UK Rail Timetable

Sunday 18 May to Saturday 13 Decen

Britain's national railway network and stations are owned by Network Rail. included in this timetable, who work together closely to provide a co-or opportunities. Details and identification codes are shown on the Train Ope over the National Rail network, together with rail and shipping connectio Channel Islands. Network Rail operate 18 managed stations but the rema... Companies. Details are shown in the station index. The Timetable Network map shows the number of the individual table for each route.

Contents

Bank Holiday Services

Altered services may apply over the relevant Bank Holiday periods and Public Holidays in Scotland. Details of services are available from National Rail Enquiries.

Engineering Works

Services may be changed, particularly at weekends, to cater for **Engineering Works.**

Passengers should check their service with their local station or by calling National Rail Enquiries (08457 48 49 50*) prior to travel.

* Calls may be recorded for training purposes.

National Rail Conditions of Carriage

A booklet containing the conditions on which tickets, including Season Tickets are issued and the Regulations and Conditions which apply to passengers' luggage can be obtained free from the National Rail website – www.nationalrail.co.uk/times_fares/nrcc/ – or from principal station ticket offices.

What's New

Welcome to the UK Rail Timetable valid from 18 May to 13 December 2008.

National Express East Anglia (NXEA) is the new name for the train operator providing services to and from London Liverpool Street and throughout East Anglia. Formerly known as 'one', the new brand was launched on 27 February 2008, and customers will notice the new brand name progressively appearing on trains and at stations.

Mitcham Eastfields station will open during the currency of this timetable. Located between Streatham and Mitcham Junction stations, services to Mitcham Eastfields will be provided by Southern and First Capital Connect.

A new Rail-Link bus service will operate between Petersfield and Waterlooville via Horndean and Cowplain – see Table 156B.

The new Southeastern timetable will deliver improvements for Sunday passengers. There will be improved frequency of services during the day to the city of Canterbury at both the East and West stations. In addition there will be improved frequency to two trains an hour on those metro routes where the evening frequency is currently hourly.

All North Yorkshire Moors Railway services will now run between Pickering and Whitby, rather than some services terminating at Goathland. Services will operate on more days, with the total number of services expected to increase by 50%. Departure times are standardised with all trains leaving at xx.00 from both Pickering and Whitby.

Please note that the information at weekends for the period Saturday 13 September to Saturday 13 December 2008 on certain tables was unavailable at the time of going to press. This information will be published in May.

Wrexham & Shropshire services are expected to start operating during the currency of this timetable. Please visit the Wrexham & Shropshire website www.wrexhamandshropshire.co.uk for updated information.

How to use this Timetable

Some tables are self-contained (such as Table 1 London–Shoeburyness) showing every train running between any two stations on the route. Train journey-lengths vary from the under-three-quarters-of-a-mile Stourbridge Town – Stourbridge Junction shuttle to the 703 mile Penzance–Dundee service. To show details of longer-distance services in a single table, short-distance services are omitted, these appearing in separate 'composite' tables.

WHICH TABLE?

General Layout of the Timetable

There are several ways of finding the correct table(s) for a journey. Tables start with the north bank of the Thames and radiate anti-clockwise around London as far as the south bank (Table 212, London-Faversham-Margate) with non-London tables (like the Cardiff Valleys) placed close to the appropriate London route. Internal Scottish routes follow from Table 216. Tables numbered 400-406 cover domestic Sleeper services. Once used to this geographic layout, required tables can usually be found with relative ease, but there are more precise methods:

Using the Index

Look up your destination. If it appears in up to five tables, those tables are listed (for example Hilsea appears in Tables 156, 157, 158, 165 and 188). If it appears in six or more then there may be sub-divisions. If your destination is sub-divided in this way and your origin is NOT shown (for example Shipley is not shown under Lancaster) then look up the origin instead as it probably has fewer tables. Alongside the station name is shown a two character code indicating which operator is responsible for operating the facilities at that station (see also Train Operator pages).

Finding and Using the Timetable Network map

If your journey is more complicated and involves several changes between tables, the Timetable Network map will be very useful. This can be found on the Network Rail website (http://www.networkrail.co.uk). Follow the link to the "Electronic National Rail Timetable" in the "For Passengers" section. The map is under "Supporting Documentation". For example, to plan a journey from North Berwick to Pontypridd one would not expect to find both in the same table. The map makes it clear that one has to change at Edinburgh and Cardiff and, as there is no through service between North Berwick and Pontypridd, allows one to look up possible routes, for example, via Crewe and Shrewsbury (Tables 65 and 131), Crewe and Birmingham (Tables 57 and 65) or York and Birmingham (Tables 51 and 57).

Using Route/Network Diagrams

For many tables a Route or Network Diagram is also provided. Route Diagrams are generally used for longer distance tables (for example Table 26) and show the route and stations served in diagrammatic form as well as the principal connecting links. Network Diagrams (for example Tables 152–154) are generally used where there is a dense network of shorter distance routes and show *all* stations and routes in the area concerned in diagrammatic form.

Using the Table

Having found the table you require make sure you look at the correct set of pages: Mondays to Fridays, Mondays to Saturdays, Saturdays, Sundays plus any relevant dates. Look for the station from which you will leave, read across until you find a suitable train, then read down to see when you will arrive at your destination.

↪ indicates the train is continued in a later column.

↩ indicates the train is continued from an earlier column.

When services in a table follow a particular pattern throughout a day or part of a day, the pattern is identified by thick downward lines at the start and end of the pattern and by a note within the lines stating "and at the same minutes past each hour until".

Bold times denote through trains whilst light, *italic*, times are connections (PLEASE READ CAREFULLY THE SECTION ON THE CONNECTIONS PAGE). Check if there is a column-heading and if there is, refer to the foot of the table for an explanation.

Because of the large number of services that 'cross' midnight, a railway timetable needs to be precise in the meaning of 'a day'. Trains starting their journeys before midnight are shown towards the end of a table – but if you are looking for the 'last' train don't stop there, as there may be later ones at the start of the table!

A train crossing midnight will be shown in full at the END of a table and any column heading denoting the day of the week applies to the day the train STARTS. For example a 2350 train headed 'SO' (see the general notes on inside front cover) commences 2350 Saturday and runs into Sunday. The train will also be shown at the front of the Sunday table with the times prior to midnight shown with note 'p', e.g. 23p50, to indicate that they refer to the previous night.

Don't worry about the ambiguity as to which day midnight itself belongs, for, to avoid this problem, all times skip from 2359 to 0001 and neither 0000 nor 2400 is ever used!

A two character code is shown at the head of each train column indicating which operator is providing the train service (see also Train Operator pages).

How to use this Timetable

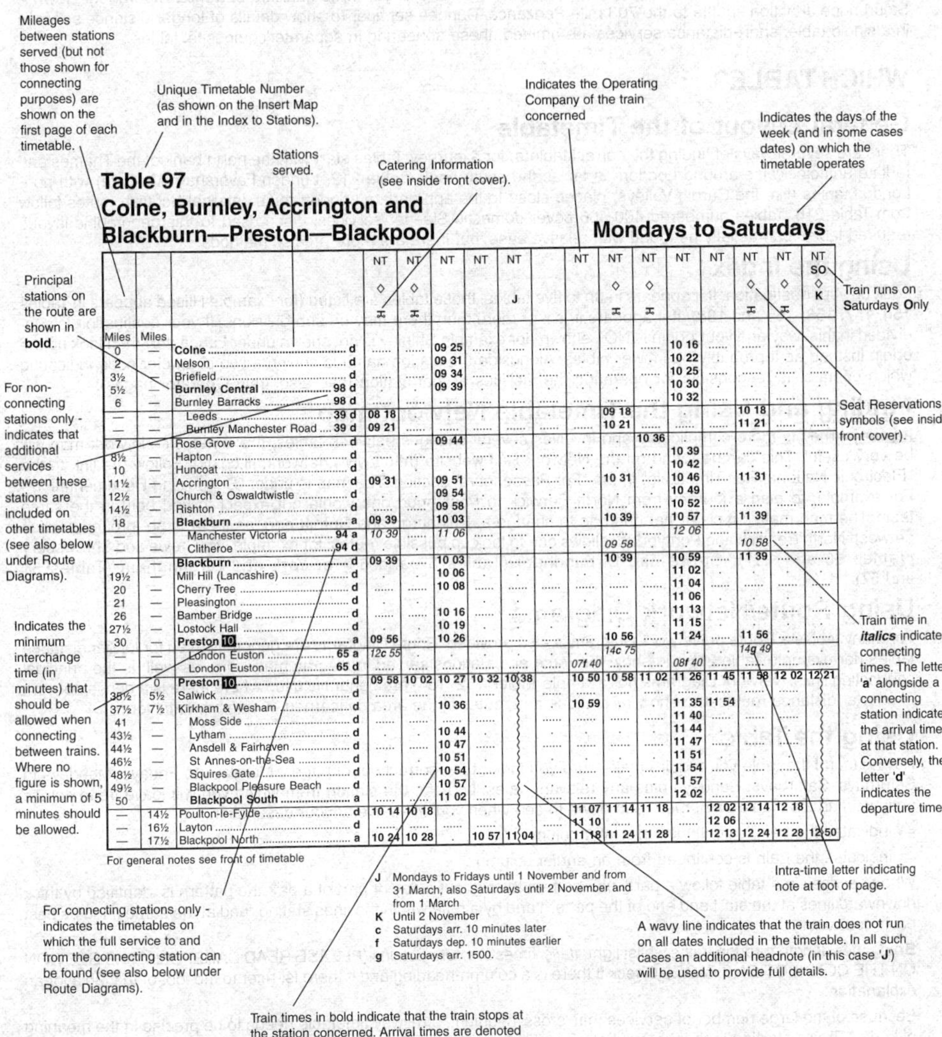

Table 97
Colne, Burnley, Accrington and Blackburn—Preston—Blackpool

Mondays to Saturdays

Miles	Miles			NT ◇	NT ◇	NT	NT	NT J		NT	NT ◇	NT ◇	NT	NT	NT ◇	NT ◇	NT SO ◇ K
0	—	**Colne**	d	.....	.....	09 25	.....	.....	.....	.....	.....	.....	10 16	.....	.....	.....	.....
2	—	Nelson	d	.	.	09 31	.	.	.	.	.	.	10 22	.	.	.	.
3½	—	Briefield	d	.....	.....	09 34	.....	.....	.....	.....	.....	.....	10 25	.....	.....	.....	.....
5½	—	**Burnley Central** 98	d	.	.	09 39	.	.	.	.	.	.	10 30	.	.	.	.
6	—	Burnley Barracks 98	d	.....	.....	.....	.....	.....	.....	.....	.....	.....	10 32	.....	.....	.....	.....
—	—	Leeds 39	d	08 18	.	.	.	.	.	.	09 18	.	.	.	10 18	.	.
—	—	Burnley Manchester Road 39	d	09 21	.....	.....	.....	.....	.....	.....	10 21	.....	.....	.....	11 21	.....	.....
7	—	Rose Grove	d	.	.	09 44	.	.	.	.	.	10 36	.	.	.	.	.
8½	—	Hapton	d	.....	.....	.....	.....	.....	.....	.....	.....	.....	10 39	.....	.....	.....	.....
10	—	Huncoat	d	.	.	.	.	.	.	.	.	.	10 42	.	.	.	.
11½	—	Accrington	d	09 31	.....	09 51	.....	.....	.....	.....	10 31	.....	10 46	.....	11 31	.....	.....
12½	—	Church & Oswaldtwistle	d	.	.	09 54	.	.	.	.	.	.	10 49	.	.	.	.
14½	—	Rishton	d	.....	.....	09 58	.....	.....	.....	.....	.....	.....	10 52	.....	.....	.....	.....
18	—	**Blackburn**	a	09 39	.	10 03	.	.	.	.	10 39	.	10 57	.	11 39	.	.
—	—	Manchester Victoria 94	a	*10 39*	.....	*11 06*	.....	.....	.....	.....	.....	.....	*12 06*	.....	.....	.....	.....
—	—	Clitheroe 94	d	.	.	.	.	.	.	.	*09 58*	.	.	.	*10 58*	.	.
—	—	**Blackburn**	d	09 39	.....	10 03	.....	.....	.....	.....	10 39	.....	10 59	.....	11 39	.....	.....
19½	—	Mill Hill (Lancashire)	d	.	.	10 06	.	.	.	.	.	.	11 02	.	.	.	.
20	—	Cherry Tree	d	.....	.....	10 08	.....	.....	.....	.....	.....	.....	11 04	.....	.....	.....	.....
21	—	Pleasington	d	.	.	.	.	.	.	.	.	.	11 06	.	.	.	.
26	—	Bamber Bridge	d	.....	.....	10 16	.....	.....	.....	.....	.....	.....	11 13	.....	.....	.....	.....
27½	—	Lostock Hall	d	.	.	10 19	.	.	.	.	.	.	11 15	.	.	.	.
30	—	**Preston** 10	a	09 56	.....	10 26	.....	.....	.....	.....	10 56	.....	11 24	.....	11 56	.....	.....
—	—	London Euston 65	a	*12c 55*	.	.	.	.	.	.	*14c 75*	.	.	.	*14g 49*	.	.
—	—	London Euston 65	d	.....	.....	.....	.....	.....	.....	*07f 40*	.....	.....	*08f 40*	.....	.....	.....	.....
—	0	**Preston** 10	d	09 58	10 02	10 27	10 32	10 38	.	10 50	10 58	11 02	11 26	11 45	11 58	12 02	12 21
35½	5½	Salwick	d	.....	.....	.....	.....		.....	.....	.....	.....	.....	.....	.....	.....	
37½	7½	Kirkham & Wesham	d	.	.	10 36	.		.	10 59	.	.	11 35	11 54	.	.	
41	—	Moss Side	d	.....	.....	.....			.....	.....	.....	.....	11 40	.....	.....	.....	
43½	—	Lytham	d	.	.	10 44	.		.	.	.	.	11 44	.	.	.	
44½	—	Ansdell & Fairhaven	d	.....	.....	10 47	.....		.....	.....	.....	.....	11 47	.....	.....	.....	
46½	—	St Annes-on-the-Sea	d	.	.	10 51	.		.	.	.	.	11 51	.	.	.	
48½	—	Squires Gate	d	.....	.....	10 54	.....		.....	.....	.....	.....	11 54	.....	.....	.....	
49½	—	Blackpool Pleasure Beach	d	.	.	10 57	.		.	.	.	.	11 57	.	.	.	
50	—	**Blackpool South**	a	.....	.....	11 02	.....		.....	.....	.....	.....	12 02	.....	.....	.....	
—	14½	Poulton-le-Fylde	d	10 14	10 18	.	.		.	11 07	11 14	11 18	.	12 02	12 14	12 18	
—	16½	Layton	d	.....	.....	.....	.....		.....	11 10	.....	.....	.....	12 06	.....	.....	
—	17½	Blackpool North	a	10 24	10 28	.	10 57	11 04	.	11 18	11 24	11 28	.	12 13	12 24	12 28	12 50

For general notes see front of timetable

J Mondays to Fridays until 1 November and from 31 March, also Saturdays until 2 November and from 1 March
K Until 2 November
c Saturdays arr. 10 minutes later
f Saturdays dep. 10 minutes earlier
g Saturdays arr. 1500.

Mileages between stations served (but not those shown for connecting purposes) are shown on the first page of each timetable.
Unique Timetable Number (as shown on the Insert Map and in the Index to Stations).
Stations served.
Catering Information (see inside front cover).
Indicates the Operating Company of the train concerned
Indicates the days of the week (and in some cases dates) on which the timetable operates
Train runs on Saturdays Only
Principal stations on the route are shown in bold.
Seat Reservations symbols (see inside front cover).
For non-connecting stations only - indicates that additional services between these stations are included on other timetables (see also below under Route Diagrams).
Indicates the minimum interchange time (in minutes) that should be allowed when connecting between trains. Where no figure is shown, a minimum of 5 minutes should be allowed.
Train time in italics indicate connecting times. The letter 'a' alongside a connecting station indicates the arrival time at that station. Conversely, the letter 'd' indicates the departure time.
Intra-time letter indicating note at foot of page.
For connecting stations only - indicates the timetables on which the full service to and from the connecting station can be found (see also below under Route Diagrams).
A wavy line indicates that the train does not run on all dates included in the timetable. In all such cases an additional headnote (in this case 'J') will be used to provide full details.
Train times in bold indicate that the train stops at the station concerned. Arrival times are denoted by 'a' against the station name and departure times by 'd'. Where there is no time shown against a station then the train concerned does not serve that station.

Route/Network Diagrams (see previous page): For many tables a Route/Network Diagram is also provided to show the routes and stations served in diagrammatic form. Where this is the case, a reference to the Route/Network Diagram will be provided at the top of each page of the timetable concerned. Timetable numbers for connecting or alternative services will not be included within the Table itself but will instead be indicated on the accompanying Route/Network Diagram.

General Information

Smoking Policy

Smoking is banned on all National Rail services and National Rail stations, including all covered and uncovered concourses, ticket halls, platforms, footbridges and subways at station premises.

Left Luggage Facilities

Details of Left Luggage facilities at stations are available from the Operator (Train Operator/Network Rail) responsible for providing facilities at the station. Please see the Station Index to identify the Station Operator and then look at the appropriate page for full details.

Penalty Fares

Penalty Fares are charged by Train Companies at some stations and on some trains. Where this is the case, warning notices will be displayed. Those stations at which Penalty Fares are in operation are indicated in the Station Index and Table numbers section (see also Train Operator pages). Please be aware that at some stations where Penalty Fare Schemes are in place not all Train Operator services calling at that station are included in the scheme.

If you can not produce a valid ticket for your entire journey when asked to do so you may be charged a Penalty Fare. This will be either twice the full single fare to the next station at which the train is due to stop, or £20, whichever is the greater. Any travel beyond the next station will be charged at the full single fare.

To avoid paying a Penalty Fare, you must purchase a valid ticket to your destination, before starting your journey. If the ticket office is closed and you can not buy the ticket you want from a self service ticket machine, you must buy a Permit to Travel paying as much of your fare as possible. This permit must be exchanged for a valid ticket at the first opportunity.

Timetable Accuracy, Contents, Presentation

Every effort is made to ensure that the information contained in the timetable is correct, but errors can still occur. If you have any questions or queries about the train services shown in this timetable, please write to the appropriate operator shown in the Directory of Train Operators.

General comments about this publication should be addressed to:–

TSO
PO Box 29
Norwich
NR3 1GN

Additional Amendments

A facility is available whereby details of any train service alterations introduced subsequent to the production of the UK Rail Timetable may be accessed through the Network Rail website (see http://www.networkrail.co.uk). Follow the link to the "Electronic National Rail Timetable" in the "For Passengers" section. Additional amendments can be found under "Supporting Documentation".

From time to time, further alterations may apply at short notice and details of these may be found through use of the links to individual Train Companies. Alternatively, the website of each company may be accessed directly at the address shown in the Directory of Train Operators.

Other National Rail Timetables

Regional and route specific timetables are available from individual train companies. Please contact the relevant train company to request the latest version of the timetable you require.

National Rail Enquiries offers an online 'Pocket Timetable' service which gives you the flexibility to create a customised timetable based around your origin and destination, your own time requirements and the days of the week that you want. Visit www.nationalrail.co.uk for more details.

Connections

Bold type times in vertical columns in the timetable show direct trains. In a few cases, where one train overtakes another, the times appear in more than one column and arrow symbols indicate where the train continues in the timetable.

Many more journey opportunities are possible by changing trains. To help plan such journeys, times in light italic type are shown in many of the timetables for departures (if the time is earlier than the bold type times for the station below in the column at which you should change trains) or arrivals (if they are later than the bold type times for the station above in the column at which you should change trains).

Where light type italic times are not shown you may have to refer to other tables in the book to work out your connecting services. In order to find the right table to reference, first look at the Route/Network Diagram that covers the table you are working from. This will show the principal connecting links and their table references, which may include the destination you are searching for. If your journey is not covered, follow the advice given on page 3 'How to use this Timetable' under the headings 'Using the loose-leaf map' and 'Using the Index'.

Connections between trains cannot be guaranteed. The nature of the integrated operation of railway passenger services means that to delay one train to await customers from a late running train arriving at a station may cause significant disruption to many other customers when they make connections at other stations along the route. Every endeavour is made to minimise the total disruption and particular attention is given to services operating infrequently and the last train services each day.

The aim of all Train Operating Companies is to run punctually, but inevitably some disruption occurs from time to time. When planning a journey you may wish to consider the effects which any disruption could have and to allow some contingency margin when planning connections.

Minimum Interchange Times at Stations

Unless a connection is shown by times printed in light type, you should generally allow a minimum of five minutes between arrival and departure.

The exceptions to this rule are indicated by minimum interchange times (e.g. **15**) alongside the station name in the tables. In certain cases the minimum interchange time is different according to the Train Operators involved.

These are detailed below:-

STATION AND 'STANDARD' MINIMUM CONNECTIONAL ALLOWANCE (Minutes)		**EXCEPTIONS** *Showing the Train Operator(s) and minimum connectional allowance applicable*		**STATION AND 'STANDARD' MINIMUM CONNECTIONAL ALLOWANCE (Minutes)**		**EXCEPTIONS** *Showing the Train Operator(s) and minimum connectional allowance applicable*		**STATION AND 'STANDARD' MINIMUM CONNECTIONAL ALLOWANCE (Minutes)**		**EXCEPTIONS** *Showing the Train Operator(s) and minimum connectional allowance applicable*	
Barnham	5	*SN*	2	Guildford	5	*GW*	4	Redhill	5	*SN*	3
Bournemouth	5	*SW*	3	Leatherhead	5	*SN*	4	St. Denys	5	*SW*	3
Brighton	10	*SN*	4	London Blackfriars	3	SE	5	Southampton Central	5	*SN, SW*	4
Cardiff Central	7	*AW*	3*	London Victoria	15	*SE, SN*	10	Tulse Hill	3	FC	4
Clapham Junction	10	*SN*	5	Luton	10	*FC*	4	Wimbledon	6	*SN, FC*	5
Gatwick Airport	10	*SE, SN*	5	Luton Airport Parkway	7	*FC*	4				

Example

At Barnham a different minimum connectional allowance applies for Train Operator SN. This means that if your journey involves changing between two trains *both of which* are operated by SN, you need only allow 2 minutes. If, however, one or both trains are provided by any other Operator then the minimum of 5 minutes (as shown after the station name) applies.

* Applicable to Valley Lines services only (table 130).

Train Information

National Rail Enquiries

Timetable and fares available at: www.nationalrail.co.uk

National Rail Enquiries provides up-to-the-minute advice on all aspects of journey planning, fares and buying tickets, live train running updates and other useful information. 0845 telephone numbers are charged at local-rate from anywhere in the UK.

For information on reservations and purchasing tickets please refer to individual train company listings in the Directory of Train Operators.

08457 48 49 50 24 Hours Daily

(calls may be recorded for training purposes)

0845 60 40 500 Welsh Language

0845 60 50 600 Textphone – 06.00 - 21.00 Daily

For live train times for today and train timetables for the next three months call TrainTracker™ on:

0871 200 49 50

Average calls to TrainTracker cost 20p a minute from a BT fixed phone. Charges from other operators may vary. Calls may be recorded for training purposes.

For live departure and arrival times direct to your mobile text station name to TrainTracker™ on:

8 49 50

TrainTracker texts cost 25p for each successful response (plus usual text costs)

Train company numbers for disabled passengers requiring assistance:–

Company	Telephone	Textphone
ARRIVA Trains Wales	08453 003 005	0870 410 0355
c2c	01702 357 640	08457 125 988
Chiltern Railways	08456 005 165	08457 078 051
CrossCountry	0844 811 0125	0844 811 0126
East Midlands Trains	08457 125 678	08457 078 051
First Capital Connect	0800 058 2844	0800 975 1052
First Great Western	08001 971 329	08002 949 209
First ScotRail	0800 912 2901	0800 912 2899
First TransPennine Express	0800 107 2149	0800 107 2061
Gatwick Express	08458 501 530	
Hull Trains	08450 710 222	08456 786 967
Island Line	0800 528 2100	0800 692 0792
London Midland	0870 609 6060	08457 078 051
London Overground	0845 601 4867	08457 125 988
Merseyrail	0151 702 2071	0870 0552681
National Express East Anglia	08000 282 878	0845 606 7245
National Express East Coast	08457 225 444	08451 202 067
Northern Rail	08456 008 008	08456 045 608
Southeastern	08007 834 524	08007 834 548
South West Trains	0800 528 2100	0800 692 0792
Southern	0800 138 1016	0800 138 1018
Virgin Trains	08457 443 366	08457 443 367

Train Information

London Travel Information

020 7222 1234 24 hours (Daily) www.tfl.gov.uk

Services to Europe on Eurostar via the Channel Tunnel

08705 186 186 0800-2100 (Daily) www.eurostar.com

Ireland

NI Railways 028 90 66 6630 0700-2000 (Daily) www.translink.co.uk.
Iarnrod Eireann (IE) (Irish Rail) 1850 366 222 www.irishrail.ie

Transport Direct

Plan journeys by car, bus, train, tube, coach, plane at www.transportdirect.info. Transport Direct is the first door-to-door on-line journey planner for Great Britain.

It's free to use; simply enter your departure point, destination and time of travel and Transport Direct will offer a number of options by different modes of transport - both public and private. Journey plans are presented as step-by-step instructions supported by detailed maps including bus stops and other points of interest to travellers. Tickets for rail and coach journeys can be booked via retail web sites without the need to re-enter journey details. Transport Direct includes live travel news for rail and car users. The car journey planner gives route information that takes account of historical traffic level data, offering the user the choice to travel at a different time, or choose public transport. When travelling by public transport, users can adjust their expected walking speed to plan rail, coach and bus connections more efficiently. You can also access Transport Direct via mobile phone and PDA to find out when your next train is due or to check road conditions.

Bus Information in Great Britain

For details of buses within Greater London ring the Transport for London line: 020 7222 1234 (24-hours).

Bus information for the rest of Great Britain is available nationally from 'Traveline' which is run by local authorities and bus operators. There are regional call centres all of which share the same telephone number and any centre will switch calls pertaining to another part of the country through to the relevant centre. Alternatively codes for reaching the appropriate centre direct can be obtained from www.traveline.org.uk/powercodes.htm.

The number is 0871 200 22 33 (calls from landlines cost 10p per minute) and centres are open at least between the hours of 0800 and 2000 daily (except Christmas Day and Boxing Day). Website: www.traveline.org.uk.

PlusBus

PlusBus provides you with a simple, easy-to-use add-on to your train ticket and gives unlimited bus travel on most bus services in the town or city. ***PlusBus*** is available to over 200 towns and cities across Great Britain with season tickets also available for many ***PlusBus*** locations. For more information visit www.plusbus.info.

Traintaxi

traintaxi

Taxi symbols on the Station index pages

Where TAXI appears against any station that has sub-entries, there will be a taxi rank outside the station from which taxis should usually be available. This also applies to Basingstoke, Bournemouth, Chelmsford, Cheltenham, Colchester, Lincoln, Middlesbrough, Milton Keynes, Northampton, Sunderland and Swindon.

Where TAXI appears against any other station, there will be a taxi rank or a cab office within 100 metres of the station. However, you are advised to check availability before travelling, and to pre-book if necessary. Indication of a rank or office is no guarantee of cabs being available.

Visit **www.traintaxi.co.uk** for information on cab firms serving **all** train, tram, metro and underground stations in Great Britain, and all bus and ferry destinations listed in this *UK Rail Timetable*.

Rail Travel for Disabled Passengers

All train operators are able to carry disabled passengers and can provide additional assistance for boarding and alighting rail services and during train journeys.

If using a wheelchair, it is recommended that passengers book assistance in advance as space on trains for wheelchair users is limited.

National Rail produce a booklet called 'Rail Travel Made Easy' which details the provisions Train Companies make for disabled people. The booklet is available from major stations or can be obtained by writing to: Disability & Inclusion Section, ATOC, 3rd Floor, 40 Bernard Street, London WC1N 1BY.

Further information is available on the **www.nationalrail.co.uk**

Seat Reservations, Luggage, Cycles and Pets

Seat Reservations

You can reserve seats on any train marked Ⓡ, 🅁, ◇ or ∝ at the top of the column in the timetable pages. Further detailed information is shown in the Directory of Train Operators. Reservations can normally be made from about 2 months in advance of the day of travel, up to about 2 hours before the train departs from its start point, or, for early morning trains, up to 1600 hours the previous evening.

Where and How to reserve

You can reserve either by visiting a station identified in the Index pages by ◇, or a rail appointed travel agent or by calling one of the telephone booking facilities listed on each Train Operator's page. Telephone reservations are only available when made in conjunction with purchasing a ticket. When reserving you will need to tell your station or agent:

1. Starting and finishing point of your journey.
2. Date of travel (Take care if your departure is soon after midnight – see How to use this Timetable).
3. Departure time of train.
4. Number of seats required.
5. You may be able to specify other preferences such as facing or back to direction of travel*, window seat, seat in Restaurant Car where available, seats round a table or airline style with fold down table where available.
   *Customers should note that some trains reverse their direction of travel during the journey.
6. First Class or Standard accommodation (if you do not specify class of travel it will be assumed that you require Standard accommodation).

Names on seats

Your name can be included in your seat reservation label or on the electronic display above your seat, if you wish, when travelling First Class on some East Midlands Trains, National Express East Anglia and National Express East Coast services or First and Standard Class on CrossCountry, First Great Western, First ScotRail, First TransPennine Express, South West Trains, and Virgin Trains services.

Connecting reservations

If your journey involves changing between trains on which seats are reservable (including journeys crossing London or other major cities), through reservations on both services are available.

Children

Seats may be reserved for children, but for a child under 5 years of age a seat may be reserved only if an appropriate child rail ticket is held.

Reservations Recommended

Trains shown 🅁 at the head of a column in the timetable pages are expected to be very busy. Seat reservations are therefore recommended for a comfortable journey and will consequently be provided free of charge to holders of valid travel tickets.

Seat Reservations, Luggage, Cycles and Pets

Reservations Compulsory
On trains shown R at the head of a column, seat reservations are compulsory and are available free of charge. Passengers may not be able to board the train if they do not have a reservation.

Trains For Weekends Away
Most long distance services after 1400 on Fridays and on Saturday mornings, also trains arriving in London on Sunday evenings and Monday mornings can be extremely busy.

Customers are advised to reserve seats in advance if planning to travel at these times.

Travelling at Peak Holiday Periods
Trains are usually extremely busy immediately before and after Bank Holidays and in some cases access to trains is only by reservation and/or boarding pass. Customers are advised to reserve seats as early as possible.

Cycles by Train
You can take your cycle on many National Rail services, however reservations may be required and restrictions may apply for peak services. Folded cycles can be carried on most train services. More information is shown in the Directory of Train Operators, the National Rail 'Cycling by Train' leaflet and online at www.nationalrail.co.uk. Cycle storage is also available at many stations.

Weekend First

Weekend First is available on many CrossCountry, East Midlands Trains, First Great Western, First ScotRail*, First TransPennine Express*, National Express East Anglia, National Express East Coast, South West Trains* and Virgin Trains (Virgin Weekend Upgrade on Virgin Trains services) services on Saturdays, Sundays and Bank Holidays. You can enjoy the luxury of special First Class accommodation on payment of a supplement. Weekend First is available to holders of most types of ticket valid in Standard accommodation, although there are certain exceptions – for full details please ring National Rail Enquiries on 08457 48 49 50 (calls may be recorded for training purposes).

If Weekend First is purchased at least a day in advance, you receive the additional benefit of a free reserved seat. Alternatively, if seats are still available, Weekend First may be purchased from a member of the on train staff.

Weekend First tickets may only be used in coaches which have Weekend First window labels. However, please note First ScotRail do not use window labels.

*may only be purchased on trains at time of travel

Customers' Luggage and Pets

Customers may take luggage provided there is space for it on the train and it is properly packed so as not to cause inconvenience or damage. Please bear in mind many trains have limited luggage space and large suitcases may not be able to be accommodated.

Excess luggage and certain more bulky items (such as skis) may be carried, subject to available space, at an extra charge.

On Gatwick Express services bulky items such as skis are conveyed free in the luggage van. There is plenty of space on board for other luggage; for further information call 0845 850 15 30.

Dogs and other pets may be taken, in most circumstances, free of charge. Animals may not be conveyed on Heathrow Express services. On First ScotRail Caledonian Sleepers dogs (except guide dogs) are not conveyed free of charge. Dogs are only permitted in the Sleeper berth providing the owner has exclusive use of the cabin and pays the relevant charge. Special arrangements are made for guide dogs.

For more information refer to the National Rail Conditions of Carriage – www.nationalrail.co.uk/times_fares/nrcc/.

Directory of Train Operators

The following pages contain details of the Train Operating Companies who operate trains included in this timetable and indicate the services they provide.

Each operator is identified by a two character code listed below. The codes are displayed in the index alongside the station name indicating which operator is responsible for operating the facilities at that station. The code is also shown at the head of each train column in the timetable pages indicating which operator is providing the train service.

18 stations are the operating responsibility of Network Rail and are shown in the index by the code NR and information about Network Rail is shown at the end of the Train Operating Company pages.

Page No	Train Company Name	Code
12	ARRIVA Trains Wales	AW
13	c2c	CC
14	CrossCountry	XC
15	Chiltern Railway Co.	CH
16	East Midlands Trains	EM
17	First Capital Connect	FC
18	First Great Western	GW
19	First ScotRail	SR
20	First TransPennine Express	TP
21	Gatwick Express	GX
22	Grand Central	GC
23	Heathrow Connect	HC
24	Heathrow Express	HX
25	Hull Trains	HT
26	Island Line	IL
27	London Midland	LM
28	London Overground	LO
29	Merseyrail	ME
30	National Express East Anglia	LE
31	National Express East Coast	GR
32	North Yorkshire Moors Railway	NY
33	Northern	NT
34	South West Trains	SW
35	Southeastern	SE
36	Southern	SN
37	Virgin Trains	VT
38	West Coast Railway Co.	WR
39	Wrexham & Shropshire	WS

AW

ARRIVA Trains Wales

ADDRESS

St Marys House, 47 Penarth Road, Cardiff CF10 5DJ
Telephone: 08456 061 660
Website: www.arrivatrainswales.co.uk
Email: customer.relations@arrivatrainswales.co.uk

MANAGING DIRECTOR

Tim Bell

RESERVATIONS AND TICKETS BY TELEPHONE

Tickets may be booked in advance and seats reserved, by telephone, from the following numbers (0800–2000 daily):
0870 9000 773 for Great Britain, tickets and reservations. 0870 9000 767 for Group and 0845 300 3005 for Disabled travel arrangements. Textphone 0845 300 6105
Please allow 5 days for delivery.

RESERVATION DETAILS

All seat reservations are free to ticket holders.

CATERING ON TRAINS

At-seat catering service of cold snacks, sandwiches and hot and cold drinks on all services marked ⊼, for all or part of the journey.

Train catering on ARRIVA Trains Wales services is provided by:

At Seat Catering (2003) Ltd,
ARRIVA Trains Wales
1st Floor
St Mary's House
47 Penarth Road
Cardiff
CF10 5DJ

CYCLES

See Cycling by Train, a guide to ARRIVA Trains Wales services leaflet for full details.

LOST PROPERTY

Contact your nearest staffed station or contact ARRIVA Trains Wales Customer Relations on 0845 6061 660.

TRAIN SERVICE UPDATE

Please consult our website at www.arrivatrainswales.co.uk for real time service updates.

PENALTY FARES

Penalty Fares are not in force on ARRIVA Trains Wales services. Customers are reminded that they must have a valid ticket when boarding at a staffed station, if not it will be necessary to charge you the full single/return fare for the journey.

DISABLED PERSON'S PROTECTION POLICY

Address as above.

CODE OF PRACTICE FOR COMMENTS, COMPLAINTS AND SUGGESTIONS

Address as above.

c2c

A member of the National Express Group plc

ADDRESS	207 Old Street, London EC1V 9NR Telephone: 0845 601 4873 Fax: 01603 214517 Website: www.c2c-online.co.uk
MANAGING DIRECTOR	Julian Drury
RESERVATIONS AND TICKETS BY TELEPHONE	Tickets may be booked in advance by telephoning 08457 44 44 22.
RESERVATION DETAILS	Reservations are not available.
CATERING ON TRAINS	Not available.
CYCLES	Cycles can be taken on off-peak trains free-of-charge when accompanied by a fare-paying passenger, subject to space availability. Bicycles are not permitted, Mondays to Fridays on services that arrive in London between 0715 and 1010, or those which leave London between 1630 and 1840. To comply with safety regulations, all cycles, with the exception of folding cycles which are completely enclosed in a container or case throughout the journey, must be conveyed in the designated area on trains. During engineering work, cycles cannot be accommodated on replacement bus services.
LOST PROPERTY	Telephone: 01702 357 699
TRAIN SERVICE UPDATE	Up to date train running information is available on the c2c website www.c2c-online.co.uk, the National Rail Enquiries website or on ceefax page 433.
PENALTY FARES	If you travel without a valid ticket you may be charged a penalty fare of £20 or twice the full single fare, whichever is the greater.
DISABLED PERSON'S PROTECTION POLICY	Available from:- Customer Relations, c2c, FREEPOST ADM3968, Southend SS1 1ZS Telephone: 0845 601 4873
CODE OF PRACTICE FOR COMMENTS, COMPLAINTS AND SUGGESTIONS	Available from Customer Relations at above address or telephone 0845 601 4873.

CrossCountry

XC

ADDRESS

CrossCountry
85 Smallbrook Queensway
Birmingham B5 4HA
Telephone: 0870 010 0084
Textphone: 0121 654 7604
Fax: 0121 654 7603
Website: www.crosscountrytrains.co.uk
Email: customer.relations@crosscountrytrains.co.uk

MANAGING DIRECTOR

Andy Cooper

RESERVATIONS AND TICKETS BY TELEPHONE

On-line at crosscountrytrains.co.uk is the easiest way to purchase your tickets. If you prefer, you can also make telephone bookings on 0844 811 0124 between 0800 and 2200 daily. Parties of 10 or more should contact Group Travel on 0871 244 2388 between 0800 and 1800 weekdays

RESERVATION DETAILS

You are strongly advised to make a seat reservation in advance; especially when travelling on trains shown ◘ in timetables. Seat reservations are free of charge.

CATERING ON TRAINS

Catering is available on most CrossCountry trains.
In First Class, on weekdays between 0600 and 2000 customers can enjoy complimentary light refreshments including hot and soft drinks, served at seat or available for collection from the on-board shop (when in operation).
In Standard we offer a range of quality snacks, sandwiches and hot drinks plus soft and alcoholic beverages between 0600 and 2000 (until mid afternoon, weekdays only, on our Nottingham - Cardiff and Birmingham - Stansted routes)
See timetables for further details.

CYCLES

We do not charge to carry your cycle. However, as space is very limited you will need to reserve in advance on nearly all our services. Please enquire before travelling. We are unable to accept powered cycles, tricycles, tandems or trailers on any of our services.

LOST PROPERTY

Contact Customer Relations on 0870 010 0084 between 0830 and 2000 weekdays, 0900 and 1600 Saturdays, or email lost.property@crosscountrytrains.co.uk

TRAIN SERVICE UPDATE

Details of major disruption to services and weekend engineering work are summarised on BBC Ceefax and BBCi on digital TV. Live travel updates are available on-line at crosscountrytrains.co.uk and details of all service disruptions can be found at nationalrail.co.uk/service_bulletins/

PENALTY FARES

A Penalty Fares scheme is not currently in operation on CrossCountry trains. Visit crosscountrytrains.co.uk for the most up to date information. Should you board one of our trains without a valid ticket you will be charged the full Single or Return fare for your journey unless the ticket office is closed and a self-service ticket machine is not available.

DISABLED PERSON'S PROTECTION POLICY

We provide a Journey Care service for the disabled, elderly and infirm. By phoning our team on 0844 811 0125, textphone 0844 811 0126, beforehand we will, where possible, arrange help for your journey. Our Disabled Persons Protection Policy is available on-line at crosscountrytrains.co.uk

CODE OF PRACTICE FOR COMMENTS, COMPLAINTS AND SUGGESTIONS

Copies of our Complaints Handling Procedure and Passenger's Charter are available on-line at crosscountrytrains.co.uk

Chiltern Railway Co.

CH

ADDRESS	Customer Services, Western House, 14 Rickfords Hill, Aylesbury HP20 2RX Telephone: 08456 005 165 (Mondays to Fridays 0830-1730) Fax: 01296 332126 Website: www.chilternrailways.co.uk
MANAGING DIRECTOR	Adrian Shooter (Acting)
RESERVATIONS AND TICKETS BY TELEPHONE	Telephone 08456 005 165 (0700-2000, 7 days a week)
RESERVATION DETAILS	Reservations are not required on Chiltern Railways services.
CATERING ON TRAINS	A trolley catering service is available on Monday to Friday peak services between Birmingham Snow Hill and London Marylebone.
CYCLES	Passengers with bicycles are welcome on Chiltern Railways. Cycles are carried off-peak free of charge but cannot be accommodated at busy times, i.e. throughout the journey on trains arriving at London Marylebone and Birmingham Snow Hill between 0745 and 1000, or throughout the journey on trains departing London Marylebone or Birmingham Snow Hill between 1630 and 1930 on Mondays to Fridays. There are no restrictions on folding bicycles. Tandems are not carried at any time.
LOST PROPERTY	Telephone 08456 005 165 (1000-1500 Mondays to Fridays).
TRAIN SERVICE UPDATE	For a recorded summary of engineering work call: 08456 005 165.
PENALTY FARES	If you do not have a valid rail ticket for the journey you are making, you will have to pay a Penalty Fare of £20 or twice the single fare, whichever is the greater, for the journey you are making on Chiltern Railways services. For full details write to the above address, or see our website.
DISABLED PERSON'S PROTECTION POLICY	Copies of the Disabled Person's Protection Policy can be obtained from the above address, or from our website.
CODE OF PRACTICE FOR COMMENTS, COMPLAINTS AND SUGGESTIONS	If you have any comments, complaints or suggestions regarding Chiltern Railways services, please write to the address shown above or telephone 08456 005 165 (0830-1730 Mondays to Fridays), Fax 01296 332126. Alternatively you can use the 'Contact Us' option on our website.

EM East Midlands Trains EM

ADDRESS	Midland House Nelson Street Derby DE1 2SA Telephone: 08457 125 678 Website: www.eastmidlandstrains.co.uk Email: getintouch@eastmidlandstrains.co.uk
MANAGING DIRECTOR	Tim Shoveller
RESERVATIONS AND TICKETS BY TELEPHONE	Buy your tickets online at eastmidlandstrains.co.uk. You can buy tickets for all rail journeys (within Great Britain) with us. Alternatively call 08457 125 678 between 0800-2000 (7 days a week).
RESERVATION DETAILS	Seat reservations on East Midlands Trains services are free. Just book in advance when you buy your ticket. We advise that you always make a reservation, as seats cannot be guaranteed without one. On our Connect services reservations are available on the Liverpool to Norwich services.
CATERING ON TRAINS	On our East Midlands Mainline services (to/from St Pancras International), our buffet provides a range of delicious healthy food options, plus snacks and Fairtrade drinks. A trolley service is available on selected East Midlands Connect services (denoted by a symbol within the timetable).
CYCLES	Bicycles are accepted for free on most East Midlands Trains services; however reservations must be made in advance.
LOST PROPERTY	Please allow a minimum of 24 hours for the items to be received at a lost property office. If your item is located you will be charged for the return of it and will be advised of this cost. To enquire about lost property, please call Customer Relations on 08457 125 678.
TRAIN SERVICE UPDATE	Details of services and real time running information, including travel alerts by email are available through our website. Visit eastmidlandstrains.co.uk. Alternatively, call National Rail Enquiries on 08457 48 49 50 (calls may be recorded for training purposes).
PENALTY FARES	You should always buy a ticket in advance of boarding your train. Penalty fares may be in operation on your service.
DISABLED PERSON'S PROTECTION POLICY	We aim to make travelling with us accessible to all our customers. If you require assistance in travelling, have special needs or mobility problems please call our team on 08457 125 678 to arrange help for your journey. A textphone service is also available on 08457 078 051.
CODE OF PRACTICE FOR COMMENTS, COMPLAINTS AND SUGGESTIONS	Our Customer Relations team is available to receive your comments, complaints or suggestions. Please write to Customer Relations at the above address, or email getintouch@eastmidlandstrains.co.uk

FC

First Capital Connect

FC

A member of the First Rail Division

ADDRESS

Freepost, RRBR-REEJ-KTKY, First Capital Connect, Customer Relations Department, PO Box 443, Plymouth PL4 6WP
Telephone: 0845 026 4700 (open 7 days a week 0700-2200 with the exception of Christmas Day)
Fax: 0845 676 9904
Website: www.firstcapitalconnect.co.uk
Email: customer.relations.fcc@firstgroup.com

CHIEF EXECUTIVE

Moir Lockhead

MANAGING DIRECTOR

Elaine Holt

RESERVATIONS AND TICKETS BY TELEPHONE

It is not necessary to pre-book on First Capital Connect services.
There is no telesales.

RESERVATION DETAILS

First Capital Connect does not operate a reservation system.

CATERING ON TRAINS

None.

CYCLES

We welcome passengers with bicycles on services where they can be safely accommodated, however restrictions apply, bicycles cannot be carried on:

- trains that are scheduled to arrive at a London terminal between 07:00 and 10:00;
- trains that are scheduled to depart from a London terminal between 16:00 and 19:00;
- trains running between Drayton Park and Moorgate;
- services between Royston and Ely that depart or arrive at Cambridge between 07:45 and 08:45, with the exception of the 07:15 and 07:45 departures from King's Cross;
- replacement bus services unless stated otherwise in any associated publicity; and
- any train where a member of our staff asks you to remove your bicycle.
- Bicycles cannot be conveyed within Travelcard zone 1 in any direction between the hours of 0700-1000 and 1600-1900 Monday to Friday

Fold up bicycles can be carried on any service at any time.

LOST PROPERTY

In order to trace lost property please contact our Customer Relations department on 0845 026 4700, between 07:00 - 22:00 Monday to Sunday.

TRAIN SERVICE UPDATE

For current train information call First Capital Connect Travel Check on 0845 330 3660, National Rail enquiries on 08457 48 49 50 (calls may be recorded for training purposes) or check our website at: www.firstcapitalconnect.co.uk/live-info

PENALTY FARES

First Capital Connect operates a Penalty Fares System. If you do not have a valid ticket or permit to travel, you will be liable to pay a penalty fare. This is £20 or twice the appropriate single fare to the next station stop, whichever is greater. This does not apply for travel from Crews Hill.

If you do not buy a ticket, you could also be prosecuted and this can lead to a criminal conviction.

DISABLED PERSON'S PROTECTION POLICY

Our Disabled Person's Protection Policy is available from Customer Relations, and is also available on our website and available at all staffed sations. First Capital Connect operates a dedicated telephone and textphone service for disabled or mobility impaired customers, the contact details are:

Telephone: 0800 058 2844

Textphone: 0800 975 1052

These are available 07:00 - 22:00, Monday to Sunday, with the exception of Christmas Day.

CODE OF PRACTICE FOR COMMENTS, COMPLAINTS AND SUGGESTIONS

Our Passenger's Charter details our code of practice and is available from all staffed stations and from our Customer Relations department. The Customer Relations department will be happy to assist with any comments, complaints or suggestions and can be contacted using the contact details above.

First Great Western

A member of the First Rail Division

ADDRESS

Milford House, 1 Milford Street, Swindon SN1 1HL
Telephone: 01793 499400
Fax: 01793 499460
Website: www.firstgreatwestern.co.uk where customers can buy tickets, check train times, obtain current information on train services, download timetables, check latest alterations to services, view promotions and offers and contact us with your comments.

CHIEF OPERATING OFFICER

Andrew Haines

RESERVATIONS AND TICKETS BY TELEPHONE

Tickets may be booked in advance using credit and debit cards and seats reserved by ringing **08457 000 125** (open 0700-2200 Mondays to Fridays and 0700-2100 Saturdays and Sundays). Allow at least 3 working days for postal delivery. A next day delivery can be arranged at £5 per transaction. Arrangements can be made for tickets to be collected from Fast Ticket machines (the credit or debit card used for purchase will be needed at many stations). For Group Travel call **08457 000 125**.

RESERVATION DETAILS

One complimentary seat reservation per single journey when purchasing a ticket, additional reservations, including those made by season ticket holders, will be subject to a £5 fee.

CATERING ON TRAINS

Most First Great Western high speed services offer a buffet or trolley service with a selection of hot and cold snacks, sandwiches, beverages, crisps and confectionery.

First Class customers also enjoy additional complimentary services:

- An at seat trolley service offering light refreshments available on Monday to Friday services between 0700 and 1900, including tea, freshly made coffee, soft drinks, mineral water, morning goods, biscuits, peanuts and fresh fruit.
- A complimentary daily newspaper (available up to 09.00) and evening paper (after 15.00) on services out of London.
- At the weekend and on weekdays after 1900 complimentary refreshments are available from the buffet on production of valid travel tickets.
- Friday night wine offers first class customers a complimentary glass of wine between 1500 and 1900.

Some weekday high speed services offer Pullman Restaurant or Travelling Chef/ Brasserie providing food freshly prepared on board by one of our own chefs. These services are available on over 200 services per week.

CYCLES

First Great Western welcomes customers with bicycles on services where they can be safely accommodated. However it is not possible to carry bicycles on some services particularly during peak periods. For full details of when bicycles cannot be carried or when reservations are required, please visit our website or pick up a leaflet at any of our staffed stations.

LOST PROPERTY

Customers who have left property on First Great Western services should contact our Customer Services team on **08457 000 125**.

TRAIN SERVICE UPDATE

For current train information including details of engineering work please visit our website: www.firstgreatwestern.co.uk

PENALTY FARES

These operate on most of our services. A penalty fare of £20 or twice the appropriate single fare to the next station stop (whichever is the greater) will be charged to anybody who is unable to produce a valid ticket or other authority when required to do so. For further information, pick up a leaflet about penalty fares from any staffed station.

DISABLED PERSON'S PROTECTION POLICY

Available from Customer Services Team
First Great Western
PO Box 313
Plymouth PL4 6YD
Tel: 08457 000 125
Email: fgwfeedback@firstgroup.com
Opening hours 0700-2200, daily.

Customers requiring assistance should contact 0800 197 1329 (0800 294 9209 textphone service) giving 24 hours notice of travel plans, if possible.

CODE OF PRACTICE FOR COMMENTS, COMPLAINTS AND SUGGESTIONS

Your views leaflets and copies of the Passenger's Charter are available to download from our website www.firstgreatwestern.co.uk, at all staffed First Great Western stations or alternatively from the Customer Services Team at the address above.

First ScotRail

A member of the First Rail Division

ADDRESS

1st Floor, Atrium Court, 50 Waterloo Street, Glasgow G2 6HQ
Telephone: 08700 00 51 51
Fax: 0141 335 4592
Website: www.firstscotrail.com
Email: enquiries@firstscotrail.com

MANAGING DIRECTOR

Mary Dickson

RESERVATIONS AND TICKETS BY TELEPHONE

Tickets may be purchased in advance and Sleepers or seats reserved, by telephone, using a debit/credit card from the following number:

08457 550033 (opening hours 0700-2200)

Please allow 3 days for tickets by post, tickets on departure arrangements available at selected stations. Tickets can also be purchased through the website - www.firstscotrail.com

First ScotRail customers can buy selected Caledonian Sleeper tickets online - and have the ticket confirmation sent to their mobile phone. Passengers simply turn up for their train, show the text message to train staff and hop on board. A confirmatory email is sent as a back-up. This free SMS service is available for 'Bargain Berth' tickets on the Caledonian Sleeper, which connects Scottish cities to Central London. Tickets can be booked up to 12 weeks in advance of travel - and right up until midday on the day of travel, subject to availability. The berths start from just £19.

RESERVATION DETAILS

Seat Reservations are free and can be made from 12 weeks in advance up to 1800 hours one day prior to the date of departure. Caledonian Sleeper reservations can be made up to 12 weeks in advance.

CATERING ON TRAINS

A Lounge Car is provided on all Caledonian Sleeper services offering a wide range of drinks, snacks and hot meals. A trolley service is available on many longer distance services as indicated in the timetable. Any comments about our daytime catering services should be made to Billy Black, Hospitality and Sleeper Manager tel: 0141 335 2066.

CYCLES

Cycles are carried free on all First ScotRail services subject to availability. Reservations are required on Caledonian Sleeper services and on longer distance routes. Tandems, tricycles, cycle trailers, motorcycles, mopeds or motorised cycles are not carried on any First ScotRail service.

LOST PROPERTY

Please phone 0141 335 3276 (0700-1900 Mon-Sat)

TRAIN SERVICE UPDATE

Register with JourneyCheck/JourneyAlert on our website: www.firstscotrail.com

PENALTY FARES

Penalty Fares are not in force on any First ScotRail services.

DISABLED PERSON'S PROTECTION POLICY

Available from the Customer Relations Manager, First ScotRail, Disabled Assistance, PO Box 7034, Fort William PH33 6WS. Tel: 0800 912 2 901 or minicom 0800 912 2 899
Fax: 0141 335 4611

Travel arrangements may be made for disabled people by calling 08 00 912 2 901*. One lightweight travel scooter, length 104cm, width 56cm with a turning radius of 99cm and combined weight of 300kg can be conveyed per train. Details of station facilities for disabled customers are also available on our website www.firstscotrail.com

*For assisted travel, an advance notice of up to 24 hours notice is appreciated.

CODE OF PRACTICE FOR COMMENTS, COMPLAINTS AND SUGGESTIONS

First ScotRail welcomes comments on the services we provide. A leaflet is available at all staffed First ScotRail stations explaining the procedures and is also available from the Customer Relations Manager at the address above. Tel: 0845 601 5929

TP **First TransPennine Express** TP

First TransPennine Express

A joint venture between First and Keolis

ADDRESS
7th Floor, Bridgewater House, 60 Whitworth Street, Manchester M1 6LT
Telephone: 08700 005151
Website: www.tpexpress.co.uk

MANAGING DIRECTOR
Vernon Barker

RESERVATIONS AND TICKETS BY TELEPHONE
Reservations and tickets are available from all local staffed stations.

RESERVATION DETAILS
Seat reservations are available at staffed stations. Seat reservations for travel on First TransPennine Express services can be booked up until the day before travel. There is no charge for making a seat reservation if you have a rail ticket, or buy one at the same time.

CATERING ON TRAINS
Catering trolley services are available between 0700 and 1900 Monday to Friday on First TransPennine Express trains between Manchester Piccadilly and York, Manchester Piccadilly and Doncaster and Manchester Piccadilly and Preston. In addition to the above, all services between Manchester Airport, Manchester Piccadilly, Carlisle, Glasgow Central and Edinburgh convey a trolley service for the whole journey. This facility is also provided at weekends.

CYCLES
Customers may take their bicycle with them on First TransPennine Express trains at no extra cost. As space is limited reservations for cycle space should be made at least 24 hours before the journey.

LOST PROPERTY
Customers who have left their property on First TransPennine Express trains or stations should contact 0845 600 1672.

TRAIN SERVICE UPDATE
Call TrainTracker on 0871 200 4950 for updated information on train departures and arrivals.

PENALTY FARES
Penalty Fares are not applicable on First TransPennine Express services. Customers are reminded that they must have a valid ticket when they travel. If not it will be necessary to charge the full Open Single or Return fare for the journey.

DISABLED PERSON'S PROTECTION POLICY
Available from:
Customer Relations,
First TransPennine Express,
ADMAIL 3878,
Freepost,
Manchester M1 9YB

Customers who have special needs and require customer assistance should contact us on 0800 107 2149.

A textphone service is available on 0800 107 2061.

CODE OF PRACTICE FOR COMMENTS, COMPLAINTS AND SUGGESTIONS
Feedback leaflets and copies of the Passenger's Charter are available from all stations served by First TransPennine Express services or alternatively contact:
Customer Relations,
First TransPennine Express,
ADMAIL 3878,
Freepost,
Manchester M1 9YB.
Telephone: 0845 600 1671
Email: tpecustomer.relations@firstgroup.com

Gatwick Express

GX

A member of the National Express Group plc

ADDRESS	207 Old Street, London EC1V 9NR Telephone: 0845 601 4873 Fax: 01603 214567 Website: www.gatwickexpress.com
MANAGING DIRECTOR	Mark Hopwood
RESERVATIONS AND TICKETS BY TELEPHONE	Reservations are not necessary on Gatwick Express services. For information and telesales please call 0845 850 1530. Tickets can also be purchased through the website - www.gatwickexpress.com
RESERVATION DETAILS	Gatwick Express is a high frequency service, so reservations are not required.
CATERING ON TRAINS	An at-seat trolley service of drinks and light refreshments is available throughout the day.
CYCLES	Cycles and other bulky items such as skis are conveyed free in the luggage van. There is plenty of space on board for other luggage – for further information call 0845 850 15 30.
LOST PROPERTY	Please call our Lost Property Office on 0845 850 15 30, select option 3.
TRAIN SERVICE UPDATE	Journey time is 30 minutes (35 minutes on Sundays). First Class and Express Class accommodation is available. From London Victoria at 0330, 0430, 0500 then every 15 minutes (xx15, xx30, xx45, xx00) until 0001, 0030. From Gatwick Airport at 0435, 0520, 0550 then every 15 minutes (xx05, xx20, xx35, xx50) until 0050, 0135. For current train information call 0845 850 15 30.
PENALTY FARES	Penalty fares are not charged on Gatwick Express services. Tickets may be bought on the train, or from our ticket offices.
DISABLED PERSON'S PROTECTION POLICY	Customers requiring assistance can book this prior to travel. Arrangements can be made by calling 0845 850 15 30, textphone available. It is advisable to give 24 hours notice of travel plans, although customers will be given assistance if they arrive at the stations without notice but please allow a little extra time.
CODE OF PRACTICE FOR COMMENTS, COMPLAINTS AND SUGGESTIONS	Initially comments or issues requiring immediate attention should be addressed to any member of Gatwick Express staff on the train or platforms. Additionally Customer Comments forms and our Passenger's Charter are available at Gatwick Express ticket offices. Alternatively you may write to the Gatwick Express Customer Relations, 52 Grosvenor Gardens, London SW1W 0AU.

Grand Central

GC

ADDRESS	Grand Central Railway Co. Ltd, 5 The Crescent, York YO24 1AW Telephone: 01904 633307 Fax: 01904 466066 Website: www.grandcentralrail.com Email: info@grandcentralrail.com
MANAGING DIRECTOR	Ian Yeowart
RESERVATIONS AND TICKETS BY TELEPHONE	Minimum transaction value: £10. Full details on the website.
RESERVATION DETAILS	All seats are reservable. No charge for reservations.
CATERING ON TRAINS	Full catering services are available. Full details on the website.
CYCLES	Normal cycles conveyed at no charge.
LOST PROPERTY	Contact the above address.
TRAIN SERVICE UPDATE	Please phone: 01904 633307 or check our website: www.grandcentralrail.com
PENALTY FARES	No penalty fares are applicable.
DISABLED PERSON'S PROTECTION POLICY	Available from the above address.
CODE OF PRACTICE FOR COMMENTS, COMPLAINTS AND SUGGESTIONS	Available from the above address.

Heathrow Connect

HC

A joint venture between First Rail Division and BAA (Heathrow Express)

ADDRESS

Full postal address for customer correspondence
Freepost RLRZ-TZXE-BYKY
Heathrow Connect
3rd Floor
30 Eastbourne Terrace
London
W2 6LE

Telephone: 0845 678 6975
Fax: 020 8745 6615
Website: www.heathrowconnect.com
Email: queries@heathrowconnect.com

MANAGING DIRECTORS

Heathrow Connect is a joint venture between First Great Western and BAA (Heathrow Express).
Andrew Haines (First Great Western)
Brian Raven (Heathrow Express)

RESERVATIONS AND TICKETS BY TELEPHONE

Reservations are not neccessary. Tickets can be booked by telephone by ringing 0845 700 0125. Open 0700-2200 (0800-1900 Saturdays and Sundays). Allow 3 working days for delivery. A next day delivery can be arranged at £5 per transaction.

RESERVATION DETAILS

Heathrow Connect services are not reservable.

CATERING ON TRAINS

Catering on trains is not available.

CYCLES

Cycles are carried free of charge, but are not allowed on trains timed to arrive at London Paddington between 0745-0945, or depart London Paddington between 1630-1830 Mondays to Fridays. In the interest of safety and customer comfort, we reserve the right to limit the number of cycles at other times.

LOST PROPERTY

For property lost on a Heathrow Connect train or at London Paddington, call the Lost Property Office at Paddington on 0207 313 1514.

For property left at Heathrow call the BAA Lost Property Office at Heathrow Central Station on 0208 745 7727.

For property left at one of the intermediate stations contact the FGW Lost Property helpline on 0845 602 4304.

TRAIN SERVICE UPDATE

For current train information call 0845 678 6975.
Website: www.heathrowconnect.com

PENALTY FARES

Penalty Fares apply at stations between Hayes & Harlington and Paddington (incl). Customers are liable to a Penalty Fare of £20 to the next station stop.

DISABLED PERSON'S PROTECTION POLICY

This is available from Customer Relations at the above address and telephone number.

CODE OF PRACTICE FOR COMMENTS, COMPLAINTS AND SUGGESTIONS

This is available from Customer Relations at the above address and telephone number.

Heathrow Express

HX

ADDRESS

Customer contact:
Freepost RLXY-ETJG-XKZS
London W2 6LG
Telephone: 0845 600 1515
(call centre)

Corporate contact:
3rd Floor, 30 Eastbourne Terrace,
London W2 6LE or
FREEPOST LON 16331, Hounslow TW6 2BR
Telephone: 020 8750 6600
Fax: 020 8750 6615
Website: www.heathrowexpress.com

MANAGING DIRECTOR

Brian Raven

RESERVATIONS AND TICKETS BY TELEPHONE

Reservations are not necessary on Heathrow Express services. Tickets may be purchased in advance from Heathrow Express sales desks, ticket machines and from a range of other appointed outlets. For details call the Customer Care Line on 0845 600 15 15. (24-hour service – local rate call)

RESERVATION DETAILS

Heathrow Express operates a 'turn up and go' service and reservations are not necessary.

CATERING ON TRAINS

As the overall journey time is only 15 minutes, or 23 minutes to Terminal 5, there is currently no catering on Heathrow Express services. Terminal 4 is served by a connecting 'shuttle' service at Heathrow Terminals 1, 2 & 3, taking a minimum 8 minutes extra.

CYCLES

Limited accommodation is available for cycles on Heathrow Express services, for passengers flying with their cycles from the airport. Heathrow Express reserve the right to limit the number of cycles conveyed on each train to no more than three at busy times. Cyclists not travelling onwards by air may use the service to and from Heathrow Terminals, subject to space being available for airline passengers.

LOST PROPERTY

Property lost at Paddington station is collected by Network Rail, who can be contacted on 020 7313 1514. For items lost at Heathrow Airport call 020 8745 7727. For items lost on Heathrow Express trains, please ask our Customer Service Representatives, or alternatively write to: Lost Property, Heathrow Express Atrium, Heathrow Airport UB3 5AP.

TRAIN SERVICE UPDATE

For current information on train services please contact our customer care line on 0845 600 15 15.

PENALTY FARES

Penalty Fares do not apply on Heathrow Express services, therefore customers may join the train without having first purchased a ticket or authority to travel. Customer Service Representatives on every train will accept cash, debit and credit cards, for ticket purchase. Please note however for tickets purchased on board there is a £2.00 premium to pay. Only full fare tickets are available to purchase on board the train. (Disabled Railcard is accepted on board however).

DISABLED PERSON'S PROTECTION POLICY

Heathrow Express trains have been specially designed with the needs of the disabled in mind. Platforms at all our stations give level access into the trains and there is space for wheelchairs on all trains.

For further information on facilities for the disabled, call the Customer Care Line on 0845 600 15 15, or write to the Managing Director at the address at the top of this page.

CODE OF PRACTICE FOR COMMENTS, COMPLAINTS AND SUGGESTIONS

It is our aim to try and resolve any problems or grievances on the spot. All our Customer Service Representatives have a supply of comment forms and our Customer Care Line on 0845 600 15 15 can deal with problems over the telephone. If you wish to write with a suggestion or complaint, please write to the Managing Director at the address at the top of this page.

Please note that Heathrow Terminal 5 station opened on 27 March 2008.

Hull Trains

HT

A joint venture between First Rail Division and Renaissance Railways Ltd.

ADDRESS	Hull Trains Customer Services, Freepost RLYY-XSTG-YXCK, Premier House, Ferensway, Kingston Upon Hull, HU1 3UF. Telephone: 08456 76 99 05 Website: www.hulltrains.co.uk Email: customer.services@hulltrains.co.uk
MANAGING DIRECTOR	Mark Leving
RESERVATIONS AND TICKETS BY TELEPHONE	Hull Trains tickets can be booked in advance and seats reserved by ringing 08450 710 222 (0700 to 2200 Monday to Friday and 0800 to 1900 Saturday and Sunday). Please allow five working days for delivery. Tickets on departure are available.
RESERVATION DETAILS	Seat reservations are free for First and Standard Class ticket holders. Season Ticket holders may reserve seats at a cost of £2 for First class and £1 for Standard class.
CATERING ON TRAINS	Hull Trains provides a buffet on all services, and a comprehensive catering package for First Class passengers. Catering is subject to availability and may be limited when services are disrupted by engineering works or Bank Holidays.
CYCLES	Cycles and tandems are carried free of charge, however, a reservation is compulsory. Please telephone 08450 710 222
LOST PROPERTY	Please contact Customer Services.
TRAIN SERVICE UPDATE	Available at www.hulltrains.co.uk, or by telephone on 08450 710222.
PENALTY FARES	Penalty fares are not in force on any Hull Trains Service
DISABLED PERSON'S PROTECTION POLICY	Available at: www.hulltrains.co.uk. Alternatively, a copy can be requested from Customer Services.
CODE OF PRACTICE FOR COMMENTS, COMPLAINTS AND SUGGESTIONS	Hull Trains' Passenger's Charter is available at www.hulltrains.co.uk. Alternatively, any comments, complaints or suggestions can be sent to Customer Services

Island Line

IL

ADDRESS	Friars Bridge Court, 41–45 Blackfriars Road, London SE1 8NZ Telephone: 08700 005151 Fax: 020 7620 5177 Website: www.southwesttrains.co.uk Email: customerrelations@swtrains.co.uk
MANAGING DIRECTOR	Stewart Palmer
RESERVATIONS AND TICKETS BY TELEPHONE	Reservations are not required on Island Line Trains services. Group travel information can be obtained by calling 023 8072 8162.
RESERVATION DETAILS	Reservations are not required.
CATERING ON TRAINS	There are no catering facilities on trains.
CYCLES	A maximum of 4 cycles may be carried in the Shanklin end of all trains at no extra charge. For the safety and comfort of our passengers, the guard may refuse to carry any further cycles on the train.
LOST PROPERTY	All items of lost property are retained at Ryde Esplanade Ticket Office. If you have lost an item please telephone the Ticket Office on 01983 562492 (0900-1700 Daily). A charge may be applicable on collection.
TRAIN SERVICE UPDATE	For current train information, please call our helpline on 0845 6000 650 or visit www.island-line.com. For details of Bank Holiday services see also the boxed note on the page immediately preceding Table 149.
PENALTY FARES	Penalty Fares are not in force on any Island Line Trains services.
DISABLED PERSON'S PROTECTION POLICY	Island Line Trains is committed to making travel easier for customers with disabilities including wheelchair users. For travel on the mainland, please call our Assisted Travel line on 0800 5282 100 (textphone 0800 692 0792), giving 24 hours notice before travelling. For journeys wholly within Island Line Trains, please telephone 01983 812591 giving 24 hours notice if assistance is required.
CODE OF PRACTICE FOR COMMENTS, COMPLAINTS AND SUGGESTIONS	Feedback leaflets are available at Ryde Esplanade or Shanklin Ticket Offices. Copies of Island Line Trains' and South West Trains' Passenger's Charters are available from any staffed station or by writing to: Customer Service Centre, South West Trains, Overline House, Southampton SO15 1GW Telephone 0845 6000 650. Fax 023 8072 8187 Email: customerrelations@swtrains.co.uk The Passenger's Charter is also featured on the website www.island-line.com and www.southwesttrains.co.uk.

London Midland

A member of the Go-Ahead Group

ADDRESS	PO Box 4323 Birmingham B2 4JB Telephone: 0121 634 2040 Website: www.londonmidland.com Email: comments@londonmidland.com
MANAGING DIRECTOR	Stephen Banaghan
RESERVATIONS AND TICKETS BY TELEPHONE	Tickets can be booked in advance on-line at www.londonmidland.com or by ringing 0845 602 4277, 0800-2000 Monday to Sunday. £5 minimum transaction, please allow 5 days for delivery.
RESERVATION DETAILS	Group travel enquiries and bookings can also be made on 0870 609 6060. Seat reservations are only available on our Birmingham–Liverpool route but are all free of charge with a valid rail ticket.
CATERING ON TRAINS	A trolley service of hot drinks and light refreshments is available for all or part of the journey on our Birmingham–Liverpool services and are indicated by a trolley symbol in the timetable pages.
CYCLES	Cycles are carried free of charge on most off-peak services, however, advance reservations are required for our Birmingham–Liverpool services. Cycles cannot be conveyed on trains arriving into London Euston between 0700 and 0959 and departing London Euston between 1600 and 1859 on Mondays to Fridays (excluding Bank Holidays). Folding cycles, completely folded down, are regarded as accompanied luggage and carried free.
LOST PROPERTY	Enquiries can be made at your nearest staffed station or by ringing Customer Relations on 0121 634 2040.
TRAIN SERVICE UPDATE	Available from National Rail Enquiries on 08457 48 49 50 (calls may be recorded for training purposes).
PENALTY FARES	A Penalty Fares system is in operation across the London Midland network. If you board a service from a staffed station without a valid ticket or permit to travel, you will be liable to a £20 penalty fare or twice the standard single fare to the next station whichever is the greater. You can only purchase a ticket on-train when travelling from an unstaffed station. Details of the scheme can be obtained by writing to Customer Relations at the address below.
DISABLED PERSON'S PROTECTION POLICY	Available from Customer Relations, London Midland PO Box 4323 Birmingham B2 4JB Telephone: 0121 634 2040
CODE OF PRACTICE FOR COMMENTS, COMPLAINTS AND SUGGESTIONS	Available from Customer Relations at the above address.

London Overground

LO

Operated by London Overground Rail Operations Ltd. (LOROL)
on behalf of Rail for London Ltd., a subsidiary of TfL

ADDRESS

125 Finchley Road
London NW3 6HY
Telephone: 0845 601 4867
Website: www.tfl.gov/overground
Email: info@lorol.co.uk

MANAGING DIRECTOR

Steve Murphy

RESERVATIONS AND TICKETS BY TELEPHONE

Tickets may be booked in advance and seats reserved on many long distance national rail services from most London Overground ticket offices. Oyster tickets may be purchased online from https://oyster.tfl.gov.uk

RESERVATION DETAILS

Seat reservations cannot be made for journeys on London Overground services.

CATERING ON TRAINS

Catering is not provided on London Overground services.

CYCLES

London Overground allows cycles on its trains and conveys them free of charge provided it is safe to do so. Due to space constraints, cycles are not permitted on services between Willesden Junction High Level and Gospel Oak and between Gospel Oak and Blackhorse Road in either direction between 0800–1000 and 1630–1830. On the Euston to Watford Line cycles are not permitted on London Overground services timed to arrive at London Euston between 0700–1000 or depart London Euston between 1630 and 1900. These restrictions apply on Mondays to Fridays only. There are no restrictions on Saturdays, Sundays and Bank Holidays. Folding bicycles can be carried on any London Overground Service at any time. Only one cycle is allowed per customer and this must be folded and within a limit of one cycle per vestibule area. Tandems and three-wheeled vehicles cannot be accommodated on any London Overground service. Cycles are not carried on buses that replace trains due to engineering work.

LOST PROPERTY

Please contact the TfL Lost Property Office at Baker Street on 0845 330 9882 or our Customer Services Team on 0845 601 4867.

TRAIN SERVICE UPDATE

Information about London Overground services and fares can be obtained by telephoning either:

- London Travel Information on 020 7222 1234 (Textphone 020 7918 3015)
- National Rail Enquiries 08457 48 49 50 (calls may be recorded for training purposes). (Textphone 08456 050 600, 0800-2000 daily)

A wide range of information about London Overground is also available from our website: www.tlf.gov/overground

PENALTY FARES

London Overground operates a Penalty Fares scheme. If you cannot produce, on request, a valid ticket for your entire journey or, when using Oyster to Pay as You Go, your Oyster card containing a record of the start of your Pay as You Go journey, you will be liable to pay a Penalty Fare of £20.00.

DISABLED PERSON'S PROTECTION POLICY

This can be obtained from our Customer Services Team at the above address.

CODE OF PRACTICE FOR COMMENTS, COMPLAINTS AND SUGGESTIONS

For a copy of the London Overground Passengers Charter please contact our Customer Services Team at the above address or ask for a copy at any London Overground station.

Merseyrail

A Serco/NedRailways company

ADDRESS	Rail House, Lord Nelson Street, Liverpool L1 1JF Telephone: 0151 702 2534 Fax: 0151 702 3074
MANAGING DIRECTOR	Bart Schmeink
RESERVATIONS AND TICKETS BY TELEPHONE	Tickets may be booked in advance and seats reserved from most Merseyrail stations for National Rail Services.
RESERVATION DETAILS	Not available.
CATERING ON TRAINS	Not available.
CYCLES	Cycles carried free of charge at any time, subject to sufficient space being available.
LOST PROPERTY	Please contact:- Station Supervisor James Street Station James Street Liverpool L2 7PQ Phone: 0151 702 2951
TRAIN SERVICE UPDATE	For current train information please call 08457 48 49 50 (calls may be recorded for training purposes). ***For details of Bank Holiday services see also the boxed note immediately preceding Table 103.***
PENALTY FARES	Please refer to notices displayed at stations for details of the penalty fare scheme in operation.
DISABLED PERSON'S PROTECTION POLICY	Available from:– Customer Relations Merseyrail Rail House, Lord Nelson Street, Liverpool L1 1JF Phone : 0151 702 2071 (Textphone 0870 0552 681) Fax : 0151 702 2413
CODE OF PRACTICE FOR COMMENTS, COMPLAINTS AND SUGGESTIONS	Available from above address

National Express East Anglia (NXEA)

LE

ADDRESS

Customer Services Centre, National Express East Anglia, Grosvenor House, 112-114 Prince of Wales Road, Norwich, NR1 1NS
Telephone: 0845 600 7245
Fax: 01603 214567
Website: www.nationalexpresseastanglia.com
Email: nxea.customerrelations@nationalexpress.com

MANAGING DIRECTOR

Andrew Chivers

RESERVATIONS AND TICKETS BY TELEPHONE

Tickets may be booked in advance by telephoning 0845 600 7245 between 0800 and 2200 (Mondays to Fridays) and 0900 and 1800 (weekends and Bank Holidays). For Business Travel, please telephone 0845 850 9080

RESERVATION DETAILS

NXEA offers seat reservations free of charge (except for season ticket holders) on main line services between London Liverpool Street and Norwich, and on direct services between London Liverpool Street and Lowestoft/Peterborough (via Ipswich).

CATERING ON TRAINS

Hot and cold drinks, sandwiches and light snacks are generally available on main line services between Norwich and London Liverpool Street and on Stansted Express services. In addition, full restaurant facilities are provided on some mainline services between Norwich and London.

CYCLES

Accompanied bicycles are conveyed free of charge on most NXEA services, but are not permitted on Stansted Express services at any time or on weekday peak services to and from London. A similar restriction also applies at Cambridge. On main line and rural services, the number of bicycles per train is limited, so a free reservation is recommended. For further details, please call NXEA customer services on 0845 600 7245.

LOST PROPERTY

If you have lost an item of property on one of our trains or stations, please contact NXEA customer services on 0845 600 7245 or email us at nxea.lostproperty@nationalexpress.com

TRAIN SERVICE UPDATE

For current train service information, please contact NXEA customer services on 0845 600 7245 or call our recorded information line on 020 7247 5488.

PENALTY FARES

NXEA operates a Penalty Fares System on most of its network, except from certain specified stations and on designated 'paytrain routes'. Stations within the Penalty Fares area are identified by warning notices at each entrance: when travelling from these stations, you must have a valid ticket for your journey. For journeys where Oyster Pay as you Go (PAYG) is accepted, you must touch in your Oyster card at the start of your journey. If travelling beyond the area where PAYG is accepted, you must have a valid ticket for the portion of the journey not covered by your Oyster card. If you cannot present a valid ticket for the journey you are making, you may be liable for a Penalty Fare (minimum £20).

DISABLED PERSON'S PROTECTION POLICY

Available from: Customer Services Centre, National Express East Anglia, Grosvenor House, 112-114 Prince of Wales Road, Norwich NR1 1NS.
Customers who require assistance are recommended to book at least 24 hours in advance through our Customer Services Centre on 0845 600 7245 or Textphone 0845 606 7245.

CODE OF PRACTICE FOR COMMENTS, COMPLAINTS AND SUGGESTIONS

Available from: Customer Services Centre, National Express East Anglia, Grosvenor House, 112-114 Prince of Wales Road, Norwich NR1 1NS. The NXEA Passenger's Charter is also available from the same address.

GR National Express East Coast (NXEC) GR

ADDRESS

Freepost YO352, York YO1 6ZZ
Telephone: 08457 225 225
Fax: 01904 524 532
Website: www.nationalexpress.com
Email: info@youreastcoast.co.uk

CHIEF EXECUTIVE OFFICER

David Franks

RESERVATIONS AND TICKETS BY TELEPHONE

Internet – purchase tickets via the internet 24 hours a day at www.nationalexpress.com.
Self service ticket machines – at all NXEC stations. Purchase tickets for today or collect pre-booked tickets.
Telesales – call 08457 225 225 – open Sunday-Thursday 0800 – 2200, Friday and Saturday 0800 – 2000. The minimum transaction is £10. Please allow 7 days from the time of booking for tickets to reach you through the post.
Business Travel – corporate credit card and account holder bookings – call 08457 225 225 – open Monday–Friday 0800 – 1800.
Group Travel – discounts are available for groups of 10 or more people – call 08457 225 225 – open Monday–Friday 0900 – 1800.

Seat reservations can only be made in conjunction with ticket purchases.

RESERVATION DETAILS

Complimentary seat reservations can usually be made on any NXEC train up to ten weeks in advance. They are available to any ticket holder upon request, and are compulsory with some ticket types. Only one reservation can be made per single journey.

CATERING ON TRAINS

Catering is available on all NXEC trains. There is a Buffet available on every service. The Restaurant is available on selected services from Monday–Friday, which are highlighted in the timetable. Website: www.nationalexpress.com.

CYCLES

Bicycles are welcome on NXEC at no extra cost. A reservation must be made and bookings are subject to space being available. Telephone 08457 225 225 or book at an NXEC ticket office. Folding cycles are welcome and no reservation is required for these.

LOST PROPERTY

If you lose something on an NXEC train or at a station please speak to a member of staff or contact us on 08457 225 333. Please note that charges are normally made for returning items of lost property. Please note that we are unable to forward items of lost property on train services.

TRAIN SERVICE UPDATE

Visit www.nationalexpress.com or call National Rail Enquiries on 08457 48 49 50 (calls may be recorded for training purposes).

PENALTY FARES

NXEC does not operate a Penalty Fares scheme. However, you should always purchase a ticket valid for travel before you board an NXEC service as only full fare tickets are sold on our trains. The only exception being Disabled Railcard holders who will be sold appropriate discounted tickets on board.

DISABLED PERSON'S PROTECTION POLICY

A copy of our DPPP can be obtained free of charge from the address at the top of this page.

Our Assisted Travel Team can help you plan your journey and organise tickets, assistance and seat reservations. To ensure the best possible levels of assistance we recommend contacting us at least 24 hours before you intend to travel. Telephone 08457 225 444 or textphone 08457 202 067 (open 7 days a week 0800-2000).

CODE OF PRACTICE FOR COMMENTS, COMPLAINTS AND SUGGESTIONS

Our Passenger's Charter is available free from all NXEC stations or from our website www.nationalexpress.com. All correspondence should be sent using the address at the top of this page.

North Yorkshire Moors Railway

NY

(Operators of the steam and heritage services between Whitby, Grosmont, Goathland and Pickering)

ADDRESS	Pickering Station, Pickering, North Yorkshire, YO18 7AJ Telephone: 01751-472508 (Customer Services and Information) Fax: 01751-476048 Website: www.nymr.co.uk Email: info@nymr.co.uk
GENERAL MANAGER	Philip Benham
RESERVATIONS AND TICKETS BY TELEPHONE	Telephone: 01751-472508 Hours of operation: 15 March to 2 November and other operating dates: 09:30-16:30 (Monday - Friday), 10:00-14:30 (Saturday and Sunday); All other times: 10:00-14:30 (Monday - Friday). At least 7 days should be allowed for receipt of tickets purchased by telephone. National Rail tickets can be booked in advance from our office in Whitby – telephone 01947 605872.
RESERVATION DETAILS	Reservations are not required on normal services. They can be made for groups of 20 or more passengers and are required on North Yorkshire Moors Railways dining train services (between Pickering and Grosmont).
CATERING ON TRAINS	An at seat trolley service of drinks and snacks is provided on most trains.
CYCLES	Cycles and dogs are carried for a charge of £2 (subject to space being available).
LOST PROPERTY	Enquiries about lost property should be made to Pickering Station at the above, or by telephone (01751-472508).
TRAIN SERVICE UPDATE	Updated train service information on all North Yorkshire Moors Railway is available on the website (see address above). A 'talking timetable' is also available giving current details of all North Yorkshire Moors Railway services by telephoning 01751-473535.
PENALTY FARES	Penalty fares are not in force on any North Yorkshire Moors Railway service.
DISABLED PERSON'S PROTECTION POLICY	Available from the address above, or Pickering and Grosmont Stations.
CODE OF PRACTICE FOR COMMENTS, COMPLAINTS AND SUGGESTIONS	North Yorkshire Moors Railway welcomes comments from passengers. Comments/suggestion cards are available from stations and on-board staff, or alternatively please write to the General Manager. Details of the company's policy are available from the above address, or Pickering and Grosmont Stations.

Northern

A Serco-NedRailways company

NT

ADDRESS

Northern Rail Ltd.,
Northern House
9 Rougier Street
York
YO1 6HZ
Telephone: 08700 005151
Website: www.northernrail.org

MANAGING DIRECTOR

Heidi Mottram

RESERVATIONS AND TICKETS BY TELEPHONE

Reservations and tickets are available from all local staffed stations.

RESERVATION DETAILS

Reservations are not required on Northern services.

For groups of 10 or more travelling together, telephone 01132 479 659.

For groups of 10 or more travelling on the Leeds-Settle-Carlisle line, blocks of seats will be reserved wherever possible. Telephone 0800 9800 766, between 0900 and 1700 on Mondays to Fridays to make a booking.

All accommodation on Northern trains is standard class.

CATERING ON TRAINS

On most Leeds-Settle-Carlisle services, food and drink can be purchased from the trolley which will pass through the train.

CYCLES

Up to two cycles can be carried on each service. This is subject to space being available, however, and cannot be booked in advance. For further details telephone 0845 000 0125.

LOST PROPERTY

Call 0870 602 3322, contact your nearest staffed station or write to Northern at the address below.

TRAIN SERVICE UPDATE

Information about Northern services and fares can be obtained by telephoning: **08457 48 49 50** (calls may be recorded for training purposes) or access the website on www.nationalrail.co.uk.

For more information on our services, please visit our website on www.northernrail.org

The latest information on train running is available by phoning TrainTracker™ from National Rail Enquiries on 0871 200 4915 or by texting TrainTracker™. Text to 484950.

PENALTY FARES

Penalty fares are not in force on any Northern service.

DISABLED PERSON'S PROTECTION POLICY

If you would like a copy of Northern's Policy or wish to arrange assistance for your journey, please phone: 0845 600 8008. (Textphone 0845 604 5608) or by writing to Customer Relations, Northern, PO Box 208, Leeds LS1 2BU, or email: assistance@northernrail.org.

CODE OF PRACTICE FOR COMMENTS, COMPLAINTS AND SUGGESTIONS

Please contact our Customer Helpline on 0845 000 0125, a textphone is available on 0845 604 5608. Alternatively you can write to us at: Customer Relations, Northern, PO Box 208, Leeds LS1 2BU.

If you would like a copy of the Northern Passenger's Charter, or Northern's Guide for Customers with Disabilities please contact our Customer Relations team.

South West Trains

ADDRESS
Friars Bridge Court, 41–45 Blackfriars Road, London SE1 8NZ
Telephone: 08700 005151 Fax: 020 7620 5177
Website: www.southwesttrains.co.uk
Email: customerrelations@swtrains.co.uk

CHAIRMAN
Ian Dobbs

MANAGING DIRECTOR
Stewart Palmer

RESERVATIONS AND TICKETS BY TELEPHONE
Tickets may be booked in advance and seats reserved by telephone, on the following number:

0845 6000 650.

Tickets may also be purchased via the South West Trains' website (see above). When ordering, please allow 5 working days for ticket delivery.

RESERVATION DETAILS
On many South West Trains' main line services (excluding peak time commuter services) seats can be reserved free of charge in First and Standard Class.

CATERING ON TRAINS
Catering on South West Trains is provided on those services marked with the symbol ☕ for all or part of the journey. Catering may be provided from a buffet area, at seat trolley service or a combination of both according to the route and time of day. All catering on South West Trains' services is provided in partnership with our contractors, Rail Gourmet (UK) Ltd. Comments on the service should be sent to the Customer Service Centre at the address below.

CYCLES
A limited number of cycles can be carried on most of our services except during the Monday to Friday peak periods. Restrictions apply on certain routes into and out of London Waterloo between 0715 and 1000 and between 1645 and 1900. At all times some services require advance reservations, as space is limited.

To obtain full details of South West Trains Cycling Policy and full details of routes and times when cycles are not carried visit www.southwesttrains.co.uk, pick up a leaflet from stations served by South West Trains or contact our Customer Service Centre at the address shown.

Cycles that can be folded to a size which allows them to be carried safely in the luggage racks on our services may be carried folded at all times.

For reasons of safety and comfort of our passengers, if the available identified cycle spaces on the train are already taken, the guard has the right to refuse to carry any further cycles on that train.

LOST PROPERTY
A lost property helpline is available between 0730-1900 Mondays to Fridays by calling 020 7401 7861

TRAIN SERVICE UPDATE
For current train information, please call our helpline on 0845 6000 650 or visit www.southwesttrains.co.uk

For details of Bank Holiday services see also the boxed note on the page immediately preceding Table 149.

PENALTY FARES
South West Trains has a duty to its fare paying passengers to ensure no-one travels for free. To this end South West Trains operates a penalty fares scheme across its network, with the only exceptions being stations west of Salisbury and Dean, Mottisfont & Dunbridge, Romsey and Chandlers Ford.

Passengers travelling to and from stations within the penalty fares area without a valid ticket may be liable to a penalty of £20 or twice the single fare to the next station at which their train stops (whichever is the greater).

DISABLED PERSON'S PROTECTION POLICY
For a copy of this publication, please contact the Customer Service Centre at the address below.

Assistance for mobility impaired passengers can be arranged by telephoning 0800 5282 100 between 0600 - 2200 daily. Please give at least 24 hours notice.

A textphone facility is available on 0800 6920 792 (calls are charged at local rates).

CODE OF PRACTICE FOR COMMENTS, COMPLAINTS AND SUGGESTIONS
Copies of South West Trains' Passenger's Charter are available from any staffed station or by writing to:
Customer Service Centre, South West Trains, Overline House, Blechynden Terrace, Southampton SO15 1GW
Telephone 0845 6000 650. Fax 023 8072 8187
Email: customerrelations@swtrains.co.uk

The Passenger's Charter is also available on our website www.southwesttrains.co.uk

Southeastern

SE

ADDRESS

Southeastern Customer Services, PO Box 286, Plymouth PL4 6WU
Telephone: 0845 000 2222
Assisted Travel: 0800 783 4524
Fax: 0845 678 6976
Textphone: 0800 783 4548

Website: www.southeasternrailway.co.uk

This customer service centre is staffed 24 hours a day, seven days a week (closed Christmas Day). Comments and complaints are dealt with here by post, fax, and web as well as on the telephone.

MANAGING DIRECTOR

Charles Horton

RESERVATIONS AND TICKETS BY TELEPHONE

Group travel (parties of 10 persons or more) on Southeastern services must be booked at least seven days in advance so that space can be allocated. To order, go to www.southeasternrailway.co.uk, select tickets, then group tickets then complete the online form.

Customers can renew six monthly and annual season tickets online at www.southeasternrailway.co.uk or at local stations. Payment may be made by debit card and by most major credit and charge cards (NB customers must hold a rail photocard).

For new monthly season ticket purchases, please complete an application form available at local stations or online at www.southeasternrailway.co.uk.

A business and continental travel and reservations account service is available from Network Business Travel Service at First Floor Offices, Cannon Street Station, London EC4N 6AP.

To open an account telephone 020 7904 0500 or visit www.nbts.co.uk

RESERVATIONS

Reservations are only needed on Southeastern services for Group Travel and mobility impaired customers who require assistance.

CATERING ON TRAINS

A light refreshment trolley is available on trains marked with ⚻.

CYCLES

Cycles are not permitted on peak time services, which are those timed to arrive in London terminals between 0700 and 0959, and those timed to leave between 1600 and 1859. Folding cycles are permitted provided they are folded.

LOST PROPERTY

Customers who have lost property on a train or at a station should contact Southeastern Customer Services on 0845 000 2222.

TRAIN SERVICE UPDATE

For current train running information contact Southeastern Customer Services on 0845 000 2222

Information is also available from national and local radio station travel updates on Ceefax page 433, and from our website: www.southeasternrailway.co.uk, select plan my journey.

PENALTY FARES

Please check notices displayed at stations for details of any penalty fares or other revenue protection systems in operation on Southeastern services.

DISABLED PERSON'S PROTECTION POLICY

Copies of the Disabled Person's Protection Policy are available from Southeastern Customer Services.
If you have any special needs and would like help with planning your journey anywhere in Great Britain please call 0800 783 4524 or use the Textphone 0800 783 4548 - open 24 hours a day.

The Southeastern Assisted Travel team will offer advice and make any special arrangements you need. If at least 24 hours' notice can be given, this will be very much appreciated.

CODE OF PRACTICE FOR COMMENTS, COMPLAINTS AND SUGGESTIONS

Southeastern Passengers' Charter leaflets are available at any Southeastern sales point or Southeastern Customer Services at the address shown above.

SN Southern SN

ADDRESS

Southern Customer Services, PO Box 277, Tonbridge TN9 2ZP
Telephone: 08451 27 29 20 (Customer Services)
Fax: 08451 27 29 30 (Customer Services)
Website: www.southernrailway.com

MANAGING DIRECTOR

Chris Burchell

RESERVATIONS AND TICKETS BY TELEPHONE

It is not necessary to pre-book on Southern services.

RESERVATION DETAILS

Reservations are not required, as Southern offer a high frequency train service.

CATERING ON TRAINS

A light refreshment of food and drinks is available on trains marked with.

CYCLES

A limited number of cycles are carried on all services except on trains due to arrive into London and Brighton on Mondays to Fridays between 0700 and 1000, or due to depart from London Stations and Brighton between 1600 and 1900 Mondays to Fridays.

LOST PROPERTY

Please call Southern Customer Services on 08451 27 29 20.

TRAIN SERVICE UPDATE

For current train information call Customer Services on 08451 27 29 20 or check our website at www.southernrailway.com

PENALTY FARES

Southern operate a Penalty Fares Scheme on all routes. You must buy a valid ticket (or permit to travel) for your journey before boarding a train. If you do not have a valid ticket or permit to travel, you may have to pay a Penalty Fare of £20.00 or twice the single fare, whichever is the greater. Please pick up a Penalty Fare leaflet from a staffed station for your information.

DISABLED PERSON'S PROTECTION POLICY

Available from Southern Customer Services at P.O. Box 277, Tonbridge TN9 2ZP. Disabled and Special needs assistance on 0800 138 1016; minicom/ textphone - 0800 138 1018; Fax - 0800 138 1017.

CODE OF PRACTICE FOR COMMENTS, COMPLAINTS AND SUGGESTIONS

Write to Southern Customer Services at the above address.
Copies of Southern Passenger's charter are available from any staffed stations. You can also obtain a copy by contacting Customer Services or from Southern's website.

VT **Virgin Trains** VT

The trading name of West Coast Trains Ltd

ADDRESS	Virgin Trains, 85 Smallbrook Queensway, Birmingham B5 4HA Telephone: 0845 000 8000 Textphone: 0121 654 7528 Website: www.virgintrains.com Email: customer.relations@virgintrains.co.uk
CHIEF EXECUTIVE	Tony Collins
MANAGING DIRECTOR	Chris Gibb
RESERVATIONS AND TICKETS BY TELEPHONE	Buy tickets for Virgin Trains and any other train company in Great Britain on the internet at www.virgintrains.com or by calling 08457 222 333 - between 0800 and 2200 7 days a week. If you have a disability or have specific needs and wish to arrange assistance on your journey call the Virgin Trains JourneyCare service on 08457 44 33 66 (Textphone 08457 44 33 67) between 0800 and 2200 every day except Christmas Day or Boxing Day.
RESERVATION DETAILS	You are strongly advised to make a seat reservation in advance. Reservations can be made for the Quiet Zone carriage, where customers should refrain from using mobile phones or creating unnecessary noise. On routes to and from London, Standard Class Quiet Zone is in coach A and in coach H for First Class. On other routes, Quiet Zone is located in Standard Class, coach F. Seat reservations are free of charge.
CATERING ON TRAINS	In First Class on a Pendolino from Monday to Friday customers can enjoy a selection of hot or cold snacks throughout the day, including a cooked breakfast on many morning peak services. In addition, Fairtrade tea, Fairtrade coffee, soft drinks and alcoholic drinks (alcohol not served with breakfast services) and a newspaper are served at seat throughout the day. In First Class on Voyager from Monday to Friday customers can enjoy complimentary light refreshments on all trains including Fairtrade tea, Fairtrade coffee, soft drinks and a newspaper with an at-seat service available. In Standard Class, we have a wide range of snacks and sandwiches, Fairtrade teas, fresh ground Fairtrade coffee, soft and alcoholic drinks and a selection of non-food items available at our onboard shop. The shop is generally open throughout. Pendolinos offer an at-seat trolley service to standard class customers on Mondays to Fridays. For more information about our onboard service pick up a copy of Travelling with Virgin Trains.
CYCLES	Subject to availability of space cycles can be carried on all trains. Most trains can carry 3 cycles, and on journeys to and from London Euston, Pendolinos can carry tandems (however, tandems are not carried on Voyager services). An advance reservation is required for all journeys.
LOST PROPERTY	Call Customer Relations on 0845 000 8000 – 0830 to 2015 Mondays to Fridays, 0900 to 1600 Saturdays, answerphone available at all other times.
TRAIN SERVICE UPDATE	Details of any disruption to services or weekend engineering work are summarised on BBC Ceefax and on BBCi on digital TV. Details of Engineering work can also be found at www.virgintrains.com.
PENALTY FARES	Penalty Fares are not applicable on any Virgin Trains service.
DISABLED PERSON'S PROTECTION POLICY	Our Customer Relations Manager (at the address above) will be pleased to supply a free copy of the Disabled Person's Protection Policy. It can also be downloaded at www.virgintrains.com. For information on station accessibility and to arrange special help please contact Virgin Trains JourneyCare (details above).
CODE OF PRACTICE FOR COMMENTS, COMPLAINTS AND SUGGESTIONS	We want you to tell us what you think of our service, good or bad. A copy of our Code of Practice for handling comments, complaints and suggestions together with Virgin Trains Passenger's Charter is available free on request from our Customer Relations Manager at the above address.

WR West Coast Railway Company WR

(Operators of the Fort William - Mallaig "Jacobite" Steam Service)

ADDRESS	Jesson Way, Carnforth, Lancashire LA5 9UR Telephone: 01524 737751/737753 Fax: 01524 735518 Website: www.steamtrain.info or www.wcrc.co.uk Email: jacobite@wcrc.co.uk
GENERAL MANAGER	Mrs Pat Marshall
COMMERCIAL MANAGER	James Shuttleworth
RESERVATIONS AND TICKETS BY TELEPHONE	Advance bookings can be made, by post (enclose SAE) to the Carnforth Office (address above) or by telephone on 01524 737751/737753, during normal office hours. Credit cards accepted. 'Jacobite' bookings can also be made in person at the Booking Office, Fort William Station.
RESERVATION DETAILS	Phone 01524 737751/737753
CATERING ON TRAINS	A buffet service, serving hot and cold drinks and cold snacks is available on all trains.
CYCLES	Cycles carried free-of-charge subject to space.
LOST PROPERTY	Telephone: 01524 737751/737753
PENALTY FARES	Penalty fares are not in force on any West Coast Railway Co. service.
TRAIN SERVICE UPDATE	For current train information please phone 08457 48 49 50 (calls may be recorded for training purposes).
DISABLED PERSON'S PROTECTION POLICY	Available from the above address.
CODE OF PRACTICE FOR COMMENTS, COMPLAINTS AND SUGGESTIONS	West Coast Railway Co. welcomes comments on services provided. Write to Carnforth office (address above).

Wrexham & Shropshire

WS

ADDRESS	Great Central House, Marylebone Station, Melcombe Place, London NW1 6JJ Telephone: 0845 260 5233 Website: www.wrexhamandshropshire.co.uk Email: info@wrexhamandshropshire.co.uk
MANAGING DIRECTOR	Andy Hamilton
RESERVATIONS AND TICKETS BY TELEPHONE	Wrexham & Shropshire tickets can be bought in advance and seats reserved. Full details will be available on the Wrexham & Shropshire website www.wrexhamandshropshire.co.uk in advance of the launch of train services.
RESERVATION DETAILS	All First and Standard Class seats are reservable at no charge.
CATERING ON TRAINS	Wrexham & Shropshire provides a comprehensive range of catering on all services. Full details will be available on the website www.wrexhamandshropshire.co.uk in advance of the launch of train services.
CYCLES	Cycles are carried free of charge.
LOST PROPERTY	Please contact the above address.
TRAIN SERVICE UPDATE	Available at www.wrexhamandshropshire.co.uk
PENALTY FARES	Wrexham & Shropshire does not operate a penalty fares policy.
DISABLED PERSON'S PROTECTION POLICY	Please contact the above address.
CODE OF PRACTICE FOR COMMENTS, COMPLAINTS AND SUGGESTIONS	Please contact the above address.

Wrexham & Shropshire services are expected to start operating during the currency of this timetable. Please visit the Wrexham & Shropshire website www.wrexhamandshropshire.co.uk for updated information.

Network Rail

NR

ADDRESS 40 Melton Street, London NW1 2EE
Telephone: 020 7557 8000
Fax: 020 7557 9000
Website: www.networkrail.co.uk

CHIEF EXECUTIVE Iain Coucher

Network Rail is responsible for operating 18 managed stations, indicated in the index by the code **NR**. Details of facilities provided, including the Disabled Peoples Protection Policy, are obtainable from the Network Rail Station Manager at the following station addresses:–

London Bridge	Network Rail Offices, Platform 14, London Bridge Station, Station Approach, London SE1 9SP.
London Cannon Street	Cannon Street Station, Cannon Street, London EC4N 6AP.
London Charing Cross	Network Rail Offices, Charing Cross Station, The Strand, London WC2 5HS.
London Euston	Room 430, Stephenson Room, East Colonnade, Euston, London NW1 2RT.
London Fenchurch Street	Network Rail Office, Fenchurch Place, London EC3M 4AJ.
London Kings Cross	Room 101, West Side Offices, Kings Cross Station, London N1 9AP.
London Liverpool Street	Ashbee House, Platform 10, Liverpool Street Station, London EC2M 7QH.
London Paddington	Room B115, Tournament House, Paddington Station, London W2 1FT.
London Victoria	3rd Floor, Kent Side Offices, Victoria Station, London SW1V 1JU.
London Waterloo	CP3-1-J General Offices, Waterloo Station, London SE1 8SW.
Birmingham New Street	Reception, Network Rail Offices, Station Forecourt, Birmingham New Street Station, Birmingham B2 4ND.
Edinburgh Waverley	Room 255, North Block, Waverley Station, Edinburgh EH1 1BB.
Gatwick Airport	Gatwick Station Manager, Gatwick Airport Station, Gatwick Airport, Sussex RH6 0RD.
Glasgow Central	Glasgow Central Station, Gordon Street, Glasgow G1 3SL.
Leeds City	Room 405, Administration Block, Leeds City Station, Leeds LS1 4DY.
Manchester Piccadilly	Room 622, Tower Block, Piccadilly Station, Manchester M60 7RA.
Liverpool Lime Street	Station Manager, The Barrier Line Building, Liverpool Lime Street Station, Liverpool L1 1JF.
St Pancras	Station Reception, St Pancras International Station, St Pancras Road, London NW1 2QP.

Staffed Left Luggage facilities, offering maximum security, are available at all Network Rail Stations.

If you wish to raise any issue concerning the rail infrastructure or the 18 managed stations operated by Network Rail (excluding matters concerning the running of trains or ticket purchase) please call the national 24 hour Helpline:- **08457 11 41 41**

Other Addresses

Department for Transport

Great Minster House, 76 Marsham Street, London SW1P 4DR

Telephone: 020 7944 8300

Email: rail@dft.gsi.gov.uk

Office of Rail Regulation

One Kemble Street, London WC2B 4AN
Telephone: 020 7282 2000 Fax: 020 7282 2040

Chairman: Chris Bolt

The main areas of the Regulator's statutory functions are:

- the issue, modification and enforcement of licences to operate trains, networks, stations and light maintenance depots;
- the approval of agreements for access by operators of railway assets to track, stations and light maintenance depots;
- the enforcement of domestic competition law; and consumer protection including a duty under the Railways Act 1993 in relation to the protection of the interests of users of railway services, including the disabled.

Publications are available from:

Sue MacSwan, The Library, ORR, 1 Waterhouse Square, 138–142 Holborn, London EC1N 2TQ (Telephone: 020 7282 2001). Email: rail.library@orr.gsi.gov.uk

Association of Train Operating Companies (ATOC)

3rd Floor, 40 Bernard Street, London WC1N 1BY. Telephone: 020 7841 8000

Director General: George Muir

ATOC represents the interests of most of the national and international passenger Train Operating Companies whose services are shown in this timetable. It manages a range of network services, products and responsibilities on behalf of these train operators including:

- the National Rail Conditions of Carriage (the passenger's contract with the train operators)
- the National Rail Enquiry Service
- the licensing of rail appointed travel agents
- national Railcards, the London Travelcard and Network Railcard.

London Underground Limited

55 Broadway, London SW1H 0BD Telephone: 020 7222 5600

Responsible for the operation of stations indicated in the index by the code **LT**

How to Cross London

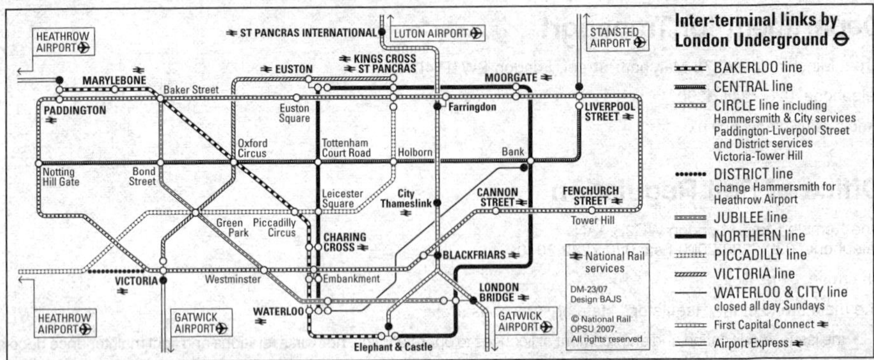

Introduction

The time taken to travel between London's stations will vary from journey to journey dependent on distance, mode of transport, time of day and the need to change en route. The quickest way to cross London is usually by the Underground network with frequent services operating between the following hours*:

- 0530 to 0015 on Monday to Friday
- 0630 to 0115 on Saturday
- 0700 to 0001 on Sunday

(* Times shown are approximate)

Buses also link many of London's main terminal stations including an extensive network of Night Bus services.

Ticket & Fares

Rail tickets for journeys routed via London are valid for transfer by London Underground or First Capital Connect services between London terminal stations, and other designated interchange stations* appropriate to the route of the through journey being made, at no extra cost. For example a Brighton to Leeds ticket is valid on London Underground services from Victoria to Kings Cross (Victoria Line), or alternatively on First Capital Connect services to St Pancras International. A Chelmsford to Southampton ticket is valid on London Underground services to Waterloo via either Liverpool Street (Circle Line) or Stratford (Jubilee Line).

(*NB. check before you travel which cross London routes your ticket is valid for before you travel. A break of journey is permitted at an intermediate Underground station, but a further ticket must be purchased in order to continue the journey)

London's Fare Zones – National Rail, Underground and Docklands Light Railway (DLR) stations within the Greater London area are in one of six Fare Zones. Single and return tickets are available for through journeys to and from all Underground and DLR stations with prices determined by the number of zones crossed or travelled through.

A range of day and longer period Travelcards are also available and provide unlimited travel on National Rail, London Underground, Docklands Light Railway and Croydon Tramlink services within the Fare Zones for which they are valid. All Travelcards, irrespective of the zones for which they are issued, can also be used on any London bus displaying this sign ⊖.

For information on ticket prices and availability contact your local staffed station, call National Rail Enquiries anytime on **08457 48 49 50*** (Textphone **0845 60 50 600**), or visit www.nationalrail.co.uk. * Calls may be recorded for training purposes.

More detailed information about London's Underground and Bus services, also Docklands Light Railway and Croydon Tramlink is available anytime from London Travel Information on **020 7222 1234** (textphone **020 7918 3015**) or visit **www.tfl.gov.uk**.

First Capital Connect

First Capital Connect operates fast, direct services from Bedford, Luton and St Albans via Central London to East Croydon, Gatwick Airport and Brighton and stopping trains between Luton, St Albans, North London, the City, Streatham, Wimbledon and Sutton. There are nine Central London First Capital Connect stations with Underground connections. First Capital Connect connects with East Midlands Trains at Luton, Luton Airport Parkway and Bedford – see Tables 52 and 53.

London Overground

Trains run daily between Willesden Junction, Kensington Olympia, West Brompton and Clapham Junction on Mondays to Sundays – see Table 186.

Southern Services

Direct services are provided from Brighton, Gatwick Airport and South London to Watford Junction. These services also call at West Brompton and Kensington Olympia. Connections for Birmingham and the West Midlands, also for North West destinations (including Manchester, Liverpool and Preston) and Glasgow are available from Watford Junction. Full details are shown on tables 66 and 186. Frequent connections from Clapham Junction or East Croydon for the rest of the Southern Network are available.

Cross London Transfer Times (in minutes)

	Blackfriars	Cannon Street	Charing Cross	Euston	Farringdon	Fenchurch Street*	Kings Cross	Liverpool Street	London Bridge	Marylebone	Paddington	St. Pancras International †	Victoria	Waterloo
Blackfriars	–	23	23	49	(b)	27	(b)	40	(b)	45	49	(b)	29	40
Cannon Street	23	–	34	60	44	30	55	43	(a)	56	60	58	40	51
Charing Cross	23	34	–	44	n/a	38	50	51	(a)	38	43	52	32	(a)
Euston	49	60	44	–	n/a	57	35	43	52	51	43	38	39	53
Farringdon	(b)	44	n/a	n/a	–	40	n/a	29	(b)	45	39	n/a	n/a	n/a
Fenchurch Street*	27	30	38	57	40	–	52	26	47	68	60	52	53	56
Kings Cross	(b)	55	50	35	n/a	52	–	41	50	50	45	30	41	55
Liverpool Street	40	43	51	43	29	26	41	–	49	56	55	41	57	62
London Bridge	(b)	(a)	(a)	52	(b)	47	50	49	–	58	62	60	n/a	(a)
Marylebone	45	56	38	51	45	68	50	56	58	–	32	53	43	47
Paddington	49	60	43	43	39	60	45	55	62	32	–	45	47	51
St. Pancras International †	(b)	58	52	38	n/a	52	30	41	60	53	45	–	41	61
Victoria	29	40	32	39	n/a	53	41	57	n/a	43	47	41	–	47
Waterloo	40	51	(a)	53	n/a	56	55	62	(a)	47	51	61	47	–

All times are based on use of London Underground services and are shown as a guide only – extra time should be allowed during the early morning/late evening and on Sundays.

* Tower Hill Underground station
† An additional 35 minutes should be allowed for Eurostar Connections
(a) Direct train services available (operated by Southeastern)
(b) Direct train services available (operated by First Capital Connect)
n/a Transfer not likely to be required as part of a through rail journey.

Some other useful transfers

If your journey requires a transfer between any of the following pairs of stations, you should allow a margin of at least the number of minutes shown when planning connections. All transfers are assumed to be by foot unless otherwise stated.

Abercynon North – South	10
Ash Vale – North Camp	19
Bicester North – Town	30
Burnley Central – Manchester Rd	25
Burscough Bridge – Junction	20
Canterbury East – West	25
Catford – Bridge	10
Clock House – Kent House	15
Dorchester South – West	15
Dorking – Deepdene	9
Edenbridge – Town	20
Enfield Chase – Town	29
Falkirk High – Grahamston	44
Farnborough Main – North	24
Forest Gate – Wanstead Park	13
Gainsborough Central – Lea Rd	33
Hackney Central – Downs	14
Harringay – Green Lanes	14
Heath High Level – Low Level	10
Hertford North – East	34
Maidstone Barracks – East	16
New Mills Central – Newtown	25
Penge East – West	19
Seven Sisters – South Tottenham	14
Southend Central – Victoria	17
Upper Warlingham – Whyteleafe	10
Walthamstow Central – Queens Rd	14
West Hampstead – Thameslink	11
Windsor & Eton Central – Riverside	14
Yeovil Junction – Pen Mill	60*

* There are no direct links by public transport between Yeovil Junction and Yeovil Pen Mill stations. Passengers are advised to seek alternative arrangements and should allow 60 minutes to make this connection.

Tyne and Wear Metro

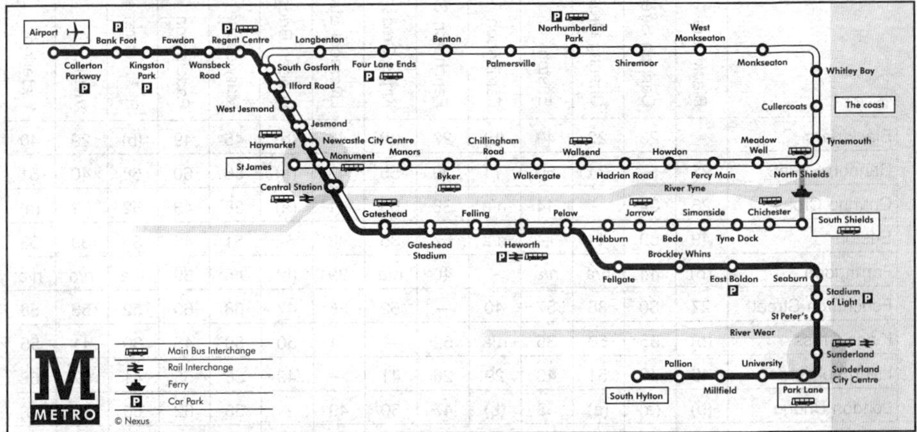

Summary Timetable

Route	Service Frequencies				
	Mon-Fri Peak	Mon-Fri Daytime	Saturday Daytime	Sunday Daytime	Evenings Daily
Airport - Monument - Pelaw - Sunderland - South Hylton	12 mins	12 mins	12 mins	15 mins	15 mins
St.James - Whitley Bay - Monument - Pelaw - South Shields	12 mins	12 mins	12 mins	15 mins	15 mins

First and last Metro trains to and from Newcastle Central Station

From Central Station to:	First Train Mon-Fri	First Train Saturday	First Train Sunday	Last Train Daily
South Hylton	0521	0524	0621	2305
Sunderland	0517	0517	0621	2320
Pelaw	0514	0517	0616	2342
South Shields	0524	0521	0634	2327
Tynemouth (via Benton)	0548	0557	0656	2337
Whitley Bay (via North Shields)	0548 ❏	0557 ❏	0656 ❏	2329 ❏
Airport	0557	0619	0641	2329

❏ Change at Monument

To Central Station from:	First Train Mon-Fri	First Train Saturday	First Train Sunday	Last Train Daily
South Hylton	0604	0605	0704	2346
Sunderland	0542	0552	0714	2356
Pelaw	0548	0549	0633	0015
South Shields	0545	0551	0703	2356
Tynemouth (via Benton)	0535	0538	0633	2310
Whitley Bay (via North Shields)	0541 ❏	0552 ❏	0636 ❏	2304 ❏
Airport	0548	0542	0627	2312

❏ Change at Monument

Ticketing

- Interchangeable tickets for both Rail and Metro are available between Sunderland and Newcastle Central Station.
- Tyne and Wear operates a Penalty Fare policy.

Information

For all travel information call
traveline public transport info
0871 200 22 33 north east
For timetable information visit **www.nexus.org.uk**

Airport Links

Aberdeen Airport

Dyce station is situated close to Aberdeen Airport and is served by services between Aberdeen and Inverness. Taxis are available - journey time approx. 5 minutes. In addition there are several through trains daily to and from Glasgow and Edinburgh (see Table 229). Journey time by taxi is 20 minutes approx. from Aberdeen Station.

Birmingham International Airport

Birmingham Airport is alongside Birmingham International station. The free Air-Rail Link transit system operates to the passenger terminals about every 2 minutes with a journey time of less than 2 minutes. Birmingham International station is served by direct trains from London Euston, Derby, Edinburgh, Glasgow, Manchester, Newcastle, Oxford, Sheffield, Southampton, York and other principal towns and cities. In addition a frequent service operates between Birmingham New Street and Birmingham International providing connections at Birmingham New Street to and from all parts of the country. (See Tables 65, 66, 68, 71, 74 and 116). Regular buses operated by Travel West Midlands (966) also run from Solihull station (see Tables 71 and 115). The journey time is approximately 20 minutes and through ticketing is available. Solihull is served by Chiltern Railways services from London Marylebone, Gerrards Cross, Beaconsfield, High Wycombe, Princes Risborough, Haddenham & Thame Parkway, Bicester North, Banbury, Leamington Spa and Warwick and by London Midland local services.

Bristol International Airport

First runs a frequent coach service from directly outside Bristol Temple Meads station. It departs every 15 minutes between 0600-1930 and at a reduced frequency between 0300-0600 and 1930-midnight. The journey time is approximately 25 minutes depending on traffic and further information is available from Traveline on **0871 200 22 33** or visit **www.traveline.org.uk.**

Cardiff International Airport

The airport is served by bus service X45 and is operated by Shamrock on Mon-Sat and First on Sundays. This operates on an hourly daytime frequency to/from Barry station, Monday to Saturday. Journey time is 7 minutes. Cardiff bus service (X91) provides an hourly daytime service from Cardiff Central Bus Station (stop E1) direct to Cardiff International Airport. Services run every hour Monday to Saturday daytimes and every 2 hours on Sundays. Journey time is 30 minutes and through ticketing is available from any rail station.

The airport is served by a free bus link from Rhoose Cardiff International Airport Station to/from the airport operated by Arriva Trains Wales. Full details of the timetable and further information can be obtained from Traveline on **0871 200 22 33** or visit **www.traveline.org.uk.**

Coventry Airport

Coventry Airport is accessible from Coventry rail station by a scheduled bus service (No. 737). A combined discounted bus and rail ticket can be purchased for travel to the airport.

For bus times call **0871 200 22 33** or visit **www.traveline.org.uk.**

Durham Tees Valley Airport

Darlington Railway station is situated just 5 miles away. Sky Express Tees Valley is a frequent dedicated shuttle bus which operates between Darlington Railway station and the airport terminal building, between 0700 and 2000. The service is free to airline passengers. Visit **www.durhamteesvalleyairport.com**.

East Midlands Airport

Bus services operate from Derby, Loughborough and Nottingham stations to East Midlands Airport. Journey times are approx 35 mins from Derby, 30 mins from Loughborough and Nottingham. A combined discounted bus and rail ticket is available from any station for travel to East Midlands Airport.

Derby is served by CrossCountry and East Midlands Trains direct services from Central and Southern England, South Wales, South Yorkshire and North Eastern England.

Loughborough is served by East Midlands Trains services from Leicester, London and the Home Counties.

Nottingham is served by East Midlands Trains services from London, North Western England, Lincolnshire, East Anglia and the West Midlands.

Combined rail and discounted bus tickets are available when travelling from Nottingham, Loughborough and Derby Stations.

For details of bus times call **01509 815637** or visit **www.kinchbus.co.uk** for Derby and Loughborough services, call **0115 950 6070** or visit **www.skylink.co.uk** for Nottingham services.

Edinburgh Airport

A frequent bus service (No. 100) links Edinburgh Waverley and Haymarket stations with Edinburgh Airport. Journey time is approx. 25 minutes. Stagecoach operate a 747 service half hourly during the day, hourly evenings and Sundays between Inverkeithing and Edinburgh Airport. Through ticketing is available. For further information telephone **0131 555 6363**.

Exeter International Airport

Stagecoach operates an hourly daytime service (56 Monday - Saturday, 379 Sundays) from Exeter St. Davids station forecourt direct to Exeter Airport. For more information call Traveline on **0871 200 22 33** or visit **www.traveline.org.uk.**

Airport Links

Glasgow Airport

Regular direct bus services are available to and from Glasgow Airport from the city centre (Central/Queen Street), Paisley Gilmour Street and Partick stations from early morning to late evening daily. Through bus/rail tickets are available between any station and Glasgow Airport via the Paisley Gilmour Street bus link, city centre bus link and First Glasgow bus service via Partick.

For further information on these services please contact the Strathclyde Passenger Transport Travel Centre at Glasgow Airport, on **0141 887 1111** or **0141 848 4330.**

Leeds Bradford International Airport

Leeds Bradford International Airport is located to the north of the cities of Bradford and Leeds, to the south of the spa town of Harrogate and to the west of the historic city of York. For more information on Leeds Bradford International Airport visit **www.lbia.co.uk**

From Leeds a direct bus service, MetroConnect 757, operates half hourly throughout the day Mondays to Saturdays (hourly early mornings, evenings and Sundays) every day from Stand S8 from outside Leeds Rail Station (Leeds Station Interchange). The journey time is approximately 40 minutes. Through ticketing is available.

From Bradford a half hourly direct bus service, MetroConnect 747, operates throughout the day Mondays to Saturdays (hourly evenings and Sundays) from Bradford Interchange and Forster Square rail stations. The journey time from Bradford is approximately 40 minutes. Through ticketing is available with a PlusBus ticket.

From Harrogate a direct bus service, Bus2Jet 767, operates daily from Harrogate, from Stand 11 in the Bus Station, to the airport. The journey time from Harrogate is approximately 35 minutes. Through ticketing is available with a PlusBus ticket.

From York an hourly direct express coach service operates daily from outside York Rail Station to the airport. The journey time from York is approximately 55 minutes. For more information telephone **01904 883 000** or visit **www.yorkaircoach.com**

For further information on the above services please telephone MetroLine **0113 245 7676** or visit **www.wymetro.com**.

Liverpool John Lennon Airport

The airport is located to the south of the city centre. A direct bus service operates between Lime Street, Moorfields and James Street stations to the airport seven days a week. Buses run every 30 minutes between 0600 & 0100 hours from the Liverpool City Centre Stations to the Airport, and between 0515 and 0015 from the Airport to the Liverpool City Centre Stations. Journey time is approximately 45 minutes. In addition regular bus services operate between Liverpool John Lennon Airport and the new Liverpool South Parkway station; journey time is 15 minutes. Liverpool South Parkway is served by direct services from North, South and East Liverpool, Manchester, Warrington, Southport, Crewe, Stafford, Wolverhampton and Birmingham. For further information please contact **0871 200 22 33,** or visit **www.traveline.org.uk**.

London City Airport

London City Airport is located in London's Docklands. There are no National Rail services direct to the airport. However the Docklands Light Railway (DLR) airport link operates from Canning Town station on the Jubilee Line of London Underground. It takes you directly to the terminal building. Journey time is just 6 minutes from Canning Town to the airport, and the DLR trains run every 7-10 minutes.

If you are travelling to or from Central London the Jubilee Line has direct connections with National Rail at London Waterloo, London Bridge, West Ham and Stratford (east London). DLR operates from Bank and Tower Gateway stations.

For further information on London City Airport telephone **020 7646 0088** or visit **www.londoncityairport.com**.

London Gatwick Airport

Gatwick has its own railway station underneath the South Terminal. Access to the North Terminal is via a free transit. Direct train services also serve many parts of the country.

Airport to/from London

Gatwick Express operate a dedicated non-stop service every 15 minutes throughout the day to/from London (Victoria) and Gatwick Airport (See Table 186).

Southern provides frequent trains throughout the day and hourly throughout the night between London Victoria and Gatwick Airport (See Table 186). Frequent train services also run between Gatwick Airport and stations throughout Sussex, Surrey and parts of Hampshire and Kent.

First Capital Connect operate direct services throughout the day between St Pancras International, Farringdon, City Thameslink, London Blackfriars, London Bridge and Gatwick Airport (generally every 15 mins, See Table 52).

A reduced frequency between London and Gatwick operates through the night.

Airport to/from Reading

First Great Western operate a direct rail service between Reading and Gatwick – (See Table 148). Customers using this route should allow at least 7 minutes at Reading to make a connection.

Other direct services to/from Airport

Southern offers direct services between Gatwick Airport and Watford Junction. Connections for Birmingham and the West Midlands, also for North West destinations (including Manchester, Liverpool and Preston) and Glasgow are available from Watford Junction.

Southern also operates direct services to/from Hastings, Southampton, Portsmouth and intermediate stations on the South Coast (See Tables 186, 187, 188, 189) Clapham Jn and East Croydon (SeeTable 186).

Southeastern operates direct services from Tonbridge (See Table 209).

First Great Western operate services from Wokingham, North Camp and Guildford (See Table 148).

First Capital Connect operate direct services to Brighton and through St Pancras International to St Albans, Luton and Bedford. Connections with East Midlands Trans services to the East Midlands and South Yorkshire and Eurostar services to Continental Europe are available at St Pancras International.

Airport Links

London Gatwick Airport continued

First Capital Connect provide regular direct services from Gatwick Airport to St. Albans, Luton, Bedford, East Croydon, Haywards Heath and Brighton (See Table 52). At Luton Airport Parkway, Luton and Bedford, they also offer convenient connections with East Midlands Trains to Leicester, Derby, Nottingham and Sheffield (See Table 53).

London Heathrow Airport

Express dedicated coaches link Reading, Watford Junction and Woking with all four terminals at Heathrow Airport. Other services link Watford, Luton, Stevenage, Feltham and Central London with the airport. For full details see the individual route information below.

Airport to/from Central London

Heathrow Express operates a direct rail service from the airport to London Paddington. Stations are located at Terminal 4, Terminal 5 and in the Central Terminal Area, serving Terminals 1, 2 and 3. Minimum journey time is 15 minutes between Paddington and Terminals 1, 2 and 3, 23 minutes to Terminal 5. Trains run every 15 minutes. (Terminal 4 is served by a connecting 'shuttle' service to/from Heathrow Terminals 1, 2 and 3, taking a minimum of 8 minutes extra.)

- 0510 to 2325 from Paddington
- 0507 to 2342 from Heathrow Terminal 5 (0503 to 2348 on Sundays)
- 0512 to 2348 from Heathrow Terminal 1, 2 and 3 (0508 to 2353 on Sundays)

For further details see Table 118.

Through tickets can be purchased from any National Rail or London Underground Station to the airport via Heathrow Express. For further information visit **www.heathrowexpress.com**.

Heathrow Connect operates a local rail service every 30 minutes between Heathrow Terminals 1,2,3 and London Paddington, calling at Hayes & Harlington, Southall, Hanwell, West Ealing and Ealing Broadway. For details see Table 117. Through tickets are available from most stations.

The London Underground Piccadilly Line connects central London with all five terminals (Terminal 1/2/3, Terminal 4 and Terminal 5). Through single and return tickets can be issued to customers travelling via a Rail terminus in Zone 1.

Sample journey time from Piccadilly Circus to the Airport is approximately one hour.

Airport to/from Reading

RailAir coaches leave from Reading railway station every 20 minutes during the daytime on Mondays to Fridays (every 30 minutes early weekday mornings and evenings, on weekends and public holidays). The luxury, air-conditioned coaches run non-stop to Terminals 1, 2 and 3 in 40-50 minutes. On the return journey from Heathrow Airport they only pick up passengers at Heathrow Central Bus Station (stands one and two) and not the terminals. Customers travelling to/from Terminal 4 should use Heathrow Express from Terminal 1.

Follow the RailAir signs from your platform at Reading station. You can buy your ticket in the RailAir lounge, or combined rail and coach tickets are also available from many stations. You should allow 15 minutes at Reading to transfer between train and coach.

For further information telephone **0118 957 9425** or visit **www.RailAir.com.**

Airport to/from Woking

Coaches leave at half-hourly intervals throughout most of the day to/from Terminal 5 and Heathrow Central Bus Station (for Terminals 1, 2 and 3) (see Table 158A).

Customers travelling to Heathrow should exit on platform 5 and the coach leaves from outside the station.

On arrival at Woking customers should allow at least 10 minutes to transfer to your train after the arrival of the coach at the station. Combined rail and coach tickets are available from most National Rail stations and from the Railair sales points at the airport. Tickets may also be booked at **www.nationalexpress.com** or by calling **08705 757 747**.

For through trains and coach times, telephone **08457 48 49 50.** (calls may be recorded for training purposes)

Airport to/from Feltham

London Buses operates frequent bus services from Feltham Station to Heathrow Airport. Route 285 operates to Hatton Cross and Heathrow Central Bus Station for Terminals 1, 2 and 3. Buses operate every 10 minutes during the day, 15 minutes in the evenings and on Sundays and 30 minutes throughout the night.

Route 490 operates to Hatton Cross and Terminals 4 and 5. Buses operate every 12 minutes during the day, 20 minutes in the evenings and on Sundays.

Customers should allow 10 minutes at Feltham to transfer between train and bus from the station forecourt adjoining platform 1.

Other direct services to/from Airport

A coach service, Green Line 724, runs throughout the day between Heathrow, West Drayton, Uxbridge, Rickmansworth, Watford, St. Albans, Hatfield, Welwyn Garden City, Hertford and Harlow. Tickets can only be purchased on the coach. A frequent bus service (route 140) runs 24 hours between Hayes & Harlington and Heathrow Airport (Central Bus Station).

For further information telephone **0870 608 7261** (Green Line Travel Information)

London Luton Airport

A frequent dedicated shuttle bus links Luton Airport with Luton Airport Parkway station – journey time 5 minutes. Luton Airport Parkway is served by frequent First Capital Connect services direct to Bedford, Central London, South London, Gatwick Airport and Brighton – see Table 52 for details. East Midlands Trains services link Luton Airport Parkway with St Pancras International and Leicester, Derby, Nottingham and Sheffield – see Table 53 for details.

In addition Virgin Trains provides an hourly dedicated coach link between the Airport, Luton railway station and town centre and Milton Keynes Central railway station and town centre (see Table 65B for details).

Airport Links

London Stansted Airport

Stansted Airport has its own railway station right in the heart of the airport terminal building.

The Stansted Express is a dedicated rail service operating between London Liverpool Street and Stansted Airport station (See Table 22). Trains run every 15 minutes throughout the day, seven days per week.

Typical journey time is 46 minutes including an intermediate stop at Tottenham Hale to enable transfer onto the Victoria Line (London Underground) for the West End. Occasionally services may be diverted via Seven Sisters at weekends.

CrossCountry operates an hourly express service seven days a week between Birmingham and Stansted Airport calling at Leicester, Peterborough and Cambridge – see Table 49 – offering connections with services to Yorkshire and the North East. Customers should be advised to arrive at the airport 1 hour 45 minutes prior to their latest check-in time.

For further information telephone **08457 48 49 50**. (calls may be recorded for training purposes)

The airport is also served by the Stansted Coachlink (Service X22) – a limited stop coach service from Colchester station – which also calls intermediately at Braintree station. Coaches run hourly throughout the day, seven days per week.

For further information telephone **0871 200 22 33** or visit **www.traveline.org.uk**

Manchester Airport

The airport railway station is right in the heart of the airport complex, linked by covered travellators. The station is served by up to 8 trains per hour from Manchester Piccadilly and direct services operate between Middlesbrough, Newcastle, York, Leeds, Huddersfield, Cleethorpes, Doncaster, Sheffield, Edinburgh, Glasgow, Carlisle, Barrow in-Furness, Windermere, Lancaster, Preston, Liverpool and the Airport. Additional regular services operate during the day, to/from many stations which can be found under the entry for Manchester Airport in the index in this timetable.

Newcastle Airport

A frequent Tyne and Wear Metro service runs between Newcastle Central Station and Newcastle Airport providing links with Northern, National Express East Coast, First TransPennine Express and CrossCountry services. Inclusive 'Train and Metro' tickets are available at discount prices.

Metro journey time approximately 20 minutes.

Metro frequency up to 6 trains each way each hour. Service operates between approx. 0600 and 2300.

Prestwick International Airport

Prestwick International Airport Station is situated directly opposite the main airport terminal buildings. A covered walkway links the station with the airport terminal. The station is served by direct trains from Glasgow Central and Ayr, with a half hourly frequency operating between the hours of 0600 and 0015 approximately. (See Table 221). Journey time is approx. 45 minutes. Discounts are available for airline users. For further information telephone **01292 678000**.

Robin Hood Airport

Robin Hood Airport, the UK's newest purpose built international airport, is built on the site of the former RAF Finningley airbase. It is situated 7 miles south of Doncaster. For more information on Robin Hood Airport visit **www.robinhoodairport.com**

From Doncaster a dedicated bus service, The Airport Arrow 707, operates hourly throughout the day from the Frenchgate Interchange (Stand A1) adjacent to Doncaster Rail Station from 0535 to 2235. The journey takes under 25 minutes.

The Airport Arrow 707 service runs alongside other local bus services which link to Robin Hood Airport, including service X19 from Barnsley.

For further information on the above services please telephone Travel South Yorkshire **01709 515151** or visit **www.travelsouthyorkshire.com**

Southampton Airport

Southampton Airport (Parkway) station is adjacent to Southampton Airport.

South West Trains operate up to 3 trains per hour between London Waterloo, Winchester and Southampton Airport with up to 2 direct services to Bournemouth, Poole, Wareham and Weymouth and most intermediate stations (See Table 158).

CrossCountry services link Southampton Airport (Parkway) with Reading, Oxford, the Midlands, North West and North East England and Scotland. (See Table 51).

10 Connection time
Ⓟ Station Car Park
🚲 Bicycle storage facility
◇ Seat reservations can be made at this station
⚠ Penalty Fare Schemes in operation on some or all services from this station
🚕 Taxi rank or cab office at station, or signposted and within 100 metres
🚶 Unstaffed station
[ ] Station Operator Code

Station index and table numbers

A

Station index and table numbers

10 Connection time
Ⓟ Station Car Park
🚲 Bicycle storage facility
◇ Seat reservations can be made at this station
⚠ Penalty Fare Schemes in operation on some or all services from this station
🚕 Taxi rank or cab office at station, or signposted and within 100 metres
Ⓤ Unstaffed station
[ ] Station Operator Code

Aughton Park [ME] ⚠ 103
Aviemore [SR] Ⓟ 🚲 ◇ 🚕 229, *Sleepers* 403
Avoncliff [GW] Ⓤ 123
Avonmouth [GW] **2** Ⓟ 🚲 Ⓤ 133
Axminster [SW] Ⓟ 🚲 ◇ 🚕 160
Aylesbury [CH] Ⓟ 🚲 ◇ ⚠ 🚕 114, 115
Aylesford [SE] Ⓤ 208
Aylesham [SE] Ⓟ 212
Ayr [SR] Ⓟ 🚲 ◇ 🚕 216, 218, 221

B

Bache [ME] Ⓤ 106
Backwell [GW] (see Nailsea)
Baglan [AW] Ⓟ 🚲 Ⓤ 128
Bagshot [SW] Ⓟ 🚲 ◇ ⚠ 149
Baildon [NT] Ⓟ Ⓤ 38
Baillieston [SR] 🚲 Ⓤ 220
Bakewell (Square) *Bus* 65H
Balcombe [SN] ◇ ⚠ 52, 186
Baldock [FC] Ⓟ ⚠ 25
Balham [SN] **4** ◇ ⚠ 🚕 177, 178, 182
Balloch [SR] 🚲 🚕 226
Balmossie [SR] 🚲 Ⓤ 229
Bamber Bridge [NT] Ⓟ Ⓤ 97
Bamford [NT] Ⓟ Ⓤ 78
Banavie [SR] Ⓟ 🚲 Ⓤ 227
Banbury [CH] Ⓟ 🚲 ◇ ⚠ 🚕 51, 71, 75, 115, 116
Bangor (Gwynedd) [AW] Ⓟ ◇ 🚕 65, 81, 102, 131
Bank Hall [ME] ⚠ 103
Banstead [SN] ⚠ Ⓤ 182
Barassie [SR] Ⓟ 🚲 Ⓤ 221
Barbican [LT] (see London)
Bardon Mill [NT] Ⓟ Ⓤ 48
Bare Lane [NT] Ⓟ Ⓤ 36, 98
Bargeddie [SR] Ⓟ 🚲 Ⓤ 220
Bargoed [AW] 🚕 130
Barking [CC] ◇ ⚠ 🚕 1, 62
Barlaston Orchard Place *Bus* 68A
Barming [SE] Ⓟ ⚠ 196
Barmouth [AW] 🚲 75
Barnehurst [SE] **4** Ⓟ ⚠ 200
Barnes [SW] 🚲 ◇ ⚠ 149
Barnes Bridge [SW] 🚲 ◇ ⚠ Ⓤ 149
Barnetby [TP] Ⓟ Ⓤ 27, 29, 30
Barnham [SN] Ⓟ 🚲 ⚠ 🚕 123, 188
Barnhill [SR] 🚲 Ⓤ 226
Barnsbury [LO] (see Caledonian Road)
Barnsley [NT] Ⓟ 🚲 ◇ 🚕 30, 34, 53
Barnsley West Bus Station *Bus* 26E
Barnstaple [GW] Ⓟ 🚲 ◇ 🚕 135, 136
Barnt Green [LM] Ⓟ ⚠ Ⓤ 69, 71
Barrhead [SR] Ⓟ 🚲 🚕 222
Barrhill [SR] Ⓟ 🚲 218
Barrow Haven [NT] Ⓤ 29
Barrow-in-Furness [TP] Ⓟ ◇ 🚕 65, 82, 100
Barrow Upon Soar [EM] Ⓤ 53
Barry [AW] **3** Ⓟ ◇ 🚕 130
Barry Docks [AW] Ⓤ 130
Barry Island [AW] Ⓤ 130
Barry Links [SR] 🚲 Ⓤ 229
Barton-on-Humber [NT] Ⓟ Ⓤ 29
Basildon [CC] 🚲 ◇ ⚠ 🚕 1
Basingstoke [SW] Ⓟ 🚲 ◇ ⚠ 🚕
Aberdeen 51
Bath 160
Birmingham 51
Bournemouth 158
Bristol 160
Brockenhurst 158
Clapham Junction 155
Coventry 51
Crewe 51
Derby 51
Dorchester 158
Dundee 51
Eastleigh 158
Edinburgh 51
Exeter 160
Fareham 158
Farnborough 158
Glasgow 51
Leeds 51
London 155
Lymington 158
Manchester 51
Newcastle 51
Oxford 51
Plymouth 160
Poole 158
Portsmouth 158
Preston 51
Reading 122
Salisbury 160
Sheffield 51
Southampton 158
Southampton Airport 158
Stoke-on-Trent 51
Surbiton 155
Torquay 160
Weymouth 158
Weybridge 155
Wimbledon 155
Winchester 158
Woking 155
Wolverhampton 51
Yeovil 160
York 51
Bat & Ball [SE] Ⓟ ⚠ Ⓤ 195
Bath Spa [GW] **7** Ⓟ 🚲 ◇ ⚠ 🚕
Bournemouth 123
Brighton 123
Bristol 132
Cardiff 132
Crewe 131
Gatwick Airport 125
Heathrow Airport 125
London 125, 160
Manchester 131
Newport 132
Oxford 125
Portsmouth 123
Reading 125
Salisbury 123
Shrewsbury 131
Slough 125
Southampton Central 123
Swindon 125
Taunton 134
Westbury 123
Weston-super-Mare 134
Weymouth 123
Yeovil 123
Bathgate [SR] Ⓟ 🚲 🚕 Ⓤ 230
Batley [NT] Ⓟ 🚲 Ⓤ 39
Battersby [NT] Ⓤ 45
Battersea Park [SN] **4** ◇ ⚠ 177, 178
Battle [SE] Ⓟ ◇ 🚕 206
Battlesbridge [LE] Ⓟ 🚲 Ⓤ 5
Bayford [FC] Ⓟ ⚠ Ⓤ 24
Beaconsfield [CH] Ⓟ 🚲 ◇ ⚠ 🚕 115
Bearley [LM] Ⓟ ⚠ Ⓤ 115
Bearsden [SR] Ⓟ 🚲 🚕 226
Bearsted [SE] Ⓟ 🚲 ◇ ⚠ 196
Beasdale [SR] 🚲 Ⓤ 227
Beaulieu Road [SW] 🚲 ⚠ Ⓤ 158
Beauly [SR] Ⓟ 🚲 Ⓤ 239
Bebington [ME] Ⓟ ⚠ 106
Beccles [LE] Ⓟ 🚲 Ⓤ 13
Beckenham Hill [SE] 🚲 ⚠ 195
Beckenham Junction [SE] **4** Ⓟ 🚲 ◇ ⚠ 🚕 177, 195, 196
Bedford [FC] **7** Ⓟ 🚲 ◇ ⚠ 🚕
Barnsley 53
Bletchley 64
Brighton 52, 186
Chesterfield 53
Derby 53
Doncaster 53
East Croydon 52
Gatwick Airport 52, 186
Haywards Heath 52, 186
Herne Hill 52
Hove 186
Kettering 53
Leeds 53
Leicester 53
London 52
Luton 52
Luton Airport Parkway 52
Meadowhall 53
Milton Keynes Central 64
Nottingham 53
Redhill 52, 186

[10] Connection time
Ⓟ Station Car Park
🚲 Bicycle storage facility
◇ Seat reservations can be made at this station
⚠ Penalty Fare Schemes in operation on some or all services from this station
🚕 Taxi rank or cab office at station, or signposted and within 100 metres
🚶 Unstaffed station
[ ] Station Operator Code

Station index and table numbers

Station index and table numbers

10 Connection time
Ⓟ Station Car Park
🚲 Bicycle storage facility
◇ Seat reservations can be made at this station
⚠ Penalty Fare Schemes in operation on some or all services from this station
🚕 Taxi rank or cab office at station, or signposted and within 100 metres
Ⓤ Unstaffed station
[ ] Station Operator Code

Peterborough 49
Plymouth 135
Preston 65
Reading 116
Redditch 69
Rugby 66
Rugeley 70
Sheffield 51
Shrewsbury 74
Solihull 71
Southampton 51
Stafford 68, 70
Stansted Airport 49
Stockport 65
Stoke-on-Trent 65
Stourbridge 71
Stratford-upon-Avon 71
Swindon 125
Telford 74
Torquay 135
Walsall 70
Warrington 65
Warwick 71
Watford 66
Wigan 65
Wolverhampton 68
Worcester 71
Wrexham 75
York 51

Birnam [SR] (see Dunkeld)
Bishop Auckland [NT] Ⓟ 🚕 Ⓤ 44
Bishopbriggs [SR] 🚲 228, 230
Bishops Stortford [LE] Ⓟ 🚲 ◇ ⚠ 🚕 22
Bishopstone [SN] Ⓤ 189
Bishopton [SR] Ⓟ 🚲 219
Bitterne [SW] Ⓟ 🚲 ⚠ Ⓤ 165
Blackburn [NT] Ⓟ ◇ 🚕 41, 94, 97
Blackfriars [FC] (see London)
Blackheath [SE] **4** ⚠ 200
Blackhorse Road [LT] ⚠ 62
Blackpool
North [NT] Ⓟ ◇ 🚕
Pleasure Beach [NT] Ⓤ
South [NT] 🚕 Ⓤ
Aberdeen 65
Birmingham 65
Birmingham International 65
Blackburn 97
Bolton 82
Bradford 41
Burnley 97
Carlisle 36, 65
Colne 97
Coventry 65
Crewe 65
Dundee 65
Edinburgh 65
Glasgow 65
Inverness 65
Lancaster 65
Leeds 41
Liverpool 65, 90
London 65
Manchester 82
Manchester Airport 82
Milton Keynes Central 65
Oxenholme Lake District 65
Preston 97
Rugby 65
St Helens 90
Stafford 65
Stockport 82
Warrington 65
Watford 65
Wigan 65
Windermere 65
Wolverhampton 65
York 41

Blackrod [NT] Ⓤ 82
Blackwater [GW] Ⓟ Ⓤ 148
Blaenau Ffestiniog [AW] Ⓤ 102
Blair Atholl [SR] Ⓟ 🚲 229, *Sleepers* 403
Blairhill [SR] Ⓟ 🚲 🚕 226
Blake Street [LM] Ⓟ ⚠ 69
Blakedown [LM] Ⓟ ⚠ Ⓤ 71
Blantyre [SR] Ⓟ 🚲 226
Blaydon [NT] Ⓤ 48
Bleasby [EM] Ⓤ 27
Bledlow, Village Hall *Bus* 115A
Bletchley [LM] Ⓟ 🚲 ◇ 🚕 64, 66
Bloxwich [LM] ⚠ Ⓤ 70
Bloxwich North [LM] ⚠ Ⓤ 70
Bluewater [SE] (see Greenhithe for Bluewater)
Blundellsands & Crosby [ME] Ⓟ ⚠ 103
Blythe Bridge [EM] Ⓟ Ⓤ 50
Bodmin Mount Folly *Bus* 135C
Bodmin Parkway [GW] Ⓟ 🚲 ◇ 🚕 51, 135, *Bus* 135C, *Sleepers* 406
Bodorgan [AW] Ⓟ Ⓤ 81
Bognor Regis [SN] **4** Ⓟ 🚲 ◇ ⚠ 🚕 188
Bogston [SR] 🚲 Ⓤ 219
Bolton [NT] 🚲 ◇ 🚕 51, 65, 82, 94, 95
Bolton-on-Dearne [NT] Ⓟ Ⓤ 31
Bookham [SW] Ⓟ 🚲 ◇ ⚠ 🚕 152, 182
Bootle [NT] Ⓤ 100
Bootle New Strand [ME] ⚠ 🚕 103
Bootle Oriel Road [ME] Ⓟ ⚠ 103
Bordesley [LM] ⚠ Ⓤ 71
Bordon Camp (Fire Station) *Bus* 156A
Borehamwood [FC] (see Elstree)
Borough Green & Wrotham [SE] Ⓟ ⚠ 🚕 196
Borth [AW] Ⓟ Ⓤ 75
Bosham [SN] 🚲 ⚠ 188
Boston [EM] Ⓟ 🚲 ◇ 🚕 19
Botley [SW] Ⓟ 🚲 ⚠ Ⓤ 158
Bottesford [EM] Ⓟ Ⓤ 19
Bourne End [GW] **3** Ⓟ 🚲 ⚠ 120
Bournemouth [SW] Ⓟ 🚲 ◇ ⚠ 🚕 51, 123, 158
Bournville [LM] ⚠ 69
Bow Brickhill [LM] Ⓤ 64
Bowes Park [FC] ⚠ 24
Bowling [SR] Ⓟ 🚲 Ⓤ 226
Boxhill & Westhumble [SN] Ⓟ ⚠ Ⓤ 152, 182
Bracknell [SW] Ⓟ 🚲 ◇ ⚠ 🚕 149
Bradford
Forster Square [NT] Ⓟ 🚲 ◇ 🚕
Interchange [NT] 🚲 ◇ 🚕
Blackpool 41
Blackburn 41
Brighouse 41
Cambridge 26
Carlisle 36
Grantham 26
Halifax 41
Huddersfield 41
Ilkley 38
Lancaster 36
Leeds 37
Liverpool 41
London 26
Manchester 41
Morecambe 36
Newark 26
Norwich 26
Peterborough 26
Preston 41
Retford 26
Rochdale 41
Selby 40
Settle 36
Shipley 37
Skipton 36
York 40

Bradford-on-Avon [GW] Ⓟ 🚲 ◇ 🚕 123, 160
Brading [IL] Ⓟ Ⓤ 167
Braintree [LE] Ⓟ 🚲 ⚠ 🚕 11
Braintree Freeport [LE] 🚲 ⚠ Ⓤ 11
Bramhall [NT] 84
Bramley (Hants) [GW] ⚠ 122
Bramley [NT] Ⓟ Ⓤ 37, 41
Brampton (Cumbria) [NT] Ⓟ Ⓤ 48
Brampton (Suffolk) [LE] Ⓤ 13
Branchton [SR] Ⓟ 🚲 Ⓤ 219
Brandon [LE] Ⓟ Ⓤ 17
Branksome [SW] Ⓟ 🚲 ◇ ⚠ 158
Braystones [NT] Ⓤ 100
Bredbury [NT] Ⓟ 🚲 78
Breich [SR] 🚲 Ⓤ 225
Brentford [SW] Ⓟ 🚲 ◇ 149
Brentwood [LE] Ⓟ 🚲 ⚠ 🚕 5
Bricket Wood [LM] Ⓤ 61
Bridge of Allan [SR] Ⓟ 🚲 Ⓤ 230

Station index and table numbers

10 Connection time
Ⓟ Station Car Park
🚲 Bicycle storage facility
◇ Seat reservations can be made at this station
⚠ Penalty Fare Schemes in operation on some or all services from this station
🚕 Taxi rank or cab office at station, or signposted and within 100 metres
Ⓤ Unstaffed station
[ ] Station Operator Code

Bridge of Orchy [SR] Ⓟ 🚲 Ⓤ 227, *Sleepers* 404
Bridgend [AW] Ⓟ 🚲 ◇ 🚕 125, 128, 130
Bridgeton [SR] 🚲 🚕 226
Bridgwater [GW] Ⓟ ◇ 134, 135
Bridlington [NT] Ⓟ 🚲 ◇ 🚕 43
Brierfield [NT] Ⓟ Ⓤ 97
Brigg [NT] Ⓟ Ⓤ 30
Brighouse [NT] Ⓟ Ⓤ 41
Brighton [SN] 10 Ⓟ 🚲 ◇ ⚠ 🚕
- Ashford International 189
- Bath Spa 123
- Bedford 52
- Birmingham 66
- Birmingham International 66
- Bognor Regis 188
- Bristol 123
- Cardiff 123
- Chichester 188
- Coventry 66
- Eastbourne 189
- East Croydon 186
- Elstree & Borehamwood 52
- Gatwick Airport 186
- Hastings 189
- Haywards Heath 186
- Hove 188
- Isle of Wight 167
- Kensington Olympia 66
- Lewes 189
- Littlehampton 188
- London 186
- Luton 52
- Luton Airport Parkway 52
- Manchester 51
- Mill Hill Broadway 52
- Milton Keynes Central 66
- Northampton 66
- Oxford 51
- Portsmouth 188
- Preston 51
- Radlett 52
- Redhill 186
- Rugby 66
- St Albans 52
- Salisbury 123, 160
- Seaford 189
- Southampton Central 188
- Watford Junction 66, 186
- West Hampstead Thameslink 52
- Wolverhampton 66
- Worthing 188

Brimsdown [LE] ⚠ 22
Brinnington [NT] 78
Bristol International Airport *Bus* 🚕 125B
Bristol
- **Parkway [GW]** 7 Ⓟ 🚲 ◇ ⚠ 🚕
- **Temple Meads [GW]** 10 Ⓟ 🚲 ◇ ⚠ 🚕
  - Aberdeen 51
  - Bath Spa 132
  - Birmingham 57
  - Bournemouth 123
  - Brighton 123
  - Bristol International Airport *Bus* 125B
  - Cardiff 132
  - Carlisle 51
  - Cheltenham Spa 57
  - Crewe 51, 131
  - Darlington 51
  - Derby 57
  - Dundee 51
  - Edinburgh 51
  - Exeter 135
  - Gatwick Airport 125
  - Glasgow 51
  - Gloucester 134
  - Heathrow Airport 125
  - Hereford 131
  - Leeds 51
  - London 125, 160
  - Manchester 51, 131
  - Newcastle 51
  - Newport (South Wales) 132
  - Nottingham 57
  - Oxford 125
  - Paignton 135
  - Penzance 135
  - Plymouth 135
  - Portsmouth 123
  - Preston 51
  - Reading 125
  - Salisbury 123
  - Severn Beach 133
  - Sheffield 51
  - Shrewsbury 131
  - Slough 125
  - Southampton Central 123
  - Stoke-on-Trent 51
  - Swindon 125
  - Taunton 134
  - Temple Meads/Parkway 134
  - Torquay 135
  - Westbury 123
  - Weston-super-Mare 134
  - Weymouth 123
  - Wolverhampton 51
  - Worcester 57
  - York 51

Brithdir [AW] Ⓤ 130
British Steel Redcar [NT] Ⓤ 44
Briton Ferry [AW] Ⓟ Ⓤ 128
Brixton [SE] ⚠ 195
Broad Green [NT] 90
Broadbottom [NT] Ⓟ 79
Broadstairs [SE] Ⓟ 🚲 🚕 207, 212
Brockenhurst [SW] 3 Ⓟ 🚲 ◇ ⚠ 🚕 51, 158
Brockholes [NT] Ⓤ 34
Brockley [SN] ⚠ 178
Brodick *Ship* 221A
Bromborough [ME] Ⓟ 🚲 ⚠ 106
Bromborough Rake [ME] ⚠ 106
Bromley Cross [NT] Ⓟ 🚲 94
Bromley North [SE] Ⓟ ⚠ 204
Bromley South [SE] 4 ◇ ⚠ 🚕 195, 196, 207, 212
Bromsgrove [LM] Ⓟ Ⓤ 69, 71
Brondesbury [LO] ⚠ 59
Brondesbury Park [LO] ⚠ 59
Brookmans Park [FC] Ⓟ 🚲 ⚠ 24
Brookwood [SW] 3 Ⓟ 🚲 ◇ ⚠ 🚕 155
Broome [AW] Ⓤ 129
Broomfleet [NT] Ⓟ Ⓤ 29
Brora [SR] Ⓟ 🚲 Ⓤ 239
Brough [TP] Ⓟ 🚲 ◇ 🚕 29, 39
Broughty Ferry [SR] 🚲 Ⓤ 229
Broxbourne [LE] 3 Ⓟ 🚲 ⚠ 🚕 22
Bruce Grove [LE] ⚠ 21
Brundall [LE] Ⓟ 🚲 15
Brundall Gardens [LE] 🚲 Ⓤ 15
Brunstane [SR] 🚲 Ⓤ 230
Brunswick [ME] Ⓟ 🚲 103
Bruton [GW] Ⓟ Ⓤ 123
Bryn [NT] Ⓤ 90
Buckenham [LE] 🚲 Ⓤ 15
Buckingham (Tesco) *Bus* 65A
Buckley [AW] Ⓟ Ⓤ 101
Bucknell [AW] Ⓤ 129
Bude Strand *Bus* 135D
Bugle [GW] 🚲 Ⓤ 142
Builth Road [AW] Ⓤ 129
Bulwell [EM] Ⓟ Ⓤ 55
Bures [LE] 🚲 Ⓤ 10
Burgess Hill [SN] 4 Ⓟ 🚲 ⚠ 🚕 52, 186, 188
Burley Park [NT] Ⓟ Ⓤ 35
Burley-in-Wharfedale [NT] Ⓟ 🚲 Ⓤ 38
Burnage [NT] 85
Burneside [TP] Ⓤ 83
Burnham [GW] Ⓟ 🚲 ⚠ 🚕 117
Burnham-on-Crouch [LE] Ⓟ 🚲 5
Burnham-on-Sea [GW] (see Highbridge)
Burnley Barracks [NT] Ⓤ 97
Burnley Central [NT] Ⓟ ◇ 97
Burnley Manchester Road [NT] Ⓟ Ⓤ 41, 97
Burnside [SR] 🚲 223
Burntisland [SR] Ⓟ 🚲 242
Burry Port [AW] (see Pembrey)
Burscough Bridge [NT] Ⓟ 82
Burscough Junction [NT] Ⓟ Ⓤ 99
Bursledon [SW] Ⓟ 🚲 ⚠ Ⓤ 165
Burton Joyce [EM] Ⓤ 27
Burton-on-Trent [EM] Ⓟ ◇ 🚕 51, 53, 57
Bury St Edmunds [LE] Ⓟ 🚲 ◇ 🚕 14
Busby [SR] Ⓟ 🚲 Ⓤ 222
Bushey [LO] Ⓟ ⚠ 🚕 60, 66
Bush Hill Park [LE] Ⓟ ⚠ 21
Butlers Lane [LM] ⚠ 69

Station index and table numbers

[10] Connection time
Ⓟ Station Car Park
🚲 Bicycle storage facility
◇ Seat reservations can be made at this station
⚠ Penalty Fare Schemes in operation on some or all services from this station
🚕 Taxi rank or cab office at station, or signposted and within 100 metres
ⓤ Unstaffed station
[ ] Station Operator Code

Station index and table numbers

■10 Connection time
Ⓟ Station Car Park
🚲 Bicycle storage facility
◇ Seat reservations can be made at this station
⚠ Penalty Fare Schemes in operation on some or all services from this station
🚕 Taxi rank or cab office at station, or signposted and within 100 metres
ⓤ Unstaffed station
[ ] Station Operator Code

Station index and table numbers

10 Connection time
Ⓟ Station Car Park
🚲 Bicycle storage facility
◇ Seat reservations can be made at this station
⚠ Penalty Fare Schemes in operation on some or all services from this station
🚕 Taxi rank or cab office at station, or signposted and within 100 metres
Ⓤ Unstaffed station
[ ] Station Operator Code

East Grinstead 184
Effingham Junction 152
Epsom 152, 182
Epsom Downs 182
Exeter 160
Gatwick Airport 186
Guildford 152, 156
Hampton Court 152
Hastings 189
Haywards Heath 186
Horsham 186
Hounslow 149
Hove 186
Kensington Olympia 66, 186
Kingston 149, 152
Lewes 189
London
Victoria 175, 177
Waterloo 149, 152
Milton Keynes Central 66
Northampton 66
Oxted 184
Portsmouth 156, 158, 188
Purley 175
Reading 149
Redhill 186
Rugby 66
Salisbury 160
Shepperton 152
Southampton 158, 188
Staines 149
Surbiton 152
Sutton (Surrey) 182
Tattenham Corner 181
Twickenham 149
Uckfield 184
Watford Junction 66, 186
West Croydon 177
Weybridge 155
Willesden Junction 186
Wimbledon 152
Windsor 149
Woking 155
Worthing 188
Yeovil Junction 160
Clapham (Nth Yorkshire) [NT] Ⓟ Ⓤ 36
Clapton [LE] ⚠ 20, 22
Clarbeston Road [AW] Ⓤ 128
Clarkston [SR] 🚲 222
Claverdon [LM] ⚠ Ⓤ 115
Claygate [SW] Ⓟ 🚲 ◇ ⚠ 🚕 152
Cleethorpes [TP] Ⓟ 🚲 ◇ 🚕 27, 29, 30
Cleland [SR] Ⓟ 🚲 Ⓤ 225
Clifton [NT] Ⓤ 82
Clifton Down [GW] Ⓟ Ⓤ 133
Clitheroe [NT] Ⓟ 94, 97
Clock House [SE] 🚲 ⚠ 203
Clunderwen [AW] Ⓟ Ⓤ 128
Clydebank [SR] 🚲 🚕 226
Coatbridge Central [SR] Ⓟ 🚲 🚕 Ⓤ 224, 226
Coatbridge Sunnyside [SR] Ⓟ 🚲 226
Coatdyke [SR] Ⓟ 🚲 Ⓤ 226
Cobham & Stoke d'Abernon [SW] Ⓟ 🚲 ◇ ⚠ 🚕 152
Cockermouth (Main Street) *Bus* 65F
Codsall [LM] Ⓟ Ⓤ 74
Cogan [AW] Ⓟ Ⓤ 130
Colchester [LE] **4** Ⓟ 🚲 ◇ ⚠ 🚕 10, 11, 13, 14
Colchester Town [LE] Ⓟ 🚲 ⚠ 11
Coleshill Parkway [LM] Ⓟ 🚲 ◇ 🚕 57
Coll *Ship* 227B
Collingham [EM] Ⓤ 27
Collington [SN] Ⓤ 189
Colne [NT] Ⓟ Ⓤ 97
Colonsay *Ship* 227B
Colwall [LM] Ⓟ ⚠ Ⓤ 71, 126
Colwyn Bay [AW] Ⓟ ◇ 🚕 81
Combe [GW] Ⓤ 126
Commondale [NT] Ⓤ 45
Congleton [NT] Ⓟ ◇ 51, 65, 84
Conisbrough [NT] Ⓟ Ⓤ 29
Connel Ferry [SR] Ⓟ 🚲 Ⓤ 227
Cononley [NT] Ⓟ Ⓤ 36
Conway Park [ME] 106
Conwy [AW] Ⓤ 81
Cooden Beach [SN] Ⓟ 🚲 ⚠ 189
Cookham [GW] Ⓟ 120
Cooksbridge [SN] Ⓟ Ⓤ 189
Coombe [GW] Ⓤ 140
Copplestone [GW] Ⓟ Ⓤ 136
Corbridge [NT] Ⓟ Ⓤ 48
Corby George Street *Bus* 26B
Corby Town Centre *Bus* 53A
Corkerhill [SR] 🚲 Ⓤ 217
Corkickle [NT] Ⓤ 100
Corpach [SR] Ⓟ 🚲 Ⓤ 227
Corrour [SR] 🚲 Ⓤ 227, *Sleepers* 404
Coryton [AW] Ⓤ 130
Coseley [LM] Ⓟ ⚠ 65, 68, 74
Cosford [LM] Ⓟ Ⓤ 74, 75
Cosham [SW] Ⓟ 🚲 ◇ ⚠ 🚕 123, 158, 165, 188
Cottingham [NT] Ⓟ 🚲 🚕 Ⓤ 43
Cottingley [NT] Ⓤ 39
Coulsdon South [SN] Ⓟ ⚠ 186
Coventry [VT] Ⓟ 🚲 ◇ ⚠ 🚕
Aberdeen 65
Barrow-in-Furness 65
Banbury 71
Basingstoke 51
Birmingham 68
Birmingham International 68
Blackpool 65
Bournemouth 51
Brighton 66
Carlisle 65
Clapham Junction 66
Crewe 65
Derby 51
Dundee 65
East Croydon 66
Edinburgh 51, 65
Gatwick Airport 66
Glasgow 51, 65
Holyhead 65
Inverness 65
Leamington Spa 71
Leeds 51
Liverpool 65
London 66
Manchester 65
Manchester Airport 65
Milton Keynes Central 66
Newcastle 51
Northampton 66
Nuneaton 67
Oxenholme Lake District 65
Oxford 51
Preston 65
Reading 51
Rugby 66
Sheffield 51
Southampton 51
Stafford 67, 68
Stoke-on-Trent 65
Watford 66
Wolverhampton 68
York 51
Cowden [SN] Ⓟ Ⓤ 184
Cowdenbeath [SR] 🚲 ◇ 242
Cowplain Shops *Bus* 156B
Cradley Heath [LM] Ⓟ 🚲 ◇ ⚠ 71, 115
Craigendoran [SR] Ⓟ 🚲 Ⓤ 226
Craignure *Ship* 227B
Cramlington [NT] Ⓟ 🚲 Ⓤ 48
Craven Arms [AW] Ⓟ Ⓤ 129, 131
Crawley [SN] Ⓟ 🚲 ◇ ⚠ 🚕 186, 188, 209
Crayford [SE] Ⓟ ⚠ 200
Crediton [GW] Ⓟ 🚲 Ⓤ 136
Cressing [LE] 🚲 ⚠ Ⓤ 11
Cressington [ME] Ⓟ ⚠ 103
Creswell [EM] Ⓤ 55
Crewe [VT] **10** Ⓟ 🚲 ◇ 🚕
Aberdeen 65, *Sleepers* 402
Aberystwyth 75
Bangor (Gwynedd) 81
Barrow-in-Furness 65
Birmingham 65
Birmingham International 65
Blackpool 65
Blaenau Ffestiniog 102
Bournemouth 51
Bristol 51, 131
Cardiff 131
Carlisle 65
Cheltenham Spa 51
Chester 81
Coventry 65
Derby 50
Douglas (IOM) 98A
Dundee 65, *Sleepers* 402
East Croydon 51

Station index and table numbers

[10] Connection time
℗ Station Car Park
🚲 Bicycle storage facility
◇ Seat reservations can be made at this station
⚠ Penalty Fare Schemes in operation on some or all services from this station
🚕 Taxi rank or cab office at station, or signposted and within 100 metres
Ⓤ Unstaffed station
[ ] Station Operator Code

Edinburgh 65
Exeter 51
Fort William *Sleepers* 404
Gatwick Airport 65
Glasgow 65
Hartford 91
Hereford 131
Holyhead 81
Inverkeithing *Sleepers* 402
Inverness 65, *Sleepers* 403
Kirkcaldy *Sleepers* 402
Lancaster 65
Liverpool 91
Liverpool South Parkway 91
Llandudno 81
London 65
Manchester 84
Manchester Airport 84
Milton Keynes Central 65
Newport (South Wales) 131
Nottingham 50
Oxenholme Lake District 65
Oxford 51
Paignton 51
Penzance 51
Perth 65, *Sleepers* 403
Plymouth 51
Preston 65
Reading 51
Rugby 65
Runcorn 91
Shrewsbury 131
Southampton 51
Stafford 65
Stirling *Sleepers* 403
Stockport 84
Stoke-on-Trent 50
Torquay 51
Watford 65
Wilmslow 84
Wolverhampton 65
Crewkerne [SW] ℗ 🚲 ◇ 160
Crews Hill [FC] ⚠ Ⓤ 24
Crianlarich [SR] ℗ 🚲 Ⓤ 227, *Sleepers* 404
Criccieth [AW] ℗ 🚲 Ⓤ 75
Cricklewood [FC] 🚲 ◇ ⚠ 52
Croftfoot [SR] 🚲 223
Crofton Park [SE] ⚠ 195
Cromer [LE] ℗ 🚲 Ⓤ 16
Cromford [EM] ℗ Ⓤ 54, 56
Crompton [NT] (see Shaw)
Crookston [SR] 🚲 Ⓤ 217
Crosby [ME] (see Blundellsands)
Crossflatts [NT] ℗ 🚲 Ⓤ 36
Cross Gates [NT] ℗ 40
Cross Keys [AW] Ⓤ 127
Crosshill [SR] 223
Crossmyloof [SR] 🚲 Ⓤ 222
Croston [NT] ℗ Ⓤ 99
Crouch Hill [LO] ⚠ 62
Crowborough [SN] ℗ 184
Crowhurst [SE] ℗ 206
Crowle [NT] Ⓤ 29
Crowthorne [GW] ℗ 🚲 148
Croy [SR] **[3]** ℗ 🚲 228, 230
Croydon
see East Croydon
see South Croydon
see West Croydon
Crystal Palace [SN] **[4]** ℗ ⚠ 177, 178
Cuddington [NT] ℗ Ⓤ 88
Cuffley [FC] ℗ 🚲 ⚠ 🚕 24
Culdrose (R.N.A.S.) *Bus* 135A
Culham [GW] ℗ 🚲 Ⓤ 116
Culrain [SR] 🚲 Ⓤ 239
Cumbernauld [SR] ℗ 🚲 🚕 224
Cupar [SR] ℗ 🚲 ◇ 51, 229
Curriehill [SR] ℗ 🚲 Ⓤ 225
Cuxton [SE] ℗ Ⓤ 208
Cwmbach [AW] ℗ Ⓤ 130
Cwmbran [AW] ℗ 🚲 ◇ 🚕 131
Cynghordy [AW] Ⓤ 129

D

Dagenham Dock [CC] ℗ ◇ ⚠ 1
Daisy Hill [NT] ℗ 🚲 82
Dalgety Bay [SR] ℗ 🚲 🚕 Ⓤ 242
Dalmally [SR] ℗ 🚲 Ⓤ 227
Dalmarnock [SR] 226
Dalmeny [SR] ℗ 🚲 242
Dalmuir [SR] ℗ 🚲 226, 227, *Sleepers* 404
Dalreoch [SR] ℗ 🚲 226
Dalry [SR] ℗ 🚲 Ⓤ 221
Dalston [NT] ℗ Ⓤ 100
Dalston Kingsland [LO] ⚠ 59
Dalton [NT] ℗ Ⓤ 82
Dalwhinnie [SR] ℗ 🚲 Ⓤ 229, *Sleepers* 403
Danby [NT] ℗ Ⓤ 45
Danescourt [AW] Ⓤ 130
Danzey [LM] ℗ ⚠ Ⓤ 71
Darfield Saltersbrook Road *Bus* 26D
Darlington [GR] **[7]** ℗ 🚲 ◇ 🚕
Aberdeen 26
Birmingham 51
Bishop Auckland 44
Bournemouth 51
Brighton 51
Bristol 51
Cambridge 26
Cardiff 51
Catterick Garrison *Bus* 26H
Derby 51
Doncaster 26
Durham 26
Durham Tees Valley Airport *Bus* 26J
Dundee 26
Edinburgh 26
Exeter 51
Glasgow 26
Grantham 26
Huddersfield 39
Leeds 26
Liverpool 39
London 26
Manchester 39
Manchester Airport 39
Middlesbrough 44
Newark 26
Newcastle 26
Newport (South Wales) 51
Norwich 26
Northallerton 26
Oxford 51
Paignton 51
Penzance 51
Peterborough 26
Plymouth 51
Reading 51
Redcar 44
Retford 26
Richmond *Bus* 26H
Saltburn 44
Sheffield 26
Southampton 51
Stansted Airport 26
Sunderland 26, 44
Torquay 51
Whitby 45
York 26
Darnall [NT] Ⓤ 30
Darnley [SR] (see Priesthill)
Darsham [LE] ℗ 🚲 Ⓤ 13
Dartford [SE] **[4]** ℗ ◇ ⚠ 🚕 200, 212
Darton [NT] ℗ Ⓤ 34
Darwen [NT] Ⓤ 94
Datchet [SW] 🚲 ◇ ⚠ 149
Davenport [NT] ℗ 86
Dawlish [GW] ℗ ◇ 🚕 51, 135, 160
Dawlish Warren [GW] ℗ 🚲 Ⓤ 135, 160
Deal [SE] ℗ 🚲 ◇ 🚕 207
Dean [GW] 🚲 Ⓤ 123, 158
Dean Lane [NT] Ⓤ 95
Deansgate [NT] 82, 84, 85, 86, 89
Deganwy [AW] Ⓤ 81, 102
Deighton [NT] Ⓤ 39
Delamere [NT] ℗ Ⓤ 88
Denby Dale [NT] ℗ Ⓤ 34
Denham [CH] ℗ 🚲 ◇ ⚠ 🚕 115
Denham Golf Club [CH] ⚠ Ⓤ 115
Denmark Hill [SE] **[4]** ⚠ 178, 195, 200
Dent [NT] ℗ Ⓤ 36
Denton [NT] Ⓤ 78
Deptford [SE] ⚠ 200
Derby [EM] **[10]** ℗ 🚲 ◇ 🚕
Barnsley 53
Bedford 53
Belper 53, 56
Birmingham 57
Birmingham International 51

Station index and table numbers

10 Connection time
Ⓟ Station Car Park
🚲 Bicycle storage facility
◇ Seat reservations can be made at this station
⚠ Penalty Fare Schemes in operation on some or all services from this station
🚕 Taxi rank or cab office at station, or signposted and within 100 metres
Ⓤ Unstaffed station
[ ] Station Operator Code

Bournemouth 51
Brighton 51
Bristol 57
Burton-on-Trent 57
Cardiff 57
Chesterfield 53
Coventry 51
Crewe 50
Doncaster 53
East Croydon 51
Edinburgh 51
Exeter 51
Gatwick Airport 53
Gloucester 57
Kettering 53
Leeds 53
Leicester 53
London 53
Long Eaton 57
Loughborough 53
Luton 53
Market Harborough 53
Matlock 56
Meadowhall 53
Newcastle 51
Newport (South Wales) 57
Nottingham 57
Oxford 51
Paignton 51
Penzance 51
Plymouth 51
Reading 51
Sheffield 53
Southampton 51
Stoke-on-Trent 50
Wakefield 53
Wellingborough 53
York 53
Derby Road [LE] 🚲 Ⓤ 13
Dereham 🚕 *Bus* 26A
Derker [NT] Ⓤ 95
Devonport [GW] Ⓟ 🚲 Ⓤ 135, 139
Dewsbury [TP] Ⓟ 🚲 ◇ 🚕 39, 41
Didcot Parkway [GW] Ⓟ 🚲 ◇ ⚠ 🚕 116, 125
Digby & Sowton [GW] Ⓟ Ⓤ 136
Dilton Marsh [GW] Ⓤ 123
Dinas Powys [AW] Ⓤ 130
Dinas Rhondda [AW] Ⓟ Ⓤ 130
Dingle Road [AW] Ⓤ 130
Dingwall [SR] Ⓟ 🚲 ◇ 🚕 239
Dinsdale [NT] Ⓤ 44
Dinting [NT] **3** Ⓟ 🚲 79
Disley [NT] Ⓟ 86
Diss [LE] Ⓟ 🚲 ◇ 🚕 11
Dockyard [GW] Ⓤ 135, 139
Dodworth [NT] Ⓟ Ⓤ 34
Dolau [AW] 🚲 Ⓤ 129
Doleham [SN] Ⓤ 189
Dolgarrog [AW] Ⓤ 102
Dolwyddelan [AW] Ⓟ Ⓤ 102
Doncaster [GR] **7** Ⓟ 🚲 ◇ 🚕
Aberdeen 26
Bedford 53
Birmingham 51
Bournemouth 51
Brighton 51
Bristol 51
Cambridge 26
Cleethorpes 29
Darlington 26
Derby 53
Dundee 26
Durham 26
Edinburgh 26
Exeter 51
Gainsborough 18
Glasgow 26
Goole 29
Grantham 26
Grimsby 29
Hull 29
Leeds 31
Leicester 53
Lincoln 18
London 26
Luton 53
Manchester 29
Manchester Airport 29
Middlesbrough 26
Newark 26
Newcastle 26
Norwich 26
Nottingham 53
Oxford 51
Paignton 51
Penzance 51
Peterborough 18, 26
Plymouth 51
Reading 51
Retford 26
Robin Hood Airport *Bus* 26F
Rotherham 29
Scunthorpe 29
Selby 29
Sheffield 29
Sleaford 18
Southampton 51
Spalding 18
Stansted Airport 26
Stevenage 26
Stockport 29
Sunderland 26
Torquay 51
Wakefield 31
York 26
Doncaster Interchange *Bus* 26E, 26F
Dorchester South [SW] Ⓟ 🚲 ◇ ⚠ 🚕 158
Dorchester West [GW] Ⓤ 123, 158
Dore [NT] Ⓟ Ⓤ 78
Dorking [SN] **4** Ⓟ 🚲 ◇ ⚠ 🚕 152, 182
Dorking Deepdene [GW] Ⓤ 148
Dorking West [GW] Ⓤ 148
Dormans [SN] ⚠ 184
Dorridge [LM] Ⓟ 🚲 ◇ ⚠ 71, 115
Douglas (IOM) *Ship* 98A
Dove Holes [NT] Ⓟ Ⓤ 86
Dovercourt [LE] Ⓟ 🚲 11
Dover Priory [SE] **4** Ⓟ 🚲 ◇ 🚕 207, 212
Dovey Junction [AW] **4** Ⓤ 75
Downham Market [FC] Ⓟ 🚲 ⚠ 🚕 17
Drayton Green [GW] Ⓤ 117
Drayton Park [FC] 🚲 ⚠ 24
Drem [SR] Ⓟ 🚲 Ⓤ 238
Driffield [NT] Ⓟ 🚲 🚕 43
Drigg [NT] Ⓤ 100
Droitwich Spa [LM] Ⓟ ◇ ⚠ 71
Dronfield [NT] Ⓟ Ⓤ 53
Drumchapel [SR] Ⓟ 🚲 🚕 226
Drumfrochar [SR] 🚲 Ⓤ 219
Drumgelloch [SR] 🚲 Ⓤ 226
Drumry [SR] Ⓟ 🚲 226
Dublin Ferryport *Ship* 81A
Duddeston [LM] ⚠ 69, 70
Dudley Port [LM] Ⓟ ⚠ 68
Duffield [EM] Ⓟ Ⓤ 56
Duirinish [SR] Ⓟ 🚲 Ⓤ 239
Duke Street [SR] 🚲 Ⓤ 226
Dullingham [LE] Ⓟ 🚲 Ⓤ 14
Dumbarton Central [SR] 🚲 ◇ 🚕 226, 227
Dumbarton East [SR] 🚲 Ⓤ 226
Dumbreck [SR] 🚲 Ⓤ 217
Dumfries [SR] Ⓟ 🚲 ◇ 🚕 216, 218
Dumpton Park [SE] Ⓤ 207, 212
Dun Laoghaire *Ship* 81A
Dunbar [GR] Ⓟ 🚲 ◇ 26, 51
Dunblane [SR] Ⓟ 🚲 ◇ 229, 230, *Sleepers* 403
Duncraig [SR] 🚲 Ⓤ 239
Dundee [SR] Ⓟ 🚲 ◇ 🚕 26, 51, 65, 229, *Sleepers* 402
Dunfermline Queen Margaret [SR] Ⓟ 🚲 Ⓤ 242
Dunfermline Town [SR] Ⓟ 🚲 ◇ 🚕 242
Dunkeld & Birnam [SR] Ⓟ 🚲 Ⓤ 229, *Sleepers* 403
Dunlop [SR] 🚲 Ⓤ 222
Dunoon *Ship* 219A
Dunrobin Castle [SR] Ⓤ *Summer only* 239
Duns *Bus* 26K
Dunstable *Bus* 52A
Dunster Steep *Bus* 135E
Dunston [NT] Ⓤ 48
Dunton Green [SE] Ⓟ ⚠ Ⓤ 204
Durham [GR] Ⓟ 🚲 ◇ 🚕 26, 39, 44, 51
Durham Tees Valley Airport *Bus* 🚕 26J
Durrington-on-Sea [SN] 🚲 ⚠ 188
Dursley [GW] (see Cam & Dursley)
Dyce [SR] Ⓟ 🚲 🚕 Ⓤ 229, 240

Station index and table numbers

⟦10⟧ Connection time
Ⓟ Station Car Park
🚲 Bicycle storage facility
◇ Seat reservations can be made at this station
⚠ Penalty Fare Schemes in operation on some or all services from this station
🚕 Taxi rank or cab office at station, or signposted and within 100 metres
⊛ Unstaffed station
[ ] Station Operator Code

Dyffryn Ardudwy [AW] ⊛ 75

E

Eaglescliffe [NT] Ⓟ 🚲 🚕 ⊛ 26, 44
Ealing Broadway [GW] ⟦3⟧ ◇ ⚠ 🚕 116, 117
Earlestown [NT] ⟦8⟧ 81, 90
Earley [SW] Ⓟ 🚲 ⚠ 149
Earlsfield [SW] 🚲 ◇ ⚠ 152, 155
Earlston *Bus* 26K
Earlswood (Surrey) [SN] 🚲 ◇ ⚠ 186
Earlswood (West Midlands) [LM] Ⓟ ⚠ ⊛ 71
East Croydon [SN] 🚲 ◇ ⚠ 🚕
  Aberdeen 51
  Bedford 52
  Bexhill 189
  Birmingham 66
  Birmingham International 66
  Bognor Regis 188
  Brighton 186
  Carlisle 51
  Caterham 181
  Chichester 188
  Clapham Junction 175
  Coventry 66
  Crewe 51
  Eastbourne 189
  East Grinstead 184
  Edinburgh 51
  Gatwick Airport 186
  Glasgow 51
  Hastings 189
  Haywards Heath 186
  Horsham 186
  Hove 186
  Kensington Olympia 66, 186
  Lewes 189
  Littlehampton 188
  London 175
  Luton 52
  Luton Airport Parkway 52
  Manchester 51
  Milton Keynes Central 66
  Northampton 66
  Norwood Junction 177, 178
  Oxford 51
  Oxted 184
  Portsmouth 188
  Preston 51
  Purley 175
  Redhill 186
  Rugby 66
  St Albans 52
  St Pancras International 52
  Seaford 189
  Southampton Central 188
  Tattenham Corner 181
  Tonbridge 186, 209
  Uckfield 184
  Watford Junction 66, 186
  West Hampstead Thameslink 52
  Wolverhampton 66
  Worthing 188
East Didsbury [NT] Ⓟ 85
East Dulwich [SN] ⚠ 177, 179
East Farleigh [SE] Ⓟ ⊛ 208
East Garforth [NT] ⊛ 40
East Grinstead [SN] Ⓟ 🚲 ◇ ⚠ 🚕 184
East Kilbride [SR] Ⓟ 🚲 ◇ 🚕 222
East Malling [SE] ⚠ ⊛ 196
East Tilbury [CC] ◇ ⚠ 1
East Worthing [SN] ⚠ ⊛ 188
Eastbourne [SN] ⟦4⟧ Ⓟ 🚲 ◇ ⚠ 🚕 189
Eastbrook [AW] Ⓟ ⊛ 130
Easterhouse [SR] Ⓟ 🚲 226
Eastham Rake [ME] Ⓟ 🚲 ⚠ 106
Eastleigh [SW] ⟦3⟧ Ⓟ 🚲 ◇ ⚠ 🚕 158
Eastrington [NT] ⊛ 29
Ebbw Vale Parkway [AW] Ⓟ ⊛ 127
Eccles [NT] Ⓟ 90
Eccles Road [LE] Ⓟ ⊛ 17
Eccleston Park [NT] 90
Edale [NT] Ⓟ ⊛ 78
Eden Camp *Bus* 26G
Eden Park [SE] ⚠ 203
Eden Project *Bus* 135B
Edenbridge [SE] Ⓟ ⊛ 209
Edenbridge Town [SN] 🚕 184
Edge Hill [NT] Ⓟ 89, 90, 91
Edinburgh [NR] ⟦10⟧ Ⓟ 🚲 ◇ 🚕
  Aberdeen 229
  Bathgate 230
  Birmingham New Street 51, 65
  Birmingham International 51, 65
  Blackpool 65
  Bournemouth 51
  Brighton 51
  Bristol 51
  Cambridge 26
  Cardiff 51
  Carlisle 65
  Carstairs 225
  Cowdenbeath 242
  Crewe 65
  Croy 228
  Cumbernauld 224
  Darlington 26
  Derby 51
  Doncaster 26
  Dunblane 230
  Dundee 229
  Dunfermline 242
  Dyce 229
  Edinburgh Park 230
  Exeter 51
  Falkirk 228, 230
  Fort William 227
  Gatwick Airport 51, 65
  Glasgow 225, 228
  Glenrothes with Thornton 242
  Grantham 26
  Inverkeithing 242
  Inverness 229
  Kirkcaldy 242
  Kyle of Lochalsh 239
  Lancaster 65
  Larbert 230
  Leeds 26
  Linlithgow 230
  Liverpool 65
  Livingston 225, 230
  London 26, *Sleepers* 400
  Mallaig 227
  Manchester 65
  Manchester Airport 65
  Markinch 242
  Motherwell 225
  Newcastle 26
  Newcraighall 230
  Newport (South Wales) 51
  North Berwick 238
  Oban 227
  Oxenholme Lake District 65
  Oxford 51
  Paignton 51
  Penzance 51
  Perth 229
  Peterborough 26
  Plymouth 51
  Polmont 230
  Preston 65
  Reading 51
  Sheffield 26
  Shotts 225
  Southampton 51
  Springburn 224
  Stafford 65
  Stirling 230
  Thurso 239
  Torquay 51
  Warrington 65
  Watford 65, *Sleepers* 400
  West Calder 225
  Western Isles *Ship* 239B
  Wick 239
  Wigan 65
  York 26
Edinburgh Park [SR] 🚲 ⊛ 230
Edmonton Green [LE] ⚠ 21
Effingham Junction [SW] ⟦6⟧ Ⓟ 🚲 ◇ ⚠ 152, 182
Eggesford [GW] Ⓟ ⊛ 136
Egham [SW] Ⓟ 🚲 ◇ ⚠ 🚕 149
Egton [NT] ⊛ 45
Eigg *Ship* 227A
Elephant & Castle [FC] 🚲 ◇ ⚠
  Ashford 196
  Bromley South 195
  Canterbury 212
  Catford 195
  Chatham 212
  Dover 212

Station index and table numbers

■10 Connection time
℗ Station Car Park
🚲 Bicycle storage facility
◇ Seat reservations can be made at this station
⚠ Penalty Fare Schemes in operation on some or all services from this station
🚕 Taxi rank or cab office at station, or signposted and within 100 metres
ⓤ Unstaffed station
[ ] Station Operator Code

F

■10 Connection time
Ⓟ Station Car Park
🚲 Bicycle storage facility
◇ Seat reservations can be made at this station
⚠ Penalty Fare Schemes in operation on some or all services from this station
🚕 Taxi rank or cab office at station, or signposted and within 100 metres
Ⓤ Unstaffed station
[ ] Station Operator Code

Station index and table numbers

G

Station index and table numbers

10 Connection time
Ⓟ Station Car Park
🚲 Bicycle storage facility
◇ Seat reservations can be made at this station
⚠ Penalty Fare Schemes in operation on some or all services from this station
🚕 Taxi rank or cab office at station, or signposted and within 100 metres
🚹 Unstaffed station
[ ] Station Operator Code

Manchester Airport 65
Maryhill 232
Milngavie 226
Milton Keynes Central 65
Motherwell 225, 226
Neilston 223
Newcastle 26, 216
Newton 223, 226
Norwich 26
Oban 227
Oxenholme Lake District 65
Oxford 51
Paignton 51
Paisley 217, 219, 221
Penzance 51
Perth 229
Peterborough 26
Plymouth 51
Preston 65
Prestwick International Airport 221
Reading 51
Sheffield 26
Shotts 225
Southampton 51
Springburn 224, 226
Stafford 65
Stirling 230
Stranraer 218
Thurso 239
Torquay 51
Warrington 51
Watford 65, *Sleepers* 401
Wemyss Bay 219
Western Isles *Ship*
via Inverness 239B
via Mallaig 227A
via Oban 227B, 227C
Whifflet 220
Wick 239
Wigan 65
York 26

Glasshoughton [NT] Ⓟ 🚲 🚹 32
Glazebrook [NT] Ⓟ 89
Gleneagles [SR] Ⓟ 🚲 🚹 229, *Sleepers* 403
Glenfinnan [SR] Ⓟ 🚲 🚹 227
Glengarnock [SR] Ⓟ 🚲 221
Glenrothes With Thornton [SR] Ⓟ 🚲 🚹 242
Glossop [NT] Ⓟ 🚲 79
Gloucester [GW] **7** Ⓟ 🚲 ◇ 🚕
Birmingham 57
Bristol 134
Cardiff 132
Carmarthen 128
Cheltenham 57
Chepstow 132
Derby 57
Didcot 125
Gatwick Airport 125
Heathrow Airport 125
Kemble 125
London 125
Lydney 132
Maesteg 128
Newcastle 51
Newport (South Wales) 132
Nottingham 57
Reading 125
Sheffield 51
Stroud 125
Swansea 128
Swindon 125
Taunton 134
Weston-super-Mare 134
Worcester 57
York 51

Glynde [SN] Ⓟ 🚹 189
Goathland [NY] 45
Gobowen [AW] Ⓟ 75
Godalming [SW] Ⓟ 🚲 ◇ ⚠ 🚕 156
Godley [NT] 🚹 79
Godstone [SE] 🚹 209
Goldthorpe [NT] Ⓟ 🚹 31
Goldthorpe Police Station *Bus* 26E
Golf Street [SR] 🚹 229
Golspie [SR] Ⓟ 🚲 🚹 239
Gomshall [GW] Ⓟ 🚹 148
Goodmayes [LE] 🚲 ⚠ 5
Goole [NT] Ⓟ 🚲 ◇ 🚕 29, 32
Goostrey [NT] Ⓟ 🚹 84
Gordon Hill [FC] Ⓟ 🚲 ⚠ 24
Goring & Streatley [GW] Ⓟ 🚲 116
Goring-by-Sea [SN] Ⓟ 🚲 ⚠ 188
Gorton [NT] 78, 79
Gospel Oak [LO] ⚠ 59, 62
Gourock [SR] Ⓟ 🚲 ◇ 🚕 219, *Ship* 219A
Gowerton [AW] Ⓟ 🚹 128, 129
Goxhill [NT] 🚹 29
Grange Park [FC] Ⓟ ⚠ 24
Grange-over-Sands [TP] ◇ 82
Grangetown [AW] 🚹 130
Grantham [GR] **7** Ⓟ 🚲 ◇ 🚕 19, 26, 49
Grateley [SW] Ⓟ 🚲 ⚠ 🚹 160
Gravelly Hill [LM] ⚠ 69
Gravesend [SE] **4** Ⓟ ◇ ⚠ 🚕 200, 209, 212
Grays [CC] Ⓟ 🚲 ◇ ⚠ 🚕 1
Great Ayton [NT] Ⓟ 🚲 🚹 45
Great Bentley [LE] 🚲 ⚠ 11
Great Chesterford [LE] ⚠ 22
Great Coates [NT] 🚹 29
Great Malvern [LM] Ⓟ ◇ ⚠ 71, 126
Great Missenden [CH] Ⓟ 🚲 ◇ ⚠ 🚕 114
Great Yarmouth [LE] Ⓟ 🚲 ◇ 🚕 15
Green Lane [ME] ⚠ 106
Green Road [NT] Ⓟ 🚹 100
Greenbank [NT] Ⓟ 🚹 88
Greenfaulds [SR] Ⓟ 🚲 🚹 224
Greenfield [NT] 🚲 39
Greenford [LT] Ⓟ ⚠ 117
Greenhithe for Bluewater [SE] ⚠ 200, 209, 212
Greenock Central [SR] Ⓟ 🚲 219
Greenock West [SR] 🚕 219
Greenwich [SE] **4** ⚠ 200
Gretna Green [SR] Ⓟ 🚲 🚹 216
Grimsby Docks [NT] 🚹 29
Grimsby Town [TP] Ⓟ 🚲 ◇ 🚕 26, 27, 29, 30
Grindleford [NT] 🚹 78
Grosmont [NT] [NY] Ⓟ 🚹 45
Grove Park [SE] **4** ⚠ 204
Guide Bridge [NT] Ⓟ 78, 79
Guildford [SW] Ⓟ 🚲 ◇ ⚠ 🚕
Ascot 149
Birmingham 51
Clapham Junction 152, 155, 156
Gatwick Airport 148
London 152, 155, 156
Portsmouth 156
Reading 148
Surbiton 152
West Croydon 182

Guiseley [NT] Ⓟ 🚲 ◇ 38
Gunnersbury [LT] 59
Gunnislake [GW] Ⓟ 🚲 🚹 139
Gunton [LE] Ⓟ 🚲 🚹 16
Gwersyllt [AW] Ⓟ 🚹 101
Gypsy Lane [NT] 🚲 🚹 45

H

Habrough [NT] Ⓟ 🚹 27, 29, 30
Hackbridge [SN] Ⓟ ◇ ⚠ 52, 179, 182
Hackney Central [LO] ⚠ 🚕 59
Hackney Downs [LE] 🚲 ⚠ 20, 21, 22
Hackney Wick [LO] ⚠ 59
Haddenham & Thame Parkway [CH] Ⓟ 🚲 ◇ ⚠ 🚕 115
Haddiscoe [LE] Ⓟ 🚲 🚹 15
Hadfield [NT] Ⓟ 🚲 79
Hadley Wood [FC] ⚠ 24
Hag Fold [NT] 82
Hagley [LM] Ⓟ ⚠ 71
Hairmyres [SR] Ⓟ 🚲 🚹 222
Hale [NT] Ⓟ 88
Halesworth [LE] Ⓟ 🚲 🚹 13
Halewood [NT] 89
Halifax [NT] Ⓟ 🚲 ◇ 🚕 41
Hall Green [LM] Ⓟ ⚠ 71
Hall I' Th' Wood [NT] 🚹 94
Hall Road [ME] 🚲 ⚠ 103
Halling [SE] 🚹 208
Haltwhistle [NT] Ⓟ 🚲 🚹 48
Ham Street [SN] Ⓟ 189
Hamble [SW] 🚲 ⚠ 🚹 165
Hamilton Central [SR] Ⓟ 🚲 ◇ 🚕 226
Hamilton Square [ME] ◇ ⚠ 🚕 106

Station index and table numbers

10 Connection time
℗ Station Car Park
🚲 Bicycle storage facility
◇ Seat reservations can be made at this station
⚠ Penalty Fare Schemes in operation on some or all services from this station
🚕 Taxi rank or cab office at station, or signposted and within 100 metres
ⓤ Unstaffed station
[ ] Station Operator Code

Hamilton West [SR] ℗ 🚲 🚕 226
Hammerton [NT] ℗ ⓤ 35
Hampden Park [SN] **4** ⚠ 189
Hampstead Heath [LO] ⚠ 59
Hampstead (South) [LO] (see South Hampstead)
Hampstead (West)
(see West Hampstead)
(see West Hampstead Thameslink)
Hampton [SW] 🚲 ⚠ 152
Hampton-in-Arden [LM] ℗ ⚠ 68
Hampton Court [SW] ℗ 🚲 ◇ ⚠ 152
Hampton Wick [SW] 🚲 ⚠ 149, 152
Hamstead [LM] ⚠ 70
Hamworthy [SW] 🚲 ◇ ⚠ 158
Hanborough [GW] ℗ 🚲 ⓤ 126
Handforth [NT] 84
Hanley Bus Station *Bus* 68A
Hanwell [GW] 🚲 ⚠ 117
Hapton [NT] ⓤ 97
Harlech [AW] ℗ 🚲 ⓤ 75
Harlesden [LT] 60
Harling Road [LE] ℗ 🚲 ⓤ 17
Harlington (Beds.) **[FC]** ℗ 🚲 ◇ ⚠ 🚕 52
Harlington (Middx.) **[GW]** (see Hayes & Harlington)
Harlow Mill [LE] ℗ 🚲 ⚠ 22
Harlow Town [LE] ℗ 🚲 ◇ ⚠ 🚕 22
Harold Wood [LE] ℗ 🚲 ⚠ 🚕 5
Harpenden [FC] ℗ 🚲 ◇ ⚠ 🚕 52
Harrietsham [SE] ℗ ⚠ 196
Harringay [FC] ⚠ 24
Harringay Green Lanes [LO] ⚠ 62
Harrington [NT] ℗ ⓤ 100
Harrogate [NT] ℗ 🚲 ◇ 🚕 26, 35
Harrow & Wealdstone [LT] ℗ ⚠ 🚕 60, 66, 186
Harrow Road [CH] (see Sudbury & Harrow Road)
Harrow Sudbury Hill [CH] (see Sudbury Hill Harrow)
Harrow-on-the-Hill [LT] **3** ℗ 🚲 ⚠ 🚕 114
Hartford [LM] ℗ ◇ 65, 91
Hartlebury [LM] ℗ ⚠ ⓤ 71
Hartlepool [NT] ℗ 🚲 ◇ 🚕 26, 44
Hartwood [SR] ℗ 🚲 ⓤ 225
Harwich International [LE] 🚲 ◇ 11, 14
Harwich Town [LE] 🚲 ⓤ 11
Haslemere [SW] **4** ℗ 🚲 ◇ ⚠ 🚕 156
Hassocks [SN] **4** ℗ 🚲 ⚠ 🚕 52, 186
Hastings [SE] **4** ℗ ◇ ⚠ 🚕 189, 206
Hatch End [LO] ℗ ⚠ 60
Hatfield [FC] ℗ 🚲 ⚠ 🚕 24, 25
Hatfield & Stainforth [NT] ℗ 🚕 ⓤ 29
Hatfield Peverel [LE] ℗ 🚲 ⚠ 11
Hathersage [NT] ℗ ⓤ 78
Hattersley [NT] 79
Hatton (Derbyshire) **[EM]** (see Tutbury & Hatton)
Hatton (Warwickshire) **[CH]** ℗ ⚠ ⓤ 71, 115
Havant [SW] ℗ 🚲 ◇ ⚠ 🚕 123, 156, 157, 165, 188
Havenhouse [EM] ⓤ 19
Haverfordwest [AW] ℗ ◇ 🚕 128
Hawarden [AW] ℗ ⓤ 101
Hawarden Bridge [AW] ⓤ 101
Hawick *Bus* 65G
Hawkhead [SR] 🚲 ⓤ 217
Haydon Bridge [NT] ℗ 🚲 ⓤ 48
Haydons Road [FC] ℗ ⚠ 52, 179
Hayes & Harlington [GW] **3** ℗ 🚲 ◇ ⚠ 117
Hayes (Kent) [SE] ℗ 🚲 ⚠ 🚕 203
Hayle [GW] ℗ ⓤ 135, *Sleepers* 406
Haymarket (Edinburgh) **[SR]** ℗ 🚲 ◇ 🚕
Aberdeen 229
Bathgate 230
Birmingham 51, 65
Birmingham International 51, 65
Blackpool 65
Bournemouth 51
Brighton 51
Bristol 51
Cambridge 26
Carlisle 65
Carstairs 225
Cowdenbeath 242
Crewe 65
Croy 228
Darlington 26
Derby 51
Doncaster 26
Dunblane 230
Dundee 229
Dunfermline 242
Edinburgh Park 230
Exeter 51
Glasgow 225, 228
Inverness 229
Lancaster 65
Larbert 230
Leeds 26
Liverpool 65
Livingston 225, 230
London 26, 65
Manchester 65
Manchester Airport 65
Motherwell 225
Newcastle 26
Newcraighall 230
North Berwick 238
Oxenholme Lake District 65
Oxford 51
Paignton 51
Penzance 51
Perth 229
Peterborough 26
Plymouth 51
Preston 65
Reading 51
Sheffield 26
Southampton 51
Stirling 230
Torquay 51
York 26
Haywards Heath [SN] **3** ℗ 🚲 ◇ ⚠ 🚕
Bedford 52
Birmingham 51
Brighton 186
Clapham Junction 186
Eastbourne 189
East Croydon 186
Edinburgh 51
Gatwick Airport 186
Glasgow 51
Hastings 189
Hove 188
Lewes 189
London 186
Littlehampton 188
Luton 52, 186
Manchester 51
Milton Keynes 66
Northampton 66
Portsmouth 188
Reading 51
Rugby 66
St Albans 52
Seaford 189
Southampton Central 188
Watford Junction 66, 186
West Hampstead Thameslink 52
Worthing 188
Hazel Grove [NT] ℗ 🚲 78, 82, 86
Headcorn [SE] **4** ℗ ⚠ 🚕 207
Headingley [NT] ℗ ⓤ 35
Headstone Lane [LO] ⚠ 60
Heald Green [NT] ℗ 🚲 82, 85
Healing [NT] ⓤ 29
Heath High Level [AW] ⓤ 130
Heath Low Level [AW] ⓤ 130
Heathrow London Airport [HX] ◇ 🚕
Bristol 125
Cardiff 125
Cheltenham Spa 125
Ealing Broadway 117
Exeter 135
Gloucester 125
London 117, 118
Penzance 135
Plymouth 135

Station index and table numbers

10 Connection time
Ⓟ Station Car Park
🚲 Bicycle storage facility
◇ Seat reservations can be made at this station
⚠ Penalty Fare Schemes in operation on some or all services from this station
🚕 Taxi rank or cab office at station, or signposted and within 100 metres
🚶 Unstaffed station
[ ] Station Operator Code

[10] Connection time
Ⓟ Station Car Park
🚲 Bicycle storage facility
◇ Seat reservations can be made at this station
⚠ Penalty Fare Schemes in operation on some or all services from this station
🚕 Taxi rank or cab office at station, or signposted and within 100 metres
Ⓤ Unstaffed station
[ ] Station Operator Code

Station index and table numbers

Station index and table numbers

[10] Connection time
Ⓟ Station Car Park
🚲 Bicycle storage facility
◇ Seat reservations can be made at this station
⚠ Penalty Fare Schemes in operation on some or all services from this station
🚕 Taxi rank or cab office at station, or signposted and within 100 metres
ⓤ Unstaffed station
[ ] Station Operator Code

L

Station index and table numbers

■10 Connection time
Ⓟ Station Car Park
🚲 Bicycle storage facility
◇ Seat reservations can be made at this station
⚠ Penalty Fare Schemes in operation on some or all services from this station
🚕 Taxi rank or cab office at station, or signposted and within 100 metres
Ⓤ Unstaffed station
[ ] Station Operator Code

Selby 40
Settle 36
Sheffield 31
Shipley 37
Skipton 36
Stansted Airport 26
Southampton 51
Torquay 51
Wakefield 31
Warrington 39
York 35, 40
Leicester [EM] Ⓟ 🚲 ◇ 🚕 49, 53, 57
Leigh (Kent) [SE] Ⓤ 209
Leigh-on-Sea [CC] Ⓟ 🚲 ◇ ⚠ 🚕 1
Leighton Buzzard [LM] Ⓟ 🚲 ◇ 🚕 66
Lelant [GW] Ⓟ Ⓤ 144
Lelant Saltings [GW] Ⓟ Ⓤ 144
Lenham [SE] Ⓟ ⚠ 196
Lenzie [SR] ■3 Ⓟ 🚲 🚕 228, 230
Leominster [AW] Ⓟ 131
Letchworth Garden City [FC] 🚲 ⚠ 🚕 24, 25
Leuchars (for St. Andrews) **[SR]** ■3 Ⓟ 🚲 ◇ 🚕 26, 51, 229, *Sleepers* 402
Levenshulme [NT] 84, 86
Lewes [SN] ■4 Ⓟ 🚲 ◇ ⚠ 🚕 186, 189
Lewisham [SE] ■4 Ⓟ 🚲 ⚠ 🚕
Bexleyheath 200
Dartford 200
Gillingham (Kent) 200
Gravesend 200
Hayes (Kent) 203
London 195, 199
Orpington 199, 204
Sidcup 200
Woolwich Arsenal 200
Leyland [NT] Ⓟ ◇ 🚕 82, 90
Leyton Midland Road [LO] ⚠ 62
Leytonstone High Road [LO] ⚠ 62
Lichfield City [LM] Ⓟ ◇ ⚠ 69
Lichfield Trent Valley [LM] Ⓟ ◇ ⚠ 65, 67, 69
Lidlington [LM] Ⓤ 64
Limehouse [CC] ⚠ 1
Lincoln [EM] Ⓟ 🚲 ◇ 🚕 18, 26, 27, 30
Lincoln Bus Station *Bus* 26D
Lindford (Liphook Road) *Bus* 156A
Lingfield [SN] Ⓟ 🚲 ⚠ 🚕 184
Lingwood [LE] Ⓟ 🚲 Ⓤ 15
Linlithgow [SR] Ⓟ 🚲 ◇ 228, 230
Liphook [SW] Ⓟ 🚲 ◇ ⚠ 🚕 156, *Bus* 156A
Liskeard [GW] ■3 Ⓟ 🚲 ◇ 51, 135, 140, *Sleepers* 406
Lismore *Ship* 227B
Liss [SW] Ⓟ 🚲 ◇ ⚠ 156
Lisvane & Thornhill [AW] Ⓟ Ⓤ 130
Litherland [ME] (see Seaforth & Litherland)
Little Kimble [CH] ⚠ Ⓤ 115
Little Sutton [ME] Ⓤ 106
Littleborough [NT] Ⓟ 41
Littlehampton [SN] ■4 Ⓟ 🚲 ⚠ 🚕 186, 188
Littlehaven [SN] ◇ ⚠ 187
Littleport [FC] 🚲 ⚠ Ⓤ 17
Liverpool
Central [ME] ■10 ⚠ 🚕
James Street [ME] ◇ ⚠
Lime Street (Main Line) **[NR]** ■10 Ⓟ 🚲 ◇ 🚕
Lime Street (Low Level) **[ME]** ■10 ◇ ⚠ 🚕
Moorfields [ME] ■10 ⚠
Aberdeen 65
Bangor (Gwynedd) 81
Barrow-in-Furness 65
Birkenhead 106
Birmingham 65
Birmingham International 65
Blackpool 65, 90
Bolton 82
Bradford 41
Cambridge 49
Cardiff 131
Carlisle 65
Chester 106
Coventry 65
Crewe 91
Darlington 39
Douglas (IOM) 98A
Dundee 65
Durham 39
Edinburgh 65
Ellesmere Port 106
Ely 49
Gatwick Airport 65
Glasgow 65
Hartford 91
Holyhead 81
Hooton 106
Huddersfield 39
Hull 39
Hunts Cross 89, 103
Inverness 65
Ipswich 49
Kirkby 103
Lancaster 65
Leeds 39, 41
Liverpool South Parkway 91
Llandudno 81
London 65
Manchester 89, 90
Manchester Airport 89
Middlesbrough 39
Milton Keynes Central 65
Mossley Hill 91
Motherwell 65
New Brighton 106
Newcastle 39
Newport (South Wales) 131
Norwich 49
Nottingham 49
Nuneaton 65
Ormskirk 103
Oxenholme Lake District 65
Peterborough 49
Preston 90, 99
Rhyl 81
Rochdale 95
Rock Ferry 106
Rugby 65
Runcorn 91
St Helens 90
Scarborough 39
Sheffield 89
Shrewsbury 131
Southport 103
Stafford 65
Stansted Airport 49
Stockport 89
Wakefield 39
Warrington 89, 90
Watford 65
West Kirby 106
Wigan 82, 90
Windermere 65
Wolverhampton 65
Wrexham 101
York 39
Liverpool Landing Stage *Ship* 98A
Liverpool South Parkway [ME] ■7 Ⓟ 🚲 ⚠ 🚕 65, 89, 91, 103
Liverpool Street [NR] (see London)
Livingston North [SR] Ⓟ 🚲 Ⓤ 230
Livingston South [SR] Ⓟ 🚲 Ⓤ 225
Llanaber [AW] Ⓤ 75
Llanbedr [AW] Ⓤ 75
Llanbister Road [AW] Ⓤ 129
Llanbradach [AW] Ⓟ Ⓤ 130
Llandaf [AW] Ⓟ 130
Llandanwg [AW] Ⓤ 75
Llandecwyn [AW] Ⓤ 75
Llandeilo [AW] Ⓟ Ⓤ 129
Llandovery [AW] Ⓟ Ⓤ 129
Llandrindod [AW] Ⓟ ◇ 129
Llandudno [AW] ◇ 🚕 65, 81, 102
Llandudno Junction [AW] Ⓟ ◇ 🚕 65, 81, 102, 131
Llandybie [AW] Ⓟ Ⓤ 129
Llanelli [AW] ◇ 128, 129
Llanfairfechan [AW] Ⓟ Ⓤ 81
Llanfairpwll [AW] Ⓟ Ⓤ 81
Llangadog [AW] Ⓤ 129
Llangammarch [AW] Ⓤ 129
Llangennech [AW] Ⓤ 129
Llangynllo [AW] Ⓤ 129
Llanharan [AW] Ⓟ Ⓤ 128
Llanhilleth [AW] Ⓟ Ⓤ 127
Llanishen [AW] Ⓟ Ⓤ 130

Station index and table numbers

■10 Connection time
Ⓟ Station Car Park
🚲 Bicycle storage facility
◇ Seat reservations can be made at this station
⚠ Penalty Fare Schemes in operation on some or all services from this station
🚕 Taxi rank or cab office at station, or signposted and within 100 metres
🚶 Unstaffed station
[ ] Station Operator Code

Llanrwst [AW] 🚶 102
Llansamlet [AW] Ⓟ 🚶 128
Llantwit Major [AW] Ⓟ 🚲 🚶 130
Llanwrda [AW] 🚶 129
Llanwrtyd [AW] Ⓟ 🚶 129
Llwyngwril [AW] 🚶 75
Llwynypia [AW] Ⓟ 🚶 130
Loch Awe [SR] Ⓟ 🚲 🚶 227
Loch Eil Outward Bound [SR] 🚲 🚶 227
Lochailort [SR] Ⓟ 🚲 🚶 227
Lochboisdale *Ship* 227C
Locheilside [SR] Ⓟ 🚲 🚶 227
Lochgelly [SR] Ⓟ 🚲 🚶 242
Lochluichart [SR] Ⓟ 🚶 239
Lochmaddy *Ship* 239B
Lochwinnoch [SR] Ⓟ 🚲 🚶 221
Lockerbie [SR] Ⓟ 🚲 ◇ 🚕 51, 65
Lockwood [NT] Ⓟ 🚶 34
London
- **Barbican [LT]** ⚠
- **Blackfriars [FC]** ■3 ◇ ⚠ 🚕
- **Cannon Street [NR]** ■4 ◇ ⚠ 🚕
- **Charing Cross [NR]** ■4 ◇ ⚠ 🚕
- **City Thameslink [FC]** ■3 ◇ ⚠ 🚕
- **Euston [NR]** ■15 Ⓟ ◇ ⚠ 🚕
- **Farringdon [LT]** ■3 ⚠
- **Fenchurch Street [NR]** ■7 ◇ ⚠ 🚕
- **Kings Cross [NR]** ■15 Ⓟ 🚲 ◇ ⚠ 🚕
- **Liverpool Street [NR]** ■15 🚲 ◇ ⚠ 🚕
- **London Bridge [NR]** ■4 🚲 ◇ ⚠ 🚕
- **Marylebone [CH]** ■10 🚲 ◇ ⚠ 🚕
- **Moorgate [LT]** ⚠
- **Paddington [NR]** ■15 Ⓟ 🚲 ◇ ⚠ 🚕
- **St Pancras International [NR]** ■15 Ⓟ ◇ ⚠ 🚕
- **Victoria [NR]** ■15 Ⓟ 🚲 ◇ ⚠ 🚕
- **Waterloo [NR]** ■15 Ⓟ 🚲 ◇ ⚠ 🚕
- **Waterloo East [SE]** ■4 ⚠

Aberdeen 26, *Sleepers* 402
Aberystwyth 75
Aldershot 149, 155
Alexandra Palace 24
Alnmouth 26
Alton 155
Amersham 114
Arbroath 26, *Sleepers* 402
Ascot 149
Ashford International 196, 207
Aviemore *Sleepers* 403
Aylesbury 114, 115
Balham 177, 178
Banbury 115, 116
Bangor (Gwynedd) 65
Barking 1
Barmouth 75
Barnsley 34, 53
Barrow-in-Furness 65
Basingstoke 155, 158
Bath Spa 125, 160
Beckenham Junction 177, 195
Bedford 52
Belper 53
Berwick-upon-Tweed 26
Bexhill 189, 206
Bicester 115, 116
Birmingham 66, 115, 116
Birmingham International 66
Bishops Stortford 22
Blackburn 97
Blackpool 65
Bletchley 66
Bodmin Parkway 135, *Sleepers* 406
Bognor Regis 188
Boston 19
Bourne End 120
Bournemouth 158
Bradford 26
Braintree 11
Brighton 186
Bristol 125, 160
Bromley North 204
Bromley South 195
Brough 29
Broxbourne 22
Burnley 97
Camborne 135, *Sleepers* 406
Cambridge 22, 25
Canterbury 207, 212
Cardiff 125
Carlisle 65, *Sleepers* 400, 401
Carstairs 65, *Sleepers* 401
Carmarthen 128
Caterham 181
Chatham 200, 212
Chelmsford 11
Cheltenham Spa 125
Chertsey 149
Chessington 152
Chester 65
Chesterfield 53
Chichester 188
Chingford 20
Clacton-on-Sea 11
Clapton 20, 22
Cleethorpes 27, 29
Colchester 11
Colne 97
Corby *Bus* 53A
Coventry 66
Crewe 65
Cromer 16
Crystal Palace 177, 178
Darlington 26
Dartford 200
Derby 53
Didcot 116
Doncaster 26, 53
Dorking 152, 182
Douglas (IOM) 98A
Dover 207, 212
Dundee 26, *Sleepers* 402
Durham 26
Eaglescliffe 26
Eastbourne 189
East Croydon 175
East Grinstead 184
Edinburgh 26, *Sleepers* 400
Effingham Junction 152
Ely 17
Enfield Town 21
Epsom 152, 182
Epsom Downs 182
Exeter 135, 160, *Sleepers* 406
Fareham 158, 188
Felixstowe 13
Finsbury Park 24, 25
Folkestone 207
Fort William *Sleepers* 404
Gatwick Airport 186
Gillingham (Kent) 200, 212
Glasgow 26, 65, *Sleepers* 401
Gloucester 125
Grantham 26
Gravesend 200
Grays 1
Great Yarmouth 15
Greenford 117
Grimsby 26, 27
Grove Park 204
Guildford 152, 155, 156
Hampton Court 152
Harrogate 26
Harrow (Sudbury Hill) 115
Harrow & Wealdstone 60, 66
Harrow-on-the-Hill 114
Hartlepool 26
Harwich 11
Haslemere 156
Hastings 189, 206
Hatfield 24
Hayes (Kent) 203
Hayle *Sleepers* 406
Haywards Heath 186
Heathrow Airport 117, 118
Hedge End 158
Henley-on-Thames 121
Hereford 125, 126
Herne Hill 195
Hertford East 22
Hertford North 24
Heysham Port 98A
High Wycombe 115
Hitchin 24, 25
Holyhead 65
Horsham 182, 186
Hounslow 149
Hove 186, 188
Howden 29
Huddersfield 26
Hull 26, 29
Huntingdon 25

Station index and table numbers

10 Connection time
Ⓟ Station Car Park
🚲 Bicycle storage facility
◇ Seat reservations can be made at this station
⚠ Penalty Fare Schemes in operation on some or all services from this station
🚕 Taxi rank or cab office at station, or signposted and within 100 metres
Ⓤ Unstaffed station
[ ] Station Operator Code

Station index and table numbers

10 Connection time
℗ Station Car Park
🚲 Bicycle storage facility
◇ Seat reservations can be made at this station
⚠ Penalty Fare Schemes in operation on some or all services from this station
🚕 Taxi rank or cab office at station, or signposted and within 100 metres
Ⓤ Unstaffed station
[ ] Station Operator Code

[10] Connection time
Ⓟ Station Car Park
🚲 Bicycle storage facility
◇ Seat reservations can be made at this station
⚠ Penalty Fare Schemes in operation on some or all services from this station
🚕 Taxi rank or cab office at station, or signposted and within 100 metres
Ⓤ Unstaffed station
[ ] Station Operator Code

Station index and table numbers

Station index and table numbers

■10 Connection time
Ⓟ Station Car Park
🚲 Bicycle storage facility
◇ Seat reservations can be made at this station
⚠ Penalty Fare Schemes in operation on some or all services from this station
🚕 Taxi rank or cab office at station, or signposted and within 100 metres
ⓤ Unstaffed station
[ ] Station Operator Code

Station index and table numbers

- **10** Connection time
- Ⓟ Station Car Park
- 🚲 Bicycle storage facility
- ◇ Seat reservations can be made at this station
- ⚠ Penalty Fare Schemes in operation on some or all services from this station
- 🚕 Taxi rank or cab office at station, or signposted and within 100 metres
- Ⓤ Unstaffed station
- [ ] Station Operator Code

O

Station index and table numbers

❿ Connection time
Ⓟ Station Car Park
🚲 Bicycle storage facility
◇ Seat reservations can be made at this station
⚠ Penalty Fare Schemes in operation on some or all services from this station
🚕 Taxi rank or cab office at station, or signposted and within 100 metres
Ⓤ Unstaffed station
[ ] Station Operator Code

P

[10] Connection time
Ⓟ Station Car Park
🚲 Bicycle storage facility
◇ Seat reservations can be made at this station
⚠ Penalty Fare Schemes in operation on some or all services from this station
🚕 Taxi rank or cab office at station, or signposted and within 100 metres
🚶 Unstaffed station
[ ] Station Operator Code

Station index and table numbers

Nottingham 49
Nuneaton 49
Oundle (Market Place) *Bus* 26B
Retford 26
Sheffield 49
Spalding 18
Stansted Airport 49
Stevenage 25
Stockport 49
Swaffham *Bus* 26A
Wakefield 26
York 26

Petersfield [SW] Ⓟ 🚲 ◇ ⚠ 🚕 156, *Bus* 156B
Petts Wood [SE] [4] Ⓟ ⚠ 195, 199, 204
Pevensey & Westham [SN] Ⓟ 🚲 ⚠ 189
Pevensey Bay [SN] 🚶 189
Pewsey [GW] Ⓟ 🚲 ◇ ⚠ 135
Pickering [NY] 45
Pickering Eastgate *Bus* 26G
Pilning [GW] Ⓟ 🚶 132
Pinhoe [SW] 🚶 160
Pitlochry [SR] Ⓟ 🚲 🚕 229, *Sleepers* 403
Pitsea [CC] Ⓟ 🚲 ◇ ⚠ 🚕 1
Pleasington [NT] Ⓟ 🚶 97
Pleasure Beach [NT] (see Blackpool)
Plockton [SR] Ⓟ 🚲 🚶 239
Pluckley [SE] Ⓟ 🚲 ⚠ 207
Plumley [NT] Ⓟ 🚶 88
Plumpton [SN] Ⓟ ⚠ 189
Plumstead [SE] ⚠ 200
Plymouth [GW] Ⓟ 🚲 ◇ ⚠ 🚕
Aberdeen 51
Basingstoke 160
Birmingham 51, 135
Bristol 135
Cardiff 135
Carlisle 51
Crewe 51
Derby 51
Dundee 51
Edinburgh 51
Exeter 135
Gatwick Airport 135
Glasgow 51
Gunnislake 139
Heathrow Airport 135
Leeds 51
London 135, 160, *Sleepers* 406
Manchester 51
Newcastle 51
Newton Abbot 135
Paignton 135
Penzance 135
Preston 51
Reading 135, *Sleepers* 406
Salisbury 160
Sheffield 51
Taunton 135
Torquay 135
Wolverhampton 51

York 51
Pokesdown [SW] 🚲 ◇ ⚠ 158
Polegate [SN] Ⓟ 🚲 ⚠ 🚕 189
Polesworth [LM] Ⓟ 🚶 67
Pollokshaws East [SR] 🚲 🚶 223
Pollokshaws West [SR] 🚲 🚶 222
Pollokshields East [SR] 🚲 223
Pollokshields West [SR] 🚲 🚶 223
Polmont [SR] [3] Ⓟ 🚲 ◇ 🚕 228, 230
Polsloe Bridge [GW] 🚶 136
Ponders End [LE] ⚠ 22
Pontarddulais [AW] Ⓟ 🚶 129
Pontefract Baghill [NT] Ⓟ 🚶 33
Pontefract Monkhill [NT] Ⓟ 🚶 32
Pontefract Tanshelf [NT] Ⓟ 🚶 32
Pontlottyn [AW] Ⓟ 🚶 130
Pont-y-Pant [AW] 🚶 102
Pontyclun [AW] Ⓟ 🚶 128
Pontypool & New Inn [AW] Ⓟ 🚶 131
Pontypridd [AW] [3] 🚲 ◇ 🚕 130
Poole [SW] [4] Ⓟ 🚲 ◇ ⚠ 🚕 158
Poppleton [NT] Ⓟ 🚲 🚶 35
Portchester [SW] 🚲 ⚠ 158, 165, 188
Port Glasgow [SR] 🚲 🚕 219
Porth [AW] Ⓟ ◇ 130
Porthmadog [AW] 🚶 75
Portlethen [SR] Ⓟ 🚲 🚶 229
Portslade [SN] Ⓟ 🚲 ⚠ 188
Portsmouth Arms [GW] Ⓟ 🚶 136
Portsmouth
Harbour [SW] 🚲 ◇ ⚠ 🚕
& Southsea [SW] Ⓟ 🚲 ◇ ⚠ 🚕
Bognor Regis 188
Brighton 188
Bristol 123
Cardiff 123
Chichester 188
Exeter 160
Fareham 165
Gatwick Airport 188
Guildford 156
Haslemere 156
Havant 157
Littlehampton 188
London 156, 158, 188
Reading
via Eastleigh 158
via Guildford 156
Ryde 167
Salisbury 123
Sandown 167
Shanklin 167
Southampton Central 165
Winchester 158
Worthing 188
Port Sunlight [ME] 🚲 ⚠ 106

Port Talbot Parkway [AW] Ⓟ 🚲 ◇ 🚕 125, 128
Possilpark & Parkhouse [SR] 🚲 🚶 232
Potters Bar [FC] Ⓟ ◇ ⚠ 🚕 24, 25
Poulton-le-Fylde [NT] Ⓟ ◇ 🚕 41, 82, 97
Poynton [NT] Ⓟ 84
Prees [AW] 🚶 131
Prescot [NT] Ⓟ 90
Prestatyn [AW] ◇ 🚕 🚶 81
Prestbury [NT] Ⓟ 🚶 84
Preston [VT] [8] Ⓟ 🚲 ◇ 🚕
Aberdeen 65, *Sleepers* 402
Barrow-in-Furness 82
Birmingham 65
Birmingham International 65
Blackburn 97
Blackpool 97
Bolton 82
Bournemouth 51
Bradford 41
Brighton 51
Bristol 51
Burnley 97
Carlisle 65
Chorley 82
Clitheroe 94, 97
Colne 97
Coventry 65
Crewe 65
Douglas (IOM) 98A
Dundee 65, *Sleepers* 402
Edinburgh 65
Exeter 51
Fort William *Sleepers* 404
Gatwick Airport 65
Glasgow 65
Inverkeithing *Sleepers* 402
Inverness 65, *Sleepers* 403
Kirkcaldy *Sleepers* 402
Lancaster 65
Leeds 41
Liverpool 90, 99
London 65
Manchester 82
Manchester Airport 82
Milton Keynes Central 65
Ormskirk 99
Oxenholme Lake District 652
Oxford 51
Paignton 51
Penzance 51
Perth 65, *Sleepers* 403
Plymouth 51
Reading 51
Rugby 65
Southampton 51
Stafford 65
Stirling *Sleepers* 403
Stockport 82
Torquay 51
Warrington 65
Watford 65

Station index and table numbers

[10] Connection time
Ⓟ Station Car Park
🚲 Bicycle storage facility
◇ Seat reservations can be made at this station
⚠ Penalty Fare Schemes in operation on some or all services from this station
🚕 Taxi rank or cab office at station, or signposted and within 100 metres
⊛ Unstaffed station
[ ] Station Operator Code

Wigan 65
Windermere 653
Wolverhampton 65
York 41
Preston Park [SN] ⚠ 52, 186
Preston (Fishergate) *Bus* 65E
Prestonpans [SR] Ⓟ 🚲 ⊛ 238
Prestwick International Airport ⊛ 218, 221
Prestwick Town [SR] Ⓟ 🚲 🚕 218, 221
Priesthill & Darnley [SR] 🚲 ⊛ 222
Princes Risborough [CH] [2] Ⓟ 🚲 ◇ ⚠ 🚕 115, 115A
Prittlewell [LE] Ⓟ 🚲 ⚠ 5
Prudhoe [NT] Ⓟ 🚲 ⊛ 48
Pulborough [SN] Ⓟ 🚲 ⚠ 🚕 188
Purfleet [CC] Ⓟ 🚲 ◇ ⚠ 1
Purley [SN] [4] Ⓟ ⚠ 🚕 175, 181, 186
Purley Oaks [SN] Ⓟ ⚠ 175, 181
Putney [SW] 🚲 ◇ ⚠ 149
Pwllheli [AW] 🚲 🚕 75
Pyle [AW] Ⓟ 🚲 ⊛ 128

Q

Quakers Yard [AW] ⊛ 130
Queenborough [SE] Ⓟ 212
Queens Park (Glasgow) **[SR]** 🚲 223
Queens Park (London) **[LT]** 60
Queens Road, Peckham [SN] 🚲 ◇ ⚠ 177, 178, 179
Queens Road, Walthamstow [LO] (see Walthamstow Queens Road)
Queenstown Road (Battersea) [SW] ⚠ ⊛ 149
Quintrell Downs [GW] ⊛ 142

R

Radcliffe (Notts.) **[EM]** Ⓟ ⊛ 19
Radlett [FC] Ⓟ 🚲 ◇ ⚠ 🚕 52
Radley [GW] Ⓟ ⊛ 116
Radyr [AW] [3] Ⓟ 🚲 ◇ 130
Rainford [NT] Ⓟ ⊛ 82
Rainham (Essex) **[CC]** Ⓟ 🚲 ◇ ⚠ 1
Rainham (Kent) [SE] Ⓟ ⚠ 🚕 212
Rainhill [NT] 90
Ramsgate [SE] [4] Ⓟ 🚲 ◇ 🚕 207, 212
Ramsgreave & Wilpshire [NT] Ⓟ ⊛ 94
Rannoch [SR] Ⓟ 🚲 ⊛ 227, *Sleepers* 404
Rauceby [EM] ⊛ 19
Ravenglass for Eskdale [NT] ⊛ 100
Ravensbourne [SE] ⚠ 195
Ravensthorpe [NT] ⊛ 39
Rawcliffe [NT] ⊛ 32
Rayleigh [LE] Ⓟ 🚲 ⚠ 🚕 5
Raynes Park [SW] [6] 🚲 ◇ ⚠ 152
Reading [GW] [7] Ⓟ 🚲 ◇ ⚠ 🚕
Aberdeen 51
Ascot 149
Banbury 116
Basingstoke 122
Bath Spa 125
Birmingham 116
Bodmin Parkway 135, *Sleepers* 406
Bournemouth 158
Brighton 148
Bristol 125
Camborne 135, *Sleepers* 406
Cardiff 125
Carlisle 51
Cheltenham Spa 125
Clapham Junction 149
Coventry 51
Crewe 51
Derby 51
Didcot 116
Dundee 51
Edinburgh 51
Exeter 135, *Sleepers* 406
Gatwick Airport 148
Glasgow 51
Gloucester 125
Guildford 148
Hayle 135, *Sleepers* 406
Heathrow Airport *Bus* 125A
Henley-on-Thames 121
Hereford 126
Leamington Spa 116
Leeds 51
Liskeard 135, *Sleepers* 406
London 116, 117, 149
Lostwithiel 135, *Sleepers* 406
Manchester 51
Marlow 120
Milford Haven 128
Moreton-in-Marsh 126
Newbury 116
Newcastle 51
Newport (South Wales) 125
Newton Abbot 135, *Sleepers* 406
Oxford 116
Paignton 135
Par 135, *Sleepers* 406
Penzance 135, *Sleepers* 406
Plymouth 135, *Sleepers* 406
Poole 158
Portsmouth
via Basingstoke 158
via Guildford 156
Preston 51
Redhill 148
Redruth 135, *Sleepers* 406
Rosslare Harbour 128
Salisbury 160
Sheffield 51
Slough 117
Southampton 158
St Austell 135, *Sleepers* 406
St Erth 135, *Sleepers* 406
Staines 149
Stratford-upon-Avon 116
Swansea 125
Swindon 125
Taunton 135
Torquay 135
Truro 135, *Sleepers* 406
Wallingford *Bus* 116A
Weston-super-Mare 125
Weymouth 158
Winchester 158
Windsor & Eton Central 117
Wolverhampton 51
Worcester 126
York 51
Reading West [GW] [3] 116, 122
Rectory Road [LE] ⚠ 21
Redbridge [SW] Ⓟ ⚠ ⊛ 158
Redcar British Steel [NT] ⊛ 44
Redcar Central [NT] Ⓟ 🚲 ◇ 🚕 44
Redcar East [NT] 🚲 ⊛ 44
Reddish North [NT] Ⓟ 🚲 78
Reddish South [NT] ⊛ 78
Redditch [LM] Ⓟ ◇ ⚠ 69
Redhill [SN] Ⓟ 🚲 ◇ ⚠ 🚕
Birmingham 51
Brighton 186
Clapham Junction 186
Dorking 148
East Croydon 186
Edenbridge 209
Gatwick Airport 186
Guildford 148
Haywards Heath 186
Horsham 186
Hove 186
Lewes 186
London 186
Manchester 51
Reading 148
Stoke-on-Trent 51
Three Bridges 186
Tonbridge 209
Tunbridge Wells 209
Wokingham 148
Wolverhampton 51
Redland [GW] 🚲 ⊛ 133
Redruth [GW] Ⓟ 🚲 ◇ 🚕 51, 135, *Sleepers* 406
Reedham (Norfolk) [LE] Ⓟ 🚲 ⊛ 15
Reedham (Surrey) **[SN]** ⚠ 181

Station index and table numbers

⑩ Connection time
Ⓟ Station Car Park
🚲 Bicycle storage facility
◇ Seat reservations can be made at this station
⚠ Penalty Fare Schemes in operation on some or all services from this station
🚕 Taxi rank or cab office at station, or signposted and within 100 metres
Ⓤ Unstaffed station
[ ] Station Operator Code

Station index and table numbers

- **10** Connection time
- Ⓟ Station Car Park
- 🚲 Bicycle storage facility
- ◇ Seat reservations can be made at this station
- ⚠ Penalty Fare Schemes in operation on some or all services from this station
- 🚕 Taxi rank or cab office at station, or signposted and within 100 metres
- Ⓤ Unstaffed station
- [ ] Station Operator Code

Station index and table numbers

10 Connection time
Ⓟ Station Car Park
🚲 Bicycle storage facility
◇ Seat reservations can be made at this station
⚠ Penalty Fare Schemes in operation on some or all services from this station
🚕 Taxi rank or cab office at station, or signposted and within 100 metres
Ⓤ Unstaffed station
[ ] Station Operator Code

Station index and table numbers

10 Connection time
Ⓟ Station Car Park
🚲 Bicycle storage facility
◇ Seat reservations can be made at this station
⚠ Penalty Fare Schemes in operation on some or all services from this station
🚕 Taxi rank or cab office at station, or signposted and within 100 metres
🚶 Unstaffed station
[ ] Station Operator Code

T

[10] Connection time
Ⓟ Station Car Park
🚲 Bicycle storage facility
◇ Seat reservations can be made at this station
⚠ Penalty Fare Schemes in operation on some or all services from this station
🚕 Taxi rank or cab office at station, or signposted and within 100 metres
Ⓤ Unstaffed station
[ ] Station Operator Code

Station index and table numbers

U

V

W

Station index and table numbers

10 Connection time
Ⓟ Station Car Park
🚲 Bicycle storage facility
◇ Seat reservations can be made at this station
⚠ Penalty Fare Schemes in operation on some or all services from this station
🚕 Taxi rank or cab office at station, or signposted and within 100 metres
Ⓤ Unstaffed station
[ ] Station Operator Code

■10 Connection time
Ⓟ Station Car Park
🚲 Bicycle storage facility
◇ Seat reservations can be made at this station
⚠ Penalty Fare Schemes in operation on some or all services from this station
🚕 Taxi rank or cab office at station, or signposted and within 100 metres
Ⓤ Unstaffed station
[ ] Station Operator Code

Station index and table numbers

Station index and table numbers

[10] Connection time
Ⓟ Station Car Park
🚲 Bicycle storage facility
◇ Seat reservations can be made at this station
⚠ Penalty Fare Schemes in operation on some or all services from this station
🚕 Taxi rank or cab office at station, or signposted and within 100 metres
Ⓤ Unstaffed station
[ ] Station Operator Code

Y

Network Diagram for Tables 1, 4

DM-1/06
Design BAJS

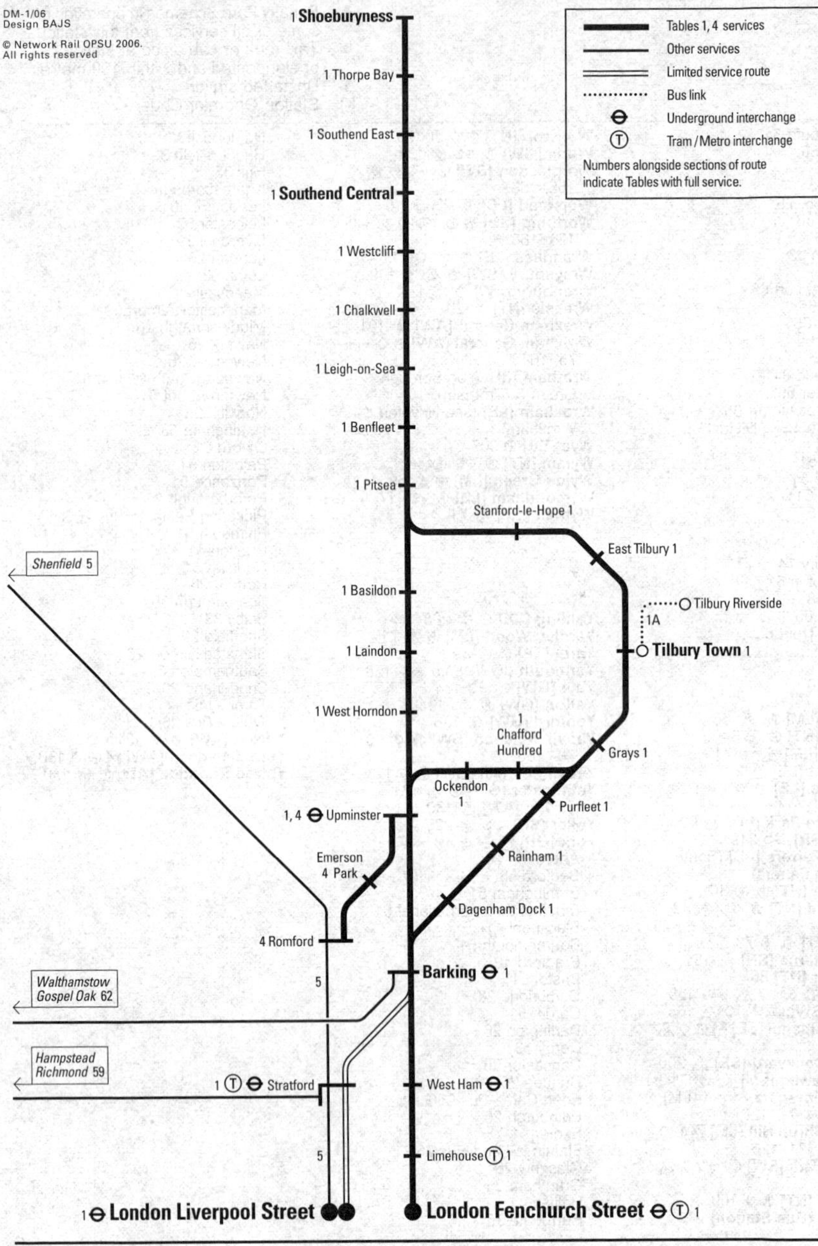
Tables 1, 4 services
Other services
Limited service route
Bus link
Underground interchange
Tram / Metro interchange
Numbers alongside sections of route indicate Tables with full service.
1 Shoeburyness
1 Thorpe Bay
1 Southend East
1 Southend Central
1 Westcliff
1 Chalkwell
1 Leigh-on-Sea
1 Benfleet
1 Pitsea
Stanford-le-Hope 1
East Tilbury 1
Tilbury Riverside
1A
Tilbury Town 1
1 Basildon
1 Laindon
1 West Horndon
1
Chafford
Hundred
Grays 1
Ockendon
1
Purfleet 1
1, 4 Upminster
Emerson
4 Park
Rainham 1
Dagenham Dock 1
4 Romford
Shenfield 5
Barking 1
5
Walthamstow
Gospel Oak 62
Hampstead
Richmond 59
1 Stratford
West Ham 1
5
Limehouse 1
1 London Liverpool Street
London Fenchurch Street 1

London → Southend Central and Shoeburyness

Network diagram - see first page of Table I

Miles	Miles	Miles	Station		CC	CC	CC	CC	CC	CC	CC	CC	CC	CC	CC	CC	CC	CC	CC	CC	CC	CC	CC	CC
					MO	MX	MO	MX	MX	MX	MO	MX	MX	MX	MX	MO	MX	MX	MX					
0	0	—	**London Fenchurch Street 7**	⊖ d	22p50	22p50	23p10	23p10	23p20	23p35	23p40	23p40	23p50	00 01		00 10	00 15		00 25	05 10			05 40	
1¾	1¾	—	Limehouse	d	22p54	22p54	23p14	23p14	23p24	23p39	23p44	23p44	23p54			00 14	00 19		00 29	05 14			05 44	
4¾	4¾	—	West Ham	⊖ d	22p59	22p59	23p19	23p19	23p29	23p44	23p49	23p49	23p59	00 09		00 19	00 24		00 34	05 19			05 49	
—	—	—	**London Liverpool Street 15**	⊖ d														00 12						
—	—	—	Stratford 7	⊖ d														00 19						
7½	7½	—	Barking	⊖ d	23p04	23p05	23p24	23p25	23p35	23p50	23p54	23p55	00 05	00 15		00 24	00 30	00a35	00 40	05 25		05 45	05 55	
15¼	—	0	Upminster	⊖ d	23p12	23p14	23p32	23p34	23p44		00 02	00 04	00 14	00 24		00 32			00 49	05 34	05 38		06 04	
—	—	3	Ockendon	d	23p18	23p19			23p49				00 19								05 43			
—	—	5	Chafford Hundred	d	23p21	23p23			23p53				00 23								05 47			
19¾	—	—	West Horndon	d			23p37	23p39			00 07	00 09				00 37			00 54	05 39			06 09	
22¾	—	—	Laindon	d			23p42	23p44			00 12	00 14		00 32		00 42			00 59	05 44			06 14	
24½	—	—	Basildon	d			23p45	23p47			00 15	00 17		00 35		00 45			01 02	05 47			06 17	
—	10½	—	Dagenham Dock	d						23p55							00 35					05 50		
—	12¾	—	Rainham	d						23p59							00 39					05 54		
—	16	—	Purfleet	d						00 04							00 44					05 59		←
—	19¾	7½	Grays	d	23p25	23p27			23p57	00a10			00 27		←		00a50				05 51	06 05		06 05
—	21½	—	**Tilbury Town 3**	d	23p28	23p30			00 01				00 30		00 30						05 55	→		06 08
—	25½	—	East Tilbury	d	23p34	23p36			00 06				→		00 36						06 01			06 14
—	27½	—	Stanford-le-Hope	d	23p37	23p40			00 10						00 40						06a06			06 18
26½	32¼	—	Pitsea	d	23p45	23p48	23p49	23p51	00 18		00 19	00 21			00 48	00 49			01 06	05 51			06 21	06 28
29¼	35	—	Benfleet	d	23p49	23p52	23p52	23p55	00 22		00 22	00 25		00 41	00 52	00 52			01 10	05 55			06 25	06 32
32½	38½	—	Leigh-on-Sea	d	23p53	23p56	23p57	23p59	00 26		00 27	00 30		00 46	00 56	00 57			01 14	06 00			06 30	06 36
34	39¾	—	Chalkwell	d	23p56	23p59	23p59	00 03	00 29		00 29	00 33		00 49	00 59	00 59			01 17	06 03			06 33	06 39
34¾	40½	—	Westcliff	d	23p58	00 02	00 02	00 05	00 32		00 32	00 35		00 51	01 02	01 02			01 20	06 05			06 35	06 42
35¾	41½	—	**Southend Central**	a	00 01	00 05	00 05	00 08	00 35		00 34	00 38		00 54	01 05	01 04			01 23	06 08			06 38	06 44
—	—	—		d	00 01	00 05	00 06	00 08	00 35		00 36	00 38		00 54	01 05	01 06			01 23	06 08			06 38	06 44
36½	42¼	—	Southend East	d	00 03	00 07	00 08	00 10	00 37		00 38	00 40		00 56	01 07	01 08			01 25	06 10			06 40	06 46
38	43¾	—	Thorpe Bay	d	00 06	00 11	00 10	00 15	00 41		00 40	00 44		01 00	01 11	01 10			01 29	06 14			06 44	06 50
39½	45¼	—	**Shoeburyness**	a	00 13	00 17	00 18	00 23	00 48		00 48	00 54		01 08	01 17	01 18			01 35	06 18			06 48	06 54

Station		CC	CC	CC	CC	CC	CC	CC	CC	CC	CC	CC	CC	CC	CC	CC	CC	CC	CC	CC	CC	CC	CC	CC
London Fenchurch Street 7	⊖ d			06 10	06 20		06 40		06 45	06 50	07 00	07 05	07 10	07 14	07 16	07 28	07 37	07 43	07 49	07 53	08 00			08 04
Limehouse	d			06 14	06 24		06 44		06 49	06 54		07 09			07 20		07 41			07 57				08 08
West Ham	⊖ d			06 19	06 29		06 49		06 54	06 59	07 08	07 14	07 18		07 25	07 36	07 46	07 51		08 02	08 08			08 13
London Liverpool Street 15	⊖ d																							
Stratford 7	⊖ d																							
Barking	⊖ d	06 05	06 16	06 25	06 35	06 52	06 55		07 00	07 05	07 14	07 20	07 24	07 27	07 31	07 42	07 52	07 57	08 01	08 08	08 14			08 19
Upminster	⊖ d		06 25	06 34			07 04		07 09		07 23	07 29	07 33		07 41	07 51	08 02		08 10	08 17	08 23			
Ockendon	d		06b34						07 14						07 47				08 17					
Chafford Hundred	d		06 38						07 18						07 51				08 21					
West Horndon	d			06 39			07 09						07 38				08 07			08 22				
Laindon	d			06 44			07 14					07a40	07 44				08 13			08a28	08 31			
Basildon	d			06 47			07 17				07 33		07 47			08 01	08 16				08 34			
Dagenham Dock	d	06 10			06 40	06 57				07 10				07 32				08 02						08 24
Rainham	d	06 14			06 44	07 01				07 14				07 36				08 06						08 28
Purfleet	d	06 19			06 49	07 06		←		07 19				07 41				08 12				←	←	08 33
Grays	d	06 25	06a42		06 55	07 12		07 12	07a23	07 26				07 47	07 55			08 17	08 25			08 17	08 25	08a39
Tilbury Town 3	d	06 28			06 58	→		07 15		07 30					07 59			→	→			08 21	08 29	
East Tilbury	d	06 34			07 04			07 21		07 36					08 05							08 27	08 35	
Stanford-le-Hope	d	06 38			07 08			07 25		07 40				07 57	08 09							08 31	08 39	
Pitsea	d	06a46		06 51	07 16		07 21	07a33		07a47			07 50	08a04	08a16		08 21				08 38	08c41	08a46	
Benfleet	d			06 55	07 20		07 25				07 39		07 54			08 07	08 25				08 42	08 45		
Leigh-on-Sea	d			07 00	07 24		07 30				07 44		07 59			08 12	08 29				08 46	08 50		
Chalkwell	d			07 03	07 27		07 33				07 47		08 02			08 15	08 32				08 49	08 53		
Westcliff	d			07 05	07 30		07 35				07 49		08 04			08 17	08 35				08 52	08 55		
Southend Central	a			07 08	07 32		07 38				07 52		08 07			08 20	08 37				08 54	08 58		
	d			07 08	07 33		07 38				07 52		08 07			08 20	08 38				08 55			
Southend East	d			07 10	07 35		07 40				07 54		08 09			08 22	08 40				08 57			
Thorpe Bay	d			07 14	07 38		07 44				07 58		08 13			08 26	08 43				09 00			
Shoeburyness	a			07 18	07 43		07 48				08 02		08 17			08 30	08 48				09 05			

Station		CC	CC	CC	CC	CC	CC	CC	CC	CC	CC	CC	CC	CC	CC	CC	CC	CC	CC	CC	CC	CC	CC	CC
London Fenchurch Street 7	⊖ d	08 10	08 17	08 20	08 32		08 40	08 50	08 53	09 00	09 04	09 10		09 20	09 30	09 35	09 40		09 50	10 00		10 05	10 10	10 20
Limehouse	d	08 14		08 24			08 44	08 54	08 57		09 08	09 14		09 24		09 39	09 44		09 54			10 09	10 14	10 24
West Ham	⊖ d	08 19	08 25	08 29	08 40		08 49	08 59		09 08	09 13	09 19		09 29	09 38	09 44	09 49		09 59	10 08		10 14	10 19	10 29
London Liverpool Street 15	⊖ d																							
Stratford 7	⊖ d																							
Barking	⊖ d	08 25	08 31	08 37	08 46		08 55	09 05	09 07	09 16	09 19	09 25		09 36	09 44	09 50	09 55		10 05	10 14		10 20	10 25	10 35
Upminster	⊖ d	08 34	08e43		08 55		09 04	09f18		09 25		09 34		09 47	09 53		10 04		10 15	10 23			10 34	10 44
Ockendon	d		08 48					09 23						09 52					10 20					10 49
Chafford Hundred	d		08 52					09 27						09 56					10 24					10 53
West Horndon	d	08 39					09 09					09 39					10 09						10 39	
Laindon	d	08 45			09 03		09 14			09 34		09 44			10 01		10 14			10 31			10 44	
Basildon	d	08 48			09 06		09 17			09 37		09 47			10 04		10 17			10 34			10 47	
Dagenham Dock	d			08 42					09 12		09 24					09 55						10 25		
Rainham	d			08 46					09 16		09 28					09 59						10 29		
Purfleet	d			08 52		←			09 21		09 33					10 04						10 34		
Grays	d		08a56	08 57		08 57		09 31	09a27		09a39		←	10 00		10a10		←	10 28		←	10a40		10 57
Tilbury Town 3	d			→		09 01		09 34					09 34	10 03				10 03	10 32		10 32			11 00
East Tilbury	d					09 07		→					09 40	→				10 09	→		10 38			→
Stanford-le-Hope	d					09 11							09 44					10 13			10 42			
Pitsea	d	08 52			09 10	09 18	09 22					09 51	09 54				10 21	10g25			10 49		10 53	
Benfleet	d	08 56			09 14	09 22	09 26			09 43		09 55	09 58		10 10		10 25	10 29		10 40	10 53		10 57	
Leigh-on-Sea	d	09 00			09 18	09 27	09 30			09 48		09 59	10 03		10 15		10 30	10 34		10 45	10 58		11 01	
Chalkwell	d	09 03			09 21	09 30	09 33			09 51		10 02	10 06		10 18		10 33	10 37		10 48	11 01		11 04	
Westcliff	d	09 06			09 24	09 32	09 36			09 53		10 05	10 08		10 20		10 35	10 39		10 50	11 03		11 07	
Southend Central	a	09 08			09 26	09 35	09 38			09 56		10 07	10 11		10 23		10 38	10 42		10 53	11 06		11 09	
	d	09 08			09 27		09 38			09 56		10 08			10 23		10 38			10 53			11 09	
Southend East	d	09 10			09 29		09 40			09 58		10 10			10 25		10 40			10 55			11 11	
Thorpe Bay	d	09 14			09 32		09 44			10 02		10 13			10 29		10 44			10 59			11 15	
Shoeburyness	a	09 18			09 38		09 48			10 06		10 18			10 34		10 48			11 04			11 19	

For general notes see front of timetable
For details of catering facilities see Directory of Train Operators

b Arr. 0630
c Arr. 0838
e Arr. 0840
f Arr. 0914
g Arr. 1021

London → Southend Central and Shoeburyness

Network diagram - see first page of Table 1

		CC	CC	CC		CC	CC	CC	CC	CC	CC	CC	CC	CC	CC	and at the same minutes past each hour until	CC	CC	CC	CC	CC	CC	CC
London Fenchurch Street 7	d	10 30		10 35		10 40	10 50	11 00		11 05	11 10	11 20	11 30		11 35		14 40	14 50	15 00		15 05	15 10	15 20
Limehouse	d			10 39		10 44	10 54			11 09	11 14	11 24			11 39		14 44	14 54			15 09	15 14	15 24
West Ham	d	10 38		10 44		10 49	10 59	11 08		11 14	11 19	11 29	11 38		11 44		14 49	14 59	15 08		15 14	15 19	15 29
London Liverpool Street 15	d																						
Stratford 7	d																						
Barking	d	10 44		10 50		10 55	11 05	11 14		11 20	11 25	11 35	11 44		11 50		14 55	15 05	15 14		15 20	15 25	15 35
Upminster	d	10 53				11 04	11 14	11 23			11 34	11 44	11 53				15 04	15 14	15 23			15 34	15 44
Ockendon	d						11 19					11 49						15 19					15 49
Chafford Hundred	d						11 23					11 53						15 23					15 53
West Horndon	d					11 09					11 39						15 09					15 39	→
Laindon	d	11 01				11 14		11 31			11 44		12 01				15 14		15 31			15 44	
Basildon	d	11 04				11 17		11 34			11 47		12 04				15 17		15 34			15 47	
Dagenham Dock	d			10 55						11 25					11 55						15 25		
Rainham	d			10 59						11 29					11 59						15 29		
Purfleet	d			11 04						11 34					12 04						15 34		
Grays	d		←	11a10			11 27		←	11a40		11 57		←	12a10			15 27		←	15a40		
Tilbury Town 3	d		11 00				11 30		11 30			12 00		12 00				15 30		15 30			
East Tilbury	d		11 06				→		11 36			→		12 06				→		15 36			
Stanford-le-Hope	d		11 10						11 40					12 10						15 40			
Pitsea	d		11 18			11 21			11 48		11 51			12 18			15 21			15 48		15 51	
Benfleet	d	11 10	11 22			11 25		11 40	11 52		11 55		12 10	12 22			15 25		15 40	15 52		15 55	
Leigh-on-Sea	d	11 15	11 26			11 30		11 45	11 56		12 00		12 15	12 26			15 30		15 45	15 56		16 00	
Chalkwell	d	11 18	11 29			11 33		11 48	11 59		12 03		12 18	12 29			15 33		15 48	15 59		16 03	
Westcliff	d	11 20	11 32			11 35		11 50	12 02		12 05		12 20	12 32			15 35		15 50	16 02		16 05	
Southend Central	a	11 23	11 35			11 38		11 53	12 05		12 08		12 23	12 35			15 38		15 52	16 04		16 09	
	d	11 23				11 38		11 53			12 08		12 23				15 38		15 52			16 09	
Southend East	d	11 25				11 40		11 55			12 10		12 25				15 40		15 54			16 11	
Thorpe Bay	d	11 29				11 44		11 59			12 14		12 29				15 44		15 59			16 15	
Shoeburyness	a	11 34				11 48		12 04			12 18		12 34				15 48		16 03			16 19	

		CC	CC	CC	CC	CC	CC	CC	CC	CC	CC	CC	CC	CC	CC	CC	CC	CC	CC	CC	CC	CC	CC	CC
London Fenchurch Street 7	d	15 27	15 30	15 33	15 40		15 47	15 51	16 00	16 07	16 10	16 18	16 21	16 27	16 30	16 33	16 37	16 45	16 48	16 51	16 57	17 02	17 04	
Limehouse	d			15 37	15 44		15 51			16 11	16 14	16 22	16 25		16 34	16 37	16 41	16 49	16 52	16 55			17 08	
West Ham	d	15 35	15 38	15 42	15 49		15 56	15 59	16 08	16 16	16 19	16 27	16 30	16 35		16 42	16 46		16 57	17 00				
London Liverpool Street 15	d																							
Stratford 7	d																							
Barking	d		15 44	15 48	15 54		16 02	16 05	16 14	16 23	16 25	16 33	16 36		16 44	16 48	16 52	16 59	17 03	17 06	17 10		17 18	
Upminster	d		15 53		16 02		16 13		16 23		16 35	16 43			16 53		17 02	17 08	17 13		17 19			
Ockendon	d					←	16 18					16 48					17b10				17 24			
Chafford Hundred	d					15 53	16 22					16 52					17 14				17 29			
West Horndon	d				16 07						16 40				16 58				17 18					
Laindon	d	15 55	16 01		16 12						16 45			16 55	17a06			17 17	17a26				17 34	
Basildon	d	15 58	16 04		16 15				16 33		16 49			16 58				17 20					17 37	
Dagenham Dock	d			15 53				16 10		16 28			16 41			16 53				17 11				
Rainham	d			15 57				16 14		16 32			16 45			16 57				17 15				
Purfleet	d			16 02				16 19		16 38			16 51			17 03				17 21				←
Grays	d			16a08		15 57	16 28	16a25		16 44		16a58	16 57			17 09	17 19			17a28	17 33			17 19
Tilbury Town 3	d					16 00	16 32			16 47			17 00			17 12	→				→			17 22
East Tilbury	d					16 06	16 38			16 53			17 06			17 18								17 28
Stanford-le-Hope	d					16 10	16 42			17a00			17 10			17a25								17 32
Pitsea	d	16 01			16 18	16c21	16a49				16 53		17a20					17 24					17 41	17a42
Benfleet	d	16 05	16 10		16 22	16 25			16 40		16 57			17 05				17 28				17 35	17 45	
Leigh-on-Sea	d	16 10	16 15		16 26	16 30			16 45		17 01			17 10				17 33				17 39	17 50	
Chalkwell	d	16 13	16 18		16 29	16 33			16 48		17 04			17 13				17 36				17 42	17 53	
Westcliff	d	16 15	16 20		16 31	16 35			16 50		17 07			17 15				17 38				17 45	17 55	
Southend Central	a	16 18	16 23		16 34	16 38			16 53		17 09			17 18				17 41				17 47	17 58	
	d		16 23		16 34				16 53		17 09			17 18				17 41				17 47	17 58	
Southend East	d		16 25		16 36				16 55		17 11			17 20				17 43				17 49	18 00	
Thorpe Bay	d		16 29		16 39				16 59		17 15			17 24				17 46				17 53	18 04	
Shoeburyness	a		16 34		16 45				17 05		17 21			17 30				17 53				18 01	18 10	

		CC	CC	CC	CC	CC	CC	CC	CC	CC	CC	CC	CC	CC	CC	CC	CC	CC	CC	CC	CC	CC	CC	CC
London Fenchurch Street 7	d	17 07	17 10	17 15	17 17	17 20		17 22	17 26	17 30	17 32	17 35		17 38	17 41	17 44	17 47	17 50		17 53	17 57	18 00		18 02
Limehouse	d	17 11	17 14		17 21	17 24		17 27	17 30			17 39		17 42	17 45	17 48	17 51			17 57	18 01			18 06
West Ham	d	17 16						17 32						17 47				17 59				18 08		
London Liverpool Street 15	d																							
Stratford 7	d																							
Barking	d	17 22	17 24			17 34		17 37	17 40		17 45	17 49		17 53	17 55					18 07	18 11			18 16
Upminster	d	17 30		17 35				17 46			17 54			18 01			18 08	18 12						18 26
Ockendon	d			17 42							17 59						18 15							18 33
Chafford Hundred	d			17 47							18 04						18 19							18 37
West Horndon	d	17 35						17 51						18 06						18 20				
Laindon	d	17a42				17 49		17a58				18 05		18a13				18 21		18 25				
Basildon	d					17 53						18 08						18 25		18 29		18 33		
Dagenham Dock	d		17 29						17 45						18 00						18 16			
Rainham	d		17 33						17 49						18 04						18 20			
Purfleet	d		17 39				←		17 54				←		18 10				←		18 26		←	
Grays	d		17a46	17 54			17 33		18a02		18 08		17 54		18a17		18 24		18 08		18a33		18 24	18 42
Tilbury Town 3	d			→			17 37				→		17 57				→		18 12				18 27	→
East Tilbury	d						17 43						18 03						18 18				18 33	
Stanford-le-Hope	d						17 47						18 07						18 22				18 37	
Pitsea	d					17 56	17a56					18 12	18a17					18 28	18a31	18 32		18 36	18a47	
Benfleet	d				17 52	18 01				18 07		18 16				18 22		18 33		18 37		18 41		
Leigh-on-Sea	d				17 57	18 05				18 11		18 21				18 26		18 37		18 41		18 45		
Chalkwell	d				18 00	18 08				18 14		18 24				18 29		18 40		18 44		18 48		
Westcliff	d				18 02	18 11				18 17		18 26				18 32		18 43		18 47		18 51		
Southend Central	a				18 05	18 13				18 19		18 29				18 34		18 45		18 49		18 53		
	d				18 05	18 14				18 20		18 29				18 34		18 45		18 49		18 53		
Southend East	d				18 07	18 16				18 22		18 31				18 36		18 47		18 51		18 55		
Thorpe Bay	d				18 11	18a21				18 25		18 34				18 40		18 51		18 55		18 59		
Shoeburyness	a				18 17					18 32		18 41				18 46		18 57		19 01		19 05		

For general notes see front of timetable
For details of catering facilities see Directory of Train Operators

b Arr. 1707
c Arr. 1618

London → Southend Central and Shoeburyness

Network diagram - see first page of Table I

Station		CC	CC	CC	CC	CC	CC	CC	CC	CC	CC	CC	CC	CC	CC	CC	CC	CC	CC	CC	CC	CC	CC	CC
London Fenchurch Street 7	⊖ ⛴ d	18 07	18 10	18 15	18 20		18 22	18 27		18 32	18 37	18 44	18 47		18 50	19 00	19 02	19 07	19 10		19 12		19 20	19 30
Limehouse	⛴ d	18 11	18 14	18 19			18 26	18 31		18 36	18 41		18 51		18 54		19 06	19 11	19 14		19 17		19 24	
West Ham	⊖ d		18 19	18 24				18 36			18 46	18 52	18 56		18 59		19 11	19 16			19 22		19 29	
London Liverpool Street 15	⊖ d																							
Stratford 7	⊖ ⛴ d																							
Barking	⊖ d	18 21	18 25	18 30				18 42		18 46	18 52		19 02		19 05		19 17	19 22	19 24		19 28		19 35	
Upminster	⊖ d		18 33				18 43	18 52			19 02		19 10				19 26		19 33		19 37		19 44	19 50
Ockendon	d						18 48				19 07						19 33						19 49	
Chafford Hundred	d						18 52				19 12						19 38						19 53	
West Horndon	d		18 38					18 57					19 15								19 42			
Laindon	d	18 37	18 43		18 47			19 02					19 20			19 26					19 47			
Basildon	d	18 40	18 46		18 50			19 06				19 14	19 24						19 43		19 50			20 00
Dagenham Dock	d			18 35						18 51					19 10			19 27						
Rainham	d			18 39						18 55					19 14			19 31		←				
Purfleet	d			18 45		←			←	19 00				←	19 20			19 36		19 20		←		
Grays	d			18a52		18 42	18 57		18 57	19 06	19a18			19 06	→		19 46	19a42		19 27		19 46	19 57	
Tilbury Town 3	d					18 45	→		19 00	→				19 10			→			19 30		19 50	20 00	
East Tilbury	d					18 51			19 06					19 16						19 36		19 56	→	
Stanford-le-Hope	d					18 55			19 10					19 20						19 40		20 00		
Pitsea	d		18 50			19 03		19 10	19a20				19 27	19a29					19 46	19 50	19 54	20a07		
Benfleet	d	18 47	18 54		18 58	19 07		19 14				19 21	19 31			19 34			19 50	19 54	19 58			20 06
Leigh-on-Sea	d	18 52	18 58		19 02	19a14		19 19				19 26	19 36			19 39			19 55	19 58	20 02			20 11
Chalkwell	d	18 55	19 01		19 05			19 22				19 29	19 38			19 42			19 58	20 01	20 05			20 14
Westcliff	d	18 57	19 03		19 08			19 24				19 31	19 41			19 44			20 00	20 04	20 08			20 16
Southend Central	a	19 00	19 06		19 10			19 27				19 34	19 43			19 47			20 03	20 09	20 10			20 19
	d	19 00	19 06		19 10			19 27				19 34	19 44			19 47			20 03		20 10			20 19
Southend East	d	19 02	19 08		19 12			19 29				19 36	19 46			19 49			20 05		20 12			20 21
Thorpe Bay	d	19 06	19 11		19 16			19 33				19 40	19 48			19 53			20a09		20 16			20 25
Shoeburyness	a	19 12	19 17		19 22			19 40				19 46	19 55			19 59					20 20			20 29

Station		CC	CC	CC	CC	CC	CC	CC	CC	CC	CC	CC	CC	CC	CC	CC	CC	CC	CC	CC	CC	CC	CC	CC
London Fenchurch Street 7	⊖ ⛴ d		19 32	19 35	19 40	19 50	20 00		20 05	20 10	20 20	20 30		20 35	20 40	20 50	21 00		21 05	21 10	21 20	21 30	21 35	
Limehouse	⛴ d			19 39	19 44	19 54			20 09	20 14	20 24			20 39	20 44	20 54			21 09	21 14	21 24		21 39	
West Ham	⊖ d		19 41	19 44	19 49	19 59	20 08		20 14	20 19	20 29	20 38		20 44	20 49	20 59	21 08		21 14	21 19	21 29	21 38	21 44	
London Liverpool Street 15	⊖ d																							21 38
Stratford 7	⊖ ⛴ d																							21 45
Barking	⊖ d		19 46	19 50	19 55	20 05	20 14		20 20	20 25	20 35	20 44		20 50	20 55	21 05	21 14		21 20	21 25	21 35	21 44	21 50	21a54
Upminster	⊖ d		19 55		20 04	20 14	20 23			20 34	20 44	20 53			21 04	21 14	21 23			21 34	21 44	21 53		
Ockendon	d					20 19					20 49					21 19					21 49			
Chafford Hundred	d					20 23					20 53					21 23					21 53			
West Horndon	d		20 00		20 09					20 39					21 09					21 39				
Laindon	d		20a06		20 14		20 31			20 44		21 01			21 14		21 31			21 44		22 01		
Basildon	d				20 17		20 34			20 47		21 04			21 17		21 34			21 47		22 04		
Dagenham Dock	d			19 55					20 25					20 55					21 25				21 55	
Rainham	d			19 59					20 29					20 59					21 29				21 59	
Purfleet	d			20 04					20 34					21 04					21 34				22 04	
Grays	d	←		20a10		20 27		←	20a40		20 57		←	21a10		21 27		←	21a40		21 57		22a10	
Tilbury Town 3	d	20 00				20 30		20 30			21 00		21 00			21 30		21 30			22 00			
East Tilbury	d	20 06				→		20 36			→		21 06			→		21 36			→			
Stanford-le-Hope	d	20 10						20 40					21 10					21 40						
Pitsea	d	20 18			20 21			20 48		20 52			21 18		21 21			21 48		21 51				
Benfleet	d	20 22			20 26		20 40	20 52		20 56		21 10	21 22		21 25		21 40	21 52		21 55		22 10		
Leigh-on-Sea	d	20 27			20 30		20 45	20 57		21 00		21 15	21 26		21 30		21 45	21 56		22 00		22 15		
Chalkwell	d	20 30			20 33		20 48	21 00		21 03		21 18	21 29		21 33		21 48	21 59		22 03		22 18		
Westcliff	d	20 32			20 36		20 50	21 02		21 06		21 20	21 32		21 35		21 50	22 02		22 05		22 20		
Southend Central	a	20 35			20 38		20 53	21 05		21 08		21 23	21 35		21 38		21 53	22 05		22 08		22 23		
	d				20 38		20 53			21 08		21 23			21 38		21 53			22 08		22 23		
Southend East	d				20 40		20 55			21 10		21 25			21 40		21 56			22 10		22 25		
Thorpe Bay	d				20 44		20 59			21 14		21 29			21 44		21 58			22 14		22 29		
Shoeburyness	a				20 48		21 04			21 18		21 34			21 48		22 04			22 18		22 34		

Station		CC	CC	CC	CC	CC	CC	CC	CC	CC	CC	CC	CC	CC	CC	CC	CC	CC	CC	CC	CC	CC		
London Fenchurch Street 7	⊖ ⛴ d		21 40	21 50	22 00		22 05	22 10	22 20	22 30		22 35	22 40	22 50	23 00		23 05	23 10	23 20	23 35	23 40	23 50		
Limehouse	⛴ d		21 44	21 54			22 09	22 14	22 24			22 39	22 44	22 54			23 09	23 14	23 24	23 39	23 44	23 54		
West Ham	⊖ d		21 49	21 59	22 08		22 14	22 19	22 29	22 38		22 44	22 49	22 59	23 08		23 14	23 19	23 29	23 44	23 49	23 59		
London Liverpool Street 15	⊖ d																							
Stratford 7	⊖ ⛴ d																							
Barking	⊖ d		21 55	22 05	22 14		22 20	22 25	22 35	22 44		22 50	22 55	23 05	23 14		23 20	23 25	23 35	23 50	23 55	00 05		
Upminster	⊖ d		22 04	22 14	22 23			22 34	22 44	22 53			23 04	23 14	23 23			23 34	23 44		00 04	00 14		
Ockendon	d			22 19					22 49					23 19					23 49			00 19		
Chafford Hundred	d			22 23					22 53					23 23					23 53			00 23		
West Horndon	d		22 09					22 39					23 09					23 39			00 09			
Laindon	d		22 14		22 31			22 44		23 01			23 14		23 31			23 44			00 14			
Basildon	d		22 17		22 34			22 47		23 04			23 17		23 34			23 47			00 17			
Dagenham Dock	d						22 25					22 55					23 25			23 55				
Rainham	d						22 29					22 59					23 29			23 59				
Purfleet	d						22 33					23 04					23 34			00 04				
Grays	d	←		22 27		←	22a40		22 57		←	23a10		23 27		←	23a40		23 57	00a10		00 27		
Tilbury Town 3	d	22 00		22 30		22 30			23 00		23 00			23 30		23 30			00 01			00 30		
East Tilbury	d	22 06		→		22 36			→		23 06			→		23 36			00 06			00 36		
Stanford-le-Hope	d	22 10				22 40					23 10					23 40			00 10			00 40		
Pitsea	d	22 18	22 21			22 48		22 51			23 18		23 21			23 48		23 51	00 18		00 21	00 48		
Benfleet	d	22 22	22 25		22 40	22 52		22 55		23 10	23 22		23 25		23 40	23 52		23 55	00 22		00 25	00 52		
Leigh-on-Sea	d	22 26	22 30		22 45	22 56		23 00		23 15	23 27		23 30		23 45	23 56		23 59	00 26		00 30	00 56		
Chalkwell	d	22 29	22 33		22 48	22 59		23 03		23 18	23 30		23 33		23 48	23 59		00 03	00 29		00 33	00 59		
Westcliff	d	22 32	22 35		22 50	23 02		23 05		23 20	23 32		23 36		23 50	00 02		00 05	00 32		00 35	01 02		
Southend Central	a	22 35	22 38		22 52	23 05		23 08		23 23	23 35		23 38		23 53	00 05		00 08	00 35		00 38	01 05		
	d		22 38		22 53	23 05		23 08		23 23	23 36		23 38		23 53	00 05		00 08	00 35		00 38	01 05		
Southend East	d		22 40		22 55	23 07		23 10		23 25	23 38		23 40		23 55	00 07		00 10	00 37		00 40	01 07		
Thorpe Bay	d		22 44		22 59	23 10		23 14		23 29	23 42		23 45		23 59	00 11		00 15	00 41		00 44	01 11		
Shoeburyness	a		22 48		23 04	23 15		23 18		23 36	23 48		23 54		00 07	00 17		00 23	00 48		00 54	01 17		

For general notes see front of timetable
For details of catering facilities see
Directory of Train Operators

London → Southend Central and Shoeburyness

Network diagram - see first page of Table 1

		CC	CC	CC	CC	CC	CC		CC	CC	CC	CC	CC	CC		CC	CC	CC	CC	CC	CC		CC	CC
London Fenchurch Street 7	⊖ d	22p50	23p10	23p20	23p35	23p40	23p50		00 01	00 15			00 25				05 10	05 35	05 50	06 05	06 10		06 20	06 35
Limehouse	d	22p54	23p14	23p24	23p39	23p44	23p54			00 19			00 29				05 14	05 39	05 54	06 09	06 14		06 24	06 39
West Ham	⊖ d	22p59	23p19	23p29	23p44	23p49	23p59		00 09	00 24			00 34				05 19	05 44	05 59	06 14	06 19		06 29	06 44
London Liverpool Street 15	⊖ d										00 12													
Stratford 7	⊖ d										00 19													
Barking	⊖ d	23p05	23p25	23p35	23p50	23p55	00 05		00 15	00 30	00a35		00 40				05 24	05 49	06 04	06 19	06 24		06 34	06 49
Upminster	⊖ d	23p14	23p34	23p44		00 04	00 14		00 24				00 49	05 05		05 28	05 32		06 12		06 32		06 42	
Ockendon	d	23p19		23p49			00 19							05a12		05 33			06 18				06 48	
Chafford Hundred	d	23p23		23p53			00 23									05 37			06 21				06 51	
West Horndon	d		23p39			00 09							00 54				05 37				06 37			
Laindon	d		23p44			00 14			00 32				00 59				05 42				06 42			
Basildon	d		23p47			00 17			00 35				01 02				05 45				06 45			
Dagenham Dock	d				23p55					00 35								05 54		06 24				06 54
Rainham	d				23p59					00 39								05 57		06 27				06 57
Purfleet	d				00 04					00 44								06 03		06 33				07 03
Grays	d	23p27		23p57	00a10		00 27			00a50		←				05a43		06a12	06 25	06a42			06 55	07a12
Tilbury Town 3	d	23p30		00 01			00 30					00 30							06 28				06 58	
East Tilbury	d	23p36		00 06			→					00 36							06 34				07 04	
Stanford-le-Hope	d	23p40		00 10								00 40							06 37				07 07	
Pitsea	d	23p48	23p51	00 18		00 21						00 48	01 06				05 50		06 45		06 49		07 15	
Benfleet	d	23p52	23p55	00 22		00 25			00 41			00 52	01 10				05 54		06 49		06 52		07 19	
Leigh-on-Sea	d	23p56	23p59	00 26		00 30			00 46			00 56	01 14				05 58		06 53		06 57		07 23	
Chalkwell	d	23p59	00 03	00 29		00 33			00 49			00 59	01 17				06 01		06 56		06 59		07 26	
Westcliff	d	00 02	00 05	00 32		00 35			00 51			01 02	01 20				06 03		06 58		07 02		07 28	
Southend Central	a	00 05	00 08	00 35		00 38			00 54			01 05	01 23				06 06		07 04		07 05		07 34	
	d	00 05	00 08	00 35		00 38			00 54			01 05	01 23				06 07				07 06			
Southend East	d	00 07	00 10	00 37		00 40			00 56			01 07	01 25				06 09				07 08			
Thorpe Bay	d	00 11	00 15	00 41		00 44			01 00			01 11	01 29				06 12				07 10			
Shoeburyness	a	00 17	00 23	00 48		00 54			01 08			01 17	01 35				06 19				07 18			

		CC	CC	CC	CC	CC	CC		CC	CC	CC	CC	CC	CC		CC	CC	CC	CC		CC	CC	CC	CC
London Fenchurch Street 7	⊖ d	06 40	06 50	07 05	07 10	07 20	07 35		07 40	07 50	08 05	08 10	08 20	08 35		08 40	08 50	09 00			09 05	09 10	09 20	09 30
Limehouse	d	06 44	06 54	07 09	07 14	07 24	07 39		07 44	07 54	08 09	08 14	08 24	08 39		08 44	08 54				09 09	09 14	09 24	
West Ham	⊖ d	06 49	06 59	07 14	07 19	07 29	07 44		07 49	07 59	08 14	08 19	08 29	08 44		08 49	08 59	09 08			09 14	09 19	09 29	09 38
London Liverpool Street 15	⊖ d																							
Stratford 7	⊖ d																							
Barking	⊖ d	06 54	07 04	07 19	07 24	07 34	07 49		07 54	08 04	08 19	08 24	08 34	08 49		08 54	09 04	09 13			09 19	09 24	09 34	09 43
Upminster	⊖ d	07 02	07 12		07 32	07 42			08 02	08 12		08 32	08 42			09 02	09 12	09 21				09 32	09 42	09 51
Ockendon	d		07 18			07 48				08 18			08 48				09 18						09 48	
Chafford Hundred	d		07 21			07 51				08 21			08 51				09 21						09 51	
West Horndon	d	07 07			07 37				08 07			08 37				09 07						09 37		
Laindon	d	07 12			07 42				08 12			08 42				09 12		09 29				09 42		09 59
Basildon	d	07 15			07 45				08 15			08 45				09 15		09 32				09 45		10 02
Dagenham Dock	d			07 24			07 54				08 24			08 54							09 24			
Rainham	d			07 27			07 57				08 27			08 57							09 27			
Purfleet	d			07 33			08 03				08 33			09 03							09 33			
Grays	d		07 25	07a42		07 55	08a12			08 25	08a42		08 55	09a12			09 25		←		09a42		09 55	
Tilbury Town 3	d		07 28			07 58				08 28			08 58				09 28		09 28				09 58	
East Tilbury	d		07 34			08 04				08 34			09 04				→		09 34				→	
Stanford-le-Hope	d		07 37			08 07				08 37			09 07						09 37					
Pitsea	d	07 19	07 45		07 49	08 15			08 19	08 45		08 49	09 15			09 19			09 45			09 49		
Benfleet	d	07 22	07 49		07 52	08 19			08 22	08 49		08 52	09 19			09 22		09 38	09 49			09 52		10 08
Leigh-on-Sea	d	07 27	07 53		07 57	08 23			08 27	08 53		08 57	09 23			09 27		09 42	09 53			09 57		10 12
Chalkwell	d	07 29	07 56		07 59	08 26			08 29	08 56		08 59	09 26			09 29		09 45	09 56			09 59		10 15
Westcliff	d	07 32	07 58		08 02	08 28			08 32	08 58		09 02	09 28			09 32		09 47	09 58			10 02		10 17
Southend Central	a	07 35	08 04		08 05	08 34			08 35	09 04		09 05	09 34			09 35		09 50	10 04			10 05		10 20
	d	07 36			08 06				08 36			09 06				09 36		09 50				10 06		10 20
Southend East	d	07 38			08 08				08 38			09 08				09 38		09 52				10 08		10 22
Thorpe Bay	d	07 40			08 10				08 40			09 10				09 40		09 55				10 10		10 25
Shoeburyness	a	07 48			08 18				08 48			09 18				09 48		10 02				10 18		10 32

		CC	CC	CC	CC	CC	CC	and at the same minutes past each hour until		CC	CC	CC	CC	CC	CC		CC	CC	CC	CC	CC	CC	CC
London Fenchurch Street 7	⊖ d		09 35	09 40	09 50	10 00				20 05	20 10	20 20	20 35	20 40	20 50		21 00		21 05	21 10	21 20	21 35	21 40
Limehouse	d		09 39	09 44	09 54					20 09	20 14	20 24	20 39	20 44	20 54				21 09	21 14	21 24	21 39	21 44
West Ham	⊖ d		09 44	09 49	09 59	10 08				20 14	20 19	20 29	20 44	20 49	20 59		21 08		21 14	21 19	21 29	21 44	21 49
London Liverpool Street 15	⊖ d																						
Stratford 7	⊖ d																						
Barking	⊖ d		09 49	09 54	10 04	10 13				20 19	20 24	20 34	20 49	20 54	21 04		21 13		21 19	21 24	21 34	21 49	21 54
Upminster	⊖ d			10 02	10 12	10 21					20 32	20 42		21 02	21 12		21 21			21 32	21 42		22 02
Ockendon	d				10 18							20 48			21 18						21 48		
Chafford Hundred	d				10 21							20 51			21 21						21 51		
West Horndon	d			10 07							20 37			21 07						21 37			22 07
Laindon	d			10 12		10 29					20 42			21 12			21 29			21 42			22 12
Basildon	d			10 15		10 32					20 45			21 15			21 32			21 45			22 15
Dagenham Dock	d		09 54							20 24			20 54						21 24			21 54	
Rainham	d		09 57							20 27			20 57						21 27			21 57	
Purfleet	d		10 03							20 33			21 03						21 33			22 03	
Grays	d	←	10a12		10 25		←			20a42		20 55	21a12		21 25			←	21a42		21 55	22a12	
Tilbury Town 3	d	09 58			10 28		10 28					20 58			21 28			21 28			21 58		
East Tilbury	d	10 04			→		10 34					21 04			→			21 34			22 04		
Stanford-le-Hope	d	10 07					10 37					21 07						21 37			22 07		
Pitsea	d	10 15		10 19			10 45				20 49	21 15		21 19				21 45		21 49	22 15		22 19
Benfleet	d	10 19		10 22		10 38	10 49				20 52	21 19		21 22			21 38	21 49		21 52	22 19		22 22
Leigh-on-Sea	d	10 23		10 27		10 42	10 53				20 57	21 23		21 27			21 42	21 53		21 57	22 23		22 27
Chalkwell	d	10 26		10 29		10 45	10 56				20 59	21 26		21 29			21 45	21 56		21 59	22 26		22 29
Westcliff	d	10 28		10 32		10 47	10 58				21 02	21 28		21 32			21 47	21 58		22 02	22 28		22 32
Southend Central	a	10 34		10 35		10 50	11 04				21 05	21 34		21 35			21 50	22 04		22 05	22 34		22 35
	d			10 36		10 50					21 06			21 36			21 50			22 06			22 36
Southend East	d			10 38		10 52					21 08			21 38			21 52			22 08			22 38
Thorpe Bay	d			10 40		10 55					21 10			21 40			21 55			22 10			22 40
Shoeburyness	a			10 48		11 02					21 18			21 48			22 02			22 18			22 48

For general notes see front of timetable
For details of catering facilities see Directory of Train Operators

Table I

Saturdays

London → Southend Central and Shoeburyness

Network diagram - see first page of Table I

Station		CC		CC	CC	CC	CC	CC	CC		CC	CC	CC	CC	CC	CC		CC	CC	CC	CC			
London Fenchurch Street 7	⊖ d	21 50		22 00		22 05	22 10	22 20	22 35		22 40	22 50	23 05	23 10		23 20		23 35	23 40		23 50			
Limehouse	d	21 54				22 09	22 14	22 24	22 39		22 44	22 54	23 09	23 14		23 24		23 39	23 44		23 54			
West Ham	⊖ d	21 59		22 08		22 14	22 19	22 29	22 44		22 49	22 59	23 14	23 19		23 29		23 44	23 49		23 59			
London Liverpool Street 15	⊖ d																							
Stratford 7	⊖ d																							
Barking	⊖ d	22 04		22 13		22 19	22 24	22 34	22 49		22 54	23 04	23 19	23 24		23 34		23 49	23 54		00 04			
Upminster	⊖ d	22 12		22 21			22 32	22 42			23 02	23 12		23 32		23 42			00 02		00 12			
Ockendon	d	22 18						22 48				23 18				23 48					00 18			
Chafford Hundred	d	22 21						22 51				23 21				23 51					00 21			
West Horndon	d						22 37				23 07			23 37					00 07					
Laindon	d			22 29			22 42				23 12			23 42					00 12					
Basildon	d			22 32			22 45				23 15			23 45					00 15					
Dagenham Dock	d					22 24			22 54				23 24					23 54						
Rainham	d					22 27			22 57				23 27		←			23 57		←				
Purfleet	d					22 33			23 03				23 33		23 33			00 03		00 03				
Grays	d	22 25			←	22a42		22 55	23a12			23 25	→		23 38	23 55		→		00 08	00 25			
Tilbury Town 3	d	22 28			22 28			22 58				23 28			23 41	23 58				00 11	00 28			
East Tilbury	d	→			22 34			23 04				23 34			23 47	00 04				00 17	00 34			
Stanford-le-Hope	d				22 37			23 07				23 37			23 50	00 07				00 20	00 37			
Pitsea	d				22 45		22 49	23 15			23 19	23 45		23 49	23 58	00 15			00 19	00 28	00 45			
Benfleet	d			22 38	22 49		22 52	23 19			23 22	23 49		23 52	00 01	00 19			00 22	00 31	00 49			
Leigh-on-Sea	d			22 42	22 53		22 57	23 23			23 27	23 53		23 57	00 06	00 23			00 27	00 36	00 53			
Chalkwell	d			22 45	22 56		22 59	23 26			23 29	23 56		23 59	00 08	00 26			00 29	00 38	00 56			
Westcliff	d			22 47	22 58		23 02	23 28			23 32	23 58		00 02	00 11	00 28			00 32	00 41	00 58			
Southend Central	a			22 50	23 04		23 05	23 31			23 35	00 01		00 05	00 13	00 31			00 35	00 43	01 01			
	d			22 50			23 06	23 31			23 36	00 01		00 06	00 14	00 31			00 36	00 44	01 01			
Southend East	d			22 52			23 08	23 33			23 38	00 03		00 08	00 16	00 33			00 38	00 46	01 03			
Thorpe Bay	d			22 55			23 10	23 36			23 40	00 06		00 10	00 18	00 36			00 40	00 48	01 06			
Shoeburyness	a			23 02			23 18	23 43			23 48	00 13		00 18	00 24	00 43			00 48	00 54	01 13			

Sundays

Station		CC	CC	CC	CC	CC	CC	CC	CC	CC	CC	CC	CC	CC	CC	CC	CC	CC	CC	CC	CC	CC	CC	CC
London Fenchurch Street 7	⊖ d	22p50	23p05	23p10		23p20	23p35	23p40		23p50	00 10	00 40	06 40		07 10	07 40	07 50	08 10			08 40	08 50	09 10	
Limehouse	d	22p54	23p09	23p14		23p24	23p39	23p44		23p54	00 14	00 44	06 44		07 14	07 44	07 54	08 14			08 44	08 54	09 14	
West Ham	⊖ d	22p59	23p14	23p19		23p29	23p44	23p49		23p59	00 19	00 49	06 49		07 19	07 49	07 59	08 19			08 49	08 59	09 19	
London Liverpool Street 15	⊖ d																							
Stratford 7	⊖ d																							
Barking	⊖ d	23p04	23p19	23p24		23p34	23p49	23p54		00 04	00 24	00 54	06 54	07 04	07 24	07 54	08 04	08 24	08 29	08 34	08 54	09 04	09 24	09 29
Upminster	⊖ d	23p12		23p32		23p42		00 02		00 12	00 32	01 02	07 02	07 12	07 32	08 02	08 12	08 32		08 42	09 02	09 12	09 32	
Ockendon	d	23p18				23p48				00 18				07 18			08 18			08 48		09 18		
Chafford Hundred	d	23p21				23p51				00 21				07 21			08 21			08 51		09 21		
West Horndon	d			23p37				00 07			00 37	01 07	07 07		07 37	08 07		08 37			09 07		09 37	
Laindon	d			23p42				00 12			00 42	01 12	07 12		07 42	08 12		08 42			09 12		09 42	
Basildon	d			23p45				00 15			00 45	01 15	07 15		07 45	08 15		08 45			09 15		09 45	
Dagenham Dock	d		23p24				23p54												08 33					09 33
Rainham	d		23p27		←		23p57		←										08 37					09 37
Purfleet	d		23p33		23p33		00 03		00 03										08 42					09 42
Grays	d	23p25	→		23p38	23p55	→		00 08	00 25				07 25			08 25		08a50	08 55		09 25		09a50
Tilbury Town 3	d	23p28			23p41	23p58			00 11	00 28				07 28			08 28			08 58		09 28		
East Tilbury	d	23p34			23p47	00 04			00 17	00 34				07 34			08 34			09 04		09 34		
Stanford-le-Hope	d	23p37			23p50	00 07			00 20	00 37				07 37			08 37			09 07		09 37		
Pitsea	d	23p45		23p49	23p58	00 15		00 19	00 28	00 45	00 49	01 19	07 19	07 45	07 49	08 19	08 45	08 49		09 15	09 19	09 45	09 49	
Benfleet	d	23p49		23p52	00 01	00 19		00 22	00 31	00 49	00 52	01 22	07 22	07 49	07 52	08 22	08 49	08 52		09 19	09 22	09 49	09 52	
Leigh-on-Sea	d	23p53		23p57	00 06	00 23		00 27	00 36	00 53	00 57	01 27	07 27	07 53	07 57	08 27	08 53	08 57		09 23	09 27	09 53	09 57	
Chalkwell	d	23p56		23p59	00 08	00 26		00 29	00 38	00 56	00 59	01 29	07 29	07 56	07 59	08 29	08 56	08 59		09 26	09 29	09 56	09 59	
Westcliff	d	23p58		00 02	00 11	00 28		00 32	00 41	00 58	01 02	01 32	07 32	07 58	08 02	08 32	08 58	09 02		09 28	09 32	09 58	10 02	
Southend Central	a	00 01		00 05	00 13	00 31		00 35	00 43	01 01	01 05	01 35	07 34	08 04	08 05	08 34	09 04	09 05		09 34	09 35	10 04	10 05	
	d	00 01		00 06	00 14	00 31		00 36	00 44	01 01	01 06	01 36	07 36		08 06	08 36		09 06			09 36		10 06	
Southend East	d	00 03		00 08	00 16	00 33		00 38	00 46	01 03	01 08	01 38	07 38		08 08	08 38		09 08			09 38		10 08	
Thorpe Bay	d	00 06		00 10	00 18	00 36		00 40	00 48	01 06	01 10	01 40	07 40		08 10	08 40		09 10			09 40		10 10	
Shoeburyness	a	00 13		00 18	00 24	00 43		00 48	00 54	01 13	01 18	01 48	07 48		08 18	08 48		09 18			09 48		10 18	

Station		CC	CC	CC		CC	CC	CC	CC	CC		CC	CC	CC	CC	CC	CC	CC	CC	CC	CC		
London Fenchurch Street 7	⊖ d		09 40	09 50		10 10		10 20	10 40	10 50		21 10		21 20	21 40	21 50	22 10	22 40	22 50	23 10	23 40		
Limehouse	d		09 44	09 54		10 14		10 24	10 44	10 54		21 14		21 24	21 44	21 54	22 14	22 44	22 54	23 14	23 44		
West Ham	⊖ d		09 49	09 59		10 19		10 29	10 49	10 59		21 19		21 29	21 49	21 59	22 19	22 49	22 59	23 19	23 49		
London Liverpool Street 15	⊖ d																						
Stratford 7	⊖ d																						
Barking	⊖ d	09 34	09 54	10 04		10 24	10 29	10 34	10 54	11 04		21 24	21 29	21 34	21 54	22 04	22 24	22 54	23 04	23 24	23 54		
Upminster	⊖ d	09 42	10 02	10 12		10 32		10 42	11 02	11 12		21 32		21 42	22 02	22 12	22 32	23 02	23 12	23 32	00 02		
Ockendon	d	09 48		10 18				10 48		11 18				21 48		22 18			23 18				
Chafford Hundred	d	09 51		10 21				10 51		11 21	and at			21 51		22 21			23 21				
West Horndon	d		10 07			10 37			11 07			21 37			22 07		22 37	23 07		23 37	00 07		
Laindon	d		10 12			10 42			11 12		the same	21 42			22 12		22 42	23 12		23 42	00 12		
Basildon	d		10 15			10 45			11 15			21 45			22 15		22 45	23 15		23 45	00 15		
Dagenham Dock	d						10 33				minutes		21 33										
Rainham	d						10 37						21 37										
Purfleet	d						10 42				past		21 42										
Grays	d	09 55		10 25			10a50	10 55		11 25			21a51	21 55		22 25			23 25				
Tilbury Town 3	d	09 58		10 28				10 58		11 28	each			21 58		22 28			23 28				
East Tilbury	d	10 04		10 34				11 04		11 34				22 04		22 34			23 34				
Stanford-le-Hope	d	10 07		10 37				11 07		11 37	hour until			22 07		22 37			23 37				
Pitsea	d	10 15	10 19	10 45		10 49		11 15	11 19	11 45		21 49		22 15	22 19	22 45	22 49	23 19	23 45	23 49	00 19		
Benfleet	d	10 19	10 22	10 49		10 52		11 19	11 22	11 49		21 52		22 19	22 22	22 49	22 52	23 22	23 49	23 52	00 22		
Leigh-on-Sea	d	10 23	10 27	10 53		10 57		11 23	11 27	11 53		21 57		22 23	22 27	22 53	22 57	23 27	23 53	23 57	00 27		
Chalkwell	d	10 26	10 29	10 56		10 59		11 26	11 29	11 56		21 59		22 26	22 29	22 56	22 59	23 29	23 56	23 59	00 29		
Westcliff	d	10 28	10 32	10 58		11 02		11 28	11 32	11 58		22 02		22 28	22 32	22 58	23 02	23 32	23 58	00 02	00 32		
Southend Central	a	10 34	10 35	11 04		11 05		11 34	11 35	12 04		22 05		22 31	22 35	23 01	23 05	23 35	00 01	00 05	00 34		
	d		10 36			11 06			11 36			22 06		22 31	22 36	23 01	23 06	23 36	00 01	00 06	00 36		
Southend East	d		10 38			11 08			11 38			22 08		22 33	22 38	23 03	23 08	23 38	00 03	00 08	00 38		
Thorpe Bay	d		10 40			11 10			11 40			22 10		22 36	22 40	23 06	23 10	23 40	00 06	00 10	00 40		
Shoeburyness	a		10 48			11 18			11 48			22 18		22 43	22 48	23 13	23 18	23 48	00 13	00 18	00 48		

For general notes see front of timetable
For details of catering facilities see Directory of Train Operators

Shoeburyness and Southend Central → London

Network diagram - see first page of Table 1

Miles	Miles	Miles			CC MX	CC MX	CC	CC	CC	CC	CC	CC	CC	CC	CC	CC	CC	CC		CC	CC	CC	CC	CC
0	0	—	**Shoeburyness**	d		23p05		04 20		04 40	04 59		05 13	05 24				05 45		05 52	05 56			06 00
1½	1½	—	Thorpe Bay	d		23p09		04 24		04 44	05 03		05 17	05 28			05 32	05 49		05 56	06 00			06 04
3	3	—	Southend East	d		23p12		04 27		04 47	05 06		05 20	05 31			05 35	05 52		05 59	06 03			06 07
3¾	3¾	—	**Southend Central**	a		23p14		04 29		04 49	05 08		05 22	05 33			05 37	05 54		06 01	06 05			06 09
—	—	—		d	22p50	23p15		04 29		04 50	05 09		05 23	05 34			05 38	05 55		06 02	06 06			06 10
4¾	4¾	—	Westcliff	d	22p53	23p17		04 31		04 52	05 11		05 25	05 36			05 40	05 57		06 04	06 08			06 12
5½	5½	—	Chalkwell	d	22p55	23p19		04 34		04 54	05 13		05 27	05 38			05 42	05 59		06 06	06 10			06 14
7	7	—	Leigh-on-Sea	d	22p58	23p22		04 37		04 57	05 16		05 30	05 41			05 45	06 02		06 09	06 13			06 17
10¼	10¼	—	Benfleet	d	23p03	23p27		04 41		05 02	05 21		05 35	05 46			05 50	06 07		06 14	06 18			06 22
13	13	—	Pitsea	d	23p07	23p32		04 45		05 06	05 25		05 39	05 50			05 54	06 11		06b23				06 26
—	18	—	Stanford-le-Hope	d	23p14		04 29			05 14			05 46				06 01			06 30			06 14	
—	20	—	East Tilbury	d	23p18		04 33			05 18			05 50				06 05			06 34			06 18	
—	23¾	—	**Tilbury Town 3**	d	23p24		04 39			05 24			05 56		←		06 11			06 40			06 24	
—	25¾	0	Grays	d	23p27		04 42		05 17	05 27		05 50	06 00 →		06 00	06 04	06 14			06 44 →		06 24	06 28	
—	29¾	—	Purfleet	d						05 33					06 05		06 20						06 33	
—	32½	—	Rainham	d						05 38					06 10		06 25						06 39	
—	34¾	—	Dagenham Dock	d						05 41					06 14		06 28						06 42	
15	—	—	Basildon	d		23p36		04 50			05 29			05 54				06 15			06 24			06 31
16¾	—	—	Laindon	d		23p39		04 53			05 32			05 57				06 18			06 27			06 34
20½	—	—	West Horndon	d		23p44		04 58			05 37			06 02				06 23						06 39
—	—	2½	Chafford Hundred	d	23p31		04 46		05 21			05 54				06 08						06 28		
—	—	4½	Ockendon	d	23p35		04 50		05 25			05 58				06 12						06 32		
24¼	—	7½	Upminster	⊖ d	23p42	23p50	04 57	05 04	05a30		05 42	06 03		06 08		06 18		06 28				06 39		06 45
32	37¾	—	Barking	⊖ d	23p50	23p58	05 06	05 13		05 47	05 51	06 12		06 16	06 20		06 34	06 37					06 50	06 54
—	—	—	Stratford 7	⊖ a			05 13																	
—	—	—	**London Liverpool Street 15**	⊖ a			05 23																	
35	40¾	—	West Ham	⊖ d	23p56	00 04		05 18		05 53	05 57	06 17		06 22	06 26	06 32	06 40	06 43				06 53	06 56	07 00
37¾	43½	—	Limehouse	d	00 01	00 09		05 23		05 58	06 02	06 22		06 27	06 31	06 37	06 45	06 48			06 51	06 58	07 01	
39½	45¼	—	**London Fenchurch Street 7**	⊖ a	00 05	00 14		05 30		06 04	06 08	06 29		06 31	06 35	06 41	06 51	06 52			06 58	07 04	07 07	07 10

		CC	CC	CC	CC	CC	CC	CC	CC	CC	CC	CC		CC	CC	CC	CC	CC	CC	CC	CC	CC	CC	CC
Shoeburyness	d		06 10		06 14	06 23			06 28					06 45				06 53			07 05			
Thorpe Bay	d	06 10	06 14		06 18	06 27			06 32					06 49				06 57			07 09			07 14
Southend East	d	06 13	06 17		06 21	06 30			06 35					06 52				07 00			07 12			07 17
Southend Central	a	06 15	06 19		06 23	06 32			06 37					06 54				07 02			07 14			07 19
	d	06 16	06 20		06 24	06 33			06 38		06 44			06 55				07 03		07 09	07 15			07 20
Westcliff	d	06 18	06 22		06 26	06 35			06 40		06 46			06 57				07 05		07 11	07 17			07 22
Chalkwell	d	06 20	06 24		06 28	06 37			06 42		06 48			06 59				07 07		07 13	07 19			07 24
Leigh-on-Sea	d	06 23	06 27		06 31	06 40			06 45		06 51	06 55		07 02				07 10		07 17	07 22			07 27
Benfleet	d	06 28	06 32		06 36	06 45			06 50		06 56	07 00		07 07				07 15		07 21	07 27			07 32
Pitsea	d	06c39			06 40				06 54	06 55	07e03	07 04					07 15	07 19		07 26				07 36
Stanford-le-Hope	d	06 46								07 02	07 10						07 22			07 33				
East Tilbury	d	06 50						←		07 06	07 14						07 26			07 37				
Tilbury Town 3	d	06 56 →		←				06 56		07 12	07 20				←		07 32		←	07 43				
Grays	d			06 44			06 51	07 00		07 16 →	07 24 →				07 16		07 36 →		07 24	07 48 →		07 32		
Purfleet	d			06 49				07 05							07 21							07 37		
Rainham	d			06 55				07 11							07 27							07 43		
Dagenham Dock	d			06 58				07 14							07 30							07 46		
Basildon	d		06 39		06 45	06 52			06 59			07 09		07 14				07 24						07 41
Laindon	d				06 48				07 02			07 12				07 20		07 27					07 37	07 44
West Horndon	d				06 53				07 07							07 25							07 42	
Chafford Hundred	d						06 55												07 28					
Ockendon	d						06 59												07 32					
Upminster	⊖ d				06 59		07 06		07 13							07 31			07 39				07 48	
Barking	⊖ d		06 58	07 05	07 08		07 15	07 21	07 23			07 29			07 37	07 40		07 44	07 48			07 53	07 56	08 01
Stratford 7	⊖ a																							
London Liverpool Street 15	⊖ a																							
West Ham	⊖ d		07 04	07 10		07 17	07 21		07 28					07 34	07 42	07 46		07 50				07 59	08 02	
Limehouse	d		07 09		07 17		07 26	07 30	07 33			07 38			07 47	07 51		07 55			08 00	08 04	08 08	08 10
London Fenchurch Street 7	⊖ a		07 15	07 21	07 24	07 27	07 32	07 36	07 40			07 44		07 47	07 54	07 57		08 01	08 03		08 06	08 10	08 14	08 17

		CC	CC	CC	CC	CC		CC	CC	CC	CC	CC	CC	CC	CC	CC	CC	CC	CC	CC	CC		CC	CC
Shoeburyness	d		07 20					07 24		07 35						07 50				07 55			08 05	
Thorpe Bay	d		07 24					07 28		07 39				07 44		07 54				07 59			08 09	
Southend East	d		07 27					07 31		07 42				07 47		07 57				08 02			08 12	
Southend Central	a		07 29					07 33		07 44				07 49		07 59				08 04			08 14	
	d		07 30					07 34		07 45				07 50		08 00				08 05			08 15	
Westcliff	d		07 32					07 36		07 47				07 52		08 02				08 07			08 17	
Chalkwell	d		07 34					07 38		07 49				07 54		08 04				08 09			08 19	
Leigh-on-Sea	d		07 37					07 41		07 52				07 57		08 07				08 12			08 22	
Benfleet	d		07 42					07 46		07 57				08 02		08 12				08 17			08 27	
Pitsea	d					07 42		07 50					07 55	08 06					08 13	08 21				
Stanford-le-Hope	d					07 49			07 44				08 02						08 20		08 12			
East Tilbury	d					07 53							08 06						08 24		08 16			
Tilbury Town 3	d	←		←		07 59					←		08 12				←		08 30		08 22			←
Grays	d	07 36		07 48		08 03 →			07 54		08 03		08 18 →		08 09		08 18		08 34 →		08 26			08 34
Purfleet	d			07 53							08 08						08 23							08 40
Rainham	d			07 59							08 14						08 29							08 45
Dagenham Dock	d			08 02							08 17						08 32							08 49
Basildon	d							07 55						08 11						08 26				
Laindon	d				07 52			07 58				08 09		08 14				08 23		08 29				
West Horndon	d				07 57							08 14						08 28						
Chafford Hundred	d	07 40							07 59						08 13						08 30			
Ockendon	d	07f49							08 03						08 19						08 34			
Upminster	⊖ d	07 56			08 03				08 10	08 14		08 19			08 26	08 29		08 33			08 41			
Barking	⊖ d			08 09	08 12			08 15	08 19		08 24	08 28		08 32			08 40	08 42		08 46	08 50			08 55
Stratford 7	⊖ a																							
London Liverpool Street 15	⊖ a																							
West Ham	⊖ d				08 17							08 33						08 47						09 01
Limehouse	d	08 13	08 16	08 19	08 22			08 25		08 31	08 34	08 38		08 41		08 46	08 49	08 52		08 55				09 06
London Fenchurch Street 7	⊖ a	08 19	08 22	08 25	08 28			08 32	08 34	08 37	08 40	08 44		08 47	08 49	08 53	08 55	08 58		09 01	09 05		09 07	09 12

For general notes see front of timetable
For details of catering facilities see Directory of Train Operators

b Arr. 0618
c Arr. 0632
e Arr. 0700
f Arr. 0744

Shoeburyness and Southend Central → London

Network diagram - see first page of Table 1

		CC	CC	CC	CC	CC	CC	CC	CC	CC	CC	CC	CC	CC	CC		CC	CC		CC	CC	CC	CC	CC
Shoeburyness	d			08 10		08 25					08 40									09 05			09 20	
Thorpe Bay	d			08 14		08 29					08 44									09 09			09 24	
Southend East	d			08 17		08 32					08 47									09 12			09 27	
Southend Central	a			08 19		08 34					08 49									09 14			09 29	
	d			08 20		08 34					08 50				09 06					09 15		09 20	09 30	
Westcliff	d			08 22		08 36					08 52				09 08					09 17		09 23	09 32	
Chalkwell	d			08 24		08 39					08 54				09 11					09 19		09 25	09 34	
Leigh-on-Sea	d			08 27		08 42					08 57			09 01	09 14					09 22		09 28	09 37	
Benfleet	d			08 32		08 47					09 02			09 06	09 19					09 27		09 33	09 42	
Pitsea	d		08 28	08 36		08 51				08 54	09 06			09 10						09 32		09 37		
Stanford-le-Hope	d		08 35							09 01				09 17								09 44		
East Tilbury	d		08 39							09 05				09 21				←				09 48		←
Tilbury Town 3	d		08 45		←					09 11		←		09 27				09 27				09 54		09 54
Grays	d		08 49		08 49		08 53	09 03		09 15		09 15		→				09 30			09 46	→		09 57
Purfleet	d		→		08 55			09 08		→		09 20									09 51			
Rainham	d				09 00			09 14				09 26									09 56			
Dagenham Dock	d				09 04			09 17				09 29									10 00			
Basildon	d			08 41		08 55					09 11				09 26					09 37			09 49	
Laindon	d	08 38		08 44					09 04		09 14		09 17				09 31			09 40			09 52	
West Horndon	d	08 43							09 10				09 22							09 45				
Chafford Hundred	d						09 01											09 34						10 03
Ockendon	d						09 05											09 38						10 07
Upminster ⊖	d	08 49		08 54		09 06	09 11		09 16				09 28				09 41	09 45		09 50			10 00	10 11
Barking ⊖	d	08 58		09 03	09 10		09 20	09 24	09 26		09 30	09 36	09 38		09 43		09 50	09 53		09 58	10 06		10 08	10 20
Stratford 7 ⊖ ⛴	a																							
London Liverpool Street 15 ⊖	a																							
West Ham ⊖	d	09 04		09 08			09 26	09 29	09 32		09 36		09 43		09 49		09 56	09 59		10 05	10 11		10 16	10 27
Limehouse ⛴	d	09 09		09 14	09 19	09 23	09 31	09 34	09 37			09 45			09 54		10 01	10 04		10 10	10 16			10 32
London Fenchurch Street 7 ⊖ ⛴	a	09 15		09 20	09 26	09 29	09 38	09 41	09 44		09 46	09 51	09 54		10 00		10 07	10 08		10 14	10 21		10 24	10 37

		CC	CC	CC	CC	CC		CC	CC	CC	CC		CC	CC	CC	CC	CC	CC	CC	CC	CC	CC	CC
Shoeburyness	d	09 35			09 50			15 05			15 20			15 34			15 50				16 05	16 15	
Thorpe Bay	d	09 39			09 54			15 09			15 24			15 38			15 54				16 09	16 19	
Southend East	d	09 42			09 57			15 12			15 27			15 41			15 57				16 12	16 22	
Southend Central	a	09 44			09 59			15 14			15 29			15 43			15 59				16 14	16 24	
	d	09 45		09 50	10 00			15 15		15 19	15 30			15 44		15 48	16 00			16 11	16 15	16 25	
Westcliff	d	09 47		09 53	10 02			15 17		15 21	15 32			15 46		15 50	16 02			16 13	16 17	16 27	
Chalkwell	d	09 49		09 55	10 04			15 19		15 24	15 34			15 48		15 53	16 04			16 15	16 19	16 29	
Leigh-on-Sea	d	09 52		09 58	10 07			15 22		15 27	15 37			15 51		15 56	16 07			16 18	16 22	16 32	
Benfleet	d	09 57		10 03	10 12		and at	15 27		15 31	15 42			15 56		16 00	16 12			16 23	16 27	16 37	
Pitsea	d	10 01		10 07				15 32		15 35				16 00		16 04				16 29	16 31		
Stanford-le-Hope	d			10 14			the same			15 42						16 11				16 36			
East Tilbury	d			10 18		←				15 46			←			16 15		←		16 40			
Tilbury Town 3	d			10 24		10 24	minutes			15 52			15 52			16 21		16 21		16 46			←
Grays	d		10 16	→		10 27			15 46	→			15 56		16 14	→		16 26	16 31	16 50			16 50
Purfleet	d		10 21				past		15 51						16 19				16 36	→			16 55
Rainham	d		10 26						15 56						16 24				16 41				17 00
Dagenham Dock	d		10 30				each		16 00						16 28				16 45				17 04
Basildon	d	10 06			10 19			15 36			15 49			16 04			16 19				16 35	16 43	
Laindon	d	10 09			10 22		hour until	15 39			15 52			16 07							16 39		
West Horndon	d	10 14						15 44						16 12							16 44		
Chafford Hundred	d					10 31							16 00					16 30					
Ockendon	d					10 35							16 04					16 34					
Upminster ⊖	d	10 20			10 30	10 40		15 50			16 00		16 09	16 18			16 30	16 40			16 50	16 54	
Barking ⊖	d	10 28	10 36		10 38	10 48		15 58	16 06		16 08		16 17	16 26	16 34		16 38	16 49	16 51		16 59	17 02	17 10
Stratford 7 ⊖ ⛴	a																						
London Liverpool Street 15 ⊖	a																						
West Ham ⊖	d	10 34	10 41		10 46	10 56		16 04	16 12		16 16		16 25	16 32			16 44		16 57		17 04	17 08	17 16
Limehouse ⛴	d	10 39	10 46			11 01		16 09	16 17				16 30	16 37	16 43			16 58	17 02		17 09	17 13	
London Fenchurch Street 7 ⊖ ⛴	a	10 43	10 51		10 54	11 05		16 13	16 21		16 24		16 34	16 41	16 47		16 52	17 02	17 06		17 14	17 18	17 24

		CC	CC	CC	CC	CC		CC	CC	CC	CC	CC	CC	CC	CC	CC	CC	CC	CC	CC	CC		CC	CC
Shoeburyness	d		16 34					16 52				17 12					17 30			17 47				18 04
Thorpe Bay	d		16 38					16 56				17 16					17 34			17 51				18 08
Southend East	d		16 41					16 59				17 19					17 37			17 54				18 11
Southend Central	a		16 43					17 01				17 21					17 39			17 56				18 13
	d	16 32	16 43			16 52		17 01				17 21					17 40			17 57				18 14
Westcliff	d	16 34	16 45			16 54		17 03				17 23					17 42			17 59				18 16
Chalkwell	d	16 37	16 48			16 57		17 06				17 26					17 44			18 01				18 18
Leigh-on-Sea	d	16 40	16 51			17 00		17 09				17 29					17 47			18 04				18 21
Benfleet	d	16 44	16 55			17 04		17 13				17 33					17 52			18 09				18 26
Pitsea	d	16 48			17 00	17 08		17 18			17 31	17 37				17 49	17 56		18 02	18 13				18 30
Stanford-le-Hope	d				17 07						17 38		17 30			17 56			18 09					
East Tilbury	d				17 11						17 42								18 13					
Tilbury Town 3	d				17 17				←		17 48							←	18 19		←			
Grays	d			17 02	17 21				17 21	17 32	17 53		17 41		←	18 07		18 07	18 23		18 23		18 25	
Purfleet	d				→				17 27		17 58		17 46		17 58	→			→		18 28			
Rainham	d								17 32		→		17 51		18 03						18 33			
Dagenham Dock	d								17 35				17 55		18 07						18 37			
Basildon	d	16 53	17 02			17 12		17 22				17 41					18 00			18 18				18 34
Laindon	d	16 56				17 15						17 44		17 48			18 05			18 21				18 37
West Horndon	d	17 01				17 20								17 53			18 10			18 26				18 42
Chafford Hundred	d			17 06						17 36								18 11					18 29	
Ockendon	d			17 10						17 42								18 15					18 33	
Upminster ⊖	d	17 06		17 17		17 26				17 48				17 59			18 15	18 22		18 32			18 40	18 47
Barking ⊖	d	17 15	17 19	17 25		17 34		17 40	17 42	17 57			18 01	18 07	18 13		18 24	18 30		18 41	18 43			18 56
Stratford 7 ⊖ ⛴	a																							
London Liverpool Street 15 ⊖	a																							
West Ham ⊖	d	17 21	17 25	17 31		17 40		17 45	17 48				18 07	18 13	18 19			18 36		18 46	18 49		18 53	19 01
Limehouse ⛴	d	17 26				17 45			17 53						18 24			18 41			18 54		18 58	19 06
London Fenchurch Street 7 ⊖ ⛴	a	17 30	17 33	17 39		17 49		17 54	17 57	18 09		18 11	18 15	18 21	18 28		18 36	18 45		18 55	18 58		19 03	19 11

For general notes see front of timetable
For details of catering facilities see
Directory of Train Operators

Shoeburyness and Southend Central → London

Network diagram - see first page of Table I

		CC	CC	CC	CC	CC	CC	CC	CC	CC	CC	CC	CC	CC	CC		CC	CC	CC	CC	CC	CC	CC	CC
Shoeburyness	d	18 18			18 35		18 50			19 05			19 20		19 35				19 50		20 05			
Thorpe Bay	d	18 22			18 39		18 54			19 09			19 24		19 39				19 54		20 09			
Southend East	d	18 25			18 42		18 57			19 12			19 27		19 42				19 57		20 12			
Southend Central	a	18 27			18 44		18 59			19 15			19 29		19 44				19 59		20 14			
	d	18 28			18 45	18 49	19 00			19 15		19 20	19 30		19 45			19 50	20 00		20 15	20 20		
Westcliff	d	18 30			18 47	18 51	19 02			19 17		19 23	19 32		19 47			19 53	20 02		20 17	20 23		
Chalkwell	d	18 32			18 49	18 53	19 04			19 19		19 25	19 34		19 49			19 55	20 04		20 19	20 25		
Leigh-on-Sea	d	18 35			18 52	18 56	19 07			19 22		19 28	19 37		19 52			19 58	20 07		20 22	20 28		
Benfleet	d	18 40			18 57	19 01	19 12			19 27		19 33	19 42		19 57			20 03	20 12		20 27	20 33		
Pitsea	d		18 37		19 02	19 05				19 32		19 37			20 02			20 07			20 32	20 37		
Stanford-le-Hope	d		18 44			19 12						19 44						20 14				20 44		
East Tilbury	d		18 48			19 16			←			19 48		←				20 18		←		20 48		
Tilbury Town 3	d		18 54			19 22			19 22			19 54		19 54				20 24		20 24		20 54		
Grays	d		18 58	18 57		→		19 23	19 25		19 48	→		19 57			20 16	→		20 27		→		20 46
Purfleet	d		19 03					19 28			19 53						20 21							20 51
Rainham	d		19 08					19 33			19 58						20 26							20 56
Dagenham Dock	d		19 12					19 37			20 02						20 30							21 00
Basildon	d	18 47			19 06		19 19			19 36			19 49		20 06				20 19		20 36			
Laindon	d	18 50			19 09		19 22			19 39			19 52		20 09				20 22		20 39			
West Horndon	d				19 14					19 44					20 14						20 44			
Chafford Hundred	d			19 01					19 29					20 01						20 31				
Ockendon	d			19 07					19 34					20 05						20 35				
Upminster	⊖ d	18 59		19 13	19 20		19 31		19 40	19 50			20 00	20 10	20 20				20 30	20 40	20 50			
Barking	⊖ d	19 08	19 18	19 22	19 28		19 40	19 43	19 50	19 58	20 08		20 08	20 18	20 28		20 36		20 38	20 48	20 58		21 03	21 06
Stratford 7	⊖ a																						21 09	
London Liverpool Street 15	⊖ a																						21 21	
West Ham	⊖ d	19 14	19 23	19 28	19 34		19 45	19 48	19 56	20 04	20 13		20 16	20 26	20 34		20 41		20 46	20 56	21 04			21 11
Limehouse	d			19 33	19 39			19 53	20 01	20 09	20 18			20 31	20 39		20 46			21 01	21 09			21 16
London Fenchurch Street 7	⊖ a	19 22	19 32	19 38	19 43		19 54	19 58	20 05	20 13	20 23		20 25	20 35	20 43		20 51		20 54	21 05	21 13			21 21

		CC	CC	CC	CC	CC	CC	CC	CC		CC	CC	CC	CC	CC	CC	CC	CC	CC	CC	CC	CC		
Shoeburyness	d	20 20		20 35			21 05				21 20		21 35			22 05			22 35			23 05		
Thorpe Bay	d	20 24		20 39			21 09				21 24		21 40			22 09			22 39			23 09		
Southend East	d	20 27		20 42			21 12				21 27		21 43			22 12			22 42			23 12		
Southend Central	a	20 29		20 44			21 14				21 29		21 45			22 14			22 44			23 14		
	d	20 30		20 45		20 50	21 15		21 20		21 30		21 46		21 50	22 15		22 20	22 45	22 50		23 15		
Westcliff	d	20 32		20 47		20 53	21 17		21 23		21 32		21 48		21 53	22 17		22 23	22 47	22 53		23 17		
Chalkwell	d	20 34		20 49		20 55	21 19		21 25		21 34		21 50		21 55	22 19		22 25	22 49	22 55		23 19		
Leigh-on-Sea	d	20 37		20 52		20 58	21 22		21 28		21 37		21 53		21 58	22 22		22 28	22 52	22 58		23 22		
Benfleet	d	20 42		20 57		21 03	21 27		21 33		21 42		21 58		22 03	22 27		22 33	22 57	23 03		23 27		
Pitsea	d			21 02		21 07	21 32		21 37				22 02		22 07	22 32		22 37	23 02	23 07		23 32		
Stanford-le-Hope	d					21 14			21 44						22 14			22 44		23 14				
East Tilbury	d		←			21 18			21 48			←			22 18			22 48		23 18				
Tilbury Town 3	d		20 54			21 24			21 54			21 54			22 24			22 54		23 24				
Grays	d		20 57		21 16	21 27		21 46	→			21 57		22 16	22 27		22 46	22 57		23 27	23 31			
Purfleet	d				21 21			21 51						22 21			22 51				23 36			
Rainham	d				21 26			21 56						22 26			22 56				23 41			
Dagenham Dock	d				21 30			22 00						22 30			23 00				23 45			
Basildon	d	20 49		21 06			21 36				21 49		22 06			22 36			23 06			23 36		
Laindon	d	20 52		21 09			21 39				21 52		22 09			22 39			23 09			23 39		
West Horndon	d			21 14			21 44						22 14			22 44			23 14			23 44		
Chafford Hundred	d		21 01			21 31						22 01			22 31			23 01		23 31				
Ockendon	d		21 05			21 35						22 05			22 35			23 05		23 35				
Upminster	⊖ d	21 00	21 10	21 20		21 40	21 50				22 00	22 10	22 20		22 42	22 50		23 12	23 20	23 42		23 50		
Barking	⊖ d	21 08	21 18	21 28	21 36	21 48	21 58	22 06			22 08	22 18	22 28	22 36	22 50	22 58	23 05	23 20	23 28	23 50	23 51	23 58		
Stratford 7	⊖ a																				23 57			
London Liverpool Street 15	⊖ a																				00 05			
West Ham	⊖ d	21 16	21 26	21 34	21 41	21 56	22 04	22 11			22 16	22 26	22 34	22 41	22 56	23 04	23 11	23 26	23 34	23 56		00 04		
Limehouse	d		21 31	21 39	21 46	22 01	22 09	22 16				22 31	22 39	22 46	23 01	23 09	23 16	23 31	23 39	00 01		00 09		
London Fenchurch Street 7	⊖ a	21 24	21 35	21 43	21 51	22 05	22 13	22 21			22 24	22 35	22 43	22 51	23 05	23 13	23 21	23 35	23 43	00 05		00 14		

Saturdays

		CC	CC	CC	CC	CC	CC	CC		CC	CC	CC	CC	CC	CC	CC		CC	CC	CC	CC	CC	CC	CC
Shoeburyness	d		23p05		04 20		05 05				05 35			06 05				06 35			07 05			07 35
Thorpe Bay	d		23p09		04 23		05 08				05 38			06 08				06 38			07 08			07 38
Southend East	d		23p12		04 26		05 11				05 41			06 11				06 41			07 11			07 41
Southend Central	a		23p14		04 28		05 13				05 43			06 13				06 43			07 13			07 43
	d	22p50	23p15		04 29		05 14			05 20	05 44		05 50	06 14		06 20		06 44		06 50	07 14		07 20	07 44
Westcliff	d	22p53	23p17		04 31		05 16			05 23	05 46		05 53	06 16		06 23		06 46		06 53	07 16		07 23	07 46
Chalkwell	d	22p55	23p19		04 33		05 18			05 25	05 48		05 55	06 18		06 25		06 48		06 55	07 18		07 25	07 48
Leigh-on-Sea	d	22p58	23p22		04 36		05 21			05 28	05 51		05 58	06 21		06 28		06 51		06 58	07 21		07 28	07 51
Benfleet	d	23p03	23p27		04 40		05 25			05 32	05 55		06 02	06 25		06 32		06 55		07 02	07 25		07 32	07 55
Pitsea	d	23p07	23p32		04 44		05 29			05 36	05 59		06 06	06 29		06 36		06 59		07 06	07 29		07 36	07 59
Stanford-le-Hope	d	23p14		04 29						05 42			06 12			06 42				07 12			07 42	
East Tilbury	d	23p18		04 32						05 45			06 15			06 45				07 15			07 45	
Tilbury Town 3	d	23p24		04 38						05 51			06 21			06 51				07 21			07 51	
Grays	d	23p27		04 41				05 48		05 54		06 18	06 24		06 48	06 54			07 18	07 24		07 48	07 54	
Purfleet	d							05 53				06 23			06 53				07 23			07 53		
Rainham	d							05 58				06 28			06 58				07 28			07 58		
Dagenham Dock	d							06 02				06 32			07 02				07 32			08 02		
Basildon	d		23p36		04 47		05 32				06 02			06 32				07 02			07 32			08 02
Laindon	d		23p39		04 50		05 35				06 05			06 35				07 05			07 35			08 05
West Horndon	d		23p44		04 55		05 40				06 10			06 40				07 10			07 40			08 10
Chafford Hundred	d	23p31		04 45						05 59			06 29			06 59				07 29			07 59	
Ockendon	d	23p35		04 49		05 16				06 02			06 32			07 02				07 32			08 02	
Upminster	⊖ d	23p42	23p50	04a57	05 02	05a23	05 46			06 09	06 16		06 39	06 46		07 09		07 16		07 39	07 46		08 09	08 16
Barking	⊖ d	23p50	23p58		05 10		05 54	06 08		06 17	06 24	06 38	06 47	06 54	07 08	07 17		07 24	07 38	07 47	07 54	08 08	08 17	08 24
Stratford 7	⊖ a																							
London Liverpool Street 15	⊖ a																							
West Ham	⊖ d	23p56	00 04		05 16		06 00	06 14		06 23	06 30	06 44	06 53	07 00	07 14	07 23		07 30	07 44	07 53	08 00	08 14	08 23	08 30
Limehouse	d	00 01	00 09		05 21		06 05	06 19		06 28	06 35	06 49	06 58	07 05	07 19	07 28		07 35	07 49	07 58	08 05	08 19	08 28	08 35
London Fenchurch Street 7	⊖ a	00 05	00 14		05 27		06 12	06 26		06 34	06 42	06 56	07 04	07 12	07 26	07 34		07 42	07 56	08 04	08 12	08 26	08 34	08 42

For general notes see front of timetable
For details of catering facilities see Directory of Train Operators

Saturdays

Shoeburyness and Southend Central → London

Network diagram - see first page of Table I

		CC	CC		CC	CC		CC	CC	CC	CC	CC	CC	CC	CC	CC	CC			CC	CC	CC	CC
Shoeburyness	d		07 50					08 05		08 20			08 35		08 50					20 05			20 35
Thorpe Bay	d		07 53					08 08		08 23			08 38		08 53					20 08			20 38
Southend East	d		07 56					08 11		08 26			08 41		08 56					20 11			20 41
Southend Central	a		07 58					08 13		08 28			08 43		08 58					20 13			20 43
	d	07 50	07 59					08 14	08 20	08 29			08 44	08 50	08 59					20 14		20 20	20 44
Westcliff	d	07 53	08 01					08 16	08 23	08 31			08 46	08 53	09 01					20 16		20 23	20 46
Chalkwell	d	07 55	08 03					08 18	08 25	08 33			08 48	08 55	09 03					20 18		20 25	20 48
Leigh-on-Sea	d	07 58	08 06					08 21	08 28	08 36			08 51	08 58	09 06					20 21		20 28	20 51
Benfleet	d	08 02	08 10					08 25	08 32	08 40			08 55	09 02	09 10			and at the same minutes past each hour until		20 25		20 32	20 55
Pitsea	d	08 06						08 29	08 36				08 59	09 06						20 29		20 36	20 59
Stanford-le-Hope	d	08 12							08 42					09 12								20 42	
East Tilbury	d	08 15				←			08 45			←		09 15			←					20 45	
Tilbury Town 3	d	08 21				08 21			08 51			08 51		09 21			09 21					20 51	
Grays	d	→			08 18	08 24			→		08 48	08 54		→		09 18	09 24				20 48	20 54	
Purfleet	d				08 23						08 53					09 23					20 53		
Rainham	d				08 28						08 58					09 28					20 58		
Dagenham Dock	d				08 32						09 02					09 32					21 02		
Basildon	d		08 16					08 32		08 46			09 02		09 16					20 32			21 02
Laindon	d		08 19					08 35		08 49			09 05		09 19					20 35			21 05
West Horndon	d							08 40					09 10							20 40			21 10
Chafford Hundred	d					08 29						08 59					09 29					20 59	
Ockendon	d					08 32						09 02					09 32					21 02	
Upminster	⊖ d		08 28			08 39		08 46		08 57		09 09	09 16		09 27		09 39			20 46		21 09	21 16
Barking	⊖ d		08 36		08 38	08 47		08 54		09 05	09 08	09 17	09 24		09 35	09 38	09 47			20 54	21 08	21 17	21 24
Stratford 7	⊖ a																						
London Liverpool Street 15	⊖ a																						
West Ham	⊖ d		08 42		08 44	08 53		09 00		09 11	09 14	09 23	09 30		09 41	09 44	09 53			21 00	21 14	21 23	21 30
Limehouse	d				08 49	08 58		09 05			09 19	09 28	09 35			09 49	09 58			21 05	21 19	21 28	21 35
London Fenchurch Street 7	⊖ a		08 53		08 56	09 04		09 12		09 22	09 26	09 34	09 42		09 52	09 56	10 04			21 12	21 26	21 34	21 42

		CC	CC	CC	CC	CC		CC	CC	CC	CC	CC	CC	CC		CC	CC	CC	CC	CC	CC			
Shoeburyness	d		20 50			21 05				21 35			22 05				22 35			23 05				
Thorpe Bay	d		20 53			21 08				21 38			22 08				22 38			23 08				
Southend East	d		20 56			21 11				21 41			22 11				22 41			23 11				
Southend Central	a		20 58			21 13				21 43			22 13				22 43			23 13				
	d	20 50	20 59			21 14			21 20	21 44		21 50	22 14			22 20	22 44		22 50	23 14	23 20			
Westcliff	d	20 53	21 01			21 16			21 23	21 46		21 53	22 16			22 23	22 46		22 53	23 16	23 23			
Chalkwell	d	20 55	21 03			21 18			21 25	21 48		21 55	22 18			22 25	22 48		22 55	23 18	23 25			
Leigh-on-Sea	d	20 58	21 06			21 21			21 28	21 51		21 58	22 21			22 28	22 51		22 58	23 21	23 28			
Benfleet	d	21 02	21 10			21 25			21 32	21 55		22 02	22 25			22 32	22 55		23 02	23 25	23 32			
Pitsea	d	21 06				21 29			21 36	21 59		22 06	22 29			22 36	22 59		23 06	23 29	23 36			
Stanford-le-Hope	d	21 12							21 42			22 12				22 42			23 12		23 42			
East Tilbury	d	21 15			←				21 45			22 15				22 45			23 15		23 45			
Tilbury Town 3	d	21 21			21 21				21 51			22 21				22 51			23 21		23 51			
Grays	d	→		21 18	21 24			21 48	21 54		22 18	22 24		22 48		22 54		23 18	23 24		23 54			
Purfleet	d			21 23				21 53			22 23			22 53				23 23						
Rainham	d			21 28				21 58			22 28			22 58				23 28						
Dagenham Dock	d			21 32				22 02			22 32			23 02				23 32						
Basildon	d		21 16			21 32				22 02			22 32				23 02			23 32				
Laindon	d		21 19			21 35				22 05			22 35				23 05			23 35				
West Horndon	d					21 40				22 10			22 40				23 10			23 40				
Chafford Hundred	d				21 29				21 59			22 29				22 59			23 29		23 59			
Ockendon	d				21 32				22 02			22 32				23 02			23 32		00 02			
Upminster	⊖ d		21 28		21 39	21 46			22 09	22 16		22 39	22 46			23 09	23 16		23 39	23 46	00 08			
Barking	⊖ d		21 36	21 38	21 47	21 54		22 08	22 17	22 24	22 38	22 47	22 54	23 08		23 17	23 24	23a39	23 47	23 55	00a18			
Stratford 7	⊖ a																							
London Liverpool Street 15	⊖ a																							
West Ham	⊖ d		21 42	21 44	21 53	22 00		22 14	22 23	22 30	22 44	22 53	23 00	23 14		23 23	23 30		23 53	00 01				
Limehouse	d			21 49	21 58	22 05		22 19	22 28	22 35	22 49	22 58	23 05	23 19		23 28	23 35		23 58	00 06				
London Fenchurch Street 7	⊖ a		21 53	21 56	22 04	22 12		22 26	22 34	22 42	22 56	23 04	23 12	23 26		23 34	23 42		00 04	00 12				

Sundays

		CC		CC		CC		CC		CC		CC		CC		CC		CC			CC	CC	CC	CC
Shoeburyness	d	23p05				05 35		06 05		06 10		06 35		07 05		07 10		07 35			08 05			08 35
Thorpe Bay	d	23p08				05 38		06 08		06 14		06 38		07 08		07 14		07 38			08 08			08 38
Southend East	d	23p11				05 41		06 11		06 16		06 41		07 11		07 16		07 41			08 11			08 41
Southend Central	a	23p13				05 43		06 13		06 19		06 43		07 13		07 19		07 43			08 13			08 43
	d	23p14		23p20		05 44		06 14		06 20		06 44		07 14		07 20		07 44			08 14	08 20		08 44
Westcliff	d	23p16		23p23		05 46		06 16		06 23		06 46		07 16		07 23		07 46			08 16	08 23		08 46
Chalkwell	d	23p18		23p25		05 48		06 18		06 25		06 48		07 18		07 25		07 48			08 18	08 25		08 48
Leigh-on-Sea	d	23p21		23p28		05 51		06 21		06 28		06 51		07 21		07 28		07 51			08 21	08 28		08 51
Benfleet	d	23p25		23p32		05 55		06 25		06 32		06 55		07 25		07 32		07 55			08 25	08 32		08 55
Pitsea	d	23p29		23p36		05 59		06 29		06 36		06 59		07 29		07 36		07 59			08 29	08 36		08 59
Stanford-le-Hope	d			23p42						06 42						07 42						08 42		
East Tilbury	d			23p45						06 45						07 45						08 45		
Tilbury Town 3	d			23p51						06 51						07 51						08 51		
Grays	d			23p54						06 54						07 54						08 54	08 59	
Purfleet	d																						09 04	
Rainham	d																						09 09	
Dagenham Dock	d																						09 13	
Basildon	d	23p32				06 02		06 32				07 02		07 32				08 02			08 32			09 02
Laindon	d	23p35				06 05		06 35				07 05		07 35				08 05			08 35			09 05
West Horndon	d	23p40				06 10		06 40				07 10		07 40				08 10			08 40			09 10
Chafford Hundred	d			23p59						06 59						07 59						08 59		
Ockendon	d			00 02						07 02						08 02						09 02		
Upminster	⊖ d	23p46		00 08		06 16		06 46		07 09		07 16		07 46		08 09		08 16			08 46	09 09		09 16
Barking	⊖ d	23p55		00a18		06 25		06 55		07 17		07 25		07 55		08 17		08 25			08 55	09 17	09a20	09 25
Stratford 7	⊖ a																							
London Liverpool Street 15	⊖ a																							
West Ham	⊖ d	00 01				06 31		07 01		07 23		07 31		08 01		08 23		08 31			09 01	09 23		09 31
Limehouse	d	00 06				06 36		07 06		07 28		07 36		08 06		08 28		08 36			09 06	09 28		09 36
London Fenchurch Street 7	⊖ a	00 12				06 42		07 12		07 34		07 42		08 12		08 34		08 42			09 12	09 34		09 42

For general notes see front of timetable
For details of catering facilities see
Directory of Train Operators

Table I

Sundays

Shoeburyness and Southend Central → London

Network diagram - see first page of Table I

		CC		CC	CC	CC	CC	CC	CC	CC
Shoeburyness	d		and at the same minutes past each hour until	21 05			21 35	22 05		22 35
Thorpe Bay	d			21 08			21 38	22 08		22 38
Southend East	d			21 11			21 41	22 11		22 41
Southend Central	a			21 13			21 43	22 13		22 43
	d	08 50		21 14	21 20		21 44	22 14	22 20	22 44
Westcliff	d	08 53		21 16	21 23		21 46	22 16	22 23	22 46
Chalkwell	d	08 55		21 18	21 25		21 48	22 18	22 25	22 48
Leigh-on-Sea	d	08 58		21 21	21 28		21 51	22 21	22 28	22 51
Benfleet	d	09 02		21 25	21 32		21 55	22 25	22 32	22 55
Pitsea	d	09 06		21 29	21 36		21 59	22 29	22 36	22 59
Stanford-le-Hope	d	09 12			21 42				22 42	
East Tilbury	d	09 15			21 45				22 45	
Tilbury Town 3	d	09 21			21 51				22 51	
Grays	d	09 24			21 54	21 59			22 54	
Purfleet	d					22 04				
Rainham	d					22 09				
Dagenham Dock	d					22 13				
Basildon	d			21 32			22 02	22 32		23 02
Laindon	d			21 35			22 05	22 35		23 05
West Horndon	d			21 40			22 10	22 40		23 10
Chafford Hundred	d	09 29			21 59				22 59	
Ockendon	d	09 32			22 02				23 02	
Upminster	⊖ d	09 39		21 46	22 09		22 16	22 46	23 09	23 16
Barking	⊖ d	09 47		21 55	22 17	22a20	22 25	22 55	23 17	23 25
Stratford 7	⊖ ⛴ a									
London Liverpool Street 15	⊖ a									
West Ham	⊖ d	09 53		22 01	22 23		22 31	23 01	23 23	23 31
Limehouse	⛴ d	09 58		22 06	22 28		22 36	23 06	23 28	23 36
London Fenchurch Street 7	⊖ ⛴ a	10 04		22 12	22 34		22 42	23 12	23 34	23 42

For general notes see front of timetable
For details of catering facilities see
Directory of Train Operators

Table 1A

Mondays to Fridays

Tilbury Town — Tilbury Riverside

Bus Service

Network diagram - see first page of Table 1

		CC	CC	CC	CC	CC	CC	CC	CC	CC	CC		CC	CC		CC	CC	CC	CC	CC	CC	CC	CC	
London Fenchurch Street 7	⊖ d	....	05b10	05b40	06 20	06 50	07 16	07 49	....	08 20	08 56	....	09 20	10 20	and every 30 minutes until	14 50	15 20	....	16 21	16 37	17 15	17 47	18 02	....
Tilbury Town 3	d	05 40	06 18	06 50	07 18	07 45	08 13	08 38	09 03	09 33	10 03	.	10 33	11 03		15 33	16 03	16 33	17 03	17 33	18 00	18 30	19 00	.
Tilbury Riverside	a	05 47	06 25	06 57	07 25	07 52	08 20	08 45	09 10	09 41	10 10	....	10 40	11 10		15 40	16 10	16 40	17 11	17 41	18 08	18 38	19 08	....

Saturdays

		CC		CC		CC			CC	CC			CC		CC									
London Fenchurch Street 7	⊖ d	....	....	....	....	06 20	....	....	06 50	07 20	and every 30 minutes until	....	17 50	....	18 20	....	....	....	....	....	....	....	....	....
Tilbury Town 3	d	05 40	.	06 15	.	07 01	.	.	07 31	08 01		.	18 31	.	19 01	.	.	.	.	.	.	.	.	.
Tilbury Riverside	a	05 47	....	06 22	....	07 08	....	....	07 38	08 08		....	18 38	....	19 08	....	....	....	....	....	....	....	....	....

Mondays to Fridays

		CC	CC	CC	CC	CC	CC	CC	CC	CC		CC	CC		CC	CC	CC	CC	CC	CC	CC	CC	CC	
Tilbury Riverside	d	05 50	06 30	07 00	07 30	07 55	08 23	08 50	09 12	09 42	....	10 12	10 42	and every 30 minutes until	15 12	15 42	16 12	16 40	17 15	17 45	18 15	18 40	19 10	....
Tilbury Town 3	a	05 55	06 35	07 05	07 35	08 00	08 28	08 55	09 17	09 49	.	10 17	10 47		15 17	15 47	16 17	16 45	17 20	17 50	18 20	18 45	19 15	.
London Fenchurch Street 7	⊖ a	06 51	07 21	07 54	08 25	08 55	09 26	09 51	10 08	10 37	....	11 05	11 35		16 05	16 34	17 02	17 57	18 28	18 58	....	19 32	20 05	....

Saturdays

		CC		CC		CC		CC		CC			CC	CC			CC		CC					
Tilbury Riverside	d	05 50	....	06 30	....	07 10	....	07 50	....	08 09	....	....	08 39	09 09	and every 30 minutes until	....	18 39	....	19 09	....	....	....	....	....
Tilbury Town 3	a	05 57	.	06 37	.	07 17	.	07 57	.	08 16	.	.	08 46	09 16		.	18 46	.	19 16	.	.	.	.	.
London Fenchurch Street 7	⊖ a	07 04	....	07 34	....	08 04	....	....	....	09 04	....	....	09 34	10 04		....	19 34	....	20 04	....	....	....	....	....

For general notes see front of timetable
For details of catering facilities see Directory of Train Operators

For full services between Tilbury Town and London Fenchurch Street refer to Table 1

b Change at Barking and Tilbury Town

No Sunday Service

Table 4

Mondays to Fridays

Romford — Upminster

Network diagram - see first page of Table 1

Miles			LE	LE	LE	LE	LE	LE	LE	LE	LE		LE	LE
0	Romford	d	06 12	06 42	07 06	07 30	07 54	08 18	08 42	09 12	09 42	and every 30 minutes until	19 12	19 42
2	Emerson Park	d	06 16	06 46	07 10	07 34	07 58	08 22	08 46	09 16	09 46		19 16	19 46
$3\frac{1}{2}$	Upminster ⊖	a	06 20	06 50	07 14	07 38	08 02	08 26	08 50	09 20	09 50		19 20	19 50

Saturdays

		LE	LE	LE	LE	LE	LE	LE	LE		LE	LE
Romford	d	06 12	06 42	07 12	07 42	08 12	08 42	09 12	09 42	and every 30 minutes until	19 12	19 42
Emerson Park	d	06 16	06 46	07 16	07 46	08 16	08 46	09 16	09 46		19 16	19 46
Upminster ⊖	a	06 20	06 50	07 20	07 50	08 20	08 50	09 20	09 50		19 20	19 50

Mondays to Fridays

Miles			LE	LE	LE	LE	LE	LE	LE	LE	LE		LE	LE
0	Upminster ⊖	d	06 24	06 54	07 18	07 42	08 06	08 30	08 54	09 24	09 54	and every 30 minutes until	19 24	19 54
$1\frac{1}{2}$	Emerson Park	d	06 28	06 58	07 22	07 46	08 10	08 34	08 58	09 28	09 58		19 28	19 58
$3\frac{1}{2}$	Romford	a	06 32	07 02	07 26	07 50	08 14	08 38	09 02	09 32	10 02		19 32	20 02

Saturdays

		LE	LE	LE	LE	LE	LE	LE	LE		LE	LE
Upminster ⊖	d	06 24	06 54	07 24	07 54	08 24	08 54	09 24	09 54	and every 30 minutes until	19 24	19 54
Emerson Park	d	06 28	06 58	07 28	07 58	08 28	08 58	09 28	09 58		19 28	19 58
Romford	a	06 32	07 02	07 32	08 02	08 32	09 02	09 32	10 02		19 32	20 02

For general notes see front of timetable
For details of catering facilities see Directory of Train Operators

No Sunday Service

Network Diagram for Tables 5, 10, 11

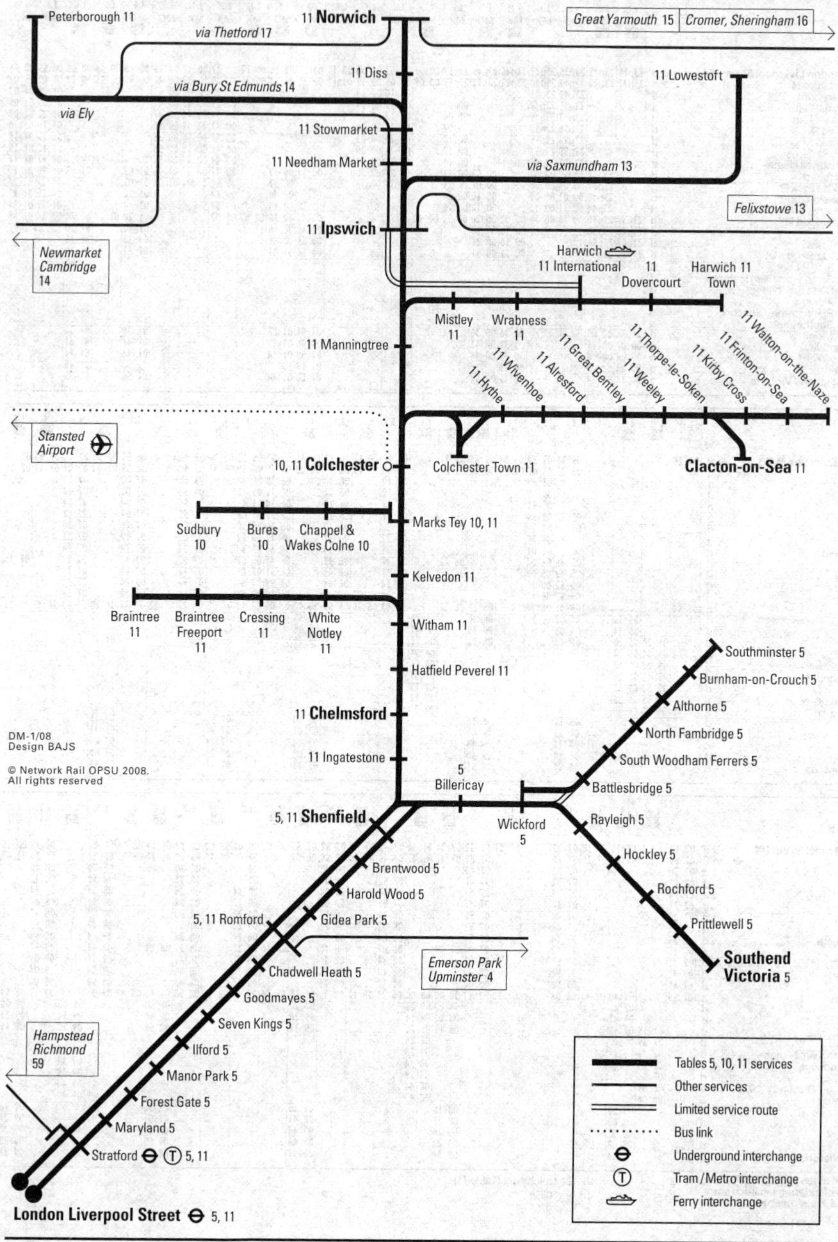

Peterborough 11
11 Norwich
via Thetford 17
Great Yarmouth 15
Cromer, Sheringham 16
11 Diss
via Bury St Edmunds 14
via Ely
11 Lowestoft
11 Stowmarket
11 Needham Market
via Saxmundham 13
Felixstowe 13
11 Ipswich
Newmarket
Cambridge
14
Harwich
11 International
11
Dovercourt
Harwich 11
Town
Mistley
11
Wrabness
11
11 Manningtree
11 Hythe
11 Wivenhoe
11 Alresford
11 Great Bentley
11 Weeley
11 Thorpe-le-Soken
11 Kirby Cross
11 Frinton-on-Sea
11 Walton-on-the-Naze
Stansted
Airport
10, 11 Colchester
Colchester Town 11
Clacton-on-Sea 11
Marks Tey 10, 11
Sudbury
10
Bures
10
Chappel &
Wakes Colne 10
Kelvedon 11
Braintree
11
Braintree
Freeport
11
Cressing
11
White
Notley
11
Witham 11
Hatfield Peverel 11
Southminster 5
Burnham-on-Crouch 5
Althorne 5
North Fambridge 5
11 Chelmsford
South Woodham Ferrers 5
11 Ingatestone
5
Billericay
Battlesbridge 5
5, 11 Shenfield
Wickford
5
Rayleigh 5
Hockley 5
Brentwood 5
Rochford 5
Harold Wood 5
5, 11 Romford
Gidea Park 5
Prittlewell 5
Southend
Victoria 5
Chadwell Heath 5
Emerson Park
Upminster 4
Goodmayes 5
Seven Kings 5
Hampstead
Richmond
59
Ilford 5
Manor Park 5
Forest Gate 5
Maryland 5
Stratford 5, 11
London Liverpool Street 5, 11
Tables 5, 10, 11 services
Other services
Limited service route
Bus link
Underground interchange
Tram / Metro interchange
Ferry interchange

DM-1/08
Design BAJS

London → Shenfield, Southminster and Southend Victoria

Network diagram - see first page of Table 5

Miles	Miles			LE MX [1]	LE MO [1]	LE MO	LE MX	LE MX [1]	LE MO [1]	LE MX	LE MO [1]	LE MX	LE MO	CC MX	LE MX [1]	LE MO [1]	LE MX [1]	LE MX	LE MX	LE MO	LE MO [1]	LE MX [1] A	LE MX [1]	LE MX	LE MO
0	—	**London Liverpool Street [15]** ⊖	d	23p15	23p15	23p35	23p37	23p45	23p45	23p52	00 02	00 02	00 05	00 12	00 15	00 15	00 18	00 22	00 32	00 35	00 45	00 48	00 50	00 55	00 55
4	—	Stratford [7] ⊖ ⛴	d	23p22	23p22	23p42	23p44	23p52	23p52	23p58	00 09	00 09	00 12	00a19	00 22	00 22	00 25	00 29	00 39	00 42	00 52	00 55	00 57	01 02	01 02
4½	—	Maryland	d			23p43	23p45			23p59		00 10	00 13					00 30	00 40	00 43				01 03	01 03
5¼	—	Forest Gate	d			23p45	23p47			00 02		00 12	00 15					00 32	00 42	00 45				01 05	01 05
6½	—	Manor Park	d			23p47	23p49			00 04		00 14	00 17					00 34	00 44	00 47				01 07	01 07
7¼	—	Ilford [2]	d			23p50	23p52			00 07		00 17	00 20					00 37	00 47	00 50				01 10	01 10
8½	—	Seven Kings	d			23p53	23p55			00 10		00 20	00 23					00 40	00 50	00 53				01 13	01 13
9¼	—	Goodmayes	d			23p55	23p57			00 12		00 22	00 25					00 42	00 52	00 55				01 15	01 15
10	—	Chadwell Heath	d			23p57	23p59			00 14		00 24	00 27					00 44	00 54	00 57				01 17	01 17
12¼	—	Romford	d		23p33	23p59	00 02		00 03	00 17		00 27	00 30		00 32	00 33		00 47	00 57	01 00	01 03		01 08	01 20	01 20
13½	—	Gidea Park [2]	d		23p37	00 04	00 06		00 07	00 21		00a31	00a36			00 37		00 51	01a01	01a06	01 07	01 07		01 24	01 24
15	—	Harold Wood	d		23p40	00 07	00 09		00 10	00 24						00 40		00 54			01 10			01 27	01 27
18¼	—	Brentwood	d		23p44	00 11	00 13		00 14	00 28						00 44		00 58			01 14			01 31	01 31
20¼	—	**Shenfield [3]**	a	23p39	23p50	00 16	00 18	00 09	00 20	00 33	00 30				00 44	00 50	00 47	01 03			01 20	01 17	01 20	01 36	01 38
—	—		d	23p40	23p50			00 10	00 20						00 45	00 50					01 20		01 20		
24¼	—	Billericay	d	23p46	23p56			00 16	00 26						00 51	00 56					01 26		01 26		
29	0	**Wickford [2]**	d	23p51	00 01			00 21	00 31						00 56	01 01					01 31		01 31		
—	2½	Battlesbridge	d																						
—	5	South Woodham Ferrers	d																						
—	8¼	North Fambridge	d																						
—	11¼	Althorne	d																						
—	14¼	Burnham-on-Crouch	d																						
—	16½	**Southminster**	a																						
33	—	Rayleigh	d	23p56	00 06			00 26	00 36						01 01	01 06					01 36		01 36		
36	—	Hockley	d	00 01	00 11			00 31	00 41						01 06	01 11					01 41		01 41		
38¾	—	Rochford	d	00 04	00 14			00 34	00 44						01 09	01 14					01 44		01 44		
41	—	Prittlewell	d	00 08				00 38							01 13								01 48		
41½	—	**Southend Victoria**	a	00 15	00 24			00 45	00 54						01 20	01 24					01 54		01 55		

		LE [1]	LE [1]	LE [1]		LE	LE	LE [1]	LE [1]	LE [1]	LE [1]	LE	LE [1]	LE	LE [1]	LE	LE	LE [1]	LE	LE [1]	LE	LE [1]	LE	LE [1]	LE [1]
London Liverpool Street [15] ⊖	d	05 25				05 26	05 39	05 52	05 55	06 02		06 02	06 12	06 12	06 15	06 22	06 32	06 34	06 42	06 48	06 52	06 55	07 02	07 04	07 08
Stratford [7] ⊖ ⛴	d	05 32				05 33	05 46	06a01	06 02	06 09		06 09	06 19	06 19	06 22	06 29	06 39	06 41	06 49	06 55	06 59	07 02	07 09	07 11	07 15
Maryland	d						05 47					06 10		06 20		06 30	06 40		06 50		07 00		07 10		
Forest Gate	d						05 49					06 12		06 22		06 32	06 42		06 52		07 02		07 12		
Manor Park	d						05 51					06 14		06 24		06 34	06 44		06 54		07 04		07 14		
Ilford [2]	d					05 38	05 54					06 17		06 27		06 37	06 47		06 57		07 07		07 17		
Seven Kings	d					05 40	05 57					06 20		06 30		06 40	06 50		07 00		07 10		07 20		
Goodmayes	d						05 59					06 22		06 32		06 42	06 52		07 02		07 12		07 22		
Chadwell Heath	d						06 01					06 24		06 34		06 44	06 54		07 04		07 14		07 24		
Romford	d	05 40				05 46	06 04			06 17		06 27		06 37		06 47	06 57	06 49	07 07		07 17		07 27		07 23
Gidea Park [2]	d					05 49	06 08					06 31		06 41		06 51	07 01		07 11		07 21		07 31		
Harold Wood	d					05 52	06 11					06 34		06 44		06 54	07 04		07 14		07 24		07 34		
Brentwood	d					05 57	06 15					06 38		06 48		06 58	07 08		07 18		07 28		07 38		
Shenfield [3]	a	05 50				06 02	06 20		06 19	06 27		06 43	06 36	06 53	06 40	07 03	07 13	07 00	07 23	07 12	07 33	07 20	07 43	07 28	07 33
	d			05 58		06 02			06 20		06 35				06 40			07 00				07 20			
Billericay	d			06 04		06 08			06 26		06 41				06 46			07 06				07 26			
Wickford [2]	d		05 20	06 10		06 13			06 31		06 47				06 51			07 11				07 31			
Battlesbridge	d		05 24	06 14							06 51														
South Woodham Ferrers	d		05 28	06 18							06 55														
North Fambridge	d		05b45	06 25							07c07														
Althorne	d		05 50	06 30							07 12														
Burnham-on-Crouch	d		05 55	06 35							07 17														
Southminster	a		06 00	06 40							07 22														
Rayleigh	d					06 19			06 36						06 56			07 16				07 36			
Hockley	d					06 23			06 41						07 01			07 21				07 41			
Rochford	d					06 27			06 44						07 04			07 24				07 44			
Prittlewell	d					06 30			06 48						07 08			07 28				07 48			
Southend Victoria	a					06 34			06 51						07 11			07 31				07 51			

		LE	LE [1]	LE [1]	LE [1]	LE		LE [1]	LE	LE [1]	LE [1]	LE	LE [1]	LE	LE [1]	LE [1]	LE	LE [1]	LE	LE [1]	LE [1]	LE	LE [1]	LE	LE [1]
London Liverpool Street [15] ⊖	d	07 12		07 15	07 18	07 22		07 27	07 32	07 34	07 40	07 42	07 48	07 52	07 55	08 02	08 02	08 08	08 12	08 14	08 18	08 22		08 32	08 35
Stratford [7] ⊖ ⛴	d	07 19		07 22	07 25	07 29			07 39	07 41	07 47	07 49	07 55	07 59	08 02		08 09	08 15	08 19	08 21	08 25	08 29		08 39	08 42
Maryland	d	07 20				07 30			07 40			07 50		08 00			08 10		08 20			08 30		08 40	
Forest Gate	d	07 22				07 32			07 42			07 52		08 02			08 12		08 22			08 32		08 42	
Manor Park	d	07 24				07 34			07 44			07 54		08 04			08 14		08 24			08 34		08 44	
Ilford [2]	d	07 27				07 37			07 47			07 57		08 07			08 17		08 27			08 37		08 47	
Seven Kings	d	07 30				07 40			07 50			08 00		08 10			08 20		08 30			08 40		08 50	
Goodmayes	d	07 32				07 42			07 52			08 02		08 12			08 22		08 32			08 42		08 52	
Chadwell Heath	d	07 34				07 44			07 54			08 04		08 14			08 24		08 34			08 44		08 54	
Romford	d	07 37				07 47			07 57	07 49		08 07		08 17		08 16	08 27		08 37	08 29		08 47		08 57	
Gidea Park [2]	d	07 41				07 51			08 01			08 11		08 21			08 31		08 41			08 51		09 01	
Harold Wood	d	07 44				07 54			08 04			08 14		08 24			08 34		08 44			08 54		09 04	
Brentwood	d	07 48				07 58			08 08			08 18		08 28			08 38		08 48			08 58		09 08	
Shenfield [3]	a	07 53		07 40	07 41	08 03		07 50	08 13	08 00	08 06	08 23	08 12	08 33	08 19	08 26	08 43	08 31	08 53	08 40	08 41	09 03		09 13	08 59
	d			07 41						08 00	08 08				08 20					08 40			09 08		09 00
Billericay	d			07 47						08 06	08 14				08 26					08 46			09 14		09 06
Wickford [2]	d		07 35	07 52						08 11	08 20				08 31					08 51			09 20		09 11
Battlesbridge	d		07 39								08 24												09 24		
South Woodham Ferrers	d		07 43								08 28												09 28		
North Fambridge	d		07 51								08 34												09 34		
Althorne	d		07 56								08 39												09 39		
Burnham-on-Crouch	d		08 01								08 44												09 44		
Southminster	a		08 06								08 49												09 49		
Rayleigh	d			07 57						08 16					08 36					08 56					09 16
Hockley	d			08 02						08 21					08 41					09 01					09 21
Rochford	d			08 05						08 24					08 44					09 04					09 24
Prittlewell	d			08 09						08 28					08 48					09 08					09 28
Southend Victoria	a			08 14						08 31					08 51					09 11					09 31

For general notes see front of timetable
For details of catering facilities see Directory of Train Operators

A To Colchester (Table 11)
b Arr. 0534
c Arr. 0701

London → Shenfield, Southminster and Southend Victoria

Network diagram - see first page of Table 5

		LE [1]	LE	LE [1]	LE	LE [1]	LE	LE [1]		LE	LE [1]	LE [1]	LE	LE	LE [1]	LE [1]	LE	LE [1]	LE	LE [1]		LE	LE [1]	LE	LE [1]
London Liverpool Street [15] ⊖	d	08 38	08 42	08 48	08 52	08 55	09 02	09 08		09 12	09 15	09 18	09 22	09 32	09 34	09 40	09 42	09 48	09 52	09 55		10 02	10 08	10 12	10 15
Stratford [7] ⊖	d		08 49	08 55	08 59	09 02	09 09	09 15		09 19	09 22	09 25	09 29	09 39	09 41	09 47	09 49	09 55	09 59	10 02		10 09	10 15	10 19	10 22
Maryland	d		08 50		09 00		09 10			09 20			09 30	09 40			09 50		10 00			10 10		10 20	
Forest Gate	d		08 52		09 02		09 12			09 22			09 32	09 42			09 52		10 02			10 12		10 22	
Manor Park	d		08 54		09 04		09 14			09 24			09 34	09 44			09 54		10 04			10 14		10 24	
Ilford [2]	d		08 57		09 07		09 17			09 27			09 37	09 47			09 57		10 07			10 17		10 27	
Seven Kings	d		09 00		09 10		09 20			09 30			09 40	09 50			10 00		10 10			10 20		10 30	
Goodmayes	d		09 02		09 12		09 22			09 32			09 42	09 52			10 02		10 12			10 22		10 32	
Chadwell Heath	d		09 04		09 14		09 24			09 34			09 44	09 54			10 04		10 14			10 24		10 34	
Romford	d		09 07		09 17		09 27	09 23		09 37			09 47	09 57	09 49		10 07		10 17			10 27	10 23	10 37	
Gidea Park [2]	d		09 11		09 21		09 31			09 41			09 51	10 01			10 11		10 21			10 31		10 41	
Harold Wood	d		09 14		09 24		09 34			09 44			09 54	10 04			10 14		10 24			10 34		10 44	
Brentwood	d		09 18		09 28		09 38			09 48			09 58	10 08			10 18		10 28			10 38		10 48	
Shenfield [3]	a	09 02	09 23	09 12	09 33	09 19	09 43	09 33		09 53	09 39	09 41	10 03	10 13	10 00	10 07	10 23	10 12	10 33	10 19		10 43	10 33	10 53	10 39
	d					09 20					09 40				10 00	10 08				10 20					10 40
Billericay	d					09 26					09 46				10 06	10 14				10 26					10 46
Wickford [2]	d					09 31					09 51				10 11	10 20				10 31					10 51
Battlesbridge	d															10 24									
South Woodham Ferrers	d															10 28									
North Fambridge	d															10 34									
Althorne	d															10 39									
Burnham-on-Crouch	d															10 44									
Southminster	a															10 49									
Rayleigh	d					09 36					09 56				10 16					10 36					10 56
Hockley	d					09 41					10 01				10 21					10 41					11 01
Rochford	d					09 44					10 04				10 24					10 44					11 04
Prittlewell	d					09 48					10 08				10 28					10 48					11 08
Southend Victoria	a					09 51					10 11				10 31					10 51					11 11

		LE [1]	LE	LE [1]	LE	LE [1]	LE	LE [1]	LE	LE [1]		LE		LE [1]	LE	LE [1]	LE [1]	LE	LE [1]	LE [1]	LE	LE [1]	LE	LE [1]
London Liverpool Street [15] ⊖	d	10 18	10 22		10 32	10 34	10 42	10 48	10 52	10 55	and at the same minutes past each hour until	15 02		15 08	15 12	15 15	15 18	15 22	15 32		15 32	15 34	15 42	15 48
Stratford [7] ⊖	d	10 25	10 29		10 39	10 41	10 49	10 55	10 59	11 02		15 09		15 15	15 19	15 22	15 25	15 29			15 39	15 41	15 49	15 55
Maryland	d		10 30		10 40		10 50		11 00			15 10			15 20			15 30			15 40		15 50	
Forest Gate	d		10 32		10 42		10 52		11 02			15 12			15 22			15 32			15 42		15 52	
Manor Park	d		10 34		10 44		10 54		11 04			15 14			15 24			15 34			15 44		15 54	
Ilford [2]	d		10 37		10 47		10 57		11 07			15 17			15 27			15 37			15 47		15 57	
Seven Kings	d		10 40		10 50		11 00		11 10			15 20			15 30			15 40			15 50		16 00	
Goodmayes	d		10 42		10 52		11 02		11 12			15 22			15 32			15 42			15 52		16 02	
Chadwell Heath	d		10 44		10 54		11 04		11 14			15 24			15 34			15 44			15 54		16 04	
Romford	d		10 47		10 57	10 49	11 07		11 17			15 27		15 23	15 37			15 47			15 57	15 49	16 07	
Gidea Park [2]	d		10 51		11 01		11 11		11 21			15 31			15 41			15 51			16 01		16 11	
Harold Wood	d		10 54		11 04		11 14		11 24			15 34			15 44			15 54			16 04		16 14	
Brentwood	d		10 58		11 08		11 18		11 28			15 38			15 48			15 58			16 08		16 18	
Shenfield [3]	a	10 41	11 03		11 13	11 00	11 23	11 12	11 33	11 19		15 43		15 33	15 53	15 39	15 41	16 03	15 54		16 13	16 00	16 23	16 12
	d			11 08		11 00				11 20						15 40				16 08		16 00		
Billericay	d			11 14		11 06				11 26						15 46				16 14		16 06		
Wickford [2]	d			11 20		11 11				11 31						15 51				16 20		16 11		
Battlesbridge	d			11 24																16 24				
South Woodham Ferrers	d			11 28																16 28				
North Fambridge	d			11 34																16 34				
Althorne	d			11 39																16 39				
Burnham-on-Crouch	d			11 44																16 44				
Southminster	a			11 49																16 49				
Rayleigh	d					11 16				11 36						15 56						16 16		
Hockley	d					11 21				11 41						16 01						16 21		
Rochford	d					11 24				11 44						16 04						16 24		
Prittlewell	d					11 28				11 48						16 08						16 28		
Southend Victoria	a					11 31				11 51						16 11						16 31		

		LE	LE [1]	LE	LE [1]	LE [1]	LE	LE [1]	LE	LE [1]	LE	LE [1]	LE [1]	LE [1]	LE		LE	LE [1]	LE	LE [1]	LE	LE [1]	LE	LE [1]	LE
London Liverpool Street [15] ⊖	d	15 52	15 55	16 02	16 02	16 10	16 12	16 17	16 22	16 25	16 32	16 36		16 40	16 42		16 46	16 47	16 52	16 55	16 56	17 02	17 02	17 04	17 06
Stratford [7] ⊖	d	15 59	16 02	16 09	16 10	16 18	16 19	16 25	16 29	16 33	16 39			16 48	16 49		16 53	16 55	16 59	17 03	17 03		17 09	17 12	17 13
Maryland	d	16 00		16 10			16 20		16 30		16 40						16 55				17 05				17 15
Forest Gate	d	16 02		16 12			16 22		16 32		16 42						16 57				17 07				17 17
Manor Park	d	16 04		16 14			16 24		16 34		16 44						16 59				17 09				17 19
Ilford [2]	d	16 07		16 17			16 27		16 37		16 47				16 55		17 02		17 05		17 12		17 15		17 22
Seven Kings	d	16 10		16 20			16 30		16 40		16 50				16 58				17 08				17 18		
Goodmayes	d	16 12		16 22			16 32		16 42		16 52				17 00				17 10				17 20		
Chadwell Heath	d	16 14		16 24			16 34		16 44		16 54				17 02		17 06		17 12		17 16		17 22		17 26
Romford	d	16 17		16 27			16 37		16 47		16 57				17 06		17 10		17 16		17 20		17 26		17 30
Gidea Park [2]	d	16 21		16 31			16 41		16 51		17 01				17a11		17 14		17a21		17 24		17a31		17 34
Harold Wood	d	16 24		16 34			16 44		16 54		17 04						17 17				17 27				17 37
Brentwood	d	16 28		16 38			16 48		16 58		17 08						17 21				17 31				17 41
Shenfield [3]	a	16 33	16 19	16 45	16 25	16 34	16 55	16 40	17 05	16 50	17 15	16 57		17 04			17 29	17 10		17 20	17 39	17 24		17 29	17 49
	d		16 20			16 35				16 50				17 05						17 20				17 29	
Billericay	d		16 26			16 41				16 56				17 11						17 26				17 36	
Wickford [2]	d		16 31			16 46				17 01			17 07	17 16						17 31				17 42	
Battlesbridge	d												17 11												
South Woodham Ferrers	d												17 15												
North Fambridge	d												17 21												
Althorne	d												17 26												
Burnham-on-Crouch	d												17 31												
Southminster	a												17 36												
Rayleigh	d		16 36			16 51				17 06				17 21						17 36				17 47	
Hockley	d		16 41			16 56				17 11				17 26						17 41				17 52	
Rochford	d		16 44			16 59				17 14				17 29						17 44				17 55	
Prittlewell	d		16 48			17 03				17 18				17 33						17 48				17 59	
Southend Victoria	a		16 51			17 09				17 23				17 39						17 53				18 04	

For general notes see front of timetable
For details of catering facilities see
Directory of Train Operators

London → Shenfield, Southminster and Southend Victoria

Network diagram - see first page of Table 5

		LE 1	LE	LE 1	LE 1	LE	LE 1	LE 1	LE	LE 1	LE	LE 1	LE	LE 1	LE	LE 1	LE		LE	LE 1	LE 1	LE	LE	LE	LE 1
London Liverpool Street 15 ⊖	d	17 08	17 12	17 12	17 15	17 16	17 17	17 22	17 22	17 25	17 26	17 32	17 32	17 34	17 36	17 38	17 39		17 42	17 42	17 45	17 46	17 49	17 52	17 52
Stratford 7 ⊖	d	17a16	17 19	17a20		17 23			17 29	17 33	17 33		17 39	17 42	17 43	17a46	17 46		17 49	17a50	17 53	17 53	17 56	17 59	
Maryland	d					17 25					17 35				17 45							17 55			
Forest Gate	d					17 27					17 37		17 42						17 52					18 02	
Manor Park	d					17 29					17 39						17 50						18 00		
Ilford 2	d		17 25			17 32			17 35		17 42		17 46		17 50		17 53		17 56			18 00	18 03	18 06	
Seven Kings	d		17 28						17 38				17 49		17 52		17 56		17 59			18 02	18 06	18 09	
Goodmayes	d		17 30						17 40				17 51		17 54		17 58		18 01			18 04	18 08	18 11	
Chadwell Heath	d		17 32			17 36			17 42		17 46		17 53		17 56		18 00		18 03			18 06	18 10	18 13	
Romford	d		17 36			17 40			17 46		17 50		17 57		18 00		18 04		18 07			18 10	18 14	18 17	
Gidea Park 2	d		17a41			17 44			17a51		17 54		18a02		18 04		18a09		18a10			18 14	18 18	18a22	
Harold Wood	d					17 47					17 57				18 07							18 17	18 21		
Brentwood	d					17 51					18 01				18 11							18 21	18 25		
Shenfield 3	a					17 59	17 41	17 44		17 51	18 09	17 54		17 59	18 19						18 10	18 29	18 31		18 14
	d						17 42			17 52				17 59							18 11		18 35		
Billericay	d						17 48			17 58				18 06							18 17		18 41		
Wickford 2	d				17 47		17 54			18 04				18 12							18 23		18 47		
Battlesbridge	d																								
South Woodham Ferrers	d				17 54																				
North Fambridge	d				18b03																				
Althorne	d				18 08																				
Burnham-on-Crouch	d				18 13																				
Southminster	a				18 20																				
Rayleigh	d						17 59			18 09				18 17							18 28		18 53		
Hockley	d						18 04			18 14				18 22							18 33		18 57		
Rochford	d						18 07			18 17				18 25							18 36		19 01		
Prittlewell	d						18 11			18 21				18 29							18 40		19 04		
Southend Victoria	a						18 16			18 26				18 34							18 45		19 10		

		LE 1	LE 1	LE	LE	LE 1	LE 1	LE	LE 1	LE	LE 1	LE 1	LE	LE 1	LE	LE 1	LE	LE	LE 1		LE 1	LE	LE 1	LE	LE 1
London Liverpool Street 15 ⊖	d	17 54	17 56	17 56	18 02	18 02	18 04	18 06	18 08	18 12	18 12	18 15	18 16	18 22	18 22	18 25	18 26	18 32	18 32		18 35	18 38	18 38	18 42	18 42
Stratford 7 ⊖	d			18 03	18 09	18a10	18 13	18 13	18a16	18 19	18a20	18 23	18 23		18 29	18 33	18 33	18 39	18a40		18 43	18 45	18 46	18 49	18 50
Maryland	d			18 05				18 15					18 25				18 35	18 40				18 46		18 50	
Forest Gate	d			18 07				18 17					18 27				18 37	18 42				18 48		18 52	
Manor Park	d			18 09				18 19					18 29				18 39	18 44				18 50		18 54	
Ilford 2	d			18 12	18 15			18 22		18 25			18 32		18 35		18 42	18 47				18 53		18 57	
Seven Kings	d				18 18					18 28					18 38			18 50				18 56		19 00	
Goodmayes	d				18 20					18 30					18 40			18 52				18 58		19 02	
Chadwell Heath	d			18 16	18 22			18 26		18 32			18 36		18 42		18 46	18 54				19 00		19 04	
Romford	d			18 20	18 26			18 30		18 36			18 40		18 46		18 50	18 57				19 03		19 07	
Gidea Park 2	d			18 24	18a31			18 34		18a41			18 44		18a51		18 54	19 01				19a09		19 11	
Harold Wood	d			18 27				18 37					18 47				18 57	19 04						19 14	
Brentwood	d			18 31				18 41					18 51				19 01	19 08						19 18	
Shenfield 3	a		18 21	18 39			18 29	18 49				18 40	18 59	18 44		18 50	19 09	19 15			19 00		19 01	19 25	
	d		18 22				18 29					18 41				18 51					19 01				
Billericay	d		18 28				18 36					18 47				18 57					19 07				
Wickford 2	d	18 29	18 34				18 42					18 53				19 03					19 13				19 17
Battlesbridge	d	18 33																							19 22
South Woodham Ferrers	d	18 37																							19 26
North Fambridge	d	18 43																							19 32
Althorne	d	18 48																							19 37
Burnham-on-Crouch	d	18 53																							19 42
Southminster	a	19 00																							19 49
Rayleigh	d		18 39				18 47					18 58				19 08					19 18				
Hockley	d		18 44				18 52					19 03				19 13					19 23				
Rochford	d		18 47				18 55					19 06				19 16					19 26				
Prittlewell	d		18 51				18 59					19 10				19 20					19 30				
Southend Victoria	a		18 56				19 04					19 15				19 25					19 35				

		LE 1	LE	LE 1	LE	LE 1	LE	LE 1	LE	LE 1	LE	LE 1	LE 1	LE	LE	LE 1	LE 1	LE	LE 1	LE	LE 1		LE 1	LE	LE 1
London Liverpool Street 15 ⊖	d	18 45	18 46	18 48	18 52	18 55	18 56	19 02	19 02	19 08	19 12	19 15	19 18	19 22	19 32	19 35	19 38	19 42	19 48	19 52			19 55	20 02	20 08
Stratford 7 ⊖	d	18 53	18 53		18 59	19 03	19 03	19 09	19 09	19a15	19 19	19 22	19 25	19 29	19 39	19 42	19 45	19 49	19 55	19 59			20 03	20 09	20 15
Maryland	d				19 00				19 10		19 20			19 30	19 40			19 50		20 00				20 10	
Forest Gate	d		18 55		19 02		19 05		19 12		19 22			19 32	19 42			19 52		20 02				20 12	
Manor Park	d		18 57		19 04		19 07		19 14		19 24			19 34	19 44			19 54		20 04				20 14	
Ilford 2	d		19 00		19 07		19 10		19 17		19 27			19 37	19 47			19 57		20 07				20 17	
Seven Kings	d		19 03		19 10		19 13		19 20		19 30			19 40	19 50			20 00		20 10				20 20	
Goodmayes	d		19 05		19 12		19 15		19 22		19 32			19 42	19 52			20 02		20 12				20 22	
Chadwell Heath	d		19 07		19 14		19 17		19 24		19 34			19 44	19 54			20 04		20 14				20 24	
Romford	d		19 10		19 17		19 20		19 27		19 37			19 47	19 57			20 07		20 17				20 27	
Gidea Park 2	d		19a16		19 21		19a26		19 31		19 41			19 51	20 01			20 11		20 21				20 31	
Harold Wood	d				19 24				19 34		19 44			19 54	20 04			20 14		20 24				20 34	
Brentwood	d				19 28				19 38		19 48			19 58	20 08			20 18		20 28				20 38	
Shenfield 3	a	19 10		19 11	19 35	19 20		19 25	19 43		19 53	19 39	19 41	20 03	20 13	19 59	20 01	20 23	20 12	20 33			20 20	20 43	20 31
	d	19 11				19 21						19 40				20 00							20 20		
Billericay	d	19 17				19 27						19 46				20 06							20 26		
Wickford 2	d	19 23				19 33						19 51				20 11					20 20		20 31		
Battlesbridge	d																				20 24				
South Woodham Ferrers	d																				20 28				
North Fambridge	d																				20 34				
Althorne	d																				20 39				
Burnham-on-Crouch	d																				20 44				
Southminster	a																				20 49				
Rayleigh	d	19 28				19 38						19 56				20 16							20 36		
Hockley	d	19 33				19 43						20 01				20 21							20 41		
Rochford	d	19 36				19 46						20 04				20 24							20 44		
Prittlewell	d	19 40				19 50						20 08				20 28							20 48		
Southend Victoria	a	19 45				19 55						20 11				20 31							20 51		

For general notes see front of timetable
For details of catering facilities see Directory of Train Operators

b Arr. 1800

London → Shenfield, Southminster and Southend Victoria

Network diagram - see first page of Table 5

		LE	LE 1	LE 1	LE	LE 1	LE	LE 1	LE 1	LE	LE 1	LE	LE 1	LE	LE 1	LE	LE 1	LE 1	LE	LE 1	LE	LE 1	CC 1		LE
London Liverpool Street 15 ⊖	d	20 12	20 15	20 18	20 22		20 32	20 34	20 38	20 42	20 48	20 52	20 55	21 02	21 08	21 12	21 15	21 18	21 22		21 32	21 34	21 38		21 42
Stratford 7 ⊖	d	20 19	20 22	20 25	20 29		20 39	20 41	20 45	20 49	20 55	20 59	21 02	21 09	21 15	21 19	21 22	21 25	21 29		21 39	21 41	21a45		21 49
Maryland	d	20 20			20 30		20 40			20 50		21 00		21 10		21 20			21 30		21 40				21 50
Forest Gate	d	20 22			20 32		20 42			20 52		21 02		21 12		21 22			21 32		21 42				21 52
Manor Park	d	20 24			20 34		20 44			20 54		21 04		21 14		21 24			21 34		21 44				21 54
Ilford 2	d	20 27			20 37		20 47			20 57		21 07		21 17		21 27			21 37		21 47				21 57
Seven Kings	d	20 30			20 40		20 50			21 00		21 10		21 20		21 30			21 40		21 50				22 00
Goodmayes	d	20 32			20 42		20 52			21 02		21 12		21 22		21 32			21 42		21 52				22 02
Chadwell Heath	d	20 34			20 44		20 54			21 04		21 14		21 24		21 34			21 44		21 54				22 04
Romford	d	20 37			20 47		20 57	20 49		21 07		21 17		21 27	21 23	21 37			21 47		21 57	21 49			22 07
Gidea Park 2	d	20 41			20 51		21 01			21 11		21 21		21 31		21 41			21 51		22 01				22 11
Harold Wood	d	20 44			20 54		21 04			21 14		21 24		21 34		21 44			21 54		22 04				22 14
Brentwood	d	20 48			20 58		21 08			21 18		21 28		21 38		21 48			21 58		22 08				22 18
Shenfield 3	a	20 53	20 39	20 41	21 03		21 13	21 00	21 01	21 23	21 12	21 33	21 19	21 43	21 33	21 53	21 39	21 41	22 03		22 13	22 00			22 23
	d		20 40			21 08		21 00					21 20				21 40			22 08		22 00			
Billericay	d		20 46			21 14		21 06					21 26				21 46			22 14		22 06			
Wickford 2	d		20 51			21 20		21 11					21 31				21 51			22 20		22 11			
Battlesbridge	d					21 24														22 24					
South Woodham Ferrers	d					21 28														22 28					
North Fambridge	d					21 34														22 34					
Althorne	d					21 39														22 39					
Burnham-on-Crouch	d					21 44														22 44					
Southminster	a					21 49														22 49					
Rayleigh	d		20 56					21 16					21 36				21 56					22 16			
Hockley	d		21 01					21 21					21 41				22 01					22 21			
Rochford	d		21 04					21 24					21 44				22 04					22 24			
Prittlewell	d		21 08					21 28					21 48				22 08					22 28			
Southend Victoria	a		21 11					21 31					21 51				22 11					22 31			

		LE 1	LE	LE 1	LE 1	LE	LE 1	LE 1	LE	LE	LE 1	LE 1	LE 1	LE	LE 1	LE	LE 1	LE 1	LE	LE	LE 1	LE 1	LE		
London Liverpool Street 15 ⊖	d	21 48	21 52	21 55	22 00	22 07	22 15	22 18	22 22	22 37		22 45	22 48	22 52	23 00	23 07	23 15	23 18	23 22	23 37	23 45	23 48	23 52		
Stratford 7 ⊖	d	21 55	21 59	22 02		22 14	22 22	22 25	22 29	22 44		22 52	22 55	22 59	23 07	23 14	23 22	23 25	23 29	23 44	23 52	23 55	23 58		
Maryland	d		22 00			22 15			22 30	22 45				23 00		23 15			23 30	23 45			23 59		
Forest Gate	d		22 02			22 17			22 32	22 47				23 02		23 17			23 32	23 47			00 02		
Manor Park	d		22 04			22 19			22 34	22 49				23 04		23 19			23 34	23 49			00 04		
Ilford 2	d		22 07			22 22			22 37	22 52				23 07		23 22			23 37	23 52			00 07		
Seven Kings	d		22 10			22 25			22 40	22 55				23 10		23 25			23 40	23 55			00 10		
Goodmayes	d		22 12			22 27			22 42	22 57				23 12		23 27			23 42	23 57			00 12		
Chadwell Heath	d		22 14			22 29			22 44	22 59				23 14		23 29			23 44	23 59			00 14		
Romford	d		22 17			22 32			22 47	23 02				23 17		23 32			23 47	00 02			00 17		
Gidea Park 2	d		22 21			22 36			22 51	23 06				23 21		23 36			23 51	00 06			00 21		
Harold Wood	d		22 24			22 39			22 54	23 09				23 24		23 39			23 54	00 09			00 24		
Brentwood	d		22 28			22 43			22 58	23 13				23 28		23 43			23 58	00 13			00 28		
Shenfield 3	a	22 12	22 33	22 19	22 22	22 48	22 39	22 41	23 03	23 18		23 09	23 12	23 33	23 23	23 48	23 39	23 41	00 03	00 18	00 09	00 12	00 33		
	d			22 20			22 40					23 10					23 40				00 10				
Billericay	d			22 26			22 46					23 16					23 46				00 16				
Wickford 2	d			22 31			22 51				22 58	23 21					23 51				00 21				
Battlesbridge	d										23 02														
South Woodham Ferrers	d										23 06														
North Fambridge	d										23 12														
Althorne	d										23 17														
Burnham-on-Crouch	d										23 22														
Southminster	a										23 27														
Rayleigh	d			22 36			22 56					23 26					23 56				00 26				
Hockley	d			22 41			23 01					23 31					00 01				00 31				
Rochford	d			22 44			23 04					23 34					00 04				00 34				
Prittlewell	d			22 48			23 08					23 38					00 08				00 38				
Southend Victoria	a			22 51			23 11					23 45					00 15				00 45				

For general notes see front of timetable
For details of catering facilities see
Directory of Train Operators

London → Shenfield, Southminster and Southend Victoria

Network diagram - see first page of Table 5

Station																									
		LE 1	LE	LE 1	LE	LE		CC 1	LE 1	LE 1	LE	LE		LE 1	LE 1	LE	LE 1	LE 1		LE	LE	LE 1	LE 1	LE	LE 1
														A											
London Liverpool Street 15 ⊖	d	23p15	23p37	23p45	23p52	00 02		00 12	00 15	00 18	00 22	00 32		00 48	00 50	00 55	05 23			05 26	05 28	05 30		05 42	06 00
Stratford 7 ⊖	d	23p22	23p44	23p52	23p58	00 09		00a19	00 22	00 25	00 29	00 39		00 55	00 57	01 02	05a32			05 33	05a36	05 37		05 49	06 07
Maryland	d		23p45		23p59	00 10					00 30	00 40				01 03								05 50	
Forest Gate	d		23p47		00 02	00 12					00 32	00 42				01 05								05 52	
Manor Park	d		23p49		00 04	00 14					00 34	00 44				01 07								05 54	
Ilford 2	d		23p52		00 07	00 17					00 37	00 47				01 10				05 38				05 57	
Seven Kings	d		23p55		00 10	00 20					00 40	00 50				01 13				05 40				06 00	
Goodmayes	d		23p57		00 12	00 22					00 42	00 52				01 15								06 02	
Chadwell Heath	d		23p59		00 14	00 24					00 44	00 54				01 17								06 04	
Romford	d		00 02		00 17	00 27			00 32		00 47	00 57			01 08	01 20				05 46		05 45		06 07	06 15
Gidea Park 2	d		00 06		00 21	00a31					00 51	01a01		01 07		01 24				05 49				06 11	
Harold Wood	d		00 09		00 24						00 54					01 27				05 52				06 14	
Brentwood	d		00 13		00 28						00 58					01 31				05 57				06 18	
Shenfield 3	a	23p39	00 18	00 09	00 33				00 44	00 47	01 03			01 17	01 20	01 36				06 02		05 55		06 23	06 25
	d	23p40		00 10					00 45						01 20					06 02			06 08		
Billericay	d	23p46		00 16					00 51						01 26					06 08			06 14		
Wickford 2	d	23p51		00 21					00 56						01 31			05 39		06 13			06 20		
Battlesbridge	d																	05 43					06 24		
South Woodham Ferrers	d																	05 47					06 28		
North Fambridge	d																	05 53					06 34		
Althorne	d																	05 58					06 39		
Burnham-on-Crouch	d																	06 03					06 44		
Southminster	a																	06 08					06 49		
Rayleigh	d	23p56		00 26					01 01						01 36					06 19					
Hockley	d	00 01		00 31					01 06						01 41					06 23					
Rochford	d	00 04		00 34					01 09						01 44					06 27					
Prittlewell	d	00 08		00 38					01 13						01 48					06 30					
Southend Victoria	a	00 15		00 45					01 20						01 55					06 34					

Station																									
		LE		LE	LE 1	LE 1	LE 1	LE 1		LE	LE 1	LE 1	LE	LE 1		LE	LE 1	LE 1	LE	LE 1		LE	LE 1	LE	LE 1
London Liverpool Street 15 ⊖	d	06 04		06 12	06 18	06 23	06 34			06 42	06 48	06 55	07 02	07 08		07 12	07 15	07 18	07 22			07 32	07 34	07 42	07 48
Stratford 7 ⊖	d	06 11		06 19	06 25	06a32	06 41			06 49	06 55	07 02	07 09	07 15		07 19	07 22	07 25	07 29			07 39	07 41	07 49	07 55
Maryland	d			06 20						06 50			07 10			07 20			07 30			07 40		07 50	
Forest Gate	d			06 22						06 52			07 12			07 22			07 32			07 42		07 52	
Manor Park	d			06 24						06 54			07 14			07 24			07 34			07 44		07 54	
Ilford 2	d			06 27						06 57			07 17			07 27			07 37			07 47		07 57	
Seven Kings	d			06 30						07 00			07 20			07 30			07 40			07 50		08 00	
Goodmayes	d			06 32						07 02			07 22			07 32			07 42			07 52		08 02	
Chadwell Heath	d			06 34						07 04			07 24			07 34			07 44			07 54		08 04	
Romford	d			06 37			06 49			07 07			07 27	07 23		07 37			07 47			07 57	07 49	08 07	
Gidea Park 2	d			06 41						07 11			07 31			07 41			07 51			08 01		08 11	
Harold Wood	d			06 44						07 14			07 34			07 44			07 54			08 04		08 14	
Brentwood	d			06 48						07 18			07 38			07 48			07 58			08 08		08 18	
Shenfield 3	a	06 30		06 53	06 41		07 00			07 23	07 12	07 19	07 43	07 33		07 53	07 39	07 41	08 03			08 13	08 00	08 23	08 12
	d	06 30					07 00	07 08				07 20					07 40			08 08			08 00		
Billericay	d	06 36					07 06	07 14				07 26					07 46			08 14			08 06		
Wickford 2	d	06 41					07 11	07 20				07 31					07 51			08 20			08 11		
Battlesbridge	d							07 24												08 24					
South Woodham Ferrers	d							07 28												08 28					
North Fambridge	d							07 34												08 34					
Althorne	d							07 39												08 39					
Burnham-on-Crouch	d							07 44												08 44					
Southminster	a							07 49												08 49					
Rayleigh	d	06 46					07 16					07 36					07 56						08 16		
Hockley	d	06 51					07 21					07 41					08 01						08 21		
Rochford	d	06 54					07 24					07 44					08 04						08 24		
Prittlewell	d	06 58					07 28					07 48					08 08						08 28		
Southend Victoria	a	07 02					07 31					07 51					08 11						08 31		

Station																								
		LE	LE 1		LE	LE 1	LE	LE 1	LE 1	LE	LE 1	LE	LE 1	LE	LE 1	LE	LE 1			LE	LE 1	LE	LE 1	LE 1
London Liverpool Street 15 ⊖	d	07 52	07 55		08 02	08 08	08 12	08 15	08 18	08 22		08 32	08 34	08 42	08 48	08 52	08 55			20 02	20 08	20 12	20 15	20 18
Stratford 7 ⊖	d	07 59	08 02		08 09	08 15	08 19	08 22	08 25	08 29		08 39	08 41	08 49	08 55	08 59	09 02			20 09	20 15	20 19	20 22	20 25
Maryland	d	08 00			08 10		08 20			08 30		08 40		08 50		09 00				20 10		20 20		
Forest Gate	d	08 02			08 12		08 22			08 32		08 42		08 52		09 02				20 12		20 22		
Manor Park	d	08 04			08 14		08 24			08 34		08 44		08 54		09 04				20 14		20 24		
Ilford 2	d	08 07			08 17		08 27			08 37		08 47		08 57		09 07				20 17		20 27		
Seven Kings	d	08 10			08 20		08 30			08 40		08 50		09 00		09 10		and at		20 20		20 30		
Goodmayes	d	08 12			08 22		08 32			08 42		08 52		09 02		09 12				20 22		20 32		
Chadwell Heath	d	08 14			08 24		08 34			08 44		08 54		09 04		09 14		the same		20 24		20 34		
Romford	d	08 17			08 27	08 23	08 37			08 47		08 57	08 49	09 07		09 17				20 27	20 23	20 37		
Gidea Park 2	d	08 21			08 31		08 41			08 51		09 01		09 11		09 21		minutes		20 31		20 41		
Harold Wood	d	08 24			08 34		08 44			08 54		09 04		09 14		09 24				20 34		20 44		
Brentwood	d	08 28			08 38		08 48			08 58		09 08		09 18		09 28				20 38		20 48		
Shenfield 3	a	08 33	08 19		08 43	08 33	08 53	08 39	08 41	09 03		09 13	09 00	09 23	09 12	09 33	09 19	past		20 43	20 33	20 53	20 39	20 41
	d		08 20					08 40			09 08		09 00				09 20						20 40	
Billericay	d		08 26					08 46			09 14		09 06				09 26	each					20 46	
Wickford 2	d		08 31					08 51			09 20		09 11				09 31	hour until					20 51	
Battlesbridge	d										09 24													
South Woodham Ferrers	d										09 28													
North Fambridge	d										09 34													
Althorne	d										09 39													
Burnham-on-Crouch	d										09 44													
Southminster	a										09 49													
Rayleigh	d		08 36					08 56					09 16				09 36						20 56	
Hockley	d		08 41					09 01					09 21				09 41						21 01	
Rochford	d		08 44					09 04					09 24				09 44						21 04	
Prittlewell	d		08 48					09 08					09 28				09 48						21 08	
Southend Victoria	a		08 51					09 11					09 31				09 51						21 11	

For general notes see front of timetable
For details of catering facilities see
Directory of Train Operators

A To Colchester (Table 11)

London → Shenfield, Southminster and Southend Victoria

Network diagram - see first page of Table 5

		LE	LE 1		LE	LE 1	LE 1	LE	LE 1		LE	LE 1	LE 1	LE	LE 1		LE 1	LE	LE	LE 1	LE 1		LE 1	LE	LE 1
London Liverpool Street 15	⊖ d	20 22			20 32	20 34	20 38	20 42	20 48		20 52	20 55	21 04	21 07	21 15		21 18	21 22	21 37	21 45	21 48			21 52	22 00
Stratford 7	⊖ d	20 29			20 39	20 41	20 45	20 49	20 55		20 59	21 02	21 11	21 14	21 22		21 25	21 29	21 44	21 52	21 55			21 59	22 07
Maryland	d	20 30			20 40			20 50			21 00			21 15				21 30	21 45					22 00	
Forest Gate	d	20 32			20 42			20 52			21 02			21 17				21 32	21 47					22 02	
Manor Park	d	20 34			20 44			20 54			21 04			21 19				21 34	21 49					22 04	
Ilford 2	d	20 37			20 47			20 57			21 07			21 22				21 37	21 52					22 07	
Seven Kings	d	20 40			20 50			21 00			21 10			21 25				21 40	21 55					22 10	
Goodmayes	d	20 42			20 52			21 02			21 12			21 27				21 42	21 57					22 12	
Chadwell Heath	d	20 44			20 54			21 04			21 14			21 29				21 44	21 59					22 14	
Romford	d	20 47			20 57	20 49		21 07			21 17		21 19	21 32				21 47	22 02					22 17	
Gidea Park 2	d	20 51			21 01			21 11			21 21			21 36				21 51	22 06					22 21	
Harold Wood	d	20 54			21 04			21 14			21 24			21 39				21 54	22 09					22 24	
Brentwood	d	20 58			21 08			21 18			21 28			21 43				21 58	22 13					22 28	
Shenfield 3	a	21 03			21 13	20 59	21 02	21 23	21 12		21 33	21 19	21 33	21 48	21 43		21 45	22 03	22 18	22 13	22 15			22 33	22 27
	d		21 08			21 00						21 20			21 43					22 13			22 22		
Billericay	d		21 14			21 06						21 26			21 49					22 19			22 28		
Wickford 2	d		21 20			21 11						21 31			21 54					22 24			22 34		
Battlesbridge	d		21 24																				22 38		
South Woodham Ferrers	d		21 28																				22 42		
North Fambridge	d		21 34																				22 48		
Althorne	d		21 39																				22 53		
Burnham-on-Crouch	d		21 44																				22 58		
Southminster	a		21 49																				23 03		
Rayleigh	d					21 16						21 36			21 59					22 29					
Hockley	d					21 21						21 41			22 04					22 34					
Rochford	d					21 24						21 44			22 07					22 37					
Prittlewell	d					21 28						21 48			22 11					22 41					
Southend Victoria	a					21 31						21 51			22 14					22 44					

		LE	LE 1	LE 1	LE		LE	LE 1	LE 1	LE	LE 1		LE	LE 1	LE 1	LE	LE		LE 1	LE 1	LE				
London Liverpool Street 15	⊖ d	22 07	22 15	22 18	22 22		22 37	22 45	22 48	22 52	23 00		23 07	23 15	23 18	23 22	23 37		23 45	23 48	23 52				
Stratford 7	⊖ d	22 14	22 22	22 25	22 29		22 44	22 52	22 55	22 59	23 07		23 14	23 22	23 25	23 29	23 44		23 52	23 55	23 58				
Maryland	d	22 15			22 30		22 45			23 00			23 15			23 30	23 45				23 59				
Forest Gate	d	22 17			22 32		22 47			23 02			23 17			23 32	23 47				00 02				
Manor Park	d	22 19			22 34		22 49			23 04			23 19			23 34	23 49				00 04				
Ilford 2	d	22 22			22 37		22 52			23 07			23 22			23 37	23 52				00 07				
Seven Kings	d	22 25			22 40		22 55			23 10			23 25			23 40	23 55				00 10				
Goodmayes	d	22 27			22 42		22 57			23 12			23 27			23 42	23 57				00 12				
Chadwell Heath	d	22 29			22 44		22 59			23 14			23 29			23 44	23 59				00 14				
Romford	d	22 32			22 47		23 02			23 17			23 32			23 47	00 02				00 17				
Gidea Park 2	d	22 36			22 51		23 06			23 21			23 36			23 51	00 06				00 21				
Harold Wood	d	22 39			22 54		23 09			23 24			23 39			23 54	00 09				00 24				
Brentwood	d	22 43			22 58		23 13			23 28			23 43			23 58	00 13				00 28				
Shenfield 3	a	22 48	22 43	22 45	23 03		23 18	23 13	23 15	23 33	23 27		23 48	23 43	23 45	00 03	00 18		00 13	00 15	00 33				
	d		22 43					23 13						23 43					00 13						
Billericay	d		22 49					23 19						23 49					00 19						
Wickford 2	d		22 54					23 24						23 54					00 24						
Battlesbridge	d																								
South Woodham Ferrers	d																								
North Fambridge	d																								
Althorne	d																								
Burnham-on-Crouch	d																								
Southminster	a																								
Rayleigh	d		22 59					23 29						23 59					00 29						
Hockley	d		23 04					23 34						00 04					00 34						
Rochford	d		23 07					23 37						00 07					00 37						
Prittlewell	d		23 11					23 41						00 11					00 41						
Southend Victoria	a		23 14					23 48						00 18					00 48						

For general notes see front of timetable
For details of catering facilities see Directory of Train Operators

London → Shenfield, Southminster and Southend Victoria

Network diagram - see first page of Table 5

		LE 1	LE	LE 1	LE	LE		LE 1	LE 1	LE	LE	LE 1		LE	LE	LE	LE 1	LE 1		LE	LE 1	LE 1	LE 1	LE	LE 1
London Liverpool Street 15 ⊖	d	23p15	23p37	23p45	23p52	00 02		00 15	00 18	00 22	00 32	00 50		00 55	06 35	07 05		07 15		07 35		07 45	08 02	08 05	08 15
Stratford 7 ⊖	d	23p22	23p44	23p52	23p58	00 09		00 22	00 25	00 29	00 39	00 57		01 02	06 42	07 12		07 22		07 42		07 52	08 09	08 12	08 22
Maryland	d		23p45		23p59	00 10				00 30	00 40			01 03	06 43	07 13				07 43				08 13	
Forest Gate	d		23p47		00 02	00 12				00 32	00 42			01 05	06 45	07 15				07 45				08 15	
Manor Park	d		23p49		00 04	00 14				00 34	00 44			01 07	06 47	07 17				07 47				08 17	
Ilford 2	d		23p52		00 07	00 17				00 37	00 47			01 10	06 50	07 20				07 50				08 20	
Seven Kings	d		23p55		00 10	00 20				00 40	00 50			01 13	06 53	07 23				07 53				08 23	
Goodmayes	d		23p57		00 12	00 22				00 42	00 52			01 15	06 55	07 25				07 55				08 25	
Chadwell Heath	d		23p59		00 14	00 24				00 44	00 54			01 17	06 57	07 27				07 57				08 27	
Romford	d		00 02		00 17	00 27		00 32		00 47	00 57	01 08		01 20	07 00	07 30		07 33		08 00		08 03		08 30	08 33
Gidea Park 2	d		00 06		00 21	00a31				00 51	01a01			01 24	07 04	07 34		07 37		08 04		08 07		08 34	08 37
Harold Wood	d		00 09		00 24					00 54				01 27	07 07	07 37		07 40		08 07		08 10		08 37	08 40
Brentwood	d		00 13		00 28					00 58				01 31	07 11	07 41		07 44		08 11		08 14		08 41	08 44
Shenfield 3	a	23p43	00 18	00 13	00 33			00 44	00 47	01 03		01 20		01 36	07 16	07 46		07 50		08 16		08 20	08 30	08 46	08 50
	d	23p43		00 13				00 45				01 20						07 50				08 20			08 50
Billericay	d	23p49		00 19				00 51				01 26						07 56				08 26			08 56
Wickford 2	d	23p54		00 24				00 56				01 31					07 30	08 01			08 05	08 31			09 01
Battlesbridge	d																07 34				08 09				
South Woodham Ferrers	d																07 38				08 13				
North Fambridge	d																07 44				08 20				
Althorne	d																07 49				08 25				
Burnham-on-Crouch	d																07 54				08 30				
Southminster	a																07 59				08 35				
Rayleigh	d	23p59		00 29				01 01				01 36						08 06				08 36			09 06
Hockley	d	00 04		00 34				01 06				01 41						08 11				08 41			09 11
Rochford	d	00 07		00 37				01 09				01 44						08 14				08 44			09 14
Prittlewell	d	00 11		00 41				01 13				01 48													
Southend Victoria	a	00 18		00 48				01 20				01 55						08 22				08 52			09 22

		LE 1		LE	LE 1	LE 1	LE		LE 1	LE	LE 1	LE	LE 1	LE	LE 1	LE 1	LE			LE 1	LE	LE 1	LE	LE 1
London Liverpool Street 15 ⊖	d	08 32		08 35		08 45	08 47		09 02	09 05	09 15	09 17	09 32	09 35		09 45	09 47	and at		19 02	19 05	19 15	19 17	19 32
Stratford 7 ⊖	d	08 39		08 42		08 52	08 54		09 09	09 12	09 22	09 24	09 39	09 42		09 52	09 54	the same		19 09	19 12	19 22	19 24	19 39
Maryland	d			08 43						09 13				09 43				minutes			19 13			
Forest Gate	d			08 45			08 57			09 15		09 27		09 45			09 57	past			19 15		19 27	
Manor Park	d			08 47			08 59			09 17		09 29		09 47			09 59	each			19 17		19 29	
Ilford 2	d			08 50			09 02			09 20		09 32		09 50			10 02	hour until			19 20		19 32	
Seven Kings	d			08 53			09 04			09 23		09 34		09 53			10 04				19 23		19 34	
Goodmayes	d			08 55			09 06			09 25		09 36		09 55			10 06				19 25		19 36	
Chadwell Heath	d			08 57			09 08			09 27		09 38		09 57			10 08				19 27		19 38	
Romford	d			09 00		09 03	09 12			09 30	09 33	09 42		10 00		10 03	10 12				19 30	19 33	19 42	
Gidea Park 2	d			09 04		09 07	09a17			09 34	09 37	09a47		10 04		10 07	10a17				19 34	19 37	19a47	
Harold Wood	d			09 07		09 10				09 37	09 40			10 07		10 10					19 37	19 40		
Brentwood	d			09 11		09 14				09 41	09 44			10 11		10 14					19 41	19 44		
Shenfield 3	a	09 00		09 16		09 20			09 30	09 46	09 50		10 00	10 16		10 20				19 30	19 46	19 50		20 00
	d					09 20					09 50					10 20						19 50		
Billericay	d					09 26					09 56					10 26						19 56		
Wickford 2	d				09 05	09 31					10 01				10 05	10 31						20 01		
Battlesbridge	d				09 09										10 09									
South Woodham Ferrers	d				09 13										10 13									
North Fambridge	d				09 20										10 20									
Althorne	d				09 25										10 25									
Burnham-on-Crouch	d				09 30										10 30									
Southminster	a				09 35										10 35									
Rayleigh	d					09 36					10 06					10 36						20 06		
Hockley	d					09 41					10 11					10 41						20 11		
Rochford	d					09 44					10 14					10 44						20 14		
Prittlewell	d																							
Southend Victoria	a					09 52					10 22					10 52						20 22		

		LE	LE 1		LE 1	LE	LE 1	LE 1	LE		LE 1	LE	LE 1	LE	LE 1		LE 1	LE	LE 1	LE	LE 1		LE	LE 1	LE
London Liverpool Street 15 ⊖	d	19 35			19 45	19 47	20 00	20 02	20 05		20 15	20 17	20 32	20 35			20 45	20 47	21 02	21 05	21 15		21 17	21 32	21 35
Stratford 7 ⊖	d	19 42			19 52	19 54		20 09	20 12		20 22	20 24	20 39	20 42			20 52	20 54	21 09	21 12	21 22		21 24	21 39	21 42
Maryland	d	19 43							20 13					20 43						21 13					21 43
Forest Gate	d	19 45				19 57			20 15			20 27		20 45				20 57		21 15			21 27		21 45
Manor Park	d	19 47				19 59			20 17			20 29		20 47				20 59		21 17			21 29		21 47
Ilford 2	d	19 50				20 02			20 20			20 32		20 50				21 02		21 20			21 32		21 50
Seven Kings	d	19 53				20 04			20 23			20 34		20 53				21 04		21 23			21 34		21 53
Goodmayes	d	19 55				20 06			20 25			20 36		20 55				21 06		21 25			21 36		21 55
Chadwell Heath	d	19 57				20 08			20 27			20 38		20 57				21 08		21 27			21 38		21 57
Romford	d	20 00			20 03	20 12			20 30		20 33	20 42		21 00			21 03	21 12		21 30	21 33		21 42		22 00
Gidea Park 2	d	20 04			20 07	20a17			20 34		20 37	20a47		21 04			21 07	21a17		21 34	21 37		21a47		22 04
Harold Wood	d	20 07			20 10				20 37		20 40			21 07			21 10			21 37	21 40				22 07
Brentwood	d	20 11			20 14				20 41		20 44			21 11			21 14			21 41	21 44				22 11
Shenfield 3	a	20 16			20 20		20 27	20 30	20 46		20 50		21 00	21 16			21 20		21 30	21 46	21 50			22 00	22 16
	d				20 20						20 50						21 20				21 50				
Billericay	d				20 26						20 56						21 26				21 56				
Wickford 2	d		20 05		20 31						21 01				21 05		21 31				22 01				
Battlesbridge	d		20 09												21 09										
South Woodham Ferrers	d		20 13												21 13										
North Fambridge	d		20 20												21 20										
Althorne	d		20 25												21 25										
Burnham-on-Crouch	d		20 30												21 30										
Southminster	a		20 35												21 35										
Rayleigh	d				20 36						21 06						21 36				22 06				
Hockley	d				20 41						21 11						21 41				22 11				
Rochford	d				20 44						21 14						21 44				22 14				
Prittlewell	d																								
Southend Victoria	a				20 52						21 22						21 52				22 22				

For general notes see front of timetable
For details of catering facilities see
Directory of Train Operators

London → Shenfield, Southminster and Southend Victoria

Network diagram - see first page of Table 5

		LE 1	LE 1	LE	LE 1		LE	LE 1	LE	LE 1	LE		LE 1	LE 1	LE	LE 1	LE 1		LE	LE 1
London Liverpool Street	d		21 45	21 47	22 02		22 05	22 15	22 17	22 32	22 35		22 45	23 02	23 05	23 15	23 32		23 35	23 45
Stratford	d		21 52	21 54	22 09		22 12	22 22	22 24	22 39	22 42		22 52	23 09	23 12	23 22	23 39		23 42	23 52
Maryland	d						22 13				22 43				23 13				23 43	
Forest Gate	d			21 57			22 15		22 27		22 45				23 15				23 45	
Manor Park	d			21 59			22 17		22 29		22 47				23 17				23 47	
Ilford	d			22 02			22 20		22 32		22 50				23 20				23 50	
Seven Kings	d			22 04			22 23		22 34		22 53				23 23				23 53	
Goodmayes	d			22 06			22 25		22 36		22 55				23 25				23 55	
Chadwell Heath	d			22 08			22 27		22 38		22 57				23 27				23 57	
Romford	d		22 03	22 12			22 30	22 33	22 42		23 00		23 03		23 30	23 33			23 59	00 03
Gidea Park	d		22 07	22a17			22 34	22 37	22a47		23 04		23 07		23 34	23 37			00 04	00 07
Harold Wood	d		22 10				22 37	22 40			23 07		23 10		23 37	23 40			00 07	00 10
Brentwood	d		22 14				22 41	22 44			23 11		23 14		23 41	23 44			00 11	00 14
Shenfield	a		22 20		22 30		22 46	22 50		23 00	23 16		23 20	23 30	23 46	23 50	00 01		00 16	00 20
	d		22 20					22 50					23 20			23 50				00 20
Billericay	d		22 26					22 56					23 26			23 56				00 26
Wickford	d	22 05	22 31					23 01					23 31			00 01				00 31
Battlesbridge	d	22 09																		
South Woodham Ferrers	d	22 13																		
North Fambridge	d	22 20																		
Althorne	d	22 25																		
Burnham-on-Crouch	d	22 30																		
Southminster	a	22 35																		
Rayleigh	d		22 36					23 06					23 36			00 06				00 36
Hockley	d		22 41					23 11					23 41			00 11				00 41
Rochford	d		22 44					23 14					23 44			00 14				00 44
Prittlewell	d																			
Southend Victoria	a		22 52					23 24					23 54			00 24				00 54

For general notes see front of timetable
For details of catering facilities see Directory of Train Operators

Southend Victoria, Southminster and Shenfield → London

Network diagram - see first page of Table 5

Miles	Miles			LE MX	LE MO	LE MX	LE	CC	LE	LE	LE	LE 1 A	LE	LE 1	LE	LE 1	LE 1	LE	LE	LE	LE 1	LE 1	LE	LE 1
0	—	**Southend Victoria**	d				04 02			04 32				05 06		05 26						05 46		
½	—	Prittlewell	d				04 04			04 34				05 08		05 28						05 48		
2¾	—	Rochford	d				04 08			04 38				05 12		05 32						05 52		
5½	—	Hockley	d				04 12			04 42				05 16		05 36						05 56		
8¼	—	Rayleigh	d				04 16			04 46				05 20		05 40						06 00		
—	0	**Southminster**	d																		05 30			
—	2¼	Burnham-on-Crouch	d																		05 34			
—	5¼	Althorne	d																		05 39			
—	8¼	North Fambridge	d																		05 45			
—	11½	South Woodham Ferrers	d																		05 50			
—	14	Battlesbridge	d																		05 54			
12½	16½	**Wickford 2**	d				04 21			04 51				05 25		05 45					06a00	06 05		
17¼	—	Billericay	d				04 28			04 58				05 31		05 51						06 11		
21¼	—	**Shenfield 3**	a				04 39			05 09				05 38		05 58						06 18		
—	—		d	23p29	23p43	23p44	04 39			05 09		05 26	05 29	05 38	05 44	05 58	06 02		06 04	06 14		06 18	06 24	06 26
23¼	—	Brentwood	d	23p32	23p46	23p47	04 42			05 12			05 32		05 47				06 07	06 17			06 27	
26½	—	Harold Wood	d	23p37	23p51	23p52	04 47			05 17			05 37		05 52				06 12	06 22			06 32	
28	—	Gidea Park 2	d	23p41	23p55	23p56	04 51			05 21		05 33	05 41		05 56			06 06	06 16	06 26			06 36	
29	—	Romford	d	23p43	23p57	23p58	04 53			05 23			05 43		05 58			06 08	06 18	06 28			06 38	
31½	—	Chadwell Heath	d	23p47	00 01	00 02	04 57			05 27			05 47		06 02			06 12	06 22	06 32			06 42	
32¼	—	Goodmayes	d	23p49	00 03	00 04	04 59			05 29			05 49		06 04			06 14	06 24	06 34			06 44	
33	—	Seven Kings	d	23p51	00 05	00 06	05 01			05 31		05 38	05 51		06 06			06 16	06 26	06 36			06 46	
34¼	—	Ilford 2	d	23p54	00 08	00 09	05 04		05 09	05 34	05 39		05 54		06 09			06 19	06 29	06 39			06 49	
35¼	—	Manor Park	d	23p56	00 10	00 11			05 11		05 41		05 56		06 11			06 21	06 31	06 41			06 51	
36¼	—	Forest Gate	d	23p58	00 12	00 13			05 13		05 43		05 58		06 13			06 23	06 33	06 43			06 53	
37	—	Maryland	d	23p59	00 14	00 15			05 15		05 45		06 00		06 15			06 25	06 35	06 45			06 55	
37½	—	Stratford 7 ⊖	d	00 02	00 16	00 17	05 09	05 13	05 17	05 39	05 47	05s44	06 02	05s53	06 17	06s15	06s18	06 27	06 37	06 47		06s32	06 57	06s41
41½	—	**London Liverpool Street 15** ⊖	a	00 10	00 25	00 25	05 17	05 23	05 25	05 47	05 55	05 57	06 10	06 01	06 25	06 24	06 27	06 35	06 45	06 55		06 41	07 07	06 49

		LE 1	LE	LE 1	LE	LE	LE 1	LE 1	LE	LE	LE	LE	LE	LE 1	LE 1	LE	LE	LE 1	LE 1	LE 1	LE 1	LE	LE
Southend Victoria	d	06 01					06 16				06 29				06 40					06 56			
Prittlewell	d	06 03					06 18				06 31				06 42					06 58			
Rochford	d	06 07					06 22				06 35				06 46					07 02			
Hockley	d	06 11					06 26				06 39				06 50					07 06			
Rayleigh	d	06 15					06 30				06 43				06 54					07 10			
Southminster	d							06 10													06 52		
Burnham-on-Crouch	d							06 14													06 56		
Althorne	d							06 19													07 01		
North Fambridge	d							06 26													07 08		
South Woodham Ferrers	d							06 32													07 14		
Battlesbridge	d							06 36													07 18		
Wickford 2	d	06 20					06 35	06 41			06 48				06 59					07 15	07 23		
Billericay	d	06 26					06 42	06 48			06 55				07 05					07 22	07 30		
Shenfield 3	a	06 33					06 48	06 54			07 01				07 12					07 28			
	d	06 33	06 34	06 39		06 44	06 48	06 54		06 54	07 01		07 04	07 06	07 12		07 15	07 16	07 20	07 28			07 28
Brentwood	d		06 37			06 47				06 57			07 07				07 18						07 31
Harold Wood	d		06 42			06 52				07 02			07 12				07 23						07 36
Gidea Park 2	d		06 46		06 49	06 56			06 59	07 06		07 09	07 16			07 22	07 28					07 34	07 40
Romford	d		06 48		06 51	06 58			07 01	07 08		07 11	07 18			07 24	07 30					07 36	07 42
Chadwell Heath	d		06 52		06 55	07 02			07 05	07 12		07 15	07 22			07 28	07 34					07 40	07 46
Goodmayes	d				06 57				07 07			07 17	07 24			07 30	07 36					07 42	07 48
Seven Kings	d				06 59				07 09			07 19	07 26			07 32	07 38					07 44	07 50
Ilford 2	d		06 57		07 02	07 07			07 12	07 17		07 22	07 29			07 35	07 41					07 47	07 53
Manor Park	d				07 05				07 15			07 25				07 38						07 50	
Forest Gate	d				07 07				07 17			07 27				07 40						07 52	
Maryland	d				07 09				07 19			07 29				07 42						07 54	
Stratford 7 ⊖	d	06s47	07 03	06s56	07 11	07 14	07s05	07s11	07 21	07 24	07s18	07 31	07 35		07s29	07 44	07 47	07s33	07s37	07s45		07 56	07 59
London Liverpool Street 15 ⊖	a	06 56	07 13	07 07	07 21	07 24	07 16	07 24	07 31	07 34	07 29	07 41	07 45	07 33	07 40	07 54	07 57	07 44	07 48	07 57	08 01	08 06	08 09

		LE 1	LE 1	LE	LE 1	LE 1	LE	LE	LE 1	LE	LE	LE	LE	LE 1	LE	LE 1	LE 1	LE 1	LE 1	LE	LE	LE	LE 1
Southend Victoria	d		07 17			07 09							07 21	07 25			07 33						07 40
Prittlewell	d		07 19			07 11							07 23	07 27			07 35						07 42
Rochford	d		07 23			07 15							07 27	07 31			07 39						07 46
Hockley	d		07 27			07 19							07 31	07 35			07 43						07 50
Rayleigh	d		07 31			07 23							07 35	07 39			07 47						07 54
Southminster	d																		07 35				
Burnham-on-Crouch	d																		07 39				
Althorne	d																		07 44				
North Fambridge	d																		07 50				
South Woodham Ferrers	d																		07b58				
Battlesbridge	d																						
Wickford 2	d		07 36			07 28							07 40	07 44			07 52		08 06				07 59
Billericay	d		07 43			07 35							07 47	07 51			07 59		08 13				08 06
Shenfield 3	a					07 42							07 55	07 58			08 06						08 13
	d	07 32		07 34	07 38	07 42		07 44	07 50		07 50		07 56	07 58	08 00	08 02	08 06	08 08				08 10	08 13
Brentwood	d			07 37				07 47			07 53		07 59		08 03							08 13	
Harold Wood	d			07 42				07 52			07 58		08 04		08 08							08 18	
Gidea Park 2	d			07 46			07 49	07 56		07 59	08 02	08 05	08 09		08 12					08 15	08 19	08 22	
Romford	d			07 48			07 51	07 58		08 01	08 04	08 07	08 11		08 14					08 17	08 21	08 24	
Chadwell Heath	d			07 52			07 55	08 02		08 05	08 08	08 11	08 15		08 18					08 21	08 25	08 28	
Goodmayes	d			07 54			07 57	08 04		08 07	08 10	08 13	08 17		08 20					08 23	08 27	08 30	
Seven Kings	d			07 56			07 59	08 06		08 09	08 12	08 15	08 19		08 22					08 25	08 29	08 32	
Ilford 2	d			07 59			08 02	08 09		08 12	08 15	08 18	08 22		08 25					08 28	08 32	08 35	
Manor Park	d						08 05					08 21								08 31			
Forest Gate	d						08 07					08 23								08 33			
Maryland	d						08 09					08 25								08 35			
Stratford 7 ⊖	d			08 05	07s55	08s00	08 11	08 15		08 18	08 21	08 27	08 30	08s15	08 33			08s25		08 37	08 40	08 43	08s30
London Liverpool Street 15 ⊖	a	07 59	08 14	08 15	08 06	08 12	08 21	08 25	08 16	08 28	08 31	08 37	08 40	08 26	08 43	08 28	08 32	08 36	08 46	08 47	08 50	08 53	08 44

For general notes see front of timetable
For details of catering facilities see
Directory of Train Operators

A From Colchester (Table 11)
b Arr. 0755

Southend Victoria, Southminster and Shenfield → London

Network diagram - see first page of Table 5

Station		LE 1		LE	LE	LE	LE 1	LE 1	LE	LE	LE	LE 1	LE 1		LE 1	LE	LE	LE 1	LE	LE 1	LE 1	LE 1	LE	LE	LE 1
Southend Victoria	d						07 53					08 03			08 11						08 26				08 46
Prittlewell	d						07 55					08 05			08 13						08 28				08 48
Rochford	d						07 59					08 09			08 17						08 32				08 52
Hockley	d						08 03					08 13			08 21						08 36				08 56
Rayleigh	d						08 07					08 17			08 25						08 40				09 00
Southminster	d																					08 17			
Burnham-on-Crouch	d																					08 21			
Althorne	d																					08 26			
North Fambridge	d																					08 34			
South Woodham Ferrers	d																					08 40			
Battlesbridge	d																					08 44			
Wickford 2	d						08 12					08 22			08 30						08 45	08 49			09 05
Billericay	d						08 19					08 29			08 37						08 52	08 56			09 12
Shenfield 3	a						08 26					08 36			08 44						08 59	09 03			09 19
	d	08 20				08 20	08 26	08 32			08 34	08 36	08 40		08 44		08 44	08 52	08 54	08 55	08 59	09 03	09 04	09 14	09 19
Brentwood	d					08 23					08 37						08 47		08 57				09 07	09 17	
Harold Wood	d					08 28					08 42						08 52		09 02				09 12	09 22	
Gidea Park 2	d				08 29	08 32				08 39	08 46						08 56		09 06				09 16	09 26	
Romford	d				08 31	08 34				08 41	08 48				08 52		08 58		09 08				09 18	09 28	
Chadwell Heath	d				08 35	08 38				08 45	08 52						09 02		09 12				09 22	09 32	
Goodmayes	d				08 37	08 40				08 47	08 54						09 04		09 14				09 24	09 34	
Seven Kings	d				08 39	08 42				08 49	08 56						09 06		09 16				09 26	09 36	
Ilford 2	d			08 38	08 42	08 45			08 48	08 52	08 59					09 02	09 09		09 19				09 29	09 39	
Manor Park	d			08 41					08 51							09 05			09 21				09 31	09 41	
Forest Gate	d			08 43					08 53							09 07			09 23				09 33	09 43	
Maryland	d			08 45					08 55							09 09			09 25				09 35	09 45	
Stratford 7 ⊖	d			08 47	08 50	08 53	08s44	08s49	08 57	09 00	09 05	08s53			09s03	09 11	09 15	09s09	09 27		09s16	09s20	09 37	09 47	09s36
London Liverpool Street 15 ⊖	a	08 48		08 57	09 00	09 03	08 56	09 01	09 07	09 10	09 15	09 04	09 06		09 14	09 21	09 25	09 20	09 37	09 22	09 28	09 31	09 47	09 57	09 47

Station		LE 1		LE	LE 1	LE	LE 1	LE 1	LE	LE 1	LE	LE 1	LE 1		LE	LE 1	LE	LE 1	LE	LE		LE 1	LE 1	LE	LE 1
Southend Victoria	d						09 06					09 26						09 46				10 06			
Prittlewell	d						09 08					09 28						09 48				10 08			
Rochford	d						09 12					09 32						09 52				10 12			
Hockley	d						09 16					09 36						09 56				10 16			
Rayleigh	d						09 20					09 40						10 00				10 20			
Southminster	d												09 17												
Burnham-on-Crouch	d												09 21												
Althorne	d												09 26												
North Fambridge	d												09 34												
South Woodham Ferrers	d												09 39												
Battlesbridge	d												09 43												
Wickford 2	d						09 25					09 45	09 49					10 05				10 25			
Billericay	d						09 31					09 51	09 55					10 11				10 31			
Shenfield 3	a						09 38					09 58	10 02					10 18				10 38			
	d	09 22		09 24	09 25	09 34	09 38	09 40	09 44	09 54	09 54	09 58	10 02		10 04	10 10	10 14	10 18	10 24	10 34		10 38	10 40	10 44	10 51
Brentwood	d			09 27		09 37			09 47		09 57				10 07		10 17		10 27	10 37				10 47	
Harold Wood	d			09 32		09 42			09 52		10 02				10 12		10 22		10 32	10 42				10 52	
Gidea Park 2	d			09 36		09 46			09 56		10 06				10 16		10 26		10 36	10 46				10 56	
Romford	d			09 38		09 48		09 48	09 58		10 08				10 18		10 28	10 26	10 38	10 48				10 58	10 59
Chadwell Heath	d			09 42		09 52			10 02		10 12				10 22		10 32		10 42	10 52				11 02	
Goodmayes	d			09 44		09 54			10 04		10 14				10 24		10 34		10 44	10 54				11 04	
Seven Kings	d			09 46		09 56			10 06		10 16				10 26		10 36		10 46	10 56				11 06	
Ilford 2	d			09 49		09 59			10 09		10 19				10 29		10 39		10 49	10 59				11 09	
Manor Park	d			09 51		10 01			10 11		10 21				10 31		10 41		10 51	11 01				11 11	
Forest Gate	d			09 53		10 03			10 13		10 23				10 33		10 43		10 53	11 03				11 13	
Maryland	d			09 55		10 05			10 15		10 25				10 35		10 45		10 55	11 05				11 15	
Stratford 7 ⊖	d	09s39		09 57		10 07	09s52	09s57	10 17	10s08	10 27	10s13	10s16		10 37	10s24	10 47	10s34	10 57	11 07		10s52	10s55	11 17	11s07
London Liverpool Street 15 ⊖	a	09 50		10 07	09 52	10 15	10 04	10 05	10 25	10 17	10 35	10 22	10 25		10 45	10 33	10 55	10 44	11 05	11 15		11 01	11 03	11 25	11 18

Station		LE	LE 1	LE 1	LE	LE 1	LE	LE 1	LE	LE			LE 1	LE 1	LE	LE 1	LE	LE 1	LE 1	LE	LE 1	LE		LE 1
Southend Victoria	d		10 26					10 46					15 06					15 26						15 46
Prittlewell	d		10 28					10 48					15 08					15 28						15 48
Rochford	d		10 32					10 52					15 12					15 32						15 52
Hockley	d		10 36					10 56					15 16					15 36						15 56
Rayleigh	d		10 40					11 00					15 20					15 40						16 00
Southminster	d			10 17															15 17					
Burnham-on-Crouch	d			10 21															15 21					
Althorne	d			10 26							and at								15 26					
North Fambridge	d			10 34															15 34					
South Woodham Ferrers	d			10 39							the same								15 39					
Battlesbridge	d			10 43															15 43					
Wickford 2	d		10 45	10 49				11 05			minutes		15 25					15 45	15 49					16 05
Billericay	d		10 51	10 55				11 11					15 31					15 51	15 55					16 11
Shenfield 3	a		10 58	11 02				11 18			past		15 38					15 58	16 02					16 18
	d	10 54	10 58		11 04	11 10	11 14	11 18	11 24	11 34			15 38	15 40	15 44	15 51	15 54	15 58		16 04	16 12	16 14		16 18
Brentwood	d	10 57			11 07		11 17		11 27	11 37	each				15 47		15 57			16 07		16 17		
Harold Wood	d	11 02			11 12		11 22		11 32	11 42					15 52		16 02			16 12		16 22		
Gidea Park 2	d	11 06			11 16		11 26		11 36	11 46	hour until				15 56		16 06			16 16		16 26		
Romford	d	11 08			11 18		11 28	11 26	11 38	11 48					15 58	15 59	16 08			16 18		16 28		16 26
Chadwell Heath	d	11 12			11 22		11 32		11 42	11 52					16 02		16 12			16 22		16 32		
Goodmayes	d	11 14			11 24		11 34		11 44	11 54					16 04		16 14			16 24		16 34		
Seven Kings	d	11 16			11 26		11 36		11 46	11 56					16 06		16 16			16 26		16 36		
Ilford 2	d	11 19			11 29		11 39		11 49	11 59					16 09		16 19			16 29		16 39		
Manor Park	d	11 21			11 31		11 41		11 51	12 01					16 11		16 21			16 31		16 41		
Forest Gate	d	11 23			11 33		11 43		11 53	12 03					16 13		16 23			16 33		16 43		
Maryland	d	11 25			11 35		11 45		11 55	12 05					16 15		16 25			16 35		16 45		
Stratford 7 ⊖	d	11 27	11s12		11 37	11s24	11 47	11s34	11 57	12 07			15s52	15s55	16 17	16s07	16 27	16s12		16 37	16s26	16 47		16s34
London Liverpool Street 15 ⊖	a	11 35	11 24		11 45	11 33	11 55	11 43	12 05	12 15			16 01	16 03	16 25	16 18	16 35	16 21		16 45	16 35	16 55		16 43

For general notes see front of timetable
For details of catering facilities see Directory of Train Operators

Southend Victoria, Southminster and Shenfield → London

Network diagram - see first page of Table 5

		LE	LE 1	LE	LE 1	LE 1	LE	LE 1	LE 1	LE	LE		LE 1	LE 1	LE 1	LE	LE	LE 1	LE	LE	LE 1	LE		LE	LE 1
Southend Victoria	d				16 06				16 21					16 35				16 51							
Prittlewell	d				16 08				16 23					16 37				16 53							
Rochford	d				16 12				16 27					16 41				16 57							
Hockley	d				16 16				16 31					16 45				17 01							
Rayleigh	d				16 20				16 35					16 49				17 05							
Southminster	d												16 17												
Burnham-on-Crouch	d												16 21												
Althorne	d												16 26												
North Fambridge	d												16 34												
South Woodham Ferrers	d												16 39												
Battlesbridge	d												16 43												
Wickford 2	d				16 25				16 40				16a50	16 54				17 10							
Billericay	d				16 31				16 46					17 00				17 16							
Shenfield 3	a				16 38				16 53					17 07				17 23							
	d	16 24	16 25	16 34	16 38	16 40	16 44	16 51	16 53	16 54	17 04			17 07	17 12		17 14	17 23		17 24	17 27			17 34	17 36
Brentwood	d	16 27		16 37			16 47			16 57	17 07						17 17			17 27				17 37	
Harold Wood	d	16 32		16 42			16 52			17 02	17 12						17 22			17 32				17 42	
Gidea Park 2	d	16 36		16 46			16 56			17 06	17 16					17 22	17 26		17 32	17 36		17 42		17 46	
Romford	d	16 38		16 48			16 58			17 08	17 18					17 24	17 28		17 34	17 38		17 44		17 48	
Chadwell Heath	d	16 42		16 52			17 02			17 12	17 22						17 32			17 42				17 52	
Goodmayes	d	16 44		16 54			17 04			17 14	17 24						17 34			17 44				17 54	
Seven Kings	d	16 46		16 56			17 06			17 16	17 26						17 36			17 46				17 56	
Ilford 2	d	16 49		16 59			17 09			17 19	17 29					17 31	17 39		17 41	17 49		17 51		17 59	
Manor Park	d	16 51		17 01			17 11			17 21						17 34			17 44			17 54			
Forest Gate	d	16 53		17 03			17 13			17 23						17 36			17 46			17 56			
Maryland	d	16 55		17 05			17 15			17 25						17 38			17 48			17 58			
Stratford 7 ⊖	d	16 57	16s39	17 07	16s52	16s55	17 17	17s05	17s08	17 27	17 34				17s26	17 40	17 44	17s37	17 50	17 54		18 00		18 05	17s50
London Liverpool Street 15 ⊖	a	17 05	16 48	17 15	17 03	17 05	17 25	17 15	17 18	17 35	17 42			17 29	17 38	17 48	17 52	17 46	17 58	18 02	17 49	18 09		18 13	18 00

		LE 1	LE	LE	LE 1	LE 1	LE 1	LE 1	LE	LE	LE		LE	LE 1	LE 1	LE	LE	LE 1	LE	LE	LE 1	LE		LE 1	LE 1
Southend Victoria	d	17 06						17 21						17 36				17 51						18 06	
Prittlewell	d	17 08						17 23						17 38				17 53						18 08	
Rochford	d	17 12						17 27						17 42				17 57						18 12	
Hockley	d	17 16						17 31						17 46				18 01						18 16	
Rayleigh	d	17 20						17 35						17 50				18 05						18 20	
Southminster	d					17 05															17 47				
Burnham-on-Crouch	d					17 09															17 51				
Althorne	d					17 14															17 56				
North Fambridge	d					17 21															18 03				
South Woodham Ferrers	d					17 26															18 08				
Battlesbridge	d					17 30															18 12				
Wickford 2	d	17 25				17 36		17 40						17 55				18 10			18 18			18 25	
Billericay	d	17 31				17 42		17 46						18 01				18 16			18 24			18 31	
Shenfield 3	a	17 38				17 49		17 53						18 08				18 23			18 31			18 38	
	d	17 38		17 44	17 46	17 49	17 51	17 53		17 54			18 04	18 08	18 12		18 14	18 23		18 24	18 31	18 34		18 38	18 40
Brentwood	d			17 47						17 57			18 07				18 17			18 27		18 37			
Harold Wood	d			17 52						18 02			18 12				18 22			18 32		18 42			
Gidea Park 2	d		17 52	17 56					18 02	18 06	18 12		18 16			18 22	18 26		18 32	18 36		18 46			
Romford	d		17 54	17 58			17 59		18 04	18 08	18 14		18 18			18 24	18 28		18 34	18 38		18 48			
Chadwell Heath	d			18 02						18 12			18 22				18 32			18 42		18 52			
Goodmayes	d			18 04						18 14			18 24				18 34			18 44		18 54			
Seven Kings	d			18 06						18 16			18 26				18 36			18 46		18 56			
Ilford 2	d		18 01	18 09					18 11	18 19	18 21		18 29			18 31	18 39		18 41	18 49		18 59			
Manor Park	d		18 04						18 14		18 24					18 34			18 44	18 51		19 01			
Forest Gate	d		18 06						18 16		18 26					18 36			18 46	18 53		19 03			
Maryland	d		18 08						18 18		18 28					18 38			18 48	18 55		19 05			
Stratford 7 ⊖	d	17s53	18 10	18 15	18s02	18s03	18s07	18s12	18 20	18 24	18 30		18 34	18s22	18s26	18 40	18 44	18s37	18 50	18 57	18s46	19 07		18s52	18s55
London Liverpool Street 15 ⊖	a	18 02	18 18	18 23	18 11	18 14	18 20	18 21	18 28	18 32	18 38		18 42	18 31	18 35	18 48	18 52	18 46	18 58	19 05	18 55	19 15		19 01	19 05

		LE	LE 1	LE	LE 1	LE	LE 1	LE 1	LE	LE 1	LE 1		LE	LE	LE 1	LE 1	LE	LE 1	LE	LE 1	LE 1	LE		LE 1	LE
Southend Victoria	d				18 26						18 46				19 06					19 26					
Prittlewell	d				18 28						18 48				19 08					19 28					
Rochford	d				18 32						18 52				19 12					19 32					
Hockley	d				18 36						18 56				19 16					19 36					
Rayleigh	d				18 40						19 00				19 20					19 40					
Southminster	d							18 27													19 17				
Burnham-on-Crouch	d							18 31													19 21				
Althorne	d							18 36													19 26				
North Fambridge	d							18 43													19 34				
South Woodham Ferrers	d							18 48													19 39				
Battlesbridge	d							18 52													19 43				
Wickford 2	d				18 45			18 58			19 05				19 25					19 45	19 49				
Billericay	d				18 51			19 04			19 11				19 31					19 51	19 55				
Shenfield 3	a				18 58			19 11			19 18				19 38					19 58	20 03				
	d	18 44	18 51	18 54	18 58	19 04	19 10		19 14	19 16	19 18		19 24	19 34	19 38	19 40	19 44	19 51	19 54	19 58		20 04		20 10	20 14
Brentwood	d	18 47		18 57		19 07			19 17				19 27	19 37			19 47		19 57			20 07			20 17
Harold Wood	d	18 52		19 02		19 12			19 22				19 32	19 42			19 52		20 02			20 12			20 22
Gidea Park 2	d	18 56		19 06		19 16			19 26				19 36	19 46			19 56		20 06			20 16			20 26
Romford	d	18 58	18 59	19 08		19 18			19 28		19 26		19 38	19 48			19 58	19 59	20 08			20 18			20 28
Chadwell Heath	d	19 02		19 12		19 22			19 32				19 42	19 52			20 02		20 12			20 22			20 32
Goodmayes	d	19 04		19 14		19 24			19 34				19 44	19 54			20 04		20 14			20 24			20 34
Seven Kings	d	19 06		19 16		19 26			19 36				19 46	19 56			20 06		20 16			20 26			20 36
Ilford 2	d	19 09		19 19		19 29			19 39				19 49	19 59			20 09		20 19			20 29			20 39
Manor Park	d	19 11		19 21		19 31			19 41				19 51	20 01			20 11		20 21			20 31			20 41
Forest Gate	d	19 13		19 23		19 33			19 43				19 53	20 03			20 13		20 23			20 33			20 43
Maryland	d	19 15		19 25		19 35			19 45				19 55	20 05			20 15		20 25			20 35			20 45
Stratford 7 ⊖	d	19 17	19s07	19 27	19s12	19 37	19s24		19 47		19s35		19 57	20 07	19s52	19s55	20 17	20s07	20 27	20s12		20 37		20s24	20 47
London Liverpool Street 15 ⊖	a	19 25	19 16	19 35	19 21	19 45	19 33		19 55	19 40	19 44		20 05	20 15	20 01	20 04	20 25	20 16	20 35	20 21		20 45		20 33	20 55

For general notes see front of timetable
For details of catering facilities see
Directory of Train Operators

Southend Victoria, Southminster and Shenfield → London

Network diagram - see first page of Table 5

Station		LE 1	LE	LE	LE 1	LE 1	CC	LE	LE 1	LE	LE 1		LE 1	LE	LE 1	LE	LE 1	LE	LE	LE 1	LE 1	LE		LE 1	LE 1
Southend Victoria	d	19 46			20 06						20 26						20 46			21 06					
Prittlewell	d	19 48			20 08						20 28						20 48			21 08					
Rochford	d	19 52			20 12						20 32						20 52			21 12					
Hockley	d	19 56			20 16						20 36						20 56			21 16					
Rayleigh	d	20 00			20 20						20 40						21 00			21 20					
Southminster	d												20 17												
Burnham-on-Crouch	d												20 21												
Althorne	d												20 26												
North Fambridge	d												20 34												
South Woodham Ferrers	d												20 39												
Battlesbridge	d												20 43												
Wickford 2	d	20 05			20 25						20 45		20 49				21 05			21 25					
Billericay	d	20 11			20 31						20 51		20 55				21 11			21 31					
Shenfield 3	a	20 18			20 38						20 58		21 02				21 18			21 38					
	d	20 18	20 24	20 34	20 38	20 40		20 44	20 51	20 54	20 58			21 04	21 10	21 14	21 18	21 24	21 34	21 38	21 40	21 44		21 51	21 58
Brentwood	d		20 27	20 37				20 47		20 57				21 07		21 17		21 27	21 37			21 47			
Harold Wood	d		20 32	20 42				20 52		21 02				21 12		21 22		21 32	21 42			21 52			
Gidea Park 2	d		20 36	20 46				20 56		21 06				21 16		21 26		21 36	21 46			21 56			
Romford	d	20 26	20 38	20 48				20 58	20 59	21 08				21 18		21 28	21 26	21 38	21 48			21 58		21 59	
Chadwell Heath	d		20 42	20 52				21 02		21 12				21 22		21 32		21 42	21 52			22 02			
Goodmayes	d		20 44	20 54				21 04		21 14				21 24		21 34		21 44	21 54			22 04			
Seven Kings	d		20 46	20 56				21 06		21 16				21 26		21 36		21 46	21 56			22 06			
Ilford 2	d		20 49	20 59				21 09		21 19				21 29		21 39		21 49	21 59			22 09			
Manor Park	d		20 51	21 01				21 11		21 21				21 31		21 41		21 51	22 01			22 11			
Forest Gate	d		20 53	21 03				21 13		21 23				21 33		21 43		21 53	22 03			22 13			
Maryland	d		20 55	21 05				21 15		21 25				21 35		21 45		21 55	22 05			22 15			
Stratford 7 ⊖ ⛴	d	20s34	20 57	21 07	20s52	20s55	21 09	21 17	21s07	21 27	21s12			21 37	21s24	21 47	21s34	21 57	22 07	21s52	21s55	22 17		22s10	22s12
London Liverpool Street 15 ⊖	a	20 43	21 05	21 15	21 01	21 04	21 21	21 25	21 17	21 35	21 21			21 45	21 33	21 55	21 43	22 05	22 15	22 01	22 03	22 25		22 19	22 23

Station		LE	LE 1	LE 1	LE 1	LE	LE	LE 1	LE 1	LE	LE 1		LE	LE 1	LE 1	LE 1	LE	CC	LE	LE 1	LE 1	LE			
Southend Victoria	d			21 36				22 06							22 36					23 06					
Prittlewell	d			21 38				22 08							22 38					23 08					
Rochford	d			21 42				22 12							22 42					23 12					
Hockley	d			21 46				22 16							22 46					23 16					
Rayleigh	d			21 50				22 20							22 50					23 20					
Southminster	d		21 17											22 17							22 56				
Burnham-on-Crouch	d		21 21											22 21							23 00				
Althorne	d		21 26											22 26							23 05				
North Fambridge	d		21 34											22 34							23 12				
South Woodham Ferrers	d		21 39											22 39							23 17				
Battlesbridge	d		21 43											22 43							23 21				
Wickford 2	d		21 49	21 55				22 25						22a49	22 55					23 25	23 29				
Billericay	d		21 55	22 01				22 31							23 01					23 31	23 35				
Shenfield 3	a		22 02	22 08				22 38							23 08					23 38	23 42				
	d	21 59		22 08	22 11	22 14	22 29	22 38	22 40	22 44	22 51		22 59		23 08	23 10	23 14		23 29	23 38	23 42	23 44			
Brentwood	d	22 02				22 17	22 32			22 47			23 02				23 17		23 32			23 47			
Harold Wood	d	22 07				22 22	22 37			22 52			23 07				23 22		23 37			23 52			
Gidea Park 2	d	22 11				22 26	22 41			22 56			23 11				23 26		23 41			23 56			
Romford	d	22 13				22 28	22 43			22 58	22 59		23 13				23 28		23 43		23 50	23 58			
Chadwell Heath	d	22 17				22 32	22 47			23 02			23 17				23 32		23 47			00 02			
Goodmayes	d	22 19				22 34	22 49			23 04			23 19				23 34		23 49			00 04			
Seven Kings	d	22 21				22 36	22 51			23 06			23 21				23 36		23 51			00 06			
Ilford 2	d	22 24				22 39	22 54			23 09			23 24				23 39		23 54			00 09			
Manor Park	d	22 26				22 41	22 56			23 11			23 26				23 41		23 56			00 11			
Forest Gate	d	22 28				22 43	22 58			23 13			23 28				23 43		23 58			00 13			
Maryland	d	22 30				22 45	23 00			23 15			23 30				23 45		23 59			00 15			
Stratford 7 ⊖ ⛴	d	22 32		22s22	22s27	22 47	23 02	22s52	22s55	23 17	23s07		23 32		23s22	23s25	23 47	23 57	00 02	23s54	23s58	00 17			
London Liverpool Street 15 ⊖	a	22 40		22 31	22 36	22 55	23 10	23 01	23 03	23 25	23 16		23 40		23 31	23 34	23 55	00 05	00 10	00 03	00 07	00 25			

For general notes see front of timetable
For details of catering facilities see
Directory of Train Operators

Southend Victoria, Southminster and Shenfield → London

Network diagram - see first page of Table 5

	LE	LE	LE	LE	LE	LE	LE 1	LE 1		LE 1	LE	LE 1	LE	LE 1	LE	LE 1	LE		LE	LE	LE 1	LE 1	LE 1	LE 1
							A																	
Southend Victoria d			04 02		04 32			05 06				05 36				06 06							06 26	
Prittlewell d			04 04		04 34			05 08				05 38				06 08							06 28	
Rochford d			04 08		04 38			05 12				05 42				06 12							06 32	
Hockley d			04 12		04 42			05 16				05 46				06 16							06 36	
Rayleigh d			04 16		04 46			05 20				05 50				06 20							06 40	
Southminster d																								06 17
Burnham-on-Crouch d																								06 21
Althorne d																								06 26
North Fambridge d																								06 34
South Woodham Ferrers d																								06 39
Battlesbridge d																								06 43
Wickford 2 d			04 21		04 51			05 25				05 55				06 25							06 45	06 49
Billericay d			04 28		04 58			05 31				06 01				06 31							06 51	06 55
Shenfield 3 a			04 39		05 09			05 38				06 08				06 38							06 58	07 02
d	23p29	23p44	04 39		05 09		05 26	05 38			05 44	06 08		06 11	06 14	06 38				06 44	06 47	06 51	06 58	
Brentwood d	23p32	23p47	04 42		05 12						05 47				06 17					06 47				
Harold Wood d	23p37	23p52	04 47		05 17						05 52				06 22					06 52				
Gidea Park 2 d	23p41	23p56	04 51		05 21		05 33				05 56		06 16		06 26		06 36		06 46	06 56				
Romford d	23p43	23p58	04 53		05 23			05 46			05 58	06 16	06 18	06 19	06 28		06 38		06 48	06 58		06 59		
Chadwell Heath d	23p47	00 02	04 57		05 27						06 02		06 22		06 32		06 42		06 52	07 02				
Goodmayes d	23p49	00 04	04 59		05 29						06 04		06 24		06 34		06 44		06 54	07 04				
Seven Kings d	23p51	00 06	05 01		05 31		05 38				06 06		06 26		06 36		06 46		06 56	07 06				
Ilford 2 d	23p54	00 09	05 04	05 09	05 34	05 39					06 09		06 29		06 39		06 49		06 59	07 09				
Manor Park d	23p56	00 11		05 11		05 41					06 11		06 31		06 41		06 51		07 01	07 11				
Forest Gate d	23p58	00 13		05 13		05 43					06 13		06 33		06 43		06 53		07 03	07 13				
Maryland d	23p59	00 15		05 15		05 45					06 15		06 35		06 45		06 55		07 05	07 15				
Stratford 7 ⊖ d	00 02	00 17	05 09	05 17	05 39	05 47	05s44	05s54		06 05	06 17	06s24	06 37	06s27	06 47	06s52	06 57		07 07	07 17	07s01	07s07	07s12	
London Liverpool Street 15 ⊖ a	00 10	00 25	05 17	05 25	05 47	05 55	05 57	06 03		06 14	06 25	06 33	06 45	06 36	06 55	07 01	07 05		07 15	07 25	07 10	07 16	07 21	

	LE	LE	LE 1	LE 1		LE	LE	LE	LE 1	LE 1	LE	LE 1	LE		LE 1	LE 1	LE	LE 1	LE 1	LE	LE 1	LE		LE
Southend Victoria d				06 46					07 06						07 26						07 46			
Prittlewell d				06 48					07 08						07 28						07 48			
Rochford d				06 52					07 12						07 32						07 52			
Hockley d				06 56					07 16						07 36						07 56			
Rayleigh d				07 00					07 20						07 40						08 00			
Southminster d																07 17								
Burnham-on-Crouch d																07 21								
Althorne d																07 26								
North Fambridge d																07 34								
South Woodham Ferrers d																07 39								
Battlesbridge d																07 43								
Wickford 2 d				07 05					07 25						07 45	07 49					08 05			
Billericay d				07 11					07 31						07 51	07 55					08 11			
Shenfield 3 a				07 18					07 38						07 58	08 02					08 18			
d		07 04	07 10	07 18			07 24	07 34	07 38	07 40	07 44	07 51	07 54		07 58		08 04	08 10	08 14	08 14	08 18	08 24		08 34
Brentwood d		07 07					07 27	07 37			07 47		07 57				08 07			08 17		08 27		08 37
Harold Wood d		07 12					07 32	07 42			07 52		08 02				08 12			08 22		08 32		08 42
Gidea Park 2 d	07 06	07 16				07 26	07 36	07 46			07 56		08 06				08 16			08 26		08 36		08 46
Romford d	07 08	07 18		07 26		07 28	07 38	07 48			07 58	07 59	08 08				08 18			08 28	08 26	08 38		08 48
Chadwell Heath d	07 12	07 22				07 32	07 42	07 52			08 02		08 12				08 22			08 32		08 42		08 52
Goodmayes d	07 14	07 24				07 34	07 44	07 54			08 04		08 14				08 24			08 34		08 44		08 54
Seven Kings d	07 16	07 26				07 36	07 46	07 56			08 06		08 16				08 26			08 36		08 46		08 56
Ilford 2 d	07 19	07 29				07 39	07 49	07 59			08 09		08 19				08 29			08 39		08 49		08 59
Manor Park d	07 21	07 31				07 41	07 51	08 01			08 11		08 21				08 31			08 41		08 51		09 01
Forest Gate d	07 23	07 33				07 43	07 53	08 03			08 13		08 23				08 33			08 43		08 53		09 03
Maryland d	07 25	07 35				07 45	07 55	08 05			08 15		08 25				08 35			08 45		08 55		09 05
Stratford 7 ⊖ d	07 27	07 37	07s24	07s34		07 47	07 57	08 07	07s52	07s55	08 17	08s07	08 27		08s12		08 37	08s24	08s30	08 47	08s34	08 57		09 07
London Liverpool Street 15 ⊖ a	07 35	07 45	07 33	07 43		07 55	08 05	08 15	08 01	08 03	08 25	08 16	08 35		08 21		08 45	08 33	08 39	08 55	08 43	09 05		09 15

	LE 1	LE 1	LE	LE 1	LE		LE 1	LE 1	LE	LE 1	LE	LE 1	LE	LE	LE 1	LE 1	LE	LE 1	LE			LE 1	LE 1
Southend Victoria d	08 06						08 26					08 46			09 06							19 26	
Prittlewell d	08 08						08 28					08 48			09 08							19 28	
Rochford d	08 12						08 32					08 52			09 12							19 32	
Hockley d	08 16						08 36					08 56			09 16							19 36	
Rayleigh d	08 20						08 40					09 00			09 20							19 40	
Southminster d								08 17															19 17
Burnham-on-Crouch d								08 21												and at			19 21
Althorne d								08 26															19 26
North Fambridge d								08 34												the same			19 34
South Woodham Ferrers d								08 39															19 39
Battlesbridge d								08 43												minutes			19 43
Wickford 2 d	08 25						08 45	08 49				09 05			09 25							19 45	19 49
Billericay d	08 31						08 51	08 55				09 11			09 31					past		19 51	19 55
Shenfield 3 a	08 38						08 58	09 02				09 18			09 38							19 58	20 02
d	08 38	08 40	08 44	08 51	08 54		08 58		09 04	09 10	09 14	09 18	09 24	09 34	09 38	09 40	09 44	09 51	09 54	each		19 58	
Brentwood d			08 47		08 57				09 07		09 17		09 27	09 37			09 47		09 57				
Harold Wood d			08 52		09 02				09 12		09 22		09 32	09 42			09 52		10 02	hour until			
Gidea Park 2 d			08 56		09 06				09 16		09 26		09 36	09 46			09 56		10 06				
Romford d			08 58	08 59	09 08				09 18		09 28	09 26	09 38	09 48			09 58	09 59	10 08				
Chadwell Heath d			09 02		09 12				09 22		09 32		09 42	09 52			10 02		10 12				
Goodmayes d			09 04		09 14				09 24		09 34		09 44	09 54			10 04		10 14				
Seven Kings d			09 06		09 16				09 26		09 36		09 46	09 56			10 06		10 16				
Ilford 2 d			09 09		09 19				09 29		09 39		09 49	09 59			10 09		10 19				
Manor Park d			09 11		09 21				09 31		09 41		09 51	10 01			10 11		10 21				
Forest Gate d			09 13		09 23				09 33		09 43		09 53	10 03			10 13		10 23				
Maryland d			09 15		09 25				09 35		09 45		09 55	10 05			10 15		10 25				
Stratford 7 ⊖ d	08s52	08s55	09 17	09s07	09 27		09s12		09 37	09s24	09 47	09s34	09 57	10 07	09s52	09s55	10 17	10s07	10 27			20s12	
London Liverpool Street 15 ⊖ a	09 01	09 03	09 25	09 16	09 35		09 21		09 45	09 33	09 55	09 43	10 05	10 15	10 01	10 03	10 25	10 16	10 35			20 21	

For general notes see front of timetable
For details of catering facilities see
Directory of Train Operators

A From Colchester (Table 11)

Southend Victoria, Southminster and Shenfield → London

Network diagram - see first page of Table 5

Station		LE	LE 1	LE	LE 1	LE	LE	LE 1	LE 1		LE	LE 1	LE	LE 1	LE 1	LE 1	LE	LE		LE 1	LE 1	LE	LE 1	LE 1	LE
Southend Victoria	d				19 46			20 06							20 36					21 06					
Prittlewell	d				19 48			20 08							20 38					21 08					
Rochford	d				19 52			20 12							20 42					21 12					
Hockley	d				19 56			20 16							20 46					21 16					
Rayleigh	d				20 00			20 20							20 50					21 20					
Southminster	d													20 17											
Burnham-on-Crouch	d													20 21											
Althorne	d													20 26											
North Fambridge	d													20 34											
South Woodham Ferrers	d													20 39											
Battlesbridge	d													20 43											
Wickford 2	d				20 05			20 25						20 49	20 55					21 25					
Billericay	d				20 11			20 31						20 55	21 01					21 31					
Shenfield 3	a				20 18			20 38						21 02	21 08					21 38					
	d	20 04	20 10	20 14	20 18	20 24	20 34	20 38	20 40		20 44	20 51	20 59		21 08	21 11	21 14	21 29		21 38	21 40	21 44	21 51	21 58	21 59
Brentwood	d	20 07		20 17		20 27	20 37				20 47		21 02				21 17	21 32				21 47			22 02
Harold Wood	d	20 12		20 22		20 32	20 42				20 52		21 07				21 22	21 37				21 52			22 07
Gidea Park 2	d	20 16		20 26		20 36	20 46				20 56		21 11				21 26	21 41				21 56			22 11
Romford	d	20 18		20 28	20 26	20 38	20 48				20 58	20 59	21 13				21 28	21 43				21 58	21 59		22 13
Chadwell Heath	d	20 22		20 32		20 42	20 52				21 02		21 17				21 32	21 47				22 02			22 17
Goodmayes	d	20 24		20 34		20 44	20 54				21 04		21 19				21 34	21 49				22 04			22 19
Seven Kings	d	20 26		20 36		20 46	20 56				21 06		21 21				21 36	21 51				22 06			22 21
Ilford 2	d	20 29		20 39		20 49	20 59				21 09		21 24				21 39	21 54				22 09			22 24
Manor Park	d	20 31		20 41		20 51	21 01				21 11		21 26				21 41	21 56				22 11			22 26
Forest Gate	d	20 33		20 43		20 53	21 03				21 13		21 28				21 43	21 58				22 13			22 28
Maryland	d	20 35		20 45		20 55	21 05				21 15		21 30				21 45	22 00				22 15			22 30
Stratford 7 ⊖	d	20 37	20s24	20 47	20s34	20 57	21 07	20s52	20s55		21 17	21s07	21 32		21s22	21s25	21 47	22 02		21s52	21s54	22 17	22s07	22s12	22 32
London Liverpool Street 15 ⊖	a	20 45	20 33	20 55	20 43	21 05	21 15	21 01	21 03		21 29	21 16	21 44		21 35	21 38	21 59	22 14		22 05	22 07	22 29	22 20	22 25	22 44

Station		LE 1	LE 1	LE 1	LE		LE	LE 1	LE 1	LE 1	LE	LE 1	LE	LE 1		LE 1	LE	LE	LE 1	LE	LE 1				
Southend Victoria	d		21 36					22 06						22 36					23 06						
Prittlewell	d		21 38					22 08						22 38					23 08						
Rochford	d		21 42					22 12						22 42					23 12						
Hockley	d		21 46					22 16						22 46					23 16						
Rayleigh	d		21 50					22 20						22 50					23 20						
Southminster	d	21 17								21 59											23 07				
Burnham-on-Crouch	d	21 21								22 03											23 11				
Althorne	d	21 26								22 08											23 16				
North Fambridge	d	21 34								22 14											23 22				
South Woodham Ferrers	d	21 39								22 19											23 27				
Battlesbridge	d	21 43								22 23											23 31				
Wickford 2	d	21 49	21 55					22 25		22 29				22 55					23 25		23a37				
Billericay	d	21 55	22 01					22 31		22 35				23 01					23 31						
Shenfield 3	a	22 02	22 08					22 38		22 42				23 08					23 38						
	d		22 08	22 11	22 14		22 29	22 38	22 40		22 44	22 51	22 59	23 08		23 10	23 14	23 29	23 38	23 44					
Brentwood	d				22 17		22 32				22 47		23 02				23 17	23 32		23 47					
Harold Wood	d				22 22		22 37				22 52		23 07				23 22	23 37		23 52					
Gidea Park 2	d				22 26		22 41				22 56		23 11				23 26	23 41		23 56					
Romford	d				22 28		22 43				22 58	22 59	23 13				23 28	23 43		23 58					
Chadwell Heath	d				22 32		22 47				23 02		23 17				23 32	23 47		00 02					
Goodmayes	d				22 34		22 49				23 04		23 19				23 34	23 49		00 04					
Seven Kings	d				22 36		22 51				23 06		23 21				23 36	23 51		00 06					
Ilford 2	d				22 39		22 54				23 09		23 24				23 39	23 54		00 09					
Manor Park	d				22 41		22 56				23 11		23 26				23 41	23 56		00 11					
Forest Gate	d				22 43		22 58				23 13		23 28				23 43	23 58		00 13					
Maryland	d				22 45		23 00				23 15		23 30				23 45	23 59		00 15					
Stratford 7 ⊖	d		22s22	22s25	22 47		23 02	22s52	22s55		23 17	23s07	23 32	23s22		23s25	23 47	00 02	23s54	00 17					
London Liverpool Street 15 ⊖	a		22 35	22 38	22 59		23 14	23 05	23 07		23 29	23 20	23 44	23 35		23 38	23 59	00 14	00 07	00 29					

For general notes see front of timetable
For details of catering facilities see
Directory of Train Operators

Southend Victoria, Southminster and Shenfield → London

Network diagram - see first page of Table 5

		LE	LE 1	LE	LE		LE	LE	LE 1	LE		LE 1	LE	LE 1	LE		LE 1	LE	LE 1	LE		LE 1	LE	LE 1	LE 1
Southend Victoria	d								06 18					06 48					07 18						07 52
Prittlewell	d																								
Rochford	d								06 22					06 52					07 22						07 56
Hockley	d								06 26					06 56					07 26						08 00
Rayleigh	d								06 30					07 00					07 30						08 04
Southminster	d																								
Burnham-on-Crouch	d																								
Althorne	d																								
North Fambridge	d																								
South Woodham Ferrers	d																								
Battlesbridge	d																								
Wickford 2	d								06 35					07 05					07 35						08 09
Billericay	d								06 41					07 11					07 41						08 15
Shenfield 3	a								06 52					07 22					07 52						08 22
	d	23p29		23p44				06 43	06 53			07 07	07 13	07 23			07 37	07 43	07 53			08 07	08 13	08 18	08 23
Brentwood	d	23p32		23p47				06 46	06 56				07 16	07 26				07 46	07 56				08 16		08 26
Harold Wood	d	23p37		23p52				06 51	07 01				07 21	07 31				07 51	08 01				08 21		08 31
Gidea Park 2	d	23p41		23p56	05 55		06 25	06 55	07 05	07 11			07 25	07 35	07 41			07 55	08 05	08 11			08 25		08 35
Romford	d	23p43		23p58	05 57		06 27	06 57	07 07	07 13			07 27	07 37	07 43			07 57	08 07	08 13			08 27		08 37
Chadwell Heath	d	23p47		00 02	06 01		06 31	07 01		07 17			07 31		07 47			08 01		08 17			08 31		
Goodmayes	d	23p49		00 04	06 03		06 33	07 03		07 19			07 33		07 49			08 03		08 19			08 33		
Seven Kings	d	23p51		00 06	06 05		06 35	07 05		07 21			07 35		07 51			08 05		08 21			08 35		
Ilford 2	d	23p54		00 09	06 08		06 38	07 08		07 24			07 38		07 54			08 08		08 24			08 38		
Manor Park	d	23p56		00 11	06 10		06 40	07 10		07 26			07 40		07 56			08 10		08 26			08 40		
Forest Gate	d	23p58		00 13	06 12		06 42	07 12		07 28			07 42		07 58			08 12		08 28			08 42		
Maryland	d	23p59		00 15	06 14		06 44	07 14					07 44					08 14					08 44		
Stratford 7	⊖ d	00 02	00 05	00 17	06 16		06 46	07 16	07 19	07 31		07s34	07 46	07 49	08 01		08s04	08 16	08 19	08 31		08s34	08 46	08s49	08 49
London Liverpool Street 15	⊖ a	00 14	00 14	00 29	06 26		06 56	07 24	07 27	07 41		07 42	07 54	07 57	08 11		08 12	08 24	08 27	08 41		08 42	08 54	08 59	08 59

		LE	LE 1		LE	LE 1	LE 1	LE		LE 1	LE		LE 1	LE	LE 1	LE	LE 1	LE 1	LE	LE 1	LE			LE 1
Southend Victoria	d						08 22						08 52					09 22						20 52
Prittlewell	d																							
Rochford	d						08 26						08 56					09 26						20 56
Hockley	d						08 30						09 00					09 30						21 00
Rayleigh	d						08 34						09 04					09 34						21 04
Southminster	d					08 05											09 05							
Burnham-on-Crouch	d					08 09											09 09					and at		
Althorne	d					08 14											09 14							
North Fambridge	d					08 20											09 20					the same		
South Woodham Ferrers	d					08 25											09 25							
Battlesbridge	d					08 29											09 29					minutes		
Wickford 2	d					08a35	08 39						09 09				09a35	09 39						21 09
Billericay	d						08 45						09 15					09 45				past		21 15
Shenfield 3	a						08 52						09 22					09 52						21 22
	d		08 41		08 43		08 53			09 11	09 13		09 23		09 41	09 43		09 53		10 11	10 13	each		21 23
Brentwood	d				08 46		08 56				09 16		09 26			09 46		09 56			10 16			21 26
Harold Wood	d				08 51		09 01				09 21		09 31			09 51		10 01			10 21	hour until		21 31
Gidea Park 2	d	08 41			08 55		09 05	09 11			09 25		09 35	09 41		09 55		10 05	10 11		10 25			21 35
Romford	d	08 43			08 57		09 07	09 13			09 27		09 37	09 43		09 57		10 07	10 13		10 27			21 37
Chadwell Heath	d	08 47			09 01			09 17			09 31			09 47		10 01			10 17		10 31			
Goodmayes	d	08 49			09 03			09 19			09 33			09 49		10 03			10 19		10 33			
Seven Kings	d	08 51			09 05			09 21			09 35			09 51		10 05			10 21		10 35			
Ilford 2	d	08 54			09 08			09 24			09 38			09 54		10 08			10 24		10 38			
Manor Park	d	08 56			09 10			09 26			09 40			09 56		10 10			10 26		10 40			
Forest Gate	d	08 58			09 12			09 28			09 42			09 58		10 12			10 28		10 42			
Maryland	d				09 14						09 44					10 14					10 44			
Stratford 7	⊖ d	09 01	09s04		09 16		09 19	09 31		09s34	09 46		09 49	10 01	10s04	10 16		10 19	10 31	10s34	10 46			21 49
London Liverpool Street 15	⊖ a	09 11	09 12		09 24		09 29	09 41		09 42	09 54		09 59	10 11	10 12	10 24		10 29	10 41	10 42	10 54			21 59

		LE 1	LE	LE 1	LE 1		LE 1	LE	LE 1	LE 1		LE	LE 1	LE 1	LE 1		LE 1	LE	LE 1	LE 1		LE			
Southend Victoria	d				21 22				21 52					22 22					22 52						
Prittlewell	d																								
Rochford	d				21 26				21 56					22 26					22 56						
Hockley	d				21 30				22 00					22 30					23 00						
Rayleigh	d				21 34				22 04					22 34					23 04						
Southminster	d			21 05									22 05							22 45					
Burnham-on-Crouch	d			21 09									22 09							22 49					
Althorne	d			21 14									22 14							22 54					
North Fambridge	d			21 20									22 20							23 00					
South Woodham Ferrers	d			21 25									22 25							23 05					
Battlesbridge	d			21 29									22 29							23 09					
Wickford 2	d			21a35	21 39				22 09				22a35	22 39					23 09	23 15					
Billericay	d				21 45				22 15					22 45					23 15						
Shenfield 3	a				21 52				22 22					22 52					23 22	23 26					
	d	21 41	21 43		21 53		22 11	22 13	22 23	22 41		22 43		22 53			23 11	23 13	23 23			23 43			
Brentwood	d		21 46		21 56			22 16	22 26			22 46		22 56				23 16	23 26			23 46			
Harold Wood	d		21 51		22 01			22 21	22 31			22 51		23 01				23 21	23 31			23 51			
Gidea Park 2	d		21 55		22 05			22 25	22 35			22 55		23 05				23 25	23 35			23 55			
Romford	d		21 57		22 07			22 27	22 37			22 57		23 07				23 27	23 37			23 57			
Chadwell Heath	d		22 01					22 31				23 01						23 31				00 01			
Goodmayes	d		22 03					22 33				23 03						23 33				00 03			
Seven Kings	d		22 05					22 35				23 05						23 35				00 05			
Ilford 2	d		22 08					22 38				23 08						23 38				00 08			
Manor Park	d		22 10					22 40				23 10						23 40				00 10			
Forest Gate	d		22 12					22 42				23 12						23 42				00 12			
Maryland	d		22 14					22 44				23 14						23 44				00 14			
Stratford 7	⊖ d	22s04	22 16		22 19		22s34	22 46	22 49	23s04		23 16		23 19	23 22		23s34	23 46	23 49			00 16			
London Liverpool Street 15	⊖ a	22 12	22 24		22 29		22 42	22 54	22 59	23 12		23 24		23 31	23 36		23 42	23 54	23 59			00 25			

For general notes see front of timetable
For details of catering facilities see
Directory of Train Operators

Mondays to Fridays

Marks Tey — Sudbury

Network diagram - see first page of Table 5

Miles			LE	LE	LE	LE		LE	LE	LE	LE		LE	LE	LE	LE		LE	LE	LE	LE	LE	LE		
0	**Colchester** 4	d	05 48	06 29	07 18	08 18	.....	09 17	10 17	11 17	12 17	.....	13 17	14 17	15 17	15 48	.....	16 53	17 49	18 49	19 33	20 15	21 17	.....	.....
—	London Liverpool Street 15 ⊖	d	.	05 25	06 38	07 38	.	08 38	09 38	10 38	11 38	.	12 38	13 38	14 38	15 18	.	16 15	17 08	18 02	18 38	19 38	20 38	.	.
5	Marks Tey 2	d	05 57	06 53	07 40	08 33	.....	09 33	10 33	11 33	12 33	.....	13 33	14 33	15 31	16 17	.....	17 07	18 05	18 59	19 45	20 33	21 33	.....	.....
8¼	Chappel & Wakes Colne	d	06 03	06 59	.	08 39	.	09 39	10 39	11 39	12 39	.	13 39	14 39	15 37	16 23	.	17 13	18 11	19 05	19 51	20 39	21 39	.	.
11¾	Bures	d	06 09	07 05	.....	08 45	.....	09 45	10 45	11 45	12 45	.....	13 45	14 45	15 43	16 29	.....	17 19	18 17	19 11	19 57	20 45	21 45	.....	.....
16¾	**Sudbury**	a	06 16	07 12	07 56	08 52	.	09 52	10 52	11 52	12 52	.	13 52	14 52	15 52	16 36	.	17 26	18 24	19 20	20 06	20 52	21 52	.	.

Saturdays

		LE	LE		LE	LE		LE	LE		LE	LE		LE	LE		LE	LE		LE	LE	LE	LE		
Colchester 4	d	06 17	07 17	.....	08 17	09 17	.....	10 17	11 17	.....	12 17	13 17	.....	14 17	15 17	.....	16 17	17 17	.....	18 17	19 17	20 17	21 17	.....	.....
London Liverpool Street 15 ⊖	d	05 30	06 38	.	07 38	08 38	.	09 38	10 38	.	11 38	12 38	.	13 38	14 38	.	15 38	16 38	.	17 38	18 38	19 38	20 38	.	.
Marks Tey 2	d	06 33	07 33	.....	08 33	09 33	.....	10 33	11 33	.....	12 33	13 33	.....	14 33	15 33	.....	16 33	17 33	.....	18 33	19 33	20 33	21 33	.....	.....
Chappel & Wakes Colne	d	06 39	07 39	.	08 39	09 39	.	10 39	11 39	.	12 39	13 39	.	14 39	15 39	.	16 39	17 39	.	18 39	19 39	20 39	21 39	.	.
Bures	d	06 45	07 45	.....	08 45	09 45	.....	10 45	11 45	.....	12 45	13 45	.....	14 45	15 45	.....	16 45	17 45	.....	18 45	19 45	20 45	21 45	.....	.....
Sudbury	a	06 52	07 52	.	08 52	09 52	.	10 52	11 52	.	12 52	13 52	.	14 52	15 52	.	16 52	17 52	.	18 52	19 52	20 52	21 52	.	.

Sundays

		LE	LE		LE	LE		LE	LE		LE	LE		LE	LE		LE	LE		LE	LE		LE		
Colchester 4	d	07 07	08 06	.....	09 06	10 06	.....	11 06	12 06	.....	13 06	14 06	.....	15 06	16 06	.....	17 06	18 06	.....	19 06	20 06	.....	21 06	.....	.....
London Liverpool Street 15 ⊖	d	.	.	.	08 02	09 02	.	10 02	11 02	.	12 02	13 02	.	14 02	15 02	.	16 02	17 02	.	18 02	19 02	.	20 02	.	.
Marks Tey 2	d	07 15	08 15	.....	09 15	10 15	.....	11 15	12 15	.....	13 15	14 15	.....	15 15	16 15	.....	17 15	18 15	.....	19 15	20 15	.....	21 15	.....	.....
Chappel & Wakes Colne	d	07 21	08 21	.	09 21	10 21	.	11 21	12 21	.	13 21	14 21	.	15 21	16 21	.	17 21	18 21	.	19 21	20 21	.	21 21	.	.
Bures	d	07 27	08 27	.....	09 27	10 27	.....	11 27	12 27	.....	13 27	14 27	.....	15 27	16 27	.....	17 27	18 27	.....	19 27	20 27	.....	21 27	.....	.....
Sudbury	a	07 34	08 34	.	09 34	10 34	.	11 34	12 34	.	13 34	14 34	.	15 34	16 34	.	17 34	18 34	.	19 34	20 34	.	21 34	.	.

Mondays to Fridays

Miles			LE	LE	LE	LE	LE		LE	LE	LE	LE	LE		LE	LE	LE	LE	LE	LE	LE	LE	LE		
0	**Sudbury**	d	05 30	06 30	07 17	08 00	09 00	.....	10 00	11 00	12 00	13 00	14 00	.....	15 00	15 54	16 40	17 31	18 31	19 22	20 08	21 00	22 00	.....	.....
5	Bures	d	05 37	06 37	07 24	08 07	09 07	.	10 07	11 07	12 07	13 07	14 07	.	15 07	16 01	.	17 38	18 38	19x29	20x15	21 07	22 07	.	.
8½	Chappel & Wakes Colne	d	05 43	06 43	07 30	08 13	09 13	.....	10 13	11 13	12 13	13 13	14 13	.....	15 13	16 07	.....	17 44	18 44	19x35	20x21	21 13	22 13	.....	.....
11¾	Marks Tey 2	a	05 49	06 49	07 36	08 19	09 19	.	10 19	11 19	12 19	13 19	14 19	.	15 19	16 13	16 56	17 50	18 50	19 41	20 27	21 19	22 19	.	.
—	London Liverpool Street 15 ⊖	a	06 49	07 51	08 48	09 22	10 17	.....	11 18	12 16	13 16	14 16	15 16	.....	16 18	17 15	17 49	18 49	19 47	20 46	21 33	22 19	23 16	.....	.....
16¾	**Colchester** 4	a	06 32	07 04	07 56	08 38	09 37	.	10 37	11 37	12 37	13 37	14 37	.	15 37	16 41	17 09	18 03	19 03	20 08	20 38	21 38	22 30	.	.

Saturdays

		LE	LE		LE	LE		LE	LE		LE	LE		LE	LE		LE	LE		LE	LE	LE	LE		
Sudbury	d	07 00	08 00	.....	09 00	10 00	.....	11 00	12 00	.....	13 00	14 00	.....	15 00	16 00	.....	17 00	18 00	.....	19 00	20 00	21 00	22 00	.....	.....
Bures	d	07 07	08 07	.	09 07	10 07	.	11 07	12 07	.	13 07	14 07	.	15 07	16 07	.	17 07	18 07	.	19 07	20 07	21 07	22 07	.	.
Chappel & Wakes Colne	d	07 13	08 13	.....	09 13	10 13	.....	11 13	12 13	.....	13 13	14 13	.....	15 13	16 13	.....	17 13	18 13	.....	19 13	20 13	21 13	22 13	.....	.....
Marks Tey 2	a	07 19	08 19	.	09 19	10 19	.	11 19	12 19	.	13 19	14 19	.	15 19	16 19	.	17 19	18 19	.	19 19	20 19	21 19	22 19	.	.
London Liverpool Street 15 ⊖	a	08 16	09 16	.....	10 16	11 16	.....	12 16	13 16	.....	14 16	15 16	.....	16 16	17 16	.....	18 16	19 16	.....	20 16	21 16	22 20	23 20	.....	.....
Colchester 4	a	07 37	08 37	.	09 37	10 37	.	11 37	12 37	.	13 37	14 37	.	15 37	16 37	.	17 37	18 36	.	19 36	20 37	21 37	22 30	.	.

Sundays

		LE	LE		LE	LE		LE	LE		LE	LE		LE	LE		LE	LE		LE	LE		LE		
Sudbury	d	07 40	08 40	.....	09 40	10 40	.....	11 40	12 40	.....	13 40	14 40	.....	15 40	16 40	.....	17 40	18 40	.....	19 40	20 40	.....	21 40	.....	.....
Bures	d	07 47	08 47	.	09 47	10 47	.	11 47	12 47	.	13 47	14 47	.	15 47	16 47	.	17 47	18 47	.	19 47	20 47	.	21 47	.	.
Chappel & Wakes Colne	d	07 53	08 53	.....	09 53	10 53	.....	11 53	12 53	.....	13 53	14 53	.....	15 53	16 53	.....	17 53	18 53	.....	19 53	20 53	.....	21 53	.....	.....
Marks Tey 2	a	07 59	08 59	.	09 59	10 59	.	11 59	12 59	.	13 59	14 59	.	15 59	16 59	.	17 59	18 59	.	19 59	20 59	.	21 59	.	.
London Liverpool Street 15 ⊖	a	09 12	10 12	.....	11 12	12 12	.....	13 12	14 12	.....	15 12	16 12	.....	17 12	18 12	.....	19 12	20 12	.....	21 12	22 12	.....	23 12	.....	.....
Colchester 4	a	.	09 12	.	10 12	11 12	.	12 12	13 12	.	14 12	15 12	.	16 12	17 12	.	18 12	19 12	.	20 12	21 12	.	22 09	.	.

For general notes see front of timetable
For details of catering facilities see Directory of Train Operators

London → Chelmsford, Colchester, Walton-on-Naze, Clacton, Harwich, Ipswich and Norwich

Network diagram - see first page of Table 5

Miles	Miles	Miles	Miles	Miles			LE MX 1 ◇	LE MO 1 ◇	LE MX 1	LE MO 1	LE FO 1	LE MFX 1	LE MX 1 ◇	LE MO 1 ◇	LE MO 1	LE MX 1	LE MO 1	LE MX 1	LE MX 1	LE A	LE 1		LE 1	LE A	LE 1
0	—	—	—	—	**London Liverpool Street 15** ⊖	d	22p30	22p30	23p00	23p02	23p18	23p18	23p30	23p30	23p32	23p48	00 02	00 18	00 48						
4	—	—	—	—	Stratford 7 ⊖	d	22b38		23p07	23p09	23p25	23p25	23b38		23p39	23p55	00 09	00 25	00 55						
12¼	—	—	—	—	Romford	d																			
20¼	—	—	—	—	Shenfield 3	d		22b57	23p24	23p31	23p42	23p42		23b57	00 01	00 12	00 31	00 47	01 17						
23½	—	—	—	—	Ingatestone	d				23p35	23p46	23p46				00 16	00 35	00 51	01 21						
29¾	—	—	—	—	**Chelmsford 3**	d	23p03		23p33	23p42	23p53	23p53	00 03		00 10	00 23	00 42	00 58	01 28						
36	—	—	—	—	Hatfield Peverel	d				23p49						00 30	00 49	01 05							
38½	0	—	—	—	**Witham 2**	d			23p42	23p54	00 03	00 03			00 19	00 35	00 54	01 10	01 38				05 21		
—	3	—	—	—	White Notley	d																	05 28		
—	4¼	—	—	—	Cressing	d																	05 30		
—	5½	—	—	—	Braintree Freeport	d																	05 33		
—	6¼	—	—	—	**Braintree**	a																	05 37		
42¼	—	—	—	—	Kelvedon	d				23p59						00 40	00 59	01 15							
46¾	—	—	—	—	Marks Tey 2	d				00 04					00 27	00 45	01 04	01 20							
51¾	—	—	—	—	**Colchester 4**	a	23p22	23p23	23p56	00 12	00 17	00 21	00 25	00 27	00 40	00 57	01 18	01 32	02 03						
—	0	0	—	—		d	23p23	23p24	23p57	00 12	00 17		00 27	00 28							05 35				05 43
—	—	2¼	—	—	Colchester Town	a																			
—	—	—	—	—		d																			
—	2¾	3¼	—	—	Hythe	d																			
—	—	5¾	—	—	Wivenhoe 3	d					00 25														
—	—	7½	—	—	Alresford (Essex)	d					00 28														
—	—	9¾	—	—	Great Bentley	d					00 32														
—	—	12½	—	—	Weeley	d																			
—	—	14¾	—	—	Thorpe-le-Soken 1	a					00 37														
—	—	—	0	—		d					00 37														
—	—	—	4¾	—	**Clacton-on-Sea**	a					00 51														
—	—	17¼	—	—	Kirby Cross	d																			
—	—	18½	—	—	Frinton-on-Sea	d																			
—	—	19¾	—	—	**Walton-on-the-Naze**	a																			
59½	—	—	—	0	Manningtree 2	d	23p32	23p33	00 04	00 20			00 36	00 37							05 44				05 51
—	—	—	—	1¾	Mistley	d																			05 55
—	—	—	—	5¾	Wrabness	d																			06 00
—	—	—	—	9½	Harwich International	d																			06 09
—	—	—	—	10¾	Dovercourt	d																			06 12
—	—	—	—	11¼	**Harwich Town**	a																			06 14
68¾	—	—	—	—	**Ipswich**	a	23p42	23p42	00 20	00 36			00 46	00 46							05 55				
—	—	—	—	—		d	23p43	23p44					00 48	00 48						05 10	06 01			06 13	
—	—	—	—	—	**Lowestoft**	a																			
77	—	—	—	—	Needham Market	d														05 20				06 23	
80¾	—	—	—	—	Stowmarket	d	23p54	23p55					00 59	00 59						05a25	06 12			06a28	
—	—	—	—	—	**Peterborough 8**	a															07 37				
95	—	—	—	—	Diss	d	00 07	00 07					01 12	01 11											
115	—	—	—	—	**Norwich**	a	00 45	00 39					01 45	01 43											

		LE 1	LE 1	LE 1	LE A	LE 1	LE 1	LE 1	LE 1	LE 1	LE 1 ◇	LE 1	LE 1	LE 1	LE 1		LE 1 ◇	LE 1	LE 1 ◇	LE 1	LE 1	LE 1 ◇	LE A	LE 1	LE 1
London Liverpool Street 15 ⊖	d							05 25			06 00		06 02	06 12			06 25		06 38	06 48		07 00			
Stratford 7 ⊖	d							05 32					06 09	06 19			06u33			06 55					
Romford	d							05 40					06 17												
Shenfield 3	d							05 51			06u23		06 28	06 37					07u02	07 12		07u23			
Ingatestone	d							05 55						06 41						07 16					
Chelmsford 3	d							06 02					06 37	06 49			06 57		07 12	07 23					⟵
Hatfield Peverel	d							06 09						06 55						07 30					07 30
Witham 2	d							06 14	06 16				06 46	07 03			07 07		07 21	⟶					07 36
White Notley	d								06 23					07 10											
Cressing	d								06 25					07 12											
Braintree Freeport	d								06 28					07 15											
Braintree	a								06 32					07 20											
Kelvedon	d							06 19					06 51						07 27						
Marks Tey 2	d							06 24					06 56						07 33						07 47
Colchester 4	a							06 32			06 48		07 04				07 20		07 41			07 49			07 56
	d	05 55	06 22					06 33		06 45	06 50		07 04		07 18		07 22	07 26	07 41		07 48	07 50			
Colchester Town	a									06 52								07 33			07 55				
	d																	07 37							
Hythe	d												07 09					07 41							
Wivenhoe 3	d							06 40					07 13		07 25			07 45							
Alresford (Essex)	d												07 16		07 29			07 48							
Great Bentley	d												07 20		07 33			07 52							
Weeley	d												07 23					07 56							
Thorpe-le-Soken 1	a							06 50					07 27		07 39			08 00							
	d			06 26			06 41	06 50				07 20	07 27		07 39			08 00							
Clacton-on-Sea	a							07 00					07 36					08 09							
Kirby Cross	d			06 30			06c49					07 24			07e46										
Frinton-on-Sea	d			06 33			06 52					07 27			07 49										
Walton-on-the-Naze	a			06 38			06 57					07 32			07 55										
Manningtree 2	d	06 03	06 31			06 36					06 59						07 32		07 50			07 59		07 35	
Mistley	d					06 40																		07 39	
Wrabness	d					06 45																		07 44	
Harwich International	d					06 52																	07 47	07 51	
Dovercourt	d					06 55																		07 54	
Harwich Town	a					06 57																		07 56	
Ipswich	a	06 17	06 41								07 08						07 41		07 59			08 08	08 15		
	d		06 42		06 52						07 09						07 42		08 03			08 09	08 16		
Lowestoft	a																								
Needham Market	d				07 02																		08 26		
Stowmarket	d		06 53		07a07						07 20						07 53		08 14			08 20	08a31		
Peterborough 8	a																		09 41						
Diss	d		07 05								07 32						08 05					08 32			
Norwich	a		07 27								07 54						08 27					08 54			

For general notes see front of timetable
For details of catering facilities see Directory of Train Operators

A To Cambridge (Table 14)
b Previous night.
Stops to pick up only

c Arr. 0645
e Arr. 0743

London → Chelmsford, Colchester, Walton-on-Naze, Clacton, Harwich, Ipswich and Norwich

Network diagram - see first page of Table 5

Station		LE 1	LE 1	LE 1	LE 1	LE 1 ◇ ☕	LE 1	LE 1	LE 1 ◇		LE 1	LE 1	LE 1 ◇ ☕	LE A	LE 1		LE 1	LE 1	LE 1	LE 1 ◇ ✕	LE 1	LE 1	LE 1	LE 1	LE 1
London Liverpool Street 15 ⊖	d	07 04	07 08	07 18	07 27	07 30			07 38		07 48		08 00		08 02		08 08		08 18	08 30			08 38	08 48	
Stratford 7 ⊖	d	07 11	07 15	07 25		07u38					07 55						08 15		08 25	08u38				08 55	
Romford	d		07 23												08 16										
Shenfield 3	d	07 28	07 34	07 42	07 51				08u02		08 12		08u23		08 26		08 32		08 42				09 02	09 12	
Ingatestone	d			07 46							08 16						08 36		08 46					09 16	
Chelmsford 3	d	07 37	07 43	07 53	08 00	08 04			08 12		08 23				08 35		08 43		08 53	09 02			09 12	09 23	
Hatfield Peverel	d							←			08 30													09 30	
Witham 2	d	07 47	07 52	08 03	08b12			08 12	08 22		08c38				08 44		08 52		09 03				09 21	09 37	
White Notley	d	07 54			→						08 44													09 43	
Cressing	d	07 56									08 47													09 46	
Braintree Freeport	d	07 59									08 49													09 48	
Braintree	a	08 04									08 54													09 53	
Kelvedon	d			08 07				08 19											09 07						
Marks Tey 2	d			08 13					08 30										09 13				09 29		
Colchester 4	a		08 06	08 20		08 23		08 30	08 38				08 49		08 58		09 06		09 20	09 23			09 37		
	d		08 06	08 21		08 24		08 31	08 38			08 46	08 50		09 02	09 04	09 07	09 14		09 24		09 30	09 38		
Colchester Town	a							08 38				08 53			09 09							09 37			
	d											08 57													
Hythe	d		08 11									09 00													
Wivenhoe 3	d		08 15									09 04					09 14								
Alresford (Essex)	d		08 18									09 08													
Great Bentley	d		08 22									09 12													
Weeley	d											09 16													
Thorpe-le-Soken 1	a		08 27									09 19					09 24				←				
	d		08 27				08 29					09 26					09 24				09 26				
Clacton-on-Sea	a		08 37									→					09 34								
Kirby Cross	d						08 33														09 30				
Frinton-on-Sea	d						08 36														09 33				
Walton-on-the-Naze	a						08 41														09 39				
Manningtree 2	d			08 29		08 34							08 59			09 12		09 22		09 34			09 46		
Mistley	d			08 33														09 26							
Wrabness	d			08 38														09 31							
Harwich International	d			08 46														09 39							
Dovercourt	d			08 49														09 42							
Harwich Town	a			08 51														09 44							
Ipswich	a					08 43			08 56				09 08			09 23				09 43			09 58		
	d					08 44			09 02				09 09	09 16						09 44					10 03
Lowestoft	a								10 32																
Needham Market	d													09 26											
Stowmarket	d					08 55								09a31						09 55					10 14
Peterborough 8	a																								11 38
Diss	d					09 07							09 30							10 07					
Norwich	a					09 27							09 52							10 27					

Station		LE 1	LE 1 ◇ ✕		LE 1	LE A	LE 1	LE 1	LE 1 ◇ ✕	LE 1	LE 1	LE 1 ◇	LE 1	LE 1	LE 1 ◇ ✕	LE 1	LE A	LE 1	LE 1		LE 1 ◇ ✕	LE 1	LE 1	LE 1 ◇	LE 1
London Liverpool Street 15 ⊖	d		09 00				09 08	09 18	09 30			09 38	09 48		10 00			10 08	10 18		10 30			10 38	10 48
Stratford 7 ⊖	d						09 15	09 25	09u38				09 55					10 15	10 25		10u38				10 55
Romford	d						09 23											10 23							
Shenfield 3	d		09u23				09 34	09 42				10u02	10 12		10u23			10 34	10 42					11u02	11 12
Ingatestone	d												10 16												11 16
Chelmsford 3	d						09 43	09 51	10 02			10 12	10 23					10 43	10 51		11 02			11 12	11 23
Hatfield Peverel	d												10 30												11 30
Witham 2	d						09 52	10 00				10 21	10 36					10 52	11 00					11 21	11 36
White Notley	d												10 43												11 43
Cressing	d												10 45												11 45
Braintree Freeport	d												10 48												11 48
Braintree	a												10 53												11 53
Kelvedon	d							10 05											11 05						
Marks Tey 2	d							10 10				10 29							11 10					11 29	
Colchester 4	a		09 49				10 06	10 18	10 21			10 37			10 49			11 06	11 18		11 21			11 37	
	d	09 46	09 50		10 00		10 07	10 21	10 24		10 30	10 38		10 46	10 50	11 00		11 07	11 18		11 22		11 30	11 38	
Colchester Town	a	09 53			10 07						10 37			10 53		11 07							11 37		
	d	09 57												10 57											
Hythe	d	10 00												11 00											
Wivenhoe 3	d	10 04					10 14							11 04				11 14							
Alresford (Essex)	d	10 08												11 08											
Great Bentley	d	10 12												11 12											
Weeley	d	10 16												11 16											
Thorpe-le-Soken 1	a	10 19					10 24			←				11 19				11 24				←			
	d	10 26					10 24			10 26				11 26				11 24				11 26			
Clacton-on-Sea	a	→					10 34							→				11 34							
Kirby Cross	d									10 30												11 30			
Frinton-on-Sea	d									10 33												11 33			
Walton-on-the-Naze	a									10 39												11 39			
Manningtree 2	d		09 59					10 29	10 34						10 59				11 26		11 31				
Mistley	d							10 33											11 30						
Wrabness	d							10 38											11 35						
Harwich International	d							10 47											11 44						
Dovercourt	d							10 50											11 47						
Harwich Town	a							10 52											11 49						
Ipswich	a		10 08						10 43			10 56			11 08						11 41			11 56	
	d		10 09			10 16			10 44			11 02			11 09		11 16				11 42			12 03	
Lowestoft	a											12 32													
Needham Market	d					10 26											11 26								
Stowmarket	d					10a31			10 55								11a31				11 53			12 14	
Peterborough 8	a																							13 38	
Diss	d		10 30						11 07						11 30						12 05				
Norwich	a		10 52						11 27						11 52						12 27				

For general notes see front of timetable
For details of catering facilities see Directory of Train Operators

A To Cambridge (Table 14)
b Arr. 0809
c Arr. 0835

London → Chelmsford, Colchester, Walton-on-Naze, Clacton, Harwich, Ipswich and Norwich

Network diagram - see first page of Table 5

Station		LE 1	LE 1◇ ☕	LE 1	LE A	LE 1	LE 1	LE 1◇ ☕	LE 1	LE 1	LE 1◇	LE 1	LE 1		LE 1◇ ☕	LE 1	LE A	LE 1	LE 1	LE 1◇ ☕	LE 1	LE 1	LE 1◇	LE 1	LE 1
London Liverpool Street 15 ⊖	d		11 00			11 08	11 18	11 30			11 38	11 48			12 00			12 08	12 18	12 30			12 38	12 48	
Stratford 7 ⊖	d					11 15	11 25	11u38				11 55						12 15	12 25	12u38				12 55	
Romford	d					11 23												12 23							
Shenfield 3	d		11u23			11 34	11 42				12u02	12 12			12u23			12 34	12 42				13u02	13 12	
Ingatestone	d											12 16												13 16	
Chelmsford 3	d					11 43	11 51	12 02			12 12	12 23						12 43	12 51	13 02			13 12	13 23	
Hatfield Peverel	d											12 30												13 30	
Witham 2	d					11 52	12 00				12 21	12 36						12 52	13 00				13 21	13 36	
White Notley	d											12 43												13 43	
Cressing	d											12 45												13 45	
Braintree Freeport	d											12 48												13 48	
Braintree	a											12 53												13 53	
Kelvedon	d						12 05												13 05						
Marks Tey 2	d						12 10				12 29								13 10				13 29		
Colchester 4	a		11 49			12 06	12 18	12 21			12 37				12 49			13 06	13 18	13 21			13 37		
	d	11 46	11 50	12 00		12 07	12 18	12 22		12 30	12 38		12 46		12 50	13 00		13 07	13 18	13 22		13 30	13 38		13 46
Colchester Town	a	11 53		12 07						12 37			12 53			13 07						13 37			13 53
	d	11 57											12 57												13 57
Hythe	d	12 00											13 00												14 00
Wivenhoe 3	d	12 04				12 14							13 04					13 14							14 04
Alresford (Essex)	d	12 08											13 08												14 08
Great Bentley	d	12 12											13 12												14 12
Weeley	d	12 16											13 16												14 16
Thorpe-le-Soken 1	a	12 19				12 24			←				13 19					13 24			←				14 19
	d	12 26 →				12 24			12 26				13 26 →					13 24			13 26				14 26 →
Clacton-on-Sea	a					12 34												13 34							
Kirby Cross	d								12 30												13 30				
Frinton-on-Sea	d								12 33												13 33				
Walton-on-the-Naze	a								12 39												13 39				
Manningtree 2	d		11 59				12 26	12 31							12 59				13 26	13 31					
Mistley	d						12 30												13 30						
Wrabness	d						12 35												13 35						
Harwich International	d						12 44												13 44						
Dovercourt	d						12 47												13 47						
Harwich Town	a						12 49												13 49						
Ipswich	a		12 08					12 41			12 56				13 08					13 41			13 56		
	d		12 09		12 16			12 42			13 02				13 09		13 16			13 42			14 03		
Lowestoft	a										14 32														
Needham Market	d				12 26												13 26								
Stowmarket	d				12a31			12 53									13a31			13 53			14 14		
Peterborough 8	a																						15 39		
Diss	d		12 30					13 05							13 30					14 05					
Norwich	a		12 52					13 27							13 52					14 27					

Station		LE 1◇ ☕	LE 1	LE A	LE 1	LE 1	LE 1◇ ✕		LE 1	LE 1	LE 1◇	LE 1	LE 1	LE 1◇ ☕	LE 1	LE A	LE 1	LE 1	LE 1◇ ✕	LE 1	LE 1	LE 1◇	LE 1		LE 1
London Liverpool Street 15 ⊖	d	13 00			13 08	13 18	13 30				13 38	13 48		14 00			14 08	14 18	14 30			14 38	14 48		
Stratford 7 ⊖	d				13 15	13 25	13u38					13 55					14 15	14 25	14u38				14 55		
Romford	d				13 23												14 23								
Shenfield 3	d	13u23			13 34	13 42					14u02	14 12		14u23			14 34	14 42				15u02	15 12		
Ingatestone	d											14 16											15 16		
Chelmsford 3	d				13 43	13 51	14 02				14 12	14 23					14 43	14 51	15 02			15 12	15 23		
Hatfield Peverel	d											14 30											15 30		
Witham 2	d				13 52	14 00					14 21	14 36					14 52	15 00				15 21	15 36		
White Notley	d											14 43											15 43		
Cressing	d											14 45											15 45		
Braintree Freeport	d											14 48											15 48		
Braintree	a											14 53											15 53		
Kelvedon	d					14 05												15 05							
Marks Tey 2	d					14 10					14 29							15 10				15 29			
Colchester 4	a	13 49			14 06	14 18	14 21				14 37			14 49			15 06	15 18	15 21			15 37			
	d	13 50	14 00		14 07	14 18	14 22			14 30	14 38		14 46	14 50	15 00		15 07	15 18	15 22		15 30	15 38			15 46
Colchester Town	a		14 07							14 37			14 53		15 07						15 37				15 53
	d												14 57												15 57
Hythe	d												15 00												16 00
Wivenhoe 3	d				14 14								15 04				15 14								16 04
Alresford (Essex)	d												15 08												16 08
Great Bentley	d												15 12												16 12
Weeley	d												15 16												16 16
Thorpe-le-Soken 1	a				14 24				←				15 19				15 24			←					16 19
	d				14 24				14 26				15 26 →				15 24			15 26					16 26 →
Clacton-on-Sea	a				14 34												15 34								
Kirby Cross	d								14 30											15 30					
Frinton-on-Sea	d								14 33											15 33					
Walton-on-the-Naze	a								14 39											15 39					
Manningtree 2	d	13 59				14 26	14 31							14 59				15 26	15 31						
Mistley	d					14 30												15 30							
Wrabness	d					14 35												15 35							
Harwich International	d					14 44												15 44							
Dovercourt	d					14 47												15 47							
Harwich Town	a					14 49												15 49							
Ipswich	a	14 08					14 41				14 56			15 08					15 41			15 56			
	d	14 09		14 16			14 42				15 02			15 09		15 16			15 42			16 03			
Lowestoft	a										16 32														
Needham Market	d			14 26												15 26									
Stowmarket	d			14a31			14 53									15a31			15 53			16 14			
Peterborough 8	a																					17 38			
Diss	d	14 30					15 05							15 30					16 05						
Norwich	a	14 52					15 27							15 52					16 27						

For general notes see front of timetable
For details of catering facilities see Directory of Train Operators

A To Cambridge (Table 14)

Table 11

Mondays to Fridays

London → Chelmsford, Colchester, Walton-on-Naze, Clacton, Harwich, Ipswich and Norwich

Network diagram - see first page of Table 5

		LE	LE	LE	LE	LE	LE	LE	LE	LE	LE	LE	LE	LE	LE	LE	LE	LE	LE	LE	LE	LE	LE
		1 ◇ ☕	1	A	1	1	R 1 ✕	1	1	1	R 1	1	R 1 ☕	1	1	1	1	A	R 1 ☕	1	1	R 1	1
London Liverpool Street 15 ⊖	d	15 00			15 08	15 18	15 30		15 32		15 38	15 48	16 00		16 02	16 15	16 17		16 30			16 32	16 36
Stratford 7 ⊖	d				15 15	15 25						15 55			16 10		16 25						
Romford	d				15 23																		
Shenfield 3	d	15u23			15 34	15 42			15 55		16u02	16 12			16 25		16 40					16u54	16 57
Ingatestone	d								15 59			16 16					16 44						
Chelmsford 3	d				15 43	15 51	15 59		16 06		16u12	16 23	16 30		16 36	16 45	16 53						17 08
Hatfield Peverel	d								16 13			16 30											17 15
Witham 2	d				15 52	16 00			16 19		16 23	16 36			16 45		17a06					17 13	17 21
White Notley	d											16 43											17 28
Cressing	d											16 45											17 30
Braintree Freeport	d											16 48											17 33
Braintree	a											16 53											17 40
Kelvedon	d					16 05			16 24						16 50	16 56							
Marks Tey 2	d					16 10					16 32					17 01							
Colchester 4	a	15 49			16 06	16 18	16 21		16 37		16 41		16 49		17 01	17 09			17 17			17 26	
	d	15 50	16 00		16 07	16 18	16 22			16 41	16 41		16 50	16 54	17 02	17 13			17 18		17 24	17 26	
Colchester Town	a		16 07							16 48				17 01							17 31		
	d									16 52											17 35		
Hythe	d									16 55											17 38		
Wivenhoe 3	d				16 14					16 59					17 09						17 42		
Alresford (Essex)	d									17 03											17 46		
Great Bentley	d									17 07											17 50		
Weeley	d									17 11											17 54		
Thorpe-le-Soken 1	a				16 24			←		17 14					17 19					←	17 57		
	d				16 24			16 26		17 21					17 19					17 21	18 03		
Clacton-on-Sea	a				16 34					→					17 31						→		
Kirby Cross	d							16 30												17 25			
Frinton-on-Sea	d							16 33												17 28			
Walton-on-the-Naze	a							16 39												17 34			
Manningtree 2	d	15 59				16 26	16 31						16 59			17 21						17 35	
Mistley	d					16 30										17 25							
Wrabness	d					16 35										17 30							
Harwich International	d					16 44										17 38							
Dovercourt	d					16 47										17 41							
Harwich Town	a					16 49										17 45							
Ipswich	a	16 08					16 41				16 58		17 08						17 33			17 47	
	d	16 09		16 16			16 42				17 02		17 09					17 16	17 34			17 49	
Lowestoft	a										18 33												
Needham Market	d			16 26														17 26				17 58	
Stowmarket	d			16a31			16 53						17 20					17a31	17 45			18 03	
Peterborough 8	a																					19 42	
Diss	d	16 30					17 05						17 32						17 57				
Norwich	a	16 52					17 27						17 55						18 20				

		LE		LE	LE	LE	LE	LE	LE	LE	LE	LE	LE	LE	LE	LE	LE	LE	LE	LE	LE	LE	LE	LE
		1		1	R 1 ☕	1	1	1	1	A	1	1	1	1	1	R 1 ☕	1	1	1	1	1	R 1 ☕	1	1
London Liverpool Street 15 ⊖	d	16 45		16 47	17 00				17 02		17 08	17 12	17 20	17 22		17 30	17 32		17 38	17 42		17 50		
Stratford 7 ⊖	d			16 55							17 16	17 20							17 46	17 50				
Romford	d																							
Shenfield 3	d			17 10					17 24					17 44			17 54							
Ingatestone	d			17 14										17 48										
Chelmsford 3	d	17 15		17 23					17 35			17 44	17 51	17 58			18 05			18 14				
Hatfield Peverel	d											17 51								18 21				
Witham 2	d			17a36					17 45		17 50	17a59		18 09			18 15		18 20	→				
White Notley	d													18 16										
Cressing	d													18 18										
Braintree Freeport	d													18 21										
Braintree	a													18 28										
Kelvedon	d	17 26							17 50		17 54						18 20		18 24					
Marks Tey 2	d	17 31							17 55		18 00								18 30					
Colchester 4	a	17 39							18 03		18 08		18 11				18 31		18 38			18 42		
	d	17 43	17 47				17 49	17 51	18 03		18 08		18 11				18 34		18 38		18 42	18 43		
Colchester Town	a						17 56										18 42							←
	d						18 00										18 48							18 48
Hythe	d						18 03										→							18 51
Wivenhoe 3	d	17 50					18 07				18 16								18 46		18 50			18 55
Alresford (Essex)	d						18 11				18 19										18 53			18 59
Great Bentley	d						18 15				18 23										18 57			19 03
Weeley	d						18 19																	19 07
Thorpe-le-Soken 1	a	18 01				←	18 22				18 28							←	18 56		19 02			19 11
	d	18 01				18 03	18 30				18 28							18 30	18 56		19 03			19 11
Clacton-on-Sea	a	18 12					→				18 40								19 07					19 22
Kirby Cross	d					18 07												18 34			19 07			
Frinton-on-Sea	d					18 10												18 37			19 10			
Walton-on-the-Naze	a					18 16												18 43			19 15			
Manningtree 2	d		17 55					17 59	18 11				18 19		18 23	18 27						18 52	18 57	
Mistley	d		17 59												18 27								19 01	
Wrabness	d		18 04												18 32								19 06	
Harwich International	d		18 12						18a29						18 39								19 13	
Dovercourt	d		18 15												18 42								19 16	
Harwich Town	a		18 19												18 44								19 18	
Ipswich	a				17 58			18 10					18 33			18 36						19 01		
	d				17 59					18 16						18 37						19 03		
Lowestoft	a																							
Needham Market	d									18 26														
Stowmarket	d									18a31						18 48								
Peterborough 8	a																							
Diss	d															19 00								
Norwich	a				18 39											19 23						19 44		

For general notes see front of timetable
For details of catering facilities see
Directory of Train Operators

A To Cambridge (Table 14)

London → Chelmsford, Colchester, Walton-on-Naze, Clacton, Harwich, Ipswich and Norwich

Network diagram - see first page of Table 5

Station		LE 1	LE 1	LE R 1 ☕	LE 1	LE A	LE 1	LE 1	LE 1	LE R 1 ✕	LE 1	LE R 1 ☕	LE 1	LE 1	LE 1	LE 1	LE 1	LE 1	LE 1	LE 1	LE R 1 ☕	LE 1	LE 1
London Liverpool Street 15 ⊖	d		17 52	18 00			18 02	18 08	18 12	18 20	18 22	18 30				18 32	18 38			18 48	19 00	19 02	
Stratford 7 ⊖	d						18 10	18 16	18 20							18 40	18 46					19 09	
Romford	d																						
Shenfield 3	d		18 14								18 44						19 01			19 11		19 26	
Ingatestone	d		18 18								18 48									19 15			
Chelmsford 3	d	←	18 28				18 35	18 40	18 44		18 58					19 05	19 13			19 24		19 35	
Hatfield Peverel	d	18 21							18 51						←	19 12						19 41	
Witham 2	d	18b30	18a41				18 45	18 50	18 57		19c11 →				19 11	19 18	19 23			19 34		19 47	
White Notley	d								19 04													19 54	
Cressing	d								19 06													19 56	
Braintree Freeport	d								19 09													19 59	
Braintree	a								19 16													20 04	
Kelvedon	d	18 36					18 50	18 54							19 17	19 23	19 27						
Marks Tey 2	d						18 55	19 00							19 23		19 33						
Colchester 4	a	18 48		18 51			19 03	19 08		19 11		19 22			19 31	19 34	19 41			19 50	19 51		
	d	18 52		18 53	18 56		19 03	19 08		19 12		19 23			19 31	19 34	19 41		19 46		19 53		
Colchester Town	a				19 03														19 53				
	d																		19 57				
Hythe	d														19 36				20 00				
Wivenhoe 3	d	18 59						19 16							19 40		19 49		20 04				
Alresford (Essex)	d	19 03													19 43				20 08				
Great Bentley	d	19 07													19 47				20 12				
Weeley	d														19 50				20 16				
Thorpe-le-Soken 1	a	19 15						19 26							19 54		19 59		20 19				
	d	19 15						19 26						19 28	19 54		19 59	20 03	20 28 →				
Clacton-on-Sea	a	19 26						19 37							20 05		20 10						
Kirby Cross	d													19 32				20 07					
Frinton-on-Sea	d													19 35				20 10					
Walton-on-the-Naze	a													19 40				20 15					
Manningtree 2	d			19 02			19 11			19 21			19 27			19 42					20 02		
Mistley	d												19 31										
Wrabness	d												19 36										
Harwich International	d												19 43										
Dovercourt	d												19 46										
Harwich Town	a												19 48										
Ipswich	a			19 11			19 24			19 30		19 39				19 56					20 11		
	d			19 12		19 16				19 32		19 40									20 12		20 16
Lowestoft	a																						
Needham Market	d					19 26																	20 25
Stowmarket	d			19 23		19a31						19 51									20 23		20 30
Peterborough 8	a																						21 58
Diss	d			19 35								20 03									20 35		
Norwich	a			19 58						20 14		20 26									20 57		

Station		LE 1	LE 1	LE 1	LE R 1 ✕	LE R 1	LE 1	LE 1	LE 1	LE 1	LE 1 ◇ ☕	LE A	LE 1	LE 1	LE	LE 1	LE 1 ◇ ✕	LE 1	LE 1	LE	LE 1	LE 1 ◇	LE B	LE 1
London Liverpool Street 15 ⊖	d		19 08	19 18	19 30	19 32		19 38	19 48		20 00		20 08			20 18	20 30	20 38	20 48			21 00		21 08
Stratford 7 ⊖	d		19 15	19 25				19 45	19 55				20 15			20 25	20u38	20 45	20 55					21 15
Romford	d																							21 23
Shenfield 3	d			19 42		19u55		20 02	20 12				20 32			20 42		21 02	21 12			21u23		21 34
Ingatestone	d			19 46					20 16							20 46			21 16					
Chelmsford 3	d		19 39	19 53	20 00			20 11	20 23				20 41			20 53	21 03	21 11	21 23					21 43
Hatfield Peverel	d								20 30										21 30					
Witham 2	d		19 50	20 03		20 12		20 20	20 36				20 50			21 03		21 20	21 36					21 52
White Notley	d								20 43										21 43					
Cressing	d								20 45										21 45					
Braintree Freeport	d								20 48										21 48					
Braintree	a								20 53										21 53					
Kelvedon	d		19 54					20 25					20 55					21 25						
Marks Tey 2	d		20 00					20 30					21 00					21 30						
Colchester 4	a		20 08	20 16	20 20	20 25		20 38			20 49		21 08			21 16	21 22	21 38				21 49		22 06
	d		20 08	20 17	20 21	20 26		20 38		20 46	20 50		21 09			21 17	21 23	21 38			21 46	21 50		22 07
Colchester Town	a									20 53											21 53			
	d									20 57											21 57			
Hythe	d									21 00											22 00			
Wivenhoe 3	d		20 16							21 04			21 16								22 04			22 14
Alresford (Essex)	d									21 08											22 08			
Great Bentley	d									21 12											22 12			
Weeley	d									21 16											22 16			
Thorpe-le-Soken 1	a		20 26				←			21 19			21 26	←							22 19			22 24
	d		20 26				20 28			21 28 →			21 26	21 28							22 26 →			22 24
Clacton-on-Sea	a		20 35										21 36											22 34
Kirby Cross	d						20 32							21 32										
Frinton-on-Sea	d						20 35							21 35										
Walton-on-the-Naze	a						20 41							21 41										
Manningtree 2	d	20 07		20 25	20 30						20 59					21 25	21 32	21 46				21 58		
Mistley	d	20 11		20 29												21 29								
Wrabness	d	20 16		20 34												21 34				←				
Harwich International	d	20 23		20 42											21 34 →	21 42		22a02		21 34				
Dovercourt	d	20 26		20 45												21 45								
Harwich Town	a	20 28		20 47												21 47								
Ipswich	a				20 40	20 44		20 57			21 08						21 42			22 00		22 07		
	d				20 41	20 52					21 09	21 16					21 43					22 15	22 16	
Lowestoft	a					22 22																23 45		
Needham Market	d											21 26											22 26	
Stowmarket	d				20 52						21 20	21a31					21 54						22a31	
Peterborough 8	a																							
Diss	d				21 04						21 32						22 06							
Norwich	a				21 26						21 54						22 28							

For general notes see front of timetable
For details of catering facilities see Directory of Train Operators

A To Cambridge (Table 14)
B To Bury St Edmunds (Table 14)
b Arr. 1826
c Arr. 1907

London → Chelmsford, Colchester, Walton-on-Naze, Clacton, Harwich, Ipswich and Norwich

Network diagram - see first page of Table 5

		LE	LE	LE	LE	LE	LE	LE		LE	LE	LE	LE	LE	LE	LE	LE	LE	LE	LE	LE	LE	LE
																				ThFO	ThFX		
		1	1 ◊	1	1	1	A	1		1	1	1	1	1 ◊	1	1	1	1	1	1	1	1 ◊	1
			☕											☕								☕	
London Liverpool Street 15 ⊖	d	21 18	21 30					21 38		21 48	22 00		22 18	22 30		22 48	23 00			23 18	23 18	23 30	23 48
Stratford 7 ⊖	d	21 25	21u38							21 55			22 25	22u38		22 55	23 07			23 25	23 25	23u38	23 55
Romford	d																						
Shenfield 3	d	21 42						22u02		22 12	22 22		22 42			23 12	23 24			23 42	23 42		00 12
Ingatestone	d									22 16						23 16				23 46	23 46		00 16
Chelmsford 3	d	21 51	22 03					22u12		22 23	22 31		22 51	23 03		23 23	23 33			23 53	23 53	00 03	00 23
Hatfield Peverel	d									22 30						23 30							00 30
Witham 2	d	22 00						22 21		22 36	22 40		23 00			23 35	23 42		23 44	00 03	00 03		00 35
White Notley	d									22 43									23 50				
Cressing	d									22 45									23 53				
Braintree Freeport	d									22 48									23 55				
Braintree	a									22 53								←	23 59				
Kelvedon	d	22 05											23 05			23 40		23 40					00 40
Marks Tey 2	d	22 10					22 21	22 29					23 10			→		23 45					00 45
Colchester 4	a	22 18	22 22			←	22 30	22 37			22 54		23 18	23 22			23 56	23 57		00 17	00 21	00 25	00 57
	d	22 26	22 23			22 26		22 38			22 54	22 58	23 19	23 23			23 57			00 17		00 27	
Colchester Town	a	→										23 05											
	d											23 09											
Hythe	d											23 12											
Wivenhoe 3	d					22 33						23 16	23 26							00 25			
Alresford (Essex)	d					22 36						23 20	23 29							00 28			
Great Bentley	d					22 40						23 24	23 33							00 32			
Weeley	d											23 28											
Thorpe-le-Soken 1	a				←	22 46						23 31	23 39							00 37			
	d				22 26	22 46						23 31	23 39							00 37			
Clacton-on-Sea	a											23 41	23 48							00 51			
Kirby Cross	d				22 30	22 51																	
Frinton-on-Sea	d				22 33	22 54																	
Walton-on-the-Naze	a				22 39	23 00																	
Manningtree 2	d		22 32	22 38							23 02			23 32	23 38		00 04					00 36	
Mistley	d			22 42											23 42								
Wrabness	d			22 47											23 47								
Harwich International	d			22 54											23 54								
Dovercourt	d			22 57											23 57								
Harwich Town	a			22 59											23 59								
Ipswich	a		22 42					22 56			23 14			23 42			00 20					00 46	
	d		22 43											23 43								00 48	
Lowestoft	a																						
Needham Market	d																						
Stowmarket	d		22 54											23 54								00 59	
Peterborough 8	a																						
Diss	d		23 06											00 07								01 12	
Norwich	a		23 28											00 45								01 45	

For general notes see front of timetable
For details of catering facilities see Directory of Train Operators

A From Sudbury (Table 10)

Table 11

London → Chelmsford, Colchester, Walton-on-Naze, Clacton, Harwich, Ipswich and Norwich

Network diagram - see first page of Table 5

		LE 1◇	LE 1	LE 1	LE 1◇	LE 1	LE 1	LE 1	LE	LE 1	LE 1	LE 1	LE	LE 1		LE 1	LE 1	LE 1	LE 1	LE	LE 1	LE 1	LE 1	LE 1◇	LE 1
		☕			☕				A				A							A					
London Liverpool Street 15 ⊖	d	22p30	23p00	23p18	23p30	23p48	00 18	00 48									05 30					06 00	06 18	06 30	
Stratford 7 ⊖	d	22b38	23p07	23p25	23b38	23p55	00 25	00 55									05 37					06 07	06 25	06u38	
Romford	d																05 45					06 15			
Shenfield 3	d		23p24	23p42		00 12	00 47	01 17									05 56					06 26	06 42		
Ingatestone	d			23p46		00 16	00 51	01 21									06 00					06 30			
Chelmsford 3	d	23p03	23p33	23p53	00 03	00 23	00 58	01 28									06 07					06 37	06 51	07 02	
Hatfield Peverel	d					00 30	01 05										06 14					06 44			
Witham 2	d		23p42	00 03		00 35	01 10	01 38				05 36					06 19	06 25				06 49	07 00		
White Notley	d											05 43						06 32							
Cressing	d											05 45						06 34							
Braintree Freeport	d											05 48						06 37							
Braintree	a											05 52						06 41							
Kelvedon	d					00 40	01 15										06 24						07 05		
Marks Tey 2	d					00 45	01 20										06 29						07 10		
Colchester 4	a	23p22	23p56	00 17	00 25	00 57	01 32	02 03									06 37					07 03	07 18	07 21	
	d	23p23	23p57	00 17	00 27					05 18	05 38			06 18			06 37				06 46	07 07	07 18	07 22	
Colchester Town	a																				06 53				
	d																				06 57				
Hythe	d																				07 00				
Wivenhoe 3	d			00 25																	07 04	07 14			
Alresford (Essex)	d			00 28																	07 08				
Great Bentley	d			00 32																	07 12				
Weeley	d																				07 16				
Thorpe-le-Soken 1	a			00 37																	07 19	07 24			←
	d			00 37												06 26					07 26	07 24			07 26
Clacton-on-Sea	a			00 51																	→	07 34			
Kirby Cross	d															06 30									07 30
Frinton-on-Sea	d															06 33									07 33
Walton-on-the-Naze	a															06 38									07 39
Manningtree 2	d	23p32	00 04		00 36					05 26	05 46			06 26			06 45						07 26	07 31	
Mistley	d									05 30				06 30									07 30		
Wrabness	d									05 35				06 35									07 35		
Harwich International	d									05 44				06 44									07 44		
Dovercourt	d									05 47				06 47									07 47		
Harwich Town	a									05 49				06 49									07 49		
Ipswich	a	23p42	00 20		00 46						05 58						06 56							07 41	
	d	23p43			00 48				05 10		06 00		06 14						07 09	07 16				07 42	
Lowestoft	a																								
Needham Market	d								05 20				06 24							07 26					
Stowmarket	d	23p54			00 59				05a25		06 11		06a29						07 20	07a31				07 53	
Peterborough 8	a										07 37														
Diss	d	00 07			01 12														07 32					08 05	
Norwich	a	00 45			01 45														07 52					08 27	

For general notes see front of timetable
For details of catering facilities see
Directory of Train Operators

A To Cambridge (Table 14)
b Previous night. Stops to pick up only

Table 11

Saturdays

London → Chelmsford, Colchester, Walton-on-Naze, Clacton, Harwich, Ipswich and Norwich

Network diagram - see first page of Table 5

Station		LE	LE	LE	LE	LE		LE	LE	LE	LE	LE	LE	LE	LE	LE	LE	LE	LE	LE		LE	LE	LE	LE
		1 ◇	1	1	1 ◇			1	1	1	1 ◇	1	1	1 ◇	1	1	1 ◇	1		1		1	1 ◇	1	1
						A					☕						☕		A				☕		
London Liverpool Street 15 ⊖	d	06 38		06 48	07 00				07 08	07 18	07 30			07 38	07 48		08 00			08 08		08 18	08 30		
Stratford 7 ⊖ ⛴	d			06 55					07 15	07 25	07u38				07 55					08 15		08 25	08u38		
Romford	d								07 23											08 23					
Shenfield 3	d	07u02		07 12	07u23				07 34	07 42				08u02	08 12		08u23			08 34		08 42			
Ingatestone	d			07 16											08 16										
Chelmsford 3	d	07 12		07 23					07 43	07 51	08 02			08 12	08 23					08 43		08 51	09 02		
Hatfield Peverel	d			07 30											08 30										
Witham 2	d	07 21		07 36					07 52	08 00				08 21	08 36					08 52		09 00			
White Notley	d			07 43											08 43										
Cressing	d			07 45											08 45										
Braintree Freeport	d			07 48											08 48										
Braintree	a			07 53											08 53										
Kelvedon	d									08 05												09 05			
Marks Tey 2	d	07 29								08 10				08 29								09 10			
Colchester 4	a	07 37			07 49				08 06	08 18	08 21			08 37			08 49			09 06		09 18	09 21		
	d	07 38	07 46		07 50			08 00	08 07	08 18	08 22		08 30	08 38		08 46	08 50	09 00		09 07		09 18	09 22		09 30
Colchester Town	a		07 53					08 07					08 37			08 53		09 07							09 37
	d		07 57													08 57									
Hythe	d		08 00													09 00									
Wivenhoe 3	d		08 04						08 14							09 04				09 14					
Alresford (Essex)	d		08 08													09 08									
Great Bentley	d		08 12													09 12									
Weeley	d		08 16													09 16									
Thorpe-le-Soken 1	a		08 19						08 24			←				09 19				09 24				←	
	d		08 26						08 24			08 26				09 26				09 24				09 26	
Clacton-on-Sea	a		→						08 34							→				09 34					
Kirby Cross	d											08 30												09 30	
Frinton-on-Sea	d											08 33												09 33	
Walton-on-the-Naze	a											08 39												09 39	
Manningtree 2	d	07 46			07 59					08 26	08 31						08 59					09 26	09 31		
Mistley	d									08 30												09 30			
Wrabness	d									08 35												09 35			
Harwich International	d					07 47				08 44												09 44			
Dovercourt	d									08 47												09 47			
Harwich Town	a									08 49												09 49			
Ipswich	a	07 58			08 08	08 15					08 41			08 56			09 08						09 41		
	d	08 03			08 09	08 16					08 42			09 02			09 09		09 16				09 42		
Lowestoft	a													10 32											
Needham Market	d					08 26													09 26						
Stowmarket	d	08 14				08a31					08 53								09a31				09 53		
Peterborough 8	a	09 38																							
Diss	d				08 30						09 05						09 30						10 05		
Norwich	a				08 52						09 27						09 52						10 27		

Station		LE	LE	LE	LE	LE	LE	LE	LE	LE	LE	LE		LE	LE	LE	LE	LE	LE	LE	LE	LE	LE	LE	LE
		1 ◇	1	1	1 ◇	1		1	1	1 ◇	1	1		R 1	1	1	R 1	1		1	1	1 ◇	1	1	R 1
					☕		A			☕							B ☕		A			☕			
London Liverpool Street 15 ⊖	d	08 38	08 48		09 00			09 08	09 18	09 30				09 38	09 48		10 00			10 08	10 18	10 30			10 38
Stratford 7 ⊖ ⛴	d		08 55					09 15	09 25	09u38					09 55					10 15	10 25	10u38			
Romford	d							09 23												10 23					
Shenfield 3	d	09u02	09 12		09u23			09 34	09 42					10u02	10 12		10u23			10 34	10 42				11u02
Ingatestone	d		09 16												10 16										
Chelmsford 3	d	09 12	09 23					09 43	09 51	10 02				10 12	10 23					10 43	10 51	11 02			11 12
Hatfield Peverel	d		09 30												10 30										
Witham 2	d	09 21	09 36					09 52	10 00					10 21	10 36					10 52	11 00				11 21
White Notley	d		09 43												10 43										
Cressing	d		09 45												10 45										
Braintree Freeport	d		09 48												10 48										
Braintree	a		09 53												10 53										
Kelvedon	d								10 05												11 05				
Marks Tey 2	d	09 29							10 10					10 29							11 10				11 29
Colchester 4	a	09 37			09 49			10 06	10 18	10 21				10 37			10 49			11 06	11 18	11 21			11 37
	d	09 38		09 46	09 50	10 00		10 07	10 18	10 22		10 30		10 38		10 46	10 50	11 00		11 07	11 18	11 22		11 30	11 38
Colchester Town	a			09 53		10 07						10 37				10 53		11 07						11 37	
	d			09 57												10 57									
Hythe	d			10 00												11 00									
Wivenhoe 3	d			10 04				10 14								11 04				11 14					
Alresford (Essex)	d			10 08												11 08									
Great Bentley	d			10 12												11 12									
Weeley	d			10 16												11 16									
Thorpe-le-Soken 1	a			10 19				10 24			←					11 19				11 24			←		
	d			10 26				10 24			10 26					11 26				11 24			11 26		
Clacton-on-Sea	a			→				10 34								→				11 34					
Kirby Cross	d										10 30												11 30		
Frinton-on-Sea	d										10 33												11 33		
Walton-on-the-Naze	a										10 39												11 39		
Manningtree 2	d	09 46			09 59				10 26	10 31							10 59				11 26	11 31			
Mistley	d								10 30												11 30				
Wrabness	d								10 35												11 35				
Harwich International	d								10 44												11 44				
Dovercourt	d								10 47												11 47				
Harwich Town	a								10 49												11 49				
Ipswich	a	09 58			10 08					10 41				10 56			11 08					11 41			11 56
	d	10 03			10 09		10 16			10 42				11 02			11 09		11 16			11 42			12 03
Lowestoft	a													12 32											
Needham Market	d						10 26												11 26						
Stowmarket	d	10 14					10a31			10 53									11a31			11 53			12 14
Peterborough 8	a	11 38																							13 38
Diss	d				10 30					11 05							11 30					12 05			
Norwich	a				10 52					11 27							11 52					12 27			

For general notes see front of timetable
For details of catering facilities see Directory of Train Operators

A To Cambridge (Table 14)
B Until 27 September to Great Yarmouth (Table 15)

Table 11

Saturdays

London → Chelmsford, Colchester, Walton-on-Naze, Clacton, Harwich, Ipswich and Norwich

Network diagram - see first page of Table 5

		LE	LE	LE	LE	LE	LE	LE	LE	LE	LE	LE	LE	LE	LE	LE	LE	LE	LE	LE	LE	LE	LE
												R			R								R
		1	1	1 ◇	1		1	1	1 ◇	1	1	1	1	1	1	1		1	1	1 ◇	1	1	1
						A									B		A						
				☕					☕						☕					☕			
London Liverpool Street [15] ⊖	d	10 48		11 00			11 08	11 18	11 30			11 38	11 48		12 00			12 08	12 18	12 30			12 38
Stratford [7] ⊖ ⛴	d	10 55					11 15	11 25	11u38				11 55					12 15	12 25	12u38			
Romford	d						11 23											12 23					
Shenfield [3]	d	11 12		11u23			11 34	11 42				12u02	12 12		12u23			12 34	12 42				13u02
Ingatestone	d	11 16											12 16										
Chelmsford [3]	d	11 23					11 43	11 51	12 02			12 12	12 23					12 43	12 51	13 02			13 12
Hatfield Peverel	d	11 30											12 30										
Witham [2]	d	11 36					11 52	12 00				12 21	12 36					12 52	13 00				13 21
White Notley	d	11 43											12 43										
Cressing	d	11 45											12 45										
Braintree Freeport	d	11 48											12 48										
Braintree	a	11 53											12 53										
Kelvedon	d							12 05											13 05				
Marks Tey [2]	d							12 10				12 29							13 10				13 29
Colchester [4]	a			11 49			12 06	12 18	12 21			12 37			12 49			13 06	13 18	13 21			13 37
	d		11 46	11 50	12 00		12 07	12 18	12 22		12 30	12 38		12 46	12 50	13 00		13 07	13 18	13 22		13 30	13 38
Colchester Town	a		11 53		12 07						12 37			12 53		13 07						13 37	
	d		11 57											12 57									
Hythe	d		12 00											13 00									
Wivenhoe [3]	d		12 04				12 14							13 04				13 14					
Alresford (Essex)	d		12 08											13 08									
Great Bentley	d		12 12											13 12									
Weeley	d		12 16											13 16									
Thorpe-le-Soken [1]	a		12 19				12 24			←				13 19				13 24			←		
	d		12 26 →				12 24			12 26				13 26 →				13 24			13 26		
Clacton-on-Sea	a						12 34											13 34					
Kirby Cross	d									12 30											13 30		
Frinton-on-Sea	d									12 33											13 33		
Walton-on-the-Naze	a									12 39											13 39		
Manningtree [2]	d			11 59				12 26	12 31						12 59				13 26	13 31			
Mistley	d							12 30											13 30				
Wrabness	d							12 35											13 35				
Harwich International	d							12 44											13 44				
Dovercourt	d							12 47											13 47				
Harwich Town	a							12 49											13 49				
Ipswich	a			12 08					12 41			12 56			13 08					13 41			13 56
	d			12 09		12 16			12 42			13 02			13 09		13 16			13 42			14 03
Lowestoft	a											14 32											
Needham Market	d					12 26											13 26						
Stowmarket	d					12a31			12 53								13a31			13 53			14 14
Peterborough [8]	a																						15 38
Diss	d			12 30					13 05						13 30					14 05			
Norwich	a			12 52					13 27						13 52					14 27			

		LE	LE	LE	LE	LE	LE	LE	LE	LE	LE	LE	LE	LE	LE	LE	LE	LE	LE	LE	LE	LE	LE	LE
												R												
		1	1	1 ◇	1		1	1	1 ◇	1	1	1	1	1	1 ◇	1		1	1	1 ◇	1	1	1 ◇	1
						A											A							
				☕					☕						☕					☕				
London Liverpool Street [15] ⊖	d	12 48		13 00			13 08	13 18	13 30			13 38	13 48		14 00			14 08	14 18	14 30			14 38	14 48
Stratford [7] ⊖ ⛴	d	12 55					13 15	13 25	13u38				13 55					14 15	14 25	14u38				14 55
Romford	d						13 23											14 23						
Shenfield [3]	d	13 12		13u23			13 34	13 42				14u02	14 12		14u23			14 34	14 42				15u02	15 12
Ingatestone	d	13 16											14 16											15 16
Chelmsford [3]	d	13 23					13 43	13 51	14 02			14 12	14 23					14 43	14 51	15 02			15 12	15 23
Hatfield Peverel	d	13 30											14 30											15 30
Witham [2]	d	13 36					13 52	14 00				14 21	14 36					14 52	15 00				15 21	15 36
White Notley	d	13 43											14 43											15 43
Cressing	d	13 45											14 45											15 45
Braintree Freeport	d	13 48											14 48											15 48
Braintree	a	13 53											14 53											15 53
Kelvedon	d							14 05											15 05					
Marks Tey [2]	d							14 10				14 29							15 10				15 29	
Colchester [4]	a			13 49			14 06	14 18	14 21			14 37			14 49			15 06	15 18	15 21			15 37	
	d		13 46	13 50	14 00		14 07	14 18	14 22		14 30	14 38		14 46	14 50	15 00		15 07	15 18	15 22		15 30	15 38	
Colchester Town	a		13 53		14 07						14 37			14 53		15 07						15 37		
	d		13 57											14 57										
Hythe	d		14 00											15 00										
Wivenhoe [3]	d		14 04				14 14							15 04				15 14						
Alresford (Essex)	d		14 08											15 08										
Great Bentley	d		14 12											15 12										
Weeley	d		14 16											15 16										
Thorpe-le-Soken [1]	a		14 19				14 24			←				15 19				15 24			←			
	d		14 26 →				14 24			14 26				15 26 →				15 24			15 26			
Clacton-on-Sea	a						14 34											15 34						
Kirby Cross	d									14 30											15 30			
Frinton-on-Sea	d									14 33											15 33			
Walton-on-the-Naze	a									14 39											15 39			
Manningtree [2]	d			13 59				14 26	14 31						14 59				15 26	15 31				
Mistley	d							14 30											15 30					
Wrabness	d							14 35											15 35					
Harwich International	d							14 44											15 44					
Dovercourt	d							14 47											15 47					
Harwich Town	a							14 49											15 49					
Ipswich	a			14 08					14 41			14 56			15 08					15 41			15 56	
	d			14 09		14 16			14 42			15 02			15 09		15 16			15 42			16 03	
Lowestoft	a											16 32												
Needham Market	d					14 26											15 26							
Stowmarket	d					14a31			14 53								15a31			15 53			16 14	
Peterborough [8]	a																						17 38	
Diss	d			14 30					15 05						15 30					16 05				
Norwich	a			14 52					15 27						15 52					16 27				

For general notes see front of timetable
For details of catering facilities see
Directory of Train Operators

A To Cambridge (Table 14)
B Until 27 September to Great Yarmouth (Table 15)

London → Chelmsford, Colchester, Walton-on-Naze, Clacton, Harwich, Ipswich and Norwich

Network diagram - see first page of Table 5

		LE		LE	LE	LE	LE	LE	LE	LE	LE	LE	LE	LE	LE	LE		LE	LE	LE	LE	LE	LE	LE	LE
												R												R	
		1		1 ◇	1		1	1	1 ◇	1	1	1	1	1	1 ◇	1			1	1	1 ◇	1	1	1	1
						A												A							
				☕					☕						☕						☕				
London Liverpool Street [15] ⊖	d			15 00			15 08	15 18	15 30			15 38	15 48		16 00				16 08	16 18	16 30			16 38	16 48
Stratford [7] ⊖ ⛴	d						15 15	15 25	15u38				15 55						16 15	16 25	16u38				16 55
Romford	d						15 23												16 23						
Shenfield [3]	d			15u23			15 34	15 42				16u02	16 12		16u23				16 34	16 42				17u02	17 12
Ingatestone	d												16 16												17 16
Chelmsford [3]	d						15 43	15 51	16 02			16 12	16 23						16 43	16 51	17 02			17 12	17 23
Hatfield Peverel	d												16 30												17 30
Witham [2]	d						15 52	16 00				16 21	16 36						16 52	17 00				17 21	17 36
White Notley	d												16 43												17 43
Cressing	d												16 45												17 45
Braintree Freeport	d												16 48												17 48
Braintree	a												16 53												17 53
Kelvedon	d							16 05												17 05					
Marks Tey [2]	d							16 10				16 29								17 10				17 29	
Colchester [4]	a			15 49			16 06	16 18	16 21			16 37			16 49				17 06	17 18	17 21			17 37	
	d	15 46		15 50	16 00		16 07	16 18	16 22		16 30	16 38		16 46	16 50	17 00			17 07	17 18	17 22		17 30	17 38	
Colchester Town	a	15 53			16 07						16 37			16 53		17 07							17 37		
	d	15 57												16 57											
Hythe	d	16 00												17 00											
Wivenhoe [3]	d	16 04					16 14							17 04					17 14						
Alresford (Essex)	d	16 08												17 08											
Great Bentley	d	16 12												17 12											
Weeley	d	16 16												17 16											
Thorpe-le-Soken [1]	a	16 19					16 24			←				17 19					17 24			←			
	d	16 26					16 24			16 26				17 26					17 24			17 26			
Clacton-on-Sea	a	→					16 34							→					17 34						
Kirby Cross	d									16 30												17 30			
Frinton-on-Sea	d									16 33												17 33			
Walton-on-the-Naze	a									16 39												17 39			
Manningtree [2]	d			15 59				16 26	16 31						16 59					17 26	17 31				
Mistley	d							16 30												17 30					
Wrabness	d							16 35												17 35					
Harwich International	d							16 44												17 44					
Dovercourt	d							16 47												17 47					
Harwich Town	a							16 49												17 49					
Ipswich	a			16 08					16 41			16 56			17 08						17 41			17 56	
	d			16 09		16 16			16 42			17 02			17 09			17 16			17 42			18 03	
Lowestoft	a											18 32													
Needham Market	d					16 26												17 26							
Stowmarket	d					16a31			16 53						17 20			17a31			17 53			18 14	
Peterborough [8]	a																							19 38	
Diss	d			16 30					17 05						17 32						18 05				
Norwich	a			16 52					17 27						17 52						18 27				

		LE	LE	LE	LE	LE	LE	LE		LE	LE	LE	LE	LE	LE	LE	LE	LE	LE	LE	LE	LE		LE	LE
													R												
		1	1 ◇	1		1	1	1 ◇		1	1	1	1	1	1	1 ◇	1		1	1	1 ◇	1		1	1
					A													A							
			☕					☕								☕					☕				
London Liverpool Street [15] ⊖	d		17 00			17 08	17 18	17 30				17 38	17 46	17 48		18 00			18 08	18 18	18 30				18 38
Stratford [7] ⊖ ⛴	d					17 15	17 25	17u38						17 55					18 15	18 25	18u38				
Romford	d					17 23													18 23						
Shenfield [3]	d		17u23			17 34	17 42					18u02		18 12		18u23			18 34	18 42					19u02
Ingatestone	d													18 16											
Chelmsford [3]	d					17 43	17 51	18 02				18 11	18u16	18 23					18 43	18 51	19 02				19 11
Hatfield Peverel	d													18 30											
Witham [2]	d					17 52	18 00					18 21		18 36					18 52	19 00					19 21
White Notley	d													18 43											
Cressing	d													18 45											
Braintree Freeport	d													18 48											
Braintree	a													18 53											
Kelvedon	d						18 05													19 05					
Marks Tey [2]	d						18 10					18 28								19 10					19 28
Colchester [4]	a		17 49			18 06	18 18	18 21				18 36	18 39			18 49			19 06	19 18	19 21				19 36
	d	17 46	17 50	18 00		18 07	18 18	18 22			18 30		18 40		18 46	18 50	19 00		19 07	19 18	19 22			19 30	
Colchester Town	a	17 53		18 07							18 37				18 53		19 07							19 37	
	d	17 57													18 57										
Hythe	d	18 00													19 00										
Wivenhoe [3]	d	18 04				18 14									19 04				19 14						
Alresford (Essex)	d	18 08													19 08										
Great Bentley	d	18 12													19 12										
Weeley	d	18 16													19 16										
Thorpe-le-Soken [1]	a	18 19				18 24				←					19 19				19 24			←			
	d	18 26				18 24				18 26					19 26				19 24			19 26			
Clacton-on-Sea	a	→				18 34									→				19 34						
Kirby Cross	d									18 30												19 30			
Frinton-on-Sea	d									18 33												19 33			
Walton-on-the-Naze	a									18 39												19 39			
Manningtree [2]	d		17 59				18 26	18 31								18 59				19 26	19 31				
Mistley	d						18 30													19 30					
Wrabness	d						18 35													19 35					
Harwich International	d						18 44													19 44					
Dovercourt	d						18 47													19 47					
Harwich Town	a						18 49													19 49					
Ipswich	a		18 08					18 41					18 56			19 08					19 41				
	d		18 09		18 16			18 42					19 02			19 09		19 16			19 42				
Lowestoft	a												20 32												
Needham Market	d				18 26													19 26							
Stowmarket	d				18a31			18 53										19a32			19 53				
Peterborough [8]	a																								
Diss	d		18 30					19 05								19 30					20 05				
Norwich	a		18 52					19 27								19 52					20 27				

For general notes see front of timetable
For details of catering facilities see Directory of Train Operators

A To Cambridge (Table 14)

London → Chelmsford, Colchester, Walton-on-Naze, Clacton, Harwich, Ipswich and Norwich

Network diagram - see first page of Table 5

Station		LE R 1	LE 1	LE 1	LE 1 ◇ ☕	LE A	LE 1	LE 1	LE 1 ◇ ☕	LE 1	LE R 1	LE 1	LE 1	LE 1 ◇ ☕		LE 1	LE 1	LE	LE 1	LE 1 ◇ ☕	LE 1	LE 1	LE	LE 1	LE 1 ◇
London Liverpool Street 15 ⊖	d	18 46	18 48		19 00		19 08	19 18	19 30		19 38		19 48	20 00		20 08			20 18	20 30	20 38	20 48			21 00
Stratford 7 ⊖	d		18 55				19 15	19 25	19u38				19 55			20 15			20 25	20u38	20 45	20 55			
Romford	d						19 23									20 23									
Shenfield 3	d		19 12		19u23		19 34	19 42			20u02		20 12	20u23		20 34			20 42		21 02	21 12			21u23
Ingatestone	d		19 16										20 16									21 16			
Chelmsford 3	d	19u16	19 23				19 43	19 51	20 03		20 12		20 23			20 43			20 51	21 03	21 12	21 23			
Hatfield Peverel	d		19 30										20 30									21 30			
Witham 2	d		19 36				19 52	20 00			20 21		20 36			20 52			21 00		21 21	21 36			
White Notley	d		19 43										20 43									21 43			
Cressing	d		19 45										20 45									21 45			
Braintree Freeport	d		19 48										20 48									21 48			
Braintree	a		19 53										20 53									21 53			
Kelvedon	d							20 05											21 05						
Marks Tey 2	d							20 10			20 29								21 10		21 29				
Colchester 4	a	19 39			19 49		20 06	20 18	20 22		20 37			20 49		21 06			21 18	21 22	21 37				21 49
	d	19 40		19 46	19 50		20 07	20 18	20 23		20 38	20 46		20 50		21 07			21 18	21 23	21 38			21 46	21 50
Colchester Town	a			19 53								20 53												21 53	
	d			19 57								20 57												21 57	
Hythe	d			20 00								21 00												22 00	
Wivenhoe 3	d			20 04			20 14					21 04				21 14								22 04	
Alresford (Essex)	d			20 08								21 08												22 08	
Great Bentley	d			20 12								21 12												22 12	
Weeley	d			20 16								21 16												22 16	
Thorpe-le-Soken 1	a			20 19			20 24			⟵		21 19				21 24	⟵							22 19	
	d			20 26 ⟶			20 24			20 26		21 26 ⟶				21 24	21 26							22 26 ⟶	
Clacton-on-Sea	a						20 34									21 34									
Kirby Cross	d									20 30							21 30								
Frinton-on-Sea	d									20 33							21 33								
Walton-on-the-Naze	a									20 39							21 39								
Manningtree 2	d				19 59			20 26	20 32					20 59					21 26	21 32	21 46				21 58
Mistley	d							20 30											21 30						
Wrabness	d							20 35											21 35				⟵		
Harwich International	d							20 44										21 34 ⟶	21 44		22a02		21 34		
Dovercourt	d							20 47											21 47						
Harwich Town	a							20 49											21 49						
Ipswich	a	19 56			20 08				20 42		20 56			21 08						21 42			22 00		22 09
	d	20 03			20 09	20 16			20 43		21 02			21 09						21 43					22 15
Lowestoft	a										22 32														23 45
Needham Market	d					20 26																			
Stowmarket	d	20 14				20a31			20 54											21 54					
Peterborough 8	a	21 38																							
Diss	d				20 30				21 06					21 30						22 06					
Norwich	a				20 52				21 28					21 52						22 28					

Station		LE B	LE 1	LE 1	LE 1 ◇ ☕	LE C		LE 1	LE 1	LE 1	LE 1	LE 1	LE 1	LE 1	LE 1 ◇ ☕	LE 1	LE 1	LE 1	LE 1	LE 1		LE 1 ◇ ☕	LE 1		
London Liverpool Street 15 ⊖	d		21 04	21 18	21 30					21 34		21 48	22 00	22 18	22 30		22 48	23 00		23 18		23 30	23 48		
Stratford 7 ⊖	d		21 11	21 25								21 55	22 07	22 25			22 55	23 07		23 25			23 55		
Romford	d		21 19																						
Shenfield 3	d		21 34	21 46						22u02		22 16	22 28	22 46			23 16	23 28		23 46			00 16		
Ingatestone	d											22 20					23 20			23 50			00 20		
Chelmsford 3	d		21 43	21 55	22 04					22 12		22 27	22 37	22 55	23 04		23 27	23 37		23 57		00 04	00 27		
Hatfield Peverel	d											22 34					23 34						00 34		
Witham 2	d		21 52	22 04						22 21		22 40	22 46	23 04			23 39	23 46	23 48	00 07			00 39		
White Notley	d											22 47							23 54						
Cressing	d											22 49							23 57						
Braintree Freeport	d											22 52							23 59						
Braintree	a											22 57							00 03						
Kelvedon	d			22 09										23 09			23 44						00 44		
Marks Tey 2	d			22 14		22 21				22 29				23 14			23 49						00 49		
Colchester 4	a		22 06	22 22	22 25	22 30				22 37			23 00	23 22	23 25		00 01	00 01		00 25		00 28	01 01		
	d		22 07		22 26					22 38	22 46		23 00	23 23	23 26			00 01				00 29			
Colchester Town	a										22 53														
	d										22 57														
Hythe	d										23 00														
Wivenhoe 3	d		22 14								23 04			23 30											
Alresford (Essex)	d										23 08			23 33											
Great Bentley	d										23 12			23 37											
Weeley	d										23 16														
Thorpe-le-Soken 1	a		22 24						⟵		23 19			23 43											
	d		22 24						22 26		23 19			23 43											
Clacton-on-Sea	a		22 34								23 29			23 52											
Kirby Cross	d								22 30																
Frinton-on-Sea	d								22 33																
Walton-on-the-Naze	a								22 39																
Manningtree 2	d				22 35			22 38					23 08		23 35	23 38		00 08				00 38			
Mistley	d							22 42								23 42									
Wrabness	d							22 47								23 47									
Harwich International	d							22 54								23 54									
Dovercourt	d							22 57								23 57									
Harwich Town	a							22 59								23 59									
Ipswich	a				22 45					22 56			23 20		23 45			00 24				00 48			
	d	22 17			22 46										23 46							00 50			
Lowestoft	a																								
Needham Market	d	22 27																							
Stowmarket	d	22a32			22 57										23 57							01 01			
Peterborough 8	a																								
Diss	d				23 10										00 10							01 14			
Norwich	a				23 32										00 32							01 36			

For general notes see front of timetable
For details of catering facilities see Directory of Train Operators

A To Cambridge (Table 14)
B To Bury St Edmunds (Table 14)
C From Sudbury (Table 10)

Sundays

London → Chelmsford, Colchester, Walton-on-Naze, Clacton, Harwich, Ipswich and Norwich

Network diagram - see first page of Table 5

		LE	LE	LE	LE	LE	LE		LE	LE	LE	LE	LE	LE		LE	LE	LE	LE	LE	LE		LE	LE	LE
		1 ◇	1	1	1 ◇	1	1		1	1	1	1				1	1	1	1	1	1		1 ◇	1	1
										A			B	C											
London Liverpool Street 15 ⊖	d	22p30	23p00	23p18	23p30	23p48	00 18													08 02			08 30	08 32	
Stratford 7 ⊖	d		23p07	23p25		23p55	00 25													08 09				08 39	
Romford	d																								
Shenfield 3	d		23p28	23p46		00 16	00 47													08 31			08u57	09 01	
Ingatestone	d			23p50		00 20	00 51													08 35					
Chelmsford 3	d	23p04	23p37	23p57	00 04	00 27	00 58													08 42				09 10	
Hatfield Peverel	d					00 34	01 05													08 49					
Witham 2	d		23p46	00 07		00 39	01 10		07 33									08 23		08 54				09 19	09 23
White Notley	d								07 39									08 29							09 29
Cressing	d								07 42									08 32							09 32
Braintree Freeport	d								07 44									08 34							09 34
Braintree	a								07 48									08 38							09 38
Kelvedon	d					00 44	01 15													08 59					
Marks Tey 2	d					00 49	01 20													09 04				09 27	
Colchester 4	a	23p25	00 01	00 25	00 28	01 01	01 32													09 12			09 23	09 35	
	d	23p26	00 01		00 29						07 40	08 12				08 18	08 35			09 12			09 24	09 35	
Colchester Town	a																								
	d																								
Hythe	d																								
Wivenhoe 3	d																08 43							09 43	
Alresford (Essex)	d																08 46							09 46	
Great Bentley	d																08 50							09 50	
Weeley	d																								
Thorpe-le-Soken 1	a																08 55							09 55	
	d																08 55		08 57					09 55	
Clacton-on-Sea	a																09 07							10 05	
Kirby Cross	d																		09 01						
Frinton-on-Sea	d																		09 04						
Walton-on-the-Naze	a																		09 09						
Manningtree 2	d	23p35	00 08		00 38						07 48	08 20				08 26				09 20	09 26		09 33		
Mistley	d															08 30					09 30				
Wrabness	d															08 35					09 35				
Harwich International	d													08 30		08 42					09 42				
Dovercourt	d															08 45					09 45				
Harwich Town	a															08 47					09 47				
Ipswich	a	23p45	00 24		00 48						08 00	08 32		08 55						09 32			09 42		
	d	23p46			00 50					07 55			08 45	09 02									09 44		
Lowestoft	a																								
Needham Market	d													09 12											
Stowmarket	d	23p57			01 01					08 07			08a58	09a17									09 55		
Peterborough 8	a									09 41															
Diss	d	00 10			01 14																		10 07		
Norwich	a	00 32			01 36																		10 29		

For general notes see front of timetable
For details of catering facilities see Directory of Train Operators

A Until 7 September
B To Bury St Edmunds (Table 14)
C To Cambridge (Table 14)

Sundays

London → Chelmsford, Colchester, Walton-on-Naze, Clacton, Harwich, Ipswich and Norwich

Network diagram - see first page of Table 5

		LE 1	LE 1	LE 1	LE 1	LE 1 ◇		LE 1	LE 1	LE	LE 1	LE 1	LE 1		LE 1 ◇	LE 1	LE 1	LE 1	LE 1	LE 1		LE 1	LE 1 ◇	LE 1	LE 1
						☕				A					☕								☕		
London Liverpool Street 15 ⊖	d			09 02		09 30		09 32				10 02			10 30	10 32				11 02			11 30	11 32	
Stratford 7 ⊖ ⛴	d			09 09				09 39				10 09				10 39				11 09				11 39	
Romford	d																								
Shenfield 3	d			09 31		09u57		10 01				10 31			10u57	11 01				11 31			11u57	12 01	
Ingatestone	d			09 35								10 35								11 35					
Chelmsford 3	d			09 42				10 10				10 42				11 10				11 42				12 10	
Hatfield Peverel	d			09 49								10 49								11 49					
Witham 2	d			09 54				10 19	10 23			10 54				11 19	11 23			11 54				12 19	12 23
White Notley	d								10 29								11 29								12 29
Cressing	d								10 32								11 32								12 32
Braintree Freeport	d								10 34								11 34								12 34
Braintree	a								10 38								11 38								12 38
Kelvedon	d			09 59								10 59								11 59					
Marks Tey 2	d			10 04				10 27				11 04				11 27				12 04				12 27	
Colchester 4	a			10 12		10 23		10 35				11 12			11 23	11 35				12 12			12 23	12 35	
	d			10 12		10 24		10 35				11 12			11 24	11 35				12 12			12 24	12 35	
Colchester Town	a																								
	d																								
Hythe	d																								
Wivenhoe 3	d							10 43								11 43								12 43	
Alresford (Essex)	d							10 46								11 46								12 46	
Great Bentley	d							10 50								11 50								12 50	
Weeley	d																								
Thorpe-le-Soken 1	a							10 55								11 55								12 55	
	d		09 57					10 55			10 57					11 55			11 57					12 55	
Clacton-on-Sea	a							11 05								12 05								13 05	
Kirby Cross	d		10 01								11 01								12 01						
Frinton-on-Sea	d		10 04								11 04								12 04						
Walton-on-the-Naze	a		10 09								11 09								12 09						
Manningtree 2	d			10 20	10 26	10 33						11 20	11 26		11 33					12 20		12 26	12 33		
Mistley	d				10 30								11 30									12 30			
Wrabness	d				10 35								11 35									12 35			
Harwich International	d				10 42								11 42									12 42			
Dovercourt	d				10 45								11 45									12 45			
Harwich Town	a				10 47								11 47									12 47			
Ipswich	a			10 32		10 42						11 32			11 42					12 32			12 42		
	d	09 55				10 44				11 02					11 44			11 55					12 44		
Lowestoft	a																								
Needham Market	d									11 12															
Stowmarket	d	10 07				10 55				11a17					11 55			12 07					12 55		
Peterborough 8	a	11 41																13 42							
Diss	d					11 07									12 07								13 07		
Norwich	a					11 29									12 29								13 29		

		LE	LE 1	LE 1	LE 1		LE 1 ◇	LE 1	LE 1	LE 1	LE 1	LE 1		LE 1	LE 1 ◇	LE 1	LE 1	LE	LE 1		LE 1	LE 1	LE 1 ◇	LE 1	LE 1
		A					☕								☕			A					☕		
London Liverpool Street 15 ⊖	d			12 02			12 30	12 32				13 02			13 30	13 32					14 02		14 30	14 32	
Stratford 7 ⊖ ⛴	d			12 09				12 39				13 09				13 39					14 09			14 39	
Romford	d																								
Shenfield 3	d			12 31			12u57	13 01				13 31			13u57	14 01					14 31		14u57	15 01	
Ingatestone	d			12 35								13 35									14 35				
Chelmsford 3	d			12 42				13 10				13 42				14 10					14 42			15 10	
Hatfield Peverel	d			12 49								13 49									14 49				
Witham 2	d			12 54				13 19	13 23			13 54				14 19	14 23				14 54			15 19	15 23
White Notley	d								13 29								14 29								15 29
Cressing	d								13 32								14 32								15 32
Braintree Freeport	d								13 34								14 34								15 34
Braintree	a								13 38								14 38								15 38
Kelvedon	d			12 59								13 59									14 59				
Marks Tey 2	d			13 04				13 27				14 04				14 27					15 04			15 27	
Colchester 4	a			13 12			13 23	13 35				14 12			14 23	14 35					15 12		15 23	15 35	
	d			13 12			13 24	13 35				14 12			14 24	14 35					15 12		15 24	15 35	
Colchester Town	a																								
	d																								
Hythe	d																								
Wivenhoe 3	d							13 43								14 43								15 43	
Alresford (Essex)	d							13 46								14 46								15 46	
Great Bentley	d							13 50								14 50								15 50	
Weeley	d																								
Thorpe-le-Soken 1	a							13 55								14 55								15 55	
	d		12 57					13 55			13 57					14 55			14 57					15 55	
Clacton-on-Sea	a							14 05								15 05								16 05	
Kirby Cross	d		13 01								14 01								15 01						
Frinton-on-Sea	d		13 04								14 04								15 04						
Walton-on-the-Naze	a		13 09								14 09								15 09						
Manningtree 2	d			13 20	13 26		13 33					14 20		14 26	14 33						15 20	15 26	15 33		
Mistley	d				13 30									14 30								15 30			
Wrabness	d				13 35									14 35								15 35			
Harwich International	d				13 42									14 42								15 42			
Dovercourt	d				13 45									14 45								15 45			
Harwich Town	a				13 47									14 47								15 47			
Ipswich	a			13 32			13 42					14 32			14 42						15 32		15 42		
	d	13 02					13 44			13 55					14 44			15 02					15 44		
Lowestoft	a																								
Needham Market	d	13 12																15 12							
Stowmarket	d	13a17					13 55			14 07					14 55			15a17					15 55		
Peterborough 8	a									15 42															
Diss	d						14 07								15 07								16 07		
Norwich	a						14 29								15 29								16 29		

For general notes see front of timetable
For details of catering facilities see
Directory of Train Operators

A To Cambridge (Table 14)

Table 11

Sundays

London → Chelmsford, Colchester, Walton-on-Naze, Clacton, Harwich, Ipswich and Norwich

Network diagram - see first page of Table 5

		LE ■1	LE ■1	LE ■1	LE ■1	LE ■1 ◇ ☕	LE ■1	LE ■1	LE A	LE ■1	LE ■1	LE ■1	LE ■1 ◇ ☕	LE ■1	LE ■1	LE ■1	LE ■1	LE ■1	LE ■1	LE ■1 ◇ ☕	LE ■1	LE ■1
London Liverpool Street ■15 ⊖	d			15 02		15 30	15 32				16 02		16 30	16 32				17 02		17 30	17 32	
Stratford ■7 ⊖ ⛴	d			15 09			15 39				16 09			16 39				17 09			17 39	
Romford	d																					
Shenfield ■3	d			15 31		15u57	16 01				16 31		16u57	17 01				17 31		17u57	18 01	
Ingatestone	d			15 35							16 35							17 35				
Chelmsford ■3	d			15 42			16 10				16 42			17 10				17 42			18 10	
Hatfield Peverel	d			15 49							16 49							17 49				
Witham ■2	d			15 54			16 19	16 23			16 54			17 19	17 23			17 54			18 19	18 23
White Notley	d							16 29							17 29							18 29
Cressing	d							16 32							17 32							18 32
Braintree Freeport	d							16 34							17 34							18 34
Braintree	a							16 38							17 38							18 38
Kelvedon	d			15 59							16 59							17 59				
Marks Tey ■2	d			16 04			16 27				17 04			17 27				18 04			18 27	
Colchester ■4	a			16 12		16 23	16 35				17 12		17 23	17 35				18 12		18 23	18 35	
	d			16 12		16 24	16 35				17 12		17 24	17 35				18 12		18 24	18 35	
Colchester Town	a																					
	d																					
Hythe	d																					
Wivenhoe ■3	d						16 43							17 43							18 43	
Alresford (Essex)	d						16 46							17 46							18 46	
Great Bentley	d						16 50							17 50							18 50	
Weeley	d																					
Thorpe-le-Soken ■1	a						16 55							17 55							18 55	
	d		15 57				16 55			16 57				17 55			17 57				18 55	
Clacton-on-Sea	a						17 05							18 05							19 05	
Kirby Cross	d		16 01							17 01							18 01					
Frinton-on-Sea	d		16 04							17 04							18 04					
Walton-on-the-Naze	a		16 09							17 09							18 09					
Manningtree ■2	d			16 20	16 26	16 33					17 20	17 26	17 33					18 20	18 26	18 33		
Mistley	d				16 30							17 30							18 30			
Wrabness	d				16 35							17 35							18 35			
Harwich International	d				16 42							17 42							18 42			
Dovercourt	d				16 45							17 45							18 45			
Harwich Town	a				16 47							17 47							18 47			
Ipswich	a			16 32		16 42					17 32		17 42					18 32		18 42		
	d	15 55				16 44			17 02				17 44			17 55				18 44		
Lowestoft	a																					
Needham Market	d								17 12													
Stowmarket	d	16 07				16 55			17a17				17 55			18 07				18 55		
Peterborough ■8	a	17 36														19 36						
Diss	d					17 07							18 07							19 07		
Norwich	a					17 29							18 29							19 29		

		LE A	LE ■1	LE ■1	LE ■1	LE ■1 ◇ ☕	LE ■1	LE ■1 ◇ ☕	LE ■1	LE ■1	LE ■1	LE ■1	LE ■1 ◇ ☕	LE ■1	LE ■1	LE A	LE ■1	LE	LE ■1	LE ■1	LE	LE ■1
London Liverpool Street ■15 ⊖	d			18 02		18 30	18 32	19 00			19 02		19 30	19 32					20 00	20 02		
Stratford ■7 ⊖ ⛴	d			18 09			18 39				19 09			19 39						20 09		
Romford	d																					
Shenfield ■3	d			18 31		18u57	19 01				19 31		19u57	20 01					20 27	20 31		
Ingatestone	d			18 35							19 35									20 35		
Chelmsford ■3	d			18 42			19 10				19 42			20 10					20 37	20 42		
Hatfield Peverel	d			18 49							19 49									20 49		
Witham ■2	d			18 54			19 19		19 23		19 54			20 19	20 23					20 54		
White Notley	d								19 29						20 29							
Cressing	d								19 32						20 32							
Braintree Freeport	d								19 34						20 34							
Braintree	a								19 38						20 38							
Kelvedon	d			18 59							19 59									20 59		
Marks Tey ■2	d			19 04			19 27				20 04			20 27						21 04		
Colchester ■4	a			19 12		19 23	19 35				20 12		20 23	20 35					20 55	21 12		
	d			19 12		19 24	19 35				20 12		20 24	20 35					20 56	21 12		
Colchester Town	a																					
	d																					
Hythe	d																					
Wivenhoe ■3	d						19 43							20 43								
Alresford (Essex)	d						19 46							20 46								
Great Bentley	d						19 50							20 50								
Weeley	d																					
Thorpe-le-Soken ■1	a						19 55							20 55								
	d		18 57				19 55			19 57				20 55			20 57					
Clacton-on-Sea	a						20 05							21 05								
Kirby Cross	d		19 01							20 01							21 01					
Frinton-on-Sea	d		19 04							20 04							21 04					
Walton-on-the-Naze	a		19 09							20 09							21 09					
Manningtree ■2	d			19 20	19 26	19 33					20 20	20 26	20 33						21 04	21 20		21 26
Mistley	d				19 30							20 30										21 30
Wrabness	d				19 35							20 35										21 35
Harwich International	d				19 42							20 42						21 10 →	21a22		← 21 10	21 42
Dovercourt	d				19 45							20 45										21 45
Harwich Town	a				19 47							20 47										21 47
Ipswich	a			19 32		19 42		20 04			20 32		20 42							21 32	21 37	
	d	19 02				19 44		20 06					20 44			21 02						
Lowestoft	a																					
Needham Market	d	19 12														21 12						
Stowmarket	d	19a17				19 55		20 17					20 55			21a17						
Peterborough ■8	a																					
Diss	d					20 07		20 29					21 07									
Norwich	a					20 29		20 51					21 29									

For general notes see front of timetable
For details of catering facilities see Directory of Train Operators

A To Cambridge (Table 14)

London → Chelmsford, Colchester, Walton-on-Naze, Clacton, Harwich, Ipswich and Norwich

Network diagram - see first page of Table 5

		LE		LE	LE	LE	LE	LE	LE		LE	LE	LE	LE	LE	LE		LE	LE	LE	LE	LE			
		1 ◇		1	1	1		1	1		1 ◇	1	1	1	1	1 ◇		1	1	1	1 ◇	1			
							A																		
		☕									☕					☕									
London Liverpool Street 15 ⊖	d	20 30		20 32				21 02			21 30	21 32			22 02	22 30		22 32		23 02	23 30	23 32			
Stratford 7 ⊖	d			20 39				21 09				21 39			22 09			22 39		23 09		23 39			
Romford	d																								
Shenfield 3	d	20u57		21 01				21 31			21u57	22 01			22 31	22u57		23 01		23 31	23u57	00 01			
Ingatestone	d							21 35							22 35					23 35					
Chelmsford 3	d			21 10				21 42				22 10			22 42			23 10		23 42		00 10			
Hatfield Peverel	d							21 49							22 49					23 49					
Witham 2	d			21 19	21 23			21 54				22 19	22 23		22 54			23 19	23 23	23 54		00 19			
White Notley	d				21 29								22 29						23 29						
Cressing	d				21 32								22 32						23 32						
Braintree Freeport	d				21 34								22 34						23 34						
Braintree	a				21 38								22 38						23 38						
Kelvedon	d							21 59							22 59					23 59					
Marks Tey 2	d			21 27			22 00	22 04				22 27			23 04			23 27		00 04		00 27			
Colchester 4	a	21 23		21 35			22 09	22 12			22 23	22 35			23 12	23 23		23 35		00 12	00 27	00 40			
	d	21 24		21 35				22 12			22 24	22 35			23 12	23 24		23 35		00 12	00 28				
Colchester Town	a																								
	d																								
Hythe	d																								
Wivenhoe 3	d			21 43								22 43						23 43							
Alresford (Essex)	d			21 46								22 46						23 46							
Great Bentley	d			21 50								22 50						23 50							
Weeley	d																								
Thorpe-le-Soken 1	a			21 55								22 55						23 55							
	d			21 55		21 57						22 55		22 57				23 55							
Clacton-on-Sea	a			22 05								23 05						00 05							
Kirby Cross	d					22 01								23 01											
Frinton-on-Sea	d					22 04								23 04											
Walton-on-the-Naze	a					22 09								23 09											
Manningtree 2	d	21 33						22 20	22 26		22 33				23 20	23 33				00 20	00 37				
Mistley	d								22 30																
Wrabness	d								22 35																
Harwich International	d								22 42																
Dovercourt	d								22 45																
Harwich Town	a								22 47																
Ipswich	a	21 42						22 32			22 42				23 32	23 42				00 36	00 46				
	d	21 44									22 44					23 44					00 48				
Lowestoft	a																								
Needham Market	d																								
Stowmarket	d	21 55									22 55					23 55					00 59				
Peterborough 8	a																								
Diss	d	22 07									23 07					00 07					01 11				
Norwich	a	22 29									23 29					00 39					01 43				

For general notes see front of timetable
For details of catering facilities see
Directory of Train Operators

A From Sudbury (Table 10)

Norwich, Ipswich, Harwich, Clacton, Walton-on-Naze, Colchester and Chelmsford → London

Network diagram - see first page of Table 5

Miles	Miles	Miles	Miles	Miles			LE MX 1	LE MO A	LE 1	LE 1	LE 1 ◇	LE 1	LE 1	LE 1	LE 1	LE 1	LE R 1 ☕	LE 1	LE B	LE 1	LE 1	LE R 1 ☕	LE 1	LE 1	LE 1
0	—	—	—	—	**Norwich**	d											05 10					05 40			
20	—	—	—	—	Diss	d											05 28					05 58			
—	—	—	—	—	**Peterborough** [8]	d																			
34¼	—	—	—	—	Stowmarket	d		00 04									05 40		05 57			06 10			
38	—	—	—	—	Needham Market	d		00 09											06 03						
—	—	—	—	—	**Lowestoft**	d																			
46¼	—	—	—	—	**Ipswich**	a		00 21									05 51		06 15			06 21			
—	—	—	—	—		d					05 23						05 53					06 23			
—	0	—	—	—	**Harwich Town**	d									05 37										
—	¾	—	—	—	Dovercourt	d									05 39										
—	1¾	—	—	—	Harwich International	d									05 42										
—	5½	—	—	—	Wrabness	d									05 48										
—	9½	—	—	—	Mistley	d									05 53										
55½	11¼	—	—	—	Manningtree [2]	d					05 33				05a58		06 03					06 33			
—	—	0	—	—	**Walton-on-the-Naze**	d								05 38							06 10				
—	—	1¼	—	—	Frinton-on-Sea	d								05 41							06 13				
—	—	2½	—	—	Kirby Cross	d								05 44							06 16				
—	—	—	0	—	**Clacton-on-Sea**	d							05 20					05 44							06 19
—	—	5	4¾	—	Thorpe-le-Soken [1]	a							05 27	05 50				05 51			06 22				06 27
—	—	—	—	—		d							05 27					05 51							06 27
—	—	7¼	—	—	Weeley	d												05 55							
—	—	10	—	—	Great Bentley	d												05 59							
—	—	12¼	—	—	Alresford (Essex)	d												06 03							
—	—	14	—	—	Wivenhoe [3]	d							05 38					06 06							06 38
—	—	16½	—	—	Hythe	d												06 10							
—	—	18	—	—	Colchester Town	a																			
—	—	—	—	—		d														06 21					
63¼	0	19¾	—	—	**Colchester** [4]	a					05 43		05 47				06 13	06 17		06 28		06 43			06 47
—	—	—	—	—		d			04 45	05 21	05 43		05 48				06 15	06 18		06 29		06 45			06 48
68¼	—	—	—	—	Marks Tey [2]	d			04 51	05 27			05 54							06 35					06 54
72¾	—	—	—	—	Kelvedon	d			04 56	05 32			06 00					06 28		06 41					07 00
—	—	—	—	0	**Braintree**	d	00 03					05 45												06 42	
—	—	—	—	¾	Braintree Freeport	d	00 05					05 47												06 44	
—	—	—	—	2	Cressing	d	00 08					05 50												06 47	
—	—	—	—	3¼	White Notley	d	00 11					05 53												06 50	
76½	—	—	—	6¼	**Witham** [2]	d	00a18		05 01	05 37	05 56	06a01	06 05			06 15	06 27	06 33		06 46				06 58	07 05
79	—	—	—	—	Hatfield Peverel	d			05 05	05 41						06 19								07 02	
85¼	—	—	—	—	**Chelmsford** [3]	d			05 12	05 48	06 05		06 14			06 26		06 42		06 55			07 03	07 09	07 14
91½	—	—	—	—	Ingatestone	d			05 19	05 55						06 33		06 48					07 10		
94¾	—	—	—	—	Shenfield [3]	a			05 25	06 01			06 25			06 39				07 06			07 16	07 20	
102¾	—	—	—	—	Romford	a																			
111¾	—	—	—	—	Stratford [7] ⊖ ⛴	a			05s44	06s18	06s29		06s41			06s56	06s59	07s08				07s26	07s33	07s37	07s40
115	—	—	—	—	**London Liverpool Street** [15] ⊖	a			05 57	06 27	06 41		06 49			07 07	07 10	07 20		07 33		07 37	07 44	07 48	07 51

		LE 1	LE 1	LE 1	LE 1	LE 1	LE 1	LE R 1 ✕	LE 1	LE 1	LE 1	LE 1	LE 1	LE 1	LE B	LE R 1 ☕	LE 1	LE 1	LE 1	LE 1	LE 1	LE 1	LE R 1 ✕		LE 1
Norwich	d							06 10								06 25							06 40		
Diss	d							06 28								06 43							06 58		
Peterborough [8]	d																								
Stowmarket	d							06 40							06 44	06 55							07 10		
Needham Market	d																								
Lowestoft	d																								
Ipswich	a							06 51							07 00	07 06							07 21		
	d		06 38					06 53							07 00	07 08							07 23		
Harwich Town	d	06 22												07 08											
Dovercourt	d	06 24												07 10											
Harwich International	d	06 27											07 10	07 13	07a25										
Wrabness	d	06 33												07 19											
Mistley	d	06 38												07 24							←				
Manningtree [2]	d	06 43	06 48					07 03					07b25 →	07a29		07 18					07 25		07 33		
Walton-on-the-Naze	d					06 43														07 04					
Frinton-on-Sea	d					06 46														07 07					
Kirby Cross	d					06 49														07 10					
Clacton-on-Sea	d			06 34	06 38					06 49									07 04						
Thorpe-le-Soken [1]	a			06 42	06 46	06 54				06 57		←							07 12	07 16					
	d			06 42	06 46	07 01 →				06 57		07 01							07 12						
Weeley	d				06 50							07 05													
Great Bentley	d				06 53							07 08													
Alresford (Essex)	d				06 58							07 13													
Wivenhoe [3]	d			06 53	07 01					07 08	←	07 16							07 23			←			
Hythe	d				07 05 →						07 05	07 20 →										07 20			
Colchester Town	a										07 09											07 24			
	d						06 59				07 13											07 28			
Colchester [4]	a	06 53	06 58	07 02			07 06	07 13		07 17	07 22					07 28			07 32		07 37	07 38	07 43		
	d		06 59	07 03			07 07	07 15		07 18						07 30			07 33		07 37		07 45		
Marks Tey [2]	d						07 13			07 24											07 43				
Kelvedon	d			07 13						07 30									07 43						
Braintree	d																	07 27							
Braintree Freeport	d																	07 29							
Cressing	d																	07 32							
White Notley	d								←									07 35							←
Witham [2]	d		07 11	07 18			07b28 →		07 28	07 35								07 43	07 48		07c58 →				07 58
Hatfield Peverel	d								07 32																08 02
Chelmsford [3]	d		07 20	07 27					07 39								07 49	07 53	07 57						08 09
Ingatestone	d		07 26														07 56								
Shenfield [3]	a		07 32	07 38					07 50								08 02		08 08						08 20
Romford	a																								
Stratford [7] ⊖ ⛴	a			07s55						08s09									08s25						
London Liverpool Street [15] ⊖	a		07 59	08 06				08 09	08 16	08 20						08 23	08 28	08 30	08 36				08 39		08 48

For general notes see front of timetable
For details of catering facilities see Directory of Train Operators

A From Cambridge (Table 14)
B From Bury St Edmunds (Table 14)
b Arr. 0722
c Arr. 0752

Table 11

Norwich, Ipswich, Harwich, Clacton, Walton-on-Naze, Colchester and Chelmsford → London

Network diagram - see first page of Table 5

		LE	LE	LE	LE	LE	LE	LE	LE	LE	LE	LE	LE	LE	LE	LE	LE	LE	LE	LE	LE	LE	LE	LE	LE
				R					R							R									
		1	1	1		1	1	1	1	1	1	1	1		1	1	1	1◇	1	1	1	1	1◇	1	1
					A									B		C									
				✕					☕									✕					✕		
Norwich	d			06 55					07 10							07 30		07 40					08 00		
Diss	d			07 13					07 28									07 58					08 17		
Peterborough 8	d																								
Stowmarket	d			07 25					07 40					07 45				08 10					08 29		
Needham Market	d													07 50											
Lowestoft	d																								
Ipswich	a			07 36					07 51					08 02		08 07		08 22					08 40		
	d			07 38					07 53							08 18		08 23					08 42		
Harwich Town	d																08 00								
Dovercourt	d																08 02								
Harwich International	d				07 47												08 06								
Wrabness	d				07 53												08 12								
Mistley	d				07a59												08 17								
Manningtree 2	d			07 48					08 03								08 22	08 33					08 52		
Walton-on-the-Naze	d		07 40												08 09							08 45			
Frinton-on-Sea	d		07 43												08 12							08 48			
Kirby Cross	d		07 46												08 15							08 51			
Clacton-on-Sea	d	07 10									07 45									08 15					08 50
Thorpe-le-Soken 1	a	07 17	07 51								07 52		←		08 21					08 22		08 56			08 57
	d	07 17	07 56								07 52		07 56							08 22		09 01			08 57
Weeley	d	07 21	→										08 00									→			
Great Bentley	d	07 25											08 03							08 28					
Alresford (Essex)	d	07 29											08 08							08 32					
Wivenhoe 3	d	07 33									08 03		08 11							08 35					09 07
Hythe	d	07 37											08 15												
Colchester Town	a												08 19												
	d							08 02				←	08 23								08 45				
Colchester 4	a	07 44		07 58				08 09	08 13		08 16	08 09	08 32				08 32	08 43		08 44	08 52		09 01		09 17
	d	07 49		08 00			08 03	→	08 15		08 18						08 37	08 45		08 48			09 03		09 17
Marks Tey 2	d						08 09				08 24									08 54					09 23
Kelvedon	d	07 59					08 15				08 30									09 00					09 29
Braintree	d									08 12														09 00	
Braintree Freeport	d									08 14														09 02	
Cressing	d									08 17														09 05	
White Notley	d									08 20														09 08	
Witham 2	d	08 04					08 20			08 28	08 35						08 49		08 58	09 05				09 15	09 34
Hatfield Peverel	d									08 32									09 02					09 20	
Chelmsford 3	d	08 13				08 19	08 29			08 39	08 44						08 58	09 02	09 09	09 14				09 27	09 43
Ingatestone	d					08 26				08 46									09 16					09 33	
Shenfield 3	a					08 32	08 40			08 52	08 55								09 22	09 25			09s29	09 40	09 54
Romford	a																							09 48	
Stratford 7 ⊖	a	08s39				08s49			08s59	09s09								09s28	09s39					09s57	10s08
London Liverpool Street 15 ⊖	a	08 50		08 55		09 01	09 06		09 10	09 20	09 22					09 25	09 33	09 40	09 50	09 52			09 56	10 05	10 17

		LE	LE	LE	LE	LE	LE	LE	LE	LE	LE	LE	LE	LE	LE	LE	LE	LE		LE	LE	LE	LE	LE	LE
				R				R			R									R					
		1		1	1	1	1	1	1	1	1	1	1	1		1◇	1	1		1	1	1	1◇	1	1
			B												B										
				☕							☕					☕							☕		
Norwich	d			08 30							09 00					09 30							10 00		
Diss	d			08 47							09 17					09 47							10 17		
Peterborough 8	d							07 52																	
Stowmarket	d		08 45					09 12			09 29				09 45								10 29		
Needham Market	d		08 51												09 50										
Lowestoft	d																			08 58					
Ipswich	a		09 03	09 07				09 26			09 40				10 03	10 07				10 26			10 40		
	d			09 08				09 30			09 42					10 08				10 30			10 42		
Harwich Town	d				09 00												10 00								
Dovercourt	d				09 02												10 02								
Harwich International	d				09 06												10 06								
Wrabness	d				09 12												10 12								
Mistley	d				09 17												10 17								
Manningtree 2	d			09 18	09 22						09 52					10 18	10 22						10 52		
Walton-on-the-Naze	d									09 45												10 45			
Frinton-on-Sea	d									09 48												10 48			
Kirby Cross	d									09 51												10 51			
Clacton-on-Sea	d												09 50												10 50
Thorpe-le-Soken 1	a					←				09 56			09 57					←				10 56			10 57
	d					09 01				10 01			09 57					10 01				11 01			10 57
Weeley	d					09 05				→								10 05				→			
Great Bentley	d					09 08												10 08							
Alresford (Essex)	d					09 13												10 13							
Wivenhoe 3	d					09 16							10 07					10 16							11 07
Hythe	d					09 20												10 20							
Colchester Town	a					09 24												10 24							
	d	09 15				09 28			09 45					10 15				10 28			10 45				
Colchester 4	a	09 22		09 27	09 32	09 37		09 48	09 52		10 01		10 17	10 22		10 27	10 32	10 37		10 48	10 52		11 01		11 17
	d			09 29	09 33		09 44	09 49			10 03		10 17			10 29	10 33			10 49			11 03		11 17
Marks Tey 2	d				09 39								10 23				10 39								11 23
Kelvedon	d				09 44												10 44								
Braintree	d											10 00												11 00	
Braintree Freeport	d											10 02												11 02	
Cressing	d											10 05												11 05	
White Notley	d											10 08												11 08	
Witham 2	d				09 49		09 56	10 02				10 15	10 31				10 49			11 02				11 15	11 31
Hatfield Peverel	d											10 20												11 20	
Chelmsford 3	d			09 47	09 58		10 05	10s10				10 27	10 40			10 46	10 58			11 11				11 27	11 40
Ingatestone	d						10 12					10 33												11 33	
Shenfield 3	a				10 09			10s22			10s29	10 40	10 51				11 09			11s22			11s29	11 40	11 51
Romford	a												10 59												11 59
Stratford 7 ⊖	a			10s11	10s24		10s32					10s55	11s07			11s10	11s24							11s55	12s07
London Liverpool Street 15 ⊖	a			10 24	10 33		10 41	10 46			10 54	11 03	11 18			11 24	11 33			11 45			11 54	12 03	12 16

For general notes see front of timetable
For details of catering facilities see Directory of Train Operators

A To Cambridge (Table 14)
B From Cambridge (Table 14)
C From Great Yarmouth (Table 15)

Norwich, Ipswich, Harwich, Clacton, Walton-on-Naze, Colchester and Chelmsford → London

Network diagram - see first page of Table 5

		LE 1	LE A	LE 1◇ ☕	LE 1	LE 1	LE 1◇	LE 1	LE 1	LE 1◇ ✕	LE 1	LE 1	LE 1	LE A	LE 1◇ ☕	LE 1	LE 1	LE 1◇	LE 1	LE 1	LE 1◇ ✕	LE 1	LE 1	LE 1	LE A
Norwich	d			10 30						11 00					11 30						12 00				
Diss	d			10 47						11 17					11 47						12 17				
Peterborough 8	d						09 47																		
Stowmarket	d		10 45				11 12			11 29				11 45							12 29				12 45
Needham Market	d		10 50											11 50											12 50
Lowestoft	d																	10 58							
Ipswich	a		11 03	11 07			11 25			11 40				12 03	12 07			12 26			12 40				13 03
	d			11 08			11 30			11 42					12 08			12 30			12 42				
Harwich Town	d				11 00											12 00									
Dovercourt	d				11 02											12 02									
Harwich International	d				11 06											12 06									
Wrabness	d				11 12											12 12									
Mistley	d				11 17											12 17									
Manningtree 2	d			11 18	11 22					11 52					12 18	12 22					12 52				
Walton-on-the-Naze	d								11 45											12 45					
Frinton-on-Sea	d								11 48											12 48					
Kirby Cross	d								11 51											12 51					
Clacton-on-Sea	d											11 50											12 50		
Thorpe-le-Soken 1	a					←			11 56			11 57					←			12 56			12 57		
	d					11 01			12 01 →			11 57					12 01			13 01 →			12 57		
Weeley	d					11 05											12 05								
Great Bentley	d					11 08											12 08								
Alresford (Essex)	d					11 13											12 13								
Wivenhoe 3	d					11 16						12 07					12 16						13 07		
Hythe	d					11 20											12 20								
Colchester Town	a					11 24											12 24								
	d	11 15				11 28		11 45					12 15				12 28		12 45					13 15	
Colchester 4	a	11 22		11 27	11 32	11 37	11 48	11 52		12 01		12 17	12 22		12 27	12 32	12 37	12 48	12 52		13 01		13 17	13 22	
	d			11 29	11 33		11 49			12 03		12 17			12 29	12 33		12 49			13 03		13 17		
Marks Tey 2	d				11 39							12 23				12 39							13 23		
Kelvedon	d				11 44											12 44									
Braintree	d										12 00											13 00			
Braintree Freeport	d										12 02											13 02			
Cressing	d										12 05											13 05			
White Notley	d										12 08											13 08			
Witham 2	d				11 49		12 02				12 15	12 31				12 49		13 02				13 15	13 31		
Hatfield Peverel	d										12 20											13 20			
Chelmsford 3	d			11 46	11 58		12 11				12 27	12 40			12 46	12 58		13 11				13 27	13 40		
Ingatestone	d										12 33											13 33			
Shenfield 3	a				12 09		12s22			12s29	12 40	12 51				13 09		13s22			13s29	13 40	13 51		
Romford	a											12 59											13 59		
Stratford 7 ⊖ ⛴	a			12s10	12s24						12s55	13s07			13s10	13s24						13s55	14s07		
London Liverpool Street 15 ⊖	a			12 24	12 33		12 45			12 54	13 03	13 16			13 24	13 33		13 45			13 54	14 03	14 16		

		LE 1◇ ☕	LE 1	LE 1	LE 1◇	LE 1	LE 1	LE 1◇ ✕	LE 1	LE 1	LE 1	LE A	LE 1◇ ☕	LE 1		LE 1	LE 1◇	LE 1	LE 1	LE 1◇ ☕	LE 1	LE 1	LE 1	LE A	LE 1◇ ☕
Norwich	d	12 30						13 00					13 30							14 00					14 30
Diss	d	12 47						13 17					13 47							14 17					14 47
Peterborough 8	d				11 48																				
Stowmarket	d				13 12			13 29				13 45								14 29				14 45	
Needham Market	d											13 50												14 50	
Lowestoft	d																12 58								
Ipswich	a	13 07			13 25			13 40				14 03	14 07				14 26			14 40				15 03	15 07
	d	13 08			13 30			13 42					14 08				14 30			14 42					15 08
Harwich Town	d		13 00											14 00											
Dovercourt	d		13 02											14 02											
Harwich International	d		13 06											14 06											
Wrabness	d		13 12											14 12											
Mistley	d		13 17											14 17											
Manningtree 2	d	13 18	13 22					13 52					14 18	14 22						14 52					15 18
Walton-on-the-Naze	d						13 45												14 45						
Frinton-on-Sea	d						13 48												14 48						
Kirby Cross	d						13 51												14 51						
Clacton-on-Sea	d									13 50												14 50			
Thorpe-le-Soken 1	a			←			13 56			13 57						←			14 56			14 57			
	d			13 01			14 01 →			13 57						14 01			15 01 →			14 57			
Weeley	d			13 05												14 05									
Great Bentley	d			13 08												14 08									
Alresford (Essex)	d			13 13												14 13									
Wivenhoe 3	d			13 16						14 07						14 16						15 07			
Hythe	d			13 20												14 20									
Colchester Town	a			13 24												14 24									
	d			13 28		13 45					14 15					14 28		14 45					15 15		
Colchester 4	a	13 27	13 32	13 37	13 48	13 52		14 01		14 17	14 22		14 27	14 32		14 37	14 48	14 52		15 01		15 17	15 22		15 27
	d	13 29	13 33		13 49			14 03		14 17			14 29	14 33			14 49			15 03		15 17			15 29
Marks Tey 2	d		13 39							14 23				14 39								15 23			
Kelvedon	d		13 44											14 44											
Braintree	d								14 00												15 00				
Braintree Freeport	d								14 02												15 02				
Cressing	d								14 05												15 05				
White Notley	d								14 08												15 08				
Witham 2	d		13 49		14 02				14 15	14 31				14 49			15 02				15 15	15 31			
Hatfield Peverel	d								14 20												15 20				
Chelmsford 3	d	13 46	13 58		14 11				14 27	14 40			14 46	14 58			15 11				15 27	15 40			15 46
Ingatestone	d								14 33												15 33				
Shenfield 3	a		14 09		14s22			14s29	14 40	14 51				15 09			15s22			15s29	15 40	15 51			
Romford	a									14 59												15 59			
Stratford 7 ⊖ ⛴	a	14s10	14s24						14s55	15s07			15s10	15s24							15s55	16s07			16s10
London Liverpool Street 15 ⊖	a	14 24	14 33		14 45			14 54	15 03	15 16			15 24	15 34			15 45			15 54	16 03	16 18			16 24

For general notes see front of timetable
For details of catering facilities see Directory of Train Operators

A From Cambridge (Table 14)

Norwich, Ipswich, Harwich, Clacton, Walton-on-Naze, Colchester and Chelmsford → London

Network diagram - see first page of Table 5

Station		LE 1	LE 1	LE 1	LE 1	LE 1	LE 1	LE 1 ◇ DP	LE 1	LE 1	LE A	LE 1	LE 1 ◇ DP	LE 1	LE 1	LE 1	LE 1	LE 1	LE 1 ◇ ✕	LE 1	LE 1	LE 1	LE 1	LE A	LE 1 ◇ DP
Norwich	d							15 00					15 30						16 00						16 30
Diss	d							15 17					15 47						16 17						16 47
Peterborough 8	d			13 47																					
Stowmarket	d			15 12				15 29			15 45								16 29					16 45	
Needham Market	d										15 50													16 50	
Lowestoft	d																								
Ipswich	a			15 25				15 40			16 03		16 07						16 40					17 03	17 07
	d			15 26				15 42					16 08				16 30		16 42						17 08
Harwich Town	d	15 00														16 05									
Dovercourt	d	15 02														16 07									
Harwich International	d	15 06														16 11									
Wrabness	d	15 12														16 17									
Mistley	d	15 17														16 22									
Manningtree 2	d	15 22						15 52					16 18			16 27			16 52						17 18
Walton-on-the-Naze	d						15 45											16 43							
Frinton-on-Sea	d						15 48											16 46							
Kirby Cross	d						15 51											16 49							
Clacton-on-Sea	d									15 50													16 48		
Thorpe-le-Soken 1	a		←				15 56			15 57					←			16 54					16 55		
	d		15 01				16 01 →			15 57					16 01			17 01 →					16 55		
Weeley	d		15 05												16 05										
Great Bentley	d		15 08												16 08										
Alresford (Essex)	d		15 13												16 13										
Wivenhoe 3	d		15 16							16 07					16 16								17 05		
Hythe	d		15 20												16 20								17 09		
Colchester Town	a		15 24												16 24										
	d		15 28			15 45						16 15			16 28						17 05				
Colchester 4	a	15 32	15 37	15 43		15 52		16 01		16 17		16 22	16 27		16 37	16 40	16 48		17 01		17 12		17 17		17 27
	d	15 36			15 48			16 03		16 17			16 29	16 33		16 53			17 03				17 17		17 29
Marks Tey 2	d				15 54					16 23				16 39		16 59							17 23		
Kelvedon	d	15 45			15 59									16 44											
Braintree	d								16 00											17 00					
Braintree Freeport	d								16 02											17 02					
Cressing	d								16 05											17 05					
White Notley	d								16 08											17 08					
Witham 2	d	15 49			16 04				16 15	16 31				16 49		17 07				17 15		17 21	17 31		
Hatfield Peverel	d								16 20													17 25			
Chelmsford 3	d	15 58			16 13				16 27	16 40			16 46	16 58		17 16				17 25		17 32	17 40		17 46
Ingatestone	d	16 05							16 33					17 05								17 39			
Shenfield 3	a	16 11			16 24			16s29	16 40	16 51				17 11		17 27			17s30	17 36		17 45	17 51		
Romford	a																						17 59		
Stratford 7 ⊖	a	16s26			16s39				16s55	17s05			17s10	17s26						17s50		18s02	18s07		18s12
London Liverpool Street 15 ⊖	a	16 35			16 48			16 54	17 05	17 15			17 24	17 38		17 49			17 54	18 00		18 11	18 20		18 24

Station		LE 1	LE 1	LE 1	LE 1 ◇	LE 1	LE 1 ◇ ✕	LE 1	LE 1	LE 1		LE A	LE 1 ◇ DP	LE 1	LE 1	LE 1	LE 1 ◇	LE 1	LE 1 ◇ ✕	LE 1	LE 1	LE 1	LE 1	LE A	LE 1
Norwich	d						17 00						17 30						18 00						
Diss	d						17 17						17 47						18 17						
Peterborough 8	d				15 47																				
Stowmarket	d				17 12		17 29					17 46	17 59						18 29					18 46	
Needham Market	d											17 52												18 52	
Lowestoft	d																16 58								
Ipswich	a				17 27		17 40					18 03	18 10				18 26		18 40					19 03	
	d				17 30		17 42						18 11				18 30		18 42			18 56			
Harwich Town	d	17 00						17 53										18 25					18 53		
Dovercourt	d	17 02						17 55										18 27					18 55		
Harwich International	d	17 06						17 58										18 30					18 58		
Wrabness	d	17 12						18 04										18 36					19 04		
Mistley	d	17 17						18 09										18 41					19 09		
Manningtree 2	d	17 22					17 52	18a14					18 21					18a46	18 52			19 06	19a14		
Walton-on-the-Naze	d					17 38										18 26									
Frinton-on-Sea	d					17 41										18 29									
Kirby Cross	d					17 44										18b35									
Clacton-on-Sea	d									17 45											18 45				
Thorpe-le-Soken 1	a		←			17 49				17 52				←		18 41					18 52				
	d		17 01			17 56 →				17 52				17 56							18 52				
Weeley	d		17 05											18 00											
Great Bentley	d		17 08							17 58				18 03							18 58				
Alresford (Essex)	d		17 13							18 02				18 08							19 02				
Wivenhoe 3	d		17 16							18 05				18 11							19 05				
Hythe	d		17 20											18 15											
Colchester Town	a		17 24											18 19											
	d		17 28											18 23											19 15
Colchester 4	a	17 32	17 37		17 48		18 01			18 14			18 30	18 32			18 48		19 01		19 14	19 17			19 22
	d	17 33			17 49		18 03			18 15			18 32	18 35			18 49		19 03		19 15				19 33 →
Marks Tey 2	d	17 39			17 55					18 21							18 55				19 21				
Kelvedon	d	17 44								18 26				18 44							19 26				
Braintree	d			17 44											18 36										
Braintree Freeport	d			17 46											18 38										
Cressing	d			17 49											18 41										
White Notley	d			17 52											18 44										
Witham 2	d	17 49		18 00	18 04				18 15	18 31				18 49	18 52		19 04			19 15	19 31				
Hatfield Peverel	d								18 20											19 20					
Chelmsford 3	d	17 58		18 09	18 13				18 27	18 40			18 49	18 58	19 02		19 13			19 27	19 40				
Ingatestone	d	18 05							18 33						19 09					19 33					
Shenfield 3	a	18 11			18s25		18s29		18 40	18 51				19 09	19 15		19s24		19s29	19 40	19 51				
Romford	a									18 59											19 59				
Stratford 7 ⊖	a	18s26							18s55	19s07			19s15	19s24						19s55	20s07				
London Liverpool Street 15 ⊖	a	18 35		18 41	18 49		18 54		19 05	19 16			19 27	19 33	19 40		19 47		19 54	20 04	20 16				

For general notes see front of timetable
For details of catering facilities see Directory of Train Operators

A From Cambridge (Table 14)
b Arr. 1832

Norwich, Ipswich, Harwich, Clacton, Walton-on-Naze, Colchester and Chelmsford → London

Network diagram - see first page of Table 5

		LE 1	LE 1 ◇	LE 1	LE 1	LE 1	LE 1 ◇	LE 1	LE 1	LE 1 ◇	LE 1	LE 1	LE 1	LE	LE 1	LE 1	LE 1	LE 1	LE 1 ◇	LE 1	LE 1 ◇	LE 1	LE 1	LE 1	LE 1
			🍴							🍴				A							🍴				
Norwich	d		18 30							19 00											20 00				
Diss	d		18 47							19 17											20 17				
Peterborough 8	d						17 47																		
Stowmarket	d						19 12			19 29				19 45							20 29				
Needham Market	d													19 50											
Lowestoft	d																		18 43						
Ipswich	a		19 07				19 25			19 40				20 03					20 16		20 40				
	d		19 08				19 27	19 35		19 42					20 08				20 30		20 42				
Harwich Town	d								19 28							20 00							20 33		21 00
Dovercourt	d								19 30							20 02							20 35		21 02
Harwich International	d								19 33							20 06							20 38		21 06
Wrabness	d								19 39							20 12							20 44		21 12
Mistley	d								19 44							20 17							20 49		21 17
Manningtree 2	d		19 18				19 37	19 46	19a49	19 52					20 18	20 22					20 52		20 56		21 22 →
Walton-on-the-Naze	d				18 48	19 24											19 51	20 24		20 45					
Frinton-on-Sea	d				18 51	19 27											19 54	20 27		20 48					
Kirby Cross	d				18 54	19b33											19 57	20c33		20 51					
Clacton-on-Sea	d												19 45											20 50	
Thorpe-le-Soken 1	a				18 59	19 39							19 52				20 02	20 39		20 56				20 57	
	d				19 01								19 52				20 03			21 01 →				20 57	
Weeley	d				19 05												20 07								
Great Bentley	d				19 08								19 58				20 10								
Alresford (Essex)	d				19 13								20 02				20 15								
Wivenhoe 3	d				19 16								20 05				20 18							21 07	
Hythe	d				19 20												20 22								
Colchester Town	a				19 24												20 26								
	d				19 28												20 30								
Colchester 4	a		19 27		19 37		19 47	19 57		20 01			20 14		20 28	20 32	20 39		20 48		21 01		21 06	21 17	
				←																					
	d		19 29	19 33			19 48			20 03			20 15		20 29	20 33			20 49		21 03			21 17	
Marks Tey 2	d			19 39			19 54						20 21			20 39								21 23	
Kelvedon	d			19 44									20 26			20 44									
Braintree	d	19 25										20 10										21 00			
Braintree Freeport	d	19 27										20 12										21 02			
Cressing	d	19 30										20 15										21 05			
White Notley	d	19 33										20 18										21 08			
Witham 2	d	19 41		19 49			20 02				20 15	20a25	20 31			20 49			21 02			21 15		21 31	
Hatfield Peverel	d										20 20											21 20			
Chelmsford 3	d	19 50	19 46	19 58			20 11				20 27		20 40		20 46	20 58			21 11			21 27		21 40	
Ingatestone	d										20 33											21 33			
Shenfield 3	a			20 09			20s23			20s29	20 40		20 51			21 09			21s23		21s29	21 40		21 51	
Romford	a												20 59											21 59	
Stratford 7 ⊖	a		20s10	20s24							20s55		21s07		21s10	21s24						21s55		22s10	
London Liverpool Street 15 ⊖	a	20 23	20 24	20 33			20 46			20 54	21 04		21 17		21 21	21 33			21 46		21 54	22 03		22 19	

		LE	LE 1	LE 1	LE 1	LE 1 ◇	LE 1	LE 1 ◇	LE 1	LE 1	LE 1	LE	LE 1	LE 1	LE 1	LE 1	LE 1	LE 1 ◇	LE 1	LE 1	LE 1	LE 1	LE
		A						🍴				A											A
Norwich	d							21 00										22 00				23 05	
Diss	d							21 17										22 17				23 22	
Peterborough 8	d					19 49															22 05		
Stowmarket	d	20 45				21 08		21 29				21 46						22 29			23 24	23 34	23 46
Needham Market	d	20 50										21 52											23 52
Lowestoft	d																						
Ipswich	a	21 03				21 25		21 40				22 03						22 40			23 37	23 48	00 03
	d	21 04	21 08			21 27		21 42					22 08					22 42		23 20	23 38		
Harwich Town	d										21 54								23 05				
Dovercourt	d										21 56								23 07				
Harwich International	d	21a28									21 59								23 10				
Wrabness	d										22 05								23 16				
Mistley	d			←							22 10								23 21				
Manningtree 2	d		21 18	21 22		21 37		21 52			22a15		22 18					22 52	23a26	23 29	23 48		
Walton-on-the-Naze	d						21 45										22 43						
Frinton-on-Sea	d						21 48										22 46						
Kirby Cross	d						21 51										22e52						
Clacton-on-Sea	d									21 50						22 24							
Thorpe-le-Soken 1	a				←		21 56			21 57				←		22 31	22 58						
	d				21 01		22 01 →			21 57				22 01		22 31							
Weeley	d				21 05									22 05		22 35							
Great Bentley	d				21 08									22 08		22 39							
Alresford (Essex)	d				21 13									22 13		22 43							
Wivenhoe 3	d				21 16					22 07				22 16		22 46							
Hythe	d				21 20									22 20		22 50							
Colchester Town	a				21 24									22 24									
	d				21 28									22 28									
Colchester 4	a		21 28	21 32	21 37	21 48		22 01		22 17			22 28	22 37		22 57		23 01		23 39	23 58		
	d		21 29	21 33		21 49		22 03		22 17			22 29					23 03					
Marks Tey 2	d			21 39						22 23			22 35										
Kelvedon	d			21 44									22 40										
Braintree	d								22 00						22 57								
Braintree Freeport	d								22 02						22 59								
Cressing	d								22 05						23 02								
White Notley	d								22 08						23 05								
Witham 2	d			21 49		22 02			22 15	22 31			22 45		23a12			23 15					
Hatfield Peverel	d								22 20				22 49										
Chelmsford 3	d		21 46	21 58		22 11			22 27	22 40			22 56					23 24					
Ingatestone	d								22 33				23 03										
Shenfield 3	a		21 58	22 11		22s22		22s29	22 40	22 51			23 09					23s36					
Romford	a									22 59													
Stratford 7 ⊖	a		22s12	22s27					22s55	23s07			23s25					23s52					
London Liverpool Street 15 ⊖	a		22 23	22 36		22 45		22 54	23 03	23 16			23 34					00 03					

For general notes see front of timetable
For details of catering facilities see Directory of Train Operators

A From Cambridge (Table 14)
b Arr. 1930
c Arr. 2030
e Arr. 2249

Table 11

Saturdays

Norwich, Ipswich, Harwich, Clacton, Walton-on-Naze, Colchester and Chelmsford → London

Network diagram - see first page of Table 5

		LE	LE	LE	LE	LE	LE	LE	LE	LE	LE		LE	LE	LE	LE	LE	LE	LE	LE	LE	LE		LE	LE
		■1	■1	■1	■1	■1	■1 ◇	■1	■1	■1 ◇	■1		■1	■1	■1	■1 ◇	■1	■1	■1	■1		A		■1 ◇	■1
							🍽			🍽						🍽								🍽	
Norwich	d						05 00			05 30						06 00								06 30	
Diss	d						05 17			05 47						06 17								06 47	
Peterborough ■8	d																								
Stowmarket	d						05 29									06 29						06 45			
Needham Market	d																					06 50			
Lowestoft	d																								
Ipswich	a						05 40			06 07						06 40						07 03		07 07	
	d						05 42			06 08				06 30		06 42					07 00			07 08	
Harwich Town	d										06 00								07 00						
Dovercourt	d										06 02								07 02						
Harwich International	d										06 06								07 06	07 15	07a25				
Wrabness	d										06 12								07 12						
Mistley	d										06 17								07 17						←
Manningtree ■2	d						05 52			06 18	06 22					06 52			07 22	07 28				07 18	07 22
Walton-on-the-Naze	d				05 45										06 45				→	→					
Frinton-on-Sea	d				05 48										06 48										
Kirby Cross	d				05 51										06 51										
Clacton-on-Sea	d								05 50									06 50							
Thorpe-le-Soken ■1	a				05 56				05 57				←		06 56			06 57							
	d				06 01 →				05 57				06 01		07 01 →			06 57							
Weeley	d												06 05												
Great Bentley	d												06 08												
Alresford (Essex)	d												06 13												
Wivenhoe ■3	d								06 07				06 16					07 07							
Hythe	d												06 20												
Colchester Town	a												06 24												
	d												06 28												
Colchester ■4	a						06 01		06 17	06 27	06 32		06 37	06 48		07 01		07 17						07 27	07 32
	d		04 45	05 30			06 03	06 06	06 17	06 29	06 33			06 49		07 03		07 17						07 29	07 33
Marks Tey ■2	d		04 51	05 36				06 12	06 23		06 39							07 23							07 39
Kelvedon	d		04 56	05 41				06 17			06 44														07 44
Braintree	d	00 03				06 00											07 00								
Braintree Freeport	d	00 05				06 02											07 02								
Cressing	d	00 08				06 05											07 05								
White Notley	d	00 11				06 08											07 08								
Witham ■2	d	00a18	05 01	05 46		06a15		06 22	06 31		06 49			07 02			07 15	07 31							07 49
Hatfield Peverel	d		05 05	05 50				06 26									07 20								
Chelmsford ■3	d		05 12	05 57				06 33	06 40	06 46	06 58			07 11			07 27	07 40						07 46	07 58
Ingatestone	d		05 19	06 04				06 40									07 33								
Shenfield ■3	a		05 25	06 10			06s29	06 46	06 51		07 09			07s22		07s29	07 40	07 51							08 09
Romford	a			06 19					06 59									07 59							
Stratford ■7 ⊖ ⛴	a		05s44	06s27				07s01	07s07	07s10	07s24						07s55	08s07						08s10	08s24
London Liverpool Street ■15 ⊖	a		05 57	06 36			06 54	07 10	07 16	07 24	07 33			07 45		07 54	08 03	08 16						08 24	08 33

For general notes see front of timetable
For details of catering facilities see
Directory of Train Operators

A From Bury St Edmunds (Table 14)

Table 11

Saturdays

Norwich, Ipswich, Harwich, Clacton, Walton-on-Naze, Colchester and Chelmsford → London

Network diagram - see first page of Table 5

		LE	LE	LE	LE	LE	LE	LE	LE	LE	LE	LE	LE	LE	LE	LE	LE	LE	LE	LE	LE	LE	LE
		1	1	R 1	1	1 ◇ ☕	A	1	1	1	B	1 ◇ ☕	1	1	R 1	1	1	1	1 ◇ ☕	1	1	1	B
Norwich	d					07 00						07 30							08 00				
Diss	d					07 17						07 47							08 17				
Peterborough 8	d																						
Stowmarket	d					07 29					07 45								08 29				08 45
Needham Market	d										07 50												08 50
Lowestoft	d			05 58											06 58								
Ipswich	a			07 26		07 40					08 03	08 07			08 26				08 40				09 03
	d			07 30		07 42						08 08			08 30				08 42				
Harwich Town	d												08 00										
Dovercourt	d												08 02										
Harwich International	d						07 47						08 06										
Wrabness	d						07 53						08 12										
Mistley	d		←				07a59						08 17										
Manningtree 2	d		07 28			07 52						08 18	08 22						08 52				
Walton-on-the-Naze	d				07 45													08 45					
Frinton-on-Sea	d				07 48													08 48					
Kirby Cross	d				07 51													08 51					
Clacton-on-Sea	d								07 50												08 50		
Thorpe-le-Soken 1	a	←			07 56				07 57					←				08 56			08 57		
	d	07 01			08 01 →				07 57					08 01				09 01 →			08 57		
Weeley	d	07 05												08 05									
Great Bentley	d	07 08												08 08									
Alresford (Essex)	d	07 13												08 13									
Wivenhoe 3	d	07 16							08 07					08 16							09 07		
Hythe	d	07 20												08 20									
Colchester Town	a	07 24												08 24									
	d	07 28								08 15				08 28			08 45					09 15	
Colchester 4	a	07 37	07 38	07 48		08 01			08 17	08 22		08 27	08 32	08 37	08 48		08 52		09 01		09 17	09 22	
	d		07 41	07 49		08 03			08 17			08 29	08 33		08 49	08 52			09 03		09 17		
Marks Tey 2	d								08 23				08 39								09 23		
Kelvedon	d												08 44										
Braintree	d							08 00												09 00			
Braintree Freeport	d							08 02												09 02			
Cressing	d							08 05												09 05			
White Notley	d							08 08												09 08			
Witham 2	d			08 02				08 15	08 31				08 49			09 04				09 15	09 31		
Hatfield Peverel	d							08 20												09 20			
Chelmsford 3	d		08 02	08 11				08 27	08 40			08 46	08 58		09s06	09 13				09 27	09 40		
Ingatestone	d							08 33												09 33			
Shenfield 3	a		08 13	08s22		08s29		08 40	08 51				09 09			09s24			09s29	09 40	09 51		
Romford	a								08 59												09 59		
Stratford 7 ⊖ ⛴	a		08s30					08s55	09s07			09s10	09s24							09s55	10s07		
London Liverpool Street 15 ⊖	a		08 39	08 45		08 54		09 03	09 16			09 24	09 33		09 38	09 47			09 54	10 03	10 16		

		LE	LE	LE	LE	LE	LE	LE	LE	LE	LE	LE	LE	LE	LE	LE	LE	LE	LE	LE	LE	LE	LE
		1 ◇ ☕	1	1	R 1	1	1	1	1 ◇ ☕	1	1	1	B	1 ◇ ☕	1	1	R 1	1	1	1	1 ◇ ☕	1	1
Norwich	d	08 30							09 00					09 30							10 00		
Diss	d	08 47							09 17					09 47							10 17		
Peterborough 8	d				07 47																		
Stowmarket	d				09 12				09 29				09 45								10 29		
Needham Market	d												09 50										
Lowestoft	d																08 58						
Ipswich	a	09 07			09 25				09 40				10 03	10 07			10 26				10 40		
	d	09 08			09 30				09 42					10 08			10 30				10 42		
Harwich Town	d		09 00												10 00								
Dovercourt	d		09 02												10 02								
Harwich International	d		09 06												10 06								
Wrabness	d		09 12												10 12								
Mistley	d		09 17												10 17								
Manningtree 2	d	09 18	09 22						09 52					10 18	10 22						10 52		
Walton-on-the-Naze	d							09 45												10 45			
Frinton-on-Sea	d							09 48												10 48			
Kirby Cross	d							09 51												10 51			
Clacton-on-Sea	d										09 50												10 50
Thorpe-le-Soken 1	a			←				09 56			09 57					←				10 56			10 57
	d			09 01				10 01 →			09 57					10 01				11 01 →			10 57
Weeley	d			09 05												10 05							
Great Bentley	d			09 08												10 08							
Alresford (Essex)	d			09 13												10 13							
Wivenhoe 3	d			09 16							10 07					10 16							11 07
Hythe	d			09 20												10 20							
Colchester Town	a			09 24												10 24							
	d			09 28			09 45					10 15				10 28			10 45				
Colchester 4	a	09 27	09 32	09 37	09 48		09 52		10 01		10 17	10 22		10 27	10 32	10 37	10 48		10 52		11 01		11 17
	d	09 29	09 33		09 49	09 52			10 03		10 17			10 29	10 33		10 49	10 52			11 03		11 17
Marks Tey 2	d		09 39								10 23				10 39								11 23
Kelvedon	d		09 44												10 44								
Braintree	d									10 00												11 00	
Braintree Freeport	d									10 02												11 02	
Cressing	d									10 05												11 05	
White Notley	d									10 08												11 08	
Witham 2	d		09 49			10 04				10 15	10 31				10 49			11 04				11 15	11 31
Hatfield Peverel	d									10 20												11 20	
Chelmsford 3	d	09 46	09 58		10s06	10 13				10 27	10 40			10 46	10 58		11s06	11 13				11 27	11 40
Ingatestone	d									10 33												11 33	
Shenfield 3	a		10 09			10s24			10s29	10 40	10 51				11 09			11s24			11s29	11 40	11 51
Romford	a										10 59												11 59
Stratford 7 ⊖ ⛴	a	10s10	10s24							10s55	11s07			11s10	11s24							11s55	12s07
London Liverpool Street 15 ⊖	a	10 24	10 33		10 38	10 47			10 54	11 03	11 16			11 24	11 33		11 42	11 47			11 54	12 03	12 16

For general notes see front of timetable
For details of catering facilities see
Directory of Train Operators

A To Cambridge (Table 14)
B From Cambridge (Table 14)

Norwich, Ipswich, Harwich, Clacton, Walton-on-Naze, Colchester and Chelmsford → London

Network diagram - see first page of Table 5

		LE	LE	LE	LE	LE	LE	LE	LE	LE	LE	LE	LE	LE	LE	LE	LE	LE	LE	LE	LE	LE	LE
		1		1◇	1	1	R 1	1	1	R 1	1	1	1		1◇	1	1	R 1	1	1	1◇	1	1
			A							B				A									
				☕						☕					☕						☕		
Norwich	d			10 30						11 00					11 30						12 00		
Diss	d			10 47						11 17					11 47						12 17		
Peterborough 8	d						09 55																
Stowmarket	d		10 45				11 14			11 29				11 45							12 29		
Needham Market	d		10 50											11 50									
Lowestoft	d																	10 58					
Ipswich	a		11 03	11 07			11 27			11 40				12 03	12 07			12 26			12 40		
	d			11 08			11 30			11 42					12 08			12 30			12 42		
Harwich Town	d				11 00											12 00							
Dovercourt	d				11 02											12 02							
Harwich International	d				11 06											12 06							
Wrabness	d				11 12											12 12							
Mistley	d				11 17											12 17							
Manningtree 2	d			11 18	11 22					11 52					12 18	12 22					12 52		
Walton-on-the-Naze	d								11 45											12 45			
Frinton-on-Sea	d								11 48											12 48			
Kirby Cross	d								11 51											12 51			
Clacton-on-Sea	d											11 50											12 50
Thorpe-le-Soken 1	a					←			11 56			11 57					←			12 56			12 57
	d					11 01			12 01 →			11 57					12 01			13 01 →			12 57
Weeley	d					11 05											12 05						
Great Bentley	d					11 08											12 08						
Alresford (Essex)	d					11 13											12 13						
Wivenhoe 3	d					11 16						12 07					12 16						13 07
Hythe	d					11 20											12 20						
Colchester Town	a					11 24											12 24						
	d	11 15				11 28		11 45					12 15				12 28		12 45				
Colchester 4	a	11 22		11 27	11 32	11 37	11 48	11 52		12 01		12 17	12 22		12 27	12 32	12 37	12 48	12 52		13 01		13 17
	d			11 29	11 33		11 49			12 03		12 17			12 29	12 33		12 49			13 03		13 17
Marks Tey 2	d				11 39							12 23				12 39							13 23
Kelvedon	d				11 44											12 44							
Braintree	d										12 00											13 00	
Braintree Freeport	d										12 02											13 02	
Cressing	d										12 05											13 05	
White Notley	d										12 08											13 08	
Witham 2	d				11 49		12 02				12 15	12 31				12 49		13 02				13 15	13 31
Hatfield Peverel	d										12 20											13 20	
Chelmsford 3	d			11 46	11 58		12 11				12 27	12 40			12 46	12 58		13 11				13 27	13 40
Ingatestone	d										12 33											13 33	
Shenfield 3	a				12 09		12s22			12s29	12 40	12 51				13 09		13s22			13s29	13 40	13 51
Romford	a											12 59											13 59
Stratford 7 ⊖	a			12s10	12s24						12s55	13s07			13s10	13s24						13s55	14s07
London Liverpool Street 15 ⊖	a			12 24	12 33		12 45			12 54	13 03	13 16			13 24	13 33		13 45			13 54	14 03	14 16

		LE	LE	LE	LE	LE	LE	LE	LE	LE	LE	LE	LE	LE	LE	LE	LE	LE	LE	LE	LE	LE	LE
		1		1◇	1	1	1◇	1	1	1◇	1	1	1		1◇	1	1	1◇	1	1	R 1	1	1
			A											A							B		
				☕						☕					☕						☕		
Norwich	d			12 30						13 00					13 30						14 00		
Diss	d			12 47						13 17					13 47						14 17		
Peterborough 8	d						11 48																
Stowmarket	d		12 45				13 12			13 29				13 45							14 29		
Needham Market	d		12 50											13 50									
Lowestoft	d																	12 58					
Ipswich	a		13 03	13 07			13 27			13 40				14 03	14 07			14 26			14 40		
	d			13 08			13 30			13 42					14 08			14 30			14 42		
Harwich Town	d				13 00											14 00							
Dovercourt	d				13 02											14 02							
Harwich International	d				13 06											14 06							
Wrabness	d				13 12											14 12							
Mistley	d				13 17											14 17							
Manningtree 2	d			13 18	13 22					13 52					14 18	14 22					14 52		
Walton-on-the-Naze	d								13 45											14 45			
Frinton-on-Sea	d								13 48											14 48			
Kirby Cross	d								13 51											14 51			
Clacton-on-Sea	d											13 50											14 50
Thorpe-le-Soken 1	a					←			13 56			13 57					←			14 56			14 57
	d					13 01			14 01 →			13 57					14 01			15 01 →			14 57
Weeley	d					13 05											14 05						
Great Bentley	d					13 08											14 08						
Alresford (Essex)	d					13 13											14 13						
Wivenhoe 3	d					13 16						14 07					14 16						15 07
Hythe	d					13 20											14 20						
Colchester Town	a					13 24											14 24						
	d	13 15				13 28		13 45					14 15				14 28		14 45				
Colchester 4	a	13 22		13 27	13 32	13 37	13 48	13 52		14 01		14 17	14 22		14 27	14 32	14 37	14 48	14 52		15 01		15 17
	d			13 29	13 33		13 49			14 03		14 17			14 29	14 33		14 49			15 03		15 17
Marks Tey 2	d				13 39							14 23				14 39							15 23
Kelvedon	d				13 44											14 44							
Braintree	d										14 00											15 00	
Braintree Freeport	d										14 02											15 02	
Cressing	d										14 05											15 05	
White Notley	d										14 08											15 08	
Witham 2	d				13 49		14 02				14 15	14 31				14 49		15 02				15 15	15 31
Hatfield Peverel	d										14 20											15 20	
Chelmsford 3	d			13 46	13 58		14 11				14 27	14 40			14 46	14 58		15 11				15 27	15 40
Ingatestone	d										14 33											15 33	
Shenfield 3	a				14 09		14s22			14s29	14 40	14 51				15 09		15s22			15s29	15 40	15 51
Romford	a											14 59											15 59
Stratford 7 ⊖	a			14s10	14s24						14s55	15s07			15s10	15s24						15s55	16s07
London Liverpool Street 15 ⊖	a			14 24	14 33		14 45			14 54	15 03	15 16			15 24	15 33		15 45			15 54	16 03	16 16

For general notes see front of timetable
For details of catering facilities see
Directory of Train Operators

A From Cambridge (Table 14)
B Until 27 September from Great Yarmouth (Table 15)

Norwich, Ipswich, Harwich, Clacton, Walton-on-Naze, Colchester and Chelmsford → London

Network diagram - see first page of Table 5

		LE	LE	LE	LE	LE	LE	LE	LE	LE	LE	LE	LE	LE	LE	LE	LE	LE	LE	LE	LE	LE	LE
		1		1 ◇	1	1	1 ◇	1	1	1 ◇	1	1	1		1 ◇	1	1	1 ◇	1	1	1 ◇	1	1
			A	🍴						🍴				A	🍴						🍴		
Norwich	d			14 30						15 00					15 30						16 00		
Diss	d			14 47						15 17					15 47						16 17		
Peterborough 8	d						13 47																
Stowmarket	d		14 45				15 12			15 29				15 45							16 29		
Needham Market	d		14 50											15 50									
Lowestoft	d																	14 58					
Ipswich	a		15 03	15 07			15 25			15 40				16 03	16 07			16 26			16 40		
	d			15 08			15 30			15 42					16 08			16 30			16 42		
Harwich Town	d				15 00											16 00							
Dovercourt	d				15 02											16 02							
Harwich International	d				15 06											16 06							
Wrabness	d				15 12											16 12							
Mistley	d				15 17											16 17							
Manningtree 2	d			15 18	15 22					15 52					16 18	16 22					16 52		
Walton-on-the-Naze	d								15 45											16 45			
Frinton-on-Sea	d								15 48											16 48			
Kirby Cross	d								15 51											16 51			
Clacton-on-Sea	d											15 50											16 50
Thorpe-le-Soken 1	a					←			15 56			15 57					←			16 56			16 57
	d					15 01			16 01 →			15 57					16 01			17 01 →			16 57
Weeley	d					15 05											16 05						
Great Bentley	d					15 08											16 08						
Alresford (Essex)	d					15 13											16 13						
Wivenhoe 3	d					15 16						16 07					16 16						17 07
Hythe	d					15 20											16 20						
Colchester Town	a					15 24											16 24						
	d	15 15				15 28		15 45					16 15				16 28		16 45				
Colchester 4	a	15 22		15 27	15 32	15 37	15 48	15 52		16 01		16 17	16 22		16 27	16 32	16 37	16 48	16 52		17 01		17 17
	d			15 29	15 33		15 49			16 03		16 17			16 29	16 33		16 49			17 03		17 17
Marks Tey 2	d				15 39							16 23				16 39							17 23
Kelvedon	d				15 44											16 44							
Braintree	d										16 00											17 00	
Braintree Freeport	d										16 02											17 02	
Cressing	d										16 05											17 05	
White Notley	d										16 08											17 08	
Witham 2	d				15 49		16 02				16 15	16 31				16 49		17 02				17 15	17 31
Hatfield Peverel	d										16 20											17 20	
Chelmsford 3	d			15 46	15 58		16 11				16 27	16 40			16 46	16 58		17 11				17 27	17 40
Ingatestone	d										16 33											17 33	
Shenfield 3	a				16 09		16s22			16s29	16 40	16 51				17 09		17s22			17s29	17 40	17 51
Romford	a											16 59											17 59
Stratford 7 ⊖	a			16s10	16s24						16s55	17s07			17s10	17s24						17s55	18s07
London Liverpool Street 15 ⊖	a			16 24	16 33		16 45			16 54	17 03	17 16			17 24	17 33		17 45			17 54	18 03	18 16

		LE	LE	LE	LE	LE	LE	LE	LE	LE	LE	LE	LE	LE	LE	LE	LE	LE	LE	LE	LE	LE	LE
		1		1 ◇	1	1	1 ◇	1	1	1 ◇	1	1	1		1 ◇	1	1	1 ◇	1	1	1 ◇	1	1
			A	🍴						🍴				A	🍴						🍴		
Norwich	d			16 30						17 00					17 30						18 00		
Diss	d			16 47						17 17					17 47						18 17		
Peterborough 8	d						15 47																
Stowmarket	d		16 45				17 12			17 29				17 46							18 29		
Needham Market	d		16 50											17 52									
Lowestoft	d																	16 58					
Ipswich	a		17 03	17 07			17 27			17 40				18 03	18 07			18 26			18 40		
	d			17 08			17 30			17 42					18 08			18 30			18 42		
Harwich Town	d				17 00											18 00							
Dovercourt	d				17 02											18 02							
Harwich International	d				17 06											18 06							
Wrabness	d				17 12											18 12							
Mistley	d				17 17											18 17							
Manningtree 2	d			17 18	17 22					17 52					18 18	18 22					18 52		
Walton-on-the-Naze	d								17 45											18 45			
Frinton-on-Sea	d								17 48											18 48			
Kirby Cross	d								17 51											18 51			
Clacton-on-Sea	d											17 50											18 50
Thorpe-le-Soken 1	a					←			17 56			17 57					←			18 56			18 57
	d					17 01			18 01 →			17 57					18 01			19 01 →			18 57
Weeley	d					17 05											18 05						
Great Bentley	d					17 08											18 08						
Alresford (Essex)	d					17 13											18 13						
Wivenhoe 3	d					17 16						18 07					18 16						19 07
Hythe	d					17 20											18 20						
Colchester Town	a					17 24											18 24						
	d	17 15				17 28		17 45					18 15				18 28		18 45				
Colchester 4	a	17 22		17 27	17 32	17 37	17 48	17 52		18 01		18 17	18 22		18 27	18 32	18 37	18 48	18 52		19 01		19 17
	d			17 29	17 33		17 49			18 03		18 17			18 29	18 33		18 49			19 03		19 17
Marks Tey 2	d				17 39							18 23				18 39							19 23
Kelvedon	d				17 44											18 44							
Braintree	d										18 00											19 00	
Braintree Freeport	d										18 02											19 02	
Cressing	d										18 05											19 05	
White Notley	d										18 08											19 08	
Witham 2	d				17 49		18 02				18 15	18 31				18 49		19 02				19 15	19 31
Hatfield Peverel	d										18 20											19 20	
Chelmsford 3	d			17 46	17 58		18 11				18 27	18 40			18 46	18 58		19 11				19 27	19 40
Ingatestone	d										18 33											19 33	
Shenfield 3	a				18 09		18s22			18s29	18 40	18 51				19 09		19s22			19s29	19 40	19 51
Romford	a											18 59											19 59
Stratford 7 ⊖	a			18s10	18s24						18s55	19s07			19s10	19s24						19s55	20s07
London Liverpool Street 15 ⊖	a			18 24	18 33		18 45			18 54	19 03	19 16			19 24	19 33		19 45			19 54	20 03	20 16

For general notes see front of timetable
For details of catering facilities see Directory of Train Operators

A From Cambridge (Table 14)

Table 11

Saturdays

Norwich, Ipswich, Harwich, Clacton, Walton-on-Naze, Colchester and Chelmsford → London

Network diagram - see first page of Table 5

		LE 1	LE A	LE 1◇ ☕	LE 1	LE 1	LE 1◇	LE 1	LE 1	LE 1◇ ☕	LE 1	LE 1	LE A	LE 1	LE 1	LE 1	LE 1◇	LE 1	LE 1◇ ☕	LE 1	LE 1	LE 1	LE A
Norwich	d			18 30						19 00									20 00				
Diss	d			18 47						19 17									20 17				
Peterborough 8	d						17 47																
Stowmarket	d		18 46				19 12			19 29			19 45						20 29				20 45
Needham Market	d		18 52										19 50										20 50
Lowestoft	d																18 58						
Ipswich	a		19 03	19 07			19 25			19 40			20 03				20 26		20 40				21 03
	d			19 08			19 27			19 42				20 08			20 30		20 42				21 04
Harwich Town	d				19 00										20 00							21 00	
Dovercourt	d				19 02										20 02							21 02	
Harwich International	d				19 06										20 06							21 06	21a28
Wrabness	d				19 12										20 12							21 12	
Mistley	d				19 17										20 17							21 17	
Manningtree 2	d			19 18	19 22		19 37			19 52				20 18	20 22				20 52			21 22 →	
Walton-on-the-Naze	d								19 45									20 45					
Frinton-on-Sea	d								19 48									20 48					
Kirby Cross	d								19 51									20 51					
Clacton-on-Sea	d											19 50									20 50		
Thorpe-le-Soken 1	a					←			19 56			19 57				←		20 56			20 57		
	d					19 01			20 01 →			19 57				20 01		21 01 →			20 57		
Weeley	d					19 05										20 05							
Great Bentley	d					19 08										20 08							
Alresford (Essex)	d					19 13										20 13							
Wivenhoe 3	d					19 16						20 07				20 16					21 07		
Hythe	d					19 20										20 20							
Colchester Town	a					19 24										20 24							
	d	19 15				19 28		19 45								20 28							
Colchester 4	a	19 22		19 27	19 32	19 37	19 48	19 52		20 01		20 17		20 28	20 32	20 37	20 48		21 01		21 17		
	d			19 29	19 33		19 49			20 03		20 17		20 29	20 33		20 49		21 03		21 17		
Marks Tey 2	d				19 39							20 23			20 39						21 23		
Kelvedon	d				19 44										20 44								
Braintree	d										20 00									21 00			
Braintree Freeport	d										20 02									21 02			
Cressing	d										20 05									21 05			
White Notley	d										20 08									21 08			
Witham 2	d				19 49		20 02				20 15	20 31			20 49		21 02			21 15	21 31		
Hatfield Peverel	d										20 20									21 20			
Chelmsford 3	d			19 46	19 58		20 11				20 27	20 40		20 46	20 58		21 11			21 27	21 40		
Ingatestone	d										20 33									21 33			
Shenfield 3	a				20 09		20s22			20s29	20 40	20 51			21 10		21s22		21s29	21 40	21 51		
Romford	a											20 59									21 59		
Stratford 7 ⊖ ⛴	a			20s10	20s24						20s55	21s07		21s10	21s25					21s54	22s07		
London Liverpool Street 15 ⊖	a			20 24	20 33		20 45			20 54	21 03	21 16		21 19	21 38		21 49		21 58	22 07	22 20		

		LE 1	LE 1	LE 1	LE 1◇	LE 1	LE 1◇ ☕	LE 1	LE 1	LE 1	LE A	LE 1	LE 1	LE 1	LE 1	LE 1◇	LE A	LE 1	LE 1	LE 1	LE 1	LE 1
Norwich	d						21 00									22 00						23 05
Diss	d						21 17									22 17						23 22
Peterborough 8	d				19 46																21 49	
Stowmarket	d				21 12		21 29				21 45					22 29	22 46				23 17	23 34
Needham Market	d										21 50						22 52				23 22	
Lowestoft	d																					
Ipswich	a				21 27		21 40				22 03					22 40	23 03				23 32	23 50
	d	21 08			21 27		21 42					22 08				22 42				23 26	23 35	
Harwich Town	d									21 54									23 10			
Dovercourt	d									21 56									23 12			
Harwich International	d									21 59									23 15			
Wrabness	d									22 05									23 21			
Mistley	d		←							22 10									23 26			
Manningtree 2	d	21 18	21 22		21 37		21 52			22a15		22 18				22 52			23a31	23 35	23 45	
Walton-on-the-Naze	d					21 45									22 45							
Frinton-on-Sea	d					21 48									22 48							
Kirby Cross	d					21 51									22 51							
Clacton-on-Sea	d								21 50					22 25								
Thorpe-le-Soken 1	a			←		21 56			21 57				←	22 32	22 57							
	d			21 01		22 01 →			21 57				22 01	22 32								
Weeley	d			21 05									22 05	22 36								
Great Bentley	d			21 08									22 08	22 40								
Alresford (Essex)	d			21 13									22 13	22 44								
Wivenhoe 3	d			21 16					22 07				22 16	22 47								
Hythe	d			21 20									22 20	22 51								
Colchester Town	a			21 24									22 24									
	d			21 28									22 28									
Colchester 4	a	21 28	21 32	21 37	21 48		22 01		22 17			22 28	22 37	22 58		23 01				23 45	23 56	
	d	21 29	21 33		21 49		22 03		22 17			22 29				23 03						
Marks Tey 2	d		21 39						22 23			22 35										
Kelvedon	d		21 44									22 40										
Braintree	d							22 00										23 07				
Braintree Freeport	d							22 02										23 09				
Cressing	d							22 05										23 12				
White Notley	d							22 08										23 15				
Witham 2	d		21 49		22 02			22 15	22 31			22 45				23 15		23a22				
Hatfield Peverel	d							22 20				22 49										
Chelmsford 3	d	21 46	21 58		22 11			22 27	22 40			22 56				23 24						
Ingatestone	d							22 33				23 03										
Shenfield 3	a	21 58	22 10		22s22		22s29	22 40	22 51			23 09				23s36						
Romford	a								22 59													
Stratford 7 ⊖ ⛴	a	22s12	22s25					22s55	23s07			23s25				23s52						
London Liverpool Street 15 ⊖	a	22 25	22 38		22 49		22 58	23 07	23 20			23 38				00 07						

For general notes see front of timetable
For details of catering facilities see Directory of Train Operators

A From Cambridge (Table 14)

Norwich, Ipswich, Harwich, Clacton, Walton-on-Naze, Colchester and Chelmsford → London

Network diagram - see first page of Table 5

		LE 1	LE 1	LE 1	LE	LE 1	LE 1	LE 1	LE 1 ◇	LE 1	LE	LE 1	LE 1	LE 1	LE 1 ◇	LE 1	LE 1	LE 1	LE 1	LE 1	LE 1 ◇	LE 1	LE 1	LE 1	LE 1
					A																				
									☕						☕						☕				
Norwich	d								07 00						08 00						09 00				
Diss	d								07 17						08 17						09 17				
Peterborough 8	d																								
Stowmarket	d								07 29						08 29						09 29				
Needham Market	d																								
Lowestoft	d																								
Ipswich	a								07 40						08 40						09 40				
	d								07 42		07 45	08 08			08 42			09 08			09 42			10 08	
Harwich Town	d																08 53						09 53		
Dovercourt	d																08 55						09 55		
Harwich International	d						07 25				08a10						08 58						09 58		
Wrabness	d																09 04						10 04		
Mistley	d																09 09						10 09		
Manningtree 2	d						07 38		07 52			08 18			08 52		09a14	09 18			09 52		10a14	10 18	
Walton-on-the-Naze	d												08 30						09 30						10 30
Frinton-on-Sea	d												08 33						09 33						10 33
Kirby Cross	d												08 36						09 36						10 36
Clacton-on-Sea	d									07 36						08 36						09 36			
Thorpe-le-Soken 1	a									07 43			08 42			08 43			09 42			09 43			10 42
	d									07 43						08 43						09 43			
Weeley	d																								
Great Bentley	d									07 49						08 49						09 49			
Alresford (Essex)	d									07 53						08 53						09 53			
Wivenhoe 3	d									07 56						08 56						09 56			
Hythe	d																								
Colchester Town	a																								
	d																								
Colchester 4	a						07 48		08 01	08 06		08 29			09 01	09 06		09 29			10 01	10 06		10 29	
	d			06 56	07 07	07 26	07 49		08 03	08 06		08 30			09 03	09 06		09 30			10 03	10 06		10 30	
Marks Tey 2	d			07 02	07a14	07 32				08 12		08 36				09 12		09 36				10 12		10 36	
Kelvedon	d			07 07		07 37						08 41						09 41						10 41	
Braintree	d	00 07						08 00						09 00						10 00					
Braintree Freeport	d	00 09						08 02						09 02						10 02					
Cressing	d	00 12						08 05						09 05						10 05					
White Notley	d	00 15						08 08						09 08						10 08					
Witham 2	d	00a22		07 12		07 42		08a16		08 20		08 46		09a16		09 20		09 46		10a16		10 20		10 46	
Hatfield Peverel	d			07 16		07 46						08 50						09 50						10 50	
Chelmsford 3	d		06 53	07 23		07 53	08 07			08 29		08 57				09 29		09 57				10 29		10 57	
Ingatestone	d		07 00	07 30		08 00						09 04						10 04						11 04	
Shenfield 3	a		07 06	07 36		08 06	08 18		08s29	08 40		09 10			09s29	09 40		10 10			10s29	10 40		11 10	
Romford	a																								
Stratford 7 ⊖	a		07s34	08s04		08s34	08s49			09s04		09s34				10s04		10s34				11s04		11s34	
London Liverpool Street 15 ⊖	a		07 42	08 12		08 42	08 59		09 03	09 12		09 42			10 01	10 12		10 42			11 03	11 12		11 42	

For general notes see front of timetable
For details of catering facilities see Directory of Train Operators

A To Sudbury (Table 10)

Table 11

Sundays

Norwich, Ipswich, Harwich, Clacton, Walton-on-Naze, Colchester and Chelmsford → London

Network diagram - see first page of Table 5

		LE		LE	LE	LE	LE	LE	LE	LE	LE	LE	LE	LE	LE	LE	LE	LE	LE	LE	LE	LE	LE	LE	LE
				[1]	[1] ◇	[1]	[1]	[1]	[1]	[1]	[1]	[1] ◇	[1]	[1]	[1]	[1]		[1]	[1] ◇	[1]	[1]	[1]	[1]	[1]	[1]
		A							B								C								
					☕							☕							☕						
Norwich	d				10 00							11 00							12 00						
Diss	d				10 17							11 17							12 17						
Peterborough [8]	d								09 47														11 46		
Stowmarket	d	10 17			10 29				11 12			11 29					12 17		12 29				13 12		
Needham Market	d	10 22															12 22								
Lowestoft	d																								
Ipswich	a	10 34			10 40				11 25			11 40					12 34		12 40				13 25		
	d				10 42			11 08				11 42			12 08				12 42			13 08			
Harwich Town	d						10 53							11 53							12 53				
Dovercourt	d						10 55							11 55							12 55				
Harwich International	d						10 58							11 58							12 58				
Wrabness	d						11 04							12 04							13 04				
Mistley	d						11 09							12 09							13 09				
Manningtree [2]	d				10 52		11a14	11 18				11 52		12a14	12 18				12 52		13a14	13 18			
Walton-on-the-Naze	d									11 30						12 30								13 30	
Frinton-on-Sea	d									11 33						12 33								13 33	
Kirby Cross	d									11 36						12 36								13 36	
Clacton-on-Sea	d					10 36							11 36							12 36					
Thorpe-le-Soken [1]	a					10 43				11 42			11 43			12 42				12 43				13 42	
	d					10 43							11 43							12 43					
Weeley	d																								
Great Bentley	d					10 49							11 49							12 49					
Alresford (Essex)	d					10 53							11 53							12 53					
Wivenhoe [3]	d					10 56							11 56							12 56					
Hythe	d																								
Colchester Town	a																								
	d																								
Colchester [4]	a				11 01	11 06		11 29				12 01	12 06		12 29				13 01	13 06		13 29			
	d				11 03	11 06		11 30				12 03	12 06		12 30				13 03	13 06		13 30			
Marks Tey [2]	d					11 12		11 36					12 12		12 36					13 12		13 36			
Kelvedon	d							11 41							12 41							13 41			
Braintree	d			11 00							12 00							13 00							14 00
Braintree Freeport	d			11 02							12 02							13 02							14 02
Cressing	d			11 05							12 05							13 05							14 05
White Notley	d			11 08							12 08							13 08							14 08
Witham [2]	d			11a16		11 20		11 46			12a16		12 20		12 46			13a16		13 20		13 46			14a16
Hatfield Peverel	d							11 50							12 50							13 50			
Chelmsford [3]	d					11 29		11 57					12 29		12 57					13 29		13 57			
Ingatestone	d							12 04							13 04							14 04			
Shenfield [3]	a				11s29	11 40		12 10				12s29	12 40		13 10				13s29	13 40		14 10			
Romford	a																								
Stratford [7] ⊖ ⛴	a					12s04		12s34					13s04		13s34					14s04		14s34			
London Liverpool Street [15] ⊖	a				12 01	12 12		12 42				13 01	13 12		13 42				14 01	14 12		14 42			

		LE	LE	LE		LE	LE	LE	LE	LE	LE	LE	LE	LE	LE	LE	LE	LE	LE	LE	LE	LE	LE	LE	LE
																								R	
		[1] ◇	[1]	[1]		[1]	[1]		[1]	[1] ◇	[1]	[1]	[1]	[1]	[1]	[1]	[1] ◇	[1]	[1]	[1]	[1]		[1]	[1]	[1]
								C														C			
		☕								☕							☕							☕	
Norwich	d	13 00								14 00							15 00							16 00	
Diss	d	13 17								14 17							15 17							16 17	
Peterborough [8]	d													13 48											
Stowmarket	d	13 29						14 17		14 29				15 12			15 29					16 17		16 29	
Needham Market	d							14 22														16 22			
Lowestoft	d																								
Ipswich	a	13 40						14 34		14 40				15 27			15 40					16 34		16 40	
	d	13 42				14 08				14 42			15 08				15 42			16 08				16 42	
Harwich Town	d			13 53								14 53							15 53						
Dovercourt	d			13 55								14 55							15 55						
Harwich International	d			13 58								14 58							15 58						
Wrabness	d			14 04								15 04							16 04						
Mistley	d			14 09								15 09							16 09						
Manningtree [2]	d	13 52		14a14		14 18				14 52		15a14	15 18				15 52		16a14	16 18				16 52	
Walton-on-the-Naze	d						14 30								15 30						16 30				
Frinton-on-Sea	d						14 33								15 33						16 33				
Kirby Cross	d						14 36								15 36						16 36				
Clacton-on-Sea	d		13 36								14 36							15 36							16 36
Thorpe-le-Soken [1]	a		13 43				14 42				14 43				15 42			15 43			16 42				16 43
	d		13 43								14 43							15 43							16 43
Weeley	d																								
Great Bentley	d		13 49								14 49							15 49							16 49
Alresford (Essex)	d		13 53								14 53							15 53							16 53
Wivenhoe [3]	d		13 56								14 56							15 56							16 56
Hythe	d																								
Colchester Town	a																								
	d																								
Colchester [4]	a	14 01	14 06			14 29				15 01	15 06		15 29				16 01	16 06		16 29				17 01	17 06
	d	14 03	14 06			14 30				15 03	15 06		15 30				16 03	16 06		16 30				17 03	17 06
Marks Tey [2]	d		14 12			14 36					15 12		15 36					16 12		16 36					17 12
Kelvedon	d					14 41							15 41							16 41					
Braintree	d								15 00							16 00							17 00		
Braintree Freeport	d								15 02							16 02							17 02		
Cressing	d								15 05							16 05							17 05		
White Notley	d								15 08							16 08							17 08		
Witham [2]	d		14 20			14 46			15a16		15 20		15 46			16a16		16 20		16 46			17a16		17 20
Hatfield Peverel	d					14 50							15 50							16 50					
Chelmsford [3]	d		14 29			14 57					15 29		15 57					16 29		16 57					17 29
Ingatestone	d					15 04							16 04							17 04					
Shenfield [3]	a	14s29	14 40			15 10				15s29	15 40		16 10				16s29	16 40		17 10				17s29	17 40
Romford	a																								
Stratford [7] ⊖ ⛴	a		15s04			15s34					16s04		16s34					17s04		17s34					18s04
London Liverpool Street [15] ⊖	a	15 01	15 12			15 42				16 01	16 12		16 42				17 01	17 12		17 42				18 01	18 12

For general notes see front of timetable
For details of catering facilities see Directory of Train Operators

A From Bury St Edmunds (Table 14)
B Until 7 September
C From Cambridge (Table 14)

Table 11

Sundays

Norwich, Ipswich, Harwich, Clacton, Walton-on-Naze, Colchester and Chelmsford → London

Network diagram - see first page of Table 5

		LE 1	LE 1 ◇ ☕	LE 1	LE 1	LE 1		LE 1	LE 1 ◇ ☕	LE 1	LE 1	LE 1	LE 1	LE A	LE 1	LE 1 ◇ ☕	LE 1	LE 1	LE 1	LE 1	LE 1	LE 1	LE 1 ◇ ☕	LE 1	LE 1
Norwich	d		16 20						17 00							18 00							19 00		
Diss	d		16 37						17 17							18 17							19 17		
Peterborough 8	d				15 47															17 47					
Stowmarket	d		16 49		17 12				17 29					18 17		18 29				19 12			19 29		
Needham Market	d													18 22											
Lowestoft	d																								
Ipswich	a		17 00		17 25				17 40					18 34		18 40				19 27			19 40		
	d		17 03	17 08					17 42			18 08				18 42			19 08				19 42		
Harwich Town	d	16 53									17 53							18 53							19 53
Dovercourt	d	16 55									17 55							18 55							19 55
Harwich International	d	16 58									17 58							18 58							19 58
Wrabness	d	17 04									18 04							19 04							20 04
Mistley	d	17 09									18 09							19 09							20 09
Manningtree 2	d	17a14		17 18					17 52		18a14	18 18				18 52		19a14	19 18				19 52		20a14
Walton-on-the-Naze	d					17 30							18 30								19 30				
Frinton-on-Sea	d					17 33							18 33								19 33				
Kirby Cross	d					17 36							18 36								19 36				
Clacton-on-Sea	d									17 36							18 36							19 36	
Thorpe-le-Soken 1	a					17 42				17 43			18 42				18 43				19 42			19 43	
	d									17 43							18 43							19 43	
Weeley	d																								
Great Bentley	d									17 49							18 49							19 49	
Alresford (Essex)	d									17 53							18 53							19 53	
Wivenhoe 3	d									17 56							18 56							19 56	
Hythe	d																								
Colchester Town	a																								
	d																								
Colchester 4	a		17 19	17 29					18 01	18 06		18 29				19 01	19 06		19 29				20 01	20 06	
	d		17 21	17 30					18 03	18 06		18 30				19 03	19 06		19 30				20 03	20 06	
Marks Tey 2	d			17 36						18 12		18 36					19 12		19 36					20 12	
Kelvedon	d			17 41								18 41							19 41						
Braintree	d							18 00							19 00							20 00			
Braintree Freeport	d							18 02							19 02							20 02			
Cressing	d							18 05							19 05							20 05			
White Notley	d							18 08							19 08							20 08			
Witham 2	d			17 46				18a16		18 20		18 46			19a16		19 20		19 46			20a16		20 20	
Hatfield Peverel	d			17 50								18 50							19 50						
Chelmsford 3	d			17 57						18 29		18 57					19 29		19 57					20 29	
Ingatestone	d			18 04								19 04							20 04						
Shenfield 3	a			18 10					18s29	18 40		19 10				19s29	19 40		20 10				20s29	20 40	
Romford	a																								
Stratford 7 ⊖ ⛴	a			18s34						19s04		19s34					20s04		20s34					21s04	
London Liverpool Street 15 ⊖	a		18 28	18 42					19 01	19 12		19 42				20 01	20 12		20 42				21 01	21 12	

		LE 1	LE 1	LE 1	LE 1	LE A	LE 1 ◇ ☕	LE 1	LE 1	LE 1	LE 1	LE 1	LE 1 ◇	LE 1	LE 1	LE 1	LE 1	LE 1	LE A	LE 1	LE 1 ◇	LE 1	LE 1		
Norwich	d						20 00						21 00								22 00		23 05		
Diss	d						20 17						21 17								22 17		23 22		
Peterborough 8	d									19 44															
Stowmarket	d					20 17	20 29			21 05			21 29						22 17		22 29		23 34		
Needham Market	d					20 22													22 22						
Lowestoft	d																								
Ipswich	a					20 34	20 40			21 18			21 40						22 34		22 40		23 48		
	d	20 08				20 35	20 42		21 08	21 19			21 42				22 08				22 42				
Harwich Town	d				20 53											21 53						22 53			
Dovercourt	d				20 55											21 55						22 55			
Harwich International	d				20 58	21a02										21 58						22 58			
Wrabness	d				21 04											22 04						23 04			
Mistley	d				21 09											22 09						23 09			
Manningtree 2	d	20 18			21a14		20 52		21 18	21 29			21 52			22a14	22 18				22 52	23 14			
Walton-on-the-Naze	d		20 30								21 30				22 13										
Frinton-on-Sea	d		20 33								21 33				22 16										
Kirby Cross	d		20 36								21 36				22 19										
Clacton-on-Sea	d							20 36						21 36				22 20							
Thorpe-le-Soken 1	a		20 42					20 43			21 42			21 43	22 25			22 27							
	d							20 43						21 43				22 27							
Weeley	d																								
Great Bentley	d							20 49						21 49											
Alresford (Essex)	d							20 53						21 53											
Wivenhoe 3	d							20 56						21 56				22 37							
Hythe	d																								
Colchester Town	a																								
	d																								
Colchester 4	a	20 29					21 01	21 06	21 29	21 40			22 01	22 06			22 29	22 47			23 01	23 24			
	d	20 30					21 03	21 06	21 30				22 03	22 06			22 30				23 03				
Marks Tey 2	d	20 36						21 12	21 36					22 12			22 36								
Kelvedon	d	20 41							21 41								22 41								
Braintree	d			21 00								22 00								22 56					
Braintree Freeport	d			21 02								22 02								22 58					
Cressing	d			21 05								22 05								23 01					
White Notley	d			21 08								22 08								23 04					
Witham 2	d	20 46		21a16				21 20	21 46			22a16		22 20			22 46			23a12	23 15				
Hatfield Peverel	d	20 50							21 50								22 50								
Chelmsford 3	d	20 57						21 29	21 57					22 29			22 57				23 24				
Ingatestone	d	21 04							22 04								23 04								
Shenfield 3	a	21 10					21s29	21 40	22 10				22s29	22 40			23 10				23s36				
Romford	a																								
Stratford 7 ⊖ ⛴	a	21s34						22s04	22s34					23s04			23s34				23s57				
London Liverpool Street 15 ⊖	a	21 42					22 01	22 12	22 42				23 01	23 12			23 42				00 07				

For general notes see front of timetable
For details of catering facilities see Directory of Train Operators

A From Cambridge (Table 14)

Network Diagram for Tables 13, 14, 15, 16, 17

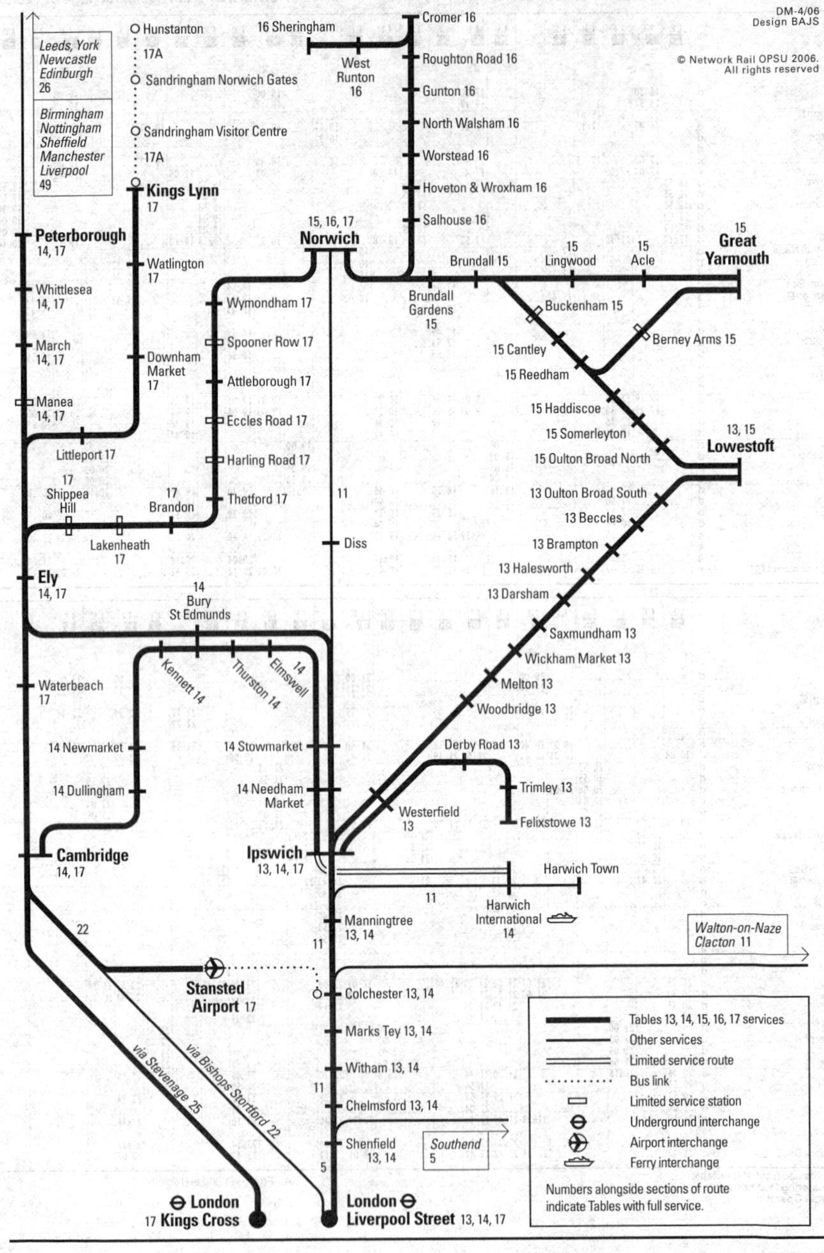

DM-4/06
Design BAJS
© Network Rail OPSU 2006.
All rights reserved
Leeds, York
Newcastle
Edinburgh
26
Birmingham
Nottingham
Sheffield
Manchester
Liverpool
49
Hunstanton
17A
Sandringham Norwich Gates
Sandringham Visitor Centre
17A
Kings Lynn
17
Watlington
17
Downham Market
17
Littleport 17
Peterborough
14, 17
Whittlesea
14, 17
March
14, 17
Manea
14, 17
17
Shippea Hill
17
Brandon
Lakenheath
17
Ely
14, 17
Waterbeach
17
14 Newmarket
14 Dullingham
Cambridge
14, 17
22
Stansted Airport 17
via Stevenage 25
via Bishops Stortford 22
London
17 Kings Cross
16 Sheringham
West Runton
16
Cromer 16
Roughton Road 16
Gunton 16
North Walsham 16
Worstead 16
Hoveton & Wroxham 16
Salhouse 16
15, 16, 17
Norwich
Wymondham 17
Spooner Row 17
Attleborough 17
Eccles Road 17
Harling Road 17
Thetford 17
11
Diss
14
Bury
St Edmunds
Kennett 14
Thurston 14
14
Elmswell
14 Stowmarket
14 Needham Market
Ipswich
13, 14, 17
Brundall Gardens
15
Brundall 15
15
Lingwood
15
Acle
15
Great Yarmouth
Buckenham 15
15 Cantley
15 Reedham
Berney Arms 15
15 Haddiscoe
15 Somerleyton
15 Oulton Broad North
13, 15
Lowestoft
13 Oulton Broad South
13 Beccles
13 Brampton
13 Halesworth
13 Darsham
Saxmundham 13
Wickham Market 13
Melton 13
Woodbridge 13
Derby Road 13
Westerfield
13
Trimley 13
Felixstowe 13
Harwich Town
11
Harwich International
14
Manningtree
13, 14
11
Walton-on-Naze
Clacton 11
Colchester 13, 14
Marks Tey 13, 14
Witham 13, 14
11
Chelmsford 13, 14
Shenfield
13, 14
Southend
5
5
London
Liverpool Street 13, 14, 17
Tables 13, 14, 15, 16, 17 services
Other services
Limited service route
Bus link
Limited service station
Underground interchange
Airport interchange
Ferry interchange
Numbers alongside sections of route indicate Tables with full service.

Ipswich → Felixstowe and Lowestoft

Network diagram - see first page of Table 13

Miles	Miles			LE	LE		LE 1	LE		LE	LE		LE 1 ◊	LE		LE	LE 1 ◊		LE	LE		LE 1 ◊	LE		LE
—	—	London Liverpool Street 15 ⊖	d					06 00			07 00		07 38	08 02		09 00	09 38		10 00	11 00		11 38	12 00		13 00
—	—	Shenfield 3	d					06 23			07 23		08u02	08 26		09 23	10u02		10 23	11 23		12u02	12 23		13 23
—	—	Chelmsford 3	d					06b02			07 12		08 12	08 35		09 12	10 12			11 12		12 12			13 12
—	—	Witham 2	d					06b14			07 21		08 22	08 44		09 21	10 21			11 21		12 21			13 21
—	—	Marks Tey 2	d					06b24			07 33		08 30			09 29	10 29			11 29		12 29			13 29
—	—	Colchester 4	d		05 35		06 22	06 50			07 50		08 38	09 04		09 50	10 38		10 50	11 50		12 38	12 50		13 50
—	—	Manningtree 2	d		05 44		06 31	06 59			07 59		08 34	09 12		09 59	10 34		10 59	11 59		12 31	12 59		13 59
0	—	**Ipswich**	d	05 04	06 04		06 47	07 13		07 32	08 27		09 02	09 27		10 27	11 02		11 27	12 27		13 02	13 27		14 27
3½	0	Westerfield	d	05 10	06 10		06 54	07 19		07 39	08 33		09 09	09 33		10 33	11 09		11 33	12 33		13 09	13 33		14 33
—	2½	Derby Road	d	05 15	06 15			07 24			08 38			09 38		10 38			11 38	12 38			13 38		14 38
—	10½	Trimley	d	05 24	06 24			07 33			08 47			09 47		10 47			11 47	12 47			13 47		14 47
—	12¼	**Felixstowe**	a	05 30	06 30			07 39			08 53			09 53		10 53			11 53	12 53			13 53		14 53
10¼	—	Woodbridge	d				07 06			07c55			09 21				11 21					13 21			
11½	—	Melton	d				07 10			07 59			09 25				11 25					13 25			
15¾	—	Wickham Market	d				07 16			08 05			09 31				11 31					13 31			
22½	—	Saxmundham	d				07 27			08a17			09 42				11 42					13 42			
26¾	—	Darsham	d				07 33						09 48				11 48					13 48			
32	—	Halesworth	d				07 43						09 58				11 58					13 58			
36	—	Brampton (Suffolk)	d				07 50						10 05				12 05					14 05			
40¼	—	Beccles	d				07 58						10 13				12 13					14 13			
46¾	—	Oulton Broad South	d				08 08						10 23				12 23					14 23			
49	—	**Lowestoft**	a				08 17						10 32				12 32					14 32			
—	—	Norwich	a				09 25						11 25				13 25					15 25			

		LE 1 ◊	LE		LE	LE R 1		LE	LE		LE	LE		LE	LE		LE R 1	LE 1 ◊		LE					
London Liverpool Street 15 ⊖	d	13 38	14 00		15 00	15 38		16 00	17 00			17 30		18 00	19 00		19 32	21 00							
Shenfield 3	d	14u02	14 23		15 23	16u02		16 02	16 54			17b24		17b54	19b01		19u55	21u23							
Chelmsford 3	d	14 12			15 12	16u12		16 30	16b45		17b15	17 51		18b14	19b13		20e00	21 11		21b11					
Witham 2	d	14 21			15 21	16 23		16 23	17 13			17b45		18b30	19b23		20 12	21 20		21b20					
Marks Tey 2	d	14 29			15 29	16 32		16 32	17b01		17b31	17b55		18b30	19b33		20 00	21 30		21b30					
Colchester 4	d	14 38	14 50		15 50	16 41		16 50	17 26		17 51	18 11		18 53	19 53		20 26	21 50							
Manningtree 2	d	14 31	14 59		15 59	16 31		16 59	17 35		17 59	18 27		19 02	20 02		20 30	21 58							
Ipswich	d	15 02	15 27		16 27	17 02		17 27	18 13		18 27	18 55		19 27	20 27		20 52	22 15		22 27					
Westerfield	d	15 09	15 33		16 33	17 09		17 33	18 20		18 33	19 02		19 33	20 33		20 59	22 22		22 33					
Derby Road	d		15 38		16 38			17 38			18 38			19 38	20 38					22 38					
Trimley	d		15 47		16 47			17 47			18 47			19 47	20 47					22 47					
Felixstowe	a		15 53		16 53			17 53			18 53			19 53	20 53					22 53					
Woodbridge	d	15 21				17 22			18 32			19 14					21 11	22 34							
Melton	d	15 25				17 26			18 36			19 18					21 15	22 38							
Wickham Market	d	15 31				17 32			18 42			19 24					21 21	22 44							
Saxmundham	d	15 42				17 43			18 53			19 35					21 32	22 55							
Darsham	d	15 48				17 49			18 59			19 41					21 38	23 01							
Halesworth	d	15 58				17 59			19f16			19 51					21 48	23 11							
Brampton (Suffolk)	d	16 05				18 06			19 23			19 58					21 55	23 18							
Beccles	d	16 13				18 14			19 31			20 06					22 03	23 26							
Oulton Broad South	d	16 23				18 24			19 41			20 16					22 13	23 36							
Lowestoft	a	16 32				18 33			19 50			20 25					22 22	23 45							
Norwich	a	17 30				19 30						21 25					23 28								

Saturdays

		LE		LE 1		LE		LE		LE 1 ◊		LE		LE		LE R 1		LE		LE		LE R 1		LE	LE
London Liverpool Street 15 ⊖	d					05 30		07 00		07 38		08 00		09 00		09 38		10 00		11 00		11 38		12 00	13 00
Shenfield 3	d					05 56		07 23		08u02		08 23		09 23		10u02		10 23		11 23		12u02		12 23	13 23
Chelmsford 3	d					06 07		07 12		08 12				09 12		10 12		10 12		11 12		12 12		12 12	13 12
Witham 2	d					06 19		07 21		08 21				09 21		10 21		10 21		11 21		12 21		12 21	13 21
Marks Tey 2	d					06 29		07 29		08 29				09 29		10 29		10 29		11 29		12 29		12 29	13 29
Colchester 4	d	05 38		05 38		06 37		07 50		08 38		08 50		09 50		10 38		10 50		11 50		12 38		12 50	13 50
Manningtree 2	d	05 46		05 46		06 45		07 59		08 31		08 59		09 59		10 31		10 59		11 59		12 31		12 59	13 59
Ipswich	d	06 27		06 50		07 27		08 27		09 02		09 27		10 27		11 02		11 27		12 27		13 02		13 27	14 27
Westerfield	d	06 33		06 57		07 33		08 33		09 09		09 33		10 33		11 09		11 33		12 33		13 09		13 33	14 33
Derby Road	d	06 38				07 38		08 38				09 38		10 38				11 38		12 38				13 38	14 38
Trimley	d	06 47				07 47		08 47				09 47		10 47				11 47		12 47				13 47	14 47
Felixstowe	a	06 53				07 53		08 53				09 53		10 53				11 53		12 53				13 53	14 53
Woodbridge	d			07 09						09 21						11 21						13 21			
Melton	d			07 13						09 25						11 25						13 25			
Wickham Market	d			07 19						09 31						11 31						13 31			
Saxmundham	d			07 30						09 42						11 42						13 42			
Darsham	d			07 36						09 48						11 48						13 48			
Halesworth	d			07 46						09 58						11 58						13 58			
Brampton (Suffolk)	d			07 53						10 05						12 05						14 05			
Beccles	d			08 01						10 13						12 13						14 13			
Oulton Broad South	d			08 11						10 23						12 23						14 23			
Lowestoft	a			08 20						10 32						12 32						14 32			
Norwich	a			09 25						11 25						13 25						15 25			

For general notes see front of timetable
For details of catering facilities see Directory of Train Operators

b Change at Colchester and Ipswich
c Arr. 0749
e Change at Colchester
f Arr. 1908

Table 13

Saturdays

Ipswich → Felixstowe and Lowestoft

Network diagram - see first page of Table 13

		LE R 1	LE	LE	LE R 1	LE	LE	LE R 1	LE	LE	LE R 1	LE 1 ◇	LE
London Liverpool Street 15	⊖ d	13 38	14 00	15 00	15 38	16 00	17 00	17 46	18 00	19 00	19 38	21 00	
Shenfield 3	d	14u02	14 23	15 23	16u02	16 23	17 23	18b02	18 23	19 23	20u02	21u23	
Chelmsford 3	d	14 12	14 12	15 12	16 12	16 12	17 12	18u16	18 16	19 16	20 12	21 12	21c12
Witham 2	d	14 21	14 21	15 21	16 21	16 21	17 21	18 21	18c21	19c21	20 21	21 21	21c21
Marks Tey 2	d	14 29	14 29	15 29	16 29	16 29	17 29	18 28	18c28	19c28	20 29	21 29	21c29
Colchester 4	d	14 38	14 50	15 50	16 38	16 50	17 50	18 40	18 50	19 50	20 38	21 50	
Manningtree 2	d	14 31	14 59	15 59	16 31	16 59	17 59	18 31	18 59	19 59	20 32	21 58	
Ipswich	d	15 02	15 27	16 27	17 02	17 27	18 27	19 02	19 27	20 27	21 02	22 15	22 27
Westerfield	d	15 09	15 33	16 33	17 09	17 33	18 33	19 09	19 33	20 33	21 09	22 22	22 33
Derby Road	d		15 38	16 38		17 38	18 38		19 38	20 38			22 38
Trimley	d		15 47	16 47		17 47	18 47		19 47	20 47			22 47
Felixstowe	a		15 53	16 53		17 53	18 53		19 53	20 53			22 53
Woodbridge	d	15 21			17 21			19 21			21 21	22 34	
Melton	d	15 25			17 25			19 25			21 25	22 38	
Wickham Market	d	15 31			17 31			19 31			21 31	22 44	
Saxmundham	d	15 42			17 42			19 42			21 42	22 55	
Darsham	d	15 48			17 48			19 48			21 48	23 01	
Halesworth	d	15 58			17 58			19 58			21 58	23 11	
Brampton (Suffolk)	d	16 05			18 05			20 05			22 05	23 18	
Beccles	d	16 13			18 13			20 13			22 13	23 26	
Oulton Broad South	d	16 23			18 23			20 23			22 23	23 36	
Lowestoft	a	16 32			18 32			20 32			22 32	23 45	
Norwich	a	17 30			19 30			21 25			23 28		

Sundays

		LE 1	LE A	LE	LE	LE	LE 1	LE	LE	LE	LE	LE	LE 1	LE	LE	LE 1	LE	LE
London Liverpool Street 15	⊖ d	08 30	09 30	10 30		11 30	12 30		13 30	14 30		15 30	16 30		17 30	18 30		20 30
Shenfield 3	d	08 57	09 57	10 57		11 57	12 57		13 57	14 57		15 57	16 57		17 57	18 57		20 57
Chelmsford 3	d	08 42	09 42	10 42		11 42	12 42		13 42	14 42		15 42	16 42		17 42	18 42		20 42
Witham 2	d	08 54	09 54	10 54		11 54	12 54		13 54	14 54		15 54	16 54		17 54	18 54		20 54
Marks Tey 2	d	09 04	10 04	11 04		12 04	13 04		14 04	15 04		16 04	17 04		18 04	19 04		21 04
Colchester 4	d	09 24	10 24	11 24		12 24	13 24		14 24	15 24		16 24	17 24		18 24	19 24		21 24
Manningtree 2	d	09 33	10 33	11 33		12 33	13 33		14 33	15 33		16 33	17 33		18 33	19 33		21 33
Ipswich	d	09 50	11 02	11 50	12 02	13 02	13 50	14 02	15 02	15 50	16 02	17 02	17 50	18 02	19 02	19 50	20 02	21 50
Westerfield	d	09 57	11 08	11 57	12 08	13 08	13 57	14 08	15 08	15 57	16 08	17 08	17 57	18 08	19 08	19 57	20 08	21 57
Derby Road	d		11 13		12 13	13 13		14 13	15 13		16 13	17 13		18 13	19 13		20 13	
Trimley	d		11 22		12 22	13 22		14 22	15 22		16 22	17 22		18 22	19 22		20 22	
Felixstowe	a		11 28		12 28	13 28		14 28	15 28		16 28	17 28		18 28	19 28		20 28	
Woodbridge	d	10 09		12 09			14 09			16 09			18 09			20 09		22 09
Melton	d	10 13		12 13			14 13			16 13			18 13			20 13		22 13
Wickham Market	d	10 19		12 19			14 19			16 19			18 19			20 19		22 19
Saxmundham	d	10 30		12 30			14 30			16 30			18 30			20 30		22 30
Darsham	d	10 36		12 36			14 36			16 36			18 36			20 36		22 36
Halesworth	d	10 46		12 46			14 46			16 46			18 46			20 46		22 46
Brampton (Suffolk)	d	10 53		12 53			14 53			16 53			18 53			20 53		22 53
Beccles	d	11 01		13 01			15 01			17 01			19 01			21 01		23 01
Oulton Broad South	d	11 11		13 11			15 11			17 11			19 11			21 11		23 11
Lowestoft	a	11 20		13 20			15 20			17 20			19 20			21 20		23 20
Norwich	a	12 33		14 33			16 33			18 33			20 33			22 33		00 03

For general notes see front of timetable
For details of catering facilities see Directory of Train Operators

A Until 7 September
b Change at Colchester
c Change at Colchester and Ipswich

Lowestoft and Felixstowe → Ipswich

Network diagram - see first page of Table 13

Miles	Miles	Station		LE	LE	LE	LE R 1	LE	LE	LE	LE	LE R 1	LE	LE	LE 1 ◇	LE	LE	LE 1 ◇
—	—	Norwich	d				05 45					07 54			09 57			11 57
0	—	**Lowestoft**	d		05 31		06 44					08 58			10 58			12 58
2¼	—	Oulton Broad South	d		05 38		06 51					09 05			11 05			13 05
8½	—	Beccles	d		05 47		07 00					09 14			11 14			13 14
13	—	Brampton (Suffolk)	d		05 55		07 08					09 22			11 22			13 22
17	—	Halesworth	d		06 03		07 16					09 30			11 30			13 30
22¼	—	Darsham	d		06 11		07 24					09 38			11 38			13 38
26½	—	Saxmundham	d		06 19		07 32		08 21			09 46			11 46			13 46
33¼	—	Wickham Market	d		06 28		07 41		08 30			09 55			11 55			13 55
37¼	—	Melton	d		06 35		07 48		08 37			10 02			12 02			14 02
38¾	—	Woodbridge	d		06 40		07 53		08 42			10 07			12 07			14 07
—	0	**Felixstowe**	d	05 34		06 38		07 50		08 56	09 56		10 56	11 56		12 56	13 56	
—	1¾	Trimley	d	05 37		06 41		07 53		08 59	09 59		10 59	11 59		12 59	13 59	
—	9¾	Derby Road	d	05 47		06 51		08 03		09 09	10 09		11 09	12 09		13 09	14 09	
45½	12¼	Westerfield	d	05 52	06 51	06 56	08 04	08 08	08 53	09 14	10 14	10 18	11 14	12 14	12 18	13 14	14 14	14 18
49	—	**Ipswich**	a	06 00	06 59	07 03	08 12	08 16	09 01	09 22	10 22	10 26	11 22	12 22	12 26	13 22	14 22	14 26
—	—	Manningtree 2	a	06 32		07 17	08 32		09 17	09 51	10 51	10 51	11 51		12 51	13 51		14 51
—	—	Colchester 4	a	06 43		07 28	08 43		09 27	09 48	10 48	10 48	11 48		12 48	13 48		14 48
—	—	Marks Tey 2	a	06b54		07b43	08b54		09b39	10b23	11b23	11 23	12b23	13b23	13 23	14b23	15b23	15 23
—	—	Witham 2	a	07b05		07b47	09b05		09b49	10 02	11 02	11 02	12 02		13 02	14 02		15 02
—	—	Chelmsford 3	a	07b14		07b56	09 02		09 46	10 10	11 10	11 10	12 10		13 10	14 10		15 10
—	—	Shenfield 3	a	07 32		08b08	09b25		10b09	10 22	11 22	11s22	12 22		13s22	14 22		15s22
—	—	London Liverpool Street 15 ⊖	a	07 37		08 23	09 25		10 24	10 46	11 45	11 45	12 45		13 45	14 45		15 45

Station		LE	LE	LE	LE	LE	LE 1 ◇	LE	LE 1 ◇	LE	LE	LE	LE
Norwich	d			13 57			15 57		16 57			19 57	
Lowestoft	d			14 58			16 58		18 43			20 58	
Oulton Broad South	d			15 05			17 05		18 50			21 05	
Beccles	d			15 14			17 14		18 59			21 14	
Brampton (Suffolk)	d			15 22			17 22		19 07			21 22	
Halesworth	d			15 30			17 30		19 15			21 30	
Darsham	d			15 38			17 38		19 23			21 38	
Saxmundham	d			15 46			17 46		19c36			21 46	
Wickham Market	d			15 55			17 55		19 45			21 55	
Melton	d			16 02			18 02		19 52			22 02	
Woodbridge	d			16 07			18 07		19 57			22 07	
Felixstowe	d	14 56	15 56		16 56	17 56		18 56		19 56	20 56		22 56
Trimley	d	14 59	15 59		16 59	17 59		18 59		19 59	20 59		22 59
Derby Road	d	15 09	16 09		17 09	18 09		19 09		20 09	21 09		23 09
Westerfield	d	15 14	16 14	16 18	17 14	18 14	18 18	19 14	20 08	20 14	21 14	22 18	23 14
Ipswich	a	15 22	16 22	16 26	17 22	18 22	18 26	19 22	20 16	20 22	21 22	22 26	23 22
Manningtree 2	a	15 51		16 51	17 51		18 51	19 36	20 51	20 51	21 36	22 51	23 47
Colchester 4	a	15 43		16 48	17 48		18 48	19 47	20 48	20 48	21 48	23 01	23 58
Marks Tey 2	a	15b54		16 59	17 55		18 55	19 54	21 23	21b23	22b23		
Witham 2	a	16b04		17 06	18 03		19 03	20 02	21 02	21 02	22 02	23 15	
Chelmsford 3	a	16b13		17 15	18 13		19 12	20 11	21 10	21 10	22 10	23 24	
Shenfield 3	a	16b24		17 27	18 25		19s24	20 23	21s23	21 23	22 22	23 36	
London Liverpool Street 15 ⊖	a	16b48		17 49	18 49		19 47	20 46	21 46	21 46	22 45	00 03	

Saturdays

Station		LE	LE R 1	LE	LE R 1	LE	LE	LE R 1	LE	LE	LE R 1	LE	LE	LE 1 ◇
Norwich	d				05 49			07 54			09 57			11 57
Lowestoft	d		05 58		06 58			08 58			10 58			12 58
Oulton Broad South	d		06 05		07 05			09 05			11 05			13 05
Beccles	d		06 14		07 14			09 14			11 14			13 14
Brampton (Suffolk)	d		06 22		07 22			09 22			11 22			13 22
Halesworth	d		06 30		07 30			09 30			11 30			13 30
Darsham	d		06 38		07 38			09 38			11 38			13 38
Saxmundham	d		06 46		07 46			09 46			11 46			13 46
Wickham Market	d		06 55		07 55			09 55			11 55			13 55
Melton	d		07 02		08 02			10 02			12 02			14 02
Woodbridge	d		07 07		08 07			10 07			12 07			14 07
Felixstowe	d	06 56		07 56		08 56	09 56		10 56	11 56		12 56	13 56	
Trimley	d	06 59		07 59		08 59	09 59		10 59	11 59		12 59	13 59	
Derby Road	d	07 09		08 09		09 09	10 09		11 09	12 09		13 09	14 09	
Westerfield	d	07 14	07 18	08 14	08 18	09 14	10 14	10 18	11 14	12 14	12 18	13 14	14 14	14 18
Ipswich	a	07 22	07 26	08 22	08 26	09 22	10 22	10 26	11 22	12 22	12 26	13 22	14 22	14 26
Manningtree 2	a	07 51	07 51	08 51	08 51	09 51	10 51	10 51	11 51	12 51	12 51	13 51		14 51
Colchester 4	a	07 48	07 48	08 48	08 48	09 48	10 48	10 48	11 48	12 48	12 48	13 48		14 48
Marks Tey 2	a	08b23	08 23	09b23	09 23	10b23	11b23	11 23	12b23	13b23	13 23	14b23	15b23	15 23
Witham 2	a	08 02	08 02	09b04	09 04	10b04	11b04	11 04	12 02	13 02	13 02	14 02		15 02
Chelmsford 3	a	08 10	08 10	09 06	09s06	10 06	11 06	11s06	12 10	13 10	13 10	14 10		15 10
Shenfield 3	a	08 22	08s22	09b24	09e24	10b24	11b24	11e24	12 22	13 22	13s22	14 22		15s22
London Liverpool Street 15 ⊖	a	08 45	08 45	09 38	09 38	10 38	11 42	11 42	12 45	13 45	13 45	14 45		15 45

For general notes see front of timetable
For details of catering facilities see Directory of Train Operators

b Change at Ipswich and Colchester
c Arr. 1930
e Change at Colchester

Table 13

Lowestoft and Felixstowe → Ipswich

Saturdays

Network diagram - see first page of Table 13

		LE	LE	LE [1] ◇	LE	LE	LE [1] ◇	LE	LE	LE [1] ◇	LE	LE	LE
Norwich	d			13 57			15 57			17 57		19 57	
Lowestoft	d			14 58			16 58			18 58		20 58	
Oulton Broad South	d			15 05			17 05			19 05		21 05	
Beccles	d			15 14			17 14			19 14		21 14	
Brampton (Suffolk)	d			15 22			17 22			19 22		21 22	
Halesworth	d			15 30			17 30			19 30		21 30	
Darsham	d			15 38			17 38			19 38		21 38	
Saxmundham	d			15 46			17 46			19 46		21 46	
Wickham Market	d			15 55			17 55			19 55		21 55	
Melton	d			16 02			18 02			20 02		22 02	
Woodbridge	d			16 07			18 07			20 07		22 07	
Felixstowe	d	14 56	15 56		16 56	17 56		18 56	19 56		20 56		22 56
Trimley	d	14 59	15 59		16 59	17 59		18 59	19 59		20 59		22 59
Derby Road	d	15 09	16 09		17 09	18 09		19 09	20 09		21 09		23 09
Westerfield	d	15 14	16 14	16 18	17 14	18 14	18 18	19 14	20 14	20 18	21 14	22 18	23 14
Ipswich	a	15 22	16 22	16 26	17 22	18 22	18 26	19 22	20 22	20 26	21 22	22 26	23 22
Manningtree [2]	a	15 51		16 51	17 51		18 51	19 36		20 51	21 37	22 51	23 35
Colchester [4]	a	15 48		16 48	17 48		18 48	19 48		20 48	21 48	23 01	23 45
Marks Tey [2]	a	16b23	17b23	17 23	18b23	19b23	19 23	20b23	21b23	21 23	22b23		
Witham [2]	a	16 02		17 02	18 02		19 02	20 02		21 02	22 02	23 15	
Chelmsford [3]	a	16 10		17 10	18 10		19 10	20 10		21 10	22 10	23 24	
Shenfield [3]	a	16 22		17s22	18 22		19s22	20 22		21s22	22 22	23 36	
London Liverpool Street [15] ⊖	a	16 45		17 45	18 45		19 45	20 45		21 49	22 49	00 07	

Sundays

		LE [1]	LE	LE A	LE	LE [1]	LE	LE	LE	LE	LE	LE [1]	LE	LE	LE [1]	LE	LE	LE
Norwich	d	07 25	08 57			10 57			12 57			14 57			16 57			18 57
Lowestoft	d	08 05	10 05			12 05			14 05			16 05			18 05			20 05
Oulton Broad South	d	08 12	10 12			12 12			14 12			16 12			18 12			20 12
Beccles	d	08 21	10 21			12 21			14 21			16 21			18 21			20 21
Brampton (Suffolk)	d	08 29	10 29			12 29			14 29			16 29			18 29			20 29
Halesworth	d	08 37	10 37			12 37			14 37			16 37			18 37			20 37
Darsham	d	08 45	10 45			12 45			14 45			16 45			18 45			20 45
Saxmundham	d	08 53	10 53			12 53			14 53			16 53			18 53			20 53
Wickham Market	d	09 02	11 02			13 02			15 02			17 02			19 02			21 02
Melton	d	09 09	11 09			13 09			15 09			17 09			19 09			21 09
Woodbridge	d	09 14	11 14			13 14			15 14			17 14			19 14			21 14
Felixstowe	d			11 32	12 32		13 32	14 32		15 32	16 32		17 32	18 32		19 32	20 32	
Trimley	d			11 35	12 35		13 35	14 35		15 35	16 35		17 35	18 35		19 35	20 35	
Derby Road	d			11 45	12 45		13 45	14 45		15 45	16 45		17 45	18 45		19 45	20 45	
Westerfield	d	09 25	11 25	11 50	12 50	13 25	13 50	14 50	15 25	15 50	16 50	17 25	17 50	18 50	19 25	19 50	20 50	21 25
Ipswich	a	09 33	11 33	11 57	12 57	13 33	13 57	14 57	15 33	15 57	16 57	17 33	17 57	18 57	19 33	19 57	20 57	21 33
Manningtree [2]	a	09 51	11 51	12 18	13 18	13 51	14 18	15 18	15 51	16 18	17 18	17 51	18 18	19 18	19 51	20 18	21 18	21 51
Colchester [4]	a	10 01	12 01	12 29	13 29	14 01	14 29	15 29	16 01	16 29	17 19	18 01	18 29	19 29	20 01	20 29	21 29	22 01
Marks Tey [2]	a	10b12	12b12	12 36	13 36	14b12	14 36	15 36	16b12	16 36	17 36	18b12	18 36	19 36	20b12	20 36	21 36	22b12
Witham [2]	a	10b20	12b20	12 46	13 46	14b20	14 46	15 46	16b20	16 46	17 46	18b20	18 46	19 46	20b20	20 46	21 46	22b20
Chelmsford [3]	a	10b29	12b29	12 57	13 57	14b29	14 57	15 57	16b29	16 57	17 57	18b29	18 57	19 57	20b29	20 57	21 57	22b29
Shenfield [3]	a	10 29	12 29	13 10	14 10	14 29	15 10	16 10	16 29	17 10	18 10	18 29	19 10	20 10	20 29	21 10	22 10	22 29
London Liverpool Street [15] ⊖	a	11 03	13 01	13 42	14 42	15 01	15 42	16 42	17 01	17 42	18 28	19 01	19 42	20 42	21 01	21 42	22 42	23 01

For general notes see front of timetable
For details of catering facilities see Directory of Train Operators

A Until 7 September
b Change at Ipswich and Colchester

Table 14

Mondays to Fridays

Ipswich → Bury St Edmunds, Cambridge, Ely and Peterborough

Network diagram - see first page of Table 13

Miles	Miles	Miles			LE	LE [1]	LE	LE	LE [1] ◇	LE	LE	LE [1]	LE	LE	LE [1] ◇
—	—	—	London Liverpool Street [15] ⊖	d					06 38		08 00	08 38	09 00	10 00	10 38
—	—	—	Shenfield	d					07u02		08 23	09 02	09 23	10 23	11u02
—	—	—	Chelmsford	d					07 12		08 12	09 12		10 12	11 12
—	—	—	Witham	d					07 21		08 22	09 21		10 21	11 21
—	—	—	Marks Tey	d					07 33		08 30	09 29		10 29	11 29
—	—	—	Colchester	d		05 35		06 22	07 41		08 50	09 38	09 50	10 50	11 38
—	—	—	Manningtree	d		05 44		06 31	07 50		08 59	09 46	09 59	10 59	
—	—	0	Harwich International	d						07 47					
0	—	18	**Ipswich**	d	05 10	06 01	06 13	06 52	08 03	08 16	09 16	10 03	10 16	11 16	12 03
8¼	—	—	Needham Market	d	05 20		06 23	07 02		08 26	09 26		10 26	11 26	
12	—	—	Stowmarket	d	05 26	06 12	06 29	07 08	08 14	08 32	09 32	10 14	10 32	11 32	12 14
17¾	—	—	Elmswell	d	05 35		06 38	07 18		08 41	09 41		10 41	11 41	
22¼	—	—	Thurston	d	05 41		06 44	07 24		08 47	09 47		10 47	11 47	
26¼	—	—	Bury St Edmunds	a	05 47	06 28	06 50	07 30	08 30	08 53	09 53	10 30	10 53	11 53	12 30
—	—	—		d	05 49	06 28	06 51	07 30	08 30	08 55	09 55	10 30	10 55	11 55	12 30
36	0	—	Kennett	d	06 00		07 02	07 42			10 06			12 06	
41	—	—	Newmarket	d	06 10		07 13	07 51		09 15	10 17		11 15	12 17	
44¼	—	—	Dullingham	d	06 15		07 18	08b00		09 20			11 20		
55¼	—	—	**Cambridge**	a	06 33		07 37	08 19		09 39	10 39		11 39	12 39	
70	14¾	—	**Ely [6]**	d		06 57			08 59			10 59			12 59
79¾	—	—	Manea	d											
85¼	—	—	March	d		07 14			09 16			11 16			13 16
93¼	—	—	Whittlesea	d		07 25			09 27			11 27			13 27
99¼	—	—	**Peterborough [8]**	a		07 37			09 41			11 38			13 38

		LE	LE	LE [1] ◇	LE	LE	LE [1] ◇	LE	LE	LE [R] [1]	LE	LE	LE [1]	LE	LE
London Liverpool Street [15] ⊖	d	11 00	12 00	12 38	13 00	14 00	14 38	15 00	16 00	16 32	17 00	18 00	19 00		21 00
Shenfield	d	11 23	12 23	13u02	13 23	14 23	15u02	15 23	16 02	16u54	16 54	17c54	19c01	20 02	21 23
Chelmsford	d		12 12	13 12		14 12	15 12		16 30	16e45	17c15	18c14	19c13	20 11	21c11
Witham	d		12 21	13 21		14 21	15 21		16 23	17 13	17 13	18c30	19c23	20 20	21c20
Marks Tey	d		12 29	13 29		14 29	15 29		16 32	17 01	17c31	18c30	19c33	20 30	21c30
Colchester	d	11 50	12 50	13 38	13 50	14 50	15 38	15 50	16 50	17 26	17 51	18 53	19 53		21 50
Manningtree	d	11 59	12 59		13 59	14 59		15 59	16 59	17 35	17 59	19 02	20 02		21 58
Harwich International	d														21 34
Ipswich	d	12 16	13 16	14 03	14 16	15 16	16 03	16 16	17 16	17 49	18 16	19 16	20 16	21 16	22 16
Needham Market	d	12 26	13 26		14 26	15 26		16 26	17 26	17 58	18 26	19 26	20 25	21 26	22 26
Stowmarket	d	12 32	13 32	14 14	14 32	15 32	16 14	16 32	17 32	18 03	18 32	19 32	20 30	21 32	22 32
Elmswell	d	12 41	13 41		14 41	15 41		16 41	17 41	18 12	18 41	19 41	20 39	21 41	22 41
Thurston	d	12 47	13 47		14 47	15 47		16 47	17 47	18 17	18 47	19 47	20 44	21 47	22 47
Bury St Edmunds	a	12 53	13 53	14 30	14 53	15 53	16 30	16 53	17 53	18 23	18 53	19 53	20 50	21 53	22 54
	d	12 55	13 55	14 30	14 55	15 55	16 30	16 55	17 55	18 23	18 55	19 55	20 50	21 55	
Kennett	d		14 06			16 06			18 06			20 06		22 06	
Newmarket	d	13 15	14 17		15 15	16 17		17 17	18 17		19 15	20 17		22 15	
Dullingham	d	13 20			15 20						19 20			22 20	
Cambridge	a	13 39	14 39		15 39	16 39		17 39	18 39		19 39	20 39		22 39	
Ely [6]	d			14 59			16 59			19f01			21 19		
Manea	d														
March	d			15 16			17 16			19 17			21 36		
Whittlesea	d			15 27			17 27			19 29			21 47		
Peterborough [8]	a			15 39			17 38			19 42			21 58		

Saturdays

		LE	LE [1]	LE	LE	LE [1] ◇	LE	LE	LE [1] ◇	LE	LE	LE [R] [1]	LE	LE
London Liverpool Street [15] ⊖	d				05 30	06 38	07g00	08 00	08 38	09 00	10 00	10 38	11 00	12 00
Shenfield	d				05 56	07u02	07g23	08 23	09u02	09 23	10 23	11u02	11 23	12 23
Chelmsford	d				06 07	07 12		08 12	09 12		10 12	11 12	11 12	12 12
Witham	d				06 19	07 21		08 21	09 21		10 21	11 21	11 21	12 21
Marks Tey	d				06 29	07 29		08 29	09 29		10 29	11 29	11 29	12 29
Colchester	d		05 38		06 37	07 38	07g50	08 50	09 38	09 50	10 50	11 38	11 50	12 50
Manningtree	d		05 46		06 45	07 46	07g59	08 59	09 46	09 59	10 59		11 59	12 59
Harwich International	d						07 47							
Ipswich	d	05 10	06 00	06 14	07 16	08 03	08 16	09 16	10 03	10 16	11 16	12 03	12 16	13 16
Needham Market	d	05 20		06 24	07 26		08 26	09 26		10 26	11 26		12 26	13 26
Stowmarket	d	05 26	06 11	06 30	07 32	08 14	08 32	09 32	10 14	10 32	11 32	12 14	12 32	13 32
Elmswell	d	05 35		06 39	07 41		08 41	09 41		10 41	11 41		12 41	13 41
Thurston	d	05 41		06 45	07 47		08 47	09 47		10 47	11 47		12 47	13 47
Bury St Edmunds	a	05 47	06 27	06 51	07 53	08 30	08 53	09 53	10 30	10 53	11 53	12 30	12 53	13 53
	d	05 49	06 27	06 53	07 55	08 30	08 55	09 55	10 30	10 55	11 55	12 30	12 55	13 55
Kennett	d	06 00		07 04	08 06			10 06			12 06			14 06
Newmarket	d	06 10		07 15	08 17		09 15	10 17		11 15	12 17		13 15	14 17
Dullingham	d	06 15		07 20	08 22		09 20			11 20			13 20	
Cambridge	a	06 36		07 39	08 39		09 39	10 39		11 39	12 39		13 39	14 39
Ely [6]	d		06 57			08 59			10 59			12 59		
Manea	d													
March	d		07 14			09 16			11 16			13 16		
Whittlesea	d		07 25			09 27			11 27			13 27		
Peterborough [8]	a		07 37			09 38			11 38			13 38		

For general notes see front of timetable
For details of catering facilities see Directory of Train Operators

b Arr. 0757
c Change at Colchester and Ipswich
e Change at Colchester
f Arr. 1852
g Change at Ipswich

Saturdays

Ipswich → Bury St Edmunds, Cambridge, Ely and Peterborough

Network diagram - see first page of Table 13

		LE R 1	LE	LE	LE 1 ◇	LE	LE	LE R 1	LE	LE	LE R 1	LE	LE
London Liverpool Street 15 ⊖	d	12 38	13 00	14 00	14 38	15 00		16 38	17 00	18 00	18 46	19 00	21 00
Shenfield	d	13u02	13 23	14 23	15u02	15 23		17u02	17 23	18 23	19b02	19 23	21 23
Chelmsford	d	13 12	13 12	14 12	15 12		16 12	17 12	17 12	18 16	19u16	19 16	21c12
Witham	d	13 21	13 21	14 21	15 21		16 21	17 21	17 21	18c21	19 21	19c21	21c21
Marks Tey	d	13 29	13 29	14 29	15 29		16 29	17 29	17 29	18c28	19 28	19c28	21c29
Colchester	d	13 38	13 50	14 50	15 38	15 50		17 38	17 50	18 50	19 40	19 50	21 50
Manningtree	d		13 59	14 59		15 59			17 59	18 59		19 59	21 58
Harwich International	d												21 34
Ipswich	d	14 03	14 16	15 16	16 03	16 16	17 16	18 03	18 16	19 16	20 03	20 16	22 17
Needham Market	d		14 26	15 26		16 26	17 26		18 26	19 26		20 26	22 27
Stowmarket	d	14 14	14 32	15 32	16 14	16 32	17 32	18 14	18 32	19 32	20 14	20 32	22 33
Elmswell	d		14 41	15 41		16 41	17 41		18 41	19 42		20 41	22 42
Thurston	d		14 47	15 47		16 47	17 47		18 47	19 48		20 47	22 48
Bury St Edmunds	a	14 30	14 53	15 53	16 30	16 53	17 53	18 30	18 53	19 53	20 30	20 53	22 55
	d	14 30	14 55	15 55	16 30	16 55	17 55	18 30	18 55	19 55	20 30	20 55	
Kennett	d			16 06			18 06			20 06		21 06	
Newmarket	d		15 15	16 17		17 17	18 17		19 15	20 17		21 15	
Dullingham	d		15 20						19 20			21 20	
Cambridge	a		15 39	16 39		17 39	18 39		19 39	20 39		21 39	
Ely 6	d	14 59			16 59			18 59			20 59		
Manea	d												
March	d	15 16			17 16			19 16			21 16		
Whittlesea	d	15 27			17 27			19 27			21 27		
Peterborough 8	a	15 38			17 38			19 38			21 38		

Sundays

		LE 1 A	LE	LE	LE 1	LE	LE 1	LE	LE 1	LE	LE 1	LE	LE 1	LE	LE
London Liverpool Street 15 ⊖	d														
Shenfield	d														
Chelmsford	d				08 42	09 42	10 42	11 42	12 42	13 42	14 42	15 42	16 42	17 42	19 42
Witham	d				08 54	09 54	10 54	11 54	12 54	13 54	14 54	15 54	16 54	17 54	19 54
Marks Tey	d				09 04	10 04	11 04	12 04	13 04	14 04	15 04	16 04	17 04	18 04	20 04
Colchester	d		08 12												
Manningtree	d		08 20												
Harwich International	d			08 30											
Ipswich	d	07 55	08 45	09 02	09 55	11 02	11 55	13 02	13 55	15 02	15 55	17 02	17 55	19 02	21 02
Needham Market	d			09 12		11 12		13 12		15 12		17 12		19 12	21 12
Stowmarket	d	08 07	08 59	09 18	10 07	11 18	12 07	13 18	14 07	15 18	16 07	17 18	18 07	19 18	21 18
Elmswell	d			09 27		11 27		13 27		15 27		17 27		19 27	21 27
Thurston	d			09 33		11 33		13 33		15 33		17 33		19 33	21 33
Bury St Edmunds	a	08 22	09 17	09 39	10 22	11 39	12 22	13 39	14 22	15 39	16 22	17 39	18 22	19 39	21 39
	d	08 23		09 40	10 23	11 40	12 23	13 40	14 23	15 40	16 23	17 40	18 23	19 40	21 40
Kennett	d			09 51		11 51		13 51		15 51		17 51		19 51	21 51
Newmarket	d			10 00		12 00		14 00		16 00		18 00		20 00	22 00
Dullingham	d			10 05		12 05		14 05		16 05		18 05		20 05	22 05
Cambridge	a			10 24		12 24		14 24		16 27		18 24		20 24	22 24
Ely 6	d	08e57			10f57		12g57		14h57		16j57		18k57		
Manea	d														
March	d	09 14			11 14		13 15		15 15		17 14		19 14		
Whittlesea	d	09 25			11 25		13 26		15 26		17 25		19 25		
Peterborough 8	a	09 41			11 41		13 42		15 42		17 36		19 36		

For general notes see front of timetable
For details of catering facilities see Directory of Train Operators

A Until 7 September
b Change at Colchester
c Change at Colchester and Ipswich
e Arr. 0851
f Arr. 1051
g Arr. 1251
h Arr. 1451
j Arr. 1651
k Arr. 1852

Peterborough, Ely, Cambridge and Bury St Edmunds → Ipswich

Network diagram - see first page of Table 13

Miles	Miles	Miles			LE MO	LE	LE	LE	LE	LE [R] [1]	LE	LE	LE [1] ◇	LE	LE	LE [1] ◇	LE	LE	LE [1]
0	—	—	**Peterborough** 8	d						07 52			09 47			11 48			13 47
6	—	—	Whittlesea	d						08 00			09 55			11 56			13 55
14	—	—	March	d						08 11			10 06			12 07			14 06
19¼	—	—	Manea	d															
29¼	0	—	**Ely** 6	d						08 30			10 30			12 30			14 30
45	—	—	**Cambridge**	d	23p00			06 41	07 43		08 43	09 43		10 43	11 43		12 43	13 43	
56	—	—	Dullingham	d	23p16				08 00			09 59			11 59			13 59	
58¼	—	—	Newmarket	d	23p21			07 01	08 04		09 03	10 04		11 03	12 04		13 03	14 04	
63¼	14¾	—	Kennett	d	23p29			07 09			09 11			11 11			13 11		
73¼	—	—	Bury St Edmunds	a	23p41			07 21	08 23	08 55	09 23	10 23	10 55	11 23	12 23	12 55	13 23	14 23	14 55
—	—	—		d	23p42	05 36	06 22	07 23	08 24	08 56	09 23	10 23	10 56	11 23	12 23	12 56	13 23	14 23	14 56
77¼	—	—	Thurston	d	23p48	05 42	06 28	07 30	08 30		09 30	10 30		11 30	12 30		13 30	14 30	
81¼	—	—	Elmswell	d	23p55	05 49	06 35	07 36	08 37		09 36	10 36		11 36	12 36		13 36	14 36	
87¼	—	—	Stowmarket	d	00 04	05 57	06 44	07 45	08 45	09 12	09 45	10 45	11 12	11 45	12 45	13 12	13 45	14 45	15 12
90¾	—	—	Needham Market	d	00 09	06 03		07 50	08 51		09 50	10 50		11 50	12 50		13 50	14 50	
99¼	—	0	**Ipswich**	a	00 21	06 15	07 00	08 02	09 03	09 26	10 03	11 03	11 25	12 03	13 03	13 25	14 03	15 03	15 25
—	—	18	Harwich International	a			07 25												
—	—	—	Manningtree	a		06 32	07b17		09 17	09 51	10 17	11 17	11 51	12 17	13 17	13 51	14 17	15 17	15 51
—	—	—	Colchester	a		06 43	07b28		09 27	09 48	10 27	11 27	11 48	12 27	13 27	13 48	14 27	15 27	15 43
—	—	—	Marks Tey	a		06c54	07c43	08c54	09c39	10 23	10c39	11c39	12 23	12c39	13c39	14 23	14c39	15c54	15 54
—	—	—	Witham	a		07c05	07c47	09c05	09c49	10 02	10c49	11c49	12 02	12c49	13c49	14 02	14c49	15c49	16 04
—	—	—	Chelmsford	a		07c14	07c56		09 46	10s10	10 45	11 45	12 10	12 45	13 45	14 10	14 45	15 45	16 13
—	—	—	Shenfield	a		07 32	08c08	09c25	10c09	10s22	11c09	12c09	12s22	13c09	14c09	14s22	15c09	16c11	16 24
—	—	—	London Liverpool Street 15 ⊖	a		07 37	08b23	09 25	10 24	10 46	11 24	12 24	12 45	13 24	14 24	14 45	15 24	16 24	16 48

		LE	LE	LE [1] ◇	LE	LE	LE [1] ◇	LE	LE	LE [1] ◇	LE	LE [1]	LE
Peterborough 8	d			15 47			17 47			19 49		22 05	
Whittlesea	d			15 55			17 55			19 57		22 13	
March	d			16 06			18 06			20 08		22 24	
Manea	d												
Ely 6	d			16 30			18 30			20 27		22 42	
Cambridge	d	14 43	15 43		16 43	17 43		18 43	19 43		20 43		22 43
Dullingham	d		15 59		16 59	17 59			19 59		20 59		22 59
Newmarket	d	15 03	16 04		17 04	18 04		19 03	20 04		21 04		23 04
Kennett	d	15 11			17 12	18 12		19 11			21 12		23 12
Bury St Edmunds	a	15 23	16 23	16 55	17 24	18 24	18 55	19 23	20 23	20 52	21 24	23 07	23 24
	d	15 23	16 23	16 56	17 25	18 25	18 56	19 23	20 23	20 52	21 25	23 08	23 25
Thurston	d	15 30	16 30		17 31	18 31		19 30	20 30		21 31		23 31
Elmswell	d	15 36	16 36		17 38	18 38		19 36	20 36		21 38		23 38
Stowmarket	d	15 45	16 45	17 12	17 46	18 46	19 12	19 45	20 45	21 08	21 46	23 24	23 46
Needham Market	d	15 50	16 50		17 52	18 52		19 50	20 50		21 52		23 52
Ipswich	a	16 03	17 03	17 27	18 03	19 03	19 25	20 03	21 03	21 25	22 03	23 37	00 03
Harwich International	a								21 28				
Manningtree	a	16 17	17 17	17 51		19 17	19 36	20 18	21b18	21 36	22 18	23 47	
Colchester	a	16 27	17 27	17 48		19 27	19 47	20 28	21b28	21 48	22 28	23 58	
Marks Tey	a	16c39	17c39	17 55	18 55	19c39	19 54	20c39	21c39	22 23	22 35		
Witham	a	16c49	17c49	18 03	18c49	19c49	20 02	20c49	21c49	22 02	22 45		
Chelmsford	a	16 45	17 45	18 13		19 45	20 11	20 46	21b46	22 10	22 56		
Shenfield	a	17c11	18c11	18s25	19c09	20c09	20s23	21c09	21b58	22s22	23 09		
London Liverpool Street 15 ⊖	a	17 24	18 24	18 49		20 24	20 46	21 21	22b23	22 45	23 34		

Saturdays

		LE	LE	LE	LE [R] [1]	LE	LE	LE [R] [1]	LE	LE	LE [1] ◇	LE	LE	LE [1] ◇
Peterborough 8	d				07 47			09 55			11 48			13 47
Whittlesea	d				07 55			10 03			11 56			13 55
March	d				08 06			10 14			12 07			14 06
Manea	d													
Ely 6	d				08 30			10 32			12 30			14 30
Cambridge	d		06 43	07 43		08 43	09 43		10 43	11 43		12 43	13 43	
Dullingham	d			07 59			09 59			11 59			13 59	
Newmarket	d		07 03	08 04		09 03	10 04		11 03	12 04		13 03	14 04	
Kennett	d		07 11			09 11			11 11			13 11		
Bury St Edmunds	a		07 23	08 23	08 55	09 23	10 23	10 57	11 23	12 23	12 55	13 23	14 23	14 55
	d	06 23	07 23	08 23	08 56	09 23	10 23	10 58	11 23	12 23	12 56	13 23	14 23	14 56
Thurston	d	06 30	07 30	08 30		09 30	10 30		11 30	12 30		13 30	14 30	
Elmswell	d	06 36	07 36	08 36		09 36	10 36		11 36	12 36		13 36	14 36	
Stowmarket	d	06 45	07 45	08 45	09 12	09 45	10 45	11 14	11 45	12 45	13 12	13 45	14 45	15 12
Needham Market	d	06 50	07 50	08 50		09 50	10 50		11 50	12 50		13 50	14 50	
Ipswich	a	07 03	08 03	09 03	09 25	10 03	11 03	11 27	12 03	13 03	13 27	14 03	15 03	15 25
Harwich International	a													
Manningtree	a	07 17	08 17	09 17	09 51	10 17	11 17	11 51	12 17	13 17	13 51	14 17	15 17	15 51
Colchester	a	07 27	08 27	09 27	09 48	10 27	11 27	11 48	12 27	13 27	13 48	14 27	15 27	15 48
Marks Tey	a	07c39	08c39	09c39	10 23	10c39	11c39	12 23	12c39	13c39	14 23	14c39	15c39	16 23
Witham	a	07c49	08c49	09c49	10 04	10c49	11c49	12 02	12c49	13c49	14 02	14c49	15c49	16 02
Chelmsford	a	07 45	08 45	09 45	10s06	10 45	11 45	12 10	12 45	13 45	14 10	14 45	15 45	16 10
Shenfield	a	08c09	09c09	10c09	10e24	11c09	12c09	12s22	13c09	14c09	14s22	15c09	16c09	16s22
London Liverpool Street 15 ⊖	a	08 24	09 24	10 24	10 38	11 24	12 24	12 45	13 24	14 24	14 45	15 24	16 24	16 45

For general notes see front of timetable
For details of catering facilities see Directory of Train Operators

b Change at Ipswich
c Change at Ipswich and Colchester
e Change at Colchester

Table 14

Saturdays

Peterborough, Ely, Cambridge and Bury St Edmunds → Ipswich

Network diagram - see first page of Table 13

		LE	LE	LE 1 ◇	LE	LE	LE 1 ◇	LE	LE	LE 1 ◇	LE	LE	LE 1
Peterborough [8]	d			15 47			17 47			19 46			21 49
Whittlesea	d			15 55			17 55			19 54			21 57
March	d			16 06			18 06			20 05			22 08
Manea	d												
Ely [6]	d			16 30			18 30			20 30			22 30
Cambridge	d	14 43	15 43		16 43	17 43		18 43	19 43		20 43	21 43	
Dullingham	d		15 59		16 59	17 59			19 59			21 59	
Newmarket	d	15 03	16 04		17 04	18 04		19 03	20 04		21 03	22 04	
Kennett	d	15 11			17 12	18 12		19 11			21 11	22 12	22 47
Bury St Edmunds	a	15 23	16 23	16 55	17 24	18 24	18 55	19 23	20 23	20 55	21 23	22 24	22 57
	d	15 23	16 23	16 56	17 25	18 25	18 56	19 23	20 23	20 56	21 23	22 25	22 58
Thurston	d	15 30	16 30		17 31	18 31		19 30	20 30		21 30	22 31	23 03
Elmswell	d	15 36	16 36		17 38	18 38		19 36	20 36		21 36	22 38	23 09
Stowmarket	d	15 45	16 45	17 12	17 46	18 46	19 12	19 45	20 45	21 12	21 45	22 46	23 17
Needham Market	d	15 50	16 50		17 52	18 52		19 50	20 50		21 50	22 52	23 22
Ipswich	a	16 03	17 03	17 27	18 03	19 03	19 25	20 03	21 03	21 27	22 03	23 03	23 32
Harwich International	a								21 28				
Manningtree	a	16 17	17 17	17 51	18 17	19 17	19 36	20 17	21b18	21 37	22 18	23 35	23 44
Colchester	a	16 27	17 27	17 48	18 27	19 27	19 48	20 28	21b28	21 48	22 28	23 45	23 56
Marks Tey	a	16c39	17c39	18 23	18c39	19c39	20 23	20c39	21c39	22 23	22 35		
Witham	a	16c49	17c49	18 02	18c49	19c49	20 02	20c49	21c49	22 02	22 45		
Chelmsford	a	16 45	17 45	18 10	18 45	19 45	20 10	20 46	21b46	22 10	22 56		
Shenfield	a	17c09	18c09	18s22	19c09	20c09	20s22	21c10	21b58	22s22	23 09		
London Liverpool Street [15] ⊖	a	17 24	18 24	18 45	19 24	20 24	20 45	21 19	22b25	22 49	23 38		

Sundays

		LE	LE 1 A	LE	LE 1	LE	LE 1	LE	LE 1	LE	LE 1	LE	LE 1	LE	LE
Peterborough [8]	d		09 47		11 46		13 48		15 47		17 47		19 44		
Whittlesea	d		09 55		11 54		13 56		15 55		17 55		19 52		
March	d		10 06		12 05		14 07		16 06		18 06		20 03		
Manea	d														
Ely [6]	d		10 30		12 30		14 30		16 30		18e30		20 22		
Cambridge	d			11 12		13 12		15 12		17 12		19 12		21 12	23 00
Dullingham	d			11 28		13 28		15 28		17 28		19 28		21 28	23 16
Newmarket	d			11 33		13 33		15 33		17 33		19 33		21 33	23 21
Kennett	d			11 41		13 41		15 41		17 41		19 41		21 41	23 29
Bury St Edmunds	a		10 55	11 53	12 55	13 53	14 55	15 53	16 55	17 53	18 55	19 53	20 47	21 53	23 41
	d	09 55	10 56	11 55	12 56	13 55	14 56	15 55	16 56	17 55	18 56	19 55	20 47	21 55	23 42
Thurston	d	10 01		12 01		14 01		16 01		18 01		20 01		22 01	23 48
Elmswell	d	10 08		12 08		14 08		16 08		18 08		20 08		22 08	23 55
Stowmarket	d	10 17	11 12	12 17	13 12	14 17	15 12	16 17	17 12	18 17	19 12	20 17	21 05	22 17	00 04
Needham Market	d	10 22		12 22		14 22		16 22		18 22		20 22		22 22	00 09
Ipswich	a	10 34	11 25	12 34	13 25	14 34	15 27	16 34	17 25	18 34	19 27	20 34	21 18	22 34	00 21
Harwich International	a											21 02			
Manningtree	a	10 51	11 51	12 51	13 51	14 51	15 51	16 51	17 51	18 51	19 51	20b51	21 28		
Colchester	a	11 01	12 01	13 01	14 01	15 01	16 01	17 01	18 01	19 01	20 01	21b01	21 40		
Marks Tey	a	11c12	12c12	13c12	14c12	15c12	16c12	17c12	18c12	19c12	20c12	21c12	22 12		
Witham	a	11c20	12c20	13c20	14c20	15c20	16c20	17c20	18c20	19c20	20c20	21c20	22 20		
Chelmsford	a	11c29	12c29	13c29	14c29	15c29	16c29	17c29	18c29	19c29	20c29	21c29	22 29		
Shenfield	a	11 29	12 29	13 29	14 29	15 29	16 29	17 29	18 29	19 29	20 29	21b29	22 29		
London Liverpool Street [15] ⊖	a	12 01	13 01	14 01	15 01	16 01	17 01	18 01	19 01	20 01	21 01	22b01	23 01		

For general notes see front of timetable
For details of catering facilities see Directory of Train Operators

A Until 7 September
b Change at Ipswich
c Change at Ipswich and Colchester
e Arr. 1827

Norwich → Great Yarmouth and Lowestoft

Network diagram - see first page of Table 13

Miles	Miles	Miles			LE 1	LE 1	LE 1	LE	LE		LE	LE 1	LE	LE	LE		LE	LE	LE	LE	LE		LE	LE	LE	LE
—	—	—	London Liverpool Street 15 ⊖	d										06 25			07 30	08 00	08 30	09 00	09 30		10 00	10 30	11 00	11 30
0	0	0	**Norwich**	d	05 15	05 45	06 24	06 36	06 55		07 05	07 36	07 54	08 36	08 57		09 36	09 57	10 36	10 57	11 36		11 57	12 36	12 57	13 36
4¾	4¾	4¾	Brundall Gardens	d		05 52		06 43			07 12		08 01	08 43			09 43		10 43		11 43			12 43		13 43
5¾	5¾	5¾	Brundall	d	05 23	05 55	06 32	06 46	07 04		07 15	07 44	08 04	08 46			09 46	10 05	10 46		11 46		12 05	12 46		13 46
8	—	—	Lingwood	d				06 51			07 20			08 51			09 51				11 51			12 51		13 51
10½	—	—	Acle	d				06 55			07b27			08 55			09 55				11 55			12 55		13 55
—	7¾	7¾	Buckenham	d																						
—	10	10	Cantley	d		06 01			07 10			07 50	08 10					10 11	10 52				12 11			
—	12¼	12¼	Reedham (Norfolk)	d		06 06	06 41		07 15			07 55	08 15					10 16	10 57				12 16			
—	16	—	Berney Arms	d								08x01							11x03							
18¼	20½	—	**Great Yarmouth**	a	05 46			07 08			07 40	08 12		09 08			10 08		11 13		12 08			13 08		14 08
—	—	16½	Haddiscoe	d		06 14			07 23				08 23					10 24					12 24			
—	—	18	Somerleyton	d		06 18			07 27				08 27					10 28					12 28			
—	—	22	Oulton Broad North	d		06 24	06 56		07 33				08 33		09 26			10 34		11 26			12 34		13 26	
—	—	23½	**Lowestoft**	a		06 30	07 03		07 42				08 38		09 36			10 41		11 33			12 41		13 33	

		LE	LE	LE		LE 1	LE	LE	LE 1	LE		LE	LE	LE 1	LE 1	LE		LE	LE 1	LE	LE 1	LE 1	LE 1	LE 1		
London Liverpool Street 15 ⊖	d	12 00	12 30	13 00		13 30	14 00	14 30	15 00			15 30		16 30	17 00	17 30		17 50	18 30		19 30		20 30			
Norwich	d	13 57	14 36	14 57		15 36	15 57	16 32	16 57	17 05		17 36	17 57	18 40	18 57	19 36		19 57	20 40	20 57	21 40	21 57	22 40	23 00		
Brundall Gardens	d		14 43			15 43		16 39		17 12		17 43		18 47		19 43			20 47		21 47					
Brundall	d	14 05	14 46			15 46	16 05	16 42	17 05	17 15		17 46	18 05	18 50	19 05	19 46		20 05	20 50	21 05	21 50	22 05	22 48	23 08		
Lingwood	d		14 51			15 51		16 47		17 20		17 51		18 55		19 51			20 55		21 55			23 13		
Acle	d		14 55			15 55		16 51		17c27		17 55		18 59		19 55			20 59		21 59			23 17		
Buckenham	d																									
Cantley	d	14 11					16 11		17 11				18 11		19 11			20 11		21 11		22 11	22 54			
Reedham (Norfolk)	d	14 16					16 16		17 16				18 16		19 16			20 16		21 16		22 16	22 59			
Berney Arms	d																									
Great Yarmouth	a		15 08			16 08		17 09		17 40		18 08		19 12		20 08			21 12		22 12			23 30		
Haddiscoe	d	14 24					16 24		17 24				18 24		19 24			20 24				22 24	23 07			
Somerleyton	d	14 28					16 28		17 28				18 28		19 28			20 28				22 28	23 11			
Oulton Broad North	d	14 34		15 26			16 34		17 34				18 34		19 34			20 34		21 31		22 34	23 17			
Lowestoft	a	14 41		15 33			16 41		17 41				18 44		19 41			20 41		21 38		22 41	23 24			

Saturdays

		LE	LE 1	LE	LE	LE	LE	LE		LE	LE	LE	LE	LE A	LE	LE		LE A	LE	LE	LE R 1 A ⊡	LE	LE	LE A		LE
London Liverpool Street 15 ⊖	d									06 30	07 00	07 30	08 00		08 30	09 00			09 30	10 00	10 00	10 30	11 00			11 30
Norwich	d	05 36	05 49	06 36	06 55	07 05	07 36	07 54		08 36	08 57	09 36	09 57	10 06	10 36	10 57		11 13	11 36	11 57	12 06	12 36	12 57	13 06		13 36
Brundall Gardens	d		05 56	06 43		07 12		08 01		08 43		09 43			10 43				11 43			12 43				13 43
Brundall	d	05 44	05 59	06 46	07 03	07 15	07 44	08 04		08 46		09 46	10 05		10 46				11 46	12 05		12 46				13 46
Lingwood	d			06 51		07 20				08 51		09 51							11 51			12 51				13 51
Acle	d			06 55		07b27				08 55		09 55							11 55			12 55				13 55
Buckenham	d												10x09													
Cantley	d		06 05		07 09		07 50	08 10					10 13		10 52					12 11						
Reedham (Norfolk)	d	05 52	06 10		07 14		07 55	08 15					10 17		10 57					12 16						
Berney Arms	d						08x01								11x03											
Great Yarmouth	a	06 08		07 08		07 40	08 12			09 08		10 08		10 38	11 13			11 43	12 08		12 40	13 08		13 40		14 08
Haddiscoe	d		06 18		07 22			08 23					10 26							12 24						
Somerleyton	d		06 22		07 26			08 27					10 29							12 28						
Oulton Broad North	d		06 28		07 32			08 33			09 26		10 35			11 26				12 34			13 26			
Lowestoft	a		06 34		07 38			08 38			09 33		10 41			11 33				12 41			13 33			

		LE	LE R 1 A ⊡	LE	LE	LE A	LE	LE		LE	LE	LE	LE	LE	LE	LE	LE	LE	LE	LE	LE	LE	LE 1	LE		
London Liverpool Street 15 ⊖	d	12 00	12 00	12 30	13 00		13 30	14 00		14 30	15 00		15 30	16 00	16 30	17 00	17 30	18 00	18 30	19 00	19 30	20 00	20 30			
Norwich	d	13 57	14 18	14 36	14 57	15 06	15 36	15 57		16 40	16 57	17 05	17 36	17 57	18 40	18 57	19 36	19 57	20 40	20 57	21 40	21 57	22 40	23 00		
Brundall Gardens	d			14 43			15 43			16 47		17 12	17 43		18 47		19 43		20 47		21 47					
Brundall	d	14 05		14 46			15 46	16 05		16 50	17 05	17 15	17 46	18 05	18 50	19 05	19 46	20 05	20 50	21 05	21 50	22 05	22 48	23 08		
Lingwood	d			14 51			15 51			16 55		17 20	17 51		18 55		19 51		20 55		21 55			23 13		
Acle	d			14 55			15 55			16 59		17c27	17 55		18 59		19 55		20 59		21 59			23 17		
Buckenham	d																									
Cantley	d	14 11						16 11			17 11			18 11		19 11		20 11		21 11		22 11	22 54			
Reedham (Norfolk)	d	14 16						16 16			17 16			18 16		19 16		20 16		21 16		22 16	22 59			
Berney Arms	d																									
Great Yarmouth	a		14 52	15 08		15 36	16 08			17 12		17 40	18 08		19 12		20 08		21 12		22 12			23 30		
Haddiscoe	d	14 24						16 24			17 24			18 24		19 24		20 24				22 24	23 07			
Somerleyton	d	14 28						16 28			17 28			18 28		19 28		20 28				22 28	23 11			
Oulton Broad North	d	14 34			15 26			16 34			17 34			18 34		19 34		20 34		21 31		22 34	23 17			
Lowestoft	a	14 41			15 33			16 41			17 41			18 41		19 41		20 41		21 38		22 41	23 24			

For general notes see front of timetable
For details of catering facilities see Directory of Train Operators

A Until 27 September
b Arr. 0724
c Arr. 1724

Table 15

Sundays

Norwich → Great Yarmouth and Lowestoft

Network diagram - see first page of Table 13

		LE 1	LE	LE	LE 1	LE	LE	LE 1	LE	LE	LE	LE	LE	LE 1
London Liverpool Street 15 ⊖	d						08 30	08 30	09 30	10 30		11 30	12 30	12 30
Norwich	d	07 25	07 36	08 45	08 57	09 36	10 45	10 57	11 36	12 45	12 57	13 36	14 45	14 57
Brundall Gardens	d			08 52			10 52			12 52			14 52	
Brundall	d		07 44	08 55	09 05	09 44	10 55	11 05	11 44	12 55	13 05	13 44	14 55	15 05
Lingwood	d			09 00			11 00			13 00			15 00	
Acle	d			09 04			11 04			13 04			15 04	
Buckenham	d					09x48			11x48					
Cantley	d		07 50		09 11	09 52		11 11	11 52		13 11	13 50		15 11
Reedham (Norfolk)	d		07 55		09 16	09 56		11 16	11 56		13 16	13 55		15 16
Berney Arms	d		08x01			10x03			12x03			14x01		
Great Yarmouth	a		08 12	09 17		10 13	11 17		12 13	13 17		14 12	15 17	
Haddiscoe	d				09 24			11 24			13 24			15 24
Somerleyton	d				09 28			11 28			13 28			15 28
Oulton Broad North	d	07 53			09 34			11 34			13 34			15 34
Lowestoft	a	07 59			09 40			11 40			13 40			15 40

		LE A	LE B	LE	LE 1 A	LE 1 B	LE	LE	LE	LE	LE	LE 1	LE	LE
London Liverpool Street 15 ⊖	d	13 30	13 30	14 30	14 30	14 30	15 30	16 30		17 30	18 30	19 00	19 30	20 30
Norwich	d	15 36	15 36	16 45	16 57	16 57	17 36	18 45	18 57	19 36	20 45	20 57	21 36	22 36
Brundall Gardens	d			16 52				18 52			20 52			22 43
Brundall	d	15 44	15 44	16 55	17 05	17 05	17 44	18 55	19 05	19 44	20 55	21 05	21 44	22 46
Lingwood	d			17 00				19 00			21 00			22 51
Acle	d			17 04				19 04			21 04			22 55
Buckenham	d	15x48	15x48		17x09									
Cantley	d	15 52	15 52		17 13	17 13	17 50		19 11	19 50		21 11	21 50	
Reedham (Norfolk)	d	15 56	15 56		17 17	17 17	17 55		19 16	19 55		21 16	21 55	
Berney Arms	d	16x03												
Great Yarmouth	a	16 13	16 13	17 17			18 10	19 17		20 10	21 17		22 10	23 08
Haddiscoe	d				17 26	17 26			19 24			21 24		
Somerleyton	d				17 29	17 29			19 28			21 28		
Oulton Broad North	d				17 35	17 35			19 34			21 34		
Lowestoft	a				17 41	17 41			19 40			21 40		

For general notes see front of timetable
For details of catering facilities see
Directory of Train Operators

A Until 7 September
B From 14 September

Lowestoft and Great Yarmouth → Norwich

Network diagram - see first page of Table 13

Miles	Miles	Miles			LE	LE	LE	LE	LE	LE	LE	LE	LE	LE	LE	LE		LE	LE	LE	LE	LE	LE	LE	LE	LE
					MX 1		1	R 1	1			1		1												
0	—	—	**Lowestoft**	d	23p30	05 36			06 40			07 40	07 55		08 42			09 42		10 50		11 42		12 50		13 42
1½	—	—	Oulton Broad North	d	23p34	05 40			06 44			07 44	07 59		08 46			09 46		10 54		11 46		12 54		13 46
5¼	—	—	Somerleyton	d		05 46			06 50			07 50			08 52			09 52				11 52				13 52
7¾	—	—	Haddiscoe	d		05 49			06 53			07 54			08 55			09 55				11 55				13 55
—	0	0	**Great Yarmouth**	d			05 55	06 42		07 17	07 44			08 17		09 17			10 17		11 17		12 17		13 17	
—	—	4½	Berney Arms	d																						
11½	—	8¼	Reedham (Norfolk)	d	23p51	05 58			07 02			08 03	08 14		09 04			10 04				12 04				14 04
13½	—	10¼	Cantley	d	23p55	06 02			07 06			08 07	08 19		09 08			10 08				12 08				14 08
15¾	—	12¼	Buckenham	d																						
—	8	—	Acle	d			06 06	06b55		07 27	07 54			08 27		09 27			10 27		11 27		12 27		13 27	
—	10½	—	Lingwood	d			06 11	07 00		07 32	07 59			08 32		09 32			10 32		11 32		12 32		13 32	
17¾	12¾	14¾	Brundall	d	00 01	06 08	06 15	07 04	07 12	07 36	08 03	08 13		08 36	09 14	09 36		10 14	10 36		11 36	12 14	12 36		13 36	14 14
18¾	13¾	15¾	Brundall Gardens	d			06 18		07 15	07 39	08 06			08 39		09 39			10 39		11 39		12 39		13 39	
23½	18½	20½	**Norwich**	a	00 12	06 19	06 28	07 14	07 25	07 50	08 19	08 25	08 38	08 50	09 25	09 50		10 28	10 50	11 25	11 50	12 25	12 50	13 25	13 50	14 25
—	—	—	London Liverpool Street 15 ⊖	a		*08 23*	*08 39*	*09 25*	*09 25*	*09 56*		*10 24*	*10 54*	*10 54*	*11 24*	*11 54*		*12 24*	*12 54*	*13 24*	*13 54*	*14 24*	*14 54*	*15 24*	*15 54*	*16 24*

		LE	LE	LE	LE	LE		LE	LE	LE	LE	LE	LE	LE	LE	LE	LE	LE	LE	LE	LE	LE	LE	LE		
			1			1				A	B	1			1	1			1		1	1	1	1		
Lowestoft	d		14 50		15 42			16 47				17 47		18 58		19 47		20 50		21 42		22 45		23 30		
Oulton Broad North	d		14 54		15 46			16 51				17 51		19 02		19 51		20 54		21 46		22 49		23 34		
Somerleyton	d				15 52			16 57				17 57		19 08		19 57				21 52		22 55				
Haddiscoe	d				15 55			17 00				18 00		19 11		20 00				21 55		22 58				
Great Yarmouth	d	14 12		15 17		16 17			17 17	17 45	17 45		18 17		19 17		20 17		21 17		22 17		23 33			
Berney Arms	d	14x19								17x52																
Reedham (Norfolk)	d	14 26			16 04			17 09		17 59	17 59	18 09		19 20		20 09				22 04		23 07	23 46	23 51		
Cantley	d	14 30			16 08			17 13		18 03	18 03	18 13		19 24		20 13				22 08		23 11		23 55		
Buckenham	d																									
Acle	d			15 27		16 27			17 27				18 27		19 27		20 27		21 27		22 27					
Lingwood	d			15 32		16 32			17 32				18 32		19 32		20 32		21 32		22 32					
Brundall	d	14 36		15 36	16 14	16 36		17 19	17 36	18 10	18 10	18 19	18 36	19 30	19 36	20 19	20 36		21 36	22 14	22 36	23 17	23 54	00 01		
Brundall Gardens	d	14 39		15 39		16 39				18 12	18 12		18 39		19 39		20 39		21 39		22 39					
Norwich	a	14 49	15 25	15 50	16 25	16 50		17 30	17 54	18 23	18 23	18 30	18 50	19 44	19 52	20 30	20 50	21 25	21 50	22 25	22 50	23 28	00 05	00 12		
London Liverpool Street 15 ⊖	a	*16 54*	*17 24*	*17 54*	*18 24*	*18 54*			*19 54*	*20 24*	*20 24*	*20 54*	*20 54*		*21 54*	*22 54*	*22 54*		*00 03*							

Saturdays

		LE	LE	LE	LE	LE	LE	LE	LE	LE	LE	LE	LE		LE	LE	LE	LE	LE	LE	LE	LE	LE	LE	LE	LE
		1		1								R 1 C ⌂			C			C				R 1 C ⌂		C		
Lowestoft	d	23p30		06 40			07 42		08 42		09 42					10 50			11 42		12 50				13 42	
Oulton Broad North	d	23p34		06 44			07 46		08 46		09 46					10 54			11 46		12 54				13 46	
Somerleyton	d			06 50			07 52		08 52		09 52								11 52						13 52	
Haddiscoe	d			06 53			07 55		08 55		09 55								11 55						13 55	
Great Yarmouth	d		06 17		07 17	07 44		08 17		09 17		10 08	10 17		10 42		11 17	11 47		12 17		13 10	13 17	13 47		14 12
Berney Arms	d																									14x19
Reedham (Norfolk)	d	23p51		07 02			08 04		09 04		10 04								12 04						14 04	14 26
Cantley	d	23p55		07 06			08 08		09 08		10 08								12 08						14 08	14 30
Buckenham	d																									
Acle	d		06 27		07 27	07 54		08 27		09 27			10 27				11 27			12 27			13 27			
Lingwood	d		06 32		07 32	07 59		08 32		09 32			10 32				11 32			12 32			13 32			
Brundall	d	00 01	06 36	07 12	07 36	08 03	08 14	08 36	09 14	09 36	10 14		10 36				11 36		12 14	12 36			13 36		14 14	14 36
Brundall Gardens	d		06 39	07 15	07 39	08 06		08 39		09 39			10 39				11 39			12 39			13 39			14 39
Norwich	a	00 12	06 50	07 25	07 50	08 19	08 25	08 50	09 25	09 50	10 25	10 44	10 52		11 08	11 25	11 50	12 16	12 25	12 50	13 25	13 44	13 52	14 16	14 25	14 49
London Liverpool Street 15 ⊖	a		*08 54*	*09 24*	*09 54*		*10 24*	*10 54*	*11 24*	*11 54*	*12 24*	*12 54*	*12 54*			*13 24*	*13 54*		*14 24*	*14 54*	*15 24*	*15 54*	*15 54*		*16 24*	*16 54*

		LE	LE		LE	LE	LE	LE	LE	LE	LE	LE	LE	LE	LE	LE	LE	LE	LE	LE	LE	LE	LE	LE		
					C					C	D							1						1		
Lowestoft	d	14 50				15 42		16 47				17 47		18 47		19 47		20 50		21 42		22 45		23 30		
Oulton Broad North	d	14 54				15 46		16 51				17 51		18 51		19 51		20 54		21 46		22 49		23 34		
Somerleyton	d					15 52		16 57				17 57		18 57		19 57				21 52		22 55				
Haddiscoe	d					15 55		17 00				18 00		19 00		20 00				21 55		22 58				
Great Yarmouth	d		15 17		15 47		16 17		17 17	17 45	17 45		18 17		19 17		20 17		21 17		22 17		23 33			
Berney Arms	d									17x52																
Reedham (Norfolk)	d					16 04		17 09		17 59	17 59	18 09		19 09		20 09				22 04		23 07	23 46	23 51		
Cantley	d					16 08		17 13		18 03	18 03	18 13		19 13		20 13				22 08		23 11		23 55		
Buckenham	d					16x11																				
Acle	d		15 27				16 27		17 27				18 27		19 27		20 27		21 27		22 27					
Lingwood	d		15 32				16 32		17 32				18 32		19 32		20 32		21 32		22 32					
Brundall	d		15 36			16 14	16 36	17 19	17 36	18 10	18 10	18 19	18 36	19 19	19 36	20 19	20 36		21 36	22 14	22 36	23 17	23 54	00 01		
Brundall Gardens	d		15 39				16 39			18 12	18 12		18 39		19 39		20 39		21 39		22 39					
Norwich	a	15 25	15 50		16 16	16 25	16 50	17 30	17 50	18 23	18 23	18 30	18 50	19 30	19 50	20 30	20 50	21 25	21 50	22 25	22 50	23 28	00 05	00 12		
London Liverpool Street 15 ⊖	a	*17 24*	*17 54*			*18 24*	*18 54*		*19 54*	*20 24*	*20 24*		*20 54*		*21 58*		*22 58*	*00 07*	*00 07*							

For general notes see front of timetable
For details of catering facilities see Directory of Train Operators

A Until 26 September
B From 29 September
C Until 27 September
D From 4 October
b Arr. 0652

Table 15

Sundays

Lowestoft and Great Yarmouth → Norwich

Network diagram - see first page of Table 13

		LE 1	LE	LE	LE 1	LE	LE	LE 1	LE	LE	LE	LE	LE	LE 1
Lowestoft	d	23p30			09 50			11 50			13 50			15 50
Oulton Broad North	d	23p34			09 54			11 54			13 54			15 54
Somerleyton	d				10 00			12 00			14 00			16 00
Haddiscoe	d				10 03			12 03			14 03			16 03
Great Yarmouth	d		08 20	09 22		10 18	11 22		12 18	13 22		14 20	15 22	
Berney Arms	d		08x27			10x25			12x25			14x27		
Reedham (Norfolk)	d	23p51	08 34		10 12	10 32		12 12	12 32		14 12	14 34		16 12
Cantley	d	23p55	08 38		10 16	10 36		12 16	12 36		14 16	14 38		16 16
Buckenham	d				10x20	10x40			12x40					
Acle	d			09 32			11 32			13 32			15 32	
Lingwood	d			09 37			11 37			13 37			15 37	
Brundall	d	00 01	08 45	09 41	10 24	10 44	11 41	12 22	12 44	13 41	14 22	14 45	15 41	16 22
Brundall Gardens	d			09 44			11 44			13 44			15 44	
Norwich	a	00 12	08 55	09 55	10 34	10 55	11 55	12 33	12 55	13 55	14 33	14 55	15 55	16 33
London Liverpool Street 15 ⊖	a		*11 03*	*12 01*	*13 01*	*13 01*	*14 01*	*15 01*	*15 01*	*16 01*		*17 01*	*18 01*	*19 01*

		LE A	LE B	LE	LE	LE	LE	LE 1	LE	LE	LE 1	LE	LE	LE
Lowestoft	d				17 50			19 50			21 50			23 25
Oulton Broad North	d				17 54			19 54			21 54			23 29
Somerleyton	d				18 00			20 00			22 00			
Haddiscoe	d				18 03			20 03			22 03			
Great Yarmouth	d	16⟆18	16⟆18	17 22		18 22	19 22		20 22	21 22		22 22	23 20	
Berney Arms	d	16x25												
Reedham (Norfolk)	d	16⟆32	16⟆32		18 12	18 34		20 12	20 34		22 12	22 34	23 32	23 44
Cantley	d	16⟆36	16⟆36		18 16	18 38		20 16	20 38		22 16	22 38	23 36	
Buckenham	d	16x40												
Acle	d			17 32			19 32			21 32				
Lingwood	d			17 37			19 37			21 37				
Brundall	d	16⟆44	16⟆44	17 41	18 22	18 45	19 41	20 22	20 45	21 41	22 22	22 45	23 43	23 53
Brundall Gardens	d			17 44			19 44			21 44			23 45	
Norwich	a	16⟆55	16⟆55	17 55	18 33	18 55	19 55	20 33	20 55	21 55	22 33	22 55	23 55	00 03
London Liverpool Street 15 ⊖	a	*19⟆01*	*19⟆01*	*20 01*		*21 01*	*22 01*	*23 01*	*23 01*	*00 07*				

For general notes see front of timetable
For details of catering facilities see
Directory of Train Operators

A Until 7 September
B From 14 September

Mondays to Saturdays

Norwich—Cromer and Sheringham

Network diagram - see first page of Table 13

Miles			LE SX	LE SO	LE SO	LE SX	LE	LE	LE	LE	LE	LE	LE	LE	LE	LE	LE	LE	LE	LE	LE
—	London Liverpool Street 15	⊖ d						06b00	07 30	08 30	09 30	10 30	11 30	12 30	13 30	14 30	15 30	17c00	17 30	19 00	20 30
0	**Norwich**	d	05 20	05 20	05 45	05 50	07 15	08 23	09 45	10 45	11 45	12 45	13 45	14 45	15 45	16 45	17 45	18 45	19 45	21 15	22 45
6	Salhouse	d		05 30	05 55	06 00	07 25	08 33	09 55		11 55		13 55		15 55	16 55	17 55	18 55	19 55	21 25	22 55
8¾	Hoveton & Wroxham	d	05 34	05 35	06 00	06 05	07 30	08 38	10 00	10 59	12 00	12 59	14 00	14 59	16 00	17 00	18 00	19 00	20 00	21 30	23 00
13	Worstead	d		05 42	06 07	06 12	07 37	08 45		11 06		13 06		15 06	16 07	17 07	18 07	19 07	20 07	21 37	23 07
16	North Walsham	a	05 44	05 48	06 13	06 18	07 43	08 51	10 10	11 11	12 10	13 11	14 10	15 11	16 13	17 13	18 13	19 13	20 13	21 43	23 13
—		d	05 44	05 48	06 13	06 21	07 46	08 53	10 13	11 14	12 13	13 14	14 13	15 14	16 15	17 15	18 16	19 15	20 16	21 43	23 13
19¾	Gunton	d		05 54	06 19	06 27	07 52	08 59	10 19		12 19		14 19		16 21	17 21	18 22	19 21	20 22	21 49	23 19
23½	Roughton Road	d		06 01	06 26	06 34	07 59	09 06		11 25		13 25		15 25	16 28	17 28	18 29	19 28	20 29	21 56	23 26
26½	**Cromer**	a	05 59	06 06	06 31	06 39	08 04	09 11	10 29	11 30	12 29	13 30	14 29	15 30	16 33	17 33	18 34	19 33	20 34	22 01	23 31
—		d	06 06	06 10	06 36	06 46	08 08	09 15	10 33	11 33	12 33	13 33	14 33	15 33	16 36	17 36	18 37	19 36	20 37	22 04	23 34
28¾	West Runton	d	06 10	06 14	06 40	06 50	08 12	09 19	10 37	11 37	12 37	13 37	14 37	15 37	16 40	17 40	18 41	19 40	20 41	22 08	23 38
30½	**Sheringham**	a	06 15	06 19	06 45	06 55	08 16	09 23	10 42	11 42	12 42	13 42	14 42	15 42	16 45	17 45	18 45	19 45	20 45	22 13	23 43

Sundays

		LE	LE A	LE	LE A	LE	LE A	LE	LE A	LE	LE A	LE	LE A	LE
London Liverpool Street 15	⊖ d			08 30	09 30	10 30	11 30	12 30	13 30	14 30	15 30	16 30	17 30	18 30
Norwich	d	08 36	09 45	10 36	11 45	12 36	13 45	14 36	15 45	16 36	17 45	18 36	19 45	20 36
Salhouse	d	08 46		10 46		12 46		14 46		16 46		18 46		20 46
Hoveton & Wroxham	d	08 51	09 59	10 51	11 59	12 51	13 59	14 51	15 59	16 51	17 59	18 51	19 59	20 51
Worstead	d	08 58		10 58		12 58		14 58		16 58		18 58		20 58
North Walsham	a	09 04	10 09	11 04	12 09	13 04	14 09	15 04	16 09	17 04	18 09	19 04	20 09	21 04
	d	09 04	10 11	11 07	12 11	13 07	14 11	15 07	16 11	17 07	18 11	19 07	20 11	21 07
Gunton	d	09 10		11 13		13 13		15 13		17 13		19 13		21 13
Roughton Road	d	09 17		11 20		13 20		15 20		17 20		19 20		21 20
Cromer	a	09 22	10 26	11 25	12 26	13 25	14 26	15 25	16 26	17 25	18 26	19 25	20 26	21 25
	d	09 26	10 30	11 29	12 30	13 29	14 30	15 29	16 30	17 29	18 30	19 29	20 30	21 29
West Runton	d	09 30		11 33		13 33		15 33		17 33		19 33		21 33
Sheringham	a	09 35	10 38	11 38	12 38	13 38	14 38	15 38	16 38	17 38	18 38	19 38	20 38	21 38

Mondays to Saturdays

Miles			LE MX	LE SX	LE SO	LE SX	LE	LE	LE	LE	LE	LE	LE	LE	LE	LE	LE	LE	LE	LE	LE	LE
0	**Sheringham**	d	23p46		06 22	06 32	07 17	08 25	09 46	10 46	11 46	12 46	13 46	14 46	15 46	16 49	17 48	18 49	19 48	20 49	22 16	23 46
1¾	West Runton	d	23p50		06 26	06 36	07 21	08 29	09 50	10 50	11 50	12 50	13 50	14 50	15 50	16 53	17 52	18 53	19 52	20 53	22 20	23 50
4	**Cromer**	a	23p54		06 30	06 40	07 25	08 33	09 54	10 54	11 54	12 54	13 54	14 54	15 54	16 57	17 56	18 57	19 56	20 57	22 24	23 54
—		d	23p57	06 03	06 33	06 43	07 28	08 36	09 57	10 57	11 57	12 57	13 57	14 57	15 57	17 00	17 59	19 00	19 59	21 00	22 27	23 57
7	Roughton Road	d		06 08	06 38	06 48	07 33	08 41	10 02		12 02		14 02	15 02	16 02		18 04		20 04	21 05	22 32	
10¾	Gunton	d		06 15	06 45	06 55	07 40	08 48		11 08		13 08			16 09		18 11		20 11	21 12	22 39	
14½	North Walsham	a	00 12	06 20	06 50	07 00	07 45	08 53	10 12	11 13	12 12	13 13	14 12	15 13	16 15	17 15	18 16	19 15	20 16	21 17	22 44	00 12
—		d	00 12	06 21	06 51	07 01	07 46	08 54	10 13	11 14	12 13	13 14	14 13	15 14	16 15	17 15	18 17	19 15	20 17	21 18	22 45	00 12
17½	Worstead	d		06 25	06 55	07 05	07 50	08 58	10 17		12 17		14 17		16 20		18 21		20 21	21 22	22 49	
21¾	Hoveton & Wroxham	d	00 22	06 33	07 03	07 13	07 58	09 06	10 25	11 24	12 25	13 24	14 25	15 24	16 27	17 26	18 29	19 26	20 29	21 30	22 57	00 22
24½	Salhouse	d		06 38	07 08	07 18	08 03	09 11		11 29		13 29		15 29	16 32		18 34		20 34	21 35	23 02	
30½	**Norwich**	a	00 37	06 49	07 19	07 29	08 14	09 22	10 41	11 41	12 41	13 41	14 41	15 41	16 44	17 41	18 45	19 41	20 45	21 46	23 13	00 37
—	London Liverpool Street 15	⊖ a		08 55	09 24	09 40	10 24	11 24	12 54	13 54	14 54	15 54	16 54	17 54	18 54	19 54	20 54	21e54	22f54	00g03		

Sundays

		LE	LE	LE B	LE	LE B	LE	LE B	LE	LE B	LE	LE B	LE	LE B	LE
Sheringham	d	23p46	09 43	10 43	11 43	12 43	13 43	14 43	15 43	16 43	17 43	18 43	19 43	20 43	21 43
West Runton	d	23p50	09 47		11 47		13 47		15 47		17 47		19 47		21 47
Cromer	a	23p54	09 51	10 49	11 51	12 49	13 51	14 49	15 51	16 49	17 51	18 49	19 51	20 49	21 51
	d	23p57	09 54	10 53	11 54	12 53	13 54	14 53	15 54	16 53	17 54	18 53	19 54	20 53	21 54
Roughton Road	d		09 59		11 59		13 59		15 59		17 59		19 59		21 59
Gunton	d		10 06		12 06		14 06		16 06		18 06		20 06		22 06
North Walsham	a	00 12	10 11	11 07	12 11	13 07	14 11	15 07	16 11	17 07	18 11	19 07	20 11	21 07	22 11
	d	00 12	10 12	11 08	12 12	13 08	14 12	15 08	16 12	17 08	18 12	19 08	20 12	21 08	22 12
Worstead	d		10 16		12 16		14 16		16 16		18 16		20 16		22 16
Hoveton & Wroxham	d	00 22	10 24	11 18	12 24	13 18	14 24	15 18	16 24	17 18	18 24	19 18	20 24	21 18	22 24
Salhouse	d		10 29		12 29		14 29		16 29		18 29		20 29		22 29
Norwich	a	00 37	10 40	11 33	12 40	13 33	14 40	15 33	16 40	17 33	18 40	19 33	20 40	21 33	22 40
London Liverpool Street 15	⊖ a		13 01	14 01	15 01	16 01	17 01	18 01	19 01	20 01	21 01	22 01	23 01	00 07	

For general notes see front of timetable
For details of catering facilities see Directory of Train Operators

- **A** Until 7 September
- **B** Until 7 September
- **b** Mondays to Fridays only
- **c** Saturdays dep. 1630
- **e** Saturdays arr. 2158
- **f** Saturdays arr. 2258
- **g** Saturdays arr. 0007

Table 17

Mondays to Fridays

London, Norwich and Cambridge → Ely, Kings Lynn and Peterborough

Network Diagram - see first page of Table 13

Miles	Miles			FC MX [1]	FC MO [1]	XC ◇ A	XC ◇ B	LE [1]	LE		FC [1]	EM ◇ C 🛒	LE [1]	XC ◇ A	FC [1]	LE [1]		LE [1]	EM ◇ C 🛒	FC [1]	XC ◇	FC [1]	LE [1]		LE [1]	EM ◇
—	—	**London Liverpool Street**	d																							
—	0	**London Kings Cross**	d	23p15	23p15										05 45					06 45		07 15				
—	—	Ipswich	d										06 01													
—	—	Stansted Airport	d				05 21														07 20					
—	—	**Norwich**	d					05 33				05 52						06 33							07 37	07 57
10¾	—	Wymondham	d					05 45				06 04						06 45							07 49	
12¾	—	Spooner Row	d																							
16	—	Attleborough	d					05 52				06 11						06 52							07 56	
19¾	—	Eccles Road	d																							
22¾	—	Harling Road	d																							
30½	—	Thetford	d					06 05				06 25						07 05							08 09	08 24
37¾	—	Brandon	d					06 13										07 13							08 17	
41½	—	Lakenheath	d																							
47	—	Shippea Hill	d																							
—	58	**Cambridge**	d	00 13	00 19	05 07	05 58		06 17		06 23			06 50	06 56	07 05			07 27	07 35	07 59	08 04	08 12			
—	63¼	Waterbeach	d	00 19	00 25						06 29				07 02					07 41		08 10				
53	72¾	**Ely** [3]	a	00 29	00 38	05 23	06 13	06 30	06 33		06 38	06 46	06 57	07 04	07 11	07 19		07 30	07 43	07 51	08 13	08 20	08 26		08 37	08 47
—	—	**Cambridge**	a					06 50										07 51							08 55	
—	—	**Ely** [3]	d			05 24	06 13				06 38	06 51	06 57	07 05	07 11				07 44	07 51	08 16	08 21				08 51
—	78¼	Littleport	d								06 45				07 18					07 58		08 28				
—	88¼	Downham Market	d								06 54				07 27					08 07		08 37				
—	93¼	Watlington	d								07 01				07 33					08 13		08 43				
—	99¼	**Kings Lynn**	a								07 10				07 43					08 22		08 52				
62¾	—	Manea	d				06x24																			
68¼	—	March	d			05 40	06 32					07 07	07 14	07 21					08 01		08 33					09 07
76½	—	Whittlesea	d			05 52	06 43						07 25	07 33					08 12							
82¼	—	**Peterborough** [8]	a			06 02	06 54					07 25	07 37	07 43					08 23		08 50					09 25

		FC [1]	LE [1] ◇	XC ◇ 🛒	LE [1]	LE [1]	FC [1]		EM ◇	XC ◇ 🛒	LE [1]	LE [1]	FC [1]	EM ◇		LE [1]	XC ◇ 🛒	LE [1]	LE [1]	FC [1]	EM ◇		XC ◇ 🛒	LE [1]	LE [1]	FC [1]
London Liverpool Street	d		06 38																							
London Kings Cross	d	07 45					08 45						09 45							10 45						11 45
Ipswich	d		08 03													10 03										
Stansted Airport	d			08 20						09 20							10 20						11 25			
Norwich	d					08 40			08 57			09 40		09 57					10 40		10 57				11 40	
Wymondham	d					08 52						09 52							10 52						11 52	
Spooner Row	d																									
Attleborough	d					08 59						09 59							10 59						11 59	
Eccles Road	d																									
Harling Road	d																									
Thetford	d					09 12			09 24			10 12		10 24					11 12		11 24				12 12	
Brandon	d					09 20						10 20							11 20						12 20	
Lakenheath	d																									
Shippea Hill	d																									
Cambridge	d	08 38		09 04	09 12		09 35			10 04	10 12		10 33				11 04	11 12		11 33			12 04	12 12		12 33
Waterbeach	d	08 44					09 41						10 39							11 39						12 39
Ely [6]	a	08 53	08 59	09 18	09 26	09 38	09 50		09 45	10 18	10 26	10 37	10 48	10 46		10 59	11 18	11 26	11 37	11 48	11 46		12 18	12 26	12 37	12 48
Cambridge	a					09 56						10 55							11 55						12 55	
Ely [6]	d	08 54	08 59	09 19			09 50		09 51	10 19			10 48	10 52		10 59	11 19			11 48	11 52		12 19			12 48
Littleport	d	09 01					09 57						10 55							11 55						12 55
Downham Market	d	09 10					10 06						11 04							12 04						13 04
Watlington	d	09 16					10 12						11 10							12 10						13 10
Kings Lynn	a	09 25					10 26						11 20							12 20						13 20
Manea	d																									
March	d		09 16	09 35						10 35						11 16	11 35						12 35			
Whittlesea	d		09 27													11 27										
Peterborough [8]	a		09 41	09 53					10 25	10 53				11 24		11 38	11 53				12 24		12 53			

For general notes see front of timetable
For details of catering facilities see Directory of Train Operators

A To Birmingham New Street (Table 49)
B To Birmingham New Street (Table 57)
C Until 5 September to Liverpool Lime Street (Table 49). From 8 September to Chesterfield (Table 49)

London, Norwich and Cambridge → Ely, Kings Lynn and Peterborough

Network Diagram - see first page of Table 13

		EM ◇	LE [1] ◇	XC ◇ 🍴	LE [1]		LE [1]	FC [1]	EM ◇	XC ◇ 🍴	LE [1]	LE [1]		FC [1]	EM ◇	LE [1] ◇	XC ◇ 🍴	LE [1]	LE [1]		FC [1]	EM ◇	XC ◇ 🍴	LE [1]	LE [1]	FC [1]
London Liverpool Street	d		10 38													12 38										
London Kings Cross	d							12 45						13 45							14 45					
Ipswich	d		12 03													14 03										
Stansted Airport	d			12 25						13 25							14 25						15 25			
Norwich	d	11 57					12 40		12 57			13 40			13 57				14 40			14 57			15 40	
Wymondham	d						12 52					13 52							14 52						15 52	
Spooner Row	d																									
Attleborough	d						12 59					13 59							14 59						15 59	
Eccles Road	d																									
Harling Road	d																									
Thetford	d	12 24					13 12		13 24			14 12			14 24				15 12			15 24			16 12	
Brandon	d						13 20					14 20							15 20						16 20	
Lakenheath	d																									
Shippea Hill	d																									
Cambridge	d			13 04	13 12			13 33		14 04	14 12			14 33			15 04	15 12			15 33		16 04	16 12		16 24
Waterbeach	d							13 39						14 39							15 39					16 30
Ely [6]	a	12 45	12 59	13 18	13 26		13 38	13 48	13 46	14 18	14 26	14 40		14 48	14 45	14 59	15 18	15 26	15 37		15 48	15 44	16 18	16 26	16 37	16 40
Cambridge	a						13 55					14 57							15 55						16 55	
Ely [6]	d	12 52	12 59	13 19				13 48	13 52	14 19				14 50	14 52	14 59	15 19				15 48	15 52	16 19			
Littleport	d							13 55						14 57							15 55					
Downham Market	d							14 04						15 06							16 04					
Watlington	d							14 10						15 12							16 10					
Kings Lynn	a							14 20						15 21							16 20					
Manea	d																									
March	d		13 16	13 35						14 35						15 16	15 35						16 35			
Whittlesea	d		13 27													15 27										
Peterborough [8]	a	13 24	13 38	13 53					14 25	14 53					15 25	15 39	15 53					16 25	16 53			

		FC [1]	EM ◇ A		LE [1] ◇	XC ◇ 🍴	LE [1]	LE [1]	LE [1]	EM ◇		FC [1]	XC ◇ B 🍴	LE [1]	LE [1]	LE [1]	LE [1]		EM ◇ C	FC [1]	LE [R] [1]	XC ◇ 🍴	FC [1]	LE [1]		LE [1]
London Liverpool Street	d				14 38				15 58						16 58						16 32			17 58		
London Kings Cross	d	15 45										16 45								17 45			18 15			
Ipswich	d				16 03																17 49					
Stansted Airport	d					16 20							17 17									18 20				
Norwich	d		15 52					16 38		16 57						17 35			17 54							18 40
Wymondham	d							16 50								17 47			18 06							18 52
Spooner Row	d							16x54																		
Attleborough	d		16 09					16 59								17 54										18 59
Eccles Road	d		16 14													17 59										
Harling Road	d		16 18													18 03										
Thetford	d		16 27					17 12		17 24						18 12			18 24							19 12
Brandon	d							17 20								18 20										19 20
Lakenheath	d																									
Shippea Hill	d																									
Cambridge	d	16 35				17 04	17 12		17 22			17 40	17 49	18 05	18 14		18 25			18 40		19 04	19 12	19 20		
Waterbeach	d	16 41							17 28			17 46			18 20		18 31			18 46				19 26		
Ely [6]	a	16 50	16 48		16 59	17 18	17 26	17 37	17 38	17 45		17 55	18 04	18 19	18 29	18 40	18 41		18 45	18 55	18 52	19 18	19 27	19 35		19 37
Cambridge	a							17 55								18 57										19 55
Ely [6]	d	16 50	16 52		16 59	17 19				17 50		17 55	18 06		18 30				18 52	18 56	19 01	19 19		19 35		
Littleport	d	16 57										18 02			18 38					19 03				19 42		
Downham Market	d	17 06										18 11			18 48					19 12				19 52		
Watlington	d	17 12										18 17			18 54					19 18				19 58		
Kings Lynn	a	17 21										18 26			19 05					19 29				20 10		
Manea	d												18x16													
March	d				17 16	17 35				18 07			18 24								19 17	19 35				
Whittlesea	d				17 27																19 29					
Peterborough [8]	a		17 26		17 38	17 53				18 24			18 43						19 31		19 42	19 53				

For general notes see front of timetable
For details of catering facilities see Directory of Train Operators

A Until 5 September to Liverpool Lime Street (Table 49). From 8 September to Chesterfield (Table 49)

B To Birmingham New Street (Table 49)

C To Nottingham (Table 49)

London, Norwich and Cambridge → Ely, Kings Lynn and Peterborough

Network Diagram - see first page of Table 13

Mondays to Fridays

		LE	EM	FC	XC	LE	LE		LE	FC	XC	LE	FC	LE		LE	FC	LE	EM	FC	FC FO		FC FX			
		■1	◇	■1	◇	■1	■1		■1	■1	◇	■1	■1	■1		■1	■1	■1		■1	■1		■1			
London Liverpool Street	d					18 58																				
London Kings Cross	d			18 45						19 45			20 15				21 15			22 15	23 15		23 15			
Ipswich	d											20 16														
Stansted Airport	d				19 18						20 20															
Norwich	d		18 57						19 45							20 48			22 10							
Wymondham	d								19 57							21 00			22 22							
Spooner Row	d																									
Attleborough	d								20 04							21 07			22 29							
Eccles Road	d																									
Harling Road	d																									
Thetford	d		19 24						20 17							21 20			22 43							
Brandon	d								20 25							21 28			22 51							
Lakenheath	d																									
Shippea Hill	d																									
Cambridge	d	19 25		19 46	19 50	20 15	20 20			20 40	20 57		21 10	21 13			22 10	22 55		23 11	00 13		00 13			
Waterbeach	d			19 52		20 21				20 46			21 16				22 16			23 17	00 19		00 19			
Ely ■6	a	19 39	19 49	20 01	20 05	20 30	20 34		20 43	20 55	21 13	21 19	21 25	21 29		21 45	22 25	23 09	23 10	23 26	00 28		00 29			
Cambridge	a								21 01							22 02			23 28							
Ely ■6	d		19 52	20 01	20 05	20 31				20 55	21 14	21 19	21 25				22 25			23 26	00 29					
Littleport	d			20 08		20 38				21 02			21 32				22 32			23 33	00 36					
Downham Market	d			20 18		20 47				21 11			21 41				22 41			23 42	00 45					
Watlington	d			20 23		20 53				21 17			21 47				22 47			23 48	00 50					
Kings Lynn	a			20 33		21 05				21 26			21 56				22 56			23 57	01 00					
Manea	d																									
March	d				20 22						21 30	21 36														
Whittlesea	d											21 47														
Peterborough ■8	a		20 25		20 39						21 52	21 58														

Saturdays

		FC	XC	XC	LE	EM	FC	EM	LE	XC	LE	LE	EM		FC	XC	LE	LE	LE	FC	EM	LE	XC	LE	LE	FC
		■1	◇	◇	■1		■1	◇	■1	◇	■1	■1	◇		■1	◇	■1	■1	■1	■1	◇	■1 ◇	◇	■1	■1	■1
			A	A				B																		
London Liverpool Street	d																	06 58				06 38				
London Kings Cross	d	23p15													06 45					07 45						08 45
Ipswich	d								06 00													08 03				
Stansted Airport	d			05 21												07 27							08 25			
Norwich	d				05 38			05 52				06 40							07 40		07 57				08 40	
Wymondham	d				05 50			06 04				06 52							07 52						08 52	
Spooner Row	d																									
Attleborough	d				05 57			06 11				06 59							07 59						08 59	
Eccles Road	d																									
Harling Road	d																									
Thetford	d				06 10			06 25				07 12							08 12		08 24				09 12	
Brandon	d				06 18							07 20							08 20						09 20	
Lakenheath	d																									
Shippea Hill	d																									
Cambridge	d	00 13	05 11	05 51		06 20	06 32			06 55	06 59		07 25		07 33	08 04	08 12	08 20		08 33			09 04	09 12		09 33
Waterbeach	d	00 19					06 38								07 39			08 26		08 39						09 39
Ely ■6	a	00 28	05 27	06 07	06 35	06 36	06 47	06 46	06 56	07 09	07 13	07 37	07 43		07 48	08 18	08 26	08 36	08 37	08 48	08 45	08 59	09 18	09 26	09 37	09 48
Cambridge	a				06 52							07 55							08 55						09 55	
Ely ■6	d	00 29	05 28	06 08			06 47	06 51	06 57	07 10			07 44		07 48	08 19				08 48	08 52	08 59	09 19			09 48
Littleport	d	00 36					06 54								07 55					08 55						09 55
Downham Market	d	00 45					07 03								08 04					09 04						10 04
Watlington	d	00 50					07 09								08 10					09 10						10 10
Kings Lynn	a	01 00					07 20								08 21					09 21						10 21
Manea	d			06x19																						
March	d		05 44	06 27				07 07	07 14	07 26			08 01			08 35					09 09	09 16	09 35			
Whittlesea	d		05 56	06 38					07 25													09 27				
Peterborough ■8	a		06 06	06 48				07 25	07 37	07 52			08 24			08 54					09 27	09 38	09 53			

For general notes see front of timetable
For details of catering facilities see
Directory of Train Operators

A To Birmingham New Street (Table 49)
B Until 6 September to Liverpool Lime Street (Table 49). From 13 September to Chesterfield (Table 49)

London, Norwich and Cambridge → Ely, Kings Lynn and Peterborough

Network Diagram - see first page of Table 13

		EM	XC	LE	LE	FC	EM	LE	XC	LE	LE	FC	EM	XC	LE	LE	FC	EM	LE	XC	LE	LE	FC	EM
		◇	◇	1	1	1	◇	1 ◇	◇	1	1	1	◇	◇	1	1	1	◇	R 1	◇	1	1	1	◇
London Liverpool Street	d							08 38											10 38					
London Kings Cross	d					09 45						10 45					11 45						12 45	
Ipswich	d							10 03											12 03					
Stansted Airport	d		09 25						10 25					11 25						12 25				
Norwich	d	08 57			09 40		09 57				10 40		10 57			11 40		11 57				12 40		12 57
Wymondham	d				09 52						10 52					11 52						12 52		
Spooner Row	d																							
Attleborough	d				09 59						10 59					11 59						12 59		
Eccles Road	d																							
Harling Road	d																							
Thetford	d	09 24			10 12		10 24				11 12		11 24			12 12		12 24				13 12		13 24
Brandon	d				10 20						11 20					12 20						13 20		
Lakenheath	d				10x25																			
Shippea Hill	d																							
Cambridge	d		10 04	10 12		10 33			11 04	11 12		11 33		12 04	12 12		12 33			13 04	13 12		13 33	
Waterbeach	d					10 39						11 39					12 39						13 39	
Ely [6]	a	09 46	10 18	10 26	10 38	10 48	10 45	10 59	11 18	11 26	11 37	11 48	11 45	12 18	12 26	12 37	12 48	12 45	12 59	13 18	13 26	13 37	13 48	13 45
Cambridge	a				10 55						11 55					12 55						13 55		
Ely [6]	d	09 53	10 19			10 48	10 53	10 59	11 19			11 48	11 52	12 19			12 48	12 53	12 59	13 19			13 48	13 52
Littleport	d					10 55						11 55					12 55						13 55	
Downham Market	d					11 04						12 04					13 04						14 04	
Watlington	d					11 10						12 10					13 10						14 10	
Kings Lynn	a					11 21						12 21					13 21						14 21	
Manea	d																							
March	d		10 35					11 16	11 35					12 35					13 16	13 35				
Whittlesea	d							11 27											13 27					
Peterborough [8]	a	10 25	10 53				11 25	11 38	11 53				12 25	12 53				13 25	13 38	13 53				14 23

		XC	LE	LE	FC	EM	LE	XC	LE	LE	FC	EM	XC	LE	LE	FC	EM	LE	XC	LE	LE	FC	EM	XC
		◇	1	1	1	◇	R 1	◇	1	1	1	◇	◇	1	1	1	◇	1 ◇	◇	1	1	1	◇	◇ A
London Liverpool Street	d						12 38											14 38						
London Kings Cross	d				13 45						14 45					15 45						16 45		
Ipswich	d						14 03											16 03						
Stansted Airport	d	13 25						14 25					15 25						16 25					17 25
Norwich	d			13 40		13 57				14 40		14 57			15 35		15 52				16 38		16 57	
Wymondham	d			13 52						14 52					15 47						16 50			
Spooner Row	d																				16x54			
Attleborough	d			13 59						14 59					15 54						16 59			
Eccles Road	d														15 59									
Harling Road	d														16 03									
Thetford	d			14 12		14 24				15 12		15 24			16 12		16 22				17 12		17 24	
Brandon	d			14 20						15 20					16 20						17 20			
Lakenheath	d																							
Shippea Hill	d																							
Cambridge	d	14 04	14 12		14 33			15 04	15 12		15 33		16 04	16 12		16 33			17 04	17 12		17 33		18 02
Waterbeach	d				14 39						15 39					16 39						17 39		
Ely [6]	a	14 18	14 26	14 37	14 48	14 45	14 59	15 18	15 26	15 37	15 48	15 45	16 18	16 26	16 37	16 48	16 43	16 59	17 18	17 26	17 37	17 48	17 45	18 16
Cambridge	a			14 55						15 55					16 55						17 55			
Ely [6]	d	14 19			14 48	14 52	14 59	15 19			15 48	15 55	16 19			16 48	16 51	16 59	17 19			17 48	17 51	18 17
Littleport	d				14 55						15 55					16 55						17 55		
Downham Market	d				15 04						16 04					17 04						18 04		
Watlington	d				15 10						16 10					17 10						18 10		
Kings Lynn	a				15 21						16 21					17 21						18 21		
Manea	d																							18x27
March	d	14 35					15 16	15 35					16 35					17 16	17 35					18 35
Whittlesea	d						15 27											17 27						
Peterborough [8]	a	14 53				15 25	15 38	15 53				16 27	16 53				17 24	17 38	17 53				18 24	18 53

		LE	LE	FC	EM	LE	XC	LE	LE	FC	EM	XC	LE	LE	FC	LE	LE	LE	FC	LE	EM	FC	FC
		1	1	1	◇	R 1	◇	1	1	1	◇	◇	1	1	1	R 1	1	1	1	1		1	1
London Liverpool Street	d					16 38										18 46							
London Kings Cross	d			17 45						18 45					19 45				20 52			21 52	23 08
Ipswich	d					18 03										20 03							
Stansted Airport	d						18 25					19 18											
Norwich	d		17 35		17 57				18 40		18 57			19 40				20 40			22 10		
Wymondham	d		17 47						18 52					19 52				20 52			22 22		
Spooner Row	d																						
Attleborough	d		17 54						18 59					19 59				20 59			22 29		
Eccles Road	d		17 59																				
Harling Road	d		18 03																				
Thetford	d		18 12		18 24				19 12		19 24			20 12				21 12			22 43		
Brandon	d		18 20						19 20					20 20				21 20			22 51		
Lakenheath	d																						
Shippea Hill	d								19x28														
Cambridge	d	18 12		18 33			19 04	19 12		19 33		19 50	20 12		20 33		21 12		21 56	22 30		22 56	00 16
Waterbeach	d			18 39						19 39					20 39				22 02			23 02	00 22
Ely [6]	a	18 26	18 37	18 48	18 45	18 59	19 18	19 26	19 37	19 48	19 46	20 04	20 26	20 37	20 48	20 59	21 26	21 37	22 11	22 44	23 06	23 11	00 31
Cambridge	a		18 55						19 55					20 55				21 55			23 26		
Ely [6]	d			18 48	18 52	18 59	19 19			19 48	19 52	20 05			20 48	20 59			22 11			23 11	00 31
Littleport	d			18 55						19 55					20 55				22 18			23 18	00 38
Downham Market	d			19 04						20 04					21 04				22 27			23 27	00 47
Watlington	d			19 10						20 10					21 10				22 32			23 32	00 53
Kings Lynn	a			19 21						20 21					21 21				22 43			23 43	01 04
Manea	d																						
March	d				19 09	19 16	19 35					20 21				21 16							
Whittlesea	d					19 27										21 27							
Peterborough [8]	a				19 26	19 38	19 53				20 25	20 39				21 38							

For general notes see front of timetable
For details of catering facilities see
Directory of Train Operators

A To Birmingham New Street (Table 49)

Table 17

Sundays

London, Norwich and Cambridge → Ely, Kings Lynn and Peterborough

Network Diagram - see first page of Table 13

		FC 1	LE 1 A	FC 1	FC 1 B		FC 1 C	LE 1	EM ◇ D	LE 1		LE 1	XC ◇	FC 1	EM ◇		LE 1	XC ◇	LE 1	LE 1		FC 1	LE 1	XC	LE 1	XC ◇
London Liverpool Street	d																									
London Kings Cross	d	23p08												10 15								12 15				
Ipswich	d		07 55							09 55									11 55							
Stansted Airport	d																	12 05								
Norwich	d							09 15	09 34						10 47		11 15						12 15			
Wymondham	d							09 27									11 27						12 27			
Spooner Row	d																									
Attleborough	d							09 34									11 34						12 34			
Eccles Road	d																									
Harling Road	d																									
Thetford	d							09 47	10 01						11 14		11 47						12 47			
Brandon	d							09 55									11 55						12 55			
Lakenheath	d							10x00									12x00									
Shippea Hill	d																									
Cambridge	d	00 16			09 07		09 16					10 44	10 48	11 02				12 36		12 46		13 02		13 09	13 38	13 43
Waterbeach	d	00 22		09 05	09 13		09 22							11 08								13 08				
Ely 6	a	00 31	08 51		09 22		09 31	10 20	10 26	10 51		11 01	11 06	11 17	11 35		12 18	12 53	12 51	13 01		13 17	13 17	13 25	13 52	13 59
Cambridge	a			09 14				10 38									12 34						13 34			
Ely 6	d	00 31	08 57		09 22		09 31		10 32	10 57			11 09	11 17	11 39			12 54	12 57			13 17		13 27		14 00
Littleport	d	00 38			09 29		09 38							11 24								13 24				
Downham Market	d	00 47			09 38		09 47							11 33								13 33				
Watlington	d	00 53			09 43		09 53							11 38								13 38				
Kings Lynn	a	01 04			09 54		10 01							11 50								13 50				
Manea	d																									
March	d		09 14							11 14			11 25					13 10	13 15					13 44		14 16
Whittlesea	d		09 25							11 25									13 26							
Peterborough 8	a		09 41						11 09	11 41			11 50		12 16			13 31	13 42					14 06		14 39

		LE 1		EM ◇	XC ◇	LE 1	LE 1		FC 1	LE 1	EM ◇ D ✠	LE 1		XC ◇	LE 1	FC 1	LE 1		EM ◇	LE 1	XC ◇	FC 1		LE 1	EM ◇ ✠	LE 1
London Liverpool Street	d																									
London Kings Cross	d								14 15							15 15						16 15				
Ipswich	d					13 55														15 55						
Stansted Airport	d				14 05									15 18							16 12					
Norwich	d	13 15		13 49						14 15	14 49				15 15				15 53					16 15	16 57	
Wymondham	d	13 27								14 27					15 27									16 27		
Spooner Row	d																									
Attleborough	d	13 34								14 34					15 34									16 34		
Eccles Road	d																									
Harling Road	d																									
Thetford	d	13 47		14 16						14 47	15 16				15 47				16 20					16 47	17 24	
Brandon	d	13 55								14 55					15 55									16 55		
Lakenheath	d														16x00											
Shippea Hill	d																									
Cambridge	d				14 36		14 46		15 02			15 38		15 47		16 02	16 38				16 47	17 02				17 44
Waterbeach	d								15 08							16 08						17 08				
Ely 6	a	14 17		14 42	14 53	14 51	15 01		15 17	15 17	15 42	15 52		16 04	16 14	16 17	16 52			16 51	17 04	17 17		17 17	17 48	17 58
Cambridge	a	14 34								15 34					16 31									17 34		
Ely 6	d			14 45	14 53	14 57			15 17		15 49			16 04		16 17				16 57	17 04	17 17			17 51	
Littleport	d								15 24							16 24						17 24				
Downham Market	d								15 33							16 33						17 33				
Watlington	d								15 38							16 38						17 38				
Kings Lynn	a								15 50							16 50						17 50				
Manea	d																									
March	d				15 10	15 15								16 21						17 14	17 21					
Whittlesea	d					15 26														17 25						
Peterborough 8	a			15 24	15 31	15 42					16 22			16 38					17 10	17 36	17 40				18 23	

For general notes see front of timetable
For details of catering facilities see Directory of Train Operators

A Until 7 September

B From 14 September. From Finsbury Park (Table 25)

C Until 7 September. From Hitchin (Table 25)

D 20 July to 7 September

Table 17

Sundays

London, Norwich and Cambridge → Ely, Kings Lynn and Peterborough

Network Diagram - see first page of Table 13

		LE [1]	FC [1]	XC ◇		EM ◇	LE [1]	LE [1]	LE [1]		FC [1]	XC ◇	LE [1]	EM ◇		FC [1]	EM ◇	LE [1]	FC [1]	EM ◇	LE [1]	FC [1]	FC [1]	FC [1]		
London Liverpool Street	d																									
London Kings Cross	d		17 15								18 15					19 15			20 15			21 15	22 15	23 15		
Ipswich	d							17 55																		
Stansted Airport	d			17 35								18 35														
Norwich	d	17 15				17 56			18 15					18 57			19 44	20 15		20 52						
Wymondham	d	17 27							18 27									20 27								
Spooner Row	d																									
Attleborough	d	17 34							18 34									20 34								
Eccles Road	d																									
Harling Road	d																									
Thetford	d	17 47				18 23			18 47					19 24			20 11	20 47		21 19						
Brandon	d	17 55							18 55									20 55								
Lakenheath	d																									
Shippea Hill	d																									
Cambridge	d		18 02	18 09			18 38				19 02	19 08	19 38			20 02			21 02		21 38	22 02	23 11	00 19		
Waterbeach	d		18 08								19 08					20 08			21 08			22 08	23 17	00 25		
Ely [6]	a	18 12	18 17	18 25		18 44	18 52	18 52	19 12		19 17	19 28	19 52	19 45		20 17	20 32	21 12	21 17	21 40	21 52	22 17	23 26	00 38		
Cambridge	a	18 29							19 30									21 29								
Ely [6]	d		18 17	18 26		18 48		18 57			19 17	19 28		19 56		20 17	20 35		21 17	21 44		22 17	23 26			
Littleport	d		18 24								19 24					20 24			21 24			22 24	23 33			
Downham Market	d		18 33								19 33					20 33			21 33			22 33	23 42			
Watlington	d		18 38								19 38					20 38			21 38			22 38	23 47			
Kings Lynn	a		18 50								19 50					20 50			21 50			22 50	23 59			
Manea	d																									
March	d			18 42				19 14				19 44														
Whittlesea	d							19 25																		
Peterborough [8]	a			19 00		19 20		19 36				20 02		20 28			21 08			22 20						

For general notes see front of timetable
For details of catering facilities see
Directory of Train Operators

Peterborough, Kings Lynn and Ely → Cambridge, Norwich and London

Network Diagram - see first page of Table 13

Miles	Miles			FC [1]	LE [1]	FC [1]	LE [1]	LE	LE [1]	FC [1]	EM ◇ A	LE [1]	FC [1]	LE [1]	LE [1]	XC ◇ B	FC [1]	LE [1]	EM ◇ A	FC [1]	LE [1]	LE [R] [1]
0	—	**Peterborough [8]**	d								06 27					07 10			07 35			07 52
6	—	Whittlesea	d													07 19						08 00
14	—	March	d								06 43					07 30			07 51			08 11
19¾	—	Manea	d													07x37						
—	0	**Kings Lynn**	d		05 18	05 53			06 18				06 53				07 23			07 55		
—	6	Watlington	d		05 25	06 00			06 25				07 00				07 30			08 02		
—	10¾	Downham Market	d		05 32	06 06			06 32				07 06				07 36			08 08		
—	21	Littleport	d		05 41	06 15			06 41				07 15				07 45			08 17		
29½	26½	**Ely [6]**	a		05 51	06 23			06 50		07 01		07 23			07 51	07 54		08 13	08 25		08 30
—	—	**Cambridge**	d					06 17				07 05									08 12	
—	—	**Ely [6]**	d	05 26	05 52	06 23	06 30	06 34	06 51	06 58	07 05	07 20	07 23	07 30	07 33	07 51	07 54	08 03	08 16	08 25	08 28	08 30
—	36	Waterbeach	d	05 35	06 01	06 33			07 00				07 33				08 04	08 12		08 35		
—	41¼	**Cambridge**	a	05 44	06 10	06 43	06 50		07 09	07 13			07 44	07 47	07 51	08 07	08 14	08 21		08 44		
35¼	—	Shippea Hill	d									07x29										
40¾	—	Lakenheath	d																			
44¼	—	Brandon	d					06 49			07 20	07 39									08 44	
51¾	—	Thetford	d					06 58			07 29	07 48							08 37		08 53	
59½	—	Harling Road	d					07 07				07 56										
62½	—	Eccles Road	d					07 12				08 00										
66¼	—	Attleborough	d					07 17			07 43	08 06							08 51		09 07	
69½	—	Spooner Row	d									08x11										
72	—	Wymondham	d					07 24			07 50	08 15							08 58		09 14	
82¼	—	**Norwich**	a					07 44			08 10	08 29							09 16		09 30	
—	—	Stansted Airport	a													08 49						
—	—	Ipswich	a																			09 26
—	99¼	**London Kings Cross**	a	06 35		07 39				08 15			08 45				09 12			09 42		
—	—	London Liverpool Street	a		07 34				08 34					09 19				09 49				10 46

		LE [1]	FC [1]	XC ◇	LE [1]	FC [1]	LE [1]	EM ◇ C	XC ◇	EM ◇	FC [1]	LE [1]	LE [1] ◇	LE [1]	XC ◇	EM ◇	FC [1]	LE [1]	LE [1]	XC ◇	EM ◇
Peterborough [8]	d			08 31				08 59	09 18	09 41			09 47		10 18	10 43				11 18	11 36
Whittlesea	d												09 55								
March	d			08 47					09 34				10 06		10 34					11 34	
Manea	d																				
Kings Lynn	d		08 27			08 59					09 56						10 56				
Watlington	d		08 34			09 06					10 03						11 03				
Downham Market	d		08 40			09 12					10 09						11 09				
Littleport	d		08 49			09 21					10 18						11 18				
Ely [6]	a		08 57	09 05		09 29		09 35	09 52	10 14	10 26		10 30		10 52	11 16	11 26			11 52	12 14
Cambridge	d				09 12							10 12						11 12			
Ely [6]	d	08 38	08 57	09 05	09 27	09 29	09 38	09 44	09 53	10 18	10 26	10 27	10 30	10 38	10 53	11 20	11 26	11 27	11 38	11 53	12 17
Waterbeach	d		09 07			09 38					10 35						11 35				
Cambridge	a	08 55	09 15	09 21		09 47	09 56		10 08		10 44			10 55	11 08		11 44		11 55	12 08	
Shippea Hill	d																				
Lakenheath	d																				
Brandon	d				09 43							10 43						11 43			
Thetford	d				09 52			10 05		10 39		10 52				11 41		11 52			12 38
Harling Road	d																				
Eccles Road	d																				
Attleborough	d				10 06							11 06						12 06			
Spooner Row	d				10x11																
Wymondham	d				10 15							11 13						12 13			
Norwich	a				10 30			10 43		11 14		11 30				12 15		12 30			13 13
Stansted Airport	a			09 59					10 49						11 49					12 49	
Ipswich	a												11 25								
London Kings Cross	a		10 12			10 46					11 35						12 33				
London Liverpool Street	a												12 45								

		FC [1]	LE [1]	LE [1] ◇	LE [1]	XC ◇	EM ◇	FC [1]	LE [1]	LE [1]	XC ◇	EM ◇	FC [1]	LE [1]	LE [1]	LE [1]	XC ◇	EM ◇	FC [1]	LE [1]	LE [1]	XC ◇
Peterborough [8]	d			11 48		12 18	12 43				13 18	13 40			13 47		14 18	14 40				15 18
Whittlesea	d			11 56											13 55							
March	d			12 07		12 34					13 34				14 06		14 34					15 34
Manea	d																					
Kings Lynn	d	11 56						12 56					13 56						14 56			
Watlington	d	12 03						13 03					14 03						15 03			
Downham Market	d	12 09						13 09					14 09						15 09			
Littleport	d	12 18						13 18					14 18						15 18			
Ely [6]	a	12 26		12 30		12 52	13 16	13 26			13 52	14 13	14 26		14 30		14 52	15 13	15 26			15 52
Cambridge	d		12 12						13 12					14 12						15 12		
Ely [6]	d	12 26	12 27	12 30	12 38	12 53	13 20	13 26	13 29	13 38	13 53	14 16	14 26	14 27	14 30	14 40	14 53	15 16	15 26	15 27	15 38	15 53
Waterbeach	d	12 35						13 35					14 35						15 35			
Cambridge	a	12 44			12 55	13 08		13 44		13 55	14 08		14 44			14 57	15 08		15 44		15 55	16 08
Shippea Hill	d																					
Lakenheath	d																					
Brandon	d		12 43						13 45					14 43						15 43		
Thetford	d		12 52				13 41		13 54			14 37		14 52				15 37		15 52		
Harling Road	d																					
Eccles Road	d																					
Attleborough	d		13 06						14 08					15 06						16 06		
Spooner Row	d																					
Wymondham	d		13 13						14 15					15 13						16 13		
Norwich	a		13 30				14 14		14 30			15 13		15 30				16 13		16 30		
Stansted Airport	a					13 49					14 49						15 49					16 49
Ipswich	a			13 25											15 25							
London Kings Cross	a	13 33						14 33					15 33						16 33			
London Liverpool Street	a			14 45																		

For general notes see front of timetable
For details of catering facilities see Directory of Train Operators

A From Nottingham (Table 49)
B From Birmingham New Street (Table 49)
C From Mansfield Woodhouse (Table 55)

Peterborough, Kings Lynn and Ely → Cambridge, Norwich and London

Network Diagram - see first page of Table 13

Station		FC 1		EM ◇	FC 1	LE 1	LE 1 ◇		LE 1	XC ◇	EM ◇	FC 1		LE 1	LE 1	XC ◇ A	FC 1		LE 1	LE 1 ◇	XC ◇	LE 1		FC 1	XC ◇	EM ◇
Peterborough 8	d			15 35			15 47			16 18	16 36					17 18				17 47	18 00				18 33	18 50
Whittlesea	d						15 55									17 26				17 55						
March	d						16 06			16 34						17 37				18 06	18 16				18 51	19 07
Manea	d															17x44										
Kings Lynn	d				15 56							16 54					17 36							18 36		
Watlington	d				16 03							17 01					17 43							18 43		
Downham Market	d				16 09							17 07					17 49							18 49		
Littleport	d				16 18							17 16					17 58							18 58		
Ely 6	a			16 08	16 26		16 30			16 52	17 09	17 24				17 58	18 06			18 28	18 34			19 06	19 09	19 25
Cambridge	d					16 12								17 12					18 05							
Ely 6	d	16 02		16 12	16 26	16 27	16 30		16 38	16 53	17 13	17 24		17 27	17 38	17 58	18 06		18 20	18 30	18 34	18 40		19 06	19 10	19 28
Waterbeach	d	16 11			16 35							17 33					18 15							19 15		
Cambridge	a	16 19			16 44				16 55	17 08		17 43			17 55	18 16	18 22				18 51	18 57		19 22	19 29	
Shippea Hill	d																									
Lakenheath	d																									
Brandon	d					16 43								17 43					18 36							
Thetford	d			16 33		16 52					17 34			17 52					18 44							19 49
Harling Road	d																									
Eccles Road	d																									
Attleborough	d					17 06								18 06					18 58							
Spooner Row	d																									
Wymondham	d					17 13								18 13					19 05							
Norwich	a			17 13		17 30					18 13			18 28					19 25							20 22
Stansted Airport	a									17 43						18 47									20 17	
Ipswich	a						17 27													19 25						
London Kings Cross	a				17 36							18 38					19 33							20 33		
London Liverpool Street	a						18 49													20 46						

Station		LE 1	LE 1	XC ◇		FC 1	EM ◇	LE 1 ◇	LE 1		LE 1	XC ◇	FC 1	LE 1		LE 1	XC ◇	FC 1	EM ◇ B	LE 1	XC ◇ A	FC 1	LE 1	EM		
Peterborough 8	d			19 19			19 37	19 49				20 17					21 18		21 37	22 05	22 17					
Whittlesea	d							19 57												22 13	22 26					
March	d			19 37				20 08				20 40					21 34			22 24	22 37					
Manea	d																									
Kings Lynn	d					19 39							20 39					21 36				22 32				
Watlington	d					19 46							20 46					21 43				22 39				
Downham Market	d					19 52							20 52					21 49				22 45				
Littleport	d					20 01							21 01					21 58				22 54				
Ely 6	a			19 56		20 09	20 13	20 26				20 58	21 09				21 52	22 06	22 10	22 42	22 55	23 02				
Cambridge	d		19 25						20 20					21 13									22 55			
Ely 6	d	19 38	19 40	19 56		20 09	20 16	20 27	20 35		20 44	20 58	21 09	21 29		21 45	21 52	22 06	22 15	22 42	22 55	23 02	23 10	23 11		
Waterbeach	d					20 18							21 18					22 15				23 11				
Cambridge	a	19 55		20 11		20 27					21 01	21 16	21 27			22 02	22 08	22 23			23 14	23 19		23 28		
Shippea Hill	d																									
Lakenheath	d																									
Brandon	d		19 56						20 51					21 45									23 26			
Thetford	d		20 04				20 37		20 59					21 54					22 36				23 34			
Harling Road	d																									
Eccles Road	d																									
Attleborough	d		20 18						21 13					22 08					22 50				23 48			
Spooner Row	d																									
Wymondham	d		20 25						21 20					22 15					22 57				23 55			
Norwich	a		20 40				21 13		21 35					22 30					23 20				00 10			
Stansted Airport	a																									
Ipswich	a							21 25												23 37						
London Kings Cross	a					21 30							22 30					23 35				00 42				
London Liverpool Street	a							22 45																		

For general notes see front of timetable
For details of catering facilities see Directory of Train Operators

A From Birmingham New Street (Table 49)
B Until 5 September from Liverpool Lime Street (Table 49). From 8 September from Nottingham (Table 49)

Table 17

Saturdays

Peterborough, Kings Lynn and Ely → Cambridge, Norwich and London

Network Diagram - see first page of Table 13

		FC	LE	EM	LE	FC	LE	XC	EM	FC	LE		LE	LE	XC	LE	EM	FC	LE	LE	XC	EM		FC	LE	LE
		1	1		1	1	1	◇ A	◇	1	1		R 1	1	◇	1	◇	1	1	1	◇	◇		1	1	R 1
Peterborough [8]	d							07 10	07 39				07 47		08 32		08 46				09 18	09 46				09 55
Whittlesea	d							07 19					07 55													10 03
March	d							07 30	07 55				08 06		08 48						09 34					10 14
Manea	d							07x37																		
Kings Lynn	d	05 56				06 56				07 56								08 56						09 56		
Watlington	d	06 03				07 03				08 03								09 03						10 03		
Downham Market	d	06 09				07 09				08 09								09 09						10 09		
Littleport	d	06 18				07 18				08 18								09 18						10 18		
Ely [6]	a	06 26				07 26		07 50	08 17	08 26			08 30		09 06		09 19	09 26			09 52	10 19		10 26		10 32
Cambridge	d			06 20	06 59						08 12								09 12						10 12	
Ely [6]	d	06 26	06 35	06 37	07 14	07 26	07 38	07 51	08 18	08 26	08 27		08 30	08 38	09 07	09 11	09 22	09 26	09 29	09 38	09 53	10 22		10 26	10 29	10 32
Waterbeach	d	06 35				07 35				08 35						09 20		09 35						10 35		
Cambridge	a	06 44	06 52			07 44	07 55	08 06		08 44				08 55	09 22	09 28		09 44		09 55	10 08			10 44		
Shippea Hill	d				07x22																					
Lakenheath	d																									
Brandon	d			06 52	07 32						08 43								09 45						10 45	
Thetford	d			07 01	07 41				08 39		08 52						09 44		09 54			10 44			10 54	
Harling Road	d			07 09	07 49																					
Eccles Road	d			07 14	07 53																					
Attleborough	d			07 19	07 59						09 06								10 08						11 08	
Spooner Row	d				08x04																					
Wymondham	d			07 26	08 08						09 13								10 15						11 15	
Norwich	a			07 44	08 23				09 12		09 30						10 17		10 30			11 12			11 30	
Stansted Airport	a							08 49							09 58						10 49					
Ipswich	a												09 25													11 27
London Kings Cross	a	07 34				08 33				09 33								10 34						11 35		
London Liverpool Street	a												10 38			10 43										12 45

		LE	XC	EM	FC	LE	LE	XC	EM	FC		LE	LE	LE	XC	EM	FC	LE	LE	XC	EM		FC	LE	LE	LE
		1	◇	◇	1	1	1	◇	◇	1		1	1 ◇	1	◇	◇	1	1	1	◇	◇		1	1	1 ◇	1
Peterborough [8]	d		10 18	10 46				11 18	11 38				11 48		12 18	12 39				13 18	13 37				13 47	
Whittlesea	d												11 56												13 55	
March	d		10 34					11 34					12 07		12 34					13 34					14 06	
Manea	d																									
Kings Lynn	d				10 56					11 56							12 56						13 56			
Watlington	d				11 03					12 03							13 03						14 03			
Downham Market	d				11 09					12 09							13 09						14 09			
Littleport	d				11 18					12 18							13 18						14 18			
Ely [6]	a		10 52	11 19	11 26			11 52	12 11	12 26			12 30		12 52	13 12	13 26			13 52	14 10		14 26		14 30	
Cambridge	d					11 12						12 12						13 12						14 12		
Ely [6]	d	10 38	10 53	11 23	11 26	11 29	11 38	11 53	12 16	12 26		12 27	12 30	12 38	12 53	13 15	13 26	13 27	13 38	13 53	14 16		14 26	14 27	14 30	14 38
Waterbeach	d				11 35					12 35							13 35						14 35			
Cambridge	a	10 55	11 08		11 44		11 55	12 08		12 44				12 55	13 08		13 44		13 55	14 08			14 44			14 55
Shippea Hill	d																									
Lakenheath	d																									
Brandon	d					11 45						12 43						13 43						14 43		
Thetford	d			11 44		11 54			12 37			12 52				13 36		13 52			14 37			14 52		
Harling Road	d																									
Eccles Road	d																									
Attleborough	d					12 08						13 06						14 06						15 06		
Spooner Row	d																									
Wymondham	d					12 15						13 13						14 13						15 13		
Norwich	a			12 17		12 30			13 13			13 30				14 13		14 30			15 13			15 30		
Stansted Airport	a		11 49					12 49							13 49					14 49						
Ipswich	a												13 27												15 25	
London Kings Cross	a				12 33					13 34							14 33						15 33			
London Liverpool Street	a												14 45												16 45	

For general notes see front of timetable
For details of catering facilities see
Directory of Train Operators

A From Birmingham New Street (Table 49)

Table 17

Saturdays

Peterborough, Kings Lynn and Ely → Cambridge, Norwich and London

Network Diagram - see first page of Table 13

		XC ◇	EM ◇	FC 1	LE 1	LE 1	XC ◇	EM ◇	FC 1		LE 1	LE 1 ◇	LE 1	XC ◇	EM ◇	FC 1	LE 1	LE 1	XC ◇ A	FC 1		LE 1	LE 1 ◇	LE 1	XC ◇	FC 1
Peterborough 8	d	14 18	14 40				15 18	15 36				15 47		16 18	16 38				17 18				17 47		18 18	
Whittlesea	d											15 55							17 26				17 55			
March	d	14 34					15 34					16 06		16 34					17 37				18 06		18 34	
Manea	d																		17x44							
Kings Lynn	d			14 56					15 56							16 56				17 56						18 34
Watlington	d			15 03					16 03							17 03				18 03						18 41
Downham Market	d			15 09					16 09							17 09				18 09						18 47
Littleport	d			15 18					16 18							17 18				18 18						18 56
Ely 6	a	14 52	15 12	15 26			15 52	16 09	16 26			16 30		16 56	17 11	17 26			17 58	18 26			18 30		18 52	19 04
Cambridge	d				15 12						16 12						17 12					18 12				
Ely 6	d	14 53	15 16	15 26	15 27	15 38	15 53	16 14	16 26		16 27	16 30	16 38	16 57	17 17	17 26	17 27	17 38	17 58	18 26		18 27	18 30	18 38	18 53	19 05
Waterbeach	d			15 35					16 35							17 35				18 35						19 15
Cambridge	a	15 08		15 44		15 55	16 08		16 44				16 55	17 15		17 44		17 55	18 15	18 44				18 55	19 13	19 21
Shippea Hill	d																									
Lakenheath	d				15x40																					
Brandon	d				15 45						16 43						17 43					18 43				
Thetford	d		15 38		15 54			16 35			16 52				17 38		17 52					18 52				
Harling Road	d																									
Eccles Road	d																									
Attleborough	d				16 08						17 06						18 06					19 06				
Spooner Row	d																									
Wymondham	d				16 15						17 13						18 13					19 13				
Norwich	a		16 13		16 30			17 13			17 30				18 13		18 30					19 30				
Stansted Airport	a	15 49					16 49							17 49					18 58							
Ipswich	a											17 27											19 25			
London Kings Cross	a			16 35					17 35							18 34				19 33						20 32
London Liverpool Street	a											18 45											20 45			

		EM ◇	LE 1	LE 1	XC ◇	FC 1	EM ◇	LE 1		LE 1 ◇	LE 1	XC ◇	FC 1	EM ◇ B	LE 1	LE 1	XC ◇	FC 1	EM ◇ C	LE 1	LE 1	XC ◇ A	EM	FC 1		
Peterborough 8	d	18 42			19 18		19 35			19 46		20 18		20 39			21 21		21 39	21 49		22 17				
Whittlesea	d									19 54										21 57		22 25				
March	d	18 58			19 34					20 05		20 34		20 55			21 37		21 55	22 08		22 36				
Manea	d																									
Kings Lynn	d					19 34							20 34					21 34						23 15		
Watlington	d					19 41							20 41					21 41						23 22		
Downham Market	d					19 47							20 47					21 47						23b31		
Littleport	d					19 56							20 56					21 56						23 40		
Ely 6	a	19 16			19 52	20 04	20 08			20 30		20 52	21 04	21 13			21 55	22 04	22 13	22 30		22 54		23 47		
Cambridge	d		19 12					20 12							21 12						22 30					
Ely 6	d	19 19	19 27	19 38	19 53	20 05	20 15	20 27		20 30	20 38	20 53	21 05	21 15	21 27	21 38	21 56	22 05	22 18	22 30	22 45	22 55	23 07	23 47		
Waterbeach	d					20 15							21 15					22 15						23 57		
Cambridge	a			19 55	20 08	20 21					20 55	21 13	21 21	21 31		21 55	22 16	22 21				23 16	23 26	00 06		
Shippea Hill	d																									
Lakenheath	d																									
Brandon	d		19 43					20 43							21 43						23 01					
Thetford	d	19 40	19 52				20 36	20 52							21 52				22 39		23 09					
Harling Road	d																									
Eccles Road	d																									
Attleborough	d		20 06					21 06							22 06				22 53		23 23					
Spooner Row	d																									
Wymondham	d		20 13					21 13							22 13				23 00		23 30					
Norwich	a	20 13	20 30				21 13	21 30							22 30				23 20		23 45					
Stansted Airport	a				20 50																					
Ipswich	a									21 27										23 32						
London Kings Cross	a					21 32							22 34					23 47								
London Liverpool Street	a									22 49																

For general notes see front of timetable
For details of catering facilities see Directory of Train Operators

A From Birmingham New Street (Table 49)
B From 13 September
C Until 6 September from Liverpool Lime Street (Table 49). From 13 September from Nottingham (Table 49)
b Arr. 2328

Peterborough, Kings Lynn and Ely → Cambridge, Norwich and London

Network Diagram - see first page of Table 13

		FC 1	LE 1	LE 1 A	FC 1	LE 1	EM ◇ B	LE 1	LE 1	FC 1	LE 1	LE 1	EM ◇ A 🛒	LE 1	FC 1	XC	LE 1	EM ◇ C	LE 1	XC
Peterborough 8	d			09 47			11 09		11 46				12 54			13 21		13 43	13 48	14 12
Whittlesea	d			09 55					11 54										13 56	
March	d			10 06			11 25		12 05							13 37			14 07	14 28
Manea	d																			
Kings Lynn	d	08 26			10 26					12 26					13 26					
Watlington	d	08 33			10 33					12 33					13 33					
Downham Market	d	08 39			10 39					12 39					13 39					
Littleport	d	08 48			10 48					12 48					13 48					
Ely 6	a	08 56		10 29	10 56		11 48		12 28	12 56			13 32		13 56	14 02		14 21	14 30	14 52
Cambridge	d					10 44					12 46			13 38						
Ely 6	d	08 56	10 21	10 30	10 56	11 01	11 51	12 18	12 30	12 56	13 01	13 17	13 36	13 53	13 56	14 02	14 17	14 28	14 30	14 53
Waterbeach	d	09 05			11 05					13 05					14 05					
Cambridge	a	09 14	10 38		11 14			12 34		13 14		13 34			14 14	14 19	14 34			15 09
Shippea Hill	d																			
Lakenheath	d					11x15					13x14									
Brandon	d					11 20	12 07				13 20			14 09						
Thetford	d					11 29	12 15				13 28		13 57	14 18				14 49		
Harling Road	d																			
Eccles Road	d																			
Attleborough	d					11 43	12 29				13 42			14 32						
Spooner Row	d																			
Wymondham	d					11 50	12 36				13 49			14 39						
Norwich	a					12 09	12 59				14 09		14 35	14 58				15 28		
Stansted Airport	a															14 58				15 44
Ipswich	a			11 25					13 25										15 27	
London Kings Cross	a	10 03			12 04					14 02					15 05					
London Liverpool Street	a																			

		FC 1	LE 1	LE 1	EM ◇ 🛒	LE 1	FC 1	XC ◇	LE 1	LE 1	EM ◇ 🛒	LE 1	FC 1	XC ◇	LE 1	EM ◇	FC 1	LE 1	XC ◇	LE 1
Peterborough 8	d				14 56			15 28		15 47	16 05			16 28		17 00			17 28	
Whittlesea	d									15 55										
March	d							15 44		16 06				16 44					17 44	
Manea	d																			
Kings Lynn	d	14 26					15 26						16 26				17 26			
Watlington	d	14 33					15 33						16 33				17 33			
Downham Market	d	14 39					15 39						16 39				17 39			
Littleport	d	14 48					15 48						16 48				17 48			
Ely 6	a	14 56			15 34		15 56	16 06		16 29	16 38		16 56	17 06		17 33	17 56		18 02	
Cambridge	d		14 46			15 38						16 38						17 44		
Ely 6	d	14 56	15 01	15 17	15 38	15 53	15 56	16 08	16 14	16 30	16 41	16 53	16 56	17 06	17 17	17 39	17 56	17 59	18 02	18 12
Waterbeach	d	15 05					16 05						17 05				18 05			
Cambridge	a	15 14		15 34			16 14	16 22	16 31				17 14	17 23	17 34		18 14		18 21	18 29
Shippea Hill	d																			
Lakenheath	d					16x06														
Brandon	d		15 17			16 12						17 09						18 15		
Thetford	d		15 26		15 59	16 20					17 02	17 18				18 00		18 24		
Harling Road	d																			
Eccles Road	d																			
Attleborough	d		15 40			16 34						17 32						18 38		
Spooner Row	d																			
Wymondham	d		15 47			16 41						17 39						18 45		
Norwich	a		16 09		16 37	16 55					17 35	17 53				18 35		18 59		
Stansted Airport	a							16 59						17 59						
Ipswich	a									17 25										
London Kings Cross	a	16 06					17 03						18 03				19 07			
London Liverpool Street	a																			

For general notes see front of timetable
For details of catering facilities see Directory of Train Operators

A Until 7 September

B Until 7 September. From Nottingham (Table 49)

C From Nottingham (Table 19)

Table 17

Sundays

Peterborough, Kings Lynn and Ely → Cambridge, Norwich and London

Network Diagram - see first page of Table 13

		LE ■1	EM ◇	LE ■1		FC ■1	XC ◇	LE ■1		EM ◇	LE ■1	FC ■1		XC ◇	LE ■1	EM ◇	FC ■1	XC ◇	LE ■1	LE ■1	FC ■1	EM ◇ A	FC ■1	XC ◇		
Peterborough 8	d	17 47	17 53				18 29			18 55				19 29	19 44	19 55		20 25				21 55		22 24		
Whittlesea	d	17 55													19 52											
March	d	18 06					18 45							19 45	20 03			20 46						22 40		
Manea	d																									
Kings Lynn	d					18 26						19 26					20 26				21 26		22 26			
Watlington	d					18 33						19 33					20 33				21 33		22 33			
Downham Market	d					18 39						19 39					20 39				21 39		22 39			
Littleport	d					18 48						19 48					20 48				21 48		22 48			
Ely 6	a	18 27	18 31			18 56	19 03			19 28		19 56		20 04	20 21	20 28	20 56	21 04			21 56	22 28	22 56	22 59		
Cambridge	d			18 38							19 38									21 38						
Ely 6	d	18 30	18 35	18 53		18 56	19 03	19 12		19 32	19 53	19 56		20 05	20 22	20 31	20 56	21 04	21 12	21 53	21 56	22 31	22 56	23 00		
Waterbeach	d					19 05						20 05					21 05				22 05		23 05			
Cambridge	a					19 14	19 20	19 30				20 14		20 21			21 14	21 19	21 29		22 14		23 13	23 17		
Shippea Hill	d																									
Lakenheath	d																									
Brandon	d			19 09							20 09									22 09						
Thetford	d		18 56	19 18						19 55	20 18					20 52				22 18		22 52				
Harling Road	d																									
Eccles Road	d																									
Attleborough	d			19 32							20 32									22 32		23 06				
Spooner Row	d																									
Wymondham	d			19 39							20 39									22 39		23 13				
Norwich	a		19 29	19 53						20 28	20 53					21 25				22 53		23 35				
Stansted Airport	a						19 59							20 59				21 53								
Ipswich	a	19 27													21 18											
London Kings Cross	a					20 03						21 05					22 03				23 15		00 32			
London Liverpool Street	a																									

For general notes see front of timetable
For details of catering facilities see Directory of Train Operators

A From Liverpool Lime Street (Table 49)

Kings Lynn → Sandringham and Hunstanton

Bus Service

This service is operated by First Eastern Counties.
Telephone Lo-call 08456-020-121

		FC	FC	FC	FC		FC	FC	FC	FC		FC	FC	FC	FC		FC	FC		FC	FC	FC			
London Kings Cross	⊖ 17 d				06 45			07 15		07 45					08 45						09 45				
London Liverpool Street	⊖ 17 d				05b58			06b28		06b58					07b58						08b58				
Cambridge	17 d			06 23	07 35			08 04		08 38					09 35						10 33				
Kings Lynn	d	06 25	06 55	07 28	08 35		08 50	09 05	09 20	09 35		09 50	10 05	10 20	10 35		10 50	11 05		11 20	11 35	11 50			
Sandringham Visitor Centre	a						09 12		09 42			10 12		10 42			11 12			11 42		12 12			
Sandringham Norwich Gates	a			07 51			09 14		09 44			10 14		10 44			11 14			11 44		12 14			
Hunstanton Bus Station	a	07 14	07 44	08 21	09 25		09 44	09 55	10 14	10 25		10 44	10 55	11 14	11 25		11 44	11 55		12 14	12 25	12 44			

		FC			FC	FC	FC	FC		FC	FC	FC	FC		FC	FC	FC	FC		FC	FC	FC	FC	FC
London Kings Cross	⊖ 17 d		and at the same minutes past each hour until			12 45		13 45					14 45					15 45				16 45	17 45	18 45
London Liverpool Street	⊖ 17 d					11b58		12b58					13b58					14b28				15b58	16 58	18 58
Cambridge	17 d					13 33		14 33					15 33					16 35				17 40	18 40	20 15
Kings Lynn	d	12 05			14 20	14 30	15 05	15 35		15 50	16 05	16 20	16 35		16 50	17 05	17 20	17 35		17 50	18 20	19 00	20 00	21 30
Sandringham Visitor Centre	a				14 42		15 27			16 12		16 42			17 12		17 42			18 12				
Sandringham Norwich Gates	a				14 44		15 29			16 14		16 44			17 14		17 44			18 14				
Hunstanton Bus Station	a	12 55			15 14	15 20	15 59	16 25		16 44	16 55	17 14	17 25		17 44	17 55	18 14	18 25		18 41	19 03	19 40	20 40	22 10

		FC
London Kings Cross	⊖ 17 d	20 15
London Liverpool Street	⊖ 17 d	19b28
Cambridge	17 d	21 10
Kings Lynn	d	23 00
Sandringham Visitor Centre	a	
Sandringham Norwich Gates	a	
Hunstanton Bus Station	a	23 40

Saturdays

This service is operated by First Eastern Counties.
Telephone Lo-call 08456-020-121

		FC	FC		FC	FC		FC	FC		FC		FC	FC	FC	FC				FC	FC		FC	FC	FC
London Kings Cross	⊖ 17 d				06 45						07 45					08 45	and at the same minutes past each hour until							13 45	
London Liverpool Street	⊖ 17 d				05b58						06b58					07b58								12b58	
Cambridge	17 d		06 32		07 33						08 33					09 33								14 33	
Kings Lynn	d	06 35	07 35		08 35	08 50		09 05	09 20		09 35		09 50	10 05	10 20	10 35				14 50	15 05		15 20	15 35	15 50
Sandringham Visitor Centre	a					09 12			09 42				10 12		10 42					15 12	15 27		15 42		16 12
Sandringham Norwich Gates	a					09 14			09 44				10 14		10 44					15 14	15 29		15 44		16 14
Hunstanton Bus Station	a	07 25	08 25		09 25	09 44		09 55	10 14		10 25		10 44	10 55	11 14	11 25				15 44	15 59		16 14	16 25	16 44

		FC		FC	FC		FC	FC		FC	FC		FC	FC		FC	FC		FC	FC					
London Kings Cross	⊖ 17 d				14 45						15 45					16 45	17 45		19 45	20 52					
London Liverpool Street	⊖ 17 d				13b58						14b58					15b58	16b58		18b58	20b28					
Cambridge	17 d				15 33						16 33					17 33	18 33		20 33	21 56					
Kings Lynn	d	16 05		16 20	16 35		16 50	17 05		17 20	17 35		17 50	18 20		19 00	20 00		21 30	23 00					
Sandringham Visitor Centre	a			16 42			17 12			17 42			18 12												
Sandringham Norwich Gates	a			16 44			17 14			17 44			18 14												
Hunstanton Bus Station	a	16 55		17 14	17 25		17 44	17 55		18 14	18 25		18 41	19 03		19 40	20 40		22 10	23 40					

Sundays

This service is operated by First Eastern Counties.
Telephone Lo-call 08456-020-121

		FC		FC		FC		FC		FC		FC		FC		FC		FC		FC	FC	FC	FC		
London Kings Cross	⊖ 17 d									10 15				12 15				14 15		15 15	18 15	19 15	21 15		
London Liverpool Street	⊖ 17 d									09b28				11b28				13b28		14b28	17b28	18b28	20b28		
Cambridge	17 d					09c16				11 02				13 02				15 02		16 02	19 02	20 02	22 02		
Kings Lynn	d	08 50		09 50		10 50		11 50		12 50		13 50		14 50		15 50		16 50		17 50	20 00	21 30	23 00		
Sandringham Visitor Centre	a	09 12		10 12		11 12		12 12		13 12		14 12		15 12		16 12		17 12		18 12					
Sandringham Norwich Gates	a	09 14		10 14		11 14		12 14		13 14		14 14		15 14		16 14		17 14		18 14					
Hunstanton Bus Station	a	09 42		10 42		11 42		12 42		13 42		14 42		15 42		16 42		17 42		18 42	20 40	22 10	23 40		

For general notes see front of timetable
For details of catering facilities see Directory of Train Operators

b Change at Cambridge and Kings Lynn
c From 14 September dep. 0907

Table 17A

Mondays to Fridays

Hunstanton and Sandringham → Kings Lynn

Bus Service

This service is operated by First Eastern Counties. Telephone Lo-call 08456-020-121

		FC	FC	FC	FC	FC	FC	FC	FC	FC		FC	FC	FC	FC	FC	FC	FC
Hunstanton Bus Station	d	06 30	07 16	07 48	08 33	08 48	09 03	09 18	09 33	09 48	and at the same minutes past each hour until	14 03	14 18	14 33	14 48	15 18	15 25	16 03
Sandringham Norwich Gates	d	06 55	07 43			09 15		09 45		10 15			14 45		15 15	15 45	15 56	
Sandringham Visitor Centre	d					09 17		09 47		10 17			14 47		15 17	15 47	15 58	
Kings Lynn	a	07 20	08 10	08 40	09 25	09 44	09 55	10 14	10 25	10 44		14 55	15 14	15 25	15 44	16 14	16 25	16 55
Cambridge	17 a	08 44	09 15	09 47		10 44				11 44					16 44		17 43	
London Liverpool Street ⊖	17 a		10b43	11b43		12b43				13b43					18b44		19b13	
London Kings Cross ⊖	17 a	09 42	10 12	10 46		11 35				12 33					17 36		18 38	

		FC	FC	FC	FC	FC	FC	FC	FC	FC	FC	FC	FC	FC	FC
Hunstanton Bus Station	d	16 18	16 33	16 48	17 08	17 18	17 33	17 48	18 03	18 44	19 14	19 44	20 44	22 14	23 44
Sandringham Norwich Gates	d	16 45		17 15		17 45		18 15							
Sandringham Visitor Centre	d	16 47		17 17		17 47		18 17							
Kings Lynn	a	17 14	17 25	17 44	18 00	18 14	18 25	18 44	18 55	19 22	19 52	20 22	21 22	22 52	00 22
Cambridge	17 a		18 22				19 22			20 27		21 27	22 23		
London Liverpool Street ⊖	17 a		20b13				21b14			22b13		23b13	23b43		
London Kings Cross ⊖	17 a		19 33				20 33			21 30		22 30	23 35		

Saturdays

This service is operated by First Eastern Counties. Telephone Lo-call 08456-020-121

		FC	FC	FC	FC	FC	FC	FC	FC		FC	FC	FC	FC	FC
Hunstanton Bus Station	d	06 30	07 30	08 33	08 48	09 03	09 18	09 33	09 48	and at the same minutes past each hour until	16 03	16 18	16 33	16 48	17 03
Sandringham Norwich Gates	d	06 55	07 55		09 15		09 45		10 15			16 45		17 15	
Sandringham Visitor Centre	d				09 17		09 47		10 17			16 47		17 17	
Kings Lynn	a	07 20	08 20	09 25	09 44	09 55	10 14	10 25	10 44		16 55	17 14	17 25	17 44	17 55
Cambridge	17 a	08 44	09 44		10 44				11 44					18 44	
London Liverpool Street ⊖	17 a	10b43	11b43		12b43				13b43						
London Kings Cross ⊖	17 a	09 33	10 34		11 35				12 33					19 33	

		FC	FC	FC	FC	FC	FC	FC	FC	FC	FC
Hunstanton Bus Station	d	17 18	17 33	17 48	18 03	18 44	19 14	19 44	20 44	22 14	23 44
Sandringham Norwich Gates	d	17 45		18 15							
Sandringham Visitor Centre	d	17 47		18 17							
Kings Lynn	a	18 14	18 25	18 44	18 55	19 22	19 52	20 22	21 22	22 52	00 22
Cambridge	17 a		19 21			20 21		21 21	22 21	00 06	
London Liverpool Street ⊖	17 a		20b43			21b43		22b43	23b43		
London Kings Cross ⊖	17 a		20 32			21 32		22 34	23 47		

Sundays

This service is operated by First Eastern Counties. Telephone Lo-call 08456-020-121

		FC	FC	FC	FC	FC	FC	FC	FC	FC	FC	FC	FC	FC
Hunstanton Bus Station	d	09 47	10 47	11 47	12 47	13 47	14 47	15 47	16 47	17 47	18 47	20 44	22 14	23 44
Sandringham Norwich Gates	d	10 14	11 14	12 14	13 14	14 14	15 14	16 14	17 14	18 14	19 14			
Sandringham Visitor Centre	d	10 16	11 16	12 16	13 16	14 16	15 16	16 16	17 16	18 16				
Kings Lynn	a	10 40	11 40	12 40	13 40	14 40	15 40	16 40	17 40	18 40	19 38	21 22	22 52	00 22
Cambridge	17 a		13 14	14 14	15 14	16 14	17 14	18 14	19 14	20 14	21 14	23 13		
London Liverpool Street ⊖	17 a		14b43	15b43	16b43	17b43	18b43	19b43	20b43	21b43	22b43			
London Kings Cross ⊖	17 a		14 02	15 05	16 06	17 03	18 03	19 07	20 03	21 05	22 03	00 32		

For general notes see front of timetable
For details of catering facilities see Directory of Train Operators

b Change at Kings Lynn and Cambridge

Network Diagram for Tables 18, 19, 27, 29, 30

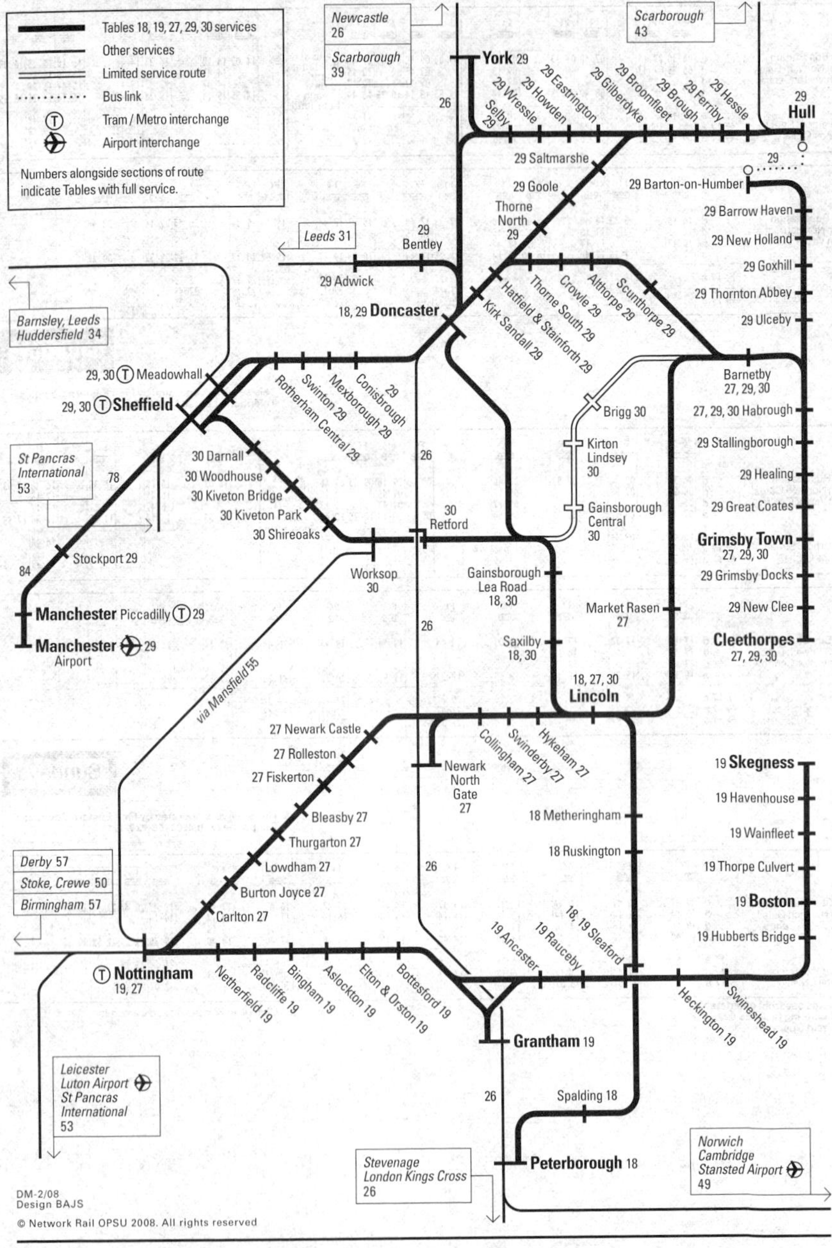

Tables 18, 19, 27, 29, 30 services
Other services
Limited service route
Bus link
Tram / Metro interchange
Airport interchange
Numbers alongside sections of route indicate Tables with full service.
Newcastle 26
Scarborough 39
Scarborough 43
York 29
Hull 29
Selby 29
29 Wressle
29 Howden
29 Eastrington
29 Gilberdyke
29 Broomfleet
29 Brough
29 Ferriby
29 Hessle
29 Saltmarshe
29 Goole
Thorne North 29
29 Barton-on-Humber
29 Barrow Haven
29 New Holland
29 Goxhill
29 Thornton Abbey
29 Ulceby
Leeds 31
29 Bentley
29 Adwick
18, 29 Doncaster
Kirk Sandall 29
Hatfield & Stainforth 29
Thorne South 29
Crowle 29
Althorpe 29
Scunthorpe 29
Barnsley, Leeds Huddersfield 34
29, 30 Meadowhall
29, 30 Sheffield
Rotherham Central 29
Swinton 29
Mexborough 29
Conisbrough 29
Barnetby 27, 29, 30
27, 29, 30 Habrough
29 Stallingborough
29 Healing
29 Great Coates
Grimsby Town 27, 29, 30
29 Grimsby Docks
29 New Clee
Cleethorpes 27, 29, 30
Brigg 30
Kirton Lindsey 30
Gainsborough Central 30
St Pancras International 53
78
30 Darnall
30 Woodhouse
30 Kiveton Bridge
30 Kiveton Park
30 Shireoaks
26
30 Retford
Worksop 30
Stockport 29
84
Manchester Piccadilly 29
Manchester Airport 29
Gainsborough Lea Road 18, 30
Market Rasen 27
Saxilby 18, 30
18, 27, 30 Lincoln
via Mansfield 55
27 Newark Castle
27 Rolleston
27 Fiskerton
Bleasby 27
Thurgarton 27
Lowdham 27
Burton Joyce 27
Carlton 27
Newark North Gate 27
Collingham 27
Swinderby 27
Hykeham 27
18 Metheringham
18 Ruskington
19 Skegness
19 Havenhouse
19 Wainfleet
19 Thorpe Culvert
19 Boston
19 Hubberts Bridge
Derby 57
Stoke, Crewe 50
Birmingham 57
Nottingham 19, 27
Netherfield 19
Radcliffe 19
Bingham 19
Aslockton 19
Elton & Orston 19
Bottesford 19
19 Ancaster
19 Rauceby
18, 19 Sleaford
Heckington 19
Swineshead 19
Grantham 19
Leicester Luton Airport St Pancras International 53
Spalding 18
Peterborough 18
Stevenage London Kings Cross 26
Norwich Cambridge Stansted Airport 49

DM-2/08
Design BAJS

Peterborough → Sleaford, Lincoln and Doncaster

Network Diagram - see first page of Table 18

Mondays to Fridays

Miles	Station		EM	NT	EM A	EM	EM	NT B	EM	NT B	EM	NT B	EM	NT B	EM	EM	NT B	EM	NT B	EM C	NT B
—	London Kings Cross 15	⊖ d					06 35				07 30		08 40			09 35		10 35		11 35	
0	**Peterborough 8**	d	06 30				07 32				08 40		09 35			10 43		11 50		12 41	
16½	Spalding	d	06a57				07a58				09 02		09 58			11 05		12 12		13 03	
35½	Sleaford	a									09 30		10 26			11 33		12 40		13 31	
—		d			06 55	07 45			08 46		09 31		10 27			11 33		12 45		13 32	
40	Ruskington	d			07 02	07 52			08 53		09 38		10 34			11 41		12 53		13 39	
47¼	Metheringham	d			07 12	08 02			09 03		09 48		10 44			11 51		13 02		13 49	
56¾	**Lincoln**	a			07 26	08 17			09 16		10 02		10 58			12 06		13 16		14 02	
—		d		07 04				08 27	09 18	09 27		10 27		11 27	11 55		12 27	13 18	13 27		14 27
62¾	Saxilby	d		07 14				08 36	09 27	09 36		10 36		11 36	12 04		12 36	13 28	13 36		14 36
72¼	Gainsborough Lea Road	d		07a26				08 49	09 40	09 49		10 49		11 49	12 17		12 49	13 40	13 49		14 49
93½	**Doncaster 7**	a						10 36	10 09	11 36		12 35		13 36	12 47		14 36	14 17	15 36		16 36

Station		EM	NT B	NT E	EM	NT	EM	EM	NT	EM	EM	EM	NT	NT	EM G	EM	NT
London Kings Cross 15	⊖ d	12 30			14 10		15 30	16 35				17 30				19 33	
Peterborough 8	d	13 48			15 09		16 25	17 32				18 35				20 28	
Spalding	d	14 10			15 32		16 47	18a01				19a02				20a54	
Sleaford	a	14 38			16 00		17 15										
	d	14 40			16 10		17 16			17 55	19 01				20 11		
Ruskington	d	14 47			16 18		17 23			18 03	19 08				20 18		
Metheringham	d	14 57			16 28		17 33			18 13	19 18				20 28		
Lincoln	a	15 11			16 45		17 48			18 26	19 31				20 41		
	d		15 27	16 27		17 22			18 24	18 29	19 33		19 43	20 27			21 27
Saxilby	d		15 36	16 36		17 31			18 33	18 41	19 42		19 52	20 36			21 36
Gainsborough Lea Road	d		15 49	16 49		17a43			18a45	18 57	19 54		20a04	20a48			21a48
Doncaster 7	a		17 36	18 35						19 26	20 24						

Saturdays

Station		EM	NT	EM A	EM	EM	NT	EM	NT B	EM	NT	EM	NT B	EM	NT B	EM	NT B	EM
London Kings Cross 15	⊖ d					06 15				07 10		08 30				10 40		11 30
Peterborough 8	d	06 28				07 30				08 40		09 34				11 50		12 43
Spalding	d	06a55				07a56				09 02		09 57				12 12		13 05
Sleaford	a									09 30		10 25				12 40		13 37
	d			06 56	07 45					09 31		10 26				12 44		13 37
Ruskington	d			07 03	07 52					09 38		10 33				12 51		13 45
Metheringham	d			07 13	08 02					09 48		10 43				13 01		13 54
Lincoln	a			07 26	08 17					10 04		10 58				13 16		14 08
	d		07 04				08 27	09 15	09 27		10 27		11 27	11 55	12 27		13 27	14 09
Saxilby	d		07 14				08 36	09 24	09 36		10 36		11 36	12 05	12 36		13 36	14 19
Gainsborough Lea Road	d		07a26				08 49	09 37	09 49		10 49		11 49	12 17	12 49		13 49	14 31
Doncaster 7	a						10 35	10 06	11 36		12 35		13 36	12 47	14 36		15 36	15 01

Station		NT B	EM	NT B	NT	EM	NT	EM	EM	EM	NT	EM	EM	EM	NT	NT	EM	EM	NT
London Kings Cross 15	⊖ d					14 00		15 00		16 30			17 40					19 30	
Peterborough 8	d					15 09		16 24		17 31			18 34					20 28	
Spalding	d					15 31		16 47		17a57			19a05					20a54	
Sleaford	a					15 59		17 16											
	d					16 07		17 16	17 33			18 11					20 20		
Ruskington	d					16 15		17 24	17 40			18 19					20 27		
Metheringham	d					16 25		17 33	17 50			18 28					20 37		
Lincoln	a					16 40		17 50	18 03			18 44					20 52		
	d	14 27	15 10	15 27	16 27		17 22				18 24			19 30	19 43	20 27			21 24
Saxilby	d	14 36	15 20	15 36	16 36		17 31				18 33			19 40	19 52	20 36			21 33
Gainsborough Lea Road	d	14 49	15 32	15 49	16 49		17a43				18a45			19 52	20a04	20a48			21a45
Doncaster 7	a	16 36	16 01	17 36	18 37									20 21					

Sundays

Station		NT	NT	NT	NT
London Kings Cross 15	⊖ d				
Peterborough 8	d				
Spalding	d				
Sleaford	a				
	d				
Ruskington	d				
Metheringham	d				
Lincoln	a				
	d	15 15	17 35	19 35	21 15
Saxilby	d	15 25	17 45	19 45	21 25
Gainsborough Lea Road	d	15a37	17a57	19a57	21a37
Doncaster 7	a				

For general notes see front of timetable
For details of catering facilities see Directory of Train Operators

- A To Leicester (Table 53)
- B To Adwick (Table 29)
- C To Newark North Gate (Table 27)
- E To Hull (Table 29)
- G To Nottingham (Table 27)

Doncaster, Lincoln and Sleaford → Peterborough

Network Diagram - see first page of Table 18

Mondays to Fridays

Miles			NT	EM	EM	EM	EM	NT	NT	EM	NT	EM	NT A	EM	EM	NT A	EM	NT A	EM B	EM	NT A	EM
0	**Doncaster** [7]	d											09 01		10 22	10 02		11 02		13 04	11 58	
21¼	Gainsborough Lea Road	d	06 25					07 38	08 24		09 38		10 38		10 52	11 38		12 38		13 30	13 39	
30¾	Saxilby	d	06 37					07 51	08 37		09 51		10 51		11 05	11 51		12 51		13 43	13 52	
36¾	**Lincoln**	a	06 53					08 06	08 52		10 06		11 06		11 18	12 05		13 05		13 56	14 06	
—		d			07 09		08 04			09 11		10 17		11 12			12 14		13 31			14 50
46¼	Metheringham	d			07 21		08 16			09 23		10 29		11 23			12 26		13 44			15 02
53½	Ruskington	d			07 31		08 26			09 33		10 39		11 33			12 36		13 53			15 11
58	Sleaford	a			07 40		08 35			09 42		10 54		11 44			12 45		14 02			15 21
—		d					08 38			09 43		10 55		11 44			12 46		14 03			15 22
77	Spalding	d		07 01		08 03	09 03			10 08		11 20		12 09			13 11		14 28			15 46
93½	**Peterborough** [8]	a		07 26		08 28	09 28			10 37		11 45		12 36			13 38		14 53			16 12
—	London Kings Cross [15] ⊖	a		08 33		09 45	10 40			11 51		13 10		13 43			14 44		15 58			17 41

		NT A	EM	EM B	NT A	NT A	EM C	EM	NT A	EM	NT A	EM	EM	NT	EM	EM D	EM	NT	EM
Doncaster [7]	d	13 02	14 25		14 01	15 02			16 02		17 00				19 34				20 33
Gainsborough Lea Road	d	14 38	14 54		15 38	16 38			17 38		18 38			19 39	20 00			20 42	21 00
Saxilby	d	14 51	15 07		15 51	16 51			17 51		18 51			19 52	20 13			20 55	21 14
Lincoln	a	15 06	15 18		16 05	17 06			18 06		19 07			20 06	20 25			21 10	21 24
	d		15 20	16 02			17 13			18 15			19 30				20 40		
Metheringham	d		15 32	16 15			17 26			18 27			19 42				20 53		
Ruskington	d		15 42	16 24			17 36			18 37			19 52				21 03		
Sleaford	a		15 53	16 33			17 47			18 48			20 08				21 14		
	d			16 34															
Spalding	d			16 58				18 02				19 53				21 00			
Peterborough [8]	a			17 24				18 28				20 21				21 26			
London Kings Cross [15] ⊖	a			18 54				19 59				21 33				23 32			

Saturdays

		NT	EM	EM	EM	EM	NT	NT	NT	EM	NT A	EM	EM	NT A	NT A	EM	EM	NT A
Doncaster [7]	d										09 02		10 19	10 02	11 02		13 04	12 02
Gainsborough Lea Road	d	06 25					07 38	08 24	09 38		10 38		10 52	11 38	12 38		13 30	13 40
Saxilby	d	06 37					07 51	08 37	09 51		10 51		11 05	11 51	12 51		13 43	13 53
Lincoln	a	06 53					08 06	08 52	10 06		11 06		11 17	12 05	13 05		13 56	14 06
	d			07 09		08 04				10 15		11 12				13 28		
Metheringham	d			07 21		08 16				10 27		11 23				13 40		
Ruskington	d			07 31		08 26				10 37		11 33				13 50		
Sleaford	a			07 40		08 35				10 46		11 43				13 59		
	d					08 38				10 51		11 43				13 59		
Spalding	d		07 01		08 03	09 03				11 16		12 08				14 24		
Peterborough [8]	a		07 26		08 28	09 29				11 41		12 34				14 53		
London Kings Cross [15] ⊖	a		08 40		09 51	10 41				13 10		13 44				15 58		

		EM	NT A	EM	NT A	EM	NT A	EM	EM	NT A	NT A	EM	EM C	NT A	EM E	NT G	NT H	EM
Doncaster [7]	d		13 01	15 07	14 02		15 02	16 27		16 02	17 02			18 02				20 33
Gainsborough Lea Road	d		14 40	15 33	15 45		16 38	16 56		17 38	18 38			19 39		20 42	20 44	21 00
Saxilby	d		14 53	15 46	15 58		16 51	17 09		17 51	18 51			19 52		20 55	20 57	21 14
Lincoln	a		15 06	15 57	16 09		17 06	17 20		18 06	19 07			20 06		21 10	21 12	21 26
	d	14 51		15 59		16 55		17 22					19 31					
Metheringham	d	15 03		16 11		17 07		17 34					19 44					
Ruskington	d	15 13		16 21		17 17		17 44					19 54					
Sleaford	a	15 22		16 30		17 28		17 55					20 05					
	d	15 23		16 31														
Spalding	d	15 47		16 56					18 04			19 53			20 58			
Peterborough [8]	a	16 13		17 21					18 29			20 22			21 23			
London Kings Cross [15] ⊖	a	17 28		18 28					19 40			21 48			22 47			

Sundays

		NT	NT J	NT K	NT J	NT K	NT L	NT N
Doncaster [7]	d							
Gainsborough Lea Road	d	14 32	16 53	16 58	18 53	18 58	20 16	20 20
Saxilby	d	14 45	17 06	17 11	19 06	19 11	20 29	20 33
Lincoln	a	15 00	17 21	17 25	19 21	19 26	20 44	20 48
	d							
Metheringham	d							
Ruskington	d							
Sleaford	a							
	d							
Spalding	d							
Peterborough [8]	a							
London Kings Cross [15] ⊖	a							

For general notes see front of timetable
For details of catering facilities see Directory of Train Operators

A From Scunthorpe (Table 29)
B From Newark North Gate (Table 27)
C From Leicester (Table 53)
D To Nottingham (Table 49)
E To Nottingham (Table 19)
G Until 6 September
H From 13 September
J Until 7 September and from 9 November
K 14 September to 2 November
L From 20 July
N Until 13 July

Skegness → Grantham and Nottingham

Network Diagram - see first page of Table 18

Miles	Miles			EM	EM	EM		EM	EM	EM		EM	EM	EM		EM	EM	EM		EM	EM	EM		EM	EM
								◇		◇			◇			◇		◇			◇			◇	
						A		B																	
0	—	**Skegness**	d						07 15			08 11		09 38			10 03			11 32		12 06			13 32
3¼	—	Havenhouse	d																			12 11			
5	—	Wainfleet	d						07 23			08 19		09 46			10 11			11 40		12 15			13 40
7	—	Thorpe Culvert	d						07 27													12 19			
23¾	—	**Boston**	d		06 16				07 50			08 45		10 14			10 40			12 06		12 42			14 06
27½	—	Hubberts Bridge	d						07 56											12 12					
30¾	—	Swineshead	d						08 01																
35¾	—	Heckington	d		06 30				08 07			08 59		10 28			10 54			12 21		12 56			14 20
40½	—	**Sleaford**	d		06 37	06 55			08 15			09 07		10 37			11 02			12 29		13 04			14 29
42½	—	Rauceby	d		06 41												11 06					13 08			
46½	0	Ancaster	d		06 47												11 12					13 14			
57¼	—	**Grantham 7**	a		07 07				08 42			09 33					11 33					13 35			
—	—	London Kings Cross 15	⊖ a		*08 33*				*10 10*			*10 51*					*12 44*					*15 20*			
—	—	**Grantham 7**	d	06 09	07 10			07 59	08 46	09 00		09 40	09 59			11 12	11 40	11 57			12 59	13 40		13 57	
65¼	12¾	Bottesford	d	06 19	07 20			08 10				09 50					11 50					13 50			
67¾	—	Elton & Orston	d	06 24																					
69½	—	Aslockton	d	06 27	07 27			08 17				09 56					11 56					13 56			
71¾	—	Bingham	d	06 32	07 31			08 21	09 03			10 01					12 01					14 01			
75¼	—	Radcliffe (Notts)	d	06 37	07 37			08 27				10 06					12 06					14 06			
77	—	Netherfield	d		07 41			08 31				10 11													
80¼	—	**Nottingham 8**	a	06 48	07 52	08 32		08 39	09 22	09 39		10 22	10 28	11 29		11 41	12 22	12 34		13 20	13 28	14 22		14 33	15 20

		EM	EM	EM		EM	EM	EM		EM	EM	EM		EM	EM	EM		EM	EM	EM		EM			
		◇		◇			◇			◇		◇			◇			◇							
Skegness	d		14 02			15 32		16 10			17 32			18 22		19 18				20 25		21 10			
Havenhouse	d							16 15																	
Wainfleet	d		14 10			15 40		16 19			17 40			18 30		19 26				20 33		21 18			
Thorpe Culvert	d							16 24														21 22			
Boston	d		14 39			16 06		16 46			18 06			18 56		19 52				20 58		21 45			
Hubberts Bridge	d													19 02											
Swineshead	d													19 07											
Heckington	d		14 53			16 20		17 00			18 20			19 14		20 10				21 12					
Sleaford	d		15 03			16 29		17 08			18 29			19 21		20 17			20 11	21 20		22 06			
Rauceby	d		15 07											19 25											
Ancaster	d		15 13											19 31		20 26									
Grantham 7	a		15 33					17 34						19 50		20 45				21 46					
London Kings Cross 15	⊖ a		*17 04*					*19 11*						*21 33*						*23 32*					
Grantham 7	d	14 58	15 40	15 56			17 02	17 40		18 00		18 56		19 54	20 04	20 49		20 56		21 52					
Bottesford	d		15 50					17 50						20 04		20 59				22 02					
Elton & Orston	d																			22 06					
Aslockton	d		15 56					17 56						20 10						22 10					
Bingham	d		16 01					18 01						20 15		21 07				22 14					
Radcliffe (Notts)	d		16 06					18 06						20 20						22 21					
Netherfield	d		16 11											20 25						22 25					
Nottingham 8	a	15 27	16 22	16 26		17 21	17 38	18 22		18 30	19 20	19 25		20 37	20 44	21 25		21 35	21 47	22 37		22 56			

Saturdays

		EM	EM		EM	EM		EM	EM		EM	EM		EM	EM		EM	EM		EM	EM		EM	EM	EM
						◇		◇			◇			◇			◇			◇			◇		◇
					A	C		D																	
Skegness	d								07 15			08 11			09 32			10 00			11 32			12 06	
Havenhouse	d																							12 11	
Wainfleet	d								07 23			08 19			09 40			10 08			11 40			12 15	
Thorpe Culvert	d								07 27															12 19	
Boston	d		06 15						07 50			08 45			10 06			10 40			12 06			12 42	
Hubberts Bridge	d								07 56												12 12				
Swineshead	d								08 01																
Heckington	d		06 29						08 07			08 59			10 20			10 54			12 21			12 56	
Sleaford	d		06 37		06 56				08 15			09 07			10 29			11 02			12 29			13 04	
Rauceby	d		06 41															11 06						13 08	
Ancaster	d		06 47															11 12						13 14	
Grantham 7	a		07 06						08 42			09 34						11 42						13 36	
London Kings Cross 15	⊖ a																								
Grantham 7	d	06 17	07 10			08 01		08 01	08 46		08 57	09 40		10 00			10 58	11 46		11 58			12 59	13 40	13 56
Bottesford	d	06 28				08 12		08 12				09 50						11 56						13 50	
Elton & Orston	d		07 23																						
Aslockton	d	06 34	07 26									09 56						12 02						13 56	
Bingham	d	06 39	07 30			08 20		08 20	09 03			10 01						12 07						14 01	
Radcliffe (Notts)	d	06 44				08 26		08 26				10 06						12 12						14 06	
Netherfield	d	06 49				08 30		08 30				10 11						12 17							
Nottingham 8	a	06 56	07 50		08 31	08 37		08 39	09 22		09 27	10 22		10 37	11 20		11 28	12 29		12 38	13 20		13 28	14 22	14 26

For general notes see front of timetable
For details of catering facilities see Directory of Train Operators

A To Leicester (Table 53)

B Until 5 September from Norwich (Table 17) to Liverpool Lime Street (Table 49). From 8 September from Norwich (Table 17) to Chesterfield (Table 49)

C Until 6 September from Norwich (Table 17) to Liverpool Lime Street (Table 49). From 13 September from Norwich (Table 17) to Chesterfield (Table 49)

D From 13 September from Norwich (Table 17) to Chesterfield (Table 49)

Saturdays

Skegness → Grantham and Nottingham

Network Diagram - see first page of Table 18

		EM		EM ◇	EM		EM ◇	EM		EM ◇	EM		EM ◇	EM		EM ◇	EM	EM ◇	EM	EM ◇	EM	EM A	EM
Skegness	d	13 32			14 05			15 32			16 11			17 32			18 21		19 18		20 20		20 59
Havenhouse	d										16 16												
Wainfleet	d	13 40			14 13			15 40			16 20			17 40			18 29		19 26		20 28		21 07
Thorpe Culvert	d										16 24										20 32		21 11
Boston	d	14 06			14 39			16 06			16 46			18 06			18 55		19 52		20 55		21 33
Hubberts Bridge	d																19 01						
Swineshead	d																19 06						
Heckington	d	14 20			14 53			16 20			17 00			18 20			19 13		20 07		21 09		
Sleaford	d	14 29			15 03			16 29			17 08			18 29			19 20		20 14		21 17		21 54
Rauceby	d				15 07												19 24						
Ancaster	d				15 13												19 30		20 23				
Grantham 7	a				15 33						17 34						19 49		20 42				22 20
London Kings Cross 15	⊖ a																						
Grantham 7	d			14 58	15 40		15 56			17 02	17 40		17 55			18 57	19 53	20 02	20 46	21 00		22 02	22 24
Bottesford	d				15 50						17 50						20 03		20 56				22 34
Elton & Orston	d																						22 38
Aslockton	d				15 56						17 56						20 09						22 42
Bingham	d				16 01						18 01						20 14		21 04				22 46
Radcliffe (Notts)	d				16 06						18 06						20 19						22 51
Netherfield	d										18 11												22 56
Nottingham 8	a	15 20		15 28	16 22		16 25	17 20		17 38	18 22		18 28	19 20		19 26	20 35	20 44	21 22	21 30	22 08	22 33	23 08

Sundays

Until 7 September

		EM	EM	EM ◇	EM		EM ◇ B	EM	EM	EM ◇		EM	EM ◇ C ✂	EM	EM ◇ D		EM ◇	EM	EM ◇	EM	EM ◇	EM	EM ◇
Skegness	d		10 11		11 10			12 35	14 10			15 09		16 13				18 06		19 13		20 44	
Havenhouse	d																						
Wainfleet	d		10 19		11 18			12 43	14 18			15 17						18 14		19 21		20 52	
Thorpe Culvert	d																						
Boston	d	09 08	10 44		11 43			13 08	14 43			15 42		16 44				18 39		19 48		21 17	
Hubberts Bridge	d																						
Swineshead	d																						
Heckington	d	09 22	10 58		11 57			13 22	14 57			15 56						18 55		20 04		21 31	
Sleaford	d	09 29	11 05		12 04			13 30	15 04			16 04		17 05				19 02		20 12		21 39	
Rauceby	d																						
Ancaster	d																						
Grantham 7	a	09 56	11 32		12 31				15 32			16 30						19 29		20 39		22 05	
London Kings Cross 15	⊖ a	*11 26*	*12 48*		*13 50*				*16 50*			*17 55*						*20 59*		*22 16*		*23 50*	
Grantham 7	d	09 59	11 35	11 56	12 34		12 51		15 39	15 59		16 34	16 53		17 49		19 00	19 36	19 57	20 42	21 03	22 09	22 51
Bottesford	d	10 09	11 45				13 01		15 49			16 44			17 59			19 46		20 52		22 19	
Elton & Orston	d																						
Aslockton	d	10 16	11 52				13 08		15 55			16 50			18 06			19 52		20 59		22 25	
Bingham	d	10 20	11 56				13 12		16 00			16 54			18 10			19 57		21 03		22 30	
Radcliffe (Notts)	d	10 26	12 02				13 18		16 05			17 00			18 16			20 02		21 09		22 35	
Netherfield	d	10 30	12 06				13 22		16 10			17 04			18 20			20 11		21 13		22 40	
Nottingham 8	a	10 43	12 19	12 25	13 09		13 29	14 20	16 21	16 29		17 17	17 22	17 55	18 27		19 30	20 22	20 31	21 26	21 32	22 52	23 29

Sundays

From 14 September

		EM ◇ E		EM ◇ G		EM		EM		EM ◇		EM		EM ◇ D		EM ◇		EM	EM ◇	EM	EM ◇	EM	EM ◇
Skegness	d							14 10				16 12						18 06		19 13			
Havenhouse	d																						
Wainfleet	d							14 18				16 20						18 14		19 21			
Thorpe Culvert	d																						
Boston	d					12 19		14 43				16 45						18 39		19 48			
Hubberts Bridge	d																						
Swineshead	d																						
Heckington	d					12 33		14 57				16 59						18 55		20 04			
Sleaford	d					12 40		15 04				17 07						19 02		20 12		21 32	
Rauceby	d																						
Ancaster	d																						
Grantham 7	a					13 09		15 32				17 33						19 29		20 39		22 00	
London Kings Cross 15	⊖ a																						
Grantham 7	d	12 51		12 51				15 39		15 59		17 37		17 49		19 00		19 36	19 57	20 42	21 03	22 04	22 51
Bottesford	d	13 01		13 01				15 49						17 59				19 46		20 52		22 14	
Elton & Orston	d																						
Aslockton	d	13 08		13 08				15 55						18 06				19 52		20 59		22 21	
Bingham	d	13 12		13 12				16 00						18 10				19 57		21 03		22 25	
Radcliffe (Notts)	d	13 18		13 18				16 05						18 16				20 02		21 09		22 31	
Netherfield	d	13 22		13 22				16 10						18 20				20 11		21 13		22 35	
Nottingham 8	a	13 29		13 31				16 21		16 29		18 07		18 27		19 30		20 22	20 31	21 26	21 32	22 43	23 29

For general notes see front of timetable
For details of catering facilities see Directory of Train Operators

- **A** From Spalding (Table 18)
- **B** From Norwich to Liverpool Lime Street (Table 49)
- **C** ✂ until 13 July
- **D** From Norwich to Manchester Piccadilly (Table 49)
- **E** Until 2 November
- **G** From 9 November

Nottingham and Grantham → Skegness

Network Diagram - see first page of Table 18

Miles	Miles			EM	EM	EM	EM	EM	EM	EM	EM	EM	EM	EM	EM	EM	EM	EM
								◇		◇		◇		◇		◇		◇
				A														
0	—	**Nottingham** 8	d	05 09		05 50	06 50	07 52	07 59	08 31	08 50	09 35	09 50	10 31	10 50	11 32	11 50	12 34
4½	—	Netherfield	d			05 56									10 56			
5	—	Radcliffe (Notts)	d			06 01					09 00				11 01			
8¾	—	Bingham	d	05 23		06 07	07 04				09 06				11 07			
10¾	—	Aslockton	d	05 27		06 11					09 10				11 11			
14½	—	Elton & Orston	d															
15	0	Bottesford	d	05 34		06 17	07 14				09 16				11 17			
22½	—	**Grantham** 7	a	05 48		06 30	07 27	08 24		09 07	09 29	10 06		11 03	11 30	12 05		13 08
—	—	London Kings Cross 15	⊖ d				*06 00*				*07 30*				*10 10*			
—	—	**Grantham** 7	d			06 37	07 31				09 35				11 36			
34	12¾	Ancaster	d				07 48				09 52							
37¾	—	Rauceby	d				07 54				09 58							
40	—	**Sleaford**	d			07 03	07 59		08 44		10 05		10 35		12 01		12 41	
44½	—	Heckington	d			07 10	08 05		08 51		10 12		10 42		12 08		12 47	
49½	—	Swineshead	d				08 12											
52¾	—	Hubberts Bridge	d				08 17											
56½	—	**Boston**	d		06 33	07 26	08 24		09 06		10b37		10 58		12 23		13 03	
73¼	—	Thorpe Culvert	d			07 47									12 44			
75¼	—	Wainfleet	d		06 56	07 52	08 48		09 30		11 01		11 22		12 49		13 27	
77	—	Havenhouse	d			07 55									12 52			
80¼	—	**Skegness**	a		07 12	08 09	09 04		09 46		11 17		11 38		13 06		13 43	

		EM	EM	EM	EM	EM	EM	EM	EM	EM	EM	EM	EM	EM	EM	EM
			◇		◇		◇				◇		◇		◇	
									B		C					
Nottingham 8	d	12 50	13 31	13 50	14 31	14 50	15 31	15 50	16 25	16 50	17 39	17 50	18 31	18 50	20 36	20 51
Netherfield	d	12 56						15 56		16 56		17 56				20 57
Radcliffe (Notts)	d	13 00				15 00		16 01		17 01	17 49	18 01		18 59		21 02
Bingham	d	13 06				15 06		16 07		17 07	17 55	18 07		19 05		21 08
Aslockton	d	13 10				15 10		16 11		17 11		18 11		19 09		21 12
Elton & Orston	d	13 14										18 14				
Bottesford	d	13 18				15 16		16 17		17 17		18 19		19 16		21 18
Grantham 7	a	13 31	14 05		15 05	15 29	16 04	16 30		17 30	18 14	18 32	19 05	19 29	21 07	21 31
London Kings Cross 15	⊖ d	*12 10*				*14 10*		*15 10*		*16 10*		*17 03*		*18 03*		*20 30*
Grantham 7	d	13 37				15 35		16 34		17 36		18 35		19 32		21 48
Ancaster	d	13 54				15 52				17 53				19 50		22 05
Rauceby	d					15 58				17 59				19 56		22 11
Sleaford	d	14 09		14 39		16 03		17c08	17a47	18 04		19 01		20 00		22 16
Heckington	d	14 16		14 45		16 09		17 14		18 11		19 08		20 07		22 22
Swineshead	d					16 16										
Hubberts Bridge	d					16 21				18 20						
Boston	d	14 36		15 01		16 28		17 31		18 28		19 24		20 22		22a39
Thorpe Culvert	d					16 49						19 45				
Wainfleet	d	15 00		15 25		16 54		17 55		18 52		19 50		20 46		
Havenhouse	d											19 53				
Skegness	a	15 16		15 41		17 10		18 11		19 08		20 07		21 02		

Saturdays

		EM	EM	EM	EM	EM	EM	EM	EM	EM	EM	EM	EM	EM	EM	EM	EM	EM
						◇		◇		◇		◇		◇		◇		◇
		A																
Nottingham 8	d	05 09		05 50	06 50	07 39	07 55	08 33	08 50	09 32	09 50	10 31	10 50	11 32	11 50	12 31	12 50	13 31
Netherfield	d			05 56													12 56	
Radcliffe (Notts)	d			06 01					09 00				11 00				13 00	
Bingham	d	05 22		06 07	07 04				09 06				11 06				13 06	
Aslockton	d	05 27		06 11					09 10				11 10				13 10	
Elton & Orston	d																13 14	
Bottesford	d	05 35		06 17	07 13				09 16				11 16				13 18	
Grantham 7	a	05 48		06 30	07 26	08 13		09 09	09 29	10 09		11 05	11 29	12 06		13 07	13 31	14 06
London Kings Cross 15	⊖ d																	
Grantham 7	d			06 37	07 30				09 35				11 35				13 36	
Ancaster	d				07 47				09 52								13 54	
Rauceby	d				07 53				09 58									
Sleaford	d			07 03	07 58		08 45		10 05		10 35		12 01		12 35		14 09	
Heckington	d			07 10	08 04		08 52		10 12		10 42		12 07		12 42		14 16	
Swineshead	d				08 11													
Hubberts Bridge	d				08 16													
Boston	d		06 33	07 26	08 23		09 08		10 34		10 58		12 23		12 58		14e39	
Thorpe Culvert	d			07 47									12 44					
Wainfleet	d		06 56	07 52	08 47		09 32		10 58		11 22		12 49		13 22		15 03	
Havenhouse	d			07 55									12 52					
Skegness	a		07 12	08 09	09 03		09 48		11 14		11 38		13 06		13 40		15 19	

For general notes see front of timetable
For details of catering facilities see Directory of Train Operators

A To Peterborough (Table 26)
B From Leicester (Table 53)
C Until 5 September from Liverpool Lime Street to Norwich (Table 49). From 8 September from Chesterfield to Norwich (Table 49)
b Arr. 1029
c Arr. 1659
e Arr. 1431

Table 19

Saturdays

Nottingham and Grantham → Skegness

Network Diagram - see first page of Table 18

		EM	EM	EM	EM	EM	EM	EM	EM	EM	EM	EM	EM	EM
			◇		◇			◇			◇		◇	
								A		B				
Nottingham 8	d	13 50	14 32	14 50	15 32	15 50	16 50	17 36	17 50	18 26	18 31	18 42	20 32	20 59
Netherfield	d					15 56	16 56		17 56					21 05
Radcliffe (Notts)	d			15 00		16 01	17 01	17 46	18 01			18 51		21 10
Bingham	d			15 06		16 07	17 07	17 52	18 07			18 57		21 16
Aslockton	d			15 10		16 11	17 11		18 11			19 01		21 20
Elton & Orston	d								18 14					21 23
Bottesford	d			15 16		16 17	17 17		18 19			19 08		21 28
Grantham 7	a		15 05	15 29	16 05	16 30	17 30	18 12	18 32		19 05	19 21	21 09	21 41
London Kings Cross 15	⊖ d													
Grantham 7	d			15 35		16 34	17 36		18 35			19 24		21 45
Ancaster	d			15 52			17 53					19 42		22 02
Rauceby	d			15 58			17 59					19 48		22 08
Sleaford	d	14 39		16 03		17b08	18 04		19 01	20a05		19 52		22 13
Heckington	d	14 45		16 09		17 14	18 11		19 08			19 59		22 19
Swineshead	d			16 16										
Hubberts Bridge	d			16 21			18 20							
Boston	d	15 01		16 28		17 31	18 28		19 24			20 14		22a34
Thorpe Culvert	d			16 49					19 45					
Wainfleet	d	15 25		16 54		17 55	18 52		19 50			20 38		
Havenhouse	d								19 53					
Skegness	a	15 41		17 10		18 11	19 08		20 07			20 54		

Sundays

Until 7 September

		EM	EM	EM	EM	EM	EM	EM	EM	EM	EM	EM	EM	EM	EM	EM	EM	EM	EM	EM	EM	EM	EM
					◇		◇		◇	◇	◇			◇	◇		◇	◇		◇		◇	
									C	D	E						E	D				G	
							🚲			🚲	🚲												
Nottingham 8	d		09 00	09 30	09 53	11 03	11 40	12 00	12 32	13 44	13 45	13 53	14 44	15 48	16 40	16 46	17 38	17 40	18 09	18 46	19 41	20 35	21 00
Netherfield	d			09 36		11 09			12 38			13 59	14 50			16 52			18 15		19 47	20 42	21 06
Radcliffe (Notts)	d			09 41		11 14			12 43			14 04	14 55			16 57			18 20		19 52	20 46	21 10
Bingham	d			09 47		11 20			12 49			14 10	15 01			17 03			18 26		19 58	20 52	21 17
Aslockton	d			09 51		11 24			12 53			14 14	15 05			17 07			18 30		20 02	20 56	21 21
Elton & Orston	d																						
Bottesford	d			09 58		11 31			13 00			14 20	15 12			17 13			18 36		20 08	21 03	21 28
Grantham 7	a			10 11	10 25	11 44	12 14	12 34	13 13	14 17	14 18	14 33	15 27	16 23	17 15	17 27	18 13	18 13	18 50	19 20	20 21	21 18	21 41
London Kings Cross 15	⊖ d			*09 00*		*10 44*		*11 10*				*13 10*	*14 10*			*16 04*			*17 44*		*19 10*		
Grantham 7	d			10 18		11 52		12 38				14 37	15 34			17 30			18 54		20 26		
Ancaster	d																						
Rauceby	d																						
Sleaford	d		09 51	10 43		12 18		13 04				15 02	16 04			17 58			19 19		20 52		
Heckington	d		09 58	10 50		12 25		13 10				15 09	16 10			18 04			19 26		20 58		
Swineshead	d																						
Hubberts Bridge	d																						
Boston	d	09 30	10 13	11 05		12 40		13 26				15 24	16 26			18 21			19 47		21a14		
Thorpe Culvert	d																						
Wainfleet	d	09 54		11 29		13 04		13 50				15 48	16 49			18 44			20 10				
Havenhouse	d																						
Skegness	a	10 10	10 52	11 45		13 20		14 06				16 04	17 05			19 00			20 26				

Sundays

From 14 September

		EM	EM	EM	EM	EM	EM	EM	EM	EM	EM	EM	EM	EM	EM
			◇		◇	◇		◇		◇	◇		◇		◇
			C		H										G
					🚲	🚲									
Nottingham 8	d	12 00	12 32		13 44	13 47	14 44	15 48	16 22	16 40	17 38	18 23	18 46	19 41	20 35
Netherfield	d		12 38				14 50		16 28			18 30		19 47	20 42
Radcliffe (Notts)	d		12 43				14 55		16 33			18 35		19 52	20 46
Bingham	d		12 49				15 01		16 39			18 41		19 58	20 52
Aslockton	d		12 53				15 05		16 43			18 45		20 02	20 56
Elton & Orston	d														
Bottesford	d		13 00				15 12		16 49			18 52		20 08	21 03
Grantham 7	a	12 34	13 13		14 17	14 20	15 27	16 23	17 03	17 15	18 13	19 07	19 20	20 21	21 18
London Kings Cross 15	⊖ d														
Grantham 7	d	12 38		13 29			15 34		17 06			19 13		20 27	
Ancaster	d														
Rauceby	d														
Sleaford	d	13 04		13 55			16 04		17 35			19 40		20a52	
Heckington	d	13 10		14 01			16 10		17 41			19 47			
Swineshead	d														
Hubberts Bridge	d														
Boston	d	13 26		14 17			16 26		17 58			20a05			
Thorpe Culvert	d														
Wainfleet	d	13 50		14 41			16 49		18 21						
Havenhouse	d														
Skegness	a	14 06		14 57			17 05		18 37						

For general notes see front of timetable
For details of catering facilities see Directory of Train Operators

- **A** Until 6 September from Liverpool Lime Street to Norwich (Table 49). From 13 September from Chesterfield to Norwich (Table 49)
- **B** From Leicester (Table 53)
- **C** To Norwich (Table 49)
- **D** Until 13 July
- **E** From 20 July
- **G** From Liverpool Lime Street (Table 49) to Norwich (Table 17)
- **H** Until 2 November
- **b** Arr. 1659

Network Diagram for Tables 20, 21, 22

DM-3/08
Design BAJS

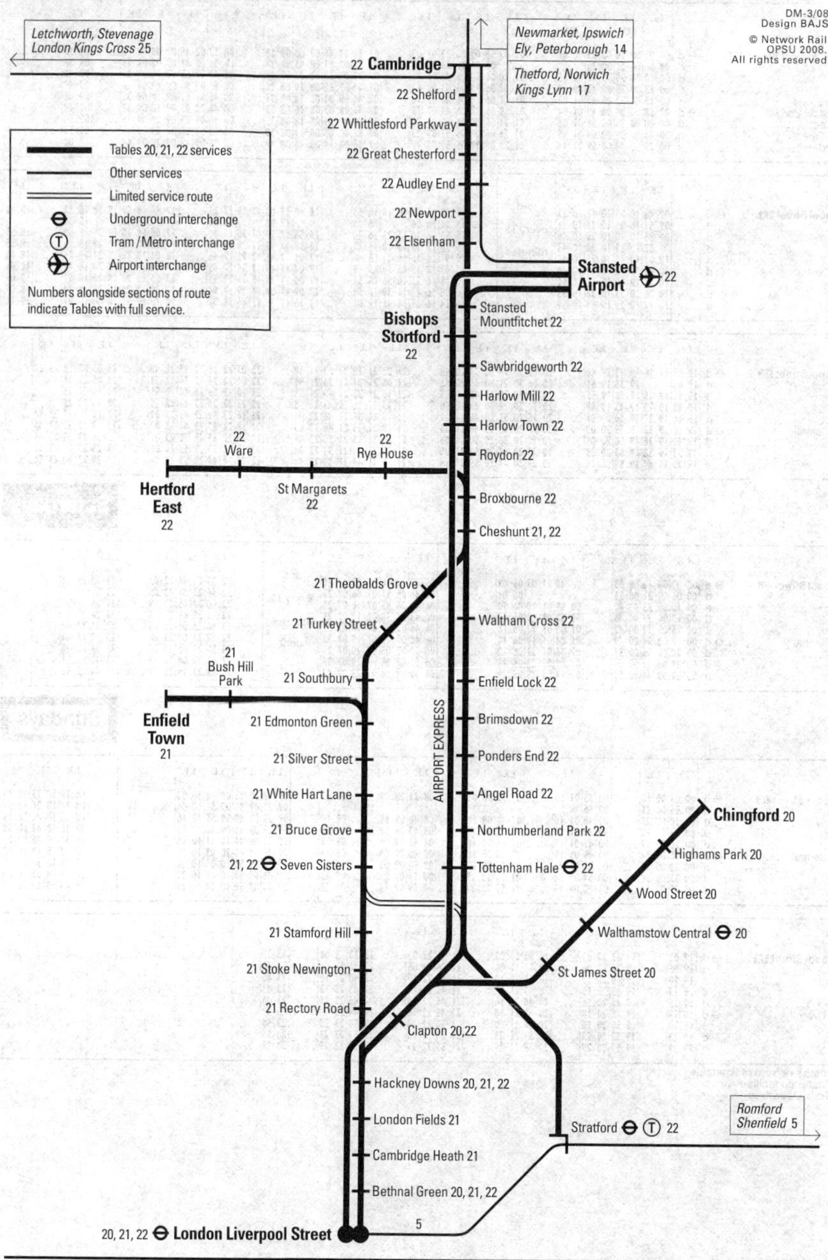
Letchworth, Stevenage
London Kings Cross 25
Newmarket, Ipswich
Ely, Peterborough 14
Thetford, Norwich
Kings Lynn 17
22 Cambridge
22 Shelford
22 Whittlesford Parkway
22 Great Chesterford
22 Audley End
22 Newport
22 Elsenham
Stansted Airport 22
Stansted Mountfitchet 22
Bishops Stortford 22
Sawbridgeworth 22
Harlow Mill 22
Harlow Town 22
Roydon 22
22 Rye House
22 Ware
St Margarets 22
Hertford East 22
Broxbourne 22
Cheshunt 21, 22
21 Theobalds Grove
21 Turkey Street
Waltham Cross 22
21 Southbury
21 Bush Hill Park
Enfield Town 21
Enfield Lock 22
21 Edmonton Green
Brimsdown 22
AIRPORT EXPRESS
21 Silver Street
Ponders End 22
21 White Hart Lane
Angel Road 22
21 Bruce Grove
Northumberland Park 22
21, 22 Seven Sisters
Tottenham Hale 22
Chingford 20
Highams Park 20
Wood Street 20
21 Stamford Hill
Walthamstow Central 20
21 Stoke Newington
St James Street 20
21 Rectory Road
Clapton 20,22
Hackney Downs 20, 21, 22
London Fields 21
Cambridge Heath 21
Bethnal Green 20, 21, 22
Stratford 22
Romford
Shenfield 5
5
20, 21, 22 London Liverpool Street
Tables 20, 21, 22 services
Other services
Limited service route
Underground interchange
Tram / Metro interchange
Airport interchange
Numbers alongside sections of route indicate Tables with full service.

Table 20

Mondays to Fridays

London → Chingford

Network diagram - see first page of Table 20

Miles			LE	LE MX	LE	LE MX	LE	LE	LE	LE	LE	LE	LE	LE	LE	LE	LE	LE	LE
0	**London Liverpool Street** 15	⊖ d	00 03	00 18	00 33	00 48	01 03	06 03	06 33	07 03	07 30	07 48	08 00	08 18	08 33	08 48	09 03	09 18	09 33
1¼	Bethnal Green	d	00 06	00 21	00 36			06 06	06 36	07 06	07 33	07 51	08 03	08 21	08 36	08 51	09 06	09 21	09 36
3	Hackney Downs	d	00 10	00 25	00 40	00 55	01 10	06 10	06 40	07 10	07 37	07 55	08 07	08 25	08 40	08 55	09 10	09 25	09 40
4	Clapton	d	00 13	00 28	00 43	00 58	01 13	06 13	06 43	07 13	07 40	07 58	08 10	08 28	08 43	08 58	09 13	09 28	09 43
5¾	St James Street	d	00 16	00 32	00 47	01 02	01 17	06 16	06 46	07 16	07 44	08 01	08 14	08 31	08 46	09 01	09 16	09 31	09 46
6¼	Walthamstow Central	⊖ d	00 18	00 34	00 49	01 04	01 19	06 18	06 48	07 18	07 46	08 03	08 16	08 33	08 48	09 03	09 18	09 33	09 48
7	Wood Street	d	00 20	00 36	00 51	01 06	01 21	06 20	06 50	07 20	07 48	08 05	08 18	08 35	08 50	09 05	09 20	09 35	09 50
8½	Highams Park	d	00 23	00 39	00 54	01 09	01 24	06 23	06 53	07 23	07 51	08 08	08 21	08 38	08 53	09 08	09 23	09 38	09 53
10½	**Chingford**	a	00 29	00 44	00 59	01 14	01 29	06 29	06 59	07 29	07 56	08 14	08 26	08 44	08 59	09 14	09 30	09 44	10 00

		LE	LE	LE	LE		LE	LE	LE	LE	LE	LE	LE	LE	LE	LE	LE	LE	LE
London Liverpool Street 15	⊖ d	09 48	10 03	10 18	10 33	and	15 48	16 03	16 18	16 33	16 48	17 03	17 18	17 33	17 48	18 03	18 18	18 33	18 48
Bethnal Green	d	09 51	10 06	10 21	10 36	every 15	15 51	16 06		16 36		17 06		17 36		18 06		18 36	
Hackney Downs	d	09 55	10 10	10 25	10 40	minutes	15 55	16 10	16 25	16 40	16 55	17 10	17 25	17 40	17 55	18 10	18 25	18 40	18 55
Clapton	d	09 58	10 13	10 28	10 43	until	15 58	16 13	16 28	16 43	16 58	17 13	17 28	17 43	17 58	18 13	18 28	18 43	18 58
St James Street	d	10 01	10 16	10 31	10 46		16 01	16 16	16 31	16 46	17 01	17 16	17 31	17 46	18 01	18 16	18 31	18 46	19 01
Walthamstow Central	⊖ d	10 03	10 18	10 33	10 48		16 03	16 19	16 34	16 49	17 04	17 19	17 34	17 49	18 04	18 19	18 34	18 49	19 04
Wood Street	d	10 05	10 20	10 35	10 50		16 05	16 21	16 36	16 51	17 06	17 21	17 36	17 51	18 06	18 21	18 36	18 51	19 06
Highams Park	d	10 08	10 23	10 38	10 53		16 08	16 24	16 39	16 54	17 09	17 24	17 39	17 54	18 09	18 24	18 39	18 54	19 09
Chingford	a	10 14	10 29	10 44	10 59		16 14	16 31	16 46	17 01	17 16	17 31	17 46	18 01	18 16	18 31	18 46	19 01	19 16

		LE	LE	LE	LE	LE	LE	LE	LE	LE	LE	LE	LE	LE	LE	LE	LE	LE	LE	LE
London Liverpool Street 15	⊖ d	19 03	19 18	19 33	19 48	20 03	20 18	20 33	20 48	21 03	21 18	21 33	21 48	22 03	22 18	22 33	22 48	23 03	23 18	23 33
Bethnal Green	d	19 06		19 36	19 51	20 06	20 21	20 36	20 51	21 06	21 21	21 36	21 51	22 06	22 21	22 36	22 51	23 06	23 21	
Hackney Downs	d	19 10	19 25	19 40	19 55	20 10	20 25	20 40	20 55	21 10	21 25	21 40	21 55	22 10	22 25	22 40	22 55	23 10	23 25	
Clapton	d	19 13	19 28	19 43	19 58	20 13	20 28	20 43	20 58	21 13	21 28	21 43	21 58	22 13	22 28	22 43	22 58	23 13	23 28	
St James Street	d	19 16	19 31	19 46	20 01	20 16	20 31	20 46	21 01	21 16	21 31	21 46	22 01	22 16	22 31	22 46	23 01	23 16	23 31	23 44
Walthamstow Central	⊖ d	19 18	19 33	19 48	20 03	20 18	20 33	20 48	21 03	21 18	21 33	21 48	22 03	22 18	22 33	22 48	23 03	23 18	23 33	23 46
Wood Street	d	19 20	19 35	19 50	20 05	20 20	20 35	20 50	21 05	21 20	21 35	21 50	22 05	22 20	22 35	22 50	23 05	23 20	23 35	23 48
Highams Park	d	19 23	19 38	19 53	20 08	20 23	20 38	20 53	21 08	21 23	21 38	21 53	22 08	22 23	22 38	22 53	23 08	23 23	23 38	23 51
Chingford	a	19 29	19 44	19 59	20 14	20 29	20 44	20 59	21 14	21 29	21 44	21 59	22 14	22 29	22 44	22 59	23 14	23 29	23 44	23 56

Saturdays

		LE	LE	LE			LE	LE	LE	LE	LE	LE		LE	LE	LE	LE	LE
London Liverpool Street 15	⊖ d	00 03	00 18	00 33	00 48	01 03	06 03	06 33	06 48	07 03	07 18	and	22 33	22 48	23 03	23 18	23 33
Bethnal Green	d	00 06	00 21	00 36			06 06	06 36	06 51	07 06	07 21	every 15	22 36	22 51	23 06	23 21	
Hackney Downs	d	00 10	00 25	00 40	00 55	01 10	06 10	06 40	06 55	07 10	07 25	minutes	22 40	22 55	23 10	23 25	
Clapton	d	00 13	00 28	00 43	00 58	01 13	06 13	06 43	06 58	07 13	07 28	until	22 43	22 58	23 13	23 28	
St James Street	d	00 16	00 32	00 47	01 02	01 17	06 16	06 46	07 01	07 16	07 31		22 46	23 01	23 16	23 31	23 44
Walthamstow Central	⊖ d	00 18	00 34	00 49	01 04	01 19	06 18	06 48	07 03	07 18	07 33		22 48	23 03	23 18	23 33	23 46
Wood Street	d	00 20	00 36	00 51	01 06	01 21	06 20	06 50	07 05	07 20	07 35		22 50	23 05	23 20	23 35	23 48
Highams Park	d	00 23	00 39	00 54	01 09	01 24	06 23	06 53	07 08	07 23	07 38		22 53	23 08	23 23	23 38	23 51
Chingford	a	00 29	00 44	00 59	01 14	01 29	06 29	06 59	07 14	07 29	07 44		22 59	23 14	23 29	23 44	23 56

Sundays

		LE	LE	LE	LE	LE	LE	LE	LE	LE	LE	LE	LE	LE		LE	LE	LE
London Liverpool Street 15	⊖ d	00 03	00 18	00 33	01 03	07 33	08 03	08 33	08 48	09 03	09 18	09 33	09 48	10 03	and	18 18	18 33	18 48
Bethnal Green	d	00 06	00 21	00 36							09 21	09 36	09 51	10 06	every 15	18 21	18 36	18 51
Hackney Downs	d	00 10	00 25	00 40	01 10	07 40	08 10	08 40	08 55	09 10	09 25	09 40	09 55	10 10	minutes	18 25	18 40	18 55
Clapton	d	00 13	00 28	00 43	01 13	07 43	08 13	08 43	08 58	09 13	09 28	09 43	09 58	10 13	until	18 28	18 43	18 58
St James Street	d	00 16	00 32	00 47	01 17	07 46	08 16	08 46	09 01	09 16	09 31	09 46	10 01	10 16		18 31	18 46	19 01
Walthamstow Central	⊖ d	00 18	00 34	00 49	01 19	07 48	08 18	08 48	09 03	09 18	09 33	09 48	10 03	10 18		18 33	18 48	19 03
Wood Street	d	00 20	00 36	00 51	01 21	07 50	08 20	08 50	09 05	09 20	09 35	09 50	10 05	10 20		18 35	18 50	19 05
Highams Park	d	00 23	00 39	00 54	01 24	07 53	08 23	08 53	09 08	09 23	09 38	09 53	10 08	10 23		18 38	18 53	19 08
Chingford	a	00 29	00 44	01 00	01 29	07 59	08 29	08 59	09 14	09 29	09 44	09 59	10 14	10 29		18 44	18 59	19 14

		LE	LE	LE	LE	LE	LE	LE	LE	LE	LE
London Liverpool Street 15	⊖ d	19 03	19 33	20 03	20 33	21 03	21 33	22 03	22 33	23 03	23 33
Bethnal Green	d	19 06	19 36	20 06	20 36	21 06	21 36	22 06	22 36	23 06	23 36
Hackney Downs	d	19 10	19 40	20 10	20 40	21 10	21 40	22 10	22 40	23 10	23 40
Clapton	d	19 13	19 43	20 13	20 43	21 13	21 43	22 13	22 43	23 13	23 43
St James Street	d	19 16	19 46	20 16	20 46	21 16	21 46	22 16	22 46	23 16	23 46
Walthamstow Central	⊖ d	19 18	19 48	20 18	20 48	21 18	21 48	22 18	22 48	23 18	23 48
Wood Street	d	19 20	19 50	20 20	20 50	21 20	21 50	22 20	22 50	23 20	23 50
Highams Park	d	19 23	19 53	20 23	20 53	21 23	21 53	22 23	22 53	23 23	23 53
Chingford	a	19 29	19 59	20 29	20 59	21 29	21 59	22 29	22 59	23 29	23 59

For general notes see front of timetable
For details of catering facilities see Directory of Train Operators

Table 20 **Mondays to Fridays**

Chingford → London

Network diagram - see first page of Table 20

Miles			LE	LE	LE	LE	LE	LE	LE	LE	LE	LE	LE	LE	LE	LE	LE	LE
0	**Chingford**	d	05 10	05 25	05 40	05 55	06 10	06 25	06 42	06 57	07 12	07 27	07 42	07 54	08 12	08 27	08 32	08 42
2	Highams Park	d	05 14	05 29	05 44	05 59	06 14	06 29	06 46	07 01	07 16	07 31	07 46	07 58	08 16	08 31	08 36	08 46
3¼	Wood Street	d	05 17	05 32	05 47	06 02	06 17	06 33	06 50	07 05	07 20	07 35	07 50	08 02	08 20	08 35	08 40	08 50
4¼	Walthamstow Central	⊖ d	05 19	05 34	05 49	06 04	06 19	06 35	06 52	07 07	07 22	07 37	07 52	08 04	08 22	08 37	08 42	08 52
4¾	St James Street	d	05 21	05 36	05 51	06 06	06 21	06 38	06 55	07 10	07 25	07 40	07 55	08 07	08 25	08 40		08 55
6½	Clapton	d	05 24	05 39	05 54	06 09	06 24	06 41	06 58	07 13	07 28	07 43	07 58	08 10	08 28	08 43		08 58
7¾	Hackney Downs	d	05 28	05 43	05 58	06 13	06 28	06 45	07 02	07 17	07 32	07 47	08 02	08 14	08 32	08 47		09 02
9¼	Bethnal Green	d	05 32	05 47	06 02	06 17	06 32	06 49		07 21		07 51		08 18		08 51		
10½	**London Liverpool Street** 15	⊖ a	05 36	05 51	06 07	06 21	06 36	06 53	07 12	07 27	07 42	07 57	08 12	08 24	08 42	08 57	09 00	09 12

		LE	LE	LE	LE	LE	LE	LE		LE	LE	LE	LE
Chingford	d	08 57	09 12	09 27	09 40	09 55	10 10	10 25	and	22 40	22 55	23 10	23 25
Highams Park	d	09 01	09 16	09 31	09 44	09 59	10 14	10 29	every 15	22 44	22 59	23 14	23 29
Wood Street	d	09 05	09 20	09 35	09 47	10 02	10 17	10 32	minutes	22 47	23 02	23 17	23 32
Walthamstow Central	⊖ d	09 07	09 22	09 37	09 49	10 04	10 19	10 34	until	22 49	23 04	23 19	23 34
St James Street	d	09 10	09 25	09 40	09 51	10 06	10 21	10 36		22 51	23 06	23 21	23 36
Clapton	d	09 13	09 28	09 43	09 54	10 09	10 24	10 39		22 54	23 09	23 24	23 39
Hackney Downs	d	09 17	09 32	09 47	09 58	10 13	10 28	10 43		22 58	23 13	23 28	23 43
Bethnal Green	d	09 21		09 51	10 02	10 17	10 32	10 47		23 02	23 17	23 32	23 47
London Liverpool Street 15	⊖ a	09 27	09 42	09 57	10 07	10 21	10 36	10 51		23 06	23 21	23 36	23 51

Saturdays

		LE	LE	LE	LE	LE	LE		LE	LE	LE	LE	LE	LE	LE
Chingford	d	05 10	05 25	05 40	05 55	06 10	06 25	and	21 40	21 55	22 10	22 25	22 55	23 10	23 25
Highams Park	d	05 14	05 29	05 44	05 59	06 14	06 29	every 15	21 44	21 59	22 14	22 29	22 59	23 14	23 29
Wood Street	d	05 17	05 32	05 47	06 02	06 17	06 32	minutes	21 47	22 02	22 17	22 32	23 02	23 17	23 32
Walthamstow Central	⊖ d	05 19	05 34	05 49	06 04	06 19	06 34	until	21 49	22 04	22 19	22 34	23 04	23 19	23 34
St James Street	d	05 21	05 36	05 51	06 06	06 21	06 36		21 51	22 06	22 21	22 36	23 06	23 21	23 36
Clapton	d	05 24	05 39	05 54	06 09	06 24	06 39		21 54	22 09	22 24	22 39	23 09	23 24	23 39
Hackney Downs	d	05 28	05 43	05 58	06 13	06 28	06 43		21 58	22 13	22 28	22 43	23 13	23 28	23 43
Bethnal Green	d	05 32	05 47	06 02	06 17	06 32	06 47		22 02	22 17	22 32	22 47	23 17	23 32	23 47
London Liverpool Street 15	⊖ a	05 36	05 51	06 06	06 21	06 36	06 51		22 06	22 21	22 36	22 51	23 22	23 36	23 51

Sundays

		LE	LE	LE	LE	LE	LE	LE	LE	LE	LE	LE	LE	LE	LE		LE
Chingford	d	06 40	06 55	07 10	07 25	07 40	07 55	08 10	08 25	08 40	08 55	09 10	09 25	09 40	09 55	and	18 10
Highams Park	d	06 44	06 59	07 14	07 29	07 44	07 59	08 14	08 29	08 44	08 59	09 14	09 29	09 44	09 59	every 15	18 14
Wood Street	d	06 47	07 02	07 17	07 32	07 47	08 02	08 17	08 32	08 47	09 02	09 17	09 32	09 47	10 02	minutes	18 17
Walthamstow Central	⊖ d	06 49	07 04	07 19	07 34	07 49	08 04	08 19	08 34	08 49	09 04	09 19	09 34	09 49	10 04	until	18 19
St James Street	d	06 51	07 06	07 21	07 36	07 51	08 06	08 21	08 36	08 51	09 06	09 21	09 36	09 51	10 06		18 21
Clapton	d	06 54	07 09	07 24	07 39	07 54	08 09	08 24	08 39	08 54	09 09	09 24	09 39	09 54	10 09		18 24
Hackney Downs	d	06 58	07 13	07 28	07 43	07 58	08 13	08 28	08 43	08 58	09 13	09 28	09 43	09 58	10 13		18 28
Bethnal Green	d										09 17	09 32	09 47	10 02	10 17		18 32
London Liverpool Street 15	⊖ a	07 06	07 21	07 37	07 52	08 06	08 21	08 38	08 51	09 06	09 21	09 36	09 51	10 06	10 21		18 36

		LE	LE	LE	LE	LE	LE	LE	LE	LE	LE	LE
Chingford	d	18 25	18 40	19 10	19 40	20 10	20 40	21 10	21 40	22 10	22 40	23 10
Highams Park	d	18 29	18 44	19 14	19 44	20 14	20 44	21 14	21 44	22 14	22 44	23 14
Wood Street	d	18 32	18 47	19 17	19 47	20 17	20 47	21 17	21 47	22 17	22 47	23 17
Walthamstow Central	⊖ d	18 34	18 49	19 19	19 49	20 19	20 49	21 19	21 49	22 19	22 49	23 19
St James Street	d	18 36	18 51	19 21	19 51	20 21	20 51	21 21	21 51	22 21	22 51	23 21
Clapton	d	18 39	18 54	19 24	19 54	20 24	20 54	21 24	21 54	22 24	22 54	23 24
Hackney Downs	d	18 43	18 58	19 28	19 58	20 28	20 58	21 28	21 58	22 28	22 58	23 28
Bethnal Green	d	18 47	19 02	19 32	20 02	20 32	21 02	21 32	22 02	22 32	23 02	23 32
London Liverpool Street 15	⊖ a	18 51	19 06	19 36	20 06	20 36	21 06	21 36	22 06	22 36	23 06	23 36

For general notes see front of timetable
For details of catering facilities see Directory of Train Operators

London → Cheshunt (via Seven Sisters) and Enfield Town

Network diagram - see first page of Table 20

Miles	Miles			LE MX A	LE MX	LE	LE	LE	LE	LE	LE	LE	LE	LE	LE	LE	LE	LE	LE	LE
0	0	**London Liverpool Street** 15	⊖ d	23p45	00 01	05 45	06 00	06 14	06 21	06 30	06 44	06 51	07 00	07 18	07 21	07 33	07 44	07 51	08 03	08 14
1¼	1¼	Bethnal Green	d	23p48	00 03	05 48	06 03		06 24	06 33		06 54	07 03		07 24	07 36		07 54	08 06	
1¾	1¾	Cambridge Heath	d	23p50	00 05	05 50	06 05		06 26	06 35		06 56	07 05		07 26	07 38		07 56	08 08	
2½	2½	London Fields	d	23p52	00 07	05 52	06 07		06 28	06 37		06 58	07 07		07 28	07 40		07 58	08 10	
3	3	Hackney Downs	d	23p54	00 09	05 54	06 09	06 22	06 30	06 39	06 52	07 00	07 09	07 25	07 30	07 42	07 52	08 00	08 12	08 22
3¾	3¾	Rectory Road	d	23p57	00 12	05 57	06 12	06 24	06 33	06 42	06 54	07 03	07 12		07 33	07 45	07 54	08 03	08 15	08 24
4¼	4¼	Stoke Newington	d	23p58	00 13	05 58	06 13	06 26	06 34	06 43	06 56	07 04	07 13		07 34	07 46	07 56	08 04	08 16	08 26
5	5	Stamford Hill	d	23p59	00 15	06 00	06 15	06 28	06 36	06 45	06 58	07 06	07 15		07 36	07 48	07 58	08 06	08 18	08 28
5½	5½	Seven Sisters	⊖ d	00 02	00 17	06 02	06 17	06 30	06 38	06 47	07 00	07 08	07 17	07 30	07 38	07 50	08 00	08 08	08 20	08 30
6¼	6¼	Bruce Grove	d	00 04	00 19	06 04	06 19	06 32	06 40	06 49	07 02	07 10	07 19	07 32	07 40	07 52	08 02	08 10	08 22	08 32
7¼	7¼	White Hart Lane	d	00 06	00 21	06 06	06 21	06 34	06 42	06 51	07 04	07 12	07 21	07 34	07 42	07 54	08 04	08 12	08 24	08 34
8	8	Silver Street	d	00 08	00 23	06 08	06 23	06 36	06 44	06 53	07 06	07 14	07 23	07 36	07 44	07 56	08 06	08 14	08 26	08 36
8½	8½	Edmonton Green	d	00 10	00 25	06 10	06 25	06 38	06 46	06 55	07 08	07 16	07 25	07 38	07 46	07 58	08 08	08 16	08 28	08 38
—	9¾	Bush Hill Park	d		00 28		06 28		06 49	06 58		07 19	07 28		07 49	08 01		08 19	08 31	
—	10¾	**Enfield Town**	a		00 33		06 33		06 54	07 03		07 24	07 33		07 54	08 06		08 24	08 36	
10½	—	Southbury	d	00 14		06 14		06 41			07 11			07 41			08 11			08 41
12¼	—	Turkey Street	d	00 17		06 17		06 44			07 14			07 44			08 14			08 44
13½	—	Theobalds Grove	d	00 19		06 19		06 47			07 17			07 47			08 17			08 47
14½	—	**Cheshunt**	a	00 22		06 24		06 51			07 21			07 51			08 21			08 51

		LE	LE	LE	LE	LE	LE	LE	LE	LE		LE	LE	LE	LE	LE	LE	LE	LE
London Liverpool Street 15	⊖ d	08 21	08 30	08 44	08 51	09 00	09 15	09 30	09 45	10 00		15 15	15 30	15 45	16 00	16 15	16 20	16 30	16 38
Bethnal Green	d	08 24	08 33		08 54	09 03	09 18	09 33	09 48	10 03		15 18	15 33	15 48	16 03	16 18	16 23	16 33	
Cambridge Heath	d	08 26	08 35		08 56	09 05	09 20	09 35	09 50	10 05		15 20	15 35	15 50	16 05	16 20	16 25	16 35	16 43
London Fields	d	08 28	08 37		08 58	09 07	09 22	09 37	09 52	10 07	and at	15 22	15 37	15 52	16 07	16 22	16 27	16 37	16 45
Hackney Downs	d	08 30	08 39	08 52	09 00	09 09	09 24	09 39	09 54	10 09		15 24	15 39	15 54	16 09	16 24	16 29	16 39	16 47
Rectory Road	d	08 33	08 42	08 54	09 03	09 12	09 27	09 42	09 57	10 12	the same	15 27	15 42	15 57	16 12	16 27	16 32	16 42	16 49
Stoke Newington	d	08 34	08 43	08 56	09 04	09 13	09 28	09 43	09 58	10 13		15 28	15 43	15 58	16 13	16 28	16 33	16 43	16 51
Stamford Hill	d	08 36	08 45	08 58	09 06	09 15	09 30	09 45	10 00	10 15	minutes	15 30	15 45	16 00	16 15	16 30	16 35	16 45	16 53
Seven Sisters	⊖ d	08 38	08 47	09 00	09 08	09 17	09 32	09 47	10 02	10 17		15 32	15 47	16 02	16 17	16 33	16 38	16 48	16 56
Bruce Grove	d	08 40	08 49	09 02	09 10	09 19	09 34	09 49	10 04	10 19	past	15 34	15 49	16 04	16 19	16 35	16 40	16 50	16 58
White Hart Lane	d	08 42	08 51	09 04	09 12	09 21	09 36	09 51	10 06	10 21		15 36	15 51	16 06	16 21	16 37	16 42	16 52	17 00
Silver Street	d	08 44	08 53	09 06	09 14	09 23	09 38	09 53	10 08	10 23	each	15 38	15 53	16 08	16 23	16 39	16 44	16 54	17 02
Edmonton Green	d	08 46	08 55	09 08	09 16	09 25	09 40	09 55	10 10	10 25		15 40	15 55	16 10	16 25	16 41	16 46	16 56	17 04
Bush Hill Park	d	08 49	08 58		09 19	09 28		09 58		10 28	hour until		15 58		16 28		16 49	16 59	
Enfield Town	a	08 54	09 03		09 24	09 33		10 03		10 33			16 03		16 34		16 55	17 06	
Southbury	d			09 11			09 44		10 14			15 44		16 14		16 45			17 08
Turkey Street	d			09 14			09 47		10 17			15 47		16 17		16 48			17 11
Theobalds Grove	d			09 17			09 49		10 19			15 49		16 19		16 50			17 14
Cheshunt	a			09 21			09 54		10 24			15 54		16 24		16 56			17 19

		LE	LE	LE	LE	LE	LE	LE	LE	LE	LE	LE	LE	LE	LE	LE	LE	LE	LE	LE
London Liverpool Street 15	⊖ d	16 50	17 00	17 08	17 20	17 30	17 38	17 50	18 00	18 08	18 20	18 30	18 38	18 50	19 00	19 08	19 20	19 30	19 45	20 00
Bethnal Green	d	16 53	17 03		17 23	17 33		17 53	18 03		18 23	18 33		18 53	19 03		19 23	19 33	19 48	20 03
Cambridge Heath	d	16 55	17 05	17 13	17 25	17 35	17 43	17 55	18 05	18 13	18 25	18 35	18 43	18 55	19 05	19 13	19 25	19 35	19 50	20 05
London Fields	d	16 57	17 07	17 15	17 27	17 37	17 45	17 57	18 07	18 15	18 27	18 37	18 45	18 57	19 07	19 15	19 27	19 37	19 52	20 07
Hackney Downs	d	16 59	17 09	17 17	17 29	17 39	17 47	17 59	18 09	18 17	18 29	18 39	18 47	18 59	19 09	19 17	19 29	19 39	19 54	20 09
Rectory Road	d	17 02	17 12	17 19	17 32	17 42	17 49	18 02	18 12	18 19	18 32	18 42	18 49	19 02	19 12	19 19	19 32	19 42	19 57	20 12
Stoke Newington	d	17 03	17 13	17 21	17 33	17 43	17 51	18 03	18 13	18 21	18 33	18 43	18 51	19 03	19 13	19 21	19 33	19 43	19 58	20 13
Stamford Hill	d	17 05	17 15	17 23	17 35	17 45	17 53	18 05	18 15	18 23	18 35	18 45	18 53	19 05	19 15	19 23	19 35	19 45	20 00	20 15
Seven Sisters	⊖ d	17 08	17 18	17 26	17 38	17 48	17 56	18 08	18 18	18 26	18 38	18 48	18 56	19 08	19 18	19 26	19 38	19 47	20 02	20 17
Bruce Grove	d	17 10	17 20	17 28	17 40	17 50	17 58	18 10	18 20	18 28	18 40	18 50	18 58	19 10	19 20	19 28	19 40	19 49	20 04	20 19
White Hart Lane	d	17 12	17 22	17 30	17 42	17 52	18 00	18 12	18 22	18 30	18 42	18 52	19 00	19 12	19 22	19 30	19 42	19 51	20 06	20 21
Silver Street	d	17 14	17 24	17 32	17 44	17 54	18 02	18 14	18 24	18 32	18 44	18 54	19 02	19 14	19 24	19 32	19 44	19 53	20 08	20 23
Edmonton Green	d	17 16	17 26	17 34	17 46	17 56	18 04	18 16	18 26	18 34	18 46	18 56	19 04	19 16	19 26	19 34	19 46	19 55	20 10	20 25
Bush Hill Park	d	17 19	17 29		17 49	17 59		18 19	18 29		18 49	18 59		19 19	19 29		19 49	19 58		20 28
Enfield Town	a	17 25	17 36		17 55	18 06		18 25	18 36		18 55	19 06		19 25	19 35		19 54	20 03		20 33
Southbury	d			17 38			18 08			18 38			19 08			19 38			20 14	
Turkey Street	d			17 41			18 11			18 41			19 11			19 41			20 17	
Theobalds Grove	d			17 44			18 14			18 44			19 14			19 44			20 19	
Cheshunt	a			17 49			18 19			18 49			19 19			19 48			20 24	

		LE	LE	LE	LE	LE	LE	LE	LE	LE	LE	LE	LE	LE	LE	LE A
London Liverpool Street 15	⊖ d	20 15	20 30	20 45	21 00	21 15	21 30	21 45	22 00	22 15	22 30	22 45	23 00	23 15	23 30	23 45
Bethnal Green	d	20 18	20 33	20 48	21 03	21 18	21 33	21 48	22 03	22 18	22 33	22 48	23 03	23 18	23 33	23 48
Cambridge Heath	d	20 20	20 35	20 50	21 05	21 20	21 35	21 50	22 05	22 20	22 35	22 50	23 05	23 20	23 35	23 50
London Fields	d	20 22	20 37	20 52	21 07	21 22	21 37	21 52	22 07	22 22	22 37	22 52	23 07	23 22	23 37	23 52
Hackney Downs	d	20 24	20 39	20 54	21 09	21 24	21 39	21 54	22 09	22 24	22 39	22 54	23 09	23 24	23 39	23 54
Rectory Road	d	20 27	20 42	20 57	21 12	21 27	21 42	21 57	22 12	22 27	22 42	22 57	23 12	23 27	23 42	23 57
Stoke Newington	d	20 28	20 43	20 58	21 13	21 28	21 43	21 58	22 13	22 28	22 43	22 58	23 13	23 28	23 43	23 58
Stamford Hill	d	20 30	20 45	21 00	21 15	21 30	21 45	22 00	22 15	22 30	22 45	23 00	23 15	23 30	23 45	23 59
Seven Sisters	⊖ d	20 32	20 47	21 02	21 17	21 32	21 47	22 02	22 17	22 32	22 47	23 02	23 17	23 32	23 47	00 02
Bruce Grove	d	20 34	20 49	21 04	21 19	21 34	21 49	22 04	22 19	22 34	22 49	23 04	23 19	23 34	23 49	00 04
White Hart Lane	d	20 36	20 51	21 06	21 21	21 36	21 51	22 06	22 21	22 36	22 51	23 06	23 21	23 36	23 51	00 06
Silver Street	d	20 38	20 53	21 08	21 23	21 38	21 53	22 08	22 23	22 38	22 53	23 08	23 23	23 38	23 53	00 08
Edmonton Green	d	20 40	20 55	21 10	21 25	21 40	21 55	22 10	22 25	22 40	22 55	23 10	23 25	23 40	23 55	00 10
Bush Hill Park	d		20 58		21 28		21 58		22 28		22 58		23 28		23 58	
Enfield Town	a		21 03		21 33		22 03		22 33		23 03		23 33		00 03	
Southbury	d	20 44		21 14		21 44		22 14		22 44		23 14		23 44		00 14
Turkey Street	d	20 47		21 17		21 47		22 17		22 47		23 17		23 47		00 17
Theobalds Grove	d	20 49		21 19		21 49		22 19		22 49		23 19		23 49		00 19
Cheshunt	a	20 54		21 24		21 54		22 24		22 54		23 24		23 54		00 22

For general notes see front of timetable
For details of catering facilities see Directory of Train Operators

A To Bishops Stortford (Table 22)

Table 21

London → Cheshunt (via Seven Sisters) and Enfield Town

Saturdays

Network diagram - see first page of Table 20

		LE A	LE	LE	LE	LE	LE	LE	LE	LE	LE		LE	LE	LE	LE	LE	LE
London Liverpool Street 15	⊖ d	23p45	00 01	05 15	05 28	05 45	06 00	06 15	06 30	06 45	07 00		22 15	22 30	22 45	23 00	23 30	23 45
Bethnal Green	d	23p48	00 03	05 18		05 48	06 03	06 18	06 33	06 48	07 03		22 18	22 33	22 48	23 03	23 33	23 48
Cambridge Heath	d	23p50	00 05	05 20		05 50	06 05	06 20	06 35	06 50	07 05		22 20	22 35	22 50	23 05	23 35	23 50
London Fields	d	23p52	00 07	05 22		05 52	06 07	06 22	06 37	06 52	07 07		22 22	22 37	22 52	23 07	23 37	23 52
Hackney Downs	d	23p54	00 09	05 24		05 54	06 09	06 24	06 39	06 54	07 09	and at	22 24	22 39	22 54	23 09	23 39	23 54
Rectory Road	d	23p57	00 12	05 27		05 57	06 12	06 27	06 42	06 57	07 12	the same	22 27	22 42	22 57	23 12	23 42	23 57
Stoke Newington	d	23p58	00 13	05 28		05 58	06 13	06 28	06 43	06 58	07 13		22 28	22 43	22 58	23 13	23 43	23 58
Stamford Hill	d	23p59	00 15	05 30		06 00	06 15	06 30	06 45	07 00	07 15	minutes	22 30	22 45	23 00	23 15	23 45	23 59
Seven Sisters	⊖ d	00 02	00 17	05 32	05 50	06 02	06 17	06 32	06 47	07 02	07 17		22 32	22 47	23 02	23 17	23 47	00 02
Bruce Grove	d	00 04	00 19	05 34	05 52	06 04	06 19	06 34	06 49	07 04	07 19	past	22 34	22 49	23 04	23 19	23 49	00 04
White Hart Lane	d	00 06	00 21	05 36	05 54	06 06	06 21	06 36	06 51	07 06	07 21	each	22 36	22 51	23 06	23 21	23 51	00 06
Silver Street	d	00 08	00 23	05 38	05 56	06 08	06 23	06 38	06 53	07 08	07 23		22 38	22 53	23 08	23 23	23 53	00 08
Edmonton Green	d	00 10	00 25	05 40	05 58	06 10	06 25	06 40	06 55	07 10	07 25	hour until	22 40	22 55	23 10	23 25	23 55	00 10
Bush Hill Park	d		00 28		06 01		06 28		06 58		07 28			22 58		23 28	23 58	
Enfield Town	a		00 33		06 06		06 33		07 03		07 33			23 03		23 33	00 03	
Southbury	d	00 14		05 44		06 14		06 44		07 14			22 44		23 14			00 14
Turkey Street	d	00 17		05 47		06 17		06 47		07 17			22 47		23 17			00 17
Theobalds Grove	d	00 19		05 49		06 19		06 49		07 19			22 49		23 19			00 19
Cheshunt	a	00 22		05 54		06 24		06 54		07 24			22 54		23 24			00 24

Sundays

		LE	LE	LE	LE B	LE	LE B	LE	LE B	LE	LE B	LE	LE B	LE
London Liverpool Street 15	⊖ d	23p45	00 01	07 30	07 52	08 00	08 22	08 30	08 52	09 00	09 22	09 30	09 52	10 00
Bethnal Green	d	23p48	00 03									09 33		10 03
Cambridge Heath	d	23p50	00 05									09 35		10 05
London Fields	d	23p52	00 07									09 37		10 07
Hackney Downs	d	23p54	00 09	07 39	07 59	08 09	08 29	08 39	08 59	09 09	09 29	09 39	09 59	10 09
Rectory Road	d	23p57	00 12	07 42		08 12		08 42		09 12		09 42		10 12
Stoke Newington	d	23p58	00 13	07 43		08 13		08 43		09 13		09 43		10 13
Stamford Hill	d	23p59	00 15	07 45		08 15		08 45		09 15		09 45		10 15
Seven Sisters	⊖ d	00 02	00 17	07 47	08 04	08 17	08 34	08 47	09 04	09 17	09 34	09 47	10 04	10 17
Bruce Grove	d	00 04	00 19	07 49		08 19		08 49		09 19		09 49		10 19
White Hart Lane	d	00 06	00 21	07 51		08 21		08 51		09 21		09 51		10 21
Silver Street	d	00 08	00 23	07 53		08 23		08 53		09 23		09 53		10 23
Edmonton Green	d	00 10	00 25	07 55	08 08	08 25	08 38	08 55	09 08	09 25	09 38	09 55	10 08	10 25
Bush Hill Park	d		00 28	07 58		08 28		08 58		09 28		09 58		10 28
Enfield Town	a		00 33	08 03		08 33		09 03		09 33		10 03		10 33
Southbury	d	00 14			08 12		08 42		09 12		09 42		10 12	
Turkey Street	d	00 17			08 15		08 45		09 15		09 45		10 15	
Theobalds Grove	d	00 19			08 17		08 47		09 17		09 47		10 17	
Cheshunt	a	00 24			08 20		08 52		09 20		09 52		10 20	

		LE B		LE	LE B	LE	LE B	LE	LE B	LE	LE B	LE	LE B	LE
London Liverpool Street 15	⊖ d	10 22		18 30	19 00	19 30	20 00	20 30	21 00	21 30	22 00	22 30	23 00	23 30
Bethnal Green	d			18 33	19 03	19 33	20 03	20 33	21 03	21 33	22 03	22 33	23 03	23 33
Cambridge Heath	d			18 35	19 05	19 35	20 05	20 35	21 05	21 35	22 05	22 35	23 05	23 35
London Fields	d			18 37	19 07	19 37	20 07	20 37	21 07	21 37	22 07	22 37	23 07	23 37
Hackney Downs	d	10 29	and at	18 39	19 09	19 39	20 09	20 39	21 09	21 39	22 09	22 39	23 09	23 39
Rectory Road	d		the same	18 42	19 12	19 42	20 12	20 42	21 12	21 42	22 12	22 42	23 12	23 42
Stoke Newington	d			18 43	19 13	19 43	20 13	20 43	21 13	21 43	22 13	22 43	23 13	23 43
Stamford Hill	d		minutes	18 45	19 15	19 45	20 15	20 45	21 15	21 45	22 15	22 45	23 15	23 45
Seven Sisters	⊖ d	10 34		18 47	19 17	19 47	20 17	20 47	21 17	21 47	22 17	22 47	23 17	23 47
Bruce Grove	d		past	18 49	19 19	19 49	20 19	20 49	21 19	21 49	22 19	22 49	23 19	23 49
White Hart Lane	d		each	18 51	19 21	19 51	20 21	20 51	21 21	21 51	22 21	22 51	23 21	23 51
Silver Street	d			18 53	19 23	19 53	20 23	20 53	21 23	21 53	22 23	22 53	23 23	23 53
Edmonton Green	d	10 38	hour until	18 55	19 25	19 55	20 25	20 55	21 25	21 55	22 25	22 55	23 25	23 55
Bush Hill Park	d			18 58		19 58		20 58		21 58		22 58		23 58
Enfield Town	a			19 03		20 03		21 03		22 03		23 03		00 03
Southbury	d	10 42			19 29		20 29		21 29		22 29		23 29	
Turkey Street	d	10 45			19 32		20 32		21 32		22 32		23 32	
Theobalds Grove	d	10 47			19 34		20 34		21 34		22 34		23 34	
Cheshunt	a	10 52			19 37		20 37		21 37		22 37		23 37	

For general notes see front of timetable
For details of catering facilities see Directory of Train Operators

A To Bishops Stortford (Table 22)
B To Hertford East (Table 22)

Cheshunt (via Seven Sisters) and Enfield Town → London

Network diagram - see first page of Table 20

Miles	Miles			LE MX	LE MO A	LE MX 1	LE 1	LE MX 1	LE 1	LE	LE	LE	LE	LE	LE	LE	LE	LE	LE	LE	LE
0	—	**Cheshunt**	d	23p31	23p31	23p51		23p58		05 16		06 01			06 33			07 03			07 33
1	—	Theobalds Grove	d	23p34	23p34					05 19		06 04			06 36			07 06			07 36
2¼	—	Turkey Street	d	23p36	23p36					05 21		06 06			06 38			07 08			07 38
4	—	Southbury	d	23p39	23p39					05 24		06 09			06 41			07 11			07 41
—	0	**Enfield Town**	d								05 52		06 20	06 32		06 48	07 02		07 18	07 32	
—	1	Bush Hill Park	d								05 55		06 23	06 35		06 51	07 05		07 21	07 35	
6	2¼	Edmonton Green	d	23p43	23p43					05 28	05 58	06 13	06 26	06 38	06 45	06 54	07 08	07 15	07 24	07 38	07 45
6½	2¾	Silver Street	d	23p45	23p45					05 30	06 00	06 15	06 28	06 40	06 47	06 56	07 10	07 17	07 26	07 40	07 47
7¼	3½	White Hart Lane	d	23p47	23p47					05 32	06 02	06 17	06 30	06 42	06 49	06 58	07 12	07 19	07 28	07 42	07 49
8¼	4½	Bruce Grove	d	23p49	23p49					05 34	06 04	06 19	06 32	06 44	06 51	07 00	07 14	07 21	07 30	07 44	07 51
9	5¼	Seven Sisters	⊖ d	23p51	23p51	00 04	00 08	00 11	00 21	05 36	06 06	06 21	06 35	06 47	06 55	07 03	07 17	07 25	07 33	07 47	07 55
9½	5¾	Stamford Hill	d	23p53	23p53					05 38	06 08	06 23	06 37	06 49	06 57	07 05	07 19	07 27	07 35	07 49	07 57
10¼	6½	Stoke Newington	d	23p55	23p55					05 40	06 10	06 25	06 39	06 51	06 59	07 07	07 21	07 29	07 37	07 51	07 59
10½	7	Rectory Road	d	23p56	23p56					05 41	06 11	06 26	06 41	06 53	07 00	07 09	07 23	07 30	07 39	07 53	08 00
11½	7¾	Hackney Downs	d	23p59	23p59			00 16		05 44	06 14	06 29	06 45	06 58	07 04	07 13	07 28	07 34	07 43	07 58	08 04
12	8¼	London Fields	d	00 01	00 01					05 46	06 16	06 31	06 47	07 00	07 06	07 15	07 30	07 36	07 45	08 00	08 06
12¾	9	Cambridge Heath	d	00 03	00 03					05 48	06 18	06 33	06 49	07 02	07 08	07 17	07 32	07 38	07 47	08 02	08 08
13¼	9½	Bethnal Green	d	00 05	00 05					05 50	06 20	06 35	06 51		07 10	07 19		07 40	07 49		08 10
14½	10¾	**London Liverpool Street 15**	⊖ a	00 10	00 11	00 18	00 22	00 25	00 36	05 55	06 25	06 40	06 55	07 10	07 16	07 25	07 40	07 46	07 55	08 10	08 16

		LE	LE	LE	LE	LE	LE	LE	LE	LE	LE	LE	LE	LE	LE	LE		LE	LE	LE
Cheshunt	d			08 03			08 33			09 03			09 31		10 01		and at	15 31		16 01
Theobalds Grove	d			08 06			08 36			09 06			09 34		10 04		the same	15 34		16 04
Turkey Street	d			08 08			08 38			09 08			09 36		10 06		minutes	15 36		16 06
Southbury	d			08 11			08 41			09 11			09 39		10 09		past	15 39		16 09
Enfield Town	d	07 50	08 02		08 18	08 32		08 48	09 02		09 18	09 29		09 52		10 22	each		15 52	
Bush Hill Park	d	07 53	08 05		08 21	08 35		08 51	09 05		09 21	09 32		09 55		10 25	hour until		15 55	
Edmonton Green	d	07 56	08 08	08 15	08 24	08 38	08 45	08 54	09 08	09 15	09 24	09 35	09 43	09 58	10 13	10 28		15 43	15 58	16 13
Silver Street	d	07 58	08 10	08 17	08 26	08 40	08 47	08 56	09 10	09 17	09 26	09 37	09 45	10 00	10 15	10 30		15 45	16 00	16 15
White Hart Lane	d	08 00	08 12	08 19	08 28	08 42	08 49	08 58	09 12	09 19	09 28	09 39	09 47	10 02	10 17	10 32		15 47	16 02	16 17
Bruce Grove	d	08 02	08 14	08 21	08 30	08 44	08 51	09 00	09 14	09 21	09 30	09 41	09 49	10 04	10 19	10 34		15 49	16 04	16 19
Seven Sisters	⊖ d	08 05	08 17	08 25	08 33	08 47	08 55	09 03	09 17	09 25	09 33	09 43	09 51	10 06	10 21	10 36		15 51	16 06	16 21
Stamford Hill	d	08 07	08 19	08 27	08 35	08 49	08 57	09 05	09 19	09 27	09 35	09 45	09 53	10 08	10 23	10 38		15 53	16 08	16 23
Stoke Newington	d	08 09	08 21	08 29	08 37	08 51	08 59	09 07	09 21	09 29	09 37	09 47	09 55	10 10	10 25	10 40		15 55	16 10	16 25
Rectory Road	d	08 10	08 23	08 30	08 39	08 53	09 00	09 09	09 23	09 30	09 39	09 49	09 56	10 11	10 26	10 41		15 56	16 11	16 26
Hackney Downs	d	08 14	08 28	08 34	08 43	08 58	09 04	09 13	09 28	09 34	09 43	09 52	09 59	10 14	10 29	10 44		15 59	16 14	16 29
London Fields	d	08 16	08 30	08 36	08 45	09 00	09 06	09 15	09 30	09 36	09 45	09 54	10 01	10 16	10 31	10 46		16 01	16 16	16 31
Cambridge Heath	d	08 18	08 32	08 38	08 47	09 02	09 08	09 17	09 32	09 38	09 47	09 56	10 03	10 18	10 33	10 48		16 03	16 18	16 33
Bethnal Green	d	08 20		08 40	08 49		09 10	09 19		09 40	09 49		10 05	10 20	10 35	10 50		16 05	16 20	16 35
London Liverpool Street 15	⊖ a	08 26	08 40	08 46	08 55	09 10	09 16	09 25	09 40	09 46	09 55	10 03	10 10	10 25	10 40	10 55		16 11	16 25	16 40

		LE	LE	LE	LE	LE	LE	LE	LE	LE	LE	LE	LE	LE	LE	LE	LE	LE	LE	LE	LE
Cheshunt	d		16 31			17 01			17 31			18 01			18 31			19 01			19 31
Theobalds Grove	d		16 34			17 04			17 34			18 04			18 34			19 04			19 34
Turkey Street	d		16 36			17 06			17 36			18 06			18 36			19 06			19 36
Southbury	d		16 39			17 09			17 39			18 09			18 39			19 09			19 39
Enfield Town	d	16 22		16 52	17 00		17 22	17 30		17 52	18 00		18 22	18 30		18 52	19 00		19 22	19 30	
Bush Hill Park	d	16 25		16 55	17 03		17 25	17 33		17 55	18 03		18 25	18 33		18 55	19 03		19 25	19 33	
Edmonton Green	d	16 28	16 43	16 58	17 06	17 13	17 28	17 36	17 43	17 58	18 06	18 13	18 28	18 36	18 43	18 58	19 06	19 13	19 28	19 36	19 43
Silver Street	d	16 30	16 45	17 00	17 08	17 15	17 30	17 38	17 45	18 00	18 08	18 15	18 30	18 38	18 45	19 00	19 08	19 15	19 30	19 38	19 45
White Hart Lane	d	16 32	16 47	17 02	17 10	17 17	17 32	17 40	17 47	18 02	18 10	18 17	18 32	18 40	18 47	19 02	19 10	19 17	19 32	19 40	19 47
Bruce Grove	d	16 34	16 49	17 04	17 12	17 19	17 34	17 42	17 49	18 04	18 12	18 19	18 34	18 42	18 49	19 04	19 12	19 19	19 34	19 42	19 49
Seven Sisters	⊖ d	16 36	16 51	17 06	17 14	17 21	17 36	17 44	17 51	18 06	18 14	18 21	18 36	18 44	18 51	19 06	19 14	19 21	19 36	19 44	19 51
Stamford Hill	d	16 38	16 53	17 08		17 23	17 38		17 53	18 08		18 23	18 38		18 53	19 08		19 23	19 38		19 53
Stoke Newington	d	16 40	16 55	17 10	17 17	17 25	17 40	17 47	17 55	18 10	18 17	18 25	18 40	18 47	18 55	19 10	19 17	19 25	19 40	19 47	19 55
Rectory Road	d	16 41	16 56	17 11		17 26	17 41		17 56	18 11		18 26	18 41		18 56	19 11		19 26	19 41		19 56
Hackney Downs	d	16 44	16 59	17 14	17 20	17 29	17 44	17 50	17 59	18 14	18 20	18 29	18 44	18 50	18 59	19 14	19 20	19 29	19 44	19 50	19 59
London Fields	d	16 46	17 01	17 16		17 31	17 46		18 01	18 16		18 31	18 46		19 01	19 16		19 31	19 46		20 01
Cambridge Heath	d	16 48	17 03	17 18		17 33	17 48		18 03	18 18		18 33	18 48		19 03	19 18		19 33	19 48		20 03
Bethnal Green	d	16 50	17 05	17 20		17 35	17 50		18 05	18 20		18 35	18 50		19 05	19 20		19 35	19 50		20 05
London Liverpool Street 15	⊖ a	16 56	17 10	17 26	17 29	17 40	17 56	17 59	18 11	18 26	18 29	18 40	18 56	18 59	19 11	19 26	19 29	19 41	19 55	19 59	20 11

		LE	LE	LE	LE	LE	LE	LE	LE	LE	LE	LE	LE	LE	LE	LE 1	LE 1
Cheshunt	d		20 01		20 31		21 01		21 31		22 01		22 31			23 31	23 51	23 58
Theobalds Grove	d		20 04		20 34		21 04		21 34		22 04		22 34			23 34		
Turkey Street	d		20 06		20 36		21 06		21 36		22 06		22 36			23 36		
Southbury	d		20 09		20 39		21 09		21 39		22 09		22 39			23 39		
Enfield Town	d	19 52		20 22		20 52		21 22		21 52		22 22		22 52	23 22			
Bush Hill Park	d	19 55		20 25		20 55		21 25		21 55		22 25		22 55	23 25			
Edmonton Green	d	19 58	20 13	20 28	20 43	20 58	21 13	21 28	21 43	21 58	22 13	22 28	22 43	22 58	23 28	23 43		
Silver Street	d	20 00	20 15	20 30	20 45	21 00	21 15	21 30	21 45	22 00	22 15	22 30	22 45	23 00	23 30	23 45		
White Hart Lane	d	20 02	20 17	20 32	20 47	21 02	21 17	21 32	21 47	22 02	22 17	22 32	22 47	23 02	23 32	23 47		
Bruce Grove	d	20 04	20 19	20 34	20 49	21 04	21 19	21 34	21 49	22 04	22 19	22 34	22 49	23 04	23 34	23 49		
Seven Sisters	⊖ d	20 06	20 21	20 36	20 51	21 06	21 21	21 36	21 51	22 06	22 21	22 36	22 51	23 06	23 36	23 51	00 04	00 11
Stamford Hill	d	20 08	20 23	20 38	20 53	21 08	21 23	21 38	21 53	22 08	22 23	22 38	22 53	23 08	23 38	23 53		
Stoke Newington	d	20 10	20 25	20 40	20 55	21 10	21 25	21 40	21 55	22 10	22 25	22 40	22 55	23 10	23 40	23 55		
Rectory Road	d	20 11	20 26	20 41	20 56	21 11	21 26	21 41	21 56	22 11	22 26	22 41	22 56	23 11	23 41	23 56		
Hackney Downs	d	20 14	20 29	20 44	20 59	21 14	21 29	21 44	21 59	22 14	22 29	22 44	22 59	23 14	23 44	23 59		00 16
London Fields	d	20 16	20 31	20 46	21 01	21 16	21 31	21 46	22 01	22 16	22 31	22 46	23 01	23 16	23 46	00 01		
Cambridge Heath	d	20 18	20 33	20 48	21 03	21 18	21 33	21 48	22 03	22 18	22 33	22 48	23 03	23 18	23 48	00 03		
Bethnal Green	d	20 20	20 35	20 50	21 05	21 20	21 35	21 50	22 05	22 20	22 35	22 50	23 05	23 20	23 50	00 05		
London Liverpool Street 15	⊖ a	20 25	20 40	20 55	21 10	21 25	21 40	21 55	22 10	22 25	22 40	22 55	23 10	23 25	23 55	00 10	00 18	00 25

For general notes see front of timetable
For details of catering facilities see
Directory of Train Operators

A From Hertford East (Table 22)

Table 21

Saturdays

Cheshunt (via Seven Sisters) and Enfield Town → London

Network diagram - see first page of Table 20

		LE	LE 1	LE 1	LE 1	LE 1	LE 1 A	LE	LE	LE	LE	LE	LE		LE	LE	LE	LE	LE
Cheshunt	d	23p31	23p51		23p58		05 16	06 01		06 31		07 01		and at the same minutes past each hour until	22 31			23 31	
Theobalds Grove	d	23p34					05 19	06 04		06 34		07 04			22 34			23 34	
Turkey Street	d	23p36					05 21	06 06		06 36		07 06			22 36			23 36	
Southbury	d	23p39					05 24	06 09		06 39		07 09			22 39			23 39	
Enfield Town	d								06 22		06 52		07 22			22 52	23 22		23 52
Bush Hill Park	d								06 25		06 55		07 25			22 55	23 25		23 55
Edmonton Green	d	23p43					05 28	06 13	06 28	06 43	06 58	07 13	07 28		22 43	22 58	23 28	23 43	23 58
Silver Street	d	23p45					05 30	06 15	06 30	06 45	07 00	07 15	07 30		22 45	23 00	23 30	23 45	23 59
White Hart Lane	d	23p47					05 32	06 17	06 32	06 47	07 02	07 17	07 32		22 47	23 02	23 32	23 47	00 02
Bruce Grove	d	23p49					05 34	06 19	06 34	06 49	07 04	07 19	07 34		22 49	23 04	23 34	23 49	00 04
Seven Sisters	⊖ d	23p51	00 04	00 07	00 11	00 21	05 36	06 21	06 36	06 51	07 06	07 21	07 36		22 51	23 06	23 36	23 51	00 06
Stamford Hill	d	23p53					05 38	06 23	06 38	06 53	07 08	07 23	07 38		22 53	23 08	23 38	23 53	00 08
Stoke Newington	d	23p55					05 40	06 25	06 40	06 55	07 10	07 25	07 40		22 55	23 10	23 40	23 55	00 10
Rectory Road	d	23p56					05 41	06 26	06 41	06 56	07 11	07 26	07 41		22 56	23 11	23 41	23 56	00 11
Hackney Downs	d	23p59			00 16		05 45	06 29	06 44	06 59	07 14	07 29	07 44		22 59	23 14	23 44	23 59	00 14
London Fields	d	00 01						06 31	06 46	07 01	07 16	07 31	07 46		23 01	23 16	23 46	00 01	00 16
Cambridge Heath	d	00 03						06 33	06 48	07 03	07 18	07 33	07 48		23 03	23 18	23 48	00 03	00 18
Bethnal Green	d	00 05					05 49	06 35	06 50	07 05	07 20	07 35	07 50		23 05	23 20	23 50	00 05	00 20
London Liverpool Street 15	⊖ a	00 10	00 18	00 21	00 25	00 36	05 54	06 40	06 55	07 10	07 25	07 40	07 55		23 10	23 25	23 55	00 10	00 25

Sundays

		LE	LE	LE	LE B	LE	LE B	LE	LE B	LE	LE B		LE	LE B	LE
Cheshunt	d	23p31			08 15		08 45		09 15		09 45	and at the same minutes past each hour until		18 15	
Theobalds Grove	d	23p34			08 18		08 48		09 18		09 48			18 18	
Turkey Street	d	23p36			08 21		08 51		09 21		09 51			18 21	
Southbury	d	23p39			08 24		08 54		09 24		09 54			18 24	
Enfield Town	d		23p52	07 57		08 27		08 57		09 27			17 57		18 27
Bush Hill Park	d		23p55	08 00		08 30		09 00		09 30			18 00		18 30
Edmonton Green	d	23p43	23p58	08 03	08 27	08 33	08 57	09 03	09 27	09 33	09 57		18 03	18 27	18 33
Silver Street	d	23p45	23p59	08 05		08 35		09 05		09 35			18 05		18 35
White Hart Lane	d	23p47	00 02	08 07		08 37		09 07		09 37			18 07		18 37
Bruce Grove	d	23p49	00 04	08 09		08 39		09 09		09 39			18 09		18 39
Seven Sisters	⊖ d	23p51	00 06	08 11	08 33	08 41	09 03	09 11	09 33	09 41	10 03		18 11	18 33	18 41
Stamford Hill	d	23p53	00 08	08 13		08 43		09 13		09 43			18 13		18 43
Stoke Newington	d	23p55	00 10	08 15		08 45		09 15		09 45			18 15		18 45
Rectory Road	d	23p56	00 11	08 16		08 46		09 16		09 46			18 16		18 46
Hackney Downs	d	23p59	00 14	08 19	08 39	08 49	09 09	09 19	09 39	09 49	10 09		18 19	18 39	18 49
London Fields	d	00 01	00 16					09 21		09 51			18 21		18 51
Cambridge Heath	d	00 03	00 18					09 23		09 53			18 23		18 53
Bethnal Green	d	00 05	00 20					09 25		09 55			18 25		18 55
London Liverpool Street 15	⊖ a	00 10	00 25	08 30	08 48	09 00	09 18	09 30	09 48	10 00	10 18		18 30	18 48	19 00

		LE B	LE	LE B	LE	LE B	LE	LE B	LE	LE B	LE	LE B
Cheshunt	d	18 45		19 31		20 31		21 31		22 31		23 31
Theobalds Grove	d	18 48		19 34		20 34		21 34		22 34		23 34
Turkey Street	d	18 51		19 36		20 36		21 36		22 36		23 36
Southbury	d	18 54		19 39		20 39		21 39		22 39		23 39
Enfield Town	d		19 08		20 08		21 08		22 08		23 08	
Bush Hill Park	d		19 11		20 11		21 11		22 11		23 11	
Edmonton Green	d	18 57	19 13	19 43	20 13	20 43	21 13	21 43	22 13	22 43	23 13	23 43
Silver Street	d		19 15	19 45	20 15	20 45	21 15	21 45	22 15	22 45	23 15	23 45
White Hart Lane	d		19 17	19 47	20 17	20 47	21 17	21 47	22 17	22 47	23 17	23 47
Bruce Grove	d		19 19	19 49	20 19	20 49	21 19	21 49	22 19	22 49	23 19	23 49
Seven Sisters	⊖ d	19 03	19 21	19 51	20 21	20 51	21 21	21 51	22 21	22 51	23 21	23 51
Stamford Hill	d		19 23	19 53	20 23	20 53	21 23	21 53	22 23	22 53	23 23	23 53
Stoke Newington	d		19 25	19 55	20 25	20 55	21 25	21 55	22 25	22 55	23 25	23 55
Rectory Road	d		19 27	19 56	20 27	20 56	21 27	21 56	22 27	22 56	23 27	23 56
Hackney Downs	d	19 09	19 30	19 59	20 30	20 59	21 30	21 59	22 30	22 59	23 30	23 59
London Fields	d		19 32	20 01	20 32	21 01	21 32	22 01	22 32	23 01	23 32	00 01
Cambridge Heath	d		19 34	20 03	20 34	21 03	21 34	22 03	22 34	23 03	23 34	00 03
Bethnal Green	d		19 36	20 05	20 36	21 05	21 36	22 05	22 36	23 05	23 36	00 05
London Liverpool Street 15	⊖ a	19 18	19 41	20 11	20 41	21 11	21 41	22 11	22 41	23 11	23 41	00 11

For general notes see front of timetable
For details of catering facilities see
Directory of Train Operators

A From Cambridge (Table 22)
B From Hertford East (Table 22)

London → Broxbourne, Hertford East, Bishops Stortford, Stansted Airport and Cambridge

Network diagram - see first page of Table 20

Miles	Miles			LE MO 1	LE MX 1	LE MO	LE MO 1	LE MX 1	LE MX 1	LE MO 1	LE MO	LE MX 1	LE MX	LE 1	LE MX	LE MO 1	LE MFO 1	XC ◇	LE 1	LE 1	LE 1	LE 1	LE
0	—	**London Liverpool Street** 15 ⊖	d		22p58	23p00	23p25	23p25	23p28	23p28		23p40	23p45	23p58	←	03 40	04 10		04 40	05 10		05 25	
1¼	—	Bethnal Green	d			23p03							23p48										
3	—	Hackney Downs	d			23p09						23p46	23p54		23p54								
—	0	Stratford 7 ⊖	d	22p45									→										
4	—	Clapton	d									23p49											
—	6¾	Seven Sisters ⊖	d			23p17									00 02								
6	—	Tottenham Hale ⊖	d	22p55	23p10		23p37	23b37	23p40	23p40		23p53		00 10					04u52	05u22		05u37	
7	—	Northumberland Park	d									23p55											
7¾	—	Angel Road	d																				
10	—	Ponders End	d	22p59						23p44		23p59											
10¾	—	Brimsdown	d	23p02						23p47		00 02											
11¾	—	Enfield Lock	d	23p04						23p49		00 04											
12¾	—	Waltham Cross	d	23p07						23p52		00 07											
14	—	Cheshunt	d	23p09	23p18	23p37			23p48	23p54		00 09		00 18	00 22								
17¼	—	Broxbourne 3	a	23p14	23p22	23p42			23p52	23p59	←	00 14		00 22	00 27								
—	0		d	23p19	23p22	00 02			23p52	23p59	00 02	00 14		00 22	00 27								05 40
—	1¾	Rye House	d			→					00 05	00 17											05 43
—	3	St Margarets (Herts)	d								00 08	00 20											05 46
—	5	Ware	d								00 12	00 24											05 50
—	7	**Hertford East**	a								00 19	00 31											05 56
20	—	Roydon	d	23p24	23p26									00 26									
22¾	—	Harlow Town	d	23p28	23p30		23p52	23p54	23p58	00 05				00 30	00 34				05 10	05 37		05 55	
24¼	—	Harlow Mill	d	23p31	23p33									00 33									
26¾	—	Sawbridgeworth	d	23p34	23p37				00 03	00 10				00 37						05 42			
30¼	—	**Bishops Stortford**	a	23p41	23p44		00 02	00 04	00 10	00 17				00 44	00 47				05 20	05 49		06 05	
—	—		d	23p42	23p44		00 03	00 04	00 11										05 20	05 50	05 55	06 05	
33¾	0	Stansted Mountfitchet	d	23p46	23p48				00 15										05 24		05 59		
—	3¾	**Stansted Airport**	a				00 12	00 13								04 30	05 00		05 39	05 59		06 15	
—	—		d															05 21					
35½	8¼	Elsenham	d	23p50	23p52				00 19												06 03		
40	—	Newport (Essex)	d	23p55	23p57				00 24												06 08		
41¾	—	Audley End	d	23p58	23p59				00 27									05 33			06 11		
45¾	—	Great Chesterford	d	00 03	00 05				00 32												06 16		
49	—	Whittlesford Parkway	d	00 08	00 10				00 37												06 21		
52½	—	Shelford	d	00 12	00 14				00 41												06 25		
55¾	—	**Cambridge**	a	00 19	00 21				00 48									05 55			06 32		

		LE 1	LE 1	LE	LE 1	LE 1	LE 1	LE 1	LE 1	LE 1	LE 1	LE 1	XC ◇	LE 1	LE	LE 1	LE 1	LE 1	LE 1	LE	LE 1	LE 1	LE 1
London Liverpool Street 15 ⊖	d	05 28	05 40	05 42	05 52	05 55	05 58		06 10	06 12	06 25	06 28		06 40	06 42	06 55	06 58	07 10		07 12	07 25	07 28	
Bethnal Green	d																						
Hackney Downs	d			05 49				←		06 18					06 49					07 19			
Stratford 7 ⊖	d				06 03 →			06 03											07 02				07 33
Clapton	d																						
Seven Sisters ⊖	d																						
Tottenham Hale ⊖	d	05 40	05u52	05 55		06u07	06 10	06 15	06u22	06 25	06u37	06 40		06u52	06 55	07u07	07 10	07u22	07 13	07 25	07u37	07 40	07 43
Northumberland Park	d							06 17											07 15				07 45
Angel Road	d							06 19											07 17				07 47
Ponders End	d			05 59						06 29					06 59					07 29			
Brimsdown	d			06 02						06 32					07 02					07 32			
Enfield Lock	d			06 04				06 24		06 34					07 04				07 22	07 34			07 52
Waltham Cross	d			06 07						06 37					07 07					07 37			
Cheshunt	d	05 48		06 09			06 18	06 28		06 39		06 48			07 09		07 18		07 26	07 39		07 48	07 56
Broxbourne 3	a	05 53		06 14			06 22	06 32		06 44		06 52			07 14		07 22		07 30	07 44		07 52	08 00
	d	05 53		06 14			06 22	06 36		06 44		06 52			07 14		07 22		07 34	07 44		07 52	
Rye House	d							06 39		06 47					07 17					07 47			
St Margarets (Herts)	d							06 42		06 50					07 20					07 50			
Ware	d							06 46		06 54					07 24					07 54			
Hertford East	a			06 27				06 53		07 01					07 31					08 01			
Roydon	d	05 57					06 26					06 56					07 26					07 56	
Harlow Town	d	06 01				06 25	06 30				06 55	07 00				07 24	07 30		07 40		07 54	08 00	
Harlow Mill	d	06 04					06 33					07 03					07 33					08 03	
Sawbridgeworth	d	06 07					06 37					07 07					07 37					08 07	
Bishops Stortford	a	06 14	06 18				06 44		06 47			07 14		07 17			07 44	07 47	07 51			08 14	
	d	06 14	06 18				06 44		06 48			07 14		07 18			07 44	07 48				08 14	
Stansted Mountfitchet	d	06 19	06 23				06 48					07 18		07 23			07 48					08 18	
Stansted Airport	a		06 29			06 43			06 59		07 13			07 29		07 42		07 59			08 13		
	d												07 20										
Elsenham	d	06 22					06 52					07 22					07 52					08 22	
Newport (Essex)	d	06 28					06 57					07 27					07 57					08 27	
Audley End	d	06 31					07 00					07 30	07 38				08 00					08 30	
Great Chesterford	d	06 36					07 05					07 35					08 05					08 35	
Whittlesford Parkway	d	06 40					07 10					07 40					08 10					08 40	
Shelford	d	06 45					07 14					07 44					08 14					08 44	
Cambridge	a	06 56					07 25					07 55	07 57				08 23					08 55	

For general notes see front of timetable
For details of catering facilities see Directory of Train Operators

b Previous night.
u Stops to pick up only

London → Broxbourne, Hertford East, Bishops Stortford, Stansted Airport and Cambridge

Network diagram - see first page of Table 20

		XC ◇ 🛒	LE 1 🛒	LE 1	LE 1 🛒	LE 1	LE 1 🛒	LE 1		LE 1	LE 1	LE 1 🛒	LE 1	XC ◇ 🛒	LE 1 🛒	LE	LE 1 🛒	LE 1		LE 1 🛒	LE 1	LE	LE 1 🛒	LE 1	XC ◇ 🛒
London Liverpool Street 15 ⊖	d		07 40	07 42	07 55	07 58	08 10			08 12		08 25	08 28		08 40	08 42	08 55	08 58		09 10		09 12	09 25	09 28	
Bethnal Green	d																								
Hackney Downs	d			07 48						08 18						08 49						09 19			
Stratford 7 ⊖ ⛴	d							08 03			08 20										08 58				
Clapton	d																								
Seven Sisters ⊖	d																								
Tottenham Hale ⊖	d		07u52	07 55	08u07	08 10	08u22	08 13		08 25	08 29	08u37	08 40		08u52	08 55	09u07	09 10		09u22	09 14	09 25	09u37	09 40	
Northumberland Park	d							08 15			08 32										09 16				
Angel Road	d							08 17			08 34										09 18				
Ponders End	d			07 59						08 29						08 59						09 29			
Brimsdown	d			08 02						08 32						09 02						09 32			
Enfield Lock	d			08 04				08 22		08 34	08 39					09 04					09 23	09 34			
Waltham Cross	d			08 07						08 37						09 07						09 37			
Cheshunt	d			08 09		08 18		08 26		08 39	08 42		08 48			09 09		09 18			09 27	09 39		09 48	
Broxbourne 3	a			08 14		08 22		08 30		08 44	08 47		08 52			09 14		09 22			09 31	09 44		09 52	
	d			08 14		08 22		08 34		08 44			08 52			09 14		09 22			09 35	09 44		09 52	
Rye House	d			08 17						08 47						09 17						09 47			
St Margarets (Herts)	d			08 20						08 50						09 20						09 50			
Ware	d			08 24						08 54						09 24						09 54			
Hertford East	a			08 31						09 01						09 31						10 01			
Roydon	d					08 26												09 26							
Harlow Town	d				08 24	08 30		08 40				08 54	08 58				09 24	09 30			09 41		09 54	09 58	
Harlow Mill	d					08 33												09 33							
Sawbridgeworth	d					08 37							09 03					09 37						10 03	
Bishops Stortford	a		08 18			08 44	08 47	08 52					09 10		09 16			09 44		09 47	09 52			10 10	
	d		08 18			08 44	08 48						09 11		09 18			09 44		09 48				10 11	
Stansted Mountfitchet	d		08 23			08 48									09 23			09 48							
Stansted Airport ✈	a		08 29		08 42		09 00					09 12			09 29		09 42			09 57			10 12		
✈	d	08 20												09 20											10 20
Elsenham	d					08 52												09 52							
Newport (Essex)	d					08 57												09 57							
Audley End	d	08 36				09 00							09 23	09 38				10 00						10 23	10 38
Great Chesterford	d					09 05												10 05							
Whittlesford Parkway	d					09 10							09 30					10 10						10 30	
Shelford	d					09 14												10 14							
Cambridge	a	08 57				09 24							09 42	09 57				10 21						10 41	10 57

		LE 1 🛒	LE 1	LE 1	LE 1 🛒	LE 1		LE 1 🛒	LE 1	LE 1	LE 1 🛒	LE 1	XC ◇ 🛒	LE 1 🛒	LE 1	LE 1		LE 1 🛒	LE 1	LE 1 🛒	LE 1	LE 1 🛒	LE 1	XC ◇ 🛒	LE 1 🛒
London Liverpool Street 15 ⊖	d	09 40		09 42	09 55	09 58		10 10		10 12	10 25	10 28		10 40		10 42		10 55	10 58	11 10	11 12	11 25	11 28		11 40
Bethnal Green	d																								
Hackney Downs	d			09 48						10 18						10 48					11 18				
Stratford 7 ⊖ ⛴	d		09 25						09 55						10 33										
Clapton	d																								
Seven Sisters ⊖	d																								
Tottenham Hale ⊖	d	09u52	09 44	09 55	10u07	10 10		10u22	10 13	10 25	10u37	10 40		10u52	10 43	10 55		11u07	11 10	11u22	11 25	11u37	11 40		11u52
Northumberland Park	d		09 46						10 15						10 45										
Angel Road	d		09 48																						
Ponders End	d			09 59						10 29						10 59					11 29				
Brimsdown	d			10 02						10 32						11 02					11 32				
Enfield Lock	d		09 53	10 04					10 21	10 34					10 51	11 04					11 34				
Waltham Cross	d			10 07						10 37						11 07					11 37				
Cheshunt	d		09 57	10 09		10 18			10 25	10 39		10 48			10 55	11 09			11 18		11 39		11 48		
Broxbourne 3	a		10 01	10 14		10 22			10 29	10 44		10 52			10 59	11 14			11 22		11 44		11 52		
	d		10 05	10 14		10 22			10 33	10 44		10 52			11 03	11 14			11 22		11 44		11 52		
Rye House	d			10 17						10 47						11 17					11 47				
St Margarets (Herts)	d			10 20						10 50						11 20					11 50				
Ware	d			10 24						10 54						11 24					11 54				
Hertford East	a			10 31						11 01						11 31					12 01				
Roydon	d		10 09			10 26									11 08				11 26						
Harlow Town	d		10 13		10 24	10 30			10 40		10 54	10 58			11 12			11 24	11 30			11 54	11 58		
Harlow Mill	d		10 16			10 33									11 15				11 33						
Sawbridgeworth	d		10 20			10 37						11 03			11 18				11 37				12 03		
Bishops Stortford	a	10 15	10 27			10 44		10 47	10 51			11 10		11 15	11 25				11 44	11 47			12 10		12 15
	d	10 15	10 27			10 44		10 48				11 11		11 15	11 26				11 44	11 48			12 11		12 15
Stansted Mountfitchet	d		10 31			10 48									11 30				11 48						
Stansted Airport ✈	a	10 29	10 39		10 42			10 57			11 12			11 25	11 39			11 42		11 57		12 12			12 25
✈	d												11 25											12 25	
Elsenham	d					10 52													11 52						
Newport (Essex)	d					10 57													11 57						
Audley End	d					11 00						11 23	11 38						12 00				12 23	12 38	
Great Chesterford	d					11 05													12 05						
Whittlesford Parkway	d					11 10						11 30							12 10				12 30		
Shelford	d					11 14													12 14						
Cambridge	a					11 21						11 40	11 57						12 21				12 40	12 57	

For general notes see front of timetable
For details of catering facilities see
Directory of Train Operators

London → Broxbourne, Hertford East, Bishops Stortford, Stansted Airport and Cambridge

Network diagram - see first page of Table 20

		LE 1	LE 1	LE 1 ⚲		LE 1	LE 1 ⚲	LE 1	LE 1 ⚲	LE 1	XC ◇ ⚲	LE 1 ⚲	LE 1	LE 1		LE 1 ⚲	LE 1	LE 1 ⚲	LE 1	LE 1 ⚲	LE 1	LE 1 ⚲	XC ◇ ⚲	LE 1	LE 1
London Liverpool Street 15 ⊖	d		11 42	11 55		11 58	12 10	12 12	12 25	12 28		12 40		12 42		12 55	12 58	13 10	13 12	13 25	13 28	13 40			13 42
Bethnal Green	d																								
Hackney Downs	d		11 48					12 18						12 48					13 18						13 48
Stratford 7 ⊖	d	11 33											12 33											13 33	
Clapton	d																								
Seven Sisters ⊖	d																								
Tottenham Hale ⊖	d	11 43	11 55	12u07		12 10	12u22	12 25	12u37	12 40		12u52	12 43	12 55		13u07	13 10	13u22	13 25	13u37	13 40	13u52		13 43	13 55
Northumberland Park	d	11 45											12 45											13 45	
Angel Road	d																								
Ponders End	d		11 59					12 29						12 59					13 29						13 59
Brimsdown	d		12 02					12 32						13 02					13 32						14 02
Enfield Lock	d	11 51	12 04					12 34					12 51	13 04					13 34					13 51	14 04
Waltham Cross	d		12 07					12 37						13 07					13 37						14 07
Cheshunt	d	11 55	12 09			12 18		12 39		12 48			12 55	13 09			13 18		13 39		13 48			13 55	14 09
Broxbourne 3	a	11 59	12 14			12 22		12 44		12 52			12 59	13 14			13 22		13 44		13 52			13 59	14 14
	d	12 03	12 14			12 22		12 44		12 52			13 03	13 14			13 22		13 44		13 52			14 03	14 14
Rye House	d		12 17					12 47						13 17					13 47						14 17
St Margarets (Herts)	d		12 20					12 50						13 20					13 50						14 20
Ware	d		12 24					12 54						13 24					13 54						14 24
Hertford East	a		12 31					13 01						13 31					14 01						14 31
Roydon	d	12 08				12 26							13 08				13 26							14 08	
Harlow Town	d	12 12		12 24		12 30			12 54	12 58			13 12			13 24	13 30			13 54	13 58			14 12	
Harlow Mill	d	12 15				12 33							13 15				13 33							14 15	
Sawbridgeworth	d	12 18				12 37				13 03			13 18				13 37				14 03			14 18	
Bishops Stortford	a	12 25				12 44	12 47			13 10		13 15	13 25				13 44	13 47			14 10	14 15		14 25	
	d	12 26				12 44	12 48			13 11		13 15	13 26				13 44	13 48			14 11	14 15		14 26	
Stansted Mountfitchet	d	12 30				12 48							13 30				13 48							14 30	
Stansted Airport ✈	a	12 39		12 42			12 57		13 12			13 25	13 39			13 42		13 57		14 12		14 25		14 39	
	d										13 25												14 25		
Elsenham	d					12 52											13 52								
Newport (Essex)	d					12 57											13 57								
Audley End	d					13 00				13 23	13 38						14 00				14 23		14 38		
Great Chesterford	d					13 05											14 05								
Whittlesford Parkway	d					13 10				13 30							14 10				14 30				
Shelford	d					13 14											14 14								
Cambridge	a					13 21				13 40	13 57						14 21				14 40		14 57		

		LE 1 ⚲		LE 1	LE 1 ⚲	LE 1	LE 1 ⚲	LE 1	XC ◇ ⚲	LE 1 ⚲	LE 1	LE 1		LE 1 ⚲	LE 1	LE 1 ⚲	LE 1	LE 1 ⚲	LE 1	XC ◇ ⚲	LE 1 ⚲	LE 1		LE 1	LE 1 ⚲
London Liverpool Street 15 ⊖	d	13 55		13 58	14 10	14 12	14 25	14 28		14 40		14 42		14 55	14 58	15 10	15 12	15 25	15 28		15 40			15 42	15 55
Bethnal Green	d																								
Hackney Downs	d					14 18						14 48					15 18							15 48	
Stratford 7 ⊖	d										14 33											15 33			
Clapton	d																								
Seven Sisters ⊖	d																								
Tottenham Hale ⊖	d	14u07		14 10	14u22	14 25	14u37	14 40		14u52	14 43	14 55		15u07	15 10	15u22	15 25	15u37	15 40		15u52	15 43		15 55	16u07
Northumberland Park	d										14 45											15 45			
Angel Road	d																					15 47			
Ponders End	d					14 29						14 59					15 29							15 59	
Brimsdown	d					14 32						15 02					15 32							16 02	
Enfield Lock	d					14 34					14 51	15 04					15 34					15 52		16 04	
Waltham Cross	d					14 37						15 07					15 37							16 07	
Cheshunt	d			14 18		14 39		14 48			14 55	15 09			15 18		15 39		15 48			15 56		16 09	
Broxbourne 3	a			14 22		14 44		14 52			14 59	15 14			15 22		15 44		15 52			16 00		16 14	
	d			14 22		14 44		14 52			15 03	15 14			15 22		15 44		15 52			16 04		16 14	
Rye House	d					14 47						15 17					15 47							16 17	
St Margarets (Herts)	d					14 50						15 20					15 50							16 20	
Ware	d					14 54						15 24					15 54							16 24	
Hertford East	a					15 01						15 31					16 01							16 31	
Roydon	d			14 26							15 08				15 26							16 08			
Harlow Town	d	14 24		14 30			14 54	14 58			15 12			15 24	15 30			15 54	15 58			16 12			16 24
Harlow Mill	d			14 33							15 15				15 33							16 15			
Sawbridgeworth	d			14 37				15 03			15 18				15 37				16 03			16 19			
Bishops Stortford	a			14 44	14 47			15 10		15 15	15 25				15 44	15 47			16 10		16 15	16 26			
	d			14 44	14 48			15 11		15 15	15 26				15 44	15 48			16 11		16 15	16 26			
Stansted Mountfitchet	d			14 48							15 30				15 48				16 15			16 30			
Stansted Airport ✈	a	14 42			14 57		15 12			15 25	15 39			15 42		15 59		16 12			16 25	16 39			16 42
	d								15 25											16 20					
Elsenham	d			14 52											15 52				16 19						
Newport (Essex)	d			14 57											15 58				16 24						
Audley End	d			15 00				15 23	15 38						16 02				16 27	16 33					
Great Chesterford	d			15 05											16 07				16 32						
Whittlesford Parkway	d			15 10				15 30							16 12				16 37						
Shelford	d			15 14											16 16				16 41						
Cambridge	a			15 21				15 40	15 57						16 28				16 49	16 58					

For general notes see front of timetable
For details of catering facilities see
Directory of Train Operators

London → Broxbourne, Hertford East, Bishops Stortford, Stansted Airport and Cambridge

Network diagram - see first page of Table 20

	LE	LE	LE	LE	LE	LE	XC	LE	LE	LE	LE	LE	LE	LE	LE	LE	LE	LE	LE	XC	LE	LE
	1 A	1 ⚲		1 ⚲	1		◇ ⚲	1 ⚲	1		1 ⚲	1 B		1 ⚲	1		1 ⚲	1		◇ ⚲	1 ⚲	1
London Liverpool Street 15 ⊖ d	15 58	16 10	16 12	16 25	16 28			16 40	16 43	16 45	16 55	16 58		17 10	17 13	17 15	17 25	17 28			17 40	17 43
Bethnal Green d																						
Hackney Downs d			16 18							16 51						17 21						
Stratford 7 ⊖ d						16 32							17 02						17 32			
Clapton d																						
Seven Sisters ⊖ d																						
Tottenham Hale ⊖ d	16 10	16u22	16 25	16u37	16 40	16 43		16u52	16 55	16 58	17u07	17 10	17 13	17u22	17 25	17 28	17u37	17 40	17 43		17u52	17 55
Northumberland Park d						16 45							17 15						17 45			
Angel Road d						16 47							17 17						17 47			
Ponders End d			16 29							17 02						17 32						
Brimsdown d			16 32							17 05						17 35						
Enfield Lock d			16 34			16 52				17 07			17 22			17 37			17 52			
Waltham Cross d			16 37			16 55				17 10			17 25			17 40			17 55			
Cheshunt d	16 18		16 39			16 57			17 04	17 12			17 27		17 34	17 42			17 57			18 04
Broxbourne 3 a	16 22		16 44		16 51	17 04			17 08	17 17		17 24	17 32		17 39	17 47		17 54	18 04			18 08
d	16 22		16 44		16 52				17 09	17 17		17 25	17 35		17 39	17 50		17 54				18 09
Rye House d			16 48							17 21			17 39			17 54						
St Margarets (Herts) d			16 51							17 24			17 42			17 57						
Ware d			16 55							17 28			17 48			18 01						
Hertford East a			17 03							17 36			17 56			18 09						
Roydon d	16 26								17 13						17 43							18 13
Harlow Town d	16 30			16 54	16 59				17 18		17 27	17 32			17 48		17 54				18 10	18 18
Harlow Mill d	16 33								17 21						17 51							18 21
Sawbridgeworth d	16 37				17 04				17 24						17 54			18 04				18 24
Bishops Stortford a	16 44	16 47			17 11			17 17	17 31			17 42		17 47	18 01		18 05	18 11			18 20	18 31
d	16 44	16 48			17 11			17 18	17 32			17 42		17 48	18 02		18 06	18 11			18 20	18 32
Stansted Mountfitchet d	16 48				17 15				17 36					17 52	18 06							18 36
Stansted Airport ✈ a		17 01		17 14				17 32			17 47			18 01			18 17				18 32	
✈ d							17 17													18 20		
Elsenham d	16 52								17 40						18 10							18 40
Newport (Essex) d	16 57								17 45						18 15							18 45
Audley End d	17 00				17 25		17 32		17 49			17 55			18 19			18 24		18 32		18 49
Great Chesterford d	17 05								17 54						18 24							18 54
Whittlesford Parkway d	17 10				17 33				17 58			18 03			18 28			18 32				18 58
Shelford d	17 14								18 03						18 33							19 03
Cambridge a	17 21				17 44		17 48		18 12			18 13			18 42			18 45		18 48		19 15

	LE	LE	LE	LE	LE	LE	LE	LE	LE	XC	LE	LE	LE	LE	LE	LE	LE	LE	LE	LE	LE	XC
		1 ⚲	1 B		1 ⚲	1		1 ⚲	1	◇ ⚲	1 ⚲		1		1 ⚲	1 B	1 ⚲		1	1	1 ⚲	◇ ⚲
London Liverpool Street 15 ⊖ d	17 45	17 55	17 58		18 10	18 13	18 15	18 25	18 28		18 40		18 43	18 45	18 55	18 58	19 10		19 13	19 15	19 25	
Bethnal Green d																						
Hackney Downs d	17 51						18 21							18 51						19 21		
Stratford 7 ⊖ d				18 02								18 32						19 02				
Clapton d																						
Seven Sisters ⊖ d																						
Tottenham Hale ⊖ d	17 58	18u07	18 10	18 13	18u22	18 25	18 28	18u37	18 40		18u52	18 43	18 55	18 58	19u07	19 10	19u22	19 13	19 25	19 28	19u37	
Northumberland Park d				18 15								18 45						19 15				
Angel Road d				18 17								18 47						19 17				
Ponders End d	18 02						18 32							19 02						19 32		
Brimsdown d	18 05						18 35							19 05						19 35		
Enfield Lock d	18 07			18 22			18 37					18 52		19 07				19 22		19 37		
Waltham Cross d	18 10			18 25			18 40					18 55		19 10				19 25		19 40		
Cheshunt d	18 12			18 27		18 34	18 42					18 57	19 04	19 12				19 27	19 34	19 42		
Broxbourne 3 a	18 17		18 24	18 32		18 39	18 47		18 54			19 02	19 09	19 17		19 24		19 32	19 39	19 47		
d	18 17		18 25	18 35		18 39	18 47		18 55			19 05	19 09	19 17		19 25		19 35	19 39	19 47		
Rye House d	18 21			18 39			18 51							19 21						19 50		
St Margarets (Herts) d	18 24			18 42			18 54							19 24						19 53		
Ware d	18 28			18 48			18 58							19 28						19 57		
Hertford East a	18 36			18 56			19 06							19 36						20 04		
Roydon d						18 43						19 10	19 13						19 43			
Harlow Town d		18 27				18 48		18 57	19 02			19 14	19 18		19 27	19 32		19 42	19 48		19 57	
Harlow Mill d						18 51						19 17	19 21						19 51			
Sawbridgeworth d			18 35			18 54			19 07			19 20	19 24					19 47	19 54			
Bishops Stortford a		18 36	18 42		18 47	19 01			19 14		19 18	19 27	19 31			19 42	19 47	19 56	20 01			
d		18 36	18 42		18 48	19 02			19 14		19 18	19 28	19 32			19 42	19 47		20 02			
Stansted Mountfitchet d					18 52	19 06						19 32	19 36						20 06			
Stansted Airport ✈ a		18 56			19 01			19 17			19 32	19 41			19 47		19 59				20 15	
✈ d										19 18												20 20
Elsenham d						19 10							19 40						20 10			
Newport (Essex) d						19 15							19 45						20 15			
Audley End d			18 55			19 19			19 27	19 32			19 49			19 55			20 19			20 32
Great Chesterford d						19 24							19 54						20 24			
Whittlesford Parkway d			19 03			19 28			19 35				19 58			20 03			20 28			
Shelford d						19 33							20 03						20 33			
Cambridge a			19 16			19 44			19 51	19 49			20 13			20 14			20 40			20 50

For general notes see front of timetable
For details of catering facilities see Directory of Train Operators

A To Ely (Table 17)
B To Kings Lynn (Table 17)

London → Broxbourne, Hertford East, Bishops Stortford, Stansted Airport and Cambridge

Network diagram - see first page of Table 20

		LE	LE	LE	LE	LE		LE	LE	LE	LE	LE	LE	LE	LE	LE		LE	LE	LE	LE	LE	LE	LE	LE
		1	1	1	1	1		1	1	1	1	1	1	1	1	1		1	1	1	1	1	1	1	1
			🛒			🛒			🛒		🛒		🛒			🛒			🛒		🛒		🛒		
London Liverpool Street 15	⊖ d	19 28	19 40		19 42	19 55		19 58	20 10	20 12	20 25	20 28	20 40		20 42	20 55		20 58	21 10	21 12	21 25	21 28	21 40		21 42
Bethnal Green	d																								
Hackney Downs	d				19 48					20 18					20 48					21 18					21 48
Stratford 7	⊖ ⛴ d			19 33										20 33										21 33	
Clapton	d																								
Seven Sisters	⊖ d																								
Tottenham Hale	⊖ d	19 40	19u52	19 43	19 55	20u07		20 10	20u22	20 25	20u37	20 40	20u52	20 43	20 55	21u07		21 10	21u22	21 25	21u37	21 40	21u52	21 43	21 55
Northumberland Park	d			19 45										20 45										21 45	
Angel Road	d																								
Ponders End	d				19 59					20 29					20 59					21 29					21 59
Brimsdown	d				20 02					20 32					21 02					21 32					22 02
Enfield Lock	d			19 51	20 04					20 34				20 51	21 04					21 34				21 51	22 04
Waltham Cross	d				20 07					20 37					21 07					21 37					22 07
Cheshunt	d	19 49		19 55	20 09			20 18		20 39		20 48		20 55	21 09			21 18		21 39		21 48		21 55	22 09
Broxbourne 3	a	19 54		19 59	20 14			20 22		20 44		20 52		20 59	21 14			21 22		21 44		21 52		21 59	22 14
	d	19 54		20 03	20 14			20 22		20 44		20 52		21 03	21 14			21 22		21 44		21 52		22 03	22 14
Rye House	d				20 17					20 47					21 17					21 47					22 17
St Margarets (Herts)	d				20 20					20 50					21 20					21 50					22 20
Ware	d				20 24					20 54					21 24					21 54					22 24
Hertford East	a				20 31					21 01					21 31					22 01					22 31
Roydon	d	19 59		20 08				20 26						21 08				21 26						22 08	
Harlow Town	d	20 03		20 12		20 24		20 30			20 54	20 58		21 12		21 24		21 30			21 54	21 58		22 12	
Harlow Mill	d	20 06		20 15				20 33						21 15				21 33						22 15	
Sawbridgeworth	d	20 09		20 18				20 37				21 03		21 18				21 37				22 03		22 18	
Bishops Stortford	a	20 16	20 20	20 25				20 44	20 48			21 10	21 15	21 25				21 44	21 47			22 10	22 15	22 25	
	d	20 17	20 21	20 26				20 44	20 48			21 11	21 15	21 26				21 44	21 48			22 11	22 15	22 26	
Stansted Mountfitchet	d	20 21		20 30				20 48			21 05			21 30				21 48			22 05			22 30	
Stansted Airport	✈ a		20 30	20 39		20 42			20 58		21 13		21 25	21 39		21 42			21 57		22 13		22 25	22 39	
	✈ d																								
Elsenham	d	20 29						20 52										21 52							
Newport (Essex)	d	20 34						20 57										21 57							
Audley End	d	20 37						21 00				21 23						22 00				22 23			
Great Chesterford	d	20 42						21 05										22 05							
Whittlesford Parkway	d	20 47						21 10				21 30						22 10				22 30			
Shelford	d	20 51						21 14										22 14							
Cambridge	a	20 58						21 22				21 40						22 21				22 40			

		LE	LE	LE		LE	LE	LE	LE	LE	LE	LE	LE	LE		LE	LE	LE	LE	LE	LE	LE			
																				FX	FO				
		1	1	1		1	1	1	1	1	1	1	1	1		1	1	1		1	1				
		🛒																							
London Liverpool Street 15	⊖ d	21 55	21 58	22 10		22 12	22 25	22 28	22 40		22 42	22 55	22 58	23 12		23 25	23 28	23 40	23 45	23 58	23 58	←			
Bethnal Green	d																		23 48						
Hackney Downs	d					22 18					22 48			23 18				23 46	23 54 →			23 54			
Stratford 7	⊖ ⛴ d									22 33															
Clapton	d																	23 49							
Seven Sisters	⊖ d																					00 02			
Tottenham Hale	⊖ d	22u07	22 10	22u22		22 25	22u37	22 40	22u52	22 43	22 55	23u07	23 10	23 25		23u37	23 40	23 53		00 10	00 10				
Northumberland Park	d									22 45								23 55							
Angel Road	d																								
Ponders End	d					22 29					22 59			23 29				23 59							
Brimsdown	d					22 32					23 02			23 32				00 02							
Enfield Lock	d					22 34				22 51	23 04			23 34				00 04							
Waltham Cross	d					22 37					23 07			23 37				00 07							
Cheshunt	d		22 18			22 39		22 48		22 55	23 09		23 18	23 39			23 48	00 09		00 18	00 18	00 22			
Broxbourne 3	a		22 22			22 44		22 52		22 59	23 14		23 22	23 44			23 52	00 14		00 22	00 22	00 27			
	d		22 22			22 44		22 52		23 03	23 14		23 22	23 44			23 52	00 14		00 22	00 22	00 27			
Rye House	d					22 47					23 17			23 47				00 17							
St Margarets (Herts)	d					22 50					23 20			23 50				00 20							
Ware	d					22 54					23 24			23 54				00 24							
Hertford East	a					23 01					23 31			00 01				00 31							
Roydon	d		22 26							23 08			23 26							00 26	00 26				
Harlow Town	d	22 24	22 30				22 54	22 58		23 12		23 24	23 30			23 54	23 58			00 30	00 30	00 34			
Harlow Mill	d		22 33							23 15			23 33							00 33	00 33				
Sawbridgeworth	d		22 37					23 03		23 18			23 37				00 03			00 37	00 37				
Bishops Stortford	a		22 44	22 47				23 10	23 15	23 26			23 44			00 04	00 10			00 44	00 44	00 47			
	d		22 44	22 48				23 11	23 15				23 44			00 04	00 11				00 44				
Stansted Mountfitchet	d		22 48				23 05					23 35	23 48				00 15				00 48				
Stansted Airport	✈ a	22 42		22 57			23 13		23 25			23 43				00 13									
	✈ d																								
Elsenham	d		22 52										23 52				00 19				00 52				
Newport (Essex)	d		22 57										23 57				00 24				00 57				
Audley End	d		23 00					23 23					23 59				00 27				01 00				
Great Chesterford	d		23 05										00 05				00 32				01 05				
Whittlesford Parkway	d		23 10					23 30					00 10				00 37				01 10				
Shelford	d		23 14										00 14				00 41								
Cambridge	a		23 22					23 40					00 21				00 48				01 19				

For general notes see front of timetable
For details of catering facilities see
Directory of Train Operators

Table 22

Saturdays

London → Broxbourne, Hertford East, Bishops Stortford, Stansted Airport and Cambridge

Network diagram - see first page of Table 20

Station		LE 1	LE 1	LE 1	LE 1	LE	LE 1	LE	LE 1		XC ◇	LE 1	LE 1	LE 1	LE 1	LE 1	LE A	LE 1		LE 1	LE 1	LE 1	LE 1	LE 1	LE 1
London Liverpool Street 15	⊖ d	22p58	23p25	23p28	23p40	23p45	23p58		04 10			04 40		05 10	05 23	05 25	05 28	05 40			05 42	05 55	05 58	06 10	06 12
Bethnal Green	d					23p48		←																	
Hackney Downs	d				23p46	23p54		23p54												←	05 48				06 18
Stratford 7	⊖ d					→									05 33 →		05 37			05 33					
Clapton	d				23p49																				
Seven Sisters	⊖ d							00 02									05a50								
Tottenham Hale	⊖ d	23p10	23b37	23p40	23p53		00 10					04u52		05u22		05u37		05u52		05 43	05 55	06u07	06 10	06u22	06 25
Northumberland Park	d				23p55															05 45					
Angel Road	d																								
Ponders End	d				23p59																05 59				06 29
Brimsdown	d				00 02																06 02				06 32
Enfield Lock	d				00 04															05 51	06 04				06 34
Waltham Cross	d				00 07																06 07				06 37
Cheshunt	d	23p18		23p48	00 09		00 18	00 22												05 55	06 09		06 18		06 39
Broxbourne 3	a	23p22		23p52	00 14		00 22	00 27												05 59	06 14		06 22		06 44
	d	23p22		23p52	00 14		00 22	00 27												06 03	06 14		06 22		06 44
Rye House	d				00 17																06 17				06 47
St Margarets (Herts)	d				00 20																06 20				06 50
Ware	d				00 24																06 24				06 54
Hertford East	a				00 31																06 31				07 01
Roydon	d	23p26					00 26													06 08			06 26		
Harlow Town	d	23p30	23p54	23p58			00 30	00 34				05 10		05 37		05 55				06 12		06 24	06 30		
Harlow Mill	d	23p33					00 33													06 15			06 33		
Sawbridgeworth	d	23p37		00 03			00 37							05 42						06 18			06 37		
Bishops Stortford	a	23p44	00 04	00 10			00 44	00 47				05 20		05 49		06 05		06 15		06 25			06 44	06 47	
	d	23p44	00 04	00 11			00 44					05 20	05 42	05 50		06 06		06 15		06 26			06 44	06 48	
Stansted Mountfitchet	d	23p48		00 15			00 48					05 25	05 46							06 30			06 48		
Stansted Airport	✈ a		00 13						05 00			05 39	05 53	05 59		06 15		06 25		06 39		06 42		06 57	
	✈ d										05 21														
Elsenham	d	23p52		00 19			00 52																06 52		
Newport (Essex)	d	23p57		00 24			00 57																06 57		
Audley End	d	23p59		00 27			01 00				05 33												07 00		
Great Chesterford	d	00 05		00 32			01 05																07 05		
Whittlesford Parkway	d	00 10		00 37			01 10																07 10		
Shelford	d	00 14		00 41																			07 14		
Cambridge	a	00 21		00 48			01 19				05 50												07 21		

Station		LE 1	LE 1	LE 1	LE 1		XC ◇	LE 1	LE 1	LE 1	LE 1 B	LE 1 ⊥	LE 1	LE 1 ⊥		LE 1	XC ◇	LE 1 ⊥	LE 1	LE 1	LE 1 ⊥	LE 1	LE 1 ⊥		LE 1
London Liverpool Street 15	⊖ d	06 23	06 25	06 28	06 40				06 42	06 55	06 58	07 10	07 12	07 25		07 28		07 40		07 42	07 55	07 58	08 10		08 12
Bethnal Green	d																								
Hackney Downs	d							←	06 48				07 18							07 48					08 18
Stratford 7	⊖ d	06 33 →						06 33											07 33						
Clapton	d																								
Seven Sisters	⊖ d																								
Tottenham Hale	⊖ d		06u37	06 40	06u52			06 43	06 55	07u07	07 10	07u22	07 25	07u37		07 40		07u52	07 43	07 55	08u07	08 10	08u22		08 25
Northumberland Park	d							06 45											07 45						
Angel Road	d																								
Ponders End	d								06 59				07 29							07 59					08 29
Brimsdown	d								07 02				07 32							08 02					08 32
Enfield Lock	d							06 51	07 04				07 34						07 51	08 04					08 34
Waltham Cross	d								07 07				07 37							08 07					08 37
Cheshunt	d			06 48				06 55	07 09		07 18		07 39			07 48			07 55	08 09		08 18			08 39
Broxbourne 3	a			06 52				06 59	07 14		07 22		07 44			07 52			07 59	08 14		08 22			08 44
	d			06 52				07 03	07 14		07 22		07 44			07 52			08 03	08 14		08 22			08 44
Rye House	d								07 17				07 47							08 17					08 47
St Margarets (Herts)	d								07 20				07 50							08 20					08 50
Ware	d								07 24				07 54							08 24					08 54
Hertford East	a								07 31				08 01							08 31					09 01
Roydon	d							07 08			07 26								08 08			08 26			
Harlow Town	d		06 54	06 58				07 12		07 24	07 30			07 54		07 58			08 12		08 24	08 30			
Harlow Mill	d							07 15			07 33								08 15			08 33			
Sawbridgeworth	d			07 03				07 18			07 37					08 03			08 18			08 37			
Bishops Stortford	a			07 10	07 15			07 25			07 44	07 47				08 10		08 15	08 25			08 44	08 47		
	d			07 11	07 15			07 26			07 44	07 48				08 11		08 15	08 26			08 44	08 48		
Stansted Mountfitchet	d		07 05					07 30			07 48			08 05					08 30			08 48			
Stansted Airport	✈ a		07 13		07 25			07 39		07 42		07 57		08 13				08 25	08 39		08 42		08 57		
	✈ d						07 27										08 25								
Elsenham	d										07 52											08 52			
Newport (Essex)	d										07 57											08 57			
Audley End	d			07 23			07 40				08 00					08 23	08 38					09 00			
Great Chesterford	d										08 05											09 05			
Whittlesford Parkway	d			07 30							08 10					08 30						09 10			
Shelford	d			07 35												08 35									
Cambridge	a			07 42			07 55				08 19					08 42	08 57					09 19			

For general notes see front of timetable
For details of catering facilities see Directory of Train Operators

A To Enfield Town (Table 21)
B To Ely (Table 17)

b Previous night.
Stops to pick up only

London → Broxbourne, Hertford East, Bishops Stortford, Stansted Airport and Cambridge

Network diagram - see first page of Table 20

		LE 1 🛒	LE 1	XC ◇	LE 1 🛒	LE 1	LE 1	LE 1 🛒	LE 1		LE 1 🛒	LE 1	LE 1 🛒	LE 1	XC ◇	LE 1 🛒	LE 1	LE 1		LE 1 🛒	LE 1	LE 1 🛒	LE 1	LE 1 🛒	LE 1
London Liverpool Street 15	⊖ d	08 25	08 28		08 40		08 42	08 55	08 58		09 10	09 12	09 25	09 28		09 40		09 42		09 55	09 58	10 10	10 12	10 25	10 28
Bethnal Green	d																								
Hackney Downs	d						08 48					09 18						09 48					10 18		
Stratford 7	⊖ d					08 33											09 33								
Clapton	d																								
Seven Sisters	⊖ d																								
Tottenham Hale	⊖ d	08u37	08 40		08u52	08 43	08 55	09u07	09 10		09u22	09 25	09u37	09 40		09u52	09 43	09 55		10u07	10 10	10u22	10 25	10u37	10 40
Northumberland Park	d					08 45											09 45								
Angel Road	d																								
Ponders End	d						08 59					09 29						09 59					10 29		
Brimsdown	d						09 02					09 32						10 02					10 32		
Enfield Lock	d					08 51	09 04					09 34					09 51	10 04					10 34		
Waltham Cross	d						09 07					09 37						10 07					10 37		
Cheshunt	d		08 48			08 55	09 09		09 18			09 39		09 48			09 55	10 09			10 18		10 39		10 48
Broxbourne 3	a		08 52			08 59	09 14		09 22			09 44		09 52			09 59	10 14			10 22		10 44		10 52
	d		08 52			09 03	09 14		09 22			09 44		09 52			10 03	10 14			10 22		10 44		10 52
Rye House	d						09 17					09 47						10 17					10 47		
St Margarets (Herts)	d						09 20					09 50						10 20					10 50		
Ware	d						09 24					09 54						10 24					10 54		
Hertford East	a						09 31					10 01						10 31					11 01		
Roydon	d					09 08			09 26								10 08				10 26				
Harlow Town	d	08 54	08 58			09 12		09 24	09 30				09 54	09 58			10 12			10 24	10 30			10 54	10 58
Harlow Mill	d					09 15			09 33								10 15				10 33				
Sawbridgeworth	d		09 03			09 18			09 37					10 03			10 18				10 37				11 03
Bishops Stortford	a		09 10		09 15	09 25			09 44		09 47			10 10		10 15	10 25				10 44	10 47			11 10
	d		09 11		09 15	09 26			09 44		09 48			10 11		10 15	10 26				10 44	10 48			11 11
Stansted Mountfitchet	d	09 05				09 30			09 48				10 05				10 30				10 48			11 05	
Stansted Airport	✈ a	09 13			09 25	09 39		09 42			09 57		10 13			10 25	10 39			10 42		10 57		11 13	
	✈ d			09 25											10 25										
Elsenham	d								09 52												10 52				
Newport (Essex)	d								09 57												10 57				
Audley End	d		09 23	09 38					10 00					10 23	10 38						11 00				11 23
Great Chesterford	d								10 05												11 05				
Whittlesford Parkway	d		09 30						10 10					10 30							11 10				11 30
Shelford	d		09 35						10 14												11 14				
Cambridge	a		09 42	09 57					10 21					10 40	10 57						11 21				11 40

		XC ◇	LE 1 🛒	LE 1	LE 1		LE 1 🛒	LE 1	LE 1 🛒	LE 1	LE 1 🛒	LE 1	XC ◇	LE 1 🛒		LE 1	LE 1	LE 1 🛒	LE 1	LE 1 🛒	LE 1	LE 1 🛒	LE 1		XC ◇
London Liverpool Street 15	⊖ d		10 40		10 42		10 55	10 58	11 10	11 12	11 25	11 28		11 40			11 42	11 55	11 58	12 10	12 12	12 25	12 28		
Bethnal Green	d																								
Hackney Downs	d				10 48					11 18							11 48				12 18				
Stratford 7	⊖ d			10 33												11 33									
Clapton	d																								
Seven Sisters	⊖ d																								
Tottenham Hale	⊖ d		10u52	10 43	10 55		11u07	11 10	11u22	11 25	11u37	11 40		11u52		11 43	11 55	12u07	12 10	12u22	12 25	12u37	12 40		
Northumberland Park	d			10 45												11 45									
Angel Road	d																								
Ponders End	d				10 59					11 29							11 59				12 29				
Brimsdown	d				11 02					11 32							12 02				12 32				
Enfield Lock	d			10 51	11 04					11 34						11 51	12 04				12 34				
Waltham Cross	d				11 07					11 37							12 07				12 37				
Cheshunt	d			10 55	11 09			11 18		11 39		11 48				11 55	12 09		12 18		12 39		12 48		
Broxbourne 3	a			10 59	11 14			11 22		11 44		11 52				11 59	12 14		12 22		12 44		12 52		
	d			11 03	11 14			11 22		11 44		11 52				12 03	12 14		12 22		12 44		12 52		
Rye House	d				11 17					11 47							12 17				12 47				
St Margarets (Herts)	d				11 20					11 50							12 20				12 50				
Ware	d				11 24					11 54							12 24				12 54				
Hertford East	a				11 31					12 01							12 31				13 01				
Roydon	d			11 08				11 26								12 08			12 26						
Harlow Town	d			11 12			11 24	11 30			11 54	11 58				12 12		12 24	12 30			12 54	12 58		
Harlow Mill	d			11 15				11 33								12 15			12 33						
Sawbridgeworth	d			11 18				11 37				12 03				12 18			12 37				13 03		
Bishops Stortford	a		11 15	11 25				11 44	11 47			12 10		12 15		12 25			12 44	12 47			13 10		
	d		11 15	11 26				11 44	11 48			12 11		12 15		12 26			12 44	12 48			13 11		
Stansted Mountfitchet	d			11 30				11 48			12 05					12 30			12 48			13 05			
Stansted Airport	✈ a		11 25	11 39			11 42		11 57		12 13			12 25		12 39		12 42		12 57		13 13			
	✈ d	11 25											12 25												13 25
Elsenham	d							11 52											12 52						
Newport (Essex)	d							11 57											12 57						
Audley End	d	11 38						12 00				12 23	12 38						13 00				13 23		13 38
Great Chesterford	d							12 05											13 05						
Whittlesford Parkway	d							12 10				12 30							13 10				13 30		
Shelford	d							12 14											13 14						
Cambridge	a	11 57						12 21				12 40	12 57						13 21				13 40		13 57

For general notes see front of timetable
For details of catering facilities see Directory of Train Operators

Table 22

Saturdays

London → Broxbourne, Hertford East, Bishops Stortford, Stansted Airport and Cambridge

Network diagram - see first page of Table 20

		LE [1] 🛒	LE [1]	LE [1]	LE [1] 🛒	LE [1]	LE [1] 🛒	LE [1]	LE [1] 🛒		LE [1]	XC ◇	LE [1] 🛒	LE [1]	LE [1]	LE [1] 🛒	LE [1]	LE [1] 🛒		LE [1]	LE [1] 🛒	LE [1]	XC ◇	LE [1] 🛒	LE [1]
London Liverpool Street [15] ⊖	d	12 40		12 42	12 55	12 58	13 10	13 12	13 25		13 28		13 40		13 42	13 55	13 58	14 10		14 12	14 25	14 28		14 40	
Bethnal Green	d																								
Hackney Downs	d			12 48				13 18							13 48					14 18					
Stratford [7] ⊖	d		12 33											13 33											14 33
Clapton	d																								
Seven Sisters ⊖	d																								
Tottenham Hale ⊖	d	12u52	12 43	12 55	13u07	13 10	13u22	13 25	13u37		13 40		13u52	13 43	13 55	14u07	14 10	14u22		14 25	14u37	14 40		14u52	14 43
Northumberland Park	d		12 45											13 45											14 45
Angel Road	d																								
Ponders End	d			12 59				13 29							13 59					14 29					
Brimsdown	d			13 02				13 32							14 02					14 32					
Enfield Lock	d		12 51	13 04				13 34						13 51	14 04					14 34					14 51
Waltham Cross	d			13 07				13 37							14 07					14 37					
Cheshunt	d		12 55	13 09		13 18		13 39			13 48			13 55	14 09		14 18			14 39		14 48			14 55
Broxbourne [3]	a		12 59	13 14		13 22		13 44			13 52			13 59	14 14		14 22			14 44		14 52			14 59
	d		13 03	13 14		13 22		13 44			13 52			14 03	14 14		14 22			14 44		14 52			15 03
Rye House	d			13 17				13 47							14 17					14 47					
St Margarets (Herts)	d			13 20				13 50							14 20					14 50					
Ware	d			13 24				13 54							14 24					14 54					
Hertford East	a			13 31				14 01							14 31					15 01					
Roydon	d		13 08			13 26								14 08			14 26								15 08
Harlow Town	d		13 12		13 24	13 30			13 54		13 58			14 12		14 24	14 30				14 54	14 58			15 12
Harlow Mill	d		13 15			13 33								14 15			14 33								15 15
Sawbridgeworth	d		13 18			13 37					14 03			14 18			14 37					15 03			15 18
Bishops Stortford	a	13 15	13 25			13 44	13 47				14 10		14 15	14 25			14 44	14 47				15 10		15 15	15 25
	d	13 15	13 26			13 44	13 48				14 11		14 15	14 26			14 44	14 48				15 11		15 15	15 26
Stansted Mountfitchet	d		13 30			13 48			14 05					14 30			14 48				15 05				15 30
Stansted Airport ✈	a	13 25	13 39		13 42		13 57		14 13				14 25	14 39		14 42		14 57			15 13			15 25	15 39
✈	d											14 25											15 25		
Elsenham	d					13 52											14 52								
Newport (Essex)	d					13 57											14 57								
Audley End	d					14 00					14 23	14 38					15 00					15 23	15 38		
Great Chesterford	d					14 05											15 05								
Whittlesford Parkway	d					14 10					14 30						15 10					15 30			
Shelford	d					14 14											15 14								
Cambridge	a					14 21					14 40	14 57					15 21					15 40	15 57		

		LE [1]	LE [1] 🛒	LE [1]	LE [1] 🛒		LE [1]	LE [1] 🛒	LE [1]	XC ◇	LE [1] 🛒	LE [1]	LE [1]	LE [1] 🛒		LE [1]	LE [1] 🛒	LE [1]	LE [1] 🛒	LE [1]	XC ◇	LE [1] 🛒	LE [1]		LE [1]
London Liverpool Street [15] ⊖	d	14 42	14 55	14 58	15 10		15 12	15 25	15 28		15 40		15 42	15 55		15 58	16 10	16 12	16 25	16 28		16 40			16 42
Bethnal Green	d																								
Hackney Downs	d	14 48					15 18						15 48					16 18							16 48
Stratford [7] ⊖	d											15 33											16 33		
Clapton	d																								
Seven Sisters ⊖	d																								
Tottenham Hale ⊖	d	14 55	15u07	15 10	15u22		15 25	15u37	15 40		15u52	15 43	15 55	16u07		16 10	16u22	16 25	16u37	16 40		16u52	16 43		16 55
Northumberland Park	d											15 45											16 45		
Angel Road	d																								
Ponders End	d	14 59					15 29						15 59					16 29							16 59
Brimsdown	d	15 02					15 32						16 02					16 32							17 02
Enfield Lock	d	15 04					15 34					15 51	16 04					16 34					16 51		17 04
Waltham Cross	d	15 07					15 37						16 07					16 37							17 07
Cheshunt	d	15 09		15 18			15 39		15 48			15 55	16 09			16 18		16 39		16 48			16 55		17 09
Broxbourne [3]	a	15 14		15 22			15 44		15 52			15 59	16 14			16 22		16 44		16 52			16 59		17 14
	d	15 14		15 22			15 44		15 52			16 03	16 14			16 22		16 44		16 52			17 03		17 14
Rye House	d	15 17					15 47						16 17					16 47							17 17
St Margarets (Herts)	d	15 20					15 50						16 20					16 50							17 20
Ware	d	15 24					15 54						16 24					16 54							17 24
Hertford East	a	15 31					16 01						16 31					17 01							17 31
Roydon	d			15 26								16 08				16 26							17 08		
Harlow Town	d		15 24	15 30				15 54	15 58			16 12		16 24		16 30			16 54	16 58			17 12		
Harlow Mill	d			15 33								16 15				16 33							17 15		
Sawbridgeworth	d			15 37					16 03			16 18				16 37				17 03			17 18		
Bishops Stortford	a			15 44	15 47				16 10		16 15	16 25				16 44	16 47			17 10		17 15	17 25		
	d			15 44	15 48				16 11		16 15	16 26				16 44	16 48			17 11		17 15	17 26		
Stansted Mountfitchet	d			15 48				16 05				16 30				16 48			17 05				17 30		
Stansted Airport ✈	a		15 42		15 57			16 13			16 25	16 39		16 42			16 57		17 13			17 25	17 39		
✈	d									16 25											17 25				
Elsenham	d			15 52												16 52									
Newport (Essex)	d			15 57												16 57									
Audley End	d			16 00					16 23	16 38						17 00				17 23	17 38				
Great Chesterford	d			16 05												17 05									
Whittlesford Parkway	d			16 10					16 30							17 10				17 30					
Shelford	d			16 14												17 14									
Cambridge	a			16 21					16 40	16 57						17 21				17 40	17 57				

For general notes see front of timetable
For details of catering facilities see Directory of Train Operators

London → Broxbourne, Hertford East, Bishops Stortford, Stansted Airport and Cambridge

Network diagram - see first page of Table 20

		LE	LE	LE	LE	LE	LE	XC	LE		LE	LE	LE	LE	LE	LE	LE	LE		XC	LE	LE	LE	LE	LE
		1	1	1	1	1	1	◇	1		1	1	1	1	1	1	1	1		◇	1	1	1	1	1
		🚲		🚲		🚲			🚲				🚲		🚲		🚲				🚲			🚲	
London Liverpool Street 15 ⊖	d	16 55	16 58	17 10	17 12	17 25	17 28		17 40			17 42	17 55	17 58	18 10	18 12	18 25	18 28			18 40		18 42	18 55	18 58
Bethnal Green	d																								
Hackney Downs	d				17 18							17 48				18 18							18 48		
Stratford 7 ⊖	d										17 33											18 33			
Clapton	d																								
Seven Sisters ⊖	d																								
Tottenham Hale ⊖	d	17u07	17 10	17u22	17 25	17u37	17 40		17u52		17 43	17 55	18u07	18 10	18u22	18 25	18u37	18 40			18u52	18 43	18 55	19u07	19 10
Northumberland Park	d										17 45											18 45			
Angel Road	d																								
Ponders End	d				17 29							17 59				18 29							18 59		
Brimsdown	d				17 32							18 02				18 32							19 02		
Enfield Lock	d				17 34						17 51	18 04				18 34						18 51	19 04		
Waltham Cross	d				17 37							18 07				18 37							19 07		
Cheshunt	d		17 18		17 39		17 48				17 55	18 09		18 18		18 39		18 48				18 55	19 09		19 18
Broxbourne 3	a		17 22		17 44		17 52				17 59	18 14		18 22		18 44		18 52				18 59	19 14		19 22
	d		17 22		17 44		17 52				18 03	18 14		18 22		18 44		18 52				19 03	19 14		19 22
Rye House	d				17 47							18 17				18 47							19 17		
St Margarets (Herts)	d				17 50							18 20				18 50							19 20		
Ware	d				17 54							18 24				18 54							19 24		
Hertford East	a				18 01							18 31				19 01							19 31		
Roydon	d		17 26								18 08			18 26								19 08			19 26
Harlow Town	d	17 24	17 30			17 54	17 58				18 12		18 24	18 30			18 54	18 58				19 12		19 24	19 30
Harlow Mill	d		17 33								18 15			18 33								19 15			19 33
Sawbridgeworth	d		17 37				18 03				18 18			18 37				19 03				19 18			19 37
Bishops Stortford	a		17 44	17 47			18 10		18 15		18 25			18 44	18 47			19 10			19 15	19 25			19 44
	d		17 44	17 48			18 11		18 15		18 26			18 44	18 48			19 11			19 15	19 26			19 44
Stansted Mountfitchet	d		17 48			18 05					18 30			18 48			19 05					19 30			19 48
Stansted Airport ✈	a	17 42		17 57		18 13			18 25		18 39		18 42		18 57		19 13				19 27	19 39		19 42	
	d							18 25												19 18					
Elsenham	d		17 52											18 52											19 52
Newport (Essex)	d		17 57											18 57											19 57
Audley End	d		18 00				18 23	18 38						19 00				19 23		19 32					20 00
Great Chesterford	d		18 05											19 05											20 05
Whittlesford Parkway	d		18 10				18 30							19 10				19 30							20 10
Shelford	d		18 14											19 14											20 14
Cambridge	a		18 21				18 40	18 57						19 21				19 40		19 49					20 21

		LE	LE	LE	LE		LE	LE	LE	LE	LE	XC	LE	LE		LE	LE	LE	LE	LE	LE	LE	LE		LE
		1	1	1	1		1	1	1	1	1		1	1		1	1	1	1	1	1	1	1		1
		🚲		🚲			🚲			🚲			🚲			🚲		🚲			🚲		🚲		
London Liverpool Street 15 ⊖	d	19 10	19 12	19 25	19 28		19 40		19 42	19 55	19 58		20 10	20 12		20 25	20 28	20 40		20 42	20 55	20 58	21 10		21 12
Bethnal Green	d																								
Hackney Downs	d		19 18						19 48					20 18						20 48					21 18
Stratford 7 ⊖	d							19 33											20 33						
Clapton	d																								
Seven Sisters ⊖	d																								
Tottenham Hale ⊖	d	19u22	19 25	19u37	19 40		19u52	19 43	19 55	20u07	20 10		20u22	20 25		20u37	20 40	20u52	20 43	20 55	21u07	21 10	21u22		21 25
Northumberland Park	d							19 45											20 45						
Angel Road	d																								
Ponders End	d		19 29						19 59					20 29						20 59					21 29
Brimsdown	d		19 32						20 02					20 32						21 02					21 32
Enfield Lock	d		19 34					19 51	20 04					20 34					20 51	21 04					21 34
Waltham Cross	d		19 37						20 07					20 37						21 07					21 37
Cheshunt	d		19 39		19 48			19 55	20 09		20 18			20 39			20 48		20 55	21 09		21 18			21 39
Broxbourne 3	a		19 44		19 52			19 59	20 14		20 22			20 44			20 52		20 59	21 14		21 22			21 44
	d		19 44		19 52			20 03	20 14		20 22			20 44			20 52		21 03	21 14		21 22			21 44
Rye House	d		19 47						20 17					20 47						21 17					21 47
St Margarets (Herts)	d		19 50						20 20					20 50						21 20					21 50
Ware	d		19 54						20 24					20 54						21 24					21 54
Hertford East	a		20 01						20 31					21 01						21 31					22 01
Roydon	d							20 08			20 26								21 08			21 26			
Harlow Town	d			19 54	19 58			20 12		20 24	20 30					20 54	20 58		21 12		21 24	21 30			
Harlow Mill	d							20 15			20 33								21 15			21 33			
Sawbridgeworth	d				20 03			20 18			20 37						21 03		21 18			21 37			
Bishops Stortford	a	19 47			20 10		20 15	20 25			20 44		20 47				21 10	21 15	21 25			21 44	21 47		
	d	19 48			20 11		20 15	20 26			20 44		20 48				21 11	21 15	21 26			21 44	21 48		
Stansted Mountfitchet	d			20 05				20 30			20 48					21 05			21 30			21 48			
Stansted Airport ✈	a	19 57		20 13			20 25	20 39		20 42			20 57			21 13		21 25	21 39		21 42		21 57		
	d											20 56													
Elsenham	d										20 52											21 52			
Newport (Essex)	d										20 57											21 57			
Audley End	d				20 23						21 00	21 10					21 23					22 00			
Great Chesterford	d										21 05											22 05			
Whittlesford Parkway	d				20 30						21 10						21 30					22 10			
Shelford	d										21 14											22 14			
Cambridge	a				20 40						21 21	21 31					21 40					22 21			

For general notes see front of timetable
For details of catering facilities see
Directory of Train Operators

Saturdays

London → Broxbourne, Hertford East, Bishops Stortford, Stansted Airport and Cambridge

Network diagram - see first page of Table 20

		LE 1 🛒	LE 1	LE 1 🛒	LE 1	LE 1	LE 1 🛒	LE 1	LE 1	LE 1	LE 1	LE 1	LE 1	LE 1	LE 1	LE 1	LE 1	LE 1	LE 1	LE 1	LE 1	LE 1
London Liverpool Street 15 ⊖	d	21 25	21 28	21 40		21 42	21 55	21 58	22 10	22 12	22 25	22 28	22 40		22 42	22 55	22 58	23 10	23 25	23 28	23 40	23 58
Bethnal Green	d																					
Hackney Downs	d					21 48				22 18					22 48			23 16			23 46	
Stratford 7 ⊖	d				21 33									22 33								
Clapton	d																					
Seven Sisters ⊖	d																				23 49	
Tottenham Hale ⊖	d	21u37	21 40	21u52	21 43	21 55	22u07	22 10	22u22	22 25	22u37	22 40	22u52	22 43	22 55	23u07	23 10	23 23	23u37	23 40	23 53	00 10
Northumberland Park	d				21 45									22 45				23 25			23 55	
Angel Road	d																					
Ponders End	d					21 59				22 29					22 59			23 29			23 59	
Brimsdown	d					22 02				22 32					23 02			23 32			00 02	
Enfield Lock	d				21 51	22 04				22 34				22 51	23 04			23 34			00 04	
Waltham Cross	d					22 07				22 37					23 07			23 37			00 07	
Cheshunt	d		21 48		21 55	22 09		22 18		22 39		22 48		22 55	23 09		23 18	23 39		23 48	00 09	00 18
Broxbourne 3	a		21 52		21 59	22 14		22 22		22 44		22 52		22 59	23 14		23 22	23 44		23 52	00 14	00 22
	d		21 52		22 03	22 14		22 22		22 44		22 52		23 03	23 14		23 22	23 44		23 52	00 14	00 22
Rye House	d					22 17				22 47					23 17			23 47			00 17	
St Margarets (Herts)	d					22 20				22 50					23 20			23 50			00 20	
Ware	d					22 24				22 54					23 24			23 54			00 24	
Hertford East	a					22 31				23 01					23 31			00 01			00 31	
Roydon	d				22 08			22 26						23 08			23 26					00 26
Harlow Town	d	21 54	21 58		22 12		22 24	22 30			22 54	22 58		23 12		23 24	23 30		23 54	23 58		00 30
Harlow Mill	d				22 15			22 33						23 15			23 33					00 33
Sawbridgeworth	d		22 03		22 18			22 37				23 03		23 18			23 37			00 03		00 37
Bishops Stortford	a		22 10	22 15	22 25			22 44	22 47			23 10	23 15	23 26			23 44		00 04	00 10		00 44
	d		22 11	22 15	22 26			22 44	22 48			23 11	23 15				23 44		00 04	00 11		00 44
Stansted Mountfitchet	d	22 05			22 30			22 48			23 05						23 48					00 48
Stansted Airport ✈	a	22 13		22 25	22 39		22 42		22 57		23 13		23 25			23 42			00 13			
✈	d																					
Elsenham	d							22 52									23 52					00 52
Newport (Essex)	d							22 57									23 57					00 57
Audley End	d		22 23					23 00				23 23					23 59			00 23		01 00
Great Chesterford	d							23 05									00 05					01 05
Whittlesford Parkway	d		22 30					23 10				23 30					00 10			00 30		01 10
Shelford	d							23 14									00 14					
Cambridge	a		22 40					23 21				23 40					00 21			00 40		01 19

Sundays

		LE 1	LE 1	LE 1	LE 1	LE 1	LE 1	LE 1	LE 1	LE 1	LE 1	LE 1	LE 1	LE 1	LE 1 🛒	LE 1 🛒	LE 1 🛒	LE	LE 1	LE 1	LE	LE 1 🛒	LE 1	LE 1 🛒
London Liverpool Street 15 ⊖	d	22p58	23p25	23p28	23p40	23p58	04 10	04 40	05 10	05 40	06 10	06 25	06 40	06 55	07 10	07 25	07 40		07 43		07 52	07 55		08 10
Bethnal Green	d																							
Hackney Downs	d				23p46																			
Stratford 7 ⊖	d																				07 59			
Clapton	d				23p49																			
Seven Sisters ⊖	d																				08 04			
Tottenham Hale ⊖	d	23p10	23b37	23p40	23p53	00 10		04u52	05u22	05u52	06u22	06u37	06u52	07 07	07 22	07 37	07 52		07 55			08 07		08 22
Northumberland Park	d				23p55																			
Angel Road	d																							
Ponders End	d				23p59														07 59					
Brimsdown	d				00 02														08 02					
Enfield Lock	d				00 04														08 04	←				
Waltham Cross	d				00 07														08 07	08 07				
Cheshunt	d	23p18		23p48	00 09	00 18													→	08 09	08 20			
Broxbourne 3	a	23p22		23p52	00 14	00 22														08 14	08 25			
	d	23p22		23p52	00 14	00 22												07 57		08 19	08 25			
Rye House	d				00 17													08 00			08 28			
St Margarets (Herts)	d				00 20													08 03			08 31			
Ware	d				00 24													08 07			08 35			
Hertford East	a				00 31													08 14			08 42		←	
Roydon	d	23p26				00 26														08 24			08 24	
Harlow Town	d	23p30	23p54	23p58		00 30		05 07	05 37	06 10		06 52		07 22		07 52				→		08 22	08 28	
Harlow Mill	d	23p33				00 33																	08 31	
Sawbridgeworth	d	23p37		00 03		00 37																	08 34	
Bishops Stortford	a	23p44	00 04	00 10		00 44		05 17	05 47	06 20	06 45		07 15		07 45		08 15						08 41	08 45
	d	23p44	00 04	00 11		00 44		05 18	05 48	06 21	06 46		07 16		07 46		08 16						08 42	08 46
Stansted Mountfitchet	d	23p48				00 48		05 22				07 03				08 03							08 46	
Stansted Airport ✈	a		00 13				04 58	05 29	05 57	06 30	06 55	07 12	07 25	07 40	07 55	08 13	08 25					08 40		08 55
✈	d																							
Elsenham	d	23p52				00 52																	08 50	
Newport (Essex)	d	23p57				00 57																	08 55	
Audley End	d	23p59		00 23		01 00																	08 58	
Great Chesterford	d	00 05				01 05																	09 03	
Whittlesford Parkway	d	00 10		00 30		01 10																	09 08	
Shelford	d	00 14																					09 12	
Cambridge	a	00 21		00 40		01 19																	09 19	

For general notes see front of timetable
For details of catering facilities see Directory of Train Operators

b Previous night.
Stops to pick up only

Table 22

Sundays

London → Broxbourne, Hertford East, Bishops Stortford, Stansted Airport and Cambridge

Network diagram - see first page of Table 20

		LE		LE 1 ⊼	LE 1	LE	LE 1 ⊼	LE 1	LE	LE 1 ⊼	LE 1	LE 1 ⊼	LE	LE 1 ⊼		LE 1	LE	LE 1 ⊼	LE 1	LE	LE 1 ⊼	LE 1	LE 1 ⊼	LE	LE 1 ⊼
London Liverpool Street 15 ⊖	d	08 22		08 25	08 28		08 40		08 52	08 55		09 10	09 22	09 25		09 28		09 40		09 52	09 55		10 10	10 22	10 25
Bethnal Green	d					←											←								
Hackney Downs	d	08 29 →				08 29			08 59				09 29 →				09 29			09 59				10 29 →	
Stratford 7 ⊖	d							08 45											09 45						
Clapton	d																								
Seven Sisters ⊖	d					08 34			09 04								09 34			10 04					
Tottenham Hale ⊖	d			08 37	08 40		08 52	08 55		09 07		09 22		09 37		09 40		09 52	09 55		10 07		10 22		10 37
Northumberland Park	d																								
Angel Road	d																								
Ponders End	d							08 59											09 59						
Brimsdown	d							09 02											10 02						
Enfield Lock	d							09 04											10 04						
Waltham Cross	d							09 07											10 07						
Cheshunt	d				08 49	08 52		09 09	09 20							09 49	09 52		10 09	10 20					
Broxbourne 3	a				08 53	08 57		09 14	09 25							09 53	09 57		10 14	10 25					
	d				08 53	08 57		09 19	09 25							09 53	09 57		10 19	10 25					
Rye House	d					09 00			09 28								10 00			10 28					
St Margarets (Herts)	d					09 03			09 31								10 03			10 31					
Ware	d					09 07			09 35								10 07			10 35					
Hertford East	a					09 14			09 42		←						10 14			10 42		←			
Roydon	d							09 24			09 24								10 24			10 24			
Harlow Town	d			08 52	08 59			→		09 22	09 28			09 52		09 59			→		10 22	10 28			10 52
Harlow Mill	d										09 31											10 31			
Sawbridgeworth	d				09 04						09 34					10 04						10 34			
Bishops Stortford	a				09 11		09 15				09 41	09 45				10 11		10 15				10 41	10 45		
	d				09 12		09 16				09 42	09 46				10 12		10 16				10 42	10 46		
Stansted Mountfitchet	d			09 03							09 46			10 03								10 46			11 03
Stansted Airport ✈	a			09 12			09 25			09 40		09 55		10 12				10 25			10 40		10 55		11 12
✈	d																								
Elsenham	d										09 50											10 50			
Newport (Essex)	d										09 55											10 55			
Audley End	d				09 24						09 58					10 24						10 58			
Great Chesterford	d										10 03											11 03			
Whittlesford Parkway	d				09 31						10 08					10 31						11 08			
Shelford	d										10 12											11 12			
Cambridge	a				09 41						10 19					10 41						11 19			

		LE 1	LE	LE 1 ⊼		LE 1	LE	LE 1 ⊼	LE 1	LE 1 ⊼	LE	XC ◇	LE 1 ⊼	LE 1	LE	LE 1 ⊼		LE 1	LE	LE 1 ⊼	LE 1	LE 1 ⊼	LE	LE 1 ⊼	LE 1
London Liverpool Street 15 ⊖	d	10 28		10 40			10 52	10 55		11 10	11 22		11 25	11 28		11 40			11 52	11 55		12 10	12 22	12 25	12 28
Bethnal Green	d		←												←										
Hackney Downs	d		10 29				10 59				11 29 →				11 29				11 59				12 29 →		
Stratford 7 ⊖	d					10 45												11 45							
Clapton	d																								
Seven Sisters ⊖	d		10 34				11 04								11 34				12 04						
Tottenham Hale ⊖	d	10 40		10 52		10 55		11 07		11 22			11 37	11 40		11 52		11 55		12 07		12 22		12 37	12 40
Northumberland Park	d																								
Angel Road	d																								
Ponders End	d					10 59												11 59							
Brimsdown	d					11 02												12 02							
Enfield Lock	d					11 04												12 04							
Waltham Cross	d					11 07												12 07							
Cheshunt	d	10 49	10 52			11 09	11 20							11 49	11 52			12 09	12 20						12 49
Broxbourne 3	a	10 53	10 57			11 14	11 25							11 53	11 57			12 14	12 25						12 53
	d	10 53	10 57			11 19	11 25							11 53	11 57			12 19	12 25						12 53
Rye House	d		11 00				11 28								12 00				12 28						
St Margarets (Herts)	d		11 03				11 31								12 03				12 31						
Ware	d		11 07				11 35								12 07				12 35						
Hertford East	a		11 14				11 42		←						12 14				12 42		←				
Roydon	d					11 24			11 24									12 24			12 24				
Harlow Town	d	10 59				→		11 22	11 28				11 52	11 59				→		12 22	12 28			12 52	12 59
Harlow Mill	d								11 31												12 31				
Sawbridgeworth	d	11 04							11 34					12 04							12 34				13 04
Bishops Stortford	a	11 11		11 15					11 41	11 45				12 11		12 15					12 41	12 45			13 11
	d	11 12		11 16					11 42	11 46				12 12		12 16					12 42	12 46			13 12
Stansted Mountfitchet	d								11 46				12 03								12 46			13 03	
Stansted Airport ✈	a			11 25				11 40		11 57			12 14			12 25				12 40		12 55		13 12	
✈	d											12 05													
Elsenham	d								11 50												12 50				
Newport (Essex)	d								11 55												12 55				
Audley End	d	11 24							11 58			12 18		12 24							12 58				13 24
Great Chesterford	d								12 03												13 03				
Whittlesford Parkway	d	11 31							12 08					12 31							13 08				13 31
Shelford	d								12 12												13 12				
Cambridge	a	11 41							12 19			12 35		12 41							13 19				13 41

For general notes see front of timetable
For details of catering facilities see
Directory of Train Operators

Sundays

London → Broxbourne, Hertford East, Bishops Stortford, Stansted Airport and Cambridge

Network diagram - see first page of Table 20

		LE	LE 1 🚲	LE 1	LE	LE 1 🚲		LE 1	LE 1 🚲	LE	XC ◇	LE 1 🚲	LE 1	LE	LE 1 🚲	LE 1	LE	LE 1 🚲		LE 1	LE 1 🚲	LE	LE 1 🚲	LE 1	LE
London Liverpool Street 15	⊖ d		12 40		12 52	12 55			13 10	13 22		13 25	13 28		13 40		13 52	13 55			14 10	14 22	14 25	14 28	
Bethnal Green	d	←												←											←
Hackney Downs	d	12 29			12 59					13 29				13 29			13 59					14 29			14 29
Stratford 7	⊖ ⛴ d			12 45						→						13 45						→			
Clapton	d																								
Seven Sisters	⊖ d	12 34			13 04									13 34			14 04								14 34
Tottenham Hale	⊖ d		12 52	12 55		13 07			13 22			13 37	13 40		13 52	13 55		14 07			14 22		14 37	14 40	
Northumberland Park	d																								
Angel Road	d																								
Ponders End	d			12 59												13 59									
Brimsdown	d			13 02												14 02									
Enfield Lock	d			13 04												14 04									
Waltham Cross	d			13 07												14 07									
Cheshunt	d	12 52		13 09	13 20								13 49	13 52		14 09	14 20							14 49	14 52
Broxbourne 3	a	12 57		13 14	13 25								13 53	13 57		14 14	14 25							14 53	14 57
	d	12 57		13 19	13 25								13 53	13 57		14 19	14 25							14 53	14 57
Rye House	d	13 00			13 28									14 00			14 28								15 00
St Margarets (Herts)	d	13 03			13 31									14 03			14 31								15 03
Ware	d	13 07			13 35									14 07			14 35								15 07
Hertford East	a	13 14			13 42			←						14 14			14 42			←					15 14
Roydon	d			13 24				13 24								14 24				14 24					
Harlow Town	d			→		13 22		13 28				13 52	13 59			→		14 22		14 28			14 52	14 59	
Harlow Mill	d							13 31												14 31					
Sawbridgeworth	d							13 34					14 04							14 34				15 04	
Bishops Stortford	a		13 15					13 41	13 45				14 11		14 15					14 41	14 45			15 11	
	d		13 16					13 42	13 46				14 12		14 16					14 42	14 46			15 12	
Stansted Mountfitchet	d							13 46				14 03								14 46			15 03		
Stansted Airport	✈ a		13 25			13 40			13 57			14 14			14 25			14 40			14 57		15 12		
	✈ d										14 05														
Elsenham	d							13 50												14 50					
Newport (Essex)	d							13 55												14 55					
Audley End	d							13 58			14 18		14 24							14 58				15 24	
Great Chesterford	d							14 03												15 03					
Whittlesford Parkway	d							14 08					14 31							15 08				15 31	
Shelford	d							14 12												15 12					
Cambridge	a							14 19			14 35		14 41							15 19				15 41	

		XC ◇	LE 1 🚲	LE 1	LE	LE 1 🚲	LE 1	LE 1 🚲		LE	XC ◇	LE 1 🚲	LE 1	LE	LE 1 🚲	LE 1	LE	LE 1 🚲	LE 1	LE 1 🚲		LE	LE 1 🚲	LE 1	LE
London Liverpool Street 15	⊖ d		14 40		14 52	14 55		15 10		15 22		15 25	15 28		15 40		15 52	15 55		16 10		16 22	16 25	16 28	
Bethnal Green	d													←											←
Hackney Downs	d				14 59					15 29				15 29			15 59					16 29			16 29
Stratford 7	⊖ ⛴ d			14 45						→						15 45						→			
Clapton	d																								
Seven Sisters	⊖ d				15 04									15 34			16 04								16 34
Tottenham Hale	⊖ d		14 52	14 55		15 07		15 22				15 37	15 40		15 52	15 55		16 07		16 22			16 37	16 40	
Northumberland Park	d																								
Angel Road	d																								
Ponders End	d			14 59												15 59									
Brimsdown	d			15 02												16 02									
Enfield Lock	d			15 04												16 04									
Waltham Cross	d			15 07												16 07									
Cheshunt	d			15 09	15 20								15 49	15 52		16 09	16 20							16 49	16 52
Broxbourne 3	a			15 14	15 25								15 53	15 57		16 14	16 25							16 53	16 57
	d			15 19	15 25								15 53	15 57		16 19	16 25							16 53	16 57
Rye House	d				15 28									16 00			16 28								17 00
St Margarets (Herts)	d				15 31									16 03			16 31								17 03
Ware	d				15 35									16 07			16 35								17 07
Hertford East	a				15 42		←							16 14			16 42		←						17 14
Roydon	d			15 24			15 24									16 24			16 24						
Harlow Town	d			→		15 22	15 28					15 52	15 59			→		16 22	16 28				16 52	16 59	
Harlow Mill	d						15 31												16 31						
Sawbridgeworth	d						15 34						16 04						16 34					17 04	
Bishops Stortford	a		15 15				15 41	15 45					16 11		16 15				16 41	16 45				17 11	
	d		15 16				15 42	15 46					16 12		16 16				16 42	16 46				17 12	
Stansted Mountfitchet	d						15 46					16 03							16 46				17 03		
Stansted Airport	✈ a		15 27			15 42		15 55				16 12			16 25			16 40		16 58			17 12		
	✈ d	15 18									16 12														
Elsenham	d						15 50												16 50						
Newport (Essex)	d						15 55												16 55						
Audley End	d	15 31					15 58				16 31		16 24						16 58					17 24	
Great Chesterford	d						16 03												17 03						
Whittlesford Parkway	d						16 08						16 31						17 08					17 31	
Shelford	d						16 12												17 12						
Cambridge	a	15 46					16 19				16 45		16 41						17 19					17 41	

For general notes see front of timetable
For details of catering facilities see Directory of Train Operators

Table 22

Sundays

London → Broxbourne, Hertford East, Bishops Stortford, Stansted Airport and Cambridge

Network diagram - see first page of Table 20

		LE 1 ✠	XC ◇	LE 1	LE	LE 1 ✠	LE 1	LE 1 ✠	LE	LE 1 ✠		LE 1	LE	LE 1 ✠	XC ◇	LE 1	LE	LE 1 ✠	LE 1	LE 1 ✠	LE	LE 1 ✠		LE 1	LE
London Liverpool Street 15 ⊖	d	16 40			16 52	16 55		17 10	17 22	17 25		17 28	←	17 40			17 52	17 55		18 10	18 22	18 25		18 28	←
Bethnal Green	d																								
Hackney Downs	d				16 59				17 29 →				17 29				17 59				18 29 →				18 29
Stratford 7 ⊖	d			16 45												17 45									
Clapton	d																								
Seven Sisters ⊖	d				17 04								17 34				18 04								18 34
Tottenham Hale ⊖	d	16 52		16 55		17 07		17 22		17 37		17 40		17 52		17 55		18 07		18 22		18 37		18 40	
Northumberland Park	d																								
Angel Road	d																								
Ponders End	d			16 59												17 59									
Brimsdown	d			17 02												18 02									
Enfield Lock	d			17 04												18 04									
Waltham Cross	d			17 07												18 07									
Cheshunt	d			17 09	17 20							17 49	17 52			18 09	18 20							18 49	18 52
Broxbourne 3	a			17 14	17 25							17 53	17 57			18 14	18 25							18 53	18 57
	d			17 19	17 25							17 53	17 57			18 19	18 25							18 53	18 57
Rye House	d				17 28								18 00				18 28								19 00
St Margarets (Herts)	d				17 31								18 03				18 31								19 03
Ware	d				17 35								18 07				18 35								19 07
Hertford East	a				17 42		←						18 14				18 42		←						19 14
Roydon	d			17 24 →			17 24									18 24 →			18 24						
Harlow Town	d					17 22	17 28			17 52		17 59						18 22	18 28			18 52		18 59	
Harlow Mill	d						17 31												18 31						
Sawbridgeworth	d						17 34					18 04							18 34					19 04	
Bishops Stortford	a	17 15					17 41	17 45				18 11		18 15					18 41	18 45				19 11	
	d	17 16					17 42	17 46				18 12		18 16					18 42	18 46				19 12	
Stansted Mountfitchet	d						17 46			18 03									18 46			19 03			
Stansted Airport ✈	a	17 25				17 44		17 57		18 12				18 25				18 44		18 55		19 12			
✈	d		17 35												18 35										
Elsenham	d						17 50												18 50						
Newport (Essex)	d						17 55												18 55						
Audley End	d		17 48				17 58					18 24			18 48				18 58					19 24	
Great Chesterford	d						18 03												19 03						
Whittlesford Parkway	d						18 08					18 31							19 08					19 31	
Shelford	d						18 12												19 12						
Cambridge	a		18 08				18 19					18 41			19 06				19 19					19 41	

		LE 1 ✠	LE 1 ✠	LE 1	LE	LE 1 ✠	LE 1 ✠	LE 1	XC	LE 1 ✠	LE	LE 1 ✠		LE 1	LE	LE 1 ✠	LE 1 ✠	LE 1	XC	LE 1 ✠	LE	LE 1 ✠	LE 1	LE	LE 1 ✠
London Liverpool Street 15 ⊖	d	18 40	18 55		19 00	19 10	19 25	19 28		19 40		19 55			20 00	20 10	20 25	20 28		20 40		20 55		21 00	21 10
Bethnal Green	d				19 03										20 03									21 03	
Hackney Downs	d				19 09										20 09									21 09	
Stratford 7 ⊖	d			18 45										19 45									20 45		
Clapton	d																								
Seven Sisters ⊖	d				19 17										20 17									21 17	
Tottenham Hale ⊖	d	18 52	19 07	18 55		19 22	19 37	19 40		19 52		20 07		19 55		20 22	20 37	20 40		20 52		21 07	20 55		21 22
Northumberland Park	d																								
Angel Road	d																								
Ponders End	d			18 59										19 59									20 59		
Brimsdown	d			19 02										20 02									21 02		
Enfield Lock	d			19 04										20 04									21 04		
Waltham Cross	d			19 07										20 07									21 07		
Cheshunt	d			19 09	19 37			19 48						20 09	20 37			20 48					21 09	21 37	
Broxbourne 3	a			19 14	19 42			19 52			←			20 14	20 42			20 52			←		21 14	21 42	
	d			19 19	19 55			19 52			19 55			20 19	20 55			20 52			20 55		21 19	21 55	
Rye House	d				→						19 59				→						20 59			→	
St Margarets (Herts)	d										20 02										21 02				
Ware	d										20 06										21 06				
Hertford East	a										20 12										21 12				
Roydon	d			19 24										20 24									21 24		
Harlow Town	d		19 22	19 28			19 52	19 58				20 22		20 28			20 52	20 58				21 22	21 28		
Harlow Mill	d			19 31										20 31									21 31		
Sawbridgeworth	d			19 34				20 03						20 34				21 03					21 34		
Bishops Stortford	a	19 15		19 41		19 45		20 10		20 15				20 41		20 45		21 10		21 15			21 41		21 45
	d	19 16		19 42		19 46		20 11		20 16				20 42		20 46		21 11		21 16			21 42		21 46
Stansted Mountfitchet	d			19 46			20 03							20 46			21 03						21 46		
Stansted Airport ✈	a	19 25	19 40			19 57	20 12			20 28		20 40				20 57	21 12			21 28		21 40			21 57
✈	d								20 19										21 19						
Elsenham	d			19 50										20 50									21 50		
Newport (Essex)	d			19 55										20 55									21 55		
Audley End	d			19 58				20 23	20 33					20 58				21 23	21 33				21 58		
Great Chesterford	d			20 03										21 03									22 03		
Whittlesford Parkway	d			20 08				20 30						21 08				21 30					22 08		
Shelford	d			20 12										21 12									22 12		
Cambridge	a			20 19				20 40	20 48					21 19				21 40	21 48				22 19		

For general notes see front of timetable
For details of catering facilities see Directory of Train Operators

Table 22

Sundays

London → Broxbourne, Hertford East, Bishops Stortford, Stansted Airport and Cambridge

Network diagram - see first page of Table 20

Station		LE 1 🚲	LE 1	XC	LE 1 🚲	LE	LE 1 🚲	LE 1	LE	LE 1	LE 1	LE 1	LE 1	LE	LE 1	LE 1	LE	LE 1	LE 1	LE	LE 1
London Liverpool Street 15 ⊖	d	21 25	21 28		21 40		21 55		22 00	22 10	22 25	22 28	22 40		22 55		23 00	23 25	23 28		23 58
Bethnal Green	d								22 03								23 03				
Hackney Downs	d								22 09								23 09				
Stratford 7 ⊖	d							21 45								22 45					
Clapton	d																				
Seven Sisters ⊖	d								22 17								23 17				
Tottenham Hale ⊖	d	21 37	21 40		21 52		22 07	21 55		22 22	22 37	22 40	22 52		23 07	22 55		23 37	23 40		00 10
Northumberland Park	d																				
Angel Road	d																				
Ponders End	d							21 59								22 59			23 44		
Brimsdown	d							22 02								23 02			23 47		
Enfield Lock	d							22 04								23 04			23 49		
Waltham Cross	d							22 07								23 07			23 52		
Cheshunt	d		21 48					22 09	22 37			22 48				23 09	23 37		23 54		00 18
Broxbourne 3	a		21 52			←		22 14	22 42			22 52		←		23 14	23 42		23 59	←	00 22
	d		21 52			21 55		22 19	22 55			22 52		22 55		23 19	00 02		23 59	00 02	00 22
Rye House	d					21 59			↪					22 59			↪			00 05	
St Margarets (Herts)	d					22 02								23 02						00 08	
Ware	d					22 06								23 06						00 12	
Hertford East	a					22 12								23 12						00 19	
Roydon	d							22 24								23 24					00 26
Harlow Town	d	21 52	21 58				22 22	22 28			22 52	22 58			23 22	23 28		23 52	00 05		00 30
Harlow Mill	d							22 31								23 31					00 33
Sawbridgeworth	d		22 03					22 34				23 03				23 34			00 10		00 37
Bishops Stortford	a		22 10		22 15			22 41		22 45		23 10	23 15			23 41		00 02	00 17		00 44
	d		22 11		22 16			22 42		22 46		23 11	23 16			23 42		00 03			
Stansted Mountfitchet	d	22 03						22 46			23 03					23 46					
Stansted Airport ✈	a	22 12			22 28		22 40			22 55	23 12		23 25		23 40			00 12			
✈	d			22 19																	
Elsenham	d							22 50								23 50					
Newport (Essex)	d							22 55								23 55					
Audley End	d		22 23					22 58				23 23				23 58					
Great Chesterford	d							23 03								00 03					
Whittlesford Parkway	d		22 30					23 08				23 30				00 08					
Shelford	d							23 12								00 12					
Cambridge	a		22 40	22 47				23 19				23 40				00 19					

For general notes see front of timetable
For details of catering facilities see Directory of Train Operators

Cambridge, Stansted Airport, Bishops Stortford, Hertford East and Broxbourne → London

Network diagram - see first page of Table 20

Miles	Miles	Station		LE MO	LE MX 1	LE MX 1	LE MO 1	LE MX 1	LE MO 1	LE MX 1	LE 1	LE 1	LE MFO 1	LE MFO 1	XC	LE 1	LE 1		LE MFO 1	LE MFX 1	LE 1	LE 1	LE 1	LE	LE 1
0	—	**Cambridge**	d		22p51										04 39	04 48						05 21			
3¼	—	Shelford	d		22p56																	05 26			
6¾	—	Whittlesford Parkway	d		23p00											04 55						05 30			
10	—	Great Chesterford	d		23p04																	05 34			
14	—	Audley End	d		23p10										04 53	05 03						05 40			
15¾	—	Newport (Essex)	d		23p13																	05 43			
20¼	0	Elsenham	d		23p19																	05 49			
—	4½	**Stansted Airport**	a												05 12										
—	—		d			23p30	23p30		23p45	23p45	23p59	00 30	01 00	01 30					05 30				06 00		
22½	8¼	Stansted Mountfitchet	d		23p22																	05 52	06 06		
25½	—	**Bishops Stortford**	a		23p28	23p39	23p39				00 08	00 39				05 16			05 39			05 58	06 10		
—	—		d		23p28	23p39	23p39				00 08	00 39				05 16			05 39	05 39	05 45	05 58	06 10		06 14
29	—	Sawbridgeworth	d		23p32											05 21					05 49	06 03			06 18
31¼	—	Harlow Mill	d		23p36											05 24					05 53	06 06			
33	—	Harlow Town	d		23p39		23p47		23p59	23p59	00 16	00 47				05 27			05 47	05 47	05 56	06 10	06 18		06 23
35¾	—	Roydon	d		23p43											05 31					06 00	06 14			
—	0	**Hertford East**	d	22p57				23p39									05 25							06 05	
—	2	Ware	d	23p01				23p43									05 29							06 09	
—	4	St Margarets (Herts)	d	23p05				23p47									05 33							06 13	
—	5¼	Rye House	d	23p08				23p50									05 36							06 16	
38½	7	Broxbourne 3	a	23p12	23p47			23p54								05 36	05 40		05 53	05 53	06 04	06 18		06 21	06 30
—	—		d	23p26	23p47			23p54								05 36	05 40		05 53	05 53	06 04	06 18		06 25	06 39
41¾	—	Cheshunt	d	23p31	23p51			23p58								05 41	05 44		05 57	05 57	06 08	06 23		06 30	⟶
43	—	Waltham Cross	d														05 47				06 10			06 32	
44	—	Enfield Lock	d														05 49				06 13			06 35	
45	—	Brimsdown	d														05 52				06 15			06 37	
45¾	—	Ponders End	d														05 54				06 17			06 39	
48	—	Angel Road	d														05 57				06 21				
48¾	—	Northumberland Park	d														05 59				06 23				
49¾	—	Tottenham Hale ⊖	d													05 49	06 03		06 07	06 07	06 26	06 31	06 34	06 45	
—	0	Seven Sisters ⊖	d	23p51	00 04	00 07	00 08	00 11	00 21	00 21															
51¾	—	Clapton	d																						
—	6¾	Stratford 7 ⊖	a																		06 39				
52¾	—	Hackney Downs	d	23p59				00 16									06 08							06 51	
54½	—	Bethnal Green	d	00 05																					
55¾	—	**London Liverpool Street 15** ⊖	a	00 11	00 18	00 22	00 22	00 25	00 35	00 36	00 51	01 21	01 50	02 20		06 03	06 17		06 23	06 23		06 47	06 49	07 02	

Station		LE 1	LE 1	LE 1	LE 1	LE 1	LE	LE 1	LE 1 A	LE 1		LE 1	LE 1	LE 1	LE	XC	LE	LE 1	LE 1	LE	LE 1	LE 1	LE	LE 1 A	LE 1
Cambridge	d	05 41			05 51				06 18				06 21			06 35		06 48			06 51			07 18	
Shelford	d	05 46			05 56								06 26								06 56				
Whittlesford Parkway	d	05 50			06 00				06 25				06 30					06 55			07 00			07 25	
Great Chesterford	d	05 54			06 04								06 34								07 04				
Audley End	d	06 00			06 10				06 34				06 40			06 49		07 04			07 10			07 34	
Newport (Essex)	d	06 03			06 13								06 43								07 13				
Elsenham	d	06 09			06 19								06 49								07 19				
Stansted Airport	a															07 09									
	d		06 15			06 30				06 43				07 00					07 15			07 30			07 43
Stansted Mountfitchet	d	06 12			06 22					06 49			06 52								07 22				07 49
Bishops Stortford	a	06 18	06 24		06 28	06 39			06 47	06 53			06 58	07 09				07 17	07 24		07 28	07 39		07 47	07 54
	d	06 18	06 24		06 28	06 39		06 42	06 48	06 54			06 58	07 09				07 17	07 24		07 28	07 39		07 48	07 54
Sawbridgeworth	d				06 33			06 46					07 03					07 22			07 33				
Harlow Mill	d				06 36			06 50					07 06								07 36				
Harlow Town	d	06 27			06 40	06 47		06 53	06 57	07 02			07 10					07 27	07 32		07 40			07 57	08 02
Roydon	d				06 44			06 57					07 14								07 44				
Hertford East	d						06 35								07 09		07 15						07 39		
Ware	d						06 39								07 13		07 19						07 43		
St Margarets (Herts)	d						06 43								07 17		07 23						07 47		
Rye House	d						06 46								07 20		07 26						07 50		
Broxbourne 3	a	06 33		⟵	06 48		06 51	07 02	07 04			⟵	07 18	07 22	07 25		07 30	07 33		⟵	07 48	07 52	07 55	08 03	
	d	06 34		06 39	06 48		06 55	07 10	07 05			07 10	07 18	07 22	07 25		07 40	07 34		07 40	07 48	07 52	07 55	08 04	
Cheshunt	d			06 43	06 53		07 00	⟶				07 14		07 27	07 30		⟶			07 44	07 53		08 00		
Waltham Cross	d			06 46			07 02					07 17			07 32					07 47		07 58	08 02		
Enfield Lock	d			06 48			07 05					07 19			07 35					07 49			08 05		
Brimsdown	d						07 07							07 31	07 37					07 52		08 02	08 07		
Ponders End	d						07 09							07 33	07 39							08 04	08 09		
Angel Road	d			06 53								07 24													
Northumberland Park	d			06 55								07 26								07 57					
Tottenham Hale ⊖	d	06 48	06 51	06 58	07 01	07 04	07 15		07 18	07 21		07 29	07 32	07 38	07 45			07 48	07 51	08 00	08 03	08 10	08 15	08 18	08 21
Seven Sisters ⊖	d																								
Clapton	d																								
Stratford 7 ⊖	a			07 12								07 43								08 13					
Hackney Downs	d						07 21								07 51								08 21		
Bethnal Green	d																								
London Liverpool Street 15 ⊖	a	07 04	07 07		07 18	07 21	07 32		07 34	07 37			07 49	07 59	08 02			08 04	08 07		08 19	08 28	08 32	08 34	08 37

For general notes see front of timetable
For details of catering facilities see Directory of Train Operators

A From Kings Lynn (Table 17)

Cambridge, Stansted Airport, Bishops Stortford, Hertford East and Broxbourne → London

Network diagram - see first page of Table 20

		LE	LE [1]		XC	LE [1]	LE	LE	LE [1]	LE [1] ⊼	LE	LE [1] A	LE [1] ⊼	LE	LE [1]	LE [1] ⊼	XC ◇	LE		LE [1] A	LE [1] ⊼	LE [1]	LE [1]	LE [1] ⊼	LE [1]
Cambridge	d		07 21		07 29				07 48			07 51			08 18		08 09			08 21					
Shelford	d		07 26									07 56								08 26					
Whittlesford Parkway	d		07 30						07 55			08 00			08 25					08 30					
Great Chesterford	d		07 34									08 04								08 34					
Audley End	d		07 40		07 44				08 04			08 10			08 34		08 24			08 40					
Newport (Essex)	d		07 43									08 13								08 43					
Elsenham	d		07 49									08 19								08 49					
Stansted Airport ✈	a				08 09												08 49								
	d					08 00				08 15			08 30			08 45					09 00			09 15	
Stansted Mountfitchet	d		07 52									08 22				08 51				08 52					
Bishops Stortford	a		07 58			08 09			08 17			08 28	08 39		08 48					08 58	09 09				
	d		07 58			08 09		08 12	08 17			08 28	08 39		08 48					08 58	09 09		09 14		
Sawbridgeworth	d		08 03					08 16	08 22			08 33								09 03			09 18		
Harlow Mill	d		08 06					08 20				08 36								09 06			09 22		
Harlow Town	d		08 10					08 23	08 27	08 31		08 40			08 57	09 02				09 10			09 25	09 30	
Roydon	d		08 14					08 27				08 44								09 14			09 29		
Hertford East	d						08 09							08 39								09 09			
Ware	d						08 13							08 43								09 13			
St Margarets (Herts)	d						08 17							08 47								09 17			
Rye House	d						08 20							08 50								09 20			
Broxbourne [3]	a		08 18				08 25	08 32	08 34		←	08 48		08 55	09 03					09 18		09 25	09 34		
	d	08 10	08 18				08 25	08 40	08 35		08 40	08 48		08 55	09 04			09 10		09 18		09 25	09 37		←
Cheshunt	d	08 14	08 23				08 30	⟶			08 44	08 53		09 00				09 14		09 23		09 30	09 42		09 42
Waltham Cross	d	08 17					08 32				08 47			09 02				09 17				09 32	⟶		
Enfield Lock	d	08 19					08 35				08 49			09 05				09 19				09 35			09 45
Brimsdown	d						08 37							09 07								09 37			
Ponders End	d						08 39							09 09								09 39			
Angel Road	d	08 24									08 54							09 24							09 50
Northumberland Park	d	08 26									08 56							09 26							09 52
Tottenham Hale ⊖	d	08 29	08 32			08 35	08 45		08 48	08 51	08 59	09 02	09 05	09 15	09 18	09 21		09 29		09 32	09 35	09 45		09 48	09 56
Seven Sisters ⊖	d																								
Clapton	d																								
Stratford [7] ⊖	a	08 43									09 13							09 43							10 08
Hackney Downs	d						08 51							09 21								09 51			
Bethnal Green	d																								
London Liverpool Street [15] ⊖	a		08 49			08 52	09 02		09 04	09 07		09 19	09 22	09 32	09 34	09 37				09 49	09 52	10 00		10 05	

		LE [1]	LE [1] ⊼	LE	LE [1] ⊼	XC ◇	LE [1]	LE [1] ⊼	LE	LE [1]	LE [1] ⊼		LE [1]	LE [1]	LE [1] ⊼	LE [1]	LE [1] ⊼	XC ◇	LE [1]	LE [1] ⊼	LE [1]	LE [1]	LE [1] ⊼	LE [1]	LE [1]
Cambridge	d	08 51				09 23	09 32							09 48				10 09	10 32						10 51
Shelford	d	08 56												09 53											10 56
Whittlesford Parkway	d	09 00					09 39							10b00					10 39						11 00
Great Chesterford	d	09 04												10 04											11 04
Audley End	d	09 10				09 37	09 47							10 10				10 23	10 47						11 10
Newport (Essex)	d	09 13												10 13											11 13
Elsenham	d	09 19												10 19											11 19
Stansted Airport ✈	a					09 59												10 49							
	d		09 30		09 45			10 00			10 15				10 30		10 45			11 00		11 03	11 15		
Stansted Mountfitchet	d	09 22			09 51									10 22								11 09			11 22
Bishops Stortford	a	09 28	09 39				10 00	10 09						10 28	10 39				11 00	11 09		11 13			11 28
	d	09 28	09 39				10 00	10 09		10 14				10 28	10 39				11 00	11 09		11 14			11 28
Sawbridgeworth	d	09 32					10 05			10 18				10 32					11 05			11 18			11 32
Harlow Mill	d	09 36								10 22				10 36								11 22			11 36
Harlow Town	d	09 39			10 02		10 10			10 25	10 30			10 39			11 00		11 10			11 25	11 30		11 39
Roydon	d	09 43								10 29				10 43								11 29			11 43
Hertford East	d			09 39					10 09							10 39					11 09				
Ware	d			09 43					10 13							10 43					11 13				
St Margarets (Herts)	d			09 47					10 17							10 47					11 17				
Rye House	d			09 50					10 20							10 50					11 20				
Broxbourne [3]	a	09 47		09 54			10 16		10 24	10 34				10 47		10 54			11 16		11 24	11 34			11 47
	d	09 47		09 54			10 16		10 24	10 37			←	10 47		10 54			11 16		11 24	11 37		←	11 47
Cheshunt	d	09 51		09 58			10 20		10 28	10 42			10 42	10 51		10 58			11 20		11 28	11 42		11 42	11 51
Waltham Cross	d			10 01					10 31	⟶						11 01					11 31	⟶			
Enfield Lock	d			10 03					10 33				10 45			11 03					11 33			11 45	
Brimsdown	d			10 06					10 36							11 06					11 36				
Ponders End	d			10 08					10 38							11 08					11 38				
Angel Road	d																								
Northumberland Park	d												10 51											11 51	
Tottenham Hale ⊖	d	10 00	10 03	10 14	10 17		10 29	10 32	10 44		10 47		10 55	11 00	11 03	11 14	11 17		11 29	11 32	11 44		11 47	11 55	12 00
Seven Sisters ⊖	d																								
Clapton	d																								
Stratford [7] ⊖	a												11 05											12 05	
Hackney Downs	d			10 20					10 50							11 20					11 50				
Bethnal Green	d																								
London Liverpool Street [15] ⊖	a	10 13	10 18	10 28	10 31		10 43	10 46	10 58		11 01			11 13	11 17	11 28	11 31		11 43	11 46	11 58		12 01		12 13

For general notes see front of timetable
For details of catering facilities see Directory of Train Operators

A From Ely (Table 17)
b Arr. 0957

Cambridge, Stansted Airport, Bishops Stortford, Hertford East and Broxbourne → London

Network diagram - see first page of Table 20

		LE 1 ⊼	LE 1	LE 1 ⊼		XC ◇	LE 1	LE 1 ⊼	LE 1	LE 1	LE 1 ⊼	LE 1	LE 1	LE 1 ⊼	LE 1	LE 1 ⊼	XC ◇	LE 1	LE 1 ⊼		LE 1	LE 1	LE 1 ⊼	LE 1	LE 1
Cambridge	d					11 09	11 32						11 51				12 09	12 32							12 51
Shelford	d												11 56												12 56
Whittlesford Parkway	d						11 39						12 00					12 39							13 00
Great Chesterford	d												12 04												13 04
Audley End	d					11 23	11 47						12 10				12 23	12 47							13 10
Newport (Essex)	d												12 13												13 13
Elsenham	d												12 19												13 19
Stansted Airport ✈	a					11 49											12 49								
	d	11 30		11 45				12 00		12 03	12 15			12 30		12 45			13 00			13 03	13 15		
Stansted Mountfitchet	d									12 09			12 22									13 09			13 22
Bishops Stortford	a	11 39					12 00	12 09		12 13			12 28	12 39				13 00	13 09			13 13			13 28
	d	11 39					12 00	12 09		12 14			12 28	12 39				13 00	13 09			13 14			13 28
Sawbridgeworth	d						12 05			12 18			12 32					13 05				13 18			13 32
Harlow Mill	d									12 22			12 36									13 22			13 36
Harlow Town	d			12 00			12 10			12 25	12 30		12 39			13 00		13 10				13 25	13 30		13 39
Roydon	d									12 29			12 43									13 29			13 43
Hertford East	d		11 39						12 09						12 39						13 09				
Ware	d		11 43						12 13						12 43						13 13				
St Margarets (Herts)	d		11 47						12 17						12 47						13 17				
Rye House	d		11 50						12 20						12 50						13 20				
Broxbourne 3	a		11 54				12 16		12 24	12 34			12 47		12 54			13 16			13 24	13 34			13 47
	d		11 54				12 16		12 24	12 37		←	12 47		12 54			13 16			13 24	13 37		←	13 47
Cheshunt	d		11 58				12 20		12 28	12 42 →		12 42	12 51		12 58			13 20			13 28	13 42 →		13 42	13 51
Waltham Cross	d		12 01						12 31						13 01						13 31				
Enfield Lock	d		12 03						12 33			12 45			13 03						13 33			13 45	
Brimsdown	d		12 06						12 36						13 06						13 36				
Ponders End	d		12 08						12 38						13 08						13 38				
Angel Road	d																								
Northumberland Park	d											12 51												13 51	
Tottenham Hale ⊖	d	12 03	12 14	12 17			12 29	12 32	12 44		12 47	12 55	13 00	13 03	13 14	13 17		13 29	13 32		13 44		13 47	13 55	14 00
Seven Sisters ⊖	d																								
Clapton	d																								
Stratford 7 ⊖	a											13 05												14 05	
Hackney Downs	d		12 20						12 50						13 20						13 50				
Bethnal Green	d																								
London Liverpool Street 15 ⊖	a	12 17	12 28	12 31			12 43	12 46	12 58		13 01		13 13	13 17	13 28	13 31		13 43	13 46		13 58		14 01		14 13

		LE 1 ⊼	LE 1	LE 1 ⊼	XC ◇	LE 1	LE 1 ⊼	LE 1	LE 1	LE 1 ⊼	LE 1	LE 1		LE 1 ⊼	LE 1	LE 1 ⊼	XC ◇	LE 1	LE 1 ⊼	LE 1	LE 1	LE 1 ⊼	LE 1	LE 1	LE 1 ⊼
Cambridge	d				13 09	13 32						13 51					14 09	14 32						14 51	
Shelford	d											13 56												14 56	
Whittlesford Parkway	d					13 39						14 00						14 39						15 00	
Great Chesterford	d											14 04												15 04	
Audley End	d				13 23	13 47						14 10					14 23	14 47						15 10	
Newport (Essex)	d											14 13												15 13	
Elsenham	d											14 19												15 19	
Stansted Airport ✈	a				13 49												14 49								
	d	13 30		13 45			14 00		14 03	14 15				14 30		14 45			15 00		15 03	15 15			15 30
Stansted Mountfitchet	d								14 09			14 22									15 09			15 22	
Bishops Stortford	a	13 39				14 00	14 09		14 13			14 28		14 39				15 00	15 09		15 13			15 28	15 39
	d	13 39				14 00	14 09		14 14			14 28		14 39				15 00	15 09		15 14			15 28	15 39
Sawbridgeworth	d					14 05			14 18			14 32						15 05			15 18			15 32	
Harlow Mill	d								14 22			14 36									15 22			15 36	
Harlow Town	d			14 00		14 10			14 25	14 30		14 39				15 00		15 10			15 25	15 30		15 39	
Roydon	d								14 29			14 43									15 29			15 43	
Hertford East	d		13 39					14 09							14 39					15 09					
Ware	d		13 43					14 13							14 43					15 13					
St Margarets (Herts)	d		13 47					14 17							14 47					15 17					
Rye House	d		13 50					14 20							14 50					15 20					
Broxbourne 3	a		13 54			14 16		14 24	14 34			14 47			14 54			15 16		15 24	15 34			15 47	
	d		13 54			14 16		14 24	14 37		←	14 47			14 54			15 16		15 24	15 37		←	15 47	
Cheshunt	d		13 58			14 20		14 28	14 42 →		14 42	14 51			14 58			15 20		15 28	15 42 →		15 42	15 51	
Waltham Cross	d		14 01					14 31							15 01					15 31					
Enfield Lock	d		14 03					14 33			14 45				15 03					15 33			15 45		
Brimsdown	d		14 06					14 36							15 06					15 36					
Ponders End	d		14 08					14 38							15 08					15 38					
Angel Road	d																						15 50		
Northumberland Park	d										14 51												15 52		
Tottenham Hale ⊖	d	14 03	14 14	14 17		14 29	14 32	14 44		14 47	14 55	15 00		15 03	15 14	15 17		15 29	15 32	15 44		15 47	15 56	16 00	16 03
Seven Sisters ⊖	d																								
Clapton	d																								
Stratford 7 ⊖	a										15 05												16 06		
Hackney Downs	d		14 20					14 50							15 20					15 50					
Bethnal Green	d																								
London Liverpool Street 15 ⊖	a	14 17	14 28	14 31		14 43	14 46	14 58		15 01		15 13		15 17	15 28	15 31		15 45	15 47	15 58		16 01		16 13	16 17

For general notes see front of timetable
For details of catering facilities see
Directory of Train Operators

Cambridge, Stansted Airport, Bishops Stortford, Hertford East and Broxbourne → London

Network diagram - see first page of Table 20

		LE 1	LE 1	LE 1 🚲	XC ◇		LE 1	LE 1	LE 1 🚲	LE 1	LE 1	LE 1 🚲	LE 1	LE 1	LE 1 🚲	LE 1	LE 1 🚲	XC ◇	LE 1	LE 1		LE 1 🚲	LE 1	LE 1	LE 1 🚲
Cambridge	d				15 09			15 21						15 51				16 09		16 21					
Shelford	d							15 26						15 56						16 26					
Whittlesford Parkway	d							15 30						16 00						16 30					
Great Chesterford	d							15 34						16 04						16 34					
Audley End	d				15 23			15 40						16 10				16 23		16 40					
Newport (Essex)	d							15 43						16 13						16 43					
Elsenham	d							15 49						16 19						16 49					
Stansted Airport ✈	a				15 49													16 49							
	d			15 45					16 00		16 03	16 15			16 30		16 45					17 00		17 03	17 15
Stansted Mountfitchet	d							15 52			16 09			16 22						16 52				17 09	
Bishops Stortford	a							15 58	16 09		16 13			16 28	16 39					16 58		17 09		17 13	
	d		15 48					15 58	16 09		16 14			16 28	16 39					16 58		17 09		17 14	
Sawbridgeworth	d							16 02			16 18			16 32						17 02				17 18	
Harlow Mill	d							16 06			16 22			16 36						17 06				17 22	
Harlow Town	d		15 56	16 00				16 09			16 25	16 30		16 39			17 00			17 09				17 25	17 30
Roydon	d							16 13			16 29			16 43						17 13				17 29	
Hertford East	d	15 39								16 09						16 39							17 12		
Ware	d	15 43								16 13						16 43							17 16		
St Margarets (Herts)	d	15 47								16 17						16 47							17 20		
Rye House	d	15 50								16 20						16 50							17 23		
Broxbourne 3	a	15 54	16 03					16 17		16 24	16 34			16 47		16 54				17 17			17 27	17 34	
	d	15 54	16 07					16 17		16 24	16 37		←	16 47		16 54			17 09	17 17			17 27	17 37	
Cheshunt	d	15 58	16 12					16 21		16 28	16 42		16 42	16 51		16 58			17 13	17 21			17 31	17 42	
Waltham Cross	d	16 01					←			16 31	→					17 01							17 34	→	
Enfield Lock	d	16 03	16 15				16 15			16 33			16 45			17 03			17 17				17 36		
Brimsdown	d	16 06	→							16 36						17 06							17 39		
Ponders End	d	16 08								16 38						17 08							17 41		
Angel Road	d						16 20						16 50						17 22						
Northumberland Park	d						16 22						16 52						17 24						
Tottenham Hale ⊖	d	16 14		16 17			16 26	16 30	16 33	16 44		16 47	16 56	17 00	17 03	17 14	17 17		17 27	17 30		17 33	17 46		17 49
Seven Sisters ⊖	d																								
Clapton	d																								
Stratford 7 ⊖	a						16 40						17 10						17 40						
Hackney Downs	d	16 20								16 50						17 20							17 52		
Bethnal Green	d																								
London Liverpool Street 15 ⊖	a	16 29		16 31				16 43	16 48	16 58		17 03		17 13	17 17	17 30	17 32			17 44		17 48	18 01		18 03

		LE 1	LE 1	LE 1 🚲	LE 1	XC ◇	LE 1 🚲	LE 1	LE 1	LE 1 🚲	LE 1	LE 1 🚲	LE 1		LE 1	LE 1 🚲	LE 1	LE 1 🚲	XC ◇	LE 1	LE 1 🚲	LE 1	LE 1 🚲	LE 1	LE 1
Cambridge	d		16 51			17 09			17 21						17 51				18 18	18 21					18 51
Shelford	d		16 56						17 26						17 56					18 26					18 56
Whittlesford Parkway	d		17 00						17 30						18 00					18 30					19 00
Great Chesterford	d		17 04						17 34						18 04					18 34					19 04
Audley End	d		17 10			17 23			17 40						18 10					18 40					19 10
Newport (Essex)	d		17 13						17 43						18 13					18 43					19 13
Elsenham	d		17 19						17 49						18 19					18 49					19 19
Stansted Airport ✈	a					17 43													18 47						
	d			17 30			17 45			18 00		18 15				18 30		18 45			19 00		19 15		
Stansted Mountfitchet	d		17 22						17 52	18 06					18 22					18 52	19 06				19 22
Bishops Stortford	a		17 28	17 39					17 58	18 10					18 28	18 39				18 58	19 10				19 28
	d		17 28	17 39					17 58	18 11					18 28	18 39				19 00	19 11				19 28
Sawbridgeworth	d		17 32						18 02						18 32					19 05					19 32
Harlow Mill	d		17 36						18 06						18 36										19 36
Harlow Town	d		17 39				18 00		18 09			18 30			18 39			19 00		19 10			19 30		19 39
Roydon	d		17 43						18 13						18 43										19 43
Hertford East	d				17 40						18 13		18 18				18 40					19 12		19 18	
Ware	d				17 44								18 22				18 44					19 16		19 22	
St Margarets (Herts)	d				17 48								18 26				18 48					19 20		19 26	
Rye House	d				17 51								18 29				18 51					19 23		19 29	
Broxbourne 3	a		17 47		17 55				18 17		18 27		18 33		18 47		18 57			19 16		19 27		19 33	19 47
	d	←	17 47		17 55			18 09	18 17		18 27		18 37		18 47		18 57			19 16		19 27		19 37	19 47
Cheshunt	d	17 42	17 51		17 59			18 13	18 21		18 31		18 42		18 51		19 01			19 20		19 31		19 42	19 51
Waltham Cross	d				18 02						18 34						19 04					19 34			
Enfield Lock	d	17 45			18 04			18 17			18 36		18 45				19 06					19 36		19 45	
Brimsdown	d				18 07						18 39						19 09					19 39			
Ponders End	d				18 09						18 41						19 11					19 41			
Angel Road	d	17 50						18 22					18 50											19 50	
Northumberland Park	d	17 52						18 24					18 52											19 52	
Tottenham Hale ⊖	d	17 56	18 00	18 03	18 14		18 18	18 27	18 30	18 33	18 46	18 49	18 56		19 00	19 03	19 16	19 19		19 29	19 32	19 46	19 49	19 56	20 00
Seven Sisters ⊖	d																								
Clapton	d																								
Stratford 7 ⊖	a	18 10						18 40					19 10											20 06	
Hackney Downs	d				18 20						18 52						19 22					19 52			
Bethnal Green	d																								
London Liverpool Street 15 ⊖	a		18 13	18 17	18 31		18 33		18 44	18 48	19 01	19 03			19 13	19 17	19 31	19 33		19 43	19 46	20 01	20 03		20 13

For general notes see front of timetable
For details of catering facilities see
Directory of Train Operators

Cambridge, Stansted Airport, Bishops Stortford, Hertford East and Broxbourne → London

Network diagram - see first page of Table 20

Station		LE 1 ⊥	LE 1	LE 1 ⊥	LE 1	LE 1 ⊥		LE 1	LE 1	LE 1 ⊥	XC ◇	LE 1	LE 1	LE 1 ⊥	LE 1	LE 1 ⊥	LE 1	LE 1	LE 1	LE 1	LE 1		LE 1	LE 1	LE 1
Cambridge	d				19 21						19 30		19 51				20 32							20 51	
Shelford	d				19 26								19 56											20 56	
Whittlesford Parkway	d				19 30								20 00				20 39							21 00	
Great Chesterford	d				19 34								20 04											21 04	
Audley End	d				19 40						19 44		20 10				20 47							21 10	
Newport (Essex)	d				19 43								20 13											21 13	
Elsenham	d				19 49								20 19											21 19	
Stansted Airport ✈	a										20 17														
	d	19 30		19 45		20 00			20 03	20 15				20 30		20 45		21 00		21 03	21 15				21 30
Stansted Mountfitchet	d				19 52				20 09				20 22							21 09				21 22	
Bishops Stortford	a	19 39			19 58	20 09			20 13				20 28	20 39			21 00	21 09		21 13				21 28	21 39
	d	19 39			20 00	20 09			20 14				20 28	20 39			21 00	21 09		21 14				21 28	21 39
Sawbridgeworth	d				20 05				20 18				20 32				21 05			21 18				21 32	
Harlow Mill	d								20 22				20 36							21 22				21 36	
Harlow Town	d			20 00	20 10				20 25	20 30			20 39			21 00	21 10			21 25	21 30			21 39	
Roydon	d								20 29				20 43							21 29				21 43	
Hertford East	d		19 40					20 10							20 39				21 09						
Ware	d		19 44					20 14							20 43				21 13						
St Margarets (Herts)	d		19 48					20 18							20 47				21 17						
Rye House	d		19 51					20 21							20 50				21 20						
Broxbourne 3	a		19 57		20 16			20 25	20 34				20 47		20 54		21 16		21 24	21 34				21 47	
	d		19 57		20 16			20 25	20 40			←	20 47		20 54		21 16		21 24	21 37			←	21 47	
Cheshunt	d		20 01		20 20			20 29	20 45			20 45	20 51		20 58		21 20		21 28	21 42			21 42	21 51	
Waltham Cross	d		20 03					20 32	→						21 01				21 31	→					
Enfield Lock	d		20 06					20 34				20 48			21 03				21 33				21 45		
Brimsdown	d		20 08					20 37							21 06				21 36						
Ponders End	d		20 10					20 39							21 08				21 38						
Angel Road	d																								
Northumberland Park	d											20 54											21 51		
Tottenham Hale	⊖ d	20 03	20 15	20 18	20 29	20 32		20 45		20 48		20 57	21 00	21 03	21 14	21 17	21 29	21 32	21 44		21 47		21 55	22 00	22 03
Seven Sisters	⊖ d																								
Clapton	d																								
Stratford 7	⊖ a											21 08											22 05		
Hackney Downs	d		20 22					20 50							21 20				21 50						
Bethnal Green	d																								
London Liverpool Street 15	⊖ a	20 17	20 31	20 33	20 45	20 47		21 01		21 03			21 14	21 17	21 28	21 31	21 43	21 46	21 58		22 01			22 13	22 17

Station		LE 1	LE 1	LE 1	LE 1	LE 1	LE 1	LE 1	LE 1	LE 1	LE 1	LE 1	LE 1	LE 1		LE 1	LE 1	LE 1	LE 1	LE 1	LE 1	LE 1	LE 1		
Cambridge	d			21 32					21 51				22 32						22 51						
Shelford	d								21 56										22 56						
Whittlesford Parkway	d			21 39					22 00				22 39						23 00						
Great Chesterford	d								22 04										23 04						
Audley End	d			21 47					22 10				22 47						23 10						
Newport (Essex)	d								22 13										23 13						
Elsenham	d								22 19										23 19						
Stansted Airport ✈	a																								
	d		21 45		22 00		22 03	22 15		22 30		22 45		23 00			23 03	23 15		23 30		23 45	23 59		
Stansted Mountfitchet	d						22 09		22 22								23 09		23 22						
Bishops Stortford	a			22 00	22 09		22 13		22 28	22 39			23 00	23 09			23 13		23 28	23 39			00 08		
	d			22 00	22 09				22 28	22 39			23 00	23 09					23 28	23 39			00 08		
Sawbridgeworth	d			22 05					22 32				23 05						23 32						
Harlow Mill	d								22 36										23 36						
Harlow Town	d		22 00	22 10				22 30	22 39			23 00	23 10					23 30	23 39			23 59	00 16		
Roydon	d								22 43										23 43						
Hertford East	d	21 39				22 09					22 39					23 09					23 39				
Ware	d	21 43				22 13					22 43					23 13					23 43				
St Margarets (Herts)	d	21 47				22 17					22 47					23 17					23 47				
Rye House	d	21 50				22 20					22 50					23 20					23 50				
Broxbourne 3	a	21 54		22 16		22 24			22 47		22 54		23 16			23 24			23 47		23 54				
	d	21 54		22 16		22 24			22 47		22 54		23 16			23 24			23 47		23 54				
Cheshunt	d	21 58		22 20		22 28			22 51		22 58		23 20			23 28			23 51		23 58				
Waltham Cross	d	22 01				22 31					23 01					23 31									
Enfield Lock	d	22 03				22 33					23 03					23 33									
Brimsdown	d	22 06				22 36					23 06					23 36									
Ponders End	d	22 08				22 38					23 08					23 38									
Angel Road	d																								
Northumberland Park	d																								
Tottenham Hale	⊖ d	22 14	22 17	22 29	22 32	22 44		22 47	23 00	23 03	23 14	23 17	23 29	23 32		23 44		23 47							
Seven Sisters	⊖ d																		00 04	00 07	00 11	00 21			
Clapton	d																								
Stratford 7	⊖ a																								
Hackney Downs	d	22 20				22 50					23 20					23 50					00 16				
Bethnal Green	d																								
London Liverpool Street 15	⊖ a	22 28	22 31	22 43	22 46	22 58		23 01	23 13	23 17	23 28	23 31	23 43	23 46		23 58		00 01	00 18	00 22	00 25	00 36	00 51		

For general notes see front of timetable
For details of catering facilities see Directory of Train Operators

Cambridge, Stansted Airport, Bishops Stortford, Hertford East and Broxbourne → London

Network diagram - see first page of Table 20

Station		LE 1	LE 1	LE 1	LE 1	LE 1	LE 1	LE 1	LE 1	LE 1	XC	LE 1	LE 1	LE 1	LE 1	LE 1	LE 1	LE 1	LE 1	LE 1	LE 1	LE 1	LE 1	XC	LE 1
Cambridge	d	22p51								04 25	04 39			05 21						05 51				06 25	06 32
Shelford	d	22p56												05 26						05 56					
Whittlesford Parkway	d	23p00								04 32				05 30						06 00					06 39
Great Chesterford	d	23p04												05 34						06 04					
Audley End	d	23p10								04 40	04 53			05 40						06 10				06 39	06 47
Newport (Essex)	d	23p13												05 43						06 13					
Elsenham	d	23p19												05 49						06 19					
Stansted Airport ✈	a										05 13													06 58	
✈	d		23p30		23p45	23p59	00 30	01 00	01 30				05 30		06 00		06 03	06 15			06 30		06 45		
Stansted Mountfitchet	d	23p22												05 52			06 09			06 22			06 51		
Bishops Stortford	a	23p28	23p39			00 08	00 39			04 53			05 39	05 58	06 09		06 13			06 28	06 39				07 00
	d	23p28	23p39			00 08	00 39			04 53		05 15	05 39	05 58	06 09		06 14			06 28	06 39				07 00
Sawbridgeworth	d	23p32								04 58		05 19		06 02			06 18			06 32					07 05
Harlow Mill	d	23p36								05 01		05 23		06 06			06 22			06 36					
Harlow Town	d	23p39			23p59	00 16	00 47			05 04		05 26		06 09			06 25	06 30		06 39			07 02		07 10
Roydon	d	23p43								05 08		05 30		06 13			06 29			06 43					
Hertford East	d			23p39												06 09						06 39			
Ware	d			23p43												06 13						06 43			
St Margarets (Herts)	d			23p47												06 17						06 47			
Rye House	d			23p50												06 20						06 50			
Broxbourne 3	a	23p47		23p54						05 12		05 34		06 17		06 24	06 34			06 47		06 54			07 16
	d	23p47		23p54						05 12		05 34		06 17		06 24	06 37		←	06 47		06 54			07 16
Cheshunt	d	23p51		23p58						05 16		05 38		06 21		06 28	06 42		06 42	06 51		06 58			07 20
Waltham Cross	d											05 40				06 31	→					07 01			
Enfield Lock	d											05 43				06 33			06 45			07 03			
Brimsdown	d											05 45				06 36						07 06			
Ponders End	d											05 47				06 38						07 08			
Angel Road	d																								
Northumberland Park	d											05 51							06 51						
Tottenham Hale ⊖	d											05 55	06 01	06 30	06 33	06 44		06 47	06 55	07 00	07 03	07 14	07 17		07 29
Seven Sisters ⊖	d	00 04	00 07	00 11	00 21					05 36															
Clapton	d																								
Stratford 7 ⊖	a											06 04							07 05						
Hackney Downs	d			00 16						05 45						06 50						07 20			
Bethnal Green	d									05 49															
London Liverpool Street 15 ⊖	a	00 18	00 22	00 25	00 36	00 51	01 21	01 50	02 20	05 54		06 14	06 15	06 43	06 47	06 58		07 01		07 13	07 17	07 28	07 31		07 43

Station		LE 1		LE 1	LE 1	LE 1	LE 1	LE 1	LE 1	LE 1	LE 1	XC	LE 1	LE 1	LE 1	LE 1	LE 1 🚲	LE 1	LE 1	LE 1 🚲	LE 1	LE 1 🚲	XC ◇	LE 1	LE 1 🚲
Cambridge	d							06 51				07 24	07 32						07 51				08 09	08 32	
Shelford	d							06 56											07 56						
Whittlesford Parkway	d							07 00					07 39						08 00					08 39	
Great Chesterford	d							07 04											08 04						
Audley End	d							07 10				07 38	07 47						08 10				08 23	08 47	
Newport (Essex)	d							07 13											08 13						
Elsenham	d							07 19											08 19						
Stansted Airport ✈	a											07 58											08 49		
✈	d	07 00			07 03	07 15			07 30		07 45			08 00		08 03	08 15			08 30		08 45			09 00
Stansted Mountfitchet	d				07 09			07 22			07 51					08 09			08 22			08 51			
Bishops Stortford	a	07 09			07 13			07 28	07 39				08 00	08 09		08 13			08 28	08 39				09 00	09 09
	d	07 09			07 14			07 28	07 39				08 00	08 09		08 14			08 28	08 39				09 00	09 09
Sawbridgeworth	d				07 18			07 32					08 05			08 18			08 32					09 05	
Harlow Mill	d				07 22			07 36								08 22			08 36						
Harlow Town	d				07 25	07 30		07 39			08 02		08 10			08 25	08 30		08 39			09 02		09 10	
Roydon	d				07 29			07 43								08 29			08 43						
Hertford East	d			07 09						07 39					08 09						08 39				
Ware	d			07 13						07 43					08 13						08 43				
St Margarets (Herts)	d			07 17						07 47					08 17						08 47				
Rye House	d			07 20						07 50					08 20						08 50				
Broxbourne 3	a			07 24	07 34			07 47		07 54			08 16		08 24	08 34			08 47		08 54			09 16	
	d			07 24	07 37		←	07 47		07 54			08 16		08 24	08 37		←	08 47		08 54			09 16	
Cheshunt	d			07 28	07 42		07 42	07 51		07 58			08 20		08 28	08 42		08 42	08 51		08 58			09 20	
Waltham Cross	d			07 31	→					08 01					08 31	→					09 01				
Enfield Lock	d			07 33			07 45			08 03					08 33			08 45			09 03				
Brimsdown	d			07 36						08 06					08 36						09 06				
Ponders End	d			07 38						08 08					08 38						09 08				
Angel Road	d																								
Northumberland Park	d						07 51											08 51							
Tottenham Hale ⊖	d	07 32		07 44		07 47	07 55	08 00	08 03	08 14	08 17		08 29	08 32	08 44		08 47	08 55	09 00	09 03	09 14	09 17		09 29	09 32
Seven Sisters ⊖	d																								
Clapton	d																								
Stratford 7 ⊖	a						08 05											09 05							
Hackney Downs	d			07 50						08 20					08 50						09 20				
Bethnal Green	d																								
London Liverpool Street 15 ⊖	a	07 46		07 58		08 01		08 13	08 17	08 28	08 31		08 43	08 46	08 58		09 01		09 13	09 17	09 28	09 31		09 43	09 46

For general notes see front of timetable
For details of catering facilities see Directory of Train Operators

Table 22

Saturdays

Cambridge, Stansted Airport, Bishops Stortford, Hertford East and Broxbourne → London

Network diagram - see first page of Table 20

Station		LE 1	LE 1	LE 1		LE 1	LE 1	LE 1	LE 1	LE 1	XC ◇	LE 1	LE 1	LE 1	LE 1	LE 1	LE 1	LE 1	LE 1	LE 1	LE 1	XC ◇	LE 1	LE 1	LE 1
												A													
				🍴				🍴		🍴			🍴			🍴			🍴		🍴			🍴	
Cambridge	d						08 51				09 24	09 32						09 51				10 09	10 32		
Shelford	d						08 56											09 56							
Whittlesford Parkway	d						09 00					09 39						10 00					10 39		
Great Chesterford	d						09 04											10 04							
Audley End	d						09 10				09 38	09 47						10 10				10 23	10 47		
Newport (Essex)	d						09 13											10 13							
Elsenham	d						09 19											10 19							
Stansted Airport ✈	a										09 58											10 49			
✈	d		09 03	09 15				09 30		09 45			10 00		10 03	10 15			10 30		10 45			11 00	
Stansted Mountfitchet	d		09 09				09 22			09 51					10 09			10 22			10 51				
Bishops Stortford	a		09 13				09 28	09 39				10 00	10 09		10 13			10 28	10 39				11 00	11 09	
	d		09 14				09 28	09 39				10 00	10 09		10 14			10 28	10 39				11 00	11 09	
Sawbridgeworth	d		09 18				09 32					10 05			10 18			10 32					11 05		
Harlow Mill	d		09 22				09 36								10 22			10 36							
Harlow Town	d		09 25	09 30			09 39			10 02		10 10			10 25	10 30		10 39			11 02		11 10		
Roydon	d		09 29				09 43								10 29			10 43							
Hertford East	d	09 09							09 39					10 09						10 39					11 09
Ware	d	09 13							09 43					10 13						10 43					11 13
St Margarets (Herts)	d	09 17							09 47					10 17						10 47					11 17
Rye House	d	09 20							09 50					10 20						10 50					11 20
Broxbourne 3	a	09 24	09 34				09 47		09 54			10 16		10 24	10 34			10 47		10 54			11 16		11 24
	d	09 24	09 37			←	09 47		09 54			10 16		10 24	10 37		←	10 47		10 54			11 16		11 24
Cheshunt	d	09 28	09 42			09 42	09 51		09 58			10 20		10 28	10 42		10 42	10 51		10 58			11 20		11 28
Waltham Cross	d	09 31	→						10 01					10 31	→					11 01					11 31
Enfield Lock	d	09 33				09 45			10 03					10 33			10 45			11 03					11 33
Brimsdown	d	09 36							10 06					10 36						11 06					11 36
Ponders End	d	09 38							10 08					10 38						11 08					11 38
Angel Road	d																								
Northumberland Park	d					09 51											10 51								
Tottenham Hale ⊖	d	09 44		09 47		09 55	10 00	10 03	10 14	10 17		10 29	10 32	10 44		10 47	10 55	11 00	11 03	11 14	11 17		11 29	11 32	11 44
Seven Sisters ⊖	d																								
Clapton	d																								
Stratford 7 ⊖ ⛴	a					10 05											11 05								
Hackney Downs	d	09 50							10 20					10 50						11 20					11 50
Bethnal Green	d																								
London Liverpool Street 15 ⊖	a	09 58		10 01			10 13	10 17	10 28	10 31		10 43	10 46	10 58		11 01		11 13	11 17	11 28	11 31		11 43	11 46	11 58

Station		LE 1	LE 1	LE 1	LE 1	LE 1		LE 1	LE 1	XC ◇	LE 1	LE 1	LE 1	LE 1	LE 1	LE 1	LE 1	LE 1	LE 1	LE 1	XC ◇	LE 1	LE 1	LE 1	LE 1
			🍴			🍴			🍴			🍴			🍴			🍴		🍴			🍴		
Cambridge	d				10 51					11 09	11 32						11 51				12 09	12 32			
Shelford	d				10 56												11 56								
Whittlesford Parkway	d				11 00						11 39						12 00					12 39			
Great Chesterford	d				11 04												12 04								
Audley End	d				11 10					11 23	11 47						12 10				12 23	12 47			
Newport (Essex)	d				11 13												12 13								
Elsenham	d				11 19												12 19								
Stansted Airport ✈	a									11 49											12 49				
✈	d	11 03	11 15			11 30			11 45			12 00		12 03	12 15			12 30		12 45			13 00		13 03
Stansted Mountfitchet	d	11 09			11 22				11 51					12 09			12 22			12 51					13 09
Bishops Stortford	a	11 13			11 28	11 39					12 00	12 09		12 13			12 28	12 39				13 00	13 09		13 13
	d	11 14			11 28	11 39					12 00	12 09		12 14			12 28	12 39				13 00	13 09		13 14
Sawbridgeworth	d	11 18			11 32						12 05			12 18			12 32					13 05			13 18
Harlow Mill	d	11 22			11 36									12 22			12 36								13 22
Harlow Town	d	11 25	11 30		11 39				12 02		12 10			12 25	12 30		12 39			13 02		13 10			13 25
Roydon	d	11 29			11 43									12 29			12 43								13 29
Hertford East	d							11 39					12 09						12 39					13 09	
Ware	d							11 43					12 13						12 43					13 13	
St Margarets (Herts)	d							11 47					12 17						12 47					13 17	
Rye House	d							11 50					12 20						12 50					13 20	
Broxbourne 3	a	11 34			11 47			11 54			12 16		12 24	12 34			12 47		12 54			13 16		13 24	13 34
	d	11 37		←	11 47			11 54			12 16		12 24	12 37		←	12 47		12 54			13 16		13 24	13 37
Cheshunt	d	11 42		11 42	11 51			11 58			12 20		12 28	12 42		12 42	12 51		12 58			13 20		13 28	13 42
Waltham Cross	d	→						12 01					12 31	→					13 01					13 31	→
Enfield Lock	d			11 45				12 03					12 33			12 45			13 03					13 33	
Brimsdown	d							12 06					12 36						13 06					13 36	
Ponders End	d							12 08					12 38						13 08					13 38	
Angel Road	d																								
Northumberland Park	d			11 51												12 51									
Tottenham Hale ⊖	d		11 47	11 55	12 00	12 03		12 14	12 17		12 29	12 32	12 44		12 47	12 55	13 00	13 03	13 14	13 17		13 29	13 32	13 44	
Seven Sisters ⊖	d																								
Clapton	d																								
Stratford 7 ⊖ ⛴	a			12 05												13 05									
Hackney Downs	d							12 20					12 50						13 20					13 50	
Bethnal Green	d																								
London Liverpool Street 15 ⊖	a		12 01		12 13	12 17		12 28	12 31		12 43	12 46	12 58		13 01		13 13	13 17	13 28	13 31		13 43	13 46	13 58	

For general notes see front of timetable
For details of catering facilities see Directory of Train Operators

A From Ely (Table 17)

Table 22

Saturdays

Cambridge, Stansted Airport, Bishops Stortford, Hertford East and Broxbourne → London

Network diagram - see first page of Table 20

		LE 1 🚲	LE 1	LE 1	LE 1 🚲	LE 1	LE 1 🚲	XC ◇		LE 1	LE 1 🚲	LE 1	LE 1	LE 1 🚲	LE 1	LE 1	LE 1 🚲	LE 1	LE 1 🚲	XC ◇	LE 1	LE 1 🚲	LE 1	LE 1	LE 1 🚲
Cambridge	d			12 51				13 09		13 32						13 51				14 09	14 32				
Shelford	d			12 56												13 56									
Whittlesford Parkway	d			13 00						13 39						14 00					14 39				
Great Chesterford	d			13 04												14 04									
Audley End	d			13 10				13 23		13 47						14 10				14 23	14 47				
Newport (Essex)	d			13 13												14 13									
Elsenham	d			13 19												14 19									
Stansted Airport ✈	a							13 49												14 49					
✈	d	13 15			13 30		13 45				14 00		14 03	14 15			14 30		14 45			15 00		15 03	15 15
Stansted Mountfitchet	d			13 22			13 51						14 09			14 22			14 51					15 09	
Bishops Stortford	a			13 28	13 39					14 00	14 09		14 13			14 28	14 39				15 00	15 09		15 13	
	d			13 28	13 39					14 00	14 09		14 14			14 28	14 39				15 00	15 09		15 14	
Sawbridgeworth	d			13 32						14 05			14 18			14 32					15 05			15 18	
Harlow Mill	d			13 36									14 22			14 36								15 22	
Harlow Town	d	13 30		13 39			14 02			14 10			14 25	14 30		14 39			15 02		15 10			15 25	15 30
Roydon	d			13 43									14 29			14 43								15 29	
Hertford East	d					13 39						14 09						14 39					15 09		
Ware	d					13 43						14 13						14 43					15 13		
St Margarets (Herts)	d					13 47						14 17						14 47					15 17		
Rye House	d					13 50						14 20						14 50					15 20		
Broxbourne 3	a			13 47		13 54				14 16		14 24	14 34			14 47		14 54			15 16		15 24	15 34	
	d		←	13 47		13 54				14 16		14 24	14 37		←	14 47		14 54			15 16		15 24	15 37	
Cheshunt	d		13 42	13 51		13 58				14 20		14 28	14 42		14 42	14 51		14 58			15 20		15 28	15 42	
Waltham Cross	d					14 01						14 31	→					15 01					15 31	→	
Enfield Lock	d		13 45			14 03						14 33			14 45			15 03					15 33		
Brimsdown	d					14 06						14 36						15 06					15 36		
Ponders End	d					14 08						14 38						15 08					15 38		
Angel Road	d																								
Northumberland Park	d		13 51												14 51										
Tottenham Hale ⊖	d	13 47	13 55	14 00	14 03	14 14	14 17			14 29	14 32	14 44		14 47	14 55	15 00	15 03	15 14	15 17		15 29	15 32	15 44		15 47
Seven Sisters ⊖	d																								
Clapton	d																								
Stratford 7 ⊖	a		14 05												15 05										
Hackney Downs	d					14 20						14 50						15 20					15 50		
Bethnal Green	d																								
London Liverpool Street 15 ⊖	a	14 01		14 13	14 17	14 28	14 31			14 43	14 46	14 58		15 01		15 13	15 17	15 28	15 31		15 43	15 46	15 58		16 01

		LE 1	LE 1	LE 1 🚲	LE 1	LE 1 🚲	XC ◇	LE 1	LE 1 🚲	LE 1		LE 1	LE 1 🚲	LE 1	LE 1	LE 1 🚲	LE 1	LE 1 🚲	XC ◇	LE 1	LE 1 🚲	LE 1	LE 1	LE 1 🚲	LE 1
Cambridge	d		14 51				15 09	15 32							15 51				16 09	16 32					
Shelford	d		14 56												15 56										
Whittlesford Parkway	d		15 00					15 39							16 00					16 39					
Great Chesterford	d		15 04												16 04										
Audley End	d		15 10				15 23	15 47							16 10				16 23	16 47					
Newport (Essex)	d		15 13												16 13										
Elsenham	d		15 19												16 19										
Stansted Airport ✈	a						15 49												16 49						
✈	d			15 30		15 45			16 00			16 03	16 15			16 30		16 45			17 00		17 03	17 15	
Stansted Mountfitchet	d		15 22			15 51						16 09			16 22			16 51					17 09		
Bishops Stortford	a		15 28	15 39				16 00	16 09			16 13			16 28	16 39				17 00	17 09		17 13		
	d		15 28	15 39				16 00	16 09			16 14			16 28	16 39				17 00	17 09		17 14		
Sawbridgeworth	d		15 32					16 05				16 18			16 32					17 05			17 18		
Harlow Mill	d		15 36									16 22			16 36								17 22		
Harlow Town	d		15 39			16 02		16 10				16 25	16 30		16 39			17 02		17 10			17 25	17 30	
Roydon	d		15 43									16 29			16 43								17 29		
Hertford East	d				15 39					16 09							16 39					17 09			
Ware	d				15 43					16 13							16 43					17 13			
St Margarets (Herts)	d				15 47					16 17							16 47					17 17			
Rye House	d				15 50					16 20							16 50					17 20			
Broxbourne 3	a		15 47		15 54			16 16		16 24		16 34			16 47		16 54			17 16		17 24	17 34		
	d	←	15 47		15 54			16 16		16 24		16 37		←	16 47		16 54			17 16		17 24	17 37		←
Cheshunt	d	15 42	15 51		15 58			16 20		16 28		16 42		16 42	16 51		16 58			17 20		17 28	17 42		17 42
Waltham Cross	d				16 01					16 31		→					17 01					17 31	→		
Enfield Lock	d	15 45			16 03					16 33				16 45			17 03					17 33			17 45
Brimsdown	d				16 06					16 36							17 06					17 36			
Ponders End	d				16 08					16 38							17 08					17 38			
Angel Road	d																								
Northumberland Park	d	15 51												16 51											17 51
Tottenham Hale ⊖	d	15 55	16 00	16 03	16 14	16 17		16 29	16 32	16 44			16 47	16 55	17 00	17 03	17 14	17 17		17 29	17 32	17 44		17 47	17 55
Seven Sisters ⊖	d																								
Clapton	d																								
Stratford 7 ⊖	a	16 05												17 05											18 05
Hackney Downs	d				16 20					16 50							17 20					17 50			
Bethnal Green	d																								
London Liverpool Street 15 ⊖	a		16 13	16 17	16 28	16 31		16 43	16 46	16 58			17 01		17 13	17 17	17 28	17 31		17 43	17 46	17 58		18 01	

For general notes see front of timetable
For details of catering facilities see
Directory of Train Operators

Cambridge, Stansted Airport, Bishops Stortford, Hertford East and Broxbourne → London

Network diagram - see first page of Table 20

		LE 1	LE 1 🚲	LE 1	LE 1 🚲	XC ◇	LE 1	LE 1 🚲	LE 1	LE 1	LE 1 🚲	LE 1		LE 1	LE 1 🚲	LE 1	LE 1 🚲	XC ◇	LE 1	LE 1 🚲	LE 1	LE 1	LE 1 🚲	LE 1	LE 1
Cambridge	d	16 51				17 18	17 32							17 51				18 18	18 32						18 51
Shelford	d	16 56												17 56											18 56
Whittlesford Parkway	d	17 00					17 39							18 00					18 39						19 00
Great Chesterford	d	17 04												18 04											19 04
Audley End	d	17 10				17 32	17 47							18 10				18 32	18 47						19 10
Newport (Essex)	d	17 13												18 13											19 13
Elsenham	d	17 19												18 19											19 19
Stansted Airport ✈	a					17 49												18 58							
	d		17 30		17 45			18 00		18 03	18 15				18 30		18 45			19 00		19 03	19 15		
Stansted Mountfitchet	d	17 22			17 51					18 09				18 22			18 51					19 09			19 22
Bishops Stortford	a	17 28	17 39				18 00	18 09		18 13				18 28	18 39				19 00	19 09		19 13			19 28
	d	17 28	17 39				18 00	18 09		18 14				18 28	18 39				19 00	19 09		19 14			19 28
Sawbridgeworth	d	17 32					18 05			18 18				18 32					19 05			19 18			19 32
Harlow Mill	d	17 36								18 22				18 36								19 22			19 36
Harlow Town	d	17 39			18 02		18 10			18 25	18 30			18 39			19 02		19 10			19 25	19 30		19 39
Roydon	d	17 43								18 29				18 43								19 29			19 43
Hertford East	d			17 39					18 09							18 39					19 09				
Ware	d			17 43					18 13							18 43					19 13				
St Margarets (Herts)	d			17 47					18 17							18 47					19 17				
Rye House	d			17 50					18 20							18 50					19 20				
Broxbourne 3	a	17 47		17 54			18 16		18 24	18 34				18 47		18 54			19 16		19 24	19 34			19 47
	d	17 47		17 54			18 16		18 24	18 37		←		18 47		18 54			19 16		19 24	19 37		←	19 47
Cheshunt	d	17 51		17 58			18 20		18 28	18 42 →		18 42		18 51		18 58			19 20		19 28	19 42 →		19 42	19 51
Waltham Cross	d			18 01					18 31							19 01					19 31				
Enfield Lock	d			18 03					18 33			18 45				19 03					19 33			19 45	
Brimsdown	d			18 06					18 36							19 06					19 36				
Ponders End	d			18 08					18 38							19 08					19 38				
Angel Road	d																								
Northumberland Park	d											18 51												19 51	
Tottenham Hale ⊖	d	18 00	18 03	18 14	18 17		18 29	18 32	18 44		18 47	18 55		19 00	19 03	19 14	19 17		19 29	19 32	19 44		19 47	19 55	20 00
Seven Sisters ⊖	d																								
Clapton	d																								
Stratford 7 ⊖ ⛴	a											19 05												20 05	
Hackney Downs	d			18 20					18 50							19 20					19 50				
Bethnal Green	d																								
London Liverpool Street 15 ⊖	a	18 13	18 17	18 28	18 31		18 43	18 46	18 58		19 01			19 13	19 17	19 28	19 31		19 43	19 46	19 58		20 01		20 13

		LE 1 🚲	LE 1	LE 1 🚲	LE 1	LE 1 🚲	LE 1	LE 1	LE 1 🚲	LE 1	LE 1	LE 1 🚲	LE 1	LE 1 🚲		XC ◇	LE 1	LE 1	LE 1	LE 1	LE 1	LE 1	LE 1	LE 1	LE 1
Cambridge	d				19 32						19 51					20 13	20 32						20 51		
Shelford	d										19 56												20 56		
Whittlesford Parkway	d				19 39						20 00						20 39						21 00		
Great Chesterford	d										20 04												21 04		
Audley End	d				19 47						20 10					20 27	20 47						21 10		
Newport (Essex)	d										20 13												21 13		
Elsenham	d										20 19												21 19		
Stansted Airport ✈	a															20 50									
	d	19 30		19 45		20 00		20 03	20 15			20 30		20 45				21 00		21 03	21 15			21 30	
Stansted Mountfitchet	d			19 51				20 09			20 22			20 51						21 09			21 22		
Bishops Stortford	a	19 39			20 00	20 09		20 13			20 28	20 39					21 00	21 09		21 13			21 28	21 39	
	d	19 39			20 00	20 09		20 14			20 28	20 39					21 00	21 09		21 14			21 28	21 39	
Sawbridgeworth	d				20 05			20 18			20 32						21 05			21 18			21 32		
Harlow Mill	d							20 22			20 36									21 22			21 36		
Harlow Town	d			20 02	20 10			20 25	20 30		20 39			21 02			21 10			21 25	21 30		21 39		
Roydon	d							20 29			20 43									21 29			21 43		
Hertford East	d		19 39				20 09						20 39						21 09						21 39
Ware	d		19 43				20 13						20 43						21 13						21 43
St Margarets (Herts)	d		19 47				20 17						20 47						21 17						21 47
Rye House	d		19 50				20 20						20 50						21 20						21 50
Broxbourne 3	a		19 54		20 16		20 24	20 34			20 47		20 54				21 16		21 24	21 34			21 47		21 54
	d		19 54		20 16		20 24	20 37		←	20 47		20 54				21 16		21 24	21 37		←	21 47		21 54
Cheshunt	d		19 58		20 20		20 28	20 42 →		20 42	20 51		20 58				21 20		21 28	21 42 →		21 42	21 51		21 58
Waltham Cross	d		20 01				20 31						21 01						21 31						22 01
Enfield Lock	d		20 03				20 33			20 45			21 03						21 33			21 45			22 03
Brimsdown	d		20 06				20 36						21 06						21 36						22 06
Ponders End	d		20 08				20 38						21 08						21 38						22 08
Angel Road	d																								
Northumberland Park	d									20 51												21 51			
Tottenham Hale ⊖	d	20 03	20 14	20 17	20 29	20 32	20 44		20 47	20 55	21 00	21 03	21 14	21 17			21 29	21 32	21 44		21 47	21 55	22 00	22 03	22 14
Seven Sisters ⊖	d																								
Clapton	d																								
Stratford 7 ⊖ ⛴	a									21 05												22 05			
Hackney Downs	d		20 20				20 50						21 20						21 50						22 20
Bethnal Green	d																								
London Liverpool Street 15 ⊖	a	20 17	20 28	20 31	20 43	20 46	20 58		21 01		21 13	21 17	21 28	21 31			21 43	21 46	21 58		22 01		22 13	22 17	22 28

For general notes see front of timetable
For details of catering facilities see
Directory of Train Operators

Table 22

Saturdays

Cambridge, Stansted Airport, Bishops Stortford, Hertford East and Broxbourne → London

Network diagram - see first page of Table 20

Station		LE 1	LE 1	LE 1	LE 1	LE 1	LE 1	LE 1	LE 1	LE 1	LE 1	LE 1	LE 1	LE 1	LE 1	LE 1	LE 1	LE 1	LE 1	LE 1	LE 1	LE 1	LE 1
Cambridge	d		21 32					21 51				22 32						22 51					
Shelford	d							21 56										22 56					
Whittlesford Parkway	d		21 39					22 00				22 39						23 00					
Great Chesterford	d							22 04										23 04					
Audley End	d		21 47					22 10				22 47						23 10					
Newport (Essex)	d							22 13										23 13					
Elsenham	d							22 19										23 19					
Stansted Airport ✈	a																						
✈	d	21 45		22 00		22 03	22 15		22 30		22 45		23 00		23 03	23 15				23 30		23 45	23 59
Stansted Mountfitchet	d	21 51				22 09		22 22			22 51				23 09			23 22					
Bishops Stortford	a		22 00	22 09		22 13		22 28	22 39			23 00	23 09		23 13			23 28		23 39			00 08
	d		22 00	22 09				22 28	22 39			23 00	23 09		23 14			23 28		23 39			00 08
Sawbridgeworth	d		22 05					22 32				23 05			23 18			23 32					
Harlow Mill	d							22 36							23 22			23 36					
Harlow Town	d	22 02	22 10				22 30	22 39			23 02	23 10			23 25	23 30		23 39				23 59	00 16
Roydon	d							22 43							23 29			23 43					
Hertford East	d				22 09					22 39				23 09							23 39		
Ware	d				22 13					22 43				23 13							23 43		
St Margarets (Herts)	d				22 17					22 47				23 17							23 47		
Rye House	d				22 20					22 50				23 20							23 50		
Broxbourne 3	a		22 16		22 24			22 47		22 54		23 16		23 24	23 34			23 47			23 54		
	d		22 16		22 24			22 47		22 54		23 16		23 24	23 37		←	23 47			23 54		
Cheshunt	d		22 20		22 28			22 51		22 58		23 20		23 28	23 42		23 42	23 51			23 58		
Waltham Cross	d				22 31					23 01				23 31	→						00 01		
Enfield Lock	d				22 33					23 03				23 33							00 03		
Brimsdown	d				22 36					23 06				23 36			23 45				00 06		
Ponders End	d				22 38					23 08				23 38							00 08		
Angel Road	d																						
Northumberland Park	d							22 58									23 51		←				
Tottenham Hale ⊖	d	22 17	22 29	22 32	22 44		22 47	23 01	23 03	23 14	23 17	23 29	23 32	23 44		23 47	23 55	23 59	23 55	00 03	00 14	00 17	
Seven Sisters ⊖	d																→						
Clapton	d																						
Stratford 7 ⊖	a																		00 04				
Hackney Downs	d				22 50					23 20				23 50							00 20		
Bethnal Green	d																						
London Liverpool Street 15 ⊖	a	22 31	22 43	22 46	22 58		23 01	23 15	23 18	23 28	23 31	23 43	23 46	23 58		00 01		00 13	00 14	00 17	00 28	00 31	00 51

Sundays

Station		LE 1	LE 1	LE 1	LE 1	LE 1	LE 1	LE 1	LE 1		LE 1	LE 1	LE 1	LE 1	LE 1	LE 1	LE 1	LE		LE 1	LE 1	LE 1	LE	LE 1	LE
Cambridge	d																				07 32				
Shelford	d																								
Whittlesford Parkway	d																				07 39				
Great Chesterford	d																								
Audley End	d																				07 47				
Newport (Essex)	d																								
Elsenham	d																								
Stansted Airport ✈	a																								
✈	d	23p03	23p30		23p45	23p59	00 30	05 30	06 00		06 30		07 00	07 15		07 30				07 45		08 00		08 15	
Stansted Mountfitchet	d	23p09																		07 51					
Bishops Stortford	a	23p13	23p39			00 08	00 39	05 39	06 09		06 39		07 09			07 39					08 00	08 09			
	d	23p14	23p39			00 08	00 39	05 39	06 09		06 39	06 42	07 09		07 28	07 39					08 00	08 09			
Sawbridgeworth	d	23p18										06 46			07 32						08 05				
Harlow Mill	d	23p22													07 36										
Harlow Town	d	23p25			23p59	00 16	00 47	05 47	06 17		06 47	06 51	07 17	07 30	07 39					08 02	08 10			08 30	
Roydon	d	23p29													07 43										
Hertford East	d			23p39														07 55							08 25
Ware	d			23p43														07 59							08 29
St Margarets (Herts)	d			23p47														08 03							08 33
Rye House	d			23p50														08 06							08 36
Broxbourne 3	a	23p34		23p54								06 57			07 48		←	08 11			08 16				08 41
	d	23p37		23p54								06 57			07 52		07 52	08 11			08 16				08 41
Cheshunt	d	23p42		23p58								07 01			→		07 57	08 15			08 20				08 45
Waltham Cross	d			00 01								07 04					07 59								
Enfield Lock	d	23p45		00 03								07 06					08 02								
Brimsdown	d			00 06								07 09					08 04								
Ponders End	d			00 08								07 11					08 06								
Angel Road	d																								
Northumberland Park	d	23p51																							
Tottenham Hale ⊖	d	23p55	00 03	00 14	00 17			06 04	06 33		07 03	07 17	07 33	07 46		08 01	08 12			08 17	08 29	08 32	←	08 46	
Seven Sisters ⊖	d																								
Clapton	d																	08 33 →					08 33		09 03
Stratford 7 ⊖	a	00 04																							
Hackney Downs	d			00 20													08 23								
Bethnal Green	d																						08 39		09 09 →
London Liverpool Street 15 ⊖	a	00 14	00 17	00 28	00 31	00 51	01 21	06 17	06 46		07 16	07 30	07 46	08 00		08 15				08 31	08 43	08 46	08 48	09 03	

For general notes see front of timetable
For details of catering facilities see
Directory of Train Operators

Cambridge, Stansted Airport, Bishops Stortford, Hertford East and Broxbourne → London

Network diagram - see first page of Table 20

		LE 1	LE 1 trolley	LE	LE 1		LE	LE 1 trolley	LE 1	LE 1 trolley	LE	LE 1 trolley	LE	LE 1		LE 1 trolley	LE	LE 1	LE	LE 1 trolley	LE 1	LE 1 trolley	LE		LE 1 trolley
Cambridge	d	07 51							08 32					08 51							09 32				
Shelford	d	07 56												08 56											
Whittlesford Parkway	d	08 00							08 39					09 00							09 39				
Great Chesterford	d	08 04												09 04											
Audley End	d	08 10							08 47					09 10							09 47				
Newport (Essex)	d	08 13												09 13											
Elsenham	d	08 19												09 19											
Stansted Airport ✈	a																								
✈	d		08 30					08 45		09 00		09 15				09 30				09 45		10 00			10 15
Stansted Mountfitchet	d	08 22						08 51						09 22						09 51					
Bishops Stortford	a	08 28	08 39						09 00	09 09				09 28		09 39					10 00	10 09			
	d	08 28	08 39						09 00	09 09				09 28		09 39					10 00	10 09			
Sawbridgeworth	d	08 32							09 05					09 32							10 05				
Harlow Mill	d	08 36												09 36											
Harlow Town	d	08 39						09 02	09 10			09 30		09 39						10 02	10 10				10 30
Roydon	d	08 43												09 43											
Hertford East	d						08 55						09 25						09 55						
Ware	d						08 59						09 29						09 59						
St Margarets (Herts)	d						09 03						09 33						10 03						
Rye House	d						09 06						09 36						10 06						
Broxbourne 3	a	08 48			←		09 11		09 16				09 41	09 48				←	10 11		10 16				
	d	08 52 →			08 52		09 11		09 16				09 41	09 52 →				09 52	10 11		10 16				
Cheshunt	d				08 57		09 15		09 20				09 45					09 57	10 15		10 20				
Waltham Cross	d				08 59													09 59							
Enfield Lock	d				09 02													10 02							
Brimsdown	d				09 04													10 04							
Ponders End	d				09 06													10 06							
Angel Road	d																								
Northumberland Park	d																								
Tottenham Hale ⊖	d		09 01		09 12			09 17	09 29	09 32	←	09 46				10 01		10 12		10 17	10 29	10 32	←		10 46
Seven Sisters ⊖	d						09 33 →				09 33		10 03						10 33 →				10 33		
Clapton	d																								
Stratford 7 ⊖	a			←	09 23												←	10 23							
Hackney Downs	d			09 09							09 39		10 09 →				10 09						10 39		
Bethnal Green	d																								
London Liverpool Street 15 ⊖	a		09 15	09 18				09 31	09 43	09 46	09 48	10 01				10 15	10 18			10 31	10 43	10 46	10 48		11 01

		LE	LE 1	LE 1 trolley	LE	LE 1	LE	LE 1 trolley	LE 1		LE 1 trolley	LE	LE 1 trolley	LE	LE 1	LE 1 trolley	LE 1	LE		LE	LE 1 trolley	XC	LE 1	LE 1 trolley	LE
Cambridge	d		09 51						10 32						10 51							11 24	11 32		
Shelford	d		09 56												10 56										
Whittlesford Parkway	d		10 00						10 39						11 00								11 39		
Great Chesterford	d		10 04												11 04										
Audley End	d		10 10						10 47						11 10							11 40	11 47		
Newport (Essex)	d		10 13												11 13										
Elsenham	d		10 19												11 19										
Stansted Airport ✈	a																					11 59			
✈	d			10 30				10 45			11 00		11 15			11 30					11 45			12 00	
Stansted Mountfitchet	d		10 22					10 51							11 22						11 51				
Bishops Stortford	a		10 28	10 39					11 00		11 09				11 28	11 39							12 00	12 09	
	d		10 28	10 39					11 00		11 09				11 28	11 39							12 00	12 09	
Sawbridgeworth	d		10 32						11 05						11 32								12 05		
Harlow Mill	d		10 36												11 36										
Harlow Town	d		10 39					11 02	11 10				11 30		11 39						12 02		12 10		
Roydon	d		10 43												11 43										
Hertford East	d	10 25					10 55							11 25				11 55							
Ware	d	10 29					10 59							11 29				11 59							
St Margarets (Herts)	d	10 33					11 03							11 33				12 03							
Rye House	d	10 36					11 06							11 36				12 06							
Broxbourne 3	a	10 41	10 48			←	11 11		11 16					11 41	11 48		←	12 11					12 16		
	d	10 41	10 52 →			10 52	11 11		11 16					11 41	11 52 →		11 52	12 11					12 16		
Cheshunt	d	10 45				10 57	11 15		11 20					11 45			11 57	12 15					12 20		
Waltham Cross	d					10 59											11 59								
Enfield Lock	d					11 02											12 02								
Brimsdown	d					11 04											12 04								
Ponders End	d					11 06											12 06								
Angel Road	d																								
Northumberland Park	d																								
Tottenham Hale ⊖	d			11 01		11 12		11 17	11 29		11 32	←	11 46			12 01	12 12				12 17		12 29	12 32	←
Seven Sisters ⊖	d	11 03					11 33 →					11 33		12 03				12 33 →							12 33
Clapton	d																								
Stratford 7 ⊖	a				←	11 23											12 23			←					
Hackney Downs	d	11 09 →			11 09							11 39		12 09 →						12 09					12 39
Bethnal Green	d																								
London Liverpool Street 15 ⊖	a			11 15	11 18			11 31	11 43		11 46	11 48	12 01			12 15				12 18	12 31		12 43	12 46	12 48

For general notes see front of timetable
For details of catering facilities see
Directory of Train Operators

Table 22

Sundays

Cambridge, Stansted Airport, Bishops Stortford, Hertford East and Broxbourne → London

Network diagram - see first page of Table 20

		LE 1 🛒	LE	LE 1	LE 1 🛒		LE	LE 1	LE	LE 1 🛒	LE 1	LE 1 🛒	LE	LE 1 🛒		LE	LE 1	LE 1 🛒	LE 1	LE	LE	LE 1 🛒	XC		LE 1
Cambridge	d			11 51							12 32						12 51						13 24		13 32
Shelford	d			11 56													12 56								
Whittlesford Parkway	d			12 00							12 39						13 00								13 39
Great Chesterford	d			12 04													13 04								
Audley End	d			12 10							12 47						13 10						13 39		13 47
Newport (Essex)	d			12 13													13 13								
Elsenham	d			12 19													13 19								
Stansted Airport ✈	a																						13 58		
	d	12 15			12 30					12 45		13 00		13 15				13 30				13 45			
Stansted Mountfitchet	d			12 22						12 51							13 22					13 51			
Bishops Stortford	a			12 28	12 39						13 00	13 09					13 28	13 39							14 00
	d			12 28	12 39						13 00	13 09					13 28	13 39							14 00
Sawbridgeworth	d			12 32							13 05						13 32								14 05
Harlow Mill	d			12 36													13 36								
Harlow Town	d	12 30		12 39						13 02	13 10			13 30			13 39					14 02			14 10
Roydon	d			12 43													13 43								
Hertford East	d		12 25						12 55							13 25				13 55					
Ware	d		12 29						12 59							13 29				13 59					
St Margarets (Herts)	d		12 33						13 03							13 33				14 03					
Rye House	d		12 36						13 06							13 36				14 06					
Broxbourne 3	a		12 41	12 48				←	13 11		13 16					13 41	13 48		←	14 11					14 16
	d		12 41	12 52 →				12 52	13 11		13 16					13 41	13 52 →		13 52	14 11					14 16
Cheshunt	d		12 45					12 57	13 15		13 20					13 45			13 57	14 15					14 20
Waltham Cross	d							12 59											13 59						
Enfield Lock	d							13 02											14 02						
Brimsdown	d							13 04											14 04						
Ponders End	d							13 06											14 06						
Angel Road	d																								
Northumberland Park	d																								
Tottenham Hale ⊖	d	12 46			13 01			13 12		13 17	13 29	13 32	←	13 46				14 01	14 12			14 17			14 29
Seven Sisters ⊖	d		13 03						13 33 →				13 33			14 03				14 33 →					
Clapton	d																								
Stratford 7 ⊖	a						←	13 23											14 23		←				
Hackney Downs	d		13 09 →				13 09						13 39			14 09 →					14 09				
Bethnal Green	d																								
London Liverpool Street 15 ⊖	a	13 01			13 15		13 18			13 31	13 43	13 46	13 48	14 01				14 15			14 18	14 31			14 43

		LE 1 🛒	LE	LE 1 🛒	LE	LE 1	LE 1 🛒	LE 1	LE		LE	LE 1 🛒	XC	LE 1	LE 1 🛒	LE	LE 1 🛒	LE		LE 1	LE 1 🛒	XC A	LE	LE 1	LE
Cambridge	d					13 51							14 20	14 32						14 51		15 09			
Shelford	d					13 56														14 56					
Whittlesford Parkway	d					14 00								14 39						15 00					
Great Chesterford	d					14 04														15 04					
Audley End	d					14 10							14 35	14 47						15 10		15 24			
Newport (Essex)	d					14 13														15 13					
Elsenham	d					14 19														15 19					
Stansted Airport ✈	a												14 58									15 44			
	d	14 00		14 15			14 30					14 45			15 00		15 15				15 30				
Stansted Mountfitchet	d					14 22						14 51								15 22					
Bishops Stortford	a	14 09				14 28	14 39							15 00	15 09					15 28	15 39				
	d	14 09				14 28	14 39							15 00	15 09					15 28	15 39				
Sawbridgeworth	d					14 32								15 05						15 32					
Harlow Mill	d					14 36														15 36					
Harlow Town	d			14 30		14 39						15 02		15 10			15 30			15 39					
Roydon	d					14 43														15 43					
Hertford East	d				14 25				14 55									15 25							15 55
Ware	d				14 29				14 59									15 29							15 59
St Margarets (Herts)	d				14 33				15 03									15 33							16 03
Rye House	d				14 36				15 06									15 36							16 06
Broxbourne 3	a				14 41	14 48		←	15 11					15 16				15 41		15 48				←	16 11
	d				14 41	14 52 →		14 52	15 11					15 16				15 41		15 52 →				15 52	16 11
Cheshunt	d				14 45			14 57	15 15					15 20				15 45						15 57	16 15
Waltham Cross	d							14 59																15 59	
Enfield Lock	d							15 02																16 02	
Brimsdown	d							15 04																16 04	
Ponders End	d							15 06																16 06	
Angel Road	d																								
Northumberland Park	d																								
Tottenham Hale ⊖	d	14 32	←	14 46			15 01	15 12				15 17		15 29	15 32	←	15 46				16 01			16 12	
Seven Sisters ⊖	d		14 33		15 03				15 33 →							15 33		16 03							16 33 →
Clapton	d																								
Stratford 7 ⊖	a							15 23			←												←	16 23	
Hackney Downs	d		14 39		15 09 →						15 09					15 39		16 09 →					16 09		
Bethnal Green	d																								
London Liverpool Street 15 ⊖	a	14 46	14 48	15 01			15 15				15 18	15 31		15 43	15 46	15 48	16 01				16 15		16 18		

For general notes see front of timetable
For details of catering facilities see
Directory of Train Operators

A From Peterborough (Table 17)

Table 22

Sundays

Cambridge, Stansted Airport, Bishops Stortford, Hertford East and Broxbourne → London

Network diagram - see first page of Table 20

		LE	LE	LE	LE		LE	LE	LE	LE	LE	LE	LE	LE		XC	LE	LE	LE	LE	LE	LE	LE		LE
		1	1	1			1		1	1	1			1		◇	1	1		1		1	1		1
		🚲		🚲			🚲			🚲				🚲				🚲		🚲			🚲		
Cambridge	d		15 32						15 51							16 24	16 32					16 51			
Shelford	d								15 56													16 56			
Whittlesford Parkway	d		15 39						16 00								16 39					17 00			
Great Chesterford	d								16 04													17 04			
Audley End	d		15 47						16 10							16 39	16 47					17 10			
Newport (Essex)	d								16 13													17 13			
Elsenham	d								16 19													17 19			
Stansted Airport ✈	a															16 59									
	d	15 45		16 00			16 15			16 30				16 45				17 00		17 15			17 30		
Stansted Mountfitchet	d	15 51							16 22					16 51								17 22			
Bishops Stortford	a		16 00	16 09					16 28	16 39							17 00	17 09				17 28	17 39		
	d		16 00	16 09					16 28	16 39							17 00	17 09				17 28	17 39		
Sawbridgeworth	d		16 05						16 32								17 05					17 32			
Harlow Mill	d								16 36													17 36			
Harlow Town	d	16 02	16 10				16 30		16 39					17 02			17 10			17 30		17 39			
Roydon	d								16 43													17 43			
Hertford East	d							16 25				16 55									17 25				
Ware	d							16 29				16 59									17 29				
St Margarets (Herts)	d							16 33				17 03									17 33				
Rye House	d							16 36				17 06									17 36				
Broxbourne 3	a		16 16					16 41	16 48		←	17 11					17 16				17 41	17 48			←
	d		16 16					16 41	16 52		16 52	17 11					17 16				17 41	17 52			17 52
Cheshunt	d		16 20					16 45	→		16 57	17 15					17 20				17 45	→			17 57
Waltham Cross	d										16 59														17 59
Enfield Lock	d										17 02														18 02
Brimsdown	d										17 04														18 04
Ponders End	d										17 06														18 06
Angel Road	d																								
Northumberland Park	d																								
Tottenham Hale ⊖	d	16 17	16 29	16 32	←		16 46			17 01	17 12			17 17			17 29	17 32	←	17 46			18 01		18 12
Seven Sisters ⊖	d				16 33			17 03				17 33 →							17 33		18 03				
Clapton	d																								
Stratford 7 ⊖	a										17 23		←												18 23
Hackney Downs	d				16 39			17 09 →					17 09						17 39		18 09 →				
Bethnal Green	d																								
London Liverpool Street 15 ⊖	a	16 31	16 43	16 46	16 48		17 01			17 15			17 18	17 31			17 43	17 46	17 48	18 01			18 15		

		LE	LE	LE	XC	LE	LE	LE	LE		LE	LE	LE	LE	LE	LE	LE	LE		LE	LE	LE	LE	LE	LE
				1	◇	1	1		1			1	1			1	1	1		1	1		1	1	1
				🚲			🚲		🚲				🚲				🚲			🚲	🚲			🚲	
Cambridge	d				17 24	17 32						17 51						18 32					18 51		
Shelford	d											17 56											18 56		
Whittlesford Parkway	d					17 39						18 00						18 39					19 00		
Great Chesterford	d											18 04											19 04		
Audley End	d				17 39	17 47						18 10						18 47					19 10		
Newport (Essex)	d											18 13											19 13		
Elsenham	d											18 19											19 19		
Stansted Airport ✈	a				17 59																				
	d			17 45			18 00		18 15				18 30				18 45			19 00	19 15			19 30	
Stansted Mountfitchet	d			17 51								18 22					18 51						19 22		
Bishops Stortford	a					18 00	18 09					18 28	18 39					19 00		19 09			19 28	19 39	
	d					18 00	18 09					18 28	18 39					19 00		19 09			19 28	19 39	
Sawbridgeworth	d					18 05						18 32						19 05					19 32		
Harlow Mill	d											18 36											19 36		
Harlow Town	d			18 02		18 10			18 30			18 39					19 02	19 10			19 30		19 39		
Roydon	d											18 43											19 43		
Hertford East	d	17 55									18 25			18 57											
Ware	d	17 59									18 29			19 01											
St Margarets (Herts)	d	18 03									18 33			19 05											
Rye House	d	18 06									18 36			19 08											
Broxbourne 3	a	18 11				18 16					18 41	18 48		19 12		←		19 16				←	19 48		←
	d	18 11				18 16					18 41	18 52		19 26		18 52		19 16				19 26	19 52		19 52
Cheshunt	d	18 15				18 20					18 45	→		→		18 57		19 20				19 31	→		19 57
Waltham Cross	d															18 59									19 59
Enfield Lock	d															19 02									20 02
Brimsdown	d															19 04									20 04
Ponders End	d															19 06									20 06
Angel Road	d																								
Northumberland Park	d																								
Tottenham Hale ⊖	d			18 18		18 29	18 32	←	18 46				19 01			19 12	19 17	19 29		19 32	19 46			20 01	20 12
Seven Sisters ⊖	d	18 33 →						18 33			19 03											19 51			
Clapton	d																								
Stratford 7 ⊖	a		←												←	19 23									20 23
Hackney Downs	d		18 09					18 39			19 09 →				19 09							19 59			
Bethnal Green	d																					20 05			
London Liverpool Street 15 ⊖	a		18 18	18 31		18 43	18 46	18 48	19 01				19 15		19 18		19 31	19 43		19 46	20 00	20 11		20 15	

For general notes see front of timetable
For details of catering facilities see Directory of Train Operators

Table 22

Sundays

Cambridge, Stansted Airport, Bishops Stortford, Hertford East and Broxbourne → London

Network diagram - see first page of Table 20

		LE	LE 1 🛒	XC ◇	LE 1		LE 1 🛒	LE 1 🛒	LE	LE 1	LE 1 🛒	LE 1	LE	LE 1 🛒		XC ◇	LE 1	LE 1	LE 1	LE	LE 1	LE 1	LE 1		LE 1
Cambridge	d			19 24	19 32					19 51						20 24	20 32				20 51				
Shelford	d									19 56											20 56				
Whittlesford Parkway	d				19 39					20 00							20 39				21 00				
Great Chesterford	d									20 04											21 04				
Audley End	d			19 39	19 47					20 10						20 39	20 47				21 10				
Newport (Essex)	d									20 13											21 13				
Elsenham	d									20 19											21 19				
Stansted Airport ✈	a			19 59												20 59									
	d		19 45				20 00	20 15			20 30			20 45				21 00	21 15			21 30			21 45
Stansted Mountfitchet	d		19 51							20 22				20 51							21 22				21 51
Bishops Stortford	a				20 00		20 09			20 28	20 39						21 00	21 09			21 28	21 39			
	d				20 00		20 09			20 28	20 39						21 00	21 09			21 28	21 39			
Sawbridgeworth	d				20 05					20 32							21 05				21 32				
Harlow Mill	d									20 36											21 36				
Harlow Town	d		20 02		20 10			20 30		20 39				21 02			21 10		21 30		21 39				22 02
Roydon	d									20 43											21 43				
Hertford East	d	19 57											20 57												
Ware	d	20 01											21 01												
St Margarets (Herts)	d	20 05											21 05												
Rye House	d	20 08											21 08												
Broxbourne 3	a	20 12			20 16				←	20 48		←	21 12				21 16			←	21 48		←		
	d	20 26			20 16				20 26	20 52		20 52	21 26				21 16			21 26	21 52		21 52		
Cheshunt	d	→			20 20				20 31	→		20 57	→				21 20			21 31	→		21 57		
Waltham Cross	d											20 59											21 59		
Enfield Lock	d											21 02											22 02		
Brimsdown	d											21 04											22 04		
Ponders End	d											21 06											22 06		
Angel Road	d																								
Northumberland Park	d																								
Tottenham Hale ⊖	d		20 17		20 29		20 32	20 46			21 01	21 12		21 17			21 29	21 32	21 46			22 01	22 12		22 17
Seven Sisters ⊖	d								20 51											21 51					
Clapton	d																								
Stratford 7 ⊖	a											21 23											22 23		
Hackney Downs	d								20 59											21 59					
Bethnal Green	d								21 05											22 05					
London Liverpool Street 15 ⊖	a		20 31		20 43		20 46	21 00	21 11		21 15			21 31			21 43	21 46	22 00	22 11		22 15			22 31

		XC ◇	LE	LE 1	LE 1	LE 1	LE	LE 1	LE 1		LE 1	LE	LE 1	LE 1	LE 1	LE 1	LE 1	LE		LE 1	LE 1	LE 1	LE 1		
Cambridge	d	21 19		21 32				21 51							22 32					22 51					
Shelford	d							21 56												22 56					
Whittlesford Parkway	d			21 39				22 00							22 39					23 00					
Great Chesterford	d							22 04												23 04					
Audley End	d	21 34		21 47				22 10							22 47					23 10					
Newport (Essex)	d							22 13												23 13					
Elsenham	d							22 19												23 19					
Stansted Airport ✈	a	21 53																							
	d				22 00	22 15			22 30				22 45			23 00	23 15				23 30	23 45	23 59		
Stansted Mountfitchet	d							22 22					22 51							23 22					
Bishops Stortford	a			22 00	22 09			22 28	22 39						23 00	23 09				23 28	23 39		00 08		
	d			22 00	22 09			22 28	22 39						23 00	23 09					23 39		00 08		
Sawbridgeworth	d			22 05				22 32							23 05										
Harlow Mill	d							22 36																	
Harlow Town	d			22 10		22 30		22 39					23 02		23 10		23 30				23 47	23 59	00 16		
Roydon	d							22 43																	
Hertford East	d		21 57									22 57													
Ware	d		22 01									23 01													
St Margarets (Herts)	d		22 05									23 05													
Rye House	d		22 08									23 08													
Broxbourne 3	a		22 12	22 16			←	22 48			←	23 12			23 16			←							
	d		22 26	22 16			22 26	22 52			22 52	23 26			23 16			23 26							
Cheshunt	d		→	22 20			22 31	→			22 57	→			23 20			23 31							
Waltham Cross	d										22 59														
Enfield Lock	d										23 02														
Brimsdown	d										23 04														
Ponders End	d										23 06														
Angel Road	d																								
Northumberland Park	d													←											
Tottenham Hale ⊖	d			22 29	22 32	22 46			23 01		23 12		23 17	23 12	23 29	23 32	23 46								
Seven Sisters ⊖	d						22 51				→							23 51			00 08	00 21			
Clapton	d																								
Stratford 7 ⊖	a													23 22											
Hackney Downs	d						22 59											23 59							
Bethnal Green	d						23 05											00 05							
London Liverpool Street 15 ⊖	a			22 43	22 46	23 00	23 11		23 15				23 31	23 36	23 43	23 46	00 01	00 11			00 22	00 35	00 51		

For general notes see front of timetable
For details of catering facilities see Directory of Train Operators

Network Diagram for Tables 24, 25

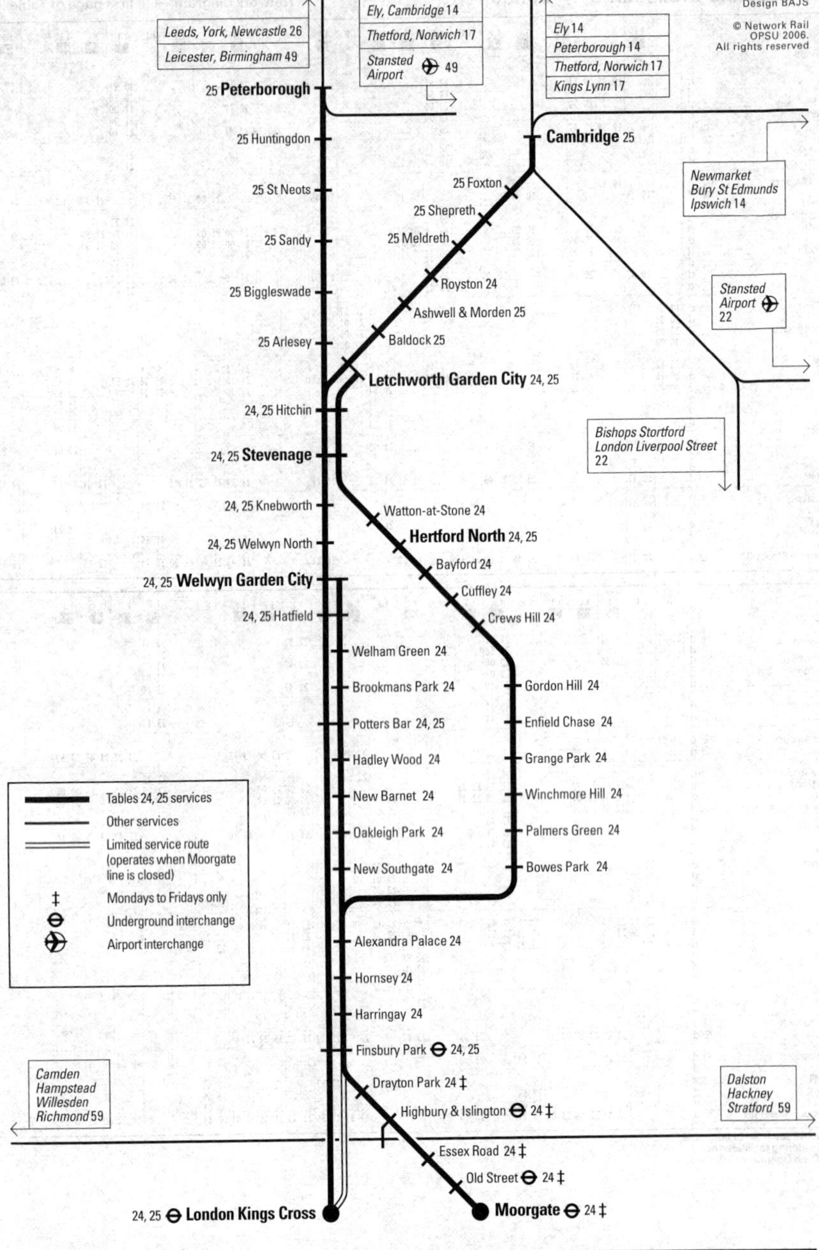

DM-23/06
Design BAJS
© Network Rail
OPSU 2006.
All rights reserved
Leeds, York, Newcastle 26
Leicester, Birmingham 49
Ely, Cambridge 14
Thetford, Norwich 17
Stansted Airport 49
Ely 14
Peterborough 14
Thetford, Norwich 17
Kings Lynn 17
25 Peterborough
25 Huntingdon
25 St Neots
25 Sandy
25 Biggleswade
25 Arlesey
Cambridge 25
25 Foxton
25 Shepreth
25 Meldreth
Royston 24
Ashwell & Morden 25
Baldock 25
Letchworth Garden City 24, 25
Newmarket
Bury St Edmunds
Ipswich 14
Stansted Airport 22
Bishops Stortford
London Liverpool Street
22
24, 25 Hitchin
24, 25 Stevenage
24, 25 Knebworth
24, 25 Welwyn North
24, 25 Welwyn Garden City
24, 25 Hatfield
Watton-at-Stone 24
Hertford North 24, 25
Bayford 24
Cuffley 24
Crews Hill 24
Welham Green 24
Brookmans Park 24
Potters Bar 24, 25
Hadley Wood 24
New Barnet 24
Oakleigh Park 24
New Southgate 24
Gordon Hill 24
Enfield Chase 24
Grange Park 24
Winchmore Hill 24
Palmers Green 24
Bowes Park 24
Tables 24, 25 services
Other services
Limited service route (operates when Moorgate line is closed)
‡ Mondays to Fridays only
Underground interchange
Airport interchange
Alexandra Palace 24
Hornsey 24
Harringay 24
Finsbury Park 24, 25
Drayton Park 24 ‡
Highbury & Islington 24 ‡
Essex Road 24 ‡
Old Street 24 ‡
Camden
Hampstead
Willesden
Richmond 59
Dalston
Hackney
Stratford 59
24, 25 London Kings Cross
Moorgate 24 ‡

London → Welwyn Garden City, Hertford North and Letchworth Garden City

Saturday service operates on Bank Holiday Mondays

Network Diagram - see first page of Table 24

Miles	Miles	Station		FC MX	FC MO A	FC MX 1	FC MO B (bus)	FC MO B (bus)	FC MO	FC MX	FC 1 C	FC MO B (bus)	FC MO 1 D	FC MX 1	FC MO 1 E	FC MO B (bus)	FC MX	FC MO A	FC MX 1	FC MO B	FC MX 1 E	FC MO 1 E	FC MO B (bus)	FC 1	FC	FC
0	—	London Kings Cross 15	⊖ d	23p26	23p28	23p36			23p41	23p41	00 07		00 07	00 36	00 36		00 41	01 06	01 06	01 06	01 36	01 36		05 22	05 26	05 56
—	0	**Moorgate**	⊖ d																							
—	½	Old Street	⊖ d																							
—	1¾	Essex Road	d																							
—	2¼	Highbury & Islington	⊖ d																							
—	2¾	Drayton Park	d																							
2½	3½	Finsbury Park	⊖ d	23p32	23p33	23p41			23p47	23p47	00 12		00 12	00 41	00 41		00 47	01 11	01 11	01 11	01 41	01 41		05 27	05 32	06 02
3½	4½	Harringay	d	23p34	23p36				23p49	23p49															05 34	06 04
4	5	Hornsey	d	23p36	23p38				23p51	23p51															05 36	06 06
5	6	Alexandra Palace	d	23p38	23p40		23p14	23p40	23p53	23p53	00 17	00 05	00 17		00 45	00 25	00 51	01 16	01 16	01 16	01 45	01 45	01 25		05 38	06 08
6½	—	New Southgate	d						23p56	23p56							00 54									
8½	—	Oakleigh Park	d						23p59	23p59					00 50		00 57				01 50	01 50				
9¾	—	New Barnet	d						00 01	00 01					00 52		00 59				01 52	01 52				
10½	—	Hadley Wood	d						00 04	00 04					00 54		01 02				01 54	01 54				
12¾	—	Potters Bar	d			23p51			00 08	00 08				00 51	00 58		01 06				01 58	01 58		05 37		
14½	—	Brookmans Park	d						00 11	00 11							01 09									
15½	—	Welham Green	d						00 13	00 13																
17¾	—	Hatfield	d			23p57			00 16	00 16				00 57	01 04		01 13				02 04	02 04		05 43		
20¼	—	**Welwyn Garden City 4**	d			00 01			00 20	00a24				01 01	01 08		01a21				02 08	02 08		05 47		
22	—	Welwyn North	d			00 04			00 23					01s04	01s16						02s11	02s16		05 50		
25	—	Knebworth	d			00 08			00 28					01s08	01s20						02s15	02s20		05 54		
—	6¾	Bowes Park	d	23p41	23p42		23p19	23p45				00 10													05 41	06 11
—	7¾	Palmers Green	d	23p43	23p44		23p29	23p55			00 20	00 20				00 36		01 18	01 19				01 36		05 43	06 13
—	8¾	Winchmore Hill	d	23p45	23p47		23p37	00 03			00 22	00 28				00 44		01 22	01 21				01 44		05 45	06 15
—	9½	Grange Park	d	23p47	23p49		23p43	00 09				00 34													05 47	06 17
—	10¼	Enfield Chase	d	23p49	23p51		23p48	00 14			00 25	00 39				00 54		01 24	01 24				01 54		05 49	06 19
—	11	Gordon Hill	d	23p51	23p53		23p54	00 20			00 27	00 45				01 00		01 26	01 26				02 00		05 51	06 21
—	12½	Crews Hill	d	23p54	23p56		00 04	00 30				00 55													05 54	06 24
—	14¼	Cuffley	d	23p57	23p59		00 12	00 38			00 31	01 03				01 15		01 30	01 30				02 15		05 57	06 27
—	17¾	Bayford	d	00 02	00 04		00 27	00 53				01 18													06 02	06 32
—	20¾	**Hertford North**	d	00 07	00 09		00 42	01 08			00 39	01 33				01 40		01 38	01 38				02s40		06a11	06a40
—	25	Watton-at-Stone	d	00 13	00 14		00 56	01 22				01 47														
27½	30	**Stevenage 4**	d	00a21	00a25	00 12	01a13	01a39	00 31		00 48	02a04	00 48	01 12	01 23	02s02		01 47	01 47	01 47	02 18	02 23	03s02	05 58		
31¾	34½	Hitchin 4	d			00 20			00a47		00 56		00 56	01a17	01a28	02s22		01 52	01 52	01 53	02a23	02a28	03s22	06a06		
34¾	37¼	**Letchworth Garden City**	a			00 29					01 00		01 00			02 37		02 06	02 06	02 06			03 37			

Station		FC 1	FC	FC	FC 1	FC	FC	FC 1	FC	FC	FC 1	FC	FC	FC 1	FC	FC	FC	FC 1	FC	FC	FC	FC 1	FC	FC	FC	FC 1
London Kings Cross 15	⊖ d	06 06	06 11	06 26	06 36			07 06			07 36			08 03				08 33				09 06				09 36
Moorgate	⊖ d					06 35	06 50		07 05	07 20		07 35	07 50		08 05	08 12	08 22		08 32	08 42	08 52		09 02	09 12	09 22	
Old Street	⊖ d					06 37	06 52		07 07	07 22		07 37	07 52		08 07	08 14	08 24		08 34	08 44	08 54		09 04	09 14	09 24	
Essex Road	d					06 40	06 55		07 10	07 25		07 40	07 55		08 10	08 17	08 27		08 37	08 47	08 57		09 07	09 17	09 27	
Highbury & Islington	⊖ d					06 42	06 57		07 12	07 27		07 42	07 57		08 12	08 19	08 29		08 39	08 49	08 59		09 09	09 19	09 29	
Drayton Park	d					06 44	06 59		07 14	07 29		07 44	07 59		08 14	08 21	08 31		08 41	08 51	09 01		09 11	09 21	09 31	
Finsbury Park	⊖ d	06 11	06 17	06 32	06 41	06 47	07 02	07 11	07 17	07 32	07 41	07 47	08 02	08 08	08 17	08 24	08 34	08 38	08 44	08 54	09 04	09 11	09 14	09 24	09 34	09 41
Harringay	d		06 19	06 34		06 49	07 04		07 19	07 34		07 49	08 04		08 19	08 26	08 36		08 46	08 56	09 06		09 16	09 26	09 36	
Hornsey	d		06 21	06 36		06 51	07 06		07 21	07 36		07 51	08 06		08 21	08 28	08 38		08 48	08 58	09 08		09 18	09 28	09 38	
Alexandra Palace	d		06 23	06 38		06 53	07 08		07 23	07 38		07 53	08 08		08 23	08 30	08 40		08 50	09 00	09 10		09 20	09 30	09 40	
New Southgate	d		06 26			06 56			07 26			07 56			08 26		08 43			09 03			09 23		09 43	
Oakleigh Park	d		06 29			06 59			07 29			07 59			08 29		08 46			09 06			09 26		09 46	
New Barnet	d		06 31			07 01			07 31			08 01			08 31		08 48			09 08			09 28		09 48	
Hadley Wood	d		06 34			07 04			07 34			08 04			08 34		08 51			09 11			09 31		09 51	
Potters Bar	d	06 21	06 38		06 51	07 08		07 21	07 38		07 51	08 08		08 19	08 38		08 55	08 48		09 15		09 21	09 35		09 55	09 51
Brookmans Park	d		06 41			07 11			07 41			08 11			08 41		08 58			09 18			09 38		09 58	
Welham Green	d		06 43			07 13			07 43			08 13			08 43		09 00			09 20			09 40		10 00	
Hatfield	d	06 27	06 46		06 57	07 16		07 27	07 46		07 57	08 16		08 25	08 46		09 03	08 54		09 23		09 27	09 43		10 03	09 57
Welwyn Garden City 4	d	06 31	06a53		07 01	07a21		07 31	07a51		08 01	08a21		08 31	08a51		09a09	09 00		09a29		09 31	09a49		10a09	10 01
Welwyn North	d	06 34			07 04			07 34			08 04			08 34				09 03				09 34				10 04
Knebworth	d	06 38			07 08			07 38			08 08			08 38				09 07				09 38				10 08
Bowes Park	d			06 41			07 10			07 41			08 11			08 33			08 53		09 12			09 33		
Palmers Green	d			06 43			07 12			07 43			08 13			08 35			08 55		09 14			09 35		
Winchmore Hill	d			06 45			07 15			07 45			08 15			08 37			08 57		09 17			09 37		
Grange Park	d			06 47			07 17			07 47			08 17			08 39			08 59		09 19			09 39		
Enfield Chase	d			06 49			07 19			07 49			08 19			08 41			09 01		09 21			09 41		
Gordon Hill	d			06 51			07 21			07 51			08 21			08 43			09 03		09 23			09 43		
Crews Hill	d			06 54			07 24			07 54			08 24			08 46			09 06		09 26			09 46		
Cuffley	d			06 57			07 27			07 57			08 27			08 49			09 09		09 29			09 49		
Bayford	d			07 02			07 32			08 02			08 32			08 54			09 14		09 34			09 54		
Hertford North	d			07 07			07a37			08 09			08 37			09b07			09a20		09 39			10a00		
Watton-at-Stone	d			07 13						08 14			08 43			09 13					09 44					
Stevenage 4	d	06 42		07a22	07 12			07 42		08a24	08 12		08a52	08 42		09 20		09 12			09 51	09 42				10 12
Hitchin 4	d	06 47			07a17			07 47			08a17			08 47		09 30		09a17			09 57	09 47				10a17
Letchworth Garden City	a	06 51						07 51						08 51		09 36					10 03	09 51				

For general notes see front of timetable
For details of catering facilities see Directory of Train Operators

A From 15 September
B Until 8 September
C All Tuesdays to Fridays, also Mondays from 15 September. To Cambridge (Table 25)
D Until 8 September. To Cambridge (Table 25)
E To Peterborough (Table 25)
b Arr. 0859

Saturday service operates on Bank Holiday Mondays

London → Welwyn Garden City, Hertford North and Letchworth Garden City

Network Diagram - see first page of Table 24

	FC	FC	FC	FC 1	FC	FC	FC	FC 1	FC	FC	FC	FC 1	FC		FC	FC	FC 1	FC	FC	FC	FC 1	FC	FC	FC	FC 1
London Kings Cross 15 ⊖ d				10 06				10 36				11 06					11 36				12 06				12 36
Moorgate ⊖ d	09 32	09 42	09 52		10 02	10 12	10 22		10 32	10 42	10 52		11 02		11 12	11 22		11 32	11 42	11 52		12 02	12 12	12 22	
Old Street ⊖ d	09 34	09 44	09 54		10 04	10 14	10 24		10 34	10 44	10 54		11 04		11 14	11 24		11 34	11 44	11 54		12 04	12 14	12 24	
Essex Road d	09 37	09 47	09 57		10 07	10 17	10 27		10 37	10 47	10 57		11 07		11 17	11 27		11 37	11 47	11 57		12 07	12 17	12 27	
Highbury & Islington ⊖ d	09 39	09 49	09 59		10 09	10 19	10 29		10 39	10 49	10 59		11 09		11 19	11 29		11 39	11 49	11 59		12 09	12 19	12 29	
Drayton Park d	09 41	09 51	10 01		10 11	10 21	10 31		10 41	10 51	11 01		11 11		11 21	11 31		11 41	11 51	12 01		12 11	12 21	12 31	
Finsbury Park ⊖ d	09 44	09 54	10 04	10 11	10 14	10 24	10 34	10 41	10 44	10 54	11 04	11 11	11 14		11 24	11 34	11 41	11 44	11 54	12 04	12 11	12 14	12 24	12 34	12 41
Harringay d	09 46	09 56	10 06		10 16	10 26	10 36		10 46	10 56	11 06		11 16		11 26	11 36		11 46	11 56	12 06		12 16	12 26	12 36	
Hornsey d	09 48	09 58	10 08		10 18	10 28	10 38		10 48	10 58	11 08		11 18		11 28	11 38		11 48	11 58	12 08		12 18	12 28	12 38	
Alexandra Palace d	09 50	10 00	10 10		10 20	10 30	10 40		10 50	11 00	11 10		11 20		11 30	11 40		11 50	12 00	12 10		12 20	12 30	12 40	
New Southgate d		10 03			10 23		10 43			11 03			11 23			11 43			12 03			12 23		12 43	
Oakleigh Park d		10 06			10 26		10 46			11 06			11 26			11 46			12 06			12 26		12 46	
New Barnet d		10 08			10 28		10 48			11 08			11 28			11 48			12 08			12 28		12 48	
Hadley Wood d		10 11			10 31		10 51			11 11			11 31			11 51			12 11			12 31		12 51	
Potters Bar d		10 15		10 21	10 35		10 55	10 51		11 15		11 21	11 35			11 55	11 51		12 15		12 21	12 35		12 55	12 51
Brookmans Park d		10 18			10 38		10 58			11 18			11 38			11 58			12 18			12 38		12 58	
Welham Green d		10 20			10 40		11 00			11 20			11 40			12 00			12 20			12 40		13 00	
Hatfield d		10 23		10 27	10 43		11 03	10 57		11 23		11 27	11 43			12 03	11 57		12 23		12 27	12 43		13 03	12 57
Welwyn Garden City 4 d		10a29		10 31	10a49		11a09	11 01		11a29		11 31	11a49			12a09	12 01		12a29		12 31	12a49		13a09	13 01
Welwyn North d				10 34				11 04				11 34					12 04				12 34				13 04
Knebworth d				10 38				11 08				11 38					12 08				12 38				13 08
Bowes Park d	09 53		10 13			10 33			10 53		11 13				11 33			11 53		12 13			12 33		
Palmers Green d	09 55		10 15			10 35			10 55		11 15				11 35			11 55		12 15			12 35		
Winchmore Hill d	09 57		10 17			10 37			10 57		11 17				11 37			11 57		12 17			12 37		
Grange Park d	09 59		10 19			10 39			10 59		11 19				11 39			11 59		12 19			12 39		
Enfield Chase d	10 01		10 21			10 41			11 01		11 21				11 41			12 01		12 21			12 41		
Gordon Hill d	10 03		10 23			10 43			11 03		11 23				11 43			12 03		12 23			12 43		
Crews Hill d	10 06		10 26			10 46			11 06		11 26				11 46			12 06		12 26			12 46		
Cuffley d	10 09		10 29			10 49			11 09		11 29				11 49			12 09		12 29			12 49		
Bayford d	10 14		10 34			10 54			11 14		11 34				11 54			12 14		12 34			12 54		
Hertford North d	10a20		10 39			11a00			11a20		11 39				12a00			12a20		12 39			13a00		
Watton-at-Stone d			10 45								11 45									12 45					
Stevenage 4 d			10 51	10 42				11 12			11 51	11 42					12 12			12 51	12 42				13 12
Hitchin 4 d			10 57	10 47				11a17			11 57	11 47					12a17			12 57	12 47				13a17
Letchworth Garden City a			11 04	10 51							12 04	11 51								13 04	12 51				

	FC	FC	FC	FC 1	FC	FC	FC	FC 1	FC	FC	FC	FC 1	FC	FC	FC	FC 1	FC	FC	FC	FC 1	FC	FC	FC	FC 1	FC
London Kings Cross 15 ⊖ d				13 06				13 36				14 06				14 36				15 06				15 36	
Moorgate ⊖ d	12 32	12 42	12 52		13 02	13 12	13 22		13 32	13 42	13 52		14 02	14 12	14 22		14 32	14 42	14 52		15 02	15 12	15 22		15 32
Old Street ⊖ d	12 34	12 44	12 54		13 04	13 14	13 24		13 34	13 44	13 54		14 04	14 14	14 24		14 34	14 44	14 54		15 04	15 14	15 24		15 34
Essex Road d	12 37	12 47	12 57		13 07	13 17	13 27		13 37	13 47	13 57		14 07	14 17	14 27		14 37	14 47	14 57		15 07	15 17	15 27		15 37
Highbury & Islington ⊖ d	12 39	12 49	12 59		13 09	13 19	13 29		13 39	13 49	13 59		14 09	14 19	14 29		14 39	14 49	14 59		15 09	15 19	15 29		15 39
Drayton Park d	12 41	12 51	13 01		13 11	13 21	13 31		13 41	13 51	14 01		14 11	14 21	14 31		14 41	14 51	15 01		15 11	15 21	15 31		15 41
Finsbury Park ⊖ d	12 44	12 54	13 04	13 11	13 14	13 24	13 34	13 41	13 44	13 54	14 04	14 11	14 14	14 24	14 34	14 41	14 44	14 54	15 04	15 11	15 14	15 24	15 34	15 41	15 44
Harringay d	12 46	12 56	13 06		13 16	13 26	13 36		13 46	13 56	14 06		14 16	14 26	14 36		14 46	14 56	15 06		15 16	15 26	15 36		15 46
Hornsey d	12 48	12 58	13 08		13 18	13 28	13 38		13 48	13 58	14 08		14 18	14 28	14 38		14 48	14 58	15 08		15 18	15 28	15 38		15 48
Alexandra Palace d	12 50	13 00	13 10		13 20	13 30	13 40		13 50	14 00	14 10		14 20	14 30	14 40		14 50	15 00	15 10		15 20	15 30	15 40		15 50
New Southgate d		13 03			13 23		13 43			14 03			14 23		14 43			15 03			15 23		15 43		
Oakleigh Park d		13 06			13 26		13 46			14 06			14 26		14 46			15 06			15 26		15 46		
New Barnet d		13 08			13 28		13 48			14 08			14 28		14 48			15 08			15 28		15 48		
Hadley Wood d		13 11			13 31		13 51			14 11			14 31		14 51			15 11			15 31		15 51		
Potters Bar d		13 15		13 21	13 35		13 55	13 51		14 15		14 21	14 35		14 55	14 51		15 15		15 21	15 35		15 55	15 51	
Brookmans Park d		13 18			13 38		13 58			14 18			14 38		14 58			15 18			15 38		15 58		
Welham Green d		13 20			13 40		14 00			14 20			14 40		15 00			15 20			15 40		16 00		
Hatfield d		13 23		13 27	13 43		14 03	13 57		14 23		14 27	14 43		15 03	14 57		15 23		15 27	15 43		16 03	15 57	
Welwyn Garden City 4 d		13a29		13 31	13a49		14a10	14 01		14a29		14 31	14a49		15a09	15 01		15a29		15 31	15a49		16a09	16 01	
Welwyn North d				13 34				14 04				14 34				15 04				15 34				16 04	
Knebworth d				13 38				14 08				14 38				15 08				15 38				16 08	
Bowes Park d	12 53		13 13			13 33			13 53		14 13			14 33			14 53		15 13			15 33			15 53
Palmers Green d	12 55		13 15			13 35			13 55		14 15			14 35			14 55		15 15			15 35			15 55
Winchmore Hill d	12 57		13 17			13 37			13 57		14 17			14 37			14 57		15 17			15 37			15 57
Grange Park d	12 59		13 19			13 39			13 59		14 19			14 39			14 59		15 19			15 39			15 59
Enfield Chase d	13 01		13 21			13 41			14 01		14 21			14 41			15 01		15 21			15 41			16 01
Gordon Hill d	13 03		13 23			13 43			14 03		14 23			14 43			15 03		15 23			15 43			16 03
Crews Hill d	13 06		13 26			13 46			14 06		14 26			14 46			15 06		15 26			15 46			16 06
Cuffley d	13 09		13 29			13 49			14 09		14 29			14 49			15 09		15 29			15 49			16 09
Bayford d	13 14		13 34			13 54			14 14		14 34			14 54			15 14		15 34			15 54			16 14
Hertford North d	13a20		13 39			14a00			14a20		14 39			15a00			15a20		15 39			16b09			16a20
Watton-at-Stone d			13 45								14 45								15 45			16 15			
Stevenage 4 d			13 51	13 42				14 12			14 51	14 42				15 12			15 51	15 42		16a23		16 12	
Hitchin 4 d			13 57	13 47				14a17			14 57	14 47				15a17			15 57	15 47				16a17	
Letchworth Garden City a			14 04	13 51							15 04	14 51							16 04	15 51					

For general notes see front of timetable
For details of catering facilities see
Directory of Train Operators

b Arr. 1559

London → Welwyn Garden City, Hertford North and Letchworth Garden City

Saturday service operates on Bank Holiday Mondays

Network Diagram - see first page of Table 24

		FC	FC	FC 1	FC	FC	FC	FC 1	FC	FC	FC	FC	FC	FC	FC 1	FC	FC	FC	FC	FC	FC	FC 1	FC	FC	FC	FC
																			A							A
London Kings Cross 15	⊖ d			16 06				16 36				16 52			17 06				17 22			17 36				17 52
Moorgate	⊖ d	15 42	15 52		16 03	16 08	16 18		16 28	16 33	16 38		16 48	16 53		16 58	17 03	17 08		17 18	17 23		17 28	17 33	17 38	
Old Street	⊖ d	15 44	15 54		16 05	16 10	16 20		16 30	16 35	16 40		16 50	16 55		17 00	17 05	17 10		17 20	17 25		17 30	17 35	17 40	
Essex Road	d	15 47	15 57		16 08	16 13	16 23		16 33	16 38	16 43		16 53	16 58		17 03	17 08	17 13		17 23	17 28		17 33	17 38	17 43	
Highbury & Islington	⊖ d	15 49	15 59		16 11	16 16	16 26		16 36	16 41	16 46		16 56	17 01		17 06	17 11	17 16		17 26	17 31		17 36	17 41	17 46	
Drayton Park	d	15 51	16 01		16 12	16 17	16 27		16 37	16 42	16 47		16 57	17 02		17 07	17 12	17 17		17 27	17 32		17 37	17 42	17 47	
Finsbury Park	⊖ d	15 54	16 04	16 11	16 15	16 20	16 30	16 41	16 40	16 45	16 50	16 57	17 00	17 05	17 11	17 10	17 15	17 20	17 27	17 30	17 35	17 41	17 40	17 45	17 50	17 57
Harringay	d	15 56	16 06		16 18	16 23	16 33			16 48	16 53		17 03	17 08				17 23		17 33	17 38			17 48		
Hornsey	d	15 58	16 08		16 20	16 25	16 35			16 50	16 55		17 05	17 10				17 25		17 35	17 40			17 50		
Alexandra Palace	d	16 00	16 10		16 22	16 28	16 38			16 52	16 58		17 08	17 12				17 28		17 38	17 42				17 56	
New Southgate	d	16 03			16 25					16 55		17 02		17 15			17 21		17 32		17 45			17 54		18 02
Oakleigh Park	d	16 06			16 29					16 59		17 06		17 19			17 24		17 36		17 49			17 57		18 06
New Barnet	d	16 08			16 31					17 01		17 08		17 21			17 26		17 38		17 51			17 59		18 08
Hadley Wood	d	16 11			16 33					17 03				17 23			17 29				17 54			18 02		
Potters Bar	d	16 15		16 21	16 37			16 51		17 07		17 13		17 27			17 33		17 43		17 58			18 06		18 13
Brookmans Park	d	16 18			16 40					17 10				17 30			17 36				18 01			18 09		
Welham Green	d	16 20			16 42					17 12				17 32			17 38				18 03			18 11		
Hatfield	d	16 23		16 27	16 46			16 57		17 16		17 19		17 36	17 29		17 42		17 49		18 06			18 15		18 19
Welwyn Garden City 4	d	16a29		16 31	16a51			17 01		17a21		17 24		17a41	17 33		17a47		17 53		18a11	17 59		18a20		18 23
Welwyn North	d			16 34				17 04				17 27			17 38				17 56			18 02				18 26
Knebworth	d			16 38				17 08				17 32			17 42				18 01			18 06				18 31
Bowes Park	d		16 13			16 30	16 40				17 00		17 10					17 30		17 40					17 58	
Palmers Green	d		16 15			16 32	16 42		16 48		17 02		17 12			17 18		17 32		17 42			17 48		18 00	
Winchmore Hill	d		16 17			16 35	16 45		16 51		17 05		17 15			17 21		17 35		17 45			17 51		18 03	
Grange Park	d		16 19			16 37	16 47				17 07		17 17					17 37		17 47					18 05	
Enfield Chase	d		16 21			16 39	16 49		16 54		17 09		17 19			17 24		17 39		17 49			17 54		18 07	
Gordon Hill	d		16 23			16 41	16a52		16 56		17 11		17a22			17 26		17 41		17 51			17 56		18 10	
Crews Hill	d		16 26			16 44					17 14							17 44							18 13	
Cuffley	d		16 29			16 47			17 01		17 17					17 31		17 47		17 56			18 01		18 16	
Bayford	d		16 34			16 52					17 22							17 52							18 21	
Hertford North	d		16 39			16a58			17 10		17a28					17 40		17a58		18a05			18 10		18a27	
Watton-at-Stone	d		16 45						17 15							17 45							18 15			
Stevenage 4	d		16a53	16 42				17 12	17a25			17 37			17 46	17a55			18 06			18 11	18a25			18 36
Hitchin 4	d			16 47				17 17				17 42			17 51				18 12			18 17				18 42
Letchworth Garden City	a			16 51				17 21				17 50			17 56				18 16			18 23				18 46

		FC	FC	FC 1	FC	FC	FC	FC	FC	FC	FC 1	FC	FC	FC	FC	FC	FC	FC 1	FC	FC	FC	FC 1	FC	FC	FC	FC
								A																		
London Kings Cross 15	⊖ d			18 06				18 22			18 36				18 52			19 06				19 36				
Moorgate	⊖ d	17 48	17 53		17 58	18 03	18 08		18 18	18 23		18 28	18 35	18 40		18 50	18 55		19 05	19 10	19 20		19 30	19 35	19 40	19 50
Old Street	⊖ d	17 50	17 55		18 00	18 05	18 10		18 20	18 25		18 30	18 37	18 42		18 52	18 57		19 07	19 12	19 22		19 32	19 37	19 42	19 52
Essex Road	d	17 53	17 58		18 03	18 08	18 13		18 23	18 28		18 33	18 40	18 45		18 55	19 00		19 10	19 15	19 25		19 35	19 40	19 45	19 55
Highbury & Islington	⊖ d	17 56	18 01		18 06	18 11	18 16		18 26	18 31		18 36	18 43	18 48		18 58	19 03		19 13	19 18	19 27		19 37	19 42	19 47	19 57
Drayton Park	d	17 57	18 02		18 07	18 12	18 17		18 27	18 32		18 37	18 44	18 49		18 59	19 04		19 14	19 19	19 29		19 39	19 44	19 49	19 59
Finsbury Park	⊖ d	18 00	18 05	18 11	18 10	18 15	18 20	18 27	18 30	18 35	18 41	18 40	18 47	18 52	18 57	19 02	19 07	19 11	19 17	19 22	19 32	19 41	19 42	19 47	19 52	20 02
Harringay	d	18 03	18 08			18 18			18 33	18 38				18 55		19 05	19 10		19 20	19 25	19 34		19 44	19 49	19 54	20 04
Hornsey	d	18 05	18 10			18 20			18 35	18 40				18 57		19 07	19 12		19 22	19 27	19 36		19 46	19 51	19 56	20 06
Alexandra Palace	d	18 08	18 12				18 26		18 38	18 42				19 00		19 10	19 14		19 24	19 30	19 38		19 48	19 53	19 58	20 08
New Southgate	d		18 15			18 24		18 32		18 45			18 53		19 02		19 17		19 27					19 56		
Oakleigh Park	d		18 19			18 27		18 36		18 49			18 56		19 06		19 21		19 31					19 59		
New Barnet	d		18 21			18 29		18 38		18 51			18 58		19 08		19 23		19 33					20 01		
Hadley Wood	d		18 24			18 32				18 54			19 01				19 26		19 36					20 04		
Potters Bar	d		18 28			18 36		18 43		18 58			19 05		19 13		19 30	19 22	19 40			19 51		20 08		
Brookmans Park	d		18 31			18 39				19 01			19 08				19 33		19 43					20 11		
Welham Green	d		18 33			18 41				19 03			19 10				19 35		19 45					20 13		
Hatfield	d		18 36			18 45		18 49		19 06			19 14		19 19		19 38	19 28	19 48			19 57		20 16		
Welwyn Garden City 4	d		18a41	18 29		18a50		18 53		19a11	18 59		19a19		19 23		19a43	19 32	19a53			20 01		20a23		
Welwyn North	d			18 32				18 56			19 02				19 26			19 35				20 04				
Knebworth	d			18 36				19 01			19 06				19 31			19 39				20 08				
Bowes Park	d	18 10					18 28		18 40					19 02		19 12				19 32	19 41		19 50		20 01	20 11
Palmers Green	d	18 12			18 18		18 30		18 42			18 48		19 04		19 14				19 34	19 43		19 52		20 03	20 13
Winchmore Hill	d	18 15			18 21		18 33		18 45			18 51		19 07		19 17				19 37	19 46		19 55		20 05	20 15
Grange Park	d	18 17					18 35		18 47					19 09		19 19				19 39	19 47		19 57		20 07	20 17
Enfield Chase	d	18 19			18 24		18 37		18 49			18 54		19 11		19 21				19 41	19 49		19 59		20 09	20 19
Gordon Hill	d	18 22			18 26		18 40		18 52			18 56		19 14		19 24				19 44	19 52		20 02		20 11	20 21
Crews Hill	d						18 43							19 17						19 47			20 05			20 24
Cuffley	d	18 26			18 31		18 46		18 56			19 01		19 20		19 28				19 50	19 56		20 08		20 16	20 27
Bayford	d						18 51							19 25						19 55			20 13			20 32
Hertford North	d	18a35			18 40		18a57		19a05			19 10		19a30		19 37				20a00	20 06		20a20		20a27	20a38
Watton-at-Stone	d				18 45							19 15				19 43					20 11					
Stevenage 4	d			18 41	18 53			19 06			19 11	19 23			19 36	19 52		19 44			20 20	20 12				
Hitchin 4	d			18 47	18 59			19 12			19 17	19 29			19 42	19 59		19 51			20 27	20 17				
Letchworth Garden City	a			18 54	19 06			19 16			19 23	19 36			19 50	20 05		19 55			20 35	20 23				

For general notes see front of timetable
For details of catering facilities see
Directory of Train Operators

A To Royston (Table 25)

Saturday service operates on Bank Holiday Mondays

London → Welwyn Garden City, Hertford North and Letchworth Garden City

Network Diagram - see first page of Table 24

		FC 1	FC	FC	FC 1	FC	FC	FC 1	FC	FC	FC 1	FC	FC	FC 1	FC	FC	FC 1	FC	FC	FC 1	FC	FC	FC 1	FC		
London Kings Cross 15 ⊖	d	20 06			20 36			21 06			21 36			22 06	22 11	22 26	22 36	22 41	22 56	23 06	23 11	23 26	23 36	23 41		
Moorgate ⊖	d		20 05	20 20		20 35	20 50		21 05	21 20		21 35	21 50													
Old Street ⊖	d		20 07	20 22		20 37	20 52		21 07	21 22		21 37	21 52													
Essex Road	d		20 10	20 25		20 40	20 55		21 10	21 25		21 40	21 55													
Highbury & Islington ⊖	d		20 12	20 27		20 42	20 57		21 12	21 27		21 42	21 57													
Drayton Park	d		20 14	20 29		20 44	20 59		21 14	21 29		21 44	21 59													
Finsbury Park ⊖	d	20 11	20 17	20 32	20 41	20 47	21 02	21 11	21 17	21 32	21 41	21 47	22 02	22 11	22 17	22 32	22 41	22 47	23 02	23 11	23 17	23 32	23 41	23 47		
Harringay	d		20 19	20 34		20 49	21 04		21 19	21 34		21 49	22 04		22 19	22 34		22 49	23 04		23 19	23 34		23 49		
Hornsey	d		20 21	20 36		20 51	21 06		21 21	21 36		21 51	22 06		22 21	22 36		22 51	23 06		23 21	23 36		23 51		
Alexandra Palace	d		20 23	20 38		20 53	21 08		21 23	21 38		21 53	22 08		22 23	22 38		22 53	23 08		23 23	23 38		23 53		
New Southgate	d		20 26			20 56			21 26			21 56			22 26			22 56			23 26			23 56		
Oakleigh Park	d		20 29			20 59			21 29			21 59			22 29			22 59			23 29			23 59		
New Barnet	d		20 31			21 01			21 31			22 01			22 31			23 01			23 31			00 01		
Hadley Wood	d		20 34			21 04			21 34			22 04			22 34			23 04			23 34			00 04		
Potters Bar	d	20 21	20 38		20 51	21 08		21 21	21 38		21 51	22 08		22 21	22 38		22 51	23 08		23 21	23 38		23 51	00 08		
Brookmans Park	d		20 41			21 11			21 41			22 11			22 41			23 11			23 41			00 11		
Welham Green	d		20 43			21 13			21 43			22 13			22 43			23 13			23 43			00 13		
Hatfield	d	20 27	20 46		20 57	21 16		21 27	21 46		21 57	22 16		22 27	22 46		22 57	23 16		23 27	23 46		23 57	00 16		
Welwyn Garden City 4	d	20 31	20a51		21 01	21a21		21 31	21a51		22 01	22a21		22 31	22a51		23 01	23a24		23 31	23a54		00 01	00a24		
Welwyn North	d	20 34			21 04			21 34			22 04			22 34			23 04			23 34			00 04			
Knebworth	d	20 38			21 08			21 38			22 08			22 38			23 08			23 38			00 08			
Bowes Park	d			20 41			21 11			21 41			22 11			22 41			23 11			23 41				
Palmers Green	d			20 43			21 13			21 43			22 13			22 43			23 13			23 43				
Winchmore Hill	d			20 45			21 15			21 45			22 15			22 45			23 15			23 45				
Grange Park	d			20 47			21 17			21 47			22 17			22 47			23 17			23 47				
Enfield Chase	d			20 49			21 19			21 49			22 19			22 49			23 19			23 49				
Gordon Hill	d			20 51			21 21			21 51			22 21			22 51			23 21			23 51				
Crews Hill	d			20 54			21 24			21 54			22 24			22 54			23 24			23 54				
Cuffley	d			20 57			21 27			21 57			22 27			22 57			23 27			23 57				
Bayford	d			21 02			21 32			22 02			22 32			23 02			23 32			00 02				
Hertford North	d			21 07			21a38			22 07			22a38			23 07			23a38			00 07				
Watton-at-Stone	d			21 13						22 13						23 13						00 13				
Stevenage 4	d	20 42		21 20	21 12			21 42		22 20	22 12			22 42		23 20	23 12			23 42		00a21	00 12			
Hitchin 4	d	20 47		21 28	21 17			21 47		22 25	22 17			22 50		23 28	23 20			23 50			00 20			
Letchworth Garden City	a	20 51		21 35	21 23			21 51		22 33	22 23			22 54		23 36	23 26			23 54			00 29			

Saturdays

		FC	FC 1	FC	FC 1 A	FC	FC	FC 1	FC	FC 1	FC 1 B	FC 1	FC	FC	FC 1	FC	FC	FC 1	FC	FC	FC 1		FC	FC	FC 1	FC
London Kings Cross 15 ⊖	d	23p26	23p36	23p41	00 07	00 11	00 26	00 36	00 41	01 06	01 36	05 22	05 26	05 56	06 06	06 11	06 26	06 36	06 41	06 56	07 06		07 11	07 26	07 36	07 41
Finsbury Park ⊖	d	23p32	23p41	23p47	00 12	00 17	00 32	00 41	00 47	01 11	01 41	05 27	05 32	06 02	06 11	06 17	06 32	06 41	06 47	07 02	07 11		07 17	07 32	07 41	07 47
Harringay	d	23p34		23p49		00 19	00 34						05 34	06 04		06 19	06 34		06 49	07 04			07 19	07 34		07 49
Hornsey	d	23p36		23p51		00 21	00 36						05 36	06 06		06 21	06 36		06 51	07 06			07 21	07 36		07 51
Alexandra Palace	d	23p38		23p53	00 17	00 23	00 38		00 51	01 16	01 45		05 38	06 08		06 23	06 38		06 53	07 08			07 23	07 38		07 53
New Southgate	d			23p56		00 26			00 54							06 26			06 56				07 26			07 56
Oakleigh Park	d			23p59		00 29			00 57		01 50					06 29			06 59				07 29			07 59
New Barnet	d			00 01		00 31			00 59		01 52					06 31			07 01				07 31			08 01
Hadley Wood	d			00 04		00 34			01 02		01 54					06 34			07 04				07 34			08 04
Potters Bar	d		23p51	00 08		00 38		00 51	01 06		01 58	05 37			06 21	06 38		06 51	07 08		07 21		07 38		07 51	08 08
Brookmans Park	d			00 11		00 41			01 09							06 41			07 11				07 41			08 11
Welham Green	d			00 13		00 43										06 43			07 13				07 43			08 13
Hatfield	d		23p57	00 16		00 46		00 57	01 13		02 04	05 43			06 27	06 46		06 57	07 16		07 27		07 46		07 57	08 16
Welwyn Garden City 4	d		00 01	00a24		00a54		01 01	01a21		02 08	05 47			06 31	06a51		07 01	07a21		07 31		07a51		08 01	08a21
Welwyn North	d		00 04					01s04			02s11	05 50			06 34			07 04			07 34				08 04	
Knebworth	d		00 08					01s08			02s15	05 54			06 38			07 08			07 38				08 08	
Bowes Park	d	23p41					00 41						05 41	06 11			06 41			07 11				07 41		
Palmers Green	d	23p43			00 20		00 43			01 19			05 43	06 13			06 43			07 13				07 43		
Winchmore Hill	d	23p45			00 22		00 45			01 21			05 45	06 15			06 45			07 15				07 45		
Grange Park	d	23p47					00 47						05 47	06 17			06 47			07 17				07 47		
Enfield Chase	d	23p49			00 25		00 49			01 24			05 49	06 19			06 49			07 19				07 49		
Gordon Hill	d	23p51			00 27		00 51			01 26			05 51	06 21			06 51			07 21				07 51		
Crews Hill	d	23p54					00 54						05 54	06 24			06 54			07 24				07 54		
Cuffley	d	23p57			00 31		00 57			01 30			05 57	06 27			06 57			07 27				07 57		
Bayford	d	00 02					01 02						06 02	06 32			07 02			07 32				08 02		
Hertford North	d	00 07			00 39		01a08			01 38			06a08	06a38			07 07			07a38				08 07		
Watton-at-Stone	d	00 13															07 13							08 13		
Stevenage 4	d	00a21	00 12		00 48			01 12		01 47	02 18	05 58			06 42		07a20	07 12			07 42			08a20	08 12	
Hitchin 4	d		00 20		00 56			01a17		01 52	02a23	06a06			06 47			07a17			07 47				08a17	
Letchworth Garden City	a		00 29		01 00					02 06					06 51						07 51					

For general notes see front of timetable
For details of catering facilities see Directory of Train Operators

A To Cambridge (Table 25)
B To Peterborough (Table 25)

There is no service between Moorgate and Finsbury Park on Saturdays

Table 24

Saturdays

London → Welwyn Garden City, Hertford North and Letchworth Garden City

Network Diagram - see first page of Table 24

		FC	FC 1	FC	FC	FC 1	FC	FC	FC 1	FC	FC	FC 1	FC	FC	FC 1	FC	FC	FC 1	FC		FC	FC 1	FC	FC	FC 1	FC
London Kings Cross 15 ⊖	d	07 56	08 06	08 11	08 26	08 36	08 41	08 56	09 06	09 11	09 26	09 36	09 41	09 56	10 06	10 11	10 26	10 36	10 41		10 56	11 06	11 11	11 26	11 36	11 41
Finsbury Park ⊖	d	08 02	08 11	08 17	08 32	08 41	08 47	09 02	09 11	09 17	09 32	09 41	09 47	10 02	10 11	10 17	10 32	10 41	10 47		11 02	11 11	11 17	11 32	11 41	11 47
Harringay	d	08 04		08 19	08 34		08 49	09 04		09 19	09 34		09 49	10 04		10 19	10 34		10 49		11 04		11 19	11 34		11 49
Hornsey	d	08 06		08 21	08 36		08 51	09 06		09 21	09 36		09 51	10 06		10 21	10 36		10 51		11 06		11 21	11 36		11 51
Alexandra Palace	d	08 08		08 23	08 38		08 53	09 08		09 23	09 38		09 53	10 08		10 23	10 38		10 53		11 08		11 23	11 38		11 53
New Southgate	d			08 26			08 56			09 26			09 56			10 26			10 56				11 26			11 56
Oakleigh Park	d			08 29			08 59			09 29			09 59			10 29			10 59				11 29			11 59
New Barnet	d			08 31			09 01			09 31			10 01			10 31			11 01				11 31			12 01
Hadley Wood	d			08 34			09 04			09 34			10 04			10 34			11 04				11 34			12 04
Potters Bar	d		08 21	08 38		08 51	09 08		09 21	09 38		09 51	10 08		10 21	10 38		10 51	11 08			11 21	11 38		11 51	12 08
Brookmans Park	d			08 41			09 11			09 41			10 11			10 41			11 11				11 41			12 11
Welham Green	d			08 43			09 13			09 43			10 13			10 43			11 13				11 43			12 13
Hatfield	d		08 27	08 46		08 57	09 16		09 27	09 46		09 57	10 16		10 27	10 46		10 57	11 16			11 27	11 46		11 57	12 16
Welwyn Garden City 4	d		08 31	08a51		09 01	09a21		09 31	09a51		10 01	10a21		10 31	10a51		11 01	11a21			11 31	11a51		12 01	12a21
Welwyn North	d		08 34			09 04			09 34			10 04			10 34			11 04				11 34			12 04	
Knebworth	d		08 38			09 08			09 38			10 08			10 38			11 08				11 38			12 08	
Bowes Park	d	08 11			08 41			09 11			09 41			10 11			10 41				11 11			11 41		
Palmers Green	d	08 13			08 43			09 13			09 43			10 13			10 43				11 13			11 43		
Winchmore Hill	d	08 15			08 45			09 15			09 45			10 15			10 45				11 15			11 45		
Grange Park	d	08 17			08 47			09 17			09 47			10 17			10 47				11 17			11 47		
Enfield Chase	d	08 19			08 49			09 19			09 49			10 19			10 49				11 19			11 49		
Gordon Hill	d	08 21			08 51			09 21			09 51			10 21			10 51				11 21			11 51		
Crews Hill	d	08 24			08 54			09 24			09 54			10 24			10 54				11 24			11 54		
Cuffley	d	08 27			08 57			09 27			09 57			10 27			10 57				11 27			11 57		
Bayford	d	08 32			09 02			09 32			10 02			10 32			11 02				11 32			12 02		
Hertford North	d	08a38			09 07			09a38			10 07			10a38			11 07				11a38			12 07		
Watton-at-Stone	d				09 13						10 13						11 13							12 13		
Stevenage 4	d		08 42		09a20	09 12			09 42		10a20	10 12			10 42		11a20	11 12				11 42		12a20	12 12	
Hitchin 4	d		08 47			09a17			09 47			10a17			10 47			11a17				11 47			12a17	
Letchworth Garden City	a		08 51						09 51						10 51							11 51				

		FC	FC 1	FC	FC	FC 1	FC	FC	FC 1	FC	FC	FC 1	FC	FC	FC 1	FC	FC		FC 1	FC	FC	FC 1	FC	FC	FC 1	FC
London Kings Cross 15 ⊖	d	11 56	12 06	12 11	12 26	12 36	12 41	12 56	13 06	13 11	13 26	13 36	13 41	13 56	14 06	14 11	14 26		14 36	14 41	14 56	15 06	15 11	15 26	15 36	15 41
Finsbury Park ⊖	d	12 02	12 11	12 17	12 32	12 41	12 47	13 02	13 11	13 17	13 32	13 41	13 47	14 02	14 11	14 17	14 32		14 41	14 47	15 02	15 11	15 17	15 32	15 41	15 47
Harringay	d	12 04		12 19	12 34		12 49	13 04		13 19	13 34		13 49	14 04		14 19	14 34			14 49	15 04		15 19	15 34		15 49
Hornsey	d	12 06		12 21	12 36		12 51	13 06		13 21	13 36		13 51	14 06		14 21	14 36			14 51	15 06		15 21	15 36		15 51
Alexandra Palace	d	12 08		12 23	12 38		12 53	13 08		13 23	13 38		13 53	14 08		14 23	14 38			14 53	15 08		15 23	15 38		15 53
New Southgate	d			12 26			12 56			13 26			13 56			14 26				14 56			15 26			15 56
Oakleigh Park	d			12 29			12 59			13 29			13 59			14 29				14 59			15 29			15 59
New Barnet	d			12 31			13 01			13 31			14 01			14 31				15 01			15 31			16 01
Hadley Wood	d			12 34			13 04			13 34			14 04			14 34				15 04			15 34			16 04
Potters Bar	d		12 21	12 38		12 51	13 08		13 21	13 38		13 51	14 08		14 21	14 38			14 51	15 08		15 21	15 38		15 51	16 08
Brookmans Park	d			12 41			13 11			13 41			14 11			14 41				15 11			15 41			16 11
Welham Green	d			12 43			13 13			13 43			14 13			14 43				15 13			15 43			16 13
Hatfield	d		12 27	12 46		12 57	13 16		13 27	13 46		13 57	14 16		14 27	14 46			14 57	15 16		15 27	15 46		15 57	16 16
Welwyn Garden City 4	d		12 31	12a51		13 01	13a21		13 31	13a51		14 01	14a21		14 31	14a51			15 01	15a21		15 31	15a51		16 01	16a21
Welwyn North	d		12 34			13 04			13 34			14 04			14 34				15 04			15 34			16 04	
Knebworth	d		12 38			13 08			13 38			14 08			14 38				15 08			15 38			16 08	
Bowes Park	d	12 11			12 41			13 11			13 41			14 11			14 41				15 11			15 41		
Palmers Green	d	12 13			12 43			13 13			13 43			14 13			14 43				15 13			15 43		
Winchmore Hill	d	12 15			12 45			13 15			13 45			14 15			14 45				15 15			15 45		
Grange Park	d	12 17			12 47			13 17			13 47			14 17			14 47				15 17			15 47		
Enfield Chase	d	12 19			12 49			13 19			13 49			14 19			14 49				15 19			15 49		
Gordon Hill	d	12 21			12 51			13 21			13 51			14 21			14 51				15 21			15 51		
Crews Hill	d	12 24			12 54			13 24			13 54			14 24			14 54				15 24			15 54		
Cuffley	d	12 27			12 57			13 27			13 57			14 27			14 57				15 27			15 57		
Bayford	d	12 32			13 02			13 32			14 02			14 32			15 02				15 32			16 02		
Hertford North	d	12a38			13 07			13a38			14 07			14a38			15 07				15a38			16 07		
Watton-at-Stone	d				13 13						14 13						15 13							16 13		
Stevenage 4	d		12 42		13a20	13 12			13 42		14a20	14 12			14 42		15a20		15 12			15 42		16a20	16 12	
Hitchin 4	d		12 47			13a17			13 47			14a17			14 47				15a17			15 47			16a17	
Letchworth Garden City	a		12 51						13 51						14 51							15 51				

For general notes see front of timetable
For details of catering facilities see
Directory of Train Operators

There is no service between Moorgate and Finsbury Park on Saturdays

Table 24

Saturdays

London → Welwyn Garden City, Hertford North and Letchworth Garden City

Network Diagram - see first page of Table 24

		FC	FC 1	FC	FC	FC 1	FC	FC	FC 1	FC	FC	FC 1	FC	FC	FC 1		FC	FC	FC 1	FC	FC	FC 1	FC	FC	FC 1	FC
London Kings Cross 15	⊖ d	15 56	16 06	16 11	16 26	16 36	16 41	16 56	17 06	17 11	17 26	17 36	17 41	17 56	18 06		18 11	18 26	18 36	18 41	18 56	19 06	19 11	19 26	19 36	19 41
Finsbury Park	⊖ d	16 02	16 11	16 17	16 32	16 41	16 47	17 02	17 11	17 17	17 32	17 41	17 47	18 02	18 11		18 17	18 32	18 41	18 47	19 02	19 11	19 17	19 32	19 41	19 47
Harringay	d	16 04		16 19	16 34		16 49	17 04		17 19	17 34		17 49	18 04			18 19	18 34		18 49	19 04		19 19	19 34		19 49
Hornsey	d	16 06		16 21	16 36		16 51	17 06		17 21	17 36		17 51	18 06			18 21	18 36		18 51	19 06		19 21	19 36		19 51
Alexandra Palace	d	16 08		16 23	16 38		16 53	17 08		17 23	17 38		17 53	18 08			18 23	18 38		18 53	19 08		19 23	19 38		19 53
New Southgate	d			16 26			16 56			17 26			17 56				18 26			18 56			19 26			19 56
Oakleigh Park	d			16 29			16 59			17 29			17 59				18 29			18 59			19 29			19 59
New Barnet	d			16 31			17 01			17 31			18 01				18 31			19 01			19 31			20 01
Hadley Wood	d			16 34			17 04			17 34			18 04				18 34			19 04			19 34			20 04
Potters Bar	d		16 21	16 38		16 51	17 08		17 21	17 38		17 51	18 08		18 21		18 38		18 51	19 08		19 21	19 38		19 51	20 08
Brookmans Park	d			16 41			17 11			17 41			18 11				18 41			19 11			19 41			20 11
Welham Green	d			16 43			17 13			17 43			18 13				18 43			19 13			19 43			20 13
Hatfield	d		16 27	16 46		16 57	17 16		17 27	17 46		17 57	18 16		18 27		18 46		18 57	19 16		19 27	19 46		19 57	20 16
Welwyn Garden City 4	d		16 31	16a51		17 01	17a21		17 31	17a51		18 01	18a21		18 31		18a51		19 01	19a21		19 31	19a51		20 01	20a21
Welwyn North	d		16 34			17 04			17 34			18 04			18 34				19 04			19 34			20 04	
Knebworth	d		16 38			17 08			17 38			18 08			18 38				19 08			19 38			20 08	
Bowes Park	d	16 11			16 41			17 11			17 41			18 11				18 41			19 11			19 41		
Palmers Green	d	16 13			16 43			17 13			17 43			18 13				18 43			19 13			19 43		
Winchmore Hill	d	16 15			16 45			17 15			17 45			18 15				18 45			19 15			19 45		
Grange Park	d	16 17			16 47			17 17			17 47			18 17				18 47			19 17			19 47		
Enfield Chase	d	16 19			16 49			17 19			17 49			18 19				18 49			19 19			19 49		
Gordon Hill	d	16 21			16 51			17 21			17 51			18 21				18 51			19 21			19 51		
Crews Hill	d	16 24			16 54			17 24			17 54			18 24				18 54			19 24			19 54		
Cuffley	d	16 27			16 57			17 27			17 57			18 27				18 57			19 27			19 57		
Bayford	d	16 32			17 02			17 32			18 02			18 32				19 02			19 32			20 02		
Hertford North	d	16a38			17 07			17a38			18 07			18a38				19 07			19a38			20 07		
Watton-at-Stone	d				17 13						18 13							19 13						20 13		
Stevenage 4	d		16 42		17a20	17 12			17 42		18a20	18 12			18 42			19a20	19 12			19 42		20a20	20 12	
Hitchin 4	d		16 47			17a17			17 47			18a17			18 47				19a17			19 47			20a17	
Letchworth Garden City	a		16 51						17 51						18 51							19 51				

		FC	FC 1	FC	FC	FC 1	FC	FC	FC 1	FC	FC	FC 1	FC	FC	FC 1	FC	FC	FC 1	FC	FC	FC 1	FC	FC	FC		
London Kings Cross 15	⊖ d	19 56	20 06	20 11	20 26	20 36	20 41	20 56	21 06	21 11	21 26	21 36	21 41	21 56	22 06	22 11	22 26	22 36	22 41	22 56	23 15	23 19	23 26	23 35		
Finsbury Park	⊖ d	20 02	20 11	20 17	20 32	20 41	20 47	21 02	21 11	21 17	21 32	21 41	21 47	22 02	22 11	22 17	22 32	22 41	22 47	23 02	23 20	23 24	23 32	23 40		
Harringay	d	20 04		20 19	20 34		20 49	21 04		21 19	21 34		21 49	22 04		22 19	22 34		22 49	23 04		23 26	23 34	23 42		
Hornsey	d	20 06		20 21	20 36		20 51	21 06		21 21	21 36		21 51	22 06		22 21	22 36		22 51	23 06		23 28	23 36	23 44		
Alexandra Palace	d	20 08		20 23	20 38		20 53	21 08		21 23	21 38		21 53	22 08		22 23	22 38		22 53	23 08		23 30	23 38	23 46		
New Southgate	d			20 26			20 56			21 26			21 56			22 26			22 56			23 33		23 49		
Oakleigh Park	d			20 29			20 59			21 29			21 59			22 29			22 59			23 37		23 52		
New Barnet	d			20 31			21 01			21 31			22 01			22 31			23 01			23 39		23 54		
Hadley Wood	d			20 34			21 04			21 34			22 04			22 34			23 04			23 41		23 57		
Potters Bar	d		20 21	20 38		20 51	21 08		21 21	21 38		21 51	22 08		22 21	22 38		22 51	23 08		23 30	23 45		00 01		
Brookmans Park	d			20 41			21 11			21 41			22 11			22 41			23 11			23 48		00 04		
Welham Green	d			20 43			21 13			21 43			22 13			22 43			23 13			23 50		00 07		
Hatfield	d		20 27	20 46		20 57	21 16		21 27	21 46		21 57	22 16		22 27	22 46		22 57	23 16		23 36	23 54		00 09		
Welwyn Garden City 4	d		20 31	20a51		21 01	21a21		21 31	21a51		22 01	22a21		22 31	22a53		23 01	23a23		23 40	00a05		00b28		
Welwyn North	d		20 34			21 04			21 34			22 04			22 34			23 04			23 45			00 31		
Knebworth	d		20 38			21 08			21 38			22 08			22 38			23 08			23 49			00 35		
Bowes Park	d	20 11			20 41			21 11			21 41			22 11			22 41			23 11			23 41			
Palmers Green	d	20 13			20 43			21 13			21 43			22 13			22 43			23 13			23 43			
Winchmore Hill	d	20 15			20 45			21 15			21 45			22 15			22 45			23 15			23 45			
Grange Park	d	20 17			20 47			21 17			21 47			22 17			22 47			23 17			23 47			
Enfield Chase	d	20 19			20 49			21 19			21 49			22 19			22 49			23 19			23 49			
Gordon Hill	d	20 21			20 51			21 21			21 51			22 21			22 51			23 21			23 51			
Crews Hill	d	20 24			20 54			21 24			21 54			22 24			22 54			23 24			23 54			
Cuffley	d	20 27			20 57			21 27			21 57			22 27			22 57			23 27			23 57			
Bayford	d	20 32			21 02			21 32			22 02			22 32			23 02			23 32			00 02			
Hertford North	d	20a38			21 07			21a38			22 07			22a38			23 07			23a38			00 07			
Watton-at-Stone	d				21 13						22 13						23 13						00 13			
Stevenage 4	d		20 42		21a20	21 12			21 42		22a20	22 12			22 42		23a21	23 12			23 55		00a23	00 41		
Hitchin 4	d		20 47			21a17			21 47			22a17			22 47			23a17			00 02			00 49		
Letchworth Garden City	a		20 51						21 51						22 51						00 06			00 57		

For general notes see front of timetable
For details of catering facilities see
Directory of Train Operators

b Arr. 0015

There is no service between Moorgate and Finsbury Park on Saturdays

Sundays until 13 July

London → Welwyn Garden City, Hertford North and Letchworth Garden City

Network Diagram - see first page of Table 24

		FC 1	FC	FC	FC 1 A	FC	FC	FC 1	FC	FC 1	FC 🚌	FC	FC	FC 1	FC 🚌	FC 🚌	FC	FC	FC 1	FC 🚌	FC		FC	FC 1	FC 🚌	FC 🚌
London Kings Cross 15	⊖ d	23p15	23p26	23p35	00 07	00 11	00 26	00 36	00 41	06 06		06 11	06 26	06 36			06 41	06 56	07 06		07 11		07 26	07 36		
Finsbury Park	⊖ d	23p20	23p32	23p40	00 12	00 17	00 32	00 41	00 47	06 11		06 17	06 32	06 41			06 47	07 02	07 11		07 17		07 32	07 41		
Harringay	d		23p34	23p42		00 19	00 34		00 49			06 19	06 34				06 49	07 04			07 19		07 34			
Hornsey	d		23p36	23p44		00 21	00 36		00 51			06 21	06 36				06 51	07 06			07 21		07 36			
Alexandra Palace	d		23p38	23p46	00 17	00 23	00 38		00 53			06 23	06 38				06 53	07 08			07 23		07 38			
New Southgate	d			23p49		00 26			00 56			06 26					06 56				07 26					
Oakleigh Park	d			23p52		00 29			00 59			06 29					06 59				07 29					
New Barnet	d			23p54		00 31			01 01			06 31					07 01				07 31					
Hadley Wood	d			23p57		00 34			01 04			06 34					07 04				07 34					
Potters Bar	d	23p30		00 01		00 38		00 51	01 08	06 21		06 38		06 51			07 08		07 21		07 38			07 51		
Brookmans Park	d			00 04		00 41			01 11			06 41					07 11				07 41					
Welham Green	d			00 07		00 43			01 13			06 43					07 13				07 43					
Hatfield	d	23p36		00 09		00 46		00 57	01 16	06 27		06 46		06 57			07 16		07 27		07 46			07 57		
Welwyn Garden City 4	d	23p40		00b28		00a57		01 03	01a26	06a34	06 41	06a55		07a04	07 11		07a25		07a34	07 41	07a55			08a04	08 11	
Welwyn North	d	23p45		00 31				01s06			06 51				07 21					07 51					08 21	
Knebworth	d	23p49		00 35				01s10			07 01				07 31					08 01					08 31	
Bowes Park	d		23p41				00 41						06 41					07 11					07 41			
Palmers Green	d		23p43		00 20		00 43						06 43					07 13					07 43			
Winchmore Hill	d		23p45		00 22		00 45						06 45					07 15					07 45			
Grange Park	d		23p47				00 47						06 47					07 17					07 47			
Enfield Chase	d		23p49		00 25		00 49						06 49					07 19					07 49			
Gordon Hill	d		23p51		00 27		00 51						06 51					07 21					07 51			
Crews Hill	d		23p54				00 54						06 54					07 24					07 54			
Cuffley	d		23p57		00 31		00 57						06 57					07 27					07 57			
Bayford	d		00 02				01 02						07 02					07 32					08 02			
Hertford North	d		00 07		00 39		01a10						07a10			07 16		07a40					08a10			08 16
Watton-at-Stone	d		00 13													07 30										08 30
Stevenage 4	d	23p55	00a23	00 41	00 48			01 14			07 08				07 38	07a47				08 08					08 38	08a47
Hitchin 4	d	00 02		00 49	00 56			01 19			07a28				07a58					08a28					08a58	
Letchworth Garden City	a	00 06		00 57	01 00			01 26																		

		FC	FC	FC 1	FC 🚌	FC	FC	FC	FC	FC 1	FC 🚌	FC	FC	FC	FC	FC 1	FC 🚌	FC	FC		FC	FC	FC 1	FC 🚌	FC	FC
London Kings Cross 15	⊖ d	07 41	07 56	08 06		08 11	08 26	08 41	08 56	09 04		09 11	09 26	09 41	09 56	10 04		10 11	10 26		10 41	10 56	11 04		11 11	11 26
Finsbury Park	⊖ d	07 47	08 02	08 11		08 17	08 32	08 47	09 02	09 09		09 17	09 32	09 47	10 02	10 09		10 17	10 32		10 47	11 02	11 09		11 17	11 32
Harringay	d	07 49	08 04			08 19	08 34	08 49	09 04			09 19	09 34	09 49	10 04			10 19	10 34		10 49	11 04			11 19	11 34
Hornsey	d	07 51	08 06			08 21	08 36	08 51	09 06			09 21	09 36	09 51	10 06			10 21	10 36		10 51	11 06			11 21	11 36
Alexandra Palace	d	07 53	08 08			08 23	08 38	08 53	09 08			09 23	09 38	09 53	10 08			10 23	10 38		10 53	11 08			11 23	11 38
New Southgate	d	07 56				08 26		08 56				09 26		09 56				10 26			10 56				11 26	
Oakleigh Park	d	07 59				08 29		08 59				09 29		09 59				10 29			10 59				11 29	
New Barnet	d	08 01				08 31		09 01				09 31		10 01				10 31			11 01				11 31	
Hadley Wood	d	08 04				08 34		09 04				09 34		10 04				10 34			11 04				11 34	
Potters Bar	d	08 08		08 21		08 38		09 08		09 19		09 38		10 08		10 19		10 38			11 08		11 19		11 38	
Brookmans Park	d	08 11				08 41		09 11				09 41		10 11				10 41			11 11				11 41	
Welham Green	d	08 13				08 43		09 13				09 43		10 13				10 43			11 13				11 43	
Hatfield	d	08 16		08 27		08 46		09 16		09 25		09 46		10 16		10 25		10 46			11 16		11 25		11 46	
Welwyn Garden City 4	d	08a25		08a34	08 38	08a55		09a21		09 29		09a51		10a21		10 29		10a51			11a21		11 29		11a51	
Welwyn North	d				08 48					09 33						10 33							11 33			
Knebworth	d				08 58					09 37						10 37							11 37			
Bowes Park	d		08 11				08 41		09 11				09 41		10 11				10 41			11 11				11 41
Palmers Green	d		08 13				08 43		09 13				09 43		10 13				10 43			11 13				11 43
Winchmore Hill	d		08 15				08 45		09 15				09 45		10 15				10 45			11 15				11 45
Grange Park	d		08 17				08 47		09 17				09 47		10 17				10 47			11 17				11 47
Enfield Chase	d		08 19				08 49		09 19				09 49		10 19				10 49			11 19				11 49
Gordon Hill	d		08 21				08 51		09 21				09 51		10 21				10 51			11 21				11 51
Crews Hill	d		08 24				08 54		09 24				09 54		10 24				10 54			11 24				11 54
Cuffley	d		08 27				08 57		09 27				09 57		10 27				10 57			11 27				11 57
Bayford	d		08 32				09 02		09 32				10 02		10 32				11 02			11 32				12 02
Hertford North	d		08a40				09a08		09a38		09 16		10a08		10a38		10 16		11a08			11a38		11 16		12a08
Watton-at-Stone	d										09 30						10 30							11 30		
Stevenage 4	d				09a05					09 40	09a47					10 40	10a47						11 40	11a47		
Hitchin 4	d									09 45						10 45							11 45			
Letchworth Garden City	a									09 49						10 49							11 49			

For general notes see front of timetable
For details of catering facilities see
Directory of Train Operators

A To Cambridge (Table 25)
b Arr. 0015

There is no service between Moorgate and Finsbury Park on Sundays

Table 24

Sundays
until 13 July

London → Welwyn Garden City, Hertford North and Letchworth Garden City

Network Diagram - see first page of Table 24

		FC	FC	FC [1]	FC (bus)	FC	FC	FC	FC	FC [1]	FC (bus)	FC	FC	FC	FC	FC [1]	FC (bus)		FC	FC	FC	FC	FC [1]	FC (bus)	FC	FC
London Kings Cross [15]	⊖ d	11 41	11 56	12 04		12 11	12 26	12 41	12 56	13 04		13 11	13 26	13 41	13 56	14 04			14 11	14 26	14 41	14 56	15 04		15 11	15 26
Finsbury Park	⊖ d	11 47	12 02	12 09		12 17	12 32	12 47	13 02	13 09		13 17	13 32	13 47	14 02	14 09			14 17	14 32	14 47	15 02	15 09		15 17	15 32
Harringay	d	11 49	12 04			12 19	12 34	12 49	13 04			13 19	13 34	13 49	14 04				14 19	14 34	14 49	15 04			15 19	15 34
Hornsey	d	11 51	12 06			12 21	12 36	12 51	13 06			13 21	13 36	13 51	14 06				14 21	14 36	14 51	15 06			15 21	15 36
Alexandra Palace	d	11 53	12 08			12 23	12 38	12 53	13 08			13 23	13 38	13 53	14 08				14 23	14 38	14 53	15 08			15 23	15 38
New Southgate	d	11 56				12 26		12 56				13 26		13 56					14 26		14 56				15 26	
Oakleigh Park	d	11 59				12 29		12 59				13 29		13 59					14 29		14 59				15 29	
New Barnet	d	12 01				12 31		13 01				13 31		14 01					14 31		15 01				15 31	
Hadley Wood	d	12 04				12 34		13 04				13 34		14 04					14 34		15 04				15 34	
Potters Bar	d	12 08		12 19		12 38		13 08		13 19		13 38		14 08		14 19			14 38		15 08		15 19		15 38	
Brookmans Park	d	12 11				12 41		13 11				13 41		14 11					14 41		15 11				15 41	
Welham Green	d	12 13				12 43		13 13				13 43		14 13					14 43		15 13				15 43	
Hatfield	d	12 16		12 25		12 46		13 16		13 25		13 46		14 16		14 25			14 46		15 16		15 25		15 46	
Welwyn Garden City [4]	d	12a21		12 29		12a51		13a21		13 29		13a51		14a21		14 29			14a51		15a21		15 29		15a51	
Welwyn North	d			12 33						13 33						14 33							15 33			
Knebworth	d			12 37						13 37						14 37							15 37			
Bowes Park	d		12 11				12 41		13 11				13 41		14 11					14 41		15 11				15 41
Palmers Green	d		12 13				12 43		13 13				13 43		14 13					14 43		15 13				15 43
Winchmore Hill	d		12 15				12 45		13 15				13 45		14 15					14 45		15 15				15 45
Grange Park	d		12 17				12 47		13 17				13 47		14 17					14 47		15 17				15 47
Enfield Chase	d		12 19				12 49		13 19				13 49		14 19					14 49		15 19				15 49
Gordon Hill	d		12 21				12 51		13 21				13 51		14 21					14 51		15 21				15 51
Crews Hill	d		12 24				12 54		13 24				13 54		14 24					14 54		15 24				15 54
Cuffley	d		12 27				12 57		13 27				13 57		14 27					14 57		15 27				15 57
Bayford	d		12 32				13 02		13 32				14 02		14 32					15 02		15 32				16 02
Hertford North	d		12a38		12 16		13a08		13a38		13 16		14a08		14a38		14 16			15a08		15a38		15 16		16a08
Watton-at-Stone	d				12 30						13 30						14 30							15 30		
Stevenage [4]	d			12 40	12a47					13 40	13a47					14 40	14a47						15 40	15a47		
Hitchin [4]	d			12 45						13 45						14 45							15 45			
Letchworth Garden City	a			12 49						13 49						14 49							15 49			

		FC	FC	FC [1]	FC (bus)	FC	FC	FC	FC	FC [1]	FC (bus)	FC	FC	FC	FC		FC [1]	FC	FC	FC	FC	FC [1]	FC	FC	FC	FC
London Kings Cross [15]	⊖ d	15 41	15 56	16 04		16 11	16 26	16 41	16 56	17 06		17 11	17 26	17 41	17 56		18 06	18 11	18 26	18 41	18 56	19 06	19 11	19 26	19 41	19 56
Finsbury Park	⊖ d	15 47	16 02	16 09		16 17	16 32	16 47	17 02	17 11		17 17	17 32	17 47	18 02		18 11	18 17	18 32	18 47	19 02	19 11	19 17	19 32	19 47	20 02
Harringay	d	15 49	16 04			16 19	16 34	16 49	17 04			17 19	17 34	17 49	18 04			18 19	18 34	18 49	19 04		19 19	19 34	19 49	20 04
Hornsey	d	15 51	16 06			16 21	16 36	16 51	17 06			17 21	17 36	17 51	18 06			18 21	18 36	18 51	19 06		19 21	19 36	19 51	20 06
Alexandra Palace	d	15 53	16 08			16 23	16 38	16 53	17 08			17 23	17 38	17 53	18 08			18 23	18 38	18 53	19 08		19 23	19 38	19 53	20 08
New Southgate	d	15 56				16 26		16 56				17 26		17 56				18 26		18 56			19 26		19 56	
Oakleigh Park	d	15 59				16 29		16 59				17 29		17 59				18 29		18 59			19 29		19 59	
New Barnet	d	16 01				16 31		17 01				17 31		18 01				18 31		19 01			19 31		20 01	
Hadley Wood	d	16 04				16 34		17 04				17 34		18 04				18 34		19 04			19 34		20 04	
Potters Bar	d	16 08		16 19		16 38		17 08		17 21		17 38		18 08			18 21	18 38		19 08		19 21	19 38		20 08	
Brookmans Park	d	16 11				16 41		17 11				17 41		18 11				18 41		19 11			19 41		20 11	
Welham Green	d	16 13				16 43		17 13				17 43		18 13				18 43		19 13			19 43		20 13	
Hatfield	d	16 16		16 25		16 46		17 16		17 27		17 46		18 16			18 27	18 46		19 16		19 27	19 46		20 16	
Welwyn Garden City [4]	d	16a21		16 29		16a51		17a21		17 31		17a51		18a21			18 31	18a51		19a21		19 31	19a51		20a21	
Welwyn North	d			16 33						17 34							18 34					19 34				
Knebworth	d			16 37						17 38							18 38					19 38				
Bowes Park	d		16 11				16 41		17 11				17 41		18 11				18 41		19 11			19 41		20 11
Palmers Green	d		16 13				16 43		17 13				17 43		18 13				18 43		19 13			19 43		20 13
Winchmore Hill	d		16 15				16 45		17 15				17 45		18 15				18 45		19 15			19 45		20 15
Grange Park	d		16 17				16 47		17 17				17 47		18 17				18 47		19 17			19 47		20 17
Enfield Chase	d		16 19				16 49		17 19				17 49		18 19				18 49		19 19			19 49		20 19
Gordon Hill	d		16 21				16 51		17 21				17 51		18 21				18 51		19 21			19 51		20 21
Crews Hill	d		16 24				16 54		17 24				17 54		18 24				18 54		19 24			19 54		20 24
Cuffley	d		16 27				16 57		17 27				17 57		18 27				18 57		19 27			19 57		20 27
Bayford	d		16 32				17 02		17 32				18 02		18 32				19 02		19 32			20 02		20 32
Hertford North	d		16a38		16 16		17a08		17a38		17 16		18 07		18a38				19 07		19a38			20 07		20a38
Watton-at-Stone	d				16 30						17 30		18 13						19 13					20 13		
Stevenage [4]	d			16 40	16a47					17 42	17a47		18a20				18 42		19a20			19 42		20a20		
Hitchin [4]	d			16 45						17 47							18 47					19 47				
Letchworth Garden City	a			16 51						17 51							18 51					19 51				

For general notes see front of timetable
For details of catering facilities see Directory of Train Operators

There is no service between Moorgate and Finsbury Park on Sundays

London → Welwyn Garden City, Hertford North and Letchworth Garden City

Sundays

until 13 July

Network Diagram - see first page of Table 24

		FC 1	FC	FC	FC	FC	FC 1	FC	FC	FC	FC	FC 1	FC	FC	FC bus	FC	FC	FC 1	FC bus	FC bus	FC	FC bus	FC	FC
London Kings Cross 15	⊖ d	20 06	20 11	20 26	20 41	20 56	21 06	21 11	21 26	21 41	21 56	22 06	22 11	22 26		22 41	22 56	23 06			23 19		23 28	23 41
Finsbury Park	⊖ d	20 11	20 17	20 32	20 47	21 02	21 11	21 17	21 32	21 47	22 02	22 11	22 17	22 32		22 47	23 02	23 11			23 25		23 33	23 47
Harringay	d		20 19	20 34	20 49	21 04		21 19	21 34	21 49	22 04		22 19	22 34		22 49	23 04				23 27		23 36	23 49
Hornsey	d		20 21	20 36	20 51	21 06		21 21	21 36	21 51	22 06		22 21	22 36		22 51	23 06				23 29		23 38	23 51
Alexandra Palace	d		20 23	20 38	20 53	21 08		21 23	21 38	21 53	22 08		22 23	22a38	22 30	22 53	23a08			23 14	23 31	23 40	23a42	23 53
New Southgate	d		20 26		20 56			21 26		21 56			22 26			22 56					23 34			23 56
Oakleigh Park	d		20 29		20 59			21 29		21 59			22 29			22 59					23 37			23 59
New Barnet	d		20 31		21 01			21 31		22 01			22 31			23 01					23 39			00 01
Hadley Wood	d		20 34		21 04			21 34		22 04			22 34			23 04					23 42			00 04
Potters Bar	d	20 21	20 38		21 08		21 21	21 38		22 08		22 21	22 38			23 08		23 21			23 46			00 08
Brookmans Park	d		20 41		21 11			21 41		22 11			22 41			23 11					23 49			00 11
Welham Green	d		20 43		21 13			21 43		22 13			22 43			23 13					23 51			00 13
Hatfield	d	20 27	20 46		21 16		21 27	21 46		22 16		22 27	22 46			23 16		23 27			23 54			00 16
Welwyn Garden City 4	d	20 31	20a51		21a21		21 31	21a51		22a21		22 31	22a54			23a24		23 31			00a04			00 20
Welwyn North	d	20 34					21 34					22 34						23 36						00 23
Knebworth	d	20 38					21 38					22 38						23 40						00 28
Bowes Park	d			20 41		21 11			21 41		22 11				22 35					23 19		23 45		
Palmers Green	d			20 43		21 13			21 43		22 13				22 45					23 29		23 55		
Winchmore Hill	d			20 45		21 15			21 45		22 15				22 53					23 37		00 03		
Grange Park	d			20 47		21 17			21 47		22 17				22 59					23 43		00 09		
Enfield Chase	d			20 49		21 19			21 49		22 19				23 04					23 48		00 14		
Gordon Hill	d			20 51		21 21			21 51		22 21				23 10				22 40	23 54		00 20		
Crews Hill	d			20 54		21 24			21 54		22 24				23 20				22 50	00 04		00 30		
Cuffley	d			20 57		21 27			21 57		22 27				23 28				22 58	00 12		00 38		
Bayford	d			21 02		21 32			22 02		22 32				23 43				23 13	00 27		00 53		
Hertford North	d			21 07		21a38			22 07		22a38				23a58				23 28	00 42		01 08		
Watton-at-Stone	d			21 13					22 13										23 42	00 56		01 22		
Stevenage 4	d	20 42		21a20			21 42		22a20			22 42						23 43	23a59	01a13		01a39		00 31
Hitchin 4	d	20 47					21 47					22 47						23 53						00a47
Letchworth Garden City	a	20 51					21 51					22 51						23 57						

Sundays

20 July to 7 September

		FC 1	FC	FC	FC 1 A	FC	FC		FC 1	FC	FC 1	FC bus	FC	FC bus		FC 1	FC bus	FC	FC 1	FC bus	FC bus		FC	FC bus	FC 1	FC bus
London Kings Cross 15	⊖ d	23p15	23p26	23p35	00 07	00 11	00 26		00 36	00 41	06 06		06 11			06 36		06 41	07 06				07 11		07 36	
Finsbury Park	⊖ d	23p20	23p32	23p40	00 12	00 17	00 32		00 41	00 47	06 11		06 17			06 41		06 47	07 11				07 17		07 41	
Harringay	d		23p34	23p42		00 19	00 34			00 49			06 19					06 49					07 19			
Hornsey	d		23p36	23p44		00 21	00 36			00 51			06 21					06 51					07 21			
Alexandra Palace	d		23p38	23p46	00 17	00 23	00 38			00 53			06 23	06 30				06 53			07 00		07 23	07 30		
New Southgate	d			23p49		00 26				00 56			06 26					06 56					07 26			
Oakleigh Park	d			23p52		00 29				00 59			06 29					06 59					07 29			
New Barnet	d			23p54		00 31				01 01			06 31					07 01					07 31			
Hadley Wood	d			23p57		00 34				01 04			06 34					07 04					07 34			
Potters Bar	d	23p30		00 01		00 38			00 51	01 08	06 21		06 38			06 51		07 08	07 21				07 38		07 51	
Brookmans Park	d			00 04		00 41				01 11			06 41					07 11					07 41			
Welham Green	d			00 07		00 43				01 13			06 43					07 13					07 43			
Hatfield	d	23p36		00 09		00 46			00 57	01 16	06 27		06 46			06 57		07 16	07 27				07 46		07 57	
Welwyn Garden City 4	d	23p40		00b28		00a57			01 03	01a26	06a34	06 41	06a55			07a04	07 11	07a25	07a34	07 41			07a55		08a04	08 11
Welwyn North	d	23p45		00 31					01s06			06 51					07 21			07 51						08 21
Knebworth	d	23p49		00 35					01s10			07 01					07 31			08 01						08 31
Bowes Park	d		23p41				00 41							06 35							07 05			07 35		
Palmers Green	d		23p43		00 20		00 43							06 45							07 15			07 45		
Winchmore Hill	d		23p45		00 22		00 45							06 53							07 23			07 53		
Grange Park	d		23p47				00 47							06 59							07 29			07 59		
Enfield Chase	d		23p49		00 25		00 49							07 04							07 34			08 04		
Gordon Hill	d		23p51		00 27		00 51							07 10							07 40			08 10		
Crews Hill	d		23p54				00 54							07 20							07 50			08 20		
Cuffley	d		23p57		00 31		00 57							07 28							07 58			08 28		
Bayford	d		00 02				01 02							07 43							08 13			08 43		
Hertford North	d		00 07		00 39		01a10							07a58							08 28			08a58		
Watton-at-Stone	d		00 13																		08 42					
Stevenage 4	d	23p55	00a23	00 41	00 48				01 14			07 08					07 38			08 08	08a59					08 38
Hitchin 4	d	00 02		00 49	00 56				01 19			07a28					07a58			08a28						08a58
Letchworth Garden City	a	00 06		00 57	01 00				01 26																	

For general notes see front of timetable
For details of catering facilities see Directory of Train Operators

A To Cambridge (Table 25)
b Arr. 0015

There is no service between Moorgate and Finsbury Park on Sundays

Table 24

Sundays

20 July to 7 September

London → Welwyn Garden City, Hertford North and Letchworth Garden City

Network Diagram - see first page of Table 24

		FC	FC **1**	FC 🚌	FC 🚌		FC	FC 🚌	FC	FC **1**	FC 🚌	FC		FC 🚌	FC	FC **1**	FC 🚌	FC	FC 🚌		FC	FC **1**	FC 🚌	FC	FC 🚌	FC
London Kings Cross 15	⊖ d	07 41	08 06				08 11		08 41	09 04		09 11			09 41	10 04		10 11			10 41	11 04		11 11		11 41
Finsbury Park	⊖ d	07 47	08 11				08 17		08 47	09 09		09 17			09 47	10 09		10 17			10 47	11 09		11 17		11 47
Harringay	d	07 49					08 19		08 49			09 19			09 49			10 19			10 49			11 19		11 49
Hornsey	d	07 51					08 21		08 51			09 21			09 51			10 21			10 51			11 21		11 51
Alexandra Palace	d	07 53			08 00		08 23	08 30	08 53		09 00	09 23		09 30	09 53		10 00	10 23	10 30		10 53		11 00	11 23	11 30	11 53
New Southgate	d	07 56					08 26		08 56			09 26			09 56			10 26			10 56			11 26		11 56
Oakleigh Park	d	07 59					08 29		08 59			09 29			09 59			10 29			10 59			11 29		11 59
New Barnet	d	08 01					08 31		09 01			09 31			10 01			10 31			11 01			11 31		12 01
Hadley Wood	d	08 04					08 34		09 04			09 34			10 04			10 34			11 04			11 34		12 04
Potters Bar	d	08 08	08 21				08 38		09 08	09 19		09 38			10 08	10 19		10 38			11 08	11 19		11 38		12 08
Brookmans Park	d	08 11					08 41		09 11			09 41			10 11			10 41			11 11			11 41		12 11
Welham Green	d	08 13					08 43		09 13			09 43			10 13			10 43			11 13			11 43		12 13
Hatfield	d	08 16	08 27				08 46		09 16	09 25		09 46			10 16	10 25		10 46			11 16	11 25		11 46		12 16
Welwyn Garden City 4	d	08a25	08a34	08 38			08a55		09a21	09 29		09a51			10a21	10 29		10a51			11a21	11 29		11a51		12a21
Welwyn North	d			08 48						09 33						10 33						11 33				
Knebworth	d			08 58						09 37						10 37						11 37				
Bowes Park	d				08 05			08 35			09 05			09 35			10 05		10 35				11 05		11 35	
Palmers Green	d				08 15			08 45			09 15			09 45			10 15		10 45				11 15		11 45	
Winchmore Hill	d				08 23			08 53			09 23			09 53			10 23		10 53				11 23		11 53	
Grange Park	d				08 29			08 59			09 29			09 59			10 29		10 59				11 29		11 59	
Enfield Chase	d				08 34			09 04			09 34			10 04			10 34		11 04				11 34		12 04	
Gordon Hill	d				08 40			09 10			09 40			10 10			10 40		11 10				11 40		12 10	
Crews Hill	d				08 50			09 20			09 50			10 20			10 50		11 20				11 50		12 20	
Cuffley	d				08 58			09 28			09 58			10 28			10 58		11 28				11 58		12 28	
Bayford	d				09 13			09 43			10 13			10 43			11 13		11 43				12 13		12 43	
Hertford North	d				09 28			09a58			10 28			10a58			11 28		11a58				12 28		12a58	
Watton-at-Stone	d				09 42						10 42						11 42						12 42			
Stevenage 4	d			09a05	09a59					09 40	10a59					10 40	11a59					11 40	12a59			
Hitchin 4	d									09 45						10 45						11 45				
Letchworth Garden City	a									09 49						10 49						11 49				

		FC **1**	FC 🚌		FC	FC 🚌	FC	FC **1**	FC 🚌	FC		FC 🚌	FC	FC **1**	FC 🚌	FC	FC 🚌		FC	FC **1**	FC 🚌	FC	FC 🚌	FC		FC **1**
London Kings Cross 15	⊖ d	12 04			12 11		12 41	13 04		13 11			13 41	14 04		14 11			14 41	15 04		15 11		15 41		16 04
Finsbury Park	⊖ d	12 09			12 17		12 47	13 09		13 17			13 47	14 09		14 17			14 47	15 09		15 17		15 47		16 09
Harringay	d				12 19		12 49			13 19			13 49			14 19			14 49			15 19		15 49		
Hornsey	d				12 21		12 51			13 21			13 51			14 21			14 51			15 21		15 51		
Alexandra Palace	d		12 00		12 23	12 30	12 53		13 00	13 23		13 30	13 53		14 00	14 23	14 30		14 53		15 00	15 23	15 30	15 53		
New Southgate	d				12 26		12 56			13 26			13 56			14 26			14 56			15 26		15 56		
Oakleigh Park	d				12 29		12 59			13 29			13 59			14 29			14 59			15 29		15 59		
New Barnet	d				12 31		13 01			13 31			14 01			14 31			15 01			15 31		16 01		
Hadley Wood	d				12 34		13 04			13 34			14 04			14 34			15 04			15 34		16 04		
Potters Bar	d	12 19			12 38		13 08	13 19		13 38			14 08	14 19		14 38			15 08	15 19		15 38		16 08		16 19
Brookmans Park	d				12 41		13 11			13 41			14 11			14 41			15 11			15 41		16 11		
Welham Green	d				12 43		13 13			13 43			14 13			14 43			15 13			15 43		16 13		
Hatfield	d	12 25			12 46		13 16	13 25		13 46			14 16	14 25		14 46			15 16	15 25		15 46		16 16		16 25
Welwyn Garden City 4	d	12 29			12a51		13a21	13 29		13a51			14a21	14 29		14a51			15a21	15 29		15a51		16a21		16 29
Welwyn North	d	12 33						13 33						14 33						15 33						16 33
Knebworth	d	12 37						13 37						14 37						15 37						16 37
Bowes Park	d		12 05			12 35			13 05			13 35			14 05		14 35				15 05		15 35			
Palmers Green	d		12 15			12 45			13 15			13 45			14 15		14 45				15 15		15 45			
Winchmore Hill	d		12 23			12 53			13 23			13 53			14 23		14 53				15 23		15 53			
Grange Park	d		12 29			12 59			13 29			13 59			14 29		14 59				15 29		15 59			
Enfield Chase	d		12 34			13 04			13 34			14 04			14 34		15 04				15 34		16 04			
Gordon Hill	d		12 40			13 10			13 40			14 10			14 40		15 10				15 40		16 10			
Crews Hill	d		12 50			13 20			13 50			14 20			14 50		15 20				15 50		16 20			
Cuffley	d		12 58			13 28			13 58			14 28			14 58		15 28				15 58		16 28			
Bayford	d		13 13			13 43			14 13			14 43			15 13		15 43				16 13		16 43			
Hertford North	d		13 28			13a58			14 28			14a58			15 28		15a58				16 28		16a58			
Watton-at-Stone	d		13 42						14 42						15 42						16 42					
Stevenage 4	d	12 40	13a59					13 40	14a59					14 40	15a59					15 40	16a59					16 40
Hitchin 4	d	12 45						13 45						14 45						15 45						16 45
Letchworth Garden City	a	12 49						13 49						14 49						15 49						16 51

For general notes see front of timetable
For details of catering facilities see Directory of Train Operators

There is no service between Moorgate and Finsbury Park on Sundays

Table 24

Sundays

London → Welwyn Garden City, Hertford North and Letchworth Garden City

20 July to 7 September

Network Diagram - see first page of Table 24

		FC 🚌	FC	FC 🚌	FC	FC 1	FC 🚌		FC	FC 🚌	FC	FC 1	FC 🚌	FC		FC 🚌	FC	FC 1	FC 🚌	FC	FC 🚌		FC	FC 1	FC 🚌	FC
London Kings Cross [15] ⊖	d		16 11		16 41	17 06			17 11		17 41	18 06		18 11			18 41	19 06		19 11			19 41	20 06		20 11
Finsbury Park ⊖	d		16 17		16 47	17 11			17 17		17 47	18 11		18 17			18 47	19 11		19 17			19 47	20 11		20 17
Harringay	d		16 19		16 49				17 19		17 49			18 19			18 49			19 19			19 49			20 19
Hornsey	d		16 21		16 51				17 21		17 51			18 21			18 51			19 21			19 51			20 21
Alexandra Palace	d	16 00	16 23	16 30	16 53		17 00		17 23	17 30	17 53		18 00	18 23		18 30	18 53		19 00	19 23	19 30		19 53		20 00	20 23
New Southgate	d		16 26		16 56				17 26		17 56			18 26			18 56			19 26			19 56			20 26
Oakleigh Park	d		16 29		16 59				17 29		17 59			18 29			18 59			19 29			19 59			20 29
New Barnet	d		16 31		17 01				17 31		18 01			18 31			19 01			19 31			20 01			20 31
Hadley Wood	d		16 34		17 04				17 34		18 04			18 34			19 04			19 34			20 04			20 34
Potters Bar	d		16 38		17 08	17 21			17 38		18 08	18 21		18 38			19 08	19 21		19 38			20 08	20 21		20 38
Brookmans Park	d		16 41		17 11				17 41		18 11			18 41			19 11			19 41			20 11			20 41
Welham Green	d		16 43		17 13				17 43		18 13			18 43			19 13			19 43			20 13			20 43
Hatfield	d		16 46		17 16	17 27			17 46		18 16	18 27		18 46			19 16	19 27		19 46			20 16	20 27		20 46
Welwyn Garden City [4]	d		16a51		17a21	17 31			17a51		18a21	18 31		18a51			19a21	19 31		19a51			20a21	20 31		20a51
Welwyn North	d					17 34						18 34						19 34						20 34		
Knebworth	d					17 38						18 38						19 38						20 38		
Bowes Park	d	16 05		16 35			17 05			17 35			18 05			18 35			19 05		19 35				20 05	
Palmers Green	d	16 15		16 45			17 15			17 45			18 15			18 45			19 15		19 45				20 15	
Winchmore Hill	d	16 23		16 53			17 23			17 53			18 23			18 53			19 23		19 53				20 23	
Grange Park	d	16 29		16 59			17 29			17 59			18 29			18 59			19 29		19 59				20 29	
Enfield Chase	d	16 34		17 04			17 34			18 04			18 34			19 04			19 34		20 04				20 34	
Gordon Hill	d	16 40		17 10			17 40			18 10			18 40			19 10			19 40		20 10				20 40	
Crews Hill	d	16 50		17 20			17 50			18 20			18 50			19 20			19 50		20 20				20 50	
Cuffley	d	16 58		17 28			17 58			18 28			18 58			19 28			19 58		20 28				20 58	
Bayford	d	17 13		17 43			18 13			18 43			19 13			19 43			20 13		20 43				21 13	
Hertford North	d	17 28		17a58			18 28			18a58			19 28			19a58			20 28		20a58				21 28	
Watton-at-Stone	d	17 42					18 42						19 42						20 42						21 42	
Stevenage [4]	d	17a59				17 42	18a59					18 42	19a59					19 42	20a59					20 42	21a59	
Hitchin [4]	d					17 47						18 47						19 47						20 47		
Letchworth Garden City	a					17 51						18 51						19 51						20 51		

		FC 🚌	FC	FC 1	FC 🚌		FC	FC 🚌	FC	FC 1	FC 🚌	FC		FC 🚌	FC	FC	FC	FC 1	FC 🚌		FC	FC 🚌	FC	FC		
London Kings Cross [15] ⊖	d		20 41	21 06			21 11		21 41	22 06		22 11			22 26	22 41	22 56	23 06			23 19		23 28	23 41		
Finsbury Park ⊖	d		20 47	21 11			21 17		21 47	22 11		22 17			22 32	22 47	23 02	23 11			23 25		23 33	23 47		
Harringay	d		20 49				21 19		21 49			22 19			22 34	22 49	23 04				23 27		23 36	23 49		
Hornsey	d		20 51				21 21		21 51			22 21			22 36	22 51	23 06				23 29		23 38	23 51		
Alexandra Palace	d	20 30	20 53		21 00		21 23	21 30	21 53		22 00	22 23		22 30	22a38	22 53	23a08		23 14		23 31	23 40	23a42	23 53		
New Southgate	d		20 56				21 26		21 56			22 26				22 56					23 34			23 56		
Oakleigh Park	d		20 59				21 29		21 59			22 29				22 59					23 37			23 59		
New Barnet	d		21 01				21 31		22 01			22 31				23 01					23 39			00 01		
Hadley Wood	d		21 04				21 34		22 04			22 34				23 04					23 42			00 04		
Potters Bar	d		21 08	21 21			21 38		22 08	22 21		22 38				23 08		23 21			23 46			00 08		
Brookmans Park	d		21 11				21 41		22 11			22 41				23 11					23 49			00 11		
Welham Green	d		21 13				21 43		22 13			22 43				23 13					23 51			00 13		
Hatfield	d		21 16	21 27			21 46		22 16	22 27		22 46				23 16		23 27			23 54			00 16		
Welwyn Garden City [4]	d		21a21	21 31			21a51		22a21	22 31		22a54				23a24		23 31			00a04			00 20		
Welwyn North	d			21 34						22 34								23 36						00 23		
Knebworth	d			21 38						22 38								23 40						00 28		
Bowes Park	d	20 35			21 05			21 35			22 05			22 35					23 19			23 45				
Palmers Green	d	20 45			21 15			21 45			22 15			22 45					23 29			23 55				
Winchmore Hill	d	20 53			21 23			21 53			22 23			22 53					23 37			00 03				
Grange Park	d	20 59			21 29			21 59			22 29			22 59					23 43			00 09				
Enfield Chase	d	21 04			21 34			22 04			22 34			23 04					23 48			00 14				
Gordon Hill	d	21 10			21 40			22 10			22 40			23 10					23 54			00 20				
Crews Hill	d	21 20			21 50			22 20			22 50			23 20					00 04			00 30				
Cuffley	d	21 28			21 58			22 28			22 58			23 28					00 12			00 38				
Bayford	d	21 43			22 13			22 43			23 13			23 43					00 27			00 53				
Hertford North	d	21a58			22 28			22a58			23 28			23a58					00 42			01 08				
Watton-at-Stone	d				22 42						23 42								00 56			01 22				
Stevenage [4]	d			21 42	22a59					22 42	23a59							23 43	01a13			01a39		00 31		
Hitchin [4]	d			21 47						22 47								23 53						00a47		
Letchworth Garden City	a			21 51						22 51								23 57								

For general notes see front of timetable
For details of catering facilities see Directory of Train Operators

There is no service between Moorgate and Finsbury Park on Sundays

Table 24

Sundays

from 14 September

London → Welwyn Garden City, Hertford North and Letchworth Garden City

Network Diagram - see first page of Table 24

	FC [1]	FC	FC	FC [1] A	FC	FC	FC [1]	FC	FC	FC	FC	FC	FC [1]	FC	FC	FC	FC	FC [1]	FC	FC	FC	FC	FC [1]	FC	FC
London Kings Cross [15] ⊖ d	23p15	23p26	23p35	00 07	00 11	00 26	00 36	00 41														08 56	09 06	09 11	09 26
Finsbury Park ⊖ d	23p20	23p32	23p40	00 12	00 17	00 32	00 41	00 47	06 17	06 32	06 47	07 02	07 11	07 17	07 32	07 47	08 02	08 11	08 17	08 32	08 47	09 02	09 11	09 17	09 32
Harringay d		23p34	23p42		00 19	00 34		00 49	06 19	06 34	06 49	07 04		07 19	07 34	07 49	08 04		08 19	08 34	08 49	09 04		09 19	09 34
Hornsey d		23p36	23p44		00 21	00 36		00 51	06 21	06 36	06 51	07 06		07 21	07 36	07 51	08 06		08 21	08 36	08 51	09 06		09 21	09 36
Alexandra Palace d		23p38	23p46	00 17	00 23	00 38		00 53	06 23	06 38	06 53	07 08		07 23	07 38	07 53	08 08		08 23	08 38	08 53	09 08		09 23	09 38
New Southgate d			23p49		00 26			00 56	06 26		06 56			07 26		07 56			08 26		08 56			09 26	
Oakleigh Park d			23p52		00 29			00 59	06 29		06 59			07 29		07 59			08 29		08 59			09 29	
New Barnet d			23p54		00 31			01 01	06 31		07 01			07 31		08 01			08 31		09 01			09 31	
Hadley Wood d			23p57		00 34			01 04	06 34		07 04			07 34		08 04			08 34		09 04			09 34	
Potters Bar d	23p30		00 01		00 38		00 51	01 08	06 38		07 08		07 21	07 38		08 08		08 21	08 38		09 08		09 21	09 38	
Brookmans Park d			00 04		00 41			01 11	06 41		07 11			07 41		08 11			08 41		09 11			09 41	
Welham Green d			00 07		00 43			01 13	06 43		07 13			07 43		08 13			08 43		09 13			09 43	
Hatfield d	23p36		00 09		00 46		00 57	01 16	06 46		07 16		07 27	07 46		08 16		08 27	08 46		09 16		09 27	09 46	
Welwyn Garden City [4] d	23p40		00b28		00a57		01 03	01a26	06a55		07a25		07 33	07a55		08a25		08 31	08a55		09a21		09 31	09a51	
Welwyn North d	23p45		00 31				01s06						07 36					08 34					09 34		
Knebworth d	23p49		00 35				01s10						07 40					08 38					09 38		
Bowes Park d		23p41				00 41				06 41		07 11			07 41		08 11			08 41		09 11			09 41
Palmers Green d		23p43		00 20		00 43				06 43		07 13			07 43		08 13			08 43		09 13			09 43
Winchmore Hill d		23p45		00 22		00 45				06 45		07 15			07 45		08 15			08 45		09 15			09 45
Grange Park d		23p47				00 47				06 47		07 17			07 47		08 17			08 47		09 17			09 47
Enfield Chase d		23p49		00 25		00 49				06 49		07 19			07 49		08 19			08 49		09 19			09 49
Gordon Hill d		23p51		00 27		00 51				06 51		07 21			07 51		08 21			08 51		09 21			09 51
Crews Hill d		23p54				00 54				06 54		07 24			07 54		08 24			08 54		09 24			09 54
Cuffley d		23p57		00 31		00 57				06 57		07 27			07 57		08 27			08 57		09 27			09 57
Bayford d		00 02				01 02				07 02		07 32			08 02		08 32			09 02		09 32			10 02
Hertford North d		00 07		00 39		01a10				07 07		07a40			08 07		08a40			09 07		09a38			10 07
Watton-at-Stone d		00 13								07 12					08 12					09 13					10 13
Stevenage [4] d	23p55	00a23	00 41	00 48			01 14			07a22			07 45		08a23			08 42		09a20			09 42		10a20
Hitchin [4] d	00 02		00 49	00 56			01a19						07 52					08 47					09 47		
Letchworth Garden City a	00 06		00 57	01 00									07 56					08 54					09 51		

	FC		FC	FC [1]	FC	FC	FC	FC	FC [1]	FC	FC	FC	FC	FC [1]	FC	FC	FC	FC	FC [1]	FC	FC	FC	FC	FC [1]	FC
London Kings Cross [15] ⊖ d	09 41		09 56	10 06	10 11	10 26	10 41	10 56	11 06	11 11	11 26	11 41	11 56	12 06	12 11	12 26	12 41	12 56	13 06	13 11	13 26	13 41	13 56	14 06	14 11
Finsbury Park ⊖ d	09 47		10 02	10 11	10 17	10 32	10 47	11 02	11 11	11 17	11 32	11 47	12 02	12 11	12 17	12 32	12 47	13 02	13 11	13 17	13 32	13 47	14 02	14 11	14 17
Harringay d	09 49		10 04		10 19	10 34	10 49	11 04		11 19	11 34	11 49	12 04		12 19	12 34	12 49	13 04		13 19	13 34	13 49	14 04		14 19
Hornsey d	09 51		10 06		10 21	10 36	10 51	11 06		11 21	11 36	11 51	12 06		12 21	12 36	12 51	13 06		13 21	13 36	13 51	14 06		14 21
Alexandra Palace d	09 53		10 08		10 23	10 38	10 53	11 08		11 23	11 38	11 53	12 08		12 23	12 38	12 53	13 08		13 23	13 38	13 53	14 08		14 23
New Southgate d	09 56				10 26		10 56			11 26		11 56			12 26		12 56			13 26		13 56			14 26
Oakleigh Park d	09 59				10 29		10 59			11 29		11 59			12 29		12 59			13 29		13 59			14 29
New Barnet d	10 01				10 31		11 01			11 31		12 01			12 31		13 01			13 31		14 01			14 31
Hadley Wood d	10 04				10 34		11 04			11 34		12 04			12 34		13 04			13 34		14 04			14 34
Potters Bar d	10 08			10 21	10 38		11 08		11 21	11 38		12 08		12 21	12 38		13 08		13 21	13 38		14 08		14 21	14 38
Brookmans Park d	10 11				10 41		11 11			11 41		12 11			12 41		13 11			13 41		14 11			14 41
Welham Green d	10 13				10 43		11 13			11 43		12 13			12 43		13 13			13 43		14 13			14 43
Hatfield d	10 16			10 27	10 46		11 16		11 27	11 46		12 16		12 27	12 46		13 16		13 27	13 46		14 16		14 27	14 46
Welwyn Garden City [4] d	10a21			10 31	10a51		11a21		11 31	11a51		12a21		12 31	12a51		13a21		13 31	13a51		14a21		14 31	14a51
Welwyn North d				10 34					11 34					12 34					13 34					14 34	
Knebworth d				10 38					11 38					12 38					13 38					14 38	
Bowes Park d			10 11			10 41		11 11			11 41		12 11			12 41		13 11			13 41		14 11		
Palmers Green d			10 13			10 43		11 13			11 43		12 13			12 43		13 13			13 43		14 13		
Winchmore Hill d			10 15			10 45		11 15			11 45		12 15			12 45		13 15			13 45		14 15		
Grange Park d			10 17			10 47		11 17			11 47		12 17			12 47		13 17			13 47		14 17		
Enfield Chase d			10 19			10 49		11 19			11 49		12 19			12 49		13 19			13 49		14 19		
Gordon Hill d			10 21			10 51		11 21			11 51		12 21			12 51		13 21			13 51		14 21		
Crews Hill d			10 24			10 54		11 24			11 54		12 24			12 54		13 24			13 54		14 24		
Cuffley d			10 27			10 57		11 27			11 57		12 27			12 57		13 27			13 57		14 27		
Bayford d			10 32			11 02		11 32			12 02		12 32			13 02		13 32			14 02		14 32		
Hertford North d			10a38			11 07		11a38			12 07		12a38			13 07		13a38			14 07		14a38		
Watton-at-Stone d						11 13					12 13					13 13					14 13				
Stevenage [4] d				10 42		11a20			11 42		12a20			12 42		13a20			13 42		14a20			14 42	
Hitchin [4] d				10 47					11 47					12 47					13 47					14 47	
Letchworth Garden City a				10 51					11 51					12 51					13 51					14 51	

For general notes see front of timetable
For details of catering facilities see Directory of Train Operators

A To Cambridge (Table 25)
b Arr. 0015

There is no service between Moorgate and Finsbury Park on Sundays

Sundays

from 14 September

London → Welwyn Garden City, Hertford North and Letchworth Garden City

Network Diagram - see first page of Table 24

	FC	FC	FC		FC 1	FC	FC	FC	FC	FC 1	FC	FC	FC	FC	FC 1	FC	FC	FC	FC	FC 1	FC	FC	FC	FC	FC 1
London Kings Cross 15 ⊖ d	14 26	14 41	14 56		15 06	15 11	15 26	15 41	15 56	16 06	16 11	16 26	16 41	16 56	17 06	17 11	17 26	17 41	17 56	18 06	18 11	18 26	18 41	18 56	19 06
Finsbury Park ⊖ d	14 32	14 47	15 02		15 11	15 17	15 32	15 47	16 02	16 11	16 17	16 32	16 47	17 02	17 11	17 17	17 32	17 47	18 02	18 11	18 17	18 32	18 47	19 02	19 11
Harringay d	14 34	14 49	15 04			15 19	15 34	15 49	16 04		16 19	16 34	16 49	17 04		17 19	17 34	17 49	18 04		18 19	18 34	18 49	19 04	
Hornsey d	14 36	14 51	15 06			15 21	15 36	15 51	16 06		16 21	16 36	16 51	17 06		17 21	17 36	17 51	18 06		18 21	18 36	18 51	19 06	
Alexandra Palace d	14 38	14 53	15 08			15 23	15 38	15 53	16 08		16 23	16 38	16 53	17 08		17 23	17 38	17 53	18 08		18 23	18 38	18 53	19 08	
New Southgate d		14 56				15 26		15 56			16 26		16 56			17 26		17 56			18 26		18 56		
Oakleigh Park d		14 59				15 29		15 59			16 29		16 59			17 29		17 59			18 29		18 59		
New Barnet d		15 01				15 31		16 01			16 31		17 01			17 31		18 01			18 31		19 01		
Hadley Wood d		15 04				15 34		16 04			16 34		17 04			17 34		18 04			18 34		19 04		
Potters Bar d		15 08			15 21	15 38		16 08		16 21	16 38		17 08		17 21	17 38		18 08		18 21	18 38		19 08		19 21
Brookmans Park d		15 11				15 41		16 11			16 41		17 11			17 41		18 11			18 41		19 11		
Welham Green d		15 13				15 43		16 13			16 43		17 13			17 43		18 13			18 43		19 13		
Hatfield d		15 16			15 27	15 46		16 16		16 27	16 46		17 16		17 27	17 46		18 16		18 27	18 46		19 16		19 27
Welwyn Garden City 4 d		15a21			15 31	15a51		16a21		16 31	16a51		17a21		17 31	17a51		18a21		18 31	18a51		19a21		19 31
Welwyn North d					15 34					16 34					17 34					18 34					19 34
Knebworth d					15 38					16 38					17 38					18 38					19 38
Bowes Park d	14 41		15 11				15 41		16 11			16 41		17 11			17 41		18 11			18 41		19 11	
Palmers Green d	14 43		15 13				15 43		16 13			16 43		17 13			17 43		18 13			18 43		19 13	
Winchmore Hill d	14 45		15 15				15 45		16 15			16 45		17 15			17 45		18 15			18 45		19 15	
Grange Park d	14 47		15 17				15 47		16 17			16 47		17 17			17 47		18 17			18 47		19 17	
Enfield Chase d	14 49		15 19				15 49		16 19			16 49		17 19			17 49		18 19			18 49		19 19	
Gordon Hill d	14 51		15 21				15 51		16 21			16 51		17 21			17 51		18 21			18 51		19 21	
Crews Hill d	14 54		15 24				15 54		16 24			16 54		17 24			17 54		18 24			18 54		19 24	
Cuffley d	14 57		15 27				15 57		16 27			16 57		17 27			17 57		18 27			18 57		19 27	
Bayford d	15 02		15 32				16 02		16 32			17 02		17 32			18 02		18 32			19 02		19 32	
Hertford North d	15 07		15a38				16 07		16a38			17 07		17a38			18 07		18a38			19 07		19a38	
Watton-at-Stone d	15 13						16 13					17 13					18 13					19 13			
Stevenage 4 d	15a20				15 42		16a20			16 42		17a20			17 42		18a20			18 42		19a20			19 42
Hitchin 4 d					15 47					16 47					17 47					18 47					19 47
Letchworth Garden City a					15 51					16 51					17 51					18 51					19 51

	FC	FC	FC	FC	FC 1	FC	FC	FC	FC	FC 1	FC	FC	FC	FC	FC 1	FC	FC	FC	FC	FC 1	FC	FC	FC		
London Kings Cross 15 ⊖ d	19 11	19 26	19 41	19 56	20 06	20 11	20 26	20 41	20 56	21 06	21 11	21 26	21 41	21 56	22 06	22 11	22 26	22 41	22 56	23 06	23 19	23 28	23 41		
Finsbury Park ⊖ d	19 17	19 32	19 47	20 02	20 11	20 17	20 32	20 47	21 02	21 11	21 17	21 32	21 47	22 02	22 11	22 17	22 32	22 47	23 02	23 11	23 25	23 33	23 47		
Harringay d	19 19	19 34	19 49	20 04		20 19	20 34	20 49	21 04		21 19	21 34	21 49	22 04		22 19	22 34	22 49	23 04		23 27	23 36	23 49		
Hornsey d	19 21	19 36	19 51	20 06		20 21	20 36	20 51	21 06		21 21	21 36	21 51	22 06		22 21	22 36	22 51	23 06		23 29	23 38	23 51		
Alexandra Palace d	19 23	19 38	19 53	20 08		20 23	20 38	20 53	21 08		21 23	21 38	21 53	22 08		22 23	22 38	22 53	23 08		23 31	23 40	23 53		
New Southgate d	19 26		19 56			20 26		20 56			21 26		21 56			22 26		22 56			23 34		23 56		
Oakleigh Park d	19 29		19 59			20 29		20 59			21 29		21 59			22 29		22 59			23 37		23 59		
New Barnet d	19 31		20 01			20 31		21 01			21 31		22 01			22 31		23 01			23 39		00 01		
Hadley Wood d	19 34		20 04			20 34		21 04			21 34		22 04			22 34		23 04			23 42		00 04		
Potters Bar d	19 38		20 08		20 21	20 38		21 08		21 21	21 38		22 08		22 21	22 38		23 08		23 21	23 46		00 08		
Brookmans Park d	19 41		20 11			20 41		21 11			21 41		22 11			22 41		23 11			23 49		00 11		
Welham Green d	19 43		20 13			20 43		21 13			21 43		22 13			22 43		23 13			23 51		00 13		
Hatfield d	19 46		20 16		20 27	20 46		21 16		21 27	21 46		22 16		22 27	22 46		23 16		23 27	23 54		00 16		
Welwyn Garden City 4 d	19a51		20a21		20 31	20a51		21a21		21 31	21a51		22a21		22 31	22a54		23a24		23 31	00a04		00 20		
Welwyn North d					20 34					21 34					22 34					23 36			00 23		
Knebworth d					20 38					21 38					22 38					23 40			00 28		
Bowes Park d		19 41		20 11			20 41		21 11			21 41		22 11			22 41		23 11			23 42			
Palmers Green d		19 43		20 13			20 43		21 13			21 43		22 13			22 43		23 13			23 44			
Winchmore Hill d		19 45		20 15			20 45		21 15			21 45		22 15			22 45		23 15			23 47			
Grange Park d		19 47		20 17			20 47		21 17			21 47		22 17			22 47		23 17			23 49			
Enfield Chase d		19 49		20 19			20 49		21 19			21 49		22 19			22 49		23 19			23 51			
Gordon Hill d		19 51		20 21			20 51		21 21			21 51		22 21			22 51		23 21			23 53			
Crews Hill d		19 54		20 24			20 54		21 24			21 54		22 24			22 54		23 24			23 56			
Cuffley d		19 57		20 27			20 57		21 27			21 57		22 27			22 57		23 27			23 59			
Bayford d		20 02		20 32			21 02		21 32			22 02		22 32			23 02		23 32			00 04			
Hertford North d		20 07		20a38			21 07		21a38			22 07		22a38			23 07		23a38			00 09			
Watton-at-Stone d		20 13					21 13					22 13					23 13					00 14			
Stevenage 4 d		20a20			20 42		21a20			21 42		22a20			22 42		23a20			23 43		00a25	00 31		
Hitchin 4 d					20 47					21 47					22 47					23 53			00a47		
Letchworth Garden City a					20 51					21 51					22 51					23 57					

For general notes see front of timetable
For details of catering facilities see Directory of Train Operators

There is no service between Moorgate and Finsbury Park on Sundays

Saturday service operates on Bank Holiday Mondays

Letchworth Garden City, Hertford North and Welwyn Garden City → London

Network Diagram - see first page of Table 24

Miles	Miles			FC	FC	FC	FC	FC	FC	FC	FC	FC	FC	FC	FC	FC	FC	FC		FC	FC	FC	FC	FC	FC	FC
				MX	MO	MO	MO	MX	MO	MO																
							1	1				1	1		1			1			1				1	
					A	B			A	A		C	C													
									Bus	Bus																
0	0	**Letchworth Garden City**	d	23p18			23p36	23p50						04 50	05 30	05 20		05 59		05 50	06 19					06 27
3	3	Hitchin 4	d	23p22			23p40	23p54				04 13	04 58	04 54	05 34	05 24		06 03		05 54	06 24				06 46	06 31
7¼	7¼	**Stevenage 4**	d	23p27		23p29	23p45	23p59	22p41	23p29		04 18	05 04	04 59	05 39	05 29		06 09		05 59	06 30				06 52	06 36
—	12¼	Watton-at-Stone	d	23p34		23p36			22p58	23p46				05 06		05 36				06 06						06 42
—	16½	**Hertford North**	d	23p40		23p42			23p12	23p59		04 28		05 12		05 42				06 12				06 34		06 50
—	19½	Bayford	d	23p44		23p46			23p27	00 15				05 16		05 46				06 16				06 38		
—	23	Cuffley	d	23p49		23p51			23p42	00 30		04 35		05 21		05 51				06 21				06 43		06 57
—	24¾	Crews Hill	d	23p52		23p54			23p50	00 38				05 24		05 54				06 24				06 46		
—	26¼	Gordon Hill	d	23p55		23p57			23p59	00 48		04 39		05 27		05 57				06 27				06 49		07 02
—	27	Enfield Chase	d	23p57		23p59			00 06	00s54		04 41		05 29		05 59				06 29				06 52		07 04
—	27¾	Grange Park	d	23p59		00 01			00 11	00s59				05 31		06 01				06 31				06 54		
—	28¾	Winchmore Hill	d	00 01		00 03			00 17	01s05				05 33		06 03				06 33				06 56		07 06
—	29½	Palmers Green	d	00 03		00 05			00 25	01s13				05 35		06 05				06 35				06 58		07 09
—	30½	Bowes Park	d	00 06		00 08			00 35	01s23				05 38		06 08				06 38				07 01		
9¾	—	Knebworth	d				23p48	00 02					05 07		05 43			06 13			06 33					
12¾	—	Welwyn North	d				23p52	00 06					05 11		05 47			06 17			06 37					
14½	—	**Welwyn Garden City 4**	d				23p56	00 09			04 15		05 15		05 50		05 58	06 20			06 40	06 25	06 35		07 00	
17	—	Hatfield	d				23p59	00 12			04 19		05 19		05 53		06 02	06 23			06 44	06 29	06 39			
19¾	—	Welham Green	d														06 06					06 33				
20¾	—	Brookmans Park	d								04 24						06 08					06 35				
22	—	Potters Bar	d				00 04	00 18			04 27		05 25		05 59		06 11	06 29			06 49	06 38	06 46			
24¼	—	Hadley Wood	d														06 15					06 42	06 49			
25¾	—	New Barnet	d								04 32		05 29				06 17					06 44	06 52			
26¾	—	Oakleigh Park	d								04 34		05 31				06 19					06 46	06 54			
28¼	—	New Southgate	d								04 37		05 34				06 22					06 49	06 57			
29¾	31¼	Alexandra Palace	d	00 08	00 10	00 10			00s40	01s28	04 40		05 37	05 40		06 10	06 25			06 40		06 52		07 03		
30¾	32¼	Hornsey	d	00 10	00 12	00 12					04 42			05 42		06 12	06 27			06 42		06 54		07 05		
31¼	32¾	Harringay	d	00 12	00 14	00 14					04 44			05 44		06 14	06 29			06 44		06 56		07 07		
32¼	33¾	Finsbury Park	⊖ d	00 15	00 16	00 17	00 20	00 29	01s00	01s48	04 47	04s50	05 41	05 47	06 08	06 17	06 32	06 41		06 47	06 58	06 59	07 03	07 10	07 14	07 16
—	34½	Drayton Park	d													06 19	06 34			06 49		07 01		07 12		07 18
—	35	Highbury & Islington	⊖ d													06 20	06 35			06 51		07 03		07 14		07 20
—	35½	Essex Road	d													06 22	06 37			06 53		07 05		07 16		07 22
—	36¾	Old Street	⊖ d													06 25	06 40			06 56		07 08		07 19		07 25
—	37¼	**Moorgate**	⊖ a													06 30	06 45			07 01		07 13		07 24		07 30
34¾	—	London Kings Cross 15	⊖ a	00 26	00 27	00 27	00 32	00 42	01 15	02 03	04 56	05 04	05 55	05 58	06 19			06 49			07 07		07 10		07 23	

		FC	FC	FC	FC	FC	FC	FC	FC	FC	FC		FC	FC	FC	FC	FC	FC	FC	FC	FC	FC	FC	FC	FC	FC
							1			1						1								1		
Letchworth Garden City	d			06 46		06 54	07 04			07 28				07 19		07 34								08 04	07 54	
Hitchin 4	d			06 50		06 58	07 08			07 32				07 23		07 38								08 08	07 58	
Stevenage 4	d			06 56		07 04	07 14			07 38				07 29		07 44	07 35							08 14	08 05	
Watton-at-Stone	d					07 10											07 42								08 12	
Hertford North	d				07 04	07 18			07 25				07 33		07 39		07 50		07 55			08 05			08 20	
Bayford	d				07 08										07 43							08 09				
Cuffley	d				07 13	07 25			07 32				07 40		07 48		07 57		08 02			08 14			08 27	
Crews Hill	d				07 16										07 51							08 17				
Gordon Hill	d		07 09		07 19	07 30			07 37				07 45		07 54		08 02		08 07		08 15	08 20			08 32	
Enfield Chase	d		07 12		07 22	07 32			07 39				07 47		07 56		08 04		08 09		08 17	08 22			08 34	
Grange Park	d		07 14		07 24				07 41				07 49		07 58				08 11		08 19	08 24				
Winchmore Hill	d		07 16		07 26	07 34			07 43				07 51		08 00				08 13		08 21	08 26				
Palmers Green	d		07 18		07 28	07 37			07 45				07 53		08 02				08 15		08 23	08 28				
Bowes Park	d		07 21		07 31				07 48				07 56		08 05		08 08		08 18		08 26	08 31			08 38	
Knebworth	d			07 00			07 18			07 41				07 33		07 47								08 17		
Welwyn North	d			07 04			07 22							07 37		07 51								08 21		
Welwyn Garden City 4	d	06 50		07 08			07 26	07 17			07 30			07 42		07 56		07 47		07 59			08 14	08 26		08 18
Hatfield	d	06 54		07 12			07 30	07 21			07 34			07 46				07 51		08 03			08 18			08 22
Welham Green	d	06 58						07 25			07 38							07 55		08 07						08 26
Brookmans Park	d	07 00						07 27			07 40							07 57		08 09						08 28
Potters Bar	d	07 03		07 18				07 30			07 43			07 52				08 00		08 12			08 25			08 31
Hadley Wood	d	07 07						07 34			07 47							08 04		08 16						08 35
New Barnet	d	07 09		07 23				07 36			07 49			07 57				08 06		08 18			08 29			08 37
Oakleigh Park	d	07 11		07 25				07 38			07 51			07 59				08 08		08 20			08 31			08 39
New Southgate	d	07 14		07 28				07 41			07 54			08 02				08 11		08 23			08 34			08 42
Alexandra Palace	d	07 17	07 23		07 33			07 44	07 50				07 58		08 07		08 11	08 14	08 20		08 28	08 33	08 37		08 41	08 45
Hornsey	d	07 19	07 25		07 35			07 46	07 52				08 00				08 13	08 16	08 22	08 27	08 30				08 43	08 47
Harringay	d	07 21	07 27		07 37			07 48	07 54				08 02				08 15	08 18	08 24	08 29	08 32				08 45	08 49
Finsbury Park	⊖ d	07 24	07 30	07 34	07 40	07 44	07 46	07 51	07 57	07 59	08 01		08 06	08 09	08 12	08 15	08 18	08 22	08 27	08 31	08 35	08 39	08 42	08 44	08 48	08 52
Drayton Park	d	07 26	07 32		07 42	07 46		07 53	07 59		08 03		08 08		08 14		08 20	08 24	08 29	08 33	08 37	08 41			08 50	08 54
Highbury & Islington	⊖ d	07 28	07 34		07 44	07 48		07 55	08 01		08 05		08 10		08 16		08 22	08 26	08 31	08 35	08 39	08 43			08 52	08 56
Essex Road	d	07 30	07 36		07 46	07 50		07 57	08 03		08 07		08 12		08 18		08 24	08 28	08 33	08 37	08 41	08 45			08 54	08 58
Old Street	⊖ d	07 33	07 39		07 49	07 53		08 00	08 06		08 10		08 15		08 21		08 27	08 31	08 36	08 40	08 44	08 48			08 57	09 01
Moorgate	⊖ a	07 39	07 44		07 54	07 59		08 05	08 11		08 16		08 20		08 27		08 32	08 36	08 41	08 46	08 50	08 55			09 02	09 06
London Kings Cross 15	⊖ a			07 41			07 56			08 07				08 17		08 24							08 50	08 53		

For general notes see front of timetable
For details of catering facilities see Directory of Train Operators

A Until 8 September
B From 15 September
C From Peterborough (Table 25)

Saturday service operates on Bank Holiday Mondays

Letchworth Garden City, Hertford North and Welwyn Garden City → London

Network Diagram - see first page of Table 24

		FC	FC	FC		FC [1]	FC	FC	FC	FC	FC [1]	FC	FC	FC	FC	FC [1]	FC	FC	FC	FC [1]		FC	FC	FC	FC [1]	FC
Letchworth Garden City	d					08 30					09 00					09 29				09 59		09 50			10 29	
Hitchin 4	d					08 34					09 04					09 33				10 03		09 54			10 33	
Stevenage 4	d					08 40		08 34			09 10	09 04				09 39				10 09		09 59			10 39	
Watton-at-Stone	d							08 41				09 11										10 06				
Hertford North	d	08 27						08 47				09 17			09 32			09 52				10 12		10 32		
Bayford	d							08 52				09 22			09 36			09 56				10 16		10 36		
Cuffley	d	08 34						08 56				09 26			09 41			10 01				10 21		10 41		
Crews Hill	d							08 59				09 29			09 44			10 04				10 24		10 44		
Gordon Hill	d	08 39					08 55	09 02	09 12			09 32			09 47			10 07				10 27		10 47		
Enfield Chase	d	08 41					08 57	09 04	09 14			09 34			09 49			10 09				10 29		10 49		
Grange Park	d	08 43					08 59	09 06	09 16			09 36			09 51			10 11				10 31		10 51		
Winchmore Hill	d	08 45					09 01	09 08	09 18			09 38			09 53			10 13				10 33		10 53		
Palmers Green	d	08 47					09 03	09 11	09 21			09 41			09 55			10 15				10 35		10 55		
Bowes Park	d	08 50					09 06	09 13	09 23			09 43			09 58			10 18				10 38		10 58		
Knebworth	d					08 44					09 13					09 43				10 13					10 43	
Welwyn North	d					08 48					09 17					09 47				10 17					10 47	
Welwyn Garden City 4	d		08 29	08 40		08 52				09 03	09 20		09 23	09 40		09 50	09 43		10 03	10 20			10 23		10 50	10 43
Hatfield	d		08 33	08 44						09 07	09 24		09 27	09 43		09 53	09 47		10 07	10 23			10 27		10 53	10 47
Welham Green	d		08 37							09 11			09 31				09 51		10 11				10 31			10 51
Brookmans Park	d		08 39							09 13			09 33				09 53		10 13				10 33			10 53
Potters Bar	d		08 43	08 51						09 16	09 30		09 36	09 49		09 59	09 56		10 16	10 29			10 36		10 59	10 56
Hadley Wood	d		08 46							09 20			09 40				10 00		10 20				10 40			11 00
New Barnet	d		08 49	08 55						09 22			09 42				10 02		10 22				10 42			11 02
Oakleigh Park	d		08 51	08 57						09 24			09 44				10 04		10 24				10 44			11 04
New Southgate	d		08 54	09 00						09 27			09 47				10 07		10 27				10 47			11 07
Alexandra Palace	d	08 52	08 57				09 09	09 16	09 26	09 30		09 46	09 50		10 00		10 10	10 20	10 30			10 40	10 50	11 00		11 10
Hornsey	d	08 54	08 59				09 11	09 18	09 28	09 32		09 48	09 52		10 02		10 12	10 22	10 32			10 42	10 52	11 02		11 12
Harringay	d	08 56	09 01				09 13	09 20	09 30	09 34		09 50	09 54		10 04		10 14	10 24	10 34			10 44	10 54	11 04		11 14
Finsbury Park	⊖ d	08 59	09 03	09 07		09 11	09 16	09 23	09 32	09 37	09 41	09 53	09 57	10 01	10 07	10 08	10 17	10 27	10 37	10 41		10 47	10 57	11 07	11 08	11 17
Drayton Park	d	09 01	09 05				09 18	09 25	09 34	09 39		09 55	09 59		10 09		10 19	10 29	10 39			10 49	10 59	11 09		11 19
Highbury & Islington	⊖ d	09 03	09 07				09 19	09 26	09 36	09 40		09 56	10 00		10 10		10 20	10 30	10 40			10 50	11 00	11 10		11 20
Essex Road	d	09 05	09 09				09 21	09 28	09 38	09 42		09 58	10 02		10 12		10 22	10 32	10 42			10 52	11 02	11 12		11 22
Old Street	⊖ d	09 08	09 12				09 24	09 31	09 41	09 45		10 01	10 05		10 15		10 25	10 35	10 45			10 55	11 05	11 15		11 25
Moorgate	⊖ a	09 13	09 18				09 29	09 36	09 46	09 50		10 06	10 10		10 20		10 30	10 40	10 50			11 00	11 10	11 20		11 30
London Kings Cross 15	⊖ a			09 14		09 19					09 50			10 10		10 19				10 49					11 19	

		FC	FC	FC [1]	FC	FC	FC	FC [1]	FC	FC	FC	FC [1]	FC		FC	FC	FC [1]	FC	FC	FC	FC [1]	FC	FC	FC	FC [1]	FC
Letchworth Garden City	d				10 50			11 29					11 50				12 29					12 50			13 29	
Hitchin 4	d			11 03	10 54			11 33				12 03	11 54				12 33				13 03	12 54			13 33	
Stevenage 4	d			11 09	10 59			11 39				12 09	11 59				12 39				13 09	12 59			13 39	
Watton-at-Stone	d				11 06								12 06									13 06				
Hertford North	d	10 52			11 12		11 32			11 52			12 12			12 32			12 52			13 12		13 32		
Bayford	d	10 56			11 16		11 36			11 56			12 16			12 36			12 56			13 16		13 36		
Cuffley	d	11 01			11 21		11 41			12 01			12 21			12 41			13 01			13 21		13 41		
Crews Hill	d	11 04			11 24		11 44			12 04			12 24			12 44			13 04			13 24		13 44		
Gordon Hill	d	11 07			11 27		11 47			12 07			12 27			12 47			13 07			13 27		13 47		
Enfield Chase	d	11 09			11 29		11 49			12 09			12 29			12 49			13 09			13 29		13 49		
Grange Park	d	11 11			11 31		11 51			12 11			12 31			12 51			13 11			13 31		13 51		
Winchmore Hill	d	11 13			11 33		11 53			12 13			12 33			12 53			13 13			13 33		13 53		
Palmers Green	d	11 15			11 35		11 55			12 15			12 35			12 55			13 15			13 35		13 55		
Bowes Park	d	11 18			11 38		11 58			12 18			12 38			12 58			13 18			13 38		13 58		
Knebworth	d			11 13				11 43				12 13					12 43				13 13				13 43	
Welwyn North	d			11 17				11 47				12 17					12 47				13 17				13 47	
Welwyn Garden City 4	d		11 03	11 20		11 23		11 50	11 43		12 03	12 20			12 23		12 50	12 43		13 03	13 20		13 23		13 50	13 43
Hatfield	d		11 07	11 23		11 27		11 53	11 47		12 07	12 23			12 27		12 53	12 47		13 07	13 23		13 27		13 53	13 47
Welham Green	d		11 11			11 31			11 51		12 11				12 31			12 51		13 11			13 31			13 51
Brookmans Park	d		11 13			11 33			11 53		12 13				12 33			12 53		13 13			13 33			13 53
Potters Bar	d		11 16	11 29		11 36		11 59	11 56		12 16	12 29			12 36		12 59	12 56		13 16	13 29		13 36		13 59	13 56
Hadley Wood	d		11 20			11 40			12 00		12 20				12 40			13 00		13 20			13 40			14 00
New Barnet	d		11 22			11 42			12 02		12 22				12 42			13 02		13 22			13 42			14 02
Oakleigh Park	d		11 24			11 44			12 04		12 24				12 44			13 04		13 24			13 44			14 04
New Southgate	d		11 27			11 47			12 07		12 27				12 47			13 07		13 27			13 47			14 07
Alexandra Palace	d	11 20	11 30		11 40	11 50	12 00		12 10	12 20	12 30		12 40		12 50	13 00		13 10	13 20	13 30		13 40	13 50	14 00		14 10
Hornsey	d	11 22	11 32		11 42	11 52	12 02		12 12	12 22	12 32		12 42		12 52	13 02		13 12	13 22	13 32		13 42	13 52	14 02		14 12
Harringay	d	11 24	11 34		11 44	11 54	12 04		12 14	12 24	12 34		12 44		12 54	13 04		13 14	13 24	13 34		13 44	13 54	14 04		14 14
Finsbury Park	⊖ d	11 27	11 37	11 41	11 47	11 57	12 07	12 11	12 17	12 27	12 37	12 41	12 47		12 57	13 07	13 08	13 17	13 27	13 37	13 41	13 47	13 57	14 07	14 08	14 17
Drayton Park	d	11 29	11 39		11 49	11 59	12 09		12 19	12 29	12 39		12 49		12 59	13 09		13 19	13 29	13 39		13 49	13 59	14 09		14 19
Highbury & Islington	⊖ d	11 30	11 40		11 50	12 00	12 10		12 20	12 30	12 40		12 50		13 00	13 10		13 20	13 30	13 40		13 50	14 00	14 10		14 20
Essex Road	d	11 32	11 42		11 52	12 02	12 12		12 22	12 32	12 42		12 52		13 02	13 12		13 22	13 32	13 42		13 52	14 02	14 12		14 22
Old Street	⊖ d	11 35	11 45		11 55	12 05	12 15		12 25	12 35	12 45		12 55		13 05	13 15		13 25	13 35	13 45		13 55	14 05	14 15		14 25
Moorgate	⊖ a	11 40	11 50		12 00	12 10	12 20		12 30	12 40	12 50		13 00		13 10	13 20		13 30	13 40	13 50		14 00	14 10	14 20		14 30
London Kings Cross 15	⊖ a			11 49				12 19				12 49					13 19				13 48				14 19	

For general notes see front of timetable
For details of catering facilities see Directory of Train Operators

Saturday service operates on Bank Holiday Mondays

Letchworth Garden City, Hertford North and Welwyn Garden City → London

Network Diagram - see first page of Table 24

		FC	FC	FC 1	FC	FC		FC	FC 1	FC	FC	FC	FC 1	FC	FC	FC	FC 1	FC	FC	FC	FC 1	FC		FC	FC	FC
Letchworth Garden City	d				13 50				14 29					14 50			15 29					15 50				
Hitchin 4	d			14 03	13 54				14 33				15 03	14 54			15 33				16 03	15 54				
Stevenage 4	d			14 09	13 59				14 39				15 09	14 59			15 39				16 09	15 59				
Watton-at-Stone	d				14 06									15 06								16 06				
Hertford North	d	13 52			14 12			14 32			14 52			15 12		15 33			15 53			16 13				16 33
Bayford	d	13 56			14 16			14 36			14 56			15 16		15 37			15 57			16 17				16 37
Cuffley	d	14 01			14 21			14 41			15 01			15 21		15 42			16 02			16 22				16 42
Crews Hill	d	14 04			14 24			14 44			15 04			15 24		15 45			16 05			16 25				16 45
Gordon Hill	d	14 07			14 27			14 47			15 07			15 27		15 48			16 08			16 28				16 48
Enfield Chase	d	14 09			14 29			14 49			15 09			15 29		15 50			16 10			16 30				16 50
Grange Park	d	14 11			14 31			14 51			15 11			15 31		15 52			16 12			16 32				16 52
Winchmore Hill	d	14 13			14 33			14 53			15 13			15 33		15 54			16 14			16 34				16 54
Palmers Green	d	14 15			14 35			14 55			15 15			15 35		15 56			16 16			16 36				16 56
Bowes Park	d	14 18			14 38			14 58			15 18			15 38		15 59			16 19			16 39				16 59
Knebworth	d			14 13					14 43				15 13				15 43				16 13					
Welwyn North	d			14 17					14 47				15 17				15 47				16 17					
Welwyn Garden City 4	d		14 03	14 20		14 23			14 50	14 43		15 03	15 20		15 23		15 50	15 44		16 04	16 20			16 24	16 40	
Hatfield	d		14 07	14 23		14 27			14 53	14 47		15 07	15 23		15 27		15 53	15 48		16 08	16 23			16 28	16 43	
Welham Green	d		14 11			14 31				14 51		15 11			15 31			15 52		16 12				16 32		
Brookmans Park	d		14 13			14 33				14 53		15 13			15 33			15 54		16 14				16 34		
Potters Bar	d		14 16	14 29		14 36			14 59	14 56		15 16	15 29		15 36		15 59	15 57		16 17	16 29			16 37	16 49	
Hadley Wood	d		14 20			14 40				15 00		15 20			15 40			16 01		16 21				16 41		
New Barnet	d		14 22			14 42				15 02		15 22			15 42			16 03		16 23				16 43		
Oakleigh Park	d		14 24			14 44				15 04		15 24			15 44			16 05		16 25				16 45		
New Southgate	d		14 27			14 47				15 07		15 27			15 47			16 08		16 28				16 48		
Alexandra Palace	d	14 20	14 30		14 40	14 50		15 00		15 10	15 20	15 30		15 40	15 50	16 01		16 11	16 21	16 31		16 41		16 51		17 01
Hornsey	d	14 22	14 32		14 42	14 52		15 02		15 12	15 22	15 32		15 42	15 52	16 03		16 13	16 23	16 33		16 43		16 53		17 03
Harringay	d	14 24	14 34		14 44	14 54		15 04		15 14	15 24	15 34		15 44	15 54	16 05		16 15	16 25	16 35		16 45		16 55		17 05
Finsbury Park	⊖ d	14 27	14 37	14 41	14 47	14 57		15 07	15 11	15 17	15 27	15 37	15 41	15 47	15 57	16 08	16 11	16 18	16 28	16 38	16 38	16 48		16 58	17 01	17 08
Drayton Park	d	14 29	14 39		14 49	14 59		15 09		15 19	15 29	15 39		15 49	15 59	16 10		16 20	16 30	16 40		16 50		17 00		17 10
Highbury & Islington	⊖ d	14 30	14 40		14 50	15 00		15 10		15 20	15 30	15 40		15 50	16 00	16 11		16 21	16 31	16 41		16 51		17 01		17 11
Essex Road	d	14 32	14 42		14 52	15 02		15 12		15 22	15 32	15 42		15 52	16 02	16 13		16 23	16 33	16 43		16 53		17 03		17 13
Old Street	⊖ d	14 35	14 45		14 55	15 05		15 15		15 25	15 35	15 45		15 55	16 05	16 16		16 26	16 36	16 46		16 56		17 06		17 16
Moorgate	⊖ a	14 40	14 50		15 00	15 10		15 20		15 30	15 40	15 50		16 00	16 10	16 21		16 31	16 41	16 51		17 01		17 11		17 21
London Kings Cross 15	⊖ a			14 49					15 20				15 49				16 19				16 48				17 11	

		FC	FC 1	FC	FC	FC	FC 1	FC	FC	FC 1	FC	FC	FC 1	FC	FC		FC 1	FC	FC	FC 1	FC	FC	FC 1	FC	FC	FC 1
Letchworth Garden City	d	16 20	16 29							17 29							18 29						19 29			
Hitchin 4	d	16 24	16 33				17 03			17 33			18 03				18 33			19 03			19 33			20 03
Stevenage 4	d	16 29	16 39				17 09	16 59		17 39	17 29		18 09	17 59			18 39	18 29		19 09			19 39	19 29		20 09
Watton-at-Stone	d	16 36						17 06			17 36			18 06				18 36						19 36		
Hertford North	d	16 43			16 53			17 13			17 42			18 12				18 42			19 12			19 42		
Bayford	d	16 47			16 57			17 17			17 46			18 16				18 46			19 16			19 46		
Cuffley	d	16 52			17 02			17 22			17 51			18 21				18 51			19 21			19 51		
Crews Hill	d	16 55			17 05			17 25			17 54			18 24				18 54			19 24			19 54		
Gordon Hill	d	16 58			17 08			17 28			17 57			18 27				18 57			19 27			19 57		
Enfield Chase	d	17 00			17 10			17 30			17 59			18 29				18 59			19 29			19 59		
Grange Park	d				17 12			17 32			18 01			18 31				19 01			19 31			20 01		
Winchmore Hill	d	17 02			17 14			17 34			18 03			18 33				19 03			19 33			20 03		
Palmers Green	d	17 05			17 16			17 36			18 05			18 35				19 05			19 35			20 05		
Bowes Park	d				17 19			17 39			18 08			18 38				19 08			19 38			20 08		
Knebworth	d		16 43				17 13			17 43			18 13				18 43			19 13			19 43			20 13
Welwyn North	d		16 47				17 17			17 47			18 17				18 47			19 17			19 47			20 17
Welwyn Garden City 4	d		16 50	16 44		17 04	17 20		17 28	17 50		17 58	18 20		18 28		18 50		18 58	19 20		19 28	19 50		19 58	20 20
Hatfield	d		16 53	16 48		17 08	17 23		17 32	17 53		18 02	18 23		18 32		18 53		19 02	19 23		19 32	19 53		20 02	20 23
Welham Green	d			16 52		17 12			17 36			18 06			18 36				19 06			19 36			20 06	
Brookmans Park	d			16 54		17 14			17 38			18 08			18 38				19 08			19 38			20 08	
Potters Bar	d		16 59	16 57		17 17	17 29		17 41	17 59		18 11	18 29		18 41		18 59		19 11	19 29		19 41	19 59		20 11	20 29
Hadley Wood	d			17 01		17 21			17 45			18 15			18 45				19 15			19 45			20 15	
New Barnet	d			17 03		17 23			17 47			18 17			18 47				19 17			19 47			20 17	
Oakleigh Park	d			17 05		17 25			17 49			18 19			18 49				19 19			19 49			20 19	
New Southgate	d			17 08		17 28			17 52			18 22			18 52				19 22			19 52			20 22	
Alexandra Palace	d			17 11	17 21	17 31		17 41	17 55		18 10	18 25		18 40	18 55			19 10	19 25		19 40	19 55		20 10	20 25	
Hornsey	d			17 13	17 23	17 33		17 43	17 57		18 12	18 27		18 42	18 57			19 12	19 27		19 42	19 57		20 12	20 27	
Harringay	d			17 15	17 25	17 35		17 45	17 59		18 14	18 29		18 44	18 59			19 14	19 29		19 44	19 59		20 14	20 29	
Finsbury Park	⊖ d	17 12	17 11	17 18	17 28	17 38	17 38	17 48	18 02	18 08	18 17	18 32	18 41	18 47	19 02		19 11	19 17	19 32	19 41	19 47	20 02	20 11	20 17	20 32	20 38
Drayton Park	d	17 14		17 20	17 30	17 40		17 50	18 04		18 19	18 34		18 49	19 04			19 19	19 34		19 49	20 04		20 19	20 34	
Highbury & Islington	⊖ d	17 15		17 21	17 31	17 41		17 51	18 05		18 20	18 35		18 50	19 05			19 20	19 35		19 50	20 05		20 20	20 35	
Essex Road	d	17 17		17 23	17 33	17 43		17 53	18 07		18 22	18 37		18 52	19 07			19 22	19 37		19 52	20 07		20 22	20 37	
Old Street	⊖ d	17 20		17 26	17 36	17 46		17 56	18 10		18 25	18 40		18 55	19 10			19 25	19 40		19 55	20 10		20 25	20 40	
Moorgate	⊖ a	17 26		17 31	17 41	17 51		18 01	18 15		18 30	18 45		19 00	19 15			19 30	19 45		20 00	20 15		20 30	20 45	
London Kings Cross 15	⊖ a		17 19				17 48			18 18			18 50				19 20			19 48			20 19			20 49

For general notes see front of timetable
For details of catering facilities see Directory of Train Operators

Letchworth Garden City, Hertford North and Welwyn Garden City → London

Saturday service operates on Bank Holiday Mondays

Network Diagram - see first page of Table 24

		FC	FC	FC 1	FC	FC	FC 1	FC		FC	FC 1	FC	FC	FC 1	FC	FC 1	FC	FC 1	FC	FC	FC	FC 1	FC	FC 1		
Letchworth Garden City	d			20 29	20 20						21 29	21 20						22 29	22 20				23 18	23 50		
Hitchin [4]	d			20 33	20 24		21 03				21 33	21 24		22 11				22 33	22 24			23 11	23 22	23 54		
Stevenage [4]	d			20 39	20 29		21 09				21 39	21 29		22 17				22 39	22 29			23 17	23 27	23 59		
Watton-at-Stone	d				20 36							21 36							22 36				23 34			
Hertford North	d	20 12			20 42			21 12				21 42			22 12				22 42		23 10		23 40			
Bayford	d	20 16			20 46			21 16				21 46			22 16				22 46		23 14		23 44			
Cuffley	d	20 21			20 51			21 21				21 51			22 21				22 51		23 19		23 49			
Crews Hill	d	20 24			20 54			21 24				21 54			22 24				22 54		23 22		23 52			
Gordon Hill	d	20 27			20 57			21 27				21 57			22 27				22 57		23 25		23 55			
Enfield Chase	d	20 29			20 59			21 29				21 59			22 29				22 59		23 27		23 57			
Grange Park	d	20 31			21 01			21 31				22 01			22 31				23 01		23 29		23 59			
Winchmore Hill	d	20 33			21 03			21 33				22 03			22 33				23 03		23 31		00 01			
Palmers Green	d	20 35			21 05			21 35				22 05			22 35				23 05		23 33		00 03			
Bowes Park	d	20 38			21 08			21 38				22 08			22 38				23 08		23 36		00 06			
Knebworth	d			20 43			21 13				21 43			22 20				22 43				23 20		00 02		
Welwyn North	d			20 47			21 17				21 47			22 24				22 47				23 24		00 06		
Welwyn Garden City [4]	d		20 28	20 50		20 58	21 20			21 28	21 50		21 58	22 27			22 30	22 50		23 00		23 27		00 09		
Hatfield	d		20 32	20 53		21 02	21 24			21 32	21 53		22 02	22 30			22 34	22 53		23 04		23 30		00 12		
Welham Green	d		20 36			21 06				21 36			22 06				22 38			23 08						
Brookmans Park	d		20 38			21 08				21 38			22 08				22 40			23 10						
Potters Bar	d		20 41	20 59		21 11	21 29			21 41	21 59		22 11	22 36			22 43	22 59		23 13		23 36		00 18		
Hadley Wood	d		20 45			21 15				21 45			22 15				22 47			23 17						
New Barnet	d		20 47			21 17				21 47			22 17				22 49			23 19						
Oakleigh Park	d		20 49			21 19				21 49			22 19				22 51			23 21						
New Southgate	d		20 52			21 22				21 52			22 22				22 54			23 24						
Alexandra Palace	d	20 40	20 55		21 10	21 25		21 40		21 55		22 10	22 25		22 40		22 57		23 10	23 27	23 38		00 08			
Hornsey	d	20 42	20 57		21 12	21 27		21 42		21 57		22 12	22 27		22 42		22 59		23 12	23 29	23 40		00 10			
Harringay	d	20 44	20 59		21 14	21 29		21 44		21 59		22 14	22 29		22 44	←	23 01		23 14	23 31	23 42		00 12			
Finsbury Park	⊖ d	20 47	21 02	21 11	21 17	21 32	21 38	21 47		22 02	22 11	22 17	22 32	22 44	22 47	22 44	23 04	23 11	23 17	23 34	23 45	23s48	00 15	00 29		
Drayton Park	d	20 49	21 04		21 19	21 34		21 49						↪												
Highbury & Islington	⊖ d	20 50	21 05		21 20	21 35		21 50																		
Essex Road	d	20 52	21 07		21 22	21 37		21 52																		
Old Street	⊖ d	20 55	21 10		21 25	21 40		21 55																		
Moorgate	⊖ a	21 00	21 15		21 30	21 45		22 00																		
London Kings Cross [15]	⊖ a			21 19			21 48			22 10	22 19	22 26	22 40		22 55	22 56	23 12	23 21	23 25	23 42	23 53	00 01	00 26	00 42		

Saturdays

		FC	FC 1	FC 1	FC 1 A	FC 1 A	FC	FC 1	FC	FC	FC 1	FC	FC	FC 1	FC	FC	FC 1	FC	FC	FC 1	FC	FC	FC 1	FC	FC	FC 1
Letchworth Garden City	d	23p18	23p50				04 50	05 30						06 29						07 29						08 29
Hitchin [4]	d	23p22	23p54		04 13	04 58	04 54	05 33			06 03			06 33			07 03			07 33			08 03			08 33
Stevenage [4]	d	23p27	23p59		04 18	05 04	04 59	05 39			06 09			06 39	06 29		07 09			07 39	07 29		08 09			08 39
Watton-at-Stone	d	23p34					05 06								06 36						07 36					
Hertford North	d	23p40			04 28		05 12		05 42			06 12			06 42			07 12			07 42			08 12		
Bayford	d	23p44					05 16		05 46			06 16			06 46			07 16			07 46			08 16		
Cuffley	d	23p49			04 35		05 21		05 51			06 21			06 51			07 21			07 51			08 21		
Crews Hill	d	23p52					05 24		05 54			06 24			06 54			07 24			07 54			08 24		
Gordon Hill	d	23p55			04 39		05 27		05 57			06 27			06 57			07 27			07 57			08 27		
Enfield Chase	d	23p57			04 41		05 29		05 59			06 29			06 59			07 29			07 59			08 29		
Grange Park	d	23p59					05 31		06 01			06 31			07 01			07 31			08 01			08 31		
Winchmore Hill	d	00 01					05 33		06 03			06 33			07 03			07 33			08 03			08 33		
Palmers Green	d	00 03					05 35		06 05			06 35			07 05			07 35			08 05			08 35		
Bowes Park	d	00 06					05 38		06 08			06 38			07 08			07 38			08 08			08 38		
Knebworth	d		00 02			05 07		05 43			06 13			06 43			07 13			07 43			08 13			08 43
Welwyn North	d		00 06			05 11		05 47			06 17			06 47			07 17			07 47			08 17			08 47
Welwyn Garden City [4]	d		00 09	04 15		05 15		05 50		05 58	06 20		06 28	06 50		06 58	07 20		07 28	07 50		07 58	08 20		08 28	08 50
Hatfield	d		00 12	04 19		05 19		05 53		06 02	06 23		06 32	06 53		07 02	07 23		07 32	07 53		08 02	08 23		08 32	08 53
Welham Green	d									06 06			06 36			07 06			07 36			08 06			08 36	
Brookmans Park	d			04 24						06 08			06 38			07 08			07 38			08 08			08 38	
Potters Bar	d		00 18	04 27		05 25		05 59		06 11	06 29		06 41	06 59		07 11	07 29		07 41	07 59		08 11	08 29		08 41	08 59
Hadley Wood	d									06 15			06 45			07 15			07 45			08 15			08 45	
New Barnet	d			04 32		05 29				06 17			06 47			07 17			07 47			08 17			08 47	
Oakleigh Park	d			04 34		05 31				06 19			06 49			07 19			07 49			08 19			08 49	
New Southgate	d			04 37		05 34				06 22			06 52			07 22			07 52			08 22			08 52	
Alexandra Palace	d	00 08		04 40		05 37	05 40		06 10	06 25		06 40	06 55		07 10	07 25		07 40	07 55		08 10	08 25		08 40	08 55	
Hornsey	d	00 10		04 42	04 47		05 42		06 12	06 27		06 42	06 57		07 12	07 27		07 42	07 57		08 12	08 27		08 42	08 57	
Harringay	d	00 12		04 44			05 44		06 14	06 29		06 44	06 59		07 14	07 29		07 44	07 59		08 14	08 29		08 44	08 59	
Finsbury Park	⊖ d	00 15	00 29	04 47	04s50	05 41	05 47	06 08	06 17	06 32	06 41	06 47	07 02	07 08	07 17	07 32	07 41	07 47	08 02	08 08	08 17	08 32	08 41	08 47	09 02	09 08
London Kings Cross [15]	⊖ a	00 26	00 42	04 56	05 04	05 55	05 58	06 19	06 25	06 40	06 49	06 55	07 10	07 19	07 25	07 40	07 49	07 55	08 10	08 19	08 25	08 40	08 49	08 55	09 10	09 19

For general notes see front of timetable
For details of catering facilities see Directory of Train Operators

A From Peterborough (Table 25)

There is no service between Finsbury Park and Moorgate on Saturdays

Table 24

Saturdays

Letchworth Garden City, Hertford North and Welwyn Garden City → London

Network Diagram - see first page of Table 24

		FC		FC	FC 1	FC	FC	FC 1	FC	FC	FC 1	FC	FC	FC 1	FC	FC	FC 1	FC	FC	FC 1	FC	FC	FC 1	FC	FC	FC 1
Letchworth Garden City	d							09 29						10 29						11 29						12 29
Hitchin 4	d				09 03			09 33			10 03			10 33			11 03			11 33			12 03			12 33
Stevenage 4	d	08 29			09 09			09 39	09 29		10 09			10 39	10 29		11 09			11 39	11 29		12 09			12 39
Watton-at-Stone	d	08 36							09 36						10 36						11 36					
Hertford North	d	08 42				09 12			09 42			10 12			10 42			11 12			11 42			12 12		
Bayford	d	08 46				09 16			09 46			10 16			10 46			11 16			11 46			12 16		
Cuffley	d	08 51				09 21			09 51			10 21			10 51			11 21			11 51			12 21		
Crews Hill	d	08 54				09 24			09 54			10 24			10 54			11 24			11 54			12 24		
Gordon Hill	d	08 57				09 27			09 57			10 27			10 57			11 27			11 57			12 27		
Enfield Chase	d	08 59				09 29			09 59			10 29			10 59			11 29			11 59			12 29		
Grange Park	d	09 01				09 31			10 01			10 31			11 01			11 31			12 01			12 31		
Winchmore Hill	d	09 03				09 33			10 03			10 33			11 03			11 33			12 03			12 33		
Palmers Green	d	09 05				09 35			10 05			10 35			11 05			11 35			12 05			12 35		
Bowes Park	d	09 08				09 38			10 08			10 38			11 08			11 38			12 08			12 38		
Knebworth	d				09 13			09 43			10 13			10 43			11 13			11 43			12 13			12 43
Welwyn North	d				09 17			09 47			10 17			10 47			11 17			11 47			12 17			12 47
Welwyn Garden City 4	d			08 58	09 20		09 28	09 50		09 58	10 20		10 28	10 50		10 58	11 20		11 28	11 50		11 58	12 20		12 28	12 50
Hatfield	d			09 02	09 23		09 32	09 53		10 02	10 23		10 32	10 53		11 02	11 23		11 32	11 53		12 02	12 23		12 32	12 53
Welham Green	d			09 06			09 36			10 06			10 36			11 06			11 36			12 06			12 36	
Brookmans Park	d			09 08			09 38			10 08			10 38			11 08			11 38			12 08			12 38	
Potters Bar	d			09 11	09 29		09 41	09 59		10 11	10 29		10 41	10 59		11 11	11 29		11 41	11 59		12 11	12 29		12 41	12 59
Hadley Wood	d			09 15			09 45			10 15			10 45			11 15			11 45			12 15			12 45	
New Barnet	d			09 17			09 47			10 17			10 47			11 17			11 47			12 17			12 47	
Oakleigh Park	d			09 19			09 49			10 19			10 49			11 19			11 49			12 19			12 49	
New Southgate	d			09 22			09 52			10 22			10 52			11 22			11 52			12 22			12 52	
Alexandra Palace	d	09 10		09 25		09 40	09 55		10 10	10 25		10 40	10 55		11 10	11 25		11 40	11 55		12 10	12 25		12 40	12 55	
Hornsey	d	09 12		09 27		09 42	09 57		10 12	10 27		10 42	10 57		11 12	11 27		11 42	11 57		12 12	12 27		12 42	12 57	
Harringay	d	09 14		09 29		09 44	09 59		10 14	10 29		10 44	10 59		11 14	11 29		11 44	11 59		12 14	12 29		12 44	12 59	
Finsbury Park	⊖ d	09 17		09 32	09 41	09 47	10 02	10 08	10 17	10 32	10 41	10 47	11 02	11 08	11 17	11 32	11 41	11 47	12 02	12 08	12 17	12 32	12 41	12 47	13 02	13 08
London Kings Cross 15	⊖ a	09 25	.	09 40	09 49	09 55	10 10	10 19	10 25	10 40	10 49	10 55	11 10	11 19	11 25	11 40	11 49	11 55	12 10	12 19	12 25	12 40	12 49	12 55	13 10	13 19

		FC	FC	FC 1		FC	FC	FC 1	FC	FC	FC 1	FC	FC	FC 1	FC	FC	FC 1	FC	FC	FC 1	FC	FC	FC 1	FC	FC	FC 1
Letchworth Garden City	d							13 29						14 29						15 29						16 29
Hitchin 4	d			13 03				13 33			14 03			14 33			15 03			15 33			16 03			16 33
Stevenage 4	d	12 29		13 09				13 39	13 29		14 09			14 39	14 29		15 09			15 39	15 29		16 09			16 39
Watton-at-Stone	d	12 36							13 36						14 36						15 36					
Hertford North	d	12 42				13 12			13 42			14 12			14 42			15 12			15 42			16 12		
Bayford	d	12 46				13 16			13 46			14 16			14 46			15 16			15 46			16 16		
Cuffley	d	12 51				13 21			13 51			14 21			14 51			15 21			15 51			16 21		
Crews Hill	d	12 54				13 24			13 54			14 24			14 54			15 24			15 54			16 24		
Gordon Hill	d	12 57				13 27			13 57			14 27			14 57			15 27			15 57			16 27		
Enfield Chase	d	12 59				13 29			13 59			14 29			14 59			15 29			15 59			16 29		
Grange Park	d	13 01				13 31			14 01			14 31			15 01			15 31			16 01			16 31		
Winchmore Hill	d	13 03				13 33			14 03			14 33			15 03			15 33			16 03			16 33		
Palmers Green	d	13 05				13 35			14 05			14 35			15 05			15 35			16 05			16 35		
Bowes Park	d	13 08				13 38			14 08			14 38			15 08			15 38			16 08			16 38		
Knebworth	d			13 13				13 43			14 13			14 43			15 13			15 43			16 13			16 43
Welwyn North	d			13 17				13 47			14 17			14 47			15 17			15 47			16 17			16 47
Welwyn Garden City 4	d		12 58	13 20			13 28	13 50		13 58	14 20		14 28	14 50		14 58	15 20		15 28	15 50		15 58	16 20		16 28	16 50
Hatfield	d		13 02	13 23			13 32	13 53		14 02	14 23		14 32	14 53		15 02	15 23		15 32	15 53		16 02	16 23		16 32	16 53
Welham Green	d		13 06				13 36			14 06			14 36			15 06			15 36			16 06			16 36	
Brookmans Park	d		13 08				13 38			14 08			14 38			15 08			15 38			16 08			16 38	
Potters Bar	d		13 11	13 29			13 41	13 59		14 11	14 29		14 41	14 59		15 11	15 29		15 41	15 59		16 11	16 29		16 41	16 59
Hadley Wood	d		13 15				13 45			14 15			14 45			15 15			15 45			16 15			16 45	
New Barnet	d		13 17				13 47			14 17			14 47			15 17			15 47			16 17			16 47	
Oakleigh Park	d		13 19				13 49			14 19			14 49			15 19			15 49			16 19			16 49	
New Southgate	d		13 22				13 52			14 22			14 52			15 22			15 52			16 22			16 52	
Alexandra Palace	d	13 10	13 25			13 40	13 55		14 10	14 25		14 40	14 55		15 10	15 25		15 40	15 55		16 10	16 25		16 39	16 55	
Hornsey	d	13 12	13 27			13 42	13 57		14 12	14 27		14 42	14 57		15 12	15 27		15 42	15 57		16 12	16 27		16 41	16 57	
Harringay	d	13 14	13 29			13 44	13 59		14 14	14 29		14 44	14 59		15 14	15 29		15 44	15 59		16 14	16 29		16 43	16 59	
Finsbury Park	⊖ d	13 17	13 32	13 41		13 47	14 02	14 08	14 17	14 32	14 41	14 47	15 02	15 08	15 17	15 32	15 41	15 47	16 02	16 08	16 17	16 32	16 41	16 47	17 02	17 08
London Kings Cross 15	⊖ a	13 25	13 40	13 49	.	13 55	14 10	14 19	14 25	14 40	14 49	14 55	15 10	15 19	15 25	15 40	15 49	15 55	16 10	16 19	16 25	16 40	16 49	16 55	17 10	17 19

For general notes see front of timetable
For details of catering facilities see Directory of Train Operators

There is no service between Finsbury Park and Moorgate on Saturdays

Table 24

Saturdays

Letchworth Garden City, Hertford North and Welwyn Garden City → London

Network Diagram - see first page of Table 24

		FC	FC	FC 1	FC	FC		FC 1	FC	FC	FC 1	FC	FC	FC 1	FC	FC	FC 1	FC	FC	FC 1	FC	FC	FC 1	FC	FC	FC 1
Letchworth Garden City	d							17 29						18 29						19 29						20 29
Hitchin 4	d			17 03				17 33			18 03			18 33			19 03			19 33			20 03			20 33
Stevenage 4	d	16 29		17 09				17 39	17 29		18 09			18 39	18 29		19 09			19 39	19 29		20 09			20 39
Watton-at-Stone	d	16 36							17 36						18 36						19 36					
Hertford North	d	16 42			17 12				17 42			18 12			18 42			19 12			19 42			20 12		
Bayford	d	16 46			17 16				17 46			18 16			18 46			19 16			19 46			20 16		
Cuffley	d	16 51			17 21				17 51			18 21			18 51			19 21			19 51			20 21		
Crews Hill	d	16 54			17 24				17 54			18 24			18 54			19 24			19 54			20 24		
Gordon Hill	d	16 57			17 27				17 57			18 27			18 57			19 27			19 57			20 27		
Enfield Chase	d	16 59			17 29				17 59			18 29			18 59			19 29			19 59			20 29		
Grange Park	d	17 01			17 31				18 01			18 31			19 01			19 31			20 01			20 31		
Winchmore Hill	d	17 03			17 33				18 03			18 33			19 03			19 33			20 03			20 33		
Palmers Green	d	17 05			17 35				18 05			18 35			19 05			19 35			20 05			20 35		
Bowes Park	d	17 08			17 38				18 08			18 38			19 08			19 38			20 08			20 38		
Knebworth	d			17 13				17 43			18 13			18 43			19 13			19 43			20 13			20 43
Welwyn North	d			17 17				17 47			18 17			18 47			19 17			19 47			20 17			20 47
Welwyn Garden City 4	d		16 58	17 20		17 28		17 50		17 58	18 20		18 28	18 50		18 58	19 20		19 28	19 50		19 58	20 20		20 28	20 50
Hatfield	d		17 02	17 23		17 32		17 53		18 02	18 23		18 32	18 53		19 02	19 23		19 32	19 53		20 02	20 23		20 32	20 53
Welham Green	d		17 06			17 36				18 06			18 36			19 06			19 36			20 06			20 36	
Brookmans Park	d		17 08			17 38				18 08			18 38			19 08			19 38			20 08			20 38	
Potters Bar	d		17 11	17 29		17 41		17 59		18 11	18 29		18 41	18 59		19 11	19 29		19 41	19 59		20 11	20 29		20 41	20 59
Hadley Wood	d		17 15			17 45				18 15			18 45			19 15			19 45			20 15			20 45	
New Barnet	d		17 17			17 47				18 17			18 47			19 17			19 47			20 17			20 47	
Oakleigh Park	d		17 19			17 49				18 19			18 49			19 19			19 49			20 19			20 49	
New Southgate	d		17 22			17 52				18 22			18 52			19 22			19 52			20 22			20 52	
Alexandra Palace	d	17 10	17 25		17 40	17 55			18 10	18 25		18 40	18 55		19 10	19 25		19 40	19 55		20 10	20 25		20 40	20 55	
Hornsey	d	17 12	17 27		17 42	17 57			18 12	18 27		18 42	18 57		19 12	19 27		19 42	19 57		20 12	20 27		20 42	20 57	
Harringay	d	17 14	17 29		17 44	17 59			18 14	18 29		18 44	18 59		19 14	19 29		19 44	19 59		20 14	20 29		20 44	20 59	
Finsbury Park	⊖ d	17 17	17 32	17 41	17 47	18 02		18 08	18 17	18 32	18 41	18 47	19 02	19 08	19 17	19 32	19 41	19 47	20 02	20 08	20 17	20 32	20 41	20 47	21 02	21 08
London Kings Cross 15	⊖ a	17 25	17 40	17 49	17 55	18 10	.	18 19	18 25	18 40	18 49	18 55	19 10	19 19	19 25	19 40	19 49	19 55	20 10	20 19	20 25	20 40	20 49	20 55	21 10	21 19

		FC	FC	FC 1	FC	FC	FC 1	FC	FC	FC 1	FC	FC	FC	FC 1	FC	FC 1 A	FC B	FC A	FC 1 C	FC 1 C	FC A	FC B	FC 1 A	FC 1 D		
Letchworth Garden City	d						21 29							22 29									23 37	23 37		
Hitchin 4	d			21 03			21 33			22 03				22 33		23 03			23 03	23 25			23 41	23 41		
Stevenage 4	d	20 29		21 09			21 39	21 29		22 09			22 29	22 39		23 09			23 09	23 30	23 29	23 29	23 46	23 46		
Watton-at-Stone	d	20 36						21 36					22 36								23 36	23 36				
Hertford North	d	20 42			21 12			21 42			22 12		22 42				23 12	23 12			23 42	23 42				
Bayford	d	20 46			21 16			21 46			22 16		22 46				23 16	23 16			23 46	23 46				
Cuffley	d	20 51			21 21			21 51			22 21		22 51				23 21	23 21			23 51	23 51				
Crews Hill	d	20 54			21 24			21 54			22 24		22 54				23 24	23 24			23 54	23 54				
Gordon Hill	d	20 57			21 27			21 57			22 27		22 57				23 27	23 27			23 57	23 57				
Enfield Chase	d	20 59			21 29			21 59			22 29		22 59				23 29	23 29			23 59	23 59				
Grange Park	d	21 01			21 31			22 01			22 31		23 01				23 31	23 31			00 01	00 01				
Winchmore Hill	d	21 03			21 33			22 03			22 33		23 03				23 33	23 33			00 03	00 03				
Palmers Green	d	21 05			21 35			22 05			22 35		23 05				23 35	23 35			00 05	00 05				
Bowes Park	d	21 08			21 38			22 08			22 38		23 08				23 38	23 38			00 08	00 14				
Knebworth	d			21 13			21 43			22 13				22 43		23 13			23 13				23 49	23 49		
Welwyn North	d			21 17			21 47			22 17				22 47		23 17			23 17				23 53	23 53		
Welwyn Garden City 4	d		20 58	21 20		21 28	21 50		21 58	22 20		22 28		22 50	22 58	23 20			23 20				23 56	23 56		
Hatfield	d		21 02	21 23		21 32	21 53		22 02	22 23		22 32		22 53	23 02	23 23			23 23				23 59	23 59		
Welham Green	d		21 06			21 36			22 06			22 36			23 06											
Brookmans Park	d		21 08			21 38			22 08			22 38			23 08											
Potters Bar	d		21 11	21 29		21 41	21 59		22 11	22 29		22 41		22 59	23 11	23 29			23 29				00 05	00 05		
Hadley Wood	d		21 15			21 45			22 15			22 45			23 15											
New Barnet	d		21 17			21 47			22 17			22 47			23 17											
Oakleigh Park	d		21 19			21 49			22 19			22 49			23 19											
New Southgate	d		21 22			21 52			22 22			22 52			23 22											
Alexandra Palace	d	21 10	21 25		21 40	21 55		22 10	22 25		22 40	22 55	23 10		23 25		23 40	23 40	23a45	23 51	00 10	00 11		00a20		
Hornsey	d	21 12	21 27		21 42	21 57		22 12	22 27		22 42	22 57	23 12		23 27		23 42	23 42			00 12	00 13				
Harringay	d	21 14	21 29		21 44	21 59		22 14	22 29		22 44	22 59	23 14		23 29		23 44	23 44			00 14	00 15				
Finsbury Park	⊖ d	21 17	21 32	21 41	21 47	22 02	22 08	22 17	22 32	22 41	22 47	23 02	23 17	23s16	23 32	23 44	23 47	23 47		23 55	00 17	00 18	00s23			
London Kings Cross 15	⊖ a	21 25	21 40	21 49	21 55	22 10	22 19	22 25	22 40	22 49	22 55	23 10	23 25	23 30	23 42	23 53	23 55	23 58	.	00 08	00 25	00 31	00 34	.	.	.

For general notes see front of timetable
For details of catering facilities see
Directory of Train Operators

A Until 6 September
B From 13 September
C From 13 September.
From Peterborough (Table 25)
D From 13 September.
From Cambridge (Table 25)

There is no service between Finsbury Park and Moorgate on Saturdays

Sundays

until 13 July

Letchworth Garden City, Hertford North and Welwyn Garden City → London

Network Diagram - see first page of Table 24

		FC	FC 1	FC	FC	FC 1	FC	FC	FC (bus)	FC 1		FC	FC	FC (bus)	FC (bus)	FC 1	FC	FC	FC (bus)	FC (bus)		FC 1	FC	FC (bus)	FC (bus)	FC 1
Letchworth Garden City	d		23p37																							
Hitchin 4	d		23p41						06 28						07 03				07 28	07 33					08 03	
Stevenage 4	d	23p29	23p46						06 48					07 08	07 23				07 48	07 53				08 08	08 23	
Watton-at-Stone	d	23p36												07 24										08 24		
Hertford North	d	23p42		06 17			06 47					07 17		07a38			07 47						08 17	08a38		
Bayford	d	23p46		06 21			06 51					07 21					07 51						08 21			
Cuffley	d	23p51		06 26			06 56					07 26					07 56						08 26			
Crews Hill	d	23p54		06 29			06 59					07 29					07 59						08 29			
Gordon Hill	d	23p57		06 32			07 02					07 32					08 02						08 32			
Enfield Chase	d	23p59		06 34			07 04					07 34					08 04						08 34			
Grange Park	d	00 01		06 36			07 06					07 36					08 06						08 36			
Winchmore Hill	d	00 03		06 38			07 08					07 38					08 08						08 38			
Palmers Green	d	00 05		06 40			07 10					07 40					08 10						08 40			
Bowes Park	d	00 08		06 43			07 13					07 43					08 13						08 43			
Knebworth	d		23p49						06 55										07 55							
Welwyn North	d		23p53						07 05										08 05							
Welwyn Garden City 4	d		23p56		06 33	06 53		07 03	07a15	07 23			07 33		07a45	07 53		08 03	08a15	08a15		08 23			09a15	08 50
Hatfield	d		23p59		06 37			07 07		07 27			07 37					08 07				08 27				
Welham Green	d				06 41			07 11					07 41					08 11								
Brookmans Park	d				06 43			07 13					07 43					08 13								
Potters Bar	d		00 05		06 46			07 16		07 33			07 46					08 16				08 33				
Hadley Wood	d				06 50			07 20					07 50					08 20								
New Barnet	d				06 52			07 22					07 52					08 22								
Oakleigh Park	d				06 54			07 24					07 54					08 24								
New Southgate	d				06 57			07 27					07 57					08 27								
Alexandra Palace	d	00 10		06 45	07 00		07 15	07 30				07 45	08 00				08 15	08 30					08 45			
Hornsey	d	00 12		06 47	07 02		07 17	07 32				07 47	08 02				08 17	08 32					08 47			
Harringay	d	00 14		06 49	07 04		07 19	07 34				07 49	08 04				08 19	08 34					08 49			
Finsbury Park	⊖ d	00 17	00s23	06 52	07 07	07 14	07 22	07 37		07 47		07 52	08 07			08 14	08 22	08 37				08 47	08 52			09 05
London Kings Cross 15	⊖ a	00 25	00 34	07 01	07 18	07 21	07 31	07 48		07 54		08 01	08 18			08 21	08 31	08 45				08 54	08 59			09 12

		FC	FC	FC 1	FC	FC	FC		FC (bus)	FC 1	FC	FC	FC	FC	FC (bus)	FC 1	FC		FC	FC	FC	FC (bus)	FC 1	FC	FC	FC
Letchworth Garden City	d			08 45						09 29						10 29							11 29			
Hitchin 4	d			08 51						09 33						10 33							11 33			
Stevenage 4	d			08 57					09 08	09 39					10 08	10 39						11 08	11 39			
Watton-at-Stone	d								09 24						10 24							11 24				
Hertford North	d		08 47			09 12			09a38		09 42		10 12		10a38		10 42			11 12		11a38		11 42		12 12
Bayford	d		08 51			09 16					09 46		10 16				10 46			11 16				11 46		12 16
Cuffley	d		08 56			09 21					09 51		10 21				10 51			11 21				11 51		12 21
Crews Hill	d		08 59			09 24					09 54		10 24				10 54			11 24				11 54		12 24
Gordon Hill	d		09 02			09 27					09 57		10 27				10 57			11 27				11 57		12 27
Enfield Chase	d		09 04			09 29					09 59		10 29				10 59			11 29				11 59		12 29
Grange Park	d		09 06			09 31					10 01		10 31				11 01			11 31				12 01		12 31
Winchmore Hill	d		09 08			09 33					10 03		10 33				11 03			11 33				12 03		12 33
Palmers Green	d		09 10			09 35					10 05		10 35				11 05			11 35				12 05		12 35
Bowes Park	d		09 13			09 38					10 08		10 38				11 08			11 38				12 08		12 38
Knebworth	d			09 01						09 43						10 43							11 43			
Welwyn North	d			09 05						09 47						10 47							11 47			
Welwyn Garden City 4	d	08 33		09 08	08 58		09 28			09 50		09 58		10 28		10 50			10 58		11 28		11 50		11 58	
Hatfield	d	08 37		09 11	09 02		09 32			09 53		10 02		10 32		10 53			11 02		11 32		11 53		12 02	
Welham Green	d	08 41			09 06		09 36					10 06		10 36					11 06		11 36				12 06	
Brookmans Park	d	08 43			09 08		09 38					10 08		10 38					11 08		11 38				12 08	
Potters Bar	d	08 46		09 17	09 11		09 41			09 59		10 11		10 41		10 59			11 11		11 41		11 59		12 11	
Hadley Wood	d	08 50			09 15		09 45					10 15		10 45					11 15		11 45				12 15	
New Barnet	d	08 52			09 17		09 47					10 17		10 47					11 17		11 47				12 17	
Oakleigh Park	d	08 54			09 19		09 49					10 19		10 49					11 19		11 49				12 19	
New Southgate	d	08 57			09 22		09 52					10 22		10 52					11 22		11 52				12 22	
Alexandra Palace	d	09 00	09 15		09 25	09 40	09 55				10 10	10 25	10 40	10 55			11 10		11 25	11 40	11 55			12 10	12 25	12 40
Hornsey	d	09 02	09 17		09 27	09 42	09 57				10 12	10 27	10 42	10 57			11 12		11 27	11 42	11 57			12 12	12 27	12 42
Harringay	d	09 04	09 19		09 29	09 44	09 59				10 14	10 29	10 44	10 59			11 14		11 29	11 44	11 59			12 14	12 29	12 44
Finsbury Park	⊖ d	09 07	09 22	09 26	09 32	09 47	10 02			10 11	10 17	10 32	10 47	11 02		11 11	11 17		11 32	11 47	12 02		12 11	12 17	12 32	12 47
London Kings Cross 15	⊖ a	09 15	09 32	09 35	09 40	09 55	10 10			10 19	10 26	10 40	10 55	11 10		11 19	11 25		11 40	11 55	12 10		12 19	12 25	12 40	12 55

For general notes see front of timetable
For details of catering facilities see Directory of Train Operators

There is no service between Finsbury Park and Moorgate on Sundays

Table 24

Sundays

until 13 July

Letchworth Garden City, Hertford North and Welwyn Garden City → London

Network Diagram - see first page of Table 24

		FC	FC 🚌	FC [1]		FC	FC	FC	FC	FC 🚌	FC [1]	FC	FC	FC		FC	FC 🚌	FC [1]	FC	FC	FC	FC	FC 🚌	FC [1]		FC
Letchworth Garden City	d			12 29							13 29							14 29						15 29		
Hitchin [4]	d			12 33							13 33							14 33						15 33		
Stevenage [4]	d		12 08	12 39						13 08	13 39						14 08	14 39					15 08	15 39		
Watton-at-Stone	d		12 24							13 24							14 24						15 24			
Hertford North	d		12a38			12 42		13 12		13a38		13 42		14 12			14a38		14 42		15 12		15a38			15 42
Bayford	d					12 46		13 16				13 46		14 16					14 46		15 16					15 46
Cuffley	d					12 51		13 21				13 51		14 21					14 51		15 21					15 51
Crews Hill	d					12 54		13 24				13 54		14 24					14 54		15 24					15 54
Gordon Hill	d					12 57		13 27				13 57		14 27					14 57		15 27					15 57
Enfield Chase	d					12 59		13 29				13 59		14 29					14 59		15 29					15 59
Grange Park	d					13 01		13 31				14 01		14 31					15 01		15 31					16 01
Winchmore Hill	d					13 03		13 33				14 03		14 33					15 03		15 33					16 03
Palmers Green	d					13 05		13 35				14 05		14 35					15 05		15 35					16 05
Bowes Park	d					13 08		13 38				14 08		14 38					15 08		15 38					16 08
Knebworth	d			12 43							13 43							14 43						15 43		
Welwyn North	d			12 47							13 47							14 47						15 47		
Welwyn Garden City [4]	d	12 28		12 50			12 58		13 28		13 50		13 58			14 28		14 50		14 58		15 28		15 50		
Hatfield	d	12 32		12 53			13 02		13 32		13 53		14 02			14 32		14 53		15 02		15 32		15 53		
Welham Green	d	12 36					13 06		13 36				14 06			14 36				15 06		15 36				
Brookmans Park	d	12 38					13 08		13 38				14 08			14 38				15 08		15 38				
Potters Bar	d	12 41		12 59			13 11		13 41		13 59		14 11			14 41		14 59		15 11		15 41		15 59		
Hadley Wood	d	12 45					13 15		13 45				14 15			14 45				15 15		15 45				
New Barnet	d	12 47					13 17		13 47				14 17			14 47				15 17		15 47				
Oakleigh Park	d	12 49					13 19		13 49				14 19			14 49				15 19		15 49				
New Southgate	d	12 52					13 22		13 52				14 22			14 52				15 22		15 52				
Alexandra Palace	d	12 55				13 10	13 25	13 40	13 55			14 10	14 25	14 40		14 55			15 10	15 25	15 40	15 55				16 10
Hornsey	d	12 57				13 12	13 27	13 42	13 57			14 12	14 27	14 42		14 57			15 12	15 27	15 42	15 57				16 12
Harringay	d	12 59				13 14	13 29	13 44	13 59			14 14	14 29	14 44		14 59			15 14	15 29	15 44	15 59				16 14
Finsbury Park	⊖ d	13 02		13 11		13 17	13 32	13 47	14 02		14 11	14 17	14 32	14 47		15 02		15 11	15 17	15 32	15 47	16 02		16 11		16 17
London Kings Cross [15]	⊖ a	13 10		13 19		13 25	13 40	13 55	14 10		14 19	14 25	14 40	14 55		15 10		15 19	15 25	15 40	15 55	16 10		16 19		16 25

		FC	FC	FC	FC 🚌	FC [1]	FC	FC	FC	FC		FC 🚌	FC [1]	FC	FC	FC	FC	FC [1]	FC	FC		FC	FC	FC [1]	FC	FC
Letchworth Garden City	d					16 29							17 29					18 29						19 29		
Hitchin [4]	d					16 33							17 33					18 33						19 33		
Stevenage [4]	d				16 08	16 39						17 08	17 39					18 39	18 29					19 39	19 29	
Watton-at-Stone	d				16 24							17 24							18 36						19 36	
Hertford North	d		16 12		16a38		16 42		17 12			17a38		17 42		18 12			18 42			19 12			19 42	
Bayford	d		16 16				16 46		17 16					17 46		18 16			18 46			19 16			19 46	
Cuffley	d		16 21				16 51		17 21					17 51		18 21			18 51			19 21			19 51	
Crews Hill	d		16 24				16 54		17 24					17 54		18 24			18 54			19 24			19 54	
Gordon Hill	d		16 27				16 57		17 27					17 57		18 27			18 57			19 27			19 57	
Enfield Chase	d		16 29				16 59		17 29					17 59		18 29			18 59			19 29			19 59	
Grange Park	d		16 31				17 01		17 31					18 01		18 31			19 01			19 31			20 01	
Winchmore Hill	d		16 33				17 03		17 33					18 03		18 33			19 03			19 33			20 03	
Palmers Green	d		16 35				17 05		17 35					18 05		18 35			19 05			19 35			20 05	
Bowes Park	d		16 38				17 08		17 38					18 08		18 38			19 08			19 38			20 08	
Knebworth	d					16 43							17 43					18 43						19 43		
Welwyn North	d					16 47							17 47					18 47						19 47		
Welwyn Garden City [4]	d	15 58		16 28		16 50		16 58		17 28			17 50		17 58		18 28	18 50		18 58			19 28	19 50		19 58
Hatfield	d	16 02		16 32		16 53		17 02		17 32			17 53		18 02		18 32	18 53		19 02			19 32	19 53		20 02
Welham Green	d	16 06		16 36				17 06		17 36					18 06		18 36			19 06			19 36			20 06
Brookmans Park	d	16 08		16 38				17 08		17 38					18 08		18 38			19 08			19 38			20 08
Potters Bar	d	16 11		16 41		16 59		17 11		17 41			17 59		18 11		18 41	18 59		19 11			19 41	19 59		20 11
Hadley Wood	d	16 15		16 45				17 15		17 45					18 15		18 45			19 15			19 45			20 15
New Barnet	d	16 17		16 47				17 17		17 47					18 17		18 47			19 17			19 47			20 17
Oakleigh Park	d	16 19		16 49				17 19		17 49					18 19		18 49			19 19			19 49			20 19
New Southgate	d	16 22		16 52				17 22		17 52					18 22		18 52			19 22			19 52			20 22
Alexandra Palace	d	16 25	16 40	16 55			17 10	17 25	17 40	17 55				18 10	18 25	18 40	18 55		19 10	19 25		19 40	19 55		20 10	20 25
Hornsey	d	16 27	16 42	16 57			17 12	17 27	17 42	17 57				18 12	18 27	18 42	18 57		19 12	19 27		19 42	19 57		20 12	20 27
Harringay	d	16 29	16 44	16 59			17 14	17 29	17 44	17 59				18 14	18 29	18 44	18 59		19 14	19 29		19 44	19 59		20 14	20 29
Finsbury Park	⊖ d	16 32	16 47	17 02		17 11	17 17	17 32	17 47	18 02			18 11	18 17	18 32	18 47	19 02	19 11	19 17	19 32		19 47	20 02	20 11	20 17	20 32
London Kings Cross [15]	⊖ a	16 40	16 55	17 10		17 19	17 25	17 40	17 55	18 10			18 19	18 25	18 40	18 55	19 10	19 19	19 25	19 40		19 55	20 10	20 19	20 25	20 40

For general notes see front of timetable
For details of catering facilities see Directory of Train Operators

There is no service between Finsbury Park and Moorgate on Sundays

Table 24

Sundays

until 13 July

Letchworth Garden City, Hertford North and Welwyn Garden City → London

Network Diagram - see first page of Table 24

Station		FC	FC	FC [1]	FC	FC	FC		FC	FC [1]	FC	FC	FC	FC	FC	FC [1]	FC [bus]	FC	FC	FC	FC [bus]	FC [1]	FC [bus]	FC [bus]		
Letchworth Garden City	d			20 29						21 29						22 29						23 36				
Hitchin [4]	d			20 33						21 33						22 33						23 40				
Stevenage [4]	d			20 39	20 29					21 39	21 29					22 39						23 45	22 41	23 29		
Watton-at-Stone	d				20 36						21 36												22 58	23 46		
Hertford North	d	20 12			20 42		21 12				21 42		22 12		22 43						22 30		23 12	23 59		
Bayford	d	20 16			20 46		21 16				21 46		22 16								22 45		23 27	00 15		
Cuffley	d	20 21			20 51		21 21				21 51		22 21								23 00		23 42	00 30		
Crews Hill	d	20 24			20 54		21 24				21 54		22 24								23 08		23 50	00 38		
Gordon Hill	d	20 27			20 57		21 27				21 57		22 27				22 40				23 18		23 59	00 48		
Enfield Chase	d	20 29			20 59		21 29				21 59		22 29				22 46				23 24		00 06	00s54		
Grange Park	d	20 31			21 01		21 31				22 01		22 31				22 51				23 29		00 11	00s59		
Winchmore Hill	d	20 33			21 03		21 33				22 03		22 33				22 57				23 35		00 17	01s05		
Palmers Green	d	20 35			21 05		21 35				22 05		22 35				23 05				23 43		00 25	01s13		
Bowes Park	d	20 38			21 08		21 38				22 08		22 38				23 15				23 53		00 35	01s23		
Knebworth	d			20 43						21 43						22 43						23 48				
Welwyn North	d			20 47						21 47						22 47						23 52				
Welwyn Garden City [4]	d		20 28	20 50		20 58			21 28	21 50		21 58		22 28		22 50		22 58				23 56				
Hatfield	d		20 32	20 53		21 02			21 32	21 53		22 02		22 32		22 53		23 02				23 59				
Welham Green	d		20 36			21 06			21 36			22 06		22 36				23 06								
Brookmans Park	d		20 38			21 08			21 38			22 08		22 38				23 08								
Potters Bar	d		20 41	20 59		21 11			21 41	21 59		22 11		22 41		22 59		23 11				00 04				
Hadley Wood	d		20 45			21 15			21 45			22 15		22 45				23 15								
New Barnet	d		20 47			21 17			21 47			22 17		22 47				23 17								
Oakleigh Park	d		20 49			21 19			21 49			22 19		22 49				23 19								
New Southgate	d		20 52			21 22			21 52			22 22		22 52				23 22								
Alexandra Palace	d	20 40	20 55		21 10	21 25	21 40		21 55		22 10	22 25	22 40	22 55	23 01		23a20	23 25	23 10	⟵	23a58		00s40	01s28		
Hornsey	d	20 42	20 57		21 12	21 27	21 42		21 57		22 12	22 27	22 42	22 57	23 03			23 27	23 12	23 27						
Harringay	d	20 44	20 59		21 14	21 29	21 44		21 59		22 14	22 29	22 44	22 59	23 05			⟶	23 14	23 29						
Finsbury Park	⊖ d	20 47	21 02	21 11	21 17	21 32	21 47		22 02	22 11	22 17	22 32	22 47	23 02	23 08	23 11			23 17	23 32		00 20	01s00	01s48		
London Kings Cross [15]	⊖ a	20 55	21 10	21 19	21 25	21 40	21 55		22 10	22 19	22 25	22 40	22 58	23 12	23 18	23 24			23 27	23 44		00 32	01 15	02 03		

Sundays

20 July to 7 September

Station		FC	FC [1]	FC [bus]	FC	FC [1]		FC [bus]	FC	FC [bus]	FC [1]	FC		FC [bus]	FC [bus]	FC [bus]	FC [bus]	FC [bus]		FC [1]	FC	FC [bus]	FC [1]	FC [1]		FC
Letchworth Garden City	d		23p37																							
Hitchin [4]	d		23p41												06 03	06 28	06 33	07 03								
Stevenage [4]	d	23p29	23p46					05 21						06 21	06 23	06 48	06 53	07 23								
Watton-at-Stone	d	23p36						05 38						06 38												
Hertford North	d	23p42		05 22				05 52		06 22				06 52								07 22				
Bayford	d	23p46		05 37				06 07		06 37				07 07								07 37				
Cuffley	d	23p51		05 52				06 22		06 52				07 22								07 52				
Crews Hill	d	23p54		06 00				06 30		07 00				07 30								08 00				
Gordon Hill	d	23p57		06 10				06 40		07 10				07 40								08 10				
Enfield Chase	d	23p59		06 16				06 46		07 16				07 46								08 16				
Grange Park	d	00 01		06 21				06 51		07 21				07 51								08 21				
Winchmore Hill	d	00 03		06 27				06 57		07 27				07 57								08 27				
Palmers Green	d	00 05		06 35				07 05		07 35				08 05								08 35				
Bowes Park	d	00 08		06 45				07 15		07 45				08 15								08 45				
Knebworth	d		23p49													06 55										
Welwyn North	d		23p53													07 05										
Welwyn Garden City [4]	d		23p56		06 33	06 53			07 03		07 23	07 33			06a45	07a15	07a15	07a45		07 53	08 03		08 23	08 50		08 33
Hatfield	d		23p59		06 37				07 07		07 27	07 37									08 07		08 27			08 37
Welham Green	d				06 41				07 11			07 41									08 11					08 41
Brookmans Park	d				06 43				07 13			07 43									08 13					08 43
Potters Bar	d		00 05		06 46				07 16		07 33	07 46									08 16		08 33			08 46
Hadley Wood	d				06 50				07 20			07 50									08 20					08 50
New Barnet	d				06 52				07 22			07 52									08 22					08 52
Oakleigh Park	d				06 54				07 24			07 54									08 24					08 54
New Southgate	d				06 57				07 27			07 57									08 27					08 57
Alexandra Palace	d	00 10		06a50	07 00			07a20	07 30	07a50		08 00		08a20							08 30	08a50				09 00
Hornsey	d	00 12			07 02				07 32			08 02									08 32					09 02
Harringay	d	00 14			07 04				07 34			08 04									08 34					09 04
Finsbury Park	⊖ d	00 17	00s23		07 07	07 14			07 37		07 47	08 07								08 14	08 37		08 47	09 05		09 07
London Kings Cross [15]	⊖ a	00 25	00 34		07 18	07 21			07 48		07 54	08 18								08 21	08 45		08 54	09 12		09 15

For general notes see front of timetable
For details of catering facilities see
Directory of Train Operators

There is no service between Finsbury Park and Moorgate on Sundays

Table 24

Sundays

Letchworth Garden City, Hertford North and Welwyn Garden City → London

20 July to 7 September

Network Diagram - see first page of Table 24

		FC 🚌	FC 🚌	FC 🚌	FC 🚌	FC 🚌	FC 1	FC	FC	FC 🚌	FC 🚌	FC 1	FC	FC	FC 🚌	FC 🚌	FC 1	FC	FC	FC 🚌	FC 🚌	FC 1
Letchworth Garden City	d						08 45					09 29					10 29					11 29
Hitchin 4	d		07 28	07 33		08 03	08 51					09 33					10 33					11 33
Stevenage 4	d	07 21	07 48	07 53		08 23	08 57			08 21		09 39			09 21		10 39			10 21		11 39
Watton-at-Stone	d	07 38								08 38					09 38					10 38		
Hertford North	d	07 52			08 22					08 52	09 22				09 52	10 22				10 52	11 22	
Bayford	d	08 07			08 37					09 07	09 37				10 07	10 37				11 07	11 37	
Cuffley	d	08 22			08 52					09 22	09 52				10 22	10 52				11 22	11 52	
Crews Hill	d	08 30			09 00					09 30	10 00				10 30	11 00				11 30	12 00	
Gordon Hill	d	08 40			09 10					09 40	10 10				10 40	11 10				11 40	12 10	
Enfield Chase	d	08 46			09 16					09 46	10 16				10 46	11 16				11 46	12 16	
Grange Park	d	08 51			09 21					09 51	10 21				10 51	11 21				11 51	12 21	
Winchmore Hill	d	08 57			09 27					09 57	10 27				10 57	11 27				11 57	12 27	
Palmers Green	d	09 05			09 35					10 05	10 35				11 05	11 35				12 05	12 35	
Bowes Park	d	09 15			09 45					10 15	10 45				11 15	11 45				12 15	12 45	
Knebworth	d		07 55				09 01					09 43					10 43					11 43
Welwyn North	d		08 05				09 05					09 47					10 47					11 47
Welwyn Garden City 4	d		08a15	08a15		08a45	09 08	08 58	09 28			09 50	09 58	10 28			10 50	10 58	11 28			11 50
Hatfield	d						09 11	09 02	09 32			09 53	10 02	10 32			10 53	11 02	11 32			11 53
Welham Green	d							09 06	09 36				10 06	10 36				11 06	11 36			
Brookmans Park	d							09 08	09 38				10 08	10 38				11 08	11 38			
Potters Bar	d						09 17	09 11	09 41			09 59	10 11	10 41			10 59	11 11	11 41			11 59
Hadley Wood	d							09 15	09 45				10 15	10 45				11 15	11 45			
New Barnet	d							09 17	09 47				10 17	10 47				11 17	11 47			
Oakleigh Park	d							09 19	09 49				10 19	10 49				11 19	11 49			
New Southgate	d							09 22	09 52				10 22	10 52				11 22	11 52			
Alexandra Palace	d	09a20			09a50			09 25	09 55	10a20	10a50		10 25	10 55	11a20	11a50		11 25	11 55	12a20	12a50	
Hornsey	d							09 27	09 57				10 27	10 57				11 27	11 57			
Harringay	d							09 29	09 59				10 29	10 59				11 29	11 59			
Finsbury Park	⊖ d						09 26	09 32	10 02			10 11	10 32	11 02			11 11	11 32	12 02			12 11
London Kings Cross 15	⊖ a						09 35	09 40	10 10			10 19	10 40	11 10			11 19	11 40	12 10			12 19

		FC	FC	FC 🚌	FC 🚌	FC 1	FC	FC	FC 🚌	FC 🚌	FC 1	FC	FC	FC 🚌	FC 🚌	FC 1	FC	FC	FC 🚌	FC 🚌	FC 1	FC
Letchworth Garden City	d					12 29					13 29					14 29					15 29	
Hitchin 4	d					12 33					13 33					14 33					15 33	
Stevenage 4	d			11 21		12 39			12 21		13 39			13 21		14 39			14 21		15 39	
Watton-at-Stone	d			11 38					12 38					13 38					14 38			
Hertford North	d			11 52	12 22				12 52	13 22				13 52	14 22				14 52	15 22		
Bayford	d			12 07	12 37				13 07	13 37				14 07	14 37				15 07	15 37		
Cuffley	d			12 22	12 52				13 22	13 52				14 22	14 52				15 22	15 52		
Crews Hill	d			12 30	13 00				13 30	14 00				14 30	15 00				15 30	16 00		
Gordon Hill	d			12 40	13 10				13 40	14 10				14 40	15 10				15 40	16 10		
Enfield Chase	d			12 46	13 16				13 46	14 16				14 46	15 16				15 46	16 16		
Grange Park	d			12 51	13 21				13 51	14 21				14 51	15 21				15 51	16 21		
Winchmore Hill	d			12 57	13 27				13 57	14 27				14 57	15 27				15 57	16 27		
Palmers Green	d			13 05	13 35				14 05	14 35				15 05	15 35				16 05	16 35		
Bowes Park	d			13 15	13 45				14 15	14 45				15 15	15 45				16 15	16 45		
Knebworth	d					12 43					13 43					14 43					15 43	
Welwyn North	d					12 47					13 47					14 47					15 47	
Welwyn Garden City 4	d	11 58	12 28			12 50	12 58	13 28			13 50	13 58	14 28			14 50	14 58	15 28			15 50	15 58
Hatfield	d	12 02	12 32			12 53	13 02	13 32			13 53	14 02	14 32			14 53	15 02	15 32			15 53	16 02
Welham Green	d	12 06	12 36				13 06	13 36				14 06	14 36				15 06	15 36				16 06
Brookmans Park	d	12 08	12 38				13 08	13 38				14 08	14 38				15 08	15 38				16 08
Potters Bar	d	12 11	12 41			12 59	13 11	13 41			13 59	14 11	14 41			14 59	15 11	15 41			15 59	16 11
Hadley Wood	d	12 15	12 45				13 15	13 45				14 15	14 45				15 15	15 45				16 15
New Barnet	d	12 17	12 47				13 17	13 47				14 17	14 47				15 17	15 47				16 17
Oakleigh Park	d	12 19	12 49				13 19	13 49				14 19	14 49				15 19	15 49				16 19
New Southgate	d	12 22	12 52				13 22	13 52				14 22	14 52				15 22	15 52				16 22
Alexandra Palace	d	12 25	12 55	13a20	13a50		13 25	13 55	14a20	14a50		14 25	14 55	15a20	15a50		15 25	15 55	16a20	16a50		16 25
Hornsey	d	12 27	12 57				13 27	13 57				14 27	14 57				15 27	15 57				16 27
Harringay	d	12 29	12 59				13 29	13 59				14 29	14 59				15 29	15 59				16 29
Finsbury Park	⊖ d	12 32	13 02			13 11	13 32	14 02			14 11	14 32	15 02			15 11	15 32	16 02			16 11	16 32
London Kings Cross 15	⊖ a	12 40	13 10			13 19	13 40	14 10			14 19	14 40	15 10			15 19	15 40	16 10			16 19	16 40

For general notes see front of timetable
For details of catering facilities see Directory of Train Operators

There is no service between Finsbury Park and Moorgate on Sundays

Table 24

Sundays

20 July to 7 September

Letchworth Garden City, Hertford North and Welwyn Garden City → London

Network Diagram - see first page of Table 24

		FC	FC (bus)	FC (bus)	FC [1]	FC	FC	FC (bus)	FC (bus)	FC [1]	FC	FC	FC (bus)	FC (bus)	FC [1]	FC	FC	FC (bus)	FC (bus)	FC [1]	FC	FC
Letchworth Garden City	d				16 29					17 29					18 29					19 29		
Hitchin [4]	d				16 33					17 33					18 33					19 33		
Stevenage [4]	d		15 21		16 39			16 21		17 39			17 21		18 39			18 21		19 39		
Watton-at-Stone	d		15 38					16 38					17 38					18 38				
Hertford North	d		15 52	16 22				16 52	17 22				17 52	18 22				18 52	19 22			
Bayford	d		16 07	16 37				17 07	17 37				18 07	18 37				19 07	19 37			
Cuffley	d		16 22	16 52				17 22	17 52				18 22	18 52				19 22	19 52			
Crews Hill	d		16 30	17 00				17 30	18 00				18 30	19 00				19 30	20 00			
Gordon Hill	d		16 40	17 10				17 40	18 10				18 40	19 10				19 40	20 10			
Enfield Chase	d		16 46	17 16				17 46	18 16				18 46	19 16				19 46	20 16			
Grange Park	d		16 51	17 21				17 51	18 21				18 51	19 21				19 51	20 21			
Winchmore Hill	d		16 57	17 27				17 57	18 27				18 57	19 27				19 57	20 27			
Palmers Green	d		17 05	17 35				18 05	18 35				19 05	19 35				20 05	20 35			
Bowes Park	d		17 15	17 45				18 15	18 45				19 15	19 45				20 15	20 45			
Knebworth	d				16 43					17 43					18 43					19 43		
Welwyn North	d				16 47					17 47					18 47					19 47		
Welwyn Garden City [4]	d	16 28			16 50	16 58	17 28			17 50	17 58	18 28			18 50	18 58	19 28			19 50	19 58	20 28
Hatfield	d	16 32			16 53	17 02	17 32			17 53	18 02	18 32			18 53	19 02	19 32			19 53	20 02	20 32
Welham Green	d	16 36				17 06	17 36				18 06	18 36				19 06	19 36				20 06	20 36
Brookmans Park	d	16 38				17 08	17 38				18 08	18 38				19 08	19 38				20 08	20 38
Potters Bar	d	16 41			16 59	17 11	17 41			17 59	18 11	18 41			18 59	19 11	19 41			19 59	20 11	20 41
Hadley Wood	d	16 45				17 15	17 45				18 15	18 45				19 15	19 45				20 15	20 45
New Barnet	d	16 47				17 17	17 47				18 17	18 47				19 17	19 47				20 17	20 47
Oakleigh Park	d	16 49				17 19	17 49				18 19	18 49				19 19	19 49				20 19	20 49
New Southgate	d	16 52				17 22	17 52				18 22	18 52				19 22	19 52				20 22	20 52
Alexandra Palace	d	16 55	17a20	17a50		17 25	17 55	18a20	18a50		18 25	18 55	19a20	19a50		19 25	19 55	20a20	20a50		20 25	20 55
Hornsey	d	16 57				17 27	17 57				18 27	18 57				19 27	19 57				20 27	20 57
Harringay	d	16 59				17 29	17 59				18 29	18 59				19 29	19 59				20 29	20 59
Finsbury Park	⊖ d	17 02			17 11	17 32	18 02			18 11	18 32	19 02			19 11	19 32	20 02			20 11	20 32	21 02
London Kings Cross [15]	⊖ a	17 10			17 19	17 40	18 10			18 19	18 40	19 10			19 19	19 40	20 10			20 19	20 40	21 10

		FC (bus)	FC (bus)	FC [1]	FC	FC	FC (bus)	FC (bus)	FC [1]	FC	FC	FC (bus)	FC [1]	FC	FC	FC	FC (bus)	FC [1]	FC (bus)	FC (bus)
Letchworth Garden City	d			20 29					21 29				22 29					23 36		
Hitchin [4]	d			20 33					21 33				22 33					23 40		
Stevenage [4]	d	19 21		20 39			20 21		21 39			21 21	22 39					23 45	22 41	23 29
Watton-at-Stone	d	19 38					20 38					21 38							22 58	23 46
Hertford North	d	19 52	20 22				20 52	21 22				21 52					22 30		23 12	23 59
Bayford	d	20 07	20 37				21 07	21 37				22 07					22 45		23 27	00 15
Cuffley	d	20 22	20 52				21 22	21 52				22 22					23 00		23 42	00 30
Crews Hill	d	20 30	21 00				21 30	22 00				22 30					23 08		23 50	00 38
Gordon Hill	d	20 40	21 10				21 40	22 10				22 40					23 18		23 59	00 48
Enfield Chase	d	20 46	21 16				21 46	22 16				22 46					23 24		00 06	00s54
Grange Park	d	20 51	21 21				21 51	22 21				22 51					23 29		00 11	00s59
Winchmore Hill	d	20 57	21 27				21 57	22 27				22 57					23 35		00 17	01s05
Palmers Green	d	21 05	21 35				22 05	22 35				23 05					23 43		00 25	01s13
Bowes Park	d	21 15	21 45				22 15	22 45				23 15					23 53		00 35	01s23
Knebworth	d			20 43					21 43				22 43					23 48		
Welwyn North	d			20 47					21 47				22 47					23 52		
Welwyn Garden City [4]	d			20 50	20 58	21 28			21 50	21 58	22 28		22 50	22 58				23 56		
Hatfield	d			20 53	21 02	21 32			21 53	22 02	22 32		22 53	23 02				23 59		
Welham Green	d				21 06	21 36				22 06	22 36			23 06						
Brookmans Park	d				21 08	21 38				22 08	22 38			23 08						
Potters Bar	d			20 59	21 11	21 41			21 59	22 11	22 41		22 59	23 11				00 04		
Hadley Wood	d				21 15	21 45				22 15	22 45			23 15						
New Barnet	d				21 17	21 47				22 17	22 47			23 17						
Oakleigh Park	d				21 19	21 49				22 19	22 49			23 19						
New Southgate	d				21 22	21 52				22 22	22 52			23 22						
Alexandra Palace	d	21a20	21a50		21 25	21 55	22a20	22a50		22 25	22 55	23a20		23 25	23 10	←	23a58		00s40	01s28
Hornsey	d				21 27	21 57				22 27	22 57			23 27	23 12	23 27				
Harringay	d				21 29	21 59				22 29	22 59			→	23 14	23 29				
Finsbury Park	⊖ d			21 11	21 32	22 02			22 11	22 32	23 02		23 11		23 17	23 32		00 20	01s00	01s48
London Kings Cross [15]	⊖ a			21 19	21 40	22 10			22 19	22 40	23 12		23 24		23 27	23 44		00 32	01 15	02 03

For general notes see front of timetable
For details of catering facilities see
Directory of Train Operators

There is no service between Finsbury Park and Moorgate on Sundays

Table 24

from 14 September

Letchworth Garden City, Hertford North and Welwyn Garden City → London

Network Diagram - see first page of Table 24

	FC	FC 1 A	FC 🚌	FC	FC	FC	FC	FC	FC		FC	FC 1	FC	FC	FC	FC 1	FC	FC	FC		FC	FC 1	FC	FC	FC
Letchworth Garden City d		23p37														08 29						09 29			
Hitchin 4 d		23p41										07 28				08 33						09 33			
Stevenage 4 d	23p29	23p46									07 29	07 33				08 39	08 29					09 39	09 29		
Watton-at-Stone d	23p36										07 36						08 36						09 36		
Hertford North d	23p42			06 12		06 42		07 12			07 42			08 12			08 42		09 12				09 42		10 12
Bayford d	23p46			06 16		06 46		07 16			07 46			08 16			08 46		09 16				09 46		10 16
Cuffley d	23p51			06 21		06 51		07 21			07 51			08 21			08 51		09 21				09 51		10 21
Crews Hill d	23p54			06 24		06 54		07 24			07 54			08 24			08 54		09 24				09 54		10 24
Gordon Hill d	23p57			06 27		06 57		07 27			07 57			08 27			08 57		09 27				09 57		10 27
Enfield Chase d	23p59			06 29		06 59		07 29			07 59			08 29			08 59		09 29				09 59		10 29
Grange Park d	00 01			06 31		07 01		07 31			08 01			08 31			09 01		09 31				10 01		10 31
Winchmore Hill d	00 03			06 33		07 03		07 33			08 03			08 33			09 03		09 33				10 03		10 33
Palmers Green d	00 05			06 35		07 05		07 35			08 05			08 35			09 05		09 35				10 05		10 35
Bowes Park d	00 14			06 38		07 08		07 38			08 08			08 38			09 08		09 38				10 08		10 38
Knebworth d		23p49										07 37				08 43						09 43			
Welwyn North d		23p53										07 40				08 47						09 47			
Welwyn Garden City 4 d		23p56			06 28		06 58		07 28			07 43	07 58		08 28	08 50		08 58			09 28	09 50		09 58	
Hatfield d		23p59			06 32		07 02		07 32				08 02		08 32	08 53		09 02			09 32	09 53		10 02	
Welham Green d					06 36		07 06		07 36				08 06		08 36			09 06			09 36			10 06	
Brookmans Park d					06 38		07 08		07 38				08 08		08 38			09 08			09 38			10 08	
Potters Bar d		00 05			06 41		07 11		07 41				08 11		08 41	08 59		09 11			09 41	09 59		10 11	
Hadley Wood d					06 45		07 15		07 45				08 15		08 45			09 15			09 45			10 15	
New Barnet d					06 47		07 17		07 47				08 17		08 47			09 17			09 47			10 17	
Oakleigh Park d					06 49		07 19		07 49				08 19		08 49			09 19			09 49			10 19	
New Southgate d					06 52		07 22		07 52				08 22		08 52			09 22			09 52			10 22	
Alexandra Palace d	00 11	00a20	00 25	06 40	06 55	07 10	07 25	07 40	07 55		08 10		08 25	08 40	08 55		09 10	09 25	09 40		09 55		10 10	10 25	10 40
Hornsey d	00 13			06 42	06 57	07 12	07 27	07 42	07 57		08 12		08 27	08 42	08 57		09 12	09 27	09 42		09 57		10 12	10 27	10 42
Harringay d	00 15			06 44	06 59	07 14	07 29	07 44	07 59		08 14		08 29	08 44	08 59		09 14	09 29	09 44		09 59		10 14	10 29	10 44
Finsbury Park ⊖ d	00 18		00s45	06a50	07a07	07a20	07a37	07a50	08a07		08a20	08a10	08 32	08 47	09 02	09 11	09 17	09 32	09 47		10 02	10 11	10 17	10 32	10 47
London Kings Cross 15 ⊖ a	00 31		01 00										08 40	08 55	09 10	09 19	09 25	09 40	09 55		10 10	10 19	10 25	10 40	10 55

	FC	FC 1	FC	FC	FC	FC		FC 1	FC	FC	FC	FC	FC 1	FC	FC	FC		FC	FC 1	FC	FC	FC	FC	FC 1	FC
Letchworth Garden City d		10 29						11 29					12 29						13 29					14 29	
Hitchin 4 d		10 33						11 33					12 33						13 33					14 33	
Stevenage 4 d		10 39	10 29					11 39	11 29				12 39	12 29					13 39	13 29				14 39	14 29
Watton-at-Stone d			10 36						11 36					12 36						13 36					14 36
Hertford North d			10 42		11 12				11 42		12 12			12 42		13 12				13 42		14 12			14 42
Bayford d			10 46		11 16				11 46		12 16			12 46		13 16				13 46		14 16			14 46
Cuffley d			10 51		11 21				11 51		12 21			12 51		13 21				13 51		14 21			14 51
Crews Hill d			10 54		11 24				11 54		12 24			12 54		13 24				13 54		14 24			14 54
Gordon Hill d			10 57		11 27				11 57		12 27			12 57		13 27				13 57		14 27			14 57
Enfield Chase d			10 59		11 29				11 59		12 29			12 59		13 29				13 59		14 29			14 59
Grange Park d			11 01		11 31				12 01		12 31			13 01		13 31				14 01		14 31			15 01
Winchmore Hill d			11 03		11 33				12 03		12 33			13 03		13 33				14 03		14 33			15 03
Palmers Green d			11 05		11 35				12 05		12 35			13 05		13 35				14 05		14 35			15 05
Bowes Park d			11 08		11 38				12 08		12 38			13 08		13 38				14 08		14 38			15 08
Knebworth d		10 43						11 43					12 43						13 43					14 43	
Welwyn North d		10 47						11 47					12 47						13 47					14 47	
Welwyn Garden City 4 d	10 28	10 50		10 58		11 28		11 50		11 58		12 28	12 50		12 58			13 28	13 50		13 58		14 28	14 50	
Hatfield d	10 32	10 53		11 02		11 32		11 53		12 02		12 32	12 53		13 02			13 32	13 53		14 02		14 32	14 53	
Welham Green d	10 36			11 06		11 36				12 06		12 36			13 06			13 36			14 06		14 36		
Brookmans Park d	10 38			11 08		11 38				12 08		12 38			13 08			13 38			14 08		14 38		
Potters Bar d	10 41	10 59		11 11		11 41		11 59		12 11		12 41	12 59		13 11			13 41	13 59		14 11		14 41	14 59	
Hadley Wood d	10 45			11 15		11 45				12 15		12 45			13 15			13 45			14 15		14 45		
New Barnet d	10 47			11 17		11 47				12 17		12 47			13 17			13 47			14 17		14 47		
Oakleigh Park d	10 49			11 19		11 49				12 19		12 49			13 19			13 49			14 19		14 49		
New Southgate d	10 52			11 22		11 52				12 22		12 52			13 22			13 52			14 22		14 52		
Alexandra Palace d	10 55		11 10	11 25	11 40	11 55			12 10	12 25	12 40	12 55		13 10	13 25	13 40		13 55		14 10	14 25	14 40	14 55		15 10
Hornsey d	10 57		11 12	11 27	11 42	11 57			12 12	12 27	12 42	12 57		13 12	13 27	13 42		13 57		14 12	14 27	14 42	14 57		15 12
Harringay d	10 59		11 14	11 29	11 44	11 59			12 14	12 29	12 44	12 59		13 14	13 29	13 44		13 59		14 14	14 29	14 44	14 59		15 14
Finsbury Park ⊖ d	11 02	11 11	11 17	11 32	11 47	12 02		12 11	12 17	12 32	12 47	13 02	13 11	13 17	13 32	13 47		14 02	14 11	14 17	14 32	14 47	15 02	15 11	15 17
London Kings Cross 15 ⊖ a	11 10	11 19	11 25	11 40	11 55	12 10		12 19	12 25	12 40	12 55	13 10	13 19	13 25	13 40	13 55		14 10	14 19	14 25	14 40	14 55	15 10	15 19	15 25

For general notes see front of timetable
For details of catering facilities see Directory of Train Operators

A From Cambridge (Table 25)

There is no service between Finsbury Park and Moorgate on Sundays

Table 24

Sundays

from 14 September

Letchworth Garden City, Hertford North and Welwyn Garden City → London

Network Diagram - see first page of Table 24

		FC	FC	FC		FC [1]	FC	FC	FC	FC	FC [1]	FC	FC	FC		FC	FC [1]	FC	FC	FC	FC	FC [1]	FC	FC		FC
Letchworth Garden City	d					15 29					16 29						17 29					18 29				
Hitchin [4]	d					15 33					16 33						17 33					18 33				
Stevenage [4]	d					15 39	15 29				16 39	16 29					17 39	17 29				18 39	18 29			
Watton-at-Stone	d						15 36					16 36						17 36					18 36			
Hertford North	d		15 12				15 42		16 12			16 42		17 12				17 42		18 12			18 42			19 12
Bayford	d		15 16				15 46		16 16			16 46		17 16				17 46		18 16			18 46			19 16
Cuffley	d		15 21				15 51		16 21			16 51		17 21				17 51		18 21			18 51			19 21
Crews Hill	d		15 24				15 54		16 24			16 54		17 24				17 54		18 24			18 54			19 24
Gordon Hill	d		15 27				15 57		16 27			16 57		17 27				17 57		18 27			18 57			19 27
Enfield Chase	d		15 29				15 59		16 29			16 59		17 29				17 59		18 29			18 59			19 29
Grange Park	d		15 31				16 01		16 31			17 01		17 31				18 01		18 31			19 01			19 31
Winchmore Hill	d		15 33				16 03		16 33			17 03		17 33				18 03		18 33			19 03			19 33
Palmers Green	d		15 35				16 05		16 35			17 05		17 35				18 05		18 35			19 05			19 35
Bowes Park	d		15 38				16 08		16 38			17 08		17 38				18 08		18 38			19 08			19 38
Knebworth	d					15 43					16 43						17 43					18 43				
Welwyn North	d					15 47					16 47						17 47					18 47				
Welwyn Garden City [4]	d	14 58		15 28		15 50		15 58		16 28	16 50		16 58			17 28	17 50		17 58		18 28	18 50		18 58		
Hatfield	d	15 02		15 32		15 53		16 02		16 32	16 53		17 02			17 32	17 53		18 02		18 32	18 53		19 02		
Welham Green	d	15 06		15 36				16 06		16 36			17 06			17 36			18 06		18 36			19 06		
Brookmans Park	d	15 08		15 38				16 08		16 38			17 08			17 38			18 08		18 38			19 08		
Potters Bar	d	15 11		15 41		15 59		16 11		16 41	16 59		17 11			17 41	17 59		18 11		18 41	18 59		19 11		
Hadley Wood	d	15 15		15 45				16 15		16 45			17 15			17 45			18 15		18 45			19 15		
New Barnet	d	15 17		15 47				16 17		16 47			17 17			17 47			18 17		18 47			19 17		
Oakleigh Park	d	15 19		15 49				16 19		16 49			17 19			17 49			18 19		18 49			19 19		
New Southgate	d	15 22		15 52				16 22		16 52			17 22			17 52			18 22		18 52			19 22		
Alexandra Palace	d	15 25	15 40	15 55			16 10	16 25	16 40	16 55		17 10	17 25	17 40		17 55		18 10	18 25	18 40	18 55		19 10	19 25		19 40
Hornsey	d	15 27	15 42	15 57			16 12	16 27	16 42	16 57		17 12	17 27	17 42		17 57		18 12	18 27	18 42	18 57		19 12	19 27		19 42
Harringay	d	15 29	15 44	15 59			16 14	16 29	16 44	16 59		17 14	17 29	17 44		17 59		18 14	18 29	18 44	18 59		19 14	19 29		19 44
Finsbury Park	⊖ d	15 32	15 47	16 02		16 11	16 17	16 32	16 47	17 02	17 11	17 17	17 32	17 47		18 02	18 11	18 17	18 32	18 47	19 02	19 11	19 17	19 32		19 47
London Kings Cross [15]	⊖ a	15 40	15 55	16 10		16 19	16 25	16 40	16 55	17 10	17 19	17 25	17 40	17 55		18 10	18 19	18 25	18 40	18 55	19 10	19 19	19 25	19 40		19 55

		FC	FC [1]	FC	FC	FC	FC	FC [1]	FC	FC		FC	FC	FC [1]	FC	FC	FC	FC	FC [1]	FC	FC	FC	FC	FC [1]		
Letchworth Garden City	d		19 29					20 29						21 29					22 29					23 36		
Hitchin [4]	d		19 33					20 33						21 33					22 33					23 40		
Stevenage [4]	d		19 39	19 29				20 39	20 29					21 39	21 29				22 39	22 29			23 29	23 45		
Watton-at-Stone	d			19 36					20 36						21 36					22 36			23 36			
Hertford North	d			19 42		20 12			20 42			21 12			21 42		22 12			22 42		23 12	23 42			
Bayford	d			19 46		20 16			20 46			21 16			21 46		22 16			22 46		23 16	23 46			
Cuffley	d			19 51		20 21			20 51			21 21			21 51		22 21			22 51		23 21	23 51			
Crews Hill	d			19 54		20 24			20 54			21 24			21 54		22 24			22 54		23 24	23 54			
Gordon Hill	d			19 57		20 27			20 57			21 27			21 57		22 27			22 57		23 27	23 57			
Enfield Chase	d			19 59		20 29			20 59			21 29			21 59		22 29			22 59		23 29	23 59			
Grange Park	d			20 01		20 31			21 01			21 31			22 01		22 31			23 01		23 31	00 01			
Winchmore Hill	d			20 03		20 33			21 03			21 33			22 03		22 33			23 03		23 33	00 03			
Palmers Green	d			20 05		20 35			21 05			21 35			22 05		22 35			23 05		23 35	00 05			
Bowes Park	d			20 08		20 38			21 08			21 38			22 08		22 38			23 08		23 38	00 08			
Knebworth	d		19 43					20 43						21 43					22 43					23 48		
Welwyn North	d		19 47					20 47						21 47					22 47					23 52		
Welwyn Garden City [4]	d	19 28	19 50		19 58		20 28	20 50		20 58			21 28	21 50		21 58		22 28	22 50		22 58			23 56		
Hatfield	d	19 32	19 53		20 02		20 32	20 53		21 02			21 32	21 53		22 02		22 32	22 53		23 02			23 59		
Welham Green	d	19 36			20 06		20 36			21 06			21 36			22 06		22 36			23 06					
Brookmans Park	d	19 38			20 08		20 38			21 08			21 38			22 08		22 38			23 08					
Potters Bar	d	19 41	19 59		20 11		20 41	20 59		21 11			21 41	21 59		22 11		22 41	22 59		23 11			00 04		
Hadley Wood	d	19 45			20 15		20 45			21 15			21 45			22 15		22 45			23 15					
New Barnet	d	19 47			20 17		20 47			21 17			21 47			22 17		22 47			23 17					
Oakleigh Park	d	19 49			20 19		20 49			21 19			21 49			22 19		22 49			23 19					
New Southgate	d	19 52			20 22		20 52			21 22			21 52			22 22		22 52			23 22					
Alexandra Palace	d	19 55		20 10	20 25	20 40	20 55		21 10	21 25		21 40	21 55		22 10	22 25	22 40	22 55		23 10	23 25	23 40	00 10			
Hornsey	d	19 57		20 12	20 27	20 42	20 57		21 12	21 27		21 42	21 57		22 12	22 27	22 42	22 57		23 12	23 27	23 42	00 12			
Harringay	d	19 59		20 14	20 29	20 44	20 59		21 14	21 29		21 44	21 59		22 14	22 29	22 44	22 59		23 14	23 29	23 44	00 14			
Finsbury Park	⊖ d	20 02	20 11	20 17	20 32	20 47	21 02	21 11	21 17	21 32		21 47	22 02	22 11	22 17	22 32	22 47	23 02	23 11	23 17	23 32	23 47	00 17	00 20		
London Kings Cross [15]	⊖ a	20 10	20 19	20 25	20 40	20 55	21 10	21 19	21 25	21 40		21 55	22 10	22 19	22 25	22 40	22 58	23 12	23 24	23 27	23 44	23 57	00 27	00 32		

For general notes see front of timetable
For details of catering facilities see
Directory of Train Operators

There is no service between Finsbury Park and Moorgate on Sundays

First Capital Connect will run a Saturday service on Bank Holiday Mondays

London → Stevenage, Cambridge and Peterborough

Network Diagram - see first page of Table 24

Miles	Miles		FC MO 1	FC MX 1	FC MO 1 A	FC MX 1 A	FC MX 1	FC MO 1	FC MX 1	FC MO 1	FC MX 1	FC MO	FC MO 1 B	FC 1 C	FC MX 1	FC MO 1	FC 1 C	FC MO B	FC MO B (bus)	FC MX 1	FC MO 1	FC MO B (bus)	FC 1	FC 1 D	GR R 1
0	0	**London Kings Cross 15** ⊖ d	23p06	23p06	23p15	23p15			23p22	23p25	23p36	23p41	00 07	00 07	00 36	00 36	01 06	01 06		01 36	01 36		05 22	05 45	06 00
2¼	2¼	Finsbury Park ⊖ d	23p11	23p11					23p27	23p30	23p41	23p47	00 12	00 12	00 41	00 41	01 11	01 11		01 41	01 41		05 27	05 50	
12¾	12¾	Potters Bar d	23p21	23p21							23p51	00 08			00 51	00 58				01 58	01 58		05 37		
17¾	17¾	Hatfield d	23p27	23p27			←	←			23p57	00 16			00 57	01 04				02 04	02 04		05 43		
20¼	20¼	Welwyn Garden City 4 d	23p31 →	23p31 →			23p31	23p31			00 01	00 20			01 01	01 08				02 08	02 08		05 47		
22	22	Welwyn North d					23p34	23p36			00 04	00 23			01s04	01s16				02s11	02s16		05 50		
25	25	Knebworth d					23p38	23p40			00 08	00 28			01s08	01s20				02s15	02s20		05 54		
—	—	Hertford North d												00 39			01 38		01 40			02 40			
27½	27½	**Stevenage 4** d					23p42	23p43	23p46	23p49	00 12	00 31	00 48	00 48	01 12	01 23	01 47	01 47	02s02	02 18	02 23	03 02	05 58	06 08	06 19
31¾	31¾	Hitchin 4 d					23p50	23p53	23p54	00 04	00 20	00a47	00 56	00 56	01 17	01 28	01 52	01 53	02s22	02 23	02 28	03 22	06 06	06 13	
34¾	—	Letchworth Garden City d			23p52	23p45	23p54	23p57			00a29		01 00	01 00			02a06	02a06	02a37			03a37		06 16	
36½	—	Baldock d					23p58	23p59					01 04	01 04										06 19	
41	—	Ashwell & Morden d					00 03	00 05					01 09	01 09										06 24	
45	—	Royston d			00 01	23p54	00 07	00 10					01 13	01 13										06 29	
48	—	Meldreth d					00 11	00 13					01 17	01 17										06 32	
50	—	Shepreth d					00 14	00 16					01 20	01 20										06 35	
51	—	Foxton d					00 17	00 18					01 23	01 23										06 38	
58	—	**Cambridge** a			00 19	00 10	00 29	00 35					01 39	01 39										06 53	
—	37	Arlesey d							23p59	00 10					01s28	01s37							06 11		
—	41	Biggleswade d							00 04	00 15					01s33	01s42				02s38	02s40		06 16 →		
—	44	Sandy d							00 08	00 18					01s37	01s46									
—	51½	St Neots d							00 15	00 26					01s45	01s53				02s48	02s50				
—	58¾	Huntingdon a							00 26	00 33					01s55	02s04				02s59	03s01				
—	—	d							00 26	00 33															
—	76¼	**Peterborough 8** a							00 42	00 55					02 17	02 26				03 21	03 23				06 50

	FC 1	FC 1	GR R 1 ✕	FC 1	FC 1	GR R 1	FC 1	FC 1	FC 1		FC 1	GR R 1 ✕	FC 1	GR R 1 ✕	FC 1	FC 1	FC 1	FC 1	GR R 1 ✕	FC 1	FC 1	FC 1	FC 1	FC 1	GR R 1 ✕
London Kings Cross 15 ⊖ d		06 06	06 15		06 22	06 35		06 36	06 45		06 52	07 00	07 06	07 10		07 15		07 22	07 30		07 36	07 45		07 52	08 00
Finsbury Park ⊖ d		06 11			06 27			06 41			06 57		07 11					07 27			07 41			07 57	
Potters Bar d		06 21		←				06 51					07 21				←				07 51				
Hatfield d		06 27 →		06 27				06 57					07 27 →				07 27				07 57				
Welwyn Garden City 4 d				06 31				07 01									07 31				08 01				
Welwyn North d				06 34				07 04									07 34				08 04				
Knebworth d				06 38				07 08									07 38				08 08				
Hertford North d																							←		
Stevenage 4 d			06 34	06 42	06 46			07 12			07 16	07 19		07 29			07 42	07 46	07 50		08 12 →		08 12	08 16	
Hitchin 4 d				06 47	06 51			07 17			07 21						07 47	07 51					08 17	08 21	
Letchworth Garden City d				06 51							07 25						07 51							08 25	
Baldock d				06 55							07 28						07 55							08 28	
Ashwell & Morden d				07 00							07 33						08 00							08 33	
Royston d				07 06							07 37						08 04							08 37	
Meldreth d				07 10							07 41						08 08							08 41	
Shepreth d				07 13							07 44						08 11							08 44	
Foxton d				07 16							07 46						08 14							08 46	
Cambridge a				07 29			←		07 31		08 01					08 02	08 28					08 35		09 01	
Arlesey d	←				06 56 →		06 56	07 23							←			07 56		←			08 23		
Biggleswade d	06 16						07 01	07 28 →							07 28			08 01 →		08 01			08 28		
Sandy d	06 20						07 05								07 32					08 05			08 32		
St Neots d	06 28						07 12								07 39					08 12			08 39		
Huntingdon a	06 35						07 20								07 47					08 20			08 47		
d	06 35						07 20								07 47					08 20			08 47		
Peterborough 8 a	06 54		07 05			07 21	07 38					07 50		08 00	08 09				08 21	08 38			09 13		08 46

For general notes see front of timetable
For details of catering facilities see Directory of Train Operators

A To Ely (Table 17)
B Until 8 September
C All Tuesdays to Fridays, also Mondays from 15 September
D To Kings Lynn (Table 17)

First Capital Connect will run a Saturday service on Bank Holiday Mondays

London → Stevenage, Cambridge and Peterborough

Network Diagram - see first page of Table 24

	FC	GR	FC	FC	GR	FC	GR	FC	FC	FC	FC	FC	FC	GR	FC	GR	FC		FC	GR	FC	FC	GR	FC	FC
	1	R 1	1	1	R 1	1	R 1	1	1	1	1	1		R 1	1	R 1	1		1	R 1	1		R 1	1	1
		✕			✕		☕							✕		✕				✕			✕		
London Kings Cross 15 ⊖ d	08 03	08 10	08 15	08 22	08 30	08 33	08 40			08 45		08 52		09 10	09 06	09 10	09 15		09 22	09 30			09 35		09 36
Finsbury Park ⊖ d	08 08			08 27		08 38						08 57	08 24		09 11				09 27			09 04			09 41
Potters Bar d	08 19					08 48									09 21										09 51
Hatfield d	08 25					08 54									09 27										09 57
Welwyn Garden City 4 d	08 31					09 00									09 31										10 01
Welwyn North d	08 34					09 03									09 34										10 04
Knebworth d	08 38					09 07									09 38										10 08
Hertford North d											⟵		09 07									09 39			
Stevenage 4 d	08 42			08 46	08 49	09 12			⟵		09 12	09 16	09 20		09 42				09 46	09 49	⟵	09 51	09 54		10 12
Hitchin 4 d	08 47			08 51		→			08 47		09 17	09 21	09 30		09 47				09 51		09 47	09 57			→
Letchworth Garden City d	→								08 54			09 25	09a36		→						09 51	10a03			
Baldock d									08 57			09 28									09 55				
Ashwell & Morden d									09 02												10 00				
Royston d									09 07			09 36									10 04				
Meldreth d									09 11												10 08				
Shepreth d									09 14												10 11				
Foxton d									09 16												10 14				
Cambridge a			09 03						09 31	09 31		09 54					10 02				10 27				
Arlesey d				08 56				⟵			09 23														
Biggleswade d				09 01				09 01			09 28								09 59					⟵	
Sandy d				→				09 05			09 32								10 03					10 03	
St Neots d								09 12			09 39								→					10 10	
Huntingdon a								09 20			09 47													10 18	
d								09 20			09 47													10 18	
Peterborough 8 a		08 59			09 20		09 27	09 38			10 04			09 47		09 56				10 20			10 26	10 34	

	FC	FC	FC	GR	FC	GR	FC	FC	GR	GR	FC	FC	FC	FC	FC	FC	FC	GR	FC	GR	FC	FC	GR	FC	FC
	1	1	1	R 1	1	R 1	1	1	R 1	R 1	1	1		1	1	1	1	R 1	1	R 1	1	1	R 1	1	
				A ✕		✕			B ✕	☕								✕		☕			✕		
London Kings Cross 15 ⊖ d	09 45		09 52	10 00	10 06	10 10	10 15	10 22	10 30	10 35				10 36	10 45		10 52	11 00	11 06	11 10	11 15	11 22	11 30		
Finsbury Park ⊖ d			09 57		10 11			10 27					10 04	10 41			10 57		11 11			11 27			11 04
Potters Bar d					10 21									10 51					11 21						
Hatfield d					10 27									10 57					11 27						
Welwyn Garden City 4 d					10 31									11 01					11 31						
Welwyn North d					10 34									11 04					11 34						
Knebworth d					10 38									11 08					11 38						
Hertford North d		⟵											10 39			⟵									11 39
Stevenage 4 d		10 12	10 16		10 42			10 46				⟵	10 51	11 12		11 12	11 16		11 42			11 46	11 50	⟵	11 51
Hitchin 4 d		10 17	10 21		10 47			10 51				10 47	10 57	→		11 17	11 21		11 47			11 51		11 47	11 57
Letchworth Garden City d			10 25		→							10 51	11a04				11 25		→					11 51	12a04
Baldock d			10 28									10 55					11 28							11 55	
Ashwell & Morden d												11 00												12 00	
Royston d			10 36									11 04					11 36							12 04	
Meldreth d												11 08												12 08	
Shepreth d												11 11												12 11	
Foxton d												11 14												12 14	
Cambridge a	10 31		10 54				11 03					11 27			11 31		11 54				12 01			12 27	
Arlesey d		10 23									⟵					11 23									
Biggleswade d		10 28						10 59			10 59					11 28						11 59			
Sandy d		10 32						→			11 03					11 32						12 03			
St Neots d		10 39									11 10					11 39						→			
Huntingdon a		10 47									11 18					11 47									
d		10 47									11 18					11 47									
Peterborough 8 a		11 05		10 45		10 56			11 16	11 22	11 34					12 04		11 46		11 56			12 21		

	GR	FC		FC	FC	FC	FC	GR	FC	GR	FC	FC	FC	FC	GR	FC	FC	FC	FC	FC	GR	FC	GR	FC	FC
	R 1	1		1	1	1	1	R 1	1	R 1	1	1	1		R 1	1	1	1	1	1	R 1	1	R 1	1	1
	☕							C ✕		✕					✕						✕		✕		
London Kings Cross 15 ⊖ d	11 35			11 36	11 45		11 52	12 00	12 06	12 10	12 15		12 22		12 30		12 36	12 45		12 52	13 00	13 06	13 10	13 15	13 22
Finsbury Park ⊖ d				11 41			11 57		12 11				12 27	12 04			12 41			12 57		13 11			13 27
Potters Bar d				11 51					12 21			⟵					12 51					13 21			
Hatfield d				11 57					12 27			12 27					12 57					13 27			
Welwyn Garden City 4 d				12 01					→			12 31					13 01					13 31			
Welwyn North d				12 04								12 34					13 04					13 34			
Knebworth d				12 08								12 38					13 08					13 38			
Hertford North d						⟵								12 39					⟵						
Stevenage 4 d	11 54			12 12		12 12	12 16			12 29		12 42	12 46	12 51			13 12		13 12	13 16		13 42			13 46
Hitchin 4 d				→		12 17	12 21					12 47	12 51	12 57			→		13 17	13 21		13 47			13 51
Letchworth Garden City d							12 25					12 51		13a04						13 25		→			
Baldock d							12 28					12 55								13 28					
Ashwell & Morden d												13 00													
Royston d							12 36					13 04								13 36					
Meldreth d												13 08													
Shepreth d												13 11													
Foxton d												13 14													
Cambridge a					12 31		12 54				13 02	13 27				⟵		13 31		13 54				14 02	
Arlesey d						12 23							12 56			12 56			13 23						13 56
Biggleswade d		⟵				12 28							→			13 01			13 28						→
Sandy d		12 03				12 32										13 05			13 32						
St Neots d		12 10				12 39										13 12			13 39						
Huntingdon a		12 18				12 47										13 20			13 47						
d		12 18				12 47										13 20			13 47						
Peterborough 8 a	12 27	12 34				13 07		12 46		13 00					13 16	13 36			14 05		13 46		13 57		

For general notes see front of timetable
For details of catering facilities see Directory of Train Operators

A The Flying Scotsman
B The Northern Lights
C The Highland Chieftain

First Capital Connect will run a Saturday service on Bank Holiday Mondays

London → Stevenage, Cambridge and Peterborough

Network Diagram - see first page of Table 24

		GR	FC	FC	FC	FC	FC	FC	FC	FC	GR		FC	FC	GR	FC	FC	FC	FC	FC	FC	FC	FC	GR	FC	FC
		R 1 ☕ 🚲	1	1		1	1	1	1	1	R 1 🍴 🚲		1	1	R 1 ☕ 🚲	1	1		1	1	1	1	1	R 1 🍴 🚲	1	1
London Kings Cross 15 ⊖	d	13 35				13 36	13 45		13 52	14 06	14 10		14 15	14 22	14 30				14 36	14 45		14 52	15 06	15 10	15 15	15 22
Finsbury Park ⊖	d				13 04	13 41			13 57	14 11				14 27				14 04	14 41			14 57	15 11			15 27
Potters Bar	d					13 51				14 21									14 51				15 21			
Hatfield	d					13 57				14 27									14 57				15 27			
Welwyn Garden City 4	d					14 01				14 31									15 01				15 31			
Welwyn North	d					14 04				14 34									15 04				15 34			
Knebworth	d					14 08				14 38									15 08				15 38			
Hertford North	d				13 39			←										14 39			←					
Stevenage 4	d			←	13 51	14 12		14 12	14 16	14 42				14 46			←	14 51	15 12		15 12	15 16	15 42			15 46
Hitchin 4	d			13 47	13 57	→		14 17	14 21	14 47				14 51			14 47	14 57	→		15 17	15 21	15 47			15 51
Letchworth Garden City	d			13 51	14a04				14 25	→							14 51	15a04				15 25	→			
Baldock	d			13 55					14 28								14 55					15 28				
Ashwell & Morden	d			14 00													15 00									
Royston	d			14 04					14 36								15 04					15 36				
Meldreth	d			14 08													15 08									
Shepreth	d			14 11													15 11									
Foxton	d			14 14													15 14									
Cambridge	a		←	14 27			14 31		14 54				15 04			←	15 27			15 31		15 54			16 03	
Arlesey	d		13 56					14 23						14 56		14 56					15 23					15 56
Biggleswade	d		14 01					14 28						→		15 01					15 28					→
Sandy	d		14 05					14 32								15 05					15 32					
St Neots	d		14 12					14 39								15 12					15 39					
Huntingdon	a		14 20					14 47								15 20					15 47					
	d		14 20					14 47								15 20					15 47					
Peterborough 8	a	14 24	14 36					15 05			14 56				15 16	15 36					16 04			15 56		

		GR	FC	FC	GR	FC	FC	FC	FC	FC	FC	GR	FC	FC	GR	FC	FC	FC	FC		FC	FC	FC	GR	FC	FC
		R 1 🍴 🚲	1		R 1 ☕ 🚲	1	1	1	1	1	1	R 1 ☕ 🚲	1	1	R 1 🍴 🚲	1	1	1	1 A			1	1	R 1 🍴 🚲	1	1
London Kings Cross 15 ⊖	d	15 30			15 35		15 36	15 45		15 52	16 06	16 10	16 15	16 23	16 35	16 36	16 40		16 45		16 52		16 53	17 03		17 06
Finsbury Park ⊖	d			15 04			15 41			15 57	16 11			16 28		16 41					16 57		16u58			17 11
Potters Bar	d						15 51				16 21					16 51					17 13					
Hatfield	d						15 57				16 27					16 57					17 19	←				17 29
Welwyn Garden City 4	d						16 01				16 31					17 01					17 24	17 01				17 33
Welwyn North	d						16 04				16 34					→					→	17 04				17 38
Knebworth	d						16 08				16 38											17 08				→
Hertford North	d			15 39					←																	
Stevenage 4	d		←	15 51	15 54		16 12		16 12	16 16	16 42			16 47				←				17 12	17 19			
Hitchin 4	d		15 47	15 57			→		16 17	16 21	16 47			16 53				16 47				17 17	17 25			
Letchworth Garden City	d		15 51	16a04						16 25	→							16 52	17 10			17 24				
Baldock	d		15 55							16 28								16 55				17 27				
Ashwell & Morden	d		16 00							16 33								17 00				17 32				
Royston	d		16 04							16 37								17 05	17 19			17 37				
Meldreth	d		16 08															17 09				17 41				
Shepreth	d		16 11															17 12				17 44				
Foxton	d		16 14															17 14				17 46				
Cambridge	a		16 30			←		16 33		16 54			17 04					17 30	17 36			18 02			←	
Arlesey	d					15 56			16 23					16 58									17 30		16 58	
Biggleswade	d					16 01			16 28					→									17 35		17 03	
Sandy	d					16 05			16 32														→		17 07	
St Neots	d					16 12			16 39								17 15								17 14	
Huntingdon	a					16 20			16 47								17 22								17 27	
	d					16 20			16 47								17 23								17 27	
Peterborough 8	a	16 16			16 25	16 37			17 04			16 56			17 24		17 41							17 51	17 55	

		FC	FC	GR	FC	FC	FC	FC	FC	GR	FC	FC	FC	FC	GR	FC	FC	FC	FC	GR	FC	FC	FC	FC	FC	FC
		1	1	R 1 B 🍴 🚲	1			1	1	R 1 🍴 🚲	1	1	1	1 A	R 1 ☕ 🚲			1	1	R 1 🍴 🚲	1	1	1	1	1 C	
London Kings Cross 15 ⊖	d	17 07	17 15	17 20			17 22		17 23	17 30		17 36	17 37	17 45	17 50		17 52		17 53	18 03			18 06	18 07	18 15	
Finsbury Park ⊖	d						17 27		17u28			17 41					17 57		17u58				18 11			
Potters Bar	d						17 43										18 13									
Hatfield	d					←	17 49									←	18 19	←								←
Welwyn Garden City 4	d					17 24	17 53	←				17 59				17 53	18 23	17 59					18 29			18 23
Welwyn North	d					17 27	→	17 38				→				17 56	→	18 02					18 32			18 26
Knebworth	d					17 32		17 42								18 01		18 06					→			18 31
Hertford North	d																									
Stevenage 4	d					17 37		17 46	17 50				18 00			18 06		18 11	18 17			←				18 36
Hitchin 4	d					17 42		17 51	17 56				18 05			18 12		18 17	18 23			18 05				18 42
Letchworth Garden City	d		17 40			17a50		17 56					→	18 10		18 16		18 24							18 40	18 46
Baldock	d							17 59										18 28							18 43	
Ashwell & Morden	d							18 04										18 33							18 48	
Royston	d		17 49					18 09						18 19		18a33		18 37							18 53	19a03
Meldreth	d							18 13										18 41								
Shepreth	d							18 16										18 44								
Foxton	d							18 18										18 47								
Cambridge	a		18 07					18 32						18 36				19 02							19 09	
Arlesey	d								18 01		←								18 28		←					
Biggleswade	d								18 06		17 35								18 33		18 06					
Sandy	d				←				→		17 39								→		18 10					
St Neots	d	17 42			17 42						17 47										18 18	18 23		18 42		
Huntingdon	a	→			17 50						17 55										18 25	18 30		18 49		
	d				17 50						17 56										18 26	18 31		18 50		
Peterborough 8	a			18 06	18 10					18 16	18 22				18 38					18 53	18 55	18 58		19 06		

For general notes see front of timetable
For details of catering facilities see Directory of Train Operators

A To Kings Lynn (Table 17)
B **The Hull Executive**
C To Ely (Table 17)

First Capital Connect will run a Saturday service on Bank Holiday Mondays

London → Stevenage, Cambridge and Peterborough

Network Diagram - see first page of Table 24

		GR	FC	FC	FC	FC	GR	FC	FC	FC	FC	FC	FC	FC	FC	FC	GR	GR	FC	FC	FC	FC	FC	FC	FC
		R 1	1		1		R 1	1	1	1	1		1		1		R 1	R 1	1	1	1	1	1		1
											A														
		✕					✕										✕	✕							
London Kings Cross 15 ⊖	d	18 20		18 22	18 23		18 33		18 36	18 37	18 45			18 52	18 53		19 00	19 03		19 06	19 07		19 15		
Finsbury Park ⊖	d			18 27	18u28	18 10			18 41					18 57	18u58	18 40				19 11					
Potters Bar	d			18 43										19 13						19 22					
Hatfield	d			18 49								←		19 19						19 28				←	←
Welwyn Garden City 4	d		←	18 53 →					18 59			18 53	←	19 23 →						19 32 →				19 23	19 32
Welwyn North	d		18 32						19 02 →			18 56	19 02											19 26	19 35
Knebworth	d		18 36									19 01	19 06											19 31	19 39
Hertford North	d					18 40										19 10									
Stevenage 4	d	18 41	18 41		18 47	18 53						19 06	19 11		19 17	19 23								19 36	19 44
Hitchin 4	d		18 47		18 53	18 59						19 12	19 17		19 23	19 29								19 42	19 51
Letchworth Garden City	d		18 54			19a06					19 10	19 16	19 24			19a36							19 40	19a50	19 55
Baldock	d		18 58								19 13		19 28												19 59
Ashwell & Morden	d		19 03								19 18		19 33												20 04
Royston	d		19 07								19 23	19a33	19 37										19 49		20 08
Meldreth	d		19 11										19 41												20 12
Shepreth	d		19 14										19 44												20 15
Foxton	d		19 17										19 47												20 18
Cambridge	a		19 32					←			19 38		20 02						←			←	20 08		20 32
Arlesey	d				18 58										19 28										
Biggleswade	d				19 03 →			18 33		19 05					19 33 →				19 03			19 33			
Sandy	d							18 37											19 07			19 37			
St Neots	d							18 47		19 14									19 19		19 41	19 45			
Huntingdon	a							18 55		19 22									19 27		19 49	19 53			
	d							18 56		19 22									19 27		19 49	19 53			
Peterborough 8	a	19 12					19 22	19 26		19 41							19 46	19 52	19 55		20 05	20 10			

		FC	FC	GR	FC	FC	FC	FC	FC	GR	GR	FC	FC	FC	FC	FC	GR	FC	FC	FC	FC	GR	FC	FC	FC
		1		R 1	1	1	1	1		R 1	R 1	1	1	1	1	1	R 1	1	1	1		R 1	1	1	1
							A							A											A
				✕						✕	✕						☕					☕			
London Kings Cross 15 ⊖	d	19 23		19 33		19 36	19 45	19 52		20 00	20 03	20 06	20 07	20 15		20 22	20 30		20 36	20 52		21 00	21 06	21 07	21 15
Finsbury Park ⊖	d	19 28	19 02			19 41		19 57	19 32			20 11				20 27			20 41	20 57	20 32		21 11		
Potters Bar	d					19 51						20 21							20 51				21 21		
Hatfield	d					19 57						20 27			←				20 57				21 27		
Welwyn Garden City 4	d					20 01						20 31 →			20 31				21 01				21 31 →		
Welwyn North	d					20 04									20 34				21 04						
Knebworth	d					20 08									20 38				21 08						
Hertford North	d		19 37						20 06												21 07				
Stevenage 4	d	19 49	19 52			20 12		20 16	20 20						20 42	20 46			21 12	21 16	21 20	21 20			
Hitchin 4	d	19 55	19 59			20 17		20 21	20 27						20 47	20 51			21 17	21 21	21 28				
Letchworth Garden City	d		20a05			20a23	20 10	20 28	20a35					20 40	20 51				21a23	21 28	21a35				21 40
Baldock	d							20 31							20 55					21 31					
Ashwell & Morden	d							20 36							21 00					21 36					
Royston	d						20 19	20 40						20 49	21 04					21 40					21 49
Meldreth	d							20 44							21 08					21 44					
Shepreth	d							20 47							21 11					21 47					
Foxton	d							20 49							21 14					21 49					
Cambridge	a				←		20 36	21 03						21 06	21 27			←		22 03					22 06
Arlesey	d	20 01 →			20 01											20 56 →		20 56							
Biggleswade	d				20 06													21 01						21 35	
Sandy	d				20 09													21 05							
St Neots	d				20 17								20 41					21 12						21 44	
Huntingdon	a				20 24								20 49					21 20						21 51	
	d				20 24								20 49					21 20						21 51	
Peterborough 8	a			20 20	20 41					20 46	20 51		21 05				21 20	21 36				21 53		22 07	

		FC	FC	GR	FC	FC	FC	FC	GR	FC	FC	FC	FC	FC	FC	FC	FC	FC	FC	FC	FC	GR	FC	FC
		1	1	R 1	1	1	1		R 1	1	1	1	1		1	1		1	1	1	1	R 1	1	1
											A								B		MX			
				☕					☕													☕		
London Kings Cross 15 ⊖	d		21 22	21 30		21 36	21 52		22 00	22 06	22 15		22 22	22 26	22 36	22 52	←	23 06	23 15		23 22	23 30		23 36
Finsbury Park ⊖	d		21 27			21 41	21 57	21 32		22 11			22 27	22 32 →	22 41	22 57	22 32	23 11			23 27			23 41
Potters Bar	d					21 51				22 21					22 51			23 21						23 51
Hatfield	d	←				21 57				22 27		←			22 57			23 27		←				23 57
Welwyn Garden City 4	d	21 31				22 01				22 31 →		22 31			23 01			23 31 →		23 31				00 01
Welwyn North	d	21 34				22 04						22 34			23 04					23 34				00 04
Knebworth	d	21 38				22 08						22 38			23 08					23 38				00 08
Hertford North	d							22 07									23 07							
Stevenage 4	d	21 42	21 46			22 12	22 16	22 20				22 42	22 46		23 12	23 16	23 20			23 42	23 46			00 12
Hitchin 4	d	21 47	21 51			22 17	22 21	22 25				22 50	22 54		23 20	23 24	23 28			23 50	23 54			00 20
Letchworth Garden City	d	21 51				22a23	22 28	22a33			22 45	22 54			23a26	23 31	23a36		23 45	23 54				00a29
Baldock	d	21 55					22 31					22 58				23 34				23 58				
Ashwell & Morden	d	22 00					22 36					23 03				23 39				00 03				
Royston	d	22 04					22 40				22 54	23 07				23 44			23 54	00 07				
Meldreth	d	22 08										23 11								00 11				
Shepreth	d	22 11										23 14								00 14				
Foxton	d	22 14										23 17								00 17				
Cambridge	a	22 27			←		22 57				23 10	23 29				00 01			00 10	00 29			←	
Arlesey	d		21 56 →		21 56								22 59								23 59 →		23 59	
Biggleswade	d				22 01								23 04										00 04	
Sandy	d				22 05								23 08										00 08	
St Neots	d				22 12								23 15										00 15	
Huntingdon	a				22 20								23 26										00 26	
	d				22 20								23 26										00 26	
Peterborough 8	a			22 16	22 36				22 46				23 42									00s23	00 42	

For general notes see front of timetable
For details of catering facilities see Directory of Train Operators

A To Kings Lynn (Table 17)
B Fridays to Kings Lynn (Table 17). Mondays to Thursdays to Ely (Table 17)

London → Stevenage, Cambridge and Peterborough

Network Diagram - see first page of Table 24

Station		FC	FC	FC	FC	FC	FC	FC	FC	FC	FC	FC	FC	GR	FC	FC	FC	FC		FC	FC	GR	FC	GR	FC	FC
		1	1	1	1	1	1	1	1	1	1	1	1	R 1	1	1	1	1		1	1	R 1	1	R 1	1	1
London Kings Cross 15 ⊖	d	23p06	23p22	23p36	00 01	00 04	00 07	00 36	01 06	01 36	05 22	05 45	06 06	06 15		06 22	06 36	06 45			06 52	07 00	07 06	07 10	07 22	07 36
Finsbury Park ⊖	d	23p11	23p27	23p41			00 12	00 41	01 11	01 41	05 27	05 50	06 11			06 27	06 41				06 57		07 11		07 27	07 41
Potters Bar	d	23p21		23p51				00 51		01 58	05 37		06 21		←		06 51						07 21			07 51
Hatfield	d	23p27		23p57				00 57		02 04	05 43		06 27		06 27		06 57						07 27			07 57
Welwyn Garden City 4	d	23p31		00 01				01 01		02 08	05 47		→		06 31		07 01						07 31			08 01
Welwyn North	d	23p34		00 04				01s04		02s11	05 50				06 34		07 04						07 34			08 04
Knebworth	d	23p38		00 08				01s08		02s15	05 54				06 38		07 08						07 38			08 08
Hertford North	d						00 39		01 38											←						
Stevenage 4	d	23p42	23p46	00 12		00s23	00 48	01 12	01 47	02 18	05 58	06 08		06 34	06 42	06 46	07 12			07 12	07 16		07 42		07 46	08 12
Hitchin 4	d	23p50	23p54	00 20		00s38	00 56	01 17	01 52	02 23	06 06	06 13			06 47	06 51	→			07 17	07 21		07 47		07 51	08 17
Letchworth Garden City	d	23p54		00a29		00s41	01 00		02a06			06 16			06 51						07 25		07 51			
Baldock	d	23p58					01 04					06 19			06 55						07 28		07 55			
Ashwell & Morden	d	00 03					01 09					06 24			07 00						07 33		08 00			
Royston	d	00 07				00s50	01 13					06 29			07 04						07 37		08 04			
Meldreth	d	00 11					01 17					06 32			07 08						07 41		08 08			
Shepreth	d	00 14					01 20					06 35			07 11						07 44		08 11			
Foxton	d	00 17					01 23					06 38			07 14						07 46		08 14			
Cambridge	a	00 29				01 07	01 39					06 50			07 27			07 31			07 59		08 27			
Arlesey	d		23p59					01s28			06 11					06 56				07 23					07 56	08 23
Biggleswade	d		00 04		00s40			01s33		02s38	06 16					07 01				07 28					08 01	08 28
Sandy	d		00 08					01s37			06 20					07 05				07 32					08 05	→
St Neots	d		00 15		00s49			01s45		02s48	06 28					07 12				07 39					08 12	
Huntingdon	a		00 26		01s00			01s55		02s59	06 35					07 20				07 47					08 20	
	d		00 26								06 35					07 20				07 47					08 20	
Peterborough 8	a		00 42		01 20			02 17		03 21	06 56			07 05		07 36				08 05		07 46		07 56	08 36	

Station		FC	FC	GR	FC	GR	FC	FC	FC	GR	FC	FC	FC		FC	FC	FC	GR	FC	FC	FC	GR	FC	FC	FC	FC
		1	1	R 1	1	R 1	1	1	1	R 1	1	1	1		1	1	1	R 1	1	1	1	R 1	1	1	1	1
London Kings Cross 15 ⊖	d	07 45	07 52	08 00	08 06	08 10		08 15	08 22	08 30			08 36		08 45		08 52	09 00	09 06	09 15	09 22	09 30			09 36	09 45
Finsbury Park ⊖	d		07 57		08 11				08 27				08 41				08 57		09 11		09 27				09 41	
Potters Bar	d				08 21								08 51						09 21						09 51	
Hatfield	d				08 27								08 57						09 27						09 57	
Welwyn Garden City 4	d				08 31								09 01						09 31						10 01	
Welwyn North	d				08 34								09 04						09 34						10 04	
Knebworth	d				08 38								09 08						09 38						10 08	
Hertford North	d															←										
Stevenage 4	d		08 16	08 20	08 42				08 46	08 49		←	09 12			09 12	09 16		09 42		09 46	09 49		←	10 12	
Hitchin 4	d		08 21		08 47				08 51			08 47	→			09 17	09 21		09 47		09 51			09 47	→	
Letchworth Garden City	d		08 25		→							08 51					09 25		→					09 51		
Baldock	d		08 28									08 55					09 28							09 55		
Ashwell & Morden	d											09 00												10 00		
Royston	d		08 36									09 04					09 36							10 04		
Meldreth	d											09 08												10 08		
Shepreth	d											09 11												10 11		
Foxton	d											09 14												10 14		
Cambridge	a	08 31	08 54					09 02				09 27			09 31		09 54			10 01				10 27		10 31
Arlesey	d						←		08 56		←					09 23					09 56		←			
Biggleswade	d						08 28		09 01		09 01					09 28					10 01		10 01			
Sandy	d						08 32		→		09 05					09 32					→		10 05			
St Neots	d						08 39				09 12					09 39							10 12			
Huntingdon	a						08 47				09 20					09 47							10 20			
	d						08 47				09 20					09 47							10 20			
Peterborough 8	a			08 51		08 56	09 05			09 20	09 37					10 05		09 46				10 20	10 39			

Station		FC	FC	GR	FC	GR	FC	FC		GR	FC	GR	FC	FC	FC	FC	FC	GR	FC	GR	FC	FC	GR	FC	FC	FC
		1	1	R 1	1	R 1	1	1		R 1	1	R 1	1	1	1	1	1	R 1	1	R 1	1	1	R 1	1	1	1
				A						B																
London Kings Cross 15 ⊖	d		09 52	10 00	10 06	10 10	10 15	10 22		10 30	10 36	10 40			10 45		10 52	11 00	11 06	11 10	11 15	11 22	11 30			11 36
Finsbury Park ⊖	d		09 57		10 11			10 27			10 41						10 57		11 11			11 27				11 41
Potters Bar	d				10 21						10 51								11 21							11 51
Hatfield	d				10 27						10 57								11 27							11 57
Welwyn Garden City 4	d				10 31						11 01								11 31							12 01
Welwyn North	d				10 34						11 04								11 34							12 04
Knebworth	d				10 38						11 08								11 38							12 08
Hertford North	d	←														←										
Stevenage 4	d	10 12	10 16		10 42			10 46			11 12			←		11 12	11 16		11 42			11 46	11 50		←	12 12
Hitchin 4	d	10 17	10 21		10 47			10 51			→			10 47		11 17	11 21		11 47			11 51			11 47	→
Letchworth Garden City	d		10 25		→									10 51			11 25		→						11 51	
Baldock	d		10 28											10 55			11 28								11 55	
Ashwell & Morden	d													11 00											12 00	
Royston	d		10 36											11 04			11 36								12 04	
Meldreth	d													11 08											12 08	
Shepreth	d													11 11											12 11	
Foxton	d													11 14											12 14	
Cambridge	a		10 54				11 01						←	11 27	11 31		11 54				12 02				12 27	
Arlesey	d	10 23						10 56					10 56			11 23						11 56		←		
Biggleswade	d	10 28						→					11 01			11 28						12 01		12 01		
Sandy	d	10 32											11 05			11 32						→		12 05		
St Neots	d	10 39											11 12			11 39								12 12		
Huntingdon	a	10 47											11 20			11 47								12 20		
	d	10 47											11 20			11 47								12 20		
Peterborough 8	a	11 05		10 46		10 56				11 16		11 26	11 38			12 05		11 46		11 56			12 21	12 39		

For general notes see front of timetable
For details of catering facilities see
Directory of Train Operators

A The Flying Scotsman
B The Northern Lights

London → Stevenage, Cambridge and Peterborough

Network Diagram - see first page of Table 24

Station		FC	FC		FC	GR	FC	GR	FC	FC	GR	FC	FC	FC	FC	FC	FC	GR	FC	GR	FC		FC	GR	FC	FC
		1	1		1	R 1	1	R 1	1	1	R 1	1	1	1	1	1	1	R 1	1	R 1	1		1	R 1	1	1
						A												B								
London Kings Cross 15 ⊖	d	11 45			11 52	12 00	12 06	12 10	12 15	12 22	12 30			12 36	12 45		12 52	13 00	13 06	13 10	13 15		13 22	13 30		
Finsbury Park ⊖	d				11 57		12 11			12 27				12 41			12 57		13 11				13 27			
Potters Bar	d						12 21							12 51					13 21							
Hatfield	d						12 27							12 57					13 27							
Welwyn Garden City 4	d						12 31							13 01					13 31							
Welwyn North	d						12 34							13 04					13 34							
Knebworth	d						12 38							13 08					13 38							
Hertford North	d		←													←										
Stevenage 4	d		12 12		12 16		12 42			12 46			←	13 12 →		13 12	13 16		13 42				13 46	13 49		←
Hitchin 4	d		12 17		12 21		12 47 →			12 51			12 47			13 17	13 21		13 47 →				13 51			13 47
Letchworth Garden City	d				12 25								12 51				13 25									13 51
Baldock	d				12 28								12 55				13 28									13 55
Ashwell & Morden	d												13 00													14 00
Royston	d				12 36								13 04				13 36									14 04
Meldreth	d												13 08													14 08
Shepreth	d												13 11													14 11
Foxton	d												13 14													14 14
Cambridge	a	12 31			12 54				13 01			←	13 27		13 31		13 54				14 01				←	14 27
Arlesey	d		12 23							12 56 →		12 56				13 23							13 56			
Biggleswade	d		12 28									13 01				13 28							14 01 →		14 01	
Sandy	d		12 32									13 05				13 32									14 05	
St Neots	d		12 39									13 12				13 39									14 12	
Huntingdon	a		12 47									13 20				13 47									14 20	
	d		12 47									13 20				13 47									14 20	
Peterborough 8	a		13 05			12 46		12 56			13 16	13 36				14 05		13 46		13 56				14 20	14 36	

Station		FC	FC	FC	FC	GR	FC	FC	FC	GR	FC	FC	FC	FC	FC	FC		GR	FC	FC	FC	GR	FC	FC	FC	FC
		1	1	1	1	R 1	1	1	1	R 1	1	1	1	1	1	1		R 1	1	1	1	R 1	1	1	1	1
London Kings Cross 15 ⊖	d	13 36	13 45		13 52	14 00	14 06	14 15	14 22	14 30			14 36	14 45		14 52		15 00	15 06	15 15	15 22	15 30			15 36	15 45
Finsbury Park ⊖	d	13 41			13 57		14 11		14 27				14 41			14 57			15 11		15 27				15 41	
Potters Bar	d	13 51					14 21						14 51						15 21						15 51	
Hatfield	d	13 57					14 27						14 57						15 27						15 57	
Welwyn Garden City 4	d	14 01					14 31						15 01						15 31						16 01	
Welwyn North	d	14 04					14 34						15 04						15 34						16 04	
Knebworth	d	14 08					14 38						15 08						15 38						16 08	
Hertford North	d			←											←											
Stevenage 4	d	14 12 →		14 12	14 16		14 42		14 46			←	15 12 →		15 12	15 16			15 42		15 46	15 49		←	16 12 →	
Hitchin 4	d			14 17	14 21		14 47 →		14 51			14 47			15 17	15 21			15 47 →		15 51			15 47		
Letchworth Garden City	d				14 25							14 51				15 25								15 51		
Baldock	d				14 28							14 55				15 28								15 55		
Ashwell & Morden	d											15 00												16 00		
Royston	d				14 36							15 04				15 36								16 04		
Meldreth	d											15 08												16 08		
Shepreth	d											15 11												16 11		
Foxton	d											15 14												16 14		
Cambridge	a		14 31		14 54			15 01			←	15 27		15 31		15 54				16 02			←	16 27		16 31
Arlesey	d			14 23					14 56 →		14 56				15 23						15 56					
Biggleswade	d			14 28							15 01				15 28						16 01 →		16 01			
Sandy	d			14 32							15 05				15 32								16 05			
St Neots	d			14 39							15 12				15 39								16 12			
Huntingdon	a			14 47							15 20				15 47								16 20			
	d			14 47							15 20				15 47								16 20			
Peterborough 8	a			15 05		14 46				15 16	15 36				16 05			15 46				16 20	16 37			

Station		FC	FC	GR	FC	FC	FC	GR	FC	FC	FC		FC	FC	FC	GR	FC	FC	FC	GR	FC	GR	FC	FC	FC	FC
		1	1	R 1	1	1	1	R 1	1	1	1		1	1	1	R 1	1	1	1	R 1	1	R 1	1	1	1	1
London Kings Cross 15 ⊖	d		15 52	16 00	16 06	16 15	16 22	16 30			16 36		16 45		16 52	17 00	17 06	17 15	17 22	17 30	17 36	17 40			17 45	
Finsbury Park ⊖	d		15 57		16 11		16 27				16 41				16 57		17 11		17 27		17 41					
Potters Bar	d				16 21						16 51						17 21				17 51					
Hatfield	d				16 27						16 57						17 27				17 57					
Welwyn Garden City 4	d				16 31						17 01						17 31				18 01					
Welwyn North	d				16 34						17 04						17 34				18 04					
Knebworth	d				16 38						17 08						17 38				18 08					
Hertford North	d	←												←												←
Stevenage 4	d	16 12	16 16		16 42		16 46			←	17 12 →			17 12	17 16		17 42		17 46	17 50	18 12 →			←		18 12
Hitchin 4	d	16 17	16 21		16 47 →		16 51			16 47				17 17	17 21		17 47 →		17 51					17 47		18 17
Letchworth Garden City	d		16 25							16 51					17 25									17 51		
Baldock	d		16 28							16 55					17 28									17 55		
Ashwell & Morden	d									17 00														18 00		
Royston	d		16 36							17 04					17 36									18 04		
Meldreth	d									17 08														18 08		
Shepreth	d									17 11														18 11		
Foxton	d									17 14														18 14		
Cambridge	a		16 54			17 01			←	17 27			17 31		17 54			18 01					←	18 27	18 31	
Arlesey	d	16 23					16 56 →		16 56					17 23					17 56							18 23
Biggleswade	d	16 28							17 01					17 28					18 01 →				18 01			18 28
Sandy	d	16 32							17 05					17 32									18 05			18 32
St Neots	d	16 39							17 12					17 39									18 12			18 39
Huntingdon	a	16 47							17 20					17 47									18 20			18 47
	d	16 47							17 20					17 47									18 20			18 47
Peterborough 8	a	17 05		16 46				17 16	17 36					18 05		17 46				18 21		18 26	18 36			19 05

For general notes see front of timetable
For details of catering facilities see Directory of Train Operators

A The Highland Chieftain
B To Glasgow Central (Table 225)

London → Stevenage, Cambridge and Peterborough

Network Diagram - see first page of Table 24

		FC	GR	GR	FC	FC		FC	FC	FC	GR	FC	GR	FC	FC	FC	FC	GR	FC	FC	FC	GR	FC	FC		FC
			R	R							R		R					R				R				
		1	1	1	1	1		1	1	1	1	1	1	1	1	1	1	1	1	1	1	1	1	1		1
			☕ 🛒	X 🛒							☕ 🛒		☕ 🛒					☕ 🛒				☕ 🛒				
London Kings Cross 15 ⊖	d	17 52	18 00	18 03	18 06	18 08		18 15		18 22	18 35	18 36	18 40		18 45		18 52	19 00	19 06	19 15	19 22	19 30				19 36
Finsbury Park ⊖	d	17 57			18 11					18 27		18 41					18 57		19 11		19 27					19 41
Potters Bar	d				18 21				←			18 51							19 21							19 51
Hatfield	d				18 27 →				18 27			18 57							19 27							19 57
Welwyn Garden City 4	d								18 31			19 01							19 31							20 01
Welwyn North	d								18 34			19 04							19 34							20 04
Knebworth	d								18 38			19 08							19 38							20 08
Hertford North	d															←										
Stevenage 4	d	18 16				18 27			18 42	18 46		19 12 →				19 12	19 16	19 19	19 42		19 46			←		20 12 →
Hitchin 4	d	18 21				18 32			18 47	18 51						19 17	19 21		19 47		19 51			19 47		
Letchworth Garden City	d	18 25							18 51								19 25		→					19 51		
Baldock	d	18 28							18 55								19 28							19 55		
Ashwell & Morden	d								19 00															20 00		
Royston	d	18 36							19 04								19 36							20 04		
Meldreth	d								19 08															20 08		
Shepreth	d								19 11															20 11		
Foxton	d								19 14															20 14		
Cambridge	a	18 54						19 01	19 27					←	19 31		19 54			20 01			←	20 27		
Arlesey	d									18 56 →				18 56		19 23					19 56 →		19 56			
Biggleswade	d													19 01		19 28							20 01			
Sandy	d													19 05		19 32							20 05			
St Neots	d					18 46								19 12		19 39							20 12			
Huntingdon	a					18 53								19 20		19 47							20 20			
	d					18 53								19 20		19 47							20 20			
Peterborough 8	a		18 46	18 52		19 09					19 21		19 26	19 36		20 05		19 50				20 16	20 36			

		FC	FC	FC	GR	FC	FC	GR	FC	FC	FC	FC	FC	FC	FC	FC	FC	FC	FC	FC	FC	FC	FC	FC
					R			R																
		1	1	1	1	1	1	1	1	1	1	1	1	1	1	1	1	1	1	1	1		1	
											A				A				A					
					☕ 🛒			☕ 🛒																
London Kings Cross 15 ⊖	d	19 45		19 52	20 00	20 06	20 22	20 30		20 36	20 52	21 06	21 22	21 36	21 52	22 06	22 22	22 36	23 08	23 12	23 15	23 35	23 50	
Finsbury Park ⊖	d			19 57		20 11	20 27			20 41	20 57	21 11	21 27	21 41	21 57	22 11	22 27	22 41	23 13	23 17	23 20	23 40	23 55	
Potters Bar	d					20 21				20 51		21 21		21 51		22 21		22 51			23 30	00 01		
Hatfield	d					20 27				20 57		21 27		21 57		22 27		22 57			23 36	00 09		←
Welwyn Garden City 4	d					20 31				21 01		21 31		22 01		22 31		23 01			23 40	00b28 →		00b28
Welwyn North	d					20 34				21 04		21 34		22 04		22 34		23 04			23 45			00 31
Knebworth	d					20 38				21 08		21 38		22 08		22 38		23 08			23 49			00 35
Hertford North	d		←																					
Stevenage 4	d		20 12	20 16		20 42	20 46			21 12	21 16	21 42	21 46	22 12	22 16	22 42	22 46	23 12		23 46	23 55			00 41
Hitchin 4	d		20 17	20 21		20 47	20 51			21 17	21 21	21 47	21 51	22 17	22 21	22 47	22 51	23 17		23 51	00 02		00s35	00 49
Letchworth Garden City	d			20 25		20 51					21 25	21 51			22 25	22 51			23 45		00 06			00a57
Baldock	d			20 28		20 55					21 28	21 55			22 28	22 55					00 09			
Ashwell & Morden	d					21 00						22 00				23 00					00 14			
Royston	d			20 36		21 04					21 36	22 04			22 36	23 04			23 55		00 19			
Meldreth	d					21 08						22 08				23 08					00 22			
Shepreth	d					21 11						22 11				23 11					00 25			
Foxton	d					21 14						22 14				23 14					00 28			
Cambridge	a	20 31		20 54		21 27			←		21 54	22 27			22 54	23 28			00 15		00 45			
Arlesey	d		20 23				20 56 →		20 56	21 23			21 56	22 23			22 56	23 23		23 56				
Biggleswade	d		20 28						21 01	21 28			22 01	22 28			23 01	23 28		00 01			00s43	
Sandy	d		20 32						21 05	21 32			22 05	22 32			23 05	23 32		00 05				
St Neots	d		20 39						21 12	21 39			22 12	22 39			23 12	23 39		00 12			00s53	
Huntingdon	a		20 47						21 20	21 47			22 20	22 47			23 20	23 47		00 20			01s00	
	d		20 47						21 20	21 47			22 20	22 47			23 20	23 47		00 20				
Peterborough 8	a		21 05		20 46			21 16	21 36	22 05			22 36	23 05			23 43	00 14		00 42			01 19	

For general notes see front of timetable
For details of catering facilities see Directory of Train Operators

A To Kings Lynn (Table 17)
b Arr. 0015

Sundays

until 13 July

London → Stevenage, Cambridge and Peterborough

Network Diagram - see first page of Table 24

		FC	FC	FC	FC	FC	FC	FC	FC	FC	FC	FC		FC	FC	FC	FC	FC	FC	FC	FC	FC	FC	GR		FC
		1	1		1	1		1	1	🚌	🚌	1		🚌	🚌	1	🚌	1 A	🚌	🚌	1	🚌	1	R 1 🍴		1
London Kings Cross 15 ⊖	d	23p12	23p15	23p35	23p50	00 04		00 07	00 36												08 30		08 48	09 00		09 04
Finsbury Park ⊖	d	23p17	23p20	23p40	23p55	00 10		00 12	00 41												08 35		08 52			09 09
Potters Bar	d		23p30	00 01					00 51																	09 19
Hatfield	d		23p36	00 09			←		00 57																	09 25
Welwyn Garden City 4	d		23p40	00b28			00b28		01 03		06 41			07 11			07 41		08 11			08 38				09 29
Welwyn North	d		23p45	→			00 31		01s06		06 51			07 21			07 51		08 21			08 48				09 33
Knebworth	d		23p49				00 35		01s10		07 01			07 31			08 01		08 31			08 58				09 37
Hertford North	d							00 39							07 16					06 16						
Stevenage 4	d	23p46	23p55			00 36	00 41	00 48	01 14		07 08			07 38	07a47		08 08		08 38	06a47	08 53	09a05	09 10	09 20		09 40
Hitchin 4	d	23p51	00 02		00s35	00 44	00 49	00 56	01 19		07a28	07 36		07a58		08 00	08a28	08 33	08a58		08 58		09 21			09 45
Letchworth Garden City	d		00 06			00s50	00a57	01 00	01a26	01 35		07 39						08 36					09 25			→
Baldock	d		00 09					01 04				07 42						08 39					09 28			
Ashwell & Morden	d		00 14					01 09				07 47						08 44								
Royston	d		00 19			01s00		01 13				07 52						08 49					09 36			
Meldreth	d		00 22					01 17				07 55						08 52								
Shepreth	d		00 25					01 20				07 58						08 55								
Foxton	d		00 28					01 23				08 01						08 58								
Cambridge	a		00 45			01 16		01 39				08 14						09 15					09 54			
Arlesey	d	23p56								01s47						08 05					09 03					
Biggleswade	d	00 01			00s43					02s07						08 10					09 08					
Sandy	d	00 05								02s17						08 14					09 12					
St Neots	d	00 12			00s53					02s37						08 21					09 19					
Huntingdon	a	00 20			01s00					03s07						08 29					09 27					
	d	00 20														08 29					09 27					
Peterborough 8	a	00 42			01 19					03 42						08 48					09 45			09 49		

		GR	FC	FC	GR	FC	FC	FC	FC	GR	FC	GR		FC	FC	FC	GR	FC	FC	FC	GR	FC	GR	FC		FC
		R 1 🍴	1	1	R 1 🍴	1	1	🚌	1	R 1 B 🍴	1	R 1 🍴		1	1	🚌	R 1 🍴	1	1	1	R 1 C 🍴	1	R 1 🍴	1		1
London Kings Cross 15 ⊖	d	09 10	09 15	09 18	09 30				09 48	10 00	10 04	10 10		10 15	10 18		10 30			10 48	11 00	11 04	11 10	11 15		
Finsbury Park ⊖	d			09 23					09 52		10 09				10 23					10 52		11 09				
Potters Bar	d										10 19											11 19				
Hatfield	d										10 25											11 25				
Welwyn Garden City 4	d										10 29											11 29				
Welwyn North	d										10 33											11 33				
Knebworth	d										10 37											11 37				
Hertford North	d							09 16								10 16										
Stevenage 4	d			09 44			←	09a47	10 10		10 40				10 44	10a47	10 49		←	11 10		11 40				←
Hitchin 4	d			09 51			09 45		10 21		10 45				10 51				10 45	11 21		11 45				11 45
Letchworth Garden City	d						09 51		10 25		→								10 51	11 25		→				11 51
Baldock	d						09 55		10 28										10 55	11 28						11 55
Ashwell & Morden	d						10 00												11 00							12 00
Royston	d						10 04		10 36										11 04	11 36						12 04
Meldreth	d						10 08												11 08							12 08
Shepreth	d						10 11												11 11							12 11
Foxton	d						10 14												11 14							12 14
Cambridge	a		10 01			←	10 27		10 54					11 01					11 27	11 54				12 01		12 27
Arlesey	d			09 56		09 56									10 56			←								
Biggleswade	d			→		10 01									11 01			11 01								
Sandy	d					10 05									→			11 05								
St Neots	d					10 12												11 12								
Huntingdon	a					10 20												11 20								
	d					10 20												11 20								
Peterborough 8	a	09 54			10 14	10 36				10 45		10 59					11 18	11 36			11 44		11 54			

For general notes see front of timetable
For details of catering facilities see Directory of Train Operators

A To Kings Lynn (Table 17)
B The Flying Scotsman
C The Northern Lights

b Arr. 0015

Table 25

Sundays until 13 July

London → Stevenage, Cambridge and Peterborough

Network Diagram - see first page of Table 24

		FC	FC	FC	GR	FC	GR	FC	FC	FC	FC	GR		FC	FC	GR	FC	GR	FC	FC	FC	GR	FC	FC		FC
					R		R					R				R		R				R				
		1		1	1	1	1	1	1	1		1		1	1	1	1	1	1	1		1	1	1		1
												A														
			[bus]								[bus]										[bus]					
					[catering]		[catering]					[catering]				[catering]		[catering]				[catering]				
London Kings Cross 15 ⊖	d	11 18		11 48	12 00	12 04	12 10	12 15		12 18		12 30			12 48	13 00	13 04	13 10	13 15	13 18		13 30				13 48
Finsbury Park ⊖	d	11 23		11 52		12 09				12 23					12 52		13 09			13 23						13 52
Potters Bar	d					12 19			←								13 19									
Hatfield	d					12 25 →			12 25								13 25									
Welwyn Garden City 4	d								12 29								13 29									
Welwyn North	d								12 33								13 33									
Knebworth	d								12 37								13 37									
Hertford North	d		11 16								12 16										13 16					
Stevenage 4	d	11 44	11a47	12 10			12 29		12 40	12 44	12a47				13 10	13 19	13 40			13 44	13a47	13 49		←		14 10
Hitchin 4	d	11 51		12 21					12 45	12 51					13 21		13 45			13 51				13 45		14 21
Letchworth Garden City	d			12 25					12 51						13 25		→							13 51		14 25
Baldock	d			12 28					12 55						13 28									13 55		14 28
Ashwell & Morden	d								13 00															14 00		
Royston	d			12 36					13 04						13 36									14 04		14 36
Meldreth	d								13 08															14 08		
Shepreth	d								13 11															14 11		
Foxton	d								13 14															14 14		
Cambridge	a			12 54				13 02	13 27					←	13 54				14 01					14 27		14 54
Arlesey	d	11 56								12 56 →				12 56						13 56			←			
Biggleswade	d	12 01												13 01						14 01 →			14 01			
Sandy	d	12 05												13 05									14 05			
St Neots	d	12 12												13 12									14 12			
Huntingdon	a	12 20												13 20									14 20			
	d	12 20												13 20									14 20			
Peterborough 8	a	12 36			12 44		12 58					13 14		13 36		13 48		13 56				14 18	14 37			

		GR	FC	GR	FC	FC	GR	FC	FC	FC	FC	GR		FC	GR	FC	FC	FC	GR	FC	FC	FC	GR	FC		GR
		R		R			R					R			R				R				R			R
		1	1	1	1	1	1	1		1	1	1		1	1	1	1		1	1	1	1	1	1		1
									[bus]									[bus]								
		[catering]		[catering]			[catering]					[catering]			[catering]				[catering]				[catering]			[catering]
London Kings Cross 15 ⊖	d	14 00	14 04	14 10	14 15	14 18	14 30				14 48	15 00		15 04	15 10	15 15	15 18		15 30			15 48	16 00	16 04		16 10
Finsbury Park ⊖	d		14 09			14 23					14 52			15 09			15 23					15 52		16 09		
Potters Bar	d		14 19											15 19										16 19		
Hatfield	d		14 25											15 25										16 25 →		
Welwyn Garden City 4	d		14 29											15 29												
Welwyn North	d		14 33											15 33												
Knebworth	d		14 37											15 37												
Hertford North	d								14 16									15 16								
Stevenage 4	d		14 40			14 44			14a47	←	15 10	15 19		15 40			15 44	15a47			←	16 10				16 29
Hitchin 4	d		14 45			14 51				14 45	15 21			15 45			15 51				15 45	16 21				
Letchworth Garden City	d		→							14 51	15 25			→							15 51	16 25				
Baldock	d									14 55	15 28										15 55	16 28				
Ashwell & Morden	d									15 00											16 00					
Royston	d									15 04	15 36										16 04	16 36				
Meldreth	d									15 08											16 08					
Shepreth	d									15 11											16 11					
Foxton	d									15 14											16 14					
Cambridge	a				15 01			←		15 27	15 54					16 01				←	16 27	16 54				
Arlesey	d					14 56 →		14 56									15 56 →			15 56						
Biggleswade	d							15 01												16 01						
Sandy	d							15 05												16 05						
St Neots	d							15 12												16 12						
Huntingdon	a							15 20												16 20						
	d							15 20												16 20						
Peterborough 8	a	14 44		14 54			15 13	15 36				15 48			15 54				16 14	16 36			16 44			16 58

		FC	FC	FC	FC	GR	GR	FC	FC	GR	FC	GR		FC	FC	FC	GR	FC	FC	FC	GR	FC	GR	FC		FC
						R	R			R		R					R				R		R			
		1	1	1		1	1	1	1	1	1	1		1	1		1	1	1	1	1	1	1	1		1
					[bus]											[bus]										
						[catering]	[restaurant]			[catering]		[catering]					[catering]				[catering]		[catering]			
London Kings Cross 15 ⊖	d	16 15		16 22		16 30	16 40		16 48	17 00	17 06	17 10		17 15	17 22		17 30			17 52	18 00	18 06	18 10	18 15		18 22
Finsbury Park ⊖	d			16 27					16 52		17 11				17 27					17 57		18 11				18 27
Potters Bar	d		←								17 21											18 21				
Hatfield	d		16 25								17 27											18 27				
Welwyn Garden City 4	d		16 29								17 31											18 31				
Welwyn North	d		16 33								17 34											18 34				
Knebworth	d		16 37								17 38											18 38				
Hertford North	d				16 16											17 16										
Stevenage 4	d		16 40	16 46	16a47	16 49			17 10		17 42				17 46	17a47	17 49		←	18 16		18 42				18 46
Hitchin 4	d		16 45	16 51					17 21		17 47				17 51				17 47	18 21		18 47				18 51
Letchworth Garden City	d		16 51						17 25		→								17 51	18 25		→				
Baldock	d		16 55						17 28										17 55	18 28						
Ashwell & Morden	d		17 00																18 00							
Royston	d		17 04						17 36										18 04	18 36						
Meldreth	d		17 08																18 08							
Shepreth	d		17 11																18 11							
Foxton	d		17 14																18 14							
Cambridge	a	17 02	17 27						17 54					18 01					18 27	18 54				19 01		
Arlesey	d			16 56				←							17 56			←								18 56
Biggleswade	d			17 01 →				17 01							18 01 →			18 01								19 01 →
Sandy	d							17 05										18 05								
St Neots	d							17 12										18 12								
Huntingdon	a							17 20										18 20								
	d							17 20										18 20								
Peterborough 8	a					17 18	17 24	17 37		17 46		17 54					18 18	18 38			18 44		18 54			

For general notes see front of timetable
For details of catering facilities see
Directory of Train Operators

A The Highland Chieftain

Table 25

Sundays
until 13 July

London → Stevenage, Cambridge and Peterborough

Network Diagram - see first page of Table 24

		GR R 1 🍴	GR R 1 🍴	FC 1	FC 1	FC 1	GR R 1 🍴	FC 1	GR R 1 🍴	FC 1	FC 1	GR R 1 🍴		GR R 1 🍴	FC 1	FC 1	FC 1	GR R 1 🍴	GR R 1 🍴	FC 1	FC 1	FC 1	GR R 1 🍴	FC 1		FC 1
London Kings Cross 15 ⊖	d	18 30	18 40			18 52	19 00	19 06	19 10	19 15	19 22	19 30		19 35			19 52	20 00	20 03	20 06	20 15	20 22	20 30			
Finsbury Park ⊖	d					18 57		19 11			19 27						19 57			20 11		20 27				
Potters Bar	d							19 21												20 21						
Hatfield	d							19 27												20 27						
Welwyn Garden City 4	d							19 31												20 31						
Welwyn North	d							19 34												20 34						
Knebworth	d							19 38												20 38						
Hertford North	d																									
Stevenage 4	d	18 50			←	19 16		19 42			19 46	19 49		19 54		←	20 16			20 42		20 46				←
Hitchin 4	d				18 47	19 21		19 47			19 51					19 47	20 21			20 47		20 51				20 47
Letchworth Garden City	d				18 51	19 25		→								19 51	20 25			→						20 51
Baldock	d				18 55	19 28										19 55	20 28									20 55
Ashwell & Morden	d				19 00											20 00										21 00
Royston	d				19 04	19 36										20 04	20 36									21 04
Meldreth	d				19 08											20 08										21 08
Shepreth	d				19 11											20 11										21 11
Foxton	d				19 14											20 14								←		21 14
Cambridge	a				19 27	19 54				20 01						20 27	20 54				21 01					21 27
Arlesey	d			←							19 56				←							20 56 →		20 56		
Biggleswade	d			19 01							20 01 →				20 01									21 01		
Sandy	d			19 05											20 05									21 05		
St Neots	d			19 12											20 12									21 12		
Huntingdon	a			19 20											20 20									21 20		
	d			19 20											20 20									21 20		
Peterborough 8	a	19 19	19 25	19 36			19 44		19 54			20 18		20 24	20 36			20 44	20 48				21 14	21 36		

		FC 1	GR R 1 🍴	FC 1	FC 1	FC 1	GR R 1 🍴	FC 1	FC 1	FC 1	GR R 1 🍴	FC 1		GR R 1 🍴	FC 1	FC 1	FC 1	FC 1	FC 1	FC 1 A	FC 1	FC 1	FC 🚌	FC		
London Kings Cross 15 ⊖	d	20 52	21 00	21 06	21 15	21 22	21 30			21 52	22 00	22 06		22 10	22 15		22 22	22 52	23 06	23 15		23 25		23 41		
Finsbury Park ⊖	d	20 57		21 11		21 27				21 57		22 11					22 27	22 57	23 11			23 30		23 47		
Potters Bar	d			21 21								22 21							23 21					00 08		
Hatfield	d			21 27								22 27							23 27		←			00 16		
Welwyn Garden City 4	d			21 31								22 31							23 31		23 31			00 20		
Welwyn North	d			21 34								22 34							→		23 36			00 23		
Knebworth	d			21 38								22 38									23 40			00 28		
Hertford North	d																						23 28			
Stevenage 4	d	21 16		21 42		21 46			←	22 16		22 42				←	22 46	23 17			23 43	23 49	23a59	00 31		
Hitchin 4	d	21 21		21 47		21 51			21 47	22 21		22 47				22 47	22 51	23 26			23 53	00 04		00a47		
Letchworth Garden City	d	21 25		→					21 51	22 25		→				22 51		23 30		23 52	23 57					
Baldock	d	21 28							21 55	22 28						22 55		23 33			23 59					
Ashwell & Morden	d								22 00							23 00					00 05					
Royston	d	21 36							22 04	22 36						23 04		23 41		00 01	00 10					
Meldreth	d								22 08							23 08					00 13					
Shepreth	d								22 11							23 11					00 16					
Foxton	d								22 14							23 14					00 18					
Cambridge	a	21 54			22 01			←	22 27	22 54					23 10	23 29		00 01		00 19	00 35					
Arlesey	d					21 56 →		21 56									22 56					00 10				
Biggleswade	d							22 01									23 01					00 15				
Sandy	d							22 05									23 05					00 18				
St Neots	d							22 12									23 12					00 26				
Huntingdon	a							22 20									23 27					00 33				
	d							22 20									23 27					00 33				
Peterborough 8	a		21 44				22 14	22 36			22 44			22s59			23 49					00 55				

For general notes see front of timetable
For details of catering facilities see
Directory of Train Operators

A To Ely (Table 17)

Table 25

Sundays

20 July to 7 September

London → Stevenage, Cambridge and Peterborough

Network Diagram - see first page of Table 24

		FC	FC	FC	FC	FC	FC	FC	FC	FC	FC	FC	FC	FC	FC	FC	FC	FC	FC	FC	GR	FC	GR	FC	FC	GR
																					R		R			R
		1	1		1	1		1	1			1		1		1		1		1	1	1	1	1	1	1
																A										
										Bus	Bus		Bus		Bus		Bus		Bus		Catering		Catering			Catering
London Kings Cross 15	⊖ d	23p12	23p15	23p35	23p50	00 04		00 07	00 36									08 30		08 48	09 00	09 04	09 10	09 15	09 18	09 30
Finsbury Park	⊖ d	23p17	23p20	23p40	23p55	00 10		00 12	00 41									08 35		08 52		09 09			09 23	
Potters Bar	d		23p30	00 01					00 51													09 19				
Hatfield	d		23p36	00 09			←		00 57													09 25				
Welwyn Garden City 4	d		23p40	00b28			00b28		01 03		06 41		07 11		07 41		08 11		08 38			09 29				
Welwyn North	d		23p45	→			00 31		01s06		06 51		07 21		07 51		08 21		08 48			09 33				
Knebworth	d		23p49				00 35		01s10		07 01		07 31		08 01		08 31		08 58			09 37				
Hertford North	d							00 39																		
Stevenage 4	d	23p46	23p55			00 36	00 41	00 48	01 14		07 08		07 38		08 08		08 38	08 53	09a05	09 10	09 20	09 40			09 44	
Hitchin 4	d	23p51	00 02		00s35	00 44	00 49	00 56	01 19		07a28	07 36	07a58	08 00	08a28	08 33	08a58	08 58		09 21		09 45			09 51	
Letchworth Garden City	d		00 06			00s50	00a57	01 00	01a26	01 35		07 39				08 36				09 25		→				
Baldock	d		00 09					01 04				07 42				08 39				09 28						
Ashwell & Morden	d		00 14					01 09				07 47				08 44										
Royston	d		00 19			01s00		01 13				07 52				08 49				09 36						
Meldreth	d		00 22					01 17				07 55				08 52										
Shepreth	d		00 25					01 20				07 58				08 55										
Foxton	d		00 28					01 23				08 01				08 58										
Cambridge	a		00 45			01 16		01 39				08 14				09 15				09 54				10 01		
Arlesey	d	23p56								01s47				08 05				09 03							09 56 →	
Biggleswade	d	00 01			00s43					02s07				08 10				09 08								
Sandy	d	00 05								02s17				08 14				09 12								
St Neots	d	00 12			00s53					02s37				08 21				09 19								
Huntingdon	a	00 20			01s00					03s07				08 29				09 27								
	d	00 20												08 29				09 27								
Peterborough 8	a	00 42			01 19					03 42				08 48				09 45			09 49		09 54			10 14

		FC	FC	FC	GR	FC	GR	FC	FC	GR	FC	FC	FC	GR	FC	GR	FC	FC	FC	FC	GR	FC	GR	FC	FC	FC
					R		R			R				R		R					R		R			
		1	1	1	1	1	1	1	1	1	1	1	1	1	1	1	1	1	1	1	1	1	1	1	1	1
					B									C												
					Catering		Catering			Catering				Catering		Catering					Catering		Catering			
London Kings Cross 15	⊖ d			09 48	10 00	10 04	10 10	10 15	10 18	10 30			10 48	11 00	11 04	11 10	11 15		11 18	11 48	12 00	12 04	12 10	12 15		12 18
Finsbury Park	⊖ d			09 52		10 09			10 23				10 52		11 09				11 23	11 52		12 09				12 23
Potters Bar	d					10 19									11 19							12 19			←	
Hatfield	d					10 25									11 25							12 25 →			12 25	
Welwyn Garden City 4	d					10 29									11 29										12 29	
Welwyn North	d					10 33									11 33										12 33	
Knebworth	d					10 37									11 37										12 37	
Hertford North	d																									
Stevenage 4	d		←	10 10		10 40			10 44	10 49		←	11 10		11 40			←	11 44	12 10			12 29		12 40	12 44
Hitchin 4	d		09 45	10 21		10 45			10 51			10 45	11 21		11 45			11 45	11 51	12 21					12 45	12 51
Letchworth Garden City	d		09 51	10 25		→						10 51	11 25		→			11 51		12 25					12 51	
Baldock	d		09 55	10 28								10 55	11 28					11 55		12 28					12 55	
Ashwell & Morden	d		10 00									11 00						12 00							13 00	
Royston	d		10 04	10 36								11 04	11 36					12 04		12 36					13 04	
Meldreth	d		10 08									11 08						12 08							13 08	
Shepreth	d		10 11									11 11						12 11							13 11	
Foxton	d		10 14									11 14						12 14							13 14	
Cambridge	a	←	10 27	10 54				11 01				11 27	11 54				12 01	12 27		12 54				13 02	13 27	
Arlesey	d	09 56							10 56		←								11 56							12 56 →
Biggleswade	d	10 01							11 01 →		11 01								12 01							
Sandy	d	10 05									11 05								12 05							
St Neots	d	10 12									11 12								12 12							
Huntingdon	a	10 20									11 20								12 20							
	d	10 20									11 20								12 20							
Peterborough 8	a	10 36			10 45		10 59			11 18	11 36			11 44		11 54			12 36		12 44		12 58			

For general notes see front of timetable
For details of catering facilities see Directory of Train Operators

A To Kings Lynn (Table 17)
B The Flying Scotsman
C The Northern Lights

b Arr. 0015

Table 25

Sundays

20 July to 7 September

London → Stevenage, Cambridge and Peterborough

Network Diagram - see first page of Table 24

	GR R 1	FC 1	FC 1	GR R 1	FC 1	GR R 1	FC 1	FC 1	GR R 1	FC 1	FC 1	FC 1	GR R 1	FC 1	GR R 1	FC 1	FC 1	GR R 1	FC 1	FC 1	FC 1	GR R 1	FC 1	GR R 1	FC 1
	A																								
London Kings Cross 15 ⊖ d	12 30		12 48	13 00	13 04	13 10	13 15	13 18	13 30			13 48	14 00	14 04	14 10	14 15	14 18	14 30			14 48	15 00	15 04	15 10	15 15
Finsbury Park ⊖ d			12 52		13 09			13 23				13 52		14 09			14 23				14 52		15 09		
Potters Bar d					13 19									14 19									15 19		
Hatfield d					13 25									14 25									15 25		
Welwyn Garden City 4 d					13 29									14 29									15 29		
Welwyn North d					13 33									14 33									15 33		
Knebworth d					13 37									14 37									15 37		
Hertford North d																									
Stevenage 4 d			13 10	13 19	13 40			13 44	13 49		←	14 10		14 40			14 44			←	15 10	15 19	15 40		
Hitchin 4 d			13 21		13 45			13 51			13 45	14 21		14 45			14 51			14 45	15 21		15 45		
Letchworth Garden City d			13 25		→						13 51	14 25		→						14 51	15 25		→		
Baldock d			13 28								13 55	14 28								14 55	15 28				
Ashwell & Morden d											14 00									15 00					
Royston d			13 36								14 04	14 36								15 04	15 36				
Meldreth d											14 08									15 08					
Shepreth d											14 11									15 11					
Foxton d											14 14									15 14					
Cambridge a		←	13 54				14 01				14 27	14 54				15 01			←	15 27	15 54				16 01
Arlesey d		12 56						13 56		←							14 56		14 56						
Biggleswade d		13 01						14 01		14 01							→		15 01						
Sandy d		13 05						→		14 05									15 05						
St Neots d		13 12								14 12									15 12						
Huntingdon a		13 20								14 20									15 20						
Huntingdon d		13 20								14 20									15 20						
Peterborough 8 a	13 14	13 36		13 48		13 56			14 18	14 37			14 44		14 54			15 13	15 36			15 48		15 54	

	FC 1	GR R 1	FC 1	FC 1	FC 1	GR R 1	FC 1	GR R 1	FC 1	FC 1	FC 1	GR R 1	GR R 1	FC 1	FC 1	GR R 1	FC 1	GR R 1	FC 1	FC 1	GR R 1	FC 1	FC 1	FC 1	GR R 1
London Kings Cross 15 ⊖ d	15 18	15 30			15 48	16 00	16 04	16 10	16 15		16 22	16 30	16 40		16 48	17 00	17 06	17 10	17 15	17 22	17 30			17 52	18 00
Finsbury Park ⊖ d	15 23				15 52		16 09				16 27				16 52		17 11			17 27				17 57	
Potters Bar d							16 19			←							17 21								
Hatfield d							16 25			16 25							17 27								
Welwyn Garden City 4 d							→			16 29							17 31								
Welwyn North d										16 33							17 34								
Knebworth d										16 37							17 38								
Hertford North d																									
Stevenage 4 d	15 44			←	16 10			16 29		16 40	16 46	16 49			17 10		17 42			17 46	17 49		←	18 16	
Hitchin 4 d	15 51			15 45	16 21					16 45	16 51				17 21		17 47			17 51			17 47	18 21	
Letchworth Garden City d				15 51	16 25					16 51					17 25		→						17 51	18 25	
Baldock d				15 55	16 28					16 55					17 28								17 55	18 28	
Ashwell & Morden d				16 00						17 00													18 00		
Royston d				16 04	16 36					17 04					17 36								18 04	18 36	
Meldreth d				16 08						17 08													18 08		
Shepreth d				16 11						17 11													18 11		
Foxton d				16 14						17 14													18 14		
Cambridge a			←	16 27	16 54				17 02	17 27					17 54				18 01				18 27	18 54	
Arlesey d	15 56		15 56								16 56			←						17 56		←			
Biggleswade d	→		16 01								17 01			17 01						18 01		18 01			
Sandy d			16 05								→			17 05						→		18 05			
St Neots d			16 12											17 12								18 12			
Huntingdon a			16 20											17 20								18 20			
Huntingdon d			16 20											17 20								18 20			
Peterborough 8 a		16 14	16 36			16 44		16 58				17 18	17 24	17 37		17 46		17 54			18 18	18 38			18 44

	FC 1	GR R 1	FC 1	FC 1	GR R 1	GR R 1	FC 1	FC 1	FC 1	GR R 1	FC 1	GR R 1	FC 1	FC 1	GR R 1	GR R 1	FC 1	FC 1	FC 1	GR R 1	GR R 1	FC 1	FC 1	FC 1	GR R 1
London Kings Cross 15 ⊖ d	18 06	18 10	18 15	18 22	18 30	18 40			18 52	19 00	19 06	19 10	19 15	19 22	19 30	19 35			19 52	20 00	20 03	20 06	20 15	20 22	20 30
Finsbury Park ⊖ d	18 11			18 27					18 57		19 11			19 27					19 57			20 11		20 27	
Potters Bar d	18 21										19 21											20 21			
Hatfield d	18 27										19 27											20 27			
Welwyn Garden City 4 d	18 31										19 31											20 31			
Welwyn North d	18 34										19 34											20 34			
Knebworth d	18 38										19 38											20 38			
Hertford North d																									
Stevenage 4 d	18 42			18 46	18 50			←	19 16		19 42			19 46	19 49	19 54		←	20 16			20 42		20 46	
Hitchin 4 d	18 47			18 51				18 47	19 21		19 47			19 51				19 47	20 21			20 47		20 51	
Letchworth Garden City d	→							18 51	19 25		→							19 51	20 25			→			
Baldock d								18 55	19 28									19 55	20 28						
Ashwell & Morden d								19 00										20 00							
Royston d								19 04	19 36									20 04	20 36						
Meldreth d								19 08										20 08							
Shepreth d								19 11										20 11							
Foxton d								19 14										20 14							
Cambridge a			19 01					19 27	19 54				20 01					20 27	20 54				21 01		
Arlesey d				18 56			←							19 56			←							20 56	
Biggleswade d				19 01			19 01							20 01			20 01							→	
Sandy d				→			19 05							→			20 05								
St Neots d							19 12										20 12								
Huntingdon a							19 20										20 20								
Huntingdon d							19 20										20 20								
Peterborough 8 a		18 54			19 19	19 25	19 36			19 44		19 54			20 18	20 24	20 36			20 44	20 48				21 14

For general notes see front of timetable
For details of catering facilities see
Directory of Train Operators

A The Highland Chieftain

Table 25

Sundays

20 July to 7 September

London → Stevenage, Cambridge and Peterborough

Network Diagram - see first page of Table 24

	FC	FC	FC	GR	FC	FC	FC	GR	FC	FC	FC	GR	FC	GR	FC	FC	FC	FC	FC	FC	FC	FC	FC
				R				R				R		R									
	1	1	1	1	1	1	1	1	1	1	1	1	1	1	1	1	1	1	1	1	1	1	
																				A			
				🍴				🍴				🍴		🍴									
London Kings Cross 15 ⊖ d			20 52	21 00	21 06	21 15	21 22	21 30			21 52	22 00	22 06	22 10	22 15		22 22	22 52	23 06	23 15		23 25	23 41
Finsbury Park ⊖ d			20 57		21 11		21 27				21 57		22 11				22 27	22 57	23 11			23 30	23 47
Potters Bar d					21 21								22 21						23 21				00 08
Hatfield d					21 27								22 27						23 27		←		00 16
Welwyn Garden City 4 d					21 31								22 31						23 31		23 31		00 20
Welwyn North d					21 34								22 34						→		23 36		00 23
Knebworth d					21 38								22 38								23 40		00 28
Hertford North d																							
Stevenage 4 d		←	21 16		21 42		21 46			←	22 16		22 42			←	22 46	23 17			23 43	23 49	00 31
Hitchin 4 d		20 47	21 21		21 47		21 51			21 47	22 21		22 47			22 47	22 51	23 26			23 53	00 04	00a47
Letchworth Garden City d		20 51	21 25		→					21 51	22 25		→			22 51		23 30		23 52	23 57		
Baldock d		20 55	21 28							21 55	22 28					22 55		23 33			23 59		
Ashwell & Morden d		21 00								22 00						23 00					00 05		
Royston d		21 04	21 36							22 04	22 36					23 04		23 41		00 01	00 10		
Meldreth d		21 08								22 08						23 08					00 13		
Shepreth d		21 11								22 11						23 11					00 16		
Foxton d		21 14								22 14						23 14					00 18		
Cambridge a	←	21 27	21 54			22 01			←	22 27	22 54				23 10	23 29		00 01		00 19	00 35		
Arlesey d	20 56						21 56 →		21 56								22 56					00 10	
Biggleswade d	21 01								22 01								23 01					00 15	
Sandy d	21 05								22 05								23 05					00 18	
St Neots d	21 12								22 12								23 12					00 26	
Huntingdon a	21 20								22 20								23 27					00 33	
d	21 20								22 20								23 27					00 33	
Peterborough 8 a	21 36			21 44				22 14	22 36			22 44		22s59			23 49					00 55	

Sundays

from 14 September

	FC	FC	FC	FC	FC	FC	FC	FC	FC	FC	FC	FC	FC	FC	FC	FC	GR	FC	GR	FC	FC	GR	FC	FC	FC
																	R		R			R			
	1	1		1	1		1	1		1	1	1	1	1	1	1	1	1	1	1	1	1	1	1	1
													B												
									🚌								🍴		🍴			🍴			
London Kings Cross 15 ⊖ d	23p12	23p15	23p35	23p50	00 04		00 07	00 36								08 52	09 00	09 06	09 10	09 15	09 22	09 30			09 52
Finsbury Park ⊖ d	23p17	23p20	23p40	23p55	00 10		00 12	00 41		06 57	07 11	07 27	07 57	08 11	08 27	08 57		09 11			09 27				09 57
Potters Bar d		23p30	00 01					00 51			07 21			08 21				09 21							
Hatfield d		23p36	00 09			←		00 57			07 27			08 27				09 27							
Welwyn Garden City 4 d		23p40	00b28			00b28		01 03			07 33			08 31				09 31							
Welwyn North d		23p45	→			00 31		01s06			07 36			08 34				09 34							
Knebworth d		23p49				00 35		01s10			07 40			08 38				09 38							
Hertford North d							00 39																		
Stevenage 4 d	23p46	23p55			00 36	00 41	00 48	01 14		07 16	07 45	07 50	08 16	08 42	08 46	09 16	09 20	09 42			09 46			←	10 16
Hitchin 4 d	23p51	00 02		00s35	00 44	00 49	00 56	01 19		07 26	07 52	08 00	08 30	08 47	08 51	09 21		09 47			09 51			09 47	10 21
Letchworth Garden City d		00 06			00s50	00a57	01 00		01 35	07 33	07 56		08 33	08 54		09 25		→						09 51	10 25
Baldock d		00 09					01 04			07 36	07 59		08 36	08 57		09 28								09 55	10 28
Ashwell & Morden d		00 14					01 09				08 04			09 02										10 00	
Royston d		00 19			01s00		01 13			07 44	08 09		08 44	09 07		09 36								10 04	10 36
Meldreth d		00 22					01 17				08 13			09 13										10 08	
Shepreth d		00 25					01 20				08 16			09 16										10 11	
Foxton d		00 28					01 23				08 18			09 18										10 14	
Cambridge a		00 45			01 16		01 39			08 03	08 34		09 03	09 31		09 54				10 01			←	10 27	10 54
Arlesey d	23p56							01s26	01s47			08 05			08 56						09 56 →		09 56		
Biggleswade d	00 01			00s43				01s31	02s07			08 10			09 01								10 01		
Sandy d	00 05							01s35	02s17			08 14			09 05								10 05		
St Neots d	00 12			00s53				01s43	02s37			08 21			09 12								10 12		
Huntingdon a	00 20			01s00				01s50	03s07			08 29			09 20								10 20		
d	00 20											08 29			09 20								10 20		
Peterborough 8 a	00 42			01 19				02 12	03 42			08 48			09 39		09 49		09 57			10 14	10 36		

For general notes see front of timetable
For details of catering facilities see Directory of Train Operators

A To Ely (Table 17)
B To Kings Lynn (Table 17)
b Arr. 0015

London → Stevenage, Cambridge and Peterborough

Network Diagram - see first page of Table 24

		GR	FC	GR	FC	FC	GR		FC	FC	FC	GR	FC	GR	FC	FC	FC	FC	GR	FC	GR	FC	FC	FC	GR	FC
		R		R			R					R		R					R		R				R	
		1	1	1	1	1	1		1	1	1	1	1	1	1	1	1	1	1	1	1	1	1	1	1	1
		A										B													C	
		☕ 🛒		☕ 🛒			☕ 🛒					☕ 🛒		☕ 🛒					☕ 🛒		☕ 🛒				☕ 🛒	
London Kings Cross 15	⊖ d	10 00	10 06	10 10	10 15	10 22	10 30				10 52	11 00	11 06	11 10	11 15		11 22	11 52	12 00	12 06	12 10	12 15		12 22	12 30	
Finsbury Park	⊖ d		10 11			10 27					10 57		11 11				11 27	11 57		12 11				12 27		
Potters Bar	d		10 21										11 21							12 21			←			
Hatfield	d		10 27										11 27							12 27			12 27			
Welwyn Garden City 4	d		10 31										11 31							→			12 31			
Welwyn North	d		10 34										11 34										12 34			
Knebworth	d		10 38										11 38										12 38			
Hertford North	d																									
Stevenage 4	d		10 42			10 46	10 49			←	11 16		11 42			←	11 46	12 16			12 29		12 42	12 46		
Hitchin 4	d		10 47			10 51				10 47	11 21		11 47			11 47	11 51	12 21					12 47	12 51		
Letchworth Garden City	d		→							10 51	11 25		→			11 51		12 25					12 51			
Baldock	d									10 55	11 28					11 55		12 28					12 55			
Ashwell & Morden	d									11 00						12 00							13 00			
Royston	d									11 04	11 36					12 04		12 36					13 04			
Meldreth	d									11 08						12 08							13 08			
Shepreth	d									11 11						12 11							13 11			
Foxton	d									11 14						12 14							13 14			
Cambridge	a				11 01				←	11 27	11 54				12 01	12 27		12 54				13 02	13 27			←
Arlesey	d					10 56											11 56							12 56		12 56
Biggleswade	d					11 01			11 01								12 01							→		13 01
Sandy	d					→			11 05								12 05									13 05
St Neots	d								11 12								12 12									13 12
Huntingdon	a								11 20								12 20									13 20
	d								11 20								12 20									13 20
Peterborough 8	a	10 45		10 59			11 18		11 36			11 44		11 54			12 36		12 44		12 58				13 14	13 36

		FC	GR	FC	GR	FC	FC	GR	FC	FC	FC	GR	FC	GR		FC	FC	GR	FC	FC	FC	GR	FC	GR	FC	FC
			R		R			R				R		R				R				R		R		
		1	1	1	1	1	1	1	1	1	1	1	1	1		1	1	1	1	1	1	1	1	1	1	1
			☕ 🛒		☕ 🛒			☕ 🛒				☕ 🛒		☕ 🛒				☕ 🛒				☕ 🛒		☕ 🛒		
London Kings Cross 15	⊖ d	12 52	13 00	13 06	13 10	13 15	13 22	13 30			13 52	14 00	14 06	14 10		14 15	14 22	14 30			14 52	15 00	15 06	15 10	15 15	15 22
Finsbury Park	⊖ d	12 57		13 11			13 27				13 57		14 11				14 27				14 57		15 11			15 27
Potters Bar	d			13 21									14 21										15 21			
Hatfield	d			13 27									14 27										15 27			
Welwyn Garden City 4	d			13 31									14 31										15 31			
Welwyn North	d			13 34									14 34										15 34			
Knebworth	d			13 38									14 38										15 38			
Hertford North	d																									
Stevenage 4	d	13 16	13 19	13 42			13 46	13 49		←	14 15		14 42				14 46			←	15 16	15 19	15 42			15 46
Hitchin 4	d	13 21		13 47			13 51			13 47	14 22		14 47				14 51			14 47	15 21		15 47			15 51
Letchworth Garden City	d	13 25		→						13 51	14 25		→							14 51	15 25		→			
Baldock	d	13 28								13 55	14 28									14 55	15 28					
Ashwell & Morden	d									14 00										15 00						
Royston	d	13 36								14 04	14 36									15 04	15 36					
Meldreth	d									14 08										15 08						
Shepreth	d									14 11										15 11						
Foxton	d									14 14										15 14						
Cambridge	a	13 54				14 01			←	14 27	14 54					15 01			←	15 27	15 54				16 01	
Arlesey	d						13 56										14 56		14 56							15 56
Biggleswade	d						14 01		14 01								→		15 01							→
Sandy	d						→		14 05										15 05							
St Neots	d								14 12										15 12							
Huntingdon	a								14 20										15 20							
	d								14 20										15 20							
Peterborough 8	a		13 48		13 56			14 18	14 37			14 44		14 54				15 14	15 36			15 48		15 54		

		GR	FC	FC	FC	GR	FC	GR	FC	FC	FC	GR	GR	FC	FC	GR	FC	GR	FC	FC	GR		FC	FC	FC	GR
		R				R		R				R	R			R		R			R					R
		1	1	1	1	1	1	1	1	1	1	1	1	1	1	1	1	1	1	1	1		1	1	1	1
		☕ 🛒				☕ 🛒		☕ 🛒				☕ 🛒	✕ 🛒			☕ 🛒		☕ 🛒			☕ 🛒					☕ 🛒
London Kings Cross 15	⊖ d	15 30			15 52	16 00	16 06	16 10	16 15		16 22	16 30	16 40		16 52	17 00	17 06	17 10	17 15	17 22	17 30				17 52	18 00
Finsbury Park	⊖ d				15 57		16 11				16 27				16 57		17 11			17 27					17 57	
Potters Bar	d						16 21			←							17 21									
Hatfield	d						16 27			16 27							17 27									
Welwyn Garden City 4	d						→			16 31							17 31									
Welwyn North	d									16 34							17 34									
Knebworth	d									16 38							17 38									
Hertford North	d																									
Stevenage 4	d			←	16 16			16 29		16 42	16 46	16 49			17 16		17 42			17 46	17 49			←	18 16	
Hitchin 4	d			15 47	16 21					16 47	16 51				17 21		17 47			17 51				17 47	18 21	
Letchworth Garden City	d			15 51	16 25					16 51					17 25		→							17 51	18 25	
Baldock	d			15 55	16 28					16 55					17 28									17 55	18 28	
Ashwell & Morden	d			16 00						17 00														18 00		
Royston	d			16 04	16 36					17 04					17 36									18 04	18 36	
Meldreth	d			16 08						17 08														18 08		
Shepreth	d			16 11						17 11														18 11		
Foxton	d			16 14						17 14														18 14		
Cambridge	a		←	16 27	16 54				17 02	17 27				←	17 54				18 01				←	18 27	18 54	
Arlesey	d		15 56								16 56									17 56						
Biggleswade	d		16 01								17 01			17 01						18 01			18 01			
Sandy	d		16 05								→			17 05						→			18 05			
St Neots	d		16 12											17 12									18 12			
Huntingdon	a		16 20											17 20									18 20			
	d		16 20											17 20									18 20			
Peterborough 8	a	16 14	16 36			16 44		16 58				17 18	17 24	17 37		17 46		17 54			18 18		18 38			18 44

For general notes see front of timetable
For details of catering facilities see Directory of Train Operators

A The Flying Scotsman
B The Northern Lights
C The Highland Chieftain

Table 25

Sundays

from 14 September

London → Stevenage, Cambridge and Peterborough

Network Diagram - see first page of Table 24

		FC	GR	FC	FC	GR	GR	FC	FC	FC	GR	FC	GR	FC	FC	GR	GR	FC	FC	FC	GR	GR	FC	FC	FC	GR
			R			R	R				R		R			R	R				R	R				R
		1	1	1	1	1	1	1	1	1	1	1	1	1	1	1	1	1	1	1	1	1	1	1	1	1
			🍴			🍴	🍴				🍴		🍴			🍴	🍴				🍴	🍴				🍴
London Kings Cross 15 ⊖	d	18 06	18 10	18 15	18 22	18 30	18 40			18 52	19 00	19 06	19 10	19 15	19 22	19 30	19 35			19 52	20 00	20 03	20 06	20 15	20 22	20 30
Finsbury Park ⊖	d	18 11			18 27					18 57		19 11			19 27					19 57			20 11		20 27	
Potters Bar	d	18 21										19 21											20 21			
Hatfield	d	18 27										19 27											20 27			
Welwyn Garden City 4	d	18 31										19 31											20 31			
Welwyn North	d	18 34										19 34											20 34			
Knebworth	d	18 38										19 38											20 38			
Hertford North	d																									
Stevenage 4	d	18 42			18 46	18 50			←	19 16		19 42			19 46	19 49	19 54		←	20 16			20 42		20 46	
Hitchin 4	d	18 47			18 51				18 47	19 21		19 47			19 51				19 47	20 21			20 47		20 51	
Letchworth Garden City	d	→							18 51	19 25		→							19 51	20 25			→			
Baldock	d								18 55	19 28									19 55	20 28						
Ashwell & Morden	d								19 00										20 00							
Royston	d								19 04	19 36									20 04	20 36						
Meldreth	d								19 08										20 08							
Shepreth	d								19 11										20 11							
Foxton	d								19 14										20 14							
Cambridge	a			19 01					19 27	19 54				20 01					20 27	20 54				21 01		
Arlesey	d				18 56			←							19 56			←							20 56	
Biggleswade	d				19 01			19 01							20 01			20 01							→	
Sandy	d				→			19 05							→			20 05								
St Neots	d							19 12										20 12								
Huntingdon	a							19 20										20 20								
	d							19 20										20 20								
Peterborough 8	a		18 54			19 19	19 25	19 36			19 44		19 54			20 18	20 24	20 36			20 44	20 48				21 14

		FC	FC	FC	GR	FC	FC	FC	GR	FC	FC	FC	GR	FC	GR	FC	FC	FC	FC	FC	FC	FC	FC	FC		
					R				R				R		R											
		1	1	1	1	1	1	1	1	1	1	1	1	1	1	1	1	1	1	1	1	1	1			
																					A					
					🍴				🍴				🍴		🍴											
London Kings Cross 15 ⊖	d			20 52	21 00	21 06	21 15	21 22	21 30			21 52	22 00	22 06	22 10	22 15		22 22	22 52	23 06	23 15		23 25	23 41		
Finsbury Park ⊖	d			20 57		21 11		21 27				21 57		22 11				22 27	22 57	23 11			23 30	23 47		
Potters Bar	d					21 21								22 21						23 21				00 08		
Hatfield	d					21 27								22 27						23 27		←		00 16		
Welwyn Garden City 4	d					21 31								22 31						23 31		23 31		00 20		
Welwyn North	d					21 34								22 34						→		23 36		00 23		
Knebworth	d					21 38								22 38								23 40		00 28		
Hertford North	d																									
Stevenage 4	d		←	21 16		21 42		21 46			←	22 16		22 42			←	22 46	23 17			23 43	23 49	00 31		
Hitchin 4	d		20 47	21 21		21 47		21 51			21 47	22 21		22 47			22 47	22 51	23 26			23 53	00 04	00a47		
Letchworth Garden City	d		20 51	21 25		→					21 51	22 25		→			22 51		23 30		23 52	23 57				
Baldock	d		20 55	21 28							21 55	22 28					22 55		23 33			23 59				
Ashwell & Morden	d		21 00								22 00						23 00					00 05				
Royston	d		21 04	21 36							22 04	22 36					23 04		23 41		00 01	00 10				
Meldreth	d		21 08								22 08						23 08					00 13				
Shepreth	d		21 11								22 11						23 11					00 16				
Foxton	d		21 14								22 14						23 14					00 18				
Cambridge	a	←	21 27	21 54			22 01			←	22 27	22 54				23 10	23 29		00 01		00 19	00 35				
Arlesey	d	20 56						21 56		21 56								22 56					00 10			
Biggleswade	d	21 01						→		22 01								23 01					00 15			
Sandy	d	21 05								22 05								23 05					00 18			
St Neots	d	21 12								22 12								23 12					00 26			
Huntingdon	a	21 20								22 20								23 27					00 33			
	d	21 20								22 20								23 27					00 33			
Peterborough 8	a	21 36			21 44				22 14	22 36			22 44		22s59			23 49					00 55			

For general notes see front of timetable
For details of catering facilities see
Directory of Train Operators

A To Ely (Table 17)

First Capital Connect will run a Saturday service on Bank Holiday Mondays

Peterborough, Cambridge and Stevenage → London

Network Diagram - see first page of Table 24

Miles	Miles			FC MX	FC MO	FC MX	FC	FC	FC	FC	FC	FC	FC	FC	FC		FC	FC	FC	FC	GR	FC	FC	FC	FC	FC
					1	1	1		1			1		1	1		1	1	1	1	R 1	1		1	1	
					A	A									B											
0	—	**Peterborough** 8	d				03 30		04 12					05 12						06 00	06 10					
17½	—	Huntingdon	a				03 44		04 26					05 26						06 14						
—	—		d				03 44		04 26					05 26						06 15						
24¾	—	St Neots	d				03 51		04 34					05 34						06 23						
32¼	—	Sandy	d						04 41					05 41						06 31						
35¼	—	Biggleswade	d				04 01		04 45					05 45						06 35					←	
39¼	—	Arlesey	d						04 50					05 50						06 40					06 40	
—	0	**Cambridge**	d		23p13	23p19									05 45					→		05 48		06 15		
—	7	Foxton	d			23p28																05 57				
—	8	Shepreth	d			23p31																05 59				
—	10	Meldreth	d			23p34																06 02				
—	13	Royston	d		23p26	23p38						05 16						06 00				06 06		06 29		
—	17	Ashwell & Morden	d			23p42						05 21										06 11				
—	21½	Baldock	d			23p47						05 26										06 16				
—	23¾	Letchworth Garden City	d	23p18	23p36	23p50		04 50			05 20	05 30	05 50				05 59	06 10				06 19	06 27	06 39		06 46
44¼	26	Hitchin 4	d	23p22	23p40	23p54	04 13	04 54	04 58	←	05 24	05 34	05 54	05 58			06 03	06 14				06 24	06 31	06 43	06 46	06 50
48¼	30¾	**Stevenage** 4	d	23p27	23p45	23p59	04 18	04 59	05 04	04 59	05 29	05 39	05 59	06 03			06 09	06 19				06 30	06 36	06 48	06 52	06 56
—	—	Hertford North	a	23p40			04 28	→		05 12	05 42		06 12										06 49			
51½	33	Knebworth	d		23p48	00 02			05 07			05 43					06 13					06 33				07 00
54¾	36	Welwyn North	d		23p52	00 06			05 11			05 47					06 17		←			06 37				07 04
56	37¾	Welwyn Garden City 4	d		23p56	00 09			05 15			05 50					06 20		06 20			06 40			07 00	07 08
58½	40¼	Hatfield	d		23p59	00 12			05 19			05 53					→		06 23			06 44				→
63½	45¼	Potters Bar	d		00 04	00 18			05 25			05 59							06 29			06 49				
73¾	55½	Finsbury Park ⊖	d	00 15	00 20	00 29	04s50		05 41	05 47	06a16	06 08	06a46	06 21	06 27			06 38	06 41			06 58	07a15	07 06	07 14	
76¼	58	**London Kings Cross** 15 ⊖	a	00 26	00 32	00 42	05 04		05 55	05 58		06 19		06 30	06 35			06 46	06 49		07 00	07 07		07 15	07 23	

		FC	FC	GR	FC		FC	FC	FC	FC	FC	FC	GR	FC	FC	FC	FC	FC		FC	FC	GR MO	GR MX	FC	FC	FC
		1	1	R 1	1			1	1	1		1	R 1	1		1	1	1		1	1	R 1	R 1	1		1
										A														B		
				✕									✕									✕	✕			
Peterborough 8	d	06 20	06 32	06 40	06 54								07 00							07 06	07 12	07 17	07 17			
Huntingdon	a	06 34	06 46		07 09											←				07 20	07 26					←
	d	06 35	06 47		07 13											07 13				07 21	07 30					07 30
St Neots	d	06 43	06 55		→											07 21				07 30	→					07 38
Sandy	d		07 03									←								07 38						
Biggleswade	d	06 52	07 07									07 07								07 42						
Arlesey	d		→									07 12								07 47						
Cambridge	d								06 27	06 45								06 57		→				07 15		
Foxton	d								06 37									07 07								
Shepreth	d								06 40									07 10								
Meldreth	d								06 43									07 13								
Royston	d							06 44	06 50	06 59							07 14	07 20						07 29		
Ashwell & Morden	d							06 49	06 55								07 19	07 25								
Baldock	d							06 54	07 00								07 24	07 30								
Letchworth Garden City	d						06 54	06 58	07 04	07 09					07 19		07 28	07 34						07 39		
Hitchin 4	d						06 58	07 02	07 08			07 18			07 23		07 32	07 38						07 43		
Stevenage 4	d						07 04	07 08	07 14			07 23			07 29		07 38	07 44						07 49		
Hertford North	a						07 16																			
Knebworth	d								07 18					←	07 33		07 41	07 47								
Welwyn North	d								07 22		←			07 22	07 37			07 51							←	
Welwyn Garden City 4	d								→		07 08			07 26	07 42			→							07 42	
Hatfield	d										07 12			07 30	→										07 46	
Potters Bar	d										07 18														07 52	
Finsbury Park ⊖	d						07a44	07 28			07 34	07 41		07 46			07 59								08 09	
London Kings Cross 15 ⊖	a	07 27		07 30				07 36		07 39	07 41	07 50	07 53	07 56		08 00	08 07					08 09	08 11	08 15	08 17	08 19

		FC	FC	FC	FC	GR	FC	FC		FC	GR	FC	FC	FC	FC	FC	GR	FC	FC	FC	FC		FC	GR	FC	FC
		1	1	1	1	R 1		1		1	R 1	1	1	1	1	1	R 1	1	1	1	1		1	R 1	1	1
												A							A							
						✕					✕						✕							✕		
Peterborough 8	d			07 26	07 34	07 40					07 46		07 59				08 04						08 16	08 33		
Huntingdon	a			07 40	07 48								08 13					←					08 31			
	d			07 40	07 50								08 13					08 13					08 31			
St Neots	d			07 47	07 58								→					08 21					08 38			
Sandy	d				08 06										←								08 46		←	
Biggleswade	d		←	07 55	08 10										08 10								08 49		08 49	
Arlesey	d		07 47		→										08 15								→		08 54	
Cambridge	d									07 26		07 45				07 54			08 15							08 24
Foxton	d									07 36						08 04										08 34
Shepreth	d									07 39						08 06										08 36
Meldreth	d									07 43						08 09										08 39
Royston	d							07 44		07 50		07 59				08 16			08 29							08 46
Ashwell & Morden	d							07 49		07 55		08 04				08 21										08 51
Baldock	d							07 54		08 00		08 09				08 26										08 56
Letchworth Garden City	d						07 54	07 58		08 04		08 12				08 30			08 39		08 44					09 00
Hitchin 4	d		07 53				07 58	08 02		08 08					08 21	08 34					08 48				09 00	09 04
Stevenage 4	d		07 59				08 05	08 08		08 14					08 27	08 40					08 53				09 05	09 10
Hertford North	a						08 19							←						←						
Knebworth	d	←								08 17				08 17		08 44				08 44						09 13
Welwyn North	d	07 51								→				08 21		→				08 48						09 17
Welwyn Garden City 4	d	07 56												08 26						08 52						→
Hatfield	d																									
Potters Bar	d																									
Finsbury Park ⊖	d	08 15	08 19				08a47							08 44	08 47					09 11	09 12				09 23	
London Kings Cross 15 ⊖	a	08 24	08 29	08 31		08 33		08 36			08 41	08 45		08 53	08 58		08 59	09 01	09 12	09 19	09 21			09 26	09 32	

For general notes see front of timetable
For details of catering facilities see Directory of Train Operators

A From Kings Lynn (Table 17)
B From Ely (Table 17)

First Capital Connect will run a Saturday service on Bank Holiday Mondays

Peterborough, Cambridge and Stevenage → London

Network Diagram - see first page of Table 24

		FC	FC	GR	FC	FC	FC	FC	FC	FC	FC		GR	FC	FC	FC	FC	GR	FC	FC	FC	FC	FC	GR		FC
		1 A	1	R 1 B ✕	1	1	1	1	1	1	1		R 1 ✕		1	1	1	R 1 ✕	1	1 A	1	1	1	R 1 ☕		1
Peterborough 8	d		08 45	08 51						09 15	09 23		09 26				09 44	09 48						10 05		
Huntingdon	a		08 59							09 29	09 38						09 58									
	d		09 00							09 30	09 41						09 59									
St Neots	d		09 07							09 37	09 49						10 06		←							
Sandy	d		09 15			←					09 57						10 14		09 57			←				
Biggleswade	d		09 18			09 18				09 45	→						10 17		10 01			10 17				
Arlesey	d		→			09 23											→		10 06			10 22				
Cambridge	d	08 45					08 54	09 20							09 28					09 50			09 55			10 20
Foxton	d						09 04																10 05			
Shepreth	d						09 06																10 07			
Meldreth	d						09 09																10 10			
Royston	d	08 59					09 15								09 43					10 04			10 15			
Ashwell & Morden	d						09 20																10 20			
Baldock	d						09 25								09 51								10 25			
Letchworth Garden City	d	09 09					09 29		←					09 50	09 54	09 59				10 14			10 29			
Hitchin 4	d					09 29	09 33		09 33					09 54	09 58	10 03			10 12			10 28	10 33			
Stevenage 4	d					09 34	→		09 39	09 56			09 57	09 59	10 03	10 09			10 18			10 33	→	10 34		
Hertford North	a													10 12												
Knebworth	d				←				09 43							10 13										
Welwyn North	d				09 17				09 47							10 17					←					
Welwyn Garden City 4	d				09 20				09 50							10 20					10 20					
Hatfield	d				09 24				09 53							→					10 23					
Potters Bar	d				09 30				09 59												10 29					
Finsbury Park ⊖	d				09 41	09 52			10 08					10a47	10 21						10 41	10 51				
London Kings Cross 15 ⊖	a	09 42		09 45	09 50	10 02		10 12	10 19	10 22			10 25		10 30			10 40	10 45	10 46	10 49	11 00		11 04		11 10

		FC	FC	FC	FC	GR	GR	FC	FC	FC	GR	FC	FC		GR	FC	FC	FC	GR	FC	GR	FC	FC	FC	FC	GR
		1		1	1	R 1 ✕	R 1 ✕	1	1	1	R 1 ✕	1	1		R 1 ☕	1	1	1	R 1 ✕	1	R 1 ✕		1	1	1	R 1 ✕
Peterborough 8	d				10 15	10 18	10 34			10 46	10 57				11 06			11 14	11 17		11 31				11 44	11 49
Huntingdon	a				10 29					11 00								11 28							11 58	
	d				10 33					11 00								11 33							12 00	
St Neots	d				10 41					11 07								11 41							12 07	
Sandy	d				10 48					11 15		←						11 48							12 15	
Biggleswade	d				10 52					11 18		11 18						→							12 18	
Arlesey	d				10 57					→															→	
Cambridge	d			10 28				10 45					10 55			11 15							11 28	11 45		
Foxton	d												11 05													
Shepreth	d												11 07													
Meldreth	d												11 10													
Royston	d			10 43									11 15										11 43			
Ashwell & Morden	d												11 20													
Baldock	d			10 51									11 25										11 51			
Letchworth Garden City	d	←	10 50	10 54									11 29				←					11 50	11 54			
Hitchin 4	d	10 33	10 54	10 58	11 03				←			11 28	11 33				11 33					11 54	11 58			
Stevenage 4	d	10 39	10 59	11 03	11 09				11 09			11 33	→				11 39		11 47			11 59	12 03			
Hertford North	a		11 12		→																	12 12				
Knebworth	d	10 43							11 13								11 43									
Welwyn North	d	10 47							11 17								11 47			←						
Welwyn Garden City 4	d	10 50							11 20								11 50			11 50						
Hatfield	d	10 53							11 23								→			11 53						
Potters Bar	d	10 59							11 29											11 59						
Finsbury Park ⊖	d	11 08	11a46	11 21					11 41			11 51								12 11		12a46	12 21			
London Kings Cross 15 ⊖	a	11 19		11 31		11 15	11 27	11 35	11 49		11 51	12 00			12 03	12 04			12 17	12 19	12 25		12 30	12 33		12 42

		FC	FC		FC	FC	GR	FC	FC	FC	FC	GR	FC	FC	GR	FC		FC	FC	GR	FC	GR	FC	FC	FC	FC
		1	1		1	1	R 1 ☕	1		1	1	R 1 ☕	1	1	R 1 ✕	1		1	1	R 1 ☕	1	R 1 ✕	1		1	1
Peterborough 8	d						12 14				12 18	12 29		12 43	12 47					13 06		13 12				
Huntingdon	a										12 33			12 57												
	d										12 33			13 00												
St Neots	d	←									12 41			13 07				←								
Sandy	d	11 48	←								12 48			13 15				13 15								
Biggleswade	d	11 52	12 18								12 52			→				13 18								
Arlesey	d	11 57									12 57															
Cambridge	d				11 55	12 15				12 28			12 45						12 55		13 15				13 28	13 45
Foxton	d				12 05														13 05							
Shepreth	d				12 07														13 07							
Meldreth	d				12 10														13 10							
Royston	d				12 15					12 43									13 15						13 43	
Ashwell & Morden	d				12 20														13 20							
Baldock	d				12 25					12 51									13 25						13 51	
Letchworth Garden City	d				12 29				12 50	12 54									13 29				←	13 50	13 54	
Hitchin 4	d	12 03	12 28		12 33				12 54	12 58	13 03					←		13 28	13 33				13 33	13 54	13 58	
Stevenage 4	d	12 09	12 33		12 39		12 43		12 59	13 03	13 09				13 16	13 09		13 33	→				13 39	13 59	14 03	
Hertford North	a								13 12		→													14 12		
Knebworth	d	12 13			12 43											13 13							13 43			
Welwyn North	d	12 17			12 47			←								13 17							13 47			
Welwyn Garden City 4	d	12 20			12 50			12 50								13 20							13 50			
Hatfield	d	12 23			→			12 53								13 23							13 53			
Potters Bar	d	12 29						12 59								13 29							13 59			
Finsbury Park ⊖	d	12 41	12 51					13 08	13a46	13 21						13 41		13 51					14 08	14a46	14 21	
London Kings Cross 15 ⊖	a	12 49	13 00			13 03	13 10	13 19		13 30		13 22	13 33		13 43	13 48		14 00		14 02	14 05	14 10	14 19		14 30	14 33

For general notes see front of timetable
For details of catering facilities see
Directory of Train Operators

A From Kings Lynn (Table 17)
B The Hull Executive

First Capital Connect will run a Saturday service on Bank Holiday Mondays

Peterborough, Cambridge and Stevenage → London

Network Diagram - see first page of Table 24

Station		FC 1	FC 1	GR R 1 ✕	FC 1	GR R 1 ✕		FC 1	FC 1	GR R 1 ⊡	FC 1	FC 1	FC	FC 1	FC 1	FC 1	GR R 1 ✕	FC 1	GR R 1 ✕		FC 1	GR R 1 ⊡	FC 1	FC 1	FC 1	FC 1
Peterborough 8	d	13 18	13 43	13 47		14 03				14 10						14 18	14 43	14 47	14 50			15 06				
Huntingdon	a	13 32	13 57													14 32		15 01								
	d	13 33	13 59													14 33		15 01								
St Neots	d	13 41	14 06					←								14 41		15 08					←			
Sandy	d	13 48	14 14					14 14								14 48		15 16								
Biggleswade	d	13 52	→					14 17								14 52		15 19					15 19			
Arlesey	d	13 57						14 22								14 57		→					15 24			
Cambridge	d								13 55		14 15			14 28	14 45									14 55	15 15	
Foxton	d								14 05															15 05		
Shepreth	d								14 07															15 07		
Meldreth	d								14 10															15 10		
Royston	d								14 15					14 43										15 15		
Ashwell & Morden	d								14 20															15 20		
Baldock	d								14 25					14 51										15 25		
Letchworth Garden City	d								14 29			←	14 50	14 54										15 29		←
Hitchin 4	d	14 03						14 28	14 33			14 33	14 54	14 58		15 03							15 30	15 33		15 33
Stevenage 4	d	14 09		14 17				14 33	→			14 39	14 59	15 03		15 09	15 12						15 35	→		15 39
Hertford North	a												15 12													
Knebworth	d	14 13										14 43				15 13										15 43
Welwyn North	d	14 17			←							14 47				15 17					←					15 47
Welwyn Garden City 4	d	14 20			14 20							14 50				15 20					15 20					15 50
Hatfield	d	→			14 23							14 53				→					15 23					15 53
Potters Bar	d				14 29							14 59									15 29					15 59
Finsbury Park	⊖ d				14 41			14 51				15 11	15a46	15 21							15 41		15 53			16 11
London Kings Cross 15	⊖ a			14 44	14 49	14 57		15 00		15 05	15 07	15 20		15 30	15 33		15 40		15 44		15 49	15 58	16 02		16 08	16 19

Station		FC 1	GR R 1 ✕	FC 1	FC	FC 1	FC 1	FC 1	GR R 1 ✕		FC 1	GR R 1 A ✕	FC	FC 1	FC 1	FC 1	FC 1	FC 1	GR R 1 ✕	FC 1	FC 1	FC 1		FC 1	GR R 1 B ✕	FC 1
Peterborough 8	d	15 18	15 23	15 44					15 47			16 02						16 14	16 17					16 45	16 48	
Huntingdon	a	15 32		15 58														16 28						16 59		
	d	15 33		15 59														16 33						16 59		
St Neots	d	15 41		16 06				←						←				16 41						17 06		←
Sandy	d	15 48		16 14				15 48						16 14				16 48						17 14		16 48
Biggleswade	d	→		→				15 52						16 17				→						17 17		16 52
Arlesey	d							15 57						16 22										→		16 57
Cambridge	d					15 28	15 45								15 55	16 15					16 24	16 45				
Foxton	d														16 05						16 33					
Shepreth	d														16 07						16 35					
Meldreth	d														16 10						16 38					
Royston	d					15 43									16 15						16 43					
Ashwell & Morden	d														16 20						16 47					
Baldock	d					15 51									16 25						16 52					
Letchworth Garden City	d				15 50	15 54							16 20		16 29		←				16 55					
Hitchin 4	d				15 54	15 58		16 03					16 24	16 28	16 33		16 33				17 00					17 03
Stevenage 4	d		15 52		15 59	16 03		16 09	16 17				16 29	16 33	→		16 39		16 48		17 05					17 09
Hertford North	a				16 12								16 42													
Knebworth	d							16 13									16 43									17 13
Welwyn North	d							16 17			←						16 47			←						17 17
Welwyn Garden City 4	d							16 20			16 20						16 50			16 50						17 20
Hatfield	d							→			16 23						→			16 53						17 23
Potters Bar	d										16 29									16 59						17 29
Finsbury Park	⊖ d				16a47	16 21					16 38		17a11	16 51						17 11	17 23					17 38
London Kings Cross 15	⊖ a		16 22			16 30	16 33		16 46		16 48	16 57		17 01		17 06			17 15	17 19	17 33	17 36			17 41	17 48

Station		GR R 1 ✕	FC 1	FC 1	GR R 1 ✕	FC 1	FC 1	FC 1	FC 1	GR R 1 ✕	FC 1	FC 1		FC 1	GR R 1 ⊡	FC 1	FC 1	FC 1	FC 1	FC 1 C	FC 1	GR R 1 ✕	FC 1	FC 1	FC 1	GR R 1 ✕
Peterborough 8	d	16 54			17 04				17 18	17 28				17 47	18 02						18 18	18 26			18 45	19 07
Huntingdon	a								17 33					18 01							18 32				18 59	
	d								17 33					18 01							18 33				18 59	
St Neots	d								17 41					18 08							18 41				19 06	
Sandy	d		←						17 48					18 16		←					18 48				19 14	
Biggleswade	d		17 17						17 52					18 19		18 19					18 52				19 17	
Arlesey	d		17 22						17 57					→		18 24					18 57				→	
Cambridge	d			16 55		17 15		17 24			17 45						17 55	18 15		18 24			18 45			
Foxton	d			17 05				17 33									18 05			18 33						
Shepreth	d			17 07				17 35									18 07			18 35						
Meldreth	d			17 10				17 38									18 10			18 38						
Royston	d			17 15				17 43									18 15			18 43						
Ashwell & Morden	d			17 20				17 47									18 20			18 47						
Baldock	d			17 25				17 52									18 25			18 52						
Letchworth Garden City	d			17 29			←	17 55									18 29		←	18 55						
Hitchin 4	d		17 28	17 33			17 33	18 00	18 03			←				18 30	18 33		18 33	19 00	19 03			←		
Stevenage 4	d		17 33	→	17 34		17 39	18 05	18 09 →			18 09				18 35	→		18 39	19 05	19 09 →			19 09		
Hertford North	a																									
Knebworth	d						17 43					18 13							18 43					19 13		
Welwyn North	d						17 47					18 17							18 47					19 17		
Welwyn Garden City 4	d						17 50					18 20							18 50					19 20		
Hatfield	d						17 53					18 23							18 53					19 23		
Potters Bar	d						17 59					18 29							18 59					19 29		
Finsbury Park	⊖ d		17 51				18 08	18 23				18 41				18 53			19 11	19 23				19 41		
London Kings Cross 15	⊖ a	17 50	18 01		18 04	18 08	18 18	18 33		18 23	18 38	18 50			18 54	19 02		19 05	19 20	19 33		19 18	19 36	19 48		19 59

For general notes see front of timetable
For details of catering facilities see Directory of Train Operators

A The Northern Lights
B The Flying Scotsman
C From Kings Lynn (Table 17)

First Capital Connect will run a Saturday service on Bank Holiday Mondays

Peterborough, Cambridge and Stevenage → London

Network Diagram - see first page of Table 24

		FC		FC	FC	FC	FC	GR	FC	GR	FC	FC	FC	FC	GR		FC	FC	FC	FC	FC	FC	GR	GR	FC	GR
								R		R					R								R	R		R
		1		1	1	1	1	1	1	1	1	1	1	1	1		1		1	1	1	1	1	1	1	1
											A										A					
								✕ 🛒		✕ 🛒					✕ 🛒								☕ 🛒	☕ 🛒		✕ 🛒
Peterborough 8	d						19 15	19 20		19 26				19 41	19 46							20 16	20 28	20 38		20 46
Huntingdon	a						19 29							19 56								20 31				
	d						19 33							19 59								20 33				
St Neots	d						19 41						←	20 06					←			20 41				
Sandy	d	←					19 48						19 48	20 14					20 14			20 48				
Biggleswade	d	19 17					→						19 52	→					20 17			20 52				
Arlesey	d	19 22											19 57						20 22			20 57				
Cambridge	d			18 55	19 15						19 24	19 45								19 55	20 28				20 45	
Foxton	d			19 05							19 33									20 05						
Shepreth	d			19 07							19 35									20 07						
Meldreth	d			19 10							19 38									20 10						
Royston	d			19 15							19 43									20 15	20 43					
Ashwell & Morden	d			19 20							19 47									20 20						
Baldock	d			19 25							19 52									20 25	20 51					
Letchworth Garden City	d			19 29		←					19 55							20 20		20 29	20 54					
Hitchin 4	d	19 28		19 33		19 33					20 00		20 03					20 24	20 28	20 33	20 58	21 03				
Stevenage 4	d	19 33		→		19 39		19 50			20 05		20 09		20 15			20 29	20 33	20 39	21 03	21 09				21 17
Hertford North	a																	20 42				→				
Knebworth	d					19 43							20 13							20 43						
Welwyn North	d					19 47			←				20 17				←			20 47						
Welwyn Garden City 4	d					19 50			19 50				20 20				20 20			20 50						
Hatfield	d					→			19 53				→				20 23			20 53						
Potters Bar	d								19 59								20 29			20 59						
Finsbury Park	⊖ d	19 52							20 11		20 23						20 38	21a16	20 51	21 11	21 21					
London Kings Cross 15	⊖ a	20 03			20 10			20 18	20 19	20 21	20 33	20 36			20 42		20 49		21 00	21 19	21 30		21 20	21 33	21 36	21 44

		FC	FC	FC	FC		GR	FC	FC	GR	FC	FC	FC	FC	FC	FC	GR	FC		FC	FC	GR	FC	FC		
							R			R							R					R				
		1		1	1		1	1	1	1		1	1		1		1	1		1		1		1		
												A						A						A		
							☕ 🛒			✕ 🛒							☕ 🛒					☕ 🛒				
Peterborough 8	d				20 55		21 12			21 21			21 28				22 15			22 25		22 59				
Huntingdon	a				21 09								21 42							22 39						
	d				21 12								21 42							22 39						
St Neots	d				21 19								21 49							22 46						
Sandy	d				21 27			←					21 57							22 54						
Biggleswade	d				21 30			21 30					22 00							22 57						
Arlesey	d				→			21 35					22 05							23 02						
Cambridge	d			20 55								21 28			21 55			22 28						23 19		
Foxton	d			21 05											22 05									23 28		
Shepreth	d			21 07											22 07									23 31		
Meldreth	d			21 10											22 10									23 34		
Royston	d			21 15								21 43			22 15			22 43						23 38		
Ashwell & Morden	d			21 20											22 20									23 42		
Baldock	d			21 25								21 51			22 25			22 51						23 47		
Letchworth Garden City	d		21 20	21 29								21 54		22 20	22 29			22 54			23 18			23 50		
Hitchin 4	d	←	21 24	21 33				21 41				21 58	22 11	22 24	22 33	←		22 58		23 11	23 22			23 54		
Stevenage 4	d	21 09	21 29	21 39				21 47		21 52	←	22 03	22 17	22 29	22 39	22 29	22s51	23 03		23 17	23 27	23s35	←	23 59		
Hertford North	a		21 42								21 42			→		22 42					23 40		23 40			
Knebworth	d	21 13	→	21 43									22 20		22 43					23 20	→			00 02		
Welwyn North	d	21 17		21 47					←				22 24		22 47					23 24				00 06		
Welwyn Garden City 4	d	21 20		21 50					21 50				22 27		22 50					23 27				00 09		
Hatfield	d	21 24		→					21 53				22 30		22 53					23 30				00 12		
Potters Bar	d	21 29							21 59				22 36		22 59					23 36				00 18		
Finsbury Park	⊖ d	21 38						22 05	22 11		22 17	22 21	22 44		23 11	23 17		23 21		23s48			00 15	00 29		
London Kings Cross 15	⊖ a	21 48					22 04	22 14	22 19	22 20	22 26	22 30	22 56		23 21	23 25	23 32	23 35		00 01		00 15	00 26	00 42		

For general notes see front of timetable
For details of catering facilities see Directory of Train Operators

A From Kings Lynn (Table 17)

Table 25

Saturdays

Peterborough, Cambridge and Stevenage → London

Network Diagram - see first page of Table 24

		FC	FC	FC	FC	FC	FC	FC	FC	FC	FC	FC	FC	GR	FC	FC	FC	GR	FC	FC	FC	FC	FC	GR	FC	FC
			1	1		1		1	1	1	1	1	1	R 1	1	1	1	R 1	1	1	1	1	1	R 1	1	1
			A																							
Peterborough 8	d			03 30		04 12			05 14	05 45			06 18	06 37			06 45	07 09				07 18	07 44	07 48		
Huntingdon	a			03 44		04 26			05 28	05 59			06 32				06 59					07 32	07 58			
	d			03 44		04 26			05 28	05 59			06 33				06 59					07 33	07 59			
St Neots	d			03 51		04 34			05 36	06 06			06 41				07 06					07 41	08 06			
Sandy	d					04 41			05 43	06 14			06 48				07 14					07 48	08 14			←
Biggleswade	d			04 01		04 45			05 47	06 17			06 52				07 17					07 52	08 17 →			08 17
Arlesey	d					04 50			05 52	06 22			06 57				07 22					07 57				08 22
Cambridge	d		23p19								05 55	06 28			06 45				06 55	07 28	07 45					
Foxton	d		23p28								06 05								07 05							
Shepreth	d		23p31								06 07								07 07							
Meldreth	d		23p34								06 10								07 10							
Royston	d		23p38					05 16			06 15	06 43							07 15	07 43						
Ashwell & Morden	d		23p42					05 21			06 20								07 20							
Baldock	d		23p47					05 26			06 25	06 51							07 25	07 51						
Letchworth Garden City	d	23p18	23p50		04 50			05 30			06 29	06 54							07 29	07 54						
Hitchin 4	d	23p22	23p54	04 13	04 54	04 58	←	05 33	06 03	06 28	06 33	06 58	07 03			←	07 28		07 33	07 58		08 03			←	08 28
Stevenage 4	d	23p27	23p59	04 18	04 59 →	05 04	04 59	05 39	06 09	06 33	06 39	07 03	07 09 →			07 09	07 33		07 39	08 03		08 09 →			08 09	08 33
Hertford North	a	23p40		04 28			05 12																			
Knebworth	d		00 02			05 07		05 43	06 13		06 43					07 13			07 43						08 13	
Welwyn North	d		00 06			05 11		05 47	06 17		06 47					07 17			07 47						08 17	
Welwyn Garden City 4	d		00 09			05 15		05 50	06 20		06 50					07 20			07 50						08 20	
Hatfield	d		00 12			05 19		05 53	06 23		06 53					07 23			07 53						08 23	
Potters Bar	d		00 18			05 25		05 59	06 29		06 59					07 29			07 59						08 29	
Finsbury Park ⊖	d	00 15	00 29	04s50		05 41	05 47	06 08	06 41	06 51	07 08	07 21				07b41	07 51		08 08	08 21					08 41	08 51
London Kings Cross 15 ⊖	a	00 26	00 42	05 04		05 55	05 58	06 19	06 49	07 02	07 19	07 32		07 29	07 34	07 49	07 59	08 04	08 19	08 32	08 33			08 40	08 49	09 02

		FC	GR	FC	FC	FC	FC	GR	GR	FC	FC	FC	GR	GR	FC	FC	FC		FC	GR	FC	FC	GR	GR	FC	FC
		1	R 1	1	1	1	1	R 1	R 1	1	1	1	R 1	R 1	1	1	1		1	R 1	1	1	R 1	R 1	1	1
Peterborough 8	d		08 09				08 18	08 26	08 32			08 45	08 57	09 07					09 12	09 15			09 26	09 33		
Huntingdon	a						08 32					08 59							09 26		←					
	d						08 33					08 59							09 26 →		09 26					
St Neots	d						08 41					09 06									09 34					
Sandy	d						08 48					09 14			←											
Biggleswade	d						08 52					09 17 →			09 17											
Arlesey	d						08 57								09 22											
Cambridge	d	07 55		08 15		08 28				08 45						08 55	09 15								09 28	09 45
Foxton	d	08 05														09 05										
Shepreth	d	08 07														09 07										
Meldreth	d	08 10														09 10										
Royston	d	08 15				08 43										09 15									09 43	
Ashwell & Morden	d	08 20														09 20										
Baldock	d	08 25				08 51										09 25									09 51	
Letchworth Garden City	d	08 29			←	08 54										09 29									09 54	
Hitchin 4	d	08 33 →			08 33	08 58	09 03				←				09 28	09 33									09 58	
Stevenage 4	d				08 39	09 03	09 09 →				09 09				09 33	09 39				09 45					10 03	
Hertford North	a																									
Knebworth	d				08 43						09 13					09 43										
Welwyn North	d				08 47						09 17					09 47						←				
Welwyn Garden City 4	d				08 50						09 20					09 50 →						09 50				
Hatfield	d				08 53						09 23											09 53				
Potters Bar	d				08 59						09 29											09 59				
Finsbury Park ⊖	d				09 08	09 21					09 41				09 51							10 08			10 21	
London Kings Cross 15 ⊖	a		09 03	09 06	09 19	09 32		09 18	09 26	09 33	09 49		09 51	10 00	10 02		10 05			10 13	10 15	10 19	10 20	10 27	10 32	10 34

		FC	FC	FC	GR	GR	FC	FC	FC	FC	GR	FC	GR	FC	FC	FC	GR	FC	FC	FC	FC	FC	GR	FC	GR	FC
		1	1	1	R 1	R 1	1	1	1	1	R 1	1	R 1	1	1	1	R 1	1	1	1	1	1	R 1	1	R 1	1
Peterborough 8	d			09 45	09 48	10 06				10 18	10 32					10 45	10 54					11 13	11 16		11 32	
Huntingdon	a			09 59						10 32						10 59						11 27				
	d		09 33	09 59						10 33						10 59						11 33				
St Neots	d		09 41	10 06						10 41					←	11 06						11 41				
Sandy	d		09 48	10 14			←			10 48 →					10 48	11 14		←				11 48 →				
Biggleswade	d		09 52	10 17 →			10 17								10 52	11 17 →		11 17								
Arlesey	d		09 57				10 22								10 57			11 22								
Cambridge	d	09 55						10 15				10 28		10 45					10 55	11 15						11 28
Foxton	d	10 05																	11 05							
Shepreth	d	10 07																	11 07							
Meldreth	d	10 10																	11 10							
Royston	d	10 15										10 43							11 15							11 43
Ashwell & Morden	d	10 20																	11 20							
Baldock	d	10 25										10 51							11 25							11 51
Letchworth Garden City	d	10 29							←			10 54							11 29		←					11 54
Hitchin 4	d	10 33 →	10 03				10 28		10 33			10 58	←		11 03			11 28	11 33 →		11 33					11 58
Stevenage 4	d		10 09				10 33		10 39		11 01 →	11 03	11 01		11 09			11 33			11 39		11 47			12 03
Hertford North	a																									
Knebworth	d		10 13						10 43						11 13						11 43					
Welwyn North	d		10 17						10 47						11 17						11 47			←		
Welwyn Garden City 4	d		10 20						10 50						11 20						11 50 →			11 50		
Hatfield	d		10 23						10 53						11 23									11 53		
Potters Bar	d		10 29						10 59						11 29									11 59		
Finsbury Park ⊖	d		10 41				10 51		11 08			11 21			11 41			11 51						12 08		12 21
London Kings Cross 15 ⊖	a		10 49		10 41	10 58	11 02	11 05	11 19			11 32	11 33	11 35	11 49		11 50	12 02		12 03			12 14	12 19	12 24	12 32

For general notes see front of timetable
For details of catering facilities see Directory of Train Operators

A From Kings Lynn (Table 17)
b Arr. 0738

Table 25

Saturdays

Peterborough, Cambridge and Stevenage → London

Network Diagram - see first page of Table 24

		FC	FC	GR	FC	FC	FC	FC	GR	FC	FC		FC	GR	FC	FC	GR	FC	GR	FC	FC	FC	FC	FC	FC	FC
		1	1	R 1	1	1	1	1	R 1	1	1		1	R 1	1	1	R 1	1	R 1	1	1	1	1	1	1	1
Peterborough [8]	d		11 45	11 48					12 15				12 18	12 34		12 45	12 50		13 07							13 18
Huntingdon	a		11 59										12 33			12 59										13 32
	d		11 59										12 33			12 59										13 33
St Neots	d		12 06		←								12 41			13 06		←								13 41
Sandy	d		12 14		11 48	←							12 48			13 14		12 48		←						13 48
Biggleswade	d		12 17		11 52	12 17							→			13 17		12 52		13 17						13 52
Arlesey	d		→		11 57	12 22										→		12 57		13 22						13 57
Cambridge	d	11 45					11 55	12 15			12 28				12 45						12 55	13 15		13 28	13 45	
Foxton	d						12 05														13 05					
Shepreth	d						12 07														13 07					
Meldreth	d						12 10														13 10					
Royston	d						12 15				12 43										13 15			13 43		
Ashwell & Morden	d						12 20														13 20					
Baldock	d						12 25				12 51										13 25			13 51		
Letchworth Garden City	d						12 29			←	12 54										13 29		←	13 54		
Hitchin [4]	d				12 03	12 28	12 33			12 33	12 58							13 03		13 28	13 33		13 33	13 58		14 03
Stevenage [4]	d				12 09	12 33	→			12 39	13 03			13 03				13 09		13 33	→		13 39	14 03		14 09
Hertford North	a																									
Knebworth	d				12 13					12 43								13 13					13 43			14 13
Welwyn North	d				12 17					12 47								13 17					13 47			14 17
Welwyn Garden City [4]	d				12 20					12 50								13 20					13 50			14 20
Hatfield	d				12 23					12 53								13 23					13 53			→
Potters Bar	d				12 29					12 59								13 29					13 59			
Finsbury Park ⊖	d				12 41	12 51				13 08	13 21							13 41		13 51			14 08	14 21		
London Kings Cross [15] ⊖	a	12 33		12 41	12 49	13 02		13 03	13 10	13 19	13 32			13 33	13 34		13 44	13 49	13 59	14 02		14 02	14 19	14 32	14 33	

		FC	GR	FC	FC	FC	FC	GR	FC	FC	FC	GR	FC	FC	GR	FC	GR	FC	FC	FC	FC	FC	FC	GR	FC	FC
		1	R 1	1	1	1	1	R 1	1	1	1	R 1	1	1	R 1	1	R 1 A	1	1	1	1	1	1	R 1	1	1
Peterborough [8]	d	13 42	13 48					14 13			14 18	14 29		14 44	14 49		15 04						15 18	15 38		15 45
Huntingdon	a	13 56									14 32			14 58									15 32			15 59
	d	13 59									14 33			14 59									15 33			15 59
St Neots	d	14 06			←						14 41			15 06				←					15 41			16 06
Sandy	d	14 14			14 14						14 48			15 14									15 48			16 14
Biggleswade	d	→			14 17						14 52			15 17				15 17					15 52			→
Arlesey	d				14 22						14 57			→				15 22					15 57			
Cambridge	d					13 55	14 15			14 28			14 45						14 55	15 15		15 28			15 45	
Foxton	d					14 05													15 05							
Shepreth	d					14 07													15 07							
Meldreth	d					14 10													15 10							
Royston	d					14 15				14 43									15 15			15 43				
Ashwell & Morden	d					14 20													15 20							
Baldock	d					14 25				14 51									15 25			15 51				
Letchworth Garden City	d					14 29			←	14 54									15 29		←	15 54				
Hitchin [4]	d				14 28	14 33			14 33	14 58	15 03					←		15 28	15 33		15 33	15 58	16 03			
Stevenage [4]	d		14 17		14 33	→			14 39	15 03	15 09					15 09		15 33	→		15 39	16 03	16 09			
Hertford North	a										→												→			
Knebworth	d								14 43							15 13					15 43					
Welwyn North	d			←					14 47							15 17					15 47					
Welwyn Garden City [4]	d			14 20					14 50							15 20					15 50					
Hatfield	d			14 23					14 53							15 23					15 53					
Potters Bar	d			14 29					14 59							15 29					15 59					
Finsbury Park ⊖	d			14 41	14 51				15 08	15 21						15 41		15 51			16 08	16 21				
London Kings Cross [15] ⊖	a		14 44	14 49	15 02		15 03	15 10	15 19	15 32		15 21	15 33		15 41	15 49	15 58	16 02		16 05	16 19	16 32		16 30	16 35	

		GR	FC	FC	FC		FC	FC	FC	GR	FC	FC	FC	FC	GR	FC	FC	FC	FC	GR	FC	FC	FC	GR	FC	FC
		R 1	1	1	1		1	1	1	R 1	1	1	1	1	R 1 B	1	1	1	1	R 1	1	1	1	R 1	1	1
Peterborough [8]	d	15 50							16 18	16 31				16 43	16 46					17 12			17 18	17 36		17 44
Huntingdon	a								16 32					16 57									17 32			17 58
	d								16 33					16 59									17 33			17 59
St Neots	d			←					16 41				←	17 06			←						17 41			18 06
Sandy	d			16 14					16 48				16 48	17 14			17 14						17 48			18 14
Biggleswade	d			16 17					→				16 52	→			17 17						17 52			→
Arlesey	d			16 22									16 57				17 22						17 57			
Cambridge	d				15 55		16 15				16 28	16 45						16 55	17 15			17 28			17 45	
Foxton	d				16 05													17 05								
Shepreth	d				16 07													17 07								
Meldreth	d				16 10													17 10								
Royston	d				16 15						16 43							17 15				17 43				
Ashwell & Morden	d				16 20													17 20								
Baldock	d				16 25						16 51							17 25				17 51				
Letchworth Garden City	d				16 29			←			16 54							17 29			←	17 54				
Hitchin [4]	d		←	16 28	16 33			16 33			16 58		17 03				17 28	17 33			17 33	17 58	18 03			
Stevenage [4]	d	16 19	16 09	16 33	→			16 39		17 00	17 03		17 09		17 16		17 33	→			17 39	18 03	18 09			
Hertford North	a																						→			
Knebworth	d		16 13					16 43					17 13								17 43					
Welwyn North	d		16 17					16 47					17 17			←					17 47					
Welwyn Garden City [4]	d		16 20					16 50					17 20			17 20					17 50					
Hatfield	d		16 23					16 53					→			17 23					17 53					
Potters Bar	d		16 29					16 59								17 29					17 59					
Finsbury Park ⊖	d		16 41	16 51				17 08			17 21					17 41	17 51				18 08	18 21				
London Kings Cross [15] ⊖	a	16 47	16 49	17 02			17 02	17 19		17 28	17 32	17 35			17 43	17 50	18 02		18 05	18 10	18 19	18 32		18 28	18 34	

For general notes see front of timetable
For details of catering facilities see
Directory of Train Operators

A The Highland Chieftain
B The Flying Scotsman

Table 25

Saturdays

Peterborough, Cambridge and Stevenage → London

Network Diagram - see first page of Table 24

		GR	FC	FC	FC	FC	FC	FC	FC	FC	FC	GR	FC	FC	FC	GR	FC	FC	FC	GR	FC	FC	FC	FC	GR	FC
		R										R				R				R					R	
		1	1	1	1	1	1	1	1	1	1	1	1	1	1	1	1	1	1	1	1	1	1	1	1	1
																			A							
Peterborough 8	d	17 50								18 18	18 43	18 48				19 12	19 18			19 38		19 45		20 14	20 17	
Huntingdon	a									18 32	18 57						19 32					19 59		20 28		
	d									18 33	18 59						19 33					19 59		20 33		
St Neots	d			←						18 41	19 06						19 41				←	20 06		20 41		
Sandy	d			18 14						18 48	19 14			←			19 48				19 48	20 14		20 48		
Biggleswade	d			18 17						18 52	19 17			19 17			→				19 52	20 17		→		
Arlesey	d			18 22						18 57	→			19 22							19 57	20 22				
Cambridge	d				17 55	18 15		18 28	18 45						18 55				19 28				19 55			
Foxton	d				18 05										19 05								20 05			
Shepreth	d				18 07										19 07								20 07			
Meldreth	d				18 10										19 10								20 10			
Royston	d				18 15			18 43							19 15				19 43				20 15			
Ashwell & Morden	d				18 20										19 20								20 20			
Baldock	d				18 25			18 51							19 25				19 51				20 25			
Letchworth Garden City	d				18 29		←	18 54							19 29				19 54				20 29			
Hitchin 4	d		←	18 28	18 33		18 33	18 58		19 03			←	19 28	19 33				19 58		20 03	20 28	20 33			
Stevenage 4	d	18 19	18 09	18 33	→		18 39	19 03		19 09			19 09	19 33	19 39	19 43			20 03	20 07	20 09	20 33	20 39		20 48	
Hertford North	a									→																
Knebworth	d		18 13				18 43						19 13		19 43						20 13		20 43			
Welwyn North	d		18 17				18 47						19 17		19 47			←			20 17		20 47			←
Welwyn Garden City 4	d		18 20				18 50						19 20		19 50			19 50			20 20		20 50			20 50
Hatfield	d		18 23				18 53						19 23		→			19 53			20 23		→			20 53
Potters Bar	d		18 29				18 59						19 29					19 59			20 29					20 59
Finsbury Park	⊖ d		18 41	18 51			19 08	19 21					19 41	19 51				20 08	20 21		20 41	20 51				21 08
London Kings Cross 15	⊖ a	18 46	18 49	19 02		19 03	19 19	19 32	19 33			19 40	19 49	20 02		20 12		20 19	20 32	20 35	20 49	21 02			21 15	21 19

		FC	FC	FC	GR	FC	FC	FC	FC	GR	FC	FC	FC	FC	GR	FC	FC	FC	FC	FC	FC	FC	FC	FC		
					R					R					R											
		1	1	1	1	1	1	1	1	1	1	1	1	1	1	1	1	1	1	1	1	1	1	1		
		A										A							A	B	C		B	C		
Peterborough 8	d			20 45	20 51				21 15	21 19				21 45	21 51					22 18	22 18	22 42				
Huntingdon	a			20 59					21 29					21 59						22 32	22 32	22 56				
	d			20 59					21 33					21 59						22 33	22 33	22 56				
St Neots	d		←	21 06			←		21 41				←	22 06			←			22 41	22 41	23 03				
Sandy	d		20 48	21 14			21 14		21 48				21 48	22 14			22 14			22 48	22 48	23 11				
Biggleswade	d		20 52	→			21 17		→				21 52	→			22 17			22 52	22 52	23 14				
Arlesey	d		20 57				21 22						21 57				22 22			22 57	22 57	23 19				
Cambridge	d	20 28						20 55				21 28						21 55	22 28				23 06	23 06		
Foxton	d							21 05										22 05					23 15	23 15		
Shepreth	d							21 07										22 07					23 18	23 18		
Meldreth	d							21 10										22 10					23 21	23 21		
Royston	d	20 43						21 15				21 43						22 15	22 43				23 25	23 25		
Ashwell & Morden	d							21 20										22 20					23 29	23 29		
Baldock	d	20 51						21 25				21 51						22 25	22 51				23 34	23 34		
Letchworth Garden City	d	20 54						21 29				21 54						22 29	22 54				23 37	23 37		
Hitchin 4	d	20 58	21 03				21 28	21 33				21 58	22 03				22 28	22 33	22 58	23 03	23 03	23 25	23 41	23 41		
Stevenage 4	d	21 03	21 09		21 20		21 33	21 39		21 51		22 03	22 09		22 20		22 33	22 39	23 03	23 09	23 09	23 30	23 46	23 46		
Hertford North	a																									
Knebworth	d		21 13					21 43					22 13					22 43		23 13	23 13		23 49	23 49		
Welwyn North	d		21 17			←		21 47			←		22 17			←		22 47		23 17	23 17		23 53	23 53		
Welwyn Garden City 4	d		21 20			21 20		21 50			21 50		22 20			22 20		22 50		23 20	23 20		23 56	23 56		
Hatfield	d		→			21 23		→			21 53		→			22 23		22 53		23 23	23 23		23 59	23 59		
Potters Bar	d					21 29					21 59					22 29		22 59		23 29	23a29		00 05	00a05		
Finsbury Park	⊖ d	21 21				21 41	21 51				22 08	22 21				22 41	23s07	23s16	23s34	23 44		23 55	00s23			
London Kings Cross 15	⊖ a	21 32			21 48	21 49	22 02			22 17	22 19	22 34			22 47	22 49	23 16	23 30	23 47	23 53		00 08	00 34			

For general notes see front of timetable
For details of catering facilities see Directory of Train Operators

A From Kings Lynn (Table 17)
B Until 6 September
C From 13 September. To Alexandra Palace (Table 24)

Table 25

Sundays

until 13 July

Peterborough, Cambridge and Stevenage → London

Network Diagram - see first page of Table 24

		FC 1	FC bus	FC bus	FC bus	FC 1	FC bus	FC bus	FC bus	FC 1	FC bus	FC 1	FC 1	FC 1	FC 1	FC 1	FC 1	FC 1	FC 1	FC 1	GR R 1 catering	FC 1	FC 1
Peterborough 8	d				05 06				06 06			08 05						08 58			09 53		
Huntingdon	a				05 41				06 41			08 19						09 12					
	d			04 50	05 41			05 50	06 41			08 19						09 12					
St Neots	d			05 20				06 20				08 26						09 19					
Sandy	d			05 40				06 40				08 34						09 27					
Biggleswade	d			05 50				06 50				08 37						09 30					
Arlesey	d			06 10				07 10				08 42						09 35					
Cambridge	d	23p06				06 28				07 28			08 11	08 28		08 55	09 15			09 28		09 55	10 15
Foxton	d	23p15											08 21			09 05						10 05	
Shepreth	d	23p18											08 23			09 07						10 07	
Meldreth	d	23p21											08 26			09 10						10 10	
Royston	d	23p25				06 43				07 43			08 31	08 43		09 15				09 43		10 15	
Ashwell & Morden	d	23p29											08 36			09 20						10 20	
Baldock	d	23p34				06 51				07 52			08 41	08 51		09 25				09 51		10 25	
Letchworth Garden City	d	23p37				06 54				07 55			08 45	08 54		09 29				09 54		10 29	
Hitchin 4	d	23p41	06 03	06 28	06 33	06a58	07 03	07 28	07 33	07a59	08 03	08 48	08 51	08 58		09 33		09 41		09 58		10 33	
Stevenage 4	d	23p46	06 23	06 48	06 53		07 23	07 48	07 53		08 23	08 53	08 57	09 03		09 39		09 46		10 03		10 39	
Hertford North	a																						
Knebworth	d	23p49		06 55				07 55					09 01			09 43						10 43	
Welwyn North	d	23p53		07 05				08 05					09 05		←	09 47			←			10 47	
Welwyn Garden City 4	d	23p56	06a45	07a15	07a15		07a45	08a15	08a15		08a45		09 08 →		09 08	09 50 →			09 50			10 50 →	
Hatfield	d	23p59													09 11				09 53				
Potters Bar	d	00 05													09 17				09 59				
Finsbury Park	⊖ d	00s23										09 11		09 21	09 26			10 05	10 11	10 21			
London Kings Cross 15	⊖ a	00 34										09 19		09 29	09 35		10 03	10 12	10 19	10 29	10 47		11 08

		FC 1	FC 1	GR R 1 catering	FC 1	FC 1	GR R 1 catering	FC 1	FC 1	FC 1	GR R 1 catering	FC 1	FC 1	GR R 1 catering	FC 1	FC 1	FC 1	GR R 1 catering	FC 1	FC 1	GR R 1 catering	FC 1	FC 1
Peterborough 8	d	09 58		10 27		10 45	11 02				11 26			11 38	11 45			12 16			12 41	12 46	
Huntingdon	a	10 12				10 59									11 59							12 59	
	d	10 12				10 59									11 59							12 59	
St Neots	d	10 20				11 06									12 06							13 06	
Sandy	d	10 27				11 14		←							12 14							13 14	
Biggleswade	d	10 31				11 17		11 17							12 17							13 17	
Arlesey	d	10 36				→		11 22							12 22							13 22	
Cambridge	d				10 28				10 55	11 15			11 28			11 55	12 15			12 28			12 55
Foxton	d								11 05							12 05							13 05
Shepreth	d								11 07							12 07							13 07
Meldreth	d								11 10							12 10							13 10
Royston	d				10 43				11 15				11 43			12 15				12 43			13 15
Ashwell & Morden	d								11 20							12 20							13 20
Baldock	d				10 51				11 25				11 51			12 25				12 51			13 25
Letchworth Garden City	d				10 54				11 29			←	11 54			12 29			←	12 54			13 29
Hitchin 4	d	10 45			10 58			11 28	11 33			11 33	11 58		12 28	12 33			12 33	12 58		13 28	13 33
Stevenage 4	d	10 50		10 58	11 03			11 33	→			11 39	12 03	12 09	12 33	→			12 39	13 03		13 33	13 39
Hertford North	a																						
Knebworth	d											11 43							12 43				13 43
Welwyn North	d		←									11 47							12 47				13 47
Welwyn Garden City 4	d		10 50									11 50							12 50				13 50 →
Hatfield	d		10 53									11 53							12 53				
Potters Bar	d		10 59									11 59							12 59				
Finsbury Park	⊖ d	11 07	11 11		11 21			11 51				12 11	12 21		12 51				13 11	13 21		13 51	
London Kings Cross 15	⊖ a	11 18	11 19	11 26	11 30		11 55	12 00		12 04	12 19	12 19	12 30	12 37	13 00		13 03	13 10	13 19	13 30	13 36	14 00	

For general notes see front of timetable
For details of catering facilities see Directory of Train Operators

Sundays

until 13 July

Peterborough, Cambridge and Stevenage → London

Network Diagram - see first page of Table 24

		FC	GR	FC	FC	FC	FC	FC	GR	GR	FC	FC	GR	FC	FC	FC	FC	GR	FC	FC	GR	FC
		1	R 1	1	1	1	1	1	R 1	R 1	1	1	R 1	1	1	1	1	R 1	1	1	R 1	1
Peterborough 8	d		13 06			13 48			14 10	14 22			14 43	14 49				15 36		15 43	15 47	
Huntingdon	a					13 59								14 59						15 59		
	d					13 59								14 59						15 59		
St Neots	d					14 06								15 06						16 06		←
Sandy	d					14 14								15 14						16 14		16 14
Biggleswade	d					14 17								15 17						→		16 17
Arlesey	d					14 22								15 22								16 22
Cambridge	d	13 15			13 28		13 55	14 15				14 28			14 55	15 15			15 28			
Foxton	d						14 05								15 05							
Shepreth	d						14 07								15 07							
Meldreth	d						14 10								15 10							
Royston	d				13 43		14 15					14 43			15 15				15 43			
Ashwell & Morden	d						14 20								15 20							
Baldock	d				13 51		14 25					14 51			15 25				15 51			
Letchworth Garden City	d				13 54		14 29				←	14 54			15 29		←		15 54			
Hitchin 4	d				13 58	14 28	14 33				14 33	14 58		15 28	15 33		15 33		15 58			16 28
Stevenage 4	d		13 42		14 03	14 33	→				14 39	15 03		15 33	→		15 39		16 04		16 17	16 33
Hertford North	a																					
Knebworth	d										14 43						15 43					
Welwyn North	d			←							14 47						15 47					
Welwyn Garden City 4	d			13 50							14 50						15 50					
Hatfield	d			13 53							14 53						15 53					
Potters Bar	d			13 59							14 59						15 59					
Finsbury Park ⊖	d			14 11	14 21	14 51					15 11	15 21		15 51			16 11		16 21			16 51
London Kings Cross 15 ⊖	a	14 02	14 10	14 19	14 30	15 02		15 05	15 11	15 15	15 19	15 30	15 37	16 03		16 06	16 19	16 29	16 34		16 45	17 00

		FC	FC	FC	GR	FC	FC	FC	GR	GR	FC	FC	FC	GR	FC	FC	GR	FC	GR	FC	FC	FC	GR
		1	1	1	R 1	1	1	1	R 1	R 1	1	1	1	R 1	1	1	R 1	1	R 1	1	1	1	R 1
									A					B									
Peterborough 8	d				16 19			16 45	16 51	17 02				17 18			17 41	17 45	18 02				18 21
Huntingdon	a							16 59										17 59					
	d							16 59										17 59					
St Neots	d							17 06			←							18 06					
Sandy	d							17 14			17 14							18 14		←			
Biggleswade	d							→			17 17							18 17		18 17			
Arlesey	d										17 22							→		18 22			
Cambridge	d	15 55	16 15				16 28					16 55	17 15			17 28					17 55	18 15	
Foxton	d	16 05										17 05									18 05		
Shepreth	d	16 07										17 07									18 07		
Meldreth	d	16 10										17 10									18 10		
Royston	d	16 15					16 43					17 15				17 43					18 15		
Ashwell & Morden	d	16 20										17 20									18 20		
Baldock	d	16 25					16 51					17 25				17 51					18 25		
Letchworth Garden City	d	16 29		←			16 54					17 29			←	17 54					18 29		
Hitchin 4	d	16 33		16 33			16 58				17 28	17 33			17 33	17 58				18 28	18 33		
Stevenage 4	d	→		16 39	16 49		17 03		17 22		17 33	→			17 39	18 03	18 11			18 33	→		
Hertford North	a																						
Knebworth	d			16 43											17 43								
Welwyn North	d			16 47		←									17 47								
Welwyn Garden City 4	d			16 50		16 50									17 50								
Hatfield	d			→		16 53									17 53								
Potters Bar	d					16 59									17 59								
Finsbury Park ⊖	d					17 11	17 21				17 51				18 11	18 21				18 51			
London Kings Cross 15 ⊖	a		17 03		17 17	17 19	17 30		17 50	17 55	18 00		18 03	18 15	18 19	18 30	18 38		18 55	19 00		19 07	19 16

		FC	FC	FC	GR	GR	FC	FC	FC	GR	FC	GR	FC	GR	GR	FC	GR	FC	FC	FC	FC	GR	FC
		1	1	1	R 1	R 1	1	1	1	R 1	1	R 1	1	R 1	R 1	1	R 1	1	1	1	1	R 1	1
Peterborough 8	d			18 45	18 50	18 58				19 19		19 29		19 33	19 41	19 47	20 02					20 23	
Huntingdon	a			18 59												19 59							
	d			18 59												19 59							
St Neots	d			19 06			←									20 06		←					
Sandy	d			19 14			19 14									20 14		20 14					
Biggleswade	d			→			19 17									→		20 17					
Arlesey	d						19 22											20 22					
Cambridge	d		18 28					18 55	19 15				19 28						19 55	20 15			20 28
Foxton	d							19 05											20 05				
Shepreth	d							19 07											20 07				
Meldreth	d							19 10											20 10				
Royston	d		18 43					19 15					19 43						20 15				20 43
Ashwell & Morden	d							19 20											20 20				
Baldock	d		18 51					19 25					19 51						20 25				20 51
Letchworth Garden City	d	←	18 54					19 29			←		19 54						20 29		←		20 54
Hitchin 4	d	18 33	18 58				19 28	19 33			19 33		19 58					20 28	20 33		20 33		20 58
Stevenage 4	d	18 39	19 03		19 21		19 33	→			19 39		20 03	20 07	20 13		20 32	20 33	→		20 39	20 54	21 03
Hertford North	a																						
Knebworth	d	18 43									19 43										20 43		
Welwyn North	d	18 47									19 47										20 47		
Welwyn Garden City 4	d	18 50									19 50										20 50		
Hatfield	d	18 53									19 53										20 53		
Potters Bar	d	18 59									19 59										20 59		
Finsbury Park ⊖	d	19 11	19 21				19 51				20 11		20 21					20 51			21 11		21 21
London Kings Cross 15 ⊖	a	19 19	19 29		19 48	19 52	20 00		20 03	20 12	20 19	20 23	20 30	20 34	20 38		20 59	21 04		21 05	21 19	21 25	21 30

For general notes see front of timetable
For details of catering facilities see Directory of Train Operators

A The Flying Scotsman
B The Highland Chieftain

Table 25

Sundays

until 13 July

Peterborough, Cambridge and Stevenage → London

Network Diagram - see first page of Table 24

		FC	GR		FC	FC	FC	FC	GR	FC		FC	GR	FC	FC	GR	FC		FC	GR	FC	FC	FC			
		1	R 1 ✕		1	1	1	1	R 1 ✕	1		1	R 1 ✕	1	1	R 1 ✕	1		1	R 1 ✕	1	1	1 A			
Peterborough 8	d	20 45	20 48						21 18				21 36	21 45		22 04				22 44		22 48				
Huntingdon	a	20 59												21 59								22 59				
	d	20 59												21 59								22 59				
St Neots	d	21 06			←									22 06								23 06				
Sandy	d	21 14			21 14									22 14								23 14				
Biggleswade	d	→			21 17									22 17								23 17				
Arlesey	d				21 22									22 22								23 22				
Cambridge	d					20 55	21 15					21 28			21 55		22 15				22 41		23 13			
Foxton	d					21 05									22 05											
Shepreth	d					21 07									22 07											
Meldreth	d					21 10									22 10											
Royston	d					21 15						21 43			22 15						22 55		23 26			
Ashwell & Morden	d					21 20									22 20											
Baldock	d					21 25						21 51			22 25						23 03					
Letchworth Garden City	d					21 29		←				21 54			22 29				←		23 06		23 36			
Hitchin 4	d				21 28	21 33		21 33				21 58		22 28	22 33				22 33		23 11	23 28	23 40			
Stevenage 4	d		21 20		21 33	→		21 39	21 48			22 03	22 09	22 33	→	22 34			22 39		23 16	23 33	23 45			
Hertford North	a																									
Knebworth	d							21 43											22 43				23 48			
Welwyn North	d							21 47		←									22 47				23 52			
Welwyn Garden City 4	d							21 50		21 50									22 50				23 56			
Hatfield	d							→		21 53									22 53				23 59			
Potters Bar	d									21 59									22 59				00 04			
Finsbury Park ⊖	d				21 51					22 11		22 21		22 56					23 11		23 38	23 58	00 20			
London Kings Cross 15 ⊖	a		21 47		22 00		22 03		22 16	22 19		22 32	22 37	23 09		23 14	23 15		23 24	23 50	23 54	00 13	00 32			

Sundays

20 July to 7 September

		FC	FC	FC	FC	FC	FC		FC	FC	FC	FC	FC	FC		FC	FC	FC	FC	FC	FC		FC	GR	FC	FC
		1	🚌	🚌	🚌	1	🚌		🚌	🚌	1	🚌	1	1		1	1	1	1	1	1		1	R 1 ✕	1	1
Peterborough 8	d				05 06					06 06			08 05							08 58				09 53		
Huntingdon	a				05 41					06 41			08 19							09 12						
	d			04 50	05 41				05 50	06 41			08 19							09 12						
St Neots	d			05 20					06 20				08 26							09 19						
Sandy	d			05 40					06 40				08 34							09 27						
Biggleswade	d			05 50					06 50				08 37							09 30						
Arlesey	d			06 10					07 10				08 42							09 35						
Cambridge	d	23p06				06 28					07 28			08 11		08 28		08 55	09 15				09 28		09 55	10 15
Foxton	d	23p15												08 21				09 05							10 05	
Shepreth	d	23p18												08 23				09 07							10 07	
Meldreth	d	23p21												08 26				09 10							10 10	
Royston	d	23p25				06 43					07 43			08 31		08 43		09 15					09 43		10 15	
Ashwell & Morden	d	23p29												08 36				09 20							10 20	
Baldock	d	23p34				06 51					07 52			08 41		08 51		09 25					09 51		10 25	
Letchworth Garden City	d	23p37				06 54					07 55			08 45		08 54		09 29					09 54		10 29	
Hitchin 4	d	23p41	06 03	06 28	06 33	06a58	07 03		07 28	07 33	07a59	08 03	08 48	08 51		08 58		09 33		09 41			09 58		10 33	
Stevenage 4	d	23p46	06 23	06 48	06 53		07 23		07 48	07 53		08 23	08 53	08 57		09 03		09 39		09 46			10 03		10 39	
Hertford North	a																									
Knebworth	d	23p49		06 55					07 55					09 01				09 43							10 43	
Welwyn North	d	23p53		07 05					08 05					09 05			←	09 47			←				10 47	
Welwyn Garden City 4	d	23p56	06a45	07a15	07a15		07a45		08a15	08a15		08a45		09 08			09 08	09 50			09 50				10 50	
Hatfield	d	23p59												→			09 11	→			09 53				→	
Potters Bar	d	00 05															09 17				09 59					
Finsbury Park ⊖	d	00s23											09 11			09 21	09 26			10 05	10 11		10 21			
London Kings Cross 15 ⊖	a	00 34											09 19			09 29	09 35		10 03	10 12	10 19		10 29	10 47		11 08

For general notes see front of timetable
For details of catering facilities see
Directory of Train Operators

A From Kings Lynn (Table 17)

Table 25

Sundays

20 July to 7 September

Peterborough, Cambridge and Stevenage → London

Network Diagram - see first page of Table 24

	FC	FC	GR	FC		FC	GR	FC	FC	FC	GR		FC	FC	GR	FC	FC	FC		GR	FC	FC	GR	FC	FC
	1	1	R 1	1		1	R 1	1	1	1	R 1		1	1	R 1	1	1	1		R 1	1	1	R 1	1	1
Peterborough 8 d	09 58		10 27			10 45	11 02				11 26				11 38	11 45				12 16			12 41	12 46	
Huntingdon a	10 12					10 59										11 59								12 59	
d	10 12					10 59										11 59								12 59	
St Neots d	10 20					11 06										12 06								13 06	
Sandy d	10 27					11 14		←								12 14								13 14	
Biggleswade d	10 31					11 17		11 17								12 17								13 17	
Arlesey d	10 36					→		11 22								12 22								13 22	
Cambridge d				10 28					10 55	11 15				11 28			11 55	12 15				12 28			12 55
Foxton d									11 05								12 05								13 05
Shepreth d									11 07								12 07								13 07
Meldreth d									11 10								12 10								13 10
Royston d				10 43					11 15					11 43			12 15					12 43			13 15
Ashwell & Morden d									11 20								12 20								13 20
Baldock d				10 51					11 25					11 51			12 25					12 51			13 25
Letchworth Garden City d				10 54					11 29				←	11 54			12 29				←	12 54			13 29
Hitchin 4 d	10 45			10 58				11 28	11 33				11 33	11 58		12 28	12 33				12 33	12 58		13 28	13 33
Stevenage 4 d	10 50		10 58	11 03				11 33	→				11 39	12 03	12 09	12 33	→				12 39	13 03		13 33	13 39
Hertford North a																									
Knebworth d													11 43								12 43				13 43
Welwyn North d		←											11 47								12 47				13 47
Welwyn Garden City 4 d		10 50											11 50								12 50				13 50
Hatfield d		10 53											11 53								12 53				→
Potters Bar d		10 59											11 59								12 59				
Finsbury Park ⊖ d	11 07	11 11		11 21				11 51					12 11	12 21		12 51					13 11	13 21		13 51	
London Kings Cross 15 ⊖ a	11 18	11 19	11 26	11 30			11 55	12 00		12 04	12 19		12 19	12 30	12 37	13 00		13 03		13 10	13 19	13 30	13 36	14 00	

	FC	GR		FC	FC	FC	FC	FC	GR		GR	FC	FC	GR	FC	FC		FC	FC	GR	FC	FC	GR		FC
	1	R 1		1	1	1	1	1	R 1		R 1	1	1	R 1	1	1		1	1	R 1	1	1	R 1		1
Peterborough 8 d		13 06				13 48			14 10		14 22			14 43	14 49					15 36		15 43	15 47		
Huntingdon a						13 59									14 59							15 59			
d						13 59									14 59							15 59			
St Neots d						14 06									15 06							16 06			←
Sandy d						14 14									15 14							16 14			16 14
Biggleswade d						14 17									15 17							→			16 17
Arlesey d						14 22									15 22										16 22
Cambridge d	13 15				13 28		13 55	14 15					14 28			14 55		15 15			15 28				
Foxton d							14 05									15 05									
Shepreth d							14 07									15 07									
Meldreth d							14 10									15 10									
Royston d					13 43		14 15						14 43			15 15					15 43				
Ashwell & Morden d							14 20									15 20									
Baldock d					13 51		14 25						14 51			15 25					15 51				
Letchworth Garden City d					13 54		14 29					←	14 54			15 29			←		15 54				
Hitchin 4 d					13 58	14 28	14 33					14 33	14 58		15 28	15 33			15 33		15 58				16 28
Stevenage 4 d		13 42			14 03	14 33	→					14 39	15 03		15 33	→			15 39		16 04		16 17		16 33
Hertford North a																									
Knebworth d												14 43							15 43						
Welwyn North d				←								14 47							15 47						
Welwyn Garden City 4 d				13 50								14 50							15 50						
Hatfield d				13 53								14 53							15 53						
Potters Bar d				13 59								14 59							15 59						
Finsbury Park ⊖ d				14 11	14 21	14 51						15 11	15 21		15 51				16 11		16 21				16 51
London Kings Cross 15 ⊖ a	14 02	14 10		14 19	14 30	15 02		15 05	15 11		15 15	15 19	15 30	15 37	16 03			16 06	16 19	16 29	16 34		16 45		17 00

	FC	FC	FC	GR	FC	FC		FC	GR	GR	FC	FC	FC		GR	FC	FC	GR	FC	GR		FC	FC	FC	GR
	1	1	1	R 1	1	1		1	R 1	R 1	1	1	1		R 1	1	1	R 1	1	R 1		1	1	1	R 1
									A						B										
Peterborough 8 d				16 19				16 45	16 51	17 02					17 18			17 41	17 45	18 02					18 21
Huntingdon a								16 59											17 59						
d								16 59											17 59						
St Neots d								17 06			←								18 06						
Sandy d								17 14			17 14								18 14			←			
Biggleswade d								→			17 17								18 17			18 17			
Arlesey d											17 22								→			18 22			
Cambridge d	15 55	16 15				16 28						16 55	17 15				17 28						17 55	18 15	
Foxton d	16 05											17 05											18 05		
Shepreth d	16 07											17 07											18 07		
Meldreth d	16 10											17 10											18 10		
Royston d	16 15					16 43						17 15					17 43						18 15		
Ashwell & Morden d	16 20											17 20											18 20		
Baldock d	16 25					16 51						17 25					17 51						18 25		
Letchworth Garden City d	16 29		←			16 54						17 29				←	17 54						18 29		
Hitchin 4 d	16 33		16 33			16 58					17 28	17 33				17 33	17 58					18 28	18 33		
Stevenage 4 d	→		16 39	16 49		17 03			17 22		17 33	→				17 39	18 03	18 11				18 33	→		
Hertford North a																									
Knebworth d			16 43													17 43									
Welwyn North d			16 47		←											17 47									
Welwyn Garden City 4 d			16 50		16 50											17 50									
Hatfield d			→		16 53											17 53									
Potters Bar d					16 59											17 59									
Finsbury Park ⊖ d					17 11	17 21					17 51					18 11	18 21					18 51			
London Kings Cross 15 ⊖ a		17 03		17 17	17 19	17 30			17 50	17 55	18 00		18 03		18 15	18 19	18 30	18 38		18 55		19 00		19 07	19 16

For general notes see front of timetable
For details of catering facilities see Directory of Train Operators

A The Flying Scotsman
B The Highland Chieftain

Sundays

20 July to 7 September

Peterborough, Cambridge and Stevenage → London

Network Diagram - see first page of Table 24

	FC	FC	FC	GR		GR	FC	FC	FC	GR	FC		GR	FC	GR	GR	FC	GR		FC	FC	FC	FC	GR	FC
	1	1	1	R 1		R 1	1	1	1	R 1	1		R 1	1	R 1	R 1	1	R 1		1	1	1	1	R 1	1
				☕ ✕		☕ ✕				☕ ✕			☕ ✕		☕ ✕	☕ ✕		☕ ✕						☕ ✕	
Peterborough 8 d			18 45	18 50		18 58				19 19			19 29		19 33	19 41	19 47	20 02						20 23	
Huntingdon a			18 59														19 59								
d			18 59														19 59								
St Neots d			19 06				←										20 06			←					
Sandy d			19 14				19 14										20 14			20 14					
Biggleswade d			→				19 17										→			20 17					
Arlesey d							19 22													20 22					
Cambridge d		18 28						18 55	19 15					19 28							19 55	20 15			20 28
Foxton d								19 05													20 05				
Shepreth d								19 07													20 07				
Meldreth d								19 10													20 10				
Royston d		18 43						19 15						19 43							20 15				20 43
Ashwell & Morden d								19 20													20 20				
Baldock d		18 51						19 25						19 51							20 25				20 51
Letchworth Garden City d	←	18 54						19 29			←			19 54							20 29		←		20 54
Hitchin 4 d	18 33	18 58					19 28	19 33			19 33			19 58						20 28	20 33		20 33		20 58
Stevenage 4 d	18 39	19 03		19 21			19 33	→			19 39			20 03	20 07	20 13		20 32		20 33	→		20 39	20 54	21 03
Hertford North a																									
Knebworth d	18 43										19 43												20 43		
Welwyn North d	18 47										19 47												20 47		
Welwyn Garden City 4 d	18 50										19 50												20 50		
Hatfield d	18 53										19 53												20 53		
Potters Bar d	18 59										19 59												20 59		
Finsbury Park ⊖ d	19 11	19 21					19 51				20 11			20 21						20 51			21 11		21 21
London Kings Cross 15 ⊖ a	19 19	19 29		19 48		19 52	20 00		20 03	20 12	20 19		20 23	20 30	20 34	20 38		20 59		21 04		21 05	21 19	21 25	21 30

	FC	GR		FC	FC	FC	FC	GR	FC		FC	GR	FC	FC	GR	FC		FC	GR	FC	FC	FC			
	1	R 1		1	1	1	1	R 1	1		1	R 1	1	1	R 1	1		1	R 1	1	1	1			
																						A			
		☕ ✕						☕ ✕				☕ ✕			☕ ✕				☕ ✕						
Peterborough 8 d	20 45	20 48						21 18				21 36	21 45		22 04				22 44		22 48				
Huntingdon a	20 59												21 59								22 59				
d	20 59												21 59								22 59				
St Neots d	21 06			←									22 06								23 06				
Sandy d	21 14			21 14									22 14								23 14				
Biggleswade d	→			21 17									22 17								23 17				
Arlesey d				21 22									22 22								23 22				
Cambridge d					20 55	21 15					21 28			21 55		22 15				22 41		23 13			
Foxton d					21 05									22 05											
Shepreth d					21 07									22 07											
Meldreth d					21 10									22 10											
Royston d					21 15						21 43			22 15						22 55		23 26			
Ashwell & Morden d					21 20									22 20											
Baldock d					21 25						21 51			22 25						23 03					
Letchworth Garden City d					21 29		←				21 54			22 29				←		23 06		23 36			
Hitchin 4 d				21 28	21 33		21 33				21 58		22 28	22 33				22 33		23 11	23 28	23 40			
Stevenage 4 d		21 20		21 33	→		21 39	21 48			22 03	22 09	22 33	→	22 34			22 39		23 16	23 33	23 45			
Hertford North a																									
Knebworth d							21 43											22 43				23 48			
Welwyn North d							21 47		←									22 47				23 52			
Welwyn Garden City 4 d							21 50		21 50									22 50				23 56			
Hatfield d							→		21 53									22 53				23 59			
Potters Bar d									21 59									22 59				00 04			
Finsbury Park ⊖ d				21 51					22 11		22 21		22 56					23 11		23 38	23 58	00 20			
London Kings Cross 15 ⊖ a		21 47		22 00		22 03		22 16	22 19		22 32	22 37	23 09		23 14	23 15		23 24	23 50	23 54	00 13	00 32			

For general notes see front of timetable
For details of catering facilities see Directory of Train Operators

A From Kings Lynn (Table 17)

Table 25

from 14 September

Peterborough, Cambridge and Stevenage → London

Network Diagram - see first page of Table 24

		FC	FC	FC	FC	FC	FC	FC	FC	FC	FC	FC	FC	GR	FC	FC	FC	FC	GR	FC	FC	GR	FC	FC	FC	GR
														R					R			R				R
		1	1	1	1	1	1	1	1	1	1	1	1	1	1	1	1	1	1	1	1	1	1	1	1	1
														☕🍴					☕🍴			☕🍴				☕🍴
Peterborough 8	d	05 50		06 45		07 45					08 58			09 53			09 58		10 27		10 45	11 02				11 26
Huntingdon	a	06 04		06 59		07 59					09 12						10 12				10 59					
	d	06 04		06 59		07 59					09 12						10 12				10 59					
St Neots	d	06 11		07 06		08 06					09 19						10 20				11 06					
Sandy	d	06 19		07 14		08 14					09 27						10 27				11 14		←			
Biggleswade	d	06 22		07 17		08 17					09 30						10 31				11 17		11 17			
Arlesey	d	06 27		07 22		08 22					09 35						10 36				→		11 22			
Cambridge	d		06 28		07 28		07 55	08 28	08 55	09 15			09 28		09 55	10 15				10 28				10 55	11 15	
Foxton	d						08 05		09 05						10 05									11 05		
Shepreth	d						08 07		09 07						10 07									11 07		
Meldreth	d						08 10		09 10						10 10									11 10		
Royston	d		06 43		07 43		08 15	08 43	09 15				09 43		10 15					10 43				11 15		
Ashwell & Morden	d						08 20		09 20						10 20									11 20		
Baldock	d		06 51		07 52		08 25	08 51	09 25				09 51		10 25					10 51				11 25		
Letchworth Garden City	d		06 54		07 55		08 29	08 54	09 29				09 54		10 29					10 54				11 29		
Hitchin 4	d	06 33	06 58	07 28	07 59	08 28	08 33	08 58	09 33		09 41		09 58		10 33		10 45			10 58			11 28	11 33		
Stevenage 4	d	06 41	07 03	07 33	08 05	08 33	08 39	09 03	09 39		09 46		10 03		10 39		10 50		10 58	11 03			11 33	→		
Hertford North	a																									
Knebworth	d			07 37			08 43		09 43						10 43											
Welwyn North	d			07 40			08 47		09 47			←			10 47			←								
Welwyn Garden City 4	d			07 43			08 50		09 50			09 50			10 50			10 50								
Hatfield	d						08 53		→			09 53			→			10 53								
Potters Bar	d						08 59					09 59						10 59								
Finsbury Park	⊖ d	07a10	07a38	08a10	08 32	08 51	09 11	09 21			10 05	10 11	10 21				11 07	11 11		11 21			11 51			
London Kings Cross 15	⊖ a				08 42	09 00	09 19	09 30		10 03	10 12	10 19	10 29	10 47		11 08	11 18	11 19	11 26	11 30		11 55	12 00		12 04	12 19

		FC	FC	GR	FC	FC	FC	GR		FC	FC	GR	FC	FC	FC	GR	FC	FC	FC	FC	FC	GR	GR	FC	FC	GR
				R				R				R				R						R	R			R
		1	1	1	1	1	1	1		1	1	1	1	1	1	1	1	1	1	1	1	1	1	1	1	1
				☕🍴				☕🍴				☕🍴				☕🍴						☕🍴	☕🍴			☕🍴
Peterborough 8	d			11 38	11 45			12 16				12 41	12 46			13 06			13 48			14 10	14 22			14 43
Huntingdon	a				11 59								12 59						13 59							
	d				11 59								12 59						13 59							
St Neots	d				12 06								13 06						14 06							
Sandy	d				12 14								13 14						14 14							
Biggleswade	d				12 17								13 17						14 17							
Arlesey	d				12 22								13 22						14 22							
Cambridge	d		11 28			11 55	12 15				12 28			12 55	13 15			13 28		13 55	14 15				14 28	
Foxton	d					12 05								13 05						14 05						
Shepreth	d					12 07								13 07						14 07						
Meldreth	d					12 10								13 10						14 10						
Royston	d		11 43			12 15					12 43			13 15				13 43		14 15					14 43	
Ashwell & Morden	d					12 20								13 20						14 20						
Baldock	d		11 51			12 25					12 51			13 25				13 51		14 25					14 51	
Letchworth Garden City	d	←	11 54			12 29				←	12 54			13 29				13 54		14 29				←	14 54	
Hitchin 4	d	11 33	11 58		12 28	12 33				12 33	12 58		13 28	13 33				13 58	14 28	14 33				14 33	14 58	
Stevenage 4	d	11 39	12 03	12 09	12 33	→				12 39	13 03		13 33	13 39		13 42		14 03	14 33	→				14 39	15 03	
Hertford North	a																									
Knebworth	d	11 43								12 43				13 43										14 43		
Welwyn North	d	11 47								12 47				13 47			←							14 47		
Welwyn Garden City 4	d	11 50								12 50				13 50			13 50							14 50		
Hatfield	d	11 53								12 53				→			13 53							14 53		
Potters Bar	d	11 59								12 59							13 59							14 59		
Finsbury Park	⊖ d	12 11	12 21		12 51					13 11	13 21		13 51				14 11	14 21	14 51					15 11	15 21	
London Kings Cross 15	⊖ a	12 19	12 30	12 37	13 00		13 03	13 10		13 19	13 30	13 36	14 00		14 02	14 10	14 19	14 30	15 02		15 05	15 11	15 15	15 19	15 30	15 37

		FC	FC	FC	FC	GR	FC	FC	GR	FC	FC	FC	FC	GR	FC	FC		FC	GR	GR	FC	FC	FC	GR	FC	FC
						R			R					R					R	R				R		
		1	1	1	1	1	1	1	1	1	1	1	1	1	1	1		1	1	1	1	1	1	1	1	1
																			A					B		
						☕🍴			☕🍴					☕🍴					☕🍴	☕🍴				☕🍴		
Peterborough 8	d	14 49				15 36		15 43	15 47					16 19				16 45	16 51	17 02				17 18		
Huntingdon	a	14 59						15 59										16 59								
	d	14 59						15 59										16 59								
St Neots	d	15 06						16 06		←								17 06			←					
Sandy	d	15 14						16 14		16 14								17 14			17 14					
Biggleswade	d	15 17						→		16 17								→			17 17					
Arlesey	d	15 22								16 22											17 22					
Cambridge	d		14 55	15 15			15 28				15 55	16 15				16 28						16 55	17 15			17 28
Foxton	d		15 05								16 05											17 05				
Shepreth	d		15 07								16 07											17 07				
Meldreth	d		15 10								16 10											17 10				
Royston	d		15 15				15 43				16 15					16 43						17 15				17 43
Ashwell & Morden	d		15 20								16 20											17 20				
Baldock	d		15 25				15 51				16 25					16 51						17 25				17 51
Letchworth Garden City	d		15 29		←		15 54				16 29		←			16 54						17 29			←	17 54
Hitchin 4	d	15 28	15 33		15 33		15 58			16 28	16 33		16 33			16 58					17 28	17 33			17 33	17 58
Stevenage 4	d	15 33	→		15 39		16 04		16 17	16 33	→		16 39	16 49		17 03			17 22		17 33	→			17 39	18 03
Hertford North	a																									
Knebworth	d				15 43								16 43												17 43	
Welwyn North	d				15 47								16 47		←										17 47	
Welwyn Garden City 4	d				15 50								16 50		16 50										17 50	
Hatfield	d				15 53								→		16 53										17 53	
Potters Bar	d				15 59										16 59										17 59	
Finsbury Park	⊖ d	15 51			16 11		16 21			16 51					17 11	17 21					17 51				18 11	18 21
London Kings Cross 15	⊖ a	16 03		16 06	16 19	16 29	16 34		16 45	17 00		17 03		17 17	17 19	17 30			17 50	17 55	18 00		18 03	18 15	18 19	18 30

For general notes see front of timetable
For details of catering facilities see
Directory of Train Operators

A The Flying Scotsman
B The Highland Chieftain

Sundays

from 14 September

Peterborough, Cambridge and Stevenage → London

Network Diagram - see first page of Table 24

		GR	FC	GR	FC	FC	FC	GR	FC	FC	FC	GR	GR	FC	FC	FC	GR	FC	GR	FC	GR	GR	FC	GR	FC	FC
		R 1 🍴	1	R 1 🍴	1	1	1	R 1 🍴	1	1	1	R 1 🍴	R 1 🍴	1	1	1	R 1 🍴	1	R 1 🍴	1	R 1 🍴	R 1 🍴	1	R 1 🍴	1	1
Peterborough 8	d	17 41	17 45	18 02				18 21			18 45	18 50	18 58				19 19		19 29		19 33	19 41	19 47	20 02		
Huntingdon	a		17 59								18 59												19 59			
	d		17 59								18 59												19 59			
St Neots	d		18 06								19 06												20 06			
Sandy	d		18 14		←						19 14 →			← 19 14									20 14 →		← 20 14	
Biggleswade	d		18 17 →		18 17									19 17											20 17	
Arlesey	d				18 22									19 22											20 22	
Cambridge	d					17 55	18 15			18 28					18 55	19 15				19 28						19 55
Foxton	d					18 05									19 05											20 05
Shepreth	d					18 07									19 07											20 07
Meldreth	d					18 10									19 10											20 10
Royston	d					18 15				18 43					19 15					19 43						20 15
Ashwell & Morden	d					18 20									19 20											20 20
Baldock	d					18 25				18 51					19 25					19 51						20 25
Letchworth Garden City	d					18 29			←	18 54					19 29			←		19 54						20 29
Hitchin 4	d				18 28	18 33 →			18 33	18 58				19 28	19 33 →			19 33		19 58					20 28	20 33 →
Stevenage 4	d	18 11			18 33				18 39	19 03		19 21		19 33				19 39		20 03	20 07	20 13		20 32	20 33	
Hertford North	a																									
Knebworth	d								18 43									19 43								
Welwyn North	d								18 47									19 47								
Welwyn Garden City 4	d								18 50									19 50								
Hatfield	d								18 53									19 53								
Potters Bar	d								18 59									19 59								
Finsbury Park ⊖	d				18 51				19 11	19 21				19 51				20 11		20 21					20 51	
London Kings Cross 15 ⊖	a	18 38		18 55	19 00		19 07	19 16	19 19	19 29		19 48	19 52	20 00		20 03	20 12	20 19	20 23	20 30	20 34	20 38		20 59	21 04	

		FC	FC	GR	FC	FC	GR	FC	FC	FC	FC	GR	FC	FC	GR	FC	FC	GR	FC	FC	GR	FC	FC	FC
		1	1	R 1 🍴	1	1	R 1 🍴	1	1	1	1	R 1 🍴	1	1	R 1 🍴	1	1	R 1 🍴	1	1	R 1 🍴	1	1	1 A
Peterborough 8	d			20 23		20 45	20 48					21 18			21 36	21 45		22 04			22 44		22 48	
Huntingdon	a					20 59										21 59							22 59	
	d					20 59										21 59							22 59	
St Neots	d					21 06										22 06							23 06	
Sandy	d					21 14 →		← 21 14								22 14							23 14	
Biggleswade	d							21 17								22 17							23 17	
Arlesey	d							21 22								22 22							23 22	
Cambridge	d	20 15			20 28				20 55	21 15				21 28			21 55		22 15			22 41		23 13
Foxton	d								21 05								22 05							
Shepreth	d								21 07								22 07							
Meldreth	d								21 10								22 10							
Royston	d				20 43				21 15					21 43			22 15					22 55		23 26
Ashwell & Morden	d								21 20								22 20							
Baldock	d				20 51				21 25					21 51			22 25					23 03		
Letchworth Garden City	d		←		20 54				21 29		←			21 54			22 29			←		23 06		23 36
Hitchin 4	d		20 33		20 58			21 28	21 33 →		21 33			21 58		22 28	22 33 →			22 33		23 11	23 28	23 40
Stevenage 4	d		20 39	20 54	21 03		21 20	21 33			21 39	21 48		22 03	22 09	22 33		22 34		22 39		23 16	23 33	23 45
Hertford North	a																							
Knebworth	d		20 43								21 43									22 43				23 48
Welwyn North	d		20 47								21 47		←							22 47				23 52
Welwyn Garden City 4	d		20 50								21 50 →		21 50							22 50				23 56
Hatfield	d		20 53										21 53							22 53				23 59
Potters Bar	d		20 59										21 59							22 59				00 04
Finsbury Park ⊖	d		21 11		21 21			21 51					22 11	22 21		22 56				23 11		23 38	23 58	00 20
London Kings Cross 15 ⊖	a	21 05	21 19	21 25	21 30		21 47	22 00		22 03		22 16	22 19	22 32	22 37	23 09		23 14	23 15	23 24	23 50	23 54	00 13	00 32

For general notes see front of timetable
For details of catering facilities see
Directory of Train Operators

A From Kings Lynn (Table 17)

Route Diagram for Table 26

DM-4/08
Design BAJS

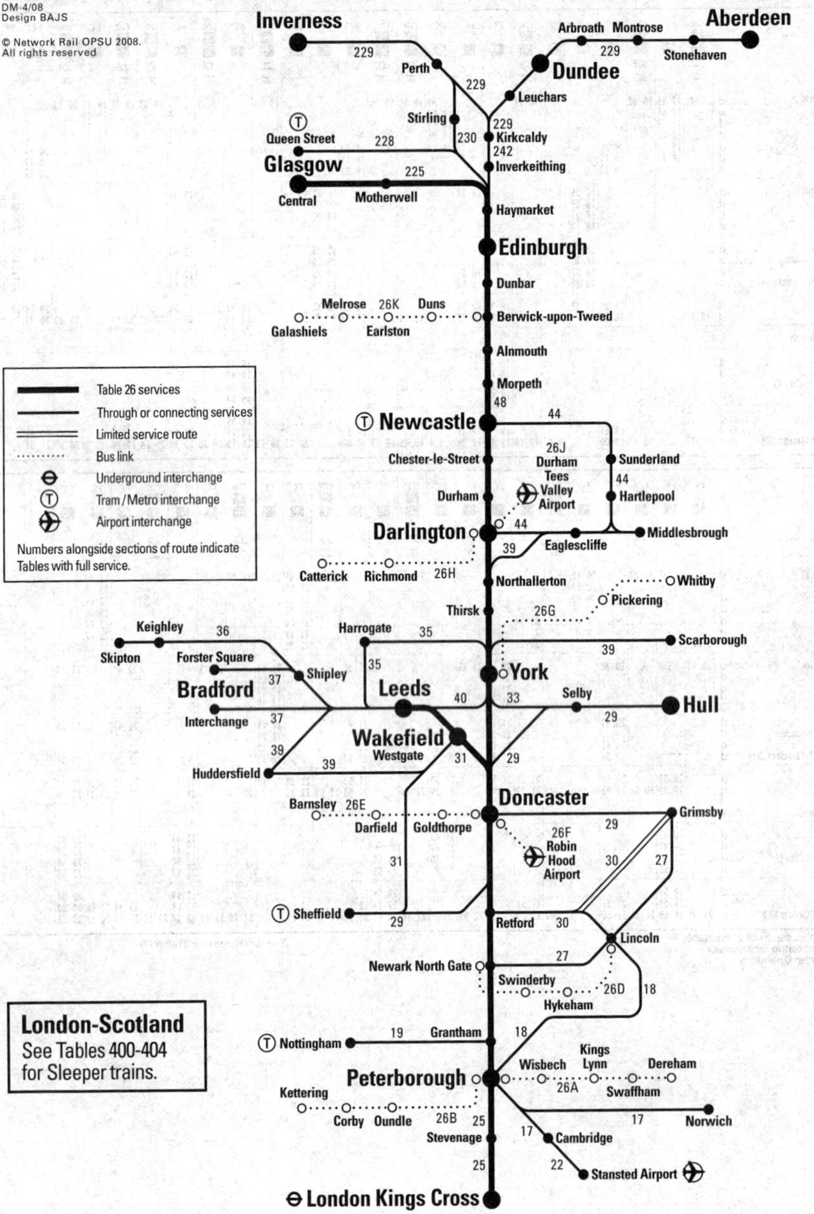

London-Scotland
See Tables 400-404 for Sleeper trains.

London → Humberside, Yorkshire, North East England and Scotland

Route Diagram - see first page of Table 26

Miles	Miles	Miles			XC	NT	GR	NT	TP	GR	NT	TP	TP	GR	NT	XC	TP	XC	GR	GR	TP	GR	XC	XC	EM
							R			R				R					R	R		R			
					1 ◇		1		1 ◇	1		1 ◇	1 ◇	1		1 ◇	1 ◇	1 ◇	1	1	1 ◇	1	1 ◇	1 ◇	◇
						A		B	C		D	E			D		C	G					H	J	K
0	—	—	**London Kings Cross 15** ⊖	d															06 00	06 15		06 35			
27½	—	—	**Stevenage 4**	d															06 19	06 34					
76¼	—	—	**Peterborough 8**	a															06 50	07 05		07 21			
—	—	—	Norwich	d																					05 52
—	—	—	Stansted Airport	d																*05 21*					
—	—	—	Cambridge	d																*05 58*					
—	—	—	**Peterborough 8**	d															06 51	07 06		07 21			07 27
105½	—	—	**Grantham 7**	a															07 10	07 25		07 40			07 58
—	—	—		d															07 10	07 25		07 40			
120	—	—	**Newark North Gate 7**	a															07 22	07 37					
—	—	—	Lincoln	a																*08 13*					
—	—	—	Grimsby Town	a																*09 15*		*09b42*			
—	—	—	**Newark North Gate 7**	d															07 22	07 37					
138½	—	—	**Retford 10**	d															07 37	07 52					
156	0	—	**Doncaster 7**	a															07 51	08 07		08 12			
—	—	—	Selby	a																					
—	—	—	Hull	a																		*09 13*			
—	19¾	—	**Wakefield Westgate 7**	a															08 10			08 36			
—	—	—	Huddersfield	a															*09 04*			*09c27*			
—	29¾	—	**Leeds 10**	a															08 32			08 52			
—	—	—	Shipley	a															*09 01*			*09 21*			
—	—	—	Bradford Forster Square	a															*09e11*			*09e28*			
—	—	—	Keighley	a															*09 11*			*09 50*			
—	—	—	Skipton	a															*09 24*			*10 07*			
—	—	—	Sheffield 7	d						*05 29*				*05 50*		*06 54*		07f10					07 54	07 46	
—	—	—	**Doncaster 7**	d						06 15						07 49				08 08			08 26	08 26	
188½	—	—	**York 8**	a						06 35						08 10				08 31			08 48	08 52	
—	—	—	Scarborough	a																					
—	—	—	Harrogate	a																*09 18*					
—	—	—	Leeds 10	d					04g50			06 35	*06 55*	07 10			07 50	07 57					*08 12*		
—	—	—	Hull	d									*06h00*							*07 07*					
—	—	—	**York 8**	d					05 40	06 37		07 06	07 32	07 37		08 12	08 22	08 27		08 33	08 42		08 50		
210¾	—	—	Thirsk	d					06 01			07 22	07 54				08 38								
218½	—	—	Northallerton	d					06 17			07 30	08 02				08 49				09 03				
232½	—	—	**Darlington 7**	a					06 28	07 05		07 41		08 05		08 38		08 53		09 02	09 14		09 20		
—	—	—	Eaglescliffe	a																					
—	—	—	Middlesbrough	a					07 01	*07 50*		*08 12*	08 32				09 20	*09 27*					*09 57*		
—	—	—	**Darlington 7**	d				06 14		07 06	07 20	07 42		08 05	08 15	08 39		08 53		09 03	09 15		09 22		
254½	—	—	**Durham**	d				06 35		07 23	07 41	07 59		08 26	08 36	08 57		09 09		09 20	09 31		09 38		
260¼	—	—	Chester-le-Street	d				06 42			07 48	08 05			08 43	09 03							09 45		
268½	—	—	**Newcastle 8**	a				06 55		07 39	08 00	08 19		08 39	08 59	09 22		09 25		09 38	09 49		10 00		
—	—	—	Hartlepool	a																					
—	—	—	Sunderland	a				*07 49*				*08 49*				*09 49*									
—	—	—	**Newcastle 8**	d		06 00	06 25			07 41				08 41				09 27		09 39					
285	—	—	Morpeth	d		06 20	06 38			*08a21*				08 55				09 42							
303¼	—	—	Alnmouth	d		06a37	06 52			08 07								09 56							
335½	—	—	**Berwick-upon-Tweed**	d			07 14			08 29				09 30						10 22					
363¾	—	—	Dunbar	d	06 40		07 38			08 52				09 55											
393	—	—	**Edinburgh 10**	a	07 13		08 06			09 19				10 20				11 02		11 13					
—	—	0	**Edinburgh**	d	07 25		08 09			09 21				10 26											
394¼	—	1¼	Haymarket	d	07 29		08 14			09 26				10 31											
437½	—	—	Motherwell	a	08 06		09 06			10 05								*12 25*							
450¼	—	—	**Glasgow Central 15**	a	08 28		09 25			10 24				*11j20*				*12k06*		*12k20*					
—	—	—	Stirling	a	*08m23*		*09m23*			*10m23*				*11m23*				*12 23*		*12 23*					
—	—	—	Perth	a	*09n36*		*09m54*			*10m56*				*12n37*				*12 56*		*12 56*					
—	—	—	**Inverness**	a	*11m59*		*11m59*			*13q35*								*15 18*		*15 18*					
—	—	13¼	Inverkeithing	a	*08m04*		*08m54*			*09m56*				10 47				*11 36*							
—	—	26	Kirkcaldy	a	*08m26*		*09m10*			*10m12*				11 04				*11 58*							
—	—	51	Leuchars 3	a	*09m09*		*10m08*			*11m12*				11 29											
—	—	59¼	**Dundee**	a	*09m22*		*10m21*			*11m24*				11 44											
—	—	76¼	Arbroath	a	*09m42*		*10m38*			*11m41*				12 01											
—	—	90	Montrose	a	*10r31*		*10m52*			*12m17*				12 17											
—	—	114¼	Stonehaven	a	*10m15*		*11m14*			*12m14*				12 40											
—	—	130½	**Aberdeen**	a	*10m35*		*11m34*			*12m35*				13 03											

For general notes see front of timetable
For details of catering facilities see Directory of Train Operators

- **A** To Chathill (Table 48)
- **B** From Middlesbrough (Table 44)
- **C** From Manchester Airport (Table 39)
- **D** From Saltburn (Table 44)
- **E** From Manchester Piccadilly (Table 39)
- **G** Until 5 September from Birmingham New Street
- **H** Until 5 September. From Birmingham New Street (Table 51)
- **J** From 8 September. From Birmingham New Street (Table 51)
- **K** To Liverpool Lime Street (from 8 September to Chesterfield) (Table 49)
- **b** Change at Doncaster
- **c** Change at Leeds
- **e** Bradford Interchange
- **f** Until 5 September dep. 0712
- **g** Mondays until 7 July and from 8 September dep. 0452, Mondays 14 July to 1 September dep. 0455
- **h** Change at Selby and York
- **j** Glasgow Queen Street. Change at Edinburgh
- **k** Glasgow Queen Street
- **m** Change at Edinburgh
- **n** Change at Edinburgh and Stirling
- **q** Change at Edinburgh and Perth
- **r** Change at Edinburgh and Arbroath

London → Humberside, Yorkshire, North East England and Scotland

Route Diagram - see first page of Table 26

		GR	TP	TP	XC	GR	HT	GR	XC	XC	EM	GR	GR	TP	GC	TP	XC	GR	GR	XC	XC	EM	TP
		R 1	1 ◇	1 ◇	R 1	R 1	BHX 1 ◇	R 1	R 1	R 1	◇	R 1	R 1	1 ◇	R 1	1 ◇	R 1	R 1	R 1	R 1	R 1	◇	1 ◇
			A	A	B				C	D	E			A		A	G			H	J	E	A
		✕				✕	⊠	✕				✕	✕		✕			✕	✕				
London Kings Cross 15 ⊖	d	07 00				07 10	07 20	07 30				07 35	08 00		08 04			08 10	08 30				
Stevenage 4	d	07 19				07 29	07u44	07 50				07 56							08 49				
Peterborough 8	a	07 50				08 00		08 21					08 46					08 59	09 20				
Norwich	d												06b33										
Stansted Airport	d																	07 20					
Cambridge	d	06 50									07 27							07 59					
Peterborough 8	d	07 51				08 01		08 21			08 30		08 46					08 59	09 21			09 27	
Grantham 7	a						08 30	08 45			08 58											09 57	
	d						08 31	08 45															
Newark North Gate 7	a					08 28													09 48				
Lincoln	a					09 00		10c02											10 21				
Grimsby Town	a							10e44											11 20				
Newark North Gate 7	d					08 28													09 48				
Retford 10	d						08 52																
Doncaster 7	a					08 58	09 05	09 16															
Selby	a						09 21																
Hull	a						10 04																
Wakefield Westgate 7	a					09 16						09 26						10 01					
Huddersfield	a					10 04						10f27						10f57					
Leeds 10	a					09 36						09 46						10 21					
Shipley	a					10 01						10 07						10 51					
Bradford Forster Square	a					10g11						10g28						10g57					
Keighley	a					10 11						10 20						11 11					
Skipton	a					10 24						10 37						11 24					
Sheffield 7	d				08 21				08 54	08 46							09 21			09 54	09 46		
Doncaster 7	d							09 17	09 22	09 22										10 17	10 17		
York 8	a	08 55						09 39	09 48	09 53			09 53		10 07				10 33	10 40	10 44		
Scarborough	a	10 30																					
Harrogate	a	09 43										10 33	10 43		11 30			11 33					
Leeds 10	d		08 27	08 57	09 05				09 12					09 27		09 57	10 05						10 27
Hull	d													08h38		09 02							
York 8	d	08 57	09 03	09 26	09 36			09 42	09 51				09 54	10 00	10 14	10 26	10 31		10 35	10 43			10 54
Thirsk	d			09 46											10 30	10 46							
Northallerton	d		09 24	09 55										10 21	10 39	10 55							11 15
Darlington 7	a	09 30	09 36		10 01			10 10	10 16				10 22	10 32			10 59		11 05	11 12			11 26
Eaglescliffe	a														10 57								
Middlesbrough	a		10 23	10 30									10 54	11 22		11 30							12 00
Darlington 7	d	09 31	09 37		10 03			10 10	10 18				10 23	10 33			11 01		11 06	11 14			11 27
Durham	d		09 54		10 19				10 34				10 40	10 50			11 18		11 23	11 30			11 44
Chester-le-Street	d								10 41					10 56									
Newcastle 8	a	10 02	10 10		10 34			10 44	10 57				10 58	11 10			11 32		11 41	11 54			11 59
Hartlepool	a														11 20								
Sunderland	a														11 50								
Newcastle 8	d	10 04			10 37								10 59				11 34						
Morpeth	d	10a35											11a35				11 49						
Alnmouth	d																12 03						
Berwick-upon-Tweed	d	10 47			11 21								11 42										
Dunbar	d				11 44																		
Edinburgh 10	a	11 30			12 17								12 30				13 16						
Edinburgh	d	11 39																					
Haymarket	d	11 44																					
Motherwell	a	12 25			14 26												14 26						
Glasgow Central 15	a	12 45			13j20								13j36				14j20						
Stirling	a	12k53			13 23								13 53				14 23						
Perth	a	13m37											14m37				14 54						
Inverness	a																17 07						
Inverkeithing	a	12k05											13 03				14 05						
Kirkcaldy	a	12k27											13 25				14 27						
Leuchars 3	a	13k12											14 11				15 12						
Dundee	a	13k24											14 23				15 24						
Arbroath	a	13k41											14 40				15 43						
Montrose	a	14n31											14 55				16n31						
Stonehaven	a	14k17											15 16				16 17						
Aberdeen	a	14k36											15 36				16 37						

For general notes see front of timetable
For details of catering facilities see Directory of Train Operators

A From Manchester Airport (Table 39)
B From Birmingham New Street (Table 51)
C Until 5 September. From Birmingham New Street (Table 51)
D From 8 September. From Birmingham New Street (Table 51)
E To Liverpool Lime Street (from 8 September to Chesterfield) (Table 49)
G From Bristol Temple Meads (from 8 September from Birmingham New Street) (Table 51)
H Until 5 September. From Bristol Temple Meads (Table 51)
J From 8 September. From Bristol Temple Meads (Table 51)

b Change at Ely and Peterborough
c Change at Peterborough
e Change at Doncaster
f Change at Leeds
g Bradford Interchange
h Change at Selby and York
j Glasgow Queen Street
k Change at Edinburgh
m Change at Edinburgh and Stirling
n Change at Edinburgh and Arbroath

London → Humberside, Yorkshire, North East England and Scotland

Route Diagram - see first page of Table 26

		GR	GR	TP	XC	GR	GR	XC	XC	GR	HT	EM	GR	XC	TP	TP	GR	GR	XC	XC	XC	GR	EM	GR
				A	B			C	D			E	G	H	A	A		J	K	L	N		E	
London Kings Cross 15 ⊖	d	08 40	09 00			09 10	09 30			09 35	09 48		10 00				10 10	10 30				10 35		11 00
Stevenage 4	d						09 49			09 54	10u09							10 12						10 46
Peterborough 8	a	09 27	09 47			09 56	10 20			10 26			10 45				10 56	11 16				11 22		11 46
Norwich	d											08 57											09 57	
Stansted Airport	d						08 20											09 19						
Cambridge	d						09 04											10 04						10b33
Peterborough 8	d	09 28	09 47			09 56	10 21			10 27		10 30	10 45				10 56	11 17				11 23	11 25	11 46
Grantham 7	a	09 49								10 46	10 53	11 10					11 15					11 42	11 56	
	d	09 49								10 46	10 54						11 15					11 42		
Newark North Gate 7	a						10 48										11 27					11 55		
Lincoln	a	10c58								12c06												12 30		
Grimsby Town	a		11e42								12e44											13 35		
Newark North Gate 7	d						10 48										11 27					11 55		
Retford 10	d	10 12									11 17						11 42							
Doncaster 7	a	10 27	10 34				11 12			11 17	11 30						11 57					12 18		
Selby	a										11 51													
Hull	a		11 53								12 32						13 06					13 52		
Wakefield Westgate 7	a	10 51				10 56				11 36							12 15					12 36		
Huddersfield	a	11f45				11f58				12f27							13 04					13f27		
Leeds 10	a	11 09				11 18				11 55							12 35					12 54		
Shipley	a	11 37				11 51				12 21							13 01					13 21		
Bradford Forster Square	a	11g42				11g57				12g28							13g11					13g28		
Keighley	a	11 50				12 20				12 50							13 11					13 52		
Skipton	a	12 07				12 37				13 07							13 24					14 09		
Sheffield 7	d				10 21			10 54	10 46										11 21	11 54	11 46			
Doncaster 7	d		10 35				11 12	11 17	11 17											12 17	12 17			
York 8	a		11 02				11 37	11 43	11 48				11 53					12 26		12 43	12 48			12 51
Scarborough	a		12 30															13 30						
Harrogate	a		11 43			12 03							12 43				13 33							13 43
Leeds 10	d			10 57	11 05			11 12							11 27	11 57		11 41	12 05	12 12				
Hull	d				10h12											11 05								
York 8	d		11 03	11 26	11 32		11 41	11 46					11 54		12 01	12 26		12 29	12 34	12 46				12 52
Thirsk	d			11 46												12 46								
Northallerton	d			11 55			12 00								12 22	12 55								
Darlington 7	a		11 33		11 58		12 14	12 20					12 25		12 33				13 00	13 11				13 20
Eaglescliffe	a																							
Middlesbrough	a			12 30	12 31			12 53							13 17	13 30								13 56
Darlington 7	d		11 34		12 00		12 14	12 21					12 26	←	12 34				13 02	13 13				13 20
Durham	d				12 23		12 32	12j45 →						12 45	12 50				13 19	13 29				
Chester-le-Street	d													12 51										
Newcastle 8	a		12 03		12 36		12 50						12 55	13 05	13 08			13 22	13 33	13 49				13 50
Hartlepool	a																							
Sunderland	a		12 49															13 49						
Newcastle 8	d		12 05		12 40								12 57					13 24	13 35					13 51
Morpeth	d		12a36										13a23											14a36
Alnmouth	d		12 31																14 01					
Berwick-upon-Tweed	d		12 53		13 22																			14 34
Dunbar	d				13 45																			
Edinburgh 10	a		13 38		14 16								14 24					14 53	15 17					15 20
Edinburgh	d		13 41															15 00						15 22
Haymarket	d																	15 04						
Motherwell	a		14 26		16 06																			16 06
Glasgow Central 15	a		14 45		15k21								15k37					16m07	16k20					16 25
Stirling	a		14n53		15 23													15n53						16n23
Perth	a		15q36		16q37													16q37						17q20
Inverness	a																							19q34
Inverkeithing	a		14n10										15 04					15 18						16n04
Kirkcaldy	a		14n42										15 26					15 35						16n26
Leuchars 3	a		15n12															16 00						17n10
Dundee	a		15n24															16 17						17n26
Arbroath	a		15n43															16 35						17n49
Montrose	a		16r31															16 51						18n03
Stonehaven	a		16n17															17 14						18n25
Aberdeen	a		16n37															17 37						18n44

For general notes see front of timetable
For details of catering facilities see Directory of Train Operators

- **A** From Manchester Airport (Table 39)
- **B** From Southampton Central (from 8 September from Bristol Temple Meads) (Table 51)
- **C** Until 5 September. From Cardiff Central (Table 51)
- **D** From 8 September. From Southampton Central (Table 51)
- **E** To Liverpool Lime Street (from 8 September to Chesterfield) (Table 49)
- **G** **The Flying Scotsman**
- **H** From Cardiff Central (from 8 September from Southampton Central) (Table 51)
- **J** **The Northern Lights**
- **K** From Plymouth (from 8 September from Cardiff Central) (Table 51)
- **L** Until 5 September. From Plymouth (Table 51)
- **N** From 8 September. From Plymouth (Table 51)

- **b** Change at Ely and Peterborough
- **c** Change at Peterborough
- **e** Change at Doncaster
- **f** Change at Leeds
- **g** Bradford Interchange
- **h** Change at Selby and York
- **j** Arr. 1238
- **k** Glasgow Queen Street
- **m** Glasgow Queen Street. Change at Edinburgh
- **n** Change at Edinburgh
- **q** Change at Edinburgh and Stirling
- **r** Change at Edinburgh and Arbroath

London → Humberside, Yorkshire, North East England and Scotland

Route Diagram - see first page of Table 26

		TP	GR	GC	TP	XC	GR	XC	XC	EM	GR	HT	TP	GR	TP	TP	XC	GR	GR	XC	XC	EM	GR	TP
		1◇ A	R 1	R 1	1◇ A	1◇ B	R 1	1◇ C	1◇ D	◇ E	R 1	1◇	1◇ A	R 1 G	1◇ A	1◇ A	1◇ H	R 1	R 1	1◇ C	1◇ J	◇ E	R 1	1◇ A
London Kings Cross 15 ⊖	d		11 10	11 27			11 30				11 35	11 48		12 00				12 10	12 30				12 35	
Stevenage 4	d						11 50				11 54							12 29					12 57	
Peterborough 8	a		11 56				12 21				12 27			12 46				13 00	13 16					
Norwich	d									10 57												11 57		
Stansted Airport	d						10 20											11 25						
Cambridge	d						11 04							11b12				12 04						
Peterborough 8	d		11 56				12 21			12 25	12 27			12 47				13 01	13 17			13 25		
Grantham 7	a		12 15							12 58	12 46	12 53						13 20				13 56	13 42	
	d		12 15								12 46	12 54						13 20					13 42	
Newark North Gate 7	a		12 27				12 50				12 58												13 55	
Lincoln	a										13 28												14 56	
Grimsby Town	a											14c44												
Newark North Gate 7	d		12 27				12 50				12 58												13 55	
Retford 10	d											13 16						13 42						
Doncaster 7	a		12 55				13 14					13 29						13 57	14 06				14 20	
Selby	a											13 44												
Hull	a		14 08									14 25							15 07					
Wakefield Westgate 7	a		13 17								13 37							14 14					14 39	
Huddersfield	a		14 04								14e27							15 04					15e45	
Leeds 10	a		13 41								13 55							14 35					15 01	
Shipley	a		14 07								14 21							15 01					15 37	
Bradford Forster Square	a		14f11								14f28							15f11					15f42	
Keighley	a		14 20								14 50							15 11					15 50	
Skipton	a		14 37								15 07							15 24					16 07	
Sheffield 7	d					12 21		12 54	12 46								13 21		13 11	11 54	14 46			
Doncaster 7	d						13 15	13 24	13 24										14 07	14 20	14 20			
York 8	a			13 19			13 39	13 46	13 54					14 00					14 34	14 45	14 50			
Scarborough	a			14 30										15 30					16 30					
Harrogate	a		14 33											14 43				15 33						
Leeds 10	d	12 27			12 57	13 05		13 12					13 27			13 57	14 05			14 12				14 27
Hull	d				11g38														13 12					
York 8	d	12 59		13 22	13 26	13 32	13 42	13 50					13 54	14 02	←	14 26	14 33		14 36	14 46				14 54 →
Thirsk	d			13 38	13 46											14 43								
Northallerton	d	13 20		13 47	13 55								14 16 →		14 16	14 54			14 58					
Darlington 7	a	13 31				14 00	14 10	14 16							14 27		14 58		15 11	15 16				
Eaglescliffe	a			14 04																				
Middlesbrough	a				14 30	14 32		14 55							15 22	15 30				15 55				
Darlington 7	d	13 32				14 02	14 11	14 18							14 34		15 00		15 11	15 18				
Durham	d	13 48				14 19	14 28	14 35							14 50		15 16		15 29	15 35				
Chester-le-Street	d	13 54						14 42																
Newcastle 8	a	14 09				14 36	14 47	14 56						14 58	15 06		15 31		15 47	15 59				
Hartlepool	a			14 23																				
Sunderland	a	14 49		14 50											15 49									
Newcastle 8	d					14 38								15 00			15 35							
Morpeth	d														15a35		15 48							
Alnmouth	d																16 02							
Berwick-upon-Tweed	d					15 22																		
Dunbar	d					15 45																		
Edinburgh 10	a					16 16								16 26			17 14							
Edinburgh	d					16 30								16 33										
Haymarket	d					16 35								16 38										
Motherwell	a																							
Glasgow Central 15	a					17h21								17h36			18j22							
Stirling	a													17 19			18 07							
Perth	a													17 55			18k48							
Inverness	a													20 08			20 58							
Inverkeithing	a					16 47								17m03			17 51							
Kirkcaldy	a					17 02								17m25			18 14							
Leuchars 3	a					17 31								18m05										
Dundee	a					17 44								18m22										
Arbroath	a					18 01								18m40										
Montrose	a					18 15								18m54										
Stonehaven	a					18 35								19m16										
Aberdeen	a					19 00								19m38										

For general notes see front of timetable
For details of catering facilities see Directory of Train Operators

A From Manchester Airport (Table 39)
B From Bournemouth (from 8 September from Plymouth) (Table 51)
C Until 5 September. From Bristol Temple Meads (Table 51)
D From 8 September. From Bournemouth (Table 51)
E To Liverpool Lime Street (from 8 September to Chesterfield) (Table 49)
G **The Highland Chieftain**
H From Plymouth (from 8 September from Bristol Temple Meads) (Table 51)
J From 8 September. From Plymouth (Table 51)

b Change at Ely and Peterborough
c Change at Doncaster
e Change at Leeds
f Bradford Interchange
g Change at Selby and York
h Glasgow Queen Street. Change at Edinburgh
j Glasgow Queen Street
k Change at Edinburgh and Stirling
m Change at Edinburgh

London → Humberside, Yorkshire, North East England and Scotland

Route Diagram - see first page of Table 26

		GR	TP	TP	GR	GR	XC	HT	XC	XC	GR	EM	GR	NT	GR	GR	TP	XC	EM	GR	XC	XC	GR
			B	B			C		D	L		E		G			B	H	E		J	K	
London Kings Cross 15 ⊖	d	13 00			13 10	13 30		13 33			13 35		14 00		14 10	14 30				14 35			15 00
Stevenage 4	d	12 46									13 12				13 46	14 12				14 54			
Peterborough 8	a	13 46			13 57						14 24				14 56	15 16							
Norwich	d											12 57							13 57				
Stansted Airport	d										12 25					13 25							
Cambridge	d	12b33									13 04					14 04							
Peterborough 8	d	13 46			13 58						14 25	14 26			14 56	15 16			15 26				
Grantham 7	a				14 17			14 34			14 44	14 56			15 15				15 55				
	d				14 17			14 35			14 44				15 15								
Newark North Gate 7	a				14 29						15 00				15 27								
Lincoln	a														16 00								
Grimsby Town	a	15c42											16c44							17c42			
Newark North Gate 7	d				14 29						15 01				15 27								
Retford 10	d					14 48		14 56															
Doncaster 7	a	14 33			14 53	15 02		15 11			15 25		15 29		15 55					16 09			
Selby	a							15 27															
Hull	a	15 51				16 04		16 10					16 49							17 08			
Wakefield Westgate 7	a				15 14	15 42					15 51				16 13					16 30			
Huddersfield	a				16 04						16e45				17 04					17e27			
Leeds 10	a				15 35	16 02					16 09				16 35					16 48			
Shipley	a				16 07						16 37				16 56					17 21			
Bradford Forster Square	a				16f11						16f42				17f11					17f28			
Keighley	a				16 20						16 51				17 10					17 45			
Skipton	a				16 37						17 07				17 26					18 01			
Sheffield 7	d					14 11	14 21		14 54	15 46								15 21			15 54	15 46	
Doncaster 7	d	14 34				15 03			15 17	16 17			15 30								16 17	16 17	
York 8	a	14 58				15 26			15 40	16 40			15 53			16 21					16 40	16 44	16 44
Scarborough	a					16 30										17 30							18 17
Harrogate	a	15 43			16 33						17 03		16 43										17 26
Leeds 10	d			14 57		14 41	15 05		15 12							15 27	15 57	16 05			16 12		
Hull	d		←													15 06							
York 8	d	15 00	14 54	15 26		15 28	15 34		15 44				15 55			16 22	16 26	16 32			16 43		16 46
Thirsk	d			15 46													16 46						
Northallerton	d		15 23	15 55													16 55						
Darlington 7	a	15 27	15 34			16 01	16 06		16 11				16 23			16 50		16 57			17 08		
Eaglescliffe	a																						
Middlesbrough	a		16 23	16 30									16 54			17 23	17 30				17 41		
Darlington 7	d	15 28	15 35			16 01	16 07		16 13				16 23			16 51		16 59			17 15 →		
Durham	d		15 51				16 25		16 30							17 08							
Chester-le-Street	d		15 57						16 37														
Newcastle 8	a	15 57	16 13			16 31	16 37		16 51				16 53			17 26		17 27					17 38
Hartlepool	a																						
Sunderland	a		16 49				17 13						17 49										
Newcastle 8	d	15 59				16 32	16 40						16 54	17 15				17 30					17 40
Morpeth	d													17 36									18a07
Alnmouth	d					16 58								18a18				17 55					
Berwick-upon-Tweed	d	16 42					17 26						17 38										18 27
Dunbar	d						17 49																
Edinburgh 10	a	17 33				18 04	18 17						18 24					18 57					19 13
Edinburgh	d	17 39											18 32					19 01					19 15
Haymarket	d	17 44											18 37					19 06					19 20
Motherwell	a	18 23																					19 57
Glasgow Central 15	a	18 41					19g21						19h36										20 17
Stirling	a	18j52					19 23						19j53										20j23
Perth	a	19k42											20k37										20j51
Inverness	a																						23j10
Inverkeithing	a	18j13											18 54					19 18					19j53
Kirkcaldy	a	18j34											19 11					19 34					20j09
Leuchars 3	a	19j13											19 35					20 04					21j28
Dundee	a	19j27											19 50					20 25					21j41
Arbroath	a	19j45											20 07					20m43					
Montrose	a												20 23					20m57					
Stonehaven	a	20j20											20 46					21m19					
Aberdeen	a	20j44											21 09					21m39					

For general notes see front of timetable
For details of catering facilities see Directory of Train Operators

- **B** From Manchester Airport (Table 39)
- **C** From Bournemouth (from 8 September from Bristol Temple Meads) (Table 51)
- **D** Until 5 September. From Paignton (Table 51)
- **E** To Liverpool Lime Street (from 8 September to Chesterfield) (Table 49)
- **G** From MetroCentre to Chathill (Table 48)
- **H** From Penzance (Table 135) (from 8 September from Paignton) (Table 51)
- **J** Until 5 September. From Bristol Temple Meads (Table 51)
- **K** From 8 September. From Brisrol Temple Meads (Table 51)
- **L** From 8 September. From Bournemouth (Table 51)
- **b** Change at Ely and Peterborough
- **c** Change at Doncaster
- **e** Change at Leeds
- **f** Bradford Interchange
- **g** Glasgow Queen Street
- **h** Glasgow Queen Street. Change at Edinburgh
- **j** Change at Edinburgh
- **k** Change at Edinburgh and Stirling
- **m** Change at Leuchars

Table 26

London → Humberside, Yorkshire, North East England and Scotland

Route Diagram - see first page of Table 26

		XC	TP	XC	GR	GR	TP	XC	XC	GR	EM	GR	TP	XC	HT	GR	GR	GR	XC	XC	GR	EM	GC	GR
														3			FO	FX						
		K	B	C			D	E	G		H		B	J					K	L		H	N	
London Kings Cross 15 ⊖	d				15 10	15 30				15 35		16 00			16 05	16 10	16 30	16 30			16 35		16 50	17 00
Stevenage 4	d				14 46	15 12				15 54							16 49	16 49			16 12			
Peterborough 8	a				15 56	16 16				16 26						16 56					17 24			
Norwich	d										14 57											15 52		
Stansted Airport	d					14 25															15 25			
Cambridge	d				14b33	15 04															16 04			
Peterborough 8	d				15 57	16 17				16 26	16 27					16 56					17 25	17 27		
Grantham 7	a				16 18					16 45	16 58				17 06	17 15	17 34	17 34				17 58		
	d				16 18					16 45					17 07	17 15	17 34	17 34						
Newark North Gate 7	a				16 29											17 27	17 46	17 46						
Lincoln	a					17 48										17 57					19c07			
Grimsby Town	a											18e46												
Newark North Gate 7	d				16 29											17 27	17 46	17 46						
Retford 10	d				16 45										17 28						18 04			
Doncaster 7	a				17 00	17 08				17 19		17 29			17 41		18 09	18 09			18 19			
Selby	a														17 59									
Hull	a				18 06										18 40		19 09	19 09			19 47			
Wakefield Westgate 7	a				17 18					17 36						18 04					18 36			
Huddersfield	a				18 05					18f27						19 04					19f27			
Leeds 10	a				17 36					17 56						18 23					18 55			
Shipley	a				18 02					18 21						18 52					19 21			
Bradford Forster Square	a				18g11					18g28						18g57					19g28			
Keighley	a				18 16					18 50						19 15					19 41			
Skipton	a				18 33					19 06						19 33					19 54			
Sheffield 7	d			16 21		16 11		16§54	16§46					17 21					17§54	17§46				
Doncaster 7	d					17 09		17§17	17§17			17 30					18 10	18 10	18§18	18§18				
York 8	a					17 34		17§40	17§45			17 54					18 34	18 34	18§41	18§44			18 44	18 51
Scarborough	a					18 51											19 31	19 31						
Harrogate	a				18 33							18 43				19 33								19 43
Leeds 10	d		16 27	17 05		16 57	17 12						17 57	18 05									18 12	
Hull	d			16 10			16 10												17§18					
York 8	d		16 58	17 33		17 36	17 43	17§46				17 56	18 26	18 32			18 39	18 39	18§44				18 47	18 53
Thirsk	d		17 14				18 00						18 46										19 05	
Northallerton	d		17 22			17 56	18 10						18 55				19 00	19 00					19 16	
Darlington 7	a		17 36	18 02		18 09		18§15				18 26		18 58			19 13	19 13	19§17					19 22
Eaglescliffe	a																						19 33	
Middlesbrough	a	←	18 28				18 42					18 56	19 30											19 55
Darlington 7	d	17§15	17 38	18 05		18 10		18§17				18 27		18 59			19 13	19 13	19§19					19 23
Durham	d	17§32	17 55	18 21		18 27		18§34						19 16			19 31	19 31	19h42					
Chester-le-Street	d		18 01					18§41											→					
Newcastle 8	a	17§53	18 15	18 36		18 45		18§55				18 57		19 33			19 49	19 49						19 52
Hartlepool	a																						20 00	
Sunderland	a											19 49											20 35	
Newcastle 8	d			18 40		18 46						18 59		19 40			19 49							19 54
Morpeth	d		18a49																					
Alnmouth	d					19 13								20 04										
Berwick-upon-Tweed	d			19 23								19 43		20 25										
Dunbar	d			19 46																				
Edinburgh 10	a			20 11		20 19						20 28		21 08			21 19							21 23
Edinburgh	d			20 15								20 31		21 15										
Haymarket	d			20 19								20 36		21 19										
Motherwell	a													21s59										
Glasgow Central 15	a			21 28		21j21						21k50		22 42			22j21							22j50
Stirling	a					21 23																		22 24
Perth	a					22m36																		23 02
Inverness	a																							
Inverkeithing	a											20 51		21n46										22 14
Kirkcaldy	a											21 08		22n08										
Leuchars 3	a											21 38		22n40										
Dundee	a											21 53		22n54										
Arbroath	a											22 10		23q18										
Montrose	a											22 26		23q32										
Stonehaven	a											22 49		23q53										
Aberdeen	a											23 12		00q17										

For general notes see front of timetable
For details of catering facilities see Directory of Train Operators

- **B** From Manchester Airport (Table 39)
- **C** From Bournemouth (from 8 September from Bristol Temple Meads) (Table 51). to Edinburgh
- **D** From Liverpool Lime Street (Table 39)
- **E** Until 5 September. From Plymouth (Table 51)
- **G** From 8 September. From Bournemouth (Table 51)
- **H** To Liverpool Lime Street (from 8 September to Chesterfield) (Table 49)
- **J** From Plymouth (Table 51). to Edinburgh
- **K** Until 5 September. From Bristol Temple Meads (Table 51)
- **L** From 8 September. From Plymouth (Table 51)
- **N** **The 21st Century Limited**

- **b** Change at Ely and Peterborough
- **c** Change at Retford
- **e** Change at Doncaster
- **f** Change at Leeds
- **g** Bradford Interchange
- **h** Arr. 1935
- **j** Glasgow Queen Street
- **k** Glasgow Queen Street. Change at Edinburgh
- **m** Change at Edinburgh and Stirling
- **n** Change at Edinburgh
- **q** Change at Edinburgh and Dundee

London → Humberside, Yorkshire, North East England and Scotland

Route Diagram - see first page of Table 26

		XC	TP	GR	GR	GR	TP	XC	GR	XC	EM	GR	GR	XC	XC	GR	GR	GR	TP	XC	GR	GR	GR	XC
																					FX	FO		
		R 1	1 ◇	R 1	R 1	R 1	1 ◇	R 1	R 1	R 1	◇	R 1	R 1	R 1	R 1	R 1	R 1	R 1	1 ◇	R 1	R 1	R 1	R 1	R 1
		A	B		C		B	D		E	G			E	D				B	H				A
London Kings Cross [15] ⊖	d			17 03	17 20	17 30			17 33			17 50	18 00				18 03	18 20			18 30	18 30	18 33	
Stevenage [4]	d				16 47				17 52			17 19						18 41						
Peterborough [8]	a			17 51	18 06	18 16						18 38					18 53	19 12					19 22	
Norwich	d										16 57													
Stansted Airport	d				16 20												17 17							
Cambridge	d			16b35	17 04							17b22					17 49							
Peterborough [8]	d			17 52	18 07	18 16					18 26	18 39					18 53	19 13					19 23	
Grantham [7]	a			18 11					18 39		18 54	19 04				←	19 14				19 36	19 36		
	d			18 11					18 39			19 05 →				19 05	19 14				19 36	19 36		
Newark North Gate [7]	a				18 35											19 17		19 40					19 52	
Lincoln	a															19 49							20 28	
Grimsby Town	a			19c58									20c43			20 52								
Newark North Gate [7]	d				18 35											19 17		19 40					19 52	
Retford [10]	d								19 01												19 58	19 58		
Doncaster [7]	a			18 41	19 04				19 16				19 27			19 41	19 47				20 14	20 14	20 18	
Selby	a				19 20																			
Hull	a				20 00											20 55	21 06							
Wakefield Westgate [7]	a			19 01					19 34							20 01	20 06						20 38	
Huddersfield	a			19e59					20e27								20e59						21e27	
Leeds [10]	a			19 21					19 53							20 21	20 25						20 54	
Shipley	a			20 07					20s11								21 07						21 37	
Bradford Forster Square	a			19f57					20 22								20f57						21f28	
Keighley	a			20 20					20g29								20s57						21 50	
Skipton	a			20 35					20g46								21 13						22 06	
Sheffield [7]	d							18 21		18h46										19j21	19 30	19 30		19h46
Doncaster [7]	d									19 19			19 28								20 15	20 15		20 22
York [8]	a					19 23				19 44			19 51					20 22			20 39	20 39		20 46
Scarborough	a					20 30												21 31						
Harrogate	a												20 43											
Leeds [10]	d		18 27				18 57	19 05		19 12								19 27	19 57	20 09	20 12	20 12		
Hull	d		17 18															19 10						
York [8]	d		18 59			19 25	19 31	19 37		19 47			19 53					20 23	20 29	20 37	20 44	20 44		20 51
Thirsk	d						19 47												20 45					
Northallerton	d		19 21				19 59												20 53		21 03	21 03		
Darlington [7]	a		19 33			19 52		20 03		20 12			20 22					20 51		21 07	21 16	21 16		21 20
Eaglescliffe	a																							
Middlesbrough	a						20 30						20 55						21 25					
Darlington [7]	d	←	19 34			19 53		20 05		20 14			20 23	←				20 51		21 09	21 16	21 16		21 22
Durham	d	19 42	19 50			20 10		20 21		20 31 →				20 31				21 09		21 26	21 34	21 34		21 39
Chester-le-Street	d		19 56											20 38										21 46
Newcastle [8]	a	20 03	20 10			20 26		20 36					20 52	20 53				21 27		21 42	21 52	21 52		22 00
Hartlepool	a																							
Sunderland	a		20 49																					
Newcastle [8]	d					20 29		20 39					20 54							21 48		21 53		
Morpeth	d					20 44								21a26						22 01				
Alnmouth	d					21 00		21 08							←					22 15				
Berwick-upon-Tweed	d					21 22		21 30 →					21 37		21 30					22 36		22 41		
Dunbar	d					21 46														22 59				
Edinburgh [10]	a					22 14							22 22		22 24					23 29		23 32		
Edinburgh	d												22 25											
Haymarket	d												22 30											
Motherwell	a												23 13											
Glasgow Central [15]	a					23k24							23 33		00k03									
Stirling	a												23m23		00 24									
Perth	a												00n15		01n20									
Inverness	a																							
Inverkeithing	a												22m56		23 29									
Kirkcaldy	a												23m18		23 51									
Leuchars [3]	a												23m51		00 21									
Dundee	a												00m05		00 36									
Arbroath	a																							
Montrose	a																							
Stonehaven	a																							
Aberdeen	a																							

For general notes see front of timetable
For details of catering facilities see Directory of Train Operators

- **A** Until 5 September. From Bristol Temple Meads (Table 51)
- **B** From Manchester Airport (Table 39)
- **C** **The Hull Executive**
- **D** From Bournemouth (from 8 September from Bristol Temple Meads) (Table 51). to Newcastle
- **E** From Paignton (from 8 September from Bournemouth (Table 51)
- **G** To Manchester Piccadilly (from 8 September to Chesterfield) (Table 49)
- **H** From Plymouth (from 8 September from Paignton) (Table 51)
- **b** Change at Ely and Peterborough
- **c** Change at Doncaster
- **e** Change at Leeds
- **f** Bradford Interchange
- **g** Change at Shipley
- **h** Until 8 September dep. 8 minutes later
- **j** Until 5 September dep. 1926
- **k** Glasgow Queen Street
- **m** Change at Edinburgh
- **n** Change at Edinburgh and Stirling

London → Humberside, Yorkshire, North East England and Scotland

Route Diagram - see first page of Table 26

		HT	EM	GR	GR	TP		XC	XC	GR	GR	GR	EM	GR	GR	HT	GR		GR	TP	GR	GR	GR			
				FX	FO						FO					BHX										
		1 ◇	◇	R 1	R 1	1 ◇		R 1	R 1	R 1	R 1	R 1	◇	R 1	R 1	1 ◇	R 1		R 1	1 ◇	R 1	R 1	R 1			
			A			B		C	D				A							B						
		⊠ ☕		✕ ⚲	✕ ⚲			☕	☕	✕ ⚲	☕ ⚲	✕ ⚲		✕ ⚲	✕ ⚲	⊠ ☕	☕ ⚲		☕ ⚲		☕ ⚲	☕ ⚲	☕ ⚲			
London Kings Cross 15 ⊖	d	18 50		19 00	19 00					19 03	19 30	19 33		20 00	20 03	20 27	20 30		21 00		21 30	22 00	23 30			
Stevenage 4	d											19 17			19 49				21 20			21 46				
Peterborough 8	a			19 46	19 46					19 52		20 20		20 46	20 51		21 20		21 53		22 16	22 46	00s23			
Norwich	d		17 54										18 57								19b45					
Stansted Airport	d											18 20		19 18							20 20					
Cambridge	d			18b14	18b14							19 04		19 50							20 57					
Peterborough 8	d		19 31	19 46	19 46					19 52		20 21	20 28	20 47	20 51		21 20		21 54		22 17	22 47				
Grantham 7	a	19 55	20 01	20 05	20 05							20 40	20 56		21 14	21 30	21 39				22 38	23 08	00s44			
	d	19 56		20 05	20 05							20 40			21 14	21 32	21 39				22 38	23 08				
Newark North Gate 7	a									20 21		20 52			21 26		21 51		22 22		22 49	23 19	00s56			
Lincoln	a	21c10										21 44									23 33					
Grimsby Town	a	21e44										22e44					23e57									
Newark North Gate 7	d									20 21		20 52			21 26		21 51		22 22		22 49	23 19				
Retford 10	d	20 17												21 27		21 53					23 05					
Doncaster 7	a	20 30		20 37	20 37					20 49		21 19		21 42	21 51	22 11	22 15		22 47		23 24	23 49	01s24			
Selby	a	20 46		21 01	21 01											22 29										
Hull	a	21 28		21 45	21 45									22 57		23 13										
Wakefield Westgate 7	a									21 14		21 37			22 13		22 34				23 42					
Huddersfield	a									22 04		22f27					23 15						03f56			
Leeds 10	a									21 34		21 56			22 33		22 53				23 59		02 35			
Shipley	a									22 07		22 37			23 07		23 30									
Bradford Forster Square	a											22g28					23g29									
Keighley	a									22 20		22 50					23 44									
Skipton	a									22 36		23 06			23 39		23 59									
Sheffield 7 ⛴	d							20 21	20h46					21j00					21k51			22 21				
Doncaster 7	d			20 38	20 38									21 42					22 47			23 49				
York 8	a			21 01	21 01				21 48		21 21			22 06					23 11			00 39				
Scarborough	a								23 02																	
Harrogate	a			21 43	21 43							23 08					00 06									
Leeds 10	d					20 45		21 10	21 12										22 12	22 42						
Hull	d					19m56																				
York 8	d			21 03	21 03	21 12		21 38	21 50		21 23			22 07					23 13	23 22						
Thirsk	d					21 28														23 39						
Northallerton	d					21 36								22 29						23 55						
Darlington 7	a			21 30	21 30	21 47		22 03	22 18		21 54			22 41					23 47	00 06		01 26				
Eaglescliffe	a																									
Middlesbrough	a			22 09	22 09				23 10																	
Darlington 7	d			21 31	21 31	21 48		22 05	22 20		21 54			22 42					23 48	00 08						
Durham	d			21 49	21 49	22 05		22 21	22 36		22 13			23 00					00 05	00 24		01n44				
Chester-le-Street	d								22 46																	
Newcastle 8 ⛴	a			22 07	22 07	22 22		22 41	22 59		22 31			23 21					00 38	00 57		02 23				
Hartlepool	a																									
Sunderland ⛴	a																									
Newcastle 8 ⛴	d				22 08																					
Morpeth	d				22 22																					
Alnmouth	d				22 38																					
Berwick-upon-Tweed	d				23 00																					
Dunbar	d																									
Edinburgh 10	a				23 54																					
Edinburgh	d																									
Haymarket	d																									
Motherwell	a																									
Glasgow Central 15	a																									
Stirling	a																									
Perth	a																									
Inverness	a																									
Inverkeithing	a																									
Kirkcaldy	a																									
Leuchars 3	a																									
Dundee	a																									
Arbroath	a																									
Montrose	a																									
Stonehaven	a																									
Aberdeen	a																									

For general notes see front of timetable
For details of catering facilities see Directory of Train Operators

- **A** To Nottingham (Table 19)
- **B** From Manchester Airport (Table 39)
- **C** From Bournemouth (from 8 September from Bristol Temple Meads) (Table 51)
- **D** From Paignton (from 8 September from Bournemouth (Table 51)
- **b** Change at Ely and Peterborough
- **c** Change at Retford
- **e** Change at Doncaster
- **f** Change at Leeds
- **g** Bradford Interchange
- **h** Until 8 September dep. 8 minutes later
- **j** From 8 September dep. 2046, change at York
- **k** From 8 September dep. 2133
- **m** Change at Selby and York
- **n** Arrival time

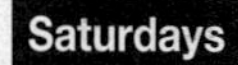

until 6 September

London → Humberside, Yorkshire, North East England and Scotland

Route Diagram - see first page of Table 26

		NT	TP	XC	GR	GR	NT	TP	TP	GR	TP		NT
					R	R				R			
			1◇	1◇	1	1		1◇	1◇	1	1◇		
		A	B				C	D			B		C
London Kings Cross 15 ⊖	d												
Stevenage 4	d												
Peterborough 8	a												
Norwich	d												
Stansted Airport	d												
Cambridge	d												
Peterborough 8	d												
Grantham 7	a												
	d												
Newark North Gate 7	a												
Lincoln	a												
Grimsby Town	a												
Newark North Gate 7	d												
Retford 10	d												
Doncaster 7	a												
Selby	a												
Hull	a												
Wakefield Westgate 7	a												
Huddersfield	a												
Leeds 10	a												
Shipley	a												
Bradford Forster Square	a												
Keighley	a												
Skipton	a												
Sheffield 7	d					05 29					06 14		
Doncaster 7	d					06 20							
York 8	a					06 40							
Scarborough	a					08 14							
Harrogate	a					07 29							
Leeds 10	d		04 49					06 35	06 55	07 10	07 50		
Hull	d								06k00		06 57		
York 8	d		05 40			06 42		07 06	07 32	07 37	08 22		
Thirsk	d		06 01					07 22	07 54		08 44		
Northallerton	d		06 17			07 01		07 30	08 02		08 55		
Darlington 7	a		06 28			07 15		07 41		08 08			
Eaglescliffe	a												
Middlesbrough	a		07 01			08 02			08 32		09 32		
Darlington 7	d					07 15	07 20	07 42		08 09			
Durham	d					07 33	07 41	07 59		08 26			
Chester-le-Street	d						07 48	08 05					
Newcastle 8	a					07 50	08 00	08 19		08 43			
Hartlepool	a												
Sunderland	a							08 49					
Newcastle 8	d	06 05			06 30	07 52				08 45			
Morpeth	d	06 25			06 43	08 06	08a44						
Alnmouth	d	06a43			06 57	08 20							
Berwick-upon-Tweed	d				07 19	08 42				09 29			
Dunbar	d				07 43	09 06				09 54			
Edinburgh 10	a				08 09	09 32				10 22			
Edinburgh	d			07 15	08 12	09 38				10 26			
Haymarket	d					09 43				10 31			
Motherwell	a			08 13	08 55	10 27							
Glasgow Central 15	a			08 38	09 15	10 48				11m36			
Stirling	a				09q23	10q53				11q23			
Perth	a				09q54	11r37				12r37			
Inverness	a				11q59								
Inverkeithing	a				08q54	10q10				10 47			
Kirkcaldy	a				09q10	10q42				11 04			
Leuchars 3	a				10q08	11q12				11 29			
Dundee	a				10q21	11q24				11 44			
Arbroath	a				10q38	11q41				12 01			
Montrose	a				10q52	12q17				12 17			
Stonehaven	a				11q14	12q14				12 40			
Aberdeen	a				11q34	12q35				13 03			

		XC	GR	TP	XC	EM	TP	GR	TP	XC		GR	EM	XC
			R					R				R		
		1◇	1	1◇	1◇	◇	1◇	1	1◇	1◇		1	◇	1◇
		E			E	G	B		B	E			G	E
London Kings Cross 15 ⊖	d		06 15					07 00				07 10		
Stevenage 4	d		06 34					06 46						
Peterborough 8	a		07 05					07 46				07 56		
Norwich	d					05 52								
Stansted Airport	d		05 21											
Cambridge	d		05 51					06b32					07 25	
Peterborough 8	d		07 06			07 28		07 46				07 56	08 25	
Grantham 7	a		07 25			07 59		08 05				08 15	08 53	
	d		07 25					08 05				08 15		
Newark North Gate 7	a		07 37					08 17				08 27		
Lincoln	a							08 54				10c04		
Grimsby Town	a		09e42									10e44		
Newark North Gate 7	d		07 37					08 17				08 27		
Retford 10	d		07 52									08 42		
Doncaster 7	a		08 07					08 41				08 57		
Selby	a													
Hull	a		09 13					09 55				10 10		
Wakefield Westgate 7	a		08 56									09 15		
Huddersfield	a		09f45									10 04		
Leeds 10	a		09 14									09 35		
Shipley	a		09f37									10 01		
Bradford Forster Square	a		09g57									10h11		
Keighley	a		09f50									10 11		
Skipton	a		10f07									10 24		
Sheffield 7	d	07 12			07 54					08 21				08 54
Doncaster 7	d		08 08		08 25			08 42						09 23
York 8	a		08 31		08 50			09 04						09 45
Scarborough	a		10j16											
Harrogate	a		09 17									10 33		
Leeds 10	d	07 57		08 12			08 27		08 57	09 05				
Hull	d													
York 8	d	08 27	08 33	08 42	08 53		08 57	09 06	09 26	09 35				09 48
Thirsk	d								09 46					
Northallerton	d			09 03			09 18		09 55					
Darlington 7	a	08 52	09 00	09 14	09 18		09 29	09 35		10 00				10 13
Eaglescliffe	a													
Middlesbrough	a	09 25		09 52				10 16	10 30					10 52
Darlington 7	d	08 54	09 01	09 15	09 20		09 30	09 36		10 02				10 15
Durham	d	09 10	09 18	09 31	09 37		09 46			10 18				10 31
Chester-le-Street	d				09 44									10 38
Newcastle 8	a	09 25	09 34	09 49	09 59		10 02	10 05		10 33				10 54
Hartlepool	a													
Sunderland	a							10 49						
Newcastle 8	d	09 27	09 36					10 07		10 37				
Morpeth	d	09 41						10a35						
Alnmouth	d	09 55												
Berwick-upon-Tweed	d		10 23					10 50		11 19				
Dunbar	d									11 42				
Edinburgh 10	a	11 01	11 12					11 37		12 15				
Edinburgh	d							11 39						
Haymarket	d							11 44						
Motherwell	a							12 28						
Glasgow Central 15	a	12n06	12n20					12 50		13n20				
Stirling	a		12 23					12q53		13 23				
Perth	a		12 56					13r37						
Inverness	a		15 18											
Inverkeithing	a	11 34	12 03					12q10		13 03				
Kirkcaldy	a	11 56	12 25					12q42		13 25				
Leuchars 3	a							13q12						
Dundee	a							13q24						
Arbroath	a							13q41						
Montrose	a							14t31						
Stonehaven	a							14q17						
Aberdeen	a							14q36						

For general notes see front of timetable
For details of catering facilities see Directory of Train Operators

- **A** To Chathill (Table 48)
- **B** From Manchester Airport (Table 39)
- **C** From Saltburn (Table 44)
- **D** From Manchester Piccadilly (Table 39)
- **E** From Birmingham New Street (Table 51)
- **G** To Liverpool Lime Street (Table 49)
- **b** Change at Ely and Peterborough
- **c** Change at Peterborough
- **e** Change at Doncaster
- **f** Change at Doncaster and Leeds
- **g** Bradford Interchange. Change at Doncaster and Leeds
- **h** Bradford Interchange
- **j** From 19 July only
- **k** Change at Selby and York
- **m** Glasgow Queen Street. Change at Edinburgh
- **n** Glasgow Queen Street
- **q** Change at Edinburgh
- **r** Change at Edinburgh and Stirling
- **t** Change at Edinburgh and Arbroath

Due to Engineering Operations in the Sheffield area, services from Saturday 13 September on this Table had not been confirmed at time of going to press. These services will be issued in a special Supplement as soon as exact timings have been confirmed.

until 6 September

London → Humberside, Yorkshire, North East England and Scotland

Route Diagram - see first page of Table 26

		TP	GC	GR	EM	TP	TP	XC	GR	GR	XC	EM	TP	GR	TP	XC	GR	GR	XC	TP	HT	EM	GR	TP
			R	R					R	R				R			R	R					R	
		1 ◇	1	1	1 ◇	1 ◇	1 ◇	1 ◇	1	1	1 ◇	◇	1 ◇	1	1 ◇	1 ◇	1	1	1 ◇	1 ◇	1 ◇	◇	1	1 ◇
		A			B	A	A	C			D	E	A		A	G			C	A		E	H	A
		🛒	☕	☕ 🛒	☕	🛒	🛒	☕	☕ 🛒	☕ 🛒	☕		🛒	☕ 🛒	🛒	☕	☕ 🛒	☕ 🛒	☕		⊠ ☕		☕ 🛒	🛒
London Kings Cross 15 ⊖	d		07 57	08 00					08 10	08 30				09 00			09 05	09 30			09 34		10 00	
Stevenage 4	d			08 20					*07 46*	08 49							09 24	09 49						
Peterborough 8	a			08 51					08 56	09 20				09 46				10 20					10 46	
Norwich	d									*06b40*		07 57										08 57		
Stansted Airport	d									*07 27*								*08 25*						
Cambridge	d									*08 04*				*08b33*				*09 04*						
Peterborough 8	d			08 51					08 57	09 21		09 29		09 46				10 21				10 26	10 46	
Grantham 7	a								09 16	09 40		09 59						10 40			10 44	10 56		
	d								09 16	09 40								10 40			10 44			
Newark North Gate 7	a								09 28								10 18							
Lincoln	a								*10 19*	*10c58*														
Grimsby Town	a								*11 17*	*11e42*													*12e44*	
Newark North Gate 7	d								09 28								10 18							
Retford 10	d													10 24							11 06			
Doncaster 7	a			09 37					09 56	10 13				10 39			10 47	11 13			11 24		11 32	
Selby	a																				11 39			
Hull	a			*10 50*						*11 12*				*11 53*			*12 08*				12 20		*12 50*	
Wakefield Westgate 7	a								10 14								11 11							
Huddersfield	a								*11 04*								*12 04*							
Leeds 10	a								10 35								11 35							
Shipley	a								*11 01*								*12 07*							
Bradford Forster Square	a								*11f11*								*12f11*							
Keighley	a								*11 11*								*12 20*							
Skipton	a								*11 24*								*12 37*							
Sheffield 7	d				09 21			09 21		*09 25*	09 54					10 21		*10 25*	10 54					
Doncaster 7	d			09 37	09 54					10 14	10 23			10 40				11 14	11 20				11 32	
York 8	a		09 57	10 01	10 16					10 39	10 45			11 03				11 39	11 45				11 56	
Scarborough	a				11 06			*11 30*						*12g30*									*13h30*	
Harrogate	a			*10 43*					*11 33*					*11 43*			*12 33*						*12 43*	
Leeds 10	d	09 27				09 57		10 05			*10 12*		10 27		10 57	11 05			*11 12*	11 27				11 57
Hull	d	*08j38*				*09 02*									*10j06*									*11 08*
York 8	d	09 56	10 00	10 03		10 26		10 34		10 42	10 47		10 54	11 04	11 26	11 34		11 41	11 48	11 54			11 57	12 26
Thirsk	d		10 21			10 46	←								11 43									12 46
Northallerton	d	10 25	10 32			10 55	10 25						11 15		11 55					12 15			12 20	12 55
Darlington 7	a	→		10 30			10 36	11 00		11 11	11 16		11 26	11 32		12 01		12 09	12 15	12 26			12 32	
Eaglescliffe	a		10 48																					
Middlesbrough	a					11 30					*11 55*			*12 32*	12 30					*12 58*			*13 23*	13 30
Darlington 7	d			10 31			10 37	11 01		11 11	11 18		11 27	11 32		12 02		12 10	12 17	12 27			12 33	
Durham	d			10 48			10 54	11 18			11 34		11 44			12 19		12 27	12 34	12 45				
Chester-le-Street	d						11 00												12 41					
Newcastle 8	a			11 04			11 14	11 32		11 43	11 53		11 59	12 02		12 35		12 44	12 56	13 00			13 02	
Hartlepool	a		11 20																					
Sunderland	a		11 50				*11 49*							*12 49*									*13 49*	
Newcastle 8	d			11 08				11 35		11 45				12 03		12 37		12 46					13 04	
Morpeth	d			*11a35*				11 48						*12a35*									*13a36*	
Alnmouth	d			11 34				12 02																
Berwick-upon-Tweed	d									12 28						13 19		13 29						
Dunbar	d															13 42								
Edinburgh 10	a			12 45				13 14		13 16				13 32		14 13		14 16					14 35	
Edinburgh	d													13 39										
Haymarket	d													13 44										
Motherwell	a													14 27										
Glasgow Central 15	a			*13k50*						*14k20*				14 47				*15k21*					*15k37*	
Stirling	a			*13 53*						*14 23*				*14m53*				*15 23*					*15 53*	
Perth	a			*14n37*						*14 54*				*15n36*									*16n37*	
Inverness	a									*17 07*														
Inverkeithing	a			*13 27*										*14m05*				*15 04*					*15 11*	
Kirkcaldy	a			*13 43*										*14m27*				*15 26*					*15 35*	
Leuchars 3	a			*14 11*										*15m12*										
Dundee	a			*14 23*										*15m24*										
Arbroath	a			*14 40*										*15m43*										
Montrose	a			*14 55*										*16q31*										
Stonehaven	a			*15 16*										*16m17*										
Aberdeen	a			*15 36*										*16m37*										

For general notes see front of timetable
For details of catering facilities see Directory of Train Operators

- **A** From Manchester Airport (Table 39)
- **B** From St Pancras International (Table 53)
- **C** From Bristol Temple Meads (Table 51)
- **D** From Birmingham New Street (Table 51)
- **E** To Liverpool Lime Street (Table 49)
- **G** From Southampton Central (Table 51)
- **H** **The Flying Scotsman**
- **b** Change at Ely and Peterborough
- **c** Change at Peterborough
- **e** Change at Doncaster
- **f** Bradford Interchange
- **g** From 19 July arr. 1214
- **h** From 19 July arr. 1314
- **j** Change at Selby and York
- **k** Glasgow Queen Street
- **m** Change at Edinburgh
- **n** Change at Edinburgh and Stirling
- **q** Change at Edinburgh and Arbroath

Due to Engineering Operations in the Sheffield area, services from Saturday 13 September on this Table had not been confirmed at time of going to press. These services will be issued in a special Supplement as soon as exact timings have been confirmed.

Table 26

London → Humberside, Yorkshire, North East England and Scotland

Route Diagram - see first page of Table 26

		GR	GR	XC	XC	GR	EM	TP	GR	TP	TP	GR	GC	XC	GR	XC	HT	EM	TP	GR	XC	TP	TP	XC
		R 1	R 1	1 ◇	1 ◇	R 1	◇	1 ◇	R 1	1 ◇	1 ◇	R 1	R 1	R 1	R 1	1 ◇	1 ◇	◇	1 ◇	R 1	1 ◇	1 ◇	1 ◇	1 ◇
			A	B	C		D	E		E	E			G		H		D	E	J	H	E	E	B
London Kings Cross 15 ⊖	d	10 10	10 30			10 40			11 00			11 10	11 27		11 30		11 48			12 00				
Stevenage 4	d		10 12						10 46						11 50									
Peterborough 8	a	10 56	11 16			11 26			11 46			11 56			12 21					12 46				
Norwich	d						09 57											10 57						
Stansted Airport	d		09 25												10 25									
Cambridge	d		10 04						10b33						11 04					11b12				
Peterborough 8	d	10 56	11 18			11 27	11 27		11 46			11 56			12 21			12 27		12 47				
Grantham 7	a	11 15				11 48	11 57					12 15			12 42		12 48	12 57						
	d	11 15				11 48						12 16			12 43		12 48							
Newark North Gate 7	a	11 27										12 28												
Lincoln	a	11 57				13c16																		
Grimsby Town	a	12 55							13e42								14e44							
Newark North Gate 7	d	11 27										12 28												
Retford 10	d											12 43					13 14							
Doncaster 7	a	11 53				12 19			12 33			12 58			13 14		13 26							
Selby	a																13 42							
Hull	a	13 07							13 50			14 10					14 22							
Wakefield Westgate 7	a	12 13										13 16												
Huddersfield	a	13 04										14 04												
Leeds 10	a	12 35										13 35												
Shipley	a	13 01										14 03												
Bradford Forster Square	a	13f11										14f11												
Keighley	a	13 11										14 13												
Skipton	a	13 24										14 26												
Sheffield 7 ⛴	d			11 21	11 54	11 41								12 21	12 25	12 54								13 21
Doncaster 7	d				12 17	12 20			12 34						13 15	13 23								
York 8	a		12 27		12 43	12 47			12 56				13 25		13 39	13 45				13 56				
Scarborough	a		13 30										14 30											
Harrogate	a	13 33							13 43			14 33								14 43				
Leeds 10	d		11 41	12 05	12 12			12 27			12 57		12 41	13 05		13 12			13 27				13 57	14 05
Hull	d									←				11g38		11g38								
York 8	d		12 29	12 35	12 46	12 49		12 54 →	12 58	12 54	13 26		13 30	13 36	13 42	13 49			13 54	13 57			14 26 →	14 33
Thirsk	d										13 43		13 51									←		
Northallerton	d									13 23	13 55		14 09						14 23 →			14 23		
Darlington 7	a			13 01	13 11	13 17			13 25	13 34				14 02	14 12	14 17						14 34		14 59
Eaglescliffe	a												14 26											
Middlesbrough	a					13 57				14 18	14 30					14 58						15 27		
Darlington 7	d			13 03	13 13	13 17			13 26	13 35				14 03	14 12	14 19					←	14 35		15 01
Durham	d			13 19	13 29	13 35				13 52				14 20	14 30	14 36 →					14 36	14 51		15 17
Chester-le-Street	d									13 58											14 43			
Newcastle 8 ⛴	a		13 24	13 34	13 49	13 53			13 59	14 12				14 34	14 46					14 54	14 56	15 10		15 32
Hartlepool	a												14 45											
Sunderland ⛴	a									14 49			15 14									15 50		
Newcastle 8 ⛴	d		13 26	13 37					14 01					14 38	14 48					14 58				15 36
Morpeth	d								14a36												15a35			15 50
Alnmouth	d			14 02																				16 04
Berwick-upon-Tweed	d								14 44					15 19						15 42				
Dunbar	d													15 42										
Edinburgh 10	a		14 54	15 10					15 33					16 19	16 19					16 30				17 14
Edinburgh	d		15 00						15 37					16 30						16 33				
Haymarket	d		15 04						15 42					16 35						16 38				
Motherwell	a			16 27					16 27															
Glasgow Central 15	a		16h07	16j20					16 50						17j21					17h36				
Stirling	a			16 23					16k53											17 19				
Perth	a			17m20					17m36						17 55					17 55				
Inverness	a			19m34											20 08					20 08				
Inverkeithing	a		15 18	16 04					16k11					16 47	16 47					17k03				
Kirkcaldy	a		15 35	16 26					16k40					17 02	17 02					17k25				
Leuchars 3	a		16 00						17k10					17 31	17 31					18k05				
Dundee	a		16 17						17k26					17 44	17 44					18k22				
Arbroath	a		16 35						17k49					18 01	18 01					18k40				
Montrose	a		16 51						18k03					18 15	18 15					18k54				
Stonehaven	a		17 14						18k24					18 35	18 35					19k16				
Aberdeen	a		17 37						18k44					19 00	19 00					19k38				

For general notes see front of timetable
For details of catering facilities see Directory of Train Operators

- **A** **The Northern Lights**
- **B** From Plymouth (Table 51)
- **C** From Bristol Temple Meads (Table 51)
- **D** To Liverpool Lime Street (Table 49)
- **E** From Manchester Airport (Table 39)
- **G** From Bournemouth (Table 51)
- **H** From Cardiff Central (Table 51)
- **J** **The Highland Chieftain**
- **b** Change at Ely and Peterborough
- **c** Change at Peterborough
- **e** Change at Doncaster
- **f** Bradford Interchange
- **g** Change at Selby and York
- **h** Glasgow Queen Street. Change at Edinburgh
- **j** Glasgow Queen Street
- **k** Change at Edinburgh
- **m** Change at Edinburgh and Stirling

Due to Engineering Operations in the Sheffield area, services from Saturday 13 September on this Table had not been confirmed at time of going to press. These services will be issued in a special Supplement as soon as exact timings have been confirmed.

Saturdays

until 6 September

don → Humberside, Yorkshire, h East England and Scotland

Route Diagram - see first page of Table 26

	GR	GR	EM	TP	XC	TP	GR		TP	TP	XC	GR	GR	XC	HT	EM	GR	TP		NT	XC	XC	GR	EM	GR
	R 1	R 1	◇	1 ◇	1 ◇	1 ◇	R 1		1 ◇	1 ◇	1 ◇	R 1	R 1	R 1	1 ◇	◇	R 1	1 ◇			R 1	1 ◇	R 1	◇	R 1
			A	B	C	B			B	B	D			E		A		B		G	H	J		A	
London Kings Cross 15 ⊖ d	12 10	12 30					13 00					13 10	13 30		13 38		14 00						14 30		15 00
Stevenage 4 d		12 12					12 46						13 49										14 12		14 46
Peterborough 8 a	12 56	13 16					13 46					13 56	14 20				14 46						15 16		15 46
Norwich d			11 57													12 57								13 57	
Stansted Airport d		11 25											12 25										13 25		
Cambridge d		12 04					12b33						13 04				13b12						14 04		14b33
Peterborough 8 d	12 56	13 16	13 26				13 46					13 56	14 21			14 24	14 47						15 16	15 26	15 46
Grantham 7 a	13 15	13 35	13 55									14 15	14 40		14 44	14 57							15 35	15 54	
d	13 15	13 35										14 15	14 40		14 44								15 35		
Newark North Gate 7 a	13 27											14 27	14 52										15 47		
Lincoln a	13 58												15 26		16c09		16 40								17 50
Grimsby Town a	15 01						15e42										16e45								17e42
Newark North Gate 7 d	13 27											14 27	14 52										15 47		
Retford 10 d												14 42			15 10								16 02		
Doncaster 7 a	13 52	14 07					14 33					14 57			15 24		15 35						16 20		16 32
Selby a															15 40										
Hull a		15 12					15 51					16 07			16 20		16 50								17 53
Wakefield Westgate 7 a	14 13	14 42										15 15											16 38		
Huddersfield a	15 04	15f45										16 04											17h45		
Leeds 10 a	14 35	15 02										15 35											17 01		
Shipley a	15 01	15f37										16 07											17 37		
Bradford Forster Square a	15j11	15k42										16j11											17j42		
Keighley a	15 11	15f50										16 20											17 51		
Skipton a	15 24	16f07										16 37											18 07		
Sheffield 7 d					13 54						14 21			14 54							15 21	15 54			
Doncaster 7 d		14 07			14 17		14 34							15 17			15 36					16 17			16 32
York 8 a		14 30			14 46		14 58						15 38	15 43			15 59					16 44			16 56
Scarborough a		15 30					16 30										17 30								18 17
Harrogate a	15 33						15 43					16 33					16 43						17 47		17 49
Leeds 10 d					14 12	14 27	14 27			14 57	15 05			15 12			15 27	15 57			16 05	16 12			
Hull d		13 12		←					←								14 51								
York 8 d		14 37		14 26	14 49	14 54	15 00		14 54	15 26	15 35		15 40	15 46			16 01	16 26			16 35	16 47			16 57
Thirsk d				14 46		→				15 46								16 46							
Northallerton d		14 56		15 01					15 23	15 55								16 55							
Darlington 7 a		15 09			15 15		15 27		15 34		16 00		16 07	16 12			16 29				17 02	17 12			17 26
Eaglescliffe a																									
Middlesbrough a				15 34	15 57				16 22	16 30				16 52			17 26	17 33				17 54			
Darlington 7 d		15 09			15 17		15 28		15 35		16 02		16 08	16 14			16 29				17 04	17 14			17 26
Durham d		15 27			15 34		15 45		15 51		16 18		16 25	16 31							17 22	17 30			17 44
Chester-le-Street d									15 57													17 37			
Newcastle 8 a		15 43			15 52		16 01		16 13		16 33		16 41	16 51			16 59				17 40	17 48			18 00
Hartlepool a																									
Sunderland a									16 49				17 13				17 50								
Newcastle 8 d		15 44					16 03				16 37		16 43				17 01			17 10		17 53			18 01
Morpeth d							16a36													17 32					
Alnmouth d							16 29													17a57		18 25			
Berwick-upon-Tweed d							16 52				17 19														18 50
Dunbar d											17 42														
Edinburgh 10 a		17 15					17 38				18 11		18 15				18 28					19 26			19 34
Edinburgh d							17 40										18 32					19 39			19 38
Haymarket d																	18 37					19 44			19 43
Motherwell a							18 27																		20 20
Glasgow Central 15 a		18m22					18 50						19m21				19n36					20m50			20 44
Stirling a		18 23					18q52						19 23				19q53								20q53
Perth a		18 54					19r42										20r37					20 51			21r42
Inverness a		20 58																				23 13			
Inverkeithing a		17 51					18q11						18 48				18 54					19 58			20q14
Kirkcaldy a		18 14					18q34										19 11					20 14			20q56
Leuchars 3 a							19q13										19 35					20 44			21q28
Dundee a							19q27										19 50					21 12			21q41
Arbroath a							19q45										20 07								22t25
Montrose a																	20 23								22t39
Stonehaven a							20q18										20 46								23t01
Aberdeen a							20q41										21 09								23t21

For general notes see front of timetable
For details of catering facilities see Directory of Train Operators

- **A** To Liverpool Lime Street (Table 49)
- **B** From Manchester Airport (Table 39)
- **C** From Weston-super-Mare (Table 51)
- **D** From Bournemouth (Table 51)
- **E** From Penzance (Table 135)
- **G** From MetroCentre to Chathill (Table 48)
- **H** From Paignton (Table 51)
- **J** From Bristol Temple Meads (Table 51)
- **b** Change at Ely and Peterborough
- **c** Change at Retford
- **e** Change at Doncaster
- **f** Change at Doncaster and Leeds
- **g** Change at Doncaster and Wakefield Westgate
- **h** Change at Leeds
- **j** Bradford Interchange
- **k** Bradford Interchange. Change at Doncaster and Leeds
- **m** Glasgow Queen Street
- **n** Glasgow Queen Street. Change at Edinburgh
- **q** Change at Edinburgh
- **r** Change at Edinburgh and Stirling
- **t** Change at Edinburgh and Dundee

Due to Engineering Operations in the Sheffield area, services from Saturday 13 September on this Table had not been confirmed at time of going to press. These services will be issued in a special Supplement as soon as exact timings have been confirmed.

Saturdays

until 6 September

London → Humberside, Yorkshire, North East England and Scotland

Route Diagram - see first page of Table 26

		TP	XC	TP	GR	EM	XC	GR	TP	XC	GR	EM	XC	GC	GR	TP	GC	TP	HT	XC	GR	XC	EM	GR
		1 ◇	R 1	1 ◇	R 1	◇	1 ◇	R 1	1 ◇	R 1	R 1	◇	1 ◇	R 1	R 1	1 ◇	R 1	1 ◇	1 ◇	1 ◇	R 1	1 ◇	◇	R 1
		A	B	C		D	E		A	G		H	E	J		A	J	A		K		G	D	
London Kings Cross 15 ⊖	d				15 30			16 00			16 30			16 50	17 00				17 05		17 30			17 40
Stevenage 4	d				15 49						16 12				16 46						17 50			17 12
Peterborough 8	a				16 20			16 46			17 16				17 46						18 21			18 26
Norwich	d					14 57						15 52											16 57	
Stansted Airport	d				14 25						15 25										16 25			
Cambridge	d				15 04			15b33			16 04				16b33						17 04			
Peterborough 8	d				16 21	16 30		16 46			17 16	17 25			17 46						18 21		18 25	18 26
Grantham 7	a				16 40	16 58					17 35	17 53							18 10		18 42		18 56	18 47
	d				16 40						17 35								18 10		18 42			18 47
Newark North Gate 7	a				16 52						17 47										18 54			18 59
Lincoln	a				18 14						19 19								20c06					
Grimsby Town	a							18e49											19e58					
Newark North Gate 7	d				16 52						17 47										18 54			18 59
Retford 10	d										18 02								18 31					
Doncaster 7	a				17 16			17 35			18 17				18 33				18 46		19 17			19 23
Selby	a																		19 07					
Hull	a							18 57			19 15								19 47					
Wakefield Westgate 7	a				17 33						18 35										19 35			19 59
Huddersfield	a				18f27						19f27										20f27			
Leeds 10	a				17 53						18 53										19 52			
Shipley	a				18 21						19 21										20 18			
Bradford Forster Square	a				18g28						19g28										20g28			
Keighley	a				18 50						19 41										20s17			
Skipton	a				19 06						19 54										20 32			
Sheffield 7	d		16 21				16 54			17 21			17 54							18 21		18 54		
Doncaster 7	d						17 22	17 35					18 23		18 33							19 21		19 25
York 8	a						17 46	18 01					18 46	18 50	18 56							19 49		19 54
Scarborough	a							19 30							20 30									
Harrogate	a				19 03			18 43			20 03				19 43									
Leeds 10	d	16 27	17 05	17 12					17 57	18 05			18 12			18 27		18 57		19 05		19 12		
Hull	d		16 10										17 18											
York 8	d	17 02	17 35	17 43			17 49	18 03	18 26	18 34			18 49	18 52	18 58	18 56	⟵	19 26		19 35		19 52		19 56
Thirsk	d	17 20		18 00					18 44					19 21			19 21	19 42						
Northallerton	d	17 28		18 10				18 22	18 55					⟶		19 21	19 30	19 50						
Darlington 7	a	17 39	18 02				18 15	18 35		18 59			19 14		19 26	19 33				20 03		20 17		20 23
Eaglescliffe	a																19 49							
Middlesbrough	a	18 25		18 42			19 00		19 30				19 52					20 23						20 55
Darlington 7	d	17 40	18 03				18 16	18 35		19 01			19 16		19 27	19 34				20 05		20 19		20 24
Durham	d	17 57	18 21				18 33			19 17			19 32		19 44	19 50				20 23		20 35		20 41
Chester-le-Street	d	18 03					18 39									19 56						20 42		
Newcastle 8	a	18 17	18 40				18 50	19 05		19 32			19 52		20 00	20 10				20 37		20 53		21 00
Hartlepool	a																20 08							
Sunderland	a	18 49						19 50								20 49	20 35							
Newcastle 8	d						18 53	19 06		19 38					20 02					20 39		20 55		
Morpeth	d	18a49														20a45						21 17		
Alnmouth	d									20 03										21 04				
Berwick-upon-Tweed	d						19 35	19 49		20 23										21 25		21 37		
Dunbar	d						19 58								21 05							22 00		
Edinburgh 10	a						20 27	20 37		21 14					21 34					22 13		22 29		
Edinburgh	d									21 15					21 39									
Haymarket	d									21s18					21 44									
Motherwell	a														22 26									
Glasgow Central 15	a							21h50		22 23					22 46					23h24				
Stirling	a									22j26										23 24				
Perth	a									23j05										00k15				
Inverness	a																							
Inverkeithing	a							21 10		21j46					22j14					22 57				
Kirkcaldy	a							21 43		22j08										23 19				
Leuchars 3	a							22 13		22j40										23 52				
Dundee	a							22 26		22j55										00 07				
Arbroath	a							22 44																
Montrose	a							22 58																
Stonehaven	a							23 20																
Aberdeen	a							23 40																

For general notes see front of timetable
For details of catering facilities see Directory of Train Operators

- **A** From Manchester Airport (Table 39)
- **B** From Newquay (Table 135)
- **C** From Liverpool Lime Street (Table 39)
- **D** To Manchester Piccadilly (Table 49)
- **E** From Bristol Temple Meads (Table 51)
- **G** From Paignton (Table 51)
- **H** To Manchester Oxford Road (Table 49)
- **J** **The 21st Century Limited**
- **K** From Bournemouth (Table 51)
- **b** Change at Ely and Peterborough
- **c** Change at Retford
- **e** Change at Doncaster
- **f** Change at Leeds
- **g** Bradford Interchange
- **h** Glasgow Queen Street
- **j** Change at Edinburgh
- **k** Change at Edinburgh and Stirling

Due to Engineering Operations in the Sheffield area, services from Saturday 13 September on this Table had not been confirmed at time of going to press. These services will be issued in a special Supplement as soon as exact timings have been confirmed.

Table 26

Saturdays

London → Humberside, Yorkshire, North East England and Scotland

until 6 September

Route Diagram - see first page of Table 26

		GR	TP	XC	GR	GR	GR	XC	GR	EM	GR	TP	XC	XC	GR	XC	HT	EM	GR	XC	GR	EM
		R 1	1 ◇	R 1	R 1	R 1	R 1	1 ◇	R 1	◇	R 1	1 ◇	1 ◇	1 ◇	R 1	1 ◇	1 ◇	◇	R 1	1 ◇	R 1	
			A	B				C		D		A	E	C		C		D		E		G
		☕ 🍸		☕	✕ 🍸	☕ 🍸	☕ 🍸	☕	☕ 🍸		☕ 🍸			☕	☕ 🍸		⊠ ☕		☕ 🍸		☕ 🍸	
London Kings Cross 15 ⊖	d	18 00			18 03	18 30	18 35		18 40		19 00				19 30		19 41		20 00		20 30	
Stevenage 4	d						18 27				19 19								19 46		20 12	
Peterborough 8	a	18 46			18 52		19 21		19 26		19 50				20 16				20 46		21 16	
Norwich	d									17 57								18 57				
Stansted Airport	d						17 25								18 25						19 18	
Cambridge	d	17b12					18 02				18b33				19 04				19b12		19 50	
Peterborough 8	d	18 46			18 52		19 21		19 27	19 28	19 51				20 16			20 27	20 46		21 17	21 27
Grantham 7	a					19 30				20 00					20 35		20 41	20 58	21 05		21 38	22 00
	d					19 30									20 35		20 43		21 05		21 38	
Newark North Gate 7	a				19 20				19 56						20 47				21 17		21 49	
Lincoln	a								20 38												22 36	
Grimsby Town	a	20c43							21c44								22c44				23c49	
Newark North Gate 7	d				19 20				19 56						20 47				21 17		21 49	
Retford 10	d								20 11								21 05		21 32			
Doncaster 7	a	19 33				20 01	20 08		20 27		20 39				21 11		21 19		21 47		22 14	
Selby	a								20 43								21 35					
Hull	a	20 52				21 04			21 27		21 45						22 15		22 58			
Wakefield Westgate 7	a				20 03	20 19			20c53		21 34						21c57		22 05		22 39	
Huddersfield	a				20e59	21 05			21f59		22f27								23e00		23f49	
Leeds 10	a				20 22	20 36			21c15		21 54						22c18		22 24		22 59	
Shipley	a					20s56			21f38		22f37								23 07		23f30	
Bradford Forster Square	a				20g57	21 06			21h57		22h28								22g57			
Keighley	a					21e20			21f51		22f50								23 20		23f44	
Skipton	a					21e36			22f07		23f06								23 39		23f59	
Sheffield 7 🚢	d			19 21				19 54					20 21		20 15	20 54					21 14	
Doncaster 7	d	19 34					20 08	20 18			20 40				21 12						22 14	
York 8	a	19 58					20 34	20 43			21 03				21 38						22 38	
Scarborough	a	21 30													23 02							
Harrogate	a	20 43				21e54									22 29		23f06				23f58	
Leeds 10	d	19 15	19 57	20 05				20 12				20 45	21 10		20 48	21 12					21 45	
Hull	d	18 46										19j56			22 29					←		
York 8	d	20 01	20 26	20 36			20 41	20 46			21 06	21 12	21 37 →		21 42	21 52				21 37	22 39	
Thirsk	d		20 43									21 28										
Northallerton	d		20 51								21 26	21 36										
Darlington 7	a	20 29		21 04			21 09	21 15			21 38	21 47			22 09	22 22					23 07	
Eaglescliffe	a																					
Middlesbrough	a		21 25					22 09						←								
Darlington 7	d	20 30		21 06			21 09	21 22 →			21 39	21 48		21 22	22 10	22 24					23 08	
Durham	d			21 23			21 27				21 56	22 05		22 12	22 27	22 43				22 49	23 25	
Chester-le-Street	d													22 19								
Newcastle 8 🚢	a	21 02		21 42			21 45				22 14	22 22		22 33	22 45	23 07				23 11	23 46	
Hartlepool	a																					
Sunderland 🚢	a																					
Newcastle 8 🚢	d	21 03																				
Morpeth	d	21 19																				
Alnmouth	d	21 35																				
Berwick-upon-Tweed	d	21 57																				
Dunbar	d																					
Edinburgh 10	a	22 48																				
Edinburgh	d																					
Haymarket	d																					
Motherwell	a																					
Glasgow Central 15	a	00k03																				
Stirling	a	00 24																				
Perth	a	01m19																				
Inverness	a																					
Inverkeithing	a	23 29																				
Kirkcaldy	a	23 51																				
Leuchars 3	a	00 21																				
Dundee	a	00 36																				
Arbroath	a																					
Montrose	a																					
Stonehaven	a																					
Aberdeen	a																					

For general notes see front of timetable
For details of catering facilities see Directory of Train Operators

- **A** From Manchester Airport (Table 39)
- **B** From Plymouth (Table 51)
- **C** From Bristol Temple Meads (Table 51)
- **D** To Nottingham (Table 19)
- **E** From Bournemouth (Table 51). ☕ to Leeds
- **G** From Spalding (Table 18) to Nottingham (Table 19)
- **b** Change at Ely and Peterborough
- **c** Change at Doncaster
- **e** Change at Leeds
- **f** Change at Doncaster and Leeds
- **g** Bradford Interchange
- **h** Bradford Interchange. Change at Doncaster and Leeds
- **j** Change at Selby and York
- **k** Glasgow Queen Street
- **m** Change at Edinburgh and Stirling

Due to Engineering Operations in the Sheffield area, services from Saturday 13 September on this Table had not been confirmed at time of going to press. These services will be issued in a special Supplement as soon as exact timings have been confirmed.

Table 26

Sundays until 13 July

London → Humberside, Yorkshire, North East England and Scotland

Route Diagram - see first page of Table 26

		GR	TP	GR	TP	GR	TP	TP	GC	GR	TP	GR	GR	XC	GR	TP	GR	EM	GR	EM	XC	HT
		R 1	1 ◇	R 1	1 ◇	R 1	1 ◇	1 ◇	R 1	R 1	1 ◇	R 1	R 1	1 ◇	R 1	1 ◇	R 1	◇	R 1	1 ◇	1 ◇	1 ◇
			A		A	B	A	C			A					A		D		E	G	
London Kings Cross 15 ⊖	d								08 55	09 00		09 10	09 30		10 00		10 10		10 30			10 44
Stevenage 4	d									09 20		08 53			09 44				10 49			
Peterborough 8	a									09 49		09 57	10 14		10 45		10 59		11 18			
Norwich	d																	09 34				
Stansted Airport	d																					
Cambridge	d																					
Peterborough 8	d									09 49		09 57	10 15		10 46		10 59	11 11	11 19			
Grantham 7	a									10 11							11 21	11 50				11 45
	d									10 11							11 21					11 46
Newark North Gate 7	a											10 31			11 16							
Lincoln	a														12 07							
Grimsby Town	a														13 09							13b38
Newark North Gate 7	d											10 31			11 16							
Retford 10	d											10 46					11 43					12 07
Doncaster 7	a									10 44		11 02	11 05		11 41		11 59		12 09			12 23
Selby	a																					12 41
Hull	a									11 46												13 21
Wakefield Westgate 7	a											11 21					12 17					
Huddersfield	a											12c19					13c27					
Leeds 10	a											11 39					12 36					
Shipley	a											12 19					13 19					
Bradford Forster Square	a											12e23					13e23					
Keighley	a											12 32					13 32					
Skipton	a											12 48					13 48					
Sheffield 7 ⛴	d					08 45							10 26						11 05	11 54	11 21	
Doncaster 7	d					09 42				10 44			11 06		11 41				12 10	12 18		
York 8	a					10 04			10 44	11 07			11 29		12 05				12 34	12 40		
Scarborough	a					11 23							12 30		13 24							
Harrogate	a														12 50		13 28					
Leeds 10	d		07 40		08 40	09 10	09 40	10 05			10 42			11 08	11 10	11 40					12 20	
Hull	d					08 54																
York 8	d		08 35	09 00	09 10	10 06	10 10	10 32	10 47	11 09	11 14		11 31	11 36	12 06	12 10			12 40		12 46	
Thirsk	d		08 52				10 27		11 03							12 27						
Northallerton	d		09 00	09 20	09 31		10 35		11 14		11 35					12 35						
Darlington 7	a			09 32	09 42	10 35		11 02		11 36	11 46		11 58	12 02	12 34				13 11		13 15	
Eaglescliffe	a								11 31													
Middlesbrough	a		09 35		10 18	11 29	11 10				12 24				13 35	13 10						
Darlington 7	d			09 33	09 43	10 36		11 03		11 37	11 47		11 59	12 04	12 34				13 12		13 17	
Durham	d			09 50	09 59	10 53		11 20		11 54	12 03			12 20	12 52						13 34	
Chester-le-Street	d							11 26														
Newcastle 8 ⛴	a			10 06	10 16	11 09		11 40		12 10	12 19		12 28	12 36	13 08				13 41		13 47	
Hartlepool	a								11 58													
Sunderland ⛴	a				11 22			12 21	12 44					13 22							14 21	
Newcastle 8 ⛴	d			10 10		11 11				12 15			12 32	12 39	13 09				13 43		13 55	
Morpeth	d			10 24																		
Alnmouth	d			10 41																	14 19	
Berwick-upon-Tweed	d			11 03		11 54				12 58				13 21					14 26			
Dunbar	d			11 27										13 44								
Edinburgh 10	a			11 57		12 39				13 46			14 01	14 13	14 35				15 10		15 25	
Edinburgh	d	09 10		12 03		12 43								14 14					15 13			
Haymarket	d	09 14		12 08		12 48								14 18					15 18			
Motherwell	a			12 47		13 33								14s58					15 56			
Glasgow Central 15	a			13 05		13 53				14f51				15 25	15f51				16 14			
Stirling	a			13g24		14g28								15g24					16g24			
Perth	a			14h46		15g12								16h46								
Inverness	a					17g38																
Inverkeithing	a	09 31		12g41		13g40				14 30			14 40		15 40							
Kirkcaldy	a	09 48		13g03		14g02							15 02		16 02							
Leuchars 3	a	10 13		13g39		14g33									16 33							
Dundee	a	10 27		13g52		14g48									16 48							
Arbroath	a	10 45		14g09		15j27									17j27							
Montrose	a	11 01		14g24		15j41									17j41							
Stonehaven	a	11 24		14g45		16j03									18j03							
Aberdeen	a	11 47		15g05		16j23									18j23							

For general notes see front of timetable
For details of catering facilities see Directory of Train Operators

- **A** From Manchester Airport (Table 39)
- **B** From Leeds (Table 31)
- **C** From Liverpool Lime Street (Table 39)
- **D** To Nottingham (Table 19)
- **E** From Leicester (Table 53)
- **G** From Birmingham New Street (Table 51)
- **b** Change at Doncaster
- **c** Change at Leeds
- **e** Bradford Interchange
- **f** Glasgow Queen Street
- **g** Change at Edinburgh
- **h** Change at Edinburgh and Stirling
- **j** Change at Edinburgh and Dundee

Table 26

Sundays

until 13 July

London → Humberside, Yorkshire, North East England and Scotland

Route Diagram - see first page of Table 26

		GR	TP	XC	GR	EM	GR	TP	GR	GR	XC	XC	GR	TP	XC	GR	GR	XC	GC	GR	TP
		R			R		R		R	R			R			R	R	R	R	R	
		1	1 ◇	1 ◇	1	◇	1	1 ◇	1	1	1 ◇	1 ◇	1	1 ◇	1 ◇	1	1	1	1	1	1 ◇
		A	B	C		D		B		E	C	G		B	G			H			B
		☕ 🍴		☕	☕ 🍴		☕ 🍴		☕ 🍴	☕ 🍴	☕	☕	☕ 🍴		☕	☕ 🍴	☕ 🍴	☕	☕	☕ 🍴	
London Kings Cross [15] ⊖	d	11 00			11 10		12 00		12 10	12 30			13 00			13 10	13 30		13 45	14 00	
Stevenage [4]	d						*11 44*		12 29				13 19				13 49				
Peterborough [8]	a	11 44			11 54		12 44		12 58	13 14			13 48			13 56	14 18			14 44	
Norwich	d					10 47							*11b15*								
Stansted Airport	d												*12 05*								
Cambridge	d						*11b02*						*12 36*								
Peterborough [8]	d	11 45			11 54	12 18	12 44		12 59	13 15			13 49			13 56	14 19			14 45	
Grantham [7]	a				12 16	12 50			13 21							14 19					
	d				12 16				13 21							14 19					
Newark North Gate [7]	a				12 28		13 14									14 31					
Lincoln	a						*13 56*		*15c00*												
Grimsby Town	a									*15e36*							*16e38*				
Newark North Gate [7]	d				12 28		13 14									14 31					
Retford [10]	d				12 43				13 43												
Doncaster [7]	a	12 38			12 59		13 39		13 59	14 07			14 39			14 56	15 09			15 39	
Selby	a																				
Hull	a	*13 48*					*14 59*						*15 57*							*16 50*	
Wakefield Westgate [7]	a				13 17				14 16							15 14					
Huddersfield	a				*14f15*					*15g27*						*16f14*					
Leeds [10]	a				13 36				14 36	*14 56*						15 33				*16 37*	
Shipley	a				*14 19*				*15 12*	*15g19*						*16 19*					
Bradford Forster Square	a				*14h23*				*15h23*	*15j53*						*16h23*				*17j10*	
Keighley	a				*14 32*				*15 23*	*15g32*						*16 32*					
Skipton	a				*14 48*				*15 36*	*15g48*						*16 48*					
Sheffield [7]	d			12 18			*12 28*			*13 24*	13 18	13 54	*14 08*		←		*14 28*	14 54			
Doncaster [7]	d	12 39					13 40			14 09		14 17 →	14 41		14 17		15 10	15 17 →		15 39	
York [8]	a	13 05					14 04			14 33			15 05				15 36		15 51	16 04	
Scarborough	a	*14 30*															*16 34*				
Harrogate	a						*14 51*		*15 28*							*16 28*				*16 50*	
Leeds [10]	d		12 40	13 20				13 40			14 20			14 40	15 08				*15 10*		15 40
Hull	d	*11 54*								*13 27*							*14 28*				
York [8]	d	13 07	13 10	13 46			14 06	14 10		14 35	14 46		15 07	15 14	15 36		15 39		15 55	16 06	16 10
Thirsk	d							14 27											16 12		
Northallerton	d		13 33				14 25	14 35						15 35					16 20		
Darlington [7]	a	13 35	13 44	14 12			14 38			15 03	15 12		15 34	15 46	16 02		16 07			16 34	16 41
Eaglescliffe	a																		16 39		
Middlesbrough	a		*14 32*				*15 27*	15 10		*15 41*			*16 04*		*16 41*		*16 41*				*17 49*
Darlington [7]	d	13 35	13 45	14 13			14 38			15 03	15 15		15 35	15 47	16 03		16 08			16 34	16 42
Durham	d	13 53	14 01	14 30			14 56				15 31		15 53	16 03	16 19		16 25				16 58
Chester-le-Street	d		14 07																		
Newcastle [8]	a	14 09	14 21	14 44			15 12			15 33	15 46		16 10	16 19	16 34		16 42			17 04	17 15
Hartlepool	a																		16 58		
Sunderland	a			*15 22*							*16 21*				*17 22*		*17 22*		17 36		
Newcastle [8]	d	14 13		14 51			15 14			15 34	15 53		16 11		16 41		16 44			17 07	
Morpeth	d										16 07						16 59				
Alnmouth	d										16 21						17 15				
Berwick-upon-Tweed	d			15 34			15 57								17 27		17 37				
Dunbar	d			15 57											17 53						
Edinburgh [10]	a	15 40		16 26			16 46			17 00	17 27		17 37		18 22		18 25			18 35	
Edinburgh	d	16 00		16 33						17 12			17 41							18 43	
Haymarket	d	16 04		16 38						17 16			17 46							18 47	
Motherwell	a												18 24		*20 19*						
Glasgow Central [15]	a	*16k51*					*17m52*			*18k22*			18 44		*19m51*					*19k51*	
Stirling	a	*17n24*								17 51					*19 27*						
Perth	a									18 27					*20q47*						
Inverness	a									20 44											
Inverkeithing	a	*16r24*		16 52			*17 22*			*17n37*			*18n07*							19 05	
Kirkcaldy	a	16 41		17 08			*17 38*			*17n59*			*18n23*							19 22	
Leuchars [3]	a	17 09		17 36			*18 01*			*18n30*										19 46	
Dundee	a	17 24		17 49			*18 14*			*18n46*										20 01	
Arbroath	a	17 41		18 06			*18 31*			*19t27*										20 18	
Montrose	a	17 59		18 20			*18 46*			*19t41*										20 34	
Stonehaven	a	18 22		18 40			*19 07*			*20t03*										20 57	
Aberdeen	a	18 46		19 05			*19 30*			*20t26*										21 21	

For general notes see front of timetable
For details of catering facilities see Directory of Train Operators

A **The Northern Lights**
B From Manchester Airport (Table 39)
C From Birmingham New Street (Table 51)
D To Liverpool Lime Street (Table 49)
E **The Highland Chieftain**
G From Bristol Temple Meads (Table 51)
H From Bournemouth (Table 51)
b Change at Ely and Peterborough
c Change at Retford
e Change at Doncaster
f Change at Leeds
g Change at Doncaster and Leeds
h Bradford Interchange
j Bradford Interchange. Change at Doncaster and Leeds
k Glasgow Queen Street. Change at Edinburgh
m Glasgow Queen Street
n Change at Edinburgh
q Change at Edinburgh and Stirling
r By changing at Edinburgh, passengers may arrive at 1617
t Change at Edinburgh and Dundee

Sundays

until 13 July

London → Humberside, Yorkshire, North East England and Scotland

Route Diagram - see first page of Table 26

	TP	GR	XC	GR	EM	HT	GR	TP	XC	GR	XC	GR	EM	GR	TP	XC	HT	GR	EM	GR
	1◇	R 1	R 1	R 1	◇	1◇	R 1	1◇	R 1	R 1	R 1	R 1	◇	R 1	1◇	R 1	1◇	R 1	◇	R 1
	A		B		C			D	E		B		G		D	B			H	
London Kings Cross 15 ⊖ d		14 10		14 30	14 30	14 44	15 00			15 10		15 30		16 00			16 04	16 10		16 30
Stevenage 4 d					13 49		15 19			14 44				15 44			16u24	16 29		16 49
Peterborough 8 a		14 54		15 14			15 48			15 54		16 14		16 44				16 58		17 18
Norwich d		12b15			13 49								14 49						15 53	
Stansted Airport d							14 05											15 18		
Cambridge d		13 43					14 36							15b02				15 47		
Peterborough 8 d		14 54		15 14	15 26		15 49			15 55		16 15	16 23	16 45				16 59	17 15	17 19
Grantham 7 a		15 16			15 56	15 44				16 17		16 39	16 51				17 13		17 47	
d		15 16				15 45				16 18		16 39					17 14			
Newark North Gate 7 a		15 28								16 30		16 50								
Lincoln a		16 58				17c20						17 51						19c21		
Grimsby Town a						17e36						18e38								19e36
Newark North Gate 7 d		15 28								16 31		16 50								
Retford 10 d		15 43				16 06											17 34	17 39		
Doncaster 7 a		15 59		16 08		16 20				16 57		17 14		17 39			17 49	17 55		18 09
Selby a						16 41											18 03			
Hull a						17 21											18 48	18 57		
Wakefield Westgate 7 a		16 17								17 14								18 12		
Huddersfield a		17f27		17g27						18f14								19f19		19g27
Leeds 10 a		16 37		16 56						17 34								18 32		18 56
Shipley a				17g19						18 19								19 19		19g19
Bradford Forster Square a		17h10		17j53						18h23								19h23		19j53
Keighley a				17g32						18 32								19 32		19g32
Skipton a				17g48						18 48								19 48		19g48
Sheffield 7 d			←	15 27				15k46	15 54		16 54	16 28		17 08		←				17 28
Doncaster 7 d			15 17	16 09					16 17		17 17 →	17 20		17 40		17 17				18 11
York 8 a				16 34			17 02		17 33			17 45		18 05						18 34
Scarborough a				17 28			18 30													19 32
Harrogate a		17 28					17 50			18 28				18 50				19 28		
Leeds 10 d	15 55		16 08					16 40	17 08			17 10			17 40	18 08				
Hull d								16 00								17 23				
York 8 d	16 23		16 36	16 40			17 05	17 10	17 36			17 47		18 07	18 10	18 36				18 39
Thirsk d	16 39														18 27					
Northallerton d	16 49							17 33							18 35					18 59
Darlington 7 a			17 02	17 07			17 32	17 44	18 01			18 15		18 35		19 01				19 11
Eaglescliffe a																				
Middlesbrough a	17 22			17 49				18 53				18 53			19 10					20 01
Darlington 7 d			17 03	17 08			17 33	17 45	18 03			18 16		18 35		19 03				19 12
Durham d			17 19					18 01	18 19			18 33				19 19				19 29
Chester-le-Street d								18 07												
Newcastle 8 a			17 34	17 37			18 02	18 21	18 34			18 52		19 05		19 34				19 47
Hartlepool a																				
Sunderland a				18 21								19 22								20 21
Newcastle 8 d			17 43	17 39			18 05		18 37					19 06		19 36				
Morpeth d																				
Alnmouth d			18 09													20 01				
Berwick-upon-Tweed d				18 22			18 48		19 21							20 21				
Dunbar d									19 44											
Edinburgh 10 a			19 15	19 08			19 34		20 12					20 34		21 07				
Edinburgh d			19 25				19 37		20 14							21 14				
Haymarket d			19 30				19 42		20 19							21 19				
Motherwell a							20 19		20s57							22s00				
Glasgow Central 15 a				20m22			20 37		21 34					21m55		22 30				
Stirling a				20 23					21n24							22n24				
Perth a									22q45											
Inverness a																				
Inverkeithing a			19 43				20n17							21 17						
Kirkcaldy a			20 05				20n59							21 33						
Leuchars 3 a			20 44											22 04						
Dundee a			21 05											22 17						
Arbroath a														22 34						
Montrose a														22 49						
Stonehaven a														23 10						
Aberdeen a														23 33						

For general notes see front of timetable
For details of catering facilities see Directory of Train Operators

- **A** From Manchester Piccadilly (Table 39)
- **B** From Bournemouth (Table 51)
- **C** To Liverpool Lime Street (Table 49)
- **D** From Manchester Airport (Table 39)
- **E** From Plymouth (Table 51)
- **G** To Nottingham (Table 19)
- **H** To Manchester Piccadilly (Table 49)
- **b** Change at Ely and Peterborough
- **c** Change at Retford
- **e** Change at Doncaster
- **f** Change at Leeds
- **g** Change at Doncaster and Leeds
- **h** Bradford Interchange
- **j** Bradford Interchange. Change at Doncaster and Leeds
- **k** Change at York
- **m** Glasgow Queen Street
- **n** Change at Edinburgh
- **q** Change at Edinburgh and Stirling

Table 26

Sundays

until 13 July

London → Humberside, Yorkshire, North East England and Scotland

Route Diagram - see first page of Table 26

		XC	GR	GR	TP	XC	GR	XC	GR	HT	EM	GR	TP	XC	GR	GR	EM	GR	XC	GR	TP	XC
		R 1	R 1	R 1	1 ◇	R 1	R 1	R 1	R 1	1 ◇	◇	R 1	1 ◇	R 1	R 1	R 1	◇	R 1	R 1	R 1	1 ◇	R 1
		A			B	A		C			D		B	C			E		G		B	G
			✕																			
London Kings Cross 15 ⊖	d		16 40	17 00			17 10		17 30	17 44		18 00			18 10	18 30		18 40		19 00		
Stevenage 4	d								17 49							18 50						
Peterborough 8	a		17 24	17 46			17 54		18 18			18 44			18 54	19 19		19 25		19 44		
Norwich	d										16 57					17b15	17 56					
Stansted Airport	d						16 12									17 35						
Cambridge	d			16b02			16 47					17b02				18 09						
Peterborough 8	d		17 25	17 46			17 54		18 19		18 30	18 44			18 55	19 19	19 22	19 25		19 44		
Grantham 7	a		17 51				18 16			18 45	18 58	19 06					19 56	19 47				
	d		17 51				18 16			18 46		19 06						19 47				
Newark North Gate 7	a			18 16					18 49						19 25							
Lincoln	a								19 50						20 20							
Grimsby Town	a									20c36										21c44		
Newark North Gate 7	d			18 16					18 49						19 26							
Retford 10	d									19 07					19 42							
Doncaster 7	a			18 41			18 49		19 14	19 23		19 42			19 58	20 12		20 20		20 35		
Selby	a									19 40												
Hull	a			19 54						20 22								21 23				
Wakefield Westgate 7	a		18 37				19 06		19 57						20 16			20 38		21 03		
Huddersfield	a		19e27				20e00		21f19									21e30		22f00		
Leeds 10	a		18 59				19 28		20 19						20 41			20 59		21 25		
Shipley	a		19 45				20 19		20f45						21 19			21 45				
Bradford Forster Square	a		19g53				20g23		20f54						21g23			21 54		21h56		
Keighley	a						20 32								21 32							
Skipton	a						20 48								21 48							
Sheffield 7 ⛴	d	17 54		18 08		←		18 54	18 28			19 08		←		19 27			19 54			←
Doncaster 7	d	18 26 →		18 42		18 26		19 18 →	19 20			19 42		19 18		20 12			20 26 →	20 35		20 26
York 8	a			19 05					19 43			20 07				20 38				21 00		
Scarborough	a			20 30								21 30										
Harrogate	a			19 50			20 28					20 50						21 51		21 58		
Leeds 10	d			18 10	18 40	19 08			19 10			19 25	19 40	20 08						20 10	20 45	21 08
Hull	d				17 23							18 53	18 53									
York 8	d			19 07	19 10	19 36			19 49			20 08	20 14	20 36		20 39				21 02	21 10	21 36
Thirsk	d												20 30								21 28	
Northallerton	d				19 31				20 08				20 38			20 59					21 38	
Darlington 7	a			19 35	19 42	20 01			20 22			20 36		21 03		21 12				21 30	21 49	22 03
Eaglescliffe	a																					
Middlesbrough	a				20 55				20 55				21 10							22 07		
Darlington 7	d			19 36	19 43	20 03			20 23			20 36		21 05		21 12				21 30	21 50	22 03
Durham	d			19 53	20 00	20 19			20 40					21 21		21 30					22 06	22 20
Chester-le-Street	d				20 06																	
Newcastle 8 ⛴	a			20 09	20 20	20 32			20 58			21 06		21 36		21 46				22 02	22 23	22 45
Hartlepool	a																					
Sunderland ⛴	a																					
Newcastle 8 ⛴	d			20 11		20 46						21 07		21 45		21 53						
Morpeth	d																					
Alnmouth	d					21 10						21 34		22 09								
Berwick-upon-Tweed	d			20 54		21 31						21 57		22 30		22 37						
Dunbar	d					21 54										23 00						
Edinburgh 10	a			21 38		22 23						22 44		23 18		23 29						
Edinburgh	d			21 41																		
Haymarket	d			21 46																		
Motherwell	a			22 23																		
Glasgow Central 15	a			22 44								23j55		00j25								
Stirling	a					23 27																
Perth	a					00 06																
Inverness	a																					
Inverkeithing	a			22k17										23 58								
Kirkcaldy	a			23k05																		
Leuchars 3	a			23k40																		
Dundee	a			23k56																		
Arbroath	a																					
Montrose	a																					
Stonehaven	a																					
Aberdeen	a																					

For general notes see front of timetable
For details of catering facilities see Directory of Train Operators

A From Penzance (Table 135)
B From Manchester Airport (Table 39)
C From Bournemouth (Table 51)
D To Manchester Piccadilly (Table 49)
E To Nottingham (Table 19)
G From Paignton (Table 51)
b Change at Ely and Peterborough
c Change at Doncaster
e Change at Leeds
f Change at Doncaster and Leeds
g Bradford Interchange
h Bradford Interchange. Change at Doncaster and Leeds
j Glasgow Queen Street
k Change at Edinburgh

Table 26

Sundays

until 13 July

London → Humberside, Yorkshire, North East England and Scotland

Route Diagram - see first page of Table 26

		GR	GR	XC	GR	EM	GR	XC	TP	GR	HT	GR	XC	GR	GR	EM	XC	GR	GR
		[R] [1]	[R] [1]	[R] [1]	[R] [1]	◇	[R] [1]	[R] [1]	[1] ◇	[R] [1]	[1] ◇	[R] [1]	[1] ◇	[R] [1]	[R] [1]	◇	[1] ◇	[R] [1]	[R] [1]
				A		B		A	C				D			B	D		
London Kings Cross [15] ⊖	d	19 10	19 30		19 35		20 00			20 03	20 10	20 30		21 00	21 30			22 00	22 10
Stevenage [4]	d		19 49		19 54						20u30			20 46				21 46	
Peterborough [8]	a	19 54	20 18		20 24		20 44			20 48		21 14		21 44	22 14			22 44	22s59
Norwich	d		18b15			18 57								19 44		20 52			
Stansted Airport	d		18 35																
Cambridge	d		19 08											20b02					
Peterborough [8]	d	19 55	20 19		20 25	20 30	20 44			20 49		21 14		21 45	22 15	22 22		22 45	
Grantham [7]	a	20 19				21 01					21 17	21 36			22 39	22 50			23s31
	d	20 19									21 18	21 36			22 39				
Newark North Gate [7]	a	20 30										21 48			22 50				23s42
Lincoln	a	21 49										22 24			23 52				
Grimsby Town	a				22c44									23c58					
Newark North Gate [7]	d	20 30										21 48			22 50				
Retford [10]	d										21 38	22 03			23 06				
Doncaster [7]	a	20 56	21 09		21 16		21 36				21 53	22 19		22 42	23 27			23 42	00s12
Selby	a	21 15									22 08								
Hull	a	21 56									22 50			00 02					
Wakefield Westgate [7]	a		21 27							21 56		22 40							
Huddersfield	a		22e27							23e20		23e27							03e03
Leeds [10]	a		21 47							22 15		23 00		00 20	00 22				01 17
Shipley	a		22 19							22 45		23 21							
Bradford Forster Square	a		22f23							22 54		23f43							
Keighley	a		22 32									23 34							
Skipton	a		22 48									23 50							
Sheffield [7] 🚢	d			20 54	20 27			←					21 54				←	22 54	
Doncaster [7]	d			21 18 →	21 20		21 36	21 18					22 26 →	22 43			22 26	23 45	
York [8]	a				21 47		22 00	22 38						23 09			23 38	00 39	
Scarborough	a						23 00												
Harrogate	a		23 00									23 59							
Leeds [10]	d				21 10				22 10										
Hull	d				20 22				20 22										
York [8]	d				21 48		22 02		22 40					23 11					
Thirsk	d								23 06										
Northallerton	d								23 16					23 46					
Darlington [7]	a				22 26		22 43		23 31					23 59				01 32	
Eaglescliffe	a																		
Middlesbrough	a				23 10														
Darlington [7]	d				22 27		22 43		23 32					00 01					
Durham	d				22 44		23 01		23 48					00 17				01a50	
Chester-le-Street	d																		
Newcastle [8] 🚢	a				23 14		23 34		00 21					00 50				02 25	
Hartlepool	a																		
Sunderland 🚢	a																		
Newcastle [8] 🚢	d																		
Morpeth	d																		
Alnmouth	d																		
Berwick-upon-Tweed	d																		
Dunbar	d																		
Edinburgh [10]	a																		
Edinburgh	d																		
Haymarket	d																		
Motherwell	a																		
Glasgow Central [15]	a																		
Stirling	a																		
Perth	a																		
Inverness	a																		
Inverkeithing	a																		
Kirkcaldy	a																		
Leuchars [3]	a																		
Dundee	a																		
Arbroath	a																		
Montrose	a																		
Stonehaven	a																		
Aberdeen	a																		

For general notes see front of timetable
For details of catering facilities see Directory of Train Operators

A From Bournemouth (Table 51)
B To Nottingham (Table 19)
C From Liverpool Lime Street (Table 39)
D From Plymouth (Table 51)

b Change at Ely and Peterborough
c Change at Doncaster
e Change at Leeds
f Bradford Interchange

Table 26

Sundays

20 July to 7 September

London → Humberside, Yorkshire, North East England and Scotland

Route Diagram - see first page of Table 26

		GR	TP	GR	TP	GR	TP	TP	GC	GR	TP	GR	GR	XC	XC	GR	TP	EM	GR	EM	GR	XC
		R 1	1 ◇	R 1	1 ◇	R 1	1 ◇	1 ◇	R 1	R 1	1 ◇	R 1	R 1	1 ◇	1 ◇	R 1	1 ◇	1 ◇	R 1	◇	R 1	1 ◇
			A		A	B		A			C				D	E	G	H		J		D
London Kings Cross [15] ⊖	d								08 55	09 00		09 10	09 30			10 00			10 10		10 30	
Stevenage [4]	d									09 20		*08 53*				*09 44*					10 49	
Peterborough [8]	a									09 49		09 57	10 14			10 45			10 59		11 18	
Norwich	d																			09 34		
Stansted Airport	d																					
Cambridge	d																					
Peterborough [8]	d									09 49		09 57	10 15			10 46			10 59	11 11	11 19	
Grantham [7]	a									10 11									11 21	11 50		
	d									10 11									11 21			
Newark North Gate [7]	a											10 31				11 16						
Lincoln	a															*12 07*						
Grimsby Town	a															*13 09*						
Newark North Gate [7]	d											10 31				11 16						
Retford [10]	d											10 46							11 43			
Doncaster [7]	a									10 44		11 02	11 05			11 41			11 59		12 09	
Selby	a																					
Hull	a									*11 46*												
Wakefield Westgate [7]	a											11 21							12 17			
Huddersfield	a											*12b19*							*13b27*			
Leeds [10]	a											11 39							12 36			
Shipley	a											*12 19*							*13 19*			
Bradford Forster Square	a											*12c23*							*13c23*			
Keighley	a											*12 32*							*13 32*			
Skipton	a											*12 48*							*13 48*			
Sheffield [7]	d					*08 45*				*09 58*			*10 26*		11 02			11 26				←
Doncaster [7]	d					09 42				10 44			11 06		11 25 →	11 41		11 55			12 10	11 25
York [8]	a					10 04			10 44	11 07			11 29			12 05		12 19			12 34	
Scarborough	a												*12 30*			*13 15*						
Harrogate	a															*12 50*			*13 28*			
Leeds [10]	d		07 40		08 40		*09 00*	09 40		*10 05*	10 25			10 57			11 22				*11 40*	12 08
Hull	d					*08 54*																
York [8]	d		08 35	09 00	09 24	10 06	10 10	10 32	10 47	11 09	11 14		11 31	11 36		12 06	12 10				12 40	12 47
Thirsk	d		08 52				10 27		11 03								12 27					
Northallerton	d		09 00	09 20	09 45		10 35		11 14		11 35						12 35					
Darlington [7]	a			09 32	09 56	10 35		11 02		11 36	11 46		11 58	12 04		12 34					13 11	13 17
Eaglescliffe	a								11 31													
Middlesbrough	a		09 35	*10 18*		*11 29*	11 10				*12 24*					*13 35*	13 10					
Darlington [7]	d			09 33	09 57	10 36		11 03		11 37	11 47		11 59	12 05		12 34					13 12	13 19
Durham	d			09 50	10 14	10 53		11 20		11 54	12 03			12 22		12 52						13 35
Chester-le-Street	d							11 26														
Newcastle [8]	a			10 06	10 31	11 09		11 40		12 10	12 19		12 28	12 36		13 08					13 41	13 50
Hartlepool	a								11 58													
Sunderland	a				*11 22*			*12 21*	12 44					*13 22*							*14 21*	
Newcastle [8]	d			10 10		11 11				12 15			12 32	12 39		13 09					13 43	13 56
Morpeth	d			10 24																		
Alnmouth	d			10 41																		14 19
Berwick-upon-Tweed	d			11 03		11 54				12 58				13 21							14 26	
Dunbar	d			11 27										13 44								
Edinburgh [10]	a			11 57		12 39				13 46			14 01	14 13		14 35					15 10	15 25
Edinburgh	d	09 10		12 03		12 43								14 14							15 13	
Haymarket	d	09 14		12 08		12 48								14 19							15 18	
Motherwell	a			12 47		13 33								14s58							15 56	
Glasgow Central [15]	a			13 05		13 53				*14e51*				15 25		*15e51*					16 14	
Stirling	a			*13f24*		*14f28*								*15f24*							*16f24*	
Perth	a			*14g46*		*15f12*								*16g46*								
Inverness	a					*17f38*																
Inverkeithing	a	09 31		*12f41*		*13f40*				*14 30*			*14 40*			*15 40*					*16f17*	
Kirkcaldy	a	09 48		*13f03*		*14f02*							*15 02*			*16 02*						
Leuchars [3]	a	10 13		*13f39*		*14f33*										*16 33*						
Dundee	a	10 27		*13f52*		*14f48*										*16 48*						
Arbroath	a	10 45		*14f09*		*15h27*										*17h27*						
Montrose	a	11 01		*14f24*		*15h41*										*17h41*						
Stonehaven	a	11 24		*14f45*		*16h03*										*18h03*						
Aberdeen	a	11 47		*15f05*		*16h23*										*18h23*						

For general notes see front of timetable
For details of catering facilities see Directory of Train Operators

- **A** From Manchester Airport (Table 39)
- **B** From Leeds (Table 31)
- **C** From Manchester Piccadilly (Table 39)
- **D** From Birmingham New Street (Table 51)
- **E** **The Flying Scotsman**
- **G** From Liverpool Lime Street (Table 39)
- **H** From Leicester (Table 53)
- **J** To Liverpool Lime Street (Table 49)
- **b** Change at Leeds
- **c** Bradford Interchange
- **e** Glasgow Queen Street
- **f** Change at Edinburgh
- **g** Change at Edinburgh and Stirling
- **h** Change at Edinburgh and Dundee

Due to Engineering Operations in the Sheffield area, services from Sunday 14 September on this Table had not been confirmed at time of going to press. These services will be issued in a special Supplement as soon as exact timings have been confirmed.

Sundays

London → Humberside, Yorkshire, North East England and Scotland

20 July to 7 September

Route Diagram - see first page of Table 26

		HT	GR	TP	XC	GR	EM	GR	TP	GR	GR	XC	XC	XC	GR	TP	GR	GR	XC	XC	GC	GR
			R			R		R		R	R				R		R	R			R	R
		1◇	1	1◇	1◇	1	◇	1	1◇	1	1	1◇	1◇	1◇	1	1◇	1	1	1◇	1◇	1	1
			A		B		C		D		E	G	B	G					H	J		
		⊠ ☕	☕ 🍴		☕	☕ 🍴		☕ 🍴		☕ 🍴	☕ 🍴	☕	☕	☕	☕ 🍴		☕ 🍴	☕ 🍴	☕	☕	☕	☕ 🍴
London Kings Cross 15 ⊖	d	10 44	11 00			11 10		12 00		12 10	12 30				13 00		13 10	13 30			13 45	14 00
Stevenage 4	d							11 44		12 29					13 19			13 49				
Peterborough 8	a		11 44			11 54		12 44		12 58	13 14				13 48		13 56	14 18				14 44
Norwich	d						10 47								11b15							
Stansted Airport	d														12 05							
Cambridge	d							11b02							12 36							
Peterborough 8	d		11 45			11 54	12 18	12 44		12 59	13 15				13 49		13 56	14 19				14 45
Grantham 7	a	11 45				12 16	12 50			13 21							14 19					
	d	11 46				12 16				13 21							14 19					
Newark North Gate 7	a					12 28		13 14									14 31					
Lincoln	a							13 56		15c00												
Grimsby Town	a	13e38									15e36							16e38				
Newark North Gate 7	d					12 28		13 14									14 31					
Retford 10	d	12 07				12 43				13 43												
Doncaster 7	a	12 23	12 38			12 59		13 39		13 59	14 07				14 39		14 56	15 09				15 39
Selby	a	12 41																				
Hull	a	13 21	13 48					14 59							15 57							16 50
Wakefield Westgate 7	a					13 17				14 16							15 14					
Huddersfield	a					14f15				15f27							16f14					
Leeds 10	a					13 36				14 36							15 33					
Shipley	a					14 19				15 12							16 19					
Bradford Forster Square	a					14g23				15g23							16g23					
Keighley	a					14 32				15 23							16 32					
Skipton	a					14 48				15 36							16 48					
Sheffield 7 🚌	d			11 26	12 21			12 28			13 24	13 54	13h21		14 08			14 28	14j21	14 54		
Doncaster 7	d		12 39					13 40			14 09	14 17			14 41			15 10		15 17		15 39
York 8	a		13 05					14 04			14 33	14 39			15 05			15 34		15 40	15 51	16 04
Scarborough	a		14 15												16 15							17 11
Harrogate	a							14 51		15 28							16 28					16 50
Leeds 10	d				13 08				13 22		13 40		14 08					14 40	15 08			15 12
Hull	d		11 54								13 27			←					14 28			
York 8	d		13 07	13 10	13 48			14 06	14 10		14 35	14 55 →	14 53	14 55	15 07	15 14		15 37	15 48	15 52	15 55	16 06
Thirsk	d								14 27												16 12	
Northallerton	d			13 33				14 25	14 35							15 35					16 20	
Darlington 7	a		13 35	13 44	14 13			14 38			15 03		15 18	15 22	15 34	15 46		16 07	16 13	16 26		16 34
Eaglescliffe	a																				16 39	
Middlesbrough	a			14 32				15 27	15 10		15 41				16 04	16 41		16 41				
Darlington 7	d		13 35	13 45	14 15			14 38			15 03		15 20	15 23	15 35	15 47		16 08	16 15	16 28		16 34
Durham	d		13 53	14 01	14 31			14 56					15 36	15 39	15 53	16 03		16 25	16 31	16 44		
Chester-le-Street	d			14 07																		
Newcastle 8 🚌	a		14 09	14 21	14 46			15 12			15 33		15 51	16 01	16 10	16 19		16 42	16 46	17 04		17 04
Hartlepool	a																				16 58	
Sunderland 🚌	a				15 22								16 21						17 22		17 36	
Newcastle 8 🚌	d		14 13		14 51			15 14			15 34		15 53		16 11			16 44	16 48			17 07
Morpeth	d												16 08					16 59				
Alnmouth	d												16 22					17 15				
Berwick-upon-Tweed	d				15 34			15 57										17 37	17 43			
Dunbar	d				15 57														18 06			
Edinburgh 10	a		15 40		16 26			16 46			17 00		17 28		17 37			18 25	18 35			18 35
Edinburgh	d		16 00		16 33						17 12				17 41							18 43
Haymarket	d		16 04		16 38						17 16				17 46							18 47
Motherwell	a														18 24							
Glasgow Central 15	a		16k51		17k52			17m52			18k22				18 44							19k51
Stirling	a		17n24		17n51						17 51				19n27							
Perth	a				18n27			18 27			18 27				20q47							
Inverness	a				20n44			20 44			20 44											
Inverkeithing	a		16r24		16 52			17 22			17n37				18n07				19 37			19 05
Kirkcaldy	a		16 41		17 08			17 38			17n59				18n23				19 59			19 22
Leuchars 3	a		17 09		17 36			18 01			18n30								20 30			19 46
Dundee	a		17 24		17 49			18 14			18n46								20 46			20 01
Arbroath	a		17 41		18 06			18 31			19t27								21t27			20 18
Montrose	a		17 59		18 20			18 46			19t41								21t42			20 34
Stonehaven	a		18 22		18 40			19 07			20t03								22t03			20 57
Aberdeen	a		18 46		19 05			19 30			20t26								22t24			21 21

For general notes see front of timetable
For details of catering facilities see Directory of Train Operators

- **A** **The Northern Lights**
- **B** From Birmingham New Street (Table 51)
- **C** To Liverpool Lime Street (Table 49)
- **D** From Liverpool Lime Street (Table 39)
- **E** **The Highland Chieftain**
- **G** From Bristol Temple Meads (Table 51)
- **H** From Bournemouth (Table 51)
- **J** From Exeter St Davids (Table 51)
- **b** Change at Ely and Peterborough
- **c** Change at Retford
- **e** Change at Doncaster
- **f** Change at Leeds
- **g** Bradford Interchange
- **h** By changing at York, passengers may depart at 1354
- **j** By changing at York, passengers may depart at 1454
- **k** Glasgow Queen Street. Change at Edinburgh
- **m** Glasgow Queen Street
- **n** Change at Edinburgh
- **q** Change at Edinburgh and Stirling
- **r** By changing at Edinburgh, passengers may arrive at 1617
- **t** Change at Edinburgh and Dundee

Due to Engineering Operations in the Sheffield area, services from Sunday 14 September on this Table had not been confirmed at time of going to press. These services will be issued in a special Supplement as soon as exact timings have been confirmed.

Table 26

Sundays

20 July to 7 September

London → Humberside, Yorkshire, North East England and Scotland

Route Diagram - see first page of Table 26

		TP	TP	GR	GR	VT		XC	HT	EM	GR	TP		GR	XC	XC	GR	EM		TP	XC	GR	HT	GR		EM
		1 ◇	1 ◇	R 1	R 1	R 1		1 ◇	1 ◇	◇	R 1	1 ◇		R 1	1 ◇	1 ◇	R 1	◇		1 ◇	1 ◇	R 1	1 ◇	R 1		◇
		A	B					C		D		A		E	E	C		D		A	C					G
London Kings Cross 15 ⊖	d			14 10	14 30				14 44		15 00			15 10			15 30					16 00	16 04	16 10		
Stevenage 4	d										15 19			14 44								15 44	16u24	16 29		
Peterborough 8	a			14 54	15 14						15 48			15 54			16 14					16 44		16 58		
Norwich	d			12b15						13 49								14 49								15 53
Stansted Airport	d										14 05													15 18		
Cambridge	d			13 43							14 36											15b02		15 47		
Peterborough 8	d			14 54	15 14					15 26	15 49			15 55			16 15	16 23				16 45		16 59		17 15
Grantham 7	a			15 16					15 44	15 56				16 17			16 39	16 51					17 13			17 47
	d			15 16					15 45					16 18			16 39						17 14			
Newark North Gate 7	a			15 28										16 30			16 50									
Lincoln	a			16 58					17c20								17 51							19c21		
Grimsby Town	a								17e36								18e38									
Newark North Gate 7	d			15 28										16 31			16 50									
Retford 10	d			15 43					16 06														17 34	17 39		
Doncaster 7	a			15 59	16 08				16 20					16 57			17 14					17 39	17 49	17 55		
Selby	a								16 41														18 03			
Hull	a								17 21														18 48	18 57		
Wakefield Westgate 7	a			16 17										17 14										18 12		
Huddersfield	a			17f27										18f14										19f19		
Leeds 10	a			16 37										17 34										18 32		
Shipley	a			17 19										18 19										19 19		
Bradford Forster Square	a			17g10										18g23										19g23		
Keighley	a			17 32										18 32										19 32		
Skipton	a			17 48										18 48										19 48		
Sheffield 7	d				15 28	15 21		15 54							16 21	16 54						17 08				
Doncaster 7	d				16 09			16 17								17 14	17 20					17 40				
York 8	a				16 34			16 44			17 02					17 38	17 45					18 05				
Scarborough	a										18 15											19 15				
Harrogate	a			17 28							17 50			18 28								18 50		19 28		
Leeds 10	d	15 12	16 00		15 40	16 08		16 10				16 10			17 08		16 40			17 12	←					
Hull	d											16 00														
York 8	d	16 10	16 38		16 40	16 48		16 55			17 05	17 10			17 44	17 56 →	17 47			17 52	17 56	18 07				
Thirsk	d		17 00																	18 14						
Northallerton	d		17 09									17 33								18 22						
Darlington 7	a	16 41			17 07	17 13		17 22			17 32	17 44			18 09		18 15				18 21	18 35				
Eaglescliffe	a																									
Middlesbrough	a		17 43		17 49															19 00	18 53					
Darlington 7	d	16 42			17 08	17 15		17 24			17 33	17 45			18 11		18 16				18 23	18 35				
Durham	d	16 58				17 31		17 40				18 01			18 27		18 33				18 39					
Chester-le-Street	d											18 07														
Newcastle 8	a	17 15			17 37	17 46		18 00			18 02	18 21			18 42		18 52				18 59	19 05				
Hartlepool	a																									
Sunderland	a				18 21												19 22									
Newcastle 8	d				17 39	17 48					18 05				18 48							19 06				
Morpeth	d																									
Alnmouth	d					18 14																				
Berwick-upon-Tweed	d				18 22						18 48				19 32											
Dunbar	d														19 55											
Edinburgh 10	a				19 08	19 20					19 34				20 24							20 34				
Edinburgh	d					19 25					19 37															
Haymarket	d					19 30					19 42				20 24											
Motherwell	a										20 19				21s09											
Glasgow Central 15	a				20h22						20 37				21 51							21h55				
Stirling	a				20 23						21j24											22 24				
Perth	a										22k45															
Inverness	a																									
Inverkeithing	a					19 43					20j17											21 17				
Kirkcaldy	a					20 05					20j59											21 33				
Leuchars 3	a					20 44																22 04				
Dundee	a					21 05																22 17				
Arbroath	a																					22 34				
Montrose	a																					22 49				
Stonehaven	a																					23 10				
Aberdeen	a																					23 33				

For general notes see front of timetable
For details of catering facilities see Directory of Train Operators

- **A** From Liverpool Lime Street (Table 39)
- **B** From Manchester Piccadilly (Table 39)
- **C** From Bristol Temple Meads (Table 51)
- **D** To Liverpool Lime Street (Table 49)
- **E** From Bournemouth (Table 51)
- **G** To Manchester Piccadilly (Table 49)
- **b** Change at Ely and Peterborough
- **c** Change at Retford
- **e** Change at Doncaster
- **f** Change at Leeds
- **g** Bradford Interchange
- **h** Glasgow Queen Street
- **j** Change at Edinburgh
- **k** Change at Edinburgh and Stirling

Due to Engineering Operations in the Sheffield area, services from Sunday 14 September on this Table had not been confirmed at time of going to press. These services will be issued in a special Supplement as soon as exact timings have been confirmed.

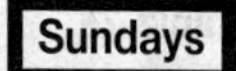

London → Humberside, Yorkshire, North East England and Scotland

20 July to 7 September

Route Diagram - see first page of Table 26

		GR	XC	XC	GR	GR	TP	GR	XC	XC	GR	TP	XC	HT	EM	GR	GR	GR	XC	XC	EM	GR
		R 1	R 1	1 ◇	R 1	R 1	1 ◇	R 1	R 1	R 1	R 1	1 ◇	R 1	1 ◇	◇	R 1	R 1	R 1	R 1	R 1	◇	R 1
			A	B			C		D	E		C	D		G				H	B	J	
London Kings Cross 15 ⊖	d	16 30			16 40	17 00		17 10			17 30			17 44		18 00	18 10	18 30				18 40
Stevenage 4	d	16 49									17 49							18 50				
Peterborough 8	a	17 18			17 24	17 46		17 54			18 18					18 44	18 54	19 19				19 25
Norwich	d														16 57			17b15			17 56	
Stansted Airport	d							16 12										17 35				
Cambridge	d					16b02		16 47								17b02		18 09				
Peterborough 8	d	17 19			17 25	17 46		17 54			18 19				18 30	18 44	18 55	19 19			19 22	19 25
Grantham 7	a				17 51			18 16						18 45	18 58	19 06					19 56	19 47
	d				17 51			18 16						18 46		19 06						19 47
Newark North Gate 7	a					18 16					18 49						19 25					
Lincoln	a										19 50						20 20					
Grimsby Town	a	19c36												20c36								
Newark North Gate 7	d					18 16					18 49						19 26					
Retford 10	d													19 07			19 42					
Doncaster 7	a	18 09				18 41		18 49			19 14			19 23		19 42	19 58	20 12				20 20
Selby	a													19 40								
Hull	a					19 55								20 22								21 23
Wakefield Westgate 7	a				18 37			19 06			19 57						20 16					20 38
Huddersfield	a				19e27			20e00			21f19											21e30
Leeds 10	a				18 59			19 28			20 19						20 41					20 59
Shipley	a				19 45			20 19			20f45						21 19					21 45
Bradford Forster Square	a				19g53			20g23			20f54						21g23					21 54
Keighley	a							20 32									21 32					
Skipton	a							20 48									21 48					
Sheffield 7 ⛴	d	17 28	17 21	17 54		18 08			18 54	18 21						19 08		19 27	19 21	19 54		
Doncaster 7	d	18 11		18 17		18 42			19 17		19 20					19 42		20 12		20 17		
York 8	a	18 34		18 41		19 05			19 40		19 43					20 07		20 38		20 43		
Scarborough	a					20 15										21 24						
Harrogate	a					19 50		20 28								20 50						21 51
Leeds 10	d	17 40	18 08			18 10	18 10			19 08	18 40	19 10	←					19 40	20 08			
Hull	d	17 23														18 53						
York 8	d	18 39	18 48	18 55		19 07	19 10		19 56 →	19 46	19 49	19 52	19 56			20 08		20 39	20 48	20 55		
Thirsk	d											20 14										
Northallerton	d	18 59					19 31				20 08	20 22						20 59				
Darlington 7	a	19 11	19 15	19 27		19 35	19 42			20 11	20 22		20 28			20 36		21 12	21 17	21 20		
Eaglescliffe	a																					
Middlesbrough	a			20 01							20 55	21 02										
Darlington 7	d	19 12	19 16	19 29		19 36	19 43			20 13	20 23		20 29			20 36		21 12	21 19	21 22		
Durham	d	19 29	19 37	19 45		19 53	20 00			20 29	20 40		20 46					21 30	21 37	21 38		
Chester-le-Street	d						20 06															
Newcastle 8 ⛴	a	19 47	19 49	20 05		20 09	20 20			20 44	20 58		21 06			21 06		21 46	21 50	21 58		
Hartlepool	a																					
Sunderland ⛴	a	20 21																				
Newcastle 8 ⛴	d		19 51			20 11				20 53						21 07		21 53	21 57			
Morpeth	d																					
Alnmouth	d		20 16							21 19						21 34						
Berwick-upon-Tweed	d		20 36			20 54				21 40						21 57		22 37	22 45			
Dunbar	d									22 03								23 00				
Edinburgh 10	a		21 24			21 38				22 32						22 44		23 29	23 36			
Edinburgh	d		21 25			21 41																
Haymarket	d		21 30			21 46																
Motherwell	a		22s11			22 23																
Glasgow Central 15	a		22 40			22 44										23h55						
Stirling	a					23j27																
Perth	a					00j06																
Inverness	a																					
Inverkeithing	a					22j17										23 58						
Kirkcaldy	a					23j05																
Leuchars 3	a					23j40																
Dundee	a					23j56																
Arbroath	a																					
Montrose	a																					
Stonehaven	a																					
Aberdeen	a																					

For general notes see front of timetable
For details of catering facilities see Directory of Train Operators

A From Penzance (Table 135)
B From Bristol Temple Meads (Table 51)
C From Liverpool Lime Street (Table 39)
D From Paignton (Table 51)
E From Bournemouth (Table 51)
G To Manchester Piccadilly (Table 49)
H From Plymouth (Table 51)
J To Nottingham (Table 19)
b Change at Ely and Peterborough
c Change at Doncaster
e Change at Leeds
f Change at Doncaster and Leeds
g Bradford Interchange
h Glasgow Queen Street
j Change at Edinburgh

Due to Engineering Operations in the Sheffield area, services from Sunday 14 September on this Table had not been confirmed at time of going to press. These services will be issued in a special Supplement as soon as exact timings have been confirmed.

Table 26

Sundays

20 July to 7 September

London → Humberside, Yorkshire, North East England and Scotland

Route Diagram - see first page of Table 26

		GR	TP	GR	GR	XC	GR	EM	XC	XC	GR	TP	GR	HT	GR	GR	GR	EM	GR	GR
		R 1	1 ◇	R 1	R 1	1 ◇	R 1	◇	R 1	1 ◇	R 1	1 ◇	R 1	1 ◇	R 1	R 1	R 1	◇	R 1	R 1
			A			B		C	D	B		A						C		
London Kings Cross 15 ⊖	d	19 00		19 10	19 30		19 35				20 00		20 03	20 10	20 30	21 00	21 30		22 00	22 10
Stevenage 4	d				19 49		19 54							20u30		20 46			21 46	
Peterborough 8	a	19 44		19 54	20 18		20 24				20 44		20 48		21 14	21 44	22 14		22 44	22s59
Norwich	d				18b15			18 57								19 44		20 52	20 52	
Stansted Airport	d				18 35															
Cambridge	d				19 08											20 02				
Peterborough 8	d	19 44		19 55	20 19		20 25	20 30			20 44		20 49		21 14	21 45	22 15	22 22	22 45	
Grantham 7	a			20 19				21 01						21 17	21 36		22 39	22 50		23s31
	d			20 19										21 18	21 36		22 39			
Newark North Gate 7	a			20 30											21 48		22 50			23s42
Lincoln	a			21 49											22 24		23 52			
Grimsby Town	a	21c44					22c44									23c58				
Newark North Gate 7	d			20 30											21 48		22 50			
Retford 10	d													21 38	22 03		23 06			
Doncaster 7	a	20 35		20 56	21 09		21 16				21 36			21 53	22 19	22 42	23 27		23 42	00s12
Selby	a			21 15										22 08						
Hull	a			21 56										22 50		00 02				
Wakefield Westgate 7	a				21 27								21 56		22 40		00 01			
Huddersfield	a				22e27								23e20		23e39					03e03
Leeds 10	a				21 47								22 15		23 00		00 22			01 17
Shipley	a				22 19								22 45		23 21					
Bradford Forster Square	a				22f23								22 54		23f43					
Keighley	a				22 32										23 34					
Skipton	a				22 48										23 50					
Sheffield 7	d	19 59				20 54	20 27		20 21		20 57					21 24			22 30	
Doncaster 7	d	20 35				21 17	21 20				21 36					22 43			23 45	
York 8	a	21 00				21 42	21 47		21 45		22 00					23 09			00 39	
Scarborough	a										23 00									
Harrogate	a	21 58			23 00					←					23 59					
Leeds 10	d	20 10	20 10				20 43		21 08	21 10		22 05				22 10				
Hull	d		18 53				20 22			20 22										
York 8	d	21 02	21 10			21 58 →	21 48		21 53	21 58	22 02	22 45				23 11				
Thirsk	d		21 28									23 10								
Northallerton	d		21 38									23 20				23 46				
Darlington 7	a	21 30	21 49				22 26		22 32	22 36	22 43	23 35				23 59			01 32	
Eaglescliffe	a																			
Middlesbrough	a	22 07								23 10										
Darlington 7	d	21 30	21 50				22 27		22 34	22 38	22 43	23 36				00 01				
Durham	d		22 06				22 44		22 51	22 57	23 01	23 53				00 17			01g50	
Chester-le-Street	d																			
Newcastle 8	a	22 02	22 23				23 14		23 23	23 29	23 34	00 25				00 50			02 25	
Hartlepool	a																			
Sunderland	a																			
Newcastle 8	d																			
Morpeth	d																			
Alnmouth	d																			
Berwick-upon-Tweed	d																			
Dunbar	d																			
Edinburgh 10	a																			
Edinburgh	d																			
Haymarket	d																			
Motherwell	a																			
Glasgow Central 15	a																			
Stirling	a																			
Perth	a																			
Inverness	a																			
Inverkeithing	a																			
Kirkcaldy	a																			
Leuchars 3	a																			
Dundee	a																			
Arbroath	a																			
Montrose	a																			
Stonehaven	a																			
Aberdeen	a																			

For general notes see front of timetable
For details of catering facilities see Directory of Train Operators

A From Liverpool Lime Street (Table 39)
B From Bristol Temple Meads (Table 51)
C To Nottingham (Table 19)
D From Bournemouth (Table 51)
b Change at Ely and Peterborough
c Change at Doncaster
e Change at Leeds
f Bradford Interchange
g Arrival time

Due to Engineering Operations in the Sheffield area, services from Sunday 14 September on this Table had not been confirmed at time of going to press. These services will be issued in a special Supplement as soon as exact timings have been confirmed.

Scotland, North East England, Yorkshire and Humberside → London

Route Diagram - see first page of Table 26

Miles	Miles	Miles			GR	EM	GR	GR	GR	GR	GR	GR		GR	HT	TP	GR	GR	HT	TP	XC		GR	TP	GR	GR
									MO	MX																
					R 1		R 1	R 1	R 1	R 1	R 1	R 1		R 1	BHX 1 ◇	1 ◇	R 1	R 1	BHX 1 ◇	1 ◇	R 1		R 1	1 ◇	R 1	R 1
						A										B				C	D			C		E
					⊡ ⊥		✕ ⊥	✕ ⊥	✕ ⊥	✕ ⊥	✕ ⊥	✕ ⊥		✕ ⊥	⊠	⊥	✕ ⊥	✕ ⊥	⊠ ⊡	⊥	⊡		✕ ⊥	⊥	✕ ⊥	✕ ⊥
—	—	0	**Aberdeen**	d																						
—	—	16¼	Stonehaven	d																						
—	—	40½	Montrose	d																						
—	—	54¼	Arbroath	d																						
—	—	71¼	**Dundee**	d																						
—	—	79½	Leuchars [3]	d																						
—	—	104½	Kirkcaldy	d																						
—	—	117¼	Inverkeithing	d																						
—	—	—	**Inverness**	d																						
—	—	—	Perth	d																						
—	—	—	Stirling	d																						
0	—	—	**Glasgow Central [15]**	d																						
12¾	—	—	Motherwell	d																						
56	—	129¼	Haymarket	d																						
57¼	—	130½	**Edinburgh [10]**	a																						
—	—	—	**Edinburgh**	d																						
86½	—	—	Dunbar	d																						
114¾	—	—	**Berwick-upon-Tweed**	d																						
147	—	—	Alnmouth	d																						
165¼	—	—	Morpeth	d																						
181¾	—	—	**Newcastle [8]** ⛴	a																						
—	—	—	Sunderland ⛴	d																						
—	—	—	Hartlepool	d																						
—	—	—	**Newcastle [8]** ⛴	d					04 10	04 20		05 25					06 00			06 13	06 19				06 30	
190	—	—	Chester-le-Street	d																	06 31					
195¾	—	—	**Durham**	d					04 27	04 36		05 38					06 12			06 29	06 38				06 42	
217¾	—	—	**Darlington [7]**	a					04 45	04 53		05 55					06 29			06 45	06 53				07 00	
—	—	—	Middlesbrough	d												05 58										
—	—	—	Eaglescliffe	d																						
—	—	—	**Darlington [7]**	d					04 45	04 54		05 56					06 30			06 46	06 55			←	07 01	
231¾	—	—	Northallerton	d					05 12	05 21		06 08				06 26				06 58 →				06 58	07 12	
239½	—	—	Thirsk	d												06 33								07 06		
261¾	—	—	**York [8]**	a					05 47	05 47		06 28				06 52	06 57				07 22			07 32	07 34	
—	—	—	Hull	a					08b20	08b20											08 45					
—	—	—	Leeds [10]	a					06 23	06 23						07 23	07 49							08 04		
—	—	—	Harrogate	d														06c06					06 30		06 45	
—	—	—	Scarborough	d																					06 30	
—	—	—	**York [8]**	d					05 50	05 50		06 30					07 00				07 27				07 36	
294¼	—	—	**Doncaster [7]**	a					06 13	06 18		06 53									07 49					
—	—	—	Sheffield [7] ⛴	a					07 03	07 03		07 40									08 20					
—	—	—	Skipton	d										05 48				06e02					06 18			
—	—	—	Keighley	d										06 01				06e15					06 31			
—	—	—	Bradford Forster Square	d										06 01				06 30					06f48			
—	—	—	Shipley	d										06 13				06u36					06 44			
—	0	—	**Leeds [10]**	d			05 05	05 30			06 05			06 40				07 00					07 20			07 00
—	—	—	Huddersfield	d			04g11	04h39			05 32							06c11					06 41			06 11
—	10	—	**Wakefield Westgate [7]**	d			05 17	05 42			06 18			06 52				07 12					07 32			
—	—	—	Hull	d								05 20			06 25											07 00
—	—	—	Selby	d								06 18			07 00											07 32
—	29¾	—	**Doncaster [7]**	d			05 35	06 00	06 14	06 18		06 54			07 18			07 30	←							07 55
311¾	—	—	**Retford [10]**	d			05 50				06 48				07 32 →				07 32							
330¼	—	—	**Newark North Gate [7]**	a			06 05	06 24	06 43	06 43	07 03			07 29												
—	—	—	Grimsby Town	d								05j26		05 58												06j26
—	—	—	Lincoln	d			05 23							06 54												
—	—	—	**Newark North Gate [7]**	d			06 05	06 24	06 43	06 43	07 04			07 29												
344¾	—	—	**Grantham [7]**	a			06 18	06 37	06 55	06 55	07 16	07 25							07 56							08 29
—	—	—		d		05 51	06 18	06 37	06 55	06 55	07 17	07 25							07 57							08 29
374	—	—	**Peterborough [8]**	a		06 27	06 37	06 58	07 15	07 15	07 37	07 45					08 03						08 32			08 50
—	—	—	Cambridge	a				08 07	08k44	08k44	08k55						09 21									10 08
—	—	—	Stansted Airport	a				08 49									09 59									10 49
—	—	—	Norwich	a					09 16	09 16							10k30									
—	—	—	**Peterborough [8]**	d	06 10		06 40	07 00	07 17	07 17	07 40	07 46					08 04						08 33			08 51
422¾	—	—	**Stevenage [4]**	a				07 58	08 26	08 26							09 05						09 34		09 06	09 56
450¼	—	—	**London Kings Cross [15]** ⊖	a	07 00		07 30	07 53	08 11	08 11	08 33	08 41		08 48			08 59	09 06	09 18				09 26		09 35	09 45

For general notes see front of timetable
For details of catering facilities see Directory of Train Operators

A From Nottingham (Table 19)
B To Manchester Airport (Table 39)
C To Liverpool Lime Street (Table 39)
D To Paignton (from 8 September to Bournemouth) (Table 51)
E **The Hull Executive**
b Change at York and Selby
c Change at Leeds
e Change at Shipley
f Bradford Interchange
g Mondays only. Change at Leeds
h Tuesdays to Fridays only. Change at Leeds
j Change at Doncaster
k Change at Peterborough and Ely

Scotland, North East England, Yorkshire and Humberside → London

Route Diagram - see first page of Table 26

Station		GR	EM	XC	GR	GR	GR	GC	EM	TP	XC	TP	GR	HT	GR	XC	GR	GR	TP	XC	XC	NT	EM	GR
		R 1	◇	R 1	R 1	R 1	R 1	R 1	◇	1 ◇	1 ◇	1 ◇	R 1	1 ◇	R 1	1 ◇	R 1	R 1	1 ◇	R 1	R 1		◇	R 1
			A	B				C	D	E	G	E				H			E	J	K	L	N	
		✕ ⊼		⊡	✕ ⊼	✕ ⊼	✕ ⊼	✕		⊼	⊡	⊼	✕ ⊼	⊠ ⊡	⊡ ⊼	⊡	✕ ⊼	✕ ⊼	⊼	⊡	⊡		⊼	✕ ⊼
Aberdeen	d																							
Stonehaven	d																							
Montrose	d																							
Arbroath	d																							
Dundee	d																							
Leuchars 3	d																							
Kirkcaldy	d																							*05 53*
Inverkeithing	d																							*06 18*
Inverness	d																							
Perth	d																							
Stirling	d																							*05 30*
Glasgow Central 15	d																							
Motherwell	d																							
Haymarket	d																							
Edinburgh 10	a																							
Edinburgh	d					05 50							06 00			06 05								07 00
Dunbar	d												06 20											
Berwick-upon-Tweed	d					06 29							06 43			06 48								07 42
Alnmouth	d												07 03			07 10						07 34		
Morpeth	d												07 19									08 00		
Newcastle 8	a					07 16							07 38			07 41						08 25		08 30
Sunderland	d							06 41												*07 55*				
Hartlepool	d							07 08																
Newcastle 8	d			06 44	07 00	07 20					07 23	07 26	07 40			07 44	07 52			08 24				08 32
Chester-le-Street	d											07 37								08 33				
Durham	d			06 56	07 12						07 37	07 43				07 56	08 04			08 40				08 45
Darlington 7	a			07 12	07 29						07 52	07 59				08 13	08 21			08 55				09 04
Middlesbrough	d				*06 49*					07 23							*07 42*		←	*08 02*				*08 26*
Eaglescliffe	d							07 28																
Darlington 7	d			07 14	07 30						07 54	08 00 →				08 14	08 22		08 00	08 57				09 05
Northallerton	d							07 45		07 54									08 12					
Thirsk	d							07 56		08 02									08 20					
York 8	a			07 41	07 58	08 09		08 14		08 19	08 24		08 34			08 41	08 49		08 55	09 24				09 34
Hull	a												*10b04*											
Leeds 10	a			08 08				*09 02*		08 50	*09 04*					09 08			09 23	*10 04*				
Harrogate	d				*07 05*		07 28										*07 49*	*08 14*						*08 16*
Scarborough	d				*07 00*												*07 47*							
York 8	d				08 00	08 12		08 16			08 27		08 36				08 51			09 27	09 25			09 35
Doncaster 7	a										08 50						09 16			09 54	09 54			10 03
Sheffield 7	a			08 51							09c25					09 51	*10e04*			10 20	10 25			
Skipton	d	06 55					*07 08*								*07 47*			*07 56*						
Keighley	d	07u05					*07 21*								*08 00*			*08 09*						
Bradford Forster Square	d	*07f05*					*07g18*								*08g05*			*08 26*						
Shipley	d	07u15					*07 35*								*08 13*			*08 33*						
Leeds 10	d	07 40					08 05								08 40			09 05						
Huddersfield	d	*06h53*					*07h25*								*07h57*			*08 37*						
Wakefield Westgate 7	d	07 52					08 17								08 52			09 18						
Hull	d													08 12										*08 56*
Selby	d													08 45										
Doncaster 7	d						08 36							09 02	09 12		09 17	09 36						10 04
Retford 10	d	08 19												09 16				09 51						
Newark North Gate 7	a	08 34													09 37		09 43	10 06						
Grimsby Town	d	*07 03*												*07j26*										*08j36*
Lincoln	d	*07 59*												*08k27*			*09 10*							*09m11*
Newark North Gate 7	d	08 34													09 37		09 43	10 06						
Grantham 7	a					09 00							09 27	09 41			09 55							10 36
	d		08 26			09 00			09 11				09 28	09 41			09 55						10 08	10 36
Peterborough 8	a		08 57				09 26		09 38				09 47		10 05		10 15	10 33					10 42	10 56
Cambridge	a						*10n44*								*11 08*			*11n44*						
Stansted Airport	a														*11 49*									
Norwich	a		10 43						11 14									*12 15*					12 15	
Peterborough 8	d						09 26						09 48		10 05		10 18	10 34						10 57
Stevenage 4	a						09 57								10 34			*11 33*						
London Kings Cross 15 ⊖	a	09 51			09 55	10 10	10 25	10 31					10 40	10 51	11 03		11 15	11 27						11 51

For general notes see front of timetable
For details of catering facilities see Directory of Train Operators

- **A** From Mansfield Woodhouse (Table 55)
- **B** To Bournemouth (from 8 September to Bristol Temple Meads) (Table 51)
- **C** **The Zephyr**
- **D** From Sheffield (from 8 September from Chesterfield) (Table 49)
- **E** To Manchester Airport (Table 39)
- **G** To Bristol Temple Meads (from 8 September to Plymouth) (Table 51)
- **H** To Plymouth (from 8 September to Paignton) (Table 51)
- **J** Until 5 September. To Paignton (Table 51)
- **K** From 8 September. To Bournemouth (Table 51)
- **L** From Chathill (Table 48)
- **N** From Liverpool Lime Street (from 8 September from Chesterfield) (Table 49)
- **b** Change at York and Selby
- **c** Until 5 September arr. 5 minutes earlier
- **e** From 8 September arr. 1007
- **f** Bradford Interchange. Change at Leeds
- **g** Bradford Interchange
- **h** Change at Leeds
- **j** Change at Doncaster
- **k** Change at Retford
- **m** Change at Peterborough
- **n** Change at Peterborough and Ely

Scotland, North East England, Yorkshire and Humberside → London

Route Diagram - see first page of Table 26

	GR	XC	TP	GR	GR	EM	TP	GR	XC	XC	HT	GR	GR	XC	TP	EM	TP	XC	XC	GR	GR	XC
		A	B			C	B		D	J				E	B	C	B	G	H			A
Aberdeen d																				06b00		
Stonehaven d																				06b16		
Montrose d																				06b38		
Arbroath d																				06b52		
Dundee d														06 38						07b11		07 35
Leuchars 3 d														06 51						07b23		07 48
Kirkcaldy d														07 25						07b57		08 20
Inverkeithing d								07b15						07 43						08b19		08 36
Inverness d																						
Perth d								05c15						06b14						07b03		
Stirling d								06b36						06b36						07b48		
Glasgow Central 15 d		06 00						06 50						07e00						07 50		08e00
Motherwell d								07 04												08 07		
Haymarket d		06 52						07 50						08 00						08 50		08 56
Edinburgh 10 a		06 56						07 55						08 06						08 55		09 02
Edinburgh d		07 05						08 00						08 10						09 00		09 05
Dunbar d		07 25																				09 25
Berwick-upon-Tweed d		07 48												08 48						09 42		09 48
Alnmouth d		08 08						08 56						09 09								
Morpeth d							08 32										09 32					
Newcastle 8 a		08 40						09 29						09 40						10 31		10 38
Sunderland d				08 30													09 30					
Hartlepool d																						
Newcastle 8 d		08 40		09 00			09 12	09 30	09 35					09 40			10 15	10 25		10 34		10 40
Chester-le-Street d							09 20											10 34				
Durham d		08 52		09 12			09 27		09 47					09 52			10 27	10 41		10 47		10 52
Darlington 7 a		09 10		09 30			09 43	09 58	10 04					10 10			10 43	10 56		11 05		11 10
Middlesbrough d			09 00	08 56											09 59					10 24		
Eaglescliffe d																						
Darlington 7 d		09 10		09 31			09 45	09 58	10 04					10 10			10 44	10 58		11 06		11 10
Northallerton d			09 28	09 43			09 56								10 27		10 56					
Thirsk d			09 36												10 35							
York 8 a		09 41	09 55	10 05			10 24	10 27	10 31					10 41	10 54		11 24	11 24		11 33		11 41
Hull a		10 56		11f33													13 02					13 02
Leeds 10 a		10 08	10 23				10 53		11 04					11 08	11 23		11 53	12 05				12 08
Harrogate d	08 30			09 05								09 44	10 14								10 44	
Scarborough d				08 47																09 47		
York 8 d				10 06				10 29	10 34	10 30								11 27	11 23	11 35		
Doncaster 7 a				10 30				10 53	10 57	10 57								11 51	11 51	12 00		
Sheffield 7 a		10 51		11 07					11 20	11 25				11 51				12 20	12 25			12 51
Skipton d	08 43											09 48									10 48	
Keighley d	08 56											10 01									11 01	
Bradford Forster Square d	09h05				09 31							10h05	10 31								11h05	
Shipley d	09 09				09 39							10 14	10 39								11 14	
Leeds 10 d	09 40				10 05							10 40	11 05								11 40	
Huddersfield d	08j57				09 35							09j57	10 35								10j57	
Wakefield Westgate 7 d	09 52				10 18							10 52	11 17								11 54	
Hull d					09 25			09 56			10 12		10 22							10 57		
Selby d											10 47											
Doncaster 7 d	10 15			10 30	10 35			10 53			11 05	11 13	11 37							12 00	12 12	
Retford 10 d								11 08			11 20											
Newark North Gate 7 a	10 38				10 59							11 41									12 37	
Grimsby Town d					09 28			09k36												10k36		
Lincoln d					10 23						10m27									11 12		
Newark North Gate 7 d	10 38				10 59							11 41									12 37	
Grantham 7 a					11 11						11 40	11 54	12 09									
d					11 11	11 04					11 40	11 54	12 09			12 07						
Peterborough 8 a	11 06			11 16	11 31	11 34		11 48				12 13	12 28			12 42				12 46	13 05	
Cambridge a	12 08			12n44	12n55			13 08					13n44									
Stansted Airport a	12 49							13 49														
Norwich a						13 13										14 14						
Peterborough 8 d	11 06			11 17	11 31			11 49				12 14	12 29							12 47	13 06	
Stevenage 4 a				11 47	12 33							12 43								13 16	14 08	
London Kings Cross 15 ⊖ a	12 03			12 17	12 25			12 42			12 44	13 10	13 22							13 43	14 02	

For general notes see front of timetable
For details of catering facilities see Directory of Train Operators

- **A** To Bournemouth (from 8 September to Bristol Temple Meads) (Table 51)
- **B** To Manchester Airport (Table 39)
- **C** From Liverpool Lime Street (from 8 September from Chesterfield) (Table 49)
- **D** Until 5 September. To Bristol Temple Meads (Table 51)
- **E** To Plymouth (Table 51)
- **G** Until 5 September. To Plymouth (Table 51)
- **H** From 8 September. To Bournemouth (Table 51)
- **J** From 8 September. To Plymouth (Table 51)

- **b** Change at Edinburgh
- **c** Change at Stirling and Edinburgh
- **e** Glasgow Queen Street. Change at Edinburgh
- **f** Change at York and Selby
- **h** Bradford Interchange
- **j** Change at Leeds
- **k** Change at Doncaster
- **m** Change at Retford
- **n** Change at Peterborough and Ely

Table 26

Mondays to Fridays

Scotland, North East England, Yorkshire and Humberside → London

Route Diagram - see first page of Table 26

		TP	GR	EM	GR	TP	XC	XC	GR	XC	GR	GR	EM	HT	GR	TP	TP	XC	XC	GR	XC	TP	GR
		1◇	R 1	◇	R 1	1◇	R 1	R 1	R 1	R 1	R 1	R 1	◇	1◇	R 1	1◇	1◇	R 1	R 1	R 1	R 1	1◇	R 1
		A		B		A	C	D		E			B			A	A	G	H		J	A	K
Aberdeen	d		06b34							07c20	07 52										08 20		08c50
Stonehaven	d		06b53							07c36	08 09										08 38		09c06
Montrose	d		07b15							07c58	08 32										08 59		09e14
Arbroath	d		07b29							08c12	08 48										09 15		09c42
Dundee	d		07 59							08c31	09 06										09 32		09c59
Leuchars 3	d		08 11							08c43	09 20										09 45		10c11
Kirkcaldy	d		08 43							09c15	09 44									09c59	10 12		10c43
Inverkeithing	d		08 59							09c24	10 00									10c20	10 27		10c59
Inverness	d									05c00	06c45												07 55
Perth	d		07f14								08c48												09 55
Stirling	d		08 06							08c36	09c06									09c36			10 29
Glasgow Central 15	d		08g30							09 00	09h15									09 50			10h30
Motherwell	d									09u14										10 04			
Haymarket	d									09 54	10 19									10 50	10 47		11 10
Edinburgh 10	a									09 59	10 26									10 56	10 54		11 16
Edinburgh	d		09 30							10 05	10 30									11 00	11 05		11 30
Dunbar	d																				11 25		
Berwick-upon-Tweed	d		10 09																	11 41	11 48		
Alnmouth	d									11 04										12 01			
Morpeth	d						10{50			11 18										11 50			
Newcastle 8	a		10 59							11 35	11 57									12 34	12 38		12 58
Sunderland	d		10 30			10 30											11 30						12 30
Hartlepool	d																						
Newcastle 8	d		11 01			11 15	11{25		11 30	11 40	11 59						12 15	12{19		12 35	12 40		13 01
Chester-le-Street	d																	12{32					
Durham	d					11 27	11{37		11 43	11 52							12 27	12{40		12 48	12 52		
Darlington 7	a		11 28			11 43	11{54		12 01	12 09							12 43	12{59		13 06	13 10		
Middlesbrough	d	11 00	10 54			10 54			11 24							12 00		12{24				12 50	
Eaglescliffe	d																						
Darlington 7	d		11 29			11 44	11{56		12 02	12 10							12 44	13{00		13 06	13 10		
Northallerton	d	11 28				11 56										12 28	12 56					13 18	
Thirsk	d	11 36														12 36						13 26	
York 8	a	11 55	11 58			12 21	12{22		12 29	12 41	12 50					12 55	13 24	13{27		13 35	13 41	13 49	13 52
Hull	a		13j33																	14 48			
Leeds 10	a	12 23	12 49			12 51			13 04	13 08						13 23	13 53	14{04			14 08	14 23	14 49
Harrogate	d		11 05		11 14						12 05				12 14								13 05
Scarborough	d		10 45								11 45												12 47
York 8	d		12 00				12{25	12{24	12 31		12 53							13{29	13{25	13 36			13 54
Doncaster 7	a						12{50	12{50	12 54									13{53	13{53	14 02			
Sheffield 7	a						13{20	13{25	13 41	13 51								14{20	14{25		14 51		
Skipton	d				10 59							11 48			12 12								
Keighley	d				11 09							12 01			12 22								
Bradford Forster Square	d				11 31							12k05			12 31								
Shipley	d				11 39							12 14			12 39								
Leeds 10	d				12 05							12 40			13 05								
Huddersfield	d				11 35							11m57			12 35								
Wakefield Westgate 7	d				12 17							12 52			13 18								
Hull	d				11 22				11 55					12 45	12 22					12 57			
Selby	d													13 20									
Doncaster 7	d				12 36				12 55			13 14		13 37	13 38					14 03			
Retford 10	d				12 51										13 55								
Newark North Gate 7	a											13 42			14 10								
Grimsby Town	d								11n36											12n36			
Lincoln	d				11q27				12 14			12 23											
Newark North Gate 7	d											13 42			14 10								
Grantham 7	a				13 14									14 08	14 23								
	d			13 08	13 14								14 06	14 09	14 23								
Peterborough 8	a		13 11	13 38					13 44		14 03	14 09	14 38		14 42					14 49			
Cambridge	a		14r44									15 08											
Stansted Airport	a											15 49											
Norwich	a			15 13									16 13										
Peterborough 8	d		13 12						13 47		14 03	14 10			14 43					14 50			
Stevenage 4	a								14 17			15 08			15 12								
London Kings Cross 15 ⊖	a		14 10		14 20				14 44		14 57	15 05		15 20	15 40					15 44			15 50

For general notes see front of timetable
For details of catering facilities see Directory of Train Operators

- **A** To Manchester Airport (Table 39)
- **B** From Liverpool Lime Street (from 8 September from Chesterfield) (Table 49)
- **C** Until 5 September. To Bristol Temple Meads (Table 51)
- **D** From 8 September. To Penzance (Table 135)
- **E** To Penzance (Table 135) (from 8 September to Plymouth) (Table 51)
- **G** Until 5 September. To Plymouth (Table 51)
- **H** From 8 September. To Bournemouth (Table 51)
- **J** To Bournemouth (from 8 September to Bristol Temple Meads) (Table 51)
- **K** **The Highland Chieftain**
- **b** Change at Dundee and Edinburgh
- **c** Change at Edinburgh
- **e** Change at Arbroath and Edinburgh
- **f** Change at Stirling and Edinburgh
- **g** Glasgow Queen Street
- **h** Glasgow Queen Street. Change at Edinburgh
- **j** Change at York and Selby
- **k** Bradford Interchange
- **m** Change at Leeds
- **n** Change at Doncaster
- **q** Change at Retford
- **r** Change at Peterborough and Ely

Scotland, North East England, Yorkshire and Humberside → London

Route Diagram - see first page of Table 26

		GR	GC	GR	EM	TP	GR	XC	XC	XC	TP	GR	GR	GR	EM	GR	TP	XC	XC	GR	GR	XC	TP	GR
					A	B		C	D	E	B	G			A		B	H	J	K		L	N	
Aberdeen	d											09 50								10b22				
Stonehaven	d											10 07								10b38				
Montrose	d											10 30								11b00				
Arbroath	d											10 47								11b14				
Dundee	d											11 04								11b30				
Leuchars 3	d											11 18								11b42				
Kirkcaldy	d						10 58					11 42								12b12				
Inverkeithing	d						11 20					11 59								12b20				
Inverness	d																							
Perth	d											10c12								11b08				
Stirling	d						10 36					11b06								11b36				
Glasgow Central 15	d						11e00					11f30								11 50				
Motherwell	d																			12 04				
Haymarket	d											12 17								12 50				
Edinburgh 10	a											12 23								12 56				
Edinburgh	d						12 00			12 05		12 30								13 00		13 05		
Dunbar	d																					13 25		
Berwick-upon-Tweed	d						12 40													13 41		13 48		
Alnmouth	d									13 02														
Morpeth	d						12 50			13 19								13 50						
Newcastle 8	a						13 27			13 40		13 58								14 30		14 37		
Sunderland	d		12 30									13 30					13 30							
Hartlepool	d		12 54																					
Newcastle 8	d					13 15	13 29	13 34		13 40		14 00				14 05	14 12	14 22		14 34		14 40		14 55
Chester-le-Street	d																	14 33						
Durham	d					13 27		13 46		13 52						14 17	14 24	14 40				14 52		15 08
Darlington 7	a					13 43	13 55	14 02		14 10						14 36	14 42	14 55		15 03		15 10		15 25
Middlesbrough	d					12 57		13 25			13 50					13 55	13 55			14 24			14 50	
Eaglescliffe	d		13 16																					
Darlington 7	d					13 44	13 56	14 03		14 10						14 37	14 44	14 57		15 04		15 10		15 26
Northallerton	d		13 38			13 56					14 18					14 49	14 56						15 18	
Thirsk	d		13 47								14 26												15 26	
York 8	a		14 07			14 22	14 24	14 29		14 41	14 48	14 51				15 09	15 25	15 26		15 33		15 41	15 51	15 53
Hull	a											15 58												17 27
Leeds 10	a					14 53		15 05		15 08	15 23	15 49					15 53	16 04				16 08	16 23	16 49
Harrogate	d			13 14								14 05		14 14							14 44			15 05
Scarborough	d											13 47												14 47
York 8	d		14 10				14 26	14 32	14 30			14 53				15 11		15 29	15 23	15 35				15 55
Doncaster 7	a						14 49	14 55	14 55							15 35		15 54	15 54	15 59				
Sheffield 7	a							15 20	15 25	15 51						16 07		16 20	16 25			16 53		17 18
Skipton	d	12 48											13 48	13 59							14 48			
Keighley	d	13 01											14 01	14 09							15 01			
Bradford Forster Square	d	13g05		13 31									14g05	14 31							15g05			
Shipley	d	13 14		13 39									14 14	14 39							15 14			
Leeds 10	d	13 40		14 05									14 40	15 05							15 40			
Huddersfield	d	12h57		13 35									13h57	14 35							14h57			
Wakefield Westgate 7	d	13 53		14 18									14 52	15 17							15 52			
Hull	d						13 25						13 57			14 25				14 57				
Selby	d																							
Doncaster 7	d	14 15					14 50						15 15			15 36				16 00				
Retford 10	d															15 51								
Newark North Gate 7	a						15 13						15 41			16 06								
Grimsby Town	d						13j36						13 52							14j36				
Lincoln	d	13 31					14 04						14 47							14 50				
Newark North Gate 7	d						15 13						15 41			16 06								
Grantham 7	a			15 03			15 26						15 54			16 19								16 44
	d			15 03	15 07		15 26						15 54		16 07	16 19								16 44
Peterborough 8	a	15 05		15 22	15 34		15 45					16 01		16 17	16 34					16 47	16 53			17 04
Cambridge	a	16 08		16k44								17 08		17k43										18 16
Stansted Airport	a	16 49										17 43												18 47
Norwich	a				17 13										18 13									19k25
Peterborough 8	d	15 06		15 23			15 47					16 02		16 17						16 48	16 54			17 04
Stevenage 4	a			15 52			16 17							16 48										17 34
London Kings Cross 15 ⊖	a	15 58	16 05	16 22			16 46					16 57	17 04	17 15		17 30				17 41	17 50			18 04

For general notes see front of timetable
For details of catering facilities see Directory of Train Operators

A From Liverpool Lime Street (from 8 September from Chesterfield) (Table 49)
B To Manchester Airport (Table 39)
C Until 5 September. To Bristol Temple Meads (Table 51)
D From 8 September. To Plymouth (Table 51)
E To Plymouth (from 8 September to Cardiff Central) (Table 51)
G **The Northern Lights**
H Until 5 September. To Cardiff Central (Table 51)
J From 8 September. To Bournemouth (Table 51)
K **The Flying Scotsman**
L To Bournemouth (from 8 September to Weston-super-Mare) (Table 51)
N To Manchester Piccadilly (Table 39)
b Change at Edinburgh
c Change at Stirling and Edinburgh
e Glasgow Queen Street
f Glasgow Queen Street. Change at Edinburgh
g Bradford Interchange
h Change at Leeds
j Change at Doncaster
k Change at Peterborough and Ely

Scotland, North East England, Yorkshire and Humberside → London

Route Diagram - see first page of Table 26

Station		HT	GR	TP	XC	XC	GR	GR	XC	TP	GR	TP	XC	GR	GR	EM	TP	XC	XC	HT	GR	XC	TP
		1◇	R 1	1◇	1◇	1◇	R 1	R 1	1◇	1◇	R 1	1◇	R 1	R 1	R 1	◇	1◇	R 1	R 1	1◇	R 1	R 1	1◇
				A	B	C			D	A		A	E			G	A	E	H			J	
Aberdeen	d						11 22															12 24	
Stonehaven	d						11 38															12 42	
Montrose	d						12 00															12b15	
Arbroath	d						12 14															13 16	
Dundee	d						12 30															13 33	
Leuchars 3	d						12 42															13 45	
Kirkcaldy	d						13 14							13c57								14 14	
Inverkeithing	d						13 30							14c18									
Inverness	d						09e19							10c52									
Perth	d						11e38							13c04									
Stirling	d						12 36							13c36									
Glasgow Central 15	d						13f00							13 50								14f00	
Motherwell	d													14 04									
Haymarket	d													14 50									
Edinburgh 10	a													14 56									
Edinburgh	d						14 00		14 05					15 00								15 05	
Dunbar	d																					15 25	
Berwick-upon-Tweed	d						14 39															15 48	
Alnmouth	d								15 04														
Morpeth	d				14 50				15 20				15 50										
Newcastle 8	a						15 28		15 38					16 26								16 39	
Sunderland	d			14 30								15 30											
Hartlepool	d																						
Newcastle 8	d			15 12	15 22		15 30		15 40		15 55	16 06	16 27	16 28								16 40	
Chester-le-Street	d			15 21								16 15	16 42					←					
Durham	d			15 27	15 34				15 52		16 08	16 22	16 49 →					16 49				16 52	
Darlington 7	a			15 43	15 50		16 01		16 09		16 26	16 38					←	17 04					
Middlesbrough	d			14 55					15 27	15 50							15 55	16 24					16 50
Eaglescliffe	d																						
Darlington 7	d			15 44	15 51		16 02		16 10		16 26	16 39 →					16 39	17 06					
Northallerton	d			15 56						16 18							16 51						17 18
Thirsk	d									16 26							17 01						17 26
York 8	a			16 20	16 23		16 30		16 41	16 51	16 54			17 20			17 27	17 32				17 41	17 50
Hull	a										18 29												
Leeds 10	a			16 53			17 04		17 08	17 23	17 50						17 53	18 04				18 08	18 23
Harrogate	d		15 14					15 44			16 05				16 14						16 44		
Scarborough	d										15 47												
York 8	d				16 25	16 25	16 32				16 56			17 21				17 34	17 34				
Doncaster 7	a				16 48	16 48					17 20							17 56	17 56				
Sheffield 7	a				17 20	17 25			17 51		18 07							18 25	18 25			18 51	
Skipton	d							15 48							16 12						16 49		
Keighley	d							16 01							16 22						17 02		
Bradford Forster Square	d		15 31					16h05							16 31						17h05		
Shipley	d		15 39					16 14							16 39						17 15		
Leeds 10	d		16 05					16 40							17 05						17 40		
Huddersfield	d		15 35					15j57							16 35						16j57		
Wakefield Westgate 7	d		16 17					16 52							17 17						17 52		
Hull	d	15 18	15 21					15 57												17 06			
Selby	d	15 57																		17 43			
Doncaster 7	d	16 15	16 36					17 10			17 20				17 37					18 03	18 11		
Retford 10	d	16 34													17 57					18 17			
Newark North Gate 7	a		17 00					17 33			17 44										18 34		
Grimsby Town	d							16 03												16k36			
Lincoln	d	15m27						16 56												17m22			
Newark North Gate 7	d		17 00					17 33			17 44										18 34		
Grantham 7	a	16 55									17 57									18 37	18 47		
	d	16 55									17 57					18 16				18 37	18 47		
Peterborough 8	a		17 27					18 01						18 26		18 49					19 06		
Cambridge	a		18 51					19 29						19n55							20 11		
Stansted Airport	a							20 17															
Norwich	a															20 22							
Peterborough 8	d		17 28					18 02						18 26							19 07		
Stevenage 4	a	17s46	18 35					19 09			18 42			19 33	19 00					19s22			
London Kings Cross 15 ⊖	a	18 12	18 23				18 27	18 54			19 11			19 18	19 29					19 47	19 59		

For general notes see front of timetable
For details of catering facilities see Directory of Train Operators

- **A** To Manchester Airport (Table 39)
- **B** Until 5 September. To Weston-super-Mare (Table 51)
- **C** From 8 September. To Plymouth (Table 51)
- **D** To Plymouth (from 8 September to Bristol Temple Meads) (Table 51)
- **E** Until 5 September. To Bristol Temple Meads (Table 51)
- **G** From Liverpool Lime Street (from 8 September from Chesterfield) (Table 49)
- **H** From 8 September. To Southampton Central (Table 51)
- **J** To Southampton Central (from 8 September to Birmingham New Street) (Table 51)
- **b** Change at Arbroath and Edinburgh
- **c** Change at Edinburgh
- **e** Change at Stirling and Edinburgh
- **f** Glasgow Queen Street
- **h** Bradford Interchange
- **j** Change at Leeds
- **k** Change at Doncaster
- **m** Change at Retford
- **n** Change at Peterborough and Ely

Scotland, North East England, Yorkshire and Humberside → London

Route Diagram - see first page of Table 26

		GR	GR	TP	XC	XC	EM	TP	GR	GR	GR	XC	TP	GC	GR	XC	XC	GR	GR	HT	GR	XC	TP	TP
		R 1	R 1	1◇	1◇	1◇	◇	1◇	R 1	R 1	R 1	1◇	1◇	R 1	R 1	1◇	1◇	R 1	R 1	BHX 1◇	R 1	1◇	1◇	1◇
				A	D	F	C	A				B	A			D	F					E		A
Aberdeen	d								13 21										14b25					
Stonehaven	d								13 37										14b41					
Montrose	d								13 59										14c15					
Arbroath	d								14 13										15b15					
Dundee	d								14 30										15b32					
Leuchars 3	d								14 42										15b44					
Kirkcaldy	d								15 14										16b14					
Inverkeithing	d								15 30										16b30					
Inverness	d																		12b40					
Perth	d								13e12										14b49					
Stirling	d								14 36										15b36					
Glasgow Central 15	d								15f00										15 50			16f00		
Motherwell	d																		16 04					
Haymarket	d																		16 50					
Edinburgh 10	a																		16 55					
Edinburgh	d								16 00			16 05							17 00			17 05		
Dunbar	d								16 20													17 25		
Berwick-upon-Tweed	d								16 43													17 48		
Alnmouth	d											17 08							17 59					
Morpeth	d								16 50			17 23												
Newcastle 8	a								17 31			17 38							18 32			18 39		
Sunderland	d			16 30										17 30										
Hartlepool	d													17 56										
Newcastle 8	d	16 55		17 10	17 17				17 32			17 40			18 10	18 20			18 35			18 40		18 58
Chester-le-Street	d				17 26											18 29								
Durham	d	17 07		17 22	17 33							17 52			18 22	18 36						18 52		19 10
Darlington 7	a	17 25		17 38	17 48				17 59			18 10			18 39	18 54			19 03			19 10		19 26
Middlesbrough	d			16 57								17 24	17 50		17 55	18 24							19 00	
Eaglescliffe	d													18 15										
Darlington 7	d	17 25		17 40	17 50			←	17 59			18 10			18 40	18 56			19 04			19 10		19 27
Northallerton	d			17 51				17 51					18 18	18 36	18 51								19 28	19 39
Thirsk	d			→				17 59					18 26	18 45									19 36	
York 8	a	17 53			18 18			18 24	18 28			18 41	18 51	19 04	19 11	19 25			19 33			19 41	19 59	20 03
Hull	a	19 32																						
Leeds 10	a	18 47						18 52	19 04			19 08	19 35		20g39	20 04						20 08		20 35
Harrogate	d		17 14							17 50				18 05					18h18		18 44			
Scarborough	d	16 47												17 45								18 46		
York 8	d	17 55			18 24	18 17			18 30					19 06	19 13	19 29	19 30		19 35					
Doncaster 7	a	18 20			18 49	18 49			18 53						19 37	19 55	19 55		19 59	20 10				
Sheffield 7	a	19 07			19 20	19 25						19 51			20 18	20 20	20 26					20 51		
Skipton	d		16 58							17 49											18 48			
Keighley	d		17 08							18 02											19 01			
Bradford Forster Square	d		17 31							18k05	18 27								18h27		19k05			
Shipley	d		17 39							18 14	18 34								18h34		19 14			
Leeds 10	d		18 05							18 40	19 05								19 05		19 40			
Huddersfield	d		17 33							17m57	18 34								18n34		18m57			
Wakefield Westgate 7	d		18 17							18 52	19 17										19 54			
Hull	d								17 56		18 22								18 53	19 18				
Selby	d								18 27											19 53				
Doncaster 7	d	18 21	18 35						18 54	19 11	19 35				19 37				20 00	20 10	20 15			
Retford 10	d	18 36																						
Newark North Gate 7	a	18 51							19 17	19 34	20 05							←			20 39			
Grimsby Town	d								17q36									18 30	18q36					
Lincoln	d	18 17																19 26						
Newark North Gate 7	d	18 51							19 17	19 34	20 05							20 05			20 39			
Grantham 7	a									19 49	→							20 17		20 42	20 51			
	d						19 09			19 49								20 17		20 42	20 51			
Peterborough 8	a	19 19	19 25				19 36		19 45						20 27			20 37	20 46		21 11			
Cambridge	a		21r01						21 16										22 08					
Stansted Airport	a																							
Norwich	a						21 13		22r30															
Peterborough 8	d	19 20	19 26						19 46						20 28			20 38	20 46		21 12			
Stevenage 4	a	19 50							20 15	20 35									21 17	21s31				
London Kings Cross 15 ⊖	a	20 18	20 21						20 42	21 03				21 09	21 20			21 33	21 44	21 59	22 04			

For general notes see front of timetable
For details of catering facilities see Directory of Train Operators

- **A** To Manchester Airport (Table 39)
- **B** To Birmingham New Street (from 8 September to Bristol Temple Meads) (Table 51)
- **C** From Liverpool Lime Street (from 8 September from Nottingham) (Table 49)
- **D** Until 5 September. To Birmingham New Street (Table 51)
- **E** To Bristol Temple Meads (from 8 September to Birmingham New Street) (Table 51)
- **F** From 8 September. To Bristol Temple Meads (Table 51)
- **b** Change at Edinburgh
- **c** Change at Arbroath and Edinburgh
- **e** Change at Stirling and Edinburgh
- **f** Glasgow Queen Street
- **g** Change at York and Selby
- **h** Change at Leeds and Doncaster
- **k** Bradford Interchange
- **m** Change at Leeds
- **n** Change at Wakefield Westgate and Doncaster
- **q** Change at Doncaster
- **r** Change at Peterborough and Ely

Scotland, North East England, Yorkshire and Humberside → London

Route Diagram - see first page of Table 26

		GR	XC	EM	GR	XC	XC	TP	NT	GR	XC	XC	GR	TP	TP	TP	NT	GR	GR	XC FX	XC FO
		R 1	1 ◇	◇	R 1	1 ◇	1 ◇	1 ◇		R 1	1 ◇	1 ◇	R 1	1 ◇	1 ◇	1 ◇		R 1	R 1	1 ◇	1 ◇
			A	B		C	D	E	G		H	J	K	L		E	N				
Aberdeen	d	14 48				15 20	15 20						16b21					18 18			19c41
Stonehaven	d	15 06				15 36	15 36						16b37					18 35			20c00
Montrose	d	15 28				16 00	16 00						16e13					18 58			20c23
Arbroath	d	15 45				16 14	16 14						17b11					19 14			20c37
Dundee	d	16 02				16 31	16 31						17b31					19 32			21b28
Leuchars 3	d	16 16				16 43	16 43						17b43					19 46			21b40
Kirkcaldy	d	16 40				17 17	17 17			17 31			18b15					20 10			22b13
Inverkeithing	d	16 57				17 33	17 33			17 47			18b12					20 26			22b36
Inverness	d									14 41									16f56		18b27
Perth	d	15g12				15g12				16 48									19b13		21g18
Stirling	d	16b06				16 36	16 36			17 06		17 36	17b36						19b36		22b06
Glasgow Central 15	d	16h15				17 00	17 00			17j15		17 30	17 50						19 50	21 55	21 55
Motherwell	d												18 04						20 04	22 25	22 25
Haymarket	d	17 16											18 49					20s44	20 50	23 10	23 10
Edinburgh 10	a	17 24											18 57					20 50	20 55	23 19	23 19
Edinburgh	d	17 30				18 05	18 05			18 35		18 45	19 00						21 00		23 22
Dunbar	d	17 54				18 25	18 25			18 57			19 24						21 20		23a58
Berwick-upon-Tweed	d	18 17								19 20			19 47						21 45		
Alnmouth	d					19 05	19 05		19 20	19 42									22 07		
Morpeth	d	18 32	18 32			19 01	19 01		19 45	19 59							21 34		22 24		
Newcastle 8	a	19 07				19 35	19 35		20 06	20 20		20 22	20 36				21 56		22 45		
Sunderland	d	18 30	18 30								19 27	19 27				20 27	21 27				
Hartlepool	d																				
Newcastle 8	d	19 08	19 25			19 40	19 37				20 26	20 26	20 38			21 47	22 00		22 46		
Chester-le-Street	d		19 36				19 46										22 09				
Durham	d		19 45			19 52	19 52				20 38	20 38	20 51			22 00	22 18		23 01		
Darlington 7	a	19 38	20 03			20 10	20 10				20 54	20 54	21 08			22 16	22 38		23 19		
Middlesbrough	d	18 54	19 25					20 00			19 55	19 55		20 50	21 40				21 55		
Eaglescliffe	d																				
Darlington 7	d	19 38	20 05			20 10	20 10	20 31			20 55	20 55	21 09		22 08	22 17			23 19		
Northallerton	d							20 42						21 18	22 19	22 29					
Thirsk	d							20 50							22 27						
York 8	a	20 06	20 31			20 41	20 42	21 10			21 21	21 21	21 37	21 42	22 52	23 04			00 16		
Hull	a													23 08							
Leeds 10	a	21 04	21 04			21 08	21 08	21 36						22 08		23 33					
Harrogate	d	19 05	19 05		19 44						20 05		20 05								
Scarborough	d										19 47		20 37								
York 8	d	20 08	20 33								21 24	21 24	21 39								
Doncaster 7	a	20 31	20 54				21 43						22 02								
Sheffield 7	a	21 18	21 30			21 51	22 19				22 21	22 22	22 54	23 57							
Skipton	d				19 48																
Keighley	d				20 01																
Bradford Forster Square	d				20k04																
Shipley	d				20 14																
Leeds 10	d				20 40																
Huddersfield	d				19m45																
Wakefield Westgate 7	d				20 55																
Hull	d				20 03								20 56								
Selby	d																				
Doncaster 7	d	20 32			21 12								22 03								
Retford 10	d				21 27																
Newark North Gate 7	a				21 42								22 26								
Grimsby Town	d				19n36								20n36								
Lincoln	d				20q40																
Newark North Gate 7	d				21 42								22 26								
Grantham 7	a				21 55								22 39								
	d			21 08	21 55								22 39								
Peterborough 8	a	21 20		21 36	22 14								22 58								
Cambridge	a	23 14																			
Stansted Airport	a																				
Norwich	a			23 20																	
Peterborough 8	d	21 21			22 15								22 59								
Stevenage 4	a	21 52			22s51								23s35								
London Kings Cross 15 ⊖	a	22 20			23 32								00 15								

For general notes see front of timetable
For details of catering facilities see Directory of Train Operators

- **A** Until 5 September
- **B** From Liverpool Lime Street (from 8 September from Nottingham) (Table 49)
- **C** Until 5 September. To Birmingham New Street (Table 51). to Leeds
- **D** From 8 September. to Leeds
- **E** To Manchester Airport (Table 39)
- **G** From Chathill to Hexham (Table 48)
- **H** Until 5 September. To Birmingham New Street (Table 51)
- **J** From 8 September. To Birmingham New Street (Table 51)
- **K** NXEC cannot guarantee connections with London Underground services
- **L** To Manchester Piccadilly (Table 39)
- **N** To Middlesbrough (Table 44)
- **b** Change at Edinburgh
- **c** Change at Dundee and Edinburgh
- **e** Change at Arbroath and Edinburgh
- **f** Change at Perth and Edinburgh
- **g** Change at Stirling and Edinburgh
- **h** Glasgow Queen Street. Change at Edinburgh
- **j** Glasgow Queen Street
- **k** Bradford Interchange
- **m** Change at Leeds
- **n** Change at Doncaster
- **q** Change at Sleaford and Grantham

Table 26

Saturdays

until 6 September

Scotland, North East England, Yorkshire and Humberside → London

Route Diagram - see first page of Table 26

Station		EM	GR	GR	GR	XC	TP	GR	XC	GR	GR	TP	XC	EM	TP	GR	GR	XC	XC	GR	GR	GR	XC
			R 1	R 1	R 1	1 ◇	1 ◇	R 1	R 1	R 1	R 1	1 ◇	R 1	◇	1 ◇	R 1	R 1	1 ◇	R 1	R 1	R 1	R 1	1 ◇
		A				B	C		D			E	G	A	E			H	D				H
Aberdeen	d																						
Stonehaven	d																						
Montrose	d																						
Arbroath	d																						
Dundee	d																						
Leuchars 3	d																						
Kirkcaldy	d																						
Inverkeithing	d																						
Inverness	d																						
Perth	d																						
Stirling	d																						
Glasgow Central 15	d																						
Motherwell	d																						
Haymarket	d																						
Edinburgh 10	a																						
Edinburgh	d																						
Dunbar	d																						
Berwick-upon-Tweed	d																						
Alnmouth	d																						
Morpeth	d																						
Newcastle 8	a																						
Sunderland	d																						
Hartlepool	d																						
Newcastle 8	d			04 30				06 00	06 08			06 13	06 19			06 35		06 50	←	07 00			←
Chester-le-Street	d												06 31										
Durham	d			04 45				06 12	06 22			06 29	06 38			06 48		07 02	06 22	07 12			07 02
Darlington 7	a			05 02				06 29	→			06 45	06 53			07 05		→	07 09	07 29			
Middlesbrough	d						05 58	*05 50*												*06 49*			
Eaglescliffe	d																						
Darlington 7	d			05 03				06 30				06 46	06 55		←	07 06			07 09	07 30			
Northallerton	d			05 30			06 26					06 57			06 57					07 41			
Thirsk	d						06 33					→			07 06								
York 8	a			05 57			06 52	06 57					07 22		07 31	07 34			07 41	08 01			08 16
Hull	a			*08b20*									*08 46*										
Leeds 10	a			*06 41*			07 23	*07 49*							08 04				08 08				
Harrogate	d									*06 06*						*06 45*				*07 14*		07 44	
Scarborough	d															*06 34*				*07 05*			
York 8	d			06 00		06 06		07 00					07 25			07 36				08 03			08 19
Doncaster 7	a			06 22		07 19		07 22					07 49			07 59							
Sheffield 7	a			*07 07*		07 51	*08c20*	08 00					08 20						08 51				09 20
Skipton	d									*05 48*							06 42				*06e48*		
Keighley	d									*06 01*							06u52				*07e01*		
Bradford Forster Square	d									*06f23*							*07g05*				07 36		
Shipley	d									*06 13*							07u00				07u41		
Leeds 10	d		05 05		06 10			*06 19*		07 00							07 40				08 05	08 15	
Huddersfield	d		*04e26*							*06e11*							*06e53*				*07 32*		
Wakefield Westgate 7	d		05 17		06 22			*06 32*		07 12							07 52				08 18		
Hull	d			*05 20*				*06 07*			06 50												
Selby	d							*06 15*			07 23												
Doncaster 7	d		05 35	06 23	06 40			07 23		07 30	07 40					08 00						08 45	
Retford 10	d		05 50		06 55												08 20						
Newark North Gate 7	a		06 05		07 10					07 54						08 24	08 34				08 54		
Grimsby Town	d							*05h26*			*06h26*					*06 59*						*07h26*	
Lincoln	d									*06 55*						*07 54*							
Newark North Gate 7	d		06 05		07 10					07 54						08 24	08 34				08 54		
Grantham 7	a		06 17		07 23					08 06						08 37	08 46				09 06		
	d	05 53	06 17		07 23					08 06				08 17		08 37	08 46				09 06		
Peterborough 8	a	06 25	06 37	07 09	07 42			08 09		08 26	08 32			08 44		08 57	09 06			09 12	09 26	09 32	
Cambridge	a		*08 06*	*08j44*				*09 22*			*09j44*						*10 08*					*10j44*	
Stansted Airport	a		*08 49*					*09 58*									*10 49*						
Norwich	a			*09 12*										10 17									
Peterborough 8	d		06 37	07 09	07 48			08 09		08 26	08 32					08 57	09 07			09 15	09 26	09 33	
Stevenage 4	a		*07 33*	*08 08*				*09 08*			*09 33*									09 45		*10 33*	
London Kings Cross 15 ⊖	a		07 29	08 04	08 40			09 03		09 18	09 26					09 51	10 00			10 13	10 20	10 27	

For general notes see front of timetable
For details of catering facilities see Directory of Train Operators

- **A** From Nottingham (Table 19)
- **B** To Birmingham New Street (Table 51)
- **C** To Manchester Airport (Table 39)
- **D** To Bournemouth (Table 51)
- **E** To Liverpool Lime Street (Table 39)
- **G** To Paignton (Table 51)
- **H** To Bristol Temple Meads (Table 51)
- **b** Change at York and Selby
- **c** Change at York
- **e** Change at Leeds
- **f** Bradford Interchange
- **g** Bradford Interchange. Change at Leeds
- **h** Change at Doncaster
- **j** Change at Peterborough and Ely

Due to Engineering Operations in the Sheffield area, services from Saturday 13 September on this Table had not been confirmed at time of going to press. These services will be issued in a special Supplement as soon as exact timings have been confirmed.

Table 26

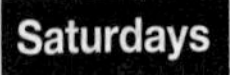
Saturdays

until 6 September

Scotland, North East England, Yorkshire and Humberside → London

Route Diagram - see first page of Table 26

	TP	EM	GR	GC	TP	XC	GC		HT	GR	GR	TP	XC	NT	EM		GR	XC	TP	GR	GR	TP	XC		EM
			R	R		R	R			R	R						R			R	R				
	1◇	◇	1	1	1◇	1	1		1◇	1	1	1◇	1◇		◇		1	1◇	1◇	1	1	1◇	1◇		◇
	A	B		C	A	D	C					A	E	G	H			J	A			A	E		H
Aberdeen d																									
Stonehaven d																									
Montrose d																									
Arbroath d																									
Dundee d																									
Leuchars 3 d																									
Kirkcaldy d																				06 16					
Inverkeithing d																				06 40			07 13		
Inverness d																									
Perth d																							05b15		
Stirling d																	05 30						06 36		
Glasgow Central 15 d																		05 50					06e30		
Motherwell d																		06u09							
Haymarket d																		06 51							
Edinburgh 10 a																		06 57							
Edinburgh d						06 05				06 15							07 00	07 05		07 30			07 50		
Dunbar d										06 35								07 25							
Berwick-upon-Tweed d						06 44				06 58							07 36	07 48		08 10			08 34		
Alnmouth d						07 04				07 18				07 34				08 11							
Morpeth d										07 34				08 00				08 00							
Newcastle 8 a						07 34				07 53				08 25			08 31	08 37		08 58			09 22		
Sunderland d				06 53									07 30				07 55					08 30			
Hartlepool d				07 17																					
Newcastle 8 d			07 30		07 33	07 40				07 54			08 24				08 33	08 40		09 00		09 12	09 25		
Chester-le-Street d					07 42								08 33									09 21			
Durham d			07 42		07 49	07 52							08 40				08 46	08 52		09 13		09 27	09 37		
Darlington 7 a			07 59		08 05	08 09				08 21			08 55				09 04	09 09		09 30		09 44	09 55		
Middlesbrough d	07 21									07 42			08 05				08 25		09 00						
Eaglescliffe d				07 45																					
Darlington 7 d			08 00		08 06	08 09				08 21		←	08 57				09 05	09 09		09 31		09 45	09 56		
Northallerton d	07 49			08 06	08 17		←					08 17							09 28	09 42		09 55			
Thirsk d	07 57			08 15	→		08 15					08 25							09 36						
York 8 a	08 19		08 28	→		08 41	08 44			08 50		08 53	09 24				09 34	09 41	09 56	10 03		10 21	10 23		
Hull a	10f33																	10 56		11f34					
Leeds 10 a	08 50		09 04			09 08						09 23	10 04					10 08	10 23	10 49		10 53			
Harrogate d						07 49					08 00						08 16			09 05	09 18				
Scarborough d							07 47													08 47					
York 8 d			08 30				08 47			08 51			09 27				09 36			10 05			10 25		
Doncaster 7 a			08 54						09 00	09 15			09 49				10 02			10 28			10 48		
Sheffield 7 a			09 41			09 51				10 04			10 20					10 51		11 07			11 20		
Skipton d											07 56									08g18	08 48				
Keighley d											08 09									08g31	09 01				
Bradford Forster Square d											08 31									08h35	09 31				
Shipley d											08 38									08g44	09 39				
Leeds 10 d										08 19	09 05									09 19	10 05				
Huddersfield d											08 37									08g45	09 35				
Wakefield Westgate 7 d										08 34	09 17									09 33	10 18				
Hull d			07 36						08 02	08 08							08 56				09 25				
Selby d									08 37																
Doncaster 7 d			08 55						09 01	09 15	09 35						10 03			10 29	10 36				
Retford 10 d			09 10						09j21																
Newark North Gate 7 a											09 59										11 00				
Grimsby Town d																	08k36				09 28				
Lincoln d			08 04						08m27		09 10										10 23				
Newark North Gate 7 d											09 59										11 00				
Grantham 7 a									09 42		10 12										11 12				
Grantham 7 d		09 10							09 42		10 12				10 16						11 12				11 07
Peterborough 8 a		09 44	09 48							10 06	10 32				10 43		10 54			11 15	11 32				11 36
Cambridge a										11 08	11n44						12 08			12n44	12n55				
Stansted Airport a										11 49							12 49								
Norwich a		11 12													12 17										13 13
Peterborough 8 d			09 48							10 06	10 32						10 54			11 16	11 32				
Stevenage 4 a											11 01									11 47	12 33				
London Kings Cross 15 ⊖ a			10 41				10 45		10 49	10 58	11 33						11 50			12 14	12 24				

For general notes see front of timetable
For details of catering facilities see Directory of Train Operators

- **A** To Manchester Airport (Table 39)
- **B** From Nottingham (Table 19)
- **C** The Zephyr
- **D** To Plymouth (Table 51)
- **E** To Bristol Temple Meads (Table 51)
- **G** From Chathill (Table 48)
- **H** From Liverpool Lime Street (Table 49)
- **J** To Bournemouth (Table 51)
- **b** Change at Stirling and Edinburgh
- **c** Change at Edinburgh
- **e** Glasgow Queen Street
- **f** Change at York and Selby
- **g** Change at Leeds and Doncaster
- **h** Bradford Interchange. Change at Leeds and Doncaster
- **j** Arr. 0916
- **k** Change at Doncaster
- **m** Change at Retford
- **n** Change at Peterborough and Ely

Due to Engineering Operations in the Sheffield area, services from Saturday 13 September on this Table had not been confirmed at time of going to press. These services will be issued in a special Supplement as soon as exact timings have been confirmed.

Table 26

Saturdays
until 6 September

Scotland, North East England, Yorkshire and Humberside → London

Route Diagram - see first page of Table 26

Station		GR	HT	XC	TP	GR	GR	TP	XC	EM	GR	XC	TP	GR	EM	GR	TP	XC	GR	XC	TP	GR	GR
		R 1	1 ◇	R 1	1 ◇	R 1	R 1	1 ◇	R 1	◇	R 1	R 1	1 ◇	R 1	◇	R 1	1 ◇	1 ◇	R 1	R 1	1 ◇	R 1	R 1
				A	B			B	C	D		E	B		D		B	G		H	B		
Aberdeen	d										06b00			06c34					07b20			07 52	
Stonehaven	d										06b16			06c53					07b36			08 09	
Montrose	d										06b38			07c15					07b58			08 32	
Arbroath	d										06b52			07c29					08b12			08 48	
Dundee	d	06b16									07b11	07 35		07 59					08b31			09 06	
Leuchars 3	d	06b28									07b23	07 48		08 11					08b43			09 20	
Kirkcaldy	d	07b01				07 44					07b50	08 20		08 43					09b15			09 44	
Inverkeithing	d	07b25				08 00					08b15	08 36		08 59					09b24			10 00	
Inverness	d																		05b00			06b45	
Perth	d					07 03								07e14								08b48	
Stirling	d					07 16								08 06					08b36			09b06	
Glasgow Central 15	d	06 50				07f30					07 50			08f30					08 50	09 00		09g15	
Motherwell	d	07 06									08 04								09 04	09u15			
Haymarket	d	07 47									08 49	08 56								09 54		10 19	
Edinburgh 10	a	07 51									08 55	09 01							09 55	09 59		10 26	
Edinburgh	d	08 00				08 35					09 00	09 05		09 30					10 00	10 05		10 30	
Dunbar	d											09 25											
Berwick-upon-Tweed	d					09 14					09 41	09 48		10 11									
Alnmouth	d	08 58																		11 04			
Morpeth	d					09 32												10 50		11 18			
Newcastle 8	a	09 31				10 02					10 31	10 36		10 58					11 27	11 35		11 58	
Sunderland	d					09 30								10 30								11 30	
Hartlepool	d																						
Newcastle 8	d	09 32		09 40		10 03		10 12	10 25		10 32	10 40		11 00			11 15	11 25	11 29	11 40		12 00	
Chester-le-Street	d								10 34														
Durham	d			09 52				10 27	10 41		10 45	10 52					11 27	11 37	11 42	11 52		12 13	
Darlington 7	a	10 00		10 09		10 31		10 43	10 56		11 03	11 08		11 26			11 43	11 55	12 00	12 08		12 31	
Middlesbrough	d				10 00	09 39					10 24		11 00	10 55					11 24		12 00	11 55	
Eaglescliffe	d																						
Darlington 7	d	10 01		10 09		10 31		10 44	10 58		11 03	11 09		11 27			11 44	11 57	12 01	12 09		12 31	
Northallerton	d				10 28			10 56					11 28				11 56				12 28		
Thirsk	d				10 36								11 36								12 36		
York 8	a	10 29		10 40	10 54	10 59		11 22	11 24		11 32	11 41	11 54	11 57			12 20	12 23	12 30	12 41	12 55	13 00	
Hull	a											12 54		13h33									
Leeds 10	a	11 04		11 08	11 23	11 49		11 53			12 04	12 08	12 23	12 49			12 53		13 04	13 08	13 23	13 49	
Harrogate	d					10 05	10 14							11 05		11 14						12 05	12 14
Scarborough	d					09 47								10 45								11 47	
York 8	d	10 31				11 00			11 27		11 33			11 59				12 25	12 31			13 02	
Doncaster 7	a	10 54				11 24			11 50		11 57			12 20				12 50	12 55				
Sheffield 7	a	11 41		11 51		12 07			12 20			12 51		13 07				13 20		13 51			
Skipton	d					09j28	09 58							10j18		10 48							12 12
Keighley	d					09j38	10 08							10j31		11 01							12 22
Bradford Forster Square	d					09k35	10 31							10k35		11 31							12 31
Shipley	d					09j49	10 39							10j44		11 39							12 39
Leeds 10	d					10 19	11 05							11 19		12 05							13 05
Huddersfield	d					09j45	10 35							10j45		11 35							12 35
Wakefield Westgate 7	d					10 32	11 17							11 32		12 17							13 17
Hull	d	09 56	10 06				10 25				10 57					11 22			11 57				12 22
Selby	d		10 41																				
Doncaster 7	d	10 55	11 02			11 24	11 39				11 57			12 21		12 35			12 57				13 38
Retford 10	d	11 10	11 17													12 50							
Newark North Gate 7	a						12 01									13 05							14 01
Grimsby Town	d	09m36									10m36					11 30			11m36				
Lincoln	d	10n27									11q12					12 23							
Newark North Gate 7	d						12 01									13 05							14 01
Grantham 7	a		11 38			11 55	12 14				12 28					13 17							
	d		11 38			11 55	12 14			12 06	12 28				13 08	13 17							
Peterborough 8	a	11 48				12 14	12 33			12 37	12 49			13 07	13 35				13 46			14 12	14 29
Cambridge	a	13 08				13r44								14 08					15 08				15r44
Stansted Airport	a	13 49												14 49					15 49				
Norwich	a									14 13					15 13								
Peterborough 8	d	11 48				12 15	12 34				12 50			13 07					13 48			14 13	14 29
Stevenage 4	a						13 03							14 08					14 17				15 33
London Kings Cross 15 ⊖	a	12 41	12 46			13 10	13 33				13 44			13 59		14 27			14 44			15 10	15 21

For general notes see front of timetable
For details of catering facilities see Directory of Train Operators

- **A** To Newquay (Table 135)
- **B** To Manchester Airport (Table 39)
- **C** To Penzance (Table 135)
- **D** From Liverpool Lime Street (Table 49)
- **E** To Bournemouth (Table 51)
- **G** To Bristol Temple Meads (Table 51)
- **H** To Paignton (Table 51)
- **b** Change at Edinburgh
- **c** Change at Dundee and Edinburgh
- **e** Change at Stirling and Edinburgh
- **f** Glasgow Queen Street
- **g** Glasgow Queen Street. Change at Edinburgh
- **h** Change at York and Selby
- **j** Change at Leeds and Doncaster
- **k** Bradford Interchange. Change at Leeds and Doncaster
- **m** Change at Doncaster
- **n** Change at Retford
- **q** Change at Peterborough
- **r** Change at Peterborough and Ely

Due to Engineering Operations in the Sheffield area, services from Saturday 13 September on this Table had not been confirmed at time of going to press. These services will be issued in a special Supplement as soon as exact timings have been confirmed.

Table 26

Scotland, North East England, Yorkshire and Humberside → London

Saturdays

until 6 September

Route Diagram - see first page of Table 26

		TP	XC	EM	XC	GR	HT	XC		TP	GR	GC	EM	GR	TP	XC		GR	XC	TP	GR	GR	EM	TP		XC
						R					R	R		R				R			R	R				
		1 ◇	1 ◇	◇	1 ◇	1	1 ◇	1 ◇		1 ◇	1	1	◇	1	1 ◇	1 ◇		1	1 ◇	1 ◇	1	1	◇	1 ◇		1 ◇
		A	B	C	D			D		A	E		C		A	B			G	A	H		C	A		J
Aberdeen	d				08 20						08b50										09 50					
Stonehaven	d				08 37						09b06										10 07					
Montrose	d				08 59						09c14										10 30					
Arbroath	d				09 15						09b42										10 47					
Dundee	d				09 32						09b59										11 04					
Leuchars [3]	d				09 45						10b11										11 18					
Kirkcaldy	d				10 12	09b59					10b43							10 58			11 42					
Inverkeithing	d				10 27	10b20					10b59							11 20			11 59					
Inverness	d										07 55															
Perth	d										09 55										10e12					
Stirling	d					09b36					10 29							10 36			11b06					
Glasgow Central [15]	d				10f00	09 50					10g15							10f45	11f00		11g15					
Motherwell	d					10 04																				
Haymarket	d				10 47	10 50					11 10										12 17					
Edinburgh [10]	a				10 51	10 55		←			11 16										12 23					
Edinburgh	d				11 05 →	11 00		11 05			11 30							12 00	12 05		12 30					
Dunbar	d							11 25																		
Berwick-upon-Tweed	d					11 41		11 48										12 39								
Alnmouth	d										12 29								13 05							
Morpeth	d					11 50										12 50			13 20							13 50
Newcastle [8]	a					12 31		12 35			13 02							13 27	13 37		13 57					
Sunderland	d										12 30	12 30												13 30		
Hartlepool	d											12 54														
Newcastle [8]	d	12 15	12 20			12 33		12 40			13 04				13 15	13 27		13 31	13 40		13 59			14 15		14 22
Chester-le-Street	d		12 29																							14 31
Durham	d	12 27	12 36			12 46		12 52							13 27	13 39		13 44	13 52		14 12			14 27		14 38
Darlington [7]	a	12 43	12 51			13 03		13 08							13 43	13 57		14 02	14 08		14 30			14 43		14 53
Middlesbrough	d					12 20				12 50					12 55			13 24		14 00	13 55					
Eaglescliffe	d											13 13														
Darlington [7]	d	12 44	12 53			13 04		13 09							13 44	13 58		14 03	14 09		14 30			14 44		14 55
Northallerton	d	12 56								13 18		13 31			13 56			14 14		14 28				14 56		
Thirsk	d									13 26		13 42								14 36						
York [8]	a	13 20	13 23			13 32		13 42		13 49	13 55	14 03			14 20	14 24		14 37	14 43	14 54	14 59			15 21		15 23
Hull	a		14 45																	16 03						
Leeds [10]	a	13 53	14 04			14 04		14 08		14 23		14 49			14 53	15 04			15 08	15 23	15 49			15 52		
Harrogate	d										13 05			13 14							14 05	14 14				
Scarborough	d										12 47										13 45					
York [8]	d		13 28			13 34					13 57	14 05				14 30		14 39			15 01					15 27
Doncaster [7]	a		13 52			13 58										14 54		15 03								15 51
Sheffield [7]	a		14 20					14 51								15 20		16 04	15 51							16 20
Skipton	d													12 48								13 59				
Keighley	d													13 01								14 09				
Bradford Forster Square	d													13 31								14 31				
Shipley	d													13 39								14 39				
Leeds [10]	d													14 05								15 05				
Huddersfield	d													13 35								14 35				
Wakefield Westgate [7]	d													14 17								15 17				
Hull	d					12 57	13 05							13 25				13 57				14 25				
Selby	d						13 40																			
Doncaster [7]	d					13 58	14 04							14 35				15 04				15 35				
Retford [10]	d						14 19							14 50								15 59				
Newark North Gate [7]	a													15 05												
Grimsby Town	d					12h36								13 25				13h36								
Lincoln	d										13 28			14 19								14j51				
Newark North Gate [7]	d													15 05								15 59				
Grantham [7]	a					14 29	14 39							15 18								16 11				
	d			14 08		14 29	14 39						15 05	15 18								16 11	16 06			
Peterborough [8]	a			14 39		14 49					15 04		15 32	15 37				15 50				16 31	16 37			
Cambridge	a										16 08			16k55				17 15								
Stansted Airport	a										16 49							17 49								
Norwich	a			16 13									17 13										18 13			
Peterborough [8]	d					14 49					15 04			15 38				15 50				16 31				
Stevenage [4]	a										16 08							16 19				17 00				
London Kings Cross [15] ⊖	a					15 41	15 49				15 58	16 02		16 30				16 47			16 58	17 28				

For general notes see front of timetable
For details of catering facilities see Directory of Train Operators

- **A** To Manchester Airport (Table 39)
- **B** To Bristol Temple Meads (Table 51)
- **C** From Liverpool Lime Street (Table 49)
- **D** To Bournemouth (Table 51)
- **E** **The Highland Chieftain**
- **G** To Penzance (Table 135)
- **H** **The Northern Lights**
- **J** To Cardiff Central (Table 51)
- **b** Change at Edinburgh
- **c** Change at Arbroath and Edinburgh
- **e** Change at Stirling and Edinburgh
- **f** Glasgow Queen Street
- **g** Glasgow Queen Street. Change at Edinburgh
- **h** Change at Doncaster
- **j** Change at Peterborough
- **k** Change at Peterborough and Ely

Due to Engineering Operations in the Sheffield area, services from Saturday 13 September on this Table had not been confirmed at time of going to press. These services will be issued in a special Supplement as soon as exact timings have been confirmed.

Table 26

Saturdays

until 6 September

Scotland, North East England, Yorkshire and Humberside → London

Route Diagram - see first page of Table 26

		GR A	HT	XC B	TP C	GR	GR	TP D	XC E	GR	XC G	TP D	EM H	TP D	XC E	GR	GR	XC J	EM K	TP C	TP D	NT	XC L
Aberdeen	d	10b22								11 22						12b24							
Stonehaven	d	10b38								11 38						12b42							
Montrose	d	11b00								12 00						12c15							
Arbroath	d	11b14								12 14						13b16							
Dundee	d	11b30								12 30						13b33							
Leuchars 3	d	11b42								12 42						13b45							
Kirkcaldy	d	12b12				12 29				13 14						14b14							
Inverkeithing	d	12b20				12 50				13 30						14b18							
Inverness	d									09e19						10b52							
Perth	d	11b08				11e12				11e38						13b04							
Stirling	d	11b36				12 06				12 36						13b36							
Glasgow Central 15	d	11 50		12f00		12f15				12f45	13f00					13 50		14f00					
Motherwell	d	12 04														14 06							
Haymarket	d	12 50														14 50							
Edinburgh 10	a	12 55														14 55							
Edinburgh	d	13 00		13 05		13 30				14 00	14 05					15 00		15 05					
Dunbar	d			13 25														15 25					
Berwick-upon-Tweed	d			13 48		14 09				14 39								15 48					
Alnmouth	d										15 05												
Morpeth	d								14 50		15 20					15 50						16 50	
Newcastle 8	a	14 27		14 36		14 57				15 26	15 38					16 27		16 37				17 13	
Sunderland	d					14 30								15 30							16 30		
Hartlepool	d																						
Newcastle 8	d	14 29		14 40		14 59		15 09	15 22	15 28	15 40			16 06	16 20	16 29		16 40			17 10		17 18
Chester-le-Street	d							15 18						16 15	16 29								17 27
Durham	d	14 42		14 52				15 25	15 34	15 41	15 52			16 22	16 36	16 42		16 52			17 22		17 34
Darlington 7	a	14 59		15 08		15 25		15 41	15 52	16 03	16 08			16 39	16 52	16 59		17 08			17 38		17 49
Middlesbrough	d	14 23			14 50			14 55		15 27		15 50		15 55		16 24				17 00			
Eaglescliffe	d																						
Darlington 7	d	15 00		15 09		15 26		15 42	15 54	16 04	16 09			16 39	16 54	17 00		17 09			17 39		17 51
Northallerton	d				15 18			15 53				16 18		16 50						17 28	17 51		
Thirsk	d				15 26							16 26		16 58						17 36	→		
York 8	a	15 28		15 41	15 52	15 55		16 20	16 23	16 32	16 41	16 49		17 18	17 22	17 29		17 41		17 55			18 22
Hull	a					17 27						18 21								19 28			
Leeds 10	a	16 04		16 08	16 23	16 49		16 53		17 04	17 08	17 23		17 53		18 04		18 08		18 23			19 04
Harrogate	d					15 05	15 14									16 05	16 44						
Scarborough	d					14 45										15 47			17 03				
York 8	d	15 30				15 57			16 25	16 34					17 25	17 31			17 49				18 25
Doncaster 7	a	15 55				16 20			16 51	16 57					17 50	17 54			18 13				18 48
Sheffield 7	a	16 41		16 51		17 07			17 18		17 51				18 20	18 41		18g51	18 45				19 20
Skipton	d					14h27	14 48									15h18	16 49						
Keighley	d					14h39	15 01									15h31	17 02						
Bradford Forster Square	d					14j35	15 31									15j35	17k05						
Shipley	d					14h50	15 39									15h44	17 15						
Leeds 10	d					15 19	16 05									16 19	17 40						
Huddersfield	d					14h45	15 35									15h45	16m57						
Wakefield Westgate 7	d					15 32	16 17									16 32	17 52						
Hull	d	14 57	15 06				15 25			15 57						16 54							
Selby	d		15 42																				
Doncaster 7	d	15 55	16 02			16 21	16 38			16 58						17 55	18 10						
Retford 10	d		16 17				16 53										18 25						
Newark North Gate 7	a						17 08									18 18	18 40						
Grimsby Town	d	14n36					15 28			15n36						16n36							
Lincoln	d		15q27				16 22										18 09						
Newark North Gate 7	d						17 08									18 18	18 40						
Grantham 7	a		16 37			16 52				17 29							18 52						
	d		16 37			16 52				17 29			18 13				18 52						
Peterborough 8	a	16 42				17 11	17 36			17 48			18 40			18 46	19 12						
Cambridge	a	18 15					18r55			19 13						20 08							
Stansted Airport	a	18 58														20 50							
Norwich	a	19r30											20 13										
Peterborough 8	d	16 46				17 12	17 36			17 50						18 48	19 12						
Stevenage 4	a	17 16								18 19							19 43						
London Kings Cross 15 ⊖	a	17 43	17 45			18 10	18 28			18 46						19 40	20 12						

For general notes see front of timetable
For details of catering facilities see Directory of Train Operators

A **The Flying Scotsman**
B To Bournemouth (Table 51)
C To Manchester Piccadilly (Table 39)
D To Manchester Airport (Table 39)
E To Bristol Temple Meads (Table 51)
G To Plymouth (Table 51)
H From Liverpool Lime Street (Table 49)
J To Southampton Central (Table 51)
K To St Pancras International (Table 53)
L To Birmingham New Street (Table 51)
b Change at Edinburgh
c Change at Arbroath and Edinburgh
e Change at Stirling and Edinburgh
f Glasgow Queen Street
g By changing at York, passengers may arrive at 1845
h Change at Leeds and Doncaster
j Bradford Interchange. Change at Leeds and Doncaster
k Bradford Interchange
m Change at Leeds
n Change at Doncaster
q Change at Retford
r Change at Peterborough and Ely

Due to Engineering Operations in the Sheffield area, services from Saturday 13 September on this Table had not been confirmed at time of going to press. These services will be issued in a special Supplement as soon as exact timings have been confirmed.

until 6 September

Scotland, North East England, Yorkshire and Humberside → London

Route Diagram - see first page of Table 26

		EM	TP	GR	HT	GR	XC	TP	GC	GR	XC	TP	TP	GR	EM	GR	XC	TP	NT	TP	GR	TP
		◇	[1]◇	[R] [1]	[1]◇	[R] [1]	[1]◇	[1]◇	[R] [1]	[R] [1]	[1]◇	[1]◇	[1]◇	[R] [1]	◇	[R] [1]	[1]◇	[1]◇		[1]◇	[R] [1]	[1]◇
		A	B				C	B			D		B		A		D	B	E	G	H	B
Aberdeen	d			13 21						14b25				14 48			15 20				16b21	
Stonehaven	d			13 37						14b41				15 06			15 36				16b37	
Montrose	d			13 59						14c15				15 28			16 00				16c13	
Arbroath	d			14 13						15b15				15 45			16 14				17b11	
Dundee	d			14 30						15b32				16 02			16 31				17b31	
Leuchars [3]	d			14 42						15b44				16 16			16 43				17b43	
Kirkcaldy	d			15 14						16b14				16 40			17 17				18b15	
Inverkeithing	d			15 30						16b30				16 57			17 33				18b12	
Inverness	d									12b40											14b41	
Perth	d			13e12						14b49				15e12							16b48	
Stirling	d			14 36						15b36				16b06			16 36				17b36	
Glasgow Central [15]	d			15f00						15 50				16g15			17f00				17 50	
Motherwell	d									16 04											18 04	
Haymarket	d									16 50				17 16							18 50	
Edinburgh [10]	a									16 56				17 25							18 55	
Edinburgh	d			16 00			16 05			17 00				17 30			18 05				19 00	
Dunbar	d													17 51			18 25				19 21	
Berwick-upon-Tweed	d			16 39										18 14			18 48				19 46	
Alnmouth	d						17 05			17 59							19 08		19 24		20 08	
Morpeth	d			16 50			17 20							18 32			19 04		19 49		20 25	
Newcastle [8]	a			17 27			17 38			18 32				19 05			19 37		20 12		20 46	
Sunderland	d								17 30					18 30							19 27	
Hartlepool	d								17 56													
Newcastle [8]	d			17 29			17 40			18 34	18 40		18 52	19 06			19 45				20 47	
Chester-le-Street	d										18 49											
Durham	d						17 52			18 47	18 56		19 04				19 56				21 00	
Darlington [7]	a			17 55			18 09			19 04	19 11		19 20	19 34			20 13				21 18	
Middlesbrough	d						17 25	18 07		18 24		19 00		18 53			19 25	20 10		20 50		21 50
Eaglescliffe	d								18 28													
Darlington [7]	d		←	17 56			18 09			19 05	19 13		19 22	19 34			20 13				21 18	22 19
Northallerton	d		17 51					18 35	18 45			19 28	19 36					20 38		21 17	21 30	22 30
Thirsk	d		17 59					18 43	18 54			19 36						20 46		21 25		22 38
York [8]	a		18 24	18 26			18 41	19 04	19 13	19 34	19 41	19 59	20 02	20 03			20 41	21 07		21 42	21 51	22 57
Hull	a								20h39					21 22				23h21				
Leeds [10]	a		18 52	19 04			19 08	19 35	20 04		20 08		20 33	20 53			21 08	21 33		22 08	22 49	23 33
Harrogate	d			17 08		17 50			18 05					19 05								
Scarborough	d								17 45					18 45								
York [8]	d			18 28					19 16	19 40				20 06							21 52	
Doncaster [7]	a			18 51						20 03				20 29							22 17	
Sheffield [7]	a			19 42			19 51				20 51			21 18			21 51	23 02			23 05	
Skipton	d					17 49								18j28		19 18						
Keighley	d					18 02								18j38		19 31						
Bradford Forster Square	d					18k05								18m48		19k35						
Shipley	d					18 14								18j48		19 44						
Leeds [10]	d					18 40								19 22		20 15						
Huddersfield	d					17n58								18j47		19 35						
Wakefield Westgate [7]	d					18 54								19 32		20 31						
Hull	d			17 55	18 12					18 53						19 24						
Selby	d			18 26	18 47																	
Doncaster [7]	d			18 52	19 05	19 14				20 04				20 30		20 48						
Retford [10]	d				19 20	19 29										21 03						
Newark North Gate [7]	a					19 44										21 18						
Grimsby Town	d			17q36		18 06				18q36						19q36						
Lincoln	d				18r24	19 10										20 41						
Newark North Gate [7]	d					19 44										21 18						
Grantham [7]	a				19 40	19 56										21 31						
	d	19 06			19 40	19 56									21 10	21 31						
Peterborough [8]	a	19 33		19 38		20 16				20 51				21 18	21 37	21 50						
Cambridge	a			20t55						22 16						23 16						
Stansted Airport	a																					
Norwich	a	21 13		22t30											23 20							
Peterborough [8]	d			19 38		20 17				20 51				21 19		21 51						
Stevenage [4]	a			20 07		20 48				21 20				21 51		22 20						
London Kings Cross [15] ⊖	a			20 35	20 46	21 15			21 18	21 48				22 17		22 47						

For general notes see front of timetable
For details of catering facilities see Directory of Train Operators

- **A** From Liverpool Lime Street (Table 49)
- **B** To Manchester Airport (Table 39)
- **C** To Bristol Temple Meads (Table 51)
- **D** To Birmingham New Street (Table 51). to Leeds
- **E** From Chathill to Hexham (Table 48)
- **G** To Manchester Piccadilly (Table 39)
- **H** To Leeds (Table 31)
- **b** Change at Edinburgh
- **c** Change at Arbroath and Edinburgh
- **e** Change at Stirling and Edinburgh
- **f** Glasgow Queen Street
- **g** Glasgow Queen Street. Change at Edinburgh
- **h** Change at York and Selby
- **j** Change at Leeds and Doncaster
- **k** Bradford Interchange
- **m** Bradford Interchange. Change at Leeds and Doncaster
- **n** Change at Leeds
- **q** Change at Doncaster
- **r** Change at Retford
- **t** Change at Peterborough and Ely

Due to Engineering Operations in the Sheffield area, services from Saturday 13 September on this Table had not been confirmed at time of going to press. These services will be issued in a special Supplement as soon as exact timings have been confirmed.

Table 26

Sundays

until 13 July

Scotland, North East England, Yorkshire and Humberside → London

Route Diagram - see first page of Table 26

		GR	GR	GR	EM	XC	GR	GR	HT	XC	GC	TP	GC	GR	TP	XC	GR	EM	GR	GR	XC	TP	EM
		R 1	R 1	R 1	◇	R 1	R 1	R 1	1 ◇	R 1	R 1	1 ◇	R 1	R 1	1 ◇	R 1	R 1	◇	R 1	R 1	R 1	1 ◇	◇
					A	B				C		D			E	G		H			G	E	A
Aberdeen	d																						
Stonehaven	d																						
Montrose	d																						
Arbroath	d																						
Dundee	d																			07 25			
Leuchars 3	d																			07 37			
Kirkcaldy	d																			08 09			
Inverkeithing	d																			08 30			
Inverness	d																						
Perth	d																						
Stirling	d																						
Glasgow Central 15	d																07b50						
Motherwell	d																						
Haymarket	d																						
Edinburgh 10	a																						
Edinburgh	d															08 50	09 00			09 30			
Dunbar	d																						
Berwick-upon-Tweed	d															09 31	09 41						
Alnmouth	d																						
Morpeth	d																						
Newcastle 8	a															10 17	10 28			10 55			
Sunderland	d										09 10					09 28				10 28			
Hartlepool	d										09 34												
Newcastle 8	d		07 58				08 55	09 25		09 30		09 33				10 25	10 30			10 57		11 03	
Chester-le-Street	d											09 42											
Durham	d		08 10				09 07			09 42		09 49				10 37				11 10		11 16	
Darlington 7	a		08 28				09 25	09 51		09 58		10 05				10 53	10 59					11 32	
Middlesbrough	d						08 45			09 15					10 15							10 53	
Eaglescliffe	d										09 55												
Darlington 7	d		08 28				09 25	09 52		09 59		10 06				10 54	10 59					11 33	
Northallerton	d						09 39				10 13	10 17	←		10 42							11 45	
Thirsk	d										10 26		10 26		10 50								
York 8	a		08 58				10 00	10 20		10 26	→	10 41	10 44		11 09	11 25	11 28			11 51		12 12	
Hull	a									11 38										13 03			
Leeds 10	a		09 38				10 38			10 52		11 08	11 32		11 38	11 51 →	12 07				← 11 51	12 38	
Harrogate	d													09 53					10 53				
Scarborough	d							09 20												10 45			
York 8	d		09 00			09 27	10 02	10 23		10 28			10 46				11 29			11 53			
Doncaster 7	a		09 25			10 32	10 26	10 47		11 31							11 53				12 30		
Sheffield 7	a		09 57			10 57		11 25		12 05							12 55				13 08		
Skipton	d			08 35					09c15										10 15				
Keighley	d			08 48					09c28										10 28				
Bradford Forster Square	d			09 02					09e21					10 02					11 02				
Shipley	d			09 10					09c40					10 08					11 10				
Leeds 10	d	08 24		09 40					10f09					10 40					11 40				
Huddersfield	d	07g12		08g12					09c12					10g02					10g44				
Wakefield Westgate 7	d	08 36		09 52					10f22					10 52					11 52				
Hull	d			08 42				09 41	10 12								10 41						
Selby	d								10 47														
Doncaster 7	d	08 54	09 26	10 10			10 29	10 48	11 04					11 13			11 53		12 10				
Retford 10	d		09 41						11 19					11 28									
Newark North Gate 7	a	09 18		10 32			10 52							11 42						12 36			
Grimsby Town	d								09f49								10f36						
Lincoln	d													11 05									
Newark North Gate 7	d	09 18		10 32			10 52							11 42						12 36			
Grantham 7	a	09 30	10 03				11 04		11 38					11 54					12 40				
	d	09 30	10 03		10 27		11 04		11 39					11 54				12 18	12 40				13 14
Peterborough 8	a	09 52	10 25	11 02	11 07		11 26	11 37						12 16			12 40	12 52		13 06			13 41
Cambridge	a		12h34					13h14									14h14			14 19			
Stansted Airport	a																			14 58			
Norwich	a				12 59			14h09										14 35					15 28
Peterborough 8	d	09 53	10 27	11 02			11 26	11 38						12 16			12 41			13 06			
Stevenage 4	a		10 58					12 09						13 33						13 42			
London Kings Cross 15 ⊖	a	10 47	11 26	11 55			12 19	12 37	12 48				12 51	13 10			13 36		13 50	14 10			

For general notes see front of timetable
For details of catering facilities see Directory of Train Operators

- **A** From Nottingham (Table 19)
- **B** To Plymouth (Table 51)
- **C** To Bournemouth (Table 51)
- **D** To Liverpool Lime Street (Table 39)
- **E** To Manchester Airport (Table 39)
- **G** To Penzance (Table 135)
- **H** From Sheffield (Table 49)
- **b** Glasgow Queen Street
- **c** Change at Leeds and Doncaster
- **e** Bradford Interchange. Change at Leeds and Doncaster
- **f** Change at Doncaster
- **g** Change at Leeds
- **h** Change at Peterborough and Ely

Scotland, North East England, Yorkshire and Humberside → London

Sundays until 13 July

Route Diagram - see first page of Table 26

		XC	GR	HT	GR	GR	XC	TP	GR	XC	GR	TP	EM	GR	GR	XC	TP	GR	XC	GR	HT	XC	TP
		R 1	R 1	1 ◇	R 1	R 1	R 1	1 ◇	R 1	R 1	R 1	1 ◇	◇	R 1	R 1	R 1	1 ◇	R 1	R 1	R 1	1 ◇	R 1	1 ◇
		A					A	B		C		B	D			C	B		A			A	E
Aberdeen	d																						
Stonehaven	d																						
Montrose	d																						
Arbroath	d																						
Dundee	d														09 25								
Leuchars 3	d														09 37								
Kirkcaldy	d														10 09								
Inverkeithing	d														10 32								
Inverness	d																						
Perth	d														09 27								
Stirling	d					09 05									10 02								
Glasgow Central 15	d	08b30								09b30									10 27	10 50			
Motherwell	d																		10u57	11 05			
Haymarket	d																		11 36	11 49			
Edinburgh 10	a																		11 41	11 54			
Edinburgh	d	09 50	10 00			10 30				10 50	11 00				11 30				11 50	12 00			
Dunbar	d									11 11													
Berwick-upon-Tweed	d		10 39			11 09				11 33										12 39			
Alnmouth	d	10 46																	12 48				
Morpeth	d														12 40								
Newcastle 8	a	11 17	11 30			11 58				12 21	12 26				13 01				13 17	13 29			
Sunderland	d					11 28									12 28								
Hartlepool	d																						
Newcastle 8	d	11 25	11 32			12 00				12 25	12 32	12 49			13 03			13 20	13 25	13 32			
Chester-le-Street	d											12 58											
Durham	d	11 37								12 37	12 45	13 05							13 37	13 45			
Darlington 7	a	11 53				12 26				12 54	13 02	13 21			13 29			13 46	13 53	14 03			
Middlesbrough	d					11 24		12 15			12 25	12 25								13 25			13 45
Eaglescliffe	d																						
Darlington 7	d	11 54				12 27				12 54	13 03	13 22			13 30		← 13 34	13 47	13 55	14 04			14 12
Northallerton	d							12 42				13 34 →			13 42								14 20
Thirsk	d							12 50															14 40
York 8	a	12 25	12 28			12 55		13 12		13 25	13 31				14 03		14 11	14 17	14 25	14 34			
Hull	a						←	14 21								←				15 43		←	
Leeds 10	a	12 51 →	13 08				12 51	13 38		13 52 →	14 07					13 52	14 38		14 51 →			14 51	15 08
Harrogate	d		11 30		11 53									12 53				13 30					
Scarborough	d					11 45									12 45								
York 8	d		12 29			12 57					13 33				14 05			14 19		14 36			
Doncaster 7	a		12 54			13 20	13 30				13 56				14 28	14 35		14 43		14 59		15 36	
Sheffield 7	a						14 03				14 52					15 03						16 02	
Skipton	d			11c15	11 30									12 15							13c15		
Keighley	d			11c28	11 40									12 28							13c28		
Bradford Forster Square	d			11e31	12 02									13 02							13e31		
Shipley	d			11c40	12 08									13 08							13c40		
Leeds 10	d			12f09	12 40									13 40							14f09		
Huddersfield	d			11c12	11g44									12g47							13c12		
Wakefield Westgate 7	d			12f22	12 52									13 52							14f22		
Hull	d		11 41	12 12							12 41							13 41			14 10		
Selby	d			12 47																	14 45		
Doncaster 7	d		12 54	13 06	13 11	13 21			←		13 57			14 10	14 29			14 48		15 00	15 05		
Retford 10	d			13 21	13h34 →				13 34					14 33							15 20		
Newark North Gate 7	a								13 48														
Grimsby Town	d			10f36							12f36							13f36					
Lincoln	d								13 05														
Newark North Gate 7	d								13 48					14 33									
Grantham 7	a		13 26	13 40					14 00						14 59						15 40		
	d		13 26	13 40					14 00				14 20		14 59						15 40		
Peterborough 8	a					14 09			14 22		14 43		14 53					15 35		15 47			
Cambridge	a										16j14									17j14			
Stansted Airport	a										16 59												
Norwich	a												16 37							17 35			
Peterborough 8	d					14 10			14 22		14 43							15 36		15 47			
Stevenage 4	a		14 14	14 29					15 33					15 28						16 17			
London Kings Cross 15 ⊖	a		14 42	14 54		15 11			15 15		15 37			15 55	16 11			16 29		16 45	16 50		

For general notes see front of timetable
For details of catering facilities see Directory of Train Operators

A To Bournemouth (Table 51)
B To Manchester Airport (Table 39)
C To Plymouth (Table 51)
D From Sheffield (Table 49)
E To Liverpool Lime Street (Table 39)
b Glasgow Queen Street
c Change at Leeds and Doncaster
e Bradford Interchange. Change at Leeds and Doncaster
f Change at Doncaster
g Change at Leeds
h Arr. 1326
j Change at Peterborough and Ely

Table 26

Sundays

until 13 July

Scotland, North East England, Yorkshire and Humberside → London

Route Diagram - see first page of Table 26

Station		GR	GR	TP	XC	GC	GR	EM	GR	TP	GR	XC	TP	XC	GR	EM	GR	HT	TP	GR	EM	GR
		R 1	R 1	1 ◇	R 1	R 1	R 1	◇	R 1	1 ◇	R 1	R 1	1 ◇	R 1	R 1	◇	R 1	1 ◇	1 ◇	R 1	1 ◇	R 1
		A		B	C		D	E		B	G	C	B	H		E			J		K	
Aberdeen	d	09 48																				11 42
Stonehaven	d	10 05																				11 59
Montrose	d	10 28																				12 22
Arbroath	d	10 44																				12 38
Dundee	d	11 02									11b25											12 59
Leuchars 3	d	11 16									11b37											13 13
Kirkcaldy	d	11 40									12b09											13 37
Inverkeithing	d	11 56									12b32											13 56
Inverness	d										09 38											
Perth	d										11 55											
Stirling	d	11b06									12 32											13b07
Glasgow Central 15	d				11 30									12c30	12 50							13e00
Motherwell	d				11u56										13 05							
Haymarket	d	12 18			12 37						13 12				13 50							14 19
Edinburgh 10	a	12 24			12 42						13 18				13 56							14 24
Edinburgh	d	12 30			12 50		13 00				13 30			13 50	14 00							14 30
Dunbar	d				13 10																	
Berwick-upon-Tweed	d				13 33		13 42				14 09											
Alnmouth	d	13 29												14 47								
Morpeth	d																					
Newcastle 8	a	14 00			14 19		14 30				15 00			15 16	15 25							15 59
Sunderland	d	13 28				13 42				14 28												15 28
Hartlepool	d					14 06																
Newcastle 8	d	14 02		14 10	14 25		14 32			14 57	15 01			15 25	15 30					15 50		16 01
Chester-le-Street	d																					
Durham	d			14 22	14 37					15 09	15 15			15 37								16 14
Darlington 7	a	14 29		14 38	14 53		14 59			15 25	15 32			15 54	15 59					16 20		16 32
Middlesbrough	d									14 38									15 45			15 50
Eaglescliffe	d					14 34																
Darlington 7	d	14 30		14 39	14 54		15 00			15 26	15 33		←	15 55	15 59					16 20		16 32
Northallerton	d					14 57	15 11			15 38 →			15 38						16 12	16 32		
Thirsk	d					15 06													16 20			
York 8	a	15 00		15 13	15 25	15 28	15 32				16 02		16 12	16 25	16 28				16 41	16 52		17 01
Hull	a						16 41					←										18 10
Leeds 10	a			15 39	15 52	16 07	16 32					15 52	16 38	16 51					17 08			
Harrogate	d				→				14 53					→	15 30							
Scarborough	d										14 45									15 45		
York 8	d	15 02				15 31	15 34				16 03				16 29					16 53	17 01	17 03
Doncaster 7	a						15 57				16 28	16 34			16 53					17 19	17 23	17 27
Sheffield 7	a						16 51					17 03			17 52						17 57	
Skipton	d								14 15								15 15					
Keighley	d								14 28								15 28					
Bradford Forster Square	d		14 02						15 02								16 02					
Shipley	d		14 08						15 08								16 08					
Leeds 10	d		14 40						15 40								16 40					
Huddersfield	d		13f44						14f44								15f44					
Wakefield Westgate 7	d		14 52						15 52								16 52					
Hull	d						14 41								15 41			16 21				
Selby	d																	16 56				
Doncaster 7	d		15 10				15 58		16 10		16 28				16 53		17 10	17 15		17 19		17 28
Retford 10	d		15 25															17 30				
Newark North Gate 7	a		15 39				16 20													17 46		
Grimsby Town	d		14 04				14g36								15g36							
Lincoln	d		14 59				15 46															
Newark North Gate 7	d		15 39				16 20													17 46		
Grantham 7	a		15 52						16 40								17 40	17 49				
	d		15 52					16 24	16 40							17 24	17 40	17 49				
Peterborough 8	a		16 13				16 50	16 55	17 01		17 18				17 40	17 51	18 02					18 21
Cambridge	a		17 23				18h14				18 21				19h14							19 20
Stansted Airport	a		17 59																			19 59
Norwich	a							18 35								19 29						
Peterborough 8	d		16 19				16 51		17 02		17 18				17 41		18 02					18 21
Stevenage 4	a		16 49				17 22								18 11					18 42		
London Kings Cross 15 ⊖	a	17 11	17 17			17 31	17 50		17 55		18 15				18 38		18 55	19 06		19 12		19 16

For general notes see front of timetable
For details of catering facilities see Directory of Train Operators

- **A** **The Northern Lights**
- **B** To Manchester Airport (Table 39)
- **C** To Plymouth (Table 51)
- **D** **The Flying Scotsman**
- **E** From Liverpool Lime Street (Table 49)
- **G** **The Highland Chieftain**
- **H** To Southampton Central (Table 51)
- **J** To Liverpool Lime Street (Table 39)
- **K** To St Pancras International (Table 53)
- **b** Change at Edinburgh
- **c** Glasgow Queen Street
- **e** Glasgow Queen Street. Change at Edinburgh
- **f** Change at Leeds
- **g** Change at Doncaster
- **h** Change at Peterborough and Ely

Table 26

Sundays

until 13 July

Scotland, North East England, Yorkshire and Humberside → London

Route Diagram - see first page of Table 26

		XC	GR	TP	XC	GR	XC	EM	GR	TP	GR	GR	GR	GR	XC	GR	XC	EM	GR	HT	TP	TP	GR
		R 1	R 1	1 ◇	1 ◇	R 1	1 ◇	◇	R 1	1 ◇	R 1	R 1	R 1	R 1	1 ◇	R 1	1 ◇	◇	R 1	1 ◇	1 ◇	1 ◇	R 1
		A		B	C		C	D		B					C		C	D			E	B	
Aberdeen	d				11 58																		13 50
Stonehaven	d				12 16																		14 07
Montrose	d				12 39																		14 30
Arbroath	d				12 55																		14 46
Dundee	d				13 12							13 25											15 04
Leuchars 3	d				13 25							13 39											15 18
Kirkcaldy	d				13 55							14 11											15 42
Inverkeithing	d				14 10							14 32											16 02
Inverness	d				09b38																		
Perth	d				11b55							13c05											
Stirling	d				13b07							14 07											15b07
Glasgow Central 15	d				13e30							14f00			14f30	14 50							15e00
Motherwell	d				13b05											15 05							
Haymarket	d				14 28											15 49							16 21
Edinburgh 10	a				14 33											15 55							16 26
Edinburgh	d				14 50	15 00						15 30			15 50	16 00							16 30
Dunbar	d				15 11																		
Berwick-upon-Tweed	d				15 33	15 41						16 09											17 09
Alnmouth	d														16 47								17 32
Morpeth	d											16 43			17 01								
Newcastle 8	a				16 21	16 31						17 01			17 20	17 27							18 07
Sunderland	d											16 28										17 28	
Hartlepool	d																						
Newcastle 8	d			16 08	16 25	16 33				16 48		17 03		17 12	17 22	17 30						17 57	18 10
Chester-le-Street	d									16 57													
Durham	d			16 20	16 37	16 46				17 04				17 24	17 34							18 09	
Darlington 7	a			16 37	16 53	17 03				17 20		17 30		17 42	17 50	17 58						18 25	
Middlesbrough	d			15 50						16 45					17 14						17 45		
Eaglescliffe	d																						
Darlington 7	d			16 38	16 54	17 04				17 21		17 31		17 42	17 51	17 58						18 26	
Northallerton	d									17 32		17 42									18 12		
Thirsk	d																				18 20		
York 8	a			17 12	17 22	17 32				17 59		18 03		18 10	18 22	18 28					18 39	18 59	19 04
Hull	a	⟵					⟵															20 08	
Leeds 10	a	16 51		17 37	17 52	18 07	17 52			18 38		18 38			18 51						19 08	19 38	19 38
Harrogate	d				⟶	16 30			16 53							17 30			17 53				
Scarborough	d											16 45					⟵						17 45
York 8	d					17 35						18 05		18 12	18 28	18 29	18 28						19 05
Doncaster 7	a	17 29				18 03	18 34					18 31		18 37	⟶	18 53	19 27						19 31
Sheffield 7	a	18 07				18 51	19g08					19 08				19 53	19 58						20 10
Skipton	d		16 15																17 15				
Keighley	d		16 28																17 28				
Bradford Forster Square	d		16h31						17 02										18 02				
Shipley	d		16 40						17 09										18 08				
Leeds 10	d		17 05						17 40										18 40				
Huddersfield	d		16j30						16j44										17j44				
Wakefield Westgate 7	d		17 18						17 52										18 52				
Hull	d					16 41					17 30					17 41				18 30			
Selby	d										18 05									19 05			
Doncaster 7	d		17 36			18 03					18 23	18 31	⟵	18 37		18 53			19 10	19 22			19 31
Retford 10	d		17 51								18k44		18 44							19 37			
Newark North Gate 7	a		18 05								⟶			19 02									
Grimsby Town	d					16m36										17m36							
Lincoln	d		17 25										17n35	18 00									
Newark North Gate 7	d		18 05											19 02									
Grantham 7	a								18 36				19 06						19 40	19 56			
	d							18 18	18 36				19 06					19 22	19 40	19 57			
Peterborough 8	a					18 49		18 54	18 58			19 18	19 28	19 33		19 40		19 51	20 01				20 22
Cambridge	a											20 21				21q14			21 19				
Stansted Airport	a											20 59							21 53				
Norwich	a							20 28										21 25	22q53				
Peterborough 8	d					18 50			18 58			19 19	19 29	19 33		19 41			20 02				20 23
Stevenage 4	a		18 59			19 21								20 07		20 13			20 32	20s45			20 54
London Kings Cross 15 ⊖	a		19 33			19 48			19 52			20 12	20 23	20 34		20 38			20 59	21 12			21 25

For general notes see front of timetable
For details of catering facilities see Directory of Train Operators

- **A** To Southampton Central (Table 51)
- **B** To Manchester Airport (Table 39)
- **C** To Bristol Temple Meads (Table 51)
- **D** From Liverpool Lime Street (Table 49)
- **E** To Liverpool Lime Street (Table 39)
- **b** Change at Edinburgh
- **c** Change at Stirling and Edinburgh
- **e** Glasgow Queen Street. Change at Edinburgh
- **f** Glasgow Queen Street
- **g** By changing at Doncaster, passengers may arrive at 1903
- **h** Bradford Interchange
- **j** Change at Leeds
- **k** Arr. 1838
- **m** Change at Doncaster
- **n** Change at Retford
- **q** Change at Peterborough and Ely

Table 26

Scotland, North East England, Yorkshire and Humberside → London

until 13 July

Route Diagram - see first page of Table 26

		XC	GR	GR	XC		GC	TP	GR	XC	EM	TP		GR	XC	TP	XC	GR	NT		XC	TP	GR	GR	
		1 ◇ A	R 1	R 1	1 ◇ A		R 1	1 ◇ B	R 1	1 ◇ A	◇ C	1 ◇ B		R 1	1 ◇ A	1 ◇ D	1 ◇ E	R 1	G		1 ◇ E	1 ◇ D	R 1	R 1	
Aberdeen	d													15 10									17 10		
Stonehaven	d													15 29									17 26		
Montrose	d													15 49									17 48		
Arbroath	d													16 03									18 02		
Dundee	d			15 25										16 25									18 19		
Leuchars 3	d			15 37										16 37									18 31		
Kirkcaldy	d		16b02	16 11										17 01			17 07						18 56	19b07	
Inverkeithing	d		16b18	16 32										17 17			17 47						19 12	19b48	
Inverness	d		13b25																					16c15	
Perth	d		15b25														15c05						17c05	18c27	
Stirling	d			16 07													17 07						18 07	19b11	
Glasgow Central 15	d	15 44	15 50	16e00						16e30							17e30	17 50					18e30	19 50	
Motherwell	d	16u00	16 05															18 05						20 04	
Haymarket	d	16 38	16 46															18 46						20 45	
Edinburgh 10	a	16 44	16 52															18 53						20 51	
Edinburgh	d	16 50	17 00	17 30						17 50				18 00			18 50	19 00					20 00	21 00	
Dunbar	d	17 11								18 11								19 20					20 20	21 21	
Berwick-upon-Tweed	d	17 33												18 39									20 43	21 44	
Alnmouth	d									18 53				19 03										22 06	
Morpeth	d																						21 17		
Newcastle 8	a	18 19	18 26	18 55						19 22				19 33			20 15	20 29					21 38	22 41	
Sunderland	d			18 28			18 42										19 28		20 28						
Hartlepool	d						19 06																		
Newcastle 8	d	18 25	18 29	18 57				19 20		19 25				19 35			20 25	20 31	21 06				21 40		
Chester-le-Street	d																		21 15						
Durham	d	18 37	18 42	19 10				19 32		19 37				19 48			20 37		21 24				21 53		
Darlington 7	a	18 53	18 59	19 27				19 48		19 53				20 05			20 53	20 57	21 44				22 10		
Middlesbrough	d			18 48				18 53								20 15						22 07			
Eaglescliffe	d						19 25																		
Darlington 7	d	18 54	19 00	19 28				19 49		19 54		←		20 06			20 54	20 58					22 11		
Northallerton	d			19 39			19 48	20 01				20 01				20 42						22 34	22 41		
Thirsk	d						19 57	→								20 50						22 42			
York 8	a	19 25	19 28	20 00			20 13			20 25		20 31		20 38		21 09	21 22	21 26				23 09	23 19		
Hull	a				←										←		22 39	22 39			←				
Leeds 10	a	19 51	20 07		19 51					20 51		21 08		21 33	20 51	21 38	21 48	22 04			21 48	23 38			
Harrogate	d	→	18 30						18 53	→				19 30			→	20 30							
Scarborough	d			18 45										19 45											
York 8	d		19 30	20 02			20 15							20 40				21 28							
Doncaster 7	a		19 53	20 25	20 32									21 05	21 30			21 51			22 30				
Sheffield 7	a		20 53		20 59							22f05		21 56	21 57			22 58			23 03				
Skipton	d								19 23																
Keighley	d								19 36																
Bradford Forster Square	d								19g31																
Shipley	d								19 48																
Leeds 10	d								20 15									20 20							
Huddersfield	d								19h32									19j44							
Wakefield Westgate 7	d								20 27									20 33							
Hull	d		18 38															20 30							
Selby	d																								
Doncaster 7	d		19 54	20 26					20 47					21 05				21 52							
Retford 10	d													21 20											
Newark North Gate 7	a		20 16											21 34											
Grimsby Town	d		18k36											20 08				20k36							
Lincoln	d													21 00											
Newark North Gate 7	d		20 16											21 34											
Grantham 7	a			20 56														22 22							
	d			20 56							21 19							22 22							
Peterborough 8	a		20 46	21 17					21 35		21 51			22 04				22 43							
Cambridge	a								23m13					23 17											
Stansted Airport	a																								
Norwich	a										23 35														
Peterborough 8	d		20 48	21 18					21 36					22 04				22 44							
Stevenage 4	a		21 20	21 48					22 09					22 34											
London Kings Cross 15 ⊖	a		21 47	22 16			22 20		22 37					23 14				23 50							

For general notes see front of timetable
For details of catering facilities see Directory of Train Operators

- **A** To Birmingham New Street (Table 51)
- **B** To Liverpool Lime Street (Table 39)
- **C** From Liverpool Lime Street (Table 49)
- **D** To Manchester Airport (Table 39)
- **E** To Derby (Table 53)
- **G** To Saltburn (Table 44)
- **b** Change at Edinburgh
- **c** Change at Stirling and Edinburgh
- **e** Glasgow Queen Street
- **f** Change at York
- **g** Bradford Interchange
- **h** Change at Leeds
- **j** Change at Leeds and Doncaster
- **k** Change at Doncaster
- **m** Change at Peterborough and Ely

Table 26

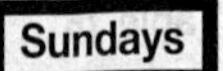

Sundays

20 July to 7 September

Scotland, North East England, Yorkshire and Humberside → London

Route Diagram - see first page of Table 26

		GR	GR	GR	EM	GR		GC	XC	GR	HT	XC		TP	GC	GR	TP	XC		GR	EM	GR	GR	TP		EM
		R 1	R 1	R 1	◇	R 1		R 1	R 1	R 1	1 ◇	R 1		1 ◇	R 1	R 1	1 ◇	1 ◇		R 1	◇	R 1	R 1	1 ◇		◇
					A				B			B		C			D	E			G			D		A
Aberdeen	d																									
Stonehaven	d																									
Montrose	d																									
Arbroath	d																									
Dundee	d																						07 25			
Leuchars 3	d																						07 37			
Kirkcaldy	d																						08 09			
Inverkeithing	d																						08 30			
Inverness	d																									
Perth	d																									
Stirling	d																									
Glasgow Central 15	d																			07b50						
Motherwell	d																									
Haymarket	d																									
Edinburgh 10	a																									
Edinburgh	d																	08 50		09 00			09 30			
Dunbar	d																									
Berwick-upon-Tweed	d																	09 31		09 41						
Alnmouth	d																									
Morpeth	d																									
Newcastle 8	a																	10 18		10 28			10 55			
Sunderland	d							09 10										09 28					10 28			
Hartlepool	d							09 34																		
Newcastle 8	d		07 58			08 55			09 10	09 25				09 33				10 25		10 30			10 57	11 03		
Chester-le-Street	d													09 42												
Durham	d		08 10			09 07			09 24					09 49				10 37					11 10	11 16		
Darlington 7	a		08 28			09 25			09 39	09 51				10 05				10 53		10 59				11 32		
Middlesbrough	d					08 45								09 15			10 15							10 53		
Eaglescliffe	d							09 55																		
Darlington 7	d		08 28			09 25			09 42	09 52				10 06				10 54		10 59				11 33		
Northallerton	d					09 39		10 13						10 17	←		10 42							11 45		
Thirsk	d							10 26 →							10 26		10 50							→		
York 8	a		08 58			10 00			10 11	10 20				10 41	10 44		11 09	11 21		11 28			11 51			
Hull	a									11 38													13 03			
Leeds 10	a		09 49						10 50					11 24			11 48			12 25						
Harrogate	d															09 53						10 53				
Scarborough	d									09 20		←											10 45			
York 8	d		09 00			10 02			10 13 →	10 23		10 13			10 46			11 24		11 29			11 53			
Doncaster 7	a		09 25			10 26				10 47		11 29						11 49		11 53						
Sheffield 7	a		09 57			11 10				11 25		12 03						12 17		12 55			13 17			
Skipton	d			08 35							09c15											10 15				
Keighley	d			08 48							09c28											10 28				
Bradford Forster Square	d			09 02							09e21					10 02						11 02				
Shipley	d			09 10							09c40					10 08						11 10				
Leeds 10	d	08 24		09 40							10f09					10 40				11 00		11 40				
Huddersfield	d	07g12		08g12							09c12					10g02				10c14		10g44				
Wakefield Westgate 7	d	08 36		09 52							10f22					10 52				11 11		11 52				
Hull	d			08 42						09 41	10 12									10 41						
Selby	d										10 47															
Doncaster 7	d	08 54	09 26	10 10		10 29				10 48	11 04					11 13				11 53		12 10				
Retford 10	d		09 41								11 19					11 28										
Newark North Gate 7	a	09 18		10 32		10 52										11 42							12 36			
Grimsby Town	d										09f49									10f36						
Lincoln	d															11 05										
Newark North Gate 7	d	09 18		10 32		10 52										11 42							12 36			
Grantham 7	a	09 30	10 03			11 04					11 38					11 54						12 40				
	d	09 30	10 03		10 27	11 04					11 39					11 54					12 18	12 40				13 14
Peterborough 8	a	09 52	10 25	11 02	11 07	11 26				11 37						12 16				12 40	12 52		13 06			13 41
Cambridge	a		12h34							13h14										14h14			14 19			
Stansted Airport	a																						14 58			
Norwich	a				12 59					14h09											14 35					15 28
Peterborough 8	d	09 53	10 27	11 02		11 26				11 38						12 16				12 41			13 06			
Stevenage 4	a		10 58							12 09						13 33							13 42			
London Kings Cross 15 ⊖	a	10 47	11 26	11 55		12 19				12 37	12 48				12 51	13 10				13 36		13 50	14 10			

For general notes see front of timetable
For details of catering facilities see Directory of Train Operators

- **A** From Nottingham (Table 19)
- **B** To Bournemouth (Table 51)
- **C** To Manchester Airport (Table 39)
- **D** To Liverpool Lime Street (Table 39)
- **E** To Plymouth (Table 51)
- **G** From Sheffield (Table 49)
- **b** Glasgow Queen Street
- **c** Change at Leeds and Doncaster
- **e** Bradford Interchange. Change at Leeds and Doncaster
- **f** Change at Doncaster
- **g** Change at Leeds
- **h** Change at Peterborough and Ely

Due to Engineering Operations in the Sheffield area, services from Sunday 14 September on this Table had not been confirmed at time of going to press. These services will be issued in a special Supplement as soon as exact timings have been confirmed.

Table 26

Sundays

Scotland, North East England, Yorkshire and Humberside → London

20 July to 7 September

Route Diagram - see first page of Table 26

		XC	TP	XC	GR	HT	GR	GR	GR	XC	TP	XC	GR	EM	GR	TP	GR	XC	GR	XC	GR	HT
		R 1	1 ◇	1 ◇	R 1	1 ◇	R 1	R 1	R 1	R 1	1 ◇	1 ◇	R 1	◇	R 1	1 ◇	R 1	R 1	R 1	1 ◇	R 1	1 ◇
		A	B	C						D	E	C		G		H		J		C		
Aberdeen	d																					
Stonehaven	d																					
Montrose	d																					
Arbroath	d																					
Dundee	d																09 25					
Leuchars 3	d																09 37					
Kirkcaldy	d																10 09					
Inverkeithing	d																10 32					
Inverness	d																					
Perth	d																09 27					
Stirling	d							09 05									10 02					
Glasgow Central 15	d				08b30								09b30					10 04			10 50	
Motherwell	d																	10u29			11 05	
Haymarket	d																	11 16			11 49	
Edinburgh 10	a																	11 21			11 54	
Edinburgh	d	09 33			10 00			10 30		10 33			11 00				11 30	11 33			12 00	
Dunbar	d									10 55												
Berwick-upon-Tweed	d				10 39			11 09		11 18												
Alnmouth	d	10 33																			12 39	
Morpeth	d																12 40	12 33				
Newcastle 8	a	11 02			11 30			11 58		12 04			12 26				13 01	13 05			13 29	
Sunderland	d							11 28									12 28					
Hartlepool	d																					
Newcastle 8	d	11 13		11 25	11 32			12 00		12 13		12 25	12 32			12 40	13 03	13 13	13 20	13 25	13 32	
Chester-le-Street	d															12 49						
Durham	d	11 25		11 37						12 25		12 37	12 45			12 56		13 25		13 37	13 45	
Darlington 7	a	11 41		11 53				12 26		12 41		12 53	13 02			13 12	13 29	13 41	13 46	13 53	14 03	
Middlesbrough	d							11 24			12 15		12 25			12 25						
Eaglescliffe	d																				13 25	
Darlington 7	d	11 42	←	11 54				12 27		12 42		12 54	13 03			13 13	13 30	13 42	13 47	13 54	14 04	
Northallerton	d		11 45								12 42					13 24	13 42					
Thirsk	d										12 50											
York 8	a	12 11	12 18	12 22	12 28			12 55		13 10	13 16	13 22	13 31			13 47	14 03	14 11	14 17	14 22	14 34	
Hull	a							14 04														
Leeds 10	a	12 51	12 54		13 24					13 51	13 55					14 26		14 51			15 43	
Harrogate	d				11 30		11 53												13 30			
Scarborough	d							11 57							12 53				13 20			
York 8	d			12 25	12 29			12 57				13 25	13 33				14 05		14 19	14 25	14 36	
Doncaster 7	a			12 49	12 54			13 20				13 49	13 56				14 28		14 43	14 50	14 59	
Sheffield 7	a	13c42		13 17				14 03		14e41		14 17	14 52				15 10	15f41		15 17		
Skipton	d					11g15	11 30								12 15							13g15
Keighley	d					11g28	11 40								12 28							13g28
Bradford Forster Square	d					11h31	12 02								13 02							13h31
Shipley	d					11g40	12 08								13 08							13g40
Leeds 10	d					12j09	12 40								13 40							14j09
Huddersfield	d					11g12	11k44								12k46							13g12
Wakefield Westgate 7	d					12j22	12 52								13 52							14j22
Hull	d				11 41	12 12																14 10
Selby	d					12 47							12 41						13 41			14 45
Doncaster 7	d				12 54	13 06	13 11	13 21	←				13 57		14 10		14 29		14 48		15 00	15 05
Retford 10	d					13 21	13m34 →		13 34													15 20
Newark North Gate 7	a								13 48						14 33							
Grimsby Town	d												12j36						13j36			
Lincoln	d								13 05													
Newark North Gate 7	d								13 48						14 33							
Grantham 7	a				13 26	13 40			14 00								14 59					15 40
	d				13 26	13 40			14 00					14 20			14 59					15 40
Peterborough 8	a							14 09	14 22				14 43	14 53					15 35		15 47	
Cambridge	a												16n14								17n14	
Stansted Airport	a												16 59									
Norwich	a													16 37							17 35	
Peterborough 8	d							14 10	14 22				14 43						15 36		15 47	
Stevenage 4	a				14 14	14 29			15 33						15 28						16 17	
London Kings Cross 15 ⊖	a				14 42	14 54		15 11	15 15				15 37		15 55		16 11		16 29		16 45	16 50

For general notes see front of timetable
For details of catering facilities see Directory of Train Operators

A To Penzance (Table 135)
B To Liverpool Lime Street (Table 39)
C To Bristol Temple Meads (Table 51)
D To Bournemouth (Table 51)
E To Manchester Piccadilly (Table 39)
G From Sheffield (Table 49)
H To Manchester Airport (Table 39)
J To Plymouth (Table 51)
b Glasgow Queen Street
c By changing at York, passengers may arrive at 1317
e By changing at York, passengers may arrive at 1417
f By changing at York, passengers may arrive at 1517
g Change at Leeds and Doncaster
h Bradford Interchange. Change at Leeds and Doncaster
j Change at Doncaster
k Change at Leeds
m Arr. 1326
n Change at Peterborough and Ely

Due to Engineering Operations in the Sheffield area, services from Sunday 14 September on this Table had not been confirmed at time of going to press. These services will be issued in a special Supplement as soon as exact timings have been confirmed.

Table 26

Scotland, North East England, Yorkshire and Humberside → London

Sundays

20 July to 7 September

Route Diagram - see first page of Table 26

		TP 1◇ A	GR R 1 B	GR R 1	XC R 1 C	TP 1◇ D	XC R 1 E	GC R 1	GR R 1 G	EM ◇ H	GR R 1	TP 1◇ A	GR R 1 J	XC R 1 K	XC 1◇ E	GR R 1	EM ◇ H	GR R 1	HT 1◇	TP 1◇ A	GR R 1	GR R 1
Aberdeen	d		09 48																			11 42
Stonehaven	d		10 05																			11 59
Montrose	d		10 28																			12 22
Arbroath	d		10 44																			12 38
Dundee	d		11 02										11b25									12 59
Leuchars 3	d		11 16										11b37									13 13
Kirkcaldy	d		11 40		11b09								12b09									13 37
Inverkeithing	d		11 56		11b48								12b32									13 56
Inverness	d												09 38									
Perth	d												11 55									
Stirling	d		11b06										12 32									13b07
Glasgow Central 15	d				11 18				11c30							12 50						13e00
Motherwell	d				11u38											13 05						
Haymarket	d		12 19										13 12			13 50						14 19
Edinburgh 10	a		12 24		12 27								13 18			13 56						14 24
Edinburgh	d		12 30		12 33				13 00				13 30	13 33		14 00						14 30
Dunbar	d				12 55																	
Berwick-upon-Tweed	d				13 18				13 42				14 09									
Alnmouth	d		13 29											14 36								
Morpeth	d																					
Newcastle 8	a		14 00		14 05				14 30				15 00	15 05		15 25						15 59
Sunderland	d		13 28					13 42					14 28									15 28
Hartlepool	d							14 06														
Newcastle 8	d	13 45	14 02		14 07		14 25		14 32			14 38	15 01	15 13	15 25	15 30				15 36	15 50	16 01
Chester-le-Street	d																					
Durham	d	13 57			14 21		14 37					14 50	15 15	15 25	15 37					15 49		16 14
Darlington 7	a	14 13	14 29		14 37		14 53		14 59			15 07	15 32	15 41	15 53	15 59				16 05	16 20	16 32
Middlesbrough	d					14 15							14 38									15 50
Eaglescliffe	d							14 34														
Darlington 7	d	14 14	14 30		14 38		14 54		15 00			15 08	15 33	15 42	15 54	15 59				16 06	16 20	16 32
Northallerton	d					14 42		14 57	15 11			15 19									16 32	
Thirsk	d					14 50		15 06														
York 8	a	14 47	15 00		15 11	15 18	15 24	15 28	15 32			15 43	16 02	16 10	16 22	16 28				16 45	16 52	17 01
Hull	a								16 41													18 10
Leeds 10	a	15 24			15 51	15 55						16 19		16 51						17 26		
Harrogate	d										14 53					15 30						
Scarborough	d															15 20						
York 8	d		15 02				15 25	15 31	15 34				16 03		16 25	16 29					16 53	17 03
Doncaster 7	a						15 47		15 57				16 28		16 49	16 53					17 19	17 27
Sheffield 7	a				16f41		16 17		16 52				17 10	17g41	17 17	17 54					18 03	18 10
Skipton	d			13 15							14 15							15 15				
Keighley	d			13 28							14 28							15 28				
Bradford Forster Square	d			14 02							15 02							16 02				
Shipley	d			14 08							15 08							16 08				
Leeds 10	d			14 40							15 40							16 40				
Huddersfield	d			13h44							14h44							15h44				
Wakefield Westgate 7	d			14 52							15 52							16 52				
Hull	d								14 41							15 41			16 21			
Selby	d																		16 56			
Doncaster 7	d			15 10					15 58		16 10		16 28			16 53		17 10	17 15		17 19	17 28
Retford 10	d			15 25															17 30			
Newark North Gate 7	a			15 39					16 20												17 46	
Grimsby Town	d			14 04					14j36							15j36						
Lincoln	d			14 59					15 46													
Newark North Gate 7	d			15 39					16 20												17 46	
Grantham 7	a			15 52							16 40							17 40	17 49			
	d			15 52						16 24	16 40						17 24	17 40	17 49			
Peterborough 8	a			16 13					16 50	16 55	17 01		17 18			17 40	17 51	18 02				18 21
Cambridge	a			17 23					18k14				18 21			19k14						19 20
Stansted Airport	a			17 59																		19 59
Norwich	a									18 35							19 29					
Peterborough 8	d			16 19					16 51		17 02		17 18			17 41		18 02				18 21
Stevenage 4	a			16 49					17 22							18 11					18 42	
London Kings Cross 15 ⊖	a		17 11	17 17				17 31	17 50		17 55		18 15			18 38		18 55	19 06		19 12	19 16

For general notes see front of timetable
For details of catering facilities see Directory of Train Operators

A To Manchester Airport (Table 39)
B The Northern Lights
C To Bournemouth (Table 51)
D To Liverpool Lime Street (Table 39)
E To Bristol Temple Meads (Table 51)
G The Flying Scotsman
H From Liverpool Lime Street (Table 49)
J The Highland Chieftain
K To Plymouth (Table 51)
b Change at Edinburgh
c Glasgow Queen Street
e Glasgow Queen Street. Change at Edinburgh
f By changing at York, passengers may arrive at 1617
g By changing at York, passengers may arrive at 1717
h Change at Leeds
j Change at Doncaster
k Change at Peterborough and Ely

Due to Engineering Operations in the Sheffield area, services from Sunday 14 September on this Table had not been confirmed at time of going to press. These services will be issued in a special Supplement as soon as exact timings have been confirmed.

Scotland, North East England, Yorkshire and Humberside → London

20 July to 7 September

Route Diagram - see first page of Table 26

		GR R 1	TP 1 ◇	XC R 1 A	XC 1 ◇ B	EM 1 ◇ C	GR R 1	EM ◇ D	GR R 1	GR R 1	TP 1 ◇ E	GR R 1	GR R 1	GR R 1	XC 1 ◇ B	XC 1 ◇ G	GR R 1	EM ◇ D	GR R 1	HT 1 ◇	TP 1 ◇	TP 1 ◇ E
Aberdeen	d			11 58																		
Stonehaven	d			12 16																		
Montrose	d			12 39																		
Arbroath	d			12 55																		
Dundee	d			13 12								13 25										
Leuchars 3	d			13 25								13 39										
Kirkcaldy	d			13 55								14 11										
Inverkeithing	d			14 10								14 32										
Inverness	d																					
Perth	d											13b05										
Stirling	d											14 07										
Glasgow Central 15	d			13c30								14e00					14 50					
Motherwell	d																15 05					
Haymarket	d			14 28													15 49					
Edinburgh 10	a			14 33													15 55					
Edinburgh	d			14 36			15 00					15 30				15 52	16 00					
Dunbar	d			14 57																		
Berwick-upon-Tweed	d			15 19			15 41					16 09										
Alnmouth	d																					
Morpeth	d			15 51								16 43										
Newcastle 8	a			16 08			16 31					17 01				17 14	17 27					
Sunderland	d											16 28										
Hartlepool	d																					
Newcastle 8	d			16 13	16 25		16 33				16 40	17 03		17 12	17 25	17 16	17 30					17 50
Chester-le-Street	d										16 49											
Durham	d			16 25	16 37		16 46				16 56			17 24	17 37	17 30						18 03
Darlington 7	a			16 41	16 55		17 03				17 12	17 30		17 42	17 53	17 47	17 58					18 19
Middlesbrough	d		16 10									16 45			17 14						17 55	
Eaglescliffe	d																					
Darlington 7	d			16 42	16 56		17 04				17 13	17 31		17 42	17 54	17 48	17 58					18 21
Northallerton	d		16 37								17 24	17 42									18 22	
Thirsk	d		16 45																		18 30	
York 8	a		17 07	17 11	17 24		17 32				17 49	18 03		18 10	18 22	18 14	18 28				18 48	18 54
Hull	a																					20 08
Leeds 10	a		17 55	17 51							18 25			18 59		18 51						19 37
Harrogate	d				16 30					16 53							17 30		17 53			
Scarborough	d				16 20												17 32					
York 8	d				17 25	17 32	17 35					18 05		18 12	18 25		18 29					
Doncaster 7	a				17 49	17 54	18 03					18 31		18 37	18 49		18 53					
Sheffield 7	a			18f41	18 17	18 27	18 52					19 10			19 17	19 41	19 53					
Skipton	d	16 15																	17 15			
Keighley	d	16 28																	17 28			
Bradford Forster Square	d	16g31								17 02									18 02			
Shipley	d	16 40								17 09									18 08			
Leeds 10	d	17 05								17 40									18 40			
Huddersfield	d	16h30								16h44									17h44			
Wakefield Westgate 7	d	17 18								17 52									18 52			
Hull	d						16 41		17 30								17 41			18 30		
Selby	d								18 05											19 05		
Doncaster 7	d	17 36					18 03		18 23			18 31	←	18 37			18 53		19 10	19 22		
Retford 10	d	17 51							18j44 →				18 44							19 37		
Newark North Gate 7	a	18 05												19 02								
Grimsby Town	d						16k36										17k36					
Lincoln	d	17 25											17m35	18 00								
Newark North Gate 7	d	18 05												19 02								
Grantham 7	a									18 36			19 06						19 40	19 56		
	d							18 18		18 36			19 06					19 22	19 40	19 57		
Peterborough 8	a						18 49	18 54		18 58		19 18	19 28	19 33			19 40	19 51	20 01			
Cambridge	a											20 21					21n14		21 19			
Stansted Airport	a											20 59							21 53			
Norwich	a							20 28										21 25	22n53			
Peterborough 8	d						18 50			18 58		19 19	19 29	19 33			19 41		20 02			
Stevenage 4	a	18 59					19 21							20 07			20 13		20 32	20s45		
London Kings Cross 15 ⊖	a	19 33					19 48			19 52		20 12	20 23	20 34			20 38		20 59	21 12		

For general notes see front of timetable
For details of catering facilities see Directory of Train Operators

- **A** To Southampton Central (Table 51)
- **B** To Bristol Temple Meads (Table 51)
- **C** To St Pancras International (Table 53)
- **D** From Liverpool Lime Street (Table 49)
- **E** To Manchester Airport (Table 39)
- **G** To Birmingham New Street (Table 51)
- **b** Change at Stirling and Edinburgh
- **c** Glasgow Queen Street. Change at Edinburgh
- **e** Glasgow Queen Street
- **f** By changing at York, passengers may arrive at 1817
- **g** Bradford Interchange
- **h** Change at Leeds
- **j** Arr. 1838
- **k** Change at Doncaster
- **m** Change at Retford
- **n** Change at Peterborough and Ely

Due to Engineering Operations in the Sheffield area, services from Sunday 14 September on this Table had not been confirmed at time of going to press. These services will be issued in a special Supplement as soon as exact timings have been confirmed.

Table 26

Sundays

20 July to 7 September

Scotland, North East England, Yorkshire and Humberside → London

Route Diagram - see first page of Table 26

		GR	XC	XC	GR	GR	TP	GC	GR	EM	TP	XC	GR	NT	TP	XC	GR	NT	TP	GR	GR
		R 1	1 ◇ A	1 ◇ B	R 1	R 1	1 ◇ C	R 1	R 1	◇ D	1 ◇ C	1 ◇ A	R 1		1 ◇ E	1 ◇ A	R 1	G	1 ◇ E	R 1	R 1
Aberdeen	d	13 50											15 10							17 10	
Stonehaven	d	14 07											15 29							17 26	
Montrose	d	14 30											15 49							17 48	
Arbroath	d	14 46											16 03							18 02	
Dundee	d	15 04				15 25							16 25							18 19	
Leuchars 3	d	15 18				15 37							16 37							18 31	
Kirkcaldy	d	15 42			16b02	16 11							17 01				17b07			18 56	19b07
Inverkeithing	d	16 02			16b18	16 32							17 17				17b47			19 12	19b48
Inverness	d				13b25																16c15
Perth	d				15b25															17c05	18c27
Stirling	d	15b07				16 07											17b07			18 07	19b11
Glasgow Central 15	d	15e00	15 44		15 50	16f00						16f30					17 50			18f30	19 50
Motherwell	d		16u00		16 05												18 05				20 04
Haymarket	d	16 21	16 38		16 46												18 46				20 45
Edinburgh 10	a	16 26	16 44		16 52												18 53				20 51
Edinburgh	d	16 30	16 50		17 00	17 30						17 50	18 00				19 00			20 00	21 00
Dunbar	d											18 13					19 20			20 20	21 21
Berwick-upon-Tweed	d	17 09										18 35	18 39							20 43	21 44
Alnmouth	d	17 32										18 55	19 03								22 06
Morpeth	d																			21 17	
Newcastle 8	a	18 07	18 13		18 26	18 55						19 24	19 33				20 29			21 38	22 41
Sunderland	d	17 28				18 28		18 42								19 28		20 28			
Hartlepool	d							19 06													
Newcastle 8	d	18 10	18 15	18 25	18 29	18 57	19 04					19 25	19 35			20 25	20 31	21 06		21 40	
Chester-le-Street	d																	21 15			
Durham	d		18 28	18 37	18 42	19 10	19 16					19 38	19 48			20 37		21 24		21 53	
Darlington 7	a		18 43	18 53	18 59	19 27	19 32					19 54	20 05			20 53	20 57	21 44		22 10	
Middlesbrough	d					18 48	18 53								19 55				22 07		
Eaglescliffe	d							19 25													
Darlington 7	d		18 45	18 54	19 00	19 28	19 33				←	19 55	20 06			20 54	20 58			22 11	
Northallerton	d					19 39	19 45	19 48			19 45				20 22				22 34	22 41	
Thirsk	d						→	19 57							20 30				22 42		
York 8	a	19 04	19 13	19 22	19 28	20 00		20 13			20 16	20 25	20 38		20 52	21 21	21 26		23 09	23 19	
Hull	a																22 39				
Leeds 10	a		19 55								20 58	21 08			21 32		23 20		23 48		
Harrogate	d			18 30					18 53				19 30				20 30				
Scarborough	d				18 30								19 30				20 30				
York 8	d	19 05		19 23	19 30	20 02		20 15					20 40	20 44		21 24	21 28				
Doncaster 7	a	19 31		19 49	19 53	20 25							21 05			21 48	21 51				
Sheffield 7	a	20 10	20g41	20 17	20 53	21 17						21 59	21 56	22 05		22 18	22 58				
Skipton	d								19 23												
Keighley	d								19 36												
Bradford Forster Square	d								19h31												
Shipley	d								19 48												
Leeds 10	d								20 15								20 20				
Huddersfield	d								19j32								19k44				
Wakefield Westgate 7	d								20 27								20 33				
Hull	d				18 38												20 30				
Selby	d																				
Doncaster 7	d	19 31			19 54	20 26			20 47				21 05				21 52				
Retford 10	d												21 20								
Newark North Gate 7	a				20 16								21 34								
Grimsby Town	d				18m36								20 08				20m36				
Lincoln	d												21 00								
Newark North Gate 7	d				20 16								21 34								
Grantham 7	a					20 56											22 22				
	d					20 56				21 19							22 22				
Peterborough 8	a	20 22			20 46	21 17			21 35	21 51			22 04				22 43				
Cambridge	a								23n13				23 17								
Stansted Airport	a																				
Norwich	a									23 35											
Peterborough 8	d	20 23			20 48	21 18			21 36				22 04				22 44				
Stevenage 4	a	20 54			21 20	21 48			22 09				22 34								
London Kings Cross 15 ⊖	a	21 25			21 47	22 16		22 20	22 37				23 14				23 50				

For general notes see front of timetable
For details of catering facilities see Directory of Train Operators

- A To Birmingham New Street (Table 51)
- B To Bristol Temple Meads (Table 51)
- C To Liverpool Lime Street (Table 39)
- D From Liverpool Lime Street (Table 49)
- E To Manchester Airport (Table 39)
- G To Saltburn (Table 44)
- b Change at Edinburgh
- c Change at Stirling and Edinburgh
- e Glasgow Queen Street. Change at Edinburgh
- f Glasgow Queen Street
- g By changing at York, passengers may arrive at 2017
- h Bradford Interchange
- j Change at Leeds
- k Change at Leeds and Doncaster
- m Change at Doncaster
- n Change at Peterborough and Ely

Due to Engineering Operations in the Sheffield area, services from Sunday 14 September on this Table had not been confirmed at time of going to press. These services will be issued in a special Supplement as soon as exact timings have been confirmed.

Mondays to Saturdays

Peterborough — Wisbech, Kings Lynn, Swaffham and Dereham
Bus Service

		GR SX 🚌	GR SX 🚌	GR 🚌	GR 🚌	GR 🚌		GR 🚌	GR 🚌	GR 🚌	GR 🚌	GR 🚌	GR 🚌	GR 🚌	GR 🚌	GR 🚌	GR 🚌
Peterborough	d	06 43	07 43	07 48	08 18	08 48	and every 30 minutes until	16 48	17 18	17 48	18 18	18 48	19 18	20 18	21 18	22 18	23 18
Wisbech Bus Station	d	07 30	08 00	08 35	09 05	09 35		17 35	18 05	18 35	19 05	19 35	20 05	21 05	22 05	23 05	00 05
Kings Lynn Bus Station	d	08 07	08 37	09 07	09 37	10 07		18 07	18 37	19 07	19 37	20 07	20 37	21 37	22 37	23 37	00 37
Swaffham Market Place	d	08 42	09 12	09 42	10 12	10 42		18 42	19 12	.	20 12	.	21 12	22 12	.	.	.
Dereham Market Place	a	09 13	09 43	10 13	10 43	11 13		19 13	19 43		20 43		21 43	22 43			

Sundays

		GR 🚌		GR 🚌	GR 🚌	GR 🚌	GR 🚌
Peterborough	d	08 18	and every hour until	20 18	21 18	22 18	23 18
Wisbech Bus Station	d	09 05		21 05	22 05	23 05	00 05
Kings Lynn Bus Station	d	09 37		21 37	22 37	23 37	00 37
Swaffham Market Place	d	10 12		22 12	.	.	.
Dereham Market Place	a	10 43		22 43			

Mondays to Saturdays

		GR SX 🚌	GR SX 🚌	GR 🚌	GR 🚌	GR 🚌	GR 🚌	GR SX 🚌	GR SO 🚌	GR SX 🚌	GR SO 🚌	GR 🚌	GR 🚌		GR 🚌	GR 🚌	GR 🚌	GR 🚌	GR 🚌
Dereham Market Place	d							07 19	07 24	07 49	07 54	08 24	08 54	and every 30 minutes until	16 54	17 54	18 54	19 54	20 54
Swaffham Market Place	d	.	.	.	.	.	.	07 49	07 54	08 19	08 24	08 54	09 24		17 24	18 24	19 24	20 24	21 24
Kings Lynn Bus Station	d	05 24	05 54	06 29	06 59	07 29	07 59	08 29	08 29	08 59	08 59	09 29	09 59		17 59	18 59	19 59	20 59	21 59
Wisbech Bus Station	d	05 56	06 26	07 01	07 31	08 01	08 31	09 01	09 01	09 31	09 31	10 01	10 31		18 31	19 31	20 31	21 31	22 31
Peterborough	a	06 38	07 08	07 43	08 13	08 43	09 13	09 43	09 43	10 13	10 13	10 43	11 13		19 13	20 13	21 13	22 13	23 13

Sundays

		GR 🚌	GR 🚌	GR 🚌	GR 🚌		GR 🚌
Dereham Market Place	d				08 54	and every hour until	20 54
Swaffham Market Place	d	.	.	.	09 24		21 24
Kings Lynn Bus Station	d	06 59	07 59	08 59	09 59		21 59
Wisbech Bus Station	d	07 31	08 31	09 31	10 31		22 31
Peterborough	a	08 13	09 13	10 13	11 13		23 13

For general notes see front of timetable
For details of catering facilities see Directory of Train Operators

Sunday service operates on Bank Holidays

This service is the X1 operated by First Eastern Counties, telephone 0845 602 0121

Table 26B

Mondays to Saturdays

Peterborough — Oundle, Corby and Kettering
Bus Service

		GR 🚌	GR 🚌	GR 🚌		GR 🚌	GR 🚌	GR 🚌	GR 🚌
Peterborough §	d	07 05	07 40	09 10	and every hour until	17 10	18 30	19 30	20 30
Oundle Market Place	a	07 27	08 22	09 32		17 32	18 57	19 57	20 57
Corby George Street	a	08 05	09 05	10 05		18 05	19 25	20 25	21 25
Kettering Library	a	08 35	09 35	10 35		18 35	19 55	20 55	21 55

Sundays

		GR 🚌	GR 🚌	GR 🚌	GR 🚌	GR 🚌	GR 🚌
Peterborough §	d	10 10	12 10	14 10	16 10	18 10	20 10
Oundle Market Place	a	10 37	12 37	14 37	16 37	18 37	20 37
Corby George Street	a	11 05	13 05	15 05	17 05	19 05	21 05
Kettering Library	a	11 35	13 35	15 35	17 35	19 35	21 35

Mondays to Saturdays

		GR 🚌	GR 🚌	GR 🚌	GR 🚌		GR 🚌	GR 🚌	GR 🚌	GR 🚌
Kettering Library	d	05 30	06 00		08 45	and every hour until	15 45	16 50	17 55	18 55
Corby George Street	d	05 55	06 25		09 10		16 10	17 15	18 20	19 20
Oundle Market Place	d	06 23	06 53	08 38	09 38		16 38	17 43	18 48	19 48
Peterborough §	a	06 40	07 25	09 00	10 00		17 00	18 05	19 10	20 20

Sundays

		GR 🚌	GR 🚌	GR 🚌	GR 🚌	GR 🚌	GR 🚌
Kettering Library	d	08 15	10 15	12 15	14 15	16 15	18 15
Corby George Street	d	08 40	10 40	12 40	14 40	16 40	18 40
Oundle Market Place	d	09 08	11 08	13 08	15 08	17 08	19 08
Peterborough §	a	09 40	11 40	13 40	15 40	17 40	19 40

For general notes see front of timetable
For details of catering facilities see Directory of Train Operators

§ Peterborough Queensgate Bus Station

Sunday service operates on Bank Holidays

This service is the X4 operated by Stagecoach East, telephone 01604 676060

Table 26D

Mondays to Fridays

Newark — Lincoln
Bus Service

		GR 🚌	GR 🚌	GR 🚌	GR 🚌	GR 🚌	GR 🚌	GR 🚌
Newark North Gate	d	15 00	16 36	17 36	18 45	19 45	22 55	23 27
Witham St Hughes	a	15 15	16 50	17 50	19 00	20 00	23 10	23 40
Hykeham Crossroads	a	15 22	16 58	17 58	19 05	20 05	23 18	23 48
Lincoln Bus Station	a	15 40	17 15	18 15	19 23	20 23	23 35	00 05

Mondays to Fridays

		GR 🚌	GR 🚌	GR 🚌	GR 🚌	GR 🚌
Lincoln Bus Station	d	05 45	06 20	07 20	11 45	16 35
Hykeham Crossroads	d	05 58	06 37	07 37	12 02	16 47
Witham St Hughes	d	06 02	06 43	07 45	12 10	16 55
Newark North Gate	a	06 15	06 55	08 00	12 25	17 10

For general notes see front of timetable
For details of catering facilities see Directory of Train Operators

No Saturday or Sunday service

This service is the 46X Raillink operated by Veolia Transport UK Limited, telephone 01522 542132

Table 26E

Mondays to Saturdays

Doncaster — Barnsley
Bus Service

		GR SX	GR	GR	GR	GR		GR	GR	GR	GR	GR	GR	GR
Doncaster Interchange	d	04 30	05 10	06 55	07 55	09 05	and every hour until	16 05	17 20	18 15	19 15	20 15	21 15	22 15
Goldthorpe Police Station	a	04 53	05 33	07 18	08 18	09 26		16 26	17 41	18 36	19 36	20 36	21 36	22 36
Darfield Roundabout	a	05 00	05 40	07 25	08 25	09 33		16 33	17 48	18 43	19 43	20 43	21 43	22 43
Barnsley West Bus Station	a	05 15	05 55	07 45	08 45	09 50		16 50	18 05	19 00	20 00	21 00	22 00	23 00

Mondays to Saturdays

		GR	GR	GR	GR	GR		GR	GR	GR	GR	GR	GR	
Barnsley West Bus Station	d	05 15	06 05	07 05	07 50	09 15	and every hour until	15 15	16 25	17 25	18 25	19 25	20 25	
Darfield Roundabout	d	05 29	06 19	07 19	08 04	09 29		15 29	16 39	17 39	18 39	19 39	20 39	
Goldthorpe Police Station	d	05 36	06 26	07 26	08 11	09 36		15 36	16 46	17 46	18 46	19 46	20 46	
Doncaster Interchange	a	06 00	06 50	07 50	08 50	10 00		16 00	17 10	18 10	19 10	20 10	21 10	

For general notes see front of timetable
For details of catering facilities see
Directory of Train Operators

No Sunday Service

This service is the X19 operated by Stagecoach East Yorkshire

Table 26F

Mondays to Fridays

Doncaster → Robin Hood Airport

Bus Service

		GR	GR		GR	GR		GR	GR		GR	GR		GR	GR		GR	GR		GR	GR		GR		GR	GR
Doncaster Interchange	d	05 35	05 55	.....	06 00	06 25	.....	06 35	06 50	.....	06 55	07 25	.....	07 35	07 45	.....	07 55	08 05	.....	08 15	08 30	.....	08 35	.....	09 00	09 05
Robin Hood Airport	a	05 59	06 20	.	06 25	06 50	.	06 59	07 15	.	07 20	07 50	.	07 59	08 10	.	08 20	08 30	.	08 40	08 55	.	08 59	.	09 25	09 30

		GR	GR	GR	and at the same minutes past each hour until		GR	GR		GR	GR		GR	GR		GR	GR		GR	GR		GR	GR		GR
Doncaster Interchange	d	09 20	09 35	09 40		.....	14 40	15 00	.....	15 05	15 20	.....	15 35	15 45	.....	16 05	16 10	.....	16 25	16 35	.....	16 40	16 55	.....	17 10
Robin Hood Airport	a	09 45	09 59	10 05		.	15 05	15 25	.	15 30	15 45	.	15 59	16 10	.	16 30	16 39	.	16 54	16 59	.	17 09	17 24	.	17 39

		GR	GR		GR	GR		GR		GR	GR	GR	and at the same minutes past each hour until		GR	GR		GR							
Doncaster Interchange	d	17 15	17 30	.....	17 35	17 50	.....	18 10	.....	18 15	18 35	18 40		.....	21 40	22 35	.....	23 00	.....	.....	.....	.....	.....	.....	.....
Robin Hood Airport	a	17 40	17 59	.	17 59	18 18	.	18 35	.	18 40	18 59	19 05		.	22 05	22 59	.	23 25	.	.	.	.	.	.	.

Saturdays

		GR	GR		GR	GR		GR	GR		GR	GR		GR	GR		GR	GR			GR	GR	GR			
Doncaster Interchange	d	05 35	05 55	.....	06 00	06 35	.....	06 40	06 50	.....	07 35	07 40	.....	07 55	08 10	.....	08 35	08 40	.....	.....	09 05	09 10	09 35	.....	.....	.....
Robin Hood Airport	a	05 59	06 20	.	06 25	06 59	.	07 05	07 15	.	07 59	08 05	.	08 20	08 35	.	08 59	09 05	.	.	09 30	09 35	09 59	.	.	.

		GR	and at the same minutes past each hour until		GR	GR		GR	GR		GR	GR			GR	GR	GR	and at the same minutes past each hour until		GR	GR		GR	
Doncaster Interchange	d	09 40		.....	16 40	17 10	.....	17 15	17 35	.....	17 40	18 10	.....	.....	18 15	18 35	18 40		.....	21 40	22 35	.....	23 00	.....
Robin Hood Airport	a	10 05		.	17 05	17 35	.	17 40	17 59	.	18 05	18 35	.	.	18 40	18 59	19 05		.	22 05	22 59	.	23 25	.

Sundays

		GR	GR	GR	GR	GR	GR	GR	GR	GR	GR	GR	GR	GR	GR	GR	GR	GR	GR	GR	GR	GR	GR	GR		
Doncaster Interchange	d	08 35	09 35	09 40	10 35	10 40	11 35	11 40	12 35	12 40	13 40	14 35	14 40	15 35	15 40	16 35	16 40	17 35	17 40	18 40	19 40	20 40	21 40	23 00	.....	.....
Robin Hood Airport	a	08 59	09 59	10 05	10 59	11 05	11 59	12 05	12 59	13 05	14 05	14 59	15 05	15 59	16 05	16 59	17 05	17 59	18 05	19 05	20 05	21 05	22 05	23 25	.	.

For general notes see front of timetable
For details of catering facilities see
Directory of Train Operators

This service is an amalgamation of routes 91 operated by First, X19 operated by Stagecoach Yorkshire and 707 operated by Wilfreda Beehive

Table 26F

Mondays to Fridays

Robin Hood Airport → Doncaster

Bus Service

		GR	GR	GR	GR	GR	GR	GR	GR	GR	GR	GR	GR	GR		GR	GR	GR	GR	GR	and at the same minutes past each hour until		GR	GR	GR
Robin Hood Airport	d	06 05	06 25	06 38	07 05	07 08	07 23	07 25	07 53	08 05	08 08	08 25	08 28	08 48	.....	09 05	09 08	09 28	09 35	09 48		.....	15 48	16 05	16 08
Doncaster Interchange	a	06 30	06 55	07 03	07 30	07 33	07 54	07 55	08 24	08 30	08 39	08 55	08 59	09 15	.	09 30	09 33	09 53	10 05	10 13		.	16 13	16 30	16 33

		GR	GR	GR	GR	GR	GR	GR	GR	GR	GR	GR	GR		GR	GR	GR	and at the same minutes past each hour until	GR	GR	GR	GR	GR		
Robin Hood Airport	d	16 38	16 45	16 58	17 05	17 18	17 38	17 45	17 58	18 05	18 28	18 45	18 58	.....	19 05	19 28	19 45		21 45	22 05	22 28	23 05	23 43	.....	.....
Doncaster Interchange	a	17 03	17 20	17 23	17 30	17 43	18 03	18 15	18 23	18 30	18 53	19 15	19 23	.	19 30	19 53	20 15		20 30	22 30	22 53	23 30	00 08	.	.

Saturdays

		GR	GR	GR	GR	GR		GR	GR	GR	GR	GR			GR	GR	GR	GR	and at the same minutes past each hour until	GR		GR	GR	GR	GR
Robin Hood Airport	d	06 05	06 25	06 38	07 05	07 28	.....	07 25	08 05	08 28	08 25	08 58	.....	.....	09 05	09 28	09 35	09 58		15 58	.....	16 05	16 28	16 45	16 58
Doncaster Interchange	a	06 30	06 55	07 03	07 30	07 53	.	07 55	08 30	08 53	08 55	09 23	.	.	09 30	09 53	10 05	10 23		16 23	.	16 30	16 53	17 20	17 23

		GR	GR	GR		GR	GR	GR	GR	GR			GR	GR	GR	and at the same minutes past each hour until	GR	GR		GR	GR	GR		
Robin Hood Airport	d	17 05	17 28	17 45	.....	17 58	18 05	18 28	18 45	18 58	.....	.....	19 05	19 28	19 45		21 45	22 05	.....	22 28	23 05	23 43	.....	.....
Doncaster Interchange	a	17 30	17 53	18 15	.	18 23	18 30	18 53	19 15	19 23	.	.	19 30	19 53	20 15		22 15	22 30	.	22 53	23 30	00 08	.	.

Sundays

		GR	GR	GR	GR	GR	GR	GR	GR	GR	GR	GR	GR	GR	GR	GR	GR	GR	GR	GR	GR	GR	GR	GR	GR	
Robin Hood Airport	d	09 05	09 28	10 05	10 28	11 05	11 28	12 05	12 28	13 28	14 05	14 28	15 05	15 28	16 05	16 28	17 05	17 28	18 05	18 28	19 28	20 28	21 28	22 28	23 43	.....
Doncaster Interchange	a	09 30	09 53	10 30	10 53	11 30	11 53	12 30	12 53	13 53	14 30	14 53	15 30	15 53	16 30	16 53	17 30	17 53	18 30	18 53	19 53	20 53	21 53	22 53	00 08	.

For general notes see front of timetable
For details of catering facilities see
Directory of Train Operators

This service is an amalgamation of routes 91 operated by First, X19 operated by Stagecoach Yorkshire and 707 operated by Wilfreda Beehive

Mondays to Fridays

York — Pickering and Whitby
Bus Service

		GR 🚌	GR 🚌	GR 🚌	GR 🚌	GR 🚌	GR 🚌	GR 🚌	GR 🚌	GR 🚌	GR 🚌	GR 🚌
York	d	08 13	09 20	10 22	11 22	12 22	13 22	14b22	15 22	16 24	17 34	18 34
Eden Camp	a	09 17	10 17	11 17	12 17	13 17	14 17	15 17	16 17	17 22	18 27	19 22
Flamingo Land	a	09 25	10 25	11 25	12 25	13 25	14 25	15 25	16 25	17 30	18 35	19 30
Pickering Eastgate	a	09 31	10 31	11 31	12 31	13 31	14 31	15 31	16 31	17 36	18 41	19 36
Whitby Bus Station	a	10 29		12 29		14 29			17 29			

Saturdays

		GR 🚌	GR 🚌	GR 🚌	GR 🚌	GR 🚌	GR 🚌	GR 🚌	GR 🚌	GR 🚌	GR 🚌	GR 🚌
York	d	08 22	09 22	10 22	11 22	12 22	13 22	14b22	15 22	16 22	17 27	18 27
Eden Camp	a	09 17	10 17	11 17	12 17	13 17	14 17	15 17	16 17	17 17	18 22	19 22
Flamingo Land	a	09 25	10 25	11 25	12 25	13 25	14 25	15 25	16 25	17 25	18 30	19 30
Pickering Eastgate	a	09 31	10 31	11 31	12 31	13 31	14 31	15 31	16 31	17 31	18 36	19 36
Whitby Bus Station	a	10 29		12 29		14 29			17 29			

Sundays

		GR 🚌	GR 🚌
York	d	10b22	15b52
Eden Camp	a	11 17	16 47
Flamingo Land	a	11 25	16 55
Pickering Eastgate	a	11 31	17 01
Whitby Bus Station	a	12 29	17 59

Mondays to Fridays

		GR 🚌	GR 🚌	GR 🚌	GR 🚌	GR 🚌	GR 🚌	GR 🚌	GR 🚌	GR 🚌	GR 🚌	GR 🚌	GR 🚌
Whitby Bus Station	d					10 45		12 45		14 45		18 18	
Pickering Eastgate	d	07 02	08 42	09 42	10 42	11 42	12 42	13 42	14 42	15 42	17 47	19 15	19 47
Flamingo Land	d	07 10	08 50	09 50	10 50	11 50	12 50	13 50	14 50	15 50	17 55	19 23	19 55
Eden Camp	d	07 18	08 58	09 58	10 58	11 58	12 58	13 58	14 58	15 58	18 03	19 31	20 03
York	a	08 13	09 56	10 56	11c56	12 56	13c56	14 56	15 56	16 58	18c53	20c25	21c25

Saturdays

		GR 🚌	GR 🚌	GR 🚌	GR 🚌	GR 🚌	GR 🚌	GR 🚌	GR 🚌	GR 🚌	GR 🚌	GR 🚌	GR 🚌
Whitby Bus Station	d					10 45		12 45		14 45		18 18	
Pickering Eastgate	d	07 02	08 42	09 42	10 42	11 42	12 42	13 42	14 42	15 42	17 42	19 15	19 47
Flamingo Land	d	07 10	08 50	09 50	10 50	11 50	12 50	13 50	14 50	15 50	17 50	19 23	19 55
Eden Camp	d	07 18	08 58	09 58	10 58	11 58	12 58	13 58	14 58	15 58	17 58	19 31	20 03
York	a	08 26	09 56	10 56	11c56	12 56	13c56	14 56	15 56	16 56	18c53	20c25	21c25

Sundays

		GR 🚌	GR 🚌	GR 🚌
Whitby Bus Station	d		13 15	18 18
Pickering Eastgate	d	09 12	14 12	19 15
Flamingo Land	d	09 20	14 20	19 23
Eden Camp	d	09 28	14 28	19 31
York	a	10c26	15c26	20c25

For general notes see front of timetable
For details of catering facilities see Directory of Train Operators

b Customers are required to change buses at Malton Bus Station

c Customers are required to change buses at Malton Bus Station

This service is the 840 operated by Yorkshire Coastliner

Please note: timings in this timetable are based upon the Winter 2007 & Spring 2008 timetable. There may be changes to the published timetable, details of which are not available at the time of going to press. For confirmation of timings, please telephone Yorkshire Coastliner on 01653 692556.

Mondays to Saturdays

Darlington — Richmond and Catterick

Bus Service

		GR SX	GR SX	GR	GR	GR	GR SX	GR	GR	GR		GR	GR	GR	GR	GR		GR	GR
Darlington	d	06 50	07 28	07 58	08 34	08 58	09 20	09 40	10 00	10 20	and at the same minutes past each hour until	17 20	17 40	18 00	18 30	19 00	and every hour until	22 00	23 00
Richmond (Market)	a	07 26	08 00	08 20	08 56	09 20	09 52	10 12	10 36	10 52		17 52	18 12	18 36	19 04	19 36		22 36	23b48
Catterick Garrison Tesco	a	....	08 13	08 51	09 25	09 51	10 08	10 25	10 51	11 08		18 08	18 25	18 51	....	19 51		22 51	23 40
Catterick Camp Centre	a	07 43	08 15	08 53	09 27	09 53	.	10 27	10 53	.		.	18 27	18 53	.	19 53		22 53	23 39
Catterick Garrison Kemmel	a	07 50	08 22	09 00	09 34	10 00	....	10 34	11 00	....		....	18 34	19 00	....	20 00		23 00	23 36

Sundays

		GR	GR		GR	GR	GR	GR		GR
Darlington	d	10 00	10 30	and at the same minutes past each hour until	16 30	17 00	17 30	18 00	and every hour until	22 00
Richmond (Market)	a	10 36	11 00		17 00	17 36	18 00	18 36		22 36
Catterick Garrison Tesco	a	10 51	11 13		17 13	17 51	18 13	18 51		22 51
Catterick Camp Centre	a	10 53	.		.	17 53	.	18 53		22 53
Catterick Garrison Kemmel	a	11 00	....		....	18 00	....	19 00		23 00

Mondays to Saturdays

		GR SX	GR SX	GR SO	GR SX	GR SX	GR SO	GR SX	GR SO	GR	GR	GR	GR	GR		GR	GR	GR	GR		GR
Catterick Garrison Kemmel	d	....	06 27	....	06 58	07 22	....	07 50	07 55	....	08 22	09 00	....	09 35	and at the same minutes past each hour until	16 35	17 00	....	18 00	and every hour until	22 00
Catterick Camp Centre	d	.	06 34	.	07 04	07 29	.	07 56	08 01	.	08 29	09 06	.	09 42		16 42	17 06	.	18 06		22 06
Catterick Garrison Tesco	d	....	06 38	....	07 06	07 31	....	07 58	08 03	08 10	08 31	09 08	09 29	09 44		16 44	17 08	17 42	18 08		22 08
Richmond (Market)	d	06 16	06 53	07 21	07 20	07 47	07 54	08 12	08 17	08 30	08 52	09 25	09 44	10 00		17 00	17 25	17 59	18 25		22 25
Darlington	a	06 49	07 26	07 54	07 55	08 27	08 27	08 52	08 52	09 05	09 27	09 55	10 14	10 35		17 35	18 00	18 29	19 00		23 00

Sundays

		GR	GR		GR	GR	GR	GR		GR
Catterick Garrison Kemmel	d	09 00	....	and at the same minutes past each hour until	....	16 00	....	17 00	and every hour until	22 00
Catterick Camp Centre	d	09 06	.		.	16 06	.	17 06		22 06
Catterick Garrison Tesco	d	09 08	09 43		15 43	16 08	16 43	17 08		22 08
Richmond (Market)	d	09 25	10 00		16 00	16 25	17 00	17 25		22 25
Darlington	a	10 00	10 30		16 30	17 00	17 30	18 00		23 00

For general notes see front of timetable
For details of catering facilities see Directory of Train Operators

b Runs via Catterick Garrison before Richmond

This service is an amalgamation of routes X26, X27 and 28 operated by Arriva North East

Table 26J

Mondays to Saturdays

Darlington — Durham Tees Valley Airport

Bus Service

		GR 🚌		GR 🚌
Darlington	d	07 00	and every hour until	22 00
Tees Valley Airport	a	07 27		22 27

Sundays

		GR 🚌		GR 🚌
Darlington	d	09 00	and every hour until	22 00
Tees Valley Airport	a	09 27		22 27

Mondays to Saturdays

		GR 🚌		GR 🚌
Tees Valley Airport	d	07 35	and every hour until	22 35
Darlington	a	07 55		22 55

Sundays

		GR 🚌		GR 🚌
Tees Valley Airport	d	09 35	and every hour until	22 35
Darlington	a	09 55		22 55

For general notes see front of timetable
For details of catering facilities see Directory of Train Operators

This is the Durham Tees Valley Airport "Skyexpress" service

Table 26K

Mondays to Fridays

Berwick-upon-Tweed — Scottish Border Towns
Bus Service

This service is operated by First Lowland under contract to Scottish Borders Council. Telephone: 01835 824000

		XC	XC	XC	XC	XC	XC	XC	XC	XC
Berwick-upon-Tweed	d	06 57	08 12	09 52	10 52	12 52	15 07	17 47	18 47	20 22
Duns	a	07 30	08 45	10 25	11 25	13 25	15 40	18 20	19 20	20 55
Earlston	a	08 08	09 33	11 03	12 03	14 03	16 28	18 58	19 58	21 33
Melrose	a	08 22	09 47	11 15	12 15	14 15	16 40	19 10	20 10	21 45
Galashiels Bus Station	a	08 40	10 02	11 30	12 30	14 30	16 55	19 25	20 25	22 00

Saturdays

This service is operated by First Lowland under contract to Scottish Borders Council. Telephone: 01835 824000

		XC	XC	XC	XC	XC	XC
Berwick-upon-Tweed	d	08 22	10 52	12 52	15 17	17 17	19 17
Duns	a	08 55	11 25	13 25	15 50	17 50	19 50
Earlston	a	09 33	12 03	14 03	16 28	18 28	20 28
Melrose	a	09 47	12 15	14 15	16 40	18 40	20 40
Galashiels Bus Station	a	10 02	12 30	14 30	16 55	18 55	20 55

Sundays

This service is operated by First Lowland under contract to Scottish Borders Council. Telephone: 01835 824000

		XC	XC	XC	XC	XC	XC
Berwick-upon-Tweed	d	10 52	12 52	15 17	17 42	19 07	20 37
Duns	a	11 25	13 25	15 50	18 15	19 40	21 10
Earlston	a	12 03	14 03	16 28	18 53	20 18	21 48
Melrose	a	12 15	14 15	16 40	19 05	20 30	22 00
Galashiels Bus Station	a	12 30	14 30	16 55	19 20	20 45	22 15

Mondays to Fridays

This service is operated by First Lowland under contract to Scottish Borders Council. Telephone: 01835 824000

		XC	XC	XC	XC	XC	XC	XC	XC
Galashiels Bus Station	d	06 25	07 40	08 10	10 50	12 50	14 40	16 32	17 20
Melrose	d	06 40	07 55	08 28	11 05	13 05	14 55	16 50	17 35
Earlston	d	06 52	08 07	08 40	11 17	13 17	15 07	17 02	17 52
Duns	d	07 30	08 55	09 20	11 55	13 55	15 55	17 40	18 30
Berwick-upon-Tweed	a	08 01	09 26	09 56	12 26	14 26	16 26	18 11	19 01

Saturdays

This service is operated by First Lowland under contract to Scottish Borders Council. Telephone: 01835 824000

		XC	XC	XC	XC	XC	XC
Galashiels Bus Station	d	06 35	08 20	10 50	12 50	14 50	17 20
Melrose	d	06 50	08 35	11 05	13 05	15 05	17 35
Earlston	d	07 02	08 47	11 17	13 17	15 17	17 52
Duns	d	07 40	09 25	11 55	13 55	15 55	18 30
Berwick-upon-Tweed	a	08 11	09 56	12 26	14 26	16 26	19 01

Sundays

This service is operated by First Lowland under contract to Scottish Borders Council. Telephone: 01835 824000

		XC	XC	XC	XC	XC	XC
Galashiels Bus Station	d	08 50	10 50	12 35	14 50	16 35	18 35
Melrose	d	09 05	11 05	12 50	15 05	16 50	18 50
Earlston	d	09 17	11 17	13 02	15 17	17 02	19 02
Duns	d	09 55	11 55	13 40	15 55	17 40	19 40
Berwick-upon-Tweed	a	10 26	12 26	14 26	16 26	18 26	20 26

For general notes see front of timetable
For details of catering facilities see Directory of Train Operators

Table 27

Mondays to Fridays

Cleethorpes → Lincoln → Newark → Nottingham

Network Diagram - see first page of Table 18

Miles	Miles			EM	EM	EM	EM A	EM	EM B	EM	EM B	EM	EM B	EM B	EM	EM B	EM B	EM C
0	—	**Cleethorpes**	d		05 51													
3¼	—	**Grimsby Town**	d		05 58			07 03				09 28			11 28			
11¼	—	Habrough	d		06 08			07 13				09 38			11 38			
17¾	—	Barnetby	d		06 17			07 22				09 47			11 47			
32¼	—	Market Rasen	d		06 34			07 39				10 03			12 03			
47	—	**Lincoln**	a		06 52			07 57				10 22			12 22			
—	—		d	05 23	06 54	07 10	07 29	07 59	08 34	09 10	09 30	10 23	10 36	11 43	12 23	12 31	13 35	14 04
51	—	Hykeham	d	05 31			07 37		08 42		09 38		10 44			12 39	13 43	
55¾	—	Swinderby	d	05 37			07 43		08 48		09 44		10 50			12 45	13 49	
58½	0	Collingham	d	05 41			07 48		08 53		09 49		10 54			12 49	13 53	
—	5	**Newark North Gate** 7	a	05 51	07 17			08 22		09 33		10 49			12 49			14 28
—	—	London Kings Cross 15	⊖ a	*07 30*	*08 48*			*09 51*		*11 15*		*12 25*			*15 05*			*16 46*
—	—	**Newark North Gate** 7	d	06 00														
63½	—	**Newark Castle**	d	06 08		07 33	07 57		09 05		09 58		11 03	12 05		12 58	14 03	
67	—	Rolleston	d	06 15		07 40	08 04				10 05		11 10			13 05		
68	—	Fiskerton	d	06 17		07 42	08 06				10 07					13 07		
69¾	—	Bleasby	d	06 21		07 45	08 10				10 11					13 10		
70¾	—	Thurgarton	d	06 24		07 48	08 13				10 14					13 13		
71½	—	Lowdham	d	06 28		07 52	08 17				10 18		11 17			13 17		
75¾	—	Burton Joyce	d	06 32		07 56	08 21				10 22		11 21			13 21		
77¾	—	Carlton	d	06 35		08 00	08 24				10 25					13 25		
80¾	—	**Nottingham** 8	a	06 48		08 12	08 32		09 30		10 33		11 31	12 28		13 33	14 28	

		EM B	EM	EM B	EM B	EM	EM	EM	EM B	EM	EM D	EM	EM
Cleethorpes	d											21 14	
Grimsby Town	d		13 52			16 03				18 30		21 21	
Habrough	d		14 02			16 12				18 40		21 30	
Barnetby	d		14 11			16 21				18 49		21 39	
Market Rasen	d		14 27			16 36				19 06		21 54	
Lincoln	a		14 46			16 54				19 24		22 15	
	d	14 38	14 47	15 32	16 40	16 56	17 29	18 17	18 33	19 26	20 43		22 31
Hykeham	d			15 40			17 37				20 51		22 39
Swinderby	d						17 44				20 57		22 45
Collingham	d			15 49		17 11	17 49	18 32			21 01		22 49
Newark North Gate 7	a		15 11			17 22		18 42		19 50			
London Kings Cross 15	⊖ a		*17 04*			*18 54*		*20 18*		*21 33*			
Newark North Gate 7	d												
Newark Castle	d	15 01		15 58	17 05		17 59		18 55		21 10		22 58
Rolleston	d	15 08		16 05			18 06		19 02		21 17		23 05
Fiskerton	d	15 10					18 08		19 04		21 19		23 07
Bleasby	d	15 13					18 12		19 08		21 22		23 10
Thurgarton	d	15 16					18 15		19 11				
Lowdham	d	15 20		16 13			18 19		19 15		21 27		23 15
Burton Joyce	d	15 24		16 17			18 23		19 19		21 31		23 19
Carlton	d	15 28		16 20			18 27		19 23		21 35		23 23
Nottingham 8	a	15 35		16 30	17 28		18 40		19 30		21 47		23 35

Saturdays

		EM	EM	EM A	EM	EM B	EM	EM B	EM	EM B	EM B	EM	EM B	EM B
Cleethorpes	d													
Grimsby Town	d				06 59				09 28			11 30		
Habrough	d				07 09				09 37			11 39		
Barnetby	d				07 18				09 46			11 48		
Market Rasen	d				07 33				10 01			12 03		
Lincoln	a				07 52				10 21			12 21		
	d	05 50	06 55	07 30	07 54	08 34	09 10	09 23	10 23	10 36	11 41	12 23	12 31	13 35
Hykeham	d	05 58	07 03	07 38		08 42		09 31		10 44			12 39	13 43
Swinderby	d	06 04	07 09	07 44		08 48		09 37		10 50			12 45	13 49
Collingham	d	06 08	07 13	07 48		08 53		09 42		10 54			12 49	13 53
Newark North Gate 7	a		07 23		08 15		09 33		10 45			12 45		
London Kings Cross 15	⊖ a													
Newark North Gate 7	d		07 27											
Newark Castle	d	06 17	07 35	07 57		09 05		09 54		11 04	12 07		12 58	14 04
Rolleston	d	06 24	07 42	08 04		09 12		10 01		11 10			13 05	
Fiskerton	d	06 26	07 44	08 06				10 03					13 07	
Bleasby	d	06 29	07 47	08 09				10 07					13 10	
Thurgarton	d	06 32	07 50	08 12				10 10					13 13	
Lowdham	d	06 36	07 54	08 16				10 14		11 18			13 17	
Burton Joyce	d	06 40	07 58	08 20				10 18		11 22			13 21	
Carlton	d	06 44	08 02	08 24				10 21		11 25			13 25	
Nottingham 8	a	06 56	08 15	08 31		09 32		10 29		11 33	12 33		13 32	14 31

For general notes see front of timetable
For details of catering facilities see
Directory of Train Operators

A From Sleaford (Table 18) to Leicester (Table 53)
B To Leicester (Table 53)
C From Peterborough (Table 18)
D From Sleaford (Table 18)

Table 27

Saturdays

Cleethorpes → Lincoln → Newark → Nottingham

Network Diagram - see first page of Table 18

		EM	EM	EM	EM	EM	EM	EM	EM	EM	EM	EM	EM
			A	A		A	A						
Cleethorpes	d												
Grimsby Town	d	13 25			15 28					18 06		19 28	
Habrough	d	13 35			15 37					18 16		19 38	
Barnetby	d	13 44			15 46					18 26		19 47	
Market Rasen	d	13 59			16 01					18 42		20 02	
Lincoln	a	14 17			16 19					19 01		20 20	
	d	14 19	14 30	15 35	16 22	16 40	17 35	18 09	18 43	19 10	19 40		20 41
Hykeham	d			15 43			17 43				19 48		20 49
Swinderby	d						17 49				19 54		20 55
Collingham	d			15 53			17 53				19 58		20 59
Newark North Gate 7	a	14 42			16 52			18 32		19 34			21 09
London Kings Cross 15	⊖ a												
Newark North Gate 7	d												21 13
Newark Castle	d		14 52	16 01		17 06	18 02		19 07		20 08		21 25
Rolleston	d		14 59	16 08			18 09				20 15		21 31
Fiskerton	d		15 01				18 11				20 17		21 33
Bleasby	d		15 05				18 15				20 21		21 36
Thurgarton	d		15 08				18 18				20 24		21 39
Lowdham	d		15 12	16 16			18 22				20 28		21 43
Burton Joyce	d		15 16	16 20			18 26				20 32		21 47
Carlton	d		15 19	16 23			18 29				20 35		21 51
Nottingham 8	a		15 33	16 31		17 30	18 36		19 33		20 51		22 03

Sundays

until 7 September

		EM	EM	EM	EM	EM	EM	EM	EM	EM	EM	EM	EM	EM
Cleethorpes	d			13 57								20 01		
Grimsby Town	d			14 04								20 08		
Habrough	d			14 13								20 18		
Barnetby	d			14 22								20 26		
Market Rasen	d			14 37								20 41		
Lincoln	a			14 55								20 59		
	d	11 05	13 05	14 59	15 46	17 10	17 25	18 00	19 10	19 25	20 12	21 00	21 26	22 12
Hykeham	d			15 07		17 18		18 08	19 18		20 20	21 08		22 20
Swinderby	d			15 13		17 24		18 14	19 24		20 26	21 14		22 26
Collingham	d			15 17		17 28		18 18	19 28		20 30	21 18	21 41	22 30
Newark North Gate 7	a	11 28	13 28	15 27	16 10		17 49	18 29		19 48		21 28	21 50	
London Kings Cross 15	⊖ a	*13 10*	*15 15*	*17 17*	*17 50*		*19 33*	*20 34*				*23 14*		
Newark North Gate 7	d			15 30				18 33				21 32		
Newark Castle	d			15 42		17 37		18 44	19 39		20 39	21 40		22 40
Rolleston	d			15 49		17 44		18 51	19 46		20 46			22 47
Fiskerton	d			15 51		17 46		18 53	19 48		20 48			22 49
Bleasby	d			15 55		17 49		18 56	19 51		20 51			22 53
Thurgarton	d			15 58		17 52		18 59	19 54		20 54			22 56
Lowdham	d			16 02		17 56		19 03	19 58		20 58			23 00
Burton Joyce	d			16 06		18 00		19 07	20 02		21 02			23 04
Carlton	d			16 09		18 04		19 11	20 06		21 06			23 07
Nottingham 8	a			16 22		18 17		19 22	20 18		21 18	22 08		23 20

Sundays

from 14 September

		EM	EM	EM	EM	EM	EM	EM	EM
Cleethorpes	d								
Grimsby Town	d								
Habrough	d								
Barnetby	d								
Market Rasen	d								
Lincoln	a								
	d	11 05	13 05	14 59	18 00	19 10	20 12	21 00	22 12
Hykeham	d			15 07	18 08	19 18	20 20	21 08	22 20
Swinderby	d			15 13	18 14	19 24	20 26	21 14	22 26
Collingham	d			15 17	18 18	19 28	20 30	21 18	22 30
Newark North Gate 7	a	11 28	13 28	15 27	18 29			21 28	
London Kings Cross 15	⊖ a								
Newark North Gate 7	d			15 30	18 33			21 32	
Newark Castle	d			15 42	18 44	19 39	20 39	21 40	22 40
Rolleston	d			15 49	18 51	19 46	20 46		22 47
Fiskerton	d			15 51	18 53	19 48	20 48		22 49
Bleasby	d			15 55	18 56	19 51	20 51		22 53
Thurgarton	d			15 58	18 59	19 54	20 54		22 56
Lowdham	d			16 02	19 03	19 58	20 58		23 00
Burton Joyce	d			16 06	19 07	20 02	21 02		23 04
Carlton	d			16 09	19 11	20 06	21 06		23 07
Nottingham 8	a			16 22	19 22	20 18	21 18	22 08	23 20

For general notes see front of timetable
For details of catering facilities see
Directory of Train Operators

A To Leicester (Table 53)

Table 27

Nottingham → Newark → Lincoln → Cleethorpes

Network Diagram - see first page of Table 18

Miles	Miles			EM	EM		EM	EM		EM	EM A		EM B	EM		EM B	EM B		EM	EM B		EM C	EM B		EM
0	—	**Nottingham 8**	d		06 02		06 58				08 09		09 26			10 23	11 26			12 26			13 26		
3	—	Carlton	d		06 08		07 04				08 15					10 32	11 32						13 32		
5	—	Burton Joyce	d		06 11		07 08				08 18					10 35	11 35			12 34			13 35		
9¼	—	Lowdham	d		06 15		07 12				08 22					10 39				12 38			13 39		
10	—	Thurgarton	d		06 19						08 26					10 43							13 43		
11	—	Bleasby	d		06 22		07 17				08 29					10 46							13 46		
12¾	—	Fiskerton	d		06 26		07 20				08 33					10 50							13 50		
13¾	—	Rolleston	d		06 28		07 22				08 35					10 52	11 45			12 46			13 52		
17¼	—	**Newark Castle**	d		06 34		07 29				08 41		09 49			10 58	11 51			12 52			13 58		
—	—	**Newark North Gate 7**	a																						
—	—	London Kings Cross 15	⊖ d					*06 15*		*07 10*				*08 30*					*10 35*			*11 35*			*12 35*
—	0	**Newark North Gate 7**	d					07 46		08 35				09 57					12 07			13 05			14 33
22½	5	Collingham	d		06 44		07 38	07 55								11 07				13 01					
25	—	Swinderby	d		06 48		07 43									11 12				13 06					
29¾	—	Hykeham	d		06 54		07 49	08 04								11 18				13 12					
33¾	—	**Lincoln**	a		07 08		08 03	08 13		09 00	09 10		10 18	10 21		11 32	12 19		12 30	13 26		13 28	14 28		14 56
—	—		d	05 57				08 17						10 22					12 38						14 57
48½	—	Market Rasen	d	06 13				08 34						10 39					12 55						15 14
63½	—	Barnetby	a	06 30				08 51						10 55					13 11						15 32
69½	—	Habrough	a	06 41				09 01						11 05					13 21						15 41
77½	—	**Grimsby Town**	a	06 57				09 15						11 20					13 35						15 56
80¾	—	**Cleethorpes**	a																						

		EM B	EM C		EM B	EM D		EM	EM		EM B	EM		EM B	EM		EM	EM B		EM					
Nottingham 8	d	14 26			15 25	16 25					17 21	17 46		18 25				20 24		22 22					
Carlton	d				15 31						17 27	17 52		18 31				20 30							
Burton Joyce	d				15 34						17 30	17 56		18 34				20 33							
Lowdham	d	14 38			15 38						17 34	18 00		18 38				20 37							
Thurgarton	d				15 42						17 38			18 42				20 41							
Bleasby	d	14 43			15 45						17 41			18 45				20 44							
Fiskerton	d	14 46			15 49						17 45			18 49				20 48							
Rolleston	d				15 51						17 47	18 07		18 51				20 50							
Newark Castle	d	14 52			15 57	16 46					17 53	18 14		18 58				20 56		22 43					
Newark North Gate 7	a																	21 06		22 54					
London Kings Cross 15	⊖ d		*14 10*						*16 10*						*17 50*		*18 33*	*19 33*		*21 30*					
Newark North Gate 7	d		15 37						17 34						19 24		20 00	21 11		22 58					
Collingham	d				16 07						18 03	18 24		19 07				21 20		23 07					
Swinderby	d				16 11							18 28		19 12				21 24		23 12					
Hykeham	d				16 17						18 12	18 34		19 18				21 30		23 18					
Lincoln	a	15 27	16 00		16 34	17 13			17 57		18 25	18 48		19 32	19 49		20 28	21 44		23 33					
	d							17 18							19 52										
Market Rasen	d							17 35							20 09										
Barnetby	a							17 51							20 30										
Habrough	a							18 01							20 40										
Grimsby Town	a							18 14							20 52										
Cleethorpes	a														21 01										

Saturdays

		EM		EM		EM		EM		EM		EM		EM B		EM		EM B		EM		EM B		EM B	EM
Nottingham 8	d			06 03		07 00						08 06		09 27				10 25				11 24		12 26	
Carlton	d			06 09		07 06						08 12						10 31						12 32	
Burton Joyce	d			06 12		07 09						08 15						10 34						12 35	
Lowdham	d			06 16		07 13						08 19						10 38						12 39	
Thurgarton	d			06 20								08 23						10 42							
Bleasby	d			06 23		07 18						08 26						10 45							
Fiskerton	d			06 27		07 22						08 30						10 49							
Rolleston	d			06 29		07 24						08 32						10 51				11 41		12 47	
Newark Castle	d			06 35		07 30						08 38		09 49				10 57				11 51		12 53	
Newark North Gate 7	a																								
London Kings Cross 15	⊖ d																								
Newark North Gate 7	d									08 31						09 56				11 34					13 35
Collingham	d			06 45		07 41						08 47												13 02	
Swinderby	d			06 49		07 45						08 52												13 06	
Hykeham	d			06 55		07 51						08 58												13 12	
Lincoln	a			07 11		08 05				08 54		09 12		10 18		10 19		11 27		11 57		12 19		13 27	13 58
	d	05 57						08 29								10 21				11 59					14 06
Market Rasen	d	06 13						08 45								10 37				12 15					14 22
Barnetby	a	06 29						09 00								10 54				12 31					14 38
Habrough	a	06 39						09 09								11 03				12 41					14 47
Grimsby Town	a	06 53						09 23								11 17				12 55					15 01
Cleethorpes	a																								

For general notes see front of timetable
For details of catering facilities see Directory of Train Operators

A From Worksop (Table 55)
B From Leicester (Table 53)
C To Peterborough (Table 18)
D From Leicester (Table 53) to Sleaford (Table 18)

Table 27

Saturdays

Nottingham → Newark → Lincoln → Cleethorpes

Network Diagram - see first page of Table 18

		EM A	EM A	EM	EM A	EM	EM A	EM	EM A	EM	EM B	EM A	EM	EM A	EM
Nottingham 8	d	13 26	14 24		15 24		16 26		17 24		18 26	19 26		20 26	21 27
Carlton	d	13 32			15 31		16 32		17 30		18 32	19 32			
Burton Joyce	d	13 35			15 34		16 35		17 33		18 35	19 35			
Lowdham	d	13 39			15 38		16 39		17 37		18 39	19 39			
Thurgarton	d	13 43			15 42		16 43		17 41		18 43	19 43			
Bleasby	d	13 46			15 45		16 46		17 44		18 46	19 46			
Fiskerton	d	13 50			15 49		16 50		17 48		18 50	19 50			
Rolleston	d	13 52			15 51		16 52		17 50		18 52	19 52			
Newark Castle	d	13 58	14 45		15 57		16 59		17 56		18 59	19 59		20 48	21 51
Newark North Gate 7	a														22 03
London Kings Cross 15	⊖ d														
Newark North Gate 7	d			15 03				17 51		18 51			20 15		22 05
Collingham	d				16 06				18 06	19 00	19 10	20 09		21 01	22 15
Swinderby	d				16 11				18 10	19 04	19 15	20 14		21 05	
Hykeham	d				16 17				18 16	19 10	19 21	20 20		21 11	
Lincoln	a	14 27	15 13	15 26	16 31		17 30	18 14	18 30	19 19	19 30	20 34	20 38	21 25	22 36
	d					16 50		18 16					20 40		
Market Rasen	d					17 07		18 33					20a56		
Barnetby	a					17 31		18 49							
Habrough	a					17 40		18 58							
Grimsby Town	a					17 54		19 14							
Cleethorpes	a														

Sundays

until 7 September

		EM	EM	EM	EM	EM	EM	EM	EM	EM	EM	EM	EM	EM
Nottingham 8	d			15 30		16 30		17 30	18 30		19 30	20 30		22 30
Carlton	d					16 36		17 36	18 36		19 36	20 36		22 36
Burton Joyce	d					16 39		17 39	18 39		19 39	20 39		22 39
Lowdham	d					16 43		17 43	18 43		19 43	20 43		22 43
Thurgarton	d					16 47		17 47	18 47		19 47	20 47		22 47
Bleasby	d					16 50		17 50	18 50		19 50	20 50		22 50
Fiskerton	d					16 54		17 54	18 54		19 54	20 54		22 54
Rolleston	d					16 56		17 56	18 56		19 56	20 56		22 56
Newark Castle	d			15 52		17 02		18 03	19 02		20 02	21 02		23 02
Newark North Gate 7	a					17 12	17 56		19 13			21 12		23 13
London Kings Cross 15	⊖ d	*10 00*	*12 00*		*14 10*	*15 30*			*17 30*	*18 10*		*19 10*	*20 30*	*21 30*
Newark North Gate 7	d	11 45	13 34		16 30	17 17			19 17	19 57		21 15	21 59	23 18
Collingham	d				16 38	17 26		18 13	19 26		20 11	21 24	22 07	23 27
Swinderby	d				16 43	17 30		18 17	19 30		20 16	21 29		23 32
Hykeham	d				16 49	17 36		18 23	19 36		20 22	21 35		23 38
Lincoln	a	12 07	13 56	16 20	16 58	17 51	18 19	18 37	19 50	20 20	20 37	21 49	22 24	23 52
	d	12 15		16 24										
Market Rasen	d	12 31		16 40										
Barnetby	a	12 47		16 55										
Habrough	a	12 55		17 03										
Grimsby Town	a	13 09		17 15										
Cleethorpes	a	13 19		17 27										

Sundays

from 14 September

		EM	EM	EM	EM	EM	EM	EM	EM
Nottingham 8	d			16 30	17 30	18 30	19 30	20 30	22 30
Carlton	d			16 36	17 36	18 36	19 36	20 36	22 36
Burton Joyce	d			16 39	17 39	18 39	19 39	20 39	22 39
Lowdham	d			16 43	17 43	18 43	19 43	20 43	22 43
Thurgarton	d			16 47	17 47	18 47	19 47	20 47	22 47
Bleasby	d			16 50	17 50	18 50	19 50	20 50	22 50
Fiskerton	d			16 54	17 54	18 54	19 54	20 54	22 54
Rolleston	d			16 56	17 56	18 56	19 56	20 56	22 56
Newark Castle	d			17 02	18 03	19 02	20 02	21 02	23 02
Newark North Gate 7	a			17 12		19 13		21 12	23 13
London Kings Cross 15	⊖ d								
Newark North Gate 7	d	11 34	13 34	17 17		19 17		21 15	23 18
Collingham	d			17 26	18 13	19 26	20 11	21 24	23 27
Swinderby	d			17 30	18 17	19 30	20 16	21 29	23 32
Hykeham	d			17 36	18 23	19 36	20 22	21 35	23 38
Lincoln	a	11 56	13 56	17 51	18 37	19 50	20 37	21 49	23 52
	d								
Market Rasen	d								
Barnetby	a								
Habrough	a								
Grimsby Town	a								
Cleethorpes	a								

For general notes see front of timetable
For details of catering facilities see Directory of Train Operators

A From Leicester (Table 53)
B From Leicester (Table 53) to Sleaford (Table 18)

Hull and Cleethorpes → Doncaster → Meadowhall, Sheffield, Manchester and Manchester Airport
Cleethorpes → Barton-on-Humber

Network Diagram - see first page of Table 18

Miles	Miles	Miles	Miles	Miles			NT	TP	NT	NT	NT	NT	NT	NT	TP	TP	EM	NT	XC	NT		NT	NT	NT
								1◊							1◊	1◊	1◊		1◊					
							A		B		C	D			E		G H	J	K	L		N		C
0	0	—	—	—	**Hull**	d							05 20		06 00								06 07	
4¾	4¾	—	—	—	Hessle	d																	06 14	
7½	7½	—	—	—	Ferriby	d																	06 19	
10½	10½	—	—	—	Brough	d							05 32		06 12								06 24	
14½	14½	—	—	—	Broomfleet	d																		
17	17	—	—	—	Gilberdyke	d									06 20								06 32	
—	19¼	—	—	—	Eastrington	d																		
—	22¼	—	—	—	Howden	d									06 27									
—	25	—	—	—	Wressle	d																		
—	31	—	—	—	**Selby**	a									06 36									
—	—	—	—	—		d								06 18	06 38									
—	—	—	—	—	York 8	33 a									07 20									
20¾	—	—	—	—	Saltmarshe	d																	06 38	
23¾	—	—	—	—	Goole	d							05 47										06 43	
31	—	—	—	—	Thorne North	d							05 56										06 51	
—	—	0	0	—	**Cleethorpes**	d										05 18								
—	—	1½	1½	—	New Clee	d																		
—	—	2¼	2¼	—	Grimsby Docks	d																		
—	—	3¼	3¼	—	**Grimsby Town**	a										05 25								
—	—	—	—	—		d										05 26								
—	—	5¼	5¼	—	Great Coates	d																		
—	—	6¼	6¼	—	Healing	d																		
—	—	7½	7½	—	Stallingborough	d																		
—	—	11¼	11¼	—	Habrough	d										05 36								
—	—	—	13	—	Ulceby	d																		
—	—	—	15¾	—	Thornton Abbey	d																		
—	—	—	17¼	—	Goxhill	d																		
—	—	—	19¼	—	New Holland	d																		
—	—	—	20¾	—	Barrow Haven	d																		
—	—	—	22¾	—	**Barton-on-Humber**	a																		
—	—	—	—	—	Barton-on-Humber	🚌 d																		
—	—	—	—	—	Hull Bus Station	🚌 a																		
—	—	17¾	—	—	Barnetby	d										05 45								
—	—	29	—	—	**Scunthorpe**	a										06 00								
—	—	—	—	—		d										06 00								
—	—	32½	—	—	Althorpe	d										06 06								
—	—	36¼	—	—	Crowle	d										06 12								
—	—	42¼	—	—	Thorne South	d										06 20								
34¼	—	45¼	—	—	Hatfield & Stainforth	d							06 03			06 25							06 57	
37	—	48	—	—	Kirk Sandall	d							06 10										07 02	
—	—	—	—	0	Adwick	31 d																		
—	—	—	—	2¼	Bentley (S.Yorks)	31 d																		
41	49¼	52	—	4	**Doncaster 7**	31 a							06 21	06 38		06 38							07 12	
—	—	—	—	—	London Kings Cross 15	⊖ 26 a										08 41							09 06	
—	—	—	—	—	York 8	26 d							05 50						06 16			06 30		
—	—	—	—	—	**Doncaster 7**	d		05 42		06 00			06 25			06 40	06 45					07 02		
45¾	—	—	—	—	Conisbrough	d				06 07			06 32									07 09		
48	—	—	—	—	Mexborough	d				06 11			06 36									07 13		
49½	—	—	—	—	Swinton (S.Yorks)	d				06 14	06 22		06 39									07 16		07 29
53¾	—	—	—	—	Rotherham Central	d				06 22	06 31		06 46									07 27		07 41
56½	—	—	—	—	**Meadowhall**	🚋 d	05 39	06 00	06 13	06 27	06 37	06 49	06 52			06 59		07 04		07 19		07 33		07 47
60	—	—	—	—	**Sheffield 7**	🚋 a	05 49	06 08	06 24	06 38	06 47	06 57	07 03			07 07	07 09	07 14	07 20	07 29		07 40		07 57
—	—	—	—	—		d		06 11								07 10								
96¾	—	—	—	—	Stockport	78 a		06 53							08b24	07 55				08 26				
102¾	—	—	—	—	**Manchester Piccadilly 10**	78 🚋 a		07 05							08 05	08 08				08 36				
112½	—	—	—	—	**Manchester Airport**	85 ✈ a		07 35							08 42	08 33				09c06				

For general notes see front of timetable
For details of catering facilities see Directory of Train Operators

- **A** From Barnsley (Table 34) to Retford (Table 30)
- **B** From Barnsley (Table 34)
- **C** From Leeds (Table 31)
- **D** From Wakefield Kirkgate (Table 34)
- **E** To Liverpool Lime Street (Table 39)
- **G** From Leeds to St Pancras International (Table 53)
- **H** **The Master Cutler**
- **J** From Leeds (Table 34)
- **K** To Bristol Temple Meads (Table 51)
- **L** From Huddersfield (Table 34)
- **N** To Worksop (Table 30)
- **b** Change at Manchester Piccadilly
- **c** Change at Sheffield and Manchester Piccadilly

Hull and Cleethorpes → Doncaster → Meadowhall, Sheffield, Manchester and Manchester Airport
Cleethorpes → Barton-on-Humber

Network Diagram - see first page of Table 18

	EM	NT	NT	NT	HT	TP	TP	NT	NT	NT	XC	GR	EM		NT	NT	NT	EM	NT	XC	NT	EM	NT
					BHX 1 ◇	1 ◇	1 ◇				R 1	R 1	1 ◇					1 ◇		1			
	A	B		bus				B			C	D	E		G	H		J	B	K		A	L
					⊠ ☕	trolley	trolley				☕	✕ trolley	☕					☕		☕			
Hull d					06 25	06 35				06 40		07 00											07 07
Hessle d										06 47													
Ferriby d										06 52													
Brough d					06 37	06 47				06 57		07 12											07 19
Broomfleet d																							07 26
Gilberdyke d										07 04													07 31
Eastrington d																							07 35
Howden d					06 49																		07 40
Wressle d																							07 48
Selby a					06 59	07 07						07 32											07 48
d					07 00	07 08						07 32											07 48
York 8 33 a																							08 22
Saltmarshe d										07 10													
Goole d										07 15													
Thorne North d										07 24													
Cleethorpes d	05 51		06 00				06 18																
New Clee d																							
Grimsby Docks d																							
Grimsby Town a	05 57		06 08				06 25																
d	05 58		06 08				06 26															07 03	
Great Coates d																							
Healing d			06 15																				
Stallingborough d			06 18																			07 13	
Habrough d	06 08		06 24				06 36																
Ulceby d			06 28																				
Thornton Abbey d																							
Goxhill d			06 35																				
New Holland d			06 40																				
Barrow Haven d			06 43																				
Barton-on-Humber a			06 48																				
Barton-on-Humber bus d				06 53																			
Hull Bus Station bus a				07 18																			
Barnetby d	06a17						06 45															07a22	
Scunthorpe a							07 00																
d							07 00								07 34								
Althorpe d															07 39								
Crowle d															07 45								
Thorne South d															07 53								
Hatfield & Stainforth d										07 30					07 59								
Kirk Sandall d										07 34					08 03								
Adwick 31 d							*06 53*		07 29												08 07		
Bentley (S.Yorks) 31 d							*06 57*		07 33												08 11		
Doncaster 7 31 a					07 16		07 33		07 37	07 45		07 53			08 13						08 15		
London Kings Cross 15 ⊖ 26 a					09b18							09 45									*10 25*		
York 8 26 d											07 27									07 44			
Doncaster 7 d							07 35		07 39	07 46	07 52		07 59								08 17		
Conisbrough d									07 46	07 53											08 24		
Mexborough d									07 50	07 57							←				08 28		
Swinton (S.Yorks) d									07 53	08 00							08 00				08 31		
Rotherham Central d									08 01	→							08c15				08 41		
Meadowhall tram d		07 48					07 53	08 03	08 07							08 17	08 22	08 24	08 34		08 49		
Sheffield 7 tram a		07 59					08 00	08 15	08 16		08 20		08 22			08 28	08 30	08 33	08 45	08 51	08 56		
d							08 05																
Stockport 78 a						*09e01*	08 50											*09 24*					
Manchester Piccadilly 10 78 tram a						08 37	09 01											*09 36*					
Manchester Airport 85 ✈ a						*09 06*	09 33											*10f01*					

For general notes see front of timetable
For details of catering facilities see Directory of Train Operators

- **A** To Newark North Gate (Table 27)
- **B** From Leeds (Table 34)
- **C** From Newcastle to Paignton (Table 51)
- **D** **The Hull Executive**
- **E** From Leeds to St Pancras International (Table 53)
- **G** To Adwick (Table 31)
- **H** From Huddersfield (Table 34)
- **J** From Barnsley to St Pancras International (Table 53)
- **K** From Newcastle to Bournemouth (Table 51)
- **L** From Beverley (Table 43)
- **b** By changing at Doncaster, passengers may arrive at 0906
- **c** Arr. 0811
- **e** Change at Manchester Piccadilly
- **f** Change at Sheffield and Manchester Piccadilly

Table 29

Mondays to Fridays

until 5 September

Hull and Cleethorpes → Doncaster → Meadowhall, Sheffield, Manchester and Manchester Airport
Cleethorpes → Barton-on-Humber

Network Diagram - see first page of Table 18

	NT	NT	TP	NT	TP	NT	NT	NT	XC	NT	NT	NT	XC	NT	NT	HT	NT	NT	TP	TP	NT	NT
			1 ◇		1 ◇				1 ◇				1 ◇			1 ◇			1 ◇	1 ◇		
				A		B	C	D	E	B	G	C	H	D	A			J			D	B
		🚌	♿		♿				⊡				⊡			⊠ ⊡			♿	♿		
Hull d			07 33			07 36				08 04						08 12		08 29	08 38			08 56
Hessle d						07 43												08 36				
Ferriby d						07 48												08 41				
Brough d			07 45			07 53				08 16						08 24		08 46	08 50			09 08
Broomfleet d						07 58																
Gilberdyke d						08 03																
Eastrington d																		08 53				
Howden d			07 56													08 36						
Wressle d																						
Selby a			08 06													08 45			09 08			
d			08 07													08 45			09 09			
York 8 33 a																			*09 48*			
Saltmarshe d						08 08																
Goole d						08 13				08 30								09 02				09 22
Thorne North d						08 22												09 10				
Cleethorpes d	07 00				07 18															08 28		
New Clee d																						
Grimsby Docks d	07 05																					
Grimsby Town a	07 07				07 25															08 35		
d	07 08				07 26															08 36		
Great Coates d	07 12																					
Healing d	07 15																					
Stallingborough d	07 18																					
Habrough d	07 24				07 36															08 46		
Ulceby d	07 28																					
Thornton Abbey d	07 32																					
Goxhill d	07 35																					
New Holland d	07 40																					
Barrow Haven d	07 43																					
Barton-on-Humber a	07 48																					
Barton-on-Humber 🚌 d		07 53																				
Hull Bus Station 🚌 a		08 18																				
Barnetby d					07 45															08 54		
Scunthorpe a					07 59															09 10		
d					08 00		08 10													09 10		
Althorpe d							08 15															
Crowle d							08 21															
Thorne South d							08 30															
Hatfield & Stainforth d						08 28	08 35											09 17				
Kirk Sandall d						08 33	08 39											09 21				
Adwick 31 d					*08 10*				*08b35*													
Bentley (S.Yorks) 31 d					*08 14*				*08b39*								09 13					
Doncaster 7 31 a					08 30	08 43	08 50			08 56						09 02	09 17					
																	09 22	09 31		09 40		09 46
London Kings Cross 15 ⊖ 26 a										*11 15*						10 51	*11 27*					
York 8 26 d									08 27			⟵	08 44				*08 51*					
Doncaster 7 d					08 42		09 01 ⟶		08 51	08 57		09 01					09 24			09 42		09 49
Conisbrough d												09 08					09 31					
Mexborough d												09 12					09 35					
Swinton (S.Yorks) d				08 34								09 15			09 35		09 42					
Rotherham Central d				08 47								09 27			09 44		09 50					
Meadowhall 🚊 d				08 53	09 00			09 03		09 15	09 21	09 33		09 49	09 51		09 56			10 00	10 03	10 07
Sheffield 7 🚊 a				09 02	09 07			09 15	09 20	09 27	09 30	09 41	09 51	09 57	10 02		10 04			10 07	10 15	10 18
d					09 11															10 11		
Stockport 78 a			*10c03*		09 53						*10 24*								*11c02*	10 53		
Manchester Piccadilly 10 78 🚊 a			09 37		10 03						*10 36*								10 35	11 03		
Manchester Airport 85 ✈ a			*10 01*		10 33						*11e01*								*11 01*	11 33		

For general notes see front of timetable
For details of catering facilities see Directory of Train Operators

- **A** From Leeds (Table 31)
- **B** From Bridlington (Table 43)
- **C** To Lincoln (Table 30)
- **D** From Leeds (Table 34)
- **E** From Newcastle to Bristol Temple Meads (Table 51)
- **G** From Huddersfield (Table 34)
- **H** From Edinburgh to Plymouth (Table 51)
- **J** From Scarborough (Table 43)
- **b** Change at Doncaster
- **c** Change at Manchester Piccadilly
- **e** Change at Sheffield and Manchester Piccadilly

Hull and Cleethorpes → Doncaster → Meadowhall, Sheffield, Manchester and Manchester Airport Cleethorpes → Barton-on-Humber

Network Diagram - see first page of Table 18

	XC 1 ◇ A		NT B	NT C	XC 1 D	NT	NT 🚌	NT	NT E	NT G	NT	NT H	EM J	TP 1 ◇	TP 1 ◇	NT E		NT K	XC 1 ◇ L	NT B	NT C	XC 1 ◇ N	NT E
	🍴				🍴									🛒	🛒				🍴			🍴	
Hull d								09 02				09 25		09 38				09 56					
Hessle d												09 32											
Ferriby d												09 37											
Brough d								09 14				09 42		09 50				10 08					
Broomfleet d																							
Gilberdyke d								09 21				09 49											
Eastrington d																							
Howden d								09 28															
Wressle d																							
Selby a								09 38						10 08									
d								09 38						10 09									
York 8 33 a								10 07															
Saltmarshe d																							
Goole d												09 58						10 22					
Thorne North d												10 06											
Cleethorpes d						09 00									09 28								
New Clee d						09x03																	
Grimsby Docks d						09 05																	
Grimsby Town a						09 08									09 35								
d						09 08							09 28		09 36								
Great Coates d						09 12																	
Healing d						09 15																	
Stallingborough d						09 18																	
Habrough d						09 24							09 38										
Ulceby d						09 28																	
Thornton Abbey d						09 32																	
Goxhill d						09 35																	
New Holland d						09 40																	
Barrow Haven d						09 43																	
Barton-on-Humber a						09 48																	
Barton-on-Humber 🚌 d							09 53																
Hull Bus Station 🚌 a							10 18																
Barnetby d													09a47		09 54								
Scunthorpe a															10 10								
d				09 17											10 10						10 18		
Althorpe d				09 22																	10 23		
Crowle d				09 29																	10 29		
Thorne South d				09 37																	10 38		
Hatfield & Stainforth d				09 42								10 12									10 43		
Kirk Sandall d				09 47								10 17									10 47		
Adwick 31 d											10 13												
Bentley (S.Yorks) 31 d											10 17												
Doncaster 7 31 a				09 57							10 22	10 27			10 40			10 45			10 58		
London Kings Cross 15 ⊖ 26 a				11 51							12 17	12 25						12 42					
York 8 26 d	09 27				09 44						09 35				10 06				10 34		10 29	10 44	
Doncaster 7 d	09 56			10 02							10 24				10 42			10 48	10 58		11 02		
Conisbrough d				10 09							10 31										11 09		
Mexborough d				10 13							10 35										11 13		
Swinton (S.Yorks) d				10 16						10 34	10b41										11 16		
Rotherham Central d				10 27						10 44	10 49										11 27		
Meadowhall 🚋 d			10 19	10 33					10 49	10 51	10 55				11 00	11 04		11 07		11 19	11 33		11 49
Sheffield 7 🚋 a	10 20		10 30	10 41	10 51				10 57	11 02	11 05				11 07	11 15		11 17	11 20	11 30	11 41	11 51	11 57
d															11 11								
Stockport 78 a			11 24											12c02	11 53					12 24			
Manchester Piccadilly 10 78 🚋 a			11 36											11 35	12 03					12 36			
Manchester Airport 85 ✈ a			12e01											12 01	12 33					13e01			

For general notes see front of timetable
For details of catering facilities see Directory of Train Operators

A From Newcastle to Paignton (Table 51)
B From Huddersfield (Table 34)
C To Lincoln (Table 30)
D From Glasgow Central to Bournemouth (Table 51)
E From Leeds (Table 34)
G From Leeds (Table 31)
H From Beverley (Table 43)
J To Newark North Gate (Table 27)
K From Bridlington (Table 43)
L From Newcastle to Bristol Temple Meads (Table 51)
N From Dundee (Table 229) to Plymouth (Table 51)
b Arr. 1038
c Change at Manchester Piccadilly
e Change at Sheffield and Manchester Piccadilly

Table 29

Mondays to Fridays
until 5 September

Hull and Cleethorpes → Doncaster → Meadowhall, Sheffield, Manchester and Manchester Airport
Cleethorpes → Barton-on-Humber

Network Diagram - see first page of Table 18

Station		NT	HT	NT	NT	TP	NT	TP	NT	XC	NT		NT	NT	NT	NT	XC	NT	NT	NT	NT	NT	EM	TP
			1 ◇			1 ◇		1 ◇		R 1							1							1 ◇
		A					B		C	D	E		G	H			J		B	A			K	
			⊠ 🍽			trolley		trolley		🍽						bus	🍽							trolley
Hull	d		10 12		10 22			10 38	10 57									11 05				11 22		11 38
Hessle	d				10 32																	11 29		
Ferriby	d				10 37																	11 34		
Brough	d		10 24		10 42			10 50	11 09									11 18				11 39		11 50
Broomfleet	d																							
Gilberdyke	d				10 49																			
Eastrington	d																					11 46		
Howden	d		10 36																					
Wressle	d																							
Selby	a		10 46					11 08										11 38						12 08
	d		10 47					11 09										11 39						12 09
York 8	33 a		*11 20*															12 10						*13 15*
Saltmarshe	d																					11 52		
Goole	d				10 58				11 23													11 58		
Thorne North	d				11 06																	12 06		
Cleethorpes	d					10 28									11 00									
New Clee	d														11x03									
Grimsby Docks	d														11 05									
Grimsby Town	a					10 35									11 08									
	d					10 36									11 08								11 28	
Great Coates	d														11 12									
Healing	d														11 15									
Stallingborough	d														11 18									
Habrough	d					10 46									11 24								11 38	
Ulceby	d														11 28									
Thornton Abbey	d														11 32									
Goxhill	d														11 35									
New Holland	d														11 40									
Barrow Haven	d														11 43									
Barton-on-Humber	a														11 48									
Barton-on-Humber (bus)	d															11 53								
Hull Bus Station (bus)	a															12 18								
Barnetby	d					10 54																	11a47	
Scunthorpe	a					11 10																		
	d					11 10								11 17										
Althorpe	d													11 22										
Crowle	d													11 28										
Thorne South	d													11 37										
Hatfield & Stainforth	d				11 12									11 42								12 12		
Kirk Sandall	d				11 17									11 46								12 17		
Adwick	31 d			11 16																	12 15			
Bentley (S.Yorks)	31 d			11 20																	12 19			
Doncaster 7	31 a		11 04	11 25	11 27	11 40			11 46					11 58							12 24	12 27		
London Kings Cross 15	⊖ 26 a		12 44		*13 22*				*13 43*					*14 02*								*14 20*		
York 8	26 d									11 27	11 03						11 44				*11 35*			
Doncaster 7	d			11 27		11 42			11 48	11 54				11 58							12 26			
Conisbrough	d			11 34										12 06							12 33			
Mexborough	d			11 38										12 10							12 37			
Swinton (S.Yorks)	d	11 34		11 41							12 02			12 16						12 34	12 42			
Rotherham Central	d	11 45		11 50							12 11			12 27						12 45	12 50			
Meadowhall	d	11 51		11 56		12 00	12 03		12 06		12 16		12 19	12 33					12 49	12 51	12 56			
Sheffield 7	a	12 02		12 05		12 07	12 15		12 18	12 20	12 26		12 30	12 41			12 51		12 57	13 02	13 06			
	d					12 11																		
Stockport	78 a					12 53		*13b01*					*13 24*											*14b02*
Manchester Piccadilly 10	78 a			*13 31*		13 03		12 35					*13 36*											13 35
Manchester Airport	85 ✈ a					13 33		*13 01*					*14c01*											*14 01*

For general notes see front of timetable
For details of catering facilities see Directory of Train Operators

- **A** From Leeds (Table 31)
- **B** From Leeds (Table 34)
- **C** From Bridlington (Table 43)
- **D** From Newcastle to Plymouth (Table 51)
- **E** Via Pontefract Baghill (Table 33)
- **G** From Huddersfield (Table 34)
- **H** To Lincoln (Table 30)
- **J** From Dundee (Table 229) to Bournemouth (Table 51)
- **K** To Newark North Gate (Table 27)
- **b** Change at Manchester Piccadilly
- **c** Change at Sheffield and Manchester Piccadilly

Table 29

Mondays to Fridays
until 5 September

Hull and Cleethorpes → Doncaster → Meadowhall, Sheffield, Manchester and Manchester Airport
Cleethorpes → Barton-on-Humber

Network Diagram - see first page of Table 18

		TP	NT	NT	XC		NT	NT	XC	NT	NT	NT	NT	TP	HT	TP	NT	NT	XC	NT		NT	XC	NT
		1 ◇			1 ◇				R 1					1 ◇	1 ◇	1 ◇			1 ◇				R 1	
			A	B	C		D	E	G	A	H						A	J	K	D		E	L	
		⊼			☕				☕					⊼	⊠ ☕	⊼			☕				☕	
Hull	d			11 55									12 22	12 38	12 45			12 57						
Hessle	d												12 29											
Ferriby	d												12 34											
Brough	d			12 07									12 39	12 50	12 57			13 09						
Broomfleet	d												12 44											
Gilberdyke	d												12 49											
Eastrington	d																							
Howden	d														13 09									
Wressle	d																							
Selby	a													13 08	13 19									
	d													13 09	13 20									
York 8	33 a																							
Saltmarshe	d																							
Goole	d			12 22									12 58					13 23						
Thorne North	d												13 06											
Cleethorpes	d	11 28														12 28								13 00
New Clee	d																							13x03
Grimsby Docks	d																							13 05
Grimsby Town	a	11 35														12 35								13 08
	d	11 36														12 36								13 08
Great Coates	d																							13 12
Healing	d																							13 15
Stallingborough	d																							13 18
Habrough	d																							13 24
Ulceby	d																							13 28
Thornton Abbey	d																							13 32
Goxhill	d																							13 35
New Holland	d																							13 40
Barrow Haven	d																							13 43
Barton-on-Humber	a																							13 48
Barton-on-Humber	🚌 d																							
Hull Bus Station	🚌 a																							
Barnetby	d	11 54														12 54								
Scunthorpe	a	12 09														13 10								
	d	12 10						12 17								13 10						13 18		
Althorpe	d							12 22														13 23		
Crowle	d							12 28														13 29		
Thorne South	d							12 37														13 38		
Hatfield & Stainforth	d							12 42					13 14									13 43		
Kirk Sandall	d							12 46					13 19									13 47		
Adwick	31 d											13 11												
Bentley (S.Yorks)	31 d											13 15												
Doncaster 7	31 a	12 40		12 46				12 57				13 20	13 29		13 37	13 40		13 46				13 58		
London Kings Cross 15	⊖ 26 a			*14 44*				*15 05*							15 20			*15 44*				*15 58*		
York 8	26 d				12 25			*12 31*	12 44							*12 31*			13 29				13 44	
Doncaster 7	d	12 42		12 48	12 55			13 02				13 24				13 42		13 48	13 54			14 01		
Conisbrough	d							13 09				13 31										14 08		
Mexborough	d							13 13				13 35										14 12		
Swinton (S.Yorks)	d							13 16			13 34	13 42										14 16		
Rotherham Central	d							13 27			13 45	13 50										14 27		
Meadowhall	🚋 d	13 00	13 03	13 07			13 21	13 33		13 49	13 51	13 56				14 00	14 03	14 06		14 19		14 33		
Sheffield 7	🚋 a	13 07	13 15	13 17	13 20		13 31	13 41	13 51	13 57	14 02	14 04				14 07	14 15	14 17	14 20	14 30		14 41	14 51	
	d	13 11														14 11								
Stockport	78 a	13 53					*14 24*							*15b01*		14 53				*15 24*				
Manchester Piccadilly 10	78 🚋 a	14 03					*14 36*							14 35		15 03				*15 36*				
Manchester Airport	85 ✈ a	14 33					*15c01*							*15 01*		15 33				*16c01*				

For general notes see front of timetable
For details of catering facilities see Directory of Train Operators

A From Leeds (Table 34)
B From Bridlington (Table 43)
C From Newcastle to Bristol Temple Meads (Table 51)
D From Huddersfield (Table 34)
E To Lincoln (Table 30)
G From Glasgow Central (Table 51) to Penzance (Table 135)
H From Leeds (Table 31)
J From Scarborough (Table 43)
K From Newcastle to Plymouth (Table 51)
L From Aberdeen (Table 229) to Bournemouth (Table 51)
b Change at Manchester Piccadilly
c Change at Sheffield and Manchester Piccadilly

Table 29

Mondays to Fridays

until 5 September

Hull and Cleethorpes → Doncaster → Meadowhall, Sheffield, Manchester and Manchester Airport
Cleethorpes → Barton-on-Humber

Network Diagram - see first page of Table 18

		NT	NT	NT	NT	NT	NT	TP	TP	NT	NT	XC	EM	NT		NT	XC	NT	NT	NT	NT	TP	TP	NT
								1 ◇	1 ◇			1 ◇					R 1					1 ◇	1 ◇	
				A	B					A	C	D	E	G		H	J	A	B					A
		[bus]						[trolley]	[trolley]			[restaurant]					[restaurant]					[trolley]	[trolley]	
Hull	d		13 12				13 25	13 38			13 57										14 25	14 38		
Hessle	d						13 32														14 32			
Ferriby	d						13 37														14 37			
Brough	d		13 24				13 42	13 50			14 09										14 42	14 50		
Broomfleet	d																							
Gilberdyke	d		13 31				13 49														14 49			
Eastrington	d		13 36																					
Howden	d		13 40																					
Wressle	d		13 45																					
Selby	a		13 55					14 08														15 08		
	d		13 56					14 09														15 09		
York 8	33 a		14 27																					
Saltmarshe	d																							
Goole	d						13 58				14 23										14 58			
Thorne North	d						14 06														15 06			
Cleethorpes	d								13 28														14 28	
New Clee	d																							
Grimsby Docks	d																							
Grimsby Town	a								13 36														14 35	
	d								13 36				13 52										14 36	
Great Coates	d																							
Healing	d																							
Stallingborough	d																							
Habrough	d												14 02										14 46	
Ulceby	d																							
Thornton Abbey	d																							
Goxhill	d																							
New Holland	d																							
Barrow Haven	d																							
Barton-on-Humber	a																							
Barton-on-Humber	[bus] d	13 53																						
Hull Bus Station	[bus] a	14 18																						
Barnetby	d								13 54				14a11										14 54	
Scunthorpe	a								14 10														15 10	
	d								14 10							14 18							15 10	
Althorpe	d															14 23								
Crowle	d															14 29								
Thorne South	d															14 38								
Hatfield & Stainforth	d						14 14									14 43					15 12			
Kirk Sandall	d						14 18									14 47					15 17			
Adwick	31 d					14 18														15 13				
Bentley (S.Yorks)	31 d					14 22														15 17				
Doncaster 7	31 a					14 26	14 29		14 40		14 46					14 58				15 22	15 27		15 40	
London Kings Cross 15	⊖ 26 a								*16 46*							*17 04*					*17 30*			
York 8	26 d					*13 36*						*14 32*					*14 44*						*15 11*	
Doncaster 7	d					14 28			14 42		14 48	14 57				15 02				15 25			15 42	
Conisbrough	d					14 35										15 09				15 32				
Mexborough	d					14 39										15 13				15 36				
Swinton (S.Yorks)	d				14 34	14 42										15 16			15 34	15 42				
Rotherham Central	d				14 45	14 50										15 27			15 43	15 50				
Meadowhall	[tram] d			14 49	14 51	14 56			15 00	15 03	15 06			15 19		15 33		15 49	15 51	15 56			16 00	16 06
Sheffield 7	[tram] a			14 57	15 02	15 06			15 07	15 15	15 18	15 20		15 30		15 41	15 51	15 57	16 02	16 04			16 07	16 15
	d								15 11														16 11	
Stockport	78 a							*16b02*	15 53					*16 24*								*17b00*	16 53	
Manchester Piccadilly 10	78 [tram] a							15 35	16 03					*16 35*								16 35	17 03	
Manchester Airport	85 [plane] a							*16 01*	16 33					*17c14*								*17 14*	17 39	

For general notes see front of timetable
For details of catering facilities see Directory of Train Operators

A From Leeds (Table 34)
B From Leeds (Table 31)
C From Bridlington (Table 43)
D From Newcastle to Bristol Temple Meads (Table 51)
E To Newark North Gate (Table 27)
G From Huddersfield (Table 34)
H To Lincoln (Table 30)
J From Edinburgh to Plymouth (Table 51)
b Change at Manchester Piccadilly
c Change at Sheffield and Manchester Piccadilly

Table 29 — Mondays to Fridays

until 5 September

Hull and Cleethorpes → Doncaster → Meadowhall, Sheffield, Manchester and Manchester Airport
Cleethorpes → Barton-on-Humber

Network Diagram - see first page of Table 18

Station		NT	XC	NT	NT	NT	XC	NT		NT	NT	NT	NT	HT	NT	NT	TP	TP	NT	NT	XC	NT	NT	XC
			R 1				R 1						bus	1 ◇			1 ◇	1 ◇			R 1			1 ◇
		A	B	C	D	E	G			H	J								H	K	L	D	E	N
Hull	d	14 57						15 06						15 18		15 21	15 38			15 57				
Hessle	d															15 28								
Ferriby	d															15 33								
Brough	d	15 09						15 18						15 30		15 38	15 50			16 09				
Broomfleet	d																							
Gilberdyke	d															15 45								
Eastrington	d																							
Howden	d													15 42										
Wressle	d																							
Selby	a							15 37						15 56			16 08							
	d							15 38						15 57			16 09							
York 8	33 a							16 06																
Saltmarshe	d																							
Goole	d	15 23														15 58				16 23				
Thorne North	d															16 06								
Cleethorpes	d											15 00						15 28						
New Clee	d											15x03												
Grimsby Docks	d											15 05												
Grimsby Town	a											15 08						15 35						
	d											15 09						15 36						
Great Coates	d											15 13												
Healing	d											15 16												
Stallingborough	d											15 19												
Habrough	d											15 25												
Ulceby	d											15 28												
Thornton Abbey	d											15 33												
Goxhill	d											15 36												
New Holland	d											15 40												
Barrow Haven	d											15 43												
Barton-on-Humber	a											15 49												
Barton-on-Humber	bus d												15 56											
Hull Bus Station	bus a												16 21											
Barnetby	d																	15 54						
Scunthorpe	a																	16 10						
	d					15 18												16 10					16 18	
Althorpe	d					15 23																	16 23	
Crowle	d					15 29																	16 29	
Thorne South	d					15 38																	16 38	
Hatfield & Stainforth	d					15 43										16 12							16 43	
Kirk Sandall	d					15 47										16 17							16 47	
Adwick	31 d														16 14									
Bentley (S.Yorks)	31 d														16 18									
Doncaster 7	31 a	15 46				15 58								16 15	16 22	16 27		16 40		16 46			16 58	
London Kings Cross 15	⊖ 26 a	*17 41*												18 12		*18 23*							*18 54*	
York 8	26 d		15 29	15 02			15 44								*15 35*						16 25			16 44
Doncaster 7	d	15 48	15 55			16 02									16 24			16 42		16 47	16 53		17 00	
Conisbrough	d					16 09									16 31								17 09	
Mexborough	d					16 13									16 35								17 13	
Swinton (S.Yorks)	d			16 01		16 16					16 34				16 42								17 16	
Rotherham Central	d			16 10		16 27					16 43				16 50								17 27	
Meadowhall	d	16 09		16 18	16 19	16 33				16 49	16 51				16 56			17 00	17 03	17 07		17 19	17 33	
Sheffield 7	a	16 17	16 20	16 25	16 30	16 41	16 51			16 57	17 02				17 04			17 07	17 15	17 17	17 18	17 30	17 41	17 51
	d																	17 11						
Stockport	78 a				*17 25*												*17b59*	17 53				*18 26*		
Manchester Piccadilly 10	78 a				*17 36*												17 35	18 03				*18 36*		
Manchester Airport	85 a				*18c05*												*18 05*	18 38				*19c09*		

For general notes see front of timetable
For details of catering facilities see Directory of Train Operators

- **A** From Scarborough (Table 43)
- **B** From Newcastle to Cardiff Central (Table 51)
- **C** Via Pontefract Baghill (Table 33)
- **D** From Huddersfield (Table 34)
- **E** To Lincoln (Table 30)
- **G** From Edinburgh to Bournemouth (Table 51)
- **H** From Leeds (Table 34)
- **J** From Leeds (Table 31)
- **K** From Bridlington (Table 43)
- **L** From Newcastle to Weston-super-Mare (Table 51)
- **N** From Edinburgh to Plymouth (Table 51)
- **b** Change at Manchester Piccadilly
- **c** Change at Sheffield and Manchester Piccadilly

Hull and Cleethorpes → Doncaster → Meadowhall, Sheffield, Manchester and Manchester Airport
Cleethorpes → Barton-on-Humber

Network Diagram - see first page of Table 18

		NT		EM	NT	NT	NT	NT	TP	TP	NT	NT	XC	NT	NT	NT	NT		TP	XC	NT	NT	HT	NT
									1 ◇	1 ◇			R 1						1 ◇	R 1			1 ◇	
				A	B	C		D			B	E	G	H					J	K	B	C		
									(trolley)	(trolley)			(buffet)				(bus)			(buffet)			⊠ (buffet)	
Hull	d	16 10						16 27	16 38			16 54							17 01				17 06	
Hessle	d							16 34																
Ferriby	d							16 39																
Brough	d	16 22						16 44	16 50			17 06							17 13				17 19	
Broomfleet	d							16 49																
Gilberdyke	d	16 29						16 54				17 13												
Eastrington	d																							
Howden	d	16 36																					17 32	
Wressle	d																							
Selby	a	16 46							17 08										17 31				17 42	
	d	16 47							17 09														17 43	
York 8	33 a	17 13																						
Saltmarshe	d							16 59																
Goole	d							17 04				17 22												
Thorne North	d							17 13																
Cleethorpes	d									16 28						17 00								
New Clee	d																							
Grimsby Docks	d															17 05								
Grimsby Town	a									16 35						17 07								
	d			16 03						16 36						17 08								
Great Coates	d															17 12								
Healing	d															17 15								
Stallingborough	d															17 18								
Habrough	d			16 12												17 24								
Ulceby	d															17 28								
Thornton Abbey	d															17 32								
Goxhill	d															17 35								
New Holland	d															17 40								
Barrow Haven	d															17 43								
Barton-on-Humber	a															17 48								
Barton-on-Humber	(bus) d																17 57							
Hull Bus Station	(bus) a																18 23							
Barnetby	d			16a21						16 54														
Scunthorpe	a									17 10														
	d									17 10					17 18									
Althorpe	d														17 23									
Crowle	d														17 29									
Thorne South	d														17 38									
Hatfield & Stainforth	d							17 19							17 43									
Kirk Sandall	d							17 23							17 47									
Adwick	31 d						16 54			17 09														17 53
Bentley (S.Yorks)	31 d						16 58			17 14														17 57
Doncaster 7	31 a							17 34		17 40		17 47			17 58								18 01	
London Kings Cross 15	⊖ 26 a														19 59								19 47	
York 8	26 d									16 56			17 34							17 44				
Doncaster 7	d						17 24			17 42		17 49	17 58		18 02									18 26
Conisbrough	d						17 31								18 09									18 33
Mexborough	d						17 35								18 13									18 37
Swinton (S.Yorks)	d					17 34	17 42								18 16							18 32		18 42
Rotherham Central	d					17 45	17 50								18 27							18 43		18 49
Meadowhall	(tram) d				17 49	17 51	17 55			18 00	18 04	18 07		18 19	18 33						18 48	18 51		18 56
Sheffield 7	(tram) a				17 57	18 02	18 04			18 07	18 15	18 18	18 20	18 30	18 41					18 51	18 57	19 02		19 05
	d									18 11														
Stockport	78 a								19b02	18 53				19 24										
Manchester Piccadilly 10	78 (tram) a								18 36	19 03				19 36										20 31
Manchester Airport	85 (air) a								19 09	19 34				20c05										21c06

For general notes see front of timetable
For details of catering facilities see Directory of Train Operators

A To Newark North Gate (Table 27)
B From Leeds (Table 34)
C From Leeds (Table 31)
D From Scarborough (Table 43)
E From Beverley (Table 43)
G From Newcastle to Bristol Temple Meads (Table 51)
H From Huddersfield (Table 34)
J To Huddersfield (Table 39)
K From Edinburgh to Southampton Central (Table 51)
b Change at Manchester Piccadilly
c Change at Sheffield and Manchester Piccadilly

Table 29

Mondays to Fridays
until 5 September

Hull and Cleethorpes → Doncaster → Meadowhall, Sheffield, Manchester and Manchester Airport
Cleethorpes → Barton-on-Humber

Network Diagram - see first page of Table 18

		TP	NT	NT	NT	NT	XC	TP	NT	NT	NT		NT	NT	XC	NT	NT	EM	NT	TP	NT	NT	NT	XC
		1 ◇					1 ◇	1 ◇							1 ◇					1 ◇				1 ◇
			A	B	B	C	D		E	B				A	G	A	H	J			A			D
		♁					⊡	♁							⊡					♁				⊡
Hull	d			17 18	17 42	17 56		18 03					18 22									18 53		
Hessle	d			17 25	17 49								18 29											
Ferriby	d			17 30	17 54								18 34											
Brough	d			17 35	17 59	18 08		18 15					18 39									19 05		
Broomfleet	d			17 40																				
Gilberdyke	d			17 45	18 06								18 46											
Eastrington	d			17 49																				
Howden	d			17 54																				
Wressle	d			17 58																				
Selby	a			18 06		18 26		18 33																
	d			18 06		18 27		18 34																
York 8	33 a			18 36																				
Saltmarshe	d				18 12					←														
Goole	d				18b20 →					18 20			18 55									19 19		
Thorne North	d									18 28			19 03											
Cleethorpes	d	17 28																		18 28				
New Clee	d																							
Grimsby Docks	d																							
Grimsby Town	a	17 35																		18 35				
	d	17 36																18 30		18 36				
Great Coates	d																							
Healing	d																							
Stallingborough	d																							
Habrough	d	17 46																18 40		18 46				
Ulceby	d																							
Thornton Abbey	d																							
Goxhill	d																							
New Holland	d																							
Barrow Haven	d																							
Barton-on-Humber	a																							
Barton-on-Humber 🚌	d																							
Hull Bus Station 🚌	a																							
Barnetby	d	17 54																18a48		18 54				
Scunthorpe	a	18 10																		19 10				
	d	18 10									18 18									19 10			19 15	
Althorpe	d										18 23												19 20	
Crowle	d										18 29												19 26	
Thorne South	d										18 38												19 34	
Hatfield & Stainforth	d									18 34	18 46		19 12										19 40	
Kirk Sandall	d									18 39	18 50		19 16										19 44	
Adwick	31 d	*18 16*																	*18 53*					
Bentley (S.Yorks)	31 d	*18 20*																	*18 57*					
Doncaster 7	31 a	18 40				18 45				18 50	19 01		19 27							19 40		19 45	19 56	
London Kings Cross 15	⊖ 26 a					*20 42*					*21 03*		*21 20*									*21 44*		
York 8	26 d	*17 55*					*18 24*								*18 44*				*18 30*			*19 13*		*19 29*
Doncaster 7	d	18 42				18 47	18 52			18 55									19 28	19 42		19 49		19 57
Conisbrough	d									19 02									19 35					
Mexborough	d									19 06									19 39					
Swinton (S.Yorks)	d									19 09							19 34		19 43					
Rotherham Central	d									19 19							19 43		19 50					
Meadowhall	🚋 d	19 00	19 04			19 07			19 16	19 25				19 34		19 49	19 52		19 57	20 00	20 04	20 08		
Sheffield 7	🚋 a	19 07	19 15			19 17	19 20		19 30	19 34				19 44	19 51	19 57	20 02		20 06	20 07	20 15	20 18		20 20
	d	19 11																		20 11				
Stockport	78 a	19 52						*20c26*		*20 26*										20 53				*21 17*
Manchester Piccadilly 10	78 🚋 a	20 03						*19 59*		*20 36*										21 03				*21 30*
Manchester Airport	85 ✈ a	20 34						*20 58*		*21e09*										21 34				*22e15*

For general notes see front of timetable
For details of catering facilities see Directory of Train Operators

A From Leeds (Table 34)
B From Beverley (Table 43)
C From Scarborough (Table 43)
D From Newcastle to Birmingham New Street (Table 51)
E From Huddersfield (Table 34)
G From Edinburgh to Bristol Temple Meads (Table 51)
H From Leeds (Table 31)
J To Newark North Gate (Table 27)
b Arr. 1817
c Change at Manchester Piccadilly
e Change at Sheffield and Manchester Piccadilly

Table 29

Mondays to Fridays
until 5 September

Hull and Cleethorpes → Doncaster → Meadowhall, Sheffield, Manchester and Manchester Airport
Cleethorpes → Barton-on-Humber

Network Diagram - see first page of Table 18

	TP	NT	NT	XC		NT	NT	NT	NT	NT	NT	HT	NT	TP	TP	XC	NT	NT	NT		XC	NT	NT
	■1 ◇ A	B	C	■1 ◇ DE 🛒			🚌		G	H	G	BHX ■1 ◇ ⊠ 🛒	J	■1 ◇	■1 ◇ A	■1 ◇ K		B	L		■1 ◇ N		G
Hull d	18 59							19 10				19 18	19 24		19 56				20 03				
Hessle d													19 31						20 10				
Ferriby d													19 36						20 15				
Brough d	19 11							19 22				19 30	19 41		20 08				20 20				
Broomfleet d																							
Gilberdyke d								19 29					19 48						20 27				
Eastrington d																							
Howden d								19 36				19 43											
Wressle d																							
Selby a	19 29							19 46				19 52			20 26								
d								19 47				19 53											
York 8 33 a								20 15							*21 00*								
Saltmarshe d																							
Goole d													19 58						20 36				
Thorne North d													20 06						20 44				
Cleethorpes d						19 00								19 28									
New Clee d																							
Grimsby Docks d						19 05																	
Grimsby Town a						19 07								19 35									
d						19 08								19 36									
Great Coates d						19 12																	
Healing d						19 15																	
Stallingborough d						19 18																	
Habrough d						19 24								19 46									
Ulceby d						19 28																	
Thornton Abbey d						19 32																	
Goxhill d						19 35																	
New Holland d						19 40																	
Barrow Haven d						19 43																	
Barton-on-Humber a						19 48																	
Barton-on-Humber 🚌 d							19 55																
Hull Bus Station 🚌 a							20 20																
Barnetby d														19 54									
Scunthorpe a														20 10									
d														20 10			20 18						
Althorpe d																	20 23						
Crowle d																	20 29						
Thorne South d																	20 38						
Hatfield & Stainforth d													20 14				20 43		20 50				
Kirk Sandall d													20 19				20 47		20 55				
Adwick 31 d														*19 53*								*20 55*	
Bentley (S.Yorks) 31 d														*19 57*								*20 59*	
Doncaster 7 31 a												20 10	20 29	20 40			20 59		21 05				
London Kings Cross 15 ⊖ 26 a												21 59							*23 32*				
York 8 26 d				19 44										*20 08*		20 33					20 44		
Doncaster 7 d			20 03											20 42		20 56			21 07			21 30	
Conisbrough d			20 10											20 48					21 14			21 37	
Mexborough d			20 14											20 52					21 18			21 41	
Swinton (S.Yorks) d			20 17							20 34				20 55					21 21			⟶	
Rotherham Central d			20 28							20 43				21 01					21 28				
Meadowhall 🚊 d		20 24	20 33						20 48	20 51	21 04			21 07				21 24	21 34				21 49
Sheffield 7 🚊 a		20 35	20 41	20 51					20 57	21 02	21 15			21 18		21 30		21 35	21 45		21 51		21 57
d																							
Stockport 78 a																							
Manchester Piccadilly 10 78 🚊 a																							
Manchester Airport 85 ✈ a																							

For general notes see front of timetable
For details of catering facilities see Directory of Train Operators

A To Leeds (Table 39)
B From Huddersfield (Table 34)
C To Worksop (Table 30)
D From Edinburgh to Bristol Temple Meads (Table 51)
E 🛒 to Leeds
G From Leeds (Table 34)
H From Leeds (Table 31)
J From Scarborough (Table 43)
K From Newcastle (Table 26)
L From Bridlington (Table 43)
N From Edinburgh to Birmingham New Street (Table 51)

Hull and Cleethorpes → Doncaster → Meadowhall, Sheffield, Manchester and Manchester Airport Cleethorpes → Barton-on-Humber

Network Diagram - see first page of Table 18

		NT	TP	NT	NT	NT	NT	EM	XC	NT	TP	NT	NT	NT		NT	NT	NT	NT	NT	NT	NT		
						ThFO														FX	FO			
			1 ◇						1 ◇		1 ◇													
		A						B	C			D		E		A		D	E			A		
						Bus																		
Hull	d						20 56				21 33									22 20	22 25			
Hessle	d																			22 27				
Ferriby	d																			22 32				
Brough	d						21 08				21 45									22 37	22 37			
Broomfleet	d																							
Gilberdyke	d										21 52													
Eastrington	d																							
Howden	d																							
Wressle	d																							
Selby	a										22 07													
	d										22 07													
York 8	33 a																							
Saltmarshe	d																							
Goole	d						21 22						21 42							22 51	22 51			
Thorne North	d												21 51							23 00	23 00			
Cleethorpes	d		20 28		21 00			21 14																
New Clee	d																							
Grimsby Docks	d				21 05																			
Grimsby Town	a		20 35		21 07			21 20																
	d		20 36		21 08			21 21																
Great Coates	d				21 12																			
Healing	d				21 15																			
Stallingborough	d				21 18																			
Habrough	d				21 24			21 30																
Ulceby	d				21 27																			
Thornton Abbey	d				21 32																			
Goxhill	d				21 35																			
New Holland	d				21 39																			
Barrow Haven	d				21 42																			
Barton-on-Humber	a				21 48																			
Barton-on-Humber	Bus d					21 55																		
Hull Bus Station	Bus a					22 20																		
Barnetby	d		20 54					21a39																
Scunthorpe	a		21 09																					
	d		21 10							21 26							22 21							
Althorpe	d									21 31							22 26							
Crowle	d									21 37							22 32							
Thorne South	d									21 45							22 41							
Hatfield & Stainforth	d									21 51			21 56				22 46			23 06	23 06			
Kirk Sandall	d									21 55			22 01				22 50			23 10	23 10			
Adwick	31 d																			22 02	22 02			
Bentley (S.Yorks)	31 d																			22 06	22 06			
Doncaster 7	31 a		21 40				21 45			22 06			22 11				23 02			23 21	23 21			
London Kings Cross 15	⊖ 26 a						00 15																	
York 8	26 d								21 24				21 39											
Doncaster 7	d		21 42				21 48						22 13							23 21	23 22			
Conisbrough	d			←									22 20							23 29	23 29			
Mexborough	d			21 41									22 24							23 33	23 33			
Swinton (S.Yorks)	d	21 35		21 44									22 29			22 34				23 36	23 36	23 55		
Rotherham Central	d	21 44		21b55									22 38			22 43				23 45	23 45	00 03		
Meadowhall	d	21 52	22 00	22 04			22 10					22 25	22 44	22 49		22 51		23 26	23 49	23 52	23 52	00 08		
Sheffield 7	a	22 07	22 07	22 12			22 18		22 21			22 35	22 54	22 57		23 02		23 35	23 57	00 01	00 01	00 23		
	d		22 11																					
Stockport	78 a		22 53									23 46												
Manchester Piccadilly 10	78 a		23 03								23 37	23 59												
Manchester Airport	85 a		23 28									00c45												

For general notes see front of timetable
For details of catering facilities see Directory of Train Operators

A From Leeds (Table 31)
B To Lincoln (Table 27)
C From Newcastle to Birmingham New Street (Table 51)
D From Huddersfield (Table 34)
E From Leeds (Table 34)
b Arr. 2151
c Change at Sheffield and Manchester Piccadilly

Hull and Cleethorpes → Doncaster → Meadowhall, Sheffield, Manchester and Manchester Airport
Cleethorpes → Barton-on-Humber

Network Diagram - see first page of Table 18

		NT	TP	NT	NT	NT	NT	NT	EM	NT	TP	TP	NT	XC	NT	NT	NT	NT	EM	NT	NT	NT	HT	TP
			1 ◇						1 ◇		1 ◇	1 ◇		R 1									BHX 1 ◇	1 ◇
		A		B		C	D		E G		H		J	K	L	N		C	Q	J				
									⊠ ☕		☕	☕		☕								🚌	⊠ ☕	☕
Hull	d							05 20			06 00						06 07						06 25	06 35
Hessle	d																06 14							
Ferriby	d																06 19							
Brough	d							05 32			06 12						06 24						06 37	06 47
Broomfleet	d																							
Gilberdyke	d										06 20						06 32							
Eastrington	d																							
Howden	d										06 27												06 49	
Wressle	d																							
Selby	a										06 36												06 59	07 07
	d									06 18	06 38												07 00	07 08
York 8	33 a										*07 20*													
Saltmarshe	d																06 38							
Goole	d							05 47									06 43							
Thorne North	d							05 56									06 51							
Cleethorpes	d											05 18							05 51		06 00			
New Clee	d																							
Grimsby Docks	d																							
Grimsby Town	a											05 25							05 57		06 08			
	d											05 26							05 58		06 08			
Great Coates	d																							
Healing	d																				06 15			
Stallingborough	d																				06 18			
Habrough	d											05 36							06 08		06 24			
Ulceby	d																				06 28			
Thornton Abbey	d																							
Goxhill	d																				06 35			
New Holland	d																				06 40			
Barrow Haven	d																				06 43			
Barton-on-Humber	a																				06 48			
Barton-on-Humber	🚌 d																					06 53		
Hull Bus Station	🚌 a																					07 18		
Barnetby	d											05 45							06a17					
Scunthorpe	a											06 00												
	d											06 00												
Althorpe	d											06 06												
Crowle	d											06 12												
Thorne South	d											06 20												
Hatfield & Stainforth	d							06 03				06 25					06 57							
Kirk Sandall	d							06 10									07 02							
Adwick	31 d																							
Bentley (S.Yorks)	31 d																							
Doncaster 7	31 a							06 21		06 38		06 38					07 12						07 16	
London Kings Cross 15	⊖ 26 a											*08 41*					*09 06*						09b18	
York 8	26 d							*05 50*						06 16		*06 30*								
Doncaster 7	d		05 42		06 00			06 25	06 34			06 40				07 02								
Conisbrough	d				06 07			06 32								07 09								
Mexborough	d				06 11			06 36								07 13								
Swinton (S.Yorks)	d				06 14	06 22		06 39								07 16		07 29						
Rotherham Central	d				06 22	06 31		06 46								07 27		07 41						
Meadowhall	🚋 d	05 39	06 00	06 13	06a27	06 37	06 49	06 52				07 00	07 04		07 19	07 33		07 47		07 48				
Sheffield 7	🚋 a	05 49	06 08	06 24		06 47	06 57	07 03	07 05			07 07	07 14	07 20	07 29	07 40		07 57		07 59				
	d		06 11									07 10												
Stockport	78 a		06 53								*08c24*	07 55			*08 26*									*09c01*
Manchester Piccadilly 10	78 🚋 a		07 05								08 05	08 08			*08 36*									08 37
Manchester Airport	85 ✈ a		07 35								*08 42*	08 33			*09e06*									*09 06*

For general notes see front of timetable
For details of catering facilities see Directory of Train Operators

- **A** From Barnsley (Table 34) to Retford (Table 30)
- **B** From Barnsley (Table 34)
- **C** From Leeds (Table 31)
- **D** From Wakefield Kirkgate (Table 34)
- **E** From Leeds to St Pancras International (Table 53)
- **G** **The Master Cutler**
- **H** To Liverpool Lime Street (Table 39)
- **J** From Leeds (Table 34)
- **K** To Plymouth (Table 51)
- **L** From Huddersfield (Table 34)
- **N** To Worksop (Table 30)
- **Q** To Newark North Gate (Table 27)
- **b** By changing at Doncaster, passengers may arrive at 0906
- **c** Change at Manchester Piccadilly
- **e** Change at Sheffield and Manchester Piccadilly

Table 29

Mondays to Fridays

from 8 September

Hull and Cleethorpes → Doncaster → Meadowhall, Sheffield, Manchester and Manchester Airport
Cleethorpes → Barton-on-Humber

Network Diagram - see first page of Table 18

		TP	NT	NT	NT	XC	NT	NT	NT	XC	GR	NT	NT	EM	NT	NT	NT	TP	NT	TP	NT		NT	EM
		1 ◇				R 1				1 ◇	R 1							1 ◇		1 ◇				1 ◇
			A			B	C		A	D	E	G		H	J				K		L		N	Q
		🛒				☕				☕	✕ 🛒						🚌	🛒		🛒				☕
Hull	d				06 40						07 00				07 07			07 33			07 36			
Hessle	d				06 47																07 43			
Ferriby	d				06 52																07 48			
Brough	d				06 57						07 12				07 19			07 45			07 53			
Broomfleet	d																				07 58			
Gilberdyke	d				07 04										07 26						08 03			
Eastrington	d														07 31									
Howden	d														07 35			07 56						
Wressle	d														07 40									
Selby	a										07 32				07 48			08 06						
	d										07 32				07 48			08 07						
York [8]	33 a														08 22									
Saltmarshe	d				07 10																08 08			
Goole	d				07 15																08 13			
Thorne North	d				07 24																08 22			
Cleethorpes	d	06 18														07 00				07 18				
New Clee	d																							
Grimsby Docks	d															07 05								
Grimsby Town	a	06 25														07 07				07 25				
	d	06 26												07 03		07 08				07 26				
Great Coates	d															07 12								
Healing	d															07 15								
Stallingborough	d															07 18								
Habrough	d	06 36												07 13		07 24				07 36				
Ulceby	d															07 28								
Thornton Abbey	d															07 32								
Goxhill	d															07 35								
New Holland	d															07 40								
Barrow Haven	d															07 43								
Barton-on-Humber	a															07 48								
Barton-on-Humber	🚌 d																07 53							
Hull Bus Station	🚌 a																08 18							
Barnetby	d	06 45												07a22						07 45				
Scunthorpe	a	07 00																		07 59				
	d	07 00										07 34								08 00			08 10	
Althorpe	d											07 39											08 15	
Crowle	d											07 45											08 21	
Thorne South	d											07 53											08 30	
Hatfield & Stainforth	d				07 30							07 59									08 28		08 35	
Kirk Sandall	d				07 34							08 03									08 33		08 39	
Adwick	31 d	*06 53*		07 29									08 07							*08 10*				
Bentley (S.Yorks)	31 d	*06 57*		07 33									08 11							*08 14*				
Doncaster [7]	31 a	07 33		07 37	07 45						07 53	08 13	08 15							08 30	08 43		08 50	
London Kings Cross [15]	⊖ 26 a										09 45		*10 25*											
York [8]	26 d	*06 30*				07 27				07 44										*07 27*				
Doncaster [7]	d	07 35		07 39	07 46	07 52							08 17							08 42			09 01 →	
Conisbrough	d			07 46	07 53								08 24											
Mexborough	d			07 50	07 57			←					08 28											
Swinton (S.Yorks)	d			07 53	08 00			08 00					08 31						08 34					
Rotherham Central	d			08 01	→			08b15					08 41						08 47					
Meadowhall	d	07 53	08 04	08a06			08 17	08 22	08 34				08a48						08 52	09 00				09 05
Sheffield [7]	a	08 00	08 15			08 20	08 28	08 30	08 45	08 51									09 01	09 07				09 11
	d	08 05																		09 11				
Stockport	78 a	08 50						*09 24*										*10c03*		09 53				
Manchester Piccadilly [10]	78 a	09 01						*09 36*										09 37		10 03				
Manchester Airport	85 a	09 33						*10e01*										*10 01*		10 33				

For general notes see front of timetable
For details of catering facilities see Directory of Train Operators

A From Leeds (Table 34)
B From Newcastle to Bournemouth (Table 51)
C From Huddersfield (Table 34)
D From Newcastle to Bristol Temple Meads (Table 51)
E **The Hull Executive**
G To Adwick (Table 31)
H To Newark North Gate (Table 27)
J From Beverley (Table 43)
K From Leeds (Table 31)
L From Bridlington (Table 43)
N To Lincoln (Table 30)
Q From Leeds to St Pancras International (Table 53)
b Arr. 0811
c Change at Manchester Piccadilly
e Change at Sheffield and Manchester Piccadilly

Table 29

Mondays to Fridays
from 8 September

Hull and Cleethorpes → Doncaster → Meadowhall, Sheffield, Manchester and Manchester Airport
Cleethorpes → Barton-on-Humber

Network Diagram - see first page of Table 18

		XC	NT	NT	NT	XC	NT	NT	HT	NT	NT	TP	TP	NT	NT	XC	NT	NT	NT	XC	NT	NT	NT	NT
		1◇				1◇			1◇			1◇	1◇			R 1				1◇				
		A	B	C	D	E	G	H			J			G	B	K		C	D	L	G	H		
		🍴				🍴			⊠ 🍴			🛒	🛒			🍴				🍴				🚌
Hull	d		08 04						08 12		08 29	08 38			08 56		09 02							
Hessle	d										08 36													
Ferriby	d										08 41													
Brough	d		08 16						08 24		08 46	08 50			09 08		09 14							
Broomfleet	d																							
Gilberdyke	d										08 53						09 21							
Eastrington	d																							
Howden	d								08 36								09 28							
Wressle	d																							
Selby	a								08 45			09 08					09 38							
	d								08 45			09 09					09 38							
York 8	33 a											*09 48*					10 07							
Saltmarshe	d																							
Goole	d		08 30								09 02				09 22									
Thorne North	d										09 10													
Cleethorpes	d												08 28										09 00	
New Clee	d																						09x03	
Grimsby Docks	d																						09 05	
Grimsby Town	a												08 35										09 08	
	d												08 36										09 08	
Great Coates	d																						09 12	
Healing	d																						09 15	
Stallingborough	d																						09 18	
Habrough	d												08 46										09 24	
Ulceby	d																						09 28	
Thornton Abbey	d																						09 32	
Goxhill	d																						09 35	
New Holland	d																						09 40	
Barrow Haven	d																						09 43	
Barton-on-Humber	a																						09 48	
Barton-on-Humber	🚌 d																							09 53
Hull Bus Station	🚌 a																							10 18
Barnetby	d												08 54											
Scunthorpe	a												09 10											
	d												09 10						09 17					
Althorpe	d																		09 22					
Crowle	d																		09 29					
Thorne South	d																		09 37					
Hatfield & Stainforth	d										09 17								09 42					
Kirk Sandall	d										09 21								09 47					
Adwick	31 d	*08b35*								09 13														
Bentley (S.Yorks)	31 d	*08b39*								09 17														
Doncaster 7	31 a		08 56						09 02	09 22	09 31		09 40		09 46				09 57					
London Kings Cross 15	⊖ 26 a		*11 15*						10 51	*11 27*									*11 51*					
York 8	26 d	08 27			⟵	08 44				*08 51*						09 25				09 44				
Doncaster 7	d	08 51	08 57		09 01					09 24			09 42		09 49	09 56			10 02					
Conisbrough	d				09 08					09 31									10 09					
Mexborough	d				09 12					09 35									10 13					
Swinton (S.Yorks)	d				09 15			09 35		09 42									10 16			10 34		
Rotherham Central	d				09 27			09 44		09 50									10 27			10 44		
Meadowhall	🚊 d		09 19	09 22	09 33		09 48	09 51		09a55			10 00	10 03	10 07			10 19	10 33		10 49	10 51		
Sheffield 7	🚊 a	09 25	09 30	09 31	09 41	09 51	09 58	10 02					10 07	10 15	10 18	10 25		10 30	10 41	10 51	10 59	11 02		
	d												10 11											
Stockport	78 a			*10 24*								*11c02*	10 53					*11 24*						
Manchester Piccadilly 10	78 🚊 a			*10 36*								10 35	11 03					*11 36*						
Manchester Airport	85 ✈ a			*11e01*								*11 01*	11 33					*12e01*						

For general notes see front of timetable
For details of catering facilities see Directory of Train Operators

A From Newcastle to Plymouth (Table 51)
B From Bridlington (Table 43)
C From Huddersfield (Table 34)
D To Lincoln (Table 30)
E From Edinburgh to Paignton (Table 51)
G From Leeds (Table 34)
H From Leeds (Table 31)
J From Scarborough (Table 43)
K To Bournemouth (Table 51)
L From Glasgow Central to Bristol Temple Meads (Table 51)
b Change at Doncaster
c Change at Manchester Piccadilly
e Change at Sheffield and Manchester Piccadilly

Table 29

Mondays to Fridays
from 8 September

Hull and Cleethorpes → Doncaster → Meadowhall, Sheffield, Manchester and Manchester Airport
Cleethorpes → Barton-on-Humber

Network Diagram - see first page of Table 18

	NT	NT	EM	TP	TP	NT	NT	XC	NT	NT	XC	HT	NT	NT	NT	NT	TP	TP	NT	NT		XC	NT
				1 ◇	1 ◇			1 ◇			R 1	1 ◇					1 ◇	1 ◇				R 1	
		A	B			C	D	E	G	H	J		C	K					C	D		L	G
				⌶	⌶			🍴			🍴	☒ 🍴					⌶	⌶				🍴	
Hull d		09 25		09 38			09 56					10 12				10 22	10 38			10 57			
Hessle d		09 32														10 32							
Ferriby d		09 37														10 37							
Brough d		09 42		09 50			10 08					10 24				10 42	10 50			11 09			
Broomfleet d																							
Gilberdyke d		09 49														10 49							
Eastrington d																							
Howden d												10 36											
Wressle d																							
Selby a				10 08								10 46					11 08						
d				10 09								10 47					11 09						
York 8 33 a												*11 20*											
Saltmarshe d																							
Goole d		09 58					10 22									10 58				11 23			
Thorne North d		10 06														11 06							
Cleethorpes d					09 28													10 28					
New Clee d																							
Grimsby Docks d																							
Grimsby Town a					09 35													10 35					
d			09 28		09 36													10 36					
Great Coates d																							
Healing d																							
Stallingborough d																							
Habrough d			09 38															10 46					
Ulceby d																							
Thornton Abbey d																							
Goxhill d																							
New Holland d																							
Barrow Haven d																							
Barton-on-Humber a																							
Barton-on-Humber 🚌 d																							
Hull Bus Station 🚌 a																							
Barnetby d			09a47		09 54													10 54					
Scunthorpe a					10 10													11 10					
d					10 10					10 18								11 10					
Althorpe d										10 23													
Crowle d										10 29													
Thorne South d										10 38													
Hatfield & Stainforth d		10 12								10 43						11 12							
Kirk Sandall d		10 17								10 47						11 17							
Adwick 31 d	10 13														11 16								
Bentley (S.Yorks) 31 d	10 17														11 20								
Doncaster 7 31 a	10 22	10 27			10 40		10 45			10 58		11 04			11 25	11 27		11 40		11 46			
London Kings Cross 15 ⊖ 26 a	*12 17*	*12 25*					*12 42*					12 44				*13 22*				*13 43*			
York 8 26 d	*09 35*				*10 06*			10 30		*10 29*	10 44											11 23	
Doncaster 7 d	10 24				10 42		10 48	10 58		11 02					11 27			11 42		11 48		11 54	
Conisbrough d	10 31									11 09					11 34								
Mexborough d	10 35									11 13					11 38								
Swinton (S.Yorks) d	10b41									11 16				11 34	11 41								
Rotherham Central d	10 49									11 27				11 45	11 50								
Meadowhall 🚊 d	10a55				11 00	11 04	11 07		11 19	11 33			11 49	11 51	11a55			12 00	12 03	12 06			12 19
Sheffield 7 🚊 a					11 07	11 15	11 17	11 25	11 30	11 41	11 51		11 58	12 02				12 07	12 15	12 17		12 25	12 30
d					11 11													12 11					
Stockport 78 a				*12c02*	11 53				*12 24*								*13c01*	12 53					*13 24*
Manchester Piccadilly 10 78 🚊 a				11 35	12 03				*12 36*								12 35	13 03					*13 36*
Manchester Airport 85 ✈ a				*12 01*	12 33				*13e01*								*13 01*	13 33					*14e01*

For general notes see front of timetable
For details of catering facilities see Directory of Train Operators

- **A** From Beverley (Table 43)
- **B** To Newark North Gate (Table 27)
- **C** From Leeds (Table 34)
- **D** From Bridlington (Table 43)
- **E** To Plymouth (Table 51)
- **G** From Huddersfield (Table 34)
- **H** To Lincoln (Table 30)
- **J** From Dundee (Table 229) to Plymouth (Table 51)
- **K** From Leeds (Table 31)
- **L** To Bournemouth (Table 51)
- **b** Arr. 1038
- **c** Change at Manchester Piccadilly
- **e** Change at Sheffield and Manchester Piccadilly

Table 29

Mondays to Fridays
from 8 September

Hull and Cleethorpes → Doncaster → Meadowhall, Sheffield, Manchester and Manchester Airport
Cleethorpes → Barton-on-Humber

Network Diagram - see first page of Table 18

		NT	XC	NT	NT	NT	NT	NT	NT	NT	EM	TP	TP	NT	NT	XC	NT	NT	XC	NT	NT	NT	NT	TP
			1 ◇									1 ◇	1 ◇			R 1			R 1					1 ◇
		A	B			🚌	C	D			E			C	G	H	J	A	K	C	D			
			☕									🍴	🍴			☕			☕					🍴
Hull	d			11 05						11 22		11 38			11 55								12 22	12 38
Hessle	d									11 29													12 29	
Ferriby	d									11 34													12 34	
Brough	d			11 18						11 39		11 50			12 07								12 39	12 50
Broomfleet	d																						12 44	
Gilberdyke	d									11 46													12 49	
Eastrington	d																							
Howden	d																							
Wressle	d																							
Selby	a			11 38								12 08												13 08
	d			11 39								12 09												13 09
York 8	33 a			12 10								*13 15*												
Saltmarshe	d									11 52														
Goole	d									11 58					12 22								12 58	
Thorne North	d									12 06													13 06	
Cleethorpes	d				11 00								11 28											
New Clee	d				11x03																			
Grimsby Docks	d				11 05																			
Grimsby Town	a				11 08								11 35											
	d				11 08						11 28		11 36											
Great Coates	d				11 12																			
Healing	d				11 15																			
Stallingborough	d				11 18																			
Habrough	d				11 24						11 38													
Ulceby	d				11 28																			
Thornton Abbey	d				11 32																			
Goxhill	d				11 35																			
New Holland	d				11 40																			
Barrow Haven	d				11 43																			
Barton-on-Humber	a				11 48																			
Barton-on-Humber	🚌 d					11 53																		
Hull Bus Station	🚌 a					12 18																		
Barnetby	d										11a47		11 54											
Scunthorpe	a												12 09											
	d	11 17											12 10					12 17						
Althorpe	d	11 22																12 22						
Crowle	d	11 28																12 28						
Thorne South	d	11 37																12 37						
Hatfield & Stainforth	d	11 42								12 12								12 42					13 14	
Kirk Sandall	d	11 46								12 17								12 46					13 19	
Adwick	31 d								12 15													13 11		
Bentley (S.Yorks)	31 d								12 19													13 15		
Doncaster 7	31 a	11 58							12 24	12 27			12 40		12 46			12 57				13 20	13 29	
London Kings Cross 15	⊖ 26 a	*14 02*								*14 20*					*14 44*			*15 05*						
York 8	26 d		11 44						*11 35*							12 24		*12 31*	12 44					
Doncaster 7	d	11 58							12 26				12 42		12 48	12 55		13 02				13 24		
Conisbrough	d	12 06							12 33									13 09				13 31		
Mexborough	d	12 10							12 37									13 13				13 35		
Swinton (S.Yorks)	d	12 16						12 34	12 42									13 16			13 34	13 42		
Rotherham Central	d	12 27						12 45	12 50									13 27			13 45	13 50		
Meadowhall	🚊 d	12 33					12 49	12 51	12a55				13 00	13 04	13 07		13 21	13 33		13 49	13 51	13a55		
Sheffield 7	🚊 a	12 41	12 51				12 58	13 02					13 07	13 14	13 17	13 25	13 29	13 41	13 51	13 58	14 02			
	d												13 11											
Stockport	78 a											*14b02*	13 53				*14 24*							*15b01*
Manchester Piccadilly 10	78 🚊 a											13 35	14 03				*14 36*							14 35
Manchester Airport	85 ✈ a											*14 01*	14 33				*15c01*							*15 01*

For general notes see front of timetable
For details of catering facilities see Directory of Train Operators

- **A** To Lincoln (Table 30)
- **B** From Dundee (Table 229) to Bristol Temple Meads (Table 51)
- **C** From Leeds (Table 34)
- **D** From Leeds (Table 31)
- **E** To Newark North Gate (Table 27)
- **G** From Bridlington (Table 43)
- **H** To Penzance (Table 135)
- **J** From Huddersfield (Table 34)
- **K** From Glasgow Central to Plymouth (Table 51)
- **b** Change at Manchester Piccadilly
- **c** Change at Sheffield and Manchester Piccadilly

Hull and Cleethorpes → Doncaster → Meadowhall, Sheffield, Manchester and Manchester Airport
Cleethorpes → Barton-on-Humber

Network Diagram - see first page of Table 18

		HT	TP	NT	NT	XC	NT	NT	XC	NT	NT	NT	NT	NT	TP	TP	NT	NT	EM	XC	NT		NT	NT
		1 ◇	1 ◇			R 1			R 1						1 ◇	1 ◇				R 1				
				A	B	C	D	E	G		A	H					A	J	K	L	D		E	
		⊠ ☕	🛒			☕			☕						🛒	🛒				☕				
Hull	d	12 45			12 57					13 12				13 25	13 38			13 57						
Hessle	d													13 32										
Ferriby	d													13 37										
Brough	d	12 57			13 09					13 24				13 42	13 50			14 09						
Broomfleet	d																							
Gilberdyke	d									13 31				13 49										
Eastrington	d									13 36														
Howden	d	13 09								13 40														
Wressle	d									13 45														
Selby	a	13 19								13 55					14 08									
	d	13 20								13 56					14 09									
York 8	33 a									14 27														
Saltmarshe	d																							
Goole	d				13 23									13 58				14 23						
Thorne North	d													14 06										
Cleethorpes	d		12 28													13 28								13 00
New Clee	d																							13x03
Grimsby Docks	d																							13 05
Grimsby Town	a		12 35													13 36								13 08
	d		12 36													13 36			13 52					13 08
Great Coates	d																							13 12
Healing	d																							13 15
Stallingborough	d																							13 18
Habrough	d																		14 02					13 24
Ulceby	d																							13 28
Thornton Abbey	d																							13 32
Goxhill	d																							13 35
New Holland	d																							13 40
Barrow Haven	d																							13 43
Barton-on-Humber	a																							13 48
Barton-on-Humber	🚌 d																							
Hull Bus Station	🚌 a																							
Barnetby	d		12 54													13 54			14a11					
Scunthorpe	a		13 10													14 10								
	d		13 10					13 18								14 10							14 18	
Althorpe	d							13 23															14 23	
Crowle	d							13 29															14 29	
Thorne South	d							13 38															14 38	
Hatfield & Stainforth	d							13 43						14 14									14 43	
Kirk Sandall	d							13 47						14 18									14 47	
Adwick	31 d												14 18											
Bentley (S.Yorks)	31 d												14 22											
Doncaster 7	31 a	13 37	13 40		13 46			13 58					14 26	14 29		14 40		14 46					14 58	
London Kings Cross 15	⊖ 26 a	15 20			*15 44*			*15 58*								*16 46*							*17 04*	
York 8	26 d					13 25			13 44				*13 36*							14 30				
Doncaster 7	d		13 42		13 48	13 54		14 01					14 28			14 42		14 48		14 57			15 02	
Conisbrough	d							14 08					14 35										15 09	
Mexborough	d							14 12					14 39										15 13	
Swinton (S.Yorks)	d							14 16				14 34	14 42										15 16	
Rotherham Central	d							14 27				14 45	14 50										15 27	
Meadowhall	🚊 d		14 00	14 03	14 06		14 19	14 33			14 48	14 51	14a55			15 00	15 03	15 06			15 19		15 33	
Sheffield 7	🚊 a		14 07	14 15	14 17	14 25	14 30	14 41	14 51		14 58	15 02				15 07	15 15	15 17		15 25	15 30		15 41	
	d		14 11													15 11								
Stockport	78 a		14 53				*15 24*								*16b02*	15 53					*16 24*			
Manchester Piccadilly 10	78 🚊 a		15 03				*15 36*								15 35	16 03					*16 35*			
Manchester Airport	85 ✈ a		15 33				*16c01*								*16 01*	16 33					*17c14*			

For general notes see front of timetable
For details of catering facilities see Directory of Train Operators

- **A** From Leeds (Table 34)
- **B** From Scarborough (Table 43)
- **C** To Bournemouth (Table 51)
- **D** From Huddersfield (Table 34)
- **E** To Lincoln (Table 30)
- **G** From Aberdeen (Table 229) to Bristol Temple Meads (Table 51)
- **H** From Leeds (Table 31)
- **J** From Bridlington (Table 43)
- **K** To Newark North Gate (Table 27)
- **L** To Plymouth (Table 51)
- **b** Change at Manchester Piccadilly
- **c** Change at Sheffield and Manchester Piccadilly

Table 29

Mondays to Fridays
from 8 September

Hull and Cleethorpes → Doncaster → Meadowhall, Sheffield, Manchester and Manchester Airport
Cleethorpes → Barton-on-Humber

Network Diagram - see first page of Table 18

		NT	NT	XC	NT	NT	NT	TP	TP	NT	NT	XC	NT	NT	XC	NT	NT	NT	HT	NT	NT	NT	NT	TP
				R 1				1 ◇	1 ◇			R 1			R 1				1 ◇					1 ◇
			A	B	C					A	D	E	G	H	J		A	C						
Hull	d						14 25	14 38			14 57					15 06			15 18		15 21			15 38
Hessle	d						14 32														15 28			
Ferriby	d						14 37														15 33			
Brough	d						14 42	14 50			15 09					15 18			15 30		15 38			15 50
Broomfleet	d																							
Gilberdyke	d						14 49														15 45			
Eastrington	d																							
Howden	d																		15 42					
Wressle	d																							
Selby	a							15 08								15 37			15 56					16 08
	d							15 09								15 38			15 57					16 09
York 8	33 a															16 06								
Saltmarshe	d																							
Goole	d						14 58				15 23										15 58			
Thorne North	d						15 06														16 06			
Cleethorpes	d								14 28													15 00		
New Clee	d																					15x03		
Grimsby Docks	d																					15 05		
Grimsby Town	a								14 35													15 08		
	d								14 36													15 09		
Great Coates	d																					15 13		
Healing	d																					15 16		
Stallingborough	d																					15 19		
Habrough	d								14 46													15 25		
Ulceby	d																					15 28		
Thornton Abbey	d																					15 33		
Goxhill	d																					15 36		
New Holland	d																					15 40		
Barrow Haven	d																					15 43		
Barton-on-Humber	a																					15 49		
Barton-on-Humber	bus d	13 53																					15 56	
Hull Bus Station	bus a	14 18																					16 21	
Barnetby	d								14 54															
Scunthorpe	a								15 10															
	d								15 10					15 18										
Althorpe	d													15 23										
Crowle	d													15 29										
Thorne South	d													15 38										
Hatfield & Stainforth	d						15 12							15 43							16 12			
Kirk Sandall	d						15 17							15 47							16 17			
Adwick	31 d					15 13														16 14				
Bentley (S.Yorks)	31 d					15 17														16 18				
Doncaster 7	31 a					15 22	15 27		15 40		15 46			15 58					16 15	16 22	16 27			
London Kings Cross 15	⊖ 26 a						*17 30*				*17 41*								18 12		*18 23*			
York 8	26 d			14 44					*15 11*			15 23			15 44					*15 35*				
Doncaster 7	d					15 25			15 42		15 48	15 55		16 02						16 24				
Conisbrough	d					15 32								16 09						16 31				
Mexborough	d					15 36								16 13						16 35				
Swinton (S.Yorks)	d				15 34	15 42								16 16				16 34		16 42				
Rotherham Central	d				15 43	15 50								16 27				16 43		16 50				
Meadowhall	d		15 49		15 51	15a55			16 00	16 04	16 09		16 19	16 33			16 49	16 51		16a55				
Sheffield 7	a		15 58	15 51	16 02				16 07	16 13	16 17	16 25	16 30	16 41	16 53		16 58	17 02						
	d								16 11															
Stockport	78 a							*17b00*	16 53				*17 25*											*17b59*
Manchester Piccadilly 10	78 a							16 35	17 03				*17 36*											17 35
Manchester Airport	85 a							*17 14*	17 39				*18c05*											*18 05*

For general notes see front of timetable
For details of catering facilities see Directory of Train Operators

A From Leeds (Table 34)
B From Edinburgh to Cardiff Central (Table 51)
C From Leeds (Table 31)
D From Scarborough (Table 43)
E To Bournemouth (Table 51)
G From Huddersfield (Table 34)
H To Lincoln (Table 30)
J From Edinburgh to Weston-super-Mare (Table 51)
b Change at Manchester Piccadilly
c Change at Sheffield and Manchester Piccadilly

Table 29

Mondays to Fridays

from 8 September

Hull and Cleethorpes → Doncaster → Meadowhall, Sheffield, Manchester and Manchester Airport
Cleethorpes → Barton-on-Humber

Network Diagram - see first page of Table 18

		TP	NT	NT	XC	NT	NT	EM	NT	XC	NT	NT	NT	NT	TP	TP	NT	NT	XC	NT	NT		TP	XC
		1 ◇			1 ◇					R 1					1 ◇	1 ◇			R 1				1 ◇	1 ◇
			A	B	C	D	E	G		H	A	J		K			A	L	N	D			Q	U
		🚲			🛒					🛒					🚲	🚲			🛒					🛒
Hull	d			15 57					16 10					16 27	16 38			16 54					17 01	
Hessle	d													16 34										
Ferriby	d													16 39										
Brough	d			16 09					16 22					16 44	16 50			17 06					17 13	
Broomfleet	d													16 49										
Gilberdyke	d								16 29					16 54				17 13						
Eastrington	d																							
Howden	d								16 36															
Wressle	d																							
Selby	a								16 46						17 08								17 31	
	d								16 47						17 09									
York 8	33 a								17 13															
Saltmarshe	d													16 59										
Goole	d			16 23										17 04				17 22						
Thorne North	d													17 13										
Cleethorpes	d	15 28														16 28								
New Clee	d																							
Grimsby Docks	d																							
Grimsby Town	a	15 35														16 35								
	d	15 36						16 03								16 36								
Great Coates	d																							
Healing	d																							
Stallingborough	d																							
Habrough	d							16 12																
Ulceby	d																							
Thornton Abbey	d																							
Goxhill	d																							
New Holland	d																							
Barrow Haven	d																							
Barton-on-Humber	a																							
Barton-on-Humber	🚌 d																							
Hull Bus Station	🚌 a																							
Barnetby	d	15 54						16a21								16 54								
Scunthorpe	a	16 10														17 10								
	d	16 10					16 18									17 10					17 18			
Althorpe	d						16 23														17 23			
Crowle	d						16 29														17 29			
Thorne South	d						16 38														17 38			
Hatfield & Stainforth	d						16 43							17 19							17 43			
Kirk Sandall	d						16 47							17 23							17 47			
Adwick	31 d												*16 54*			*17 09*								
Bentley (S.Yorks)	31 d												*16 58*			*17 14*								
Doncaster 7	31 a	16 40		16 46			16 58							17 34		17 40		17 47			17 58			
London Kings Cross 15	⊖ 26 a						*18 54*														*19 59*			
York 8	26 d				16 25					16 44						*16 56*			17 34					17 44
Doncaster 7	d	16 42		16 47	16 53		17 00						17 24			17 42		17 49	17 58		18 02			
Conisbrough	d						17 09						17 31								18 09			
Mexborough	d						17 13						17 35								18 13			
Swinton (S.Yorks)	d						17 16					17 34	17 42								18 16			
Rotherham Central	d						17 27					17 45	17 50								18 27			
Meadowhall	🚊 d	17 00	17 03	17 07		17 19	17 33				17 48	17 51	17a55			18 00	18 04	18 07		18 19	18 33			
Sheffield 7	🚊 a	17 07	17 15	17 17	17 25	17 29	17 41			17 51	17 58	18 02				18 07	18 15	18 18	18 25	18 30	18 43			18 51
	d	17 11														18 11								
Stockport	78 a	17 53				*18 26*									*19b02*	18 53				*19 24*				
Manchester Piccadilly 10	78 🚊 a	18 03				*18 36*									*18 36*	19 03				*19 36*				
Manchester Airport	85 ✈ a	18 38				*19c09*									*19 09*	19 34				*20c05*				

For general notes see front of timetable
For details of catering facilities see Directory of Train Operators

A From Leeds (Table 34)
B From Bridlington (Table 43)
C To Plymouth (Table 51)
D From Huddersfield (Table 34)
E To Lincoln (Table 30)
G To Newark North Gate (Table 27)
H From Edinburgh to Bristol Temple Meads (Table 51)
J From Leeds (Table 31)
K From Scarborough (Table 43)
L From Beverley (Table 43)
N To Southampton Central (Table 51)
Q To Huddersfield (Table 39)
U From Edinburgh to Birmingham New Street (Table 51)
b Change at Manchester Piccadilly
c Change at Sheffield and Manchester Piccadilly

Hull and Cleethorpes → Doncaster → Meadowhall, Sheffield, Manchester and Manchester Airport
Cleethorpes → Barton-on-Humber

Network Diagram - see first page of Table 18

		NT	NT	NT	NT	HT	NT	TP	NT	NT	NT	NT	XC	TP	NT	NT	NT	NT	NT	XC	NT	NT	EM	NT
						1 ◇		1 ◇					1 ◇	1 ◇						1 ◇				
				A	B				A	C	C	D	E		G	C			A	H	A	B	J	
			🚌			⊠ 🍵		🍴					🍵	🍴						🍵				
Hull	d					17 06				17 18	17 42	17 56		18 03				18 22						
Hessle	d									17 25	17 49							18 29						
Ferriby	d									17 30	17 54							18 34						
Brough	d					17 19				17 35	17 59	18 08		18 15				18 39						
Broomfleet	d									17 40														
Gilberdyke	d									17 45	18 06							18 46						
Eastrington	d									17 49														
Howden	d					17 32				17 54														
Wressle	d									17 58														
Selby	a					17 42				18 06		18 26		18 33										
	d					17 43				18 06		18 27		18 34										
York 8	33 a									18 36														
Saltmarshe	d										18 12					←								
Goole	d										18b20					18 20		18 55						
Thorne North	d										→					18 28		19 03						
Cleethorpes	d	17 00						17 28																
New Clee	d																							
Grimsby Docks	d	17 05																						
Grimsby Town	a	17 07						17 35																
	d	17 08						17 36																
Great Coates	d	17 12																					18 30	
Healing	d	17 15																						
Stallingborough	d	17 18																						
Habrough	d	17 24						17 46															18 40	
Ulceby	d	17 28																						
Thornton Abbey	d	17 32																						
Goxhill	d	17 35																						
New Holland	d	17 40																						
Barrow Haven	d	17 43																						
Barton-on-Humber	a	17 48																						
Barton-on-Humber	🚌 d		17 57																					
Hull Bus Station	🚌 a		18 23																					
Barnetby	d							17 54															18a48	
Scunthorpe	a							18 10																
	d							18 10									18 18							
Althorpe	d																18 23							
Crowle	d																18 29							
Thorne South	d																18 38							
Hatfield & Stainforth	d															18 34	18 46	19 12						
Kirk Sandall	d															18 39	18 50	19 16						
Adwick	31 d						17 53	18 16																18 53
Bentley (S.Yorks)	31 d						17 57	18 20																18 57
Doncaster 7	31 a					18 01		18 40				18 44				18 50	19 01	19 27						
London Kings Cross 15	⊖ 26 a					19 47						20 42					21 03	21 20						
York 8	26 d							17 55					18 17							18 44				18 30
Doncaster 7	d						18 26	18 42				18 46	18 52			18 55								19 28
Conisbrough	d						18 33									19 02								19 35
Mexborough	d						18 37									19 06								19 39
Swinton (S.Yorks)	d				18 34		18 42									19 09						19 34		19 43
Rotherham Central	d				18c45		18 49									19 19						19 45		19 50
Meadowhall	🚊 d			18 48	18 51		18a56	19 00	19 04			19 08			19 16	19a24			19 34		19 48	19 51		19a56
Sheffield 7	🚊 a			18 57	19 02			19 07	19 15			19 18	19 25		19 30				19 44	19 51	19 57	20 02		
	d							19 11																
Stockport	78 a							19 52						20e26	20 26									
Manchester Piccadilly 10	78 🚊 a							20 03						19 59	20 36									
Manchester Airport	85 ✈ a							20 34						20 58	21f09									

For general notes see front of timetable
For details of catering facilities see Directory of Train Operators

A From Leeds (Table 34)
B From Leeds (Table 31)
C From Beverley (Table 43)
D From Scarborough (Table 43)
E To Bristol Temple Meads (Table 51)
G From Huddersfield (Table 34)
H From Edinburgh to Birmingham New Street (Table 51)
J To Newark North Gate (Table 27)
b Arr. 1817
c Arr. 1841
e Change at Manchester Piccadilly
f Change at Sheffield and Manchester Piccadilly

Table 29

Mondays to Fridays
from 8 September

Hull and Cleethorpes → Doncaster → Meadowhall, Sheffield, Manchester and Manchester Airport
Cleethorpes → Barton-on-Humber

Network Diagram - see first page of Table 18

		TP	NT	NT	NT	XC	TP	NT	XC	NT	NT	NT	NT	NT	NT	HT	NT	TP	NT	TP	NT	NT	NT	NT
																BHX								
		1 ◇				1 ◇	1 ◇		1 ◇							1 ◇		1 ◇		1 ◇				
			A			B	C		D E		A	G			A		H			C	J	K		A
														🚌										
		trolley				catering			catering							⊠ catering								
Hull	d			18 53			18 59			19 10						19 18	19 24			19 56		20 03		
Hessle	d																19 31					20 10		
Ferriby	d																19 36					20 15		
Brough	d			19 05			19 11			19 22						19 30	19 41			20 08		20 20		
Broomfleet	d																							
Gilberdyke	d									19 29							19 48					20 27		
Eastrington	d																							
Howden	d									19 36						19 43								
Wressle	d																							
Selby	a						19 29			19 46						19 52				20 26				
	d									19 47						19 53								
York 8	33 a									20 15										*21 00*				
Saltmarshe	d																							
Goole	d			19 19													19 58					20 36		
Thorne North	d																20 06					20 44		
Cleethorpes	d	18 28											19 00					19 28						
New Clee	d																							
Grimsby Docks	d												19 05											
Grimsby Town	a	18 35											19 07					19 35						
	d	18 36											19 08					19 36						
Great Coates	d												19 12											
Healing	d												19 15											
Stallingborough	d												19 18											
Habrough	d	18 46											19 24					19 46						
Ulceby	d												19 28											
Thornton Abbey	d												19 32											
Goxhill	d												19 35											
New Holland	d												19 40											
Barrow Haven	d												19 43											
Barton-on-Humber	a												19 48											
Barton-on-Humber	🚌 d													19 55										
Hull Bus Station	🚌 a													20 20										
Barnetby	d	18 54																19 54						
Scunthorpe	a	19 10																20 10						
	d	19 10			19 15													20 10	20 18					
Althorpe	d				19 20														20 23					
Crowle	d				19 26														20 29					
Thorne South	d				19 34														20 38					
Hatfield & Stainforth	d				19 40												20 14		20 43			20 50		
Kirk Sandall	d				19 44												20 19		20 47			20 55		
Adwick	31 d																	*19 53*					*20 55*	
Bentley (S.Yorks)	31 d																	*19 57*					*20 59*	
Doncaster 7	31 a	19 40		19 45	19 56											20 10	20 29	20 40	20 59			21 05		
London Kings Cross 15	⊖ 26 a			*21 44*												21 59						*23 32*		
York 8	26 d			*19 13*		19 30			19 44									*20 08*						
Doncaster 7	d	19 42		19 49		19 57		20 03										20 42				21 07	21 30	
Conisbrough	d							20 10										20 48				21 14	21 37	
Mexborough	d							20 14										20 52				21 18	21 41	
Swinton (S.Yorks)	d							20 17				20 34						20 55				21 21	→	
Rotherham Central	d							20 28				20 43						21 01				21 28		
Meadowhall	🚋 d	20 00	20 04	20 08				20 33			20 48	20 51			21 04			21 07			21 24	21 34		21 49
Sheffield 7	🚋 a	20 07	20 15	20 18		20 26		20 44	20 50		20 57	21 02			21 15			21 18			21 35	21 45		21 57
	d	20 11																						
Stockport	78 a	20 53				22b26																		
Manchester Piccadilly 10	78 🚋 a	21 03				22 03																		
Manchester Airport	85 ✈ a	21 34				22b39																		

For general notes see front of timetable
For details of catering facilities see Directory of Train Operators

A From Leeds (Table 34)
B To Bristol Temple Meads (Table 51)
C To Leeds (Table 39)
D catering to Leeds
E From Edinburgh to Birmingham New Street (Table 51)
G From Leeds (Table 31)
H From Scarborough (Table 43)
J From Huddersfield (Table 34)
K From Bridlington (Table 43)
b Change at Sheffield and Manchester Piccadilly

Table 29

Mondays to Fridays

from 8 September

Hull and Cleethorpes → Doncaster → Meadowhall, Sheffield, Manchester and Manchester Airport
Cleethorpes → Barton-on-Humber

Network Diagram - see first page of Table 18

		NT	TP	NT	XC	NT	NT ThFO	NT	EM	XC	NT	TP	NT	NT	NT	NT	NT	NT	NT	NT FX	NT FO	NT
			1 ◇		1 ◇					1 ◇		1 ◇										
		A			B		🚌		C	D			E		G	A		E	G			A
Hull	d							20 56				21 33								22 20	22 25	
Hessle	d																			22 27		
Ferriby	d																			22 32		
Brough	d							21 08				21 45								22 37	22 37	
Broomfleet	d																					
Gilberdyke	d											21 52										
Eastrington	d																					
Howden	d																					
Wressle	d																					
Selby	a											22 07										
	d											22 07										
York 8	33 a																					
Saltmarshe	d																					
Goole	d							21 22						21 42						22 51	22 51	
Thorne North	d													21 51						23 00	23 00	
Cleethorpes	d		20 28			21 00			21 14													
New Clee	d																					
Grimsby Docks	d					21 05																
Grimsby Town	a		20 35			21 07			21 20													
	d		20 36			21 08			21 21													
Great Coates	d					21 12																
Healing	d					21 15																
Stallingborough	d					21 18																
Habrough	d					21 24			21 30													
Ulceby	d					21 27																
Thornton Abbey	d					21 32																
Goxhill	d					21 35																
New Holland	d					21 39																
Barrow Haven	d					21 42																
Barton-on-Humber	a					21 48																
Barton-on-Humber	🚌 d						21 55															
Hull Bus Station	🚌 a						22 20															
Barnetby	d		20 54						21a39													
Scunthorpe	a		21 09																			
	d		21 10								21 26						22 21					
Althorpe	d										21 31						22 26					
Crowle	d										21 37						22 32					
Thorne South	d										21 45						22 41					
Hatfield & Stainforth	d										21 51			21 56			22 46			23 06	23 06	
Kirk Sandall	d										21 55			22 01			22 50			23 10	23 10	
Adwick	31 d																			*22 02*	*22 02*	
Bentley (S.Yorks)	31 d																			*22 06*	*22 06*	
Doncaster 7	31 a		21 40					21 45			22 06			22 11			23 02			23 21	23 21	
London Kings Cross 15	⊖ 26 a							*00 15*														
York 8	26 d				20 44					21 24				*21 39*								
Doncaster 7	d		21 42	←	21 45			21 48						22 13						23 21	23 22	
Conisbrough	d													22 20						23 29	23 29	
Mexborough	d			21 41										22 24						23 33	23 33	
Swinton (S.Yorks)	d	21 35		21 44										22 29		22 34				23 36	23 36	23 55
Rotherham Central	d	21 44		21b55										22 38		22 43				23 45	23 45	00 03
Meadowhall	🚊 d	21 51	22 00	22 04				22 10					22 25	22 44	22 48	22 51		23 26	23 49	23 52	23 52	00 08
Sheffield 7	🚊 a	22 02	22 07	22 11	22 19			22 19		22 22			22 35	22 54	22 58	23 02		23 35	23 57	00 01	00 01	00 23
	d		22 11																			
Stockport	78 a		22 53										*23 46*									
Manchester Piccadilly 10	78 🚊 a		23 03									23 37	*23 59*									
Manchester Airport	85 ✈ a		23 28									*00 45*	*00c45*									

For general notes see front of timetable
For details of catering facilities see Directory of Train Operators

A From Leeds (Table 31)
B From Edinburgh (Table 26). 🍴 to Leeds
C To Lincoln (Table 27)
D From Edinburgh to Birmingham New Street (Table 51)
E From Huddersfield (Table 34)
G From Leeds (Table 34)
b Arr. 2151
c Change at Sheffield and Manchester Piccadilly

Table 29

until 6 September

Hull and Cleethorpes → Doncaster → Meadowhall, Sheffield, Manchester and Manchester Airport
Cleethorpes → Barton-on-Humber

Network Diagram - see first page of Table 18

		NT	TP	NT	NT	NT	NT	NT	TP	TP	NT	NT	NT	XC	NT	TP	NT	NT	TP	NT	NT	NT	GR	NT
			1 ◇						1 ◇	1 ◇				1 ◇		1 ◇			1 ◇				R 1	
		A		B		B			C		D			E			G	H				H		
									⊼	⊼				⊡					⊼				⊡ ⊼	
Hull	d						05 20		06 00				06 07			06 36				06 40			06 50	
Hessle	d												06 14							06 47				
Ferriby	d												06 19							06 52				
Brough	d						05 32		06 12				06 24			06 48				06 57			07 02	
Broomfleet	d																							
Gilberdyke	d								06 20				06 31							07 04				
Eastrington	d																							
Howden	d								06 27															
Wressle	d																							
Selby	a								06 36							07 06							07 23	
	d							06 15	06 38							07 07							07 23	
York 8	33 a								*07 20*															
Saltmarshe	d												06 37							07 10				←
Goole	d						05 47						06 42							07 15 →				07 15
Thorne North	d						05 56						06 51											07 24
Cleethorpes	d									05 18					06 00				06 18					
New Clee	d																							
Grimsby Docks	d																							
Grimsby Town	a									05 25					06 08				06 25					
	d									05 26					06 08				06 26					
Great Coates	d																							
Healing	d														06 15									
Stallingborough	d														06 18									
Habrough	d									05 36					06 24				06 36					
Ulceby	d														06 28									
Thornton Abbey	d																							
Goxhill	d														06 35									
New Holland	d														06 40									
Barrow Haven	d														06 43									
Barton-on-Humber	a														06 48									
Barton-on-Humber	🚌 d																							
Hull Bus Station	🚌 a																							
Barnetby	d									05 45									06 45					
Scunthorpe	a									06 00									07 00					
	d									06 00									07 00					
Althorpe	d									06 06														
Crowle	d									06 12														
Thorne South	d									06 20														
Hatfield & Stainforth	d						06 03			06 25			06 57											07 30
Kirk Sandall	d						06 10						07 01											07 34
Adwick	31 d													*06b53*							07 29			
Bentley (S.Yorks)	31 d													*06b57*							07 33			
Doncaster 7	31 a						06 16	06 36		06 38			07 14						07 33		07 37		07 40	07 45
London Kings Cross 15	⊖ 26 a						*08 04*						*09 03*										09 26	*09 51*
York 8	26 d									*06 00*				06 06					*07 00*					
Doncaster 7	d		05 42		06 00		06 27			06 40		07 02		07 26					07 35		07 39			07 46
Conisbrough	d				06 07		06 34					07 09									07 46			07 53
Mexborough	d				06 11		06 38					07 13									07 50			07 57
Swinton (S.Yorks)	d				06 14		06 41					07 16					07 29				07 53			08 00 →
Rotherham Central	d				06 22		06 49					07c27					07 41				08 00			
Meadowhall	🚊 d	05 39	06 00	06 13	06 27	06 49	06 55			07 00	07 19	07 33					07 47	07 48	07 53		08 06	08 03		
Sheffield 7	🚊 a	05 49	06 08	06 25	06 38	06 57	07 06			07 07	07 29	07 45		07 51			07 57	07 59	08 00		08 14	08 15		
	d		06 11							07 10									08 05					
Stockport	78 a		06 53						*08e25*	07 55	*08 25*					*09e01*			08 50					
Manchester Piccadilly 10	78 🚊 a		07 05						08 05	08 08	*08 36*					08 36			09 01					
Manchester Airport	85 ✈ a		07 35						*08 42*	08 33	*09f06*					*09 06*			09 33					

For general notes see front of timetable
For details of catering facilities see Directory of Train Operators

A From Barnsley (Table 34) to Retford (Table 30)
B From Barnsley (Table 34)
C To Liverpool Lime Street (Table 39). ⊼ from Leeds
D From Huddersfield (Table 34)
E To Birmingham New Street (Table 51)
G From Leeds (Table 31)
H From Leeds (Table 34)
b Change at Doncaster
c Arr. 0723
e Change at Manchester Piccadilly
f Change at Sheffield and Manchester Piccadilly

Due to Engineering Operations in the Sheffield area, services from Saturday 13 September on this Table had not been confirmed at time of going to press. These services will be issued in a special Supplement as soon as exact timings have been confirmed.

Table 29

Saturdays until 6 September

Hull and Cleethorpes → Doncaster → Meadowhall, Sheffield, Manchester and Manchester Airport
Cleethorpes → Barton-on-Humber

Network Diagram - see first page of Table 18

	XC	EM	NT	NT	NT	NT	XC	EM	NT	NT	NT	TP	EM	NT		NT	TP	NT	NT	HT	NT	XC	NT
	R 1	1 ◇					R 1					1 ◇	1 ◇				1 ◇			1 ◇		1 ◇	
	A	B	C	D		E	G	H	J		🚌		K			L		N	Q		E	U	N
	☕	☕					☕						☕				🍴			⊠ ☕		☕	
Hull d									06 57			07 33						07 36		08 02			08 08
Hessle d																		07 43					
Ferriby d																		07 48					
Brough d									07 09			07 45						07 53		08 14			08 20
Broomfleet d																		07 58					
Gilberdyke d									07 17									08 03					
Eastrington d									07 21														
Howden d									07 26			07 56								08 26 →			
Wressle d									07 31														
Selby a									07 40			08 06											
d									07 40			08 07											
York [8] 33 a									08 14														
Saltmarshe d																		08 08					
Goole d																		08 13					08 34
Thorne North d																		08 22					
Cleethorpes d										07 00							07 18						
New Clee d																							
Grimsby Docks d										07 05													
Grimsby Town a										07 07							07 25						
d								06 59		07 08							07 26						
Great Coates d										07 12													
Healing d										07 15													
Stallingborough d										07 18													
Habrough d								07 09		07 24							07 36						
Ulceby d										07 28													
Thornton Abbey d										07 32													
Goxhill d										07 35													
New Holland d										07 40													
Barrow Haven d										07 43													
Barton-on-Humber a										07 48													
Barton-on-Humber 🚌 d											07 53												
Hull Bus Station 🚌 a											08 18												
Barnetby d								07a18									07 45						
Scunthorpe a																	07 59						
d			07 34														08 00		08 10				
Althorpe d			07 39																08 15				
Crowle d			07 45																08 21				
Thorne South d			07 53																08 30				
Hatfield & Stainforth d			07 59															08 28	08 35				
Kirk Sandall d			08 03															08 32	08 39				
Adwick 31 d														08 07			*08 12*						*08 35*
Bentley (S.Yorks) 31 d														08 11			*08 16*						*08 39*
Doncaster [7] 31 a			08 13											08 15			08 30	08 43	08 52				08 57
London Kings Cross [15] ⊖ 26 a																	*10 27*	*10 41*					*10 58*
York [8] 26 d	07 25						07 44							*07 36*								08 19	
Doncaster [7] d	07 52	07 59												08 17			08 42		09 02 →				08 59
Conisbrough d														08 24									
Mexborough d					←									08 28									
Swinton (S.Yorks) d					08 00									08 31		08 34							
Rotherham Central d					08b12									08 41		08 47							
Meadowhall 🚊 d				08 17	08b22	08 37							08 47	08 49		08 53	09 00				09 03		09 19
Sheffield [7] 🚊 a	08 20	08 21		08 28	08 31	08 47	08 51						08 54	08 57		09 02	09 07				09 15	09 20	09 27
d																	09 11						
Stockport 78 a					*09 25*							*10c03*					09 53						
Manchester Piccadilly [10] 78 🚊 a					*09 36*							09 37					10 03						
Manchester Airport 85 ✈ a					*10e02*							*10 02*					10 33						

For general notes see front of timetable
For details of catering facilities see Directory of Train Operators

- **A** From Newcastle to Paignton (Table 51)
- **B** From Leeds to St Pancras International (Table 53)
- **C** To Adwick (Table 31)
- **D** From Huddersfield (Table 34)
- **E** From Leeds (Table 34)
- **G** From Newcastle to Bournemouth (Table 51)
- **H** To Newark North Gate (Table 27)
- **J** From Beverley (Table 43)
- **K** From Barnsley to St Pancras International (Table 53)
- **L** From Leeds (Table 31)
- **N** From Bridlington (Table 43)
- **Q** To Lincoln (Table 30)
- **U** From Newcastle to Bristol Temple Meads (Table 51)
- **b** Arr. 3 minutes earlier
- **c** Change at Manchester Piccadilly
- **e** Change at Sheffield and Manchester Piccadilly

Due to Engineering Operations in the Sheffield area, services from Saturday 13 September on this Table had not been confirmed at time of going to press. These services will be issued in a special Supplement as soon as exact timings have been confirmed.

Table 29

until 6 September

Hull and Cleethorpes → Doncaster → Meadowhall, Sheffield, Manchester and Manchester Airport
Cleethorpes → Barton-on-Humber

Network Diagram - see first page of Table 18

	NT	HT	NT	XC	NT	NT	NT	NT	TP	TP	NT	NT	XC	NT	NT	NT	NT	XC	NT	NT	NT	NT	NT
		1 ◇		R 1					1 ◇	1 ◇			1 ◇					1 ◇					
	A		B	C	D	E		G			D	H	J		(bus)	A	B	K		D	E		L
		⊠ ☕		☕						trolley			☕					☕					
Hull d								08 29	08 38			08 56							09 02				09 25
Hessle d								08 36															09 32
Ferriby d								08 41															09 37
Brough d								08 46	08 50			09 08							09 14				09 42
Broomfleet d																							
Gilberdyke d								08 53											09 21				09 49
Eastrington d		←																					
Howden d		08 26																	09 28				
Wressle d																							
Selby a		08 36							09 08										09 38				
d		08 37							09 09										09 38				
York 8 33 a									*09 41*										10 10				
Saltmarshe d																							
Goole d								09 02				09 22											09 58
Thorne North d								09 10															10 06
Cleethorpes d										08 28				09 00									
New Clee d														09x03									
Grimsby Docks d														09 05									
Grimsby Town a										08 35				09 08									
d										08 36				09 08									
Great Coates d														09 12									
Healing d														09 15									
Stallingborough d														09 18									
Habrough d										08 46				09 24									
Ulceby d														09 28									
Thornton Abbey d														09 32									
Goxhill d														09 35									
New Holland d														09 40									
Barrow Haven d														09 43									
Barton-on-Humber a														09 48									
Barton-on-Humber (bus) d															09 53								
Hull Bus Station (bus) a															10 18								
Barnetby d										08 54													
Scunthorpe a										09 10													
d										09 10							09 17						
Althorpe d																	09 22						
Crowle d																	09 29						
Thorne South d																	09 37						
Hatfield & Stainforth d								09 16									09 42						10 12
Kirk Sandall d								09 21									09 47						10 17
Adwick 31 d							09 13															10 10	
Bentley (S.Yorks) 31 d							09 17															10 14	
Doncaster 7 31 a		09 00					09 22	09 31		09 40		09 46					09 57					10 19	10 27
London Kings Cross 15 ⊖ 26 a		10 49	←				*11 33*					*11 50*										*12 14*	*12 24*
York 8 26 d			*08 30*	08 44			*08 51*						09 27					09 44				*09 36*	
Doncaster 7 d			09 02				09 24			09 42		09 48	09 51				10 02					10 24	
Conisbrough d			09 09				09 31										10 09					10 31	
Mexborough d			09 13				09 35										10 13					10 35	
Swinton (S.Yorks) d			09 16			09 35	09 42										10 16				10 34	10b41	
Rotherham Central d			09 27			09 44	09 50										10 27				10 45	10 50	
Meadowhall (tram) d	09 22		09 33		09 49	09 51	09 56			10 00	10 03	10 07				10 19	10 33			10 49	10 51	10 56	
Sheffield 7 (tram) a	09 30		09 41	09 51	09 57	10 02	10 04			10 07	10 15	10 18	10 20			10 30	10 41	10 51		10 57	11 02	11 05	
d										10 11													
Stockport 78 a	*10 24*								*11c02*	10 53						*11 24*							
Manchester Piccadilly 10 78 (tram) a	*10 36*								10 35	11 03						*11 36*						*12 31*	
Manchester Airport 85 (air) a	*11e01*								*11 01*	11 33						*12e01*							

For general notes see front of timetable
For details of catering facilities see Directory of Train Operators

- **A** From Huddersfield (Table 34)
- **B** To Lincoln (Table 30)
- **C** From Edinburgh to Plymouth (Table 51)
- **D** From Leeds (Table 34)
- **E** From Leeds (Table 31)
- **G** From Scarborough (Table 43)
- **H** From Bridlington (Table 43)
- **J** From Newcastle to Bristol Temple Meads (Table 51)
- **K** From Glasgow Central to Bournemouth (Table 51)
- **L** From Beverley (Table 43)
- **b** Arr. 1038
- **c** Change at Manchester Piccadilly
- **e** Change at Sheffield and Manchester Piccadilly

Due to Engineering Operations in the Sheffield area, services from Saturday 13 September on this Table had not been confirmed at time of going to press. These services will be issued in a special Supplement as soon as exact timings have been confirmed.

Table 29

Saturdays

until 6 September

Hull and Cleethorpes → Doncaster → Meadowhall, Sheffield, Manchester and Manchester Airport Cleethorpes → Barton-on-Humber

Network Diagram - see first page of Table 18

		EM	TP	TP	NT	NT	XC	NT	NT		XC	HT	NT	NT	NT	NT	TP	NT	TP	NT	NT	NT	XC	NT
			1◇	1◇			1◇				R 1	1◇					1◇		1◇				R 1	
		A			B	C	D	E	G		H		B	J				B				C	K	L
				[trolley]			[buffet]				[buffet]	[restaurant] [buffet]					[trolley]				[bus]		[buffet]	
Hull	d		09 38			09 56						10 06				10 25			10 38			10 57		
Hessle	d															10 32								
Ferriby	d															10 37								
Brough	d		09 50			10 08						10 18				10 42			10 50			11 09		
Broomfleet	d																							
Gilberdyke	d															10 49								
Eastrington	d																							
Howden	d											10 30												
Wressle	d																							
Selby	a		10 08									10 40							11 08					
	d		10 09									10 41							11 09					
York 8	33 a											*11 16*												
Saltmarshe	d																							
Goole	d					10 22										10 58						11 23		
Thorne North	d															11 06								
Cleethorpes	d			09 28													10 28			11 00				
New Clee	d																			11x03				
Grimsby Docks	d																			11 05				
Grimsby Town	a			09 35													10 35			11 08				
	d	09 28		09 36													10 36			11 08				
Great Coates	d																			11 12				
Healing	d																			11 15				
Stallingborough	d																			11 18				
Habrough	d	09 37															10 46			11 24				
Ulceby	d																			11 28				
Thornton Abbey	d																			11 32				
Goxhill	d																			11 35				
New Holland	d																			11 40				
Barrow Haven	d																			11 43				
Barton-on-Humber	a																			11 48				
Barton-on-Humber	[bus] d																				11 53			
Hull Bus Station	[bus] a																				12 18			
Barnetby	d	09a46		09 54													10 54							
Scunthorpe	a			10 10													11 10							
	d			10 10					10 18								11 10							
Althorpe	d								10 23															
Crowle	d								10 29															
Thorne South	d								10 38															
Hatfield & Stainforth	d								10 43							11 11								
Kirk Sandall	d								10 47							11 17								
Adwick	31 d														11 08									
Bentley (S.Yorks)	31 d														11 12									
Doncaster 7	31 a			10 40		10 46			10 58			11 01			11 20	11 28	11 40					11 46		
London Kings Cross 15	⊖ 26 a					*12 41*			*13 10*			12 46				*13 33*						*13 44*		
York 8	26 d			*10 05*			10 25		*10 31*		10 44						*11 00*						11 27	11 01
Doncaster 7	d			10 42		10 48	10 53		11 02						11 24		11 42					11 48	11 55	
Conisbrough	d								11 09						11 31									
Mexborough	d								11 13						11 35									
Swinton (S.Yorks)	d								11 16					11 34	11 41									12 01
Rotherham Central	d								11 27					11 45	11 50									12 11
Meadowhall	[tram] d			11 00	11 04	11 06		11 19	11 33				11 49	11 51	11 56		12 00	12 03				12 06		12 16
Sheffield 7	[tram] a			11 07	11 15	11 17	11 20	11 30	11 41		11 51		11 57	12 02	12 05		12 07	12 15				12 17	12 20	12 25
	d			11 11													12 11							
Stockport	78 a		*12b02*	11 53				*12 24*									12 53		*13b02*					
Manchester Piccadilly 10	78 [tram] a		11 35	12 03				*12 36*							*13 31*		13 03		12 35					
Manchester Airport	85 [plane] a		*12 01*	12 33				*13c01*									13 33		*13 01*					

For general notes see front of timetable
For details of catering facilities see Directory of Train Operators

A To Newark North Gate (Table 27)

B From Leeds (Table 34)
C From Bridlington (Table 43)
D From Edinburgh to Bristol Temple Meads (Table 51)
E From Huddersfield (Table 34)
G To Lincoln (Table 30)
H From Newcastle (Table 51) to Newquay (Table 135)

J From Leeds (Table 31)
K From Newcastle (Table 51) to Penzance (Table 135)
L Via Pontefract Baghill (Table 33)
b Change at Manchester Piccadilly
c Change at Sheffield and Manchester Piccadilly

Due to Engineering Operations in the Sheffield area, services from Saturday 13 September on this Table had not been confirmed at time of going to press. These services will be issued in a special Supplement as soon as exact timings have been confirmed.

until 6 September

Hull and Cleethorpes → Doncaster → Meadowhall, Sheffield, Manchester and Manchester Airport
Cleethorpes → Barton-on-Humber

Network Diagram - see first page of Table 18

Station		NT	NT	XC	NT	NT	NT	NT	NT	NT	EM	TP	TP	NT	NT	XC	NT	NT	XC	NT	NT	NT	NT	NT
				R 1								1 ◇	1 ◇			1 ◇			R 1					
		A	B	C	D		E	G			H			E	J	K	A	B	L		E	G		
				catering								trolley	trolley			catering			catering					
Hull	d					11 08				11 22		11 38			11 57									12 22
Hessle	d									11 29														12 29
Ferriby	d									11 34														12 34
Brough	d					11 20				11 39		11 50			12 09									12 39
Broomfleet	d																							12 44
Gilberdyke	d									11 46														12 49
Eastrington	d																							
Howden	d																							
Wressle	d																							
Selby	a					11 39						12 08												
	d					11 40						12 09								12 51				
York 8	33 a					12 10						13 23								13 23				
Saltmarshe	d									11 52														
Goole	d									11 58					12 23									12 58
Thorne North	d									12 06														13 06
Cleethorpes	d				11 13								11 28											
New Clee	d																							
Grimsby Docks	d																							
Grimsby Town	a				11 19								11 35											
	d				11 20						11 30		11 36											
Great Coates	d																							
Healing	d																							
Stallingborough	d																							
Habrough	d				11 30						11 39													
Ulceby	d																							
Thornton Abbey	d																							
Goxhill	d																							
New Holland	d																							
Barrow Haven	d																							
Barton-on-Humber	a																							
Barton-on-Humber	bus d																							
Hull Bus Station	bus a																							
Barnetby	d				11a39						11a48		11 54											
Scunthorpe	a												12 10											
	d		11 17										12 10					12 18						
Althorpe	d		11 22															12 23						
Crowle	d		11 29															12 29						
Thorne South	d		11 37															12 38						
Hatfield & Stainforth	d		11 42							12 12								12 43						13 12
Kirk Sandall	d		11 47							12 17								12 47						13 17
Adwick	31 d								12 13														13 12	
Bentley (S.Yorks)	31 d								12 17														13 16	
Doncaster 7	31 a		11 58						12 22	12 27			12 40		12 45			12 59					13 23	13 27
London Kings Cross 15	⊖ 26 a		13 59							14 27					14 44									15 21
York 8	26 d		11 27	11 44					11 33				11 59			12 25			12 44				12 31	
Doncaster 7	d		12 02						12 24				12 42		12 48	12 52		13 01					13 25	
Conisbrough	d		12 09						12 31									13 09					13 32	
Mexborough	d		12 13						12 35									13 13					13 36	
Swinton (S.Yorks)	d		12 16					12 34	12 42									13 16				13 34	13 42	
Rotherham Central	d		12 27					12 45	12 50									13 27				13 45	13 50	
Meadowhall	tram d	12 19	12 33				12 49	12 51	12 56				13 00	13 03	13 06		13 21	13 33			13 49	13 51	13 56	
Sheffield 7	tram a	12 30	12 41	12 51			12 57	13 02	13 04				13 07	13 15	13 17	13 20	13 31	13 41	13 51		13 57	14 02	14 04	
	d												13 11											
Stockport	78 a	13 24										14b02	13 53				14 25							
Manchester Piccadilly 10	78 tram a	13 36										13 35	14 03				14 36							
Manchester Airport	85 ✈ a	14c01										14 01	14 33				15c01							

For general notes see front of timetable
For details of catering facilities see Directory of Train Operators

A From Huddersfield (Table 34)
B To Lincoln (Table 30)
C From Dundee (Table 229) to Bournemouth (Table 51)
D To Sheffield via Retford (Table 30)
E From Leeds (Table 34)
G From Leeds (Table 31)
H To Newark North Gate (Table 27)
J From Bridlington (Table 43)
K From Newcastle to Bristol Temple Meads (Table 51)
L From Glasgow Central to Paignton (Table 51)
b Change at Manchester Piccadilly
c Change at Sheffield and Manchester Piccadilly

Due to Engineering Operations in the Sheffield area, services from Saturday 13 September on this Table had not been confirmed at time of going to press. These services will be issued in a special Supplement as soon as exact timings have been confirmed.

Saturdays

until 6 September

Hull and Cleethorpes → Doncaster → Meadowhall, Sheffield, Manchester and Manchester Airport Cleethorpes → Barton-on-Humber

Network Diagram - see first page of Table 18

	TP	TP		NT	NT	XC	NT	NT	XC	NT	NT	NT	NT	HT	NT	NT	NT	EM	TP	TP	NT	NT	XC
	1 ◇	1 ◇				1 ◇			1 ◇					1 ◇					1 ◇	1 ◇			1 ◇
				A	B	C	D	E	G		🚌	A	H					J			A	K	C
		🚲				☕			☕					☒ ☕						🚲			☕
Hull d	12 38				12 57									13 05		13 12	13 25		13 38			13 57	
Hessle d																	13 32						
Ferriby d																	13 37						
Brough d	12 50				13 09									13 17		13 24	13 42		13 50			14 09	
Broomfleet d																							
Gilberdyke d																13 31	13 49						
Eastrington d																13 36							
Howden d														13 29		13 40							
Wressle d																13 45							
Selby a	13 08													13 39		13 53			14 08				
d	13 09													13 40		13 54			14 09				
York 8 33 a																14 26							
Saltmarshe d																							
Goole d					13 23												13 58					14 23	
Thorne North d																	14 06						
Cleethorpes d		12 28								13 00										13 28			
New Clee d										13x03													
Grimsby Docks d										13 05													
Grimsby Town a		12 35								13 08										13 35			
d		12 36								13 08								13 25		13 36			
Great Coates d										13 12													
Healing d										13 15													
Stallingborough d										13 18													
Habrough d										13 24								13 35					
Ulceby d										13 28													
Thornton Abbey d										13 32													
Goxhill d										13 35													
New Holland d										13 40													
Barrow Haven d										13 43													
Barton-on-Humber a										13 48													
Barton-on-Humber 🚌 d											13 53												
Hull Bus Station 🚌 a											14 18												
Barnetby d		12 54																13a43		13 54			
Scunthorpe a		13 10																		14 10			
d		13 10						13 17												14 10			
Althorpe d								13 22															
Crowle d								13 29															
Thorne South d								13 37															
Hatfield & Stainforth d								13 42									14 12						
Kirk Sandall d								13 47									14 17						
Adwick 31 d															14 14								
Bentley (S.Yorks) 31 d															14 18								
Doncaster 7 31 a		13 40			13 46			13 58						14 03	14 22		14 27			14 40		14 46	
London Kings Cross 15 ⊖ 26 a					*15 41*									15 49			*16 30*					*16 47*	
York 8 26 d		*12 31*				13 28			13 44						*13 34*								14 30
Doncaster 7 d		13 42			13 48	13 54		14 02							14 24					14 42		14 48	14 56
Conisbrough d								14 09							14 31								
Mexborough d								14 13							14 35								
Swinton (S.Yorks) d								14 16					14 34		14 42								
Rotherham Central d								14 27					14 45		14 50								
Meadowhall 🚊 d		14 00		14 03	14 07		14 19	14 33				14 49	14 51		14 56					15 00	15 03	15 06	
Sheffield 7 🚊 a		14 07		14 15	14 17	14 20	14 30	14 41	14 51			14 57	15 02		15 04					15 07	15 15	15 17	15 20
d		14 11																		15 11			
Stockport 78 a	*15b02*	14 53					*15 24*												*16b02*	15 53			
Manchester Piccadilly 10 78 🚊 a	14 37	15 03					*15 36*												15 35	16 03			
Manchester Airport 85 ✈ a	*15 01*	15 33					*16c01*												*16 01*	16 33			

For general notes see front of timetable
For details of catering facilities see Directory of Train Operators

A From Leeds (Table 34)
B From Scarborough (Table 43)
C From Newcastle to Bristol Temple Meads (Table 51)
D From Huddersfield (Table 34)
E To Lincoln (Table 30)
G From Aberdeen (Table 229) to Bournemouth (Table 51)
H From Leeds (Table 31)
J To Newark North Gate (Table 27)
K From Bridlington (Table 43)
b Change at Manchester Piccadilly
c Change at Sheffield and Manchester Piccadilly

Due to Engineering Operations in the Sheffield area, services from Saturday 13 September on this Table had not been confirmed at time of going to press. These services will be issued in a special Supplement as soon as exact timings have been confirmed.

Table 29

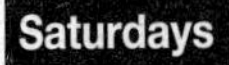

until 6 September

Hull and Cleethorpes → Doncaster → Meadowhall, Sheffield, Manchester and Manchester Airport
Cleethorpes → Barton-on-Humber

Network Diagram - see first page of Table 18

		NT	NT	XC	NT	NT	NT	NT	TP	TP	NT	NT	NT	XC	NT	NT	NT	XC		NT	NT	NT	HT	NT
				1 ◇					1 ◇	1 ◇				1 ◇				1 ◇					1 ◇	
		A	B	C	D	E					D		G	H	A	J	B	K		D	E	L		
				☕						🍴				☕				☕					⊠ ☕	
Hull	d							14 25	14 38			14 51	14 57										15 06	
Hessle	d							14 32																
Ferriby	d							14 37																
Brough	d							14 42	14 50			15 03	15 09										15 18	
Broomfleet	d																							
Gilberdyke	d							14 49																
Eastrington	d																							
Howden	d																						15 31	
Wressle	d																							
Selby	a								15 08			15 22											15 41	
	d								15 09			15 22											15 42	
York 8	33 a											15 53												
Saltmarshe	d																							
Goole	d							14 58					15 23											
Thorne North	d							15 06																
Cleethorpes	d									14 28												14 56		
New Clee	d																							
Grimsby Docks	d																							
Grimsby Town	a									14 35												15 02		
	d									14 36												15 04		
Great Coates	d																							
Healing	d																							
Stallingborough	d																							
Habrough	d									14 46												15 14		
Ulceby	d																							
Thornton Abbey	d																							
Goxhill	d																							
New Holland	d																							
Barrow Haven	d																							
Barton-on-Humber	a																							
Barton-on-Humber	🚌 d																							
Hull Bus Station	🚌 a																							
Barnetby	d									14 54												15a23		
Scunthorpe	a									15 10														
	d		14 18							15 10							15 17							
Althorpe	d		14 23														15 22							
Crowle	d		14 29														15 29							
Thorne South	d		14 38														15 37							
Hatfield & Stainforth	d		14 43					15 12									15 42							
Kirk Sandall	d		14 47					15 17									15 47							
Adwick	31 d						15 13																	16 13
Bentley (S.Yorks)	31 d						15 17																	16 17
Doncaster 7	31 a		14 58				15 22	15 27		15 40			15 47				15 58						16 01	16 22
London Kings Cross 15	⊖ 26 a							*17 28*					*17 43*				*18 10*						17 45	
York 8	26 d			14 44			*14 39*							15 27		15 12	*15 30*	15 44						
Doncaster 7	d		15 02				15 24			15 42			15 48	15 55			16 02							16 24
Conisbrough	d		15 09				15 31										16 09							16 31
Mexborough	d		15 13				15 35										16 13							16 35
Swinton (S.Yorks)	d		15 16			15 34	15 42									16 10	16 16				16 34			16 42
Rotherham Central	d		15 27			15 43	15 50									16 18	16 27				16 43			16 50
Meadowhall	🚋 d	15 19	15 33		15 49	15 51	15 56			16 00	16 06		16 09		16 19	16 24	16 33			16 49	16 51			16 56
Sheffield 7	🚋 a	15 30	15 41	15 51	15 57	16 02	16 04			16 07	16 15		16 17	16 20	16 30	16 35	16 41	16 51		16 57	17 02			17 04
	d									16 11														
Stockport	78 a	*16 24*							*17b02*	16 53						*17 24*								
Manchester Piccadilly 10	78 🚋 a	*16 36*							*16 35*	17 03						*17 35*								
Manchester Airport	85 ✈ a	*17c11*							*17 11*	17 39						*18c05*								

For general notes see front of timetable
For details of catering facilities see Directory of Train Operators

A From Huddersfield (Table 34)
B To Lincoln (Table 30)
C From Edinburgh (Table 51) to Penzance (Table 135)
D From Leeds (Table 34)
E From Leeds (Table 31)
G From Scarborough (Table 43)
H From Newcastle to Cardiff Central (Table 51)
J Via Pontefract Baghill (Table 33)
K From Edinburgh to Bournemouth (Table 51)
L To Sheffield via Retford (Table 30)
b Change at Manchester Piccadilly
c Change at Sheffield and Manchester Piccadilly

Due to Engineering Operations in the Sheffield area, services from Saturday 13 September on this Table had not been confirmed at time of going to press. These services will be issued in a special Supplement as soon as exact timings have been confirmed.

Table 29

until 6 September

Hull and Cleethorpes → Doncaster → Meadowhall, Sheffield, Manchester and Manchester Airport
Cleethorpes → Barton-on-Humber

Network Diagram - see first page of Table 18

Station		NT	NT	NT	EM	TP	TP	NT	NT	XC	NT	NT	XC	NT	NT	NT	NT	NT	TP	TP	NT	NT	XC	NT
			Bus		A	1 ◇	1 ◇	B	C	1 ◇ D	E	G	1 ◇ H		B	J		K	1 ◇	1 ◇	B	L	1 ◇ D	E
Hull	d			15 25		15 38			15 57					16 10				16 27	16 38			16 54		
Hessle	d			15 32														16 34						
Ferriby	d			15 37														16 39						
Brough	d			15 42		15 50			16 09					16 22				16 44	16 50			17 06		
Broomfleet	d																	16 49						
Gilberdyke	d			15 49										16 29				16 54				17 13		
Eastrington	d																							
Howden	d													16 36										
Wressle	d																							
Selby	a					16 08								16 46					17 08					
	d					16 09								16 47					17 09					
York 8	33 a													17 13										
Saltmarshe	d																	16 59						
Goole	d			15 58					16 24									17 04				17 22		
Thorne North	d			16 06														17 13						
Cleethorpes	d	15 00					15 28													16 28				
New Clee	d	15x03																						
Grimsby Docks	d	15 05																						
Grimsby Town	a	15 09					15 35													16 35				
	d	15 10			15 28		15 36													16 36				
Great Coates	d	15 14																						
Healing	d	15 17																						
Stallingborough	d	15 20																						
Habrough	d	15 26			15 37																			
Ulceby	d	15 29																						
Thornton Abbey	d	15 34																						
Goxhill	d	15 37																						
New Holland	d	15 41																						
Barrow Haven	d	15 44																						
Barton-on-Humber	a	15 50																						
Barton-on-Humber	Bus d		15 56																					
Hull Bus Station	Bus a		16 21																					
Barnetby	d				15a46		15 54													16 54				
Scunthorpe	a						16 10													17 09				
	d						16 10					16 18								17 10				
Althorpe	d											16 23												
Crowle	d											16 29												
Thorne South	d											16 38												
Hatfield & Stainforth	d			16 12								16 43						17 19						
Kirk Sandall	d			16 17								16 47						17 23						
Adwick	31 d																17 05							
Bentley (S.Yorks)	31 d																17 09							
Doncaster 7	31 a			16 28			16 40		16 46			16 58						17 34		17 40		17 45		
London Kings Cross 15	⊖ 26 a			18 28					18 46													19 40		
York 8	26 d						15 57			16 25			16 44				16 34						17 25	
Doncaster 7	d						16 42		16 48	16 53		17 02					17 24			17 42		17 48	17 55	
Conisbrough	d											17 09					17 31							
Mexborough	d											17 13					17 35							
Swinton (S.Yorks)	d											17 16				17 34	17 42							
Rotherham Central	d											17 27				17 45	17 50							
Meadowhall	d						17 00	17 03	17 06		17 19	17 33			17 49	17 51	17 56			18 00	18 04	18 06		18 19
Sheffield 7	a						17 07	17 15	17 17	17 18	17 30	17 41	17 51		17 57	18 02	18 05			18 07	18 15	18 18	18 20	18 30
	d						17 11													18 11				
Stockport	78 a					18b01	17 53				18 26								19b02	18 52				19 24
Manchester Piccadilly 10	78 a					17 35	18 03				18 35						19 33		18 35	19 03				19 35
Manchester Airport	85 ✈ a					18 05	18 38				19c08								19 08	19 34				20c05

For general notes see front of timetable
For details of catering facilities see Directory of Train Operators

A To Newark North Gate (Table 27)
B From Leeds (Table 34)
C From Bridlington (Table 43)
D From Newcastle to Bristol Temple Meads (Table 51)
E From Huddersfield (Table 34)
G To Lincoln (Table 30)
H From Edinburgh to Plymouth (Table 51)
J From Leeds (Table 31)
K From Scarborough (Table 43)
L From Beverley (Table 43)
b Change at Manchester Piccadilly
c Change at Sheffield and Manchester Piccadilly

Due to Engineering Operations in the Sheffield area, services from Saturday 13 September on this Table had not been confirmed at time of going to press. These services will be issued in a special Supplement as soon as exact timings have been confirmed.

Table 29

until 6 September

Hull and Cleethorpes → Doncaster → Meadowhall, Sheffield, Manchester and Manchester Airport
Cleethorpes → Barton-on-Humber

Network Diagram - see first page of Table 18

		NT	TP	EM	NT	NT	XC	NT	NT	NT	TP	NT	NT	EM	NT	NT	XC	NT	NT	TP	NT	NT	XC
			1 ◇	1 ◇			1 ◇				1 ◇						1 ◇			1 ◇			1 ◇
		A	B	C			D	E	G			E	H	J	H	K	L	H	N		Q		U
						🚌																	
Hull	d		17 00										17 18		17 42	17 55				18 03			
Hessle	d												17 25		17 49								
Ferriby	d												17 30		17 54								
Brough	d		17 12										17 35		17 59	18 07				18 15			
Broomfleet	d												17 40										
Gilberdyke	d												17 45		18 06								
Eastrington	d												17 49										
Howden	d												17 54										
Wressle	d												17 58										
Selby	a		17 30										18 06			18 25				18 33			
	d												18 06			18 26				18 34			
York 8	33 a												18 36										
Saltmarshe	d														18 12								
Goole	d														18 19 →			← 18 19					
Thorne North	d																	18 28					
Cleethorpes	d				17 00						17 28								18 06				
New Clee	d																						
Grimsby Docks	d				17 05																		
Grimsby Town	a				17 07						17 35								18 12				
	d				17 08						17 36			18 06					18 13				
Great Coates	d				17 12																		
Healing	d				17 15																		
Stallingborough	d				17 18																		
Habrough	d				17 24						17 46			18 16					18 23				
Ulceby	d				17 28																		
Thornton Abbey	d				17 32																		
Goxhill	d				17 35																		
New Holland	d				17 40																		
Barrow Haven	d				17 43																		
Barton-on-Humber	a				17 48																		
Barton-on-Humber	🚌 d					17 57																	
Hull Bus Station	🚌 a					18 23																	
Barnetby	d										17 54			18a25					18a34				
Scunthorpe	a										18 10												
	d	17 18									18 10											18 17	
Althorpe	d	17 23																				18 22	
Crowle	d	17 29																				18 29	
Thorne South	d	17 38																				18 37	
Hatfield & Stainforth	d	17 43																18 34				18 45	
Kirk Sandall	d	17 47																18 39				18 50	
Adwick	31 d			*17b54*							*18 14*												
Bentley (S.Yorks)	31 d			*17b58*							*18 18*												
Doncaster 7	31 a	17 58									18 40					18 45		18 51				19 01	
London Kings Cross 15	⊖ 26 a	*20 12*									*20 35*					*20 35*						*21 15*	
York 8	26 d	*17 31*		17 49			17 44										18 25					*18 28*	18 44
Doncaster 7	d	18 02		18 15						18 24	18 42					18 47	18 51					19 03	
Conisbrough	d	18 09								18 31												19 10	
Mexborough	d	18 13								18 35												19 14	
Swinton (S.Yorks)	d	18 16							18 34	18 41												19 17	
Rotherham Central	d	18 27							18 43	18 48												19 27	
Meadowhall	d	18 33		18 38				18 48	18 51	18 54	19 00	19 04				19 06					19 19	19 33	
Sheffield 7	a	18 41		18 45			18 51	18 57	19 02	19 04	19 07	19 15				19 15	19 20				19 30	19 42	19 51
	d										19 11												
Stockport	78 a										19 53									*20c28*	20 25		
Manchester Piccadilly 10	78 a										20 03									19 59	*20 36*		
Manchester Airport	85 a										20 34									*20 58*	*21e09*		

For general notes see front of timetable
For details of catering facilities see Directory of Train Operators

A To Lincoln (Table 30)
B To Huddersfield (Table 39)
C From Scarborough (Table 39) to St Pancras International (Table 53)
D From Edinburgh to Southampton Central (Table 51)
E From Leeds (Table 34)
G From Leeds (Table 31)
H From Beverley (Table 43)
J To Newark North Gate (Table 27)
K From Scarborough (Table 43)
L From Newcastle to Birmingham New Street (Table 51)
N To Sheffield via Retford (Table 30)
Q From Huddersfield (Table 34)
U From Edinburgh to Bristol Temple Meads (Table 51)
b Change at Doncaster
c Change at Manchester Piccadilly
e Change at Sheffield and Manchester Piccadilly

Due to Engineering Operations in the Sheffield area, services from Saturday 13 September on this Table had not been confirmed at time of going to press. These services will be issued in a special Supplement as soon as exact timings have been confirmed.

Table 29

Saturdays until 6 September

Hull and Cleethorpes → Doncaster → Meadowhall, Sheffield, Manchester and Manchester Airport
Cleethorpes → Barton-on-Humber

Network Diagram - see first page of Table 18

		NT	NT	HT	NT	NT	TP	NT	NT	NT	NT	TP	NT	NT	NT	NT	XC	NT	NT	EM	NT	TP	NT	TP
				1 ◇			1 ◇					1 ◇					1 ◇					1 ◇		1 ◇
		A	B					A				D			E	G	H J	K	A	L	B	D	A	
				⊠ ☕			trolley							bus			☕							
Hull	d			18 12		18 24			18 46	18 53		19 00						19 24				19 56		
Hessle	d					18 31												19 31						
Ferriby	d					18 36												19 36						
Brough	d			18 25		18 41			18 58	19 05		19 12						19 41				20 08		
Broomfleet	d																							
Gilberdyke	d					18 48			19 05									19 48						
Eastrington	d																							
Howden	d			18 37					19 12															
Wressle	d																							
Selby	a			18 46					19 22			19 30										20 26		
	d			18 47					19 22															
York 8	33 a								19 50													*21 00*		
Saltmarshe	d																							
Goole	d					18 57				19 19								19 58						
Thorne North	d					19 05												20 06						
Cleethorpes	d						18 28						19 00											19 28
New Clee	d																							
Grimsby Docks	d												19 05											
Grimsby Town	a						18 35						19 07											19 35
	d						18 36						19 08							19 28				19 36
Great Coates	d												19 12											
Healing	d												19 15											
Stallingborough	d												19 18											
Habrough	d						18 46						19 24							19 38				19 46
Ulceby	d												19 28											
Thornton Abbey	d												19 32											
Goxhill	d												19 35											
New Holland	d												19 40											
Barrow Haven	d												19 43											
Barton-on-Humber	a												19 48											
Barton-on-Humber	bus d													19 55										
Hull Bus Station	bus a													20 20										
Barnetby	d						18 54													19a46				19 54
Scunthorpe	a						19 10																	20 10
	d						19 10				19 15													20 10
Althorpe	d										19 20													
Crowle	d										19 26													
Thorne South	d										19 35													
Hatfield & Stainforth	d					19 12					19 40							20 13						
Kirk Sandall	d					19 17					19 44							20 17						
Adwick	31 d				*18 53*																			*19 53*
Bentley (S.Yorks)	31 d				*18 57*																			*19 57*
Doncaster 7	31 a			19 04		19 26	19 40			19 46	19 56							20 30						20 40
London Kings Cross 15	⊖ 26 a			20 46			*21 48*				*21 48*													*22 47*
York 8	26 d																19 44							*20 06*
Doncaster 7	d				19 25		19 42			19 49						20 03								20 42
Conisbrough	d				19 32											20 10								20 48
Mexborough	d				19 36											20 14								20 52
Swinton (S.Yorks)	d		19 34		19 43											20 17					20 34			20 55
Rotherham Central	d		19 43		19 51											20 29					20 43			21 01
Meadowhall	tram d	19 49	19 52		19 56		20 00	20 04		20 07					20 24	20 35			20 48		20 51		21 03	21 07
Sheffield 7	tram a	19 57	20 02		20 05		20 07	20 15		20 18					20 35	20 42	20 51		20 57		21 02		21 15	21 18
	d						20 11																	
Stockport	78 a						20 53			*21 16*														
Manchester Piccadilly 10	78 tram a						21 03			*21 26*														
Manchester Airport	85 ✈ a						21 34			*21b58*														

For general notes see front of timetable
For details of catering facilities see Directory of Train Operators

A From Leeds (Table 34)
B From Leeds (Table 31)
D To Leeds (Table 39)
E From Huddersfield (Table 34)
G To Worksop (Table 30)
H From Newcastle to Birmingham New Street (Table 51)
J ☕ to Leeds
K From Scarborough (Table 43)
L To Lincoln (Table 27)
b Change at Sheffield and Manchester Piccadilly

Due to Engineering Operations in the Sheffield area, services from Saturday 13 September on this Table had not been confirmed at time of going to press. These services will be issued in a special Supplement as soon as exact timings have been confirmed.

Table 29

until 6 September

Hull and Cleethorpes → Doncaster → Meadowhall, Sheffield, Manchester and Manchester Airport Cleethorpes → Barton-on-Humber

Network Diagram - see first page of Table 18

		NT	NT	NT	XC	NT	NT	TP	NT	NT	NT	NT	NT	TP	NT	NT	NT	NT	NT	NT	NT	NT
					1 ◇			1 ◇						1 ◇								
			A	B	C	D	E				🚌				A	D	E			A	E	B
Hull	d			20 03					20 51					21 33								22 22
Hessle	d			20 10																		
Ferriby	d			20 15																		
Brough	d			20 20					21 03					21 45								22 34
Broomfleet	d																					
Gilberdyke	d			20 27										21 52								
Eastrington	d																					
Howden	d																					
Wressle	d																					
Selby	a													22 07								
	d													22 07								
York 8	33 a													22 53								
Saltmarshe	d																					
Goole	d			20 36					21 17													22 48
Thorne North	d			20 44					21 26													22 57
Cleethorpes	d							20 28		21 00												
New Clee	d																					
Grimsby Docks	d									21 05												
Grimsby Town	a							20 35		21 07												
	d							20 36		21 08												
Great Coates	d									21 12												
Healing	d									21 15												
Stallingborough	d									21 18												
Habrough	d									21 24												
Ulceby	d									21 27												
Thornton Abbey	d									21 32												
Goxhill	d									21 35												
New Holland	d									21 39												
Barrow Haven	d									21 42												
Barton-on-Humber	a									21 48												
Barton-on-Humber	🚌 d										21 55											
Hull Bus Station	🚌 a										22 20											
Barnetby	d							20 54														
Scunthorpe	a							21 09														
	d	20 18						21 10					21 21						22 21			
Althorpe	d	20 23											21 26						22 26			
Crowle	d	20 30											21 32						22 32			
Thorne South	d	20 38											21 40						22 41			
Hatfield & Stainforth	d	20 43		20 51					21 31				21 46						22 46			23 03
Kirk Sandall	d	20 48		20 56					21 36				21 50						22 50			23 07
Adwick	31 d							*20 57*														*22 50*
Bentley (S.Yorks)	31 d							*21 01*														*22 54*
Doncaster 7	31 a	20 59		21 05				21 40	21 46				22 02						23 02			23 18
London Kings Cross 15	⊖ 26 a																					
York 8	26 d				20 44													21 52				
Doncaster 7	d			21 07				21 42	21 49			21 54						22 24				23 19
Conisbrough	d			21 14								22 01						22 31				23 26
Mexborough	d			21 18								22 05						22 35				23 30
Swinton (S.Yorks)	d			21 21			21 35					22 08					22 34	22 38			23 30	23 33
Rotherham Central	d			21 28			21 44					22 16					22 43	22 48			23 38	23 43
Meadowhall	🚊 d		21 24	21 35		21 49	21 52	22 00	22 09			22 22			22 25	22 49	22 51	22 56		23 26	23 43	23 48
Sheffield 7	🚊 a		21 35	21 45	21 51	21 57	22 07	22 07	22 18			22 32			22 35	22 57	23 02	23 05		23 35	23 58	23 58
	d																					
Stockport	78 a							*23 21*														
Manchester Piccadilly 10	78 🚊 a							*23 37*						23 37								
Manchester Airport	85 ✈ a													*00 45*								

For general notes see front of timetable
For details of catering facilities see Directory of Train Operators

A From Huddersfield (Table 34)
B From Bridlington (Table 43)
C From Edinburgh to Birmingham New Street (Table 51)
D From Leeds (Table 34)
E From Leeds (Table 31)

Due to Engineering Operations in the Sheffield area, services from Saturday 13 September on this Table had not been confirmed at time of going to press. These services will be issued in a special Supplement as soon as exact timings have been confirmed.

Table 29

Sundays

Hull and Cleethorpes → Doncaster → Meadowhall, Sheffield, Manchester and Manchester Airport Cleethorpes → Barton-on-Humber

until 13 July

Network Diagram - see first page of Table 18

	NT	TP	VT	NT	NT	EM	NT	NT	NT	NT	XC	NT	TP	NT	TP	NT	TP	NT	HT	NT
		1 ◇	1 ◇			1 ◇					R 1		1 ◇		1 ◇		1 ◇		1 ◇	
			A ☕		B	C ☕	D		E		G ☕		H			B		B	⊠ ☕	
Hull d								08 42				08 54	09 05	09 41					10 12	
Hessle d								08 49												
Ferriby d								08 54												
Brough d								08 59				09 06	09 17	09 53					10 24	
Broomfleet d																				
Gilberdyke d								09 06						10 00						
Eastrington d																				
Howden d																				
Wressle d																			10 36	
Selby a												09 25	09 36						10 46	
d												09 25	09 36						10 47	
York 8 33 a												09 54								
Saltmarshe d																				
Goole d								09 15		09 43				10 09						
Thorne North d										09 51										
Cleethorpes d																	09 41			
New Clee d																				
Grimsby Docks d																				
Grimsby Town a																	09 49			
d																	09 49			
Great Coates d																				
Healing d																				
Stallingborough d																				
Habrough d																	09 59			
Ulceby d																				
Thornton Abbey d																				
Goxhill d																				
New Holland d																				
Barrow Haven d																				
Barton-on-Humber a																				
Barton-on-Humber 🚌 d																				
Hull Bus Station 🚌 a																				
Barnetby d																	10 08			
Scunthorpe a																	10 23			
d																	10 23			
Althorpe d																				
Crowle d																				
Thorne South d																				
Hatfield & Stainforth d										09 57				10 21						
Kirk Sandall d										10 02				10 26						
Adwick 31 d																				*10 43*
Bentley (S.Yorks) 31 d																				*10 47*
Doncaster 7 31 a								09 38		10 11				10 36			10 53		11 03	
London Kings Cross 15 ⊖ 26 a								*11 55*		*12 19*				*12 37*					12 48	
York 8 26 d						*09 00*					09b27				*10 02*		*10 23*			
Doncaster 7 d	08 03		09 03	09 13		09 33		09 39		10 13	10 33				10 42		10 55			11 13
Conisbrough d	08 10			09 20						10 20										11 20
Mexborough d	08 14			09 24						10 24										11 24
Swinton (S.Yorks) d	08 17			09 28			09 36			10 27										11 29
Rotherham Central d	08 25			09 35			09c48			10 36										11 37
Meadowhall 🚊 d	08 30	09 00		09 41	09 41		09 54	10 00	10 33	10 42					11 00	11 05	11 13	11 33		11 42
Sheffield 7 🚊 a	08 41	09 10	09 26	09 51	09 51	09 57	10 04	10 11	10 43	10 52	10 57				11 10	11 15	11 25	11 43		11 51
d		09 13													11 13					
Stockport 78 a		09 58						*11 18*					*11e38*		11 58		*12 23*			
Manchester Piccadilly 10 78 🚊 a		10 08						*11 32*					*11 05*		12 08		*12 36*			
Manchester Airport 85 ✈ a		10 36						*12f11*					*11 33*		12 37		*13f10*			

For general notes see front of timetable
For details of catering facilities see Directory of Train Operators

A From Leeds to Bournemouth (Table 51)
B From Leeds (Table 34)
C From Leeds to St Pancras International (Table 53)
D From Leeds (Table 31)
E From Huddersfield (Table 34)
G To Plymouth (Table 51)
H To Liverpool Lime Street (Table 39)
b By changing at Doncaster, passengers may depart at 1002
c Arr. 0945
e Change at Manchester Piccadilly
f Change at Sheffield and Manchester Piccadilly

Table 29

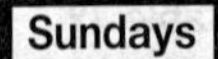

Sundays

until 13 July

Hull and Cleethorpes → Doncaster → Meadowhall, Sheffield, Manchester and Manchester Airport
Cleethorpes → Barton-on-Humber

Network Diagram - see first page of Table 18

	NT	XC	NT	NT	TP	TP	NT	NT	NT	NT	NT	XC	TP	NT	NT	HT	NT	NT	XC
		R 1			1 ◇	1 ◇						R 1	1 ◇			1 ◇			R 1
	A	B		Bus			C	D	E			G		H				J	K
Hull d	10 41				11 01						11 41				11 54	12 12		12 41	
Hessle d																			
Ferriby d																			
Brough d	10 53				11 13						11 53				12 06	12 24		12 53	
Broomfleet d																			
Gilberdyke d	11 00										12 00							13 00	
Eastrington d																			
Howden d																12 36			
Wressle d																			
Selby a					11 31										12 25	12 46			
Selby d					11 32										12 25	12 47			
York 8 33 a															12 56				
Saltmarshe d																			
Goole d	11 09									11 43	12 09							13 09	
Thorne North d										11 51									
Cleethorpes d			09 56			10 28													
New Clee d			09x59																
Grimsby Docks d			10 01																
Grimsby Town a			10 04			10 35													
Grimsby Town d			10 04			10 36													
Great Coates d			10 08																
Healing d			10 11																
Stallingborough d			10 14																
Habrough d			10 20			10 46													
Ulceby d			10 24																
Thornton Abbey d			10 28																
Goxhill d			10 31																
New Holland d			10 36																
Barrow Haven d			10 39																
Barton-on-Humber a			10 45																
Barton-on-Humber (bus) d				10 55															
Hull Bus Station (bus) a				11 19															
Barnetby d						10 54													
Scunthorpe a						11 10													
Scunthorpe d						11 10													
Althorpe d																			
Crowle d																			
Thorne South d																			
Hatfield & Stainforth d										11 57									
Kirk Sandall d										12 02									
Adwick 31 d																	*12 43*		
Bentley (S.Yorks) 31 d																	*12 47*		
Doncaster 7 31 a	11 32					11 41				12 13	12 32					13 05		13 32	
London Kings Cross 15 ⊖ 26 a						*13 36*					*14 42*					14 54			
York 8 26 d		10 28								*11 29*		11 28					*12 29*	*12 57*	12b28
Doncaster 7 d	11 33	11 38				11 42				12 16		12 33	12 42				13 13	13 33	13 38
Conisbrough d										12 23							13 20		
Mexborough d										12 27							13 24		
Swinton (S.Yorks) d								11 55		12 30							13 29		
Rotherham Central d								12 04		12 38							13 36		
Meadowhall d	11 51					12 00	12 05	12 10	12 33	12 43			13 00	13 33			13 42	13 51	
Sheffield 7 a	12 03	12 05				12 10	12 14	12 21	12 43	12 55		13 08	13 10	13 43			13 55	14 03	14 03
Sheffield 7 d						12 13							13 13						
Stockport 78 a					*13c21*	12 56		*13 23*	*13 57*				14 01						
Manchester Piccadilly 10 78 a					12 57	13 10		*13 36*	*14 10*				14 11						
Manchester Airport 85 a					*13 33*	13 39		14e14					14 36						

For general notes see front of timetable
For details of catering facilities see Directory of Train Operators

A From Bridlington (Table 43)
B From Newcastle to Bournemouth (Table 51)
C From Leeds (Table 34)
D From Leeds (Table 31)
E From Huddersfield (Table 34)
G From Edinburgh (Table 51) to Penzance (Table 135)
H From Leeds (Table 34) to Lincoln (Table 30)
J From Scarborough (Table 43)
K From Edinburgh to Bournemouth (Table 51)
b By changing at Doncaster, passengers may depart at 1257
c Change at Manchester Piccadilly
e Change at Sheffield and Manchester Piccadilly

Table 29

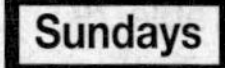

Sundays

until 13 July

Hull and Cleethorpes → Doncaster → Meadowhall, Sheffield, Manchester and Manchester Airport
Cleethorpes → Barton-on-Humber

Network Diagram - see first page of Table 18

		TP	TP	NT	NT	NT	NT	NT	NT	NT	NT	XC	TP	NT	HT	NT	EM	NT	NT	XC	TP
		1 ◇	1 ◇	A	B		bus	C			D	R 1 E ☕	1 ◇	A	1 ◇ ☒ ☕		G		H	R 1 J ☕	1 ◇
Hull	d	12 50								13 27	13 41				14 10			14 28	14 41		14 50
Hessle	d																	14 35			
Ferriby	d																	14 40			
Brough	d	13 02								13 39	13 53				14 22			14 45	14 53		15 02
Broomfleet	d																				
Gilberdyke	d										14 00								15 00		
Eastrington	d																				
Howden	d														14 34						
Wressle	d																				
Selby	a	13 21								13 58					14 44			15 04			15 21
	d	13 21								13 58					14 45			15 04			15 21
York 8	33 a									14 22								15 30			
Saltmarshe	d																				
Goole	d								13 43		14 09								15 09		
Thorne North	d								13 51												
Cleethorpes	d		12 28			12 56							13 28				13 57				
New Clee	d					12x59															
Grimsby Docks	d					13 01															
Grimsby Town	a		12 35			13 04							13 35				14 03				
	d		12 36			13 04							13 36				14 04				
Great Coates	d					13 08															
Healing	d					13 11															
Stallingborough	d					13 14															
Habrough	d					13 20											14 13				
Ulceby	d					13 24															
Thornton Abbey	d					13 29															
Goxhill	d					13 32															
New Holland	d					13 36															
Barrow Haven	d					13 39															
Barton-on-Humber	a					13 45															
Barton-on-Humber	bus d						13 55														
Hull Bus Station	bus a						14 19														
Barnetby	d		12 54										13 54				14a22				
Scunthorpe	a		13 10										14 10								
	d		13 10										14 10								
Althorpe	d																				
Crowle	d																				
Thorne South	d																				
Hatfield & Stainforth	d								13 57												
Kirk Sandall	d								14 02												
Adwick	31 d															*14 43*					
Bentley (S.Yorks)	31 d															*14 47*					
Doncaster 7	31 a		13 41						14 11		14 32		14 41		15 05				15 32		
London Kings Cross 15	⊖ 26 a		*15 37*						*16 11*				*16 29*		16 50						
York 8	26 d								*13 33*			13b28	*14 05*			*14 36*				14c28	
Doncaster 7	d		13 42						14 13		14 33	14 39	14 42			15 13			15 33	15 38	
Conisbrough	d								14 20							15 20					
Mexborough	d								14 24							15 24					
Swinton (S.Yorks)	d				13 58				14 29							15 29					
Rotherham Central	d				14 06				14 36							15 37					
Meadowhall	⇌ d		14 00	14 05	14 11			14 33	14 42		14 52		15 00	15 33		15 42			15 52		
Sheffield 7	⇌ a		14 09	14 15	14 21			14 43	14 52		15 03	15 03	15 10	15 44		15 51			16 01	16 02	
	d		14 12										15 13								
Stockport	78 a	*15e14*	15 01		*15 24*								16 03								*17e14*
Manchester Piccadilly 10	78 ⇌ a	14 52	15 13		*15 34*								16 13								16 50
Manchester Airport	85 ✈ a	*15 18*	15 37		*16f11*								16 36								*17 18*

For general notes see front of timetable
For details of catering facilities see Directory of Train Operators

- **A** From Leeds (Table 34)
- **B** From Leeds (Table 31)
- **C** From Huddersfield (Table 34)
- **D** From Scarborough (Table 43)
- **E** From Edinburgh to Plymouth (Table 51)
- **G** To Nottingham (Table 27)
- **H** From Bridlington (Table 43)
- **J** From Glasgow Central to Bournemouth (Table 51)
- **b** By changing at Doncaster, passengers may depart at 1405
- **c** By changing at Doncaster, passengers may depart at 1436
- **e** Change at Manchester Piccadilly
- **f** Change at Sheffield and Manchester Piccadilly

Table 29

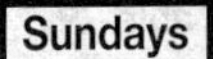

Sundays until 13 July

Hull and Cleethorpes → Doncaster → Meadowhall, Sheffield, Manchester and Manchester Airport
Cleethorpes → Barton-on-Humber

Network Diagram - see first page of Table 18

		TP	NT		NT	NT	NT	NT	NT		XC	TP	NT	NT	NT		HT	EM	NT	XC	TP		TP	NT
		1 ◇									R 1	1 ◇					1 ◇	1 ◇		R 1	1 ◇		1 ◇	
			A		B				C		D		E					G	H	J				A
								bus																
Hull	d								15 41						16 00		16 21		16 41		16 50			
Hessle	d																							
Ferriby	d																							
Brough	d								15 53						16 12		16 33		16 53		17 02			
Broomfleet	d																							
Gilberdyke	d								16 00										17 00					
Eastrington	d																							
Howden	d																16 45							
Wressle	d																							
Selby	a														16 31		16 55				17 20			
	d														16 31		16 56				17 21			
York 8	33 a														16 57									
Saltmarshe	d																							
Goole	d					15 43			16 09										17 09					
Thorne North	d					15 51																		
Cleethorpes	d	14 28					15 02					15 28											16 28	
New Clee	d						15x05																	
Grimsby Docks	d						15 07																	
Grimsby Town	a	14 35					15 10					15 35											16 35	
	d	14 36					15 10					15 36											16 36	
Great Coates	d						15 14																	
Healing	d						15 17																	
Stallingborough	d						15 20																	
Habrough	d	14 46					15 26																	
Ulceby	d						15 30																	
Thornton Abbey	d						15 34																	
Goxhill	d						15 37																	
New Holland	d						15 42																	
Barrow Haven	d						15 45																	
Barton-on-Humber	a						15 50																	
Barton-on-Humber	bus d							15 55																
Hull Bus Station	bus a							16 19																
Barnetby	d	14 54										15 54											16 54	
Scunthorpe	a	15 10										16 10											17 10	
	d	15 10										16 10											17 10	
Althorpe	d																							
Crowle	d																							
Thorne South	d																							
Hatfield & Stainforth	d					15 57																		
Kirk Sandall	d					16 02																		
Adwick	31 d													16 43										
Bentley (S.Yorks)	31 d													16 47										
Doncaster 7	31 a	15 41				16 11			16 32			16 41					17 14		17 31				17 41	
London Kings Cross 15	⊖ 26 a	17 50				18 15						18 38					19 06						19 48	
York 8	26 d	14 36				15 34					15b28	16 03		16 29				17 01		16c28			17 03	
Doncaster 7	d	15 42				16 13			16 33		16 39	16 42		17 13				17 25	17 32	17 38			17 42	
Conisbrough	d					16 20								17 21										
Mexborough	d					16 24								17 25										
Swinton (S.Yorks)	d		15 55			16 29								17 29										17 55
Rotherham Central	d		16 05			16 37								17 36										18 05
Meadowhall	tram d	16 00	16 11		16 33	16 42			16 52			17 00	17 33	17 42					17 52				18 00	18 11
Sheffield 7	tram a	16 10	16 21		16 43	16 51			17 03		17 03	17 10	17 43	17 52				17 57	18 02	18 07			18 10	18 23
	d	16 13										17 13											18 13	
Stockport	78 a	16 56	17 21									17 55	18 56								19e17		19 00	19 20
Manchester Piccadilly 10	78 tram a	17 11	17 36									18 12	19 10								18 52		19 12	19 32
Manchester Airport	85 ✈ a	17 36	18f11									18 36									19 18		19 36	20f11

For general notes see front of timetable
For details of catering facilities see Directory of Train Operators

A From Leeds (Table 31)
B From Huddersfield (Table 34)
C From Scarborough (Table 43)
D From Glasgow Central to Plymouth (Table 51)
E From Leeds (Table 34)
G To St Pancras International (Table 53)
H From Bridlington (Table 43)
J From Edinburgh to Southampton Central (Table 51)
b By changing at Doncaster, passengers may depart at 1603
c By changing at Doncaster, passengers may depart at 1703
e Change at Manchester Piccadilly
f Change at Sheffield and Manchester Piccadilly

Table 29

Sundays

until 13 July

Hull and Cleethorpes → Doncaster → Meadowhall, Sheffield, Manchester and Manchester Airport Cleethorpes → Barton-on-Humber

Network Diagram - see first page of Table 18

		NT	NT	NT	NT	GR		NT	XC	TP	TP	NT		NT	NT	NT	HT	XC		NT	TP	NT	NT	NT
						R 1			1◇	1◇	1◇						1◇	1◇			1◇			
		A	B					C	D			E						G		H		J	B	
						catering			catering							bus	catering	catering						
Hull	d				17 23	17 30		17 41			18 10						18 30			18 38				
Hessle	d																							
Ferriby	d																							
Brough	d				17 35	17 42		17 53			18 22						18 42			18 50				
Broomfleet	d																							
Gilberdyke	d							18 00																
Eastrington	d																			18 57				
Howden	d																18 54							
Wressle	d																							
Selby	a				17 54	18 05					18 41						19 04							
	d				17 54	18 05					18 41						19 05							
York 8	33 a				18 23																			
Saltmarshe	d																							
Goole	d			17 43				18 09												19 06				
Thorne North	d			17 51																19 14				
Cleethorpes	d									17 28					17 56						18 28			
New Clee	d														17x59									
Grimsby Docks	d														18 01									
Grimsby Town	a									17 35					18 04						18 35			
	d									17 36					18 04						18 36			
Great Coates	d														18 08									
Healing	d														18 11									
Stallingborough	d														18 14									
Habrough	d									17 46					18 20									
Ulceby	d														18 24									
Thornton Abbey	d														18 28									
Goxhill	d														18 31									
New Holland	d														18 36									
Barrow Haven	d														18 39									
Barton-on-Humber	a														18 45									
Barton-on-Humber	bus d															18 55								
Hull Bus Station	bus a															19 19								
Barnetby	d									17 54											18 54			
Scunthorpe	a									18 10											19 10			
	d									18 10											19 10			
Althorpe	d																							
Crowle	d																							
Thorne South	d																							
Hatfield & Stainforth	d			17 57																19 20				
Kirk Sandall	d			18 02																19 25				
Adwick	31 d													18 43										
Bentley (S.Yorks)	31 d													18 47										
Doncaster 7	31 a			18 11		18 23		18 33		18 41							19 21			19 35	19 41			
London Kings Cross 15	⊖ 26 a			20 12		20b23				20 38							21 12				21 47			
York 8	26 d	17 17		17 35					17c28	18 05				18 29				18 28			19 05			19 30
Doncaster 7	d			18 13				18 34	18 38	18 42				19 15				19 34		19 37	19 42			20 14
Conisbrough	d			18 20										19 22										20 21
Mexborough	d			18 24										19 26										20 25
Swinton (S.Yorks)	d	18 11		18 29										19 29								19 55		20 32
Rotherham Central	d	18 20		18 37										19 39								20 06		20 39
Meadowhall	tram d	18 26	18 33	18 42				18 52		19 00		19 33		19 44						19 56	20 00	20 11	20 37	20 45
Sheffield 7	tram a	18 35	18 42	18 51				19 03	19 08	19 10		19 44		19 53				19 58		20 07	20 10	20 23	20 45	20 53
	d									19 13											20 13			
Stockport	78 a	19 46								20 00	20e38										20 54	21 16		
Manchester Piccadilly 10	78 tram a	19 59								20 09	20 11										21 04	21 31		
Manchester Airport	85 ✈ a	20f33								20 36	20 52										21 36	22f11		

For general notes see front of timetable
For details of catering facilities see Directory of Train Operators

- **A** Via Pontefract Baghill (Table 33)
- **B** From Huddersfield (Table 34)
- **C** From Scarborough (Table 43)
- **D** From Aberdeen (Table 229) to Bristol Temple Meads (Table 51)
- **E** From Leeds (Table 34)
- **G** From Edinburgh to Bristol Temple Meads (Table 51)
- **H** From Bridlington (Table 43)
- **J** From Leeds (Table 31)
- **b** By changing at Doncaster, passengers may arrive at 2012
- **c** By changing at Doncaster, passengers may depart at 1805
- **e** Change at Manchester Piccadilly
- **f** Change at Sheffield and Manchester Piccadilly

Table 29

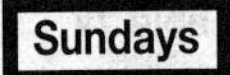

Sundays

until 13 July

Hull and Cleethorpes → Doncaster → Meadowhall, Sheffield, Manchester and Manchester Airport
Cleethorpes → Barton-on-Humber

Network Diagram - see first page of Table 18

		XC	TP		NT	TP	EM	NT	NT		NT	XC	NT	TP	TP		NT	NT	NT	XC	NT			
		1 ◇	1 ◇			1 ◇						1 ◇		1 ◇	1 ◇					1 ◇				
		A				B	C	D				E	G		B		H	J	K	L	D			
		☕																						
Hull	d				18 53	19 04			20 22		20 30				21 00				21 15					
Hessle	d																		21 22					
Ferriby	d																		21 27					
Brough	d				19 05	19 16			20 34		20 42				21 12				21 32					
Broomfleet	d																							
Gilberdyke	d										20 49								21 39					
Eastrington	d																							
Howden	d																							
Wressle	d																							
Selby	a				19 24	19 35			20 53						21 31									
	d				19 24				20 53															
York 8	33 a				19 52				21 18															
Saltmarshe	d																							
Goole	d										20 58								21 48					
Thorne North	d																		21 56					
Cleethorpes	d		19 28				20 01							20 28										
New Clee	d																							
Grimsby Docks	d																							
Grimsby Town	a		19 35				20 07							20 35										
	d		19 36				20 08							20 36										
Great Coates	d																							
Healing	d																							
Stallingborough	d																							
Habrough	d		19 46				20 18							20 46										
Ulceby	d																							
Thornton Abbey	d																							
Goxhill	d																							
New Holland	d																							
Barrow Haven	d																							
Barton-on-Humber	a																							
Barton-on-Humber	🚌 d																							
Hull Bus Station	🚌 a																							
Barnetby	d		19 54				20a26							20 54										
Scunthorpe	a		20 10											21 10										
	d		20 10											21 10										
Althorpe	d																							
Crowle	d																							
Thorne South	d																							
Hatfield & Stainforth	d																		22 02					
Kirk Sandall	d																		22 07					
Adwick	31 d										20 54								21 43					
Bentley (S.Yorks)	31 d										20 58								21 47					
Doncaster 7	31 a		20 41								21 21			21 41					22 17					
London Kings Cross 15	⊖ 26 a		23 14											23 50										
York 8	26 d	19b28	20 02								20 40	20c28	20 44						21 28	21 25				
Doncaster 7	d	20 34	20 42								21 23	21 33		21 42					22 20	22 33				
Conisbrough	d		20 49																22 27					
Mexborough	d		20 53																22 31					
Swinton (S.Yorks)	d		20 56										21 38					22 32	22 37					
Rotherham Central	d		21 02								21 39		21 49					22 40	22 44					
Meadowhall	🚊 d		21 08					21 32			21 45		21 54	22 00			22 41	22 45	22 50		23 33			
Sheffield 7	🚊 a	20 59	21 17					21 43			21 56	21 57	22 05	22 10			22 52	22 54	22 58	23 03	23 43			
	d		21 19																					
Stockport	78 a		22 00					23 00																
Manchester Piccadilly 10	78 🚊 a		22 14					23 13																
Manchester Airport	85 ✈ a		22 36					23e49																

For general notes see front of timetable
For details of catering facilities see Directory of Train Operators

A ☕ to Leeds
B To Leeds (Table 39)
C To Nottingham (Table 27)
D From Leeds (Table 34)
E From Edinburgh to Birmingham New Street (Table 51)
G Via Pontefract Baghill (Table 33)
H From Barnsley (Table 34)
J From Leeds (Table 31)
K From Scarborough (Table 43)
L From Edinburgh (Table 26) to Derby (Table 53)
b By changing at Doncaster, passengers may depart at 2002
c By changing at Doncaster, passengers may depart at 2040
e Change at Sheffield and Manchester Piccadilly

Table 29

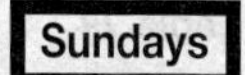

Sundays

Hull and Cleethorpes → Doncaster → Meadowhall, Sheffield, Manchester and Manchester Airport
Cleethorpes → Barton-on-Humber

20 July to 7 September

Network Diagram - see first page of Table 18

	NT	TP	NT	NT	XC	NT	NT	EM		NT	XC	NT	NT	TP	NT	TP	NT		TP	NT	HT	NT	NT
		1 ◇			1 ◇			1 ◇			R 1			1 ◇		1 ◇			1 ◇		1 ◇		
				A	B	C		D		E	G						A			A			🚌
					☕			☕			☕										☒ ☕		
Hull d							08 42						08 54	09 20	09 41						10 12		
Hessle d							08 49																
Ferriby d							08 54																
Brough d							08 59						09 06	09 32	09 53						10 24		
Broomfleet d																							
Gilberdyke d							09 06								10 00								
Eastrington d																							
Howden d																					10 36		
Wressle d																							
Selby a													09 25	09 51							10 46		
Selby d													09 25	09 51							10 47		
York 8 33 a													09 54										
Saltmarshe d																							
Goole d							09 15					09 43			10 09								
Thorne North d												09 51											
Cleethorpes d																			09 41			09 56	
New Clee d																						09x59	
Grimsby Docks d																						10 01	
Grimsby Town a																			09 49			10 04	
Grimsby Town d																			09 49			10 04	
Great Coates d																						10 08	
Healing d																						10 11	
Stallingborough d																						10 14	
Habrough d																			09 59			10 20	
Ulceby d																						10 24	
Thornton Abbey d																						10 28	
Goxhill d																						10 31	
New Holland d																						10 36	
Barrow Haven d																						10 39	
Barton-on-Humber a																						10 45	
Barton-on-Humber 🚌 d																							10 55
Hull Bus Station 🚌 a																							11 19
Barnetby d																			10 08				
Scunthorpe a																			10 23				
Scunthorpe d																			10 23				
Althorpe d																							
Crowle d																							
Thorne South d																							
Hatfield & Stainforth d												09 57			10 21								
Kirk Sandall d												10 02			10 26								
Adwick 31 d																							
Bentley (S.Yorks) 31 d																							
Doncaster 7 31 a							09 38					10 11			10 36				10 53		11 03		
London Kings Cross 15 ⊖ 26 a							11 55					12 19			12 37						12 48		
York 8 26 d					09 00						09 13					10 02			10 23				
Doncaster 7 d	08 03		09 13		09 34		09 39	10 05				10 13				10 42			10 55				
Conisbrough d	08 10		09 20									10 20											
Mexborough d	08 14		09 24									10 24											
Swinton (S.Yorks) d	08 17		09 28			09 36						10 27											
Rotherham Central d	08 25		09 35			09b48						10 36											
Meadowhall 🚊 d	08 30	09 00	09 41	09 41		09 54	10 00			10 33		10 42				11 00	11 05		11 13	11 33			
Sheffield 7 🚊 a	08 41	09 10	09 51	09 51	09 57	10 04	10 09	10 30		10 43	10 46	10 52				11 10	11 15		11 25	11 43			
Sheffield d		09 13														11 13							
Stockport 78 a		09 58					11 18							12c00		11 58			12 23				
Manchester Piccadilly 10 78 🚊 a		10 08					11 32							11 33		12 08			12 36				
Manchester Airport 85 ✈ a		10 33					12e02							12 02		12 33			13e11				

For general notes see front of timetable
For details of catering facilities see Directory of Train Operators

A From Leeds (Table 34)
B From Leeds to Bournemouth (Table 51)
C From Leeds (Table 31)
D From Leeds to St Pancras International (Table 53)
E From Huddersfield (Table 34)
G To Plymouth (Table 51)
b Arr. 0945
c Change at Manchester Piccadilly
e Change at Sheffield and Manchester Piccadilly

Due to Engineering Operations in the Sheffield area, services from Sunday 14 September on this Table had not been confirmed at time of going to press. These services will be issued in a special Supplement as soon as exact timings have been confirmed.

Table 29

Sundays

20 July to 7 September

Hull and Cleethorpes → Doncaster → Meadowhall, Sheffield, Manchester and Manchester Airport Cleethorpes → Barton-on-Humber

Network Diagram - see first page of Table 18

		NT	NT	XC	TP	TP	NT	XC	NT	NT	NT	NT	TP	XC	XC	NT	NT	HT	TP	NT	NT	TP
				R 1	1 ◇	1 ◇		1 ◇					1 ◇	1 ◇	R 1			1 ◇	1 ◇			1 ◇
			A	B			C	D	E	G				H	J		K		L		N	
				🍴				🍴						🍴	🍴			⊠ 🍴				
Hull	d		10 41		10 50							11 41				11 54		12 12	12 35		12 41	
Hessle	d																					
Ferriby	d																					
Brough	d		10 53		11 02							11 53				12 06		12 24	12 47		12 53	
Broomfleet	d																					
Gilberdyke	d		11 00									12 00									13 00	
Eastrington	d																					
Howden	d																	12 36				
Wressle	d																					
Selby	a				11 20											12 25		12 46	13 06			
	d				11 21											12 25		12 47	13 06			
York 8	33 a															12 56						
Saltmarshe	d																					
Goole	d		11 09								11 43	12 09									13 09	
Thorne North	d										11 51											
Cleethorpes	d					10 28																12 28
New Clee	d																					
Grimsby Docks	d																					
Grimsby Town	a					10 35																12 35
	d					10 36																12 36
Great Coates	d																					
Healing	d																					
Stallingborough	d																					
Habrough	d					10 46																
Ulceby	d																					
Thornton Abbey	d																					
Goxhill	d																					
New Holland	d																					
Barrow Haven	d																					
Barton-on-Humber	a																					
Barton-on-Humber	🚌 d																					
Hull Bus Station	🚌 a																					
Barnetby	d					10 54																12 54
Scunthorpe	a					11 10																13 10
	d					11 10																13 10
Althorpe	d																					
Crowle	d																					
Thorne South	d																					
Hatfield & Stainforth	d										11 57											
Kirk Sandall	d										12 02											
Adwick	31 d	10 43																		12 43		
Bentley (S.Yorks)	31 d	10 47																		12 47		
Doncaster 7	31 a		11 32			11 41					12 13	12 32						13 05			13 32	13 41
London Kings Cross 15	⊖ 26 a					13 36						14 42						14 54				15 37
York 8	26 d			10b13				11 24			11 29			12 25	12 13					12 29	12 57	
Doncaster 7	d	11 13	11 33	11 37		11 42		11 50			12 16		12 42	12 50						13 13	13 33	13 42
Conisbrough	d	11 20									12 23									13 20		
Mexborough	d	11 24									12 27									13 24		
Swinton (S.Yorks)	d	11 29							11 55		12 30									13 30		
Rotherham Central	d	11 38							12 06		12 38									13 38		
Meadowhall	🚊 d	11 44	11 51			12 00	12 05		12 11	12 33	12 43		13 00				13 33			13 44	13 51	14 00
Sheffield 7	🚊 a	11 52	12 03	12 03		12 10	12 14	12 17	12 20	12 43	12 55		13 10	13 17	13 42		13 43			13 55	14 03	14 09
	d					12 13							13 13									14 12
Stockport	78 a				13c21	12 56			13 23	13 57			14 01	14 20					15c23			15 01
Manchester Piccadilly 10	78 🚊 a				12 57	13 10			13 36	14 10			14 11	14 33					15 05			15 13
Manchester Airport	85 ✈ a				13 36	13 39			14e14				14 33	15e11					15 36			15 37

For general notes see front of timetable
For details of catering facilities see Directory of Train Operators

- **A** From Bridlington (Table 43)
- **B** From Newcastle to Bournemouth (Table 51)
- **C** From Leeds (Table 34)
- **D** From Edinburgh to Plymouth (Table 51)
- **E** From Leeds (Table 31)
- **G** From Huddersfield (Table 34)
- **H** From Newcastle to Bristol Temple Meads (Table 51)
- **J** From Edinburgh (Table 51) to Penzance (Table 135)
- **K** From Leeds (Table 34) to Lincoln (Table 30)
- **L** To Liverpool Lime Street (Table 39)
- **N** From Scarborough (Table 43)
- **b** By changing at Doncaster, passengers may depart at 1023
- **c** Change at Manchester Piccadilly
- **e** Change at Sheffield and Manchester Piccadilly

Due to Engineering Operations in the Sheffield area, services from Sunday 14 September on this Table had not been confirmed at time of going to press. These services will be issued in a special Supplement as soon as exact timings have been confirmed.

Table 29

Sundays

Hull and Cleethorpes → Doncaster → Meadowhall, Sheffield, Manchester and Manchester Airport Cleethorpes → Barton-on-Humber

20 July to 7 September

Network Diagram - see first page of Table 18

		NT	XC	NT	XC	NT	NT	NT	NT	NT	NT	TP	XC	XC	NT	HT	EM	TP	NT	NT	NT
			■1 ◇		🅁 ■1							■1 ◇	■1 ◇	🅁 ■1		■1 ◇		■1 ◇			
		A	B	C	D		bus	E			G		B	H	A		J				K
			(catering)		(catering)								(catering)	(catering)		⊠ (catering)					
Hull	d									13 27	13 41					14 10		14 25		14 28	14 41
Hessle	d																			14 35	
Ferriby	d																			14 40	
Brough	d									13 39	13 53					14 22		14 37		14 45	14 53
Broomfleet	d																				
Gilberdyke	d										14 00										15 00
Eastrington	d																				
Howden	d															14 34					
Wressle	d																				
Selby	a									13 58						14 44		14 56		15 04	
	d									13 58						14 45		14 56		15 04	
York 8	33 a									14 22										15 30	
Saltmarshe	d																				
Goole	d								13 43		14 09										15 09
Thorne North	d								13 51												
Cleethorpes	d					12 56						13 28					13 57				
New Clee	d					12x59															
Grimsby Docks	d					13 01															
Grimsby Town	a					13 04						13 35					14 03				
	d					13 04						13 36					14 04				
Great Coates	d					13 08															
Healing	d					13 11															
Stallingborough	d					13 14															
Habrough	d					13 20											14 13				
Ulceby	d					13 24															
Thornton Abbey	d					13 29															
Goxhill	d					13 32															
New Holland	d					13 36															
Barrow Haven	d					13 39															
Barton-on-Humber	a					13 45															
Barton-on-Humber	bus d						13 55														
Hull Bus Station	bus a						14 19														
Barnetby	d											13 54					14a22				
Scunthorpe	a											14 10									
	d											14 10									
Althorpe	d																				
Crowle	d																				
Thorne South	d																				
Hatfield & Stainforth	d								13 57												
Kirk Sandall	d								14 02												
Adwick	31 d																		14 43		
Bentley (S.Yorks)	31 d																		*14 47*		
Doncaster 7	31 a								14 11		14 32	14 41				15 05					15 32
London Kings Cross 15	⊖ 26 a								*16 11*			*16 29*				16 50					
York 8	26 d		13 25		13 13				*13 33*			*14 05*	14 25	14 14					*14 36*		
Doncaster 7	d		13 50						14 13		14 33	14 42	14 50						15 13		15 33
Conisbrough	d								14 20										15 20		
Mexborough	d								14 24										15 24		
Swinton (S.Yorks)	d			14 01					14 30										15 30		
Rotherham Central	d			14 09					14 37										15 37		
Meadowhall	tram d	14 04		14 14				14 33	14 43		14 53	15 00			15 34				15 43		15 52
Sheffield 7	tram a	14 14	14 17	14 24	14 41			14 43	14 52		15 04	15 10	15 17	15 41	15 44				15 51		16 01
	d											15 13									
Stockport	78 a			*15 20*								16 03	*16 20*					17b23			
Manchester Piccadilly 10	78 tram a			*15 34*								16 13	*16 33*					16 50			
Manchester Airport	85 ✈ a			*16c11*								16 33	*17c11*								

For general notes see front of timetable
For details of catering facilities see Directory of Train Operators

A From Leeds (Table 34)
B From Newcastle to Bristol Temple Meads (Table 51)
C From Leeds (Table 31)
D From Edinburgh to Bournemouth (Table 51)
E From Huddersfield (Table 34)
G From Scarborough (Table 43)
H From Glasgow Central to Plymouth (Table 51)
J To Nottingham (Table 27)
K From Bridlington (Table 43)
b Change at Manchester Piccadilly
c Change at Sheffield and Manchester Piccadilly

Due to Engineering Operations in the Sheffield area, services from Sunday 14 September on this Table had not been confirmed at time of going to press. These services will be issued in a special Supplement as soon as exact timings have been confirmed.

Table 29

Sundays

20 July to 7 September

Hull and Cleethorpes → Doncaster → Meadowhall, Sheffield, Manchester and Manchester Airport
Cleethorpes → Barton-on-Humber

Network Diagram - see first page of Table 18

		TP	XC	NT	NT	NT	XC	NT	NT		NT	TP	XC	XC	NT	NT	NT	HT		TP	NT	TP	XC	NT
		1 ◇	R 1				R 1					1 ◇	1 ◇	R 1				1 ◇		1 ◇		1 ◇	1 ◇	
			A	B			C	D			E		A	G		H					J		A	B
			☕			🚌	☕						☕	☕				⊠ ☕					☕	
Hull	d										15 41				16 00			16 21		16 35	16 41			
Hessle	d																							
Ferriby	d																							
Brough	d										15 53				16 12			16 33		16 47	16 53			
Broomfleet	d																							
Gilberdyke	d										16 00										17 00			
Eastrington	d																							
Howden	d																	16 45						
Wressle	d																							
Selby	a														16 31			16 55		17 05				
	d														16 31			16 56		17 06				
York 8	33 a														16 57									
Saltmarshe	d																							
Goole	d								15 43		16 09										17 09			
Thorne North	d								15 51															
Cleethorpes	d	14 28			15 02							15 28										16 28		
New Clee	d				15x05																			
Grimsby Docks	d				15 07																			
Grimsby Town	a	14 35			15 10							15 35										16 35		
	d	14 36			15 10							15 36										16 36		
Great Coates	d				15 14																			
Healing	d				15 17																			
Stallingborough	d				15 20																			
Habrough	d	14 46			15 26																			
Ulceby	d				15 30																			
Thornton Abbey	d				15 34																			
Goxhill	d				15 37																			
New Holland	d				15 42																			
Barrow Haven	d				15 45																			
Barton-on-Humber	a				15 50																			
Barton-on-Humber	🚌 d					15 55																		
Hull Bus Station	🚌 a					16 19																		
Barnetby	d	14 54										15 54										16 54		
Scunthorpe	a	15 10										16 10										17 10		
	d	15 10										16 10										17 10		
Althorpe	d																							
Crowle	d																							
Thorne South	d																							
Hatfield & Stainforth	d								15 57															
Kirk Sandall	d								16 02															
Adwick	31 d																*16 43*							
Bentley (S.Yorks)	31 d																*16 47*							
Doncaster 7	31 a	15 41							16 11		16 32	16 41						17 14			17 31	17 41		
London Kings Cross 15	⊖ 26 a	*17 50*							*18 15*			*18 38*						19 06				*19 48*		
York 8	26 d		15 25				15 13		*15 34*			*16 03*	16 25	16 13			*16 29*				*16 53*	*17 03*	17 25	
Doncaster 7	d	15 42	15 48						16 13		16 33	16 42	16 50				17 13				17 32	17 42	17 50	
Conisbrough	d								16 20								17 21							
Mexborough	d								16 24								17 25							
Swinton (S.Yorks)	d			15 55					16 29								17 30							17 55
Rotherham Central	d			16 05					16 37								17 38							18 05
Meadowhall	🚋 d	16 00		16 11				16 34	16 42		16 53	17 00				17 34	17 43				17 53	18 00		18 11
Sheffield 7	🚋 a	16 10	16 17	16 26			16 41	16 43	16 52		17 03	17 10	17 17	17 41		17 44	17 54				18 03	18 10	18 17	18 23
	d	16 13										17 13										18 13		
Stockport	78 a	16 56		*17 21*								17 55	*18 24*							19b22		19 01		
Manchester Piccadilly 10	78 🚋 a	17 11		*17 36*								18 12	*18 35*							18 52		19 12		
Manchester Airport	85 ✈ a	17 32		*18c11*								18 33	*19c11*									19 32		

For general notes see front of timetable
For details of catering facilities see Directory of Train Operators

A From Newcastle to Bristol Temple Meads (Table 51)
B From Leeds (Table 31)
C From Glasgow Central to Bournemouth (Table 51)
D From Huddersfield (Table 34)
E From Scarborough (Table 43)
G From Edinburgh to Plymouth (Table 51)
H From Leeds (Table 34)
J From Bridlington (Table 43)
b Change at Manchester Piccadilly
c Change at Sheffield and Manchester Piccadilly

Due to Engineering Operations in the Sheffield area, services from Sunday 14 September on this Table had not been confirmed at time of going to press. These services will be issued in a special Supplement as soon as exact timings have been confirmed.

Table 29

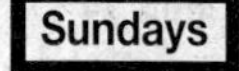

Sundays

Hull and Cleethorpes → Doncaster → Meadowhall, Sheffield, Manchester and Manchester Airport
Cleethorpes → Barton-on-Humber

20 July to 7 September

Network Diagram - see first page of Table 18

		EM	NT	XC	NT	NT		NT	GR	NT	TP	XC	XC	TP	NT		NT	NT	NT	HT	NT	TP	XC	NT
		1 ◇		R 1					R 1		1 ◇	1 ◇	1 ◇	1 ◇						1 ◇		1 ◇	1 ◇	
		A	B	C	D					E		G	H		J						K		H	L
		⊡		⊡					⊡ ⚲			⊡	⊡						🚌	⊠ ⊡			⊡	
Hull	d							17 23	17 30	17 41				18 21						18 30	18 38			
Hessle	d																							
Ferriby	d																							
Brough	d							17 35	17 42	17 53				18 33						18 42	18 50			
Broomfleet	d																							
Gilberdyke	d									18 00											18 57			
Eastrington	d																							
Howden	d																			18 54				
Wressle	d																							
Selby	a							17 54	18 05					18 52						19 04				
	d							17 54	18 05					18 52						19 05				
York 8	33 a							18 23																
Saltmarshe	d																							
Goole	d					17 43				18 09											19 06			
Thorne North	d					17 51															19 14			
Cleethorpes	d										17 28							17 56				18 28		
New Clee	d																	17x59						
Grimsby Docks	d																	18 01						
Grimsby Town	a										17 35							18 04				18 35		
	d										17 36							18 04				18 36		
Great Coates	d																	18 08						
Healing	d																	18 11						
Stallingborough	d																	18 14						
Habrough	d										17 46							18 20						
Ulceby	d																	18 24						
Thornton Abbey	d																	18 28						
Goxhill	d																	18 31						
New Holland	d																	18 36						
Barrow Haven	d																	18 39						
Barton-on-Humber	a																	18 45						
Barton-on-Humber	🚌 d																		18 55					
Hull Bus Station	🚌 a																		19 19					
Barnetby	d										17 54											18 54		
Scunthorpe	a										18 10											19 10		
	d										18 10											19 10		
Althorpe	d																							
Crowle	d																							
Thorne South	d																							
Hatfield & Stainforth	d					17 57															19 20			
Kirk Sandall	d					18 02															19 25			
Adwick	31 d																18 43							
Bentley (S.Yorks)	31 d																18 47							
Doncaster 7	31 a					18 11			18 23	18 33	18 41									19 21	19 35	19 41		
London Kings Cross 15	⊖ 26 a					20 12			20b23		20 38									21 12		21 47		
York 8	26 d	17 32	17 17	17 14		17 35					18 05	18 15	18 25				18 29					19 05	19 23	
Doncaster 7	d	18 00				18 13				18 34	18 42		18 50				19 15				19 37	19 42	19 50	
Conisbrough	d					18 20											19 22							
Mexborough	d					18 24											19 26							
Swinton (S.Yorks)	d		18 11			18 30											19 30							19 55
Rotherham Central	d		18 20			18 37											19 39							20 06
Meadowhall	🚊 d		18 26		18 34	18 43				18 53	19 00				19 33		19 44				19 56	20 00		20 11
Sheffield 7	🚊 a	18 27	18 35	18 41	18 46	18 52				19 03	19 10	19 41	19 17		19 44		19 53				20 07	20 10	20 17	20 23
	d										19 13											20 13		
Stockport	78 a	19 20	19 46								20 00		20 24	20c52								20 54		21 16
Manchester Piccadilly 10	78 🚊 a	19 32	19 59								20 09		20 35	20 23								21 04		21 31
Manchester Airport	85 ✈ a	20e11									20 32		21e11	20 54								21 32		22e11

For general notes see front of timetable
For details of catering facilities see Directory of Train Operators

- **A** To St Pancras International (Table 53)
- **B** Via Pontefract Baghill (Table 33)
- **C** From Aberdeen (Table 229) to Southampton Central (Table 51)
- **D** From Huddersfield (Table 34)
- **E** From Scarborough (Table 43)
- **G** From Edinburgh to Birmingham New Street (Table 51)
- **H** From Newcastle to Bristol Temple Meads (Table 51)
- **J** From Leeds (Table 34)
- **K** From Bridlington (Table 43)
- **L** From Leeds (Table 31)
- **b** By changing at Doncaster, passengers may arrive at 2012
- **c** Change at Manchester Piccadilly
- **e** Change at Sheffield and Manchester Piccadilly

Due to Engineering Operations in the Sheffield area, services from Sunday 14 September on this Table had not been confirmed at time of going to press. These services will be issued in a special Supplement as soon as exact timings have been confirmed.

Table 29

Sundays

20 July to 7 September

Hull and Cleethorpes → Doncaster → Meadowhall, Sheffield, Manchester and Manchester Airport
Cleethorpes → Barton-on-Humber

Network Diagram - see first page of Table 18

		XC	NT		NT	NT	TP	NT	NT	EM	NT	XC		NT	TP	TP	XC	NT	NT	NT	NT
		1 ◇					1 ◇					1 ◇			1 ◇	1 ◇	1 ◇				
		A			B			C		D		E		G		H	J	K	L	N	C
		⊡																			
Hull	d		18 53						20 22		20 30					20 45				21 15	
Hessle	d																			21 22	
Ferriby	d																			21 27	
Brough	d		19 05						20 34		20 42					20 57				21 32	
Broomfleet	d																				
Gilberdyke	d										20 49									21 39	
Eastrington	d																				
Howden	d																				
Wressle	d																				
Selby	a		19 24						20 53							21 16					
	d		19 24						20 53												
York 8	33 a		19 52						21 18												
Saltmarshe	d																				
Goole	d										20 58									21 48	
Thorne North	d																			21 56	
Cleethorpes	d						19 28			20 01					20 28						
New Clee	d																				
Grimsby Docks	d																				
Grimsby Town	a						19 35			20 07					20 35						
	d						19 36			20 08					20 36						
Great Coates	d																				
Healing	d																				
Stallingborough	d																				
Habrough	d						19 46			20 18					20 46						
Ulceby	d																				
Thornton Abbey	d																				
Goxhill	d																				
New Holland	d																				
Barrow Haven	d																				
Barton-on-Humber	a																				
Barton-on-Humber	🚌 d																				
Hull Bus Station	🚌 a																				
Barnetby	d						19 54			20a26					20 54						
Scunthorpe	a						20 10								21 10						
	d						20 10								21 10						
Althorpe	d																				
Crowle	d																				
Thorne South	d																				
Hatfield & Stainforth	d																			22 02	
Kirk Sandall	d																			22 07	
Adwick	31 d										*20 54*									*21 43*	
Bentley (S.Yorks)	31 d										*20 58*									*21 47*	
Doncaster 7	31 a						20 41				21 21				21 41					22 17	
London Kings Cross 15	⊖ 26 a						*23 14*								*23 50*						
York 8	26 d	19 15				*19 30*	*20 02*				*20 40*	20 30		20 44			21 24			*21 28*	
Doncaster 7	d					20 14	20 42				21 23				21 42		21 51			22 20	
Conisbrough	d					20 21	20 49													22 27	
Mexborough	d					20 25	20 53													22 31	
Swinton (S.Yorks)	d					20 32	20 56							21 38					22 32	22 37	
Rotherham Central	d					20 39	21 02				21 39			21 49					22 40	22 44	
Meadowhall	🚊 d				20 38	20 45	21 08	21 32			21 45			21 54	22 00			22 41	22 45	22 50	23 33
Sheffield 7	🚊 a	20 41			20 46	20 53	21 17	21 43			21 56	21 59		22 05	22 10		22 18	22 51	22 54	22 58	23 43
	d						21 19														
Stockport	78 a						22 00	*23 00*													
Manchester Piccadilly 10	78 🚊 a						22 14	*23 13*													
Manchester Airport	85 ✈ a						22 34	*23b49*													

For general notes see front of timetable
For details of catering facilities see Directory of Train Operators

A ⊡ to Leeds
B From Huddersfield (Table 34)
C From Leeds (Table 34)
D To Nottingham (Table 27)
E From Edinburgh to Birmingham New Street (Table 51)
G Via Pontefract Baghill (Table 33)
H To Leeds (Table 39)
J From Newcastle to Birmingham New Street (Table 51)
K From Barnsley (Table 34)
L From Leeds (Table 31)
N From Scarborough (Table 43)
b Change at Sheffield and Manchester Piccadilly

Due to Engineering Operations in the Sheffield area, services from Sunday 14 September on this Table had not been confirmed at time of going to press. These services will be issued in a special Supplement as soon as exact timings have been confirmed.

Table 29

Mondays to Fridays

until 5 September

Manchester Airport, Manchester, Sheffield and Meadowhall → Doncaster → Cleethorpes and Hull
Barton-on-Humber → Cleethorpes

Network Diagram - see first page of Table 18

Miles	Miles	Miles	Miles	Miles	Station		TP	TP	TP	NT	NT	NT	NT	NT	NT	EM	NT	NT	NT	NT		NT	NT	NT
							MX	MO	MO															
							1 ◇	1 ◇	1 ◇															
								A	B	C	D		E	G	H	J	H	🚌					C	G
0	—	—	—	—	**Manchester Airport**	85 ✈ d	03 21	03 18	03 21															
9¾	—	—	—	—	**Manchester Piccadilly** 10	78 🚢 d	03 40	03 37	03 44															
15¾	—	—	—	—	Stockport	78 d																		
52½	—	—	—	—	**Sheffield** 7	🚢 a	04 31	04 37	04 37															
—	—	—	—	—		d	04 40	04 40	04 40	05 10	05 16		05 29	05 36	05 50		06 14					06 18	06 28	06 36
56	—	—	—	—	**Meadowhall**	🚢 d				05 16	05a21		05 35	05a42	05a55		06a19					06 24	06 34	06a41
58¾	—	—	—	—	Rotherham Central	d				05 22			05 41									06 30	06 40	
63¼	—	—	—	—	Swinton (S.Yorks)	d				05a30			05 49									06 38	06a48	
64½	—	—	—	—	Mexborough	d							05 52									06 41		
66¾	—	—	—	—	Conisbrough	d							05 56									06 45		
71½	—	—	—	—	**Doncaster** 7	a	05 14	05 14	05 14				06 06									06 56		
—	—	—	—	—	York 8	26 a							*06 35*											
—	—	—	—	—	London Kings Cross 15	⊖ 26 d																		
—	0	0	—	0	**Doncaster**	31 d						05 55	06 14							06 47		06 59		
—	—	—	—	1¾	Bentley (S.Yorks)	31 a							*06 28*									07 02		
—	—	—	—	4	Adwick	31 a							*06 32*									07 08		
75½	—	4	—	—	Kirk Sandall	d							06 20							06 53				
78¼	—	6¾	—	—	Hatfield & Stainforth	d							06 25							06 58				
—	—	9¾	—	—	Thorne South	d														07 03				
—	—	15¾	—	—	Crowle	d														07 11				
—	—	19½	—	—	Althorpe	d														07 17				
—	—	23	—	—	**Scunthorpe**	a														07 26				
—	—	—	—	—		d																		
—	—	34¼	—	—	Barnetby	d										06 31								
—	—	—	—	—	Hull Bus Station	🚌 d												06 25						
—	—	—	—	—	Barton-on-Humber	🚌 a												06 50						
—	—	—	0	—	**Barton-on-Humber**	d													06 58					
—	—	—	2	—	Barrow Haven	d													07 03					
—	—	—	3½	—	New Holland	d													07 07					
—	—	—	5½	—	Goxhill	d													07 11					
—	—	—	7	—	Thornton Abbey	d																		
—	—	—	9¾	—	Ulceby	d													07 19					
—	—	40¾	11½	—	Habrough	d										06 41			07 23					
—	—	44½	15¼	—	Stallingborough	d													07 28					
—	—	45½	16¼	—	Healing	d													07 31					
—	—	45½	17¼	—	Great Coates	d																		
—	—	48¾	19½	—	**Grimsby Town**	a										06 57			07 37					
—	—	—	—	—		d													07 38					
—	—	49¾	20½	—	Grimsby Docks	d																		
—	—	50½	21¼	—	New Clee	d																		
—	—	52	22¾	—	**Cleethorpes**	a													07 50					
81½	—	—	—	—	Thorne North	d							06 30											
88¾	—	—	—	—	Goole	d							06 41											
92¼	—	—	—	—	Saltmarshe	d							06 46											
—	—	—	—	—	York 8	33 d																		
—	18¼	—	—	—	**Selby**	a						06 14												
—	—	—	—	—		d																		
—	24½	—	—	—	Wressle	d																		
—	27	—	—	—	Howden	d																		
—	30	—	—	—	Eastrington	d																		
95½	32¼	—	—	—	Gilberdyke	d							06 53											
98	34¾	—	—	—	Broomfleet	d							06 57											
102	38¾	—	—	—	Brough	d							07 03											
105	41¾	—	—	—	Ferriby	d							07 07											
107¾	44½	—	—	—	Hessle	d							07 12											
112	49¼	—	—	—	**Hull**	a							07 22											

For general notes see front of timetable
For details of catering facilities see Directory of Train Operators

A Until 14 July
B From 21 July
C To Leeds (Table 31)
D To Barnsley (Table 34)
E To Beverley (Table 43)
G To Huddersfield (Table 34)
H To Leeds (Table 34)
J From Lincoln (Table 27)

Manchester Airport, Manchester, Sheffield and Meadowhall → Doncaster → Cleethorpes and Hull Barton-on-Humber → Cleethorpes

Network Diagram - see first page of Table 18

Station		NT A	NT	TP 1◇	NT A	NT B	NT 🚌	NT	TP 1◇	NT C	NT	NT	XC 1◇ D	NT E		NT	EM 1◇ G	NT H	NT J	NT K	EM L	TP 1◇	XC 1◇ N	NT A
Manchester Airport	85 d			05 15					05 47													07 02		
Manchester Piccadilly 10	78 d			05 49					06 21				05 52									07 35		
Stockport	78 d			05 58					05b53				06 01									07b13		
Sheffield 7	a			06 48																				
	d	06 49	06 52	06 54	07 04								07 12	07 14		07 23	07 25	07 36	07 41	07 51			07 54	08 08
Meadowhall	d	06a54	06 58	07 02	07a09									07 21		07 29	07a31	07a41	07 47	07a57				08a13
Rotherham Central	d		07 05									←		07 27		07 35			07 55					
Swinton (S.Yorks)	d		07 15									07 15		07a35		07 45			08 03					
Mexborough	d		→									07 18				07 48			08 06					
Conisbrough	d											07 22				07 52			08 10					
Doncaster 7	a			07 22								07 30				08 02			08 20				08 24	
York 8	26 a											08 10	08 24										08 48	
London Kings Cross 15	⊖ 26 d															06 00			06 35					
Doncaster	31 d			07 24						07 28		07 32				08 04			08 22					
Bentley (S.Yorks)	31 a											07 35				08 19								
Adwick	31 a											07 41				08 25								
Kirk Sandall	d									07 34						08 10								
Hatfield & Stainforth	d									07 39						08 15								
Thorne South	d															08 20								
Crowle	d															08 29								
Althorpe	d															08 35								
Scunthorpe	a			07 49												08 43								
	d			07 50																				
Barnetby	d			08 04																	08 52			
Hull Bus Station	🚌 d						07 25																	
Barton-on-Humber	🚌 a						07 50																	
Barton-on-Humber	d							08 00																
Barrow Haven	d							08 05																
New Holland	d							08 08																
Goxhill	d							08 13																
Thornton Abbey	d							08 16																
Ulceby	d							08 20																
Habrough	d			08 13				08 25													09 01			
Stallingborough	d							08 30																
Healing	d							08 33																
Great Coates	d							08 36																
Grimsby Town	a			08 26				08 41													09 15			
	d			08 35				08 41																
Grimsby Docks	d							08 44																
New Clee	d							08x46																
Cleethorpes	a			08 46				08 51																
Thorne North	d									07 44														
Goole	d									07 53									08 43					
Saltmarshe	d									07 58														
York 8	33 d								06 09		07 30													
Selby	a								07 42		07 49											08 57		
	d								07 42		07 49											08 58		
Wressle	d										07 57													
Howden	d								07 51		08 02													
Eastrington	d										08 07													
Gilberdyke	d					07 39				08 04	08 11													
Broomfleet	d					07 43					08 15													
Brough	d					07 49			08 03	08 12	08 21								08 57					
Ferriby	d					07 53				08 16	08 26													
Hessle	d					07 58				08 21	08 30													
Hull	a					08 11			08 20	08 34	08 45								09 13			09 30		

For general notes see front of timetable
For details of catering facilities see Directory of Train Operators

A To Leeds (Table 34)
B To Scarborough (Table 43)
C To Beverley (Table 43)
D From Birmingham New Street to Edinburgh (Table 51)
E To Leeds (Table 31)
G From Derby (Table 53) to Barnsley (Table 34)
H To Huddersfield (Table 34)
J To Bridlington (Table 43)
K From Retford (Table 30) to Leeds (Table 34)
L From Newark North Gate (Table 27)
N From Birmingham New Street to Newcastle (Table 51)
b Change at Manchester Piccadilly

Table 29

Mondays to Fridays

until 5 September

Manchester Airport, Manchester, Sheffield and Meadowhall → Doncaster → Cleethorpes and Hull Barton-on-Humber → Cleethorpes

Network Diagram - see first page of Table 18

		TP	NT	NT	HT	XC	NT	NT	NT	NT	XC	NT	NT	NT	NT	TP	TP	NT	NT	NT	NT	XC	NT
		1 ◇			BHX 1 ◇	R 1					1 ◇					1 ◇	1 ◇					R 1
			A			B		C	D	E	G			H	E			A			H	J	
Manchester Airport	85 d	06 44							07b05							07 52	*08 07*						
Manchester Piccadilly 10	78 d	07 19							*07 43*							08 17	08 41						
Stockport	78 d	07 27							*07 54*							08 26	*08c21*						
Sheffield 7	a	08 09														09 09							
	d	08 11	08 14			08 21	08 25	08 36	08 41	08 51	08 54			08 57	09 08	09 11		09 14				09 21	09 25
Meadowhall	d	08 17	08 23				08 31	08a41	08 47	08a56				09 03	09a13	09 17		09 21					09 31
Rotherham Central	d		08 29				08 37							09 10				09 27					09 37
Swinton (S.Yorks)	d		08a38				08 47							09 18				09a36					09 48
Mexborough	d						08 50							09 21									09 51
Conisbrough	d						08 54							09 25									09 55
Doncaster 7	a	08 40					09 05		09 12		09 19			09 35		09 40							10 04
York 8	26 a					09 33	*09 39*				09 48											10 29	
London Kings Cross 15	⊖ 26 d				07 20											*07 30*					←		
Doncaster	31 d	08 42		08 56	09 06		09 12		09 17					09 49 →		09 42			09 46		09 49		10 06
Bentley (S.Yorks)	31 a	*08 55*					*09 17*														09 52		*10 17*
Adwick	31 a	*09 01*					*09 21*														09 58		*10 21*
Kirk Sandall	d			09 02			09 18												09 52				10 12
Hatfield & Stainforth	d			09 07			09 23												09 57				10 17
Thorne South	d						09 28																10 22
Crowle	d						09 36																10 31
Althorpe	d						09 42																10 37
Scunthorpe	a	09 08					09 51									10 07							10 45
	d	09 08														10 08							
Barnetby	d	09 22														10 22							
Hull Bus Station	🚌 d											09 25											
Barton-on-Humber	🚌 a											09 50											
Barton-on-Humber	d												09 58										
Barrow Haven	d												10 03										
New Holland	d												10 06										
Goxhill	d												10 11										
Thornton Abbey	d												10 14										
Ulceby	d												10 18										
Habrough	d												10 23			10 31							
Stallingborough	d												10 28										
Healing	d												10 31										
Great Coates	d												10 34										
Grimsby Town	a	09 42											10 39			10 44							
	d	09 43											10 39			10 45							
Grimsby Docks	d												10 42										
New Clee	d												10x44										
Cleethorpes	a	09 58											10 49			10 59							
Thorne North	d			09 12															10 02				
Goole	d			09 21					09 39										10 11				
Saltmarshe	d																						
York 8	33 d				*08 43*															09 53			
Selby	a				09 21												09 57			10 12			
	d				09 22												09 58			10 12			
Wressle	d																						
Howden	d				09 32																		
Eastrington	d																			10 22			
Gilberdyke	d			09 29															10 19	10 29			
Broomfleet	d																						
Brough	d			09 37	09 44				09 56								10 16		10 27	10 37			
Ferriby	d			09 42															10 32				
Hessle	d			09 46															10 36				
Hull	a			09 59	10 04				10 10								10 33		10 49	10 56			

For general notes see front of timetable
For details of catering facilities see Directory of Train Operators

A To Leeds (Table 31)
B From Birmingham New Street to Edinburgh (Table 51)
C To Huddersfield (Table 34)
D To Bridlington (Table 43)
E To Leeds (Table 34)
G From Birmingham New Street to Newcastle (Table 51)
H From Worksop (Table 30)
J From Bristol Temple Meads to Edinburgh (Table 51)
b Change at Manchester Piccadilly and Sheffield
c Change at Manchester Piccadilly

Table 29

Mondays to Fridays

until 5 September

Manchester Airport, Manchester, Sheffield and Meadowhall → Doncaster → Cleethorpes and Hull
Barton-on-Humber → Cleethorpes

Network Diagram - see first page of Table 18

		NT		NT	NT	EM	NT	XC 1 ◇	NT	NT	TP 1 ◇	NT	TP 1 ◇	NT	XC 1 ◇	NT	NT		NT	NT	NT	XC 1 ◇	HT 1 ◇	NT
		A		B	C	D	E	G	H	E		H		J	K				B	L	E	N		H
								🛒			🛒		🛒		🛒							🛒	⊠ 🛒	
Manchester Airport	85 ⇋ d						*08b07*				08 52		*09 07*								*09b07*			
Manchester Piccadilly 10	78 🚉 d						*08 42*				09 20		09 42	*08 44*							*09 42*			
Stockport	78 d						*08 53*				09 28		*09c20*								*09 55*			
Sheffield 7	🚉 a										10 08													
	d	09 29		09 36	09 41		09 51	09 54	09 57	10 08	10 11			10 14	10 21		10 25		10 36	10 41	10 51	10 54		10 57
Meadowhall	🚉 d	09 35		09a41	09 45		09a56		10 03	10a13	10 17			10 21			10 31		10a41	10 47	10a56			11 03
Rotherham Central	d	09 42							10 10					10 27			10 37							11 10
Swinton (S.Yorks)	d	09 51							10 18					10a36			10 47							11 20
Mexborough	d								10 21								10 50							11 23
Conisbrough	d								10 25								10 54							11 27
Doncaster 7	a				10 12			10 15	10 36		10 40						11 04			11 08		11 15		11 35
York 8	26 a	10 51			*11 02*			10 40			*11 37*				11 29		*11 37*					11 42		
London Kings Cross 15	⊖ 26 d										*09 00*	←											09 48	
Doncaster	31 d				10 16				10 44 →		10 42	10 44				10 47	11 07			11 17			11 36	11 38
Bentley (S.Yorks)	31 a											10 47										*11e29*		11 41
Adwick	31 a											10 53										*11e33*		11 47
Kirk Sandall	d															10 53	11 13							
Hatfield & Stainforth	d															10 58	11 18							
Thorne South	d																11 23							
Crowle	d																11 31							
Althorpe	d																11 37							
Scunthorpe	a										11 07						11 45							
	d										11 08													
Barnetby	d					10 56					11 22													
Hull Bus Station	🚌 d																							
Barton-on-Humber	🚌 a																							
Barton-on-Humber	d																							
Barrow Haven	d																							
New Holland	d																							
Goxhill	d																							
Thornton Abbey	d																							
Ulceby	d																							
Habrough	d					11 05																		
Stallingborough	d																							
Healing	d																							
Great Coates	d																							
Grimsby Town	a					11 20					11 42													
	d										11 43													
Grimsby Docks	d																							
New Clee	d																							
Cleethorpes	a										11 54													
Thorne North	d															11 03								
Goole	d				10 35											11 12				11 38				
Saltmarshe	d																							
York 8	33 d												*10 20*											
Selby	a												10 57										11 51	
	d												10 58										11 52	
Wressle	d																							
Howden	d																						12 02	
Eastrington	d																							
Gilberdyke	d															11 20								
Broomfleet	d															11 25								
Brough	d				10 49								11 16			11 31				11 52			12 15	
Ferriby	d															11 35								
Hessle	d															11 40								
Hull	a				11 06								11 33			11 53				12 09			12 32	

For general notes see front of timetable
For details of catering facilities see Directory of Train Operators

- **A** Via Pontefract Baghill (Table 33)
- **B** To Huddersfield (Table 34)
- **C** To Scarborough (Table 43)
- **D** From Newark North Gate (Table 27)
- **E** To Leeds (Table 34)
- **G** From Bristol Temple Meads to Newcastle (Table 51)
- **H** From Lincoln (Table 30)
- **J** To Leeds (Table 31)
- **K** From Southampton Central to Edinburgh (Table 51)
- **L** To Bridlington (Table 43)
- **N** From Cardiff Central to Newcastle (Table 51)
- **b** Change at Manchester Piccadilly and Sheffield
- **c** Change at Manchester Piccadilly
- **e** Change at Doncaster

Manchester Airport, Manchester, Sheffield and Meadowhall → Doncaster → Cleethorpes and Hull Barton-on-Humber → Cleethorpes

Network Diagram - see first page of Table 18

	NT	NT	NT	TP	TP	NT	NT	NT	XC	NT		NT	NT	NT	XC	NT	EM	NT	TP	TP	NT	NT	XC
				1 ◇	1 ◇				1 ◇						1 ◇				1 ◇	1 ◇			1 ◇
			A			B			C			D	E	A	G	H	J	A			B		K
	[bus]			[trolley]	[trolley]				[buffet]						[buffet]				[trolley]	[trolley]			[buffet]
Manchester Airport 85 d				09 52	*10 07*									*10b07*					10 52	*11 07*			
Manchester Piccadilly 10 78 d				10 20	10 42									*10 42*					11 20	11 42	*10 46*		
Stockport 78 d				10 28	*10c18*									*10 55*					11 27	*11c19*			
Sheffield 7 a				11 08															12 08				
d			11 08	11 11		11 14			11 21	11 25		11 36	11 41	11 51	11 54	11 57		12 08	12 11		12 14		12 21
Meadowhall d			11a13	11 17		11 21				11 31		11a41	11 47	11a56		12 03		12a13	12 17		12 21		
Rotherham Central d						11 27				11 37						12 10					12 27		
Swinton (S.Yorks) d						11a36				11 48						12 19					12a36		
Mexborough d										11 51						12 22							
Conisbrough d										11 55						12 26							
Doncaster 7 a				11 40						12 04			12 11		12 15	12 35			12 38				
York 8 26 a									12 29						12 43								13 29
London Kings Cross 15 ⊖ 26 d										*10 10*						*10 35*							
Doncaster 31 d				11 42			11 49			12 07			12 14			12 36			12 42			12 49	
Bentley (S.Yorks) 31 a															*12e28*	12 40							
Adwick 31 a															*12e32*	12 45							
Kirk Sandall d							11 55			12 14												12 55	
Hatfield & Stainforth d							12 00			12 19												13 00	
Thorne South d										12 24													
Crowle d										12 32													
Althorpe d										12 38													
Scunthorpe a				12 07						12 46									13 07				
d				12 08															13 08				
Barnetby d				12 22													13 12		13 22				
Hull Bus Station [bus] d	11 25																						
Barton-on-Humber [bus] a	11 50																						
Barton-on-Humber d		11 58																					
Barrow Haven d		12 03																					
New Holland d		12 06																					
Goxhill d		12 11																					
Thornton Abbey d		12 14																					
Ulceby d		12 18																					
Habrough d		12 23		12 31													13 21						
Stallingborough d		12 28																					
Healing d		12 31																					
Great Coates d		12 34																					
Grimsby Town a		12 39		12 44													13 35		13 42				
d		12 39		12 45															13 43				
Grimsby Docks d		12 42																					
New Clee d		12x44																					
Cleethorpes a		12 49		12 57															13 54				
Thorne North d							12 05															13 05	
Goole d							12 14						12 35									13 14	
Saltmarshe d																							
York 8 33 d								11 53												*12 18*			
Selby a					11 57			12 17												12 57			
d					11 58			12 18												12 58			
Wressle d																							
Howden d								12 27															
Eastrington d																							
Gilberdyke d							12 22	12 34														13 22	
Broomfleet d																							
Brough d					12 15		12 30	12 42					12 49							13 16		13 30	
Ferriby d							12 35															13 35	
Hessle d							12 39															13 39	
Hull a					12 36		12 52	13 02					13 06							13 33		13 52	

For general notes see front of timetable
For details of catering facilities see Directory of Train Operators

A To Leeds (Table 34)
B To Leeds (Table 31)
C From Plymouth to Edinburgh (Table 51)
D To Huddersfield (Table 34)
E To Scarborough (Table 43)
G From Plymouth to Newcastle (Table 51)
H From Lincoln (Table 30)
J From Newark North Gate (Table 27)
K From Bournemouth (Table 51) to Aberdeen (Table 229)
b Change at Manchester Piccadilly and Sheffield
c Change at Manchester Piccadilly
e Change at Doncaster

Table 29

Mondays to Fridays

until 5 September

Manchester Airport, Manchester, Sheffield and Meadowhall → Doncaster → Cleethorpes and Hull Barton-on-Humber → Cleethorpes

Network Diagram - see first page of Table 18

		NT	NT	NT	NT	NT	NT	XC	HT	NT	NT	TP	TP	NT	NT	XC	NT	NT	NT	NT	NT	NT
								1◇	1◇			1◇	1◇			1◇						
			A	B	C			D		E	C			G		H			J	A	B	C
Manchester Airport	85 d				11b07							11 52	12 07									12b07
Manchester Piccadilly 10	78 d				11 42							12 20	12 42									12 42
Stockport	78 d				11 55							12 28	12c19									12 55
Sheffield 7	a											13 08										
	d	12 25	12 36	12 41	12 51			12 54		12 57	13 08	13 11		13 14		13 21		13 25	13 28	13 36	13 41	13 51
Meadowhall	d	12 31	12a41	12 47	12a56					13 03	13a13	13 17		13 21				13 31	13 35	13a41	13 46	13a57
Rotherham Central	d	12 37								13 10				13 27				13 37	13 42			
Swinton (S.Yorks)	d	12 47								13 18				13a36				13 47	13 50			
Mexborough	d	12 50								13 21								13 50				
Conisbrough	d	12 54								13 25								13 54				
Doncaster 7	a	13 04		13 11				13 22		13 35		13 38						14 04			14 14	
York 8	26 a	13 39						13 46				14 34				14 29			14 50		14 58	
London Kings Cross 15	⊖ 26 d	11 10							11 48									12 10			12 30	
Doncaster	31 d	13 06		13 18					13 29	13 38		13 42					13 46	14 06			14 17	
Bentley (S.Yorks)	31 a			13 30						13 41												
Adwick	31 a			13 34						13 47												
Kirk Sandall	d	13 12															13 52	14 13				
Hatfield & Stainforth	d	13 17															13 57	14 18				
Thorne South	d	13 22																14 23				
Crowle	d	13 31																14 32				
Althorpe	d	13 37																14 38				
Scunthorpe	a	13 45										14 07						14 45				
	d											14 08										
Barnetby	d											14 22										
Hull Bus Station	🚌 d					13 25																
Barton-on-Humber	🚌 a					13 50																
Barton-on-Humber	d						13 58															
Barrow Haven	d						14 03															
New Holland	d						14 06															
Goxhill	d						14 11															
Thornton Abbey	d						14 14															
Ulceby	d						14 18															
Habrough	d						14 23					14 31										
Stallingborough	d						14 28															
Healing	d						14 31															
Great Coates	d						14 34															
Grimsby Town	a						14 39					14 44										
	d						14 39					14 45										
Grimsby Docks	d						14 42															
New Clee	d						14x44															
Cleethorpes	a						14 49					14 57										
Thorne North	d																14 02					
Goole	d			13 37													14 12				14 36	
Saltmarshe	d																14 17					
York 8	33 d														13 45							
Selby	a								13 44				13 57		14 09							
	d								13 45				13 58		14 09							
Wressle	d																					
Howden	d								13 55													
Eastrington	d																					
Gilberdyke	d																14 28					
Broomfleet	d																					
Brough	d			13 51					14 08				14 15		14 29		14 36				14 52	
Ferriby	d																14 40					
Hessle	d																14 45					
Hull	a			14 08					14 25				14 33		14 48		14 56				15 07	

For general notes see front of timetable
For details of catering facilities see Directory of Train Operators

A To Huddersfield (Table 34)
B To Bridlington (Table 43)
C To Leeds (Table 34)
D From Bristol Temple Meads to Newcastle (Table 51)
E From Lincoln (Table 30)
G To Leeds (Table 31)
H From Plymouth to Edinburgh (Table 51)
J Via Pontefract Baghill (Table 33)
b Change at Manchester Piccadilly and Sheffield
c Change at Manchester Piccadilly

Table 29

Manchester Airport, Manchester, Sheffield and Meadowhall → Doncaster → Cleethorpes and Hull Barton-on-Humber → Cleethorpes

Mondays to Fridays
until 5 September

Network Diagram - see first page of Table 18

	XC	NT	NT	TP	TP	NT	NT	EM	NT	XC	NT	HT	NT		NT	NT	HT	XC	NT	NT	NT	NT	TP
	1 ◇			1 ◇	1 ◇					R 1		1 ◇					1 ◇	1 ◇					1 ◇
	A	B	C			D	E	G		H			J			C		K	B	C			
	☕			🛒	🛒					☕		⊠ ☕					⊠ ☕	☕			🚌		🛒
Manchester Airport 85 ✈ d				12 52	*13 07*											*13b07*							13 52
Manchester Piccadilly [10] 78 🚊 d				13 20	13 42	*12 46*										*13 42*							14 20
Stockport 78 d				13 28	*13c19*											*13 55*							14 28
Sheffield [7] 🚊 a				14 08																			15 08
d	13 54	13 57	14 08	14 11		14 14				14 21	14 25		14 36		14 41	14 51		14 54	14 57	15 08			15 11
Meadowhall 🚊 d		14 03	14a13	14 17		14 21					14 31		14a41		14 47	14a56			15 03	15a13			15 17
Rotherham Central d		14 10				14 27					14 37								15 10				
Swinton (S.Yorks) d		14 18				14a36					14 48								15 18				
Mexborough d		14 21									14 51								15 21				
Conisbrough d		14 25									14 55								15 25				
Doncaster [7] a	14 18	14 35		14 38							15 04				15 09			15 15	15 36				15 38
York [8] 26 a	14 45			*15 26*						15 29								15 40					
London Kings Cross [15] ⊖ 26 d		*12 35*		*13 00*							*13 10*	13 33			*13 30*				*14 00*				
Doncaster 31 d		14 38		14 42			14 46				15 06	15 12			15 14				15 38				15 42
Bentley (S.Yorks) 31 a	*14e30*	14 41									*15 17*								15 41				
Adwick 31 a	*14e34*	14 47									*15 21*								15 47				
Kirk Sandall d							14 54				15 12												
Hatfield & Stainforth d							14 59				15 17												
Thorne South d											15 22												
Crowle d											15 30												
Althorpe d											15 36												
Scunthorpe a				15 07							15 45												16 07
d				15 08																			16 08
Barnetby d				15 22				15 32															16 22
Hull Bus Station 🚌 d																					15 25		
Barton-on-Humber 🚌 a																					15 50		
Barton-on-Humber d																						15 58	
Barrow Haven d																						16 03	
New Holland d																						16 06	
Goxhill d																						16 11	
Thornton Abbey d																						16 14	
Ulceby d																						16 18	
Habrough d								15 42														16 23	16 31
Stallingborough d																						16 28	
Healing d																						16 31	
Great Coates d																						16 34	
Grimsby Town a				15 42				15 56														16 39	16 44
d				15 43																		16 39	16 45
Grimsby Docks d																						16 42	
New Clee d																							
Cleethorpes a				15 54																		16 48	16 56
Thorne North d							15 04																
Goole d							15 13								15 33								
Saltmarshe d																							
York [8] 33 d									14 59														
Selby a					14 57				15 19			15 27											
d					14 58				15 19			15 28											
Wressle d																	←						
Howden d												15 38 →					15 38						
Eastrington d																							
Gilberdyke d							15 21																
Broomfleet d																							
Brough d					15 16		15 29		15 39						15 47		15 53						
Ferriby d							15 34																
Hessle d							15 38																
Hull a					15 33		15 51		15 58						16 04		16 10						

For general notes see front of timetable
For details of catering facilities see Directory of Train Operators

A From Bristol Temple Meads to Newcastle (Table 51)
B From Lincoln (Table 30)
C To Leeds (Table 34)
D To Leeds (Table 31)
E To Scarborough (Table 43)
G From Newark North Gate (Table 27)
H From Bournemouth to Edinburgh (Table 51)
J To Huddersfield (Table 34)
K From Paignton to Newcastle (Table 51)
b Change at Manchester Piccadilly and Sheffield
c Change at Manchester Piccadilly
e Change at Doncaster

Manchester Airport, Manchester, Sheffield and Meadowhall → Doncaster → Cleethorpes and Hull
Barton-on-Humber → Cleethorpes

Network Diagram - see first page of Table 18

		TP	NT	NT	XC	NT	NT	NT		NT	NT	XC	NT	NT	TP	TP	NT	NT	XC	NT	NT	NT	EM	NT
		1 ◇			R 1							1 ◇			1 ◇	1 ◇			R 1					
			A	B	C		D			E	G	H	J	E			A	B	K		D		L	E
		⚮			🍴							🍴			⚮	⚮			🍴					
Manchester Airport 85 ✈	d	14 07								14b07					14 52	15 07								15b07
Manchester Piccadilly 10 78 🚌	d	14 42								14 42					15 20	15 42	14 46							15 42
Stockport 78	d	14c19								14 55					15 28	15c19								15 51
Sheffield 7 🚌	a														16 08									
	d		15 14		15 21	15 25	15 36	15 41		15 51		15 54	15 57	16 08	16 11		16 14		16 21	16 25	16 36	16 41		16 51
Meadowhall 🚌	d		15 21			15 31	15a41	15 47		15a56			16 03	16a13	16 17		16 21			16 31	16a41	16 47		16a56
Rotherham Central	d		15 27			15 37							16 10				16 27			16 37				
Swinton (S.Yorks)	d		15a36			15 47							16 18				16a36			16 47				
Mexborough	d					15 50							16 21							16 50				
Conisbrough	d					15 54							16 25							16 54				
Doncaster 7	a					16 04		16 12				16 15	16 35		16 38					17 07		17 11		
York 8 26	a				16 29							16 40			17 34				17 29			17 54		
London Kings Cross 15 ⊖ 26	d					14 10		14 35							14 35							15 10		
Doncaster 31	d			15 46		16 09		16 18					16 38		16 42			16 46				17 14		
Bentley (S.Yorks) 31	a					16 17							16 41											
Adwick 31	a					16 21							16 47											
Kirk Sandall	d			15 52		16 15												16 52						
Hatfield & Stainforth	d			15 57		16 20												16 57						
Thorne South	d					16 25																		
Crowle	d					16 34																		
Althorpe	d					16 40																		
Scunthorpe	a					16 48									17 07									
	d														17 08									
Barnetby	d														17 22								17 52	
Hull Bus Station 🚌	d																							
Barton-on-Humber 🚌	a																							
Barton-on-Humber	d																							
Barrow Haven	d																							
New Holland	d																							
Goxhill	d																							
Thornton Abbey	d																							
Ulceby	d																							
Habrough	d																						18 01	
Stallingborough	d																							
Healing	d																							
Great Coates	d																							
Grimsby Town	a														17 42								18 14	
	d														17 43									
Grimsby Docks	d																							
New Clee	d																							
Cleethorpes	a														17 54									
Thorne North	d			16 02														17 02				17 26		
Goole	d			16 11				16 37										17 11				17 35		
Saltmarshe	d																	17 16						
York 8 33	d										16 12													
Selby	a	15 57									16 38					16 57								
	d	15 58									16 39					16 58								
Wressle	d										16 46													
Howden	d										16 51													
Eastrington	d																							
Gilberdyke	d			16 20							16 58							17 23						
Broomfleet	d																							
Brough	d	16 16		16 28				16 51			17 06					17 16		17 31				17 49		
Ferriby	d			16 32							17 10							17 36						
Hessle	d			16 37														17 40						
Hull	a	16 33		16 49				17 08			17 27					17 35		17 53				18 06		

For general notes see front of timetable
For details of catering facilities see Directory of Train Operators

A To Leeds (Table 31)
B To Bridlington (Table 43)
C From Penzance (Table 135) to Dundee (Table 229)
D To Huddersfield (Table 34)
E To Leeds (Table 34)
G To Scarborough (Table 43)
H From Bristol Temple Meads to Newcastle (Table 51)
J From Lincoln (Table 30)
K From Bournemouth to Glasgow Central (Table 51)
L From Lincoln (Table 27)
b Change at Manchester Piccadilly and Sheffield
c Change at Manchester Piccadilly

Manchester Airport, Manchester, Sheffield and Meadowhall → Doncaster → Cleethorpes and Hull Barton-on-Humber → Cleethorpes

Network Diagram - see first page of Table 18

Station		NT		XC	NT	NT	NT	NT	HT	NT	TP	TP	NT	NT	XC	NT	NT		NT	NT	NT	XC	NT	TP
				1 ◇					1 ◇		1 ◇	1 ◇			R 1							R 1		1 ◇
				A	B	C	bus			D			E	G	H		J			D		K	B	
Manchester Airport	85 d										15 52	16 07								16b07				17 04
Manchester Piccadilly 10	78 d										16 20	16 42	15 46							16 42				17 42
Stockport	78 d										16 28	16c19								16 53				17c18
Sheffield 7	a										17 08													
	d			16 54		16 57				17 08	17 11		17 14		17 21	17 25	17 36		17 41	17 51		17 54		
Meadowhall	d					17 03				17a13	17 17		17 21			17 31	17a41		17 47	17a56				
Rotherham Central	d					17 10							17 27			17 38								
Swinton (S.Yorks)	d					17 18							17a36			17 47								
Mexborough	d					17 21										17 50								
Conisbrough	d					17 25										17 54								
Doncaster 7	a			17 15		17 35					17 38					18 07			18 13			18 16		
York 8	26 a			17 40							18 34				18 29							18 41		
London Kings Cross 15	⊖ 26 d				15 30	16 00			16 05										16 30				16 35	
Doncaster	31 d				17 22	17 38			17 42		17 42			17 56					18 16				18 27	
Bentley (S.Yorks)	31 a			17e30		17 41																18e30		
Adwick	31 a			17e34		17 47																18e34		
Kirk Sandall	d				17 29									18 02									18 34	
Hatfield & Stainforth	d				17 34									18 07									18 39	
Thorne South	d				17 39																		18 44	
Crowle	d				17 47																		18 52	
Althorpe	d				17 53																		18 58	
Scunthorpe	a				18 01						18 08												19 06	
	d										18 08													
Barnetby	d										18 22													
Hull Bus Station	bus d						17 30																	
Barton-on-Humber	bus a						17 55																	
Barton-on-Humber	d							18 00																
Barrow Haven	d							18 05																
New Holland	d							18 08																
Goxhill	d							18 13																
Thornton Abbey	d							18 16																
Ulceby	d							18 20																
Habrough	d							18 25			18 31													
Stallingborough	d							18 30																
Healing	d							18 33																
Great Coates	d							18 36																
Grimsby Town	a							18 41			18 46													
	d							18 41			18 46													
Grimsby Docks	d							18 44																
New Clee	d																							
Cleethorpes	a							18 50			19 00													
Thorne North	d													18 12										
Goole	d													18 21					18 36					
Saltmarshe	d													18 26										
York 8	33 d	17 27																			18 14			
Selby	a	17 45							17 59			18 04									18 43			19 00
	d	17 46							18 00			18 06									18 43			19 01
Wressle	d																				18 51			
Howden	d	17 55							18 10			18 16									18 56			
Eastrington	d																				19 00			
Gilberdyke	d	18 01												18 37							19 05			
Broomfleet	d													18 41										
Brough	d	18 09							18 23			18 28		18 47					18 53		19 13			19 19
Ferriby	d													18 51										
Hessle	d													18 56										
Hull	a	18 29							18 40			18 45		19 06					19 09		19 32			19 36

For general notes see front of timetable
For details of catering facilities see Directory of Train Operators

A From Plymouth to Newcastle (Table 51)
B From Adwick (Table 31)
C From Lincoln (Table 30)
D To Leeds (Table 34)
E To Leeds (Table 31)
G To Scarborough (Table 43)
H From Plymouth to Glasgow Central (Table 51)
J To Huddersfield (Table 34)
K From Bristol Temple Meads to Newcastle (Table 51)
b Change at Manchester Piccadilly and Sheffield
c Change at Manchester Piccadilly
e Change at Doncaster

Manchester Airport, Manchester, Sheffield and Meadowhall → Doncaster → Cleethorpes and Hull Barton-on-Humber → Cleethorpes

Network Diagram - see first page of Table 18

		NT	NT	NT	XC	TP	GR	NT	NT	NT	NT		XC	NT	NT	NT	NT	NT	TP	TP	EM	NT	NT	XC
					R 1	1 ◊	R 1						R 1						1 ◊	1 ◊				R 1
		A	B	C	D		E		G	H	B		J		K			B			L	C		N Q
							✕									🚌								
Manchester Airport	85 d					16 52					*17b04*								17 52	*18 10*				
Manchester Piccadilly 10	78 d					17 20					*17 42*								18 18	18 42				
Stockport	78 d					17 28					*17 53*								18 26	*18c19*				
Sheffield 7	a					18 15													19 08					
	d	17 57	18 08	18 14	18 21	18 24		18 29	18 36	18 41	18 51		18 54		18 57			19 08	19 11			19 18		19 26
Meadowhall	d	18 03	18a13	18 21		18 29		18 35	18a41	18 47	18a56				19 03			19a13	19 17			19 25		
Rotherham Central	d	18 09		18 27				18 42							19 10							19 31		
Swinton (S.Yorks)	d	18 17		18a36				18 50							19 20							19a40		
Mexborough	d	18 20						18 53							19 23									
Conisbrough	d	18 24						18 57							19 27									
Doncaster 7	a	18 35				18 53		19 08		19 11			19 17		19 39				19 41					
York 8	26 a				19 29					*19 44*			19 44											20 34
London Kings Cross 15	⊖ 26 d					*17 03*	17 20												*18 00*					
Doncaster	31 d	18 41				18 55	19 05			19 14				19 20					19 42				19 51	
Bentley (S.Yorks)	31 a												*19e32*											
Adwick	31 a												*19e36*											
Kirk Sandall	d	18 47												19 27									19 57	
Hatfield & Stainforth	d	18 52												19 32									20 02	
Thorne South	d													19 37										
Crowle	d													19 46										
Althorpe	d													19 52										
Scunthorpe	a					19 22								19 59					20 07					
	d					19 23													20 08					
Barnetby	d					19 37													20 22		20 31			
Hull Bus Station	🚌 d															19 25								
Barton-on-Humber	🚌 a															19 50								
Barton-on-Humber	d																19 58							
Barrow Haven	d																20 03							
New Holland	d																20 06							
Goxhill	d																20 11							
Thornton Abbey	d																20 14							
Ulceby	d																20 18							
Habrough	d																20 23				20 40			
Stallingborough	d																20 28							
Healing	d																20 31							
Great Coates	d																20 34							
Grimsby Town	a					19 58											20 39		20 43		20 52			
	d					19 58											20 39		20 44		20 53			
Grimsby Docks	d																20 42							
New Clee	d																							
Cleethorpes	a					20 09											20 48		20 57		21 01			
Thorne North	d	18 57																					20 08	
Goole	d	19 06								19 34													20 17	
Saltmarshe	d																							
York 8	33 d																			*19 23*				
Selby	a						19 20													20 00				
	d						19 21													20 01				
Wressle	d																							
Howden	d																			20 10				
Eastrington	d																							
Gilberdyke	d	19 15																					20 25	
Broomfleet	d																							
Brough	d	19 23					19 43			19 49										20 22			20 33	
Ferriby	d	19 27																					20 37	
Hessle	d	19 32																					20 42	
Hull	a	19 47					20 00			20 07										20 39			20 55	

For general notes see front of timetable
For details of catering facilities see Directory of Train Operators

- **A** From Lincoln (Table 30)
- **B** To Leeds (Table 34)
- **C** To Leeds (Table 31)
- **D** From Bournemouth to Edinburgh (Table 51)
- **E** **The Hull Executive**
- **G** To Huddersfield (Table 34)
- **H** To Bridlington (Table 43)
- **J** From Paignton to Newcastle (Table 51)
- **K** From Retford Low Level (Table 30)
- **L** From Newark North Gate (Table 27)
- **N** From Plymouth to Edinburgh (Table 51)
- **Q** to Leeds
- **b** Change at Manchester Piccadilly and Sheffield
- **c** Change at Manchester Piccadilly
- **e** Change at Doncaster

Table 29

Mondays to Fridays

until 5 September

Manchester Airport, Manchester, Sheffield and Meadowhall → Doncaster → Cleethorpes and Hull Barton-on-Humber → Cleethorpes

Network Diagram - see first page of Table 18

	NT	NT	NT	NT		XC	NT	HT	NT	NT	TP	NT	NT	NT	XC	NT	NT	NT	XC		EM	NT	NT ThFO
						R 1		1 ◇			1 ◇				R 1				1 ◇		1 ◇		
		A	B	C		D				C		E			G	H		A	J		K	C	🚌
Manchester Airport 85 d			18b10								18 52								19b12				
Manchester Piccadilly 10 78 d			18 44								19 18								19 42				
Stockport 78 d			18 55								19 26								19 55				
Sheffield 7 a											20 08												
Sheffield d	19 30	19 38	19 44	19 51		19 54			19 57	20 08	20 11			20 15	20 21	20 27	20 39	20 41	20 54		21 00	21 08	
Meadowhall d	19 36	19a43	19 50	19a56					20 03	20a13	20 17			20 21		20 35	20 45	20a47				21a13	
Rotherham Central d	19 42								20 10					20 27		20 41	20 52						
Swinton (S.Yorks) d	19 51								20 19					20 36		20a50	21 00						
Mexborough d	19 54								20 22					20 39			21 03						
Conisbrough d	19 58								20 26					20 43			21 07						
Doncaster 7 a	20 08		20 11			20 20			20 36		20 41			20 55			21 18				21 26		
York 8 26 a	*20 39*					20 46									21 35				21 48		*22 06*		
London Kings Cross 15 ⊖ 26 d			*18 03*				*18 33*	18 50				*19 00*					*19 03*						
Doncaster 31 d			20 15				20 25	20 31			20 42	20 44	20 49				21 18						
Bentley (S.Yorks) 31 a						*20c41*															*21 41*		
Adwick 31 a						*20c45*															*21 45*		
Kirk Sandall d							20 31						20 55				21 26						
Hatfield & Stainforth d							20 36						21 00				21 31						
Thorne South d							20 41										21 38						
Crowle d							20 50										21 46						
Althorpe d							20 56										21 52						
Scunthorpe a							21 04				21 07						22 01						
Scunthorpe d											21 08												
Barnetby d											21 22												
Hull Bus Station 🚌 d																							21 25
Barton-on-Humber 🚌 a																							21 50
Barton-on-Humber d																							
Barrow Haven d																							
New Holland d																							
Goxhill d																							
Thornton Abbey d																							
Ulceby d																							
Habrough d											21 31												
Stallingborough d																							
Healing d																							
Great Coates d																							
Grimsby Town a											21 44												
Grimsby Town d											21 45												
Grimsby Docks d																							
New Clee d																							
Cleethorpes a											21 59												
Thorne North d													21 06										
Goole d			20 36										21a17										
Saltmarshe d																							
York 8 33 d																							
Selby a								20 46				21 01											
Selby d								20 47				21 02											
Wressle d																							
Howden d								20 57															
Eastrington d																							
Gilberdyke d												21 15											
Broomfleet d																							
Brough d			20 49					21 09				21 23											
Ferriby d												21 28											
Hessle d												21 32											
Hull a			21 06					21 28				21 45											

For general notes see front of timetable
For details of catering facilities see Directory of Train Operators

A To Huddersfield (Table 34)
B To Beverley (Table 43)
C To Leeds (Table 34)
D From Bristol Temple Meads to Newcastle (Table 51)
E To Bridlington (Table 43)
G From Bournemouth to Newcastle (Table 51)
H To Leeds (Table 31)
J From Paignton to Newcastle (Table 51)
K From St Pancras International to Leeds (Table 53)
b Change at Manchester Piccadilly and Sheffield
c Change at Doncaster

Table 29

Mondays to Fridays
until 5 September

Manchester Airport, Manchester, Sheffield and Meadowhall → Doncaster → Cleethorpes and Hull Barton-on-Humber → Cleethorpes

Network Diagram - see first page of Table 18

		NT	TP	TP	NT	NT	HT	XC	NT	NT	EM	NT	TP	NT		TP	NT	NT	NT	NT	NT	NT		
							BHX														FX			
			1 ◇	1 ◇			1 ◇	1 ◇			1 ◇		1 ◇			1 ◇								
			A		B			C	D	E	G	H		D		A		E		D	J			
							⊠ ☕				☕													
Manchester Airport 85 ✈	d			19 52						20b15			20 52								21 52	21 52		
Manchester Piccadilly 10 78 🚌	d			20 18						20 42			21 18	20 46							22 18	22 18		
Stockport 78	d			20 26						20 55			21 26								22 26	22 26		
Sheffield 7 🚌	a			21 08									22 09											
	d			21 11	21 15			21 21	21 31	21 41	21 51	22 08	22 11	22 15			22 21	22 41		23 15	23 24	23 27		
Meadowhall 🚌	d			21 17	21 21				21 37	21a46		22a13	22 17	22 21			22 31	22a46		23 21	23a29	23 33		
Rotherham Central	d				21 27				21 43					22 27			22 37			23 27		23 39		
Swinton (S.Yorks)	d				21 36				21a51					22a36			22 48			23a36		23 47		
Mexborough	d				21 39												22 51					23 50		
Conisbrough	d				21 43												22 55					23 54		
Doncaster 7	a			21 40	21 54						22 12		22 42				23 04					00 07		
York 8 26	a							22 58			23 12						00 39							
London Kings Cross 15 ⊖ 26	d			*19 33*	*20 00*		*20 27*						*20 30*						*21 00*					
Doncaster 31	d			21 42	21 56		22 12						22 42						23 25					
Bentley (S.Yorks) 31	a										22 33													
Adwick 31	a										22 37													
Kirk Sandall	d				22 02								22 49						23 31					
Hatfield & Stainforth	d				22 07								22 53						23 36					
Thorne South	d												22 58											
Crowle	d												23 07											
Althorpe	d												23 13											
Scunthorpe	a			22 07									23 18											
	d			22 08									23 18											
Barnetby	d			22 23									23 36											
Hull Bus Station 🚌	d																							
Barton-on-Humber 🚌	a																							
Barton-on-Humber	d	21 58																						
Barrow Haven	d	22 03																						
New Holland	d	22 06																						
Goxhill	d	22 11																						
Thornton Abbey	d	22 14																						
Ulceby	d	22 18																						
Habrough	d	22 23		22 31									23 44											
Stallingborough	d	22 28																						
Healing	d	22 31																						
Great Coates	d	22 34																						
Grimsby Town	a	22 39		22 44									23 57											
	d	22 39		22 45									23 58											
Grimsby Docks	d	22 42																						
New Clee	d																							
Cleethorpes	a	22 48		22 59									00 09											
Thorne North	d				22 13														23 42					
Goole	d				22 22														23a53					
Saltmarshe	d				22 26																			
York 8 33	d					22 03																		
Selby	a					22 22	22 29																	
	d		21 27			22 22	22 30									22 44								
Wressle	d																							
Howden	d		21 36				22 40																	
Eastrington	d																							
Gilberdyke	d				22 31	22 38																		
Broomfleet	d																							
Brough	d		21 48		22 39	22 46	22 54									23 04								
Ferriby	d					22 51																		
Hessle	d					22 55																		
Hull	a		22 05		22 57	23 08	23 13									23 21								

For general notes see front of timetable
For details of catering facilities see Directory of Train Operators

- **A** From Leeds (Table 39)
- **B** To Beverley (Table 43)
- **C** From Plymouth (Table 51)
- **D** To Leeds (Table 31)
- **E** To Huddersfield (Table 34)
- **G** From St Pancras International to Leeds (Table 53)
- **H** To Leeds (Fridays to Barnsley) (Table 34)
- **J** To Wakefield Westgate (Table 31)
- **b** Change at Manchester Piccadilly and Sheffield

Manchester Airport, Manchester, Sheffield and Meadowhall → Doncaster → Cleethorpes and Hull Barton-on-Humber → Cleethorpes

Network Diagram - see first page of Table 18

Station		TP	TP	TP	NT	NT	NT	NT	NT	NT	EM	NT	NT	NT	NT	NT	NT	NT	NT	TP	NT	TP	NT	NT
		MX 1 ◇	MO 1 ◇	MO 1 ◇																1 ◇		1 ◇		
			A	B	C	D		E	G	H	J	H	🚌				C	G	H		K		🚌	
Manchester Airport	85 ✈ d	03 21	03 18	03 21																05 15		*05 47*		
Manchester Piccadilly 10	78 🚇 d	03 40	03 37	03 44																05 49		06 21		
Stockport	78 d																			05 58		05b53		
Sheffield 7	🚇 a	04 31	04 37	04 37																06 48				
	d	04 40	04 40	04 40	05 10	05 16		05 29	05 36	05 50		06 14				06 18	06 28	06 36	06 49	06 54				
Meadowhall	🚇 d				05 16	05a21		05 35	05a41	05a55		06a19				06 24	06 34	06a41	06a54	07 02				
Rotherham Central	d				05 22			05 41								06 30	06 40							
Swinton (S.Yorks)	d				05a30			05 49								06 38	06a48							
Mexborough	d							05 52								06 41								
Conisbrough	d							05 56								06 45								
Doncaster 7	a	05 14	05 14	05 14				06 06								06 56				07 22				
York 8	26 a							*06 35*																
London Kings Cross 15	⊖ 26 d																							
Doncaster	31 d						05 55	06 14							06 47	06 59				07 24				
Bentley (S.Yorks)	31 a							*06 28*								07 02				*07 35*				
Adwick	31 a							*06 32*								07 08				*07 40*				
Kirk Sandall	d							06 20							06 53									
Hatfield & Stainforth	d							06 25							06 58									
Thorne South	d														07 03									
Crowle	d														07 11									
Althorpe	d														07 17									
Scunthorpe	a														07 26					07 49				
	d																			07 50				
Barnetby	d										06 31									08 04				
Hull Bus Station	🚌 d												06 25										07 25	
Barton-on-Humber	🚌 a												06 50										07 50	
Barton-on-Humber	d													06 58										08 00
Barrow Haven	d													07 03										08 05
New Holland	d													07 07										08 08
Goxhill	d													07 11										08 13
Thornton Abbey	d																							08 16
Ulceby	d													07 19										08 20
Habrough	d										06 41			07 23						08 13				08 25
Stallingborough	d													07 28										08 30
Healing	d													07 31										08 33
Great Coates	d																							08 36
Grimsby Town	a										06 57			07 37						08 26				08 41
	d													07 38						08 35				08 41
Grimsby Docks	d																							08 44
New Clee	d																							08x46
Cleethorpes	a													07 50						08 46				08 51
Thorne North	d							06 30																
Goole	d							06 41																
Saltmarshe	d							06 46																
York 8	33 d																					*06 09*		
Selby	a						06 14															07 42		
	d																					07 42		
Wressle	d																							
Howden	d																					07 51		
Eastrington	d																							
Gilberdyke	d							06 53													07 39			
Broomfleet	d							06 57													07 43			
Brough	d							07 03													07 49	08 03		
Ferriby	d							07 07													07 53			
Hessle	d							07 12													07 58			
Hull	a							07 22													08 11	08 20		

For general notes see front of timetable
For details of catering facilities see Directory of Train Operators

A From 15 September
B 8 September
C To Leeds (Table 31)
D To Barnsley (Table 34)
E To Beverley (Table 43)
G To Huddersfield (Table 34)
H To Leeds (Table 34)
J From Lincoln (Table 27)
K To Scarborough (Table 43)
b Change at Manchester Piccadilly

Manchester Airport, Manchester, Sheffield and Meadowhall → Doncaster → Cleethorpes and Hull Barton-on-Humber → Cleethorpes

Network Diagram - see first page of Table 18

Station		NT	NT	NT	NT	XC	NT	NT	NT	NT	EM	TP	XC	NT	NT	TP	NT	NT	HT	NT	XC	NT	NT	XC
						1 ◇						1 ◇	1 ◇			1 ◇			BHX 1 ◇		1 ◇			R 1
		A		B		C	D		E	G	H		J	K	B		D				L	E	G	J
Manchester Airport	85 d											07 02				06 44								07b05
Manchester Piccadilly	78 d					05 52						07 35				07 19								07 43
Stockport	78 d					06 01						07c13				07 27								07 54
Sheffield	a															08 09								
	d			06 57		07 10	07 14	07 22	07 36	07 41			07 46	07 51	08 07	08 11	08 14				08 21	08 36	08 41	08 46
Meadowhall	d		06 58	07a05			07 21	07 29	07a41	07 47				07a57	08a13	08 17	08 23			08 31		08a41	08 47	
Rotherham Central	d		07 04				07 27	07 35		07 55							08 29			08 37				
Swinton (S.Yorks)	d		07 14				07a35	07 45		08 03							08a38			08 47				
Mexborough	d		07 17					07 48		08 06										08 50				
Conisbrough	d		07 21					07 52		08 10										08 54				
Doncaster	a		07 30					08 02		08 20			08 24			08 40				09 05			09 12	09 19
York	26 a		08 10			08 24							08 50			09 39				09 39	09 33		09 48	09 49
London Kings Cross	⊖ 26 d							06 00		06 35									07 20					
Doncaster	31 d	07 28	07 32					08 04		08 23						08 42		08 56	09 06	09 12			09 16	
Bentley (S.Yorks)	31 a		07 35					08 19								08 55				09 17				
Adwick	31 a		07 40					08 25								09 01				09 21				
Kirk Sandall	d	07 34						08 10										09 02		09 18				
Hatfield & Stainforth	d	07 39						08 15										09 07		09 23				
Thorne South	d							08 20												09 28				
Crowle	d							08 29												09 36				
Althorpe	d							08 35												09 42				
Scunthorpe	a							08 43								09 08				09 51				
	d															09 08								
Barnetby	d										08 52					09 22								
Hull Bus Station	d																							
Barton-on-Humber	a																							
Barton-on-Humber	d																							
Barrow Haven	d																							
New Holland	d																							
Goxhill	d																							
Thornton Abbey	d																							
Ulceby	d																							
Habrough	d										09 01													
Stallingborough	d																							
Healing	d																							
Great Coates	d																							
Grimsby Town	a										09 15					09 42								
	d															09 43								
Grimsby Docks	d																							
New Clee	d																							
Cleethorpes	a															09 58								
Thorne North	d	07 44																09 12						
Goole	d	07 53								08 43								09 21					09 39	
Saltmarshe	d	07 58																						
York	33 d				07 30														08 43					
Selby	a				07 49							08 57							09 21					
	d				07 49							08 58							09 22					
Wressle	d				07 57																			
Howden	d				08 02														09 32					
Eastrington	d				08 07																			
Gilberdyke	d	08 04			08 11													09 29						
Broomfleet	d				08 15																			
Brough	d	08 12			08 21					08 57								09 37	09 44				09 56	
Ferriby	d	08 16			08 26													09 42						
Hessle	d	08 21			08 30													09 46						
Hull	a	08 34			08 45					09 13		09 30						09 59	10 04				10 10	

For general notes see front of timetable
For details of catering facilities see Directory of Train Operators

- **A** To Beverley (Table 43)
- **B** To Leeds (Table 34)
- **C** To Edinburgh (Table 26)
- **D** To Leeds (Table 31)
- **E** To Huddersfield (Table 34)
- **G** To Bridlington (Table 43)
- **H** From Newark North Gate (Table 27)
- **J** From Birmingham New Street (Table 51)
- **K** From Retford (Table 30) to Leeds (Table 34)
- **L** From Birmingham New Street to Edinburgh (Table 51)
- **b** Change at Manchester Piccadilly and Sheffield
- **c** Change at Manchester Piccadilly

Manchester Airport, Manchester, Sheffield and Meadowhall → Doncaster → Cleethorpes and Hull Barton-on-Humber → Cleethorpes

Network Diagram - see first page of Table 18

		NT	NT	NT	NT	NT	TP	TP	NT		NT	NT	NT	NT	XC	NT	NT	EM	XC	NT	NT	NT	TP	TP
							1 ◇	1 ◇							1 ◇				R 1				1 ◇	1 ◇
		A	bus		B	A			C				B		D	E	G	H	J	A	K	A		
							trolley	trolley							buffet				buffet				trolley	trolley
Manchester Airport	85 d						07 52	*08 07*											*08b07*				08 52	*09 07*
Manchester Piccadilly 10	78 d						08 17	08 41											*08 42*				09 20	09 42
Stockport	78 d						08 26	*08c21*											*08 53*				09 28	*09c20*
Sheffield 7	a						09 09																10 08	
	d	08 51			08 56	09 05	09 11		09 14						09 21	09 36	09 41		09 46	09 51	09 58	10 08	10 11	
Meadowhall	d	08a56			09 03	09a10	09 17		09 21					09 31		09a41	09 45			09a58	10 04	10a13	10 17	
Rotherham Central	d				09 10				09 27					09 37							10 10			
Swinton (S.Yorks)	d				09 18				09a36					09 48							10 18			
Mexborough	d				09 21									09 51							10 21			
Conisbrough	d				09 25									09 55							10 25			
Doncaster 7	a				09 35		09 40							10 04			10 12		10 15		10 36		10 40	
York 8	26 a													*10 40*	10 29		*11 02*		10 41					
London Kings Cross 15	⊖ 26 d						*07 30*						⟵										*09 00*	
Doncaster	31 d				09 49 ⟶		09 42				09 46		09 49	10 06			10 16				10 44 ⟶		10 42	
Bentley (S.Yorks)	31 a												09 52	*10 17*										
Adwick	31 a												09 58	*10 21*										
Kirk Sandall	d										09 52			10 12										
Hatfield & Stainforth	d										09 57			10 17										
Thorne South	d													10 22										
Crowle	d													10 31										
Althorpe	d													10 37										
Scunthorpe	a						10 07							10 45									11 07	
	d						10 08																11 08	
Barnetby	d						10 22											10 56					11 22	
Hull Bus Station	bus d		09 25																					
Barton-on-Humber	bus a		09 50																					
Barton-on-Humber	d			09 58																				
Barrow Haven	d			10 03																				
New Holland	d			10 06																				
Goxhill	d			10 11																				
Thornton Abbey	d			10 14																				
Ulceby	d			10 18																				
Habrough	d			10 23			10 31											11 05						
Stallingborough	d			10 28																				
Healing	d			10 31																				
Great Coates	d			10 34																				
Grimsby Town	a			10 39			10 44											11 20					11 42	
	d			10 39			10 45																11 43	
Grimsby Docks	d			10 42																				
New Clee	d			10x44																				
Cleethorpes	a			10 49			10 59																11 54	
Thorne North	d										10 02													
Goole	d										10 11						10 35							
Saltmarshe	d																							
York 8	33 d											09 53												*10 20*
Selby	a							09 57				10 12												10 57
	d							09 58				10 12												10 58
Wressle	d																							
Howden	d											10 22												
Eastrington	d																							
Gilberdyke	d										10 19	10 29												
Broomfleet	d																							
Brough	d							10 16			10 27	10 37					10 49							11 16
Ferriby	d										10 32													
Hessle	d										10 36													
Hull	a							10 33			10 49	10 56					11 06							11 33

For general notes see front of timetable
For details of catering facilities see Directory of Train Operators

- **A** To Leeds (Table 34)
- **B** From Worksop (Table 30)
- **C** To Leeds (Table 31)
- **D** From Birmingham New Street to Edinburgh (Table 51)
- **E** To Huddersfield (Table 34)
- **G** To Scarborough (Table 43)
- **H** From Newark North Gate (Table 27)
- **J** From Bristol Temple Meads (Table 51)
- **K** From Lincoln (Table 30)
- **b** Change at Manchester Piccadilly and Sheffield
- **c** Change at Manchester Piccadilly

Manchester Airport, Manchester, Sheffield and Meadowhall → Doncaster → Cleethorpes and Hull
Barton-on-Humber → Cleethorpes

Network Diagram - see first page of Table 18

		NT	NT	XC	NT	NT	NT	NT	XC	HT	NT	NT	NT	NT	NT	TP	TP	NT	NT	NT	NT	XC	NT	NT
				1 ◇					1 ◇	1 ◇						1 ◇	1 ◇					1 ◇		
		A	B	C			D	E	G		H	B	🚌		H			A				J	D	K
				☕					☕	⊠ ☕						🍴	🍴					☕		
Manchester Airport	85 ✈ d								09b07							09 52	10 07							
Manchester Piccadilly 10	78 🚆 d	08 44							09 42							10 20	10 42							
Stockport	78 d								09 55							10 28	10c18							
Sheffield 7	🚆 a															11 08								
	d	10 14		10 21			10 36	10 41	10 46		10 51	10 58			11 08	11 11		11 14				11 21	11 36	11 41
Meadowhall	🚆 d	10 21				10 31	10a41	10 47			10a56	11 04			11a13	11 17		11 21		11 32			11a41	11 47
Rotherham Central	d	10 27				10 37						11 10						11 27		11 38				
Swinton (S.Yorks)	d	10a36				10 47						11 20						11a36		11 48				
Mexborough	d					10 50						11 23								11 51				
Conisbrough	d					10 54						11 27								11 55				
Doncaster 7	a					11 04		11 08	11 15			11 36				11 40				12 04				12 11
York 8	26 a			11 29		11 37			11 43													12 29		
London Kings Cross 15	⊖ 26 d		←							09 48										10 10				
Doncaster	31 d		10 44		10 47	11 07		11 17		11 36		11 38				11 42			11 49	12 07				12 14
Bentley (S.Yorks)	31 a		10 47						11e29			11 41												
Adwick	31 a		10 53						11e33			11 47												
Kirk Sandall	d				10 53	11 13													11 55	12 14				
Hatfield & Stainforth	d				10 58	11 18													12 00	12 19				
Thorne South	d					11 23														12 24				
Crowle	d					11 31														12 32				
Althorpe	d					11 37														12 38				
Scunthorpe	a					11 45										12 07				12 46				
	d															12 08								
Barnetby	d															12 22								
Hull Bus Station	🚌 d												11 25											
Barton-on-Humber	🚌 a												11 50											
Barton-on-Humber	d													11 58										
Barrow Haven	d													12 03										
New Holland	d													12 06										
Goxhill	d													12 11										
Thornton Abbey	d													12 14										
Ulceby	d													12 18										
Habrough	d													12 23		12 31								
Stallingborough	d													12 28										
Healing	d													12 31										
Great Coates	d													12 34										
Grimsby Town	a													12 39		12 44								
	d													12 39		12 46								
Grimsby Docks	d													12 42										
New Clee	d													12x44										
Cleethorpes	a													12 49		12 57								
Thorne North	d				11 03														12 05					
Goole	d				11 12			11 38											12 14					12 35
Saltmarshe	d																							
York 8	33 d																				11 53			
Selby	a									11 51							11 57				12 17			
	d									11 52							11 58				12 18			
Wressle	d																							
Howden	d									12 02											12 27			
Eastrington	d																							
Gilberdyke	d				11 20														12 22		12 34			
Broomfleet	d				11 25																			
Brough	d				11 31			11 52		12 15							12 15		12 30		12 42			12 49
Ferriby	d				11 35														12 35					
Hessle	d				11 40														12 39					
Hull	a				11 53			12 09		12 32							12 36		12 52		13 02			13 06

For general notes see front of timetable
For details of catering facilities see Directory of Train Operators

A To Leeds (Table 31)
B From Lincoln (Table 30)
C From Bristol Temple Meads to Edinburgh (Table 51)
D To Huddersfield (Table 34)
E To Bridlington (Table 43)
G From Southampton Central (Table 51)
H To Leeds (Table 34)
J From Cardiff Central to Edinburgh (Table 51)
K To Scarborough (Table 43)
b Change at Manchester Piccadilly and Sheffield
c Change at Manchester Piccadilly
e Change at Doncaster

Table 29

Mondays to Fridays
from 8 September

Manchester Airport, Manchester, Sheffield and Meadowhall → Doncaster → Cleethorpes and Hull Barton-on-Humber → Cleethorpes

Network Diagram - see first page of Table 18

		XC	NT	EM	NT	NT	TP	TP	NT	NT	NT	XC	NT	NT	NT	NT	XC	HT		NT	NT	NT	TP	TP
		1 ◇					1 ◇	1 ◇				1 ◇					1 ◇	1 ◇					1 ◇	1 ◇
		A	B	C	D	B			E			G	H	J			K			B	D	B		
															🚌									
		☕					🛒	🛒				☕					☕	⊠ ☕					🛒	🛒
Manchester Airport	85 ✈ d	10b07					10 52	11 07									11b07						11 52	12 07
Manchester Piccadilly 10	78 🚆 d	10 42					11 20	11 42	10 46								11 42						12 20	12 42
Stockport	78 d	10 55					11 27	11c19									11 55						12 28	12c19
Sheffield 7	🚆 a						12 08																13 08	
	d	11 46	11 51		11 58	12 08	12 11		12 14			12 21	12 36	12 41			12 46			12 51	12 58	13 08	13 11	
Meadowhall	🚆 d		11a56		12 04	12a13	12 17		12 21		12 31		12a41	12 47						12a56	13 04	13a13	13 17	
Rotherham Central	d				12 10				12 27		12 37										13 10			
Swinton (S.Yorks)	d				12 19				12a36		12 47										13 18			
Mexborough	d				12 22						12 50										13 21			
Conisbrough	d				12 26						12 54										13 25			
Doncaster 7	a	12 15			12 35		12 38				13 04			13 11			13 22				13 36		13 38	
York 8	26 a	12 43									13 39	13 30					13 49						14 34	
London Kings Cross 15	⊖ 26 d				10 35						11 10							11 48						
Doncaster	31 d				12 36		12 42			12 49	13 06			13 18				13 29			13 38		13 42	
Bentley (S.Yorks)	31 a	12e28			12 40									13 30							13 41			
Adwick	31 a	12e32			12 45									13 34							13 47			
Kirk Sandall	d									12 55	13 12													
Hatfield & Stainforth	d									13 00	13 17													
Thorne South	d										13 22													
Crowle	d										13 31													
Althorpe	d										13 37													
Scunthorpe	a						13 07				13 45												14 07	
	d						13 08																14 08	
Barnetby	d			13 12			13 22																14 22	
Hull Bus Station	🚌 d														13 25									
Barton-on-Humber	🚌 a														13 50									
Barton-on-Humber	d															13 58								
Barrow Haven	d															14 03								
New Holland	d															14 06								
Goxhill	d															14 11								
Thornton Abbey	d															14 14								
Ulceby	d															14 18								
Habrough	d			13 21												14 23							14 31	
Stallingborough	d															14 28								
Healing	d															14 31								
Great Coates	d															14 34								
Grimsby Town	a			13 35			13 42									14 39							14 44	
	d						13 43									14 39							14 45	
Grimsby Docks	d															14 42								
New Clee	d															14x44								
Cleethorpes	a						13 54									14 49							14 57	
Thorne North	d									13 05														
Goole	d									13 14				13 37										
Saltmarshe	d																							
York 8	33 d							12 18																
Selby	a							12 57										13 44						13 57
	d							12 58										13 45						13 58
Wressle	d																							
Howden	d																	13 55						
Eastrington	d																							
Gilberdyke	d									13 22														
Broomfleet	d																							
Brough	d							13 16		13 30				13 51				14 08						14 15
Ferriby	d									13 35														
Hessle	d									13 39														
Hull	a							13 33		13 52				14 08				14 25						14 33

For general notes see front of timetable
For details of catering facilities see Directory of Train Operators

A From Plymouth (Table 51)
B To Leeds (Table 34)
C From Newark North Gate (Table 27)
D From Lincoln (Table 30)
E To Leeds (Table 31)
G From Plymouth (Table 51) to Aberdeen (Table 229)
H To Huddersfield (Table 34)
J To Bridlington (Table 43)
K From Bournemouth (Table 51)
b Change at Manchester Piccadilly and Sheffield
c Change at Manchester Piccadilly
e Change at Doncaster

Table 29

Mondays to Fridays
from 8 September

Manchester Airport, Manchester, Sheffield and Meadowhall → Doncaster → Cleethorpes and Hull
Barton-on-Humber → Cleethorpes

Network Diagram - see first page of Table 18

		NT	NT	NT	NT	XC	NT	NT	XC	NT	NT	NT	TP	TP	NT	NT	XC	EM	NT	NT	HT	NT	NT	XC
						1 ◇			1 ◇				1 ◇	1 ◇			1 ◇				1 ◇			R 1
		A				B	C	D	E	G	H	G			A	J	B	K				C		L
Manchester Airport	85 ✈ d								12b07				12 52	13 07										13b07
Manchester Piccadilly 10	78 d								12 42				13 20	13 42	12 46									13 42
Stockport	78 d								12 55				13 28	13c19										13 55
Sheffield 7	a												14 08											
	d	13 14				13 21	13 36	13 41	13 46	13 51	13 58	14 08	14 11		14 14		14 21					14 36	14 41	14 46
Meadowhall	d	13 21			13 31		13a41	13 46		13a56	14 04	14a13	14 17		14 21					14 31		14a41	14 47	
Rotherham Central	d	13 27			13 37						14 10				14 27					14 37				
Swinton (S.Yorks)	d	13a36			13 47						14 18				14a36					14 48				
Mexborough	d				13 50						14 21									14 51				
Conisbrough	d				13 54						14 25									14 55				
Doncaster 7	a				14 04			14 14	14 18		14 36		14 38							15 04			15 09	15 15
York 8	26 a					14 30		*14 58*	14 50				*15 26*				15 29							15 40
London Kings Cross 15	⊖ 26 d				*12 10*			*12 30*			*12 35*		*13 00*							*13 10*	13 33		*13 30*	
Doncaster	31 d			13 46	14 06			14 16			14 38		14 42			14 46				15 06	15 12		15 14	
Bentley (S.Yorks)	31 a								*14e30*		14 41									*15 17*				
Adwick	31 a								*14e34*		14 47									*15 21*				
Kirk Sandall	d			13 52	14 12											14 54				15 12				
Hatfield & Stainforth	d			13 57	14 17											14 59				15 17				
Thorne South	d				14 23															15 22				
Crowle	d				14 32															15 30				
Althorpe	d				14 38															15 36				
Scunthorpe	a				14 45								15 07							15 45				
	d												15 08											
Barnetby	d												15 22					15 32						
Hull Bus Station	🚌 d																							
Barton-on-Humber	🚌 a																							
Barton-on-Humber	d																							
Barrow Haven	d																							
New Holland	d																							
Goxhill	d																							
Thornton Abbey	d																							
Ulceby	d																							
Habrough	d																	15 42						
Stallingborough	d																							
Healing	d																							
Great Coates	d																							
Grimsby Town	a												15 42					15 56						
	d												15 43											
Grimsby Docks	d																							
New Clee	d																							
Cleethorpes	a												15 54											
Thorne North	d			14 02												15 04								
Goole	d			14 12				14 36								15 13							15 33	
Saltmarshe	d			14 17																				
York 8	33 d		13 45																14 59					
Selby	a		14 09											14 57					15 19		15 27			
	d		14 09											14 58					15 19		15 28			
Wressle	d																							
Howden	d																				15 38 ↦			
Eastrington	d																							
Gilberdyke	d			14 28												15 21								
Broomfleet	d																							
Brough	d		14 29	14 36				14 52						15 16		15 29			15 39				15 47	
Ferriby	d			14 40												15 34								
Hessle	d			14 45												15 38								
Hull	a		14 48	14 56				15 07						15 33		15 51			15 58				16 04	

For general notes see front of timetable
For details of catering facilities see Directory of Train Operators

A To Leeds (Table 31)
B From Bristol Temple Meads to Edinburgh (Table 51)
C To Huddersfield (Table 34)
D To Bridlington (Table 43)
E From Plymouth (Table 51)
G To Leeds (Table 34)
H From Lincoln (Table 30)
J To Scarborough (Table 43)
K From Newark North Gate (Table 27)
L From Bournemouth (Table 51)
b Change at Manchester Piccadilly and Sheffield
c Change at Manchester Piccadilly
e Change at Doncaster

Manchester Airport, Manchester, Sheffield and Meadowhall → Doncaster → Cleethorpes and Hull Barton-on-Humber → Cleethorpes

Network Diagram - see first page of Table 18

		NT	HT	NT	NT	NT	NT	TP	TP	NT	NT	NT	XC	NT	NT	NT	XC	NT	NT	NT	TP	TP	NT	NT
			1 ◇					1 ◇	1 ◇				1 ◇				R 1				1 ◇	1 ◇		
		A		B	A	🚌				C	D		E	G		H	J	A	B	A			C	D
			⊠ ☕					🍴	🍴				☕				☕				🍴	🍴		
Manchester Airport	85 ✈ d							13 52	*14 07*								*14b07*				14 52	*15 07*		
Manchester Piccadilly 10	78 🚆 d							14 20	14 42								*14 42*				15 20	15 42	*14 46*	
Stockport	78 d							14 28	*14c19*								*14 55*				15 28	*15c19*		
Sheffield 7	🚆 a							15 08													16 08			
	d	14 51		14 58	15 08			15 11		15 14			15 21	15 36	15 41		15 46	15 51	15 58	16 08	16 11		16 14	
Meadowhall	🚆 d	14a56		15 04	15a13			15 17		15 21		15 31		15a41	15 47			15a56	16 04	16a13	16 17		16 21	
Rotherham Central	d			15 10						15 27		15 37							16 10				16 27	
Swinton (S.Yorks)	d			15 18						15a36		15 47							16 18				16a36	
Mexborough	d			15 21								15 50							16 21					
Conisbrough	d			15 25								15 54							16 25					
Doncaster 7	a			15 36				15 38				16 04			16 12		16 15		16 36		16 38			
York 8	26 a												16 29				16 40				*17 34*			
London Kings Cross 15	⊖ 26 d			*14 00*								*14 10*			*14 35*									
Doncaster	31 d			15 38				15 42			15 46	16 09			16 18				16 38		16 42			16 46
Bentley (S.Yorks)	31 a			15 41								*16 17*							16 41					
Adwick	31 a			15 47								*16 21*							16 47					
Kirk Sandall	d										15 52	16 15												16 52
Hatfield & Stainforth	d										15 57	16 20												16 57
Thorne South	d											16 25												
Crowle	d											16 34												
Althorpe	d											16 40												
Scunthorpe	a							16 07				16 48									17 07			
	d							16 08													17 08			
Barnetby	d							16 22													17 22			
Hull Bus Station	🚌 d					15 25																		
Barton-on-Humber	🚌 a					15 50																		
Barton-on-Humber	d						15 58																	
Barrow Haven	d						16 03																	
New Holland	d						16 06																	
Goxhill	d						16 11																	
Thornton Abbey	d						16 14																	
Ulceby	d						16 18																	
Habrough	d						16 23	16 31																
Stallingborough	d						16 28																	
Healing	d						16 31																	
Great Coates	d						16 34																	
Grimsby Town	a						16 39	16 44													17 42			
	d						16 39	16 45													17 43			
Grimsby Docks	d						16 42																	
New Clee	d																							
Cleethorpes	a						16 48	16 56													17 54			
Thorne North	d										16 02													17 02
Goole	d										16 11				16 37									17 11
Saltmarshe	d																							17 16
York 8	33 d															16 12								
Selby	a								15 57							16 38						16 57		
	d								15 58							16 39						16 58		
Wressle	d		←													16 46								
Howden	d		15 38													16 51								
Eastrington	d																							
Gilberdyke	d										16 20					16 58								17 23
Broomfleet	d																							
Brough	d		15 53						16 16		16 28				16 51	17 06						17 16		17 31
Ferriby	d										16 32					17 10								17 36
Hessle	d										16 37													17 40
Hull	a		16 10						16 33		16 49				17 08	17 27						17 35		17 53

For general notes see front of timetable
For details of catering facilities see Directory of Train Operators

A To Leeds (Table 34)
B From Lincoln (Table 30)
C To Leeds (Table 31)
D To Bridlington (Table 43)
E From Paignton (Table 51) to Dundee (Table 229)
G To Huddersfield (Table 34)
H To Scarborough (Table 43)
J From Penzance (Table 135)
b Change at Manchester Piccadilly and Sheffield
c Change at Manchester Piccadilly

Table 29

Mondays to Fridays
from 8 September

Manchester Airport, Manchester, Sheffield and Meadowhall → Doncaster → Cleethorpes and Hull Barton-on-Humber → Cleethorpes

Network Diagram - see first page of Table 18

		NT	EM	XC	NT	NT		NT	XC	NT	NT	NT	NT	NT	HT	NT	TP	TP	NT	NT	NT	XC	NT	NT
				R 1					R 1			🚌			1 ◇		1 ◇	1 ◇				R 1		
			A	B	C				D	E	G			H		E			J	K		L	C	
				☕					☕						⊠ ☕		🍴	🍴				☕		
Manchester Airport	85 ✈ d								15b07								15 52	16 07						
Manchester Piccadilly 10	78 🚆 d								15 42								16 20	16 42	15 46					
Stockport	78 d								15 51								16 28	16c19						
Sheffield 7	🚆 a																17 08							
	d			16 21	16 36	16 41			16 46	16 51				16 58		17 08	17 11		17 14			17 21	17 36	17 41
Meadowhall	🚆 d	16 31			16a41	16 47				16a56				17 04		17a13	17 17		17 21		17 31		17a41	17 47
Rotherham Central	d	16 37												17 10					17 27		17 38			
Swinton (S.Yorks)	d	16 47												17 18					17a36		17 47			
Mexborough	d	16 50												17 21							17 50			
Conisbrough	d	16 54												17 25							17 54			
Doncaster 7	a	17 07				17 11			17 15					17 36			17 38				18 07			18 13
York 8	26 a			17 29		17 54			17 45								18 34					18 29		
London Kings Cross 15	⊖ 26 d					15 10					15 30			16 00	16 05									16 30
Doncaster	31 d					17 14					17 22			17 38	17 42		17 42			17 56				18 16
Bentley (S.Yorks)	31 a								17e30					17 41										
Adwick	31 a								17e34					17 47										
Kirk Sandall	d										17 29									18 02				
Hatfield & Stainforth	d										17 34									18 07				
Thorne South	d										17 39													
Crowle	d										17 47													
Althorpe	d										17 53													
Scunthorpe	a										18 01						18 08							
	d																18 08							
Barnetby	d		17 52														18 22							
Hull Bus Station	🚌 d											17 30												
Barton-on-Humber	🚌 a											17 55												
Barton-on-Humber	d												18 00											
Barrow Haven	d												18 05											
New Holland	d												18 08											
Goxhill	d												18 13											
Thornton Abbey	d												18 16											
Ulceby	d												18 20											
Habrough	d		18 01										18 25				18 31							
Stallingborough	d												18 30											
Healing	d												18 33											
Great Coates	d												18 36											
Grimsby Town	a		18 14										18 41				18 46							
	d												18 41				18 46							
Grimsby Docks	d												18 44											
New Clee	d																							
Cleethorpes	a												18 50				19 00							
Thorne North	d					17 26														18 12				18 36
Goole	d					17 35														18 21				
Saltmarshe	d																			18 26				
York 8	33 d							17 27																
Selby	a							17 45							17 59			18 04						
	d							17 46							18 00			18 06						
Wressle	d																							
Howden	d							17 55							18 10			18 16						
Eastrington	d																							
Gilberdyke	d							18 01												18 37				
Broomfleet	d																			18 41				
Brough	d					17 49		18 09							18 23			18 28		18 47				18 53
Ferriby	d																			18 51				
Hessle	d																			18 56				
Hull	a					18 06		18 29							18 40			18 45		19 06				19 09

For general notes see front of timetable
For details of catering facilities see Directory of Train Operators

A From Lincoln (Table 27)
B From Bristol Temple Meads to Glasgow Central (Table 51)
C To Huddersfield (Table 34)
D From Bournemouth (Table 51)
E To Leeds (Table 34)
G From Adwick (Table 31)
H From Lincoln (Table 30)
J To Leeds (Table 31)
K To Scarborough (Table 43)
L From Plymouth to Glasgow Central (Table 51)
b Change at Manchester Piccadilly and Sheffield
c Change at Manchester Piccadilly
e Change at Doncaster

Manchester Airport, Manchester, Sheffield and Meadowhall → Doncaster → Cleethorpes and Hull Barton-on-Humber → Cleethorpes

Network Diagram - see first page of Table 18

Station		NT	XC R 1 A	NT B	NT C	TP 1 ◇	NT D	NT B	NT E	XC R 1 G	TP 1 ◇	GR R 1 H	NT	NT J	NT K	NT (bus)	NT	XC R 1 L	NT B	NT B	NT	TP 1 ◇	TP 1 ◇	NT E
Manchester Airport	85 d		16b07			17 04					16 52								17b04			17 52	18 10	
Manchester Piccadilly 10	78 d		16 42			17 42					17 20								17 42			18 18	18 42	
Stockport	78 d		16 53			17c18					17 28								17 53			18 26	18c19	
Sheffield 7	a										18 15											19 08		
	d		17 46	17 51			17 57	18 08	18 14	18 21	18 24			18 36	18 41			18 46	18 51	19 08		19 11		19 15
Meadowhall	d			17a59			18 03	18a13	18 21		18 29		18 35	18a41	18 47				18a56	19a13		19 17		19e25
Rotherham Central	d						18 09		18 27				18 42											19 31
Swinton (S.Yorks)	d						18 17		18a36				18 50											19a40
Mexborough	d						18 20						18 53											
Conisbrough	d						18 24						18 57											
Doncaster 7	a		18 16				18 35				18 53		19 08		19 11			19 17				19 41		
York 8	26 a		18 41							19 29					19 44			19 44						
London Kings Cross 15	⊖ 26 d				16 35						17 03	17 20										18 00		
Doncaster	31 d				18 27		18 41				18 55	19 05			19 14						19 20	19 42		
Bentley (S.Yorks)	31 a		18f30															19f32						
Adwick	31 a		18f34															19f36						
Kirk Sandall	d				18 34		18 47														19 27			
Hatfield & Stainforth	d				18 39		18 52														19 32			
Thorne South	d				18 44																19 37			
Crowle	d				18 52																19 46			
Althorpe	d				18 58																19 52			
Scunthorpe	a				19 06						19 22										19 59	20 07		
	d										19 23											20 08		
Barnetby	d										19 37											20 22		
Hull Bus Station	(bus) d															19 25								
Barton-on-Humber	(bus) a															19 50								
Barton-on-Humber	d																19 58							
Barrow Haven	d																20 03							
New Holland	d																20 06							
Goxhill	d																20 11							
Thornton Abbey	d																20 14							
Ulceby	d																20 18							
Habrough	d																20 23							
Stallingborough	d																20 28							
Healing	d																20 31							
Great Coates	d																20 34							
Grimsby Town	a										19 58						20 39					20 43		
	d										19 58						20 39					20 44		
Grimsby Docks	d																20 42							
New Clee	d																							
Cleethorpes	a										20 09						20 48					20 57		
Thorne North	d						18 57																	
Goole	d						19 06								19 34									
Saltmarshe	d																							
York 8	33 d	18 14																					19 23	
Selby	a	18 43				19 00						19 20											20 00	
	d	18 43				19 01						19 21											20 01	
Wressle	d	18 51																						
Howden	d	18 56																					20 10	
Eastrington	d	19 00																						
Gilberdyke	d	19 05					19 15																	
Broomfleet	d																							
Brough	d	19 13				19 19	19 23					19 43			19 49								20 22	
Ferriby	d						19 27																	
Hessle	d						19 32																	
Hull	a	19 32				19 36	19 47					20 00			20 07								20 39	

For general notes see front of timetable
For details of catering facilities see Directory of Train Operators

- **A** From Plymouth (Table 51)
- **B** To Leeds (Table 34)
- **C** From Adwick (Table 31)
- **D** From Lincoln (Table 30)
- **E** To Leeds (Table 31)
- **G** From Bristol Temple Meads to Edinburgh (Table 51)
- **H** **The Hull Executive**
- **J** To Huddersfield (Table 34)
- **K** To Bridlington (Table 43)
- **L** From Bournemouth to Newcastle (Table 51)
- **b** Change at Manchester Piccadilly and Sheffield
- **c** Change at Manchester Piccadilly
- **e** Arr. 1922
- **f** Change at Doncaster

Table 29

Mondays to Fridays
from 8 September

Manchester Airport, Manchester, Sheffield and Meadowhall → Doncaster → Cleethorpes and Hull Barton-on-Humber → Cleethorpes

Network Diagram - see first page of Table 18

		NT	XC	EM	NT	NT	NT	NT	XC	NT	HT	NT	NT	NT	TP	NT	NT	NT	XC	NT	TP	NT	XC	NT
			R 1						R 1		1 ◇				1 ◇				R 1		1 ◇		R 1	ThFO
			A B	C	D		E	G	H				J	J		K			L	N	Q		U	bus
			⊡								⊠ ⊡													
Manchester Airport	85 d												18b10		18 52								19b12	
Manchester Piccadilly 10	78 d												18 44		19 18								19 42	
Stockport	78 d												18 55		19 26								19 55	
Sheffield 7	a														20 08									
	d		19 21		19 25	19 30	19 38	19 41	19 46				19 53	20 08	20 11				20 21	20 27		20 40	20 46	
Meadowhall	d				19 31	19 36	19a43	19 47				19 56	19a58	20a13	20 17			20 21		20 35		20 46		
Rotherham Central	d				19 37	19 42						20 09						20 27		20 41		20 52		
Swinton (S.Yorks)	d				19 47	19 51						20 18						20 36		20a50		21 00		
Mexborough	d				19 50	19 54						20 21						20 39				21 03		
Conisbrough	d				19 54	19 58						20 25						20 43				21 07		
Doncaster 7	a				20 04	20 08		20 11	20 20			20 35			20 41			20 55				21 18		
York 8	26 a		20 34			*20 39*			20 46										21 35			*22 06*	21 48	
London Kings Cross 15	⊖ 26 d									*18 33*	18 50					*19 00*						*19 03*		
Doncaster	31 d	19 51						20 15		20 25	20 31				20 42	20 44	20 49					21 18		
Bentley (S.Yorks)	31 a							*20 41*														*21 41*		
Adwick	31 a							*20 45*														*21 45*		
Kirk Sandall	d	19 57								20 31							20 55					21 26		
Hatfield & Stainforth	d	20 02								20 36							21 00					21 31		
Thorne South	d									20 41												21 38		
Crowle	d									20 50												21 46		
Althorpe	d									20 56												21 52		
Scunthorpe	a									21 04					21 07							22 01		
	d														21 08									
Barnetby	d			20 31											21 22									
Hull Bus Station	bus d																							21 25
Barton-on-Humber	bus a																							21 50
Barton-on-Humber	d																							
Barrow Haven	d																							
New Holland	d																							
Goxhill	d																							
Thornton Abbey	d																							
Ulceby	d																							
Habrough	d			20 40											21 31									
Stallingborough	d																							
Healing	d																							
Great Coates	d																							
Grimsby Town	a			20 52											21 44									
	d			20 53											21 45									
Grimsby Docks	d																							
New Clee	d																							
Cleethorpes	a			21 01											21 59									
Thorne North	d	20 08															21 06							
Goole	d	20 17						20 36									21a17							
Saltmarshe	d																							
York 8	33 d																							
Selby	a										20 46					21 01								
	d										20 47					21 02					21 27			
Wressle	d																							
Howden	d										20 57										21 36			
Eastrington	d																							
Gilberdyke	d	20 25														21 15								
Broomfleet	d																							
Brough	d	20 33						20 49			21 09					21 23					21 48			
Ferriby	d	20 37														21 28								
Hessle	d	20 42														21 32								
Hull	a	20 55						21 06			21 28					21 45					22 05			

For general notes see front of timetable
For details of catering facilities see Directory of Train Operators

A ⊡ to Leeds
B From Paignton to Edinburgh (Table 51)
C From Newark North Gate (Table 27)
D From Retford Low Level (Table 30)
E To Huddersfield (Table 34)
G To Beverley (Table 43)
H From Plymouth to Newcastle (Table 51)
J To Leeds (Table 34)
K To Bridlington (Table 43)
L From Bristol Temple Meads to Newcastle (Table 51)
N To Leeds (Table 31)
Q From Leeds (Table 39)
U From Bournemouth to Newcastle (Table 51)
b Change at Manchester Piccadilly and Sheffield

Manchester Airport, Manchester, Sheffield and Meadowhall → Doncaster → Cleethorpes and Hull Barton-on-Humber → Cleethorpes

Network Diagram - see first page of Table 18

		NT	NT	TP	NT	NT	XC	NT	EM	HT	NT	XC	NT	TP	NT	TP	NT	NT	NT	NT	NT	NT
										BHX											FX	
				1 ◇			1 ◇		1 ◇	1 ◇		1 ◇		1 ◇		1 ◇						
			A		B		C	D	E		G	H	J		D	K		G		D	L	
Manchester Airport	85 d			19 52							20b15			20 52							21 52	21 52
Manchester Piccadilly 10	78 d			20 18							20 42			21 18	20 46						22 18	22 18
Stockport	78 d			20 26							20 55			21 26							22 26	22 26
Sheffield 7	a			21 08										22 09								
	d		21 06	21 11	21 15		21 21	21 30	21 33		21 41	21 47	22 08	22 11	22 15		22 21	22 41		23 15	23 24	23 27
Meadowhall	d		21a13	21 17	21 21			21 36			21a47		22a13	22 17	22 21		22 31	22a46		23 21	23a29	23 33
Rotherham Central	d				21 27			21 43							22 27		22 37			23 27		23 39
Swinton (S.Yorks)	d				21 36			21a51							22a36		22 48			23a36		23 47
Mexborough	d				21 39												22 51					23 50
Conisbrough	d				21 43												22 55					23 54
Doncaster 7	a			21 40	21 54				21 57					22 42			23 04					00 07
York 8	26 a						22 58		23 12			23 09					00 39					
London Kings Cross 15	⊖ 26 d			19 33	20 00					20 27				20 30					21 00			
Doncaster	31 d			21 42	21 56					22 12				22 42					23 25			
Bentley (S.Yorks)	31 a								22 33													
Adwick	31 a								22 37													
Kirk Sandall	d				22 02									22 49					23 31			
Hatfield & Stainforth	d				22 07									22 53					23 36			
Thorne South	d													22 58								
Crowle	d													23 07								
Althorpe	d													23 13								
Scunthorpe	a			22 07										23 18								
	d			22 08										23 18								
Barnetby	d			22 23										23 36								
Hull Bus Station	d																					
Barton-on-Humber	a																					
Barton-on-Humber	d	21 58																				
Barrow Haven	d	22 03																				
New Holland	d	22 06																				
Goxhill	d	22 11																				
Thornton Abbey	d	22 14																				
Ulceby	d	22 18																				
Habrough	d	22 23		22 31										23 44								
Stallingborough	d	22 28																				
Healing	d	22 31																				
Great Coates	d	22 34																				
Grimsby Town	a	22 39		22 44										23 57								
	d	22 39		22 45										23 58								
Grimsby Docks	d	22 42																				
New Clee	d																					
Cleethorpes	a	22 48		22 59										00 09								
Thorne North	d				22 13														23 42			
Goole	d				22 22														23a53			
Saltmarshe	d				22 26																	
York 8	33 d					22 03																
Selby	a					22 22				22 29												
	d					22 22				22 30						22 44						
Wressle	d																					
Howden	d									22 40												
Eastrington	d																					
Gilberdyke	d				22 31	22 38																
Broomfleet	d																					
Brough	d				22 39	22 46				22 54						23 04						
Ferriby	d					22 51																
Hessle	d					22 55																
Hull	a				22 57	23 08				23 13						23 21						

For general notes see front of timetable
For details of catering facilities see Directory of Train Operators

A To Leeds (Table 34)
B To Beverley (Table 43)
C From Paignton (Table 51)
D To Leeds (Table 31)
E From St Pancras International to Leeds (Table 53)
G To Huddersfield (Table 34)
H From Plymouth (Table 51)
J To Leeds (Fridays to Barnsley)(Table 34)
K From Leeds (Table 39)
L To Wakefield Westgate (Table 31)
b Change at Manchester Piccadilly and Sheffield

Table 29

until 6 September

Manchester Airport, Manchester, Sheffield and Meadowhall → Doncaster → Cleethorpes and Hull Barton-on-Humber → Cleethorpes

Network Diagram - see first page of Table 18

Station		TP 1 ◇	NT A	NT	NT B	NT A	EM C	NT D	NT	NT	NT	NT E	NT G	NT	TP 1 ◇	NT D	NT H	TP 1 ◇	NT (bus)	NT	NT B	NT	NT	XC 1 ◇ J
Manchester Airport	85 d	03 21													05 15			*05 47*						
Manchester Piccadilly 10	78 d	03 40													05 49	*05 52*		06 21						*05 52*
Stockport	78 d														05 58	*06 01*		*05b53*						*06 01*
Sheffield 7	a	04 31													06 48									
	d	04 40	05 16		05 29	05 48		06 14			06 18	06 28	06 36	06 52	06 54	07 08								07 12
Meadowhall	d		05a21		05 35	05a53		06a19			06 24	06 34	06a41	06 58	07 02	07a13							←	
Rotherham Central	d				05 41						06 30	06 40		07 04										
Swinton (S.Yorks)	d				05 49						06 38	06a48		07 14 →									07 14	
Mexborough	d				05 52						06 41												07 17	
Conisbrough	d				05 56						06 45												07 21	
Doncaster 7	a	05 14			06 06						06 57				07 22								07 31	
York 8	26 a				*06 40*										*08 31*								*08 31*	08 24
London Kings Cross 15	⊖ 26 d																							
Doncaster	31 d			05 50	06 14					06 47	07 00				07 24						07 28		07 32	
Bentley (S.Yorks)	31 a				*06 28*						07 03				*07 35*								07 35	
Adwick	31 a				*06 32*						07 09				*07 41*								07 41	
Kirk Sandall	d				06 20					06 53											07 34			
Hatfield & Stainforth	d				06 25					06 58											07 39			
Thorne South	d									07 03														
Crowle	d									07 11														
Althorpe	d									07 17														
Scunthorpe	a									07 25					07 49									
	d														07 50									
Barnetby	d						06 30								08 04									
Hull Bus Station	(bus) d																		07 25					
Barton-on-Humber	(bus) a																		07 50					
Barton-on-Humber	d								06 58											08 00				
Barrow Haven	d								07 03											08 05				
New Holland	d								07 07											08 08				
Goxhill	d								07 11											08 13				
Thornton Abbey	d																			08 16				
Ulceby	d								07 19											08 20				
Habrough	d						06 39		07 23						08 13					08 25				
Stallingborough	d								07 28											08 30				
Healing	d								07 31											08 33				
Great Coates	d																			08 36				
Grimsby Town	a						06 53		07 37						08 26					08 41				
	d								07 38						08 35					08 43				
Grimsby Docks	d																			08 45				
New Clee	d																			08x48				
Cleethorpes	a								07 50						08 46					08 52				
Thorne North	d				06 30																07 44			
Goole	d				06 39																07 53			
Saltmarshe	d				06 44																07 58			
York 8	33 d																	*06 05*				07 30		
Selby	a			06 10														07 42				07 50		
	d																	07 42				07 50		
Wressle	d																					07 58		
Howden	d																	07 51				08 03		
Eastrington	d																					08 08		
Gilberdyke	d				06 50												07 39				08 04	08 12		
Broomfleet	d				06 54												07 43					08 16		
Brough	d				07 00												07 49	08 03			08 12	08 22		
Ferriby	d				07 04												07 53				08 16	08 27		
Hessle	d				07 09												07 58				08 21	08 31		
Hull	a				07 22												08 11	08 20			08 34	08 46		

For general notes see front of timetable
For details of catering facilities see Directory of Train Operators

- **A** To Barnsley (Table 34)
- **B** To Beverley (Table 43)
- **C** From Lincoln (Table 27)
- **D** To Leeds (Table 34)
- **E** To Leeds (Table 31)
- **G** To Huddersfield (Table 34)
- **H** To Scarborough (Table 43)
- **J** From Birmingham New Street to Edinburgh (Table 51)
- **b** Change at Manchester Piccadilly

Due to Engineering Operations in the Sheffield area, services from Saturday 13 September on this Table had not been confirmed at time of going to press. These services will be issued in a special Supplement as soon as exact timings have been confirmed.

Table 29

Saturdays

until 6 September

Manchester Airport, Manchester, Sheffield and Meadowhall → Doncaster → Cleethorpes and Hull
Barton-on-Humber → Cleethorpes

Network Diagram - see first page of Table 18

Station		NT	EM	NT	NT	NT	NT	EM	XC	NT	TP	TP	NT	XC	NT	NT	NT	NT	NT	NT	XC	NT	NT	NT
			1 ◇						1 ◇		1 ◇	1 ◇		1 ◇							1 ◇			
		A	B		C	D	E	G	H	J			A	K	L			C	D	J	H		J	
			☕						☕		🍴	🍴		☕							☕			🚌
Manchester Airport	85 ✈ d									05b47	06 44	07 02								07b05				
Manchester Piccadilly 10	78 🚆 d									06 32	07 19	07 35								07 43				
Stockport	78 d										07 27	07c07								07 54				
Sheffield 7	🚆 a										08 09													
	d	07 14	07 17	07 23	07 36	07 41	07 51		07 54	08 08	08 11		08 14	08 21			08 23	08 36	08 41	08 51	08 54	08 57	09 08	
Meadowhall	🚆 d	07 21	07a23	07 29	07a41	07 47	07a57			08a13	08 17		08 23				08 31	08a41	08 47	08a56		09 03	09a13	
Rotherham Central	d	07 27		07 37		07 55							08 29				08 37					09 10		
Swinton (S.Yorks)	d	07a35		07 46		08 03							08a38				08 47					09 19		
Mexborough	d			07 49		08 06											08 50					09 22		
Conisbrough	d			07 53		08 10											08 54					09 26		
Doncaster 7	a			08 02		08 20			08 23		08 40						09 05		09 09		09 21	09 36		
York 8	26 a					*09 04*			08 50					09 30							09 45			
London Kings Cross 15	⊖ 26 d					*06 15*										*07 00*	*07 10*							
Doncaster	31 d			08 04		08 22					08 42					08 48	09 10		09 16			09 37		
Bentley (S.Yorks)	31 a			*08 19*							*08 53*						*09 17*					09 44		
Adwick	31 a			*08 25*							*08 59*						*09 21*					09 50		
Kirk Sandall	d			08 10												08 55	09 18							
Hatfield & Stainforth	d			08 15												09 00	09 23							
Thorne South	d			08 19													09 28							
Crowle	d			08 28													09 36							
Althorpe	d			08 34													09 42							
Scunthorpe	a			08 43							09 08						09 49							
	d										09 08													
Barnetby	d							09 00			09 22				09 40									
Hull Bus Station	🚌 d																							09 25
Barton-on-Humber	🚌 a																							09 50
Barton-on-Humber	d																							
Barrow Haven	d																							
New Holland	d																							
Goxhill	d																							
Thornton Abbey	d																							
Ulceby	d																							
Habrough	d							09 09							09 49									
Stallingborough	d																							
Healing	d																							
Great Coates	d																							
Grimsby Town	a							09 23			09 42				10 01									
	d										09 43				10 01									
Grimsby Docks	d																							
New Clee	d																							
Cleethorpes	a										09 58				10 14									
Thorne North	d															09 05								
Goole	d					08 42										09 14			09 39					
Saltmarshe	d																							
York 8	33 d																							
Selby	a											08 57												
	d											08 58												
Wressle	d																							
Howden	d																							
Eastrington	d																							
Gilberdyke	d															09 22								
Broomfleet	d																							
Brough	d					08 56										09 30			09 53					
Ferriby	d															09 35								
Hessle	d															09 39								
Hull	a					09 13						09 33				09 55			10 10					

For general notes see front of timetable
For details of catering facilities see Directory of Train Operators

- **A** To Leeds (Table 31)
- **B** From Derby (Table 53) to Barnsley (Table 34)
- **C** To Huddersfield (Table 34)
- **D** To Bridlington (Table 43)
- **E** From Retford (Table 30) to Leeds (Table 34)
- **G** From Lincoln (Table 27)
- **H** From Birmingham New Street to Newcastle (Table 51)
- **J** To Leeds (Table 34)
- **K** From Birmingham New Street to Edinburgh (Table 51)
- **L** From Sheffield via Retford (Table 30)
- **b** Change at Manchester Piccadilly and Sheffield
- **c** Change at Manchester Piccadilly

Due to Engineering Operations in the Sheffield area, services from Saturday 13 September on this Table had not been confirmed at time of going to press. These services will be issued in a special Supplement as soon as exact timings have been confirmed.

Table 29

until 6 September

Manchester Airport, Manchester, Sheffield and Meadowhall → Doncaster → Cleethorpes and Hull Barton-on-Humber → Cleethorpes

Network Diagram - see first page of Table 18

		NT	TP	TP	NT	NT	NT	EM	EM	XC	NT	NT	NT	NT	NT	XC	NT	NT	TP	TP	NT		NT	XC
			1 ◇	1 ◇				1 ◇		1 ◇						1 ◇			1 ◇	1 ◇				1 ◇
					A			B	C	D		E	G	H	J	K	L	J			A			N
Manchester Airport	85 d		07 52	08 07											08b07				08 52	09 07				
Manchester Piccadilly 10	78 d		08 17	08 42	07 46										08 42				09 20	09 42	08 46			
Stockport	78 d		08 26	08c20											08 55				09 28	09c21				
Sheffield 7	a		09 09																10 08					
	d		09 11		09 14			09 21		09 21	09 25	09 31	09 36	09 41	09 51	09 54	09 57	10 08	10 11		10 14			10 21
Meadowhall	d		09 17		09 21			09 29			09 32	09 37	09a41	09 47	09a56		10 03	10a13	10 17		10 21			
Rotherham Central	d				09 27						09 39	09 44					10 10				10 27			
Swinton (S.Yorks)	d				09a36						09 48	09 52					10 18				10a36			
Mexborough	d										09 51						10 21							
Conisbrough	d										09 55						10 25							
Doncaster 7	a		09 40					09 52			10 05			10 11		10 18	10 35		10 40					
York 8	26 a							10 16		10 29	10 39	10 53				10 45								11 31
London Kings Cross 15	⊖ 26 d					08 00					08 10			08 30									09 00	
Doncaster	31 d		09 42			09 46					10 07			10 21			10 37		10 42				10 46	
Bentley (S.Yorks)	31 a										10 17						10 41							
Adwick	31 a										10 21						10 47							
Kirk Sandall	d					09 53					10 14												10 52	
Hatfield & Stainforth	d					09 58					10 19												10 57	
Thorne South	d										10 24													
Crowle	d										10 33													
Althorpe	d										10 39													
Scunthorpe	a		10 07								10 46								11 07					
	d		10 08																11 08					
Barnetby	d		10 22						10 55										11 22					
Hull Bus Station	d																							
Barton-on-Humber	a																							
Barton-on-Humber	d	09 58																						
Barrow Haven	d	10 03																						
New Holland	d	10 06																						
Goxhill	d	10 11																						
Thornton Abbey	d	10 14																						
Ulceby	d	10 18																						
Habrough	d	10 23	10 31						11 03															
Stallingborough	d	10 28																						
Healing	d	10 31																						
Great Coates	d	10 34																						
Grimsby Town	a	10 39	10 44						11 17										11 42					
	d	10 39	10 45																11 43					
Grimsby Docks	d	10 42																						
New Clee	d	10x44																						
Cleethorpes	a	10 49	10 56																11 54					
Thorne North	d					10 03																	11 02	
Goole	d					10 12								10 40									11 12	
Saltmarshe	d																							
York 8	33 d			08 34			09 52													10 17				
Selby	a			09 57			10 12													10 59				
	d			09 58			10 12													10 59				
Wressle	d																							
Howden	d						10 22																	
Eastrington	d																							
Gilberdyke	d					10 20	10 29																11 20	
Broomfleet	d																						11 25	
Brough	d			10 16		10 28	10 37							10 54						11 17			11 31	
Ferriby	d					10 33																	11 35	
Hessle	d					10 37																	11 40	
Hull	a			10 33		10 50	10 56							11 12						11 34			11 53	

For general notes see front of timetable
For details of catering facilities see Directory of Train Operators

A To Leeds (Table 31)
B From St Pancras International (Table 53) to Scarborough (Table 39)
C From Newark North Gate (Table 27)
D From Bristol Temple Meads to Edinburgh (Table 51)
E Via Pontefract Baghill (Table 33)
G To Huddersfield (Table 34)
H To Scarborough (Table 43)
J To Leeds (Table 34)
K From Birmingham New Street to Newcastle (Table 51)
L From Lincoln (Table 30)
N From Southampton Central to Edinburgh (Table 51)
b Change at Manchester Piccadilly and Sheffield
c Change at Manchester Piccadilly

Due to Engineering Operations in the Sheffield area, services from Saturday 13 September on this Table had not been confirmed at time of going to press. These services will be issued in a special Supplement as soon as exact timings have been confirmed.

Table 29

until 6 September

Manchester Airport, Manchester, Sheffield and Meadowhall → Doncaster → Cleethorpes and Hull Barton-on-Humber → Cleethorpes

Network Diagram - see first page of Table 18

		NT	NT	NT	NT	XC	HT	NT	NT	NT	NT	TP	TP	NT	NT	NT	EM	XC	NT	NT	NT	NT	XC	NT
						1 ◇	1 ◇					1 ◇	1 ◇					1 ◇					1 ◇	
			A	B	C	D		E	bus		C			G			H	J		A	K	C	D	E
Manchester Airport	85 ✈ d				09b07							09 52	10 07									10b07		
Manchester Piccadilly 10	78 d				09 42							10 20	10 42	09 46								10 42		
Stockport	78 d				09 55							10 28	10c18									10 55		
Sheffield 7	a											11 08												
	d	10 25	10 36	10 41	10 51	10 54		10 57			11 08	11 11		11 14				11 21	11 25	11 36	11 41	11 51	11 54	11 57
Meadowhall	d	10 31	10a41	10 47	10a56			11 03			11a13	11 17		11 21					11 31	11a41	11 47	11a56		12 03
Rotherham Central	d	10 37						11 10						11 27					11 37					12 10
Swinton (S.Yorks)	d	10 47						11 20						11a36					11 48					12 19
Mexborough	d	10 50						11 23											11 51					12 22
Conisbrough	d	10 54						11 27											11 55					12 26
Doncaster 7	a	11 04		11 09		11 16		11 35				11 38							12 04		12 11		12 15	12 35
York 8	26 a	11 39				11 45												12 29			12 47		12 43	
London Kings Cross 15	⊖ 26 d	09 05					09 34					10 00							10 10					10 40
Doncaster	31 d	11 07		11 18			11 24	11 38				11 42			11 46				12 08		12 16			12 36
Bentley (S.Yorks)	31 a	11 17						11 41											12 17					12 40
Adwick	31 a	11 21						11 47											12 21					12 45
Kirk Sandall	d	11 13													11 52				12 14					
Hatfield & Stainforth	d	11 18													11 57				12 19					
Thorne South	d	11 23																	12 24					
Crowle	d	11 31																	12 32					
Althorpe	d	11 37																	12 38					
Scunthorpe	a	11 45										12 07							12 47					
	d											12 08												
Barnetby	d											12 22					12 32							
Hull Bus Station	bus d								11 25															
Barton-on-Humber	bus a								11 50															
Barton-on-Humber	d									11 58														
Barrow Haven	d									12 03														
New Holland	d									12 06														
Goxhill	d									12 11														
Thornton Abbey	d									12 14														
Ulceby	d									12 18														
Habrough	d									12 23		12 31					12 41							
Stallingborough	d									12 28														
Healing	d									12 31														
Great Coates	d									12 34														
Grimsby Town	a									12 39		12 44					12 55							
	d									12 39		12 45												
Grimsby Docks	d									12 42														
New Clee	d									12x44														
Cleethorpes	a									12 49		12 56												
Thorne North	d														12 02									
Goole	d			11 37											12 12						12 35			
Saltmarshe	d																							
York 8	33 d															11 49								
Selby	a						11 39						11 57			12 09								
	d						11 40						11 58			12 09								
Wressle	d																							
Howden	d						11 50									12 19								
Eastrington	d																							
Gilberdyke	d														12 20	12 27								
Broomfleet	d																							
Brough	d			11 51			12 03						12 16		12 28	12 35					12 49			
Ferriby	d														12 33									
Hessle	d														12 37									
Hull	a			12 08			12 20						12 33		12 50	12 54					13 07			

For general notes see front of timetable
For details of catering facilities see Directory of Train Operators

- **A** To Huddersfield (Table 34)
- **B** To Bridlington (Table 43)
- **C** To Leeds (Table 34)
- **D** From Bristol Temple Meads to Newcastle (Table 51)
- **E** From Lincoln (Table 30)
- **G** To Leeds (Table 31)
- **H** From Newark North Gate (Table 27)
- **J** From Plymouth to Edinburgh (Table 51)
- **K** To Scarborough (Table 43)
- **b** Change at Manchester Piccadilly and Sheffield
- **c** Change at Manchester Piccadilly

Due to Engineering Operations in the Sheffield area, services from Saturday 13 September on this Table had not been confirmed at time of going to press. These services will be issued in a special Supplement as soon as exact timings have been confirmed.

Table 29

Saturdays

until 6 September

Manchester Airport, Manchester, Sheffield and Meadowhall → Doncaster → Cleethorpes and Hull Barton-on-Humber → Cleethorpes

Network Diagram - see first page of Table 18

		NT	TP	TP	NT	NT	XC	NT	NT	NT	NT	NT	NT	NT	XC	HT	NT	NT	TP	TP	NT	NT	EM	XC
			1 ◇	1 ◇			R 1								1 ◇	1 ◇			1 ◇	1 ◇				1 ◇
		A			B		C	D		E	G	A	bus		H		J	A			B		K	L
			trolley				buffet								buffet	restaurant, buffet			trolley					buffet
Manchester Airport	85 ✈ d		10 52	*11 07*								*11b07*							11 52	*12 07*				
Manchester Piccadilly 10	78 ⇌ d		11 20	11 42	*10 46*							*11 42*							12 20	12 42	*11 46*			
Stockport	78 d		11 28	*11c19*								*11 55*							12 28	*12c19*				
Sheffield 7	⇌ a		12 08																13 08					
	d	12 08	12 11		12 14		12 21		12 25	12 36	12 41	12 51			12 54		12 57	13 08	13 11		13 14			13 21
Meadowhall	⇌ d	12a13	12 17		12 21				12 31	12a41	12 47	12a56					13 03	13a13	13 17		13 21			
Rotherham Central	d				12 27				12 37								13 10				13 27			
Swinton (S.Yorks)	d				12a36				12 47								13 18				13a36			
Mexborough	d								12 50								13 21							
Conisbrough	d								12 54								13 25							
Doncaster 7	a		12 38						13 04		13 11				13 19		13 35		13 38					
York 8	26 a						13 31		*13 39*						13 45				*14 30*					14 29
London Kings Cross 15	⊖ 26 d		*11 00*						*11 10*							11 48								
Doncaster	31 d		12 42			12 46			13 06		13 20					13 27	13 38		13 42					
Bentley (S.Yorks)	31 a								*13 17*								13 41		*14 17*					
Adwick	31 a								*13 21*								13 47		*14 21*					
Kirk Sandall	d					12 52			13 12															
Hatfield & Stainforth	d					12 57			13 17															
Thorne South	d								13 22															
Crowle	d								13 31															
Althorpe	d								13 37															
Scunthorpe	a		13 07						13 45										14 07					
	d		13 08																14 08					
Barnetby	d		13 22					13 43											14 22				14 39	
Hull Bus Station	bus d												13 25											
Barton-on-Humber	bus a												13 50											
Barton-on-Humber	d													13 58										
Barrow Haven	d													14 03										
New Holland	d													14 06										
Goxhill	d													14 11										
Thornton Abbey	d													14 14										
Ulceby	d													14 18										
Habrough	d							13 52						14 23					14 31				14 47	
Stallingborough	d													14 28										
Healing	d													14 31										
Great Coates	d													14 34										
Grimsby Town	a		13 42					14 05						14 39					14 44				15 01	
	d		13 43					14 05						14 39					14 45					
Grimsby Docks	d													14 42										
New Clee	d													14x44										
Cleethorpes	a		13 54					14 16						14 49					14 57					
Thorne North	d					13 02																		
Goole	d					13 11					13 39													
Saltmarshe	d																							
York 8	33 d			*12 18*																		13 38		
Selby	a			12 57												13 42				13 57		14 03		
	d			12 58												13 43				13 58		14 04		
Wressle	d																							
Howden	d															13 53						14 13		
Eastrington	d																							
Gilberdyke	d					13 20																		
Broomfleet	d																							
Brough	d			13 16		13 28					13 53					14 05				14 16		14 25		
Ferriby	d					13 32																		
Hessle	d					13 37																		
Hull	a			13 33		13 50					14 10					14 22				14 33		14 45		

For general notes see front of timetable
For details of catering facilities see Directory of Train Operators

A To Leeds (Table 34)
B To Leeds (Table 31)
C From Bournemouth (Table 51) to Aberdeen (Table 229)
D From Sheffield via Retford (Table 30)
E To Huddersfield (Table 34)
G To Bridlington (Table 43)
H From Cardiff Central to Newcastle (Table 51)
J From Lincoln (Table 30)
K From Newark North Gate (Table 27)
L From Plymouth to Edinburgh (Table 51)
b Change at Manchester Piccadilly and Sheffield
c Change at Manchester Piccadilly

Due to Engineering Operations in the Sheffield area, services from Saturday 13 September on this Table had not been confirmed at time of going to press. These services will be issued in a special Supplement as soon as exact timings have been confirmed.

Manchester Airport, Manchester, Sheffield and Meadowhall → Doncaster → Cleethorpes and Hull Barton-on-Humber → Cleethorpes

until 6 September

Network Diagram - see first page of Table 18

	NT	NT	NT	NT	NT	NT	XC	NT	NT	TP	TP	NT	NT	NT	XC	NT	NT	NT	NT	XC		HT	NT
							1 ◇			1 ◇	1 ◇				1 ◇					R 1		1 ◇	
			A	B	C	D	E	G	D			H	J		K		B		D	L			G
Manchester Airport 85 d						12b07				12 52	13 07								13b07				
Manchester Piccadilly [10] 78 d						12 42				13 20	13 42	12 46							13 42				
Stockport 78 d						12 55				13 28	13c19								13 55				
Sheffield [7] a										14 08													
d		13 25	13 28	13 36	13 41	13 51	13 54	13 57	14 08	14 11		14 14			14 21	14 25	14 36	14 41	14 51	14 54			14 57
Meadowhall d		13 31	13 35	13a41	13 47	13a57		14 03	14a13	14 17		14 21				14 31	14a41	14 47	14a56				15 03
Rotherham Central d		13 37	13 42					14 10				14 27				14 37							15 10
Swinton (S.Yorks) d		13 47	13 50					14 18				14a36				14 47							15 18
Mexborough d		13 50						14 21								14 50							15 21
Conisbrough d		13 54						14 25								14 54							15 25
Doncaster [7] a		14 04			14 11		14 15	14 35		14 38						15 04		15 11		15 15			15 36
York [8] 26 a			14 50		*14 58*		14 46								15 29			*15 59*		15 43			
London Kings Cross [15] ⊖ 26 d		*12 10*			*12 30*					*13 00*						*13 10*						13 38	
Doncaster 31 d	13 46	14 06			14 18			14 38		14 42			14 46			15 07		15 16				15 25	15 38
Bentley (S.Yorks) 31 a		*14 17*						14 41								*15 17*							15 41
Adwick 31 a		*14 21*						14 47								*15 21*							15 47
Kirk Sandall d	13 52	14 12											14 52			15 13							
Hatfield & Stainforth d	13 57	14 17											14 57			15 18							
Thorne South d		14 22														15 23							
Crowle d		14 31														15 31							
Althorpe d		14 37														15 37							
Scunthorpe a		14 45								15 07						15 46							
d										15 08													
Barnetby d										15 22													
Hull Bus Station d																							
Barton-on-Humber a																							
Barton-on-Humber d																							
Barrow Haven d																							
New Holland d																							
Goxhill d																							
Thornton Abbey d																							
Ulceby d																							
Habrough d																							
Stallingborough d																							
Healing d																							
Great Coates d																							
Grimsby Town a										15 42													
d										15 43													
Grimsby Docks d																							
New Clee d																							
Cleethorpes a										15 54													
Thorne North d	14 02												15 02										
Goole d	14 12				14 37								15 13					15 37					
Saltmarshe d	14 17																						
York [8] 33 d														15 05									
Selby a											14 57			15 24								15 40	
d											14 58			15 24								15 41	
Wressle d																							
Howden d																						15 51	
Eastrington d																							
Gilberdyke d	14 26												15 21										
Broomfleet d																							
Brough d	14 34				14 54						15 16		15 29	15 44				15 51				16 03	
Ferriby d	14 39												15 34										
Hessle d	14 43												15 38										
Hull a	14 56				15 12						15 33		15 51	16 03				16 07				16 20	

For general notes see front of timetable
For details of catering facilities see Directory of Train Operators

- **A** Via Pontefract Baghill (Table 33)
- **B** To Huddersfield (Table 34)
- **C** To Bridlington (Table 43)
- **D** To Leeds (Table 34)
- **E** From Weston-super-Mare to Newcastle (Table 51)
- **G** From Lincoln (Table 30)
- **H** To Leeds (Table 31)
- **J** To Scarborough (Table 43)
- **K** From Bournemouth to Edinburgh (Table 51)
- **L** From Penzance (Table 135) to Newcastle (Table 51)
- **b** Change at Manchester Piccadilly and Sheffield
- **c** Change at Manchester Piccadilly

Due to Engineering Operations in the Sheffield area, services from Saturday 13 September on this Table had not been confirmed at time of going to press. These services will be issued in a special Supplement as soon as exact timings have been confirmed.

Table 29

until 6 September

Manchester Airport, Manchester, Sheffield and Meadowhall → Doncaster → Cleethorpes and Hull
Barton-on-Humber → Cleethorpes

Network Diagram - see first page of Table 18

	NT	NT	NT	TP	TP	NT	NT	XC	NT	NT	NT	NT	NT	NT	XC	NT	NT	TP	TP	NT	NT	EM	XC
				1 ◇	1 ◇			R 1							1 ◇			1 ◇	1 ◇				R 1
			A			B	C	D		E		A	G	H	J	K	A			B	C	L	N
	bus			trolley				restaurant							restaurant			trolley					restaurant
Manchester Airport 85 ✈ d				13 52	*14 07*							*14b07*						14 52	*15 07*				
Manchester Piccadilly 10 78 d				14 20	14 42	*13 46*						*14 42*						15 18	15 42	*14 46*			
Stockport 78 d				14 28	*14c19*							*14 55*						15 26	*15c19*				
Sheffield 7 a				15 08														16 08					
d			15 08	15 11		15 14		15 21	15 25	15 36	15 40	15 51			15 54	15 57	16 08	16 11		16 14			16 21
Meadowhall d			15a13	15 17		15 21			15 31	15a41	15 46	15a56				16 03	16a13	16 17		16 21			
Rotherham Central d						15 27			15 37							16 10				16 27			
Swinton (S.Yorks) d						15a36			15 47							16 18				16a36			
Mexborough d									15 50							16 21							
Conisbrough d									15 54							16 25							
Doncaster 7 a				15 38					16 04		16 11				16 15	16 35		16 38					
York 8 26 a								16 29			*16 56*				16 44								17 31
London Kings Cross 15 ⊖ 26 d				*14 00*												*14 30*		*15 00*					
Doncaster 31 d				15 42			15 46		16 06		16 14					16 38		16 42			16 47		
Bentley (S.Yorks) 31 a															*16e31*	16 41							
Adwick 31 a															*16e35*	16 47							
Kirk Sandall d							15 52		16 13												16 53		
Hatfield & Stainforth d							15 57		16 18												16 58		
Thorne South d									16 24														
Crowle d									16 33														
Althorpe d									16 39														
Scunthorpe a				16 07					16 46									17 07					
d				16 08														17 08					
Barnetby d				16 22										17 07				17 22				17 31	
Hull Bus Station bus d	15 25																						
Barton-on-Humber bus a	15 50																						
Barton-on-Humber d		15 58																					
Barrow Haven d		16 03																					
New Holland d		16 06																					
Goxhill d		16 11																					
Thornton Abbey d		16 14																					
Ulceby d		16 18																					
Habrough d		16 23		16 31										17 19								17 40	
Stallingborough d		16 28																					
Healing d		16 31																					
Great Coates d		16 34																					
Grimsby Town a		16 39		16 45										17 37				17 42				17 54	
d		16 39		16 46										17 38				17 43					
Grimsby Docks d		16 42																					
New Clee d																							
Cleethorpes a		16 48		16 56										17 46				17 54					
Thorne North d							16 02														17 03		
Goole d							16 12				16 36										17 12		
Saltmarshe d																					17 17		
York 8 33 d													16 12										
Selby a					15 57								16 38						16 57				
d					15 58								16 39						16 58				
Wressle d													16 46										
Howden d													16 51										
Eastrington d																							
Gilberdyke d							16 20						16 58								17 23		
Broomfleet d																							
Brough d					16 16		16 28				16 50		17 06						17 16		17 31		
Ferriby d							16 33						17 10								17 36		
Hessle d							16 37														17 40		
Hull a					16 33		16 50				17 07		17 27						17 34		17 53		

For general notes see front of timetable
For details of catering facilities see Directory of Train Operators

A To Leeds (Table 34)
B To Leeds (Table 31)
C To Bridlington (Table 43)
D From Paignton to Newcastle (Table 51)
E To Huddersfield (Table 34)
G To Scarborough (Table 43)
H From Sheffield via Retford (Table 30)
J From Bristol Temple Meads (Table 51) to Dundee (Table 229)
K From Lincoln (Table 30)
L From Lincoln (Table 27)
N From Newquay (Table 135) to Newcastle (Table 51)
b Change at Manchester Piccadilly and Sheffield
c Change at Manchester Piccadilly
e Change at Doncaster

Due to Engineering Operations in the Sheffield area, services from Saturday 13 September on this Table had not been confirmed at time of going to press. These services will be issued in a special Supplement as soon as exact timings have been confirmed.

until 6 September

Manchester Airport, Manchester, Sheffield and Meadowhall → Doncaster → Cleethorpes and Hull Barton-on-Humber → Cleethorpes

Network Diagram - see first page of Table 18

		NT	NT	NT	NT	NT	XC	NT	NT	NT	NT	NT	TP	TP	NT	NT	EM	XC	NT	NT	NT	NT	XC	NT
							1 ◇						1 ◇	1 ◇				R 1					1 ◇	
			A		B		C	D			E	B			G		H	J		A		B	K	D
							☕		🚌				🍴					☕					☕	
Manchester Airport	85 ✈ d				15b07								15 52	16 07								16b07		
Manchester Piccadilly 10	78 🚆 d				15 42								16 20	16 42	15 46							16 42		
Stockport	78 d				15 55								16 28	16c19								16 53		
Sheffield 7	🚆 a												17 08											
	d	16 25	16 36	16 41	16 51		16 54				16 57	17 08	17 11		17 14			17 21	17 25	17 36	17 41	17 51	17 54	
Meadowhall	🚆 d	16 31	16a41	16 47	16a56						17 03	17a13	17 17		17 21				17 31	17a41	17 47	17a56		
Rotherham Central	d	16 37									17 10				17 27				17 38					
Swinton (S.Yorks)	d	16 47									17 18				17a36				17 47					
Mexborough	d	16 50									17 21								17 50					
Conisbrough	d	16 54									17 25								17 54					
Doncaster 7	a	17 08		17 11			17 19				17 35		17 38						18 07		18 12		18 21	
York 8	26 a						17 46											18 29					18 46	
London Kings Cross 15	⊖ 26 d										15 30		16 00								16 30			
Doncaster	31 d			17 14				17 22			17 38		17 42			17 48					18 24			18 28
Bentley (S.Yorks)	31 a						17e30				17 41												18e32	
Adwick	31 a						17e34				17 47												18e36	
Kirk Sandall	d							17 28								17 54								18 35
Hatfield & Stainforth	d							17 33								17 59								18 40
Thorne South	d							17 38																18 45
Crowle	d							17 47																18 53
Althorpe	d							17 53																18 59
Scunthorpe	a							18 01					18 08											19 07
	d												18 08											
Barnetby	d												18 22				18 49							
Hull Bus Station	🚌 d								17 30															
Barton-on-Humber	🚌 a								17 55															
Barton-on-Humber	d									18 00														
Barrow Haven	d									18 05														
New Holland	d									18 08														
Goxhill	d									18 13														
Thornton Abbey	d									18 16														
Ulceby	d									18 20														
Habrough	d									18 25			18 31				18 58							
Stallingborough	d									18 30														
Healing	d									18 33														
Great Coates	d									18 36														
Grimsby Town	a									18 41			18 49				19 14							
	d									18 41			18 49											
Grimsby Docks	d									18 44														
New Clee	d																							
Cleethorpes	a									18 50			18 59											
Thorne North	d			17 28												18 04								
Goole	d			17 37												18 13					18 44			
Saltmarshe	d															18 18								
York 8	33 d					17 18																		
Selby	a					17 37								17 58										
	d					17 37								17 59										
Wressle	d																							
Howden	d					17 47								18 08										
Eastrington	d																							
Gilberdyke	d					17 57										18 22								
Broomfleet	d															18 26								
Brough	d			17 56		18 05								18 20		18 32					18 58			
Ferriby	d															18 37								
Hessle	d															18 42								
Hull	a			18 10		18 21								18 37		18 57					19 15			

For general notes see front of timetable
For details of catering facilities see Directory of Train Operators

A To Huddersfield (Table 34)
B To Leeds (Table 34)
C From Bristol Temple Meads to Edinburgh (Table 51)
D From Adwick (Table 31)
E From Lincoln (Table 30)
G To Leeds (Table 31)
H From Newark North Gate (Table 27)
J From Paignton to Glasgow Central (Table51)
K From Bristol Temple Meads to Newcastle (Table 51)
b Change at Manchester Piccadilly and Sheffield
c Change at Manchester Piccadilly
e Change at Doncaster

Due to Engineering Operations in the Sheffield area, services from Saturday 13 September on this Table had not been confirmed at time of going to press. These services will be issued in a special Supplement as soon as exact timings have been confirmed.

Table 29

until 6 September

Manchester Airport, Manchester, Sheffield and Meadowhall → Doncaster → Cleethorpes and Hull Barton-on-Humber → Cleethorpes

Network Diagram - see first page of Table 18

		NT	NT	NT	NT	TP	HT	TP	XC	TP	NT	NT	NT	NT	NT	XC	NT	EM	NT	NT	NT	NT	TP	TP
						■1 ◇	■1 ◇	■1 ◇	■1 ◇	■1 ◇						■1 ◇		■1 ◇					■1 ◇	■1 ◇
			A	B	C				D				E	G	B	H	J	K	B	J				
Manchester Airport	85 d					17 04		16 52							17b04								17 52	18 10
Manchester Piccadilly 10	78 d				16 46	17 42		17 20							17 42								18 17	18 41
Stockport	78 d					17c16		17 28		←					17 55								18 26	18e16
Sheffield 7	a							18 12		18 12													19 08	
	d		17 57	18 08	18 14			→	18 21	18 24		18 29	18 36	18 41	18 51	18 54	19 00	19 04	19 08				19 11	
Meadowhall	d		18 03	18a13	18 21					18 29		18 35	18a41	18 47	18a56		19 06		19a13	←			19 17	
Rotherham Central	d		18 10		18 27							18 42					19 13							
Swinton (S.Yorks)	d		18 18		18a36							18 50					19 22			19 22				
Mexborough	d		18 21									18 53					→			19 25				
Conisbrough	d		18 25									18 57								19 29				
Doncaster 7	a		18 37							18 53		19 08		19 10		19 18		19 29		19 40			19 41	
York 8	26 a								19 32							19 49							20 34	
London Kings Cross 15	⊖ 26 d						17 05																18 00	
Doncaster	31 d						18 48			18 55	18 58	19 13		19 13									19 42	
Bentley (S.Yorks)	31 a															19f30								
Adwick	31 a															19f34								
Kirk Sandall	d										19 06	19 20												
Hatfield & Stainforth	d										19 11	19 25												
Thorne South	d											19 30												
Crowle	d											19 39												
Althorpe	d											19 45												
Scunthorpe	a									19 22		19 52											20 08	
	d									19 23													20 08	
Barnetby	d									19 37													20 22	
Hull Bus Station	bus d																				19 25			
Barton-on-Humber	bus a																				19 50			
Barton-on-Humber	d																					19 58		
Barrow Haven	d																					20 03		
New Holland	d																					20 06		
Goxhill	d																					20 11		
Thornton Abbey	d																					20 14		
Ulceby	d																					20 18		
Habrough	d																					20 23		
Stallingborough	d																					20 28		
Healing	d																					20 31		
Great Coates	d																					20 34		
Grimsby Town	a									19 58												20 39	20 43	
	d									19 58												20 39	20 44	
Grimsby Docks	d																					20 42		
New Clee	d																							
Cleethorpes	a									20 09												20 48	20 57	
Thorne North	d										19 16													
Goole	d										19 25													
Saltmarshe	d																							
York 8	33 d	18 13																						19 23
Selby	a	18 41				19 00	19 07							19 34										20 00
	d	18 42				19 01	19 08							19 34										20 01
Wressle	d																							
Howden	d	18 51					19 18																	20 10
Eastrington	d	18 56																						
Gilberdyke	d	19 00									19 33													
Broomfleet	d																							
Brough	d	19 08				19 19	19 30				19 41			19 54										20 22
Ferriby	d										19 46													
Hessle	d										19 50													
Hull	a	19 28				19 36	19 47				20 03			20 11										20 39

For general notes see front of timetable
For details of catering facilities see Directory of Train Operators

- **A** From Lincoln (Table 30)
- **B** To Leeds (Table 34)
- **C** To Leeds (Table 31)
- **D** From Bournemouth to Edinburgh (Table 51)
- **E** To Huddersfield (Table 34)
- **G** To Bridlington (Table 43)
- **H** From Paignton to Edinburgh (Table 51)
- **J** From Retford Low Level (Table 30)
- **K** From St Pancras International to Leeds (Table 53)
- **b** Change at Manchester Piccadilly and Sheffield
- **c** Change at Manchester Piccadilly. From 19 July dep. 1718
- **e** Change at Manchester Piccadilly. From 19 July dep. 1819
- **f** Change at Doncaster

Due to Engineering Operations in the Sheffield area, services from Saturday 13 September on this Table had not been confirmed at time of going to press. These services will be issued in a special Supplement as soon as exact timings have been confirmed.

Table 29

Manchester Airport, Manchester, Sheffield and Meadowhall → Doncaster → Cleethorpes and Hull Barton-on-Humber → Cleethorpes

until 6 September

Network Diagram - see first page of Table 18

Station			NT	NT	XC	NT	NT	NT	NT	NT	XC	NT	GR	NT	NT	EM	TP	NT	NT	XC	NT	NT	NT	EM	NT
					R 1						1 ◇		R 1			1 ◇	1 ◇			1 ◇				1 ◇	
			A		B		C	D	E		G				E	H		J		K	A		C	L	
Manchester Airport	85 ✈	d						18b10									18 52						19b12		
Manchester Piccadilly 10	78	d	17 46					18 44								18 46	19 18						19 42		
Stockport		78 d						18 55									19 26						19 55		
Sheffield 7		a															20 08								
		d	19 14		19 21	19 30	19 38	19 44	19 51		19 54			19 57	20 08	20 11	20 11		20 15	20 21	20 31	20 38	20 41	20 48	
Meadowhall		d	19 21			19 36	19a43	19 50	19a56					20 03	20a13		20 17		20 20		20 37	20 44	20a47	20a53	
Rotherham Central		d	19 27			19 42								20 09					20 26		20 43	20 53			
Swinton (S.Yorks)		d	19a40			19 51								20 17					20 36		20a50	21 05 →			
Mexborough		d				19 54								20 20					20 39						
Conisbrough		d				19 58								20 24					20 43						
Doncaster 7		a				20 09		20 11			20 16			20 36		20 36	20 41		20 56						
York 8	26	a			20 29						20 43								21 38	21 35					
London Kings Cross 15	⊖ 26	d						18 30				18 35	18 40					19 00							
Doncaster	31	d		19 47				20 14				20 25	20 28				20 42	20 46							21 07
Bentley (S.Yorks)	31	a														20 48									
Adwick	31	a														20 52									
Kirk Sandall		d		19 53								20 31						20 52							21 13
Hatfield & Stainforth		d		19 58								20 36						20 57							21 18
Thorne South		d										20 41													21 23
Crowle		d										20 50													21 31
Althorpe		d										20 56													21 37
Scunthorpe		a										21 04					21 08								21 46
		d															21 08								
Barnetby		d															21 22								
Hull Bus Station	🚌	d																							
Barton-on-Humber	🚌	a																							
Barton-on-Humber		d																							
Barrow Haven		d																							
New Holland		d																							
Goxhill		d																							
Thornton Abbey		d																							
Ulceby		d																							
Habrough		d															21 31								
Stallingborough		d																							
Healing		d																							
Great Coates		d																							
Grimsby Town		a															21 44								
		d															21 45								
Grimsby Docks		d																							
New Clee		d																							
Cleethorpes		a															21 59								
Thorne North		d		20 03														21 02							
Goole		d		20 12				20 33										21 11							
Saltmarshe		d																							
York 8	33	d								20 17															
Selby		a								20 36			20 43												
		d								20 36			20 45												
Wressle		d																							
Howden		d																							
Eastrington		d																							
Gilberdyke		d		20 22						20 50								21 19							
Broomfleet		d																							
Brough		d		20 30				20 47		20 58			21 07					21 27							
Ferriby		d		20 35						21 02															
Hessle		d		20 39						21 07															
Hull		a		20 52				21 04		21 22			21 27					21 45							

For general notes see front of timetable
For details of catering facilities see Directory of Train Operators

A To Leeds (Table 31)
B From Plymouth to Newcastle (Table 51)
C To Huddersfield (Table 34)
D To Beverley (Table 43)
E To Leeds (Table 34)
G From Bristol Temple Meads to Newcastle (Table 51)
H From St Pancras International to Leeds (Table 53)
J To Bridlington (Table 43)
K From Bournemouth to Newcastle (Table 51)
L From St Pancras International to Barnsley (Table 53)
b Change at Manchester Piccadilly and Sheffield

Due to Engineering Operations in the Sheffield area, services from Saturday 13 September on this Table had not been confirmed at time of going to press. These services will be issued in a special Supplement as soon as exact timings have been confirmed.

Table 29

Saturdays

until 6 September

Manchester Airport, Manchester, Sheffield and Meadowhall → Doncaster → Cleethorpes and Hull Barton-on-Humber → Cleethorpes

Network Diagram - see first page of Table 18

Station		EM	TP	HT	NT	NT	NT	XC	NT	TP	NT	XC	NT	NT	EM	NT	TP	TP	NT	NT	NT	NT
		1 ◇	1 ◇	1 ◇				1 ◇		1 ◇		R 1			1 ◇		1 ◇	1 ◇				
		A	B					C	D		E	G	H	J	A	K	B			H	J	
		(catering)		(catering)		(bus)									(catering)							
Manchester Airport 85	d									19 52				20b15				20 52			21b04	
Manchester Piccadilly 10 78	d									20 20				20 42				21 18			21 42	
Stockport 78	d									20 28				20 55				21 26			21 52	
Sheffield 7	a									21 08								22 09				
	d	20 51						20 54	21 08	21 11	21 14	21 21	21 26	21 41	21 57	22 08		22 11	22 26	22 31	22 41	23 24
Meadowhall	d								21a13	21 17	21 22		21 32	21a46		22a13		22 17	22 32	22 37	22a46	23 31
Rotherham Central	d				(connection)						21 28		21 38						22 39	22 43		23 37
Swinton (S.Yorks)	d				21 05						21 40		21a48						22 47	22a50		23 45
Mexborough	d				21 08						21 43								22 50			23 48
Conisbrough	d				21 12						21 47								22 54			23 52
Doncaster 7	a	21 13			21 23					21 40	21 55				22 21			22 36	23 04			00 03
York 8 26	a							21 49			22 38	22 36										
London Kings Cross 15 ⊖ 26	d			19 41							20 00							20 30				
Doncaster 31	d			21 20						21 42	21 57							22 38	23 05			
Bentley (S.Yorks) 31	a	21 31																22 52				
Adwick 31	a	21 35																22 56				
Kirk Sandall	d										22 03							22 44	23 12			
Hatfield & Stainforth	d										22 08							22 48	23 17			
Thorne South	d																	22 53				
Crowle	d																	23 02				
Althorpe	d																	23 08				
Scunthorpe	a									22 07								23 13				
	d									22 08								23 13				
Barnetby	d									22 22								23 28				
Hull Bus Station (bus)	d					21 25																
Barton-on-Humber (bus)	a					21 50																
Barton-on-Humber	d						21 58															
Barrow Haven	d						22 03															
New Holland	d						22 06															
Goxhill	d						22 11															
Thornton Abbey	d						22 14															
Ulceby	d						22 18															
Habrough	d						22 23			22 31								23 36				
Stallingborough	d						22 28															
Healing	d						22 31															
Great Coates	d						22 34															
Grimsby Town	a						22 39			22 44								23 49				
	d						22 39			22 45								23 50				
Grimsby Docks	d						22 42															
New Clee	d																					
Cleethorpes	a						22 48			22 59								00 02				
Thorne North	d										22 13								23 22			
Goole	d										22 22								23a33			
Saltmarshe	d										22 27											
York 8 33	d																21 45					
Selby	a			21 35																		
	d		21 27	21 36													22 45					
Wressle	d																					
Howden	d		21 36	21 46																		
Eastrington	d																					
Gilberdyke	d										22 33											
Broomfleet	d																					
Brough	d		21 48	21 58							22 41						23 05					
Ferriby	d																					
Hessle	d																					
Hull	a		22 05	22 15							22 58						23 21					

For general notes see front of timetable
For details of catering facilities see Directory of Train Operators

A From St Pancras International to Leeds (Table 53)

B From Leeds (Table 39)
C From Bristol Temple Meads to Newcastle (Table 51)
D To Leeds (Table 34)
E To Beverley (Table 43)
G From Paignton (Table 51)

H To Leeds (Table 31)
J To Huddersfield (Table 34)
K To Barnsley (Table 34)
b Change at Manchester Piccadilly and Sheffield

Due to Engineering Operations in the Sheffield area, services from Saturday 13 September on this Table had not been confirmed at time of going to press. These services will be issued in a special Supplement as soon as exact timings have been confirmed.

Table 29

Sundays

until 13 July

Manchester Airport, Manchester, Sheffield and Meadowhall → Doncaster → Cleethorpes and Hull Barton-on-Humber → Cleethorpes

Network Diagram - see first page of Table 18

		NT	NT	NT	NT	NT	NT	TP		NT	TP	TP	NT	NT	NT	NT		NT	NT	NT	NT	TP	XC	NT
								1 ◇			1 ◇	1 ◇										1 ◇	1 ◇	
			A		B	C	D			E				B	A								G	A
																(bus)							(catering)	
Manchester Airport	85 ✈ d					07b36					08 40	08 51								08b51		10 47		
Manchester Piccadilly 10	78 d					08 12					09 00	09 30								09 43		11 12		
Stockport	78 d					08 22					09 09	08c39								09 56		10c36		
Sheffield 7	a										09 55													
	d	08 00	08 39		08 45	09 36	09 39	09 42			09 58			10 26	10 39					11 05			11 21	11 32
Meadowhall	d	08 06	08a44		08 51	09 42	09a44	09 48			10 03			10 32	10a44					11 12				11a37
Rotherham Central	d	08 12			08 57	09 48		09 57												11 18				
Swinton (S.Yorks)	d	08 20			09 05	09a58		10 05												11 28				
Mexborough	d	08 23			09 08			10 08												11 31				
Conisbrough	d	08 27			09 12			10 12												11 35				
Doncaster 7	a	08 38			09 22			10 20			10 26			10 51						11 47				
York 8	26 a				10 04						11 07			11 29						12 34			12 44	
London Kings Cross 15	⊖ 26 d													09 00					09 10					
Doncaster	31 d			09 07	09 26					10 21	10 27			10 53					11 07					
Bentley (S.Yorks)	31 a	09 13												11 13										
Adwick	31 a	09 17												11 17										
Kirk Sandall	d			09 13															11 13					
Hatfield & Stainforth	d			09 18															11 18					
Thorne South	d																							
Crowle	d																							
Althorpe	d																							
Scunthorpe	a										10 53													
	d										10 53													
Barnetby	d										11 08													
Hull Bus Station	(bus) d															10 25								
Barton-on-Humber	(bus) a															10 50								
Barton-on-Humber	d																	11 00						
Barrow Haven	d																	11 05						
New Holland	d																	11 08						
Goxhill	d																	11 13						
Thornton Abbey	d																	11 16						
Ulceby	d																	11 20						
Habrough	d																	11 25						
Stallingborough	d																	11 30						
Healing	d																	11 33						
Great Coates	d																	11 36						
Grimsby Town	a										11 27							11 41						
	d										11 28							11 41						
Grimsby Docks	d																	11 44						
New Clee	d																	11x46						
Cleethorpes	a										11 39							11 51						
Thorne North	d			09 24	09 38														11 25					
Goole	d			09a35	09 47					10 40				11 12					11a36					
Saltmarshe	d																							
York 8	33 d												10 40								12 05			
Selby	a											10 47	10 59								12 24	12 32		
	d											10 48	10 59								12 24	12 32		
Wressle	d																							
Howden	d																							
Eastrington	d																							
Gilberdyke	d				09 58					10 48				11 23										
Broomfleet	d																							
Brough	d				10 06					10 56		11 07	11 19	11 31							12 44	12 54		
Ferriby	d																							
Hessle	d																							
Hull	a				10 21					11 14		11 24	11 38	11 46							13 03	13 11		

For general notes see front of timetable
For details of catering facilities see Directory of Train Operators

- **A** To Leeds (Table 34)
- **B** To Scarborough (Table 43)
- **C** To Leeds (Table 31)
- **D** To Huddersfield (Table 34)
- **E** To Bridlington (Table 43)
- **G** From Birmingham New Street to Edinburgh (Table 51)
- **b** Change at Manchester Piccadilly and Sheffield
- **c** Change at Manchester Piccadilly

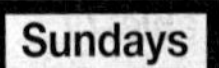

until 13 July

Manchester Airport, Manchester, Sheffield and Meadowhall → Doncaster → Cleethorpes and Hull Barton-on-Humber → Cleethorpes

Network Diagram - see first page of Table 18

	NT	NT	EM	EM	HT	TP	XC	NT	NT	NT	NT	NT	NT	NT	XC	NT	TP	NT	NT	NT
				1 ◇	1 ◇	1 ◇	1 ◇								1 ◇		1 ◇			
	A	B	C	D			E		G	H		(bus)			J	K	L	H	A	B
				(catering)	⊠ (catering)		(catering)								(catering)					
Manchester Airport 85 ✈ d				10b01		10 52											12 45		11b27	
Manchester Piccadilly 10 78 ⇌ d				10 30		11 12											13 11		12 09	
Stockport 78 d				10 46		11 21											12c45		12 23	
Sheffield 7 ⇌ a						12 03														
d	11 36	11 39		11 54		12 08	12 18	12 24	12 28	12 39					13 18	13 24		13 32	13 36	13 39
Meadowhall ⇌ d	11 42	11a44				12 14		12 30	12 34	12a44	←					13 30		13a37	13 42	13a44
Rotherham Central d	11 48							12 36								13 36			13 48	
Swinton (S.Yorks) d	11a57							12 47 →			12 47					13 44			13a56	
Mexborough d											12 50					13 47				
Conisbrough d											12 54					13 51				
Doncaster 7 a				12 17		12 33			12 54		13 03					14 01				
York 8 26 a				12 40			13 44				14 04				14 44	14 33				
London Kings Cross 15 ⊖ 26 d					10 44				11 00							12 00				
Doncaster 31 d					12 24	12 36			12 55		13 05					14 03				
Bentley (S.Yorks) 31 a											13 13									
Adwick 31 a											13 17									
Kirk Sandall d											13 11									
Hatfield & Stainforth d											13 16									
Thorne South d																				
Crowle d																				
Althorpe d																				
Scunthorpe a						13 01														
d						13 02														
Barnetby d			12 47			13 16														
Hull Bus Station (bus) d												13 25								
Barton-on-Humber (bus) a												13 55								
Barton-on-Humber d													14 00							
Barrow Haven d													14 05							
New Holland d													14 08							
Goxhill d													14 13							
Thornton Abbey d													14 16							
Ulceby d													14 20							
Habrough d			12 56			13 25							14 25							
Stallingborough d													14 30							
Healing d													14 33							
Great Coates d													14 36							
Grimsby Town a			13 09			13 38							14 41							
d			13 10			13 39							14 41							
Grimsby Docks d													14 44							
New Clee d													14x46							
Cleethorpes a			13 19			13 51							14 51							
Thorne North d											13 25									
Goole d									13 15		13a35					14 25				
Saltmarshe d																				
York 8 33 d														13 23						
Selby a					12 41									13 42			14 32			
d					12 42									13 42			14 32			
Wressle d																				
Howden d					12 52															
Eastrington d																				
Gilberdyke d									13 23							14 33				
Broomfleet d																				
Brough d					13 04				13 31					14 02		14 41	14 53			
Ferriby d																				
Hessle d																				
Hull a					13 21				13 48					14 21		14 59	15 11			

For general notes see front of timetable
For details of catering facilities see Directory of Train Operators

A To Leeds (Table 31)
B To Huddersfield (Table 34)
C From Newark North Gate (Table 27)
D From Leicester (Table 53)
E From Birmingham New Street (Table 51) to Aberdeen (Table 229)
G To Scarborough (Table 43)
H To Leeds (Table 34)
J From Birmingham New Street to Edinburgh (Table 51)
K To Bridlington (Table 43)
L From Liverpool Lime Street (Table 39)
b Change at Manchester Piccadilly and Sheffield
c Change at Manchester Piccadilly

Table 29

until 13 July

Manchester Airport, Manchester, Sheffield and Meadowhall → Doncaster → Cleethorpes and Hull Barton-on-Humber → Cleethorpes

Network Diagram - see first page of Table 18

		NT	XC	TP	NT	NT	NT	NT	XC	TP	NT	NT	NT	TP	NT	NT	NT	NT	NT	NT	NT
			1 ◇	1 ◇						1 ◇				1 ◇							
			A			B	C						D	E	C				G	H	J
			⊡						⊡								🚌				
Manchester Airport	85 d		12b13	12 52						13 52				14 47							14b00
Manchester Piccadilly 10	78 d		12 43	13 12						14 15				15 12					14 19		14 43
Stockport	78 d		12 53	13 21						14 23				14c49					14 28		14 54
Sheffield 7	a			14 06						15 05											
	d		13 54	14 08	14 22	14 28	14 39		14 54	15 08		15 24	15 27		15 30				15 33	15 39	15 46
Meadowhall	d			14 14	14 28	14 34	14a44			15 14		15 30	15 34		15a37				15 42	15a44	15 52
Rotherham Central	d				14 34			←				15 36				←			15 48		15 58
Swinton (S.Yorks)	d				14 45			14 45				15 46				15 46			15a56		16 08
Mexborough	d				→			14 48				→				15 49					
Conisbrough	d							14 52								15 53					
Doncaster 7	a		14 15	14 33		14 56		15 01	15 15	15 33			15 54			16 03					
York 8	26 a		15e33	15 05				15 36	16 33				16 34			17 33					17 00
London Kings Cross 15	⊖ 26 d			12 30		13 00		13 10		13 30			14 00								
Doncaster	31 d			14 36		14 59		15 05		15 36			15 56								
Bentley (S.Yorks)	31 a							15 13													
Adwick	31 a							15 17													
Kirk Sandall	d							15 13													
Hatfield & Stainforth	d							15 18													
Thorne South	d																				
Crowle	d																				
Althorpe	d																				
Scunthorpe	a			15 01						16 01											
	d			15 02						16 02											
Barnetby	d			15 16						16 16											
Hull Bus Station	🚌 d																15 30				
Barton-on-Humber	🚌 a																15 55				
Barton-on-Humber	d																	16 10			
Barrow Haven	d																	16 15			
New Holland	d																	16 18			
Goxhill	d																	16 23			
Thornton Abbey	d																	16 26			
Ulceby	d																	16 30			
Habrough	d									16 25								16 35			
Stallingborough	d																	16 40			
Healing	d																	16 43			
Great Coates	d																	16 46			
Grimsby Town	a			15 36						16 38								16 51			
	d			15 37						16 39								16 51			
Grimsby Docks	d																	16 54			
New Clee	d																	16x56			
Cleethorpes	a			15 48						16 50								17 01			
Thorne North	d							15 25													
Goole	d					15 19		15a33					16 17								
Saltmarshe	d																				
York 8	33 d	14 45									15 43										
Selby	a	15 04									16 01			16 34							
	d	15 04									16 02			16 34							
Wressle	d																				
Howden	d																				
Eastrington	d																				
Gilberdyke	d					15 27							16 25								
Broomfleet	d																				
Brough	d	15 24				15 35					16 21		16 33	16 54							
Ferriby	d					15 40															
Hessle	d					15 44															
Hull	a	15 43				15 57					16 41		16 50	17 11							

For general notes see front of timetable
For details of catering facilities see Directory of Train Operators

A From Bristol Temple Meads to Edinburgh (Table 51)
B To Scarborough (Table 43)
C To Leeds (Table 34)
D To Bridlington (Table 43)
E From Liverpool Lime Street (Table 39)
G To Leeds (Table 31)
H From Retford Low Level (Table 30) to Huddersfield (Table 34)
J Via Pontefract Baghill (Table 33)
b Change at Manchester Piccadilly and Sheffield
c Change at Manchester Piccadilly
e By changing at Doncaster, passengers may arrive at 1505

Table 29

Sundays

until 13 July

Manchester Airport, Manchester, Sheffield and Meadowhall → Doncaster → Cleethorpes and Hull
Barton-on-Humber → Cleethorpes

Network Diagram - see first page of Table 18

		EM	XC	HT	TP	NT	NT	TP	NT	NT	NT	XC	TP	HT	TP	NT	NT	NT	NT	NT	XC	TP
			R 1	1 ◇	1 ◇			1 ◇				R 1	1 ◇	1 ◇	1 ◇						R 1	1 ◇
		A	B				C		D			E					G		H	J	K	
			☕	⊠ ☕								☕		⊠ ☕							☕	
Manchester Airport	85 ✈ d				14 52			15 27				15b08	15 52		16 27						16b01	16 52
Manchester Piccadilly 10	78 🚆 d				15 15			16 00				15 43	16 15		17 00						16 43	17 15
Stockport	78 d				15 23			15c29	15 27			15 54	16 23		16c29						16 54	17 23
Sheffield 7	🚆 a				16 04								17 05									18 04
	d		15 54		16 08	16 24	16 28		16 39			16 54	17 08			17 24	17 28		17 34	17 39	17 54	18 08
Meadowhall	🚆 d				16 14	16 30	16 34		16a44				17 14			17 30	17 34		17 42	17a44		18 14
Rotherham Central	d					16 36					←					17 36		←	17 48			
Swinton (S.Yorks)	d					16 46					16 46					17 46		17 46	17a56			
Mexborough	d					→					16 49					→		17 49				
Conisbrough	d										16 53							17 53				
Doncaster 7	a		16 15		16 33		16 54				17 02	17 15	17 33				17 57	18 06			18 15	18 33
York 8	26 a		17 33								17 45	18e33	18 05				18 34				19f33	19 05
London Kings Cross 15	⊖ 26 d			14 44							15 10		15 30	16 04			16 10					16 30
Doncaster	31 d			16 21	16 36		16 55				17 04		17 36	17 49			18 03					18 36
Bentley (S.Yorks)	31 a										17 13											
Adwick	31 a										17 17											
Kirk Sandall	d										17 13											
Hatfield & Stainforth	d										17 18											
Thorne South	d																					
Crowle	d																					
Althorpe	d																					
Scunthorpe	a				17 01								18 01									19 01
	d				17 02								18 02									19 02
Barnetby	d	16 55			17 16								18 16									19 16
Hull Bus Station	🚌 d																					
Barton-on-Humber	🚌 a																					
Barton-on-Humber	d																					
Barrow Haven	d																					
New Holland	d																					
Goxhill	d																					
Thornton Abbey	d																					
Ulceby	d																					
Habrough	d	17 03											18 25									
Stallingborough	d																					
Healing	d																					
Great Coates	d																					
Grimsby Town	a	17 15			17 36								18 38									19 36
	d	17 16			17 37								18 39									19 37
Grimsby Docks	d																					
New Clee	d																					
Cleethorpes	a	17 27			17 48								18 50									19 50
Thorne North	d										17 25											
Goole	d						17 15				17a34						18 22					
Saltmarshe	d																					
York 8	33 d									17 10												
Selby	a			16 41				17 13		17 30				18 03	18 16							
	d			16 42				17 14		17 31				18 03	18 16							
Wressle	d																					
Howden	d			16 52										18 15								
Eastrington	d																					
Gilberdyke	d						17 23										18 35					
Broomfleet	d																					
Brough	d			17 04			17 31	17 37		17 51				18 26	18 36		18 43					
Ferriby	d																					
Hessle	d																					
Hull	a			17 21			17 48	17 53		18 10				18 48	18 53		18 57					

For general notes see front of timetable
For details of catering facilities see Directory of Train Operators

A From Nottingham (Table 27)
B From Plymouth to Glasgow Central (Table 51)
C To Scarborough (Table 43)
D From Lincoln (Table 30) to Leeds (Table 34)
E From Bournemouth to Glasgow Central (Table 51)
G To Bridlington (Table 43)
H To Leeds (Table 31)
J To Huddersfield (Table 34)
K From Penzance (Table 135) to Edinburgh (Table 51)
b Change at Manchester Piccadilly and Sheffield
c Change at Manchester Piccadilly
e By changing at Doncaster, passengers may arrive at 1805
f By changing at Doncaster, passengers may arrive at 1905

until 13 July

Manchester Airport, Manchester, Sheffield and Meadowhall → Doncaster → Cleethorpes and Hull Barton-on-Humber → Cleethorpes

Network Diagram - see first page of Table 18

		NT	NT		NT	NT	NT	NT	NT	XC	HT		NT	TP	TP	NT	NT	NT	XC		NT	TP	EM	GR
										R 1	1 ◇			1 ◇	1 ◇				R 1			1 ◇	1 ◇	R 1
			A		B		bus			C			D				E	G	H				J	
Manchester Airport	85 ✈ d									17b05				17 52	18 27						18b01	18 52		
Manchester Piccadilly 10	78 d									17 43				18 15	19 00						18 42	19 15		
Stockport	78 d									17 54				18 23	18c29		18 27				18 56	19 22		
Sheffield 7	a													19 05								20 04		
	d	18 24	18 28		18 38					18 54			18 58	19 08		19 27	19 35	19 39	19 54		20 03	20 08	20 24	
Meadowhall	d	18 30	18 34		18a44								19 04	19 14		19 33	19 42	19a44			20 09	20 14		
Rotherham Central	d	18 36				←							19 10			19 39	19 48							
Swinton (S.Yorks)	d	18 46				18 46							19 18			19 47	19a56							
Mexborough	d	→				18 49										19 50								
Conisbrough	d					18 53										19 54								
Doncaster 7	a		18 54			19 04				19 15				19 33		20 05			20 15		20 30	20 34	20 45	
York 8	26 a					19 46				20e33			20 16	20 07		20 38			21 33					
London Kings Cross 15	⊖ 26 d		17 00								17 44										18 40	19 00		19 10
Doncaster	31 d		18 55								19 25			19 36							20 30	20 42		20 58
Bentley (S.Yorks)	31 a									19f32														
Adwick	31 a									19f36														
Kirk Sandall	d		19 01																					
Hatfield & Stainforth	d		19 06																					
Thorne South	d																							
Crowle	d																							
Althorpe	d																							
Scunthorpe	a													20 01								21 07		
	d													20 02								21 08		
Barnetby	d													20 16								21 22		
Hull Bus Station	bus d						18 30																	
Barton-on-Humber	bus a						18 55																	
Barton-on-Humber	d							19 10																
Barrow Haven	d							19 15																
New Holland	d							19 18																
Goxhill	d							19 23																
Thornton Abbey	d							19 26																
Ulceby	d							19 30																
Habrough	d							19 35														21 31		
Stallingborough	d							19 40																
Healing	d							19 43																
Great Coates	d							19 46																
Grimsby Town	a							19 51						20 36								21 44		
	d							19 51						20 37								21 45		
Grimsby Docks	d							19 54																
New Clee	d							19x56																
Cleethorpes	a							20 01						20 50								21 56		
Thorne North	d		19 12																					
Goole	d		19 21																		20 49			
Saltmarshe	d																							
York 8	33 d								19 10															
Selby	a								19 29		19 40				20 18									21 15
	d								19 29		19 40				20 18									21 15
Wressle	d																							
Howden	d										19 52													
Eastrington	d																							
Gilberdyke	d		19 29																		20 57			
Broomfleet	d																							
Brough	d		19 37						19 49		20 03				20 37						21 05			21 36
Ferriby	d																							
Hessle	d																							
Hull	a		19 54						20 08		20 22				20 54						21 23			21 56

For general notes see front of timetable
For details of catering facilities see Directory of Train Operators

- **A** To Beverley (Table 43)
- **B** To Leeds (Table 34)
- **C** From Bournemouth to Edinburgh (Table 51)
- **D** Via Pontefract Baghill (Table 33)
- **E** To Leeds (Table 31)
- **G** To Huddersfield (Table 34)
- **H** From Paignton to Newcastle (Table 51)
- **J** From St Pancras International to Leeds (Table 53)
- **b** Change at Manchester Piccadilly and Sheffield
- **c** Change at Manchester Piccadilly
- **e** By changing at Doncaster, passengers may arrive at 2007
- **f** Change at Doncaster

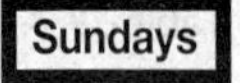

Sundays

until 13 July

Manchester Airport, Manchester, Sheffield and Meadowhall → Doncaster → Cleethorpes and Hull Barton-on-Humber → Cleethorpes

Network Diagram - see first page of Table 18

		NT	NT	NT	XC	TP	EM	HT	NT	NT	NT	TP	XC	NT	TP	NT	NT	XC	NT
					R 1	1 ◇	1 ◇	1 ◇				1 ◇	1 ◇		1 ◇			1 ◇	
			A		B		C			D	E	G	H			J		K	
Manchester Airport	85 d				19b05	19 52							20b01	20 52					21 52
Manchester Piccadilly 10	78 d				19 42	20 15				20 19			20 43	21 15					22 15
Stockport	78 d				19 54	20 23				20 29			20 53	21 22					22 22
Sheffield 7	a					21 06													
	d	20 27	20 39		20 54	21 08	21 15		21 24	21 36	21 43		21 54	22 26	22 30	22 39		22 54	23 20
Meadowhall	d	20 33	20a44			21 14			21 30	21 42	21a48			22 32	22 36	22a44	←		23 26
Rotherham Central	d	20 39							21 37	21 48				22 38					23 32
Swinton (S.Yorks)	d	20 47							21 46	21a56				22 48			22 48		23 43
Mexborough	d	20 50							21 49					→			22 51		23 46
Conisbrough	d	20 54							21 53								22 55		23 50
Doncaster 7	a	21 04			21 15	21 34	21 37		22 02				22 15		22 55		23 03	23 15	23 58
York 8	26 a	21 47			22c38				23 09				23e38					00 39	
London Kings Cross 15	⊖ 26 d					19 35		20 10							21 00				
Doncaster	31 d	21 06				21 42		21 54	22 04						22 58		23 07		
Bentley (S.Yorks)	31 a						21 52												
Adwick	31 a						21 56												
Kirk Sandall	d	21 12																	
Hatfield & Stainforth	d	21 17																	
Thorne South	d																		
Crowle	d																		
Althorpe	d																		
Scunthorpe	a					22 07									23 23				
	d					22 08									23 24				
Barnetby	d					22 22									23 38				
Hull Bus Station	🚌 d																		
Barton-on-Humber	🚌 a																		
Barton-on-Humber	d																		
Barrow Haven	d																		
New Holland	d																		
Goxhill	d																		
Thornton Abbey	d																		
Ulceby	d																		
Habrough	d					22 31													
Stallingborough	d																		
Healing	d																		
Great Coates	d																		
Grimsby Town	a					22 44									23 58				
	d					22 45									23 59				
Grimsby Docks	d																		
New Clee	d																		
Cleethorpes	a					22 56									00 10				
Thorne North	d	21 23															23 19		
Goole	d	21a34							22 23								23 28		
Saltmarshe	d																		
York 8	33 d			21 41															
Selby	a			22 00				22 08											
	d			22 00				22 08				22 39							
Wressle	d																		
Howden	d							22 20											
Eastrington	d																		
Gilberdyke	d								22 31								23 36		
Broomfleet	d																		
Brough	d			22 20				22 31	22 39			22 59					23 44		
Ferriby	d																		
Hessle	d																		
Hull	a			22 39				22 50	22 56			23 16					00 02		

For general notes see front of timetable
For details of catering facilities see Directory of Train Operators

A To Leeds (Table 34)
B From Bournemouth (Table 51)
C From St Pancras International to Leeds (Table 53)
D To Leeds (Table 31)
E To Barnsley (Table 34)
G From Leeds (Table 39)
H From Plymouth (Table 51)
J From Lincoln (Table 30) to Leeds (Table 34)
K From Bournemouth to Leeds (Table 51)
b Change at Manchester Piccadilly and Sheffield
c By changing at Doncaster, passengers may arrive at 2200
e By changing at Doncaster, passengers may arrive at 2309

Table 29

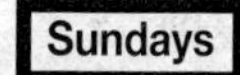

Sundays

Manchester Airport, Manchester, Sheffield and Meadowhall → Doncaster → Cleethorpes and Hull Barton-on-Humber → Cleethorpes

20 July to 7 September

Network Diagram - see first page of Table 18

Station		NT	NT	NT	NT	NT	NT	TP	NT	NT	TP	NT		TP	NT	NT	NT	NT	XC	NT	NT	EM	EM	HT
								1 ◇			1 ◇			1 ◇					1 ◇			1 ◇		1 ◇
			A		B	C	D		E			B			A				G			H	J	
																🚌			☕			☕		⊠ ☕
Manchester Airport	85 ✈ d					06b22					08 40			09 25						08b47				
Manchester Piccadilly 10	78 🚆 d					07 39					09 00	09 04		09 42						09 35				
Stockport	78 d										09 09	09 17		09c10										
Sheffield 7	🚆 a										09 55													
	d	08 00	08 39		08 45	09 36	09 39	09 42			09 58	10 26			10 39				11 02	11 05		11 26		
Meadowhall	🚆 d	08 06	08a44		08 51	09 42	09a44	09 48			10 03	10 32			10a44					11 12				
Rotherham Central	d	08 12			08 57	09 48		09 57												11 18				
Swinton (S.Yorks)	d	08 20			09 05	09a58		10 05												11 28				
Mexborough	d	08 23			09 08			10 08												11 31				
Conisbrough	d	08 27			09 12			10 12												11 35				
Doncaster 7	a	08 38			09 22			10 20			10 26	10 51							11 23	11 47		11 54		
York 8	26 a				*10 04*						*11 07*	*11 29*							⟶			12 19		
London Kings Cross 15	⊖ 26 d											*09 00*						*09 10*						10 44
Doncaster	31 d			09 07	09 26				10 21		10 27	10 53						11 07						12 24
Bentley (S.Yorks)	31 a	*09 13*										*11 13*												
Adwick	31 a	*09 17*										*11 17*												
Kirk Sandall	d			09 13														11 13						
Hatfield & Stainforth	d			09 18														11 18						
Thorne South	d																							
Crowle	d																							
Althorpe	d																							
Scunthorpe	a										10 53													
	d										10 53													
Barnetby	d										11 08												12 47	
Hull Bus Station	🚌 d															10 25								
Barton-on-Humber	🚌 a															10 50								
Barton-on-Humber	d																11 00							
Barrow Haven	d																11 05							
New Holland	d																11 08							
Goxhill	d																11 13							
Thornton Abbey	d																11 16							
Ulceby	d																11 20							
Habrough	d																11 25						12 56	
Stallingborough	d																11 30							
Healing	d																11 33							
Great Coates	d																11 36							
Grimsby Town	a										11 27						11 41						13 09	
	d										11 28						11 41						13 10	
Grimsby Docks	d																11 44							
New Clee	d																11x46							
Cleethorpes	a										11 39						11 51						13 19	
Thorne North	d			09 24	09 38													11 25						
Goole	d			09a35	09 47				10 40			11 12						11a36						
Saltmarshe	d																							
York 8	33 d									10 40											12 05			
Selby	a									10 59				11 15							12 24			12 41
	d									10 59				11 16							12 24			12 42
Wressle	d																							
Howden	d																							12 52
Eastrington	d																							
Gilberdyke	d				09 58				10 48			11 23												
Broomfleet	d																							
Brough	d				10 06				10 56	11 19		11 31		11 37							12 44			13 04
Ferriby	d																							
Hessle	d																							
Hull	a				10 21				11 14	11 38		11 46		11 52							13 03			13 21

For general notes see front of timetable
For details of catering facilities see Directory of Train Operators

- **A** To Leeds (Table 34)
- **B** To Scarborough (Table 43)
- **C** To Leeds (Table 31)
- **D** To Huddersfield (Table 34)
- **E** To Bridlington (Table 43)
- **G** From Birmingham New Street to Edinburgh (Table 51)
- **H** From Leicester (Table 53)
- **J** From Newark North Gate (Table 27)
- **b** Change at Manchester Piccadilly and Sheffield
- **c** Change at Manchester Piccadilly

Due to Engineering Operations in the Sheffield area, services from Sunday 14 September on this Table had not been confirmed at time of going to press. These services will be issued in a special Supplement as soon as exact timings have been confirmed.

Table 29

Sundays

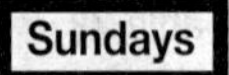

20 July to 7 September

Manchester Airport, Manchester, Sheffield and Meadowhall → Doncaster → Cleethorpes and Hull Barton-on-Humber → Cleethorpes

Network Diagram - see first page of Table 18

	TP	XC		NT	NT	NT	TP	XC	NT	NT	NT	NT	NT	NT		NT	XC	NT	TP	NT	NT	NT	XC
	1 ◇	1 ◇					1 ◇	1 ◇									1 ◇		1 ◇				1 ◇
		A		B	C	D		E		G	B			🚌			A	H	J	B	C	D	K
		☕						☕									☕						☕
Manchester Airport 85 ✈ d	*10 46*						10 49												*12 46*		*11b22*		*12b13*
Manchester Piccadilly 10 78 🚆 d	11 12						11 12												13 12		*12 01*		*12 43*
Stockport 78 d	*10c42*						11 21												*12c42*		*11b32*		*12 53*
Sheffield 7 🚆 a							12 03																
d				11 32	11 36	11 39	12 08	12 21	12 24	12 28	12 39						13 21	13 24		13 32	13 36	13 39	13 54
Meadowhall 🚆 d				11a37	11 42	11a44	12 14		12 30	12 34	12a44							13 30		13a37	13 42	13a44	
Rotherham Central d					11 48				12 36				←					13 37			13 48		
Swinton (S.Yorks) d					11a57				12 48				12 48					13 45			13a56		
Mexborough d									→				12 51					13 48					
Conisbrough d		←											12 55					13 52					
Doncaster 7 a		11 23					12 33			12 54			13 03					14 02					14 16
York 8 26 a		12 44						13 45					*14 04*				14 47	*14 33*					14 39
London Kings Cross 15 ⊖ 26 d										*11 00*								*12 00*					
Doncaster 31 d							12 36			12 55			13 05					14 04					
Bentley (S.Yorks) 31 a													*13 13*										
Adwick 31 a													*13 17*										
Kirk Sandall d													13 11										
Hatfield & Stainforth d													13 16										
Thorne South d																							
Crowle d																							
Althorpe d																							
Scunthorpe a							13 01																
d							13 02																
Barnetby d							13 16																
Hull Bus Station 🚌 d														13 25									
Barton-on-Humber 🚌 a														13 55									
Barton-on-Humber d																14 00							
Barrow Haven d																14 05							
New Holland d																14 08							
Goxhill d																14 13							
Thornton Abbey d																14 16							
Ulceby d																14 20							
Habrough d							13 25									14 25							
Stallingborough d																14 30							
Healing d																14 33							
Great Coates d																14 36							
Grimsby Town a							13 38									14 41							
d							13 39									14 41							
Grimsby Docks d																14 44							
New Clee d																14x46							
Cleethorpes a							13 51									14 51							
Thorne North d													13 25										
Goole d										13 15			13a35					14 25					
Saltmarshe d																							
York 8 33 d												13 06											
Selby a	12 45											13 25							14 45				
d	12 46											13 25							14 46				
Wressle d																							
Howden d																							
Eastrington d																							
Gilberdyke d										13 23								14 33					
Broomfleet d																							
Brough d	13 12									13 31		13 45						14 41	15 06				
Ferriby d																							
Hessle d																							
Hull a	13 26									13 48		14 04						14 59	15 23				

For general notes see front of timetable
For details of catering facilities see Directory of Train Operators

A From Birmingham New Street to Edinburgh (Table 51)
B To Leeds (Table 34)
C To Leeds (Table 31)
D To Huddersfield (Table 34)
E From Birmingham New Street (Table 51) to Aberdeen (Table 229)
G To Scarborough (Table 43)
H To Bridlington (Table 43)
J From Liverpool Lime Street (Table 39)
K From Bristol Temple Meads to Newcastle (Table 51)
b Change at Manchester Piccadilly and Sheffield
c Change at Manchester Piccadilly

Due to Engineering Operations in the Sheffield area, services from Sunday 14 September on this Table had not been confirmed at time of going to press. These services will be issued in a special Supplement as soon as exact timings have been confirmed.

Table 29

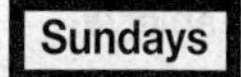

Manchester Airport, Manchester, Sheffield and Meadowhall → Doncaster → Cleethorpes and Hull Barton-on-Humber → Cleethorpes

20 July to 7 September

Network Diagram - see first page of Table 18

Station		TP	NT	XC	NT	NT	NT	NT	XC	TP	NT	XC	NT	NT	NT	NT	NT	NT	NT	NT	EM	NT
		1 ◇		1 ◇					1 ◇	1 ◇		R 1										
				A		B	C		D			E		G	C				H	J	K	L
				☕					☕			☕					🚌					
Manchester Airport	85 ✈ d	12 49							13b22	13 49												13b58
Manchester Piccadilly 10	78 🚊 d	13 12							13 48	14 15												14 43
Stockport	78 d	13 21							13 58	14 23												14 54
Sheffield 7	🚊 a	14 06								15 05												
	d	14 08		14 21	14 22	14 28	14 39		14 54	15 08		15 21	15 24	15 28	15 30				15 36	15 39		15 46
Meadowhall	🚊 d	14 14			14 28	14 34	14a44			15 14			15 30	15 34	15a37				15 42	15a44		15 52
Rotherham Central	d				14 35			←					15 37			←			15 48			15 58
Swinton (S.Yorks)	d				14 46			14 46					15 47			15 47			15a56			16 08
Mexborough	d				→			14 49					→			15 50						
Conisbrough	d							14 53								15 54						
Doncaster 7	a	14 33				14 56		15 03	15 16	15 33				15 54		16 04						
York 8	26 a	*15 05*		15 45				*15 34*	15 40			16 45		*16 34*								17 00
London Kings Cross 15	⊖ 26 d	*12 30*				*13 00*		*13 10*		*13 30*				*14 00*								
Doncaster	31 d	14 36				14 59		15 05		15 36				15 56								
Bentley (S.Yorks)	31 a							*15 13*														
Adwick	31 a							*15 17*														
Kirk Sandall	d							15 13														
Hatfield & Stainforth	d							15 18														
Thorne South	d																					
Crowle	d																					
Althorpe	d																					
Scunthorpe	a	15 01								16 01												
	d	15 02								16 02												
Barnetby	d	15 16								16 16											16 55	
Hull Bus Station	🚌 d																15 30					
Barton-on-Humber	🚌 a																15 55					
Barton-on-Humber	d																	16 10				
Barrow Haven	d																	16 15				
New Holland	d																	16 18				
Goxhill	d																	16 23				
Thornton Abbey	d																	16 26				
Ulceby	d																	16 30				
Habrough	d									16 25								16 35			17 03	
Stallingborough	d																	16 40				
Healing	d																	16 43				
Great Coates	d																	16 46				
Grimsby Town	a	15 36								16 38								16 51			17 15	
	d	15 37								16 39								16 51			17 16	
Grimsby Docks	d																	16 54				
New Clee	d																	16x56				
Cleethorpes	a	15 48								16 50								17 01			17 27	
Thorne North	d							15 25														
Goole	d					15 19		15a33						16 17								
Saltmarshe	d																					
York 8	33 d		14 45								15 43											
Selby	a		15 04								16 01											
	d		15 04								16 02											
Wressle	d																					
Howden	d																					
Eastrington	d																					
Gilberdyke	d					15 27								16 25								
Broomfleet	d																					
Brough	d		15 24			15 35					16 21			16 33								
Ferriby	d					15 40																
Hessle	d					15 44																
Hull	a		15 43			15 57					16 41			16 50								

For general notes see front of timetable
For details of catering facilities see Directory of Train Operators

A From Bournemouth to Edinburgh (Table 51)
B To Scarborough (Table 43)
C To Leeds (Table 34)
D From Exeter St Davids to Newcastle (Table 51)
E From Plymouth (Table 51) to Dundee (Table 229)
G To Bridlington (Table 43)
H To Leeds (Table 31)
J From Retford Low Level (Table 30) to Huddersfield (Table 34)
K From Nottingham (Table 27)
L Via Pontefract Baghill (Table 33)
b Change at Manchester Piccadilly and Sheffield

Due to Engineering Operations in the Sheffield area, services from Sunday 14 September on this Table had not been confirmed at time of going to press. These services will be issued in a special Supplement as soon as exact timings have been confirmed.

Table 29

Sundays

20 July to 7 September

Manchester Airport, Manchester, Sheffield and Meadowhall → Doncaster → Cleethorpes and Hull Barton-on-Humber → Cleethorpes

Network Diagram - see first page of Table 18

		XC	HT	TP	XC	NT	NT	NT	TP		NT	NT	XC	TP	HT	XC	NT	NT	TP	NT	NT		NT	XC
		1 ◇	1 ◇	1 ◇	R 1				1 ◇				1 ◇	1 ◇	1 ◇	R 1			1 ◇					1 ◇
		A			B		C				D		A			E		G			H		J	A
		☕	⊠ ☕		☕								☕		⊠ ☕	☕								☕
Manchester Airport	85 ✈ d			14 49					15 20				14b58	15 49					16 22					15b58
Manchester Piccadilly 10	78 🚌 d			15 15					16 00				15 43	16 15					17 00					16 43
Stockport	78 d			15 23					15c29		15 27		15 54	16 23					16c29					16 54
Sheffield 7	🚌 a			16 04										17 05										
	d	15 54		16 08	16 21	16 24	16 28				16 39		16 54	17 08		17 21	17 24	17 28			17 36		17 39	17 54
Meadowhall	🚌 d			16 14		16 30	16 34				16a44	←		17 14			17 30	17 34		←	17 42		17a44	
Rotherham Central	d					16 37											17 37				17 48			
Swinton (S.Yorks)	d					16 47 →						16 47					17 47 →			17 47	17a56			
Mexborough	d											16 50								17 50				
Conisbrough	d											16 54								17 54				
Doncaster 7	a	16 16		16 33			16 54					17 04	17 14	17 33				17 57		18 06				18 16
York 8	26 a	16 44			17 41								17 38	18 05		18 45		18 34						18 41
London Kings Cross 15	⊖ 26 d		14 44									15 10		15 30	16 04			16 10						
Doncaster	31 d		16 21	16 36			16 55					17 05		17 36	17 49			18 03						
Bentley (S.Yorks)	31 a						17 13																	
Adwick	31 a						17 17																	
Kirk Sandall	d											17 13												
Hatfield & Stainforth	d											17 18												
Thorne South	d																							
Crowle	d																							
Althorpe	d																							
Scunthorpe	a			17 01										18 01										
	d			17 02										18 02										
Barnetby	d			17 16										18 16										
Hull Bus Station	🚌 d																							
Barton-on-Humber	🚌 a																							
Barton-on-Humber	d																							
Barrow Haven	d																							
New Holland	d																							
Goxhill	d																							
Thornton Abbey	d																							
Ulceby	d																							
Habrough	d													18 25										
Stallingborough	d																							
Healing	d																							
Great Coates	d																							
Grimsby Town	a			17 36										18 38										
	d			17 37										18 39										
Grimsby Docks	d																							
New Clee	d																							
Cleethorpes	a			17 48										18 50										
Thorne North	d											17 25												
Goole	d						17 15					17a34						18 22						
Saltmarshe	d																							
York 8	33 d							17 10																
Selby	a		16 41					17 30	17 35						18 03				18 31					
	d		16 42					17 31	17 35						18 03				18 31					
Wressle	d																							
Howden	d		16 52												18 15									
Eastrington	d																							
Gilberdyke	d						17 23											18 35						
Broomfleet	d																							
Brough	d		17 04				17 31	17 51	17 55						18 26			18 43	18 51					
Ferriby	d																							
Hessle	d																							
Hull	a		17 21				17 48	18 10	18 11						18 48			18 57	19 08					

For general notes see front of timetable
For details of catering facilities see Directory of Train Operators

A From Bristol Temple Meads to Newcastle (Table 51)
B From Bournemouth to Glasgow Central (Table 51)
C To Scarborough (Table 43)
D From Lincoln (Table 30) to Leeds (Table 34)
E From Penzance (Table 135) to Glasgow Central (Table 51)
G To Bridlington (Table 43)
H To Leeds (Table 31)
J To Huddersfield (Table 34)
b Change at Manchester Piccadilly and Sheffield
c Change at Manchester Piccadilly

Due to Engineering Operations in the Sheffield area, services from Sunday 14 September on this Table had not been confirmed at time of going to press. These services will be issued in a special Supplement as soon as exact timings have been confirmed.

Table 29

Sundays

Manchester Airport, Manchester, Sheffield and Meadowhall → Doncaster → Cleethorpes and Hull Barton-on-Humber → Cleethorpes

20 July to 7 September

Network Diagram - see first page of Table 18

Station		TP	XC	NT	NT	NT	NT	NT	NT	NT	XC	HT	NT	TP	TP	XC	NT	NT	NT	XC	EM	NT	TP
		1 ◇	R 1								R 1	1 ◇		1 ◇	1 ◇					R 1	1 ◇		1 ◇
			A		B	C		bus			D		E			G		H	J	K	L		
Manchester Airport	85 ✈ d	16 49									*16b58*			17 49	*18 22*					*17b58*			18 49
Manchester Piccadilly 10	78 d	17 15									*17 43*			18 15	19 00					*18 42*			19 15
Stockport	78 d	17 23									*17 54*			18 23	*18c29*					*18 56*			19 22
Sheffield 7	a	18 04												19 05									20 04
	d	18 08	18 21	18 24	18 28	18 39					18 54		18 58	19 08		19 21	19 27	19 36	19 39	19 54	19 59	20 03	20 08
Meadowhall	d	18 14		18 30	18 34	18a44							19 04	19 14			19 33	19 42	19a44			20 09	20 14
Rotherham Central	d			18 37			←						19 10				19 39	19 48					
Swinton (S.Yorks)	d			18 47			18 47						19 18				19 47	19a56					
Mexborough	d			→			18 50										19 50						
Conisbrough	d						18 54										19 54						
Doncaster 7	a	18 33			18 54		19 04				19 16			19 33			20 05			20 16	20 22	20 30	20 34
York 8	26 a	*19 05*	19 43								19 40		20 16	*20 07*		20 45	*20 38*			20 43	*21 00*		
London Kings Cross 15	⊖ 26 d	*16 30*			*17 00*							17 44										*18 40*	*19 00*
Doncaster	31 d	18 36			18 55							19 25		19 36								20 30	20 42
Bentley (S.Yorks)	31 a										*19e32*												
Adwick	31 a										*19e36*												
Kirk Sandall	d				19 01																		
Hatfield & Stainforth	d				19 06																		
Thorne South	d																						
Crowle	d																						
Althorpe	d																						
Scunthorpe	a	19 01												20 01									21 07
	d	19 02												20 02									21 08
Barnetby	d	19 16												20 16									21 22
Hull Bus Station	bus d							18 30															
Barton-on-Humber	bus a							18 55															
Barton-on-Humber	d								19 10														
Barrow Haven	d								19 15														
New Holland	d								19 18														
Goxhill	d								19 23														
Thornton Abbey	d								19 26														
Ulceby	d								19 30														
Habrough	d								19 35														21 31
Stallingborough	d								19 40														
Healing	d								19 43														
Great Coates	d								19 46														
Grimsby Town	a	19 36							19 51					20 36									21 44
	d	19 37							19 51					20 37									21 45
Grimsby Docks	d								19 54														
New Clee	d								19x56														
Cleethorpes	a	19 50							20 01					20 50									21 56
Thorne North	d				19 12																		
Goole	d				19 21																	20 49	
Saltmarshe	d																						
York 8	33 d									19 10													
Selby	a									19 29		19 40			20 28								
	d									19 29		19 40			20 28								
Wressle	d																						
Howden	d											19 52											
Eastrington	d																						
Gilberdyke	d				19 29																	20 57	
Broomfleet	d																						
Brough	d				19 37					19 49		20 03			20 46							21 05	
Ferriby	d																						
Hessle	d																						
Hull	a				19 55					20 08		20 22			21 03							21 23	

For general notes see front of timetable
For details of catering facilities see Directory of Train Operators

- **A** From Bournemouth to Edinburgh (Table 51)
- **B** To Beverley (Table 43)
- **C** To Leeds (Table 34)
- **D** From Paignton to Newcastle (Table 51)
- **E** Via Pontefract Baghill (Table 33)
- **G** From Plymouth to Edinburgh (Table 51)
- **H** To Leeds (Table 31)
- **J** To Huddersfield (Table 34)
- **K** From Bristol Temple Meads to Newcastle (Table 51)
- **L** From St Pancras International to Leeds (Table 53)
- **b** Change at Manchester Piccadilly and Sheffield
- **c** Change at Manchester Piccadilly
- **e** Change at Doncaster

Due to Engineering Operations in the Sheffield area, services from Sunday 14 September on this Table had not been confirmed at time of going to press. These services will be issued in a special Supplement as soon as exact timings have been confirmed.

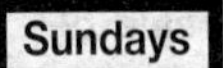

Sundays

20 July to 7 September

Manchester Airport, Manchester, Sheffield and Meadowhall → Doncaster → Cleethorpes and Hull Barton-on-Humber → Cleethorpes

Network Diagram - see first page of Table 18

		GR	NT		XC	NT	NT	XC	EM	TP	HT	XC	NT	NT	NT		NT	TP	NT	TP	NT	NT		
		R 1			R 1			1 ◇	1 ◇	1 ◇	1 ◇	R 1						1 ◇		1 ◇				
					A		B	C	D			E		G	H				J	K				
		☕							☕		⊠ ☕													
Manchester Airport	85 ✈ d							18b58		19 49							20 49					21 49		
Manchester Piccadilly 10	78 ⇌ d							19 42		20 15							21 15					22 15		
Stockport	78 d							19 54		20 23							21 22					22 22		
Sheffield 7	⇌ a									21 06														
	d				20 21	20 27	20 39	20 54	20 57	21 08		21 21	21 24	21 36	21 43		22 26	22 30	22 39			23 20		
Meadowhall	⇌ d					20 33	20a44			21 14			21 30	21 42	21a48		22 32	22 36	22a44		←	23 26		
Rotherham Central	d					20 39							21 37	21 48			22 38					23 32		
Swinton (S.Yorks)	d					20 47							21 46	21a56			22 48				22 48	23 43		
Mexborough	d					20 50							21 49				→				22 51	23 46		
Conisbrough	d					20 54							21 53								22 55	23 50		
Doncaster 7	a					21 04		21 16	21 20	21 34			22 02					22 55			23 03	23 58		
York 8	26 a				21 45			21 42	22 00			22 53	23 09								00 39			
London Kings Cross 15	⊖ 26 d	19 10								19 35	20 10							21 00						
Doncaster	31 d	20 58				21 06				21 42	21 54		22 04					22 58			23 07			
Bentley (S.Yorks)	31 a									21 52														
Adwick	31 a									21 56														
Kirk Sandall	d					21 12																		
Hatfield & Stainforth	d					21 17																		
Thorne South	d																							
Crowle	d																							
Althorpe	d																							
Scunthorpe	a									22 07								23 23						
	d									22 08								23 24						
Barnetby	d									22 22								23 38						
Hull Bus Station	🚌 d																							
Barton-on-Humber	🚌 a																							
Barton-on-Humber	d																							
Barrow Haven	d																							
New Holland	d																							
Goxhill	d																							
Thornton Abbey	d																							
Ulceby	d																							
Habrough	d									22 31														
Stallingborough	d																							
Healing	d																							
Great Coates	d																							
Grimsby Town	a									22 44								23 58						
	d									22 45								23 59						
Grimsby Docks	d																							
New Clee	d																							
Cleethorpes	a									22 56								00 10						
Thorne North	d					21 23															23 19			
Goole	d					21a34							22 23								23 28			
Saltmarshe	d																							
York 8	33 d		21 41																					
Selby	a	21 15	22 00								22 08													
	d	21 15	22 00								22 08									23 09				
Wressle	d																							
Howden	d										22 20													
Eastrington	d																							
Gilberdyke	d												22 31								23 36			
Broomfleet	d																							
Brough	d	21 36	22 20								22 31		22 39							23 29	23 44			
Ferriby	d																							
Hessle	d																							
Hull	a	21 56	22 39								22 50		22 56							23 43	00 02			

For general notes see front of timetable
For details of catering facilities see Directory of Train Operators

A From Bournemouth to Newcastle (Table 51)
B To Leeds (Table 34)
C From Bristol Temple Meads to Newcastle (Table 51)
D From St Pancras International to Leeds (Table 53)
E From Plymouth (Table 51)
G To Leeds (Table 31)
H To Barnsley (Table 34)
J From Lincoln (Table 30) to Leeds (Table 34)
K From Leeds (Table 39)
b Change at Manchester Piccadilly and Sheffield

Due to Engineering Operations in the Sheffield area, services from Sunday 14 September on this Table had not been confirmed at time of going to press. These services will be issued in a special Supplement as soon as exact timings have been confirmed.

Table 30

Sheffield → Retford and Lincoln

Mondays to Fridays
until 5 September

Network Diagram - see first page of Table 18

Miles		NT	NT	NT	NT		NT A	NT	NT B	NT B	NT B	NT B	NT B	NT B	NT B	NT B	NT	NT B	NT	NT	NT A	NT	NT	
—	Huddersfield 34 d						06 10	07 10	08 10	09 13	10 13	11 13	12 13	13 13	14 13	15 13		16 13	17 13	17 56	19 18	20 18	21 18	
—	Barnsley 34 d		05 18	05 53	06 46		06 58	08 06	08 58	10 01	11 01	12 01	13 01	14 01	15 01	16 01	16 26	17 01	18 01	18 58	20 06	21 06	22 06	
—	Meadowhall 29 ⛴ d		05 39	06 13	07 04		07 33	08 24	09 33	10 33	11 33	12 33	13 33	14 33	15 33	16 33	17 00	17 33	18 19	19 25	20 33	21 24	22 25	
0	**Sheffield** 7 ⛴ d	05 39	05 53	06 44	07 30		07 44	08 44	09 44	10 44	11 44	12 44	13 44	14 44	15 44	16 44	17 18	17 44	18 45	19 48	20 44	21 44	22 44	
2¼	Darnall d		05 58	06 49	07 35			08 49	09 49	10 49	11 49	12 49	13 49	14 49	15 49	16 49	17 23	17 49	18 50	19 53	20 49	21 49	22 49	
5¼	Woodhouse d		06 03	06 54	07 40			08 54	09 54	10 54	11 54	12 54	13 54	14 54	15 54	16 54	17 28	17 54	18 55	19 58	20 54	21 54	22 54	
9½	Kiveton Bridge d		06 10	07 01	07 47			09 01	10 01	11 01	12 01	13 01	14 01	15 01	16 01	17 01	17 35	18 01	19 02	20 05	21 01	22 01	23 01	
10¾	Kiveton Park d	05 54	06 13	07 04	07 50		07 59	09 04	10 04	11 04	12 04	13 04	14 04	15 04	16 04	17 04	17 38	18 04	19 05	20 08	21 04	22 04	23 04	
13¾	Shireoaks d		06 18	07 09	07 55			09 09	10 09	11 09	12 09	13 09	14 09	15 09	16 09	17 09	17 43	18 09	19 10	20 13	21 09	22 09	23 09	
15¾	Worksop d	06 01	06 24	07 14	07 59		08a10	09 13	10 13	11 13	12 13	13 13	14 13	15 13	16 13	17 13	17 47	18 13	19 14	20 17	21a21	22 15	23a18	
23½	**Retford Low Level** 10 a	06 10	06b38	07 23	08 09			09 23	10 23	11 23	12 23	13 23	14 23	15 23	16 23	17 23	18 01	18 23	19 24	20 27		22b30		
—	London Kings Cross 15 ⊖ 26 a		08 33		09 51			11 27	12 42		14 20	15 40		17 30	18 12	19 29	19 47	20 18		23 32				
—	**Retford Low Level** 10 d	06 10		07 24	08 09			09 23	10 23	11 24	12 23	13 23	14 23	15 23	16 23	17 23		18 23	19 24	20 27				
33	Gainsborough Lea Road 18 d	06 25		07 38	08 24			09 38	10 38	11 38	12 38	13 39	14 38	15 38	16 38	17 38		18 38	19 39	20 42				
42½	Saxilby 18 d	06 37		07 51	08 37			09 51	10 51	11 51	12 51	13 52	14 51	15 51	16 51	17 51		18 51	19 52	20 55				
48½	**Lincoln** 18 a	06 53		08 06	08 52			10 06	11 06	12 05	13 05	14 06	15 06	16 05	17 06	18 06		19 07	20 06	21 10				

Mondays to Fridays
from 8 September

	NT	NT	NT	NT		NT A	NT	NT B	NT B	NT B	NT B	NT B	NT B	NT B	NT B	NT	NT B	NT	NT	NT	NT	NT		
Huddersfield 34 d						06 05	07 08	08 07	09 08	10 08	11 08	12 08	13 08	14 08	15 08		16 08	17 08	17 56	18 22	20 15	21 18		
Barnsley 34 d		05 18	05 53	06 46		06 58	07 58	08 58	10 01	11 01	12 01	13 01	14 01	15 01	16 01	16 48	17 01	18 01	18 58	19 48	21 06	22 06		
Meadowhall 29 ⛴ d		05 39	06 13	07 04		07 33	08 22	09 33	10 33	11 33	12 33	13 33	14 33	15 33	16 33	17 03	17 33	18 19	19 16	20 08	21 24	22 25		
Sheffield 7 ⛴ d	05 39	05 53	06 44	07 30		07 44	08 43	09 43	10 43	11 43	12 43	13 43	14 43	15 43	16 43	17 23	17 43	18 43	19 48	20 44	21 44	22 44		
Darnall d		05 58	06 49	07 35			08 49	09 49	10 49	11 49	12 49	13 49	14 49	15 49	16 49	17 30	17 49	18 50	19 53	20 50	21 49	22 49		
Woodhouse d		06 03	06 54	07 40			08 54	09 54	10 54	11 54	12 54	13 54	14 54	15 54	16 54	17 35	17 54	18 55	19 58	20 55	21 54	22 54		
Kiveton Bridge d		06 10	07 01	07 47			09 01	10 01	11 01	12 01	13 01	14 01	15 01	16 01	17 01	17 42	18 01	19 02	20 05	21 02	22 01	23 01		
Kiveton Park d	05 54	06 13	07 04	07 50		07 59	09 04	10 04	11 04	12 04	13 04	14 04	15 04	16 04	17 04	17 45	18 04	19 05	20 08	21 05	22 04	23 04		
Shireoaks d		06 18	07 09	07 55			09 09	10 09	11 09	12 09	13 09	14 09	15 09	16 09	17 09	17 50	18 09	19 10	20 13	21 09	22 09	23 09		
Worksop d	06 01	06 24	07 14	07 59		08a10	09 13	10 13	11 13	12 13	13 13	14 13	15 13	16 13	17 13	17 54	18 13	19 14	20 17	21a22	22 15	23a18		
Retford Low Level 10 a	06 10	06b38	07 23	08 09			09 23	10 23	11 23	12 23	13 23	14 23	15 23	16 23	17 23	18 08	18 23	19 24	20 27		22b30			
London Kings Cross 15 ⊖ 26 a		08 33		09 51			11 27	12 42		14 20	15 40		17 30	18 12	19 29		20 18		23 32					
Retford Low Level 10 d	06 10		07 24	08 09			09 23	10 23	11 24	12 23	13 23	14 23	15 23	16 23	17 23		18 23	19 24	20 27					
Gainsborough Lea Road 18 d	06 25		07 38	08 24			09 38	10 38	11 38	12 38	13 39	14 38	15 38	16 38	17 38		18 38	19 39	20 42					
Saxilby 18 d	06 37		07 51	08 37			09 51	10 51	11 51	12 51	13 52	14 51	15 51	16 51	17 51		18 51	19 52	20 55					
Lincoln 18 a	06 53		08 06	08 52			10 06	11 06	12 05	13 05	14 06	15 06	16 05	17 06	18 06		19 07	20 06	21 10					

Saturdays
until 6 September

	NT	NT	NT	NT	NT	NT	NT B	NT B	NT B	NT	NT B	NT B	NT B	NT	NT B	NT B	NT	NT B	NT B	NT	NT A	NT	NT	
Huddersfield 34 d					06 10	07 10	08 10	09 13	10 13		11 13	12 13	13 13	13 13	14 13	15 13		16 13	17 13	18 13	19 18	20 18	21 18	
Barnsley 34 d		05 18	05 53	06 27	06 58	07 58	08 58	10 01	11 01		12 01	13 01	14 01	14 48	15 01	16 01	16 26	17 01	18 01	19 01	20 06	21 06	22 06	
Meadowhall 29 ⛴ d		05 39	06 13	07 00	07 33	08 22	09 33	10 33	11 33		12 33	13 33	14 33	15 06	15 33	16 33	17 00	17 33	18 33	19 19	20 35	21 24	22 25	
Sheffield 7 ⛴ d	05 39	05 51	06 44	07 30	08 02	08 44	09 44	10 44	11 44	12 01	12 44	13 44	14 44	15 30	15 44	16 44	17 18	17 44	18 44	19 48	20 44	21 44	22 44	
Darnall d		05 57	06 49	07 35	08 08	08 49	09 49	10 49	11 49	12 07	12 49	13 49	14 49	15 35	15 49	16 49	17 23	17 49	18 50	19 53	20 49	21 49	22 49	
Woodhouse d		06 02	06 54	07 40	08 13	08 54	09 54	10 54	11 54	12 12	12 54	13 54	14 54	15 40	15 54	16 54	17 28	17 54	18 55	19 58	20 54	21 54	22 54	
Kiveton Bridge d		06 09	07 01	07 47	08 20	09 01	10 01	11 01	12 01	12 19	13 01	14 01	15 01	15 47	16 01	17 01	17 35	18 01	19 02	20 05	21 01	22 01	23 01	
Kiveton Park d	05 54	06 12	07 04	07 50	08 23	09 04	10 04	11 04	12 04	12 22	13 04	14 04	15 04	15 50	16 04	17 04	17 38	18 04	19 05	20 08	21 04	22 04	23 04	
Shireoaks d		06 16	07 09	07 55	08 28	09 09	10 09	11 09	12 09	12 27	13 09	14 09	15 09	15 55	16 09	17 09	17 43	18 09	19 10	20 13	21 09	22 09	23 09	
Worksop d	06 01	06 23	07 14	07 59	08 32	09 13	10 13	11 13	12 13	12 35	13 13	14 13	15 13	15 59	16 13	17 13	17 47	18 13	19 14	20 17	21a21	22 15	23a18	
Retford Low Level 10 a	06 10	06b38	07 23	08 09	08 42	09 23	10 23	11 23	12 23	12 44	13 23	14 23	15 23	16 09	16 23	17 23	18 01	18 23	19 24	20 27		22b30		
London Kings Cross 15 ⊖ 26 a		08 40		10 00	10 41		12 41		14 27		15 49	16 30	17 45		18 28		20 12	20 46		22 47				
Retford Low Level 10 d	06 10		07 24	08 09	08 42	09 24	10 23	11 24	12 23	12 45	13 23	14 23	15 23	16 09	16 23	17 23		18 23	19 24	20 27				
Gainsborough Lea Road 18 d	06 25		07 38	08 24		09 38	10 38	11 38	12 38		13 40	14 40	15 45		16 38	17 38		18 38	19 39	20 42				
Saxilby 18 d	06 37		07 51	08 37		09 51	10 51	11 51	12 51		13 53	14 53	15 58		16 51	17 51		18 51	19 52	20 55				
Lincoln 18 a	06 53		08 06	08 52		10 06	11 06	12 05	13 05		14 06	15 06	16 09		17 06	18 06		19 07	20 06	21 10				
Gainsborough Central d					08 57					13 00				16 24										
Kirton Lindsey d					09 16					13 18				16 43										
Brigg d					09 29					13 32				16 56										
Barnetby 29 a					09 40					13 42				17 07										
Habrough 29 a					09 49					13 52				17 19										
Grimsby Town 29 a					10 01					14 05				17 37										
Cleethorpes 29 a					10 14					14 16				17 46										

For general notes see front of timetable
For details of catering facilities see Directory of Train Operators

A From Doncaster (Table 29)
B From Scunthorpe (Table 29)
b Retford High Level

Due to Engineering Operations in the Sheffield area, services from Saturday 13 September on this Table had not been confirmed at time of going to press. These services will be issued in a special Supplement as soon as exact timings have been confirmed.

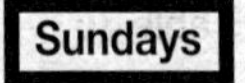

until 7 September

Sheffield → Retford and Lincoln

Network Diagram - see first page of Table 18

	NT A	NT	NT	NT B	NT C	NT C	NT B	NT
Huddersfield 34 d	11 19		13 19	15 19	15 19	17 19	17 19	19 19
Barnsley 34 d	13 12		15 12	17 12	17 12	18 12	18 12	20 12
Meadowhall 29 ⛴ d	13 33		15b42	17 42	17 43	19 00	19 00	20 45
Sheffield 7 ⛴ d	13 48	14 01	16 00	18 00	18 01	19 24	19 24	21 06
Darnall d		14 06	16 05	18 05	18 06	19 29	19 33	21 11
Woodhouse d		14 11	16 10	18 10	18 11	19 34	19 38	21 16
Kiveton Bridge d		14 18	16 17	18 17	18 18	19 41	19 45	21 23
Kiveton Park d		14 21	16 20	18 20	18 21	19 44	19 48	21 26
Shireoaks d		14 25	16 24	18 24	18 25	19 48	19 52	21 30
Worksop d	14 08	14 29	16 29	18 29	18 29	19 52	19 56	21 34
Retford Low Level 10 a	14 17	14 44	16 38	18 38	18 38	20 01	20 05	21 49
London Kings Cross 15 ⊖ 26 a		16 50	19 06	21 12	21 12	23 14	23 14	
Retford Low Level 10 d	14 18		16 39	18 39	18 39	20 02	20 06	
Gainsborough Lea Road 18 d	14 32		16 53	18 53	18 53	20 16	20 20	
Saxilby 18 d	14 45		17 06	19 06	19 06	20 29	20 33	
Lincoln 18 a	15 00		17 20	19 21	19 21	20 44	20 48	

For general notes see front of timetable
For details of catering facilities see Directory of Train Operators

A From Leeds (Table 34)
B Until 13 July
C From 20 July

b From 20 July dep. 1543

Due to Engineering Operations in the Sheffield area, services from Sunday 14 September on this Table had not been confirmed at time of going to press. These services will be issued in a special Supplement as soon as exact timings have been confirmed.

Table 30

Mondays to Fridays
until 5 September

Lincoln and Retford → Sheffield

Network Diagram - see first page of Table 18

Miles			NT	NT A	NT	NT B	NT B	NT B	NT B	NT B	NT B	NT B	NT B	NT B	NT C	NT	NT D	NT	NT	NT	NT	NT	NT	NT		
0	**Lincoln**	18 d			07 04		08 27	09 27	10 27	11 27	12 27	13 27	14 27	15 27	16 27	17 22		18 24	19 43	20 27		21 27				
6	Saxilby	18 d			07 14		08 36	09 36	10 36	11 36	12 36	13 36	14 36	15 36	16 36	17 31		18 33	19 52	20 36		21 36				
15½	Gainsborough Lea Road	18 d			07 26		08 49	09 49	10 49	11 49	12 49	13 49	14 49	15 49	16 49	17 44		18 46	20 05	20 49		21 49				
25	**Retford Low Level** 10	a			07 40		09 03	10 03	11 03	12 03	13 03	14 03	15 03	16 03	17 02	17 58		19 04	20 19	21 03		22 03				
—	London Kings Cross 15	⊖ 26 d					07 20		08 40	10 10		12 10	13 33		15 10	16 05		16 35	18 30	18 50		20 27				
—	**Retford Low Level** 10	d		07b03	07 40		09 03	10 03	11 03	12 03	13 03	14 03	15 03	16 03	17 03	17 58	18 10	19 04	20 19	21 03		22 03	22b45			
32¾	Worksop	d	06 30	07 16	07 52	08 14	09 15	10 15	11 15	12 15	13 15	14 15	15 15	16 15	17 15	18 10	18 21	19 16	20 31	21 15	21 26	22 15	22 58	23 28		
34¾	Shireoaks	d	06 33	07 20	07 55	08 19	09 19	10 19	11 19	12 19	13 19	14 19	15 19	16 19	17 19		18 25	19 20	20 35		21 31	22 19	23 02	23 32		
37¼	Kiveton Park	d	06 39	07 25	08 01	08 25	09 25	10 25	11 25	12 25	13 25	14 25	15 25	16 25	17 25		18 31	19 26	20 41	21 23	21 37	22 25	23 08	23 38		
39	Kiveton Bridge	d	06 42	07 28	08 04	08 28	09 28	10 28	11 28	12 28	13 28	14 28	15 28	16 28	17 28		18 34	19 29	20 44		21 40	22 28	23 11	23 41		
43¼	Woodhouse	d	06 48	07 34	08 10	08 34	09 34	10 34	11 34	12 34	13 34	14 34	15 34	16 34	17 34		18 41	19 35	20 50		21 46	22 34	23 17	23 52		
46¼	Darnall	d	06 53	07 39	08 15	08 39	09 39	10 39	11 39	12 39	13 39	14 39	15 39	16 39	17 39		18 46	19 40	20 55		21 51	22 39	23 22	23 57		
48½	**Sheffield** 7	a	07 02	07 47	08 26	08 48	09 48	10 48	11 48	12 48	13 48	14 48	15 48	16 48	17 47	18 35	18 54	19 54	21 05	21 43	22 00	22 50	23 31	00 03		
—	Meadowhall	29 a	07 20	07 57	08 41	09 03	10 03	11 03	12 03	13 03	14 03	15 03	16 03	17 03	18 03	18 56	19 03	20 13	21 21		22 13	23 20				
—	Barnsley	34 a	07 48	08 11	09 00	09 34	10 34	11 34	12 34	13 34	14 34	15 34	16 34	17 34	18 34	19 15	19 34	20 34	22 05		22 34	23c50				
—	Huddersfield	34 a	08 49		09 49	10 49	11 49	12 49	13 49	14 49	15 49	16 49	17 50	18 57	19 57		20 54	21 54	22 54		23 59					

Mondays to Fridays
from 8 September

		NT	NT A	NT	NT B	NT B	NT B	NT B		NT B	NT B	NT B	NT B	NT B	NT C	NT	NT D	NT	NT	NT	NT	NT	NT	NT		
Lincoln	18 d			07 04		08 27	09 27	10 27		11 27	12 27	13 27	14 27	15 27	16 27	17 22		18 24	19 43	20 27		21 27				
Saxilby	18 d			07 14		08 36	09 36	10 36		11 36	12 36	13 36	14 36	15 36	16 36	17 31		18 33	19 52	20 36		21 36				
Gainsborough Lea Road	18 d			07 26		08 49	09 49	10 49		11 49	12 49	13 49	14 49	15 49	16 49	17 44		18 46	20 05	20 49		21 49				
Retford Low Level 10	a			07 40		09 03	10 03	11 03		12 03	13 03	14 03	15 03	16 03	17 02	17 58		19 04	20 19	21 03		22 03				
London Kings Cross 15	⊖ 26 d					07 20		08 40		10 10		12 10	13 33		15 10	16 05	16 35		18 30	18 50		20 27				
Retford Low Level 10	d		07b03	07 40		09 03	10 03	11 03		12 03	13 03	14 03	15 03	16 03	17 03	17 58	18 20	19 04	20 19	21 03		22 03	22b45			
Worksop	d	06 30	07 16	07 52	08 14	09 15	10 15	11 15		12 15	13 15	14 15	15 15	16 15	17 15	18 10	18 31	19 16	20 31	21 15	21 26	22 15	22 58	23 28		
Shireoaks	d	06 33	07 20	07 55	08 19	09 19	10 19	11 19		12 19	13 19	14 19	15 19	16 19	17 19		18 35	19 20	20 35		21 31	22 19	23 02	23 32		
Kiveton Park	d	06 39	07 25	08 01	08 25	09 25	10 25	11 25		12 25	13 25	14 25	15 25	16 25	17 25		18 41	19 26	20 41	21 23	21 37	22 25	23 08	23 38		
Kiveton Bridge	d	06 42	07 28	08 04	08 28	09 28	10 28	11 28		12 28	13 28	14 28	15 28	16 28	17 28		18 44	19 29	20 44		21 40	22 28	23 11	23 41		
Woodhouse	d	06 48	07 34	08 10	08 34	09 34	10 34	11 34		12 34	13 34	14 34	15 34	16 34	17 34		18 52	19 35	20 50		21 47	22 34	23 17	23 52		
Darnall	d	06 53	07 39	08 15	08 39	09 39	10 39	11 39		12 39	13 39	14 39	15 39	16 39	17 39		18 57	19 40	20 55		21 52	22 39	23 22	23 57		
Sheffield 7	a	07 03	07 47	08 26	08 48	09 48	10 48	11 48		12 48	13 48	14 48	15 48	16 48	17 48	18 34	19 05	19 53	21 04	21 43	22 00	22 50	23 31	00 03		
Meadowhall	29 a	07 20	07 57	08 41	09 03	10 03	11 03	12 03		13 03	14 03	15 03	16 03	17 03	18 03	18 46		20 13	21 17		22 13	23 20				
Barnsley	34 a	08 00	08 11	09 00	09 34	10 34	11 34	12 34		13 34	14 34	15 34	16 34	17 34	18 34	19 15		20 34	22 05		22 34	23c50				
Huddersfield	34 a		09 52	09 52	10 52	11 52	12 52	13 52		14 52	15 52	16 52	17 54	19 02	20 02			21e59	22 58		23 59					

Saturdays
until 6 September

		NT	NT A	NT	NT B	NT B	NT B	NT B	NT	NT B	NT B	NT B	NT B	NT	NT D	NT	NT D	NT	NT	NT	NT	NT	NT	NT	NT	
Cleethorpes	29 d								11 13					14 56					18 06							
Grimsby Town	29 d								11 20					15 04					18 13							
Habrough	29 d								11 30					15 14					18 23							
Barnetby	29 d								11 40					15 23					18 34							
Brigg	d								11 50					15 34					18 46							
Kirton Lindsey	d								12 04					15 48					19 00							
Gainsborough Central	d								12 22					16 06					19 18							
Lincoln	18 d			07 04	08 27	09 27	10 27	11 27		12 27	13 27	14 27	15 27		16 27	17 22		18 24		19 43	20 27		21 24			
Saxilby	18 d			07 14	08 36	09 36	10 36	11 36		12 36	13 36	14 36	15 36		16 36	17 31		18 33		19 52	20 36		21 33			
Gainsborough Lea Road	18 d			07 26	08 49	09 49	10 49	11 49		12 49	13 49	14 49	15 49		16 49	17 44		18 46		20 05	20 49		21 46			
Retford Low Level 10	a			07 40	09 03	10 03	11 03	12 03	12 37	13 03	14 03	15 03	16 03	16 20	17 03	17 58		19 04	19 32	20 19	21 03		22 00			
London Kings Cross 15	⊖ 26 d				07 10		09 00	09 34		11 10	11 48	13 10	13 38	14 30				17 05			18 40		20 00			
Retford Low Level 10	d		07b03	07 40	09 03	10 03	11 03	12 03	12 37	13 03	14 03	15 03	16 03	16 21	17 03	17 58	18 10	19 04	19 33	20 19	21 03		22 00	22b45		
Worksop	d	06 30	07 16	07 52	09 15	10 15	11 15	12 15	12 49	13 15	14 15	15 15	16 15	16 32	17 15	18 10	18 21	19 16	19 44	20 31	21 15	21 26	22 12	22 58	23 28	
Shireoaks	d	06 33	07 20	07 55	09 19	10 19	11 19	12 19	12 53	13 19	14 19	15 19	16 19	16 36	17 19		18 25	19 20	19 48	20 35		21 31	22 16	23 02	23 32	
Kiveton Park	d	06 39	07 25	08 01	09 25	10 25	11 25	12 25	12 59	13 25	14 25	15 25	16 25	16 42	17 25		18 31	19 26	19 54	20 41	21 23	21 37	22 22	23 08	23 38	
Kiveton Bridge	d	06 42	07 28	08 04	09 28	10 28	11 28	12 28	13 02	13 28	14 28	15 28	16 28	16 45	17 28		18 34	19 29	19 57	20 44		21 40	22 25	23 11	23 41	
Woodhouse	d	06 48	07 34	08 10	09 34	10 34	11 34	12 34	13 08	13 34	14 34	15 34	16 34	16 52	17 34		18 41	19 35	20 04	20 50		21 46	22 31	23 17	23 47	
Darnall	d	06 53	07 39	08 15	09 39	10 39	11 39	12 39	13 13	13 39	14 39	15 39	16 39	16 57	17 39		18 46	19 40	20 09	20 55		21 51	22 36	23 22	23 52	
Sheffield 7	a	07 02	07 47	08 26	09 48	10 48	11 48	12 48	13 26	13 48	14 48	15 48	16 48	17 06	17 48	18 35	18 54	19 54	20 21	21 05	21 43	22 02	22 46	23 31	00 01	
Meadowhall	29 a	07 20	07 57	08 41	10 03	11 03	12 03	13 03	13 41	14 03	15 03	16 03	17 03	17 20	18 03	18 56	19 06	20 13	20 36	21 21	22 13	22 17	23 30			
Barnsley	34 a	07 43	08 11	09 00	10 34	11 34	12 34	13 34	14 00	14 34	15 34	16 34	17 34	18 02	18 34	19 15	19 34	20 34	21 06	22 05	22 34	23 06				
Huddersfield	34 a	08 49		09 49	11 49	12 49	13 49		14 49	15 49	16 49	17 50		18 50	19 51		20 54		21 54	22 54		23 55				

For general notes see front of timetable
For details of catering facilities see Directory of Train Operators

- **A** To Leeds (Table 31)
- **B** To Adwick (Table 29)
- **C** To Hull (Table 29)
- **D** To Doncaster (Table 29)
- **b** Retford High Level
- **c** Mondays to Thursdays only
- **e** Change at Sheffield and Barnsley

Due to Engineering Operations in the Sheffield area, services from Saturday 13 September on this Table had not been confirmed at time of going to press. These services will be issued in a special Supplement as soon as exact timings have been confirmed.

Table 30

Sundays

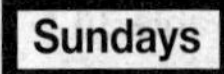

until 7 September

Lincoln and Retford → Sheffield

Network Diagram - see first page of Table 18

		NT A	NT B	NT C	NT A	NT	NT D	NT
Lincoln	18 d		15 15	17 35	17 35	19 35	21 15	
Saxilby	18 d		15 25	17 45	17 45	19 45	21 25	
Gainsborough Lea Road	18 d		15 37	17 57	17 57	19 57	21 37	
Retford Low Level 10	a		15 51	18 11	18 11	20 11	21 51	
London Kings Cross 15	⊖ 26 d	*12 10*		*16 10*	*16 10*	*18 10*	*20 10*	*20 30*
Retford Low Level 10	d	14 50	15 51	18 11	18 11	20 11	21 51	22 24
Worksop	d	15 01	16 03	18 23	18 23	20 23	22 03	22 35
Shireoaks	d	15 05	16 06	18 26	18 26	20 26	22 06	22 39
Kiveton Park	d	15 10	16 12	18 32	18 32	20 32	22 12	22 44
Kiveton Bridge	d	15 13	16 15	18 35	18 35	20 35	22 15	22 47
Woodhouse	d	15 19	16 21	18 41	18 46	20 41	22 21	22 53
Darnall	d	15 24	16 26	18 46	18 51	20 46	22 26	22 58
Sheffield 7	🚋 a	15b38	16 35	18 55	18 58	20 56	22 34	23 07
Meadowhall	29 🚋 a	15 44	16 44	*19 13*	*19 13*	*21 13*	22 44	*23 25*
Barnsley	34 a	16 06	17 05	*20 05*	*20 05*	*22 09*	23 05	
Huddersfield	34 a	16 55	*18 54*	*20 53*	*20 53*			

For general notes see front of timetable
For details of catering facilities see Directory of Train Operators

A Until 13 July
B From 20 July. To Leeds (Table 34)
C From 20 July
D To Leeds (Table 34)
b From 20 July arr. 1533

Due to Engineering Operations in the Sheffield area, services from Sunday 14 September on this Table had not been confirmed at time of going to press. These services will be issued in a special Supplement as soon as exact timings have been confirmed.

Network Diagram for Tables 31, 32, 33, 34

DM-5/08
Design BAJS

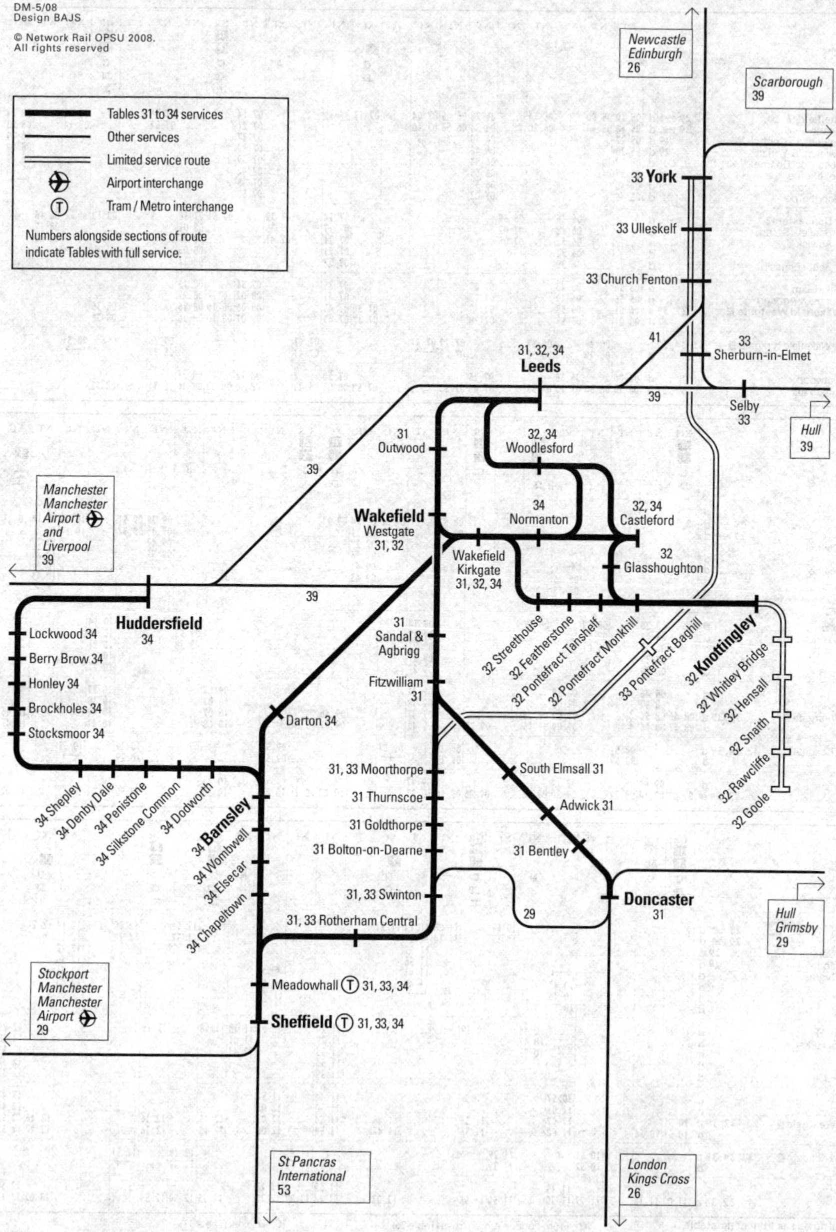

Sheffield, Doncaster and Wakefield → Leeds

Network Diagram - see first page of Table 31

Miles	Miles		NT	NT	NT	NT	NT	NT	NT	NT		XC	NT	NT	NT	NT	GR	NT	NT		GR	NT	NT	NT
												1 ◇					R 1				R 1			
							A					G			A		C		D		C		E	
—	0	**Sheffield 7** 29 d	05 10	05 50		06 14		06 28	06 49	07 04		07 12				07 14			07 51			08 08		08 14
—	3¼	Meadowhall 29 d	05 16	05 56		06 20		06 34	06 55	07 10						07 21			07 57			08 14		08 23
—	6¼	Rotherham Central 29 d	05 22					06 40								07 27								08 29
—	10¾	Swinton (S.Yorks) 29 d	05 30					06 48								07 35								08 38
—	13	Bolton-on-Dearne d	05 34					06 53								07 39								08 42
—	14½	Goldthorpe d	05 37					06 55								07 42								08 45 →
—	15	Thurnscoe d	05 40					06 58								07 45								
—	18½	Moorthorpe d	05 45					07 03								07 50								
0	—	**Doncaster 7** d			06 25		06 59						07 14		07 32		07 51	07 58			08 12		08 16	
1¾	—	Bentley (S.Yorks) d			06 28		07 02						07 17		07 35			08 01					08 19	
4	—	Adwick a			06 32		07 08						07 21		07 41			08 05					08 25	
—	—	d			06 32								07 21					08 05						
8¾	—	South Elmsall d			06 38								07 27					08 11						
13¼	22¼	Fitzwilliam d	05 50		06 43			07 09					07 35			07 56		08 16						
18	27	Sandal & Agbrigg d	05 56		06 49			07 15					07 41			08 02		08 22						
19¾	28¾	**Wakefield Westgate 7** 32, 39 a	06 01		06 53			07 19				07 36	07 45			08 06	08 10	08 26			08 36			
—	—	d	06 01		06 53			07 20				07 37	07 45	←		08 07	08 10	08 26			08 36			
—	—	Wakefield Kirkgate 4 32, 34, 39 a		06 28		06 57			07 29	07 47				07 47					08 28			08 51		
—	—	d		06 29		06 58			07 29	→				07 47					08 29			→		
22¼	31¼	Outwood d	06 06		06 58			07 25					07 50			08 12		08 31						
29¾	38¾	**Leeds 10** 32, 34 a	06 26	06 50	07 13	07 33		07 44	07 50			07 52	08 03	08 23		08 30	08 32	08 46	08 51		08 52			

	XC	NT	NT	NT	NT	GR		GR	NT	NT	NT	NT	XC	GR	NT		NT	NT	NT	NT	NT	NT	NT	XC
	R 1					R 1		R 1					R 1	R 1										1 ◇
	G					C		C					H	C				J	K					L
Sheffield 7 29 d	08 21								08 51		09 08	09 14	09 21						09 29	09 51		10 08	10 14	10 21
Meadowhall 29 d									08 57		09 14	09 21							09 35	09 57		10 14	10 21	
Rotherham Central 29 d												09 27							09 42				10 27	
Swinton (S.Yorks) 29 d												09 36							09 51				10 36	
Bolton-on-Dearne d					←							09 41					←						10 41	
Goldthorpe d					08 45							09 43 →					09 43						10 43 →	
Thurnscoe d					08 48												09 46							
Moorthorpe d					08 53												09 51		10a01					
Doncaster 7 d		08 26		08 52		08 58				09 14								09 49			10 14			
Bentley (S.Yorks) d		08 29		08 55						09 17								09 52			10 17			
Adwick a		08 33		09 01						09 21								09 58			10 21			
d		08 33								09 21											10 21			
South Elmsall d		08 39								09 27											10 27			
Fitzwilliam d		08 46			08 59					09 32							09 57				10 32			
Sandal & Agbrigg d		08 52			09 05					09 38							10 03				10 38			
Wakefield Westgate 7 32, 39 a	08 46	08 56			09 09	09 16				09 42			09 46				10 07				10 42			10 46
d	08 47	08 56	←		09 09	09 16		09 27		09 42			09 47	10 01	←		10 08				10 42			10 47
Wakefield Kirkgate 4 32, 34, 39 a			08 51						09 29		09 51				09 51					10 29		10 51		
d			08 52						09 29		→				09 52					10 29		→		
Outwood d		09 01			09 14					09 47							10 13				10 47			
Leeds 10 32, 34 a	09 02	09 14	09 27		09 30	09 36		09 46	09 50	10 02			10 02	10 21	10 27		10 30			10 50	11 02			11 02

	GR	GR		NT	NT	NT	NT	GR	NT	NT	XC		NT	NT	NT	NT	GR	NT	GR	NT		NT	XC	NT
	R 1	R 1						R 1			1 ◇						R 1		R 1				1 ◇	
	C	C				N		C			Q					N	C		C				U	
Sheffield 7 29 d							10 51		11 08	11 14	11 21							11 51		12 08		12 14	12 21	
Meadowhall 29 d							10 57		11 14	11 21								11 57		12 14		12 21		
Rotherham Central 29 d										11 27												12 27		
Swinton (S.Yorks) 29 d										11 36												12 36		
Bolton-on-Dearne d					←					11 41					←							12 41		
Goldthorpe d					10 43					11 43 →					11 43							12 43 →		
Thurnscoe d					10 46										11 46									
Moorthorpe d					10 51										11 51									
Doncaster 7 d	10 28					10 44		11 19					11 26			11 38	11 58		12 19					12 25
Bentley (S.Yorks) d						10 47							11 29			11 41								12 28
Adwick a						10 53							11 33			11 47								12 32
d													11 33											12 32
South Elmsall d													11 39											12 38
Fitzwilliam d					10 57								11 44		11 57									12 43
Sandal & Agbrigg d					11 03								11 50		12 03									12 49
Wakefield Westgate 7 32, 39 a	10 51				11 07			11 36			11 46		11 54		12 07		12 15		12 36				12 46	12 53
d	10 51	10 56		←	11 08			11 36			11 47		11 54	←	12 08		12 15		12 36				12 47	12 53
Wakefield Kirkgate 4 32, 34, 39 a				10 51			11 29		11 51					11 51				12 29		12 51				
d				10 52			11 29							11 52				12 29		→				
Outwood d					11 13								11 59		12 13									12 58
Leeds 10 32, 34 a	11 09	11 18		11 27	11 30		11 50	11 55			12 02		12 14	12 27	12 30		12 35	12 50	12 54				13 02	13 13

For general notes see front of timetable
For details of catering facilities see Directory of Train Operators

A From Sheffield (Table 29)
C From London Kings Cross (Table 26)
D From Retford (Table 30)
E From Scunthorpe (Table 29)
G From Birmingham New Street to Edinburgh (Table 51)
H From Bristol Temple Meads to Edinburgh (Table 51)
J From Worksop (Table 30)
K To York (Table 33)
L From Southampton Central to Edinburgh (Table 51)
N From Lincoln (Table 30)
Q From Plymouth to Edinburgh (Table 51)
U From Bournemouth (Table 51) to Aberdeen (Table 229)

Sheffield, Doncaster and Wakefield → Leeds

Network Diagram - see first page of Table 31

		NT	NT	NT	GR	NT	GR	NT		NT	XC	NT	NT	NT	NT	GR	NT		NT	GR	NT	NT	XC	NT	NT
					R 1		R 1				1 ◇					R 1				R 1			R 1		
				A	B		B				C				A	B	D			B			E		
					☕ 🍴						☕					☕ 🍴				☕ 🍴			☕		
Sheffield 7	29 🚊 d					12 51		13 08		13 14	13 21						13 28		13 51		14 08	14 14	14 21		
Meadowhall	29 🚊 d					12 57		13 14		13 21							13 35		13 57		14 14	14 21			
Rotherham Central	29 d									13 27							13 42					14 27			
Swinton (S.Yorks)	29 d									13 36							13 50					14 36			
Bolton-on-Dearne	d		←							13 41				←								14 41			
Goldthorpe	d		12 43							13 43				13 43								14 43			
Thurnscoe	d		12 46							→				13 46								→			
Moorthorpe	d		12 51											13 51			14a01								
Doncaster 7	d			12 36	12 57							13 27			13 38	13 57				14 21				14 27	
Bentley (S.Yorks)	d			12 40								13 30			13 41									14 30	
Adwick	a			12 45								13 34			13 47									14 34	
	d											13 34												14 34	
South Elmsall	d											13 40												14 40	
Fitzwilliam	d		12 57									13 45		13 57										14 45	
Sandal & Agbrigg	d		13 03									13 51		14 03										14 51	
Wakefield Westgate 7	32, 39 a		13 07		13 17						13 46	13 55		14 07		14 14				14 39			14 46	14 55	
	d	←	13 08		13 17		13 37				13 47	13 55	←	14 08		14 14				14 39			14 47	14 55	←
Wakefield Kirkgate 4	32, 34, 39 a	12 51				13 29		13 51					13 51						14 28		14 51				14 51
	d	12 52				13 29		→					13 52						14 29		→				14 52
Outwood	d		13 13									14 00		14 13										15 00	
Leeds 10	32, 34 a	13 27	13 33		13 41	13 50	13 55				14 02	14 14	14 27	14 30		14 35			14 50	15 01			15 02	15 15	15 27

		NT	NT	GR		NT	NT	NT	NT	XC	GR	NT	NT		NT	GR	GR	NT	NT	NT	NT	NT		XC	NT
				R 1						R 1	R 1					R 1	R 1							R 1	
			A	B						G	B				A	B	B			A				H	
				☕ 🍴						☕	☕ 🍴					☕ 🍴	☕ 🍴							☕	
Sheffield 7	29 🚊 d					14 51		15 08	15 14	15 21								15 51			16 08	16 14		16 21	
Meadowhall	29 🚊 d					14 57		15 14	15 21									15 57			16 14	16 21			
Rotherham Central	29 d								15 27													16 27			
Swinton (S.Yorks)	29 d								15 36													16 36			
Bolton-on-Dearne	d	←							15 41				←									16 41			
Goldthorpe	d	14 43							15 43				15 43									16 43			
Thurnscoe	d	14 46							→				15 46									→			
Moorthorpe	d	14 51											15 51												
Doncaster 7	d		14 38	14 53			15 14				15 29				15 38	15 55	16 10		16 14	16 38					
Bentley (S.Yorks)	d		14 41				15 17								15 41				16 17	16 41					
Adwick	a		14 47				15 21								15 47				16 21	16 47					
	d						15 21												16 21						
South Elmsall	d						15 27												16 27						
Fitzwilliam	d	14 57					15 32						15 57						16 32						
Sandal & Agbrigg	d	15 03					15 38						16 03						16 38						
Wakefield Westgate 7	32, 39 a	15 07		15 14			15 42			15 46	15 51		16 08			16 13	16 30		16 42					16 46	
	d	15 08		15 14			15 42			15 47	15 51	←	16 08			16 14	16 30		16 43					16 47	←
Wakefield Kirkgate 4	32, 34, 39 a					15 29		15 51				15 51						16 27			16 51				16 51
	d					15 29		→				15 52						16 27			→				16 52
Outwood	d	15 13					15 47						16 13						16 50						
Leeds 10	32, 34 a	15 30		15 35		15 50	16 02			16 02	16 09	16 27	16 30			16 35	16 48	16 50	17 02					17 02	17 27

		NT	GR	NT	GR	NT	NT	XC	NT		GR	NT	NT	NT	NT	GR	NT	NT		XC	NT	GR	NT	NT	GR
			R 1		R 1			R 1			R 1					R 1				R 1		R 1			R 1
			B		B			J			B			A		B				E		B			K
			☕ 🍴		☕ 🍴			☕								☕ 🍴				☕		☕ 🍴			☕ 🍴
Sheffield 7	29 🚊 d			16 51		17 08	17 14	17 21							17 51		18 08	18 14		18 21					
Meadowhall	29 🚊 d			16 57		17 14	17 21								17 57		18 14	18 21							
Rotherham Central	29 d						17 27											18 27							
Swinton (S.Yorks)	29 d						17 36											18 36							
Bolton-on-Dearne	d	←					17 41						←					18 41						←	
Goldthorpe	d	16 43					17 43						17 43					18 43						18 43	
Thurnscoe	d	16 46					→						17 46					→						18 46	
Moorthorpe	d	16 51											17 51											18 51	
Doncaster 7	d		17 01		17 19				17 27					17 38		18 19					18 27	18 43			19 17
Bentley (S.Yorks)	d								17 30					17 41							18 30				
Adwick	a								17 34					17 47							18 34				
	d								17 34												18 34				
South Elmsall	d								17 40												18 40				
Fitzwilliam	d	16 57							17 45				18 02								18 46			19 01	
Sandal & Agbrigg	d	17 03							17 51				18 08								18 51			19 07	
Wakefield Westgate 7	32, 39 a	17 07	17 18		17 36			17 46	17 55				18 12			18 36				18 46	18 55	19 01		19 12	19 34
	d	17 08	17 18		17 36			17 47	17 55		18 04	←	18 13			18 36				18 47	18 56	19 01	←	19 12	19 34
Wakefield Kirkgate 4	32, 34, 39 a			17 29		17 51						17 51			18 36		18 51						18 51		
	d			17 29		→						17 52			18 36		→						18 52		
Outwood	d	17 13							18 00				18 18								19 00			19 17	
Leeds 10	32, 34 a	17 30	17 36	17 50	17 56			18 02	18 15		18 23	18 27	18 33		18 55	18 55				19 02	19 15	19 21	19 27	19 33	19 53

For general notes see front of timetable
For details of catering facilities see Directory of Train Operators

A From Lincoln (Table 30)
B From London Kings Cross (Table 26)
C From Plymouth to Edinburgh (Table 51)
D To York (Table 33)
E From Bournemouth to Edinburgh (Table 51)
G From Penzance (Table 135) to Dundee (Table 229)
H From Bournemouth to Glasgow Central (Table 51)
J From Plymouth to Glasgow Central (Table 51)
K From London Kings Cross to Bradford Forster Square (Table 26)

Table 31

Mondays to Fridays
until 5 September

Sheffield, Doncaster and Wakefield → Leeds

Network Diagram - see first page of Table 31

Station		NT	NT	EM	NT		XC	NT	GR	GR	NT	NT	NT	GR		NT	XC	NT	EM	NT	NT	GR	NT		GR
				1 ◇ A B			R 1 C		R 1 D	R 1 E				R 1 D			R 1 G		1 ◇ A			R 1 D			R 1 D
Sheffield 7	29 d	18 51	19 08	19 15	19 18		19 26						19 51			20 08	20 21	20 27	20 35						
Meadowhall	29 d	18 57	19 14		19 25								19 57			20 14		20 35							
Rotherham Central	29 d				19 31													20 41							
Swinton (S.Yorks)	29 d				19 40													20 50							
Bolton-on-Dearne	d				19 44							←						20 55					←		
Goldthorpe	d				19 47 →							19 47						20 57 →					20 57		
Thurnscoe	d											19 50											21 00		
Moorthorpe	d											19 55											21 05		
Doncaster 7	d							19 29	19 42	19 47				20 19						20 38		20 50			21 20
Bentley (S.Yorks)	d							19 32												20 41					
Adwick	a							19 36												20 45					
	d							19 36												20 45					
South Elmsall	d							19 42												20 51					
Fitzwilliam	d							19 48				20 04								21 01			21 11		
Sandal & Agbrigg	d							19 53				20 10								21 06			21 17		
Wakefield Westgate 7	32, 39 a			19 44			19 49	19 57	20 01	20 06		20 14		20 38			20 53		21 01	21 10		21 14	21 22		21 37
	d			19 44			19 50	19 58	20 01	20 06	←	20 15		20 38			20 54		21 01	21 11	←	21 14	21 22		21 37
Wakefield Kirkgate 4	32, 34, 39 a	19 36	19 51 →								19 51		20 28			20 51 →					20 51				
	d	19 36									19 52		20 29								20 52				
Outwood	d							20 02				20 20								21 15			21 27		
Leeds 10	32, 34 a	19 57		20 06			20 06	20 17	20 21	20 25	20 27	20 37	20 50	20 54			21 09		21 21	21 27	21 27	21 34	21 47		21 56

Station		EM	NT	XC	NT	NT	GR	NT	EM		GR	NT FX	NT	XC	NT	NT FX	NT FO	NT		GR	NT FX	NT FO	NT FX		
		1 ◇ A		1 ◇ H			R 1 D		1 ◇ A		R 1 D			1 ◇ J						R 1 D					
Sheffield 7	29 d	21 00	21 08	21 21				21 31	21 51			22 08	22 15	22 21							23 15	23 15	23 24		
Meadowhall	29 d		21 14					21 37				22 14	22 21								23 21	23 21	23 30		
Rotherham Central	29 d							21 43					22 27								23 27	23 27			
Swinton (S.Yorks)	29 d							21 51					22 36								23 36	23 36			
Bolton-on-Dearne	d							21 55					22 41					←			23 41	23 41			
Goldthorpe	d							21 58					22 43 →					22 43			23 44	23 44			
Thurnscoe	d							22 01										22 46			23 47	23 47			
Moorthorpe	d							22 06										22 51			23 52	23 52			
Doncaster 7	d	21 27				21 38	21 53		22 13		22 18				22 30					23 24					
Bentley (S.Yorks)	d					21 41									22 33										
Adwick	a					21 45									22 37										
	d					21 45									22 37										
South Elmsall	d					21 51									22 43										
Fitzwilliam	d					21 58		22 12							22 48			22 57							
Sandal & Agbrigg	d					22 04		22 18							22 54			23 03							
Wakefield Westgate 7	32, 39 a	21 44		21 49		22 08	22 13	22 22	22 30		22 34			22s46	22 58			23 07		23 42	00 09		00 17		
	d	21 44		21 50	←	22 09	22 13	22 23	22 30		22 35				22 58	←		23 08		23 42	00 10				
Wakefield Kirkgate 4	32, 34, 39 a		21 51 →		21 51							22 51 →				22 51							00s10		
	d				21 52											22 52	22 52								
Outwood	d					22 14		22 28							23 03			23 13							
Leeds 10	32, 34 a	22 05		22 05	22 27	22 28	22 33	22 46	22 50		22 53			23 05	23 18	23 27	23 27	23 30		23 59	00 30	00 30			

Mondays to Fridays
from 8 September

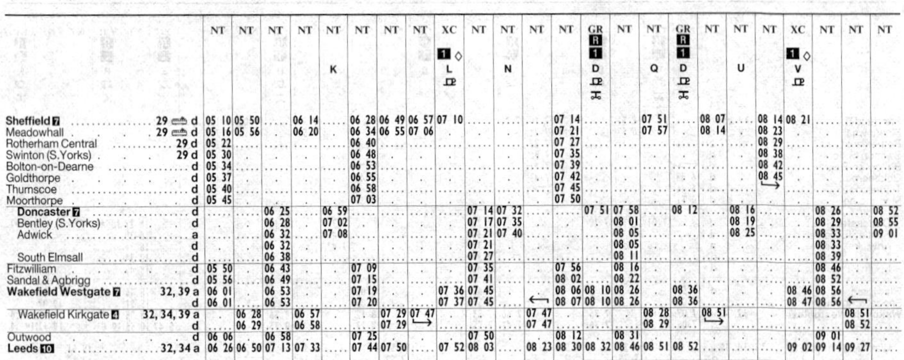

Station		NT	NT	NT	NT	NT	NT	NT	NT	XC	NT	NT	NT	NT	GR	NT	NT	GR	NT	NT	NT	XC	NT	NT	NT
						K				1 ◇ L		N			R 1 D		Q	R 1 D		U		1 ◇ V			
Sheffield 7	29 d	05 10	05 50		06 14		06 28	06 49	06 57	07 10				07 14			07 51		08 07		08 14	08 21			
Meadowhall	29 d	05 16	05 56		06 20		06 34	06 55	07 06					07 21			07 57		08 14		08 23				
Rotherham Central	29 d	05 22					06 40							07 27							08 29				
Swinton (S.Yorks)	29 d	05 30					06 48							07 35							08 38				
Bolton-on-Dearne	d	05 34					06 53							07 39							08 42				
Goldthorpe	d	05 37					06 55							07 42							08 45 →				
Thurnscoe	d	05 40					06 58							07 45											
Moorthorpe	d	05 45					07 03							07 50											
Doncaster 7	d			06 25		06 59					07 14	07 32			07 51	07 58		08 12		08 16			08 26		08 52
Bentley (S.Yorks)	d			06 28		07 02					07 17	07 35				08 01				08 19			08 29		08 55
Adwick	a			06 32		07 08					07 21	07 40				08 05				08 25			08 33		09 01
	d			06 32							07 21					08 05							08 33		
South Elmsall	d			06 38							07 27					08 11							08 39		
Fitzwilliam	d	05 50		06 43			07 09				07 35			07 56		08 16							08 46		
Sandal & Agbrigg	d	05 56		06 49			07 15				07 41			08 02		08 22							08 52		
Wakefield Westgate 7	32, 39 a	06 01		06 53			07 19			07 36	07 45			08 06	08 10	08 26		08 36				08 46	08 56		
	d	06 01		06 53			07 20			07 37	07 45		←	08 07	08 10	08 26		08 36				08 47	08 56	←	
Wakefield Kirkgate 4	32, 34, 39 a		06 28		06 57			07 29	07 47 →				07 47				08 28		08 51 →					08 51	
	d		06 29		06 58			07 29					07 47				08 29							08 52	
Outwood	d	06 06		06 58			07 25				07 50			08 12		08 31							09 01		
Leeds 10	32, 34 a	06 26	06 50	07 13	07 33		07 44	07 50		07 52	08 03		08 23	08 30	08 32	08 46	08 51	08 52				09 02	09 14	09 27	

For general notes see front of timetable
For details of catering facilities see Directory of Train Operators

- **A** From St Pancras International (Table 53)
- **B** **The Master Cutler**
- **C** From Plymouth to Edinburgh (Table 51)
- **D** From London Kings Cross (Table 26)
- **E** From London Kings Cross to Skipton (Table 26)
- **G** From Bournemouth to Newcastle (Table 51)
- **H** From Plymouth to York (Table 51)
- **J** From Bournemouth to Birmingham New Street (Table 51)
- **K** From Sheffield (Table 29)
- **L** To Edinburgh (Table 26)
- **N** From Meadowhall (Table 29)
- **Q** From Retford (Table 30)
- **U** From Scunthorpe (Table 29)
- **V** From Birmingham New Street to Edinburgh (Table 51)

Sheffield, Doncaster and Wakefield → Leeds

Network Diagram - see first page of Table 31

	NT	GR	GR	NT	NT	NT	XC	GR	NT	NT	NT	NT	NT	NT	NT	GR	GR	NT	XC	NT	NT	NT	GR	NT
		R 1	R 1				1 ◇	R 1								R 1	R 1		1 ◇				R 1	
		A	A				B	A			C		D 🚌			A	A		E		G		A	
		☕ ⚲					☕									🍴 ⚲	🍴 ⚲		☕				☕ ⚲	
Sheffield 7 — 29 d					09 05	09 14	09 21							10 08	10 14				10 21			10 51		11 08
Meadowhall — 29 d					09 14	09 21							*09 31*	10 14	10 21							10 57		11 14
Rotherham Central — 29 d						09 27							*09 37*		10 27									
Swinton (S.Yorks) — 29 d						09 36							09 55		10 36									
Bolton-on-Dearne d	←					09 41				←					10 41					←				
Goldthorpe d	08 45					09 43				09 43					10 43					10 43				
Thurnscoe d	08 48					→				09 46					→					10 46				
Moorthorpe d	08 53									09 53			10a25							10 51				
Doncaster 7 d		08 58		09 14							09 49	10 14				10 28					10 44		11 19	
Bentley (S.Yorks) d				09 17							09 52	10 17									10 47			
Adwick a				09 21							09 58	10 21									10 53			
d				09 21								10 21												
South Elmsall d				09 27								10 27												
Fitzwilliam d	08 59			09 32						10 00		10 32								10 57				
Sandal & Agbrigg d	09 05			09 38						10 06		10 38								11 03				
Wakefield Westgate 7 — 32, 39 a	09 09	09 16		09 42			09 46			10 10		10 42				10 51			10 46	11 07			11 36	
d	09 09	09 16	09 27	09 42			09 47	10 01	←	10 11		10 42				10 51	10 56	←	10 47	11 08			11 36	
Wakefield Kirkgate 4 — 32, 34, 39 a					09 51				09 51					10 51				10 51				11 29		11 51
d					→				09 52					→				10 52				11 29		→
Outwood d	09 14			09 47						10 16		10 47								11 13				
Leeds 10 — 32, 34 a	09 30	09 36	09 46	10 02			10 02	10 21	10 27	10 30		11 02				11 09	11 18	11 27	11 02	11 30		11 50	11 55	

	NT	XC	NT	NT	NT	NT	GR	NT	GR	NT	NT	XC	NT	NT	NT	NT	GR	NT	GR	NT	NT	XC	NT	NT
		1 ◇					R 1		R 1			1 ◇					R 1		R 1			1 ◇		
		H				G	A		A			J				G	A		A			E		
		☕					☕ ⚲		☕ ⚲			☕					☕ ⚲					☕		
Sheffield 7 — 29 d	11 14	11 21						11 51		12 08	12 14	12 21						12 51		13 08	13 14	13 21		
Meadowhall — 29 d	11 21							11 57		12 14	12 21							12 57		13 14	13 21			
Rotherham Central — 29 d	11 27										12 27										13 27			
Swinton (S.Yorks) — 29 d	11 36										12 36										13 36			
Bolton-on-Dearne d	11 41				←						12 41				←						13 41			
Goldthorpe d	11 43				11 43						12 43				12 43						13 43			
Thurnscoe d	→				11 46						→				12 46						→			
Moorthorpe d					11 51										12 51									
Doncaster 7 d			11 26			11 38	11 58		12 19				12 25			12 36	12 57						13 27	
Bentley (S.Yorks) d			11 29			11 41							12 28			12 40							13 30	
Adwick a			11 33			11 47							12 32			12 45							13 34	
d			11 33										12 32										13 34	
South Elmsall d			11 39										12 38										13 40	
Fitzwilliam d			11 44		11 57								12 43		12 57								13 45	
Sandal & Agbrigg d			11 50		12 03								12 49		13 03								13 51	
Wakefield Westgate 7 — 32, 39 a		11 46	11 54		12 07		12 15		12 36			12 46	12 53		13 07		13 17					13 46	13 55	
d		11 47	11 54	←	12 08		12 15		12 36			12 47	12 53	←	13 08		13 17		13 37			13 47	13 55	←
Wakefield Kirkgate 4 — 32, 34, 39 a				11 51				12 29		12 51				12 51				13 29		13 51				13 51
d				11 52				12 29		→				12 52				13 29		→				13 52
Outwood d			11 59		12 13								12 58		13 13								14 00	
Leeds 10 — 32, 34 a		12 02	12 14	12 27	12 30		12 35	12 50	12 54			13 02	13 13	13 27	13 33		13 41	13 50	13 55			14 02	14 14	14 27

	NT	NT	GR	NT	NT	GR	NT	NT	XC	NT	NT	NT	NT	GR	NT	NT	NT	NT	XC	GR	NT	NT	NT	GR
			R 1			R 1			1 ◇					R 1					1 ◇	R 1				R 1
		G	A	D 🚌		A			E				G	A					K	A			G	A
			☕ ⚲			☕ ⚲			☕					☕ ⚲					☕	☕ ⚲				☕ ⚲
Sheffield 7 — 29 d					13 51		14 08	14 14	14 21						14 51		15 08	15 14	15 21					
Meadowhall — 29 d				*13 31*	13 57		14 14	14 21							14 57		15 14	15 21						
Rotherham Central — 29 d				*13 37*				14 27										15 27						
Swinton (S.Yorks) — 29 d				13 55				14 36										15 36						
Bolton-on-Dearne d	←							14 41				←						15 38				←		
Goldthorpe d	13 43							14 43				14 43						15 43				15 43		
Thurnscoe d	13 46							→				14 46						→				15 46		
Moorthorpe d	13 51			14a25								14 51										15 51		
Doncaster 7 d		13 38	13 57			14 21				14 27			14 38	14 53		15 14				15 29			15 38	15 55
Bentley (S.Yorks) d		13 41								14 30			14 41			15 17							15 41	
Adwick a		13 47								14 34			14 47			15 21							15 47	
d										14 34						15 21								
South Elmsall d										14 40						15 27								
Fitzwilliam d	13 57									14 45		14 57				15 32						15 57		
Sandal & Agbrigg d	14 03									14 51		15 03				15 38						16 03		
Wakefield Westgate 7 — 32, 39 a	14 07		14 14			14 39			14 46	14 55		15 07		15 14		15 42			15 46			16 08		16 13
d	14 08		14 14			14 39			14 47	14 55	←	15 08		15 14		15 42			15 47	15 51	←	16 08		16 14
Wakefield Kirkgate 4 — 32, 34, 39 a					14 28		14 51				14 51				15 29		15 51				15 51			
d					14 29		→				14 52				15 29		→				15 52			
Outwood d	14 13									15 00		15 13				15 47						16 13		
Leeds 10 — 32, 34 a	14 30		14 35		14 50	15 01			15 02	15 15	15 27	15 30		15 35	15 50	16 02			16 02	16 09	16 27	16 30		16 35

For general notes see front of timetable
For details of catering facilities see Directory of Train Operators

A From London Kings Cross (Table 26)
B From Birmingham New Street to Edinburgh (Table 51)
C From Worksop (Table 30)
D To York (Table 33)
E From Bristol Temple Meads to Edinburgh (Table 51)
G From Lincoln (Table 30)
H From Cardiff Central to Edinburgh (Table 51)
J From Plymouth (Table 51) to Aberdeen (Table 229)
K From Paignton (Table 51) to Dundee (Table 229)

Sheffield, Doncaster and Wakefield → Leeds

Network Diagram - see first page of Table 31

		GR R 1 A	NT	NT	NT	NT	XC R 1 B	NT	NT	NT C	GR R 1 A	NT	GR R 1 A	NT	NT	XC R 1 D	NT	GR R 1 A	NT	NT	NT C	NT	GR R 1 A	NT	NT
Sheffield 7	29 d		15 51		16 08	16 14	16 21					16 51		17 08	17 14	17 21						17 51		18 08	18 14
Meadowhall	29 d		15 57		16 14	16 21						16 57		17 14	17 21							18 00		18 14	18 21
Rotherham Central	29 d					16 27									17 27										18 27
Swinton (S.Yorks)	29 d					16 36									17 36										18 36
Bolton-on-Dearne	d					16 41			←						17 41					←					18 41
Goldthorpe	d					16 43 →			16 43						17 43 →					17 43					18 43 →
Thurnscoe	d								16 46											17 46					
Moorthorpe	d								16 51											17 51					
Doncaster 7	d	16 10		16 14						16 38	17 01		17 19				17 27				17 38		18 19		
Bentley (S.Yorks)	d			16 17						16 41							17 30				17 41				
Adwick	a			16 21						16 47							17 34				17 47				
	d			16 21													17 34								
South Elmsall	d			16 27													17 40								
Fitzwilliam	d			16 32					16 57								17 45			18 02					
Sandal & Agbrigg	d			16 38					17 03								17 51			18 08					
Wakefield Westgate 7	32, 39 a	16 30		16 42			16 46		17 07		17 18		17 36			17 46	17 55			18 12			18 36		
	d	16 30		16 43			16 47	←	17 08		17 18		17 36			17 47	17 55	18 04	←	18 13			18 36		
Wakefield Kirkgate 4	32, 34, 39 a		16 27		16 51 →			16 51				17 29		17 51 →					17 51			18 36		18 51 →	
	d		16 27					16 52				17 29							17 52			18 36			
Outwood	d			16 50					17 13								18 00			18 18					
Leeds 10	32, 34 a	16 48	16 50	17 02			17 02	17 27	17 30		17 36	17 50	17 56			18 02	18 15	18 23	18 27	18 33		18 55	18 55		

		XC R 1 E	NT	GR R 1 A	NT	NT	GR R 1 G	NT	NT	NT	XC R 1 H	NT	GR R 1 A	GR R 1 J	NT	NT	NT	EM 1 ◊ K L	GR R 1 A	NT	XC R 1 N	NT	NT	GR R 1 A	NT
Sheffield 7	29 d	18 21						18 51	19 08		19 21						19 53	19 55		20 08	20 21				20 27
Meadowhall	29 d							18 57	19 14	19 25							19 59			20 14					20 35
Rotherham Central	29 d									19 31															20 41
Swinton (S.Yorks)	29 d									19 40															20 50
Bolton-on-Dearne	d					←				19 44						←									20 55
Goldthorpe	d					18 43				19 47 →						19 47									20 57
Thurnscoe	d					18 46										19 50									21 00
Moorthorpe	d					18 51										19 55									21 05
Doncaster 7	d		18 27	18 43			19 17					19 29	19 42	19 47					20 19			20 38		20 50	
Bentley (S.Yorks)	d		18 30									19 32										20 41			
Adwick	a		18 34									19 36										20 45			
	d		18 34									19 36										20 45			
South Elmsall	d		18 40									19 42										20 51			
Fitzwilliam	d		18 46			19 01						19 48				20 04						21 01			21 11
Sandal & Agbrigg	d		18 51			19 07						19 53				20 10						21 06			21 17
Wakefield Westgate 7	32, 39 a	18 46	18 55	19 01		19 12	19 34				19 49	19 57	20 01	20 06		20 14		20 30	20 38		20 53	21 10		21 14	21 21
	d	18 47	18 56	19 01	←	19 12	19 34				19 50	19 58	20 01	20 06	←	20 15		20 30	20 38		20 54	21 11	←	21 14	21 22
Wakefield Kirkgate 4	32, 34, 39 a				18 51			19 36	19 51 →						19 51		20 29			20 51 →			20 51		
	d				18 52			19 36							19 52		20 29						20 52		
Outwood	d		19 00			19 17						20 02				20 20						21 15			21 27
Leeds 10	32, 34 a	19 02	19 15	19 21	19 27	19 33	19 53	19 56			20 06	20 17	20 21	20 25	20 27	20 37	20 50	20 52	20 54		21 09	21 27	21 27	21 34	21 46

		EM 1 ◊ K	GR R 1 A	NT	XC 1 ◊ Q	NT	NT	GR R 1 A	NT	EM 1 ◊ K	NT	GR R 1 A	NT FX	NT	EM 1 ◊ K	NT	NT FX	NT FO	NT	XC 1 ◊ U	GR R 1 A	NT FX	NT FO	NT FX
Sheffield 7	29 d	20 57		21 06	21 21				21 30	21 33			22 08	22 15	22 19					22 46		23 15	23 15	23 24
Meadowhall	29 d			21 14					21 36				22 14	22 21								23 21	23 21	23 30
Rotherham Central	29 d								21 43					22 27								23 27	23 27	
Swinton (S.Yorks)	29 d								21 51					22 36								23 36	23 36	
Bolton-on-Dearne	d								21 55		←			22 41					←			23 41	23 41	
Goldthorpe	d								21 58 →		21 58			22 43 →					22 43			23 44	23 44	
Thurnscoe	d										22 01								22 46			23 47	23 47	
Moorthorpe	d										22 06								22 51			23 52	23 52	
Doncaster 7	d		21 20				21 38	21 53		21 58		22 18				22 30					23 24			
Bentley (S.Yorks)	d						21 41									22 33								
Adwick	a						21 45									22 37								
	d						21 45									22 37								
South Elmsall	d						21 51									22 43								
Fitzwilliam	d						21 58				22 14					22 48			22 57					
Sandal & Agbrigg	d						22 04				22 20					22 54			23 03					
Wakefield Westgate 7	32, 39 a	21 26	21 37		21 49		22 08	22 13		22 17	22 24	22 34			22 46	22 58			23 07	23s17	23 42	00 09		00 17
	d	21 28	21 37		21 50	←	22 09	22 13		22 19	22 25	22 35			22 46	22 58	←		23 08		23 42	00 10		
Wakefield Kirkgate 4	32, 34, 39 a			21 51 →		21 51							22 51 →				22 51							00s10
	d					21 52											22 52	22 52						
Outwood	d						22 14				22 31					23 03			23 13					
Leeds 10	32, 34 a	21 52	21 56		22 05	22 27	22 28	22 33		22 40	22 47	22 53			23 07	23 18	23 27	23 27	23 30	23 39	23 59	00 30	00 30	

For general notes see front of timetable
For details of catering facilities see Directory of Train Operators

A From London Kings Cross (Table 26)
B From Bristol Temple Meads to Glasgow Central (Table 51)
C From Lincoln (Table 30)
D From Plymouth to Glasgow Central (Table 51)
E From Bristol Temple Meads to Edinburgh (Table 51)
G From London Kings Cross to Bradford Forster Square (Table 26)
H From Paignton to Edinburgh (Table 51)
J From London Kings Cross to Skipton (Table 26)
K From St Pancras International (Table 53)
L **The Master Cutler**
N From Bristol Temple Meads to Newcastle (Table 51)
Q From Paignton to York (Table 51)
U From Bournemouth (Table 51)

Table 31

Saturdays

until 6 September

Sheffield, Doncaster and Wakefield → Leeds

Network Diagram - see first page of Table 31

	NT	NT	NT	NT	NT	NT	XC	NT	NT	NT	NT	NT	NT	NT	XC	NT	NT	NT	NT	GR	NT	NT	NT	NT
			A		A		1 ◇ B				C		D		1 ◇ B					R 1 E				
Sheffield 7 29 d		06 14		06 28		07 08	07 12			07 14	07 51	08 08		08 14	08 21						08 51		09 08	09 14
Meadowhall 29 d		06 20		06 34		07 14				07 21	07 57	08 14		08 23							08 57		09 14	09 21
Rotherham Central 29 d				06 40						07 27				08 29										09 27
Swinton (S.Yorks) 29 d				06 48						07 35				08 38										09 36
Bolton-on-Dearne d				06 52						07 39				08 42					←					09 41
Goldthorpe d				06 55						07 42				08 45					08 45					09 43
Thurnscoe d				06 58						07 45				→					08 48					→
Moorthorpe d				07 03						07 50									08 53					
Doncaster 7 d	06 25		07 00		07 32			07 14					08 16			08 26		08 50		08 58		09 14		
Bentley (S.Yorks) d	06 28		07 03		07 35			07 17					08 19			08 29		08 53				09 17		
Adwick a	06 32		07 09		07 41			07 21					08 25			08 33		08 59				09 21		
d	06 32							07 21								08 33						09 21		
South Elmsall d	06 38							07 27								08 39						09 27		
Fitzwilliam d	06 43			07 09				07 35		07 56						08 46			08 59			09 32		
Sandal & Agbrigg d	06 49			07 15				07 41		08 02						08 52			09 05			09 38		
Wakefield Westgate 7 32, 39 a	06 53			07 19			07 36	07 45		08 06					08 46	08 56			09 09	09 15		09 42		
d	06 53			07 19			07 37	07 45	←	08 07					08 47	08 56	←		09 09	09 15		09 42		
Wakefield Kirkgate 4 32, 34, 39 a		06 57				07 51			07 51		08 28	08 51					08 51				09 29		09 51	
d		06 58				→			07 51		08 29	→					08 52				09 29		→	
Outwood d	06 58			07 24				07 50		08 12						09 01			09 14			09 47		
Leeds 10 32, 34 a	07 15	07 33		07 44			07 52	08 04	08 27	08 30	08 51				09 02	09 14	09 27		09 30	09 35	09 50	10 02		

	XC	NT	NT	NT	GR	NT	NT	NT	NT	NT	XC	NT	NT	NT	GR	NT	NT	NT	NT	XC	NT	NT	GR	NT
	1 ◇ G			A	R 1 E	H					1 ◇ J			K	R 1 E					1 ◇ L		K	R 1 E	
Sheffield 7 29 d	09 21					09 31	09 51		10 08	10 14	10 21					10 51		11 08	11 14	11 21				11 51
Meadowhall 29 d						09 37	09 57		10 14	10 21						10 57		11 14	11 21					11 57
Rotherham Central 29 d						09 44				10 27									11 27					
Swinton (S.Yorks) 29 d						09 52				10 36									11 36					
Bolton-on-Dearne d			←							10 41			←						11 41					
Goldthorpe d			09 43							10 43			10 43						11 43					
Thurnscoe d			09 46							→			10 46						→					
Moorthorpe d			09 51			10a01							10 51											
Doncaster 7 d				09 37	09 57			10 14						10 37	10 48		11 14					11 38	11 54	
Bentley (S.Yorks) d				09 44				10 17						10 41			11 17					11 41		
Adwick a				09 50				10 21						10 47			11 21					11 47		
d								10 21									11 21							
South Elmsall d								10 27									11 27							
Fitzwilliam d			09 57					10 32					10 57				11 32							
Sandal & Agbrigg d			10 03					10 38					11 03				11 38							
Wakefield Westgate 7 32, 39 a	09 46		10 07		10 14			10 42			10 46		11 07		11 11		11 42			11 46			12 13	
d	09 47	←	10 08		10 16			10 42			10 47	←	11 08		11 13		11 42			11 47	←		12 13	
Wakefield Kirkgate 4 32, 34, 39 a		09 51					10 29		10 51			10 51				11 29		11 51			11 51			12 29
d		09 52					10 29		→			10 52				11 29		→			11 52			12 29
Outwood d			10 13					10 47					11 13				11 47							
Leeds 10 32, 34 a	10 02	10 27	10 30		10 35		10 50	11 02			11 02	11 27	11 30		11 35	11 50	12 02			12 02	12 27		12 35	12 50

	NT	NT	NT	XC	NT	NT	NT	GR	NT	NT	NT	NT	XC	NT	NT	NT	GR	NT	NT	NT	NT	NT	XC	NT
				R 1 N			K	R 1 E					1 ◇ L			K	R 1 E	H					1 ◇ Q	
Sheffield 7 29 d		12 08	12 14	12 21					12 51		13 08	13 14	13 21					13 28	13 51		14 08	14 14	14 21	
Meadowhall 29 d		12 14	12 21						12 57		13 14	13 21						13 35	13 57		14 14	14 21		
Rotherham Central 29 d			12 27									13 27						13 42				14 27		
Swinton (S.Yorks) 29 d			12 36									13 36						13 50				14 36		
Bolton-on-Dearne d			12 41			←						13 41			←							14 41		
Goldthorpe d			12 43			12 43						13 43			13 43							14 43		
Thurnscoe d			→			12 46						→			13 46							→		
Moorthorpe d						12 51									13 51			14a00						
Doncaster 7 d	12 14						12 36	12 59		13 14						13 38	13 53			14 14				
Bentley (S.Yorks) d	12 17						12 40			13 17						13 41				14 17				
Adwick a	12 21						12 45			13 21						13 47				14 21				
d	12 21									13 21										14 21				
South Elmsall d	12 27									13 27										14 27				
Fitzwilliam d	12 32					12 57				13 32					13 57					14 32				
Sandal & Agbrigg d	12 38					13 03				13 38					14 03					14 38				
Wakefield Westgate 7 32, 39 a	12 42			12 46		13 07		13 16		13 42			13 46		14 07		14 13			14 42			14 46	
d	12 42			12 47	←	13 08		13 16		13 42			13 47	←	14 08		14 13			14 42			14 47	←
Wakefield Kirkgate 4 32, 34, 39 a		12 51			12 51				13 29		13 51			13 51					14 28		14 51			14 51
d		→			12 52				13 29		→			13 52					14 29		→			14 52
Outwood d	12 47					13 13				13 47					14 13					14 47				
Leeds 10 32, 34 a	13 02			13 02	13 27	13 33		13 35	13 50	14 02			14 02	14 27	14 30		14 35		14 50	15 02			15 02	15 27

For general notes see front of timetable
For details of catering facilities see Directory of Train Operators

- **A** From Sheffield (Table 29)
- **B** From Birmingham New Street (Table 51) to Edinburgh (Table 26)
- **C** From Retford (Table 30)
- **D** From Scunthorpe (Table 29)
- **E** From London Kings Cross (Table 26)
- **G** From Bristol Temple Meads to Edinburgh (Table 51)
- **H** To York (Table 33)
- **J** From Southampton Central to Edinburgh (Table 51)
- **K** From Lincoln (Table 30)
- **L** From Plymouth to Edinburgh (Table 51)
- **N** From Bournemouth to Aberdeen (Table 51)
- **Q** From Bournemouth to Edinburgh (Table 51)

Due to Engineering Operations in the Sheffield area, services from Saturday 13 September on this Table had not been confirmed at time of going to press. These services will be issued in a special Supplement as soon as exact timings have been confirmed.

Saturdays
until 6 September

Sheffield, Doncaster and Wakefield → Leeds

Network Diagram - see first page of Table 31

		NT	NT	GR	NT	NT	NT	NT	XC	NT	NT	NT	NT	GR	NT	NT	XC	NT	NT	NT	NT	NT	GR	NT	NT
				R 1					R 1					R 1			R 1						R 1		
			A	B					C			A		B			D				A		B		
Sheffield [7]	29 d				14 51		15 08	15 14	15 21				15 51		16 08	16 14	16 21					16 51		17 08	17 14
Meadowhall	29 d				14 57		15 14	15 21					15 57		16 14	16 21						16 57		17 14	17 21
Rotherham Central	29 d							15 27								16 27									17 27
Swinton (S.Yorks)	29 d							15 36								16 36									17 36
Bolton-on-Dearne	d	←						15 41			←					16 41				←					17 41
Goldthorpe	d	14 43						15 43 →			15 43					16 43 →				16 43					17 43 →
Thurnscoe	d	14 46									15 46									16 46					
Moorthorpe	d	14 51									15 51									16 51					
Doncaster [7]	d		14 38	14 58		15 14						15 38		16 21				16 28			16 38		17 16		
Bentley (S.Yorks)	d		14 41			15 17						15 41						16 31			16 41				
Adwick	a		14 47			15 21						15 47						16 35			16 47				
	d					15 21												16 35							
South Elmsall	d					15 27												16 41							
Fitzwilliam	d	14 57				15 32					15 57							16 47		16 57					
Sandal & Agbrigg	d	15 03				15 38					16 03							16 53		17 03					
Wakefield Westgate [7]	32, 39 a	15 07		15 15		15 42			15 46		16 08			16 38			16 46	16 57		17 07			17 33		
	d	15 08		15 15		15 42			15 47	←	16 08			16 38			16 47	16 57	←	17 08			17 33		
Wakefield Kirkgate [4]	32, 34, 39 a				15 29		15 51			15 51			16 27		16 51				16 51			17 29		17 51	
	d				15 29		→			15 52			16 27		→				16 52			17 29		→	
Outwood	d	15 13				15 47					16 13							17 02		17 13					
Leeds [10]	32, 34 a	15 30		15 35	15 50	16 02			16 02	16 27	16 30		16 50	17 01			17 02	17 16	17 27	17 30		17 50	17 53		

		XC	NT	NT	NT	NT	GR	NT	NT	NT	XC	NT	NT	NT	GR	NT	EM	NT	NT	XC	NT	EM	GR	NT	NT
		R 1					R 1				1 ◇				R 1		1 ◇			R 1		1 ◇	R 1		
		E				A	B				G				H		J			K		J	B		
Sheffield [7]	29 d	17 21						17 51	18 08	18 14	18 21					18 51	19 04	19 08	19 14	19 21					
Meadowhall	29 d							17 57	18 14	18 21						18 57		19 14	19 21						
Rotherham Central	29 d									18 27									19 27						
Swinton (S.Yorks)	29 d									18 36									19 40						
Bolton-on-Dearne	d				←					18 41				←					19 44						←
Goldthorpe	d				17 43					18 43				18 43					19 47						19 47
Thurnscoe	d				17 46					→				18 46					→						19 50
Moorthorpe	d				17 51									18 51								←			19 55
Doncaster [7]	d		17 27			17 38	18 18					18 29			19 18		19 31				19 27	19 31			
Bentley (S.Yorks)	d		17 30			17 41						18 32					→				19 30				
Adwick	a		17 34			17 47						18 36									19 34				
	d		17 34									18 36									19 34				
South Elmsall	d		17 40									18 42									19 40				
Fitzwilliam	d		17 45		17 57							18 47		18 57							19 45				20 01
Sandal & Agbrigg	d		17 51		18 03							18 53		19 03							19 55				20 07
Wakefield Westgate [7]	32, 39 a	17 46	17 55		18 07		18 35				18 46	18 57		19 07	19 35					19 46	19 55	19 59			20 11
	d	17 47	17 55	←	18 08		18 35				18 47	18 57	←	19 08	19 35					19 47		19 59	20 03	←	20 11
Wakefield Kirkgate [4]	32, 34, 39 a			17 51				18 36	18 51				18 51			19 36		19 51						19 51	
	d			17 52				18 36	→				18 52			19 36		→						19 52	
Outwood	d		18 00		18 13							19 02		19 13							20 00				20 16
Leeds [10]	32, 34 a	18 02	18 15	18 27	18 30		18 53	18 55			19 02	19 17	19 27	19 31	19 52	19 57				20 02	20 13	20 22	20 22	20 27	20 32

		GR	NT	NT	EM	XC	EM	NT	NT	NT	EM	NT	XC	NT	GR	NT	NT	EM	GR	XC	NT	NT	NT		
		R 1			1 ◇	1 ◇	1 ◇				1 ◇		R 1		R 1			1 ◇	R 1	1 ◇					
		L			J	N	J				J		Q		B			J	U	V					
Sheffield [7]	29 d		19 51	20 08	20 11	20 21				20 31	20 51	21 08	21 21				21 26	21 57		22 21			22 31		
Meadowhall	29 d		19 57	20 14						20 37		21 14					21 32						22 37		
Rotherham Central	29 d									20 43							21 38						22 43		
Swinton (S.Yorks)	29 d									20 50							21 48						22 51		
Bolton-on-Dearne	d									20 55							21 52						22 55		
Goldthorpe	d									20 57							21 55						22 58		
Thurnscoe	d									21 00							21 58						23 01		
Moorthorpe	d						←			21 05							22 03						23 06		
Doncaster [7]	d	20 02			20 36		20 36		20 45		21 15			21 28	21 48			22 22	22 25			22 49			
Bentley (S.Yorks)	d				→				20 48					21 31								22 52			
Adwick	a								20 52					21 35								22 56			
	d								20 52					21 35								22 56			
South Elmsall	d								20 58					21 41								23 02			
Fitzwilliam	d								21 03	21 11				21 48			22 09					23 07	23 12		
Sandal & Agbrigg	d								21 09	21 17				21 53			22 15					23 13	23 18		
Wakefield Westgate [7]	32, 39 a	20 19				20 48	20 53		21 13	21 22	21 34		21 46	21 57	22 05		22 19	22 39	22 43	22s46		23 17	23 22		
	d	20 19				20 49	20 53	←	21 13	21 22	21 34		21 47	21 58	22 05	←	22 19	22 39	22 43			23 17	23 23		
Wakefield Kirkgate [4]	32, 34, 39 a		20 28	20 51				20 51				21 51				21 51									
	d		20 29	→				20 52				→				21 52					22 52				
Outwood	d								21 18	21 27				22 02			22 26					23 22	23 28		
Leeds [10]	32, 34 a	20 36	20 50			21 05	21 15	21 27	21 33	21 47	21 54		22 02	22 18	22 24	22 27	22 42	22 59	23 03	23 09	23 27	23 37	23 47		

For general notes see front of timetable
For details of catering facilities see Directory of Train Operators

- **A** From Lincoln (Table 30)
- **B** From London Kings Cross (Table 26)
- **C** From Paignton to Newcastle (Table 51)
- **D** From Newquay to Newcastle (Table 51)
- **E** From Paignton to Glasgow Central (Table 51)
- **G** From Bournemouth to Edinburgh (Table 51)
- **H** From London Kings Cross to Skipton (Table 26)
- **J** From St Pancras International (Table 53)
- **K** From Plymouth to Newcastle (Table 51)
- **L** From London Kings Cross to Bradford Forster Square Table 37)
- **N** From Bournemouth to Newcastle (Table 51)
- **Q** From Paignton to York (Table 51)
- **U** From Glasgow Central (Table 26)
- **V** From Bournemouth (Table 51)

Due to Engineering Operations in the Sheffield area, services from Saturday 13 September on this Table had not been confirmed at time of going to press. These services will be issued in a special Supplement as soon as exact timings have been confirmed.

Sundays until 13 July

Sheffield, Doncaster and Wakefield → Leeds

Network Diagram - see first page of Table 31

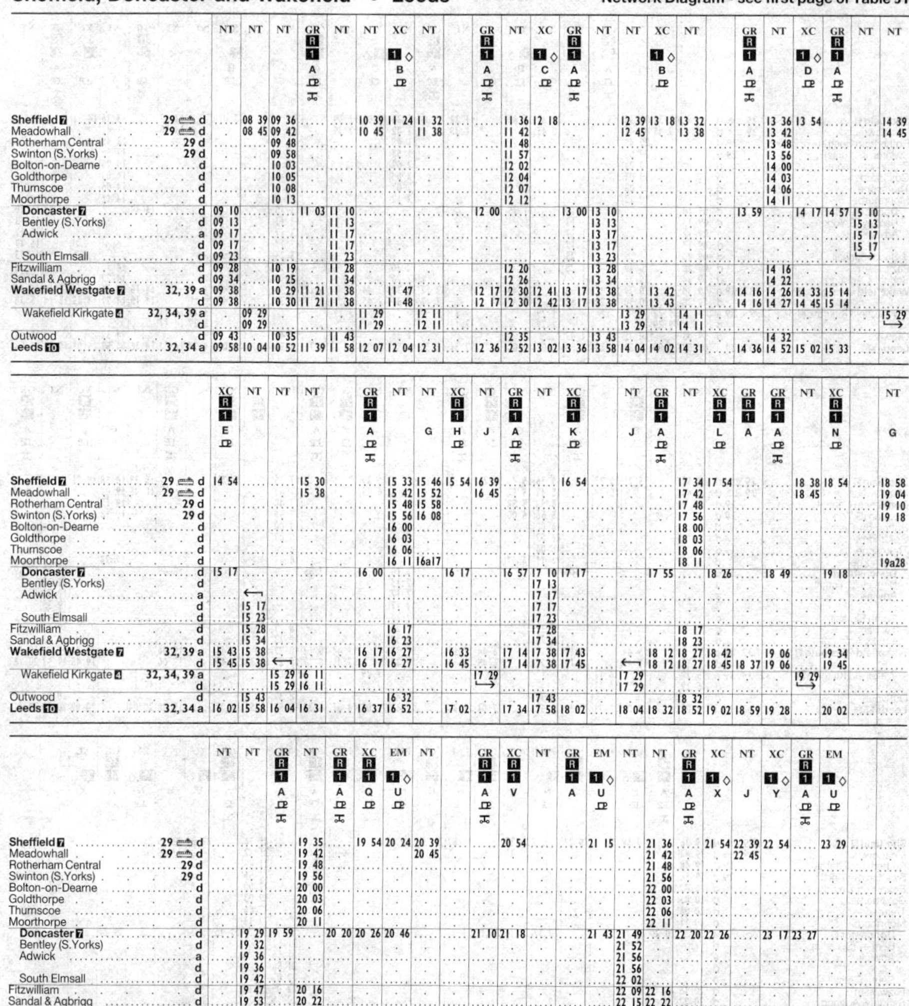

Station		NT	NT	NT	GR	NT	NT	XC	NT		GR	NT	XC	GR	NT	NT	XC	NT		GR	NT	XC	GR	NT	NT
					R 1 A ☕ 🍴			1 ◇ B ☕			R 1 A ☕ 🍴		1 ◇ C ☕	R 1 A ☕ 🍴			1 ◇ B ☕			R 1 A ☕ 🍴		1 ◇ D ☕	R 1 A ☕ 🍴		
Sheffield 7	29 🚋 d		08 39	09 36			10 39	11 24	11 32			11 36	12 18			12 39	13 18	13 32			13 36	13 54			14 39
Meadowhall	29 🚋 d		08 45	09 42			10 45		11 38			11 42				12 45		13 38			13 42				14 45
Rotherham Central	29 d			09 48								11 48									13 48				
Swinton (S.Yorks)	29 d			09 58								11 57									13 56				
Bolton-on-Dearne	d			10 03								12 02									14 00				
Goldthorpe	d			10 05								12 04									14 03				
Thurnscoe	d			10 08								12 07									14 06				
Moorthorpe	d			10 13								12 12									14 11				
Doncaster 7	d	09 10			11 03	11 10					12 00			13 00	13 10					13 59		14 17	14 57	15 10	
Bentley (S.Yorks)	d	09 13				11 13									13 13									15 13	
Adwick	a	09 17				11 17									13 17									15 17	
	d	09 17				11 17									13 17									15 17 →	
South Elmsall	d	09 23				11 23									13 23										
Fitzwilliam	d	09 28		10 19		11 28						12 20			13 28						14 16				
Sandal & Agbrigg	d	09 34		10 25		11 34						12 26			13 34						14 22				
Wakefield Westgate 7	32, 39 a	09 38		10 29	11 21	11 38		11 47			12 17	12 30	12 41	13 17	13 38		13 42			14 16	14 26	14 33	15 14		
	d	09 38		10 30	11 21	11 38		11 48			12 17	12 30	12 42	13 17	13 38		13 43			14 16	14 27	14 45	15 14		
Wakefield Kirkgate 4	32, 34, 39 a		09 29				11 29		12 11							13 29		14 11							15 29 →
	d		09 29				11 29		12 11							13 29		14 11							
Outwood	d	09 43		10 35		11 43						12 35			13 43						14 32				
Leeds 10	32, 34 a	09 58	10 04	10 52	11 39	11 58	12 07	12 04	12 31		12 36	12 52	13 02	13 36	13 58	14 04	14 02	14 31		14 36	14 52	15 02	15 33		

Station		XC	NT	NT	NT		GR	NT	NT	XC	NT	GR	NT	XC		NT	GR	NT	XC	GR	GR	NT	XC		NT
		R 1 E ☕					R 1 A ☕ 🍴		G	R 1 H ☕	J	R 1 A ☕ 🍴		R 1 K ☕		J	R 1 A ☕ 🍴		R 1 L ☕	R 1 A	R 1 A ☕ 🍴		R 1 N ☕		G
Sheffield 7	29 🚋 d	14 54			15 30			15 33	15 46	15 54	16 39			16 54				17 34	17 54			18 38	18 54		18 58
Meadowhall	29 🚋 d				15 38			15 42	15 52		16 45							17 42				18 45			19 04
Rotherham Central	29 d							15 48	15 58									17 48							19 10
Swinton (S.Yorks)	29 d							15 56	16 08									17 56							19 18
Bolton-on-Dearne	d							16 00										18 00							
Goldthorpe	d							16 03										18 03							
Thurnscoe	d							16 06										18 06							
Moorthorpe	d							16 11	16a17									18 11							19a28
Doncaster 7	d	15 17					16 00			16 17		16 57	17 10	17 17			17 55		18 26		18 49		19 18		
Bentley (S.Yorks)	d												17 13												
Adwick	a		←										17 17												
	d		15 17										17 17												
South Elmsall	d		15 23										17 23												
Fitzwilliam	d		15 28					16 17					17 28					18 17							
Sandal & Agbrigg	d		15 34					16 23					17 34					18 23							
Wakefield Westgate 7	32, 39 a	15 43	15 38				16 17	16 27		16 33		17 14	17 38	17 43			18 12	18 27	18 42		19 06		19 34		
	d	15 45	15 38	←			16 17	16 27		16 45		17 14	17 38	17 45		←	18 12	18 27	18 45	18 37	19 06		19 45		
Wakefield Kirkgate 4	32, 34, 39 a			15 29	16 11						17 29 →					17 29						19 29 →			
	d			15 29	16 11											17 29									
Outwood	d		15 43					16 32					17 43					18 32							
Leeds 10	32, 34 a	16 02	15 58	16 04	16 31		16 37	16 52		17 02		17 34	17 58	18 02		18 04	18 32	18 52	19 02	18 59	19 28		20 02		

Station		NT	NT	GR	NT	GR	XC	EM	NT		GR	XC	NT	GR	EM	NT	NT	GR	XC	NT	XC	GR	EM		
				R 1 A ☕ 🍴		R 1 A ☕ 🍴	R 1 Q ☕	1 ◇ U ☕			R 1 A ☕ 🍴	R 1 V		R 1 A	1 ◇ U ☕			R 1 A ☕ 🍴	1 ◇ X	J	1 ◇ Y	R 1 A ☕ 🍴	1 ◇ U ☕		
Sheffield 7	29 🚋 d				19 35		19 54	20 24	20 39			20 54			21 15		21 36		21 54	22 39	22 54		23 29		
Meadowhall	29 🚋 d				19 42				20 45								21 42			22 45					
Rotherham Central	29 d				19 48												21 48								
Swinton (S.Yorks)	29 d				19 56												21 56								
Bolton-on-Dearne	d				20 00												22 00								
Goldthorpe	d				20 03												22 03								
Thurnscoe	d				20 06												22 06								
Moorthorpe	d				20 11												22 11								
Doncaster 7	d		19 29	19 59		20 20	20 26	20 46			21 10	21 18			21 43	21 49		22 20	22 26		23 17	23 27			
Bentley (S.Yorks)	d		19 32													21 52									
Adwick	a		19 36													21 56									
	d		19 36													21 56									
South Elmsall	d		19 42													22 02									
Fitzwilliam	d		19 47		20 16											22 09	22 16								
Sandal & Agbrigg	d		19 53		20 22											22 15	22 22								
Wakefield Westgate 7	32, 39 a		19 57	20 16	20 26	20 38	20 45	21 03			21 27	21 34			22 01	22 19	22 26	22 40	22 45				23 53		
	d	←	19 57	20 16	20 27	20 38	20 45	21 03			21 27	21 45	←	21 56	22 01	22 20	22 27	22 40	22 46				23 53		
Wakefield Kirkgate 4	32, 34, 39 a	19 29							21 29 →				21 29							23 28					
	d	19 29											21 29							23 29					
Outwood	d		20 02		20 32											22 25	22 32								
Leeds 10	32, 34 a	20 04	20 19	20 41	20 52	20 59	21 02	21 25			21 47	22 02	22 04	22 15	22 23	22 39	22 52	23 00	23 02	00 04	00 20	00 22	00 30		

For general notes see front of timetable
For details of catering facilities see Directory of Train Operators

- **A** From London Kings Cross (Table 26)
- **B** From Birmingham New Street to Edinburgh (Table 51)
- **C** From Birmingham New Street (Table 51) to Aberdeen (Table 229)
- **D** From Bristol Temple Meads (Table 51) to Edinburgh (Table 26)
- **E** From Bournemouth (Table 51) to Dundee (Table 229)
- **G** To York (Table 33)
- **H** From Plymouth to Glasgow Central (Table51)
- **J** From Lincoln (Table 30)
- **K** From Bournemouth to Glasgow Central (Table 51)
- **L** From Penzance (Table 135) to Edinburgh (Table 51)
- **N** From Bournemouth to Edinburgh (Table 51)
- **Q** From Paignton to Newcastle (Table 51)
- **U** From St Pancras International (Table 53)
- **V** From Bournemouth to York (Table 51)
- **X** From Plymouth to York (Table 51)
- **Y** From Bournemouth (Table 51)

Table 31

Sundays

20 July to 7 September

Sheffield, Doncaster and Wakefield → Leeds

Network Diagram - see first page of Table 31

	NT	NT	NT	GR R 1 A	NT	NT	XC 1◇ B		NT	GR R 1 A	NT	XC 1◇ C	NT	GR R 1 A	NT		XC 1◇ B	NT	NT	GR R 1 A	NT	XC 1◇ D	GR R 1 A	NT
Sheffield 7 29 ⇌ d		08 39	09 36			10 39	11 02		11 32		11 36	12 02	12 39				13 02		13 32		13 36	14 21		
Meadowhall 29 ⇌ d		08 45	09 42			10 45			11 38		11 42		12 45						13 38		13 42			
Rotherham Central 29 d			09 48								11 48										13 48			
Swinton (S.Yorks) 29 d			09 58								11 57										13 56			
Bolton-on-Dearne d			10 03								12 02										14 00			
Goldthorpe d			10 05								12 04										14 03			
Thurnscoe d			10 08								12 07										14 06			
Moorthorpe d			10 13								12 12										14 11			
Doncaster 7 d	09 10			11 03	11 10		11 25			12 00				13 00	13 10					13 59			14 57	15 10
Bentley (S.Yorks) d	09 13				11 13										13 13									15 13
Adwick a	09 17				11 17										13 17									15 17
d	09 17				11 17										13 17									15 17
South Elmsall d	09 23				11 23										13 23									15 23
Fitzwilliam d	09 28		10 19		11 28						12 20				13 28						14 16			15 28
Sandal & Agbrigg d	09 34		10 25		11 34						12 26				13 34						14 22			15 34
Wakefield Westgate 7 32, 39 a	09 38		10 29	11 21	11 38		11 44			12 17	12 30	12 44		13 17	13 38		13 44			14 16	14 26	14 44	15 14	15 38
d	09 38		10 30	11 21	11 38		11 45			12 17	12 30	12 45		13 17	13 38		13 45	←		14 16	14 27	14 45	15 14	15 38
Wakefield Kirkgate 4 32, 34, 39 a		09 29				11 29			12 11				13 29					13 29	14 11					
d		09 29				11 29			12 11				→					13 29	14 11					
Outwood d	09 43		10 35		11 43						12 35				13 43						14 32			15 43
Leeds 10 32, 34 a	09 58	10 04	10 52	11 39	11 58	12 07	12 02		12 31	12 36	12 52	13 01		13 36	13 58		14 03	14 07	14 31	14 36	14 52	15 01	15 33	15 58

	NT		XC R 1 E	NT	GR R 1 A	NT	NT G	XC R 1 H	GR R 1 A		NT	NT J	XC R 1 K	GR R 1 A	NT	GR R 1 A	XC R 1 D		GR R 1 A	NT	NT G	XC R 1 L	NT	GR R 1 A
Sheffield 7 29 ⇌ d	14 39		15 21	15 32		15 36	15 46	16 21				16 39	17 21		17 36		18 21			18 39	18 58	19 21		
Meadowhall 29 ⇌ d	14 45			15 38		15 42	15 52					16 45			17 42					18 45	19 04			
Rotherham Central 29 d						15 48	15 58								17 48						19 10			
Swinton (S.Yorks) 29 d						15 56	16 08								17 56						19 18			
Bolton-on-Dearne d						16 00									18 00									
Goldthorpe d						16 03									18 03									
Thurnscoe d						16 06									18 06									
Moorthorpe d						16 11	16a17								18 11						19a28			
Doncaster 7 d					16 00				16 57		17 10			17 55					18 49				19 29	19 59
Bentley (S.Yorks) d											17 13												19 32	
Adwick a											17 17												19 36	
d											17 17												19 36	
South Elmsall d											17 23												19 42	
Fitzwilliam d						16 17					17 28				18 17								19 47	
Sandal & Agbrigg d						16 23					17 34				18 23								19 53	
Wakefield Westgate 7 32, 39 a			15 44		16 17	16 27		16 44	17 14		17 38		17 44	18 12	18 27		18 44		19 06			19 44	19 57	20 16
d			15 45		16 17	16 27		16 45	17 14		17 38		17 45	18 12	18 27	18 37	18 45		19 06			19 45	19 57	20 16
Wakefield Kirkgate 4 32, 34, 39 a	15 29			16 11								17 29								19 29				
d	15 29			16 11								17 29								19 29				
Outwood d						16 32					17 43				18 32								20 02	
Leeds 10 32, 34 a	16 05		16 01	16 31	16 37	16 52		17 01	17 34		17 58	18 05	18 01	18 32	18 52	18 59	19 02		19 28	20 04		20 02	20 19	20 41

	NT	GR R 1 A	EM 1◇ N		XC R 1 Q	EM 1◇ N	NT	GR R 1 A	EM 1◇ N	XC R 1 U	EM 1◇ N		NT	GR R 1 A	NT	NT	GR R 1 A	XC 1◇ V	NT J	EM 1◇ N	GR R 1 A	XC 1◇ X		
Sheffield 7 29 ⇌ d	19 36		19 59		20 21		20 39		20 57	21 21						21 36		22 21	22 39	23 14		23 29		
Meadowhall 29 ⇌ d	19 42						20 45									21 42			22 45					
Rotherham Central 29 d	19 48															21 48								
Swinton (S.Yorks) 29 d	19 56															21 56								
Bolton-on-Dearne d	20 00															22 00								
Goldthorpe d	20 03															22 03								
Thurnscoe d	20 06															22 06								
Moorthorpe d	20 11					←										22 11								
Doncaster 7 d		20 20	20 27			20 27		21 10	21 21						21 49		22 20				23 27			
Bentley (S.Yorks) d			→												21 52									
Adwick a															21 56									
d															21 56									
South Elmsall d															22 02									
Fitzwilliam d	20 16														22 09	22 16								
Sandal & Agbrigg d	20 22														22 15	22 22								
Wakefield Westgate 7 32, 39 a	20 26	20 38			20 44	20 49		21 27	21 39	21 44	←				22 19	22 26	22 40	22s45		23 39		23s52		
d	20 27	20 38			20 45	20 49		21 27	21 39	21 45	21 39		←	21 56	22 20	22 27	22 40			23 39				
Wakefield Kirkgate 4 32, 34, 39 a							21 29						21 29						23 28					
d							→						21 29						23 29					
Outwood d	20 32														22 25	22 32								
Leeds 10 32, 34 a	20 52	20 59			21 01	21 10		21 47	22 02	22 01	22 02		22 04	22 15	22 39	22 52	23 00	23 09	00 04	00 16	00 22	00 34		

For general notes see front of timetable
For details of catering facilities see Directory of Train Operators

- **A** From London Kings Cross (Table 26)
- **B** From Birmingham New Street to Edinburgh (Table 51)
- **C** From Birmingham New Street (Table 51) to Aberdeen (Table 229)
- **D** From Bournemouth to Edinburgh (Table 51)
- **E** From Plymouth (Table 51) to Dundee (Table 229)
- **G** To York (Table 33)
- **H** From Bournemouth to Glasgow Central (Table 51)
- **J** From Lincoln (Table 30)
- **K** From Penzance (Table 135) to Glasgow Central (Table 51)
- **L** From Plymouth to Edinburgh (Table 51)
- **N** From St Pancras International (Table 53)
- **Q** From Bournemouth to Newcastle (Table 51)
- **U** From Plymouth to York (Table 51)
- **V** From Bournemouth (Table 51)
- **X** From Plymouth (Table 51)

Due to Engineering Operations in the Sheffield area, services from Sunday 14 September on this Table had not been confirmed at time of going to press. These services will be issued in a special Supplement as soon as exact timings have been confirmed.

Leeds → Wakefield, Doncaster and Sheffield

Network Diagram - see first page of Table 31

Miles	Miles	Station	GR	GR	NT	XC	NT	GR	NT		NT	EM	NT	NT	NT	GR	NT		GR	XC	NT	NT	NT	NT
			R 1	R 1		1 ◇		R 1				1 ◇				R 1			R 1	R 1				
			A	A		B		A				C D				A			E	G				H
0	0	**Leeds** 10 32, 34 d	05 05	05 30	05 33	06 00		06 05			06 05	06 14	06 19		06 38	06 40	06 43		07 00	07 05			07 16	
7½	7½	Outwood d			05 44								06 28				06 54							
—	—	Wakefield Kirkgate 4 32, 34, 39 a									06 22			←	07 09							←	07 32	
—	—	d							06 10		06 22			06 22	07 10							07 10	07 32	
10	10	**Wakefield Westgate** 7 32, 39 a	05 17	05 42	05 49	06 11		06 18			→	06 26	06 32		→	06 52	06 58		07 12	07 18				
—	—	d	05 17	05 42	05 49	06 12						06 26	06 33				06 58		07 12	07 19				
11¾	11¾	Sandal & Agbrigg d			05 53								06 36				07 02							
16½	16½	Fitzwilliam d			06 00								06 42				07 09							
21	—	South Elmsall d											06 47											
25¾	—	Adwick a											06 53											
—	—	d											06 53											07 29
28	—	Bentley (S.Yorks) d											06 57											07 33
29¾	—	**Doncaster** 7 a	05 35	05 59								06 44	07 07						07 29					07 37
—	20¼	Moorthorpe d			06 06		←										07 14				←			
—	23¾	Thurnscoe d			06 12		06 12										07 20				07 20			
—	24½	Goldthorpe d			→		06 14										→				07 22			
—	25¾	Bolton-on-Dearne d					06 17														07 25			
—	28	Swinton (S.Yorks) 29 a					06 22														07 29			
—	32½	Rotherham Central 29 a					06 30														07 39			
—	35¼	Meadowhall 29 a					06 37		06 48					07 03							07 46	07 48	08 03	
—	38¾	**Sheffield** 7 29 a				06 40	06 47		06 57			07 09		07 14						07 51	07 57	07 59	08 15	

Station	GR	NT	EM		NT	NT	NT	GR	NT	GR	XC		NT	NT	NT	NT	EM	NT	GR		NT	NT	GR	XC
	R 1		1 ◇					R 1		R 1	R 1						1 ◇		R 1				R 1	1 ◇
	A		C			H		J		K	L						C		A			H	A	N
Leeds 10 32, 34 d	07 20	07 23	07 26				07 27	07 40	07 47	08 05	08 10				08 16	08 19	08 28	08 34	08 40		08 48		09 05	09 10
Outwood d							07 36		07 59							08 28					08 59			
Wakefield Kirkgate 4 32, 34, 39 a		07 54			←										08 32			09 03						
d		07 55			07 55										08 32			09 03						
Wakefield Westgate 7 32, 39 a	07 32	→	07 38				07 42	07 52	08 03	08 17	08 23					08 33	08 39	→	08 52		09 03		09 18	09 23
d			07 38				07 42		08 03	08 17	08 23					08 34	08 39				09 03		09 18	09 23
Sandal & Agbrigg d							07 45		08 07							08 37					09 07			
Fitzwilliam d							07 51		08 14							08 43					09 12			
South Elmsall d							08 06									08 48								
Adwick a							08 10									08 54								
d						08 07	08 10						08 35			08 54						09 13		
Bentley (S.Yorks) d						08 11	08 14						08 39			08 58						09 17		
Doncaster 7 a			07 58			08 15	08 24			08 36			08 44			09 07			09 11			09 22	09 35	
Moorthorpe d									08 19					←							09 20			
Thurnscoe d									08 25					08 25							09 26			
Goldthorpe d									→					08 27							→			
Bolton-on-Dearne d														08 30										
Swinton (S.Yorks) 29 a														08 34										
Rotherham Central 29 a														08 46										
Meadowhall 29 a					08 33									08 52	09 03									
Sheffield 7 29 a			08 22		08 45						08 51			09 02	09 15		09 15							09 51

Station	NT	NT	NT	NT	NT		GR	NT	NT	GR	XC	NT	NT		NT	NT	NT	GR	NT	NT	GR		XC	NT
							R 1			R 1	R 1							R 1			R 1		1 ◇	
							A		H	A	Q							A		H	A		U	
Leeds 10 32, 34 d			09 16	09 19	09 34		09 40	09 48		10 05	10 10				10 16	10 19	10 34	10 40	10 48		11 05		11 10	
Outwood d				09 28				09 59								10 28			10 59					
Wakefield Kirkgate 4 32, 34, 39 a	←		09 32		10 03							←			10 32		11 03							←
d	09 03		09 32		10 03							10 03			10 32		11 03							11 03
Wakefield Westgate 7 32, 39 a				09 32	→		09 52	10 03		10 18	10 23					10 32	→	10 52	11 03		11 17		11 23	
d				09 33			09 52	10 03		10 18	10 23					10 32		10 52	11 03		11 17		11 23	
Sandal & Agbrigg d				09 36				10 07								10 35			11 07					
Fitzwilliam d				09 42				10 14								10 42			11 14					
South Elmsall d				09 49												10 47								
Adwick a				09 54												10 52								
d				09 55					10 13							10 53				11 16				
Bentley (S.Yorks) d				09 59					10 17							10 57				11 20				
Doncaster 7 a				10 08			10 14		10 22	10 35						11 07		11 12		11 25	11 37			
Moorthorpe d		←						10 19					←						11 19					
Thurnscoe d		09 26						10 25					10 25						11 25					
Goldthorpe d		09 28						→					10 27						→					
Bolton-on-Dearne d		09 31											10 30											
Swinton (S.Yorks) 29 a		09 35											10 34											
Rotherham Central 29 a		09 44											10 42											
Meadowhall 29 a	09 48	09 51	10 03									10 48	10 51		11 03									11 48
Sheffield 7 29 a	09 57	10 02	10 15								10 51	10 57	11 02		11 15								11 51	11 57

For general notes see front of timetable
For details of catering facilities see Directory of Train Operators

- **A** To London Kings Cross (Table 26)
- **B** To Bournemouth (Table 51)
- **C** To St Pancras International (Table 53)
- **D** The Master Cutler
- **E** From Bradford Forster Square to London Kings Cross (Table 26)
- **G** To Plymouth (Table 51)
- **H** To Sheffield (Table 29)
- **J** From Skipton to London Kings Cross (Table 26)
- **K** From Harrogate to London Kings Cross (Table 26)
- **L** From Newcastle to Bournemouth (Table 51)
- **N** From Edinburgh to Plymouth (Table 51)
- **Q** From Glasgow Central to Bournemouth (Table 51)
- **U** From Dundee (Table 229) to Bournemouth (Table 51)

Leeds → Wakefield, Doncaster and Sheffield

Network Diagram - see first page of Table 31

		NT	NT	NT A	NT	NT	GR R 1 B	NT		NT C	GR R 1 B	XC R 1 D	NT	NT	NT	NT		NT	GR R 1 B	NT	NT C	GR R 1 B	XC R 1 E	NT	NT
Leeds 10	32, 34 d		11 16		11 19	11 34	11 40	11 48			12 05	12 10			12 16	12 19		12 34	12 40	12 48		13 05	13 10		
Outwood	d				11 28			11 59								12 28				12 59					
Wakefield Kirkgate 4	32, 34, 39 a		11 32			12 04							←		12 32			13 03						←	
	d		11 32			12 05							12 05		12 32			13 03						13 03	
Wakefield Westgate 7	32, 39 a				11 32	→	11 54	12 03			12 17	12 23				12 32		→	12 52	13 03		13 18	13 23		
	d				11 32		11 54	12 03			12 17	12 23				12 32			12 52	13 03		13 18	13 23		
Sandal & Agbrigg	d				11 35			12 07								12 35				13 07					
Fitzwilliam	d				11 42			12 14								12 42				13 14					
South Elmsall	d				11 47											12 47									
Adwick	a				11 52											12 52									
	d				11 53					12 15						12 53					13 11				
Bentley (S.Yorks)	d				11 57					12 19						12 57					13 15				
Doncaster 7	a				12 07		12 12			12 24	12 36					13 07			13 11		13 20	13 37			
Moorthorpe	d	←		11 51				12 19						←						13 19					←
Thurnscoe	d	11 25						12 25 →						12 25						13 25 →					13 25
Goldthorpe	d	11 27												12 27											13 27
Bolton-on-Dearne	d	11 30												12 30											13 30
Swinton (S.Yorks)	29 a	11 34		12 01										12 34											13 34
Rotherham Central	29 a	11 44		12 10										12 44											13 44
Meadowhall	29 🚋 a	11 51	12 03	12 16									12 48	12 51	13 03									13 48	13 51
Sheffield 7	29 🚋 a	12 02	12 15	12 26								12 51	12 57	13 02	13 15								13 51	13 57	14 02

		NT		NT	NT	GR R 1 B	NT	GR R 1 B	XC R 1 G	NT		NT	NT C	NT	NT	NT	GR R 1 B	NT		GR R 1 B	XC R 1 H	NT	NT	NT C	NT
Leeds 10	32, 34 d	13 16		13 19	13 34	13 40	13 48	14 05	14 10					14 16	14 19	14 34	14 40	14 48		15 05	15 10				15 16
Outwood	d			13 28			13 59								14 28			14 59							
Wakefield Kirkgate 4	32, 34, 39 a	13 32			14 03					←				14 32		15 03						←			15 32
	d	13 32			14 03					14 03				14 32		15 03						15 03			15 32
Wakefield Westgate 7	32, 39 a			13 32	→	13 53	14 03	14 18	14 23						14 32	→	14 52	15 03		15 17	15 23				
	d			13 32		13 53	14 03		14 23						14 32		14 52	15 03			15 23				
Sandal & Agbrigg	d			13 35			14 07								14 35			15 07							
Fitzwilliam	d			13 42			14 14								14 42			15 14							
South Elmsall	d			13 47											14 47										
Adwick	a			13 52											14 52										
	d			13 53									14 18		14 53									15 13	
Bentley (S.Yorks)	d			13 57									14 22		14 57									15 17	
Doncaster 7	a			14 07		14 15							14 26		15 07		15 13							15 22	
Moorthorpe	d						14 19					←						15 19					←		
Thurnscoe	d						14 25 →					14 25						15 25 →					15 25		
Goldthorpe	d											14 27											15 27		
Bolton-on-Dearne	d											14 30											15 30		
Swinton (S.Yorks)	29 a											14 34											15 34		
Rotherham Central	29 a											14 44											15 42		
Meadowhall	29 🚋 a	14 03								14 48		14 51		15 03								15 48	15 51		16 05
Sheffield 7	29 🚋 a	14 15							14 51	14 57		15 02		15 15							15 51	15 57	16 02		16 15

		NT A	NT	NT		GR R 1 B	NT	NT C	GR R 1 B	XC R 1 J	NT	NT		NT	NT	NT	GR R 1 B	NT K	NT	GR R 1 B		XC 1 ◇ H	NT	NT	NT
Leeds 10	32, 34 d		15 19	15 34		15 40	15 48		16 05	16 10				16 16	16 19	16 34	16 40		16 48	17 05		17 10			17 16
Outwood	d		15 28				15 59								16 28				16 59						
Wakefield Kirkgate 4	32, 34, 39 a			16 03							←			16 32		17 03							←		17 32
	d			16 03							16 03			16 32		17 03							17 03		17 32
Wakefield Westgate 7	32, 39 a		15 32	→		15 52	16 03		16 17	16 23					16 33	→	16 52		17 03	17 17		17 23			
	d		15 32				16 03		16 17	16 23					16 33		16 52		17 03	17 17		17 23			
Sandal & Agbrigg	d		15 35				16 07								16 36				17 07						
Fitzwilliam	d		15 42				16 14								16 43				17 14						
South Elmsall	d		15 47												16 48										
Adwick	a		15 52												16 53										
	d		15 53					16 14							16 54			17 09							
Bentley (S.Yorks)	d		15 57					16 18							16 58			17 14							
Doncaster 7	a		16 07					16 22	16 36						17 07		17 10	17 19		17 36					
Moorthorpe	d	15 50					16 19					←							17 19					←	
Thurnscoe	d						16 25 →					16 25							17 25 →					17 25	
Goldthorpe	d											16 27												17 27	
Bolton-on-Dearne	d											16 30												17 30	
Swinton (S.Yorks)	29 a	16 01										16 34												17 34	
Rotherham Central	29 a	16 10										16 43												17 44	
Meadowhall	29 🚋 a	16 18									16 48	16 51		17 03									17 48	17 51	18 03
Sheffield 7	29 🚋 a	16 25								16 51	16 57	17 02		17 15								17 51	17 57	18 02	18 15

For general notes see front of timetable
For details of catering facilities see Directory of Train Operators

- **A** From York (Table 33)
- **B** To London Kings Cross (Table 26)
- **C** To Sheffield (Table 29)
- **D** From Dundee (Table 229) to Plymouth (Table 51)
- **E** From Glasgow Central (Table 51) to Penzance (Table 135)
- **G** From Aberdeen (Table 229) to Bournemouth (Table 51)
- **H** From Edinburgh to Plymouth (Table 51)
- **J** From Edinburgh to Bournemouth (Table 51)
- **K** To Scunthorpe (Table 29)

Mondays to Fridays
until 5 September

Leeds → Wakefield, Doncaster and Sheffield

Network Diagram - see first page of Table 31

	NT	NT	GR	NT	NT		GR	XC	NT	NT	NT	NT	NT		GR	NT	GR	XC	NT	NT	NT		NT	NT
			R 1 A		B		R 1 A	R 1 C							R 1 A		R 1 A	1 ◇ D						
Leeds 10 32, 34 d	17 19	17 34	17 40	17 46			18 05	18 10			18 16	18 19	18 34		18 40	18 48	19 05	19 10			19 16		19 19	19 34
Outwood d	17 28			17 57								18 28				18 59							19 28	
Wakefield Kirkgate 4 32, 34, 39 a		18 03							←		18 32		19 03						←		19 32			20 03
d		18 03							18 03		18 32		19 03						19 03		19 32			20 03
Wakefield Westgate 7 32, 39 a	17 32	→	17 52	18 01			18 17	18 23				18 32	→		18 52	19 03	19 17	19 23					19 32	→
d	17 32		17 52	18 01			18 17	18 23				18 32			18 52	19 03	19 17	19 23					19 32	
Sandal & Agbrigg d	17 35			18 05								18 35				19 07							19 35	
Fitzwilliam d	17 42			18 12								18 42				19 14							19 42	
South Elmsall d	17 47											18 47											19 47	
Adwick a	17 52											18 52											19 52	
d	17 53				18 16							18 53											19 53	
Bentley (S.Yorks) d	17 57				18 20							18 57											19 57	
Doncaster 7 a	18 07		18 09		18 25		18 34					19 07			19 10		19 34						20 07	
Moorthorpe d				18 17						←						19 19				←				
Thurnscoe d				18 23						18 23						19 25				19 25				
Goldthorpe d				→						18 25						→				19 27				
Bolton-on-Dearne d										18 28										19 30				
Swinton (S.Yorks) 29 a										18 32										19 34				
Rotherham Central 29 a										18 43										19 43				
Meadowhall 29 a									18 47	18 51	19 03								19 48	19 51	20 03			
Sheffield 7 29 a								18 51	18 57	19 02	19 15							19 51	19 57	20 02	20 15			

	GR	NT	XC	NT	NT	NT	NT		NT	GR	NT	XC	NT	NT	NT		NT	NT	NT	NT	NT			
	R 1 A		1 ◇ D							R 1 A		1 ◇ E												
Leeds 10 32, 34 d	19 40	19 48	20 10			20 16	20 21		20 34	20 40	20 48	21 10			21 28		21 34	21 48	22 34	22 39	23 09			
Outwood d		19 59					20 30				20 59				21 37			21 59		22 48	23 20			
Wakefield Kirkgate 4 32, 34, 39 a				←		20 32			21 03				←				22 03		23 03					
d				20 03		20 32			21 03				21 03				22 03		23 03					
Wakefield Westgate 7 32, 39 a	19 54	20 03	20 23				20 34		→	20 55	21 03	21 23			21 41			22 03		22 53	23 24			
d	19 54	20 03	20 23				20 34			20 55	21 03	21 23			21 42			22 03		22 54	23 24			
Sandal & Agbrigg d		20 07					20 37				21 07				21 45			22 07		22 57	23 28			
Fitzwilliam d		20 14					20 44				21 13				21 51			22 14		23 03	23 35			
South Elmsall d							20 49								21 56					23 08				
Adwick a							20 54								22 02					23 14				
d							20 55								22 02					23 14				
Bentley (S.Yorks) d							20 59								22 06					23 18				
Doncaster 7 a	20 14						21 09			21 12					22 16					23 27				
Moorthorpe d		20 19			←						21 20			←				22 19			23 40			
Thurnscoe d		20 25			20 25						21 26			21 26				22 25			23 46			
Goldthorpe d		→			20 27						→			21 28				22 27			23 48			
Bolton-on-Dearne d					20 30									21 31				22 30			23 51			
Swinton (S.Yorks) 29 a					20 34									21 35				22 34			23 55			
Rotherham Central 29 a					20 42									21 44				22 43			00 02			
Meadowhall 29 a				20 47	20 50	21 03							21 48	21 52			22 48	22 51	23 48		00 08			
Sheffield 7 29 a			20 51	20 57	21 02	21 15						21 51	21 57	22 07			22 57	23 02	23 57		00 23			

Mondays to Fridays
from 8 September

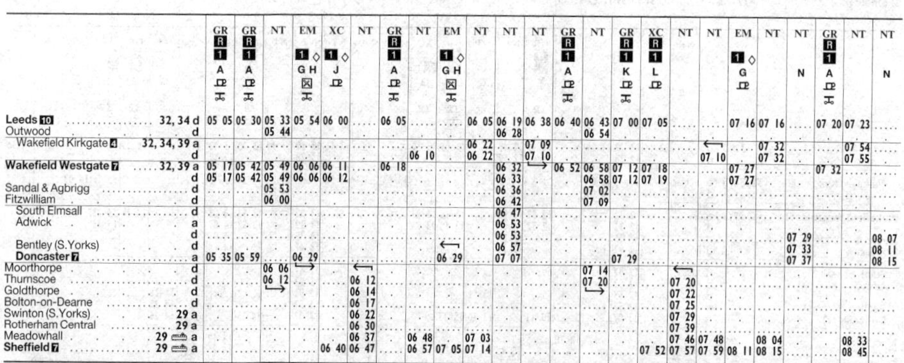

	GR	GR	NT	EM	XC	NT	GR	NT	EM	NT	NT	NT	GR	NT	GR	XC	NT	NT	EM	NT	NT	GR	NT	NT
	R 1 A	R 1 A		1 ◇ G H	1 ◇ J		R 1 A		1 ◇ G H				R 1 A		R 1 K	R 1 L			1 ◇ G		N	R 1 A		N
Leeds 10 32, 34 d	05 05	05 30	05 33	05 54	06 00		06 05			06 05	06 19	06 38	06 40	06 43	07 00	07 05			07 16	07 16		07 20	07 23	
Outwood d			05 44								06 28			06 54										
Wakefield Kirkgate 4 32, 34, 39 a										06 22		07 09						←		07 32			07 54	
d								06 10		06 22		07 10						07 10		07 32			07 55	
Wakefield Westgate 7 32, 39 a	05 17	05 42	05 49	06 06	06 11		06 18				06 32	→	06 52	06 58	07 12	07 18			07 27			07 32		
d	05 17	05 42	05 49	06 06	06 12						06 33			06 58	07 12	07 19			07 27					
Sandal & Agbrigg d			05 53								06 36			07 02										
Fitzwilliam d			06 00								06 42			07 09										
South Elmsall d											06 47													
Adwick a											06 53													
d											06 53										07 29			08 07
Bentley (S.Yorks) d									←		06 57										07 33			08 11
Doncaster 7 a	05 35	05 59		06 29					06 29		07 07				07 29						07 37			08 15
Moorthorpe d			06 06	→		←								07 14			←							
Thurnscoe d			06 12			06 12								07 20			07 20							
Goldthorpe d			→			06 14								→			07 22							
Bolton-on-Dearne d						06 17											07 25							
Swinton (S.Yorks) 29 a						06 22											07 29							
Rotherham Central 29 a						06 30											07 39							
Meadowhall 29 a						06 37		06 48		07 03							07 46	07 48		08 04			08 33	
Sheffield 7 29 a					06 40	06 47		06 57	07 05	07 14						07 52	07 57	07 59	08 11	08 15			08 45	

For general notes see front of timetable
For details of catering facilities see Directory of Train Operators

- **A** To London Kings Cross (Table 26)
- **B** To Scunthorpe (Table 29)
- **C** From Edinburgh to Southampton Central (Table 51)
- **D** From Edinburgh to Bristol Temple Meads (Table 51)
- **E** From Edinburgh to Birmingham New Street (Table 51)
- **G** To St Pancras International (Table 53)
- **H** **The Master Cutler**
- **J** To Bristol Temple Meads (Table 51)
- **K** From Bradford Forster Square to London Kings Cross (Table 26)
- **L** To Paignton (Table 51)
- **N** To Meadowhall (Table 29)

Leeds → Wakefield, Doncaster and Sheffield

Network Diagram - see first page of Table 31

Station		NT	GR	NT	GR	XC		NT	EM	NT	NT	NT	GR	NT	NT	GR	XC	NT	NT	NT	NT	NT	GR	NT	NT
			R 1 A		R 1 B	1 ◇ C			1 ◇ D				R 1 E		G	R 1 E	1 ◇ H						R 1 E		G
Leeds 10	32, 34 d	07 27	07 40	07 47	08 05	08 10			08 16		08 19	08 34	08 40	08 48		09 05	09 10			09 16	09 19	09 34	09 40	09 48	
Outwood	d	07 36		07 59							08 28			08 59							09 28			09 59	
Wakefield Kirkgate 4	32, 34, 39 a								08 32			09 03						←		09 32		10 03			
	d								08 33			09 03						09 03		09 32		10 03			
Wakefield Westgate 7	32, 39 a	07 42	07 52	08 03	08 17	08 23					08 33	→	08 52	09 03		09 18	09 23				09 32	→	09 52	10 03	
	d	07 42		08 03	08 17	08 23					08 34			09 03		09 18	09 23				09 33		09 52	10 03	
Sandal & Agbrigg	d	07 45		08 07							08 37			09 07							09 36			10 07	
Fitzwilliam	d	07 51		08 14							08 43			09 12							09 42			10 14	
South Elmsall	d	08 06									08 48										09 49				
Adwick	a	08 10									08 54										09 54				
	d	08 10								08 35	08 54				09 13						09 55				10 13
Bentley (S.Yorks)	d	08 14								08 39	08 58				09 17						09 59				10 17
Doncaster 7	a	08 24			08 36					08 44	09 07		09 11		09 22	09 35					10 08		10 14		10 22
Moorthorpe	d			08 19				←						09 20					←					10 19	
Thurnscoe	d			08 25				08 25						09 26					09 26					10 25	
Goldthorpe	d			→				08 27						→					09 28					→	
Bolton-on-Dearne	d							08 30											09 31						
Swinton (S.Yorks)	29 a							08 34											09 35						
Rotherham Central	29 a							08 46											09 44						
Meadowhall	29 🚊 a							08 52	09 03									09 48	09 51	10 03					
Sheffield 7	29 🚊 a					08 51		09 01	09 11								09 51	09 58	10 02	10 15					

Station		GR	XC	NT	NT	NT	NT	NT	GR	NT	NT	GR		XC	NT	NT	NT	NT	NT	GR	NT	NT	GR	XC	NT
		R 1 E	1 ◇ J						R 1 E		G	R 1 E		R 1 K						R 1 E		G	R 1 E	1 ◇ L	
Leeds 10	32, 34 d	10 05	10 10			10 16	10 19	10 34	10 40	10 48		11 05		11 10			11 16	11 19	11 34	11 40	11 48		12 05	12 10	
Outwood	d			←			10 28			10 59								11 28			11 59				
Wakefield Kirkgate 4	32, 34, 39 a			10 03		10 32		11 03							←		11 32		12 04						←
	d					10 32		11 03							11 03		11 32		12 05						12 05
Wakefield Westgate 7	32, 39 a	10 18	10 23				10 32	→	10 52	11 03		11 17		11 23				11 32	→	11 54	12 03		12 17	12 23	
	d	10 18	10 23				10 32		10 52	11 03		11 17		11 23				11 32		11 54	12 03		12 17	12 23	
Sandal & Agbrigg	d						10 35			11 07								11 35			12 07				
Fitzwilliam	d						10 42			11 14								11 42			12 14				
South Elmsall	d						10 47											11 47							
Adwick	a						10 52											11 52							
	d						10 53				11 16							11 53				12 15			
Bentley (S.Yorks)	d						10 57				11 20							11 57				12 19			
Doncaster 7	a	10 35					11 07		11 12		11 25	11 37						12 07		12 12		12 24	12 36		
Moorthorpe	d				←					11 19						←					12 19				
Thurnscoe	d				10 25					11 25						11 25					12 25				
Goldthorpe	d				10 27					→						11 27					→				
Bolton-on-Dearne	d				10 30											11 30									
Swinton (S.Yorks)	29 a				10 34											11 34									
Rotherham Central	29 a				10 42											11 44									
Meadowhall	29 🚊 a			10 48	10 51	11 03									11 48	11 51	12 03								12 48
Sheffield 7	29 🚊 a		10 51	10 59	11 02	11 15								11 51	11 58	12 02	12 15							12 51	12 58

Station		NT	NT	NT	NT	NT	GR	NT	NT	GR	XC	NT	NT	NT	NT	NT	GR	NT		NT	GR	XC	NT	NT	NT
						N 🚌	R 1 E		G	R 1 E	1 ◇ Q						R 1 E			G	R 1 E	1 ◇ U			
Leeds 10	32, 34 d		12 16	12 19	12 34		12 40	12 48		13 05	13 10			13 16	13 19	13 34	13 40	13 48			14 05	14 10			14 16
Outwood	d			12 28				12 59				←			13 28			13 59					←		
Wakefield Kirkgate 4	32, 34, 39 a		12 32		13 03							13 03		13 32		14 03							14 03		14 32
	d		12 32		13 03									13 32		14 03									14 32
Wakefield Westgate 7	32, 39 a			12 32	→		12 52	13 03		13 18	13 23				13 32	→	13 53	14 03			14 18	14 23			
	d			12 32			12 52	13 03		13 18	13 23				13 32		13 53	14 03				14 23			
Sandal & Agbrigg	d			12 35				13 07							13 35			14 07							
Fitzwilliam	d			12 42				13 14							13 42			14 14							
South Elmsall	d			12 47											13 47										
Adwick	a			12 52											13 52										
	d			12 53					13 11						13 53					14 18					
Bentley (S.Yorks)	d			12 57					13 15						13 57					14 22					
Doncaster 7	a			13 07			13 11		13 20	13 37					14 07		14 15			14 26					
Moorthorpe	d	←				12 30		13 19										14 19							
Thurnscoe	d	12 25						13 25					←					14 25						←	
Goldthorpe	d	12 27						→					13 27					→						14 27	
Bolton-on-Dearne	d	12 30											13 30											14 30	
Swinton (S.Yorks)	29 a	12 34				13 05							13 34											14 34	
Rotherham Central	29 a	12 44				*13 26*							13 44											14 44	
Meadowhall	29 🚊 a	12 51	13 03			*13 32*						13 48	13 51	14 03									14 48	14 51	15 03
Sheffield 7	29 🚊 a	13 02	13 14			*13 41*					13 51	13 58	14 02	14 15								14 51	14 58	15 02	15 15

For general notes see front of timetable
For details of catering facilities see Directory of Train Operators

- **A** From Skipton to London Kings Cross (Table 26)
- **B** From Harrogate to London Kings Cross (Table 26)
- **C** From Newcastle to Bristol Temple Meads (Table 51)
- **D** To St Pancras International (Table 53)
- **E** To London Kings Cross (Table 26)
- **G** To Meadowhall (Table 29)
- **H** From Edinburgh to Paignton (Table 51)
- **J** From Glasgow Central to Bournemouth (Table 51)
- **K** From Dundee to Plymouth (Table 51)
- **L** From Dundee (Table 229) to Bristol Temple Meads (Table 51)
- **N** From York (Table 33)
- **Q** From Glasgow Central to Plymouth (Table 51)
- **U** From Aberdeen (Table 229) to Bristol Temple Meads (Table 51)

Table 31

Mondays to Fridays
from 8 September

Leeds → Wakefield, Doncaster and Sheffield

Network Diagram - see first page of Table 31

Station			NT	NT	GR	NT	NT	GR	XC	NT	NT	NT	NT	NT	GR	NT	NT	GR	XC	NT	NT	NT	NT	NT	GR	NT
					R 1			R 1	R 1						R 1			R 1	R 1						R 1	bus
					A		B	A	C						A		B	A	D						A	
Leeds 10	32, 34	d	14 19	14 34	14 40	14 48		15 05	15 10			15 16	15 19	15 34	15 40	15 48		16 05	16 10			16 16	16 19	16 34	16 40	
Outwood		d	14 28			14 59				←			15 28			15 59							16 28			
Wakefield Kirkgate 4	32, 34, 39	a		15 03						15 03		15 32		16 03						←		16 32		17 03		
		d		15 03								15 32		16 03						16 03		16 32		17 03		
Wakefield Westgate 7	32, 39	a	14 32		14 52	15 03		15 17	15 23				15 32	→	15 52	16 03		16 17	16 23				16 33	→	16 52	
		d	14 32		14 52	15 03			15 23				15 32			16 03		16 17	16 23				16 33		16 52	
Sandal & Agbrigg		d	14 35			15 07							15 35			16 07							16 36			
Fitzwilliam		d	14 42			15 14							15 42			16 14							16 43			
South Elmsall		d	14 47										15 47										16 48			
Adwick		a	14 52										15 52										16 53			
		d	14 53				15 13						15 53				16 14						16 54			
Bentley (S.Yorks)		d	14 57				15 17						15 57				16 18						16 58			
Doncaster 7		a	15 07		15 13		15 22						16 07				16 22	16 36					17 07		17 10	
Moorthorpe		d				15 19										16 19										16 30
Thurnscoe		d				15 25					←					16 25					←					
Goldthorpe		d				→					15 27					→					16 27					
Bolton-on-Dearne		d									15 30										16 30					
Swinton (S.Yorks)	29	a									15 34										16 34					17 05
Rotherham Central	29	a									15 42										16 43					*17 26*
Meadowhall	29	a		15 48						15 48	15 51	16 03								16 48	16 51	17 03				*17 32*
Sheffield 7	29	a		15 58					15 51	15 58	16 02	16 13							16 53	16 58	17 02	17 15				*17 41*

Station			NT		NT	GR	XC	NT	NT	NT	NT	NT	GR	NT	NT	GR	XC	NT	NT	NT	NT	NT	GR	NT	GR	XC
						R 1	R 1						R 1			R 1	1 ◇						R 1		R 1	1 ◇
			E			A	G						A		E	A	H						A		A	H
Leeds 10	32, 34	d			16 48	17 05	17 10			17 16	17 19	17 34	17 40	17 48		18 05	18 10			18 16	18 19	18 34	18 40	18 48	19 05	19 10
Outwood		d			16 59						17 28			17 59							18 28			18 59		
Wakefield Kirkgate 4	32, 34, 39	a								17 32		18 03						←		18 32		19 03				
		d						←		17 32		18 03						18 03		18 32		19 03				
Wakefield Westgate 7	32, 39	a			17 03	17 17	17 23	17 03			17 32	→	17 52	18 03		18 17	18 23				18 32	→	18 52	19 03	19 17	19 23
		d			17 03	17 17	17 23				17 32		17 52	18 03		18 17	18 23				18 32		18 52	19 03	19 17	19 23
Sandal & Agbrigg		d			17 07						17 35			18 07							18 35			19 07		
Fitzwilliam		d			17 14						17 42			18 14							18 42			19 14		
South Elmsall		d									17 47										18 47					
Adwick		a									17 52										18 52					
		d	17 09								17 53				18 16						18 53					
Bentley (S.Yorks)		d	17 14								17 57				18 20						18 57					
Doncaster 7		a	17 19			17 36					18 07		18 09		18 25	18 34					19 07		19 10		19 34	
Moorthorpe		d			17 19									18 19					←					19 19		
Thurnscoe		d			17 25				←					18 25					18 25					19 25		
Goldthorpe		d			→				17 27					→					18 27					→		
Bolton-on-Dearne		d							17 30										18 30							
Swinton (S.Yorks)	29	a							17 34										18 34							
Rotherham Central	29	a							17 44										18 41							
Meadowhall	29	a						17 48	17 51	18 03								18 47	18 51	19 03						
Sheffield 7	29	a					17 51	17 58	18 02	18 15							18 51	18 57	19 02	19 15						19 51

Station			NT	NT	NT	NT	NT	GR	NT	XC	NT	NT	NT	NT	NT	GR	NT	XC	NT	NT	NT	NT	NT	NT		
								R 1		1 ◇						R 1		1 ◇								
								A		H						A		J								
Leeds 10	32, 34	d			19 16	19 19	19 34	19 40	19 48	20 10			20 16	20 21	20 34	20 40	20 48	21 10	21 28	21 34	21 48	22 34	22 39	23 09		
Outwood		d				19 28			19 59					20 30			20 59		21 37		21 59		22 48	23 20		
Wakefield Kirkgate 4	32, 34, 39	a	←		19 32		20 03				←		20 32		21 03					22 03		23 03				
		d	19 03		19 32		20 03				20 03		20 32		21 03					22 03		23 03				
Wakefield Westgate 7	32, 39	a				19 32	→	19 54	20 03	20 23				20 34		20 55	21 03	21 23	21 41		22 03		22 53	23 24		
		d				19 32		19 54	20 03	20 23				20 34		20 55	21 03	21 23	21 42		22 03		22 54	23 24		
Sandal & Agbrigg		d				19 35			20 07					20 37			21 07		21 45		22 07		22 57	23 28		
Fitzwilliam		d				19 42			20 14					20 44			21 13		21 51		22 14		23 03	23 35		
South Elmsall		d				19 47								20 49					21 56				23 08			
Adwick		a				19 52								20 54					22 02				23 14			
		d				19 53								20 55					22 02				23 14			
Bentley (S.Yorks)		d				19 57								20 59					22 06				23 18			
Doncaster 7		a				20 07		20 14						21 09		21 12		21 43	22 16				23 27			
Moorthorpe		d		←					20 19			←					21 20				22 19			23 40		
Thurnscoe		d		19 25					20 25			20 25					21 26				22 25			23 46		
Goldthorpe		d		19 27					→			20 27					21 28				22 27			23 48		
Bolton-on-Dearne		d		19 30								20 30					21 31				22 30			23 51		
Swinton (S.Yorks)	29	a		19 34								20 34					21 35				22 34			23 55		
Rotherham Central	29	a		19 44								20 42					21 44				22 43			00 02		
Meadowhall	29	a	19 46	19 51	20 03						20 47	20 50	21 03		21 48		21 50			22 47	22 51	23 48		00 08		
Sheffield 7	29	a	19 57	20 02	20 15					20 50	20 57	21 02	21 15		21 57		22 02	22 19		22 58	23 02	23 57		00 23		

For general notes see front of timetable
For details of catering facilities see Directory of Train Operators

- **A** To London Kings Cross (Table 26)
- **B** To Meadowhall (Table 29)
- **C** From Edinburgh to Cardiff Central (Table 51)
- **D** From Edinburgh to Weston-Super-Mare (Table 51)
- **E** To Scunthorpe (Table 29)
- **G** From Edinburgh to Bristol Temple Meads (Table 51)
- **H** From Edinburgh to Birmingham New Street (Table 51)
- **J** From Edinburgh (Table 26)

Table 31

until 6 September

Leeds → Wakefield, Doncaster and Sheffield

Network Diagram - see first page of Table 31

	GR R 1 A	XC 1◇ B	GR R 1 A	NT	NT	NT	GR R 1 A	NT	NT C	NT	EM 1◇ D	NT	NT C	NT	GR R 1 E	NT	GR R 1 G	XC R 1 H	NT	GR R 1	NT	NT	NT	NT
Leeds 10 32, 34 d	05 05	06 00	06 10	06 19	06 38	06 43	07 00			07 16	07 19	07 23		07 26	07 40	07 47	08 05	08 10		08 15		08 16	08 19	08 34
Outwood d				06 28		06 54								07 35		07 59							08 28	
Wakefield Kirkgate 4 32, 34, 39 a					07 09			←		07 32		07 54										08 32		09 03
d					07 10			07 10		07 32		07 55										08 32		09 03
Wakefield Westgate 7 32, 39 a	05 17	06 11	06 22	06 32	→	06 58	07 12				07 32			07 39	07 52	08 03	08 18	08 23					08 33	→
d	05 17	06 11	06 22	06 32		06 58	07 12				07 32			07 39		08 03		08 23					08 34	
Sandal & Agbrigg d				06 35		07 02								07 42		08 07							08 37	
Fitzwilliam d				06 42		07 09								07 49		08 14							08 43	
South Elmsall d				06 47										08 06									08 48	
Adwick a				06 52										08 12									08 54	
d				06 53					07 29				08 07	08 12					08 35				08 54	
Bentley (S.Yorks) d				06 57					07 33				08 11	08 16					08 39				08 58	
Doncaster 7 a	05 34		06 40	07 07			07 30		07 37		07 58		08 15	08 22					08 43	08 44			09 07	
Moorthorpe d						07 14										08 19					←			
Thurnscoe d						07 20										08 25					08 25			
Goldthorpe d						07 22										→					08 27			
Bolton-on-Dearne d						07 25															08 30			
Swinton (S.Yorks) 29 a						07 29															08 34			
Rotherham Central 29 a						07 39															08 46			
Meadowhall 29 a						07 46		07 48		08 03		08 36									08 52	09 03		
Sheffield 7 29 a		06 41				07 57		07 59		08 15	08 21	08 47						08 51			09 02	09 15		

	EM 1◇ D	NT	NT C	GR R 1 A	XC R 1 J	NT	NT	NT	NT	NT	NT	NT C	GR R 1 A	XC 1◇ K	NT	NT	NT	NT	NT	NT	NT C	GR R 1 A	XC R 1 L	NT
Leeds 10 32, 34 d	08 40	08 48		09 05	09 10			09 16	09 19	09 34	09 48		10 05	10 10			10 16	10 19	10 34	10 48		11 05	11 10	
Outwood d		08 59							09 28		09 59							10 28		10 59				
Wakefield Kirkgate 4 32, 34, 39 a						←		09 32		10 03					←		10 32		11 03					←
d						09 03		09 32		10 03					10 03		10 32		11 03					11 03
Wakefield Westgate 7 32, 39 a	08 51	09 03		09 17	09 22				09 33	→	10 03		10 18	10 22				10 32	→	11 03		11 17	11 23	
d	08 52	09 03		09 17	09 23				09 33		10 03		10 18	10 23				10 32		11 03		11 17	11 23	
Sandal & Agbrigg d		09 07							09 36		10 07							10 35		11 07				
Fitzwilliam d		09 14							09 43		10 14							10 42		11 14				
South Elmsall d									09 48									10 47						
Adwick a									09 53									10 52						
d			09 13						09 54			10 10						10 53			11 08			
Bentley (S.Yorks) d			09 17						09 58			10 14						10 57			11 12			
Doncaster 7 a			09 22	09 35					10 07			10 19	10 36					11 07			11 20	11 38		
Moorthorpe d		09 20					←				10 19					←				11 19				
Thurnscoe d		09 26					09 26				10 25					10 25				11 25				
Goldthorpe d		→					09 28				→					10 27				→				
Bolton-on-Dearne d							09 31									10 30								
Swinton (S.Yorks) 29 a							09 35									10 34								
Rotherham Central 29 a							09 44									10 44								
Meadowhall 29 a						09 48	09 51	10 03							10 48	10 51	11 03							11 48
Sheffield 7 29 a	09 21				09 51	09 57	10 02	10 15						10 51	10 57	11 02	11 15						11 51	11 57

	NT	NT	NT N	NT	NT	NT	NT C	GR R 1 A	XC R 1 Q	NT	NT	NT	NT	NT	NT	NT C	GR R 1 A	XC R 1 U	NT	NT	NT	NT	NT	NT
Leeds 10 32, 34 d		11 16		11 19	11 34	11 48		12 05	12 10			12 16	12 19	12 34	12 48		13 05	13 10			13 16	13 19	13 34	13 48
Outwood d				11 28		11 59							12 28		12 59							13 28		13 59
Wakefield Kirkgate 4 32, 34, 39 a		11 32			12 04					←		12 32		13 03					←		13 32		14 03	
d		11 32			12 05					12 05		12 32		13 03					13 03		13 32		14 03	
Wakefield Westgate 7 32, 39 a				11 32	→	12 03		12 17	12 23				12 32	→	13 03		13 17	13 22				13 32	→	14 03
d				11 32		12 03		12 17	12 23				12 32		13 03		13 17	13 23				13 32		14 03
Sandal & Agbrigg d				11 35		12 07							12 35		13 07							13 35		14 07
Fitzwilliam d				11 42		12 14							12 42		13 14							13 42		14 14
South Elmsall d				11 47									12 47									13 47		
Adwick a				11 52									12 52									13 52		
d				11 53			12 13						12 53			13 12						13 53		
Bentley (S.Yorks) d				11 57			12 17						12 57			13 16						13 57		
Doncaster 7 a				12 07			12 22	12 34					13 07			13 23	13 37					14 07		
Moorthorpe d	←		11 49			12 19					←				13 19					←				14 19
Thurnscoe d	11 25					12 25					12 25				13 25					13 25				14 25
Goldthorpe d	11 27					→					12 27				→					13 27				→
Bolton-on-Dearne d	11 30										12 30									13 30				
Swinton (S.Yorks) 29 a	11 34		11 59								12 34									13 34				
Rotherham Central 29 a	11 44		12 10								12 44									13 44				
Meadowhall 29 a	11 51	12 03	12 16							12 48	12 51	13 03							13 48	13 51	14 03			
Sheffield 7 29 a	12 02	12 15	12 25						12 51	12 57	13 02	13 15						13 51	13 57	14 02	14 15			

For general notes see front of timetable
For details of catering facilities see Directory of Train Operators

- **A** To London Kings Cross (Table 26)
- **B** To Plymouth (Table 51)
- **C** To Sheffield (Table 29)
- **D** To St Pancras International (Table 53)
- **E** From Skipton to London Kings Cross (Table 26)
- **G** From Bradford Forster Square to London Kings Cross (Table 26)
- **H** From Newcastle to Bournemouth (Table 51)
- **J** From Edinburgh to Plymouth (Table 51)
- **K** From Glasgow Central to Bournemouth (Table 51)
- **L** From Newcastle (Table 51) to Newquay (Table 135)
- **N** From York (Table 33)
- **Q** From Dundee (Table 229) to Bournemouth (Table 51)
- **U** From Glasgow Central to Paignton (Table 51)

Due to Engineering Operations in the Sheffield area, services from Saturday 13 September on this Table had not been confirmed at time of going to press. These services will be issued in a special Supplement as soon as exact timings have been confirmed.

Table 31

Saturdays
until 6 September

Leeds → Wakefield, Doncaster and Sheffield

Network Diagram - see first page of Table 31

	NT	GR	XC	NT	NT	NT	NT	NT	NT	NT	GR	XC	NT	NT	NT	NT	NT	NT	NT	NT	GR	XC	NT	NT
		R 1	1 ◇								R 1	1 ◇									R 1	1 ◇		
	A	B	C							A	B	D				E				A	B	G		
Leeds 10 32, 34 d		14 05	14 10			14 16	14 19	14 34	14 48		15 05	15 10			15 16		15 19	15 34	15 48		16 05	16 10		
Outwood d							14 28		14 59								15 28		15 59					
Wakefield Kirkgate 4 32, 34, 39 a				←		14 32		15 03					←		15 32			16 03					←	
d				14 03		14 32		15 03					15 03		15 32			16 03					16 03	
Wakefield Westgate 7 32, 39 a		14 17	14 22				14 32	→	15 03		15 17	15 22					15 32	→	16 03		16 17	16 22		
d		14 17	14 23				14 32		15 03		15 17	15 23					15 32		16 03		16 17	16 23		
Sandal & Agbrigg d							14 35		15 07								15 35		16 07					
Fitzwilliam d							14 42		15 14								15 42		16 14					
South Elmsall d							14 47										15 47							
Adwick a							14 52										15 52							
d	14 14						14 53			15 13							15 53			16 13				
Bentley (S.Yorks) d	14 18						14 57			15 17							15 57			16 17				
Doncaster 7 a	14 22	14 34					15 07			15 22	15 35						16 07			16 22	16 38			
Moorthorpe d					←				15 19					←		16 01			16 19					←
Thurnscoe d					14 25				15 25					15 25					16 25					16 25
Goldthorpe d					14 27				→					15 27					→					16 27
Bolton-on-Dearne d					14 30									15 30										16 30
Swinton (S.Yorks) 29 a					14 34									15 34		16 10								16 34
Rotherham Central 29 a					14 44									15 42		16 17								16 43
Meadowhall 29 a				14 48	14 51	15 03							15 48	15 51	16 05	16 23							16 48	16 51
Sheffield 7 29 a			14 51	14 57	15 02	15 15						15 51	15 57	16 02	16 15	16 35						16 51	16 57	17 02

	NT	NT	NT	NT	NT	XC	NT	NT	NT	NT	NT	GR	NT	NT	XC	NT	NT	NT	NT	NT	GR	NT	XC	NT
						1 ◇						R 1			1 ◇						R 1		1 ◇	
				H		J						B		H	K						B		L	
Leeds 10 32, 34 d	16 16	16 19	16 34		16 48	17 10			17 16	17 19	17 34	17 40	17 46		18 10			18 16	18 19	18 34	18 40	18 48	19 10	
Outwood d		16 28			16 59					17 28			17 57						18 28			18 59		
Wakefield Kirkgate 4 32, 34, 39 a	16 32		17 03				←		17 32		18 03					←		18 32		19 03				←
d	16 32		17 03				17 03		17 32		18 03					18 03		18 32		19 03				19 03
Wakefield Westgate 7 32, 39 a		16 32	→		17 03	17 22				17 33	→	17 52	18 01		18 22				18 32	→	18 54	19 03	19 22	
d		16 32			17 03	17 23				17 33		17 52	18 01		18 23				18 33		18 54	19 03	19 23	
Sandal & Agbrigg d		16 35			17 07					17 36			18 05						18 36			19 07		
Fitzwilliam d		16 42			17 14					17 43			18 12						18 42			19 14		
South Elmsall d		16 47								17 48									18 47					
Adwick a		16 52								17 53									18 53					
d		16 53		17 05						17 54				18 14					18 53					
Bentley (S.Yorks) d		16 57		17 09						17 58				18 18					18 57					
Doncaster 7 a		17 07		17 14						18 07		18 09		18 23					19 07		19 11			
Moorthorpe d					17 19			←					18 17				←					19 19		
Thurnscoe d					17 25			17 25					18 23				18 23					19 25		
Goldthorpe d					→			17 27					→				18 25					→		
Bolton-on-Dearne d								17 30									18 28							
Swinton (S.Yorks) 29 a								17 34									18 34							
Rotherham Central 29 a								17 44									18 43							
Meadowhall 29 a	17 03						17 48	17 51	18 03							18 47	18 51	19 03						19 48
Sheffield 7 29 a	17 15					17 51	17 57	18 02	18 15						18 51	18 57	19 02	19 15					19 51	19 57

	NT	NT	NT	NT	NT	XC	NT	NT	GR	NT	NT	NT	NT	XC	NT	NT	NT	NT	NT	NT	NT	NT		
						1 ◇			R 1					1 ◇										
						N			B					Q										
Leeds 10 32, 34 d		19 16	19 22	19 34	19 48	20 10			20 15	20 16	20 21	20 34	20 48	21 10			21 34	21 34	21 48	22 16	22 34	22 44		
Outwood d			19 28		19 59						20 30		20 59				21 43		21 59	22 25		22 55		
Wakefield Kirkgate 4 32, 34, 39 a		19 32		20 03			←			20 32		21 03			←			22 03			23 03			
d		19 32		20 03			20 03			20 32		21 03			21 03			22 03						
Wakefield Westgate 7 32, 39 a			19 32	→	20 03	20 23			20 31		20 36	→	21 03	21 22			21 47		22 03	22 29		22 59		
d			19 32		20 03	20 23			20 31		20 36		21 03	21 23			21 47		22 03	22 30		22 59		
Sandal & Agbrigg d			19 35		20 07						20 39		21 07				21 50		22 07	22 33		23 03		
Fitzwilliam d			19 42		20 14						20 46		21 13				21 57		22 14	22 39		23 10		
South Elmsall d			19 47								20 51						22 02			22 44				
Adwick a			19 53								20 56						22 07			22 50				
d			19 53								20 57						22 08			22 50				
Bentley (S.Yorks) d			19 57								21 01						22 12			22 54				
Doncaster 7 a			20 10						20 48		21 09						22 22			23 04				
Moorthorpe d	←				20 19			←					21 20			←			22 19			23 15		
Thurnscoe d	19 25				20 25			20 25					21 26			21 26			22 25			23 21		
Goldthorpe d	19 27				→			20 27					→			21 28			22 27			23 23		
Bolton-on-Dearne d	19 30							20 30								21 31			22 30			23 26		
Swinton (S.Yorks) 29 a	19 34							20 34								21 35			22 34			23 30		
Rotherham Central 29 a	19 43							20 42								21 44			22 43			23 37		
Meadowhall 29 a	19 51	20 03					20 47	20 50		21 03					21 48	21 52		22 48	22 51			23 43		
Sheffield 7 29 a	20 02	20 15				20 51	20 57	21 02		21 15				21 51	21 57	22 07		22 57	23 02			23 58		

For general notes see front of timetable
For details of catering facilities see Directory of Train Operators

- **A** To Sheffield (Table 29)
- **B** To London Kings Cross (Table 26)
- **C** From Aberdeen (Table 229) to Bournemouth (Table 51)
- **D** From Edinburgh (Table 51) to Penzance (Table 135)
- **E** From York (Table 33)
- **G** From Edinburgh to Bournemouth (Table 51)
- **H** To Scunthorpe (Table 29)
- **J** From Edinburgh to Plymouth (Table 51)
- **K** From Edinburgh to Southampton Central (Table 51)
- **L** From Edinburgh to Bristol Temple Meads (Table 51)
- **N** From Newcastle to Birmingham New Street (Table 51)
- **Q** From Edinburgh to Birmingham New Street (Table 51)

Due to Engineering Operations in the Sheffield area, services from Saturday 13 September on this Table had not been confirmed at time of going to press. These services will be issued in a special Supplement as soon as exact timings have been confirmed.

Sundays
until 13 July

Leeds → Wakefield, Doncaster and Sheffield

Network Diagram - see first page of Table 31

		GR R 1 A	XC 1 ◇ B	NT	NT	EM 1 ◇ C	NT		GR R 1 D	GR R 1 A	XC R 1 E	NT	NT	NT		GR R 1 A	EM 1 ◇ C	NT	XC R 1 G	NT	NT		NT	GR R 1 A	XC R 1 H
Leeds 10	32, 34 d	08 24	08 30	08 30	08 50	09 00			09 05	09 40	10 00	10 09	10 14	10 17		10 40	10 57		11 00	11 09	11 14			11 40	12 00
Outwood	d				09 01							10 18								11 20					
Wakefield Kirkgate 4	32, 34, 39 a			08 59									10 30	10 46				←			11 30				
	d			09 00									10 30	10 46				10 46			11 30				
Wakefield Westgate 7	32, 39 a	08 36	08 42		09 05	09 11			09 17	09 52	10 11	10 22		→		10 52	11 08		11 11	11 24				11 52	12 11
	d	08 36	08 43		09 05	09 11			09 17	09 52	10 12	10 22				10 52	11 08		11 12	11 24				11 52	12 12
Sandal & Agbrigg	d				09 09							10 25								11 28					
Fitzwilliam	d				09 16							10 32								11 35					
South Elmsall	d											10 37													
Adwick	a											10 42													
	d											10 43													
Bentley (S.Yorks)	d											10 47													
Doncaster 7	a	08 54	09 00			09 32			09 37	10 09	10 32	10 57				11 12			11 31					12 09	12 30
Moorthorpe	d				09 21		←													11 40			←		
Thurnscoe	d				09 27 →		09 27													11 46 →			11 46		
Goldthorpe	d						09 29																11 48		
Bolton-on-Dearne	d						09 32																11 51		
Swinton (S.Yorks)	29 a						09 36																11 55		
Rotherham Central	29 a						09 45																12 04		
Meadowhall	29 a			09 41			09 53						11 04					11 32			12 04		12 09		
Sheffield 7	29 a		09 26	09 51		09 57	10 04				10 57		11 15				11 37	11 43	12 05		12 14		12 21		13 08

		NT	NT J	GR R 1 A	XC R 1 K	NT		NT	NT	GR R 1 A	XC R 1 L	NT	NT		GR R 1 A	XC R 1 N	NT	GR R 1 A	XC R 1 Q	NT		NT	GR R 1 A	XC R 1 U	GR R 1 A
Leeds 10	32, 34 d	12 09	12 17	12 40	13 00	13 09		13 14		13 40	14 00	14 09	14 17		14 40	15 00	15 09	15 40	16 00	16 09		16 17	16 40	17 00	17 05
Outwood	d	12 18				13 20						14 18					15 20			16 18					
Wakefield Kirkgate 4	32, 34, 39 a		12 46					13 30					14 46									16 46			
	d		12 46					13 30					14 46									16 46			
Wakefield Westgate 7	32, 39 a	12 22		12 52	13 11	13 24				13 52	14 11	14 22			14 52	15 11	15 24	15 52	16 11	16 22			16 52	17 11	17 18
	d	12 22		12 52	13 12	13 24				13 52	14 12	14 22			14 52	15 12	15 24	15 52	16 12	16 22			16 52	17 12	17 18
Sandal & Agbrigg	d	12 25				13 28						14 25					15 28			16 25					
Fitzwilliam	d	12 32				13 35						14 32					15 35			16 32					
South Elmsall	d	12 37										14 37								16 37					
Adwick	a	12 42										14 42								16 42					
	d	12 43										14 43								16 43					
Bentley (S.Yorks)	d	12 47										14 47								16 47					
Doncaster 7	a	12 57		13 11	13 30					14 09	14 35	14 57			15 10	15 32		16 09	16 34	16 57			17 10	17 29	17 35
Moorthorpe	d					13 40			←								15 40								
Thurnscoe	d					13 46 →			13 46								15 46								
Goldthorpe	d								13 48								15 48								
Bolton-on-Dearne	d								13 51								15 51								
Swinton (S.Yorks)	29 a								13 58								15 55								
Rotherham Central	29 a								14 05								16 05								
Meadowhall	29 a		13 32					14 03	14 11				15 32				16 10					17 32			
Sheffield 7	29 a		13 43		14 03			14 15	14 21		15 03		15 44			16 02	16 21		17 03			17 43		18 07	

		NT	GR R 1 A	NT V	XC 1 ◇ X		NT	NT	GR R 1 A	XC 1 ◇ Y	NT	XC 1 ◇ Z		GR R 1 A	NT	NT	XC 1 ◇ K	NT V	NT		NT	XC 1 ◇ AA	NT		
Leeds 10	32, 34 d	17 09	17 40		18 00		18 09	18 17	18 40	19 00	19 09	20 00		20 15	20 17	20 20	21 00		21 09		21 40	22 00	22 17		
Outwood	d	17 20					18 18				19 20					20 29			21 18		21 51				
Wakefield Kirkgate 4	32, 34, 39 a							18 46							20 46								22 46		
	d							18 46							20 46								22 46		
Wakefield Westgate 7	32, 39 a	17 24	17 52		18 11		18 22		18 52	19 11	19 24	20 11		20 27		20 33	21 11		21 22		21 55	22 11			
	d	17 24			18 12		18 22		18 52	19 12	19 24	20 12		20 27		20 33	21 12		21 22		21 55	22 12			
Sandal & Agbrigg	d	17 28					18 25				19 28					20 36			21 25		21 59				
Fitzwilliam	d	17 35					18 32				19 35					20 43			21 32		22 06				
South Elmsall	d						18 37									20 48			21 37						
Adwick	a						18 42									20 53			21 42						
	d						18 43									20 54			21 43						
Bentley (S.Yorks)	d						18 47									20 58			21 47						
Doncaster 7	a				18 34		18 57		19 09	19 28		20 32		20 47		21 08	21 30		21 57			22 30			
Moorthorpe	d	17 40		18 02							19 40							21 29			22 11				
Thurnscoe	d	17 46									19 46										22 17				
Goldthorpe	d	17 48									19 48										22 19				
Bolton-on-Dearne	d	17 51									19 51										22 22				
Swinton (S.Yorks)	29 a	17 55		18 11							19 55							21 38			22 32				
Rotherham Central	29 a	18 05		18 20							20 04							21 48			22 39				
Meadowhall	29 a	18 10		18 25				19 32			20 11				21 32			21 54			22 45		23 32		
Sheffield 7	29 a	18 23		18 35	19 08			19 44		19 58	20 23	20 59			21 43		21 57	22 05			22 54	23 03	23 43		

For general notes see front of timetable
For details of catering facilities see Directory of Train Operators

- **A** To London Kings Cross (Table 26)
- **B** To Bournemouth (Table 51)
- **C** To St Pancras International (Table 53)
- **D** To Glasgow Central (Table 26)
- **E** From York to Plymouth (Table 51)
- **G** From Newcastle to Bournemouth (Table 51)
- **H** From Edinburgh (Table 51) to Penzance (Table 135)
- **J** To Lincoln (Table 30)
- **K** From Edinburgh to Birmingham New Street (Table 51)
- **L** From Edinburgh to Plymouth (Table 51)
- **N** From Glasgow Central to Bournemouth (Table 51)
- **Q** From Glasgow Central to Plymouth (Table 51)
- **U** From Edinburgh to Southampton Central (Table 51)
- **V** From York (Table 33)
- **X** From Aberdeen (Table 229) to Bristol Temple Meads (Table 51)
- **Y** From Edinburgh to Bristol Temple Meads (Table 51)
- **Z** From Glasgow Central to Birmingham New Street (Table 51)
- **AA** From Edinburgh to Derby (Table 51)

Table 31

Sundays
20 July to 7 September

Leeds → Wakefield, Doncaster and Sheffield

Network Diagram - see first page of Table 31

		GR	NT	NT	NT	GR	XC	EM		GR	XC	NT	NT	NT	GR	XC		EM	XC	NT	NT	NT	GR	NT	NT
		R 1				R 1	1 ◇	1 ◇		R 1	R 1				R 1	R 1		1 ◇	R 1				R 1		
		A				B	C	D		A	E				A	G		D	G				A		H
Leeds 10	32, 34 d	08 24	08 30	08 50		09 05	09 20	09 32		09 40	10 00	10 09	10 14	10 17	10 40	11 00		11 06		11 09	11 14		11 40	12 09	12 17
Outwood	d			09 01								10 18								11 20				12 18	
Wakefield Kirkgate 4	32, 34, 39 a		08 59										10 30	10 46							11 30				12 46
	d		09 00										10 30	10 46							11 30				12 46
Wakefield Westgate 7	32, 39 a	08 36		09 05		09 17	09 31	09 46		09 52	10 11	10 22			10 52	11 11		11 17		11 24			11 52	12 22	→
	d	08 36		09 05		09 17	09 31	09 46		09 52	10 12	10 22			10 52	11 12		11 17		11 24			11 52	12 22	
Sandal & Agbrigg	d			09 09								10 25								11 28				12 25	
Fitzwilliam	d			09 16								10 32								11 35				12 32	
South Elmsall	d											10 37												12 37	
Adwick	a											10 42												12 42	
	d											10 43												12 43	
Bentley (S.Yorks)	d											10 47							←					12 47	
Doncaster 7	a	08 54				09 37	09 50	10 03		10 09		10 57			11 12	11 29			11 29				12 09	12 57	
Moorthorpe	d			09 21	←											→				11 40		←			
Thurnscoe	d			09 27	09 27															11 46		11 46			
Goldthorpe	d			→	09 29															→		11 48			
Bolton-on-Dearne	d				09 32																	11 51			
Swinton (S.Yorks)	29 a				09 36																	11 55			
Rotherham Central	29 a				09 45																	12 05			
Meadowhall	29 a		09 41		09 53								11 04	11 32							12 04	12 11			
Sheffield 7	29 a		09 51		10 04		10 12	10 30			10 46		11 15	11 43				11 47	12 03		12 14	12 20			

		GR		XC	NT	NT	NT	NT	GR	XC		NT	NT	GR	XC	NT	NT	GR		XC	NT	NT	GR	XC	NT
		R 1		R 1					R 1	R 1				R 1	R 1			R 1		R 1			R 1	R 1	
		A		J	H				A	K				A	L			A		N			A	Q	
Leeds 10	32, 34 d	12 40		13 00		13 09	13 14		13 40	14 00		14 09	14 17	14 40	15 00		15 09	15 40		16 00	16 09	16 17	16 40	17 00	
Outwood	d					13 20						14 18					15 20				16 18				
Wakefield Kirkgate 4	32, 34, 39 a				←		13 30						14 46			←						16 46			←
	d				12 46		13 30						14 46			14 46						16 46			16 46
Wakefield Westgate 7	32, 39 a	12 52		13 11		13 24			13 52	14 11		14 22	→	14 52	15 11		15 24	15 52		16 11	16 22	→	16 52	17 11	
	d	12 52		13 12		13 24			13 52	14 12		14 22		14 52	15 12		15 24	15 52		16 12	16 22		16 52	17 12	
Sandal & Agbrigg	d					13 28						14 25					15 28				16 25				
Fitzwilliam	d					13 35						14 32					15 35				16 32				
South Elmsall	d											14 37									16 37				
Adwick	a											14 42									16 42				
	d											14 43									16 43				
Bentley (S.Yorks)	d											14 47									16 47				
Doncaster 7	a	13 11						←	14 09			14 57		15 10				16 09			16 57		17 10		
Moorthorpe	d					13 40		13 40									15 40								
Thurnscoe	d					13 46		13 46									15 46								
Goldthorpe	d					→		13 48									15 48								
Bolton-on-Dearne	d							13 51									15 51								
Swinton (S.Yorks)	29 a							13 58									15 55								
Rotherham Central	29 a							14 08									16 05								
Meadowhall	29 a				13 32		14 03	14 14								15 32	16 10								17 32
Sheffield 7	29 a			13 42	13 43		14 15	14 24		14 41					15 41	15 44	16 26			16 41				17 41	17 44

		GR	NT	GR		NT	XC	NT	NT	GR	XC	NT		NT	XC	GR	NT	NT	NT	XC	NT	NT	NT		
		R 1		R 1			R 1			R 1	1 ◇				1 ◇	R 1				1 ◇					
		A		A		U	V			A					X	A				Y	U				
Leeds 10	32, 34 d	17 05	17 09	17 40			18 00	18 09	18 17	18 40	19 00			19 09	20 00	20 15	20 17	20 20	21 09	21 15		21 40	22 17		
Outwood	d		17 20					18 18						19 20				20 29	21 18			21 51			
Wakefield Kirkgate 4	32, 34, 39 a								18 46			←					20 46						22 46		
	d								18 46			18 46					20 46						22 46		
Wakefield Westgate 7	32, 39 a	17 18	17 24	17 52			18 11	18 22	→	18 52	19 11			19 24	20 11	20 27		20 33	21 22	21 26		21 55			
	d	17 18	17 24				18 12	18 22		18 52	19 12			19 24	20 12	20 27		20 33	21 22	21 26		21 55			
Sandal & Agbrigg	d		17 28					18 25						19 28				20 36	21 25			21 59			
Fitzwilliam	d		17 35					18 32						19 35				20 43	21 32			22 06			
South Elmsall	d							18 37										20 48	21 37						
Adwick	a							18 42										20 53	21 42						
	d							18 43										20 54	21 43						
Bentley (S.Yorks)	d							18 47										20 58	21 47						
Doncaster 7	a	17 35						18 57		19 09						20 47		21 08	21 57						
Moorthorpe	d		17 40			18 02								19 40							21 29	22 11			
Thurnscoe	d		17 46											19 46								22 17			
Goldthorpe	d		17 48											19 48								22 19			
Bolton-on-Dearne	d		17 51											19 51								22 22			
Swinton (S.Yorks)	29 a		17 55			18 11								19 55							21 38	22 32			
Rotherham Central	29 a		18 05			18 20								20 04							21 48	22 39			
Meadowhall	29 a		18 10			18 25						19 32		20 11			21 32				21 54	22 45	23 32		
Sheffield 7	29 a		18 23			18 35	18 41				19 41	19 44		20 23	20 41		21 43			21 59	22 05	22 54	23 43		

For general notes see front of timetable
For details of catering facilities see Directory of Train Operators

- **A** To London Kings Cross (Table 26)
- **B** To Glasgow Central (Table 26)
- **C** To Bournemouth (Table 51)
- **D** To St Pancras International (Table 53)
- **E** From York to Plymouth (Table 51)
- **G** From Newcastle to Bournemouth (Table 51)
- **H** To Lincoln (Table 30)
- **J** From Edinburgh (Table 51) to Penzance (Table 135)
- **K** From Edinburgh to Bournemouth (Table 51)
- **L** From Glasgow Central to Plymouth (Table 51)
- **N** From Glasgow Central to Bournemouth (Table 51)
- **Q** From Edinburgh to Plymouth (Table 51)
- **U** From York (Table 33)
- **V** From Aberdeen (Table 229) to Southampton Central (Table 51)
- **X** From Glasgow Central to Birmingham New Street (Table 51)
- **Y** From Edinburgh to Birmingham New Street (Table 51)

Due to Engineering Operations in the Sheffield area, services from Sunday 14 September on this Table had not been confirmed at time of going to press. These services will be issued in a special Supplement as soon as exact timings have been confirmed.

Table 32

Mondays to Saturdays

Leeds and Wakefield → Pontefract, Knottingley and Goole

Network Diagram - see first page of Table 31

Miles	Miles			NT SX	NT	NT	NT	NT		NT	NT	NT	NT	NT	NT
0	—	**Leeds** [10]	31, 34 d	05 46		07 04		08 04	and at the same minutes past each hour until	16 04		17 19		18 04	
6	—	Woodlesford	34 d	05 54		07 12		08 12		16 12		17 28		18 12	
10¾	—	Castleford	a	06 03		07 23		08 21		16 21		17 37		18 21	
—	—		34 d	06 05		07 26		08 23		16 23		17 40		18 23	
12¼	—	Glasshoughton	d	06 10		07 30		08 28		16 28		17 44		18 28	
—	0	**Wakefield Westgate** [7]	31, 39 d		06 25										
—	1	Wakefield Kirkgate [4]	31, 34, 39 a		06 29										
—	—		d		06 29		07 38				16 38		17 38		18 38
—	5¼	Streethouse	d		06 36		07 46				16 46		17 46		18 46
—	7	Featherstone	d		06 40		07 50				16 50		17 50		18 50
—	9	Pontefract Tanshelf	d		06 44		07 53				16 53		17 53		18 53
14	9¾	Pontefract Monkhill	a	06 14	06 47	07 35	07 56	08 32		16 32	16 56	17 49	17 56	18 32	18 56
—	—		d	06 14	06 47	07 35	07 56	08 32		16 32	16 56	17 49	17 56	18 32	18 56
16	—	**Knottingley**	a	06 22	06 54	07 42	08 03	08 39		16 39	17 03	17 55	18 03	18 39	19 03
—	—		d									17 55			
20¼	—	Whitley Bridge	d									18 01			
22	—	Hensall	d									18 06			
25¾	—	Snaith	d									18 12			
28½	—	Rawcliffe	d									18 17			
32½	—	**Goole**	a									18 29			

		NT	NT	NT	NT	NT	NT	NT	NT SX	NT SO
Leeds [10]	31, 34 d	19 04		20 04		21 04		22 04		
Woodlesford	34 d	19 12		20 12		21 12		22 12		
Castleford	a	19 21		20 21		21 21		22 21		
	34 d	19 23		20 23		21 23		22 23		
Glasshoughton	d	19 28		20 28		21 28		22 28		
Wakefield Westgate [7]	31, 39 d						21 57		23 04	23 04
Wakefield Kirkgate [4]	31, 34, 39 a						22 00		23 07	23 07
	d		19 38		20 38		22 00		23 07	23 07
Streethouse	d		19 46		20 46		22 08		23 15	23 15
Featherstone	d		19 50		20 50		22 12		23 19	23 19
Pontefract Tanshelf	d		19 53		20 53		22 16		23 23	23 23
Pontefract Monkhill	a	19 32	19 56	20 32	20 56	21 32	22 18	22 32	23 29	23 29
	d	19 32	19 56	20 32	20 56	21 32	22 19	22 32	23 29	
Knottingley	a	19 39	20 03	20 39	21 03	21 39	22 25	22 39	23 33	
	d									
Whitley Bridge	d									
Hensall	d									
Snaith	d									
Rawcliffe	d									
Goole	a									

Sundays

		NT	NT	NT	NT	NT	NT	NT
Leeds [10]	34 d	09 30	11 17	13 17	15 17	17 17	19 17	21 17
Woodlesford	34 d	09 38	11 25	13 25	15 25	17 25	19 25	21 25
Castleford	34 a	09 46	11 33	13 33	15 33	17 33	19 35	21 33
	d	09 49	11 36	13 36	15 36	17 36	19 36	21 36
Glasshoughton	d	09 53	11 40	13 40	15 40	17 40	19 40	21 40
Pontefract Monkhill	d	09 58	11 45	13 45	15 45	17 45	19 45	21 45
Knottingley	a	10 04	11 52	13 52	15 52	17 52	19 52	21 52

For general notes see front of timetable
For details of catering facilities see Directory of Train Operators

Goole, Knottingley and Pontefract → Wakefield and Leeds

Network Diagram - see first page of Table 31

Miles	Miles	Station		NT SX	NT	NT SO	NT SX	NT	NT	NT	NT	and at the same minutes past each hour until	NT	NT	NT
0	—	**Goole**	d			07 04	07 11								
4	—	Rawcliffe	d			07 11	07 18								
6¾	—	Snaith	d			07 16	07 23								
10½	—	Hensall	d			07 23	07 30								
12¼	—	Whitley Bridge	d			07 27	07 34								
16½	—	**Knottingley**	a			07 35	07 42								
—	—		d	06 25	06 56	07 35	07 46	07 56	08 18	08 56	09 18		17 18	18 05	18 43
18½	0	Pontefract Monkhill	a	06 29	07 00	07 39	07 50	08 00	08 22	09 00	09 22		17 22	18 09	18 47
—	—		d	06 29	07 00	07 39	07 50	08 00	08 22	09 00	09 22		17 22	18 09	18 47
—	¾	Pontefract Tanshelf	d		07 03			08 03		09 03				18 12	
—	2¾	Featherstone	d		07 06			08 06		09 06				18 15	
—	4½	Streethouse	d		07 10			08 10		09 10				18 19	
—	8¾	Wakefield Kirkgate 4	31, 34, 39 a		07 22			08 21		09 21				18 32	
—	—		d												
—	9¾	**Wakefield Westgate 7**	...31, 39 a												
20	—	Glasshoughton	d	06 34		07 44	07 55		08 27		09 27		17 27		18 52
21½	—	Castleford	a	06 38		07 49	08 04		08 31		09 31		17 31		18 56
—	—		34 d	06 41		07 51	08 06		08 34		09 34		17 34		18 59
26½	—	Woodlesford	34 d	06 50		08 00	08 15		08 43		09 43		17 43		19 08
32½	—	**Leeds 10**	31, 34 a	07 03		08 13	08 27		09 00		09 55		17 55		19 21

Station		NT	NT	NT	NT	NT	NT	NT	NT	NT
Goole	d		18 49							
Rawcliffe	d		18 56							
Snaith	d		19 01							
Hensall	d		19 08							
Whitley Bridge	d		19 12							
Knottingley	a		19 20							
	d	19 05	19 27	19 56	20 18	21 18	21 23	22 18	22 30	23 18
Pontefract Monkhill	a	19 09	19 31	20 00	20 22	21 22	21 27	22 25	22 34	23 22
	d	19 09	19 31	20 00	20 22	21 22	21 27	22 25	22 34	23 22
Pontefract Tanshelf	d	19 12		20 03			21 30		22 37	
Featherstone	d	19 15		20 06			21 33		22 40	
Streethouse	d	19 19		20 10			21 37		22 44	
Wakefield Kirkgate 4	31, 34, 39 a	19 31		20 22			21 47		22 55	
	d						21 47		22 55	
Wakefield Westgate 7	...31, 39 a						21 52		23 00	
Glasshoughton	d		19 36		20 27	21 27		22 30		23 27
Castleford	a		19 40		20 31	21 31		22 34		23 31
	34 d		19 43		20 34	21 34		22 37		23 34
Woodlesford	34 d		19 52		20 43	21 43		22 46		23 43
Leeds 10	31, 34 a		20 04		20 55	21 55		23 01		23 55

Sundays

Station		NT	NT	NT	NT	NT	NT	NT
Knottingley	d	10 26	12 26	14 26	16 26	18 26	20 26	22 26
Pontefract Monkhill	d	10 30	12 30	14 30	16 30	18 30	20 30	22 30
Glasshoughton	d	10 35	12 35	14 35	16 35	18 35	20 35	22 35
Castleford	a	10 39	12 39	14 39	16 39	18 39	20 36	22 39
	34 d	10 42	12 42	14 42	16 42	18 42	20 42	22 42
Woodlesford	34 d	10 51	12 51	14 51	16 51	18 51	20 51	22 51
Leeds 10	34 a	11 06	13 06	15 04	17 04	19 06	21 04	23 04

For general notes see front of timetable
For details of catering facilities see Directory of Train Operators

Table 33

Sheffield and Selby → York

Local services only

Mondays to Fridays
until 5 September

Network Diagram - see first page of Table 31

Miles	Miles		NT	NT A	NT B	NT A	NT	NT	NT A	NT	NT	NT	NT A	NT
0	—	**Sheffield 7** 29, 31 d								09 29				
3½	—	Meadowhall 29, 31 d								09 35				
6¼	—	Rotherham Central 29, 31 d								09 42				
10¾	—	Swinton (S.Yorks) 29, 31 d								09 51				
18½	—	Moorthorpe 31 d								10 01				
25½	—	Pontefract Baghill d								10 10				
—	—	Hull 29 d	06 00		07 07		08 38	09 02			10 12	11 05		11 38
—	0	**Selby** d	06 48		07 48		09 16	09 38			10 54	11 39		12 51
33¾	8¼	Sherburn-in-Elmet d	07 00		08 02		09 28			10 27				
36	10½	Church Fenton d	07 04	08 04		09 09			10 05	10 31			12 05	
38	12½	Ulleskelf d			08 08					10 35				
46¾	21	**York 8** 29 a	07 20	08 19	08 22	09 23	09 48	10 07	10 20	10 51	11 20	12 10	12 20	13 15

	NT A	NT	NT	NT	NT A	NT	NT A	NT B	NT A	NT	NT	NT A	NT A
Sheffield 7 29, 31 d			13 28										
Meadowhall 29, 31 d			13 35										
Rotherham Central 29, 31 d			13 42										
Swinton (S.Yorks) 29, 31 d			13 50										
Moorthorpe 31 d			14 01										
Pontefract Baghill d			14 10										
Hull 29 d		13 12		15 06		16 10		17 18		19 10	19 56		
Selby d		13 56		15 38		16 47		18 06		19 47	20 37		
Sherburn-in-Elmet d		14 10	14 27										
Church Fenton d	14 05		14 31		16 05		18 06		19 05			21 12	23 16
Ulleskelf d			14 35				18 10					21 16	
York 8 29 a	14 20	14 27	14 50	16 06	16 22	17 13	18 24	18 36	19 20	20 15	21 00	21 29	23 34

Mondays to Fridays
from 8 September

	NT	NT A	NT B	NT A	NT	NT	NT A	NT	NT Bus	NT	NT A	NT	NT A	NT	NT Bus	NT	NT A	NT	NT A	NT B	NT A	NT	NT	NT A	NT A
Sheffield 7 29, 31 d									09 14						13 14										
Meadowhall 29, 31 d									09 31						13 31										
Rotherham Central 29, 31 d									09 37						13 37										
Swinton (S.Yorks) 29, 31 d									09 55						13 55										
Moorthorpe 31 d									10 25						14 25										
Pontefract Baghill d									10 40						14 40										
Hull 29 d	06 00		07 07		08 38	09 02		10 12		11 05		11 38		13 12		15 06		16 10		17 18		19 10	19 56		
Selby d	06 48		07 48		09 16	09 38		10 54		11 39		12 51		13 56		15 38		16 47		18 06		19 47	20 37		
Sherburn-in-Elmet d	07 00		08 02		09 28				11 00					14 10	15 00										
Church Fenton d	07 04	08 04		09 09			10 05		11 10		12 05		14 05		15 10		16 05		18 06		19 05			21 12	23 16
Ulleskelf d			08 08						11 20						15 20				18 10					21 16	
York 8 29 a	07 20	08 19	08 22	09 23	09 48	10 07	10 20	11 20	11 50	12 10	12 20	13 15	14 20	14 27	15 50	16 06	16 22	17 13	18 24	18 36	19 20	20 15	21 00	21 29	23 34

Saturdays
until 6 September

	NT	NT B	NT A	NT A	NT	NT	NT A	NT	NT	NT	NT A	NT	NT A
Sheffield 7 29, 31 d								09 31					
Meadowhall 29, 31 d								09 37					
Rotherham Central 29, 31 d								09 44					
Swinton (S.Yorks) 29, 31 d								09 52					
Moorthorpe 31 d								10 02					
Pontefract Baghill d								10 11					
Hull 29 d	06 00	06 57			08 38	09 02			10 06	11 08		11 38	
Selby d	06 48	07 40			09 14	09 38			10 54	11 40		12 51	
Sherburn-in-Elmet d	07 00	07 54			09 26			10 27				13 03	
Church Fenton d	07 04		08 04	09 05			10 05	10 32			12 05		14 05
Ulleskelf d		08 00						10 36					
York 8 29 a	07 20	08 14	08 19	09 20	09 41	10 10	10 20	10 53	11 16	12 10	12 20	13 23	14 20

	NT	NT	NT	NT A	NT	NT A	NT B	NT A	NT	NT	NT A	NT	NT A
Sheffield 7 29, 31 d		13 28											
Meadowhall 29, 31 d		13 35											
Rotherham Central 29, 31 d		13 42											
Swinton (S.Yorks) 29, 31 d		13 50											
Moorthorpe 31 d		14 00											
Pontefract Baghill d		14 09											
Hull 29 d	13 12		14 51		16 10		17 18		18 46	19 56		21 33	
Selby d	13 54		15 22		16 47		18 06		19 22	20 35		22 28	
Sherburn-in-Elmet d		14 26											
Church Fenton d		14 30		16 05		18 06		19 05			21 13		23 19
Ulleskelf d		14 34				18 10					21 18		
York 8 29 a	14 26	14 50	15 53	16 22	17 13	18 24	18 36	19 19	19 50	21 00	21 30	22 53	23 36

For general notes see front of timetable
For details of catering facilities see Directory of Train Operators

A From Blackpool North (Table 41)
B From Beverley (Table 43)

Due to Engineering Operations in the Sheffield area, services from Saturday 13 September on this Table had not been confirmed at time of going to press. These services will be issued in a special Supplement as soon as exact timings have been confirmed.

Table 33

Sundays

until 13 July

Sheffield and Selby → York

Local services only

Network Diagram - see first page of Table 31

	NT A	NT	NT B		NT	NT B	NT		NT B	NT	NT		NT	NT B	NT		NT B	NT	NT		NT C	NT	NT D		
Sheffield 7 29, 31 🚊 d													15 46						18 58						
Meadowhall 29, 31 🚊 d													15 52						19 04						
Rotherham Central 29, 31 d													15 58						19 10						
Swinton (S.Yorks) 29, 31 d													16 08						19 18						
Moorthorpe 31 d													16 18						19 28						
Pontefract Baghill d													16 26						19 37						
Hull 29 d		08 54			11 54		13 27			14 28	16 00				17 23			18 53				20 22			
Selby d		09 25			12 25		13 58			15 04	16 31				17 54			19 24				20 53			
Sherburn-in-Elmet d													16 42						19 54						
Church Fenton d	09 19		10 53			12 49			14 49				16 46	16 49			18 49		19 58		20 49		22 59		
Ulleskelf d																									
York 8 29 a	09 33	09 54	11 07		12 56	13 03	14 22		15 03	15 30	16 57		17 00	17 04	18 23		19 03	19 52	20 16		21 02	21 18	23 17		

Sundays

20 July to 7 September

	NT Bus	NT	NT Bus		NT	NT Bus	NT		NT Bus	NT	NT		NT	NT Bus	NT		NT Bus	NT	NT	NT Bus	NT	NT D Bus	NT D Bus		
Sheffield 7 29, 31 🚊 d													15 46						18 58						
Meadowhall 29, 31 🚊 d													15 52						19 04						
Rotherham Central 29, 31 d													15 58						19 10						
Swinton (S.Yorks) 29, 31 d													16 08						19 18						
Moorthorpe 31 d													16 18						19 28						
Pontefract Baghill d													16 26						19 37						
Hull 29 d		08 54			11 54		13 27			14 28	16 00				17 23			18 53			20 22				
Selby d		09 25			12 25		13 58			15 04	16 31				17 54			19 24			20 53				
Sherburn-in-Elmet d													16 42						19 54						
Church Fenton d	09 20		10 35			12 35			14 35				16 46	16 35			18 35		19 58	20 35		22 40	23 50		
Ulleskelf d																									
York 8 29 a	09 50	09 54	11 05		12 56	13 05	14 22		15 05	15 30	16 57		17 00	17 05	18 23		19 05	19 52	20 16	21 05	21 18	23 10	00 20		

For general notes see front of timetable
For details of catering facilities see Directory of Train Operators

A From Bradford Interchange (Table 37)
B From Huddersfield (Table 41)
C From Blackpool North (Table 41)
D From Leeds (Table 40)

Due to Engineering Operations in the Sheffield area, services from Sunday 14 September on this Table had not been confirmed at time of going to press. These services will be issued in a special Supplement as soon as exact timings have been confirmed.

Table 33

York → Selby and Sheffield

Local services only

Mondays to Fridays

until 5 September

Network Diagram - see first page of Table 31

Miles	Miles			NT	NT A	NT	NT B	NT	NT A	NT	NT	NT	NT A	NT	NT
0	0	**York 8**	29 d	06 09	07 06	07 30	07 48	08 43	09 09	09 53	10 20	11 03	11 09	11 53	12 18
8¾	8¾	Ulleskelf	d		07 15							11 13			
10¾	10¾	Church Fenton	d		07a20		08a00		09a20			11 17	11a20		
12¾	12¾	Sherburn-in-Elmet	d									11 21			
—	21	**Selby**	a	06 30		07 49		09 08		10 12	10 40			12 17	12 38
—	—	Hull	29 a	*08 20*		08 45		*10 04*		10 56	*11 33*			13 02	*13 33*
21¼	—	Pontefract Baghill	d									11 39			
28¼	—	Moorthorpe	31 a									11 51			
36	—	Swinton (S.Yorks)	29, 31 a									12 01			
40½	—	Rotherham Central	29, 31 a									12 10			
43¼	—	Meadowhall	29, 31 a									12 16			
46¾	—	**Sheffield 7**	29, 31 a									12 26			

		NT A	NT	NT	NT	NT A	NT C	NT A	NT	NT	NT A	NT	NT B	NT B	NT	NT B
York 8	29 d	13 09	13 45	14 59	15 02	15 09	16 12	17 07	17 27	18 14	19 04	19 23	20 13	21 10	22 03	23 13
Ulleskelf	d				15 12					18 23				21 22		
Church Fenton	d	13a20			15 16	15a20	16 23	17a19		18 28	19a15		20a24	21a28		23a28
Sherburn-in-Elmet	d		13 57		15 20		16 27			18 31						
Selby	a		14 09	15 19			16 38		17 45	18 43		19 44			22 22	
Hull	29 a		14 48	15 58			17 27		18 29	19 32		*20 39*			23 08	
Pontefract Baghill	d				15 38											
Moorthorpe	31 a				15 50											
Swinton (S.Yorks)	29, 31 a				16 01											
Rotherham Central	29, 31 a				16 10											
Meadowhall	29, 31 a				16 18											
Sheffield 7	29, 31 a				16 25											

Mondays to Fridays

from 8 September

		NT	NT A	NT	NT B	NT	NT A	NT	NT	NT A	NT 🚌	NT	NT	NT A
York 8	29 d	06 09	07 06	07 30	07 48	08 43	09 09	09 53	10 20	11 09	11 10	11 53	12 18	13 09
Ulleskelf	d		07 15								11 35			
Church Fenton	d		07a20		08a00		09a20			11a20	11 45			13a20
Sherburn-in-Elmet	d										11 55			
Selby	a	06 30		07 49		09 08		10 12	10 40			12 17	12 38	
Hull	29 a	*08 20*		08 45		*10 04*		10 56	*11 33*			13 02	*13 33*	
Pontefract Baghill	d										12 15			
Moorthorpe	31 a										12 30			
Swinton (S.Yorks)	29, 31 a										13 05			
Rotherham Central	29, 31 a										*13 26*			
Meadowhall	29, 31 a										*13 32*			
Sheffield 7	29, 31 a										*13 41*			

		NT	NT	NT A	NT 🚌	NT C	NT A	NT	NT	NT A	NT	NT B	NT B	NT	NT B
York 8	29 d	13 45	14 59	15 09	15 10	16 12	17 07	17 27	18 14	19 04	19 23	20 13	21 10	22 03	23 13
Ulleskelf	d				15 35				18 23				21 22		
Church Fenton	d			15a20	15 45	16 23	17a19		18 28	19a15		20a24	21a28		23a28
Sherburn-in-Elmet	d	13 57			15 55	16 27			18 31						
Selby	a	14 09	15 19			16 38		17 45	18 43		19 44			22 22	
Hull	29 a	14 48	15 58			17 27		18 29	19 32		*20 39*			23 08	
Pontefract Baghill	d				16 15										
Moorthorpe	31 a				16 30										
Swinton (S.Yorks)	29, 31 a				17 05										
Rotherham Central	29, 31 a				*17 26*										
Meadowhall	29, 31 a				*17 32*										
Sheffield 7	29, 31 a				*17 41*										

Saturdays

until 6 September

		NT	NT A	NT	NT A	NT	NT A	NT	NT	NT	NT A	NT	NT	NT A
York 8	29 d	06 05	07 06	07 30	08 07	08 34	09 09	09 52	10 17	11 01	11 09	11 49	12 18	13 09
Ulleskelf	d		07 15							11 11				
Church Fenton	d		07a20		08a19		09a20			11 15	11a20			13a20
Sherburn-in-Elmet	d									11 19				
Selby	a	06 26		07 50		08 54		10 12	10 37			12 09	12 38	
Hull	29 a	*08 20*		08 46		*10 33*		10 56	*11 34*			12 54	*13 33*	
Pontefract Baghill	d									11 37				
Moorthorpe	31 a									11 49				
Swinton (S.Yorks)	29, 31 a									11 59				
Rotherham Central	29, 31 a									12 10				
Meadowhall	29, 31 a									12 16				
Sheffield 7	29, 31 a									12 25				

For general notes see front of timetable
For details of catering facilities see Directory of Train Operators

A To Blackpool North (Table 41)
B To Leeds (Table 40)
C To Scarborough (Table 43)

Due to Engineering Operations in the Sheffield area, services from Saturday 13 September on this Table had not been confirmed at time of going to press. These services will be issued in a special Supplement as soon as exact timings have been confirmed.

Table 33

Saturdays

until 6 September

York → Selby and Sheffield

Local services only

Network Diagram - see first page of Table 31

	NT	NT	NT	NT	NT	NT	NT	NT	NT	NT	NT	NT	NT	NT	NT
			A		B	A			A		C		C		C
York 8 29 d	13 38	15 05	15 09	15 12	16 12	17 09	17 18	18 13	19 04	19 23	20 13	20 17	21 13	21 45	23 13
Ulleskelf d				15 23				18 22					21 22		
Church Fenton d			15a20	15 27	16 23	17a20		18 27	19a15		20a24		21a28		23a27
Sherburn-in-Elmet d	13 52			15 31	16 27			18 30							
Selby a	14 03	15 24			16 38		17 37	18 41		19 44		20 36		22 05	
Hull 29 a	14 45	16 03			17 27		18 21	19 28		*20 39*		21 22		*23 21*	
Pontefract Baghill d				15 49											
Moorthorpe 31 a				16 01											
Swinton (S.Yorks) 29, 31 a				16 10											
Rotherham Central 29, 31 a				16 17											
Meadowhall 29, 31 🚊 a				16 23											
Sheffield 7 29, 31 🚊 a				16 35											

Sundays

until 13 July

	NT	NT	NT	NT	NT	NT	NT	NT	NT	NT	NT	NT	NT	NT	NT	NT	NT	NT
	A	D		D			D			A			D		D			C
York 8 29 d	08 48	09 52	10 40	11 52	12 05	13 23	13 52	14 45	15 43	15 52	17 10	17 17	17 52	19 10	19 52	20 44	21 41	21 52
Ulleskelf d																		
Church Fenton d	09a00	10a04		12a04			14a04			16a03		17 29	18a04		20a04	20 55		22a04
Sherburn-in-Elmet d												17 33				20 59		
Selby a			10 59		12 24	13 42		15 04	16 01		17 30			19 29			22 00	
Hull 29 a			11 38		13 03	14 21		15 43	16 41		18 10			20 08			22 39	
Pontefract Baghill d												17 49				21 17		
Moorthorpe 31 a												18 01				21 29		
Swinton (S.Yorks) 29, 31 a												18 11				21 38		
Rotherham Central 29, 31 a												18 20				21 48		
Meadowhall 29, 31 🚊 a												18 25				21 54		
Sheffield 7 29, 31 🚊 a												18 35				22 05		

Sundays

20 July to 7 September

	NT	NT	NT	NT	NT	NT	NT	NT	NT	NT	NT	NT	NT	NT	NT	NT	NT	NT
																		C
	🚌	🚌		🚌			🚌			🚌			🚌		🚌			🚌
York 8 29 d	08 45	10 00	10 40	12 00	12 05	13 06	14 00	14 45	15 43	16 00	17 10	17 17	18 00	19 10	20 00	20 44	21 41	21 50
Ulleskelf d																		
Church Fenton d	09a15	10a30		12a30			14a30			16a30		17 29	18a30		20a30	20 55		22a20
Sherburn-in-Elmet d												17 33				20 59		
Selby a			10 59		12 24	13 25		15 04	16 01		17 30			19 29			22 00	
Hull 29 a			11 38		13 03	14 04		15 43	16 41		18 10			20 08			22 39	
Pontefract Baghill d												17 49				21 17		
Moorthorpe 31 a												18 01				21 29		
Swinton (S.Yorks) 29, 31 a												18 11				21 38		
Rotherham Central 29, 31 a												18 20				21 48		
Meadowhall 29, 31 🚊 a												18 25				21 54		
Sheffield 7 29, 31 🚊 a												18 35				22 05		

For general notes see front of timetable
For details of catering facilities see
Directory of Train Operators

A To Blackpool North (Table 41)
B To Scarborough (Table 43)
C To Leeds (Table 40)
D To Huddersfield (Table 41)

Due to Engineering Operations in the Sheffield area, services from Saturday 13 September on this Table had not been confirmed at time of going to press. These services will be issued in a special Supplement as soon as exact timings have been confirmed.

Due to Engineering Operations in the Sheffield area, services from Sunday 14 September on this Table had not been confirmed at time of going to press. These services will be issued in a special Supplement as soon as exact timings have been confirmed.

Sheffield → Barnsley → Huddersfield and Leeds

Network Diagram - see first page of Table 31

Miles	Miles		NT	NT	NT	NT A		NT	NT	NT	NT		NT	EM 1 ◇ B	NT C	NT		NT D	NT A	NT	NT		NT	NT A
—	—	St Pancras International ⊖ 53 d																						
0	0	**Sheffield 7** 29, 31 d	05 16	05 36	05 50			06 14	06 36	06 49			07 04	07 25		07 36		07 51		08 08	08 36		08 51	
3½	3½	Meadowhall 29, 31 d	05 22	05 42	05 56			06 20	06 42	06 55			07 10	07 31		07 42		07 57		08 14	08 42		08 57	
7¼	7¼	Chapeltown d	05 28	05 48				06 26	06 48				07 16			07 48				08 20	08 48			
10½	10½	Elsecar d	05 33					06 31					07 21							08 25				
12	12	Wombwell d	05 37	05 55				06 35	06 55				07 25			07 55				08 29	08 55			
16	16	**Barnsley** a	05 42	06 01	06 10			06 40	07 00	07 09			07 30	07 48		08 00		08 11		08 34	09 00		09 11	
—	—	d		06 01	06 11			06 41	07 01	07 10			07 31			08 01		08 12		08 35	09 01		09 12	
—	19	Dodworth d		06 07					07 07							08 07					09 07			
—	20¼	Silkstone Common d		06 11					07 11							08 11					09 11			
—	23½	Penistone d		06 18					07 18							08 18					09 18			
—	27¼	Denby Dale d		06 25					07 24							08 24					09 24			
—	29¾	Shepley d		06 30					07 29							08 29					09 29			
—	30¾	Stocksmoor d		06 32					07 32							08 32					09 32			
—	32¾	Brockholes d		06 36					07 36							08 36					09 36			
—	33¾	Honley d		06 39					07 38							08 38					09 38			
—	34¾	Berry Brow d		06 42					07 41							08 41					09 41			
—	35¾	Lockwood d		06 44					07 44							08 44					09 44			
—	37	**Huddersfield** a		06 50					07 49							08 49					09 49			
19½	—	Darton d						06 46					07 36							08 40				
27	—	Wakefield Kirkgate 4 31 d			06 29			06 58		07 29			07 47					08 29		08 52			09 29	
30	—	Normanton d			06 33			07 02		07 33			07 52							08 56				
33½	—	Castleford a						07 08					07 58							09 02				
—	—	d				06 41		07 10			07 38		08 00		08 06				08 34	09 04				09 34
38¼	—	Woodlesford d				06 50		07 19			07 47		08 09		08 15				08 43	09 13				09 43
44¼	—	**Leeds 10** 31 a			06 50	07 03		07 33		07 50	08 01		08 23		08 27			08 51	09 00	09 27			09 50	09 55

	NT	NT	NT	NT A		NT	NT	NT	NT A		NT	NT	NT	NT A		NT	NT	NT	NT A		NT	NT	NT	NT A
St Pancras International ⊖ 53 d		*06 10*				*07 25*					*08 25*					*09 25*					*10 25*			
Sheffield 7 29, 31 d	09 08	09 36	09 51			10 08	10 36	10 51			11 08	11 36	11 51			12 08	12 36	12 51			13 08	13 36	13 51	
Meadowhall 29, 31 d	09 14	09 42	09 57			10 14	10 42	10 57			11 14	11 42	11 57			12 14	12 42	12 57			13 14	13 42	13 57	
Chapeltown d	09 20	09 48				10 20	10 48				11 20	11 48				12 20	12 48				13 20	13 48		
Elsecar d	09 25					10 25					11 25					12 25					13 25			
Wombwell d	09 29	09 55				10 29	10 55				11 29	11 55				12 29	12 55				13 29	13 55		
Barnsley a	09 34	10 00	10 11			10 34	11 00	11 11			11 34	12 00	12 11			12 34	13 00	13 11			13 34	14 00	14 12	
d	09 35	10 01	10 12			10 35	11 01	11 12			11 35	12 01	12 12			12 35	13 01	13 12			13 35	14 01	14 12	
Dodworth d		10 07					11 07					12 07					13 07					14 07		
Silkstone Common d		10 11					11 11					12 11					13 11					14 11		
Penistone d		10 18					11 18					12 18					13 18					14 18		
Denby Dale d		10 24					11 24					12 24					13 24					14 24		
Shepley d		10 29					11 29					12 29					13 29					14 29		
Stocksmoor d		10 32					11 32					12 32					13 32					14 32		
Brockholes d		10 36					11 36					12 36					13 36					14 36		
Honley d		10 38					11 38					12 38					13 38					14 38		
Berry Brow d		10 41					11 41					12 41					13 41					14 41		
Lockwood d		10 44					11 44					12 44					13 44					14 44		
Huddersfield a		10 49					11 49					12 49					13 49					14 49		
Darton d	09 40					10 40					11 40					12 40					13 40			
Wakefield Kirkgate 4 31 d	09 52		10 29			10 52		11 29			11 52		12 29			12 52		13 29			13 52		14 29	
Normanton d	09 56					10 56					11 56					12 56					13 56			
Castleford a	10 02					11 02					12 02					13 02					14 02			
d	10 04			10 34		11 04			11 34		12 04			12 34		13 04			13 34		14 04			14 34
Woodlesford d	10 13			10 43		11 13			11 43		12 13			12 43		13 13			13 43		14 13			14 43
Leeds 10 31 a	10 27		10 50	10 55		11 27		11 50	11 55		12 27		12 50	12 55		13 27		13 50	13 55		14 27		14 50	14 55

	NT	NT		NT	NT A	NT	NT		NT	NT A	NT	NT		NT	NT A	NT	NT		NT	NT A	NT	NT		NT
St Pancras International ⊖ 53 d	*11 25*					*12 25*					*13 25*					*14 25*					*15 25*			
Sheffield 7 29, 31 d	14 08	14 36		14 51		15 08	15 36		15 51		16 08	16 36		16 51		17 08	17 36		17 51		18 08	18 36		18 51
Meadowhall 29, 31 d	14 14	14 42		14 57		15 14	15 42		15 57		16 14	16 42		16 57		17 14	17 42		17 57		18 14	18 42		18 57
Chapeltown d	14 20	14 48				15 20	15 48				16 20	16 48				17 20	17 48				18 20	18 48		
Elsecar d	14 25					15 25					16 25	16 53				17 25	17 53				18 25	18 53		
Wombwell d	14 29	14 55				15 29	15 55				16 29	16 57				17 29	17 57				18 29	18 57		
Barnsley a	14 34	15 00		15 11		15 34	16 00		16 11		16 34	17 02		17 11		17 34	18 02		18 11		18 34	19 02		19 15
d	14 35	15 01		15 12		15 35	16 01		16 12		16 35	17 03		17 12		17 35	18 03		18 18		18 35	19 09		19 18
Dodworth d		15 07					16 07					17 09					18 09					19 15		
Silkstone Common d		15 11					16 11					17 13					18 13					19 19		
Penistone d		15 18					16 18					17 20					18b27					19 26		
Denby Dale d		15 24					16 24					17 26					18 33					19 33		
Shepley d		15 29					16 29					17 31					18 38					19 38		
Stocksmoor d		15 32					16 32					17 34					18 41					19 40		
Brockholes d		15 36					16 36					17 38					18 45					19 44		
Honley d		15 38					16 38					17 40					18 47					19 47		
Berry Brow d		15 41					16 41					17 43					18 50					19 50		
Lockwood d		15 44					16 44					17 46					18 53					19 52		
Huddersfield a		15 49					16 49					17 50					18 57					19 57		
Darton d	14 40					15 40					16 40					17 40					18 40			
Wakefield Kirkgate 4 31 d	14 52			15 29		15 52			16 27		16 52			17 29		17 52			18 36		18 52			19 36
Normanton d	14 56					15 56					16 56					17 56					18 56			
Castleford a	15 02					16 02					17 02					18 02					19 02			
d	15 04				15 34	16 04				16 34	17 04				17 34	18 04				18 59	19 04			
Woodlesford d	15 13				15 43	16 13				16 43	17 13				17 43	18 13				19 08	19 13			
Leeds 10 31 a	15 27			15 50	15 55	16 27			16 50	16 55	17 27			17 50	17 55	18 27			18 55	19 21	19 27			19 57

For general notes see front of timetable
For details of catering facilities see Directory of Train Operators

A From Knottingley (Table 32)
B From Derby (Table 53)
C From Goole (Table 32)
D From Retford (Table 30)
b Arr. 1819

Mondays to Fridays
until 5 September

Sheffield → Barnsley → Huddersfield and Leeds

Network Diagram - see first page of Table 31

			NT A	NT	NT	NT	NT B	NT	NT B	NT	NT	NT B	NT	NT FX	NT FO	NT FO	NT B	NT	NT FX C
St Pancras International	⊖ 53	d		16 25	16 55					17 45	18 25			19 25	19 25				20 25
Sheffield 7	29, 31	d		19 08	19 38	19 51		20 08		20 41	21 08		21 41	22 08	22 08			22 41	23 24
Meadowhall	29, 31	d		19 14	19 44	19 57		20 14		20 47	21 14		21 47	22 14	22 14			22 47	23 30
Chapeltown		d		19 20	19 50			20 20		20 53	21 20		21 53	22 20	22 20			22 53	23 36
Elsecar		d		19 25	19 55			20 25			21 25			22 25	22 25			22 58	23 41
Wombwell		d		19 29	19 59			20 29		21 00	21 29		22 00	22 29	22 29			23 00	23 45
Barnsley		a		19 34	20 04	20 12		20 34		21 06	21 34		22 05	22 34	22 34			23 06	23 50
		d		19 35	20 07	20 12		20 35		21 06	21 35		22 06	22 35				23 06	23 51
Dodworth		d			20 13					21 12			22 12					23 12	
Silkstone Common		d			20 17					21 16			22 16					23 16	
Penistone		d			20 24					21 23			22 23					23 23	
Denby Dale		d			20 30					21 29			22 29					23 29	
Shepley		d			20 35					21 34			22 34					23 34	
Stocksmoor		d			20 38					21 37			22 37					23 37	
Brockholes		d			20 42					21 41			22 41					23 41	
Honley		d			20 44					21 43			22 43					23 43	
Berry Brow		d			20 47					21 46			22 46					23 46	
Lockwood		d			20 50					21 49			22 49					23 49	
Huddersfield		a			20 54					21 54			22 54					23 59	
Darton		d		19 40				20 40			21 40			22 40					23 56
Wakefield Kirkgate 4	31	d		19 52		20 29		20 52			21 52			22 52		22 52			00s10
Normanton		d		19 56				20 56			21 56			22 56		22 56			
Castleford		a		20 02				21 02			22 02			23 02		23 02			
		d	19 43	20 04			20 34	21 04	21 34		22 04	22 37		23 04		23 04	23 34		
Woodlesford		d	19 52	20 13			20 43	21 13	21 43		22 13	22 46		23 13		23 13	23 43		
Leeds 10	31	a	20 04	20 27		20 50	20 55	21 27	21 55		22 27	23 01		23 27		23 27	23 55		

Mondays to Fridays
from 8 September

			NT	NT	NT	NT B	NT	NT	NT	NT	NT	NT A	NT	NT D	NT B	NT	NT	NT	NT B	NT	NT
St Pancras International	⊖ 53	d																			06 10
Sheffield 7	29, 31	d	05 16	05 36	05 50		06 14	06 36	06 49		06 57		07 36	07 51		08 07	08 36	08 51		09 05	09 36
Meadowhall	29, 31	d	05 22	05 42	05 56		06 20	06 42	06 55		07 06		07 42	07 57		08 14	08 42	08 57		09 14	09 42
Chapeltown		d	05 28	05 48			06 26	06 48			07 12		07 48			08 20	08 48			09 20	09 48
Elsecar		d	05 33				06 31				07 17					08 25				09 25	
Wombwell		d	05 37	05 55			06 35	06 55			07 21		07 55			08 29	08 55			09 29	09 55
Barnsley		a	05 42	06 00	06 10		06 40	07 00	07 09		07 30		08 00	08 11		08 34	09 00	09 11		09 34	10 00
		d		06 01	06 11		06 41	07 01	07 10		07 31		08 01	08 12		08 35	09 01	09 12		09 35	10 01
Dodworth		d		06 07				07 07					08 07				09 07				10 07
Silkstone Common		d		06 11				07 11					08 11				09 11				10 11
Penistone		d		06 18				07 17					08 18				09 18				10 18
Denby Dale		d		06 24				07 23					08 24				09 24				10 24
Shepley		d		06 29				07 29					08 29				09 29				10 29
Stocksmoor		d		06 32				07 32					08 32				09 32				10 32
Brockholes		d		06 36				07 36					08 36				09 36				10 36
Honley		d		06 38				07 38					08 38				09 38				10 38
Berry Brow		d		06 41				07 41					08 41				09 41				10 41
Lockwood		d		06 44				07 44					08 44				09 44				10 44
Huddersfield		a		06 53				07 53					08 52				09 52				10 52
Darton		d					06 46				07 36					08 40				09 40	
Wakefield Kirkgate 4	31	d			06 29		06 58		07 29		07 47			08 29		08 52				09 52	
Normanton		d			06 33		07 02		07 33		07 52					08 56				09 56	
Castleford		a					07 08				07 58					09 02				10 02	
		d				06 41	07 10			07 38	08 00	08 06			08 34	09 04			09 34	10 04	
Woodlesford		d				06 50	07 19			07 47	08 09	08 15			08 43	09 13			09 43	10 13	
Leeds 10	31	a			06 50	07 03	07 33		07 50	08 01	08 23	08 27		08 51	09 00	09 27		09 50	09 55	10 27	

			NT	NT B	NT	NT	NT	NT B	NT	NT	NT	NT B	NT	NT	NT	NT B	NT	NT	NT	NT B
St Pancras International	⊖ 53	d			07 25				08 25				09 25				10 25			
Sheffield 7	29, 31	d	09 51		10 08	10 36	10 51		11 08	11 36	11 51		12 08	12 36	12 51		13 08	13 36	13 51	
Meadowhall	29, 31	d	09 58		10 14	10 42	10 57		11 14	11 42	11 57		12 14	12 42	12 57		13 14	13 42	13 57	
Chapeltown		d			10 20	10 48			11 20	11 48			12 20	12 48			13 20	13 48		
Elsecar		d			10 25				11 25				12 25				13 25			
Wombwell		d			10 29	10 55			11 29	11 55			12 29	12 55			13 29	13 55		
Barnsley		a	10 13		10 34	11 00	11 11		11 34	12 00	12 11		12 34	13 00	13 11		13 34	14 00	14 11	
		d	10 13		10 35	11 01	11 12		11 35	12 01	12 12		12 35	13 01	13 12		13 35	14 01	14 12	
Dodworth		d				11 07				12 07				13 07				14 07		
Silkstone Common		d				11 11				12 11				13 11				14 11		
Penistone		d				11 18				12 18				13 18				14 18		
Denby Dale		d				11 24				12 24				13 24				14 24		
Shepley		d				11 29				12 29				13 29				14 29		
Stocksmoor		d				11 32				12 32				13 32				14 32		
Brockholes		d				11 36				12 36				13 36				14 36		
Honley		d				11 38				12 38				13 38				14 38		
Berry Brow		d				11 41				12 41				13 41				14 41		
Lockwood		d				11 44				12 44				13 44				14 44		
Huddersfield		a				11 52				12 52				13 52				14 52		
Darton		d			10 40				11 40				12 40				13 40			
Wakefield Kirkgate 4	31	d			10 52		11 29		11 52		12 29		12 52		13 29		13 52		14 29	
Normanton		d			10 56				11 56				12 56				13 56			
Castleford		a			11 02				12 02				13 02				14 02			
		d		10 34	11 04			11 34	12 04			12 34	13 04			13 34	14 04			14 34
Woodlesford		d		10 43	11 13			11 43	12 13			12 43	13 13			13 43	14 13			14 43
Leeds 10	31	a	10 50	10 55	11 27		11 50	11 55	12 27		12 50	12 55	13 27		13 50	13 55	14 27		14 50	14 55

For general notes see front of timetable
For details of catering facilities see Directory of Train Operators

A From Goole (Table 32)
B From Knottingley (Table 32)
C To Wakefield Westgate (Table 31)
D From Retford (Table 30)

Sheffield → Barnsley → Huddersfield and Leeds

Network Diagram - see first page of Table 31

	NT	NT	NT		NT	NT	NT		NT	NT	NT		NT	NT	NT		NT	NT	NT		NT	NT	NT	NT
					A					A					A						A			
St Pancras International ⊖ 53 d	11 25					12 25					13 25						14 25					15 25		
Sheffield 7 29, 31 d	14 08	14 36	14 51			15 08	15 36		15 51		16 08		16 36	16 51			17 08	17 36	17 51			18 08	18 36	18 51
Meadowhall 29, 31 d	14 14	14 42	14 57			15 14	15 42		15 57		16 14		16 42	16 57			17 14	17 42	18 00			18 14	18 42	18 57
Chapeltown d	14 20	14 48				15 20	15 48				16 20		16 48				17 20	17 48				18 20	18 48	
Elsecar d	14 25					15 25					16 25		16 53				17 25	17 53				18 25	18 53	
Wombwell d	14 29	14 55				15 29	15 55				16 29		16 57				17 29	17 57				18 29	18 57	
Barnsley a	14 34	15 00	15 11			15 34	16 00		16 11		16 34		17 02	17 11			17 34	18 02	18 14			18 34	19 02	19 15
d	14 35	15 01	15 12			15 35	16 01		16 12		16 35		17 03	17 12			17 35	18 03	18 18			18 35	19 09	19 18
Dodworth d		15 07					16 07						17 09					18 09					19 15	
Silkstone Common d		15 11					16 11						17 13					18 13					19 19	
Penistone d		15 18					16 18						17 20					18b27					19 26	
Denby Dale d		15 24					16 24						17 26					18 33					19 33	
Shepley d		15 29					16 29						17 31					18 38					19 38	
Stocksmoor d		15 32					16 32						17 34					18 41					19 40	
Brockholes d		15 36					16 36						17 38					18 45					19 44	
Honley d		15 38					16 38						17 40					18 47					19 47	
Berry Brow d		15 41					16 41						17 43					18 50					19 50	
Lockwood d		15 44					16 44						17 46					18 53					19 52	
Huddersfield a		15 52					16 52						17 54					19 02					20 02	
Darton d	14 40					15 40					16 40						17 40					18 40		
Wakefield Kirkgate 4 31 d	14 52		15 29			15 52			16 27		16 52			17 29			17 52		18 36			18 52		19 36
Normanton d	14 56					15 56					16 56						17 56					18 56		
Castleford a	15 02					16 02					17 02						18 02					19 02		
d	15 04				15 34	16 04				16 34	17 04				17 34		18 04				18 59	19 04		
Woodlesford d	15 13				15 43	16 13				16 43	17 13				17 43		18 13				19 08	19 13		
Leeds 10 31 a	15 27		15 50		15 55	16 27			16 50	16 55	17 27			17 50	17 55		18 27		18 55		19 21	19 27		19 56

	NT		NT	NT	NT		NT	NT	NT		NT	NT	NT		NT	NT	NT		NT	NT	NT	NT		
																FX	FO		FO			FX		
	B						A		A				A							A		C		
St Pancras International ⊖ 53 d			16 25	16 55								17 45			18 25						19 25	20 25		
Sheffield 7 29, 31 d			19 08	19 38	19 53			20 08				21 06			21 41	22 08	22 08				22 41	23 24		
Meadowhall 29, 31 d			19 14	19 44	19 59			20 14			20 48	21 14			21 47	22 14	22 14				22 47	23 30		
Chapeltown d			19 20	19 50				20 20			20 54	21 20			21 53	22 20	22 20				22 53	23 36		
Elsecar d			19 25	19 55				20 25				21 25				22 25	22 25				22 58	23 41		
Wombwell d			19 29	19 59				20 29			21 00	21 29			22 00	22 29	22 29				23 00	23 45		
Barnsley a			19 34	20 04	20 13			20 34			21 06	21 34			22 05	22 34	22 34				23 06	23 50		
d			19 35	20 07	20 13			20 35			21 07	21 35			22 06	22 35					23 06	23 51		
Dodworth d				20 13							21 13				22 12						23 12			
Silkstone Common d				20 17							21 17				22 16						23 16			
Penistone d				20 24							21 24				22 23						23 23			
Denby Dale d				20 30							21 30				22 29						23 29			
Shepley d				20 35							21 35				22 34						23 34			
Stocksmoor d				20 38							21 38				22 37						23 37			
Brockholes d				20 42							21 42				22 41						23 41			
Honley d				20 44							21 44				22 43						23 43			
Berry Brow d				20 47							21 47				22 46						23 46			
Lockwood d				20 50							21 50				22 49						23 49			
Huddersfield a				20 59							21 59				22 58						23 59			
Darton d			19 40					20 40				21 40				22 40						23 56		
Wakefield Kirkgate 4 31 d			19 52		20 29			20 52				21 52				22 52			22 52			00s10		
Normanton d			19 56					20 56				21 56				22 56			22 56					
Castleford a			20 02					21 02				22 02				23 02			23 02					
d	19 43		20 04				20 34	21 04	21 34			22 04	22 37			23 04			23 04	23 34				
Woodlesford d	19 52		20 13				20 43	21 13	21 43			22 13	22 46			23 13			23 13	23 43				
Leeds 10 31 a	20 04		20 27		20 50		20 55	21 27	21 55			22 27	23 01			23 27			23 27	23 55				

Saturdays
until 6 September

	NT	NT	NT	NT	NT	NT	EM	NT	NT	NT	NT	NT	NT	NT	NT	NT	NT	NT	NT	NT	NT	NT	NT	NT
							1 ◇																	
					B		D		E	A				A				A				A		
							⊡																	
St Pancras International ⊖ 53 d																06 20			07 25				08 25	
Sheffield 7 29, 31 d	05 16	05 48	06 14	06 36		07 08	07 17	07 36	07 51		08 08	08 36	08 51		09 08	09 36	09 51		10 08	10 36	10 51		11 08	11 36
Meadowhall 29, 31 d	05 22	05 54	06 20	06 42		07 14	07 23	07 42	07 57		08 14	08 42	08 57		09 14	09 42	09 57		10 14	10 42	10 57		11 14	11 42
Chapeltown d	05 28	06 00	06 26	06 48		07 20		07 48			08 20	08 48			09 20	09 48			10 20	10 48			11 20	11 48
Elsecar d	05 33	06 05	06 31			07 25					08 25				09 25				10 25				11 25	
Wombwell d	05 37	06 09	06 35	06 55		07 29		07 55			08 29	08 55			09 29	09 55			10 29	10 55			11 29	11 55
Barnsley a	05 42	06 14	06 40	07 00		07 34	07 43	08 00	08 11		08 34	09 00	09 11		09 34	10 00	10 11		10 34	11 00	11 11		11 34	12 00
d			06 41	07 01		07 35		08 01	08 12		08 35	09 01	09 12		09 35	10 01	10 12		10 35	11 01	11 12		11 35	12 01
Dodworth d				07 07				08 07				09 07				10 07				11 07				12 07
Silkstone Common d				07 11				08 11				09 11				10 11				11 11				12 11
Penistone d				07 18				08 18				09 18				10 18				11 18				12 18
Denby Dale d				07 24				08 24				09 24				10 24				11 24				12 24
Shepley d				07 29				08 29				09 29				10 29				11 29				12 29
Stocksmoor d				07 32				08 32				09 32				10 32				11 32				12 32
Brockholes d				07 36				08 36				09 36				10 36				11 36				12 36
Honley d				07 38				08 38				09 38				10 38				11 38				12 38
Berry Brow d				07 41				08 41				09 41				10 41				11 41				12 41
Lockwood d				07 44				08 44				09 44				10 44				11 44				12 44
Huddersfield a				07 49				08 49				09 49				10 49				11 49				12 49
Darton d			06 46			07 40					08 40				09 40				10 40				11 40	
Wakefield Kirkgate 4 31 d			06 58			07 51			08 29		08 52		09 29		09 52		10 29		10 52		11 29		11 52	
Normanton d			07 02			07 56					08 56				09 56				10 56				11 56	
Castleford a			07 08			08 02					09 02				10 02				11 02				12 02	
d			07 10		07 51	08 04				08 34	09 04			09 34	10 04			10 34	11 04			11 34	12 04	
Woodlesford d			07 19		08 00	08 13				08 43	09 13			09 43	10 13			10 43	11 13			11 43	12 13	
Leeds 10 31 a			07 33		08 13	08 27			08 51	09 00	09 27		09 50	09 55	10 27		10 50	10 55	11 27		11 50	11 55	12 27	

For general notes see front of timetable
For details of catering facilities see Directory of Train Operators

- **A** From Knottingley (Table 32)
- **B** From Goole (Table 32)
- **C** To Wakefield Westgate (Table 31)
- **D** From Derby (Table 53)
- **E** From Retford (Table 30)
- **b** Arr. 1819

Due to Engineering Operations in the Sheffield area, services from Saturday 13 September on this Table had not been confirmed at time of going to press. These services will be issued in a special Supplement as soon as exact timings have been confirmed.

Table 34

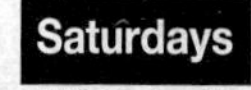

until 6 September

Sheffield → Barnsley → Huddersfield and Leeds

Network Diagram - see first page of Table 31

		NT		NT A	NT	NT	NT	NT A	NT	NT	NT	NT A	NT	NT	NT	NT A	NT	NT	NT	NT A	NT	NT	NT	NT A	NT
St Pancras International	⊖ 53 d				09 25				10 25				11 25				12 25				13 25				14 25
Sheffield 7	29, 31 d	11 51			12 08	12 36	12 51		13 08	13 36	13 51		14 08	14 36	14 51		15 08	15 36	15 51		16 08	16 36	16 51		17 08
Meadowhall	29, 31 d	11 57			12 14	12 42	12 57		13 14	13 42	13 57		14 14	14 42	14 57		15 14	15 42	15 57		16 14	16 42	16 57		17 14
Chapeltown	d				12 20	12 48			13 20	13 48			14 20	14 48			15 20	15 48			16 20	16 48			17 20
Elsecar	d				12 25				13 25				14 25				15 25				16 25	16 53			17 25
Wombwell	d				12 29	12 55			13 29	13 55			14 29	14 55			15 29	15 55			16 29	16 57			17 29
Barnsley	a	12 11			12 34	13 00	13 11		13 34	14 00	14 12		14 34	15 00	15 11		15 34	16 00	16 11		16 34	17 02	17 11		17 34
	d	12 12			12 35	13 01	13 12		13 35	14 01	14 12		14 35	15 01	15 12		15 35	16 01	16 12		16 35	17 03	17 12		17 35
Dodworth	d					13 07				14 07				15 07				16 07				17 09			
Silkstone Common	d					13 11				14 11				15 11				16 11				17 13			
Penistone	d					13 18				14 18				15 18				16 18				17 20			
Denby Dale	d					13 24				14 24				15 24				16 24				17 26			
Shepley	d					13 29				14 29				15 29				16 29				17 31			
Stocksmoor	d					13 32				14 32				15 32				16 32				17 34			
Brockholes	d					13 36				14 36				15 36				16 36				17 38			
Honley	d					13 38				14 38				15 38				16 38				17 40			
Berry Brow	d					13 41				14 41				15 41				16 41				17 43			
Lockwood	d					13 44				14 44				15 44				16 44				17 46			
Huddersfield	a					13 49				14 49				15 49				16 49				17 50			
Darton	d				12 40				13 40				14 40				15 40				16 40				17 40
Wakefield Kirkgate 4	31 d	12 29			12 52		13 29		13 52		14 29		14 52		15 29		15 52		16 27		16 52		17 29		17 52
Normanton	d				12 56				13 56				14 56				15 56				16 56				17 56
Castleford	a				13 02				14 02				15 02				16 02				17 02				18 02
	d			12 34	13 04			13 34	14 04			14 34	15 04			15 34	16 04			16 34	17 04			17 34	18 04
Woodlesford	d			12 43	13 13			13 43	14 13			14 43	15 13			15 43	16 13			16 43	17 13			17 43	18 13
Leeds 10	31 a	12 50		12 55	13 27		13 50	13 55	14 27		14 50	14 55	15 27		15 50	15 55	16 27		16 50	16 55	17 27		17 50	17 55	18 27

		NT	NT	NT A	NT	NT	NT	NT B	NT	NT	NT	NT A	NT	NT	EM 1 ◇	NT A	NT	NT A	NT	NT	NT	NT A	NT		
St Pancras International	⊖ 53 d		15 25						16 25					17 40	18 00		18 25			19 25					
Sheffield 7	29, 31 d	17 36	17 51		18 08	18 36	18 51		19 08	19 38	19 51		20 08	20 41	20 48		21 08		21 41	22 08			22 41		
Meadowhall	29, 31 d	17 42	17 57		18 14	18 42	18 57		19 14	19 44	19 57		20 14	20 47	20 54		21 14		21 47	22 14			22 47		
Chapeltown	d	17 48			18 20	18 48			19 20	19 50			20 20	20 53			21 20		21 53	22 20			22 53		
Elsecar	d	17 53			18 25	18 53			19 25	19 55			20 25				21 25			22 25			22 58		
Wombwell	d	17 57			18 29	18 57			19 29	19 59			20 29	21 00			21 29		22 00	22 29			23 00		
Barnsley	a	18 02	18 11		18 34	19 02	19 15		19 34	20 04	20 12		20 34	21 06	21 14		21 34		22 05	22 34			23 06		
	d	18 03	18 18		18 35	19 03	19 18		19 35	20 07	20 12		20 35	21 06			21 35		22 06				23 06		
Dodworth	d	18 09				19 09				20 13				21 12					22 12				23 12		
Silkstone Common	d	18 13				19 13				20 17				21 16					22 16				23 16		
Penistone	d	18 20				19 20				20 24				21 23					22 23				23 23		
Denby Dale	d	18 26				19 26				20 30				21 29					22 29				23 29		
Shepley	d	18 31				19 31				20 35				21 34					22 34				23 34		
Stocksmoor	d	18 34				19 34				20 38				21 37					22 37				23 37		
Brockholes	d	18 38				19 38				20 42				21 41					22 41				23 41		
Honley	d	18 40				19 41				20 44				21 43					22 43				23 43		
Berry Brow	d	18 43				19 44				20 47				21 46					22 46				23 46		
Lockwood	d	18 46				19 46				20 50				21 49					22 49				23 49		
Huddersfield	a	18 50				19 51				20 54				21 54					22 54				23 55		
Darton	d				18 40				19 40				20 40				21 40								
Wakefield Kirkgate 4	31 d		18 36		18 52		19 36		19 52		20 29		20 52				21 52				22 52				
Normanton	d				18 56				19 56				20 56				21 56				22 56				
Castleford	a				19 02				20 02				21 02				22 02				23 02				
	d			18 59	19 04			19 43	20 04			20 34	21 04			21 34	22 04	22 37			23 04	23 34			
Woodlesford	d			19 08	19 13			19 52	20 13			20 43	21 13			21 43	22 13	22 46			23 13	23 43			
Leeds 10	31 a		18 55	19 21	19 27		19 57	20 04	20 27		20 50	20 55	21 27			21 55	22 27	23 01			23 27	23 55			

For general notes see front of timetable
For details of catering facilities see Directory of Train Operators

A From Knottingley (Table 32)
B From Goole (Table 32)

Due to Engineering Operations in the Sheffield area, services from Saturday 13 September on this Table had not been confirmed at time of going to press. These services will be issued in a special Supplement as soon as exact timings have been confirmed.

Table 34

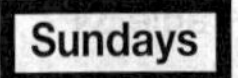

until 7 September

Sheffield → Barnsley → Huddersfield and Leeds

Network Diagram - see first page of Table 31

		NT	NT A	NT	NT	NT	NT A	NT	NT	NT	NT	NT A	NT	NT
St Pancras International	⊖ 53 d									*09b30*	*09c30*			*10 30*
Sheffield 7	29, 31 ⛴ d	08 39		09 39	10 39	11 32		11 39	12 32	12 39	13 32		13 39	14 39
Meadowhall	29, 31 ⛴ d	08 45		09 45	10 45	11 38		11 45	12 38	12 45	13 38		13 45	14 45
Chapeltown	d	08 51		09 51	10 51			11 51		12 51			13 51	14 51
Elsecar	d	08 56		09 56	10 56			11 56		12 56			13 56	14 56
Wombwell	d	09 00		10 00	11 00			12 00		13 00			14 00	15 00
Barnsley	a	09 05		10 05	11 05	11 52		12 06	12 52	13 05	13 52		14 05	15 05
	d	09 09		10 06	11 09	11 53		12 06	12 57	13 09	13 53		14 06	15 09
Dodworth	d			10 12				12 12	13 03				14 12	
Silkstone Common	d			10 16				12 16	13 07				14 16	
Penistone	d			10 23				12 23	13 14				14 23	
Denby Dale	d			10 29				12 29	13 20				14 29	
Shepley	d			10 34				12 34	13 25				14 34	
Stocksmoor	d			10 37				12 37	13e35				14 37	
Brockholes	d			10 41				12 41	13 39				14 41	
Honley	d			10 43				12 43	13 42				14 43	
Berry Brow	d			10 46				12 46	13 45				14 46	
Lockwood	d			10 49				12 49	13 47				14 49	
Huddersfield	a			10 53				12 54	13 52				14 53	
Darton	d	09 14			11 14					13 14				15 14
Wakefield Kirkgate 4	31 d	09 29			11 29	12 11				13 29	14 11			15 29
Normanton	d	09 34			11 34					13 34				15 34
Castleford	a	09 39			11 39					13 39				15 39
	d	09 42	10 42		11 42		12 42			13 42		14 42		15 42
Woodlesford	d	09 51	10 51		11 51		12 51			13 51		14 51		15 51
Leeds 10	31 a	10 04	11 06		12 07	12 31	13 06			14f07	14 31	15 04		16 04

		NT	NT A	NT B	NT	NT C	NT A	NT	NT D	NT A	NT	NT	NT	NT	NT C
St Pancras International	⊖ 53 d	*11 30*				*12 30*		*13g30*	*14 30*		*15h30*	*17 25*	*18 25*		*19j25*
Sheffield 7	29, 31 ⛴ d	15 30		15 39	16 32	16 39		17 39	18 38		19 39	20 39	21 43		22 39
Meadowhall	29, 31 ⛴ d	15 38		15 45	16 38	16 45		17 45	18 45		19 45	20 45	21 49		22 45
Chapeltown	d			15 51		16 51		17 51	18 51		19 51	20 51	21 55		22 51
Elsecar	d			15 56		16 56		17 56	18 56		19 56	20 56	22 00		22 56
Wombwell	d			16 00		17 00		18 00	19 00		20 00	21 00	22 04		23 00
Barnsley	a	15 52		16 06	16 52	17 05		18 05	19 05		20 05	21 06	22 09		23 05
	d	15 53		16 06	16 57	17 09		18 07	19 09		20 06	21 09			23 09
Dodworth	d			16 12	17 03			18 13			20 12				
Silkstone Common	d			16 16	17 07			18 17			20 16				
Penistone	d			16 23	17 14			18 24			20 23				
Denby Dale	d			16 29	17 20			18 30			20 29				
Shepley	d			16 34	17 25			18 35			20 34				
Stocksmoor	d			16 37	17k35			18 38			20 37				
Brockholes	d			16 41	17 39			18 42			20 41				
Honley	d			16 43	17 42			18 44			20 43				
Berry Brow	d			16 46	17 45			18 47			20 46				
Lockwood	d			16 49	17 47			18 50			20 49				
Huddersfield	a			16 55	17 52			18 54			20 53				
Darton	d					17 14			19 14			21 14			23 14
Wakefield Kirkgate 4	31 d	16 11				17 29			19 29			21 29			23 29
Normanton	d					17 34			19 34			21 34			23 34
Castleford	a					17 39			19 41			21 39			23 39
	d		16 42			17 42	18 42		19 42	20 42		21 42		22 42	23 42
Woodlesford	d		16 51			17 51	18 51		19 51	20 51		21 51		22 51	23 51
Leeds 10	31 a	16 31	17 04			18 04	19 06		20 04	21 04		22 04		23 04	00 04

For general notes see front of timetable
For details of catering facilities see Directory of Train Operators

A From Knottingley (Table 32)
B From Retford Low Level (Table 30)
C From Lincoln (Table 30)
D From 20 July dep. 1530
b From 20 July only
c From 20 July dep. 1030
e Arr. 1328
f Until 13 July arr. 1404
g From 20 July dep. 1430
h From 20 July dep. 1630
j From 20 July dep. 1930
k Arr. 1728

Due to Engineering Operations in the Sheffield area, services from Sunday 14 September on this Table had not been confirmed at time of going to press. These services will be issued in a special Supplement as soon as exact timings have been confirmed.

Leeds and Huddersfield → Barnsley → Sheffield

Network Diagram - see first page of Table 31

Miles	Miles			NT A	NT	NT B	NT	NT	NT	NT	NT B	NT	NT	EM 1 ◇	NT	NT B	NT	NT	NT	NT B
0	—	**Leeds 10**	31 d			05 46		06 05		06 38	07 04	07 16			07 23	08 04	08 16		08 34	09 04
6	—	Woodlesford	d			05 54				06 46	07 12				07 31	08 12			08 42	09 12
10¾	—	Castleford	a			06 03				06 57	07 23				07 42	08 21			08 50	09 21
—	—		d							06 59					07 44				08 53	
14¼	—	Normanton	d							07 05					07 50				08 58	
17¼	—	Wakefield Kirkgate 4	31 d				06 10	06 22		07 10		07 32			07 55		08 32		09 03	
24¼	—	Darton	d				06 21			07 21					08 06				09 14	
—	0	**Huddersfield**	d						06 10				07 10					08 10		
—	1¼	Lockwood	d						06 13				07 13					08 13		
—	2¼	Berry Brow	d						06 16				07 16					08 16		
—	3¾	Honley	d						06 19				07 19					08 19		
—	4¾	Brockholes	d						06 22				07 22					08 22		
—	6¼	Stocksmoor	d						06 26				07 26					08 26		
—	7¼	Shepley	d						06 28				07 28					08 28		
—	9¼	Denby Dale	d						06 34				07 33					08 34		
—	13¼	Penistone	d						06 42				07 42					08 42		
—	16¾	Silkstone Common	d						06 47				07 47					08 47		
—	18	Dodworth	d						06 51				07 51					08 51		
28¼	21	**Barnsley**	a				06 27	06 44	06 57	07 27		07 48	07 57		08 13		08 48	08 57	09 22	
—	—		d	05 18	05 53		06 27	06 46	06 58	07 28		07 48	07 58	08 06	08 14		08 48	08 58	09 26	
32¼	25	Wombwell	d	05 23	05 58		06 32		07 03	07 33			08 03		08 19			09 03	09 31	
33¼	26½	Elsecar	d	05 27	06 02		06 36		07 07	07 37			08 07		08 23			09 07	09 35	
37	29¾	Chapeltown	d	05 33	06 07		06 41		07 12	07 42			08 12		08 28			09 12	09 40	
40¾	33½	Meadowhall	29, 31 a	05 38	06 13		06 48	07 03	07 19	07 48		08 03	08 17	08 24	08 33		09 03	09 19	09 48	
44¼	37	**Sheffield 7**	29, 31 a	05 49	06 24		06 57	07 14	07 29	07 59		08 15	08 28	08 33	08 45		09 15	09 30	09 57	
—	—	St Pancras International	⊖ 53 a	*08 42*			*09 29*	*09 33*				*10 48*		11 34			*11 51*			

		NT	NT	NT	NT B	NT	NT	NT	NT B	NT	NT	NT	NT B	NT	NT	NT	NT B	NT	NT	NT
Leeds 10	31 d	09 16		09 34	10 04	10 16		10 34	11 04	11 16		11 34	12 04	12 16		12 34	13 04	13 16		13 34
Woodlesford	d			09 42	10 12			10 42	11 12			11 42	12 12			12 42	13 12			13 42
Castleford	a			09 50	10 21			10 50	11 21			11 50	12 21			12 50	13 21			13 50
	d			09 53				10 53				11 53				12 53				13 53
Normanton	d			09 58				10 58				11 58				12 58				13 58
Wakefield Kirkgate 4	31 d	09 32		10 03		10 32		11 03		11 32		12 05		12 32		13 03		13 32		14 03
Darton	d			10 14				11 14				12 16				13 14				14 14
Huddersfield	d		09 13				10 13				11 13				12 13				13 13	
Lockwood	d		09 16				10 16				11 16				12 16				13 16	
Berry Brow	d		09 19				10 19				11 19				12 19				13 19	
Honley	d		09 22				10 22				11 22				12 22				13 22	
Brockholes	d		09 25				10 25				11 25				12 25				13 25	
Stocksmoor	d		09 29				10 29				11 29				12 29				13 29	
Shepley	d		09 31				10 31				11 31				12 31				13 31	
Denby Dale	d		09 36				10 36				11 36				12 36				13 36	
Penistone	d		09 44				10 44				11 44				12 44				13 44	
Silkstone Common	d		09 49				10 49				11 49				12 49				13 49	
Dodworth	d		09 53				10 53				11 53				12 53				13 53	
Barnsley	a	09 48	10 00	10 21		10 48	11 00	11 21		11 48	12 00	12 22		12 48	13 00	13 21		13 48	14 00	14 21
	d	09 48	10 01	10 26		10 48	11 01	11 26		11 48	12 01	12 26		12 48	13 01	13 26		13 48	14 01	14 26
Wombwell	d		10 06	10 31			11 06	11 31			12 06	12 31			13 06	13 31			14 06	14 31
Elsecar	d			10 35				11 35				12 35				13 35				14 35
Chapeltown	d		10 13	10 40			11 13	11 40			12 13	12 40			13 13	13 40			14 13	14 40
Meadowhall	29, 31 a	10 03	10 19	10 48		11 03	11 19	11 48		12 03	12 19	12 48		13 03	13 20	13 48		14 03	14 19	14 48
Sheffield 7	29, 31 a	10 15	10 30	10 57		11 15	11 30	11 57		12 15	12 30	12 57		13 15	13 31	13 57		14 15	14 30	14 57
St Pancras International	⊖ 53 a	*12 51*				*13 45*				*14 44*				*15 50*				*16 45*		

		NT B	NT	NT	NT	NT B	NT	NT	NT	NT B	NT	NT	NT	NT	NT	NT C	NT	NT	NT B
Leeds 10	31 d	14 04	14 16		14 34	15 04	15 16		15 34	16 04	16 16		16 34	17 16		17 19	17 34	17 43	18 04
Woodlesford	d	14 12			14 42	15 12			15 42	16 12			16 42			17 28	17 42		18 12
Castleford	a	14 21			14 50	15 21			15 50	16 21			16 50			17 37	17 50		18 21
	d				14 53				15 53				16 53				17 53		
Normanton	d				14 58				15 58				16 58	17 28			17 58		
Wakefield Kirkgate 4	31 d		14 32		15 03		15 32		16 03		16 32		17 03	17 32			18 03		
Darton	d				15 14				16 14				17 14				18 14		
Huddersfield	d			14 13				15 13				16 13			17 13			18 22	
Lockwood	d			14 16				15 16				16 16			17 16				
Berry Brow	d			14 19				15 19				16 19			17 19				
Honley	d			14 22				15 22				16 22			17 22				
Brockholes	d			14 25				15 25				16 25			17 25				
Stocksmoor	d			14 29				15 29				16 29			17 29				
Shepley	d			14 31				15 31				16 31			17 31				
Denby Dale	d			14 36				15 36				16 36			17 36				
Penistone	d			14 44				15 44				16 44			17 44				
Silkstone Common	d			14 49				15 49				16 49			17 49				
Dodworth	d			14 53				15 53				16 53			17 53				
Barnsley	a		14 48	15 00	15 21		15 48	16 00	16 21		16 48	17 00	17 21	17 48	18 00		18 22		
	d		14 48	15 01	15 26		15 48	16 01	16 26		16 48	17 01	17 26	17 48	18 01		18 26		
Wombwell	d			15 06	15 31			16 06	16 31			17 06	17 31		18 06		18 31		
Elsecar	d				15 35				16 35				17 35				18 35		
Chapeltown	d			15 13	15 40			16 13	16 40			17 13	17 40		18 13		18 40		
Meadowhall	29, 31 a		15 03	15 19	15 48		16 05	16 19	16 48		17 03	17 19	17 48	18 03	18 19		18 47		
Sheffield 7	29, 31 a		15 15	15 30	15 57		16 15	16 30	16 57		17 15	17 30	17 57	18 15	18 30		18 57		
St Pancras International	⊖ 53 a		*17 53*				*18 51*				*19 52*			*20 41*					

For general notes see front of timetable
For details of catering facilities see Directory of Train Operators

A To Retford (Table 30)
B To Knottingley (Table 32)
C To Goole (Table 32)

Table 34

Mondays to Fridays
until 5 September

Leeds and Huddersfield → Barnsley → Sheffield

Network Diagram - see first page of Table 31

	NT	NT	NT		NT	NT	NT		NT	NT	NT		NT	NT	NT		NT	NT	NT	NT	NT	NT		
						A					A							A			A			
Leeds 10 31 d	18 16				18 34	19 04	19 16			19 34	20 04		20 16		20 34			21 04	21 34		22 04	22 34		
Woodlesford d					18 42	19 12				19 42	20 12				20 42			21 12	21 42		22 12	22 42		
Castleford a					18 50	19 21				19 50	20 21				20 51			21 21	21 50		22 21	22 50		
d					18 53					19 53					20 53				21 53			22 53		
Normanton d					18 58					19 58					20 58				21 58			22 58		
Wakefield Kirkgate 4 31 d	18 32				19 03		19 32			20 03			20 32		21 03				22 03			23 03		
Darton d			←		19 14					20 14					21 14				22 14			23 14		
Huddersfield d		17 56	18 22						19 18					20 18			21 18			22 18				
Lockwood d		17 59	18 25						19 21					20 21			21 21			22 21				
Berry Brow d		18 02	18 28						19 24					20 24			21 24			22 24				
Honley d		18 05	18 31						19 27					20 27			21 27			22 27				
Brockholes d		18 08	18 34						19 30					20 30			21 30			22 30				
Stocksmoor d		18 12	18 38						19 34					20 34			21 34			22 34				
Shepley d		18 14	18 40						19 36					20 36			21 36			22 36				
Denby Dale d		18 19	18 45						19 41					20 41			21 41			22 41				
Penistone d		18b36	18 53						19 49					20 49			21 49			22 49				
Silkstone Common d		18 41	18 58						19 54					20 54			21 54			22 54				
Dodworth d		18 45	19 02						19 58					20 58			21 58			22 58				
Barnsley a	18 48	18 52	19 09		19 21		19 48		20 05	20 22			20 48	21 05	21 22		22 05		22 25	23 05		23 24		
d	18 48	18 58	19 16		19 26		19 48		20 06	20 26			20 48	21 06	21 26		22 06		22 26	23 06		23 26		
Wombwell d		19 03	19 21		19 31				20 11	20 31				21 11	21 31		22 11		22 31	23 11		23 31		
Elsecar d		19 07			19 35					20 35					21 35				22 35	23 15		23 35		
Chapeltown d		19 12	19 28		19 40				20 18	20 40				21 18	21 41		22 18		22 40	23 20		23 40		
Meadowhall 29, 31 🚋 a	19 03	19 16	19 34		19 48		20 03		20 23	20 47			21 03	21 24	21 48		22 23		22 48	23 25		23 48		
Sheffield 7 29, 31 🚋 a	19 15	19 30	19 44		19 57		20 15		20 35	20 57			21 15	21 35	21 57		22 35		22 57	23 35		23 57		
St Pancras International ⊖ 53 a	*21 53*						*23 04*																	

Mondays to Fridays
from 8 September

	NT	NT	NT	NT	NT	NT	NT	NT	NT	NT	NT	NT	EM	NT	NT	NT	NT	NT	NT	NT	NT	NT	NT	NT
													1 ◇											
	B		A					A				A	☕			A				A				A
Leeds 10 31 d			05 46		06 05		06 38	07 04	07 16		07 23	08 04	08 16		08 34	09 04	09 16		09 34	10 04	10 16		10 34	11 04
Woodlesford d			05 54				06 46	07 12			07 31	08 12			08 42	09 12			09 42	10 12			10 42	11 12
Castleford a			06 03				06 57	07 23			07 42	08 21			08 50	09 21			09 50	10 21			10 50	11 21
d							06 59				07 44				08 53				09 53				10 53	
Normanton d							07 05				07 50				08 58				09 58				10 58	
Wakefield Kirkgate 4 31 d				06 10	06 22		07 10		07 32		07 55				09 03		09 32		10 03		10 32		11 03	
Darton d				06 21			07 21				08 06				09 14				10 14				11 14	
Huddersfield d						06 05				07 08				08 07				09 08				10 08		
Lockwood d						06 08				07 11				08 10				09 11				10 11		
Berry Brow d						06 11				07 14				08 13				09 14				10 14		
Honley d						06 14				07 17				08 16				09 17				10 17		
Brockholes d						06 17				07 20				08 19				09 20				10 20		
Stocksmoor d						06 21				07 24				08 23				09 24				10 24		
Shepley d						06 23				07 26				08 25				09 26				10 26		
Denby Dale d						06 29				07 32				08 31				09 31				10 31		
Penistone d						06 42				07 42				08 42				09 44				10 44		
Silkstone Common d						06 47				07 47				08 47				09 49				10 49		
Dodworth d						06 51				07 51				08 51				09 53				10 53		
Barnsley a				06 27	06 44	06 57	07 27		07 48	07 57	08 13			08 57	09 22		09 48	10 00	10 21		10 48	11 00	11 21	
d	05 18	05 53		06 27	06 46	06 58	07 28		07 49	07 58	08 14			08 58	09 26		09 48	10 01	10 26		10 48	11 01	11 26	
Wombwell d	05 23	05 58		06 32		07 03	07 33			08 03	08 19			09 03	09 31			10 06	10 31			11 06	11 31	
Elsecar d	05 27	06 02		06 36		07 07	07 37			08 07	08 23			09 07	09 35				10 35				11 35	
Chapeltown d	05 33	06 07		06 41		07 12	07 42			08 12	08 28			09 12	09 40			10 13	10 40			11 13	11 40	
Meadowhall 29, 31 🚋 a	05 38	06 13		06 48	07 03	07 19	07 48		08 04	08 17	08 33			09 19	09 48		10 03	10 19	10 48		11 03	11 19	11 48	
Sheffield 7 29, 31 🚋 a	05 49	06 24		06 57	07 14	07 29	07 59		08 15	08 28	08 45		09 11	09 31	09 58		10 15	10 30	10 59		11 15	11 30	11 58	
St Pancras International ⊖ 53 a	*08 55*			*09 33*			*10 48*						*11 51*		*12 51*				*13 45*				*14 44*	

	NT	NT	NT	NT	NT	NT	NT	NT	NT	NT	NT	NT	NT	NT	NT	NT	NT	NT	NT	NT	NT	NT	NT	NT
				A				A				A				A				A				
Leeds 10 31 d	11 16		11 34	12 04	12 16		12 34	13 04	13 16		13 34	14 04	14 16		14 34	15 04	15 16		15 34	16 04	16 16		16 34	17 16
Woodlesford d			11 42	12 12			12 42	13 12			13 42	14 12			14 42	15 12			15 42	16 12			16 42	
Castleford a			11 50	12 21			12 50	13 21			13 50	14 21			14 50	15 21			15 50	16 21			16 50	
d			11 53				12 53				13 53				14 53				15 53				16 53	
Normanton d			11 58				12 58				13 58				14 58				15 58				16 58	17 28
Wakefield Kirkgate 4 31 d	11 32		12 05		12 32		13 03		13 32		14 03		14 32		15 03		15 32		16 03		16 32		17 03	17 32
Darton d			12 16				13 14				14 14				15 14				16 14				17 14	
Huddersfield d		11 08				12 08				13 08				14 08				15 08				16 08		
Lockwood d		11 11				12 11				13 11				14 11				15 11				16 11		
Berry Brow d		11 14				12 14				13 14				14 14				15 14				16 14		
Honley d		11 17				12 17				13 17				14 17				15 17				16 17		
Brockholes d		11 20				12 20				13 20				14 20				15 20				16 20		
Stocksmoor d		11 24				12 24				13 24				14 24				15 24				16 24		
Shepley d		11 26				12 26				13 26				14 26				15 26				16 26		
Denby Dale d		11 31				12 31				13 31				14 31				15 31				16 31		
Penistone d		11 44				12 44				13 44				14 44				15 44				16 44		
Silkstone Common d		11 49				12 49				13 49				14 49				15 49				16 49		
Dodworth d		11 53				12 53				13 53				14 53				15 53				16 53		
Barnsley a	11 48	12 00	12 22		12 48	13 00	13 21		13 48	14 00	14 21		14 48	15 00	15 21		15 48	16 00	16 25		16 48	17 00	17 21	17 48
d	11 48	12 01	12 26		12 48	13 01	13 26		13 48	14 01	14 26		14 48	15 01	15 26		15 48	16 01	16 26		16 48	17 01	17 26	17 48
Wombwell d		12 06	12 31			13 06	13 31			14 06	14 31			15 06	15 31			16 06	16 31			17 06	17 31	
Elsecar d			12 35				13 35				14 35				15 35				16 35				17 35	
Chapeltown d		12 13	12 40			13 13	13 40			14 13	14 40			15 13	15 40			16 13	16 40			17 13	17 40	
Meadowhall 29, 31 🚋 a	12 03	12 19	12 48		13 03	13 20	13 48		14 03	14 19	14 48		15 03	15 19	15 48		16 03	16 19	16 48		17 03	17 19	17 48	18 03
Sheffield 7 29, 31 🚋 a	12 15	12 30	12 58		13 14	13 29	13 58		14 15	14 30	14 58		15 15	15 30	15 58		16 13	16 30	16 58		17 15	17 29	17 58	18 15
St Pancras International ⊖ 53 a			*15 50*				*16 45*				*17 53*				*18 51*				*19 52*				*20 41*	

For general notes see front of timetable
For details of catering facilities see Directory of Train Operators

A To Knottingley (Table 32)
B To Retford (Table 30)
b Arr. 1826

Mondays to Fridays

from 8 September

Leeds and Huddersfield → Barnsley → Sheffield

Network Diagram - see first page of Table 31

		NT	NT	NT	NT	NT	NT	NT	NT	NT	NT	NT	NT	NT	NT	NT	NT	NT	NT	NT	NT	NT	NT	NT
			A			B					B				B					B			B	
Leeds 10	31 d		17 19	17 34	17 43	18 04	18 16			18 34	19 04	19 16		19 34	20 04	20 16		20 34		21 04	21 34		22 04	22 34
Woodlesford	d		17 28	17 42		18 12				18 42	19 12			19 42	20 12			20 42		21 12	21 42		22 12	22 42
Castleford	a		17 37	17 50		18 21				18 50	19 21			19 50	20 21			20 51		21 21	21 50		22 21	22 50
	d			17 53						18 53				19 53				20 53			21 53			22 53
Normanton	d			17 58						18 58				19 58				20 58			21 58			22 58
Wakefield Kirkgate 4	31 d			18 03			18 32			19 03		19 32		20 03		20 32		21 03			22 03			23 03
Darton	d			18 14					←	19 14				20 14				21 14			22 14			23 14
Huddersfield	d	17 08			18 22			17 56	18 22				19 15				20 15		21 18			22 15		
Lockwood	d	17 11						17 59	18 25				19 18				20 18		21 21			22 18		
Berry Brow	d	17 14						18 02	18 28				19 21				20 21		21 24			22 21		
Honley	d	17 17						18 05	18 31				19 24				20 24		21 27			22 24		
Brockholes	d	17 20						18 08	18 34				19 27				20 27		21 30			22 27		
Stocksmoor	d	17 24						18 12	18 38				19 31				20 31		21 34			22 31		
Shepley	d	17 26						18 14	18 40				19 33				20 33		21 36			22 33		
Denby Dale	d	17 31						18 19	18 45				19 38				20 38		21 41			22 38		
Penistone	d	17 44						18b36	18 53				19 49				20 49		21 49			22 49		
Silkstone Common	d	17 49						18 41	18 58				19 54				20 54		21 54			22 54		
Dodworth	d	17 53						18 45	19 02				19 58				20 58		21 58			22 58		
Barnsley	a	18 00		18 25			18 48	18 52	19 09	19 21		19 48	20 05	20 22		20 48	21 05	21 22	22 05		22 25	23 05		23 24
	d	18 01		18 26			18 48	18 58	19 16	19 26		19 48	20 06	20 26		20 48	21 06	21 26	22 06		22 26	23 06		23 26
Wombwell	d	18 06		18 31				19 03	19 21	19 31			20 11	20 31			21 11	21 31	22 11		22 31	23 11		23 31
Elsecar	d			18 35				19 07		19 35				20 35				21 35			22 35	23 15		23 35
Chapeltown	d	18 13		18 40				19 12	19 28	19 40			20 18	20 40			21 18	21 41	22 18		22 40	23 20		23 40
Meadowhall	29, 31 ⇌ a	18 19		18 47			19 03	19 16	19 34	19 46		20 03	20 28	20 47		21 03	21 24	21 48	22 23		22 47	23 25		23 48
Sheffield 7	29, 31 ⇌ a	18 30		18 57			19 15	19 30	19 44	19 57		20 15		20 57		21 15	21 35	21 57	22 35		22 58	23 35		23 57
St Pancras International	⊖ 53 a			*21 53*						*23 04*														

Saturdays

until 6 September

		NT	NT	NT	NT	NT	NT	NT	NT	NT	NT	EM	NT	NT	NT	NT	NT	NT		NT	NT	NT	NT	NT	NT
												1 ◇													
		C					B				B					B					B				B
												⊡													
Leeds 10	31 d					06 38	07 04	07 16		07 23	08 04		08 16		08 34	09 04	09 16			09 34	10 04	10 16		10 34	11 04
Woodlesford	d					06 46	07 12			07 31	08 12				08 42	09 12				09 42	10 12			10 42	11 12
Castleford	a					06 57	07 23			07 42	08 21				08 50	09 21				09 50	10 21			10 50	11 21
	d					06 59				07 44					08 53					09 53				10 53	
Normanton	d					07 05				07 50					08 58					09 58				10 58	
Wakefield Kirkgate 4	31 d					07 10		07 32		07 55			08 32		09 03		09 32			10 03		10 32		11 03	
Darton	d					07 21				08 06					09 14					10 14				11 14	
Huddersfield	d				06 10				07 10					08 10				09 13					10 13		
Lockwood	d				06 13				07 13					08 13				09 16					10 16		
Berry Brow	d				06 16				07 16					08 16				09 19					10 19		
Honley	d				06 19				07 19					08 19				09 22					10 22		
Brockholes	d				06 22				07 22					08 22				09 25					10 25		
Stocksmoor	d				06 26				07 26					08 26				09 29					10 29		
Shepley	d				06 28				07 28					08 28				09 31					10 31		
Denby Dale	d				06 34				07 33					08 34				09 36					10 36		
Penistone	d				06 42				07 42					08 42				09 44					10 44		
Silkstone Common	d				06 47				07 47					08 47				09 49					10 49		
Dodworth	d				06 51				07 51					08 51				09 53					10 53		
Barnsley	a				06 57	07 27		07 48	07 57	08 16			08 48	08 57	09 22		09 48	10 00		10 21		10 48	11 00	11 21	
	d	05 18	05 53	06 27	06 58	07 28		07 48	07 58	08 17		08 30	08 48	08 58	09 26		09 48	10 01		10 26		10 48	11 01	11 26	
Wombwell	d	05 23	05 58	06 32	07 03	07 33			08 03	08 22				09 03	09 31			10 06		10 31			11 06	11 31	
Elsecar	d	05 27	06 02	06 36	07 07	07 37			08 07	08 26				09 07	09 35					10 35				11 35	
Chapeltown	d	05 33	06 07	06 41	07 12	07 42			08 12	08 31				09 12	09 40			10 13		10 40			11 13	11 40	
Meadowhall	29, 31 ⇌ a	05 38	06 13	06 48	07 19	07 48		08 03	08 17	08 36		08 45	09 03	09 19	09 48		10 03	10 19		10 48		11 03	11 19	11 48	
Sheffield 7	29, 31 ⇌ a	05 49	06 25	06 57	07 29	07 59		08 15	08 28	08 47		08 54	09 15	09 30	09 57		10 15	10 30		10 57		11 15	11 30	11 57	
St Pancras International	⊖ 53 a	*08 45*	*09 17*	*09 49*				*10 46*				11 34	*11 59*				*12 51*					*13 44*			

For general notes see front of timetable
For details of catering facilities see
Directory of Train Operators

A To Goole (Table 32)
B To Knottingley (Table 32)
C To Retford (Table 30)

b Arr. 1826

Due to Engineering Operations in the Sheffield area, services from Saturday 13 September on this Table had not been confirmed at time of going to press. These services will be issued in a special Supplement as soon as exact timings have been confirmed.

Table 34

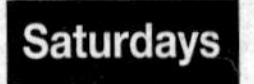

until 6 September

Leeds and Huddersfield → Barnsley → Sheffield

Network Diagram - see first page of Table 31

	NT	NT	NT	NT A	NT	NT	NT	NT A	NT	NT	NT	NT A	NT	NT	NT	NT A	NT	NT	NT	NT A	NT	NT	NT
Leeds 10 31 d	11 16		11 34	12 04	12 16		12 34	13 04	13 16		13 34	14 04	14 16		14 34	15 04	15 16		15 34	16 04	16 16		16 34
Woodlesford d			11 42	12 12			12 42	13 12			13 42	14 12			14 42	15 12			15 42	16 12			16 42
Castleford a			11 50	12 21			12 50	13 21			13 50	14 21			14 50	15 21			15 50	16 21			16 50
d			11 53				12 53				13 53				14 53				15 53				16 53
Normanton d			11 58				12 58				13 58				14 58				15 58				16 58
Wakefield Kirkgate 4 31 d	11 32		12 05		12 32		13 03		13 32		14 03		14 32		15 03		15 32		16 03		16 32		17 03
Darton d			12 16				13 14				14 14				15 14				16 14				17 14
Huddersfield d		11 13				12 13				13 13				14 13				15 13				16 13	
Lockwood d		11 16				12 16				13 16				14 16				15 16				16 16	
Berry Brow d		11 19				12 19				13 19				14 19				15 19				16 19	
Honley d		11 22				12 22				13 22				14 22				15 22				16 22	
Brockholes d		11 25				12 25				13 25				14 25				15 25				16 25	
Stocksmoor d		11 29				12 29				13 29				14 29				15 29				16 29	
Shepley d		11 31				12 31				13 31				14 31				15 31				16 31	
Denby Dale d		11 36				12 36				13 36				14 36				15 36				16 36	
Penistone d		11 44				12 44				13 44				14 44				15 44				16 44	
Silkstone Common d		11 49				12 49				13 49				14 49				15 49				16 49	
Dodworth d		11 53				12 53				13 53				14 53				15 53				16 53	
Barnsley a	11 48	12 00	12 22		12 48	13 00	13 21		13 48	14 00	14 21		14 48	15 00	15 21		15 48	16 00	16 21		16 48	17 00	17 21
d	11 48	12 01	12 26		12 48	13 01	13 26		13 48	14 01	14 26		14 48	15 01	15 26		15 48	16 01	16 26		16 48	17 01	17 26
Wombwell d		12 06	12 31			13 06	13 31			14 06	14 31			15 06	15 31			16 06	16 31			17 06	17 31
Elsecar d			12 35				13 35				14 35				15 35				16 35				17 35
Chapeltown d		12 13	12 40			13 13	13 40			14 13	14 40			15 13	15 40			16 13	16 40			17 13	17 40
Meadowhall 29, 31 a	12 03	12 19	12 48		13 03	13 20	13 48		14 03	14 19	14 48		15 03	15 19	15 48		16 05	16 19	16 48		17 03	17 19	17 48
Sheffield 7 29, 31 a	12 15	12 30	12 57		13 15	13 31	13 57		14 15	14 30	14 57		15 15	15 30	15 57		16 15	16 30	16 57		17 15	17 30	17 57
St Pancras International ⊖ 53 a	*14 45*				*15 51*				*16 45*				*17 51*				*18 51*				*19 45*		

	NT	NT	NT B	NT	NT A	NT	NT	NT	NT A	NT	NT	NT	NT A	NT	NT	NT	NT	NT A	NT	NT	NT A	NT
Leeds 10 31 d	17 16		17 19	17 34	18 04	18 16		18 34	19 04	19 16		19 34	20 04	20 16		20 34		21 04	21 34		22 04	22 34
Woodlesford d			17 28	17 42	18 12			18 42	19 12			19 42	20 12			20 42		21 12	21 42		22 12	22 42
Castleford a			17 37	17 50	18 21			18 50	19 21			19 50	20 21			20 51		21 21	21 50		22 21	22 50
d				17 53				18 53				19 53				20 53			21 53			22 53
Normanton d	17 28			17 58				18 58				19 58				20 58			21 58			22 58
Wakefield Kirkgate 4 31 d	17 32			18 03		18 32		19 03		19 32		20 03		20 32		21 03			22 03			23a03
Darton d				18 14				19 14				20 14				21 14			22 14			
Huddersfield d		17 13					18 13				19 18				20 18		21 18			22 18		
Lockwood d		17 16					18 16				19 21				20 21		21 21			22 21		
Berry Brow d		17 19					18 19				19 24				20 24		21 24			22 24		
Honley d		17 22					18 22				19 27				20 27		21 27			22 27		
Brockholes d		17 25					18 25				19 30				20 30		21 30			22 30		
Stocksmoor d		17 29					18 29				19 34				20 34		21 34			22 34		
Shepley d		17 31					18 31				19 36				20 36		21 36			22 36		
Denby Dale d		17 36					18 36				19 41				20 41		21 41			22 41		
Penistone d		17 44					18 44				19 49				20 49		21 49			22 49		
Silkstone Common d		17 49					18 49				19 54				20 54		21 54			22 54		
Dodworth d		17 53					18 53				19 58				20 58		21 58			22 58		
Barnsley a	17 48	18 00		18 22		18 48	19 00	19 21		19 48	20 05	20 22		20 48	21 05	21 22	22 05		22 25	23 05		
d	17 48	18 01		18 26		18 48	19 01	19 26		19 48	20 06	20 26		20 48	21 06	21 26	22 06		22 26	23 06		
Wombwell d		18 06		18 31			19 06	19 31			20 11	20 31			21 11	21 31	22 11		22 31	23 11		
Elsecar d				18 35				19 35				20 35				21 35			22 35	23 15		
Chapeltown d		18 13		18 40			19 13	19 40			20 18	20 40			21 18	21 41	22 18		22 40	23 20		
Meadowhall 29, 31 a	18 03	18 19		18 47		19 03	19 19	19 48		20 03	20 23	20 47		21 03	21 24	21 48	22 23		22 48	23 25		
Sheffield 7 29, 31 a	18 15	18 30		18 57		19 15	19 30	19 57		20 15	20 35	20 57		21 15	21 35	21 57	22 35		22 57	23 35		
St Pancras International ⊖ 53 a	*20 48*			*21 52*																		

For general notes see front of timetable
For details of catering facilities see Directory of Train Operators

A To Knottingley (Table 32)
B To Goole (Table 32)

Due to Engineering Operations in the Sheffield area, services from Saturday 13 September on this Table had not been confirmed at time of going to press. These services will be issued in a special Supplement as soon as exact timings have been confirmed.

Table 34

until 7 September

Leeds and Huddersfield → Barnsley → Sheffield

Network Diagram - see first page of Table 31

	NT	NT	NT A	NT	NT	NT	NT	NT	NT A	NT B	NT	NT	NT A
Leeds 10 31 d	08 30		09 30	10 14		10 17	11 14		11 17	12 17	13 14		13 17
Woodlesford d	08 38		09 38			10 25			11 25	12 25			13 25
Castleford a	08 47		09 46			10 33			11 33	12 33			13 33
d	08 49					10 36				12 36			
Normanton d	08 55					10 41				12 41			
Wakefield Kirkgate 4 31 d	09 00			10 30		10 46	11 30			12 46	13 30		
Darton d	09 14					11 00				13 00			
Huddersfield d		09 19			10 14			11 19				13 19	
Lockwood d		09 22			10 17			11 22				13 22	
Berry Brow d		09 25			10 20			11 25				13 25	
Honley d		09 28			10 23			11 28				13 28	
Brockholes d		09 31			10 26			11 31				13 31	
Stocksmoor d		09 35			10 11			11 35				13 35	
Shepley d		09 37			10 34			11 37				13 37	
Denby Dale d		09 42			10 39			11 42				13 42	
Penistone d		09 50			10 47			11 50				13 50	
Silkstone Common d		09 55			10 52			11 55				13 55	
Dodworth d		09 59			10 56			11 59				13 59	
Barnsley a	09 20	10 06		10 49	11 03	11 07	11 49	12 06		13 07	13 49	14 06	
d	09 21	10 12		10 49	11 04	11 12	11 49	12 12		13 12	13 49	14 12	
Wombwell d	09 26	10 17				11 17		12 17		13 17		14 17	
Elsecar d	09 30	10 21				11 21		12 21		13 21		14 21	
Chapeltown d	09 35	10 26				11 26		12 26		13 26		14 26	
Meadowhall 29, 31 ⛴ a	09 41	10 32		11 04	11 20	11 32	12 04	12 32		13 32	14 03	14 32	
Sheffield 7 29, 31 ⛴ a	09 51	10 43		11 15	11 30	11 43	12 14	12 43		13 43	14 14	14 43	
St Pancras International ⊖ 53 a	*13b48*	*14 18*		*14 55*		*16c06*		*16 06*		*17e06*	*17f06*	*17g55*	

	NT	NT	NT	NT A	NT	NT	NT A	NT	NT	NT A	NT	NT A	NT	NT
Leeds 10 31 d		14 17		15 17	16 17		17 17	18 17		19 17	20 17	21 17		22 17
Woodlesford d		14 25		15 25	16 25		17 25	18 25		19 25	20 25	21 25		22 25
Castleford a		14 33		15 33	16 33		17 33	18 33		19 35	20 33	21 33		22 33
d		14 36			16 36			18 36			20 36			22 36
Normanton d		14 41			16 41			18 41			20 41			22 41
Wakefield Kirkgate 4 31 d		14 46			16 46			18 46			20 46			22 46
Darton d		15 00			17 00			19 00			21 00			23 00
Huddersfield d	14 14		15 19			17 19			19 19					
Lockwood d	14 17		15 22			17 22			19 22					
Berry Brow d	14 20		15 25			17 25			19 25					
Honley d	14 23		15 28			17 28			19 28					
Brockholes d	14 26		15 31			17 31			19 31					
Stocksmoor d	14 30		15 35			17 35			19 35					
Shepley d	14 34		15 37			17 37			19 37					
Denby Dale d	14 39		15 42			17 42			19 42					
Penistone d	14 47		15 50			17 50			19 50					
Silkstone Common d	14 52		15 55			17 55			19 55					
Dodworth d	14 56		15 59			17 59			19 59					
Barnsley a	15 03	15 07	16 06		17 07	18 06		19 06	20 06		21 07			23 07
d	15 04	15 12	16 12		17 12	18 12		19 11	20 12		21 12		22 21	23 12
Wombwell d		15 17	16 17		17 17	18 17		19 17	20 17		21 17		22 26	23 17
Elsecar d		15 21	16 21		17 21	18 21		19 21	20 21		21 21		22 30	23 21
Chapeltown d		15 26	16 26		17 26	18 26		19 26	20 26		21 26		22 35	23 26
Meadowhall 29, 31 ⛴ a	15 20	15 32	16 32		17 32	18 32		19 32	20 33		21 32		22 40	23 32
Sheffield 7 29, 31 ⛴ a	15 30	15 44	16 43		17h44	18j46		19 44	20 46		21 43		22 51	23 43
St Pancras International ⊖ 53 a		*19k59*	*20m49*		*20 49*	*22 18*								

For general notes see front of timetable
For details of catering facilities see Directory of Train Operators

A To Knottingley (Table 32)
B To Lincoln (Table 30)
b From 20 July arr. 1318
c From 20 July arr. 1455
e Until 13 July only
f From 20 July only
g From 20 July arr. 1724
h Until 13 July arr. 1743
j Until 13 July arr. 1842
k From 20 July arr. 1857
m From 20 July arr. 1956

Due to Engineering Operations in the Sheffield area, services from Sunday 14 September on this Table had not been confirmed at time of going to press. These services will be issued in a special Supplement as soon as exact timings have been confirmed.

Network Diagram for Tables 35, 36, 37, 38

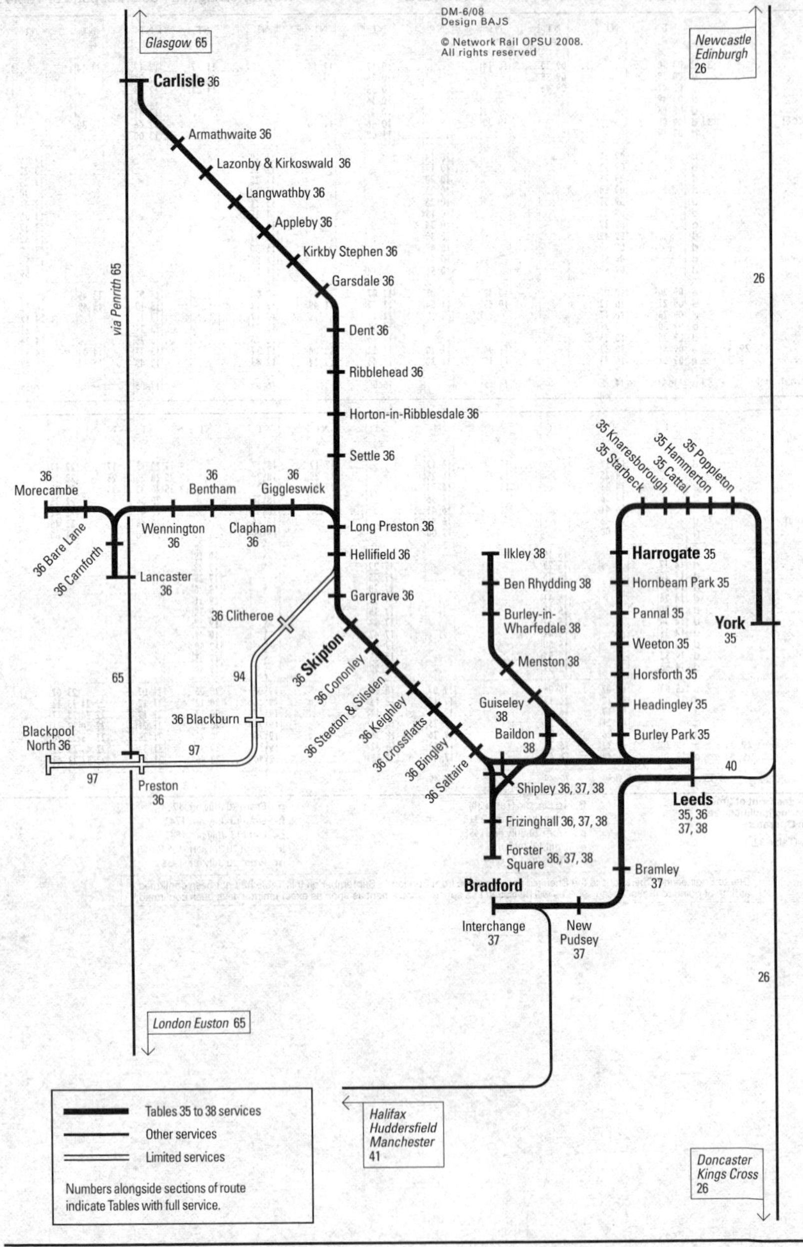
DM-6/08
Design BAJS
© Network Rail OPSU 2008.
All rights reserved
Glasgow 65
Carlisle 36
Armathwaite 36
Lazonby & Kirkoswald 36
Langwathby 36
Appleby 36
Kirkby Stephen 36
Garsdale 36
Dent 36
Ribblehead 36
Horton-in-Ribblesdale 36
Settle 36
via Penrith 65
Newcastle
Edinburgh
26
36 Morecambe
36 Bentham
36 Giggleswick
Wennington 36
Clapham 36
Long Preston 36
36 Bare Lane
36 Carnforth
Lancaster 36
Hellifield 36
Gargrave 36
36 Clitheroe
36 Skipton
36 Cononley
36 Steeton & Silsden
36 Keighley
36 Crossflatts
36 Bingley
36 Saltaire
94
65
36 Blackburn
Blackpool North 36
97
Preston 36
Ilkley 38
Ben Rhydding 38
Burley-in-Wharfedale 38
Menston 38
Guiseley 38
Baildon 38
Shipley 36, 37, 38
Frizinghall 36, 37, 38
Forster Square 36, 37, 38
Bradford
Interchange 37
New Pudsey 37
Bramley 37
Leeds 35, 36 37, 38
40
35 Knaresborough
35 Starbeck
35 Hammerton
35 Cattal
35 Poppleton
Harrogate 35
Hornbeam Park 35
Pannal 35
Weeton 35
Horsforth 35
Headingley 35
Burley Park 35
York 35
London Euston 65
Halifax
Huddersfield
Manchester
41
Doncaster
Kings Cross
26
Tables 35 to 38 services
Other services
Limited services
Numbers alongside sections of route indicate Tables with full service.

Table 35

Mondays to Fridays

York → Harrogate → Leeds

Network Diagram - see first page of Table 35

Miles				NT	NT	NT	GR 🅁 1 A ✕ ⇆	NT	NT	NT	NT	NT	NT	NT	NT	NT	NT	NT	NT	NT	NT
0	York 8	41	d					06 52				07 57		08 45	09 10		10 11		11 11		12 11
3	Poppleton		d					06 56				08 01		08 50	09 14		10 15		11 15		12 15
8¾	Hammerton		d					07 04				08 09		08 58	09 22		10 23		11 23		12 23
10¼	Cattal		d					07 07				08 12		09 01	09 26		10 26		11 26		12 26
16¾	Knaresborough		a									08 21		09 09	09 34		10 34		11 34		12 34
—			d			07 00			07 42	07 56		08 21	08 56	09 10	09 35	10 05	10 35	11 05	11 35	12 05	12 35
18¼	Starbeck		d			07 03		07 27	07 45	07 59		08 24	08 59	09 13	09 38	10 08	10 38	11 08	11 38	12 08	12 38
20¼	Harrogate		a			07 08		07 32	07 50	08 04		08 29	09 04	09 18	09 43	10 13	10 43	11 13	11 43	12 13	12 43
—			d	06 06	06 30	07 11	07 28	07 40	07 51	08 06	08 14	08 30	09 05	09 19	09 44	10 14	10 44	11 14	11 44	12 14	12 44
21½	Hornbeam Park		d	06 08	06 32	07 14		07 42	07 54		08 17	08 33		09 22	09 47	10 17	10 47	11 17	11 47	12 17	12 47
23¾	Pannal		d	06 13	06 37	07 19		07 47	07 59		08 22	08 38		09 27	09 52	10 22	10 52	11 22	11 52	12 22	12 52
27	Weeton		d	06 18	06 42	07 23		07 51	08 03		08 26	08 42		09 31	09 56	10 26	10 56	11 26	11 56	12 26	12 56
33	Horsforth		d	06 28	06 50	07 32	07u46	08 00	08 12	08 22	08 35	08 51	09 21	09 40	10 05	10 35	11 05	11 35	12 05	12 35	13 05
35¾	Headingley		d	06 32	06 54	07 36		08 04	08 16	08 26	08 39	08 55	09 25	09 44	10 09	10 39	11 09	11 39	12 09	12 39	13 09
36½	Burley Park		d	06 34	06 56	07 38		08 06	08 18	08 29	08 41	08 57	09 27	09 47	10 11	10 41	11 11	11 41	12 11	12 41	13 11
38¾	Leeds 10	41	a	06 44	07 08	07 48	07 58	08 17	08 29	08 40	08 52	09 08	09 37	09 56	10 22	10 52	11 22	11 52	12 22	12 52	13 22

			NT	NT	NT	NT	NT	NT	NT	NT	NT	NT	NT	NT	NT	NT	NT	NT	NT	NT
York 8	41	d		13 11		14 11		15 11		16 11		16 54	17 17		18 11		19 11	20 11	21 11	22 11
Poppleton		d		13 15		14 15		15 15		16 15		16 58	17 21		18 15		19 15	20 15	21 16	22 15
Hammerton		d		13 23		14 23		15 23		16 23		17 06	17 29		18 23		19 23	20 23	21 23	22 23
Cattal		d		13 26		14 26		15 26		16 26		17 09	17 32		18 26		19 26	20 26	21 27	22 27
Knaresborough		a		13 34		14 34		15 34		16 34		17 17	17 40		18 34		19 34	20 34	21 34	22 35
		d	13 05	13 35	14 05	14 35	15 05	15 35	16 05	16 35	17 05	17 18	17 41	18 05	18 35	19 05	19 35	20 35	21 35	22 36
Starbeck		d	13 08	13 38	14 08	14 38	15 08	15 38	16 08	16 38	17 08	17 21	17 44	18 12	18 38	19 08	19 38	20 38	21 39	22 40
Harrogate		a	13 13	13 43	14 13	14 43	15 13	15 43	16 13	16 43	17 14	17 26	17 49	18 17	18 43	19 13	19 43	20 43	21 43	22 45
		d	13 14	13 44	14 14	14 44	15 14	15 44	16 14	16 44	17 14	17 30	17 50	18 18	18 44	19 14	19 44	20 44	21 45	22 47
Hornbeam Park		d	13 17	13 47	14 17	14 47	15 17	15 47	16 17	16 47	17 17	17 32	17 53	18 21	18 47	19 17	19 47	20 47	21 48	22 49
Pannal		d	13 22	13 52	14 22	14 52	15 22	15 52	16 22	16 52	17 22	17 37	17 58	18 26	18 52	19 22	19 52	20 52	21 53	22 54
Weeton		d	13 26	13 56	14 26	14 56	15 26	15 56	16 26	16 56	17 26	17 42	18 02	18 30	18 56	19 26	19 56	20 56	21 58	22 59
Horsforth		d	13 35	14 05	14 35	15 05	15 35	16 05	16 35	17 05	17 38	17 50	18 11	18 39	19 05	19 35	20 05	21 05	22 06	23 08
Headingley		d	13 39	14 09	14 39	15 09	15 39	16 09	16 39	17 09	17 42	17 54	18 15	18 43	19 09	19 39	20 09	21 09	22 10	23 12
Burley Park		d	13 41	14 11	14 41	15 11	15 41	16 11	16 41	17 11	17 44	17 57	18 17	18 45	19 11	19 41	20 11	21 11	22 13	23 15
Leeds 10	41	a	13 52	14 22	14 52	15 22	15 52	16 22	16 52	17 22	17 55	18 07	18 28	18 55	19 22	19 52	20 22	21 22	22 23	23 25

Saturdays

			NT	NT	NT	GR 🅁 1 A 🅿 ⇆	NT	NT	NT	NT	NT	NT	NT	NT	NT	NT
York 8	41	d			06 52			07 57		08 45	09 10		10 11		11 11	
Poppleton		d			06 56			08 01		08 49	09 14		10 15		11 15	
Hammerton		d			07 04			08 09		08 57	09 22		10 23		11 23	
Cattal		d			07 07			08 12		09 00	09 26		10 26		11 26	
Knaresborough		a			07 15			08 21		09 08	09 34		10 34		11 34	
		d		06 47	07 21		07 51	08 21	08 51	09 09	09 35	10 05	10 35	11 05	11 35	12 05
Starbeck		d		06 50	07 24		07 54	08 24	08 54	09 12	09 38	10 08	10 38	11 08	11 38	12 08
Harrogate		a		06 55	07 29		07 59	08 29	08 59	09 17	09 43	10 13	10 43	11 13	11 43	12 13
		d	06 06	06 56	07 31	07 44	08 00	08 30	09 00	09 18	09 44	10 14	10 44	11 14	11 44	12 14
Hornbeam Park		d	06 08	06 59	07 33		08 03	08 33	09 03	09 21	09 47	10 17	10 47	11 17	11 47	12 17
Pannal		d	06 13	07 04	07 38		08 08	08 38	09 08	09 26	09 52	10 22	10 52	11 22	11 52	12 22
Weeton		d	06 18	07 08	07 42		08 12	08 42	09 12	09 30	09 56	10 26	10 56	11 26	11 56	12 26
Horsforth		d	06 28	07 17	07 51		08 21	08 51	09 21	09 39	10 05	10 35	11 05	11 35	12 05	12 35
Headingley		d	06 32	07 21	07 55		08 25	08 55	09 25	09 43	10 09	10 39	11 09	11 39	12 09	12 39
Burley Park		d	06 34	07 23	07 57		08 27	08 57	09 27	09 47	10 11	10 41	11 11	11 41	12 11	12 41
Leeds 10	41	a	06 44	07 34	08 08	08 12	08 38	09 08	09 37	09 55	10 22	10 52	11 22	11 52	12 22	12 52

			NT	NT	NT	NT	NT	NT	NT	NT	NT	NT	NT	NT	NT	NT	NT	NT	NT
York 8	41	d	12 11		13 11		14 11		15 11		16 11		16 54	17 17		18 11	19 11	20 11	21 57
Poppleton		d	12 15		13 15		14 15		15 15		16 15		16 58	17 21		18 15	19 15	20 15	22 01
Hammerton		d	12 23		13 23		14 23		15 23		16 23		17 06	17 29		18 23	19 23	20 23	22 09
Cattal		d	12 26		13 26		14 26		15 26		16 26		17 09	17 32		18 26	19 26	20 26	22 12
Knaresborough		a	12 34		13 34		14 34		15 34		16 34		17 17	17 40		18 34	19 34	20 34	22 20
		d	12 35	13 05	13 35	14 05	14 35	15 05	15 35	16 05	16 35	17 05	17 18	17 41	18 05	18 35	19 35	20 35	22 21
Starbeck		d	12 38	13 08	13 38	14 08	14 38	15 08	15 38	16 08	16 38	17 08	17 21	17 44	18 12	18 38	19 38	20 38	22 24
Harrogate		a	12 43	13 13	13 43	14 13	14 43	15 13	15 43	16 13	16 43	17 14	17 26	17 49	18 17	18 43	19 43	20 43	22 29
		d	12 44	13 14	13 44	14 14	14 44	15 14	15 44	16 14	16 44	17 14	17 30	17 50	18 18	18 44	19 44	20 44	22 37
Hornbeam Park		d	12 47	13 17	13 47	14 17	14 47	15 17	15 47	16 17	16 47	17 17	17 32	17 53	18 21	18 47	19 47	20 47	22 39
Pannal		d	12 52	13 22	13 52	14 22	14 52	15 22	15 52	16 22	16 52	17 22	17 37	17 58	18 26	18 52	19 52	20 52	22 44
Weeton		d	12 56	13 26	13 56	14 26	14 56	15 26	15 56	16 26	16 56	17 26	17 42	18 02	18 30	18 56	19 56	20 56	22 49
Horsforth		d	13 05	13 35	14 05	14 35	15 05	15 35	16 05	16 35	17 05	17 38	17 50	18 11	18 39	19 05	20 05	21 05	22 57
Headingley		d	13 09	13 39	14 09	14 39	15 09	15 39	16 09	16 39	17 09	17 42	17 54	18 15	18 43	19 09	20 09	21 09	23 01
Burley Park		d	13 11	13 41	14 11	14 41	15 11	15 41	16 11	16 41	17 11	17 44	17 57	18 17	18 45	19 11	20 11	21 11	23 04
Leeds 10	41	a	13 22	13 52	14 22	14 52	15 22	15 52	16 22	16 52	17 22	17 55	18 07	18 28	18 55	19 22	20 22	21 22	23 14

For general notes see front of timetable
For details of catering facilities see
Directory of Train Operators

A To London Kings Cross (Table 26)

Table 35

Sundays

York → Harrogate → Leeds

Network Diagram - see first page of Table 35

			NT	NT	NT	NT	NT	NT	NT	NT	NT	NT	NT	NT
York 8	41	d				12 18	14 19	16 18	17 17	18 17	19 17	20 18	21 26	
Poppleton		d				12 22	14 23	16 22	17 21	18 21	19 21	20 22	21 30	
Hammerton		d				12 30	14 31	16 30	17 29	18 29	19 29	20 30	21 38	
Cattal		d				12 33	14 34	16 33	17 32	18 32	19 32	20 33	21 41	
Knaresborough		a				12 41	14 42	16 41	17 40	18 40	19 40	20 41	21 49	
		d			11 42	12 42	14 43	16 42	17 42	18 42	19 42	20 42	21 50	
Starbeck		d			11 45	12 45	14 46	16 45	17 45	18 45	19 45	20 45	21 53	
Harrogate		a			11 50	12 50	14 51	16 50	17 50	18 50	19 50	20 50	21 58	
		d	09 53	10 53	11 53	12 53	14 53	16 53	17 53	18 53	19 53	20 53	22 02	23 05
Hornbeam Park		d	09 56	10 56	11 56	12 56	14 56	16 56	17 56	18 56	19 56	20 56	22 04	23 08
Pannal		d	10 01	11 01	12 01	13 01	15 01	17 01	18 01	19 01	20 01	21 01	22 09	23 13
Weeton		d	10 05	11 05	12 05	13 05	15 05	17 05	18 05	19 05	20 05	21 05	22 14	23 17
Horsforth		d	10 14	11 14	12 14	13 14	15 14	17 14	18 14	19 14	20 14	21 14	22 22	23 26
Headingley		d	10 18	11 18	12 18	13 18	15 18	17 18	18 18	19 18	20 18	21 18	22 26	23 30
Burley Park		d	10 20	11 20	12 20	13 20	15 20	17 20	18 20	19 20	20 20	21 20	22 29	23 32
Leeds 10	41	a	10 30	11 28	12 30	13 30	15 30	17 30	18 30	19 30	20 30	21 30	22 40	23 43

For general notes see front of timetable
For details of catering facilities see Directory of Train Operators

Table 35

Leeds → Harrogate → York

Network Diagram - see first page of Table 35

Miles			NT	NT		NT	NT		NT	NT		NT	NT		NT	NT		NT	NT		NT	NT		NT	NT		NT	NT
0	**Leeds** 10	41 d	06 06	06 29		07 13	07 43		07 59	08 29		08 59	09 29		09 59	10 29		10 59	11 29		11 59	12 29		12 59	13 29		13 59	14 29
2¼	Burley Park	d	06 10	06 33		07 17	07 47		08 03	08 33		09 03	09 33		10 03	10 33		11 03	11 33		12 03	12 33		13 03	13 33		14 03	14 33
3	Headingley	d	06 13	06 36		07 20	07 50		08 06	08 36		09 06	09 36		10 06	10 36		11 06	11 36		12 06	12 36		13 06	13 36		14 06	14 36
5¾	Horsforth	d	06 18	06 41		07 25	07 55		08 11	08 41		09 11	09 41		10 11	10 41		11 11	11 41		12 11	12 41		13 11	13 41		14 11	14 41
11¾	Weeton	d	06 26	06 49		07 33			08 19	08 49		09 19	09 49		10 19	10 49		11 19	11 49		12 19	12 49		13 19	13 49		14 19	14 49
15	Pannal	d	06 32	06 55		07 39			08 25	08 55		09 25	09 55		10 25	10 55		11 25	11 55		12 25	12 55		13 25	13 55		14 25	14 55
17¼	Hornbeam Park	d	06 37	07 00		07 44	08 10		08 30	09 00		09 30	10 00		10 30	11 00		11 30	12 00		12 30	13 00		13 30	14 00		14 30	15 00
18¾	**Harrogate**	a	06 40	07 04		07 49	08 13		08 33	09 03		09 33	10 03		10 33	11 03		11 33	12 03		12 33	13 03		13 33	14 03		14 33	15 03
—		d	06 45	07 05		07 49	08 16		08 34	09 05		09 35	10 05		10 35	11 05		11 35	12 05		12 35	13 05		13 35	14 05		14 35	15 05
20½	Starbeck	d	06 49	07 08		07 52	08 19		08 38	09 08		09 38	10 08		10 38	11 08		11 38	12 08		12 38	13 08		13 38	14 08		14 38	15 08
22	**Knaresborough**	a	06 54	07 15		07 59	08 25		08 45	09 14		09 45	10 14		10 45	11 14		11 45	12 14		12 45	13 14		13 45	14 14		14 45	15 14
—		d	06 55	07 19		07 59	08 28			09 15			10 14			11 14			12 14			13 14			14 14			15 14
28½	Cattal	d	07 03	07 27		08 07	08 36			09 23			10 22			11 22			12 22			13 22			14 22			15 22
30	Hammerton	d	07 06	07 30		08 11	08 39			09 27			10 26			11 26			12 26			13 26			14 26			15 26
35¾	Poppleton	d	07 13	07 37		08 18	08 46			09 34			10 33			11 33			12 33			13 33			14 33			15 33
38½	**York** 8	41 a	07 21	07 49		08 29	08 58			09 45			10 46			11 45			12 45			13 45			14 44			15 47

		NT	NT		NT	NT		NT	NT		NT	NT		NT	NT		NT	NT		NT	NT		NT	NT		NT		
Leeds 10	41 d	14 59	15 29		15 59	16 29		16 42	16 59		17 13	17 29		17 44	17 59		18 29	18 59		19 29	20 29		21 29	22 29		23 29		
Burley Park	d	15 03	15 33		16 03	16 33		16 46	17 03		17 17	17 33		17 48	18 03		18 33	19 03		19 33	20 33		21 33	22 33		23 33		
Headingley	d	15 06	15 36		16 06	16 36		16 49	17 06		17 20	17 36		17 51	18 06		18 36	19 06		19 36	20 36		21 36	22 36		23 36		
Horsforth	d	15 11	15 41		16 11	16 41		16a54	17 11		17 25	17 41		17 56	18 11		18 41	19 11		19 41	20 41		21 41	22 41		23 41		
Weeton	d	15 19	15 49		16 19	16 49			17 19		17 33	17 49			18 19		18 49	19 19		19 49	20 49		21 49	22 49		23 49		
Pannal	d	15 25	15 55		16 25	16 55			17 25		17 39	17 55			18 25		18 55	19 25		19 55	20 55		21 55	22 55		23 55		
Hornbeam Park	d	15 30	16 00		16 30	17 00			17 30		17 44	18 00			18 30		19 00	19 30		20 00	21 00		22 00	23 01		23 59		
Harrogate	a	15 33	16 03		16 33	17 03			17 33		17 47	18 03		18 15	18 33		19 03	19 33		20 03	21 03		22 03	23 08		00 06		
	d	15 35	16 05		16 35	17 08			17 35		17 49	18 05		18 16	18 35		19 05	19 35		20 05	21 05		22 05					
Starbeck	d	15 38	16 08		16 38	17 11			17 38		17 52	18 08		18 20	18 39		19 08	19 38		20 08	21 08		22 08					
Knaresborough	a	15 45	16 14		16 45	17 17			17 45		17 59	18 14		18 26	18 45		19 14	19 45		20 14	21 14		22 15					
	d		16 14			17 21						18 14					19 14			20 14	21 14							
Cattal	d		16 22			17 29						18 22					19 22			20 22	21 22							
Hammerton	d		16 26			17 32						18 26					19 26			20 26	21 26							
Poppleton	d		16 33			17 39						18 33					19 33			20 33	21 33							
York 8	41 a		16 45			17 48						18 46					19 45			20 44	21 46							

Saturdays

		NT		NT		NT		NT		NT		NT		NT		NT		NT		NT		NT		NT		NT		NT
Leeds 10	41 d	06 08		06 37		07 13		07 39		07 54		08 29		08 59		09 29		09 59		10 29		10 59		11 29		11 59		12 29
Burley Park	d	06 12		06 41		07 17		07 43		07 58		08 33		09 03		09 33		10 03		10 33		11 03		11 33		12 03		12 33
Headingley	d	06 15		06 44		07 20		07 46		08 01		08 36		09 06		09 36		10 06		10 36		11 06		11 36		12 06		12 36
Horsforth	d	06 20		06 49		07 25		07 51		08 06		08 41		09 11		09 41		10 11		10 41		11 11		11 41		12 11		12 41
Weeton	d	06 28		06 57		07 33		07 59		08 14		08 49		09 19		09 49		10 19		10 49		11 19		11 49		12 19		12 49
Pannal	d	06 34		07 03		07 39		08 05		08 20		08 55		09 25		09 55		10 25		10 55		11 25		11 55		12 25		12 55
Hornbeam Park	d	06 39		07 08		07 44		08 10		08 25		09 00		09 30		10 00		10 30		11 00		11 30		12 00		12 30		13 00
Harrogate	a	06 42		07 11		07 49		08 13		08 28		09 03		09 33		10 03		10 33		11 03		11 33		12 03		12 33		13 03
	d	06 45		07 14		07 49		08 16		08 29		09 05		09 35		10 05		10 35		11 05		11 35		12 05		12 35		13 05
Starbeck	d	06 49		07 17		07 52		08 19		08 33		09 08		09 38		10 08		10 38		11 08		11 38		12 08		12 38		13 08
Knaresborough	a	06 54		07 23		07 59		08 25		08 40		09 14		09 45		10 14		10 45		11 14		11 45		12 14		12 45		13 14
	d	06 55		07 23		07 59		08 28				09 15				10 14				11 14				12 14				13 14
Cattal	d	07 03		07 31		08 07		08 36				09 23				10 22				11 22				12 22				13 22
Hammerton	d	07 06		07 35		08 11		08 39				09 27				10 26				11 26				12 26				13 26
Poppleton	d	07 13		07 42		08 19		08 46				09 34				10 33				11 33				12 33				13 33
York 8	41 a	07 21		07 49		08 26		08 58				09 45				10 42				11 45				12 45				13 42

		NT		NT		NT		NT		NT		NT		NT		NT	NT	NT	NT	NT	NT	NT	NT	NT	NT	NT		
Leeds 10	41 d	12 59		13 29		13 59		14 29		14 59		15 29		15 59		16 29	16 59	17 13	17 29	17 59	18 29	19 29	20 29	21 20	22 29	23 21		
Burley Park	d	13 03		13 33		14 03		14 33		15 03		15 33		16 03		16 33	17 03	17 17	17 33	18 03	18 33	19 33	20 33	21 24	22 33	23 25		
Headingley	d	13 06		13 36		14 06		14 36		15 06		15 36		16 06		16 36	17 06	17 20	17 36	18 06	18 36	19 36	20 36	21 27	22 36	23 28		
Horsforth	d	13 11		13 41		14 11		14 41		15 11		15 41		16 11		16 41	17 11	17 25	17 41	18 11	18 41	19 41	20 41	21 32	22 41	23 33		
Weeton	d	13 19		13 49		14 19		14 49		15 19		15 49		16 19		16 49	17 19	17 33	17 49	18 19	18 49	19 49	20 49	21 40	22 49	23 41		
Pannal	d	13 25		13 55		14 25		14 55		15 25		15 55		16 25		16 55	17 25	17 39	17 55	18 25	18 55	19 55	20 55	21 46	22 55	23 47		
Hornbeam Park	d	13 30		14 00		14 30		15 00		15 30		16 00		16 30		17 00	17 30	17 44	18 00	18 30	19 00	20 00	21 00	21 51	23 00	23 52		
Harrogate	a	13 33		14 03		14 33		15 03		15 33		16 03		16 33		17 03	17 33	17 47	18 03	18 33	19 03	20 03	21 03	21 54	23 06	23 58		
	d	13 35		14 05		14 35		15 05		15 35		16 05		16 35		17 08	17 35	17 49	18 05	18 35	19 05	20 05	21 05	21 56				
Starbeck	d	13 38		14 08		14 38		15 08		15 38		16 08		16 38		17 11	17 38	17 52	18 08	18 38	19 08	20 08	21 08	21 59				
Knaresborough	a	13 45		14 14		14 45		15 14		15 45		16 14		16 45		17 17	17 45	17 59	18 14	18 45	19 14	20 14	21 14	22 06				
	d			14 14				15 14				16 14				17 21			18 14		19 14	20 14	21 14					
Cattal	d			14 22				15 22				16 22				17 29			18 22		19 22	20 22	21 22					
Hammerton	d			14 26				15 26				16 26				17 33			18 26		19 26	20 26	21 26					
Poppleton	d			14 33				15 33				16 33				17 40			18 33		19 33	20 33	21 33					
York 8	41 a			14 46				15 45				16 45				17 47			18 46		19 45	20 42	21 48					

For general notes see front of timetable
For details of catering facilities see
Directory of Train Operators

Table 35

Sundays

Leeds → Harrogate → York

Network Diagram - see first page of Table 35

Station			NT	NT	NT	NT	NT	NT	NT	NT	NT	NT	NT	NT
Leeds 10	41	d	09 54	10 54	12 54	14 54	15 54	16 54	17 54	18 54	19 54	21 16	22 23	23 22
Burley Park		d	09 59	10 59	12 59	14 59	15 59	16 59	17 59	18 59	19 59	21 21	22 28	23 27
Headingley		d	10 01	11 01	13 01	15 01	16 01	17 01	18 01	19 01	20 01	21 23	22 30	23 29
Horsforth		d	10 07	11 07	13 07	15 07	16 07	17 07	18 07	19 07	20 07	21 29	22 36	23 35
Weeton		d	10 14	11 14	13 14	15 14	16 14	17 14	18 14	19 14	20 14	21 37	22 43	23 42
Pannal		d	10 20	11 20	13 20	15 20	16 20	17 20	18 20	19 20	20 20	21 43	22 49	23 48
Hornbeam Park		d	10 25	11 25	13 25	15 25	16 25	17 25	18 25	19 25	20 25	21 48	22 54	23 53
Harrogate		a	10 31	11 28	13 28	15 28	16 28	17 28	18 28	19 28	20 28	21 51	23 00	23 59
		d		11 30	13 30	15 30	16 30	17 30	18 30	19 30	20 30	21 53		
Starbeck		d		11 34	13 34	15 34	16 34	17 34	18 34	19 34	20 34	21 57		
Knaresborough		a		11 39	13 39	15 39	16 39	17 39	18 39	19 39	20 39	22 03		
		d		11 40	13 40	15 40	16 45	17 44	18 44	19 44	20 45			
Cattal		d		11 48	13 48	15 48	16 53	17 52	18 52	19 52	20 53			
Hammerton		d		11 51	13 51	15 51	16 56	17 55	18 55	19 55	20 56			
Poppleton		d		11 58	13 58	15 58	17 03	18 02	19 02	20 02	21 03			
York 8	41	a		12 08	14 08	16 08	17 10	18 12	19 12	20 10	21 13			

For general notes see front of timetable
For details of catering facilities see
Directory of Train Operators

Leeds and Bradford → Skipton, Lancaster, Morecambe and Carlisle

Network Diagram - see first page of Table 35

Miles	Miles	Miles		NT	NT	NT	NT	NT	NT	NT	NT	NT	NT	NT	NT	NT	NT	NT	NT	NT	NT	NT
—	—	—	London Kings Cross 15 ⊖ 26 d																06 00			06 35
0	0	—	**Leeds 10** 37 d		05 55		06 21			06 56		07 25		07 51		08 19	08 25		08 49	08 56		09 26
—	—	0	**Bradford Forster Square** 37 d			06 10	06 15	06 40		06 55	07 15		07 42	07 46	08 11	08 16		08 41	08 46		09 11	09 16
—	—	1¾	Frizinghall 37 d			06 13	06 18	06 43		06 58	07 18		07 45	07 49	08 14	08 19		08 44	08 49		09 14	09 19
10¾	10¾	2¾	Shipley 37 a		06 07	06 17	06 32	06 47		07 09	07 22	07 36	07 49	08 02	08 18	08 31	08 37	08 48	09 01	09 07	09 18	09 37
—	—	—	d		06 08	06 19	06 33	06 48		07 10	07 23	07 37	07 50	08 03	08 19	08 32	08 37	08 49	09 02	09 09	09 19	09 38
11½	11½	—	Saltaire d		06 10	06 21	06 35	06 50		07 12	07 25	07 39	07 52	08 05	08 21		08 39	08 51		09 11	09 21	09 40
13¾	13¾	—	Bingley d		06 14	06 25	06 39	06 54		07 16	07 29	07 43	07 56	08 09	08 25	08 37	08 43	08 55	09 06	09 15	09 25	09 44
14½	14½	—	Crossflatts d		06 16	06 27	06 41	06 56		07 18	07 31	07 45	07 58	08 11	08 27		08 45	08 57		09 17	09 27	09 46
17	17	—	Keighley d		06 21	06 32	06 45	07 01		07 22	07 36	07 49	08 03	08 15	08 32	08 42	08 49	09 02	09 12	09 21	09 32	09 50
20	20	—	Steeton & Silsden d		06 26	06 36	06 49	07 05		07 26	07 40	07 53	08 07	08 19	08 36		08 53	09 06		09 25	09 36	09 54
23¼	23¼	—	Cononley d		06 30	06 40	06 53	07 09		07 30	07 44	07 57	08 11	08 23	08 40		08 57	09 10		09 29	09 40	09 58
26¼	26¼	—	**Skipton** a		06 38	06 48	07 00	07 17		07 37	07 51	08 05	08 19	08 32	08 47	08 55	09 07	09 18	09 24	09 37	09 47	10 07
—	—	—	d	05 43												08 56			09 26			
30	30	—	Gargrave d	05 48												09 02			09 32			
36¼	36¼	—	Hellifield d	05 57												09 10			09 40			
37½	37½	—	Long Preston d	06 00												09 13			09 43			
—	41¼	—	Giggleswick d	06 09												09 20						
—	48	—	Clapham (Nth Yorkshire) d	06 16												09 28						
—	51¼	—	Bentham d	06 22												09 33						
—	54½	—	Wennington d	06 27												09 39						
—	64	—	Carnforth 83 a	06 43												09 54						
—	70¼	—	**Lancaster 6** 65, 83, 98 a	06 53												10 04						
—	72¾	—	Bare Lane 98 a	07 16												10 16						
—	75½	—	**Morecambe** 98 a	07 20												10 22						
41¼	—	—	Settle d																09 50			
47½	—	—	Horton In Ribblesdale d																09 58			
52¼	—	—	Ribblehead d																10 06			
58¼	—	—	Dent d																10 16			
61¾	—	—	Garsdale d																10 21			
71½	—	—	Kirkby Stephen d						07 28										10 34			
82¼	—	—	Appleby d						07 40										10 47			
93¼	—	—	Langwathby d						07 54										11 01			
97½	—	—	Lazonby & Kirkoswald d						08 00										11 07			
103	—	—	Armathwaite d						08 08										11 15			
113	—	—	**Carlisle 8** 65 a						08 24										11 34			
—	—	—	Glasgow Central 15 65 a	10 18					10 18							13b14			13 14			

	NT	NT	NT	NT	NT	NT	NT	NT	NT	NT	NT	NT	NT	NT	NT	NT	NT	NT	NT	NT	NT	NT
London Kings Cross 15 ⊖ 26 d		07 10			07c20						08 40				09 35		10 10			10 35		
Leeds 10 37 d		09 47	09 56		10 19	10 26		10 49	10 56		11 26		11 56		12 26		12 49	12 56		13 26		13 49
Bradford Forster Square 37 d	09 41	09 46		10 11	10 16		10 41	10 46		11 11	11 16	11 41	11 46	12 11	12 16	12 41	12 46		13 11	13 16	13 41	13 46
Frizinghall 37 d	09 44	09 49		10 14	10 19		10 44	10 49		11 14	11 19	11 44	11 49	12 14	12 19	12 44	12 49		13 14	13 19	13 44	13 49
Shipley 37 a	09 48	10 01	10 07	10 18	10 31	10 37	10 48	11 01	11 07	11 18	11 37	11 48	12 07	12 18	12 37	12 48	13 01	13 07	13 18	13 37	13 48	14 03
d	09 49	10 02	10 08	10 19	10 32	10 38	10 49	11 02	11 08	11 19	11 38	11 49	12 08	12 19	12 38	12 49	13 02	13 08	13 19	13 38	13 49	14 03
Saltaire d	09 51		10 10	10 21		10 40	10 51		11 10	11 21	11 40	11 51	12 10	12 21	12 40	12 51		13 10	13 21	13 41	13 51	
Bingley d	09 55	10 06	10 14	10 25		10 44	10 55	11 06	11 14	11 25	11 44	11 55	12 14	12 25	12 44	12 55	13 06	13 14	13 25	13 45	13 55	14 08
Crossflatts d	09 57		10 16	10 27		10 46	10 57		11 16	11 27	11 46	11 57	12 16	12 27	12 46	12 57		13 16	13 27	13 47	13 57	
Keighley d	10 02	10 12	10 20	10 32	10 40	10 50	11 02	11 12	11 20	11 32	11 50	12 02	12 20	12 32	12 50	13 02	13 12	13 20	13 32	13 52	14 02	14 13
Steeton & Silsden d	10 06		10 24	10 36		10 54	11 06		11 24	11 36	11 54	12 06	12 24	12 36	12 54	13 06		13 24	13 36	13 56	14 06	
Cononley d	10 10		10 28	10 40		10 58	11 10		11 28	11 40	11 58	12 10	12 28	12 40	12 58	13 10		13 28	13 40	14 00	14 10	
Skipton a	10 17	10 24	10 37	10 47	10 52	11 07	11 17	11 24	11 37	11 47	12 07	12 17	12 37	12 47	13 07	13 17	13 24	13 37	13 47	14 09	14 17	14 26
d		10 26			10 54			11 26									13 26					14 27
Gargrave d					10 59												13 31					14 33
Hellifield d					11 08			11 37									13 40					14 41
Long Preston d					11 11												13 42					14 44
Giggleswick d					11 18																	14 51
Clapham (Nth Yorkshire) d					11 25																	14 59
Bentham d					11 31																	15 04
Wennington d					11 36																	15 10
Carnforth 83 a					11 52																	15 25
Lancaster 6 65, 83, 98 a					12 01																	15 38
Bare Lane 98 a					12 16																	16 08
Morecambe 98 a					12 21																	16 13
Settle d		10 44						11 46									13 48					
Horton In Ribblesdale d								11 54									13 57					
Ribblehead d								12 02									14 05					
Dent d								12 12									14 14					
Garsdale d								12 17									14 20					
Kirkby Stephen d		11 22						12 30									14 32					
Appleby d		11 36						12 43									14 45					
Langwathby d								12 57									14 59					
Lazonby & Kirkoswald d								13 03									15 04					
Armathwaite d								13 11									15 12					
Carlisle 8 65 a		12 17						13 29									15 32					
Glasgow Central 15 65 a		13 46			15b25			14 54									17 21					18b46

For general notes see front of timetable
For details of catering facilities see Directory of Train Operators

b Change at Lancaster
c Change at Doncaster and Leeds

Leeds and Bradford → Skipton, Lancaster, Morecambe and Carlisle

Network Diagram - see first page of Table 35

		NT	NT	NT	NT	NT	NT	NT	NT	NT	NT	NT	NT	NT	NT	NT	NT	NT	NT	NT	NT	NT
London Kings Cross 15	⊖ 26 d	11 10		11b30		12 10			12 35		13 10		13 35		14 10			14 35		15 10		
Leeds 10	37 d	13 56		14 26		14 49	14 56		15 26		15 56		16 26		16 45	16 52		17 20		17 51	17 56	
Bradford Forster Square	37 d		14 11	14 16	14 41	14 46		15 11	15 16	15 41	15 46	16 11	16 16	16 40	16 44		17 11	17 16	17 38	17 46		18 11
Frizinghall	37 d		14 14	14 19	14 44	14 49		15 14	15 19	15 44	15 49	16 14	16 19	16 43	16 48		17 14	17 19	17 41	17 49		18 14
Shipley	37 a	14 07	14 18	14 37	14 48	15 01	15 07	15 18	15 37	15 48	16 07	16 18	16 37	16 48	16 56	17 04	17 18	17 31	17 45	18 02	18 07	18 18
	d	14 08	14 19	14 38	14 49	15 02	15 08	15 19	15 38	15 49	16 08	16 19	16 38	16 49	16 57	17 05	17 19	17 32	17 46	18 03	18 08	18 19
Saltaire	d	14 10	14 21	14 40	14 51		15 10	15 21	15 40	15 51	16 10	16 22	16 40	16 52	16 59		17 22	17 34	17 49	18 05		18 21
Bingley	d	14 14	14 25	14 44	14 55	15 06	15 14	15 25	15 44	15 55	16 14	16 26	16 44	16 56	17 03	17 10	17 26	17 38	17 53	18 09	18 14	18 25
Crossflatts	d	14 16	14 27	14 46	14 57		15 16	15 27	15 46	15 57	16 16	16 28	16 47	16 58	17 06		17 28	17 41	17 55	18 12		18 27
Keighley	d	14 20	14 32	14 50	15 02	15 12	15 20	15 32	15 50	16 02	16 20	16 33	16 51	17 03	17 10	17 15	17 33	17 45	18 00	18 16	18 21	18 32
Steeton & Silsden	d	14 24	14 36	14 54	15 06		15 24	15 36	15 54	16 06	16 24	16 37	16 56	17 07	17 15	17 20	17 37	17 50	18 04	18 21	18 26	18 36
Cononley	d	14 28	14 40	14 58	15 10		15 28	15 40	15 58	16 10	16 28	16 41	17 00	17 11	17 19		17 41	17 54	18 08	18 25		18 40
Skipton	a	14 37	14 47	15 07	15 17	15 24	15 37	15 47	16 07	16 17	16 37	16 49	17 07	17 19	17 26	17 31	17 49	18 01	18 16	18 33	18 39	18 47
	d					15 26										17 32					18 40	
Gargrave	d															17 38					18 46	
Hellifield	d					15 37										17 46					18 54	
Long Preston	d															17 49					18 57	
Giggleswick	d															17 56						
Clapham (Nth Yorkshire)	d															18 04						
Bentham	d															18 09						
Wennington	d															18 15						
Carnforth	83 a															18 30						
Lancaster 6	65, 83, 98 a															18 43						
Bare Lane	98 a															18 51						
Morecambe	98 a															18 57						
Settle	d					15 45															19 03	
Horton In Ribblesdale	d					15 53															19 11	
Ribblehead	d					16 01															19 19	
Dent	d					16 11															19 29	
Garsdale	d					16 16															19 34	
Kirkby Stephen	d					16 29															19 47	
Appleby	d					16 41															19 59	
Langwathby	d					16 55															20 13	
Lazonby & Kirkoswald	d					17 01															20 19	
Armathwaite	d					17 09															20 27	
Carlisle 8	65 a					17 28															20 47	
Glasgow Central 15	65 a					19 37										21c11					22 31	

		NT	NT	NT	NT	NT	NT	NT	NT	NT	NT	GR R 1 ✕	NT	NT	NT	NT	NT	NT	NT	NT	NT
London Kings Cross 15	⊖ 26 d	15 35				16 35			17 03	17e33		18 03			18 33	19 03		19 33	20 03		20 30
Leeds 10	37 d	18 26		18 50		19 19	19 25		19 56	19e59	20 26	20 33	20 55		21 26	21 56		22 26	22 56		23 18
Bradford Forster Square	37 d	18 16	18 41	18 46	19 07			19 36	19 41	20 06	20 25		20 38	21 05	21 25	21 38	22 05	22 25	22 38	23 09	23 20
Frizinghall	37 d	18 19	18 44	18 49	19 10			19 39	19 44	20 09	20 28		20 41	21 08	21 28	21 41	22 08	22 28	22 41	23 12	23 23
Shipley	37 a	18 37	18 48	19 03	19 14	19 31	19 37	19 43	20 07	20 16	20 37		21 07	21 12	21 37	22 07	22 12	22 37	23 07	23 16	23 30
	d	18 38	18 49	19 03	19 15	19 32	19 38	19 44	20 08	20 16	20 38		21 08	21 14	21 38	22 08	22 14	22 38	23 08	23 17	23 32
Saltaire	d	18 40	18 51	19 05	19 17		19 40	19 46	20 10	20 19	20 40		21 10	21 16	21 40	22 10	22 16	22 40	23 10	23 19	23 34
Bingley	d	18 44	18 55	19 09	19 21	19 36	19 44	19 50	20 14	20 23	20 44		21 14	21 20	21 44	22 14	22 20	22 44	23 14	23 23	23 38
Crossflatts	d	18 46	18 57	19 11	19 23		19 46	19 52	20 16	20 25	20 46		21 16	21 22	21 46	22 16	22 22	22 46	23 16	23 25	23 40
Keighley	d	18 50	19 02	19 15	19 28	19 42	19 50	19 57	20 20	20 29	20 50	20s57	21 20	21 27	21 50	22 20	22 27	22 50	23 20	23 30	23 44
Steeton & Silsden	d	18 54	19 06	19 19	19 32		19 54	20 01	20 24	20 33	20 54		21 24	21 31	21 54	22 24	22 31	22 54	23 24	23 34	23 48
Cononley	d	18 58	19 10	19 23	19 36		19 58	20 05	20 28	20 37	20 58		21 28	21 35	21 58	22 28	22 35	22 58	23 29	23 38	23 52
Skipton	a	19 06	19 17	19 33	19 44	19 54	20 06	20 12	20 35	20 46	21 06	21 13	21 36	21 42	22 06	22 36	22 42	23 06	23 39	23 45	23 59
	d					19 59															
Gargrave	d					20 05															
Hellifield	d					20 14															
Long Preston	d					20 16															
Giggleswick	d																				
Clapham (Nth Yorkshire)	d																				
Bentham	d																				
Wennington	d																				
Carnforth	83 a																				
Lancaster 6	65, 83, 98 a																				
Bare Lane	98 a																				
Morecambe	98 a																				
Settle	d					20 22															
Horton In Ribblesdale	d					20 31															
Ribblehead	d					20a41															
Dent	d																				
Garsdale	d																				
Kirkby Stephen	d																				
Appleby	d																				
Langwathby	d																				
Lazonby & Kirkoswald	d																				
Armathwaite	d																				
Carlisle 8	65 a																				
Glasgow Central 15	65 a																				

For general notes see front of timetable
For details of catering facilities see Directory of Train Operators

b Change at Doncaster and Leeds
c Change at Lancaster
e Change at Shipley

Table 36

Saturdays

Leeds and Bradford → Skipton, Lancaster, Morecambe and Carlisle

Network Diagram - see first page of Table 35

Station		NT	NT	NT	NT	NT	NT	NT	NT	NT	NT	NT	NT	NT	NT	NT	NT	NT	NT	NT	NT
London Kings Cross 15	⊖ 26 d														*06b15*		*07 10*				
Leeds 10	37 d	05 55		06 19	06 56		07 56		08 19	08 25		08 49	08 56		09 26		09 47	09 56		10 19	10 26
Bradford Forster Square	37 d		06 10	*06 15*		07 11	*07 15*	08 11	*08 16*		08 41	*08 46*		09 11	*09 16*	09 41	*09 46*		10 11	*10 16*	
Frizinghall	37 d		06 13	*06 18*		07 14	*07 18*	08 14	*08 19*		08 44	*08 49*		09 14	*09 19*	09 44	*09 49*		10 14	*10 19*	
Shipley	37 a	06 07	06 17	06 31	07 07	07 18	08 08	08 18	08 31	08 37	08 48	09 01	09 07	09 18	09 37	09 48	10 01	10 07	10 18	10 31	10 37
	d	06 08	06 19	06 32	07 08	07 19	08 08	08 19	08 32	08 37	08 49	09 02	09 09	09 19	09 38	09 49	10 02	10 08	10 19	10 32	10 38
Saltaire	d	06 10	06 21		07 10	07 21	08 10	08 21		08 39	08 51		09 11	09 21	09 40	09 51		10 10	10 21		10 40
Bingley	d	06 14	06 25	06 36	07 14	07 25	08 14	08 25	08 37	08 43	08 55	09 06	09 15	09 25	09 44	09 55	10 06	10 14	10 25		10 44
Crossflatts	d	06 16	06 27		07 16	07 27	08 16	08 27		08 45	08 57		09 17	09 27	09 46	09 57		10 16	10 27		10 46
Keighley	d	06 21	06 32	06 42	07 20	07 32	08 20	08 32	08 42	08 49	09 02	09 12	09 21	09 32	09 50	10 02	10 12	10 20	10 32	10 40	10 50
Steeton & Silsden	d	06 26	06 36		07 24	07 36	08 24	08 36		08 53	09 06		09 25	09 36	09 54	10 06		10 24	10 36		10 54
Cononley	d	06 30	06 40		07 28	07 40	08 28	08 40		08 57	09 10		09 29	09 40	09 58	10 10		10 28	10 40		10 58
Skipton	a	06 38	06 48	06 55	07 37	07 47	08 37	08 47	08 55	09 07	09 18	09 24	09 37	09 47	10 07	10 17	10 24	10 37	10 47	10 52	11 07
	d	06 40		06 56					08 56			09 26					10 26			10 54	
Gargrave	d	06 45							09 02			09 32								10 59	
Hellifield	d	06 54		07 08					09 10			09 40								11c11	
Long Preston	d	06 57							09 13			09 43								11 14	
Giggleswick	d	07 05							09 20											11 21	
Clapham (Nth Yorkshire)	d	07 13							09 28											11 28	
Bentham	d	07 18							09 33											11 34	
Wennington	d	07 24							09 39											11 39	
Carnforth	83 a	07 39							09 53											11 55	
Lancaster 6	65, 83, 98 a	07 53							10 04											12 04	
Bare Lane	98 a	*08 25*							10 16											12 20	
Morecambe	98 a	*08 29*							10 22											12 25	
Settle	d			07 15								09 51					10 44				
Horton In Ribblesdale	d			07 24								10 00									
Ribblehead	d			07 32								10 08									
Dent	d			07 41								10 17									
Garsdale	d			07 47								10 23									
Kirkby Stephen	d			07 59								10 35					11 22				
Appleby	d			08 12								10 49					11 36				
Langwathby	d			08 26								11 03									
Lazonby & Kirkoswald	d			08 31								11 08									
Armathwaite	d			08 39								11 16									
Carlisle 8	65 a			08 58								11 35					12 17				
Glasgow Central 15	65 a																				

Station		NT	NT	NT	NT	NT	NT	NT	NT	NT	NT	NT	NT	NT	NT	NT	NT	NT	NT	NT
London Kings Cross 15	⊖ 26 d		*08 10*					*09 05*				*10 10*					*11 10*			
Leeds 10	37 d		10 49	10 56		11 26		11 56		12 26		12 49	12 56		13 26		13 49	13 56		14 26
Bradford Forster Square	37 d	10 41	*10 46*		11 11	*11 16*	11 41	*11 46*	12 11	*12 16*	12 41	*12 46*		13 11	*13 16*	13 41	*13 46*		14 11	*14 16*
Frizinghall	37 d	10 44	*10 49*		11 14	*11 19*	11 44	*11 49*	12 14	*12 19*	12 44	*12 49*		13 14	*13 19*	13 44	*13 49*		14 14	*14 19*
Shipley	37 a	10 48	11 01	11 07	11 18	11 37	11 48	12 07	12 18	12 37	12 48	13 01	13 07	13 18	13 37	13 48	14 03	14 07	14 18	14 37
	d	10 49	11 02	11 08	11 19	11 38	11 49	12 08	12 19	12 38	12 49	13 02	13 08	13 19	13 38	13 49	14 03	14 08	14 19	14 38
Saltaire	d	10 51		11 10	11 21	11 40	11 51	12 10	12 21	12 40	12 51		13 10	13 21	13 40	13 51		14 10	14 21	14 40
Bingley	d	10 55	11 06	11 14	11 25	11 44	11 55	12 14	12 25	12 44	12 55	13 06	13 14	13 25	13 44	13 55	14 08	14 14	14 25	14 44
Crossflatts	d	10 57		11 16	11 27	11 46	11 57	12 16	12 27	12 46	12 57		13 16	13 27	13 46	13 57		14 16	14 27	14 46
Keighley	d	11 02	11 12	11 20	11 32	11 50	12 02	12 20	12 32	12 50	13 02	13 12	13 20	13 32	13 51	14 02	14 13	14 20	14 32	14 50
Steeton & Silsden	d	11 06		11 24	11 36	11 54	12 06	12 24	12 36	12 54	13 06		13 24	13 36	13 56	14 06		14 24	14 36	14 54
Cononley	d	11 10		11 28	11 40	11 58	12 10	12 28	12 40	12 58	13 10		13 28	13 40	14 00	14 10		14 28	14 40	14 58
Skipton	a	11 17	11 24	11 37	11 47	12 07	12 17	12 37	12 47	13 07	13 17	13 24	13 37	13 47	14 09	14 17	14 26	14 37	14 47	15 07
	d		11 26									13 26					14 27			
Gargrave	d											13 31					14 33			
Hellifield	d		11 37									13 41					14 41			
Long Preston	d											13 43					14 44			
Giggleswick	d																14 51			
Clapham (Nth Yorkshire)	d																14 59			
Bentham	d																15 04			
Wennington	d																15 10			
Carnforth	83 a																15 25			
Lancaster 6	65, 83, 98 a																15 38			
Bare Lane	98 a																16 08			
Morecambe	98 a																16 13			
Settle	d		11 46									13 49								
Horton In Ribblesdale	d		11 54									13 58								
Ribblehead	d		12 02									14 06								
Dent	d		12 12									14 15								
Garsdale	d		12 17									14 21								
Kirkby Stephen	d		12 30									14 33								
Appleby	d		12 43									14 46								
Langwathby	d		12 57									15 00								
Lazonby & Kirkoswald	d		13 03									15 05								
Armathwaite	d		13 11									15 13								
Carlisle 8	65 a		13 29									15 32								
Glasgow Central 15	65 a																			

For general notes see front of timetable
For details of catering facilities see Directory of Train Operators

b Change at Doncaster and Leeds
c Arr. 1107

Table 36

Saturdays

Leeds and Bradford → Skipton, Lancaster, Morecambe and Carlisle

Network Diagram - see first page of Table 35

		NT	NT	NT	NT	NT	NT	NT	NT	NT	NT	NT	NT	NT	NT	NT	NT	NT	NT	NT	NT
London Kings Cross 15	⊖ 26 d		*12 10*			*12b30*		*13 10*							*14 30*					*15 30*	
Leeds 10	37 d		14 49	14 56		15 26		15 56		16 26		16 49	16 56		17 26		17 49	17 56		18 26	
Bradford Forster Square	37 d	14 41	*14 46*		15 11	*15 16*	15 41	*15 46*	16 11	*16 16*	16 40	*16 44*		17 11	*17 16*	17 41	*17 46*		18 11	*18 16*	18 41
Frizinghall	37 d	14 44	*14 49*		15 14	*15 19*	15 44	*15 49*	16 14	*16 19*	16 43	*16 48*		17 14	*17 19*	17 44	*17 49*		18 14	*18 19*	18 44
Shipley	37 a	14 48	15 01	15 07	15 18	15 37	15 48	16 07	16 18	16 37	16 48	17 01	17 07	17 18	17 37	17 48	18 02	18 07	18 18	18 37	18 48
	d	14 49	15 02	15 08	15 19	15 38	15 49	16 08	16 19	16 38	16 49	17 02	17 08	17 19	17 38	17 49	18 02	18 08	18 19	18 38	18 49
Saltaire	d	14 51		15 10	15 21	15 40	15 51	16 10	16 22	16 40	16 52		17 10	17 22	17 40	17 51		18 10	18 21	18 40	18 51
Bingley	d	14 55	15 06	15 14	15 25	15 44	15 55	16 14	16 26	16 44	16 56	17 07	17 14	17 26	17 44	17 55	18 07	18 14	18 25	18 44	18 55
Crossflatts	d	14 57		15 16	15 27	15 46	15 57	16 16	16 28	16 47	16 58		17 17	17 28	17 47	17 57		18 17	18 27	18 46	18 57
Keighley	d	15 02	15 12	15 20	15 32	15 50	16 02	16 20	16 33	16 51	17 03	17 12	17 21	17 33	17 51	18 02	18 13	18 21	18 32	18 50	19 02
Steeton & Silsden	d	15 06		15 24	15 36	15 54	16 06	16 24	16 37	16 56	17 07	17 17	17 26	17 37	17 56	18 06	18 18	18 26	18 36	18 54	19 06
Cononley	d	15 10		15 28	15 40	15 58	16 10	16 28	16 41	17 00	17 11		17 30	17 41	18 00	18 10		18 30	18 40	18 58	19 10
Skipton	a	15 17	15 24	15 37	15 47	16 07	16 17	16 37	16 49	17 07	17 19	17 27	17 37	17 49	18 07	18 17	18 28	18 39	18 47	19 06	19 17
	d		15 26									17 31					18 30				
Gargrave	d											17 37					18 37				
Hellifield	d		15 37									17 45					18 46				
Long Preston	d											17 48					18 48				
Giggleswick	d											17 55									
Clapham (Nth Yorkshire)	d											18 03									
Bentham	d											18 08									
Wennington	d											18 14									
Carnforth	83 a											18 29									
Lancaster 6	65, 83, 98 a											18 43									
Bare Lane	98 a											18 51									
Morecambe	98 a											18 57									
Settle	d		15 45														18 54				
Horton In Ribblesdale	d		15 53														19 03				
Ribblehead	d		16 01														19 11				
Dent	d		16 11														19 20				
Garsdale	d		16 16														19 26				
Kirkby Stephen	d		16 29														19 38				
Appleby	d		16 41														19 51				
Langwathby	d		16 55														20 05				
Lazonby & Kirkoswald	d		17 01														20 10				
Armathwaite	d		17 09														20 18				
Carlisle 8	65 a		17 28														20 37				
Glasgow Central 15	65 a																				

		NT	NT	NT	NT	NT	GR R 1	NT	NT	NT	NT	NT	NT	NT	NT	NT	NT	NT	NT
London Kings Cross 15	⊖ 26 d			*16 30*			17 30				*18c30*		*18b40*			*19b00*	*20 00*		*20b30*
Leeds 10	37 d	18 56		19 19	19 25		19 57		20 06	20 26	20 55		21 26	21 56		22 26	22 56		23 18
Bradford Forster Square	37 d	*18 46*	19 07			19 36		20 07		*20 25*	*20 38*	21 05	*21 25*	*21 38*	22 05	*22 25*	*22 38*	23 05	*23 20*
Frizinghall	37 d	*18 49*	19 10			19 39		20 10		*20 28*	*20 41*	21 08	*21 28*	*21 41*	22 08	*22 28*	*22 41*	23 08	*23 23*
Shipley	37 a	19 07	19 14	19 31	19 37	19 43		20 12	20 18	20 37	21 07	21 12	21 38	22 07	22 12	22 37	23 07	23 12	23 30
	d	19 08	19 15	19 32	19 38	19 44		20 12	20 20	20 38	21 08	21 14	21 39	22 08	22 14	22 38	23 08	23 14	23 32
Saltaire	d	19 10	19 17		19 40	19 46		20 14	20 22	20 40	21 10	21 16	21 41	22 10	22 16	22 40	23 10	23 16	23 34
Bingley	d	19 14	19 21	19 36	19 44	19 50		20 18	20 26	20 44	21 14	21 20	21 45	22 14	22 20	22 44	23 14	23 20	23 38
Crossflatts	d	19 16	19 23		19 46	19 52		20 20	20 28	20 46	21 16	21 22	21 47	22 16	22 22	22 46	23 16	23 22	23 40
Keighley	d	19 20	19 28	19 42	19 50	19 57	20s17	20 25	20 33	20 50	21 20	21 27	21 51	22 20	22 27	22 50	23 20	23 27	23 44
Steeton & Silsden	d	19 24	19 32		19 54	20 01		20 29	20 37	20 54	21 24	21 31	21 55	22 24	22 31	22 54	23 24	23 31	23 48
Cononley	d	19 28	19 36		19 58	20 05		20 33	20 41	20 58	21 28	21 35	21 59	22 28	22 35	22 58	23 28	23 35	23 52
Skipton	a	19 37	19 44	19 54	20 06	20 12	20 32	20 43	20 49	21 06	21 36	21 42	22 07	22 36	22 42	23 06	23 39	23 41	23 59
	d			19 59															
Gargrave	d			20 05															
Hellifield	d			20 14															
Long Preston	d			20 16															
Giggleswick	d																		
Clapham (Nth Yorkshire)	d																		
Bentham	d																		
Wennington	d																		
Carnforth	83 a																		
Lancaster 6	65, 83, 98 a																		
Bare Lane	98 a																		
Morecambe	98 a																		
Settle	d			20 22															
Horton In Ribblesdale	d			20 31															
Ribblehead	d			20a40															
Dent	d																		
Garsdale	d																		
Kirkby Stephen	d																		
Appleby	d																		
Langwathby	d																		
Lazonby & Kirkoswald	d																		
Armathwaite	d																		
Carlisle 8	65 a																		
Glasgow Central 15	65 a																		

For general notes see front of timetable
For details of catering facilities see Directory of Train Operators

b Change at Doncaster and Leeds
c Change at Shipley

Table 36

Sundays

Leeds and Bradford → Skipton, Lancaster, Morecambe and Carlisle

Network Diagram - see first page of Table 35

	NT A	NT	NT B ⚮	NT A ⚮	NT	NT	NT A	NT	NT	NT	NT	NT	NT	NT	NT	NT	
London Kings Cross 15 ⊖ 26 d									09 10		10 10		11 10		12 10	12b30	13 10
Leeds 10 37 d	08 40	09 00			10 08	10c34	10 54	11 08	12 08	12c34	13 08	13 15	14 08	14c34	15 00	15 08	16 08
Bradford Forster Square 37 d		09 02			10 02	10 48		11 02	12 02	12 48	13 02		14 02	14 48	15 02		16 02
Frizinghall 37 d		09 05			10 05	10 51		11 05	12 05	12 51	13 05		14 05	14 51	15 05		16 05
Shipley 37 a	08 52	09 13			10 19	10 54	11 06	11 19	12 19	12 54	13 19	13 28	14 19	14 54	15 12	15 19	16 19
d	08 53	09 14			10 20	10 55	11 07	11 20	12 20	12 55	13 20	13 29	14 20	14 55	15 13	15 20	16 20
Saltaire d	08 55	09 16			10 22	10 57		11 22	12 22	12 57	13 22		14 22	14 57		15 22	16 22
Bingley d	08 59	09 20			10 26	11 01	11 12	11 26	12 26	13 01	13 26	13 34	14 26	15 01	15 18	15 26	16 26
Crossflatts d	09 01	09 22			10 28	11 03		11 28	12 28	13 03	13 28		14 28	15 03		15 28	16 28
Keighley d	09 06	09 28			10 32	11 08	11 17	11 32	12 32	13 08	13 32	13 39	14 32	15 08	15 23	15 32	16 32
Steeton & Silsden d	09 11	09 32			10 36	11 12		11 36	12 36	13 12	13 36		14 36	15 12		15 36	16 36
Cononley d	09 16	09 37			10 40	11 16		11 40	12 40	13 16	13 40		14 40	15 16		15 40	16 40
Skipton a	09 23	09 44			10 48	11 23	11 30	11 48	12 48	13 23	13 48	13 53	14 48	15 23	15 36	15 48	16 48
d	09 30	09 46					11 34					13 54			15 37		
Gargrave d	09 35						11 40					14 00			15 43		
Blackpool North 97 d			08 42														
Preston 8 94, 97 d			09 10	10 00													
Blackburn 94 d			09 30	10 22													
Clitheroe 94 d			09 53	10 45													
Hellifield d	09 44	09 57	10 16	11 08			11 48					14 08			15 51		
Long Preston d	09 46						11 51					14 11			15 55		
Giggleswick d	09 55						11 58								16 02		
Clapham (Nth Yorkshire) d	10 03						12 06								16 09		
Bentham d	10 09						12 12								16 15		
Wennington d	10 14						12 17								16 20		
Carnforth 83 a	10 30						12 33								16 36		
Lancaster 6 65, 83, 98 a	10 39						12 43								16 46		
Bare Lane 98 a	10 51						12 58								16 56		
Morecambe 98 a	10 55						13 02								17 01		
Settle d		10 06	10 36	11 17								14 17					
Horton In Ribblesdale d		10 15	10 45	11 26								14 26					
Ribblehead d		10 23	10 53	11 34								14 34					
Dent d		10 33	11 03	11 44								14 44					
Garsdale d		10 39	11 08	11 49								14 50					
Kirkby Stephen d		10 52	11 21	12 02								15 03					
Appleby d		11 05	11 35	12 16								15 15					
Langwathby d		11 19	11 49	12 30								15 29					
Lazonby & Kirkoswald d		11 25	11 55	12 36								15 35					
Armathwaite d		11 33	12 03	12 44								15 43					
Carlisle 8 65 a		11 49	12 18	12 59								16 00					
Glasgow Central 15 65 a																	

	NT	NT	NT C	NT D	NT E	NT	NT	NT	NT	NT	NT	NT	NT	NT	NT
London Kings Cross 15 ⊖ 26 d		14e30					15 10			17 10		18 10	19 30		20 30
Leeds 10 37 d	16c35	17 08	17 23	17 23	17 23	17 33	18 08	18c34	19 08	20 08	20c34	21 08	22 08	22c34	23 10
Bradford Forster Square 37 d	16 48	17 02					18 02	18 48	19 02	20 02	20 48	21 02	22 02	22 48	23 02
Frizinghall 37 d	16 51	17 05					18 05	18 51	19 05	20 05	20 51	21 05	22 05	22 51	23 05
Shipley 37 a	16 54	17 19	17 35	17 35	17 35	17 45	18 19	18 54	19 19	20 19	20 54	21 19	22 19	22 54	23 21
d	16 55	17 20	17 36	17 36	17 36	17 46	18 20	18 55	19 20	20 20	20 55	21 20	22 20	22 55	23 22
Saltaire d	16 57	17 22					18 22	18 57	19 22	20 22	20 57	21 22	22 22	22 57	23 24
Bingley d	17 01	17 26	17 40	17 40	17 40	17 50	18 26	19 01	19 26	20 26	21 01	21 26	22 26	23 01	23 28
Crossflatts d	17 03	17 28					18 28	19 03	19 28	20 28	21 03	21 28	22 28	23 03	23 30
Keighley d	17 08	17 32	17 46	17 46	17 46	17 56	18 32	19 08	19 32	20 32	21 08	21 32	22 32	23 08	23 34
Steeton & Silsden d	17 12	17 36					18 36	19 12	19 36	20 36	21 12	21 36	22 36	23 12	23 38
Cononley d	17 16	17 40					18 40	19 16	19 40	20 40	21 16	21 40	22 40	23 16	23 42
Skipton a	17 23	17 48	17 59	17 59	17 59	18 08	18 48	19 23	19 48	20 48	21 23	21 48	22 48	23 23	23 50
d			18 00	18 00	18 00	18 11									
Gargrave d			18 06	18 06	18 06										
Blackpool North 97 d															
Preston 8 94, 97 d															
Blackburn 94 d															
Clitheroe 94 d															
Hellifield d			18 14	18 14	18 14	18 22									
Long Preston d			18 18	18 18	18 18										
Giggleswick d			18 25	18 25	18 25										
Clapham (Nth Yorkshire) d			18 32	18 32	18 32										
Bentham d			18 38	18 38	18 38										
Wennington d			18 43	18 43	18 43										
Carnforth 83 a			18 57	18 57	18 59										
Lancaster 6 65, 83, 98 a			19 11	19 11	19 13										
Bare Lane 98 a			19 20	19 29	19 22										
Morecambe 98 a			19 24	19 33	19 26										
Settle d						18 30									
Horton In Ribblesdale d						18 39									
Ribblehead d						18 47									
Dent d						18 57									
Garsdale d						19 02									
Kirkby Stephen d						19 15									
Appleby d						19 28									
Langwathby d						19 42									
Lazonby & Kirkoswald d						19 48									
Armathwaite d						19 56									
Carlisle 8 65 a						20 13									
Glasgow Central 15 65 a															

For general notes see front of timetable
For details of catering facilities see Directory of Train Operators

- **A** Until 14 September
- **B** Until 19 October
- **C** Until 13 July
- **D** 20 July to 7 September
- **E** From 14 September
- **b** Until 13 July only.
- **c** Change at Shipley

Carlisle, Morecambe, Lancaster and Skipton → Bradford and Leeds

Network Diagram - see first page of Table 35

Miles	Miles	Miles			NT	NT	NT	NT	NT	GR R 1 ✕	NT		NT	NT	NT	NT	NT	NT	NT		NT	NT	NT	NT	NT
—	—	—	Glasgow Central [15]	65 d																					
0	—	—	**Carlisle** [8]	65 d														06 20							
10	—	—	Armathwaite	d														06 34							
15½	—	—	Lazonby & Kirkoswald	d														06 41							
19¾	—	—	Langwathby	d														06 47							
30¾	—	—	Appleby	d														07 03							
41½	—	—	Kirkby Stephen	d														07a17							
51¼	—	—	Garsdale	d																					
54¾	—	—	Dent	d																					
60¾	—	—	Ribblehead	d													07 14								
65½	—	—	Horton In Ribblesdale	d													07 21								
71¾	—	—	Settle	d													07 29								
—	0	—	**Morecambe**	98 d																		06 55			
—	1¾	—	Bare Lane	98 d																		06 59			
—	4¼	—	**Lancaster** [6]	65, 83, 98 d																		07 15			
—	11½	—	Carnforth	83 d																		07 24			
—	21	—	Wennington	d																		07 38			
—	24¼	—	Bentham	d																		07 43			
—	27½	—	Clapham (Nth Yorkshire)	d																		07 49			
—	34¼	—	Giggleswick	d																		07 57			
75½	38	—	Long Preston	d													07 34					08 05			
76¾	39¼	—	Hellifield	d													07 37					08 08			
83	45½	—	Gargrave	d													07 46					08 16			
86¾	49¼	—	**Skipton**	a													07 54					08 25			
—	—	—		d	05 48	06 02	06 18	06 27	06 42	06 55	07 01		07 08	07 24	07 32	07 47	07 56		08 01		08 15	08 27	08 32	08 43	09 02
89¾	52¼	—	Cononley	d	05 52	06 06	06 22	06 31	06 46		07 05		07 12	07 28	07 36	07 51			08 05		08 19		08 36	08 47	09 06
93	55½	—	Steeton & Silsden	d	05 56	06 10	06 26	06 35	06 51		07 10		07 17	07 33	07 41	07 56	08 04		08 10		08 24		08 40	08 51	09 10
96	58½	—	Keighley	d	06 01	06 15	06 31	06 40	06 56	07u05	07 15		07 21	07 37	07 45	08 00	08 09		08 14		08 28	08 37	08 45	08 56	09 15
98¼	61	—	Crossflatts	d	06 04	06 18	06 34	06 43	07 00		07 19		07 26	07 41	07 49	08 04			08 18		08 32		08 48	08 59	09 18
99¼	61¾	—	Bingley	d	06 07	06 21	06 37	06 46	07 02		07 22		07 28	07 44	07 52	08 07	08 14		08 21		08 35	08 42	08 51	09 02	09 21
101¼	64	—	Saltaire	d	06 10	06 24	06 40	06 49	07 06		07 25		07 32	07 48	07 56	08 11			08 25		08 39		08 54	09 05	09 24
102¼	64¾	0	Shipley	a	06 12	06 27	06 42	06 53	07 08		07 28		07 34	07 50	07 58	08 13	08 18		08 27		08 41	08 47	08 58	09 07	09 27
—	—	—		37 d	06 13	06 28	06 44	06 53	07 09	07u15	07 28		07 35	07 50	08 00	08 13	08 19		08 28		08 41	08 47	08 58	09 08	09 28
—	—	1	Frizinghall	37 a		06 32		06 57	07 17		07 32		07 49		08 03		08 25		08 31		08 50	08 54	09 02	09 21	09 32
—	—	2¾	**Bradford Forster Square**	37 a		06 38		07 03	07 22		07 39		07 56		08 09		08 31		08 38		08 56	09 00	09 09	09 27	09 38
113	75½	—	**Leeds** [10]	37 a	06 27	06b53	06 58	07b16	07 23	07 29			07 49	08 05	08b24	08 27	08 37		08b49		08 56	09 04		09 23	09b53
—	—	—	London Kings Cross [15]	⊖ 26 a	08 48	09b06				09 51			10 25	11c15			11 27							12 03	

		NT	NT	NT	NT		NT	NT	NT	NT	NT	NT	NT		NT	NT	NT	NT	NT	NT	NT		NT	NT	NT
Glasgow Central [15]	65 d									07 10							08e10								
Carlisle [8]	65 d									08 53															
Armathwaite	d									09 07															
Lazonby & Kirkoswald	d									09 14															
Langwathby	d									09 20															
Appleby	d									09 35															
Kirkby Stephen	d									09 48															
Garsdale	d									10 01															
Dent	d									10 06															
Ribblehead	d									10 17															
Horton In Ribblesdale	d									10 23															
Settle	d									10 31															
Morecambe	98 d																10 45								
Bare Lane	98 d																10 49								
Lancaster [6]	65, 83, 98 d																11 02								
Carnforth	83 d																11 11								
Wennington	d																11 25								
Bentham	d																11 30								
Clapham (Nth Yorkshire)	d																11 37								
Giggleswick	d																11 44								
Long Preston	d																11 52								
Hellifield	d									10 39							11 55								
Gargrave	d																12 03								
Skipton	a									10 54							12 11								
	d	09 18	09 32	09 48	10 02		10 18	10 32	10 48	10 59	11 02	11 18	11 33		11 48	12 02	12 12	12 18	12 32	12 48	13 02		13 18	13 32	13 48
Cononley	d	09 22	09 36	09 52	10 06		10 22	10 36	10 52		11 06	11 22	11 37		11 52	12 06		12 22	12 36	12 52	13 06		13 22	13 36	13 52
Steeton & Silsden	d	09 26	09 40	09 56	10 10		10 26	10 40	10 56		11 10	11 26	11 41		11 56	12 10		12 26	12 40	12 56	13 10		13 26	13 40	13 56
Keighley	d	09 31	09 45	10 01	10 15		10 31	10 45	11 01	11 09	11 15	11 31	11 46		12 01	12 15	12 22	12 31	12 45	13 01	13 15		13 31	13 45	14 01
Crossflatts	d	09 34	09 48	10 04	10 18		10 34	10 48	11 04		11 18	11 34	11 49		12 05	12 18		12 34	12 48	13 04	13 18		13 34	13 48	14 04
Bingley	d	09 37	09 51	10 07	10 21		10 37	10 51	11 07	11 13	11 21	11 37	11 52		12 07	12 21	12 27	12 37	12 51	13 07	13 21		13 37	13 51	14 07
Saltaire	d	09 40	09 54	10 10	10 24		10 40	10 54	11 10		11 24	11 40	11 55		12 11	12 24		12 40	12 54	13 10	13 24		13 40	13 54	14 10
Shipley	a	09 42	09 57	10 12	10 27		10 42	10 57	11 12	11 19	11 28	11 42	11 58		12 14	12 27	12 32	12 42	12 57	13 12	13 27		13 42	13 57	14 12
	37 d	09 44	09 58	10 14	10 28		10 44	10 58	11 14	11 19	11 28	11 44	11 58		12 14	12 28	12 32	12 44	12 58	13 14	13 28		13 44	13 58	14 14
Frizinghall	37 a	09 54	10 02	10 24	10 32		10 54	11 02	11 24		11 32	11 54	12 02		12 24	12 32	12 47	12 54	13 02	13 24	13 32		13 54	14 02	14 24
Bradford Forster Square	37 a	10 00	10 08	10 30	10 38		11 00	11 08	11 30		11 38	12 00	12 10		12 30	12 38	12 53	13 00	13 08	13 30	13 38		14 00	14 08	14 30
Leeds [10]	37 a	09 59	10b24	10 28	10b53		10 58	11b24	11 28	11 36	11b55	11 58	12b24		12 29		12 50	12 58	13b24	13 28	13b54		13 58	14b24	14 28
London Kings Cross [15]	⊖ 26 a			13 10					14 02	14 20					15 05		15 40			15 58					17 04

For general notes see front of timetable
For details of catering facilities see Directory of Train Operators

b Change at Shipley
c Change at Leeds and Doncaster
e Change at Lancaster

Carlisle, Morecambe, Lancaster and Skipton → Bradford and Leeds

Network Diagram - see first page of Table 35

	NT	NT	NT	NT	NT	NT		NT	NT	NT	NT	NT	NT	NT		NT	NT	NT	NT	NT	NT	NT		NT
Glasgow Central 15 65 d	10 10												12 10					12 49						
Carlisle 8 65 d	11 51												14 00					15 03						
Armathwaite d	12 05												14 14											
Lazonby & Kirkoswald d	12 12												14 21											
Langwathby d	12 18												14 27											
Appleby d	12 33												14 43					15 40						
Kirkby Stephen d	12 45												14 55					15 53						
Garsdale d	12 59												15 09											
Dent d	13 04												15 14											
Ribblehead d	13 13												15 23											
Horton In Ribblesdale d	13 20												15 29											
Settle d	13 28												15 38					16 35						
Morecambe 98 d				12 44																				
Bare Lane 98 d				12 48																				
Lancaster 6 65, 83, 98 d				13 15																				
Carnforth 83 d				13 25																				
Wennington d				13 38																				
Bentham d				13 44																				
Clapham (Nth Yorkshire) d				13 50																				
Giggleswick d				13 58																				
Long Preston d	13 33			14 07																				
Hellifield d	13 36			14 10									15 46											
Gargrave d	13 44			14 18																				
Skipton a	13 53			14 26									16 05					16 55						
d	13 59	14 02	14 18	14 27	14 32	14 48		15 02	15 18	15 32	15 48	16 02	16 12	16 18		16 36	16 49	16 58	17 02	17 19	17 30	17 49		18 02
Cononley d		14 06	14 22		14 36	14 52		15 06	15 22	15 36	15 52	16 06		16 22		16 40	16 53		17 06	17 23	17 34	17 53		18 06
Steeton & Silsden d		14 10	14 27		14 40	14 56		15 10	15 26	15 40	15 56	16 10		16 26		16 44	16 57		17 10	17 27	17 38	17 57		18 10
Keighley d	14 09	14 15	14 31	14 39	14 45	15 01		15 15	15 31	15 45	16 01	16 15	16 22	16 31		16 49	17 02	17 08	17 15	17 32	17 43	18 02		18 15
Crossflatts d		14 18	14 35		14 48	15 04		15 18	15 34	15 48	16 04	16 18		16 34		16 52	17 05		17 18	17 35	17 46	18 05		18 18
Bingley d	14 13	14 21	14 38	14 43	14 51	15 07		15 21	15 37	15 51	16 07	16 21	16 26	16 37		16 55	17 08	17 16	17 21	17 38	17 49	18 08		18 21
Saltaire d		14 24	14 42		14 54	15 10		15 24	15 40	15 54	16 10	16 24		16 40		16 58	17 11		17 24	17 41	17 52	18 11		18 24
Shipley a	14 19	14 28	14 44	14 49	14 57	15 12		15 27	15 42	15 57	16 12	16 27	16 31	16 42		17 02	17 13	17 19	17 28	17 43	17 55	18 13		18 28
37 d	14 19	14 28	14 45	14 51	14 58	15 14		15 28	15 44	15 58	16 14	16 28	16 31	16 44		17 02	17 15	17 20	17 28	17 45	17 56	18 14		18 28
Frizinghall 37 a		14 32	14 54		15 02	15 24		15 32	15 55	16 02	16 24	16 32	16 47	16 53		17 06	17 24		17 32	17 52	18 00	18 24		18 32
Bradford Forster Square 37 a		14 38	15 00		15 08	15 30		15 38	16 01	16 08	16 30	16 38	16 53	16 59		17 12	17 30		17 38	17 58	18 08	18 31		18 38
Leeds 10 37 a	14 37	14b53	14 59	15 06	15b24	15 28		15b53	15 58	16b24	16 28	16b53	16 51	16 58		17b24	17 29	17 40	17b55	18 00	18b24	18 29		18b48
London Kings Cross 15 ⊖ 26 a			18c12			18 23					18 54		19 29				19 59	20 21				21 03		

	NT	NT	NT	NT	NT	NT	NT		NT	NT	NT	NT	NT	NT	NT		NT	NT	NT	NT	NT	NT		
Glasgow Central 15 65 d	14e10		14 10									16 10		16e46										
Carlisle 8 65 d			16 18									17 55												
Armathwaite d			16 32									18 09												
Lazonby & Kirkoswald d			16 39									18 16												
Langwathby d			16 45									18 22												
Appleby d			17 01									18 37												
Kirkby Stephen d			17 14									18 49												
Garsdale d			17 28									19 03												
Dent d			17 33									19 08												
Ribblehead d			17 42									19 17							21 00					
Horton In Ribblesdale d			17 49									19 24							21 06					
Settle d			17 58									19 32							21 14					
Morecambe 98 d	16 38													19 05										
Bare Lane 98 d	16 42													19 09										
Lancaster 6 65, 83, 98 d	16 54													19 24										
Carnforth 83 d	17 03													19 33										
Wennington d	17 16													19 47										
Bentham d	17 22													19 52										
Clapham (Nth Yorkshire) d	17 28													19 59										
Giggleswick d	17 36													20 06										
Long Preston d	17 44		18 03											20 14					21 20					
Hellifield d	17 47		18 06									19 39		20 17					21 23					
Gargrave d	17 55		18 15											20 25					21 31					
Skipton a	18 03		18 23									19 54		20 34					21 40					
d		18 16	18 28	18 32	18 48	19 00	19 18		19 32	19 48	19 54	20 06	20 18	20 37	20 48		20 54	21 18		21 48	21 54	22 18		
Cononley d		18 20		18 36	18 52	19 04	19 22		19 36	19 52	19 58		20 22		20 52		20 58	21 22		21 52	21 58	22 22		
Steeton & Silsden d		18 25		18 40	18 56	19 08	19 26		19 40	19 56	20 02		20 26		20 56		21 02	21 26		21 56	22 02	22 26		
Keighley d		18 29	18 38	18 45	19 01	19 13	19 31		19 45	20 01	20 07	20 16	20 31	20 47	21 01		21 07	21 31		22 01	22 07	22 31		
Crossflatts d		18 33		18 48	19 04	19 16	19 34		19 48	20 04	20 10		20 34		21 04		21 10	21 34		22 04	22 10	22 34		
Bingley d		18 35	18 42	18 51	19 07	19 19	19 37		19 51	20 07	20 13	20 21	20 37	20 52	21 07		21 13	21 37		22 07	22 13	22 37		
Saltaire d		18 39		18 54	19 10	19 22	19 40		19 54	20 10	20 16		20 40		21 10		21 16	21 40		22 10	22 16	22 40		
Shipley a		18 42	18 48	18 58	19 12	19 25	19 42		19 57	20 12	20 19	20 27	20 42	20 57	21 12		21 19	21 42		22 13	22 19	22 42		
37 d		18 44	18 48	18 58	19 14	19 26	19 44		19 58	20 14	20 20	20 28	20 43	20 57	21 14		21 19	21 43		22 14	22 19	22 43		
Frizinghall 37 a		18 54		19 02	19 24	19 29			20 01		20 24		20 51	21 05			21 23	21 51			22 23	22 51		
Bradford Forster Square 37 a		19 01		19 08	19 30	19 35			20 08		20 32		20 57	21 12			21 29	21 57			22 31	22 57		
Leeds 10 37 a		18 59	19 07	19b26	19 29	19b55	19 59			20 28		20 44	21 00	21 15	21 30			21 59		22 32		23 01		
London Kings Cross 15 ⊖ 26 a					22 04					23 32			00c15											

For general notes see front of timetable
For details of catering facilities see Directory of Train Operators

b Change at Shipley
c Change at Leeds and Doncaster
e Change at Lancaster

Carlisle, Morecambe, Lancaster and Skipton → Bradford and Leeds

Network Diagram - see first page of Table 35

		NT	NT	GR R 1	NT	NT	NT	NT	NT	NT	NT	NT	NT	NT	NT	NT	NT	NT	NT	NT	NT
Glasgow Central 15	65 d																		06 10		
Carlisle 8	65 d																		07 52		
Armathwaite	d																		08 06		
Lazonby & Kirkoswald	d																		08 13		
Langwathby	d																		08 19		
Appleby	d																		08 34		
Kirkby Stephen	d																		08 46		
Garsdale	d																		09 00		
Dent	d																		09 05		
Ribblehead	d								07 14										09 14		
Horton In Ribblesdale	d								07 21										09 21		
Settle	d								07 29										09 29		
Morecambe	98 d															07 34					
Bare Lane	98 d															07 38					
Lancaster 6	65, 83, 98 d															08 12					
Carnforth	83 d															08 21					
Wennington	d															08 35					
Bentham	d															08 40					
Clapham (Nth Yorkshire)	d															08 46					
Giggleswick	d															08 54					
Long Preston	d								07 34							09 02					
Hellifield	d								07 37							09 05			09 36		
Gargrave	d								07 46							09 13					
Skipton	a								07 54							09 23			09 53		
	d	05 48	06 02	06 42	06 48	07 01	07 32	07 47	07 56	08 01	08 18	08 32	08 48	09 02	09 18	09 28	09 32	09 48	09 58	10 02	10 18
Cononley	d	05 52	06 06		06 52	07 05	07 36	07 51		08 05	08 22	08 36	08 52	09 06	09 22		09 36	09 52		10 06	10 22
Steeton & Silsden	d	05 56	06 10		06 56	07 10	07 41	07 56	08 04	08 10	08 27	08 40	08 56	09 10	09 26		09 40	09 56		10 10	10 26
Keighley	d	06 01	06 15	06u52	07 01	07 15	07 45	08 00	08 09	08 14	08 31	08 45	09 01	09 15	09 31	09 38	09 45	10 01	10 08	10 15	10 31
Crossflatts	d	06 04	06 18		07 04	07 19	07 49	08 04		08 18	08 35	08 48	09 04	09 18	09 34		09 48	10 04		10 18	10 34
Bingley	d	06 07	06 21		07 07	07 22	07 52	08 07	08 14	08 21	08 38	08 51	09 07	09 21	09 37		09 51	10 07	10 12	10 21	10 37
Saltaire	d	06 10	06 24		07 10	07 25	07 56	08 11		08 25	08 42	08 54	09 10	09 24	09 40		09 54	10 10		10 24	10 40
Shipley	a	06 12	06 27		07 14	07 28	07 58	08 13	08 18	08 27	08 44	08 57	09 12	09 27	09 42	09 49	09 57	10 12	10 18	10 27	10 42
	37 d	06 13	06 28	07u00	07 14	07 28	08 00	08 13	08 19	08 28	08 44	08 58	09 14	09 28	09 44	09 49	09 58	10 14	10 19	10 28	10 44
Frizinghall	37 a		06 32		07 24	07 32	08 03		08 25	08 31	08 54	09 02	09 24	09 32	09 54		10 02	10 24		10 32	10 54
Bradford Forster Square	37 a		06 38		07 30	07 39	08 09		08 31	08 38	09 00	09 09	09 31	09 38	10 00		10 08	10 30		10 38	11 00
Leeds 10	37 a	06 27		07 15	07 28	07b58	08b24	08 27	08 37	08b53	08 58	09b26	09 28	09b53	09 59	10 08	10b24	10 28	10 37	10b53	10 58
London Kings Cross 15	⊖ 26 a	09 18		10 00		10b20			11 33		12c14		12 24			13c10			13 33		13c59

		NT	NT	NT	NT	NT	NT	NT	NT	NT	NT	NT	NT	NT	NT	NT	NT	NT	NT	NT
Glasgow Central 15	65 d																			
Carlisle 8	65 d					09 28												11 51		
Armathwaite	d					09 42												12 05		
Lazonby & Kirkoswald	d					09 49												12 12		
Langwathby	d					09 55												12 18		
Appleby	d					10 10												12 33		
Kirkby Stephen	d					10 22												12 45		
Garsdale	d					10 36												13 02		
Dent	d					10 41												13 07		
Ribblehead	d					10 50												13 16		
Horton In Ribblesdale	d					10 57												13 23		
Settle	d					11 05												13 31		
Morecambe	98 d									10 34										
Bare Lane	98 d									10 38										
Lancaster 6	65, 83, 98 d									10 56										
Carnforth	83 d									11 05										
Wennington	d									11 19										
Bentham	d									11 24										
Clapham (Nth Yorkshire)	d									11 31										
Giggleswick	d									11 38										
Long Preston	d									11 51								13 36		
Hellifield	d					11 12				11 54								13 39		
Gargrave	d									12 02								13 47		
Skipton	a					11 29				12 12								13 56		
	d	10 32	10 48	11 02	11 18	11 30	11 33	11 48	12 02	12 12	12 18	12 32	12 48	13 02	13 18	13 32	13 48	13 59	14 02	14 18
Cononley	d	10 36	10 52	11 06	11 22		11 37	11 52	12 06		12 22	12 36	12 52	13 06	13 22	13 36	13 52		14 06	14 22
Steeton & Silsden	d	10 40	10 56	11 10	11 26		11 41	11 56	12 10		12 26	12 40	12 56	13 10	13 26	13 40	13 56		14 10	14 27
Keighley	d	10 45	11 01	11 15	11 31	11 40	11 46	12 01	12 15	12 22	12 31	12 45	13 01	13 15	13 31	13 45	14 01	14 09	14 15	14 31
Crossflatts	d	10 48	11 04	11 18	11 34		11 49	12 04	12 18		12 34	12 48	13 04	13 18	13 34	13 48	14 04		14 18	14 35
Bingley	d	10 51	11 07	11 21	11 37	11 44	11 52	12 07	12 21	12 27	12 37	12 51	13 07	13 21	13 37	13 51	14 07	14 13	14 21	14 38
Saltaire	d	10 54	11 10	11 24	11 40		11 55	12 10	12 24		12 40	12 54	13 10	13 24	13 40	13 54	14 10		14 24	14 42
Shipley	a	10 57	11 12	11 27	11 42	11 49	11 58	12 14	12 27	12 32	12 42	12 57	13 12	13 27	13 42	13 57	14 12	14 19	14 28	14 44
	37 d	10 58	11 14	11 28	11 44	11 49	11 58	12 14	12 28	12 32	12 44	12 58	13 14	13 28	13 44	13 58	14 14	14 19	14 28	14 45
Frizinghall	37 a	11 02	11 24	11 32	11 54		12 02	12 24	12 32	12 47	12 54	13 02	13 24	13 32	13 54	14 02	14 24		14 32	14 54
Bradford Forster Square	37 a	11 08	11 30	11 38	12 00		12 10	12 30	12 38	12 53	13 00	13 08	13 30	13 38	14 00	14 08	14 30		14 38	15 00
Leeds 10	37 a	11b24	11 28	11b55	11 58	12 06	12b24	12 29		12 50	12 58	13b24	13 28	13b54	13 58	14b24	14 28	14 37	14b53	14 59
London Kings Cross 15	⊖ 26 a		14 27										16 30					17 28		

For general notes see front of timetable
For details of catering facilities see Directory of Train Operators

b Change at Shipley
c Change at Leeds and Doncaster

Carlisle, Morecambe, Lancaster and Skipton → Bradford and Leeds

Network Diagram - see first page of Table 35

		NT	NT	NT	NT		NT	NT	NT	NT		NT	NT	NT	NT		NT	NT	NT	NT		NT	NT	NT	NT
Glasgow Central 15	65 d																								
Carlisle 8	65 d												14 26							15 48					
Armathwaite	d												14 40												
Lazonby & Kirkoswald	d												14 47												
Langwathby	d												14 53												
Appleby	d												15 09							16 25					
Kirkby Stephen	d												15 21							16 38					
Garsdale	d												15 35												
Dent	d												15 40												
Ribblehead	d												15 49												
Horton In Ribblesdale	d												15 56												
Settle	d												16 05							17 15					
Morecambe	98 d	12 47																						16 38	
Bare Lane	98 d	12 51																						16 42	
Lancaster 6	65, 83, 98 d	13 13																						16 53	
Carnforth	83 d	13 23																						17 02	
Wennington	d	13 36																						17 16	
Bentham	d	13 42																						17 21	
Clapham (Nth Yorkshire)	d	13 48																						17 28	
Giggleswick	d	13 56																						17 35	
Long Preston	d	14 07																						17 43	
Hellifield	d	14 10											16 12											17 46	
Gargrave	d	14 18																						17 54	
Skipton	a	14 26											16 27							17 36				18 03	
	d	14 27	14 32	14 48	15 02		15 18	15 32	15 48	16 02		16 18	16 29	16 32	16 49		17 02	17 19	17 30	17 41		17 49	18 02		18 16
Cononley	d		14 36	14 52	15 06		15 22	15 36	15 52	16 06		16 22		16 36	16 53		17 06	17 23	17 34			17 53	18 06		18 20
Steeton & Silsden	d		14 40	14 56	15 10		15 26	15 40	15 56	16 10		16 26		16 40	16 57		17 10	17 27	17 38			17 57	18 10		18 25
Keighley	d	14 39	14 45	15 01	15 15		15 31	15 45	16 01	16 15		16 31	16 39	16 45	17 02		17 15	17 32	17 43	17 51		18 02	18 15		18 29
Crossflatts	d		14 48	15 04	15 18		15 34	15 48	16 04	16 18		16 34		16 48	17 05		17 18	17 35	17 46			18 05	18 18		18 33
Bingley	d	14 43	14 51	15 07	15 21		15 37	15 51	16 07	16 21		16 37	16 45	16 51	17 08		17 21	17 38	17 49	17 55		18 08	18 21		18 35
Saltaire	d		14 54	15 10	15 24		15 40	15 54	16 10	16 24		16 40		16 54	17 11		17 24	17 41	17 52			18 11	18 24		18 39
Shipley	a	14 49	14 58	15 12	15 27		15 42	15 57	16 12	16 27		16 42	16 49	16 58	17 13		17 27	17 43	17 55	18 00		18 13	18 28		18 42
	37 d	14 50	14 58	15 14	15 28		15 44	15 58	16 14	16 28		16 44	16 50	16 58	17 15		17 28	17 45	17 56	18 00		18 14	18 28		18 44
Frizinghall	37 a		15 02	15 24	15 32		15 55	16 02	16 24	16 32		16 53		17 02	17 24		17 32	17 54	18 00	18 17		18 24	18 32		18 54
Bradford Forster Square	37 a		15 08	15 30	15 38		16 01	16 08	16 30	16 38		16 59		17 08	17 30		17 38	18 00	18 08	18 23		18 31	18 38		19 01
Leeds 10	37 a	15 07	15b24	15 28	15b53		15 58	16b24	16 28	16b53		16 58	17 07	17b24	17 29		17b55	18 00		18 17		18 29	18b52		18 59
London Kings Cross 15	⊖ 26 a	18c10		18 28			19c40								20 12							21 15			

		NT	NT		NT	NT	NT	NT		NT	NT	NT	NT		NT	NT	NT	NT		NT	NT	NT	NT		
Glasgow Central 15	65 d																								
Carlisle 8	65 d	16 14										18 00													
Armathwaite	d	16 28										18 14													
Lazonby & Kirkoswald	d	16 35										18 21													
Langwathby	d	16 41										18 27													
Appleby	d	16 57										18 42													
Kirkby Stephen	d	17 09										18 54													
Garsdale	d	17 23										19 08													
Dent	d	17 28										19 13													
Ribblehead	d	17 37										19 23								21 00					
Horton In Ribblesdale	d	17 44										19 29								21 06					
Settle	d	17 53										19 37								21 14					
Morecambe	98 d														19 00										
Bare Lane	98 d														19 05										
Lancaster 6	65, 83, 98 d														19 19										
Carnforth	83 d														19 31										
Wennington	d														19 45										
Bentham	d														19 50										
Clapham (Nth Yorkshire)	d														19 57										
Giggleswick	d														20 04										
Long Preston	d	17 58													20 15					21 20					
Hellifield	d	18 06										19 46			20 18					21 23					
Gargrave	d	18 15													20 26					21 31					
Skipton	a	18 23										20 05			20 35					21 40					
	d	18 28	18 32		18 48	19 00	19 18	19 32		48	19 54	20 06	20 18		20 37	20 48	20 54	21 18			21 48	21 54	22 18		
Cononley	d		18 36		18 52	19 04	19 22	19 36		52	19 58		20 22			20 52	20 58	21 22			21 52	21 58	22 22		
Steeton & Silsden	d		18 40		18 56	19 08	19 26	19 40		19 56	20 02		20 26			20 56	21 02	21 26			21 56	22 02	22 26		
Keighley	d	18 38	18 45		19 01	19 13	19 31	19 45		20 01	20 07	20 16	20 31		20 47	21 01	21 07	21 31			22 01	22 07	22 31		
Crossflatts	d		18 48		19 04	19 16	19 34	19 48		20 04	20 10		20 34			21 04	21 10	21 34			22 04	22 10	22 34		
Bingley	d	18 42	18 51		19 07	19 19	19 37	19 51		20 07	20 13	20 21	20 37		20 52	21 07	21 13	21 37			22 07	22 13	22 37		
Saltaire	d		18 54		19 10	19 22	19 40	19 54		20 10	20 16		20 40			21 10	21 16	21 40			22 10	22 16	22 40		
Shipley	a	18 48	18 58		19 12	19 25	19 42	19 57		20 12	20 20	20 27	20 42		20 57	21 12	21 19	21 42			22 12	22 19	22 42		
	37 d	18 48	18 58		19 14	19 26	19 44	19 58		20 14	20 20	20 28	20 43		20 57	21 14	21 19	21 43			22 14	22 19	22 43		
Frizinghall	37 a		19 02		19 24	19 29		20 01			20 24		20 51		21 05		21 23	21 51				22 23	22 51		
Bradford Forster Square	37 a		19 08		19 30	19 35		20 08			20 32		20 57		21 12		21 29	21 57				22 31	22 57		
Leeds 10	37 a	19 07	19b26		19 29	19b55	19 59			20 28		20 44	21 00		21 15	21 30		21 59			22 32		23 01		
London Kings Cross 15	⊖ 26 a	22c17					22 47																		

For general notes see front of timetable
For details of catering facilities see
Directory of Train Operators

b Change at Shipley
c Change at Leeds and Doncaster

Table 36

Sundays

Carlisle, Morecambe, Lancaster and Skipton → Bradford and Leeds

Network Diagram - see first page of Table 35

		NT	NT	NT	NT	NT	NT	NT	NT	NT	NT	NT A	NT	NT	NT	NT	NT B	NT C	NT	NT
Glasgow Central 15	65 d																			
Carlisle 8	65 d						09 24									13 51				
Armathwaite	d						09 38									14 05				
Lazonby & Kirkoswald	d						09 45									14 12				
Langwathby	d						09 52									14 19				
Appleby	d						10 06									14 33				
Kirkby Stephen	d						10 19									14 46				
Garsdale	d						10 33									15 00				
Dent	d						10 38									15 05				
Ribblehead	d						10 48									15 15				
Horton In Ribblesdale	d						10 55									15 22				
Settle	d						11 03									15 30				
Morecambe	98 d											12 23					14 28	14 28		
Bare Lane	98 d											12 27					14 32	14 32		
Lancaster 6	65, 83, 98 d											12 48					14 43	14 54		
Carnforth	83 d											12 57					14b58	15 06		
Wennington	d											13 10					15 11	15 19		
Bentham	d											13 16					15 17	15 25		
Clapham (Nth Yorkshire)	d											13 22					15 23	15 31		
Giggleswick	d											13 30					15 31	15 39		
Long Preston	d						11 09					13 38				15 35	15 45	15 47		
Hellifield	d						11 12					13 41				15 38	15 48	15 50		
Clitheroe	94 a																			
Blackburn	94, 97 a																			
Preston 8	97 a																			
Blackpool North	97 a																			
Gargrave	d						11 20					13 49				15 46	15 56	15 58		
Skipton	a						11 28					13 59				15 55	16 04	16 06		
	d	08 35	09 15	09 36	10 15	11 15	11 30	11 37	12 15	13 15	13 37	13 59	14 15	15 15	15 37	15 57	16 06	16 08	16 15	17 15
Cononley	d	08 39	09 19	09 40	10 19	11 19		11 41	12 19	13 19	13 41		14 19	15 19	15 41				16 19	17 19
Steeton & Silsden	d	08 44	09 23	09 44	10 23	11 23		11 45	12 23	13 23	13 45		14 23	15 23	15 45				16 23	17 23
Keighley	d	08 48	09 28	09 49	10 28	11 28	11 40	11 50	12 28	13 28	13 50	14 09	14 28	15 28	15 50	16 07	16 16	16 18	16 28	17 28
Crossflatts	d	08 52	09 31	09 52	10 31	11 31		11 53	12 31	13 31	13 53		14 31	15 31	15 53				16 31	17 31
Bingley	d	08 54	09 34	09 55	10 34	11 34	11 44	11 56	12 34	13 34	13 56	14 14	14 34	15 34	15 56	16 11	16 21	16 23	16 34	17 34
Saltaire	d	08 58	09 37	09 58	10 37	11 37		11 59	12 37	13 37	13 59		14 37	15 37	15 59				16 37	17 37
Shipley	a	09 00	09 39	10 01	10 39	11 39	11 49	12 02	12 39	13 39	14 02	14 19	14 39	15 39	16 02	16 16	16 25	16 27	16 39	17 39
	37 d	09 00	09 40	10 01	10 40	11 40	11 49	12 02	12 40	13 40	14 02	14 19	14 40	15 40	16 02	16 16	16 27	16 29	16 40	17 40
Frizinghall	37 a		09 48	10 05	10 48	11 48		12 06	12 48	13 48	14 06		14 48	15 48	16 06				16 48	17 51
Bradford Forster Square	37 a		09 54	10 12	10 54	11 54		12 12	12 54	13 54	14 12		14 54	15 54	16 12				16 55	17 58
Leeds 10	37 a	09 14	09 54	10c22	10 54	11 54	12 06	12c22	12 54	13 54	14c22	14 39	14 54	15 54	16c22	16 34	16 45	16 47	16 54	17 54
London Kings Cross 15	⊖ 26 a	11 55	12e48		13 50	14f54	15f11		15 55	16f50			17 55	18 55					19 33	20 59

		NT	NT	NT A ✠	NT	NT D	NT E	NT	NT	NT	NT G ✠	NT	NT H	NT J	NT	NT	NT
Glasgow Central 15	65 d																
Carlisle 8	65 d			15 29	16 37						17 30						
Armathwaite	d			15 45	16 51						17 44						
Lazonby & Kirkoswald	d			15 52	16 58						17 52						
Langwathby	d			15 59	17 05						17 58						
Appleby	d			16 14	17 20						18 14						
Kirkby Stephen	d			16 27	17 33						18 27						
Garsdale	d			16 41	17 47						18 40						
Dent	d			16 46	17 52						18 46						
Ribblehead	d			16 56	18 02						18 55						
Horton In Ribblesdale	d			17 03	18 09						19 02						
Settle	d			17 12	18 18						19 10						
Morecambe	98 d					17 42	17 54						20 00	20 00			
Bare Lane	98 d					17 46	17 58						20 04	20 04			
Lancaster 6	65, 83, 98 d					18 04	18 06						20 15	20 17			
Carnforth	83 d					18 12	18 15						20 24	20 26			
Wennington	d					18 25	18 28						20 37	20 39			
Bentham	d					18 31	18 34						20 43	20 45			
Clapham (Nth Yorkshire)	d					18 39	18 41						20 50	20 52			
Giggleswick	d					18 47	18 49						20 58	21 00			
Long Preston	d					18 59	18 59						21 06	21 08			
Hellifield	d			17 20	18 25	19 02	19 02				19 20		21 09	21 11			
Clitheroe	94 a			17 46							19 47						
Blackburn	94, 97 a			18 15							20 14						
Preston 8	97 a			18 39							20 34						
Blackpool North	97 a										21 03						
Gargrave	d					19 10	19 10						21 17	21 19			
Skipton	a				18 40	19 18	19 18						21 25	21 27			
	d	17 37	18 15		18 42	19 18	19 18	19 23	19 37	20 15		21 15	21 26	21 28	21 37	22 15	23 15
Cononley	d	17 41	18 19					19 27	19 41	20 19		21 19			21 41	22 19	23 19
Steeton & Silsden	d	17 45	18 23					19 31	19 45	20 23		21 23			21 45	22 23	23 23
Keighley	d	17 50	18 28		18 52	19 28	19 28	19 36	19 50	20 28		21 28	21 36	21 38	21 50	22 28	23 28
Crossflatts	d	17 53	18 31					19 39	19 53	20 31		21 31			21 53	22 31	23 31
Bingley	d	17 56	18 34		18 56	19 32	19 32	19 42	19 56	20 34		21 34	21 41	21 43	21 56	22 34	23 34
Saltaire	d	17 59	18 37					19 45	19 59	20 37		21 37			21 59	22 37	23 37
Shipley	a	18 02	18 39		19 01	19 37	19 37	19 47	20 02	20 39		21 39	21 46	21 48	22 02	22 39	23 40
	37 d	18 02	18 40		19 02	19 38	19 38	19 48	20 02	20 40		21 40	21 47	21 49	22 02	22 40	23 40
Frizinghall	37 a	18 06	18 48			19 48	19 48		20 06	20 48		21 48			22 06	22 48	
Bradford Forster Square	37 a	18 12	18 54			19 54	19 54		20 12	20 54		21 54			22 12	22 54	
Leeds 10	37 a	18c23	18 54		19 19	19 56	19 56	20 02	20c22	20 54		21 54	22 03	22 05	22c22	22 54	23 58
London Kings Cross 15	⊖ 26 a							22 37									

For general notes see front of timetable
For details of catering facilities see Directory of Train Operators

A Until 14 September
B Until 13 July
C 20 July to 14 September
D From 14 September
E Until 7 September
G Until 19 October
H Until 13 July and from 14 September
J 20 July to 7 September
b Arr. 1452
c Change at Shipley
e Change at Leeds and Doncaster
f Until 7 September only.

Leeds → Shipley and Bradford

Network Diagram - see first page of Table 35

Miles	Miles			NT	NT	NT	NT	NT	NT	NT	NT	NT	NT		NT	NT	NT	NT	NT	NT	NT	NT	NT	NT		NT
0	0	**Leeds 10**	d	05 08	05 51	05 55	06 03		06 21	06 22		06 37			06 49	06 51	06 56	07 09		07 23		07 25	07 37			07 39
10¾	—	**Shipley**	a			06 07			06 32						07 01		07 09					07 36				07 50
—	—		d					06 28			06 41		06 53		07 02				07 15		07 28			07 47		07 51
11¾	—	Frizinghall	d					06 32			06 44		06 57		07 04				07 17		07 32			07 49		07 53
—	4	Bramley	d	05 15	05 58					06 29		06 44						07 16		07 30			07 44			
—	5¾	New Pudsey	d	05 20	06 03		06 12			06 34		06 49				07 01		07 21		07 35			07 49			
—	9½	**Bradford Interchange**	a	05 28	06 11		06 23			06 42		06 57				07 11		07 29		07 43			07 57			
13½	—	**Bradford Forster Square**	a					06 38			06 50		07 03		07 10				07 22		07 39			07 56		07 59

		NT	NT	NT	NT	NT	NT	NT	NT	NT	NT		NT	NT	NT	NT	NT	NT	NT	NT	NT	NT		NT	NT	NT
Leeds 10	d	07 51		07 51	08 08		08 10		08 19	08 22	08 25		08 37		08 40		08 49	08 51	08 56	09 08		09 10		09 22		09 26
Shipley	a			08 02			08 22		08 31		08 37				08 51		09 01		09 07			09 21				09 37
	d		08 00			08 13	08 23	08 28						08 48	08 52	08 58					09 18	09 22			09 28	
Frizinghall	d		08 03			08 16	08 25	08 31						08 50	08 54	09 02					09 21	09 24			09 32	
Bramley	d				08 15					08 29			08 44							09 15				09 29		
New Pudsey	d	08 01			08 20					08 34			08 49					09 00		09 20				09 34		
Bradford Interchange	a	08 11			08 28					08 42			08 57					09 11		09 28				09 42		
Bradford Forster Square	a		08 09			08 22	08 31	08 38						08 56	09 00	09 09					09 27	09 30			09 38	

		NT	NT	NT	NT	NT	NT	NT	NT	NT		NT	NT	NT	NT	NT	NT	NT	NT	NT	NT		NT	NT	NT	NT
Leeds 10	d	09 37		09 40		09 47	09 51	09 56	10 08			10 10		10 19	10 22	10 26	10 37		10 40		10 49		10 51	10 56	11 08	
Shipley	a			09 51		10 01		10 07				10 21		10 31		10 37			10 51		11 01			11 07		
	d		09 44	09 52	09 58					10 14		10 22	10 28					10 44	10 52	10 58						11 14
Frizinghall	d		09 47	09 54	10 02					10 17		10 24	10 32					10 47	10 54	11 02						11 17
Bramley	d	09 44							10 15						10 29		10 44								11 15	
New Pudsey	d	09 49					10 01		10 20						10 34		10 49						11 01		11 20	
Bradford Interchange	a	09 57					10 11		10 28						10 42		10 57						11 11		11 28	
Bradford Forster Square	a		09 53	10 00	10 08					10 23		10 30	10 38					10 53	11 00	11 08						11 23

		NT	NT	NT	NT	NT	NT	NT	NT		NT	NT	NT	NT	NT	NT	NT	NT	NT	NT		NT	NT	NT	NT	NT
Leeds 10	d	11 10	11 22		11 26	11 37		11 40	11 51			11 56	12 08		12 10	12 22		12 26	12 37			12 40		12 49	12 51	12 56
Shipley	a	11 21			11 37			11 51				12 07			12 21			12 37				12 51		13 01		13 07
	d	11 22		11 28			11 44	11 52			11 58			12 14	12 22		12 28			12 44		12 52	12 58			
Frizinghall	d	11 24		11 32			11 47	11 54			12 02			12 17	12 24		12 32			12 47		12 54	13 02			
Bramley	d		11 29			11 44							12 15			12 29			12 44							
New Pudsey	d		11 34			11 49			12 01				12 20			12 34			12 49						13 01	
Bradford Interchange	a		11 42			11 57			12 11				12 28			12 42			12 57						13 11	
Bradford Forster Square	a	11 30		11 38			11 53	12 00			12 10			12 24	12 30		12 38			12 53		13 00	13 08			

		NT	NT	NT	NT	NT	NT	NT		NT	NT	NT	NT	NT	NT	NT	NT	NT	NT		NT	NT	NT	NT	NT	NT
Leeds 10	d	13 08		13 10	13 22		13 26	13 37			13 40		13 49	13 51	13 56	14 08		14 10	14 22			14 26	14 37		14 40	
Shipley	a			13 21			13 37				13 51		14 03		14 07			14 21				14 37			14 51	
	d		13 14	13 22		13 28				13 44	13 52	13 58					14 14	14 22			14 28			14 44	14 52	14 58
Frizinghall	d		13 17	13 24		13 32				13 47	13 54	14 02					14 17	14 24			14 32			14 47	14 54	15 02
Bramley	d	13 15			13 29			13 44								14 15			14 29				14 44			
New Pudsey	d	13 20			13 34			13 49						14 01		14 20			14 34				14 49			
Bradford Interchange	a	13 28			13 42			13 57						14 11		14 28			14 42				14 57			
Bradford Forster Square	a		13 23	13 30		13 38				13 53	14 00	14 08					14 23	14 30			14 38			14 53	15 00	15 08

		NT	NT	NT	NT	NT	NT		NT	NT	NT	NT	NT	NT	NT	NT	NT	NT		NT	NT	NT	NT	NT	NT	NT
Leeds 10	d	14 49	14 51	14 56	15 08		15 10		15 22		15 26	15 37		15 40	15 51		15 56	16 08			16 10	16 22		16 26	16 37	
Shipley	a	15 01		15 07			15 21				15 37			15 52			16 07				16 21			16 37		
	d					15 14	15 22			15 28			15 44	15 52		15 58				16 14	16 22		16 28			16 44
Frizinghall	d					15 17	15 24			15 32			15 47	15 55		16 02				16 17	16 24		16 32			16 47
Bramley	d				15 15				15 29			15 44						16 15				16 29			16 44	
New Pudsey	d		15 01		15 20				15 34			15 49			16 01			16 20				16 34			16 49	
Bradford Interchange	a		15 11		15 28				15 42			15 57			16 11			16 28				16 42			16 57	
Bradford Forster Square	a					15 23	15 30			15 38			15 53	16 01		16 08				16 23	16 30		16 38			16 53

		NT	NT	NT	NT	NT		NT	NT	NT	NT	NT	NT	NT	NT	NT	NT		NT	NT	NT	NT	NT	NT	NT	NT
Leeds 10	d	16 39	16 45	16 51		16 52		17 08		17 10		17 20	17 22		17 36	17 37			17 51	17 51	17 56	18 08		18 10	18 22	
Shipley	a	16 50	16 56			17 04				17 21		17 31			17 49					18 02	18 07			18 21		
	d	16 51			17 02				17 15	17 22	17 28			17 45	17 50		17 56						18 14	18 22		18 28
Frizinghall	d	16 53			17 06				17 17	17 24	17 32			17 47	17 52		18 00						18 17	18 24		18 32
Bramley	d							17 15					17 29			17 44						18 15			18 30	
New Pudsey	d			17 01				17 20					17 34			17 49			18 01			18 20			18 35	
Bradford Interchange	a			17 11				17 28					17 42			17 57			18 11			18 28			18 43	
Bradford Forster Square	a	16 59			17 12				17 23	17 30	17 38			17 53	17 58		18 08						18 23	18 31		18 38

For general notes see front of timetable
For details of catering facilities see
Directory of Train Operators

Leeds → Shipley and Bradford

Network Diagram - see first page of Table 35

Mondays to Fridays

		NT	NT	NT	NT		NT	NT	NT	NT	NT	NT	NT	NT	NT	NT		NT	NT	NT	NT	NT	GR R 1 A	NT	NT	NT
Leeds 10	d	18 26	18 37		18 40			18 50	18 51	19 08		19 10		19 19	19 22	19 25		19 37			19 51	19 56	19 59	20 08		
Shipley	a	18 37			18 52			19 03				19 21		19 31		19 37						20 07	20s11			
	d			18 44	18 52		18 58				19 14	19 22	19 26						19 44	19 58					20 20	20 28
Frizinghall	d			18 46	18 55		19 02				19 17	19 24	19 29						19 47	20 01					20 24	20 30
Bramley	d		18 44							19 15					19 29			19 44						20 15		
New Pudsey	d		18 49						19 01	19 20					19 34			19 49			20 01			20 20		
Bradford Interchange	a		18 57						19 11	19 28					19 45			19 57			20 11			20 28		
Bradford Forster Square	a			18 52	19 01		19 08				19 23	19 30	19 35						19 53	20 08			20 22		20 32	20 36

		NT	NT	NT		NT	NT	NT	NT	NT	NT	NT	NT	NT	NT		NT	NT	NT	NT	NT	NT	NT	NT		
Leeds 10	d	20 26	20 37				20 55	21 08		21 26	21 37			21 56	22 08			22 26	22 37			22 56	23 08	23 18		
Shipley	a	20 37					21 07			21 37				22 07				22 37				23 07		23 30		
	d			20 48		21 03			21 19			21 48	22 03				22 19			22 48	23 03					
Frizinghall	d			20 51		21 05			21 23			21 51	22 05				22 23			22 51	23 05					
Bramley	d		20 44					21 15			21 44				22 15				22 44				23 15			
New Pudsey	d		20 49					21 20			21 49				22 20				22 49				23 20			
Bradford Interchange	a		20 57					21 28			21 57				22 28				22 57				23 29			
Bradford Forster Square	a			20 57		21 12			21 29			21 57	22 11				22 31			22 57	23 13					

Saturdays

		NT	NT	NT	NT	NT	NT	NT	NT	NT	NT	NT	NT	NT	NT	NT	NT	NT	NT	NT	NT	NT	NT	NT	NT	NT
Leeds 10	d	05 51	05 55	06 03		06 19	06 22	06 37		06 51	06 56	07 09	07 10	07 23		07 37		07 51		07 56	08 08	08 10		08 19	08 22	08 25
Shipley	a		06 07			06 31					07 07		07 21							08 08		08 22		08 31		08 37
	d				06 28				06 44				07 22		07 28		07 47		08 00			08 23	08 28			
Frizinghall	d				06 32				06 47				07 24		07 32		07 49		08 03			08 25	08 31			
Bramley	d	05 58					06 29	06 44				07 16		07 30		07 44					08 15				08 29	
New Pudsey	d	06 03		06 12			06 34	06 49		07 01		07 21		07 35		07 49		08 01			08 20				08 34	
Bradford Interchange	a	06 11		06 23			06 42	06 57		07 11		07 29		07 43		07 57		08 11			08 28				08 42	
Bradford Forster Square	a				06 38				06 55				07 30		07 39		07 56		08 09			08 31	08 38			

		NT	NT	NT	NT	NT	NT	NT	NT	NT	NT	NT	NT	NT	NT	NT	NT	NT	NT	NT	NT	NT	NT	NT	NT	NT
Leeds 10	d	08 37		08 40		08 49	08 51	08 56	09 08		09 10	09 22		09 26	09 37		09 40		09 47	09 51	09 56	10 08		10 10		10 19
Shipley	a			08 51		09 01		09 07			09 21			09 37			09 51		10 01		10 07			10 21		10 31
	d		08 44	08 52	08 58					09 14	09 22		09 28			09 44	09 52	09 58					10 14	10 22	10 28	
Frizinghall	d		08 46	08 54	09 02					09 17	09 24		09 32			09 47	09 54	10 02					10 17	10 24	10 32	
Bramley	d	08 44							09 15			09 29			09 44							10 15				
New Pudsey	d	08 49					09 00		09 20			09 34			09 49					10 01		10 20				
Bradford Interchange	a	08 57					09 11		09 28			09 42			09 57					10 11		10 28				
Bradford Forster Square	a		08 53	09 00	09 09					09 24	09 31		09 38			09 53	10 00	10 08					10 23	10 30	10 38	

		NT	NT	NT	NT	NT	NT	NT	NT	NT	NT	NT	NT	NT	NT	NT	NT	NT	NT	NT	NT	NT	NT	NT	NT	NT
Leeds 10	d	10 22	10 26	10 37		10 40		10 49	10 51	10 56	11 08		11 10	11 22		11 26	11 37		11 40	11 51		11 56	12 08		12 10	12 22
Shipley	a		10 37			10 51		11 01		11 07			11 21			11 37			11 51			12 07			12 21	
	d				10 44	10 52	10 58					11 14	11 22		11 28			11 44	11 52		11 58			12 14	12 22	
Frizinghall	d				10 47	10 54	11 02					11 17	11 24		11 32			11 47	11 54		12 02			12 17	12 24	
Bramley	d	10 29		10 44							11 15			11 29			11 44						12 15			12 29
New Pudsey	d	10 34		10 49					11 01		11 20			11 34			11 49			12 01			12 20			12 34
Bradford Interchange	a	10 42		10 57					11 11		11 28			11 42			11 57			12 11			12 28			12 42
Bradford Forster Square	a				10 53	11 00	11 08					11 23	11 30		11 38			11 53	12 00		12 10			12 24	12 30	

		NT	NT	NT	NT	NT	NT	NT	NT	NT	NT	NT	NT	NT	NT	NT	NT	NT	NT	NT	NT	NT	NT	NT	NT	NT
Leeds 10	d		12 26	12 37		12 40		12 49	12 51	12 56	13 08		13 10	13 22		13 26	13 37		13 40		13 49	13 51	13 56	14 08		14 10
Shipley	a		12 37			12 51		13 01		13 07			13 21			13 37			13 51		14 03		14 07			14 21
	d	12 28			12 44	12 52	12 58					13 14	13 22		13 28			13 44	13 52	13 58					14 14	14 22
Frizinghall	d	12 32			12 47	12 54	13 02					13 17	13 24		13 32			13 47	13 54	14 02					14 17	14 24
Bramley	d			12 44							13 15			13 29			13 44							14 15		
New Pudsey	d			12 49					13 01		13 20			13 34			13 49					14 01		14 20		
Bradford Interchange	a			12 57					13 11		13 28			13 42			13 57					14 11		14 28		
Bradford Forster Square	a	12 38			12 53	13 00	13 08					13 23	13 30		13 38			13 53	14 00	14 08					14 23	14 30

For general notes see front of timetable
For details of catering facilities see
Directory of Train Operators

A From London Kings Cross (Table 26)

Table 37

Saturdays

Leeds → Shipley and Bradford

Network Diagram - see first page of Table 35

		NT	NT	NT	NT	NT	NT	NT	NT	NT	NT	NT	NT	NT	NT	NT	NT	NT	NT	NT	NT	NT	NT	NT	NT	NT
Leeds 10	d	14 22		14 26	14 37		14 40		14 49	14 51	14 56	15 08		15 10	15 22		15 26	15 37		15 40	15 51		15 56	16 08		16 10
Shipley	a			14 37			14 51		15 01		15 07			15 21			15 37			15 52			16 07			16 21
	d		14 28			14 44	14 52	14 58					15 14	15 22		15 28			15 44	15 52		15 58			16 14	16 22
Frizinghall	d		14 32			14 47	14 54	15 02					15 17	15 24		15 32			15 47	15 55		16 02			16 17	16 24
Bramley	d	14 29			14 44							15 15			15 29			15 44						16 15		
New Pudsey	d	14 34			14 49					15 01		15 20			15 34			15 49			16 01			16 20		
Bradford Interchange	a	14 42			14 57					15 11		15 28			15 42			15 57			16 11			16 28		
Bradford Forster Square	a		14 38			14 53	15 00	15 08					15 23	15 30		15 38			15 53	16 01		16 08			16 23	16 30

		NT	NT	NT	NT	NT	NT	NT	NT	NT	NT	NT	NT	NT	NT	NT	NT	NT	NT	NT	NT	NT	NT	NT	NT	NT
Leeds 10	d	16 22		16 26	16 37		16 39		16 49	16 51	16 56	17 08		17 10	17 22		17 26	17 37		17 40		17 49	17 51	17 56	18 08	
Shipley	a			16 37			16 50		17 01		17 07			17 21			17 37			17 51		18 02		18 07		
	d		16 28			16 44	16 51	16 58					17 15	17 22		17 28			17 45	17 52	17 56					18 14
Frizinghall	d		16 32			16 47	16 53	17 02					17 17	17 24		17 32			17 47	17 54	18 00					18 17
Bramley	d	16 29			16 44							17 15			17 29			17 44							18 15	
New Pudsey	d	16 34			16 49					17 01		17 20			17 34			17 49					18 01		18 20	
Bradford Interchange	a	16 42			16 57					17 11		17 28			17 42			17 57					18 11		18 28	
Bradford Forster Square	a		16 38			16 53	16 59	17 08					17 23	17 30		17 38			17 53	18 00	18 08					18 23

		NT	NT	NT	NT	NT	NT	NT	NT	NT	NT	NT	NT	NT	NT	NT	NT	NT	NT	NT	NT	NT	NT	NT	NT	NT
Leeds 10	d	18 10	18 22		18 26	18 37		18 40	18 51		18 56	19 08		19 10		19 19	19 22	19 25	19 37			19 51	20 06	20 08		
Shipley	a	18 21			18 37			18 52			19 07			19 21		19 31		19 37					20 18			
	d	18 22		18 28			18 44	18 52		18 58			19 14	19 22	19 26					19 44	19 58				20 20	20 28
Frizinghall	d	18 24		18 32			18 46	18 55		19 02			19 17	19 24	19 29					19 47	20 01				20 24	20 30
Bramley	d		18 30			18 44						19 15					19 29		19 44					20 15		
New Pudsey	d		18 35			18 49			19 01			19 20					19 34		19 49			20 01		20 20		
Bradford Interchange	a		18 43			18 57			19 11			19 28					19 45		19 57			20 11		20 28		
Bradford Forster Square	a	18 31		18 38			18 52	19 01		19 08			19 23	19 30	19 35					19 53	20 08				20 32	20 36

		NT	NT	NT	GR R 1 A	NT	NT	NT	NT	NT	NT	NT	NT	NT	NT	NT	NT	NT	NT	NT	NT	NT B	NT C	NT		
Leeds 10	d	20 26	20 37		20 43		20 55	21 08		21 26	21 37			21 56	22 08		22 26	22 37			22 56	23 00	23 08	23 18		
Shipley	a	20 37			20s56		21 07			21 38				22 07			22 37				23 07			23 30		
	d			20 48		21 03			21 19			21 48	22 03			22 19			22 48	23 03						
Frizinghall	d			20 51		21 05			21 23			21 51	22 05			22 23			22 51	23 05						
Bramley	d		20 44					21 15			21 44				22 15			22 44				23 07	23 15			
New Pudsey	d		20 49					21 20			21 49				22 20			22 49				23 12	23 20			
Bradford Interchange	a		20 57					21 28			21 57				22 28			22 57				23 20	23 28			
Bradford Forster Square	a			20 57	21 06	21 12			21 29			21 57	22 11			22 31			22 57	23 13						

Sundays

		NT	NT D	NT E	NT	NT G	NT		NT	NT	NT	NT	NT	NT		NT	NT	NT	NT	NT	NT G		NT	NT	NT	NT
Leeds 10	d	08 02	08 11	08 21	08 34	08 40	08 45		09 00	09 02	09 25	09 34	09 35			10 02		10 08	10 34	10 34	10 54		11 02	11 08	11 34	11 35
Shipley	a				08 45	08 52			09 13			09 45						10 19	10 45		11 06			11 19	11 45	
	d				08 46							09 46		10 01			10 15		10 46						11 46	
Frizinghall	d				08 48							09 48		10 05			10 18		10 48						11 48	
Bramley	d	08 10	08 18	08 28						09 10	09 32					10 10				10 42			11 10			
New Pudsey	d	08 15	08 23	08 33			08 54			09 15	09 37		09 45			10 15				10 47			11 15			11 44
Bradford Interchange	a	08 23	08 31	08 41			09 03			09 23	09 45		09 54			10 23				10 55			11 23			11 53
Bradford Forster Square	a				08 54							09 54		10 12			10 24		10 54						11 54	

		NT	NT	NT	NT		NT	NT	NT	NT	NT	NT		NT	NT	NT	NT	NT	NT		NT	NT	NT	NT	NT	NT
Leeds 10	d		12 02		12 08		12 34	12 35	13 02	13 08	13 15	13 34		13 35		14 02		14 08	14 34		14 35	15 00	15 02	15 08	15 34	15 35
Shipley	a				12 19		12 45			13 19	13 28	13 45						14 19	14 45			15 12		15 19	15 45	
	d	12 02		12 15			12 46					13 46			14 02		14 15		14 46						15 46	
Frizinghall	d	12 06		12 18			12 48					13 48			14 06		14 18		14 48						15 48	
Bramley	d		12 10					12 42	13 10							14 10					14 42		15 10			
New Pudsey	d		12 15					12 47	13 15					13 44		14 15					14 47		15 15			15 44
Bradford Interchange	a		12 23					12 55	13 23					13 53		14 23					14 55		15 23			15 53
Bradford Forster Square	a	12 12		12 24			12 54					13 54			14 12		14 24		14 54						15 54	

For general notes see front of timetable
For details of catering facilities see Directory of Train Operators

- **A** From London Kings Cross (Table 26)
- **B** From 13 September
- **C** Until 6 September
- **D** 20 July to 7 September
- **E** Until 13 July and from 14 September
- **G** Until 14 September

Leeds → Shipley and Bradford

Network Diagram - see first page of Table 35

		NT	NT		NT	NT	NT	NT	NT	NT		NT	NT	NT	NT	NT	NT		NT	NT	NT	NT	NT	NT		NT
Leeds 10	d		16 02			16 08	16 35	16 35	16 50	17 02		17 08	17 23	17 33	17 35	17 37			18 02		18 08	18 34	18 35	19 02		19 08
Shipley	a					16 19		16 46				17 19	17 35	17 45		17 49					18 19	18 45				19 19
	d	16 02			16 15			16 46								17 49	18 02			18 15		18 46				
Frizinghall	d	16 06			16 18			16 48								17 51	18 06			18 18		18 48				
Bramley	d		16 10						16 57	17 10									18 10				18 42	19 10		
New Pudsey	d		16 15				16 44		17 02	17 15					17 44				18 15				18 47	19 15		
Bradford Interchange	a		16 23				16 53		17 10	17 23					17 53				18 23				18 55	19 23		
Bradford Forster Square	a	16 12			16 24			16 55								17 58	18 12			18 24		18 54				

		NT	NT	NT	NT	NT	NT		NT	NT	NT	NT	NT	NT		NT	NT	NT	NT	NT	NT		NT	NT		
Leeds 10	d	19 34	19 35		20 02		20 08		20 34	20 35	21 02	21 08	21 34	21 35			22 02		22 08	22 34	22 35		23 10	23 22		
Shipley	a	19 45					20 19		20 45			21 19	21 45						22 19	22 45			23 21			
	d	19 46		20 02		20 15			20 46				21 46			22 02		22 15		22 46						
Frizinghall	d	19 48		20 06		20 18			20 48				21 48			22 06		22 18		22 48						
Bramley	d				20 10					20 42	21 10			21 43			22 10				22 42			23 29		
New Pudsey	d		19 44		20 15					20 47	21 14			21 47			22 15				22 47			23 34		
Bradford Interchange	a		19 53		20 23					20 55	21 23			21 56			22 23				22 55			23 43		
Bradford Forster Square	a	19 54		20 12		20 24			20 54				21 54			22 12		22 24		22 54						

For general notes see front of timetable
For details of catering facilities see
Directory of Train Operators

Bradford and Shipley → Leeds

Network Diagram - see first page of Table 35

Miles	Miles			NT MX	NT	NT	NT	NT	NT	GR R 1 A ✕	NT	NT	NT		NT	NT	NT	NT	GR R 1 B ✕	NT	NT	NT	NT	NT		NT
0	—	**Bradford Forster Square**	d		06 01		06 10	06 15		06 30		06 40	06 44			06 55				07 11	07 15					07 42
—	0	**Bradford Interchange**	d	00 35					06 18						06 48		07 05					07 18		07 35		
—	3¼	New Pudsey	d						06 26						06 57		07 14					07 27		07 44		
—	5½	Bramley	d						06 30						07 01		07 18							07 48		
1¾	—	Frizinghall	d		06 04		06 13	06 18				06 43	06 47			06 58				07 14	07 18					07 45
2¾	—	**Shipley**	a		06 08		06 17	06 22				06 47	06 51			07 02				07 18	07 22					07 49
—	—		d		06 08	06 13				06u36	06 44					07 02	07 09		07u15				07 35			
13½	9½	**Leeds** 10	a	00 54	06 22	06 27			06 37	06 53	06 58				07 09	07 16	07 23	07 27	07 29			07 37	07 49	07 59		

		NT	NT	NT	NT	NT	NT	NT	NT	NT	NT		NT	NT	NT	NT	NT	NT	NT	NT	NT	NT		NT	NT	NT
Bradford Forster Square	d		07 46		07 59			08 11		08 16			08 26				08 41	08 46			09 01			09 11	09 16	
Bradford Interchange	d			07 49			08 05				08 18				08 35				08 47			09 05				09 18
New Pudsey	d			07 57			08 14				08 27				08 44				08 57			09 14				09 27
Bramley	d			08 01			08 18								08 48				09 01			09 18				
Frizinghall	d		07 49		08 02			08 14		08 19			08 29				08 44	08 49			09 04			09 14	09 19	
Shipley	a		07 53		08 06			08 18		08 23			08 33				08 48	08 53			09 08			09 18	09 23	
	d	07 50			08 07	08 13			08 19				08 33	08 41		08 47				09 08	09 09					
Leeds 10	a	08 05		08 13	08 24	08 27	08 28		08 37		08 39		08 49	08 56	08 57	09 04			09 12	09 23	09 26	09 28				09 39

		NT	NT	NT	NT	NT	NT	NT	NT	NT		NT	NT	NT	NT	NT	NT	NT	NT	NT	NT		NT	NT	NT	NT
Bradford Forster Square	d	09 31			09 41	09 46		10 01				10 11	10 16		10 31			10 41	10 46		11 01				11 11	
Bradford Interchange	d		09 35				09 48		10 05					10 18		10 35				10 48			11 05			
New Pudsey	d		09 44				09 57		10 14					10 27		10 44				10 57			11 14			
Bramley	d		09 48				10 01		10 18							10 48				11 01			11 18			
Frizinghall	d	09 34			09 44	09 49		10 04				10 14	10 19		10 34			10 44	10 49		11 04				11 14	
Shipley	a	09 38			09 48	09 53		10 08				10 18	10 23		10 38			10 48	10 53		11 08				11 18	
	d	09 39		09 44				10 09		10 14					10 39		10 44				11 09			11 14		11 19
Leeds 10	a	09 53	09 58	09 59			10 10	10 24	10 28	10 28				10 37	10 53	10 58	10 58			11 10	11 24		11 28	11 28		11 36

		NT	NT	NT	NT	NT	NT	NT	NT		NT	NT	NT	NT	NT	NT	NT	NT	NT	NT		NT	NT	NT	NT	NT
Bradford Forster Square	d	11 16		11 31			11 41	11 46			12 01			12 11	12 16			12 31				12 41	12 46		13 01	
Bradford Interchange	d		11 18		11 35				11 48			12 05				12 18			12 35					12 48		13 05
New Pudsey	d		11 27		11 44				11 57			12 14				12 27			12 44					12 57		13 14
Bramley	d				11 48				12 01			12 18							12 48					13 01		13 18
Frizinghall	d	11 19		11 34			11 44	11 49			12 04			12 14	12 19			12 34				12 44	12 49		13 04	
Shipley	a	11 23		11 38			11 48	11 53			12 08			12 18	12 23			12 38				12 48	12 53		13 08	
	d			11 39		11 44					12 09		12 14				12 32	12 39		12 44					13 09	
Leeds 10	a		11 39	11 55	11 58	11 58			12 10		12 24	12 28	12 29			12 38	12 50	12 55	12 58	12 58				13 10	13 24	13 28

		NT	NT	NT	NT	NT	NT	NT		NT	NT	NT	NT	NT	NT	NT	NT	NT	NT		NT	NT	NT	NT	NT	NT
Bradford Forster Square	d		13 11	13 16		13 31				13 41	13 46		14 01			14 11		14 16			14 31			14 41	14 46	
Bradford Interchange	d				13 18		13 35					13 48		14 05					14 18			14 35				14 48
New Pudsey	d				13 27		13 44					13 57		14 14					14 27			14 44				14 57
Bramley	d						13 48					14 01		14 18								14 48				15 01
Frizinghall	d		13 14	13 19		13 34				13 44	13 49		14 04			14 14		14 19			14 34			14 44	14 49	
Shipley	a		13 18	13 23		13 38				13 48	13 53		14 08			14 18		14 23			14 38			14 48	14 53	
	d	13 14				13 39		13 44					14 09		14 14		14 19				14 39		14 45			
Leeds 10	a	13 28			13 37	13 54	13 58	13 58				14 10	14 24	14 28	14 28		14 37		14 39		14 53	14 58	14 59			15 12

		NT	NT	NT	NT	NT	NT		NT	NT	NT	NT	NT	NT	NT	NT	NT	NT		NT	NT	NT	NT	NT	NT	NT
Bradford Forster Square	d	15 01			15 11	15 16			15 31			15 41	15 46		16 01			16 11		16 16			16 31			16 40
Bradford Interchange	d		15 05				15 18			15 35				15 48		16 05					16 18			16 35		
New Pudsey	d		15 14				15 27			15 44				15 57		16 14					16 27			16 44		
Bramley	d		15 18							15 48				16 01		16 18								16 48		
Frizinghall	d	15 04			15 14	15 19			15 34			15 44	15 49		16 04			16 14		16 19			16 34			16 43
Shipley	a	15 08			15 18	15 23			15 38			15 48	15 53		16 08			16 18		16 23			16 38			16 48
	d	15 09		15 14					15 39		15 44				16 09		16 14					16 31	16 39		16 44	
Leeds 10	a	15 24	15 28	15 28			15 37		15 53	15 58	15 58			16 10	16 24	16 28	16 28				16 37	16 51	16 53	16 58	16 58	

For general notes see front of timetable
For details of catering facilities see Directory of Train Operators

A To London Kings Cross (Table 26)
B From Skipton to London Kings Cross (Table 26)

Bradford and Shipley → Leeds

Network Diagram - see first page of Table 35

		NT	NT	NT	NT	NT		NT	NT	NT	NT	NT	NT	NT	NT	NT	NT		NT	NT	NT	NT	NT	NT	NT	NT
Bradford Forster Square	d	16 44		17 01				17 11			17 16	17 31			17 38	17 46			18 01			18 11	18 16		18 27	
Bradford Interchange	d		16 48		17 05				17 18				17 35				17 48			18 05				18 18		18 35
New Pudsey	d		16 57		17 14				17 27				17 44				17 57			18 14				18 27		18 44
Bramley	d		17 01		17 18								17 48				18 01			18 18						18 48
Frizinghall	d	16 48		17 04				17 14			17 19	17 34			17 41	17 49			18 04			18 14	18 19		18 30	
Shipley	a	16 51		17 08				17 18			17 23	17 38			17 45	17 53			18 08			18 18	18 23		18 34	
	d			17 09		17 15				17 20		17 39		17 45					18 09		18 14				18 34	
Leeds 10	a		17 10	17 24	17 28	17 29			17 37	17 40		17 55	17 58	18 00			18 10		18 24	18 28	18 29			18 37	18 48	18 59

		NT	NT	NT	NT		NT	NT	NT	NT	NT	NT	NT	NT	NT	NT		NT	NT	NT	NT	NT	NT	NT	NT	NT
Bradford Forster Square	d			18 41	18 46			19 01			19 07		19 31		19 36			19 41			20 06			20 25		
Bradford Interchange	d						18 48		19 05			19 18		19 35						20 04		20 18			20 35	
New Pudsey	d						18 57		19 14			19 27		19 44						20 13		20 27			20 44	
Bramley	d						19 01		19 18					19 48						20 17					20 48	
Frizinghall	d			18 44	18 49			19 04			19 10		19 34		19 39			19 44			20 09			20 28		
Shipley	a			18 48	18 53			19 08			19 14		19 38		19 43			19 48			20 16			20 32		
	d	18 44	18 48					19 09		19 14			19 39			19 44			20 14				20 28			20 43
Leeds 10	a	18 59	19 07				19 10	19 26	19 28	19 29		19 37	19 55	19 58		19 59			20 28	20 29		20 37	20 44		20 57	21 00

		NT	NT	NT		NT	NT	NT	NT	NT	NT	NT	NT	NT	NT		NT	NT	NT	NT	NT	NT	NT	NT		
Bradford Forster Square	d	20 38				21 05		21 25			21 38		22 05				22 25			22 38		23 09	23 20			
Bradford Interchange	d			21 04					21 35			22 04			22 18			22 35			23 04			23 35		
New Pudsey	d			21 13					21 44			22 13			22 27			22 44			23 13			23 44		
Bramley	d			21 17					21 48			22 17						22 48			23 17			23 48		
Frizinghall	d	20 41				21 08		21 28			21 41		22 08				22 28			22 41		23 12	23 23			
Shipley	a	20 45				21 12		21 32			21 45		22 12				22 32			22 45		23 16	23 27			
	d		20 57				21 14			21 43				22 14					22 43							
Leeds 10	a		21 15	21 25			21 30		21 58	21 59		22 25		22 32	22 38			22 58	23 01		23 25			23 58		

Saturdays

		NT	NT	NT	NT	NT	NT	GR R 1 A	NT	NT	NT	NT	NT	NT	GR R 1 B	NT	NT	NT	NT	NT	NT	NT	NT	NT	NT	NT
Bradford Forster Square	d		06 01		06 10	06 15			07 01			07 11	07 15		07 36			07 59			08 11		08 16		08 31	
Bradford Interchange	d	00 35					06 23			07 05				07 18		07 35	07 49			08 05				08 18		08 35
New Pudsey	d						06 32			07 14				07 27		07 44	07 57			08 14				08 27		08 44
Bramley	d						06 36			07 18						07 48	08 01			08 18						08 48
Frizinghall	d		06 04		06 13	06 18			07 04			07 14	07 18					08 02			08 14		08 19		08 34	
Shipley	a		06 08		06 17	06 22			07 08			07 18	07 22					08 05			08 18		08 23		08 38	
	d		06 08	06 13				07u00	07 09		07 14				07u41			08 07	08 13			08 19			08 38	
Leeds 10	a	00 54	06 22	06 27			06 44	07 15	07 23	07 27	07 28			07 37	07 58	07 59	08 13	08 24	08 27	08 28		08 37		08 39	08 53	08 57

		NT	NT	NT	NT	NT	NT	NT	NT	NT	NT	NT	NT	NT	NT	NT	NT	NT	NT	NT	NT	NT	NT	NT	NT	NT
Bradford Forster Square	d		08 41	08 46		09 01			09 11	09 16		09 31			09 41		09 46		10 01			10 11			10 16	10 31
Bradford Interchange	d				08 47		09 05				09 18		09 35					09 48		10 05			10 18			
New Pudsey	d				08 57		09 14				09 27		09 44					09 57		10 14			10 27			
Bramley	d				09 01		09 18						09 48					10 01		10 18						
Frizinghall	d		08 44	08 49		09 04			09 14	09 19		09 34			09 44		09 49		10 04			10 14			10 19	10 34
Shipley	a		08 48	08 53		09 08			09 18	09 23		09 38			09 48		09 53		10 08			10 18			10 23	10 38
	d	08 44				09 09		09 14				09 39		09 44		09 49			10 09		10 14			10 19		10 39
Leeds 10	a	08 58			09 12	09 26	09 28	09 28			09 39	09 53	09 58	09 59		10 08		10 10	10 24	10 28	10 28		10 37	10 37		10 53

		NT	NT	NT		NT	NT	NT	NT	NT	NT	NT	NT	NT	NT	NT	NT	NT	NT	NT	NT	NT	NT	NT	NT	NT
Bradford Forster Square	d			10 41		10 46		11 01			11 11	11 16		11 31			11 41		11 46		12 01			12 11	12 16	
Bradford Interchange	d	10 35					10 48		11 05				11 18		11 35					11 48		12 05				12 18
New Pudsey	d	10 44					10 57		11 14				11 27		11 44					11 57		12 14				12 27
Bramley	d	10 48					11 01		11 18						11 48					12 01		12 18				
Frizinghall	d			10 44		10 49		11 04			11 14	11 19		11 34			11 44		11 49		12 04			12 14	12 19	
Shipley	a			10 48		10 53		11 08			11 18	11 23		11 38			11 48		11 53		12 08			12 18	12 23	
	d		10 44					11 09		11 14				11 39		11 44		11 49			12 09		12 14			
Leeds 10	a	10 58	10 58				11 10	11 24	11 28	11 28			11 39	11 55	11 58	11 58		12 06		12 10	12 24	12 28	12 29			12 38

For general notes see front of timetable
For details of catering facilities see Directory of Train Operators

A From Skipton to London Kings Cross (Table 26)
B To London Kings Cross (Table 26)

Table 37

Saturdays

Bradford and Shipley → Leeds

Network Diagram - see first page of Table 35

		NT	NT	NT	NT	NT	NT	NT	NT	NT	NT	NT	NT	NT	NT	NT	NT	NT	NT	NT	NT	NT	NT	NT	NT	NT
Bradford Forster Square	d		12 31			12 41	12 46		13 01			13 11	13 16		13 31			13 41	13 46		14 01			14 11		14 16
Bradford Interchange	d			12 35				12 48		13 05				13 18		13 35				13 48		14 05				
New Pudsey	d			12 44				12 57		13 14				13 27		13 44				13 57		14 14				
Bramley	d			12 48				13 01		13 18						13 48				14 01		14 18				
Frizinghall	d		12 34			12 44	12 49		13 04			13 14	13 19		13 34			13 44	13 49		14 04			14 14		14 19
Shipley	a		12 38			12 48	12 53		13 08			13 18	13 23		13 38			13 48	13 53		14 08			14 18		14 23
	d	12 32	12 39		12 44				13 09		13 14				13 39		13 44				14 09		14 14		14 19	
Leeds 10	a	12 50	12 55	12 58	12 58			13 10	13 24	13 28	13 28			13 37	13 54	13 58	13 58			14 10	14 24	14 28	14 28		14 37	

		NT	NT	NT	NT	NT	NT	NT		NT	NT	NT	NT	NT	NT	NT	NT	NT	NT	NT	NT	NT	NT	NT	NT	NT
Bradford Forster Square	d		14 31			14 41		14 46			15 01			15 11	15 16		15 31			15 41	15 46		16 01			16 11
Bradford Interchange	d	14 18		14 35						14 48		15 05				15 18		15 35				15 48		16 05		
New Pudsey	d	14 27		14 44						14 57		15 14				15 27		15 44				15 57		16 14		
Bramley	d			14 48						15 01		15 18						15 48				16 01		16 18		
Frizinghall	d		14 34			14 44		14 49			15 04			15 14	15 19		15 34			15 44	15 49		16 04			16 14
Shipley	a		14 38			14 48		14 53			15 08			15 18	15 23		15 38			15 48	15 53		16 08			16 18
	d		14 39		14 45		14 50				15 09		15 14				15 39		15 44				16 09		16 14	
Leeds 10	a	14 39	14 53	14 58	14 59		15 07			15 12	15 24	15 28	15 28			15 37	15 53	15 58	15 58			16 10	16 24	16 28	16 28	

		NT	NT	NT	NT	NT	NT	NT	NT	NT	NT	NT	NT	NT	NT	NT	NT	NT	NT	NT	NT	NT	NT	NT	NT	NT
Bradford Forster Square	d	16 16		16 31			16 40		16 44		17 01			17 11	17 16		17 31			17 41	17 46			18 01		
Bradford Interchange	d		16 18		16 35					16 48		17 05				17 18		17 35				17 48			18 05	
New Pudsey	d		16 27		16 44					16 57		17 14				17 27		17 44				17 57			18 14	
Bramley	d				16 48					17 01		17 18						17 48				18 01			18 18	
Frizinghall	d	16 19		16 34			16 43		16 48		17 04			17 14	17 19		17 34			17 44	17 49			18 04		
Shipley	a	16 23		16 38			16 48		16 51		17 08			17 18	17 23		17 38			17 48	17 53			18 08		
	d			16 39		16 44		16 50			17 09		17 15				17 39		17 45				18 00	18 09		18 14
Leeds 10	a		16 37	16 53	16 58	16 58		17 07		17 10	17 24	17 28	17 29			17 37	17 55	17 58	18 00			18 10	18 17	18 24	18 28	18 29

		NT	NT	NT	NT	NT	NT	NT	NT	NT	NT	NT	NT	NT	NT	NT	NT	NT	NT	NT	NT	NT	NT	NT	NT	NT
Bradford Forster Square	d	18 11	18 16		18 31				18 41	18 46		19 01			19 07		19 31		19 36		19 41	20 07				
Bradford Interchange	d			18 18		18 35					18 48		19 05			19 18		19 35						20 04	20 21	
New Pudsey	d			18 27		18 44					18 57		19 14			19 27		19 44						20 13	20 30	
Bramley	d					18 48					19 01		19 18					19 48						20 17		
Frizinghall	d	18 14	18 19		18 34				18 44	18 49		19 04			19 10		19 34		19 39		19 44	20 10				
Shipley	a	18 18	18 23		18 38				18 48	18 53		19 08			19 14		19 38		19 43		19 48	20 12				
	d				18 38		18 44	18 48				19 09		19 14			19 39			19 44			20 14			20 28
Leeds 10	a			18 37	18 52	18 59	18 59	19 07			19 10	19 26	19 28	19 29		19 37	19 55	19 58		19 59			20 28	20 29	20 40	20 44

		NT	NT	NT	NT	NT	NT	NT	NT	NT	NT	NT	NT	NT	NT	NT	NT	NT	NT	NT	NT	NT	NT	NT		
Bradford Forster Square	d	20 25		20 38				21 05		21 25			21 38		22 05			22 25			22 38		23 05	23 20		
Bradford Interchange	d				20 43		21 04				21 35			22 04			22 18		22 35			23 04				
New Pudsey	d				20 52		21 13				21 44			22 13			22 27		22 44			23 13				
Bramley	d				20 56		21 17				21 48			22 17					22 48			23 17				
Frizinghall	d	20 28		20 41				21 08		21 28			21 41		22 08			22 28			22 41		23 08	23 23		
Shipley	a	20 32		20 45				21 12		21 32			21 45		22 12			22 32			22 45		23 12	23 27		
	d		20 43			20 57			21 14			21 43				22 14				22 43						
Leeds 10	a		21 00		21 07	21 15	21 25		21 30		21 58	21 59		22 25		22 32	22 38		22 58	23 01		23 25				

Sundays

		NT	NT	NT	NT	NT	NT	NT		NT	NT	NT	NT	NT	NT	NT		NT	NT	NT	NT	NT	NT	NT		NT
Bradford Forster Square	d				09 02			10 02					10 38	10 48		11 02						12 02				12 38
Bradford Interchange	d	00 05	08 31			09 21				10 02	10 31				11 02			11 31			12 01		12 31			
New Pudsey	d	00 14	08 39			09 30				10 10	10 39				11 10			11 39			12 09		12 39			
Bramley	d	00 18	08 43			09 34				10 14	10 43							11 43			12 13		12 43			
Frizinghall	d				09 05			10 05					10 41	10 51		11 05						12 05				12 41
Shipley	a				09 08			10 08					10 44	10 54		11 09						12 08				12 44
	d			09 00	09 10		09 40	10 08				10 40				11 10			11 40	11 49		12 08		12 40		
Leeds 10	a	00 28	08 52	09 14	09 24	09 42	09 54	10 22		10 24	10 52	10 54			11 21	11 24		11 54	11 54	12 06	12 21	12 22	12 52	12 54		

For general notes see front of timetable
For details of catering facilities see
Directory of Train Operators

Table 37

Sundays

Bradford and Shipley → Leeds

Network Diagram - see first page of Table 35

		NT	NT	NT	NT	NT	NT	NT		NT A	NT	NT	NT	NT	NT	NT		NT	NT	NT	NT	NT	NT B	NT C		NT
Bradford Forster Square	d	12 48		13 02			14 02						14 38	14 48		15 02					16 02					
Bradford Interchange	d		13 02		13 31			14 02			14 31				15 02			15 31		16 01						16 31
New Pudsey	d		13 10		13 39			14 10			14 39				15 10			15 39		16 09						16 39
Bramley	d				13 43			14 14			14 43							15 43		16 13						16 43
Frizinghall	d	12 51		13 05			14 05						14 41	14 51		15 05					16 05					
Shipley	a	12 54		13 08			14 08						14 44	14 54		15 08					16 08					
	d			13 08		13 40	14 08			14 19		14 40				15 08			15 40		16 08	16 16	16 27	16 29		
Leeds 10	a		13 21	13 22	13 52	13 54	14 22	14 22		14 39	14 53	14 54			15 21	15 22		15 52	15 54	16 21	16 22	16 34	16 45	16 47		16 54

		NT	NT	NT	NT	NT	NT	NT		NT	NT	NT	NT	NT	NT	NT		NT	NT	NT	NT	NT	NT	NT		NT
Bradford Forster Square	d		16 38	16 48		17 02					18 02			18 38	18 48				19 02					20 02		
Bradford Interchange	d				17 02		17 31			18 02		18 31						19 02		19 31			20 02			20 14
New Pudsey	d				17 10		17 39			18 10		18 39						19 10		19 39			20 10			20 22
Bramley	d						17 43			18 14		18 43								19 43						20 26
Frizinghall	d		16 41	16 51		17 05					18 05			18 41	18 51				19 05					20 05		
Shipley	a		16 44	16 54		17 08					18 08			18 44	18 54				19 08					20 08		
	d	16 40				17 09		17 40			18 08		18 40			19 02			19 08		19 38	19 48		20 08		
Leeds 10	a	16 54			17 21	17 23	17 52	17 54		18 22	18 23	18 54	18 54			19 19		19 21	19 22	19 53	19 56	20 02	20 22	20 22		20 34

		NT	NT	NT	NT	NT	NT	NT		NT	NT D	NT E	NT	NT	NT	NT		NT	NT	NT	NT	NT D	NT	NT E		
Bradford Forster Square	d			20 38	20 48		21 02						22 02					22 38	22 48		23 02					
Bradford Interchange	d	20 31				21 02		21 31						22 02	22 31					23 02		23 31		23 52		
New Pudsey	d	20 39				21 10		21 39						22 10	22 39					23 10		23 39		00 01		
Bramley	d	20 43						21 43						22 14	22 43							23 43		00 04		
Frizinghall	d			20 41	20 51		21 05						22 05					22 41	22 51		23 05					
Shipley	a			20 44	20 54		21 08						22 08					22 44	22 54		23 08					
	d		20 40				21 08			21 40	21 47	21 49	22 08			22 40					23 08		23 40			
Leeds 10	a	20 54	20 54			21 21	21 24	21 54		21 54	22 03	22 05	22 22	22 23	22 53	22 54				23 21	23 22	23 52	23 58	00 13		

For general notes see front of timetable
For details of catering facilities see Directory of Train Operators

A Until 14 September
B Until 13 July
C 20 July to 14 September
D Until 13 July and from 14 September
E 20 July to 7 September

Leeds and Bradford → Ilkley

Network Diagram - see first page of Table 35

Miles	Miles			NT	NT	NT	NT	NT	NT	NT	NT	NT	NT	NT	NT	NT	NT	NT	NT	NT	NT	NT	NT	NT	NT
						SX	SX		SX	SO	SX	SX	SX			SO	SX								
0	—	**Leeds** 10	d	06 02		06 27		07 02			07 29	07 35		08 02		08 32	08 35		09 02		09 32		10 02		10 32
—	0	**Bradford Forster Square**	37 d		06 15		06 44		07 11	07 15			07 46		08 16			08 46		09 16		09 46		10 16	
—	1¾	Frizinghall	37 d		06 18		06 47		07 14	07 18			07 49		08 19			08 49		09 19		09 49		10 19	
—	2¾	Shipley	37 d		06 22		06 51		07 18	07 23			07 53		08 23			08 53		09 23		09 53		10 23	
—	4¼	Baildon	d		06 25		06 54		07 21	07 26			07 56		08 26			08 56		09 26		09 56		10 26	
10¼	7½	Guiseley	d	06 14	06 31	06b41	07 00	07 14	07 27	07 32	07 41	07 48	08 02	08 14	08 32	08 44	08 47	09 02	09 14	09 32	09 45	10 02	10 14	10 32	10 44
11½	8¾	Menston	d	06 17	06 34	06 44	07 03	07 17	07 30	07 35	07 44	07 51	08 05	08 17	08 35	08 47	08 50	09 05	09 17	09 35	09 48	10 05	10 17	10 35	10 47
13	10¼	Burley-in-Wharfedale	d	06 20	06 37	06 47	07 06	07 20	07 33	07 38	07 47	07 56	08 09	08 20	08 38	08 50	08 53	09 08	09 20	09 38	09 52	10 08	10 20	10 38	10 50
15¼	12½	Ben Rhydding	d	06 23	06 40	06 51	07 09	07 24	07 36	07 41	07 51	07 59	08 12	08 23	08 41	08 53	08 56	09 11	09 24	09 41	09 55	10 11	10 23	10 41	10 53
16¼	13½	**Ilkley**	a	06 29	06 46	06 56	07 15	07 29	07 42	07 47	07 56	08 05	08 18	08 29	08 49	08 59	09 02	09 17	09 33	09 47	10 01	10 17	10 29	10 47	10 59

		NT	NT	NT	NT	NT	NT	NT	NT	NT	NT	NT	NT	NT	NT	NT	NT	NT	NT	NT	NT	NT	NT	NT	NT
Leeds 10	d		11 02		11 32		12 02		12 32		13 02		13 32		14 02		14 32		15 02		15 32		16 02		16 32
Bradford Forster Square	37 d	10 46		11 16		11 46		12 16		12 46		13 16		13 46		14 16		14 46		15 16		15 46		16 16	
Frizinghall	37 d	10 49		11 19		11 49		12 19		12 49		13 19		13 49		14 19		14 49		15 19		15 49		16 19	
Shipley	37 d	10 53		11 23		11 53		12 23		12 53		13 23		13 53		14 23		14 53		15 23		15 53		16 23	
Baildon	d	10 56		11 26		11 56		12 26		12 56		13 26		13 56		14 26		14 56		15 26		15 56		16 26	
Guiseley	d	11 02	11 14	11 32	11 44	12 02	12 14	12 32	12 44	13 02	13 14	13 32	13 44	14 02	14 14	14 32	14 44	15 02	15 14	15 32	15 44	16 02	16 14	16 32	16 44
Menston	d	11 05	11 17	11 35	11 47	12 05	12 17	12 35	12 47	13 05	13 17	13 35	13 47	14 05	14 17	14 35	14 47	15 05	15 17	15 35	15 47	16 05	16 17	16 35	16 47
Burley-in-Wharfedale	d	11 08	11 20	11 38	11 50	12 08	12 20	12 38	12 50	13 08	13 20	13 38	13 50	14 08	14 20	14 38	14 50	15 08	15 20	15 38	15 50	16 08	16 20	16 38	16 50
Ben Rhydding	d	11 11	11 23	11 41	11 53	12 11	12 23	12 41	12 53	13 11	13 23	13 41	13 53	14 11	14 23	14 41	14 53	15 11	15 23	15 41	15 53	16 11	16 23	16 41	16 53
Ilkley	a	11 17	11 29	11 47	11 59	12 17	12 29	12 47	13 00	13 17	13 29	13 47	13 59	14 17	14 29	14 47	15 01	15 17	15 29	15 47	15 59	16 17	16 29	16 47	16 59

		NT	NT	NT	NT	NT	NT	NT	NT	NT	NT	NT	NT	NT	NT	NT	NT	NT	NT	NT	NT	NT	NT	NT
				SX	SO	SX												SO	SX					
Leeds 10	d		17 02	17 15			17 32		18 02		18 32		19 02	19 32		20 02		21 02	21 06		22 02		23 15	
Bradford Forster Square	37 d	16 44			17 16	17 16		17 46		18 16		18 46			19 41		20 38			21 38		22 38		23 20
Frizinghall	37 d	16 48			17 19	17 19		17 49		18 19		18 49			19 44		20 41			21 41		22 41		23 23
Shipley	37 d	16 52			17 23	17 25		17 53		18 23		18 53			19 48		20 45			21 45		22 45		23 27
Baildon	d	16 55			17 26	17 28		17 57		18 26		18 56			19 51		20 48			21 48		22 48		23 30
Guiseley	d	17 01	17 14	17 28	17 32	17 35	17 44	18 02	18 14	18 32	18 44	19 02	19 14	19 44	19 56	20 14	20 54	21 14	21 18	21 54	22 14	22 54	23 27	23 36
Menston	d	17 04	17 17	17 31	17 35	17 38	17 47	18 05	18 17	18 35	18 47	19 05	19 17	19 47	19 59	20 17	20 57	21 17	21 21	21 57	22 17	22 57	23 30	23 39
Burley-in-Wharfedale	d	17 07	17 20	17 34	17 38	17 42	17 51	18 08	18 20	18 38	18 50	19 08	19 20	19 50	20 02	20 20	21 00	21 20	21 24	22 00	22 20	23 00	23 33	23 42
Ben Rhydding	d	17 10	17 23	17 37	17 41	17 46	17 54	18 12	18 23	18 41	18 53	19 11	19 24	19 53	20 06	20 23	21 03	21 23	21 27	22 03	22 23	23 03	23 36	23 45
Ilkley	a	17 17	17 29	17 43	17 47	17 51	18 00	18 17	18 29	18 47	19 00	19 17	19 29	20 00	20 12	20 30	21 09	21 29	21 33	22 09	22 29	23 09	23 42	23 51

Sundays

		NT	NT	NT	NT	NT	NT	NT	NT	NT	NT	NT	NT	NT	NT	NT	NT	NT	NT	NT	NT	NT	NT
Leeds 10	d	09 12	10 12		11 12	12 12		13 12	14 12		15 12	16 12		17 12	18 12		19 12	20 12		21 12	22 12		23 14
Bradford Forster Square	37 d			10 38			12 38			14 38			16 38			18 38			20 38			22 38	
Frizinghall	37 d			10 41			12 41			14 41			16 41			18 41			20 41			22 41	
Shipley	37 d			10 44			12 44			14 44			16 44			18 44			20 44			22 44	
Baildon	d			10 47			12 47			14 47			16 47			18 47			20 47			22 47	
Guiseley	d	09 23	10 23	10 52	11 23	12 23	12 52	13 23	14 23	14 52	15 23	16 23	16 52	17 23	18 23	18 52	19 23	20 23	20 52	21 23	22 23	22 52	23 25
Menston	d	09 26	10 26	10 55	11 26	12 26	12 55	13 26	14 26	14 55	15 26	16 26	16 55	17 26	18 26	18 55	19 26	20 26	20 55	21 26	22 26	22 55	23 28
Burley-in-Wharfedale	d	09 29	10 29	10 58	11 29	12 29	12 58	13 29	14 29	14 58	15 29	16 29	16 58	17 29	18 29	18 58	19 29	20 29	20 58	21 29	22 29	22 58	23 31
Ben Rhydding	d	09 33	10 33	11 02	11 33	12 33	13 02	13 33	14 33	15 02	15 33	16 33	17 02	17 33	18 33	19 02	19 33	20 33	21 02	21 33	22 33	23 02	23 35
Ilkley	a	09 38	10 38	11 07	11 38	12 38	13 07	13 38	14 38	15 07	15 38	16 38	17 07	17 38	18 38	19 07	19 38	20 38	21 07	21 38	22 38	23 07	23 40

For general notes see front of timetable
For details of catering facilities see Directory of Train Operators

b Arr. 0638

Ilkley → Bradford and Leeds

Network Diagram - see first page of Table 35

Miles	Miles			NT	NT SX	NT SO	NT SX	NT SX	NT	NT	NT SX	NT SX	NT SX	NT SO	NT SX	NT SO	NT SX	NT	NT SO	NT SX
0	0	**Ilkley**	d	06 09	06 17	06 19	06 40	06 50	07 10	07 22	07 40	07 50	08 05	08 10	08 17	08 21	08 24	08 40	08 51	08 54
1	1	Ben Rhydding	d	06 11	06 19	06 21	06 42	06 52	07 12	07 24	07 42	07 52	08 07	08 12	08 19	08 23	08 26	08 42	08 53	08 56
3½	3½	Burley-in-Wharfedale	d	06 17	06 25	06 27	06 48	06 58	07 18	07 30	07 48	07 58	08 13	08 18	08 25	08 29	08 32	08 48	08 59	09 02
4¾	4¾	Menston	d	06 20	06 28	06 30	06 51	07 01	07 21	07 33	07 51	08 01	08 16	08 21	08 28	08 32	08 35	08 51	09 02	09 05
6	6	Guiseley	d	06 23	06 31	06 34	06 54	07 04	07 24	07 36	07 54	08 04	08 19	08 24	08 31	08 35	08 39	08 54	09 05	09 08
—	9½	Baildon	d		06 36	06 39		07 09		07 41		08 09				08 40	08 44		09 10	09 13
—	10¾	Shipley	37 a		06 41	06 44		07 14		07 47		08 12				08 43	08 47		09 14	09 18
—	11¾	Frizinghall	37 a		06 44	06 47		07 17		07 49		08 16				08 46	08 50		09 17	09 21
—	13½	**Bradford Forster Square**	37 a		06 50	06 55		07 22		07 56		08 22				08 53	08 56		09 24	09 27
16¼	—	**Leeds [10]**	a	06 39			07 10		07 38		08 09		08 34	08 39	08 46			09 11		

		NT	NT	NT SX	NT SO	NT	NT	NT	NT	NT	NT	NT	NT	NT	NT	NT	NT	NT	NT	NT
Ilkley	d	09 10	09 21	09 40	09 40	09 51	10 10	10 21	10 40	10 51	11 10	11 21	11 40	11 51	12 10	12 21	12 40	12 51	13 10	13 21
Ben Rhydding	d	09 12	09 23	09 42	09 42	09 53	10 12	10 23	10 42	10 53	11 12	11 23	11 42	11 53	12 12	12 23	12 42	12 53	13 12	13 23
Burley-in-Wharfedale	d	09 18	09 29	09 48	09 48	09 59	10 18	10 29	10 48	10 59	11 18	11 29	11 48	11 59	12 18	12 29	12 48	12 59	13 18	13 29
Menston	d	09 21	09 32	09 51	09 51	10 02	10 21	10 32	10 51	11 02	11 21	11 32	11 51	12 02	12 21	12 32	12 51	13 02	13 21	13 32
Guiseley	d	09 24	09 35	09 54	09 54	10 05	10 25	10 35	10 54	11 05	11 24	11 35	11 54	12 05	12 24	12 35	12 54	13 05	13 24	13 35
Baildon	d		09 40			10 10		10 40		11 10		11 40		12 10		12 40		13 10		13 40
Shipley	37 a		09 44			10 14		10 44		11 14		11 44		12 14		12 44		13 14		13 44
Frizinghall	37 a		09 47			10 17		10 47		11 17		11 47		12 17		12 47		13 17		13 47
Bradford Forster Square	37 a		09 53			10 23		10 53		11 23		11 53		12 24		12 53		13 23		13 53
Leeds [10]	a	09 39		10 08	10 15		10 41		11 08		11 39		12 08		12 39		13 08		13 38	

		NT	NT	NT	NT	NT	NT	NT	NT	NT	NT	NT	NT	NT	NT	NT SO	NT SX	NT	NT
Ilkley	d	13 40	13 51	14 10	14 21	14 40	14 51	15 10	15 21	15 40	15 51	16 10	16 21	16 40	16 51	17 10	17 14	17 21	17 40
Ben Rhydding	d	13 42	13 53	14 12	14 23	14 42	14 53	15 12	15 23	15 42	15 53	16 12	16 23	16 42	16 53	17 12	17 16	17 23	17 42
Burley-in-Wharfedale	d	13 48	13 59	14 18	14 29	14 48	14 59	15 18	15 29	15 48	15 59	16 18	16 29	16 48	16 59	17 18	17 22	17 29	17 48
Menston	d	13 51	14 02	14 21	14 32	14 51	15 02	15 21	15 32	15 51	16 02	16 21	16 32	16 51	17 02	17 21	17 25	17 32	17 51
Guiseley	d	13 54	14 05	14 24	14 35	14 54	15 05	15 24	15 35	15 54	16 05	16 24	16 35	16 54	17 05	17 24	17 29	17 35	17 54
Baildon	d		14 10		14 40		15 10		15 40		16 10		16 40		17 10			17 40	
Shipley	37 a		14 14		14 44		15 14		15 44		16 14		16 44		17 14			17 44	
Frizinghall	37 a		14 17		14 47		15 17		15 47		16 17		16 47		17 17			17 47	
Bradford Forster Square	37 a		14 23		14 53		15 23		15 53		16 23		16 53		17 23			17 53	
Leeds [10]	a	14 09		14 39		15 10		15 40		16 08		16 38		17 09		17 38	17 44		18 09

		NT	NT SX	NT	NT	NT	NT	NT	NT	NT	NT	NT	NT	NT	NT	NT	NT	NT
Ilkley	d	17 51	18 04	18 10	18 21	18 40	18 51	19 10	19 21	19 40	20 05	20 21	20 40	21 21	21 40	22 21	22 40	23 21
Ben Rhydding	d	17 53	18 06	18 12	18 23	18 42	18 53	19 12	19 23	19 42	20 07	20 23	20 42	21 23	21 42	22 23	22 42	23 23
Burley-in-Wharfedale	d	17 59	18 12	18 18	18 29	18 48	18 59	19 18	19 29	19 48	20 13	20 29	20 48	21 29	21 48	22 29	22 48	23 29
Menston	d	18 02	18 15	18 21	18 32	18 51	19 02	19 21	19 32	19 51	20 16	20 32	20 51	21 32	21 51	22 32	22 51	23 32
Guiseley	d	18 05	18 18	18 24	18 35	18 54	19 05	19 24	19 35	19 54	20 19	20 35	20 54	21 35	21 54	22 35	22 54	23 35
Baildon	d	18 10			18 40		19 10		19 40		20 24		20 59		21 59		22 59	
Shipley	37 a	18 14			18 43		19 14		19 44		20 27		21 03		22 02		23 02	
Frizinghall	37 a	18 17			18 46		19 17		19 47		20 30		21 05		22 05		23 05	
Bradford Forster Square	37 a	18 23			18 52		19 23		19 53		20 36		21 12		22 11		23 13	
Leeds [10]	a		18 35	18 40		19 09		19 40		20 09		20 53		21 49		22 49		23 49

Sundays

		NT	NT	NT	NT	NT	NT	NT	NT	NT	NT	NT	NT	NT	NT	NT	NT	NT	NT	NT	NT	NT	NT
Ilkley	d	09 30	09 53	10 21	11 21	11 53	12 21	13 21	13 53	14 21	15 21	15 53	16 21	17 21	17 53	18 21	19 21	19 53	20 21	21 21	21 53	22 21	23 21
Ben Rhydding	d	09 32	09 55	10 23	11 23	11 55	12 23	13 23	13 55	14 23	15 23	15 55	16 23	17 23	17 55	18 23	19 23	19 55	20 23	21 23	21 55	22 23	23 23
Burley-in-Wharfedale	d	09 38	10 01	10 29	11 29	12 01	12 29	13 29	14 01	14 29	15 29	16 01	16 29	17 29	18 01	18 29	19 29	20 01	20 29	21 29	22 01	22 29	23 29
Menston	d	09 41	10 04	10 32	11 32	12 04	12 32	13 32	14 04	14 32	15 32	16 04	16 32	17 32	18 04	18 32	19 32	20 04	20 32	21 32	22 04	22 32	23 32
Guiseley	d	09 44	10 07	10 35	11 35	12 07	12 35	13 35	14 07	14 35	15 35	16 07	16 35	17 35	18 07	18 35	19 35	20 07	20 35	21 35	22 07	22 35	23 35
Baildon	d		10 12			12 12			14 12			16 12			18 12			20 12			22 12		
Shipley	37 a		10 15			12 15			14 15			16 15			18 15			20 15			22 15		
Frizinghall	37 a		10 18			12 18			14 18			16 18			18 18			20 18			22 18		
Bradford Forster Square	37 a		10 24			12 24			14 24			16 24			18 24			20 24			22 24		
Leeds [10]	a	09 58		10 49	11 49		12 49	13 49		14 49	15 49		16 49	17 49		18 49	19 49		20 49	21 49		22 49	23 49

For general notes see front of timetable
For details of catering facilities see
Directory of Train Operators

Network Diagram for Tables 39, 40, 41, 43

DM-7/08
Design BAJS

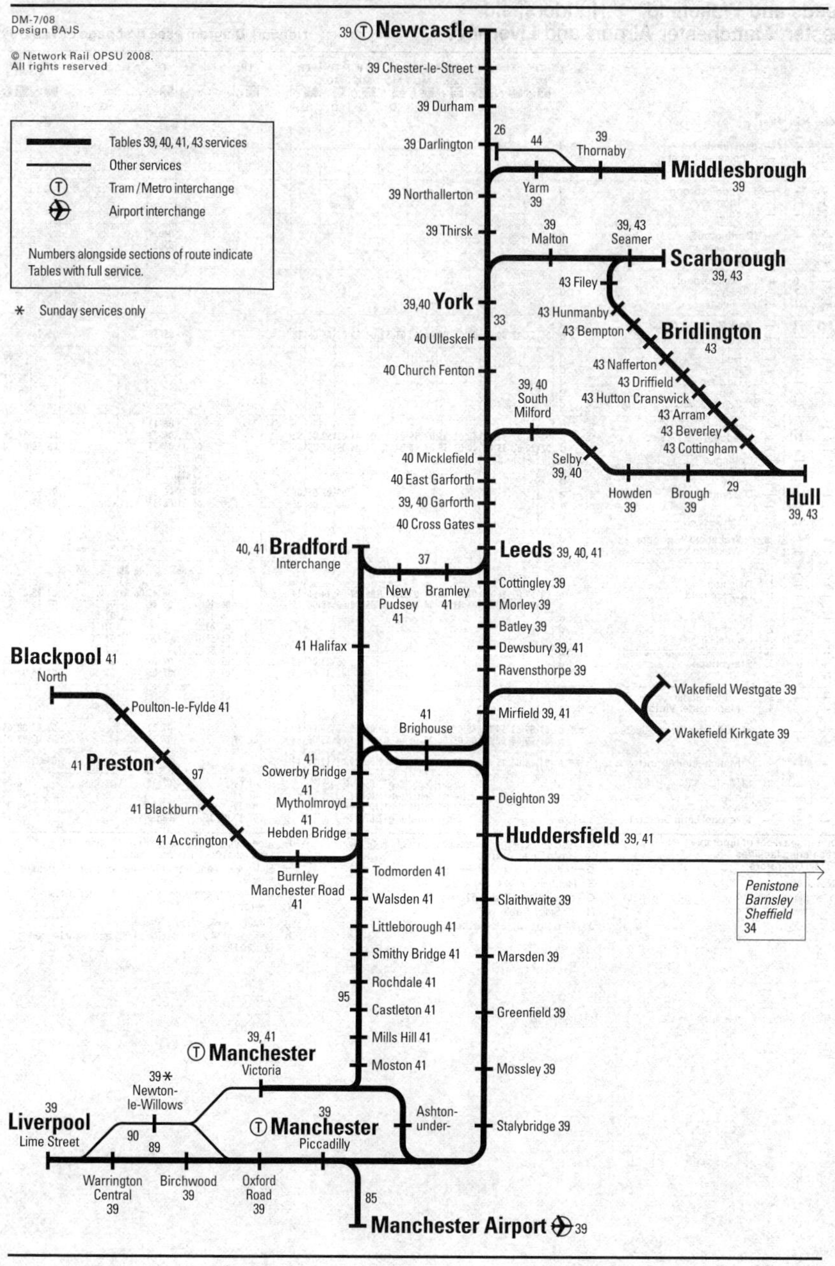
Tables 39, 40, 41, 43 services
Other services
Tram / Metro interchange
Airport interchange
Numbers alongside sections of route indicate Tables with full service.
* Sunday services only
39 Newcastle
39 Chester-le-Street
39 Durham
39 Darlington
26
44
39 Thornaby
Middlesbrough 39
Yarm 39
39 Northallerton
39 Thirsk
39 Malton
39, 43 Seamer
Scarborough 39, 43
43 Filey
39,40 York
33
43 Hunmanby
43 Bempton
Bridlington 43
40 Ulleskelf
40 Church Fenton
43 Nafferton
43 Driffield
43 Hutton Cranswick
43 Arram
43 Beverley
43 Cottingham
39, 40 South Milford
Selby 39, 40
40 Micklefield
40 East Garforth
39, 40 Garforth
40 Cross Gates
Howden 39
Brough 39
29
Hull 39, 43
40, 41 Bradford Interchange
37
New Pudsey 41
Bramley 41
Leeds 39, 40, 41
Cottingley 39
Morley 39
Batley 39
Dewsbury 39, 41
Ravensthorpe 39
41 Halifax
Blackpool 41 North
Poulton-le-Fylde 41
Wakefield Westgate 39
Mirfield 39, 41
41 Brighouse
Wakefield Kirkgate 39
41 Preston
97
41 Sowerby Bridge
41 Mytholmroyd
41 Blackburn
Deighton 39
41 Hebden Bridge
41 Accrington
Huddersfield 39, 41
Burnley Manchester Road 41
Todmorden 41
Walsden 41
Slaithwaite 39
Penistone
Barnsley
Sheffield
34
Littleborough 41
Smithy Bridge 41
Marsden 39
Rochdale 41
95
Castleton 41
Greenfield 39
Mills Hill 41
39, 41 Manchester Victoria
Moston 41
Mossley 39
39* Newton-le-Willows
39 Liverpool Lime Street
90
89
39 Manchester Piccadilly
Ashton-under-
Stalybridge 39
Warrington Central 39
Birchwood 39
Oxford Road 39
85
Manchester Airport 39

Newcastle, Middlesbrough, Scarborough, York, Hull, Leeds and Wakefield → Huddersfield → Manchester, Manchester Airport and Liverpool

Network Diagram - see first page of Table 39

Miles	Miles	Miles	Miles	Miles			TP	TP	TP	TP	TP	TP	TP	TP	TP		TP	NT	NT	TP	NT	NT	NT	TP	TP
							MO	MX	MO	MX	MO	MO	MX	MO											
							1◇	1◇	1◇	1◇	1◇	1◇	1◇	1◇	1◇		1◇			1◇				1◇	1◇
							A		B			C	C	D	E							G	H		J
																				♿				♿	♿
0	—	—	—	—	Newcastle 8	d														04b20					
8¾	—	—	—	—	Chester-le-Street	d																			
14	—	—	—	—	Durham	d														04b36					
—	—	0	—	—	**Middlesbrough**	d																			
—	—	3¼	—	—	Thornaby	d																			
—	—	8½	—	—	Yarm	d																			
36	—	—	—	—	**Darlington 7**	d														04b54					
50	—	20¾	—	—	Northallerton	d														05b21					
57¾	—	28½	—	—	Thirsk	d																			
—	—	—	0	—	**Scarborough**	d																			
—	—	—	2¾	—	Seamer	d																			
—	—	—	21	—	Malton	d																			
80	—	50¾	42	—	**York 8**	a																			
—	—	—	—	—		d	01 53	02 00	02c00	03 00	03c00	03e57	04 09	05 05	05 26					05 58				06 28	
—	0	—	—	—	**Hull**	d																			06 00
—	10½	—	—	—	Brough	d																			06 12
—	22¼	—	—	—	Howden	d																			06 27
—	31	—	—	—	Selby	d																			06 38
—	38¾	—	—	—	South Milford	d																			
98¼	44½	—	60¼	—	Garforth	d														06 13					
105½	51¾	—	67½	—	**Leeds 10**	a	02 19	02 33	02 40	03 33	03 39	04 38	04 41	05 52	05 52					06 23				06 53	07 05
—	—	—	—	—		d	02 20	02 35	02 40	03 35	03 40	04 40	04 44	05 55	05 55				06 13	06 25				06 55	07 10
108½	—	—	—	—	Cottingley	d													06 18						
110	—	—	—	—	Morley	d													06 22						
113¼	—	—	—	—	Batley	d													06 27						
114¾	—	—	—	—	**Dewsbury**	a								06 05	06 05				06 30	06 36				07 06	
—	—	—	—	—		d								06 06	06 06				06 31	06 37				07 07	
116	—	—	—	—	Ravensthorpe	d													06 34						
—	—	—	—	0	**Wakefield Westgate**	d																	06 29		
—	—	—	—	1	Wakefield Kirkgate	d															←		06 35		
117½	—	—	—	10½	Mirfield	d													06 38		06 38		06 48		
120¾	—	—	—	13¼	Deighton	d													→		06 43		06 52		
122¼	—	—	—	15½	**Huddersfield**	a	02 57	02 56	03 03	03 56	04 03	05 27	05 27	06 14	06 14					06 45	06 51		07 00	07 15	07 27
—	—	—	—	—		d	02 59	03 00	03 04	03 59	04 04	05 28	05 28	06 15	06 15			06 30		06 46		06 56		07 16	07 28
127¼	—	—	—	20	Slaithwaite	d												06 37				07 03			
129¾	—	—	—	22½	Marsden	d												06 43				07f11			
135¼	—	—	—	28¼	Greenfield	d												06 51				07 20			
138	—	—	—	30¾	Mossley (Grtr Manchester)	d												06 55				07 24			
140¾	—	—	—	33½	**Stalybridge**	a								06 33	06 33			07 00		07 05		07 29		07 35	07 48
—	—	—	—	—		d								06 33	06 33			07 00		07 05		07 30		07 35	07 48
—	—	—	—	34¾	Ashton-under-Lyne	d												07 04				07 34			
—	—	—	—	41¼	**Manchester Victoria**	a												07 18				07 46			
148¼	—	—	—	—	**Manchester Piccadilly 10**	a	03 59	03 59	03 59	04 58	04 58	06 00	06 00	06 50	06 50					07 22				07 53	08 05
—	—	—	—	—		d	04 00	04 00	04 00	05 00	05 00	06 07	06 07	06 53	06 53		07 07			07 30				08 03	08 07
—	—	—	—	—	**Manchester Airport**	a	04 15	04 15	04 15	05 19	05 19	06 29	06 29	07 12	07 12					07 48				08 22	08 42
148¾	—	—	—	—	Manchester Oxford Road	a				06g02	06g02	06g31	06g31				07 09			07g38					08 09
161¼	—	—	—	—	Birchwood	a				06h51	06h51	07h11	07h11				07 24								08 24
164½	—	—	—	—	Warrington Central	a				06h58	06h58	07h19	07h19				07 29			07g54					08 29
183	—	—	—	—	**Liverpool Lime Street 10**	a				07h44	07h44	07g47	07g47				07 57	08 35		08g29					08 57

For general notes see front of timetable
For details of catering facilities see Directory of Train Operators

A From 10 November
B Until 3 November
C Also stops at East Didsbury 0615, Gatley 0618 and Heald Green 0621
D 21 July to 8 September
E Not Mondays 21 July to 8 September
G To Southport (Table 82)
H To Selby (Table 41)
J Also stops at Gilberdyke 0620

b Mondays dep. Newcastle 0410, Durham 0427, Darlington 0445, Northallerton 0512,
c Until 14 July and from 15 September dep. 13 minutes later
e Until 14 July and from 15 September dep. 0405
f Arr. 0708
g Change at Manchester Piccadilly
h Change at Manchester Piccadilly and Manchester Oxford Road

Newcastle, Middlesbrough, Scarborough, York, Hull, Leeds and Wakefield → Huddersfield → Manchester, Manchester Airport and Liverpool

Network Diagram - see first page of Table 39

		NT	NT		TP	TP	NT	NT	NT	NT	TP	NT	TP		NT	NT	TP	TP	NT	NT	TP	NT	NT		TP
					1 ◇	1 ◇					1 ◇		1 ◇				1 ◇	1 ◇			1 ◇				1 ◇
		A	B						C		D				B				C						
					🛒	🛒					🛒		🛒				🛒	🛒			🛒				🛒
Newcastle 8 ⛴	d				05b25						06c00		06 13				06c44				07c20				07c23
Chester-le-Street	d												06c31												
Durham	d				05b38						06c12		06 29				06c56				07c12				07c37
Middlesbrough	d				05 58																07 23				
Thornaby	d				06 03																07 28				
Yarm	d				06 10																07 39				
Darlington 7	d				05 56						06c30		06 46				07c14				07c30				07c54
Northallerton	d				06 26								06 58				07c12				07 54				
Thirsk	d				06 33								07 06								08 02				
Scarborough	d										06 30						07 00								07 47
Seamer	d										06 35						07 05								07 52
Malton	d										06 53						07 23								08 10
York 8	a				06 52						07 21		07 32				07 51				08 19				08 37
	d				06 58						07 24		07 40				07 54				08 24				08 40
Hull	d					06 35												07 33							
Brough	d					06 47												07 45							
Howden	d					06 49												07 56							
Selby	d					07 08												08 07							
South Milford	d																								
Garforth	d				07 13	07 24											08u13				08 41				
Leeds 10	a				07 23	07 35					07 52		08 04				08 23	08 37			08 50				09 04
	d		07 13		07 25	07 38				07 43	07 55		08 10		08 13		08 25	08 40		08 43	08 55				09 10
Cottingley	d		07 18							07 48					08 18					08 48					
Morley	d		07 22							07 52					08 22					08 52					
Batley	d		07 27							07 57					08 27					08 57					
Dewsbury	a		07 30		07 36					08 00	08 06				08 30		08 36			09 00	09 06				
	d		07 31		07 37					08 01	08 07				08 31		08 37			09 01	09 07				
Ravensthorpe	d		07 34							08 04					08 34					09 04					
Wakefield Westgate	d								07 29										08 29						
Wakefield Kirkgate	d								07 35			←							08 35			←			
Mirfield	d		07a37						07 50	08 08		08 08			08a37				08 51	09 08		09 08			
Deighton	d								07 56	→		08 14							08 57	→		09 16			
Huddersfield	a				07 45	07 56			08 03		08 15	08 21	08 27				08 45	08 57	09 04		09 15	09 21			09 27
	d	07 32			07 46	07 57		08 02			08 16		08 28			08 32	08 46	08 58			09 16				09 28
Slaithwaite	d	07 39						08 09								08 39									
Marsden	d	07 45						08 15								08 45									
Greenfield	d	07 53						08 23								08 53									
Mossley (Grtr Manchester)	d	07 57						08 27								08 57									
Stalybridge	a	08 02			08 08	08 16		08 32					08 45			09 02									09 45
	d	08 03			08 08	08 16	08 22	08 33					08 46			09 03							09 42		09 46
Ashton-under-Lyne	d	08 07					08 26	08 37								09 07							09 46		
Manchester Victoria ⛴	a	08 20					08 35	08 50								09 20							09 57		
Manchester Piccadilly 10 ⛴	a				08 28	08 37					08 52		09 05				09 23	09 37			09 50				10 05
	d				08 30						08 55		09 07				09 27				09 53				10 07
Manchester Airport ✈	a				08 51	09 06					09 18		09 40				09 44	10 01			10 14				10 40
Manchester Oxford Road	a				08e47	08 52							09 09				09e36	09 51			10e05				10 09
Birchwood	a												09 24				10f02								10 23
Warrington Central	a												09 29				09e57								10 28
Liverpool Lime Street 10	a						09 39	10 05					09 57				10e29	10 39					11 05		10 57

For general notes see front of timetable
For details of catering facilities see Directory of Train Operators

- **A** To Wigan Wallgate (Table 82)
- **B** To Brighouse (Table 41)
- **C** To Selby (Table 41)
- **D** Also stops at Cross Gates 0744
- **b** Change at Northallerton
- **c** Change at York
- **e** Change at Manchester Piccadilly
- **f** Change at Manchester Piccadilly and Manchester Oxford Road

Newcastle, Middlesbrough, Scarborough, York, Hull, Leeds and Wakefield → Huddersfield → Manchester, Manchester Airport and Liverpool

Network Diagram - see first page of Table 39

Station		NT	NT	TP	TP	NT	NT	TP	NT	NT	TP	NT	NT	TP	TP	NT	NT	TP	NT	NT	TP	NT	NT
				1 ◇	1 ◇			1 ◇			1 ◇			1 ◇	1 ◇			1 ◇			1 ◇		
		A				B						A				B						A	
				⚲	⚲			⚲			⚲			⚲	⚲			⚲			⚲		
Newcastle 8 ⛴	d			07 26				*07 52*			*08b24*			*08b40*				09 12			*09b35*		
Chester-le-Street	d			07 37							*08b33*							09 20					
Durham	d			07 43				*08 04*			*08b40*			*08b52*				09 27			*09b47*		
Middlesbrough	d													09 00									
Thornaby	d													09 05									
Yarm	d													09 13									
Darlington 7	d			08 00				*08 22*			*08b57*			*09b10*				09 45			*10b04*		
Northallerton	d			08 12										09 28				09 56					
Thirsk	d			08 20										09 36									
Scarborough	d										08 47										09 47		
Seamer	d										08 52										09 52		
Malton	d										09 10										10 10		
York 8	a			08 55							09 37			09 55				10 24			10 37		
	d			08 58				09 28			09 40			09 58				10 27			10 40		
Hull	d				08 38										09 38								
Brough	d				08 50										09 50								
Howden	d				*08 36*										*09 28*								
Selby	d				09 09										10 09								
South Milford	d																						
Garforth	d			09 13										10 13									
Leeds 10	a			09 23	09 35			09 53			10 04			10 23	10 37			10 53			11 04		
	d	09 13		09 25	09 40		09 43	09 55			10 10	10 13		10 25	10 40		10 43	10 55			11 10	11 13	
Cottingley	d						09 48										10 48						
Morley	d	09 21					09 52					10 21					10 52					11 21	
Batley	d	09 26					09 57					10 26					10 57					11 26	
Dewsbury	a	09 29		09 36			10 00	10 06				10 29		10 36			11 00	11 06				11 29	
	d	09 29		09 37			10 01	10 07				10 29		10 37			11 01	11 07				11 29	
Ravensthorpe	d						10 04										11 04						
Wakefield Westgate	d					09 29										10 29							
Wakefield Kirkgate	d					09 35			←							10 35			←				
Mirfield	d	09a35				09 51	10 08		10 08			10a35				10 51	11 08		11 08			11a35	
Deighton	d					09 57	→		10 14							10 58	→		11 14				
Huddersfield	a			09 45	09 57	10 04		10 15	10 21		10 27			10 45	10 57	11 04		11 15	11 21		11 27		
	d		09 32	09 46	09 58			10 16			10 28		10 32	10 46	10 58			11 16			11 28		11 32
Slaithwaite	d		09 39										10 39										11 39
Marsden	d		09 45										10 45										11 45
Greenfield	d		09 53										10 53										11 53
Mossley (Grtr Manchester)	d		09 57										10 57										11 57
Stalybridge	a		10 02								10 45		11 02								11 45		12 02
	d		10 03							10 42	10 46		11 03							11 42	11 46		12 03
Ashton-under-Lyne	d		10 07							10 46			11 07							11 46			12 07
Manchester Victoria ⛴	a		10 20							10 57			11 20							11 57			12 20
Manchester Piccadilly 10 ⛴	a			10 22	10 35			10 50			11 05			11 22	11 35			11 50			12 05		
	d			10 27				10 53			11 07			11 27				11 53			12 07		
Manchester Airport ✈	a			10 44	*11 01*			11 14			*11 40*			11 44	*12 01*			12 14			*12 40*		
Manchester Oxford Road	a			*10c40*	*10 47*						11 09			*11c40*	*11 47*						12 09		
Birchwood	a										11 23										12 23		
Warrington Central	a			*10c57*							11 28			*11c57*							12 28		
Liverpool Lime Street 10	a			*11c29*	*11 39*					12 05	11 57			*12c29*	*12 39*					13 05	12 57		

For general notes see front of timetable
For details of catering facilities see Directory of Train Operators

A To Hebden Bridge (Table 41)
B To Selby (Table 41)
b Change at York
c Change at Manchester Piccadilly

Newcastle, Middlesbrough, Scarborough, York, Hull, Leeds and Wakefield → Huddersfield → Manchester, Manchester Airport and Liverpool

Network Diagram - see first page of Table 39

		TP [1]◇	TP [1]◇	NT A	NT	TP [1]◇	NT	NT	TP [1]◇	NT B	NT	TP [1]◇	TP [1]◇	NT A	NT	TP [1]◇	NT	NT	TP [1]◇	NT B	NT	TP [1]◇	TP [1]◇
Newcastle [8]	d	09b40				10 15			10b25			10b40				11 15			11b30			11b59	
Chester-le-Street	d								10b34			10c50											
Durham	d	09b52				10 27			10b41			10e52				11 27			11b43			11b52	
Middlesbrough	d	09 59										11 00										12 00	
Thornaby	d	10 04										11 05										12 05	
Yarm	d	10 12										11 13										12 13	
Darlington [7]	d	10b10				10 44			10b58			11e10				11 44			12b02			12b10	
Northallerton	d	10 27				10 56						11 28				11 56						12 28	
Thirsk	d	10 35										11 36										12 36	
Scarborough	d								10 45										11 45				
Seamer	d								10 50										11 50				
Malton	d								11 08										12 08				
York [8]	a	10 54				11 24			11 37			11 55				12 21			12 35			12 55	
	d	10 58				11 28			11 39			11 58				12 28			12 38			12 58	
Hull	d		10 38										11 38										12 38
Brough	d		10 50										11 50										12 50
Howden	d		10 36																				
Selby	d		11 09										12 09										13 09
South Milford	d																						
Garforth	d	11 13										12 13										13 13	
Leeds [10]	a	11 23	11 33			11 53			12 05			12 23	12 33			12 51			13 04			13 23	13 33
	d	11 25	11 40		11 43	11 55			12 10	12 13		12 25	12 40		12 43	12 55			13 10	13 13		13 25	13 40
Cottingley	d				11 48										12 48								
Morley	d				11 52					12 21					12 52					13 21			
Batley	d				11 57					12 26					12 57					13 26			
Dewsbury	a	11 36			12 00	12 06				12 29		12 36			13 00	13 06				13 29		13 36	
	d	11 37			12 01	12 07				12 29		12 37			13 01	13 07				13 29		13 37	
Ravensthorpe	d				12 04										13 04								
Wakefield Westgate	d			11 29										12 29									
Wakefield Kirkgate	d			11 34			←							12 35			←						
Mirfield	d			11 49	12 08		12 08			12a35				12 50	13 08		13 08			13a35			
Deighton	d			11 57	→		12 15							12 57	→		13 14						
Huddersfield	a	11 45	11 58	12 04		12 15	12 21		12 27			12 45	12 57	13 04		13 15	13 21		13 27			13 45	13 57
	d	11 46	11 59			12 16			12 28		12 32	12 46	12 58			13 16			13 28		13 32	13 46	13 58
Slaithwaite	d										12 39										13 39		
Marsden	d										12 45										13 45		
Greenfield	d										12 53										13 53		
Mossley (Grtr Manchester)	d										12 57										13 57		
Stalybridge	a								12 45		13 02								13 45		14 02		
	d							12 42	12 46		13 03							13 42	13 46		14 03		
Ashton-under-Lyne	d							12 46			13 07							13 46			14 07		
Manchester Victoria	a							12 57			13 20							13 57			14 20		
Manchester Piccadilly [10]	a	12 22	12 35			12 50			13 05			13 22	13 35			13 50			14 05			14 22	14 35
	d	12 27				12 53			13 07			13 27				13 53			14 07			14 27	
Manchester Airport	a	12 51	13 01			13 14			13 40			13 44	14 01			14 14			14 40			14 44	15 01
Manchester Oxford Road	a	12f40	12 47						13 09			13f40	13 47						14 09			14f40	14 47
Birchwood	a								13 23										14 23				
Warrington Central	a	12f57							13 28			13f57							14 28			14f57	
Liverpool Lime Street [10]	a	13f29	13 39					14 05	13 57			14f29	14 39					15 05	14 57			15f29	15 39

For general notes see front of timetable
For details of catering facilities see Directory of Train Operators

A To Selby (Table 41)
B To Hebden Bridge (Table 41)
b Change at York
c From 8 September only. Change at York
e Change at York. From8 September dep. Durham 1056, Darlington 1111
f Change at Manchester Piccadilly

Newcastle, Middlesbrough, Scarborough, York, Hull, Leeds and Wakefield → Huddersfield → Manchester, Manchester Airport and Liverpool

Network Diagram - see first page of Table 39

		NT	NT	TP	NT	NT		TP	NT	NT	TP	TP	NT	NT	TP	NT		NT	TP	NT	NT	TP	TP	NT	NT
				1 ◇				1 ◇			1 ◇	1 ◇			1 ◇				1 ◇			1 ◇	1 ◇		
		A							B				A		C					B		D		A	
Newcastle 8	d			12 15				12b19			12b40				13 15				13b34			13c40			
Chester-le-Street	d							12b32																	
Durham	d			12 27				12b40			12b52				13 27				13b46			13e52			
Middlesbrough	d										12 50											13 50			
Thornaby	d										12 55											13 55			
Yarm	d										13 03											14 03			
Darlington 7	d			12 44				13b00			13b10				13 44				14b03			14f10			
Northallerton	d			12 56							13 18				13 56							14 18			
Thirsk	d										13 26				13 47							14 26			
Scarborough	d							12 47											13 47						
Seamer	d							12 52											13 52						
Malton	d							13 10											14 10						
York 8	a			13 24				13 37			13 49				14 22				14 37			14 48			
	d			13 28				13 40			13 58				14g28				14 40			14 58			
Hull	d											13 38											14 38		
Brough	d											13 50											14 50		
Howden	d											13 40													
Selby	d											14 09											15 09		
South Milford	d																								
Garforth	d										14 13											15 13			
Leeds 10	a			13 53				14 04			14 23	14 34			14 53				15 05			15 23	15 33		
	d		13 43	13 55				14 10	14 13		14 25	14 40		14 43	14 55				15 10	15 13		15 25	15 40		15 43
Cottingley	d		13 48											14 48											15 48
Morley	d		13 52						14 21					14 52						15 21					15 52
Batley	d		13 57						14 26					14 57						15 26					15 57
Dewsbury	a		14 00	14 06					14 29		14 36			15 00	15 06					15 29		15 36			16 00
	d		14 01	14 07					14 29		14 37			15 01	15 07					15 29		15 37			16 01
Ravensthorpe	d		14 04											15 04						15 32					16 04
Wakefield Westgate	d	13 29											14 29											15 29	
Wakefield Kirkgate	d	13 35			←								14 35			←								15 35	
Mirfield	d	13 51	14 08		14 08				14a35				14 51	15 08		15 08				15a36				15 51	16 08
Deighton	d	13 57	→		14 14								14 57	→		15 15								15 57	→
Huddersfield	a	14 04		14 15	14 21			14 27			14 45	14 57	15 04		15 15	15 21			15 27			15 45	15 57	16 04	
	d			14 16				14 28		14 32	14 46	14 58			15 16				15 28		15 32	15 46	15 58		
Slaithwaite	d									14 39											15 39				
Marsden	d									14 45											15 45				
Greenfield	d									14 53											15 53				
Mossley (Grtr Manchester)	d									14 57											15 57				
Stalybridge	a							14 45		15 02									15 45		16 02				
	d					14 42		14 46		15 03								15 42	15 46		16 03				
Ashton-under-Lyne	d					14 46				15 07								15 46			16 07				
Manchester Victoria	a					14 57				15 20								15 57			16 20				
Manchester Piccadilly 10	a			14 50				15 05			15 22	15 35			15 50				16 05			16 22	16 35		
	d			14 53				15 07			15 27				15 53				16 07			16 27			
Manchester Airport ✈	a			15 14				15 40			15 44	16 01			16 14				16 40			16 51			
Manchester Oxford Road	a							15 09			15h40	15 47							16 09			16h39	16 50		
Birchwood	a							15 23											16 23						
Warrington Central	a							15 28			15h57								16 28			16h57			
Liverpool Lime Street 10	a					16 05		15 57			16h27	16 39						17 04	16 57			17h27	17 38		

For general notes see front of timetable
For details of catering facilities see Directory of Train Operators

- **A** To Selby (Table 41)
- **B** To Hebden Bridge (Table 41)
- **C** Until 5 September
- **D** Also stops at Heald Green 1638
- **b** Change at York
- **c** Change at York. From 8 September dep. 1334
- **e** Change at York. From 8 September dep. 1346
- **f** Change at York. From 8 September dep. 1403
- **g** From 8 September dep. 1425
- **h** Change at Manchester Piccadilly

Newcastle, Middlesbrough, Scarborough, York, Hull, Leeds and Wakefield → Huddersfield → Manchester, Manchester Airport and Liverpool

Network Diagram - see first page of Table 39

		TP	NT		NT	TP	NT	NT	TP	TP	NT	NT	TP		NT	TP	NT	NT	TP	TP	NT	NT	NT	TP
		1 ◇			BHX	1 ◇			1 ◇	1 ◇			1 ◇			1 ◇			1 ◇	1 ◇				1 ◇
					C	D	E	G			H						E		J			K	L	N
		⚲				⚲			⚲	⚲			⚲			⚲			⚲	⚲				⚲
Newcastle 8 ⛴	d	14 12				14b22			14b40				15 12			15b30			15b40					16 06
Chester-le-Street	d					14b33							15 21											16 15
Durham	d	14 24				14b40			14b52				15 27			15b34			15b52					16 22
Middlesbrough	d								14 50										15 50					
Thornaby	d								14 55										15 55					
Yarm	d								15 03										16 03					
Darlington 7	d	14 44				14b57			15b10				15 44			16b02			16b10					16 39
Northallerton	d	14 56							15 18				15 56						16 18					16 51
Thirsk	d								15 26										16 26					17 01
Scarborough	d					14 47										15 47								
Seamer	d					14 52										15 52								
Malton	d					15 10										16 10								
York 8	a	15 25				15 37			15 51				16 20			16 37			16 51					17 27
	d	15c28				15 40			15 58				16 28			16 40			16 58					17 28
Hull	d									15 38										16 38				
Brough	d									15 50										16 50				
Howden	d									15 42										16 36				
Selby	d									16 09										17 09				
South Milford	d																							
Garforth	d								16 13										17 13					
Leeds 10	a	15 53				16 04			16 23	16 36			16 53			17 04			17 23	17 35				17 53
	d	15 55				16 10	16 13		16 25	16 40		16 43	16 55			17 10	17 13		17 25	17 40			17 43	17 55
Cottingley	d						16 18					16 48											17 48	
Morley	d						16 22					16 52					17 21						17 52	
Batley	d						16 27					16 57					17 26						17 57	
Dewsbury	a	16 06					16 30		16 36			17 00	17 06				17 29		17 36	17 51			18 00	18 06
	d	16 07					16 31		16 37			17 01	17 07				17 29		17 37	17 51			18 01	18 07
Ravensthorpe	d						16 34					17 04					17 32						18 04	
Wakefield Westgate	d										16 29											17 29		
Wakefield Kirkgate	d		←								16 35				←							17 35		
Mirfield	d		16 08				16a37				16 51	17 08			17 08		17a36					17 52	18 08	
Deighton	d		16 15								16 57	→			17 14							17 57	→	
Huddersfield	a	16 15	16 21			16 27			16 45	16 57	17 04		17 15		17 21	17 27			17 45	18 00		18 05		18 15
	d	16 16				16 28		16 32	16 46	16 58			17 16			17 28		17 32	17 46	18 01	18 05			18 16
Slaithwaite	d							16 39										17 39			18 12			
Marsden	d							16 45										17 45			18 17			
Greenfield	d							16 53										17 53			18 25			
Mossley (Grtr Manchester)	d							16 57										17 57			18 29			
Stalybridge	a					16 46		17 02	17 06							17 45		18 02	18 06		18 34			
	d				16 42	16 47		17 03	17 07							17 46		18 03	18 07		18 34			
Ashton-under-Lyne	d				16 46			17 07										18 07			18 38			
Manchester Victoria ⛴	a				16 57			17 21										18 20			18 52			
Manchester Piccadilly 10 ⛴	a	16 50				17 05			17 24	17 35			17 51			18 05			18 22	18 36				18 52
	d	16 53				17 07							17 58			18 07			18 27					18 55
Manchester Airport ✈	a	17 14				17 40				18 05			18 14			18 42			18 46	19 09				19 14
Manchester Oxford Road	a					17 09			17 39	17 47						18 09			18e39	18 51				
Birchwood	a					17 23			17 56							18 23								
Warrington Central	a					17 28			18 02							18 28			18e57					
Liverpool Lime Street 10	a					18 00			18 32	18 40						18 57			19e29	19 38				

For general notes see front of timetable
For details of catering facilities see Directory of Train Operators

C To Blackpool North (Table 82)
D Also stops at Hunts Cross 1740
E To Hebden Bridge (Table 41)
G To Wigan North Western (Table 82)
H To Selby (Table 41)
J Also stops at Heald Green 1840
K To Leeds (Table 41)
L To Sheffield (Table 34)
N Also stops at Heald Green 1907
b Change at York
c From 8 September dep. 1526
e Change at Manchester Piccadilly

Newcastle, Middlesbrough, Scarborough, York, Hull, Leeds and Wakefield → Huddersfield → Manchester, Manchester Airport and Liverpool

Network Diagram - see first page of Table 39

Station		NT		TP	TP	NT	NT	TP	NT	NT	NT	TP		NT	TP	TP	NT	NT	TP	NT	TP	TP		TP	NT
				1 ◇	1 ◇			1 ◇				1 ◇			1 ◇	1 ◇			1 ◇		1 ◇	1 ◇		1 ◇	
		A				B																			
					🛒			🛒				🛒			🛒										
Newcastle 8	d				16b27							17 10				17b32			17b40			18b20			
Chester-le-Street	d				16b42											17b26						18b29			
Durham	d				16b49							17 22				17b33			17b52			18b36			
Middlesbrough	d							16 50											17 50					19 00	
Thornaby	d							16 55											17 55					19 05	
Yarm	d							17 03											18 03					19 13	
Darlington 7	d				17b06							17 40				17b59						18b56			
Northallerton	d							17 18				17 51							18 18			18b51		19 28	
Thirsk	d							17 26				17 59							18 26			18b45		19 36	
Scarborough	d				16 47											17 45						18 46			
Seamer	d				16 52											17 50						18 51			
Malton	d				17 10											18 08						19 11			
York 8	a				17 37			17 50				18 24				18 35			18 51			19 36		19 59	
	d				17 40			17 58				18 28				18 38			19 10			19 39			
Hull	d			17 01											18 03						18 59				
Brough	d			17 13											18 15						19 11				
Howden	d														17 54										
Selby	d			17 32					18 02						18 34						19 30				
South Milford	d																								
Garforth	d							18 13											19 23						
Leeds 10	a			17 59	18 04			18 23	18 29			18 52			18 58	19 04			19 35		19 56	20 04			
	d			18 02	18 10	18 13		18 25			18 40	18 52			19 02	19 10		19 13	19 40			20 10			
Cottingley	d										18 45							19 18							
Morley	d					18 21					18 49							19 22							
Batley	d					18 26					18 54							19 27							
Dewsbury	a			18 13		18 29		18 36			18 57			←	19 13			19 30	19 50						
	d			18 13		18 29		18 37			18 58			18 58	19 13			19 31	19 51						
Ravensthorpe	d					18 32					→			19 01				19 34							
Wakefield Westgate	d									18 29										19 29					
Wakefield Kirkgate	d	←								18 35										19 35					
Mirfield	d	18 08				18a36				18 52				19 05				19 38		19 52					
Deighton	d	18 13								18 57				19 10				19 45		20 01					
Huddersfield	a	18 21		18 25	18 27			18 45		19 04		19 12		19 18	19 22	19 27		19 49	19 59	20 06		20 27			
	d				18 28		18 32	18 46				19 13			19 23	19 28	19 32		20 00			20 28			20 32
Slaithwaite	d						18 39										19 39								20 39
Marsden	d						18 45										19 45								20 45
Greenfield	d						18 53										19 53								20 53
Mossley (Grtr Manchester)	d						18 57										19 57								20 57
Stalybridge	a				18 45		19 02	19 06								19 46	20 02					20 45			21 02
	d				18 46		19 03	19 07								19 46	20 03					20 46			21 03
Ashton-under-Lyne	d						19 07										20 07								21 07
Manchester Victoria	a						19 21										20 20								21 20
Manchester Piccadilly 10	a				19 05			19 24				19 50			19 59	20 05			20 35			21 05			
	d				19 07							19 53				20 07			20 38			21 07			
Manchester Airport ✈	a				19 40			20 05				20 12							20 58			21 37			
Manchester Oxford Road	a				19 09			19 40								20 09			20c54			21 09			
Birchwood	a				19 23											20 23						21 23			
Warrington Central	a				19 28			19 57								20 28						21 28			
Liverpool Lime Street 10	a				19 57			20 29								20 55						21 55			

For general notes see front of timetable
For details of catering facilities see Directory of Train Operators

A To Sheffield (Table 34)
B To Hebden Bridge (Table 41)
b Change at York
c Change at Manchester Piccadilly

Newcastle, Middlesbrough, Scarborough, York, Hull, Leeds and Wakefield → Huddersfield → Manchester, Manchester Airport and Liverpool

Network Diagram - see first page of Table 39

		NT	TP	NT	TP	TP	NT	NT	TP	NT		TP	TP	NT	NT	TP	NT	TP	TP	NT		NT	TP	
			1 ◇		1 ◇	1 ◇			1 ◇			1 ◇	1 ◇			1 ◇		1 ◇	1 ◇				1 ◇	
																A								
			✕																					
Newcastle 8	d		18 58			19b25			19c40				20e38										21 47	
Chester-le-Street	d					19e36			19c36															
Durham	d		19 10			19e45			19e52				20e51										22 00	
Middlesbrough	d								20 00				20 50					21 40						
Thornaby	d								20 06				20 55					21 45						
Yarm	d												21 03											
Darlington 7	d		19 27			20b05			20 31				21e09					22 08					22 17	
Northallerton	d		19 39						20 42				21 18					22 19					22 29	
Thirsk	d		19 36						20 50									22 27						
Scarborough	d					19 47						20 37							22 07					
Seamer	d					19 52						20 42							22 12					
Malton	d					20 10						21 00							22 30					
York 8	a		20 03			20 37			21 10			21 28	21 42					22 52	22 57				23 04	
	d		20 10			20 40			21 10			21 30	21 45										23 07	
Hull	d				19 56											21 33								
Brough	d				20 08											21 45								
Howden	d				19 43																			
Selby	d				20 27											22 07								
South Milford	d				20 36											22 17								
Garforth	d																							
Leeds 10	a		20 35		20 57	21 04			21 36			22 18	22 08			22 35							23 33	
	d	20 13	20 40			21 10		21 13	21 40				22 10		22 13	22 40						23 13	23 35	
Cottingley	d	20 18						21 18							22 18							23 18		
Morley	d	20 22						21 22							22 22							23 22		
Batley	d	20 27						21 27							22 27							23 27		
Dewsbury	a	20 30	20 50					21 30	21 50						22 30	22 51						23 30	23 46	
	d	20 31	20 51					21 31	21 51						22 31	22 51						23 31	23 46	
Ravensthorpe	d	20 34						21 34							22 34							23 34		
Wakefield Westgate	d			20 29						21 29							22 42							
Wakefield Kirkgate	d			20 35						21 35							22 47							
Mirfield	d	20 38		20 51				21 38		21 48					22 38		23 03					23 38		
Deighton	d	20 44		21 00				21 45		22 00					22 44		23 10					23 45		
Huddersfield	a	20 51	20 59	21 05		21 27		21 49	21 59	22 04			22 27		22 52	23 00	23 15					23 49	23 55	
	d		21 00			21 28	21 32		22 00				22 28	22 32		23 00				23 22			23 56	
Slaithwaite	d						21 39							22 39						23 29				
Marsden	d						21 45							22 45						23 35				
Greenfield	d						21 53							22 53						23 43				
Mossley (Grtr Manchester)	d						21 57							22 57						23 47				
Stalybridge	a					21 45	22 02						22 45	23 02						23 52				
	d					21 46	22 03						22 46	23 03						23 53				
Ashton-under-Lyne	d						22 07							23 07						23 57				
Manchester Victoria	a						22 20							23 20						00 11				
Manchester Piccadilly 10	a		21 35			22 05			22 35				23 05			23 37							00 55	
	d		21 38			22 07			22 38														00 55	
Manchester Airport ✈	a		21 58			22 39			22 58				23 56			00 45							01 11	
Manchester Oxford Road	a		21f49			22 09			22f51				23 22											
Birchwood	a					22 24							23g54											
Warrington Central	a					22 29							00g01											
Liverpool Lime Street 10	a		22f41			22 55							00g38											

For general notes see front of timetable
For details of catering facilities see Directory of Train Operators

A Also stops at Gilberdyke 2152

b Change at York. From 8 September dep. Newcastle 1908, Darlington 1938

c Change at York. From 8 September dep. Newcastle 1937, Chester-le-Street 1946

e Change at York

f Change at Manchester Piccadilly

g Change at Manchester Piccadilly and Manchester Oxford Road

Table 39

Saturdays

Newcastle, Middlesbrough, Scarborough, York, Hull, Leeds and Wakefield → Huddersfield → Manchester, Manchester Airport and Liverpool

Network Diagram - see first page of Table 39

		TP	TP	TP	TP	TP	TP	TP	TP	NT	NT	TP	TP	NT	NT	TP	TP	NT	NT	TP	TP	NT	NT	TP	NT
		[1] ◇	[1] ◇	[1] ◇	[1] ◇	[1] ◇	[1] ◇	[1] ◇	[1] ◇			[1] ◇	[1] ◇			[1] ◇	[1] ◇			[1] ◇	[1] ◇			[1] ◇	
				A					B C	D	E				G			E				G			
									[trolley]								[trolley]							[trolley]	
Newcastle [8]	d																06 13								
Chester-le-Street	d																								
Durham	d																06 29								
Middlesbrough	d											05 58												07 21	
Thornaby	d											06 03												07 26	
Yarm	d											06 10												07 34	
Darlington [7]	d																06 46								
Northallerton	d											06 26					06 57							07 49	
Thirsk	d											06 33					07 06							07 57	
Scarborough	d															06 34				07 05					
Seamer	d															06 39				07 10					
Malton	d															06 57				07 28					
York [8]	a											06 52				07 24	07 31			07 55				08 19	
	d	02 00	03 00	04 17	05 26		05 58	06 28				06 58				07 28	07 40			07 58				08 25	
Hull	d								06 00				06 36								07 33				
Brough	d								06 12				06 48								07 45				
Howden	d								06 27												07 56				
Selby	d								06 38				07 07								08 07				
South Milford	d																								
Garforth	d						06 13					07 13								08 13					
Leeds [10]	a	02 33	03 33	04 45	05 52		06 23	06 53	07 05			07 23	07 35			07 52	08 04			08 23	08 37			08 50	
	d	02 35	03 35	04 47	05 55		06 25	06 55	07 10		07 13	07 25	07 38			07 55	08 10	08 13		08 25	08 40		08 43	08 55	
Cottingley	d																						08 48		
Morley	d										07 21							08 21					08 52		
Batley	d										07 26							08 26					08 57		
Dewsbury	a				06 05		06 36	07 06			07 29	07 36				08 06		08 29		08 36			09 00	09 06	
	d				06 06		06 37	07 07			07 29	07 37				08 07		08 29		08 37			09 01	09 07	
Ravensthorpe	d										07 32							08 32					09 04		
Wakefield Westgate	d														07 29							08 29			←
Wakefield Kirkgate	d														07 35							08 35			
Mirfield	d										07a36				07 50			08a36				08 51	09 08		09 08
Deighton	d														07 54							08 57	→		09 14
Huddersfield	a	02 56	03 56	05 27	06 14		06 45	07 15	07 27			07 45	07 56		08 02	08 15	08 27			08 45	08 57	09 04		09 15	09 21
	d	02 59	03 59	05 28	06 15		06 46	07 16	07 28	07 32		07 46	07 57	08 02		08 16	08 28		08 32	08 46	08 58			09 16	
Slaithwaite	d									07 39				08 09					08 39						
Marsden	d									07 45				08 15					08 45						
Greenfield	d									07 53				08 23					08 53						
Mossley (Grtr Manchester)	d									07 57				08 27					08 57						
Stalybridge	a				06 33		07 05	07 34	07 45	08 02		08 08	08 16	08 32			08 45		09 02						
	d				06 33		07 05	07 35	07 46	08 03		08 08	08 16	08 33			08 46		09 03						
Ashton-under-Lyne	d									08 07				08 37					09 07						
Manchester Victoria	a									08 20				08 50					09 20						
Manchester Piccadilly [10]	a	03 59	04 58	06 00	06 50		07 22	07 53	08 05			08 28	08 36			08 52	09 05			09 23	09 37			09 50	
	d	04 00	04 59	06 07	06 53	07 07	07 30	08 03	08 07			08 30				08 55	09 07			09 27				09 53	
Manchester Airport	a	04 15	05 19	06 29	07 12		07 48	08 22	*08 42*			08 51	*09 06*			09 20	*09 40*			09 44	*10 02*			10 14	
Manchester Oxford Road	a		*06b02*	*06b31*	*07b09*	07 09	*07b38*		08 09			*08b47*	*08 52*				09 09			*09b36*	*09 51*			*10b05*	
Birchwood	a		*06c56*			07 24			08 23								09 24			*10c02*					
Warrington Central	a		*07c03*			07 29	*07b54*		08 29								09 29			*09b57*					
Liverpool Lime Street [10]	a			*07b47*		07 57	*08b29*		08 57				*09 42*	10 05			09 57			*10b27*	*10 39*				

For general notes see front of timetable
For details of catering facilities see Directory of Train Operators

A Also stops at East Didsbury 0615, Gatley 0618 and Heald Green 0621
B Also stops at Gilberdyke 0620
C [trolley] from Leeds
D To Wigan Wallgate (Table 82)
E To Hebden Bridge (Table 41)
G To Selby (Table 41)
b Change at Manchester Piccadilly
c Change at Manchester Piccadilly and Manchester Oxford Road

Newcastle, Middlesbrough, Scarborough, York, Hull, Leeds and Wakefield → Huddersfield → Manchester, Manchester Airport and Liverpool

Network Diagram - see first page of Table 39

		NT		TP	NT	NT	TP	TP	NT	NT	TP	NT	NT	TP	NT	NT	TP	TP	NT	NT	TP	NT	NT	TP	NT
				1 ◇			1 ◇	1 ◇			1 ◇			1 ◇			1 ◇	1 ◇			1 ◇			1 ◇	
					A				B										B						A
				✠			✠				✠			✠			✠							✠	
Newcastle 8	d						07 33														09 12				
Chester-le-Street	d						07 42														09 21				
Durham	d						07 49														09 27				
Middlesbrough	d																09 00								
Thornaby	d																09 05								
Yarm	d																09 13								
Darlington 7	d						08 06														09 45				
Northallerton	d						08 17										09 28				09 55				
Thirsk	d						08 25										09 36								
Scarborough	d			07 47										08 47										09 47	
Seamer	d			07 52										08 52										09 52	
Malton	d			08 10										09 10										10 10	
York 8	a			08 37			08 53							09 37			09 56				10 21			10 37	
	d			08 40			08 58				09 28			09 40			09 58				10 28			10 40	
Hull	d							08 38										09 38							
Brough	d							08 50										09 50							
Howden	d																								
Selby	d							09 09										10 09							
South Milford	d																								
Garforth	d						09 13										10 13								
Leeds 10	a			09 04			09 23	09 35			09 53			10 04			10 23	10 37			10 53			11 04	
	d			09 10	09 13		09 25	09 40		09 43	09 55			10 10	10 13		10 25	10 40		10 43	10 55			11 10	11 13
Cottingley	d									09 48										10 48					
Morley	d				09 21					09 52					10 21					10 52					11 21
Batley	d				09 26					09 57					10 26					10 57					11 26
Dewsbury	a				09 29		09 36			10 00	10 06				10 29		10 36			11 00	11 06				11 29
	d				09 29		09 37			10 01	10 07				10 29		10 37			11 01	11 07				11 29
Ravensthorpe	d									10 04										11 04					
Wakefield Westgate	d								09 29										10 29						
Wakefield Kirkgate	d								09 35			←							10 35			←			
Mirfield	d				09a35				09 51	10 08		10 08			10a35				10 51	11 08		11 08			11a35
Deighton	d								09 57	→		10 14							10 58	→		11 14			
Huddersfield	a			09 27			09 45	09 57	10 04		10 15	10 21		10 27			10 45	10 57	11 04		11 15	11 21		11 27	
	d			09 28		09 32	09 46	09 58			10 16			10 28		10 32	10 46	10 58			11 16			11 28	
Slaithwaite	d					09 39										10 39									
Marsden	d					09 45										10 45									
Greenfield	d					09 53										10 53									
Mossley (Grtr Manchester)	d					09 57										10 57									
Stalybridge	a			09 45		10 02								10 45		11 02								11 45	
	d	09 42		09 46		10 03							10 42	10 46		11 03							11 42	11 46	
Ashton-under-Lyne	d	09 46				10 07							10 46			11 07							11 46		
Manchester Victoria ⇌	a	09 57				10 20							10 57			11 20							11 57		
Manchester Piccadilly 10 ⇌	a			10 05			10 22	10 35			10 50			11 05			11 22	11 35			11 50			12 05	
	d			10 07			10 27				10 53			11 07			11 27				11 53			12 07	
Manchester Airport ✈	a			*10 40*			10 44	*11 01*			11 14			*11 40*			11 44	*12 01*			12 14			*12 40*	
Manchester Oxford Road	a			10 09			*10b40*	*10 47*			*11c05*			11 09			*11b40*	*11 47*						12 09	
Birchwood	a			10 23										11 23										12 23	
Warrington Central	a			10 28			*10b57*							11 28			*11b57*							12 28	
Liverpool Lime Street 10	a	11 05		10 57			*11b29*	*11 39*					12 05	11 57			*12b29*	*12 39*					13 05	12 57	

For general notes see front of timetable
For details of catering facilities see Directory of Train Operators

A To Hebden Bridge (Table 41)
B To Selby (Table 41)
b Change at Manchester Piccadilly
c Until 6 September only

Newcastle, Middlesbrough, Scarborough, York, Hull, Leeds and Wakefield → Huddersfield → Manchester, Manchester Airport and Liverpool

Network Diagram - see first page of Table 39

		NT	TP	TP		TP	NT	NT	TP	NT	NT	TP	NT	NT	TP	TP	NT	NT	TP	TP	NT	NT	TP	NT	NT
			1 ◇	1 ◇		1 ◇			1 ◇			1 ◇			1 ◇	1 ◇			1 ◇	1 ◇			1 ◇		
						A	B						C				B			A				C	
			🛒						🛒			🛒			🛒	🛒			🛒						
Newcastle 8	d								10 12										11 15						
Chester-le-Street	d																								
Durham	d								10 27										11 27						
Middlesbrough	d		10 00												11 00										
Thornaby	d		10 05												11 05										
Yarm	d		10 13												11 13										
Darlington 7	d								10 44										11 44						
Northallerton	d		10 28						10 56						11 28				11 56						
Thirsk	d		10 36												11 36										
Scarborough	d					10 30						10 45								11 37			11 47		
Seamer	d											10 50											11 52		
Malton	d											11 08											12 10		
York 8	a		10 54			11 16			11 22			11 35			11 54				12 20	12 23			12 37		
	d		10 58						11 28			11 40			11 58				12 28				12 40		
Hull	d			10 38												11 38									
Brough	d			10 50												11 50									
Howden	d																								
Selby	d			11 09												12 09									
South Milford	d																								
Garforth	d		11 13												12 13										
Leeds 10	a		11 23	11 33					11 53			12 04			12 23	12 33			12 53				13 04		
	d		11 25	11 40				11 43	11 55			12 10	12 13		12 25	12 40		12 43	12 55				13 10	13 13	
Cottingley	d							11 48										12 48							
Morley	d							11 52					12 21					12 52						13 21	
Batley	d							11 57					12 26					12 57						13 26	
Dewsbury	a		11 36					12 00	12 06				12 29		12 36			13 00	13 06					13 29	
	d		11 37					12 01	12 07				12 29		12 37			13 01	13 07					13 29	
Ravensthorpe	d							12 04										13 04							
Wakefield Westgate	d						11 29										12 29								
Wakefield Kirkgate	d						11 35			←							12 35				←				
Mirfield	d						11 51	12 08		12 08			12a35				12 51	13 08			13 08			13a35	
Deighton	d						11 57	→		12 14							12 57	→			13 14				
Huddersfield	a		11 45	11 58			12 04		12 15	12 21		12 27			12 45	12 57	13 04		13 15		13 21		13 27		
	d	11 32	11 46	11 59					12 16			12 28		12 32	12 46	12 58			13 16				13 28		13 32
Slaithwaite	d	11 39												12 39											13 39
Marsden	d	11 45												12 45											13 45
Greenfield	d	11 53												12 53											13 53
Mossley (Grtr Manchester)	d	11 57												12 57											13 57
Stalybridge	a	12 02										12 45		13 02									13 45		14 02
	d	12 03									12 42	12 46		13 03								13 42	13 46		14 03
Ashton-under-Lyne	d	12 07									12 46			13 07								13 46			14 07
Manchester Victoria	a	12 20									12 57			13 20								13 57			14 20
Manchester Piccadilly 10	a		12 22	12 35					12 50			13 05			13 22	13 35			13 50				14 05		
	d		12 27						12 53			13 07			13 27				13 53				14 07		
Manchester Airport ✈	a		12 51	*13 01*					13 14			*13 40*			13 44	*14 01*			14 14				*14 40*		
Manchester Oxford Road	a		*12c40*	*12 47*								13 09			*13c40*	*13 47*							14 09		
Birchwood	a											13 23											14 23		
Warrington Central	a		*12c57*									13 28			*13c57*								14 28		
Liverpool Lime Street 10	a		*13c27*	*13 39*							14 05	13 57			*14c27*	*14 39*						15 05	14 57		

For general notes see front of timetable
For details of catering facilities see Directory of Train Operators

A 19 July to 6 September
B To Selby (Table 41)
C To Hebden Bridge (Table 41)

c Change at Manchester Piccadilly

Table 39

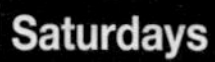

Newcastle, Middlesbrough, Scarborough, York, Hull, Leeds and Wakefield → Huddersfield → Manchester, Manchester Airport and Liverpool

Network Diagram - see first page of Table 39

		TP	TP	NT	NT	TP		NT	NT	TP	NT	NT	TP	TP	NT	NT	TP	NT	NT	TP	NT	NT	TP	TP	NT
		1 ◇	1 ◇			1 ◇				1 ◇			1 ◇	1 ◇			1 ◇			1 ◇			1 ◇	1 ◇	
				A							B				A						B		C		A
		🛒				🛒							🛒				🛒			🛒			🛒		
Newcastle 8	d					12 15											13 15								
Chester-le-Street	d																								
Durham	d					12 27											13 27								
Middlesbrough	d	12 00											12 50										14 00		
Thornaby	d	12 05											12 55										14 05		
Yarm	d	12 13											13 03										14 13		
Darlington 7	d					12 44											13 44								
Northallerton	d	12 28				12 56							13 18				13 56						14 28		
Thirsk	d	12 36											13 26										14 36		
Scarborough	d									12 47										13 45					
Seamer	d									12 52										13 50					
Malton	d									13 10										14 08					
York 8	a	12 55				13 20				13 37			13 49				14 20			14 35			14 54		
	d	12 58				13 28				13 40			13 58				14 28			14 38			14 58		
Hull	d		12 38											13 38										14 38	
Brough	d		12 50											13 50										14 50	
Howden	d																								
Selby	d		13 09											14 09										15 09	
South Milford	d																								
Garforth	d	13 13											14 13										15 13		
Leeds 10	a	13 23	13 33			13 53				14 04			14 23	14 33			14 53			15 04			15 23	15 33	
	d	13 25	13 40		13 43	13 55				14 10	14 13		14 25	14 40		14 43	14 55			15 10	15 13		15 25	15 40	
Cottingley	d				13 48											14 48									
Morley	d				13 52						14 21					14 52					15 21				
Batley	d				13 57						14 26					14 57					15 26				
Dewsbury	a	13 36			14 00	14 06					14 29		14 36			15 00	15 06				15 29		15 36		
	d	13 37			14 01	14 07					14 29		14 37			15 01	15 07				15 29		15 37		
Ravensthorpe	d				14 04											15 04					15 32				
Wakefield Westgate	d			13 29											14 29										15 29
Wakefield Kirkgate	d			13 35				←							14 35			←							15 35
Mirfield	d			13 51	14 08			14 08			14a35				14 51	15 08		15 08			15a36				15 51
Deighton	d			13 57	→			14 14							14 57	→		15 14							15 57
Huddersfield	a	13 45	13 57	14 04		14 15		14 21		14 27			14 45	14 57	15 04		15 15	15 21		15 27			15 45	15 57	16 04
	d	13 46	13 58			14 16				14 28		14 32	14 46	14 58			15 16			15 28		15 32	15 46	15 58	
Slaithwaite	d											14 39										15 39			
Marsden	d											14 45										15 45			
Greenfield	d											14 53										15 53			
Mossley (Grtr Manchester)	d											14 57										15 57			
Stalybridge	a									14 45		15 02								15 45		16 02			
	d								14 42	14 46		15 03							15 42	15 46		16 03			
Ashton-under-Lyne	d								14 46			15 07							15 46			16 07			
Manchester Victoria	a								14 57			15 20							15 57			16 20			
Manchester Piccadilly 10	a	14 22	14 37			14 50				15 05			15 22	15 35			15 50			16 05			16 22	16 35	
	d	14 27				14 53				15 07			15 27				15 53			16 07			16 27		
Manchester Airport ✈	a	14 44	*15 01*			15 14				*15 40*			15 44	*16 01*			16 14			*16 40*			16 51		
Manchester Oxford Road	a	*14b40*	*14 51*							15 09			*15b40*	*15 47*						16 09			*16b40*	*16 50*	
Birchwood	a									15 23										16 23					
Warrington Central	a	*14b57*								15 28			*15b57*							16 28			*16b57*		
Liverpool Lime Street 10	a	*15b25*	*15 39*						16 05	15 57			*16b29*	*16 39*					17 04	16 57			*17b29*	*17 38*	

For general notes see front of timetable
For details of catering facilities see Directory of Train Operators

A To Selby (Table 41)
B To Hebden Bridge (Table 41)
C Also stops at Heald Green 1638

b Change at Manchester Piccadilly

Table 39

Saturdays

Newcastle, Middlesbrough, Scarborough, York, Hull, Leeds and Wakefield → Huddersfield → Manchester, Manchester Airport and Liverpool

Network Diagram - see first page of Table 39

		NT	TP 1◇ ⊼	NT	NT A	TP 1◇ B ⊼	NT C	NT D		TP 1◇ ⊼	TP 1◇ ⊼	NT	NT E	NT	TP 1◇ ⊼	NT	NT	TP 1◇ ⊼	NT C	NT	TP 1◇ G ⊼	TP 1◇	NT H	NT	TP 1◇ J ⊼
Newcastle 8	d		14 15												15 09										16 06
Chester-le-Street	d														15 18										16 15
Durham	d		14 27												15 25										16 22
Middlesbrough	d									14 50											15 50				
Thornaby	d									14 55											15 55				
Yarm	d									15 03											16 03				
Darlington 7	d		14 44												15 42										16 39
Northallerton	d		14 56							15 18					15 53						16 18				16 50
Thirsk	d									15 26											16 26				16 58
Scarborough	d					14 45												15 47							
Seamer	d					14 50												15 52							
Malton	d					15 08												16 10							
York 8	a		15 21			15 35				15 52					16 20			16 37			16 49				17 18
	d		15 28			15 39				15 58					16 28			16 40			16 58				17 28
Hull	d										15 38											16 38			
Brough	d										15 50											16 50			
Howden	d																								
Selby	d										16 09											17 09			
South Milford	d																								
Garforth	d									16 13											17 13				
Leeds 10	a		15 52			16 04				16 23	16 36				16 53			17 04			17 23	17 35			17 53
	d	15 43	15 55			16 10	16 13			16 25	16 40			16 43	16 55			17 10	17 13		17 25	17 40		17 43	17 55
Cottingley	d	15 48												16 48										17 48	
Morley	d	15 52					16 21							16 52					17 21					17 52	
Batley	d	15 57					16 26							16 57					17 26					17 57	
Dewsbury	a	16 00	16 06				16 29			16 36				17 00	17 06				17 29		17 36	17 51		18 00	18 06
	d	16 01	16 07				16 29			16 37				17 01	17 07				17 29		17 37	17 51		18 01	18 07
Ravensthorpe	d	16 04					16 32							17 04					17 32					18 04	
Wakefield Westgate	d												16 29										17 29		
Wakefield Kirkgate	d			←									16 35			←							17 35		
Mirfield	d	16 08		16 08			16a36						16 51	17 08		17 08			17a36				17 52	18 08	
Deighton	d	→		16 15									16 57	→		17 14							17 57	→	
Huddersfield	a		16 15	16 21		16 27				16 45	16 57		17 05		17 15	17 21		17 27			17 45	18 00	18 05		18 15
	d		16 16			16 28		16 32		16 46	16 58	17 04			17 16			17 28		17 32	17 46	18 01			18 16
Slaithwaite	d							16 39				17 11								17 39					
Marsden	d							16 45				17a17								17 45					
Greenfield	d							16 53												17 53					
Mossley (Grtr Manchester)	d							16 57												17 57					
Stalybridge	a					16 45		17 02		17 06								17 45		18 02	18 06				
	d				16 28	16 46		17 03		17 07							17 41	17 46		18 03	18 07				
Ashton-under-Lyne	d				16 32			17 07									17 45			18 07					
Manchester Victoria	a				16 42			17 21									17 59			18 20					
Manchester Piccadilly 10	a		16 50			17 05				17 24	17 35				17 52			18 05			18 22	18 35			18 52
	d		16 53			17 07									17 58			18 07			18 27				18 55
Manchester Airport	a		17 11			*17 40*					18b05				18 14			*18 42*			18 46	*19 08*			19 14
Manchester Oxford Road	a					17 09				*17 39*	17 47							18 09			18c39	18 47			
Birchwood	a					17 23				*17 56*								18 23							
Warrington Central	a					17 28				*18 02*								18 28			18c57				
Liverpool Lime Street 10	a					18 00				*18 32*	*18 40*						19 05	18 57			19c29	*19 38*			

For general notes see front of timetable
For details of catering facilities see Directory of Train Operators

A To Southport (Table 82)
B Also stops at Hunts Cross 1740
C To Hebden Bridge (Table 41)
D To Wigan Wallgate (Table 82)
E To Selby (Table 41)
G Also stops at Heald Green 1840
H To York (Table 41)
J Also stops at Heald Green 1907
b From 13 September arr. 1801
c Change at Manchester Piccadilly

Table 39

Saturdays

Newcastle, Middlesbrough, Scarborough, York, Hull, Leeds and Wakefield → Huddersfield → Manchester, Manchester Airport and Liverpool

Network Diagram - see first page of Table 39

Station		NT	TP 1 ◇	NT	TP 1 ◇	EM 1 ◇	NT	NT	TP 1 ◇	NT		NT	TP 1 ◇	NT	TP 1 ◇	TP 1 ◇	NT	NT	TP 1 ◇	NT	TP 1 ◇	TP 1 ◇	TP 1 ◇	NT	NT
						A 🍴	B																		
Newcastle 8 ⛴	d												17 10												
Chester-le-Street	d																								
Durham	d												17 22												
Middlesbrough	d								17 00										18 07				19 00		
Thornaby	d								17 06										18 12				19 05		
Yarm	d								17 13										18 20				19 13		
Darlington 7	d												17 39												
Northallerton	d								17 28				17 51						18 35				19 28		
Thirsk	d								17 36				17 59						18 43				19 36		
Scarborough	d				16 47	17 03										17 45						18 45			
Seamer	d				16 52											17 50						18 51			
Malton	d				17 10											18 08						19 09			
York 8	a				17 37	17 46			17 55				18 24			18 36			19 04			19 36	19 59		
	d				17 40				17 58				18 28			18 38			19 10			19 38			
Hull	d		17 00												18 03						19 00				
Brough	d		17 12												18 15						19 12				
Howden	d																								
Selby	d		17 31												18 34						19 31				
South Milford	d																								
Garforth	d								18 13										19 23						
Leeds 10	a		17 59		18 04				18 23				18 52		18 58	19 04			19 35		19 56	20 04			
	d		18 02		18 10		18 13		18 25			18 40	18 52		19 02	19 10		19 13	19 40			20 10			20 13
Cottingley	d											18 45						19 18							20 18
Morley	d						18 21					18 49						19 22							20 22
Batley	d						18 26					18 54						19 27							20 27
Dewsbury	a		18 13				18 29		18 36			18 57		←	19 13			19 30	19 50						20 30
	d		18 13				18 29		18 37			18 58 →		18 58	19 13			19 31	19 51						20 31
Ravensthorpe	d						18 32							19 01				19 34							20 34
Wakefield Westgate	d									18 29										19 29					
Wakefield Kirkgate	d	←								18 35										19 35					
Mirfield	d	18 08					18a36			18 52				19 05				19 38		19 52					20 38
Deighton	d	18 13								18 57				19 10				19 45		20 01					20 44
Huddersfield	a	18 21	18 25		18 27				18 45	19 04			19 12	19 18	19 22	19 27		19 49	19 59	20 06		20 27			20 48
	d				18 28			18 32	18 46				19 13		19 23	19 28	19 32		20 00			20 28		20 32	20 48
Slaithwaite	d							18 39									19 39							20 39	20 55
Marsden	d							18 45									19 45							20 45	21a02
Greenfield	d							18 53									19 53							20 53	
Mossley (Grtr Manchester)	d							18 57									19 57							20 57	
Stalybridge	a				18 45			19 02	19 06							19 46	20 02					20 45		21 02	
	d			18 41	18 46			19 03	19 07							19 46	20 03					20 46		21 03	
Ashton-under-Lyne	d			18 45				19 07									20 07							21 07	
Manchester Victoria ⛴	a			18 59				19 21									20 20							21 20	
Manchester Piccadilly 10 ⛴	a				19 05				19 23				19 50		19 59	20 05			20 35			21 05			
	d				19 07								19 53			20 07			20 38			21 07			
Manchester Airport ✈	a				*19 40*				*20 05*				20 12						20 58			*21 37*			
Manchester Oxford Road	a				19 09				*19 35*							20 09			*20b54*			21 09			
Birchwood	a				19 23				*20c11*							20 23						21 23			
Warrington Central	a				19 28				*20c17*							20 28						21 28			
Liverpool Lime Street 10	a			20 05	19 57				*20 38*							20 55						21 55			

For general notes see front of timetable
For details of catering facilities see Directory of Train Operators

- **A** Until 6 September. To St Pancras International (Table 53)
- **B** To Hebden Bridge (Table 41)
- **b** Change at Manchester Piccadilly
- **c** Change at Manchester Piccadilly and Manchester Oxford Road

Table 39

Saturdays

Newcastle, Middlesbrough, Scarborough, York, Hull, Leeds and Wakefield → Huddersfield → Manchester, Manchester Airport and Liverpool

Network Diagram - see first page of Table 39

		TP	NT	TP	TP	NT	NT	TP	TP	NT	TP	NT	NT	TP	NT	TP	NT	NT	NT	TP	TP	TP	TP
		1◇		1◇	1◇			1◇	1◇		1◇			1◇		1◇				1◇	1◇	1◇	
														A				B	C	B	C	B	B 🚌
Newcastle 8 🚢	d	18 52																					
Chester-le-Street	d																						
Durham	d	19 04																					
Middlesbrough	d							20 10			20 50										21 50	21 50	
Thornaby	d							20 15			20 55										21 55	21 55	
Yarm	d							20 23			21 03												
Darlington 7	d	19 22																			22 19	22 19	
Northallerton	d	19 36						20 38			21 17										22 30	22 30	
Thirsk	d							20 46			21 25										22 38	22 38	
Scarborough	d				19 47				20 37							22 07							
Seamer	d				19 52				20 42							22 12							
Malton	d				20 10				21 00							22 30							
York 8	a	20 02			20 37			21 07	21 28		21 42					22 57					22 57	22 57	
	d	20 10			20 40			21 10			21 45										23 07	23 07	
Hull	d			19 56										21 33									
Brough	d			20 08										21 45									
Howden	d																						
Selby	d			20 27										22 07									
South Milford	d			20 36										22 17									
Garforth	d																						
Leeds 10	a	20 33		20 59	21 04			21 33			22 08			22 35							23 33	23 33	
	d	20 40			21 10		21 13	21 40			22 10		22 13	22 40				23 05	23 13		23 35		23 45
Cottingley	d						21 18						22 18					23 10	23 18				
Morley	d						21 22						22 22					23 14	23 22				
Batley	d						21 27						22 27					23 19	23 27				
Dewsbury	a	20 50					21 30	21 50					22 30	22 51				23 22	23 30		23 46		00 05
	d	20 51					21 31	21 51					22 31	22 51				23 23	23 31		23 46		00 05
Ravensthorpe	d						21 34						22 34					23 26	23 34				
Wakefield Westgate	d		20 29							21 29					22 42								
Wakefield Kirkgate	d		20 35							21 35					22 47								
Mirfield	d		20 51				21 38			21 48			22 38		23 00			23 30	23 38				
Deighton	d		21 01				21 45			22 01			22 44		23 08			23 37	23 45				
Huddersfield	a	20 59	21 05		21 27		21 49	21 59		22 05	22 27		22 52	23 00	23 12			23 41	23 49		23 55		00 30
	d	21 00			21 28	21 32		22 00			22 28	22 32		23 00			23 22			23 54	23 56		00 30
Slaithwaite	d					21 39						22 39					23 29						
Marsden	d					21 45						22 45					23 35						
Greenfield	d					21 53						22 53					23 43						
Mossley (Grtr Manchester)	d					21 57						22 57					23 47						
Stalybridge	a				21 45	22 02					22 45	23 02					23 52						
	d				21 46	22 03					22 46	23 03					23 53						
Ashton-under-Lyne	d					22 07						23 07					23 57						
Manchester Victoria 🚢	a					22 20						23 20					00 11			00 42			
Manchester Piccadilly 10 🚢	a	21 35			22 05			22 35			23 05			23 37						00 58	00 29		02 00
	d	21 38			22 07			22 38												00 59	00 38		
Manchester Airport ✈	a	21 58			22 39			22 58			23 56			00 45						01 14	00 57		01 30
Manchester Oxford Road	a	21b48			22 09			22b51			23c22												
Birchwood	a				22 23			23e47															
Warrington Central	a				22 28			23e54															
Liverpool Lime Street 10	a	22b41			22 57			00f31															

For general notes see front of timetable
For details of catering facilities see Directory of Train Operators

A Also stops at Gilberdyke 2152

B From 13 September

C Until 6 September

b Change at Manchester Piccadilly

c Until 6 September only

e Change at Manchester Piccadilly and Manchester Oxford Road. From 13 September arr. 5 minutes earlier

f Change at Manchester Piccadilly and Manchester Oxford Road

Table 39

Sundays

until 13 July

Newcastle, Middlesbrough, Scarborough, York, Hull and Leeds → Huddersfield → Manchester, Manchester Airport and Liverpool

Network Diagram - see first page of Table 39

		TP 1◇	TP 1◇	TP 1◇	TP 1◇	TP 1◇	TP 1◇		NT	NT	TP 1	TP 1◇	TP 1◇	TP 1◇		TP 1◇	NT	NT	TP 1◇	TP 1◇	TP 1◇		TP 1◇	TP 1◇	NT
Newcastle 8	d																		09 33					11 03	
Chester-le-Street	d																		09 42						
Durham	d																		09 49					11 16	
Middlesbrough	d																			10 15					
Thornaby	d																			10 20					
Yarm	d																			10 28					
Darlington 7	d																		10 06					11 33	
Northallerton	d																		10 17	10 42				11 45	
Thirsk	d																			10 50					
Scarborough	d															09 20							10 45		
Seamer	d															09 25							10 50		
Malton	d															09 43							11 08		
York 8	a															10 10			10 41	11 09			11 35	12 12	
	d	02 09	03 09	04 09	05 05	06 05	07 46				08 15		09 15			10 15			10 45	11 15			11 40	12 15	
Hull	d													09 05							11 01				
Brough	d													09 17							11 13				
Howden	d																								
Selby	d													09 36							11 32				
South Milford	d													09 46							11 41				
Garforth	d																						11 57		
Leeds 10	a	02 58	04 00	04 59	05 55	06 55	08 38				08 47		09 38	10 03		10 38			11 08	11 38	12 01		12 07	12 38	
	d	03 00	04 00	05 00	05 55	06 55	08 40			08 44		09 10	09 40	10 10		10 40		10 44	11 10	11 40	12 02		12 10	12 40	
Cottingley	d									08 49								10 49							
Morley	d									08 53								10 53							
Batley	d									08 58								10 58							
Dewsbury	a				06 06	07 06	08 51			09 01			09 51			10 51		11 01		11 51				12 51	
	d				06 07	07 07	08 51			09 02			09 51			10 51		11 02		11 51				12 51	
Ravensthorpe	d									09 05								11 05							
Mirfield	d									09 09								11 09							
Deighton	d									09 15								11 15							
Huddersfield	a	03 16	04 16	05 16	06 16	07 16	09 00			09 19		09 27	10 00	10 27		11 00		11 19	11 27	12 00	12 19		12 27	13 00	
	d	03 17	04 17	05 17	06 17	07 17	09 01		09 07	09 19		09 28	10 01	10 28		11 01	11 09	11 19	11 28	12 01	12 20		12 28	13 01	13 09
Slaithwaite	d								09 14	09 26							11 16	11 26							13 16
Marsden	d								09 20	09a33							11 22	11a33							13 22
Greenfield	d								09 28								11 30								13 30
Mossley (Grtr Manchester)	d								09 32								11 34								13 34
Stalybridge	a				06 34	07 34	09 18		09 37			09 46		10 46			11 39		11 46				12 46		13 39
	d				06 35	07 35	09 19		09 38			09 46		10 46			11 40		11 46				12 46		13 40
Ashton-under-Lyne	d								09 42								11 44								13 44
Manchester Victoria	a								09 56								11 58								13 58
	d																								
Manchester Piccadilly 10	a	04 02	05 05	06 04	07 04	08 04	09 34					10 05	10 34	11 05		11 33			12 05	12 33	12 57		13 05	13 33	
	d	04 05	05 05	06 05	07 05	08 05	09 39					10 07	10 42	11 07		11 39			12 07	12 39			13 07	13 40	
Manchester Airport	a	04 21	05 21	06 21	07 21	08 26	09 58					*10 33*	11 04	*11 33*		11 58			*12 33*	12 58			*13 33*	13 58	
Manchester Oxford Road	a											10 09		11 09					12 09				13 09		
Newton-le-Willows	a																								
Birchwood	a				*08b20*	*09b34*						10 23		11 23					12 23				13 23		
Warrington Central	a				*08b25*	*09b39*						10 28		11 28					12 28				13 28		
Liverpool Lime Street 10	a				*09b20*	*10b20*						10 57		11 57					12 57				13 57		

For general notes see front of timetable
For details of catering facilities see Directory of Train Operators

b Change at Manchester Piccadilly and Manchester Oxford Road

Table 39

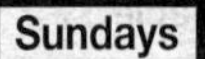

Sundays

until 13 July

Newcastle, Middlesbrough, Scarborough, York, Hull and Leeds → Huddersfield → Manchester, Manchester Airport and Liverpool

Network Diagram - see first page of Table 39

		NT	TP 1 ◇	TP 1 ◇	TP 1 ◇	TP 1 ◇		TP 1 ◇	TP 1 ◇	NT	NT	TP 1 ◇	TP 1 ◇		TP 1 ◇	TP 1 ◇	TP 1 ◇	NT	NT	TP 1 ◇		TP 1 ◇	TP 1 ◇	TP 1 ◇	TP 1 ◇
Newcastle 8	d								12 49				14 10				14 57						16 08		
Chester-le-Street	d								12 58																
Durham	d								13 05				14 22				15 09						16 20		
Middlesbrough	d				12 15							13 45										15 45			
Thornaby	d				12 20							13 50										15 50			
Yarm	d				12 28							13 58										15 58			
Darlington 7	d								13 22				14 39				15 26						16 38		
Northallerton	d				12 42				13 34			14 12					15 38					16 12			
Thirsk	d				12 50							14 20										16 20			
Scarborough	d		11 45					12 45								14 45				15 45					16 45
Seamer	d							12 50								14 50									16 50
Malton	d							13 08								15 08									17 08
York 8	a		12 30		13 12			13 35	14 11			14 40	15 13			15 35	16 12			16 30		16 41	17 12		17 35
	d			12 45	13 15			13 42	14 15			14 45	15 15			15 37	16 15					16 45	17 14		17 42
Hull	d					12 50									14 50									16 50	
Brough	d					13 02									15 02									17 02	
Howden	d																								
Selby	d					13 21									15 21									17 21	
South Milford	d					13 31									15 31									17 30	
Garforth	d							13 57								15 57									17 57
Leeds 10	a			13 08	13 38	13 49		14 07	14 38			15 08	15 39		15 49	16 07	16 38					17 08	17 37	17 48	18 07
	d	12 44		13 10	13 40	13 58		14 10	14 40		14 44	15 10	15 40		15 57	16 10	16 40		16 44			17 10	17 40	17 57	18 10
Cottingley	d	12 49									14 49								16 49						
Morley	d	12 53									14 53								16 53						
Batley	d	12 58									14 58								16 58						
Dewsbury	a	13 01			13 51				14 51		15 01		15 51				16 51		17 01				17 50		
	d	13 02			13 51				14 51		15 02		15 51				16 51		17 02				17 51		
Ravensthorpe	d	13 05									15 05								17 05						
Mirfield	d	13 09									15 09								17 09						
Deighton	d	13 15									15 15								17 15						
Huddersfield	a	13 19		13 27	14 00	14 15		14 27	15 00		15 19	15 27	16 01		16 14	16 27	17 00		17 19			17 27	17 59	18 14	18 27
	d	13 19		13 28	14 01	14 16		14 28	15 01	15 09	15 19	15 28	16 01		16 15	16 28	17 01	17 09	17 19			17 28	18 01	18 15	18 28
Slaithwaite	d	13 26								15 16	15 26							17 16	17 26						
Marsden	d	13a33								15 22	15a33							17 22	17a33						
Greenfield	d									15 30								17 30							
Mossley (Grtr Manchester)	d									15 34								17 34							
Stalybridge	a			13 46				14 45		15 39		15 46				16 45		17 39				17 46			18 45
	d			13 46				14 46		15 40		15 46				16 46		17 40				17 46			18 46
Ashton-under-Lyne	d									15 44								17 44							
Manchester Victoria	a									15 58								17 58							
	d																								
Manchester Piccadilly 10	a			14 05	14 33	14 52		15 05	15 33			16 05	16 34		16 50	17 05	17 33					18 05	18 33	18 52	19 05
	d			14 07	14 37			15 07	15 39			16 07	16 39			17 07	17 39					18 07	18 39		19 07
Manchester Airport	a			*14 33*	14 58	*15 18*		*15 33*	15 58			*16 33*	16 58		*17 18*	*17 33*	17 58					*18 33*	18 58		*19 33*
Manchester Oxford Road	a			14 09				15 09				16 09				17 09						18 09			19 09
Newton-le-Willows	a																								
Birchwood	a			14 23				15 23				16 23				17 23						18 23			19 24
Warrington Central	a			14 28				15 28				16 28				17 28						18 28			19 29
Liverpool Lime Street 10	a			14 57				15 57				16 57				17 57						18 57			19 57

For general notes see front of timetable
For details of catering facilities see
Directory of Train Operators

Table 39

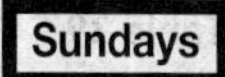

Newcastle, Middlesbrough, Scarborough, York, Hull and Leeds → Huddersfield → Manchester, Manchester Airport and Liverpool

until 13 July

Network Diagram - see first page of Table 39

		TP	NT	NT	TP		TP	TP	TP	TP	TP	NT		NT	TP	TP	TP	TP	TP		NT	TP	TP		
		1 ◇			1 ◇		1 ◇	1 ◇	1 ◇	1 ◇	1 ◇				1 ◇	1 ◇	1 ◇	1 ◇	1 ◇			1 ◇	1 ◇		
Newcastle 8	d	16 48							17 57							19 20									
Chester-le-Street	d	16 57																							
Durham	d	17 04							18 09							19 32									
Middlesbrough	d						17 45										20 15						22 07		
Thornaby	d						17 50										20 20						22 12		
Yarm	d						17 58										20 28						22 20		
Darlington 7	d	17 21							18 26							19 49									
Northallerton	d	17 32					18 12									20 01	20 42						22 34		
Thirsk	d						18 20										20 50						22 42		
Scarborough	d				17 45						18 45				19 45				20 45			21 45			
Seamer	d										18 50								20 50			21 50			
Malton	d										19 08								21 08			22 08			
York 8	a	17 59			18 30		18 39		18 59		19 35				20 30	20 31	21 09		21 35			22 35	23 09		
	d	18 15					18 45		19 15		19 42					20 45	21 15		21 38			22 42	23 12		
Hull	d							18 10		19 04								21 00							
Brough	d							18 22		19 16								21 12							
Howden	d																								
Selby	d							18 41		19 35								21 31							
South Milford	d							18 53										21 40							
Garforth	d										19 57								21 54						
Leeds 10	a	18 38					19 08	19 12	19 38	19 59	20 07					21 08	21 38	22 00	22 04			23 08	23 38		
	d	18 40		18 44			19 10	19 16	19 40		20 10			20 44		21 10	21 40		22 10		22 44	23 10	23 40		
Cottingley	d			18 49										20 49							22 49				
Morley	d			18 53										20 53							22 53				
Batley	d			18 58										20 58							22 58				
Dewsbury	a	18 51		19 01					19 51		20 20			21 01		21 21	21 51				23 01		23 51		
	d	18 51		19 02					19 51		20 21			21 02		21 21	21 51				23 02		23 51		
Ravensthorpe	d			19 05										21 05							23 05				
Mirfield	d			19 09										21 09							23 09				
Deighton	d			19 15										21 15							23 15				
Huddersfield	a	19 00		19 19			19 27	19 33	20 00		20 29			21 19		21 30	22 00		22 27		23 20	23 27	23 59		
	d	19 01	19 09	19 19			19 28	19 34	20 01		20 30	21 09		21 19		21 30	22 01		22 28			23 28	00 01		
Slaithwaite	d		19 16	19 26								21 16		21 26											
Marsden	d		19 22	19a33								21 22		21a33											
Greenfield	d		19 30									21 30													
Mossley (Grtr Manchester)	d		19 34									21 34													
Stalybridge	a		19 39				19 46				20 48	21 39				21 48			22 45						
	d		19 40				19 46				20 48	21 40				21 48			22 46						
Ashton-under-Lyne	d		19 44									21 44													
Manchester Victoria	a		19 58									21 58													
	d																								
Manchester Piccadilly 10	a	19 33					20 05	20 11	20 33		21 05					22 05	22 33		23 03			00 03	00 33		
	d	19 39					20 07		20 39		21 07					22 07	22 39						00 35		
Manchester Airport	a	19 58					*20 33*	*20 52*	20 58		*21 33*					*22 33*	22 58		*23 33*			*00 33*	00 54		
Manchester Oxford Road	a						20 09				21 09					22 09									
Newton-le-Willows	a																								
Birchwood	a						20 23				21 23					22 23									
Warrington Central	a						20 28				21 28					22 28									
Liverpool Lime Street 10	a						20 57				21 57					22 57									

For general notes see front of timetable
For details of catering facilities see Directory of Train Operators

Table 39

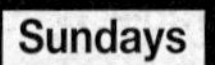

Sundays

20 July to 7 September

Newcastle, Middlesbrough, Scarborough, York, Hull and Leeds → Huddersfield → Manchester, Manchester Airport and Liverpool

Network Diagram - see first page of Table 39

		TP	TP	TP	TP	TP	TP	NT	NT	NT	TP	TP	TP	TP	NT	NT	NT	TP		TP	TP	TP	TP	TP	NT
		1 ◇	1 ◇	1 ◇	1 ◇	1 ◇	1 ◇		bus		1 ◇	1 ◇	1 ◇	1 ◇		bus		1 ◇		1 ◇	1 ◇	1 ◇	1 ◇	1 ◇	
Newcastle 8	d																			09 33					
Chester-le-Street	d																			09 42					
Durham	d																			09 49					
Middlesbrough	d																				10 15				
Thornaby	d																				10 20				
Yarm	d																				10 28				
Darlington 7	d																			10 06					
Northallerton	d																			10 17	10 42				
Thirsk	d																				10 50				
Scarborough	d																	09 20						10 45	
Seamer	d																	09 25						10 50	
Malton	d																	09 43						11 08	
York 8	a																	10 10		10 41	11 09			11 35	
	d	02 16	03 31	04 46	05 46	06 58	07 46					08 57	09 25					10 20		10 50	11 14			11 47	
Hull	d													09 20								10 50			
Brough	d													09 32								11 02			
Howden	d																								
Selby	d													09 51								11 21			
South Milford	d																								
Garforth	d																								
Leeds 10	a	03 08	04 23	05 38	06 38	07 50	08 38					09 31	10 07	10 26				10 54		11 24	11 48	11 58	←	12 25	
	d	03 10	04 25	05 40	06 40	07 52	08 40			08 44	09 10	09 40	10 10	10 40			10 44	11 10		11 40	12 10 →	12 02	12 10	12 40	
Cottingley	d									08 49							10 49								
Morley	d									08 53							10 53								
Batley	d									08 58							10 58								
Dewsbury	a			05 51	06 51	08 03	08 51			09 01		09 51		10 51			11 01			11 51				12 51	
	d			05 51	06 51	08 03	08 51			09 02		09 51		10 51			11 02			11 51				12 51	
Ravensthorpe	d									09 05							11 05								
Mirfield	d									09 09							11 09								
Deighton	d									09 15							11 15								
Huddersfield	a	03 27	04 42	06 00	07 00	08 12	09 00			09 19	09 27	10 00	10 27	11 00			11 19	11 27		12 00		12 19	12 27	13 00	
	d	03 28	04 43	06 01	07 01	08 13	09 01	09 09		09 19	09 28	10 01	10 28	11 01	11 09		11 19	11 28		12 01		12 20	12 28	13 01	13 09
Slaithwaite	d							09 16		09 26					11 16		11 26								13 16
Marsden	d							09 22		09a33					11 22		11a33								13 22
Greenfield	d							09 30							11 30										13 30
Mossley (Grtr Manchester)	d							09 34							11 34										13 34
Stalybridge	a				07 18	08 30	09 18	09 39			09 46		10 46		11 39			11 46					12 46		13 39
	d				07 19	08 31	09 19	09 40	09 45		09 46		10 46		11 40	11 45		11 46					12 46		13 40
Ashton-under-Lyne	d								09 55							11 55									
Manchester Victoria	a								10 15							12 15									
	d																								
Manchester Piccadilly 10	a	04 00	05 15	06 33	07 34	08 46	09 34	09 57			10 05	10 34	11 05	11 33	11 57			12 05		12 33		12 57	13 06	13 33	13 57
	d	04 05	05 20	06 35	07 41	08 50	09 39				10 07	10 39	11 07	11 42				12 07		12 39			13 07	13 40	
Manchester Airport	a	04 21	05 36	06 51	07 58	09 05	10 02				*10 33*	11 02	*11 36*	12 02				*12 33*		13 02			*13 36*	14 02	
Manchester Oxford Road	a										10 09		11 09					12 09					13 09		
Newton-le-Willows	a																								
Birchwood	a				*08b20*	*09b34*					10 23		11 23		*12 23*			12 23					13 23		
Warrington Central	a				*08b25*	*09b39*					10 28		11 28		*12 28*			12 28					13 28		
Liverpool Lime Street 10	a				*09b20*	*10b20*					10 57		11 57		*12 57*			12 57					13 57		

For general notes see front of timetable
For details of catering facilities see Directory of Train Operators

b Change at Manchester Piccadilly and Manchester Oxford Road

Table 39

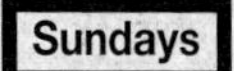

20 July to 7 September

Newcastle, Middlesbrough, Scarborough, York, Hull and Leeds → Huddersfield → Manchester, Manchester Airport and Liverpool

Network Diagram - see first page of Table 39

		NT	NT	TP	TP	TP	TP	TP	TP	NT	NT	NT	TP	TP		TP	TP	TP	NT	NT	NT	TP	TP	TP	TP
		(bus)		1◇	1◇	1◇	1◇	1◇	1◇		(bus)		1◇	1◇		1◇	1◇	1◇		(bus)		1◇	1◇	1◇	1◇
Newcastle 8	d			11 03					12 40					13 45				14 38					15 36		
Chester-le-Street	d								12 49																
Durham	d			11 16					12 56					13 57				14 50					15 49		
Middlesbrough	d						12 15										14 15								16 10
Thornaby	d						12 20										14 20								16 15
Yarm	d						12 28										14 28								16 23
Darlington 7	d			11 33					13 13					14 14				15 08					16 06		
Northallerton	d			11 45			12 42		13 24								14 42	15 19							16 37
Thirsk	d						12 50										14 50								16 45
Scarborough	d				11 57								13 20									15 20			
Seamer	d				12 02								13 25									15 25			
Malton	d				12 20								13 43									15 43			
York 8	a			12 18	12 47		13 16		13 47				14 10	14 47			15 18	15 43				16 10	16 45		17 07
	d			12 20	12 50		13 20		13 50				14 20	14 50			15 20	15 45				16 20	16 50		
Hull	d					12 35										14 25								16 35	
Brough	d					12 47										14 37								16 47	
Howden	d																								
Selby	d					13 06										14 56								17 06	
South Milford	d																								
Garforth	d																								
Leeds 10	a			12 54	13 24	13 45	13 55	←	14 26				14 55	15 24		15 32	15 55	16 19				16 55	17 26	17 44	
	d		12 44	13 10	13 40	14 10	13 58	14 10	14 40			14 44	15 10	15 40		15 57	16 10	16 40			16 44	17 10	17 40	17 57	
Cottingley	d		12 49			→						14 49									16 49				
Morley	d		12 53									14 53									16 53				
Batley	d		12 58									14 58									16 58				
Dewsbury	a		13 01		13 51				14 51			15 01		15 51				16 51			17 01		17 50		
	d		13 02		13 51				14 51			15 02		15 51				16 51			17 02		17 51		
Ravensthorpe	d		13 05									15 05									17 05				
Mirfield	d		13 09									15 09									17 09				
Deighton	d		13 15									15 15									17 15				
Huddersfield	a		13 19	13 27	14 00		14 15	14 27	15 00			15 19	15 27	16 01		16 14	16 27	17 00			17 19	17 27	17 59	18 14	
	d		13 19	13 28	14 01		14 16	14 28	15 01	15 09		15 19	15 28	16 01		16 15	16 28	17 01	17 09		17 19	17 28	18 01	18 15	
Slaithwaite	d		13 26							15 16		15 26							17 16		17 26				
Marsden	d		13a33							15 22		15a33							17 22		17a33				
Greenfield	d									15 30									17 30						
Mossley (Grtr Manchester)	d									15 34									17 34						
Stalybridge	a			13 46				14 45		15 39			15 46				16 45		17 39			17 46			
	d	13 45		13 46				14 46		15 40	15 45		15 46				16 46		17 40	17 45		17 46			
Ashton-under-Lyne	d	13 55									15 55									17 55					
Manchester Victoria	a	14 15									16 15									18 15					
	d																								
Manchester Piccadilly 10	a			14 05	14 33		14 52	15 05	15 33	15 57			16 05	16 34		16 50	17 05	17 33	17 58			18 05	18 33	18 52	
	d			14 07	14 39			15 07	15 39				16 07	16 39			17 07	17 39				18 07	18 39		
Manchester Airport	a			*14 33*	15 02			*15 36*	16 02				*16 33*	17 02			*17 32*	18 02				*18 33*	19 02		
Manchester Oxford Road	a			14 09				15 09					16 09				17 09					18 09			
Newton-le-Willows	a																								
Birchwood	a			14 23				15 23					16 23				17 23					18 23			
Warrington Central	a			14 28				15 28					16 28				17 28					18 28			
Liverpool Lime Street 10	a			14 57				15 57					16 57				17 57					18 57			

For general notes see front of timetable
For details of catering facilities see Directory of Train Operators

Table 39

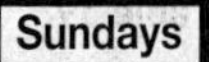
Sundays

20 July to 7 September

Newcastle, Middlesbrough, Scarborough, York, Hull and Leeds → Huddersfield → Manchester, Manchester Airport and Liverpool

Network Diagram - see first page of Table 39

		TP 1◇	TP 1◇	TP 1◇	NT	NT 🚌	NT	TP 1◇	TP 1◇	TP 1◇	TP 1◇	TP 1◇	NT	TP 1◇	NT 🚌	NT	TP 1◇	TP 1◇	TP 1◇	TP 1◇	NT	TP 1◇	TP 1◇
Newcastle 8 🚢	d			16 40							17 50						19 04						
Chester-le-Street	d			16 49																			
Durham	d			16 56							18 03						19 16						
Middlesbrough	d									17 55								19 55					22 07
Thornaby	d									18 00								20 00					22 12
Yarm	d									18 08								20 08					22 20
Darlington 7	d			17 13							18 21						19 33						
Northallerton	d			17 24						18 22							19 45	20 22					22 34
Thirsk	d									18 30								20 30					22 42
Scarborough	d	16 20	16 20					17 32				18 30		19 30						20 30		21 45	
Seamer	d	16 25	16 25									18 35								20 35		21 50	
Malton	d	16 43	16 43									18 53								20 53		22 08	
York 8	a	17 10	17 10	17 49				18 17		18 48	18 54	19 20		20 15			20 16	20 52		21 20		22 35	23 09
	d	17 17	17 17	17 51				18 23			19 00	19 25					20 24	20 55		21 26		22 42	23 12
Hull	d	↪							18 21										20 45				
Brough	d								18 33										20 57				
Howden	d																						
Selby	d								18 52										21 16				
South Milford	d																						
Garforth	d																						
Leeds 10	a		17 55	18 25				18 59	19 25		19 37	19 59					20 58	21 32	21 49	22 07		23 20	23 48
	d		18 10	18 40			18 44	19 10	19 30		19 40	20 10				20 44	21 10	21 40		22 10	22 44	23 21	23 51
Cottingley	d						18 49									20 49					22 49		
Morley	d						18 53									20 53					22 53		
Batley	d						18 58									20 58					22 58		
Dewsbury	a			18 51			19 01				19 51	20 20				21 01	21 21	21 51			23 01		00 01
	d			18 51			19 02				19 51	20 21				21 02	21 21	21 51			23 02		00 02
Ravensthorpe	d						19 05									21 05					23 05		
Mirfield	d						19 09									21 09					23 09		
Deighton	d						19 15									21 15					23 15		
Huddersfield	a		18 27	19 00			19 19	19 27	19 47		20 00	20 29				21 19	21 30	22 00		22 27	23 20	23 39	00 09
	d		18 28	19 01	19 09		19 19	19 28	19 48		20 01	20 30	21 09			21 19	21 30	22 01		22 28		23 40	00 11
Slaithwaite	d				19 16		19 26						21 16			21 26							
Marsden	d				19 22		19a33						21 22			21a33							
Greenfield	d				19 30								21 30										
Mossley (Grtr Manchester)	d				19 34								21 34										
Stalybridge	a		18 45		19 39			19 46				20 48	21 39				21 48			22 45			
	d		18 46		19 40	19 45		19 46				20 48	21 40		21 45		21 48			22 46			
Ashton-under-Lyne	d					19 55									21 55								
Manchester Victoria 🚢	a					20 15									22 15								
	d																						
Manchester Piccadilly 10 🚢	a		19 05	19 33	19 57			20 05	20 23		20 33	21 05	21 56				22 05	22 34		23 03		00 14	00 44
	d		19 07	19 39				20 07			20 39	21 07					22 07	22 39					00 54
Manchester Airport ✈	a		*19 32*	20 04				*20 32*	*20 54*		21 02	*21 32*					*22 34*	23 02		23 33			01 11
Manchester Oxford Road	a		19 09					20 09				21 09					22 09						
Newton-le-Willows	a																						
Birchwood	a		19 24					20 23				21 23					22 23						
Warrington Central	a		19 29					20 28				21 28					22 28						
Liverpool Lime Street 10	a		19 57					20 57				21 57					22 57						

For general notes see front of timetable
For details of catering facilities see
Directory of Train Operators

Table 39

Sundays

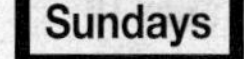

Newcastle, Middlesbrough, Scarborough, York, Hull and Leeds → Huddersfield → Manchester, Manchester Airport and Liverpool

14 September to 2 November

Network Diagram - see first page of Table 39

		TP 🚌	TP 🚌	TP 🚌	TP 🚌		TP 🚌	TP [1]	NT	NT		TP [1]	TP [1] ◇	TP [1] ◇	TP [1] ◇		TP [1] ◇	NT	NT	TP [1] ◇		TP [1] ◇	TP [1] ◇	TP [1] ◇	TP [1] ◇
Newcastle [8] 🚢	d																			09 33					11 03
Chester-le-Street	d																			09 42					
Durham	d																			09 49					11 16
Middlesbrough	d																					10 15			
Thornaby	d																					10 20			
Yarm	d																					10 28			
Darlington [7]	d																			10 06					11 33
Northallerton	d																			10 17		10 42			11 45
Thirsk	d																					10 50			
Scarborough	d																09 20							10 45	
Seamer	d																09 25							10 50	
Malton	d																09 43							11 08	
York [8]	a																10 10			10 41		11 09		11 35	12 11
	d	02 30	04 30		06 00			07 46				08 15		09 15			10 15			10 45		11 15		11 40	12 15
Hull	d														09 05								11 01		
Brough	d														09 17								11 13		
Howden	d																								
Selby	d														09 36								11 32		
South Milford	d														09 46								11 41		
Garforth	d																							11 57	
Leeds [10]	a	03 15	05 15		06 45			08 13				08 47		09 38	10 03		10 38			11 08		11 38	12 01	12 07	12 38
	d	03 15	05 15	06 15	06 45		07 35						09 10	09 40	10 10		10 40		10 44	11 10		11 40	12 02	12 10	12 40
Cottingley	d																		10 49						
Morley	d																		10 53						
Batley	d																		10 58						
Dewsbury	a			06 40			08 00							09 51			10 51		11 01			11 51			12 51
	d			06 40			08 00							09 51			10 51		11 02			11 51			12 51
Ravensthorpe	d																		11 05						
Mirfield	d																		11 09						
Deighton	d																		11 15						
Huddersfield	a	03 50	05 50	07 05			08 25						09 27	10 00	10 27		11 00		11 19	11 27		12 00	12 19	12 27	13 00
	d	03 50	05 50	07 05			08 25		09 19				09 28	10 01	10 28		11 01	11 09	11 19	11 28		12 01	12 20	12 28	13 01
Slaithwaite	d								09 26									11 16	11 26						
Marsden	d								09a33									11 22	11a33						
Greenfield	d																	11 30							
Mossley (Grtr Manchester)	d																	11 34							
Stalybridge	a		06 35	07 50			09 10						09 46		10 46			11 39		11 46				12 46	
	d		06 35	07 50			09 10			09 38			09 46		10 46			11 40		11 46				12 46	
Ashton-under-Lyne	d									09 42								11 44							
Manchester Victoria 🚢	a									09 56								11 58							
	d																								
Manchester Piccadilly [10] 🚢	a	04 50	06 55	08 10			09 30						10 05	10 33	11 05		11 33			12 05		12 33	12 57	13 05	13 33
	d	04 50	06 55	08 10			09 30						10 07	10 47	11 07		11 40			12 07		12 39		13 07	13 41
Manchester Airport ✈	a	05 15	07 20	08 35	08 05		09 55						*10 33*	11 04	*11 33*		11 58			*12 33*		12 58		*13 33*	13 58
Manchester Oxford Road	a												10 09		11 09					12 09				13 09	
Newton-le-Willows	a																								
Birchwood	a		*08b20*	*09b34*									10 23		11 23					12 23				13 23	
Warrington Central	a		*08b25*	*09b39*									10 28		11 28					12 28				13 28	
Liverpool Lime Street [10]	a		*09b20*	*10b20*									10 57		11 57					12 57				13 57	

For general notes see front of timetable
For details of catering facilities see Directory of Train Operators

b Change at Manchester Piccadilly and Manchester Oxford Road

Table 39

Sundays

Newcastle, Middlesbrough, Scarborough, York, Hull and Leeds → Huddersfield → Manchester, Manchester Airport and Liverpool

14 September to 2 November

Network Diagram - see first page of Table 39

		NT	NT		TP 1◇	TP 1◇	TP 1◇	TP 1◇		TP 1◇	NT	NT	TP 1◇		TP 1◇	TP 1◇	TP 1◇	TP 1◇		NT	NT	TP 1◇	TP 1◇		TP 1◇
Newcastle 8	d									12 49					14 10			14 57					16 08		
Chester-le-Street	d									12 58															
Durham	d									13 05					14 22			15 09					16 20		
Middlesbrough	d					12 15							13 45									15 45			
Thornaby	d					12 20							13 50									15 50			
Yarm	d					12 28							13 58									15 58			
Darlington 7	d									13 22					14 39			15 26					16 37		
Northallerton	d					12 42				13 34			14 12					15 38				16 12			
Thirsk	d					12 50							14 20									16 20			
Scarborough	d							12 45									14 45								
Seamer	d							12 50									14 50								
Malton	d							13 08									15 08								
York 8	a					13 12		13 35		14 11			14 40		15 13		15 35	16 12				16 41	17 12		
	d				12 45	13 15		13 42		14 15			14 45		15 15		15 39	16 15				16 45	17 14		
Hull	d						12 50									14 50									16 50
Brough	d						13 02									15 02									17 02
Howden	d																								
Selby	d						13 21									15 21									17 21
South Milford	d						13 31									15 31									17 30
Garforth	d							13 57									15 57								
Leeds 10	a				13 08	13 38	13 48	14 07		14 38			15 08		15 39	15 48	16 07	16 38				17 08	17 37		17 48
	d		12 44		13 10	13 40	13 58	14 10		14 40		14 44	15 10		15 40	15 57	16 10	16 40			16 44	17 10	17 40		17 57
Cottingley	d		12 49									14 49									16 49				
Morley	d		12 53									14 53									16 53				
Batley	d		12 58									14 58									16 58				
Dewsbury	a		13 01			13 51				14 51		15 01			15 51			16 51			17 01		17 50		
	d		13 02			13 51				14 51		15 02			15 51			16 51			17 02		17 51		
Ravensthorpe	d		13 05									15 05									17 05				
Mirfield	d		13 09									15 09									17 09				
Deighton	d		13 15									15 15									17 15				
Huddersfield	a		13 19		13 27	14 00	14 15	14 27		15 00		15 19	15 27		16 01	16 14	16 27	17 00			17 19	17 27	17 59		18 14
	d	13 09	13 19		13 28	14 01	14 16	14 28		15 01	15 09	15 19	15 28		16 01	16 15	16 28	17 01		17 09	17 19	17 28	18 01		18 15
Slaithwaite	d	13 16	13 26								15 16	15 26								17 16	17 26				
Marsden	d	13 22	13a33								15 22	15a33								17 22	17a33				
Greenfield	d	13 30									15 30									17 30					
Mossley (Grtr Manchester)	d	13 34									15 34									17 34					
Stalybridge	a	13 39			13 46			14 45			15 39		15 46				16 45			17 39		17 46			
	d	13 40			13 46			14 46			15 40		15 46				16 46			17 40		17 46			
Ashton-under-Lyne	d	13 44									15 44									17 44					
Manchester Victoria	a	13 58									15 58									17 58					
	d																								
Manchester Piccadilly 10	a				14 05	14 33	14 52	15 05		15 33			16 05		16 34	16 50	17 05	17 33				18 05	18 33		18 52
	d				14 07	14 39		15 07		15 39			16 07		16 39		17 07	17 39				18 07	18 39		
Manchester Airport	a				*14 33*	14 58	*15 21*	*15 33*		15 58			*16 33*		16 58	*17 18*	*17 33*	17 58				*18 33*	18 58		*19 18*
Manchester Oxford Road	a				14 09			15 09					16 09				17 09					18 09			
Newton-le-Willows	a																								
Birchwood	a				14 23			15 23					16 23				17 23					18 23			
Warrington Central	a				14 28			15 28					16 28				17 28					18 28			
Liverpool Lime Street 10	a				14 57			15 57					16 57				17 57					18 57			

For general notes see front of timetable
For details of catering facilities see Directory of Train Operators

Table 39

Sundays

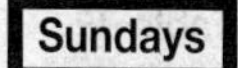

Newcastle, Middlesbrough, Scarborough, York, Hull and Leeds → Huddersfield → Manchester, Manchester Airport and Liverpool

14 September to 2 November

Network Diagram - see first page of Table 39

		TP 1◇	TP 1◇	NT	NT		TP 1◇	TP 1◇	TP 1◇	TP 1◇		TP 1◇	NT	NT	TP 1◇		TP 1◇	TP 1◇	TP 1◇	NT		TP 1◇	TP 1◇		
Newcastle 8 ⛴	d		16 48						17 57						19 20										
Chester-le-Street	d		16 57																						
Durham	d		17 04						18 09						19 32										
Middlesbrough	d						17 45										20 15						22 07		
Thornaby	d						17 50										20 20						22 12		
Yarm	d						17 58										20 28						22 20		
Darlington 7	d		17 21						18 26						19 49										
Northallerton	d		17 32				18 12								20 01		20 42						22 34		
Thirsk	d						18 20										20 50						22 42		
Scarborough	d	16 45										18 45							20 45			21 45			
Seamer	d	16 50										18 50							20 50			21 50			
Malton	d	17 08										19 08							21 08			22 08			
York 8	a	17 35	17 59				18 40		18 59			19 35			20 31		21 09		21 35			22 35	23 09		
	d	17 42	18 15				18 45		19 15			19 42			20 45		21 15		21 38			22 42	23 12		
Hull	d							18 10		19 04								21 00							
Brough	d							18 22		19 16								21 12							
Howden	d																								
Selby	d							18 41		19 35								21 31							
South Milford	d							18 53										21 40							
Garforth	d	17 57										19 57							21 54						
Leeds 10	a	18 07	18 38				19 08	19 12	19 38	19 59		20 07			21 08		21 38	22 00	22 04			23 08	23 38		
	d	18 10	18 40		18 44		19 10	19 16	19 40			20 10		20 44	21 10		21 40		22 10	22 44		23 10	23 40		
Cottingley	d				18 49									20 49						22 49					
Morley	d				18 53									20 53						22 53					
Batley	d				18 58									20 58						22 58					
Dewsbury	a		18 51		19 01				19 51			20 20		21 01	21 21		21 51			23 01			23 51		
	d		18 51		19 02				19 51			20 21		21 02	21 21		21 51			23 02			23 51		
Ravensthorpe	d				19 05									21 05						23 05					
Mirfield	d				19 09									21 09						23 09					
Deighton	d				19 15									21 15						23 15					
Huddersfield	a	18 27	19 00		19 19		19 27	19 33	20 00			20 29		21 19	21 30		22 00		22 27	23 20		23 27	23 59		
	d	18 28	19 01	19 09	19 19		19 28	19 34	20 01			20 30	21 09	21 19	21 30		22 01		22 28			23 28	00 01		
Slaithwaite	d			19 16	19 26								21 16	21 26											
Marsden	d			19 22	19a33								21 22	21a33											
Greenfield	d			19 30									21 30												
Mossley (Grtr Manchester)	d			19 34									21 34												
Stalybridge	a	18 45		19 39			19 45					20 48	21 39		21 48				22 45						
	d	18 46		19 40			19 46					20 48	21 40		21 48				22 46						
Ashton-under-Lyne	d			19 44									21 44												
Manchester Victoria ⛴	a			19 58									21 58												
	d																								
Manchester Piccadilly 10 ⛴	a	19 05	19 33				20 05	20 11	20 33			21 05			22 05		22 33		23 03			00 03	00 33		
	d	19 07	19 39				20 07		20 39			21 07			22 07		22 39						00 35		
Manchester Airport ✈	a	*19 33*	19 58				*20 33*	*20 52*	20 58			*21 33*			*22 33*		22 58		*23 33*			*00 33*	00 54		
Manchester Oxford Road	a	19 09					20 09					21 09			22 09										
Newton-le-Willows	a																								
Birchwood	a	19 24					20 23					21 23			22 23										
Warrington Central	a	19 29					20 28					21 28			22 28										
Liverpool Lime Street 10	a	19 57					20 57					21 57			22 57										

For general notes see front of timetable
For details of catering facilities see Directory of Train Operators

Table 39

Sundays

from 9 November

Newcastle, Middlesbrough, Scarborough, York, Hull and Leeds → Huddersfield → Manchester, Manchester Airport and Liverpool

Network Diagram - see first page of Table 39

		TP	TP	TP	TP	TP	TP		TP	NT	TP	TP	TP	TP		TP	TP	TP	NT	TP	TP		TP	TP	TP
		🚌	🚌	🚌	🚌	🚌	1		🚌		1 ◇	1 ◇	1 ◇	🚌		1 ◇	1 ◇	1 ◇		🚌	1 ◇		1 ◇	🚌	1 ◇
Newcastle 8	d																				09 33				
Chester-le-Street	d																				09 42				
Durham	d																				09 49				
Middlesbrough	d																						10 15		
Thornaby	d																						10 20		
Yarm	d																						10 28		
Darlington 7	d																				10 06				
Northallerton	d																				10 17		10 42		
Thirsk	d																						10 50		
Scarborough	d																	09 20							10 45
Seamer	d																	09 25							10 50
Malton	d																	09 43							11 08
York 8	a																	10 10			10 41		11 09		11 35
	d	02 30	04 30		06 00		07 46				08 30		09 15					10 15			10 45		11 15		11 40
Hull	d															09 05	09 30								
Brough	d															09 17	09 42								
Howden	d																								
Selby	d															09 36	10 01								
South Milford	d															09 46	10 10								
Garforth	d																								11 57
Leeds 10	a	03 15	05 15		06 45		08 13				08 54		09 38			10 03	10 34	10 38			11 07		11 38		12 07
	d	03 15	05 15	06 15	06 45	07 35			08 25		09 00		09 40			10 10		10 40	10 44		11 10		11 40		12 10
Cottingley	d																		10 49						
Morley	d																		10 53						
Batley	d																		10 58						
Dewsbury	a			06 40		08 00			08 50				09 51					10 51	11 01				11 51		
	d			06 40		08 00			08 50				09 51					10 51	11 02				11 51		
Ravensthorpe	d																		11 05						
Mirfield	d																		11 09						
Deighton	d																		11 15						
Huddersfield	a	03 50	05 50	07 05		08 25			09 15		09 18		10 00					11 00	11 19				12 00		
	d	03 50	05 50	07 05		08 25			09 15	09 19	09 20		10 03					11 02	11 19				12 02		
Slaithwaite	d									09 26									11 26						
Marsden	d									09a33									11a33						
Greenfield	d																								
Mossley (Grtr Manchester)	d																								
Stalybridge	a		06 35	07 50		09 10			10 00																
	d		06 35	07 50		09 10			10 00					10 30						11 40				12 30	
Ashton-under-Lyne	d													10 37										12 37	
Manchester Victoria 🚢	a										10 11		10 55	10 57		11 07		11 51		12 00	12 04		12 51	12 57	13 06
	d										10 13	10 16	11 05			11 09		11 53			12 09		12 52		13 09
Manchester Piccadilly 10 🚢	a	04 50	06 55	08 10		09 30			10 20			10 31	11 28					12 07					13 07		
	d	04 50	06 55	08 10		09 30			10 20			10 32	11 32					12 08					13 08		
Manchester Airport ✈	a	05 15	07 20	08 35	08 05	09 55			10 45			10 47	11 47					12 24					13 24		
Manchester Oxford Road	a																								
Newton-le-Willows	a										10 34					11 27					12 28				13 28
Birchwood	a		08b20	09b34		10b34						11b34	12b34					13b34					14b34		
Warrington Central	a		08b25	09b39		10b39					11c05	11b39				11c55					12c55				13c55
Liverpool Lime Street 10	a		09b20	10b20							10 54					11 56					12 51				13 55

For general notes see front of timetable
For details of catering facilities see Directory of Train Operators

b Change at Manchester Piccadilly and Manchester Oxford Road

c By bus

Table 39

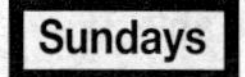

from 9 November

Newcastle, Middlesbrough, Scarborough, York, Hull and Leeds → Huddersfield → Manchester, Manchester Airport and Liverpool

Network Diagram - see first page of Table 39

Station		TP 1 ◇	NT	TP 1 ◇	TP (bus)	TP 1 ◇		TP 1 ◇	TP (bus)	TP 1 ◇	TP 1 ◇	NT	TP 1 ◇		TP (bus)	TP 1 ◇	TP 1 ◇	TP (bus)	TP 1 ◇	TP 1 ◇		NT	TP 1 ◇	TP (bus)	TP 1 ◇
Newcastle 8	d	11 03									12 49						14 10			14 57					
Chester-le-Street	d										12 58														
Durham	d	11 16									13 05						14 22			15 09					
Middlesbrough	d							12 15								13 45									15 45
Thornaby	d							12 20								13 50									15 50
Yarm	d							12 28								13 58									15 58
Darlington 7	d	11 33									13 23						14 39			15 26					
Northallerton	d	11 45						12 42			13 34					14 12				15 38					16 12
Thirsk	d							12 50								14 20									16 20
Scarborough	d									12 45									14 45						
Seamer	d									12 50									14 50						
Malton	d									13 08									15 08						
York 8	a	12 11						13 12		13 35	14 11					14 40	15 13		15 35	16 12					16 41
	d	12 15				12 40		13 15		13 42	14 15					14 45	15 15		15 39	16 15					16 45
Hull	d			12 00									14 00										16 00		
Brough	d			12 12									14 12										16 12		
Howden	d																								
Selby	d			12 31									14 31										16 31		
South Milford	d			12 40									14 40										16 40		
Garforth	d									13 57									15 57						
Leeds 10	a	12 38		13 00		13 03		13 38		14 07	14 38		15 00			15 08	15 39		16 07	16 38			17 00		17 08
	d	12 40	12 44			13 10		13 40		14 10	14 40	14 44				15 10	15 40		16 10	16 40		16 44			17 10
Cottingley	d		12 49									14 49										16 49			
Morley	d		12 53									14 53										16 53			
Batley	d		12 58									14 58										16 58			
Dewsbury	a	12 51	13 01					13 51			14 51	15 01					15 50			16 51		17 01			
	d	12 51	13 02					13 51			14 51	15 02					15 51			16 51		17 02			
Ravensthorpe	d		13 05									15 05										17 05			
Mirfield	d		13 09									15 09										17 09			
Deighton	d		13 15									15 15										17 15			
Huddersfield	a	13 00	13 19					14 00			15 00	15 19					16 01			17 00		17 19			
	d	13 02	13 19					14 02			15 01	15 19					16 02			17 01		17 19			
Slaithwaite	d		13 26									15 26										17 26			
Marsden	d		13a33									15a33										17a33			
Greenfield	d																								
Mossley (Grtr Manchester)	d																								
Stalybridge	a																								
	d				13 40				14 30						15 40			16 30						17 40	
Ashton-under-Lyne	d								14 37									16 37							
Manchester Victoria	a	13 51			14 00	14 06		14 51	14 57	15 06	15 51				16 00	16 07	16 51	16 57	17 06	17 51				18 00	18 04
	d	13 52				14 09		14 52		15 09	15 52					16 15	16 52		17 09	17 52					18 09
Manchester Piccadilly 10	a	14 07						15 07			16 08						17 08			18 07					
	d	14 08						15 08			16 08						17 08			18 08					
Manchester Airport ✈	a	14 24						15 29			16 24						17 24			18 24					
Manchester Oxford Road	a																								
Newton-le-Willows	a					14 27				15 27						16 33			17 27						18 27
Birchwood	a	15b34						16b34			17b34						18b34			19b34					
Warrington Central	a					14c55				15c55						17c05			17c55						18c55
Liverpool Lime Street 10	a					14 51				15 51						16 55			17 51						18 51

For general notes see front of timetable
For details of catering facilities see Directory of Train Operators

b Change at Manchester Piccadilly and Manchester Oxford Road
c By bus

Table 39

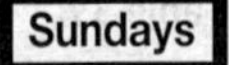

Sundays

from 9 November

Newcastle, Middlesbrough, Scarborough, York, Hull and Leeds → Huddersfield → Manchester, Manchester Airport and Liverpool

Network Diagram - see first page of Table 39

		TP	TP	TP	TP		NT	TP	TP	TP	TP	TP		TP	TP	TP	NT	TP	TP	TP	TP	NT	TP		
		1 ◇	bus	1 ◇	1 ◇			1 ◇	bus	1 ◇	1 ◇	1 ◇		bus	1 ◇	bus		1 ◇	1 ◇	1 ◇	1 ◇		1 ◇		
Newcastle 8 ⛴	d	16 08			16 48						17 57							19 20							
Chester-le-Street	d				16 57																				
Durham	d	16 20			17 04						18 09							19 32							
Middlesbrough	d									17 45									20 15				22 07		
Thornaby	d									17 50									20 20				22 12		
Yarm	d									17 58									20 28				22 20		
Darlington 7	d	16 37			17 21						18 26							19 49							
Northallerton	d				17 32					18 12								20 01	20 42				22 34		
Thirsk	d									18 20									20 50				22 42		
Scarborough	d			16 45											18 45						20 45				
Seamer	d			16 50											18 50						20 50				
Malton	d			17 08											19 08						21 08				
York 8	a	17 12		17 35	17 59					18 40	18 59				19 35			20 30	21 09		21 35		23 09		
	d	17 14		17 42	18 15					18 45	19 15				19 42			20 34	21 15		21 38		23 12		
Hull	d							18 00				19 04								21 00					
Brough	d							18 12				19 16								21 12					
Howden	d																								
Selby	d							18 31				19 35								21 31					
South Milford	d							18 40												21 40					
Garforth	d			17 57											19 57						21 54				
Leeds 10	a	17 37		18 07	18 38			19 00		19 08	19 38	19 59			20 07			20 58	21 38	22 00	22 04		23 38		
	d	17 40		18 10	18 40		18 44			19 10	19 40				20 10		20 44	21 00	21 40		22 10	22 44	23 40		
Cottingley	d						18 49										20 49					22 49			
Morley	d						18 53										20 53					22 53			
Batley	d						18 58										20 58					22 58			
Dewsbury	a	17 50			18 51		19 01				19 51				20 20		21 01	21 11			22 20	23 01	23 51		
	d	17 51			18 51		19 02				19 51				20 21		21 02	21 11			22 21	23 02	23 51		
Ravensthorpe	d						19 05										21 05					23 05			
Mirfield	d						19 09										21 09					23 09			
Deighton	d						19 15										21 15					23 15			
Huddersfield	a	17 59			19 00		19 19				20 00						21 19	21 22			22 29	23 20			
	d	18 01			19 02		19 19				20 01						21 19	21 24			22 31				
Slaithwaite	d						19 26										21 26								
Marsden	d						19a33										21a33								
Greenfield	d																								
Mossley (Grtr Manchester)	d																								
Stalybridge	a																								
	d		18 30						19 40					20 30		21 35									
Ashton-under-Lyne	d		18 37											20 37		21 42									
Manchester Victoria ⛴	a	18 51	18 57	19 06	19 51				20 00	20 05	20 51			20 57	21 09	22 02		22 11	22 35		23 24		00 36		
	d	18 52		19 09	19 52					20 09	20 53				21 09			22 13	22 38				00 38		
Manchester Piccadilly 10 ⛴	a	19 07			20 07						21 07								22 54				00 54		
	d	19 08			20 08						21 08								22 54				00 54		
Manchester Airport ✈	a	19 24			20 24						21 24								23 09				01 11		
Manchester Oxford Road	a																								
Newton-le-Willows	a			19 27						20 27					21 27			22 31							
Birchwood	a	20b34			21b34						22b34														
Warrington Central	a			19c55						20c55					22c02			23c05							
Liverpool Lime Street 10	a			19 51						20 51					21 51			22 54							

For general notes see front of timetable
For details of catering facilities see Directory of Train Operators

b Change at Manchester Piccadilly and Manchester Oxford Road

c By bus

Liverpool, Manchester Airport and Manchester → Huddersfield → Wakefield, Leeds, Hull, York, Scarborough, Middlesbrough and Newcastle

Network Diagram - see first page of Table 39

Miles	Miles	Miles	Miles	Miles	Station		TP	TP	TP	TP	TP	TP	TP	NT	TP	TP	TP	NT	NT	NT	TP	NT	NT	TP	NT
							MO	MX	MO	MO	MO	MO	MX												
							1 ◇	1 ◇	1 ◇	1 ◇	1 ◇	1 ◇	1 ◇		1 ◇	1 ◇	1 ◇				1 ◇			1 ◇	
							A		B	B	C	D													
																🚲	🚲				🚲				
0	—	—	—	—	**Liverpool Lime Street** [10]	d																			
18½	—	—	—	—	Warrington Central	d																			
21¾	—	—	—	—	Birchwood	d																			
34¼	—	—	—	—	Manchester Oxford Road	d																			
—	—	—	—	—	**Manchester Airport** ✈	d	00 55	01 00	00 55	02 56	03 17	03 22	03 17			*04 34*	05 34				*05 47*				
34¾	—	—	—	—	**Manchester Piccadilly** [10]	a	01 10	01 13	01 10	03 09	03 31	03 36	03 31				05 48								
—	—	—	—	—		d	01 15	01 15	01 10	03 10	03 41	03 41	03 38			05 39	05 57				06 21				
—	—	—	—	0	**Manchester Victoria**	d																			
—	—	—	—	6½	Ashton-under-Lyne	d																			
42¼	—	—	—	7¾	**Stalybridge**	a										05 52									
—	—	—	—	—		d										05 52							06 42		
45	—	—	—	10½	Mossley (Grtr Manchester)	d																	06 46		
47¼	—	—	—	12¾	Greenfield	d																	06 50		
53¼	—	—	—	18¾	Marsden	d																06 48	06 59		
55¾	—	—	—	21¼	Slaithwaite	d																06 52	07 03		
60¼	—	—	—	25¾	**Huddersfield**	a	01 44	02 03	02 03	04 10	04 10	04 10	04 35			06 10	06 26				06 52	07 00	07 11		
—	—	—	—	—		d	01 45	02 06	02 06	04 11	04 11	04 11	04 39	05 32		06 11	06 27	06 31	06 41		06 53	07 00			07 16
62¼	—	—	—	27¾	Deighton	d								05 36				06 34	06 45			07 03			07 19
65¼	—	—	—	30¾	Mirfield	d								05 41				06 39	06 50			07 08			07 24
—	—	—	—	40¼	Wakefield Kirkgate	a								05 57					07 03						
—	—	—	—	41¼	**Wakefield Westgate**	a								06 05					07 10						
66¾	—	—	—	—	Ravensthorpe	d												06 42				07 11			07 27
68¼	—	—	—	—	**Dewsbury**	a											06 36	06 46			07 03	07 15			07 31
—	—	—	—	—		d											06 37	06 46			07 03	07 15			07 35 →
69¾	—	—	—	—	Batley	d												06 49				07 18			
73	—	—	—	—	Morley	d												06 55				07 24			
74½	—	—	—	—	Cottingley	d												06 59				07 28			
77½	0	—	0	—	**Leeds** [10]	a	02 24	02 40	02 40	04 50	04 50	04 50	05 00			06 32	06 52	07 07			07 18	07 38			
—	—	—	—	—		d	02 26	02 45	02 45	04 52	04 52	04 52	05 03			06 35	06 55			07 13	07 23				
84¾	7¼	—	7¼	—	Garforth	d																			
—	12¾	—	—	—	South Milford	a																			
—	20¾	—	—	—	Selby	a														07 39	07 42				
—	29½	—	—	—	Howden	a															07 51				
—	41¼	—	—	—	Brough	a															08 03				
—	51¾	—	—	—	**Hull**	a															08 20				
103	—	0	25½	—	**York** [8]	a	03b06	03 13	03 19	05 18	05 36	05 18	05 32			07 03	07 22								
—	—	—	—	—		d				05 40	05 40	05 40	05 40		06 38	07 06	07 25							07 32	
—	—	—	46½	—	Malton	d									07 02		07 49								
—	—	—	64¾	—	Seamer	a									07 19		08 06								
—	—	—	67½	—	**Scarborough**	a									07 30		08 14								
125¼	—	22¼	—	—	Thirsk	a				06 01	06 01	06 01	06 01			07 22	*07c52*							07 52	
133	—	30	—	—	Northallerton	a				06 17	06 17	06 17	06 17			07 30								08 01	
147	—	—	—	—	**Darlington** [7]	a				06 28	06 28	06 28	06 28			07 41	*08c05*								
—	—	42¼	—	—	Yarm	d																		08 16	
—	—	47½	—	—	Thornaby	a				06 52	06 52	06 52	06 52											08 25	
—	—	50¾	—	—	**Middlesbrough**	a				07 01	07 01	07 01	07 01											08 32	
169	—	—	—	—	Durham	a										07 58	*08c26*								
174¾	—	—	—	—	Chester-le-Street	a										08 04	*08e43*								
183	—	—	—	—	**Newcastle** [8]	a										08 19	*08c39*								

For general notes see front of timetable
For details of catering facilities see Directory of Train Operators

A Until 3 November
B From 10 November
C 21 July to 8 September
D Until 14 July and 15 September to 3 November

b Until 14 July and from 15 September arr. 0252
c Change at York
e Change at York and Durham

Liverpool, Manchester Airport and Manchester → Huddersfield → Wakefield, Leeds, Hull, York, Scarborough, Middlesbrough and Newcastle

Network Diagram - see first page of Table 39

		TP	NT	NT	TP		NT	NT	TP	TP	NT	NT	TP	NT	NT	NT	TP		NT	TP	NT	NT	TP	NT	TP
		1 ◇			1 ◇				1 ◇	1 ◇			1 ◇				1 ◇			1 ◇			1 ◇		1 ◇
								A				B		C		D					E			B	G
		🛒			🛒				🛒	🛒			🛒				🛒			🛒			🛒		🛒
Liverpool Lime Street 10	d				06 18						06 39		*06b47*				07 15				07 18	07 47			*07b47*
Warrington Central	d				06 42								*07b15*				07 39								*08b16*
Birchwood	d				06 47								*07b20*				07 44								*08b21*
Manchester Oxford Road	d	*06b24*			07 07				*07b13*				*07b43*				08 07						*08 20*		*08b45*
Manchester Airport ✈	d	06 23			*06 44*				07 02				07 34							08 04			*08 07*		08 33
Manchester Piccadilly 10 ⛴	a	06 39			07 10				07 19				07 48				08 10			08 19					08 49
	d	06 53			07 12				07 25	07 35			07 55				08 12			08 25			08 41		08 57
Manchester Victoria ⛴	d			06 57							07 39			07 57							08 27	08 57			
Ashton-under-Lyne	d			07 07							07 49			08 07							08 37	09 07			
Stalybridge	a	07 06		07 11	07 25				07 38		07 54		08 07	08 13			08 24				08 41	09 13			
	d	07 06		07 12	07 25				07 38		07 54		08 08				08 25				08 42				
Mossley (Grtr Manchester)	d			07 16							07 59										08 46				
Greenfield	d			07 20							08 03										08 50				
Marsden	d			07 29							08 11										08 59				
Slaithwaite	d			07 33							08 16										09 03				
Huddersfield	a	07 24		07 41	07 44				07 56	08 07	08 24		08 25				08 44			08 55	09 11		09 14		09 26
	d	07 25			07 45		07 49		07 57	08 10			08 27		08 33	08 37	08 45			08 57			09 16		09 27
Deighton	d						07 53								08 36	08 40									
Mirfield	d						07 59	07 54				08 19			08 41	08 45								09 13	
Wakefield Kirkgate	a						08 13									09 00									
Wakefield Westgate	a						08 22									09 08									
Ravensthorpe	d											08 23			08 44									09 17	
Dewsbury	a		⟵		07 54			07 59	08 06	08 19		08 26	08 37		08 48				⟵	09 06				09 20	09 36
	d		07 35		07 55			08 00	08 07	08 20		08 31	08 37		08 55 ⟶				08 55	09 07				09 24	09 37
Batley	d		07 38					08 03				08 34							08 58					09 27	
Morley	d		07 44					08 09				08 40							09 04					09 33	
Cottingley	d		07 47									08 43							09 08						
Leeds 10	a	07 47	07 55		08 10			08 18	08 23	08 35		08 51	08 54				09 06		09 16	09 22			09 36	09 44	09 52
	d	07 50			08 12				08 27	08 38			08 57				09 12			09 27			09 38		09 57
Garforth	d	08 00											09 05												10 05
South Milford	a																								
Selby	a									08 57													09 57		
Howden	a									*09 31*													*10 22*		
Brough	a																						10 15		
Hull	a									09 30													10 33		
York 8	a	08 20			08 35				08 55				09 25				09 36			09 55					10 23
	d	08 22			08 38	08 42			09 03				09 26				09 38			10 00					10 26
Malton	d				09 02												10 02								
Seamer	a				09 19												10 19								
Scarborough	a				09 30												10 30								
Thirsk	a	08 38											09 45							*10 29*					10 45
Northallerton	a	08 48				09 02			09 23				09 55							10 20					10 55
Darlington 7	a	*09e02*				09 14			09 36				*10e01*				*10e16*			10 32					*10e59*
Yarm	d	09 03											10 10												11 10
Thornaby	a	09 11											10 20												11 20
Middlesbrough	a	09 20											10 30												11 30
Durham	a	*09e20*				09 31			09 53				*10e18*				*10e33*			10 50					*11e17*
Chester-le-Street	a				*09e44*												*10e40*			10 56					
Newcastle 8 ⛴	a	*09e38*				09 49			10 10				*10e34*				*10e57*			11 10					*11e32*

For general notes see front of timetable
For details of catering facilities see Directory of Train Operators

- **A** From Hebden Bridge (Table 41)
- **B** From Brighouse (Table 41)
- **C** From Wigan Wallgate (Table 82)
- **D** From Selby (Table 41)
- **E** Also stops at Widnes 0732 and Irlam 0749
- **G** Also stops at Heald Green 0837
- **b** Change at Manchester Piccadilly
- **e** Change at York

Liverpool, Manchester Airport and Manchester → Huddersfield → Wakefield, Leeds, Hull, York, Scarborough, Middlesbrough and Newcastle

Network Diagram - see first page of Table 39

		NT	NT	TP	TP	NT	NT	NT	TP	TP	NT	NT	TP	TP	NT	NT	NT	TP	TP	NT	NT	TP	TP	NT	NT
				1 ◇	1 ◇				1 ◇	1 ◇			1 ◇	1 ◇				1 ◇	1 ◇			1 ◇	1 ◇		
			A			B						A			B						A			B	
				🍴	🍴				🍴	🍴			🍴	🍴				🍴	🍴			🍴	🍴		
Liverpool Lime Street 10	d			08 22				08 48		*08b52*			09 22				09 48		*09b52*			10 22			
Warrington Central	d			08 44						*09b17*			09 44						*10b17*			10 44			
Birchwood	d			08 49						*09c03*			09 49						*10c03*			10 49			
Manchester Oxford Road	d			09 07					*09 27*	*09b43*			10 07					*10 27*	*10b43*			11 07			
Manchester Airport ✈	d				09 04				*09 07*	09 34				10 04				*10 07*	10 34				11 04		
Manchester Piccadilly 10	a			09 10	09 19					09 48			10 10	10 19					10 48			11 10	11 19		
	d			09 12	09 25				09 42	09 57			10 12	10 27				10 42	10 57			11 12	11 27		
Manchester Victoria	d						09 27	09 57								10 27	10 57								11 27
Ashton-under-Lyne	d						09 37	10 07								10 37	11 07								11 37
Stalybridge	a			09 25			09 41	10 13					10 25			10 41	11 13					11 25			11 41
	d			09 25			09 42						10 25			10 42						11 25			11 42
Mossley (Grtr Manchester)	d						09 46									10 47									11 47
Greenfield	d						09 51									10 51									11 51
Marsden	d						09 59									10 59									11 59
Slaithwaite	d						10 04									11 04									12 04
Huddersfield	a			09 43	09 56		10 12		10 15	10 26			10 44	10 56		11 12		11 15	11 26			11 44	11 56		12 12
	d	09 31	09 35	09 45	09 57				10 16	10 27	10 31	10 35	10 45	10 57				11 16	11 27	11 31	11 35	11 45	11 57		
Deighton	d	09 34	09 38								10 34	10 38								11 34	11 38				
Mirfield	d	09 39	09 43			10 07					10 39	10 43			11 07					11 39	11 43			12 07	
Wakefield Kirkgate	a		09 58									10 56									11 56				
Wakefield Westgate	a		10 10									11 08									12 08				
Ravensthorpe	d	09 42									10 42									11 42					
Dewsbury	a	09 46			10 06	10 12				10 36	10 46			11 06	11 12				11 36	11 46			12 06	12 12	
	d	09 46			10 07	10 12				10 37	10 46			11 07	11 12				11 37	11 46			12 07	12 12	
Batley	d	09 49				10 15					10 49				11 15					11 49				12 15	
Morley	d	09 55				10 21					10 55				11 21					11 55				12 21	
Cottingley	d	09 59									10 59									11 59					
Leeds 10	a	10 07		10 09	10 22	10 31			10 36	10 52	11 07		11 09	11 22	11 33			11 36	11 52	12 07		12 09	12 22	12 32	
	d			10 12	10 27				10 38	10 57			11 12	11 27				11 38	11 57			12 12	12 27		
Garforth	d									11 05									12 05						
South Milford	a																								
Selby	a								10 57									11 57							
Howden	a								*12 01*									*12 27*							
Brough	a								11 15									12 15							
Hull	a								11 33									12 36							
York 8	a			10 36	10 49					11 23			11 35	11 52					12 23			12 35	12 55		
	d			10 38	10 54					11 26			11 38	12 01					12 26			12 38	12 59		
Malton	d			11 02									12 02									13 02			
Seamer	a			11 19									12 19									13 19			
Scarborough	a			11 30									12 30									13 30			
Thirsk	a									11 45									12 46				*13 37*		
Northallerton	a				11 15					11 55				12 21					12 55				13 19		
Darlington 7	a				11 26					*11e58*			*12e20*	12 33					*13e00*			*13e11*	13 31		
Yarm	d									12 10									13 10						
Thornaby	a									12 18									13 20						
Middlesbrough	a									12 30									13 30						
Durham	a				11 43					*12e22*			*12e38*	12 50					*13e18*			*13e28*	13 48		
Chester-le-Street	a												*12e50*										13 54		
Newcastle 8	a				11 59					*12e36*			*12e55*	13 08					*13e33*			*13e49*	14 09		

For general notes see front of timetable
For details of catering facilities see Directory of Train Operators

- **A** From Selby (Table 41)
- **B** From Hebden Bridge (Table 41)
- **b** Change at Manchester Piccadilly
- **c** Change at Manchester Oxford Road and Manchester Piccadilly
- **e** Change at York

Liverpool, Manchester Airport and Manchester → Huddersfield → Wakefield, Leeds, Hull, York, Scarborough, Middlesbrough and Newcastle

Network Diagram - see first page of Table 39

		NT	TP	TP	NT	NT	TP		TP	NT	NT	NT	TP	TP	NT	NT	TP	TP	NT	NT	NT	TP	TP	NT	NT
			1 ◇	1 ◇			1 ◇		1 ◇				1 ◇	1 ◇			1 ◇	1 ◇				1 ◇	1 ◇		
						A				B						C			B						A
			🛒	🛒			🛒		🛒				🛒	🛒			🛒	🛒				🛒	🛒		
Liverpool Lime Street 10	d	10 48		10b52			11 22					11 48		11b52			12 22				12 48		12b52		
Warrington Central	d			11b17			11 44							12b17			12 44						13b17		
Birchwood	d			11c03			11 49							12c03			12 49						13c03		
Manchester Oxford Road	d		11 27	11b43			12 07						12 27	12b43			13 07					13 27	13b43		
Manchester Airport ✈	d		11 07	11 34					12 04				12 07	12 34				13 04				13 07	13 34		
Manchester Piccadilly 10	a			11 48			12 10		12 19					12 48			13 10	13 19					13 48		
	d		11 42	11 57			12 12		12 27				12 42	12 57			13 12	13 27				13 42	13 57		
Manchester Victoria	d	11 57									12 27	12 57								13 27	13 57				
Ashton-under-Lyne	d	12 07									12 37	13 07								13 37	14 07				
Stalybridge	a	12 13					12 25				12 41	13 13					13 25			13 41	14 13				
	d						12 25				12 42						13 25			13 42					
Mossley (Grtr Manchester)	d										12 47									13 47					
Greenfield	d										12 51									13 51					
Marsden	d										12 59									13 59					
Slaithwaite	d										13 04									14 04					
Huddersfield	a		12 15	12 26			12 44		12 56		13 12		13 15	13 26			13 44	13 56		14 12		14 15	14 26		
	d		12 16	12 27	12 31	12 35	12 45		12 57				13 16	13 27	13 31	13 35	13 45	13 57				14 16	14 27	14 31	14 35
Deighton	d				12 34	12 38									13 34	13 38								14 34	14 38
Mirfield	d				12 39	12 43				13 07					13 39	13 43			14 07					14 39	14 43
Wakefield Kirkgate	a					12 56										13 56									14 58
Wakefield Westgate	a					13 08										14 08									15 08
Ravensthorpe	d				12 42										13 42									14 42	
Dewsbury	a			12 36	12 46				13 06	13 12				13 36	13 46			14 06	14 12				14 36	14 46	
	d			12 37	12 46				13 07	13 12				13 37	13 46			14 07	14 12				14 37	14 46	
Batley	d				12 49					13 15					13 49				14 15					14 49	
Morley	d				12 55					13 21					13 55				14 21					14 55	
Cottingley	d				12 59										13 59									14 59	
Leeds 10	a		12 36	12 52	13 07		13 09		13 22	13 32			13 36	13 52	14 07		14 09	14 22	14 32			14 36	14 52	15 07	
	d		12 38	12 57			13 12		13 27				13 38	13 57			14 12	14 27				14 38	14 57		
Garforth	d			13 05										14 05									15 05		
South Milford	a																								
Selby	a		12 57										13 57									14 57			
Howden	a		*13 54*																			*15 37*			
Brough	a		13 15										14 14									15 15			
Hull	a		13 33										14 33									15 33			
York 8	a			13 24			13 35		13 52					14 23			14 37	14 53					15 23		
	d			13 26			13 38		13 54					14 26			14 38	14 54					15 26		
Malton	d						14 02										15 02								
Seamer	a						14 19										15 19								
Scarborough	a						14 30										15 30								
Thirsk	a			13 46										14 42									15 46		
Northallerton	a			13 55					14 15					14 53				15 22					15 55		
Darlington 7	a			*14e00*			*14e16*		14 27					*14e58*			*15e16*	15 34					*16f06*		
Yarm	d			14 10										15 08									16 09		
Thornaby	a			14 18										15 20									16 20		
Middlesbrough	a			14 30										15 30									16 30		
Durham	a			*14e18*			*14e34*		14 50					*15e15*			*15e34*	15 51					*16g24*		
Chester-le-Street	a						*14e41*											15 57							
Newcastle 8	a			*14e36*			*14e56*		15 06					*15e31*			*15e57*	16 13					*16j37*		

For general notes see front of timetable
For details of catering facilities see Directory of Train Operators

A From Selby (Table 41)
B From Hebden Bridge (Table 41)
C From Leeds (Table 41)
b Change at Manchester Piccadilly
c Change at Manchester Oxford Road and Manchester Piccadilly
e Change at York
f Change at York. From 8 September arr. 1611
g Change at York. From 8 September arr. 1629
j Change at York. From 8 September arr. 1651

Liverpool, Manchester Airport and Manchester → Huddersfield → Wakefield, Leeds, Hull, York, Scarborough, Middlesbrough and Newcastle

Network Diagram - see first page of Table 39

		TP	TP	NT	NT	NT	TP	TP	NT	NT	TP	TP	NT	NT	NT	TP	TP	NT	NT		TP	NT	TP	NT	NT
		1 ◇	1 ◇				1 ◇	1 ◇			1 ◇	1 ◇				1 ◇	1 ◇				1 ◇		1 ◇		
				A						B			A						B		C			A	
Liverpool Lime Street 10	d	13 22				13 48		13b52			14 22				14 48		14b52				15 22				
Warrington Central	d	13 44						14b17			14 44						15b17				15 44				
Birchwood	d	13 49						14c03			14 49						15c03				15 49				
Manchester Oxford Road	d	14 07					14 27	14b43			15 07					15 27	15b43				16 07				
Manchester Airport ✈	d		14 04				14 07	14 34				15 04				15 07	15 34						16 04		
Manchester Piccadilly 10	a	14 10	14 19					14 48			15 10	15 19					15 48				16 10		16 19		
	d	14 12	14 27				14 42	14 57			15 12	15 27				15 42	15 57				16 12		16 27		
Manchester Victoria	d				14 27	14 57								15 27	15 57							16 18			16 27
Ashton-under-Lyne	d				14 37	15 07								15 37	16 07							16 28			16 37
Stalybridge	a	14 25			14 41	15 13					15 25			15 41	16 13						16 25	16 34			16 41
	d	14 25			14 42						15 25			15 42							16 25				16 42
Mossley (Grtr Manchester)	d				14 47									15 47											16 47
Greenfield	d				14 51									15 51											16 51
Marsden	d				14 59									15 59											16 59
Slaithwaite	d				15 04									16 04											17 04
Huddersfield	a	14 44	14 56		15 12		15 15	15 26			15 44	15 56		16 12		16 15	16 26				16 44		16 56		17 12
	d	14 45	14 57				15 16	15 27	15 31	15 35	15 45	15 57				16 16	16 27	16 31	16 35		16 45		16 57		
Deighton	d								15 34	15 38								16 34	16 38						
Mirfield	d			15 07					15 39	15 43			16 07					16 39	16 43					17 07	
Wakefield Kirkgate	a									15 58									16 58						
Wakefield Westgate	a									16 08									17 08						
Ravensthorpe	d								15 42									16 42							
Dewsbury	a		15 06	15 12				15 36	15 46			16 06	16 12				16 36	16 46					17 06	17 12	
	d		15 07	15 12				15 37	15 46			16 07	16 12				16 37	16 46					17 07	17 12	
Batley	d			15 15					15 49				16 15					16 49						17 15	
Morley	d			15 21					15 55				16 21					16 55						17 21	
Cottingley	d								15 59									16 59							
Leeds 10	a	15 09	15 22	15 31			15 36	15 52	16 07		16 10	16 22	16 32			16 36	16 52	17 07			17 09		17 22	17 31	
	d	15 12	15 27				15 38	15 57			16 12	16 27				16 38	16 57				17 12		17 24		
Garforth	d							16 05									17 05						17 34		
South Milford	a																								
Selby	a						15 57									16 57									
Howden	a						16 51									17 54									
Brough	a						16 15									17 15									
Hull	a						16 33									17 35									
York 8	a	15 35	15 52					16 23			16 35	16 52					17 22				17 38		17 57		
	d	15 38						16 26			16 38	16 58					17 26				17 43		18 00		
Malton	d	16 02									17 02						17 50						18 24		
Seamer	a	16 19									17 19						18 07						18 41		
Scarborough	a	16 30									17 30						18 17						18 51		
Thirsk	a							16 46				17 14									17 59				
Northallerton	a		16 55					16 55				17 22					17e56				18 09				
Darlington 7	a	16e11	16 50					16e57			17e08	17 36					18e02				18e15		18e58		
Yarm	d							17 09													18 24				
Thornaby	a							17 19													18 32				
Middlesbrough	a							17 30													18 42				
Durham	a	16e29	17 08								17e31	17 55					18e20				18e33		19e15		
Chester-le-Street	a	16e36										18 01									18e40				
Newcastle 8	a	16e51	17 26					17e27			17e38	18 15					18e36				18e55		19e33		

For general notes see front of timetable
For details of catering facilities see Directory of Train Operators

A From Hebden Bridge (Table 41)
B From Selby (Table 41)
C Also stops at Cross Gates 1718
b Change at Manchester Piccadilly
c Change at Manchester Oxford Road and Manchester Piccadilly
e Change at York

Liverpool, Manchester Airport and Manchester → Huddersfield → Wakefield, Leeds, Hull, York, Scarborough, Middlesbrough and Newcastle

Network Diagram - see first page of Table 39

		TP	TP	NT	NT	NT	TP	NT	NT	TP	NT	NT	TP	NT	TP	NT	NT	TP	NT	TP	NT	TP	TP	NT	NT
		1 ◇	1 ◇				1 ◇			1 ◇			1 ◇		1 ◇			1 ◇		1 ◇		1 ◇	1 ◇		
				A				B								A			C						A
		🍴	🍴				🍴			🍴			🍴		🍴			🍴		🍴		🍴			
Liverpool Lime Street 10	d		15b52			15 48	16 22					16 18			16b52		16 48	17 22					17b52		
Warrington Central	d		16b17				16 44								17b17			17 44					18b17		
Birchwood	d						16 49											17 49					18c08		
Manchester Oxford Road	d	16 27	16b38				17 07			17b13			17 27		17b38			18 07				18 18	18b40		
Manchester Airport ✈	d	16 07	16 34							17 04					17 34					17 52		18 10	18 34		
Manchester Piccadilly 10	a		16 48				17 10			17 19					17 49			18 10					18 49		
	d	16 42	16 55				17 12			17 25			17 42		17 55			18 12		18 25		18 42	18 57		
Manchester Victoria	d					16 57		17 14				17 27					17 57				18 27				
Ashton-under-Lyne	d					17 07		17 24				17 37					18 07				18 37				
Stalybridge	a		17 07			17 12	17 25	17 28		17 38		17 41			18 08		18 12	18 25			18 41				
	d		17 08			17 12	17 25	17 29		17 38		17 42			18 08		18 12	18 25			18 42				
Mossley (Grtr Manchester)	d					17 17		17 33				17 46					18 17				18 47				
Greenfield	d					17 21		17 37				17 50					18 21				18 51				
Marsden	d					17 29						17 59					18 29				18 59				
Slaithwaite	d					17 34						18 03					18 34				19 04				
Huddersfield	a	17 15	17 26			17 42	17 44	17 55		17 56		18 11	18 15		18 26		18 42	18 45		18 56	19 12	19 15	19 26		
	d	17 16	17 27	17 33	17 37		17 45			17 57	18 06		18 16		18 27	18 34		18 45		18 57		19 16	19 27	19 31	19 35
Deighton	d			17 36	17 40						18 09					18 38								19 34	19 38
Mirfield	d			17 41	17 45						18 14					18 43			18 47					19 39	19 43
Wakefield Kirkgate	a			17 58												18 58									19 58
Wakefield Westgate	a			18 08												19 08									20 08
Ravensthorpe	d				17 48						18 17								18 50					19 42	
Dewsbury	a		17 36		17 52				←	18 07	18 21			←	18 36				18 54	19 06			19 36	19 46	
	d		17 37		17 55 →				17 55	18 07	18 25 →			18 25	18 37				18 57	19 07			19 37	19 46	
Batley	d								17 58					18 28					19 00					19 49	
Morley	d								18 04					18 34					19 06					19 55	
Cottingley	d								18 08					18 37										19 59	
Leeds 10	a	17 37	17 52				18 09		18 18	18 22			18 36	18 45	18 53			19 09	19 17	19 23		19 36	19 52	20 07	
	d	17 38	17 57				18 12			18 27			18 38		18 57			19 12		19 27		19 38	19 57		
Garforth	d		18 05												19 05								20 05		
South Milford	a												18 51									19 51			
Selby	a	18 04											19 00									20 00			
Howden	a	18 15																				20 09			
Brough	a	18 27											19 18									20 21			
Hull	a	18 45											19 36									20 39			
York 8	a		18 25				18 37			18 52					19 25			19 35		19 55			20 23		
	d		18 26				18 43			18 59					19 31			19 38					20 29		
Malton	d						19 07											20 02							
Seamer	a						19 24											20 19							
Scarborough	a						19 31											20 30							
Thirsk	a		18 46				19e04								19 47								20 45		
Northallerton	a		18 55				19e15			19 20					19 58								20 53		
Darlington 7	a		19 13				19e22			19 33					20e03			20e12		20 51			21e07		
Yarm	d		19 09												20 13								21 07		
Thornaby	a		19 17												20 21								21 16		
Middlesbrough	a		19 30												20 30								21 25		
Durham	a		19f31							19 50					20e20			20e30		21 09			21e25		
Chester-le-Street	a									19 56								20e37							
Newcastle 8	a		19g49				19e52			20 10					20e36			20e52		21 27			21e42		

For general notes see front of timetable
For details of catering facilities see Directory of Train Operators

A From Selby (Table 41)

B From Wigan Wallgate (Table 82)

C From Hebden Bridge (Table 41)

b Change at Manchester Piccadilly

c Change at Manchester Oxford Road and Manchester Piccadilly

e Change at York

f Change at Northallerton

g Change at Northallerton. Fridays arr. 1948

Liverpool, Manchester Airport and Manchester → Huddersfield → Wakefield, Leeds, Hull, York, Scarborough, Middlesbrough and Newcastle

Network Diagram - see first page of Table 39

Station		TP	NT	NT	TP	TP	NT	NT	TP	NT	TP	NT	NT	TP	NT	TP	TP	NT	NT	TP	NT	TP	TP
		1 ◇			1 ◇	1 ◇			1 ◇		1 ◇			1 ◇		1 ◇	1 ◇			1 ◇		1 ◇	1 ◇
			A					B													C		
Liverpool Lime Street 10	d	18 22							19 22					20 22						21b35		22 30	
Warrington Central	d	18 44							19 44					20 44						22b01		22 52	
Birchwood	d	18 49							19 49					20 49						21c39		22 57	
Manchester Oxford Road	d	19 07			19b17				20 07					21 07			21b28			22b23		23 15	23b26
Manchester Airport ✈	d				19 22				*19 30*		20 22						21 22			22 22		*22 47*	23 22
Manchester Piccadilly 10	a	19 10			19 38				20 10		20 38			21 10			21 38			22 38		23 17	23 38
	d	19 12			19 42				20 12		20 42			21 12			21 42			22 42		23 19	23 40
Manchester Victoria	d			19 27						20 27					21 27				22 27		23 00		
Ashton-under-Lyne	d			19 37						20 37					21 37				22 37		23 09		
Stalybridge	a	19 25		19 41					20 25	20 41				21 25	21 41		21 55		22 41	22 55	23 14	23 33	
	d	19 25		19 42					20 25	20 42				21 25	21 42		21 55		22 42	22 55	23 14	23 33	
Mossley (Grtr Manchester)	d			19 46						20 46					21 46				22 46		23 19		
Greenfield	d			19 50						20 50					21 50				22 50		23 23		
Marsden	d			19 59						20 59					21 59				22 59		23 31		
Slaithwaite	d			20 03						21 03					22 03				23 03		23 36		
Huddersfield	a	19 44		20 11	20 14				20 44	21 11	21 15			21 44	22 11		22 14		23 11	23 14	23 45	23 50	00 23
	d	19 45			20 16		20 31	20 35	20 45		21 16	21 31	21 35	21 45			22 16	22 31		23 15		23 51	00 24
Deighton	d						20 34	20 38				21 34	21 39					22 34					
Mirfield	d		20 07				20 39	20 43				21 39	21 44					22 39					
Wakefield Kirkgate	a							20 58					21 58										
Wakefield Westgate	a							21 08					22 10										
Ravensthorpe	d						20 42					21 42						22 42					
Dewsbury	a		20 12		20 25		20 46				21 25	21 46					22 25	22 46		23 25			00 33
	d		20 12		20 25		20 46				21 25	21 46					22 25	22 46		23 25			00 33
Batley	d		20 15				20 49					21 49						22 49					
Morley	d		20 21				20 55					21 55						22 55					
Cottingley	d						20 59					21 59						22 59					
Leeds 10	a	20 09	20 31		20 40		21 07		21 09		21 39	22 08		22 09			22 39	23 07		23 39		00 34	00 55
	d	20 12			20 45	21 05			21 12		21 42			22 12		22 22	22 42			23 42		00 38	01 03
Garforth	d																						
South Milford	a					21 17										22 34							
Selby	a					21 27										22 44							
Howden	a					21 36																	
Brough	a					21 48										23 03							
Hull	a					22 05										23 21							
York 8	a	20 36			21 09				21 40		22 08			22 38			23 12			00 08		01 15	01 52
	d	20 38			21 12						22 15						23 22						
Malton	d	21 03									22 39												
Seamer	a	21 20									22 56												
Scarborough	a	21 31									23 04												
Thirsk	a				21 28												23 38						
Northallerton	a	21e03			21 36				*22 27*								23 55						
Darlington 7	a	21e16			21 47				*22 18*					*23 49*			00 06			*01 26*			
Yarm	d																						
Thornaby	a																						
Middlesbrough	a																						
Durham	a	21e34			22 04				*22 35*					*00 07*			00 24			*01 44*			
Chester-le-Street	a	21e45							*22 45*														
Newcastle 8	a	21e52			22 22				*22 59*					*00 40*			00 57			*02 23*			

For general notes see front of timetable
For details of catering facilities see Directory of Train Operators

A From Hebden Bridge (Table 41)
B From Leeds (Table 41)
C From Wigan Wallgate (Table 82)
b Change at Manchester Piccadilly
c Change at Manchester Oxford Road and Manchester Piccadilly
e Change at York

Table 39

Saturdays

Liverpool, Manchester Airport and Manchester → Huddersfield → Wakefield, Leeds, Hull, York, Scarborough, Middlesbrough and Newcastle

Network Diagram - see first page of Table 39

		TP	TP	TP	TP	TP	NT	NT	TP	TP	TP	NT	NT		TP	NT	TP	TP	NT	NT	TP	NT	NT	TP	TP
		1◇	1◇	1◇	1◇	1◇			1◇	1◇	1◇				1◇		1◇	1◇			1◇			1◇	1◇
																A							B	C	D
											trolley				trolley		trolley	trolley			trolley				trolley
Liverpool Lime Street 10	d														06 18					06 39	06b47				07 18
Warrington Central	d														06 42						07b15				07 43
Birchwood	d														06 47						07b20				07 48
Manchester Oxford Road	d										06b32				07 07		07b13				07b43				08 07
Manchester Airport	d	01 00	03 17		04 34	05 34				05 47	06 23				06 44		07 02				07 34				
Manchester Piccadilly 10	a	01 14	03 31			05 48					06 40				07 10		07 19				07 48				08 10
	d	01 15	03 38		05 39	05 57				06 21	06 53				07 12		07 25	07 35			07 55				08 12
Manchester Victoria	d												06 57							07 39					
Ashton-under-Lyne	d												07 07							07 49					
Stalybridge	a				05 52						07 06		07 11		07 25		07 38			07 54	08 08				08 24
	d				05 52						07 06		07 12		07 25		07 38			07 54	08 08				08 25
Mossley (Grtr Manchester)	d												07 16							07 59					
Greenfield	d												07 20							08 03					
Marsden	d											07 20	07 29							08 11					
Slaithwaite	d											07 24	07 33							08 16					
Huddersfield	a	02 00	04 22		06 10	06 26				06 52	07 24	07 31	07 41		07 44		07 56	08 07		08 24	08 25				08 44
	d	02 04	04 26		06 11	06 27	06 31	06 41		06 53	07 25	07 32			07 45		07 57	08 10	08 14		08 27	08 33	08 37		08 45
Deighton	d						06 34	06 45				07 36							08 17			08 36	08 40		
Mirfield	d						06 39	06 50				07 41				07 54			08 22			08 41	08 45		
Wakefield Kirkgate	a							07 03				07 57											09 00		
Wakefield Westgate	a							07 10				08 08											09 08		
Ravensthorpe	d						06 42												08 25			08 44			
Dewsbury	a					06 36	06 46			07 03					07 54	07 59	08 06	08 19	08 28		08 37	08 48			
	d					06 37	06 46			07 03					07 55	08 00	08 07	08 20	08 28		08 37	08 53 ↳			
Batley	d						06 49									08 03			08 31						
Morley	d						06 55									08 09			08 37						
Cottingley	d						06 59												08 40						
Leeds 10	a	02 40	04 47		06 32	06 52	07 07			07 20	07 47				08 10	08c18	08 23	08 35	08 51		08 54				09 06
	d	02 45	04 49		06 35	06 55				07 23	07 50				08 12		08 27	08 38			08 57				09 12
Garforth	d										08 00						08 35				09 05				
South Milford	a																								
Selby	a									07 42								08 57							
Howden	a									07 51															
Brough	a									08 03															
Hull	a									08 20								09 33							
York 8	a	03 14	05 30		07 02	07 22					08 20				08 34		08 53				09 25				09 36
	d		05 40	06 38	07 06	07 25			07 32		08 22				08 38		08 57				09 26			09 28	09 38
Malton	d			07 02		07 49									09 02										10 02
Seamer	a			07 19		08 06									09 19										10 19
Scarborough	a			07 30		08 14									09 30									10 16	10 30
Thirsk	a		06 01		07 22				07 54		08 44										09 45				
Northallerton	a		06 17		07 30				08 02		08 55						09 17				09 54				
Darlington 7	a		06 28		07 41												09 29								
Yarm	d								08 16		09 12										10 10				
Thornaby	a		06 52						08 24		09 22										10 20				
Middlesbrough	a		07 01						08 32		09 32										10 30				
Durham	a				07 58												09 46								
Chester-le-Street	a				08 04																				
Newcastle 8	a				08 19												10 02								

For general notes see front of timetable
For details of catering facilities see Directory of Train Operators

A Until 6 September. From Hebden Bridge (Table 41)
B From Selby (Table 41)
C 19 July to 6 September
D Also stops at Widnes 0736 and Irlam 0753
b Change at Manchester Piccadilly
c From 13 September arr. 0820

Liverpool, Manchester Airport and Manchester → Huddersfield → Wakefield, Leeds, Hull, York, Scarborough, Middlesbrough and Newcastle

Network Diagram - see first page of Table 39

		NT	TP	NT		NT	NT	TP	EM	TP	NT	NT	TP	TP	NT	NT	NT		TP	TP	NT	NT	TP	TP	TP
			1 ◇					1 ◇	1 ◇	1 ◇			1 ◇	1 ◇					1 ◇	1 ◇			1 ◇	1 ◇	1 ◇
				A					B	C		D			A							D	E		
			🛒						🍽	🛒			🛒	🛒						🛒				🛒	
Liverpool Lime Street 10	d					07 18	07 47			07b47			08 21				08 48			08b52				09 22	
Warrington Central	d									08b16			08 44							09b17				09 44	
Birchwood	d									08b21			08 49							09c03				09 49	
Manchester Oxford Road	d							08 21		08b45			09 07						09 27	09b43				10 07	
Manchester Airport ✈	d		08 04					08 07		08 33				09 04					09 07	09 34					10 04
Manchester Piccadilly 10	a		08 20							08 50			09 10	09 20						09 48				10 10	10 19
	d		08 25					08 42		08 57			09 12	09 27					09 42	09 57				10 12	10 27
Manchester Victoria	d					08 27	08 57									09 27	09 57								
Ashton-under-Lyne	d					08 37	09 07									09 37	10 07								
Stalybridge	a					08 41	09 13						09 25			09 42	10 13							10 25	
	d					08 42							09 25			09 42								10 25	
Mossley (Grtr Manchester)	d					08 46										09 47									
Greenfield	d					08 51										09 51									
Marsden	d					08 59										09 59									
Slaithwaite	d					09 03										10 04									
Huddersfield	a		08 55			09 11		09 14		09 26			09 44	09 56		10 12			10 15	10 26				10 44	10 56
	d		08 57					09 15		09 27	09 31	09 35	09 45	09 57					10 16	10 27	10 31	10 35		10 45	10 57
Deighton	d										09 34	09 38									10 34	10 38			
Mirfield	d			09 07							09 39	09 43			10 07						10 39	10 43			
Wakefield Kirkgate	a											09 58										10 56			
Wakefield Westgate	a											10 10										11 08			
Ravensthorpe	d										09 42										10 42				
Dewsbury	a	⟵	09 06	09 12						09 36	09 46			10 06	10 12					10 36	10 46				11 06
	d	08 53	09 07	09 12						09 37	09 46			10 07	10 12					10 37	10 46				11 07
Batley	d	08 56		09 15							09 49				10 15						10 49				
Morley	d	09 02		09 21							09 55				10 21						10 55				
Cottingley	d	09 06									09 59										10 59				
Leeds 10	a	09 16	09 22	09 31				09 36		09 52	10 07		10 09	10 22	10 31				10 36	10 52	11 07			11 09	11 22
	d		09 27					09 38		09 57			10 12	10 27					10 38	10 57				11 12	11 27
Garforth	d									10 05										11 05					
South Milford	a																								
Selby	a							09 57											10 59						
Howden	a																								
Brough	a							10 15											11 17						
Hull	a							10 33											11 34						
York 8	a		09 52							10 23			10 35	10 52						11 23				11 35	11 52
	d		09 56						10 24	10 26			10 38	10 54						11 26			11 28	11 38	11 54
Malton	d												11 02											12 02	
Seamer	a												11 19											12 19	
Scarborough	a								11 06				11 30										12 14	12 30	
Thirsk	a									10 45										11 42					
Northallerton	a		10 25							10 55				11 15						11 55					12 15
Darlington 7	a		10 36											11 26											12 26
Yarm	d									11 10										12 10					
Thornaby	a									11 20										12 18					
Middlesbrough	a									11 30										12 30					
Durham	a		10 53											11 43											12 44
Chester-le-Street	a		10 59																						
Newcastle 8	a		11 14											11 59											13 00

For general notes see front of timetable
For details of catering facilities see Directory of Train Operators

A From Hebden Bridge (Table 41)
B Until 6 September. From St Pancras International (Table 53)
C Also stops at Heald Green 0837
D From Selby (Table 41)
E 19 July to 6 September
b Change at Manchester Piccadilly
c Change at Manchester Oxford Road and Manchester Piccadilly

Liverpool, Manchester Airport and Manchester → Huddersfield → Wakefield, Leeds, Hull, York, Scarborough, Middlesbrough and Newcastle

Network Diagram - see first page of Table 39

Station		NT	NT	NT	TP	TP	NT	NT		TP	TP	TP	NT	NT	NT	TP	TP	NT	NT	TP	TP		NT	NT	NT
					1 ◇	1 ◇				1 ◇	1 ◇	1 ◇				1 ◇	1 ◇			1 ◇	1 ◇				
		A						B		C			A						B				A		
					🍴	🍴					🍴	🍴					🍴			🍴	🍴				
Liverpool Lime Street 10	d			09 48		09b52					10 22				10 48		10b52			11 22					11 48
Warrington Central	d					10b17					10 44						11b17			11 44					
Birchwood	d					10c03					10 49						11c03			11 49					
Manchester Oxford Road	d				10 27	10b43					11 07					11 27	11b43			12 07					
Manchester Airport ✈	d				10 07	10 34						11 04				11 07	11 34				12 04				
Manchester Piccadilly 10	a					10 48					11 10	11 19					11 48			12 10	12 19				
	d				10 42	10 57					11 12	11 27				11 42	11 57			12 12	12 27				
Manchester Victoria	d		10 27	10 57										11 27	11 57									12 27	12 57
Ashton-under-Lyne	d		10 37	11 07										11 37	12 07									12 37	13 07
Stalybridge	a		10 41	11 13							11 25			11 41	12 13					12 25				12 41	13 13
	d		10 42								11 25			11 42						12 25				12 42	
Mossley (Grtr Manchester)	d		10 47											11 47										12 47	
Greenfield	d		10 51											11 51										12 51	
Marsden	d		10 59											11 59										12 59	
Slaithwaite	d		11 04											12 04										13 04	
Huddersfield	a		11 12		11 15	11 26					11 44	11 56		12 12		12 15	12 26			12 44	12 56			13 12	
	d				11 16	11 27	11 31	11 35			11 45	11 57				12 16	12 27	12 31	12 35	12 45	12 57				
Deighton	d						11 34	11 38										12 34	12 38						
Mirfield	d	11 07					11 39	11 43					12 07					12 39	12 43				13 07		
Wakefield Kirkgate	a							11 56											12 56						
Wakefield Westgate	a							12 08											13 08						
Ravensthorpe	d						11 42											12 42							
Dewsbury	a	11 12				11 36	11 46					12 06	12 12				12 36	12 46			13 06		13 12		
	d	11 12				11 37	11 46					12 07	12 12				12 37	12 46			13 07		13 12		
Batley	d	11 15					11 49						12 15					12 49					13 15		
Morley	d	11 21					11 55						12 21					12 55					13 21		
Cottingley	d						11 59											12 59							
Leeds 10	a	11 31			11 36	11 52	12 07				12 09	12 22	12 31			12 36	12 52	13 07		13 09	13 22		13 31		
	d				11 38	11 57					12 12	12 27				12 38	12 57			13 12	13 27				
Garforth	d					12 05											13 05								
South Milford	a																								
Selby	a				11 57											12 57									
Howden	a																								
Brough	a				12 15											13 15									
Hull	a				12 33											13 33									
York 8	a					12 23					12 35	12 52					13 23			13 35	13 52				
	d					12 26				12 28	12 38	12 54					13 26			13 38	13 54				
Malton	d										13 02									14 02					
Seamer	a										13 19									14 19					
Scarborough	a									13 14	13 30									14 30					
Thirsk	a					12 46											13 43								
Northallerton	a					12 55						13 23					13 55				14 22				
Darlington 7	a											13 34									14 34				
Yarm	d					13 10											14 10								
Thornaby	a					13 20											14 18								
Middlesbrough	a					13 30											14 30								
Durham	a											13 51									14 51				
Chester-le-Street	a											13 57													
Newcastle 8	a											14 12									15 10				

For general notes see front of timetable
For details of catering facilities see Directory of Train Operators

A From Hebden Bridge (Table 41)
B From Selby (Table 41)
C 19 July to 6 September
b Change at Manchester Piccadilly
c Change at Manchester Oxford Road and Manchester Piccadilly

Liverpool, Manchester Airport and Manchester → Huddersfield → Wakefield, Leeds, Hull, York, Scarborough, Middlesbrough and Newcastle

Network Diagram - see first page of Table 39

		TP	TP	NT	NT	TP	TP	NT	NT	NT	TP	TP		NT	NT	TP	TP	NT	NT	NT	TP	TP	NT	NT	TP
		1 ◇	1 ◇			1 ◇	1 ◇				1 ◇	1 ◇				1 ◇	1 ◇				1 ◇	1 ◇			1 ◇
					A			B							A			B						A	
			⊼			⊼	⊼				⊼	⊼				⊼	⊼								⊼
Liverpool Lime Street 10	d		11b52			12 22				12 48		12b52				13 22				13 48		13b52			14 22
Warrington Central	d		12b17			12 44						13b17				13 44						14b17			14 44
Birchwood	d		12c03			12 49						13c03				13 49						14c03			14 49
Manchester Oxford Road	d	12 27	12b43			13 07					13 27	13b43				14 07					14 27	14b43			15 07
Manchester Airport	d	12 07	12 34				13 04				13 07	13 34					14 04				14 07	14 34			
Manchester Piccadilly 10	a		12 48			13 10	13 19					13 48				14 10	14 19					14 48			15 10
	d	12 42	12 57			13 12	13 27				13 42	13 57				14 12	14 27				14 42	14 57			15 12
Manchester Victoria	d								13 27	13 57									14 27	14 57					
Ashton-under-Lyne	d								13 37	14 07									14 37	15 07					
Stalybridge	a					13 25			13 41	14 13						14 25			14 41	15 13					15 25
	d					13 25			13 42							14 25			14 42						15 25
Mossley (Grtr Manchester)	d								13 47										14 47						
Greenfield	d								13 51										14 51						
Marsden	d								13 59										14 59						
Slaithwaite	d								14 04										15 04						
Huddersfield	a	13 15	13 26			13 44	13 56		14 12		14 15	14 26				14 44	14 56		15 12		15 15	15 26			15 44
	d	13 16	13 27	13 31	13 35	13 45	13 57				14 16	14 27		14 31	14 35	14 45	14 57				15 16	15 27	15 31	15 35	15 45
Deighton	d			13 34	13 38									14 34	14 38								15 34	15 38	
Mirfield	d			13 39	13 43			14 07						14 39	14 43			15 07					15 39	15 43	
Wakefield Kirkgate	a				13 56										14 58									15 58	
Wakefield Westgate	a				14 08										15 08									16 08	
Ravensthorpe	d			13 42										14 42									15 42		
Dewsbury	a		13 36	13 46			14 06	14 12				14 36		14 46			15 06	15 12				15 36	15 46		
	d		13 37	13 46			14 07	14 12				14 37		14 46			15 07	15 12				15 37	15 46		
Batley	d			13 49				14 15						14 49				15 15					15 49		
Morley	d			13 55				14 21						14 55				15 21					15 55		
Cottingley	d			13 59										14 59									15 59		
Leeds 10	a	13 36	13 52	14 07		14 09	14 22	14 31			14 36	14 52		15 07		15 09	15 22	15 31			15 36	15 52	16 07		16 09
	d	13 38	13 57			14 12	14 27				14 38	14 57				15 12	15 27				15 38	15 57			16 12
Garforth	d		14 05									15 05										16 05			
South Milford	a																								
Selby	a	13 57									14 57										15 57				
Howden	a																								
Brough	a	14 15									15 15										16 15				
Hull	a	14 33									15 33										16 33				
York 8	a		14 23			14 35	14 52					15 23				15 35	15 52					16 23			16 35
	d		14 26			14 38	14 54					15 26				15 38						16 26			16 38
Malton	d					15 02										16 02									17 02
Seamer	a					15 19										16 19									17 19
Scarborough	a					15 30										16 30									17 30
Thirsk	a		14 45									15 45										16 44			
Northallerton	a		15 00				15 22					15 55										16 55			
Darlington 7	a						15 34																		
Yarm	d		15 15									16 09										17 09			
Thornaby	a		15 27									16 21										17 22			
Middlesbrough	a		15 34									16 30										17 33			
Durham	a						15 51																		
Chester-le-Street	a						15 57																		
Newcastle 8	a						16 13																		

For general notes see front of timetable
For details of catering facilities see Directory of Train Operators

A From Selby (Table 41)
B From Hebden Bridge (Table 41)
b Change at Manchester Piccadilly
c Change at Manchester Oxford Road and Manchester Piccadilly

Table 39

Saturdays

Liverpool, Manchester Airport and Manchester → Huddersfield → Wakefield, Leeds, Hull, York, Scarborough, Middlesbrough and Newcastle

Network Diagram - see first page of Table 39

		TP	NT		NT	NT	NT	TP	TP	NT	NT	TP	TP	NT	NT	TP		TP	NT	NT	NT	NT	TP	NT	TP
		1 ◇						1 ◇	1 ◇			1 ◇	1 ◇			1 ◇		1 ◇					1 ◇		1 ◇
			A		B						C	D		B						C					
		🛒							🛒																
Liverpool Lime Street [10]	d						14 48		14b52			15 22						15b52	15 48				16 22		
Warrington Central	d								15b17			15 44						16b17					16 44		
Birchwood	d								15c03			15 49											16 49		
Manchester Oxford Road	d							15 27	15b43			16 07				16 27		16b38					17 07		
Manchester Airport ✈	d	15 04						15 07	15 34				16 04			16 07		16 34							17 04
Manchester Piccadilly [10]	a	15 19							15 48			16 10	16 19					16 48					17 10		17 19
	d	15 27						15 42	15 57			16 12	16 27			16 42		16 55					17 12		17 25
Manchester Victoria	d					15 27	15 57								16 27				16 57						
Ashton-under-Lyne	d					15 37	16 07								16 37				17 07						
Stalybridge	a					15 41	16 13					16 25			16 41			17 08	17 13				17 25		17 38
	d					15 42						16 25			16 42			17 08					17 25		17 38
Mossley (Grtr Manchester)	d					15 47									16 47										
Greenfield	d					15 51									16 51										
Marsden	d					15 59									16 59							17 29			
Slaithwaite	d					16 04									17 04							17 33			
Huddersfield	a	15 56				16 12		16 15	16 26			16 44	16 56		17 12	17 15		17 26				17 41	17 44		17 56
	d	15 57	16 10					16 16	16 27	16 31	16 35	16 45	16 57			17 16		17 27		17 33	17 37		17 45		17 58
Deighton	d									16 34	16 38									17 36	17 40				
Mirfield	d		15 51		16 07					16 39	16 43			17 07						17 41	17 45				
Wakefield Kirkgate	a		↪								16 58									17 58					
Wakefield Westgate	a										17 08									18 06					
Ravensthorpe	d									16 42											17 48				
Dewsbury	a	16 06			16 12				16 36	16 46			17 06	17 12				17 36			17 52			←	18 07
	d	16 07			16 12				16 37	16 46			17 07	17 12				17 37			17 55 ↪			17 55	18 07
Batley	d				16 15					16 49				17 15										17 58	
Morley	d				16 21					16 55				17 21										18 04	
Cottingley	d									16 59														18 08	
Leeds [10]	a	16 22			16 31			16 36	16 52	17 07		17 09	17 22	17 31		17 37		17 52					18 09	18 18	18 22
	d	16 27						16 38	16 57			17 12	17 24			17 38		17 57					18 12		18 27
Garforth	d								17 05				17 34					18 05							
South Milford	a																								
Selby	a							16 57								17 58									
Howden	a															18 07									
Brough	a							17 15								18 19									
Hull	a							17 34								18 37									
York [8]	a	16 52							17 22			17 38	17 57					18 25					18 35		18 52
	d	17 02							17 26			17 43	18 00					18 26					18 38		18 56
Malton	d								17 50				18 24										19 02		
Seamer	a								18 07				18 41										19 19		
Scarborough	a								18 17				18 51										19 30		
Thirsk	a	17 20										17 59						18 44							
Northallerton	a	17 28										18 09						18 55							19 20
Darlington [7]	a	17 39																							19 33
Yarm	d											18 24						19 09							
Thornaby	a											18 32						19 17							
Middlesbrough	a											18 42						19 30							
Durham	a	17 56																							19 50
Chester-le-Street	a	18 02																							19 56
Newcastle [8]	a	18 17																							20 10

For general notes see front of timetable
For details of catering facilities see Directory of Train Operators

- **A** From Wakefield Westgate
- **B** From Hebden Bridge (Table 41)
- **C** From Selby (Table 41)
- **D** Also stops at Cross Gates 1718
- **b** Change at Manchester Piccadilly
- **c** Change at Manchester Oxford Road and Manchester Piccadilly

Table 39

Saturdays

Liverpool, Manchester Airport and Manchester → Huddersfield → Wakefield, Leeds, Hull, York, Scarborough, Middlesbrough and Newcastle

Network Diagram - see first page of Table 39

		NT	NT	TP 1 ◇	NT	TP 1 ◇	NT		NT A	TP 1 ◇	NT B	TP 1 ◇	NT	TP 1 ◇	TP 1 ◇	NT	NT A	TP 1 ◇	NT B	NT		TP 1 ◇	TP 1 ◇	NT	NT A
Liverpool Lime Street 10	d		16 18			16b52	16 48			17 22					17b52			18 22							
Warrington Central	d					17b17				17 44					18b17			18 44							
Birchwood	d									17 49					18c08			18 49							
Manchester Oxford Road	d			17 27		17b38				18 07				18 18	18b39			19 07				19b17			
Manchester Airport ✈	d					17 34						17 52		18 10	18 34							19 15			
Manchester Piccadilly 10	a					17 49				18 10					18 52			19 10				19 38			
	d			17 42		17 55				18 12		18 27		18 41	18 57			19 12				19 42			
Manchester Victoria	d		17 27				17 57						18 27							19 27					
Ashton-under-Lyne	d		17 37				18 07						18 37							19 37					
Stalybridge	a		17 41			18 08	18 13			18 25			18 41					19 25		19 41					
	d		17 42			18 08				18 25			18 42					19 25		19 42					
Mossley (Grtr Manchester)	d		17 47										18 47							19 46					
Greenfield	d		17 51										18 51							19 50					
Marsden	d		17 59										18 59							19 59					
Slaithwaite	d		18 04										19 04							20 03					
Huddersfield	a		18 12	18 15		18 26				18 45		18 56	19 12	19 15	19 26			19 44		20 11		20 14			
	d	18 07		18 16		18 27			18 34	18 47		18 57		19 16	19 27	19 31	19 35	19 45				20 16		20 31	20 35
Deighton	d	18 10							18 37							19 34	19 38							20 34	20 38
Mirfield	d	18 15							18 42		18 47					19 39	19 43		20 07					20 39	20 43
Wakefield Kirkgate	a								18 58								19 58								20 58
Wakefield Westgate	a								19 08								20 08								21 07
Ravensthorpe	d	18 18									18 50					19 42								20 42	
Dewsbury	a	18 22			←	18 36					18 54	19 06			19 36	19 46			20 12			20 25		20 46	
	d	18 25			18 25	18 37					18 57	19 07			19 37	19 46			20 12			20 25		20 46	
Batley	d	↳			18 28						19 00					19 49			20 15					20 49	
Morley	d				18 34						19 06					19 55			20 21					20 55	
Cottingley	d				18 37											19 59								20 59	
Leeds 10	a			18 36	18 45	18 53				19 09	19 18	19 24		19 36	19 52	20 07		20 09	20 32			20 40		21 07	
	d			18 38		18 57				19 12		19 27		19 38	19 57			20 12				20 45	21 05		
Garforth	d					19 05									20 05										
South Milford	a			18 51										19 51									21 17		
Selby	a			19 00										20 00									21 27		
Howden	a													20 09									21 36		
Brough	a			19 18										20 21									21 48		
Hull	a			19 36										20 39									22 05		
York 8	a					19 22				19 35		19 58			20 24			20 36				21 09			
	d					19 26				19 38					20 26			20 38				21 12			
Malton	d									20 02								21 02							
Seamer	a									20 19								21 19							
Scarborough	a									20 30								21 30							
Thirsk	a					19 42									20 43							21 28			
Northallerton	a					19 50									20 51							21 36			
Darlington 7	a																					21 47			
Yarm	d					20 04									21 05										
Thornaby	a					20 12									21 14										
Middlesbrough	a					20 23									21 25										
Durham	a																					22 04			
Chester-le-Street	a																								
Newcastle 8	a																					22 22			

For general notes see front of timetable
For details of catering facilities see Directory of Train Operators

A From Selby (Table 41)
B From Hebden Bridge (Table 41)
b Change at Manchester Piccadilly
c Change at Manchester Oxford Road and Manchester Piccadilly

Liverpool, Manchester Airport and Manchester → Huddersfield → Wakefield, Leeds, Hull, York, Scarborough, Middlesbrough and Newcastle

Network Diagram - see first page of Table 39

		TP 1 ◇	NT	TP 1 ◇	NT	NT	TP 1 ◇	NT	TP 1 ◇	TP 1 ◇	NT A	NT B	NT	TP 1 ◇	NT C	NT D	TP 1 ◇ E	TP 1 ◇ G	TP 1 ◇ A	TP 1 ◇ B	NT A (bus)	TP A (bus)
Liverpool Lime Street 10	d	19 22					20 22										22 30	22 30	22 30			
Warrington Central	d	19 44					20 44										22 52	22 52	22 52			
Birchwood	d	19 49					20 49										22 57	22 57	22 57			
Manchester Oxford Road	d	20 07					21 07			21b27				22b16			23 15	23 15	23 15	23b26		23b33
Manchester Airport ✈	d	19 30		20 22						21 22				22 22			22 47	22 47	22 47	23 22		23 25
Manchester Piccadilly 10	a	20 10		20 38			21 10			21 37				22 38			23 17	23 17	23 17	23 38		23 50
	d	20 12		20 42			21 12			21 42				22 42			23 19	23 19	23 19	23 42		23 50
Manchester Victoria	d		20 27					21 27					22 27		23 00	23 00						
Ashton-under-Lyne	d		20 37					21 37					22 37		23 09	23 09						
Stalybridge	a	20 25	20 41				21 25	21 41		21 55			22 41	22 55	23 14	23 14	23 33	23 33	23 33			
	d	20 25	20 42				21 25	21 42		21 55			22 42	22 55	23 14	23 14	23 33	23 33	23 33			
Mossley (Grtr Manchester)	d		20 46					21 46					22 46		23 19	23 19						
Greenfield	d		20 50					21 50					22 50		23 23	23a25					23 32	
Marsden	d		20 59		21 19			21 59					22 59		23 31						23 57	
Slaithwaite	d		21 03		21 23			22 03					23 03		23 36						00 04	
Huddersfield	a	20 44	21 11	21 15	21 30		21 44	22 12		22 15			23 11	23 14	23 44		23 51	23 51	23 52	00 14	00 22	00 50
	d	20 45		21 16	21 31	21 35	21 45			22 16	22 19	22 31		23 16			23 51	23 51		00 15		00 50
Deighton	d				21 34	21 39					22 22	22 34										
Mirfield	d				21 39	21 44					22 27	22 39										
Wakefield Kirkgate	a					21 58																
Wakefield Westgate	a					22 10																
Ravensthorpe	d				21 42						22 30	22 42										
Dewsbury	a			21 25	21 46					22 25	22 34	22 46		23 25						00 24		01 10
	d			21 25	21 46					22 25	22 34	22 46		23 25						00 24		01 10
Batley	d				21 49						22 37	22 49										
Morley	d				21 55						22 43	22 55										
Cottingley	d				21 59						22 47	22 59										
Leeds 10	a	21 09		21 39	22 07		22 09			22 39	22 55	23 07		23 39			00 13	00 13		00 39		01 35
	d	21 12		21 42			22 12		22 22	22 42				23 42			00 15	00 15		00 43		01 35
Garforth	d																					
South Milford	a								22 35													
Selby	a								22 45													
Howden	a																					
Brough	a								23 04													
Hull	a								23 21													
York 8	a	21 40		22 05			22 38			23 09				00 08			00 41	01 08		01 35		02 20
	d			22 08																		
Malton	d			22 32																		
Seamer	a			22 49																		
Scarborough	a			23 02																		
Thirsk	a																					
Northallerton	a																					
Darlington 7	a																					
Yarm	d																					
Thornaby	a																					
Middlesbrough	a																					
Durham	a																					
Chester-le-Street	a																					
Newcastle 8	a																					

For general notes see front of timetable
For details of catering facilities see Directory of Train Operators

- **A** From 13 September
- **B** Until 6 September
- **C** Until 6 September. From Wigan Wallgate (Table 82)
- **D** From 13 September. From Wigan Wallgate (Table 82)
- **E** Until 12 July
- **G** 19 July to 6 September
- **b** Change at Manchester Piccadilly

Table 39

until 13 July

Liverpool, Manchester Airport and Manchester → Huddersfield → Leeds, Hull, York, Scarborough, Middlesbrough and Newcastle

Network Diagram - see first page of Table 39

		TP 1◇	TP 1◇	TP 1◇	NT	TP 1◇	NT		TP 1◇	TP 1◇	TP 1◇	TP 1◇	NT	TP 1◇		NT	TP 1◇	TP 1◇	NT	TP 1◇	TP 1◇		TP 1◇	NT	TP 1◇
Liverpool Lime Street [10]	d										08 22							09 22			*09 30*				*09b57*
Warrington Central	d										08 44							09 45							*10b32*
Birchwood	d										08 49							09 50							*10b37*
Newton-le-Willows	d																								
Manchester Oxford Road	d										09 07							10 07							
Manchester Airport ✈	d	01 22	04 37	06 09		07 09				08 22	*08 47*			*08 51*			09 25	*09 47*		10 22	*10 47*				11 22
Manchester Piccadilly [10] 🚢	a	01 35	04 50	06 25		07 23				08 38	09 10						09 41	10 10		10 38					11 38
	d	01 37	04 52	06 29		07 26				08 42	09 12			09 30			09 42	10 12		10 42	11 12				11 42
Manchester Victoria 🚢	a																								
	d						08 18												10 18						
Ashton-under-Lyne	d						08 28												10 28						
Stalybridge	a			06 55		07 55	08 32			08 55				09 43				10 25	10 32		11 25				
	d			06 55		07 55	08 33			08 55				09 43				10 25	10 33		11 25				
Mossley (Grtr Manchester)	d						08 37												10 37						
Greenfield	d						08 41												10 41						
Marsden	d						08 50						09 40						10 50					11 47	
Slaithwaite	d						08 54						09 44						10 54					11 51	
Huddersfield	a	02 20	05 36	07 11		08 11	09 02			09 11	09 41		09 51	10 01			10 14	10 43	11 02	11 11	11 43			11 58	12 11
	d	02 21	05 37	07 12	07 48	08 12				09 12	09 42		09 51	10 02			10 14	10 44		11 12	11 44			11 58	12 12
Deighton	d				07 51								09 55											12 02	
Mirfield	d				07 56								10 00											12 07	
Ravensthorpe	d				07 59								10 03											12 10	
Dewsbury	a			07 22	08 03	08 22				09 22			10 06			←	10 25			11 21				12 13	12 21
	d			07 22	08 08	08 22				09 22			10 10 →			10 10	10 25			11 22				12 14	12 22
Batley	d				08 11											10 13								12 17	
Morley	d				08 17											10 19								12 23	
Cottingley	d				08 20											10 22								12 26	
Leeds [10]	a	02 42	05 58	07 39	08 28	08 39				09 38	10 03			10 23		10 30	10 41	11 05		11 38	12 05			12 34	12 37
	d	02 44	06 01	07 40		08 40			09 10	09 40	10 05			10 25			10 42	11 10		11 40	12 10				12 40
Garforth	d								09 18									11 18							
South Milford	a													10 38							12 22				
Selby	a													10 47							12 32				
Howden	a																								
Brough	a													11 07							12 53				
Hull	a													11 24							13 11				
York [8]	a	03 37	06 53	08 34		09 07			09 35	10 06	10 28						11 09	11 36		12 05					13 07
	d			08 35		09 10			09 38	10 10	10 32	10 36					11 14	11 38		12 10			12 38		13 10
Malton	d								10 02									12 02							
Seamer	a								10 19			11 14						12 19							
Scarborough	a								10 27			11 23						12 30					13 24		
Thirsk	a			08 51						10 27										12 27					
Northallerton	a			08 59		09 30				10 35							11 34			12 35					13 32
Darlington [7]	a					09 42					11 02						11 46								13 44
Yarm	d			09 14						10 49										12 49					
Thornaby	a			09 22						10 57										12 57					
Middlesbrough	a			09 35						11 10										13 10					
Durham	a					09 59					11 19						12 03								14 01
Chester-le-Street	a										11 25														14 07
Newcastle [8] 🚢	a					10 16					11 40						12 19								14 21

For general notes see front of timetable
For details of catering facilities see Directory of Train Operators

b Change at Manchester Oxford Road and Manchester Piccadilly

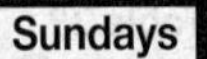

until 13 July

Liverpool, Manchester Airport and Manchester → Huddersfield → Leeds, Hull, York, Scarborough, Middlesbrough and Newcastle

Network Diagram - see first page of Table 39

		TP 1◇	NT	TP 1◇	TP 1◇	NT		TP 1◇	TP 1◇	NT	TP 1◇	TP 1◇	TP 1◇		TP 1◇	NT	TP 1◇	TP 1◇	TP 1◇	NT		TP 1◇	TP 1◇	TP 1◇	TP 1◇
Liverpool Lime Street 10	d	11 22			12 22				13 22		13b30	13 52	14 22					14 52	15 22				15 52	16 22	
Warrington Central	d	11 44			12 45				13 44		13b44	14 18	14 44					15 18	15 44				16 18	16 44	
Birchwood	d	11 49							13 49		13b49		14 49						15 49					16 49	
Newton-le-Willows	d																								
Manchester Oxford Road	d	12 07			13 05				14 07				15 07						16 07					17 07	
Manchester Airport ✈	d	11 47		12 22	12 45			13 22	13 47		14 22	14 27	14 47				15 17	15 27	15 47			16 22	16 27	16 47	
Manchester Piccadilly 10	a	12 10		12 37	13 07			13 37	14 10		14 37		15 10				15 39		16 10			16 38		17 10	
	d	12 15		12 42	13 11			13 42	14 12		14 42	15 00	15 12				15 42	16 00	16 12			16 42	17 00	17 12	
Manchester Victoria	a																								
	d		12 18							14 18										16 18					
Ashton-under-Lyne	d		12 28							14 28										16 28					
Stalybridge	a	12 28	12 32		13 25				14 25	14 32			15 25						16 25	16 32				17 25	
	d	12 28	12 33		13 25				14 25	14 33			15 25						16 25	16 33				17 25	
Mossley (Grtr Manchester)	d		12 37							14 37										16 37					
Greenfield	d		12 41							14 41										16 41					
Marsden	d		12 50			13 47				14 50						15 48				16 50					
Slaithwaite	d		12 54			13 51				14 54						15 52				16 54					
Huddersfield	a	12 46	13 02	13 11	13 44	13 58		14 11	14 43	15 02	15 11	15 29	15 43			15 59	16 11	16 29	16 43	17 02		17 11	17 29	17 43	
	d	12 47		13 12	13 44	13 58		14 12	14 44		15 12	15 30	15 44			15 59	16 12	16 30	16 44			17 12	17 30	17 44	
Deighton	d					14 02										16 03									
Mirfield	d					14 07										16 08									
Ravensthorpe	d					14 10										16 11									
Dewsbury	a			13 21		14 13		14 21			15 21					16 14	16 21					17 21			
	d			13 22		14 14		14 22			15 22					16 15	16 22					17 22			
Batley	d					14 17										16 18									
Morley	d					14 23										16 24									
Cottingley	d					14 26										16 27									
Leeds 10	a	13 08		13 37	14 07	14 34		14 37	15 06		15 37	15 52	16 06			16 35	16 37	16 51	17 06			17 37	17 51	18 06	
	d	13 10		13 40	14 10			14 40	15 10		15 40	15 55	16 10				16 40	16 54	17 10			17 40	17 54	18 10	
Garforth	d	13 18							15 18										17 18						
South Milford	a				14 22								16 24										18 06		
Selby	a				14 32								16 34					17 13					18 16		
Howden	a																								
Brough	a				14 53								16 53					17 36					18 35		
Hull	a				15 11								17 11					17 53					18 53		
York 8	a	13 37		14 05				15 07	15 40		16 05	16 19					17 09		17 37			18 09		18 37	
	d	13 38		14 10				15 14	15 44		16 10	16 23			16 42		17 10		17 38			18 10			18 45
Malton	d	14 02							16 08										18 02						
Seamer	a	14 19							16 25										18 19						
Scarborough	a	14 30							16 34						17 28				18 30						19 32
Thirsk	a			14 27								16 39										18 27			
Northallerton	a			14 35				15 34				16 47					17 32					18 35			
Darlington 7	a							15 46			16 41						17 44								
Yarm	d			14 49								17 03										18 49			
Thornaby	a			14 57								17 11										18 58			
Middlesbrough	a			15 10								17 22										19 10			
Durham	a							16 03			16 58						18 01								
Chester-le-Street	a																18 07								
Newcastle 8	a							16 19			17 15						18 21								

For general notes see front of timetable
For details of catering facilities see Directory of Train Operators

b Change at Manchester Piccadilly

Table 39

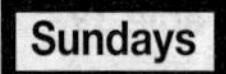

Liverpool, Manchester Airport and Manchester → Huddersfield → Leeds, Hull, York, Scarborough, Middlesbrough and Newcastle

until 13 July

Network Diagram - see first page of Table 39

		NT	TP 1◇	TP 1◇	NT		TP 1◇	TP 1◇	TP 1◇	NT	TP 1◇	TP 1◇		NT	TP 1◇	TP 1◇	TP 1◇	NT	TP 1◇		NT	TP 1◇	TP 1◇		
Liverpool Lime Street 10	d			17 22				*17 52*	18 22			19 22				20 22						21 52	*21b57*		
Warrington Central	d			17 44				*18 18*	18 44			19 44				20 44						22 15	*22b32*		
Birchwood	d			17 49					18 49			19 49				20 49						22 20	*22b37*		
Newton-le-Willows	d																								
Manchester Oxford Road	d			18 07					19 07			20 07				21 07						22 37			
Manchester Airport ✈	d		17 22	*17 47*			18 22	*18 27*	*18 47*		19 22	*19 47*			20 22	*20 47*			21 22			*22 01*	23 22		
Manchester Piccadilly 10	a		17 38	18 10			18 39		19 10		19 38	20 10			20 38	21 10			21 38			22 40	23 36		
	d		17 42	18 12			18 42	19 00	19 12		19 42	20 12			20 42	21 12			21 42			22 42	23 42		
Manchester Victoria	a																								
	d				18 18									20 18							22 18				
Ashton-under-Lyne	d				18 28									20 28							22 28				
Stalybridge	a			18 25	18 32				19 25			20 25		20 32		21 25					22 33	22 55			
	d			18 25	18 33				19 25			20 25		20 33		21 25						22 55			
Mossley (Grtr Manchester)	d				18 37									20 37											
Greenfield	d				18 41									20 41											
Marsden	d	17 47			18 50					19 48				20 50				21 48							
Slaithwaite	d	17 51			18 54					19 52				20 54				21 52							
Huddersfield	a	17 58	18 11	18 43	19 02		19 11	19 31	19 43	19 59	20 11	20 43		21 02	21 11	21 43		21 59	22 11			23 11	00 11		
	d	17 58	18 12	18 44			19 12	19 32	19 44	19 59	20 12	20 44			21 12	21 44		21 59	22 12			23 12	00 12		
Deighton	d	18 02								20 03								22 03							
Mirfield	d	18 07								20 08								22 08							
Ravensthorpe	d	18 10								20 11								22 11							
Dewsbury	a	18 13	18 21				19 21			20 14	20 21				21 21			22 14	22 21			23 22			
	d	18 14	18 22				19 22			20 15	20 22				21 22			22 15	22 22			23 22			
Batley	d	18 17								20 18								22 18							
Morley	d	18 23								20 24								22 24							
Cottingley	d	18 26								20 27								22 27							
Leeds 10	a	18 34	18 37	19 06			19 37	19 53	20 06	20 35	20 39	21 07			21 37	22 05		22 35	22 37			23 38	00 33		
	d		18 40	19 10			19 40	19 56	20 10		20 45	21 10			21 40	22 10	22 17		22 50			23 40	00 36		
Garforth	d			19 18								21 18													
South Milford	a							20 08									22 29								
Selby	a							20 18									22 39								
Howden	a																								
Brough	a							20 37									22 58								
Hull	a							20 54									23 16								
York 8	a		19 07	19 38			20 05		20 37		21 09	21 38			22 06	22 38			23 21			00 08	01 02		
	d		19 10	19 38			20 14		20 38		21 10				22 08	22 40									
Malton	d			20 02					21 02						22 32										
Seamer	a			20 19					21 19						22 49										
Scarborough	a			20 30					21 30						23 00										
Thirsk	a						20 30				21 27					23 05									
Northallerton	a		19 30				20 38				21 37					23 15									
Darlington 7	a		19 42								21 49					23 31									
Yarm	d						20 52																		
Thornaby	a						21 00																		
Middlesbrough	a						21 10																		
Durham	a		19 59								22 06					23 48									
Chester-le-Street	a		20 05																						
Newcastle 8	a		20 20								22 23					00 21									

For general notes see front of timetable
For details of catering facilities see Directory of Train Operators

b Change at Manchester Oxford Road and Manchester Piccadilly

Table 39

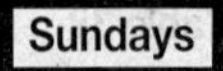

20 July to 7 September

Liverpool, Manchester Airport and Manchester → Huddersfield → Leeds, Hull, York, Scarborough, Middlesbrough and Newcastle

Network Diagram - see first page of Table 39

Station		TP 1 ◇	TP 1 ◇	TP 1 ◇	NT	NT (bus)	TP 1 ◇	NT	TP 1 ◇	TP 1 ◇	TP 1 ◇	TP 1 ◇		NT	TP 1 ◇	NT	TP 1 ◇	NT (bus)	TP 1 ◇	TP 1 ◇	NT	TP 1 ◇	TP 1 ◇	NT	NT (bus)
Liverpool Lime Street 10	d											08 22								09 22	*08 30*		*09 30*		
Warrington Central	d											08 44								09 45					
Birchwood	d											08 49								09 50					
Newton-le-Willows	d																								
Manchester Oxford Road	d											09 07								10 07					
Manchester Airport ✈	d	01 22	04 42	06 22			07 22				08 18	*08 47*					09 25			*09 46*		10 22	*10 46*		
Manchester Piccadilly 10	a	01 36	04 56	06 38			07 37				08 37	09 10					09 41			10 10		10 38			
	d	01 42	05 02	06 42			07 42	07 45			08 42	09 12			09 30		09 42			10 12	10 19	10 42	11 12		
Manchester Victoria	a																								
	d					07 20												09 55							11 55
Ashton-under-Lyne	d					07 40												10 15							12 15
Stalybridge	a			06 55		07 50	07 55	07 59			08 55				09 43			10 25		10 25	10 32		11 25		12 25
	d			06 55			07 55	08 00			08 55				09 43					10 25	10 33		11 25		
Mossley (Grtr Manchester)	d							08 04													10 37				
Greenfield	d							08 08													10 41				
Marsden	d							08 17						09 40							10 50			11 47	
Slaithwaite	d							08 21						09 44							10 54			11 51	
Huddersfield	a	02 12	05 31	07 11			08 11	08 29			09 11	09 41		09 51	10 01		10 14			10 43	11 02	11 11	11 43	11 58	
	d	02 13	05 32	07 12	07 48		08 12				09 12	09 42		09 51	10 02		10 14			10 44		11 12	11 44	11 58	
Deighton	d				07 51									09 55										12 02	
Mirfield	d				07 56									10 00										12 07	
Ravensthorpe	d				07 59									10 03										12 10	
Dewsbury	a			07 22	08 03		08 22				09 22			10 06		←	10 25					11 21		12 13	
	d			07 22	08 08		08 22				09 22			10 10 →		10 10	10 25					11 22		12 14	
Batley	d				08 11											10 13								12 17	
Morley	d				08 17											10 19								12 23	
Cottingley	d				08 20											10 22								12 26	
Leeds 10	a	02 34	05 54	07 39	08 28		08 39				09 38	10 03			10 23	10 31	10 41			11 05		11 38	12 05	12 34	
	d	02 38	05 58	07 40			08 40		09 00		09 40	10 05			10 25		10 42			11 22		11 40	12 10		
Garforth	d																								
South Milford	a																								
Selby	a																11 15						12 45		
Howden	a																*12 51*								
Brough	a																11 37						13 12		
Hull	a																11 52						13 26		
York 8	a	03 30	06 50	08 34			09 19		09 37		10 16	10 41			11 08					12 09		12 17			
	d			08 35			09 24		09 38	10 10	10 32	10 45			11 14				11 38	12 10		12 23			
Malton	d								10 02			11 12							12 02			12 47			
Seamer	a								10 19			11 29							12 19			13 04			
Scarborough	a								10 30			11 39							12 30			13 15			
Thirsk	a			08 51						10 27										12 27					
Northallerton	a			08 59			09 45			10 35					11 34					12 35					
Darlington 7	a						09 56				11 02				11 46										
Yarm	d			09 14						10 49										12 49					
Thornaby	a			09 22						10 57										12 57					
Middlesbrough	a			09 35						11 10										13 10					
Durham	a						10 13				11 19				12 03										
Chester-le-Street	a										11 25														
Newcastle 8	a						10 31				11 40				12 19										

For general notes see front of timetable
For details of catering facilities see
Directory of Train Operators

Table 39

Liverpool, Manchester Airport and Manchester → Huddersfield → Leeds, Hull, York, Scarborough, Middlesbrough and Newcastle

20 July to 7 September

Network Diagram - see first page of Table 39

		TP		TP	NT	TP	TP	NT	NT	TP	TP	NT	TP	TP		TP	NT	NT	TP	TP	TP	NT	TP	TP	TP
		1 ◇		1 ◇		1 ◇	1 ◇		🚌	1 ◇	1 ◇		1 ◇	1 ◇		1 ◇		🚌	1 ◇	1 ◇	1 ◇		1 ◇	1 ◇	1 ◇
Liverpool Lime Street 10	d	09b57		11 22			12 22				13 22	12 52	13c30	13 52		14 22				14 52	15 22			15 52	16 22
Warrington Central	d	10b32		11 44			12 45				13 44	13 18		14 18		14 44				15 18	15 44			16 18	16 44
Birchwood	d	10b37		11 49			12 50				13 49					14 49					15 49				16 49
Newton-le-Willows	d																								
Manchester Oxford Road	d			12 07			13 07				14 07					15 07					16 07				17 07
Manchester Airport ✈	d	11 22		11 46		12 22	12 46			13 22	13 46	13 49	14 22			14 46			15 20		15 46	15 49	16 22		16 46
Manchester Piccadilly 10	a	11 38		12 10		12 37	13 10			13 37	14 10		14 38			15 10			15 39		16 10		16 38		17 10
	d	11 42		12 14	12 19	12 42	13 12			13 42	14 12	14 19	14 42	14 56		15 12			15 42	16 00	16 12	16 19	16 42	17 00	17 12
Manchester Victoria	a																								
	d								13 55									15 55							
Ashton-under-Lyne	d								14 15									16 15							
Stalybridge	a			12 27	12 32		13 25		14 25		14 25	14 32				15 25		16 25			16 25	16 32			17 25
	d			12 27	12 33		13 25				14 25	14 33				15 25					16 25	16 33			17 25
Mossley (Grtr Manchester)	d				12 37							14 37										16 37			
Greenfield	d				12 41							14 41										16 41			
Marsden	d				12 50			13 47				14 50					15 48					16 50			
Slaithwaite	d				12 54			13 51				14 54					15 52					16 54			
Huddersfield	a	12 11		12 45	13 02	13 11	13 43	13 58		14 11	14 43	15 02	15 11	15 29		15 43	15 59		16 11	16 29	16 43	17 02	17 11	17 29	17 43
	d	12 12		12 46		13 12	13 44	13 58		14 12	14 44		15 12	15 30		15 44	15 59		16 12	16 30	16 44		17 12	17 30	17 44
Deighton	d							14 02									16 03								
Mirfield	d							14 07									16 08								
Ravensthorpe	d							14 10									16 11								
Dewsbury	a	12 21				13 21		14 13		14 21			15 21				16 14		16 21				17 21		
	d	12 22				13 22		14 14		14 22			15 22				16 15		16 22				17 22		
Batley	d							14 17									16 18								
Morley	d							14 23									16 24								
Cottingley	d							14 26									16 27								
Leeds 10	a	12 37		13 07		13 37	14 09	14 34		14 37	15 07		15 37	15 52		16 06	16 35		16 37	16 52	17 06		17 37	17 51	18 06
	d	12 40		13 22		13 40	14 10			14 40	15 12		15 40	16 00		16 10			16 40	16 54	17 12		17 40	18 00	18 10
Garforth	d																								
South Milford	a																								
Selby	a						14 45													17 35				18 31	
Howden	a																								
Brough	a						15 05													17 54				18 50	
Hull	a						15 23													18 11				19 08	
York 8	a	13 19		13 59		14 21				15 20	15 50		16 20	16 35		16 47			17 21		17 47		18 20		18 49
	d	13 23		14 10						15 23	16 10		16 23	16 38		17 10			17 23		17 52		18 23		19 10
Malton	d	13 47								15 47									17 47				18 47		
Seamer	a	14 04								16 04									18 04				19 04		
Scarborough	a	14 15								16 15			17 11						18 15				19 15		
Thirsk	a			14 27										17 00							18 14				
Northallerton	a			14 35										17 09		17 32					18 22				19 30
Darlington 7	a										16 41					17 44									19 42
Yarm	d			14 49										17 23							18 37				
Thornaby	a			14 57										17 34							18 48				
Middlesbrough	a			15 10										17 43							19 00				
Durham	a										16 58					18 01									19 59
Chester-le-Street	a															18 07									20 05
Newcastle 8	a										17 15					18 21									20 20

For general notes see front of timetable
For details of catering facilities see Directory of Train Operators

b Change at Manchester Oxford Road and Manchester Piccadilly

c Change at Manchester Piccadilly

Table 39

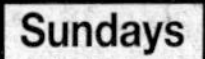

20 July to 7 September

Liverpool, Manchester Airport and Manchester → Huddersfield → Leeds, Hull, York, Scarborough, Middlesbrough and Newcastle

Network Diagram - see first page of Table 39

		NT	NT	TP		TP	NT	TP	TP	TP	NT	NT	TP	TP	NT	TP	TP	TP	NT	TP	NT	TP	TP		
			🚌	1 ◇		1 ◇		1 ◇	1 ◇	1 ◇		🚌	1 ◇	1 ◇		1 ◇	1 ◇	1 ◇		1 ◇	🚌	1 ◇	1 ◇		
Liverpool Lime Street 10	d					17 22			*17 52*	18 22				19 22			20 22					21 52	21b57		
Warrington Central	d					17 44			*18 18*	18 44				19 44			20 44					22 15	22b32		
Birchwood	d					17 49				18 49				19 49			20 49					22 20	22b37		
Newton-le-Willows	d																								
Manchester Oxford Road	d					18 07				19 07				20 07			21 07					22 37			
Manchester Airport ✈	d			17 22		*17 46*	*17 49*	18 22		*18 46*			19 22	*19 46*	*19 49*	20 22	*20 46*			21 22		*21 58*	23 22		
Manchester Piccadilly 10 🚢	a			17 38		18 10		18 39		19 10			19 38	20 10		20 38	21 10			21 38		22 40	23 36		
	d			17 42		18 12	18 19	18 42	19 00	19 12			19 42	20 12	20 19	20 42	21 12			21 42		22 42	23 42		
Manchester Victoria 🚢	a																								
	d		17 55									19 55									22 18				
Ashton-under-Lyne	d		18 15									20 15									22 38				
Stalybridge	a		18 25			18 25	18 32			19 25		20 25		20 25	20 32		21 25				22 48	22 55			
	d					18 25	18 33			19 25				20 25	20 33		21 25					22 55			
Mossley (Grtr Manchester)	d						18 37								20 37										
Greenfield	d						18 41								20 41										
Marsden	d	17 47					18 50				19 48				20 50				21 48						
Slaithwaite	d	17 51					18 54				19 52				20 54				21 52						
Huddersfield	a	17 58		18 11		18 43	19 02	19 11	19 31	19 43	19 59		20 11	20 43	21 02	21 11	21 43		21 59	22 11		23 11	00 11		
	d	17 58		18 12		18 44		19 12	19 32	19 44	19 59		20 12	20 44		21 12	21 44		21 59	22 12		23 12	00 12		
Deighton	d	18 02									20 03								22 03						
Mirfield	d	18 07									20 08								22 08						
Ravensthorpe	d	18 10									20 11								22 11						
Dewsbury	a	18 13		18 21				19 21			20 14		20 21			21 21			22 14	22 21		23 22			
	d	18 14		18 22				19 22			20 15		20 22			21 22			22 15	22 22		23 22			
Batley	d	18 17									20 18								22 18						
Morley	d	18 23									20 24								22 24						
Cottingley	d	18 26									20 27								22 27						
Leeds 10	a	18 34		18 37		19 06		19 37	19 53	20 07	20 35		20 39	21 06		21 37	22 05		22 35	22 37		23 38	00 33		
	d			18 40		19 10		19 40	19 56	20 10			20 43	21 10		21 40	22 05	22 27		22 40		23 40	00 36		
Garforth	d																								
South Milford	a																								
Selby	a								20 28									23 09							
Howden	a																								
Brough	a								20 46									23 28							
Hull	a								21 03									23 43							
York 8	a			19 21		19 51		20 21		20 49			21 19	21 50		22 17	22 44			23 21		00 24	01 15		
	d			19 23		19 52		20 31		21 10				22 08			22 45								
Malton	d			19 47				20 57						22 32											
Seamer	a			20 04				21 14						22 49											
Scarborough	a			20 15				21 24						23 00											
Thirsk	a					20 14				21 27							23 10								
Northallerton	a					20 22				21 37							23 20								
Darlington 7	a									21 49							23 35								
Yarm	d					20 37																			
Thornaby	a					20 50																			
Middlesbrough	a					21 02																			
Durham	a									22 06							23 52								
Chester-le-Street	a																								
Newcastle 8 🚢	a									22 23							00 25								

For general notes see front of timetable
For details of catering facilities see Directory of Train Operators

b Change at Manchester Oxford Road and Manchester Piccadilly

Table 39

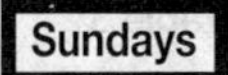

Liverpool, Manchester Airport and Manchester → Huddersfield → Leeds, Hull, York, Scarborough, Middlesbrough and Newcastle

14 September to 2 November

Network Diagram - see first page of Table 39

		TP 1 ◇	TP (bus)	TP (bus)	TP 1 ◇	TP (bus)		TP 1 ◇	TP 1 ◇	TP 1 ◇	TP 1 ◇	NT		NT	TP 1 ◇	NT	TP 1 ◇	TP 1 ◇		NT	TP 1 ◇	TP 1 ◇	NT	TP 1 ◇	TP 1 ◇
Liverpool Lime Street 10	d										08 22							09 22				*09 30*		*09b57*	11 22
Warrington Central	d										08 44							09 45						*10b32*	11 44
Birchwood	d										08 49							09 50						*10b37*	11 49
Newton-le-Willows	d																								
Manchester Oxford Road	d										09 07							10 07							12 07
Manchester Airport ✈	d		01 35	05 30		06 20				07 41	*08 44*				*08 51*		09 25	*09 47*			10 22	*10 47*		11 22	*11 47*
Manchester Piccadilly 10	a		02 00	05 55		06 40				07 54	09 10						09 41	10 10			10 38			11 38	12 10
	d		02 00	05 55		06 40				07 57	09 12				09 30		09 42	10 12			10 42	11 12		11 42	12 12
Manchester Victoria	a									08 11															
	d									08 30		09 18								10 18					
Ashton-under-Lyne	d											09 28								10 28					
Stalybridge	a					07 00						09 33			09 43			10 25		10 32		11 25			12 25
	d					07 00									09 43			10 25		10 33		11 25			12 25
Mossley (Grtr Manchester)	d																			10 37					
Greenfield	d																			10 41					
Marsden	d													09 40						10 50			11 47		
Slaithwaite	d													09 44						10 54			11 51		
Huddersfield	a		03 00	06 55		07 45				09 15	09 41			09 51	10 01		10 14	10 43		11 02	11 11	11 43	11 58	12 11	12 43
	d		03 00	06 55		07 45				09 18	09 42			09 51	10 02		10 14	10 44			11 12	11 44	11 58	12 12	12 44
Deighton	d													09 55									12 02		
Mirfield	d													10 00									12 07		
Ravensthorpe	d													10 03									12 10		
Dewsbury	a					08 05				09 27				10 06		←	10 25				11 21		12 13	12 21	
	d					08 05				09 28				10 10 →		10 10	10 25				11 22		12 14	12 22	
Batley	d															10 13							12 17		
Morley	d															10 19							12 23		
Cottingley	d															10 22							12 26		
Leeds 10	a		03 35	07 30		08 30				09 42	10 03				10 23	10 30	10 41	11 05			11 38	12 05	12 34	12 37	13 06
	d	00 42	03 35		07 40			08 40	09 10	09 42	10 06				10 25		10 42	11 10			11 40	12 10		12 40	13 10
Garforth	d								09 18									11 18							13 18
South Milford	a														10 38							12 22			
Selby	a														10 47							12 32			
Howden	a																								
Brough	a														11 07							12 53			
Hull	a														11 24							13 11			
York 8	a	01 08	04 20		08 09			09 07	09 35	10 08	10 30						11 09	11 36			12 05			13 07	13 37
	d				08 10			09 10	09 38	10 10	10 33						11 14	11 38			12 10			13 10	13 38
Malton	d								10 02									12 02							14 02
Seamer	a								10 19									12 19							14 19
Scarborough	a								10 30									12 30							14 30
Thirsk	a				08 27					10 27											12 27				
Northallerton	a				08 35			09 30		10 35							11 34				12 35			13 32	
Darlington 7	a							09 42			11 03						11 46							13 44	
Yarm	d				08 49					10 49											12 49				
Thornaby	a				09 02					10 59											12 57				
Middlesbrough	a				09 14					11 12											13 10				
Durham	a							09 59			11 20						12 03							14 01	
Chester-le-Street	a										11 26													14 07	
Newcastle 8	a							10 16			11 41						12 19							14 21	

For general notes see front of timetable
For details of catering facilities see
Directory of Train Operators

b Change at Manchester Oxford Road and Manchester Piccadilly

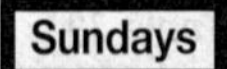

Liverpool, Manchester Airport and Manchester → Huddersfield → Leeds, Hull, York, Scarborough, Middlesbrough and Newcastle

14 September to 2 November

Network Diagram - see first page of Table 39

		NT		TP	TP	NT	TP	TP		NT	TP	TP	TP	NT		TP	TP	TP	NT	TP		TP	TP	NT	TP
				1 ◇	1 ◇		1 ◇	1 ◇			1 ◇	1 ◇	1 ◇			1 ◇	1 ◇	1 ◇		1 ◇		1 ◇	1 ◇		1 ◇
Liverpool Lime Street 10	d				12 22			13 22			*13b30*	*13 52*	14 22				*14 52*	15 22				*15 52*	16 22		
Warrington Central	d				12 45			13 44				*14 18*	14 44				*15 18*	15 44				*16 18*	16 44		
Birchwood	d				12 50			13 49					14 49					15 49					16 49		
Newton-le-Willows	d																								
Manchester Oxford Road	d				13 07			14 07					15 07					16 07					17 07		
Manchester Airport ✈	d			12 22	*12 46*		13 22	*13 47*			14 22	*14 26*	*14 47*			15 17	*15 27*	*15 47*		16 22		*16 27*	*16 47*		17 22
Manchester Piccadilly 10	a			12 37	13 10		13 37	14 10			14 38		15 10			15 39		16 10		16 38			17 10		17 38
	d			12 42	13 12		13 42	14 12			14 42	14 56	15 12			15 42	16 00	16 12		16 42		17 00	17 12		17 42
Manchester Victoria	a																								
	d	12 18								14 18									16 18						
Ashton-under-Lyne	d	12 28								14 28									16 28						
Stalybridge	a	12 32			13 25			14 25		14 32			15 25					16 25	16 32				17 25		
	d	12 33			13 25			14 25		14 33			15 25					16 25	16 33				17 25		
Mossley (Grtr Manchester)	d	12 37								14 37									16 37						
Greenfield	d	12 41								14 41									16 41						
Marsden	d	12 50				13 47				14 50				15 48					16 50					17 47	
Slaithwaite	d	12 54				13 51				14 54				15 52					16 54					17 51	
Huddersfield	a	13 02		13 11	13 43	13 58	14 11	14 43		15 02	15 11	15 29	15 43	15 59		16 11	16 29	16 43	17 02	17 11		17 29	17 43	17 58	18 11
	d			13 12	13 44	13 58	14 12	14 44			15 12	15 30	15 44	15 59		16 12	16 30	16 44		17 12		17 30	17 44	17 58	18 12
Deighton	d					14 02								16 03										18 02	
Mirfield	d					14 07								16 08										18 07	
Ravensthorpe	d					14 10								16 11										18 10	
Dewsbury	a			13 21		14 13	14 21				15 21			16 14		16 21				17 21				18 13	18 21
	d			13 22		14 14	14 22				15 22			16 15		16 22				17 22				18 14	18 22
Batley	d					14 17								16 18										18 17	
Morley	d					14 23								16 24										18 23	
Cottingley	d					14 26								16 27										18 26	
Leeds 10	a			13 37	14 09	14 34	14 37	15 06			15 37	15 52	16 06	16 35		16 37	16 51	17 06		17 37		17 51	18 06	18 34	18 37
	d			13 40	14 10		14 40	15 10			15 40	15 55	16 10			16 40	16 54	17 10		17 40		17 54	18 10		18 40
Garforth	d							15 18										17 18							
South Milford	a				14 22								16 24									18 06			
Selby	a				14 32								16 34				17 13					18 16			
Howden	a																								
Brough	a				14 51								16 53				17 36					18 35			
Hull	a				15 11								17 11				17 53					18 53			
York 8	a			14 05			15 07	15 40			16 05	16 19				17 09		17 37		18 09			18 37		19 07
	d			14 10			15 14	15 44			16 10	16 23				17 10		17 38		18 10					19 10
Malton	d							16 08										18 02							
Seamer	a							16 25										18 19							
Scarborough	a							16 34										18 30							
Thirsk	a			14 27								16 39								18 27					
Northallerton	a			14 35			15 34					16 47				17 32				18 35					19 30
Darlington 7	a						15 46				16 41					17 44									19 42
Yarm	d			14 49								17 03								18 49					
Thornaby	a			14 57								17 11								18 58					
Middlesbrough	a			15 10								17 22								19 10					
Durham	a						16 03				16 58					18 01									19 59
Chester-le-Street	a															18 07									20 05
Newcastle 8	a						16 19				17 15					18 21									20 20

For general notes see front of timetable
For details of catering facilities see Directory of Train Operators

b Change at Manchester Piccadilly

Sundays

Liverpool, Manchester Airport and Manchester → Huddersfield → Leeds, Hull, York, Scarborough, Middlesbrough and Newcastle

14 September to 2 November

Network Diagram - see first page of Table 39

		TP	NT	TP		TP	TP	NT	TP	TP		NT	TP	TP	TP	NT		NT	TP	NT	TP	TP		
		1 ◇		1 ◇		1 ◇	1 ◇		1 ◇	1 ◇			1 ◇	1 ◇	1 ◇				1 ◇		1 ◇	1 ◇		
Liverpool Lime Street 10	d	17 22				*17 52*	18 22			19 22				20 22							21 52	21b57		
Warrington Central	d	17 44				*18 18*	18 44			19 44				20 44							22 15	22b32		
Birchwood	d	17 49					18 49			19 49				20 49							22 20	22b37		
Newton-le-Willows	d																							
Manchester Oxford Road	d	18 07					19 07			20 07				21 07							22 37			
Manchester Airport	d	*17 47*		18 22		*18 27*	*18 47*		19 22	*19 47*			20 22	*20 47*					21 22		*22 01*	23 22		
Manchester Piccadilly 10	a	18 10		18 39			19 10		19 38	20 10			20 38	21 10					21 38		22 40	23 36		
	d	18 12		18 42		19 00	19 12		19 42	20 12			20 42	21 12					21 42		22 42	23 42		
Manchester Victoria	a																							
	d		18 18									20 18								22 18				
Ashton-under-Lyne	d		18 28									20 28								22 28				
Stalybridge	a	18 25	18 32				19 25			20 25		20 32		21 25						22 33	22 55			
	d	18 25	18 33				19 25			20 25		20 33		21 25							22 55			
Mossley (Grtr Manchester)	d		18 37									20 37												
Greenfield	d		18 41									20 41												
Marsden	d		18 50					19 48				20 50						21 48						
Slaithwaite	d		18 54					19 52				20 54						21 52						
Huddersfield	a	18 43	19 02	19 11		19 31	19 43	19 59	20 11	20 43		21 02	21 11	21 43				21 59	22 11		23 11	00 11		
	d	18 44		19 12		19 32	19 44	19 59	20 12	20 44			21 12	21 44				21 59	22 12		23 12	00 12		
Deighton	d							20 03										22 03						
Mirfield	d							20 08										22 08						
Ravensthorpe	d							20 11										22 11						
Dewsbury	a			19 21				20 14	20 21				21 21					22 14	22 21		23 22			
	d			19 22				20 15	20 22				21 22					22 15	22 22		23 22			
Batley	d							20 18										22 18						
Morley	d							20 24										22 24						
Cottingley	d							20 27										22 27						
Leeds 10	a	19 06		19 37		19 53	20 06	20 35	20 39	21 07			21 37	22 05				22 35	22 37		23 38	00 33		
	d	19 10		19 40		19 56	20 10		20 45	21 10			21 40	22 10	22 17	22 35			22 50		23 40	00 36		
Garforth	d	19 18								21 18						22 47								
South Milford	a					20 08									22 29									
Selby	a					20 18									22 39									
Howden	a																							
Brough	a					20 37									22 58									
Hull	a					20 54									23 16									
York 8	a	19 38		20 05			20 37		21 09	21 38			22 06	22 38		23 17			23 21		00 08	01 02		
	d	19 38		20 14			20 38		21 10				22 08	22 40										
Malton	d	20 02					21 02						22 32											
Seamer	a	20 19					21 19						22 49											
Scarborough	a	20 30					21 30						23 00											
Thirsk	a			20 30					21 27					23 05										
Northallerton	a			20 38					21 37					23 15										
Darlington 7	a								21 49					23 31										
Yarm	d			20 52																				
Thornaby	a			21 00																				
Middlesbrough	a			21 10																				
Durham	a								22 06					23 48										
Chester-le-Street	a																							
Newcastle 8	a								22 23					00 21										

For general notes see front of timetable
For details of catering facilities see Directory of Train Operators

b Change at Manchester Oxford Road and Manchester Piccadilly

Table 39

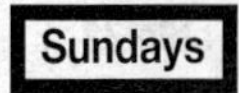

from 9 November

Liverpool, Manchester Airport and Manchester → Huddersfield → Leeds, Hull, York, Scarborough, Middlesbrough and Newcastle

Network Diagram - see first page of Table 39

Station		TP 1 ◊	TP bus	TP bus	TP 1 ◊	TP bus	TP 1 ◊	TP bus	TP 1 ◊	TP 1 ◊		TP 1 ◊	TP bus	NT	TP 1 ◊	TP 1 ◊	TP 1 ◊	TP bus	TP 1 ◊	TP 1 ◊		TP bus	NT	TP 1 ◊	TP 1 ◊
Liverpool Lime Street 10	d											08 10					09 10							09b30	11 10
Warrington Central	d											07c57					08c57							09e32	09c57
Birchwood	d																							09e37	
Newton-le-Willows	d											08 27					09 27								11 27
Manchester Oxford Road	d																								
Manchester Airport	✈ d		01 35	05 30		06 20				07 41					08 48				09 56					10 56	
Manchester Piccadilly 10	a		02 00	05 55		06 40				07 55					09 06				10 09					11 09	
	d		02 00	05 55		06 40				07 57					09 08				10 11					11 10	
Manchester Victoria	a									08 11		08 48			09 24		09 48		10 27					11 25	11 49
	d							08 25		08 30		08 55	09 05		09 30		09 55	10 05	10 32	10 53		11 05		11 32	11 55
Ashton-under-Lyne	d												09 25									11 25			
Stalybridge	a					07 00		08 45					09 32					10 25				11 32			
	d					07 00																			
Mossley (Grtr Manchester)	d																								
Greenfield	d																								
Marsden	d													09 40									11 47		
Slaithwaite	d													09 44									11 51		
Huddersfield	a		03 00	06 55		07 45				09 15		09 42		09 51			10 44			11 43			11 58		12 43
	d		03 00	06 55		07 45				09 18		09 45		09 51			10 45			11 46			11 58		12 45
Deighton	d													09 55									12 02		
Mirfield	d													10 00									12 07		
Ravensthorpe	d													10 03									12 10		
Dewsbury	a					08 05				09 27				10 06	10 25				11 21				12 13	12 21	
	d					08 05				09 28				10 10	10 25				11 22				12 14	12 22	
Batley	d													10 13									12 17		
Morley	d													10 19									12 23		
Cottingley	d													10 22									12 26		
Leeds 10	a		03 35	07 30		08 30				09 42		10 05		10 30	10 40		11 07		11 37	12 09			12 34	12 37	13 06
	d	00 42	03 35		07 40		08 40		09 10	09 42		10 06			10 42	10 51	11 10		11 40	12 10				12 40	13 10
Garforth	d								09 18								11 18								13 18
South Milford	a															11 03				12 22					
Selby	a															11 13				12 32					
Howden	a																								
Brough	a															11 36				12 53					
Hull	a															11 51				13 11					
York 8	a	01 08	04 20		08 09		09 07		09 35	10 08		10 30			11 09		11 36		12 05					13 07	13 37
	d				08 10		09 10		09 38	10 10		10 33			11 14		11 38		12 10					13 10	13 38
Malton	d								10 02								12 02								14 02
Seamer	a								10 19								12 19								14 19
Scarborough	a								10 30								12 30								14 30
Thirsk	a				08 27					10 27									12 27						
Northallerton	a				08 35		09 30			10 35					11 34				12 35					13 32	
Darlington 7	a						09 42					11 02			11 46									13 44	
Yarm	d				08 49					10 49									12 49						
Thornaby	a				09 02					10 57									12 57						
Middlesbrough	a				09 14					11 10									13 10						
Durham	a						09 59					11 19			12 03									14 01	
Chester-le-Street	a											11 25												14 07	
Newcastle 8	a						10 16					11 40			12 19									14 21	

For general notes see front of timetable
For details of catering facilities see Directory of Train Operators

b Change at Manchester Piccadilly
c By bus
e Change at Manchester Oxford Road and Manchester Piccadilly

Table 39

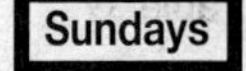

Sundays

from 9 November

Liverpool, Manchester Airport and Manchester → Huddersfield → Leeds, Hull, York, Scarborough, Middlesbrough and Newcastle

Network Diagram - see first page of Table 39

		TP	TP	TP	TP	NT	TP	TP		TP	TP	TP	TP	TP	NT	TP	TP	TP		TP	TP	TP	TP	TP	NT
		(bus)	1 ◇	1 ◇	(bus)		1 ◇	1 ◇		(bus)	1 ◇	1 ◇	1 ◇	(bus)		1 ◇	1 ◇	(bus)		1 ◇	1 ◇	1 ◇	(bus)	1 ◇	
Liverpool Lime Street 10	d			12 10				13 10					14 10				15 10					16 10			
Warrington Central	d		10b32	11c57				12c57			13e18		13c57			14e18	14c57				15e18	15c57			
Birchwood	d		10b37				11b37				12b37					13b37					14b37				
Newton-le-Willows	d			12 27				13 27					14 27				15 27					16 27			
Manchester Oxford Road	d																								
Manchester Airport ✈	d		11 56				12 49				13 56					14 56					15 56				
Manchester Piccadilly 10	a		12 09				13 04				14 09					15 09					16 10				
	d		12 11				13 11				14 11					15 11					16 12				
Manchester Victoria	a		12 26	12 49			13 26	13 49			14 27		14 49			15 25	15 48				16 25	16 48			
	d	12 05	12 32	12 54	13 05		13 32	13 55		14 05	14 32		14 55	15 05		15 32	15 55	16 05			16 32	16 53	17 05		
Ashton-under-Lyne	d				13 25									15 25									17 25		
Stalybridge	a	12 25			13 32					14 25				15 32				16 25					17 32		
	d																								
Mossley (Grtr Manchester)	d																								
Greenfield	d																								
Marsden	d					13 47									15 48										17 47
Slaithwaite	d					13 51									15 52										17 51
Huddersfield	a			13 42		13 58		14 42					15 42		15 59		16 42					17 39			17 58
	d			13 46		13 58		14 44					15 45		15 59		16 45					17 41			17 58
Deighton	d					14 02									16 03										18 02
Mirfield	d					14 07									16 08										18 07
Ravensthorpe	d					14 10									16 11										18 10
Dewsbury	a		13 21			14 13	14 21				15 21				16 14	16 21					17 21				18 13
	d		13 22			14 14	14 22				15 22				16 15	16 22					17 22				18 14
Batley	d					14 17									16 18										18 17
Morley	d					14 23									16 24										18 23
Cottingley	d					14 26									16 27										18 26
Leeds 10	a		13 37	14 08		14 34	14 37	15 06			15 37		16 06		16 35	16 37	17 07				17 37	18 06			18 34
	d		13 40	14 10			14 40	15 10			15 40	15 55	16 10			16 40	17 10			17 17	17 40	18 10		18 17	
Garforth	d							15 18									17 18								
South Milford	a			14 22									16 24											18 34	
Selby	a			14 32									16 34							17 41				18 44	
Howden	a																								
Brough	a			14 51									16 53							18 01				19 03	
Hull	a			15 11									17 11							18 15				19 18	
York 8	a		14 05				15 07	15 40			16 05	16 19				17 09	17 37				18 09	18 37			
	d		14 10				15 14	15 44			16 10	16 23				17 10	17 38				18 10				
Malton	d							16 08									18 02								
Seamer	a							16 25									18 19								
Scarborough	a							16 34									18 30								
Thirsk	a		14 27									16 39									18 27				
Northallerton	a		14 35				15 34					16 47				17 32					18 35				
Darlington 7	a						15 46				16 41					17 44									
Yarm	d		14 49									17 03									18 49				
Thornaby	a		14 57									17 11									18 58				
Middlesbrough	a		15 10									17 22									19 10				
Durham	a						16 03				16 58					18 01									
Chester-le-Street	a															18 07									
Newcastle 8	a						16 19				17 15					18 21									

For general notes see front of timetable
For details of catering facilities see Directory of Train Operators

b Change at Manchester Oxford Road and Manchester Piccadilly

c By bus

e Change at Manchester Piccadilly

Table 39

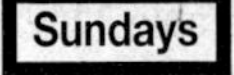

Sundays

from 9 November

Liverpool, Manchester Airport and Manchester → Huddersfield → Leeds, Hull, York, Scarborough, Middlesbrough and Newcastle

Network Diagram - see first page of Table 39

	TP 1 ◇	TP 1 ◇	TP (bus)	NT	TP 1 ◇		TP 1 ◇	TP (bus)	TP 1 ◇	NT	TP 1 ◇	TP 1 ◇	TP (bus)	TP 1 ◇	TP 1 ◇	TP (bus)	TP 1 ◇	NT	TP 1 ◇	TP 1 ◇	TP (bus)	TP 1 ◇
Liverpool Lime Street 10 d		17 10					18 09					19 10			20 10					21 50		
Warrington Central d	16b18	16c57			17b18		17c57				18b18	18c57		19b18	19c57				20b18	21 20		21 47
Birchwood d	15e37				16e37						17e37			18e37					19e37			21e37
Newton-le-Willows d		17 27					18 26					19 27			20 27					22 11		
Manchester Oxford Road d																						
Manchester Airport ✈ d	16 56				17 56						18 56			19 54					20 55			22 56
Manchester Piccadilly 10 a	17 09				18 09						19 09			20 07					21 08			23 09
d	17 11				18 11						19 11			20 09					21 10			23 10
Manchester Victoria a	17 25	17 49			18 27		18 48				19 25	19 48		20 26	20 48				21 26	22 32		23 24
d	17 32	17 55	18 05	18 18	18 32		18 55	19 05			19 32	19 55	20 05	20 32	20 55	21 05			21 32	22 37	22 45	23 26
Ashton-under-Lyne d				18 28				19 25								21 25					23 05	
Stalybridge a			18 25	18 32				19 32					20 25			21 32					23 12	
d				18 33																		
Mossley (Grtr Manchester) d				18 37																		
Greenfield d				18 41																		
Marsden d				18 50						19 48								21 48				
Slaithwaite d				18 54						19 52								21 52				
Huddersfield a		18 42		19 02			19 43			19 59		20 42			21 46			21 59		23 24		00 11
d		18 45					19 45			19 59		20 45			21 47			21 59		23 24		00 12
Deighton d										20 03								22 03				
Mirfield d										20 08								22 08				
Ravensthorpe d										20 11								22 11				
Dewsbury a	18 21				19 21					20 14	20 21			21 21				22 14	22 21	23 34		
d	18 22				19 22					20 15	20 22			21 22				22 15	22 22	23 34		
Batley d										20 18								22 18				
Morley d										20 24								22 24				
Cottingley d										20 27								22 27				
Leeds 10 a	18 37	19 09			19 36		20 07			20 35	20 39	21 06		21 37	22 07			22 35	22 37	23 51		00 33
d	18 40	19 10			19 40		20 10		20 17		20 45	21 10		21 40	22 10		22 17		22 50	23 53		00 36
Garforth d		19 18										21 18										
South Milford a									20 29								22 29					
Selby a									20 39								22 39					
Howden a																						
Brough a									20 58								22 58					
Hull a									21 14								23 16					
York 8 a	19 07	19 38			20 05		20 37				21 09	21 38		22 06	22 38				23 21	00 20		01 02
d	19 10	19 38			20 14		20 38				21 10			22 08	22 40							
Malton d		20 02					21 02							22 32								
Seamer a		20 19					21 19							22 49								
Scarborough a		20 30					21 30							23 00								
Thirsk a					20 30						21 27				23 05							
Northallerton a	19 30				20 38						21 37				23 15							
Darlington 7 a	19 42										21 49				23 31							
Yarm d					20 52																	
Thornaby a					21 00																	
Middlesbrough a					21 10																	
Durham a	19 59										22 06				23 48							
Chester-le-Street a	20 05																					
Newcastle 8 a	20 20										22 23				00 21							

For general notes see front of timetable
For details of catering facilities see Directory of Train Operators

b Change at Manchester Piccadilly
c By bus
e Change at Manchester Oxford Road and Manchester Piccadilly

York and Selby → Leeds

Network Diagram - see first page of Table 39

Miles	Miles	Station		TP	TP	TP	TP	TP	TP	TP		TP	TP	TP	TP	TP	NT	TP		NT	TP	TP	NT	TP	TP	NT
				MO	MX	MO	MO	MX	MO	MO		MO	MO	MX	MO											
				1 ◇	1 ◇	1 ◇	1 ◇	1 ◇	1 ◇	1 ◇		1 ◇	1 ◇	1 ◇	1 ◇	1 ◇		1 ◇			1 ◇	1 ◇		1 ◇	1 ◇	
				AB	A	A C	A D	A	A C	A E		A C	A E	A	A C	A G		A		H	A	J	K	L	N	H
0	—	**York** 8	33 d	01 53	02 00	02 00	02 13	03 00	03 00	03 13		03 57	04 05	04 09	05 05	05 26	05 40	05 58		06 13	06 28			06 58		07 06
8¾	—	Ulleskelf	33 d																							07 15
10½	—	Church Fenton	33 d																							07 21
—	0	**Selby**	d																			06 38	06 43		07 08	
—	7¾	South Milford	d																				06 53			
15¾	11	Micklefield	d														05 58			06 28			06 58			07 28
17½	12¾	East Garforth	d														06 02			06 32			07 02			07 32
18¼	13½	Garforth	d														06 05	06 13		06 35			07 05	07 13	07 24	07 35
21	16¼	Cross Gates	d														06 10			06 40			07 10			07 40
25½	20¾	**Leeds** 10	a	02 19	02 33	02 40	02 40	03 33	03 39	03 39		04 38	04 38	04 41	05 52	05 52	06 18	06 23		06 49	06 53	07 05	07 19	07 23	07 35	07 49
—	—	Bradford Interchange	37 a									*05 28*	*05 28*	*05 28*		*06 23*		*06 57*		07 11	*07 29*		07 43	*07 57*		08 11

Station		TP	NT		TP	XC	NT	NT	TP	NT	TP		NT	TP	NT	TP	XC	NT	TP		TP	NT	TP	TP	XC	NT
		1 ◇			1 ◇	R 1			1 ◇		1 ◇			1 ◇		1 ◇	1 ◇		1 ◇		1 ◇		1 ◇	1 ◇	R 1	
		Q	U		V	X	K		Q		N		H	L		Y	Z	K	AA		N	H	A	Y	BB	K
York 8	33 d	07 24			07 40	07 44		07 48	07 54	←				08 24	08 27	08 40	08 44		08 58			09 09	09 28	09 40	09 44	
Ulleskelf	33 d																									
Church Fenton	33 d							08 05		08 05												09 21				
Selby	d		07 26				07 43	→			08 07		08 12					08 42			09 09					09 43
South Milford	d		07 35				07 53						08 22					08 52								09 53
Micklefield	d		07 41				07 58			08 13			08 28		08 42			08 58				09 28				09 58
East Garforth	d		07 46				08 02			08 17			08 32		08 46			09 02				09 32				10 04
Garforth	d		07 48				08 05		08u13	08 20			08 35	08 41	08 48			09 05	09 13			09 35				10 05
Cross Gates	d	07 44	07 53				08 10			08 25			08 40		08 53			09 10				09 40				10 10
Leeds 10	a	07 52	08 02		08 04	08 08	08 19		08 23	08 34	08 37		08 48	08 50	09 02	09 04	09 08	09 19	09 23		09 35	09 49	09 53	10 04	10 08	10 19
Bradford Interchange	37 a		08 28				08 42		*08 57*				09 11	*09 28*				09 42	*09 57*			10 11	*10 28*			10 42

Station		TP	TP	NT		TP	TP	XC	NT	TP	TP	NT		TP	TP	XC	NT	TP	TP	NT		TP	TP	XC	NT	TP
		1 ◇	1 ◇			1 ◇	1 ◇	R 1		1 ◇	1 ◇			1 ◇	1 ◇	R 1		1 ◇	1 ◇			1 ◇	1 ◇	R 1		1 ◇
		L	N	H		AA	Y	CC	K	L	N	H		AA	Y	DD	K	L	N	H		AA	Y	EE	K	L
York 8	33 d	09 58		10 11		10 27	10 40	10 44		10 58		11 09		11 28	11 39	11 44		11 58		12 13		12 28	12 38	12 44		12 58
Ulleskelf	33 d																									
Church Fenton	33 d											11 21														
Selby	d		10 09						10 43		11 09						11 43		12 09						12 43	
South Milford	d								10 53								11 53								12 53	
Micklefield	d			10 28					10 58			11 28					11 58			12 28					12 58	
East Garforth	d			10 32					11 02			11 32					12 02			12 32					13 02	
Garforth	d	10 13		10 35					11 05	11 13		11 35					12 05	12 13		12 35					13 05	13 13
Cross Gates	d			10 40					11 10			11 40					12 10			12 40					13 10	
Leeds 10	a	10 23	10 37	10 49		10 53	11 04	11 08	11 19	11 23	11 33	11 49		11 53	12 05	12 08	12 19	12 23	12 33	12 49		12 51	13 04	13 08	13 19	13 23
Bradford Interchange	37 a	*10 57*		11 11		*11 28*			11 42	*11 57*		12 11		*12 28*		*12 42*		*12 57*		13 11		*13 28*			13 42	*13 57*

Station		TP	NT	TP	TP		XC	NT	TP	TP	NT	TP	TP		TP	XC	NT	TP	TP	NT	TP		TP	TP	XC	NT
		1 ◇		1 ◇	1 ◇		R 1		1 ◇	1 ◇		1 ◇	1 ◇		1 ◇	R 1		1 ◇	1 ◇		1 ◇		1 ◇	1 ◇	R 1	
		N	H	AA	Y		FF	K	L	N	H	GG	HH		Y	JJ	K	L	N	H	GG		HH	Y	KK	K
York 8	33 d		13 09	13 28	13 40		13 44		13 58		14 13	14 25	14 28		14 40	14 44		14 58		15 09	15 26		15 28	15 40	15 44	
Ulleskelf	33 d																									
Church Fenton	33 d		13 21																	15 21						
Selby	d	13 09						13 43		14 09							14 43		15 09							15 43
South Milford	d							13 53									14 53									15 53
Micklefield	d		13 28					13 58			14 28						14 58			15 28						15 58
East Garforth	d		13 32					14 02			14 32						15 02			15 32						16 02
Garforth	d		13 35					14 05	14 13		14 35						15 05	15 13		15 35						16 05
Cross Gates	d		13 40					14 10			14 40						15 10			15 40						16 10
Leeds 10	a	13 33	13 49	13 53	14 04		14 08	14 19	14 23	14 34	14 49	14 53	14 53		15 05	15 08	15 19	15 23	15 33	15 49	15 53		15 53	16 04	16 08	16 19
Bradford Interchange	37 a		14 11	*14 28*				14 42	*14 57*		15 11	*15 28*	*15 28*				15 42	*15 57*		16 11	*16 28*		*16 28*			16 42

For general notes see front of timetable
For details of catering facilities see Directory of Train Operators

- **A** To Manchester Airport (Table 39)
- **B** From 10 November
- **C** 21 July to 8 September
- **D** Until 14 July and 15 September to 3 November
- **E** Until 14 July and from 15 September
- **G** Not Mondays 21 July to 8 September
- **H** To Blackpool North (Table 41)
- **J** From Hull to Liverpool Lime Street (Table 39)
- **K** To Wakefield Westgate (Table 39)
- **L** From Middlesbrough to Manchester Airport (Table 39)
- **N** From Hull to Manchester Piccadilly (Table 39)
- **Q** From Scarborough to Manchester Airport (Table 39)
- **U** To Manchester Victoria (Table 41)
- **V** From Newcastle to Liverpool Lime Street(Table 39)
- **X** From Newcastle to Bournemouth (from 8 September to Bristol Temple Meads) (Table 51)
- **Y** From Scarborough to Liverpool Lime Street (Table 39)
- **Z** From Edinburgh to Plymouth (from 8 September to Paignton) (Table 51)
- **AA** From Newcastle to Manchester Airport (Table 39)
- **BB** From Glasgow Central to Bournemouth (from 8 September to Bristol Temple Meads) (Table 51)
- **CC** From Dundee (Table 229) to Plymouth (Table 51)
- **DD** From Dundee (Table 229) to Bournemouth (from 8 September to Bristol Temple Meads) (Table 51)
- **EE** From Glasgow Central (Table 26)to Penzance (from 8 September to Plymouth) (Table 135)
- **FF** From Aberdeen (Table 228) to Bournemouth (from 8 September to Bristol Temple Meads) (Table 51)
- **GG** From 8 September. From Newcastle to Manchester Airport (Table 39)
- **HH** Until 5 September. From Newcastle to Manchester Airport (Table 39)
- **JJ** From Edinburgh to Plymouth (from 8 September to Cardiff Central) (Table 51)
- **KK** From Edinburgh to Bournemouth (from 8 September to Weston-Super-Mare) (Table 51)

York and Selby → Leeds

Network Diagram - see first page of Table 39

		TP	TP	NT	TP	TP		XC	NT	TP	TP	NT	TP	TP		TP	XC	NT	TP	NT	TP	TP		TP	XC	NT
		1 ◇	1 ◇		1 ◇	1 ◇		1 ◇		1 ◇	1 ◇		1 ◇	1 ◇		1 ◇	R 1		1 ◇		1 ◇	1 ◇		1 ◇	1 ◇	
		A	B	C	D	E		G	H	J	B	C	D	K		E	L	H	A	C	D	B		E	N	
		trolley	trolley		trolley	trolley		buffet		trolley	trolley		trolley			trolley	buffet		trolley		trolley	trolley			buffet	
York 8	33 d	15 58		16 13	16 28	16 40		16 44		16 58		17 07	17 28			17 40	17 44		17 58	18 10	18 28			18 38	18 44	
Ulleskelf	33 d																									
Church Fenton	33 d											17 20														
Selby	d		16 09						16 43		17 09			17 32				17 43				18 34				18 43
South Milford	d								16 53									17 53								18 53
Micklefield	d			16 28					16 58			17 28						17 58		18 24						18 58
East Garforth	d			16 32					17 02			17 32						18 02		18 28						19 02
Garforth	d	16 13		16 35					17 05	17 13		17 35						18 05	18 13	18 31						19 05
Cross Gates	d			16 40					17 10			17 40						18 10		18 36						19 10
Leeds 10	a	16 23	16 36	16 49	16 53	17 04	.	17 08	17 19	17 23	17 35	17 50	17 53	17 59	.	18 04	18 08	18 20	18 23	18 47	18 52	18 58	.	19 04	19 08	19 21
Bradford Interchange	37 a	*16 57*		17 11	*17 28*				17 42	*17 57*		18 11	*18 28*	18b31				18 43	*18 57*	19 11		*19 28*			*19 45*	

		NT	NT	TP	NT	TP	TP		XC	TP	NT	TP	TP	XC	TP		NT	TP	TP	TP	NT	TP	NT			
				1 ◇		1 ◇	1 ◇		1 ◇	1 ◇		1 ◇	1 ◇	1 ◇	1 ◇			1 ◇	1 ◇	1 ◇		1 ◇				
			C	J	C	Q	E		N	D		Q	E	V	J			A	X	B		D				
									buffet																	
York 8	33 d		19 04	19 10			19 39		19 44	20 10	20 13		20 40	20 44	21 10		21 10	21 45	21 30		22 13	23 07	23 13			
Ulleskelf	33 d				←												21 22									
Church Fenton	33 d		19 20		19 20						20 25						21 28						23 28			
Selby	d	18 55	→			19 30						20 27								22 07						
South Milford	d											20 36								22 17						
Micklefield	d				19 27						20 32						21 36				22 28		23 36			
East Garforth	d				19 31						20 36						21 40				22 33		23 40			
Garforth	d	19 12		19 23	19 35						20 39						21 42				22 35		23 43			
Cross Gates	d				19 40						20 44						21 47				22 40		23 47			
Leeds 10	a	19 24		19 35	19 49	19 56	20 04	.	20 08	20 35	20 53	20 57	21 04	21 08	21 36	.	21 57	22 08	22 18	22 35	22 49	23 33	23 55			
Bradford Interchange	37 a	*19 57*			20 11	*20 28*			*20 57*			*21 28*		*21 57*			22 28		*22 57*		23 29					

Saturdays

until 6 September

		TP	TP	TP	TP	TP	XC	NT	TP	TP	NT		TP	TP	NT	TP	TP	XC	NT	TP	TP	NT		TP	TP	XC
		1 ◇	1 ◇	1 ◇	1 ◇	1 ◇	1 ◇		1 ◇	1 ◇			1 ◇	1 ◇		1 ◇	1 ◇	R 1		1 ◇	1 ◇			1 ◇	1 ◇	R 1
		Y	Y	Y	Y	Y	Z	C	Y	AA	H		J	B	C	BB	CC	DD	H	BB	B	C		J	E	EE
							buffet										trolley	buffet						trolley	trolley	buffet
York 8	33 d	02 00	03 00	04 17	05 26	05 58	06 06	06 13	06 28				06 58		07 06	07 28	07 40	07 44		07 58		08 07		08 25	08 40	08 44
Ulleskelf	33 d														07 15											
Church Fenton	33 d														07 21							08 20				
Selby	d									06 38	06 43			07 07					07 43		08 07					
South Milford	d										06 53								07 53							
Micklefield	d							06 28			06 58				07 28				07 58			08 27				
East Garforth	d							06 32			07 02				07 32				08 02			08 32				
Garforth	d					06 13		06 35			07 05		07 13		07 35				08 05	08 13		08 35				
Cross Gates	d							06 40			07 10				07 40				08 10			08 40				
Leeds 10	a	02 33	03 33	04 45	05 52	06 23	06 41	06 49	06 53	07 05	07 17	.	07 23	07 35	07 49	07 52	08 04	08 08	08 19	08 23	08 37	08 49	.	08 50	09 04	09 08
Bradford Interchange	37 a			*06 11*	*06 23*	*06 57*		07 11	*07 29*		07 43		*07 57*		08 11	*08 28*			08 42	*08 57*		09 11		*09 28*		

		NT	TP	TP	NT	TP	TP	XC	NT	TP		TP	NT	TP	TP	XC	NT	TP	TP	NT	TP		TP	XC	NT	TP
			1 ◇	1 ◇		1 ◇	1 ◇	1 ◇		1 ◇		1 ◇		1 ◇	1 ◇	R 1		1 ◇	1 ◇		1 ◇		1 ◇	R 1		1 ◇
		H	D	B	C	Y	E	FF	H	J		B	C	D	E	GG	H	J	B	C	D		E	HH	H	J
			trolley			trolley	trolley	buffet		trolley					trolley	buffet		trolley			trolley		trolley	buffet		trolley
York 8	33 d		08 58		09 09	09 28	09 40	09 44		09 58			10 11	10 28	10 40	10 44		10 58		11 09	11 28		11 40	11 44		11 58
Ulleskelf	33 d																									
Church Fenton	33 d				09 21															11 21						
Selby	d	08 43		09 09					09 43			10 09					10 43		11 09						11 43	
South Milford	d	08 53							09 53								10 53								11 53	
Micklefield	d	08 58			09 28				09 58				10 28				10 58			11 28					11 58	
East Garforth	d	09 02			09 32				10 02				10 32				11 02			11 32					12 02	
Garforth	d	09 05	09 13		09 35				10 05	10 13			10 35				11 05	11 13		11 35					12 05	12 13
Cross Gates	d	09 10			09 40				10 10				10 40				11 10			11 40					12 10	
Leeds 10	a	09 19	09 23	09 35	09 49	09 53	10 04	10 08	10 19	10 23	.	10 37	10 49	10 53	11 04	11 08	11 19	11 23	11 33	11 49	11 53	.	12 04	12 08	12 19	12 23
Bradford Interchange	37 a	09 42	*09 57*		10 11	*10 28*			10 42	*10 57*			11 11	*11 28*			11 42	*11 57*		12 11	*12 28*				12 42	*12 57*

For general notes see front of timetable
For details of catering facilities see Directory of Train Operators

- **A** From Middlesbrough to Manchester Piccadilly (Table 39)
- **B** From Hull to Manchester Piccadilly (Table 39)
- **C** To Blackpool North (Table 41)
- **D** From Newcastle to Manchester Airport (Table 39)
- **E** From Scarborough to Liverpool Lime Street (Table 39)
- **G** From Edinburgh to Plymouth (from 8 September to Bristol Temple Meads) (Table 51)
- **H** To Wakefield Westgate (Table 39)
- **J** From Middlesbrough to Manchester Airport (Table 39)
- **K** From Hull to Huddersfield (Table 39)
- **L** From Edinburgh to Southampton Central (from 8 September to Birmingham New Street) (Table 51)
- **N** From Edinburgh to Bristol Temple Meads (from 8 September to Birmingham New Street) (Table 51)
- **Q** From Hull (Table 39)
- **V** From Edinburgh to Birmingham New Street (from 8 September to Sheffield) (Table 51)
- **X** From Scarborough (Table 39)
- **Y** To Manchester Airport (Table 39)
- **Z** To Birmingham New Street (Table 51)
- **AA** From Hull to Liverpool Lime Street (Table 39)
- **BB** From Scarborough to Manchester Airport (Table 39)
- **CC** From Newcastle to Liverpool Lime Street(Table 39)
- **DD** From Newcastle to Bournemouth (Table 51)
- **EE** From Edinburgh to Plymouth (Table 51)
- **FF** From Glasgow Central to Bournemouth (Table 51)
- **GG** From Newcastle (Table 51) to Newquay (Table 135)
- **HH** From Dundee (Table 229) to Bournemouth (Table 51)
- **b** Bradford Forster Square

Due to Engineering Operations in the Sheffield area, services from Saturday 13 September on this Table had not been confirmed at time of going to press. These services will be issued in a special Supplement as soon as exact timings have been confirmed.

Table 40

Saturdays

until 6 September

York and Selby → Leeds

Network Diagram - see first page of Table 39

	TP	NT	TP	TP	XC	NT	TP	TP		NT	TP	TP	XC	NT	TP	TP	NT	TP	TP		XC	NT	TP	TP	NT
	1◇		1◇	1◇	R 1		1◇	1◇			1◇	1◇	1◇		1◇	1◇		1◇	1◇		1◇		1◇	1◇	
	A	B	C	D	E	G	H	A		B	C	D	J	G	H	A	B	C	D		K	G	H	A	B
	🛒		🛒		🍴		🛒				🛒		🍴		🛒			🛒	🛒		🍴		🛒		
York 8 33 d		12 13	12 28	12 40	12 44		12 58			13 09	13 28	13 40	13 44		13 58		14 13	14 28	14 38		14 44		14 58		15 09
Ulleskelf 33 d																									
Church Fenton 33 d										13 21															15 21
Selby d	12 09					12 43		13 09						13 43		14 09						14 43		15 09	
South Milford d						12 53								13 53								14 53			
Micklefield d		12 28				12 58				13 28				13 58			14 28					14 58			15 28
East Garforth d		12 32				13 02				13 32				14 02			14 32					15 02			15 32
Garforth d		12 35				13 05	13 13			13 35				14 05	14 13		14 35					15 05	15 13		15 35
Cross Gates d		12 40				13 10				13 40				14 10			14 40					15 10			15 40
Leeds 10 a	12 33	12 49	12 53	13 04	13 08	13 19	13 23	13 33		13 49	13 53	14 04	14 08	14 19	14 23	14 33	14 49	14 53	15 04		15 08	15 19	15 23	15 33	15 49
Bradford Interchange 37 a		13 11	*13 28*			13 42	*13 57*			14 11	*14 28*			14 42	*14 57*		15 11	*15 28*				15 42	*15 57*		16 11

	TP	TP	XC	NT	TP	TP	NT		TP	TP	XC	NT	TP	TP	NT	TP	TP	TP		XC	NT	TP	NT	TP	TP
	1◇	1◇	1◇		1◇	1◇			1◇	1◇	1◇		1◇	1◇		1◇	1◇	1◇		1◇		1◇		1◇	1◇
	C	D	L	G	N	A	B		C	D	Q	G	H	A	B	C	U	D		V	G	N	B	C	A
	🛒	🛒	🍴		🛒	🛒			🛒	🛒	🍴		🛒			🛒				🍴					
York 8 33 d	15 28	15 39	15 44		15 58		16 13		16 28	16 40	16 44		16 58		17 09	17 28		17 40		17 44		17 58	18 10	18 28	
Ulleskelf 33 d																									
Church Fenton 33 d															17 21										
Selby d				15 43		16 09						16 43		17 09			17 31				17 43				18 34
South Milford d				15 53								16 53									17 53				
Micklefield d				15 58			16 28					16 58			17 28						17 58		18 24		
East Garforth d				16 02			16 32					17 02			17 32						18 02		18 28		
Garforth d				16 05	16 13		16 35					17 05	17 13		17 35						18 05	18 13	18 31		
Cross Gates d				16 10			16 40					17 10			17 40						18 10		18 36		
Leeds 10 a	15 52	16 04	16 08	16 19	16 23	16 36	16 49		16 53	17 04	17 08	17 19	17 23	17 35	17 49	17 53	17 59	18 04		18 08	18 20	18 23	18 45	18 52	18 58
Bradford Interchange 37 a	*16 28*			16 42	*16 57*		17 11		*17 28*			17 42	*17 57*		18 11	*18 28*	*18b31*				18 43	*18 57*	19 11		*19 28*

	TP	XC	NT	NT	TP	NT		TP	TP	XC	TP	NT	TP	TP	XC	TP	NT	TP	GR	TP	NT	TP	NT		
	1◇	1◇			1◇			1◇	1◇	1◇	1◇		1◇	1◇	1◇	1◇		1◇	R 1	1◇		1◇			
	D	X	G	B	H	B		Y	D	Z	C		Y	D	AA	H		N		A		H			
		🍴								🍴									🍴 🛒						
York 8 33 d	18 38	18 44		19 04	19 10				19 38	19 44	20 10	20 13		20 40	20 44	21 10	21 13	21 45			22 13	23 07	23 13		
Ulleskelf 33 d						←											21 22								
Church Fenton 33 d				19 21 →		19 21						20 25					21 28						23 28		
Selby d			18 43					19 31					20 27							22 07					
South Milford d			18 53										20 36							22 17					
Micklefield d			18 58			19 28						20 32					21 36				22 28		23 35		
East Garforth d			19 02			19 32						20 36					21 40				22 32		23 39		
Garforth d			19 05		19 23	19 35						20 39					21 42				22 35		23 42		
Cross Gates d			19 10			19 40						20 44					21 47				22 40		23 47		
Leeds 10 a	19 04	19 08	19 21		19 35	19 49		19 56	20 04	20 08	20 33	20 53	20 59	21 04	21 08	21 33	21 54	22 08		22 35	22 49	23 33	23 56		
Bradford Interchange 37 a			19 45			20 11		*20 28*		*20 57*	*21b06*	*21 28*			*21 57*		*22 28*	*22 57*			*23 28*				

Sundays

until 13 July

	TP	TP	TP	TP	TP	TP	TP	NT	TP	XC		TP	NT	TP	XC	TP	NT	TP	XC	TP	TP		NT	TP	XC
	1◇	1◇	1◇	1◇	1◇	1◇	1		1◇	R 1		1◇		1◇	R 1	1◇		1◇	R 1	1◇	1◇			1◇	R 1
	DD	DD	DD	DD	DD	DD		B	DD	FF		GG	HH	JJ	KK	LL	B	CC	K	BB	D		HH	C	L
										🍴					🍴				🍴						🍴
York 8 33 d	02 09	03 09	04 09	05 05	06 05	07 46	08 15	08 48	09 15	09 27			09 52	10 15	10 28	10 45	10 57	11 15	11 28		11 40		11 52	12 15	12 28
Ulleskelf 33 d																									
Church Fenton 33 d								09 01					10 04										12 04		
Selby d												09 36								11 32					
South Milford d												09 46								11 41					
Micklefield d								09 09					10 12				11 12						12 12		
East Garforth d								09 13					10 16				11 16						12 16		
Garforth d								09 16					10 19				11 18				11 57		12 19		
Cross Gates d								09 21					10 23				11 23						12 23		
Leeds 10 a	02 58	04 00	04 59	05 55	06 55	08 38	08 47	09 30	09 38	09 53		10 03	10 32	10 38	10 52	11 08	11 32	11 38	11 51	12 01	12 07		12 32	12 38	12 51
Bradford Interchange 37 a					*08 23*	*09 23*		09 54	*10 23*			*10b54*	10 55		*11 23*		11 53		*12 23*		*12b54*		12 55		*13 23*

For general notes see front of timetable
For details of catering facilities see Directory of Train Operators

- **A** From Hull to Manchester Piccadilly (Table 39)
- **B** To Blackpool North (Table 41)
- **C** From Newcastle to Manchester Airport (Table 39)
- **D** From Scarborough to Liverpool Lime Street (Table 39)
- **E** From Glasgow Central to Paignton (Table51)
- **G** To Wakefield Westgate (Table 39)
- **H** From Middlesbrough to Manchester Airport (Table 39)
- **J** From Aberdeen (Table 229) to Bournemouth (Table 51)
- **K** From Edinburgh (Table 51) to Penzance (Table 135)
- **L** From Edinburgh to Bournemouth (Table 51)
- **N** From Middlesbrough to Manchester Piccadilly (Table 39)
- **Q** From Edinburgh to Plymouth (Table 51)
- **U** From Hull to Huddersfield (Table 39)
- **V** From Edinburgh to Southampton Central (Table 51)
- **X** From Edinburgh to Bristol Temple Meads (Table 51)
- **Y** From Hull (Table 39)
- **Z** From Newcastle to Birmingham New Street(Table 51)
- **AA** From Edinburgh to Birmingham New Street (Table 51)
- **DD** To Manchester Airport (Table 39)
- **FF** To Plymouth (Table 51)
- **GG** From Hull to Liverpool Lime Street (Table 39)
- **HH** To Huddersfield (Table 41)
- **JJ** From Scarborough to Manchester Airport (Table 39)
- **KK** From Newcastle to Bournemouth (Table 51)
- **LL** From Newcastle to Liverpool Lime Street(Table 39)
- **b** Bradford Forster Square

Due to Engineering Operations in the Sheffield area, services from Saturday 13 September on this Table had not been confirmed at time of going to press. These services will be issued in a special Supplement as soon as exact timings have been confirmed.

Table 40

Sundays

until 13 July

York and Selby → Leeds

Network Diagram - see first page of Table 39

		TP	NT	TP	TP	XC	TP	NT	TP	XC	TP	NT	TP	TP	XC	TP	NT	TP	XC	TP	NT	TP	TP	XC
		1◇		1◇	1◇	R 1	1◇		1◇	R 1	1◇		1◇	1◇	R 1	1◇		1◇	R 1	1◇		1◇	1◇	1◇
		A	B	C	D	E	G	H	J	K	L	B	J	D	N	G	B	J	Q	L	B	J	D	U
York 8	33 d	12 45	12 57	13 15		13 28	13 42	13 52	14 15	14 28	14 45	14 57	15 15		15 28	15 37	15 52	16 15	16 28	16 45	16 55	17 14		17 28
Ulleskelf	33 d																							
Church Fenton	33 d							14 04									16 04							
Selby	d				13 21									15 21									17 21	
South Milford	d				13 31									15 31									17 30	
Micklefield	d		13 12					14 12				15 12					16 12				17 10			
East Garforth	d		13 16					14 16				15 16					16 16				17 14			
Garforth	d		13 18				13 57	14 19				15 18				15 57	16 18				17 16			
Cross Gates	d		13 23					14 23				15 23					16 23				17 21			
Leeds 10	a	13 08	13 32	13 38	13 49	13 52	14 07	14 32	14 38	14 51	15 08	15 32	15 39	15 49	15 52	16 07	16 32	16 38	16 51	17 08	17 31	17 37	17 48	17 52
Bradford Interchange	37 a		13 53			14 23	14b54	14 55		15 23		15 53			16 23		16 53	17 10	17 23		17 53			18 23

		TP	NT	TP	XC	TP	TP	NT	TP	XC	TP	TP	NT	XC	TP	NT	TP	XC	TP	TP	NT	TP	TP
		1◇		1◇	1◇	1◇	1◇		1◇	1◇	1◇	1◇		1◇	1◇		1◇	1◇	1◇	1◇		1◇	1◇
		G	H	J	V	L	D	B	J	X	Y	G	H	Z	AA	BB	C	CC	Y	DD		DD	C
York 8	33 d	17 42	17 52	18 15	18 28	18 45		18 57	19 15	19 28		19 42	19 52	20 28	20 45	20 57	21 15	21 25		21 38	21 52	22 42	23 12
Ulleskelf	33 d																						
Church Fenton	33 d		18 04										20 04								22 04		
Selby	d						18 41				19 35								21 31				
South Milford	d						18 53												21 40				
Micklefield	d		18 12					19 12					20 12			21 12					22 12		
East Garforth	d		18 16					19 16					20 16			21 17					22 16		
Garforth	d	17 57	18 19					19 18				19 57	20 19			21 19				21 54	22 19		
Cross Gates	d		18 23					19 23					20 23			21 24					22 23		
Leeds 10	a	18 07	18 32	18 38	18 51	19 08	19 12	19 32	19 38	19 51	19 59	20 07	20 32	20 51	21 08	21 33	21 38	21 48	22 00	22 04	22 32	23 08	23 38
Bradford Interchange	37 a	18b54	18 55		19 23			19 53		20 23		20b54	20 55	21 23	21b54	21 56		22 23		22b54		23 43	

Sundays

20 July to 7 September

		TP	TP	TP	TP	TP	TP	NT	TP	NT	XC	TP	NT	TP	NT	XC	TP	TP	NT	NT	TP	TP
		1◇	1◇	1◇	1◇	1◇	1◇		1◇		R 1	1◇		1◇		R 1	1◇	1◇			1◇	1◇
		EE	EE	EE	EE	EE	EE	bus	EE	bus	FF	A	bus	GG	bus	HH	G	J	bus	bus	L	D
York 8	33 d	02 16	03 31	04 46	05 46	06 58	07 46		08 57	09 00	09 13	09 25			10 00	10 13	10 20	10 50		11 00	11 14	
Ulleskelf	33 d																					
Church Fenton	33 d							08 20														
Selby	d													09 51								11 21
South Milford	d																					
Micklefield	d							08 40		09 40			←		10 40				←	11 40		
East Garforth	d							08 50		09 50			09 50		10 50				10 50	11 50		
Garforth	d							08 59		→			09 59		→				10 59	→		
Cross Gates	d							09 10					10 10						11 10			
Leeds 10	a	03 08	04 23	05 38	06 38	07 50	08 38	09 25	09 31		09 49	10 07	10 25	10 26		10 50	10 54	11 24	11 25		11 48	11 58
Bradford Interchange	37 a					08 23	09 23	09 54			10 23	10b54				11 23			11 53		12 23	12b54

		TP	NT	NT	XC	TP	TP	NT	TP	NT	XC	TP	NT	TP	NT	XC	TP	TP	NT	TP	NT
		1◇			R 1	1◇	1◇		1◇		R 1	1◇		1◇		R 1	1◇	1◇		1◇	
		JJ	bus	bus	KK	AA	JJ	bus	MM	bus	NN	OO	bus	J	bus	N	G	J	bus	D	bus
York 8	33 d	11 47		12 00	12 13	12 20	12 50			13 00	13 13	13 20		13 50	14 00	14 14	14 20	14 50			15 00
Ulleskelf	33 d																				
Church Fenton	33 d																				
Selby	d								13 06											14 56	
South Milford	d																				
Micklefield	d		←	12 40				←		13 40			←		14 40				←		15 40
East Garforth	d		11 50	12 50				12 50		13 50			13 50		14 50				14 50		15 50
Garforth	d		11 59	→				12 59		→			13 59		→				14 59		→
Cross Gates	d		12 10					13 10					14 10						15 10		
Leeds 10	a	12 25	12 25		12 51	12 54	13 24	13 25	13 45		13 51	13 55	14 25	14 26		14 51	14 55	15 24	15 25	15 32	
Bradford Interchange	37 a		12 55		13 23			13 53	14 23		14 23	14b54	14 55			15 23			15 53		

For general notes see front of timetable
For details of catering facilities see Directory of Train Operators

- **A** To Liverpool Lime Street (Table 39)
- **B** To Blackpool North (Table 41)
- **C** From Middlesbrough to Manchester Airport (Table 39)
- **D** From Hull to Manchester Piccadilly (Table 39)
- **E** From Edinburgh to Plymouth (Table 51)
- **G** From Scarborough to Liverpool Lime Street (Table 39)
- **H** To Huddersfield (Table 41)
- **J** From Newcastle to Manchester Airport (Table 39)
- **K** From Glasgow Central to Bournemouth (Table 51)
- **L** From Middlesbrough to Liverpool Lime Street (Table 39)
- **N** From Glasgow Central to Plymouth (Table 51)
- **Q** From Edinburgh to Southampton Central (Table 51)
- **U** From Aberdeen (Table 229) to Bristol Temple Meads (Table 51)
- **V** From Edinburgh to Bristol Temple Meads(Table 51)
- **X** From Glasgow Central to Birmingham New Street (Table 51)
- **Y** From Hull (Table 39)
- **Z** From Edinburgh to Birmingham New Street(Table 51)
- **AA** From Newcastle to Liverpool Lime Street(Table 39)
- **BB** To Manchester Victoria (Table 41)
- **CC** From Edinburgh to Derby (Table 51)
- **DD** From Scarborough to Manchester Piccadilly (Table 39)
- **EE** To Manchester Airport (Table 39)
- **FF** To Plymouth (Table 51)
- **GG** From Hull to Manchester Airport (Table 39)
- **HH** From Newcastle to Bournemouth (Table 51)
- **JJ** From Scarborough to Manchester Airport (Table 39)
- **KK** From Edinburgh (Table 51) to Penzance (Table 135)
- **MM** From Hull to Liverpool Lime Street (Table 39)
- **NN** From Edinburgh to Bournemouth (Table 51)
- **OO** From Middlesbrough to Manchester Piccadilly (Table 39)
- **b** Bradford Forster Square

Due to Engineering Operations in the Sheffield area, services from Sunday 14 September on this Table had not been confirmed at time of going to press. These services will be issued in a special Supplement as soon as exact timings have been confirmed.

Table 40

Sundays

20 July to 7 September

York and Selby → Leeds

Network Diagram - see first page of Table 39

		XC	TP	TP		NT	NT	XC	TP		NT	TP	TP	NT		XC	TP	TP	NT		NT	XC	TP	TP		NT
		R 1	1 ◇	1 ◇				R 1	1 ◇			1 ◇	1 ◇			R 1	1 ◇	1 ◇				1 ◇	1 ◇	1 ◇		
		A	B	C				D	E			C	G			H	E	C				J	E	G		
						bus	bus				bus			bus					bus		bus					bus
		☕						☕								☕						☕				
York 8	33 d	15 13	15 20	15 45			16 00	16 13	16 20			16 50		17 00		17 14	17 17	17 51			18 00	18 15	18 23			
Ulleskelf	33 d																									
Church Fenton	33 d																									
Selby	d												17 06											18 52		
South Milford	d																									
Micklefield	d					←	16 40				←			17 40					←		18 40					←
East Garforth	d					15 50	16 50				16 50			17 50					17 50		18 50					18 50
Garforth	d					15 59	→				16 59			→					17 59		→					18 59
Cross Gates	d					16 10					17 10								18 10							19 10
Leeds 10	a	15 51	15 55	16 19		16 25		16 51	16 55		17 25	17 26	17 44			17 51	17 55	18 25	18 25			18 51	18 59	19 25		19 25
Bradford Interchange	37 a	*16 23*				*16 53*		*17 23*			*17 53*	*17b58*				*18 23*	*18b54*		*18 55*							*19 53*

		NT	TP	XC	TP		NT	NT	TP	XC		NT	TP	TP	NT		TP	NT	NT	TP		NT	TP			
			1 ◇	1 ◇	1 ◇				1 ◇	1 ◇			1 ◇	1 ◇			1 ◇			1 ◇			1 ◇			
			C	K	E				L	J			Q	U			V			V			Q			
		bus					bus	bus				bus			bus			bus	bus			bus				
				☕																						
York 8	33 d	19 00	19 00	19 15	19 25			20 00	20 24	20 30			20 55		21 00		21 26		21 50	22 42			23 12			
Ulleskelf	33 d																									
Church Fenton	33 d																		22 20							
Selby	d													21 16												
South Milford	d																									
Micklefield	d	19 40					←	20 40				←			21 40			←	22 40			←				
East Garforth	d	19 50					19 50	20 50				20 50			21 50			21 50	22 50			22 50				
Garforth	d	→					19 59	→				20 59			→			21 59	→			22 59				
Cross Gates	d						20 10					21 10						22 10				23 10				
Leeds 10	a		19 37	19 55	19 59		20 25		20 58	21 08		21 25	21 32	21 49			22 07	22 25		23 20		23 25	23 48			
Bradford Interchange	37 a		*20 23*		*20b54*		*20 55*			*21b54*		*21 56*		*22 23*			*22b54*	*22 55*								

For general notes see front of timetable
For details of catering facilities see Directory of Train Operators

- **A** From Glasgow Central to Bournemouth (Table 51)
- **B** From Middlesbrough to Liverpool Lime Street (Table 39)
- **C** From Newcastle to Manchester Airport (Table 39)
- **D** From Edinburgh to Plymouth (Table 51)
- **E** From Scarborough to Liverpool Lime Street (Table 39)
- **G** From Hull to Manchester Piccadilly (Table 39)
- **H** From Aberdeen (Table 229) to Southampton Central (Table 51)
- **J** From Edinburgh to Birmingham New Street (Table 51)
- **K** From Glasgow Central to Birmingham New Street (Table 51)
- **L** From Newcastle to Liverpool Lime Street(Table 39)
- **Q** From Middlesbrough to Manchester Airport (Table 39)
- **U** From Hull (Table 39)
- **V** From Scarborough to Manchester Piccadilly (Table 39)
- **b** Bradford Forster Square

Due to Engineering Operations in the Sheffield area, services from Sunday 14 September on this Table had not been confirmed at time of going to press. These services will be issued in a special Supplement as soon as exact timings have been confirmed.

Leeds → Selby and York

Network Diagram - see first page of Table 39

Miles	Miles		TP	TP	TP	TP	TP	TP	TP	TP	TP	TP	TP	TP	NT	NT	TP	GR	TP	NT	NT	TP	XC	NT	TP
			MO	MO	MX	MX	MO	MO	MX	MO	MO	MO	MX												
			1◇	1◇	1◇	1◇	1◇	1◇	1◇	1◇	1◇	1◇	1◇	1◇			1◇	R 1	1◇			1◇	1◇		1◇
			A B	A C	D	A	A E	A C	A	A G	B H	C H	H	J			K	L	N	Q	U	H	V		X
—	—	Bradford Interchange 37 d												06b01			06 18	06b30	06 48	07 05	07 18				07 35
0	0	**Leeds 10** d	00 36	00 36	00 38	01 03	02 26	02 26	02 45	02 45	04 52	04 52	05 03	06 35	06 39	06 42	06 55	07 10	07 23	07 29	07 40	07 50	07 57	07 58	08 12
4¼	4¼	Cross Gates d													06 45					07 36	07 47			08 04	
7¼	7¼	Garforth d													06 51	06 53				07 41	07 52	08 00		08 10	
8	8	East Garforth d													06 53					07 43	07 55			08 12	
9¾	9¾	Micklefield d													06 57					07 47	07 58			08 16	
—	12¾	South Milford d														07 04				07 52				08 20	
—	20¾	**Selby** a														07 18			07 42	08 05				08 35	
14¾	—	Church Fenton 33 a																			08 04				
16½	—	Ulleskelf 33 a																							
25½	—	**York 8** 33 a	01 02	01 15	01 15	01 52	02 52	03 06	03 13	03 19	05 18	05 36	05 32	07 03	07 15		07 22	07 35			08 19	08 20	08 24		08 35

	NT	TP	TP	NT	TP	XC	TP	NT	TP	TP	NT	TP	XC	TP	NT	TP	TP	NT	TP	XC	TP	NT	TP	TP	NT
		1◇	1◇		1◇	R 1	1◇		1◇	1◇		1◇	R 1	1◇		1◇	1◇		1◇	1◇	1◇		1◇	1◇	
	Y	Z	N	U	H	AA	BB	Y	Z	N	U	H	CC	BB	Y	Z	N	U	H	DD	BB	Y	Z	N	U
Bradford Interchange 37 d	07 49		08 05	08 18		08b26	08 35	08 47		09 05	09 18		09b31	09 35	09 48		10 05	10 18		10b31	10 35	10 48		11 05	11 18
Leeds 10 d	08 15	08 27	08 38	08 45	08 57	09 05	09 12	09 15	09 27	09 38	09 41	09 57	10 05	10 12	10 15	10 27	10 38	10 41	10 57	11 05	11 12	11 15	11 27	11 38	11 41
Cross Gates d	08 22			08 52				09 22			09 48				10 22			10 48				11 22			11 48
Garforth d	08 27	08a35		08 57	09 05			09 27			09 53	10 05			10 27			10 53	11 05			11 27			11 53
East Garforth d	08 29			08 59				09 29			09 56				10 29			10 56				11 29			11 56
Micklefield d	08 33			09 03				09 33			09 59				10 33			10 59				11 33			11 59
South Milford d	08 38							09 38							10 38							11 38			
Selby a	08 53		08 57					09 54		09 57					10 53		10 57					11 55		11 57	
Church Fenton 33 a				09 08							10 05														12 05
Ulleskelf 33 a																									
York 8 33 a		08 55		09 23	09 25	09 33	09 36		09 55		10 20	10 23	10 29	10 36		10 49		11 17	11 23	11 29	11 35		11 52		12 20

	TP	XC	TP	NT	TP	TP	NT	TP	XC	TP	NT	TP	TP	NT	TP	XC	TP	NT	TP	TP	NT	TP	XC	TP	NT
	1◇	1◇	1◇		1◇	1◇		1◇	1◇	1◇		1◇	1◇		1◇	1◇	1◇		1◇	1◇		1◇	R 1	1◇	
	H	EE	BB	Y	Z	N	U	H	HH	BB	Y	Z	N	U	H	JJ	BB	Y	Z	N	U	H	KK	BB	Y
Bradford Interchange 37 d		11b31	11 35	11 48		12 05	12 18		12b31	12 35	12 48		13 05	13 18		13b31	13 35	13 48		14 05	14 18		14b31	14 35	14 48
Leeds 10 d	11 57	12 05	12 12	12 15	12 27	12 38	12 41	12 57	13 05	13 12	13 15	13 27	13 38	13 41	13 57	14 05	14 12	14 15	14 27	14 38	14 41	14 57	15 05	15 12	15 15
Cross Gates d				12 22			12 48				13 22			13 48				14 22			14 48				15 22
Garforth d	12 05			12 27			12 53	13 05			13 27			13 53	14 05			14 27			14 53	15 05			15 27
East Garforth d				12 29			12 56				13 29			13 56				14 29			14 56				15 29
Micklefield d				12 33			12 59				13 33			13 59				14 33			14 59				15 33
South Milford d				12 38							13 38							14 38							15 38
Selby a				12 53		12 57					13 53		13 57					14 52		14 57					15 53
Church Fenton 33 a														14 05											
Ulleskelf 33 a																									
York 8 33 a	12 23	12 29	12 35		12 55		13 17	13 24	13 29	13 35		13 52		14 20	14 23	14 29	14 37		14 53		15 17	15 23	15 29	15 35	

	TP	TP	NT	TP	XC	TP	NT	TP	TP	NT	TP	XC	TP	NT	TP	NT	TP	NT	NT	TP	XC	TP	NT	TP	TP
	1◇	1◇		1◇	R 1	1◇		1◇	1◇		1◇	R 1	1◇		1◇		1◇			1◇	R 1	1◇		1◇	1◇
	A	N	U	H	LL	BB	Y	Z	N	U	K	MM	NN	Y	K		N	U		H	OO	BB	Y	Z	N
Bradford Interchange 37 d		15 05	15 18		15b31	15 35	15 48		16 05	16 18		16b31	16 35	16 48			17 05	17 18			17b31	17 35	17 48		18 05
Leeds 10 d	15 27	15 38	15 41	15 57	16 05	16 12	16 15	16 27	16 38	16 41	16 57	17 05	17 12	17 15	17 24	17 28	17 38	17 41	17 49	17 57	18 05	18 12	18 15	18 27	18 38
Cross Gates d			15 48				16 22			16 48			17 18	17 24		17 34		17 48	17 56				18 22		
Garforth d			15 53	16 05			16 28			16 53	17 05			17 29	17 34	17 40		17 53	18 01	18 05			18 27		
East Garforth d			15 56				16 30			16 56				17 31		17 42		17 56	18 04				18 29		
Micklefield d			15 59				16 34			16 59				17 35		17 46		17 59	18 08				18 33		
South Milford d							16 39							17 40					18 12				18 38		18 51
Selby a		15 57					16 55		16 57					17 54			18 04		18 25				18 50		19 00
Church Fenton 33 a			16 05															18 05							
Ulleskelf 33 a																		18 10							
York 8 33 a	15 52		16 22	16 23	16 29	16 35		16 52		17 18	17 22	17 29	17 38		17 57	18 06		18 24		18 25	18 29	18 37		18 52	

For general notes see front of timetable
For details of catering facilities see Directory of Train Operators

- **A** From Manchester Airport (Table 39)
- **B** Until 14 July and from 15 September
- **C** 21 July to 8 September
- **D** From Liverpool Lime Street (Table 39)
- **E** Until 14 July and 8 September to 3 November
- **G** From 10 November
- **H** From Manchester Airport to Middlesbrough (Table 39)
- **J** From Manchester Piccadilly to Newcastle(Table 39)
- **K** From Manchester Airport to Scarborough (Table 39)
- **L** To Aberdeen (Table 229)
- **N** From Manchester Piccadilly to Hull (Table 39)
- **Q** From Manchester Victoria (Table 41)
- **U** From Blackpool North (Table 41)
- **V** From Birmingham New Street (from 8 September from Sheffield) (Table 51)
- **X** From Liverpool Lime Street to Scarborough and to Newcastle (Table 39)
- **Y** From Wakefield Westgate (Table 39)
- **Z** From Manchester Airport to Newcastle (Table 39)
- **AA** From Birmingham New Street to Edinburgh (Table 51)
- **BB** From Liverpool Lime Street to Scarborough (Table 39)
- **CC** From Bristol Temple Meads (from 8 September from Birmingham New Street) to Edinburgh (Table 51)
- **DD** From Southampton Central (from 8 September from Bristol Temple Meads) to Edinburgh (Table 51)
- **EE** From Plymouth to Edinburgh (Table 51) (from 8 September from Cardiff Central)
- **HH** From Bournemouth to Aberdeen (Table 229) (from 8 September from Plymouth) (Table 51)
- **JJ** From Plymouth to Edinburgh (Table 51) (from 8 September from Bristol Temple Meads)
- **KK** From Bournemouth (from 8 September from Bristol Temple Meads) to Edinburgh (table 51)
- **LL** From Penzance (from 8 September from Paignton) (Table 135) to Dundee (Table 229)
- **MM** From Bournemouth (from 8 September from Bristol Temple Meads) to Glasgow Central (Table 51)
- **NN** From Liverpool Lime Street to Middlesbrough (Table 39)
- **OO** From Plymouth to Glasgow Central (Table 51)
- **b** Bradford Forster Square

Leeds → Selby and York

Network Diagram - see first page of Table 39

	NT	TP	XC	TP	NT	TP	TP	NT	TP	XC	TP	TP	NT	TP	XC	TP	TP	NT	XC	TP	TP	TP	NT	TP
		1◇	R 1◇	1◇		1◇	1◇		1◇	R 1◇	1◇	1◇		1◇	R 1◇	1◇	1◇		1◇	1◇	1◇	1◇		1◇
	A	B	C	D		E	G	A	B	J	D	K	A	L	N	Q	U		V	Q	L	K	A	X
		🛒	🍴	🛒		🛒	🛒								🍴									
Bradford Interchange 37 d	18 18		18b27	18 35		18 48	19 05	19 18		19 35		20 04	20 18				21 04		21 35			22 04	22 18	23 04
Leeds 10 d	18 41	18 57	19 05	19 12	19 15	19 27	19 38	19 41	19 57	20 09	20 12	20 45	20 48	21 05	21 10	21 12	21 42	21 51	22 10	22 12	22 22	22 42	22 51	23 42
Cross Gates d	18 48				19 22			19 48					20 55					21 58					22 58	
Garforth d	18 53	19 05			19 27			19 53	20 05				21 00					22 04					23 03	
East Garforth d	18 56				19 29			19 56					21 02					22 06					23 06	
Micklefield d	18 59				19 33			19 59					21 06					22 10					23 10	
South Milford d							19 51							21 18							22 35			
Selby a							20 00							21 27							22 44			
Church Fenton 33 a	19 05												21 11										23 16	
Ulleskelf 33 a													21 16											
York 8 33 a	19 20	19 25	19 29	19 35	19 53	19 55		20 20	20 23	20 34	20 36	21 09	21 29		21 35	21 40	22 08	22 27	22 58	22 38		23 12	23 34	00 08

Saturdays

until 6 September

	TP	TP	TP	TP	TP	NT	TP	GR	TP	NT	TP	XC	NT	TP	NT	TP	TP	NT	TP	XC	TP	NT	TP
	1◇	1◇	1◇	1◇	1◇		1◇	R 1	1◇		1◇	1◇		1◇		1◇	1◇		1◇	1◇	1◇		1◇
	Q	X	X	B	Y		U	Z	G	A	B	BB		D		K	G	A	B	BB	D	CC	K
								🍴 🛒			🛒	🍴		🛒		🛒	🛒		🛒	🍴	🛒		🛒
Bradford Interchange 37 d					06b01		06 23			07 18				07b36		07 49	08 05	08 18		08b31		08 47	
Leeds 10 d	00 38	01 03	02 45	04 49	06 35	06 38	06 55	07 10	07 23	07 40	07 50	07 57	08 00	08 12	08 15	08 27	08 38	08 41	08 57	09 05	09 12	09 15	09 27
Cross Gates d						06 44				07 47			08 06		08 22			08 48				09 22	
Garforth d						06 50				07 52	08 00		08 12		08 27			08 53	09 05			09 27	
East Garforth d						06 52				07 55			08 14		08 29			08 56				09 29	
Micklefield d						06 56				07 58			08 18		08 34			08 59				09 33	
South Milford d													08 22		08 38							09 38	
Selby a									07 42				08 35		08 53		08 57					09 54	
Church Fenton 33 a										08 04								09 05					
Ulleskelf 33 a																							
York 8 33 a	01 15	01 47	03 14	05 30	07 02	07 14	07 22	07 35		08 19	08 20	08 24		08 34		08 53		09 20	09 25	09 30	09 36		09 52

	TP	NT	TP	XC	TP	NT	TP	TP	NT	TP	XC	TP	NT	TP	TP	NT	TP	XC	TP	NT	TP	TP
	1◇		1◇	1◇	1◇		1◇	1◇		1◇	1◇	1◇		1◇	1◇		1◇	1◇	1◇		1◇	1◇
	G	A	B	DD	D	CC	K	G	A	B	EE	D	CC	K	G	A	B	FF	D	CC	K	G
			🛒	🍴	🛒		🛒			🛒	🍴	🛒			🛒		🛒	🍴	🛒		🛒	
Bradford Interchange 37 d	09 05	09 18		09b31	09 35	09 48		10 05	10 18		10b31	10 35	10 48		11 05	11 18		11b31	11 35	11 48		12 05
Leeds 10 d	09 38	09 41	09 57	10 05	10 12	10 15	10 27	10 38	10 41	10 57	11 05	11 12	11 15	11 27	11 38	11 41	11 57	12 05	12 12	12 15	12 27	12 38
Cross Gates d		09 48				10 22			10 48				11 22			11 48				12 22		
Garforth d		09 53	10 05			10 27			10 53	11 05			11 27			11 53	12 05			12 27		
East Garforth d		09 56				10 29			10 56				11 29			11 56				12 29		
Micklefield d		09 59				10 33			10 59				11 33			11 59				12 33		
South Milford d						10 38							11 38							12 38		
Selby a	09 57					10 53		10 59					11 53		11 57					12 53		12 57
Church Fenton 33 a		10 05														12 05						
Ulleskelf 33 a																						
York 8 33 a		10 20	10 23	10 29	10 35		10 52		11 17	11 23	11 31	11 35		11 52		12 20	12 23	12 29	12 35		12 52	

	NT	TP	XC	TP	NT	TP	TP	NT	TP	XC	TP	NT	TP	TP	NT	TP	XC	TP	NT	TP	TP	NT	TP
		1◇	R 1	1◇		1◇	1◇		1◇	1◇	1◇		1◇	1◇		1◇	1◇	1◇		1◇	1◇		1◇
	A	B	GG	D	CC	K	G	A	B	FF	D	CC	K	G	A	B	HH	D	CC	X	G	A	B
		🛒	🍴	🛒		🛒			🛒	🍴	🛒		🛒	🛒		🛒	🍴	🛒		🛒			
Bradford Interchange 37 d	12 18		12b31	12 35	12 48		13 05	13 18		13b31	13 35	13 48		14 05	14 18		14b31	14 35	14 48		15 05	15 18	
Leeds 10 d	12 41	12 57	13 05	13 12	13 15	13 27	13 38	13 41	13 57	14 05	14 12	14 15	14 27	14 38	14 41	14 57	15 05	15 12	15 15	15 27	15 38	15 41	15 57
Cross Gates d	12 48				13 22			13 48				14 22			14 48				15 22			15 48	
Garforth d	12 53	13 05			13 27			13 53	14 05			14 27			14 53	15 05			15 27			15 53	16 05
East Garforth d	12 56				13 29			13 56				14 29			14 56				15 29			15 56	
Micklefield d	12 59				13 33			13 59				14 33			14 59				15 33			15 59	
South Milford d					13 38							14 38							15 38				
Selby a					13 53		13 57					14 52		14 57					15 53		15 57		
Church Fenton 33 a								14 05														16 05	
Ulleskelf 33 a																							
York 8 33 a	13 17	13 23	13 31	13 35		13 52		14 20	14 23	14 29	14 35		14 52		15 19	15 23	15 29	15 35		15 52		16 22	16 23

For general notes see front of timetable
For details of catering facilities see Directory of Train Operators

- **A** From Blackpool North (Table 41)
- **B** From Manchester Airport to Middlesbrough (Table 39)
- **C** From Bournemouth (from 8 September from Bristol Temple Meads) to Edinburgh (table 51)
- **D** From Liverpool Lime Street to Scarborough (Table 39)
- **E** From Manchester Piccadilly (Table 39)
- **G** From Manchester Piccadilly to Hull (Table 39)
- **J** From Plymouth (from 8 September from Paignton) to Edinburgh (Table 51) to Leeds
- **K** From Manchester Airport to Newcastle (Table 39)
- **L** To Hull (Table 39)
- **N** From Bournemouth (from 8 September from Bristol Temple Meads) to Newcastle (Table 51)
- **Q** From Liverpool Lime Street (Table 39)
- **U** From Manchester Airport to Scarborough (Table 39)
- **V** From Plymouth (from 8 September from Paignton) (Table 51)
- **X** From Manchester Airport (Table 39)
- **Y** From Manchester Piccadilly to Newcastle(Table 39)
- **Z** To Aberdeen (Table 229)
- **BB** From Birmingham New Street to Edinburgh (Table 51)
- **CC** From Wakefield Westgate (Table 39)
- **DD** From Bristol Temple Meads to Edinburgh (Table 51)
- **EE** From Southampton Central to Edinburgh (Table 51)
- **FF** From Plymouth to Edinburgh (Table 51)
- **GG** From Bournemouth (Table 51) to Aberdeen (Table 228
- **HH** From Bournemouth to Edinburgh (Table 51)
- **b** Bradford Forster Square

Due to Engineering Operations in the Sheffield area, services from Saturday 13 September on this Table had not been confirmed at time of going to press. These services will be issued in a special Supplement as soon as exact timings have been confirmed.

Saturdays

until 6 September

Leeds → Selby and York

Network Diagram - see first page of Table 39

		XC	TP		NT	TP	TP	NT	TP	XC	TP	NT		TP	TP	NT	TP	XC	TP	NT	TP		TP	NT	TP	XC
		R 1	1◇			1◇	1◇		1◇	R 1	1◇			1◇	1◇		1◇	R 1	1◇		1◇		1◇		1◇	1◇
		A	B		C	D	E	G	H	J	K	C		H	E	G	L	N	B	C	D		E	G	L	U
Bradford Interchange	37 d	15b31	15 35		15 48		16 05	16 18		16b31	16 35	16 48			17 05	17 18		17b31	17 35	17 48			18 05	18 18		18b31
Leeds 10	d	16 05	16 12		16 15	16 27	16 38	16 41	16 57	17 05	17 12	17 15		17 24	17 38	17 41	17 57	18 05	18 12	18 15	18 27		18 38	18 41	18 57	19 05
Cross Gates	d				16 22			16 48			17 18	17 24				17 48				18 22				18 48		
Garforth	d				16 28			16 53	17 05			17 29		17 34		17 53	18 05			18 27				18 53	19 05	
East Garforth	d				16 30			16 56				17 31				17 56				18 29				18 56		
Micklefield	d				16 34			16 59				17 35				17 59				18 33				18 59		
South Milford	d				16 39							17 40								18 38			18 51			
Selby	a				16 54		16 57					17 53			17 58					18 50			19 00			
Church Fenton	33 a															18 06								19 05		
Ulleskelf	33 a															18 10										
York 8	33 a	16 29	16 35			16 52		17 17	17 22	17 31	17 38			17 57		18 24	18 25	18 29	18 35		18 52			19 19	19 22	19 32

		TP	NT	TP	TP	NT	TP		XC	TP	TP	NT	TP	XC	TP	TP		NT	XC	TP	TP	TP	NT	TP		
		1◇		1◇	1◇		1◇		R 1	1◇	1◇		1◇	1◇	1◇	1◇			R 1	1◇	1◇	1◇		1◇		
		B	C	V	E	G	L		Y	B	D	G	Z	AA	BB	H			CC	BB	Z	DD	G	DD		
Bradford Interchange	37 d	18 35	18 48		19 05	19 18			19b31	19 35	20 04	20 21				21 04				21 35		22 04	22 18	23 04		
Leeds 10	d	19 12	19 15	19 27	19 38	19 41	19 57		20 05	20 12	20 45	20 48	21 05	21 10	21 12	21 42		21 45	22 05	22 12	22 22	22 42	22 54	23 42		
Cross Gates	d		19 22			19 48						20 55						21 52					23 01			
Garforth	d		19 27			19 53	20 05					21 00						21 57					23 06			
East Garforth	d		19 29			19 56						21 03						21 59					23 09			
Micklefield	d		19 33			19 59						21 07						22 03					23 13			
South Milford	d				19 51								21 18								22 36					
Selby	a				20 00								21 27								22 45					
Church Fenton	33 a											21 13											23 19			
Ulleskelf	33 a											21 18														
York 8	33 a	19 35	19 53	19 58		20 21	20 24		20 29	20 36	21 09	21 30		21 35	21 40	22 05		22 19	22 36	22 38		23 09	23 36	00 08		

Sundays

until 13 July

		TP	TP	TP	TP	TP	TP	NT	GR	TP	TP	NT	TP	TP	NT		TP	XC	TP	NT	TP	TP	XC	NT	TP	TP
		1◇	1◇	1◇	1◇	1◇	1◇		R 1	1◇	1◇		1◇	1◇			1◇	1◇	1◇		1◇	1◇	1◇		1◇	1◇
		BB	DD	DD	DD	L	D		EE	FF	L	GG	HH	E	JJ		D	EE	B	G	L	E	KK	JJ	D	B
Bradford Interchange	37 d		00 05					08 31			09b02	09 21			10 02			10 31		11 02		11 31		12 01	12b02	12 31
Leeds 10	d	00 15	00 43	02 44	06 01	07 40	08 40	08 55	09 05	09 10	09 40	09 48	10 05	10 25	10 29		10 42	11 08	11 10	11 25	11 40	12 10	12 20	12 25	12 40	13 10
Cross Gates	d							09 02				09 54			10 36					11 32				12 31		
Garforth	d							09 07		09 18		10 00			10 41				11 18	11 37				12 37		13 18
East Garforth	d							09 09				10 02			10 43					11 39				12 39		
Micklefield	d							09 13				10 06			10 47					11 43				12 43		
South Milford	d													10 38								12 23				
Selby	a													10 47								12 32				
Church Fenton	33 a							09 19							10 53									12 49		
Ulleskelf	33 a																									
York 8	33 a	00 41	01 35	03 37	06 53	08 34	09 07	09 33	10 04	09 35	10 06	10 23	10 28		11 07		11 09	11 33	11 36	11 59	12 05		12 44	13 03	13 07	13 37

		XC	NT	TP	TP	XC	NT		TP	XC	TP	NT	TP	TP	XC	TP	NT	TP	TP	XC	TP	NT		TP	TP	XC
		1◇		1◇	1◇	1◇			1◇	1◇	1◇		1◇	1◇	R 1	1◇		1◇	1◇	R 1	1◇			1◇	1◇	R 1
		LL	G	L	MM	KK	JJ		D	NN	B	G	D	OO	PP	MM	JJ	D	E	RR	B	G		L	E	SS
Bradford Interchange	37 d		13 02		13 31		14 02			14 31		15 02			15 31		16 01	16b02		16 31		17 02				17 31
Leeds 10	d	13 20	13 25	13 40	14 10	14 20	14 25		14 40	15 08	15 10	15 25	15 40	15 55	16 08	16 10	16 25	16 40	16 54	17 08	17 10	17 25		17 40	17 54	18 08
Cross Gates	d		13 32				14 31					15 32					16 31					17 32				
Garforth	d		13 37				14 37				15 18	15 37					16 37				17 18	17 37				
East Garforth	d		13 39				14 39					15 39					16 39					17 39				
Micklefield	d		13 43				14 43					15 43					16 43					17 43				
South Milford	d				14 23											16 25									18 07	
Selby	a				14 32											16 34			17 13						18 16	
Church Fenton	33 a						14 49										16 49									
Ulleskelf	33 a																									
York 8	33 a	13 44	13 59	14 05		14 44	15 03		15 07	15 33	15 40	15 59	16 05	16 19	16 33		17 04	17 09		17 33	17 37	18 00		18 09		18 33

For general notes see front of timetable
For details of catering facilities see Directory of Train Operators

- **A** From Paignton to Newcastle (Table 51)
- **B** From Liverpool Lime Street to Scarborough (Table 39)
- **C** From Wakefield Westgate (Table 39)
- **D** From Manchester Airport to Newcastle (Table 39)
- **E** From Manchester Piccadilly to Hull (Table 39)
- **G** From Blackpool North (Table 41)
- **H** From Manchester Airport to Scarborough (Table 39)
- **J** From Newquay (Table 135) to Newcastle (Table 51)
- **K** From Liverpool Lime Street to Middlesbrough (Table 39)
- **L** From Manchester Airport to Middlesbrough (Table 39)
- **N** From Paignton to Glasgow Central (Table 51)
- **U** From Bournemouth to Edinburgh (Table 51)
- **V** From Manchester Piccadilly (Table 39)
- **Y** From Plymouth to Newcastle (Table 51)
- **Z** To Hull (Table 39)
- **AA** From Bournemouth to Newcastle (Table 51)
- **BB** From Liverpool Lime Street (Table 39)
- **CC** From Paignton (Table 51)
- **DD** From Manchester Airport (Table 39)
- **EE** To Glasgow Central (Table 26)
- **FF** To Scarborough (Table 39)
- **GG** From Halifax (Table 41)
- **HH** From Liverpool Lime Street to Newcastle(Table 39)
- **JJ** From Huddersfield (Table 41)
- **KK** From Birmingham New Street to Edinburgh (Table 51)
- **LL** From Birmingham New Street (Table 51) to Aberdeen (Table 229)
- **MM** From Liverpool Lime Street to Hull (Table 39)
- **NN** From Bristol Temple Meads to Edinburgh (Table 51)
- **OO** From Manchester Piccadilly to Middlesbrough (Table 39)
- **PP** From Bournemouth (Table 51) to Dundee (Table 229)
- **RR** From Plymouth to Glasgow Central (Table 51)
- **SS** From Bournemouth to Glasgow Central (Table 51)
- **b** Bradford Forster Square

Due to Engineering Operations in the Sheffield area, services from Saturday 13 September on this Table had not been confirmed at time of going to press. These services will be issued in a special Supplement as soon as exact timings have been confirmed.

Table 40

Sundays until 13 July

Leeds → Selby and York

Network Diagram - see first page of Table 39

	TP 1◊ A	NT B	TP 1◊ C	XC R 1 D 🛒	TP 1◊ E	NT G	TP 1◊ H	TP 1◊ J	XC R 1 K	TP 1◊ E	NT G	TP 1◊ C	XC R 1 L	TP 1◊ A	NT G	TP 1◊ N	XC R 1 Q	TP 1◊ U	TP 1◊ V	NT	TP 1◊ X	XC 1◊ Y	TP 1◊ A
Bradford Interchange 37 d		18 02		*18 31*		19 02			*19 31*		20 02	*20 14*	*20 31*		21 02		*21 31*			*22 02*		*22 31*	*23 02*
Leeds 10 d	18 10	18 25	18 40	19 08	19 10	19 25	19 40	19 56	20 08	20 10	20 25	20 45	21 08	21 10	21 25	21 40	22 08	22 10	22 17	22 35	22 50	23 08	23 40
Cross Gates d		18 31				19 32					20 32				21 32					22 41			
Garforth d		18 37			19 18	19 37					20 37			21 18	21 37					22 47			
East Garforth d		18 39				19 39					20 39				21 39					22 49			
Micklefield d		18 43				19 43					20 43				21 43					22 53			
South Milford d								20 09											22 30				
Selby a								20 18											22 39				
Church Fenton 33 a		18 49									20 48									22 59			
Ulleskelf 33 a																							
York 8 33 a	18 37	19 03	19 07	19 33	19 38	19 59	20 05		20 33	20 37	21 02	21 09	21 33	21 38	21 59	22 06	22 38	22 38		23 17	23 21	23 38	00 08

Sundays 20 July to 7 September

	TP 1◊ A	TP 1◊ X	TP 1◊ X	TP 1◊ X	TP 1◊ H	TP 1◊ C	TP 1◊ Z	GR R 1 AA 🛒	NT 🚌	TP 1◊ BB	NT 🚌	NT 🚌	TP 1◊ E	TP 1◊ CC	NT 🚌	NT 🚌	TP 1◊ DD	XC 1◊ AA 🛒	TP 1◊ EE	NT 🚌	NT 🚌
Bradford Interchange 37 d		*00 05*						*08 31*		*09b02*		*09 21*				*10 02*			*10 31*		*11 02*
Leeds 10 d	00 15	00 43	02 38	05 58	07 40	08 40	09 00	09 05	09 05	09 40		10 00	10 05	10 25		10 40	10 42	10 57	11 22		11 35
Cross Gates d									09 20			10 15				10 55					11 50
Garforth d									09 30			10 25				11 05					12 00
East Garforth d									09 45		←	10 40			←	11 20				←	12 15
Micklefield d									09 55 →		09 55	10 50 →			10 50	11 30 →				11 30	12 25 →
South Milford d																					
Selby a																	11 15				
Church Fenton 33 a																					
Ulleskelf 33 a																					
York 8 33 a	01 08	01 35	03 30	06 50	08 34	09 19	09 37	10 04		10 16	10 35		10 41	11 08	11 30			11 33	12 09	12 10	

	TP 1◊ N	NT 🚌	XC 1◊ FF 🛒	TP 1◊ J	NT 🚌	TP 1◊ N	XC 1◊ GG 🛒	TP 1◊ EE	NT 🚌	NT 🚌	TP 1◊ X	XC 1◊ FF 🛒	NT 🚌	TP 1◊ JJ	NT 🚌	TP 1◊ N	XC 1◊ K 🛒	TP 1◊ U	NT 🚌	NT 🚌	TP 1◊ N
Bradford Interchange 37 d	*11 02*			*11 31*	*12b02*		*12 31*			*13 02*		*13 31*			*14 02*		*14 31*			*15 02*	
Leeds 10 d	11 40		12 08	12 10	12 35	12 40	13 08	13 22		13 35	13 40	14 08		14 10	14 35	14 40	15 08	15 12		15 35	15 40
Cross Gates d					12 50					13 50					14 50					15 50	
Garforth d					13 00					14 00					15 00					16 00	
East Garforth d		←			13 15				←	14 15			←		15 15				←	16 15	
Micklefield d		12 25			13 25 →				13 25	14 25 →			14 25		15 25 →				15 25	16 25 →	
South Milford d																					
Selby a				12 45										14 45							
Church Fenton 33 a																					
Ulleskelf 33 a																					
York 8 33 a	12 17	13 05	12 44			13 19	13 45	13 59	14 05		14 21	14 47	15 05			15 20	15 45	15 50	16 05		16 20

	TP 1◊ KK	XC 1◊ LL 🛒	TP 1◊ U	NT 🚌	NT 🚌	TP 1◊ N	TP 1◊ MM	XC R 1 NN 🛒	TP 1◊ EE	NT 🚌	NT 🚌	TP 1◊ N	TP 1◊ J	XC R 1 OO 🛒	TP 1◊ U	NT 🚌	NT 🚌	TP 1◊ N	XC R 1 K 🛒	TP 1◊ EE	NT 🚌
Bradford Interchange 37 d		*15 31*			*16b02*				*16 31*		*17 02*				*17 31*		*18 02*		*18 31*		
Leeds 10 d	16 00	16 08	16 10		16 35	16 40	16 54	17 08	17 12		17 35	17 40	18 00	18 08	18 10		18 35	18 40	19 08	19 10	
Cross Gates d					16 50						17 50						18 50				
Garforth d					17 00						18 00						19 00				
East Garforth d				←	17 15					←	18 15					←	19 15				←
Micklefield d				16 25	17 25 →					17 25	18 25 →					18 25	19 25 →				19 25
South Milford d																					
Selby a							17 35						18 31								
Church Fenton 33 a																					
Ulleskelf 33 a																					
York 8 33 a	16 35	16 45	16 47	17 05		17 21		17 41	17 47	18 05		18 20		18 45	18 49	19 05		19 21	19 43	19 51	20 05

For general notes see front of timetable
For details of catering facilities see Directory of Train Operators

- **A** From Liverpool Lime Street (Table 39)
- **B** From Huddersfield (Table 41)
- **C** From Manchester Airport to Newcastle (Table 39)
- **D** From Penzance (Table 135) to Edinburgh (Table 51)
- **E** From Liverpool Lime Street to Scarborough (Table 39)
- **G** From Blackpool North (Table 41)
- **H** From Manchester Airport to Middlesbrough (Table 39)
- **J** From Manchester Piccadilly to Hull (Table 39)
- **K** From Bournemouth to Edinburgh (Table 51)
- **L** From Paignton to Newcastle (Table 51)
- **N** From Manchester Airport to Scarborough (Table 39)
- **Q** From Bournemouth (Table 51)
- **U** From Liverpool Lime Street to Newcastle(Table 39)
- **V** To Hull (Table 39)
- **X** From Manchester Airport (Table 39)
- **Y** From Plymouth (Table 51)
- **Z** To Scarborough (Table 39)
- **AA** To Glasgow Central (Table 26)
- **BB** From Manchester Airport (Table 39) to Newcastle (Table 26)
- **CC** From Manchester Piccadilly to Newcastle (Table 39)
- **DD** From Manchester Airport to Hull (Table 39)
- **EE** From Liverpool Lime Street to Middlesbrough (Table 39)
- **FF** From Birmingham New Street to Edinburgh (Table 51)
- **GG** From Birmingham New Street (Table 51) to Aberdeen (Table 229)
- **JJ** From Liverpool Lime Street to Hull (Table 39)
- **KK** From Manchester Piccadilly to Middlesbrough (Table 39)
- **LL** From Plymouth (Table 51) to Dundee (Table 229)
- **MM** From Manchester Piccadilly (Table 39) to Hull (Table 29)
- **NN** From Bournemouth to Glasgow Central (Table 51)
- **OO** From Penzance (Table 135) to Glasgow Central (Table 51)
- **b** Bradford Forster Square

Due to Engineering Operations in the Sheffield area, services from Sunday 14 September on this Table had not been confirmed at time of going to press. These services will be issued in a special Supplement as soon as exact timings have been confirmed.

Table 40

Sundays

20 July to 7 September

Leeds → Selby and York

Network Diagram - see first page of Table 39

		NT	TP	TP	XC	TP		NT	NT	TP	XC	TP		NT	NT	TP	TP	XC		NT	TP	TP	NT	TP		
			1 ◇	1 ◇	R 1	1 ◇				1 ◇	R 1	1 ◇				1 ◇	1 ◇	R 1			1 ◇	1 ◇		1 ◇		
			A	B	C	D				E	G	H				E	D	J			K	E		L		
		bus						bus	bus					bus	bus					bus			bus			
Bradford Interchange	37 d	*19 02*				*19 31*			*20 02*		*20 31*				*21 02*		*21 31*					*22 02*		*23 02*		
Leeds 10	d	19 35	19 40	19 56	20 08	20 10			20 35	20 43	21 08	21 10			21 35	21 40	22 05	22 10			22 27	22 40	22 45	23 40		
Cross Gates	d	19 50							20 50						21 50								23 00			
Garforth	d	20 00							21 00						22 00								23 10			
East Garforth	d	20 15						←	21 15					←	22 15					←			23 25			
Micklefield	d	20 25						20 25	21 25					21 25	22 25					22 25			23 35			
South Milford	d	↪							↪						↪											
Selby	a			20 28																	23 09					
Church Fenton	33 a																			22 40			23 50			
Ulleskelf	33 a																									
York 8	33 a		20 21		20 45	20 49		21 05		21 19	21 45	21 50		22 05		22 17	22 44	22 53		23 10		23 21	00 20	00 24		

For general notes see front of timetable
For details of catering facilities see
Directory of Train Operators

A From Manchester Airport to Scarborough (Table 39)
B From Manchester Piccadilly to Hull (Table 39)
C From Plymouth to Edinburgh (Table 51)
D From Liverpool Lime Street to Newcastle(Table 39)
E From Manchester Airport (Table 39)
G From Bournemouth to Newcastle (Table 51)
H From Liverpool Lime Street to Scarborough (Table 39)
J From Plymouth (Table 51)
K To Hull (Table 39)
L From Liverpool Lime Street (Table 39)

Due to Engineering Operations in the Sheffield area, services from Sunday 14 September on this Table had not been confirmed at time of going to press. These services will be issued in a special Supplement as soon as exact timings have been confirmed.

Leeds and Bradford → Huddersfield, Blackpool North, Rochdale and Manchester Victoria via Halifax and Brighouse

Network Diagram - see first page of Table 39

Miles	Miles	Miles	Miles			NT	NT	NT A	NT B	NT	NT	NT	NT C	NT D		NT	NT	NT	NT E	NT	NT	NT	NT	NT	NT E
—	—	—	—	York 8	40 d											06 13					07 06				
—	—	—	—	Selby	40 d														06 43			07 26			07 43
0	0	—	0	**Leeds 10**	37, 39 d	05 08	05 51			06 03	06 22	06 37				06 51	07 09	07 13	07 23	07 37	07 51	08 08	08 13		08 22
4	4	—	—	Bramley	37 d	05 15	05 58				06 29	06 44					07 16		07 30	07 44		08 15			08 29
5¾	5¾	—	—	New Pudsey	37 d	05 20	06 03			06 12	06 34	06 49				07 01	07 21		07 35	07 49	08 01	08 20			08 34
9½	9½	—	—	**Bradford Interchange**	37 a	05 28	06 11			06 23	06 42	06 57				07 11	07 29		07 43	07 57	08 11	08 28			08 42
—	—	—	—		d	05 31	06 14			06 25	06 45	07 00				07 14	07 32		07 46	08 00	08 14	08 31			08 45
17½	17½	—	—	**Halifax**	a	05 43	06 26			06 37	06 57	07 12				07 25	07 44		07 59	08 12	08 25	08 43			08 58
—	—	0	—		d	05 43	06 27			06 37	06 57	07 12				07 26	07 44		08 07	08 12	08 26	08 43		09 03	09 07
—	—	—	9¼	Dewsbury	39 d													07 31					08 31		
—	—	—	12¼	Mirfield	39 d													07 38					08 38		
—	—	5¼	16¼	Brighouse	d													07a48	08 17				08a48		09 17
—	—	10½	—	**Huddersfield**	39 a														08 30						09 30
21	21	—	22	Sowerby Bridge	d	05 50	06 33				07 04	07 19					07 51			08 19		08 50		09 10	
25	25	—	26	Mytholmroyd	d	05 56	06 39				07 10	07 25					07 57			08 25		08 56		09 16	
26¼	26¼	—	27¼	**Hebden Bridge**	a	05 59	06 42			06 49	07 14	07 28				07 37	08 00			08 28	08 37	08 59		09 20	
—	—	—	—		d	05 59	06 42			06 49		07 28				07 38	08 00			08 28	08 38	08 59			
—	39	—	—	Burnley Manchester Road	97 a					07 08						07 57					08 57				
—	45¼	—	—	Accrington	97 a					07 17						08 06					09 06				
—	51½	—	—	Blackburn	97 a					07 25						08 14					09 14				
—	63½	—	—	**Preston 8**	97 a					07 46						08 33					09 34				
—	78	—	—	Poulton-le-Fylde	97 a					08 04						08 54					09 53				
—	81	—	—	**Blackpool North**	97 a					08 12						09 04					10 02				
30½	—	—	—	Todmorden	d	06 06	06 50	07 14	07 18			07 35	07 46	07 48			08 07			08 35		09 06			
32	—	—	—	Walsden	d	06 09	06 53	07 17	07 21			07 38	07 49	07 51			08 10			08 38		09 09			
36	—	—	—	Littleborough	d	06 16	06 59	07 24	07 28			07 45	07 56	07 58			08 17			08 45		09 16			
37	—	—	—	Smithy Bridge	d	06 18	07 02	07 26	07 30			07 47	07 58	08 00			08 19			08 47		09 18			
39¼	—	—	—	**Rochdale**	a	06 23	07 06	07 30	07 34			07 51	08 02	08 04			08 23			08 51		09 22			
—	—	—	—		95 d	06 24	07 06	07 31	07 35			07 52	08 05	08 05			08 24			08 52		09 23			
41	—	—	—	Castleton	95 a	06 27	07 09	07 34	07 38			07 55	08 08	08 08			08 27								
43¾	—	—	—	Mills Hill	95 a	06 31	07 14	07 37	07 41			07 59	08 12	08 12			08 31								
45¾	—	—	—	Moston	95 a	06 35	07 17	07 41	07 45			08 03	08 15	08 15			08 35								
49¾	—	—	—	**Manchester Victoria**	95 ⛴ a	06 46	07 29	07 53	07 57			08 16	08 25	08 25			08 46			09 09		09 40			
—	—	—	—	Liverpool Lime Street 10	90 a	*08 13*		09 05	09 05				09 39	09 39			*10 05*					*11 05*			

		NT		NT	NT	NT	NT E	NT	NT	NT	NT	NT E		NT	NT	NT	NT	NT E	NT	NT	NT	NT		NT E	NT
York 8	40 d								09 09						10 11					11 09					
Selby	40 d			08 12			08 42					09 43						10 43							
Leeds 10	37, 39 d	08 37		08 51	09 08	09 13	09 22	09 37	09 51	10 08	10 13	10 22		10 37	10 51	11 08	11 13	11 22	11 37	11 51	12 08	12 13		12 22	12 37
Bramley	37 d	08 44			09 15		09 29	09 44		10 15		10 29		10 44		11 15		11 29	11 44		12 15			12 29	12 44
New Pudsey	37 d	08 49		09 00	09 20		09 34	09 49	10 01	10 20		10 34		10 49	11 01	11 20		11 34	11 49	12 01	12 20			12 34	12 49
Bradford Interchange	37 a	08 57		09 11	09 28		09 42	09 57	10 11	10 28		10 42		10 57	11 11	11 28		11 42	11 57	12 11	12 28			12 42	12 57
	d	09 00		09 11	09 31		09 45	10 00	10 14	10 31		10 45		11 00	11 14	11 31		11 45	12 00	12 14	12 31			12 45	13 00
Halifax	a	09 12		09 23	09 43		09 58	10 12	10 25	10 43		10 58		11 12	11 25	11 43		11 58	12 12	12 25	12 43			12 58	13 12
	d	09 12		09 25	09 43		10 06	10 12	10 26	10 43		11 06		11 12	11 26	11 43		12 06	12 12	12 26	12 43			13 06	13 12
Dewsbury	39 d					09 29					10 29						11 29					12 29			
Mirfield	39 d					09 35					10 35						11 35					12 35			
Brighouse	d					09 48	10 16				10 48	11 16					11 48	12 16				12 48		13 16	
Huddersfield	39 a						10 30					11 30						12 31						13 30	
Sowerby Bridge	d	09 19			09 50	09 58		10 19		10 50	10 58			11 19		11 50	11 58		12 19		12 50	12 58			13 19
Mytholmroyd	d	09 25			09 56	10 04		10 25		10 56	11 04			11 25		11 56	12 04		12 25		12 56	13 04			13 25
Hebden Bridge	a	09 28		09 37	09 59	10 08		10 28	10 37	10 59	11 08			11 28	11 37	11 59	12 08		12 28	12 37	12 59	13 08			13 28
	d	09 28		09 37	09 59			10 28	10 38	10 59				11 28	11 38	11 59			12 28	12 38	12 59				13 28
Burnley Manchester Road	97 a			09 56					10 57						11 57					12 57					
Accrington	97 a			10 05					11 06						12 06					13 06					
Blackburn	97 a			10 13					11 14						12 14					13 14					
Preston 8	97 a			10 32					11 34						12 32					13 32					
Poulton-le-Fylde	97 a			10 52					11 52						12 52					13 52					
Blackpool North	97 a			11 02					12 01						13 00					13 59					
Todmorden	d	09 36			10 06			10 35		11 06				11 35		12 06			12 36		13 06				13 35
Walsden	d				10 09					11 09						12 09					13 09				
Littleborough	d	09 46			10 16			10 43		11 16				11 43		12 16			12 44		13 16				13 43
Smithy Bridge	d	09 48			10 18			10 45		11 18				11 45		12 18			12 46		13 18				13 45
Rochdale	a	09 52			10 22			10 49		11 22				11 49		12 22			12 51		13 22				13 49
	95 d	09 53			10 23			10 50		11 23				11 50		12 23			12 52		13 23				13 50
Castleton	95 a																								
Mills Hill	95 a																								
Moston	95 a																								
Manchester Victoria	95 ⛴ a	10 10			10 40			11 09		11 40				12 07		12 40			13 09		13 40				14 09
Liverpool Lime Street 10	90 a				*12 05*					*13 05*						*14 05*					*15 05*				

For general notes see front of timetable
For details of catering facilities see Directory of Train Operators

A From 6 October
B Until 3 October
C From 6 October. To Kirkby (Table 82)
D Until 3 October. To Kirkby (Table 82)
E To Wakefield Westgate (Table 39)

Leeds and Bradford → Huddersfield, Blackpool North, Rochdale and Manchester Victoria via Halifax and Brighouse

Network Diagram - see first page of Table 39

		NT	NT	NT	NT	NT	NT	NT	NT	NT		NT	NT	NT	NT	NT	NT	NT	NT	NT		NT	NT	NT	NT
					A					A						A						A			
York [8]	40 d	12 13					13 09						14 13					15 09						16 13	
Selby	40 d				12 43					13 43						14 43						15 43			
Leeds [10]	37, 39 d	12 51	13 08	13 13	13 22	13 37	13 51	14 08	14 13	14 22		14 37	14 51	15 08	15 13	15 22	15 37	15 51	16 08	16 13		16 22	16 37	16 51	17 08
Bramley	37 d		13 15		13 29	13 44		14 15		14 29		14 44		15 15		15 29	15 44		16 15			16 29	16 44		17 15
New Pudsey	37 d	13 01	13 20		13 34	13 49	14 01	14 20		14 34		14 49	15 01	15 20		15 34	15 49	16 01	16 20			16 34	16 49	17 01	17 20
Bradford Interchange	37 a	13 11	13 28		13 42	13 57	14 11	14 28		14 42		14 57	15 11	15 28		15 42	15 57	16 11	16 28			16 42	16 57	17 11	17 28
	d	13 14	13 31		13 45	14 00	14 14	14 31		14 45		15 00	15 14	15 31		15 45	16 00	16 14	16 31			16 45	17 00	17 14	17 31
Halifax	a	13 25	13 43		13 58	14 12	14 25	14 43		14 58		15 12	15 25	15 43		15 58	16 12	16 25	16 43			16 58	17 12	17 25	17 43
	d	13 26	13 43		14 06	14 12	14 26	14 43		15 06		15 12	15 26	15 43		16 06	16 12	16 26	16 43			17 06	17 12	17 26	17 43
Dewsbury	39 d			13 29					14 29						15 29					16 31					
Mirfield	39 d			13 35					14 35						15 36					16 38					
Brighouse	d			13 48	14 16				14 49	15 16					15 48	16 16				16 48		17 16			
Huddersfield	39 a				14 30					15 30						16 30						17 30			
Sowerby Bridge	d		13 50	13 58		14 19		14 50	14 59			15 19		15 50	15 58		16 19		16 50	16 58			17 19		17 50
Mytholmroyd	d		13 56	14 04		14 25		14 56	15 05			15 25		15 56	16 04		16 25		16 56	17 04			17 25		17 56
Hebden Bridge	a	13 37	13 59	14 08		14 28	14 37	14 59	15 09			15 28	15 37	15 59	16 08		16 28	16 37	16 59	17 08			17 28	17 37	17 59
	d	13 38	13 59			14 28	14 38	14 59				15 28	15 38	15 59			16 28	16 38	16 59				17 28	17 38	17 59
Burnley Manchester Road	97 a	13 57					14 57						15 57					16 57						17 57	
Accrington	97 a	14 06					15 06						16 06					17 06						18 06	
Blackburn	97 a	14 14					15 14						16 14					17 14						18 14	
Preston [8]	97 a	14 32					15 32						16 33					17 34						18 34	
Poulton-le-Fylde	97 a	14 52					15 52						16 52					17 53						18 54	
Blackpool North	97 a	15 00					16 00						17 00					18 03						19 03	
Todmorden	d		14 06			14 36		15 06				15 36		16 06			16 35		17 06				17 35		18 06
Walsden	d		14 09					15 09						16 09			16 38		17 09				17 38		18 09
Littleborough	d		14 16			14 44		15 16				15 46		16 16			16 45		17 16				17 45		18 16
Smithy Bridge	d		14 18			14 46		15 18				15 48		16 18			16 47		17 18				17 47		18 18
Rochdale	a		14 22			14 51		15 22				15 53		16 22			16 51		17 22				17 51		18 22
	95 d		14 23			14 52		15 23				15 54		16 23			16 52		17 23				17 52		18 23
Castleton	95 a																								
Mills Hill	95 a																								
Moston	95 a																								
Manchester Victoria	95 a		14 40			15 09		15 40				16 10		16 40			17 10		17 40				18 10		18 41
Liverpool Lime Street [10]	90 a		*16 05*					*17 04*						*18 05*					*19 05*				*19 35*		*20 05*

		NT	NT	NT	NT	NT	NT	NT		NT	NT	NT	NT	NT	NT	NT	NT	NT		NT	NT	NT	NT		
			A					A					A												
York [8]	40 d				17 07						18 10				19 04										
Selby	40 d		16 43					17 43																	
Leeds [10]	37, 39 d	17 13	17 22	17 37	17 51	18 08	18 13	18 22		18 37	18 51	19 08	19 22	19 37	19 51	20 08	20 37	21 08		21 37	22 08	22 37	23 08		
Bramley	37 d		17 29	17 44		18 15		18 30		18 44		19 15	19 29	19 44		20 15	20 44	21 15		21 44	22 15	22 44	23 15		
New Pudsey	37 d		17 34	17 49	18 01	18 20		18 35		18 49	19 01	19 20	19 34	19 49	20 01	20 20	20 49	21 20		21 49	22 20	22 49	23 20		
Bradford Interchange	37 a		17 42	17 57	18 11	18 28		18 43		18 57	19 11	19 28	19 45	19 57	20 11	20 28	20 57	21 28		21 57	22 28	22 57	23 29		
	d		17 45	18 00	18 14	18 31		18 46		19 00	19 14	19 31	19 45	20 00	20 14	20 31	21 00	21 31		22 00	22 31	23 00	23 31		
Halifax	a		17 58	18 12	18 26	18 43		18 59		19 12	19 25	19 43	20 01	20 12	20 25	20 44	21 12	21 44		22 12	22 44	23 12	23 44		
	d		18 06	18 12	18 26	18 43		19 06		19 12	19 26	19 43	20 04	20 12	20 26	20 44	21 12	21 44		22 12	22 44	23 12	23 44		
Dewsbury	39 d	17 29					18 29																		
Mirfield	39 d	17 36					18 36																		
Brighouse	d	17 50	18 16				18 49	19 16					20 14			20 55		21 55			22 55		23 55		
Huddersfield	39 a		18 31					19 30					20 30			21 08		22 07			23 07		00 09		
Sowerby Bridge	d	17 59		18 19		18 50	18 59			19 19		19 50		20 19			21 19			22 19		23 19			
Mytholmroyd	d	18 05		18 25		18 56	19 05			19 25		19 56		20 25			21 25			22 25		23 25			
Hebden Bridge	a	18 09		18 28	18 38	18 59	19 09			19 28	19 37	19 59		20 28	20 37		21 28			22 28		23 28			
	d			18 28	18 38	18 59				19 28	19 38			20 28	20 38		21 28			22 28		23 28			
Burnley Manchester Road	97 a				18 58						19 57				20 57										
Accrington	97 a				19 07						20 06				21 06										
Blackburn	97 a				19 15						20 14				21 14										
Preston [8]	97 a				19 36						20 31				21 31										
Poulton-le-Fylde	97 a				19 54						20 49				21 49										
Blackpool North	97 a				20 03						20 56				21 56										
Todmorden	d			18 35		19 06				19 35				20 35			21 35			22 35		23 35			
Walsden	d			18 38		19 09				19 38				20 38			21 38			22 38		23 38			
Littleborough	d			18 45		19 16				19 45				20 45			21 45			22 45		23 45			
Smithy Bridge	d			18 47		19 18				19 47				20 47			21 47			22 47		23 47			
Rochdale	a			18 51		19 22				19 51				20 51			21 51			22 51		23 51			
	95 d			18 52		19 23				19 52				20 52			21 52			22 52		23 52			
Castleton	95 a			18 55						19 55				20 55			21 55			22 55					
Mills Hill	95 a			18 59						19 59				20 59			21 59			22 59					
Moston	95 a			19 03						20 03				21 03			22 03			23 03					
Manchester Victoria	95 a			19 14		19 40				20 14				21 14			22 14			23 14		00 08			
Liverpool Lime Street [10]	90 a					*21 05*				*22 05*				*23 05*			*00 14*								

For general notes see front of timetable
For details of catering facilities see Directory of Train Operators

A To Wakefield Westgate (Table 39)

Table 41

Saturdays

Leeds and Bradford → Huddersfield, Blackpool North, Rochdale and Manchester Victoria via Halifax and Brighouse

Network Diagram - see first page of Table 39

		NT	NT A	NT B	NT	NT		NT	NT C	NT D	NT	NT		NT	NT E	NT	NT	NT		NT	NT E	NT	NT	NT	NT
York 8	40 d										06 13						07 06						08 07		
Selby	40 d														06 43						07 43				
Leeds 10	37, 39 d	05 51			06 03	06 22		06 37			06 51	07 09		07 13	07 23	07 37	07 51	08 08		08 13	08 22	08 37	08 51	09 08	09 13
Bramley	37 d	05 58				06 29		06 44				07 16			07 30	07 44		08 15			08 29	08 44		09 15	
New Pudsey	37 d	06 03			06 12	06 34		06 49			07 01	07 21			07 35	07 49	08 01	08 20			08 34	08 49	09 00	09 20	
Bradford Interchange	37 a	06 11			06 23	06 42		06 57			07 11	07 29			07 43	07 57	08 11	08 28			08 42	08 57	09 11	09 28	
	d	06 14			06 25	06 45		07 00			07 14	07 32			07 46	08 00	08 14	08 31			08 45	09 00	09 14	09 31	
Halifax	a	06 26			06 37	06 57		07 12			07 25	07 44			07 59	08 12	08 25	08 43			08 58	09 12	09 26	09 43	
	d	06 27			06 37	06 57		07 12			07 26	07 44			08 07	08 12	08 26	08 43			09 06	09 12	09 26	09 43	
Dewsbury	39 d													07 29						08 29					09 29
Mirfield	39 d													07 36						08 36					09 35
Brighouse	d													07 49	08 17					08 49	09 16				09 49
Huddersfield	39 a														08 30						09 30				
Sowerby Bridge	d	06 33				07 04		07 19				07 51		07 59		08 19		08 50		08 59		09 19		09 50	09 59
Mytholmroyd	d	06 39				07 10		07 25				07 57		08 05		08 25		08 56		09 05		09 25		09 56	10 05
Hebden Bridge	a	06 42			06 49	07 14		07 28			07 37	08 00		08 09		08 28	08 37	08 59		09 09		09 28	09 38	09 59	10 09
	d	06 42			06 49			07 28			07 38	08 00				08 28	08 38	08 59				09 28	09 38	09 59	
Burnley Manchester Road	97 a				07 08						07 57						08 57						09 58		
Accrington	97 a				07 17						08 06						09 06						10 07		
Blackburn	97 a				07 25						08 14						09 14						10 15		
Preston 8	97 a				07 47						08 33						09 33						10 32		
Poulton-le-Fylde	97 a				08 04						08 54						09 54						10 53		
Blackpool North	97 a				08 12						09 03						10 02						11 03		
Todmorden	d	06 50	07 14	07 18				07 35	07 46	07 48		08 07				08 35		09 06				09 35		10 06	
Walsden	d	06 53	07 17	07 21				07 38	07 49	07 51		08 10				08 38		09 09						10 09	
Littleborough	d	06 59	07 24	07 28				07 45	07 56	07 58		08 17				08 45		09 16				09 43		10 16	
Smithy Bridge	d	07 02	07 26	07 30				07 47	07 58	08 00		08 19				08 47		09 18				09 45		10 18	
Rochdale	a	07 06	07 30	07 34				07 51	08 02	08 04		08 23				08 51		09 22				09 49		10 22	
	95 d	07 06	07 31	07 35				07 52	08 05	08 05		08 24				08 52		09 23				09 50		10 23	
Castleton	95 a	07 09	07 34	07 38				07 55	08 08	08 08		08 27													
Mills Hill	95 a	07 14	07 37	07 41				07 59	08 12	08 12		08 31													
Moston	95 a	07 17	07 41	07 45				08 03	08 15	08 15		08 35													
Manchester Victoria	95 ⛴ a	07 29	07 53	07 57				08 16	08 25	08 25		08 46				09 09		09 40				10 10		10 40	
Liverpool Lime Street 10	90 a		09 05	09 05					*09 39*	*09 39*		*10 05*						*11 05*						*12 05*	

		NT E		NT	NT	NT	NT	NT E		NT	NT	NT	NT	NT E		NT	NT	NT	NT	NT E		NT	NT	NT	NT
York 8	40 d				09 09						10 11						11 09						12 13		
Selby	40 d	08 43						09 43						10 43						11 43					
Leeds 10	37, 39 d	09 22		09 37	09 51	10 08	10 13	10 22		10 37	10 51	11 08	11 13	11 22		11 37	11 51	12 08	12 13	12 22		12 37	12 51	13 08	13 13
Bramley	37 d	09 29		09 44		10 15		10 29		10 44		11 15		11 29		11 44		12 15		12 29		12 44		13 15	
New Pudsey	37 d	09 34		09 49	10 01	10 20		10 34		10 49	11 01	11 20		11 34		11 49	12 01	12 20		12 34		12 49	13 01	13 20	
Bradford Interchange	37 a	09 42		09 57	10 11	10 28		10 42		10 57	11 11	11 28		11 42		11 57	12 11	12 28		12 42		12 57	13 11	13 28	
	d	09 45		10 00	10 14	10 31		10 45		11 00	11 14	11 31		11 45		12 00	12 14	12 31		12 45		13 00	13 14	13 31	
Halifax	a	09 58		10 12	10 25	10 43		10 58		11 12	11 25	11 43		11 58		12 12	12 25	12 43		12 58		13 12	13 25	13 43	
	d	10 06		10 12	10 26	10 43		11 06		11 12	11 26	11 43		12 06		12 12	12 26	12 43		13 06		13 12	13 26	13 43	
Dewsbury	39 d						10 29						11 29						12 29						13 29
Mirfield	39 d						10 35						11 35						12 35						13 35
Brighouse	d	10 16					10 49	11 16					11 49	12 16					12 49	13 16					13 49
Huddersfield	39 a	10 30						11 30						12 30						13 30					
Sowerby Bridge	d			10 19		10 50	10 59			11 19		11 50	11 59			12 19		12 50	12 59			13 19		13 50	13 59
Mytholmroyd	d			10 25		10 56	11 05			11 25		11 56	12 05			12 25		12 56	13 05			13 25		13 56	14 05
Hebden Bridge	a			10 28	10 37	10 59	11 09			11 28	11 37	11 59	12 09			12 28	12 37	12 59	13 09			13 28	13 37	13 59	14 09
	d			10 28	10 38	10 59				11 28	11 38	11 59				12 28	12 38	12 59				13 28	13 38	13 59	
Burnley Manchester Road	97 a				10 57						11 57						12 57						13 57		
Accrington	97 a				11 06						12 06						13 06						14 06		
Blackburn	97 a				11 14						12 14						13 14						14 14		
Preston 8	97 a				11 34						12 32						13 32						14 32		
Poulton-le-Fylde	97 a				11 52						12 52						13 52						14 52		
Blackpool North	97 a				12 01						13 01						14 00						15 01		
Todmorden	d			10 35		11 06				11 35		12 06				12 36		13 06				13 35		14 06	
Walsden	d					11 09						12 09						13 09						14 09	
Littleborough	d			10 43		11 16				11 43		12 16				12 45		13 16				13 43		14 16	
Smithy Bridge	d			10 45		11 18				11 45		12 18				12 47		13 18				13 45		14 18	
Rochdale	a			10 49		11 23				11 49		12 22				12 51		13 22				13 49		14 22	
	95 d			10 50		11 24				11 50		12 23				12 52		13 23				13 50		14 23	
Castleton	95 a																								
Mills Hill	95 a																								
Moston	95 a																								
Manchester Victoria	95 ⛴ a			11 09		11 40				12 09		12 40				13 09		13 40				14 09		14 40	
Liverpool Lime Street 10	90 a					*13 05*						*14 05*						*15 05*						*16 05*	

For general notes see front of timetable
For details of catering facilities see Directory of Train Operators

A From 11 October
B Until 4 October
C From 11 October. To Kirkby (Table 82)
D Until 4 October. To Kirkby (Table 82)
E To Wakefield Westgate (Table 39)

Table 41

Saturdays

Leeds and Bradford → Huddersfield, Blackpool North, Rochdale and Manchester Victoria via Halifax and Brighouse

Network Diagram - see first page of Table 39

Station		NT A	NT	NT	NT	NT	NT A	NT	NT	NT	NT	NT A	NT	NT	NT	NT	NT A	NT	NT	NT	NT
York 8	40 d			13 09					14 13					15 09					16 13		
Selby	40 d	12 43					13 43					14 43					15 43				
Leeds 10	37, 39 d	13 22	13 37	13 51	14 08	14 13	14 22	14 37	14 51	15 08	15 13	15 22	15 37	15 51	16 08	16 13	16 22	16 37	16 51	17 08	17 13
Bramley	37 d	13 29	13 44		14 15		14 29	14 44		15 15		15 29	15 44		16 15		16 29	16 44		17 15	
New Pudsey	37 d	13 34	13 49	14 01	14 20		14 34	14 49	15 01	15 20		15 34	15 49	16 01	16 20		16 34	16 49	17 01	17 20	
Bradford Interchange	37 a	13 42	13 57	14 11	14 28		14 42	14 57	15 11	15 28		15 42	15 57	16 11	16 28		16 42	16 57	17 11	17 28	
	d	13 45	14 00	14 14	14 31		14 45	15 00	15 14	15 31		15 45	16 00	16 14	16 31		16 45	17 00	17 14	17 31	
Halifax	a	13 58	14 12	14 25	14 43		14 58	15 12	15 25	15 43		15 58	16 12	16 25	16 43		16 58	17 12	17 25	17 43	
	d	14 06	14 12	14 26	14 43		15 06	15 12	15 26	15 43		16 06	16 12	16 26	16 43		17 06	17 12	17 26	17 43	
Dewsbury	39 d					14 29					15 29					16 29					17 29
Mirfield	39 d					14 35					15 36					16 36					17 36
Brighouse	d	14 16				14 49	15 16				15 49	16 16				16 49	17 16				17 50
Huddersfield	39 a	14 30					15 30					16 30					17 30				
Sowerby Bridge	d		14 19		14 50	14 59		15 19		15 50	15 59		16 19		16 50	16 59		17 19		17 50	17 59
Mytholmroyd	d		14 25		14 56	15 05		15 25		15 56	16 05		16 25		16 56	17 05		17 25		17 56	18 05
Hebden Bridge	a		14 28	14 37	14 59	15 09		15 28	15 37	15 59	16 09		16 28	16 37	16 59	17 09		17 28	17 37	17 59	18 10
	d		14 28	14 38	14 59			15 28	15 38	15 59			16 28	16 38	16 59			17 28	17 38	17 59	
Burnley Manchester Road	97 a			14 57					15 57					16 57					17 57		
Accrington	97 a			15 06					16 06					17 06					18 06		
Blackburn	97 a			15 14					16 14					17 14					18 14		
Preston 8	97 a			15 32					16 33					17 34					18 34		
Poulton-le-Fylde	97 a			15 52					16 52					17 53					18 55		
Blackpool North	97 a			16 01					17 01					18 03					19 04		
Todmorden	d		14 36		15 06			15 36		16 06			16 35		17 06			17 35		18 06	
Walsden	d				15 09					16 09			16 38		17 09			17 38		18 09	
Littleborough	d		14 44		15 16			15 46		16 16			16 45		17 16			17 45		18 16	
Smithy Bridge	d		14 46		15 18			15 48		16 18			16 47		17 18			17 47		18 18	
Rochdale	a		14 51		15 22			15 53		16 22			16 51		17 22			17 51		18 22	
	95 d		14 52		15 23			15 54		16 23			16 52		17 23			17 52		18 23	
Castleton	95 a																				
Mills Hill	95 a																				
Moston	95 a																				
Manchester Victoria	95 ⇌ a		15 09		15 40			16 10		16 40			17 08		17 40			18 08		18 41	
Liverpool Lime Street 10	90 a				*17 04*					*18 05*					*19 05*			*19 35*		*20 05*	

Station		NT A	NT	NT	NT	NT	NT A	NT	NT	NT	NT A	NT	NT	NT	NT	NT	NT	NT	NT	NT B	NT C
York 8	40 d			17 09					18 10				19 04								
Selby	40 d	16 43					17 43				18 43										
Leeds 10	37, 39 d	17 22	17 37	17 51	18 08	18 13	18 22	18 37	18 51	19 08	19 22	19 37	19 51	20 08	20 37	21 08	21 37	22 08	22 37	23 00	23 08
Bramley	37 d	17 29	17 44		18 15		18 30	18 44		19 15	19 29	19 44		20 15	20 44	21 15	21 44	22 15	22 44	23 07	23 15
New Pudsey	37 d	17 34	17 49	18 01	18 20		18 35	18 49	19 01	19 20	19 34	19 49	20 01	20 20	20 49	21 20	21 49	22 20	22 49	23 12	23 20
Bradford Interchange	37 a	17 42	17 57	18 11	18 28		18 43	18 57	19 11	19 28	19 45	19 57	20 11	20 28	20 57	21 28	21 57	22 28	22 57	23 20	23 28
	d	17 45	18 00	18 14	18 31		18 46	19 00	19 14	19 31	19 45	20 00	20 14	20 31	21 00	21 31	22 00	22 31	23 00	23 23	23 31
Halifax	a	17 58	18 12	18 26	18 43		18 59	19 12	19 25	19 43	20 01	20 12	20 25	20 44	21 12	21 44	22 12	22 44	23 12	23 36	23 44
	d	18 06	18 12	18 26	18 43		19 06	19 12	19 26	19 43	20 06	20 12	20 26	20 44	21 12	21 44	22 12	22 44	23 12	23 36	23 44
Dewsbury	39 d					18 29															
Mirfield	39 d					18 36															
Brighouse	d	18 16				18 49	19 16				20 16			20 55		21 55		22 55		23 47	23 55
Huddersfield	39 a	18 30					19 30				20 30			21 08		22 08		23 07		23 59	00 09
Sowerby Bridge	d		18 19		18 50	18 59		19 19		19 50		20 19			21 19		22 19		23 19		
Mytholmroyd	d		18 25		18 56	19 05		19 25		19 56		20 25			21 25		22 25		23 25		
Hebden Bridge	a		18 28	18 38	18 59	19 09		19 28	19 37	19 59		20 28	20 37		21 28		22 28		23 28		
	d		18 28	18 38	18 59			19 28	19 38			20 28	20 38		21 28		22 28		23 28		
Burnley Manchester Road	97 a			18 57					19 57				20 57								
Accrington	97 a			19 06					20 06				21 06								
Blackburn	97 a			19 14					20 14				21 14								
Preston 8	97 a			19 35					20 31				21 31								
Poulton-le-Fylde	97 a			19 58					20 49				21 49								
Blackpool North	97 a			20 07					20 56				21 56								
Todmorden	d		18 35		19 06			19 35				20 35			21 35		22 35		23 35		
Walsden	d		18 38		19 09			19 38				20 38			21 38		22 38		23 38		
Littleborough	d		18 45		19 16			19 45				20 45			21 45		22 45		23 45		
Smithy Bridge	d		18 47		19 18			19 47				20 47			21 47		22 47		23 47		
Rochdale	a		18 53		19 23			19 51				20 51			21 51		22 51		23 51		
	95 d		18 54		19 24			19 52				20 52			21 52		22 52		23 52		
Castleton	95 a		18 57					19 55				20 55			21 55		22 55				
Mills Hill	95 a		19 01					19 59				20 59			21 59		22 59				
Moston	95 a		19 05					20 03				21 03			22 03		23 03				
Manchester Victoria	95 ⇌ a		19 15		19 40			20 14				21 14			22 14		23 14		00 08		
Liverpool Lime Street 10	90 a				*21 05*			*22 06*				*23 05*			*00 14*						

For general notes see front of timetable
For details of catering facilities see Directory of Train Operators

A To Wakefield Westgate (Table 39)
B From 13 September
C Until 6 September

Table 41

Sundays

Leeds and Bradford → Huddersfield, Blackpool North, Rochdale and Manchester Victoria via Halifax and Brighouse

until 13 July and from 14 September

Network Diagram - see first page of Table 39

		NT	NT		NT	NT		NT	NT		NT	NT		NT	NT		NT	NT		NT	NT		NT	NT	NT
York 8	40 d							08 48			09 52			10 57			11 52			12 57			13 52		14 57
Selby	40 d																								
Leeds 10	37, 39 d	08 21	08 45		09 02	09 25		09 35	10 02		10 34	11 02		11 35	12 02		12 35	13 02		13 35	14 02		14 35	15 02	15 35
Bramley	37 d	08 28			09 10	09 32			10 10		10 42	11 10			12 10		12 42	13 10			14 10		14 42	15 10	
New Pudsey	37 d	08 33	08 54		09 15	09 37		09 45	10 15		10 47	11 15		11 44	12 15		12 47	13 15		13 44	14 15		14 47	15 15	15 44
Bradford Interchange	37 a	08 41	09 03		09 23	09 45		09 54	10 23		10 55	11 23		11 53	12 23		12 55	13 23		13 53	14 23		14 55	15 23	15 53
	d	08 45	09 05		09 26	09 48		09 57	10 26		10 58	11 26		11 55	12 26		12 58	13 26		13 55	14 26		14 58	15 26	15 55
Halifax	a	08 57	09 17		09 38	10 01		10 09	10 38		11 11	11 38		12 07	12 38		13 11	13 38		14 07	14 38		15 11	15 38	16 07
	d	09 01	09 17		09 39	10 01		10 09	10 38		11 15	11 38		12 07	12 38		13 15	13 38		14 07	14 38		15 14	15 38	16 07
Dewsbury	39 d																								
Mirfield	39 d																								
Brighouse	d					10 11					11 25						13 25						15 26		
Huddersfield	39 a					10 24					11b39						13 39						15b39		
Sowerby Bridge	d	09 08			09 45				10 45			11 45			12 45			13 45			14 45			15 45	
Mytholmroyd	d	09 14			09 51				10 51			11 51			12 51			13 51			14 51			15 51	
Hebden Bridge	a	09 17	09 29		09 54			10 21	10 54			11 54		12 19	12 54			13 54		14 19	14 54			15 54	16 19
	d	09 17	09 29		09 54			10 21	10 54			11 54		12 19	12 54			13 54		14 19	14 54			15 54	16 19
Burnley Manchester Road	97 a		09 48					10 41						12 38						14 38					16 38
Accrington	97 a		09 57					10 50						12 47						14 47					16 47
Blackburn	97 a		10 05					10 58						12 55						14 55					16 55
Preston 8	97 a		10 29					11 15						13 13						15 13					17 13
Poulton-le-Fylde	97 a		10 47					11 33						13 31						15 32					17 31
Blackpool North	97 a		10 54					11 40						13 39						15 40					17 40
Todmorden	d	09 24			10 01				11 01			12 01			13 01			14 01			15 01			16 01	
Walsden	d	09 27			10 04				11 04			12 04			13 04			14 04			15 04			16 04	
Littleborough	d	09 34			10 11				11 11			12 11			13 11			14 11			15 11			16 11	
Smithy Bridge	d	09 36			10 13				11 13			12 13			13 13			14 13			15 13			16 13	
Rochdale	a	09 41			10 17				11 17			12 17			13 17			14 17			15 17			16 17	
	95 d	09 41			10 18				11 18			12 18			13 18			14 18			15 18			16 18	
Castleton	95 a	09 44			10 21				11 21			12 21			13 21			14 21			15 21			16 21	
Mills Hill	95 a	09 48			10 25				11 25			12 25			13 25			14 25			15 25			16 25	
Moston	95 a	09 52			10 29				11 29			12 29			13 29			14 29			15 29			16 29	
Manchester Victoria	95 ⛴ a	10 01			10 38				11 38			12 38			13 38			14 38			15 38			16 38	
Liverpool Lime Street 10	90 a	*10c54*			*11c56*				*12c51*			*13c55*			*14c51*			*15c51*			*16c55*			*17c51*	

		NT		NT	NT		NT	NT		NT	NT		NT	NT		NT	NT		NT	NT		NT	NT		
York 8	40 d			15 52				16 55			17 52			18 57			19 52			20 57					
Selby	40 d																								
Leeds 10	37, 39 d	16 02		16 35	16 50		17 02	17 35		18 02	18 35		19 02	19 35		20 02	20 35		21 02	21 35		22 02	22 35		
Bramley	37 d	16 10			16 57		17 10			18 10	18 42		19 10			20 10	20 42		21 10	21 43		22 10	22 42		
New Pudsey	37 d	16 15		16 44	17 02		17 15	17 44		18 15	18 47		19 15	19 44		20 15	20 47		21 14	21 47		22 15	22 47		
Bradford Interchange	37 a	16 23		16 53	17 10		17 23	17 53		18 23	18 55		19 23	19 53		20 23	20 55		21 23	21 56		22 23	22 55		
	d	16 26		16 55	17 13		17 26	17 55		18 26	18 58		19 26	19 55		20 26	20 58		21 26	21 58		22 26	22 58		
Halifax	a	16 38		17 07	17 26		17 38	18 07		18 38	19 11		19 38	20 07		20 38	21 11		21 38	22 10		22 39	23 11		
	d	16 38		17 07	17 26		17 38	18 07		18 38	19 15		19 38	20 07		20 38	21 15		21 38	22 11		22 39	23 11		
Dewsbury	39 d																								
Mirfield	39 d																								
Brighouse	d				17 36						19 25						21 25					22 49	23a22		
Huddersfield	39 a				17 49						19 40						21e39					23 02			
Sowerby Bridge	d	16 45					17 45			18 45			19 45			20 45			21 45	22 17					
Mytholmroyd	d	16 51					17 51			18 51			19 51			20 51			21 51	22 23					
Hebden Bridge	a	16 54		17 19			17 54	18 19		18 54			19 54	20 19		20 54			21 55	22 27					
	d	16 54		17 19			17 54	18 19		18 54			19 54	20 19		20 54				22 27					
Burnley Manchester Road	97 a			17 38				18 38						20 38											
Accrington	97 a			17 47				18 47						20 47											
Blackburn	97 a			17 55				18 55						20 55											
Preston 8	97 a			18 13				19 13						21 13											
Poulton-le-Fylde	97 a			18 31				19 31						21 31											
Blackpool North	97 a			18 38				19 38						21 38											
Todmorden	d	17 01					18 01			19 01			20 01			21 01				22 34					
Walsden	d	17 04					18 04			19 04			20 04			21 04				22 37					
Littleborough	d	17 11					18 11			19 11			20 11			21 11				22 44					
Smithy Bridge	d	17 13					18 13			19 13			20 13			21 13				22 46					
Rochdale	a	17 17					18 17			19 17			20 17			21 17				22 50					
	95 d	17 18					18 18			19 18			20 18			21 18				22 51					
Castleton	95 a	17 21					18 21			19 21			20 21			21 21				22 54					
Mills Hill	95 a	17 25					18 25			19 25			20 25			21 25				22 58					
Moston	95 a	17 29					18 29			19 29			20 29			21 29				23 02					
Manchester Victoria	95 ⛴ a	17 38					18 38			19 38			20 38			21 38				23 11					
Liverpool Lime Street 10	90 a	*18c51*					*19c51*			*20c51*			*21c51*			*22c54*									

For general notes see front of timetable
For details of catering facilities see Directory of Train Operators

b From 9 November arr. 1 minute later
c From 9 November only
e From 9 November arr. 2143

Table 41

Sundays

20 July to 7 September

Leeds and Bradford → Huddersfield, Blackpool North, Rochdale and Manchester Victoria via Halifax and Brighouse

Network Diagram - see first page of Table 39

		NT	NT	NT 🚌	NT 🚌	NT	NT		NT 🚌	NT 🚌	NT	NT	NT	NT 🚌		NT 🚌	NT	NT	NT 🚌	NT 🚌	NT		NT	NT 🚌	NT 🚌
York 8	40 d																								
Selby	40 d																								
Leeds 10	37, 39 d	08 02	08 11			08 45	09 02				09 25	09 35	10 02				10 34	11 02			11 35		12 02		
Bramley	37 d	08 10	08 18				09 10				09 32		10 10				10 42	11 10					12 10		
New Pudsey	37 d	08 15	08 23			08 54	09 15				09 37	09 45	10 15				10 47	11 15			11 44		12 15		
Bradford Interchange	37 a	08 23	08 31			09 03	09 23				09 45	09 54	10 23				10 55	11 23			11 53		12 23		
	d		08 38			09 05	09 26				09 48	09 57	10 26				10 58	11 26			11 55		12 26		
Halifax	a		08 50			09 17	09 38				10 01	10 09	10 38				11 11	11 38			12 07		12 38		
	d		08 51			09 17	09 39				10 01	10 09	10 38				11 15	11 38			12 07		12 38		
Dewsbury	39 d																								
Mirfield	39 d																								
Brighouse	d										10 11						11 25								
Huddersfield	39 a										10 24						11 39								
Sowerby Bridge	d		08 58				09 45						10 45					11 45					12 45		
Mytholmroyd	d		09 04				09 51						10 51					11 51					12 51		
Hebden Bridge	a		09 07			09 29	09 54					10 21	10 54					11 54			12 19		12 54		
	d		09 07			09 29	09 54					10 21	10 54					11 54			12 19		12 54		
Burnley Manchester Road	97 a					09 48						10 41									12 38				
Accrington	97 a					09 57						10 50									12 47				
Blackburn	97 a					10 05						10 58									12 55				
Preston 8	97 a					10 29						11 15									13 13				
Poulton-le-Fylde	97 a					10 47						11 33									13 31				
Blackpool North	97 a					10 54						11 40									13 39				
Todmorden	d		09 14				10 01						11 01					12 01					13 01		
Walsden	d		09 17				10 04						11 04					12 04					13 04		
Littleborough	d		09 24				10 11						11 11					12 11					13 11		
Smithy Bridge	d		09 26				10 13						11 13					12 13					13 13		
Rochdale	a		09 31				10 17						11 17					12 17					13 17		
	95 d			09 36	09 36				10 22	10 22				11 22		11 22			12 22	12 22				13 22	13 22
Castleton	95 a				09 42					10 28						11 28				12 28					13 28
Mills Hill	97 a				09 52					10 38						11 38				12 38					13 38
Moston	95 a				10 07					10 53						11 53				12 53					13 53
Manchester Victoria	95 ⛴ a			10 01	10 27				10 47	11 13				11 47		12 13			12 47	13 13				13 47	14 13
Liverpool Lime Street 10	90 a																								

		NT	NT	NT 🚌	NT 🚌	NT		NT	NT 🚌	NT 🚌	NT	NT	NT 🚌		NT 🚌	NT	NT	NT 🚌	NT 🚌	NT		NT	NT	NT 🚌	NT 🚌
York 8	40 d																								
Selby	40 d																								
Leeds 10	37, 39 d	12 35	13 02			13 35		14 02			14 35	15 02				15 35	16 02			16 35		16 50	17 02		
Bramley	37 d	12 42	13 10					14 10			14 42	15 10					16 10					16 57	17 10		
New Pudsey	37 d	12 47	13 15			13 44		14 15			14 47	15 15				15 44	16 15			16 44		17 02	17 15		
Bradford Interchange	37 a	12 55	13 23			13 53		14 23			14 55	15 23				15 53	16 23			16 53		17 10	17 23		
	d	12 58	13 26			13 55		14 26			14 58	15 26				15 55	16 26			16 55		17 13	17 26		
Halifax	a	13 11	13 38			14 07		14 38			15 11	15 38				16 07	16 38			17 07		17 26	17 38		
	d	13 15	13 38			14 07		14 38			15 14	15 38				16 07	16 38			17 07		17 26	17 38		
Dewsbury	39 d																								
Mirfield	39 d																								
Brighouse	d	13 25									15 26											17 36			
Huddersfield	39 a	13 39									15 39											17 49			
Sowerby Bridge	d		13 45					14 45				15 45					16 45						17 45		
Mytholmroyd	d		13 51					14 51				15 51					16 51						17 51		
Hebden Bridge	a		13 54			14 19		14 54				15 54				16 19	16 54			17 19			17 54		
	d		13 54			14 19		14 54				15 54				16 19	16 54			17 19			17 54		
Burnley Manchester Road	97 a					14 38										16 38				17 38					
Accrington	97 a					14 47										16 47				17 47					
Blackburn	97 a					14 55										16 55				17 55					
Preston 8	97 a					15 13										17 13				18 13					
Poulton-le-Fylde	97 a					15 32										17 31				18 31					
Blackpool North	97 a					15 40										17 40				18 38					
Todmorden	d		14 01					15 01				16 01					17 01						18 01		
Walsden	d		14 04					15 04				16 04					17 04						18 04		
Littleborough	d		14 11					15 11				16 11					17 11						18 11		
Smithy Bridge	d		14 13					15 13				16 13					17 13						18 13		
Rochdale	a		14 17					15 17				16 17					17 17						18 17		
	95 d			14 22	14 22				15 22	15 22			16 22		16 22			17 22	17 22					18 22	18 22
Castleton	95 a				14 28					15 28					16 28				17 28						18 28
Mills Hill	97 a				14 38					15 38					16 38				17 38						18 38
Moston	95 a				14 53					15 53					16 53				17 53						18 53
Manchester Victoria	95 ⛴ a			14 47	15 13				15 47	16 13			16 47		17 13			17 47	18 13					18 47	19 13
Liverpool Lime Street 10	90 a																								

For general notes see front of timetable
For details of catering facilities see Directory of Train Operators

Table 41

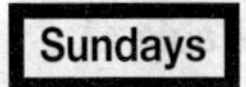

Sundays

Leeds and Bradford → Huddersfield, Blackpool North, Rochdale and Manchester Victoria via Halifax and Brighouse

20 July to 7 September

Network Diagram - see first page of Table 39

	NT	NT	NT 🚌	NT 🚌		NT	NT	NT 🚌	NT 🚌	NT	NT		NT 🚌	NT 🚌	NT	NT	NT	NT 🚌		NT 🚌	NT	NT		
York [8] 40 d																								
Selby 40 d																								
Leeds [10] 37, 39 d	17 35	18 02				18 35	19 02			19 35	20 02				20 35	21 02	21 35				22 02	22 35		
Bramley 37 d		18 10				18 42	19 10				20 10				20 42	21 10	21 43				22 10	22 42		
New Pudsey 37 d	17 44	18 15				18 47	19 15			19 44	20 15				20 47	21 14	21 47				22 15	22 47		
Bradford Interchange 37 a	17 53	18 23				18 55	19 23			19 53	20 23				20 55	21 23	21 56				22 23	22 55		
d	17 55	18 26				18 58	19 26			19 55	20 26				20 58	21 26	21 58				22 26	22 58		
Halifax a	18 07	18 38				19 11	19 38			20 07	20 38				21 11	21 38	22 10				22 39	23 11		
d	18 07	18 38				19 15	19 38			20 07	20 38				21 15	21 38	22 11				22 39	23 11		
Dewsbury 39 d																								
Mirfield 39 d																								
Brighouse d						19 25									21 25						22 49	23a22		
Huddersfield 39 a						19 40									21 39						23 02			
Sowerby Bridge d		18 45					19 45				20 45					21 45	22 17							
Mytholmroyd d		18 51					19 51				20 51					21 51	22 23							
Hebden Bridge a	18 19	18 54					19 54			20 19	20 54					21 55	22 27							
d	18 19	18 54					19 54			20 19	20 54						22 27							
Burnley Manchester Road 97 a	18 38									20 38														
Accrington 97 a	18 47									20 47														
Blackburn 97 a	18 55									20 55														
Preston [8] 97 a	19 13									21 13														
Poulton-le-Fylde 97 a	19 31									21 31														
Blackpool North 97 a	19 38									21 38														
Todmorden d		19 01					20 01				21 01						22 34							
Walsden d		19 04					20 04				21 04						22 37							
Littleborough d		19 11					20 11				21 11						22 44							
Smithy Bridge d		19 13					20 13				21 13						22 46							
Rochdale a		19 17					20 17				21 17						22 50							
95 d			19 22	19 22				20 22	20 22				21 22	21 22				22 55		22 55				
Castleton 95 a				19 28					20 28					21 28						23 01				
Mills Hill 97 a				19 38					20 38					21 38						23 11				
Moston 95 a				19 53					20 53					21 53						23 26				
Manchester Victoria 95 ⛴ a			19 47	20 13				20 47	21 13				21 47	22 13				23 20		23 46				
Liverpool Lime Street [10] 90 a																								

For general notes see front of timetable
For details of catering facilities see Directory of Train Operators

Manchester Victoria, Rochdale, Blackpool North and Huddersfield → Bradford and Leeds via Brighouse and Halifax

Network Diagram - see first page of Table 39

Miles	Miles	Miles	Miles			NT	NT	NT	NT	NT	NT A	NT	NT	NT	NT	NT	NT A	NT	NT	NT	NT	NT A	NT
—	—	—	—	Liverpool Lime Street 10	90 d											*05 47*		*06 39*					*07 47*
0	—	—	—	**Manchester Victoria**	95 d			05 54		06 18			06 49			07 18		07 47			08 19		08 54
4	—	—	—	Moston	95 d					06 25			06 55			07 25		07 53			08 25		
6	—	—	—	Mills Hill	95 d					06 30			07 00			07 30		07 58			08 30		
8¾	—	—	—	Castleton	95 d					06 35			07 05			07 35		08 03			08 35		
10½	—	—	—	**Rochdale**	95 a			06 08		06 38			07 08			07 38		08 06			08 38		09 08
—	—	—	—		d			06 09		06 39			07 09			07 39		08 07			08 39		09 09
12¾	—	—	—	Smithy Bridge	d			06 13		06 43			07 13			07 43		08 11			08 43		09 13
13¾	—	—	—	Littleborough	d			06 16		06 46			07 16			07 46		08 14			08 46		09 16
17¾	—	—	—	Walsden	d			06 22		06 52			07 22			07 52		08 20			08 52		09 22
19¼	—	—	—	Todmorden	d			06 26		06 56			07 26			07 56		08 24			08 56		09 26
—	0	—	—	**Blackpool North**	97 d				05 30					06 28					07 30				
—	3	—	—	Poulton-le-Fylde	97 d				05 36					06 34					07 36				
—	17½	—	—	**Preston 8**	97 d				05 55					06 54					07 55				
—	29½	—	—	Blackburn	97 d				06 11					07 11					08 11				
—	35¾	—	—	Accrington	97 d				06 19					07 18					08 19				
—	42	—	—	Burnley Manchester Road	97 d				06 28					07 27					08 28				
23½	54¾	—	0	**Hebden Bridge**	a			06 32	06 49	07 02			07 32	07 49		08 02		08 30	08 49		09 02		09 32
—	—	—	—		d		06 17	06 33	06 50	07 03		07 27	07 33	07 50		08 03		08 34	08 50		09 03		09 33
24¾	56	—	1¼	Mytholmroyd	d		06 20	06 36		07 06		07 30	07 36			08 06		08 37			09 06		09 36
28¾	60	—	5¼	Sowerby Bridge	d		06 26	06 42		07 12		07 36	07 42			08 12		08 43			09 12		09 42
—	—	0	—	**Huddersfield**	39 d						07 11						08 06					09 11	
—	—	5¼	11	Brighouse	d	05 52					07 21	07 44			08 11		08b20			09 07		09 21	
—	—	—	15	Mirfield	39 a							07 54			08 19					09 13			
—	—	—	18	Dewsbury	39 a							07 59			08 26					09 20			
32¼	63½	10½	—	**Halifax**	a	06 02	06 32	06 48	07 01	07 18	07 32		07 48	08 02		08 18	08 32	08 49	09 01		09 18	09 32	09 48
—	—	—	—		d	06 02	06 33	06 49	07 02	07 19	07 33		07 49	08 02		08 19	08 33	08 50	09 02		09 19	09 33	09 49
40¼	71½	—	—	**Bradford Interchange**	a	06 15	06 46	07 03	07 16	07 33	07 47		08 03	08 16		08 33	08 46	09 04	09 16		09 33	09 46	10 03
—	—	—	—		37 d	06 18	06 48	07 05	07 18	07 35	07 49		08 05	08 18		08 35	08 47	09 05	09 18		09 35	09 48	10 05
43¾	75	—	—	New Pudsey	37 a	06 26	06 57	07 14	07 26	07 44	07 57		08 14	08 26		08 44	08 57	09 14	09 26		09 44	09 57	10 14
45¾	77	—	—	Bramley	37 a	06 30	07 00	07 17		07 47	08 01		08 17			08 47	09 00	09 17			09 47	10 00	10 17
49¾	81	—	27¼	**Leeds 10**	37, 39 a	06 37	07 09	07 27	07 37	07 59	08 13	08 18	08 28	08 39	08 51	08 57	09 12	09 28	09 39	09 44	09 58	10 10	10 28
—	—	—	—	Selby	40 a			08 05			08 53						09 54					10 53	
—	—	—	—	York 8	40 a				08 19					09 23					10 20				

		NT	NT	NT	NT A	NT	NT	NT	NT	NT A	NT	NT	NT	NT	NT A	NT	NT	NT	NT	NT A	NT	NT
Liverpool Lime Street 10	90 d					*08 48*					*09 48*					*10 48*					*11 48*	
Manchester Victoria	95 d			09 24		09 54			10 24		10 54			11 24		11 54			12 24		12 54	
Moston	95 d																					
Mills Hill	95 d																					
Castleton	95 d																					
Rochdale	95 a			09 38		10 08			10 38		11 08			11 38		12 08			12 38		13 08	
	d			09 39		10 08			10 39		11 09			11 39		12 08			12 39		13 09	
Smithy Bridge	d			09 43		10 12			10 43		11 13			11 43		12 12			12 43		13 13	
Littleborough	d			09 46		10 16			10 46		11 16			11 46		12 16			12 46		13 16	
Walsden	d			09 52					10 52					11 52					12 52			
Todmorden	d			09 56		10 23			10 56		11 26			11 56		12 25			12 56		13 26	
Blackpool North	97 d		08 29					09 30					10 30					11 30				
Poulton-le-Fylde	97 d		08 35					09 36					10 36					11 36				
Preston 8	97 d		08 54					09 55					10 55					11 55				
Blackburn	97 d		09 11					10 11					11 11					12 11				
Accrington	97 d		09 19					10 19					11 19					12 19				
Burnley Manchester Road	97 d		09 28					10 28					11 28					12 28				
Hebden Bridge	a		09 49	10 02		10 32		10 49	11 02		11 32		11 49	12 02		12 32		12 49	13 02		13 32	
	d	09 40	09 50	10 03		10 33	10 40	10 50	11 03		11 33	11 40	11 50	12 03		12 33	12 40	12 50	13 03		13 33	13 40
Mytholmroyd	d	09 43		10 06		10 36	10 43		11 06		11 36	11 43		12 06		12 36	12 43		13 06		13 36	13 43
Sowerby Bridge	d	09 49		10 12		10 42	10 49		11 12		11 42	11 49		12 12		12 42	12 49		13 12		13 42	13 49
Huddersfield	39 d				10 10					11 10					12 10					13 10		
Brighouse	d	09 57			10 20		10 57			11 20		11 57			12 20		12 57			13 20		13 57
Mirfield	39 a	10 06					11 06					12 06					13 06					14 06
Dewsbury	39 a	10 12					11 12					12 12					13 12					14 12
Halifax	a		10 01	10 18	10 32	10 48		11 01	11 18	11 32	11 48		12 01	12 18	12 32	12 48		13 01	13 18	13 32	13 48	
	d		10 02	10 19	10 33	10 49		11 02	11 19	11 33	11 49		12 02	12 19	12 33	12 49		13 02	13 19	13 33	13 49	
Bradford Interchange	a		10 16	10 33	10 46	11 03		11 16	11 33	11 46	12 03		12 16	12 33	12 46	13 03		13 16	13 33	13 46	14 03	
	37 d		10 18	10 35	10 48	11 05		11 18	11 35	11 48	12 05		12 18	12 35	12 48	13 05		13 18	13 35	13 48	14 05	
New Pudsey	37 a		10 26	10 44	10 57	11 14		11 26	11 44	11 57	12 14		12 26	12 44	12 57	13 14		13 26	13 44	13 57	14 14	
Bramley	37 a			10 47	11 00	11 17			11 47	12 00	12 17			12 47	13 00	13 17			13 47	14 00	14 17	
Leeds 10	37, 39 a	10 31	10 37	10 58	11 10	11 28	11 33	11 39	11 58	12 10	12 28	12 32	12 38	12 58	13 10	13 28	13 32	13 37	13 58	14 10	14 28	14 32
Selby	40 a				11 55					12 53					13 53					14 52		
York 8	40 a		11 17					12 20					13 17					14 20				

For general notes see front of timetable
For details of catering facilities see Directory of Train Operators

A From Wakefield Westgate (Table 39)
b Arr. 0816

Manchester Victoria, Rochdale, Blackpool North and Huddersfield → Bradford and Leeds via Brighouse and Halifax

Network Diagram - see first page of Table 39

		NT		NT	NT A	NT	NT	NT	NT		NT A	NT	NT	NT	NT	NT A		NT	NT	NT	NT	NT A	NT		NT
Liverpool Lime Street 10	90 d					12 48						13 48						14 48					15 48		
Manchester Victoria	95 d			13 24		13 54			14 24			14 54			15 24			15 54			16 24		16 54		
Moston	95 d																								
Mills Hill	95 d																								
Castleton	95 d																								
Rochdale	95 a			13 38		14 08			14 38			15 08			15 38			16 08			16 38		17 08		
	d			13 39		14 09			14 39			15 09			15 39			16 09			16 39		17 09		
Smithy Bridge	d			13 43		14 13			14 43			15 13			15 43			16 13			16 43		17 13		
Littleborough	d			13 46		14 16			14 46			15 16			15 46			16 16			16 46		17 16		
Walsden	d			13 52					14 52						15 52			16 22			16 52		17 22		
Todmorden	d			13 56		14 26			14 56			15 26			15 56			16 26			16 56		17 26		
Blackpool North	97 d	12 30						13 30						14 30						15 30					16 30
Poulton-le-Fylde	97 d	12 36						13 36						14 36						15 36					16 36
Preston 8	97 d	12 55						13 55						14 55						15 55					16 55
Blackburn	97 d	13 11						14 11						15 11						16 11					17 11
Accrington	97 d	13 19						14 19						15 19						16 19					17 19
Burnley Manchester Road	97 d	13 28						14 28						15 28						16 28					17 28
Hebden Bridge	a	13 49		14 02		14 32		14 49	15 02			15 32		15 49	16 02			16 32		16 49	17 02		17 32		17 49
	d	13 50		14 03		14 33	14 40	14 50	15 03			15 33	15 40	15 50	16 03			16 33	16 40	16 50	17 03		17 33		17 50
Mytholmroyd	d			14 06		14 36	14 43		15 06			15 36	15 43		16 06			16 36	16 43		17 06		17 36		
Sowerby Bridge	d			14 12		14 42	14 49		15 12			15 42	15 49		16 12			16 42	16 49		17 12		17 42		
Huddersfield	39 d				14 10						15 10					16 10						17 10			
Brighouse	d				14 20		14 57				15 20		15 57			16 20			16 57			17 20			
Mirfield	39 a						15 06						16 06						17 06						
Dewsbury	39 a						15 12						16 12						17 12						
Halifax	a	14 01		14 18	14 32	14 48		15 01	15 18		15 32	15 48		16 01	16 18	16 32		16 48		17 01	17 18	17 32	17 48		18 01
	d	14 02		14 19	14 33	14 49		15 02	15 19		15 33	15 49		16 02	16 19	16 33		16 49		17 02	17 19	17 33	17 49		18 02
Bradford Interchange	a	14 16		14 33	14 46	15 03		15 16	15 33		15 46	16 03		16 16	16 33	16 46		17 03		17 16	17 33	17 46	18 03		18 16
	37 d	14 18		14 35	14 48	15 05		15 18	15 35		15 48	16 05		16 18	16 35	16 48		17 05		17 18	17 35	17 48	18 05		18 18
New Pudsey	37 a	14 26		14 44	14 57	15 14		15 26	15 44		15 57	16 14		16 26	16 44	16 57		17 14		17 26	17 44	17 57	18 14		18 26
Bramley	37 a			14 47	15 00	15 17			15 47		16 00	16 17			16 47	17 00		17 17			17 47	18 00	18 17		
Leeds 10	37, 39 a	14 39		14 58	15 12	15 28	15 31	15 37	15 58		16 10	16 28	16 32	16 37	16 58	17 10		17 28	17 31	17 37	17 58	18 10	18 28		18 37
Selby	40 a				15 53						16 55					17 54						18 50			
York 8	40 a	15 17						16 22						17 18						18 24					19 20

		NT	NT A	NT	NT	NT	NT		NT	NT	NT	NT	NT	NT		NT	NT	NT	NT	NT	NT		NT		
Liverpool Lime Street 10	90 d				16 18		17 12			17 35			17 50			18 48			19 18		20 18		21 18		
Manchester Victoria	95 d	17 18			17 49		18 19			18 47			19 18			20 19			21 19		22 19		23 19		
Moston	95 d	17 25			17 55		18 25			18 53			19 25			20 25			21 25		22 25		23 25		
Mills Hill	95 d	17 30			18 00		18 30			18 57			19 30			20 30			21 30		22 30		23 30		
Castleton	95 d	17 35			18 05		18 35			19 02			19 35			20 35			21 35		22 35		23 35		
Rochdale	95 a	17 38			18 08		18 38			19 05			19 38			20 38			21 38		22 38		23 38		
	d	17 39			18 09		18 39			19 06			19 39			20 39			21 39		22 39		23 39		
Smithy Bridge	d	17 43			18 13		18 43			19 10			19 43			20 43			21 43		22 43		23 43		
Littleborough	d	17 46			18 16		18 46			19 13			19 46			20 46			21 46		22 46		23 46		
Walsden	d	17 52			18 22		18 52			19 19			19 52			20 52			21 52		22 52		23 52		
Todmorden	d	17 56			18 26		18 56			19a24			19 56			20 56			21 56		22 56		23 56		
Blackpool North	97 d					17 19						18 30						20 28							
Poulton-le-Fylde	97 d					17 25						18 36						20 34							
Preston 8	97 d					17 44						18 55						20 54							
Blackburn	97 d					18 11						19 11						21 11							
Accrington	97 d					18 19						19 19						21 18							
Burnley Manchester Road	97 d					18 28						19 28						21 27							
Hebden Bridge	a	18 02			18 32	18 49	19 02					19 49	20 02			21 02		21 49	22 02		23 02		00 02		
	d	18 03		18 23	18 33	18 50	19 03				19 40	19 50	20 03			21 03		21 50	22 03		23 03		00 03		
Mytholmroyd	d	18 06		18 26	18 36		19 06				19 43		20 06			21 06			22 06		23 06		00 06		
Sowerby Bridge	d	18 12		18 32	18 42		19 12				19 49		20 12			21 12			22 12		23 12		00 12		
Huddersfield	39 d		18 12						19 23					20 25			21 27			22 25					
Brighouse	d		18 23	18 40					19 33		19 57			20 35			21 37			22 35					
Mirfield	39 a			18 47							20 06														
Dewsbury	39 a			18 54							20 12														
Halifax	a	18 18	18 33		18 48	19 01	19 18		19 43			20 01	20 18	20 45		21 18	21 47	22 02	22 18	22 45	23 18		00 18		
	d	18 19	18 33		18 49	19 02	19 19		19 49			20 02	20 19	20 49		21 19	21 49	22 02	22 19	22 49	23 19		00 19		
Bradford Interchange	a	18 33	18 46		19 03	19 16	19 33		20 02			20 16	20 33	21 02		21 33	22 02	22 16	22 33	23 02	23 33		00 33		
	37 d	18 35	18 48		19 05	19 18	19 35		20 04			20 18	20 35	21 04		21 35	22 04	22 18	22 35	23 04	23 35		00 35		
New Pudsey	37 a	18 44	18 57		19 14	19 26	19 44		20 13			20 26	20 44	21 13		21 44	22 13	22 26	22 44	23 13	23 44				
Bramley	37 a	18 47	19 00		19 17		19 47		20 16				20 47	21 16		21 47	22 16		22 47	23 16	23 47				
Leeds 10	37, 39 a	18 59	19 10	19 17	19 28	19 37	19 58		20 29		20 31	20 37	20 57	21 25		21 58	22 25	22 38	22 58	23 25	23 58		00 54		
Selby	40 a																								
York 8	40 a					20 20						21 29						23 34							

For general notes see front of timetable
For details of catering facilities see
Directory of Train Operators

A From Wakefield Westgate (Table 39)

Manchester Victoria, Rochdale, Blackpool North and Huddersfield → Bradford and Leeds via Brighouse and Halifax

Network Diagram - see first page of Table 39

		NT	NT	NT	NT		NT	NT	NT	NT		NT	NT	NT	NT		NT	NT	NT	NT		NT	NT	NT	NT
													A						A						A
Liverpool Lime Street 10	90 d											*05 47*		*06 39*						*07 47*					
Manchester Victoria	95 d		05 54		06 24				06 49			07 18		07 47				08 19		08 54				09 24	
Moston	95 d								06 55			07 25		07 53				08 25							
Mills Hill	95 d								07 00			07 30		07 58				08 30							
Castleton	95 d								07 05			07 35		08 03				08 35							
Rochdale	95 a		06 08		06 38				07 08			07 38		08 06				08 38		09 08				09 38	
	d		06 09		06 39				07 09			07 39		08 07				08 39		09 09				09 39	
Smithy Bridge	d		06 13		06 43				07 13			07 43		08 11				08 43		09 13				09 43	
Littleborough	d		06 16		06 46				07 16			07 46		08 14				08 46		09 16				09 46	
Walsden	d		06 22		06 52				07 22			07 52		08 20				08 52		09 22				09 52	
Todmorden	d		06 26		06 56				07 26			07 56		08 24				08 56		09 26				09 56	
Blackpool North	97 d			05 30						06 27							07 30						08 27		
Poulton-le-Fylde	97 d			05 36						06 33							07 36						08 33		
Preston 8	97 d			05 55						06 54							07 55						08 52		
Blackburn	97 d			06 11						07 11							08 11						09 11		
Accrington	97 d			06 19						07 19							08 19						09 19		
Burnley Manchester Road	97 d			06 28						07 28							08 28						09 28		
Hebden Bridge	a		06 32	06 49	07 02				07 32	07 49		08 02		08 30			08 49	09 02		09 32			09 49	10 02	
	d		06 33	06 50	07 03			07 27	07 33	07 50		08 03		08 33	08 40		08 50	09 03		09 33		09 40	09 50	10 03	
Mytholmroyd	d		06 36		07 06			07 30	07 36			08 06		08 36	08 43			09 06		09 36		09 43		10 06	
Sowerby Bridge	d		06 42		07 12			07 36	07 42			08 12		08 42	08 49			09 12		09 42		09 49		10 12	
Huddersfield	39 d						07 10						08 06						09 10						10 10
Brighouse	d	05 56					07 19	07 44					08b20		08 57				09 20			09 57			10 20
Mirfield	39 a							07 54							09 06							10 06			
Dewsbury	39 a							07 59							09 12							10 12			
Halifax	a	06 06	06 48	07 01	07 18		07 32		07 48	08 01		08 18	08 32	08 48			09 01	09 18	09 32	09 48			10 01	10 18	10 32
	d	06 06	06 49	07 02	07 19		07 33		07 49	08 02		08 19	08 33	08 49			09 02	09 19	09 33	09 49			10 02	10 19	10 33
Bradford Interchange	a	06 19	07 03	07 16	07 33		07 47		08 03	08 16		08 33	08 46	09 04			09 16	09 33	09 46	10 03			10 16	10 33	10 46
	37 d	06 23	07 05	07 18	07 35		07 49		08 05	08 18		08 35	08 47	09 05			09 18	09 35	09 48	10 05			10 18	10 35	10 48
New Pudsey	37 a	06 32	07 14	07 26	07 44		07 57		08 14	08 26		08 44	08 57	09 14			09 26	09 44	09 57	10 14			10 26	10 44	10 57
Bramley	37 a	06 35	07 17		07 47		08 01		08 17			08 47	09 00	09 17				09 47	10 00	10 17				10 47	11 00
Leeds 10	37, 39 a	06 44	07 27	07 37	07 59		08 13	08c18	08 28	08 39		08 57	09 12	09 28	09 31		09 39	09 58	10 10	10 28		10 31	10 37	10 58	11 10
Selby	40 a												09 54						10 53						11 53
York 8	40 a			08 19						09 20							10 20						11 17		

		NT	NT		NT	NT	NT	NT		NT	NT	NT	NT		NT	NT	NT	NT		NT	NT	NT	NT		NT
							A						A							A					
Liverpool Lime Street 10	90 d	*08 48*						*09 48*							*10 48*						*11 48*				
Manchester Victoria	95 d	09 54				10 24		10 54				11 24			11 54			12 24			12 54				13 24
Moston	95 d																								
Mills Hill	95 d																								
Castleton	95 d																								
Rochdale	95 a	10 08				10 38		11 08				11 38			12 08			12 38			13 08				13 38
	d	10 08				10 39		11 09				11 39			12 08			12 39			13 09				13 39
Smithy Bridge	d	10 12				10 43		11 13				11 43			12 12			12 43			13 13				13 43
Littleborough	d	10 16				10 46		11 16				11 46			12 16			12 46			13 16				13 46
Walsden	d					10 52						11 52						12 52							13 52
Todmorden	d	10 25				10 56		11 26				11 56			12 25			12 56			13 26				13 56
Blackpool North	97 d				09 30						10 30						11 30						12 30		
Poulton-le-Fylde	97 d				09 36						10 36						11 36						12 36		
Preston 8	97 d				09 55						10 55						11 55						12 55		
Blackburn	97 d				10 11						11 11						12 11						13 11		
Accrington	97 d				10 19						11 19						12 19						13 19		
Burnley Manchester Road	97 d				10 28						11 28						12 28						13 28		
Hebden Bridge	a	10 32			10 49	11 02		11 32			11 49	12 02			12 32		12 49	13 02			13 32		13 49		14 02
	d	10 33	10 40		10 50	11 03		11 33		11 40	11 50	12 03			12 33	12 40	12 50	13 03			13 33	13 40	13 50		14 03
Mytholmroyd	d	10 36	10 43			11 06		11 36		11 43		12 06			12 36	12 43		13 06			13 36	13 43			14 06
Sowerby Bridge	d	10 42	10 49			11 12		11 42		11 49		12 12			12 42	12 49		13 12			13 42	13 49			14 12
Huddersfield	39 d						11 10						12 10							13 10					
Brighouse	d		10 57				11 20			11 57			12 20			12 57				13 20		13 57			
Mirfield	39 a		11 06							12 06						13 06						14 06			
Dewsbury	39 a		11 12							12 12						13 12						14 12			
Halifax	a	10 48			11 01	11 18	11 32	11 48			12 01	12 18	12 32		12 48		13 01	13 18		13 32	13 48		14 01		14 18
	d	10 49			11 02	11 19	11 33	11 49			12 02	12 19	12 33		12 49		13 02	13 19		13 33	13 49		14 02		14 19
Bradford Interchange	a	11 03			11 16	11 33	11 46	12 03			12 16	12 33	12 46		13 03		13 16	13 33		13 46	14 03		14 16		14 33
	37 d	11 05			11 18	11 35	11 48	12 05			12 18	12 35	12 48		13 05		13 18	13 35		13 48	14 05		14 18		14 35
New Pudsey	37 a	11 14			11 26	11 44	11 57	12 14			12 26	12 44	12 57		13 14		13 26	13 44		13 57	14 14		14 26		14 44
Bramley	37 a	11 17				11 47	12 00	12 17				12 47	13 00		13 17			13 47		14 00	14 17				14 47
Leeds 10	37, 39 a	11 28	11 31		11 39	11 58	12 10	12 28		12 31	12 38	12 58	13 10		13 28	13 31	13 37	13 58		14 10	14 28	14 31	14 39		14 58
Selby	40 a						12 53						13 53							14 52					
York 8	40 a				12 20						13 17						14 20						15 19		

For general notes see front of timetable
For details of catering facilities see Directory of Train Operators

A From Wakefield Westgate (Table 39)
b Arr. 0816
c From 13 September arr. 0820

Table 41

Saturdays

Manchester Victoria, Rochdale, Blackpool North and Huddersfield → Bradford and Leeds via Brighouse and Halifax

Network Diagram - see first page of Table 39

		NT A	NT	NT	NT		NT	NT A	NT	NT		NT	NT	NT A	NT		NT	NT	NT	NT A		NT	NT	NT	NT A
Liverpool Lime Street [10]	90 d		*12 48*						*13 48*						*14 48*							*15 48*			
Manchester Victoria	95 d		13 54				14 24		14 54				15 24		15 54				16 24			16 54		17 18	
Moston	95 d																							17 25	
Mills Hill	95 d																							17 30	
Castleton	95 d																							17 35	
Rochdale	95 a		14 08				14 38		15 08				15 38		16 08				16 38			17 08		17 38	
	d		14 09				14 39		15 09				15 39		16 09				16 39			17 09		17 39	
Smithy Bridge	d		14 13				14 43		15 13				15 43		16 13				16 43			17 13		17 43	
Littleborough	d		14 16				14 46		15 16				15 46		16 16				16 46			17 16		17 46	
Walsden	d						14 52						15 52		16 22				16 52			17 22		17 52	
Todmorden	d		14 26				14 56		15 26				15 56		16 26				16 56			17 26		17 56	
Blackpool North	97 d				13 30							14 30						15 30					16 30		
Poulton-le-Fylde	97 d				13 36							14 36						15 36					16 36		
Preston [8]	97 d				13 55							14 55						15 55					16 55		
Blackburn	97 d				14 11							15 11						16 11					17 11		
Accrington	97 d				14 19							15 19						16 19					17 19		
Burnley Manchester Road	97 d				14 28							15 28						16 28					17 28		
Hebden Bridge	a		14 32		14 49		15 02		15 32			15 49	16 02		16 32			16 49	17 02			17 32	17 49	18 02	
	d		14 33	14 40	14 50		15 03		15 33	15 40		15 50	16 03		16 33		16 40	16 50	17 03			17 33	17 50	18 03	
Mytholmroyd	d		14 36	14 43			15 06		15 36	15 43			16 06		16 36		16 43		17 06			17 36		18 06	
Sowerby Bridge	d		14 42	14 49			15 12		15 42	15 49			16 12		16 42		16 49		17 12			17 42		18 12	
Huddersfield	39 d	14 10						15 10						16 10						17 10					18 10
Brighouse	d	14 20		14 57				15 20		15 57				16 20			16 57			17 20					18 20
Mirfield	39 a			15 06						16 06							17 06								
Dewsbury	39 a			15 12						16 12							17 12								
Halifax	a	14 32	14 48		15 01		15 18	15 32	15 48			16 01	16 18	16 32	16 48			17 01	17 18	17 32		17 48	18 01	18 18	18 32
	d	14 33	14 49		15 02		15 19	15 33	15 49			16 02	16 19	16 33	16 49			17 02	17 19	17 33		17 49	18 02	18 19	18 33
Bradford Interchange	a	14 46	15 03		15 16		15 33	15 46	16 03			16 16	16 33	16 46	17 03			17 16	17 33	17 46		18 03	18 16	18 33	18 46
	37 d	14 48	15 05		15 18		15 35	15 48	16 05			16 18	16 35	16 48	17 05			17 18	17 35	17 48		18 05	18 18	18 35	18 48
New Pudsey	37 a	14 57	15 14		15 26		15 44	15 57	16 14			16 26	16 44	16 57	17 14			17 26	17 44	17 57		18 14	18 26	18 44	18 57
Bramley	37 a	15 00	15 17				15 47	16 00	16 17				16 47	17 00	17 17				17 47	18 00		18 17		18 47	19 00
Leeds [10]	37, 39 a	15 12	15 28	15 31	15 37		15 58	16 10	16 28	16 31		16 37	16 58	17 10	17 28		17 31	17 37	17 58	18 10		18 28	18 37	18 59	19 10
Selby	40 a	15 53						16 54						17 53						18 50					
York [8]	40 a				16 22							17 17						18 24					19 19		19 53

		NT	NT		NT	NT	NT	NT		NT	NT	NT	NT		NT	NT	NT	NT		NT	NT				
Liverpool Lime Street [10]	90 d		*16 18*			*17 12*		*17 35*				*17 48*			*18 48*			*19 18*			*21 18*				
Manchester Victoria	95 d		17 49			18 19		18 47				19 26			20 19			21 19			22 49				
Moston	95 d		17 55			18 25		18 53				19 32			20 25			21 25			22 55				
Mills Hill	95 d		18 00			18 30		18 57				19 37			20 30			21 30			23 00				
Castleton	95 d		18 05			18 35		19 02				19 42			20 35			21 35			23 05				
Rochdale	95 a		18 08			18 38		19 05				19 45			20 38			21 38			23 08				
	d		18 09			18 39		19 06				19 47			20 39			21 39			23 09				
Smithy Bridge	d		18 13			18 43		19 10				19 51			20 43			21 43			23 13				
Littleborough	d		18 16			18 46		19 13				19 54			20 46			21 46			23 16				
Walsden	d		18 22			18 52		19 19				20 00			20 52			21 52			23 22				
Todmorden	d		18 26			18 56		19a24				20 04			20 56			21 56			23 26				
Blackpool North	97 d				17 19						18 30						20 30								
Poulton-le-Fylde	97 d				17 25						18 36						20 37								
Preston [8]	97 d				17 44						18 56						20 55								
Blackburn	97 d				18 11						19 13						21 11								
Accrington	97 d				18 19						19 20						21 19								
Burnley Manchester Road	97 d				18 28						19 29						21 28								
Hebden Bridge	a		18 32		18 49	19 02					19 51	20 10			21 02		21 49	22 02			23 32				
	d	18 23	18 33		18 50	19 03				19 40	19 52	20 11			21 03		21 50	22 03			23 33				
Mytholmroyd	d	18 26	18 36			19 06				19 43		20 14			21 06			22 06			23 36				
Sowerby Bridge	d	18 32	18 42			19 12				19 49		20 20			21 12			22 12			23 42				
Huddersfield	39 d						19 23						20 25			21 25				22 25					
Brighouse	d	18 40					19 33			19 57			20 35			21 35				22 35					
Mirfield	39 a	18 47								20 06															
Dewsbury	39 a	18 54								20 12															
Halifax	a		18 48		19 01	19 18	19 43				20 04	20 26	20 45		21 18	21 45	22 01	22 18		22 45	23 48				
	d		18 49		19 02	19 19	19 49				20 04	20 27	20 49		21 19	21 49	22 02	22 19		22 49	23 49				
Bradford Interchange	a		19 03		19 16	19 33	20 02				20 18	20 41	21 02		21 33	22 02	22 16	22 33		23 02	00 03				
	37 d		19 05		19 18	19 35	20 04				20 21	20 43	21 04		21 35	22 04	22 18	22 35		23 04	00 05				
New Pudsey	37 a		19 14		19 26	19 44	20 13				20 29	20 52	21 13		21 44	22 13	22 26	22 44		23 13	00 14				
Bramley	37 a		19 17			19 47	20 16					20 55	21 16		21 47	22 16		22 47		23 16	00 17				
Leeds [10]	37, 39 a	19 18	19 28		19 37	19 58	20 29			20 32	20 40	21 07	21 25		21 58	22 25	22 38	22 58		23 25	00 28				
Selby	40 a																								
York [8]	40 a				20 21						21 30						23 36								

For general notes see front of timetable
For details of catering facilities see
Directory of Train Operators

A From Wakefield Westgate (Table 39)

Table 41

Sundays

Manchester Victoria, Rochdale, Blackpool North and Huddersfield → Bradford and Leeds via Brighouse and Halifax

until 13 July and from 14 September

Network Diagram - see first page of Table 39

		NT	NT	NT	NT	NT	NT	NT	NT	NT	NT	NT	NT	NT	NT	NT	NT	NT	NT	NT	NT	NT	NT	NT	NT
			A	B	B	A		B	A		B	A		B	A		B	A		B	A		B	A	
Liverpool Lime Street 10	90 d				08 10			09 10						11 10			12 10			13 10			14 10		
Manchester Victoria	95 d				09 09	09 14		10 09	10 15		11 08	11 15		12 09	12 15		13 08	13 15		14 09	14 15		15 09	15 15	
Moston	95 d				09 16	09 21		10 15	10 21		11 15	11 21		12 15	12 21		13 15	13 21		14 15	14 21		15 15	15 21	
Mills Hill	95 d				09 20	09 25		10 19	10 25		11 19	11 25		12 19	12 25		13 19	13 25		14 19	14 25		15 19	15 25	
Castleton	95 d				09 25	09 30		10 24	10 30		11 24	11 30		12 24	12 30		13 24	13 30		14 24	14 30		15 24	15 30	
Rochdale	95 a				09 29	09 34		10 28	10 34		11 28	11 34		12 28	12 34		13 28	13 34		14 28	14 34		15 28	15 34	
	d				09 29	09 34		10 28	10 34		11 28	11 34		12 28	12 34		13 28	13 34		14 28	14 34		15 28	15 34	
Smithy Bridge	d				09 33	09 38		10 32	10 38		11 32	11 38		12 32	12 38		13 32	13 38		14 32	14 38		15 32	15 38	
Littleborough	d				09 37	09 42		10 36	10 42		11 36	11 42		12 36	12 42		13 36	13 42		14 36	14 42		15 36	15 42	
Walsden	d				09 43	09 48		10 42	10 48		11 42	11 48		12 42	12 48		13 42	13 48		14 42	14 48		15 42	15 48	
Todmorden	d				09 46	09 51		10 45	10 51		11 45	11 51		12 45	12 51		13 45	13 51		14 45	14 51		15 45	15 51	
Blackpool North	97 d						09 10						11 12						13 12						15 12
Poulton-le-Fylde	97 d						09 16						11 18						13 18						15 18
Preston 8	97 d						09 35						11 37						13 37						15 37
Blackburn	97 d						09 51						11 53						13 53						15 53
Accrington	97 d						09 59						12 01						14 01						16 01
Burnley Manchester Road	97 d						10 10						12 10						14 10						16 10
Hebden Bridge	a				09 53	09 58	10 31	10 52	10 58		11 52	11 58	12 31	12 52	12 58		13 52	13 58	14 31	14 52	14 58		15 52	15 58	16 31
	d				09 53	09 58	10 32	10 52	10 58		11 52	11 58	12 32	12 52	12 58		13 52	13 58	14 32	14 52	14 58		15 52	15 58	16 32
Mytholmroyd	d				09 56	10 01		10 55	11 01		11 55	12 01		12 55	13 01		13 55	14 01		14 55	15 01		15 55	16 01	
Sowerby Bridge	d				10 02	10 07		11 01	11 07		12 01	12 07		13 01	13 07		14 01	14 07		15 01	15 07		16 01	16 07	
Huddersfield	39 d		09 20	09 25						11 20						13 20						15 20			
Brighouse	d		09 30	09 35						11 30						13 30						15 30			
Mirfield	39 a																								
Dewsbury	39 a																								
Halifax	a		09 42	09 46	10 09	10 14	10 43	11 08	11 14	11 44	12 08	12 14	12 43	13 08	13 14	13 44	14 08	14 14	14 43	15 08	15 14	15 44	16 08	16 14	16 43
	d	09 06	09 47	09 47	10 14	10 14	10 45	11 14	11 14	11 45	12 14	12 14	12 45	13 14	13 14	13 45	14 14	14 14	14 45	15 14	15 14	15 45	16 14	16 14	16 45
Bradford Interchange	a	09 19	09 59	09 59	10 28	10 28	10 59	11 28	11 28	11 58	12 28	12 28	12 59	13 28	13 28	13 59	14 28	14 28	14 59	15 28	15 28	15 58	16 28	16 28	16 59
	37 d	09 21	10 02	10 02	10 31	10 31	11 02	11 31	11 31	12 01	12 31	12 31	13 02	13 31	13 31	14 02	14 31	14 31	15 02	15 31	15 31	16 01	16 31	16 31	17 02
New Pudsey	37 a	09 30	10 10	10 10	10 39	10 39	11 10	11 39	11 39	12 09	12 39	12 39	13 10	13 39	13 39	14 10	14 39	14 39	15 10	15 39	15 39	16 09	16 39	16 39	17 10
Bramley	37 a	09 33	10 14	10 14	10 43	10 43		11 43	11 43	12 13	12 43	12 43		13 43	13 43	14 14	14 43	14 43		15 43	15 43	16 13	16 43	16 43	
Leeds 10	37, 39 a	09 42	10 24	10 24	10 52	10 52	11 21	11 54	11 54	12 21	12 52	12 52	13 21	13 52	13 52	14 22	14 53	14 53	15 21	15 52	15 52	16 21	16 54	16 54	17 21
Selby	40 a																								
York 8	40 a	10 23	11 07	11 07			11 59			13 03			13 59			15 03			15 59			17 04			18 00

		NT	NT	NT	NT	NT	NT	NT	NT	NT	NT	NT	NT	NT	NT	NT	NT	NT	NT	NT	NT	NT	NT
		B	A		B	A		B	A			B	A		B	A	B	A	B	A		B	A
Liverpool Lime Street 10	90 d	15 10			16 10			17 10				18 09			19 10				20 10				
Manchester Victoria	95 d	16 09	16 15		17 09	17 15		18 09	18 15			19 09	19 15		20 09	20 15			21 09	21 15		22 09	22 15
Moston	95 d	16 15	16 21		17 15	17 21		18 15	18 21			19 15	19 21		20 15	20 21			21 15	21 21		22 15	22 21
Mills Hill	95 d	16 19	16 25		17 19	17 25		18 19	18 25			19 19	19 25		20 19	20 25			21 19	21 25		22 19	22 25
Castleton	95 d	16 24	16 30		17 24	17 30		18 24	18 30			19 24	19 30		20 24	20 30			21 24	21 30		22 24	22 30
Rochdale	95 a	16 28	16 34		17 28	17 34		18 28	18 34			19 28	19 34		20 28	20 34			21 28	21 34		22 28	22 34
	d	16 28	16 34		17 28	17 34		18 28	18 34			19 28	19 34		20 28	20 34			21 28	21 34		22 28	22 34
Smithy Bridge	d	16 32	16 38		17 32	17 38		18 32	18 38			19 32	19 38		20 32	20 38			21 32	21 38		22 32	22 38
Littleborough	d	16 36	16 42		17 36	17 42		18 36	18 42			19 36	19 42		20 36	20 42			21 36	21 42		22 36	22 42
Walsden	d	16 42	16 48		17 42	17 48		18 42	18 48			19 42	19 48		20 42	20 48			21 42	21 48		22 42	22 48
Todmorden	d	16 45	16 51		17 45	17 51		18 45	18 51			19 45	19 51		20 45	20 51			21 45	21 51		22 45	22 51
Blackpool North	97 d						17 10			18 10				19 12							21 12		
Poulton-le-Fylde	97 d						17 16			18 16				19 18							21 18		
Preston 8	97 d						17 37			18 37				19 37							21 37		
Blackburn	97 d						17 53			18 53				19 53							21 53		
Accrington	97 d						18 01			19 01				20 01							22 01		
Burnley Manchester Road	97 d						18 10			19 10				20 10							22 10		
Hebden Bridge	a	16 52	16 58		17 52	17 58	18 31	18 52	18 58	19 31		19 52	19 58	20 31	20 52	20 58			21 52	21 58	22 31	22 52	22 58
	d	16 52	16 58		17 52	17 58	18 32	18 52	18 58	19 32		19 52	19 58	20 32	20 52	20 58			21 52	21 58	22 32	22 52	22 58
Mytholmroyd	d	16 55	17 01		17 55	18 01		18 55	19 01			19 55	20 01		20 55	21 01			21 55	22 01		22 55	23 01
Sowerby Bridge	d	17 01	17 07		18 01	18 07	18 39	19 01	19 07			20 01	20 07		21 01	21 07			22 01	22 07		23 01	23 07
Huddersfield	39 d			17 20							19 36						21 15	21 20					
Brighouse	d			17 30							19 46						21 25	21 30					
Mirfield	39 a																						
Dewsbury	39 a																						
Halifax	a	17 08	17 14	17 44	18 08	18 14	18 45	19 08	19 14	19 43	19 55	20 08	20 14	20 43	21 08	21 14	21 35	21 45	22 08	22 14	22 43	23 08	23 14
	d	17 14	17 14	17 45	18 14	18 14	18 45	19 14	19 14	19 45	19 55	20 14	20 14	20 45	21 14	21 14	21 45	21 45	22 14	22 14	22 45	23 14	23 14
Bradford Interchange	a	17 28	17 28	17 59	18 28	18 28	18 59	19 28	19 28	19 59	20 11	20 28	20 28	20 59	21 28	21 28	21 59	21 59	22 28	22 28	22 59	23 28	23 28
	37 d	17 31	17 31	18 02	18 31	18 31	19 02	19 31	19 31	20 02	20 14	20 31	20 31	21 02	21 31	21 31	22 02	22 02	22 31	22 31	23 02	23 31	23 31
New Pudsey	37 a	17 39	17 39	18 10	18 39	18 39	19 10	19 39	19 39	20 10	20 22	20 39	20 39	21 10	21 39	21 39	22 10	22 10	22 39	22 39	23 10	23 39	23 39
Bramley	37 a	17 43	17 43	18 14	18 43	18 43		19 43	19 43		20 26	20 43	20 43		21 43	21 43	22 14	22 14	22 43	22 43		23 43	23 43
Leeds 10	37, 39 a	17 52	17 52	18 22	18 54	18 54	19 21	19 53	19 53	20 22	20 34	20 54	20 54	21 21	21 54	21 54	22 22	22 22	22 53	22 53	23 21	23 52	23 52
Selby	40 a																						
York 8	40 a			19 03			19 59			21 02				21 59									

For general notes see front of timetable
For details of catering facilities see Directory of Train Operators

A Until 2 November
B From 9 November

Table 41

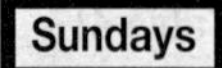

Sundays

20 July to 7 September

Manchester Victoria, Rochdale, Blackpool North and Huddersfield → Bradford and Leeds via Brighouse and Halifax

Network Diagram - see first page of Table 39

	NT	NT	NT 🚌	NT 🚌		NT	NT	NT 🚌	NT 🚌		NT	NT	NT 🚌	NT 🚌		NT	NT	NT 🚌	NT 🚌		NT	NT	NT 🚌	NT 🚌
Liverpool Lime Street 10 90 d																								
Manchester Victoria 95 ⛴ d			08 38	09 04				09 38	10 04				10 38	11 04				11 38	12 04				12 38	13 04
Moston 95 d			08 58					09 58					10 58					11 58					12 58	
Mills Hill 95 d			09 13					10 13					11 13					12 13					13 13	
Castleton 95 d			09 23					10 23					11 23					12 23					13 23	
Rochdale 95 a			09 29	09 29				10 29	10 29				11 29	11 29				12 29	12 29				13 29	13 29
d						09 34					10 34					11 34					12 34			
Smithy Bridge d						09 38					10 38					11 38					12 38			
Littleborough d						09 42					10 42					11 42					12 42			
Walsden d						09 48					10 48					11 48					12 48			
Todmorden d						09 51					10 51					11 51					12 51			
Blackpool North 97 d							09 10										11 12							
Poulton-le-Fylde 97 d							09 16										11 18							
Preston 8 97 d							09 35										11 37							
Blackburn 97 d							09 51										11 53							
Accrington 97 d							09 59										12 01							
Burnley Manchester Road 97 d							10 10										12 10							
Hebden Bridge a						09 58	10 31				10 58					11 58	12 31				12 58			
d						09 58	10 32				10 58					11 58	12 32				12 58			
Mytholmroyd d						10 01					11 01					12 01					13 01			
Sowerby Bridge d						10 07					11 07					12 07					13 07			
Huddersfield 39 d		09 20										11 20										13 20		
Brighouse d		09 30										11 30										13 30		
Mirfield 39 a																								
Dewsbury 39 a																								
Halifax a		09 42				10 14	10 43				11 14	11 44				12 14	12 43				13 14	13 44		
d	09 06	09 47				10 14	10 45				11 14	11 45				12 14	12 45				13 14	13 45		
Bradford Interchange a	09 19	09 59				10 28	10 59				11 28	11 58				12 28	12 59				13 28	13 59		
37 d	09 21	10 02				10 31	11 02				11 31	12 01				12 31	13 02				13 31	14 02		
New Pudsey 37 a	09 30	10 10				10 39	11 10				11 39	12 09				12 39	13 10				13 39	14 10		
Bramley 37 a	09 33	10 14				10 43					11 43	12 13				12 43					13 43	14 14		
Leeds 10 37, 39 a	09 42	10 24				10 52	11 21				11 54	12 21				12 52	13 21				13 52	14 22		
Selby 40 a																								
York 8 40 a																								

	NT	NT		NT 🚌	NT 🚌	NT	NT		NT 🚌	NT 🚌	NT	NT		NT 🚌	NT 🚌	NT	NT		NT 🚌	NT 🚌	NT	NT		NT 🚌
Liverpool Lime Street 10 90 d																								
Manchester Victoria 95 ⛴ d				13 38	14 04				14 38	15 04				15 38	16 04				16 38	17 04				17 38
Moston 95 d				13 58					14 58					15 58					16 58					17 58
Mills Hill 95 d				14 13					15 13					16 13					17 13					18 13
Castleton 95 d				14 23					15 23					16 23					17 23					18 23
Rochdale 95 a				14 29	14 29				15 29	15 29				16 29	16 29				17 29	17 29				18 29
d	13 34					14 34					15 34					16 34					17 34			
Smithy Bridge d	13 38					14 38					15 38					16 38					17 38			
Littleborough d	13 42					14 42					15 42					16 42					17 42			
Walsden d	13 48					14 48					15 48					16 48					17 48			
Todmorden d	13 51					14 51					15 51					16 51					17 51			
Blackpool North 97 d		13 12										15 12										17 10		
Poulton-le-Fylde 97 d		13 18										15 18										17 16		
Preston 8 97 d		13 37										15 37										17 37		
Blackburn 97 d		13 53										15 53										17 53		
Accrington 97 d		14 01										16 01										18 01		
Burnley Manchester Road 97 d		14 10										16 10										18 10		
Hebden Bridge a	13 58	14 31				14 58					15 58	16 31				16 58					17 58	18 31		
d	13 58	14 32				14 58					15 58	16 32				16 58					17 58	18 32		
Mytholmroyd d	14 01					15 01					16 01					17 01					18 01			
Sowerby Bridge d	14 07					15 07					16 07					17 07					18 07	18 39		
Huddersfield 39 d							15 20										17 20							
Brighouse d							15 30										17 30							
Mirfield 39 a																								
Dewsbury 39 a																								
Halifax a	14 14	14 43				15 14	15 44				16 14	16 43				17 14	17 44				18 14	18 45		
d	14 14	14 45				15 14	15 45				16 14	16 45				17 14	17 45				18 14	18 45		
Bradford Interchange a	14 28	14 59				15 28	15 58				16 28	16 59				17 28	17 59				18 28	18 59		
37 d	14 31	15 02				15 31	16 01				16 31	17 02				17 31	18 02				18 31	19 02		
New Pudsey 37 a	14 39	15 10				15 39	16 09				16 39	17 10				17 39	18 10				18 39	19 10		
Bramley 37 a	14 43					15 43	16 13				16 43					17 43	18 14				18 43			
Leeds 10 37, 39 a	14 53	15 21				15 52	16 21				16 54	17 21				17 52	18 22				18 54	19 21		
Selby 40 a																								
York 8 40 a																								

For general notes see front of timetable
For details of catering facilities see Directory of Train Operators

Table 41

Sundays

Manchester Victoria, Rochdale, Blackpool North and Huddersfield → Bradford and Leeds via Brighouse and Halifax

20 July to 7 September

Network Diagram - see first page of Table 39

		NT 🚌	NT	NT	NT		NT 🚌	NT 🚌	NT	NT		NT 🚌	NT 🚌	NT	NT		NT 🚌	NT 🚌	NT	NT	NT 🚌	NT 🚌	NT		
Liverpool Lime Street 10	90 d																								
Manchester Victoria	95 ⛴ d	18 04					18 38	19 04				19 38	20 04				20 38	21 04			21 59	22 25			
Moston	95 d						18 58					19 58					20 58				22 19				
Mills Hill	95 d						19 13					20 13					21 13				22 34				
Castleton	95 d						19 23					20 23					21 23				22 44				
Rochdale	95 a	18 29					19 29	19 29				20 29	20 29				21 29	21 29			22 50	22 50			
	d		18 34						19 34					20 34					21 34				22 55		
Smithy Bridge	d		18 38						19 38					20 38					21 38				22 59		
Littleborough	d		18 42						19 42					20 42					21 42				23 03		
Walsden	d		18 48						19 48					20 48					21 48				23 09		
Todmorden	d		18 51						19 51					20 51					21 51				23 12		
Blackpool North	97 d			18 10						19 12										21 12					
Poulton-le-Fylde	97 d			18 16						19 18										21 18					
Preston 8	97 d			18 37						19 37										21 37					
Blackburn	97 d			18 53						19 53										21 53					
Accrington	97 d			19 01						20 01										22 01					
Burnley Manchester Road	97 d			19 10						20 10										22 10					
Hebden Bridge	a		18 58	19 31					19 58	20 31				20 58					21 58	22 31			23 19		
	d		18 58	19 32					19 58	20 32				20 58					21 58	22 32			23 19		
Mytholmroyd	d		19 01						20 01					21 01					22 01				23 22		
Sowerby Bridge	d		19 07						20 07					21 07					22 07				23 28		
Huddersfield	39 d				19 36										21 20										
Brighouse	d				19 46										21 30										
Mirfield	39 a																								
Dewsbury	39 a																								
Halifax	a		19 14	19 43	19 55				20 14	20 43				21 14	21 45				22 14	22 43			23 35		
	d		19 14	19 45	19 55				20 14	20 45				21 14	21 45				22 14	22 45			23 35		
Bradford Interchange	a		19 28	19 59	20 11				20 28	20 59				21 28	21 59				22 28	22 59			23 49		
	37 d		19 31	20 02	20 14				20 31	21 02				21 31	22 02				22 31	23 02			23 52		
New Pudsey	37 a		19 39	20 10	20 22				20 39	21 10				21 39	22 10				22 39	23 10			23 59		
Bramley	37 a		19 43		20 26				20 43					21 43	22 14				22 43				00 04		
Leeds 10	37, 39 a		19 53	20 22	20 34				20 54	21 21				21 54	22 23				22 53	23 21			00 13		
Selby	40 a																								
York 8	40 a																								

For general notes see front of timetable
For details of catering facilities see Directory of Train Operators

Mondays to Saturdays

until 6 September

Hull → Beverley, Bridlington and Scarborough

Network Diagram - see first page of Table 39

Miles			NT	TP 1◇ A	TP 1◇ B	NT	NT	NT C	NT SO	NT SX	TP 1◇ D	NT E	NT G	NT C	TP 1◇ D	NT	NT C	TP 1◇ D	NT	TP 1◇ D	NT C
0	**Hull**	d	06 24			06 54	07 14	07 36	07 52	07 52		08 14	08 37	09 15		09 44	10 14		10 44		11 14
4	Cottingham	d	06 30			07 00	07 20	07 42	07 58	07 58		08 20	08 43	09 21		09 50	10 20		10 50		11 20
8¼	**Beverley**	d	06 37			07 07	07 27	07a48	08 05	08 05		08 27	08a49	09 28		09 57	10 27		10 57		11 27
11¼	Arram	d				07 11				08 09											
16½	Hutton Cranswick	d				07 18	07 36		08 14	08 16		08 36		09 37		10 06			11 06		
19½	Driffield	d	06 49			07 24	07 41		08 19	08 22		08 41		09 42		10 11	10 39		11 11		11 39
21½	Nafferton	d				07 27	07 45		08 23	08 25		08 45		09 46		10 15			11 15		
31	**Bridlington**	a	07 04			07 39	07 58		08 36	08 39		08 56		10 01		10 26	10 54		11 28		11 52
—		d				07 49						09 00				10 36					12 04
34½	Bempton	d				07 56						09 07				10 43					12 11
41¾	Hunmanby	d				08 06						09 17				10 53					12 21
44½	Filey	d				08 11						09 22				10 58					12 26
51	Seamer	d		07 19	08 06	08 22					09 19	09 34			10 19	11 12		11 19		12 19	12 37
53½	**Scarborough**	a		07 30	08 14	08 29					09 30	09 40			10 30	11 18		11 30		12 30	12 43

		NT	NT C	TP 1◇ D	NT	TP 1◇ D	NT C	NT	NT C	TP 1◇ D	NT	NT C	TP 1◇ D	TP 1◇ D	NT G	NT	NT	NT G	NT	TP 1◇ B	TP 1◇ B
Hull	d	11 44	12 14		12 44		13 14	13 44	14 14		14 44	15 20			16 00	16 14	16 29	16 52	17 07		
Cottingham	d	11 50	12 20		12 50		13 20	13 50	14 20		14 50	15 26			16 07	16 21	16 36	16 59	17 14		
Beverley	d	11 57	12 27		12 57		13 27	13 57	14 27		14 57	15 33			16 13	16a27	16a42	17 05	17a20		
Arram	d				13 01										16 18						
Hutton Cranswick	d	12 06			13 08			14 06			15 06				16 25			17 14			
Driffield	d	12 11	12 39		13 14		13 39	14 11	14 39		15 11	15 45			16 30			17 20			
Nafferton	d	12 15			13 17			14 15			15 15				16 34			17 23			
Bridlington	a	12 28	12 54		13 31		13 52	14 28	14 54		15 26	16 02			16 45			17 37			
	d						14 04				15 30				16 54						
Bempton	d						14 11				15 37				17 01						
Hunmanby	d						14 21				15 47				17 11						
Filey	d						14 26				15 52				17 16						
Seamer	d			13 19		14 19	14 37			15 19	16 03		16 19	17 19	17 27					18 07	18 41
Scarborough	a			13 30		14 30	14 45			15 30	16 10		16 30	17 30	17 35					18 17	18 51

		NT H	NT	NT G	NT SX	NT SO	NT SX	TP SO 1◇ D	TP SX 1◇ D	TP 1◇ D	NT J	NT SX C	NT SO C	TP SO 1◇ D	TP SX 1◇ D	NT C	NT G	TP SO 1◇ B	TP SX 1◇ B	NT C
Hull	d	17 30	17 44	18 00	18 25	18 45	18 50				19 14	20 10	20 14			21 09	21 48			23 00
Cottingham	d	17 37	17 51	18 07	18 31	18 51	18 56				19 20	20 16	20 21			21 15	21 54			23 06
Beverley	d	17 43	17a57	18 13	18a37	18a57	19a02				19 27	20 23	20 27			21a21	22 01			23a12
Arram	d	17 48										20 27	20 32							
Hutton Cranswick	d	17 55		18 22							19 36	20 34	20 39				22 10			
Driffield	d	18 00		18 28							19 41	20 40	20 44				22 15			
Nafferton	d	18 04		18 31							19 45	20 43	20 48				22 19			
Bridlington	a	18 15		18 45							19 57	20 57	21 01				22 32			
	d	18 18									19 59									
Bempton	d	18 25									20 06									
Hunmanby	d	18 35									20 16									
Filey	d	18 40									20 21									
Seamer	d	18 50						19 19	19 24	20 19	20 33			21 19	21 20			22 49	22 56	
Scarborough	a	18 57						19 30	19 31	20 30	20 39			21 30	21 31			23 02	23 04	

Mondays to Saturdays

from 8 September

		NT	TP 1◇ A	TP 1◇ B	NT	NT	NT C	NT SO	NT SX	TP 1◇ D	NT E	NT G	NT C	TP 1◇ D	NT	NT C	TP 1◇ D	NT	TP 1◇ D	NT C	NT
Hull	d	06 24			06 54	07 14	07 36	07 52	07 52		08 14	08 37	09 15		09 44	10 14		10 44		11 14	11 44
Cottingham	d	06 30			07 00	07 20	07 42	07 58	07 58		08 20	08 43	09 21		09 50	10 20		10 50		11 20	11 50
Beverley	d	06 38			07 07	07 28	07a50	08 06	08 06		08 28	08a50	09 29		09 57	10 28		10 58		11 27	11 58
Arram	d				07 11				08 10												
Hutton Cranswick	d				07 18	07 37		08 15	08 17		08 37		09 38		10 06			11 07			12 07
Driffield	d	06 50			07 24	07 42		08 20	08 23		08 43		09 43		10 11	10 40		11 12		11 39	12 12
Nafferton	d				07 27	07 46		08 24	08 26		08 46		09 47		10 15			11 16			12 16
Bridlington	a	07 06			07 39	08 00		08 39	08 41		09 00		10 03		10 28	10 57		11 30		11 52	12 30
	d				07 47						09 02				10 36					12 04	
Bempton	d				07 54						09 09				10 43					12 11	
Hunmanby	d				08 04						09 19				10 53					12 21	
Filey	d				08 09						09 24				10 58					12 26	
Seamer	d		07 19	08 06	08 22					09 19	09 35			10 19	11 09		11 19		12 19	12 37	
Scarborough	a		07 30	08 14	08 29					09 30	09 41			10 30	11 16		11 30		12 30	12 43	

For general notes see front of timetable
For details of catering facilities see Directory of Train Operators

A From York (Table 39)
B From Manchester Airport (Table 39)
C From Sheffield (Table 29)
D From Liverpool Lime Street (Table 39)
E From Gilberdyke (Table 29)
G From Doncaster (Table 29)
H From York via Selby (Table 29)
J Mondays to Fridays from Doncaster (Table 29)

Mondays to Saturdays
from 8 September

Hull → Beverley, Bridlington and Scarborough

Network Diagram - see first page of Table 39

		NT A	TP 1◇ B	NT	TP 1◇ B	NT A	NT	NT A	TP 1◇ B	NT	NT A	TP 1◇ B	TP 1◇ B	NT C	NT	NT	NT D	NT	TP 1◇ E	TP 1◇ E	NT SO G
Hull	d	12 14		12 44		13 14	13 44	14 14		14 44	15 20			16 00	16 14	16 29	16 52	17 07			17 29
Cottingham	d	12 20		12 50		13 20	13 50	14 20		14 50	15 26			16 07	16 21	16 36	16 59	17 14			17 36
Beverley	d	12 28		12 58		13 28	13 58	14 28		14 57	15 33			16 15	16a27	16a43	17 06	17a20			17 44
Arram	d			13 02										16 19							17 48
Hutton Cranswick	d			13 09			14 07			15 06				16 26			17 15				17 55
Driffield	d	12 40		13 15		13 40	14 12	14 40		15 11	15 45			16 32			17 21				18 01
Nafferton	d			13 18			14 16			15 15				16 35			17 24				18 04
Bridlington	a	12 56		13 33		13 55	14 30	14 56		15 28	16 02			16 48			17 39				18 19
	d					14 04				15 30				16 54							18 22
Bempton	d					14 11				15 37				17 01							18 29
Hunmanby	d					14 21				15 47				17 11							18 39
Filey	d					14 26				15 52				17 16							18 44
Seamer	d		13 19		14 19	14 39			15 19	16 03		16 19	17 19	17 27					18 07	18 41	18 55
Scarborough	a		13 30		14 30	14 45			15 30	16 10		16 30	17 30	17 35					18 17	18 51	19 01

		NT SX G	NT	NT D	NT SX	NT SO	NT SX	TP SO 1◇ B	TP SX 1◇ B	TP 1◇ B	NT H	NT SX A	NT SO A	TP SO 1◇ B	TP SX 1◇ B	NT A	NT D	TP SO 1◇ E	TP SX 1◇ E	NT A
Hull	d	17 30	17 44	18 00	18 25	18 45	18 50				19 14	20 10	20 14			21 09	21 48			23 00
Cottingham	d	17 37	17 51	18 07	18 31	18 51	18 56				19 20	20 16	20 21			21 15	21 54			23 06
Beverley	d	17 45	17a58	18 14	18a38	18a58	19a03				19 28	20 24	20 28			21a23	22 02			23a13
Arram	d	17 49										20 28	20 33							
Hutton Cranswick	d	17 56		18 23							19 37	20 35	20 40				22 11			
Driffield	d	18 02		18 29							19 42	20 41	20 45				22 16			
Nafferton	d	18 05		18 32							19 46	20 44	20 49				22 20			
Bridlington	a	18 18		18 48							19 59	21 00	21 04				22 34			
	d	18 21									20 01									
Bempton	d	18 28									20 08									
Hunmanby	d	18 38									20 18									
Filey	d	18 43									20 23									
Seamer	d	18 54						19 19	19 24	20 19	20 36			21 19	21 20			22 49	22 56	
Scarborough	a	19 01						19 30	19 31	20 30	20 42			21 30	21 31			23 02	23 04	

Sundays
until 28 September

		NT	TP 1◇ J	TP 1◇ K	NT	TP 1◇ L	TP 1◇ N	NT A	NT D	TP 1◇ Q	TP 1◇ U	NT A	NT	TP 1◇ U	TP 1◇ V	NT A	NT A	TP 1◇ U	TP 1◇ V
Hull	d	09 00			09 25			10 25	11 30			12 00	13 00			14 00	15 05		
Cottingham	d	09 06			09 31			10 31	11 36			12 06	13 06			14 06	15 11		
Beverley	d	09 13			09 38			10 38	11 43			12 13	13 13			14 13	15 18		
Arram	d				09 42														
Hutton Cranswick	d				09 49			10 47				12 22				14 22			
Driffield	d	09 25			09 55			10 52	11 55			12 27	13 25			14 27	15 30		
Nafferton	d				09 58			10 56				12 31				14 31			
Bridlington	a	09 40			10 10			11 07	12 10			12 42	13 40			14 42	15 45		
	d				10 12			11 10				12 45				14 45			
Bempton	d				10 19			11 17				12 52				14 52			
Hunmanby	d				10 29			11 27				13 02				15 02			
Filey	d				10 34			11 32				13 07				15 07			
Seamer	d		10∫19	10∫19	10 45	11∫14	11∫29	11 43		12 19	13∫04	13 22		14∫04	14∫19	15 18		16∫04	16∫25
Scarborough	a		10∫27	10∫30	10 52	11∫23	11∫39	11 50		12 30	13∫15	13 28		14∫15	14∫30	15 25		16∫15	16∫34

		NT A	NT A	TP 1◇ U	NT	TP 1◇ V	TP 1◇ U	NT A	NT A	TP 1◇ U	NT A	TP 1◇ V	TP 1◇ U	TP 1◇ V	TP 1◇ X
Hull	d	16 05	16 57		17 20			18 00	19 00		20 00				
Cottingham	d	16 11	17 03		17 26			18 06	19 06		20 06				
Beverley	d	16 18	17 10		17 33			18 13	19 13		20a12				
Arram	d														
Hutton Cranswick	d	16 27	17 19		17 42				19 22						
Driffield	d	16 32	17 24		17 47			18 25	19 27						
Nafferton	d	16 36	17 28		17 51				19 31						
Bridlington	a	16 47	17 41		18 04			18 38	19 44						
	d	16 53						18 45							
Bempton	d	17 00						18 52							
Hunmanby	d	17 10						19 02							
Filey	d	17 15						19 07							
Seamer	d	17 26		18∫04		18∫19	19∫04	19 22		20∫04		20∫19	21∫14	21∫19	22 49
Scarborough	a	17 33		18∫15		18∫30	19∫15	19 27		20∫15		20∫30	21∫24	21∫30	23 00

For general notes see front of timetable
For details of catering facilities see Directory of Train Operators

- **A** From Sheffield (Table 29)
- **B** From Liverpool Lime Street (Table 39)
- **C** From Doncaster (Table 26)
- **D** From Doncaster (Table 29)
- **E** From Manchester Airport (Table 39)
- **G** From York via Selby (Table 29)
- **H** Mondays to Fridays from Doncaster (Table 29)
- **J** Until 13 July. From Leeds (Table 39)
- **K** From 20 July. From Leeds (Table 39)
- **L** Until 13 July. From York (Table 39)
- **N** 20 July to 7 September. From Liverpool Lime Street (Table 39)
- **Q** Fom Liverpool Lime Street (20 July to 7 September from York) (Table 39)
- **U** 20 July to 7 September. From Manchester Airport (Table 39)
- **V** Until 13 July and from 14 September. From Liverpool Lime Street (Table 39)
- **X** From Manchester Airport (20 July to 7 September from Liverpool Lime Street) (Table 39)

Sundays

from 5 October

Hull → Beverley, Bridlington and Scarborough

Network Diagram - see first page of Table 39

		TP ■1 ◇	TP ■1 ◇	NT	TP ■1 ◇	NT	NT	TP ■1 ◇	NT	TP ■1 ◇	NT	NT	TP ■1 ◇	TP ■1 ◇	TP ■1 ◇
		A	B	C	B	C	C	B	C	B	C	C	B	B	D
Hull	d			12 00		14 00	16 05		16 57		19 00	20 00			
Cottingham	d			12 06		14 06	16 11		17 03		19 06	20 06			
Beverley	d			12 13		14 13	16a17		17 10		19 13	20a12			
Arram	d														
Hutton Cranswick	d			12 22		14 22			17 19		19 22				
Driffield	d			12 27		14 27			17 24		19 27				
Nafferton	d			12 31		14 31			17 28		19 31				
Bridlington	a			12 44		14 44			17 41		19 44				
	d														
Bempton	d														
Hunmanby	d														
Filey	d														
Seamer	d	10 19	12 19		14 19			16 25		18 19			20 19	21 19	22 49
Scarborough	a	10 30	12 30		14 30			16 34		18 30			20 30	21 30	23 00

For general notes see front of timetable
For details of catering facilities see Directory of Train Operators

A From Leeds (Table 39)
B From Liverpool Lime Street (Table 39)
C From Sheffield (Table 29)
D From Manchester Airport (Table 39)

Mondays to Saturdays

until 6 September

Scarborough, Bridlington and Beverley → Hull

Network Diagram - see first page of Table 39

Miles			NT SO A	NT SX A	TP SX 1◇ B	TP SO 1◇ B		NT SX	NT C	NT D	NT		NT C	TP SX 1◇ B	TP SO 1◇ B	TP 1◇ E		NT D	TP 1◇ E	NT C	NT D		NT	TP 1◇ E	NT D	NT	TP 1◇ E
0	**Scarborough**	d			06 30	06 34							06 50	07 00	07 05	07 47			08 47				09 03	09 47		10 00	10 45
2¾	Seamer	d			06a35	06a39							06 55	07a05	07a10	07a52			08a52				09 08	09a52		10 05	10a50
9¼	Filey	d											07 04										09 17			10 14	
12	Hunmanby	d											07 09										09 21			10 18	
19½	Bempton	d											07 19										09 31			10 28	
22¾	**Bridlington**	a											07 26										09 39			10 36	
—		d							06 46	07 14			07 34					08 08			09 06		09 42		10 12	10 42	
32¼	Nafferton	d							06 56	07 24			07 45					08 18			09 16		09 52			10 52	
34¾	Driffield	d							07 01	07 29			07 49					08 23			09 21		09 57		10 25	10 57	
37½	Hutton Cranswick	d							07 05	07 33			07 54					08 27			09 25		10 01			11 01	
42½	Arram	d											08 01								09 32						
45½	**Beverley**	d	06 30	06 40				06 58	07 15	07 43	07 57		08 07					08 37		09 00	09 37		10 11		10 37	11 11	
49¾	Cottingham	d	06 35	06 45				07 03	07 21	07 49	08 03		08 13					08 43		09 05	09 43		10 16		10 43	11 16	
53¾	**Hull**	a	06 44	06 53				07 12	07 31	07 59	08 13		08 23					08 53		09 14	09 53		10 26		10 53	11 26	

		NT D		NT	NT D	TP SX 1◇ E	TP SO 1◇ E		NT	TP 1◇ E	NT D	NT		NT D	TP SO 1◇ E	TP SX 1◇ E	NT		TP SO 1◇ E	TP SX 1◇ E	NT D	NT C		TP 1◇ E	NT D	NT	NT A
Scarborough	d				11 28	11 45	11 47			12 47				13 28	13 45	13 47			14 45	14 47		14 54		15 47			
Seamer	d				11 33	11a50	11a52			12a52				13 33	13a50	13a52			14a50	14a52		14 59		15a52			
Filey	d				11 42									13 42								15 08					
Hunmanby	d				11 46									13 46								15 12					
Bempton	d				11 56									13 56								15 22					
Bridlington	a				12 04									14 04								15 30					
	d	11 12		11 42	12 12				12 42		13 12	13 42		14 12			14 42				15 12	15 40				16 14	
Nafferton	d			11 52					12 52			13 52					14 52					15 50				16 24	
Driffield	d	11 25		11 57	12 25				12 57		13 25	13 57		14 25			14 57				15 25	15 55				16 29	
Hutton Cranswick	d			12 01					13 01			14 01					15 01					15 59				16 33	
Arram	d			12 08																							
Beverley	d	11 37		12 13	12 37				13 11		13 37	14 11		14 37			15 11				15 37	16 09			16 32	16 43	17 00
Cottingham	d	11 43		12 19	12 43				13 16		13 43	14 16		14 43			15 16				15 43	16 14			16 37	16 48	17 05
Hull	a	11 53		12 29	12 54				13 26		13 53	14 26		14 53			15 29				15 53	16 24			16 46	16 58	17 14

		NT G	NT D		TP 1◇ E	NT	NT	NT C		TP 1◇ E	TP SO 1◇ E	TP SX 1◇ E	NT		NT D	TP 1◇ E	NT	TP 1◇ H		NT	NT J	TP 1◇ K	NT				
Scarborough	d		16 18		16 47			17 38		17 45	18 45	18 46				19 47	20 00	20 37				22 07					
Seamer	d		16 22		16a52			17 43		17a50	18a50	18a51				19a52	20 05	20a42				22a12					
Filey	d		16 32					17 52									20 14										
Hunmanby	d		16 36					17 56									20 19										
Bempton	d		16 46					18 06									20 28										
Bridlington	a		16 53					18 14									20 36										
	d		17 06				17 46	18 25							19 10		20 38				21 35		22 40				
Nafferton	d		17 16				17 56	18 36							19 20		20 48				21 45		22 50				
Driffield	d		17 20				18 01	18 40							19 25		20 53				21 50		22 55				
Hutton Cranswick	d		17 24				18 05	18 45							19 29		20 57				21 54		22 59				
Arram	d						18 12																				
Beverley	d	17 25	17 34			18 03	18 17	18 54					19 15		19 39		21 07			21 43	22 04		23 09				
Cottingham	d	17 30	17 39			18 08	18 23	19 00					19 20		19 44		21 13			21 48	22 09		23 14				
Hull	a	17 39	17 49			18 17	18 33	19 12					19 29		19 54		21 23			21 57	22 19		23 25				

Mondays to Saturdays

from 8 September

		NT SO A	NT SX A	TP SX 1◇ B	TP SO 1◇ B		NT SX	NT C	NT SX D	NT SO D		NT	NT		TP SX 1◇ B		TP SO 1◇ B	TP 1◇ E	NT D	TP 1◇ E		NT C	NT D	NT	TP 1◇ E		NT D
Scarborough	d			06 30	06 34								06b48		07 00		07 05	07 47		08 47				09 00	09 47		
Seamer	d			06a35	06a39								06b53		07a05		07a10	07a52		08a52				09 05	09a52		
Filey	d												07 04											09 14			
Hunmanby	d												07 09											09 20			
Bempton	d												07 19											09 30			
Bridlington	a												07 26											09 37			
	d							06 44	07 12	07 14			07 31						08 06				09 03	09 40			10 10
Nafferton	d							06 54	07 22	07 24			07 42						08 16				09 13	09 50			
Driffield	d							06 59	07 27	07 29			07 46						08 21				09 18	09 55			10 23
Hutton Cranswick	d							07 03	07 31	07 33			07 51						08 25				09 22	09 59			
Arram	d												07 58										09 29				
Beverley	d	06 30	06 38				06 58	07 13	07 42	07 44		07 57	08 06						08 36			09 00	09 36	10 10			10 36
Cottingham	d	06 35	06 43				07 03	07 20	07 48	07 50		08 03	08 12						08 42			09 05	09 41	10 15			10 42
Hull	a	06 45	06 53				07 14	07 31	07 59	08 00		08 13	08 24						08 53			09 14	09 53	10 26			10 53

For general notes see front of timetable
For details of catering facilities see Directory of Train Operators

A To York via Selby (Table 29)
B To Manchester Airport (Table 39)
C To Doncaster (Table 29)
D To Sheffield (Table 29)
E To Liverpool Lime Street (Table 39)
G To Sheffield (Saturdays to Doncaster) (Table 29)
H To Leeds (Saturdays to York) (Table 39)
J Saturdays to Sheffield (Table 29)
K To York (Table 39)
b Saturdays dep. 2 minutes later

Table 43

Mondays to Saturdays
from 8 September

Scarborough, Bridlington and Beverley → Hull

Network Diagram - see first page of Table 39

		NT	TP	NT	NT	NT	TP	TP	NT	TP	NT	NT	NT	TP	TP	NT	TP	TP	NT	NT	TP	NT
							SX	SO						SO	SX		SO	SX				
			1 ◇				1 ◇	1 ◇		1 ◇				1 ◇	1 ◇		1 ◇	1 ◇			1 ◇	
			A	B		B	A	A		A	B		B	A	A		A	A	B	C	A	B
Scarborough	d	09 57	10 45			11 28	11 45	11 47		12 47			13 26	13 45	13 47		14 45	14 47		14 54	15 47	
Seamer	d	10 02	10a50			11 33	11a50	11a52		12a52			13 31	13a50	13a52		14a50	14a52		14 59	15a52	
Filey	d	10 11				11 42							13 40							15 08		
Hunmanby	d	10 15				11 46							13 44							15 12		
Bempton	d	10 25				11 56							13 54							15 22		
Bridlington	a	10 34				12 04							14 04							15 30		
	d	10 39		11 09	11 39	12 09			12 39		13 09	13 39	14 09			14 39			15 09	15 37		
Nafferton	d	10 49			11 49				12 49			13 49				14 49				15 47		
Driffield	d	10 54		11 22	11 54	12 22			12 54		13 22	13 54	14 22			14 54			15 22	15 52		
Hutton Cranswick	d	10 58			11 58				12 58			13 58				14 58				15 56		
Arram	d				12 05																	
Beverley	d	11 09		11 36	12 12	12 36			13 09		13 36	14 09	14 36			15 09			15 36	16 07		16 32
Cottingham	d	11 15		11 41	12 17	12 41			13 15		13 41	14 15	14 41			15 15			15 41	16 13		16 37
Hull	a	11 26		11 54	12 29	12 54			13 26		13 53	14 26	14 53			15 29			15 53	16 24		16 46

		NT	NT	NT	NT	TP	NT	NT	NT	TP	TP	TP	NT	NT	TP	NT	TP	NT	NT	NT	TP	NT
											SO	SX							SX	SO		
						1 ◇				1 ◇	1 ◇	1 ◇			1 ◇		1 ◇				1 ◇	
			D	E	B	A			C	A	A	A		B	A		G			B	H	
Scarborough	d				16 15	16 47			17 38	17 45	18 45	18 46			19 47	20 00	20 37				22 07	
Seamer	d				16 19	16a52			17 43	17a50	18a50	18a51			19a52	20 05	20a42				22a12	
Filey	d				16 29				17 52							20 14						
Hunmanby	d				16 33				17 56							20 21						
Bempton	d				16 43				18 06							20 30						
Bridlington	a				16 53				18 16							20 38						
	d	16 11			17 03			17 44	18 22					19 07		20 40			21 32	21 35		22 40
Nafferton	d	16 21			17 13			17 54	18 33					19 17		20 50			21 42	21 45		22 50
Driffield	d	16 26			17 17			17 59	18 37					19 22		20 55			21 47	21 50		22 55
Hutton Cranswick	d	16 30			17 21			18 03	18 42					19 26		20 59			21 51	21 54		22 59
Arram	d							18 10														
Beverley	d	16 41	17 00	17 25	17 32		18 03	18 16	18 53				19 14	19 37		21 11		21 42	22 02	22 04		23 09
Cottingham	d	16 47	17 05	17 30	17 38		18 08	18 22	18 58				19 19	19 43		21 16		21 47	22 08	22 09		23 14
Hull	a	16 58	17 15	17 39	17 51		18 17	18 33	19 12				19 29	19 54		21 28		21 57	22 19	22 19		23 25

Sundays
until 28 September

		TP	NT	TP	NT	TP	NT	TP	TP	NT	NT	TP	TP	NT	NT
		1 ◇		1 ◇		1 ◇		1 ◇	1 ◇			1 ◇	1 ◇		
		J	B	J	B	K	B	L	N	B	B	L	N	B	B
Scarborough	d	09 20		10 45	11 14	11∫57	12 08	12∫45	13∫20		14 08	14∫45	15∫20		16 08
Seamer	d	09a25		10a50	11 19	12a02	12 13	12a50	13a25		14 13	14a50	15a25		16 13
Filey	d				11 28		12 22				14 22				16 22
Hunmanby	d				11 32		12 26				14 26				16 26
Bempton	d				11 42		12 36				14 36				16 36
Bridlington	a				11 50		12 44				14 44				16 44
	d		09 53		11 53		12 53			13 53	14 53			15 50	16 53
Nafferton	d		10 03		12 03					14 03				16 00	
Driffield	d		10 08		12 08		13 06			14 08	15 06			16 05	17 06
Hutton Cranswick	d		10 12		12 12					14 12				16 09	
Arram	d														
Beverley	d		10 22		12 22		13 18			14 22	15 18			16 19	17 18
Cottingham	d		10 27		12 27		13 24			14 27	15 24			16 24	17 24
Hull	a		10 37		12 37		13 34			14 37	15 34			16 35	17 34

		TP	TP	NT	NT	NT	NT	TP	TP	NT	NT	TP	TP	TP
		1 ◇	1 ◇					1 ◇	1 ◇			1 ◇	1 ◇	1 ◇
		N	L		B			N	L		B	Q	U	V
Scarborough	d	16∫20	16∫45				18 08	18∫30	18∫45		19 37	20∫30	20∫45	21 45
Seamer	d	16a25	16a50				18 13	18a35	18a50		19 42	20a35	20a50	21a50
Filey	d						18 22				19 51			
Hunmanby	d						18 27				19 56			
Bempton	d						18 36				20 05			
Bridlington	a						18 44				20 13			
	d			17 16	17 53	18 14	18 53			19 57	20 15			
Nafferton	d			17 26			19 03				20 25			
Driffield	d			17 31	18 06	18 27	19 08			20 10	20 30			
Hutton Cranswick	d			17 35			19 12				20 34			
Arram	d						19 19							
Beverley	d			17 45	18 18	18 39	19 24			20 22	20 44			
Cottingham	d			17 50	18 24	18 45	19 30			20 28	20 49			
Hull	a			18 00	18 34	18 55	19 40			20 38	20 59			

For general notes see front of timetable
For details of catering facilities see Directory of Train Operators

A To Liverpool Lime Street (Table 39)
B To Sheffield (Table 29)
C To Doncaster (Table 29)
D To York via Selby (Table 29)
E To Meadowhall (Saturdays to Doncaster) (Table 29)
G To Leeds (Saturdays to York) (Table 39)
H To York (Table 39)
J To Manchester Airport (20 July to 7 September to Liverpool Lime Street) (Table 39)
K 20 July to 7 September. To Manchester Airport (Table 39)
L Until 13 July and from 14 September. To Liverpool Lime Street (Table 39)
N 20 July to 7 September. To Liverpool Lime Street (Table 39)
Q 20 July to 7 September. To Manchester Piccadilly (Table 39)
U Until 13 July and from 14 September. To Manchester Piccadilly (Table 39)
V To Manchester Piccadilly (Table 39)

Table 43

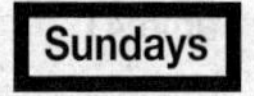

Sundays

from 5 October

Scarborough, Bridlington and Beverley → Hull

Network Diagram - see first page of Table 39

		TP ◇ A	TP ◇ B	NT C	TP ◇ B	NT C	TP ◇ B	NT C	TP ◇ B	NT C	TP ◇ B	NT C	TP ◇ D	TP ◇ E
Scarborough	d	09 20	10 45		12 45		14 45		16 45		18 45		20 45	21∫45
Seamer	d	09a25	10a50		12a50		14a50		16a50		18a50		20a50	21a50
Filey	d													
Hunmanby	d													
Bempton	d													
Bridlington	a													
	d					12 53		14 53		17 50		20 15		
Nafferton	d					13 03		15 03		18 00		20 25		
Driffield	d					13 08		15 08		18 05		20 30		
Hutton Cranswick	d					13 12		15 12		18 09		20 34		
Arram	d													
Beverley	d			12 22		13 22		15 22		18 19		20 44		
Cottingham	d			12 27		13 27		15 27		18 24		20 49		
Hull	a			12 37		13 37		15 37		18 34		20 59		

For general notes see front of timetable
For details of catering facilities see Directory of Train Operators

A To Manchester Airport (Table 39)
B To Liverpool Lime Street (Table 39)
C To Sheffield (Table 29)
D To Manchester Piccadilly (from 9 November to Manchester Victoria) (Table 39)
E Until 2 November.
To Manchester Piccadilly (Table 39)

Network Diagram for Tables 44, 45, 48

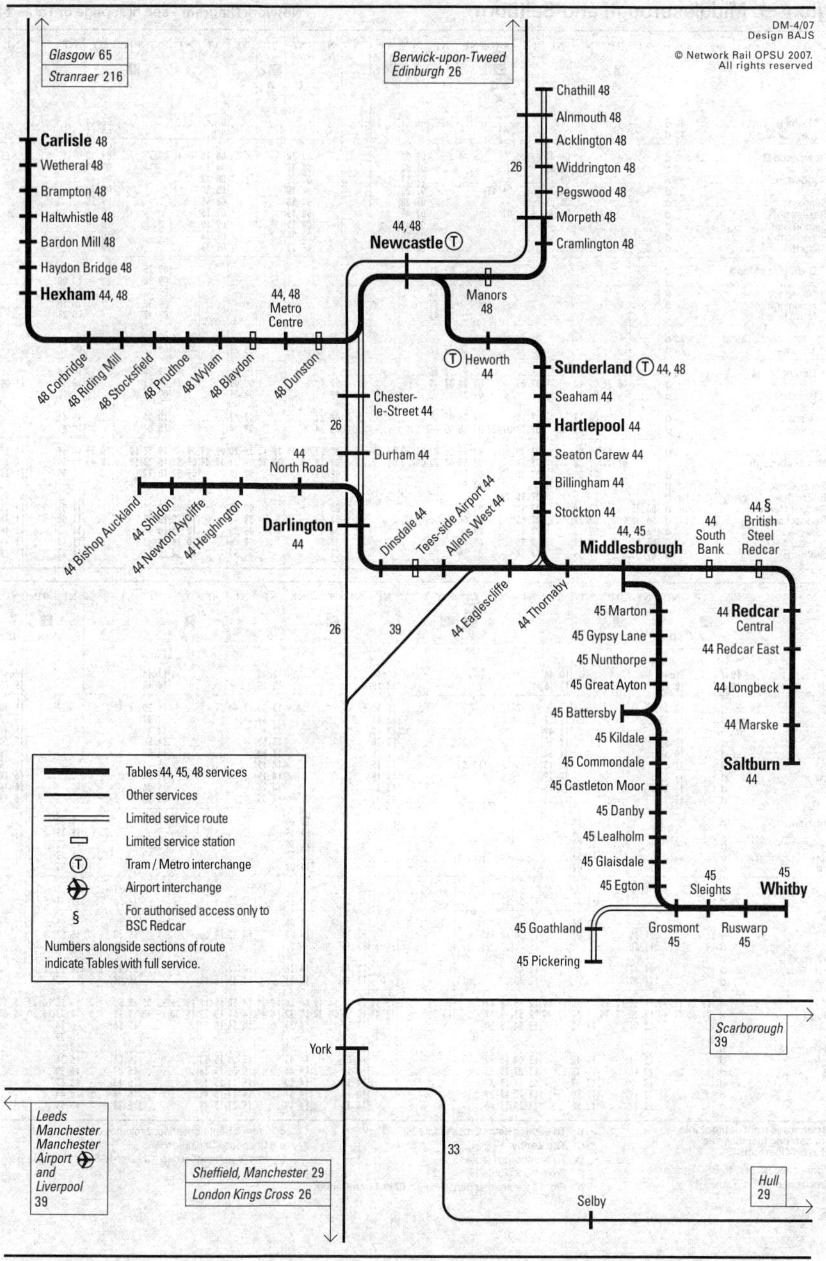

DM-4/07
Design BAJS
© Network Rail OPSU 2007.
All rights reserved
Glasgow 65
Stranraer 216
Berwick-upon-Tweed
Edinburgh 26
Chathill 48
Alnmouth 48
Acklington 48
Widdrington 48
Pegswood 48
Morpeth 48
Cramlington 48
26
Carlisle 48
Wetheral 48
Brampton 48
Haltwhistle 48
Bardon Mill 48
Haydon Bridge 48
Hexham 44, 48
44, 48
Newcastle
Manors
48
44, 48
Metro
Centre
48 Corbridge
48 Riding Mill
48 Stocksfield
48 Prudhoe
48 Wylam
48 Blaydon
48 Dunston
Heworth
44
Sunderland 44, 48
Seaham 44
Hartlepool 44
Seaton Carew 44
Billingham 44
Stockton 44
Chester-
le-Street 44
26
Durham 44
44
North Road
44 Bishop Auckland
44 Shildon
44 Newton Aycliffe
44 Heighington
Darlington
44
Dinsdale 44
Tees-side Airport 44
Allens West 44
44 Eaglescliffe
44 Thornaby
44, 45
Middlesbrough
44
South
Bank
44 §
British
Steel
Redcar
26
39
45 Marton
45 Gypsy Lane
45 Nunthorpe
45 Great Ayton
45 Battersby
45 Kildale
45 Commondale
45 Castleton Moor
45 Danby
45 Lealholm
45 Glaisdale
45 Egton
44 Redcar
Central
44 Redcar East
44 Longbeck
44 Marske
Saltburn
44
45
Sleights
45
Whitby
45 Goathland
45 Pickering
Grosmont
45
Ruswarp
45
Tables 44, 45, 48 services
Other services
Limited service route
Limited service station
Tram / Metro interchange
Airport interchange
For authorised access only to
BSC Redcar
Numbers alongside sections of route
indicate Tables with full service.
Scarborough
39
York
Leeds
Manchester
Manchester
Airport
and
Liverpool
39
33
Sheffield, Manchester 29
London Kings Cross 26
Hull
29
Selby

Newcastle, Sunderland, Bishop Auckland and Darlington → Middlesbrough and Saltburn

Network Diagram - see first page of Table 44

Miles	Miles		NT	TP	NT	NT	NT	GC	NT	NT	NT	TP		NT	NT	TP	NT	NT	NT	NT	TP	NT	NT		NT
				1 ◇ A				R 1 B C ✕		D		1 ◇ E			D	1 ◇ A					1 ◇ A				
—	—	Hexham 48 d									06 13							07b42				08c44			
—	—	MetroCentre 48 d																08b15				09 15			
—	0	**Newcastle** 8 26 ⛴ d		06 00		06 00	06 30		06 44	07e00	07 00			07 26	07 30		07 52	08 30	08 40	09e12		09 30	09e40		10 15
—	2¾	Heworth ⛴ d				06 07					07 07				07 37			08 37				09 37			
—	12	**Sunderland** ⛴ a				06 19					07 19				07 49			08 49				09 49			
—	—	d				06 20		06 45			07 20				07 50			08 50				09 50			
—	17¼	Seaham d				06 28					07 28				07 58			08 58				09 58			
—	30	**Hartlepool** d				06a46		07 08			07 45				08 15			09 15				10 15			
—	32¼	Seaton Carew d									07 49				08 19			09 19				10 19			
—	37¼	Billingham d									07 56				08 26			09 26				10 26			
—	41¾	Stockton d									08 04				08 33			09 33				10 33			
0	—	**Bishop Auckland** d								07 21										09 25			10 03		
2¾	—	Shildon d								07 26										09 30			10 08		
5	—	Newton Aycliffe d								07 31										09 35			10 13		
6¼	—	Heighington d								07 34										09 38			10 16		
10¾	—	North Road d								07 43										09 47			10 25		
—	—	Chester-le-Street 26 d					06 31							07 37					08 33	09 20					
—	—	Durham 26 d		06 12			06 42		06 56	07 12				07 43			08 04		08 52	09 27			09 52		10 27
12	—	**Darlington** 7 26 a								07 46										09 50			10 28		
—	—	d		06 36	06 40		07 05		07 24	07 48				08 10			09 00		09 36	09 53			10 30		11 00
15¾	—	Dinsdale d			06 46				07 29					08 15			09 05			09 58					
17½	—	Tees-side Airport d																							
20	—	Allens West d			06 53		07 15		07 36	07 59				08 22			09 12			10 05			10 41		
20¾	—	Eaglescliffe d			06 55		07 18	07a27	07 38	08 01				08 24			09 14			10 07			10 43		
23¾	44	Thornaby d		06 53	07 01		07 23		07 45	08 07	08 12	08 25		08 33	08 39	09 12	09 20	09 39	09 52	10 18	10 21	10 39	10 48		11 17
27	47¼	**Middlesbrough** a		07 01	07 08		07 28		07 50	08 12	08 20	08 32		08 38	08 48	09 20	09 27	09 48	09 57	10 23	10 30	10 48	10 54		11 22
—	—	d	06 34		07 08		07 30		07 51					08 39			09 28		09 57	10 24			10 55		11 23
29½	—	South Bank d							07 56					08 43											
32¾	—	British Steel Redcar § d					07 38																		
34½	—	**Redcar Central** d	06 45		07 19		07 42		08 03					08 51			09 38		10 08	10 35			11 05		11 33
35½	—	Redcar East d	06 48		07 21		07 45		08 06					08 53			09 41		10 10	10 37			11 08		11 36
37	—	Longbeck d	06 52		07 25		07 49		08 10					08 57			09 45		10 14	10 41			11 12		11 40
37½	—	Marske d	06 54		07 27		07 50		08 11					08 59			09 46		10 16	10 43			11 13		11 41
39½	—	**Saltburn** a	07 03		07 35		07 58		08 19					09 07			09 54		10 24	10 52			11 22		11 49

	TP	NT	NT	TP	NT	NT	NT	NT	GC	TP		NT	NT	TP	NT	NT	NT	NT	TP	NT	NT		NT	TP	NT
	1 ◇ A	D		1 ◇ A					R 1 B ✕	1 ◇ A				1 ◇ A		D			1 ◇ A					1 ◇ A	D
Hexham 48 d		09c44				10 44						11c44				12c44				13c44					14c44
MetroCentre 48 d		10 15				11 15						12 15				13 15				14 15					15 15
Newcastle 8 26 ⛴ d		10 30	11 01		11e25	11 30	11 40	12 15				12 30	12 40		13e29	13 30	13 40	14 12		14 30	14 40		15e22		15 30
Heworth ⛴ d		10 37				11 37						12 37				13 37				14 37					15 37
Sunderland ⛴ a		10 49				11 49						12 49				13 49				14 49					15 49
d		10 50				11 50			12 30			12 50				13 50				14 50					15 50
Seaham d		10 58				11 58						12 58				13 58				14 58					15 58
Hartlepool d		11 15				12 15			12 54			13 15				14 15				15 15					16 15
Seaton Carew d		11 19				12 19						13 19				14 19				15 19					16 19
Billingham d		11 26				12 26						13 26				14 26				15 26					16 26
Stockton d		11 33				12 33						13 33				14 33				15 33					16 33
Bishop Auckland d					11 40										13 40								15 30		
Shildon d					11 45										13 45								15 35		
Newton Aycliffe d					11 50										13 50								15 40		
Heighington d					11 53										13 53								15 43		
North Road d					12 02										14 02								15 52		
Chester-le-Street 26 d			10f34										12 32								14 33		15 21		
Durham 26 d			10f52		11 37		11 52	12 27					12 52		13 27		13 52	14 24			14 52		15 34		
Darlington 7 26 a					12 06										14 06								15 55		
d			11 35		12 07		12 30	12 56					13 30		14 08		14 32	15 00			15 30		15 57		
Dinsdale d			11 40										13 35								15 35		16 03		
Tees-side Airport d																									
Allens West d			11 47				12 40						13 42		14 18		14 42				15 42		16 10		
Eaglescliffe d			11 49				12 43		13a15				13 44		14 21		14 45	15 11			15 44		16 12		
Thornaby d	11 21	11 39	11 55	12 19	12 25	12 39	12 48	13 12		13 21		13 39	13 51	14 19	14 26	14 39	14 50	15 17	15 21	15 39	15 50		16 18	16 21	16 41
Middlesbrough a	11 30	11 48	12 00	12 30	12 31	12 49	12 53	13 17		13 30		13 48	13 56	14 30	14 32	14 48	14 55	15 22	15 30	15 48	15 55		16 23	16 30	16 47
d			12 01		12 32		12 54	13 20					13 57		14 33		14 56	15 23			15 56		16 24		
South Bank d																							16 29		
British Steel Redcar § d																									
Redcar Central d			12 11		12 42		13 04	13 30					14 07		14 43		15 06	15 33			16 06		16 36		
Redcar East d			12 14		12 45		13 07	13 33					14 10		14 46		15 09	15 36			16 09		16 39		
Longbeck d			12 18		12 49		13 11	13 37					14 14		14 50		15 13	15 40			16 13		16 43		
Marske d			12 19		12 50		13 12	13 38					14 15		14 51		15 14	15 41			16 14		16 44		
Saltburn a			12 27		12 58		13 20	13 46					14 23		14 59		15 22	15 49			16 22		16 55		

For general notes see front of timetable
For details of catering facilities see Directory of Train Operators

§ For authorised access only to BSC Redcar
A From Manchester Airport (Table 39)
B To London Kings Cross (Table 26)
C **The Zephyr**
D To Nunthorpe (Table 45)
E From York (Table 39)
b From 8 September dep. Hexham 0739, MetroCentre 0817
c From 8 September dep. 2 minutes earlier
e Change at Darlington
f from 8 September dep. Chester-le-Street 1050, Durham 1056

Newcastle, Sunderland, Bishop Auckland and Darlington → Middlesbrough and Saltburn

Network Diagram - see first page of Table 44

	NT	NT	TP	NT	NT	NT	GC	NT	TP		NT	NT	TP	NT	NT	TP	NT	NT	NT	TP	NT	NT	NT
			■1 ◇				R ■1		■1 ◇				■1 ◇			■1 ◇				■1 ◇			
			A		B	C	D ✕		E				A	B		A				A			G
Hexham 48 d					15b44	16c16					16b44			17 42				18c44					
MetroCentre 48 d					16 15	16 39					17 15			18 13				19 17			20 15		
Newcastle 8 26 d	15 40	16e06		16 27	16 30	16 53		17 17			17 30	17e40		18 30	18e40		19 08	19 30	19f40		20 30	20e38	22 00
Heworth d					16 37	17 00					17 37			18 37				19 37			20 37		
Sunderland a					16 49	17 13					17 49			18 49				19 49			20 49		
d					16 50	17 15	17 30				17 50			18 50				19 50			20 50		
Seaham d					16 58	17 22					17 58			18 58				19 58			20 58		
Hartlepool d					17 15	17 39	17 56				18 15			19 15				20 15			21 15		
Seaton Carew d					17 19	17 43					18 19			19 19				20 19			21 19		
Billingham d					17 26	17 50					18 26			19 26				20 26			21 26		
Stockton d					17 33	17 57					18 33			19 33				20 33			21 33		
Bishop Auckland d		16 30										18 03			19 03							21 15	
Shildon d		16 35										18 08			19 08							21 20	
Newton Aycliffe d		16 40										18 13			19 13							21 25	
Heighington d		16 43										18 16			19 16							21 28	
North Road d		16 52										18 25			19 25							21 37	
Chester-le-Street 26 d		16 15		16 42				17 26							18 29				19f36				22 09
Durham 26 d	15 52	16 22		16 49				17 33				17 52			18 52		19 10		19 52			20 51	22 18
Darlington 7 26 a		16 57										18 31			19 30							21 40	22 38
d	16 30	16 59		17 15				18 03				18 33			19 31		20 07		20 30			21 44	22 42
Dinsdale d				17 20				18 08									20 12					21 49	
Tees-side Airport d																							
Allens West d	16 41	17 09		17 27				18 15				18 43			19 42		20 19					21 56	22 53
Eaglescliffe d	16 44	17 12		17 29			18a14	18 17				18 46			19 44		20 21		20 41			21 58	22 55
Thornaby d	16 49	17 17	17 19	17 35	17 39	18 03		18 23	18 32		18 39	18 51	19 18	19 39	19 50	20 21	20 26	20 39	20 50	21 17	21 39	22 04	23 00
Middlesbrough a	16 54	17 23	17 30	17 41	17 49	18 13		18 28	18 42		18 48	18 56	19 30	19 48	19 55	20 30	20 35	20 50	20 55	21 25	21 48	22 09	23 10
d	16 56	17 24		17 43				18 30				18 59			19 56				20 55			22 09	
South Bank d				17 47																			
British Steel Redcar § d																							
Redcar Central d	17 06	17 35		17 55				18 40				19 09			20 06				21 05			22 20	
Redcar East d	17 09	17 37		17 57				18 43				19 12			20 09				21 08			22 22	
Longbeck d	17 13	17 41		18 01				18 47				19 16			20 13				21 12			22 26	
Marske d	17 14	17 43		18 03				18 48				19 17			20 14				21 13			22 28	
Saltburn a	17 22	17 52		18 11				18 56				19 26			20 23				21 22			22 37	

Saturdays

	NT	TP	NT	NT	NT	NT	GC		NT	NT	TP	NT	NT	NT	TP		NT	NT	NT	TP	NT	NT	NT		TP
		■1 ◇					R ■1				■1 ◇				■1 ◇					■1 ◇					■1 ◇
		A					D H		B		J		B		A					A					A
Hexham 48 d										06 13											08g44				
MetroCentre 48 d																					09g15				
Newcastle 8 26 d		06h00		06 00	06h13	06h35			07h00	07 00		07j30	07 30	07h54			08 30	08h40	09j12		09 30	09j40	10h03		
Heworth d				06 07						07 07			07 37				08 37				09 37				
Sunderland a				06 19						07 19			07 49				08 49				09 49				
d				06 20			06 53			07 20			07 50				08 50				09 50				
Seaham d				06 28						07 28			07 58				08 58				09 58				
Hartlepool d				06a46			07 17			07 45			08 15				09 15				10 15				
Seaton Carew d										07 49			08 19				09 19				10 19				
Billingham d										07 56			08 26				09 26				10 26				
Stockton d										08 04			08 33				09 33				10 33				
Bishop Auckland d												07 35							09 23			09 53			
Shildon d												07 40							09 28			09 58			
Newton Aycliffe d												07 45							09 33			10 03			
Heighington d												07 48							09 36			10 06			
North Road d												07 57							09 45			10 15			
Chester-le-Street 26 d						06h31								07h42				08h33	09h21						
Durham 26 d		06h12			06h29	06h48			07h12			07h42		07h52				08h52	09h27			09h52			
Darlington 7 26 a												08 00							09 48			10 18			
d		06 36	06 40		06 58	07 19			07 38			08 09		09 00				09 23	09 51			10 20	10 47		
Dinsdale d			06 46			07 24						08 15		09 05				09 28	09 56						
Tees-side Airport d																						10 28			
Allens West d			06 53		07 08	07 31			07 49			08 22		09 12				09 35	10 03			10 33			
Eaglescliffe d			06 55		07 11	07 32	07a44		07 51			08 24		09 14				09 37	10 05			10 35			
Thornaby d		06 53	07 01		07 16	07 39			07 56	08 09	08 25	08 30	08 39	09 20	09 23		09 39	09 45	10 11	10 21	10 39	10 45	11 03		11 21
Middlesbrough a		07 01	07 09		07 21	07 44			08 02	08 20	08 32	08 36	08 48	09 25	09 32		09 48	09 52	10 16	10 30	10 48	10 52	11 08		11 30
d	06 40		07 10		07 22	07 45						08 36		09 27				09 54	10 20			10 54	11 14		
South Bank d						07 49						08 41													
British Steel Redcar § d																									
Redcar Central d	06 50		07 20		07 32	07 57						08 48		09 37				10 04	10 30			11 04	11 24		
Redcar East d	06 53		07 23		07 35	07 59						08 51		09 40				10 07	10 33			11 07	11 27		
Longbeck d	06 57		07 27		07 39	08 03						08 55		09 44				10 11	10 37			11 11	11 31		
Marske d	06 58		07 28		07 40	08 05						08 56		09 45				10 12	10 38			11 12	11 32		
Saltburn a	07 05		07 35		07 48	08 14						09 05		09 53				10 20	10 47			11 20	11 40		

For general notes see front of timetable
For details of catering facilities see Directory of Train Operators

- § For authorised access only to BSC Redcar
- A From Manchester Airport (Table 39)
- B To Nunthorpe (Table 45)
- C From Carlisle (Table 48)
- D To London Kings Cross (Table 26)
- E From Liverpool Lime Street (Table 39)
- G From Morpeth (Table 48)
- H **The Zephyr**
- J From York (Table 39)
- b From 8 September dep. 2 minutes earlier
- c From 8 September dep. 4 minutes earlier
- e Change at Darlington
- f From 8 September dep. Newcastle 1937, Chester-le-Street 1946
- g From 13 September dep. 1 minute earlier
- h Until 6 September only
- j Until 6 September only. Change at Darlington

For details of connecting services from Newcastle, Chester-le-Street and Durham via Darlington from 13 September, please refer to the re-issued Table 26 contained in the September supplement.

Newcastle, Sunderland, Bishop Auckland and Darlington → Middlesbrough and Saltburn

Network Diagram - see first page of Table 44

	NT	NT	TP	NT	NT	NT	GC		NT	TP	NT	NT	NT	TP	NT		NT	NT	TP	NT	NT	NT	TP		NT
			1◇				R 1			1◇				1◇					1◇				1◇		
	A		B				C			B				B	A				B				B		A
Hexham 48 d	09b44				10c44						11b44				12 44					13b44					14e44
MetroCentre 48 d	10 15				11c15						12c15				13 15					14c15					15 15
Newcastle 8 26 d	10 30	10f40		11g25	11 30	11f40			12f20		12 30	12f40	13g15		13 30		13f40	14f22		14 30	14f59	15g22			15 30
Heworth d	10 37				11 37						12 37				13 37					14 37					15 37
Sunderland a	10 49				11 49						12 49				13 49					14 49					15 50
d	10 50				11 50		12 30				12 50				13 50					14 50					15 50
Seaham d	10 58				11 58						12 58				13 58					14 58					15 58
Hartlepool d	11 15				12 15		12 54				13 15				14 15					15 15					16 15
Seaton Carew d	11 19				12 19						13 19				14 19					15 19					16 19
Billingham d	11 26				12 26						13 26				14 26					15 26					16 26
Stockton d	11 33				12 33						13 33				14 33					15 33					16 33
Bishop Auckland d				11 40									13 26									15 32			
Shildon d				11 45									13 31									15 37			
Newton Aycliffe d				11 50									13 36									15 42			
Heighington d				11 53									13 39									15 45			
North Road d				12 02									13 48									15 54			
Chester-le-Street 26 d		10f34							12f29									14f31				15f18			
Durham 26 d		10f52		11f37		11f52			12f36			12f52	13f27				13f52	14f38			14f52	15f34			
Darlington 7 26 a				12 06									13 51									15 58			
d		11 30		12 06		12 35			12 58			13 31	13 53				14 35	15 04			15 32	16 00			
Dinsdale d		11 35							13 03			13 36									15 37				
Tees-side Airport d																									
Allens West d		11 42				12 45			13 10			13 43	14 04				14 45	15 14			15 44				
Eaglescliffe d		11 44				12 48	13a12		13 12			13 45	14 06				14 48	15 17			15 46	16 12			
Thornaby d	11 39	11 50	12 19	12 25	12 39	12 53			13 18	13 21	13 39	13 52	14 13	14 19	14 39		14 53	15 22	15 27	15 39	15 52	16 17	16 21		16 39
Middlesbrough a	11 48	11 55	12 30	12 32	12 49	12 58			13 23	13 30	13 48	13 57	14 18	14 30	14 48		14 58	15 27	15 34	15 48	15 57	16 22	16 30		16 47
d		11 56		12 33		12 58			13 24			13 58	14 20				14 58	15 28			15 58	16 23			
South Bank d																						16 27			
British Steel Redcar § d																									
Redcar Central d		12 06		12 43		13 09			13 34			14 08	14 31				15 09	15 39			16 08	16 35			
Redcar East d		12 09		12 46		13 11			13 37			14 11	14 33				15 11	15 41			16 11	16 37			
Longbeck d		12 13		12 50		13 15			13 41			14 15	14 37				15 15	15 45			16 15	16 41			
Marske d		12 14		12 51		13 17			13 42			14 16	14 39				15 17	15 47			16 16	16 43			
Saltburn a		12 22		12 59		13 25			13 50			14 24	14 48				15 25	15 55			16 24	16 52			

	NT	NT	TP	NT	NT	NT	NT		GC	TP	NT	NT	TP	NT	NT		TP	NT	NT	NT	TP	NT	NT		
			1◇						R 1	1◇			1◇				1◇				1◇				
			B	A		D			C	E			B	A			B				B				
Hexham 48 d				15b44		16 16					16e44			17 42					18h44						
MetroCentre 48 d				16c15		16 40					17 15			18 13					19 17			20 15			
Newcastle 8 26 d	15f40	16f20		16 30	16g40	16 53	17f18				17 29	17g40		18 30	18g52			19f06	19 28	19f45		20 30	20g47		
Heworth d				16 37		17 00					17 37			18 37					19 36			20 37			
Sunderland a				16 49		17 13					17 50			18 49					19 50			20 49			
d				16 50		17 15			17 30		17 50			18 50					19 50			20 50			
Seaham d				16 58		17 22					17 58			18 58					19 58			20 58			
Hartlepool d				17 15		17 39			17 56		18 15			19 15					20 15			21 15			
Seaton Carew d				17 19		17 43					18 19			19 19					20 19			21 19			
Billingham d				17 26		17 50					18 26			19 26					20 26			21 26			
Stockton d				17 33		17 57					18 33			19 33					20 33			21 33			
Bishop Auckland d					17 00							18 00			18 59								21 17		
Shildon d					17 05							18 05			19 04								21 22		
Newton Aycliffe d					17 10							18 10			19 09								21 27		
Heighington d					17 13							18 13			19 12								21 30		
North Road d					17 22							18 22			19 21								21 39		
Chester-le-Street 26 d		16f29					17f27								18f49										
Durham 26 d	15f52	16f36			16f52		17f34					17f52			19f04					19f56			21f00		
Darlington 7 26 a					17 26							18 25			19 25								21 42		
d	16 27	17 04			17 27		18 00					18 30			19 27			20 07		20 30			21 44		
Dinsdale d					17 33		18 05											20 12					21 49		
Tees-side Airport d																									
Allens West d	16 37				17 40		18 12					18 41			19 38			20 19					21 56		
Eaglescliffe d	16 40	17 15			17 42		18 14		18a27			18 45			19 40			20 21		20 41			21 58		
Thornaby d	16 45	17 21	17 23	17 39	17 47	18 03	18 20			18 32	18 39	18 50	19 18	19 39	19 45		20 13	20 27	20 39	20 48	21 15	21 39	22 04		
Middlesbrough a	16 52	17 26	17 33	17 49	17 54	18 12	18 25			18 42	18 48	19 00	19 30	19 48	19 52		20 23	20 38	20 50	20 55	21 25	21 48	22 09		
d	16 54	17 28			17 54		18 25					19 01			19 54					20 55			22 09		
South Bank d					17 59																				
British Steel Redcar § d																									
Redcar Central d	17 04	17 38			18 06		18 36					19 11			20 04					21 05			22 20		
Redcar East d	17 07	17 41			18 09		18 38					19 14			20 07					21 08			22 22		
Longbeck d	17 11	17 45			18 13		18 42					19 18			20 11					21 12			22 26		
Marske d	17 12	17 46			18 14		18 44					19 19			20 12					21 13			22 28		
Saltburn a	17 20	17 54			18 23		18 52					19 28			20 21					21 22			22 37		

For general notes see front of timetable
For details of catering facilities see Directory of Train Operators

§ For authorised access only to BSC Redcar
A To Nunthorpe (Table 45)
B From Manchester Airport (Table 39)
C To London Kings Cross (Table 26)
D From Carlisle (Table 48)
E From Liverpool Lime Street (Table 39)
b From 13 September dep. 1 minute earlier
c From 13 September dep. 1 minute later
e From 13 September dep. 2 minutes earlier
f Until 6 September only
g Until 6 September only. Change at Darlington
h From 13 September dep. 1840

For details of connecting services from Newcastle, Chester-le-Street and Durham via Darlington from 13 September, please refer to the re-issued Table 26 contained in the September supplement.

Table 44

Sundays

Newcastle, Sunderland, Bishop Auckland and Darlington → Middlesbrough and Saltburn

Network Diagram - see first page of Table 44

	NT	NT	TP	TP	NT	NT	GC	NT	NT	NT	TP	TP	NT	NT	NT	NT	TP
			1 ◇	1 ◇			R 1				1 ◇	1 ◇					1 ◇
	A	B	C	D	A		E			A	G	H	J				K
Hexham 48 d																	
MetroCentre 48 d															10 48		
Newcastle 8 26 d		07b58						09 00	08c55	09 45			10 00	10e25	11 00	11b25	
Heworth d								09 07		09 52			10 07		11 06		
Sunderland a								09 22		10 05			10 21		11 22		
d							09 10			10 06			10 21				
Seaham d										10 14			10 29				
Hartlepool d							09 34			10 31			10 45				
Seaton Carew d										10 35			10 50				
Billingham d										10 42			10 57				
Stockton d										10 49			11 04				
Bishop Auckland d					08 40									10 29			
Shildon d					08 45									10 34			
Newton Aycliffe d					08 50									10 39			
Heighington d					08 54									10 42			
North Road d					09 02									10 51			
Chester-le-Street 26 d														09b42			
Durham 26 d		08b10							09c07					10b37		11b37	
Darlington 7 26 a					09 05									10 54			
d	08 18	08 41			09 07	09 20			09 56					11 04		12 02	
Dinsdale d	08 23	08 46			09 12	09 25								11 09			
Tees-side Airport d																	
Allens West d	08 30	08 53			09 19	09 32								11 16			
Eaglescliffe d	08 32	08 55			09 21	09 34	09a54		10 07					11 18		12 13	
Thornaby d	08 38	09 01	09 03	09 22	09 31	09 43			10 13	10 55	10 58	11 00	11 09	11 24		12 19	12 58
Middlesbrough a	08 44	09 06	09 14	09 35	09 39	09 49			10 18	11 03	11 10	11 12	11 17	11 29		12 24	13 10
d		09 07				09 50			10 22					11 30		12 25	
South Bank d																	
British Steel Redcar § d																	
Redcar Central d		09 17				10 00			10 33					11 41		12 35	
Redcar East d		09 20				10 03			10 35					11 43		12 38	
Longbeck d		09 24				10 07			10 39					11 47		12 42	
Marske d		09 25				10 08			10 41					11 49		12 43	
Saltburn a		09 32				10 15			10 48					11 57		12 50	

	NT	NT	NT	NT	NT	GC	TP	TP	NT	NT	NT	NT	NT	NT	NT	TP	NT
						R 1	1 ◇	1 ◇								1 ◇	
						E	L	N		A						Q	
Hexham 48 d																	
MetroCentre 48 d	11 48		12 48						13 48			14 48					15 48
Newcastle 8 26 d	12 00	12e25	13 00	13b32					14 00	14b32		15 00	15b01	15f30			16 00
Heworth d	12 06		13 06						14 06			15 06					16 06
Sunderland a	12 21		13 22						14 21			15 22					16 21
d	12 21					13 42			14 21								16 21
Seaham d	12 29								14 29								16 29
Hartlepool d	12 45				13 30	14 06			14 45						16 22		16 45
Seaton Carew d	12 50				13 34				14 50						16 26		16 50
Billingham d	12 57				13 41				14 57						16 33		16 57
Stockton d	13 04				13 48				15 04						16 40		17 04
Bishop Auckland d		12 40									14 49						
Shildon d		12 45									14 54						
Newton Aycliffe d		12 50									14 59						
Heighington d		12 53									15 02						
North Road d		13 02									15 11						
Chester-le-Street 26 d				12g58													
Durham 26 d		12b37		13b45						14b37			15b15	15f37			
Darlington 7 26 a		13 05			14 14						15 14				17 01		
d		13 07		14 10						15 06	15 16		15 42	16 19			
Dinsdale d		13 15									15 21						
Tees-side Airport d																	
Allens West d		13 22									15 28						
Eaglescliffe d		13 24		14 21		14a33					15 30		15 53	16 30			
Thornaby d	13 09	13 30		14 27			14 57	14 58	15 09	15 22	15 36		15 59	16 36		17 11	17 17
Middlesbrough a	13 20	13 35		14 32			15 10	15 10	15 20	15 27	15 41		16 04	16 41		17 22	17 25
d		13 35		14 33							15 42		16 05	16 45			
South Bank d																	
British Steel Redcar § d																	
Redcar Central d		13 46		14 43							15 52		16 15	16 55			
Redcar East d		13 48		14 46							15 55		16 18	16 58			
Longbeck d		13 52		14 50							15 59		16 22	17 02			
Marske d		13 54		14 51							16 00		16 23	17 03			
Saltburn a		14 02		14 58							16 08		16 30	17 11			

For general notes see front of timetable
For details of catering facilities see Directory of Train Operators

§ For authorised access only to BSC Redcar
A Until 14 September. To Whitby (Table 45)
B Until 14 September
C From 14 September. From Leeds (Table 39)
D Until 7 September. From Manchester Airport (Table 39)
E To London Kings Cross (Table 26)
G Until 7 September and from 9 November. From Manchester Airport (20 July to 7 September from York) (Table 39)
H 14 September to 2 November. From Manchester Airport (Table 39)
J From 21 September
K From Manchester Airport (20 July to 7 September from Liverpool Lime Street) (Table 39)
L Until 13 July. From Manchester Airport (Table 39)
N From 20 July. From Manchester Airport (20 July to 7 September from Liverpool Lime Street) (Table 39)
Q Until 13 July and from 14 September. From Manchester Piccadilly (from 9 November from Leeds) (Table 39)
b Until 7 September only
c Until 7 September only. From 20 July dep. Newcastle 0910, Durham 0924
e Until 7 September only. Change at Darlington
f Until 7 September only. From 20 July dep. Newcastle 1536, Durham 1549
g Until 7 September only. 20 July to 7 September dep. 1249

For details of connecting services from Newcastle, Chester-le-Street and Durham via Darlington from 14 September, please refer to the re-issued Table 26 contained in the September supplement.

Newcastle, Sunderland, Bishop Auckland and Darlington → Middlesbrough and Saltburn

Network Diagram - see first page of Table 44

	NT	TP	NT	NT	TP	TP	NT	NT	GC	NT	NT	NT	NT	TP	TP	NT	NT	NT
		1 ◇			1 ◇	1 ◇			R 1					1 ◇	1 ◇			
		A			B	C			D			E	G	B	C			
									🍴									
Hexham 48 d																		
MetroCentre 48 d	16 48							17 48		18 48								
Newcastle 8 26 ⛴ d	17 00		16b33	17c30				18 00		19 00	18e57		19f35			20 00	21 06	21e40
Heworth ⛴ d	17 06							18 06		19 06						20 07		
Sunderland ⛴ a	17 22							18 21		19 22						20 21		
d								18 21	18 42							20 21		
Seaham d								18 29								20 29		
Hartlepool d								18 45	19 06							20 45		
Seaton Carew d								18 50								20 50		
Billingham d								18 57								20 57		
Stockton d								19 04								21 04		
Bishop Auckland d			16 56				18 49						19 55					
Shildon d			17 01				18 54						20 00					
Newton Aycliffe d			17 06				18 59						20 05					
Heighington d			17 09				19 02						20 08					
North Road d			17 18				19 11						20 17					
Chester-le-Street 26 d			16g49	16c57													21 15	
Durham 26 d			16b46	17c37							19e10		19e48				21 24	21e53
Darlington 7 26 a			17 23				19 16						20 20				21 44	
d			17 24	18 31							19 36	20 30	20 30				21 45	22 45
Dinsdale d			17 30								19 41	20 35	20 35					
Tees-side Airport d																		
Allens West d			17 37								19 48	20 42	20 42					
Eaglescliffe d			17 39	18 42					19a24		19 50	20 44	20 44				21 57	22 56
Thornaby d		17 35	17 44	18 48	18 49	18 58		19 11			19 56	20 50	20 50	20 51	21 01	21 08	22 02	23 02
Middlesbrough a		17 43	17 49	18 53	19 00	19 10		19 20			20 01	20 55	20 55	21 02	21 10	21 20	22 07	23 10
d			17 50	18 54							20 02	20 56	20 56				22 08	
South Bank d																		
British Steel Redcar § d																		
Redcar Central d			18 01	19 04							20 12	21 06	21 06				22 18	
Redcar East d			18 03	19 07							20 15	21 09	21 09				22 21	
Longbeck d			18 07	19 11							20 19	21 13	21 13				22 25	
Marske d			18 09	19 12							20 20	21 14	21 14				22 26	
Saltburn a			18 17	19 19							20 27	21 21	21 22				22 34	

For general notes see front of timetable
For details of catering facilities see Directory of Train Operators

§ For authorised access only to BSC Redcar
A 20 July to 7 September. From Manchester Piccadilly (Table 39)
B 20 July to 7 September. From Liverpool Lime Street (Table 39)
C Until 13 July and from 14 September. From Manchester Airport (Table 39)
D To London Kings Cross (Table 26)
E From 21 September
G Until 14 September
b Until 7 September only. Change at Darlington. From 20 July dep. Newcastle 1640, Durham 1656
c Until 7 September only. From 20 July dep. Newcastle 1750, Chester-le-Street 1649, Durham 1803
e Until 7 September only
f Until 7 September only. Change at Darlington
g 20 July to 7 September only

For details of connecting services from Newcastle, Chester-le-Street and Durham via Darlington from 14 September, please refer to the re-issued Table 26 contained in the September supplement.

Saltburn and Middlesbrough → Darlington, Bishop Auckland, Sunderland and Newcastle

Network Diagram - see first page of Table 44

Miles	Miles			NT	TP	NT	NT	NT	NT	TP	NT	NT	NT		NT	NT	NT	TP	NT	NT	TP	NT	NT	GC		NT
					1 ◇					1 ◇								1 ◇			1 ◇			R 1		
					A				B	A	C							A	C		A			D ✕		
0	—	**Saltburn**	d					06 24				07 17	07 38		08 02		08 30			09 21		10 00				10 30
2	—	Marske	d					06 28				07 21	07 42		08 06		08 34			09 25		10 04				10 34
2½	—	Longbeck	d					06 31				07 24	07 45		08 09		08 37			09 28		10 07				10 37
4	—	Redcar East	d					06 34				07 27	07 48		08 12		08 40			09 31		10 10				10 40
5	—	**Redcar Central**	d					06 37				07 30	07 51		08 15		08 43			09 34		10 13				10 43
6¾	—	British Steel Redcar §	d																							
10	—	South Bank	d														08 50									
12½	0	**Middlesbrough**	a					06 47				07 40	08 01		08 25		08 55			09 45		10 23				10 53
—	—		d	05 45	05 58			06 49	06 56	07 23	07 32	07 42	08 02		08 26	08 32	08 56	09 00	09 32	09 46	09 59	10 24	10 32			10 54
15¾	3¼	Thornaby	d	05 50	06a03			06 54	07 02	07a28	07 37	07 47	08 07		08 31	08 37	09 01	09a04	09 37	09 51	10a04	10 29	10 37			10 59
18¾	—	Eaglescliffe	d	05 55				06 59				07 52	08 13		08 37		09 07			09 57		10 35		10 58		
19½	—	Allens West	d	05 58				07 02				07 55	08 15				09 09			09 59		10 37				
22	—	Tees-side Airport	d																							
23¾	—	Dinsdale	d					07 08				08 01	08 22									10 44				
27½	—	**Darlington** 7	a	06 14				07 19				08 11	08 31		08 53		09 24			10 17		10 53				11 19
—	—		26 d	06 14			06 47	07 20				08 15	08 33				09 26					10 55				
—	—	Durham	26 a	06 35				07 41				08 35	08 56		09 20		09 53			10 50		11 17				11 43
—	—	Chester-le-Street	26 a	06 42				07 48				08 43	09 02		09 44		10 40			10 56						
28¾	—	North Road	d				06 50						08 36				09 29					10 58				
33¼	—	Heighington	d				06 58						08 44				09 37					11 06				
34½	—	Newton Aycliffe	d				07 02						08 48				09 40					11 10				
36¾	—	Shildon	d				07 06						08 52				09 45					11 14				
39½	—	**Bishop Auckland**	a				07 18						08 59				09 52					11 21				
—	5½	Stockton	d						07 08		07 43					08 43			09 43				10 43			
—	10	Billingham	d						07 15		07 50					08 50			09 50				10 50			
—	15	Seaton Carew	d						07 21		07 56					08 56			09 56				10 56			
—	17¼	**Hartlepool**	d			07 03			07 27		08 02					09 02			10 02				11 02	11b23		
—	30	Seaham	d			07 18			07 42		08 17					09 17			10 17				11 17			
—	35¼	**Sunderland**	⛴ a			07 28			07 53		08 28					09 28			10 28				11 28	11 50		
—	—		d			07 30			07 55		08 30					09 30			10 30				11 30			
—	44½	Heworth	⛴ d			07 41			08 06		08 41					09 42			10 42				11 42			
—	47¼	**Newcastle** 8	26 ⛴ a	06 55		07 51		08 00	08 16		08 51	08 59	09c22		09 38	09 52	10c02		10 52	11 10		11c32	11 52			11 59
—	—	MetroCentre	48 a			08 03			08 31		09 01								11 01				12 01			
—	—	Hexham	48 a			08 40			08e58		09f37								11f36				12f36			

		TP	NT	NT	NT	TP	NT	NT	TP	NT	NT		NT	TP	NT	GC	NT	NT	TP	NT	NT	NT		TP	NT	NT
		1 ◇				1 ◇			1 ◇					1 ◇		R 1			1 ◇					1 ◇		
		A				A		E	A					A		D ✕			G			C		A		
Saltburn	d		11 00		11 30		12 00			12 30	13 00				13 30		14 00			14 30	15 03				15 30	16 00
Marske	d		11 04		11 34		12 04			12 34	13 04				13 34		14 04			14 35	15 07				15 34	16 04
Longbeck	d		11 07		11 37		12 07			12 37	13 07				13 37		14 07			14 38	15 10				15 37	16 07
Redcar East	d		11 10		11 40		12 10			12 40	13 10				13 40		14 10			14 41	15 13				15 40	16 10
Redcar Central	d		11 13		11 43		12 13			12 43	13 13				13 43		14 13			14 44	15 16				15 43	16 13
British Steel Redcar §	d																									
South Bank	d																									
Middlesbrough	a		11 23		11 55		12 23			12 56	13 24				13 54		14 23			14 54	15 26				15 54	16 23
	d	11 00	11 24	11 32	11 55	12 00	12 24	12 32	12 50	12 57	13 25		13 32	13 50	13 55		14 24	14 32	14 50	14 55	15 27	15 32		15 50	15 55	16 24
Thornaby	d	11a05	11 30	11 37	12 00	12a05	12 29	12 37	12a55	13 02	13 30		13 37	13a55	14 00		14 29	14 37	14a55	15 00	15 32	15 37		15a55	16 00	16 29
Eaglescliffe	d		11 35				12 35				13 35					14 05	14 35				15 37				16 05	16 35
Allens West	d		11 38				12 37				13 38						14 37				15 40				16 08	16 37
Tees-side Airport	d																									
Dinsdale	d						12 44				13 44										15 46				16 14	
Darlington 7	a		11 52		12 19		12 53			13 22	13 54				14 21		14 52			15 20	15 56				16 24	16 52
	26 d						12 55										14 54				15 57					
Durham	26 a		12 22		12 50		13 18			13 48	14 18				14 50		15 15			15 51	16 24				17 08	17 31
Chester-le-Street	26 a		12 50							13 54	14 41									15 57	16 36					
North Road	d						12 58										14 57				16 01					
Heighington	d						13 06										15 05				16 09					
Newton Aycliffe	d						13 10										15 09				16 12					
Shildon	d						13 14										15 13				16 16					
Bishop Auckland	a						13 21										15 19				16 24					
Stockton	d			11 43				12 43					13 43					14 43				15 43				
Billingham	d			11 50				12 50					13 50					14 50				15 50				
Seaton Carew	d			11 56				12 56					13 56					14 56				15 56				
Hartlepool	d			12 02				13 02					14 02			14 24		15 02				16 02				
Seaham	d			12 17				13 17					14 17					15 17				16 17				
Sunderland	⛴ a			12 29				13 28					14 28			14 50		15 28				16 27				
	d			12 30				13 30					14 30					15 30				16 30				
Heworth	⛴ d			12 42				13 42					14 42					15 42				16 42				
Newcastle 8	26 ⛴ a		12 36	12 51	12 55		13c33	13 51		14 09	14 36		14 51		15 06		15c31	15 51		15 57	16c37	16 51			17 26	17 27
MetroCentre	48 a			13 01				14 01					15 01					16 01				17 01				
Hexham	48 a			13f36				14f36					15f36					16 36				17 36				

For general notes see front of timetable
For details of catering facilities see Directory of Train Operators

§ For authorised access only to BSC Redcar
A To Manchester Airport (Table 39)
B To Carlisle (Table 48)
C From Nunthorpe (Table 45)
D From London Kings Cross (Table 26)
E Until 5 September
G To Manchester Piccadilly (Table 39)
b Arr. 1120
c Change at Darlington
e From 8 September arr. 0901
f From 8 September arr. 2 minutes later

Saltburn and Middlesbrough → Darlington, Bishop Auckland, Sunderland and Newcastle

Network Diagram - see first page of Table 44

		NT	TP	NT	NT	NT	TP	NT	NT	NT	NT	TP	NT	GC	NT	NT	TP	NT	TP	NT	TP	NT	NT
			1 ◇				1 ◇					1 ◇		R 1			1 ◇		1 ◇		1 ◇		
		A	B				C					D		E G ✕			C	H	B		D		
Saltburn	d			16 30	17 00			17 30	18 00		18 30				19 00	19 30				20 30		21 30	22 40
Marske	d			16 34	17 04			17 34	18 04		18 34				19 04	19 34				20 34		21 34	22 44
Longbeck	d			16 37	17 07			17 37	18 07		18 37				19 07	19 37				20 37		21 37	22 47
Redcar East	d			16 40	17 10			17 40	18 10		18 40				19 10	19 40				20 40		21 40	22 50
Redcar Central	d			16 43	17 13			17 43	18 13		18 43				19 13	19 43				20 43		21 43	22 53
British Steel Redcar §	d			16 46																			
South Bank	d			16 52																			
Middlesbrough	a			16 57	17 23			17 53	18 23		18 53				19 23	19 54				20 54		21 54	23 03
	d	16 32	16 50	16 57	17 24	17 32	17 50	17 55	18 24	18 30	18 54	19 00	19 20		19 25	19 55	20 00	20 30	20 50	20 55	21 40	21 55	23 05
Thornaby	d	16 37	16a55	17 02	17 29	17 37	17a55	18 00	18 29	18 35	18 59	19a05	19 25		19 30	20 00	20 06	20 35	20a55	21 00	21 45	22 00	23 10
Eaglescliffe	d			17 08	17 35			18 05			19 05			19 34	19 35	20 05				21 06		22 05	
Allens West	d			17 10	17 37			18 08			19 07				19 38	20 08				21 08		22 08	
Tees-side Airport	d																						
Dinsdale	d			17 17	17 44			18 14			19 14				19 44					21 15		22 14	
Darlington 7	a			17 26	17 54			18 24	18 49		19 29				19 56	20 25	20 29			21 24	22 04	22 28	23 31
26	d			17 28				18 32								20 30							
Durham 26	a			17 55	18 20				19 15		20 10				20 20	21 09				21 49	22 35	23 00	00 07
Chester-le-Street 26	a			18 01	18 40				19 56						20 37	21 45					22 45		
North Road	d			17 31				18 35								20 33							
Heighington	d			17 39				18 43								20 41							
Newton Aycliffe	d			17 43				18 47								20 45							
Shildon	d			17 47				18 51								20 49							
Bishop Auckland	a			17 55				18 58								20 56							
Stockton	d	16 44				17 43				18 41			19 31					20 41					
Billingham	d	16 51				17 50				18 48			19 38					20 48					
Seaton Carew	d	16 57				17 56				18 54			19 44					20 54					
Hartlepool	d	17 03				18 02				19 00			19 49	20b08				21 00					
Seaham	d	17 18				18 18				19 15			20c10					21 15					
Sunderland ⛴	a	17 29				18 28				19 26			20 20	20 35				21 26					
	d	17 30				18 30				19 27			20 27					21 27					
Heworth ⛴	d	17 42				18 42				19 38			20 38					21 38					
Newcastle 8 26 ⛴	a	17 51		18e15	18 36	18 53			19 33	19 47	20 26		20 47		20 36	21e27		21 47		22 07	22 59	23 21	00 40
MetroCentre 48	a	18 01								19 57													
Hexham 48	a	18 31																					

Saturdays

		NT	TP	NT	NT	NT	NT	TP	NT	NT	NT	NT	NT	NT	TP	NT	NT	TP	NT	NT	GC	NT	TP
			1 ◇					1 ◇							1 ◇			1 ◇			R 1		1 ◇
			C				A	C	H						C	H		C		J	E 🅿		C
Saltburn	d					06 24				07 17	07 40	08 00		08 30			09 13		10 00			10 30	
Marske	d					06 28				07 21	07 44	08 04		08 34			09 17		10 04			10 34	
Longbeck	d					06 31				07 24	07 47	08 07		08 37			09 20		10 07			10 37	
Redcar East	d					06 34				07 27	07 50	08 10		08 40			09 23		10 10			10 40	
Redcar Central	d					06 37				07 30	07 53	08 13		08 43			09 26		10 13			10 43	
British Steel Redcar §	d																						
South Bank	d													08 50									
Middlesbrough	a					06 47				07 40	08 03	08 23		08 55			09 36		10 23			10 54	
	d	05 50	05 58			06 49	06 56	07 21	07 32	07 42	08 05	08 25	08 32	08 55	09 00	09 32	09 39	10 00	10 24	10 32		10 55	11 00
Thornaby	d	05 55	06a03			06 54	07 02	07a26	07 37	07 47	08 10	08 30	08 37	09 00	09a05	09 37	09 44	10a05	10 29	10 37		11 00	11a05
Eaglescliffe	d	06 00				07 01				07 56	08 12	08 35		09 06			09 49		10 34		10 49		
Allens West	d	06 03				07 03				07 59	08 15			09 08			09 52		10 37				
Tees-side Airport	d																						
Dinsdale	d					07 10				08 07	08 21								10 43				
Darlington 7	a	06 18				07 20				08 14	08 37	08 51		09 22			10 06		10 54			11 19	
26	d				06 48	07 20				08 16	08 38			09 24					10 57				
Durham 26	a	07f33				07 40				08 36	09f09	09f18		09f46			10f30		11f17			11f43	
Chester-le-Street 26	a					07 48				08 44		09f43					10f37						
North Road	d				06 51						08 42			09 27					11 00				
Heighington	d				06 59						08 50			09 35					11 08				
Newton Aycliffe	d				07 02						08 53			09 39					11 12				
Shildon	d				07 07						08 57			09 43					11 16				
Bishop Auckland	a				07 19						09 04			09 50					11 23				
Stockton	d						07 08		07 43				08 43			09 43				10 43			
Billingham	d						07 15		07 50				08 50			09 50				10 50			
Seaton Carew	d						07 21		07 56				08 56			09 56				10 56			
Hartlepool	d			07 03			07 27		08 02				09 02			10 02				11 02	11 21		
Seaham	d			07 18			07 42		08 17				09 17			10 17				11 17			
Sunderland ⛴	a			07 28			07 53		08 30				09 28			10 28				11 28	11 50		
	d			07 30			07 55		08 30				09 30			10 30				11 30			
Heworth ⛴	d			07 42			08 07		08 42				09 42			10 42				11 42			
Newcastle 8 26 ⛴	a	07f50		07 53		08 00	08 17		08 53	08 55	09g25	09f34	09 54	10g02		10 52	10f54		11g32	11 52		11f59	
MetroCentre 48	a			08 03			08 31		09 02							11 01				12 01			
Hexham 48	a			08 40			08h58		09h38							11j36				12k36			

For general notes see front of timetable
For details of catering facilities see Directory of Train Operators

§ For authorised access only to BSC Redcar
A To Carlisle (Table 48)
B To Manchester Piccadilly (Table 39)
C To Manchester Airport (Table 39)
D To York (Table 39)
E From London Kings Cross (Table 26)
G **The 21st Century Limited**
H From Nunthorpe (Table 45)
J Until 6 September
b Arr. 2000
c Arr. 2005
e Change at Darlington
f Until 6 September only
g Until 6 September only. Change at Darlington
h From 13 September arr. 2 minutes later
j From 13 September arr. 1140
k From 13 September arr. 3 minutes later

For details of connecting services via Darlington to Durham, Chester-le-Street and Newcastle from 13 September, please refer to the re-issued Table 26 contained in the September supplement.

Table 44

Saturdays

Saltburn and Middlesbrough → Darlington, Bishop Auckland, Sunderland and Newcastle

Network Diagram - see first page of Table 44

		NT	NT	NT	TP 1◇ A	NT	NT B	TP 1◇ A		NT	NT	NT	NT	TP 1◇ A	GC R 1 C	NT		NT	TP 1◇ D	NT	NT	NT B	TP 1◇ A	NT		NT
Saltburn	d	11 00		11 30		11 56				12 30	13 00		13 30			13 58				14 30	15 00			15 30		16 00
Marske	d	11 04		11 34		12 00				12 34	13 04		13 34			14 02				14 34	15 04			15 34		16 04
Longbeck	d	11 07		11 37		12 03				12 37	13 07		13 37			14 05				14 37	15 07			15 37		16 07
Redcar East	d	11 10		11 40		12 06				12 40	13 10		13 40			14 08				14 40	15 10			15 40		16 10
Redcar Central	d	11 13		11 43		12 09				12 43	13 13		13 43			14 11				14 43	15 13			15 43		16 13
British Steel Redcar §	d																									
South Bank	d																									
Middlesbrough	a	11 23		11 54		12 19				12 54	13 23		13 53			14 21				14 54	15 23			15 53		16 23
	d	11 24	11 32	11 55	12 00	12 20	12 32	12 50		12 55	13 24	13 32	13 55	14 00		14 23		14 32	14 50	14 55	15 27	15 32	15 50	15 55		16 24
Thornaby	d	11 29	11 37	12 00	12a05	12 25	12 37	12a55		13 00	13 29	13 37	14 00	14a05		14 28		14 37	14a55	15 00	15 32	15 37	15a55	16 00		16 29
Eaglescliffe	d	11 35				12 30					13 34				14 27	14 33					15 37			16 05		16 34
Allens West	d	11 37				12 33					13 37					14 36					15 40			16 08		16 37
Tees-side Airport	d										13 41															
Dinsdale	d					12 39					13 45										15 46			16 14		
Darlington 7	a	11 51		12 20		12 49				13 21	13 55		14 20			14 50				15 20	15 55			16 24		16 51
	26 d					12 50										14 53								16 25		
Durham	26 a	12b18		12b44		13b18				13b51	14b19		14b51			15b16				15b45	16b17					17b21
Chester-le-Street	26 a	12b40								13b57	14b42									15b57						17b36
North Road	d					12 54										14 57								16 28		
Heighington	d					13 02										15 05								16 37		
Newton Aycliffe	d					13 05										15 08								16 40		
Shildon	d					13 09										15 12								16 44		
Bishop Auckland	a					13 16										15 20								16 52		
Stockton	d		11 43				12 43					13 43						14 43				15 43				
Billingham	d		11 50				12 50					13 50						14 50				15 50				
Seaton Carew	d		11 56				12 56					13 56						14 56				15 56				
Hartlepool	d		12 02				13 02					14 02			14 46			15 02				16 02				
Seaham	d		12 17				13 17					14 17						15 17				16 17				
Sunderland 🚇	a		12 29				13 28					14 28			15 14			15 28				16 27				
	d		12 30				13 30					14 30						15 30				16 30				
Heworth 🚇	d		12 42				13 42					14 42						15 42				16 42				
Newcastle 8	26 🚇 a	12b35	12 52	13b00		13c34	13 52			14b12	14b34	14 51	15b10			15c32		15 52		16b01	16b33	16 52				17b40
MetroCentre	48 a		13 01				14 01					15 01						16 01				17 01				
Hexham	48 a		13e36				14 36					15e36						16 36				17 36				

		NT E	NT	TP 1◇ D	NT	NT B	NT	TP 1◇ A		NT	NT	NT	TP 1◇ G	NT	NT	GC R 1 C H	NT	TP 1◇ A	NT B	TP 1◇ D	NT	TP 1◇ J	NT	NT
Saltburn	d		16 30		16 59		17 28			18 00		18 28			19 00		19 35				20 30		21 30	22 40
Marske	d		16 34		17 03		17 32			18 04		18 32			19 04		19 39				20 34		21 34	22 44
Longbeck	d		16 37		17 06		17 35			18 07		18 35			19 07		19 42				20 37		21 37	22 47
Redcar East	d		16 40		17 09		17 38			18 10		18 38			19 10		19 45				20 40		21 40	22 50
Redcar Central	d		16 43		17 12		17 41			18 13		18 41			19 13		19 48				20 43		21 43	22 53
British Steel Redcar §	d																							
South Bank	d				17 19																			
Middlesbrough	a		16 54		17 24		17 55			18 23		18 51			19 23		19 58				20 54		21 53	23 04
	d	16 32	16 55	17 00	17 25	17 30	17 56	18 07		18 24	18 30	18 53	19 00	19 20	19 25		19 59	20 10	20 30	20 50	20 55	21 50	21 55	23 05
Thornaby	d	16 37	17 00	17a05	17 30	17 35	18 01	18a12		18 29	18 35	18 58	19a05	19 25	19 30		20 04	20a15	20 35	20a55	21 00	21 55	22 00	23 10
Eaglescliffe	d		17 05		17 35		18 06					19 03			19 35	19 50	20 10				21 06		22 05	
Allens West	d		17 08		17 38		18 09					19 06			19 38		20 12				21 08		22 08	
Tees-side Airport	d																							
Dinsdale	d		17 14				18 15					19 12			19 44		20 19				21 15		22 14	
Darlington 7	a		17 24		17 52		18 25			18 49		19 23			19 54		20 28				21 24	22 15	22 24	23 30
	26 d		17 30				18 26										20 36							
Durham	26 a		17b56		18b20					19b16		19b50			20b22		21b22				21b56	22b42	23b25	
Chester-le-Street	26 a		18b02		18b38							19b56			20b41		22b18							
North Road	d		17 34				18 30										20 39							
Heighington	d		17 42				18 38										20 47							
Newton Aycliffe	d		17 45				18 41										20 51							
Shildon	d		17 49				18 45										20 55							
Bishop Auckland	a		17 57				18 53										21 02							
Stockton	d	16 43				17 41					18 41			19 31					20 41					
Billingham	d	16 50				17 48					18 48			19 38					20 48					
Seaton Carew	d	16 56				17 54					18 54			19 44					20 54					
Hartlepool	d	17 02				18 02					19 00			19 49		20 09			21 00					
Seaham	d	17 17				18 18					19 15			20f10					21 15					
Sunderland 🚇	a	17 27				18 28					19 26			20 20		20 35			21 26					
	d	17 30				18 30					19 27			20 27					21 27					
Heworth 🚇	d	17 42				18 42					19 38			20 38					21 38					
Newcastle 8	26 🚇 a	17 52	18c17		18b40	18 53	19c05			19b32	19 48	20b10		20 48	20b37		21c42		21 48		22b14	23b07	23b46	
MetroCentre	48 a	18 01									19 58													
Hexham	48 a	18 32																						

For general notes see front of timetable
For details of catering facilities see Directory of Train Operators

§ For authorised access only to BSC Redcar
A To Manchester Airport (Table 39)
B From Nunthorpe (Table 45)
C From London Kings Cross (Table 26)
D To Manchester Piccadilly (Table 39)
E To Carlisle (Table 48)
G To York (Table 39)
H **The 21st Century Limited**
J To Manchester Airport (from 13 September to Leeds) (Table 39)
b Until 6 September only
c Until 6 September only. Change at Darlington
e From 13 September arr. 3 minutes later
f Arr. 2005

For details of connecting services via Darlington to Durham, Chester-le-Street and Newcastle from 13 September, please refer to the re-issued Table 26 contained in the September supplement.

Table 44

Sundays

Saltburn and Middlesbrough → Darlington, Bishop Auckland, Sunderland and Newcastle

Network Diagram - see first page of Table 44

		NT	NT	NT	NT	NT	NT	NT	TP	NT	NT	NT	NT	GC	GC	NT	TP	NT
									1 ◇					R 1	R 1		1 ◇	
		A					A	B	C					D	E		G	
Saltburn	d						09 36			10 28		11 00						12 01
Marske	d						09 40			10 32		11 04						12 05
Longbeck	d						09 43			10 35		11 07						12 08
Redcar East	d						09 46			10 38		11 10						12 11
Redcar Central	d						09 49			10 41		11 13						12 14
British Steel Redcar §	d																	
South Bank	d																	
Middlesbrough	a						09 59			10 51		11 23						12 24
	d		08 45		09 15	09 30	10 00	10 00	10 15	10 53		11 24	11 30				12 15	12 25
Thornaby	d		08 50		09 20	09 35	10 05	10 05	10a20	10 58		11 29	11 35				12a20	12 30
Eaglescliffe	d		08 55		09 25		10 10	10 10		11 03		11 34		11 32	12 02			12 36
Allens West	d		08 58		09 28							11 37						
Tees-side Airport	d																	
Dinsdale	d				09 34							11 43						
Darlington 7	a		09 12		09 49		10 28	10 28		11 22		11 54						12 53
	26 d	08 05			09 51							11 55				12 20		
Durham	26 a		*09b50*		*10c13*		*10b53*			*11b54*		*12e19*						*13f33*
Chester-le-Street	26 a						*11b25*											*14b07*
North Road	d	08 08			09 54							11 58						
Heighington	d	08 16			10 02							12 07						
Newton Aycliffe	d	08 19			10 05							12 10						
Shildon	d	08 24			10 10							12 14						
Bishop Auckland	a	08 34			10 20							12 20						
Stockton	d					09 41							11 41			12 36		
Billingham	d					09 48							11 48			12 43		
Seaton Carew	d					09 54							11 54			12 49		
Hartlepool	d					10 00							12 00	12g09	12g31	12a57		
Seaham	d					10 15							12 15					
Sunderland	⛴ a					10 26							12 26	12 44	12 56			
	d			09 28		10 28					11 28		12 28					
Heworth	⛴ d			09 39		10 39					11 39		12 39					
Newcastle 8	26 ⛴ a		*10b06*	09 48	*10h31*	10 48	*11b09*			*12b10*	11 48	*12j36*	12 48					*13b41*
MetroCentre	48 a			10 01		10 59					11 57		12 59					
Hexham	48 a																	

For general notes see front of timetable
For details of catering facilities see Directory of Train Operators

- § For authorised access only to BSC Redcar
- **A** Until 14 September
- **B** From 21 September
- **C** To Manchester Airport (20 July to 7 September to Liverpool Lime Street) (Table 39)
- **D** Until 7 September. From London Kings Cross (Table 26)
- **E** From 14 September. From London Kings Cross (Table 26)
- **G** To Manchester Airport (20 July to 7 September to Manchester Piccadilly) (Table 39)
- **b** Until 7 September only
- **c** 20 July to 7 September only
- **e** Until 7 September only. (From 20 July arr. 1221)
- **f** Until 7 September only. From 20 July arr. 1353
- **g** Arr. 11 minutes earlier
- **h** 20 July to 7 September only. Change at Darlington
- **j** Until 7 September only. Change at Darlington

For details of connecting services via Darlington to Durham, Chester-le-Street and Newcastle from 14 September, please refer to the re-issued Table 26 contained in the September supplement.

Saltburn and Middlesbrough → Darlington, Bishop Auckland, Sunderland and Newcastle

Network Diagram - see first page of Table 44

		NT	NT	NT	TP	TP	NT	NT	NT	NT	TP	NT	TP	NT	GC	NT	NT	NT
					1 ◇ A	1 ◇ B					1 ◇ A		1 ◇ C		R 1 D			E
Saltburn	d		13 00				14 14					15 20				16 21	16 48	
Marske	d		13 04				14 18					15 24				16 25	16 52	
Longbeck	d		13 07				14 21					15 27				16 28	16 55	
Redcar East	d		13 10				14 24					15 30				16 31	16 58	
Redcar Central	d		13 13				14 27					15 33				16 34	17 01	
British Steel Redcar §	d																	
South Bank	d																	
Middlesbrough	a		13 23				14 37					15 48				16 44	17 11	
	d		13 25	13 30	13 45	14 15	14 38		15 30		15 45	15 50	16 10			16 45	17 14	17 25
Thornaby	d		13 30	13 35	13a50	14a20	14 43		15 35		15a50	15 55	16a15			16 50	17 19	17 30
Eaglescliffe	d		13 35				14 49					16 00			16 40	16 56	17 25	17 37
Allens West	d		13 38									16 03						17 40
Tees-side Airport	d																	
Dinsdale	d		13 45									16 09						17 50
Darlington 7	a		13 54				15 06					16 20				17 11	17 31	18 05
	26 d		14 09							15 37		16 22						18 15
Durham	26 a		14b29				15c30					16e58				18f01	18g18	18h33
Chester-le-Street	26 a															18h07		
North Road	d		14 12									16 25						18 18
Heighington	d		14 20									16 33						18 26
Newton Aycliffe	d		14 23									16 36						18 29
Shildon	d		14 28									16 41						18 34
Bishop Auckland	a		14 33									16 46						18 39
Stockton	d			13 41					15 41	15 53								
Billingham	d			13 48					15 48	16 00								
Seaton Carew	d			13 54					15 54	16 06								
Hartlepool	d			14 00					16 00	16a14					17j10			
Seaham	d			14 15					16 15									
Sunderland	a			14 26					16 26						17 36			
	d	13 28		14 28				15 28	16 28					17 28				
Heworth	d	13 39		14 39				15 39	16 39					17 39				
Newcastle 8	26 a	13 49	14k44	14 48			15c46	15 48	16 48			17m04		17 48		18f02	18g34	18m52
MetroCentre	48 a	13 59		14 59				15 59	16 57					17 59				
Hexham	48 a																	

		NT	TP	NT	NT	TP	NT	NT	NT	NT	NT	TP	TP	NT	NT	TP	NT
			1 ◇ A	G	H	1 ◇ C	E			J		1 ◇ K	1 ◇ L			1 ◇ N	
Saltburn	d			17 20	17 20			18 27			19 23			20 31	21 30		22 38
Marske	d			17 24	17 24			18 31			19 27			20 35	21 34		22 42
Longbeck	d			17 27	17 27			18 34			19 30			20 38	21 37		22 45
Redcar East	d			17 30	17 30			18 37			19 33			20 41	21 40		22 48
Redcar Central	d			17 33	17 33			18 40			19 36			20 44	21 43		22 51
British Steel Redcar §	d																
South Bank	d																
Middlesbrough	a			17 48	17 48			18 52			19 46			20 54	21 53		23 01
	d	17 30	17 45	17 49	17 49	17 55	18 48	18 53		19 30	19 47	19 55	20 15	20 55	21 55	22 07	23 02
Thornaby	d	17 35	17a50	17 54	17 54	18a00	18 53	18 58		19 35	19 52	20a00	20a20	21 00	22 00	22a12	23 07
Eaglescliffe	d			17 59	17 59		18 59				19 58			21 06	22 05		23 12
Allens West	d			18 02	18 02		19 02				20 00				22 08		
Tees-side Airport	d																
Dinsdale	d			18 08	18 08		19 08				20 07				22 14		
Darlington 7	a			18 18	18 18		19 16	19 25			20 17			21 23	22 26		23 30
	26 d				18 20		19 21										
Durham	26 a			19n18				19h53			21q20			22h06			
Chester-le-Street	26 a							20h05									
North Road	d				18 23		19 24										
Heighington	d				18 31		19 32										
Newton Aycliffe	d				18 34		19 35										
Shildon	d				18 39		19 40										
Bishop Auckland	a				18 44		19 45										
Stockton	d	17 41								19 41							
Billingham	d	17 48								19 48							
Seaton Carew	d	17 54								19 54							
Hartlepool	d	18 00								20 00							
Seaham	d	18 15								20 15							
Sunderland	a	18 26								20 25							
	d	18 28							19 28	20 28							
Heworth	d	18 39							19 39	20 39							
Newcastle 8	26 a	18 48		19h05				20h09	19 52	20 49	21h06			22h02			
MetroCentre	48 a	18 59															
Hexham	48 a																

For general notes see front of timetable
For details of catering facilities see Directory of Train Operators

§ For authorised access only to BSC Redcar
A Until 13 July and from 14 September. To Liverpool Lime Street (Table 39)
B 20 July to 7 September. To Liverpool Lime Street (Table 39)
C 20 July to 7 September. To York (Table 39)
D From London Kings Cross (Table 26)
E Until 14 September. From Whitby (Table 45)
G Until 14 September
H From 21 September
J Until 14 September from Whitby (Table 45)
K 20 July to 7 September. To Manchester Airport (Table 39)
L Until 13 July and from 14 September. To Manchester Airport (Table 39)
N To Manchester Airport (Table 39)
b Until 7 September only. From 20 July arr. 1430
c Until 7 September only. From 20 July arr. 5 minutes later
e Until 7 September only. 20 July to 7 September arr. 1643
f Until 7 September only. From 20 July arr. Durham 1739, Newcastle 1800
g Until 13 July only
h Until 7 September only
j Arr. 1658
k Until 7 September only. Change at Darlington. From 20 July arr. 1446
m Until 7 September only. Change at Darlington
n Until 7 September only. From 20 July arr. 1929
q Until 7 September only. 20 July to 7 September arr. 2045

For details of connecting services via Darlington to Durham, Chester-le-Street and Newcastle from 14 September, please refer to the re-issued Table 26 contained in the September supplement.

Middlesbrough and Pickering → Whitby

Network Diagram - see first page of Table 44

Mondays to Fridays

Miles			NT	NT A	NT	NY MFX B 🍴	NT	NT C	NY MFX B 🍴	NT	NT C	NT C	NY MFX B 🍴	NT	NT C	NT C
—	Newcastle 8	44 d	06b00	*07 00*	07 30		09b12	10 30		12b40	13 30	15 30		16b06	16 30	18 30
—	Darlington 7	44 d	*06 36*	07 48	*08 10*		*09 53*	*11 00*		*13 30*	*14 08*	*15 57*		*16 59*	*17 15*	*18 33*
0	**Middlesbrough**	d	07 08	08 13	08 49		10 38	11 49		14 16	14 49	16 47		17 40	17 54	19 49
3	Marton	d	07 13	08 18	08 54		10 43	11 54		14 21	14 54	16 52		17 45	17 59	19 54
4	Gypsy Lane	d	07 16	08 21	08 58		10 46	11 57		14 24	14 57	16 55		17 48	18 02	19 57
4½	Nunthorpe	d	07 19	08a28	09a01		10 49	12a01		14 27	15a03	16a59		17 51	18a08	20a03
8½	Great Ayton	d	07 25				10 55			14 33				17 57		
11	Battersby	a	07 31				11 01			14 39				18 03		
—		d	07 39				11 05			14 43				18 07		
12¾	Kildale	d	07 44				11 10			14 48				18 12		
16¾	Commondale	d	07 51				11 17			14 55				18 19		
18½	Castleton Moor	d	07 55				11 20			14 58				18 22		
20	Danby	d	07 58				11 23			15 01				18 25		
23½	Lealholm	d	08 05				11 30			15 08				18 32		
25½	Glaisdale	a	08 10				11 34			15 12				18 36		
—		d	08 12				11 37			15 15				18 39		
27¼	Egton	d	08 16				11 40			15 18				18 42		
—	**Pickering §**	d														
—	Goathland §	d														
28¾	Grosmont	d	08 20			10 10	11 44		13 10	15 22			17 10	18 46		
32	Sleighs	d	08 29				11 53			15 31				18 55		
33½	Ruswarp	d	08 34				11 58			15 36				19 00		
35	**Whitby**	a	08 41			10 35	12 05		13 35	15 43			17 35	19 07		

Saturdays

		NT	NT	NT	NY D 🍴	NT	NT C	NY D 🍴	NT	NT C	NT C	NY D 🍴	NT	NT C	NT C
Newcastle 8	44 d			07 30			10 30			13 30	15 30			16 30	18 30
Darlington 7	44 d	*06 36*	07 38	*08 09*		*09 51*	*10 47*		*13 31*	*13 53*	*16 00*		*17 04*		*18 30*
Middlesbrough	d	07 06	08 04	08 49		10 38	11 49		14 12	14 49	16 47		17 38	17 50	19 48
Marton	d	07 11	08 09	08 54		10 43	11 54		14 17	14 54	16 52		17 43	17 55	19 53
Gypsy Lane	d	07 14	08 12	08 58		10 46	11 57		14 20	14 57	16 55		17 46	17 58	19 56
Nunthorpe	d	07 17	08a18	09a01		10 49	12a01		14 23	15a01	16a59		17 49	18a01	20a01
Great Ayton	d	07 23				10 55			14 29				17 55		
Battersby	a	07 29				11 01			14 35				18 01		
	d	07 33				11 05			14 39				18 05		
Kildale	d	07 38				11 10			14 44				18 10		
Commondale	d	07 45				11 17			14 51				18 17		
Castleton Moor	d	07 49				11 20			14 54				18 20		
Danby	d	07 52				11 23			14 57				18 23		
Lealholm	d	07 59				11 30			15 04				18 30		
Glaisdale	a	08 04				11 34			15 08				18 34		
	d	08 06				11 37			15 11				18 37		
Egton	d	08 10				11 40			15 14				18 40		
Pickering §	d														
Goathland §	d														
Grosmont	d	08 14			10 10	11 44		13 10	15 18			17 10	18 44		
Sleighs	d	08 23				11 53			15 27				18 53		
Ruswarp	d	08 28				11 58			15 32				18 58		
Whitby	a	08 35			10 35	12 05		13 35	15 39			17 35	19 05		

Sundays

until 14 September

		NT	NT A	NT	NT	NT
Newcastle 8	44 d			09 45		
Darlington 7	44 d	08 18	09 07	*09 56*	*13 07*	15 06
Middlesbrough	d	08 47	09 45	11 06	14 17	15 29
Marton	d	08 52	09 50	11 11	14 22	15 34
Gypsy Lane	d	08 55	09 53	11 14	14 25	15 37
Nunthorpe	d	08 58	09 56	11 17	14 28	15 40
Great Ayton	d	09 04	10 02	11 24	14 34	15 46
Battersby	a	09 10	10 08	11 29	14 40	15 52
	d	09 14	10 12	11 34	14 44	15 56
Kildale	d	09 19	10 17	11 38	14 49	16 01
Commondale	d	09 26	10 24	11 45	14 56	16 08
Castleton Moor	d	09 29	10 27	11 49	14 59	16 11
Danby	d	09 32	10 30	11 52	15 02	16 14
Lealholm	d	09 39	10 37	11 58	15 09	16 21
Glaisdale	a	09 43	10 41	12 03	15 13	16 25
	d	09 46	10 50	12 05	15 16	16 30
Egton	d	09 49	10 53	12 09	15 19	16 33
Pickering §	d					
Goathland §	d					
Grosmont	d	09 53	10 57	12 13	15 23	16 37
Sleighs	d	10 02	11 06	12 22	15 32	16 46
Ruswarp	d	10 07	11 11	12 26	15 37	16 51
Whitby	a	10 14	11 18	12 33	15 44	16 58

For general notes see front of timetable
For details of catering facilities see Directory of Train Operators

§ North Yorkshire Moors Railway. For full service between Pickering, Goathland and Grosmont, please refer to separate publicity.

A From Bishop Auckland (Table 44)
B Until 23 October
C From Hexham (Table 48)
D Until 27 September, 11 October and 1 November
b Change at Darlington and Middlesbrough

Table 45

Sundays

from 21 September

Middlesbrough and Pickering → Whitby

Network Diagram - see first page of Table 44

		NY A	NY A	NY A
Newcastle 8	44 d			
Darlington 7	44 d			
Middlesbrough	d			
Marton	d			
Gypsy Lane	d			
Nunthorpe	d			
Great Ayton	d			
Battersby	a			
	d			
Kildale	d			
Commondale	d			
Castleton Moor	d			
Danby	d			
Lealholm	d			
Glaisdale	a			
	d			
Egton	d			
Pickering §	d			
Goathland §	d			
Grosmont	d	10 10	13 10	17 10
Sleights	d			
Ruswarp	d			
Whitby	a	10 35	13 35	17 35

For general notes see front of timetable
For details of catering facilities see
Directory of Train Operators

§ North Yorkshire Moors Railway. For full service between Pickering, Goathland and Grosmont, please refer to separate publicity.

A 28 September to 2 November and 7 December

No Sunday service operated by Northern Trains

Whitby → Pickering and Middlesbrough

Network Diagram - see first page of Table 44

Mondays to Fridays

Miles			NT A	NT	NT A	NT	NY MFX B	NT A	NT	NY MFX B	NT A	NT	NT	NY MFX B	NT	NT	NT
0	**Whitby**	d				08 52	11 00		12 41	14 00			16 05	18 00			19 15
1½	Ruswarp	d				08 56			12 45				16 09				19 19
3	Sleights	d				09 01			12 50				16 14				19 24
6¼	Grosmont	d				09 09	11a20		12 58	14a20			16 22	18a20			19 32
—	Goathland §	a															
—	**Pickering §**	a															
7¾	Egton	d				09 12			13 01				16 26				19 35
9½	Glaisdale	a				09 16			13 05				16 30				19 39
—		d				09 19			13 08				16 33				19 42
11½	Lealholm	d				09 24			13 13				16 38				19 47
15	Danby	d				09 30			13 19				16 45				19 53
16½	Castleton Moor	d				09 33			13 22				16 49				19 56
18¼	Commondale	d				09 37			13 26				16 52				20 00
22¼	Kildale	d				09 44			13 33				16 59				20 07
24	Battersby	a				09 49			13 38				17 04				20 12
—		d				09 53			13 42				17 09				20 16
26½	Great Ayton	d				09 58			13 47				17 14				20 21
30½	Nunthorpe	d	07 19	08 30	09 16	10 05		12 16	13 54		15 16	17 02	17 21		18 24	20 14	20 28
31	Gypsy Lane	d	07 21	08 32	09 18	10 07		12 18	13 56		15 18	17 04	17 23		18 26	20 16	20 30
32	Marton	d	07 23	08 34	09 21	10 10		12 21	13 59		15 21	17 06	17 25		18 29	20 19	20 33
35	**Middlesbrough**	a	07 29	08 43	09 27	10 18		12 28	14 07		15 30	17 13	17 35		18 35	20 25	20 39
—	Darlington 7	44 a	08 11	09 24	10 17	10 53		13 22	14 52		16 24	17 54	18 24		19 29		21 24
—	Newcastle 8	44 a	08 51	10b02	10 52	11b32		13 51	15b31		16 51	18b36	19b33		20b26	21 47	22b07

Saturdays

		NT A	NT	NT A	NT	NY C	NT A	NT	NY C	NT A	NT	NT	NY C	NT	NT	NT
Whitby	d				08 45	11 00		12 41	14 00		15 50		18 00			19 15
Ruswarp	d				08 49			12 45			15 54					19 19
Sleights	d				08 54			12 50			15 59					19 24
Grosmont	d				09 02	11a20		12 58	14a20		16 07		18a20			19 32
Goathland §	a															
Pickering §	a															
Egton	d				09 05			13 01			16 10					19 35
Glaisdale	a				09 09			13 05			16 14					19 39
	d				09 12			13 08			16 17					19 42
Lealholm	d				09 17			13 13			16 22					19 47
Danby	d				09 23			13 19			16 28					19 53
Castleton Moor	d				09 26			13 22			16 31					19 56
Commondale	d				09 30			13 26			16 35					20 00
Kildale	d				09 37			13 33			16 42					20 07
Battersby	a				09 42			13 38			16 47					20 12
	d				09 46			13 42			16 51					20 16
Great Ayton	d				09 51			13 47			16 56					20 21
Nunthorpe	d	07 19	08 26	09 16	09 58		12 16	13 54		15 16	17 03	17 16		18 24	20 14	20 28
Gypsy Lane	d	07 21	08 28	09 18	10 00		12 18	13 56		15 18	17 05	17 18		18 26	20 16	20 30
Marton	d	07 23	08 30	09 21	10 03		12 21	13 59		15 21	17 08	17 20		18 29	20 19	20 33
Middlesbrough	a	07 29	08 39	09 27	10 11		12 27	14 07		15 30	17 16	17 29		18 35	20 25	20 41
Darlington 7	44 a	08 14	09 22	10 06	10 54		13 21	14 50		16 24	17 52	18 25		19 23		21 24
Newcastle 8	44 a	08 53		10 52			13 52			16 52		18 53			21 48	

Sundays

until 14 September

		NT	NT	NT D	NT D	NT
Whitby	d	10 24	12 43	15 57	17 20	18 00
Ruswarp	d	10 28	12 47	16 01	17 24	18 04
Sleights	d	10 33	12 52	16 06	17 29	18 09
Grosmont	d	10 41	13 00	16 14	17 37	18 17
Goathland §	a					
Pickering §	a					
Egton	d	10 44	13 03	16 17	17 40	18 20
Glaisdale	a	10 48	13 07	16 21	17 44	18 24
	d	10 53	13 10	16 26	17 47	18 27
Lealholm	d	10 58	13 15	16 31	17 52	18 32
Danby	d	11 04	13 21	16 37	17 58	18 38
Castleton Moor	d	11 07	13 24	16 40	18 01	18 41
Commondale	d	11 11	13 28	16 44	18 05	18 45
Kildale	d	11 18	13 35	16 51	18 12	18 52
Battersby	a	11 23	13 40	16 56	18 17	18 57
	d	11 37	13 44	17 00	18 21	19 01
Great Ayton	d	11 42	13 49	17 05	18 26	19 06
Nunthorpe	d	11 49	13 56	17 12	18 33	19 13
Gypsy Lane	d	11 51	13 58	17 14	18 35	19 15
Marton	d	11 53	14 01	17 17	18 38	19 18
Middlesbrough	a	12 02	14 09	17 25	18 46	19 28
Darlington 7	44 a	12 53	15 06	18 05	19 16	20 17
Newcastle 8	44 a					20 49

For general notes see front of timetable
For details of catering facilities see Directory of Train Operators

§ North Yorkshire Moors Railway. For full service between Grosmont, Goathland and Pickering, please refer to separate publicity.

A To Hexham (Table 48)
B Until 23 October
C Until 27 September, 11 October and 1 November
D To Bishop Auckland (Table 44)
b Change at Middlesbrough and Darlington

Table 45

Sundays

from 21 September

Whitby → Pickering and Middlesbrough

Network Diagram - see first page of Table 44

		NY A ⊡	NY A ⊡	NY A ⊡
Whitby	d	11 00	14 00	18 00
Ruswarp	d	}	}	}
Sleights	d	}	}	}
Grosmont	d	11a20	14a20	18a20
Goathland §	a			
Pickering §	a			
Egton	d			
Glaisdale	a			
	d			
Lealholm	d			
Danby	d			
Castleton Moor	d			
Commondale	d			
Kildale	d			
Battersby	a			
	d			
Great Ayton	d			
Nunthorpe	d			
Gypsy Lane	d			
Marton	d			
Middlesbrough	a			
Darlington 7 44	a			
Newcastle 8 44	a			

For general notes see front of timetable
For details of catering facilities see Directory of Train Operators

§ North Yorkshire Moors Railway. For full service between Grosmont, Goathland and Pickering, please refer to separate publicity.

A 28 September to 2 November and 7 December

No Sunday service operated by Northern Trains

Chathill and Morpeth → Newcastle → MetroCentre, Hexham and Carlisle

Network Diagram - see first page of Table 44

Miles	Miles			NT	NT	GR	NT	NT	NT	NT		NT	NT	NT	NT	NT	NT	NT		NT	NT	XC	NT	NT	NT
					A	R 1 B ✕	C	D		E								E				R 1 G		D	
0	—	**Chathill**	d						07 22																
11¼	—	Alnmouth	26 d			07 03			07 34													11 04			
17½	—	Acklington	d						07 42																
22¾	—	Widdrington	d						07 49																
27½	—	Pegswood	d						07 55																
29½	—	**Morpeth**	26 d			07 19			08 00			08 32			09 32					10 50		11 18			11 50
36¼	—	Cramlington	d						08 08			08 40			09 41					10 58					11 58
45½	—	Manors	d						08 21			08 53													
46	—	**Newcastle** 8	26 a			07 38			08 25			08 57			09 55					11 14		11 35			12 13
—	—	Sunderland	44 d				07 30	07 55		08 30					*09 30*			10 30						11 30	
—	—	London Kings Cross 15	⊖ 26 d												*06 15*	*07 00*		*07 30*		*08 00*				*08 30*	*09 01*
—	0	**Newcastle** 8	d	06 30	06 54		07 56	08 24		08 54			09 24	09 44	10 00	10 24	10 44	10 54		11 14	11 24		11 44	11 54	12 14
48½	2¼	Dunston	d												10 05										
49½	3½	**MetroCentre**	a				08 03	08 31		09 01			09 31	09 51	10 08	10 32	10 52	11 01		11 21	11 32		11 53	12 01	12 22
—	—		d				08 04	08 32		09 02			09 32		10 09	10 33		11 02			11 33			12 02	
—	5½	Blaydon	d				08 08			09 05															
—	9¾	Wylam	d	06 44			08 14	08 40		09 12					10 17			11 10						12 10	
—	12	Prudhoe	d	06 48			08 18	08 44		09 15			09 42		10 21	10 43		11 14			11 43			12 14	
—	14½	Stocksfield	d	06 53			08 23	08 48		09 20					10 25			11 18						12 18	
—	16¾	Riding Mill	d	06 57			08 27			09 24					10 30			11 23						12 23	
—	19¼	Corbridge	d	07 01			08 31			09 28					10 33			11 26						12 26	
—	22¼	**Hexham**	a	07 10	07 20		08 40	08 58		09 37			09 55		10 42	10 56		11 36			11 56			12 36	
—	—		d		07 20			08 59					09 55			10 56					11 56				
—	30	Haydon Bridge	d		07 29			09 08													12 05				
—	33¾	Bardon Mill	d		07 36			09 14													12 12				
—	38¼	Haltwhistle	d		07 43			09 21					10 14			11 15					12 19				
—	50¾	Brampton (Cumbria)	d		07 58			09 37													12 34				
—	57¼	Wetheral	d		08 07			09 45													12 43				
—	61¾	**Carlisle** 8	a		08 17			09 56					10 44			11 46					12 53				

		NT	NT	NT		NT	NT	NT	XC	NT	NT	NT		NT	NT	NT	NT	NT	XC	NT		NT	NT	NT	NT
			H			D			R 1 J		E					D			1 ◇ J			D		K	
Chathill	d																								
Alnmouth	26 d								13 06										15 04						
Acklington	d																								
Widdrington	d																								
Pegswood	d																								
Morpeth	26 d						12 50		13 23			13 50					14 50		15 20				15 50		
Cramlington	d						12 58					13 58					14 58						15 58		
Manors	d						13 11					14 10													
Newcastle 8	26 a						13 13		13 40			14 13					15 13		15 38				16 13		
Sunderland	44 d					12 30					13 30					14 30						15 30			
London Kings Cross 15	⊖ 26 d						*10 00*			*10 30*		*11 00*					*12 00*						*13 00*		*13 30*
Newcastle 8	d	12 24	12 39	12 44		12 54	13 14	13 24		13 44	13 54	14 14		14 24	14 44	14 54	15 14	15 24		15 44		15 54	16 14	16 24	16 44
Dunston	d																								
MetroCentre	a	12 32	12 46	12 52		13 01	13 22	13 31		13 51	14 01	14 22		14 31	14 52	15 01	15 21	15 32		15 51		16 01	16 21	16 31	16 51
	d		12 46			13 02		13 32			14 02			14 32		15 02		15 32				16 02		16 32	
Blaydon	d																								
Wylam	d					13 10					14 10			14 40		15 10						16 10		16 40	
Prudhoe	d					13 14		13 42			14 14			14 44		15 14						16 14		16 44	
Stocksfield	d					13 18					14 18					15 18						16 18		16 48	
Riding Mill	d					13 23					14 23					15 23						16 23		16 53	
Corbridge	d					13 26					14 26					15 26						16 26		16 56	
Hexham	a		13 06			13 36		13 55			14 36			14 56		15 36		15 54				16 36		17 02	
	d		13 08					13 55						14 57				15 54						17 03	
Haydon Bridge	d																	16 04						17 12	
Bardon Mill	d																	16 10							
Haltwhistle	d		13 26					14 14						15 16				16 17						17 23	
Brampton (Cumbria)	d																	16 33							
Wetheral	d																	16 42							
Carlisle 8	a		13 59					14 45						15 47				16 53						17 55	

For general notes see front of timetable
For details of catering facilities see Directory of Train Operators

A To Glasgow Central (Table 216)
B From Edinburgh to London Kings Cross (Table 26)
C From Hartlepool (Table 44)
D From Middlesbrough (Table 44)
E From Nunthorpe (Table 45)
G From Glasgow Central (Table 51) to Penzance (Table 135)
H To Stranraer (Table 216)
J From Edinburgh to Plymouth (Table 51)
K To Whitehaven (Table 100)

Mondays to Fridays

until 5 September

Chathill and Morpeth → Newcastle → MetroCentre, Hexham and Carlisle

Network Diagram - see first page of Table 44

		NT	NT	NT	NT	XC		NT	NT	NT	NT	NT	NT	NT		NT	GR	NT	NT	NT	NT	NT	GR	
						1 ◇											R 1						R 1	
		A		B		C		D						D			E				G		H	
Chathill	d															19 08								
Alnmouth	26 d					17 08										19 20	19 42						22 07	
Acklington	d															19 28								
Widdrington	d															19 35								
Pegswood	d															19 41								
Morpeth	26 d		16 50			17 23					18 32		19 01			19 45	19 59				21 34		22 24	
Cramlington	d		16 58								18 40		19 09			19 54					21 42			
Manors	d																							
Newcastle 8	26 a		17 12			17 38					18 55		19 25			20 06	20 20				21 56		22 45	
Sunderland	44 d	16 30						17 30				*18 30*		19 27				*20 27*		*21 27*				
London Kings Cross 15	⊖ 26 d			*14 00*				*15 00*				*16 00*				*17 00*		*17 30*	*18 00*	*18 20*		*19 00*		
Newcastle 8	d	16 54		17 13	17 26			17 54	18 01	18 24		19 10		19 50		20 10		20 55	21 10	21 55		22 30		
Dunston	d								18 07															
MetroCentre	a	17 01		17 20	17 33			18 01	18 10	18 31		19 17		19 57		20 17		21 03	21 17	22 04		22 37		
	d	17 02		17 20	17 34			18 01		18 32		19 18				20 18			21 18			22 38		
Blaydon	d				17 39																			
Wylam	d	17 10		17 29	17 46			18 09		18 40		19 26				20 26			21 26			22 46		
Prudhoe	d	17 14		17 32	17 49			18 13		18 44		19 30				20 30			21 30			22 50		
Stocksfield	d	17 18			17 54			18 18		18 48		19 34				20 34			21 34			22 54		
Riding Mill	d	17 23			17 58			18 22		18 53		19 39				20 39			21 39			22 59		
Corbridge	d	17 26			18 02			18 26		18 56		19 42				20 42			21 42			23 02		
Hexham	a	17 36		17 45	18 10			18 31		19 02		19 48				20 51			21 48			23 11		
	d			17 45				18 31		19 03		19 49							21 49					
Haydon Bridge	d			17 54				18 40				19 58							21 58					
Bardon Mill	d			18 01				18 47											22 04					
Haltwhistle	d			18 08				18 54		19 21		20 09							22 11					
Brampton (Cumbria)	d			18 23						19 37									22 27					
Wetheral	d			18 32						19 45									22 35					
Carlisle 8	a			18 45				19 28		19 57		20 42							22 46					

Mondays to Fridays

from 8 September

		NT	NT	GR	NT	NT	NT		NT	NT	NT	NT	NT	NT		NT	NT	NT	NT	XC	NT		NT	NT	NT
				R 1																1 ◇					
			J	K	L	D			A								A			N			D		
Chathill	d						07 22																		
Alnmouth	26 d			07 03			07 34													11 04					
Acklington	d						07 42																		
Widdrington	d						07 49																		
Pegswood	d						07 55																		
Morpeth	26 d			07 19			08 00			08 32			09 32					10 50		11 18				11 50	
Cramlington	d						08 08			08 40			09 41					10 58						11 58	
Manors	d						08 21			08 53															
Newcastle 8	26 a			07 38			08 25			08 57			09 55					11 14		11 35				12 13	
Sunderland	44 d				07 30	07 55			08 30				*09 30*				10 30						11 30		
London Kings Cross 15	⊖ 26 d												*06 15*	*07 00*			*07 30*	*08 00*					*08 30*	*09 00*	
Newcastle 8	d	06 24	06 49		07 56	08 24			08 54		09 24	09 44	10 00	10 24		10 44	10 54	11 14	11 24		11 44		11 54	12 14	12 24
Dunston	d												10 05												
MetroCentre	a				08 03	08 31			09 01		09 31	09 51	10 08	10 31		10 52	11 01	11 21	11 32		11 53		12 01	12 22	12 32
	d				08 04	08 32			09 02		09 32		10 09	10 32			11 02		11 33				12 02		
Blaydon	d				08 08				09 05																
Wylam	d	06 38			08 14	08 40			09 12				10 17				11 10						12 10		
Prudhoe	d	06 42			08 18	08 44			09 15				10 21	10 42			11 14		11 43				12 14		
Stocksfield	d	06 47			08 23	08 48			09 20				10 25				11 18						12 18		
Riding Mill	d	06 51			08 27				09 24				10 30				11 23						12 23		
Corbridge	d	06 55			08 31				09 28				10 33				11 26						12 26		
Hexham	a	07 06	07 16		08 40	09 01			09 39		09 53		10 42	10 55			11 38		11 58				12 38		
	d		07 16			09 02					09 54			10 55					11 59						
Haydon Bridge	d		07 25			09 11													12 08						
Bardon Mill	d		07 32			09 17													12 14						
Haltwhistle	d		07 39			09 24					10 12			11 14					12 21						
Brampton (Cumbria)	d		07 54			09 40													12 37						
Wetheral	d		08 03			09 48													12 46						
Carlisle 8	a		08 16			10 00					10 45			11 46					12 56						

For general notes see front of timetable
For details of catering facilities see Directory of Train Operators

A From Nunthorpe (Table 45)
B To Stranraer (Table 216)
C From Edinburgh to Bristol Temple Meads (Table 51)
D From Middlesbrough (Table 44)
E From Edinburgh (Table 26)
G To Middlesbrough (Table 44)
H From Glasgow Central to York (Table 26)
J To Glasgow Central (Table 216)
K From Edinburgh to London Kings Cross (Table 26)
L From Hartlepool (Table 44)
N From Glasgow Central to Plymouth (Table 51)

Chathill and Morpeth → Newcastle → MetroCentre, Hexham and Carlisle

Network Diagram - see first page of Table 44

	NT A	NT	NT B	NT	NT		XC R 1 C ⊡	NT	NT D	NT	NT	NT		NT B	NT	NT	XC R 1 E ⊡	NT	NT B		NT	NT G	NT	NT D
Chathill d																								
Alnmouth 26 d							13 02										15 04							
Acklington d																								
Widdrington d																								
Pegswood d																								
Morpeth 26 d				12 50			13 19			13 50					14 50		15 20				15 50			
Cramlington d				12 58						13 58					14 58						15 58			
Manors d				13 11						14 10														
Newcastle 8 26 ⛴ a				13 13			13 40			14 13					15 13		15 38				16 13			
Sunderland 44 ⛴ d			12 30						13 30					14 30					15 30					16 30
London Kings Cross 15 ⊖ 26 d				*10 00*				*10 30*		*11 00*					*12 00*						*13 00*		*13 30*	
Newcastle 8 ⛴ d	12 39	12 44	12 54	13 14	13 24			13 44	13 54	14 14	14 24	14 44		14 54	15 14	15 24		15 44	15 54		16 14	16 24	16 44	16 54
Dunston d																								
MetroCentre a	12 46	12 52	13 01	13 22	13 31			13 51	14 01	14 22	14 31	14 52		15 01	15 21	15 32		15 51	16 01		16 21	16 31	16 51	17 01
d	12 46		13 02		13 32				14 02		14 32			15 02		15 32			16 02			16 32		17 02
Blaydon d																								
Wylam d			13 10						14 10		14 40			15 10					16 10			16 40		17 10
Prudhoe d			13 14		13 42				14 14		14 44			15 14					16 14			16 44		17 14
Stocksfield d			13 18						14 18					15 18					16 18			16 48		17 18
Riding Mill d			13 23						14 23					15 23					16 23			16 53		17 23
Corbridge d			13 26						14 26					15 26					16 26			16 56		17 26
Hexham a	13 06		13 38		13 56				14 38		14 56			15 38		15 54			16 36			17 02		17 36
d	13 08				13 57						14 57					15 54						17 03		
Haydon Bridge d																16 04						17 12		
Bardon Mill d																16 10								
Haltwhistle d	13 26				14 15						15 16					16 17						17 23		
Brampton (Cumbria) d																16 33								
Wetheral d																16 42								
Carlisle 8 a	13 59				14 55						15 47					16 53						17 55		

	NT	NT A	NT	XC 1 ◇ H ⊡		NT B	NT	NT	NT	NT	NT		NT B	NT	GR R 1 J ⊡	NT	NT	NT		NT K	NT	GR R 1 L ⊡		
Chathill d														19 08										
Alnmouth 26 d				17 08										19 20	19 42							22 07		
Acklington d														19 28										
Widdrington d														19 35										
Pegswood d														19 41										
Morpeth 26 d	16 50			17 23					18 32		19 01			19 45	19 59					21 34		22 24		
Cramlington d	16 58								18 40		19 09			19 54						21 42				
Manors d																								
Newcastle 8 26 ⛴ a	17 12			17 38					18 55		19 25			20 06	20 20					21 56		22 45		
Sunderland 44 ⛴ d						17 30				*18 30*			19 27			*20 27*		*21 27*						
London Kings Cross 15 ⊖ 26 d		*14 00*				*15 00*				*16 00*				*17 00*		*17 30*	*18 00*	*18 20*			*19 00*			
Newcastle 8 ⛴ d		17 13	17 26			17 54	18 01	18 24		19 10			19 50	20 10		20 55	21 06	21 55			22 26			
Dunston d							18 07																	
MetroCentre a		17 20	17 33			18 01	18 10	18 31		19 17			19 57	20 17		21 03	21 13	22 04			22 33			
d		17 20	17 34			18 01		18 32		19 18				20 18			21 14				22 34			
Blaydon d			17 39																					
Wylam d		17 29	17 46			18 09		18 40		19 26				20 26			21 22				22 42			
Prudhoe d		17 32	17 49			18 13		18 44		19 30				20 30			21 26				22 46			
Stocksfield d			17 54			18 18		18 48		19 34				20 34			21 30				22 50			
Riding Mill d			17 58			18 22		18 53		19 39				20 39			21 35				22 55			
Corbridge d			18 02			18 26		18 56		19 42				20 42			21 38				22 58			
Hexham a		17 45	18 14			18 31		19 04		19 48				20 53			21 45				23 09			
d		17 45				18 31		19 05		19 49							21 46							
Haydon Bridge d		17 54				18 40				19 58							21 55							
Bardon Mill d		18 01				18 47											22 01							
Haltwhistle d		18 08				18 54		19 23		20 09							22 08							
Brampton (Cumbria) d		18 23						19 39									22 24							
Wetheral d		18 32						19 47									22 32							
Carlisle 8 a		18 45				19 28		19 59		20 42							22 45							

For general notes see front of timetable
For details of catering facilities see Directory of Train Operators

A To Stranraer (Table 216)

B From Middlesbrough (Table 44)

C From Edinburgh to Cardiff Central (Table 51)

D From Nunthorpe (Table 45)

E From Edinburgh to Bristol Temple Meads (Table 51)

G To Whitehaven (Table 100)

H From Edinburgh to Birmingham New Street (Table 51)

J From Edinburgh (Table 26)

K To Middlesbrough (Table 44)

L From Glasgow Central to York (Table 26)

Table 48

Saturdays

until 6 September

Chathill and Morpeth → Newcastle → MetroCentre, Hexham and Carlisle

Network Diagram - see first page of Table 44

		NT	GR	NT	NT		NT	NT	NT	NT		NT	NT	NT	NT		NT	NT	XC	NT		NT	NT	NT	NT
			R 1																R 1						
		A	B	C	D			E							E				G			D			H
Chathill	d						07 22																		
Alnmouth	26 d		07 19				07 34												11 04						
Acklington	d						07 42																		
Widdrington	d						07 49																		
Pegswood	d						07 55																		
Morpeth	26 d		07 35				08 00					09 32					10 50		11 18				11 50		
Cramlington	d						08 08					09 40					10 58						11 58		
Manors	d						08 21																		
Newcastle 8	26 a		07 53				08 25					09 55					11 14		11 35				12 13		
Sunderland	44 d			07 30	07 55			08 30					*09 30*		10 30							11 30			
London Kings Cross 15	⊖ 26 d									*06 15*			*07 00*				*08 00*					*08 30*	*09 00*		
Newcastle 8	d	06 34		07 56	08 24			08 54	09 24	09 44		10 00	10 24	10 44	10 54		11 14	11 22		11 44		11 54	12 14	12 24	12 39
Dunston	d											10 05													
MetroCentre	a			08 03	08 31			09 02	09 31	09 51		10 08	10 31	10 53	11 01		11 21	11 32		11 52		12 01	12 22	12 31	12 46
	d			08 04	08 32			09 02	09 32			10 09	10 32		11 02			11 33				12 02			12 46
Blaydon	d			08 08				09 05																	
Wylam	d	06 49		08 14	08 40			09 11				10 17			11 10							12 10			
Prudhoe	d	06 53		08 18	08 44			09 15	09 42			10 21	10 42		11 14			11 43				12 14			
Stocksfield	d	06 57		08 23	08 48			09 20				10 25			11 18							12 18			
Riding Mill	d	07 02		08 27				09 24				10 30			11 23							12 23			
Corbridge	d	07 05		08 31				09 28				10 33			11 26							12 26			
Hexham	a	07 10		08 40	08 58			09 38	09 55			10 42	10 55		11 36			11 56				12 36			13 06
	d	07 11			08 59				09 56				10 55					11 57							13 08
Haydon Bridge	d	07 20			09 08													12 06							
Bardon Mill	d	07 26			09 14													12 12							
Haltwhistle	d	07 33			09 21				10 14				11 14					12 19							13 26
Brampton (Cumbria)	d	07 49			09 37													12 35							
Wetheral	d	07 57			09 45													12 44							
Carlisle 8	a	08 09			09 56				10 45				11 45					12 54							13 59

		NT	NT		NT	NT	XC	NT		NT	NT	NT	NT		NT	NT	NT	XC		NT	NT	NT	NT		NT
							1 ◇											1 ◇							
			D				J			E					D			K			D		L		
Chathill	d																								
Alnmouth	26 d						13 05											15 05							
Acklington	d																								
Widdrington	d																								
Pegswood	d																								
Morpeth	26 d				12 50		13 20				13 50					14 50		15 20				15 50			
Cramlington	d				12 58						13 58					14 58						15 58			
Manors	d				13 11																				
Newcastle 8	26 a				13 13		13 37				14 13					15 13		15 38				16 13			
Sunderland	44 d		12 30							13 30					14 30						15 30				
London Kings Cross 15	⊖ 26 d		*09 30*		*10 00*			*10 30*			*11 00*				*11 30*	*12 00*					*12 30*	*13 00*			
Newcastle 8	d	12 44	12 54		13 14	13 24		13 44		13 54	14 14	14 24	14 44		14 54	15 14	15 24			15 44	15 54	16 14	16 24		16 44
Dunston	d																								
MetroCentre	a	12 52	13 01		13 22	13 31		13 51		14 01	14 22	14 31	14 52		15 01	15 21	15 31			15 51	16 01	16 21	16 31		16 51
	d		13 02			13 32				14 02		14 32			15 02		15 32				16 02		16 32		
Blaydon	d																								
Wylam	d		13 10							14 10		14 40			15 10						16 10		16 40		
Prudhoe	d		13 14			13 42				14 14		14 44			15 14		15 42				16 14		16 44		
Stocksfield	d		13 18							14 18					15 18						16 18		16 48		
Riding Mill	d		13 23							14 23					15 23						16 23		16 53		
Corbridge	d		13 26							14 26					15 26						16 26		16 56		
Hexham	a		13 36			13 55				14 36		14 56			15 36		15 55				16 36		17 02		
	d					13 56						14 57					15 56						17 03		
Haydon Bridge	d																16 05						17 12		
Bardon Mill	d																16 11								
Haltwhistle	d					14 14						15 16					16 18						17 23		
Brampton (Cumbria)	d																16 34								
Wetheral	d																16 43								
Carlisle 8	a					14 45						15 47					16 54						17 55		

For general notes see front of timetable
For details of catering facilities see Directory of Train Operators

A To Glasgow Central (Table 216)
B From Edinburgh to London Kings Cross (Table 26)
C From Hartlepool (Table 44)
D From Middlesbrough (Table 44)
E From Nunthorpe (Table 45)
G From Glasgow Central to Paignton (Table 51)
H To Stranraer (Table 216)
J From Edinburgh (Table 51) to Penzance (Table 135)
K From Edinburgh to Plymouth (Table 51)
L To Whitehaven (Table 100)

Due to Engineering Operations in the Sheffield area, services from Saturday 13 September on this Table had not been confirmed at time of going to press. These services will be issued in a special Supplement as soon as exact timings have been confirmed.

Table 48

Saturdays
until 6 September

Chathill and Morpeth → Newcastle → MetroCentre, Hexham and Carlisle

Network Diagram - see first page of Table 44

		NT	NT	NT	NT	XC	NT	NT	NT	NT	NT	NT	NT	NT	GR	NT	NT	NT	NT
		A	B			1 ◇ C	D						D		R 1 E				
Chathill	d													19 12					
Alnmouth	26 d					17 05								19 24	20 08				
Acklington	d													19 32					
Widdrington	d													19 39					
Pegswood	d													19 45					
Morpeth	26 d			16 50		17 20				18 32		19 04		19 49	20b25			21 15	
Cramlington	d			16 58						18 40		19 12		19 58				21 23	
Manors	d																		
Newcastle 8	26 a			17 13		17 38				18 56		19 26		20 12	20 46			21 40	
Sunderland	44 d	16 30					17 30				*18 30*		19 27			20 27			*21 27*
London Kings Cross 15	⊖ 26 d	*13 30*	*14 00*						*15 00*				*16 00*	*17 00*			*18 00*		*18 35*
Newcastle 8	d	16 54	17 11		17 24		17 54	18 02	18 24		19 10		19 50	20 14		20 56	21 10		21 56
Dunston	d				17 30			18 07											
MetroCentre	a	17 01	17 18		17 32		18 01	18 12	18 31		19 17		19 58	20 21		21 05	21 17		22 04
	d	17 02	17 18		17 33		18 02		18 32		19 18			20 22			21 18		
Blaydon	d				17 37														
Wylam	d	17 10	17 27		17 44		18 10		18 40		19 26			20 30			21 26		
Prudhoe	d	17 14	17 30		17 47		18 14		18 44		19 30			20 34			21 30		
Stocksfield	d	17 18			17 52		18 18		18 48		19 34			20 38			21 34		
Riding Mill	d	17 23			17 56		18 23		18 53		19 39			20 43			21 39		
Corbridge	d	17 26			18 00		18 26		18 56		19 42			20 46			21 42		
Hexham	a	17 36	17 45		18 08		18 32		19 02		19 48			20 55			21 48		
	d		17 45				18 33		19 03		19 49						21 49		
Haydon Bridge	d		17 54				18 42				19 58						21 58		
Bardon Mill	d		18 01				18 48										22 04		
Haltwhistle	d		18 08				18 55		19 21		20 09						22 11		
Brampton (Cumbria)	d		18 23						19 37								22 27		
Wetheral	d		18 32						19 45								22 35		
Carlisle 8	a		18 43				19 29		19 57		20 42						22 45		

Sundays
until 7 September

		NT	NT	NT	NT	NT	NT	NT	NT	NT	NT	NT	NT	NT	NT	NT	NT	NT
						D						D						D
Sunderland	44 d		09 28			10 28			11 28			12 28			13 28			14 28
London Kings Cross 15	⊖ 26 d										*09 00*	*09 30*		*10 00*	*10 30*		*11 00*	
Newcastle 8	d	09 10	09 53	10 10	10 30	10 50	11 10	11 30	11 50	12 10	12 30	12 50	13 10	13 30	13 50	14 10	14 30	14 50
MetroCentre	a	09 17	10 01	10 17	10 37	10 59	11 17	11 37	11 57	12 17	12 37	12 59	13 17	13 37	13 59	14 17	14 37	14 59
	d	09 18		10 18			11 18			12 18			13 18			14 18		
Wylam	d	09 26		10 26			11 26			12 26			13 26			14 26		
Prudhoe	d	09 30		10 30			11 30			12 30			13 30			14 30		
Stocksfield	d	09 34		10 34			11 34			12 34			13 34			14 34		
Riding Mill	d	09 39		10 39			11 39			12 39			13 39			14 39		
Corbridge	d	09 42		10 42			11 42			12 42			13 42			14 42		
Hexham	a	09 48		10 48			11 48			12 48			13 48			14 48		
	d	09 49		10 49			11 49			12 49			13 49			14 49		
Haydon Bridge	d	09 58		10 58						12 58								
Bardon Mill	d	10 04		11 04						13 04								
Haltwhistle	d	10 11		11 11			12 08			13 11			14 08			15 08		
Brampton (Cumbria)	d	10 27		11 27						13 27								
Wetheral	d	10 35		11 35						13 35								
Carlisle 8	a	10 45		11 45			12 38			13 45			14 38			15 38		

		NT	NT	NT	NT	NT	NT	NT	NT	NT	NT	NT	NT	NT
							D						D	
Sunderland	44 d			15 28			16 28			17 28			18 28	*19 28*
London Kings Cross 15	⊖ 26 d		*12 00*	*12 30*		*13 00*	*13 30*		*14 00*	*14 30*	*15 00*			*16 30*
Newcastle 8	d	15 10	15 30	15 50	16 10	16 30	16 50	17 10	17 30	17 50	18 10	18 30	18 50	20 15
MetroCentre	a	15 17	15 37	15 59	16 19	16 37	16 57	17 17	17 37	17 59	18 17	18 37	18 59	20 22
	d	15 18			16 20			17 18			18 18			20 23
Wylam	d	15 26			16 28			17 26			18 26			20 31
Prudhoe	d	15 30			16 32			17 30			18 30			20 35
Stocksfield	d	15 34			16 36			17 34			18 34			20 39
Riding Mill	d	15 39			16 41			17 39			18 39			20 44
Corbridge	d	15 42			16 44			17 42			18 42			20 47
Hexham	a	15 48			16 50			17 48			18 48			20 53
	d	15 49			16 51			17 49			18 49			20 54
Haydon Bridge	d	15 58									18 58			21 03
Bardon Mill	d	16 04									19 04			21 09
Haltwhistle	d	16 11			17 10			18 08			19 11			21 16
Brampton (Cumbria)	d	16 27									19 27			21 32
Wetheral	d	16 35									19 35			21 40
Carlisle 8	a	16 45			17 40			18 38			19 45			21 50

For general notes see front of timetable
For details of catering facilities see Directory of Train Operators

A From Nunthorpe (Table 45)
B To Stranraer (Table 216)
C From Edinburgh to Bristol Temple Meads (Table 51)
D From Middlesbrough (Table 44)
E From Glasgow Central to Leeds (Table 26)
b Arr. 2022

For Sunday service from Morpeth to Newcastle, please see Table 26

Due to Engineering Operations in the Sheffield area, services from Saturday 13 September on this Table had not been confirmed at time of going to press. These services will be issued in a special Supplement as soon as exact timings have been confirmed.

Due to Engineering Operations in the Sheffield area, services from Sunday 14 September on this Table had not been confirmed at time of going to press. These services will be issued in a special Supplement as soon as exact timings have been confirmed.

Table 48

Mondays to Fridays

until 5 September

Carlisle, Hexham and MetroCentre → Newcastle → Morpeth and Chathill

Network Diagram - see first page of Table 44

Miles	Miles			NT	GR	NT	NT	NT	NT	GR	NT		NT	XC	NT	NT	NT	NT		NT		NT	XC	NT	NT
					R 1					R 1				1 ◇									R 1		
					A	B			B	C	D			E	B			G	H			B	J		
0	—	**Carlisle 8**	d					06 25			07 13					08 30			09 33						10 36
4¼	—	Wetheral	d					06 32			07 20					08 37									
11	—	Brampton (Cumbria)	d					06 42			07 30					08 47									
23¼	—	Haltwhistle	d					06 56			07 45					09 01			10 01						11 04
28	—	Bardon Mill	d					07 04			07 52					09 09									
31¾	—	Haydon Bridge	d					07 09			07 57					09 14									
39½	—	**Hexham**	a					07 18			08 06					09 23			10 19						11 22
—	—		d			06 13		07 19	07 42		08 07				08 44	09 23		09 44	10 19			10 44			11 22
42½	—	Corbridge	d			06 17		07 23	07 46		08 11				08 48			09 48				10 48			
45	—	Riding Mill	d			06 22		07 28	07 51		08 16				08 53			09 53				10 53			
47¼	—	Stocksfield	d			06 26		07 32	07 55		08 20				08 57			09 57				10 57			
49¾	—	Prudhoe	d			06 30		07 36	07 59		08 24				09 01	09 35		10 01				11 01			11 34
52	—	Wylam	d			06 34		07 40	08 03		08 28				09 05			10 05				11 05			
56½	—	Blaydon	d						08 09		08 34														
58¼	0	**MetroCentre**	a					07 49	08 14		08 43				09 14	09 46		10 14	10 40			11 15			11 45
—	—		d					07 50	08 15		08 44				09 15	09 47		10 15	10 40	11 00		11 15		11 30	11 46
59½	1¼	Dunston	d								08 47														
61¾	3½	**Newcastle 8**	a			06 52		08 03	08 25		08 57				09 27	09 59		10 25	10 55	11 09		11 25		11 39	11 59
—	—	London Kings Cross 15	⊖ 26 a			09 55		11 51	12 17		12 42				12b44			13 43		14 44				14 57	
—	—	Sunderland	44 a			07 19			08 49						09 49			10 49				11 49			
—	—	**Newcastle 8**	26 d	06 00	06 25		07 58			08 41			09 00	09 27			10 15			11 15			11 34		
—	4	Manors	d																						
—	13¼	Cramlington	d	06 12			08 11						09 12				10 27			11 27					
—	20	**Morpeth**	26 d	06 20	06 38		08a21			08a55			09a20	09 42			10a35			11a35			11 49		
—	22	Pegswood	d																						
—	26¾	Widdrington	d																						
—	32	Acklington	d																						
—	38¼	Alnmouth	26 d	06 37	06a52									09a55									12a02		
—	49½	**Chathill**	a	06 53																					

		NT	NT	NT	NT	NT	NT		NT	NT	NT	NT	NT	NT	NT	NT		NT	XC	NT	NT	NT	NT	NT	NT
																			1 ◇						
			B						G				B		K			G	L				G		B
Carlisle 8	d				11 34						12 30				13 37						14 36				15 30
Wetheral	d										12 37														
Brampton (Cumbria)	d										12 47														
Haltwhistle	d				12 02						13 01				14 05						15 04				15 58
Bardon Mill	d										13 09														
Haydon Bridge	d				12 13						13 14														
Hexham	a				12 22						13 23				14 23						15 22				16 16
	d		11 44		12 23				12 44		13 23		13 44		14 24			14 44			15 22		15 44		16 16
Corbridge	d		11 48						12 48				13 48					14 48					15 48		
Riding Mill	d		11 53						12 53				13 53					14 53					15 53		
Stocksfield	d		11 57						12 57				13 57					14 57					15 57		
Prudhoe	d		12 01		12 34				13 01		13 35		14 01					15 01			15 34		16 01		16 28
Wylam	d		12 05						13 05				14 05					15 05					16 05		
Blaydon	d																								
MetroCentre	a		12 14		12 45				13 14		13 46		14 14		14 44			15 14			15 46		16 14		16 39
	d	12 05	12 15	12 30	12 45	12 40	13 00		13 15	13 30	13 47	14 00	14 15	14 30	14 45	15 00		15 15		15 30	15 46	16 00	16 15	16 30	16 39
Dunston	d																	15 18							
Newcastle 8	a	12 13	12 28	12 40	12 57	12 51	13 10		13 26	13 38	13 59	14 09	14 26	14 40	14 57	15 09		15 27		15 38	15 58	16 11	16 25	16 40	16 50
London Kings Cross 15	⊖ 26 a	15 44				15 51	16 46			16 57			17 41	18 04		18 26				19 11		19 18		20 18	
Sunderland	44 a		12 49						13 49				14 49					15 49					16 49		17 13
Newcastle 8	26 d	12 15				13 03						14 15				15 15			15 35			16 15			
Manors	d																					16 17			
Cramlington	d	12 26				13 15						14 27				15 27						16 28			
Morpeth	26 d	12a36				13a23						14a36				15a35			15 48			16a36			
Pegswood	d																								
Widdrington	d																								
Acklington	d																								
Alnmouth	26 d																		16 02						
Chathill	a																								

For general notes see front of timetable
For details of catering facilities see Directory of Train Operators

A To Glasgow Central (Table 26)
B To Middlesbrough (Table 44)
C From Leeds (Table 26) to Aberdeen (Table 229)
D From Dumfries (Table 216)
E From Birmingham New Street to Edinburgh (Table 51)
G To Nunthorpe (Table 45)
H From Girvan (Table 216)
J From Bristol Temple Meads to Edinburgh (Table 51)
K From Stranraer (Table 216)
L From Plymouth to Edinburgh (Table 51)
b Change at Newcastle and Doncaster

Table 48

Carlisle, Hexham and MetroCentre → Newcastle → Morpeth and Chathill

Mondays to Fridays

until 5 September

Network Diagram - see first page of Table 44

	NT	NT		NT	NT	NT	NT	NT	NT	NT	NT		GR	NT	NT	NT	XC	NT	GR	NT	NT	NT		
		A				B			A	C	A		R 1 D ✕				R 1 E		FO R 1 D ✕					
Carlisle 8 d					16 37			17 20		18 18				19 32							21 20			
Wetheral d					16 44			17 27													21 27			
Brampton (Cumbria) d					16 54			17 37													21 37			
Haltwhistle d					17 08			17 52		18 46				20 00							21 52			
Bardon Mill d					17 16			17 59													21 59			
Haydon Bridge d					17 21			18 04													22 04			
Hexham a					17 30			18 13		19 04				20 19							22 13			
d		16 44			17 31	17 42		18 14	18 44	19 04				20 19				21 14			22 14	23 14		
Corbridge d		16 48				17 46		18 18	18 48	19 09				20 24				21 18			22 18	23 18		
Riding Mill d		16 53				17 51		18 23	18 53	19 13				20 28				21 23			22 23	23 23		
Stocksfield d		16 57			17 40	17 55		18 27	18 57	19 17				20 32				21 27			22 27	23 27		
Prudhoe d		17 01			17 44	17 59		18 31	19 01	19 22				20 37				21 31			22 31	23 31		
Wylam d		17 05				18 03		18 35	19 05	19 26				20 40				21 35			22 35	23 35		
Blaydon d									19 11															
MetroCentre a		17 14			17 56	18 12		18 43	19 16	19 34				20 49				21 44			22 44	23 45		
d	17 00	17 15		17 35	17 56	18 13	18 18	18 44	19 17	19 35	20 15			20 50		21 10		21 45		22 15	22 45	23 45		
Dunston d																								
Newcastle 8 a	17 08	17 25		17 43	18 08	18 23	18 26	18 55	19 27	19 47	20 23			21 02		21 18		21 56		22 23	22 59	23 57		
London Kings Cross 15 ⊖ 26 a	20 42			21 20			21 44	22 20			00 15													
Sunderland 44 a		17 49				18 49			19 49		20 49													
Newcastle 8 26 d	17 15			17 46			18 28						20 29		21 05		21 48		22 08					
Manors d	17 17			17 48			18 30																	
Cramlington d	17 28			17 59			18 41								21 17									
Morpeth 26 d	17 36			18a07			18a49						20 44		21a26		22 01		22 22					
Pegswood d	17 48																							
Widdrington d	17 54																							
Acklington d	18 10																							
Alnmouth 26 d	18 18												20a58				22a14		22a36					
Chathill a	18 32																							

Mondays to Fridays

from 8 September

	NT	GR	NT	NT	NT	NT		GR	NT	NT	XC	NT	NT		NT	NT	NT	NT	NT	XC		NT	NT	NT
		R 1 G	A			A		R 1 H	J		1 ◇ K	A				B	L		A	1 ◇ N				
Carlisle 8 d					06 25				07 13				08 30				09 33						10 30	
Wetheral d					06 32				07 20				08 37											
Brampton (Cumbria) d					06 42				07 30				08 47											
Haltwhistle d					06 56				07 45				09 01				10 01						10 58	
Bardon Mill d					07 04				07 52				09 09											
Haydon Bridge d					07 09				07 57				09 14											
Hexham a					07 18				08 06				09 23				10 19						11 20	
d			06 13		07 19	07 39			08 07			08 42	09 23			09 42	10 19		10 44				11 20	
Corbridge d			06 17		07 23	07 45			08 11			08 46				09 46			10 48					
Riding Mill d			06 22		07 28	07 50			08 16			08 51				09 51			10 53					
Stocksfield d			06 26		07 32	07 54			08 20			08 55				09 55			10 57					
Prudhoe d			06 32		07 36	08 00			08 24			09 00	09 35			10 00			11 01				11 32	
Wylam d			06 36		07 40	08 04			08 28			09 04				10 04			11 05					
Blaydon d						08 10			08 34															
MetroCentre a					07 49	08 16			08 43			09 14	09 46			10 14	10 40		11 15				11 45	
d					07 50	08 17			08 44			09 15	09 47			10 15	10 40	11 00	11 15			11 30	11 46	12 05
Dunston d									08 47															
Newcastle 8 a			06 57		08 08	08 27			08 57			09 27	09 59			10 25	10 55	11 09	11 25			11 39	11 59	12 13
London Kings Cross 15 ⊖ 26 a			10 10		11 51	12 17			12 42			12b44				13 43		14 44				14 57		15 44
Sunderland 44 a			07 19			08 49						09 49				10 49			11 49					
Newcastle 8 26 d	06 00	06 25		07 58				08 41		09 00	09 27				10 15			11 15		11 34				12 15
Manors d																								
Cramlington d	06 12			08 11						09 12					10 27			11 27						12 26
Morpeth 26 d	06 20	06 38		08a21				08a55		09a20	09 42				10a35			11a35		11 49				12a36
Pegswood d																								
Widdrington d																								
Acklington d																								
Alnmouth 26 d	06 37	06a52									09a55									12a02				
Chathill a	06 53																							

For general notes see front of timetable
For details of catering facilities see Directory of Train Operators

- **A** To Middlesbrough (Table 44)
- **B** To Nunthorpe (Table 45)
- **C** From Glasgow Central (Table 216)
- **D** From London Kings Cross to Edinburgh (Table 26)
- **E** From Plymouth to Edinburgh (Table 51)
- **G** To Glasgow Central (Table 26)
- **H** From Leeds (Table 26) to Aberdeen (Table 229)
- **J** From Dumfries (Table 216)
- **K** From Sheffield to Edinburgh (Table 26)
- **L** From Girvan (Table 216)
- **N** From Birmingham New Street to Edinburgh (Table 51)
- **b** Change at Newcastle and Doncaster

Carlisle, Hexham and MetroCentre → Newcastle → Morpeth and Chathill

Network Diagram - see first page of Table 44

Station		NT	NT	NT	NT	NT		NT	NT	NT	NT	NT	NT		NT	NT	NT	XC	NT	NT		NT	NT	NT	NT
		A						B				A			C		B	[1] ◇ D [bicycle]					B		A
Carlisle [8]	d			11 27						12 30					13 37					14 35					15 22
Wetheral	d									12 37															
Brampton (Cumbria)	d									12 47															
Haltwhistle	d			11 55						13 01					14 05					15 03					15 50
Bardon Mill	d									13 09															
Haydon Bridge	d			12 06						13 14															
Hexham	a			12 18						13 23					14 23					15 21					16 12
	d	11 42		12 19				12 42		13 23		13 42			14 24		14 42			15 21			15 42		16 12
Corbridge	d	11 46						12 46				13 46					14 46						15 46		
Riding Mill	d	11 51						12 51				13 51					14 51						15 51		
Stocksfield	d	11 55						12 55				13 55					14 55						15 55		
Prudhoe	d	12 00		12 30				13 00		13 35		14 00					15 00			15 33			16 00		16 24
Wylam	d	12 04						13 04				14 04					15 04						16 04		
Blaydon	d																								
MetroCentre	a	12 14		12 44				13 14		13 46		14 14			14 44		15 14			15 46			16 14		16 39
	d	12 15	12 30	12 44	12 40	13 00		13 15	13 30	13 47	14 00	14 15	14 30		14 45	15 00	15 15		15 30	15 46		16 00	16 15	16 30	16 39
Dunston	d																15 18								
Newcastle [8] [bus]	a	12 28	12 40	12 57	12 51	13 10		13 26	13 38	13 59	14 09	14 26	14 40		14 57	15 09	15 27		15 38	15 58		16 11	16 25	16 40	16 50
London Kings Cross [15] ⊖ 26	a				*15 51*	*16 46*			*16 57*			*17 41*	*18 04*			*18 26*			*19 11*			*19 18*		*20 18*	
Sunderland 44 [bus]	a	12 49						13 49				14 49					15 49						16 49		17 13
Newcastle [8] 26 [bus]	d				13 03						14 15					15 15		15 35				16 15			
Manors	d																					16 17			
Cramlington	d				13 15						14 27					15 27						16 28			
Morpeth 26	d				13a23						14a36					15a35		15 48				16a36			
Pegswood	d																								
Widdrington	d																								
Acklington	d																								
Alnmouth 26	d																	16a01							
Chathill	a																								

Station		NT	NT	NT	NT		NT	NT	NT	NT	NT	NT		GR	NT	NT	NT	XC	NT	GR	NT	NT	NT		
			A				B			A	E	A		[R] [1] G ✕ [bicycle]				[R] [1] H		FO [R] [1] G ✕ [bicycle]					
Carlisle [8]	d				16 29				17 12		18 18				19 32							21 18			
Wetheral	d				16 36				17 19													21 25			
Brampton (Cumbria)	d				16 46				17 29													21 35			
Haltwhistle	d				17 03				17 44		18 46				20 00							21 50			
Bardon Mill	d				17 10				17 51													21 57			
Haydon Bridge	d				17 15				17 56													22 02			
Hexham	a				17 27				18 09		19 04				20 19							22 13			
	d		16 42		17 28		17 42		18 10	18 40	19 04				20 19				21 10			22 14	23 14		
Corbridge	d		16 46				17 46		18 14	18 44	19 09				20 24				21 14			22 18	23 18		
Riding Mill	d		16 51				17 51		18 19	18 49	19 13				20 28				21 19			22 23	23 23		
Stocksfield	d		16 55		17 37		17 55		18 23	18 53	19 17				20 32				21 23			22 27	23 27		
Prudhoe	d		17 00		17 41		17 59		18 27	18 59	19 22				20 37				21 29			22 31	23 33		
Wylam	d		17 04				18 03		18 31	19 03	19 26				20 40				21 33			22 35	23 37		
Blaydon	d									19 09															
MetroCentre	a		17 14		17 55		18 12		18 43	19 16	19 34				20 49				21 44			22 44	23 49		
	d	17 00	17 15	17 35	17 55		18 13	18 18	18 44	19 17	19 35	20 15			20 50		21 10		21 45		22 15	22 45	23 49		
Dunston	d																								
Newcastle [8] [bus]	a	17 08	17 25	17 43	18 07		18 23	18 26	18 54	19 27	19 47	20 23			21 02		21 18		21 56		22 23	22 59	00 01		
London Kings Cross [15] ⊖ 26	a	*20 42*		*21 20*				*21 44*	*22 20*			*00 15*													
Sunderland 44 [bus]	a		17 49				18 49			19 49		20 49													
Newcastle [8] 26 [bus]	d	17 15		17 46				18 28						20 29		21 05		21 48		22 08					
Manors	d	17 17		17 48				18 30																	
Cramlington	d	17 28		17 59				18 41								21 17									
Morpeth 26	d	17 36		18a07				18a49						20 44		21a26		22 01		22 22					
Pegswood	d	17 48																							
Widdrington	d	17 54																							
Acklington	d	18 10																							
Alnmouth 26	d	18 18												20a58				22a14		22a36					
Chathill	a	18 32																							

For general notes see front of timetable
For details of catering facilities see Directory of Train Operators

- **A** To Middlesbrough (Table 44)
- **B** To Nunthorpe (Table 45)
- **C** From Stranraer (Table 216)
- **D** From Bristol Temple Meads to Edinburgh (Table 51)
- **E** From Glasgow Central (Table 216)
- **G** From London Kings Cross to Edinburgh (Table 26)
- **H** From Paignton to Edinburgh (Table 51)

Table 48

Saturdays

until 6 September

Carlisle, Hexham and MetroCentre → Newcastle → Morpeth and Chathill

Network Diagram - see first page of Table 44

		NT	GR	NT	GR	NT	NT	NT	NT	XC	NT	NT	NT	NT	NT	NT	XC	NT	NT	NT	NT
			R 1		R 1					1 ◇							1 ◇				
			A	B	C			D	B	E			G	H		B	J				B
			☕ ✠		☕ ✠					☕							☕				
Carlisle 8	d					06 25		07 13			08 30			09 33					10 35		
Wetheral	d					06 32		07 20			08 37										
Brampton (Cumbria)	d					06 42		07 30			08 47										
Haltwhistle	d					06 56		07 45			09 01			10 01					11 03		
Bardon Mill	d					07 04		07 52			09 09										
Haydon Bridge	d					07 09		07 57			09 14										
Hexham	a					07 18		08 06			09 23			10 19					11 21		
	d			06 13		07 18		08 07	08 44		09 23		09 44	10 19		10 44			11 21		11 44
Corbridge	d			06 17		07 23		08 11	08 48				09 48			10 48					11 48
Riding Mill	d			06 22		07 27		08 16	08 53				09 53			10 53					11 53
Stocksfield	d			06 26		07 31		08 20	08 57				09 57			10 57					11 57
Prudhoe	d			06 30		07 36		08 24	09 01		09 35		10 01			11 01			11 33		12 01
Wylam	d			06 34		07 40		08 28	09 05		09 39		10 05			11 05					12 05
Blaydon	d							08 34													
MetroCentre	a					07 49		08 43	09 14		09 48		10 14	10 40		11 14			11 45		12 14
	d					07 49		08 44	09 15		09 49		10 15	10 40	11 00	11 15		11 30	11 45	12 00	12 15
Dunston	d							08 47													
Newcastle 8	🚇 a			06 52		08 03		08 57	09 25		10 01		10 25	10 55	11 10	11 25		11 38	11 59	12 08	12 25
London Kings Cross 15	⊖ 26 a			*10 13*		*11 50*		*12 41*	*13 10*		*13 44*		*13 59*		*14 44*			*15 10*			*15 41*
Sunderland	44 🚇 a			07 19		08 49			09 49				10 49			11 49					12 49
Newcastle 8	26 🚇 d	06 05	06 30		07 52		08 24			09 27		10 15			11 15		11 35			12 15	
Manors	d																				
Cramlington	d	06 17					08 36					10 27			11 27					12 27	
Morpeth	26 d	06 25	06 43		08 06		08a44			09 41		10a35			11a35		11 48			12a35	
Pegswood	d																				
Widdrington	d																				
Acklington	d																				
Alnmouth	26 d	06 43	06a57		08a20					09a54							12a01				
Chathill	a	06 58																			

		NT	NT	NT	NT	NT	NT	NT	NT	NT	NT	NT	NT	NT	NT	XC	NT	NT	NT	NT
																1 ◇				
							G				B		K		G	L				G
																☕				
Carlisle 8	d			11 34					12 30				13 36					14 36		
Wetheral	d								12 37											
Brampton (Cumbria)	d								12 47											
Haltwhistle	d			12 02					13 01				14 06					15 04		
Bardon Mill	d								13 09											
Haydon Bridge	d			12 13					13 14											
Hexham	a			12 22					13 23				14 24					15 22		
	d			12 23			12 44		13 23		13 44		14 24		14 44			15 22		15 44
Corbridge	d						12 48				13 48				14 48					15 48
Riding Mill	d						12 53				13 53				14 53					15 53
Stocksfield	d						12 57				13 57				14 57					15 57
Prudhoe	d			12 34			13 01		13 35		14 01				15 01			15 34		16 01
Wylam	d						13 05				14 05				15 05					16 05
Blaydon	d																			
MetroCentre	a			12 45			13 14		13 46		14 14		14 45		15 14			15 46		16 14
	d	12 30	12 40	12 45	13 00		13 15	13 30	13 47	14 00	14 15	14 30	14 45	15 00	15 15		15 30	15 46	16 00	16 15
Dunston	d														15 18					
Newcastle 8	🚇 a	12 38	12 52	12 57	13 11		13 26	13 39	14 00	14 13	14 25	14 40	14 59	15 09	15 28		15 38	16 00	16 11	16 25
London Kings Cross 15	⊖ 26 a		*15 58*		*16 47*			*16 58*		*17 43*		*18 10*		*18 46*					*19 40*	
Sunderland	44 🚇 a						13 49				14 49				15 50					16 49
Newcastle 8	26 🚇 d					13 15				14 15				15 15		15 36			16 15	
Manors	d																		16 17	
Cramlington	d					13 26				14 26				15 27					16 28	
Morpeth	26 d					13a36				14a36				15a35		15 50			16a36	
Pegswood	d																			
Widdrington	d																			
Acklington	d																			
Alnmouth	26 d															16a03				
Chathill	a																			

For general notes see front of timetable
For details of catering facilities see Directory of Train Operators

A To Glasgow Central (Table 26)
B To Middlesbrough (Table 44)
C From Doncaster to Glasgow Central (Table 26)
D From Dumfries (Table 216)
E From Birmingham New Street to Edinburgh (Table 51)
G To Nunthorpe (Table 45)
H From Girvan (Table 216)
J From Bristol Temple Meads to Edinburgh (Table 51)
K From Stranraer (Table 216)
L From Plymouth to Edinburgh (Table 51)

Due to Engineering Operations in the Sheffield area, services from Saturday 13 September on this Table had not been confirmed at time of going to press. These services will be issued in a special Supplement as soon as exact timings have been confirmed.

Saturdays
until 6 September

Carlisle, Hexham and MetroCentre → Newcastle → Morpeth and Chathill

Network Diagram - see first page of Table 44

		NT	NT	NT	NT	NT	NT	NT	NT	NT	NT	NT	NT	NT	NT	GR	NT	NT	NT	NT
			A		A			B			A	C	A			R 1 D				
Carlisle 8	d		15 30				16 29			17 20		18 18			19 33					21 20
Wetheral	d						16 36			17 27										21 27
Brampton (Cumbria)	d						16 46			17 37										21 37
Haltwhistle	d		15 58				17 00			17 52		18 46			20 01					21 52
Bardon Mill	d						17 08			17 59										21 59
Haydon Bridge	d						17 13			18 04										22 04
Hexham	a		16 16				17 22			18 13		19 04			20 19					22 13
	d		16 16		16 44		17 22	17 42		18 14	18 44	19 04			20 19			21 14		22 14
Corbridge	d				16 48			17 46		18 18	18 48	19 09			20 24			21 18		22 18
Riding Mill	d				16 53			17 51		18 23	18 53	19 13			20 28			21 23		22 23
Stocksfield	d				16 57		17 31	17 55		18 27	18 57	19 17			20 32			21 27		22 27
Prudhoe	d		16 28		17 01		17 35	17 59		18 31	19 01	19 22			20 37			21 31		22 31
Wylam	d				17 05			18 03		18 35	19 05	19 26			20 40			21 35		22 35
Blaydon	d										19 11									
MetroCentre	a		16 40		17 14		17 45	18 12		18 44	19 16	19 34			20 49			21 44		22 44
	d	16 30	16 40	17 00	17 15	17 35	17 45	18 13	18 18	18 45	19 17	19 34	20 15		20 50		21 10	21 45	22 10	22 45
Dunston	d																			
Newcastle 8	a	16 38	16 50	17 08	17 26	17 43	17 59	18 23	18 26	18 55	19 27	19 46	20 23		21 01		21 18	21 55	22 20	22 59
London Kings Cross 15 ⊖ 26	a			*20 35*					*21 48*	*22 17*										
Sunderland 44	a		17 13		17 50			18 49			19 50		20 49							
Newcastle 8 26	d			17 10		17 44			18 28					20 24		21 03				
Manors	d			17 13		17 47			18 30											
Cramlington	d			17 24		17 58			18 41					20 36						
Morpeth 26	d			17 32		18a06			18a49					20a45		21 19				
Pegswood	d			17 35																
Widdrington	d			17 41																
Acklington	d			17 48																
Alnmouth 26	d			17 57												21a33				
Chathill	a			18 13																

Sundays
until 7 September

		NT	NT	NT	NT	NT	NT	NT	NT	NT	NT	NT	NT	NT	NT	NT	NT	NT
							A						A					
Carlisle 8	d		09 05			10 05			11 12			12 05			13 12			14 12
Wetheral	d		09 12			10 12						12 12						
Brampton (Cumbria)	d		09 22			10 22						12 22						
Haltwhistle	d		09 36			10 36			11 40			12 36			13 40			14 40
Bardon Mill	d		09 44			10 44						12 44						
Haydon Bridge	d		09 49			10 49						12 49						
Hexham	a		09 58			10 58			11 58			12 58			13 58			14 58
	d		09 59			10 59			11 59			12 59			13 59			14 59
Corbridge	d		10 03			11 03			12 03			13 03			14 03			15 03
Riding Mill	d		10 08			11 08			12 08			13 08			14 08			15 08
Stocksfield	d		10 12			11 12			12 12			13 12			14 12			15 12
Prudhoe	d		10 16			11 16			12 16			13 16			14 16			15 16
Wylam	d		10 20			11 20			12 20			13 20			14 20			15 20
MetroCentre	a		10 29			11 29			12 29			13 29			14 29			15 29
	d	10 10	10 30	10 48	11 10	11 30	11 48	12 10	12 30	12 48	13 10	13 30	13 48	14 10	14 30	14 48	15 10	15 30
Newcastle 8	a	10 18	10 40	10 56	11 18	11 40	11 56	12 18	12 40	12 57	13 18	13 40	13 56	14 18	14 40	14 56	15 18	15 40
London Kings Cross 15 ⊖ 26	a	*13 36*	*14 10*		*14 42*	*15 11*		*15 37*	*16 11*	*16 29*	*16 45*	*17 11*		*17 50*	*18 15*		*18 38*	*19 12*
Sunderland 44	a			11 22			12 21			13 22			14 21			15 22		

		NT	NT	NT	NT	NT	NT	NT	NT	NT	NT	NT	NT	NT
		A						A						
Carlisle 8	d			15 05			16 12			17 12			18 05	20 15
Wetheral	d			15 12									18 12	
Brampton (Cumbria)	d			15 22									18 22	
Haltwhistle	d			15 36			16 40			17 40			18 36	20 43
Bardon Mill	d			15 44									18 44	
Haydon Bridge	d			15 49									18 49	
Hexham	a			15 58			16 58			17 58			18 58	20 58
	d			15 59			16 59			17 59			18 59	20 59
Corbridge	d			16 03			17 03			18 03			19 03	21 03
Riding Mill	d			16 08			17 08			18 08			19 08	21 08
Stocksfield	d			16 12			17 12			18 12			19 12	21 12
Prudhoe	d			16 16			17 16			18 16			19 16	21 16
Wylam	d			16 20			17 20			18 20			19 20	21 20
MetroCentre	a			16 29			17 29			18 29			19 29	21 29
	d	15 48	16 10	16 30	16 48	17 10	17 30	17 48	18 10	18 30	18 48	19 10	19 30	21 30
Newcastle 8	a	15 58	16 18	16 40	16 56	17 18	17 40	17 56	18 18	18 40	18 56	19 18	19 40	21 43
London Kings Cross 15 ⊖ 26	a		*19 48*	*20 12*	*20 34*	*20 38*		*21 25*	*21 47*	*22 16*		*23 14*	*23 50*	
Sunderland 44	a	16 21			17 22			18 21			19 22		*20 21*	

For general notes see front of timetable
For details of catering facilities see Directory of Train Operators

A To Middlesbrough (Table 44)
B To Nunthorpe (Table 45)
C From Glasgow Central (Table 216)
D From London Kings Cross to Edinburgh (Table 26)

For Sunday service from Newcastle to Morpeth, please see Table 26

Due to Engineering Operations in the Sheffield area, services from Saturday 13 September on this Table had not been confirmed at time of going to press. These services will be issued in a special Supplement as soon as exact timings have been confirmed.

Due to Engineering Operations in the Sheffield area, services from Sunday 14 September on this Table had not been confirmed at time of going to press. These services will be issued in a special Supplement as soon as exact timings have been confirmed.

Route Diagram for Table 49

DM-7/05
Design BAJS

This table summarises through services which, with their associated connecting services at Peterborough, link together The North, Midlands and East Anglia. In certain instances a faster journey is possible via London and the relevant Table(s) should be consulted.

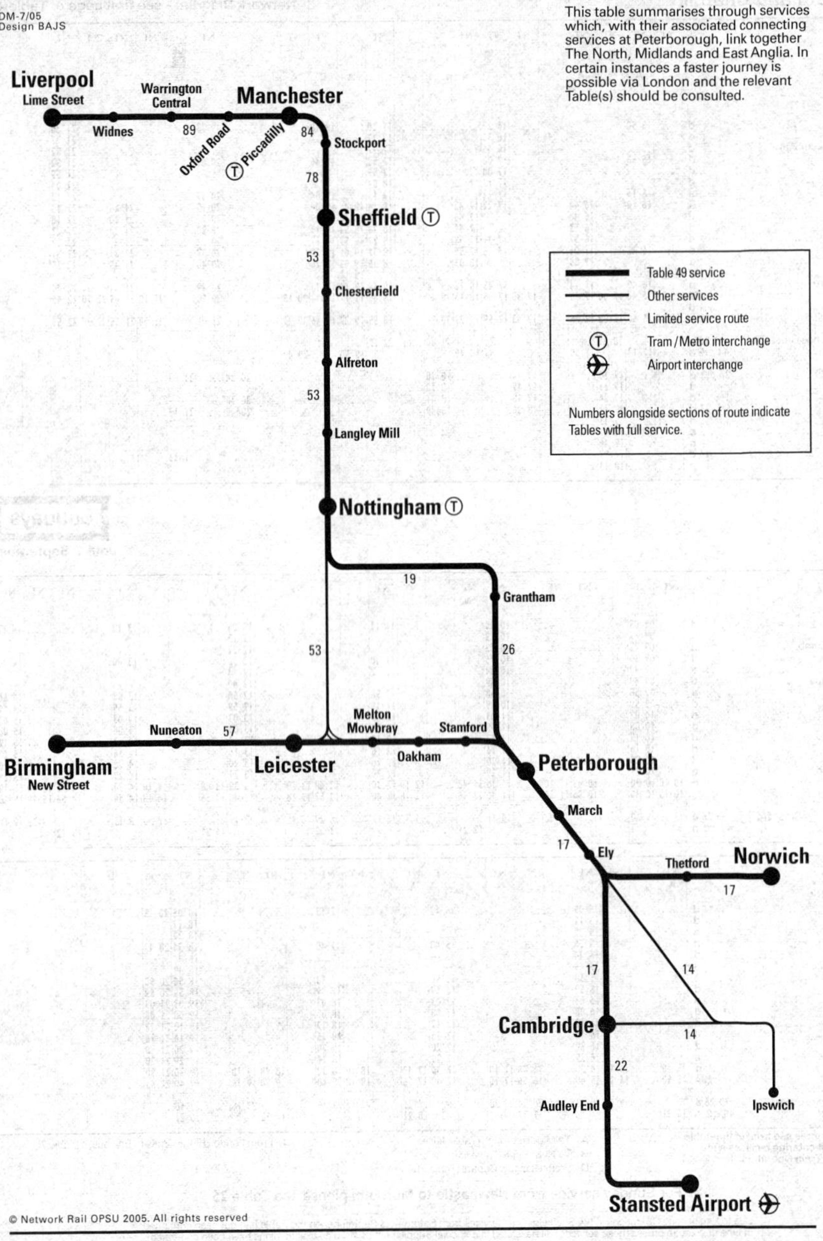

Stansted Airport → East Anglia → East Midlands → Birmingham and North West England

Route Diagram - see first page of Table 49

Miles	Miles	Miles	Miles			EM	EM	XC	XC		EM	EM	XC	EM		XC	EM	XC	EM		XC	EM	XC	EM	XC
						◇	◇	◇	◇		◇	◇	◇	◇		◇	◇	◇	◇		◇	◇	◇	◇	◇
												A		A			A		A			A		A	
						🍴	🍴		🍴		🍴		🍴			🍴		🍴			🍴		🍴		🍴
0	0	—	0	**Norwich**	d							05 52					07 57		08 57			09 57		10 57	
30½	30½	—	30½	Thetford	d							06 25					08 24		09 24			10 24		11 24	
—	—	—	—	Ipswich	d								*06b01*	*06 01*		*06c13*	*06e13*	*08b03*			*08c16*	*08e16*	*10b03*		*10c16*
—	—	0	—	**Stansted Airport** ✈	d				05 21							07 20		08 20			09 20		10 20		11 25
—	—	10¾	—	Audley End	d				05 33							07 38		08 36			09 38		10 38		11 38
—	—	24¾	—	**Cambridge**	d			05 07	05 58			*06 23*	06 50	07 27		07 59	*08 12*	09 04	*09 12*		10 04	*10 12*	11 04	*11 12*	12 04
53¾	53¾	39½	53¾	Ely [6]	d			05 24	06 13			06 51	07 05	07 44		08 16	08 51	09 19	09 51		10 19	10 52	11 19	11 52	12 19
61¼	61¼	—	61¼	March	d			05 40	06 32			07 07	07 21	08 01		08 33	09 07	09 35			10 35		11 35		12 35
75¼	75¼	—	75¼	**Peterborough** [8]	a			06 02	06 54			07 25	07 43	08 23		08 50	09 25	09 53	10 25		10 53	11 24	11 53	12 24	12 53
—	—	—	—		d			06 08	06 55			07 27	07 46	08 30		08 54	09 27	09 54	10 30		10 54	11 25	11 54	12 25	12 54
87¾	—	—	—	Stamford	d			06 21	07 08				07 59			09 07		10 07			11 07		12 07		13 07
101¼	—	—	—	Oakham	d			06 39	07 24				08 15			09 23		10 23			11 23		12 23		13 23
112¾	—	—	—	Melton Mowbray	d			06 50	07 35				08 26			09 34		10 34			11 34		12 34		13 34
127¾	—	—	—	**Leicester**	d			07 09	07 52				08 52			09 52		10 52			11 52		12 52		13 52
146½	—	—	—	Nuneaton	a			07 35	08 17				09 11			10 14		11 13			12 13		13 13		14 13
167½	—	—	—	**Birmingham New Street** [12]	a			08 09	08 51				09 47			10 47		11 47			12 47		13 47		14 47
—	104½	—	—	Grantham [7]	d							07 59		09 00			09 59		11 12			11 57		12 59	
—	127¼	—	145	**Nottingham** [8] ⛴	a			*08f20*	*09f20*			08 39	*09f26*	09 39		*10f36*	10 28	*11f36*	11 41		*12f35*	12 34	*13f36*	13 28	*14f36*
—	—	—	—		d	05 19	06 34				07 42	08 42		09 40			10 42		11 42			12 42		13 45	
—	139¼	—	157	Langley Mill	d		06 53				07 58	08 58		09 57			10 58					12 58			
—	145½	—	163¼	Alfreton	d		07 01				08 06	09 06		10 05			11 06		12 04			13 06		14 07	
—	155½	—	173¼	Chesterfield	d	05 54	07 14				08 18	09 18		10 18			11 18		12 18			13 18		14 18	
—	167¼	—	185½	**Sheffield** [7] ⛴	a	06 10	07 32				08 38	09 38		10 38			11 38		12 38			13 38		14 38	
—	—	—	—		d	06 20	07 37				08 42	09 42		10 42			11 42		12 42			13 42		14 42	
—	204½	—	222¼	Stockport	a	07 23	08 26				09 24	10 24		11 24			12 24		13 24			14 24		15 24	
—	210½	—	228¼	**Manchester Piccadilly** [10] ⛴	a	07 35	08 36				09 36	10 36		11 36			12 36		13 36			14 36		15 36	
—	211	—	228¾	Manchester Oxford Road	a	07 38	08 40				09 40	10 40		11 40			12 40		13 40			14 40		15 40	
—	226¾	—	244½	Warrington Central	a	07 54	08 57				09 57	10 57		11 57			12 57		13 57			14 57		15 57	
—	233	—	250¾	Widnes	a	08 02	09 05				10 05	11 05		12 05			13 05		14 05			15 05		16 05	
—	245¼	—	263	**Liverpool Lime Street** [10]	a	08 29	09 29				10 29	11 29		12 29			13 29		14 29			15 29		16 27	

		EM		XC	EM	XC	EM		XC	EM	XC	EM		XC	EM	XC	EM		XC	EM	XC	EM	XC		
		◇		◇	◇	◇	◇		◇	◇	◇	◇		◇	◇	◇	◇		◇	◇	◇		◇		
		A			A		A			A												B			
				🍴					🍴																
Norwich	d	11 57			12 57		13 57			14 57		15 52			16 57		17 54			18 57					
Thetford	d	12 24			13 24		14 24			15 24		16 27			17 24		18 24			19 24					
Ipswich	d	*10e16*		*12b03*		*12c16*	*12e16*		*14b03*	*14 03*	*14c16*	*14e16*		*16b03*		*16c16*	*16e16*		*17b49*		*18c16*		*19c16*		
Stansted Airport ✈	d			12 25		13 25			14 25		15 25			16 20		17 17			18 20		19 16		20 20		
Audley End	d			12 38		13 38			14 38		15 38			16 33		17 32			18 32		19 32		20 32		
Cambridge	d	*12 12*		13 04	*13 12*	14 04	*14 12*		15 04	*15 12*	16 04	*16 24*		17 04	*17 22*	17 49	*18 25*		19 04	*19 25*	19 50		20 57		
Ely [6]	d	12 52		13 19	13 52	14 19	14 52		15 19	15 52	16 19	16 52		17 19	17 50	18 06	18 52		19 19	19 52	20 05		21 14		
March	d			13 35		14 35			15 35		16 35			17 35	18 07	18 24			19 35		20 22		21 30		
Peterborough [8]	a	13 24		13 53	14 25	14 53	15 25		15 53	16 25	16 53	17 26		17 53	18 24	18 43	19 31		19 53	20 25	20 39		21 52		
	d	13 25		13 54	14 26	14 54	15 26		15 54	16 27	16 54	17 27		17 54	18 26	18 44	19 31		19 54	20 28	20 41	21 30	21 54		
Stamford	d			14 07		15 07			16 07		17 07			18 07		18 57			20 07		20 54	21 43	22 07		
Oakham	d			14 23		15 23			16 23		17 23			18 23		19 13			20 23		21 09	21 58	22 23		
Melton Mowbray	d			14 34		15 34			16 34		17 34			18 34		19 24			20 34		21 20	22 11	22 34		
Leicester	d			14 52		15 52			16 52		17 52			18 52		19 41			20 52		21 41		22 49		
Nuneaton	a			15 13		16 13			17 13		18 17			19 13		20 00			21 13		22 00		23 08		
Birmingham New Street [12]	a			15 47		16 47			17 47		18 48			19 47		20 37			21 47		22 36		23 41		
Grantham [7]	d	13 57			14 58		15 56			17 02		18 00			18 56		20 04			20 56					
Nottingham [8] ⛴	a	14 33		*15f36*	15 27	*16f35*	16 26		*17f50*	17 38	*18f48*	18 30		*19f35*	19 25	*20f27*	20 44		*21f37*	21 35	*22f28*	22 56	*23f31*		
	d	14 42			15 42		16 42			17 42		18 40			19 27										
Langley Mill	d	14 58					16 58			17 58		18 56													
Alfreton	d	15 06			16 06		17 06			18 06		19 06			19 57										
Chesterfield	d	15 18			16 18		17 18			18 18		19 18			20 08										
Sheffield [7] ⛴	a	15 38			16 38		17 34			18 38		19 39			20 27										
	d	15 42			16 42		17 42			18 42		19 42			20 31										
Stockport	a	16 24			17 25		18 26			19 24		20 26			21 17										
Manchester Piccadilly [10] ⛴	a	16 35			17 36		18 36			19 36		20 36			21 30										
Manchester Oxford Road	a	16 39			17 39		18 39			19 40		20 39													
Warrington Central	a	16 57			18 02		18 57			19 57		20 57													
Widnes	a	17 05			18 10		19 05			20 05		21 05													
Liverpool Lime Street [10]	a	17 27			18 32		19 29			20 29		21 29													

For general notes see front of timetable
For details of catering facilities see
Directory of Train Operators

- **A** 🍴 from Nottingham
- **B** From Spalding (Table 18)
- **b** Change at Ely
- **c** Change at Cambridge
- **e** Change at Cambridge and Ely
- **f** Change at Leicester

Table 49

Mondays to Fridays
from 8 September

Stansted Airport → East Anglia → East Midlands → Birmingham and North West England

Route Diagram - see first page of Table 49

		EM ◇ 🛒	EM ◇ 🛒	XC ◇	XC ◇ 🛒	EM ◇ 🛒	EM A	EM ◇	XC ◇ 🛒	EM ◇ A	EM ◇	XC ◇ 🛒	EM ◇ A	EM ◇	XC ◇ 🛒	EM ◇ A	EM ◇	XC ◇ 🛒	EM ◇ A	EM ◇	XC ◇ 🛒	EM ◇ A	EM ◇	XC ◇ 🛒	EM ◇ A
Norwich	d						05 52						07 57			08 57			09 57			10 57			11 57
Thetford	d						06 25						08 24			09 24			10 24			11 24			12 24
Ipswich	d								06b01			06c13	06e13		08b03			08c16	08e16		10b03			10c16	10e16
Stansted Airport ✈	d				05 21							07 20			08 20			09 20			10 20			11 25	
Audley End	d				05 33							07 38			08 36			09 38			10 38			11 38	
Cambridge	d			05 07	05 58		06 23		06 50	07 27		07 59	08 12		09 04	09 12		10 04	10 12		11 04	11 12		12 04	12 12
Ely 6	d			05 24	06 13		06 51		07 05	07 44		08 16	08 51		09 19	09 51		10 19	10 52		11 19	11 52		12 19	12 52
March	d			05 40	06 32		07 07		07 21	08 01		08 33	09 07		09 35			10 35			11 35			12 35	
Peterborough 8	a			06 02	06 54		07 25		07 43	08 23		08 50	09 25		09 53	10 25		10 53	11 24		11 53	12 24		12 53	13 24
	d			06 08	06 55		07 27		07 46	08 30		08 54	09 27		09 54	10 30		10 54	11 25		11 54	12 25		12 54	13 25
Stamford	d			06 21	07 08				07 59			09 07			10 07			11 07			12 07			13 07	
Oakham	d			06 39	07 24				08 15			09 23			10 23			11 23			12 23			13 23	
Melton Mowbray	d			06 50	07 35				08 26			09 34			10 34			11 34			12 34			13 34	
Leicester	d			07 09	07 52				08 52			09 52			10 52			11 52			12 52			13 52	
Nuneaton	a			07 35	08 17				09 11			10 14			11 13			12 13			13 13			14 13	
Birmingham New Street 12	a			08 09	08 51				09 47			10 47			11 47			12 47			13 47			14 47	
Grantham 7	d						07 59			09 00			09 59			11 12			11 57			12 59			13 57
Nottingham 8	a			08f20	09f20		08 39		09f26	09 39		10f36	10 28		11f36	11 41		12f35	12 34		13f36	13 28		14f36	14 33
	d	05 19	06 24			07 38	08 42			09 40			10 42			11 42			12 42			13 45			14 42
Langley Mill	d		06 43			07 54	08 58			09 57			10 58						12 58						14 58
Alfreton	d		06 51			08 02	09 06			10 05			11 06			12 04			13 06			14 07			15 06
Chesterfield	d	05 56	07 05			08 14	09a18			10a18			11a18			12a18			13a18			14a19			15a17
Sheffield 7	a	06 18	07 35			08 40																			
	d	06 20	07 37			08 42		09 42			10 42			11 42			12 42			13 42			14 42		
Stockport	a	07 23	08 26			09 24		10 24			11 24			12 24			13 24			14 24			15 24		
Manchester Piccadilly 10	a	07 35	08 36			09 36		10 36			11 36			12 36			13 36			14 36			15 36		
Manchester Oxford Road	a	07 38	08 40			09 40		10 40			11 40			12 40			13 40			14 40			15 40		
Warrington Central	a	07 54	08 57			09 57		10 57			11 57			12 57			13 57			14 57			15 57		
Widnes	a	08 02	09 05			10 05		11 05			12 05			13 05			14 05			15 05			16 05		
Liverpool Lime Street 10	a	08 29	09 29			10 29		11 29			12 29			13 29			14 29			15 29			16 25		

		EM ◇	XC ◇ 🛒	EM ◇ A	EM ◇	XC ◇ 🛒	EM ◇ A	EM ◇	XC ◇ 🛒	EM ◇ A	EM ◇	XC ◇	EM ◇	EM ◇	XC ◇	EM ◇	XC ◇	EM ◇	XC ◇	EM ◇	XC ◇	EM B	XC ◇		
Norwich	d			12 57			13 57			14 57			15 52			16 57		17 54		18 57					
Thetford	d			13 24			14 24			15 24			16 27			17 24		18 24		19 24					
Ipswich	d		12b03			12c16	12e16		14b03	14 03		14c16	14e16		16b03		16c16	16e16	17b49		18c16		19c16		
Stansted Airport ✈	d		12 25			13 25			14 25			15 25			16 20		17 17		18 20		19 16		20 20		
Audley End	d		12 38			13 38			14 38			15 38			16 33		17 32		18 32		19 32		20 32		
Cambridge	d		13 04	13 12		14 04	14 12		15 04	15 12		16 04	16 24		17 04	17 22	17 49	18 25	19 04	19 25	19 50		20 57		
Ely 6	d		13 19	13 52		14 19	14 52		15 19	15 52		16 19	16 52		17 19	17 50	18 06	18 52	19 19	19 52	20 05		21 14		
March	d		13 35			14 35			15 35			16 35			17 35	18 07	18 24		19 35		20 22		21 30		
Peterborough 8	a		13 53	14 25		14 53	15 25		15 53	16 25		16 53	17 26		17 53	18 24	18 43	19 31	19 53	20 25	20 39		21 52		
	d		13 54	14 26		14 54	15 26		15 54	16 27		16 54	17 27		17 54	18 26	18 44	19 31	19 54	20 28	20 41	21 30	21 54		
Stamford	d		14 07			15 07			16 07			17 07			18 07		18 57		20 07		20 54	21 43	22 07		
Oakham	d		14 23			15 23			16 23			17 23			18 23		19 13		20 23		21 09	21 58	22 23		
Melton Mowbray	d		14 34			15 34			16 34			17 34			18 34		19 24		20 34		21 20	22 11	22 34		
Leicester	d		14 52			15 52			16 52			17 52			18 52		19 41		20 52		21 41		22 49		
Nuneaton	a		15 13			16 13			17 13			18 17			19 13		20 00		21 13		22 00		23 08		
Birmingham New Street 12	a		15 47			16 47			17 47			18 48			19 47		20 37		21 47		22 36		23 41		
Grantham 7	d			14 58			15 56			17 02			18 00			18 56		20 04		20 56					
Nottingham 8	a		15f36	15 27		16f35	16 26		17f50	17 38		18f48	18 30		19f35	19 25	20f27	20 44	21f37	21 35	22f28	22 56	23f31		
	d			15 42			16 42			17 42			18 40			19 27									
Langley Mill	d						16 58			17 58			18 56												
Alfreton	d			16 06			17 06			18 06			19 06			19 57									
Chesterfield	d			16a18			17a18			18a18			19a22			20a11									
Sheffield 7	a																								
	d	15 42			16 42			17 42			18 42			19 42											
Stockport	a	16 24			17 25			18 26			19 24			20 26											
Manchester Piccadilly 10	a	16 35			17 36			18 36			19 36			20 36											
Manchester Oxford Road	a	16 39			17 39			19 39			19 40			20 39											
Warrington Central	a	16 57			18 02			19 57			19 57			20 57											
Widnes	a	17 05			18 10			19 05			20 05			21 05											
Liverpool Lime Street 10	a	17 27			18 32			19 29			20 29			21 29											

For general notes see front of timetable
For details of catering facilities see Directory of Train Operators

A 🛒 from Nottingham
B From Spalding (Table 18)
b Change at Ely
c Change at Cambridge
e Change at Cambridge and Ely
f Change at Leicester

Saturdays

until 6 September

Stansted Airport → East Anglia → East Midlands → Birmingham and North West England

Route Diagram - see first page of Table 49

		EM ◇	EM ◇	XC ◇	XC ◇	EM ◇	EM ◇	XC ◇	EM ◇	XC ◇	EM ◇	XC ◇	EM ◇	XC ◇	EM ◇	XC ◇	EM ◇	XC ◇
Norwich	d						05 52				07 57		08 57		09 57		10 57	
Thetford	d						06 25				08 24		09 24		10 24		11 24	
Ipswich	d							*06b00*		*06c14*	*06e14*	*08b03*		*08c16*	*08e16*	*10b03*		*10c16*
Stansted Airport	d				05 21					07 25		08 25		09 25		10 25		11 25
Audley End	d				05 33					07 40		08 38		09 38		10 38		11 38
Cambridge	d			05 11	05 51		*06 20*	06 55	07 25	08 04	*08 20*	09 04	*09 12*	10 04	*10 12*	11 04	*11 12*	12 04
Ely 6	d			05 28	06 08		06 51	07 10	07 44	08 19	08 52	09 19	09 53	10 19	10 53	11 19	11 52	12 19
March	d			05 44	06 27		07 07	07 26	08 01	08 35	09 09	09 35		10 35		11 35		12 35
Peterborough 8	a			06 06	06 48		07 25	07 52	08 24	08 54	09 27	09 53	10 25	10 53	11 25	11 53	12 25	12 53
	d			06 08	06 50		07 28	07 54	08 25	08 54	09 29	09 54	10 26	10 54	11 27	11 54	12 27	12 54
Stamford	d			06 21	07 03			08 07		09 07		10 07		11 07		12 07		13 07
Oakham	d			06 35	07 18			08 23		09 23		10 23		11 23		12 23		13 23
Melton Mowbray	d			06 46	07 29			08 34		09 34		10 34		11 34		12 34		13 34
Leicester	d			07 08	07 46			08 52		09 52		10 52		11 52		12 52		13 52
Nuneaton	a			07 32	08 11			09 14		10 14		11 13		12 14		13 14		14 14
Birmingham New Street 12	a			08 08	08 47			09 47		10 47		11 47		12 47		13 47		14 47
Grantham 7	d						08 01		08 57		10 00		10 58		11 58		12 59	
Nottingham 8	a			*08f16*	*08f56*		08 37	*09f38*	09 27	*10f34*	10 37	*11f27*	11 28	*12f27*	12 38	*13f25*	13 28	*14f37*
	d	05 23	06 34			07 42	08 42		09 42		10 42		11 42		12 47		13 42	
Langley Mill	d		06 50			07 58	08 59		09 59						13 03		13 59	
Alfreton	d		06 58			08 06	09 07		10 07		11 04		12 04		13 11		14 07	
Chesterfield	d	05 54	07 10			08 18	09 18		10 18		11 18		12 18		13 22		14 18	
Sheffield 7	a	06 10	07 31			08 38	09 38		10 38		11 38		12 38		13 39		14 38	
	d	06 20	07 36			08 42	09 42		10 42		11 42		12 42		13 42		14 42	
Stockport	a	07 22	08 25			09 25	10 24		11 24		12 24		13 24		14 25		15 24	
Manchester Piccadilly 10	a	07 35	08 36			09 36	10 36		11 36		12 36		13 36		14 36		15 36	
Manchester Oxford Road	a	07 38	08 40			09 40	10 40		11 40		12 40		13 40		14 40		15 40	
Warrington Central	a	07 54	08 57			09 57	10 57		11 57		12 57		13 57		14 57		15 57	
Widnes	a	08 02	09 05			10 05	11 05		12 05		13 05		14 05		15 05		16 05	
Liverpool Lime Street 10	a	08 29	09 27			10 27	11 29		12 29		13 27		14 27		15 25		16 29	

		EM ◇	XC ◇	EM ◇	XC ◇	EM ◇	XC ◇	EM ◇	XC ◇	EM ◇	XC ◇	EM ◇	XC ◇	EM ◇	XC ◇	EM ◇	XC ◇
Norwich	d	11 57		12 57		13 57		14 57		15 52		16 57		17 57		18 57	
Thetford	d	12 24		13 24		14 24		15 24		16 22		17 24		18 24		19 24	
Ipswich	d	*10e16*	*12b03*		*12c16*	*12e16*	*14b03*		*14c16*	*14e16*	*16b03*		*16c16*	*16e16*	*18b03*		*18c16*
Stansted Airport	d		12 25		13 25		14 25		15 25		16 25		17 25		18 25		19 18
Audley End	d		12 38		13 38		14 38		15 38		16 38		17 38		18 38		19 32
Cambridge	d	*12 12*	13 04	*13 12*	14 04	*14 12*	15 04	*15 12*	16 04	*16 12*	17 04	*17 12*	18 02	*18 12*	19 04	*19 12*	19 50
Ely 6	d	12 53	13 19	13 52	14 19	14 52	15 19	15 55	16 19	16 51	17 19	17 51	18 17	18 52	19 19	19 52	20 05
March	d		13 35		14 35		15 35		16 35		17 35		18 35	19 09	19 35		20 21
Peterborough 8	a	13 25	13 53	14 23	14 53	15 25	15 53	16 27	16 53	17 24	17 53	18 24	18 53	19 26	19 53	20 25	20 39
	d	13 26	13 54	14 24	14 54	15 26	15 54	16 30	16 54	17 25	17 54	18 25	18 54	19 28	19 54	20 27	20 45
Stamford	d		14 07		15 07		16 07		17 07		18 07		19 07		20 07		20 58
Oakham	d		14 23		15 23		16 23		17 23		18 23		19 23		20 23		21 13
Melton Mowbray	d		14 34		15 34		16 34		17 34		18 34		19 34		20 34		21 24
Leicester	d		14 52		15 52		16 52		17 52		18 52		19 52		20 52		21 39
Nuneaton	a		15 13		16 13		17 14		18 13		19 14		20 13		21 13		22 00
Birmingham New Street 12	a		15 47		16 47		17 47		18 47		19 47		20 47		21 47		22 35
Grantham 7	d	13 56		14 58		15 56		17 02		17 55		18 57		20 02		21 00	
Nottingham 8	a	14 26	*15f26*	15 28	*16f26*	16 25	*17f28*	17 38	*18f26*	18 28	*19f52*	19 26	*20f39*	20 44	*21f39*	21 30	*22f26*
	d	14 42		15 44		16 42		17 42		18 42		19 28					
Langley Mill	d	14 59				16 58		17 58		18 59							
Alfreton	d	15 07		16 06		17 06		18 06		19 07		19 52					
Chesterfield	d	15 18		16 18		17 18		18 18		19 18		20 08					
Sheffield 7	a	15 38		16 38		17 34		18 38		19 39		20 25					
	d	15 42		16 42		17 42		18 42		19 42		20 29					
Stockport	a	16 24		17 24		18 26		19 24		20 25		21 16					
Manchester Piccadilly 10	a	16 36		17 35		18 35		19 35		20 36		21 26					
Manchester Oxford Road	a	16 40		17 39		18 39				20 39							
Warrington Central	a	16 57		18 02		18 57											
Widnes	a	17 05		18 10		19 05											
Liverpool Lime Street 10	a	17 29		18 32		19 29											

For general notes see front of timetable
For details of catering facilities see Directory of Train Operators

b Change at Ely
c Change at Cambridge
e Change at Cambridge and Ely
f Change at Leicester

Table 49

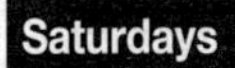

Saturdays

from 13 September

Stansted Airport → East Anglia → East Midlands → Birmingham and North West England

Route Diagram - see first page of Table 49

		EM ◇	EM ◇	XC ◇	XC ◇	EM ◇	EM ◇	EM ◇	XC ◇	EM ◇	EM ◇	XC ◇		EM ◇	EM ◇	XC ◇	EM ◇	EM ◇	XC ◇	EM ◇	EM ◇	XC ◇	EM ◇	EM ◇	XC ◇
Norwich	d						05 52								07 57		08 57			09 57			10 57		
Thetford	d						06 25								08 24		09 24			10 24			11 24		
Ipswich	d								*06*b*00*			*06*c*14*			*06*e*14*	*08*b*03*			*08*c*16*	*08*e*16*		*10*b*03*			*10*c*16*
Stansted Airport	d				05 21							07 25				08 25			09 25			10 25			11 25
Audley End	d				05 33							07 40				08 38			09 38			10 38			11 38
Cambridge	d			05 11	05 51		*06 20*		06 55	07 25		08 04			*08 20*	09 04	*09 12*		10 04	*10 12*		11 04	*11 12*		12 04
Ely 6	d			05 28	06 08		06 51		07 10	07 44		08 19			08 52	09 19	09 53		10 19	10 53		11 19	11 52		12 19
March	d			05 44	06 27		07 07		07 26	08 01		08 35			09 09	09 35			10 35			11 35			12 35
Peterborough 8	a			06 06	06 48		07 25		07 52	08 24		08 54			09 27	09 53	10 25		10 53	11 25		11 53	12 25		12 53
	d			06 08	06 50		07 28		07 54	08 25		08 54			09 29	09 54	10 26		10 54	11 27		11 54	12 27		12 54
Stamford	d			06 21	07 03				08 07			09 07				10 07			11 07			12 07			13 07
Oakham	d			06 35	07 18				08 23			09 23				10 23			11 23			12 23			13 23
Melton Mowbray	d			06 46	07 29				08 34			09 34				10 34			11 34			12 34			13 34
Leicester	d			07 08	07 46				08 52			09 52				10 52			11 52			12 52			13 52
Nuneaton	a			07 32	08 11				09 14			10 14				11 13			12 14			13 14			14 14
Birmingham New Street 12	a			08 08	08 47				09 47			10 47				11 47			12 47			13 47			14 47
Grantham 7	d						08 01			08 57					10 00		10 58			11 58			12 59		
Nottingham 8	a						08 37			09 27					10 37		11 28			12 38			13 28		
	d	05 23	06 22			07 38	08 42			09 42					10 42		11 42			12 47			13 42		
Langley Mill	d		06 43			07 54	08 58			09 59										13 03			13 59		
Alfreton	d		06 51			08 02	09 06			10 07					11 04		12 04			13 11			14 07		
Chesterfield	d	05 56	07 05			08 14	09a18			10a18					11a19		12a18			13a23			14a20		
Sheffield 7	a	06 18	07 35			08 40																			
	d	06 20	07 36			08 42		09 42			10 42			11 42				12 42			13 42			14 42	
Stockport	a	07 23	08 25			09 25		10 24			11 24			12 24				13 24			14 25			15 24	
Manchester Piccadilly 10	a	07 35	08 36			09 36		10 36			11 36			12 36				13 36			14 36			15 36	
Manchester Oxford Road	a	07 38	08 40			09 40		10 40			11 40			12 40				13 40			14 40			15 40	
Warrington Central	a	07 54	08 57			09 57		10 57			11 57			12 57				13 57			14 57			15 57	
Widnes	a	08 02	09 05			10 05		11 05			12 05			13 05				14 05			15 05			16 05	
Liverpool Lime Street 10	a	08 29	09 27			10 27		11 29			12 29			13 29				14 27			15 25			16 29	

		EM ◇		EM ◇	XC ◇	EM ◇	EM ◇	XC ◇	EM ◇	EM ◇	XC ◇	EM ◇	EM ◇	XC ◇	EM ◇	EM ◇	XC ◇	EM ◇	XC ◇	EM ◇	XC ◇	EM ◇	XC ◇		
Norwich	d	11 57				12 57			13 57			14 57			15 52			16 57		17 57		18 57			
Thetford	d	12 24				13 24			14 24			15 24			16 22			17 24		18 24		19 24			
Ipswich	d	*10*e*16*			*12*b*03*			*12*c*16*	*12*e*16*		*14*b*03*			*14*c*16*	*14*e*16*		*16*b*03*		*16*c*16*	*16*e*16*	*18*b*03*		*18*c*16*		
Stansted Airport	d				12 25			13 25			14 25			15 25			16 25		17 25		18 25		19 18		
Audley End	d				12 38			13 38			14 38			15 38			16 38		17 38		18 38		19 32		
Cambridge	d	*12 12*			13 04	*13 12*		14 04	*14 12*		15 04	*15 12*		16 04	*16 12*		17 04	*17 12*	18 02	*18 12*	19 04	*19 12*	19 50		
Ely 6	d	12 53			13 19	13 52		14 19	14 52		15 19	15 55		16 19	16 51		17 19	17 51	18 17	18 52	19 19	19 52	20 05		
March	d				13 35			14 35			15 35			16 35			17 35		18 35	19 09	19 35		20 21		
Peterborough 8	a	13 25			13 53	14 23		14 53	15 25		15 53	16 27		16 53	17 24		17 53	18 24	18 53	19 26	19 53	20 25	20 39		
	d	13 26			13 54	14 24		14 54	15 26		15 54	16 30		16 54	17 25		17 54	18 25	18 54	19 28	19 54	20 27	20 45		
Stamford	d				14 07			15 07			16 07			17 07			18 07		19 07		20 07		20 58		
Oakham	d				14 23			15 23			16 23			17 23			18 23		19 23		20 23		21 13		
Melton Mowbray	d				14 34			15 34			16 34			17 34			18 34		19 34		20 34		21 24		
Leicester	d				14 52			15 52			16 52			17 52			18 52		19 52		20 52		21 39		
Nuneaton	a				15 13			16 13			17 14			18 13			19 14		20 13		21 13		22 00		
Birmingham New Street 12	a				15 47			16 47			17 47			18 47			19 47		20 47		21 47		22 35		
Grantham 7	d	13 56				14 58			15 56			17 02			17 55			18 57		20 02		21 00			
Nottingham 8	a	14 26				15 28			16 25			17 38			18 28			19 26		20 44		21 30			
	d	14 42				15 44			16 42			17 42			18 42			19 28							
Langley Mill	d	14 59							16 58			17 58			18 59										
Alfreton	d	15 07				16 06			17 06			18 06			19 07			19 55							
Chesterfield	d	15a18				16a18			17a18			18a18			19a19			20a10							
Sheffield 7	a																								
	d			15 42			16 42			17 42			18 42			19 42									
Stockport	a			16 24			17 24			18 26			19 24			20 24									
Manchester Piccadilly 10	a			16 36			17 35			18 35			19 35			20 36									
Manchester Oxford Road	a			16 40			17 39			18 39						20 39									
Warrington Central	a			16 57			18 02			18 57															
Widnes	a			17 05			18 10			19 05															
Liverpool Lime Street 10	a			17 29			18 32			19 29															

For general notes see front of timetable
For details of catering facilities see Directory of Train Operators

b Change at Ely
c Change at Cambridge
e Change at Cambridge and Ely

Table 49

Stansted Airport → East Anglia → East Midlands → Birmingham and North West England

Route Diagram - see first page of Table 49

		EM ◇	EM ◇	EM ◇	EM ◇	EM ◇	XC ◇	EM ◇	EM ◇	XC ◇	XC ◇	EM ◇	EM ◇	XC ◇
Norwich	d					09 34		10 47					13 49	
Thetford	d					10 01		11 14					14 16	
Ipswich	d						09b55			11c02	11e02			13c02
Stansted Airport	d									12 05				14 05
Audley End	d									12 18				14 18
Cambridge	d						10 48	*11 02*		12 36	13 43			14 36
Ely 6	d					10 32	11 09	11 39		12 54	14 00		14 45	14 53
March	d						11 25			13 10	14 16			15 10
Peterborough 8	a					11 09	11 50	12 16		13 31	14 39		15 24	15 31
	d					11 11	11 52	12 18		13 35	14 41		15 26	15 33
Stamford	d						12 05			13 48	14 54			15 46
Oakham	d						12 19			14 09	15 08			16 00
Melton Mowbray	d						12 30			14 21	15 19			16 11
Leicester	d						12 48			14 40	15 44			16 30
Nuneaton	a						13 11			15 01	16 11			16 57
Birmingham New Street 12	a						13 48			15 37	16 48			17 34
Grantham 7	d					11 56		12 51					15 59	
Nottingham 8	a					12 25	*14f12*	13 29		*16f11*			16 29	*17f17*
	d	09 13	10 32	11 27	12 20			13 37	14 23			15 29	16 32	
Langley Mill	d				12 40			13 51	14 41				16 47	
Alfreton	d		10 54	11 50	12 48			14 00	14 49			15 48	16 55	
Chesterfield	d													
Sheffield 7	a	10 20	11 32	12 32	13 26			14 40	15 26			16 26	17 32	
	d	10 26	11 40	12 39	13 37			14 43	15 34			16 36	17 42	
Stockport	a	11 18	12 23	13 23	14 20			15 24	16 20			17 21	18 24	
Manchester Piccadilly 10	a	11 32	12 36	13 36	14 33			15 34	16 33			17 36	18 35	
Manchester Oxford Road	a	11 39	12 39	13 39	14 39			15 39	16 39			17 39	18 39	
Warrington Central	a	11 56	12 56	13 56	14 56			15 56	16 56			17 56	18 56	
Widnes	a	12 04	13 04	14 04	15 04			16 04	17 04			18 04	19 04	
Liverpool Lime Street 10	a	12 29	13 29	14 29	15 29			16 29	17 29			18 29	19 29	

		EM ◇	EM ◇ ⚲	XC ◇	EM ◇	XC ◇	EM ◇ ⚲	XC ◇	EM ◇	XC ◇	EM ◇	EM ◇	EM ◇
Norwich	d		14 49		15 53		16 57		17 56		18 57	19 44	20 52
Thetford	d		15 16		16 20		17 24		18 23		19 24	20 11	21 19
Ipswich	d		*13 55*	13e02		15b55				17b55	17e02		19e02
Stansted Airport	d			15 18		16 12		17 35		18 35			
Audley End	d			15 31		16 31		17 48		18 48			
Cambridge	d		*15 02*	15 47		16 47	*17 02*	18 09		19 08		*20 02*	*21 02*
Ely 6	d		15 49	16 04		17 04	17 51	18 26	18 48	19 28	19 56	20 35	21 44
March	d			16 21		17 21		18 42		19 44			
Peterborough 8	a		16 22	16 38	17 10	17 40	18 23	19 00	19 20	20 02	20 28	21 08	22 20
	d		16 23	16 40	17 15	17 41	18 30	19 01	19 22	20 06	20 30	21 10	22 22
Stamford	d			16 53		17 54		19 14		20 19		21 23	
Oakham	d			17 07		18 08		19 28		20 33		21 37	
Melton Mowbray	d			17 18		18 19		19 39		20 44		21 48	
Leicester	d			17 43		18 38		20 09		21 02			
Nuneaton	a			18 03		18 58		20 29		21 22			
Birmingham New Street 12	a			18 38		19 36		21 06		22 00			
Grantham 7	d		16 53		17 49		19 00		19 57		21 03		22 51
Nottingham 8	a		17 22	*19f06*	18 27	*20f05*	19 30	*20f38*	20 31	*22f11*	21 32	22 31	23 29
	d	17 15			18 30		19 32						
Langley Mill	d	17 32			18 45								
Alfreton	d	17 40			18 53		19 52						
Chesterfield	d												
Sheffield 7	a	18 17			19 31		20 30						
	d	18 35			19 35		20 35						
Stockport	a	19 20			20 24		21 16						
Manchester Piccadilly 10	a	19 32			20 35		21 31						
Manchester Oxford Road	a	19 39											
Warrington Central	a	19 56											
Widnes	a	20 04											
Liverpool Lime Street 10	a	20 29											

For general notes see front of timetable
For details of catering facilities see Directory of Train Operators

b Change at Ely
c Change at Cambridge
e Change at Cambridge and Ely
f Change at Leicester

Table 49

Stansted Airport → East Anglia → East Midlands → Birmingham and North West England

Sundays

20 July to 7 September

Route Diagram - see first page of Table 49

		EM	EM	EM	EM	XC	EM	EM	XC	XC	EM	EM	XC	EM	XC	EM	XC	EM	XC	EM	XC	EM	EM	EM
		◇	◇	◇	◇	◇	◇	◇	◇	◇	◇	◇	◇	◇	◇	◇	◇	◇	◇	◇	◇	◇	◇	◇
Norwich	d				09 34		10 47					13 49		14 49		15 53		16 57		17 56		18 57	19 44	20 52
Thetford	d				10 01		11 14					14 16		15 16		16 20		17 24		18 23		19 24	20 11	21 19
Ipswich	d					09b55			11c02	11e02			13c02	13 55	13e02		15b55				17b55	17e02		19e02
Stansted Airport ✈	d								12 05				14 05		15 18		16 12		17 35		18 35			
Audley End	d								12 18				14 18		15 31		16 31		17 48		18 48			
Cambridge	d					10 48	*11 02*		12 36	13 43			14 36	*15 02*	15 47		16 47	*17 02*	18 09		19 08		*20 02*	*21 02*
Ely 6	d				10 32	11 09	11 39		12 54	14 00		14 45	14 53	15 49	16 04		17 04	17 51	18 26	18 48	19 28	19 56	20 35	21 44
March	d					11 25			13 10	14 16			15 10		16 21		17 21		18 42		19 44			
Peterborough 8	a				11 09	11 50	12 16		13 31	14 39		15 24	15 31	16 22	16 38	17 10	17 40	18 23	19 00	19 20	20 02	20 28	21 08	22 20
	d				11 11	11 52	12 18		13 35	14 41		15 26	15 33	16 23	16 40	17 15	17 41	18 30	19 01	19 22	20 06	20 30	21 10	22 22
Stamford	d					12 05			13 48	14 54			15 46		16 53		17 54		19 14		20 19		21 23	
Oakham	d					12 19			14 09	15 08			16 00		17 07		18 08		19 28		20 33		21 37	
Melton Mowbray	d					12 30			14 21	15 19			16 11		17 18		18 19		19 39		20 44		21 48	
Leicester	d					12 48			14 40	15 44			16 30		17 43		18 38		20 09		21 02			
Nuneaton	a					13 11			15 01	16 11			16 57		18 03		18 58		20 29		21 22			
Birmingham New Street 12	a					13 48			15 37	16 48			17 34		18 38		19 36		21 06		22 00			
Grantham 7	d				11 56		12 51					15 59		16 53		17 49		19 00		19 57		21 03		22 51
Nottingham 8 🚋	a				12 25	14f12	13 29		16f11			16 29	17f17	17 22	19f06	18 27	20f05	19 30	20f38	20 31	22f11	21 32	22 31	23 29
	d	09 20	10 34	11 41	12 36		13 36	14 33			15 30	16 45		17 35		18 34		19 40						
Langley Mill	d				12 57		13 57	14 54				17 01		17 52		18 52								
Alfreton	d		10 58	12 09	13 05		14 06	15 02			15 56	17 09		18 00		19 00		20 03						
Chesterfield	d	09 54	11 13	12 20	13 17		14 17	15 14			16 13	17 20		18 14		19 14		20 14						
Sheffield 7 🚋	a	10 15	11 32	12 36	13 34		14 33	15 31			16 32	17 38		18 31		19 32		20 31						
	d	10 26	11 40	12 39	13 37		14 37	15 34			16 36	17 42		18 35		19 35		20 35						
Stockport	a	11 18	12 23	13 23	14 20		15 20	16 20			17 21	18 24		19 20		20 24		21 16						
Manchester Piccadilly 10 🚋	a	11 32	12 36	13 36	14 33		15 34	16 33			17 36	18 35		19 32		20 35		21 31						
Manchester Oxford Road	a	11 39	12 39	13 39	14 39		15 39	16 39			17 39	18 39		19 39										
Warrington Central	a	11 56	12 56	13 56	14 56		15 56	16 56			17 56	18 56		19 56										
Widnes	a	12 04	13 04	14 04	15 04		16 04	17 04			18 04	19 04		20 04										
Liverpool Lime Street 10	a	12 29	13 29	14 29	15 29		16 29	17 29			18 29	19 29		20 29										

Sundays

14 September to 2 November

		EM	EM	EM	XC	EM	EM	EM	XC	XC	EM	EM	XC	XC	EM	EM	XC	EM	XC	EM	XC	EM	EM	EM
		◇	◇	◇	◇	◇	◇	◇	◇	◇	◇	◇	◇	◇	◇	◇	◇	◇	◇	◇	◇	◇	◇	◇
Norwich	d						10 47					13 49				15 53		16 57		17 56		18 57	19 44	20 52
Thetford	d						11 14					14 16				16 20		17 24		18 23		19 24	20 11	21 19
Ipswich	d				09b55				11c02	11e02			13c02	13e02			15b55				17b55	17e02		19e02
Stansted Airport ✈	d								12 05				14 05	15 18			16 12		17 35		18 35			
Audley End	d								12 18				14 18	15 31			16 31		17 48		18 48			
Cambridge	d				10 48		*11 02*		12 36	13 43			14 36	15 47			16 47	*17 02*	18 09	*18 02*	19 08		*20 02*	*21 02*
Ely 6	d				11 09		11 39		12 54	14 00		14 45	14 53	16 04			17 04	17 51	18 26	18 48	19 28	19 56	20 35	21 44
March	d				11 25				13 10	14 16			15 10	16 21			17 21		18 42		19 44			
Peterborough 8	a				11 50		12 16		13 31	14 39		15 24	15 31	16 38		17 10	17 40	18 23	19 00	19 20	20 02	20 28	21 08	22 20
	d				11 52		12 18		13 35	14 41		15 26	15 33	16 40		17 15	17 41	18 30	19 01	19 22	20 06	20 30	21 10	22 22
Stamford	d				12 05				13 48	14 54			15 46	16 53			17 54		19 14		20 19		21 23	
Oakham	d				12 19				14 09	15 08			16 00	17 07			18 08		19 28		20 33		21 37	
Melton Mowbray	d				12 30				14 21	15 19			16 11	17 18			18 19		19 39		20 44		21 48	
Leicester	d				12 48				14 40	15 44			16 30	17 43			18 38		20a02		21a01			
Nuneaton	a				13 11				15 01	16 11			16 57	18 03			18 58							
Birmingham New Street 12	a				13 48				15 37	16 48			17 34	18 38			19 36							
Grantham 7	d						12 51					15 59				17 49		19 00		19 57		21 03		22 51
Nottingham 8 🚋	a						13 29					16 29				18 27		19 30	*20 35*	20 31		21 32	22 31	23 29
	d	09 14	10 36	11 40		12 35	13 37	14 25			15 29	16 32			17 31	18 30		19 38						
Langley Mill	d					12 51	13 51	14 41				16 47			17 48	18 45								
Alfreton	d		10 58	12 02		12 59	14 00	14 49			15 48	16 55			17 56	18 53		19 59						
Chesterfield	d	09 49	11 13	12 13		13 11	14 16	15 01			16 01	17 06			18 07	19 06		20 10						
Sheffield 7 🚋	a	10 12	11 35	12 35		13 33	14 37	15 23			16 26	17 28			18 29	19 28		20 32						
	d	10 26	11 40	12 39		13 37	14 43	15 34			16 36	17 42			18 35	19 35		20 35						
Stockport	a	11 18	12 23	13 23		14 20	15 24	16 20			17 21	18 24			19 20	20 24		21 16						
Manchester Piccadilly 10 🚋	a	11 32	12 36	13 36		14 33	15 34	16 33			17 36	18 35			19 32	20 35		21 31						
Manchester Oxford Road	a	11 39	12 39	13 39		14 39	15 39	16 39			17 39	18 39			19 39									
Warrington Central	a	11 56	12 56	13 56		14 56	15 56	16 56			17 56	18 56			19 56									
Widnes	a	12 04	13 04	14 04		15 04	16 04	17 04			18 04	19 04			20 04									
Liverpool Lime Street 10	a	12 29	13 29	14 29		15 29	16 29	17 29			18 29	19 29			20 29									

For general notes see front of timetable
For details of catering facilities see Directory of Train Operators

b Change at Ely
c Change at Cambridge
e Change at Cambridge and Ely
f Change at Leicester

Table 49

Sundays

from 9 November

Stansted Airport → East Anglia → East Midlands → Birmingham and North West England

Route Diagram - see first page of Table 49

		EM ◇	EM ◇	EM ◇	XC ◇	EM ◇	EM ◇	EM ◇	XC ◇	XC ◇	EM ◇	EM ◇	XC ◇	XC ◇	EM ◇	EM ◇	XC ◇	EM ◇ ✠		XC ◇	EM ◇	XC ◇	EM ◇	EM ◇	EM ◇
Norwich	d						10 47					13 49				15 53		16 57			17 56		18 57	19 44	20 52
Thetford	d						11 14					14 16				16 20		17 24			18 23		19 24	20 11	21 19
Ipswich	d				09b55				*11c02*	*11e02*			*13c02*	*13e02*			*15b55*					*17b55*	*17e02*		*19e02*
Stansted Airport ✈	d								12 05				14 05	15 18			16 12			17 35		18 35			
Audley End	d								12 18				14 18	15 31			16 31			17 48		18 48			
Cambridge	d				10 48		*11 02*		12 36	13 43			14 36	15 47			16 47	*17 02*		18 09	*18 02*	19 08		*20 02*	*21 02*
Ely 6	d				11 09		11 39		12 54	14 00		14 45	14 53	16 04			17 04	17 51		18 26	18 48	19 28	19 56	20 35	21 44
March	d				11 25				13 10	14 16			15 10	16 21			17 21			18 42		19 44			
Peterborough 8	a				11 50		12 16		13 31	14 39		15 24	15 31	16 38		17 10	17 40	18 23		19 00	19 20	20 02	20 28	21 08	22 20
	d				11 52		12 18		13 35	14 41		15 26	15 33	16 40		17 15	17 41	18 30		19 01	19 22	20 06	20 30	21 10	22 22
Stamford	d				12 05				13 48	14 54			15 46	16 53			17 54			19 14		20 19		21 23	
Oakham	d				12 19				14 09	15 08			16 00	17 07			18 08			19 28		20 33		21 37	
Melton Mowbray	d				12 30				14 21	15 19			16 11	17 18			18 19			19 39		20 44		21 48	
Leicester	d				12 48				14 40	15 44			16 30	17 43			18 38			20a02		21a01			
Nuneaton	a				13 11				15 01	16 11			16 57	18 03			18 58								
Birmingham New Street 12	a				13 48				15 37	16 48			17 34	18 38			19 36								
Grantham 7	d						12 51					15 59				17 49		19 00			19 57		21 03		22 51
Nottingham 8	a						13 29					16 29				18 27		19 30		*20 35*	20 31		21 32	22 31	23 29
	d	09 19	10 40	11 40		12 34	13 37	14 25			15 28	16 36			17 35	18 34		19 37							
Langley Mill	d	09 35	10 56	11 56		12 50	13 52	14 41			15 44	16 52			17 51	18 50		19 53							
Alfreton	d	09 42	11 04	12 03		12 58	14 01	14 49			15 51	17 00			17 59	18 58		20 00							
Chesterfield	d	09 54	11 15	12 15		13 09	14 12	15 01			16 03	17 11			18 10	19 09		20 12							
Sheffield 7	a	10 17	11 37	12 37		13 33	14 33	15 23			16 29	17 33			18 32	19 31		20 34							
	d	10 26	11 40	12 39		13 37	14 43	15 34			16 36	17 42			18 35	19 35		20 35							
Stockport	a	11 18	12 23	13 23		14 20	15 24	16 20			17 21	18 24			19 20	20 24		21 23							
Manchester Piccadilly 10	a	11 32	12 36	13 36		14 33	15 34	16 33			17 36	18 35			19 32	20 35		21 33							
Manchester Oxford Road	a	11 39	12 39	13 39		14 39	15 39	16 39			17 39	18 39			19 39										
Warrington Central	a	11 56	12 56	13 56		14 56	15 56	16 56			17 56	18 56			19 56										
Widnes	a	12 04	13 04	14 04		15 04	16 04	17 04			18 04	19 04			20 04										
Liverpool Lime Street 10	a	12 29	13 29	14 29		15 29	16 29	17 29			18 29	19 29			20 29										

For general notes see front of timetable
For details of catering facilities see Directory of Train Operators

b Change at Ely
c Change at Cambridge
e Change at Cambridge and Ely

Table 49

Mondays to Fridays

until 5 September

North West England and Birmingham → East Midlands → East Anglia → Stansted Airport

Route Diagram - see first page of Table 49

Miles	Miles	Miles	Miles			EM	EM	XC	EM	XC	EM		XC	EM	XC	EM	XC	EM		XC	EM	XC	EM	XC	EM
						◇		◇	◇	◇	◇		◇	◇	◇	◇	◇	◇		◇	◇	◇	◇	◇	◇
											A					B		B			B		B		B
										(trolley)			(trolley)		(trolley)		(trolley)			(trolley)		(trolley)		(trolley)	
—	0	—	0	**Liverpool Lime Street** 10	d											06 47		07 47			08 52		09 52		10 52
—	12¼	—	12¼	Widnes	d											07 07		08 08			09 09		10 09		11 09
—	18½	—	18½	Warrington Central	d											07 15		08 16			09 17		10 17		11 17
—	34¼	—	34¼	Manchester Oxford Road	d											07 39		08 38			09 38		10 38		11 38
—	34¾	—	34¾	**Manchester Piccadilly** 10	d											07 43		08 42			09 42		10 42		11 42
—	40¾	—	40¾	Stockport	d											07 54		08 53			09 55		10 55		11 55
—	77½	—	77½	**Sheffield** 7	a											08 34		09 35			10 35		11 35		12 35
—	—	—	—		d									07 40		08 38		09 38			10 38		11 38		12 38
—	89¾	—	89¾	Chesterfield	d									07 53		08 52		09 53			10 53		11 53		12 53
—	99¾	—	99¾	Alfreton	d									08 06		09 07		10 04			11 04		12 04		13 04
—	106	—	106	Langley Mill	d									08 13		09 14					11 11				13 11
—	118	—	118	**Nottingham** 8	a									08 29		09 30		10 25			11 30		12 29		13 29
—	—	—	—		d	04 56	05 09	*05b30*	06 13	*06b53*	07 52		*07b30*	08 31	*08b26*	09 35	*09b30*	10 31		*10b30*	11 32	*11b30*	12 34	*12b30*	13 31
—	140¾	—	—	Grantham 7	d		05 51				08 26			09 11		10 08		11 04			12 07		13 08		14 06
0	—	—	—	**Birmingham New Street** 12	d			05 20		06 37			07 21		08 24		09 24			10 24		11 24		12 24	
21	—	—	—	Nuneaton	d			05 48		07 05			07 48		08 53		09 53			10 53		11 53		12 53	
39¾	—	—	—	**Leicester**	d			06 12		07 29			08 14		09 14		10 14			11 14		12 14		13 14	
54¾	—	—	—	Melton Mowbray	d	05 29		06 28	06 52	07 45			08 30		09 30		10 30			11 30		12 30		13 30	
66¼	—	—	—	Oakham	d	05 41		06 41	07 04	07 57			08 41		09 41		10 41			11 41		12 41		13 41	
79¾	—	—	—	Stamford	d	06 02		06 55	07 18	08 13			08 57		09 57		10 57			11 57		12 57		13 57	
92¼	170	—	187¾	**Peterborough** 8	a	06 17	06 27	07 08	07 33	08 28	08 57		09 14	09 38	10 14	10 42	11 14	11 34		12 14	12 42	13 14	13 38	14 14	14 38
—	—	—	—		d	06 27		07 10	07 35	08 31	08 59		09 18	09 41	10 18	10 43	11 18	11 36		12 18	12 43	13 18	13 40	14 18	14 40
106¼	184	—	201¾	March	a	06 42		07 30	07 50	08 46			09 33		10 33		11 33			12 33		13 33		14 33	
113¾	191½	0	209¼	Ely 6	a	07 01		07 51	08 13	09 05	09 35		09 52	10 14	10 52	11 16	11 52	12 14		12 52	13 16	13 52	14 13	14 52	15 13
—	—	14¾	—	**Cambridge**	a	*07 44*		08 07	*08 44*	09 21			10 08	*10 44*	11 08	*11 44*	12 08	*12 44*		13 08	*13 44*	14 08	*14 44*	15 08	*15 44*
—	—	28¾	—	Audley End	a			08 23		09 37			10 22		11 22		12 22			13 22		14 23		15 23	
—	—	39½	—	**Stansted Airport** ✈	a			08 49		09 58			10 49		11 49		12 49			13 49		14 49		15 49	
—	—	—	—	Ipswich	a	*10c03*			*09 26*	*11e03*				*11 25*	*13e03*	*14c03*		*13 25*		*15e03*	*16c03*	*16f03*	*15 25*	*17e03*	*18c03*
137	214¾	—	232¾	Thetford	a	07 28			08 37		10 04			10 38		11 40		12 38			13 40		14 37		15 37
167½	245¼	—	263	**Norwich**	a	08 10			09 16		10 43			11 14		12 15		13 13			14 14		15 13		16 13

		XC	EM		XC	EM	XC	XC	XC	EM		EM	XC	EM	XC	XC	EM		EM	XC	EM	EM	EM		
		◇	◇		◇	◇	◇	◇	◇	◇		◇	◇	◇	◇	◇	◇		◇	◇	◇	◇	◇		
			B			B						B		B			B		B						
		(trolley)			(trolley)		(trolley)	(trolley)		(trolley)											(trolley)	(trolley)			
Liverpool Lime Street 10	d		11 52			12 52				13 52		14 52		15 52			16 52		17 52		18 52	19 52	21 35		
Widnes	d		12 09			13 09				14 09		15 09		16 09			17 09		18 09		19 09	20 09	21 53		
Warrington Central	d		12 17			13 17				14 17		15 17		16 17			17 17		18 17		19 17	20 17	22 01		
Manchester Oxford Road	d		12 38			13 38				14 38		15 38		16 38			17 38		18 40		19 38	20 38	22 23		
Manchester Piccadilly 10	d		12 42			13 42				14 42		15 42		16 42			17 42		18 44		19 42	20 42	22 27		
Stockport	d		12 55			13 55				14 55		15 51		16 53			17 53		18 55		19 55	20 55	22 38		
Sheffield 7	a		13 35			14 35				15 35		16 35		17 38			18 43		19 36		20 39	21 34	23 35		
	d		13 38			14 38				15 38		16 38		17 41			18 45		19 38		20 40	21 38	23 38		
Chesterfield	d		13 53			14 53				15 55		16 55		17 55			19 01		19 56		20 55	21 53	23 59		
Alfreton	d		14 04			15 04				16 06		17 06		18 06			19 12		20 07		21 06	22 04			
Langley Mill	d					15 11						17 13		18 13					20 16		21 13	22 11			
Nottingham 8	a		14 29			15 29				16 34		17 29		18 29			19 37		20 31		21 38	22 36	00 46		
	d	*13b30*	14 31		*14b30*	15 31	*15b30*	*16b07*	*16b30*			17 39	*17b30*	18 31	*18b30*	*19b30*			20 36	*20b07*					
Grantham 7	d		15 07			16 07						18 16		19 09					21 08						
Birmingham New Street 12	d	13 24			14 24		15 24	16 12	16 24				17 24		18 24	19 24				20 24					
Nuneaton	d	13 53			14 53		15 53	16 41	16 56				17 55		18 53	19 51				20 54					
Leicester	d	14 14			15 14		16 14	17 03	17 31				18 16		19 14	20 17				21 15					
Melton Mowbray	d	14 30			15 30		16 30	17 19	17 46				18 32		19 30	20 32				21 32					
Oakham	d	14 41			15 41		16 41	17 30	17 57				18 44		19 41	20 44				21 44					
Stamford	d	14 57			15 57		16 57	17 45	18 14				19 02		19 57	21 00				21 59					
Peterborough 8	a	15 14	15 34		16 14	16 34	17 16	17 58	18 32			18 49	19 19	19 36	20 15	21 16			21 36	22 15					
	d	15 18	15 35		16 18	16 36	17 18	18 00	18 33			18 50	19 19	19 37	20 17	21 18			21 37	22 17					
March	a	15 33			16 33		17 37	18 15	18 51			19 06	19 36		20 38	21 33				22 36					
Ely 6	a	15 52	16 08		16 52	17 09	17 58	18 34	19 09			19 25	19 56	20 13	20 58	21 52			22 10	22 55					
Cambridge	a	16 08	*16 44*		17 08	*17 43*	18 16	18 51	19 29			*19 55*	20 11	*21 01*	21 16	22 08				23 14					
Audley End	a	16 22			17 23				19 43																
Stansted Airport ✈	a	16 49			17 43		18 47		20 08																
Ipswich	a		*17 27*		*19e03*	*20c03*	*19f25*		*21e03*			*22c03*		*21 25*	*00c03*				*23 37*						
Thetford	a		16 33			17 33						19 49		20 36					22 35						
Norwich	a		17 13			18 13						20 22		21 13					23 20						

For general notes see front of timetable
For details of catering facilities see Directory of Train Operators

- **A** From Mansfield Woodhouse (Table 55)
- **B** (trolley) to Nottingham
- **b** Change at Leicester
- **c** Change at Ely and Cambridge
- **e** Change at Cambridge
- **f** Change at Ely

North West England and Birmingham → East Midlands → East Anglia → Stansted Airport

Route Diagram - see first page of Table 49

		EM	EM	XC	EM	XC	EM	XC	EM	XC	EM	EM	XC	EM	EM	XC	EM	EM	XC	EM	EM	XC	EM	EM	XC
		◇		◇	◇	◇	◇	◇	◇	◇	◇	◇	◇	◇	◇	◇	◇	◇	◇	◇	◇	◇	◇	◇	◇
							A					B			B			B			B			B	
						🛒		🛒		🛒	🛒		🛒	🛒		🛒	🛒		🛒	🛒		🛒	🛒		🛒
Liverpool Lime Street [10]	d										06 47			07 47			08 52			09 52			10 52		
Widnes	d										07 07			08 08			09 09			10 09			11 09		
Warrington Central	d										07 15			08 16			09 17			10 17			11 17		
Manchester Oxford Road	d										07 39			08 38			09 38			10 38			11 38		
Manchester Piccadilly [10] 🚊	d										07 43			08 42			09 42			10 42			11 42		
Stockport	d										07 54			08 53			09 55			11 55			11 55		
Sheffield [7] 🚊	a										08 36			09 38			10 38			11 38			12 38		
	d																								
Chesterfield	d								07 53			08 52			09 53			10 53			11 53			12 53	
Alfreton	d								08 06			09 07			10 04			11 04			12 04			13 04	
Langley Mill	d								08 13			09 14						11 11						13 11	
Nottingham [8] 🚊	a								08 29			09 30			10 25			11 30			12 29			13 29	
	d	04 56	05 09	05b30	06 13	06b53	07 52	07b30	08 31	08b26		09 35	09b30		10 31	10b30		11 32	11b30		12 34	12b30		13 31	13b30
Grantham [7]	d		05 51				08 26		09 11			10 08			11 04			12 07			13 08			14 06	
Birmingham New Street [12]	d			05 20		06 37		07 21		08 24			09 24			10 24			11 24			12 24			13 24
Nuneaton	d			05 48		07 05		07 48		08 53			09 53			10 53			11 53			12 53			13 53
Leicester	d			06 12		07 29		08 14		09 14			10 14			11 14			12 14			13 14			14 14
Melton Mowbray	d	05 29		06 28	06 52	07 45		08 30		09 30			10 30			11 30			12 30			13 30			14 30
Oakham	d	05 41		06 41	07 04	07 57		08 41		09 41			10 41			11 41			12 41			13 41			14 41
Stamford	d	06 02		06 55	07 18	08 13		08 57		09 57			10 57			11 57			12 57			13 57			14 57
Peterborough [8]	a	06 17	06 27	07 08	07 33	08 28	08 57	09 14	09 38	10 14		10 42	11 14		11 34	12 14		12 42	13 14		13 38	14 14		14 38	15 14
	d	06 27		07 10	07 35	08 31	08 59	09 18	09 41	10 18		10 43	11 18		11 36	12 18		12 43	13 18		13 40	14 18		14 40	15 18
March	a	06 42		07 30	07 50	08 46		09 33		10 33			11 33			12 33			13 33			14 33			15 33
Ely [6]	a	07 01		07 51	08 13	09 05	09 35	09 52	10 14	10 52		11 16	11 52		12 14	12 52		13 16	13 52		14 13	14 52		15 13	15 52
Cambridge	a	07 44		08 07	08 44	09 21		10 08	10 44	11 08		11 44	12 08		12 44	13 08		13 44	14 08		14 44	15 08		15 44	16 08
Audley End	a			08 23		09 37		10 22		11 22			12 22			13 22			14 22			15 23			16 22
Stansted Airport ✈	a			08 49		09 58		10 49		11 49			12 49			13 49			14 49			15 49			16 49
Ipswich	a	10f03			09 26	11g03			11 25	13g03		14f03			13 25	15g03		16f03	16h03		15 25	17g03		18f03	
Thetford	a	07 28			08 37		10 04		10 38			11 40			12 38			13 40			14 37			15 37	
Norwich	a	08 10			09 16		10 43		11 14			12 15			13 13			14 14			15 13			16 13	

		EM	EM	XC	EM	EM	XC	EM	XC	XC	EM	EM	XC	EM	EM	XC	EM	XC	EM	XC	EM	EM	EM	EM
		◇	◇	◇	◇	◇	◇	◇	◇	◇	◇	◇	◇	◇	◇	◇	◇	◇	◇	◇	◇	◇	◇	◇
			B			B						B												
		🛒		🛒	🛒		🛒	🛒	🛒		🛒			🛒			🛒				🛒	🛒	🛒	
Liverpool Lime Street [10]	d	11 52			12 52			13 52			14 52			15 52			16 52				17 52	18 52	19 52	21 35
Widnes	d	12 09			13 09			14 09			15 09			16 09			17 09				18 09	19 09	20 09	21 53
Warrington Central	d	12 17			13 17			14 17			15 17			16 17			17 17				18 17	19 17	20 17	22 01
Manchester Oxford Road	d	12 38			13 38			14 38			15 38			16 38			17 38				18 40	19 38	20 38	22 23
Manchester Piccadilly [10] 🚊	d	12 42			13 42			14 42			15 42			16 42			17 42				18 44	19 42	20 42	22 27
Stockport	d	12 55			13 55			14 55			15 51			16 53			17 53				18 55	19 55	20j55	22 38
Sheffield [7] 🚊	a	13 38			14 38			15 38			16 38			17 38			18 43				19 40	20 35	21 34	23 35
	d																				19 43	20 37	21 36	23 38
Chesterfield	d		13 53			14 53						16 57									20 06	21 03	21 58	23 59
Alfreton	d		14 04			15 04						17 08									20 17	21 14	22 10	
Langley Mill	d					15 11						17 15									20 26	21 22	22 18	
Nottingham [8] 🚊	a		14 29			15 29						17 31									20 41	21 45	22 41	00 46
	d		14 31	14b30		15 31	15b30		16b07	16b30		17 39	17b30		18 31	18b30		19b30	20 36	20b07				
Grantham [7]	d		15 07			16 07						18 16			19 09				21 08					
Birmingham New Street [12]	d			14 24			15 24		16 12	16 24			17 24			18 24		19 24		20 24				
Nuneaton	d			14 53			15 53		16 41	16 56			17 55			18 53		19 51		20 54				
Leicester	d			15 14			16 14		17 03	17 31			18 16			19 14		20 17		21 15				
Melton Mowbray	d			15 30			16 30		17 19	17 46			18 32			19 30		20 32		21 32				
Oakham	d			15 41			16 41		17 30	17 57			18 44			19 41		20 44		21 44				
Stamford	d			15 57			16 57		17 45	18 14			19 02			19 57		21 00		21 59				
Peterborough [8]	a		15 34	16 14		16 34	17 16		17 58	18 32		18 49	19 19		19 36	20 15		21 16	21 36	22 15				
	d		15 35	16 18		16 36	17 18		18 00	18 33		18 50	19 19		19 37	20 17		21 18	21 37	22 17				
March	a			16 33			17 37		18 15	18 51		19 06	19 36			20 38		21 33		22 36				
Ely [6]	a		16 08	16 52		17 09	17 58		18 34	19 09		19 25	19 56		20 13	20 58		21 52	22 10	22 55				
Cambridge	a		16 44	17 08		17 43	18 16		18 51	19 29		19 55	20 11		21 01	21 16		22 08		23 14				
Audley End	a			17 23						19 43														
Stansted Airport ✈	a			17 43			18 47			20 08														
Ipswich	a		17 27	19g03		20f03	19h25			21g03		22f03			21 25	00f03			23 37					
Thetford	a		16 33			17 33						19 49			20 36				22 35					
Norwich	a		17 13			18 13						20 22			21 13				23 20					

For general notes see front of timetable
For details of catering facilities see Directory of Train Operators

- **A** From Mansfield Woodhouse (Table 55)
- **B** 🛒 to Nottingham
- **b** Change at Leicester
- **f** Change at Ely and Cambridge
- **g** Change at Cambridge
- **h** Change at Ely

Table 49

until 6 September

North West England and Birmingham → East Midlands → East Anglia → Stansted Airport

Route Diagram - see first page of Table 49

		EM	XC ◇	EM ◇		XC ◇	EM ◇	XC ◇		EM ◇	XC ◇	EM ◇		XC ◇	EM ◇	XC ◇		EM ◇	XC ◇	EM ◇		XC ◇	EM ◇	XC ◇	EM ◇
Liverpool Lime Street 10	d											06 47			07 47			08 52		09 52			10 52		11 52
Widnes	d											07 07			08 08			09 09		10 09			11 09		12 09
Warrington Central	d											07 15			08 16			09 17		10 17			11 17		12 17
Manchester Oxford Road	d											07 39			08 38			09 38		10 38			11 38		12 38
Manchester Piccadilly 10	d											07 43			08 42			09 42		10 42			11 42		12 42
Stockport	d											07 54			08 55			09 55		10 55			11 55		12 55
Sheffield 7	a											08 35			09 35			10 35		11 35			12 35		13 35
	d											08 38			09 38			10 38		11 38			12 38		13 38
Chesterfield	d											08 54			09 53			10 53		11 53			12 53		13 53
Alfreton	d											09 07			10 04			11 04		12 04			13 04		14 04
Langley Mill	d											09 14						11 11					13 11		
Nottingham 8	a											09 30			10 24			11 30		12 29			13 29		14 30
	d	05 09	*05b29*	06 19		*06b25*	07 39	*07b30*		08 33	*08b35*	09 32		*09b30*	10 31	*10b30*		11 32	*11b30*	12 31		*12b30*	13 31	*13b30*	14 32
Grantham 7	d	05 53					08 17			09 10		10 16			11 07			12 06		13 08			14 08		15 05
Birmingham New Street 12	d		05 20			06 36		07 24			08 24			09 24		10 24			11 24			12 24		13 24	
Nuneaton	d		05 46			07 04		07 53			08 53			09 53		10 53			11 53			12 53		13 53	
Leicester	d		06 07			07 29		08 14			09 14			10 14		11 14			12 14			13 14		14 14	
Melton Mowbray	d		06 25	06 56		07 45		08 30			09 30			10 30		11 30			12 30			13 30		14 30	
Oakham	d		06 37	07 08		07 57		08 41			09 41			10 41		11 41			12 41			13 41		14 41	
Stamford	d		06 53	07 23		08 13		08 57			09 57			10 57		11 57			12 57			13 57		14 57	
Peterborough 8	a	06 25	07 08	07 38		08 31	08 44	09 14		09 44	10 14	10 43		11 14	11 36	12 14		12 37	13 14	13 35		14 14	14 39	15 14	15 32
	d		07 10	07 39		08 32	08 46	09 18		09 46	10 18	10 46		11 18	11 38	12 18		12 39	13 18	13 37		14 18	14 40	15 18	15 36
March	a		07 29	07 55		08 48		09 33			10 33			11 33		12 33			13 33			14 33		15 33	
Ely 6	a		07 50	08 17		09 06	09 19	09 52		10 19	10 52	11 19		11 52	12 11	12 52		13 12	13 52	14 10		14 52	15 12	15 52	16 09
Cambridge	a		08 06	*08 44*		09 22	*09 44*	10 08		*10 44*	11 08	*11 44*		12 08	*12 44*	13 08		*13 44*	14 08	*14 44*		15 08	*15 44*	16 08	*16 44*
Audley End	a		08 22			09 37		10 22			11 22			12 22		13 22			14 22			15 22		16 22	
Stansted Airport ✈	a		08 49			09 58		10 49			11 49			12 49		13 49			14 49			15 49		16 49	
Ipswich	a			*09 25*		*11c03*	*12e03*			*11 27*	*13c03*	*14e03*			*13 27*	*15c03*		*16e03*		*15 25*		*17c03*	*18e03*		*17 27*
Thetford	a			08 38			09 44			10 44		11 44			12 37			13 36		14 37			15 37		16 35
Norwich	a			09 12			10 17			11 12		12 17			13 13			14 13		15 13			16 13		17 13

		XC ◇		EM ◇	XC ◇	XC ◇		EM ◇	EM ◇	XC ◇		EM ◇	XC ◇	XC ◇		EM ◇	EM ◇	XC ◇		EM ◇	EM ◇	EM ◇			
Liverpool Lime Street 10	d			12 52				13 52	14 52			15 52				16 52	17 52			18 52	19 52				
Widnes	d			13 09				14 09	15 09			16 09				17 09	18 09			19 09	20 09				
Warrington Central	d			13 17				14 17	15 17			16 17				17 17	18 17			19 17	20 17				
Manchester Oxford Road	d			13 38				14 38	15 38			16 38				17 38	18 39			19 38	20 38				
Manchester Piccadilly 10	d			13 42				14 42	15 42			16 42				17 42	18 44			19 42	20 42	21 42			
Stockport	d			13 55				14 55	15 55			16 53				17 55	18 55			19 55	20 55	21 52			
Sheffield 7	a			14 35				15 35	16 35			17 38				18 35	19 35			20 34	21 34	22 31			
	d			14 38				15 38	16 38			17 41				18 38	19 38			20 40	21 37	22 36			
Chesterfield	d			14 53				15 53	16 55			17 55				18 53	19 53			20 55	21 53	22 50			
Alfreton	d			15 04				16 04	17 06			18 06				19 04	20 04			21 06	22 04				
Langley Mill	d			15 11				16 11	17 13			18 13								21 13	22 11				
Nottingham 8	a			15 30				16 35	17 31			18 29				19 29	20 29			21 35	22 38	23 26			
	d	*14b30*		15 32	*15b30*	*16b30*			17 36	*17b30*		18 31	*18b30*	*19b30*			20 32	*20b30*							
Grantham 7	d			16 06					18 13			19 06					21 10								
Birmingham New Street 12	d	14 24			15 24	16 24				17 24			18 24	19 24				20 27							
Nuneaton	d	14 53			15 53	16 53				17 53			18 53	19 53				20 54							
Leicester	d	15 14			16 14	17 14				18 14			19 14	20 19				21 15							
Melton Mowbray	d	15 30			16 30	17 30				18 30			19 30	20 36				21 33							
Oakham	d	15 41			16 41	17 41				18 41			19 41	20 47				21 45							
Stamford	d	15 57			16 57	17 57				18 57			19 57	21 04				21 59							
Peterborough 8	a	16 14		16 37	17 14	18 14			18 40	19 14		19 33	20 14	21 20			21 37	22 15							
	d	16 18		16 38	17 18	18 18			18 42	19 18		19 35	20 18	21 21			21 39	22 17							
March	a	16 33			17 37	18 33			18 57	19 33			20 33	21 37			21 54	22 36							
Ely 6	a	16 56		17 11	17 58	18 52			19 16	19 52		20 08	20 52	21 55			22 13	22 54							
Cambridge	a	17 15		*17 44*	18 15	19 13			*19 55*	20 08		*20 55*	21 13	22 16				23 16							
Audley End	a	17 36			18 36					20 27															
Stansted Airport ✈	a	17 58			18 55					20 50															
Ipswich	a	*19c03*		*20e03*	*19f25*	*21 03*			*22e03*			*21 27*	*23 03*				*23 32*								
Thetford	a			17 38					19 40			20 36					22 38								
Norwich	a			18 13					20 13			21 13					23 20								

For general notes see front of timetable
For details of catering facilities see Directory of Train Operators

b Change at Leicester
c Change at Cambridge
e Change at Ely and Cambridge
f Change at Ely

Table 49

from 13 September

North West England and Birmingham → East Midlands → East Anglia → Stansted Airport

Route Diagram - see first page of Table 49

		EM	XC	EM	XC	EM	XC	EM	XC	EM	EM	XC	EM	EM	XC	EM	EM	XC	EM	EM	XC	EM	EM	XC	EM
			◇	◇	◇	◇	◇	◇	◇	◇	◇	◇	◇	◇	◇	◇	◇	◇	◇	◇	◇	◇	◇	◇	◇
Liverpool Lime Street 10	d									06 47			07 47			08 52			09 52			10 52			11 52
Widnes	d									07 07			08 08			09 09			10 09			11 09			12 09
Warrington Central	d									07 15			08 16			09 17			10 17			11 17			12 17
Manchester Oxford Road	d									07 39			08 38			09 38			10 38			11 38			12 38
Manchester Piccadilly 10	d									07 43			08 42			09 42			10 42			11 42			12 42
Stockport	d									07 54			08 55			09 55			10 55			11 55			12 55
Sheffield 7	a									08 35			09 38			10 38			11 38			12 38			13 38
	d																								
Chesterfield	d										08 54			09 53			10 53			11 53			12 53		
Alfreton	d										09 07			10 04			11 04			12 04			13 04		
Langley Mill	d										09 14						11 11						13 11		
Nottingham 8	a										09 30			10 24			11 30			12 29			13 29		
	d	05 09		06 19		07 39		08 33			09 32			10 31			11 32			12 31			13 31		
Grantham 7	d	05 53				08 17		09 10			10 16			11 07			12 06			13 08			14 08		
Birmingham New Street 12	d		05 20		06 36		07 24		08 24			09 24			10 24			11 24			12 24			13 24	
Nuneaton	d		05 46		07 04		07 53		08 53			09 53			10 53			11 53			12 53			13 53	
Leicester	d		06 07		07 29		08 14		09 14			10 14			11 14			12 14			13 14			14 14	
Melton Mowbray	d		06 25	06 56	07 45		08 30		09 30			10 30			11 30			12 30			13 30			14 30	
Oakham	d		06 37	07 08	07 57		08 41		09 41			10 41			11 41			12 41			13 41			14 41	
Stamford	d		06 53	07 23	08 13		08 57		09 57			10 57			11 57			12 57			13 57			14 57	
Peterborough 8	a	06 25	07 08	07 38	08 31	08 44	09 14	09 44	10 14		10 43	11 14		11 36	12 14		12 37	13 14		13 35	14 14		14 39	15 14	
	d		07 10	07 39	08 32	08 46	09 18	09 46	10 18		10 46	11 18		11 38	12 18		12 39	13 18		13 37	14 18		14 40	15 18	
March	a		07 29	07 55	08 48		09 33		10 33			11 33			12 33			13 33			14 33			15 33	
Ely 6	a		07 50	08 17	09 06	09 19	09 52	10 19	10 52		11 19	11 52		12 11	12 52		13 12	13 52		14 10	14 52		15 12	15 52	
Cambridge	a		08 06	*08 44*	09 22	*09 44*	10 08	*10 44*	11 08		*11 44*	12 08		*12 44*	13 08		*13 44*	14 08		*14 44*	15 08		*15 44*	16 08	
Audley End	a		08 22		09 37		10 22		11 22			12 22			13 22			14 22			15 22			16 22	
Stansted Airport ✈	a		08 49		09 58		10 49		11 49			12 49			13 49			14 49			15 49			16 49	
Ipswich	a			*09 25*	*11b03*	*12c03*		*11 27*	*13b03*		*14c03*			*13 27*	*15b03*		*16c03*			*15 25*	*17b03*		*18c03*		
Thetford	a			08 38		09 44		10 44			11 44			12 37			13 36			14 37			15 37		
Norwich	a			09 12		10 17		11 12			12 17			13 13			14 13			15 13			16 13		

		EM	XC	EM	EM	XC	EM	XC	EM	EM	XC	EM	EM	XC	EM	EM	XC	EM	XC	EM	EM	EM	EM
		◇	◇	◇	◇	◇	◇	◇	◇	◇	◇	◇	◇	◇	◇	◇	◇	◇	◇	◇	◇	◇	◇
Liverpool Lime Street 10	d			12 52			13 52		14 52			15 52			16 52					17 52	18 52	19 52	
Widnes	d			13 09			14 09		15 09			16 09			17 09					18 09	19 09	20 09	
Warrington Central	d			13 17			14 17		15 17			16 17			17 17					18 17	19 17	20 17	
Manchester Oxford Road	d			13 38			14 38		15 38			16 38			17 38					18 39	19 38	20 38	
Manchester Piccadilly 10	d			13 42			14 42		15 42			16 42			17 42					18 44	19 42	20 42	21 42
Stockport	d			13 55			14 55		15 55			16 53			17 55					18 55	19 55	20 55	21 52
Sheffield 7	a			14 38			15 38		16 38			17 38			18 38					19 35	20 34	21 34	22 31
	d																			19 43	20 36	21 36	22 34
Chesterfield	d	13 53			14 53					16 55										20 06	21 03	21 58	22 54
Alfreton	d	14 04			15 04					17 06										20 17	21 14	22 10	
Langley Mill	d				15 11					17 13										20 26	21 22	22 18	
Nottingham 8	a	14 30			15 30					17 31										20 41	21 45	22 41	23 36
	d	14 32			15 32					17 36			18 31			19 32		20 32					
Grantham 7	d	15 05			16 06					18 13			19 06			20 11		21 10					
Birmingham New Street 12	d		14 24			15 24		16 24			17 24			18 24			19 24		20 27				
Nuneaton	d		14 53			15 53		16 53			17 53			18 53			19 53		20 54				
Leicester	d		15 14			16 14		17 14			18 14			19 14			20 19		21 15				
Melton Mowbray	d		15 30			16 30		17 30			18 30			19 30			20 36		21 33				
Oakham	d		15 41			16 41		17 41			18 41			19 41			20 47		21 45				
Stamford	d		15 57			16 57		17 57			18 57			19 57			21 04		21 59				
Peterborough 8	a	15 32	16 14		16 37	17 14		18 14		18 40	19 14		19 33	20 14		20 38	21 20	21 37	22 15				
	d	15 36	16 18		16 38	17 18		18 18		18 42	19 18		19 35	20 18		20 39	21 21	21 39	22 17				
March	a		16 33			17 37		18 33		18 57	19 33			20 33		20 55	21 37	21 54	22 36				
Ely 6	a	16 09	16 56		17 11	17 58		18 52		19 16	19 52		20 08	20 52		21 13	21 55	22 13	22 54				
Cambridge	a	*16 44*	17 15		*17 44*	18 15		19 13		*19 55*	20 08		*20 55*	21 13		21 31	22 16		23 16				
Audley End	a		17 36			18 36					20 27												
Stansted Airport ✈	a		17 58			18 55					20 50												
Ipswich	a	*17 27*	*19b03*		*20c03*	*19e25*		*21 03*		*22c03*			*21 27*			*23 03*		*23 32*					
Thetford	a	16 35			17 38					19 40			20 36					22 38					
Norwich	a	17 13			18 13					20 13			21 13					23 20					

For general notes see front of timetable
For details of catering facilities see Directory of Train Operators

b Change at Cambridge
c Change at Ely and Cambridge
e Change at Ely

Table 49

Sundays
until 13 July

North West England and Birmingham → East Midlands → East Anglia → Stansted Airport

Route Diagram - see first page of Table 49

		EM ◇	EM ◇ ⚲	XC	EM ◇	EM ◇ ⚲	XC ◇	EM ◇ ⚲	XC ◇	EM ◇	XC ◇	EM ◇	XC ◇	EM ◇	XC ◇	EM ◇	XC ◇	EM ◇	EM ◇	XC ◇	EM ◇	EM ◇	EM ◇
Liverpool Lime Street 10	d									12 52		13 52		14 52		15 52		16 52	17 52		18 52	19 52	21 22
Widnes	d									13 10		14 10		15 10		16 10		17 10	18 10		19 10	20 10	21 40
Warrington Central	d									13 18		14 18		15 18		16 18		17 18	18 18		19 18	20 18	21 47
Manchester Oxford Road	d									13 41		14 39		15 39		16 39		17 39	18 39		19 39	20 39	22 08
Manchester Piccadilly 10	d							12 43		13 46		14 43		15 43		16 43		17 43	18 42		19 42	20 43	22 12
Stockport	d							12 53		13 57		14 54		15 54		16 54		17 54	18 56		19 54	20 53	22 26
Sheffield 7	a							13 38		14 36		15 34		16 34		17 34		18 36	19 35		20 35	21 38	23 23
	d		10 36			12 43		13 41		14 44		15 36		16 36		17 36		18 40	19 37		20 37	21 40	23 26
Chesterfield	d																						
Alfreton	d		11 10			13 17		14 24		15 18		16 10		17 13		18 10		19 14	20 11		21 13	22 15	00 01
Langley Mill	d									15 26		16 18		17 21		18 18		19 22			21 20	22 23	00 08
Nottingham 8	a		11 30			13 38		14 46		15 44		16 33		17 36		18 36		19 43	20 32		21 41	22 44	00 30
	d	09 53	11 40	11b19	12 32	13 44	13b26	14 50	14b18	15 48	15b39	16 40	16b39	17 40	17b06	18 46	18b17		20 35	19b36			
Grantham 7	d	10 27	12 18		13 14	14 20				16 24		17c24		18 18		19 22			21 19				
Birmingham New Street 12	d			11 26			13 36		14 34		15 32		16 34		17 34		18 34			20 28			
Nuneaton	d			11 53			14 04		15 02		16 01		17 03		18 03		19 02			20 58			
Leicester	d			12 21			14 28		15 24		16 27		17 27		18 28		19 24			21 21			
Melton Mowbray	d			12 38			14 45		15 43		16 44		17 46		18 46		19 41			21 38			
Oakham	d			12 51			14 57		15 55		16 56		17 58		18 59		19 52			21 50			
Stamford	d			13 04			15 11		16 09		17 10		18 12		19 13		20 08			22 04			
Peterborough 8	a	11 07	12 52	13 19	13 41	14 53	15 25	16 04	16 26	16 55	17 26	17 51	18 27	18 54	19 28	19 51	20 23		21 51	22 19			
	d	11 09	12 54	13 21	13 43	14 56	15 28	16 05	16 28	17 00	17 28	17 53	18 29	18 55	19 29	19 55	20 25		21 55	22 24			
March	a	11 24		13 36			15 43		16 43		17 43		18 44		19 45		20 45			22 40			
Ely 6	a	11 48	13 32	14 02	14 21	15 34	16 06	16 38	17 06	17 33	18 02	18 31	19 03	19 28	20 04	20 28	21 04		22 28	22 59			
Cambridge	a	12 34	14 14	14 19	15 09	16 14	16 22	17 14	17 23	18 14	18 21	19 14	19 20	20 14	20 21	21 14	21 19		23 13	23 17			
Audley End	a			14 34			16 39		17 38				19 38		20 38		21 34						
Stansted Airport ✈	a			14 58			16 59		17 59				19 59		20 59		21 54						
Ipswich	a	13 25			15 27		17e25		20f34		19e27		22f34		21e18		00f21						
Thetford	a	12 15	13 56		14 48	15 58		17 02		18 00		18 55		19 54		20 52			22 52				
Norwich	a	12 59	14 35		15 28	16 37		17 35		18 35		19 29		20 28		21 25			23 35				

Sundays
20 July to 7 September

		EM ◇	EM ◇ ⚲	XC	EM ◇	EM ◇ ⚲	XC ◇	EM ◇ ⚲	XC ◇	EM ◇	XC ◇	EM ◇	XC ◇	EM ◇	XC ◇	EM ◇	XC ◇	EM ◇	EM ◇	XC ◇	EM ◇	EM ◇	EM ◇
Liverpool Lime Street 10	d									12 52		13 52		14 52		15 52		16 52	17 52		18 52	19 52	21 22
Widnes	d									13 10		14 10		15 10		16 10		17 10	18 10		19 10	20 10	21 40
Warrington Central	d									13 18		14 18		15 18		16 18		17 18	18 18		19 18	20 18	21 47
Manchester Oxford Road	d									13 41		14 39		15 39		16 39		17 39	18 39		19 39	20 39	22 08
Manchester Piccadilly 10	d							12 43		13 48		14 43		15 43		16 43		17 43	18 42		19 42	20 43	22 12
Stockport	d							12 53		13 58		14 54		15 54		16 54		17 54	18 56		19 54	20 53	22 26
Sheffield 7	a							13 38		14 38		15 34		16 34		17 34		18 36	19 35		20 35	21 38	23 23
	d		10 34			12 52		13 58		14 41		15 39		16 39		17 39		18 40	19 37		20 38	21 41	23 27
Chesterfield	d		10 47			13 06		14 13		14 56		15 54		16 54		17 53		18 54	19 53		20 54	21 56	23 41
Alfreton	d					13 18		14 24		15 07		16 05		17 08		18 04		19 05	20 05		21 05	22 08	23 52
Langley Mill	d									15 15		16 12		17 17		18 12		19 17			21 16	22 19	00 01
Nottingham 8	a		11 18			13 40		14 47		15 36		16 33		17 32		18 30		19 39	20 29		21 38	22 41	00 23
	d	09 53	11 40	10b16	12 32	13 45	13b26	14 53	14b18	15 48	15b39	16 40	16b39	17 38	17b07	18 46	18b17		20 35	19b36			
Grantham 7	d	10 27	12 18		13 14	14 20				16 24		17c24		18 18		19 22			21 19				
Birmingham New Street 12	d			11 26			13 36		14 34		15 32		16 34		17 34		18 34			20 28			
Nuneaton	d			11 53			14 04		15 02		16 01		17 03		18 03		19 02			20 58			
Leicester	d			12 21			14 28		15 24		16 27		17 27		18 28		19 24			21 21			
Melton Mowbray	d			12 38			14 45		15 43		16 44		17 46		18 46		19 41			21 38			
Oakham	d			12 51			14 57		15 55		16 56		17 58		18 59		19 52			21 50			
Stamford	d			13 04			15 11		16 09		17 10		18 12		19 13		20 08			22 04			
Peterborough 8	a	11 07	12 52	13 19	13 41	14 53	15 25	16 04	16 26	16 55	17 26	17 51	18 27	18 54	19 28	19 51	20 23		21 51	22 19			
	d	11 09	12 54	13 21	13 43	14 56	15 28	16 05	16 28	17 00	17 28	17 53	18 29	18 55	19 29	19 55	20 25		21 55	22 24			
March	a	11 24		13 36			15 43		16 43		17 43		18 44		19 45		20 45			22 40			
Ely 6	a	11 48	13 32	14 02	14 21	15 34	16 06	16 38	17 06	17 33	18 02	18 31	19 03	19 28	20 04	20 28	21 04		22 28	22 59			
Cambridge	a	12 34	14 14	14 19	15 09	16 14	16 22	17 14	17 23	18 14	18 21	19 14	19 20	20 14	20 21	21 14	21 19		23 13	23 17			
Audley End	a			14 34			16 39		17 38				19 38		20 38		21 34						
Stansted Airport ✈	a			14 58			16 59		17 59				19 59		20 59		21 54						
Ipswich	a	13 25			15 27		17e25		20f34		19e27		22f34		21e18		00f21						
Thetford	a	12 15	13 56		14 48	15 58		17 02		18 00		18 55		19 54		20 52			22 52				
Norwich	a	12 59	14 35		15 28	16 37		17 35		18 35		19 29		20 28		21 25			23 35				

For general notes see front of timetable
For details of catering facilities see Directory of Train Operators

b Change at Leicester
c Arr. 1715
e Change at Ely
f Change at Ely and Cambridge

Table 49

Sundays

14 September to 2 November

North West England and Birmingham → East Midlands → East Anglia → Stansted Airport

Route Diagram - see first page of Table 49

		XC	EM ◇	EM ◇	XC ◇	EM ◇	XC ◇	EM ◇	XC ◇	EM ◇	XC ◇	EM ◇	XC ◇	EM ◇	XC ◇	EM ◇	EM ◇	XC ◇	EM ◇	EM ◇	EM ◇
Liverpool Lime Street 10	d							12 52		13 52		14 52		15 52		16 52	17 52		18 52	19 52	21 22
Widnes	d							13 10		14 10		15 10		16 10		17 10	18 10		19 10	20 10	21 40
Warrington Central	d							13 18		14 18		15 18		16 18		17 18	18 18		19 18	20 18	21 47
Manchester Oxford Road	d							13 41		14 39		15 39		16 39		17 39	18 39		19 39	20 39	22 08
Manchester Piccadilly 10	d					12 43		13 48		14 43		15 43		16 43		17 43	18 42		19 42	20 43	22 12
Stockport	d					12 53		13 58		14 54		15 54		16 54		17 54	18 56		19 54	20 53	22 26
Sheffield 7	a					13 37		14 38		15 34		16 34		17 34		18 36	19 35		20 35	21 38	23 23
	d			12 43		13 42		14 46		15 36		16 36		17 36		18 40	19 37		20 37	21 40	23 27
Chesterfield	d			13 05		14 04		15 09		15 59		16 58		17 58		19 03	19 59		21 00	22 05	23 49
Alfreton	d			13 21		14 15		15 20		16 10		17 12		18 09		19 14	20 10		21 12	22 17	23 59
Langley Mill	d							15 27		16 17		17 20		18 18		19 21			21 20	22 25	00 07
Nottingham 8	a			13 42		14 37		15 45		16 33		17 35		18 35		19 43	20 31		21 41	22 46	00 30
	d		12 32	13 44		14 50		15 48		16 40		17 38		18 46			20 35				
Grantham 7	d		13 14	14 20				16 24		17b24		18 18		19 22			21 19				
Birmingham New Street 12	d	11 26			13 36		14 34		15 32		16 34		17 34		18 34						
Nuneaton	d	11 53			14 04		15 02		16 01		17 03		18 03		19 02						
Leicester	d	12 21			14 28		15 24		16 27		17 27		18 28		19 24			21 19			
Melton Mowbray	d	12 38			14 45		15 43		16 44		17 46		18 46		19 41			21 36			
Oakham	d	12 51			14 57		15 55		16 56		17 58		18 59		19 52			21 48			
Stamford	d	13 04			15 11		16 09		17 10		18 12		19 13		20 08			22 02			
Peterborough 8	a	13 19	13 41	14 53	15 25	16 04	16 26	16 55	17 26	17 51	18 27	18 54	19 28	19 51	20 23		21 51	22 18			
	d	13 21	13 43	14 56	15 28	16 05	16 28	17 00	17 28	17 53	18 29	18 55	19 29	19 55	20 25		21 55	22 24			
March	a	13 36			15 43		16 43		17 43		18 44		19 45		20 45			22 40			
Ely 6	a	14 02	14 21	15 34	16 06	16 38	17 06	17 33	18 02	18 31	19 03	19 28	20 04	20 28	21 04		22 28	22 59			
Cambridge	a	14 19	*15 09*	*16 14*	16 22	*17 14*	17 23	*18 14*	18 21	*19 14*	19 20	*20 14*	20 21	*21 14*	21 19		*23 13*	23 17			
Audley End	a	14 34			16 39		17 38				19 38		20 38		21 34						
Stansted Airport ✈	a	14 58			16 59		17 59				19 59		20 59		21 54						
Ipswich	a		*15 27*		*17c25*		*20e34*		*19c27*		*22e34*		*21c18*		*00e21*						
Thetford	a		14 48	15 58		17 02		18 00		18 55		19 54		20 52			22 52				
Norwich	a		15 28	16 37		17 35		18 35		19 29		20 28		21 25			23 35				

Sundays

from 9 November

		XC	EM ◇	EM ◇	XC ◇	EM ◇	XC ◇	EM ◇	XC ◇	EM ◇	XC ◇	EM ◇	XC ◇	EM ◇	XC ◇	EM ◇	EM ◇	XC ◇	EM ◇	EM ◇	EM ◇
Liverpool Lime Street 10	d							12 52		13 52		14 52		15 52		16 52	17 52		18 52	19 52	21 22
Widnes	d							13 10		14 10		15 10		16 10		17 10	18 10		19 10	20 10	21 40
Warrington Central	d							13 18		14 18		15 18		16 18		17 18	18 18		19 18	20 18	21 47
Manchester Oxford Road	d							13 41		14 39		15 39		16 39		17 39	18 39		19 39	20 39	22 08
Manchester Piccadilly 10	d					12 43		13 48		14 43		15 43		16 43		17 43	18 42		19 42	20 43	22 12
Stockport	d					12 53		13 58		14 54		15 54		16 54		17 54	18 56		19 54	20 53	22 26
Sheffield 7	a					13 38		14 38		15 34		16 34		17 34		18 36	19 35		20 35	21 38	23 23
	d			12 43		13 41		14 44		15 36		16 36		17 36		18 40	19 37		20 37	21 40	23 26
Chesterfield	d			13 05		14 04		15 09		15 59		16 58		17 58		19 03	19 59		21 01	22 03	23 48
Alfreton	d					14 15		15 20		16 10		17 12		18 09		19 14	20 10		21 12	22 15	23 59
Langley Mill	d							15 27		16 17		17 20		18 18		19 21			21 20	22 22	00 07
Nottingham 8	a			13 35		14 37		15 45		16 33		17 35		18 35		19 43	20 31		21 41	22 43	00 29
	d		12 32	13 47		14 50		15 48		16 40		17 38		18 46			20 35				
Grantham 7	d		13 14	14 20				16 24		17b24		18 18		19 22			21 19				
Birmingham New Street 12	d	11 26			13 36		14 34		15 32		16 34		17 34		18 34						
Nuneaton	d	11 53			14 04		15 02		16 01		17 03		18 03		19 02						
Leicester	d	12 21			14 28		15 24		16 27		17 27		18 28		19 24			21 19			
Melton Mowbray	d	12 38			14 45		15 43		16 44		17 46		18 46		19 41			21 36			
Oakham	d	12 51			14 57		15 55		16 56		17 58		18 59		19 52			21 48			
Stamford	d	13 04			15 11		16 09		17 10		18 12		19 13		20 08			22 02			
Peterborough 8	a	13 19	13 41	14 53	15 25	16 04	16 26	16 55	17 26	17 51	18 27	18 54	19 28	19 51	20 23		21 51	22 18			
	d	13 21	13 43	14 56	15 28	16 05	16 28	17 00	17 28	17 53	18 29	18 55	19 29	19 55	20 25		21 55	22 24			
March	a	13 36			15 43		16 43		17 43		18 44		19 45		20 45			22 40			
Ely 6	a	14 02	14 21	15 34	16 06	16 38	17 06	17 33	18 02	18 31	19 03	19 28	20 04	20 28	21 04		22 28	22 59			
Cambridge	a	14 19	*15 09*	*16 14*	16 22	*17 14*	17 23	*18 14*	18 21	*19 14*	19 20	*20 14*	20 21	*21 14*	21 19		*23 13*	23 17			
Audley End	a	14 34			16 39		17 38				19 38		20 38		21 34						
Stansted Airport ✈	a	14 58			16 59		17 59				19 59		20 59		21 54						
Ipswich	a		*15 27*		*17c25*		*20e34*		*19c27*		*22e34*		*21c18*		*00e21*						
Thetford	a		14 48	15 58		17 02		18 00		18 55		19 54		20 52			22 52				
Norwich	a		15 28	16 37		17 35		18 35		19 29		20 28		21 25			23 35				

For general notes see front of timetable
For details of catering facilities see Directory of Train Operators

b Arr. 1715
c Change at Ely
e Change at Ely and Cambridge

Network Diagram for Tables 50, 55, 56, 57

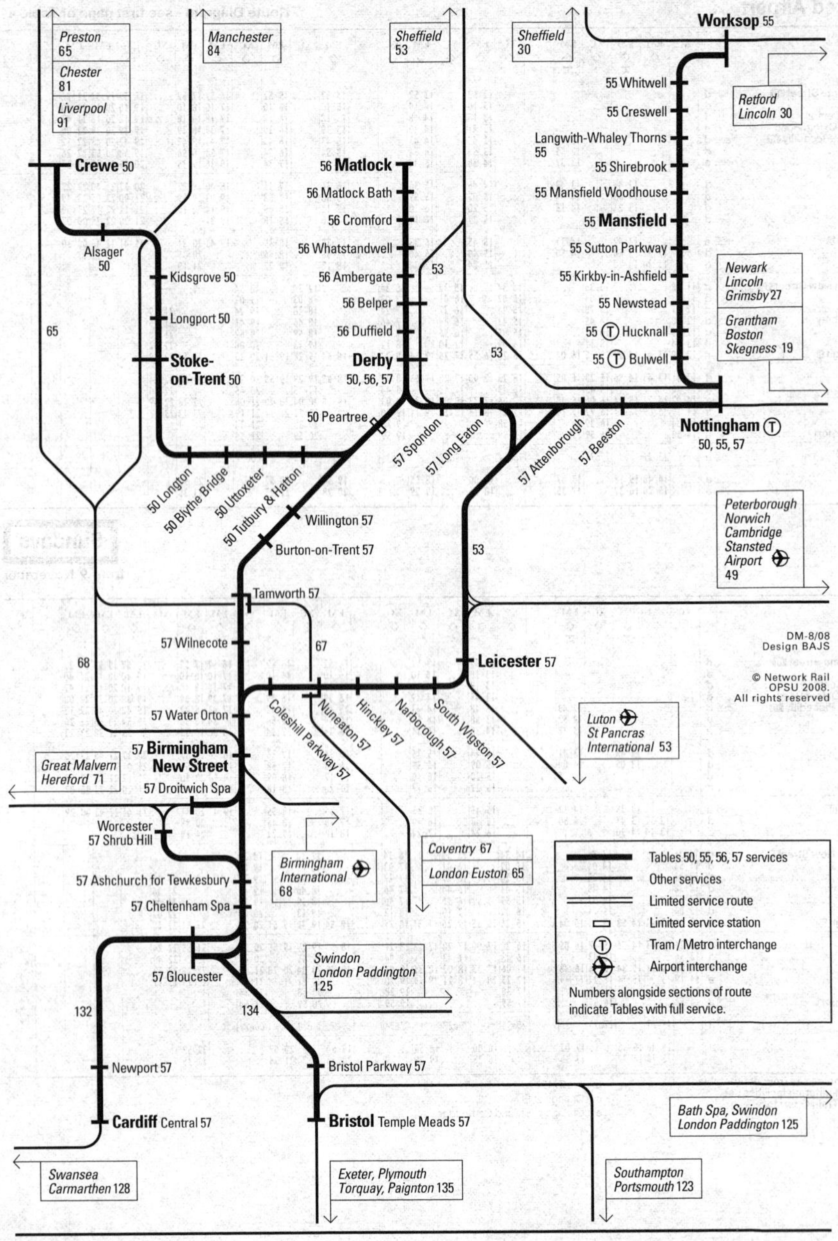

Preston 65
Chester 81
Liverpool 91
Manchester 84
Sheffield 53
Sheffield 30
Worksop 55
Retford Lincoln 30
55 Whitwell
55 Creswell
Langwith-Whaley Thorns 55
55 Shirebrook
55 Mansfield Woodhouse
55 Mansfield
55 Sutton Parkway
55 Kirkby-in-Ashfield
55 Newstead
55 Hucknall
55 Bulwell
Newark Lincoln Grimsby 27
Grantham Boston Skegness 19
Nottingham
50, 55, 57
Crewe 50
Alsager 50
Kidsgrove 50
Longport 50
Stoke-on-Trent 50
65
56 Matlock
56 Matlock Bath
56 Cromford
56 Whatstandwell
56 Ambergate
56 Belper
56 Duffield
Derby
50, 56, 57
53
50 Peartree
57 Spondon
57 Long Eaton
57 Attenborough
57 Beeston
50 Longton
50 Blythe Bridge
50 Uttoxeter
50 Tutbury & Hatton
Willington 57
Burton-on-Trent 57
Peterborough Norwich Cambridge Stansted Airport 49
Tamworth 57
57 Wilnecote
67
68
Leicester 57
DM-8/08
Design BAJS
© Network Rail OPSU 2008. All rights reserved
57 Water Orton
Coleshill Parkway 57
Nuneaton 57
Hinckley 57
Narborough 57
South Wigston 57
Luton St Pancras International 53
Great Malvern Hereford 71
57 Birmingham New Street
57 Droitwich Spa
Worcester 57 Shrub Hill
Birmingham International 68
Coventry 67
London Euston 65
57 Ashchurch for Tewkesbury
57 Cheltenham Spa
57 Gloucester
Swindon London Paddington 125
132
134
Tables 50, 55, 56, 57 services
Other services
Limited service route
Limited service station
Tram / Metro interchange
Airport interchange
Numbers alongside sections of route indicate Tables with full service.
Newport 57
Bristol Parkway 57
Cardiff Central 57
Bristol Temple Meads 57
Bath Spa, Swindon London Paddington 125
Swansea Carmarthen 128
Exeter, Plymouth Torquay, Paignton 135
Southampton Portsmouth 123

Nottingham and Derby → Stoke-on-Trent and Crewe

Network Diagram - see first page of Table 50

Miles			NT	NT	EM A	EM B	NT	EM	EM	EM	EM	EM	EM	EM	EM	EM	EM	EM	NT	EM	EM	EM
0	**Nottingham** 8 🚌	d			05 55	05 55																
16	**Derby** 10	d			06 31	06 39		07 30	08 28	09 28	10 28	11 28	12 28	13 28	14 28	15 28	16 28	17 45		18 44	19 28	20 28
17¼	Peartree	d						07 33									16 31					
27½	Tutbury & Hatton	d			06 52	06 52		07 45	08 44	09 41	10 41	11 41	12 41	13 41	14 42	15 41	16 43	17 58		18 57	19 41	20 46
35¼	Uttoxeter	d			07 02	07 02		07 54	08 53	09 51	10 51	11 51	12 51	13 51	14 52	15 51	16 52	18 08		19 07	19 51	20 55
46½	Blythe Bridge	d			07 15	07 15		08 07	09 06	10 04	11 04	12 04	13 04	14 04	15 05	16 04	17 05	18 21		19 20	20 04	21 08
49½	Longton	d			07 20	07 20		08 13	09 12	10 09	11 09	12 09	13 09	14 09	15 10	16 09	17 11			19 25	20 09	21 14
51	**Stoke-on-Trent**	a			07 27	07 27		08 21	09 18	10 17	11 17	12 17	13 17	14 18	15 17	16 17	17 17	18 32		19 32	20 17	21 21
—		d	06 56	07 13	07 27	07 27	07 40	08 21	09 19	10 18	11 18	12 18	13 18	14 18	15 18	16 18	17 18	18 32	19 19	19 32	20 18	21 22
55	Longport	d	07 00	07 20	07 32	07 32		08 26	09 24	10 23	11 23	12 23	13 23	14 23	15 23	16 23	17 23			19 37	20 23	21 27
58¼	Kidsgrove	d	07a05	07a24	07 39	07 39	07a48	08 33	09 30	10 29	11 29	12 29	13 29	14 30	15 29	16 29	17 29	18 41	19a27	19 44	20 29	21 33
60¾	Alsager	d			07 42	07 42		08 36	09 34	10 33	11 33	12 33	13 33	14 33	15 33	16 33	17 33	18 45		19 47	20 33	21 37
66½	**Crewe** 10	a			07 56	07 56		08 50	09 48	10 47	11 47	12 47	13 47	14 47	15 47	16 47	17 47	18 59		20 01	20 47	21 51

Saturdays

		NT	EM	EM	EM	EM	EM	EM	EM	EM	EM	EM	EM	EM	NT	EM	EM	EM
Nottingham 8 🚌	d		05 52															
Derby 10	d		06 39	07 30	08 28	09 28	10 28	11 28	12 28	13 28	14 28	15 28	16 28	17 28		18 28	19 28	20 32
Peartree	d			07 33										17 31				
Tutbury & Hatton	d		06 53	07 45	08 45	09 41	10 41	11 41	12 41	13 41	14 43	15 41	16 42	17 43		18 41	19 41	20 46
Uttoxeter	d		07 03	07 54	08 56	09 51	10 51	11 51	12 51	13 51	14 52	15 51	16 51	17 52		18 51	19 51	20 56
Blythe Bridge	d		07 16	08 07	09 09	10 04	11 04	12 04	13 04	14 04	15 05	16 04	17 04	18 05		19 04	20 04	21 09
Longton	d		07 21	08 13	09 14	10 09	11 09	12 09	13 09	14 09	15 11	16 09	17 10	18 11		19 09	20 10	21 14
Stoke-on-Trent	a		07 28	08 21	09 21	10 17	11 17	12 17	13 17	14 17	15 17	16 17	17 17	18 21		19 17	20 17	21 22
	d	06 45	07 28	08 21	09 21	10 18	11 18	12 18	13 18	14 18	15 18	16 18	17 18	18 21	19 19	19 22	20 18	21 23
Longport	d	06 49	07 33	08 26	09 26	10 23	11 23	12 23	13 23	14 23	15 23	16 23	17 23	18 26		19 27	20 23	21 28
Kidsgrove	d	06a54	07 40	08 33	09 33	10 29	11 29	12 29	13 29	14 29	15 28	16 29	17 29	18 33	19a27	19 33	20 29	21 33
Alsager	d		07 43	08 36	09 36	10 33	11 33	12 33	13 33	14 33	15 33	16 33	17 33	18 36		19 37	20 33	21 38
Crewe 10	a		07 57	08 50	09 50	10 47	11 47	12 47	13 47	14 47	15 47	16 47	17 47	18 50		19 51	20 47	21 52

Sundays

until 13 July

		EM	NT	EM	EM	EM	NT	EM	EM	EM	NT
Nottingham 8 🚌	d										
Derby 10	d	14 43		15 43	16 38	17 45		18 45	19 44	20 44	
Peartree	d										
Tutbury & Hatton	d	14 56		15 56	16 54	17 59		18 58	19 57	20 57	
Uttoxeter	d	15 06		16 06	17 04	18 08		19 08	20 07	21 07	
Blythe Bridge	d	15 19		16 19	17 17	18 21		19 21	20 20	21 20	
Longton	d	15 24		16 24	17 22	18 27		19 26	20 25	21 25	
Stoke-on-Trent	a	15 30		16 31	17 30	18 32		19 36	20 31	21 34	
	d	15 31	16 19	16 31	17 30	18 32	19 20	19 36	20 32	21 34	22 15
Longport	d	15 36	16 23	16 36	17 35	18 37	19 24	19 42	20 37	21 39	22 19
Kidsgrove	d	15 42	16a27	16 41	17 41	18 43	19a28	19 47	20 44	21 45	22a23
Alsager	d	15 46		16 45	17 45	18 47		19 51	20 47	21 49	
Crewe 10	a	16 03		17 02	17 59	19 04		20 05	21 04	22 06	

Sundays

20 July to 7 September

		EM	NT	EM	EM	EM	NT	EM	EM	EM	NT
Nottingham 8 🚌	d										
Derby 10	d	14 43		15 43	16 38	17 45		18 45	19 44	20 44	
Peartree	d										
Tutbury & Hatton	d	14 56		15 56	16 54	17 59		18 58	19 57	20 57	
Uttoxeter	d	15 06		16 06	17 04	18 08		19 08	20 07	21 07	
Blythe Bridge	d	15 19		16 19	17 17	18 21		19 21	20 20	21 20	
Longton	d	15 24		16 24	17 22	18 27		19 26	20 25	21 25	
Stoke-on-Trent	a	15 30		16 29	17 35	18 32		19 36	20 31	21 36	
	d	15 31	16 19	16 29	17 35	18 32	19 20	19 36	20 32	21 37	22 15
Longport	d	15 36	16 23	16 36	17 40	18 37	19 24	19 42	20 37	21 42	22 19
Kidsgrove	d	15 42	16a27	16 41	17 46	18 43	19a28	19 47	20 44	21 48	22a23
Alsager	d	15 46		16 45	17 50	18 47		19 51	20 47	21 52	
Crewe 10	a	16 03		17 02	18 06	19 04		20 05	21 04	22 09	

For general notes see front of timetable
For details of catering facilities see Directory of Train Operators

A Until 5 September
B From 8 September

Table 50

from 14 September

Nottingham and Derby → Stoke-on-Trent and Crewe

Network Diagram - see first page of Table 50

		EM	NT	EM	EM	EM	NT	EM	EM	EM	NT
Nottingham 8	d										
Derby 10	d	14 43		15 43	16 39	17 45		18 44	19 44	20 44	
Peartree	d										
Tutbury & Hatton	d	14 56		15 56	16 55	17 59		18 57	19 57	20 57	
Uttoxeter	d	15 06		16 06	17 05	18 08		19 07	20 07	21 07	
Blythe Bridge	d	15 19		16 19	17 18	18 21		19 20	20 20	21 20	
Longton	d	15 24		16 24	17 23	18 27		19 25	20 25	21 25	
Stoke-on-Trent	a	15 31		16 31	17 30	18 32		19 34	20 32	21 32	
	d	15 31	16 19	16 31	17 30	18 32	19 20	19 34	20 32	21 32	22 15
Longport	d	15 36	16 23	16 36	17 35	18 37	19 24	19 40	20 37	21 37	22 19
Kidsgrove	d	15 42	16a27	16 41	17 41	18 43	19a28	19 45	20 44	21 43	22a23
Alsager	d	15 46		16 45	17 45	18 47		19 49	20 47	21 47	
Crewe 10	a	16 03		17 02	17 59	19 04		20 03	21 05	22 04	

For general notes see front of timetable
For details of catering facilities see
Directory of Train Operators

Crewe and Stoke-on-Trent → Derby and Nottingham

Network Diagram - see first page of Table 50

Miles			XC 1 ◇ ☕	EM	NT	EM	NT	EM	EM	EM	EM	EM	EM	EM	EM	EM	EM	EM	NT	EM	EM
0	Crewe 10	d	05 45	05 50		06 39		08 07	09 07	10 07	11 07	12 07	13 07	14 07	15 07	16 07	17 07	18 07		19 07	20 49
6½	Alsager	d		06 01		06 48		08 15	09 15	10 15	11 15	12 15	13 15	14 15	15 15	16 15	17 15	18 15		19 15	20 57
8¾	Kidsgrove	d		06 07	06 17	06 53	07 10	08 21	09 21	10 21	11 21	12 21	13 21	14 21	15 21	16 21	17 21	18 21	18 52	19 21	21 02
11¾	Longport	d		06 13			07 14	08 27	09 27	10 27	11 27	12 27	13 27	14 27	15 27	16 27	17 27	18 27	18 57	19 27	21 08
15¼	Stoke-on-Trent	a	06 03	06 22	06 27	07 02	07 19	08 32	09 32	10 32	11 32	12 32	13 32	14 32	15 32	16 32	17 32	18 32	19 02	19 32	21 13
—		d		06 23		07 02		08 33	09 33	10 33	11 33	12 33	13 33	14 33	15 33	16 33	17 33	18 33		19 33	21 14
17½	Longton	d		06 28				08 39	09 39	10 39	11 39	12 39	13 39	14 39	15 39	16 39	17 39	18 39		19 39	21 19
20¾	Blythe Bridge	d		06 34		07 12		08 45	09 45	10 45	11 45	12 45	13 45	14 45	15 45	16 45	17 45	18 45		19 45	21 25
31¼	Uttoxeter	d		06 46		07 25		08 58	09 58	10 58	11 58	12 58	13 58	14 58	15 58	16 58	17 58	18 58		19 58	21 37
39¼	Tutbury & Hatton	d		06 55		07 33		09 06	10 06	11 06	12 06	13 06	14 06	15 06	16 06	17 06	18 06	19 06		20 06	21 46
49½	Peartree	d				07 48									16 19						
50¾	Derby 10	a		07 15		07 51		09 26	10 26	11 26	12 26	13 26	14 26	15 26	16 28	17 26	18 26	19 26		20 26	22 11
66¾	Nottingham 8	a																			

Saturdays

		XC 1 ◇ ☕	NT	EM	EM	NT	EM A	EM B	EM	EM	EM	EM	EM	EM	EM	EM	EM	EM	NT A	NT B	EM	EM
Crewe 10	d	05 45		06 07	06 52		08 07	08 07	09 07	10 07	11 07	12 07	13 07	14 07	15 07	16 07	17 07	18 07			19 07	20 50
Alsager	d			06 15	07 00		08 15	08 15	09 15	10 15	11 15	12 15	13 15	14 15	15 15	16 15	17 15	18 15			19 15	20 58
Kidsgrove	d		06 17	06 21	07 05	07 10	08 22	08 23	09 21	10 22	11 22	12 22	13 22	14 22	15 22	16 22	17 22	18 22	18 44	18 51	19 22	21 03
Longport	d			06 27	07 10	07 14	08 28	08 29	09 27	10 28	11 28	12 28	13 27	14 28	15 28	16 28	17 28	18 28	18 48	18 56	19 28	21 08
Stoke-on-Trent	a	06 03	06 27	06 32	07 15	07 19	08 33	08 34	09 32	10 33	11 33	12 33	13 32	14 33	15 33	16 33	17 33	18 33	18 53	19 01	19 33	21 13
	d			06 33	07 16		08 34	08 34	09 33	10 33	11 33	12 33	13 33	14 33	15 33	16 33	17 33	18 33			19 33	21 14
Longton	d			06 38	07 21		08 39	08 39	09 38	10 38	11 38	12 38	13 38	14 38	15 38	16 38	17 38	18 38			19 38	21 19
Blythe Bridge	d			06 44	07 27		08 45	08 45	09 44	10 44	11 44	12 44	13 44	14 44	15 44	16 44	17 44	18 44			19 44	21 25
Uttoxeter	d			06 56	07 39		08 58	08 58	09 56	10 57	11 57	12 57	13 56	14 57	15 57	16 57	17 57	18 57			19 57	21 37
Tutbury & Hatton	d			07 05	07 48		09 06	09 06	10 05	11 05	12 05	13 05	14 05	15 05	16 05	17 05	18 05	19 05			20 05	21 46
Peartree	d			07 18											16 20							
Derby 10	a			07 26	08 10		09 28	09 28	10 26	11 27	12 27	13 27	14 26	15 27	16 29	17 27	18 27	19 27			20 27	22 07
Nottingham 8	a																					

Sundays
until 13 July

		EM	EM	NT	EM	EM	EM	NT	EM	EM	EM	NT
Crewe 10	d	14 16	15 16		16 16	17 16	18 16		19 16	20 16	21 23	
Alsager	d	14 25	15 25		16 24	17 26	18 25		19 26	20 25	21 31	
Kidsgrove	d	14 29	15 29	15 52	16 30	17 31	18 30	18 54	19 31	20 30	21 36	21 42
Longport	d	14 34	15 34	15 56	16 35	17 36	18 36	18 58	19 36	20 35	21 41	21 46
Stoke-on-Trent	a	14 39	15 39	16 03	16 40	17 41	18 41	19 04	19 41	20 40	21 46	21 51
	d	14 40	15 40		16 40	17 41	18 41		19 41	20 40	21 47	
Longton	d	14 45	15 45		16 45	17 47	18 46		19 46	20 45	21 53	
Blythe Bridge	d	14 51	15 51		16 51	17 53	18 52		19 52	20 51	21 59	
Uttoxeter	d	15 03	16 03		17 04	18 05	19 05		20 05	21 04	22 11	
Tutbury & Hatton	d	15 12	16 12		17 12	18 14	19 13		20 13	21 12	22 20	
Peartree	d											
Derby 10	a	15 33	16 34		17 32	18 32	19 37		20 35	21 32	22 34	
Nottingham 8	a										23 06	

Sundays
20 July to 7 September

		XC 1 ◇ ☕	EM	EM	NT	EM	EM	EM	NT	EM	EM	EM	NT
Crewe 10	d	08 46	13 59	14 59		16 16	17 16	18 19		19 16	20 16	21 23	
Alsager	d		14 08	15 08		16 24	17 27	18 29		19 26	20 26	21 31	
Kidsgrove	d		14 12	15 12	15 52	16 30	17 32	18 33	18 49	19 31	20 31	21 36	21 42
Longport	d		14 17	15 17	15 57	16 35	17 37	18 39	18 54	19 36	20 36	21 41	21 46
Stoke-on-Trent	a	09 04	14 22	15 22	16 03	16 40	17 42	18 44	18 59	19 41	20 41	21 46	21 53
	d		14 23	15 23		16 40	17 42	18 45		19 41	20 41	21 47	
Longton	d		14 28	15 28		16 45	17 47	18 50		19 46	20 46	21 53	
Blythe Bridge	d		14 34	15 34		16 51	17 53	18 56		19 52	20 52	21 59	
Uttoxeter	d		14 46	15 46		17 04	18 06	19 08		20 05	21 05	22 11	
Tutbury & Hatton	d		14 58	15 55		17 12	18 14	19 17		20 13	21 13	22 20	
Peartree	d												
Derby 10	a		15 19	16 17		17 32	18 33	19 38		20 35	21 33	22 34	
Nottingham 8	a											23 06	

For general notes see front of timetable
For details of catering facilities see
Directory of Train Operators

A From 13 September
B Until 6 September.

from 14 September

Crewe and Stoke-on-Trent → Derby and Nottingham

Network Diagram - see first page of Table 50

		XC 1 ◇	EM	EM	NT	EM	EM	EM	NT	EM	EM	EM	NT
Crewe 10	d	08 46	14 16	15 16		16 16	17 16	18 16		19 16	20 16	21 23	
Alsager	d		14 25	15 25		16 24	17 26	18 25		19 25	20 25	21 31	
Kidsgrove	d		14 29	15 29	15 51	16 30	17 31	18 30	18 49	19 31	20 30	21 36	21 42
Longport	d		14 34	15 34	15 56	16 35	17 36	18 36	18 53	19 36	20 35	21 41	21 46
Stoke-on-Trent	a	09 04	14 39	15 39	16 03	16 40	17 41	18 41	19 03	19 41	20 40	21 46	21 51
	d		14 40	15 40		16 40	17 41	18 41		19 41	20 40	21 47	
Longton	d		14 45	15 45		16 45	17 47	18 46		19 46	20 45	21 53	
Blythe Bridge	d		14 51	15 51		16 51	17 53	18 52		19 52	20 51	21 59	
Uttoxeter	d		15 03	16 03		17 04	18 05	19 05		20 05	21 04	22 11	
Tutbury & Hatton	d		15 12	16 12		17 12	18 14	19 13		20 13	21 12	22 20	
Peartree	d												
Derby 10	a		15 33	16 34		17 32	18 32	19 38		20 35	21 32	22 34	
Nottingham 8	a											23 17	

For general notes see front of timetable
For details of catering facilities see Directory of Train Operators

Route Diagram for Table 51

DM-3/07
Design BAJS

This Table summarises through services which, with their associated connecting services at Birmingham New Street, link centres in the North and South of the country. In certain instances a faster journey is possible via London and the relevant Table(s) should be consulted.

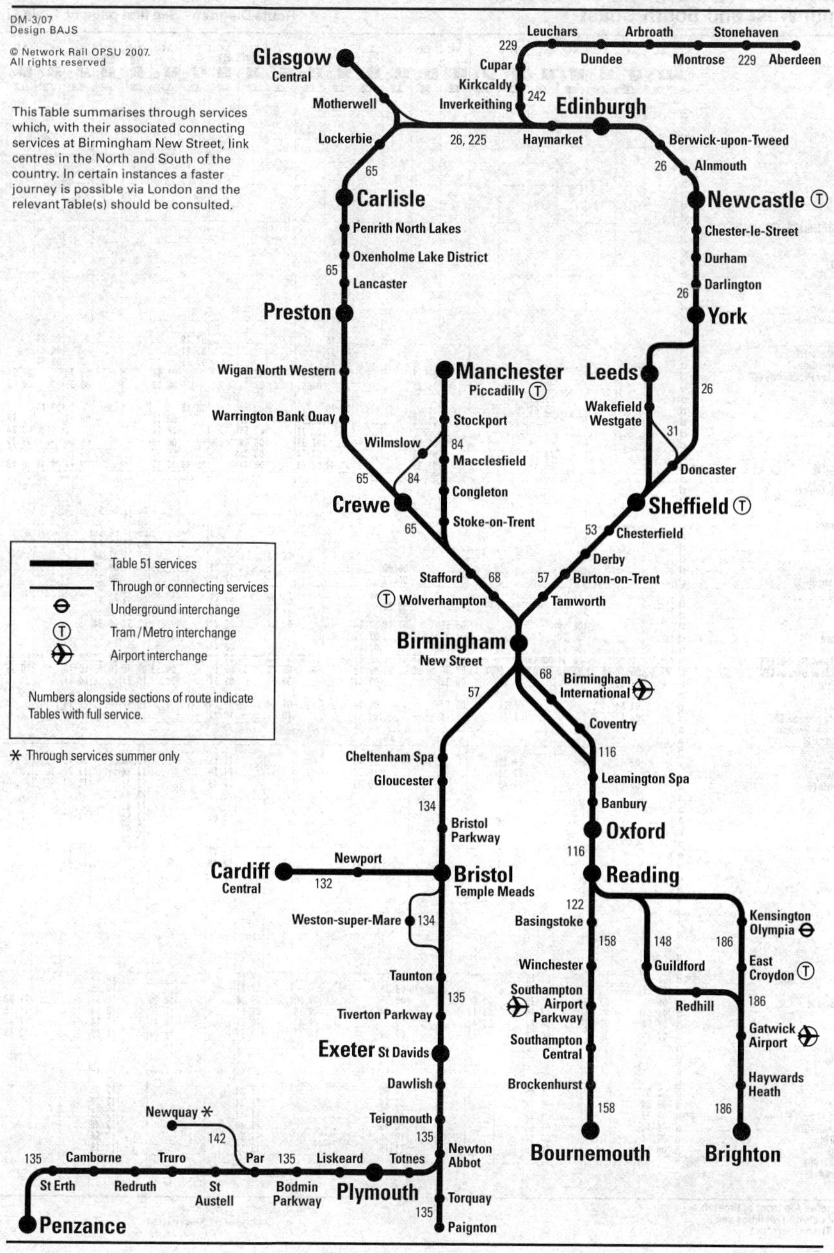

until 5 September

Scotland, The North East, North West England → The South West and South Coast

Route Diagram - See first page of Table 51

		XC	XC	XC	XC	XC	XC	XC	XC	VT	XC	XC	VT	XC	XC	XC	XC	VT	XC	XC	XC	XC	VT	XC
																R	R			R	R			
		1 ◇	1 ◇	1 ◇	1 ◇	1 ◇	1 ◇	1 ◇	1 ◇	1 ◇	1 ◇	1 ◇	1 ◇	1 ◇	1 ◇	1	1	1 ◇	1 ◇	1	1	1 ◇	1 ◇	1 ◇
		☕	☕	☕	☕	☕	☕	☕	☕	⊠	☕	☕	☕	☕	☕	☕	☕	☕	☕	☕	☕	☕	☕	☕
Aberdeen	d																							
Stonehaven	d																							
Montrose	d																							
Arbroath	d																							
Dundee	d																							
Leuchars [8]	d																							
Cupar	d																							
Markinch	d																							
Kirkcaldy	d																							
Inverkeithing	d																							
Glasgow Central [15]	d																							
Motherwell	d																							
Haymarket	d																							
Edinburgh [10]	d																							
Haymarket	d																							
Lockerbie	d																							
Carlisle [8]	d																							
Penrith North Lakes	d																							
Oxenholme Lake District	d																							
Lancaster [6]	d																							
Preston [8]	d												06 15					07 29					08 29	
Wigan North Western	d												06 27					07 41					08 41	
Warrington Bank Quay	d												06 45					07 53					08 52	
Manchester Piccadilly [10]	d					05b20				06 17				06 54		07 24			07 54			08 24		08 54
Stockport	d					05b31				06 25				06c53		07 33			08 03			08 33		09 03
Wilmslow	d					05b39																		
Crewe [10]	d					05 45							07 10					08 15					09 15	
Macclesfield	d									06 38				07c09		07 47			08 16			08 47		09 16
Congleton	d													07 21		07 55			08 24					09 24
Stoke-on-Trent	d					06 04				06 54				07 33		08 08			08 39			09 04		09 39
Stafford	d					06 24				07 15				07 54		08 26			08 57			09 26		
Wolverhampton [7]	d					06 41				07 35			07 49	08 13		08 41		08 49	09 13			09 41	09 49	10 13
Dunbar	d																							
Berwick-upon-Tweed	d																							
Alnmouth	d																							
Newcastle [8]	d																			06 19	06 44			
Chester-le-Street	d																			06 31				
Durham	d																			06 38	06 56			
Darlington [7]	d																			06 55	07 14			
York [8]	d														06 16					07 27	07 44			
Leeds [10]	d										06 00						07 05				08 10			
Wakefield Westgate [7]	d										06 12						07 19				08 23			
Doncaster [7]	d																			07 52				
Sheffield [7]	d										06 45				07 23		07 53			08 23	08 53			
Chesterfield	d										06 57				07 35		08 05			08 35				
Derby [10]	d				06 10				06 55		07 19	07 24			07 57		08 27			08 57	09 24			
Burton-on-Trent	d				06 20				07 07			07 35					08 37							
Tamworth	d				06 31				07 18			07 46					08 48							
Birmingham New Street [12]	a				06 51	06 58	←		07 36	07 55	07 58	08 07	08 11	08 30	08 36	08 58	09 06	09 11	09 30	09 36	09 58	09 58	10 11	10 30
Birmingham New Street [12]	d	06 03	06 10	06 33	07 10	07 03	07 10	07 33	07 40	08 00	08 03	08 10		08 33	08 40	09 03	09 10		09 33	09 40	10 03	10 10		10 33
Cheltenham Spa	a		07 21		→		07 51		08 21			08 51			09 21		09 51			10 21		10 51		
Gloucester [7]	a																							
Bristol Parkway [7]	a		07 54				08 24		08 54			09 24			09 54		10 24			10 54		11 24		
Bristol Temple Meads [10]	a		08 11				08 41		09 11			09 41			10 11		10 41			11 11		11 41		
Newport (South Wales)	a																							
Cardiff Central [7]	a																							
Weston-super-Mare	a																			11 32				
Taunton	a		08 42				09 15					10 15					11 15			12 03		12 15		
Tiverton Parkway	a						09 28					10 28					11 28			12 16		12 28		
Exeter St Davids [6]	a		09 07				09 43					10 43					11 43			12 31		12 43		
Dawlish	a																			12 44				
Teignmouth	a																			12 49				
Newton Abbot	a						10 02					11 02					12 02			12 56		13 02		
Torquay	a		09 34																	13 07				
Paignton	a		09 47																	13 20				
Totnes	a						10 16					11 16					12 16					13 16		
Plymouth	a						10 48					11 48					12 48					13 48		
Liskeard [3]	a																							
Bodmin Parkway	a																							
Par [3]	a																							
St Austell	a																							
Truro	a																							
Redruth	a																							
Camborne	a																							
St Erth [2]	a																							
Penzance	a																							
Birmingham International ✈	d	06 15				07 15				08 10	08 15					09 15					10 15			
Coventry	d	06 25				07 25				08a20	08 25					09 25					10 25			
Leamington Spa [8]	d	06 38		07 00		07 38		08 00			08 38			09 00		09 38			10 00		10 38			11 00
Banbury	a	06 54		07 18		07 54		08 18			08 54			09 18		09 54			10 18		10 54			11 18
Oxford	a	07 14		07 41		08 14		08 41			09 14			09 41		10 14			10 41		11 14			11 41
Reading [7]	a	07 39		08 13		08 39		09 13			09 39			10 13		10 39			11 09		11 39			12 13
Kensington Olympia	a																		11 56					
East Croydon	a																		12 16					
Guildford	a																							
Redhill	a																							
Basingstoke	a	08 08				09 08					10 08					11 08					12 08			
Winchester	a	08 24				09 24					10 24					11 24					12 24			
Southampton Airport Parkwy ✈	a	08 33				09 33					10 33					11 33					12 33			
Southampton Central	a	08 40				09 40					10 40					11 40					12 40			
Brockenhurst [3]	a	08 56				09 56					10 56					11 56					12 56			
Bournemouth	a	09 15				10 15					11 15					12 15					13 15			
Gatwick Airport [10] ✈	a																		12 33					
Haywards Heath [3]	a																		12 49					
Brighton [10]	a																		13 15					

For general notes see front of timetable
For details of catering facilities see Directory of Train Operators

b Change at Stafford
c Change at Stoke-on-Trent

until 5 September

Scotland, The North East, North West England → The South West and South Coast

Route Diagram - See first page of Table 51

		XC		XC	XC	VT	XC	XC	XC	XC	VT	XC	XC	XC	XC	VT	XC	XC	XC	XC	XC	XC	XC	VT
				R					R					R		R		R	R	R			R	R
		1◇		1	1◇	1◇	1◇	1◇	1	1◇	1◇	1◇	1◇	1	1◇	1	1◇	1	1	1	1◇	1◇	1	1
Aberdeen	d																							
Stonehaven	d																							
Montrose	d																							
Arbroath	d																							
Dundee	d														06 38				07 35					
Leuchars 8	d														06 51				07 48					
Cupar	d														06 58				07 56					
Markinch	d														07 13				08 11					
Kirkcaldy	d														07 25				08 20					
Inverkeithing	d														07 43				08 36					
Glasgow Central 15	d								06 00		07 45												09 00	10 10
Motherwell	d																						09u14	
Haymarket	d								06 52						08 00				08 56				09 54	
Edinburgh 10	d				06 05	06 36			07 05						08 10	08 51			09 05				10 05	
Haymarket	d					06u40										08u56								
Lockerbie	d																							
Carlisle 8	d					07 53					09 13					10 17								11 22
Penrith North Lakes	d					08 09					09 29													
Oxenholme Lake District	d					08 33					09 54					10 53								
Lancaster 6	d					09 09					10 09					11 10								12 12
Preston 8	d					09 29					10 28					11 29								12 32
Wigan North Western	d					09 41					10 42					11 41								12 45
Warrington Bank Quay	d					09 53					10 53					11 52								12 59
Manchester Piccadilly 10	d			09 24			09 54			10 24		10 54		11 24			11 54			12 24	12 54			
Stockport	d			09 33			10 03			10 33		11 03		11 33			12 03			12 33	13 03			
Wilmslow	d																							
Crewe 10	d					10 15					11 14					12 13								13 33
Macclesfield	d			09 47			10 16			10 47		11 16		11 47			12 16			12 47	13 16			
Congleton	d											11 24									13 24			
Stoke-on-Trent	d			10 04			10 39			11 04		11 39		12 04			12 39			13 04	13 39			
Stafford	d			10 26						11 26				12 26						13 26				
Wolverhampton 7	d			10 41		10 49	11 13			11 41	11 49	12 13		12 41		12 49	13 13			13 41	14 13			14 18
Dunbar	d								07 25										09 25					
Berwick-upon-Tweed	d				06 48				07 48						08 48				09 48					
Alnmouth	d				07 10				08 08						09 09									
Newcastle 8	d	07 23			07 44			08 24	08 40				09 35		09 40			10 25	10 40			11 25	11 04 11 40 →	
Chester-le-Street	d							08 33										10 34						
Durham	d	07 37			07 56			08 40	08 52				09 47		09 52			10 41	10 52			11 37		
Darlington 7	d	07 54			08 14			08 57	09 10				10 04		10 10			10 58	11 10			11 56		
York 8	d	08 27			08 44			09 27	09 44				10 34		10 44			11 27	11 44			12 25		
Leeds 10	d				09 10				10 10						11 10				12 10					
Wakefield Westgate 7	d				09 23				10 23						11 23				12 23					
Doncaster 7	d	08 51						09 56					10 58					11 54				12 55		
Sheffield 7	d	09 23			09 53			10 23	10 53				11 23		11 53			12 23	12 53			13 23		
Chesterfield	d	09 35						10 35					11 35					12 35				13 35		
Derby 10	d	09 57			10 24			10 57	11 24				11 57		12 24			12 57	13 24			13 57		
Burton-on-Trent	d	10 07											12 07									14 07		
Tamworth	d	10 18											12 18									14 18		
Birmingham New Street 12	a	10 36		10 58	11 04	11 11	11 30	11 36	11 58	11 58	12 11	12 30	12 36	12 58	13 04	13 11	13 30	13 36	13 58	13 58	14 30	14 36		14 41
Birmingham New Street 12	d	10 40		11 03	11 10		11 33	11 40	12 03	12 10		12 33	12 40	13 03	13 10		13 33	13 40	14 03	14 10	14 33	14 40		
Cheltenham Spa	a	11 21			11 51			12 21		12 51			13 21		13 51			14 21		14 51		15 21		
Gloucester 7	a																							
Bristol Parkway 7	a	11 54			12 24			12 54		13 24			13 54		14 24			14 54		15 24		15 54		
Bristol Temple Meads 10	a	12 11			12 41			13 11		13 41			14 11		14 41			15 11		15 41		16 11		
Newport (South Wales)	a																							
Cardiff Central 7	a																							
Weston-super-Mare	a																							
Taunton	a				13 15			13 42		14 15					15 15			15 42		16 15				
Tiverton Parkway	a				13 28			14 01		14 28					15 28			15 54		16 28				
Exeter St Davids 6	a				13 43			14 16		14 43					15 43			16 10		16 43				
Dawlish	a							14 29																
Teignmouth	a							14 34																
Newton Abbot	a				14 02			14 41		15 02					16 02			16 30		17 02				
Torquay	a							14 52																
Paignton	a							15 05																
Totnes	a				14 16					15 16					16 16			16 43		17 16				
Plymouth	a				14 48					15 48					16 48			17 15		17 48				
Liskeard 3	a																			18 17				
Bodmin Parkway	a																			18 29				
Par 3	a																			18 40				
St Austell	a																			18 46				
Truro	a																			19 04				
Redruth	a																			19 16				
Camborne	a																			19 23				
St Erth 2	a																			19 33				
Penzance	a																			19 49				
Birmingham International ✈	d			11 15					12 15					13 15					14 15					
Coventry	d			11 25					12 25					13 25					14 25					
Leamington Spa 8	d			11 38			12 00		12 38			13 00		13 38			14 00		14 38		15 00			
Banbury	a			11 54			12 18		12 54			13 18		13 54			14 18		14 54		15 18			
Oxford	a			12 14			12 41		13 14			13 41		14 14			14 41		15 14		15 41			
Reading 7	a			12 39			13 13		13 39			14 13		14 39			15 13		15 39		16 11			
Kensington Olympia	a																							
East Croydon	a																							
Guildford	a																				16 59			
Redhill	a																				*17 38*			
Basingstoke	a			13 08					14 08					15 08					16 08					
Winchester	a			13 24					14 24					15 24					16 24					
Southampton Airport Parkwy ✈	a			13 33					14 33					15 33					16 33					
Southampton Central	a			13 40					14 40					15 40					16 40					
Brockenhurst 3	a			13 56					14 56					15 56					16 56					
Bournemouth	a			14 15					15 15					16 15					17 15					
Gatwick Airport 10 ✈	a																				*17 50*			
Haywards Heath 3	a																							
Brighton 10	a																							

For general notes see front of timetable
For details of catering facilities see
Directory of Train Operators

until 5 September

Scotland, The North East, North West England → The South West and South Coast

Route Diagram - See first page of Table 51

		XC	XC	VT	XC	XC	XC	XC	VT	XC	XC	XC	XC	VT	XC	XC	XC	XC	VT	XC	XC	XC	XC
			R				R	R	R	R		R	R	R	R	R	R			R	R	R	
		1◇	1	1◇	1◇	1◇	1	1	1	1	1◇	1	1	1	1	1	1	1◇	1◇	1	1	1	1◇
		🍴	🍴	🍴	🍴	🍴	🍴	🍴	🍴	🍴	🍴	🍴	🍴	🍴	🍴	🍴	🍴	🍴	🍴	🍴	🍴	🍴	🍴
Aberdeen	d						08 20																
Stonehaven	d						08 37																
Montrose	d						08 59																
Arbroath	d						09 15																
Dundee	d						09 32																
Leuchars [3]	d						09 45																
Cupar	d						09 52																
Markinch	d						10 04																
Kirkcaldy	d						10 12																
Inverkeithing	d						10 27																
Glasgow Central [15]	d								12 10										14 10				
Motherwell	d																						
Haymarket	d						10 47																
Edinburgh [10]	d			10 51			11 05						12 05	12 52			13 05						14 05
Haymarket	d			10u57										12u56									
Lockerbie	d													13 53									
Carlisle [8]	d			12 13					13 21					14 14					15 21				
Penrith North Lakes	d			12 29										14 29									
Oxenholme Lake District	d			12 53					13 59					14 53									
Lancaster [6]	d			13 09										15 08					16 09				
Preston [8]	d			13 29					14 30					15 29					16 29				
Wigan North Western	d			13 41					14 42					15 41					16 41				
Warrington Bank Quay	d			13 53					14 54					15 52					16 53				
Manchester Piccadilly [10]	d	13 24			13 54			14 24		14 54		15 24			15 54			16 24		16 54		17 24	
Stockport	d	13 33			14 03			14 33		15 03		15 33			16 03			16 33		17 03		17 33	
Wilmslow	d																						
Crewe [10]	d			14 14					15 15					16 11					17 15				
Macclesfield	d	13 47			14 16			14 47		15 16		15 47			16 16			16 47		17 16		17 47	
Congleton	d									15 24										17 24			
Stoke-on-Trent	d	14 04			14 39			15 04		15 39		16 04			16 39			17 04		17 39		18 04	
Stafford	d	14 26						15 26				16 26						17 26				18 26	
Wolverhampton [7]	d	14 41		14 49	15 13			15 41	15 49	16 13		16 41		16 49	17 13			17 41	17 49	18 13		18 41	
Dunbar	d						11 25										13 25						
Berwick-upon-Tweed	d						11 48										13 48						
Alnmouth	d		←										13 06										15 04
Newcastle [8]	d		11 40			12 19	12 40				13 34		13 40			14 22	14 40				15 22		15 40
Chester-le-Street	d					12 32										14 33							
Durham	d		11 52			12 40	12 52				13 46		13 52			14 40	14 52				15 34		15 52
Darlington [7]	d		12 10			13 00	13 10				14 03		14 10			14 57	15 10				15 51		16 10
York [8]	d		12 44			13 29	13 44				14 32		14 44			15 29	15 44				16 25		16 44
Leeds [10]	d		13 10				14 10						15 10				16 10						17 10
Wakefield Westgate [7]	d		13 23				14 23						15 23				16 23						17 23
Doncaster [7]	d					13 54					14 57					15 55					16 53		
Sheffield [7]	d		13 53			14 23	14 53				15 23		15 53			16 23	16 53				17 20		17 53
Chesterfield	d					14 35					15 35					16 35					17 35		
Derby [10]	d		14 24			14 57	15 24				15 57		16 24			16 57	17 24				17 57		18 24
Burton-on-Trent	d										16 07										18 07		
Tamworth	d										16 18										18 18		
Birmingham New Street [12]	a	14 58	15 04	15 11	15 30	15 36	15 58	15 58	16 11	16 30	16 36	16 58	17 04	17 11	17 30	17 36	17 58	17 58	18 11	18 30	18 36	18 58	19 08
Birmingham New Street [12]	d	15 03	15 10		15 33	15 40	16 03	16 10		16 33	16 40	17 03	17 10		17 33	17 40	18 03	18 10		18 33	18 40	19 03	19 10
Cheltenham Spa	a		15 51			16 21		16 51			17 21		17 51			18 21		18 51			19 21		19 51
Gloucester [7]	a															18 34							
Bristol Parkway [7]	a		16 24			16 54		17 24			17 54		18 24			19 05		19 24			19 54		20 24
Bristol Temple Meads [10]	a		16 41			17 11		17 41			18 11		18 41			19 22		19 41			20 11		20 41
Newport (South Wales)	a															19 59							
Cardiff Central [7]	a															20 19							
Weston-super-Mare	a																				20 39		
Taunton	a		17 15			17 42		18 15					19 15					20 15					21 15
Tiverton Parkway	a		17 28			17 55		18 28					19 28					20 28					21 28
Exeter St Davids [6]	a		17 43			18 10		18 43					19 43					20 43					21 43
Dawlish	a					18 23																	
Teignmouth	a					18 28																	
Newton Abbot	a		18 08			18 35		19 02					20 02					21 02					22 02
Torquay	a																						
Paignton	a																						
Totnes	a		18 21			18 48		19 16					20 16					21 16					22 16
Plymouth	a		18 48			19 20		19 48					20 48					21 48					22 48
Liskeard [3]	a		19 22					20 12															
Bodmin Parkway	a		19 34					20 24															
Par [3]	a		19 46					20 35															
St Austell	a		19 53					20 41															
Truro	a		20 10					20 59															
Redruth	a		20 21					21 13															
Camborne	a		20 28					21 20															
St Erth [2]	a		20 39					21 30															
Penzance	a		20 56					21 47															
Birmingham International ✈	d	15 15					16 15					17 15					18 15					19 15	
Coventry	d	15 25					16 25					17 25					18 25					19 25	
Leamington Spa [8]	d	15 38			16 00		16 38			17 00		17 38			18 00		18 38			19 00		19 38	
Banbury	a	15 54			16 18		16 54			17 18		17 54			18 18		18 54			19 18		19 54	
Oxford	a	16 14			16 41		17 14			17 41		18 14			18 41		19 14			19 41		20 14	
Reading [7]	a	16 39			17 13		17 39			18 11		18 39			19 13		19 39			20 09		20 39	
Kensington Olympia	a									19 01										20 52			
East Croydon	a									19 33										21 15			
Guildford	a																						
Redhill	a																			21 34			
Basingstoke	a	17 08					18 08					19 08					20 08					21 08	
Winchester	a	17 24					18 24					19 24					20 24					21 24	
Southampton Airport Parkwy ✈	a	17 33					18 33					19 33					20 33					21 33	
Southampton Central	a	17 40					18 40					19 40					20 40					21 40	
Brockenhurst [3]	a	17 56					18 56					19 56					20 56					21 56	
Bournemouth	a	18 15					19 15					20 24					21 26					22 26	
Gatwick Airport [10] ✈	a									19 52										21 47			
Haywards Heath [3]	a									20 04										21b45			
Brighton [10]	a									20 30										22b00			

For general notes see front of timetable
For details of catering facilities see Directory of Train Operators

b Change at East Croydon

until 5 September

Scotland, The North East, North West England → The South West and South Coast

Route Diagram - See first page of Table 51

		VT	XC	XC	XC	XC	VT	XC	XC	XC	XC	VT	XC	XC	XC	XC	VT	XC	VT	XC	XC	XC
				R	R																	
		1 ◇	1 ◇	1	1	1 ◇	1 ◇	1 ◇	1 ◇	1 ◇	1 ◇	1 ◇	1 ◇	1 ◇	1 ◇	1 ◇	1 ◇	1 ◇	1 ◇	1 ◇	1 ◇	1 ◇
		☕	☕	☕	☕	☕	☕	☕	☕	☕	☕	☕		☕		☕	☕	☕	☕	☕		
Aberdeen	d																					
Stonehaven	d																					
Montrose	d																					
Arbroath	d																					
Dundee	d																					
Leuchars 3	d																					
Cupar	d																					
Markinch	d																					
Kirkcaldy	d																					
Inverkeithing	d																					
Glasgow Central 15	d						16 10										18 10					
Motherwell	d																18u27					
Haymarket	d																					
Edinburgh 10	d	14 52			15 05						16 05	16 51				17 05		18 05	18 52			
Haymarket	d	14u57										16u56							18u56			
Lockerbie	d	15 53										17 49							19 49			
Carlisle 8	d	16 14					17 21					18 11					19 32		20 11			
Penrith North Lakes	d	16 29					17 36					18 27							20 27			
Oxenholme Lake District	d	16 53					18 00					18 51					20 07		20 52			
Lancaster 6	d	17 09										19 08					20 23		21 07			
Preston 8	d	17 29					18 29					19 29					20 49		21 29			
Wigan North Western	d	17 41					18 42					19 41					21 01		21 42			
Warrington Bank Quay	d	17 53					18 53					19 53					21 13		21 54			
Manchester Piccadilly 10 ⛴	d		17 54			18 24		18 54		19 24			19 54		20 24						21 54	
Stockport	d		18 03			18 33		19 03		19 33			20 03		20 33						22 03	
Wilmslow	d																					
Crewe 10	d	18 15					19 15					20 15					21 35		22 16			
Macclesfield	d		18 16			18 47		19 16		19 47			20 16		20 47						22 16	
Congleton	d		18 24					19 24					20 24								22 24	
Stoke-on-Trent	d		18 39			19 04		19 39		20 04			20 39		21 04						22 39	
Stafford	d					19 25		19 58		20 26			20 57		21 26		21 55		22 36		22 57	
Wolverhampton 7 ⛴	d	18 49	19 13			19 41	19 49	20 13		20 41		20 49	21 13		21 41		22 16		22 49		23 13	
Dunbar	d				15 25											17 25		18 25				
Berwick-upon-Tweed	d				15 48											17 48				←		
Alnmouth	d										17 08							19 05		19 05		
Newcastle 8	d			16 27	16 40				17 17		17 40			18 20		18 40		→		19 40		20 26
Chester-le-Street	d			16 42					17 26					18 29								
Durham	d			16 49	16 52				17 33		17 52			18 36		18 52				19 52		20 38
Darlington 7	d			17 06					17 50		18 10			18 56		19 10				20 10		20 55
York 8	d			17 34	17 44				18 24		18 44			19 29		19 44				20 44		21 24
Leeds 10	d				18 10						19 10					20 10				21 10		
Wakefield Westgate 7	d				18 23						19 23					20 23				21 23		
Doncaster 7	d			17 58					18 52					19 57								
Sheffield 7	d			18 23	18 53				19 23		19 53			20 23		20 53				21 53		22 27
Chesterfield	d			18 35					19 35		20 05			20 35		21 05				22 05		22 53
Derby 10	d			18 57	19 24				19 57		20 27			20 57		21 27				22 27		23 15
Burton-on-Trent	d								20 07							21 37				22 37		23 26
Tamworth	d								20 18							21 48				22 48		23 37
Birmingham New Street 12	a	19 11	19 30	19 36	19 58	19 58	20 11	20 35	20 43	20 58	21 04	21 11	21 35	21 44	22 04	22 08	22 38		23 11	23 21	23 47	23 59
Birmingham New Street 12	d		19 33	19 40	20 03	20 10				21 03	21 10					22 10						
Cheltenham Spa	a			20 21		20 51					21 51					22 51						
Gloucester 7	a																					
Bristol Parkway 7	a			20 54		21 24					22 24					23 24						
Bristol Temple Meads 10	a			21 11		21 41					22 41					23 41						
Newport (South Wales)	a																					
Cardiff Central 7	a																					
Weston-super-Mare	a																					
Taunton	a					22 15																
Tiverton Parkway	a					22 28																
Exeter St Davids 6	a					23 24																
Dawlish	a																					
Teignmouth	a																					
Newton Abbot	a					23 44																
Torquay	a																					
Paignton	a																					
Totnes	a					23 57																
Plymouth	a					00 29																
Liskeard 3	a																					
Bodmin Parkway	a																					
Par 3	a																					
St Austell	a																					
Truro	a																					
Redruth	a																					
Camborne	a																					
St Erth 2	a																					
Penzance	a																					
Birmingham International ✈	d				20 15					21 15												
Coventry	d				20 25					21 25												
Leamington Spa 8	d		20 00		20 38					21 38												
Banbury	a		20 18		20 54					21 54												
Oxford	a		20 41		21 14					22 14												
Reading 7	a		21 06		21 39					22 39												
Kensington Olympia	a																					
East Croydon ⛴	a																					
Guildford	a		21 33																			
Redhill	a		22 11																			
Basingstoke	a				22 08					23 08												
Winchester	a				22 24					23 24												
Southampton Airport Parkwy ✈	a				22 33					23 33												
Southampton Central	a				22 46					23 47												
Brockenhurst 3	a				23b04					00b04												
Bournemouth	a				23b23					00b22												
Gatwick Airport 10 ✈	a		22 37																			
Haywards Heath 3	a		22c52																			
Brighton 10	a		23c15																			

For general notes see front of timetable
For details of catering facilities see Directory of Train Operators

b Change at Winchester
c Change at Redhill

from 8 September

Scotland, The North East, North West England → The South West and South Coast

Route Diagram - See first page of Table 51

		XC	XC	XC	XC	XC	XC	XC	XC	VT	XC	XC	VT	XC	XC	XC	XC	VT	XC	XC	XC	XC	VT	XC
																R	R			R	R			
		1◇	1◇	1◇	1◇	1◇	1◇	1◇	1◇	1◇	1◇	1◇	1◇	1◇	1◇	1	1	1◇	1◇	1	1	1◇	1◇	1◇
		☕	☕	☕	☕	☕	☕	☕	☕	⊠	☕	☕	☕	☕	☕	☕	☕	☕	☕	☕	☕	☕	☕	☕
Aberdeen	d																							
Stonehaven	d																							
Montrose	d																							
Arbroath	d																							
Dundee	d																							
Leuchars (3)	d																							
Cupar	d																							
Markinch	d																							
Kirkcaldy	d																							
Inverkeithing	d																							
Glasgow Central (15)	d																							
Motherwell	d																							
Haymarket	d																							
Edinburgh (10)	d																							
Haymarket	d																							
Lockerbie	d																							
Carlisle (8)	d																							
Penrith North Lakes	d																							
Oxenholme Lake District	d																							
Lancaster (6)	d																							
Preston (8)	d												06 15					07 29					08 29	
Wigan North Western	d												06 27					07 41					08 41	
Warrington Bank Quay	d												06 45					07 53					08 52	
Manchester Piccadilly (10)	d					05b20				06 17				06 54		07 24			07 54			08 24		08 54
Stockport	d					05b31				06 25				06c53		07 33			08 03			08 33		09 03
Wilmslow	d					05b39																		
Crewe (10)	d					05 45							07 10					08 15					09 15	
Macclesfield	d									06 38				07c09		07 47			08 16			08 47		09 16
Congleton	d													07 21		07 55			08 24					09 24
Stoke-on-Trent	d					06 04				06 54				07 33		08 08			08 39			09 04		09 39
Stafford	d					06 24				07 15				07 54		08 26			08 57			09 26		
Wolverhampton (7)	d					06 41				07 35			07 49	08 13		08 41		08 49	09 13			09 41	09 49	10 13
Dunbar	d																							
Berwick-upon-Tweed	d																							
Alnmouth	d																							
Newcastle (8)	d																				06 19			
Chester-le-Street	d																				06 31			
Durham	d																				06 38			
Darlington (7)	d																				06 55			
York (8)	d																06 16				07 27			
Leeds (10)	d														06 00					07 05				
Wakefield Westgate (7)	d														06 12					07 19				
Doncaster (7)	d																				07 52			
Sheffield (7)	d										06 31				07 07		07 33			07 59	08 31			
Chesterfield	d										06 57				07 35		08 02			08 35	09 02			
Derby (10)	d				06 10				06 55		07 20	07 24			07 57		08 27			08 57	09 24			
Burton-on-Trent	d				06 20				07 07			07 35					08 37							
Tamworth	d				06 31				07 18			07 46					08 48							
Birmingham New Street (12)	a				06 51	06 58	←		07 36	07 55	07 58	08 07	08 11	08 30	08 36	08 58	09 06	09 11	09 30	09 36	09 58	09 58	10 11	10 30
Birmingham New Street (12)	d	06 03	06 10	06 33	07 10	07 03	07 10	07 33	07 40	08 00	08 03	08 10		08 33	08 40	09 03	09 10		09 33	09 40	10 03	10 10		10 33
Cheltenham Spa	a		07 21		→		07 51		08 21			08 51			09 21		09 51			10 21		10 51		
Gloucester (7)	a																							
Bristol Parkway (7)	a		07 54				08 24		08 54			09 24			09 54		10 24			10 54		11 24		
Bristol Temple Meads (10)	a		08 11				08 41		09 11			09 41			10 11		10 41			11 11		11 41		
Newport (South Wales)	a																							
Cardiff Central (7)	a																							
Weston-super-Mare	a																			11 32				
Taunton	a		08 42				09 15					10 15					11 15			12 03		12 15		
Tiverton Parkway	a						09 28					10 28					11 28			12 16		12 28		
Exeter St Davids (6)	a		09 07				09 43					10 43					11 43			12 31		12 43		
Dawlish	a																			12 44				
Teignmouth	a																			12 49				
Newton Abbot	a						10 02					11 02					12 02			12 56		13 02		
Torquay	a		09 34																	13 07				
Paignton	a		09 47																	13 20				
Totnes	a						10 16					11 16					12 16					13 16		
Plymouth	a						10 48					11 48					12 48					13 48		
Liskeard (3)	a																							
Bodmin Parkway	a																							
Par (3)	a																							
St Austell	a																							
Truro	a																							
Redruth	a																							
Camborne	a																							
St Erth (2)	a																							
Penzance	a																							
Birmingham International	d	06 15				07 15				08 10	08 15					09 15					10 15			
Coventry	d	06 25				07 25				08a20	08 25					09 25					10 25			
Leamington Spa (8)	d	06 38		07 00		07 38		08 00			08 38			09 00		09 38			10 00		10 38			11 00
Banbury	a	06 54		07 18		07 54		08 18			08 54			09 18		09 54			10 18		10 54			11 18
Oxford	a	07 14		07 41		08 14		08 41			09 14			09 41		10 14			10 41		11 14			11 41
Reading (7)	a	07 39		08 13		08 39		09 13			09 39			10 13		10 39			11 09		11 39			12 13
Kensington Olympia	a																		11 56					
East Croydon	a																		12 16					
Guildford	a																							
Redhill	a																							
Basingstoke	a	08 08				09 08					10 08					11 08					12 08			
Winchester	a	08 24				09 24					10 24					11 24					12 24			
Southampton Airport Parkwy	a	08 33				09 33					10 33					11 33					12 33			
Southampton Central	a	08 40				09 40					10 40					11 40					12 40			
Brockenhurst (3)	a	08 56				09 56					10 56					11 56					12 56			
Bournemouth	a	09 15				10 15					11 15					12 15					13 15			
Gatwick Airport (10)	a																		12 33					
Haywards Heath (3)	a																		12 49					
Brighton (10)	a																		13 15					

For general notes see front of timetable
For details of catering facilities see Directory of Train Operators

b Change at Stafford
c Change at Stoke-on-Trent

from 8 September

Scotland, The North East, North West England → The South West and South Coast

Route Diagram - See first page of Table 51

		XC	XC	XC	XC	VT	XC	XC	XC	XC	XC	VT	XC	XC	XC	XC	XC	VT	XC	XC	XC	XC	XC	XC
			R						R						R		R	R		R	R	R		
		1 ◇	1	1 ◇	1 ◇	1 ◇	1 ◇	1 ◇	1	1 ◇	1 ◇	1 ◇	1 ◇	1 ◇	1	1 ◇	1	1	1 ◇	1	1	1	1 ◇	1 ◇
Aberdeen	d																							
Stonehaven	d																							
Montrose	d																							
Arbroath	d																							
Dundee	d																06 38							07 35
Leuchars [3]	d																06 51							07 48
Cupar	d																06 58							07 56
Markinch	d																07 13							08 11
Kirkcaldy	d																07 25							08 20
Inverkeithing	d																07 43							08 36
Glasgow Central [15]	d										06 00	07 45												
Motherwell	d																							
Haymarket	d										06 52						08 00							08 56
Edinburgh [10]	d				06 05	06 36					07 05						08 10	08 51						09 05
Haymarket	d					06u40												08u56						
Lockerbie	d																							
Carlisle [8]	d					07 53						09 13						10 17						
Penrith North Lakes	d					08 09						09 29												
Oxenholme Lake District	d					08 33						09 54						10 53						
Lancaster [6]	d					09 09						10 09						11 10						
Preston [8]	d					09 29						10 28						11 29						
Wigan North Western	d					09 41						10 42						11 41						
Warrington Bank Quay	d					09 53						10 53						11 52						
Manchester Piccadilly [10]	d		09 24				09 54			10 24			10 54		11 24				11 54			12 24	12 54	
Stockport	d		09 33				10 03			10 33			11 03		11 33				12 03			12 33	13 03	
Wilmslow	d																							
Crewe [10]	d					10 15						11 14						12 13						
Macclesfield	d		09 47				10 16			10 47			11 16		11 47				12 16			12 47	13 16	
Congleton	d												11 24										13 24	
Stoke-on-Trent	d		10 04				10 39			11 04			11 39		12 04				12 39			13 04	13 39	
Stafford	d		10 26							11 26					12 26							13 26		
Wolverhampton [7]	d		10 41			10 49	11 13			11 41		11 49	12 13	←	12 41			12 49	13 13			13 41	14 13	
Dunbar	d										07 25 →			07 25						←				09 25
Berwick-upon-Tweed	d				06 48			←						07 48			08 48			08 48				09 48
Alnmouth	d				07 10			07 10						08 08			→			09 09				
Newcastle [8]	d	06 44		07 23	→			07 44						08 40						09 40				10 40
Chester-le-Street	d																							
Durham	d	06 56		07 37				07 56						08 52						09 52				10 52
Darlington [7]	d	07 14		07 54				08 13						09 10						10 10				11 10
York [8]	d	07 44		08 27				08 44	09 25					09 44		10 30				10 44	11 23			11 44
Leeds [10]	d	08 10						09 10						10 10						11 10				12 10
Wakefield Westgate [7]	d	08 23						09 23						10 23						11 23				12 23
Doncaster [7]	d			08 51					09 56							10 58					11 54			
Sheffield [7]	d	08 57		09 31				10 00	10 31					11 00		11 31				12 01	12 31			13 01
Chesterfield	d	09 35		10 02				10 35	11 02					11 35		12 02				12 34	13 01			13 35
Derby [10]	d	09 57		10 24				10 57	11 24					11 57		12 24				12 57	13 24			13 57
Burton-on-Trent	d	10 07												12 07										14 07
Tamworth	d	10 18												12 18										14 18
Birmingham New Street [12]	a	10 36	10 58	11 04		11 11	11 30	11 36	11 58	11 58		12 11	12 30	12 36	12 58	13 04		13 11	13 30	13 36	13 58	13 58	14 30	14 36
Birmingham New Street [12]	d	10 40	11 03	11 10			11 33	11 40	12 03	12 10			12 33	12 40	13 03	13 10			13 33	13 40	14 03	14 10	14 33	14 40
Cheltenham Spa	a	11 21		11 51				12 21		12 51				13 21		13 51				14 21		14 51		15 21
Gloucester [7]	a																							
Bristol Parkway [7]	a	11 54		12 24				12 54		13 24				13 54		14 24				14 54		15 24		15 54
Bristol Temple Meads [10]	a	12 11		12 41				13 11		13 41				14 11		14 41				15 11		15 41		16 11
Newport (South Wales)	a																							
Cardiff Central [7]	a																							
Weston-super-Mare	a																							
Taunton	a			13 15				13 42		14 15						15 15				15 42		16 15		
Tiverton Parkway	a			13 28				14 01		14 28						15 28				15 54		16 28		
Exeter St Davids [6]	a			13 43				14 16		14 43						15 43				16 10		16 43		
Dawlish	a							14 29																
Teignmouth	a							14 34																
Newton Abbot	a			14 02				14 41		15 02						16 02				16 30		17 02		
Torquay	a							14 52																
Paignton	a							15 05																
Totnes	a			14 16						15 16						16 16				16 43		17 16		
Plymouth	a			14 48						15 48						16 48				17 15		17 48		
Liskeard [3]	a																					18 17		
Bodmin Parkway	a																					18 29		
Par [3]	a																					18 40		
St Austell	a																					18 46		
Truro	a																					19 04		
Redruth	a																					19 16		
Camborne	a																					19 23		
St Erth [2]	a																					19 33		
Penzance	a																					19 49		
Birmingham International	d		11 15						12 15						13 15						14 15			
Coventry	d		11 25						12 25						13 25						14 25			
Leamington Spa [8]	d		11 38				12 00		12 38				13 00		13 38				14 00		14 38		15 00	
Banbury	a		11 54				12 18		12 54				13 18		13 54				14 18		14 54		15 18	
Oxford	a		12 14				12 41		13 14				13 41		14 14				14 41		15 14		15 41	
Reading [7]	a		12 39				13 13		13 39				14 13		14 39				15 13		15 39		16 11	
Kensington Olympia	a																							
East Croydon	a																							
Guildford	a																						16 59	
Redhill	a																						*17 38*	
Basingstoke	a		13 08						14 08						15 08						16 08			
Winchester	a		13 24						14 24						15 24						16 24			
Southampton Airport Parkway	a		13 33						14 33						15 33						16 33			
Southampton Central	a		13 40						14 40						15 40						16 40			
Brockenhurst [3]	a		13 56						14 56						15 56						16 56			
Bournemouth	a		14 15						15 15						16 15						17 15			
Gatwick Airport [10]	a																						*17 50*	
Haywards Heath [3]	a																							
Brighton [10]	a																							

For general notes see front of timetable
For details of catering facilities see Directory of Train Operators

from 8 September

Scotland, The North East, North West England → The South West and South Coast

Route Diagram - See first page of Table 51

		XC	VT	XC	XC	VT	XC	XC	XC	XC	VT	XC	XC	XC	XC	VT	XC	XC	XC	XC	VT	XC	XC	XC
		1◇	R 1	1◇	R 1	1◇	1◇	1◇	R 1	R 1	R 1	R 1	1◇	R 1	R 1	R 1	R 1	R 1	R 1	1◇	1◇	R 1	R 1	R 1
Aberdeen	d												08 20											
Stonehaven	d												08 37											
Montrose	d												08 59											
Arbroath	d												09 15											
Dundee	d												09 32											
Leuchars 3	d												09 45											
Cupar	d												09 52											
Markinch	d												10 04											
Kirkcaldy	d												10 12											
Inverkeithing	d												10 27											
Glasgow Central 15	d	09 00	10 10								12 10										14 10			
Motherwell	d	09u14																						
Haymarket	d	09 54											10 47											
Edinburgh 10	d	10 05				10 51							11 05			12 52		12 05					13 05	
Haymarket	d					10u57										12u56								
Lockerbie	d															13 53								
Carlisle 8	d		11 22			12 13					13 21					14 14					15 21			
Penrith North Lakes	d					12 29										14 29								
Oxenholme Lake District	d					12 53					13 59					14 53								
Lancaster 6	d		12 12			13 09										15 08					16 09			
Preston 8	d		12 32			13 29					14 30					15 29					16 29			
Wigan North Western	d		12 45			13 41					14 42					15 41					16 41			
Warrington Bank Quay	d		12 59			13 53					14 54					15 52					16 53			
Manchester Piccadilly 10	d			13 24			13 54			14 24		14 54		15 24			15 54			16 24		16 54		17 24
Stockport	d			13 33			14 03			14 33		15 03		15 33			16 03			16 33		17 03		17 33
Wilmslow	d																							
Crewe 10	d		13 33			14 14					15 15					16 11					17 15			
Macclesfield	d			13 47			14 16			14 47		15 16		15 47			16 16			16 47		17 16		17 47
Congleton	d											15 24										17 24		
Stoke-on-Trent	d			14 04			14 39			15 04		15 39		16 04			16 39			17 04		17 39		18 04
Stafford	d			14 26						15 26				16 26						17 26				18 26
Wolverhampton 7	d		14 18	14 41		14 49	15 13			15 41	15 49	16 13		16 41		16 49	17 13			17 41	17 49	18 13		18 41
Dunbar	d												11 25										13 25	
Berwick-upon-Tweed	d												11 48										13 48	
Alnmouth	d	11 04						←										13 02						
Newcastle 8	d	11 40						11 40					12 40					13 40					14 40	
Chester-le-Street	d	→																						
Durham	d							11 52					12 52					13 52					14 52	
Darlington 7	d							12 10					13 10					14 10					15 10	
York 8	d				12 24			12 44	13 25				13 44		14 30			14 44	15 23				15 44	
Leeds 10	d							13 10					14 10					15 10					16 10	
Wakefield Westgate 7	d							13 23					14 23					15 23					16 23	
Doncaster 7	d				12 55				13 54						14 57				15 55					
Sheffield 7	d				13 31			14 00	14 31				15 00		15 31			16 00	16 31				17 00	
Chesterfield	d				14 02			14 33	15 03				15 35		16 02			16 35	17 02				17 35	
Derby 10	d				14 24			14 57	15 24				15 57		16 24			16 57	17 24				17 57	
Burton-on-Trent	d												16 07										18 07	
Tamworth	d												16 18										18 18	
Birmingham New Street 12	a		14 41	14 58	15 04	15 11	15 30	15 36	15 58	15 58	16 11	16 30	16 36	16 58	17 04	17 11	17 30	17 36	17 58	17 58	18 11	18 30	18 36	18 58
Birmingham New Street 12	d			15 03	15 10		15 33	15 40	16 03	16 10		16 33	16 40	17 03	17 10		17 33	17 40	18 03	18 10		18 33	18 40	19 03
Cheltenham Spa	a				15 51			16 21		16 51			17 21		17 51			18 21		18 51			19 21	
Gloucester 7	a																	18 34						
Bristol Parkway 7	a				16 24			16 54		17 24			17 54		18 24			19 05		19 24			19 54	
Bristol Temple Meads 10	a				16 41			17 11		17 41			18 11		18 41			19 22		19 41			20 11	
Newport (South Wales)	a																	19 59						
Cardiff Central 7	a																	20 19						
Weston-super-Mare	a																						20 39	
Taunton	a				17 15			17 42		18 15					19 15					20 15				
Tiverton Parkway	a				17 28			17 55		18 28					19 28					20 28				
Exeter St Davids 6	a				17 43			18 10		18 43					19 43					20 43				
Dawlish	a							18 23																
Teignmouth	a							18 28																
Newton Abbot	a				18 08			18 35		19 02					20 02					21 02				
Torquay	a																							
Paignton	a																							
Totnes	a				18 21			18 48		19 16					20 16					21 16				
Plymouth	a				18 48			19 20		19 48					20 48					21 48				
Liskeard 3	a				19 22					20 12														
Bodmin Parkway	a				19 34					20 24														
Par 3	a				19 46					20 35														
St Austell	a				19 53					20 41														
Truro	a				20 10					20 59														
Redruth	a				20 21					21 13														
Camborne	a				20 28					21 20														
St Erth 2	a				20 39					21 30														
Penzance	a				20 56					21 47														
Birmingham International ✈	d			15 15					16 15					17 15					18 15					19 15
Coventry	d			15 25					16 25					17 25					18 25					19 25
Leamington Spa 8	d			15 38			16 00		16 38			17 00		17 38			18 00		18 38			19 00		19 38
Banbury	a			15 54			16 18		16 54			17 18		17 54			18 18		18 54			19 18		19 54
Oxford	a			16 14			16 41		17 14			17 41		18 14			18 41		19 14			19 41		20 14
Reading 7	a			16 39			17 13		17 39			18 11		18 39			19 13		19 39			20 09		20 39
Kensington Olympia	a											19 01										20 52		
East Croydon	a											19 33										21 15		
Guildford	a																							
Redhill	a																					21 34		
Basingstoke	a			17 08					18 08					19 08					20 08					21 08
Winchester	a			17 24					18 24					19 24					20 24					21 24
Southampton Airport Parkwy ✈	a			17 33					18 33					19 33					20 33					21 33
Southampton Central	a			17 40					18 40					19 40					20 40					21 40
Brockenhurst 3	a			17 56					18 56					19 56					20 56					21 56
Bournemouth	a			18 15					19 15					20 24					21 26					22 26
Gatwick Airport 10 ✈	a											19 52										21 47		
Haywards Heath 3	a											20 04										21b45		
Brighton 10	a											20 30										22b00		

For general notes see front of timetable
For details of catering facilities see Directory of Train Operators

b Change at East Croydon

from 8 September

Scotland, The North East, North West England → The South West and South Coast

Route Diagram - See first page of Table 51

		XC	VT	XC	XC	XC	XC	VT	XC	XC	XC	XC	XC	VT	XC	XC	XC	XC	VT	XC	VT	XC	XC
					R	R																	
		1 ◇	1 ◇	1 ◇	1	1	1 ◇	1 ◇	1 ◇	1 ◇	1 ◇	1 ◇	1 ◇	1 ◇	1 ◇	1 ◇	1 ◇	1 ◇	1 ◇	1 ◇	1 ◇	1 ◇	1 ◇
		☕	☕	☕	☕	☕	☕	☕	☕	☕	☕	☕	☕	☕		☕		☕	☕	☕	☕		
Aberdeen	d																						
Stonehaven	d																						
Montrose	d																						
Arbroath	d																						
Dundee	d																						
Leuchars [3]	d																						
Cupar	d																						
Markinch	d																						
Kirkcaldy	d																						
Inverkeithing	d																						
Glasgow Central [15]	d							16 10											18 10				
Motherwell	d																		18u27				
Haymarket	d																						
Edinburgh [10]	d		14 52		14 05					15 05			16 05	16 51						17 05	18 52		18 45
Haymarket	d		14u57											16u56							18u56		
Lockerbie	d		15 53											17 49							19 49		
Carlisle [8]	d		16 14					17 21						18 11					19 32		20 11		
Penrith North Lakes	d		16 29					17 36						18 27							20 27		
Oxenholme Lake District	d		16 53					18 00						18 51					20 07		20 52		
Lancaster [6]	d		17 09											19 08					20 23		21 07		
Preston [8]	d		17 29					18 29						19 29					20 49		21 29		
Wigan North Western	d		17 41					18 42						19 41					21 01		21 42		
Warrington Bank Quay	d		17 53					18 53						19 53					21 13		21 54		
Manchester Piccadilly [10]	d			17 54			18 24		18 54		19 24				19 54		20 24					21 54	
Stockport	d			18 03			18 33		19 03		19 33				20 03		20 33					22 03	
Wilmslow	d																						
Crewe [10]	d		18 15					19 15						20 15					21 35		22 16		
Macclesfield	d			18 16			18 47		19 16		19 47				20 16		20 47					22 16	
Congleton	d			18 24					19 24						20 24							22 24	
Stoke-on-Trent	d			18 39			19 04		19 39		20 04				20 39		21 04					22 39	
Stafford	d						19 25		19 58		20 26				20 57		21 26		21 55		22 36	22 57	
Wolverhampton [7]	d		18 49	19 13			19 41	19 49	20 13		20 41			20 49	21 13		21 41		22 16		22 49	23 13	
Dunbar	d									15 25										17 25			
Berwick-upon-Tweed	d									15 48						←				17 48			
Alnmouth	d				15 04								17 08			17 08							
Newcastle [8]	d				15 40					16 40			→			17 40				18 40			20 26
Chester-le-Street	d																						
Durham	d				15 52					16 52						17 52				18 52			20 38
Darlington [7]	d				16 10											18 10				19 10			20 55
York [8]	d	16 25			16 44	17 34				17 44		18 17				18 44		19 30		19 44			21 24
Leeds [10]	d				17 10					18 10						19 10				20 10			
Wakefield Westgate [7]	d				17 23					18 23						19 23				20 23			
Doncaster [7]	d	16 53				17 58						18 52						19 57					
Sheffield [7]	d	17 31			18 00	18 31				19 00		19 31				20 00		20 31		21 00			22 27
Chesterfield	d	18 02			18 35	19 02				19 33		20 01				20 35		20 57		21 35			22 53
Derby [10]	d	18 24			18 57	19 24				19 57		20 27				20 57		21 27		21 57			23 15
Burton-on-Trent	d									20 07								21 37		22 07			23 26
Tamworth	d									20 18								21 48		22 18			23 37
Birmingham New Street [12]	a	19 08	19 11	19 30	19 36	19 58	19 58	20 11	20 35	20 43	20 58	21 04		21 11	21 35	21 44	22 04	22 08	22 38	22 50	23 11	23 47	23 59
Birmingham New Street [12]	d	19 10		19 33	19 40	20 03	20 10				21 03	21 10						22 10					
Cheltenham Spa	a	19 51			20 21		20 51					21 51						22 51					
Gloucester [7]	a																						
Bristol Parkway [7]	a	20 24			20 54		21 24					22 24						23 24					
Bristol Temple Meads [10]	a	20 41			21 11		21 41					22 41						23 41					
Newport (South Wales)	a																						
Cardiff Central [7]	a																						
Weston-super-Mare	a																						
Taunton	a	21 15					22 15																
Tiverton Parkway	a	21 28					22 28																
Exeter St Davids [6]	a	21 43					23 24																
Dawlish	a																						
Teignmouth	a																						
Newton Abbot	a	22 02					23 44																
Torquay	a																						
Paignton	a																						
Totnes	a	22 16					23 57																
Plymouth	a	22 48					00 29																
Liskeard [3]	a																						
Bodmin Parkway	a																						
Par [3]	a																						
St Austell	a																						
Truro	a																						
Redruth	a																						
Camborne	a																						
St Erth [2]	a																						
Penzance	a																						
Birmingham International	d					20 15					21 15												
Coventry	d					20 25					21 25												
Leamington Spa [8]	d			20 00		20 38					21 38												
Banbury	a			20 18		20 54					21 54												
Oxford	a			20 41		21 14					22 14												
Reading [7]	a			21 06		21 39					22 39												
Kensington Olympia	a																						
East Croydon	a																						
Guildford	a			21 33																			
Redhill	a			22 11																			
Basingstoke	a					22 08					23 08												
Winchester	a					22 24					23 24												
Southampton Airport Parkwy	a					22 33					23 33												
Southampton Central	a					22 46					23 47												
Brockenhurst [3]	a					23b04					00b04												
Bournemouth	a					23b23					00b22												
Gatwick Airport [10]	a			22 37																			
Haywards Heath [3]	a			22c52																			
Brighton [10]	a			23c15																			

For general notes see front of timetable
For details of catering facilities see Directory of Train Operators

b Change at Winchester
c Change at Redhill

Scotland, The North East, North West England → The South West and South Coast

Route Diagram - See first page of Table 51

		XC	XC	XC	XC	XC	XC	XC	VT	XC	XC	VT	XC	XC	XC	XC	XC	XC	XC	VT	XC	VT
		1◇	1◇	1◇	1◇	1◇	1◇	1◇	1◇	1◇	R 1	R 1	R 1	1◇	1◇	R 1	R 1	R 1	R 1	1◇	1◇	1◇
													A									
Aberdeen	d																					
Stonehaven	d																					
Montrose	d																					
Arbroath	d																					
Dundee	d																					
Leuchars 3	d																					
Cupar	d																					
Markinch	d																					
Kirkcaldy	d																					
Inverkeithing	d																					
Glasgow Central 15	d																				05 50	06 10
Motherwell	d																				06u09	06u25
Haymarket	d																				06 51 →	
Edinburgh 10	d																					
Haymarket	d																					
Lockerbie	d																					
Carlisle 8	d																					07 28
Penrith North Lakes	d																					07 43
Oxenholme Lake District	d																					08 07
Lancaster 6	d																					08 23
Preston 8	d								06 15			07 20								08 29		08 47
Wigan North Western	d								06 27			07 32								08 40		08 59
Warrington Bank Quay	d								06 47			07 44								08 52		09 10
Manchester Piccadilly 10	d			05b10						06 54			07 24		07 54				08 24			
Stockport	d			05b19						07 03			07 33		08 03				08 33			
Wilmslow	d			05b27									07 42									
Crewe 10	d			05 45					07 10			08 06	08 10							09 14		09 31
Macclesfield	d									07 16					08 16				08 46			
Congleton	d									07 24					08 24							
Stoke-on-Trent	d			06 06						07 39					08 39				09 06			
Stafford	d			06 26						07 58			08 33		08 58				09 26			
Wolverhampton 7	d			06 41					07 48	08 13		08 43	08 49		09 13				09 41	09 49		
Dunbar	d																					
Berwick-upon-Tweed	d																					
Alnmouth	d																					
Newcastle 8	d															06 08	06 19					
Chester-le-Street	d																06 31					
Durham	d															06 22	06 38	←				
Darlington 7	d															07 09	06 55	07 09				
York 8	d													06 06		→	07 25	07 44				
Leeds 10	d							06 00						06 48				08 10				
Wakefield Westgate 7	d							06 11						*06 32*				08 23				
Doncaster 7	d													07 26			07 52					
Sheffield 7	d						06 01	06 53						07 53			08 23	08 53				
Chesterfield	d						06 24	07 05						08 05			08 35					
Derby 10	d		06 10				07 15	07 27						08 27			08 57	09 24				
Burton-on-Trent	d		06 20					07 37						08 37								
Tamworth	d		06 31					07 48						08 48								
Birmingham New Street 12	a		06 51	06 58	←		07 58	08 06	08 10	08 30		09 05	09 06	09 11	09 30		09 36	09 58	09 58	10 11		10 24
Birmingham New Street 12	d	06 03	07 10	07 03	07 10	07 33	08 03	08 10		08 33	09 03		09 10		09 33		09 40	10 03	10 10			10 30
Cheltenham Spa	a		→		07 51			08 51					09 51				10 21		10 51			
Gloucester 7	a																					
Bristol Parkway 7	a				08 24			09 24					10 24				10 54		11 24			
Bristol Temple Meads 10	a				08 41			09 41					10 41				11 11		11 41			
Newport (South Wales)	a																					
Cardiff Central 7	a																					
Weston-super-Mare	a																11 28					
Taunton	a				09 15			10 15									12 00		12 15			
Tiverton Parkway	a				09 28			10 28									12 13					
Exeter St Davids 6	a				09 43			10 43					11 43				12 28		12 43			
Dawlish	a				09 57												12 41		12 57			
Teignmouth	a				10 02												12 48		13 03			
Newton Abbot	a				10 10			11 03									12 56		13 10			
Torquay	a				10 21												13 07		13 24			
Paignton	a				10 34												13 21		13 38			
Totnes	a							11 16														
Plymouth	a							11 48					12 48									
Liskeard 3	a												13 10									
Bodmin Parkway	a												13 22									
Par 3	a																					
St Austell	a																					
Truro	a																					
Redruth	a																					
Camborne	a																					
St Erth 2	a																					
Penzance	a																					
Birmingham International	d	06 15		07 15			08 15				09 15							10 15				10 40
Coventry	d	06 25		07 25			08 25				09 25							10 25				10a49
Leamington Spa 8	d	06 38		07 38		08 00	08 38			09 00	09 38				10 00			10 38				
Banbury	a	06 54		07 54		08 17	08 54			09 17	09 54				10 17			10 54				
Oxford	a	07 14		08 14		08 41	09 14			09 41	10 14				10 41			11 14				
Reading 7	a	07 44		08 39		09 13	09 39			10 13	10 39				11 13			11 39				
Kensington Olympia	a														11 56							
East Croydon	a														12 37							
Guildford	a																					
Redhill	a																					
Basingstoke	a			09 08			10 08				11 08							12 08				
Winchester	a			09 24			10 24				11 24							12 24				
Southampton Airport Parkwy	a			09 33			10 33				11 33							12 33				
Southampton Central	a			09 40			10 40				11 40							12 40				
Brockenhurst 3	a			09 56			10 56				11 56							12 56				
Bournemouth	a			10 15			11 15				12 15							13 15				
Gatwick Airport 10	a														12 53							
Haywards Heath 3	a														13 13							
Brighton 10	a														13 37							

For general notes see front of timetable
For details of catering facilities see Directory of Train Operators

A To Newquay arr. 1449 (Table 135)
b Change at Stafford

Table 51 SUMMARY OF SERVICES **Saturdays**

Scotland, The North East, North West England → The South West and South Coast

until 12 July

Route Diagram - See first page of Table 51

		XC	XC	VT	XC	XC	VT	VT	XC	XC	VT	XC	XC	VT	VT	XC	XC	VT	XC	XC	VT	VT
						R							R	R						R	R	
		1◇	1◇	1◇	1◇	1	1◇	1◇	1◇	1◇	1◇	1◇	1	1	1◇	1◇	1◇	1◇	1◇	1	1	1◇
																				A		
		☕	☕	☕	☕	☕	☕	☕	☕	☕	☕	☕	☕	☕	☕	☕	☕	☕	☕	☕	☕	☕
Aberdeen	d																					
Stonehaven	d																					
Montrose	d																					
Arbroath	d																					
Dundee	d																					
Leuchars 3	d																					
Cupar	d																					
Markinch	d																					
Kirkcaldy	d																					
Inverkeithing	d																					
Glasgow Central 15	d							07 10						07 40	08 07							
Motherwell	d											←			08u26							
Haymarket	d											06 51										
Edinburgh 10	d					06 05	06 51					07 05					07 50				08 52	
Haymarket	d						06u55														08u56	
Lockerbie	d						07 52															
Carlisle 8	d						08 13	08 39						09 11	09 32						10 10	
Penrith North Lakes	d						08 29							09 26	09 47							
Oxenholme Lake District	d						08 53							09 51	10 11						10 47	
Lancaster 6	d						09 09	09 27						10 09	10 27						11 06	11 24
Preston 8	d						09 29	09 47						10 29	10 47						11 28	11 47
Wigan North Western	d						09 41	09 59						10 41	10 59						11 40	11 59
Warrington Bank Quay	d						09 53	10 10						10 53	11 10						11 53	12 10
Manchester Piccadilly 10	d	08 54		09 15	09 24				09 54		10 15		10 24			10 54		11 15	11 24			
Stockport	d	09 03		09u24	09 33				10 03		10u24		10 33			11 03		11u24	11 33			
Wilmslow	d																					
Crewe 10	d						10 15	10 31						11 15	11 31						12 13	12 31
Macclesfield	d	09 16			09 46				10 16				10 46			11 16			11 46			
Congleton	d	09 24														11 24						
Stoke-on-Trent	d	09 39		09 50	10 06				10 39		10 50		11 06			11 39		11 50	12 06			
Stafford	d	09 58			10 26				10 58				11 26			11 58			12 26			
Wolverhampton 7	d	10 13			10 41		10 49		11 13				11 41	11 49		12 13			12 41		12 49	
Dunbar	d											07 25										
Berwick-upon-Tweed	d					06 44						07 48					08 34					
Alnmouth	d					07 04						08 11										
Newcastle 8	d		06 50			07 40				08 24		08 40					09 25			09 40		
Chester-le-Street	d									08 33												
Durham	d		07 02			07 52				08 40		08 52					09 37			09 52		
Darlington 7	d					08 09				08 57		09 09					09 56			10 09		
York 8	d		08 19			08 44				09 27		09 44					10 25			10 44		
Leeds 10	d					09 10						10 10								11 10		
Wakefield Westgate 7	d					09 23						10 23								11 23		
Doncaster 7	d									09 51							10 53					
Sheffield 7	d		09 23			09 53				10 23		10 53					11 23			11 53		
Chesterfield	d		09 35							10 35							11 35					
Derby 10	d		09 57			10 24				10 57		11 24					11 57			12 30		
Burton-on-Trent	d		10 07														12 07					
Tamworth	d		10 18														12 18					
Birmingham New Street 12	a	10 30	10 36	10 47	10 58	11 04	11 11	11 24	11 30	11 36	11 47	11 58	11 58	12 11	12 24	12 30	12 36	12 47	12 58	13 09	13 11	13 24
Birmingham New Street 12	d	10 33	10 40	10 51	11 03	11 10		11 30	11 33	11 40	11 51	12 03	12 10		12 30	12 33	12 40	12 51	13 03	13 10		13 30
Cheltenham Spa	a		11 21			11 51				12 21			12 51				13 21					
Gloucester 7	a																					
Bristol Parkway 7	a		11 54			12 24				12 54			13 24				13 54					
Bristol Temple Meads 10	a		12 11			12 41				13 11			13 41				14 11			14 41		
Newport (South Wales)	a																					
Cardiff Central 7	a																					
Weston-super-Mare	a												14 01									
Taunton	a					13 15							14 27									
Tiverton Parkway	a					13 28							14 40									
Exeter St Davids 6	a					13 43							14 55									
Dawlish	a												15 11									
Teignmouth	a												15 18									
Newton Abbot	a					14 03							15 26									
Torquay	a												15 40									
Paignton	a												15 52									
Totnes	a					14 16																
Plymouth	a					14 48														16 43		
Liskeard 3	a																			17 07		
Bodmin Parkway	a																			17 19		
Par 3	a																					
St Austell	a																					
Truro	a																					
Redruth	a																					
Camborne	a																					
St Erth 2	a																					
Penzance	a																					
Birmingham International ✈	d			11 04	11 15			11 40			12 04	12 15			12 40			13 04	13 15			13 40
Coventry	d			11a13	11 25			11a49			12a13	12 25			12a49			13a13	13 25			13a49
Leamington Spa 8	d	11 00			11 38				12 00			12 38				13 00			13 38			
Banbury	a	11 17			11 54				12 17			12 54				13 17			13 54			
Oxford	a	11 41			12 14				12 41			13 14				13 41			14 14			
Reading 7	a	12 13			12 39				13 13			13 39				14 13			14 39			
Kensington Olympia	a																					
East Croydon	a																					
Guildford	a																					
Redhill	a																					
Basingstoke	a				13 08							14 08							15 08			
Winchester	a				13 24							14 24							15 24			
Southampton Airport Parkwy ✈	a				13 33							14 33							15 33			
Southampton Central	a				13 40							14 40							15 40			
Brockenhurst 3	a				13 56							14 56							15 56			
Bournemouth	a				14 15							15 15							16 15			
Gatwick Airport 10 ✈	a																					
Haywards Heath 3	a																					
Brighton 10	a																					

For general notes see front of timetable
For details of catering facilities see Directory of Train Operators

A To Newquay arr. 1840 (Table 135)

Scotland, The North East, North West England → The South West and South Coast

until 12 July

Route Diagram - See first page of Table 51

		XC	XC	VT	XC	XC	XC	VT	VT	XC	XC	VT	XC	XC	VT	VT	XC	XC	VT	XC	XC	VT
			R		R	R	R	R						R								R
		1 ◇	1	1 ◇	1	1	1	1	1 ◇	1 ◇	1 ◇	1 ◇	1 ◇	1	1 ◇	1 ◇	1 ◇	1 ◇	1 ◇	1 ◇	1 ◇	1
		🛒	🛒	🛒	🛒	🛒	🛒	🛒	🛒	🛒	🛒	🛒	🛒	🛒	🛒	🛒	🛒	🛒	🛒	🛒	🛒	🛒
Aberdeen	d																			08 20		
Stonehaven	d																			08 37		
Montrose	d																			08 59		
Arbroath	d																			09 15		
Dundee	d				07 35															09 32		
Leuchars [3]	d				07 48															09 45		
Cupar	d				07 56															09 52		
Markinch	d				08 11															10 04		
Kirkcaldy	d				08 20															10 12		
Inverkeithing	d				08 36															10 27		
Glasgow Central [15]	d						09 00	10 10	10 20							11 10						12 10
Motherwell	d						09u15							←		11u23						
Haymarket	d				08 56		09 54 →							09 54						10 47		
Edinburgh [10]	d				09 05									10 05	10 52					11 05		
Haymarket	d														10u56							
Lockerbie	d																					
Carlisle [8]	d							11 22	11 32						12 13	12 32						13 21
Penrith North Lakes	d								11 47						12 29	12 47						
Oxenholme Lake District	d								12 11						12 53	13 11						13 58
Lancaster [6]	d							12 11	12 27						13 09	13 27						
Preston [8]	d							12 29	12 47						13 29	13 47						14 29
Wigan North Western	d							12 41	12 59						13 41	13 59						14 41
Warrington Bank Quay	d							12 53	13 10						13 53	14 10						14 52
Manchester Piccadilly [10] 🚊	d	11 54		12 15		12 24				12 54		13 15	13 24				13 54		14 15		14 24	
Stockport	d	12 03		12u24		12 33				13 03		13u24	13 33				14 03		14u24		14 33	
Wilmslow	d																					
Crewe [10]	d							13 15	13 31						14 15	14 31						15 13
Macclesfield	d	12 16				12 46				13 16			13 46				14 16				14 46	
Congleton	d									13 24												
Stoke-on-Trent	d	12 39		12 50		13 06				13 39		13 50	14 06				14 39		14 50		15 06	
Stafford	d	12 58				13 26				13 58			14 26				14 58				15 26	
Wolverhampton [7] 🚊	d	13 13				13 41		13 49		14 13			14 41		14 49		15 13				15 41	15 47
Dunbar	d				09 25															11 25		
Berwick-upon-Tweed	d				09 48															11 48		
Alnmouth	d													11 04								
Newcastle [8]	d		10 25		10 40						11 25			11 40				12 20		12 40		
Chester-le-Street	d		10 34															12 29				
Durham	d		10 41		10 52						11 37			11 52				12 36		12 52		
Darlington [7]	d		10 58		11 09						11 57			12 09				12 53		13 09		
York [8]	d		11 27		11 44						12 25			12 44				13 28		13 44		
Leeds [10]	d				12 10									13 10						14 10		
Wakefield Westgate [7]	d				12 23									13 23						14 23		
Doncaster [7]	d		11 55								12 52							13 54				
Sheffield [7]	d		12 23		12 53						13 23			13 53				14 23		14 53		
Chesterfield	d		12 35								13 35							14 35				
Derby [10]	d		12 57		13 24						13 57			14 24				14 57		15 24		
Burton-on-Trent	d										14 07											
Tamworth	d										14 18											
Birmingham New Street [12]	a	13 30	13 36	13 47	13 58	13 58		14 11	14 24	14 30	14 36	14 47	14 58	15 04	15 11	15 24	15 30	15 36	15 47	15 58	15 58	16 11
Birmingham New Street [12]	d	13 33	13 40	13 51	14 03	14 10			14 30	14 33	14 40	14 51	15 03	15 10		15 30	15 33	15 40	15 51	16 03	16 10	
Cheltenham Spa	a		14 21			14 51					15 21			15 51				16 21			16 51	
Gloucester [7]	a																					
Bristol Parkway [7]	a		14 54			15 24					15 54			16 24				16 54			17 24	
Bristol Temple Meads [10]	a		15 11			15 41					16 11			16 41				17 11			17 41	
Newport (South Wales)	a																					
Cardiff Central [7]	a																					
Weston-super-Mare	a																					
Taunton	a					16 15								17 15							18 15	
Tiverton Parkway	a					16 28								17 28							18 28	
Exeter St Davids [6]	a		16 03			16 43								17 43							18 43	
Dawlish	a													17 57								
Teignmouth	a													18 03								
Newton Abbot	a													18 11							19 03	
Torquay	a					17 15								18 25								
Paignton	a					17 29								18 39								
Totnes	a																				19 16	
Plymouth	a		17 07																		19 48	
Liskeard [3]	a																				20 17	
Bodmin Parkway	a																				20 29	
Par [3]	a		17 55																		20 40	
St Austell	a		18 02																		20 46	
Truro	a		18 19																		21 03	
Redruth	a		18 31																		21 15	
Camborne	a		18 38																		21 21	
St Erth [2]	a		18 48																		21 31	
Penzance	a		19 05																		21 48	
Birmingham International ✈	d			14 04					14 40			15 01	15 15			15 40			16 04	16 15		
Coventry	d			14a13					14a49			15a13	15 25			15a49			16a13	16 25		
Leamington Spa [8]	d	14 00								15 00			15 38				16 00			16 38		
Banbury	a	14 17								15 17			15 54				16 17			16 54		
Oxford	a	14 41			15 14					15 41			16 14				16 41			17 14		
Reading [7]	a	15 13			15 39					16 13			16 39				17 13			17 39		
Kensington Olympia	a																					
East Croydon 🚊	a																					
Guildford	a									16 58												
Redhill	a									*17 38*												
Basingstoke	a				16 08								17 08							18 08		
Winchester	a				16 24								17 24							18 24		
Southampton Airport Parkway ✈	a				16 33								17 33							18 33		
Southampton Central	a				16 40								17 40							18 40		
Brockenhurst [3]	a				16 56								17 56							18 56		
Bournemouth	a				17 15								18 15							19 15		
Gatwick Airport [10] ✈	a									*17 50*												
Haywards Heath [3]	a																					
Brighton [10]	a																					

For general notes see front of timetable
For details of catering facilities see Directory of Train Operators

Scotland, The North East, North West England → The South West and South Coast

until 12 July

Route Diagram - See first page of Table 51

		VT	XC	XC	VT	XC	XC	VT	VT	XC	XC	VT	XC	XC	VT	VT	XC	XC	VT	XC	XC	VT
		1 ◇	1 ◇	1 ◇	1 ◇	1 ◇	1 ◇	R 1	1 ◇	1 ◇	1 ◇	1 ◇	1 ◇	1 ◇	1 ◇	1 ◇	1 ◇	1 ◇	1 ◇	1 ◇	1 ◇	1 ◇
Aberdeen	d																					
Stonehaven	d																					
Montrose	d																					
Arbroath	d																					
Dundee	d																					
Leuchars 3	d																					
Cupar	d																					
Markinch	d																					
Kirkcaldy	d																					
Inverkeithing	d																					
Glasgow Central 15	d								13 10						14 10							
Motherwell	d								13u25													
Haymarket	d																					
Edinburgh 10	d						12 05	12 52					13 05								14 05	14 52
Haymarket	d							12u56														14u56
Lockerbie	d							13 52														
Carlisle 8	d							14 13	14 32						15 21	15 27						16 09
Penrith North Lakes	d							14 28	14 47							15 41						16 24
Oxenholme Lake District	d							14 53	15 11							16 05						16 48
Lancaster 6	d	14 27						15 09	15 27						16 10	16 27						17 04
Preston 8	d	14 47						15 29	15 47						16 29	16 47						17 24
Wigan North Western	d	14 59						15 41	15 59						16 41	16 59						17 36
Warrington Bank Quay	d	15 10						15 52	16 10						16 52	17 10						17 48
Manchester Piccadilly 10	d		14 54		15 15	15 24				15 54		16 15		16 24			16 54		17 15	17 24		
Stockport	d		15 03		15u24	15 33				16 03		16u24		16 33			17 03		17u24	17 33		
Wilmslow	d																					
Crewe 10	d	15 31						16 12	16 31						17 15	17 31						18 13
Macclesfield	d		15 16			15 46				16 16				16 46			17 16			17 46		
Congleton	d		15 24														17 24					
Stoke-on-Trent	d		15 39		15 50	16 06				16 39		16 50		17 06			17 39		17 50	18 06		
Stafford	d		15 58			16 26				16 58				17 26			17 58			18 26		
Wolverhampton 7	d		16 13			16 41		16 49		17 13				17 41	17 49		18 13			18 41		18 49
Dunbar	d												13 25									
Berwick-upon-Tweed	d												13 48									
Alnmouth	d						13 05														15 05	
Newcastle 8	d			13 27			13 40				14 22		14 40					15 22			15 40	
Chester-le-Street	d										14 31											
Durham	d			13 39			13 52				14 38		14 52					15 34			15 52	
Darlington 7	d			13 58			14 09				14 55		15 09					15 54			16 09	
York 8	d			14 30			14 44				15 27		15 44					16 25			16 44	
Leeds 10	d						15 10						16 10								17 10	
Wakefield Westgate 7	d						15 23						16 23								17 23	
Doncaster 7	d			14 56							15 55							16 53				
Sheffield 7	d			15 23			15 53				16 23		16 53					17 20			17 53	
Chesterfield	d			15 35							16 35							17 35				
Derby 10	d			15 57			16 24				16 57		17 24					17 57			18 24	
Burton-on-Trent	d			16 07														18 07				
Tamworth	d			16 18														18 18				
Birmingham New Street 12	a	16 24	16 30	16 36	16 47	16 58	17 04	17 11	17 24	17 30	17 36	17 47	17 58	17 58	18 11	18 24	18 30	18 36	18 47	18 58	19 04	19 11
Birmingham New Street 12	d	16 30	16 33	16 40	16 51	17 03	17 10		17 30	17 33	17 40	17 51	18 03	18 10		18 30	18 33	18 40	18 51	19 03	19 10	
Cheltenham Spa	a			17 21			17 51				18 21			18 51				19 21			19 51	
Gloucester 7	a										18 33											
Bristol Parkway 7	a			17 54			18 24				19 09			19 24				19 54			20 24	
Bristol Temple Meads 10	a			18 11			18 41				19 26			19 41				20 11			20 41	
Newport (South Wales)	a										19 59											
Cardiff Central 7	a										20 19											
Weston-super-Mare	a						19 04															
Taunton	a						19 26							20 15							21 15	
Tiverton Parkway	a						19 39							20 28							21 28	
Exeter St Davids 6	a						19 54							20 43							21 43	
Dawlish	a																					
Teignmouth	a																					
Newton Abbot	a						20 14							21 03							22 03	
Torquay	a																					
Paignton	a																					
Totnes	a						20 27							21 16							22 20	
Plymouth	a						20 54							21 48							22 55	
Liskeard 3	a																					
Bodmin Parkway	a																					
Par 3	a						21 46															
St Austell	a						21 53															
Truro	a						22 11															
Redruth	a						22 29															
Camborne	a						22 36															
St Erth 2	a						22 46															
Penzance	a						23 03															
Birmingham International	d	16 40			17 04	17 15			17 40			18 04	18 15			18 40			19 04	19 15		
Coventry	d	16a49			17a13	17 25			17a49			18a13	18 25			18a49			19a13	19 25		
Leamington Spa 8	d		17 00			17 38				18 00			18 38				19 00			19 38		
Banbury	a		17 17			17 54				18 17			18 54				19 17			19 54		
Oxford	a		17 41			18 14				18 41			19 14				19 41			20 14		
Reading 7	a		18 13			18 39				19 13			19 39				20 13			20 39		
Kensington Olympia	a		19 01																			
East Croydon	a		19 36																			
Guildford	a																20 58					
Redhill	a																21 28					
Basingstoke	a					19 08							20 08							21 08		
Winchester	a					19 24							20 24							21 24		
Southampton Airport Parkwy	a					19 33							20 33							21 33		
Southampton Central	a					19 40							20 40							21 40		
Brockenhurst 3	a					19 56							20 56							21 56		
Bournemouth	a					20 15							21 15							22 15		
Gatwick Airport 10	a		19 52														21 47					
Haywards Heath 3	a		20 04														22 24					
Brighton 10	a		20 28														22 48					

For general notes see front of timetable
For details of catering facilities see Directory of Train Operators

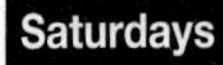
Saturdays

until 12 July

Scotland, The North East, North West England → The South West and South Coast

Route Diagram - See first page of Table 51

		XC	XC	VT	XC	XC		VT	XC	XC	VT	XC	XC	VT	XC	VT		XC	VT	XC	VT	XC		
		1 ◇	1 ◇	1 ◇	1 ◇	1 ◇		1 ◇	1 ◇	1 ◇	1 ◇	1 ◇	1 ◇	1 ◇	1 ◇	1 ◇		1 ◇	1 ◇	1 ◇	1 ◇	1 ◇		
		☕	☕	☕	☕	☕		☕	☕	☕	☕	☕	☕	☕		☕		☕	☕		☕	☕		
Aberdeen	d																							
Stonehaven	d																							
Montrose	d																							
Arbroath	d																							
Dundee	d																							
Leuchars 3	d																							
Cupar	d																							
Markinch	d																							
Kirkcaldy	d																							
Inverkeithing	d																							
Glasgow Central 15	d							16 03											18 10					
Motherwell	d																		18u27					
Haymarket	d																							
Edinburgh 10	d				15 05								16 05	16 52								18 05		
Haymarket	d													16u56										
Lockerbie	d													17 50					19 12					
Carlisle 8	d							17 21						18 11					19 32					
Penrith North Lakes	d							17 36						18 27										
Oxenholme Lake District	d							18 00						18 51					20 08					
Lancaster 6	d													19 07					20 21					
Preston 8	d							18 30						19 29					20 43		21 22			
Wigan North Western	d							18 42						19 41					20 55		21 34			
Warrington Bank Quay	d							18 53						19 53					21 06		21 46			
Manchester Piccadilly 10	d	17 54		18 15		18 24			18 54		19 15	19 24			19 54	20 15				20 54				
Stockport	d	18 03		18u24		18 33			19 03		19u24	19 33			20 03	20u24				21 03				
Wilmslow	d																							
Crewe 10	d							19 15						20 15					21 28		22 08			
Macclesfield	d	18 16				18 46			19 16			19 46			20 16	20 38				21 16				
Congleton	d	18 24							19 24						20 24					21 24				
Stoke-on-Trent	d	18 39		18 50		19 06			19 39		19 50	20 06			20 39	20 56				21 39				
Stafford	d	18 58				19 25			19 58			20 26			20 58	21 18			21 51	21 58	22 33			
Wolverhampton 7	d	19 13				19 41		19 49	20 13			20 41		20 49	21 13	21 35			22 09	22 13	22 49			
Dunbar	d				15 25																	18 25		
Berwick-upon-Tweed	d				15 48																	18 48		
Alnmouth	d												17 05									19 08		
Newcastle 8	d		16 20		16 40					17 18			17 40					18 40				19 45		
Chester-le-Street	d		16 29							17 27								18 49						
Durham	d		16 36		16 52					17 34			17 52					18 56				19 56		
Darlington 7	d		16 54		17 09					17 51			18 09					19 13				20 13		
York 8	d		17 25		17 44					18 25			18 44					19 44				20 44		
Leeds 10	d				18 10								19 10					20 10				21 10		
Wakefield Westgate 7	d				18 23								19 23					20 23				21 23		
Doncaster 7	d		17 55							18 51														
Sheffield 7	d		18 23		18 53					19 23			19 53					20 53				21 53		
Chesterfield	d		18 35							19 35			20 05					21 05				22 05		
Derby 10	d		18 57		19 24					19 57			20 27					21 27				22 27		
Burton-on-Trent	d									20 07								21 37				22 37		
Tamworth	d									20 18								21 48				22 48		
Birmingham New Street 12	a	19 35	19 36	19 47	19 58	19 58		20 11	20 35	20 43	20 49	20 58	21 04	21 11	21 35	21 56		22 13	22 30	22 35	23 10	23 15		
Birmingham New Street 12	d		19 40	19 51	20 03	20 10					20 53	21 03	21 10			22 00								
Cheltenham Spa	a		20 21			20 51							21 51											
Gloucester 7	a																							
Bristol Parkway 7	a		20 54			21 24							22 24											
Bristol Temple Meads 10	a		21 11			21 41							22 41											
Newport (South Wales)	a																							
Cardiff Central 7	a																							
Weston-super-Mare	a																							
Taunton	a					22 15																		
Tiverton Parkway	a					22 28																		
Exeter St Davids 6	a					22 43																		
Dawlish	a																							
Teignmouth	a																							
Newton Abbot	a					23 11																		
Torquay	a																							
Paignton	a																							
Totnes	a					23 26																		
Plymouth	a					23 59																		
Liskeard 3	a																							
Bodmin Parkway	a																							
Par 3	a																							
St Austell	a																							
Truro	a																							
Redruth	a																							
Camborne	a																							
St Erth 2	a																							
Penzance	a																							
Birmingham International ✈	d			20 04	20 15						21 04	21 15				22 10								
Coventry	d			20a13	20 25						21a13	21 25				22a19								
Leamington Spa 8	d				20 38							21 38												
Banbury	a				20 54							21 54												
Oxford	a				21 14							22 14												
Reading 7	a				21 39							22 39												
Kensington Olympia	a																							
East Croydon	a																							
Guildford	a																							
Redhill	a																							
Basingstoke	a				22 08							23 08												
Winchester	a				22 24							23 24												
Southampton Airport Parkwy ✈	a				22 33							23 33												
Southampton Central	a				22 50							23 45												
Brockenhurst 3	a				23b04							00b04												
Bournemouth	a				23b23							00b22												
Gatwick Airport 10 ✈	a																							
Haywards Heath 3	a																							
Brighton 10	a																							

For general notes see front of timetable
For details of catering facilities see Directory of Train Operators

b Change at Winchester

Scotland, The North East, North West England → The South West and South Coast

19 July to 6 September

Route Diagram - See first page of Table 51

		XC	XC	XC	XC	XC	XC	XC	VT	XC	XC	VT	XC	XC	XC	XC	XC	XC	XC	VT	XC	XC
		1 ◇	1 ◇	1 ◇	1 ◇	1 ◇	1 ◇	1 ◇	1 ◇	1 ◇	R 1	R 1	R 1	1 ◇	1 ◇	R 1	R 1	R 1	R 1	1 ◇	1 ◇	1 ◇
													A									
Aberdeen	d																					
Stonehaven	d																					
Montrose	d																					
Arbroath	d																					
Dundee	d																					
Leuchars 3	d																					
Cupar	d																					
Markinch	d																					
Kirkcaldy	d																					
Inverkeithing	d																					
Glasgow Central 15	d																					
Motherwell	d																					
Haymarket	d																					
Edinburgh 10	d																					
Haymarket	d																					
Lockerbie	d																					
Carlisle 8	d																					
Penrith North Lakes	d																					
Oxenholme Lake District	d																					
Lancaster 6	d																					
Preston 8	d								06 15			07 20								08 29		
Wigan North Western	d								06 27			07 32								08 40		
Warrington Bank Quay	d								06 47			07 44								08 52		
Manchester Piccadilly 10	d			05b10						06 54			07 24		07 54				08 24		08 54	
Stockport	d			05b19						07 03			07 33		08 03				08 33		09 03	
Wilmslow	d			05b27									07 42									
Crewe 10	d			05 45					07 10			08 06	08 10							09 14		
Macclesfield	d									07 16					08 16				08 46		09 16	
Congleton	d									07 24					08 24						09 24	
Stoke-on-Trent	d			06 06						07 39					08 39				09 06		09 39	
Stafford	d			06 26						07 58			08 33		08 58				09 26		09 58	
Wolverhampton 7	d			06 41					07 48	08 13		08 43	08 49		09 13				09 41	09 49	10 13	
Dunbar	d																					
Berwick-upon-Tweed	d																					
Alnmouth	d																					
Newcastle 8	d															06 08	06 19					06 50
Chester-le-Street	d																06 31					
Durham	d															06 22	06 38	←				07 02
Darlington 7	d															07 09	06 55	07 09				
York 8	d													06 06		→	07 25	07 44				08 19
Leeds 10	d							06 00						06 48				08 10				
Wakefield Westgate 7	d							06 11						*06 32*				08 23				
Doncaster 7	d													07 26			07 52					
Sheffield 7	d						06 01	06 53						07 53			08 23	08 53				09 23
Chesterfield	d						06 24	07 05						08 05			08 35					09 35
Derby 10	d		06 10				07 15	07 27						08 27			08 57	09 24				09 57
Burton-on-Trent	d		06 20					07 37						08 37								10 07
Tamworth	d		06 31					07 48						08 48								10 18
Birmingham New Street 12	a		06 51	06 58	←		07 58	08 06	08 10	08 30		09 05	09 06	09 11	09 30		09 36	09 58	09 58	10 11	10 30	10 36
Birmingham New Street 12	d	06 03	07 10	07 03	07 10	07 33	08 03	08 10		08 33	09 03		09 10		09 33		09 40	10 03	10 10		10 33	10 40
Cheltenham Spa	a		→		07 51			08 51					09 51				10 21		10 51			11 21
Gloucester 7	a																					
Bristol Parkway 7	a				08 24			09 24					10 24				10 54		11 24			11 54
Bristol Temple Meads 10	a				08 41			09 41					10 41				11 11		11 41			12 11
Newport (South Wales)	a																					
Cardiff Central 7	a																					
Weston-super-Mare	a																11 28					
Taunton	a				09 15			10 15									12 00		12 15			
Tiverton Parkway	a				09 28			10 28									12 13					
Exeter St Davids 6	a				09 43			10 43					11 43				12 28		12 43			
Dawlish	a				09 57												12 41		12 57			
Teignmouth	a				10 02												12 48		13 03			
Newton Abbot	a				10 10			11 03									12 56		13 10			
Torquay	a				10 21												13 07		13 24			
Paignton	a				10 34												13 21		13 38			
Totnes	a							11 16														
Plymouth	a							11 48					12 48									
Liskeard 3	a												13 10									
Bodmin Parkway	a												13 22									
Par 3	a																					
St Austell	a																					
Truro	a																					
Redruth	a																					
Camborne	a																					
St Erth 2	a																					
Penzance	a																					
Birmingham International	d	06 15		07 15			08 15				09 15							10 15				
Coventry	d	06 25		07 25			08 25				09 25							10 25				
Leamington Spa 8	d	06 38		07 38		08 00	08 38			09 00	09 38				10 00			10 38			11 00	
Banbury	a	06 54		07 54		08 17	08 54			09 17	09 54				10 17			10 54			11 17	
Oxford	a	07 14		08 14		08 41	09 14			09 41	10 14				10 41			11 14			11 41	
Reading 7	a	07 44		08 39		09 13	09 39			10 13	10 39				11 13			11 39			12 13	
Kensington Olympia	a														11 56							
East Croydon	a														12 37							
Guildford	a																					
Redhill	a																					
Basingstoke	a			09 08			10 08				11 08							12 08				
Winchester	a			09 24			10 24				11 24							12 24				
Southampton Airport Parkwy	a			09 33			10 33				11 33							12 33				
Southampton Central	a			09 40			10 40				11 40							12 40				
Brockenhurst 3	a			09 56			10 56				11 56							12 56				
Bournemouth	a			10 15			11 15				12 15							13 15				
Gatwick Airport 10	a														12 53							
Haywards Heath 3	a														13 13							
Brighton 10	a														13 37							

For general notes see front of timetable
For details of catering facilities see Directory of Train Operators

A To Newquay arr. 1449 (Table 135)
b Change at Stafford

Due to Engineering Operations, services from Saturday 13 September on this Table had not been confirmed at time of going to press. These services will be issued in a special Supplement as soon as exact timings have been confirmed

Scotland, The North East, North West England → The South West and South Coast

19 July to 6 September

Route Diagram - See first page of Table 51

		XC	XC	VT	XC	XC	XC	XC	VT	XC	XC	XC	XC	VT	XC	XC	XC	XC	XC	VT	XC
			R					R	R				R	R		R	R	R	R	R	
		1 ◇	1	1 ◇	1 ◇	1 ◇	1 ◇	1	1	1 ◇	1 ◇	1 ◇	1	1	1 ◇	1	1	1	1	1	1 ◇
													A								
		☕	☕	☕	☕	☕	☕	☕	☕	☕	☕	☕	☕	☕	☕	☕	☕	☕	☕	☕	☕
Aberdeen	d																				
Stonehaven	d																				
Montrose	d																				
Arbroath	d																				
Dundee	d																07 35				
Leuchars 3	d																07 48				
Cupar	d																07 56				
Markinch	d																08 11				
Kirkcaldy	d																08 20				
Inverkeithing	d																08 36				
Glasgow Central 15	d						05 50		07 40										09 00	10 10	
Motherwell	d						06u09												09u15		
Haymarket	d						06 51										08 56		09 54		
Edinburgh 10	d		06 05	06 51			07 05				07 50			08 52			09 05		10 05 ↳		
Haymarket	d			06u55										08u56							
Lockerbie	d			07 52																	
Carlisle 8	d			08 13					09 11					10 10						11 22	
Penrith North Lakes	d			08 29					09 26												
Oxenholme Lake District	d			08 53					09 51					10 47							
Lancaster 6	d			09 09					10 09					11 06						12 11	
Preston 8	d			09 29					10 29					11 28						12 29	
Wigan North Western	d			09 41					10 41					11 40						12 41	
Warrington Bank Quay	d			09 53					10 53					11 53						12 53	
Manchester Piccadilly 10	d	09 24			09 54			10 24		10 54		11 24			11 54			12 24			12 54
Stockport	d	09 33			10 03			10 33		11 03		11 33			12 03			12 33			13 03
Wilmslow	d																				
Crewe 10	d			10 15					11 15					12 13						13 15	
Macclesfield	d	09 46			10 16			10 46		11 16		11 46			12 16			12 46			13 16
Congleton	d									11 24											13 24
Stoke-on-Trent	d	10 06			10 39			11 06		11 39		12 06			12 39			13 06			13 39
Stafford	d	10 26			10 58			11 26		11 58		12 26			12 58			13 26			13 58
Wolverhampton 7	d	10 41		10 49	11 13			11 41	11 49	12 13		12 41		12 49	13 13			13 41		13 49	14 13
Dunbar	d						07 25										09 25				
Berwick-upon-Tweed	d		06 44				07 48				08 34						09 48				
Alnmouth	d		07 04				08 11														
Newcastle 8	d		07 40			08 24	08 40				09 25		09 40			10 25	10 40				
Chester-le-Street	d					08 33										10 34					
Durham	d		07 52			08 40	08 52				09 37		09 52			10 41	10 52				
Darlington 7	d		08 09			08 57	09 09				09 56		10 09			10 58	11 09				
York 8	d		08 44			09 27	09 44				10 25		10 44			11 27	11 44				
Leeds 10	d		09 10				10 10						11 10				12 10				
Wakefield Westgate 7	d		09 23				10 23						11 23				12 23				
Doncaster 7	d					09 51					10 53					11 55					
Sheffield 7	d		09 53			10 23	10 53				11 23		11 53			12 23	12 53				
Chesterfield	d					10 35					11 35					12 35					
Derby 10	d		10 24			10 57	11 24				11 57		12 30			12 57	13 24				
Burton-on-Trent	d										12 07										
Tamworth	d										12 18										
Birmingham New Street 12	a	10 58	11 04	11 11	11 30	11 36	11 58	11 58	12 11	12 30	12 36	12 58	13 09	13 11	13 30	13 36	13 58	13 58		14 11	14 30
Birmingham New Street 12	d	11 03	11 10		11 33	11 40	12 03	12 10		12 33	12 40	13 03	13 10		13 33	13 40	14 03	14 10			14 33
Cheltenham Spa	a		11 51			12 21		12 51			13 21					14 21		14 51			
Gloucester 7	a																				
Bristol Parkway 7	a		12 24			12 54		13 24			13 54					14 54		15 24			
Bristol Temple Meads 10	a		12 41			13 11		13 41			14 11		14 41			15 11		15 41			
Newport (South Wales)	a																				
Cardiff Central 7	a																				
Weston-super-Mare	a							14 01													
Taunton	a		13 15					14 27										16 15			
Tiverton Parkway	a		13 28					14 40										16 28			
Exeter St Davids 6	a		13 43					14 55								16 03		16 43			
Dawlish	a							15 11													
Teignmouth	a							15 18													
Newton Abbot	a		14 03					15 26													
Torquay	a							15 40										17 15			
Paignton	a							15 52										17 29			
Totnes	a		14 16																		
Plymouth	a		14 48										16 43			17 07					
Liskeard 3	a												17 07								
Bodmin Parkway	a												17 19								
Par 3	a															17 55					
St Austell	a															18 02					
Truro	a															18 19					
Redruth	a															18 31					
Camborne	a															18 38					
St Erth 2	a															18 48					
Penzance	a															19 05					
Birmingham International ✈	d	11 15					12 15					13 15									
Coventry	d	11 25					12 25					13 25									
Leamington Spa 8	d	11 38			12 00		12 38			13 00		13 38			14 00						15 00
Banbury	a	11 54			12 17		12 54			13 17		13 54			14 17						15 17
Oxford	a	12 14			12 41		13 14			13 41		14 14			14 41		15 14				15 41
Reading 7	a	12 39			13 13		13 39			14 13		14 39			15 13		15 39				16 13
Kensington Olympia	a																				
East Croydon	a																				
Guildford	a																				16 58
Redhill	a																				*17 38*
Basingstoke	a	13 08					14 08					15 08					16 08				
Winchester	a	13 24					14 24					15 24					16 24				
Southampton Airport Parkwy ✈	a	13 33					14 33					15 33					16 33				
Southampton Central	a	13 40					14 40					15 40					16 40				
Brockenhurst 3	a	13 56					14 56					15 56					16 56				
Bournemouth	a	14 15					15 15					16 15					17 15				
Gatwick Airport 10 ✈	a																				*17 50*
Haywards Heath 3	a																				
Brighton 10	a																				

For general notes see front of timetable
For details of catering facilities see
Directory of Train Operators

A To Newquay arr. 1840 (Table 135)

Due to Engineering Operations, services from Saturday 13 September on this Table had not been confirmed at time of going to press. These services will be issued in a special Supplement as soon as exact timings have been confirmed

Scotland, The North East, North West England → The South West and South Coast

19 July to 6 September

Route Diagram - See first page of Table 51

		XC	XC	XC	VT	XC	XC	XC	XC	VT	XC	XC	XC	XC	VT	XC	XC	XC	XC	VT	XC
				R						R					R						
		1 ◇	1 ◇	1	1 ◇	1 ◇	1 ◇	1 ◇	1 ◇	1	1 ◇	1 ◇	1 ◇	1 ◇	1	1 ◇	1 ◇	1 ◇	1 ◇	1 ◇	1 ◇
Aberdeen	d							08 20													
Stonehaven	d							08 37													
Montrose	d							08 59													
Arbroath	d							09 15													
Dundee	d							09 32													
Leuchars 3	d							09 45													
Cupar	d							09 52													
Markinch	d							10 04													
Kirkcaldy	d							10 12													
Inverkeithing	d							10 27													
Glasgow Central 15	d									12 10										14 10	
Motherwell	d																				
Haymarket	d			←				10 47													
Edinburgh 10	d			10 05	10 52			11 05						12 05	12 52			13 05			
Haymarket	d				10u56										12u56						
Lockerbie	d														13 52						
Carlisle 8	d				12 13					13 21					14 13					15 21	
Penrith North Lakes	d				12 29										14 28						
Oxenholme Lake District	d				12 53					13 58					14 53						
Lancaster 6	d				13 09										15 09					16 10	
Preston 8	d				13 29					14 29					15 29					16 29	
Wigan North Western	d				13 41					14 41					15 41					16 41	
Warrington Bank Quay	d				13 53					14 52					15 52					16 52	
Manchester Piccadilly 10	d		13 24			13 54			14 24		14 54		15 24			15 54			16 24		16 54
Stockport	d		13 33			14 03			14 33		15 03		15 33			16 03			16 33		17 03
Wilmslow	d																				
Crewe 10	d				14 15					15 13					16 12					17 15	
Macclesfield	d		13 46			14 16			14 46		15 16		15 46			16 16			16 46		17 16
Congleton	d										15 24										17 24
Stoke-on-Trent	d		14 06			14 39			15 06		15 39		16 06			16 39			17 06		17 39
Stafford	d		14 26			14 58			15 26		15 58		16 26			16 58			17 26		17 58
Wolverhampton 7	d		14 41		14 49	15 13			15 41	15 47	16 13		16 41		16 49	17 13			17 41	17 49	18 13
Dunbar	d							11 25										13 25			
Berwick-upon-Tweed	d							11 48										13 48			
Alnmouth	d			11 04										13 05							
Newcastle 8	d	11 25		11 40			12 20	12 40				13 27		13 40			14 22	14 40			
Chester-le-Street	d						12 29										14 31				
Durham	d	11 37		11 52			12 36	12 52				13 39		13 52			14 38	14 52			
Darlington 7	d	11 57		12 09			12 53	13 09				13 58		14 09			14 55	15 09			
York 8	d	12 25		12 44			13 28	13 44				14 30		14 44			15 27	15 44			
Leeds 10	d			13 10				14 10						15 10				16 10			
Wakefield Westgate 7	d			13 23				14 23						15 23				16 23			
Doncaster 7	d	12 52					13 54					14 56					15 55				
Sheffield 7	d	13 23		13 53			14 23	14 53				15 23		15 53			16 23	16 53			
Chesterfield	d	13 35					14 35					15 35					16 35				
Derby 10	d	13 57		14 24			14 57	15 24				15 57		16 24			16 57	17 24			
Burton-on-Trent	d	14 07										16 07									
Tamworth	d	14 18										16 18									
Birmingham New Street 12	a	14 36	14 58	15 04	15 11	15 30	15 36	15 58	15 58	16 11	16 30	16 36	16 58	17 04	17 11	17 30	17 36	17 58	17 58	18 11	18 30
Birmingham New Street 12	d	14 40	15 03	15 10		15 33	15 40	16 03	16 10		16 33	16 40	17 03	17 10		17 33	17 40	18 03	18 10		18 33
Cheltenham Spa	a	15 21		15 51			16 21		16 51			17 21		17 51			18 21		18 51		
Gloucester 7	a																18 33				
Bristol Parkway 7	a	15 54		16 24			16 54		17 24			17 54		18 24			19 09		19 24		
Bristol Temple Meads 10	a	16 11		16 41			17 11		17 41			18 11		18 41			19 26		19 41		
Newport (South Wales)	a																19 59				
Cardiff Central 7	a																20 19				
Weston-super-Mare	a													19 04							
Taunton	a			17 15					18 15					19 26					20 15		
Tiverton Parkway	a			17 28					18 28					19 39					20 28		
Exeter St Davids 6	a			17 43					18 43					19 54					20 43		
Dawlish	a			17 57																	
Teignmouth	a			18 03																	
Newton Abbot	a			18 11					19 03					20 14					21 03		
Torquay	a			18 25																	
Paignton	a			18 39																	
Totnes	a								19 16					20 27					21 16		
Plymouth	a								19 48					20 54					21 48		
Liskeard 3	a								20 17												
Bodmin Parkway	a								20 29												
Par 3	a								20 40					21 46							
St Austell	a								20 46					21 53							
Truro	a								21 03					22 11							
Redruth	a								21 15					22 29							
Camborne	a								21 21					22 36							
St Erth 2	a								21 31					22 46							
Penzance	a								21 48					23 03							
Birmingham International	d		15 15					16 15					17 15					18 15			
Coventry	d		15 25					16 25					17 25					18 25			
Leamington Spa 8	d		15 38			16 00		16 38			17 00		17 38			18 00		18 38			19 00
Banbury	a		15 54			16 17		16 54			17 17		17 54			18 17		18 54			19 17
Oxford	a		16 14			16 41		17 14			17 41		18 14			18 41		19 14			19 41
Reading 7	a		16 39			17 13		17 39			18 13		18 39			19 13		19 39			20 13
Kensington Olympia	a										19 01										
East Croydon	a										19 36										
Guildford	a																				20 58
Redhill	a																				21 28
Basingstoke	a		17 08					18 08					19 08					20 08			
Winchester	a		17 24					18 24					19 24					20 24			
Southampton Airport Parkwy	a		17 33					18 33					19 33					20 33			
Southampton Central	a		17 40					18 40					19 40					20 40			
Brockenhurst 3	a		17 56					18 56					19 56					20 56			
Bournemouth	a		18 15					19 15					20 15					21 15			
Gatwick Airport 10	a										19 52										21 47
Haywards Heath 3	a										20 04										22 24
Brighton 10	a										20 28										22 48

For general notes see front of timetable
For details of catering facilities see
Directory of Train Operators

Due to Engineering Operations, services from Saturday 13 September on this Table had not been confirmed at time of going to press. These services will be issued in a special Supplement as soon as exact timings have been confirmed

Scotland, The North East, North West England → The South West and South Coast

19 July to 6 September

Route Diagram - See first page of Table 51

		XC	XC	XC	VT	XC	XC	XC		XC	VT	XC	XC	XC	XC	VT	XC	XC	VT	XC	VT	XC		
		1◇	1◇	1◇	1◇	1◇	1◇	1◇		1◇	1◇	1◇	1◇	1◇	1◇	1◇	1◇	1◇	1◇	1◇	1◇	1◇		
Aberdeen	d																							
Stonehaven	d																							
Montrose	d																							
Arbroath	d																							
Dundee	d																							
Leuchars 3	d																							
Cupar	d																							
Markinch	d																							
Kirkcaldy	d																							
Inverkeithing	d																							
Glasgow Central 15	d										16 03								18 10					
Motherwell	d																		18u27					
Haymarket	d																							
Edinburgh 10	d			14 05	14 52			15 05							16 05	16 52						18 05		
Haymarket	d				14u56											16u56								
Lockerbie	d															17 50			19 12					
Carlisle 8	d				16 09						17 21					18 11			19 32					
Penrith North Lakes	d				16 24						17 36					18 27								
Oxenholme Lake District	d				16 48						18 00					18 51			20 08					
Lancaster 6	d				17 04											19 07			20 21					
Preston 8	d				17 24						18 30					19 29			20 43		21 22			
Wigan North Western	d				17 36						18 42					19 41			20 55		21 34			
Warrington Bank Quay	d				17 48						18 53					19 53			21 06		21 46			
Manchester Piccadilly 10	d		17 24			17 54				18 24		18 54		19 24			19 54			20 54				
Stockport	d		17 33			18 03				18 33		19 03		19 33			20 03			21 03				
Wilmslow	d																							
Crewe 10	d				18 13						19 15					20 15			21 28		22 08			
Macclesfield	d		17 46			18 16				18 46		19 16		19 46			20 16			21 16				
Congleton	d					18 24						19 24					20 24			21 24				
Stoke-on-Trent	d		18 06			18 39				19 06		19 39		20 06			20 39			21 39				
Stafford	d		18 26			18 58				19 25		19 58		20 26			20 58		21 51	21 58	22 33			
Wolverhampton 7	d		18 41		18 49	19 13				19 41	19 49	20 13		20 41		20 49	21 13		22 09	22 13	22 49			
Dunbar	d							15 25														18 25		
Berwick-upon-Tweed	d							15 48														18 48		
Alnmouth	d			15 05											17 05							19 08		
Newcastle 8	d	15 22		15 40			16 20	16 40					17 18		17 40			18 40				19 45		
Chester-le-Street	d						16 29						17 27					18 49						
Durham	d	15 34		15 52			16 36	16 52					17 34		17 52			18 56				19 56		
Darlington 7	d	15 54		16 09			16 54	17 09					17 51		18 09			19 13				20 13		
York 8	d	16 25		16 44			17 25	17 44					18 25		18 44			19 44				20 44		
Leeds 10	d			17 10				18 10							19 10			20 10				21 10		
Wakefield Westgate 7	d			17 23				18 23							19 23			20 23				21 23		
Doncaster 7	d	16 53					17 55						18 51											
Sheffield 7	d	17 20		17 53			18 23	18 53					19 23		19 53			20 53				21 53		
Chesterfield	d	17 35					18 35						19 35		20 05			21 05				22 05		
Derby 10	d	17 57		18 24			18 57	19 24					19 57		20 27			21 27				22 27		
Burton-on-Trent	d	18 07											20 07					21 37				22 37		
Tamworth	d	18 18											20 18					21 48				22 48		
Birmingham New Street 12	a	18 36	18 58	19 04	19 11	19 35	19 36	19 58		19 58	20 11	20 35	20 43	20 58	21 04	21 11	21 35	22 13	22 30	22 35	23 10	23 15		
Birmingham New Street 12	d	18 40	19 03	19 10			19 40	20 03		20 10				21 03	21 10									
Cheltenham Spa	a	19 21		19 51			20 21			20 51					21 51									
Gloucester 7	a																							
Bristol Parkway 7	a	19 54		20 24			20 54			21 24					22 24									
Bristol Temple Meads 10	a	20 11		20 41			21 11			21 41					22 41									
Newport (South Wales)	a																							
Cardiff Central 7	a																							
Weston-super-Mare	a																							
Taunton	a			21 15						22 15														
Tiverton Parkway	a			21 28						22 28														
Exeter St Davids 6	a			21 43						22 43														
Dawlish	a																							
Teignmouth	a																							
Newton Abbot	a			22 03						23 11														
Torquay	a																							
Paignton	a																							
Totnes	a			22 20						23 26														
Plymouth	a			22 55						23 59														
Liskeard 3	a																							
Bodmin Parkway	a																							
Par 3	a																							
St Austell	a																							
Truro	a																							
Redruth	a																							
Camborne	a																							
St Erth 2	a																							
Penzance	a																							
Birmingham International ✈	d		19 15					20 15						21 15										
Coventry	d		19 25					20 25						21 25										
Leamington Spa 8	d		19 38					20 38						21 38										
Banbury	a		19 54					20 54						21 54										
Oxford	a		20 14					21 14						22 14										
Reading 7	a		20 39					21 39						22 39										
Kensington Olympia	a																							
East Croydon	a																							
Guildford	a																							
Redhill	a																							
Basingstoke	a		21 08					22 08						23 08										
Winchester	a		21 24					22 24						23 24										
Southampton Airport Parkwy ✈	a		21 33					22 33						23 33										
Southampton Central	a		21 40					22 50						23 45										
Brockenhurst 3	a		21 56					23b04						00b04										
Bournemouth	a		22 15					23b23						00b22										
Gatwick Airport 10 ✈	a																							
Haywards Heath 3	a																							
Brighton 10	a																							

For general notes see front of timetable
For details of catering facilities see Directory of Train Operators

b Change at Winchester

Due to Engineering Operations, services from Saturday 13 September on this Table had not been confirmed at time of going to press. These services will be issued in a special Supplement as soon as exact timings have been confirmed

Table 51 — SUMMARY OF SERVICES

Sundays until 13 July

Scotland, The North East, North West England → The South West and South Coast

Route Diagram - See first page of Table 51

Station		XC	XC	XC	XC	XC	XC	XC	VT	XC	XC	VT	XC	XC	VT	XC	XC
											R		R	R		R	R
		1◇	1◇	1◇	1◇	1◇	1◇	1◇	1◇	1◇	1	1◇	1	1	1◇	1	1
		☕	☕	☕	☕	☕	☕	☕	☕	☕	☕	☕	☕	☕	☕	☕	☕
Aberdeen	d																
Stonehaven	d																
Montrose	d																
Arbroath	d																
Dundee	d																
Leuchars 3	d																
Cupar	d																
Markinch	d																
Kirkcaldy	d																
Inverkeithing	d																
Glasgow Central 15	d																
Motherwell	d																
Haymarket	d																
Edinburgh 10	d																08 50
Haymarket	d																
Lockerbie	d																
Carlisle 8	d																
Penrith North Lakes	d																
Oxenholme Lake District	d																
Lancaster 6	d																
Preston 8	d								10 24			11 24			12 23		
Wigan North Western	d								10 36			11 36			12 35		
Warrington Bank Quay	d								10 47			11 48			12 47		
Manchester Piccadilly 10	d			08 10	09 08			10 04		11 06				12 06		13 06	
Stockport	d				09 18			10 13		11 15				12 15		13 16	
Wilmslow	d			08 24	09 27			10 20		11 22				12 23			
Crewe 10	d			08 48	09 48			10 42	11 09	11 42		12 10		12 43	13 08		
Macclesfield	d															13 31	
Congleton	d																
Stoke-on-Trent	d															13 50	
Stafford	d			09 15	10 15			11 09		12 09				13 08		14 14	
Wolverhampton 7	d			09 31	10 31			11 31	11 49	12 31		12 49		13 31	13 49	14 31	
Dunbar	d																
Berwick-upon-Tweed	d																09 31
Alnmouth	d																
Newcastle 8	d												09 30				10 25
Chester-le-Street	d																
Durham	d												09 42				10 37
Darlington 7	d												09 59				10 54
York 8	d										09 27		10 28				11 28
Leeds 10	d						08 30				10 00		11 00				12 00
Wakefield Westgate 7	d						08 43				10 12		11 12				12 12
Doncaster 7	d						09 03				10 33		11 38				12 33
Sheffield 7	d						09 32				11 21		12 21				13 21
Chesterfield	d																
Derby 10	d						10 40				12 20		13 20				14 20
Burton-on-Trent	d										12 30						14 30
Tamworth	d										12 41						14 41
Birmingham New Street 12	a			09 58	10 58		11 53	11 58	12 17	12 58	13 03	13 17	13 53	13 58	14 17	14 58	15 04
Birmingham New Street 12	d	09 03	10 03	10 10	11 03	11 10	12 03	12 10		13 03	13 10		14 03	14 10		15 03	15 10
Cheltenham Spa	a			10 51		11 51		12 51			13 51			14 51			15 51
Gloucester 7	a																
Bristol Parkway 7	a			11 25		12 25		13 25			14 25			15 25			16 25
Bristol Temple Meads 10	a			11 38		12 38		13 38			14 38			15 38			16 38
Newport (South Wales)	a																
Cardiff Central 7	a																
Weston-super-Mare	a			12 01													
Taunton	a			12 23		13 15		14 15			15 15			16 15			17 15
Tiverton Parkway	a			12 35		13 28		14 28			15 28			16 28			17 28
Exeter St Davids 6	a			12 51		13 43		14 43			15 43			16 43			17 43
Dawlish	a			13 05													
Teignmouth	a			13 10													
Newton Abbot	a			13 21		14 03		15 03			16 03			17 03			18 03
Torquay	a			13 33													
Paignton	a			13 46													
Totnes	a					14 16		15 16			16 16			17 16			18 16
Plymouth	a					14 48		15 48			16 48			17 48			18 48
Liskeard 3	a													18 17			19 17
Bodmin Parkway	a													18 30			19 29
Par 3	a													18 40			19 40
St Austell	a													18 47			19 46
Truro	a													19 04			20 04
Redruth	a													19 16			20 20
Camborne	a													19 22			20 27
St Erth 2	a													19 32			20 37
Penzance	a													19 49			20 53
Birmingham International ✈	d																
Coventry	d																
Leamington Spa 8	d	09 38	10 38		11 38		12 38			13 38			14 38			15 38	
Banbury	a	09 54	10 54		11 54		12 54			13 54			14 54			15 54	
Oxford	a	10 14	11 14		12 14		13 14			14 14			15 14			16 14	
Reading 7	a	10 44	11 44		12 44		13 44			14 44			15 44			16 44	
Kensington Olympia	a																
East Croydon	a																
Guildford	a																
Redhill	a																
Basingstoke	a	11 08	12 08		13 08		14 08			15 08			16 08			17 08	
Winchester	a	11 24	12 24		13 24		14 24			15 24			16 24			17 24	
Southampton Airport Parkway ✈	a	11 33	12 33		13 33		14 33			15 33			16 33			17 33	
Southampton Central	a	11 42	12 42		13 42		14 42			15 42			16 42			17 42	
Brockenhurst 3	a	12 02	13 02		14 02		15 02			16 02			17 02			18 02	
Bournemouth	a	12 32	13 32		14 32		15 32			16 32			17 32			18 32	
Gatwick Airport 10 ✈	a																
Haywards Heath 3	a																
Brighton 10	a																

For general notes see front of timetable
For details of catering facilities see Directory of Train Operators

Scotland, The North East, North West England → The South West and South Coast

Route Diagram - See first page of Table 51

		XC	XC	XC	XC	VT	XC	XC	VT	XC	XC	XC	VT	XC	XC	XC	VT
		R 1	R 1	R 1	R 1	R 1	R 1	R 1	R 1	1 ◇	R 1	R 1	R 1	R 1	R 1	R 1	R 1
Aberdeen	d																
Stonehaven	d																
Montrose	d																
Arbroath	d																
Dundee	d																
Leuchars 3	d																
Cupar	d																
Markinch	d																
Kirkcaldy	d																
Inverkeithing	d																
Glasgow Central 15	d		10 27		11 30	11 55							14 03				
Motherwell	d		10u57		11u56	12u11					←						
Haymarket	d		11 36		12 37						11 36				←		
Edinburgh 10	d	09 50	→		12 50			10 50	12 52		11 50				12 50	13 50	14 53
Haymarket	d				→				12u57								14u58
Lockerbie	d								13 51								15 53
Carlisle 8	d					13 16			14 13				15 20				16 14
Penrith North Lakes	d					13 32			14 28								16 29
Oxenholme Lake District	d								14 53								16 53
Lancaster 6	d					14 09			15 09				16 08				17 09
Preston 8	d					14 27			15 28				16 27				17 29
Wigan North Western	d					14 41			15 41				16 40				17 41
Warrington Bank Quay	d					14 52			15 52				16 51				17 53
Manchester Piccadilly 10	d			14 08			15 06					16 08		17 06			
Stockport	d			14 18			15 16					16 18		17 16			
Wilmslow	d																
Crewe 10	d					15 13			16 14				17 13				18 15
Macclesfield	d			14 32			15 31					16 31		17 31			
Congleton	d																
Stoke-on-Trent	d			14 50			15 49					16 49		17 49			
Stafford	d			15 14			16 08					17 09		18 15			
Wolverhampton 7	d			15 31		15 49	16 31		16 49			17 31	17 49	18 31			18 52
Dunbar	d							11 11							13 10		
Berwick-upon-Tweed	d							11 33							13 33		
Alnmouth	d	10 46									12 48					14 47	
Newcastle 8	d	11 25						12 25			13 25				14 25	→	
Chester-le-Street	d																
Durham	d	11 37						12 37			13 37				14 37		
Darlington 7	d	11 54						12 54			13 55				14 54		
York 8	d	12 28						13 28			14 28				15 28		
Leeds 10	d	13 00						14 00			15 00				16 00		
Wakefield Westgate 7	d	13 12						14 12			15 12				16 12		
Doncaster 7	d	13 38						14 39			15 38				16 39		
Sheffield 7	d	14 21						15 21			16 21				17 21		
Chesterfield	d																
Derby 10	d	15 20						16 20			17 20				18 20		
Burton-on-Trent	d							16 30							18 30		
Tamworth	d							16 41							18 41		
Birmingham New Street 12	a	15 53		15 58		16 17	16 58	17 04	17 17		17 54	17 58	18 17	18 58	19 04		19 20
Birmingham New Street 12	d	16 03		16 10			17 03	17 10		17 33	18 03	18 10		19 03	19 10		
Cheltenham Spa	a			16 51				17 51				18 51			19 51		
Gloucester 7	a																
Bristol Parkway 7	a			17 25				18 25				19 25			20 25		
Bristol Temple Meads 10	a			17 38				18 38				19 38			20 38		
Newport (South Wales)	a																
Cardiff Central 7	a																
Weston-super-Mare	a																
Taunton	a			18 15				19 15				20 15			21 15		
Tiverton Parkway	a			18 28				19 28				20 28			21 28		
Exeter St Davids 6	a			18 43				19 43				20 43			21 43		
Dawlish	a																
Teignmouth	a																
Newton Abbot	a			19 03				20 03				21 03			22 03		
Torquay	a																
Paignton	a																
Totnes	a			19 16				20 16				21 16			22 16		
Plymouth	a			19 48				20 48				21 48			22 48		
Liskeard 3	a			20 17													
Bodmin Parkway	a			20 29													
Par 3	a			20 40													
St Austell	a			20 46													
Truro	a			21 04													
Redruth	a			21 15													
Camborne	a			21 22													
St Erth 2	a			21 32													
Penzance	a			21 48													
Birmingham International	d																
Coventry	d																
Leamington Spa 8	d	16 38					17 38			18 00	18 38			19 38			
Banbury	a	16 54					17 54			18 18	18 54			19 54			
Oxford	a	17 14					18 14			18 41	19 14			20 14			
Reading 7	a	17 44					18 44			19 13	19 44			20 44			
Kensington Olympia	a																
East Croydon	a																
Guildford	a									19 54							
Redhill	a									20 27							
Basingstoke	a	18 08					19 08				20 08			21 08			
Winchester	a	18 24					19 24				20 24			21 24			
Southampton Airport Parkwy	a	18 33					19 33				20 33			21 33			
Southampton Central	a	18 42					19 42				20 42			21 42			
Brockenhurst 3	a	19 02					20 02				21 02			22 02			
Bournemouth	a	19 32					20 32				21 32			22 32			
Gatwick Airport 10	a									20 44							
Haywards Heath 3	a									20 54							
Brighton 10	a									21 13							

For general notes see front of timetable
For details of catering facilities see Directory of Train Operators

Sundays

until 13 July

Scotland, The North East, North West England → The South West and South Coast

Route Diagram - See first page of Table 51

		XC	XC		XC	VT		XC	XC		XC	VT		XC	VT		XC	XC	XC	VT	XC	XC		
		R	R			R																		
		1	1		1◇	1		1◇	1◇		1◇	1◇		1◇	1◇		1◇	1◇	1◇	1◇	1◇	1◇		
		⊐	⊐		⊐	⊐		⊐	⊐		⊐	⊐		⊐	⊐			⊐	⊐	⊐		⊐		
Aberdeen	d								11 58															
Stonehaven	d								12 17															
Montrose	d								12 39															
Arbroath	d								12 55															
Dundee	d								13 12															
Leuchars 8	d								13 25															
Cupar	d								13 32															
Markinch	d								13 47															
Kirkcaldy	d								13 55															
Inverkeithing	d								14 10															
Glasgow Central 15	d				15 44	15 54									18 04									
Motherwell	d				16u00													←						
Haymarket	d				16 38				14 29									16 38						
Edinburgh 10	d				→				14b50		15 50	16 56						16 50	17 50	18 52				
Haymarket	d											17u01								18u57				
Lockerbie	d											17 58								19 58				
Carlisle 8	d					17 17						18 21			19 15					20 18				
Penrith North Lakes	d											18 36								20 34				
Oxenholme Lake District	d					17 53						19 00			19 52					20 58				
Lancaster 6	d					18 10						19 15			20 08					21 14				
Preston 8	d					18 29						19 35			20 28					21 34				
Wigan North Western	d					18 41						19 47			20 40					21 46				
Warrington Bank Quay	d					18 52						19 58			20 52					21 58				
Manchester Piccadilly 10	d		18 08					19 10									20 55				21 55			
Stockport	d		18 18					19 18									21 04				22 04			
Wilmslow	d																							
Crewe 10	d					19 13						20 19			21 13					22 20				
Macclesfield	d		18 31					19 34									21 16				22 16			
Congleton	d																							
Stoke-on-Trent	d		18 49					19 53									21 35				22 35			
Stafford	d		19 15					20 13							21 33		21 53			22 40	22 53			
Wolverhampton 7	d		19 31			19 49		20 31				20 52			21 49		22 09			22 55	23 09	←		
Dunbar	d								15 11									17 11	18 11			18 11		
Berwick-upon-Tweed	d	←							15 33					←				17 33	→					
Alnmouth	d	14 47									16 47			16 47								18 53		
Newcastle 8	d	15 25							16 25		→			17 22				18 25				19 25		
Chester-le-Street	d																							
Durham	d	15 37							16 37					17 34				18 37				19 37		
Darlington 7	d	15 55							16 54					17 51				18 54				19 54		
York 8	d	16 28							17 28					18 28				19 28				20 28		
Leeds 10	d	17 00							18 00					19 00				20 00				21 00		
Wakefield Westgate 7	d	17 12							18 12					19 12				20 12				21 12		
Doncaster 7	d	17 38							18 38					19 34				20 34				21 33		
Sheffield 7	d	18 21							19 21					20 21				21 21				22 04		
Chesterfield	d																							
Derby 10	d	19 20							20 20					21 20				22 15				22 57		
Burton-on-Trent	d								20 30					21 30				22 27				23 07		
Tamworth	d								20 41					21 41				22 38				23 18		
Birmingham New Street 12	a	19 54	19 58			20 17		20 58	21 04			21 21		22 04	22 17		22 41	23 14		23 23	23 42	23 51		
Birmingham New Street 12	d	20 03	20 10					21 03	21 10					22 10										
Cheltenham Spa	a		20 51						21 51					22 51										
Gloucester 7	a																							
Bristol Parkway 7	a		21 25						22 25					23 25										
Bristol Temple Meads 10	a		21 38						22 41					23 41										
Newport (South Wales)	a																							
Cardiff Central 7	a																							
Weston-super-Mare	a																							
Taunton	a		22 15																					
Tiverton Parkway	a		22 28																					
Exeter St Davids 6	a		22 43																					
Dawlish	a																							
Teignmouth	a																							
Newton Abbot	a		23 03																					
Torquay	a																							
Paignton	a																							
Totnes	a		23 16																					
Plymouth	a		23 48																					
Liskeard 3	a																							
Bodmin Parkway	a																							
Par 3	a																							
St Austell	a																							
Truro	a																							
Redruth	a																							
Camborne	a																							
St Erth 2	a																							
Penzance	a																							
Birmingham International ✈	d																							
Coventry	d																							
Leamington Spa 8	d	20 38						21 38																
Banbury	a	20 54						21 54																
Oxford	a	21 14						22 14																
Reading 7	a	21 44						22 44																
Kensington Olympia	a																							
East Croydon	a																							
Guildford	a																							
Redhill	a																							
Basingstoke	a	22 08						23 08																
Winchester	a	22 43						23 24																
Southampton Airport Parkwy ✈	a	23 18						23 33																
Southampton Central	a	23 31						23 47																
Brockenhurst 3	a	23c16						00 53																
Bournemouth	a	23c35						01 16																
Gatwick Airport 10 ✈	a																							
Haywards Heath 3	a																							
Brighton 10	a																							

For general notes see front of timetable
For details of catering facilities see Directory of Train Operators

b Arr. 1434
c Change at Basingstoke

Table 51 — SUMMARY OF SERVICES — Sundays

Scotland, The North East, North West England → The South West and South Coast

20 July to 7 September

Route Diagram - See first page of Table 51

		XC	XC	XC	XC	XC	XC	XC	XC	XC	VT	XC	XC	XC	XC	XC	XC	VT	XC
		1◇	1◇	1◇	1◇	1◇	1◇	1◇	1◇	1◇	1◇	1◇	1◇	R 1	R 1	1◇	1◇	1◇	R 1
Aberdeen	d																		
Stonehaven	d																		
Montrose	d																		
Arbroath	d																		
Dundee	d																		
Leuchars 3	d																		
Cupar	d																		
Markinch	d																		
Kirkcaldy	d																		
Inverkeithing	d																		
Glasgow Central 15	d																		
Motherwell	d																		
Haymarket	d																		
Edinburgh 10	d																08 50		
Haymarket	d																		
Lockerbie	d																		
Carlisle 8	d																		
Penrith North Lakes	d																		
Oxenholme Lake District	d																		
Lancaster 6	d																		
Preston 8	d										10 24							11 22	
Wigan North Western	d										10 36							11 36	
Warrington Bank Quay	d										10 47							11 48	
Manchester Piccadilly 10	d			08 10		09 24		09 53		10 24		10 53	11 23			11 53			
Stockport	d					09 33		10 04		10 33		11 04	11 33			12 04			
Wilmslow	d			08 24															
Crewe 10	d			08 46	09 17						11 09							12 16	
Macclesfield	d					09 46		10 16		10 46		11 16	11 47			12 16			
Congleton	d																		
Stoke-on-Trent	d			09 05		10 05		10 35		11 03		11 35	12 05			12 35			
Stafford	d			09 26	09 53	10 26		10 53		11 21		11 53	12 26			12 53			
Wolverhampton 7	d			09 41	10 09	10 41		11 09		11 36	12 01	12 09	12 41			13 09		13 26	
Dunbar	d																		
Berwick-upon-Tweed	d																09 31		
Alnmouth	d																		
Newcastle 8	d														09 10		10 25		
Chester-le-Street	d																		
Durham	d														09 24		10 37		
Darlington 7	d														09 42		10 54		
York 8	d													09 13	10 13		11 24		
Leeds 10	d								09 00					10 00	11 00				
Wakefield Westgate 7	d								09 12					10 12	11 12				
Doncaster 7	d								09 34						11 37		11 50		
Sheffield 7	d								10 00					11 23	12 06		12 23		
Chesterfield	d								10 12					11 35			12 35		
Derby 10	d								10 40					12 20	12 39		12 57		
Burton-on-Trent	d													12 30					
Tamworth	d													12 41					
Birmingham New Street 12	a			09 58	10 31	10 58		11 28	11 53	11 58	12 17	12 31	12 58	13 04	13 25	13 31	13 36	13 55	←
Birmingham New Street 12	d	09 03	10 03	10 10	10 33	11 03	11 10	11 33	12 03	12 10		12 33	13 03	13 10	14 03	13 33	13 40		14 03
Cheltenham Spa	a			10 51			11 51			12 51				13 51	→		14 20		
Gloucester 7	a																		
Bristol Parkway 7	a			11 25			12 25			13 25				14 25			14 58		
Bristol Temple Meads 10	a			11 38			12 38			13 38				14 38			15 11		
Newport (South Wales)	a																		
Cardiff Central 7	a																		
Weston-super-Mare	a			12 01															
Taunton	a			12 23			13 15			14 15				15 15			15 43		
Tiverton Parkway	a			12 35			13 28			14 28				15 28			15 55		
Exeter St Davids 6	a			12 51			13 43			14 43				15 43			16 10		
Dawlish	a			13 05															
Teignmouth	a			13 10															
Newton Abbot	a			13 21			14 03			15 03				16 03			16 30		
Torquay	a			13 33															
Paignton	a			13 46															
Totnes	a						14 16			15 16				16 16			16 43		
Plymouth	a						14 48			15 48				16 48			17 16		
Liskeard 3	a																		
Bodmin Parkway	a																		
Par 3	a																		
St Austell	a																		
Truro	a																		
Redruth	a																		
Camborne	a																		
St Erth 2	a																		
Penzance	a																		
Birmingham International	d																		
Coventry	d																		
Leamington Spa 8	d	09 38	10 38		11 00	11 38		12 00	12 38			13 00	13 38			14 00			14 38
Banbury	a	09 54	10 54		11 18	11 54		12 18	12 54			13 18	13 54			14 18			14 54
Oxford	a	10 14	11 14		11 41	12 14		12 41	13 14			13 41	14 14			14 41			15 14
Reading 7	a	10 44	11 44		12 13	12 44		13 13	13 44			14 13	14 44			15 13			15 44
Kensington Olympia	a																		
East Croydon	a																		
Guildford	a																		
Redhill	a																		
Basingstoke	a	11 08	12 08			13 08			14 08				15 08						16 08
Winchester	a	11 24	12 24			13 24			14 24				15 24						16 24
Southampton Airport Parkwy	a	11 33	12 33			13 33			14 33				15 33						16 33
Southampton Central	a	11 42	12 42			13 42			14 42				15 42						16 42
Brockenhurst 3	a	12 02	13 02			14 02			15 02				16 02						17 02
Bournemouth	a	12 32	13 32			14 32			15 32				16 32						17 32
Gatwick Airport 10	a																		
Haywards Heath 3	a																		
Brighton 10	a																		

For general notes see front of timetable
For details of catering facilities see Directory of Train Operators

Due to Engineering Operations, services from Sunday 14 September on this Table had not been confirmed at time of going to press. These services will be issued in a special Supplement as soon as exact timings have been confirmed

Table 51 SUMMARY OF SERVICES

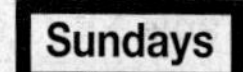

Scotland, The North East, North West England → The South West and South Coast

20 July to 7 September

Route Diagram - See first page of Table 51

		XC	VT		XC	XC	XC		XC	XC	XC		XC	XC	XC		XC	XC	VT		XC	XC	XC	XC
		R 1	1 ◇		1 ◇	R 1	1 ◇		R 1	R 1	1 ◇		R 1	1 ◇	R 1		R 1	R 1	R 1		1 ◇	1 ◇	R 1	R 1
Aberdeen	d																							
Stonehaven	d																							
Montrose	d																							
Arbroath	d																							
Dundee	d																							
Leuchars 3	d																							
Cupar	d																							
Markinch	d																							
Kirkcaldy	d																							
Inverkeithing	d																							
Glasgow Central 15	d																	10 04	11 55					
Motherwell	d																	10u29	12u10					
Haymarket	d																	11 16						
Edinburgh 10	d					09 33							10 33					11 33						
Haymarket	d																							
Lockerbie	d																							
Carlisle 8	d																		13 16					
Penrith North Lakes	d																		13 31					
Oxenholme Lake District	d																							
Lancaster 6	d																		14 08					
Preston 8	d		12 23																14 27					
Wigan North Western	d		12 35																14 40					
Warrington Bank Quay	d		12 47																14 52					
Manchester Piccadilly 10	d	12 24			12 53				13 17		13 53						14 24				14 51		15 24	
Stockport	d	12 33			13 04				13 33		14 04						14 33				15 04		15 33	
Wilmslow	d																							
Crewe 10	d		13 09																15 13					
Macclesfield	d	12 47			13 16				13 47		14 16						14 46				15 16		15 46	
Congleton	d																							
Stoke-on-Trent	d	13 05			13 35				14 05		14 35						15 05				15 36		16 07	
Stafford	d	13 24			13 53				14 26		14 53						15 26				15 53		16 26	
Wolverhampton 7	d	13 41	14 02		14 09				14 41		15 09						15 41		16 07		16 09		16 41	
Dunbar	d												10 55											
Berwick-upon-Tweed	d												11 18											
Alnmouth	d					10 33												12 33						
Newcastle 8	d					11 13	11 25						12 13	12 25				13 13				13 25		
Chester-le-Street	d																							
Durham	d					11 25	11 37						12 25	12 37				13 25				13 37		
Darlington 7	d					11 42	11 54						12 42	12 54				13 42				13 54		
York 8	d					12 13	12 25						13 13	13 25				14 14				14 25		
Leeds 10	d					13 00				←			14 00					15 00						
Wakefield Westgate 7	d					13 12				13 12			14 12					15 12						
Doncaster 7	d					→	12 50							13 50	←							14 50		←
Sheffield 7	d						13 23			13 48			14 48	14 23	14 48			15 48				15 23		15 48
Chesterfield	d						13 35						→	14 35				→				15 35		
Derby 10	d						13 57			14 20				14 57	15 20							15 57		16 20
Burton-on-Trent	d						14 07															16 07		
Tamworth	d						14 18															16 18		
Birmingham New Street 12	a	13 58	14 24		14 31		14 36		14 58	14 54	15 31			15 36	15 55		15 58		16 28		16 31	16 36	16 58	16 54
Birmingham New Street 12	d	14 10			14 33		14 40		15 03	15 10	15 33			15 40	16 03		16 10				16 33	16 40	17 03	17 10
Cheltenham Spa	a	14 51					15 20			15 51				16 20			16 51					17 20		17 51
Gloucester 7	a																							
Bristol Parkway 7	a	15 25					15 58			16 25				16 58			17 25					17 58		18 25
Bristol Temple Meads 10	a	15 38					16 14			16 38				17 13			17 38					18 13		18 38
Newport (South Wales)	a																							
Cardiff Central 7	a																							
Weston-super-Mare	a																							
Taunton	a	16 15								17 15							18 15							19 15
Tiverton Parkway	a	16 28								17 28							18 28							19 28
Exeter St Davids 6	a	16 43								17 43							18 43							19 43
Dawlish	a																							
Teignmouth	a																							
Newton Abbot	a	17 03								18 03							19 03							20 03
Torquay	a																							
Paignton	a																							
Totnes	a	17 16								18 16							19 16							20 16
Plymouth	a	17 48								18 48							19 48							20 48
Liskeard 3	a	18 17								19 17							20 17							
Bodmin Parkway	a	18 30								19 29							20 29							
Par 3	a	18 40								19 40							20 40							
St Austell	a	18 47								19 46							20 46							
Truro	a	19 04								20 04							21 04							
Redruth	a	19 16								20 20							21 15							
Camborne	a	19 22								20 27							21 22							
St Erth 2	a	19 32								20 37							21 32							
Penzance	a	19 49								20 53							21 48							
Birmingham International ✈	d																							
Coventry	d																							
Leamington Spa 8	d				15 00				15 38		16 00				16 38						17 00		17 38	
Banbury	a				15 18				15 54		16 18				16 54						17 18		17 54	
Oxford	a				15 41				16 14		16 41				17 14						17 41		18 14	
Reading 7	a				16 13				16 44		17 13				17 44						18 13		18 44	
Kensington Olympia	a																							
East Croydon	a																							
Guildford	a																							
Redhill	a																							
Basingstoke	a								17 08						18 08								19 08	
Winchester	a								17 24						18 24								19 24	
Southampton Airport Parkwy ✈	a								17 33						18 33								19 33	
Southampton Central	a								17 42						18 42								19 42	
Brockenhurst 3	a								18 02						19 02								20 02	
Bournemouth	a								18 32						19 32								20 32	
Gatwick Airport 10 ✈	a																							
Haywards Heath 3	a																							
Brighton 10	a																							

For general notes see front of timetable
For details of catering facilities see
Directory of Train Operators

Due to Engineering Operations, services from Sunday 14 September on this Table had not been confirmed at time of going to press. These services will be issued in a special Supplement as soon as exact timings have been confirmed

SUMMARY OF SERVICES

Sundays

Scotland, The North East, North West England → The South West and South Coast

20 July to 7 September

Route Diagram - See first page of Table 51

		XC R 1	VT R 1	XC 1 ◇	XC R 1	XC R 1	XC R 1	VT R 1	XC 1 ◇	XC R 1	XC 1 ◇	XC R 1	XC R 1	XC 1 ◇	XC R 1	XC 1 ◇	XC R 1	XC R 1
Aberdeen	d														11 58			
Stonehaven	d														12 17			
Montrose	d														12 39			
Arbroath	d														12 55			
Dundee	d														13 12			
Leuchars [3]	d														13 25			
Cupar	d														13 32			
Markinch	d														13 47			
Kirkcaldy	d														13 55			
Inverkeithing	d														14 10			
Glasgow Central [15]	d	11 18						14 03										
Motherwell	d	11u38																
Haymarket	d														14 29			
Edinburgh [10]	d	12 33	12 39							13 33					14 36			
Haymarket	d		12u44															
Lockerbie	d		13 40															
Carlisle [8]	d		14 01					15 15										
Penrith North Lakes	d		14 17															
Oxenholme Lake District	d		14 41															
Lancaster [6]	d		14 57					16 04										
Preston [8]	d		15 18					16 26										
Wigan North Western	d		15 30					16 38										
Warrington Bank Quay	d		15 42					16 49										
Manchester Piccadilly [10]	d			15 55			16 24		16 55			17 24		17 55				18 24
Stockport	d			16 04			16 33		17 04			17 33		18 04				18 33
Wilmslow	d																	
Crewe [10]	d		16 07					17 10										
Macclesfield	d			16 16			16 46		17 16			17 46		18 16				18 47
Congleton	d																	
Stoke-on-Trent	d			16 35			17 05		17 35			18 03		18 35				19 05
Stafford	d			16 53			17 26		17 53			18 22		18 53				19 26
Wolverhampton [7]	d		17 02	17 09			17 41	18 02	18 09			18 41		19 09				19 41
Dunbar	d	12 55													14 57			
Berwick-upon-Tweed	d	13 18													15 19			
Alnmouth	d									14 36								
Newcastle [8]	d	14 07			14 25					15 13	15 25				16 13	16 25		
Chester-le-Street	d																	
Durham	d	14 21			14 37					15 25	15 37				16 25	16 37		
Darlington [7]	d	14 38			14 54					15 42	15 54				16 42	16 56		
York [8]	d	15 13			15 25	←				16 13	16 25				17 14	17 25	←	
Leeds [10]	d	16 00				16 00				17 00			←		18 00		18 00	
Wakefield Westgate [7]	d	→				16 12				17 12			17 12		→		18 12	
Doncaster [7]	d				15 48					→	16 50					17 50		
Sheffield [7]	d				16 23	16 48					17 23		17 48			18 23	18 48	
Chesterfield	d				16 35						17 35					18 35		
Derby [10]	d				16 57	17 20					17 57		18 20			18 57	19 20	
Burton-on-Trent	d										18 07					19 07		
Tamworth	d										18 18					19 18		
Birmingham New Street [12]	a		17 23	17 31	17 36	17 54	17 58	18 23	18 31		18 36	18 58	18 54	19 34		19 36	19 54	19 58
Birmingham New Street [12]	d			17 33	17 40	18 03	18 10		18 33		18 40	19 03	19 10			19 40	20 03	20 10
Cheltenham Spa	a				18 20		18 51				19 20		19 51			20 20		20 51
Gloucester [7]	a				18 34													
Bristol Parkway [7]	a				19 07		19 25				19 58		20 25			20 58		21 25
Bristol Temple Meads [10]	a				19 24		19 38				20 13		20 38			21 13		21 38
Newport (South Wales)	a																	
Cardiff Central [7]	a																	
Weston-super-Mare	a																	
Taunton	a						20 15						21 15					22 15
Tiverton Parkway	a						20 28						21 28					22 28
Exeter St Davids [6]	a						20 43						21 43					22 43
Dawlish	a																	
Teignmouth	a																	
Newton Abbot	a						21 03						22 03					23 03
Torquay	a																	
Paignton	a																	
Totnes	a						21 16						22 16					23 16
Plymouth	a						21 48						22 48					23 48
Liskeard [3]	a																	
Bodmin Parkway	a																	
Par [3]	a																	
St Austell	a																	
Truro	a																	
Redruth	a																	
Camborne	a																	
St Erth [2]	a																	
Penzance	a																	
Birmingham International	d																	
Coventry	d																	
Leamington Spa [8]	d			18 00		18 38			19 00			19 38					20 38	
Banbury	a			18 18		18 54			19 18			19 54					20 54	
Oxford	a			18 41		19 14			19 41			20 14					21 14	
Reading [7]	a			19 13		19 44			20 13			20 44					21 44	
Kensington Olympia	a																	
East Croydon	a																	
Guildford	a			19 54					20 50									
Redhill	a			20 27					21 31									
Basingstoke	a					20 08						21 08					22 08	
Winchester	a					20 24						21 24					22 43	
Southampton Airport Parkwy	a					20 33						21 33					23 18	
Southampton Central	a					20 42						21 42					23 31	
Brockenhurst [3]	a					21 02						22 02					23b16	
Bournemouth	a					21 32						22 32					23b35	
Gatwick Airport [10]	a			20 44					21 47									
Haywards Heath [3]	a			20 54					22 28									
Brighton [10]	a			21 13					22 50									

For general notes see front of timetable
For details of catering facilities see Directory of Train Operators

b Change at Basingstoke

Due to Engineering Operations, services from Sunday 14 September on this Table had not been confirmed at time of going to press. These services will be issued in a special Supplement as soon as exact timings have been confirmed

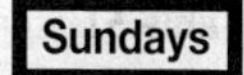

Scotland, The North East, North West England → The South West and South Coast

20 July to 7 September

Route Diagram - See first page of Table 51

		VT	XC	XC		XC	XC	XC		XC	XC	VT		XC	XC	XC	VT	XC	XC	XC	VT	XC
		R 1	1 ◇	1 ◇		1 ◇	1 ◇	1 ◇		1 ◇	1 ◇	1 ◇		1 ◇	1 ◇	1 ◇	1 ◇	1 ◇	1 ◇	1 ◇	1 ◇	1 ◇
		☕	☕	☕		☕	☕	☕		☕	☕	☕		☕	☕	☕	☕		☕		☕	☕
Aberdeen	d																					
Stonehaven	d																					
Montrose	d																					
Arbroath	d																					
Dundee	d																					
Leuchars [8]	d																					
Cupar	d																					
Markinch	d																					
Kirkcaldy	d																					
Inverkeithing	d																					
Glasgow Central [15]	d	15 54					15 44										18 04					
Motherwell	d						16u00															
Haymarket	d						16 38															
Edinburgh [10]	d			15 52			16 50					16 49							17 50		18 56	
Haymarket	d											16u54									19u01	
Lockerbie	d											17 48									19 58	
Carlisle [8]	d	17 15										18 11					19 15				20 18	
Penrith North Lakes	d											18 26									20 34	
Oxenholme Lake District	d	17 51										18 50					19 52				20 58	
Lancaster [6]	d	18 10										19 07					20 08				21 14	
Preston [8]	d	18 29										19 27					20 28				21 35	
Wigan North Western	d	18 41										19 39					20 40				21 46	
Warrington Bank Quay	d	18 52										19 50					20 52				21 59	
Manchester Piccadilly [10]	d		18 55					19 24						19 55				20 55		21 55		
Stockport	d		19 04					19 33						20 04				21 04		22 04		
Wilmslow	d																					
Crewe [10]	d	19 11										20 10					21 13				22 19	
Macclesfield	d		19 16					19 46						20 16				21 16		22 16		
Congleton	d																					
Stoke-on-Trent	d		19 35					20 05						20 35				21 35		22 35		
Stafford	d		19 53					20 26						20 53			21 50	21 53		22 53	23 00	
Wolverhampton [7]	d	20 04	20 09					20 41				21 02		21 09			22 06	22 17		23 09	23 19	
Dunbar	d																		18 13			
Berwick-upon-Tweed	d																		18 35			
Alnmouth	d																		18 55			
Newcastle [8]	d			17 16		17 25	18 15								18 25				19 25			20 25
Chester-le-Street	d																					
Durham	d			17 30		17 37	18 28								18 37				19 37			20 37
Darlington [7]	d			17 48		17 54	18 45								18 54				19 54			20 54
York [8]	d			18 15		18 25	19 15								19 23	←			20 28			21 24
Leeds [10]	d			19 00			20 00									20 00			21 15			
Wakefield Westgate [7]	d			19 12			→									20 12			21 26			
Doncaster [7]	d					18 50					←				19 50							21 51
Sheffield [7]	d			19 48		19 23					19 48				20 23	20 48			22 00			22 23
Chesterfield	d			→		19 35					20 00				20 35	21 00			22 12			22 35
Derby [10]	d					19 57					20 24				20 57	21 24			22 36			22 57
Burton-on-Trent	d					20 07					20 34				21 08	21 34			22 47			23 07
Tamworth	d					20 18					20 45				21 19	21 45			22 58			23 19
Birmingham New Street [12]	a	20 26	20 31			20 36		20 58		←	21 11	21 25		21 31	21 45	22 11	22 27	22 41	23 22	23 30	23 41	23 45
Birmingham New Street [12]	d					21 10		21 03		21 10					22 10							
Cheltenham Spa	a					→				21 51					22 51							
Gloucester [7]	a																					
Bristol Parkway [7]	a									22 25					23 25							
Bristol Temple Meads [10]	a									22 41					23 41							
Newport (South Wales)	a																					
Cardiff Central [7]	a																					
Weston-super-Mare	a																					
Taunton	a																					
Tiverton Parkway	a																					
Exeter St Davids [6]	a																					
Dawlish	a																					
Teignmouth	a																					
Newton Abbot	a																					
Torquay	a																					
Paignton	a																					
Totnes	a																					
Plymouth	a																					
Liskeard [3]	a																					
Bodmin Parkway	a																					
Par [3]	a																					
St Austell	a																					
Truro	a																					
Redruth	a																					
Camborne	a																					
St Erth [2]	a																					
Penzance	a																					
Birmingham International	d																					
Coventry	d																					
Leamington Spa [8]	d							21 38														
Banbury	a							21 54														
Oxford	a							22 14														
Reading [7]	a							22 44														
Kensington Olympia	a																					
East Croydon	a																					
Guildford	a																					
Redhill	a																					
Basingstoke	a							23 08														
Winchester	a							23 24														
Southampton Airport Parkwy	a							23 33														
Southampton Central	a							23 47														
Brockenhurst [3]	a							*00 53*														
Bournemouth	a							*01 16*														
Gatwick Airport [10]	a																					
Haywards Heath [3]	a																					
Brighton [10]	a																					

For general notes see front of timetable
For details of catering facilities see Directory of Train Operators

Due to Engineering Operations, services from Sunday 14 September on this Table had not been confirmed at time of going to press. These services will be issued in a special Supplement as soon as exact timings have been confirmed

South Coast and the South West → North West England, The North East and Scotland

Route Diagram - See first page of Table 51

		VT	XC	XC	XC	XC	XC	VT	XC	XC	XC	VT	XC	XC	XC	XC	XC	VT	XC	XC	XC	XC	VT	XC
		1 ◇	1 ◇	1 ◇	1 ◇	1 ◇	R 1	1 ◇	1 ◇	1 ◇	1 ◇	1 ◇	R 1	1 ◇	1 ◇	1 ◇	1 ◇	1 ◇	1 ◇	1 ◇	1 ◇	1 ◇	1 ◇	1 ◇
																A								
		⊠	☕	☕	☕	☕	☕	☕	☕	☕	☕	☕	☕	☕	☕	☕	☕	☕	☕	☕	☕	☕	☕	☕
Brighton 10	d													*03 50*										
Haywards Heath 3	d													*04 25*										
Gatwick Airport 10 ✈	d													05 15						05 45				
Bournemouth	d																*05 12*					06 30		
Brockenhurst 3	d																*05 38*					06 48		
Southampton Central	d										05 15						06 15					07 15		
Southampton Airport Parkwy ✈	d										05 22						06 22					07 22		
Winchester	d										05 31						06 31					07 31		
Basingstoke	d										05 47						06 47					07 47		
Redhill	d													05 33						06 04				
Guildford	d													06 00						06 51				
East Croydon	d																							
Kensington Olympia	d																							
Reading 7	d										06 10			06 40			07 10			07 40		08 10		
Oxford	d										06 36			07 06			07 36			08 06		08 36		
Banbury	d										06 53			07 25			07 53			08 25		08 53		
Leamington Spa 8	d										07 11			07 43			08 11			08 43		09 11		
Coventry	d										07 23						08 23					09 23		
Birmingham International ✈	d										07 34						08 34					09 34		
Penzance	d																							
St Erth 2	d																							
Camborne	d																							
Redruth	d																							
Truro	d																							
St Austell	d																							
Par 3	d																							
Bodmin Parkway	d																							
Liskeard 3	d																							
Plymouth	d																							06 25
Totnes	d																							06 50
Paignton	d																							
Torquay	d																							
Newton Abbot	d																							07 03
Teignmouth	d																							
Dawlish	d																							
Exeter St Davids 6	d																		06 23					07 23
Tiverton Parkway	d																		06 37					07 37
Taunton	d																		06 51					07 51
Weston-super-Mare	d																							
Cardiff Central 7	d																				07 00			
Newport (South Wales)	d																				07 15			
Bristol Temple Meads 10	d												06 15		07 00				07 30		08 00			08 30
Bristol Parkway 7	d												06 25		07 10				07 40		08 10			08 40
Gloucester 7	d												07 02											
Cheltenham Spa	d												07 12		07 42				08 12		08 42			09 12
Birmingham New Street 12	a										07 45		07 57	08 18	08 26		08 48		09 00	09 18	09 26	09 45		09 57
Birmingham New Street 12	d	05 30	06 00	06 03	06 30	06 30	07 03	07 03	07 18	07 30	07 48	08 03	08 03	08 18	08 30	08 48	09 03	09 03	09 18		09 30	09 48	10 03	10 03
Tamworth	d		06 15		06 47		07 19			07 47			08 19		08 47									
Burton-on-Trent	d		06 25		06 58		07 29			07 58			08 29		08 58									
Derby 10	a		06 38		07 11		07 42			08 11			08 42		09 16		09 39				10 11			10 39
Chesterfield	a				07 32		08 02			08 32					09 36						10 32			
Sheffield 7	a		07 09		07 50		08 17			08 50			09 18		09 50		10 15				10 50			11 15
Doncaster 7	a				08 24					09 19					10 15						11 15			
Wakefield Westgate 7	a		07 36				08 46						09 46				10 46							11 46
Leeds 10	a		07 52				09 02						10 02				11 02							12 02
York 8	a		08 24		08 48		09 33			09 48			10 29		10 40		11 29				11 42			12 29
Darlington 7	a		08 53		09 20		10 01			10 16			10 59		11 12		11 58				12 20			13 00
Durham	a		09 08		09 37		10 18			10 33			11 17		11 29		12 22				12 38			13 18
Chester-le-Street	a				09 44					10 40											12 50			
Newcastle 8	a		09 25		10 00		10 34			10 57			11 32		11 54		12 36				13 05			13 33
Alnmouth	a		09 55										12 02											14 00
Berwick-upon-Tweed	a						11 20										13 21							
Dunbar	a						11 43										13 44							
Wolverhampton 7	d	05 49		06 21		07b06		07 21	07 39		08 06	08 21		08 39		09 06		09 21	09 39			10 06	10 21	
Stafford	a	06 04		06 33		07 17		07 33	07 53		08 17			08 53		09 17						10 17		
Stoke-on-Trent	a			06 52		07 36			08 12		08 36			09 12		09 36			10 12			10 36		
Congleton	a			07 04		07 48			08 24										10 24					
Macclesfield	a			07 13		07 56			08 32		08 52			09 31		09 52			10 32			10 52		
Crewe 10	a	06 25						07 53				08 54						09 53					10 53	
Wilmslow	a																							
Stockport	a			07 30		08 09			08 46		09 05			09 46		10 05			10 46			11 05		
Manchester Piccadilly 10	a			07 47		08 27			09 02		09 20			10 02		10 20			11 02			11 20		
Warrington Bank Quay	a	06 44						08 12				09 12						10 11					11 11	
Wigan North Western	a	07 03						08 23				09 23						10 22					11 22	
Preston 8	a	07 17						08 41				09 38						10 37					11 37	
Lancaster 6	a	07 34						09 00				09 55											11 54	
Oxenholme Lake District	a	07 47						09 17				10 10						11 11						
Penrith North Lakes	a	08 13						09 43				10 35											12 33	
Carlisle 8	a	08 34						10 01				10 52						11 56					12 51	
Lockerbie	a	08 54						10 21				11 12											13 10	
Haymarket	a											12s08											14s08	
Edinburgh 10	a		11 02				12 17					12 19	13 16				14 16						14 19	15 17
Haymarket	a																							
Motherwell	a	09s50						11s04																
Glasgow Central 15	a	10 18						11 28										13 22						
Inverkeithing	a																							
Kirkcaldy	a																							
Markinch	a																							
Cupar	a																							
Leuchars 3	a																							
Dundee	a																							
Arbroath	a																							
Montrose	a																							
Stonehaven	a																							
Aberdeen	a																							

For general notes see front of timetable
For details of catering facilities see Directory of Train Operators

A From Derby (Table 57)
b Arr. 0700

until 5 September

South Coast and the South West → North West England, The North East and Scotland

Route Diagram - See first page of Table 51

Station		XC	XC	XC	XC	VT	XC	XC	XC	XC	VT	XC	XC	XC	XC	XC	VT	XC	XC	XC	XC	VT	XC	XC
							R			R						R		R			R		R	
		1◇	1◇	1◇	1◇	1◇	1	1◇	1◇	1	1◇	1◇	1◇	1◇	1◇	1	1◇	1	1◇	1◇	1	1◇	1	1◇
Brighton 10	d																		09 21					
Haywards Heath 3	d																		09 33					
Gatwick Airport 10 ✈	d																		09 46					
Bournemouth	d				07 30					08 45						09 45					10 45			
Brockenhurst 3	d				07 47					09 00						10 00					11 00			
Southampton Central	d				08 15					09 15						10 15					11 15			
Southampton Airport Parkwy ✈	d				08 22					09 22						10 22					11 22			
Winchester	d				08 31					09 31						10 31					11 31			
Basingstoke	d				08 47					09 47						10 47					11 47			
Redhill	d																							
Guildford	d																							
East Croydon	d																		10 08					
Kensington Olympia	d																		10 37					
Reading 7	d	08 40			09 10			09 40		10 10			10 40			11 10			11 40		12 10			12 40
Oxford	d	09 06			09 36			10 06		10 36			11 06			11 36			12 06		12 36			13 06
Banbury	d	09 25			09 53			10 25		10 53			11 25			11 53			12 25		12 53			13 25
Leamington Spa 8	d	09 43			10 11			10 43		11 11			11 43			12 11			12 43		13 11			13 43
Coventry	d				10 23					11 23						12 23					13 23			
Birmingham International ✈	d			10 18	10 34					11 34					12 18	12 34					13 34			
Penzance	d																	07 30					08 30	
St Erth 2	d																	07 38					08 38	
Camborne	d																	07 48					08 48	
Redruth	d																	07 54					08 54	
Truro	d																	08 06					09 06	
St Austell	d																	08 22					09 22	
Par 3	d																	08 29					09 29	
Bodmin Parkway	d																	08 40					09 40	
Liskeard 3	d																	08 52					09 52	
Plymouth	d		06 40				07 25					08 25						09 25					10 25	
Totnes	d		07 05				07 50					08 50						09 50					10 50	
Paignton	d																			10 04				
Torquay	d																			10 10				
Newton Abbot	d		07 18				08 03					09 03						10 03		10 21			11 03	
Teignmouth	d																			10 28				
Dawlish	d																			10 33				
Exeter St Davids 6	d		07 38				08 23					09 23						10 23		10 48			11 23	
Tiverton Parkway	d		07 52				08 37					09 37						10 37		11 01			11 37	
Taunton	d		08 06				08 51					09 51						10 51		11 16			11 51	
Weston-super-Mare	d		08 30																					
Cardiff Central 7	d																							
Newport (South Wales)	d																							
Bristol Temple Meads 10	d		09 00				09 30		10 00			10 30		11 00				11 30		12 00			12 30	
Bristol Parkway 7	d		09 10				09 40		10 10			10 40		11 10				11 40		12 10			12 40	
Gloucester 7	d																							
Cheltenham Spa	d		09 42				10 12		10 42			11 12		11 42				12 12		12 42			13 12	
Birmingham New Street 12	a	10 18	10 26	10 30	10 45		10 57	11 18	11 26	11 45		11 57	12 18	12 26	12 30	12 45		12 57	13 18	13 26	13 45		13 57	14 18
Birmingham New Street 12	d	10 18	10 30	10 48	11 03	11 03	11 18		11 30	11 48	12 03	12 03	12 18	12 30	12 48	13 03	13 03	13 18		13 30	13 48	14 03	14 03	14 18
Tamworth	d		10 47											12 47										
Burton-on-Trent	d		10 58											12 58										
Derby 10	a		11 11		11 39				12 11			12 39		13 11		13 39				14 11			14 39	
Chesterfield	a		11 32						12 32					13 32						14 32				
Sheffield 7	a		11 50		12 15				12 50			13 15		13 50		14 15				14 50			15 15	
Doncaster 7	a		12 15						13 22					14 18						15 15				
Wakefield Westgate 7	a				12 46							13 46				14 46							15 46	
Leeds 10	a				13 02							14 02				15 02							16 02	
York 8	a		12 43		13 29				13 46			14 29		14 45		15 29				15 40			16 29	
Darlington 7	a		13 11		14 00				14 16			14 58		15 16		16 06				16 11			16 57	
Durham	a		13 28		14 18				14 34			15 15		15 34		16 24				16 29				
Chester-le-Street	a								14 41											16 36				
Newcastle 8	a		13 49		14 36				14 56			15 31		15 59		16 37				16 51			17 27	
Alnmouth	a											16 01											17 54	
Berwick-upon-Tweed	a				15 21											17 25								
Dunbar	a				15 44											17 48								
Wolverhampton 7	d	10 39		11 06		11 21	11 39				12 21		12 39		13 06		13 21	13 39			14 06	14 21		14 39
Stafford	a			11 17						12 17					13 17						14 17			
Stoke-on-Trent	a	11 12		11 36			12 12			12 36			13 12		13 36			14 12			14 36			15 12
Congleton	a						12 24											14 24						
Macclesfield	a	11 31		11 52			12 32			12 52			13 31		13 52			14 32			14 52			15 31
Crewe 10	a					11 55					12 53						13 53					14 53		
Wilmslow	a																							
Stockport	a	11 46		12 05			12 46			13 05			13 46		14 05			14 46			15 05			15 46
Manchester Piccadilly 10	a	12 02		12 20			13 02			13 20			14 02		14 20			15 02			15 20			16 02
Warrington Bank Quay	a					12 13					13 11						14 14					15 11		
Wigan North Western	a					12 24					13 22						14 26					15 22		
Preston 8	a					12 47					13 37						14 41					15 37		
Lancaster 6	a					13 04					13 54						14 57					15 56		
Oxenholme Lake District	a										14 08						15 12							
Penrith North Lakes	a					13 43																16 33		
Carlisle 8	a					14 00					14 51						15 53					16 51		
Lockerbie	a					14 21					15 12													
Haymarket	a										16s08											18s09		
Edinburgh 10	a				16b16						16 16	17 14				18 17						18 19	18 57	
Haymarket	a				16 33																		19 04	
Motherwell	a																							
Glasgow Central 15	a					15 25											17 21							
Inverkeithing	a				16 47																		19 18	
Kirkcaldy	a				17 02																		19 34	
Markinch	a				17 11																		19 43	
Cupar	a				17 24																		19 57	
Leuchars 3	a				17 31																		20 04	
Dundee	a				17 44																		20 25	
Arbroath	a				18 01																			
Montrose	a				18 15																			
Stonehaven	a				18 35																			
Aberdeen	a				19 00																			

For general notes see front of timetable
For details of catering facilities see Directory of Train Operators

b Dep. 1630

until 5 September

South Coast and the South West → North West England, The North East and Scotland

Route Diagram - See first page of Table 51

		XC	XC	VT	XC	XC	XC	XC	XC	VT	XC	XC	XC	XC	LM	XC	VT	XC	XC	XC	XC	XC	XC	VT
		1 ◇	1 ◇	1 ◇	R 1	R 1	1 ◇	1 ◇	R 1	1 ◇	R 1	R 1	R 1	1 ◇	1 ◇	R 1	1 ◇	R 1	R 1	R 1	R 1	R 1	R 1	1 ◇
Brighton 10	d																							
Haywards Heath 3	d																							
Gatwick Airport 10 ✈	d																							
Bournemouth	d				11 45				12 45							13 45							14 45	
Brockenhurst 3	d				12 00				13 00							14 00							15 00	
Southampton Central	d				12 15				13 15							14 15							15 15	
Southampton Airport Parkwy ✈	d				12 22				13 22							14 22							15 22	
Winchester	d				12 31				13 31							14 31							15 31	
Basingstoke	d				12 47				13 47							14 47							15 47	
Redhill	d																							
Guildford	d																							
East Croydon	d																							
Kensington Olympia	d																							
Reading 7	d				13 10		13 40		14 10			14 40				15 10			15 40				16 10	
Oxford	d				13 36		14 06		14 36			15 06				15 36			16 06				16 36	
Banbury	d				13 53		14 25		14 53			15 25				15 53			16 25				16 53	
Leamington Spa 8	d				14 11		14 43		15 11			15 43				16 11			16 43				17 11	
Coventry	d				14 23				15 23							16 23							17 23	
Birmingham International ✈	d		14 18		14 34				15 34					16 18		16 34							17 34	
Penzance	d					09 30																		
St Erth 2	d					09 38																		
Camborne	d					09 48																		
Redruth	d					09 54																		
Truro	d					10 06																		
St Austell	d					10 22																		
Par 3	d					10 29																		
Bodmin Parkway	d					10 40																		
Liskeard 3	d					10 52																		
Plymouth	d					11 25		11 50			12 25							13 25						
Totnes	d					11 50		12 15			12 50							13 50						
Paignton	d																			14 01				
Torquay	d																			14 07				
Newton Abbot	d					12 03		12 28			13 03							14 03		14 18				
Teignmouth	d																			14 25				
Dawlish	d																			14 30				
Exeter St Davids 6	d					12 23		12 48			13 23							14 23		14 44				
Tiverton Parkway	d					12 37		13 02			13 37							14 37		14 57				
Taunton	d					12 51		13 16			13 51							14 51		15 12				
Weston-super-Mare	d																			15 36				
Cardiff Central 7	d																							
Newport (South Wales)	d																							
Bristol Temple Meads 10	d	13 00				13 30		14 00			14 30		15 00					15 30		16 00				
Bristol Parkway 7	d	13 10				13 40		14 10			14 40		15 10					15 40		16 10				
Gloucester 7	d																							
Cheltenham Spa	d	13 42				14 12		14 42			15 12		15 42					16 12		16 42				
Birmingham New Street 12	a	14 26	14 30		14 45	14 57	15 18	15 26	15 45		15 57	16 18	16 26	16 30		16 45		16 57	17 18	17 26	←		17 45	
Birmingham New Street 12	d	14 30	14 48	15 03	15 03	15 18		15 30	15 48	16 03	16 03	16 18	16 30	16 48	16 51	17 03	17 03	17 18	17 39 →	17 30	17 39		17 48	18 03
Tamworth	d	14 47																			18 06			
Burton-on-Trent	d	14 58																			18 16			
Derby 10	a	15 11			15 39			16 11			16 39		17 16			17 39				18 16	18 34			
Chesterfield	a	15 32						16 32					17 37							18 37				
Sheffield 7	a	15 50			16 15			16 50			17 15		17 50			18 15				18 50				
Doncaster 7	a	16 15						17 15					18 16							19 17				
Wakefield Westgate 7	a				16 46						17 46					18 46								
Leeds 10	a				17 02						18 02					19 02								
York 8	a	16 40			17 29			17 40			18 29		18 41			19 29				19 44				
Darlington 7	a	17 08			18 02			18 15			18 58		19 17			20 03				20 12				
Durham	a	17 31			18 20			18 33			19 15		19 35			20 20				20 30				
Chester-le-Street	a							18 40												20 37				
Newcastle 8	a	17 53			18 36			18 55			19 33		20 03			20 36				20 53				
Alnmouth	a										20 03					21 07								
Berwick-upon-Tweed	a				19 22						20 24					21 29								
Dunbar	a				19 45																			
Wolverhampton 7	d		15 06	15 21		15 39				16 21		16 39		17 06	17 10			17 39					18 06	18 21
Stafford	a		15 17						16 17					17 17	17 26								18 17	
Stoke-on-Trent	a		15 36			16 12			16 36			17 12		17 36				18 12					18 36	
Congleton	a					16 24						17 24						18 24						
Macclesfield	a		15 52			16 32			16 52			17 32		17 52				18 32					18 52	
Crewe 10	a			15 55						16 53					17 48		17 53							18 54
Wilmslow	a																							
Stockport	a		16 05			16 46			17 05			17 46		18 05				18 46					19 05	
Manchester Piccadilly 10	a		16 20			17 02			17 20			18 02		18 20				19 02					19 20	
Warrington Bank Quay	a			16 14						17 11					18 06									19 12
Wigan North Western	a			16 25						17 22					18 17									19 23
Preston 8	a			16 40						17 37					18 39		18 39							19 42
Lancaster 6	a			16 59						17 54							18 58							19 59
Oxenholme Lake District	a			17 15						18 11							19 13							20 13
Penrith North Lakes	a									18 37														20 39
Carlisle 8	a			17 57						18 55							19 54							20 58
Lockerbie	a																							
Haymarket	a									20s08														22s13
Edinburgh 10	a				20 11					20 19	21 08					22 24						←		22 24
Haymarket	a				20 18						21 18 →											21 18		
Motherwell	a			19s14																		21s59		
Glasgow Central 15	a			19 37	21 28												21 11					22 42		
Inverkeithing	a																							
Kirkcaldy	a																							
Markinch	a																							
Cupar	a																							
Leuchars 3	a																							
Dundee	a																							
Arbroath	a																							
Montrose	a																							
Stonehaven	a																							
Aberdeen	a																							

For general notes see front of timetable
For details of catering facilities see Directory of Train Operators

until 5 September

South Coast and the South West → North West England, The North East and Scotland

Route Diagram - See first page of Table 51

		XC	XC	XC	VT	XC	VT	XC	XC	XC	XC	XC	XC	XC	XC	VT	XC	XC	XC	XC	XC	XC	XC
		R 1 ⊡	R 1 ⊡	R 1 ⊡	1 ◇ ⊡	R 1 ⊡	1 ◇ ⊡	R 1 ⊡	R 1 ⊡	1 ◇ ⊡	R 1 ⊡	1 ◇ ⊡	1 ◇ ⊡	1 ◇ ⊡	1 ◇ ⊡	1 ◇ ⊡	1 ◇ ⊡	1 ◇ ⊡	1 ◇ ⊡	1 ◇ ⊡	1 ◇ ⊡	1 ◇ ⊡	1 ◇
Brighton 10	d		14 22																				
Haywards Heath 3	d		14b31																				
Gatwick Airport 10 ✈	d		14 51										17 03										
Bournemouth	d					15 45					16 45				17 45				18 45			19 45	
Brockenhurst 3	d					16 00					17 00				18 00				19 00			20 00	
Southampton Central	d					16 15					17 15				18 15				19 15			20 15	
Southampton Airport Parkwy ✈	d					16 22					17 22				18 22				19 22			20 22	
Winchester	d					16 31					17 31				18 31				19 31			20 31	
Basingstoke	d					16 47					17 47				18 47				19 47			20 47	
Redhill	d												17 14										
Guildford	d												17 57										
East Croydon 🚌	d		15 09																				
Kensington Olympia	d		15 36																				
Reading 7	d		16 40			17 10			17 40		18 10		18 40		19 10			19 40	20 10			21 10	
Oxford	d		17 06			17 36			18 06		18 36		19 06		19 36			20 06	20 36			21 36	
Banbury	d		17 25			17 53			18 25		18 53		19 25		19 53			20 25	20 53			21 53	
Leamington Spa 8	d		17 43			18 11			18 43		19 11		19 43		20 11			20 43	21 11			22 11	
Coventry	d				18c09	18 23					19 23				20 23				21 23			22 23	
Birmingham International ✈	d				18c21	18 34					19 34				20 34				21 34			22 34	
Penzance	d																						
St Erth 2	d																						
Camborne	d																						
Redruth	d																						
Truro	d																						
St Austell	d																						
Par 3	d																						
Bodmin Parkway	d																						
Liskeard 3	d																						
Plymouth	d	14 25						15 25				16 25					17 25			18 25			
Totnes	d	14 50						15 50				16 50					17 50			18 50			
Paignton	d									16 15													
Torquay	d									16 21													
Newton Abbot	d	15 03						16 03		16 33		17 03					18 03			19 03			
Teignmouth	d																						
Dawlish	d																						
Exeter St Davids 6	d	15 23						16 23		16 53		17 23					18 23			19 23			
Tiverton Parkway	d	15 37						16 37		17 07		17 37					18 37			19 37			
Taunton	d	15 51						16 51		17 21		17 51					18 51			19 51			
Weston-super-Mare	d																						
Cardiff Central 7	d																						
Newport (South Wales)	d																						
Bristol Temple Meads 10	d	16 30		17 00				17 30		18 00		18 30		19 00			19 30			20 30			22 00
Bristol Parkway 7	d	16 40		17 10				17 40		18 10		18 40		19 10			19 40			20 40			22 10
Gloucester 7	d																						
Cheltenham Spa	d	17 12		17 42				18 12		18 42		19 12		19 42			20 12			21 12			22 42
Birmingham New Street 12	a	17 57	18 18	18 26	18c32	18 45		18 57	19 18	19 26	19 45	19 57	20 18	20 42	20 48		20 57	21 18	21 45	21 57	⟵	22 52	23 43
Birmingham New Street 12	d	18 03	18 18	18 30	18 43	19 03	19 03	19 18		19 30	20 03	20 03	20 18	20 48	21 03	21 03	21 18		22 18	22 03	22 18		
Tamworth	d			18 47						19 47		20 19			21 19				⟶	22 19			
Burton-on-Trent	d			18 58						19 58		20 29			21 29					22 29			
Derby 10	a	18 39		19 11		19 39				20 11		20 42			21 42					22 42			
Chesterfield	a	19 02		19 32		20 02				20 32		21 02			22 02					23 27			
Sheffield 7	a	19 17		19 50		20 17				20 50		21 17			22 17					23 54			
Doncaster 7	a			20 20																			
Wakefield Westgate 7	a	19 49				20 53						21 49			22s46								
Leeds 10	a	20 06				21 09						22 05			23 05					01 01			
York 8	a	20 34		20 46		21 35				21 48		22 58											
Darlington 7	a	21 07		21 20		22 03				22 18													
Durham	a	21 25		21 38		22 20				22 35													
Chester-le-Street	a			21 45						22 45													
Newcastle 8	a	21 42		22 00		22 41				22 59													
Alnmouth	a	22 14																					
Berwick-upon-Tweed	a	22 35																					
Dunbar	a	22 58																					
Wolverhampton 7 🚌	d		18 39		19 06		19 21	19 39			20 21		20 39	21 11		21 21	21 39				22 39		
Stafford	a				19 21		19 36				20 34			21 23		21 36	21 53				22 53		
Stoke-on-Trent	a		19 12		19 45			20 12					21 12	21 45			22 12				23s12		
Congleton	a							20 24									22 24						
Macclesfield	a		19 31		20 01			20 32					21 31	22 02			22 32						
Crewe 10	a						19 58				20 54					21 58							
Wilmslow	a										21 15												
Stockport	a		19 46		20 16			20 46			21 25		21 46	22 15			22 46						
Manchester Piccadilly 10 🚌	a		20 02		20 35			21 02			21 39		22 02	22 32			23 02				00 07		
Warrington Bank Quay	a						20 16									22 17							
Wigan North Western	a						20 27									22 43							
Preston 8	a						20 42									23 04							
Lancaster 6	a						21 00																
Oxenholme Lake District	a						21 14																
Penrith North Lakes	a						21 41																
Carlisle 8	a						21 58																
Lockerbie	a						22 17																
Haymarket	a																						
Edinburgh 10	a	23 29																					
Haymarket	a																						
Motherwell	a						23s04																
Glasgow Central 15	a						23 33																
Inverkeithing	a																						
Kirkcaldy	a																						
Markinch	a																						
Cupar	a																						
Leuchars 3	a																						
Dundee	a																						
Arbroath	a																						
Montrose	a																						
Stonehaven	a																						
Aberdeen	a																						

For general notes see front of timetable
For details of catering facilities see Directory of Train Operators

b Change at East Croydon

c Until 25 July and from 25 August dep. Coventry 1814, Birmingham International 1828, Birmingham New Street arr. 1839

from 8 September

South Coast and The South West → North West England, The North East and Scotland

Route Diagram - See first page of Table 51

		VT	XC	XC	XC	XC	XC	VT	XC	XC	XC	XC	VT	XC	XC	XC	XC	VT	XC	XC
		1 ◇	1 ◇	1 ◇	1 ◇	1 ◇	R 1	1 ◇	1 ◇	1 ◇	1 ◇	R 1	1 ◇	1 ◇	1 ◇	1 ◇	1 ◇	1 ◇	1 ◇	1 ◇
																A				
		☒	☕	☕	☕	☕	☕	☕	☕	☕	☕	☕	☕	☕	☕	☕	☕	☕	☕	☕
Brighton 10	d													03 50						
Haywards Heath 3	d													04 25						
Gatwick Airport 10 ✈	d													05 15						05 45
Bournemouth	d																05 12			
Brockenhurst 3	d																05 38			
Southampton Central	d										05 15						06 15			
Southampton Airport Parkwy ✈	d										05 22						06 22			
Winchester	d										05 31						06 31			
Basingstoke	d										05 47						06 47			
Redhill	d													05 33						06 04
Guildford	d													06 00						06 51
East Croydon	d																			
Kensington Olympia	d																			
Reading 7	d										06 10			06 40			07 10			07 40
Oxford	d										06 36			07 06			07 36			08 06
Banbury	d										06 53			07 25			07 53			08 25
Leamington Spa 8	d										07 11			07 43			08 11			08 43
Coventry	d										07 23						08 23			
Birmingham International ✈	d										07 34						08 34			
Penzance	d																			
St Erth 2	d																			
Camborne	d																			
Redruth	d																			
Truro	d																			
St Austell	d																			
Par 3	d																			
Bodmin Parkway	d																			
Liskeard 3	d																			
Plymouth	d																			
Totnes	d																			
Paignton	d																			
Torquay	d																			
Newton Abbot	d																			
Teignmouth	d																			
Dawlish	d																			
Exeter St Davids 6	d																		06 23	
Tiverton Parkway	d																		06 37	
Taunton	d																		06 51	
Weston-super-Mare	d																			
Cardiff Central 7	d																			
Newport (South Wales)	d																			
Bristol Temple Meads 10	d											06 15			07 00				07 30	
Bristol Parkway 7	d											06 25			07 10				07 40	
Gloucester 7	d											07 02								
Cheltenham Spa	d											07 12			07 42				08 12	
Birmingham New Street 12	a										07 45	07 57		08 18	08 26		08 48		09 00	09 18
Birmingham New Street 12	d	05 30	06 00	06 03	06 30	06 30	07 03	07 03	07 18	07 30	07 48	08 03	08 03	08 18	08 30	08 48	09 03	09 03	09 18	
Tamworth	d		06 15			06 47	07 19			07 47		08 19			08 47					
Burton-on-Trent	d		06 25			06 58	07 29			07 58		08 29			08 58					
Derby 10	a		06 38			07 11	07 42			08 11		08 42			09 11		09 39			
Chesterfield	a		06 57			07 34	08 01			08 32		09 02			09 36		10 03			
Sheffield 7	a		07 27			08 06	08 36			09 06		09 36			10 06		10 36			
Doncaster 7	a		08 24				09 19					10 15					11 15			
Wakefield Westgate 7	a					08 46				09 46					10 46					
Leeds 10	a					09 02				10 02					11 02					
York 8	a		08 50			09 33	09 49			10 29		10 41			11 29		11 43			
Darlington 7	a					10 01				10 59					11 58					
Durham	a					10 18				11 17					12 22					
Chester-le-Street	a									11 25										
Newcastle 8	a					10 34				11 34					12 36					
Alnmouth	a									12 03										
Berwick-upon-Tweed	a					11 20									13 21					
Dunbar	a					11 43									13 44					
Wolverhampton 7	d	05 49		06 21	07b06			07 21	07 39		08 06		08 21	08 39		09 06		09 21	09 39	
Stafford	a	06 04		06 33	07 17			07 33	07 53		08 17			08 53		09 17				
Stoke-on-Trent	a			06 52	07 36				08 12		08 36			09 12		09 36			10 12	
Congleton	a			07 04	07 48				08 24										10 24	
Macclesfield	a			07 13	07 56				08 32		08 52			09 31		09 52			10 32	
Crewe 10	a	06 25						07 53					08 54					09 53		
Wilmslow	a																			
Stockport	a			07 30	08 09				08 46		09 05			09 46		10 05			10 46	
Manchester Piccadilly 10	a			07 47	08 27				09 02		09 20			10 02		10 20			11 02	
Warrington Bank Quay	a	06 44						08 12					09 12					10 11		
Wigan North Western	a	07 03						08 23					09 23					10 22		
Preston 8	a	07 17						08 41					09 38					10 37		
Lancaster 6	a	07 34						09 00					09 55							
Oxenholme Lake District	a	07 47						09 17					10 10					11 11		
Penrith North Lakes	a	08 13						09 43					10 35							
Carlisle 8	a	08 34						10 01					10 52					11 56		
Lockerbie	a	08 54						10 21					11 12							
Haymarket	a												12s08							
Edinburgh 10	a					12 17				13 16			12 19		14 16					
Haymarket	a																			
Motherwell	a	09s50						11s04												
Glasgow Central 15	a	10 18						11 28										13 22		
Inverkeithing	a																			
Kirkcaldy	a																			
Markinch	a																			
Cupar	a																			
Leuchars 3	a																			
Dundee	a																			
Arbroath	a																			
Montrose	a																			
Stonehaven	a																			
Aberdeen	a																			

For general notes see front of timetable
For details of catering facilities see Directory of Train Operators

A From Derby (Table 57)
b Arr. 0700

from 8 September

South Coast and The South West → North West England, The North East and Scotland

Route Diagram - See first page of Table 51

		XC	XC	XC	VT	XC	XC	XC	XC	VT	XC	XC	XC	XC	XC	VT	XC	XC	XC	XC
											R			R						R
		1◇	1◇	1◇	1◇	1◇	1◇	1◇	1◇	1◇	1	1◇	1◇	1	1◇	1◇	1◇	1◇	1◇	1
		⊡	⊡	⊡	⊡	⊡	⊡	⊡	⊡	⊡	⊡	⊡	⊡	⊡	⊡	⊡	⊡	⊡	⊡	⊡
Brighton 10	d																			
Haywards Heath 3	d																			
Gatwick Airport 10 ✈	d																			
Bournemouth	d		06 30						07 30					08 45						09 45
Brockenhurst 3	d		06 48						07 47					09 00						10 00
Southampton Central	d		07 15						08 15					09 15						10 15
Southampton Airport Parkwy ✈	d		07 22						08 22					09 22						10 22
Winchester	d		07 31						08 31					09 31						10 31
Basingstoke	d		07 47						08 47					09 47						10 47
Redhill	d																			
Guildford	d																			
East Croydon	d																			
Kensington Olympia	d																			
Reading 7	d		08 10			08 40			09 10			09 40		10 10			10 40			11 10
Oxford	d		08 36			09 06			09 36			10 06		10 36			11 06			11 36
Banbury	d		08 53			09 25			09 53			10 25		10 53			11 25			11 53
Leamington Spa 8	d		09 11			09 43			10 11			10 43		11 11			11 43			12 11
Coventry	d		09 23						10 23					11 23						12 23
Birmingham International ✈	d		09 34					10 18	10 34					11 34					12 18	12 34
Penzance	d																			
St Erth 2	d																			
Camborne	d																			
Redruth	d																			
Truro	d																			
St Austell	d																			
Par 3	d																			
Bodmin Parkway	d																			
Liskeard 3	d																			
Plymouth	d			06 25			06 40				07 25				08 25					
Totnes	d			06 50			07 05				07 50				08 50					
Paignton	d																			
Torquay	d																			
Newton Abbot	d			07 03			07 18				08 03				09 03					
Teignmouth	d																			
Dawlish	d																			
Exeter St Davids 6	d			07 23			07 38				08 23				09 23					
Tiverton Parkway	d			07 37			07 52				08 37				09 37					
Taunton	d			07 51			08 06				08 51				09 51					
Weston-super-Mare	d						08 30													
Cardiff Central 7	d	07 00																		
Newport (South Wales)	d	07 15																		
Bristol Temple Meads 10	d	08 00		08 30			09 00				09 30		10 00		10 30			11 00		
Bristol Parkway 7	d	08 10		08 40			09 10				09 40		10 10		10 40			11 10		
Gloucester 7	d																			
Cheltenham Spa	d	08 42		09 12			09 42				10 12		10 42		11 12			11 42		
Birmingham New Street 12	a	09 26	09 45	09 57		10 18	10 26	10 30	10 45		10 57	11 18	11 26	11 45	11 57		12 18	12 26	12 30	12 45
Birmingham New Street 12	d	09 30	09 48	10 03	10 03	10 18	10 30	10 48	11 03	11 03	11 18		11 30	11 48	12 03	12 03	12 18	12 30	12 48	13 03
Tamworth	d						10 47											12 47		
Burton-on-Trent	d						10 58											12 58		
Derby 10	a	10 11		10 39			11 11		11 39				12 11		12 39			13 11		13 39
Chesterfield	a	10 36		11 00			11 33		12 00				12 35		13 00			13 34		14 00
Sheffield 7	a	11 06		11 36			12 06		12 36				13 06		13 36			14 06		14 36
Doncaster 7	a			12 15					13 22						14 18					15 15
Wakefield Westgate 7	a	11 46					12 46						13 46					14 46		
Leeds 10	a	12 02					13 02						14 02					15 02		
York 8	a	12 34		12 43			13 30		13 49				14 30		14 45			15 29		15 40
Darlington 7	a	13 00					14 00						14 58					16 06		
Durham	a	13 18					14 18						15 15					16 24		
Chester-le-Street	a																			
Newcastle 8	a	13 33					14 36						15 31					16 37		
Alnmouth	a	14 00											16 01							
Berwick-upon-Tweed	a						15 21											17 25		
Dunbar	a						15 44											17 48		
Wolverhampton 7	d		10 06		10 21	10 39		11 06		11 21	11 39					12 21	12 39		13 06	
Stafford	a		10 17					11 17						12 17					13 17	
Stoke-on-Trent	a		10 36			11 12		11 36			12 12			12 36			13 12		13 36	
Congleton	a										12 24									
Macclesfield	a		10 52			11 31		11 52			12 32			12 52			13 31		13 52	
Crewe 10	a				10 53					11 55						12 53				
Wilmslow	a																			
Stockport	a		11 05			11 46		12 05			12 46			13 05			13 46		14 05	
Manchester Piccadilly 10	a		11 20			12 02		12 20			13 02			13 20			14 02		14 20	
Warrington Bank Quay	a				11 11					12 13						13 11				
Wigan North Western	a				11 22					12 24						13 22				
Preston 8	a				11 37					12 47						13 37				
Lancaster 6	a				11 54					13 04						13 54				
Oxenholme Lake District	a															14 08				
Penrith North Lakes	a				12 33					13 43										
Carlisle 8	a				12 51					14 00						14 51				
Lockerbie	a				13 10					14 21						15 12				
Haymarket	a				14s08											16s08				
Edinburgh 10	a	15 17			14 19		16b16						17 14			16 16		18 17		
Haymarket	a						16 33													
Motherwell	a																			
Glasgow Central 15	a									15 25										
Inverkeithing	a						16 47													
Kirkcaldy	a						17 02													
Markinch	a						17 11													
Cupar	a						17 24													
Leuchars 3	a						17 31													
Dundee	a						17 44													
Arbroath	a						18 01													
Montrose	a						18 15													
Stonehaven	a						18 35													
Aberdeen	a						19 00													

For general notes see front of timetable
For details of catering facilities see
Directory of Train Operators

b Dep. 1630

from 8 September

South Coast and The South West → North West England, The North East and Scotland

Route Diagram - See first page of Table 51

		VT	XC	XC	XC	XC	XC	VT	XC	XC	XC	XC	VT	XC	XC	XC	XC	XC	VT	XC
		1 ◇	R 1	1 ◇	1 ◇	R 1	R 1	1 ◇	1 ◇	R 1	1 ◇	R 1	1 ◇	R 1	1 ◇	R 1	R 1	R 1	1 ◇	R 1
		⊏P	⊏P	⊏P	⊏P	⊏P	⊏P	⊏P	⊏P	⊏P	⊏P	⊏P	⊏P	⊏P	⊏P	⊏P	⊏P	⊏P	⊏P	⊏P
Brighton [10]	d			09 21																
Haywards Heath [3]	d			09 33																
Gatwick Airport [10] ✈	d			09 46																
Bournemouth	d					10 45						11 45					12 45			
Brockenhurst [3]	d					11 00						12 00					13 00			
Southampton Central	d					11 15						12 15					13 15			
Southampton Airport Parkwy ✈	d					11 22						12 22					13 22			
Winchester	d					11 31						12 31					13 31			
Basingstoke	d					11 47						12 47					13 47			
Redhill	d																			
Guildford	d																			
East Croydon	d			10 08																
Kensington Olympia	d			10 37																
Reading [7]	d			11 40		12 10			12 40			13 10			13 40		14 10			14 40
Oxford	d			12 06		12 36			13 06			13 36			14 06		14 36			15 06
Banbury	d			12 25		12 53			13 25			13 53			14 25		14 53			15 25
Leamington Spa [8]	d			12 43		13 11			13 43			14 11			14 43		15 11			15 43
Coventry	d					13 23						14 23					15 23			
Birmingham International ✈	d					13 34					14 18	14 34					15 34			
Penzance	d		07 30				08 30							09 30						
St Erth [2]	d		07 38				08 38							09 38						
Camborne	d		07 48				08 48							09 48						
Redruth	d		07 54				08 54							09 54						
Truro	d		08 06				09 06							10 06						
St Austell	d		08 22				09 22							10 22						
Par [3]	d		08 29				09 29							10 29						
Bodmin Parkway	d		08 40				09 40							10 40						
Liskeard [3]	d		08 52				09 52							10 52						
Plymouth	d		09 25				10 25							11 25		11 50		12 25		
Totnes	d		09 50				10 50							11 50		12 15		12 50		
Paignton	d				10 04															
Torquay	d				10 10															
Newton Abbot	d		10 03		10 21		11 03							12 03		12 28		13 03		
Teignmouth	d				10 28															
Dawlish	d				10 33															
Exeter St Davids [6]	d		10 23		10 48		11 23							12 23		12 48		13 23		
Tiverton Parkway	d		10 37		11 01		11 37							12 37		13 02		13 37		
Taunton	d		10 51		11 16		11 51							12 51		13 16		13 51		
Weston-super-Mare	d																			
Cardiff Central [7]	d																			
Newport (South Wales)	d																			
Bristol Temple Meads [10]	d		11 30		12 00		12 30			13 00				13 30		14 00		14 30		
Bristol Parkway [7]	d		11 40		12 10		12 40			13 10				13 40		14 10		14 40		
Gloucester [7]	d																			
Cheltenham Spa	d		12 12		12 42		13 12			13 42				14 12		14 42		15 12		
Birmingham New Street [12]	a		12 57	13 18	13 26	13 45	13 57		14 18	14 26	14 30	14 45		14 57	15 18	15 26	15 45	15 57		16 18
Birmingham New Street [12]	d	13 03	13 18		13 30	13 48	14 03	14 03	14 18	14 30	14 48	15 03	15 03	15 18		15 30	15 48	16 03	16 03	16 18
Tamworth	d									14 47										
Burton-on-Trent	d									14 58										
Derby [10]	a				14 11		14 39			15 11		15 39				16 11		16 39		
Chesterfield	a				14 35		15 00			15 37		16 00				16 34		17 01		
Sheffield [7]	a				15 06		15 36			16 06		16 36				17 06		17 36		
Doncaster [7]	a						16 15					17 15						18 16		
Wakefield Westgate [7]	a				15 46					16 46						17 46				
Leeds [10]	a				16 02					17 02						18 02				
York [8]	a				16 29		16 40			17 29		17 45				18 29		18 39		
Darlington [7]	a				16 57					18 02						18 58				
Durham	a									18 20						19 15				
Chester-le-Street	a																			
Newcastle [8]	a				17 27					18 36						19 33				
Alnmouth	a				17 54											20 03				
Berwick-upon-Tweed	a									19 22						20 24				
Dunbar	a									19 45										
Wolverhampton [7]	d	13 21	13 39			14 06		14 21	14 39		15 06		15 21	15 39					16 21	16 39
Stafford	a					14 17					15 17						16 17			
Stoke-on-Trent	a		14 12			14 36			15 12		15 36			16 12			16 36			17 12
Congleton	a		14 24											16 24						17 24
Macclesfield	a		14 32			14 52			15 31		15 52			16 32			16 52			17 32
Crewe [10]	a	13 53						14 53					15 55						16 53	
Wilmslow	a																			
Stockport	a		14 46			15 05			15 46		16 05			16 46			17 05			17 46
Manchester Piccadilly [10]	a		15 02			15 20			16 02		16 20			17 02			17 20			18 02
Warrington Bank Quay	a	14 14						15 11					16 14						17 11	
Wigan North Western	a	14 26						15 22					16 25						17 22	
Preston [8]	a	14 41						15 37					16 40						17 37	
Lancaster [6]	a	14 57						15 56					16 59						17 54	
Oxenholme Lake District	a	15 12											17 15						18 11	
Penrith North Lakes	a							16 33											18 37	
Carlisle [8]	a	15 53						16 51					17 57						18 55	
Lockerbie	a																			
Haymarket	a							18s09											20s08	
Edinburgh [10]	a				18 57			18 19		20 11						21 08			20 19	
Haymarket	a				19 04					20 18 ⟶						21 18 ⟶				
Motherwell	a												19s14							
Glasgow Central [15]	a	17 21											19 37							
Inverkeithing	a				19 18															
Kirkcaldy	a				19 34															
Markinch	a				19 43															
Cupar	a				19 57															
Leuchars [3]	a				20 04															
Dundee	a				20 25															
Arbroath	a																			
Montrose	a																			
Stonehaven	a																			
Aberdeen	a																			

For general notes see front of timetable
For details of catering facilities see Directory of Train Operators

from 8 September

South Coast and The South West → North West England, The North East and Scotland

Route Diagram - See first page of Table 51

		XC	XC	LM	XC	VT	XC	XC	XC	XC	XC	XC	XC	XC	VT	XC	XC	VT	XC
		R 1	1◇	1◇	R 1	1◇	R 1	R 1	R 1	R 1	R 1	R 1	R 1	1◇	1◇	R 1	R 1	1◇	R 1
Brighton 10	d															14 22			
Haywards Heath 3	d															*14b31*			
Gatwick Airport 10 ✈	d															14 51			
Bournemouth	d				13 45								14 45						15 45
Brockenhurst 3	d				14 00								15 00						16 00
Southampton Central	d				14 15								15 15						16 15
Southampton Airport Parkwy ✈	d				14 22								15 22						16 22
Winchester	d				14 31								15 31						16 31
Basingstoke	d				14 47								15 47						16 47
Redhill	d																		
Guildford	d																		
East Croydon	d															15 09			
Kensington Olympia	d															15 36			
Reading 7	d				15 10					15 40			16 10			16 40			17 10
Oxford	d				15 36					16 06			16 36			17 06			17 36
Banbury	d				15 53					16 25			16 53			17 25			17 53
Leamington Spa 8	d				16 11					16 43			17 11			17 43			18 11
Coventry	d				16 23								17 23					18 14	18 23
Birmingham International ✈	d		16 18		16 34								17 34					18 28	18 34
Penzance	d																		
St Erth 2	d																		
Camborne	d																		
Redruth	d																		
Truro	d																		
St Austell	d																		
Par 3	d																		
Bodmin Parkway	d																		
Liskeard 3	d																		
Plymouth	d							13 25						14 25					
Totnes	d							13 50						14 50					
Paignton	d										14 01								
Torquay	d										14 07								
Newton Abbot	d							14 03			14 18			15 03					
Teignmouth	d										14 25								
Dawlish	d										14 30								
Exeter St Davids 6	d							14 23			14 44			15 23					
Tiverton Parkway	d							14 37			14 57			15 37					
Taunton	d							14 51			15 12			15 51					
Weston-super-Mare	d										15 36								
Cardiff Central 7	d																		
Newport (South Wales)	d																		
Bristol Temple Meads 10	d	15 00						15 30			16 00			16 30			17 00		
Bristol Parkway 7	d	15 10						15 40			16 10			16 40			17 10		
Gloucester 7	d																		
Cheltenham Spa	d	15 42						16 12			16 42			17 12			17 42		
Birmingham New Street 12	a	16 26	16 30		16 45			16 57		17 18	17 26	←	17 45	17 57		18 18	18 26	18 39	18 45
Birmingham New Street 12	d	16 30	16 48	16 51	17 03	17 03		17 18		17 39 ↳	17 30	17 39	17 48	18 03	18 03	18 18	18 30	18 43	19 03
Tamworth	d											18 06					18 47		
Burton-on-Trent	d											18 16					18 58		
Derby 10	a	17 14			17 39						18 11	18 34		18 39			19 11		19 39
Chesterfield	a	17 37			18 04						18 36			19 04			19 38		20 02
Sheffield 7	a	18 06			18 40						19 12			19 36			20 06		20 36
Doncaster 7	a				19 17									20 20					
Wakefield Westgate 7	a	18 46									19 49						20 53		
Leeds 10	a	19 02									20 06						21 09		
York 8	a	19 29			19 44						20 34			20 46			21 35		21 48
Darlington 7	a	20 03			20 12						21 07			21 20			22 03		22 18
Durham	a	20 20			20 30						21 25			21 38			22 20		22 35
Chester-le-Street	a				20 37									21 45					22 45
Newcastle 8	a	20 36			20 53						21 42			22 00			22 41		22 59
Alnmouth	a	21 07									22 14								
Berwick-upon-Tweed	a	21 29									22 35								
Dunbar	a										22 58								
Wolverhampton 7	d		17 06	17 10				17 39					18 06		18 21	18 39		19 06	
Stafford	a		17 17	17 26									18 17					19 21	
Stoke-on-Trent	a		17 36					18 12					18 36			19 12		19 45	
Congleton	a							18 24											
Macclesfield	a		17 52					18 32					18 52			19 31		20 01	
Crewe 10	a			17 48		17 53									18 54				
Wilmslow	a																		
Stockport	a		18 05					18 46					19 05			19 46		20 16	
Manchester Piccadilly 10	a		18 20					19 02					19 20			20 02		20 35	
Warrington Bank Quay	a			18 06											19 12				
Wigan North Western	a			18 17											19 23				
Preston 8	a			18 39		18 39									19 42				
Lancaster 6	a					18 58									19 59				
Oxenholme Lake District	a					19 13									20 13				
Penrith North Lakes	a														20 39				
Carlisle 8	a					19 54									20 58				
Lockerbie	a																		
Haymarket	a														22s13				
Edinburgh 10	a	22 24			22 34		←		←		23 29				22 24				
Haymarket	a						20 18		21 18										
Motherwell	a								21s59										
Glasgow Central 15	a					21 11	21 28		22 42										
Inverkeithing	a																		
Kirkcaldy	a																		
Markinch	a																		
Cupar	a																		
Leuchars 3	a																		
Dundee	a																		
Arbroath	a																		
Montrose	a																		
Stonehaven	a																		
Aberdeen	a																		

For general notes see front of timetable
For details of catering facilities see Directory of Train Operators

b Change at East Croydon

from 8 September

South Coast and The South West → North West England, The North East and Scotland

Route Diagram - See first page of Table 51

		VT	XC	XC	XC	XC	XC	XC	XC	XC	XC	VT	XC	XC	XC	XC	XC	XC	XC
									FX	FO									
			R	R		R													
		1 ◇	1	1	1 ◇	1	1 ◇	1 ◇	1 ◇	1 ◇	1 ◇	1 ◇	1 ◇	1 ◇	1 ◇	1 ◇	1 ◇	1 ◇	1 ◇
		☕	☕	☕	☕	☕	☕	☕	☕	☕	☕	☕	☕	☕	☕	☕	☕	☕	
Brighton 10	d																		
Haywards Heath 3	d																		
Gatwick Airport 10 ✈	d							*17 03*											
Bournemouth	d					16 45					17 45				18 45			19 45	
Brockenhurst 3	d					17 00					18 00				19 00			20 00	
Southampton Central	d					17 15					18 15				19 15			20 15	
Southampton Airport Parkwy ✈	d					17 22					18 22				19 22			20 22	
Winchester	d					17 31					18 31				19 31			20 31	
Basingstoke	d					17 47					18 47				19 47			20 47	
Redhill	d							*17 14*											
Guildford	d							17 57											
East Croydon 🚊	d																		
Kensington Olympia	d																		
Reading 7	d			17 40		18 10		18 40			19 10			19 40	20 10			21 10	
Oxford	d			18 06		18 36		19 06			19 36			20 06	20 36			21 36	
Banbury	d			18 25		18 53		19 25			19 53			20 25	20 53			21 53	
Leamington Spa 8	d			18 43		19 11		19 43			20 11			20 43	21 11			22 11	
Coventry	d					19 23					20 23				21 23			22 23	
Birmingham International ✈	d					19 34					20 34				21 34			22 34	
Penzance	d																		
St Erth 2	d																		
Camborne	d																		
Redruth	d																		
Truro	d																		
St Austell	d																		
Par 3	d																		
Bodmin Parkway	d																		
Liskeard 3	d																		
Plymouth	d		15 25				16 25						17 25			18 25			
Totnes	d		15 50				16 50						17 50			18 50			
Paignton	d				16 15														
Torquay	d				16 21														
Newton Abbot	d		16 03		16 33		17 03						18 03			19 03			
Teignmouth	d																		
Dawlish	d																		
Exeter St Davids 6	d		16 23		16 53		17 23						18 23			19 23			
Tiverton Parkway	d		16 37		17 07		17 37						18 37			19 37			
Taunton	d		16 51		17 21		17 51						18 51			19 51			
Weston-super-Mare	d																		
Cardiff Central 7	d																		
Newport (South Wales)	d																		
Bristol Temple Meads 10	d		17 30		18 00		18 30		19 00	19 00			19 30			20 30			22 00
Bristol Parkway 7	d		17 40		18 10		18 40		19 10	19 10			19 40			20 40			22 10
Gloucester 7	d																		
Cheltenham Spa	d		18 12		18 42		19 12		19 42	19 42			20 12			21 12			22 42
Birmingham New Street 12	a		18 57	19 18	19 26	19 45	19 57	20 18	20 42	20 42	20 48		20 57	21 18	21 45	21 57	⟵	22 52	23 43
Birmingham New Street 12	d	19 03	19 18		19 30	20 03	20 03	20 18		20 48	21 03	21 03	21 18		22 18 ⟶	22 03	22 18		
Tamworth	d				19 47		20 19				21 19					22 19			
Burton-on-Trent	d				19 58		20 29				21 29					22 29			
Derby 10	a				20 11		20 42				21 42					22 42			
Chesterfield	a				20 34		21 04				22 02					23 27			
Sheffield 7	a				21 11		21 38				22 36					23 54			
Doncaster 7	a																		
Wakefield Westgate 7	a				21 49						23s17								
Leeds 10	a				22 05						23 39					01 01			
York 8	a				22 58		23 09												
Darlington 7	a																		
Durham	a																		
Chester-le-Street	a																		
Newcastle 8	a																		
Alnmouth	a																		
Berwick-upon-Tweed	a																		
Dunbar	a																		
Wolverhampton 7 🚊	d	19 21	19 39			20 21		20 39		21 11		21 21	21 39				22 39		
Stafford	a	19 36				20 34				21 23		21 36	21 53				22 53		
Stoke-on-Trent	a		20 12					21 12		21 45			22 12				23s12		
Congleton	a		20 24										22 24						
Macclesfield	a		20 32					21 31		22 02			22 32						
Crewe 10	a	19 58				20 54						21 58							
Wilmslow	a					21 15													
Stockport	a		20 46			21 25		21 46		22 15			22 46						
Manchester Piccadilly 10 🚊	a		21 02			21 39		22 02		22 32			23 02				00 07		
Warrington Bank Quay	a	20 16										22 17							
Wigan North Western	a	20 27										22 43							
Preston 8	a	20 42										23 04							
Lancaster 6	a	21 00																	
Oxenholme Lake District	a	21 14																	
Penrith North Lakes	a	21 41																	
Carlisle 8	a	21 58																	
Lockerbie	a	22 17																	
Haymarket	a																		
Edinburgh 10	a																		
Haymarket	a																		
Motherwell	a	23s04																	
Glasgow Central 15	a	23 33																	
Inverkeithing	a																		
Kirkcaldy	a																		
Markinch	a																		
Cupar	a																		
Leuchars 3	a																		
Dundee	a																		
Arbroath	a																		
Montrose	a																		
Stonehaven	a																		
Aberdeen	a																		

For general notes see front of timetable
For details of catering facilities see Directory of Train Operators

South Coast and The South West → North West England, The North East and Scotland

until 12 July

Route Diagram - See first page of Table 51

		VT	XC	XC	XC	XC	VT	XC	XC		XC	VT	XC	XC	XC	XC	XC	VT		XC	XC	XC	VT	XC
		1◇	1◇	1◇	1◇	1◇	1◇	1◇	1◇		1◇	1◇	1◇	1◇	1◇	1◇	1◇	1◇		1◇	1◇	1◇	1◇	1◇
Brighton 10	d													*03 50*										
Haywards Heath 3	d													*04 25*										
Gatwick Airport 10 ✈	d													05 15							05 45			
Bournemouth	d																							06 37
Brockenhurst 3	d																							06 54
Southampton Central	d																06 15							07 15
Southampton Airport Parkwy ✈	d																06 22							07 22
Winchester	d																06 31							07 31
Basingstoke	d																06 47							07 47
Redhill	d													05 33							05 52			
Guildford	d													06 00										
East Croydon	d																				06 07			
Kensington Olympia	d																				06 51			
Reading 7	d													06 40			07 10				07 40			08 10
Oxford	d													07 07			07 36				08 07			08 36
Banbury	d													07 25			07 53				08 25			08 53
Leamington Spa 8	d													07 43			08 11				08 43			09 11
Coventry	d																08 23						09 10	09 23
Birmingham International ✈	d																08 34						09 22	09 34
Penzance	d																							
St Erth 2	d																							
Camborne	d																							
Redruth	d																							
Truro	d																							
St Austell	d																							
Par 3	d																							
Bodmin Parkway	d																							
Liskeard 3	d																							
Plymouth	d																							
Totnes	d																							
Paignton	d																							
Torquay	d																							
Newton Abbot	d																							
Teignmouth	d																							
Dawlish	d																							
Exeter St Davids 6	d																							
Tiverton Parkway	d																							
Taunton	d																							
Weston-super-Mare	d																							
Cardiff Central 7	d																							
Newport (South Wales)	d																							
Bristol Temple Meads 10	d												06 15							07 30		08 00		
Bristol Parkway 7	d												06 25							07 40		08 10		
Gloucester 7	d												07 01											
Cheltenham Spa	d												07 12							08 12		08 42		
Birmingham New Street 12	a												07 57	08 18			08 45			08 57	09 18	09 26	09 36	09 45
Birmingham New Street 12	d	05 30	06 00	06 20	06 30	07 03	07 03	07 20	07 30		07 48	08 03	08 03	08 20	08 30	08 48	09 03	09 03		09 20		09 30	09 40	09 48
Tamworth	d		06 16		06 47	07 19			07 47				08 19		08 47							09 47		
Burton-on-Trent	d		06 26		06 58	07 29			07 58				08 29		08 58							09 58		
Derby 10	a		06 39		07 11	07 42			08 11				08 42		09 11		09 39					10 11		
Chesterfield	a				07 32	08 01			08 32				09 01		09 32							10 32		
Sheffield 7	a		07 09		07 50	08 17			08 50				09 17		09 50		10 15					10 50		
Doncaster 7	a				08 23				09 21						10 18							11 16		
Wakefield Westgate 7	a		07 36			08 46							09 46				10 46							
Leeds 10	a		07 52			09 02							10 02				11 02							
York 8	a		08 24		08 50	09 30			09 45				10 29		10 45		11 31					11 45		
Darlington 7	a		08 52		09 18	10 00			10 13				11 00		11 16		12 01					12 15		
Durham	a		09 09		09 36	10 17			10 30				11 17		11 33		12 18					12 33		
Chester-le-Street	a				09 43				10 37													12 40		
Newcastle 8	a		09 25		09 59	10 33			10 54				11 32		11 53		12 35					12 56		
Alnmouth	a		09 54										12 01											
Berwick-upon-Tweed	a					11 18											13 18							
Dunbar	a					11 41											13 41							
Wolverhampton 7	d	05 49		06 40			07 21	07 40			08 06	08 21		08 40		09 08		09 21		09 40				10 08
Stafford	a	06 04		06 52			07 33	07 52			08 17			08 52		09 22				09 52			10 17	10 22
Stoke-on-Trent	a			07 12				08 12			08 41			09 12		09 41				10 12				10 41
Congleton	a			07 24				08 24						09 24										
Macclesfield	a			07 33				08 33			08 58			09 33		09 57				10 32				10 57
Crewe 10	a	06 25					07 54					08 54						09 54					10 38	
Wilmslow	a																							
Stockport	a			07 46				08 46			09 11			09 46		10 11				10 46				11 11
Manchester Piccadilly 10	a			08 02				09 02			09 27			10 02		10 27				11 02				11 27
Warrington Bank Quay	a	06 43					08 12					09 11						10 12					10 57	
Wigan North Western	a	07 02					08 23					09 22						10 23					11 08	
Preston 8	a	07 17					08 39					09 38						10 38					11 22	
Lancaster 6	a	07 33					08 59					09 53											11 40	
Oxenholme Lake District	a	07 47					09 16					10 08						11 11					11 53	
Penrith North Lakes	a	08 13					09 42					10 34											12 19	
Carlisle 8	a	08 31					10 00					10 52						11 50					12 37	
Lockerbie	a	08 51					10 20					11 11												
Haymarket	a											12s08												
Edinburgh 10	a		11 01			12 15						12 19	13 14				14 13							
Haymarket	a																							
Motherwell	a	09s33					11s03																	
Glasgow Central 15	a	09 59					11 27											13 16					13 59	
Inverkeithing	a																							
Kirkcaldy	a																							
Markinch	a																							
Cupar	a																							
Leuchars 3	a																							
Dundee	a																							
Arbroath	a																							
Montrose	a																							
Stonehaven	a																							
Aberdeen	a																							

For general notes see front of timetable
For details of catering facilities see Directory of Train Operators

South Coast and The South West → North West England, The North East and Scotland

Saturdays until 12 July

Route Diagram - See first page of Table 51

		VT	XC	XC	XC	XC		VT	XC	XC	VT	XC	XC	XC	VT		XC	VT	XC	XC	XC	XC	VT	XC
		1 ◇ ☕	1 ◇ ☕	1 ◇ ☕	1 ◇ ☕	1 ◇ ☕		1 ◇ ☕	1 ◇ ☕	R 1 ☕	R 1 ☕	1 ◇ ☕	1 ◇ ☕	1 ◇ ☕	1 ◇ ☕		R 1 ☕	1 ◇ ☕	1 ◇ ☕	1 ◇ ☕	1 ◇ ☕	1 ◇ ☕	1 ◇ ☕	1 ◇ ☕
Brighton 10	d																							
Haywards Heath 3	d																							
Gatwick Airport 10 ✈	d																							
Bournemouth	d									07 45							08 45							
Brockenhurst 3	d									08 00							09 00							
Southampton Central	d									08 15							09 15							
Southampton Airport Parkwy ✈	d									08 22							09 22							
Winchester	d									08 31							09 31							
Basingstoke	d									08 47							09 47							
Redhill	d																							
Guildford	d																							
East Croydon	d																							
Kensington Olympia	d																							
Reading 7	d			08 40						09 10			09 40				10 10			10 40				
Oxford	d			09 07						09 36			10 07				10 36			11 07				
Banbury	d			09 25						09 53			10 25				10 53			11 25				
Leamington Spa 8	d			09 43						10 11			10 43				11 11			11 43				
Coventry	d							10 10		10 23					11 10		11 23						12 10	
Birmingham International ✈	d					10 12		10 22		10 34					11 22		11 34					12 12	12 22	
Penzance	d																							
St Erth 2	d																							
Camborne	d																							
Redruth	d																							
Truro	d																							
St Austell	d																							
Par 3	d																							
Bodmin Parkway	d																							
Liskeard 3	d																							
Plymouth	d		06 25									07 25							08 25					
Totnes	d		06 50									07 50							08 50					
Paignton	d																							
Torquay	d																							
Newton Abbot	d		07 03									08 03							09 03					
Teignmouth	d																							
Dawlish	d																							
Exeter St Davids 6	d		07 23									08 23							09 23					
Tiverton Parkway	d		07 37									08 37							09 37					
Taunton	d		07 51									08 51							09 51					
Weston-super-Mare	d																				10 27			
Cardiff Central 7	d													09 00										
Newport (South Wales)	d													09 15										
Bristol Temple Meads 10	d		08 30		09 00							09 30		10 00					10 30		11 00			
Bristol Parkway 7	d		08 40		09 10							09 40		10 10					10 40		11 10			
Gloucester 7	d																							
Cheltenham Spa	d		09 12		09 42							10 12		10 42					11 12		11 42			
Birmingham New Street 12	a		09 57	10 18	10 26	10 30		10 36	⟵	10 45		10 57	11 18	11 26	11 36		11 45		11 57	12 18	12 26	12 30	12 36	⟵
Birmingham New Street 12	d	10 03	10 03	10 20	10 30	10 48		10 40	10 48	11 03	11 03	11 20		11 30	11 40		11 48	12 03	12 03	12 20	12 30	12 48	12 40	12 48
Tamworth	d				10 47	⟶															12 47	⟶		
Burton-on-Trent	d				10 58																12 58			
Derby 10	a		10 39		11 11					11 39				12 11					12 39		13 11			
Chesterfield	a				11 32									12 32							13 32			
Sheffield 7	a		11 15		11 50					12 15				12 50					13 15		13 50			
Doncaster 7	a				12 15									13 19							14 15			
Wakefield Westgate 7	a		11 46							12 46									13 46					
Leeds 10	a		12 02							13 02									14 02					
York 8	a		12 29		12 43					13 31				13 45					14 29		14 46			
Darlington 7	a		13 01		13 11					14 02				14 17					14 59		15 15			
Durham	a		13 18		13 28					14 19				14 35					15 16		15 33			
Chester-le-Street	a													14 42										
Newcastle 8	a		13 34		13 49					14 34				14 56					15 32		15 52			
Alnmouth	a		14 01																16 03					
Berwick-upon-Tweed	a									15 19														
Dunbar	a									15 42														
Wolverhampton 7	d	10 21		10 40					11 08		11 21	11 40					12 08	12 21		12 40				13 08
Stafford	a			10 52				11 17	11 22			11 52			12 17		12 22			12 52			13 17	13 22
Stoke-on-Trent	a			11 12					11 41			12 12					12 41			13 12				13 41
Congleton	a			11 24																13 24				
Macclesfield	a			11 33					11 57			12 32					12 57			13 33				13 57
Crewe 10	a	10 54						11 38			11 54				12 38			12 54					13 38	
Wilmslow	a																							
Stockport	a			11 46					12 11			12 46					13 11			13 46				14 11
Manchester Piccadilly 10	a			12 02					12 27			13 02					13 27			14 02				14 27
Warrington Bank Quay	a	11 11						11 57			12 13				12 56			13 11					13 57	
Wigan North Western	a	11 22						12 08			12 24				13 07			13 22					14 08	
Preston 8	a	11 37						12 22			12 39				13 24			13 36					14 23	
Lancaster 6	a	11 54						12 39			12 55				13 39			13 55					14 39	
Oxenholme Lake District	a							12 54										14 10					14 53	
Penrith North Lakes	a	12 31						13 20			13 32												15 19	
Carlisle 8	a	12 49						13 38			13 52							14 50					15 37	
Lockerbie	a	13 09									14 12							15 09						
Haymarket	a	14s04																16s09						
Edinburgh 10	a	14 14	15 10							16b19								16 19	17 14					
Haymarket	a									16 33														
Motherwell	a																						16s34	
Glasgow Central 15	a							14 58			15 17												16 58	
Inverkeithing	a									16 47														
Kirkcaldy	a									17 02														
Markinch	a									17 11														
Cupar	a									17 24														
Leuchars 3	a									17 31														
Dundee	a									17 44														
Arbroath	a									18 01														
Montrose	a									18 15														
Stonehaven	a									18 35														
Aberdeen	a									19 00														

For general notes see front of timetable
For details of catering facilities see Directory of Train Operators

b Dep. 1630

Saturdays

South Coast and The South West → North West England, The North East and Scotland

until 12 July

Route Diagram - See first page of Table 51

Station		XC	VT	XC	XC	XC	VT	XC	XC	VT	XC	XC	XC	VT	XC	XC	XC	VT	XC	XC	XC
			R			R			R	R							R	R			
		1 ◇	1	1 ◇	1 ◇	1	1 ◇	1 ◇	1	1	1 ◇	1 ◇	1 ◇	1 ◇	1 ◇	1 ◇	1	1	1 ◇	1 ◇	1 ◇
																	A				
		🍴	🍴	🍴	🍴	🍴	🍴	🍴	🍴	🍴	🍴	🍴	🍴	🍴	🍴	🍴	🍴	🍴	🍴	🍴	🍴
Brighton 10	d				09 15																
Haywards Heath 3	d				09 34																
Gatwick Airport 10	d				09 46																
Bournemouth	d	09 45						10 45								11 45					
Brockenhurst 3	d	10 00						11 00								12 00					
Southampton Central	d	10 15						11 15								12 15					
Southampton Airport Parkwy	d	10 22						11 22								12 22					
Winchester	d	10 31						11 31								12 31					
Basingstoke	d	10 47						11 47								12 47					
Redhill	d																				
Guildford	d																				
East Croydon	d				10 03																
Kensington Olympia	d				10 33																
Reading 7	d				11 40						12 40					13 10			13 40		
Oxford	d				12 07						13 07					13 36			14 07		
Banbury	d				12 25						13 25					13 53			14 25		
Leamington Spa 8	d				12 43						13 43					14 11			14 43		
Coventry	d						13 10							14 10		14 23					
Birmingham International	d						13 22						14 12	14 22		14 34					
Penzance	d					08 05															
St Erth 2	d					08 14															
Camborne	d					08 24															
Redruth	d					08 31															
Truro	d					08 44															
St Austell	d					09 00															
Par 3	d																				
Bodmin Parkway	d					09 16															
Liskeard 3	d					09 29															
Plymouth	d					09 57											11 25				
Totnes	d																				
Paignton	d			09 30					10 32												
Torquay	d			09 37					10 39												
Newton Abbot	d			09 51																	
Teignmouth	d			09 59																	
Dawlish	d			10 06																	
Exeter St Davids 6	d			10 23		11 00			11 10								12 23				
Tiverton Parkway	d																				
Taunton	d								11 33												
Weston-super-Mare	d								12 00												
Cardiff Central 7	d																				
Newport (South Wales)	d																				
Bristol Temple Meads 10	d			11 30		12 00			12 30			13 00					13 30				14 00
Bristol Parkway 7	d			11 40		12 10			12 40			13 10									14 10
Gloucester 7	d																				
Cheltenham Spa	d			12 12		12 42			13 12			13 42									14 42
Birmingham New Street 12	a	12 45		12 57	13 18	13 26	13 36	13 45	13 57		14 18	14 26	14 30	14 36	←	14 45	14 57		15 18	←	15 26
Birmingham New Street 12	d	13 03	13 03	13 20		13 30	13 40	13 48	14 03	14 03	14 20	14 30	14 48	14 40	14 48	15 20	15 03	15 03		15 20	15 30
Tamworth	d											14 47	→			→					
Burton-on-Trent	d											14 58									
Derby 10	a	13 39				14 11			14 39			15 11					15 39				16 11
Chesterfield	a					14 32						15 32									16 32
Sheffield 7	a	14 15				14 50			15 15			15 50					16 15				16 50
Doncaster 7	a					15 15						16 15									17 19
Wakefield Westgate 7	a	14 46							15 46								16 46				
Leeds 10	a	15 02							16 02								17 02				
York 8	a	15 29				15 43			16 29			16 44					17 31				17 46
Darlington 7	a	16 00				16 12			17 02			17 12					18 02				18 15
Durham	a	16 17				16 30			17 21			17 29					18 20				18 32
Chester-le-Street	a											17 36									18 38
Newcastle 8	a	16 33				16 51			17 40			17 48					18 40				18 50
Alnmouth	a											18 24									
Berwick-upon-Tweed	a	17 18																			19 34
Dunbar	a	17 41																			19 57
Wolverhampton 7	d		13 21	13 40				14 08		14 21	14 40				15 08			15 21		15 40	
Stafford	a			13 52			14 18	14 22			14 52			15 17	15 22					15 52	
Stoke-on-Trent	a			14 12				14 41			15 12				15 41					16 12	
Congleton	a										15 24										
Macclesfield	a			14 32				14 57			15 33				15 57					16 32	
Crewe 10	a		13 54				14 39			14 54				15 38				15 54			
Wilmslow	a																				
Stockport	a			14 46				15 11			15 46				16 11					16 46	
Manchester Piccadilly 10	a			15 02				15 27			16 02				16 27					17 02	
Warrington Bank Quay	a		14 12				14 57			15 12				15 56				16 12			
Wigan North Western	a		14 23				15 08			15 23				16 07				16 23			
Preston 8	a		14 39				15 22			15 39				16 22				16 39			
Lancaster 6	a		14 54				15 39			15 54				16 38				16 57			
Oxenholme Lake District	a		15 09				15 52							16 52				17 12			
Penrith North Lakes	a		15 36				16 18			16 33				17 18				17 38			
Carlisle 8	a		15 54				16 36			16 49				17 36				17 56			
Lockerbie	a																	18 17			
Haymarket	a									18s05											
Edinburgh 10	a	18 11								18 15		19b26									20 27
Haymarket	a											19 43									
Motherwell	a		16s53				17s34											19s00			
Glasgow Central 15	a		17 18				17 57							18 58				19 27			
Inverkeithing	a											19 58									
Kirkcaldy	a											20 14									
Markinch	a											20 23									
Cupar	a											20 37									
Leuchars 3	a											20 44									
Dundee	a											21 12									
Arbroath	a																				
Montrose	a																				
Stonehaven	a																				
Aberdeen	a																				

For general notes see front of timetable
For details of catering facilities see Directory of Train Operators

A From Newquay dep. 0940 (Table 135)
b Dep. 1939

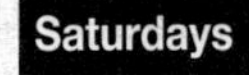

until 12 July

South Coast and The South West → North West England, The North East and Scotland

Route Diagram - See first page of Table 51

		VT	XC	VT	XC	XC	XC	XC	VT	XC	XC	VT	XC	XC	XC	VT	XC	XC	VT	XC	XC	XC
			R		R							R	R					R	R			
		1 ◇	1	1 ◇	1	1 ◇	1 ◇	1 ◇	1 ◇	1 ◇	1 ◇	1	1	1 ◇	1 ◇	1 ◇	1 ◇	1	1	1 ◇	1 ◇	1 ◇
Brighton 10	d																			14 22		
Haywards Heath 3	d																			14b32		
Gatwick Airport 10 ✈	d																			14 52		
Bournemouth	d		12 45								13 45						14 45					
Brockenhurst 3	d		13 00								14 00						15 00					
Southampton Central	d		13 15								14 15						15 15					
Southampton Airport Parkwy ✈	d		13 22								14 22						15 22					
Winchester	d		13 31								14 31						15 31					
Basingstoke	d		13 47								14 47						15 47					
Redhill	d																					
Guildford	d																					
East Croydon	d																			15 08		
Kensington Olympia	d																			15 40		
Reading 7	d		14 10			14 40					15 10			15 40			16 10			16 40		
Oxford	d		14 36			15 07					15 36			16 07			16 36			17 07		
Banbury	d		14 53			15 25					15 53			16 25			16 53			17 25		
Leamington Spa 8	d		15 11			15 43					16 11			16 43			17 11			17 43		
Coventry	d	15 10	15 23						16 10		16 23					17 10	17 23					
Birmingham International ✈	d	15 22	15 34					16 12	16 22		16 34					17 22	17 34					18 12
Penzance	d												11 37									
St Erth 2	d												11 46									
Camborne	d												11 56									
Redruth	d												12 03									
Truro	d												12 15									
St Austell	d												12 31									
Par 3	d												12 39									
Bodmin Parkway	d												12 50									
Liskeard 3	d												13 02									
Plymouth	d												13 30					14 25				
Totnes	d																	14 50				
Paignton	d				12 30										14 10							
Torquay	d				12 39										14 17							
Newton Abbot	d				12 50													15 03				
Teignmouth	d				12 59										14 34							
Dawlish	d				13 05										14 41							
Exeter St Davids 6	d				13 23								14 23		14 55			15 23				
Tiverton Parkway	d				13 37										15 08			15 37				
Taunton	d				13 51										15 23			15 51				
Weston-super-Mare	d																					
Cardiff Central 7	d																					
Newport (South Wales)	d																					
Bristol Temple Meads 10	d				14 30		15 00						15 30		16 00			16 30			17 00	
Bristol Parkway 7	d				14 40		15 10						15 40		16 10			16 40			17 10	
Gloucester 7	d																					
Cheltenham Spa	d				15 12		15 42						16 12		16 42			17 12			17 42	
Birmingham New Street 12	a	15 36	15 45		15 57	16 18	16 26	16 30	16 36	←	16 45		16 57	17 18	17 26	17 36	17 45	17 57		18 18	18 26	18 30
Birmingham New Street 12	d	15 40	15 48	16 03	16 03	16 20	16 30	16 48 →	16 40	16 48	17 03	17 03	17 20		17 30	17 40	17 48	18 03	18 03	18 20	18 30	18 48 →
Tamworth	d						16 47											18 19			18 47	
Burton-on-Trent	d						16 58											18 29			18 58	
Derby 10	a				16 39		17 11				17 39				18 11			18 42			19 11	
Chesterfield	a						17 32								18 32			19 01			19 32	
Sheffield 7	a				17 15		17 50				18 15				18 50			19 16			19 50	
Doncaster 7	a						18 21								19 18						20 16	
Wakefield Westgate 7	a				17 46						18 46							19 46				
Leeds 10	a				18 02						19 02							20 02				
York 8	a				18 29		18 46				19 32				19 49			20 29			20 43	
Darlington 7	a				18 59		19 14				20 03				20 17			21 04			21 15	
Durham	a				19 16		19 31				20 22				20 34			21 22			22 11	
Chester-le-Street	a														20 41						22 18	
Newcastle 8	a				19 32		19 52				20 37				20 53			21 42			22 33	
Alnmouth	a				20 02						21 03											
Berwick-upon-Tweed	a				20 22						21 24				21 36							
Dunbar	a														21 59							
Wolverhampton 7	d		16 08	16 21		16 40				17 08		17 21	17 40				18 08		18 20	18 40		
Stafford	a	16 17	16 22			16 52			17 17	17 22			17 52			18 17	18 22			18 52		
Stoke-on-Trent	a		16 41			17 12				17 41			18 12				18 41			19 12		
Congleton	a					17 24														19 24		
Macclesfield	a		16 57			17 33				17 57			18 32				18 57			19 33		
Crewe 10	a	16 38		16 54					17 38			17 54				18 38			18 54			
Wilmslow	a																					
Stockport	a		17 11			17 46				18 11			18 46				19 11			19 46		
Manchester Piccadilly 10	a		17 27			18 02				18 27			19 02				19 27			20 02		
Warrington Bank Quay	a	16 57		17 12					17 57			18 12				18 57			19 12			
Wigan North Western	a	17 08		17 23					18 08			18 23				19 08			19 24			
Preston 8	a	17 23		17 39					18 22			18 39				19 25			19 43			
Lancaster 6	a	17 40		17 55					18 39			18 59				19 39						
Oxenholme Lake District	a			18 09					18 52			19 14				19 52						
Penrith North Lakes	a								19 19							20 18						
Carlisle 8	a	18 29		18 55					19 36			19 55				20 41						
Lockerbie	a			19 15																		
Haymarket	a			20s12																		
Edinburgh 10	a			20 22	21 14						22 13				22 29							
Haymarket	a				21s18																	
Motherwell	a								20s39													
Glasgow Central 15	a	19 57			22 23				21 00			21 13										
Inverkeithing	a																					
Kirkcaldy	a																					
Markinch	a																					
Cupar	a																					
Leuchars 3	a																					
Dundee	a																					
Arbroath	a																					
Montrose	a																					
Stonehaven	a																					
Aberdeen	a																					

For general notes see front of timetable
For details of catering facilities see Directory of Train Operators

b Change at East Croydon

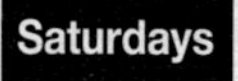

until 12 July

South Coast and The South West → North West England, The North East and Scotland

Route Diagram - See first page of Table 51

Station		VT	XC	XC	VT	XC	XC	XC	VT	XC	XC	XC	XC	XC	XC	XC	XC	XC	XC	XC
		1 ◇	1 ◇	1 ◇	R 1	R 1	1 ◇	1 ◇	1 ◇	1 ◇	R 1	1 ◇	1 ◇	1 ◇	R 1	1 ◇	1 ◇	1 ◇	1 ◇	1 ◇
															A					
Brighton 10	d																			
Haywards Heath 3	d																			
Gatwick Airport 10 ✈	d											*17 03*								
Bournemouth	d			15 45						16 45				17 45			18 45			19 45
Brockenhurst 3	d			16 00						17 00				18 00			19 00			20 00
Southampton Central	d			16 15						17 15				18 15			19 15			20 15
Southampton Airport Parkwy ✈	d			16 22						17 22				18 22			19 22			20 22
Winchester	d			16 31						17 31				18 31			19 31			20 31
Basingstoke	d			16 47						17 47				18 47			19 47			20 47
Redhill	d											*17 14*								
Guildford	d											17 58								
East Croydon	d																			
Kensington Olympia	d																			
Reading 7	d			17 10			17 40			18 10		18 40		19 10		19 40	20 10			21 10
Oxford	d			17 36			18 07			18 36		19 07		19 36		20 07	20 36			21 36
Banbury	d			17 53			18 25			18 53		19 25		19 53		20 25	20 53			21 53
Leamington Spa 8	d			18 11			18 43			19 11		19 43		20 11		20 43	21 11			22 11
Coventry	d	18 10		18 23					19 16	19 23				20 23			21 23			22 23
Birmingham International ✈	d	18 22		18 34					19 28	19 34				20 34			21 34			22 34
Penzance	d																			
St Erth 2	d																			
Camborne	d																			
Redruth	d																			
Truro	d																			
St Austell	d																			
Par 3	d																			
Bodmin Parkway	d														16 29					
Liskeard 3	d														16 44					
Plymouth	d														17 25			18 25		
Totnes	d														17 50			18 50		
Paignton	d					15 39					16 35								19 03	
Torquay	d					15 46					16 42								19 09	
Newton Abbot	d					15 59					16 53							19 03	19 20	
Teignmouth	d					16 07					17 02								19 27	
Dawlish	d					16 12					17 08								19 32	
Exeter St Davids 6	d					16 26					17 23				18 23			19 23	19 45	
Tiverton Parkway	d										17 37							19 36	19 59	
Taunton	d					16 50					17 51							19 51	20 13	
Weston-super-Mare	d																		20 39	
Cardiff Central 7	d																			
Newport (South Wales)	d																			
Bristol Temple Meads 10	d					17 30		18 00			18 30		19 00		19 30			20 30	21 00	
Bristol Parkway 7	d					17 40		18 10			18 40		19 10		19 40			20 40	21 10	
Gloucester 7	d																			
Cheltenham Spa	d					18 12		18 42			19 12		19 42		20 12			21 12	21 42	
Birmingham New Street 12	a	18 36	⟵	18 45		18 57	19 18	19 26	19 39	19 45	19 57	20 18	20 26	20 45	20 57	21 22	21 45	22 03	22 26	22 50
Birmingham New Street 12	d	18 40	18 48	19 03	19 03	19 20		19 30	19 48	20 03	20 03	20 20	20 48	20 50	21 20		22 20		22 33	
Tamworth	d							19 47			20 19			21 23					22 49	
Burton-on-Trent	d							19 58			20 29			21 33					22 59	
Derby 10	a			19 39				20 11			20 42			21 45					23 16	
Chesterfield	a			20 01				20 36			21 01			22 04						
Sheffield 7	a			20 18				20 50			21 18			22 19						
Doncaster 7	a																			
Wakefield Westgate 7	a			20 48							21 46			22s46						
Leeds 10	a			21 05							22 02			23 09						
York 8	a			21 35				21 49			22 36									
Darlington 7	a							22 22												
Durham	a			22 48				22 42												
Chester-le-Street	a																			
Newcastle 8	a			23 11				23 07												
Alnmouth	a																			
Berwick-upon-Tweed	a																			
Dunbar	a																			
Wolverhampton 7	d		19 08		19 21	19 40			20 09	20 21		20 40	21 08		21 40		22 40			
Stafford	a	19 17	19 22		19 33	19 52			20 23	20 33		20 52	21 22		21 52		22 52			
Stoke-on-Trent	a		19 41			20 12			20 43			21 12								
Congleton	a											21 24								
Macclesfield	a		19 57			20 32			20 59			21 33								
Crewe 10	a	19 38			19 54					20 55					22 20					
Wilmslow	a									21 12			21 57		22 40		23 39			
Stockport	a		20 11			20 46			21s13	21 22		21 46	22 11		22 50		23s49			
Manchester Piccadilly 10	a		20 27			21 02			21 26	21 36		22 02	22 27		23 07		00 06			
Warrington Bank Quay	a	19 57			20 12															
Wigan North Western	a	20 08			20 23															
Preston 8	a	20 26			20 43															
Lancaster 6	a																			
Oxenholme Lake District	a																			
Penrith North Lakes	a																			
Carlisle 8	a																			
Lockerbie	a																			
Haymarket	a																			
Edinburgh 10	a																			
Haymarket	a																			
Motherwell	a																			
Glasgow Central 15	a																			
Inverkeithing	a																			
Kirkcaldy	a																			
Markinch	a																			
Cupar	a																			
Leuchars 3	a																			
Dundee	a																			
Arbroath	a																			
Montrose	a																			
Stonehaven	a																			
Aberdeen	a																			

For general notes see front of timetable
For details of catering facilities see Directory of Train Operators

A From Newquay dep. 1522 (Table 135)

South Coast and The South West → North West England, The North East and Scotland

19 July to 6 September

Route Diagram - See first page of Table 51

		VT	XC	XC	XC	XC	VT	XC	XC	XC	VT	XC	XC	XC	XC	XC	VT	XC	XC	XC	XC	VT	XC
		1 ◇	1 ◇	1 ◇	1 ◇	1 ◇	1 ◇	1 ◇	1 ◇	1 ◇	1 ◇	1 ◇	1 ◇	1 ◇	1 ◇	1 ◇	1 ◇	1 ◇	1 ◇	1 ◇	1 ◇	1 ◇	1 ◇
Brighton 10	d												03 50										
Haywards Heath 3	d												04 25										
Gatwick Airport 10 ✈	d												05 15						05 45				
Bournemouth	d																				06 37		
Brockenhurst 3	d																				06 54		
Southampton Central	d															06 15					07 15		
Southampton Airport Parkway ✈	d															06 22					07 22		
Winchester	d															06 31					07 31		
Basingstoke	d															06 47					07 47		
Redhill	d												05 33						05 52				
Guildford	d												06 00										
East Croydon	d																		06 07				
Kensington Olympia	d																		06 51				
Reading 7	d												06 40			07 10			07 40		08 10		
Oxford	d												07 07			07 36			08 07		08 36		
Banbury	d												07 25			07 53			08 25		08 53		
Leamington Spa 8	d												07 43			08 11			08 43		09 11		
Coventry	d															08 23					09 23		
Birmingham International ✈	d															08 34					09 34		
Penzance	d																						
St Erth 2	d																						
Camborne	d																						
Redruth	d																						
Truro	d																						
St Austell	d																						
Par 3	d																						
Bodmin Parkway	d																						
Liskeard 3	d																						
Plymouth	d																						06 25
Totnes	d																						06 50
Paignton	d																						
Torquay	d																						
Newton Abbot	d																						07 03
Teignmouth	d																						
Dawlish	d																						
Exeter St Davids 6	d																						07 23
Tiverton Parkway	d																						07 37
Taunton	d																						07 51
Weston-super-Mare	d																						
Cardiff Central 7	d																						
Newport (South Wales)	d																						
Bristol Temple Meads 10	d											06 15						07 30		08 00			08 30
Bristol Parkway 7	d											06 25						07 40		08 10			08 40
Gloucester 7	d											07 01											
Cheltenham Spa	d											07 12						08 12		08 42			09 12
Birmingham New Street 12	a											07 57	08 18			08 45		08 57	09 18	09 26	09 45		09 57
Birmingham New Street 12	d	05 30	06 00	06 20	06 30	07 03	07 03	07 20	07 30	07 48	08 03	08 03	08 20	08 30	08 48	09 03	09 03	09 20		09 30	09 48	10 03	10 03
Tamworth	d		06 16		06 47	07 19			07 47			08 19		08 47						09 47			
Burton-on-Trent	d		06 26		06 58	07 29			07 58			08 29		08 58						09 58			
Derby 10	a		06 39		07 11	07 42			08 11			08 42		09 11		09 39				10 11			10 39
Chesterfield	a				07 32	08 01			08 32			09 01		09 32						10 32			
Sheffield 7	a		07 09		07 50	08 17			08 50			09 17		09 50		10 15				10 50			11 15
Doncaster 7	a				08 23				09 21					10 18						11 16			
Wakefield Westgate 7	a		07 36			08 46						09 46				10 46							11 46
Leeds 10	a		07 52			09 02						10 02				11 02							12 02
York 8	a		08 24		08 50	09 30			09 45			10 29		10 45		11 31				11 45			12 29
Darlington 7	a		08 52		09 18	10 00			10 13			11 00		11 16		12 01				12 15			13 01
Durham	a		09 09		09 36	10 17			10 30			11 17		11 33		12 18				12 33			13 18
Chester-le-Street	a				09 43				10 37											12 40			
Newcastle 8	a		09 25		09 59	10 33			10 54			11 32		11 53		12 35				12 56			13 34
Alnmouth	a		09 54									12 01											14 01
Berwick-upon-Tweed	a					11 18										13 18							
Dunbar	a					11 41										13 41							
Wolverhampton 7 🚊	d	05 49		06 40			07 21	07 40		08 06	08 21		08 40		09 08		09 21	09 40			10 08	10 21	
Stafford	a	06 04		06 52			07 33	07 52		08 17			08 52		09 22			09 52			10 22		
Stoke-on-Trent	a			07 12				08 12		08 36			09 12		09 41			10 12			10 41		
Congleton	a			07 24				08 24					09 24										
Macclesfield	a			07 33				08 33		08 52			09 33		09 57			10 32			10 57		
Crewe 10	a	06 25					07 54				08 54						09 54					10 54	
Wilmslow	a																						
Stockport	a			07 46				08 46		09 05			09 46		10 11			10 46			11 11		
Manchester Piccadilly 10 🚊	a			08 02				09 02		09 20			10 02		10 27			11 02			11 27		
Warrington Bank Quay	a	06 43					08 12				09 11						10 12					11 11	
Wigan North Western	a	07 02					08 23				09 22						10 23					11 22	
Preston 8	a	07 17					08 39				09 38						10 38					11 37	
Lancaster 6	a	07 33					08 59				09 53											11 54	
Oxenholme Lake District	a	07 47					09 16				10 08						11 11						
Penrith North Lakes	a	08 13					09 42				10 34											12 31	
Carlisle 8	a	08 31					10 00				10 52						11 50					12 49	
Lockerbie	a	08 51					10 20				11 11											13 09	
Haymarket	a										12s08											14s04	
Edinburgh 10	a		11 01			12 15					12 19	13 14				14 13						14 14	15 10
Haymarket	a																						
Motherwell	a	09s33					11s03																
Glasgow Central 15	a	09 59					11 27										13 16						
Inverkeithing	a																						
Kirkcaldy	a																						
Markinch	a																						
Cupar	a																						
Leuchars 3	a																						
Dundee	a																						
Arbroath	a																						
Montrose	a																						
Stonehaven	a																						
Aberdeen	a																						

For general notes see front of timetable
For details of catering facilities see Directory of Train Operators

Due to Engineering Operations, services from Saturday 13 September on this Table had not been confirmed at time of going to press. These services will be issued in a special Supplement as soon as exact timings have been confirmed

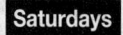

South Coast and The South West → North West England, The North East and Scotland

19 July to 6 September

Route Diagram - See first page of Table 51

		XC	XC	XC	XC	VT	XC	XC	XC	XC	VT	XC	XC	XC	XC	XC	VT	XC	XC	XC	XC	XC	VT
		1◇	1◇	1◇	R 1	R 1	1◇	1◇	1◇	R 1	1◇	1◇	1◇	1◇	1◇	1◇	R 1	1◇	1◇	R 1	1◇	R 1	R 1
Brighton [10]	d																		09 15				
Haywards Heath [3]	d																		09 34				
Gatwick Airport [10] ✈	d																		09 46				
Bournemouth	d				07 45					08 45						09 45					10 45		
Brockenhurst [3]	d				08 00					09 00						10 00					11 00		
Southampton Central	d				08 15					09 15						10 15					11 15		
Southampton Airport Parkwy ✈	d				08 22					09 22						10 22					11 22		
Winchester	d				08 31					09 31						10 31					11 31		
Basingstoke	d				08 47					09 47						10 47					11 47		
Redhill	d																						
Guildford	d																						
East Croydon	d																		10 03				
Kensington Olympia	d																		10 33				
Reading [7]	d	08 40			09 10			09 40		10 10			10 40						11 40				
Oxford	d	09 07			09 36			10 07		10 36			11 07						12 07				
Banbury	d	09 25			09 53			10 25		10 53			11 25						12 25				
Leamington Spa [8]	d	09 43			10 11			10 43		11 11			11 43						12 43				
Coventry	d				10 23					11 23													
Birmingham International ✈	d			10 09	10 34					11 34					12 09								
Penzance	d																			08 05			
St Erth [2]	d																			08 14			
Camborne	d																			08 24			
Redruth	d																			08 31			
Truro	d																			08 44			
St Austell	d																			09 00			
Par [3]	d																						
Bodmin Parkway	d																			09 16			
Liskeard [3]	d																			09 29			
Plymouth	d						07 25					08 25								09 57			
Totnes	d						07 50					08 50											
Paignton	d																	09 30				10 32	
Torquay	d																	09 37				10 39	
Newton Abbot	d						08 03					09 03						09 51					
Teignmouth	d																	09 59					
Dawlish	d																	10 06					
Exeter St Davids [6]	d						08 23					09 23						10 23		11 00		11 10	
Tiverton Parkway	d						08 37					09 37											
Taunton	d						08 51					09 51										11 33	
Weston-super-Mare	d													10 27								12 00	
Cardiff Central [7]	d								09 00														
Newport (South Wales)	d								09 15														
Bristol Temple Meads [10]	d		09 00				09 30		10 00			10 30		11 00				11 30		12 00		12 30	
Bristol Parkway [7]	d		09 10				09 40		10 10			10 40		11 10				11 40		12 10		12 40	
Gloucester [7]	d																						
Cheltenham Spa	d		09 42				10 12		10 42			11 12		11 42				12 12		12 42		13 12	
Birmingham New Street [12]	a	10 18	10 26	10 20	10 45		10 57	11 18	11 26	11 45		11 57	12 18	12 26	12 20	12 45		12 57	13 18	13 26	13 45	13 57	
Birmingham New Street [12]	d	10 20	10 30	10 48	11 03	11 03	11 20		11 30	11 48	12 03	12 03	12 20	12 30	12 48	13 03	13 03	13 20		13 30	13 48	14 03	14 03
Tamworth	d		10 47											12 47									
Burton-on-Trent	d		10 58											12 58									
Derby [10]	a		11 11		11 39				12 11			12 39		13 11		13 39				14 11		14 39	
Chesterfield	a		11 32						12 32					13 32						14 32			
Sheffield [7]	a		11 50		12 15				12 50			13 15		13 50		14 15				14 50		15 15	
Doncaster [7]	a		12 15						13 19					14 15						15 15			
Wakefield Westgate [7]	a				12 46							13 46				14 46						15 46	
Leeds [10]	a				13 02							14 02				15 02						16 02	
York [8]	a		12 43		13 31				13 45			14 29		14 46		15 29				15 43		16 29	
Darlington [7]	a		13 11		14 02				14 17			14 59		15 15		16 00				16 12		17 02	
Durham	a		13 28		14 19				14 35			15 16		15 33		16 17				16 30		17 21	
Chester-le-Street	a								14 42														
Newcastle [8]	a		13 49		14 34				14 56			15 32		15 52		16 33				16 51		17 40	
Alnmouth	a											16 03											
Berwick-upon-Tweed	a				15 19											17 18							
Dunbar	a				15 42											17 41							
Wolverhampton [7] 🚢	d	10 40		11 08		11 21	11 40			12 08	12 21		12 40		13 08		13 21	13 40			14 08		14 21
Stafford	a	10 52		11 22			11 52			12 22			12 52		13 22			13 52			14 22		
Stoke-on-Trent	a	11 12		11 41			12 12			12 41			13 12		13 41			14 12			14 41		
Congleton	a	11 24											13 24										
Macclesfield	a	11 33		11 57			12 32			12 57			13 33		13 57			14 32			14 57		
Crewe [10]	a					11 54					12 54						13 54						14 54
Wilmslow	a																						
Stockport	a	11 46		12 11			12 46			13 11			13 46		14 11			14 46			15 11		
Manchester Piccadilly [10] 🚢	a	12 02		12 27			13 02			13 27			14 02		14 27			15 02			15 27		
Warrington Bank Quay	a					12 13					13 11						14 12						15 12
Wigan North Western	a					12 24					13 22						14 23						15 23
Preston [8]	a					12 39					13 36						14 39						15 39
Lancaster [6]	a					12 55					13 55						14 54						15 54
Oxenholme Lake District	a										14 10						15 09						
Penrith North Lakes	a					13 32											15 36						16 33
Carlisle [8]	a					13 52					14 50						15 54						16 49
Lockerbie	a					14 12					15 09												
Haymarket	a										16s09												18s05
Edinburgh [10]	a				16b19						16 19	17 14				18 11							18 15
Haymarket	a				16 33																		
Motherwell	a																16s53						
Glasgow Central [15]	a					15 17											17 18						
Inverkeithing	a				16 47																		
Kirkcaldy	a				17 02																		
Markinch	a				17 11																		
Cupar	a				17 24																		
Leuchars [3]	a				17 31																		
Dundee	a				17 44																		
Arbroath	a				18 01																		
Montrose	a				18 15																		
Stonehaven	a				18 35																		
Aberdeen	a				19 00																		

For general notes see front of timetable
For details of catering facilities see
Directory of Train Operators

b Dep. 1630

Due to Engineering Operations, services from Saturday 13 September on this Table had not been confirmed at time of going to press. These services will be issued in a special Supplement as soon as exact timings have been confirmed

South Coast and The South West → North West England, The North East and Scotland

19 July to 6 September

Route Diagram - See first page of Table 51

		XC	XC	XC	XC	XC	VT	XC	XC	XC	XC	VT	XC	XC	XC	XC	XC	VT	XC	XC	XC	XC
						R	R				R		R					R	R			
		1◇	1◇	1◇	1◇	1	1	1◇	1◇	1◇	1	1◇	1	1◇	1◇	1◇	1◇	1	1	1◇	1◇	1◇
						A																
Brighton 10	d																					
Haywards Heath 3	d																					
Gatwick Airport 10 ✈	d																					
Bournemouth	d				11 45						12 45						13 45					14 45
Brockenhurst 3	d				12 00						13 00						14 00					15 00
Southampton Central	d				12 15						13 15						14 15					15 15
Southampton Airport Parkwy ✈	d				12 22						13 22						14 22					15 22
Winchester	d				12 31						13 31						14 31					15 31
Basingstoke	d				12 47						13 47						14 47					15 47
Redhill	d																					
Guildford	d																					
East Croydon	d																					
Kensington Olympia	d																					
Reading 7	d	12 40			13 10			13 40			14 10			14 40			15 10			15 40		16 10
Oxford	d	13 07			13 36			14 07			14 36			15 07			15 36			16 07		16 36
Banbury	d	13 25			13 53			14 25			14 53			15 25			15 53			16 25		16 53
Leamington Spa 8	d	13 43			14 11			14 43			15 11			15 43			16 11			16 43		17 11
Coventry	d				14 23						15 23						16 23					17 23
Birmingham International ✈	d			14 09	14 34						15 34					16 09	16 34					17 34
Penzance	d																		11 37			
St Erth 2	d																		11 46			
Camborne	d																		11 56			
Redruth	d																		12 03			
Truro	d																		12 15			
St Austell	d																		12 31			
Par 3	d																		12 39			
Bodmin Parkway	d																		12 50			
Liskeard 3	d																		13 02			
Plymouth	d					11 25													13 30			
Totnes	d																					
Paignton	d												12 30								14 10	
Torquay	d												12 39								14 17	
Newton Abbot	d												12 50									
Teignmouth	d												12 59								14 34	
Dawlish	d												13 05								14 41	
Exeter St Davids 6	d					12 23							13 23						14 23		14 55	
Tiverton Parkway	d												13 37								15 08	
Taunton	d												13 51								15 23	
Weston-super-Mare	d																					
Cardiff Central 7	d																					
Newport (South Wales)	d																					
Bristol Temple Meads 10	d		13 00			13 30				14 00			14 30		15 00				15 30		16 00	
Bristol Parkway 7	d		13 10							14 10			14 40		15 10				15 40		16 10	
Gloucester 7	d																					
Cheltenham Spa	d		13 42							14 42			15 12		15 42				16 12		16 42	
Birmingham New Street 12	a	14 18	14 26	14 20	14 45	14 57		15 18	←	15 26	15 45		15 57	16 18	16 26	16 20	16 45		16 57	17 18	17 26	17 45
Birmingham New Street 12	d	14 20	14 30	14 48	15 20 →	15 03	15 03		15 20	15 30	15 48	16 03	16 03	16 20	16 30	16 48	17 03	17 03	17 20		17 30	17 48
Tamworth	d		14 47												16 47							
Burton-on-Trent	d		14 58												16 58							
Derby 10	a		15 11			15 39				16 11			16 39		17 11		17 39				18 11	
Chesterfield	a		15 32							16 32					17 32						18 32	
Sheffield 7	a		15 50			16 15				16 50			17 15		17 50		18 15				18 50	
Doncaster 7	a		16 15							17 19					18 21						19 18	
Wakefield Westgate 7	a					16 46							17 46				18 46					
Leeds 10	a					17 02							18 02				19 02					
York 8	a		16 44			17 31				17 46			18 29		18 46		19 32				19 49	
Darlington 7	a		17 12			18 02				18 15			18 59		19 14		20 03				20 17	
Durham	a		17 29			18 20				18 32			19 16		19 31		20 22				20 34	
Chester-le-Street	a		17 36							18 38											20 41	
Newcastle 8	a		17 48			18 40				18 50			19 32		19 52		20 37				20 53	
Alnmouth	a		18 24										20 02				21 03					
Berwick-upon-Tweed	a									19 34			20 22				21 24				21 36	
Dunbar	a									19 57											21 59	
Wolverhampton 7	d	14 40		15 08			15 21		15 40		16 08	16 21		16 40		17 08		17 21	17 40			18 08
Stafford	a	14 52		15 22					15 52		16 22			16 52		17 22			17 52			18 22
Stoke-on-Trent	a	15 12		15 41					16 12		16 41			17 12		17 41			18 12			18 41
Congleton	a	15 24												17 24								
Macclesfield	a	15 33		15 57					16 32		16 57			17 33		17 57			18 32			18 57
Crewe 10	a						15 54					16 54						17 54				
Wilmslow	a																					
Stockport	a	15 46		16 11					16 46		17 11			17 46		18 11			18 46			19 11
Manchester Piccadilly 10	a	16 02		16 27					17 02		17 27			18 02		18 27			19 02			19 27
Warrington Bank Quay	a						16 12					17 12						18 12				
Wigan North Western	a						16 23					17 23						18 23				
Preston 8	a						16 39					17 39						18 39				
Lancaster 6	a						16 57					17 55						18 59				
Oxenholme Lake District	a						17 12					18 09						19 14				
Penrith North Lakes	a						17 38															
Carlisle 8	a						17 56					18 55						19 55				
Lockerbie	a						18 17					19 15										
Haymarket	a											20s12										
Edinburgh 10	a		19b26							20 27		20 22	21 14				22 13				22 29	
Haymarket	a		19 43										21s18									
Motherwell	a						19s00															
Glasgow Central 15	a						19 27						22 23					21 13				
Inverkeithing	a		19 58																			
Kirkcaldy	a		20 14																			
Markinch	a		20 23																			
Cupar	a		20 37																			
Leuchars 3	a		20 44																			
Dundee	a		21 12																			
Arbroath	a																					
Montrose	a																					
Stonehaven	a																					
Aberdeen	a																					

For general notes see front of timetable
For details of catering facilities see Directory of Train Operators

A From Newquay dep. 0940 (Table 135)
b Dep. 1939

Due to Engineering Operations, services from Saturday 13 September on this Table had not been confirmed at time of going to press. These services will be issued in a special Supplement as soon as exact timings have been confirmed

Table 51 **SUMMARY OF SERVICES**

Saturdays

South Coast and The South West → North West England, The North East and Scotland

19 July to 6 September

Route Diagram - See first page of Table 51

		XC	VT	XC	XC	XC	XC	VT	XC	XC	XC	XC	XC	XC	XC	XC	XC	XC	XC	XC	XC	XC
		R	R					R	R				R				R					
		1	1	1 ◇	1 ◇	1 ◇	1 ◇	1	1	1 ◇	1 ◇	1 ◇	1	1 ◇	1 ◇	1 ◇	1	1 ◇	1 ◇	1 ◇	1 ◇	1 ◇
																	A					
		☕	☕	☕	☕	☕	☕	☕	☕	☕	☕	☕	☕	☕	☕	☕	☕	☕	☕	☕	☕	
Brighton 10	d			14 22																		
Haywards Heath 3	d			14b32																		
Gatwick Airport 10 ✈	d			14 52										*17 03*								
Bournemouth	d						15 45					16 45				17 45			18 45			19 45
Brockenhurst 3	d						16 00					17 00				18 00			19 00			20 00
Southampton Central	d						16 15					17 15				18 15			19 15			20 15
Southampton Airport Parkwy ✈	d						16 22					17 22				18 22			19 22			20 22
Winchester	d						16 31					17 31				18 31			19 31			20 31
Basingstoke	d						16 47					17 47				18 47			19 47			20 47
Redhill	d													*17 14*								
Guildford	d													17 58								
East Croydon ⛴	d			15 08																		
Kensington Olympia	d			15 40																		
Reading 7	d			16 40			17 10			17 40		18 10		18 40		19 10		19 40	20 10			21 10
Oxford	d			17 07			17 36			18 07		18 36		19 07		19 36		20 07	20 36			21 36
Banbury	d			17 25			17 53			18 25		18 53		19 25		19 53		20 25	20 53			21 53
Leamington Spa 8	d			17 43			18 11			18 43		19 11		19 43		20 11		20 43	21 11			22 11
Coventry	d						18 23					19 23				20 23			21 23			22 23
Birmingham International ✈	d					18 09	18 34					19 34				20 34			21 34			22 34
Penzance	d																					
St Erth 2	d																					
Camborne	d																					
Redruth	d																					
Truro	d																					
St Austell	d																					
Par 3	d																					
Bodmin Parkway	d																16 29					
Liskeard 3	d																16 44					
Plymouth	d	14 25															17 25			18 25		
Totnes	d	14 50															17 50			18 50		
Paignton	d								15 39				16 35								19 03	
Torquay	d								15 46				16 42								19 09	
Newton Abbot	d	15 03							15 59				16 53							19 03	19 20	
Teignmouth	d								16 07				17 02								19 27	
Dawlish	d								16 12				17 08								19 32	
Exeter St Davids 6	d	15 23							16 26				17 23				18 23			19 23	19 45	
Tiverton Parkway	d	15 37											17 37							19 36	19 59	
Taunton	d	15 51							16 50				17 51							19 51	20 13	
Weston-super-Mare	d																				20 39	
Cardiff Central 7	d																					
Newport (South Wales)	d																					
Bristol Temple Meads 10	d	16 30			17 00				17 30		18 00		18 30		19 00		19 30			20 30	21 00	
Bristol Parkway 7	d	16 40			17 10				17 40		18 10		18 40		19 10		19 40			20 40	21 10	
Gloucester 7	d																					
Cheltenham Spa	d	17 12			17 42				18 12		18 42		19 12		19 42		20 12			21 12	21 42	
Birmingham New Street 12	a	17 57		18 18	18 26	18 20	18 45		18 57	19 18	19 26	19 45	19 57	20 18	20 26	20 45	20 57	21 22	21 45	22 03	22 26	22 50
Birmingham New Street 12	d	18 03	18 03	18 20	18 30	18 48	19 03	19 03	19 20		19 30	20 03	20 03	20 20	20 48	20 50	21 20		22 20		22 33	
Tamworth	d	18 19			18 47						19 47		20 19			21 23					22 49	
Burton-on-Trent	d	18 29			18 58						19 58		20 29			21 33					22 59	
Derby 10	a	18 42			19 11		19 39				20 11		20 42			21 45					23 16	
Chesterfield	a	19 01			19 32		20 01				20 36		21 01			22 04						
Sheffield 7	a	19 16			19 50		20 18				20 50		21 18			22 19						
Doncaster 7	a				20 16																	
Wakefield Westgate 7	a	19 46					20 48						21 46			22s46						
Leeds 10	a	20 02					21 05						22 02			23 09						
York 8	a	20 29			20 43		21 35				21 49		22 36									
Darlington 7	a	21 04			21 15						22 22											
Durham	a	21 22			22 11		22 48				22 42											
Chester-le-Street	a				22 18																	
Newcastle 8	a	21 42			22 33		23 11				23 07											
Alnmouth	a																					
Berwick-upon-Tweed	a																					
Dunbar	a																					
Wolverhampton 7 ⛴	d		18 20	18 40		19 08		19 21	19 40			20 21		20 40	21 08		21 40		22 40			
Stafford	a			18 52		19 22		19 33	19 52			20 33		20 52	21 22		21 52		22 52			
Stoke-on-Trent	a			19 12		19 41			20 12					21 12	21 41				23s12			
Congleton	a			19 24										21 24								
Macclesfield	a			19 33		19 57			20 32					21 33	21 57				23s32			
Crewe 10	a		18 54					19 54				20 55					22 20					
Wilmslow	a											21 12					22 40					
Stockport	a			19 46		20 11			20 46			21 22		21 46	22 11		22 50		23s44			
Manchester Piccadilly 10 ⛴	a			20 02		20 27			21 02			21 36		22 02	22 27		23 07		00 04			
Warrington Bank Quay	a		19 12					20 12														
Wigan North Western	a		19 24					20 23														
Preston 8	a		19 43					20 43														
Lancaster 6	a																					
Oxenholme Lake District	a																					
Penrith North Lakes	a																					
Carlisle 8	a																					
Lockerbie	a																					
Haymarket	a																					
Edinburgh 10	a																					
Haymarket	a																					
Motherwell	a																					
Glasgow Central 15	a																					
Inverkeithing	a																					
Kirkcaldy	a																					
Markinch	a																					
Cupar	a																					
Leuchars 3	a																					
Dundee	a																					
Arbroath	a																					
Montrose	a																					
Stonehaven	a																					
Aberdeen	a																					

For general notes see front of timetable
For details of catering facilities see Directory of Train Operators

A From Newquay dep. 1522 (Table 135)
b Change at East Croydon

Due to Engineering Operations, services from Saturday 13 September on this Table had not been confirmed at time of going to press. These services will be issued in a special Supplement as soon as exact timings have been confirmed

South Coast and The South West → North West England, The North East and Scotland

until 13 July

Route Diagram - See first page of Table 51

		VT	XC	XC	VT	XC	XC	XC	VT	XC	XC	VT	XC	XC	XC	XC	VT	XC	XC
																		R	
		1◇	1◇	1◇	1◇	1◇	1◇	1◇	1◇	1◇	1◇	1◇	1◇	1◇	1◇	1◇	1◇	1	1◇
		🍴	🍴	🍴	🍴	🍴	🍴	🍴	🍴	🍴	🍴	🍴	🍴	🍴	🍴	🍴	🍴	🍴	🍴
Brighton 10	d																		
Haywards Heath 3	d																		
Gatwick Airport 10 ✈	d																		
Bournemouth	d													08b06				09 40	
Brockenhurst 3	d													08b34				09 57	
Southampton Central	d													08 39				10 15	
Southampton Airport Parkway ✈	d													08 46				10 22	
Winchester	d													09 23				10 31	
Basingstoke	d													09 47				10 47	
Redhill	d																		
Guildford	d																		
East Croydon	d																		
Kensington Olympia	d																		
Reading 7	d													10 10				11 10	
Oxford	d													10 36				11 36	
Banbury	d													10 53				11 53	
Leamington Spa 8	d													11 11				12 11	
Coventry	d																		
Birmingham International ✈	d																		
Penzance	d																		
St Erth 2	d																		
Camborne	d																		
Redruth	d																		
Truro	d																		
St Austell	d																		
Par 3	d																		
Bodmin Parkway	d																		
Liskeard 3	d																		
Plymouth	d																		09 25
Totnes	d																		09 50
Paignton	d																		
Torquay	d																		
Newton Abbot	d																		10 03
Teignmouth	d																		
Dawlish	d																		
Exeter St Davids 6	d																		10 23
Tiverton Parkway	d																		10 37
Taunton	d																		10 51
Weston-super-Mare	d																		
Cardiff Central 7	d																		
Newport (South Wales)	d																		
Bristol Temple Meads 10	d									09 15					10 30				11 30
Bristol Parkway 7	d									09 25					10 40				11 40
Gloucester 7	d									10 00									
Cheltenham Spa	d									10 12					11 12				12 12
Birmingham New Street 12	a									10 51				11 51	11 51	←		12 46	12 51
Birmingham New Street 12	d	08 52	09 03	09 03	09 52		10 03	10 03	10 52	11 03	11 03	11 40		12 03 →	12 03	12 03	12 52	13 03 →	13 03
Tamworth	d														12 19				
Burton-on-Trent	d														12 29				
Derby 10	a			10 24				11 22			12 22				12 46				
Chesterfield	a																		
Sheffield 7	a			11 17				12 11			13 11				13 46				
Doncaster 7	a														14 15				
Wakefield Westgate 7	a			11 47				12 41			13 42				14 33				
Leeds 10	a			12 04				13 02			14 02				15 02				
York 8	a			12 44				13 44			14 44				15 33				
Darlington 7	a			13 15				14 12			15 12				16 02				
Durham	a			13 33				14 29			15 30				16 19				
Chester-le-Street	a					←													
Newcastle 8	a			13 47 →		13 47		14 44			15 46		←		16 34				
Alnmouth	a					14 18					16 21 →		16 21						
Berwick-upon-Tweed	a							15 33							17 26				
Dunbar	a							15 56							17 52				
Wolverhampton 7	d	09 21	09 32		10 21		10 32		11 21	11 32		12 15				12 32	13 21		13c38
Stafford	a	09 33	09 44				10 44			11 44						12 44			13 51
Stoke-on-Trent	a																		14 12
Congleton	a																		
Macclesfield	a																		14 27
Crewe 10	a	10 01			10 59				11 59			12 59					13 54		
Wilmslow	a		10 25				11 25			12 24						13 25			
Stockport	a		10 35				11 35			12 34						13 35			14 41
Manchester Piccadilly 10	a		10 52				11 52			12 49						13 56			14 56
Warrington Bank Quay	a	10 18			11 17				12 15			13 16					14 11		
Wigan North Western	a	10 29			11 28				12 27			13 27					14 22		
Preston 8	a	10 44			11 42				12 44			13 42					14 38		
Lancaster 6	a				11 58				13 01			13 58					14 57		
Oxenholme Lake District	a				12 13							14 13					15 11		
Penrith North Lakes	a				12 40				13 38								15 39		
Carlisle 8	a				12 58				13 56			14 54					15 56		
Lockerbie	a				13 20							15 14							
Haymarket	a											16s12							
Edinburgh 10	a				14 29	15 25		16 26				16 19	17 27		18 22				
Haymarket	a							16 36											
Motherwell	a																		
Glasgow Central 15	a								15 16								17 19		
Inverkeithing	a							16 52											
Kirkcaldy	a							17 08											
Markinch	a							17 17											
Cupar	a							17 29											
Leuchars 3	a							17 36											
Dundee	a							17 49											
Arbroath	a							18 06											
Montrose	a							18 20											
Stonehaven	a							18 40											
Aberdeen	a							19 05											

For general notes see front of timetable
For details of catering facilities see
Directory of Train Operators

b Change at Basingstoke
c Arr. five minutes earlier

South Coast and The South West → North West England, The North East and Scotland

until 13 July

Route Diagram - See first page of Table 51

		XC	XC	VT	XC	XC	VT	XC	XC	VT	XC	XC	VT	XC	XC	XC	XC	VT	XC
		R 1	1 ◇	R 1	R 1	R 1	R 1	R 1	R 1	R 1	R 1	R 1	R 1	R 1	R 1	R 1	R 1	R 1	R 1
																A			
		🍴	🍴	🍴	🍴	🍴	🍴	🍴	🍴	🍴	🍴	🍴	🍴	🍴	🍴	🍴	🍴	🍴	🍴
Brighton 10	d		09 40																
Haywards Heath 3	d		09 52																
Gatwick Airport 10 ✈	d		10 12																
Bournemouth	d					10 40		11 40				12 40			13 40				
Brockenhurst 3	d					10 57		11 57				12 57			13 57				
Southampton Central	d					11 15		12 15				13 15			14 15				
Southampton Airport Parkwy ✈	d					11 22		12 22				13 22			14 22				
Winchester	d					11 31		12 31				13 31			14 31				
Basingstoke	d					11 47		12 47				13 47			14 47				
Redhill	d		10 33																
Guildford	d		11 03																
East Croydon	d																		
Kensington Olympia	d																		
Reading 7	d		11 40			12 10		13 10				14 10			15 10				
Oxford	d		12 07			12 36		13 36				14 36			15 36				
Banbury	d		12 25			12 53		13 53				14 53			15 53				
Leamington Spa 8	d		12 43			13 11		14 11				15 11			16 11				
Coventry	d																		
Birmingham International ✈	d																		
Penzance	d								09 30		10 30								
St Erth 2	d								09 38		10 38								
Camborne	d								09 48		10 48								
Redruth	d								09 54		10 54								
Truro	d								10 06		11 06								
St Austell	d								10 22		11 22								
Par 3	d								10 29		11 29					12 29			
Bodmin Parkway	d								10 40		11 40					12 40			
Liskeard 3	d								10 52		11 52					12 52			
Plymouth	d				10 25				11 25		12 25					13 25			
Totnes	d				10 50				11 50		12 50					13 50			
Paignton	d																		14 11
Torquay	d																		14 17
Newton Abbot	d				11 03				12 03		13 03					14 03			14 28
Teignmouth	d																		14 35
Dawlish	d																		14 40
Exeter St Davids 6	d				11 23				12 23		13 23					14 23			15 08
Tiverton Parkway	d				11 37				12 37		13 37					14 37			15 22
Taunton	d				11 51				12 51		13 51					14 51			15 36
Weston-super-Mare	d																		16 05
Cardiff Central 7	d																		
Newport (South Wales)	d																		
Bristol Temple Meads 10	d				12 30				13 30		14 30					15 30			16 30
Bristol Parkway 7	d				12 40				13 40		14 40					15 40			16 40
Gloucester 7	d																		
Cheltenham Spa	d				13 12				14 12		15 12					16 12			17 12
Birmingham New Street 12	a	←	13 15		13 51	13 57		14 57	14 57		15 51	15 57			16 57	16 57			17 51
Birmingham New Street 12	d	13 03		13 52	14 03	14 03	14 52	15 03	15 03	15 40	16 03	16 03	16 40		17 03	17 03		17 52	18 03
Tamworth	d				14 19						16 19								18 19
Burton-on-Trent	d				14 29						16 29								18 29
Derby 10	a	13 39			14 42			15 39			16 46				17 46				18 42
Chesterfield	a																		
Sheffield 7	a	14 25			15 46			16 44			17 47				18 37				19 47
Doncaster 7	a	15 15			16 15			17 15			18 15				19 15				20 15
Wakefield Westgate 7	a	15 43			16 33			17 43			18 42				19 34				20 45
Leeds 10	a	16 02			17 02			18 02			19 02				20 02				21 02
York 8	a	16 33			17 33			18 33			19 33				20 33				21 33
Darlington 7	a	17 02			18 01			19 01			20 01				21 03				22 03
Durham	a	17 19			18 18			19 18			20 18				21 20				22 19
Chester-le-Street	a																		
Newcastle 8	a	17 34			18 34			19 34			20 38				21 36				22 45
Alnmouth	a	18 08						20 00			21 09				22 08				
Berwick-upon-Tweed	a				19 20			20 20			21 30				22 29				
Dunbar	a				19 43						21 53				→				
Wolverhampton 7	d			14 21		14b38	15 21		15b38	16 15		16b38	17 15			17b38		18 21	
Stafford	a					14 51			15 51			16 51				17 51			
Stoke-on-Trent	a					15 12			16 12			17 12				18 12			
Congleton	a																		
Macclesfield	a					15 27			16 27			17 27				18 27			
Crewe 10	a			14 52			15 53			16 54			17 53					18 52	
Wilmslow	a																		
Stockport	a					15 41			16 41			17 41				18 41			
Manchester Piccadilly 10	a					15 56			16 56			17 56				18 56			
Warrington Bank Quay	a			15 11			16 11			17 10			18 12					19 10	
Wigan North Western	a			15 22			16 22			17 21			18 23					19 21	
Preston 8	a			15 38			16 37			17 37			18 37					19 41	
Lancaster 6	a			15 55			16 53			17 53			18 53					19 55	
Oxenholme Lake District	a						17 08						19 08					20 10	
Penrith North Lakes	a			16 31						18 30			19 35					20 36	
Carlisle 8	a			16 48			17 49			18 48			19 52					20 52	
Lockerbie	a																		
Haymarket	a			18s03						20s04								22s08	
Edinburgh 10	a	19c15		18 14	20 12			21 07		20 14	22 23						←	22 19	
Haymarket	a	19 28			20 18			21 18						←			21 18		
Motherwell	a				20s57		18s52	→						20s57			22s00		
Glasgow Central 15	a				→		19 16						21 18	21 34			22 30		
Inverkeithing	a	19 43																	
Kirkcaldy	a	20 05																	
Markinch	a	20 14																	
Cupar	a	20 34																	
Leuchars 3	a	20 44																	
Dundee	a	21 05																	
Arbroath	a																		
Montrose	a																		
Stonehaven	a																		
Aberdeen	a																		

For general notes see front of timetable
For details of catering facilities see Directory of Train Operators

A From Newquay dep. 1134 (Table 135)
b Arr. five minutes earlier
c Dep. 1925

until 13 July

South Coast and The South West → North West England, The North East and Scotland

Route Diagram - See first page of Table 51

Station		XC	VT	XC	XC	XC	XC	XC	XC	XC	XC	XC	XC	XC	XC	XC	XC
		R 1	R 1	R 1	R 1	R 1	1 ◇	R 1	1 ◇	1 ◇	1 ◇	1 ◇	1 ◇	1 ◇	1 ◇	1 ◇	1 ◇
Brighton 10	d																
Haywards Heath 3	d																
Gatwick Airport 10 ✈	d																
Bournemouth	d	14 40			15 40			16 40		17 40			18 40		19 40	20 40	
Brockenhurst 3	d	14 57			15 57			16 57		17 57			18 57		19 57	20 57	
Southampton Central	d	15 15			16 15			17 15		18 15			19 15		20 15	21 15	
Southampton Airport Parkway ✈	d	15 22			16 22			17 22		18 22			19 22		20 22	21 22	
Winchester	d	15 31			16 31			17 31		18 31			19 31		20 31	21 31	
Basingstoke	d	15 47			16 47			17 47		18 47			19 47		20 47	21 47	
Redhill	d																
Guildford	d																
East Croydon	d																
Kensington Olympia	d																
Reading 7	d	16 10			17 10			18 10		19 10			20 10		21 10	22 10	
Oxford	d	16 36			17 36			18 36		19 36			20 36		21 36	22 36	
Banbury	d	16 53			17 53			18 53		19 53			20 53		21 53	22 53	
Leamington Spa 8	d	17 11			18 11			19 11		20 11			21 11		22 11	23 11	
Coventry	d																
Birmingham International ✈	d																
Penzance	d																
St Erth 2	d																
Camborne	d																
Redruth	d																
Truro	d																
St Austell	d																
Par 3	d																
Bodmin Parkway	d																
Liskeard 3	d																
Plymouth	d					15 25	16 25				17 25	18 25					
Totnes	d					15 50	16 50				17 50	18 50					
Paignton	d																
Torquay	d																
Newton Abbot	d					16 03	17 03				18 03	19 03					
Teignmouth	d																
Dawlish	d																
Exeter St Davids 6	d					16 23	17 23				18 23	19 23					
Tiverton Parkway	d					16 37	17 37				18 37	19 37					
Taunton	d					16 51	17 51				18 51	19 51					
Weston-super-Mare	d																
Cardiff Central 7	d																
Newport (South Wales)	d																
Bristol Temple Meads 10	d					17 30	18 30				19 30	20 30					22 10
Bristol Parkway 7	d					17 40	18 40				19 40	20 40					22 20
Gloucester 7	d																
Cheltenham Spa	d					18 12	19 12				20 12	21 12					22 52
Birmingham New Street 12	a	17 57			18 51	18 57	19 51	19 51	←	20 51	20 57	21 51	21 51	←	22 51	23 43	23 44
Birmingham New Street 12	d	18 03	18 41		19 03	19 03	20 03 →	20 03	20 03	21 03	21 03	22 03 →	22 03	22 03	23 03		
Tamworth	d								20 19	21 19					23 19		
Burton-on-Trent	d								20 29	21 29				22 39	23 29		
Derby 10	a				19 39				20 42	21 42				22 55	23 50		
Chesterfield	a																
Sheffield 7	a				20 47				21 37	22 40							
Doncaster 7	a				21 15				22 15	23 15							
Wakefield Westgate 7	a				21 34				22 45								
Leeds 10	a				22 02				23 02	00 20							
York 8	a				22 38				23 38								
Darlington 7	a																
Durham	a																
Chester-le-Street	a																
Newcastle 8	a																
Alnmouth	a			←													
Berwick-upon-Tweed	a			22 29													
Dunbar	a																
Wolverhampton 7	d	18b38	19 15			19b38		20b38			21b38		22b38				
Stafford	a	18 51	19 33			19 51		20 51			21 51		22 51				
Stoke-on-Trent	a	19 12				20 12		21 12			22 12		23 12				
Congleton	a																
Macclesfield	a	19 27				20 27		21 27			22 27		23 27				
Crewe 10	a		19 54														
Wilmslow	a																
Stockport	a	19 41				20 41		21 41			22 41		23 41				
Manchester Piccadilly 10	a	19 56				20 56		21 56			22 56		23 56				
Warrington Bank Quay	a		20 12														
Wigan North Western	a		20 23														
Preston 8	a		20 38														
Lancaster 6	a		20 54														
Oxenholme Lake District	a		21 09														
Penrith North Lakes	a		21 35														
Carlisle 8	a		22 13														
Lockerbie	a		22 33														
Haymarket	a																
Edinburgh 10	a			23 18													
Haymarket	a																
Motherwell	a		23s16														
Glasgow Central 15	a		23 38														
Inverkeithing	a																
Kirkcaldy	a																
Markinch	a																
Cupar	a																
Leuchars 3	a																
Dundee	a																
Arbroath	a																
Montrose	a																
Stonehaven	a																
Aberdeen	a																

For general notes see front of timetable
For details of catering facilities see Directory of Train Operators

b Arr. five minutes earlier

South Coast and The South West → North West England, The North East and Scotland

20 July to 7 September

Route Diagram - See first page of Table 51

		VT 1 ◇ ☕	XC 1 ◇ ☕	XC 1 ◇ ☕	XC 1 ◇ ☕	XC 1 ◇ ☕	VT 1 ◇ ☕	XC 1 ◇ ☕	XC 1 ◇ ☕	XC 1 ◇ ☕	VT 1 ◇ ☕	XC 1 ◇ ☕	XC 1 ◇ ☕	XC 1 ◇ ☕	XC 1 ◇ ☕	XC 1 ◇ ☕	VT 1 ◇ ☕	XC 1 ◇ ☕	XC 1 ◇ ☕	XC 1 ◇ ☕	VT 1 ◇ ☕	XC 1 ◇ ☕	XC 1 ◇ ☕	XC 1 ◇ ☕
Brighton 10	d																							09 40
Haywards Heath 3	d																							09 52
Gatwick Airport 10 ✈	d																							10 12
Bournemouth	d																	08b06				09 40		
Brockenhurst 3	d																	08b34				09 57		
Southampton Central	d																	08 39				10 15		
Southampton Airport Parkwy ✈	d																	08 46				10 22		
Winchester	d																	09 23				10 31		
Basingstoke	d																	09 47				10 47		
Redhill	d																							10 33
Guildford	d																							11 03
East Croydon	d																							
Kensington Olympia	d																							
Reading 7	d																	10 10				11 10		11 40
Oxford	d																	10 36				11 36		12 07
Banbury	d																	10 53				11 53		12 25
Leamington Spa 8	d																	11 11				12 11		12 43
Coventry	d																							
Birmingham International ✈	d																							
Penzance	d																							
St Erth 2	d																							
Camborne	d																							
Redruth	d																							
Truro	d																							
St Austell	d																							
Par 3	d																							
Bodmin Parkway	d																							
Liskeard 3	d																							
Plymouth	d																			09 25				
Totnes	d																			09 50				
Paignton	d																							
Torquay	d																							
Newton Abbot	d																			10 03				
Teignmouth	d																							
Dawlish	d																							
Exeter St Davids 6	d																			10 23				
Tiverton Parkway	d																			10 37				
Taunton	d																			10 51				
Weston-super-Mare	d																							
Cardiff Central 7	d																							
Newport (South Wales)	d																							
Bristol Temple Meads 10	d									09 15						10 30				11 30				
Bristol Parkway 7	d									09 25						10 40				11 40				
Gloucester 7	d									10 00														
Cheltenham Spa	d									10 12						11 12				12 12			←	
Birmingham New Street 12	a									10 51				←		11 51		11 51		12 51		12 46	12 51	13 15
Birmingham New Street 12	d	09 03	09 03	09 18	09 48	10 03	10 03	10 18	10 48	11 18 →	11 03		11 03	11 18	11 48	12 03	12 03	12 18	12 48	→	13 03	13 03	13 18	
Tamworth	d															12 19								
Burton-on-Trent	d															12 29								
Derby 10	a		10 24			11 22							12 22			12 42						13 39		
Chesterfield	a		10 45													13 22						14 00		
Sheffield 7	a		10 59			11 58							12 57			13 41						14 14		
Doncaster 7	a		11 23													14 16								
Wakefield Westgate 7	a		11 44			12 44							13 44									14 44		
Leeds 10	a		12 02			13 01							14 03									15 01		
York 8	a		12 44			13 45							14 47			14 39						15 45		
Darlington 7	a		13 17			14 13							15 18			15 22						16 13		
Durham	a		13 34			14 30							15 35			15 39						16 30		
Chester-le-Street	a																							
Newcastle 8	a		13 50			14 46							15 51			16 01						16 46		
Alnmouth	a		14 18										16 21											
Berwick-upon-Tweed	a					15 33						←										17 42		
Dunbar	a					15 56						15 56										18 05		
Wolverhampton 7	d	09 21		09 38	10 08	→	10 21	10 38	11 08		11 21			11 38	12 08		12 21	12 38	13 08		13 21		13 38	
Stafford	a	09 33		09 50	10 23		10 33	10 50	11 20		11 33			11 50	12 20		12 33	12 51	13 20		13 36		13 50	
Stoke-on-Trent	a			10 09	10 42			11 09	11 39					12 09	12 39			13 12	13 43				14 12	
Congleton	a																							
Macclesfield	a			10 27	11 00			11 27	11 57					12 27	12 57			13 30	14 01				14 28	
Crewe 10	a	10 12					11 12				12 17						13 13				14 15			
Wilmslow	a																							
Stockport	a			10 41	11 14			11 41	12 11					12 40	13 11			13 41	14 16				14 41	
Manchester Piccadilly 10	a			10 56	11 32			11 56	12 26					13 02	13 26			13 59	14 30				14 56	
Warrington Bank Quay	a	10 29					11 30				12 35						13 30				14 32			
Wigan North Western	a	10 40					11 41				12 47						13 41				14 47			
Preston 8	a	10 57					11 55				13 06						13 56				15 02			
Lancaster 6	a						12 11				13 23						14 13				15 17			
Oxenholme Lake District	a						12 26										14 27				15 31			
Penrith North Lakes	a						12 53				14 01										15 59			
Carlisle 8	a						13 11				14 18						15 08				16 16			
Lockerbie	a						13 32										15 28							
Haymarket	a										15 31										17 29			
Edinburgh 10	a		15 25								15 41	16 26	17 28								17 36	18 35		
Haymarket	a											16 36												
Motherwell	a																							
Glasgow Central 15	a						14 34										16 33							
Inverkeithing	a											16 52												
Kirkcaldy	a											17 08												
Markinch	a											17 17												
Cupar	a											17 29												
Leuchars 3	a											17 36												
Dundee	a											17 49												
Arbroath	a											18 06												
Montrose	a											18 20												
Stonehaven	a											18 40												
Aberdeen	a											19 05												

For general notes see front of timetable
For details of catering facilities see
Directory of Train Operators

b Change at Basingstoke

Due to Engineering Operations, services from Sunday 14 September on this Table had not been confirmed at time of going to press. These services will be issued in a special Supplement as soon as exact timings have been confirmed

South Coast and The South West → North West England, The North East and Scotland

20 July to 7 September

Route Diagram - See first page of Table 51

		XC	XC	XC	VT	XC	XC	XC	VT	XC	XC	XC	XC	XC	XC	XC	XC	XC	XC	VT	XC	XC	XC	XC
		1◇	R 1	R 1	R 1	1◇	1◇	1◇	R 1	R 1	R 1	1◇	1◇	R 1	R 1	1◇	1◇	1◇	R 1	R 1	R 1	1◇	R 1	R 1
																					A			
		☕	☕	☕	☕	☕	☕	☕	☕	☕	☕	☕	☕	☕	☕	☕	☕	☕	☕	☕	☕	☕	☕	☕
Brighton 10	d																							
Haywards Heath 3	d																							
Gatwick Airport 10 ✈	d																							
Bournemouth	d		10 40							11 40				12 40					13 40					14 40
Brockenhurst 3	d		10 55							11 57				12 57					13 57					14 57
Southampton Central	d		11 15							12 15				13 15					14 15					15 15
Southampton Airport Parkwy ✈	d		11 22							12 22				13 22					14 22					15 22
Winchester	d		11 31							12 31				13 31					14 31					15 31
Basingstoke	d		11 47							12 47				13 47					14 47					15 47
Redhill	d																							
Guildford	d																							
East Croydon	d																							
Kensington Olympia	d																							
Reading 7	d		12 10			12 40				13 10		13 40		14 10		14 40			15 10			15 40		16 10
Oxford	d		12 36			13 07				13 36		14 07		14 36		15 07			15 36			16 07		16 36
Banbury	d		12 53			13 25				13 53		14 25		14 53		15 25			15 53			16 25		16 53
Leamington Spa 8	d		13 11			13 43				14 11		14 43		15 11		15 43			16 11			16 43		17 11
Coventry	d																							
Birmingham International ✈	d																							
Penzance	d										09 30				10 30									
St Erth 2	d										09 38				10 38									
Camborne	d										09 48				10 48									
Redruth	d										09 54				10 54									
Truro	d										10 06				11 06									
St Austell	d										10 22				11 22									
Par 3	d										10 29				11 29						12 29			
Bodmin Parkway	d										10 40				11 40						12 40			
Liskeard 3	d										10 52				11 52						12 52			
Plymouth	d			10 25							11 25				12 25						13 25			
Totnes	d			10 50							11 50				12 50						13 50			
Paignton	d																						13 59	
Torquay	d																						14 05	
Newton Abbot	d			11 03							12 03				13 03						14 03		14 16	
Teignmouth	d																						14 24	
Dawlish	d																						14 29	
Exeter St Davids 6	d	10 48		11 23							12 23				13 23						14 23		14 43	
Tiverton Parkway	d	11 01		11 37							12 37				13 37						14 37			
Taunton	d	11 16		11 51							12 51				13 51						14 51		15 07	
Weston-super-Mare	d																						15 30	
Cardiff Central 7	d																							
Newport (South Wales)	d																							
Bristol Temple Meads 10	d	12 00		12 30			13 00				13 30		14 00		14 30		15 00				15 30		16 00	
Bristol Parkway 7	d	12 10		12 40			13 10				13 40		14 10		14 40		15 10				15 40		16 10	
Gloucester 7	d																							
Cheltenham Spa	d	12 42		13 12			13 42				14 12		14 42		15 12		15 42				16 12		16 42	
Birmingham New Street 12	a	13 26	13 45	13 51		14 15	14 26			14 54	14 57	15 15	15 26	15 46	15 51	16 15	16 26		16 57		16 57	17 15	17 26	17 46
Birmingham New Street 12	d	13 30	13 48	14 03	14 03	14 18	14 30	14 48	15 03	15 03	15 18		15 30	15 48	16 03	16 18	16 30	16 48	17 03	17 03	17 18		17 30	17 48
Tamworth	d						14 47										16 47							
Burton-on-Trent	d						14 58										16 58							
Derby 10	a	14 11		14 39			15 11			15 39			16 11		16 39		17 11		17 39				18 11	
Chesterfield	a	14 32					15 32						16 32				17 32						18 32	
Sheffield 7	a	14 48		15 13			15 48			16 13			16 48		17 13		17 48		18 16				18 48	
Doncaster 7	a	15 16					16 16						17 14				18 16						19 16	
Wakefield Westgate 7	a			15 44						16 44					17 44				18 44					
Leeds 10	a			16 01						17 01					18 01				19 02					
York 8	a	15 40		16 45			16 44			17 41			17 38		18 45		18 41		19 43				19 40	
Darlington 7	a	16 26		17 13			17 22			18 09			18 21		19 15		19 27		20 11				20 28	
Durham	a	16 43		17 30			17 39			18 26			18 38		19 36		19 44		20 28				20 45	
Chester-le-Street	a																							
Newcastle 8	a	17 04		17 46			18 00			18 42			18 59		19 49		20 05		20 44				21 06	
Alnmouth	a			18 13											20 15				21 18					
Berwick-upon-Tweed	a									19 31					20 35				21 39					
Dunbar	a									19 54									22 02					
Wolverhampton 7	d		14 08		14 21	14 38		15 08	15 21		15 38			16 08		16 38		17 08		17 21	17 38			18 06
Stafford	a		14 20		14 33	14 51		15 20	15 33		15 50			16 21		16 51		17 20		17 33	17 50			18 19
Stoke-on-Trent	a		14 39			15 12		15 42			16 13			16 45		17 15		17 45			18 14			18 43
Congleton	a																							
Macclesfield	a		14 57			15 30		16 00			16 34			17 03		17 34		18 04			18 31			19 01
Crewe 10	a				15 15				16 12											18 15				
Wilmslow	a																							
Stockport	a		15 12			15 43		16 15			16 48			17 17		17 48		18 19			18 50			19 15
Manchester Piccadilly 10	a		15 32			15 59		16 30			17 05			17 32		18 03		18 34			19 04			19 30
Warrington Bank Quay	a				15 32				16 29											18 33				
Wigan North Western	a				15 43				16 40											18 47				
Preston 8	a				15 59				16 55											19 01				
Lancaster 6	a				16 16				17 11											19 18				
Oxenholme Lake District	a								17 26											19 32				
Penrith North Lakes	a				16 52															19 59				
Carlisle 8	a				17 09				18 07											20 17				
Lockerbie	a																							
Haymarket	a																							
Edinburgh 10	a			19 20						20 24					21 24				22 32					
Haymarket	a			19 28											21 29									
Motherwell	a								19s10	21s09					22s11									
Glasgow Central 15	a				18 22				19 32	21 51					22 40					21 34				
Inverkeithing	a			19 43																				
Kirkcaldy	a			20 05																				
Markinch	a			20 14																				
Cupar	a			20 34																				
Leuchars 3	a			20 44																				
Dundee	a			21 05																				
Arbroath	a																							
Montrose	a																							
Stonehaven	a																							
Aberdeen	a																							

For general notes see front of timetable
For details of catering facilities see Directory of Train Operators

A From Newquay dep. 1134 (Table 135)

Due to Engineering Operations, services from Sunday 14 September on this Table had not been confirmed at time of going to press. These services will be issued in a special Supplement as soon as exact timings have been confirmed

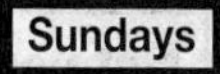

South Coast and The South West → North West England, The North East and Scotland

20 July to 7 September

Route Diagram - See first page of Table 51

		XC	VT	XC	XC	XC	XC	VT	XC	XC	XC	XC	XC	XC	XC	XC	XC	XC	XC	XC	XC	XC	XC
		R	R		R		R	R	R			R	R										
		1	1	1 ◇	1	1 ◇	1	1	1	1 ◇	1 ◇	1	1	1 ◇	1 ◇	1 ◇	1 ◇	1 ◇	1 ◇	1 ◇	1 ◇	1 ◇	1 ◇
		☕	☕	☕	☕	☕	☕	☕	☕	☕	☕	☕	☕	☕	☕	☕	☕	☕	☕	☕			☕
Brighton 10	d																						
Haywards Heath 3	d																						
Gatwick Airport 10 ✈	d																						
Bournemouth	d						15 40					16 40				17 40		18 40			19 40	20 40	
Brockenhurst 3	d						15 57					16 57				17 57		18 55			19 57	20 57	
Southampton Central	d						16 15					17 15				18 15		19 15			20 15	21 15	
Southampton Airport Parkwy ✈	d						16 22					17 22				18 22		19 22			20 22	21 22	
Winchester	d						16 31					17 31				18 31		19 31			20 31	21 31	
Basingstoke	d						16 47					17 47				18 47		19 47			20 47	21 47	
Redhill	d																						
Guildford	d																						
East Croydon	d																						
Kensington Olympia	d																						
Reading 7	d			16 40			17 10			17 40		18 10		18 40		19 10		20 10			21 10	22 10	
Oxford	d			17 07			17 36			18 07		18 36		19 07		19 36		20 36			21 36	22 36	
Banbury	d			17 25			17 53			18 25		18 53		19 25		19 53		20 53			21 53	22 53	
Leamington Spa 8	d			17 43			18 11			18 43		19 11		19 43		20 11		21 11			22 11	23 11	
Coventry	d																						
Birmingham International ✈	d																						
Penzance	d																						
St Erth 2	d																						
Camborne	d																						
Redruth	d																						
Truro	d																						
St Austell	d																						
Par 3	d																						
Bodmin Parkway	d																						
Liskeard 3	d																						
Plymouth	d	14 25							15 25				16 25				17 25		18 25				
Totnes	d	14 50							15 50				16 50				17 50		18 50				
Paignton	d																						
Torquay	d																						
Newton Abbot	d	15 03							16 03				17 03				18 03		19 03				
Teignmouth	d																						
Dawlish	d																						
Exeter St Davids 6	d	15 23							16 23				17 23				18 23		19 23				
Tiverton Parkway	d	15 37							16 37				17 37				18 37		19 37				
Taunton	d	15 51							16 51				17 51				18 51		19 51				
Weston-super-Mare	d																						
Cardiff Central 7	d																						
Newport (South Wales)	d																						
Bristol Temple Meads 10	d	16 30			17 00				17 30		18 00		18 30		19 00		19 30		20 30				22 10
Bristol Parkway 7	d	16 40			17 10				17 40		18 10		18 40		19 10		19 40		20 40				22 20
Gloucester 7	d																						
Cheltenham Spa	d	17 12			17 42				18 12		18 42		19 12		19 42		20 12		21 12				22 52
Birmingham New Street 12	a	17 51		18 15	18 26		18 51		18 57	19 15	19 26	19 46	19 51	20 15	20 26	20 51	20 57	21 51	21 51	⟵	22 51	23 43	23 44
Birmingham New Street 12	d	18 03	18 03	18 18	18 30	18 48	19 03	19 03	19 18		19 30	19 48	20 03	20 18	20 48	21 03	21 18	22 18	22 03	22 18	23 03		
Tamworth	d				18 47						19 47		20 19			21 19		⟶			23 20		
Burton-on-Trent	d				18 58						19 58		20 29			21 29			22 39		23 29		
Derby 10	a	18 39			19 11		19 39				20 11		20 42			21 40			22 50		23 50		
Chesterfield	a	19 00			19 32		20 00				20 32		21 01			22 02			23 11				
Sheffield 7	a	19 14			19 48		20 14				20 48		21 15			22 18			23 26				
Doncaster 7	a				20 16						21 16												
Wakefield Westgate 7	a	19 44					20 44						21 44			22s45			23s52				
Leeds 10	a	20 02					21 01						22 01			23 09			00 34				
York 8	a	20 45			20 43		21 45				21 42		22 53										
Darlington 7	a	21 17			21 20		22 32				22 36												
Durham	a	21 36			21 37		22 50				22 56												
Chester-le-Street	a																						
Newcastle 8	a	21 50			21 58		23 23				23 29												
Alnmouth	a	22 23																					
Berwick-upon-Tweed	a	22 44																					
Dunbar	a																						
Wolverhampton 7	d		18 21	18 38		19 08		19 21	19 36			20 08		20 38	21 06		21 38			22 38			
Stafford	a		18 33	18 51		19 20		19 33	19 49			20 20		20 51	21 19		21 50			22 50			
Stoke-on-Trent	a			19 13		19 40			20 07			20 42		21 12	21 43		22 09			23s09			
Congleton	a																						
Macclesfield	a			19 31		20 01			20 25			21 01		21 30	22 04		22 27			23s27			
Crewe 10	a		19 12					20 15															
Wilmslow	a																						
Stockport	a			19 46		20 15			20 41			21 16		21 42	22 18		22 40			23s41			
Manchester Piccadilly 10	a			20 01		20 32			20 56			21 31		21 56	22 32		22 56			23 56			
Warrington Bank Quay	a		19 30					20 32															
Wigan North Western	a		19 41					20 46															
Preston 8	a		19 57					21 01															
Lancaster 6	a		20 12					21 18															
Oxenholme Lake District	a		20 26					21 32															
Penrith North Lakes	a		20 52					21 58															
Carlisle 8	a		21 08					22 17															
Lockerbie	a							22 36															
Haymarket	a		22s30																				
Edinburgh 10	a	23 36	22 41																				
Haymarket	a																						
Motherwell	a							23s19															
Glasgow Central 15	a							23 41															
Inverkeithing	a																						
Kirkcaldy	a																						
Markinch	a																						
Cupar	a																						
Leuchars 3	a																						
Dundee	a																						
Arbroath	a																						
Montrose	a																						
Stonehaven	a																						
Aberdeen	a																						

For general notes see front of timetable
For details of catering facilities see Directory of Train Operators

Due to Engineering Operations, services from Sunday 14 September on this Table had not been confirmed at time of going to press. These services will be issued in a special Supplement as soon as exact timings have been confirmed

Network Diagram for Table 52

DM-9/08
Design BAJS

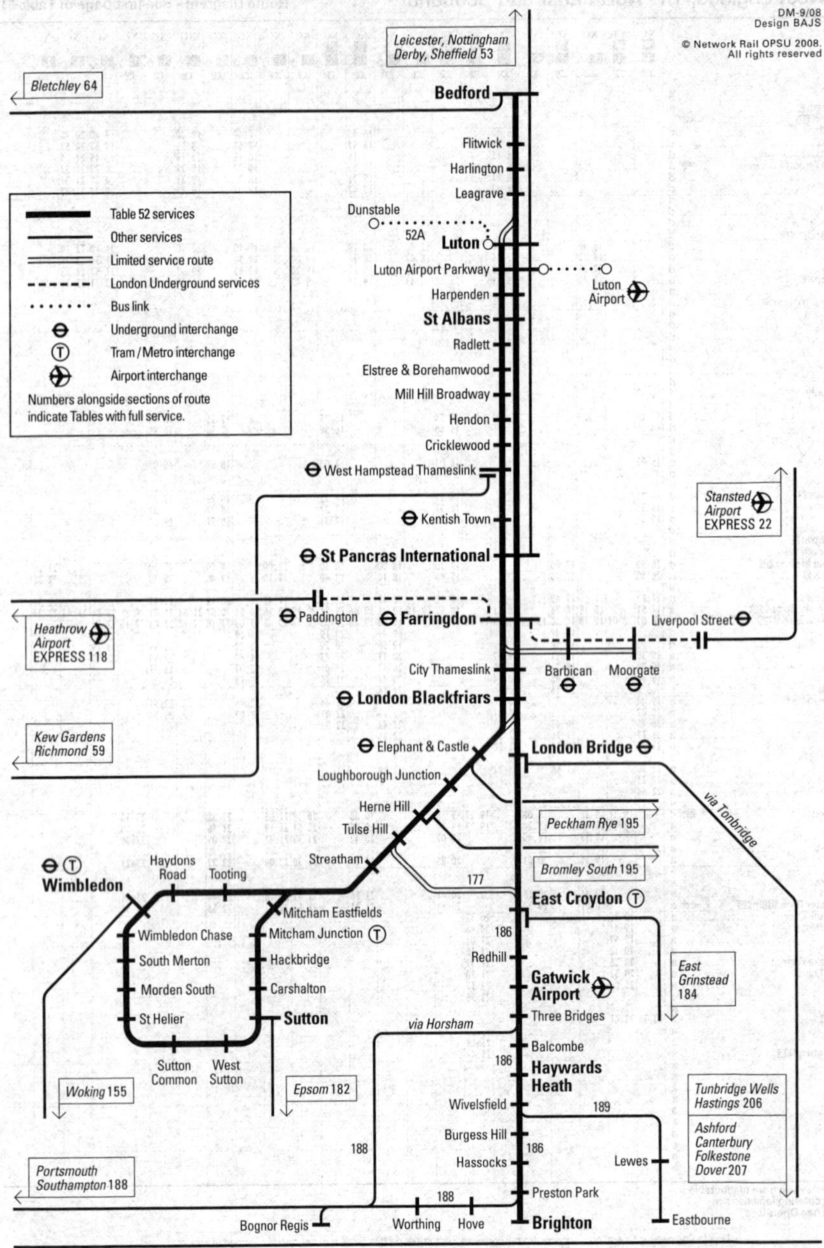

Bedford, Luton, St.Albans and City of London → South London, Gatwick Airport and Brighton

Network Diagram - see first page of Table 52

Miles	Miles	Miles	Miles	Miles	Station		FC MO 1	FC MX 1	FC MO 1	FC	FC MO	FC MX	FC MX	FC MO 1	FC MX 1	FC 1	FC	FC 1	FC 1		FC 1	FC 1	FC 1	FC 1	SN
0	0	—	—	—	**Bedford** 7	d	21p40	21p50		22p10	22p40	22p40	23p10	23p40	23p40	00 40	01 40		02 40			03 40	04 10	04 20	
9½	—	—	—	—	Flitwick	d	21p49	21p59		22p19	22p49	22p49	23p19	23p49	23p49	00 49	01 49		02 49			03 49	04 19	04 29	
12½	—	—	—	—	Harlington	d	21p53	22p03		22p23	22p53	22p53	23p23	23p53	23p53	00 53	01 53		02 53			03 53	04 23	04 33	
17	—	—	—	—	Leagrave	d	21p59	22p09		22p29	22p59	22p59	23p29	23p59	23p59	00 59	01 59		02 59			03 59	04 29	04 39	
19½	19½	—	—	—	**Luton** 10	d	22p04	22p14		22p34	23p04	23p04	23p34	00 04	00 04	01 04	02 04		03 04			04 04	04 34	04 44	
20½	—	—	—	—	Luton Airport Parkway 7 ✈	d	22p06	22p16		22p36	23p06	23p06	23p36	00 06	00 06	01 06	02 06		03 06			04 06	04 36	04 46	
25	—	—	—	—	Harpenden	d	22p12	22p22		22p42	23p12	23p12	23p42	00 12	00 12	01 12	02 12		03 12			04 12	04 42	04 52	
29¾	—	—	—	—	**St Albans City**	d	22p18	22p29		22p48	23p18	23p18	23p48	00 18	00 18	01 18	02 18		03 18			04 18	04 48	04 58	
34¼	—	—	—	—	Radlett	d	22p23			22p53	23p23	23p23	23p53	00 23	00 23	01 23	02 23		03 23			04 23		05 03	
37¼	—	—	—	—	Elstree & Borehamwood	d	22p27			22p57	23p27	23p27	23p57	00 27	00 27	01 27	02 27		03 27			04 27		05 07	
40½	—	—	—	—	Mill Hill Broadway	d	22p31			23p01	23p31	23p31	00 01	00 31	00 31	01 31	02 31		03 31			04 31		05 11	
42¾	—	—	—	—	Hendon	d	22p34			23p04	23p34	23p34	00 04	00 34	00 34	01 34	02 34		03 34			04 34		05 14	
44¾	—	—	—	—	Cricklewood	d	22p38		←	23p08	23p38	23p38	00 08	00 38	00 38	01 38	02 38		03 38			04 38		05 18	
45¾	—	—	—	—	West Hampstead Thameslink	⊖ d	22p42	22p42	22p42	23p12	23p42	23p42	00 12	00 42	00 42	01 42	02 42		03 42			04 42	05 02	05 22	
48¼	—	—	—	—	Kentish Town	⊖ d	→		22p46	23p16	23p46	23p46	00 16	00 46	00 46	01 46	02 46		03 46			04 46		05 26	
—	49¾	—	—	—	**St Pancras International**	⊖ a																			
50	0	—	—	—	**St Pancras International** 15	⊖ d		22p54	22p54	23p24	23p54	23p54	00 24	00 54	00 54	01 54	02 54	03 25	03 54		04 25	04 54	05 14	05 34	
51	0	—	—	—	Farringdon 3	⊖ d		22p59	22p59	23p29	23p59	23p59	00 29									04 59	05 19	05 39	
—	¼	—	—	—	Barbican	⊖ a																			
—	¾	—	—	—	**Moorgate**	⊖ a																			
51¾	—	—	—	—	City Thameslink 3	d		23p01																	
52¼	0	0	0	—	**London Blackfriars** 3	⊖ d		23p04	23p04	23p34	00 04	00 04	00 34	01 04	01 04	02 04	03 04	03 34	04 04		04 34	05 04	05 24	05 44	
—	1	1	—	—	Elephant & Castle	⊖ d																			
—	3	3	—	—	Loughborough Jn	d																			
—	4	4	—	—	Herne Hill 4	d																			
53	—	—	—	—	**London Bridge** 4	⊖ d		23p11	23p11	23p41	00 11	00 11	00 41										05 31	05 50	
—	5	5	5	—	Tulse Hill 3	d																			
—	6½	6½	—	0	Streatham 4	d																			
—	—	—	—	1	Mitcham Eastfields	d																			
—	—	—	—	2	Mitcham Junction 🚊	d																			
—	—	—	—	4	Hackbridge	d																			
—	—	—	—	4¾	Carshalton	d																			
—	8	—	—	—	Tooting	d																			
—	9¼	—	—	—	Haydons Road	d																			
—	10½	—	—	—	**Wimbledon** 6 ⊖ 🚊	d																			05 57
—	11½	—	—	—	Wimbledon Chase	d																			06 00
—	12	—	—	—	South Merton	d																			06 02
—	12½	—	—	—	Morden South	d																			06 04
—	13	—	—	—	St Helier	d																			06 06
—	14	—	—	—	Sutton Common	d																			06 08
—	15	—	—	—	West Sutton	d																			06 11
—	16	12½	—	6	**Sutton (Surrey)** 4	a																			06 14
63¼	—	—	10	—	**East Croydon** 🚊	d		23p24	23p27	23p57	00 27	00 27	00 57	01 32	01 32	02 32	03 32	04 02	04 32		05 02	05 32	05 52	06 04	
73¾	—	—	—	—	Redhill	d		*00 03*	*00 03*		*00 50*										*05 39*	*06 06*		*06 36*	
79½	—	—	—	—	**Gatwick Airport** 10 ✈	d		23p41	23p50	00 17	00 47	00 50	01 17	01 52	01 52	02 52	03 52	04 24	04 52		05 22	05 54	06 08	06 20	
82¼	—	—	—	—	Three Bridges 4	d		23p47	23p54	00a24	00a54	00a54	01a24	01a58	01a58	02a58	03a58	04a30	04 58		05 26	06 00	06 14	06 26	
86¾	—	—	—	—	Balcombe	d		23p53	*00 25*									*06b00*			*06 00*		06 20	06 32	
90¾	—	—	—	—	**Haywards Heath** 3	d		23p58	00 03	*01 00*	*02 03*		*02 04*					*05 00*	05 08		05 36	06 10	06 25	06 38	
93¾	—	—	—	—	Wivelsfield 4	d		00 02	*00 34*									*05 40*			05 40	06 14	06 29	06 42	
94½	—	—	—	—	Burgess Hill 4	d		00 04	00 08									*05 42*	*05 42*		05 42	06 16	06 32	06 44	
96½	—	—	—	—	Hassocks 4	d		00 08	*00 40*									*05 46*	*05 46*		05 46	06 19	06 35	06 47	
102¼	—	—	—	—	Preston Park	d		00 15	*00 47*									*05 53*	*05 53*		05 53	06 26	06 42	06 54	
103¾	—	—	—	—	**Brighton** 10	a		00 20	00 22	*01 17*	*02 30*		*02 30*					*05 16*	05 29		05 59	06 32	06 46	06 59	

For general notes see front of timetable
For details of catering facilities see
Directory of Train Operators

b Change at Gatwick Airport and Three Bridges

Bedford, Luton, St.Albans and City of London → South London, Gatwick Airport and Brighton

Network Diagram - see first page of Table 52

Station		SN	FC	FC 1	SN	FC 1	FC	FC 1	FC	EM 1 ◇ A	FC	FC 1	FC 1	EM 1 ◇ B	SN	FC	FC 1	FC 1	FC 1	FC	FC	SN C	FC
Bedford 7	d			04 50		05 20		05 40	05 48	05 50		06 00		06 19			06 16		06 20		06 26		06 36
Flitwick	d			04 59		05 29		05 49	05 56			06 09					06 25		06 29		06 35		06 46
Harlington	d			05 03		05 33		05 53	06 01			06 13							06 33		06 39		
Leagrave	d			05 09		05 39		05 59	06 07			06 19							06 39		06 45		
Luton 10	d			05 14		05 44	05 48	06 04	06 12		06 18	06 24	06 30	06 35			06 36		06 44		06 50		06 56
Luton Airport Parkway 7 ✈	d			05 16		05 46	05 50	06 06		06 08	06 20	06 26	06 32						06 46		06 52		
Harpenden	d			05 22		05 52	05 56	06 12	06 18		06 26	06 32	06 38				06 42		06 52		06 58		07 02
St Albans City	d			05 28		05 58	06 02	06 18	06 24		06 32	06 38	06 44				06 48		06 58	06 52	07 04		07 08
Radlett	d			05 33			06 07				06 37		06 49					←		06 57	07 09		
Elstree & Borehamwood	d			05 37			06 11				06 41		06 54 →			←		06 54		07 01	07 14 →		
Mill Hill Broadway	d			05 41			06 15				06 45 →					06 45		06 57		07 05			
Hendon	d			05 44			06 18									06 48				07 08			
Cricklewood	d			05 48			06 22									06 52				07 12			
West Hampstead Thameslink	⊖ d			05 52		06 12	06 25	06 32				06 50				06 55		07 04	07 10	07 15			
Kentish Town	⊖ d			05 56			06 29									06 59				07 19			
St Pancras International	⊖ a									06 41				07 05									
St Pancras International 15	⊖ d			06 04		06 24	06 33	06 39	06 44			06 57				07 03	07 07	07 12	07 17	07 24			07 28
Farringdon 3	⊖ d			06 09		06 29	06 38	06 44	06 48			07 02				07 08	07 12	07 16	07 22	07 28			07 32
Barbican	⊖ a								06 49									07 18		07 30			
Moorgate	⊖ a								06 54									07 25		07 35			
City Thameslink 3	d			06 11		06 31	06 41	06 47				07 07				07 11	07 17		07 27				07 37
London Blackfriars 3	⊖ d		06 11	06 14		06 36	06 46	06 50				07 10				07 16	07 23		07 32				07 40
Elephant & Castle	⊖ d		06 14				06 49									07 19	07 27						07 43
Loughborough Jn	d		06 18				06 53									07 23	07 31						07 47
Herne Hill 4	d		06b24				06 57									07 28	07 35						07 52
London Bridge 4	⊖ d	06 00		06 21	06 30	06 43		07c00				07 16			07 00				07 40			07 31	
Tulse Hill 3	d	06 17	06 29		06 47		07 02								07 17	07 32	07 38					07 48	07 56
Streatham 4	d	06 21	06 32		06 51		07 06								07 21	07 36	07 42					07 52	07 59
Mitcham Eastfields	d		06 36				07 10									07 40							08 03
Mitcham Junction 🚊	d		06 39				07 13									07 43							08 07
Hackbridge	d		06 43				07 17									07 44							08 10
Carshalton	d		06 45				07 19									07 49							08 13
Tooting	d	06 27			06 57										07 25		07 46					07 56	
Haydons Road	d	06 30			07 00										07 28		07 49					07 59	
Wimbledon 6	⊖ 🚊 d	06 33			07a03										07 32		07a54					08 02	
Wimbledon Chase	d	06 36			07e10										07 35							08 05	
South Merton	d	06 38			07 12										07 37							08 07	
Morden South	d	06 40			07 14										07 39							08 09	
St Helier	d	06 42			07 16										07 41							08 11	
Sutton Common	d	06 44			07 18										07 43							08 13	
West Sutton	d	06 47			07 21										07 46							08 16	
Sutton (Surrey) 4	a	06 50	06 49		07 25		07 23								07 49	07 53						08 19	08 16
East Croydon	🚊 d			06 36		06 56		07 16				07 32							07 56				
Redhill	d			*07 06*				*07 39*				*08 05*							*08 31*				
Gatwick Airport 10 ✈	d			06 52		07 12		07 32				07 50							08 12				
Three Bridges 4	d			06 56		07 18		07 38				07 54							08 16				
Balcombe	d			*07 15*		*07 35*						08 00							08 22				
Haywards Heath 3	d			07 06		07 28		07 48				08 06							08 28				
Wivelsfield 4	d			07 10		07 32						08 10							08 32				
Burgess Hill 4	d			07 12		07 34		07 54				08 12							08 34				
Hassocks 4	d			07 15		07 37						08 15							08 37				
Preston Park	d			07 22		07 44		*08 22*				08 22							08 44				
Brighton 10	a			07 27		07 49		08 06				08 27							08 49				

For general notes see front of timetable
For details of catering facilities see Directory of Train Operators

A From Leicester (Table 53)
B From Derby (Table 53)
C To London Victoria (Table 177)
b Arr. 0622
c Arr. 0656
e Arr. 0706

Bedford, Luton, St.Albans and City of London → South London, Gatwick Airport and Brighton

Network Diagram - see first page of Table 52

		FC	FC		FC	EM	FC	FC	FC	FC	SN	FC	FC	EM	FC	EM	FC		SN	FC	FC	FC	FC	EM	FC
						1 ◇			1				1	1 ◇	1	1 ◇					1	1	1	1 ◇	
						A								B		A			C					A	
						⊠ ✠								⊠ ✠		⊓								⊠ ✠	
Bedford [7]	d				06 40	06 51			06 56				07 00		07 08						07 16	07 22	07 28		
Flitwick	d				06 49				07 05				07 09								07 25	07 31	07 37		
Harlington	d				06 53								07 13								07 29	07 35			
Leagrave	d				07 00								07 19		07 25						07 35	07 41			
Luton [10]	d		06 56		07 04	07 08		07 08	07 16	07 20			07 24	07 29	07 30						07 40	07 46	07 48	07 52	
Luton Airport Parkway [7] ✈	d		06 58		07 06			07 10		07 22			07 26			07 38					07 42	07 48			
Harpenden	d		07 04		07 12			07 16	07 22	07 28			07 32		07 36						07 48	07 54	07 54		
St Albans City	d		07 10		07 18			07 22	07 28	07 34			07 38		07 44					07 44	07 56	08 00	08 00		07 54
Radlett	d	←	07 15					07 27		07 39										07 49		08 05			07 59
Elstree & Borehamwood	d	07 14	07 19					07 31		07 43										07 54		08 10 →			08 03
Mill Hill Broadway	d		07 23				←	07 35		07 47		←					←								08 07
Hendon	d		07 27 →				07 27	07 39 →		07 51 →		07 39					07 51								08 10
Cricklewood	d						07 30					07 42					07 54								08 14
West Hampstead Thameslink ⊖	d	07 23					07 33					07 45					07 57			08 03					08 17
Kentish Town ⊖	d						07 37					07 49					08 01								08 21
St Pancras International ⊖	a					07 36								07 59		08 06								08 24	
St Pancras International [15] ⊖	d	07 32			07 40		07 44		07 48			07 56	08 00		08 04		08 08			08 12	08 16		08 20		08 26
Farringdon [3] ⊖	d	07 37			07 44		07 48		07 52			08 00	08 04		08 08		08 12			08 16	08 20		08 24		08 30
Barbican ⊖	a	07 38			07 46		07 51										08 15				08 23				08 33
Moorgate ⊖	a	07 43			07 52		07 56										08 20				08 28				08 38
City Thameslink [3]	d								07 55			08 03	08 09		08 13					08 19			08 27		
London Blackfriars [3] ⊖	d								08 00			08 08	08 12		08a19					08 24			08 32		
Elephant & Castle ⊖	d											08 11								08 27			08 35		
Loughborough Jn	d											08 15								08 31			08 39		
Herne Hill [4]	d								08 09			08 22								08 38			08 43		
London Bridge [4] ⊖	d										08 02		08 19						08 24						
Tulse Hill [3]	d								08 13		08 19	08 26							08 38	08 44			08 47		
Streatham [4]	d										08 23	08 29							08 42	08 47					
Mitcham Eastfields	d											08 33								08 51					
Mitcham Junction 🚋	d											08 37								08 55					
Hackbridge	d											08 40								08 58					
Carshalton	d											08 43								09 01					
Tooting	d										08 27								08 46						
Haydons Road	d										08 30								08 49						
Wimbledon [6] ⊖ 🚋	d										08 32								08 55						
Wimbledon Chase	d										08 35								08 58						
South Merton	d										08 37								09 00						
Morden South	d										08 39								09 02						
St Helier	d										08 41								09 04						
Sutton Common	d										08 43								09 06						
West Sutton	d										08 46								09 09						
Sutton (Surrey) [4]	a										08 49	08 46							09 13	09 05					
East Croydon 🚋	d								08 26				08 36										09 06		
Redhill	d												08 49										*09 30*		
Gatwick Airport [10] ✈	d								08 42				08 56										09 23		
Three Bridges [4]	d								08 46				09 00										09 28		
Balcombe	d								08 52																
Haywards Heath [3]	d								08 58				09 10										09b40		
Wivelsfield [4]	d								09 02				*09 17*												
Burgess Hill [4]	d								09 04				*09 24*										*10 03*		
Hassocks [4]	d								09 07				*09 27*										*10 06*		
Preston Park	d								09 14				*09 34*										*10 13*		
Brighton [10]	a								09 20				09 24										09 54		

For general notes see front of timetable
For details of catering facilities see Directory of Train Operators

A From Nottingham (Table 53)
B From Sheffield (Table 53)
C To London Victoria (Table 177)
b Arr. 0936

Bedford, Luton, St.Albans and City of London → South London, Gatwick Airport and Brighton

Network Diagram - see first page of Table 52

		FC 1	FC	FC	FC	FC	EM 1 ◇ A ⊠	FC 1	FC 1		EM 1 ◇ B ⊠	FC	FC	FC 1	FC 1	FC	FC 1	EM 1 ◇ C	FC	FC	FC 1	FC	FC		FC 1
Bedford 7	d		07 32	07 42				07 48	07 52		07 53	07 58			08 04		08 20	08 25	08 32		08 40				08 55
Flitwick	d		07 41					07 57	08 01			08 07			08 13		08 29		08 41		08 49				09 04
Harlington	d		07 45					08 01	08 05						08 17		08 33				08 53				09 08
Leagrave	d		07 51	07 57				08 07	08 11						08 23		08 39				08 59				09 14
Luton 10	d		07 56	08 02		08 02	08 10	08 12	08 16			08 20			08 28		08 44		08 54		09 04		09 14		09 19
Luton Airport Parkway 7 ✈	d		07 58			08 04		08 14	08 18						08 30		08 46				09 06		09 16		09 21
Harpenden	d		08 04	08 09		08 10		08 20	08 24			08 26			08 36		08 52		09 00		09 12		09 22		09 27
St Albans City	d		08 12	08 16	08 07	08 16		08 27	08 32			08 32	08 22		08 44	08 40	09 00		09 06	08 56	09 18	09 12	09 28		09 33
Radlett	d	←			08 12	08 21			08 37				08 27	←		08 45				09 01		09 17	09 33		
Elstree & Borehamwood	d	08 10			08 16	08 26			08 42				08 31	08 42		08 49				09 05		09 21	09 37		
Mill Hill Broadway	d				08 21				→				08 36			08 54				09 10		09 26	09 42		
Hendon	d				08 24								08 39			08 57				09 13		09 29	09 45		
Cricklewood	d				08 28								08 43			09 01				09 17		09 33	→		
West Hampstead Thameslink ⊖	d	08 20			08 31	08 35							08 47	08 51		09 05				09 21		09 36			
Kentish Town ⊖	d				08 35								08 51			09 09				09 25		09 40			
St Pancras International ⊖	a						08 42				08 38							09 06							
St Pancras International 15 ⊖	d	08 29	08 33	08 36	08 40	08 44		08 47				08 52	08 56	09 00	09 04	09 14	09 20		09 26	09 32	09 39	09 48			09 54
Farringdon 3 ⊖	d	08 33	08 37	08 40	08 44	08 48		08 52				08 56	09 00	09 04	09 08	09 18	09 24		09 30	09 36	09 44	09 52			09 59
Barbican ⊖	a	08 36		08 43		08 51								09 07					09 33						
Moorgate ⊖	a	08 41		08 48		08 56								09 12					09 38						
City Thameslink 3	d		08 40		08 47			08 55				08 59	09 03		09 13	09 21	09 27			09 39	09 46	09 55			10 01
London Blackfriars 3 ⊖	d		08 45		08 52			08 58				09 03	09 08		09 17	09 26	09 34			09 44	09 49	10 00			10 05
Elephant & Castle ⊖	d				08 55							09 06	09 11			09 29				09 47		10 03			
Loughborough Jn	d				08 59							09 10	09 15			09 33				09 51		10 07			
Herne Hill 4	d		08 55		09b06							09 14	09 22			09 38				09 57		10 12			
London Bridge 4 ⊖	d							09 06							09 25		09 42				09 56				10 11
Tulse Hill 3	d		09c02		09 14							09 18	09 28			09 44				10 02		10 16			
Streatham 4	d		09 05		09 19							09 22	09 31			09 47				10 05		10 19			
Mitcham Eastfields	d				09 23											09 51						10 23			
Mitcham Junction 🚊	d				09 27											09 55						10 27			
Hackbridge	d				09 30											09 58						10 30			
Carshalton	d				09 33											10 01						10 33			
Tooting	d		09 10									09 26	09 36							10 10					
Haydons Road	d		09 13									09 29	09 39							10 13					
Wimbledon 6 ⊖ 🚊	d		09 17									09 32	09 47							10 17					
Wimbledon Chase	d		09 20										09 50							10 20					
South Merton	d		09 22										09 52							10 22					
Morden South	d		09 24										09 54							10 24					
St Helier	d		09 26										09 56							10 26					
Sutton Common	d		09 28										09 58							10 28					
West Sutton	d		09 31										10 01							10 31					
Sutton (Surrey) 4	a		09 37		09 37								10 05			10 05				10 35		10 37			
East Croydon 🚊	d							09 24							09 39		09 54				10 09				10 24
Redhill	d														*10 00*						*10 30*				
Gatwick Airport 10 ✈	d							09 41							09 56		10 11				10 26				10 41
Three Bridges 4	d							09 45							10 00		10 15				*10 44*				10 45
Balcombe	d							09 51									10 21								
Haywards Heath 3	d							09 57							10 10		10 27				10 38				10 55
Wivelsfield 4	d							10 01							*10 22*		10 31				*10 50*				10 59
Burgess Hill 4	d							10 03							*10 24*		10 33				*10 52*				11 01
Hassocks 4	d							10 06							*10 27*		10 36				*10 55*				11 04
Preston Park	d							10 13							*10 34*		10 43				*11 02*				11 11
Brighton 10	a							10 19							10 24		10 51				10 54				11 17

For general notes see front of timetable
For details of catering facilities see Directory of Train Operators

A From Sheffield (Table 53)
B From Derby (Table 53)
C From Nottingham (Table 53)

b Arr. 0903
c Arr. 0859

Bedford, Luton, St.Albans and City of London → South London, Gatwick Airport and Brighton

Network Diagram - see first page of Table 52

Station		EM 1 ◇ A ☕	FC	FC 1	EM 1 ◇ B ☕	FC 1	FC	FC	FC 1	FC	FC 1	FC 1	EM 1 ◇ A ☕	FC	FC	FC 1	FC	FC 1	FC	EM 1 ◇ B ☕	FC	FC	FC 1	FC
Bedford 7	d	09 03		09 10	09 23	09 20			09 25		09 40	09 50	09 53			09 57		10 10	10 20	10 21			10 27	
Flitwick	d			09 19		09 29			09 34		09 49	09 59				10 06		10 19	10 29				10 36	
Harlington	d			09 23					09 38		09 53					10 10		10 23					10 40	
Leagrave	d			09 29					09 44		09 59					10 15		10 29					10 45	
Luton 10	d			09 34	09 38	09 39		09 44	09 49		10 04	10 09			10 14	10 19		10 34	10 39	10 39		10 44	10 49	
Luton Airport Parkway 7 ✈	d	09 21		09 36				09 46	09 51		10 06		10 09		10 16	10 21		10 36				10 46	10 51	
Harpenden	d			09 42		09 47		09 52	09 57		10 12	10 17			10 22	10 27		10 42	10 47			10 52	10 57	
St Albans City	d			09 48		09 53	09 43	09 58	10 03		10 18	10 23		10 13	10 28	10 33		10 48	10 52		10 43	10 58	11 03	
Radlett	d						09 48	10 03						10 18	10 33						10 48	11 03		
Elstree & Borehamwood	d						09 53	10 08						10 23	10 38						10 53	11 08		
Mill Hill Broadway	d		←				09 57	10 12		←				10 27	10 42		←				10 57	11 12		←
Hendon	d		09 45				10 01	10 16		10 16				10 31	10 46		10 46				11 01	11 16		11 16
Cricklewood	d		09 49				10 04	→		10 19				10 34	→		10 49				11 04	→		11 19
West Hampstead Thameslink	⊖ d		09 52				10 08			10 22				10 38			10 52				11 08			11 22
Kentish Town	⊖ d		09 56				10 12			10 26				10 42			10 56				11 12			11 26
St Pancras International	⊖ a	09 45			10 04								10 34							11 04				
St Pancras International 15	⊖ d		10 02	10 09		10 14	10 17		10 24	10 32	10 39	10 44		10 47		10 54	11 02	11 09	11 14		11 18		11 24	11 32
Farringdon 3	⊖ d		10 07	10 14		10 18	10 22		10 29	10 37	10 44	10 48		10 52		10 59	11 07	11 14	11 18		11 22		11 29	11 37
Barbican	⊖ a					10 20						10 50							11 20					
Moorgate	⊖ a					10 24						10 54							11 24					
City Thameslink 3	d		10 09	10 16			10 26		10 31	10 39	10 46			10 56		11 01	11 09	11 16			11 26		11 31	11 39
London Blackfriars 3	⊖ d		10 16	10 20			10 30		10 35	10 46	10 50			11 00		11 05	11 16	11 20			11 30		11 35	11 46
Elephant & Castle	⊖ d		10 19				10 33			10 49				11 03			11 19				11 33			11 49
Loughborough Jn	d		10 23				10 37			10 53				11 07			11 23				11 37			11 53
Herne Hill 4	d		10 27				10 42			10 57				11 12			11 27				11 42			11 57
London Bridge 4	⊖ d			10 26					10 41		10 56					11 11		11 26					11 41	
Tulse Hill 3	d		10 32				10 46			11 02				11 16			11 32				11 46			12 02
Streatham 4	d		10 35				10 49			11 05				11 19			11 35				11 49			12 05
Mitcham Eastfields	d						10 53							11 23							11 53			
Mitcham Junction	🚊 d						10 57							11 27							11 57			
Hackbridge	d						11 00							11 30							12 00			
Carshalton	d						11 03							11 33							12 03			
Tooting	d		10 40							11 10							11 40							12 10
Haydons Road	d		10 43							11 13							11 43							12 13
Wimbledon 6	⊖ 🚊 d		10 47							11 17							11 47							12 17
Wimbledon Chase	d		10 50							11 20							11 50							12 20
South Merton	d		10 52							11 22							11 52							12 22
Morden South	d		10 54							11 24							11 54							12 24
St Helier	d		10 56							11 26							11 56							12 26
Sutton Common	d		10 58							11 28							11 58							12 28
West Sutton	d		11 01							11 31							12 01							12 31
Sutton (Surrey) 4	a		11 05				11 06			11 35				11 36			12 05				12 06			12 35
East Croydon	🚊 d			10 39					10 54		11 09					11 24		11 39					11 54	
Redhill	d			*11 00*							*11 30*							*12 00*						
Gatwick Airport 10 ✈	d			10 56					11 11		11 26					11 41		11 56					12 11	
Three Bridges 4	d			*11 14*					11 15		*11 44*					11 45		*12 14*					12 15	
Balcombe	d			*11 21*					11 21									*12 21*					12 21	
Haywards Heath 3	d			11 08					11 27		11 38					11 55		12 08					12 27	
Wivelsfield 4	d								11 31		*11 50*					11 59							12 31	
Burgess Hill 4	d			*11 33*					11 33		*11 52*					12 01		*12 33*					12 33	
Hassocks 4	d			*11 36*					11 36		*11 55*					12 04		*12 36*					12 36	
Preston Park	d			*11 43*					11 43		*12 02*					12 11		*12 43*					12 43	
Brighton 10	a			11 24					11 49		11 54					12 17		12 24					12 49	

For general notes see front of timetable
For details of catering facilities see Directory of Train Operators

A From Burton-on-Trent (Table 53)
B From Nottingham (Table 53)

Bedford, Luton, St.Albans and City of London → South London, Gatwick Airport and Brighton

Network Diagram - see first page of Table 52

		FC 1	EM 1 ◇ A	FC	FC	FC 1		FC	FC 1	EM 1 ◇ B	EM 1 ◇ C	FC	FC	FC 1	FC	FC 1	EM 1 ◇ D	FC	FC	FC 1		EM 1 ◇ E	FC	FC 1	EM 1 ◇ C
Bedford 7	d	10 40	10 51			10 55			11 10	11 12	11 21			11 25		11 40	11 51			11 55				12 10	12 21
Flitwick	d	10 49				11 04			11 19					11 34		11 49				12 04				12 19	
Harlington	d	10 53				11 08			11 23					11 38		11 53				12 08				12 23	
Leagrave	d	10 59				11 14			11 29					11 44		11 59				12 14				12 29	
Luton 10	d	11 04			11 14	11 19			11 34		11 36		11 44	11 49		12 04			12 14	12 19		12 20		12 34	12 36
Luton Airport Parkway 7 ✈	d	11 06	11 07		11 16	11 21			11 36				11 46	11 51		12 06	12 07		12 16	12 21				12 36	
Harpenden	d	11 12			11 22	11 27			11 42				11 52	11 57		12 12			12 22	12 27				12 42	
St Albans City	d	11 18		11 13	11 28	11 33			11 48			11 43	11 58	12 03		12 18		12 13	12 28	12 33				12 48	
Radlett	d			11 18	11 33							11 48	12 03					12 18	12 33						
Elstree & Borehamwood	d			11 23	11 38							11 53	12 08					12 23	12 38						
Mill Hill Broadway	d			11 27	11 42			←				11 57	12 12		←			12 27	12 42				←		
Hendon	d			11 31	11 46			11 46				12 01	12 16		12 16			12 31	12 46				12 46		
Cricklewood	d			11 34	→			11 49				12 04	→		12 19			12 34	→				12 49		
West Hampstead Thameslink	⊖ d			11 37				11 52				12 07			12 22			12 37					12 52		
Kentish Town	⊖ d			11 41				11 56				12 11			12 26			12 41					12 56		
St Pancras International	⊖ a		11 34							11 51	12 04						12 34					12 51			13 04
St Pancras International 15	⊖ d	11 39		11 47		11 54		12 02	12 09			12 17		12 24	12 32	12 39		12 47		12 54			13 02	13 09	
Farringdon 3	⊖ d	11 44		11 52		11 59		12 07	12 14			12 22		12 29	12 37	12 44		12 52		12 59			13 07	13 14	
Barbican	⊖ a																								
Moorgate	⊖ a																								
City Thameslink 3	d	11 46		11 54		12 01		12 09	12 16			12 24		12 31	12 39	12 46		12 54		13 01			13 09	13 16	
London Blackfriars 3	⊖ d	11 50		12 00		12 05		12 16	12 20			12 30		12 35	12 46	12 50		13 00		13 05			13 16	13 20	
Elephant & Castle	⊖ d			12 03				12 19				12 33			12 49			13 03					13 19		
Loughborough Jn	d			12 07				12 23				12 37			12 53			13 07					13 23		
Herne Hill 4	d			12 12				12 27				12 42			12 57			13 12					13 27		
London Bridge 4	⊖ d	11 56				12 11			12 26					12 41		12 56				13 11				13 26	
Tulse Hill 3	d			12 16				12 32				12 46			13 02			13 16					13 32		
Streatham 4	d			12 19				12 35				12 49			13 05			13 19					13 35		
Mitcham Eastfields	d			12 23								12 53						13 23							
Mitcham Junction	🚋 d			12 27								12 57						13 27							
Hackbridge	d			12 30								13 00						13 30							
Carshalton	d			12 33								13 03						13 33							
Tooting	d							12 40							13 10								13 40		
Haydons Road	d							12 43							13 13								13 43		
Wimbledon 6	⊖ 🚋 d							12 47							13 17								13 47		
Wimbledon Chase	d							12 50							13 20								13 50		
South Merton	d							12 52							13 22								13 52		
Morden South	d							12 54							13 24								13 54		
St Helier	d							12 56							13 26								13 56		
Sutton Common	d							12 57							13 28								13 58		
West Sutton	d							13 01							13 31								14 01		
Sutton (Surrey) 4	a			12 36				13 05				13 06			13 35			13 36					14 05		
East Croydon	🚋 d	12 09				12 24			12 39					12 54		13 09				13 24				13 39	
Redhill	d	*12 30*							*13 00*							*13 30*								*14 00*	
Gatwick Airport 10	✈ d	12 26				12 41			12 56					13 11		13 26				13 41				13 56	
Three Bridges 4	d	*12 44*				12 45			*13 14*					13 15		*13 44*				13 45				*14 14*	
Balcombe	d								*13 21*					13 21										*14 21*	
Haywards Heath 3	d	12 38				12 55			13 08					13 27		13 38				13 55				14 08	
Wivelsfield 4	d	*12 50*				12 59								13 31		*13 50*				13 59					
Burgess Hill 4	d	*12 52*				13 01			*13 33*					13 33		*13 52*				14 01				*14 33*	
Hassocks 4	d	*12 55*				13 04			*13 36*					13 36		*13 55*				14 04				*14 36*	
Preston Park	d	*13 02*				13 11			*13 43*					13 43		*14 02*				14 11				*14 43*	
Brighton 10	a	12 54				13 17			13 24					13 49		13 54				14 17				14 25	

For general notes see front of timetable
For details of catering facilities see Directory of Train Operators

A Until 5 September from Barnsley (Table 53). From 8 September from Derby (Table 53)
B From Leeds (Table 53)
C From Nottingham (Table 53)
D From Derby (Table 53)
E From Sheffield (Table 53)

Bedford, Luton, St.Albans and City of London → South London, Gatwick Airport and Brighton

Network Diagram - see first page of Table 52

	FC	FC	FC 1	FC	FC 1	EM 1 ◇ A	FC	FC	FC 1	FC	FC 1		EM 1 ◇ B	FC	FC	FC 1	FC	FC 1	EM 1 ◇ A	FC	FC	FC 1	FC	FC 1
Bedford 7 d			12 25		12 40	12 51			12 55		13 10		13 21			13 25		13 40	13 51			13 55		14 10
Flitwick d			12 34		12 49				13 04		13 19					13 34		13 49				14 04		14 19
Harlington d			12 38		12 53				13 08		13 23					13 38		13 53				14 08		14 23
Leagrave d			12 44		12 59				13 14		13 29					13 44		13 59				14 14		14 29
Luton 10 d		12 44	12 49		13 04			13 14	13 19		13 34		13 36		13 44	13 49		14 04			14 14	14 19		14 34
Luton Airport Parkway 7 ✈ d		12 46	12 51		13 06	13 07		13 16	13 21		13 36				13 46	13 51		14 06	14 07		14 16	14 21		14 36
Harpenden d		12 52	12 57		13 12			13 22	13 27		13 42				13 52	13 57		14 12			14 22	14 27		14 42
St Albans City d	12 43	12 58	13 03		13 18		13 13	13 28	13 33		13 48			13 43	13 58	14 03		14 18		14 13	14 28	14 33		14 48
Radlett d	12 48	13 03					13 18	13 33						13 48	14 03					14 18	14 33			
Elstree & Borehamwood d	12 53	13 08					13 23	13 38						13 53	14 08					14 23	14 38			
Mill Hill Broadway d	12 57	13 12		←			13 27	13 42		←				13 57	14 12		←			14 27	14 42		←	
Hendon d	13 01	13 16		13 16			13 31	13 46		13 46				14 01	14 16		14 16			14 31	14 46		14 46	
Cricklewood d	13 04	→		13 19			13 34	→		13 49				14 04	→		14 19			14 34	→		14 49	
West Hampstead Thameslink ⊖ d	13 07			13 22			13 37			13 52				14 07			14 22			14 37			14 52	
Kentish Town ⊖ d	13 11			13 26			13 41			13 56				14 11			14 26			14 41			14 56	
St Pancras International ⊖ a						13 34							14 04						14 34					
St Pancras International 15 ⊖ d	13 17		13 24	13 32	13 39		13 47		13 54	14 02	14 09			14 17		14 24	14 32	14 39		14 47		14 54	15 02	15 09
Farringdon 3 ⊖ d	13 22		13 29	13 37	13 44		13 52		13 59	14 07	14 14			14 22		14 29	14 37	14 44		14 52		14 59	15 07	15 14
Barbican ⊖ a																								
Moorgate ⊖ a																								
City Thameslink 3 d	13 24		13 31	13 39	13 46		13 54		14 01	14 09	14 16			14 24		14 31	14 39	14 46		14 54		15 01	15 09	15 16
London Blackfriars 3 ⊖ d	13 30		13 35	13 46	13 50		14 00		14 05	14 16	14 20			14 30		14 35	14 46	14 50		15 00		15 05	15 16	15 20
Elephant & Castle ⊖ d	13 33			13 49			14 03			14 19				14 33			14 49			15 03			15 19	
Loughborough Jn d	13 37			13 53			14 07			14 23				14 37			14 53			15 07			15 23	
Herne Hill 4 d	13 42			13 57			14 12			14 27				14 42			14 57			15 12			15 27	
London Bridge 4 ⊖ d			13 41		13 56				14 11		14 26					14 41		14 56				15 11		15 26
Tulse Hill 3 d	13 46			14 02			14 16			14 32				14 46			15 02			15 16			15 32	
Streatham 4 d	13 49			14 05			14 19			14 35				14 49			15 05			15 19			15 35	
Mitcham Eastfields d	13 53						14 23							14 53						15 23				
Mitcham Junction 🚋 d	13 57						14 27							14 57						15 27				
Hackbridge d	14 00						14 30							15 00						15 30				
Carshalton d	14 03						14 33							15 03						15 33				
Tooting d				14 10						14 40							15 10						15 40	
Haydons Road d				14 13						14 43							15 13						15 43	
Wimbledon 6 ⊖ 🚋 d				14 17						14 47							15 17						15 47	
Wimbledon Chase d				14 20						14 50							15 20						15 50	
South Merton d				14 22						14 52							15 22						15 52	
Morden South d				14 24						14 54							15 24						15 54	
St Helier d				14 26						14 56							15 26						15 56	
Sutton Common d				14 28						14 58							15 28						15 58	
West Sutton d				14 31						15 01							15 31						16 01	
Sutton (Surrey) 4 a	14 06			14 33			14 36			15 05				15 06			15 35			15 36			16 05	
East Croydon 🚋 d			13 54		14 09				14 24		14 39					14 54		15 09				15 24		15 39
Redhill d					*14 30*						*15 00*							*15 30*						*16 00*
Gatwick Airport 10 ✈ d			14 11		14 26				14 41		14 56					15 11		15 26				15 41		15 56
Three Bridges 4 d			14 15		*14 44*				14 45		*15 14*					15 15		*15 44*				15 45		16 00
Balcombe d			14 21								*15 21*					15 21		*16 21*						
Haywards Heath 3 d			14 27		14 38				14 55		15 08					15 27		15 38				15 55		16 10
Wivelsfield 4 d			14 31		*14 50*				14 59							15 31		*15 50*				15 59		
Burgess Hill 4 d			14 33		*14 52*				15 01		*15 33*					15 33		*15 52*				16 01		*16 33*
Hassocks 4 d			14 36		*14 55*				15 04		*15 36*					15 36		*15 55*				16 04		*16 36*
Preston Park d			14 43		*15 02*				15 11		*15 43*					15 43		*16 02*				16 11		*16 43*
Brighton 10 a			14 49		14 54				15 17		15 24					15 49		15 54				16 17		16 24

For general notes see front of timetable
For details of catering facilities see
Directory of Train Operators

A From Derby (Table 53)
B From Nottingham (Table 53)

Bedford, Luton, St.Albans and City of London → South London, Gatwick Airport and Brighton

Network Diagram - see first page of Table 52

Station		EM	FC	FC		FC	FC	FC	EM	FC	FC	FC	EM	FC	FC	EM	FC	FC		FC	FC	FC	FC	EM	FC
		1 ◇				1		1	1 ◇			1	1 ◇		1	1 ◇				1		1	1	1 ◇	
		A							B				C			A								B	
		⊡							⊡				⊡			⊡								⊡	
Bedford 7	d	14 21				14 25		14 40	14 51			14 55			15 10	15 21				15 25		15 35	15 40	15 51	
Flitwick	d					14 34		14 49				15 04			15 19					15 34			15 49		
Harlington	d					14 38		14 53				15 08			15 23					15 38			15 53		
Leagrave	d					14 44		14 59				15 14			15 29					15 44			15 59		
Luton 10	d	14 36		14 44		14 49		15 04			15 14	15 19	15 20		15 34	15 36		15 44		15 49		15 55	16 04		
Luton Airport Parkway 7 ✈	d			14 46		14 51		15 06	15 07		15 16	15 21			15 36			15 46		15 51		15 57	16 06	16 07	
Harpenden	d			14 52		14 57		15 12			15 22	15 27			15 42			15 52		15 57		16 03	16 12		
St Albans City	d		14 43	14 58		15 03		15 18		15 13	15 28	15 33			15 48		15 42	15 58		16 03		16 10	16 18		16 13
Radlett	d		14 48	15 03						15 18	15 33						15 47	16 03							16 18
Elstree & Borehamwood	d		14 53	15 08						15 23	15 38						15 52	16 08			←				16 23
Mill Hill Broadway	d		14 57	15 12			←			15 27	15 42			←			15 56	16 12			16 12				16 27
Hendon	d		15 01	15 16			15 16			15 31	15 46			15 46			16 00	→			16 16				16 31
Cricklewood	d		15 04	→			15 19			15 34	→			15 49			16 03				16 19				16 34
West Hampstead Thameslink	⊖ d		15 07				15 22			15 37				15 52			16 06			16 16	16 22				16 37
Kentish Town	⊖ d		15 11				15 26			15 41				15 56			16 10				16 26				16 41
St Pancras International	⊖ a	15 04							15 34				15 50			16 04								16 34	
St Pancras International 15	⊖ d		15 17			15 24	15 32	15 39		15 47		15 54		16 02	16 09		16 14			16 27	16 32	16 36	16 39		16 45
Farringdon 3	⊖ d		15 22			15 29	15 37	15 44		15 52		15 59		16 07	16 14		16 15			16 32	16 37	16 40	16 44		16 50
Barbican	⊖ a																						16 46		
Moorgate	⊖ a																						16 51		
City Thameslink 3	d		15 24			15 31	15 39	15 46		15 54		16 01		16 09	16 16		16 21			16 34	16 39	16 43			16 52
London Blackfriars 3	⊖ d		15 30			15 35	15 46	15 50		16 00		16 05		16 16	16 20		16 26			16 37	16 42	16 46			16 58
Elephant & Castle	⊖ d		15 33				15 49			16 03				16 19			16 30				16 45	16 50			17 02
Loughborough Jn	d		15 37				15 53			16 07				16 23			16 34				16 49	16 54			17 06
Herne Hill 4	d		15 42				15 57			16 12				16 27			16 38				16 53	16 58			17 11
London Bridge 4	⊖ d					15 41		15 56				16 11			16 26					16b46					
Tulse Hill 3	d		15 46				16 02			16 16				16 32			16 42				16 58	17c08			17 16
Streatham 4	d		15 49				16 05			16 19				16 35			16 45				17 01	17 11			17 19
Mitcham Eastfields	d		15 53							16 23							16 49								17 23
Mitcham Junction 🚋	d		15 57							16 27							16 52								17 27
Hackbridge	d		16 00							16 30							16 56								17 30
Carshalton	d		16 03							16 33							16 58								17 33
Tooting	d						16 10							16 39							17 06	17 16			
Haydons Road	d						16 13							16 42							17 09	17 19			
Wimbledon 6	⊖ 🚋 d						16 17							16 46							17 13	17a23			
Wimbledon Chase	d						16 20							16 49							17 16				
South Merton	d						16 22							16 51							17 18				
Morden South	d						16 24							16 53							17 20				
St Helier	d						16 26							16 55							17 22				
Sutton Common	d						16 28							16 57							17 24				
West Sutton	d						16 31							17 00							17 27				
Sutton (Surrey) 4	a		16 06				16 35			16 36				17 05			17 02				17 31				17 38
East Croydon 🚋	d					15 54		16 09				16 24			16 40					17 00					
Redhill	d							*16 30*							*17 00*					*17 27*					
Gatwick Airport 10 ✈	d					16 11		16 26				16 41			16 56					17 16					
Three Bridges 4	d					16 15		16 30				16 45			17 00					17 20					
Balcombe	d					16 21														17 26					
Haywards Heath 3	d					16 27		16 40				16 55			17 10					17 32					
Wivelsfield 4	d					16 31		*16 50*				16 59			*17 28*					17 36					
Burgess Hill 4	d					16 33		*16 52*				17 01			*17 30*					17 39					
Hassocks 4	d					16 36		*16 55*				17 04			*17 34*					17 43					
Preston Park	d					16 43		*17 02*				17 11			*17 41*					17 50					
Brighton 10	a					16 49		16 54				17 17			17 26					17 54					

For general notes see front of timetable
For details of catering facilities see Directory of Train Operators

A From Nottingham (Table 53)
B From Derby (Table 53)
C From Sheffield (Table 53)

b Arr. 1643
c Arr. 1702

Bedford, Luton, St.Albans and City of London → South London, Gatwick Airport and Brighton

Network Diagram - see first page of Table 52

	FC	FC 1	FC	FC 1	EM 1◇ A ☕	FC	FC	FC 1	FC		FC 1	FC	EM 1◇ B ☕	FC 1	FC	FC	FC	FC 1	EM 1◇ C ☕	EM 1◇ A ☕	FC	FC 1	FC	FC 1
Bedford 7 d		15 55		16 10	16 21			16 25			16 36	16 50	16 51	17 00				17 10	17 12	17 21		17 20		17 36
Flitwick d		16 04		16 19				16 34			16 45	16 59						17 19				17 29		17 45
Harlington d		16 08		16 23				16 38			16 49	17 03						17 23				17 33		17 49
Leagrave d		16 14		16 29				16 44			16 55	17 09						17 29				17 39		17 55
Luton 10 d	16 14	16 19		16 34	16 36		16 44	16 49			17 00	17 14		17 18			17 18	17 34		17 36		17 44	17 48	18 00
Luton Airport Parkway 7 ✈ d	16 16	16 21		16 36			16 46	16 51			17 02	17 16	17 07			←	17 20	17 36				17 46	17 50	18 02
Harpenden d	16 22	16 27		16 42			16 52	16 57			17 08	17 22				17 22	17 26	17 42				17 52	17 56	18 08
St Albans City d	16 28	16 33		16 48		16 43	16 58	17 03			17 14	→		17 28	17 18	17 28	17 32	17 48			17 44	17 58	18 02	18 14
Radlett d	16 33					16 48	17 03								17 23		17 37				17 49		18 07	
Elstree & Borehamwood d	16 38		←			16 53	17 08		←						17 28		17 41				17 53		18 11	
Mill Hill Broadway d	16 42		16 42			16 57	17 12		17 12						17 32		17 45				17 57		18 15	
Hendon d	→		16 46			17 01	→		17 16						17 36		17 48				18 00		18 18	
Cricklewood d			16 49			17 04			17 19						17 39		17 52				18 04		18 22	
West Hampstead Thameslink ⊖ d		16 48	16 52			17 08		17 16	17 22						17 42	17 46	17 55				18 07	18 12	18 25	
Kentish Town ⊖ d			16 56			17 12			17 26						17 46		17 59				18 11		18 29	
St Pancras International ⊖ a					17 04								17 34						17 53	18 04				
St Pancras International 15 ⊖ d		16 55	17 01	17 09		17 17		17 25	17 31		17 35			17 46	17 51	17 55	18 03	18 09			18 15	18 19	18 33	18 39
Farringdon 3 ⊖ d		17 00	17 06	17 14		17 22		17 30	17 36		17 40			17 50	17 56	18 00	18 08	18 14			18 20	18 24	18 38	18 44
Barbican ⊖ a		17 02						17 34								18 04						18 26		
Moorgate ⊖ a		17 07						17 39								18 09						18 31		
City Thameslink 3 d			17 11	17 16		17 24			17 38		17 42			17 53	17 58		18 10	18 16			18 22		18 40	18 46
London Blackfriars 3 ⊖ d			17 14	17 20		17 30			17 42		17 46			17 57	18 02		18 14	18 20			18 26		18 44	18 49
Elephant & Castle ⊖ d			17 17			17 34			17 45						18 06		18 18				18 30		18 48	
Loughborough Jn d			17 21			17 38			17 49						18 10		18 22				18 34		18 52	
Herne Hill 4 d			17 25			17 42			17 53					18 06	18 14		18 26				18 38		18 56	
London Bridge 4 ⊖ d				17 32							17 52							18 26						18 56
Tulse Hill 3 d			17 29			17 46			17 58						18 18		18 31				18 44		19 02	
Streatham 4 d			17 33			17 50			18 01						18 22		18 34				18 47		19 05	
Mitcham Eastfields d						17 54									18 26						18 51			
Mitcham Junction d						17 57									18 30						18 55			
Hackbridge d						18 00									18 33						18 58			
Carshalton d						18 03									18 36						19 01			
Tooting d			17 38						18 06								18 38						19 10	
Haydons Road d			17 41						18 09								18 41						19 13	
Wimbledon 6 ⊖ d			17 45						18b14								18 45						19 17	
Wimbledon Chase d			17 48						18 17								18 48						19 20	
South Merton d			17 50						18 19								18 50						19 22	
Morden South d			17 52						18 21								18 52						19 24	
St Helier d			17 54						18 23								18 54						19 26	
Sutton Common d			17 56						18 25								18 56						19 28	
West Sutton d			17 59						18 28								18 59						19 31	
Sutton (Surrey) 4 a			18 03			18 07			18 31						18 39		19 03				19 04		19 38	
East Croydon d				17 50							18 08			18 20				18 40						19 10
Redhill d				18 02							18 29			18 32				19 07						19 30
Gatwick Airport 10 ✈ d				18 12							18 24			18 42				18 56						19 26
Three Bridges 4 d				18 18							18c35			18a51				19 02						19 32
Balcombe d				18 24							18c50							19 08						
Haywards Heath 3 d				18 30							18 36			18e58				19 12						19 40
Wivelsfield 4 d				18 34							18 42			19e09				19 28						
Burgess Hill 4 d				18 37							18 43			19e04				19 17						19 46
Hassocks 4 d				18 41							18 47			19e08				19 21						19 50
Preston Park d				18 48							18 56			19e15				19 43						
Brighton 10 a				18 54							19 02			19e25				19 32						20 00

For general notes see front of timetable
For details of catering facilities see Directory of Train Operators

A From Nottingham (Table 53)
B From Derby (Table 53)
C From Sheffield (Table 53)
b Arr. 1811
c Change at East Croydon
e Change at Gatwick Airport

Bedford, Luton, St.Albans and City of London → South London, Gatwick Airport and Brighton

Network Diagram - see first page of Table 52

		FC		FC 1	EM 1 ◇ A	FC	EM 1 ◇ B	FC 1	EM 1 ◇ C	FC	FC	FC 1	FC	FC 1	FC	FC 1		EM 1 ◇ A	FC	EM 1 ◇ B	EM 1 ◇ C	FC	FC 1	FC	FC 1
Bedford 7	d			17 50	17 51			18 10	18 23			18 30		18 40		18 50		18 53			19 23		19 20		19 50
Flitwick	d			17 59				18 19				18 39		18 49		18 59							19 29		19 59
Harlington	d			18 03				18 23						18 53		19 03							19 33		20 03
Leagrave	d			18 09				18 29						18 59		19 09							19 39		20 09
Luton 10	d			18 14		18 20	18 21	18 34	18 39		18 50	18 52	←	19 04		19 14			19 20	19 22	19 39		19 44	19 50	20 14
Luton Airport Parkway 7 ✈	d			18 16	18 07	18 22		18 36			18 52		18 52	19 06		19 16		19 07	19 22				19 46	19 52	20 16
Harpenden	d			18 22		18 28		18 42			→	18 58	18 58	19 12		19 22			19 28				19 52	19 58	20 22
St Albans City	d	18 18		18 28		18 34		18 48		18 52		19 03	19 04	19 18	19 22	19 28			19 34			19 52	19 58	20 04	20 28
Radlett	d	18 23				18 39				18 57			19 09		19 27				19 39			19 57		20 09	
Elstree & Borehamwood	d	18 27				18 43				19 01			19 13		19 31				19 43			20 01		20 13	
Mill Hill Broadway	d					18 47							19 17						19 47					20 17	
Hendon	d					18 50							19 20						19 50					20 20	
Cricklewood	d					18 54							19 24						19 54					20 24	
West Hampstead Thameslink	⊖ d	18 35		18 42		18 57				19 09			19 27		19 39	19 42			19 57			20 09	20 12	20 27	20 42
Kentish Town	⊖ d					19 01							19 31						20 01					20 31	
St Pancras International	⊖ a				18 34		18 51		19 04									19 34		19 52	20 04				
St Pancras International 15	⊖ d	18 45		18 54		19 05		19 09		19 17		19 24	19 35	19 39	19 48	19 54			20 05			20 17	20 24	20 35	20 54
Farringdon 3	⊖ d	18 50		18 59		19 10		19 14		19 22		19 29	19 40	19 44	19 52	19 59			20 10			20 22	20 29	20 40	20 59
Barbican	⊖ a																								
Moorgate	⊖ a																								
City Thameslink 3	d	18 52		19 01		19 12		19 16		19 24		19 31	19 42	19 47	19 55	20 01			20 12			20 24	20 31	20 42	21 01
London Blackfriars 3	⊖ d	18 56		19 04		19 16		19 19		19 30		19 34	19 46	19b54	20 00	20 04			20 16			20 30	20 34	20 46	21 04
Elephant & Castle	⊖ d	19 00				19 19				19 33			19 49		20 03				20 19			20 33		20 49	
Loughborough Jn	d	19 04				19 23				19 37			19 53		20 07				20 23			20 37		20 53	
Herne Hill 4	d	19 08				19 28				19 42			19 58		20 12				20 27			20 42		20 57	
London Bridge 4	⊖ d			19 12				19 27				19 41		20 01		20 11							20 41		21 11
Tulse Hill 3	d	19 14				19 32				19 47			20 02		20 16				20 32			20 46		21 02	
Streatham 4	d	19 17				19 35				19 50			20 05		20 19				20 35			20 49		21 05	
Mitcham Eastfields	d	19 21								19 53					20 23							20 53			
Mitcham Junction	🚋 d	19 25								19 57					20 27							20 57			
Hackbridge	d	19 28								20 00					20 30							21 00			
Carshalton	d	19 31								20 04					20 33							21 03			
Tooting	d					19 40							20 10						20 40					21 10	
Haydons Road	d					19 43							20 13						20 43					21 13	
Wimbledon 6	⊖ 🚋 d					19 47							20 17						20 47					21 17	
Wimbledon Chase	d					19 50							20 20						20 50					21 20	
South Merton	d					19 52							20 22						20 52					21 22	
Morden South	d					19 54							20 24						20 54					21 24	
St Helier	d					19 56							20 26						20 56					21 26	
Sutton Common	d					19 58							20 28						20 58					21 28	
West Sutton	d					20 01							20 31						21 01					21 31	
Sutton (Surrey) 4	a	19 34				20 08				20 08			20 38		20 38				21 05			21 08		21 38	
East Croydon	🚋 d			19 24				19 39				19 54		20 14		20 23							20 54		21 24
Redhill	d							*20 00*				*20 24*		*20 30*		*20 46*							*21 30*		*21 59*
Gatwick Airport 10	✈ d			19 41				19 55				20 11		20 31		20 40							21 11		21 41
Three Bridges 4	d			19 45				20 01				20 15		*20 40*		20 43							21 15		21 45
Balcombe	d			19 51										*20 49*		20 49									21 51
Haywards Heath 3	d			19 58				20 09				20 26		20 42		20 58							21 26		21 58
Wivelsfield 4	d			20 02				*20 17*				20 30				21 02							21 30		22 02
Burgess Hill 4	d			20 04				20 15				20 32		*21 04*		21 04							21 32		22 04
Hassocks 4	d			20 07				20 19				20 35		*21 07*		21 07							21 35		22 08
Preston Park	d			20 14								20 42		*21 14*		21 15							21 42		22 15
Brighton 10	a			20 20				20 29				20 46		20 58		21 20							21 48		22 20

For general notes see front of timetable
For details of catering facilities see Directory of Train Operators

A From Derby (Table 53)
B From Sheffield (Table 53)
C From Nottingham (Table 53)
b Arr. 1951

Bedford, Luton, St.Albans and City of London → South London, Gatwick Airport and Brighton

Network Diagram - see first page of Table 52

		EM [1] ◇ A	FC	EM [1] ◇ B	FC [1]	FC	FC [1]	EM [1] ◇ A		EM [1] ◇ C	FC	EM [1] ◇ B	FC [1]	FC	FC [1]	EM [1] ◇ B	FC	FC [1]	EM [1] ◇ B	FC	FC	FC [1]			
Bedford [7]	d	19 51		20 23	20 20		20 50	20 51		21 11		21 23	21 20		21 50	22 00		22 10	22 45	22 40	23 10	23 40			
Flitwick	d				20 29		20 59						21 29		21 59			22 19		22 49	23 19	23 49			
Harlington	d				20 33		21 03						21 33		22 03			22 23		22 53	23 23	23 53			
Leagrave	d				20 39		21 09						21 39		22 09			22 29		22 59	23 29	23 59			
Luton [10]	d		20 20	20 39	20 44	20 50	21 14				21 20	21 39	21 44	21 50	22 14	22 16	22 20	22 34	23 01	23 04	23 34	00 04			
Luton Airport Parkway [7] ✈	d	20 07	20 22		20 46	20 52	21 16	21 07			21 22		21 46	21 52	22 16		22 22	22 36		23 06	23 36	00 06			
Harpenden	d		20 28		20 52	20 58	21 22				21 28		21 52	21 58	22 22		22 28	22 42		23 12	23 42	00 12			
St Albans City	d		20 34		20 58	21 04	21 28				21 34		21 59	22 04	22 29		22 34	22 48		23 18	23 48	00 18			
Radlett	d		20 39			21 09					21 39			22 09			22 39	22 53		23 23	23 53	00 23			
Elstree & Borehamwood	d		20 43			21 13					21 43			22 13			22 43	22 57		23 27	23 57	00 27			
Mill Hill Broadway	d		20 47			21 17					21 47			22 17			22 47	23 01		23 31	00 01	00 31			
Hendon	d		20 50			21 20					21 50			22 20			22 50	23 04		23 34	00 04	00 34			
Cricklewood	d		20 54			21 24					21 54			22 24			22 54	23 08		23 38	00 08	00 38			
West Hampstead Thameslink ⊖	d		20 57		21 12	21 27	21 42				21 57		22 12	22 27	22 42		22 57	23 12		23 42	00 12	00 42			
Kentish Town ⊖	d		21 01			21 31					22 01			22 31			23 01	23 16		23 46	00 16	00 46			
St Pancras International ⊖	a	20 34		21 04				21 34		21 53		22 04				22 40			23 32						
St Pancras International [15] ⊖	d		21 05		21 24	21 35	21 54				22 05		22 24	22 36	22 54		23 06	23 24		23 54	00 24	00 54			
Farringdon [3] ⊖	d		21 10		21 29	21 40	21 59				22 10		22 29	22 40	22 59		23 10	23 29		23 59	00 29				
Barbican ⊖	a																								
Moorgate ⊖	a																								
City Thameslink [3]	d		21 12		21 31	21 42	22 01				22 12		22 31	22 42	23 01										
London Blackfriars [3] ⊖	d		21 16		21 34	21 46	22 04				22 16		22 34	22 46	23 04		23 16	23 34		00 04	00 34	01 04			
Elephant & Castle ⊖	d		21 19			21 49					22 19			22 49			23 19								
Loughborough Jn	d		21 23			21 53					22 23			22 53			23s23								
Herne Hill [4]	d		21 27			21 57					22 27			22 57			23 27								
London Bridge [4] ⊖	d				21 41		22 11						22 41		23 11			23 41		00 11	00 41				
Tulse Hill [3]	d		21 32			22 02					22 32			23 02			23 32								
Streatham [4]	d		21 35			22 05					22 35			23 04			23 35								
Mitcham Eastfields	d																								
Mitcham Junction	d																								
Hackbridge	d																								
Carshalton	d																								
Tooting	d		21 40			22 10					22 40			23 10			23 40								
Haydons Road	d		21 43			22 13					22 43			23 13			23 43								
Wimbledon [6] ⊖	d		21 47			22 17					22 47			23 17			23 46								
Wimbledon Chase	d		21 50			22 20					22 50			23 20			23 49								
South Merton	d		21 52			22 22					22 52			23 22			23 51								
Morden South	d		21 54			22 24					22 54			23 24			23 53								
St Helier	d		21 56			22 26					22 56			23 26			23 55								
Sutton Common	d		21 58			22 28					22 58			23 28			23 57								
West Sutton	d		22 01			22 31					23 01			23 31			23 59								
Sutton (Surrey) [4]	a		22 05			22 38					23 05			23 35			00 03								
East Croydon	d				21 54		22 24						22 54		23 24			23 57		00 27	00 57	01 32			
Redhill	d				*22 30*		*23 00*						*23 30*		*00 03*			*00 24*		*00 50*					
Gatwick Airport [10] ✈	d				22 11		22 41						23 11		23 41			00 17		00 50	01 17	01 52			
Three Bridges [4]	d				22 15		22 45						23 15		23 47			00a24		00a54	01a24	01a58			
Balcombe	d						22 51								23 53										
Haywards Heath [3]	d				22 26		22 58						23 26		23 58			*01 00*			*02 04*				
Wivelsfield [4]	d				22 30		23 02						23 30		00 02										
Burgess Hill [4]	d				22 32		23 04						23 32		00 04										
Hassocks [4]	d				22 35		23 08						23 35		00 08										
Preston Park	d				22 42		23 15						23 42		00 15										
Brighton [10]	a				22 48		23 20						23 48		00 20			*01 17*			*02 30*				

For general notes see front of timetable
For details of catering facilities see Directory of Train Operators

A From Derby (Table 53)
B From Nottingham (Table 53)
C From Sheffield (Table 53)

Bedford, Luton, St.Albans and City of London → South London, Gatwick Airport and Brighton

Network Diagram - see first page of Table 52

		FC 1	FC 1	FC	FC	FC 1	FC 1	FC 1	FC 1	FC 1	FC 1	FC 1	FC	FC 1		FC 1	FC	FC 1	FC 1	FC	FC 1	EM 1 ◇ A	FC	FC	FC 1
Bedford 7	d	21p50	22p10	22p40	23p10	23p40	00 40	01 40	02 40	03 10	03 40	04 20		04 50		05 20		05 40	05 50		06 10	06 16			06 25
Flitwick	d	21p59	22p19	22p49	23p19	23p49	00 49	01 49	02 49	03 19	03 49	04 29		04 59		05 29		05 49	05 59		06 19				06 34
Harlington	d	22p03	22p23	22p53	23p23	23p53	00 53	01 53	02 53	03 23	03 53	04 33		05 03		05 33		05 53	06 03		06 23				06 38
Leagrave	d	22p09	22p29	22p59	23p29	23p59	00 59	01 59	02 59	03 29	03 59	04 39		05 09		05 39		05 59	06 09		06 29				06 44
Luton 10	d	22p14	22p34	23p04	23p34	00 04	01 04	02 04	03 04	03 34	04 04	04 44		05 14		05 44	05 50	06 04	06 14	06 20	06 34	06 37	06 44		06 49
Luton Airport Parkway 7 ✈	d	22p16	22p36	23p06	23p36	00 06	01 06	02 06	03 06	03 36	04 06	04 46		05 16		05 46	05 52	06 06	06 16	06 22	06 36		06 46		06 51
Harpenden	d	22p22	22p42	23p12	23p42	00 12	01 12	02 12	03 12	03 42	04 12	04 52		05 22		05 52	05 58	06 12	06 22	06 28	06 42		06 52		06 57
St Albans City	d	22p29	22p48	23p18	23p48	00 18	01 18	02 18	03 18	03 48	04 18	04 58		05 28		05 58	06 04	06 18	06 28	06 34	06 48		06 58		07 03
Radlett	d		22p53	23p23	23p53	00 23	01 23	02 23	03 23	03 53	04 23	05 03		05 33			06 09			06 39			07 03		
Elstree & Borehamwood	d		22p57	23p27	23p57	00 27	01 27	02 27	03 27	03 57	04 27	05 07		05 37			06 13			06 43			07 08		
Mill Hill Broadway	d		23p01	23p31	00 01	00 31	01 31	02 31	03 31	04 01	04 31	05 11		05 41			06 17			06 47			07 12		
Hendon	d		23p04	23p34	00 04	00 34	01 34	02 34	03 34	04 04	04 34	05 14		05 44			06 20			06 50			07 16 →		
Cricklewood	d		23p08	23p38	00 08	00 38	01 38	02 38	03 38	04 08	04 38	05 18		05 48			06 24			06 54					
West Hampstead Thameslink ⊖	d	22p42	23p12	23p42	00 12	00 42	01 42	02 42	03 42	04 12	04 42	05 22		05 52		06 12	06 27		06 42	06 57					
Kentish Town ⊖	d		23p16	23p46	00 16	00 46	01 46	02 46	03 46	04 16	04 46	05 26		05 56			06 31			07 01					
St Pancras International ⊖	a																					07 05			
St Pancras International 15 ⊖	d	22p54	23p24	23p54	00 24	00 54	01 54	02 54	03 54	04 23	04 54	05 34		06 04		06 24	06 35	06 39	06 54	07 05	07 09				07 24
Farringdon 3 ⊖	d	22p59	23p29	23p59	00 29						04 59	05 39		06 09		06 29	06 40	06 44	06 59	07 10	07 14				07 29
Barbican ⊖	a																								
Moorgate ⊖	a																								
City Thameslink 3	d	23p01																							
London Blackfriars 3 ⊖	d	23p04	23p34	00 04	00 34	01 04	02 04	03 04	04 04	04 34	05 04	05 44	06 16	06b20		06 35	06 46	06 50	07 05	07 16	07 20			07 30	07 35
Elephant & Castle ⊖	d												06 19				06 49			07 19				07 33	
Loughborough Jn	d																06 53			07 23				07 37	
Herne Hill 4	d												06 27				06 57			07 27				07 42	
London Bridge 4 ⊖	d	23p11	23p41	00 11	00 41							05 50		06 26		06 41		06 56	07 11		07 26				07 41
Tulse Hill 3	d												06 32				07 02			07 32				07 46	
Streatham 4	d												06 35				07 05			07 35				07 49	
Mitcham Eastfields	d																							07 53	
Mitcham Junction 🚋	d																							07 57	
Hackbridge	d																							08 00	
Carshalton	d																							08 05	
Tooting	d												06 40				07 10			07 40					
Haydons Road	d												06 43				07 13			07 43					
Wimbledon 6 ⊖ 🚋	d												06 47				07 17			07 47					
Wimbledon Chase	d												06 50				07 20			07 50					
South Merton	d												06 52				07 22			07 52					
Morden South	d												06 54				07 24			07 54					
St Helier	d												06 56				07 26			07 56					
Sutton Common	d												06 58				07 28			07 58					
West Sutton	d												07 01				07 31			08 01					
Sutton (Surrey) 4	a												07 05				07 35			08 05				08 06	
East Croydon 🚋	d	23p24	23p57	00 27	00 57	01 32	02 32	03 32	04 32	05 02	05 32	06 05		06 39		06 54		07 09	07 24		07 39				07 54
Redhill	d	*00 03*	*00 24*	*00 50*						*05 39*	*06 06*	*06 45*		*07 15*					*07 48*		*08 00*				
Gatwick Airport 10 ✈	d	23p41	00 17	00 50	01 17	01 52	02 52	03 52	04 52	05 22	05 54	06 20		06 56		07 11		07 26	07 41		07 56				08 11
Three Bridges 4	d	23p47	00a24	00a54	01a24	01a58	02a58	03a58	04a58	05 28	06 00	06 26		07 00		07 15		*07 39*	07 45		*08 14*				08 15
Balcombe	d	23p53						*05c35*		05 35	06 06	06 32				07 21					*08 21*				08 21
Haywards Heath 3	d	23p58	*01 00*		*02 06*			*05 00*	*05 40*	05 42	06 12	06 38		07 08		07 27		07 38	07 55		08 08				08 27
Wivelsfield 4	d	00 02							*05 46*	05 46	06 16	*06 45*				07 31		*07 50*	07 59						08 31
Burgess Hill 4	d	00 04							*05 48*	05 48	06 18	*06 47*		*07 33*		07 33		*07 52*	08 01		*08 33*				08 33
Hassocks 4	d	00 08							*05 52*	05 52	06 22	*06 51*		*07 36*		07 36		*07 55*	08 04		*08 36*				08 36
Preston Park	d	00 15							*05 59*	05 59	06 29	*06 58*		*07 43*		07 43		*08 02*	08 11		*08 43*				08 43
Brighton 10	a	00 20	*01 17*		*02 32*			*05 16*	*06 07*	06 07	06 34	06 51		07 24		07 49		07 54	08 17		08 24				08 49

For general notes see front of timetable
For details of catering facilities see Directory of Train Operators

A From Derby (Table 53)
b Arr. 0614
c Change at Gatwick Airport and Three Bridges

Table 52

Saturdays

Bedford, Luton, St.Albans and City of London → South London, Gatwick Airport and Brighton

Network Diagram - see first page of Table 52

		FC	FC	FC 1	EM 1 ◇ A	FC		FC	FC 1	FC	FC	EM 1 ◇ B	FC 1	FC	EM 1 ◇ A	FC	FC 1	FC	FC	FC 1		FC	FC	FC 1	FC
Bedford 7	d			06 40	06 50				06 55				07 10		07 26		07 25			07 40				07 55	
Flitwick	d			06 49					07 04				07 19				07 34			07 49				08 04	
Harlington	d			06 53					07 08				07 23				07 38			07 53				08 08	
Leagrave	d			06 59					07 14				07 29				07 44			07 59				08 14	
Luton 10	d		06 59	07 04	07 08			07 14	07 19		07 26	07 30	07 34			07 44	07 49		07 59	08 04			08 14	08 19	
Luton Airport Parkway 7 ✈	d		07 01	07 06				07 16	07 21		07 28		07 36		07 42	07 46	07 51		08 01	08 06			08 16	08 21	
Harpenden	d		07 07	07 12				07 22	07 27		07 34		07 42			07 52	07 57		08 07	08 12			08 22	08 27	
St Albans City	d		07 13	07 18				07 28	07 33		07b43		07 48			07 58	08 03		08 13	08 18			08 28	08 33	
Radlett	d		07 18					07 33			07 48					08 03			08 18				08 33		
Elstree & Borehamwood	d		07 23					07 38			07 53					08 08			08 23				08 38		
Mill Hill Broadway	d	←	07 27			←		07 42		←	07 57			←		08 12		←	08 27			←	08 42		←
Hendon	d	07 16	07 31			07 31		07 46		07 46	08 01			08 01		08 16		08 16	08 31			08 31	08 46		08 46
Cricklewood	d	07 19	→			07 34		→		07 50	→			08 04		→		08 19	→			08 34	→		08 49
West Hampstead Thameslink ⊖	d	07 22				07 37				07 52				08 07				08 22				08 37			08 52
Kentish Town ⊖	d	07 26				07 41				07 56				08 11				08 26				08 41			08 56
St Pancras International ⊖	a				07 38							08 05			08 09										
St Pancras International 15 ⊖	d	07 32		07 39		07 47			07 54	08 02			08 10	08 17			08 24	08 32		08 39		08 47		08 54	09 02
Farringdon 3 ⊖	d	07 37		07 44		07 52			07 59	08 07			08 14	08 22			08 29	08 37		08 44		08 52		08 59	09 07
Barbican ⊖	a																								
Moorgate ⊖	a																								
City Thameslink 3	d																							09 01	09 09
London Blackfriars 3 ⊖	d	07c46		07 50		08 00			08 05	08e16			08 20	08 30			08 35	08f46		08 50		09 00		09 05	09 16
Elephant & Castle ⊖	d	07 49				08 03				08 19				08 33				08 49				09 03			09 19
Loughborough Jn	d	07 53				08 07				08 23				08 37				08 53				09 07			09 23
Herne Hill 4	d	07 57				08 12				08 27				08 42				08 57				09 12			09 27
London Bridge 4 ⊖	d			07 56					08 11				08 26				08 41			08 56				09 11	
Tulse Hill 3	d	08 02				08 16				08 32				08 46				09 02				09 16			09 32
Streatham 4	d	08 05				08 19				08 35				08 49				09 05				09 19			09 35
Mitcham Eastfields	d					08 23								08 53								09 23			
Mitcham Junction	d					08 27								08 57								09 27			
Hackbridge	d					08 30								09 00								09 30			
Carshalton	d					08 33								09 03								09 33			
Tooting	d	08 10								08 40								09 10							09 40
Haydons Road	d	08 13								08 43								09 13							09 43
Wimbledon 6 ⊖	d	08 17								08 47								09 17							09 47
Wimbledon Chase	d	08 20								08 50								09 20							09 50
South Merton	d	08 22								08 52								09 22							09 52
Morden South	d	08 24								08 54								09 24							09 54
St Helier	d	08 26								08 56								09 26							09 56
Sutton Common	d	08 28								08 58								09 28							09 58
West Sutton	d	08 31								09 01								09 31							10 01
Sutton (Surrey) 4	a	08 35				08 36				09 05				09 06				09 35				09 36			10 05
East Croydon	d			08 09					08 24				08 39				08 54			09 09				09 24	
Redhill	d			*08 30*									*09 00*							*09 30*					
Gatwick Airport 10 ✈	d			08 26					08 41				08 56				09 11			09 26				09 41	
Three Bridges 4	d			*08 44*					08 45				*09 14*				09 15			*09 44*				09 45	
Balcombe	d												*09 21*				09 21								
Haywards Heath 3	d			08 38					08 55				09 08				09 27			09 38				09 55	
Wivelsfield 4	d			*08 50*					08 59								09 31			*09 50*				09 59	
Burgess Hill 4	d			*08 54*					09 01				*09 33*				09 33			*09 52*				10 01	
Hassocks 4	d			*08 57*					09 04				*09 36*				09 36			*09 55*				10 04	
Preston Park	d			*09 04*					09 11				*09 43*				09 43			*10 02*				10 11	
Brighton 10	a			08 54					09 18				09 24				09 49			09 54				10 17	

For general notes see front of timetable
For details of catering facilities see Directory of Train Operators

A From Nottingham (Table 53)
B From Sheffield (Table 53)
b Arr. 0739
c Arr. 0743
e Arr. 0813
f Arr. 0843

Table 52

Saturdays

Bedford, Luton, St.Albans and City of London → South London, Gatwick Airport and Brighton

Network Diagram - see first page of Table 52

Station		FC 1	EM 1 ◇ A ⊡	FC	FC	FC 1	FC	FC 1	EM 1 ◇ B ⊡	FC	FC	FC 1		FC	FC 1	EM 1 ◇ A ⊡	FC	FC	FC 1	FC	FC 1	EM 1 ◇ C ⊡	EM 1 ◇ D ⊡	FC	FC
Bedford 7	d	08 10	08 21			08 25		08 40	08 51			08 55			09 10	09 21			09 25		09 40	09 46	09 51		
Flitwick	d	08 19				08 34		08 49				09 04			09 19				09 34		09 49				
Harlington	d	08 23				08 38		08 53				09 08			09 23				09 38		09 53				
Leagrave	d	08 29				08 44		08 59				09 14			09 29				09 44		09 59				
Luton 10	d	08 34	08 36		08 44	08 49		09 04			09 14	09 19			09 34	09 36		09 44	09 49		10 04				10 14
Luton Airport Parkway 7 ✈	d	08 36			08 46	08 51		09 06	09 07		09 16	09 21			09 36			09 46	09 51		10 06		10 07		10 16
Harpenden	d	08 42			08 52	08 57		09 12			09 22	09 27			09 42			09 52	09 57		10 12				10 22
St Albans City	d	08 48		08 43	08 58	09 03		09 18		09 13	09 28	09 33			09 48		09 43	09 58	10 03		10 18			10 13	10 28
Radlett	d			08 48	09 03					09 18	09 33						09 48	10 03						10 18	10 33
Elstree & Borehamwood	d			08 53	09 08					09 23	09 38						09 53	10 08						10 23	10 38
Mill Hill Broadway	d			08 57	09 12		←			09 27	09 42			←			09 57	10 12		←				10 27	10 42
Hendon	d			09 01	09 16		09 16			09 31	09 46			09 46			10 01	10 16		10 16				10 31	10 46
Cricklewood	d			09 04	→		09 19			09 34	→			09 49			10 04	→		10 19				10 34	→
West Hampstead Thameslink	⊖ d			09 07			09 22			09 37				09 52			10 07			10 22				10 37	
Kentish Town	⊖ d			09 11			09 26			09 41				09 56			10 11			10 26				10 41	
St Pancras International	⊖ a		09 04						09 34							10 04						10 29	10 36		
St Pancras International 15	⊖ d	09 09		09 17		09 24	09 32	09 39		09 47		09 54		10 02	10 09		10 17		10 24	10 32	10 39			10 47	
Farringdon 3	⊖ d	09 14		09 22		09 29	09 37	09 44		09 52		09 59		10 07	10 14		10 22		10 29	10 37	10 44			10 52	
Barbican	⊖ a																								
Moorgate	⊖ a																								
City Thameslink 3	d	09 16		09 24		09 31	09 39	09 46		09 54		10 01		10 09	10 16		10 24		10 31	10 39	10 46			10 54	
London Blackfriars 3	⊖ d	09 20		09 30		09 35	09 46	09 50		10 00		10 05		10 16	10 20		10 30		10 35	10 46	10 50			11 00	
Elephant & Castle	⊖ d			09 33			09 49			10 03				10 19			10 33			10 49				11 03	
Loughborough Jn	d			09 37			09 53			10 07				10 23			10 37			10 53				11 07	
Herne Hill 4	d			09 42			09 57			10 12				10 27			10 42			10 57				11 12	
London Bridge 4	⊖ d	09 26				09 41		09 56				10 11			10 26				10 41		10 56				
Tulse Hill 3	d			09 46			10 02			10 16				10 32			10 46			11 02				11 16	
Streatham 4	d			09 49			10 05			10 19				10 35			10 49			11 05				11 19	
Mitcham Eastfields	d			09 53						10 23							10 53							11 23	
Mitcham Junction 🚊	d			09 57						10 27							10 57							11 27	
Hackbridge	d			10 00						10 30							11 00							11 30	
Carshalton	d			10 03						10 33							11 03							11 33	
Tooting	d						10 10							10 40						11 10					
Haydons Road	d						10 13							10 43						11 13					
Wimbledon 6	⊖ 🚊 d						10 17							10 47						11 17					
Wimbledon Chase	d						10 20							10 50						11 20					
South Merton	d						10 22							10 52						11 22					
Morden South	d						10 24							10 54						11 24					
St Helier	d						10 26							10 56						11 26					
Sutton Common	d						10 28							10 58						11 28					
West Sutton	d						10 31							11 01						11 31					
Sutton (Surrey) 4	a			10 06			10 35			10 36				11 05			11 06			11 35				11 36	
East Croydon	🚊 d	09 39				09 54		10 09				10 24			10 39				10 54		11 09				
Redhill	d	*10 00*						*10 30*							*11 00*						*11 30*				
Gatwick Airport 10	✈ d	09 56				10 11		10 26				10 41			10 56				11 11		11 26				
Three Bridges 4	d	*10 14*				10 15		*10 44*				10 45			*11 14*				11 15		*11 44*				
Balcombe	d	*10 21*				10 21									*11 21*				11 21						
Haywards Heath 3	d	10 08				10 27		10 38				10 55			11 08				11 27		11 38				
Wivelsfield 4	d					10 31		*10 50*				10 59							11 31		*11 50*				
Burgess Hill 4	d	*10 33*				10 33		*10 52*				11 01			*11 33*				11 33		*11 52*				
Hassocks 4	d	*10 36*				10 36		*10 55*				11 04			*11 36*				11 36		*11 55*				
Preston Park	d	*10 43*				10 43		*11 02*				11 11			*11 43*				11 43		*12 02*				
Brighton 10	a	10 24				10 49		10 54				11 17			11 24				11 49		11 54				

For general notes see front of timetable
For details of catering facilities see Directory of Train Operators

A From Nottingham (Table 53)
B From Derby (Table 53)
C Until 1 November from Sheffield (Table 53). From 8 November from Nottingham (Table 53)
D From Burton-on-Trent (Table 53)

Bedford, Luton, St.Albans and City of London → South London, Gatwick Airport and Brighton

Network Diagram - see first page of Table 52

		FC	FC	FC		EM	FC	FC	FC	FC	FC	EM	FC	FC	FC	FC	FC	EM		EM	FC	FC	FC	FC	FC
		1		1		1 ◇			1		1	1 ◇			1		1	1 ◇		1 ◇			1		1
						A						B						C		A					
						🍴						🍴						🍴		🍴					
Bedford 7	d	09 55		10 10		10 21			10 25		10 40	10 51			10 55		11 10	11 17		11 21			11 25		11 40
Flitwick	d	10 04		10 19					10 34		10 49				11 04		11 19						11 34		11 49
Harlington	d	10 08		10 23					10 38		10 53				11 08		11 23						11 38		11 53
Leagrave	d	10 14		10 29					10 44		10 59				11 14		11 29						11 44		11 59
Luton 10	d	10 19		10 34		10 36		10 44	10 49		11 04			11 14	11 19		11 34			11 36		11 44	11 49		12 04
Luton Airport Parkway 7 ✈	d	10 21		10 36				10 46	10 51		11 06	11 07		11 16	11 21		11 36					11 46	11 51		12 06
Harpenden	d	10 27		10 42				10 52	10 57		11 12			11 22	11 27		11 42					11 52	11 57		12 12
St Albans City	d	10 33		10 48			10 43	10 58	11 03		11 18		11 13	11 28	11 33		11 48				11 43	11 58	12 03		12 18
Radlett	d						10 48	11 03					11 18	11 33							11 48	12 03			
Elstree & Borehamwood	d						10 53	11 08					11 23	11 38							11 53	12 08			
Mill Hill Broadway	d		←				10 57	11 12		←			11 27	11 42		←					11 57	12 12		←	
Hendon	d		10 46				11 01	11 16		11 16			11 31	11 46		11 46					12 01	12 16		12 16	
Cricklewood	d		10 49				11 04	→		11 19			11 34	→		11 49					12 04	→		12 19	
West Hampstead Thameslink	⊖ d		10 52				11 07			11 22			11 37			11 52					12 07			12 22	
Kentish Town	⊖ d		10 56				11 11			11 26			11 41			11 56					12 11			12 26	
St Pancras International	⊖ a					11 04						11 34						11 59		12 04					
St Pancras International 15	⊖ d	10 54	11 02	11 09			11 17		11 24	11 32	11 39		11 47		11 54	12 02	12 09				12 17		12 24	12 32	12 39
Farringdon 3	⊖ d	10 59	11 07	11 14			11 22		11 29	11 37	11 44		11 52		11 59	12 07	12 14				12 22		12 29	12 37	12 44
Barbican	⊖ a																								
Moorgate	⊖ a																								
City Thameslink 3	d	11 01	11 09	11 16			11 24		11 31	11 39	11 46		11 54		12 01	12 09	12 16				12 24		12 31	12 39	12 46
London Blackfriars 3	⊖ d	11 05	11 16	11 20			11 30		11 35	11 46	11 50		12 00		12 05	12 16	12 20				12 30		12 35	12 46	12 50
Elephant & Castle	⊖ d		11 19				11 33			11 49			12 03			12 19					12 33			12 49	
Loughborough Jn	d		11 23				11 37			11 53			12 07			12 23					12 37			12 53	
Herne Hill 4	d		11 27				11 42			11 57			12 12			12 27					12 42			12 57	
London Bridge 4	⊖ d	11 11		11 26					11 41		11 56				12 11		12 26						12 41		12 56
Tulse Hill 3	d		11 32				11 46			12 02			12 16			12 32					12 46			13 02	
Streatham 4	d		11 35				11 49			12 05			12 19			12 35					12 49			13 05	
Mitcham Eastfields	d						11 53						12 23								12 53				
Mitcham Junction	🚊 d						11 57						12 27								12 57				
Hackbridge	d						12 00						12 30								13 00				
Carshalton	d						12 03						12 33								13 03				
Tooting	d		11 40							12 10						12 40								13 10	
Haydons Road	d		11 43							12 13						12 43								13 13	
Wimbledon 6	⊖ 🚊 d		11 47							12 17						12 47								13 17	
Wimbledon Chase	d		11 50							12 20						12 50								13 20	
South Merton	d		11 52							12 22						12 52								13 22	
Morden South	d		11 54							12 24						12 54								13 24	
St Helier	d		11 56							12 26						12 56								13 26	
Sutton Common	d		11 58							12 28						12 58								13 28	
West Sutton	d		12 01							12 31						13 01								13 31	
Sutton (Surrey) 4	a		12 05				12 06			12 35			12 36			13 05					13 06			13 35	
East Croydon	🚊 d	11 24		11 39					11 54		12 09				12 24		12 39						12 54		13 09
Redhill	d			*12 00*							*12 30*						*13 00*								*13 30*
Gatwick Airport 10	✈ d	11 41		11 56					12 11		12 26				12 40		12 56						13 11		13 26
Three Bridges 4	d	11 45		*12 14*					12 15		*12 44*				12 45		*13 14*						13 15		*13 44*
Balcombe	d			*12 21*					12 21								*13 21*						13 21		
Haywards Heath 3	d	11 55		12 08					12 27		12 38				12 55		13 08						13 27		13 38
Wivelsfield 4	d	11 59							12 31		*12 50*				12 59								13 31		*13 50*
Burgess Hill 4	d	12 01		*12 33*					12 33		*12 52*				13 01		*13 33*						13 33		*13 52*
Hassocks 4	d	12 04		*12 36*					12 36		*12 55*				13 04		*13 36*						13 36		*13 55*
Preston Park	d	12 11		*12 43*					12 43		*13 02*				13 11		*13 43*						13 43		*14 02*
Brighton 10	a	12 17		12 24					12 49		12 54				13 17		13 24						13 49		13 54

For general notes see front of timetable
For details of catering facilities see Directory of Train Operators

A From Nottingham (Table 53)

B Until 6 September from Barnsley (Table 53). From 13 September from Derby

C From Leeds (Table 53)

Bedford, Luton, St.Albans and City of London → South London, Gatwick Airport and Brighton

Network Diagram - see first page of Table 52

Station		EM	FC	FC	FC	EM	FC	FC	EM	FC		FC	FC	FC	FC	EM	FC	FC	FC	FC	FC	EM	FC	FC	FC
		1 ◇			1	1 ◇		1	1 ◇				1		1	1 ◇			1		1	1 ◇			1
		A				B			C							A						C			
Bedford [7]	d	11 51			11 55			12 10	12 21				12 25		12 40	12 51			12 55		13 10	13 21			13 25
Flitwick	d				12 04			12 19					12 34		12 49				13 04		13 19				13 34
Harlington	d				12 08			12 23					12 38		12 53				13 08		13 23				13 38
Leagrave	d				12 14			12 29					12 44		12 59				13 14		13 29				13 44
Luton [10]	d			12 14	12 19	12 21		12 34	12 36			12 44	12 49		13 04			13 14	13 19		13 34	13 36		13 44	13 49
Luton Airport Parkway [7] ✈	d	12 07		12 16	12 21			12 36				12 46	12 51		13 06	13 07		13 16	13 21		13 36			13 46	13 51
Harpenden	d			12 22	12 27			12 42				12 52	12 57		13 12			13 22	13 27		13 42			13 52	13 57
St Albans City	d		12 13	12 28	12 33			12 48		12 43		12 58	13 03		13 18		13 13	13 28	13 33		13 48		13 43	13 58	14 03
Radlett	d		12 18	12 33						12 48		13 03					13 18	13 33					13 48	14 03	
Elstree & Borehamwood	d		12 23	12 38						12 53		13 08					13 23	13 38					13 53	14 08	
Mill Hill Broadway	d		12 27	12 42			←			12 57		13 12		←			13 27	13 42		←			13 57	14 12	
Hendon	d		12 31	12 46			12 46			13 01		13 16		13 16			13 31	13 46		13 46			14 01	14 16	
Cricklewood	d		12 34	→			12 49			13 04		→		13 19			13 34	→		13 49			14 04	→	
West Hampstead Thameslink ⊖	d		12 37				12 52			13 07				13 22			13 37			13 52			14 07		
Kentish Town ⊖	d		12 41				12 56			13 11				13 26			13 41			13 56			14 11		
St Pancras International ⊖	a	12 34				12 51			13 04							13 34						14 04			
St Pancras International [15] ⊖	d		12 47		12 54		13 02	13 09		13 17			13 24	13 32	13 39		13 47		13 54	14 02	14 09		14 17		14 24
Farringdon [3] ⊖	d		12 52		12 59		13 07	13 14		13 22			13 29	13 37	13 44		13 52		13 59	14 07	14 14		14 22		14 29
Barbican ⊖	a																								
Moorgate ⊖	a																								
City Thameslink [3]	d		12 54		13 01		13 09	13 16		13 24			13 31	13 39	13 46		13 54		14 01	14 09	14 16		14 24		14 31
London Blackfriars [3] ⊖	d		13 00		13 05		13 16	13 20		13 30			13 35	13 46	13 50		14 00		14 05	14 16	14 20		14 30		14 35
Elephant & Castle ⊖	d		13 03				13 19			13 33				13 49			14 03			14 19			14 33		
Loughborough Jn	d		13 07				13 23			13 37				13 53			14 07			14 23			14 37		
Herne Hill [4]	d		13 12				13 27			13 42				13 57			14 12			14 27			14 42		
London Bridge [4] ⊖	d				13 11			13 26					13 41		13 56				14 11		14 26				14 41
Tulse Hill [3]	d		13 16				13 32			13 46				14 02			14 16			14 32			14 46		
Streatham [4]	d		13 19				13 35			13 49				14 05			14 19			14 35			14 49		
Mitcham Eastfields	d		13 23							13 53							14 23						14 53		
Mitcham Junction 🚋	d		13 27							13 57							14 27						14 57		
Hackbridge	d		13 30							14 00							14 30						15 00		
Carshalton	d		13 33							14 03							14 33						15 03		
Tooting	d						13 40							14 10						14 40					
Haydons Road	d						13 43							14 13						14 43					
Wimbledon [6] ⊖ 🚋	d						13 47							14 17						14 47					
Wimbledon Chase	d						13 50							14 20						14 50					
South Merton	d						13 52							14 22						14 52					
Morden South	d						13 54							14 24						14 54					
St Helier	d						13 56							14 26						14 56					
Sutton Common	d						13 58							14 28						14 58					
West Sutton	d						14 01							14 31						15 01					
Sutton (Surrey) [4]	a		13 36				14 05			14 06				14 35			14 36			15 05			15 06		
East Croydon 🚋	d				13 24			13 39					13 54		14 09				14 24		14 39				14 54
Redhill	d							*14 00*							*14 30*						*15 00*				
Gatwick Airport [10] ✈	d				13 41			13 56					14 11		14 26				14 41		14 56				15 11
Three Bridges [4]	d				13 45			*14 14*					14 15		*14 44*				14 45		*15 14*				15 15
Balcombe	d							*14 21*					14 21								*15 21*				15 21
Haywards Heath [3]	d				13 55			14 08					14 27		14 38				14 55		15 08				15 27
Wivelsfield [4]	d				13 59								14 31		*14 50*				14 59						15 31
Burgess Hill [4]	d				14 01			*14 33*					14 33		*14 52*				15 01		*15 33*				15 33
Hassocks [4]	d				14 04			*14 36*					14 36		*14 55*				15 04		*15 36*				15 36
Preston Park	d				14 11			*14 43*					14 43		*15 02*				15 11		*15 43*				15 43
Brighton [10]	a				14 17			14 24					14 49		14 54				15 17		15 24				15 49

For general notes see front of timetable
For details of catering facilities see Directory of Train Operators

A From Derby (Table 53)
B From Sheffield (Table 53)
C From Nottingham (Table 53)

Table 52

Saturdays

Bedford, Luton, St.Albans and City of London → South London, Gatwick Airport and Brighton

Network Diagram - see first page of Table 52

Station		FC		FC 1	EM 1 ◇ A	FC	FC	FC 1	FC	FC 1	EM 1 ◇ B	FC	FC	FC 1	FC	FC 1		EM 1 ◇ A	FC	FC	FC 1	EM 1 ◇ C	FC	FC 1	EM 1 ◇ B
Bedford 7	d			13 40	13 51			13 55		14 10	14 21			14 25		14 40		14 51			14 55			15 10	15 21
Flitwick	d			13 49				14 04		14 19				14 34		14 49					15 04			15 19	
Harlington	d			13 53				14 08		14 23				14 38		14 53					15 08			15 23	
Leagrave	d			13 59				14 14		14 29				14 44		14 59					15 14			15 29	
Luton 10	d			14 04			14 14	14 19		14 34	14 36		14 44	14 49		15 04				15 14	15 19	15 21		15 34	15 36
Luton Airport Parkway 7 ✈	d			14 06	14 07		14 16	14 21		14 36			14 46	14 51		15 06		15 07		15 16	15 21			15 36	
Harpenden	d			14 12			14 22	14 28		14 42			14 52	14 57		15 12				15 22	15 27			15 42	
St Albans City	d			14 18		14 13	14 28	14 34		14 48		14 43	14 58	15 03		15 18			15 13	15 28	15 33			15 48	
Radlett	d					14 18	14 33					14 48	15 03						15 18	15 33					
Elstree & Borehamwood	d					14 23	14 38					14 53	15 08						15 23	15 38					
Mill Hill Broadway	d	←				14 27	14 42		←			14 57	15 12		←				15 27	15 42			←		
Hendon	d	14 16				14 31	14 46		14 46			15 01	15 16		15 16				15 31	15 46			15 46		
Cricklewood	d	14 19				14 34	→		14 49			15 04	→		15 19				15 34	→			15 49		
West Hampstead Thameslink	⊖ d	14 22				14 37			14 52			15 07			15 22				15 37				15 52		
Kentish Town	⊖ d	14 26				14 41			14 56			15 11			15 26				15 41				15 56		
St Pancras International	⊖ a				14 34						15 04							15 34				15 51			16 04
St Pancras International 15	⊖ d	14 32		14 39		14 47		14 54	15 02	15 09		15 17		15 24	15 32	15 39			15 47		15 54		16 02	16 09	
Farringdon 3	⊖ d	14 37		14 44		14 52		14 59	15 07	15 14		15 22		15 29	15 37	15 44			15 52		15 59		16 07	16 14	
Barbican	⊖ a																								
Moorgate	⊖ a																								
City Thameslink 3	d	14 39		14 46		14 54		15 01	15 09	15 16		15 24		15 31	15 39	15 46			15 54		16 01		16 09	16 16	
London Blackfriars 3	⊖ d	14 46		14 50		15 00		15 05	15 16	15 20		15 30		15 35	15 46	15 50			16 00		16 05		16 16	16 20	
Elephant & Castle	⊖ d	14 49				15 03			15 19			15 33			15 49				16 03				16 19		
Loughborough Jn	d	14 53				15 07			15 23			15 37			15 53				16 07				16 23		
Herne Hill 4	d	14 57				15 12			15 27			15 42			15 57				16 12				16 27		
London Bridge 4	⊖ d			14 56				15 11		15 26				15 41		15 56					16 11			16 26	
Tulse Hill 3	d	15 02				15 16			15 32			15 46			16 02				16 16				16 32		
Streatham 4	d	15 05				15 19			15 35			15 49			16 05				16 19				16 35		
Mitcham Eastfields	d					15 23						15 53							16 23						
Mitcham Junction	🚋 d					15 27						15 57							16 27						
Hackbridge	d					15 30						16 00							16 30						
Carshalton	d					15 33						16 03							16 33						
Tooting	d	15 10							15 40						16 10								16 40		
Haydons Road	d	15 13							15 43						16 13								16 43		
Wimbledon 6	⊖ 🚋 d	15 17							15 47						16 17								16 47		
Wimbledon Chase	d	15 20							15 50						16 20								16 50		
South Merton	d	15 22							15 52						16 22								16 52		
Morden South	d	15 24							15 54						16 24								16 54		
St Helier	d	15 26							15 56						16 26								16 56		
Sutton Common	d	15 28							15 58						16 28								16 58		
West Sutton	d	15 31							16 01						16 31								17 01		
Sutton (Surrey) 4	a	15 35				15 36			16 05			16 06			16 35				16 36				17 05		
East Croydon	🚋 d			15 09				15 24		15 39				15 54		16 09					16 24			16 39	
Redhill	d			*15 30*						*16 00*						*16 30*								*17 00*	
Gatwick Airport 10 ✈	d			15 26				15 41		15 56				16 11		16 26					16 41			16 56	
Three Bridges 4	d			*15 44*				15 45		*16 14*				16 15		*16 44*					16 45			*17 14*	
Balcombe	d									*16 21*				16 21										*17 21*	
Haywards Heath 3	d			15 38				15 55		16 08				16 27		16 38					16 55			17 08	
Wivelsfield 4	d			*15 50*				15 59						16 31		*16 50*					16 59				
Burgess Hill 4	d			*15 52*				16 01		*16 33*				16 33		*16 52*					17 01			*17 33*	
Hassocks 4	d			*15 55*				16 04		*16 36*				16 36		*16 55*					17 04			*17 36*	
Preston Park	d			*16 02*				16 11		*16 43*				16 43		*17 02*					17 11			*17 43*	
Brighton 10	a			15 54				16 17		16 24				16 49		16 54					17 17			17 24	

For general notes see front of timetable
For details of catering facilities see Directory of Train Operators

A From Derby (Table 53)
B From Nottingham (Table 53)
C From Sheffield (Table 53)

Table 52

Saturdays

Bedford, Luton, St.Albans and City of London → South London, Gatwick Airport and Brighton

Network Diagram - see first page of Table 52

	FC	FC	FC	FC	FC	EM	FC		FC	FC	FC	FC	EM	FC	FC	FC	FC	FC	EM	FC	FC		FC	FC
			1		1	1 ◇				1		1	1 ◇			1		1	1 ◇				1	
						A ⎍							B ⎍						A ⎍					
Bedford 7 d			15 25		15 40	15 51				15 55		16 10	16 21			16 25		16 40	16 51				16 55	
Flitwick d			15 34		15 49					16 04		16 19				16 34		16 49					17 04	
Harlington d			15 38		15 53					16 08		16 23				16 38		16 53					17 08	
Leagrave d			15 44		15 59					16 14		16 29				16 44		16 59					17 14	
Luton 10 d		15 44	15 49		16 04				16 14	16 19		16 34	16 36		16 44	16 49		17 04			17 14		17 19	
Luton Airport Parkway 7 ✈ d		15 46	15 51		16 06	16 07			16 16	16 21		16 36			16 46	16 51		17 06	17 07		17 16		17 21	
Harpenden d		15 52	15 57		16 12				16 22	16 27		16 42			16 52	16 57		17 12			17 22		17 27	
St Albans City d	15 43	15 58	16 03		16 18		16 13		16 28	16 33		16 48		16 43	16 58	17 03		17 18		17 13	17 28		17 33	
Radlett d	15 48	16 03					16 18		16 33					16 48	17 03					17 18	17 33			
Elstree & Borehamwood d	15 53	16 08					16 23		16 38					16 53	17 08					17 23	17 38			
Mill Hill Broadway d	15 57	16 12		←			16 27		16 42		←			16 57	17 12		←			17 27	17 42			←
Hendon d	16 01	16 16		16 16			16 31		16 46		16 46			17 01	17 16		17 16			17 31	17 46			17 46
Cricklewood d	16 04	→		16 19			16 34		→		16 49			17 04	→		17 19			17 34	→			17 49
West Hampstead Thameslink ⊖ d	16 07			16 22			16 37				16 52			17 07			17 22			17 37				17 52
Kentish Town ⊖ d	16 11			16 26			16 41				16 56			17 11			17 26			17 41				17 56
St Pancras International ⊖ a						16 34							17 04						17 34					
St Pancras International 15 ⊖ d	16 17		16 24	16 32	16 39		16 47			16 54	17 02	17 09		17 17		17 24	17 32	17 39		17 47			17 54	18 02
Farringdon 3 ⊖ d	16 22		16 29	16 37	16 44		16 52			16 59	17 07	17 14		17 22		17 29	17 37	17 44		17 52			17 59	18 07
Barbican ⊖ a																								
Moorgate ⊖ a																								
City Thameslink 3 d	16 24		16 31	16 39	16 46		16 54			17 01	17 09	17 16		17 24		17 31	17 39	17 46		17 54			18 01	18 09
London Blackfriars 3 ⊖ d	16 30		16 35	16 46	16 50		17 00			17 05	17 16	17 20		17 30		17 35	17 46	17 50		18 00			18 05	18 16
Elephant & Castle ⊖ d	16 33			16 49			17 03				17 19			17 33			17 49			18 03				18 19
Loughborough Jn d	16 37			16 53			17 07				17 23			17 37			17 53			18 07				18 23
Herne Hill 4 d	16 42			16 57			17 12				17 27			17 42			17 57			18 12				18 27
London Bridge 4 ⊖ d			16 41		16 56					17 11		17 26				17 41		17 56					18 11	
Tulse Hill 3 d	16 46			17 02			17 16				17 32			17 46			18 02			18 16				18 32
Streatham 4 d	16 49			17 05			17 19				17 35			17 49			18 05			18 19				18 35
Mitcham Eastfields d	16 53						17 23							17 53						18 23				
Mitcham Junction 🚋 d	16 57						17 27							17 57						18 27				
Hackbridge d	17 00						17 30							18 00						18 30				
Carshalton d	17 03						17 33							18 03						18 33				
Tooting d				17 10							17 40						18 10							18 40
Haydons Road d				17 13							17 43						18 13							18 43
Wimbledon 6 ⊖ 🚋 d				17 17							17 47						18 17							18 47
Wimbledon Chase d				17 20							17 50						18 20							18 50
South Merton d				17 22							17 52						18 22							18 52
Morden South d				17 24							17 54						18 24							18 54
St Helier d				17 26							17 56						18 26							18 56
Sutton Common d				17 28							17 58						18 28							18 58
West Sutton d				17 31							18 01						18 31							19 01
Sutton (Surrey) 4 a	17 06			17 35			17 36				18 05			18 06			18 35			18 36				19 05
East Croydon 🚋 d			16 54		17 09					17 24		17 39				17 54		18 09					18 24	
Redhill d					*17 30*							*18 00*						*18 30*						
Gatwick Airport 10 ✈ d			17 11		17 26					17 41		17 56				18 11		18 26					18 41	
Three Bridges 4 d			17 15		*17 44*					17 45		*18 14*				18 15		*18 40*					18 45	
Balcombe d			17 21									*18 21*				18 21								
Haywards Heath 3 d			17 27		17 38					17 55		18 08				18 27		18 38					18 55	
Wivelsfield 4 d			17 31		*17 50*					17 59						18 31		*18 50*					18 59	
Burgess Hill 4 d			17 33		*17 52*					18 01		*18 33*				18 33		*18 52*					19 01	
Hassocks 4 d			17 36		*17 55*					18 04		*18 36*				18 36		*18 55*					19 04	
Preston Park d			17 43		*18 02*					18 11		*18 43*				18 43		*19 02*					19 11	
Brighton 10 a			17 49		17 54					18 17		18 24				18 49		18 54					19 17	

For general notes see front of timetable
For details of catering facilities see Directory of Train Operators

A From Derby (Table 53)
B From Nottingham (Table 53)

Table 52 **Saturdays**

Bedford, Luton, St.Albans and City of London → South London, Gatwick Airport and Brighton

Network Diagram - see first page of Table 52

		FC 1	EM 1◇ A 🍴	EM 1◇ B 🍴	FC	FC	FC 1	FC	FC 1	FC	FC 1	EM 1◇ A 🍴	FC	EM 1◇ C 🍴		FC 1	EM 1◇ D 🍴	FC 1	FC	FC 1	FC 1	EM 1◇ A 🍴	FC	EM 1◇ D 🍴	FC 1
Bedford 7	d	17 10	17 13	17 21			17 25		17 40		17 50	17 51				18 10	18 21	18 20		18 40	18 50	18 51		19 25	19 20
Flitwick	d	17 19					17 34		17 49		17 59					18 19		18 29		18 49	18 59				19 29
Harlington	d	17 23					17 38		17 53		18 03					18 23		18 33		18 53	19 03				19 33
Leagrave	d	17 29					17 44		17 59		18 09					18 29		18 39		18 59	19 09				19 39
Luton 10	d	17 34		17 36		17 44	17 49		18 04		18 14		18 20	18 21		18 34	18 36	18 44	18 50	19 04	19 14		19 20	19 41	19 44
Luton Airport Parkway 7 ✈	d	17 36				17 46	17 51		18 06		18 16	18 07	18 22			18 36		18 46	18 52	19 06	19 16	19 07	19 22		19 46
Harpenden	d	17 42				17 52	17 57		18 12		18 22		18 28			18 42		18 52	18 58	19 12	19 22		19 28		19 52
St Albans City	d	17 48			17 43	17 58	18 03		18 18	18 13	18 28		18 34			18 48		18 58	19 04	19 18	19 28		19 34		19 58
Radlett	d				17 48	18 03				18 18			18 39						19 09				19 39		
Elstree & Borehamwood	d				17 53	18 08				18 23			18 43						19 13				19 43		
Mill Hill Broadway	d				17 57	18 12		←		18 27			18 47						19 17				19 47		
Hendon	d				18 01	18 16 →		18 16		18 31			18 50						19 20				19 50		
Cricklewood	d				18 04			18 19		18 34			18 54						19 24				19 54		
West Hampstead Thameslink	⊖ d				18 07			18 22		18 37	18 42		18 57					19 12	19 27		19 42		19 57		20 12
Kentish Town	⊖ d				18 11			18 26		18 41			19 01						19 31				20 01		
St Pancras International	⊖ a		17 51	18 04								18 34		18 51			19 04					19 35		20 09	
St Pancras International 15	⊖ d	18 09			18 17		18 24	18 32	18 39	18 47	18 54		19 05			19 09		19 24	19 35	19 39	19 54		20 05		20 24
Farringdon 3	⊖ d	18 14			18 22		18 29	18 37	18 44	18 52	18 59		19 10			19 14		19 29	19 40	19 44	19 59		20 10		20 29
Barbican	⊖ a																								
Moorgate	⊖ a																								
City Thameslink 3	d	18 16			18 24		18 31	18 39	18 46	18 54	19 01		19 12			19 16		19 30	19 42	19 46	20 01		20 12		20 31
London Blackfriars 3	⊖ d	18 20			18 30		18 35	18 46	18 50	19 00	19 04		19 16			19 20		19 35	19 46	19 50	20 04		20 16		20 34
Elephant & Castle	⊖ d				18 33			18 49		19 03			19 19						19 49				20 19		
Loughborough Jn	d				18 37			18 53		19 07			19 23						19 53				20 23		
Herne Hill 4	d				18 42			18 57		19 12			19 27						19 57				20 27		
London Bridge 4	⊖ d	18 26					18 41		18 56		19 11					19 26		19 41		19 56	20 11				20 41
Tulse Hill 3	d				18 46			19 02		19 16			19 32						20 02				20 32		
Streatham 4	d				18 49			19 05		19 19			19 35						20 05				20 35		
Mitcham Eastfields	d				18 53					19 23															
Mitcham Junction 🚋	d				18 57					19 27															
Hackbridge	d				19 00					19 30															
Carshalton	d				19 03					19 33															
Tooting	d							19 10					19 40						20 10				20 40		
Haydons Road	d							19 13					19 43						20 13				20 43		
Wimbledon 6 ⊖ 🚋	d							19 17					19 47						20 17				20 47		
Wimbledon Chase	d							19 20					19 50						20 20				20 50		
South Merton	d							19 22					19 52						20 22				20 52		
Morden South	d							19 24					19 54						20 24				20 54		
St Helier	d							19 26					19 56						20 26				20 56		
Sutton Common	d							19 28					19 58						20 28				20 58		
West Sutton	d							19 31					20 01						20 31				21 01		
Sutton (Surrey) 4	a				19 06			19 38		19 38			20 05						20 38				21 05		
East Croydon 🚋	d	18 39					18 54		19 09		19 24					19 39		19 54		20 09	20 24				20 54
Redhill	d	*19 00*							*19 30*							*20 00*				*20 30*	*21 00*				*21 30*
Gatwick Airport 10 ✈	d	18 56					19 11		19 26		19 41					19 56		20 11		20 26	20 41				21 11
Three Bridges 4	d	*19 14*					19 15		*19 40*		19 45					*20 14*		20 15		*20 40*	20 45				21 15
Balcombe	d	*19 21*					19 21									*20 21*		20 21		*20 51*	20 51				
Haywards Heath 3	d	19 08					19 27		19 38		19 55					20 11		20 27		20 38	20 58				21 26
Wivelsfield 4	d						19 31		*19 50*		19 59							20 31		*20 50*	21 02				21 30
Burgess Hill 4	d	*19 33*					19 33		*19 52*		20 01					*20 33*		20 33		*20 52*	21 04				21 32
Hassocks 4	d	*19 36*					19 36		*19 55*		20 04					*20 36*		20 36		*20 55*	21 08				21 35
Preston Park	d	*19 43*					19 43		*20 02*		20 11					*20 43*		20 43		*21 02*	21 15				21 42
Brighton 10	a	19 24					19 49		19 54		20 17					20 26		20 49		20 54	21 20				21 48

For general notes see front of timetable
For details of catering facilities see Directory of Train Operators

A From Derby (Table 53)
B Until 6 September from Sheffield (Table 53). From 13 September from Nottingham (Table 53)
C From Sheffield (Table 53)
D From Nottingham (Table 53)

Bedford, Luton, St.Albans and City of London → South London, Gatwick Airport and Brighton

Network Diagram - see first page of Table 52

		FC	FC 1	EM 1 ◇ A ☕	FC	EM 1 ◇ B ☕		FC 1	FC 1	FC 1	EM 1 ◇ A ☕	FC	EM 1 ◇ C ☕	EM 1 ◇ B ☕	FC 1	FC	EM 1 ◇ B ☕	FC 1	FC	FC	FC	FC 1	FC 1		
Bedford 7	d		19 50	19 51		20 25		20 20		20 50	20 51		21 13	21 23	21 20		21 52	21 50		22 10	22 40	23 10	23 40		
Flitwick	d		19 59					20 29		20 59					21 29			21 59		22 19	22 49	23 19	23 49		
Harlington	d		20 03					20 33		21 03					21 33			22 03		22 23	22 53	23 23	23 53		
Leagrave	d		20 09					20 39		21 09					21 39			22 09		22 29	22 59	23 29	23 59		
Luton 10	d	19 50	20 14		20 20	20 41		20 44	20 50	21 14		21 20	21 29	21 39	21 44	21 50	22 09	22 14	22 20	22 34	23 04	23 34	00 04		
Luton Airport Parkway 7 ✈	d	19 52	20 16	20 07	20 22			20 46	20 52	21 16	21 09	21 22			21 46	21 52		22 16	22 22	22 36	23 06	23 36	00 06		
Harpenden	d	19 58	20 22		20 28			20 52	20 58	21 22		21 28			21 52	21 58		22 22	22 28	22 42	23 12	23 42	00 12		
St Albans City	d	20 04	20 28		20 34			20 58	21 04	21 28		21 34			21 58	22 04		22 28	22 34	22 48	23 18	23 48	00 18		
Radlett	d	20 09			20 39				21 09			21 39				22 09			22 39	22 53	23 23	23 53	00 23		
Elstree & Borehamwood	d	20 13			20 43				21 13			21 43				22 13			22 43	22 57	23 27	23 57	00 27		
Mill Hill Broadway	d	20 17			20 47				21 17			21 47				22 17			22 47	23 01	23 31	00 01	00 31		
Hendon	d	20 20			20 50				21 20			21 50				22 20			22 50	23 04	23 34	00 04	00 34		
Cricklewood	d	20 24			20 54				21 24			21 54				22 24			22 54	23 08	23 38	00 08	00 38		
West Hampstead Thameslink ⊖	d	20 27	20 42		20 57			21 12	21 27	21 42		21 57			22 12	22 27		22 42	22 57	23 12	23 42	00 12	00 42		
Kentish Town ⊖	d	20 31			21 01				21 31			22 01				22 31			23 01	23 16	23 46	00 16	00 46		
St Pancras International ⊖	a			20 35		21 08					21 35		21 52	22 04			22 43								
St Pancras International 15 ⊖	d	20 35	20 54		21 05			21 24	21 35	21 54		22 05			22 24	22 36		22 54	23 06	23 24	23 54	00 24	00 54		
Farringdon 3 ⊖	d	20 40	20 59		21 10			21 29	21 40	21 59		22 10			22 29	22 40		22 59	23 10	23 29	23 59	00 29			
Barbican ⊖	a																								
Moorgate ⊖	a																								
City Thameslink 3	d	20 42	21 01																						
London Blackfriars 3 ⊖	d	20 46	21 04		21 16			21 34	21 46	22 04		22 16			22 34	22 46		23 04	23 16	23 34	00 04	00 34	01a03		
Elephant & Castle ⊖	d	20 49			21 19				21 49			22 19				22 49			23 19						
Loughborough Jn	d	20 53			21 23				21 53			22 23				22 53			23s23						
Herne Hill 4	d	20 57			21 27				21 57			22 27				22 57			23 27						
London Bridge 4 ⊖	d		21 11					21 41		22 11					22 41			23 11		23 41	00 16	00 41			
Tulse Hill 3	d	21 02			21 32				22 02			22 32				23 02			23 32						
Streatham 4	d	21 05			21 35				22 05			22 35				23 05			23 35						
Mitcham Eastfields	d																								
Mitcham Junction 🚋	d																								
Hackbridge	d																								
Carshalton	d																								
Tooting	d	21 10			21 40				22 10			22 40				23 10			23 40						
Haydons Road	d	21 13			21 43				22 13			22 43				23 13			23 43						
Wimbledon 6 ⊖ 🚋	d	21 17			21 47				22 17			22 47				23 17			23 47						
Wimbledon Chase	d	21 20			21 50				22 20			22 50				23 20			23 50						
South Merton	d	21 22			21 52				22 22			22 52				23 22			23 52						
Morden South	d	21 24			21 54				22 24			22 54				23 24			23 54						
St Helier	d	21 26			21 56				22 26			22 56				23 26			23 56						
Sutton Common	d	21 28			21 58				22 28			22 58				23 28			23 58						
West Sutton	d	21 31			22 01				22 31			23 01				23 31			00 01						
Sutton (Surrey) 4	a	21 38			22 05				22 38			23 05				23 35			00 05						
East Croydon 🚋	d		21 24					21 54		22 24					22 54			23 24		23 57	00 29	00 57			
Redhill	d		*21 59*					*22 30*		*23 00*					*23 30*			*00 03*		*00 24*					
Gatwick Airport 10 ✈	d		21 41					22 11		22 41					23 11			23 41		00 18	00 47	01 17			
Three Bridges 4	d		21 45					22 15		22 45					23 15			23 45		00a24	00a54	01a24			
Balcombe	d		21 51							22 51								23 53							
Haywards Heath 3	d		21 58					22 26		22 58					23 26			23 58		*01 00*					
Wivelsfield 4	d		22 02					22 30		23 02					23 30			00 02							
Burgess Hill 4	d		22 04					22 32		23 04					23 32			00 04							
Hassocks 4	d		22 08					22 35		23 08					23 35			00 08							
Preston Park	d		22 15					22 42		23 15					23 42			00 15							
Brighton 10	a		22 20					22 48		23 20					23 48			00 20		*01 17*		*02 20*			

For general notes see front of timetable
For details of catering facilities see Directory of Train Operators

A From Derby (Table 53)
B From Nottingham (Table 53)
C Until 6 September from Scarborough (Table 26). From 13 September from York

Table 52

Sundays

Bedford, Luton, St.Albans and City of London → South London, Gatwick Airport and Brighton

Network Diagram - see first page of Table 52

		FC 1	FC	FC	FC 1	FC 1	FC 1	FC 1	FC 1	FC 1	FC 1	FC	FC	EM 1 ◇ A	FC 1	FC	FC 1	EM 1 ◇ B	FC 1	FC		FC 1	EM 1 ◇ A	FC 1	FC
Bedford 7	d	21p50	22p10	22p40	23p10	23p40	05 40	06 10	06 40	07 10	07 50		08 10	08 16	08 20		08 40	08 46	08 50			09 10	09 15	09 20	
Flitwick	d	21p59	22p19	22p49	23p19	23p49	05 49	06 19	06 49	07 19	07 59		08 19		08 29		08 50		08 59			09 19		09 29	
Harlington	d	22p03	22p23	22p53	23p23	23p53	05 53	06 23	06 53	07 23	08 03		08 23		08 33		08 54		09 03			09 23		09 33	
Leagrave	d	22p09	22p29	22p59	23p29	23p59	05 59	06 29	06 59	07 29	08 09		08 29		08 39		09 00		09 09			09 29		09 39	
Luton 10	d	22p14	22p34	23p04	23p34	00 04	06 04	06 34	07 04	07 34	08 14	08 20	08 34	08 37	08 44	08 50	09 04	09 08	09 14	09 20		09 34		09 44	09 50
Luton Airport Parkway 7 ✈	d	22p16	22p36	23p06	23p36	00 06	06 06	06 36	07 06	07 36	08 16	08 22	08 36		08 46	08 52	09 06		09 16	09 22		09 36	09 43	09 46	09 52
Harpenden	d	22p22	22p42	23p12	23p42	00 12	06 12	06 42	07 12	07 42	08 22	08 28	08 42		08 52	08 58	09 12		09 22	09 28		09 42		09 52	09 58
St Albans City	d	22p28	22p48	23p18	23p48	00 18	06 18	06 48	07 18	07 48	08 28	08 34	08 48		08 58	09 04	09 18		09 28	09 34		09 48		09 58	10 04
Radlett	d		22p53	23p23	23p53	00 23	06 23	06 53	07 23	07 53		08 39				09 09				09 39					10 09
Elstree & Borehamwood	d		22p57	23p27	23p57	00 27	06 27	06 57	07 27	07 57		08 43				09 13				09 43					10 13
Mill Hill Broadway	d		23p01	23p31	00 01	00 31	06 31	07 01	07 31	08 01		08 47				09 17				09 47					10 17
Hendon	d		23p04	23p34	00 04	00 34	06 34	07 04	07 34	08 04		08 50				09 20				09 50					10 20
Cricklewood	d		23p08	23p38	00 08	00 38	06 38	07 08	07 38	08 08		08 54				09 24				09 54					10 24
West Hampstead Thameslink ⊖	d	22p42	23p12	23p42	00 12	00 42	06 42	07 12	07 42	08 12	08 44	08 57			09 14	09 27			09 44	09 57				10 14	10 27
Kentish Town ⊖	d		23p16	23p46	00 16	00 46	06 46	07 16	07 46	08 16		09 01				09 31				10 01					10 31
St Pancras International ⊖	a													09 16				09 45					10 16		
St Pancras International 15 ⊖	d	22p54	23p24	23p54	00 24	00 54	06 54	07 24	07 54	08 24	08 54	09 06	09 10		09 24	09 36	09 40		09 54	10 06		10 10		10 24	10 36
Farringdon 3 ⊖	d	22p59	23p29	23p59	00 29		06 59	07 29	07 59	08 29	08 59	09 10	09 14		09 29	09 40	09 44		09 59	10 10		10 14		10 29	10 40
Barbican ⊖	a																								
Moorgate ⊖	a																								
City Thameslink 3	d																								
London Blackfriars 3 ⊖	d	23p04	23p34	00 04	00 34	01a03	07 04	07 34	08 04	08 34	09 04	09 16	09 19		09 34	09 46	09 49		10 04	10 16		10 19		10 34	10 46
Elephant & Castle ⊖	d											09 19				09 49				10 19					10 49
Loughborough Jn	d											09 23				09 53				10 23					10 53
Herne Hill 4	d											09 27				09 57				10 27					10 57
London Bridge 4 ⊖	d	23p11	23p41	00 16	00 41		07 11	07 41	08 11	08 41	09 11		09 26		09 41		09 56		10 11			10 26		10 41	
Tulse Hill 3	d											09 31				10 01				10 31					11 01
Streatham 4	d											09 34				10 04				10 34					11 04
Mitcham Eastfields	d																								
Mitcham Junction 🚋	d																								
Hackbridge	d																								
Carshalton	d																								
Tooting	d											09 38				10 08				10 38					11 08
Haydons Road	d											09 41				10 11				10 41					11 11
Wimbledon 6 ⊖ 🚋	d											09 44				10 14				10 44					11 14
Wimbledon Chase	d											09 47				10 17				10 47					11 17
South Merton	d											09 49				10 19				10 49					11 19
Morden South	d											09 51				10 21				10 51					11 21
St Helier	d											09 53				10 23				10 53					11 23
Sutton Common	d											09 55				10 25				10 55					11 25
West Sutton	d											09 58				10 28				10 58					11 28
Sutton (Surrey) 4	a											10 01				10 31				11 01					11 31
East Croydon 🚋	d	23p24	23p57	00 29	00 57		07 27	07 57	08 27	08 57	09 27		09a45		09 57		10a15		10 27			10a45		10 57	
Redhill	d	*00 03*	*00 50*				*07 50*	*08 37*	*08 50*	*09 37*	*09 50*		*10 03*				*10 37*		*10 50*			*11 03*			
Gatwick Airport 10 ✈	d	23p41	00 18	00 47	01 17		07 50	08 20	08 50	09 20	09 50		*10 11*		10 20		*10 41*		10 50			*11 11*		11 20	
Three Bridges 4	d	23p45	00a24	00a54	01a24		07 54	08 24	08 54	09 24	09 54		*10 16*		10 24		*10 52*		10 54			*11 16*		11 24	
Balcombe	d	23p53					*08 23*		*09 23*		*10 23*		*10 23*						*11 23*			*11 23*			
Haywards Heath 3	d	23p58	*01 00*				08 03	08 33	09 03	09 33	10 03		*10 28*		10 33		*11 03*		11 03			*11 28*		11 33	
Wivelsfield 4	d	00 02					*08 32*		*09 32*	*09 45*	*10 32*		*10 32*		*10 45*				*11 32*			*11 32*		*11 45*	
Burgess Hill 4	d	00 04					08 08	08 38	09 08	09 38	10 08		*10 34*		10 38		*11 08*		11 08			*11 34*		11 38	
Hassocks 4	d	00 08					*08 38*	08 42	*09 38*	09 42	*10 38*		*10 38*		10 42				*11 38*			*11 38*		11 42	
Preston Park	d	00 15					*08 45*	*09 45*	*09 45*	*10 45*	*10 45*		*10 45*		*11 45*				*11 45*			*11 45*		*12 45*	
Brighton 10	a	00 20	*01 17*		*02 20*		08 22	08 52	09 22	09 52	10 22		*10 50*		10 52		*11 05*		11 22			*11 50*		11 52	

For general notes see front of timetable
For details of catering facilities see
Directory of Train Operators

A From Derby (Table 53)

B Until 13 July and from 14 September from Nottingham (Table 53). 20 July to 7 September from Leicester (table 53)

Table 52

Sundays

Bedford, Luton, St.Albans and City of London → South London, Gatwick Airport and Brighton

Network Diagram - see first page of Table 52

		FC 1	EM 1 ◇ A ☕	FC 1	FC	FC 1	EM 1 ◇ B ☕	FC 1	FC	FC 1	EM 1 ◇ C ☕	FC 1	FC	FC 1	EM 1 ◇ B ☕	FC 1	FC	FC 1		EM 1 ◇ D ☕	FC 1	FC	FC	EM 1 ◇ E ☕	FC 1
Bedford 7	d	09 40	09 45	09 50		10 10	10 15	10 20		10 40	10 46	10 50		11 10	11 16	11 20		11 40		11 46	11 50		12 10	12 16	12 20
Flitwick	d	09 49		09 59		10 19		10 29		10 49		10 59		11 19		11 29		11 49			11 59		12 19		12 29
Harlington	d	09 53		10 03		10 23		10 33		10 53		11 03		11 23		11 33		11 53			12 03		12 23		12 33
Leagrave	d	09 59		10 09		10 29		10 39		10 59		11 09		11 29		11 39		11 59			12 09		12 29		12 39
Luton 10	d	10 04	10 08	10 14	10 20	10 34		10 44	10 50	11 04	11 07	11 14	11 20	11 34		11 44	11 50	12 04		12 08	12 14	12 20	12 34	12 38	12 44
Luton Airport Parkway 7 ✈	d	10 06		10 16	10 22	10 36		10 46	10 52	11 06		11 16	11 22	11 36	11 41	11 46	11 52	12 06			12 16	12 22	12 36		12 46
Harpenden	d	10 12		10 22	10 28	10 42		10 52	10 58	11 12		11 22	11 28	11 42		11 52	11 58	12 12			12 22	12 28	12 42		12 52
St Albans City	d	10 18		10 28	10 34	10 48		10 58	11 04	11 18		11 28	11 34	11 48		11 58	12 04	12 18			12 28	12 34	12 48		12 58
Radlett	d				10 39				11 09				11 39				12 09					12 39			
Elstree & Borehamwood	d				10 43				11 13				11 43				12 13					12 43			
Mill Hill Broadway	d				10 47				11 17				11 47				12 17					12 47			
Hendon	d				10 50				11 20				11 50				12 20					12 50			
Cricklewood	d				10 54				11 24				11 54				12 24					12 54			
West Hampstead Thameslink ⊖	d			10 44	10 57			11 14	11 27			11 44	11 57			12 14	12 27				12 44	12 57			13 14
Kentish Town ⊖	d				11 01				11 31				12 01				12 31					13 01			
St Pancras International ⊖	a		10 46				11 19				11 49				12 19					12 50				13 18	
St Pancras International 15 ⊖	d	10 40		10 54	11 06	11 10		11 24	11 36	11 40		11 54	12 06	12 10		12 24	12 36	12 40			12 54	13 06	13 10		13 24
Farringdon 3 ⊖	d	10 44		10 59	11 10	11 14		11 29	11 40	11 44		11 59	12 10	12 14		12 29	12 40	12 44			12 59	13 10	13 14		13 29
Barbican ⊖	a																								
Moorgate ⊖	a																								
City Thameslink 3	d																								
London Blackfriars 3 ⊖	d	10 49		11 04	11 16	11 19		11 34	11 46	11 49		12 04	12 16	12 19		12 34	12 46	12 49			13 04	13 16	13 19		13 34
Elephant & Castle ⊖	d				11 19				11 49				12 19				12 49					13 19			
Loughborough Jn	d				11 23				11 53				12 23				12 53					13 23			
Herne Hill 4	d				11 27				11 57				12 27				12 57					13 27			
London Bridge 4 ⊖	d	10 56		11 11		11 26		11 41		11 56		12 11		12 26		12 41		12 56			13 11		13 26		13 41
Tulse Hill 3	d				11 31				12 01				12 31				13 01					13 31			
Streatham 4	d				11 34				12 04				12 34				13 04					13 34			
Mitcham Eastfields	d																								
Mitcham Junction 🚋	d																								
Hackbridge	d																								
Carshalton	d																								
Tooting	d				11 38				12 08				12 38				13 08					13 38			
Haydons Road	d				11 41				12 11				12 41				13 11					13 41			
Wimbledon 6 ⊖ 🚋	d				11 44				12 14				12 44				13 14					13 44			
Wimbledon Chase	d				11 47				12 17				12 47				13 17					13 47			
South Merton	d				11 49				12 19				12 49				13 19					13 49			
Morden South	d				11 51				12 21				12 51				13 21					13 51			
St Helier	d				11 53				12 23				12 53				13 23					13 53			
Sutton Common	d				11 55				12 25				12 55				13 25					13 55			
West Sutton	d				11 58				12 28				12 58				13 28					13 58			
Sutton (Surrey) 4	a				12 01				12 31				13 01				13 31					14 01			
East Croydon 🚋	d	11a15		11 27		11a45		11 57		12a15		12 27		12a45		12 57		13a15			13 27		13a45		13 57
Redhill	d	*11 37*		*11b50*		*12 03*				*12 37*		*12 50*		*13 03*				*13 37*			*13 50*		*14 03*		
Gatwick Airport 10 ✈	d	*11 41*		11 50		*12 11*		12 20		*12 41*		12 50		*13 11*		13 20		*13 41*			13 50		*14 11*		14 20
Three Bridges 4	d	*11 52*		11 54		*12 16*		12 24		*12 52*		12 54		*13 16*		13 24		*13 52*			13 54		*14 16*		14 24
Balcombe	d			*12 23*		*12 23*						*13 23*		*13 23*				*14 23*			*14 23*		*14 23*		
Haywards Heath 3	d	*12 03*		12 03		*12 28*		12 33		*13 03*		13 03		*13 28*		13 33		*14 03*			14 03		*14 28*		14 33
Wivelsfield 4	d			*12 32*		*12 32*		*12 45*				*13 32*		*13 32*		*13 45*		*14 32*			*14 32*		*14 32*		*14 45*
Burgess Hill 4	d	*12 08*		12 08		*12 34*		12 38		*13 08*		13 08		*13 34*		13 38		*14 08*			14 08		*14 34*		14 38
Hassocks 4	d			*12 38*		*12 38*		12 42				*13 38*		*13 38*		13 42		*14 38*			*14 38*		*14 38*		14 42
Preston Park	d			*12 45*		*12 45*		*13 45*				*13 45*		*13 45*		*14 45*		*14 45*			*14 45*		*14 45*		*15 45*
Brighton 10	a	*12 05*		12 22		*12 49*		12 52		*13 05*		13 22		*13 50*		13 52		*14 05*			14 22		*14 50*		14 52

For general notes see front of timetable
For details of catering facilities see Directory of Train Operators

A Until 13 July and from 14 September from Nottingham (Table 53). 20 July to 7 September from Leicester (table 53)

B From Derby (Table 53)

C Until 13 July and from 14 September from Nottingham (Table 53). 20 July to 7 September from Loughborough (Table 53)

D From Nottingham (Table 53)

E From Sheffield (Table 53)

b From 14 September arr. 1203

Bedford, Luton, St.Albans and City of London → South London, Gatwick Airport and Brighton

Network Diagram - see first page of Table 52

Station		FC	FC 1	EM 1 ◇ A	FC 1	FC	FC 1	EM 1 ◇ B	FC 1	FC	FC 1	EM 1 ◇ C	FC 1	FC	EM 1 ◇ A	FC 1		FC 1	FC	EM 1 ◇ C	FC 1	FC 1	FC	FC 1	EM 1 ◇ B
Bedford 7	d		12 40	12 45	12 50	13 00	13 10	13 16	13 20	13 30	13 40	13 45	13 50	14 00	14 07	14 10		14 20	14 30	14 44	14 40	14 50	15 00	15 10	15 15
Flitwick	d		12 49		12 59		13 19		13 29		13 49		13 59			14 19		14 29			14 49	14 59		15 19	
Harlington	d		12 53		13 03		13 23		13 33		13 53		14 03			14 23		14 33			14 53	15 03		15 23	
Leagrave	d		12 59		13 09		13 29		13 39		13 59		14 09			14 29		14 39			14 59	15 09		15 30	
Luton 10	d	12 50	13 04	13 08	13 14	13 20	13 34		13 44	13 50	14 04	14 09	14 14	14 18		14 34		14 44	14 50	14 59	15 04	15 14	15 20	15 34	
Luton Airport Parkway 7 ✈	d	12 52	13 06		13 16	13 22	13 36		13 46	13 52	14 06		14 16	14 20		14 36		14 46	14 52		15 06	15 16	15 22	15 36	
Harpenden	d	12 58	13 12		13 22	13 28	13 42		13 52	13 58	14 12		14 22	14 26		14 42		14 52	14 58		15 12	15 22	15 28	15 42	
St Albans City	d	13 04	13 18		13 28	13 34	13 48		13 58	14 04	14 18		14 28	14 32		14 48		14 58	15 04		15 18	15 28	15 34	15 48	
Radlett	d	13 09				13 39				14 09				14 37					15 09				15 39		
Elstree & Borehamwood	d	13 13				13 43				14 13				14 43					15 13				15 43		
Mill Hill Broadway	d	13 17				13 47				14 17				14 47					15 17				15 47		
Hendon	d	13 20				13 50				14 20				14 50					15 20				15 50		
Cricklewood	d	13 24				13 54				14 24				14 54					15 24				15 54		
West Hampstead Thameslink ⊖	d	13 27			13 44	13 57			14 14	14 27			14 44	14 57				15 14	15 27			15 44	15 57		
Kentish Town ⊖	d	13 31				14 01				14 31				15 01					15 31				16 01		
St Pancras International ⊖	a			13 48				14 18				14 44			14 55					15 29					16 06
St Pancras International 15 ⊖	d	13 36	13 40		13 54	14 06	14 10		14 24	14 36	14 40		14 54	15 06		15 10		15 24	15 36		15 40	15 54	16 06	16 10	
Farringdon 3 ⊖	d	13 40	13 44		13 59	14 10	14 14		14 29	14 40	14 44		14 59	15 10		15 14		15 29	15 40		15 44	15 59	16 10	16 14	
Barbican ⊖	a																								
Moorgate ⊖	a																								
City Thameslink 3	d																								
London Blackfriars 3 ⊖	d	13 46	13 49		14 04	14 16	14 19		14 34	14 46	14 49		15 04	15 16		15 19		15 34	15 46		15 49	16 04	16 16	16 19	
Elephant & Castle ⊖	d	13 49				14 19				14 49				15 19					15 49				16 19		
Loughborough Jn	d	13 53				14 23				14 53				15 23					15 53				16 23		
Herne Hill 4	d	13 57				14 27				14 57				15 27					15 57				16 27		
London Bridge 4 ⊖	d		13 56		14 11		14 26		14 41		14 56		15 11			15 26		15 41			15 56	16 11		16 26	
Tulse Hill 3	d	14 01				14 31				15 01				15 31					16 01				16 31		
Streatham 4	d	14 04				14 34				15 04				15 34					16 04				16 34		
Mitcham Eastfields	d																								
Mitcham Junction	d																								
Hackbridge	d																								
Carshalton	d																								
Tooting	d	14 08				14 38				15 08				15 38					16 08				16 38		
Haydons Road	d	14 11				14 41				15 11				15 41					16 11				16 41		
Wimbledon 6 ⊖	d	14 14				14 44				15 14				15 44					16 14				16 44		
Wimbledon Chase	d	14 17				14 47				15 17				15 47					16 17				16 47		
South Merton	d	14 19				14 49				15 19				15 49					16 19				16 49		
Morden South	d	14 21				14 51				15 21				15 51					16 21				16 51		
St Helier	d	14 23				14 53				15 23				15 53					16 23				16 53		
Sutton Common	d	14 25				14 55				15 25				15 55					16 25				16 55		
West Sutton	d	14 28				14 58				15 28				15 58					16 28				16 58		
Sutton (Surrey) 4	a	14 31				15 01				15 31				16 01					16 31				17 01		
East Croydon	d		14a15		14 27		14a45		14 57		15a15		15 27			15a45		15 57			16a15	16 27		16a45	
Redhill	d		*14 37*		*14 53*		*15 03*				*15 37*		*15 53*			*16 03*					*16 37*	*16 50*		*17 03*	
Gatwick Airport 10 ✈	d		*14b41*		14 50		*15 11*		15 20		*15 41*		15 50			*16 11*		16 20			*16 41*	16 50		*17 11*	
Three Bridges 4	d		*14 52*		14 54		*15 16*		15 24		*15 52*		15 54			*16 16*		16 24			*16 52*	16 54		*17 16*	
Balcombe	d				*15 23*		*15 23*						*16 23*			*16 23*						*17 23*		*17 23*	
Haywards Heath 3	d		*15 03*		15 03		*15 28*		15 33		*16 03*		16 03			*16 28*		16 33			*17 03*	17 03		*17 28*	
Wivelsfield 4	d				*15 32*		*15 32*		*15 45*				*16 32*			*16 32*		*16 45*				*17 32*		*17 32*	
Burgess Hill 4	d		*15 08*		15 08		*15 34*		15 38		*16 08*		16 08			*16 34*		16 38			*17 08*	17 08		*17 34*	
Hassocks 4	d				*15 38*		*15 38*		15 42				*16 38*			*16 38*		16 42				*17 38*		*17 38*	
Preston Park	d				*15 45*		*15 45*		*16 45*				*16 45*			*16 45*		*17 45*				*17 45*		*17 45*	
Brighton 10	a		*15c05*		15 22		*15 50*		15 52		*16 05*		16 22			*16 50*		16 52			*17 05*	17 22		*17 50*	

For general notes see front of timetable
For details of catering facilities see Directory of Train Operators

A From Leeds (Table 153)
B From Sheffield (Table 53)
C From Nottingham (Table 53)

b From 14 September arr. 1446
c From 14 September arr. 1522

Bedford, Luton, St.Albans and City of London → South London, Gatwick Airport and Brighton

Network Diagram - see first page of Table 52

	FC	FC	EM	FC	FC	FC	EM	FC	FC	FC	EM	FC	FC		EM	FC	EM	FC	FC	FC	EM	FC	FC	EM
	1		1 ◇ A ☕	1	1		1 ◇ B ☕		1		1 ◇ A ☕	1			1 ◇ B ☕	1	1 ◇ A ☕		1		1 ◇ B ☕	1		1 ◇ C ☕
Bedford 7 d	15 20	15 30	15 35	15 40	15 50	16 00		16 10	16 20	16 30	16 54	16 50	17 00		17 09	17 20	17 25		17 50		18 06	18 20		18 34
Flitwick d	15 29			15 49	15 59			16 20	16 29			16 59				17 29			17 59			18 29		
Harlington d	15 33			15 53	16 03			16 24	16 33			17 03				17 33			18 03			18 33		
Leagrave d	15 39			15 59	16 09			16 29	16 39			17 09				17 39			18 09			18 39		
Luton 10 d	15 44	15 50	15 55	16 04	16 14	16 20		16 35	16 44	16 50	17 11	17 14	17 20			17 44		17 50	18 14	18 20	18 27	18 44	18 50	18 55
Luton Airport Parkway 7 ✈ d	15 46	15 52		16 06	16 16	16 22	16 35	16 38	16 46	16 52		17 16	17 22			17 46	17 42	17 52	18 16	18 22		18 46	18 52	
Harpenden d	15 52	15 58		16 12	16 22	16 28		16 43	16 52	16 58		17 22	17 28			17 52		17 58	18 22	18 28		18 52	18 58	
St Albans City d	15 58	16 04		16 18	16 28	16 34		16 49	16 58	17 04		17 28	17 34			17 58		18 04	18 28	18 34		18 58	19 04	
Radlett d		16 09				16 39				17 09			17 39					18 09		18 39			19 09	
Elstree & Borehamwood d		16 13				16 43				17 13			17 43					18 14		18 44			19 14	
Mill Hill Broadway d		16 17				16 47				17 17			17 47					18 18		18 48			19 18	
Hendon d		16 20				16 50				17 20			17 50					18 21		18 51			19 21	
Cricklewood d		16 24				16 54				17 24			17 54					18 25		18 55			19 25	
West Hampstead Thameslink ⊖ d	16 14	16 27			16 44	16 57			17 14	17 27		17 44	17 57			18 14		18 27	18 44	18 57		19 14	19 27	
Kentish Town ⊖ d		16 31				17 01				17 31			18 01					18 31		19 01			19 31	
St Pancras International ⊖ a			16 27				17 06				17 41				17 55		18 11				18 57			19 24
St Pancras International 15 ⊖ d	16 24	16 36		16 40	16 54	17 06		17 09	17 24	17 36		17 54	18 06			18 24		18 36	18 54	19 06		19 24	19 36	
Farringdon 3 ⊖ d	16 29	16 40		16 44	16 59	17 10		17 14	17 29	17 40		17 59	18 10			18 29		18 40	18 59	19 10		19 29	19 40	
Barbican ⊖ a																								
Moorgate ⊖ a																								
City Thameslink 3 d																								
London Blackfriars 3 ⊖ d	16 34	16 46		16 49	17 04	17 16		17 19	17 34	17 46		18 04	18 16			18 34		18 46	19 04	19 16		19 34	19 46	
Elephant & Castle ⊖ d		16 49				17 19				17 49			18 19					18 49		19 19			19 49	
Loughborough Jn d		16 53				17 23				17 53			18 23					18 53		19 23			19 53	
Herne Hill 4 d		16 57				17 27				17 57			18 27					18 57		19 27			19 57	
London Bridge 4 ⊖ d	16 41			16 56	17 11			17 26	17 41			18 11				18 41			19 11			19 41		
Tulse Hill 3 d		17 01				17 31				18 01			18 31					19 01		19 31			20 01	
Streatham 4 d		17 04				17 34				18 04			18 34					19 04		19 34			20 04	
Mitcham Eastfields d																								
Mitcham Junction 🚋 d																								
Hackbridge d																								
Carshalton d																								
Tooting d		17 08				17 38				18 08			18 38					19 08		19 38			20 08	
Haydons Road d		17 11				17 41				18 11			18 41					19 11		19 41			20 11	
Wimbledon 6 ⊖ 🚋 d		17 14				17 44				18 14			18 44					19 14		19 44			20 14	
Wimbledon Chase d		17 17				17 47				18 17			18 47					19 17		19 47			20 17	
South Merton d		17 19				17 49				18 19			18 49					19 19		19 49			20 19	
Morden South d		17 21				17 51				18 21			18 51					19 21		19 51			20 21	
St Helier d		17 23				17 53				18 23			18 53					19 23		19 53			20 23	
Sutton Common d		17 25				17 55				18 25			18 55					19 25		19 55			20 25	
West Sutton d		17 28				17 58				18 28			18 58					19 28		19 58			20 28	
Sutton (Surrey) 4 a		17 31				18 01				18 31			19 01					19 31		20 01			20 31	
East Croydon 🚋 d	16 57			17a15	17 27			17a45	17 57			18 27				18 57			19 27			19 57		
Redhill d				17 37	17 50			18 03	18 37			18 50				19 37			19 50			20 37		
Gatwick Airport 10 ✈ d	17 20			17 41	17 50			18 11	18 20			18 50				19 20			19 50			20 20		
Three Bridges 4 d	17 24			17 52	17 54			18 16	18 24			18 54				19 24			19 54			20 24		
Balcombe d				18 23	18 23			18 23				19 23							20 23					
Haywards Heath 3 d	17 33			18 03	18 03			18 28	18 33			19 03				19 33			20 03			20 33		
Wivelsfield 4 d	17 45			18 32	18 32			18 32	18 45			19 32				19 45			20 32			20 45		
Burgess Hill 4 d	17 38			18 08	18 08			18 34	18 38			19 08				19 38			20 08			20 38		
Hassocks 4 d	17 42			18 38	18 38			18 38	18 42			19 38				19 42			20 38			20 42		
Preston Park d	18 45			18 45	18 45			18 45	19 45			19 45				20 45			20 45			21 45		
Brighton 10 a	17 52			18 05	18 22			18 50	18 52			19 22				19 52			20 22			20 52		

For general notes see front of timetable
For details of catering facilities see Directory of Train Operators

A From Nottingham (Table 53)
B From Sheffield (Table 53)
C Until 13 July from Nottingham (Table 53). From 20 July from Sheffield (Table 53)

Table 52

Sundays

Bedford, Luton, St.Albans and City of London → South London, Gatwick Airport and Brighton

Network Diagram - see first page of Table 52

		FC	EM	EM	FC	FC	FC	EM	EM	FC	EM	EM	FC	FC	FC	EM	FC	EM	FC	FC	EM	FC	FC
		1	1 ◇	1 ◇		1		1 ◇	1 ◇	1	1 ◇	1 ◇	1	1	1	1 ◇	1	1 ◇	1		1 ◇		1
			A	B				C	D		E	B				G		H			C		
			☕	☕				☕	☕		☕	☕				☕		☕			☕		
Bedford 7	d	18 50	19 10	19 13		19 20		19 36	19 49	19 50	19 55	19 57	20 00	20 10	20 40	20 49	21 10	21 30	21 40	22 10	22 31	22 40	23 40
Flitwick	d	18 59				19 29				19 59				20 19	20 49		21 19		21 49	22 19		22 49	23 49
Harlington	d	19 03				19 33				20 03				20 23	20 53		21 23		21 53	22 23		22 53	23 53
Leagrave	d	19 09				19 39				20 09				20 29	20 59		21 29		21 59	22 29		22 59	23 59
Luton 10	d	19 14			19 20	19 44	19 50	19 52		20 14			20 20	20 34	21 04	21 08	21 34	21 49	22 04	22 34	22 50	23 04	00 04
Luton Airport Parkway 7	✈ d	19 16			19 22	19 46	19 52			20 16			20 22	20 36	21 06		21 36		22 06	22 36		23 06	00 06
Harpenden	d	19 22			19 28	19 52	19 58			20 22			20 28	20 42	21 12		21 42		22 12	22 42		23 12	00 12
St Albans City	d	19 28			19 34	19 58	20 04			20 28			20 34	20 48	21 18		21 48		22 18	22 48		23 18	00 18
Radlett	d				19 39		20 09						20 39	20 53	21 23		21 53		22 23	22 53		23 23	00 23
Elstree & Borehamwood	d				19 44		20 14						20 43	20 57	21 27		21 57		22 27	22 57		23 27	00 27
Mill Hill Broadway	d				19 48		20 18						20 47	21 01	21 31		22 01		22 31	23 01		23 31	00 31
Hendon	d				19 51		20 21						20 50	21 04	21 34		22 04		22 34	23 04		23 34	00 34
Cricklewood	d				19 55		20 25						20 54	21 08	21 38		22 08		22 38	23 08		23 38	00 38
West Hampstead Thameslink	⊖ d	19 44			19 57	20 14	20 27			20 44			20 57	21 12	21 42		22 12		22 42	23 12		23 42	00 42
Kentish Town	⊖ d				20 01		20 31						21 01	21 16	21 46		22 16		22 46	23 16		23 46	00 46
St Pancras International	⊖ a		19 56	19 59				20 21	20 49		20 49	20 49				21 37		22 18			23 22		
St Pancras International 15	⊖ d	19 54			20 06	20 24	20 36			20 54			21b10	21 24	21 54		22 24		22 54	23 24		23 54	00 54
Farringdon 3	⊖ d	19 59			20 10	20 29	20 40			20 59			21 14	21 29	21 59		22 29		22 59	23 29		23 59	
Barbican	⊖ a																						
Moorgate	⊖ a																						
City Thameslink 3	d																						
London Blackfriars 3	⊖ d	20 04			20 16	20 34	20 46			21 04			21 19	21 34	22 04		22 34		23 04	23 34		00 04	01 04
Elephant & Castle	⊖ d				20 19		20 49																
Loughborough Jn	d				20 23		20 53																
Herne Hill 4	d				20 27		20 57																
London Bridge 4	⊖ d	20 11				20 41				21 11			21 26	21 41	22 11		22 41		23 11	23 41		00 11	
Tulse Hill 3	d				20 31		21 01																
Streatham 4	d				20 34		21 04																
Mitcham Eastfields	d																						
Mitcham Junction	d																						
Hackbridge	d																						
Carshalton	d																						
Tooting	d				20 38		21 08																
Haydons Road	d				20 41		21 11																
Wimbledon 6	⊖ d				20 44		21 14																
Wimbledon Chase	d				20 47		21 17																
South Merton	d				20 49		21 19																
Morden South	d				20 51		21 21																
St Helier	d				20 53		21 23																
Sutton Common	d				20 55		21 25																
West Sutton	d				20 58		21 28																
Sutton (Surrey) 4	a				21 01		21 31																
East Croydon	d	20 27				20 57				21 27			21a47	21 57	22 27		22 57		23 27	23 57		00 27	01 32
Redhill	d	20 50				21 37				21 50			22 12	22 37	22c50		23 42		00 05	00 50		00 50	
Gatwick Airport 10	✈ d	20 50				21 20				21 50				22 20	22 50		23 20		23 50	00 17		00 47	01 52
Three Bridges 4	d	20 54				21 24				21 54			22 24	22 24	22 54		23 24		23 54	00a24		00a54	01a58
Balcombe	d	21 23								22 23			23e23		23 23		00 25		00 25				
Haywards Heath 3	d	21 03				21 33				22 03			22 33	22 33	23 03		23 33		00 03	02f03		02 03	
Wivelsfield 4	d	21 32				21 45				22 32			22 45	22 45	23 32		23 45		00 34				
Burgess Hill 4	d	21 08				21 38				22 08			22 38	22 38	23 08		23 38		00 08				
Hassocks 4	d	21 38				21 42				22 38			22 42	22 42	23 38		23 42		00 40				
Preston Park	d	21 45				22 45				22 45			23g45	23 45	23 45		00 47		00 47				
Brighton 10	a	21 22				21 52				22 22			22 52	22 52	23 22		23 52		00 22	02f30		02 30	

For general notes see front of timetable
For details of catering facilities see Directory of Train Operators

- **A** From 20 July from Sheffield (Table 53)
- **B** Until 13 July. From Sheffield (Table 53)
- **C** From Nottingham (Table 53)
- **D** 20 July to 7 September. From Sheffield (Table 53)
- **E** from 14 September From Sheffield (Table 53)
- **G** From York (Table 53)
- **H** From Sheffield (Table 53)
- **b** Arr. 2107
- **c** From 14 September arr. 2303
- **e** Change at East Croydon and Gatwick Airport
- **f** Change at Gatwick Airport and Three Bridges
- **g** Change at East Croydon and Burgess Hill

Brighton, Gatwick Airport and South London → City of London, St.Albans, Luton and Bedford

Network Diagram - see first page of Table 52

Miles	Miles	Miles	Miles	Miles			FC MO 1	FC MX	FC MX 1	FC MO 1	FC MX 1	FC MO 1	FC MX	FC MX 1	FC MO 1	FC MX 1	FC MO 1	FC MO	FC MX	FC MX 1	FC MO 1	FC 1	FC 1	FC	EM 1 ◇ A
0	—	—	—	—	**Brighton** 10	d	21p44		22p07	22p16				22p33	22p44					23p37	23p44				
1½	—	—	—	—	Preston Park	d			22p11					22p37						23p41	*23 06*				
7¼	—	—	—	—	Hassocks 4	d	21p52		22p17					22p43	22p52					23p47	23p52				
9¼	—	—	—	—	Burgess Hill 4	d	21p56		22p21	22p26				22p47	22p56					23p51	23p56				
10	—	—	—	—	Wivelsfield 4	d			22p23					22p49						23p53	*23 53*				
13	—	—	—	—	**Haywards Heath** 3	d	22p01		22p32	22p31				22p54	23p01					23p59	00 01				
17	—	—	—	—	Balcombe	d			22p37					23p00						00 04	*23 29*				
21½	—	—	—	—	Three Bridges 4	d	22p10		22p42	22p40				23p12	23p10					00 10	00 10	02 25	03 25	04 25	
24¼	—	—	—	—	**Gatwick Airport** 10 ✈	d	22p15		22p46	22p45				23p16	23p15					00 15	00 15	02 30	03 30	04 30	
30	—	—	—	—	Redhill	d														00 22	00 22				
40½	—	—	0	—	**East Croydon**	d	22p32		23p02	23p02				23p32	23p32					00 36	00 36	02 47	03 47	04 47	
—	0	0	—	0	**Sutton (Surrey)** 4	d																			
—	1	—	—	—	West Sutton	d																			
—	2	—	—	—	Sutton Common	d																			
—	3	—	—	—	St Helier	d																			
—	3½	—	—	—	Morden South	d																			
—	4	—	—	—	South Merton	d																			
—	4½	—	—	—	Wimbledon Chase	d																			
—	5¾	—	—	—	**Wimbledon** 6 ⊖	d																			
—	6¾	—	—	—	Haydons Road	d																			
—	8	—	—	—	Tooting	d																			
—	—	—	—	1¼	Carshalton	d																			
—	—	—	—	2	Hackbridge	d																			
—	—	—	—	4	Mitcham Junction	d																			
—	—	—	—	5	Mitcham Eastfields	d																			
—	9½	6	—	6	Streatham 4	d																			
—	11	7½	5	—	Tulse Hill 3	d																			
50¾	—	—	—	—	**London Bridge** 4 ⊖	d	22p45		23p15	23p15				23p45	23p45			00 20	00 20	00 52	00 52				
—	12	8½	—	—	Herne Hill 4	d																			
—	13	9½	—	—	Loughborough Jn	d																			
—	15	11½	—	—	Elephant & Castle	d					←					←									
51½	16	12½	10	—	**London Blackfriars** 3 ⊖	d	22p53	23p08	23p23 →	23p23	23p23		23p38	23p53 →	23p53	23p53		00 28	00 28	01 00	01 00	03 13	04 13	05 13	
52	—	—	—	—	City Thameslink 3	d																			
—	0	—	—	—	**Moorgate** ⊖	d																			
—	½	—	—	—	Barbican ⊖	d																			
52¾	¾	—	—	—	Farringdon 3 ⊖	d	22p58	23p14		23p28	23p29		23p44		23p58	23p59		00 30	00 34					05 18	
53¾	0	—	—	—	**St Pancras International** 15 ⊖	d	23p02	23p18		23p32	23p33		23p48		00 02	00 03		00b38	00 38	01 08	01 08	03 22	04 22	05 22	06 10
55½	—	—	—	—	Kentish Town ⊖	d	23p06	23p22		23p36			23p52		00 06			00 42	00 42	01 12	01 12	03 26	04 26	05 26	
58	—	—	—	—	West Hampstead Thameslink ⊖	d	23p10	23p26		23p40	23p40		23p56		00 10	00 10		00 46	00 46	01 16	01 16	03 30	04 30	05 30	
59	—	—	—	—	Cricklewood	d	23p13	23p29		23p43		←	23p59		00 13		←	00 49	00 49	01 19	01 19	03 33	04 33	05 33	
61	—	—	—	—	Hendon	d	23p16	23p32		23p46 →		23p46	00 02		00 16 →		00 16	00 52	00 52	01 22	01 22	03 36	04 36	05 36	
63¼	—	—	—	—	Mill Hill Broadway	d	23p19	23p35				23p49	00 05				00 19	00 55	00 55	01 25	01 25	03 39	04 39	05 39	
66½	—	—	—	—	Elstree & Borehamwood	d	23p24	23p40				23p54	00 10				00 24	01 00	01 00	01 30	01 30	03 44	04 44	05 44	
69½	—	—	—	—	Radlett	d	23p28	23p44				23p58	00 14				00 28	01 04	01 04	01 34	01 34	03 48	04 48	05 48	
74	—	—	—	—	**St Albans City**	d	23p34	23p50			23p54	00 04	00 20			00 24	00 34	01 10	01 10	01 40	01 40	03 54	04 54	05 54	
78¾	—	—	—	—	Harpenden	d	23p39	23p55			00 01	00 09	00 25			00 31	00 39	01 15	01 15	01 45	01 45	03 59	04 59	05 59	
83¼	—	—	—	—	Luton Airport Parkway 7 ✈	d	23p45	00 01			00 07	00 15	00 31			00 37	00 45	01 21	01 21	01 51	01 51	04 05	05 05	06 05	
84¼	30¼	—	—	—	**Luton** 10	d	23p49	00 05			00 10	00 19	00 35			00 40	00 49	01 25	01 25	01 55	01 55	04 10	05 10	06 10	06 33
86¾	—	—	—	—	Leagrave	d	23p53	00 09			00 14	00 23	00 39			00 44	00 53	01 29	01 29	01 59	01 59	04 14	05 14	06 14	
91¼	—	—	—	—	Harlington	d	23p59	00 14			00 20	00 29	00 44			00 50	00 59	01 34	01 34	02 04	02 04	04 20	05 20	06 20	
94¼	—	—	—	—	Flitwick	d	00 03	00 18			00 24	00 33	00 48			00 54	01 03	01 38	01 38	02 08	02 08	04 24	05 24	06 24	
103¾	49¾	—	—	—	**Bedford** 7	a	00 15	00 30			00 35	00 45	01 00			01 05	01 15	01 50	01 50	02 20	02 20	04 35	05 35	06 35	06 47

For general notes see front of timetable
For details of catering facilities see Directory of Train Operators

A To Sheffield (Table 53)
b Arr. 0035

Brighton, Gatwick Airport and South London → City of London, St.Albans, Luton and Bedford

Network Diagram - see first page of Table 52

Station		FC 1	EM 1 ◊ A	FC B	FC 1		FC B	EM 1 ◊ C	FC 1	FC	EM 1 ◊ D	FC 1	EM 1 ◊ A	FC	FC	FC B	FC 1	FC B	FC	EM 1 ◊ C	FC	FC 1	FC 1	SN	FC
Brighton 10	d	*03 50*			05 09				05 39			05 49					06 09						06 24		
Preston Park	d				05 13				05 43			05 53					06 13						06 28		
Hassocks 4	d				05 19				05 49			05 59					06 19						06 34		
Burgess Hill 4	d				05 23				05 53			06 03					06 23						06 38		
Wivelsfield 4	d				05 26				05 56			06 05					*06 15*						06 40		
Haywards Heath 3	d	*04 25*			05 30				06 00			06 09					06 30						06 45		
Balcombe	d								06 05								06 35						06 51		
Three Bridges 4	d	04 55			05 40				06 12			06 20					06 40						06 56		
Gatwick Airport 10	✈ d	05 00			05 46				06 16			06 24					06 46						07 01		
Redhill	d				*05 28*				*05 48*			06 33											07 10		
East Croydon	d	05 17			06 02				06 32			06 44					07 02						07 24		
Sutton (Surrey) 4	d														06 23						06 49			07 25	
West Sutton	d														06 26						06 52				
Sutton Common	d														06 28						06 55				
St Helier	d														06 31						06 57				
Morden South	d														06 33						06 59				
South Merton	d														06 35						07 01				
Wimbledon Chase	d														06 37						07 03				
Wimbledon 6	⊖ d									06 28					06 40						07 07				
Haydons Road	d									06 30					06 43						07 08				
Tooting	d									06 33					06 46						07 11				
Carshalton	d																							07 28	
Hackbridge	d																							07 31	
Mitcham Junction	d																							07 34	
Mitcham Eastfields	d																							07 38	
Streatham 4	d			05 46			06 06			06 36					06 50	06 56					07 16			07 42	
Tulse Hill 3	d			05 50			06 10			06 40					06 54	07 00					07 20		07 35	07 46	
London Bridge 4	⊖ d	05 34			06 15				06 46			06 59					07 16							08a02	
Herne Hill 4	d			05 54			06 14			06 44					06 59	07 04					07 24				
Loughborough Jn	d						06 17			06 48					07 02	07 07					07 27				
Elephant & Castle	d			06 02			06 22			06 53					07 07	07 12					07 32				
London Blackfriars 3	⊖ d	05 43		06b08	06 24		06 28		06 53	06 58		07 07			07 12	07 18	07 23				07 38		07c53		
City Thameslink 3	d			06 10	06 25		06 30		06 56	07 00		07 09			07 14	07 20	07 25				07 40		07 55		
Moorgate	⊖ d																		07 30			07 50			08 00
Barbican	⊖ d																								
Farringdon 3	⊖ d	05 48		06 14	06 29		06 34		06 59	07 04		07 12			07 16	07 24	07 28		07 32		07 44	07 52	07 58		08 04
St Pancras International 15	⊖ d	05 52	06 35	06 18	06 33		06 38	07 00	07 03	07 08	07 25	07 16	07 30		07 21	07 28	07 32		07 36	08 00	07 48	07 56	08 02		08 08
Kentish Town	⊖ d	05 56		06 22			06 42			07 12									07 40			08 00			08 12
West Hampstead Thameslink	⊖ d	06 00		06 26	06 40		06 46		07 10	07 16						07 36	07 40		07 44		07 56	08 04	08 09		08 16
Cricklewood	d	06 03		06 29			06 49			07 19				←					07 47			08 07			08 19
Hendon	d	06 06		06 32			06 52			07 22				07 22					07 50			08 10			08 22
Mill Hill Broadway	d	06 09		06 35			06 55			→				07 25				←	07 53			08 13			→
Elstree & Borehamwood	d	06 14		06 40			07 00							07 30		07 46		07 46	07 58		08 06	→			
Radlett	d	06 18		06 44			07 04							07 34		→		07 50	08 02		08 10				
St Albans City	d	06 24		06 50	06 54		07 10		07 24			07 36		07 40	07a43		07 54	07a57	08a10		08 16		08 23		
Harpenden	d	06 29		06 55	07 01		07 15		07 29			07 43		07 47			07 59				08 21		08 30		
Luton Airport Parkway 7	✈ d	06 35	06a56	07 01	07 07		07 21	07 22	07 35			07 49		07 54			08 05			08 22	08 27		08 36		
Luton 10	d	06 40		07 04	07 10		07 24		07 38		07a49	07 52	07 53	07 57			08 08				08 30		08 39		
Leagrave	d	06 44		07 08	07 14		07 28		07 43			07 56		08 00			08 12				08 34				
Harlington	d	06 50		07 14	07 20		07 34		07 48			08 02		08 06			08 18				08 40				
Flitwick	d	06 54		07 18	07 24		07 38		07 52			08 06		08 10			08 22				08 44		08 49		
Bedford 7	a	07 07		07 31	07 37		07 51	07 37	08 05			08 18	08 08	08 22			08 35			08 37	08 55		09 00		

For general notes see front of timetable
For details of catering facilities see Directory of Train Operators

- **A** To Nottingham (Table 53)
- **B** From Selhurst (Table 177)
- **C** To Derby (Table 53)
- **D** To Sheffield (Table 53)
- **b** Arr. 0605
- **c** Arr. 0750

Brighton, Gatwick Airport and South London → City of London, St.Albans, Luton and Bedford

Network Diagram - see first page of Table 52

		FC	EM	EM	FC		FC	FC	FC	FC	FC	FC	FC	EM	FC	FC	FC	FC	EM	FC	FC	EM	FC	FC	FC
		1	1 ◇	1 ◇	1				1					1 ◇		1		1	1 ◇			1 ◇	1		
			A	B										C					A			B			
			⊠ ⚲	☕										☕					⊠ ⚲			☕			
Brighton 10	d								07 00									07 26					07 50		
Preston Park	d								07 04									07 30					07 54		
Hassocks 4	d								07 10									07 36					08 00		
Burgess Hill 4	d								07 14									07 40					*08 00*		
Wivelsfield 4	d								07 18									*07 39*					*07 49*		
Haywards Heath 3	d								07 23									07 47					08 09		
Balcombe	d								*07 19*														08 14		
Three Bridges 4	d								07 32									07 56					*08 09*		
Gatwick Airport 10 ✈	d								07 37									08 01					08 22		
Redhill	d								*07 26*									08 14							
East Croydon 🚊	d								07 54									08 28					08 38		
Sutton (Surrey) 4	d						07 23						07 53								08 17				
West Sutton	d						07 26						07 56								08 20				
Sutton Common	d						07 29						07 59								08 22				
St Helier	d						07 31						08 01								08 25				
Morden South	d						07 33						08 03								08 27				
South Merton	d						07 35						08 05								08 29				
Wimbledon Chase	d						07 37						08 07								08 31				
Wimbledon 6 ⊖ 🚊	d						07 42					07 58	08 12								08 35				
Haydons Road	d						07 44					08 00	08 14								08 38				
Tooting	d						07 47					08 03	08 17								08 41				
Carshalton	d																								
Hackbridge	d																								
Mitcham Junction 🚊	d																								
Mitcham Eastfields	d																								
Streatham 4	d						07 52					08 11	08 21								08 45				
Tulse Hill 3	d						07 57		08 05			08 15	08 27					08 39			08 49		08 55		
London Bridge 4 ⊖	d																								
Herne Hill 4	d						08 01					08 22	08 31					08 43			08 53		09 00		
Loughborough Jn	d						08 03					08 25	08 34								08 56				
Elephant & Castle	d						08 09					08 30	08 40								09 00				
London Blackfriars 3 ⊖	d						08 13		08b23			08 35	08 45					08c57			09 05		09 09		
City Thameslink 3	d						08 15		08 25			08 37	08 47					08 59			09 07		09 11		
Moorgate ⊖	d				08 10					08 32						08 52				09 04				09 14	
Barbican ⊖	d																								
Farringdon 3 ⊖	d				08 12		08 20		08 29	08 34		08 42	08 50			08 58		09 02		09 06	09 10		09 14	09e20	
St Pancras International 15 ⊖	d		08 25	08 30	08 16		08 24		08 33	08 38		08 46	08 54	09 00		09 02		09 06	09 25	09 10	09 14	09 30	09 18	09 24	
Kentish Town ⊖	d						08 28			08 42			08 58								09 18			09 28	
West Hampstead Thameslink ⊖	d						08 32			08 48			09 02							09 16	09 22			09 32	
Cricklewood	d						08 35	←		08 51	←		09 05		←		←				09 25			09 35	←
Hendon	d	←					08 38	08 22		08 54	08 38		09 08		08 54		09 08				09 28			09 38	09 28
Mill Hill Broadway	d	08 13					→	08 25		→	08 41		→		08 57		09 11				→			→	09 31
Elstree & Borehamwood	d	08 18						08 30			08 46				09 02		09 16			09 26					09 36
Radlett	d	08 22						08 36			08 50				09 08		09 20			09 30					09 40
St Albans City	d	08a29			08 36			08a42	08 54		08a57	09 09			09 14	09 22	09a27	09 28		09 38			09 42		09a49
Harpenden	d				08 43				08 59			09 14			09 19	09 28		09 34		09 43			09 47		
Luton Airport Parkway 7 ✈	d				08 49				09 05			09 20		09 22	09 25			09 40		09 49			09 53		
Luton 10	d			08 53	08 54				09 08			09 24			09a29	09 34		09 44	09a48	09a52		09 53	09 56		
Leagrave	d				08 57				09 12			09 27						09 47					09 59		
Harlington	d				09 03				09 18			09 33						09 53					10 05		
Flitwick	d				09 07				09 22			09 37				09 45		09 57					10 09		
Bedford 7	a		09 00	09 07	09 18				09 35			09 48		09 37		09 58		10 08				10 08	10 20		

For general notes see front of timetable
For details of catering facilities see Directory of Train Operators

A To Sheffield (Table 53)
B To Nottingham (Table 53)
C To Derby (Table 53)
b Arr. 0819
c Arr. 0852
e Arr. 0917

Brighton, Gatwick Airport and South London → City of London, St.Albans, Luton and Bedford

Network Diagram - see first page of Table 52

		FC 1	FC	FC	FC 1		FC	EM 1 ◇ A	FC	FC 1	FC	FC	EM 1 ◇ B	FC 1	FC	FC	FC 1	FC	FC	FC 1	FC	EM 1 ◇ A	FC	FC 1	FC
Brighton 10	d	08 02			08 16					08 36				09 00			09 04			09 34				09 37	
Preston Park	d	08 06			08 20					08 40							09 08			*09 08*				09 41	
Hassocks 4	d	08 12			08 26					08 46				09 08			09 14			*09 14*				09 47	
Burgess Hill 4	d	08 16			08 30					08 50				09 12			09 18			*09 35*				09 51	
Wivelsfield 4	d	08 18			08 33					*08 39*				*08 59*			09 20			*09 33*				09 53	
Haywards Heath 3	d	08 23			08 38					09 00				09 16			09 25			09 48				09 58	
Balcombe	d	*08 21*								09 06							09 31			*09 31*					
Three Bridges 4	d	08 34			08 47					09 12				09 27			09 37			*09 48*				10 10	
Gatwick Airport 10	d	08 38			08 52					09 16				09 31			09 41			10 01				10 16	
Redhill	d	*08 18*			*08 35*					*08 51*				*09 22*						*09 48*				*10 05*	
East Croydon	d	08 54			09 08					09 32				09 47			09 57			10 17				10 32	
Sutton (Surrey) 4	d		08 47								09 05					09 38		09 37			10 06				10 05
West Sutton	d		08 50								09 08							09 40							10 08
Sutton Common	d		08 52								09 10							09 42							10 10
St Helier	d		08 55								09 13							09 45							10 13
Morden South	d		08 57								09 15							09 47							10 15
South Merton	d		08 59								09 17							09 49							10 17
Wimbledon Chase	d		09 01								09 19							09 51							10 19
Wimbledon 6	d		09 04								09 24							09 56							10 23
Haydons Road	d		09 06								09 26							09 58							10 25
Tooting	d		09 09								09 29							10 01							10 28
Carshalton	d															09 41					10 09				
Hackbridge	d															09 43					10 11				
Mitcham Junction	d															09 46					10 14				
Mitcham Eastfields	d															09 50					10 18				
Streatham 4	d		09 15								09 34					09 54		10 06			10 23				10 33
Tulse Hill 3	d		09 19		09 25						09 38					09 58		10 12			10 27				10 42
London Bridge 4	d	09 11								09 45				10 00			10 15			10 30				10 45	
Herne Hill 4	d		09 23								09 42					10 02		10 16			10 31				10 46
Loughborough Jn	d		09 26								09 45					10 05		10 19			10 34				10 49
Elephant & Castle	d		09 30								09 50					10 10		10 24			10 39				10 54
London Blackfriars 3	d	09 19	09 34		09 38					09 53	09 58			10 08		10b14	10 23	10 28		10 38	10 43			10 53	10 58
City Thameslink 3	d	09 21	09 36		09 40					09 55	10 00			10 10		10 16	10 25	10 30		10 40	10 45			10 55	11 00
Moorgate	d						09 48																		
Barbican	d																								
Farringdon 3	d	09c29	09 40		09 44		09 50			09 59	10 04			10 14		10 19	10 29	10 34		10 44	10 49			10 59	11 04
St Pancras International 15	d	09 33	09 44		09 48		09 54	10 00		10 03	10 08		10 30	10 18		10 23	10 33	10 38		10 48	10 53	11 00		11 03	11 08
Kentish Town	d		09 48				09 58				10 12					10 27		10 42			10 57				11 12
West Hampstead Thameslink	d		09 52				10 02				10 16					10 31		10 46			11 01				11 16
Cricklewood	d		09 55	←			10 05		←		10 19	←			←	10 34		10 49	←		11 04		←		11 19
Hendon	d		09 58 →	09 38			10 08 →		09 58		10 22 →	10 08			10 22	10 37 →		10 52 →	10 37		11 07 →		10 52		11 22 →
Mill Hill Broadway	d			09 41					10 01			10 11			10 25				10 40				10 55		
Elstree & Borehamwood	d			09 46					10 06			10 16			10 30				10 45				11 00		
Radlett	d			09 50					10 10			10 20			10 38				10 50				11 08		
St Albans City	d	09 54		09 58	10 09				10a17	10 24		10 28		10 39	10 44		10 54		10a57	11 09			11 14	11 24	
Harpenden	d	09 59		10 03	10 14					10 29		10 37		10 44	10 51		10 59			11 14			11 19	11 29	
Luton Airport Parkway 7	d	10 05		10 09	10 20			10 22		10 35		10 43		10 50	10 57		11 05			11 20		11 22	11 25	11 35	
Luton 10	d	10 08		10a17	10 24					10 38		10a47	10 53	10 54	11a01		11 08			11 24			11a29	11 38	
Leagrave	d	10 12			10 28					10 42				10 58			11 12			11 28				11 42	
Harlington	d	10 18			10 34					10 48				11 04			11 18			11 34				11 48	
Flitwick	d	10 22			10 38					10 52				11 08			11 22			11 38				11 52	
Bedford 7	a	10 35			10 50			10 37		11 05			11 07	11 20			11 35			11 50		11 37		12 05	

For general notes see front of timetable
For details of catering facilities see Directory of Train Operators

A To Derby (Table 53)
B To Nottingham (Table 53)
b Arr. 1010
c Arr. 0926

Brighton, Gatwick Airport and South London → City of London, St.Albans, Luton and Bedford

Network Diagram - see first page of Table 52

		FC	EM	FC	FC		FC	FC	FC	FC	FC	FC	EM	FC	FC	FC	FC	EM	FC	FC	FC	FC	FC	FC	FC
			1 ◇	1				1			1		1 ◇		1			1 ◇	1			1			1
			A										B					A							
			☕										☕					☕							
Brighton 10	d			10 04				10 07			10 34				10 37				11 04			11 07			11 34
Preston Park	d			09 58				10 11			10 11				10 41				10 58			11 11			11 11
Hassocks 4	d			10 05				10 17			10 17				10 47				11 05			11 17			11 17
Burgess Hill 4	d			10 08				10 21			10 21				10 51				11 08			11 21			11 21
Wivelsfield 4	d			10 11				10 23			10 35				10 53				11 11			11 23			11 34
Haywards Heath 3	d			10 18				10 32			10 48				11 02				11 18			11 32			11 48
Balcombe	d							10 37			10 37											11 37			11 37
Three Bridges 4	d			10 18				10 42			10 48				11 12				11 18			11 42			11 48
Gatwick Airport 10 ✈	d			10 31				10 46			11 01				11 16				11 31			11 46			12 01
Redhill	d			10 18				10 37			10 48				11 16							11 37			11 49
East Croydon	d			10 47				11 02			11 17				11 32				11 47			12 02			12 17
Sutton (Surrey) 4	d				10 36				10 37			11 06				11 07				11 36			11 37		
West Sutton	d								10 40							11 10							11 40		
Sutton Common	d								10 42							11 12							11 42		
St Helier	d								10 45							11 15							11 45		
Morden South	d								10 47							11 17							11 47		
South Merton	d								10 49							11 19							11 49		
Wimbledon Chase	d								10 51							11 21							11 52		
Wimbledon 6 ⊖	d								10 56							11 26							11 55		
Haydons Road	d								10 58							11 28							11 58		
Tooting	d								11 01							11 31							12 01		
Carshalton	d				10 39							11 09								11 39					
Hackbridge	d				10 41							11 11								11 41					
Mitcham Junction	d				10 44							11 14								11 44					
Mitcham Eastfields	d				10 48							11 18								11 48					
Streatham 4	d				10 53				11 06			11 23				11 36				11 53			12 06		
Tulse Hill 3	d				10 57				11 12			11 27				11 42				11 57			12 12		
London Bridge 4 ⊖	d			11 00				11 15			11 30				11 45				12 00			12 15			12 30
Herne Hill 4	d				11 00				11 16			11 30				11 46				12 00			12 16		
Loughborough Jn	d				11 04				11 19			11 34				11 49				12 04			12 19		
Elephant & Castle	d				11 09				11 24			11 39				11 54				12 09			12 24		
London Blackfriars 3 ⊖	d			11 08	11 13			11 23	11 28		11 38	11 43			11 53	11 58			12 08	12 13		12 23	12 28		12 38
City Thameslink 3	d			11 10	11 15			11 25	11 30		11 40	11 45			11 55	12 00			12 10	12 15		12 25	12 30		12 40
Moorgate ⊖	d																								
Barbican ⊖	d																								
Farringdon 3 ⊖	d			11 14	11 19			11 29	11 34		11 44	11 49			11 59	12 04			12 14	12 19		12 29	12 34		12 44
St Pancras International 15 ⊖	d		11 30	11 18	11 23			11 33	11 38		11 48	11 53	12 00		12 03	12 08		12 30	12 18	12 23		12 33	12 38		12 48
Kentish Town ⊖	d				11 27				11 42			11 57				12 12				12 27			12 42		
West Hampstead Thameslink ⊖	d				11 31				11 46			12 01				12 16				12 31			12 46		
Cricklewood	d	←			11 34		←		11 49	←		12 04		←		12 19	←			12 34	←		12 49	←	
Hendon	d	11 07			11 37 →		11 22		11 52 →	11 37		12 07 →		11 52		12 22 →	12 07			12 37 →	12 22		12 52 →	12 37	
Mill Hill Broadway	d	11 10					11 25			11 40				11 55			12 10				12 25			12 40	
Elstree & Borehamwood	d	11 15					11 30			11 45				12 00			12 15				12 30			12 45	
Radlett	d	11 20					11 38			11 50				12 08			12 20				12 38			12 50	
St Albans City	d	11a27		11 39			11 44	11 54		11a57	12 09			12 14	12 24		12a27		12 39		12 44	12 54		12a57	13 09
Harpenden	d			11 44			11 49	11 59			12 14			12 19	12 29				12 44		12 49	12 59			13 14
Luton Airport Parkway 7 ✈	d			11 50			11 55	12 05			12 20		12 22	12 25	12 35				12 50		12 55	13 05			13 20
Luton 10	d		11 53	11 54			11a59	12 08			12 24			12a29	12 38			12 53	12 54		12a59	13 08			13 24
Leagrave	d			11 58				12 12			12 28				12 42				12 58			13 12			13 28
Harlington	d			12 04				12 18			12 34				12 48				13 04			13 18			13 34
Flitwick	d			12 08				12 22			12 38				12 52				13 08			13 22			13 38
Bedford 7	a		12 07	12 20				12 35			12 50		12 37		13 05			13 07	13 20			13 35			13 50

For general notes see front of timetable
For details of catering facilities see Directory of Train Operators

A To Nottingham (Table 53)
B To Derby (Table 53)

Brighton, Gatwick Airport and South London → City of London, St.Albans, Luton and Bedford

Network Diagram - see first page of Table 52

		FC	EM 1 ◇ A	FC	FC 1		FC	FC	EM 1 ◇ B	FC 1	FC	FC	FC 1	FC	FC	FC 1	FC	EM 1 ◇ A	FC	EM 1 ◇ C	FC 1	FC	FC	EM 1 ◇ B	FC 1
Brighton 10	d				11 37					12 04			12 07			12 34					12 37				13 04
Preston Park	d				11 41					11 58			12 11			12 11					12 41				12 58
Hassocks 4	d				11 47					12 05			12 17			12 17					12 47				13 05
Burgess Hill 4	d				11 51					12 08			12 21			12 21					12 51				13 08
Wivelsfield 4	d				11 53					12 11			12 23			12 34					12 53				13 11
Haywards Heath 3	d				12 02					12 18			12 32			12 48					13 02				13 18
Balcombe	d												12 37			12 37									
Three Bridges 4	d				12 12					12 18			12 42			12 48					13 12				13 18
Gatwick Airport 10 ✈	d				12 16					12 31			12 46			13 01					13 16				13 31
Redhill	d				12 16								12 37			12 48					13 16				
East Croydon	d				12 32					12 47			13 02			13 17					13 32				13 47
Sutton (Surrey) 4	d	12 06					12 07				12 36			12 37			13 06					13 07			
West Sutton	d						12 10							12 40								13 10			
Sutton Common	d						12 12							12 42								13 12			
St Helier	d						12 15							12 45								13 15			
Morden South	d						12 17							12 47								13 17			
South Merton	d						12 19							12 49								13 19			
Wimbledon Chase	d						12 21							12 51								13 21			
Wimbledon 6 ⊖	d						12 26							12 56								13 26			
Haydons Road	d						12 28							12 58								13 28			
Tooting	d						12 31							13 01								13 31			
Carshalton	d	12 09									12 39						13 09								
Hackbridge	d	12 11									12 41						13 11								
Mitcham Junction	d	12 14									12 44						13 14								
Mitcham Eastfields	d	12 18									12 48						13 18								
Streatham 4	d	12 23					12 36				12 53			13 06			13 23					13 36			
Tulse Hill 3	d	12 27					12 42				12 57			13 12			13 27					13 42			
London Bridge 4 ⊖	d				12 45					13 00			13 15			13 30					13 45				14 00
Herne Hill 4	d	12 30					12 46				13 00			13 16			13 30					13 46			
Loughborough Jn	d	12 34					12 49				13 04			13 19			13 34					13 49			
Elephant & Castle	d	12 39					12 54				13 09			13 24			13 39					13 54			
London Blackfriars 3 ⊖	d	12 43			12 53		12 58			13 08	13 13		13 23	13 28		13 38	13 43				13 53	13 58			14 08
City Thameslink 3	d	12 45			12 55		13 00			13 10	13 15		13 25	13 30		13 40	13 45				13 55	14 00			14 10
Moorgate ⊖	d																								
Barbican ⊖	d																								
Farringdon 3 ⊖	d	12 49			12 59		13 04			13 14	13 19		13 29	13 34		13 44	13 49				13 59	14 04			14 14
St Pancras International 15 ⊖	d	12 53	13 00		13 03		13 08		13 30	13 18	13 23		13 33	13 38		13 48	13 53	14 00		14 25	14 03	14 08		14 30	14 18
Kentish Town ⊖	d	12 57					13 12				13 27			13 42			13 57					14 12			
West Hampstead Thameslink ⊖	d	13 01					13 16				13 31			13 46			14 01					14 16			
Cricklewood	d	13 04		←			13 19	←			13 34	←		13 49	←		14 04		←			14 19	←		
Hendon	d	13 07		12 52			13 22	13 07			13 37	13 22		13 52	13 37		14 07		13 52			14 22	14 07		
Mill Hill Broadway	d	→		12 55			→	13 10			→	13 25		→	13 40		→		13 55			→	14 10		
Elstree & Borehamwood	d			13 00				13 15				13 30			13 45				14 00				14 15		
Radlett	d			13 08				13 20				13 38			13 50				14 08				14 20		
St Albans City	d			13 14	13 24			13a27		13 39		13 44	13 54		13a57	14 09			14 14		14 24		14a27		14 39
Harpenden	d			13 19	13 29					13 44		13 49	13 59			14 14			14 19		14 29				14 44
Luton Airport Parkway 7 ✈	d		13 22	13 25	13 35					13 50		13 55	14 05			14 20		14 22	14 25		14 35				14 50
Luton 10	d			13a29	13 38				13 53	13 54		13a59	14 08			14 24			14a29		14 38			14 53	14 54
Leagrave	d				13 42					13 58			14 12			14 28					14 42				14 58
Harlington	d				13 48					14 04			14 18			14 34					14 48				15 04
Flitwick	d				13 52					14 08			14 22			14 38					14 52				15 08
Bedford 7	a		13 37		14 05				14 07	14 20			14 35			14 50		14 37		15 00	15 05			15 07	15 20

For general notes see front of timetable
For details of catering facilities see Directory of Train Operators

A To Derby (Table 53)
B To Nottingham (Table 53)
C To Sheffield (Table 53)

Brighton, Gatwick Airport and South London → City of London, St.Albans, Luton and Bedford

Network Diagram - see first page of Table 52

Station		FC	FC	FC 1	FC		FC	FC 1	FC	EM 1 ◇ A 🍴	FC	FC 1	FC	FC	FC	EM 1 ◇ B 🍴	EM 1 ◇ C 🍴	FC 1	FC	FC	FC 1	FC	FC	FC 1	EM 1 ◇ C 🍴
Brighton 10	d			13 07				13 34				13 37						14 04			14 07				
Preston Park	d			13 11				*13 11*				13 41						*13 58*			14 11				
Hassocks 4	d			13 17				*13 17*				13 47						*14 05*			14 17				
Burgess Hill 4	d			13 21				*13 21*				13 51						*14 08*			14 21				
Wivelsfield 4	d			13 23				*13 34*				13 53						*14 11*			14 23				
Haywards Heath 3	d			13 32				13 48				14 02						14 18			14 31				
Balcombe	d			13 37				*13 37*													14 37				
Three Bridges 4	d			13 42				*13 48*				14 12						*14 18*			14 41				
Gatwick Airport 10 ✈	d			13 46				14 01				14 16						14 31			14 46				
Redhill	d			*13 37*				*13 48*				*14 16*									*14 37*				
East Croydon	d			14 02				14 17				14 32						14 47			15 01				
Sutton (Surrey) 4	d	13 36			13 37				14 06				14 07						14 36			14 37			
West Sutton	d				13 40								14 10									14 40			
Sutton Common	d				13 42								14 12									14 42			
St Helier	d				13 45								14 15									14 45			
Morden South	d				13 47								14 17									14 47			
South Merton	d				13 49								14 19									14 49			
Wimbledon Chase	d				13 51								14 21									14 51			
Wimbledon 6 ⊖	d				13 56								14 26									14 56			
Haydons Road	d				13 58								14 28									14 58			
Tooting	d				14 01								14 31									15 01			
Carshalton	d	13 39							14 09										14 39						
Hackbridge	d	13 41							14 11										14 41						
Mitcham Junction	d	13 44							14 14										14 44						
Mitcham Eastfields	d	13 48							14 18										14 48						
Streatham 4	d	13 53			14 06				14 23				14 36						14 53			15 06			
Tulse Hill 3	d	13 57			14 12				14 27				14 42						14 57			15 12			
London Bridge 4 ⊖	d			14 15				14 30				14 45						15 00			15 15				
Herne Hill 4	d	14 00			14 16				14 30				14 46						15 00			15 16			
Loughborough Jn	d	14 04			14 19				14 34				14 49						15 04			15 19			
Elephant & Castle	d	14 09			14 24				14 39				14 54						15 09			15 24			
London Blackfriars 3 ⊖	d	14 13		14 23	14 28			14 38	14 43			14 53	14 58					15 08	15 13		15 22	15 28			
City Thameslink 3	d	14 15		14 25	14 30			14 40	14 45			14 55	15 00					15 10	15 15		15 25	15 30			
Moorgate ⊖	d														15 06									15 35	
Barbican ⊖	d																								
Farringdon 3 ⊖	d	14 19		14 29	14 34			14 44	14 49			14 59	15 04		15 10			15 14	15 19		15 29	15 34		15 39	
St Pancras International 15 ⊖	d	14 23		14 33	14 38			14 48	14 53	15 00		15 03	15 08		15 15	15 25	15 30	15 18	15 23		15 33	15 38		15 44	15 55
Kentish Town ⊖	d	14 27			14 42				14 57				15 12						15 27			15 42			
West Hampstead Thameslink ⊖	d	14 31			14 46				15 01				15 16						15 31			15 46			
Cricklewood	d	14 34	←		14 49		←		15 04		←		15 19	←					15 34	←		15 49	←		
Hendon	d	14 37	14 22		14 52		14 37		15 07		14 52		15 22	15 07					15 37	15 22		15 52	15 37		
Mill Hill Broadway	d	→	14 25		→		14 40		→		14 55		→	15 10					→	15 25		→	15 40		
Elstree & Borehamwood	d		14 30				14 45				15 00			15 15						15 30			15 45		
Radlett	d		14 38				14 50				15 08			15 20						15 38			15 50		
St Albans City	d		14 44	14 54			14a57	15 09			15 14	15 24		15a27	15 34			15 39		15 44	15 54		15a57	16 02	
Harpenden	d		14 49	14 59				15 14			15 20	15 29			15 40			15 44		15 49	15 59			16 09	
Luton Airport Parkway 7 ✈	d		14 55	15 05				15 20		15 22	15 25	15 35						15 50		15 55	16 05				
Luton 10	d		14a59	15 08				15 24			15a29	15 38			15 47	15a48	15 53	15 54		15a59	16 08			16 17	16a18
Leagrave	d			15 12				15 28				15 42						15 58			16 12				
Harlington	d			15 18				15 34				15 48						16 04			16 18				
Flitwick	d			15 22				15 38				15 52			15 58			16 08			16 22			16 27	
Bedford 7	a			15 35				15 50		15 37		16 05			16 10		16 08	16 20			16 35			16 40	

For general notes see front of timetable
For details of catering facilities see Directory of Train Operators

A To Derby (Table 53)
B To Sheffield (Table 53)
C To Nottingham (Table 53)

Brighton, Gatwick Airport and South London → City of London, St.Albans, Luton and Bedford

Network Diagram - see first page of Table 52

		FC 1	FC	EM 1 ◇ A	FC		EM 1 ◇	FC 1	FC	FC	EM 1 ◇ B	FC 1	FC	FC	FC 1	FC 1	FC	FC	FC 1	FC	FC	FC 1	EM 1 ◇ A	EM 1 ◇ C	FC 1
Brighton 10	d	14 34						14 37				15 04				15 07						15 34			15 37
Preston Park	d	*14 11*						14 41				*14 58*				15 11						*15 11*			15 41
Hassocks 4	d	*14 17*						14 47				*15 05*				15 17						*15 17*			15 47
Burgess Hill 4	d	*14 21*						14 51				*15 08*				15 21						*15 21*			15 51
Wivelsfield 4	d	*14 34*						14 53				*15 11*				15 23						*15 35*			15 53
Haywards Heath 3	d	14 48						15 02				15 18				15 32						15 48			15 58
Balcombe	d	*14 37*														15 37						*15 37*			
Three Bridges 4	d	*14 48*						15 12				*15 18*				15 42						*15 48*			16 07
Gatwick Airport 10 ✈	d	15 01						15 16				15 31				15 46						16 01			16 11
Redhill	d	*14 48*						*15 16*								*15 37*						*15 48*			
East Croydon	d	15 17						15 32				15 47				16 02						16 17			16 27
Sutton (Surrey) 4	d		15 06						15 07				15 36				15 37			16 06					
West Sutton	d								15 10								15 40								
Sutton Common	d								15 12								15 42								
St Helier	d								15 15								15 45								
Morden South	d								15 17								15 47								
South Merton	d								15 19								15 49								
Wimbledon Chase	d								15 21								15 51								
Wimbledon 6 ⊖	d								15 26								15 56								
Haydons Road	d								15 28								15 58								
Tooting	d								15 31								16 01								
Carshalton	d		15 09										15 39							16 09					
Hackbridge	d		15 11										15 41							16 11					
Mitcham Junction	d		15 14										15 44							16 14					
Mitcham Eastfields	d		15 18										15 48							16 18					
Streatham 4	d		15 23						15 36				15 53				16 06			16 23					
Tulse Hill 3	d		15 27						15 42				15 57				16 12			16 27		16 33			
London Bridge 4 ⊖	d	15 30						15 45				16 00				16 15									16 42
Herne Hill 4	d		15 30						15 46				16 00				16 16			16 31		16 37			
Loughborough Jn	d		15 34						15 49				16 04				16 19			16 34					
Elephant & Castle	d		15 39						15 54				16 09				16 24			16 40		16 43			
London Blackfriars 3 ⊖	d	15 38	15 43					15 53	15 58			16 08	16 14			16 26	16 30			16 44		16 50			16 54
City Thameslink 3	d	15 40	15 45					15 55	16 00			16 10	16 16			16 28	16 32			16 46		16 52			16 56
Moorgate ⊖	d														16 24				16 38						
Barbican ⊖	d																								
Farringdon 3 ⊖	d	15 44	15 49					15 59	16 04			16 14	16 20		16 28	16 32	16 36		16 42	16 50		16 58			17 02
St Pancras International 15 ⊖	d	15 48	15 53	16 00			16 08	16 03	16 08		16 30	16 18	16 25		16 32	16 36	16 40		16 46	16 54		17 02	17 15	17 30	17 06
Kentish Town ⊖	d		15 57						16 12				16 28				16 44			16 58					
West Hampstead Thameslink ⊖	d		16 01						16 16				16 32				16 48			17 02					
Cricklewood	d		16 04		←				16 19	←			16 35	←			16 51	←		17 05	←				
Hendon	d		16 07		15 52				16 22	16 07			16 38	16 22			16 54	16 38		17 08	16 54				
Mill Hill Broadway	d		→		15 55				→	16 11			→	16 27			→	16 43		→	16 59				
Elstree & Borehamwood	d				16 00					16 16				16 32				16 48			17 04				
Radlett	d				16 08					16 20				16 38				16 52			17 08				
St Albans City	d	16 09			16 14			16 24		16a27		16 40		16 44	16 52	16 56		17a00	17 06		17 14	17 22			17 26
Harpenden	d	16 14			16 19			16 30				16 46		16 50	16 58	17 04			17 14		17 20	17 28			17 34
Luton Airport Parkway 7 ✈	d	16 20		16a21	16 25			16 36				16 52		16 56		17 10			17 20		17 26	17 34	17a38		17 40
Luton 10	d	16 24			16a29		16 38	16 40			16 53	16 55		16a59	17 04	17 13			17 23		17a29	17 36			17 43
Leagrave	d	16 28						16 44				16 58				17 16			17 26						17 46
Harlington	d	16 34						16 50				17 04				17 22			17 32						17 52
Flitwick	d	16 38						16 54				17 08			17 15	17 26			17 36			17 47			17 56
Bedford 7	a	16 50					16 56	17 05			17 07	17 20			17 28	17 38			17 48			18 00		18 07	18 08

For general notes see front of timetable
For details of catering facilities see Directory of Train Operators

- **A** To Derby (Table 53)
- **B** To Nottingham (Table 53)
- **C** To Sheffield (Table 53)

Brighton, Gatwick Airport and South London → City of London, St.Albans, Luton and Bedford

Network Diagram - see first page of Table 52

Station		FC	FC	FC	FC		FC	FC 1	FC 1	FC	FC 1	EM 1 ◇ A ☕	FC 1	FC	EM 1 ◇ B ☕	FC 1	EM 1 ◇ C ☕	FC	EM 1 ◇ D ☕	FC	FC	FC 1	FC 1	FC	FC
Brighton 10	d												16 07			16 14									
Preston Park	d												16 11			*16 11*									
Hassocks 4	d												16 17												
Burgess Hill 4	d												16 21			16 25									
Wivelsfield 4	d												*16 11*												
Haywards Heath 3	d												16 26			16 38									
Balcombe	d												16 31												
Three Bridges 4	d												16 37			16 47									
Gatwick Airport 10 ✈	d												16 41			16 53									
Redhill	d												*16 18*			*16 48*									
East Croydon 🚋	d												16 57			17 09									
Sutton (Surrey) 4	d		16 07	16 38	16 37															17 06	17 02				
West Sutton	d		16 10		16 40																17 05				
Sutton Common	d		16 12		16 42																17 07				
St Helier	d		16 15		16 45																17 10				
Morden South	d		16 17		16 47																17 12				
South Merton	d		16 19		16 49																17 14				
Wimbledon Chase	d		16 21		16 51																17 16				
Wimbledon 6 ⊖ 🚋	d		16 28		16 55																17 20				
Haydons Road	d		16 30		16 57																17 22				
Tooting	d		16 33		17 00																17 25				
Carshalton	d			16 41																17 09					
Hackbridge	d			16 43																17 11					
Mitcham Junction 🚋	d			16 46																17 14					
Mitcham Eastfields	d			16 50																17 18					
Streatham 4	d		16 38	16 55	17 05															17 23	17 29				
Tulse Hill 3	d		16 41	17 02	17 09								17 14							17 27	17 33				
London Bridge 4 ⊖	d															17 29									
Herne Hill 4	d		16 46	17 06	17 14															17 31	17 37				
Loughborough Jn	d		16 49	17 10	17 17															17 34	17 40				
Elephant & Castle	d		16 54	17 14	17 22															17 39	17 44				
London Blackfriars 3 ⊖	d		17 00	17 18	17 32								17 26			17 36				17 44	17 48	17 52			
City Thameslink 3	d		17 02	17 20	17 34								17 28			17 39				17 46	17 50	17 54			
Moorgate ⊖	d						17 04	17 10	17 14		17 24												17 58		18 04
Barbican ⊖	d																								
Farringdon 3 ⊖	d		17 06	17 24	17 38		17 10	17 14	17 18		17 28		17 32			17 42				17 50	17 54	17 58	18 02		18 08
St Pancras International 15 ⊖	d		17 10	17 28	17 42		17 14	17 18	17 22		17 32	17 45	17 36		17 55	17 46	18 00		18 15	17 54	17 58	18 02	18 06		18 12
Kentish Town ⊖	d			17 32	17 46		17 18														18 02				18 16
West Hampstead Thameslink ⊖	d		17 18	17 36	17 50		17 22													18 02	18 06				18 20
Cricklewood	d	←		17 39	17 53		17 25			←				←				←			18 09			←	18 23
Hendon	d	17 08		17 42	17 56		17 28			17 28				17 42				17 56			18 12			18 12	18 26
Mill Hill Broadway	d	17 13		→	→		→			17 33				17 47				18 01			→			18 17	→
Elstree & Borehamwood	d	17 18	17 28							17 38				17 52				18 06		18 12				18 22	
Radlett	d	17 22	17 32							17 42				17 56				18 10		18 16				18 26	
St Albans City	d	17a30	17 38					17 38	17 42	17 48	17 52		17 56	18a04		18 06		18 16		18 22		18 22	18 26	18a34	
Harpenden	d		17 44					17 44	17 50	17 54	17 58		18 04			18 14		18 22		18 28		18 28	18 34		
Luton Airport Parkway 7 ✈	d		17 50						17 56	18 00			18 10			18 20	18 23	18 28		18 34			18 40		
Luton 10	d		17 54					17 50	17 59	18a05	18 04	18a09	18 13		18a19	18 23		18a33		18 38		18 34	18 43		
Leagrave	d		17 58						18 02				18 16			18 26				18 42			18 46		
Harlington	d		18 04						18 08				18 22			18 32				18 48			18 52		
Flitwick	d		18 08					18 01	18 12		18 15		18 26			18 36				18 52		18 45	18 56		
Bedford 7	a		18 20					18 14	18 24		18 28		18 38			18 48	18 38		18 54	19 04		18 58	19 08		

For general notes see front of timetable
For details of catering facilities see Directory of Train Operators

A To Leeds (Table 53)
B To Nottingham (Table 53)
C To Burton-on-Trent (Table 53)
D Until 5 September to Sheffield (Table 53). From 8 September to Derby (Table 53)

Brighton, Gatwick Airport and South London → City of London, St.Albans, Luton and Bedford

Network Diagram - see first page of Table 52

		FC 1	EM 1 ◇ A ☕	FC	FC		FC	FC 1	SN	EM 1 ◇ A ☕	FC 1	FC	FC	FC 1	FC	EM 1 ◇ B ☕	FC	FC 1	SN	FC 1	FC	FC	FC 1	SN	EM 1 ◇ C ☕
Brighton 10	d	16 29									17 03							17 23		17 37					
Preston Park	d	16 33									*16 58*							17 27		17 41					
Hassocks 4	d	16 39									*17 05*							17 33		17 47					
Burgess Hill 4	d	16 43									17 13							17 37		17 51					
Wivelsfield 4	d	16 46									*17 11*							17 40							
Haywards Heath 3	d	16 50									17 18							17 46		17 56					
Balcombe	d	16 56																*17 27*		18 02					
Three Bridges 4	d	17 02									17 27							17 56		18 12					
Gatwick Airport 10 ✈	d	17 07									17 31							18 01		18 16					
Redhill	d										*17 22*							*17 53*		*18 07*					
East Croydon 🚋	d	17 27									17 47							18 17		18 32					
Sutton (Surrey) 4	d						17 32		17 30			17 40			18 04				18 04		18 08			18 31	
West Sutton	d								17 34			17 43							18 07		18 13			18 34	
Sutton Common	d								17 36			17 45									18 14			18 37	
St Helier	d								17 39			17 48									18 18			18 39	
Morden South	d								17 41			17 50									18 20			18 41	
South Merton	d								17 43			17 52									18 22			18 43	
Wimbledon Chase	d								17 45			17 54									18 24			18 45	
Wimbledon 6 ⊖ 🚋	d								17 51			17 58							18 21		18 28			18 50	
Haydons Road	d								17 53			18 00							18 23		18 30			18 52	
Tooting	d								17 56			18 03							18 26		18 33			18 55	
Carshalton	d						17 35								18 07										
Hackbridge	d						17 37								18 09										
Mitcham Junction 🚋	d						17 40								18 12										
Mitcham Eastfields	d						17 44								18 16										
Streatham 4	d						17 49		18 01			18 08			18 20				18 32		18 38			18 59	
Tulse Hill 3	d						17 54		18 05			18 12			18 24			18 32	18 36		18 42			19 05	
London Bridge 4 ⊖	d								18a24		18 11								18a53	18 45				19a22	
Herne Hill 4	d						17 57					18 16			18 28			18 37			18 48				
Loughborough Jn	d						18 01					18 19			18 31			18 40			18 51				
Elephant & Castle	d	17 52					18 06					18 24			18 36			18 45			18 56				
London Blackfriars 3 ⊖	d	18b06					18c14				18 26	18 32			18e46			18f52		18 56	19 02				
City Thameslink 3	d	18 08					18g20				18 28	18 34			18 48			18 54		18 58	19 04				
Moorgate ⊖	d				18 16			18 24						18 38									19 08		
Barbican ⊖	d																								
Farringdon 3 ⊖	d	18 12			18 20		18 24	18 28			18 32	18 38		18 42	18 52			18 58		19 02	19 08		19 12		
St Pancras International 15 ⊖	d	18 16	18 30		18 24		18 28	18 32		18 55	18 36	18 42		18 46	18 56	19 00		19 02		19 06	19 12		19 16		19 25
Kentish Town ⊖	d						18 32					18 46			19 00						19 16				
West Hampstead Thameslink ⊖	d				18 32		18 36					18 50			19 04					19 14	19 20				
Cricklewood	d			←			18 39					18 53	←		19 07		←				19 23	←			
Hendon	d			18 26			18 42					18 56	18 42		19 10		18 56				19 26	19 10			
Mill Hill Broadway	d			18 31			→					→	18 47		→		19 01				→	19 15			
Elstree & Borehamwood	d			18 36	18 42								18 52				19 06					19 20			
Radlett	d			18 40	18 46								18 56				19 10					19 24			
St Albans City	d	18 36		18 46	18 52			18 52			18 56		19a04	19 06			19 16	19 22		19 28		19a32	19 36		
Harpenden	d	18 44		18 52	18 58			18 58			19 04			19 14			19 22	19 28		19 34			19 44		
Luton Airport Parkway 7 ✈	d	18 50		18 58	19 04						19 10			19 20		19 22	19 28			19 40					
Luton 10	d	18 53	18a54	19a03	19 08			19 04			19 13			19 23			19a33	19 34		19 43			19 50		19a50
Leagrave	d	18 56			19 12						19 16			19 26						19 46			19 54		
Harlington	d	19 02			19 18						19 22			19 32						19 52					
Flitwick	d	19 06			19 22			19 15			19 26			19 36				19 45		19 56					
Bedford 7	a	19 18			19 34			19 28		19 30	19 38			19 48		19 37		19 58		20 09			20 12		

For general notes see front of timetable
For details of catering facilities see Directory of Train Operators

- **A** To Nottingham (Table 53)
- **B** To Burton-on-Trent (Table 53)
- **C** To Leeds (Table 53)
- **b** Arr. 1756
- **c** Arr. 1809
- **e** Arr. 1840
- **f** Arr. 1849
- **g** Arr. 1816

Brighton, Gatwick Airport and South London → City of London, St.Albans, Luton and Bedford

Network Diagram - see first page of Table 52

		EM 1◇ A ☕	FC 1	FC	FC		FC 1	FC	FC	FC 1	EM 1◇ B ☕	FC	FC	FC 1	FC	FC	EM 1◇ A ☕	FC 1	FC	FC 1	FC	FC 1	EM 1◇ B ☕	FC	FC 1
Brighton 10	d		18 03				18 07			18 34				18 37				18b49		19 07		19 34			19 37
Preston Park	d		17 58				18 11			18 11				18 41				18 41		19 11		19 11			19 41
Hassocks 4	d		18 05				18 17			18 17				18 47				18 47		19 17		19 17			19 47
Burgess Hill 4	d		18 13				18 21			18 33				18 51				18 51		19 21		19 33			19 51
Wivelsfield 4	d		18 11				18 23			18 34				18 53				19c05		19 23					19 53
Haywards Heath 3	d		18 18				18 32			18 48				19 02				19c14		19 32		19 48			20 02
Balcombe	d		18 02				18 37			18 37										19 37		19 37			
Three Bridges 4	d		18 18				18 42			18 48				19 12				19 27		19 42		19 51			20 12
Gatwick Airport 10 ✈	d		18 31				18 46			19 01				19 16				19 31		19 46		20 01			20 16
Redhill	d		18 21				18 37			18 47				19 07				19 18		19 37		19 47			20 08
East Croydon	d		18 47				19 02			19 17				19 32				19 47		20 02		20 17			20 32
Sutton (Surrey) 4	d							18 40					19 04		19 05						19 37				
West Sutton	d							18 43							19 08						19 40				
Sutton Common	d							18 45							19 10						19 42				
St Helier	d							18 48							19 13						19 45				
Morden South	d							18 50							19 15						19 47				
South Merton	d							18 52							19 17						19 49				
Wimbledon Chase	d							18 54							19 19						19 51				
Wimbledon 6 ⊖	d							18 58							19 26						19 56				
Haydons Road	d							19 00							19 28						19 58				
Tooting	d							19 03							19 31						20 01				
Carshalton	d												19 07												
Hackbridge	d												19 09												
Mitcham Junction	d												19 12												
Mitcham Eastfields	d												19 16												
Streatham 4	d							19 08					19 21		19 36						20 06				
Tulse Hill 3	d							19 12					19 27		19 42						20 12				
London Bridge 4 ⊖	d		19 00				19 16			19 30				19 45				20 00		20 15		20 30			20 45
Herne Hill 4	d							19 18					19 32		19 48						20 16				
Loughborough Jn	d							19 21					19 35		19 51						20 19				
Elephant & Castle	d							19 26					19 40		19 56						20 24				
London Blackfriars 3 ⊖	d		19e10				19 23	19 30		19 38			19 44	19 53	20 00			20 08		20 23	20 30	20 38			20 53
City Thameslink 3	d		19 12				19 25	19 32		19 40			19 46	19 55	20 02			20 10		20 25	20 32	20 40			20 55
Moorgate ⊖	d				19 18																				
Barbican ⊖	d																								
Farringdon 3 ⊖	d		19 16		19 22		19 29	19 36		19 44			19 50	19 59	20 06			20 14		20 29	20 36	20 44			20 59
St Pancras International 15 ⊖	d	19 30	19 20		19 26		19 33	19 40		19 48	20 00		19 54	20 03	20 10		20 30	20 18		20 33	20 40	20 48	21 00		21 03
Kentish Town ⊖	d				19 30			19 44					19 58		20 14						20 44				
West Hampstead Thameslink ⊖	d				19 34		19 40	19 48					20 02	20 10	20 18					20 40	20 48				21 10
Cricklewood	d			←	19 37			19 51				←	20 05		20 21				←		20 51			←	
Hendon	d			19 26	19 40			19 54	←			19 54	20 08		20 24	←			20 24		20 54			20 54	
Mill Hill Broadway	d			19 31	19 45			→	19 45			19 59	20 13		→	20 13			20 27		→			20 57	
Elstree & Borehamwood	d			19 36	→				19 50			20 04	→			20 18			20 32					21 02	
Radlett	d			19 40					19 54			20 08				20 22			20 38					21 08	
St Albans City	d		19 42	19 46			19 54		20 00	20 09		20 14		20 24		20 30		20 39	20 44	20 54		21 09		21 14	21 24
Harpenden	d		19 48	19 52			20 01		20 06	20 14		20 19		20 31		20 36		20 44	20 49	21 01		21 14		21 19	21 31
Luton Airport Parkway 7 ✈	d		19 54	19 58			20 07		20 12	20 20	20 22	20 25		20 37		20 42		20 50	20 55	21 07		21 20	21 22	21 25	21 37
Luton 10	d	19 53	19 57	20a01			20 10		20 15	20 24		20a29		20 40		20 45	20 53	20 54	20a59	21 10		21 24		21a29	21 40
Leagrave	d		20 00				20 14		20 18	20 28				20 44		20 48		20 58		21 14		21 28			21 44
Harlington	d		20 06				20 20		20 24	20 34				20 50		20 54		21 04		21 20		21 34			21 50
Flitwick	d		20 10				20 24		20 28	20 38				20 54		20 58		21 08		21 24		21 38			21 54
Bedford 7	a	20 08	20 22				20 35		20 40	20 50	20 37			21 05		21 10	21 07	21 20		21 35		21 50	21 37		22 05

For general notes see front of timetable
For details of catering facilities see Directory of Train Operators

A To Nottingham (Table 53)
B To Derby (Table 53)
b Change at East Croydon
c Change at Gatwick Airport
e Arr. 1907

Brighton, Gatwick Airport and South London → City of London, St.Albans, Luton and Bedford

Network Diagram - see first page of Table 52

		FC	EM 1 ◇ A	FC 1	FC		FC 1	FC	EM 1 ◇ A	FC 1	FC	FC 1	EM 1 ◇ B	FC	FC 1	FC	FC 1	EM 1 ◇ C	FC	FC 1	FC	FC 1	FC 1		
Brighton 10	d			20 04			20 07			20 34		20 37			21 07		21 37			22 07		22 33	23 37		
Preston Park	d			*19 41*			20 11			*20 11*		20 41			21 11		21 41			22 11		22 37	23 41		
Hassocks 4	d			*19 47*			20 17			*20 17*		20 47			21 17		21 47			22 17		22 43	23 47		
Burgess Hill 4	d			*19 51*			20 21			*20 33*		20 51			21 21		21 51			22 21		22 47	23 51		
Wivelsfield 4	d			*20 05*			20 23					20 53			21 23		21 53			22 23		22 49	23 53		
Haywards Heath 3	d			20 18			20 32			20 48		21 02			21 32		22 02			22 32		22 54	23 59		
Balcombe	d						20 37			*20 37*					21 37					22 37		23 00	00 04		
Three Bridges 4	d			*20 18*			20 42			*20 51*		21 12			21 42		22 12			22 42		23 12	00 10		
Gatwick Airport 10 ✈	d			20 31			20 46			21 01		21 16			21 46		22 16			22 46		23 16	00 15		
Redhill	d			*20 18*			*20 37*			*20 47*		*21 08*			*21 37*		*22 08*			*22 40*		*22 47*	00 22		
East Croydon	d			20 47			21 02			21 17		21 32			22 02		22 32			23 02		23 32	00 36		
Sutton (Surrey) 4	d	20 09						20 39						21 09		21 49									
West Sutton	d	20 12						20 42						21 12		21 52									
Sutton Common	d	20 14						20 44						21 14		21 54									
St Helier	d	20 17						20 47						21 17		21 57									
Morden South	d	20 19						20 49						21 19		21 59									
South Merton	d	20 21						20 51						21 21		22 01									
Wimbledon Chase	d	20 23						20 53						21 23		22 03									
Wimbledon 6 ⊖	d	20 28						20 58						21b38		22 08									
Haydons Road	d	20 30						21 00						21 40		22 10									
Tooting	d	20 33						21 03						21 43		22 13									
Carshalton	d																								
Hackbridge	d																								
Mitcham Junction	d																								
Mitcham Eastfields	d																								
Streatham 4	d	20 40						21 10						21 48		22 18									
Tulse Hill 3	d	20 44						21 14						21 52		22 22									
London Bridge 4 ⊖	d			21 00			21 15			21 30		21 45			22 15		22 45			23 15		23 45	00 52		
Herne Hill 4	d	20 48						21 18						21 56		22 26									
Loughborough Jn	d	20 51						22 21						21 59		22 29									
Elephant & Castle	d	20 56						21 26						22 04		22 34									
London Blackfriars 3 ⊖	d	21 00		21 08			21 23	21 32		21 38		21 53		22 08	22 23	22 38	22 53		23 10	23 23	23 40	23 53	01 00		
City Thameslink 3	d	21 02		21 10			21 25	21 34		21 40		21 55		22 10	22 25	22 40	22 55								
Moorgate ⊖	d																								
Barbican ⊖	d																								
Farringdon 3 ⊖	d	21 06		21 14			21 29	21 39		21 44		21 59		22 14	22 29	22 44	22 59		23 14	23 29	23 44	23 59			
St Pancras International 15 ⊖	d	21 10	21 30	21 18			21 33	21 43	22 00	21 48		22 03	22 25	22 18	22 33	22 48	23 03	23 15	23 18	23 33	23 48	00 03	01 08		
Kentish Town ⊖	d	21 14						21 47						22 22		22 52			23 22		23 52		01 12		
West Hampstead Thameslink ⊖	d	21 18					21 40	21 51				22 10		22 26	22 40	22 56	23 10		23 26	23 40	23 56	00 10	01 16		
Cricklewood	d	21 21			←			21 54			←			22 29		22 59			23 29		23 59		01 19		
Hendon	d	21 24			21 24			21 57			21 57			22 32		23 02			23 32		00 02		01 22		
Mill Hill Broadway	d	→			21 27			→			22 00			22 35		23 05			23 35		00 05		01 25		
Elstree & Borehamwood	d				21 32						22 05			22 40		23 10			23 40		00 10		01 30		
Radlett	d				21 38						22 09			22 44		23 14			23 44		00 14		01 34		
St Albans City	d			21 39	21 44		21 54			22 08	22 14	22 24		22 50	22 54	23 20	23 24		23 50	23 54	00 20	00 24	01 40		
Harpenden	d			21 44	21 49		22 01			22 14	22 19	22 31		22 55	23 01	23 25	23 31		23 55	00 01	00 25	00 31	01 45		
Luton Airport Parkway 7 ✈	d			21 50	21 56		22 07			22 20	22 25	22 37		23 01	23 07	23 31	23 37		00 01	00 07	00 31	00 37	01 51		
Luton 10	d		21 53	21 54	22 00		22 10		22 22	22 24	22 30	22 40	22 48	23 05	23 10	23 35	23 40	23 45	00 05	00 10	00 35	00 40	01 55		
Leagrave	d			21 58	22 04		22 14			22 28	22 34	22 44		23 09	23 14	23 39	23 44		00 09	00 14	00 39	00 44	01 59		
Harlington	d			22 04	22 10		22 20			22 34	22 40	22 50		23 14	23 20	23 44	23 50		00 14	00 20	00 44	00 50	02 04		
Flitwick	d			22 08	22 14		22 24			22 38	22 44	22 54		23 18	23 24	23 48	23 54		00 18	00 24	00 48	00 54	02 08		
Bedford 7	a		22 07	22 20	22 25		22 35		22 37	22 50	22 55	23 05	23 04	23 30	23 35	00 01	00 05	00 09	00 30	00 35	01 00	01 05	02 20		

For general notes see front of timetable
For details of catering facilities see Directory of Train Operators

A To Nottingham (Table 53)
B To Sheffield (Table 53)
C To Derby (Table 53)

b Arr. 11 minutes earlier

Brighton, Gatwick Airport and South London → City of London, St.Albans, Luton and Bedford

Network Diagram - see first page of Table 52

		FC	FC 1	FC	FC 1	FC	FC 1	FC	FC 1	FC 1	FC 1	FC 1	EM 1 ◇	FC 1	FC	FC 1	EM 1 ◇	FC	EM 1 ◇	EM 1 ◇	FC 1	FC	FC	FC 1	FC
													A		B		C	B	D	C		B			
													🍴				🍴		🍴	🍴					
Brighton 10	d		22p07		22p33		23p37					*03 50*				05 24					06 04			06 24	
Preston Park	d		22p11		22p37		23p41									05 28					06b*00*			06 28	
Hassocks 4	d		22p17		22p43		23p47									05 34					06b*06*			06 34	
Burgess Hill 4	d		22p21		22p47		23p51									05 38					06 14			06 38	
Wivelsfield 4	d		22p23		22p49		23p53									05 40					*06 11*			06 40	
Haywards Heath 3	d		22p32		22p54		23p59					*04 25*				05 45					06 18			06 45	
Balcombe	d		22p37		23p00		00 04									05 51					*05 51*			06 51	
Three Bridges 4	d		22p42		23p12		00 10		02 25	03 25	04 25	04 55		05 20		05 56					*06 20*			06 56	
Gatwick Airport 10 ✈	d		22p46		23p16		00 15		02 30	03 30	04 30	05 00		05 25		06 01					06 31			07 01	
Redhill	d						00 22									*05 52*					*06 08*			*06 37*	
East Croydon	d		23p02		23p32		00 36		02 47	03 47	04 47	05 17		05 42		06 17					06 47			07 17	
Sutton (Surrey) 4	d																								07 06
West Sutton	d																								
Sutton Common	d																								
St Helier	d																								
Morden South	d																								
South Merton	d																								
Wimbledon Chase	d																								
Wimbledon 6 ⊖	d																						06 56		
Haydons Road	d																						06 58		
Tooting	d																						07 01		
Carshalton	d																								07 09
Hackbridge	d																								07 11
Mitcham Junction	d																								07 14
Mitcham Eastfields	d																								07 18
Streatham 4	d														05 49			06 19				06 49	07 06		07 23
Tulse Hill 3	d														05 58			06 23				06 53	07 12		07 27
London Bridge 4 ⊖	d		23p15		23p45	00 20	00 52									06 31					07 01			07 31	
Herne Hill 4	d														06 02			06 26				06 56	07 16		07 30
Loughborough Jn	d																	06 30				07 00	07 19		07 34
Elephant & Castle	d														06 07			06 35				07 05	07 24		07 39
London Blackfriars 3 ⊖	d	23p08	23p23	23p38	23p53	00 28	01 00		03 13	04 13	05 13	05 43		06 08	06 13	06 38		06 43			07 08	07 13	07 28	07 38	07 43
City Thameslink 3	d																								
Moorgate ⊖	d																								
Barbican ⊖	d																								
Farringdon 3 ⊖	d	23p14	23p29	23p44	23p59	00 34					05 18	05 48		06 14	06 19	06 42		06 49			07 14	07 19	07 34	07 44	07 49
St Pancras International 15 ⊖	d	23p18	23p33	23p48	00 03	00 38	01 08	01 52	03 22	04 22	05 22	05 52	06 20	06 18	06 23	06 46	07 00	06 53	07 25	07 30	07 18	07 23	07 38	07 48	07 53
Kentish Town ⊖	d	23p22		23p52		00 42	01 12	01 56	03 26	04 26	05 26	05 56			06 27			06 57				07 27	07 42		07 57
West Hampstead Thameslink ⊖	d	23p26	23p40	23p56	00 10	00 46	01 16	02 00	03 30	04 30	05 30	06 00		06 25	06 31	06 53		07 01			07 25	07 31	07 46		08 01
Cricklewood	d	23p29		23p59		00 49	01 19	02 03	03 33	04 33	05 33	06 03			06 34			07 04				07 34	07 49		08 04
Hendon	d	23p32		00 02		00 52	01 22	02 06	03 36	04 36	05 36	06 06			06 37			07 07				07 37	07 52 →		08 07 →
Mill Hill Broadway	d	23p35		00 05		00 55	01 25	02 09	03 39	04 39	05 39	06 09			06 40			07 10				07 40			
Elstree & Borehamwood	d	23p40		00 10		01 00	01 30	02 14	03 44	04 44	05 44	06 14			06 45			07 15				07 45			
Radlett	d	23p44		00 14		01 04	01 34	02 18	03 48	04 48	05 48	06 18			06 49			07 19				07 49			
St Albans City	d	23p50	23p54	00 20	00 24	01 10	01 40	02 24	03 54	04 54	05 54	06 24		06 41	06 55	07 09		07 25			07 41	07 57		08 09	
Harpenden	d	23p55	00 01	00 25	00 31	01 15	01 45	02 29	03 59	04 59	05 59	06 29		06 47	07 00	07 15		07 30			07 47	08 02		08 14	
Luton Airport Parkway 7 ✈	d	00 01	00 07	00 31	00 37	01 21	01 51	02 35	04 05	05 05	06 05	06 35		06 52	07 06	07 20	07 25	07 36			07 52	08 08		08 20	
Luton 10	d	00 05	00 10	00 35	00 40	01 25	01 55	02 40	04 10	05 10	06 10	06 40	06 44	06 56	07a10	07 24		07a40	07a49	07 53	07 56	08 11		08 24	
Leagrave	d	00 09	00 14	00 39	00 44	01 29	01 59	02 44	04 14	05 14	06 14	06 44		07 00		07 28					08 00	08 14		08 28	
Harlington	d	00 14	00 20	00 44	00 50	01 34	02 04	02 50	04 20	05 20	06 20	06 50		07 06		07 34					08 06	08 20		08 34	
Flitwick	d	00 18	00 24	00 48	00 54	01 38	02 08	02 54	04 24	05 24	06 24	06 54		07 10		07 38					08 10	08 24		08 38	
Bedford 7	a	00 30	00 35	01 00	01 05	01 50	02 20	03 05	04 35	05 35	06 35	07 05	07 01	07 22		07 50	07 41			08 08	08 22	08 37		08 50	

For general notes see front of timetable
For details of catering facilities see Directory of Train Operators

A Until 6 September to Scarborough (Table 26). From 13 September to York
B From Selhurst (Table 177)
C To Nottingham (Table 53)
D To Sheffield (Table 53)
b Change at Haywards Heath

Table 52

Saturdays

Brighton, Gatwick Airport and South London → City of London, St.Albans, Luton and Bedford

Network Diagram - see first page of Table 52

	EM 1 ◇ A 🍴	FC	EM 1 ◇ B 🍴	FC 1	FC	FC	EM 1 ◇ C 🍴	FC 1	FC	FC	FC 1		FC	FC	FC 1	FC	EM 1 ◇ A 🍴	FC	FC 1	FC	FC	EM 1 ◇ B 🍴	EM 1 ◇ C 🍴	FC 1
Brighton 10 d				06 37				07 04			07 07				07 34				07 37					08 04
Preston Park d				06 41				*06 58*			07 11				*07 11*				07 41					*07 58*
Hassocks 4 d				06 47				*07 05*			07 17				*07 17*				07 47					*08 05*
Burgess Hill 4 d				06 51				*07 08*			07 21				*07 21*				07 51					*08 08*
Wivelsfield 4 d				06 53				*07 11*			07 23				*07 34*				07 53					*08 11*
Haywards Heath 3 d				07 02				07 18			07 32				07 48				08 02					08 18
Balcombe d								*06 51*			07 37				*07 37*									
Three Bridges 4 d				07 12				*07 18*			07 42				*07 48*				08 12					*08 18*
Gatwick Airport 10 ✈ d				07 16				07 31			07 46				08 01				08 16					08 31
Redhill d				*07 16*							*07 37*				*07 48*				*08 16*					
East Croydon 🚋 d				07 32				07 47			08 02				08 17				08 32					08 47
Sutton (Surrey) 4 d						07 07			07 36				07 37			08 06				08 07				
West Sutton d						07 10							07 40							08 10				
Sutton Common d						07 12							07 42							08 12				
St Helier d						07 15							07 45							08 15				
Morden South d						07 17							07 47							08 17				
South Merton d						07 19							07 49							08 19				
Wimbledon Chase d						07 21							07 51							08 21				
Wimbledon 6 ⊖ 🚋 d						07 26							07 56							08 26				
Haydons Road d						07 28							07 58							08 28				
Tooting d						07 31							08 01							08 31				
Carshalton d									07 39							08 09								
Hackbridge d									07 41							08 11								
Mitcham Junction 🚋 d									07 44							08 14								
Mitcham Eastfields d									07 48							08 18								
Streatham 4 d						07 36			07 53				08 06			08 23				08 36				
Tulse Hill 3 d						07 42			07 57				08 12			08 27				08 42				
London Bridge 4 ⊖ d				07 45				08 01			08 15				08 31				08 45					09 01
Herne Hill 4 d						07 46			08 00				08 16			08 31				08 46				
Loughborough Jn d						07 49			08 04				08 19			08 34				08 49				
Elephant & Castle d						07 54			08 09				08 24			08 39				08 54				
London Blackfriars 3 ⊖ d				07 53		07 58		08 08	08 13		08 23		08 28		08 38	08 43			08 53	08 58				09 08
City Thameslink 3 d																				09 00				09 10
Moorgate ⊖ d																								
Barbican ⊖ d																								
Farringdon 3 ⊖ d				07 59		08 04		08 14	08 19		08 29		08 34		08 44	08 49			08 59	09 04				09 14
St Pancras International 15 ⊖ d	08 00		08 25	08 03		08 08	08 30	08 18	08 23		08 33		08 38		08 48	08 53	09 00		09 03	09 08		09 25	09 30	09 18
Kentish Town ⊖ d						08 12			08 27				08 42			08 57				09 12				
West Hampstead Thameslink ⊖ d						08 16			08 31				08 46			09 01				09 16				
Cricklewood d		←			←	08 19			08 34	←			08 49	←		09 04		←		09 19	←			
Hendon d		07 52			08 07	08 22			08 37	08 22			08 52	08 37		09 07		08 52		09 22	09 07			
Mill Hill Broadway d		07 55			08 10	→			→	08 25			→	08 40		→		08 55		→	09 10			
Elstree & Borehamwood d		08 00			08 15					08 30				08 45				09 00			09 15			
Radlett d		08 08			08 20					08 38				08 50				09 08			09 20			
St Albans City d		08 14		08 24	08a27			08 39		08 44	08 54			08a57	09 09			09 14	09 24		09a27			09 39
Harpenden d		08 19		08 29				08 44		08 49	08 59				09 14			09 19	09 29					09 44
Luton Airport Parkway 7 ✈ d	08 22	08 25		08 35				08 50		08 55	09 05				09 20		09 22	09 25	09 35					09 50
Luton 10 d		08a29		08 38			08 53	08 54		08a59	09 08				09 24			09a29	09 38			09a48	09 53	09 54
Leagrave d				08 42				08 58			09 12				09 28				09 42					09 58
Harlington d				08 48				09 04			09 18				09 34				09 48					10 04
Flitwick d				08 52				09 08			09 22				09 38				09 52					10 08
Bedford 7 a	08 37		09 00	09 05			09 07	09 20			09 35				09 50		09 37		10 05				10 07	10 20

For general notes see front of timetable
For details of catering facilities see Directory of Train Operators

A To Derby (Table 53)
B To Sheffield (Table 53)
C To Nottingham (Table 53)

Table 52

Saturdays

Brighton, Gatwick Airport and South London → City of London, St.Albans, Luton and Bedford

Network Diagram - see first page of Table 52

		FC	FC	FC 1	FC	FC	FC 1	FC	EM 1◇ A	FC	FC 1	FC	FC	EM 1◇ B	FC 1	FC	FC	FC 1	FC	FC	FC 1	FC	EM 1◇ A	FC	FC 1
Brighton 10	d			08 07			08 34				08 37				09 04			09 07			09 34				09 37
Preston Park	d			08 11			*08 11*				08 41				*08 58*			09 11			*09 11*				09 41
Hassocks 4	d			08 17			*08 17*				08 47				*09 05*			09 17			*09 17*				09 47
Burgess Hill 4	d			08 21			*08 21*				08 51				*09 08*			09 21							09 51
Wivelsfield 4	d			08 23			*08 34*				08 53				*09 11*						*09 34*				09 53
Haywards Heath 3	d			08 32			08 49				09 02				09 18			09 26			09 48				10 02
Balcombe	d			08 37			*08 37*											09 32			*09 32*				
Three Bridges 4	d			08 42			*08 48*				09 12				*09 18*			09 37			*09 48*				10 12
Gatwick Airport 10 ✈	d			08 46			09 01				09 16				09 31			09 41			10 01				10 16
Redhill	d			*08 37*			*08 48*				*09 16*										*09 48*				*10 16*
East Croydon	d			09 02			09 17				09 32				09 47			09 57			10 17				10 32
Sutton (Surrey) 4	d	08 36			08 37			09 06				09 07				09 36			09 37			10 06			
West Sutton	d				08 40							09 10							09 40						
Sutton Common	d				08 42							09 12							09 42						
St Helier	d				08 45							09 15							09 45						
Morden South	d				08 47							09 17							09 47						
South Merton	d				08 49							09 19							09 49						
Wimbledon Chase	d				08 51							09 21							09 51						
Wimbledon 6 ⊖	d				08 56							09 26							09 56						
Haydons Road	d				08 58							09 28							09 58						
Tooting	d				09 01							09 31							10 01						
Carshalton	d	08 39						09 09								09 39						10 09			
Hackbridge	d	08 41						09 11								09 41						10 11			
Mitcham Junction	d	08 44						09 14								09 44						10 14			
Mitcham Eastfields	d	08 48						09 18								09 48						10 18			
Streatham 4	d	08 53			09 06			09 23				09 36				09 53			10 06			10 23			
Tulse Hill 3	d	08 57			09 12			09 27				09 42				09 57			10 12			10 27			
London Bridge 4 ⊖	d			09 15			09 30				09 45				10 00			10 15			10 30				10 45
Herne Hill 4	d	09 00			09 16			09 30				09 46				10 00			10 16			10 30			
Loughborough Jn	d	09 04			09 19			09 34				09 49				10 04			10 19			10 34			
Elephant & Castle	d	09 09			09 24			09 39				09 54				10 09			10 24			10 39			
London Blackfriars 3 ⊖	d	09 13		09 23	09 28		09 38	09 43			09 53	09 58			10 08	10 13		10 23	10 28		10 38	10 43			10 53
City Thameslink 3	d	09 15		09 25	09 30		09 40	09 45			09 55	10 00			10 10	10 15		10 25	10 30		10 40	10 45			10 55
Moorgate ⊖	d																								
Barbican ⊖	d																								
Farringdon 3 ⊖	d	09 19		09 29	09 34		09 44	09 49			09 59	10 04			10 14	10 19		10 29	10 34		10 44	10 49			10 59
St Pancras International 15 ⊖	d	09 23		09 33	09 38		09 48	09 53	10 00		10 03	10 08		10 30	10 18	10 23		10 33	10 38		10 48	10 53	11 00		11 03
Kentish Town ⊖	d	09 27			09 42			09 57				10 12				10 27			10 42			10 57			
West Hampstead Thameslink ⊖	d	09 31			09 46			10 01				10 16				10 31			10 46			11 01			
Cricklewood	d	09 34	←		09 49	←		10 04		←		10 19	←			10 34	←		10 49	←		11 04		←	
Hendon	d	09 37	09 22		09 52	09 37		10 07		09 52		10 22	10 07			10 37	10 22		10 52	10 37		11 07		10 52	
Mill Hill Broadway	d	→	09 25		→	09 40		→		09 55		→	10 10			→	10 25		→	10 40		→		10 55	
Elstree & Borehamwood	d		09 30			09 45				10 00			10 15				10 30			10 45				11 00	
Radlett	d		09 38			09 50				10 08			10 20				10 38			10 50				11 08	
St Albans City	d		09 44	09 54		09a57	10 09			10 14	10 24		10a27		10 39		10 44	10 54		10a57	11 09			11 14	11 24
Harpenden	d		09 49	09 59			10 14			10 19	10 29				10 44		10 49	10 59			11 14			11 19	11 29
Luton Airport Parkway 7 ✈	d		09 55	10 05			10 20		10 22	10 25	10 35				10 50		10 55	11 05			11 20		11 22	11 25	11 35
Luton 10	d		09a59	10 08			10 24			10a29	10 38			10 53	10 54		10a59	11 08			11 24			11a29	11 38
Leagrave	d			10 12			10 28				10 42				10 58			11 12			11 28				11 42
Harlington	d			10 18			10 34				10 48				11 04			11 18			11 34				11 48
Flitwick	d			10 22			10 38				10 52				11 08			11 22			11 38				11 52
Bedford 7	a			10 35			10 50		10 37		11 05			11 07	11 20			11 35			11 50		11 37		12 05

For general notes see front of timetable
For details of catering facilities see Directory of Train Operators

A To Derby (Table 53)

B Until 6 September to Sheffield (Table 53). From 13 September to Nottingham

Table 52

Saturdays

Brighton, Gatwick Airport and South London → City of London, St.Albans, Luton and Bedford

Network Diagram - see first page of Table 52

		FC		FC	EM 1 ◇ A ☕	FC 1	FC	FC	FC 1	FC	FC	FC 1	FC	EM 1 ◇ B ☕	FC	FC 1	FC	FC	EM 1 ◇ A ☕	FC 1	FC	FC	FC 1	FC	FC
Brighton 10	d					10 04			10 07			10 34				10 37				11 04			11 07		
Preston Park	d					*09 58*			10 11			*10 11*				10 41				*10 58*			11 11		
Hassocks 4	d					*10 05*			10 17			*10 17*				10 47				*11 05*			11 17		
Burgess Hill 4	d					*10 08*			10 21			*10 21*				10 51				*11 08*			11 21		
Wivelsfield 4	d					*10 11*			10 23			*10 34*				10 53				*11 11*			11 23		
Haywards Heath 3	d					10 18			10 32			10 48				11 02				11 18			11 32		
Balcombe	d								10 37			*10 37*											11 37		
Three Bridges 4	d					*10 18*			10 42			*10 48*				11 12				*11 18*			11 42		
Gatwick Airport 10 ✈	d					10 31			10 46			11 01				11 16				11 31			11 46		
Redhill	d								*10 37*			*10 48*				*11 16*							*11 37*		
East Croydon	d					10 47			11 02			11 17				11 32				11 47			12 02		
Sutton (Surrey) 4	d	10 07					10 36			10 37			11 06				11 07				11 36			11 37	
West Sutton	d	10 10								10 40							11 10							11 40	
Sutton Common	d	10 12								10 42							11 12							11 42	
St Helier	d	10 15								10 45							11 15							11 45	
Morden South	d	10 17								10 47							11 17							11 47	
South Merton	d	10 19								10 49							11 19							11 49	
Wimbledon Chase	d	10 21								10 51							11 21							11 51	
Wimbledon 6 ⊖	d	10 26								10 56							11 26							11 56	
Haydons Road	d	10 28								10 58							11 28							11 58	
Tooting	d	10 31								11 01							11 31							12 01	
Carshalton	d						10 39						11 09								11 39				
Hackbridge	d						10 41						11 11								11 41				
Mitcham Junction	d						10 44						11 14								11 44				
Mitcham Eastfields	d						10 48						11 18								11 48				
Streatham 4	d	10 36					10 53			11 06			11 23				11 36				11 53			12 06	
Tulse Hill 3	d	10 42					10 57			11 12			11 27				11 42				11 57			12 12	
London Bridge 4 ⊖	d					11 00			11 15			11 30				11 45				12 00			12 15		
Herne Hill 4	d	10 46					11 00			11 16			11 30				11 46				12 00			12 16	
Loughborough Jn	d	10 49					11 04			11 19			11 34				11 49				12 04			12 19	
Elephant & Castle	d	10 54					11 09			11 24			11 39				11 54				12 09			12 24	
London Blackfriars 3 ⊖	d	10 58				11 08	11 13		11 23	11 28		11 38	11 43			11 53	11 58			12 08	12 13		12 23	12 28	
City Thameslink 3	d	11 00				11 10	11 15		11 25	11 30		11 40	11 45			11 55	12 00			12 10	12 15		12 25	12 30	
Moorgate ⊖	d																								
Barbican ⊖	d																								
Farringdon 3 ⊖	d	11 04				11 14	11 19		11 29	11 34		11 44	11 49			11 59	12 04			12 14	12 19		12 29	12 34	
St Pancras International 15 ⊖	d	11 08			11 30	11 18	11 23		11 33	11 38		11 48	11 53	12 00		12 03	12 08		12 30	12 18	12 23		12 33	12 38	
Kentish Town ⊖	d	11 12					11 27			11 42			11 57				12 12				12 27			12 42	
West Hampstead Thameslink ⊖	d	11 16					11 31			11 46			12 01				12 16				12 31			12 46	
Cricklewood	d	11 19		←			11 34	←		11 49	←		12 04		←		12 19	←			12 34	←		12 49	←
Hendon	d	11 22		11 07			11 37	11 22		11 52	11 37		12 07		11 52		12 22	12 07			12 37	12 22		12 52	12 37
Mill Hill Broadway	d	→		11 10			→	11 25		→	11 40		→		11 55		→	12 10			→	12 25		→	12 40
Elstree & Borehamwood	d			11 15				11 30			11 45				12 00			12 15				12 30			12 45
Radlett	d			11 20				11 38			11 50				12 08			12 20				12 38			12 50
St Albans City	d			11a27		11 39		11 44	11 54		11a57	12 09			12 14	12 24		12a27		12 39		12 44	12 54		12a57
Harpenden	d					11 44		11 49	11 59			12 14			12 19	12 29				12 44		12 49	12 59		
Luton Airport Parkway 7 ✈	d					11 50		11 55	12 05			12 20		12 22	12 25	12 35				12 50		12 55	13 05		
Luton 10	d				11 53	11 54		11a59	12 08			12 24			12a29	12 38			12 53	12 54		12a59	13 08		
Leagrave	d					11 58			12 12			12 28				12 42				12 58			13 12		
Harlington	d					12 04			12 18			12 34				12 48				13 04			13 18		
Flitwick	d					12 08			12 22			12 38				12 52				13 08			13 22		
Bedford 7	a				12 07	12 20			12 35			12 50		12 37		13 05			13 07	13 20			13 35		

For general notes see front of timetable
For details of catering facilities see Directory of Train Operators

A To Nottingham (Table 53)
B To Derby (Table 53)

Brighton, Gatwick Airport and South London → City of London, St.Albans, Luton and Bedford

Network Diagram - see first page of Table 52

		FC 1	FC	EM 1 ◇ A ☕	FC	FC 1	FC	FC	EM 1 ◇ B ☕	FC 1	FC	FC	FC 1	FC		FC	FC 1	FC	EM 1 ◇ A ☕	FC	EM 1 ◇ C ☕	FC 1	FC	FC	EM 1 ◇ B ☕
Brighton 10	d	11 34				11 37				12 04			12 07				12 34					12 37			
Preston Park	d	*11 11*				11 41				*11 58*			12 11				*12 11*					12 41			
Hassocks 4	d	*11 17*				11 47				*12 05*			12 17				*12 17*					12 47			
Burgess Hill 4	d	*11 21*				11 51				*12 08*			12 21				*12 21*					12 51			
Wivelsfield 4	d	*11 34*				11 53				*12 11*			12 23				*12 34*					12 53			
Haywards Heath 3	d	11 48				12 02				12 18			12 32				12 48					13 02			
Balcombe	d	*11 37*											12 37				*12 37*								
Three Bridges 4	d	*11 48*				12 12				*12 18*			12 42				*12 48*					13 12			
Gatwick Airport 10 ✈	d	12 01				12 16				12 31			12 46				13 01					13 16			
Redhill	d	*11 48*				*12 16*							*12 37*				*12 48*					*13 16*			
East Croydon 🚋	d	12 17				12 32				12 47			13 02				13 17					13 32			
Sutton (Surrey) 4	d		12 06				12 07				12 36			12 37				13 06					13 07		
West Sutton	d						12 10							12 40									13 10		
Sutton Common	d						12 12							12 42									13 12		
St Helier	d						12 15							12 45									13 15		
Morden South	d						12 17							12 47									13 17		
South Merton	d						12 19							12 49									13 19		
Wimbledon Chase	d						12 21							12 51									13 21		
Wimbledon 6 ⊖ 🚋	d						12 26							12 56									13 26		
Haydons Road	d						12 28							12 58									13 28		
Tooting	d						12 31							13 01									13 31		
Carshalton	d		12 09								12 39							13 09							
Hackbridge	d		12 11								12 41							13 11							
Mitcham Junction 🚋	d		12 14								12 44							13 14							
Mitcham Eastfields	d		12 18								12 48							13 18							
Streatham 4	d		12 23				12 36				12 53			13 06				13 23					13 36		
Tulse Hill 3	d		12 27				12 42				12 57			13 12				13 27					13 42		
London Bridge 4 ⊖	d	12 30				12 45				13 00			13 15				13 30					13 45			
Herne Hill 4	d		12 30				12 46				13 00			13 16				13 30					13 46		
Loughborough Jn	d		12 34				12 49				13 04			13 19				13 34					13 49		
Elephant & Castle	d		12 39				12 54				13 09			13 24				13 39					13 54		
London Blackfriars 3 ⊖	d	12 38	12 43			12 53	12 58			13 08	13 13		13 23	13 28			13 38	13 43				13 53	13 58		
City Thameslink 3	d	12 40	12 45			12 55	13 00			13 10	13 15		13 25	13 30			13 40	13 45				13 55	14 00		
Moorgate ⊖	d																								
Barbican ⊖	d																								
Farringdon 3 ⊖	d	12 44	12 49			12 59	13 04			13 14	13 19		13 29	13 34			13 44	13 49				13 59	14 04		
St Pancras International 15 ⊖	d	12 48	12 53	13 00		13 03	13 08		13 30	13 18	13 23		13 33	13 38			13 48	13 53	14 00		14 25	14 03	14 08		14 30
Kentish Town ⊖	d		12 57				13 12				13 27			13 42				13 57					14 12		
West Hampstead Thameslink ⊖	d		13 01				13 16				13 31			13 46				14 01					14 16		
Cricklewood	d		13 04		←		13 19	←			13 34	←		13 49		←		14 04		←			14 19	←	
Hendon	d		13 07		12 52		13 22	13 07			13 37	13 22		13 52		13 37		14 07		13 52			14 22	14 07	
Mill Hill Broadway	d		→		12 55		→	13 10			→	13 25		→		13 40		→		13 55			→	14 10	
Elstree & Borehamwood	d				13 00			13 15				13 30				13 45				14 00				14 15	
Radlett	d				13 08			13 20				13 38				13 50				14 08				14 20	
St Albans City	d	13 09			13 14	13 24		13a27		13 39		13 44	13 54			13a57	14 09			14 14		14 24		14a27	
Harpenden	d	13 14			13 19	13 29				13 44		13 49	13 59				14 14			14 19		14 29			
Luton Airport Parkway 7 ✈	d	13 20		13 22	13 25	13 35				13 50		13 55	14 05				14 20		14 22	14 25		14 35			
Luton 10	d	13 24			13a29	13 38			13 53	13 54		13a59	14 08				14 24			14a29		14 38			14 53
Leagrave	d	13 28				13 42				13 58			14 12				14 28					14 42			
Harlington	d	13 34				13 48				14 04			14 18				14 34					14 48			
Flitwick	d	13 38				13 52				14 08			14 22				14 38					14 52			
Bedford 7	a	13 50		13 37		14 05			14 07	14 20			14 35				14 50		14 37		15 00	15 05			15 07

For general notes see front of timetable
For details of catering facilities see
Directory of Train Operators

A To Derby (Table 53)
B To Nottingham (Table 53)
C To Sheffield (Table 53)

Table 52

Saturdays

Brighton, Gatwick Airport and South London → City of London, St.Albans, Luton and Bedford

Network Diagram - see first page of Table 52

		FC	FC	FC	FC	FC	FC	FC	FC	EM	FC	FC	FC	FC	EM	EM	FC	FC	FC	FC	FC	FC	EM	FC	FC
		1			1			1		1 ◇		1			1 ◇	1 ◇	1			1			1 ◇	1	
										A					B	C							C		
Brighton 10	d	13 04			13 07			13 34				13 37					14 04			14 07				14 34	
Preston Park	d	12 58			13 11			13 11				13 41					13 58			14 11				14 11	
Hassocks 4	d	13 05			13 17			13 17				13 47					14 05			14 17				14 17	
Burgess Hill 4	d	13 08			13 21			13 21				13 51					14 08			14 21				14 21	
Wivelsfield 4	d	13 11			13 23			13 34				13 53					14 11			14 23				14 34	
Haywards Heath 3	d	13 18			13 32			13 48				14 02					14 18			14 32				14 48	
Balcombe	d				13 37			13 37												14 37				14 37	
Three Bridges 4	d	13 18			13 42			13 48				14 12					14 18			14 42				14 48	
Gatwick Airport 10 ✈	d	13 31			13 46			14 01				14 16					14 31			14 46				15 01	
Redhill	d				13 37			13 48				14 16								14 37				14 48	
East Croydon	d	13 47			14 02			14 17				14 32					14 47			15 02				15 17	
Sutton (Surrey) 4	d		13 36			13 37			14 06				14 07					14 36			14 37				15 06
West Sutton	d					13 40							14 10								14 40				
Sutton Common	d					13 42							14 12								14 42				
St Helier	d					13 45							14 15								14 45				
Morden South	d					13 47							14 17								14 47				
South Merton	d					13 49							14 19								14 49				
Wimbledon Chase	d					13 51							14 21								14 51				
Wimbledon 6 ⊖	d					13 56							14 26								14 56				
Haydons Road	d					13 58							14 28								14 58				
Tooting	d					14 01							14 31								15 01				
Carshalton	d		13 39						14 09									14 39							15 09
Hackbridge	d		13 41						14 11									14 41							15 11
Mitcham Junction	d		13 44						14 14									14 44							15 14
Mitcham Eastfields	d		13 48						14 18									14 48							15 18
Streatham 4	d		13 53			14 06			14 23				14 36					14 53			15 06				15 23
Tulse Hill 3	d		13 57			14 12			14 27				14 42					14 57			15 12				15 27
London Bridge 4 ⊖	d	14 00			14 15			14 30				14 45					15 00			15 15				15 30	
Herne Hill 4	d		14 00			14 16			14 30				14 46					15 00			15 16				15 30
Loughborough Jn	d		14 04			14 19			14 34				14 49					15 04			15 19				15 34
Elephant & Castle	d		14 09			14 24			14 39				14 54					15 09			15 24				15 39
London Blackfriars 3 ⊖	d	14 08	14 13		14 23	14 28		14 38	14 43			14 53	14 58				15 08	15 13		15 23	15 28			15 38	15 43
City Thameslink 3	d	14 10	14 15		14 25	14 30		14 40	14 45			14 55	15 00				15 10	15 15		15 25	15 30			15 40	15 45
Moorgate ⊖	d																								
Barbican ⊖	d																								
Farringdon 3 ⊖	d	14 14	14 19		14 29	14 34		14 44	14 49			14 59	15 04				15 14	15 19		15 29	15 34			15 44	15 49
St Pancras International 15 ⊖	d	14 18	14 23		14 33	14 38		14 48	14 53	15 00		15 03	15 08		15 25	15 30	15 18	15 23		15 33	15 38		15 55	15 48	15 53
Kentish Town ⊖	d		14 27			14 42			14 57				15 12					15 27			15 42				15 57
West Hampstead Thameslink ⊖	d		14 31			14 46			15 01				15 16					15 31			15 46				16 01
Cricklewood	d		14 34	←		14 49	←		15 04		←		15 19	←				15 34	←		15 49	←			16 04
Hendon	d		14 37	14 22		14 52	14 37		15 07		14 52		15 22	15 07				15 37	15 22		15 52	15 37			16 07
Mill Hill Broadway	d		→	14 25		→	14 40		→		14 55		→	15 10				→	15 25		→	15 40			→
Elstree & Borehamwood	d			14 30			14 45				15 00			15 15					15 30			15 45			
Radlett	d			14 38			14 50				15 08			15 20					15 38			15 50			
St Albans City	d	14 39		14 44	14 54		14a57	15 09			15 14	15 24		15a27			15 39		15 44	15 54		15a57		16 09	
Harpenden	d	14 44		14 49	14 59			15 14			15 19	15 29					15 44		15 49	15 59				16 14	
Luton Airport Parkway 7 ✈	d	14 50		14 55	15 05			15 20		15 22	15 25	15 35					15 50		15 55	16 05				16 20	
Luton 10	d	14 54		14a59	15 08			15 24			15a29	15 38			15a48	15 53	15 54		15a59	16 08			16a18	16 24	
Leagrave	d	14 58			15 12			15 28				15 42					15 58			16 12				16 28	
Harlington	d	15 04			15 18			15 34				15 48					16 04			16 18				16 34	
Flitwick	d	15 08			15 22			15 38				15 52					16 08			16 22				16 38	
Bedford 7	a	15 20			15 35			15 50		15 37		16 05				16 07	16 20			16 35				16 50	

For general notes see front of timetable
For details of catering facilities see Directory of Train Operators

A To Derby (Table 53)
B To Sheffield (Table 53)
C To Nottingham (Table 53)

Brighton, Gatwick Airport and South London → City of London, St.Albans, Luton and Bedford

Network Diagram - see first page of Table 52

	EM 1 ◊ A	FC	FC 1		FC	FC	EM 1 ◊ B	FC 1	FC	FC	FC 1	FC	FC	FC 1	FC	EM 1 ◊ C	FC	FC 1	FC	FC	EM 1 ◊ D	EM 1 ◊ E	FC 1	FC
Brighton 10 d			14 37					15 04			15 07			15 34				15 37					16 04	
Preston Park d			14 41					*14 58*			15 11			*15 11*				15 41					*15 58*	
Hassocks 4 d			14 47					*15 05*			15 17			*15 17*				15 47					*16 05*	
Burgess Hill 4 d			14 51					*15 08*			15 21			*15 21*				15 51					*16 08*	
Wivelsfield 4 d			14 53					*15 11*			15 23			*15 34*				15 53					*16 11*	
Haywards Heath 3 d			15 02					15 18			15 32			15 48				16 02					16 18	
Balcombe d											15 37			*15 37*										
Three Bridges 4 d			15 12					*15 18*			15 42			*15 48*				16 12					*16 18*	
Gatwick Airport 10 ✈ d			15 16					15 31			15 46			16 01				16 16					16 31	
Redhill d			*15 16*								*15 37*			*15 48*				*16 16*						
East Croydon d			15 32					15 47			16 02			16 17				16 32					16 47	
Sutton (Surrey) 4 d					15 07				15 36			15 37			16 06				16 07					16 36
West Sutton d					15 10							15 40							16 10					
Sutton Common d					15 12							15 42							16 12					
St Helier d					15 15							15 45							16 15					
Morden South d					15 17							15 47							16 17					
South Merton d					15 19							15 49							16 19					
Wimbledon Chase d					15 21							15 51							16 21					
Wimbledon 6 ⊖ d					15 26							15 56							16 26					
Haydons Road d					15 28							15 58							16 28					
Tooting d					15 31							16 01							16 31					
Carshalton d									15 39						16 09									16 39
Hackbridge d									15 41						16 11									16 41
Mitcham Junction d									15 44						16 14									16 44
Mitcham Eastfields d									15 48						16 18									16 48
Streatham 4 d					15 36				15 53			16 06			16 23				16 36					16 53
Tulse Hill 3 d					15 42				15 57			16 12			16 27				16 42					16 57
London Bridge 4 ⊖ d			15 45					16 00			16 15			16 30				16 45					17 00	
Herne Hill 4 d					15 46				16 00			16 16			16 30				16 46					17 00
Loughborough Jn d					15 49				16 04			16 19			16 34				16 49					17 04
Elephant & Castle d					15 54				16 09			16 24			16 39				16 54					17 09
London Blackfriars 3 ⊖ d			15 53		15 58			16 08	16 13		16 23	16 28		16 38	16 43			16 53	16 58				17 08	17 13
City Thameslink 3 d			15 55		16 00			16 10	16 15		16 25	16 30		16 40	16 45			16 55	17 00				17 10	17 15
Moorgate ⊖ d																								
Barbican ⊖ d																								
Farringdon 3 ⊖ d			15 59		16 04			16 14	16 19		16 29	16 34		16 44	16 49			16 59	17 04				17 14	17 19
St Pancras International 15 ⊖ d	16 00		16 03		16 08		16 30	16 18	16 23		16 33	16 38		16 48	16 53	17 00		17 03	17 08		17 30	17 40	17 18	17 23
Kentish Town ⊖ d					16 12				16 27			16 42			16 57				17 12					17 27
West Hampstead Thameslink ⊖ d					16 16				16 31			16 46			17 01				17 16					17 31
Cricklewood d		←			16 19	←			16 34	←		16 49	←		17 04		←		17 19	←				17 34
Hendon d		15 52			16 22	16 07			16 37	16 22		16 52	16 37		17 07		16 52		17 22	17 07				17 37
Mill Hill Broadway d		15 55			→	16 10			→	16 25		→	16 40		→		16 55		→	17 10				→
Elstree & Borehamwood d		16 00				16 15				16 30			16 45				17 00			17 15				
Radlett d		16 08				16 20				16 38			16 50				17 08			17 20				
St Albans City d		16 14	16 24			16a27		16 39		16 44	16 54		16a57	17 09			17 14	17 24		17a27			17 39	
Harpenden d		16 19	16 29					16 44		16 49	16 59			17 14			17 19	17 29					17 44	
Luton Airport Parkway 7 ✈ d	16 22	16 25	16 35					16 50		16 55	17 05			17 20		17 22	17 25	17 35					17 50	
Luton 10 d		16a29	16 38				16 53	16 54		16a59	17 08			17 24			17a29	17 38			17 53		17 54	
Leagrave d			16 42					16 58			17 12			17 28				17 42					17 58	
Harlington d			16 48					17 04			17 18			17 34				17 48					18 04	
Flitwick d			16 52					17 08			17 22			17 38				17 52					18 08	
Bedford 7 a	16 37		17 05				17 07	17 20			17 35			17 50		17 37		18 05			18 07	18 19	18 20	

For general notes see front of timetable
For details of catering facilities see Directory of Train Operators

A To Burton-on-Trent (Table 53)
B To Nottingham (Table 53)
C To Derby (Table 53)
D Until 1 November to Sheffield (Table 53). From 8 November to Nottingham
E To Leeds (Table 53)

Brighton, Gatwick Airport and South London → City of London, St.Albans, Luton and Bedford

Network Diagram - see first page of Table 52

		FC	FC [1]	FC	FC	EM [1] ◇ A ☕	FC [1]	FC	EM [1] ◇ B ☕	FC	FC [1]	FC	FC	EM [1] ◇ A ☕	FC [1]	FC		FC	FC [1]	FC	FC	EM [1] ◇ A ☕	FC [1]	FC	EM [1] ◇ C ☕
Brighton [10]	d		16 07				16 34				16 37				17 04				17 07				17 34		
Preston Park	d		16 11				*16 11*				16 41				*16 58*				17 11				*17 11*		
Hassocks [4]	d		16 17				*16 17*				16 47				*17 05*				17 17				*17 17*		
Burgess Hill [4]	d		16 21				*16 21*				16 51				*17 08*				17 21				*17 21*		
Wivelsfield [4]	d		16 23				*16 34*				16 53				*17 11*				17 23				*17 34*		
Haywards Heath [3]	d		16 32				16 48				17 02				17 18				17 32				17 48		
Balcombe	d		16 37				*16 37*												17 37				*17 37*		
Three Bridges [4]	d		16 42				*16 48*				17 12				*17 18*				17 42				*17 48*		
Gatwick Airport [10] ✈	d		16 46				17 01				17 16				17 31				17 46				18 01		
Redhill	d		*16 37*				*16 48*				*17 16*								*17 37*				*17 48*		
East Croydon	d		17 02				17 17				17 32				17 47				18 02				18 17		
Sutton (Surrey) [4]	d			16 37				17 06				17 07				17 36				17 37				18 06	
West Sutton	d			16 40								17 10								17 40					
Sutton Common	d			16 42								17 12								17 42					
St Helier	d			16 45								17 15								17 45					
Morden South	d			16 47								17 17								17 47					
South Merton	d			16 49								17 19								17 49					
Wimbledon Chase	d			16 51								17 21								17 51					
Wimbledon [6] ⊖	d			16 56								17 26								17 56					
Haydons Road	d			16 58								17 28								17 58					
Tooting	d			17 01								17 31								18 01					
Carshalton	d							17 09								17 39								18 09	
Hackbridge	d							17 11								17 41								18 11	
Mitcham Junction	d							17 14								17 44								18 14	
Mitcham Eastfields	d							17 18								17 48								18 18	
Streatham [4]	d			17 06				17 23				17 36				17 53				18 06				18 23	
Tulse Hill [3]	d			17 12				17 27				17 42				17 57				18 12				18 27	
London Bridge [4] ⊖	d		17 15				17 30				17 45				18 00				18 15				18 30		
Herne Hill [4]	d			17 16				17 30				17 46				18 00				18 16				18 30	
Loughborough Jn	d			17 19				17 34				17 49				18 04				18 19				18 34	
Elephant & Castle	d			17 24				17 39				17 54				18 09				18 24				18 39	
London Blackfriars [3] ⊖	d		17 23	17 28			17 38	17 43			17 53	17 58			18 08	18 13			18 23	18 28			18 38	18 43	
City Thameslink [3]	d		17 25	17 30			17 40	17 45			17 55	18 00			18 10	18 15			18 25	18 30			18 40	18 45	
Moorgate ⊖	d																								
Barbican ⊖	d																								
Farringdon [3] ⊖	d		17 29	17 34			17 44	17 49			17 59	18 04			18 14	18 19			18 29	18 34			18 44	18 49	
St Pancras International [15] ⊖	d		17 33	17 38		17 55	17 48	17 53	18 00		18 03	18 08		18 30	18 18	18 23			18 33	18 38		18 55	18 48	18 53	19 00
Kentish Town ⊖	d			17 42				17 57				18 12				18 27				18 42				18 57	
West Hampstead Thameslink ⊖	d			17 46				18 01				18 16				18 31				18 46				19 01	
Cricklewood	d	←		17 49	←			18 04		←		18 19	←			18 34		←		18 49	←			19 04	
Hendon	d	17 22		17 52	17 37			18 07		17 52		18 22	18 07			18 37		18 22		18 52	18 37			19 07	
Mill Hill Broadway	d	17 25		→	17 40			→		17 55		→	18 10			→		18 25		→	18 40			→	
Elstree & Borehamwood	d	17 30			17 45					18 00			18 15					18 30			18 45				
Radlett	d	17 38			17 50					18 08			18 20					18 38			18 50				
St Albans City	d	17 44	17 54		17a57		18 09			18 14	18 24		18b29		18 39			18 44	18 54		18c59		19 09		
Harpenden	d	17 49	17 59				18 14			18 19	18 29		18 34		18 44			18 49	18 59		19 04		19 14		
Luton Airport Parkway [7] ✈	d	17 55	18 05				18 20		18 22	18 25	18 35		18 40		18 50			18 55	19 05		19 10		19 20		19 22
Luton [10]	d	17a59	18 08			18a18	18 24			18a29	18 38		18 44	18 53	18 54			18a59	19 08		19 14	19a18	19 24		
Leagrave	d		18 12				18 28				18 44		18 48		18 58				19 12		19 18		19 28		
Harlington	d		18 18				18 34				18 49		18 54		19 04				19 18		19 24		19 34		
Flitwick	d		18 22				18 38				18 53		18 58		19 08				19 22		19 28		19 38		
Bedford [7]	a		18 35				18 50		18 37		19 05		19 10	19 07	19 20				19 35		19 40		19 50		19 37

For general notes see front of timetable
For details of catering facilities see Directory of Train Operators

A To Nottingham (Table 53)
B Until 6 September to Barnsley (Table 53). From 13 September to Sheffield (Table 53)
C To Derby (Table 53)
b Arr. 1826
c Arr. 1856

Table 52

Saturdays

Brighton, Gatwick Airport and South London → City of London, St.Albans, Luton and Bedford

Network Diagram - see first page of Table 52

Station		FC	FC	FC	FC	EM	EM	FC	FC	FC	FC	FC	FC	FC	EM	FC	FC	FC	FC	FC	EM	FC	FC	FC	FC
			1			1 ◇	1 ◇	1			1			1	1 ◇			1			1 ◇	1		1	
						A	B								C						B				
Brighton [10]	d		17 37					18 04			18 07			18 34				18 37				19 04		19 07	
Preston Park	d		17 41					17 58			18 11			18 11				18 41				18 58		19 11	
Hassocks [4]	d		17 47					18 05			18 17			18 17				18 47				19 05		19 17	
Burgess Hill [4]	d		17 51					18 08			18 21			18 21				18 51				19 08		19 21	
Wivelsfield [4]	d		17 53					18 11			18 23			18 34				18 53				19 11		19 23	
Haywards Heath [3]	d		18 02					18 18			18 32			18 48				19 02				19 18		19 32	
Balcombe	d										18 37			18 37										19 37	
Three Bridges [4]	d		18 12					18 18			18 42			18 51				19 12				19 18		19 42	
Gatwick Airport [10] ✈	d		18 16					18 31			18 46			19 01				19 16				19 31		19 46	
Redhill	d		18 16								18 37			18 48				19 06				19 18		19 37	
East Croydon	d		18 32					18 47			19 02			19 17				19 32				19 47		20 02	
Sutton (Surrey) [4]	d			18 07					18 36			18 37					19 06		19 07						19 39
West Sutton	d			18 10								18 40							19 10						19 42
Sutton Common	d			18 12								18 42							19 12						19 44
St Helier	d			18 15								18 45							19 15						19 47
Morden South	d			18 17								18 47							19 17						19 49
South Merton	d			18 19								18 49							19 19						19 51
Wimbledon Chase	d			18 21								18 51							19 21						19 53
Wimbledon [6] ⊖	d			18 26								18 56							19 28						19 58
Haydons Road	d			18 28								18 58							19 30						20 00
Tooting	d			18 31								19 01							19 33						20 03
Carshalton	d								18 39								19 09								
Hackbridge	d								18 41								19 11								
Mitcham Junction	d								18 44								19 14								
Mitcham Eastfields	d								18 48								19 18								
Streatham [4]	d			18 36					18 53			19 06					19 23		19 40						20 10
Tulse Hill [3]	d			18 42					18 57			19 12					19 27		19 44						20 14
London Bridge [4] ⊖	d		18 45					19 00			19 15			19 30				19 45				20 00		20 15	
Herne Hill [4]	d			18 46					19 00			19 16					19 30		19 47						20 17
Loughborough Jn	d			18 49					19 04			19 19					19 34		19 51						20 21
Elephant & Castle	d			18 54					19 09			19 24					19 39		19 56						20 26
London Blackfriars [3] ⊖	d		18 53	18 58				19 08	19 13		19 23	19 28		19 38			19 43	19 53	20 00			20 08		20 23	20 30
City Thameslink [3]	d		18 55	19 00				19 10	19 15		19 25	19 30		19 40			19 45	19 55	20 02			20 10		20 25	20 32
Moorgate ⊖	d																								
Barbican ⊖	d																								
Farringdon [3] ⊖	d		18 59	19 04				19 14	19 19		19 29	19 34		19 44			19 49	19 59	20 06			20 14		20 29	20 36
St Pancras International [15] ⊖	d		19 03	19 08		19 25	19 30	19 18	19 23		19 33	19 38		19 48	20 00		19 53	20 03	20 10		20 30	20 18		20 33	20 40
Kentish Town ⊖	d			19 12					19 27			19 42					19 57		20 14						20 44
West Hampstead Thameslink ⊖	d			19 16					19 31			19 46					20 01	20 10	20 18					20 40	20 48
Cricklewood	d	←		19 19	←				19 34	←		19 49	←			←	20 04		20 21				←		20 51
Hendon	d	18 52		19 22	19 07				19 37	19 22		19 52	19 37			19 52	20 07		20 24	←			20 24		20 54
Mill Hill Broadway	d	18 55		→	19 10				→	19 25		→	19 40			19 55	20 10		→	20 10			20 27		→
Elstree & Borehamwood	d	19 00			19 15					19 30			19 45			20 00	→			20 15			20 32		
Radlett	d	19 08			19 20					19 38			19 50			20 08				20 20			20 38		
St Albans City	d	19 14	19 24		19b29			19 39		19 44	19 54		19c59	20 09		20 14		20 24		20e29		20 40	20 44	20 54	
Harpenden	d	19 19	19 31		19 35			19 44		19 49	20 01		20 04	20 14		20 19		20 31		20 35		20 44	20 49	21 01	
Luton Airport Parkway [7] ✈	d	19 25	19 37		19 41			19 50		19 55	20 07		20 10	20 20	20 22	20 25		20 37		20 41		20 50	20 55	21 07	
Luton [10]	d	19a29	19 40		19 44	19a48	19 53	19 54		19a59	20 10		20 14	20 24		20a29		20 40		20a43	20 53	20 54	20a59	21 10	
Leagrave	d		19 44		19 48			19 58			20 14		20 18	20 28				20 44				20 58		21 14	
Harlington	d		19 50		19 54			20 04			20 20		20 24	20 34				20 50				21 04		21 20	
Flitwick	d		19 54		19 58			20 08			20 24		20 28	20 38				20 54				21 08		21 24	
Bedford [7]	a		20 05		20 10		20 07	20 20			20 35		20 40	20 50	20 37			21 05			21 07	21 20		21 35	

For general notes see front of timetable
For details of catering facilities see Directory of Train Operators

A To Leeds (Table 53)
B To Nottingham (Table 53)
C To Derby (Table 53)
b Arr. 1926
c Arr. 1956
e Arr. 2026

Table 52

Saturdays

Brighton, Gatwick Airport and South London → City of London, St.Albans, Luton and Bedford

Network Diagram - see first page of Table 52

		FC 1	EM 1 ◊ A ☕	FC	FC 1	FC	FC 1	FC	FC 1	FC	FC 1	FC	FC 1	EM 1 ◊ A ☕	FC	FC 1	FC	FC 1	FC	FC 1	FC	FC 1	FC 1
Brighton 10	d	19 34			19 37		20 04		20 07		20 34		20 37			21 07		21 37		22 07		22 33	23 37
Preston Park	d	*19 11*			19 41		*19 41*		20 11		*20 11*		20 41			21 11		21 41		22 11		22 37	23 41
Hassocks 4	d	*19 17*			19 47		*19 47*		20 17		*20 17*		20 47			21 17		21 47		22 17		22 43	23 47
Burgess Hill 4	d	*19 21*			19 51		*20 02*		20 21		*20 21*		20 51			21 21		21 51		22 21		22 47	23 51
Wivelsfield 4	d	*19 34*			19 53		*20 03*		20 23				20 53			21 23		21 53		22 23		22 49	23 53
Haywards Heath 3	d	19 48			20 02		20 18		20 32		20 48		21 02			21 32		22 02		22 32		22 54	23 59
Balcombe	d	*19 37*							20 37		*20 37*					21 37				22 37		23 00	00 04
Three Bridges 4	d	*19 51*			20 12		*20 18*		20 42		*20 51*		21 12			21 42		22 12		22 42		23 12	00 10
Gatwick Airport 10 ✈	d	20 01			20 16		20 31		20 46		21 01		21 16			21 46		22 16		22 46		23 16	00 15
Redhill	d	*19 47*			*20 08*		*20 18*		*20 37*		*20 47*		*21 08*			*21 38*		*22 08*		*22 40*		*22 47*	00 22
East Croydon	d	20 17			20 32		20 47		21 02		21 17		21 32			22 02		22 32		23 02		23 32	00 36
Sutton (Surrey) 4	d					20 09				20 39					21 09		21 49						
West Sutton	d					20 12				20 42					21 12		21 52						
Sutton Common	d					20 14				20 44					21 14		21 54						
St Helier	d					20 17				20 47					21 17		21 57						
Morden South	d					20 19				20 49					21 19		21 59						
South Merton	d					20 21				20 51					21 21		22 01						
Wimbledon Chase	d					20 23				20 53					21 23		22 03						
Wimbledon 6 ⊖	d					20 27				20 57					21b38		22 08		22 38				
Haydons Road	d					20 29				20 59					21 40		22 10		22 40				
Tooting	d					20 32				21 02					21 43		22 13		22 43				
Carshalton	d																						
Hackbridge	d																						
Mitcham Junction	d																						
Mitcham Eastfields	d																						
Streatham 4	d					20 39				21 09					21 48		22 18		22 48				
Tulse Hill 3	d					20 43				21 13					21 52		22 22		22 52				
London Bridge 4 ⊖	d	20 30			20 45		21 00		21 15		21 30		21 45			22 15		22 45		23 15		23 45	00 52
Herne Hill 4	d					20 47				21 17					21 55		22 26		22 55				
Loughborough Jn	d					20 51				21 21					21 59		22 30						
Elephant & Castle	d					20 56				21 26					22 04		22 34		23 04				
London Blackfriars 3 ⊖	d	20 38			20 53	21 00	21 08		21 23	21c32	21 38		21 53		22 07	22 23	22 37	22 53	23 09	23 23	23 38	23 53	01 00
City Thameslink 3	d	20 40			20 55	21 02																	
Moorgate ⊖	d																						
Barbican ⊖	d																						
Farringdon 3 ⊖	d	20 44			20 59	21 06	21 14		21 29	21 39	21 44		21 59		22 14	22 29	22 44	22 59	23 14	23 29	23 44	23 59	
St Pancras International 15 ⊖	d	20 48	21 00		21 03	21 10	21 18		21 33	21 43	21 48		22 03	22 10	22 18	22 33	22 48	23 03	23 18	23 33	23 48	00 03	01 08
Kentish Town ⊖	d					21 14				21 47					22 22		22 52		23 22		23 52		01 12
West Hampstead Thameslink ⊖	d				21 10	21 18			21 40	21 51			22 10		22 26	22 40	22 56	23 10	23 26	23 40	23 56	00 10	01 16
Cricklewood	d			←		21 21		←		21 54		←			22 29		22 59		23 29		23 59		01 19
Hendon	d			20 54		21 24		21 24		21 57		21 57			22 32		23 02		23 32		00 02		01 22
Mill Hill Broadway	d			20 57		→		21 27		→		22 00			22 35		23 05		23 35		00 05		01 25
Elstree & Borehamwood	d			21 02				21 32				22 05			22 40		23 10		23 40		00 10		01 30
Radlett	d			21 08				21 38				22 09			22 44		23 14		23 44		00 14		01 34
St Albans City	d	21 09		21 14	21 24		21 39	21 44	21 54		22 10	22 15	22 24		22 50	22 54	23 20	23 24	23 50	23 54	00 20	00 24	01 40
Harpenden	d	21 14		21 19	21 31		21 44	21 49	22 01		22 14	22 21	22 31		22 55	23 01	23 25	23 31	23 55	00 01	00 25	00 31	01 45
Luton Airport Parkway 7 ✈	d	21 20	21 22	21 25	21 37		21 50	21 55	22 07		22 20	22 27	22 37		23 01	23 07	23 31	23 37	00 01	00 07	00 31	00 37	01 51
Luton 10	d	21 24		21a29	21 40		21 54	22 00	22 10		22 24	22 30	22 40	22 45	23 05	23 10	23 35	23 40	00 05	00 10	00 35	00 40	01 55
Leagrave	d	21 28			21 44		21 58	22 04	22 14		22 28	22 34	22 44		23 09	23 14	23 39	23 44	00 09	00 14	00 39	00 44	01 59
Harlington	d	21 34			21 50		22 04	22 10	22 20		22 34	22 40	22 50		23 14	23 20	23 44	23 50	00 14	00 20	00 44	00 50	02 04
Flitwick	d	21 38			21 54		22 08	22 14	22 24		22 38	22 44	22 54		23 18	23 24	23 48	23 54	00 18	00 24	00 48	00 54	02 08
Bedford 7	a	21 50	21 37		22 05		22 20	22 25	22 35		22 50	22 55	23 05	23 07	23 30	23 35	00 01	00 05	00 30	00 35	01 00	01 05	02 20

For general notes see front of timetable
For details of catering facilities see Directory of Train Operators

A To Derby (Table 53)
b Arr. 2127
c Arr. 2126

Table 52

Sundays

Brighton, Gatwick Airport and South London → City of London, St.Albans, Luton and Bedford

Network Diagram - see first page of Table 52

		FC	FC 1	FC	FC 1	FC	FC 1	FC 1	FC 1	FC 1	FC 1	FC 1	EM 1 ◇ A		FC 1	EM 1 ◇ B	FC 1	EM 1 ◇ A	FC 1	EM 1 ◇ B	FC 1	FC	EM 1 ◇ A	FC 1	FC
Brighton 10	d		22p07		22p33		23p37	*03 50*	05 44	06 13	06 44	07 16			07 44		08 16		08 44		09 16	*09 16*		09 44	
Preston Park	d		22p11		22p37		23p41				*06 19*	*07 03*			*07 03*		*08 03*		*08 03*		*09 03*	*09 03*		*09 03*	
Hassocks 4	d		22p17		22p43		23p47		05 52		06 52	*07 10*			07 52		*08 10*		08 52		*09 10*	*09 10*		09 52	
Burgess Hill 4	d		22p21		22p47		23p51		05 56	06 26	06 56	07 26			07 56		08 26		08 56		09 26	*09 26*		09 56	
Wivelsfield 4	d		22p23		22p49		23p53				*06 32*	*07 16*			*07 32*		*08 16*		*08 31*		*09 16*	*09 16*		*09 31*	
Haywards Heath 3	d		22p32		22p54		23p59		06 01	06 31	07 01	07 31			08 01		08 31		09 01		09 31	*09 31*		10 01	
Balcombe	d		22p37		23p00		00 04					*07 26*					*08 26*				*09 26*	*09 26*			
Three Bridges 4	d		22p42		23p12		00 10	05 10	06 10	06 40	07 10	07 40			08 10		08 40		09 10		09 40	*09 40*		10 10	
Gatwick Airport 10 ✈	d		22p46		23p16		00 15	05 15	06 15	06 45	07 15	07 45			08 15		08 45		09 15		09 45			10 15	
Redhill	d						00 22		*05 46*		*07 07*				*08 09*				*09 09*			*09 46*		*10 09*	
East Croydon	d		23p02		23p32		00 36	05 32	06 32	07 02	07 32	08 02			08 32		09 02		09 32		10 02	10 12		10 32	
Sutton (Surrey) 4	d																								10 10
West Sutton	d																								10 13
Sutton Common	d																								10 15
St Helier	d																								10 17
Morden South	d																								10 19
South Merton	d																								10 21
Wimbledon Chase	d																								10 22
Wimbledon 6 ⊖	d	22p39																							10 26
Haydons Road	d	22p41																							10 28
Tooting	d	22p44																							10 31
Carshalton	d																								
Hackbridge	d																								
Mitcham Junction	d																								
Mitcham Eastfields	d																								
Streatham 4	d	22p49																							10 35
Tulse Hill 3	d	22p53																							10 38
London Bridge 4 ⊖	d		23p15		23p45	00 20	00 52			07 15	07 45	08 15			08 45		09 15		09 45		10 15	10 30		10 45	
Herne Hill 4	d	22p56																							10 42
Loughborough Jn	d																								10 45
Elephant & Castle	d	23p05																							10 50
London Blackfriars 3 ⊖	d	23p08	23p23	23p38	23p53	00 28	01 00	05 55	06 55	07 23	07 53	08 23			08 53		09 23		09 53		10 23	10 38		10 53	10 58
City Thameslink 3	d																								
Moorgate ⊖	d																								
Barbican ⊖	d																								
Farringdon 3 ⊖	d	23p14	23p29	23p44	23p59	00 34			06 58	07 28	07 58	08 28			08 58		09 28		09 58		10 28	10 44		10 58	11 02
St Pancras International 15 ⊖	d	23p18	23p33	23p48	00 03	00 38	01 08	06 02	07 02	07 32	08 02	08 32	09 00		09 02	09 30	09 32	10 00	10 02	10 30	10 32	10 48	11 00	11 02	11 06
Kentish Town ⊖	d	23p22		23p52		00 42	01 12	06 06	07 06	07 36	08 06	08 36			09 06		09 36		10 06		10 36				11 10
West Hampstead Thameslink ⊖	d	23p26	23p40	23p56	00 10	00 46	01 16	06 10	07 10	07 40	08 10	08 40			09 10		09 40		10 10		10 40	10 55			11 14
Cricklewood	d	23p29		23p59		00 49	01 19	06 13	07 13	07 43	08 13	08 43			09 13		09 43		10 13		10 43				11 17
Hendon	d	23p32		00 02		00 52	01 22	06 16	07 16	07 46	08 16	08 46			09 16		09 46		10 16		10 46				11 20
Mill Hill Broadway	d	23p35		00 05		00 55	01 25	06 19	07 19	07 49	08 19	08 49			09 19		09 49		10 19		10 49				11 23
Elstree & Borehamwood	d	23p40		00 10		01 00	01 30	06 24	07 24	07 54	08 24	08 54			09 24		09 54		10 24		10 54				11 28
Radlett	d	23p44		00 14		01 04	01 34	06 28	07 28	07 58	08 28	08 58			09 28		09 58		10 28		10 58				11 32
St Albans City	d	23p50	23p54	00 20	00 24	01 10	01 40	06 34	07 34	08 04	08 34	09 04			09 34		10 04		10 34		11 04	11 11		11 24	11 37
Harpenden	d	23p55	00 01	00 25	00 31	01 15	01 45	06 39	07 39	08 09	08 39	09 09			09 39		10 09		10 39		11 09	11 17		11 29	11 43
Luton Airport Parkway 7 ✈	d	00 01	00 07	00 31	00 37	01 21	01 51	06 45	07 45	08 15	08 45	09 15			09 45		10 15		10 45		11 15	11 22	11 28	11 35	11 48
Luton 10	d	00 05	00 10	00 35	00 40	01 25	01 55	06 49	07 49	08 19	08 49	09 19	09 30		09 49	10 02	10 19	10 30	10 49		11 19	11 26	11 33	11 39	11a53
Leagrave	d	00 09	00 14	00 39	00 44	01 29	01 59	06 53	07 53	08 23	08 53	09 23			09 53		10 23		10 53		11 23	11 30		11 43	
Harlington	d	00 14	00 20	00 44	00 50	01 34	02 04	06 59	07 59	08 29	08 59	09 29			09 59		10 29		10 59		11 29	11 36		11 49	
Flitwick	d	00 18	00 24	00 48	00 54	01 38	02 08	07 03	08 03	08 33	09 03	09 33			10 03		10 33		11 03		11 33	11 40		11 53	
Bedford 7	a	00 30	00 35	01 00	01 05	01 50	02 20	07 17	08 15	08 45	09 15	09 45	09 50		10 15	10 22	10 45	10 50	11 15	11 24	11 45	11 53	11 55	12 05	

For general notes see front of timetable
For details of catering facilities see
Directory of Train Operators

A To Nottingham (Table 53)
B To Sheffield (Table 53)

Table 52

Sundays

Brighton, Gatwick Airport and South London → City of London, St.Albans, Luton and Bedford

Network Diagram - see first page of Table 52

		FC	EM	FC		FC	FC	EM	FC	FC	FC	EM	FC	FC	FC	EM	FC		FC	FC	EM	FC	FC	FC	EM
		1	1 ◇	1			1	1 ◇	1		1	1 ◇	1		1	1 ◇	1			1	1 ◇	1		1	1 ◇
			A									A				B					A				B
			🍴					🍴				🍴				🍴					🍴				🍴
Brighton 10	d	09 51		10 16			10 16		10 44		10 51		11 16		11 16		11 44			11 51		12 16		12 16	
Preston Park	d	09 03		10 03			10 03		10 03				11 03		11 03		11 03					12 03		12 03	
Hassocks 4	d	09 52		10 10			10 10		10 52		10 52		11 10		11 10		11 52			11 52		12 10		12 10	
Burgess Hill 4	d	09 56		10 26			10 26		10 56		10 56		11 26		11 26		11 56			11 56		12 26		12 26	
Wivelsfield 4	d	09 31		10 16			10 16		10 31		10 31		11 16		11 16		11 31			11 31		12 16		12 16	
Haywards Heath 3	d	10 01		10 31			10 31		11 01		11 01		11 31		11 31		12 01			12 01		12 31		12 31	
Balcombe	d	09 26		10 26			10 26						11 26		11 26							12 26		12 26	
Three Bridges 4	d	10 10		10 40			10 40		11 10		11 10		11 40		11 40		12 10			12 10		12 40		12 40	
Gatwick Airport 10 ✈	d	10 18		10 45					11 15		11 18		11 45				12 15			12 18		12 45			
Redhill	d						10 46		11 09						11 46		12 09							12 46	
East Croydon 🚌	d	10 42		11 02			11 12		11 32		11 42		12 02		12 12		12 32			12 42		13 02		13 12	
Sutton (Surrey) 4	d					10 40				11 10				11 40					12 10				12 40		
West Sutton	d					10 43				11 13				11 43					12 13				12 43		
Sutton Common	d					10 45				11 15				11 45					12 15				12 45		
St Helier	d					10 47				11 17				11 47					12 17				12 47		
Morden South	d					10 49				11 19				11 49					12 19				12 49		
South Merton	d					10 51				11 21				11 51					12 21				12 51		
Wimbledon Chase	d					10 52				11 22				11 52					12 22				12 52		
Wimbledon 6 ⊖ 🚌	d					10 56				11 26				11 56					12 26				12 56		
Haydons Road	d					10 58				11 28				11 58					12 28				12 58		
Tooting	d					11 01				11 31				12 01					12 31				13 01		
Carshalton	d																								
Hackbridge	d																								
Mitcham Junction 🚌	d																								
Mitcham Eastfields	d																								
Streatham 4	d					11 05				11 35				12 05					12 35				13 05		
Tulse Hill 3	d					11 08				11 38				12 08					12 38				13 08		
London Bridge 4 ⊖	d	11 00		11 15			11 30		11 45		12 00		12 15		12 30		12 45			13 00		13 15		13 30	
Herne Hill 4	d					11 12				11 42				12 14					12 44				13 12		
Loughborough Jn	d					11 15				11 45				12 17					12 47				13 15		
Elephant & Castle	d					11 20				11 50				12 22					12 52				13 20		
London Blackfriars 3 ⊖	d	11 08		11 23		11 28	11 38		11 53	11 58	12 08		12 23	12 28	12 38		12 53		12 58	13 08		13 23	13 28	13 38	
City Thameslink 3	d																								
Moorgate ⊖	d																								
Barbican ⊖	d																								
Farringdon 3 ⊖	d	11 14		11 28		11 32	11 44		11 58	12 02	12 14		12 28	12 32	12 44		12 58		13 02	13 14		13 28	13 32	13 44	
St Pancras International 15 ⊖	d	11 18	11 30	11 32		11 36	11 48	12 00	12 02	12 06	12 18	12 30	12 32	12 36	12 48	13 00	13 02		13 06	13 18	13 30	13 32	13 36	13 48	14 00
Kentish Town ⊖	d					11 40				12 10				12 40					13 10				13 40		
West Hampstead Thameslink ⊖	d	11 25				11 44	11 55			12 14	12 25			12 44	12 55				13 14	13 25			13 44	13 55	
Cricklewood	d					11 47				12 17				12 47					13 17				13 47		
Hendon	d					11 50				12 20				12 50					13 20				13 50		
Mill Hill Broadway	d					11 53				12 23				12 53					13 23				13 53		
Elstree & Borehamwood	d					11 58				12 28				12 58					13 28				13 58		
Radlett	d					12 02				12 32				13 02					13 32				14 02		
St Albans City	d	11 41		11 54		12 07	12 11		12 24	12 37	12 41		12 54	13 07	13 11		13 24		13 37	13 41		13 54	14 07	14 11	
Harpenden	d	11 47		11 59		12 13	12 17		12 29	12 43	12 47		12 59	13 13	13 17		13 29		13 43	13 47		13 59	14 13	14 17	
Luton Airport Parkway 7 ✈	d	11 52		12 05		12 18	12 22		12 35	12 48	12 52		13 05	13 18	13 23	13 27	13 35		13 48	13 53		14 05	14 18	14 23	
Luton 10	d	11 56		12 09		12a23	12 26	12 31	12 39	12 52	12 56		13 09	13 22	13 26	13 33	13 39		13 52	13 56		14 09	14 22	14 26	14 32
Leagrave	d	12 00		12 13			12 30		12 43		13 00		13 13		13 30		13 43			14 00		14 13		14 30	
Harlington	d	12 06		12 19			12 36		12 49		13 06		13 19		13 36		13 49			14 06		14 19		14 36	
Flitwick	d	12 10		12 23			12 40		12 53		13 10		13 23		13 40		13 53			14 10		14 23		14 40	
Bedford 7	a	12 23	12 23	12 35			12 53	12 55	13 05	13 13	13 23	13 23	13 35	13 43	13 53	13 54	14 05		14 13	14 23	14 23	14 35	14 43	14 53	14 46

For general notes see front of timetable
For details of catering facilities see Directory of Train Operators

A To Sheffield (Table 53)
B To Nottingham (Table 53)

Table 52

Sundays

Brighton, Gatwick Airport and South London → City of London, St.Albans, Luton and Bedford

Network Diagram - see first page of Table 52

		FC 1	FC	EM 1 ◇ A	FC 1	FC 1	FC	FC		EM 1 ◇ B	FC 1	FC	EM 1 ◇ A	FC 1	FC 1	FC	FC 1	EM 1 ◇ B	FC 1	FC	FC 1		EM 1 ◇	FC 1	FC
Brighton 10	d	12 44			12 51	13 16		13 16			13 44			13 51	14 16		14 16		14 44		14 51			15 16	
Preston Park	d	12 03				13 03		13 03			13 03			13 03	14 03		14 03		14 03					15 03	
Hassocks 4	d	12 52			12 52	13 10		13 10			13 52			13 52	14 10		14 10		14 52		14 52			15 10	
Burgess Hill 4	d	12 56			12 56	13 26		13 26			13 56			13 56	14 26		14 26		14 56		14 56			15 26	
Wivelsfield 4	d	12 31			12 31	13 16		13 16			13 31			13 31	14 16		14 16		14 31		14 31			15 16	
Haywards Heath 3	d	13 01			13 01	13 31		13 31			14 01			14 01	14 31		14 31		15 01		15 01			15 31	
Balcombe	d					13 26		13 26						13 26	14 26		14 26							15 26	
Three Bridges 4	d	13 10			13 10	13 40		13 40			14 10			14 10	14 40		14 40		15 10		15 10			15 40	
Gatwick Airport 10 ✈	d	13 15			13 18	13 45					14 15			14 18	14 45				15 15		15 18			15 45	
Redhill	d	13 09						13 46			14 09						14 46		15 09						
East Croydon	d	13 32			13 42	14 02		14 12			14 32			14 42	15 02		15 12		15 32		15 42			16 02	
Sutton (Surrey) 4	d		13 10				13 40					14 10				14 40				15 10					15 40
West Sutton	d		13 13				13 43					14 13				14 43				15 13					15 43
Sutton Common	d		13 15				13 45					14 15				14 45				15 15					15 45
St Helier	d		13 17				13 47					14 17				14 47				15 17					15 47
Morden South	d		13 19				13 49					14 19				14 49				15 19					15 49
South Merton	d		13 21				13 51					14 21				14 51				15 21					15 51
Wimbledon Chase	d		13 22				13 52					14 22				14 52				15 22					15 52
Wimbledon 6 ⊖	d		13 26				13 56					14 26				14 56				15 26					15 56
Haydons Road	d		13 28				13 58					14 28				14 58				15 28					15 58
Tooting	d		13 31				14 01					14 31				15 01				15 31					16 01
Carshalton	d																								
Hackbridge	d																								
Mitcham Junction	d																								
Mitcham Eastfields	d																								
Streatham 4	d		13 35				14 05					14 35				15 05				15 35					16 05
Tulse Hill 3	d		13 38				14 08					14 38				15 08				15 38					16 08
London Bridge 4 ⊖	d	13 45			14 00	14 15		14 30			14 45			15 00	15 15		15 30		15 45		16 00			16 15	
Herne Hill 4	d		13 42				14 12					14 42				15 12				15 42					16 14
Loughborough Jn	d		13 45				14 15					14 45				15 15				15 45					16 17
Elephant & Castle	d		13 50				14 20					14 50				15 20				15 50					16 22
London Blackfriars 3 ⊖	d	13 53	13 58		14 08	14 23	14 28	14 38			14 53	14 58		15 08	15 23	15 28	15 38		15 53	15 58	16 08			16 23	16 28
City Thameslink 3	d																								
Moorgate ⊖	d																								
Barbican ⊖	d																								
Farringdon 3 ⊖	d	13 58	14 02		14 14	14 28	14 32	14 44			14 58	15 02		15 14	15 28	15 32	15 44		15 58	16 02	16 14			16 28	16 32
St Pancras International 15 ⊖	d	14 02	14 06	14 30	14 18	14 32	14 36	14 48		15 00	15 02	15 06	15 30	15 18	15 32	15 36	15 48	16 00	16 02	16 06	16 18		16 30	16 32	16 36
Kentish Town ⊖	d		14 10				14 40					15 10				15 40				16 10					16 40
West Hampstead Thameslink ⊖	d		14 14		14 25		14 44	14 55				15 14		15 25		15 44	15 55			16 14	16 25				16 44
Cricklewood	d		14 17				14 47					15 17				15 47				16 17					16 47
Hendon	d		14 20				14 50					15 20				15 50				16 20					16 50
Mill Hill Broadway	d		14 23				14 53					15 23				15 53				16 23					16 53
Elstree & Borehamwood	d		14 28				14 58					15 28				15 58				16 28					16 58
Radlett	d		14 32				15 02					15 32				16 02				16 32					17 02
St Albans City	d	14 24	14 37		14 41	14 54	15 07	15 11			15 24	15 37		15 41	15 54	16 07	16 11		16 24	16 37	16 41			16 54	17 07
Harpenden	d	14 29	14 43		14 47	14 59	15 13	15 17			15 29	15 43		15 47	15 59	16 13	16 17		16 31	16 43	16 47			16 59	17 13
Luton Airport Parkway 7 ✈	d	14 35	14 48		14 53	15 05	15 18	15 23		15 29	15 35	15 48		15 53	16 05	16 18	16 23		16 37	16 48	16 53			17 05	17 18
Luton 10	d	14 39	14 52		14 56	15 09	15 22	15 26		15 34	15 39	15 52		15 56	16 09	16 22	16 26	16 32	16 40	16 52	16 56		17 01	17 09	17a23
Leagrave	d	14 43			15 00	15 13		15 30			15 43			16 00	16 13		16 30		16 43		17 00			17 13	
Harlington	d	14 49			15 06	15 19		15 36			15 49			16 06	16 19		16 36		16 49		17 06			17 19	
Flitwick	d	14 53			15 10	15 23		15 40			15 53			16 10	16 23		16 40		16 53		17 10			17 23	
Bedford 7	a	15 05	15 13	15 15	15 23	15 35	15 43	15 53		15 51	16 05	16 13	16 15	16 23	16 36	16 43	16 53	16 47	17 06	17 13	17 23		17 15	17 35	

For general notes see front of timetable
For details of catering facilities see Directory of Train Operators

A To Sheffield (Table 53)
B To Nottingham (Table 53)

Table 52

Sundays

Brighton, Gatwick Airport and South London → City of London, St.Albans, Luton and Bedford

Network Diagram - see first page of Table 52

		FC 1	EM 1 ◇ A ☕	FC 1	EM 1 ◇ B ☕	FC	FC 1	FC 1	EM 1 ◇ C ☕	FC	FC 1	FC 1		FC	FC 1	EM 1 ◇ B ☕	FC 1	FC	FC	EM 1 ◇ A ☕	FC 1	FC	EM 1 ◇ C ☕	FC 1	FC
Brighton 10	d	15 16		15 44			15 51	16 16			16 16	16 44			16 51		17 16		17 16		17 44			18 16	
Preston Park	d	15 03		15 03				16 03			16 03	16 03					17 03		17 03		17 03			18 03	
Hassocks 4	d	15 10		15 52			15 52	16 10			16 10	16 52			16 52		17 10		17 10		17 52			18 10	
Burgess Hill 4	d	15 26		15 56			15 56	16 26			16 26	16 56			16 56		17 26		17 26		17 56			18 26	
Wivelsfield 4	d	15 16		15 31			15 31	16 16			16 16	16 31			16 31		17 16		17 16		17 31			18 16	
Haywards Heath 3	d	15 31		16 01			16 01	16 31			16 31	17 01			17 01		17 31		17 31		18 01			18 31	
Balcombe	d	15 26						16 26			16 26						17 26		17 26					18 26	
Three Bridges 4	d	15 40		16 10			16 10	16 40			16 40	17 10			17 10		17 40		17 40		18 10			18 40	
Gatwick Airport 10 ✈	d			16 15			16 18	16 45				17 15			17 18		17 45				18 15			18 45	
Redhill	d	15 46		16 09							16 46	17 09							17 46		18 09				
East Croydon	d	16 12		16 32			16 42	17 02			17 12	17 32			17 42		18 02		18 12		18 32			19 02	
Sutton (Surrey) 4	d					16 10				16 40				17 10				17 40				18 10			18 40
West Sutton	d					16 13				16 43				17 13				17 43				18 13			18 43
Sutton Common	d					16 15				16 45				17 15				17 45				18 15			18 45
St Helier	d					16 17				16 47				17 17				17 47				18 17			18 47
Morden South	d					16 19				16 49				17 19				17 49				18 19			18 49
South Merton	d					16 21				16 51				17 21				17 51				18 21			18 51
Wimbledon Chase	d					16 22				16 52				17 22				17 52				18 22			18 52
Wimbledon 6 ⊖	d					16 26				16 56				17 26				17 56				18 26			18 56
Haydons Road	d					16 28				16 58				17 28				17 58				18 28			18 58
Tooting	d					16 31				17 01				17 31				18 01				18 31			19 01
Carshalton	d																								
Hackbridge	d																								
Mitcham Junction	d																								
Mitcham Eastfields	d																								
Streatham 4	d					16 35				17 05				17 35				18 05				18 35			19 05
Tulse Hill 3	d					16 38				17 08				17 38				18 08				18 38			19 08
London Bridge 4 ⊖	d	16 30		16 45			17 00	17 15			17 30	17 45			18 00		18 15		18 30		18 45			19 15	
Herne Hill 4	d					16 42				17 14				17 42				18 12				18 42			19 12
Loughborough Jn	d					16 45				17 17				17 45				18 15				18 44			19 14
Elephant & Castle	d					16 50				17 22				17 50				18 20				18 50			19 20
London Blackfriars 3 ⊖	d	16 38		16 53		16 58	17 08	17 23		17 28	17 38	17 53		17 58	18 08		18 23	18 28	18 38		18 53	18 58		19 23	19 28
City Thameslink 3	d																								
Moorgate ⊖	d																								
Barbican ⊖	d																								
Farringdon 3 ⊖	d	16 44		16 58		17 02	17 14	17 28		17 32	17 44	17 58		18 02	18 14		18 28	18 32	18 44		18 58	19 02		19 28	19 32
St Pancras International 15 ⊖	d	16 48	17 00	17 02	17 30	17 06	17 18	17 32	18 00	17 36	17 48	18 02		18 06	18 18	18 30	18 32	18 36	18 48	19 00	19 02	19 06	19 30	19 32	19 36
Kentish Town ⊖	d					17 10				17 40				18 10				18 40				19 10			19 40
West Hampstead Thameslink ⊖	d	16 55				17 14	17 25			17 44	17 55			18 14	18 25			18 44	18 55		19 10	19 14		19 40	19 44
Cricklewood	d					17 17				17 47				18 17				18 47				19 17			19 47
Hendon	d					17 20				17 50				18 20				18 50				19 20			19 50
Mill Hill Broadway	d					17 23				17 53				18 23				18 53				19 23			19 53
Elstree & Borehamwood	d					17 28				17 58				18 28				18 58				19 28			19 58
Radlett	d					17 32				18 02				18 32				19 02				19 31			20 01
St Albans City	d	17 11		17 24		17 37	17 41	17 54		18 07	18 11	18 24		18 37	18 41		18 54	19 07	19 11		19 24	19 36		19 54	20 06
Harpenden	d	17 17		17 29		17 43	17 47	17 59		18 13	18 17	18 29		18 43	18 47		18 59	19 13	19 17		19 29	19 42		19 59	20 12
Luton Airport Parkway 7 ✈	d	17 22		17 35		17 48	17 52	18 05		18 18	18 22	18 35		18 48	18 52	18 56	19 05	19 18	19 22		19 35	19 47		20 05	20 17
Luton 10	d	17 26	17 31	17 39	17 51	17a53	17 56	18 09	18 22	18a23	18 26	18 39		18a53	18 56		19 09	19a23	19 26	19 27	19 39	19 52	19 55	20 09	20 22
Leagrave	d	17 30		17 43			18 00	18 13			18 30	18 43			19 00		19 13		19 30		19 43			20 13	
Harlington	d	17 36		17 49			18 06	18 19			18 36	18 49			19 06		19 19		19 36		19 49			20 19	
Flitwick	d	17 40		17 53			18 10	18 23			18 40	18 53			19 10		19 23		19 40		19 53			20 23	
Bedford 7	a	17 53	17 47	18 05	18 15		18 23	18 35	18 46		18 53	19 05			19 23	19 17	19 35		19 53	19 45	20 05	20 13	20 17	20 35	20 43

For general notes see front of timetable
For details of catering facilities see Directory of Train Operators

A To Nottingham (Table 53)
B To Derby (Table 53)
C To Sheffield (Table 53)

Table 52

Sundays

Brighton, Gatwick Airport and South London → City of London, St.Albans, Luton and Bedford

Network Diagram - see first page of Table 52

		EM	FC		FC	EM	FC	FC	EM	FC	FC	EM	FC	FC	FC	FC	EM	FC	EM	FC	FC	FC	FC		
		1 ◇	1			1 ◇	1		1 ◇	1		1 ◇	1		1		1 ◇	1	1 ◇	1	1	1	1		
		A				B			A			C					A		C						
		☕				☕			☕			☕					☕		☕						
Brighton 10	d		18 44				19 16			19 44			20 16		20 44			21 16		21 44	22 16	22 44	23 44		
Preston Park	d		*18 03*				*19 03*			*19 03*			*20 03*		*20 03*			*21 03*		*21 03*	*22 03*	*22 03*	*23 06*		
Hassocks 4	d		18 52				*19 10*			19 52			*20 10*		20 52			*21 10*		21 52	*22 10*	22 52	23 52		
Burgess Hill 4	d		18 56				19 26			19 56			20 26		20 56			21 26		21 56	22 26	22 56	23 56		
Wivelsfield 4	d		*18 31*				*19 16*			*19 31*			*20 16*		*20 31*			*21 16*		*21 31*	*22 16*		*23 19*		
Haywards Heath 3	d		19 01				19 31			20 01			20 31		21 01			21 31		22 01	22 31	23 01	00 01		
Balcombe	d						*19 26*						*20 26*					*21 26*			*22 26*		*23 29*		
Three Bridges 4	d		19 10				19 40			20 10			20 40		21 10			21 40		22 10	22 40	23 10	00 10		
Gatwick Airport 10 ✈	d		19 15				19 45			20 15			20 45		21 15			21 45		22 15	22 45	23 15	00 15		
Redhill	d		*19 09*							*20 09*					*21 13*					*22 09*		*23 09*	00 22		
East Croydon	d		19 32				20 02			20 32			21 02		21 32			22 02		22 32	23 02	23 32	00 36		
Sutton (Surrey) 4	d				19 10			19 40			20 10			20 40		21 10									
West Sutton	d				19 13			19 43			20 13			20 43		21 13									
Sutton Common	d				19 15			19 45			20 15			20 45		21 15									
St Helier	d				19 17			19 47			20 17			20 47		21 17									
Morden South	d				19 19			19 49			20 19			20 49		21 19									
South Merton	d				19 21			19 51			20 21			20 51		21 21									
Wimbledon Chase	d				19 22			19 52			20 22			20 52		21 22									
Wimbledon 6 ⊖	d				19 26			19 56			20 26			20 56		21 26									
Haydons Road	d				19 28			19 58			20 28			20 58		21 28									
Tooting	d				19 31			20 01			20 31			21 01		21 31									
Carshalton	d																								
Hackbridge	d																								
Mitcham Junction	d																								
Mitcham Eastfields	d																								
Streatham 4	d				19 35			20 05			20 35			21 05		21 35									
Tulse Hill 3	d				19 38			20 08			20 38			21 08		21 38									
London Bridge 4 ⊖	d		19 45				20 15			20 45			21 15		21 45			22 15		22 45	23 15	23 45	00 52		
Herne Hill 4	d				19 42			20 12			20 42			21 12		21 42									
Loughborough Jn	d				19 44			20 14			20 44			21 14		21 44									
Elephant & Castle	d				19 50			20 20			20 50			21 20		21 50									
London Blackfriars 3 ⊖	d		19 53		19 58		20 23	20 28		20 53	20 58		21 23	21 28	21 53	21 58		22 23		22 53	23 23	23 53	01 00		
City Thameslink 3	d																								
Moorgate ⊖	d																								
Barbican ⊖	d																								
Farringdon 3 ⊖	d		19 58		20 02		20 28	20 32		20 58	21 02		21 28	21 32	21 58	22 02		22 28		22 58	23 28	23 58			
St Pancras International 15 ⊖	d	20 00	20 02		20 06	20 30	20 32	20 36	21 00	21 02	21 06	21 30	21 32	21 36	22 02	22 06	22 30	22 32	23 00	23 02	23 32	00 02	01 08		
Kentish Town ⊖	d				20 10			20 40			21 10			21 40		22 10		22 36		23 06	23 36	00 06	01 12		
West Hampstead Thameslink ⊖	d		20 10		20 14		20 40	20 44		21 10	21 14		21 40	21 44	22 10	22 14		22 40		23 10	23 40	00 10	01 16		
Cricklewood	d				20 17			20 47			21 17			21 47		22 17		22 43		23 13	23 43	00 13	01 19		
Hendon	d				20 20			20 50			21 20			21 50		22 20		22 46		23 16	23 46	00 16	01 22		
Mill Hill Broadway	d				20 23			20 53			21 23			21 53		22 23		22 49		23 19	23 49	00 19	01 25		
Elstree & Borehamwood	d				20 28			20 58			21 28			21 58		22 28		22 54		23 24	23 54	00 24	01 30		
Radlett	d				20 31			21 01			21 31			22 01		22 31		22 58		23 28	23 58	00 28	01 34		
St Albans City	d		20 24		20 36		20 54	21 06		21 24	21 36		21 54	22 06	22 24	22 36		23 04		23 34	00 04	00 34	01 40		
Harpenden	d		20 29		20 42		20 59	21 12		21 29	21 42		21 59	22 12	22 29	22 42		23 09		23 39	00 09	00 39	01 45		
Luton Airport Parkway 7 ✈	d		20 35		20 47		21 05	21 17		21 35	21 47		22 05	22 17	22 35	22 47		23 15		23 45	00 15	00 45	01 51		
Luton 10	d	20 26	20 39		20 52		21 09	21 22	21 23	21 39	21 50		22 09	22 22	22 39	22 50	22 55	23 19	23 26	23 49	00 19	00 49	01 55		
Leagrave	d		20 43				21 13			21 43			22 13		22 43			23 23		23 53	00 23	00 53	01 59		
Harlington	d		20 49				21 19			21 49			22 19		22 49			23 29		23 59	00 29	00 59	02 04		
Flitwick	d		20 53				21 23			21 53			22 23		22 53			23 33		00 03	00 33	01 03	02 08		
Bedford 7	a	20 47	21 05		21 13	21 13	21 35	21 43	21 47	22 05	22 13	22 18	22 35	22 43	23 05	23 13	23 18	23 45	23 52	00 15	00 45	01 15	02 20		

For general notes see front of timetable
For details of catering facilities see Directory of Train Operators

A To Nottingham (Table 53)
B To Leeds (Table 53)
C To Derby (Table 53)

Table 52A

Luton → Dunstable
Bus Service

		FC	FC		FC	FC		FC	FC		FC	FC		FC	FC		FC	FC		FC	FC		FC	FC		FC	FC		FC
Luton	d	05 57	06 15		06 40	07 10		07 32	07 53		08 06	08 27		08 47	09 08		09 27	09 34		09 52	10 04		10 22	10 34		10 52	11 04		11 22
Dunstable	a	06 20	06 50		07 10	07 45		08 05	08 25		08 45	09 00		09 25	09 40		09 55	10 10		10 25	10 40		10 55	11 10		11 25	11 40		11 55

		FC	FC		FC	FC		FC	FC		FC	FC		FC	FC		FC	FC		FC	FC		FC	FC		FC	FC		FC
Luton	d	11 34	11 52		12 04	12 22		12 34	12 52		13 04	13 22		13 34	13 52		14 04	14 22		14 34	14 52		15 04	15 22		15 36	15 52		16 04
Dunstable	a	12 10	12 29		12 40	12 55		13 10	13 25		13 40	13 55		14 10	14 29		14 40	14 55		15 10	15 25		15 40	15 55		16 10	16 25		16 40

		FC	FC		FC	FC		FC	FC		FC	FC		FC	FC		FC	FC		FC	FC		FC	FC		FC	FC		
Luton	d	16 22	16 37		16 50	17 07		17 25	17 40		17 57	18 27		18 43	19 15		19 30	20 02		20 32	21 00		21 17	21 45		22 15	22 45		
Dunstable	a	16 59	17 14		17 34	17 46		18 00	18 12		18 32	18 55		19 08	19 42		19 54	20 32		21 02	21 20		21 41	22 09		22 37	23 08		

Saturdays

		FC	FC		FC	FC		FC	FC		FC	FC		FC	FC		FC	FC		FC	FC		FC	FC		FC	FC		FC
Luton	d	05 55	06 30		07 07	07 37		08 07	08 37		09 07	09 27		09 42	10 02		10 22	10 42		11 02	11 22		11 42	12 02		12 22	12 42		13 02
Dunstable	a	06 13	06 48		07 35	08 05		08 40	09 10		09 40	09 57		10 15	10 35		10 55	11 15		11 35	11 55		12 15	12 39		12 55	13 15		13 35

		FC	FC		FC	FC		FC	FC		FC	FC		FC	FC		FC	FC		FC	FC	FC	FC	FC	FC	FC	FC		
Luton	d	13 22	13 42		14 02	14 22		14 42	15 02		15 22	15 42		16 02	16 13		16 22	16 42		17 12	17 42	19 00	19 30	20 02	20 30	21 17	21 45		
Dunstable	a	13 55	14 15		14 39	14 55		15 15	15 35		15 55	16 15		16 31	16 47		17 00	17 11		17 45	18 11	19 18	19 54	20 32	21 02	21 41	21 59		

Sundays

		FC					FC					FC					FC					FC							
Luton	d	18 42					19 42					20 42					21 42					22 42							
Dunstable	a	19 04					20 04					21 04					22 04					23 06							

For general notes see front of timetable
For details of catering facilities see
Directory of Train Operators

Table 52A

Mondays to Fridays

Dunstable → Luton

Bus Service

		FC	FC	FC	FC	FC	FC	FC	FC	FC	FC	FC	FC	FC	FC	FC	FC	FC	FC	FC	FC	FC	FC	FC	FC	FC	FC	FC	FC
Dunstable	d	05 15	05 45	05 50	06 00	06 05	06 25	06 40	06 50	06 55	07 15	07 30	07 36	07 53	08 00	08 08	08 10	08 18	08 28	08 30	08 49	09 00	09 05	09 17	09 30	09 35	09 47	10 00	10 05
Luton	a	05 40	06 04	06 04	06 15	06 30	06 40	07 06	07 04	07 10	07 32	08 04	07 53	08 12	08 36	08 27	08 46	08 37	08 47	09 06	09 08	09 34	09 27	09 34	10 04	09 52	10 04	10 34	10 22

		FC		FC	FC	FC	FC	FC	FC	FC	FC	FC	FC	FC	FC	FC	FC	FC	FC	FC	FC	FC	FC	FC	FC	FC	FC	FC	FC
Dunstable	d	10 17	.....	10 30	10 35	10 47	11 00	11 05	11 17	11 30	11 35	11 47	12 00	12 05	12 17	12 30	12 35	12 47	13 00	13 05	13 17	13 35	13 47	14 00	14 05	14 17	14 30	14 35	14 47
Luton	a	10 34	.	11 04	10 52	11 04	11 34	11 22	11 34	12 04	11 52	12 04	12 34	12 22	12 34	13 04	12 52	13 04	13 34	13 22	13 34	13 52	14 04	14 34	14 22	14 34	15 04	14 52	15 04

		FC	FC	FC	FC	FC	FC	FC	FC	FC	FC	FC	FC	FC	FC	FC	FC	FC	FC	FC	FC	FC	FC	FC	FC	FC	FC		
Dunstable	d	15 00	15 05	15 19	15 35	15 40	15 47	16 05	16 10	16 20	16 33	16 40	16 50	17 08	17 10	17 20	17 23	17 40	17 40	18 10	18 20	18 45	19 15	20 15	20 45	21 45	23 08	.....	.....
Luton	a	15 34	15 22	15 36	15 52	16 15	16 04	16 22	16 47	16 37	16 50	17 17	17 07	17 25	17 47	17 59	17 40	17 57	18 17	18 27	18 51	19 16	19 44	20 35	21 10	22 07	23 31	.	.

Saturdays

		FC	FC	FC		FC	FC	FC		FC	FC	FC		FC	FC	FC		FC	FC	FC		FC	FC	FC		FC	FC	FC	FC
Dunstable	d	06 00	06 15	06 20	.....	06 50	07 00	07 15	.....	07 40	07 50	08 10	.....	08 20	08 40	08 50	.....	09 05	09 10	09 25	.....	09 30	09 45	10 00	.....	10 05	10 25	10 30	10 45
Luton	a	06 26	06 30	06 44	.	07 07	07 34	07 28	.	08 10	08 07	08 40	.	08 37	09 10	09 07	.	09 27	09 34	09 42	.	10 04	10 02	10 34	.	10 22	10 42	11 04	11 02

		FC		FC	FC	FC		FC	FC	FC		FC	FC	FC		FC	FC	FC		FC	FC	FC		FC	FC	FC		FC	FC
Dunstable	d	11 00	.....	11 05	11 25	11 30	.....	11 45	12 00	12 05	.....	12 25	12 30	12 45	.....	13 00	13 05	13 25	.....	13 30	13 45	14 00	.....	14 05	14 25	14 30	.....	14 45	15 00
Luton	a	11 34	.	11 22	11 42	12 04	.	12 02	12 34	12 22	.	12 42	13 04	13 02	.	13 34	13 22	13 42	.	14 04	14 02	14 34	.	14 22	14 42	15 04	.	15 02	15 34

		FC	FC	FC		FC	FC	FC		FC	FC	FC		FC	FC	FC		FC	FC	FC		FC	FC						
Dunstable	d	15 05	15 25	15 30	.....	15 45	16 00	16 05	.....	16 25	16 40	16 55	.....	17 10	17 23	17 40	.....	18 00	18 45	19 15	.....	20 45	23 08	.....	.....	.....	.....	.....	.....
Luton	a	15 22	15 42	16 04	.	16 02	16 34	16 22	.	16 42	17 14	17 12	.	17 44	17 40	18 10	.	18 33	19 16	19 44	.	21 10	23 31	.	.	.	.	.	.

For general notes see front of timetable
For details of catering facilities see
Directory of Train Operators

No Sunday Service

Route Diagram for Table 53

DM-23/08
Design BAJS

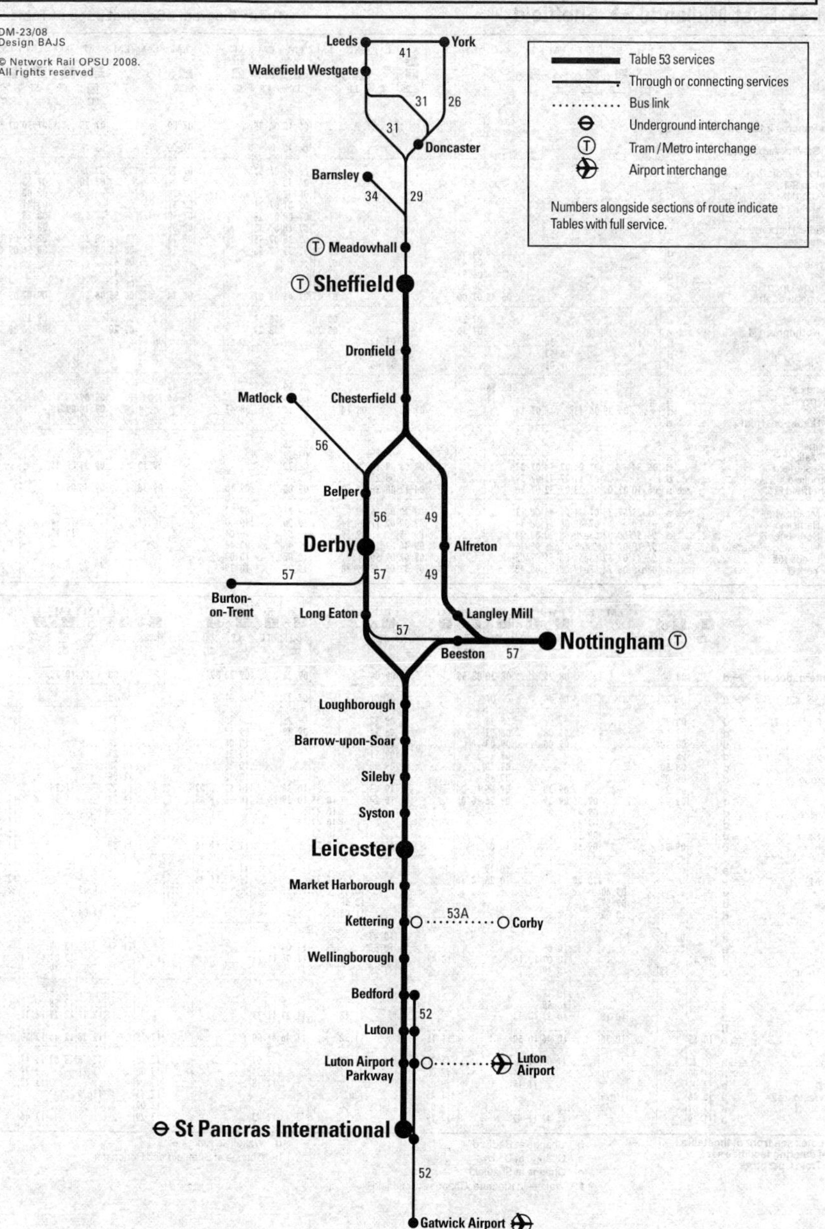
Leeds
York
41
Wakefield Westgate
31
26
31
Doncaster
Barnsley
34
29
Meadowhall
Sheffield
Dronfield
Matlock
Chesterfield
56
Belper
56
49
Derby
Alfreton
57
57
49
Burton-on-Trent
Long Eaton
Langley Mill
57
Nottingham
Beeston
57
Loughborough
Barrow-upon-Soar
Sileby
Syston
Leicester
Market Harborough
Kettering
53A
Corby
Wellingborough
Bedford
52
Luton
Luton Airport Parkway
Luton Airport
St Pancras International
52
Gatwick Airport
Table 53 services
Through or connecting services
Bus link
Underground interchange
Tram / Metro interchange
Airport interchange
Numbers alongside sections of route indicate Tables with full service.

London → East Midlands → Sheffield

Route Diagram - See first page of Table 53

Miles	Miles			EM ◇	XC 1 ◇	EM 1 ◇	EM ◇	XC 1 ◇	XC	EM		XC R 1	EM ◇	XC 1 ◇	EM	EM 1 ◇	EM 1 ◇	XC R 1		EM 1 ◇	EM ◇	EM	EM 1 ◇ ⊠	XC 1 ◇	EM 1 ◇	EM 1 ◇ ⊠
0	0	**St Pancras International** ⊖	d													06 10	06 35			07 00			07 25		07 30	07 55
—	—	Gatwick Airport 10 ✈	d													04 30				05b00			06 16			
—	—	Luton Airport Parkway 7	d													06 05	06 57			07 22			07 35			
30¼	30¼	**Luton** 10	d													06 33				07 04			07 50		07 53	
49¾	49¾	Bedford 7	d													06 48				07 38					08 08	
65¼	65¼	Wellingborough	d													07 01	07 21			07 51					08 21	
72	72	Kettering	d													07 08	07 28			07 58					08 28	
83	83	Market Harborough	d													07 18	07 38			08 08					08 38	
99¼	99¼	**Leicester**	a													07 35	07 55			08 23			08 38		08 55	09 04
—	—		d						06 30	06 40					07 24	07 35	07 56			08 24		08 35	08 39		08 56	09 05
103	103	Syston	d							06 47					07 31							08 42				
105¾	105¾	Sileby	d							06 52					07 38							08 47				
107¾	107¾	Barrow Upon Soar	d							06 56					07 43							08 51				
111¾	111¾	Loughborough	d						06 45	07 00					07 47	07 46	08 07			08 34		08 55	08 50		09 07	09 16
123¼	—	Beeston	a							07 21					08 10		08 19								09 19	
126½	—	**Nottingham** 8	a							07 30					08 20		08 29					09 20			09 26	09 36
—	—		d	05 19			06 34						07 42								08 42					
138¼	—	Langley Mill	d				06 53						07 58								08 58					
144¾	—	Alfreton	d				07 01						08 06								09 06					
—	120½	Long Eaton	a						06 56							07 59				08 43						
—	128½	**Derby** 10	a						07 11							08 13				08 56			09 09			
—	—		d		06 39	06 43		07 14				07 42		08 14		08 16		08 42					09 10	09 18		
—	—	Burton-on-Trent	a													08 37							09 49			
—	136½	Belper	a													08 25										
—	—	Matlock	a													08c59										
—	152¾	Chesterfield	d	05 54		07 04	07 14	07 33				08 03	08 18	08 33		08 39					09 18		09 31	09 36		
160¼	158	Dronfield	d			07 11	07 21	07 39					08 25													
167¼	165	**Sheffield** 7	a	06 10	07 09	07 23	07 32	07 50				08 17	08 38	08 50		09 05		09 18			09 38		09 46	09 50		
—	—	Meadowhall	a	06 23	07 28	07 31	07 46	08 13				08 30	08 56	09 03		09 21		09 30			09 56			10 03		
—	—	Barnsley	a	07 00		07 48	08 11	08 34				09 00	09 11	09 34		10 00		10 00			10 11			10 34		
—	—	Doncaster 7	a	06 56	08 02	08e20	08 20	08 24				09 05		09 19		10 04		10 04						10 15		
—	—	Wakefield Westgate 7	a	07 19	07 36	08f28	08g28	08e46				08 46	09g29			09 46		09 46			10g29					
—	—	Leeds 10	a	07 44	07 52	08e51	08 51	09e02				09 02	09 50			10 02		10 02			10 50					
—	—	York 8	a	08h10	08 24	08e48	08 48	08 48				09 33	09 48	09 48		10 29		10 29					10 40	10 40		

		XC 1 ◇	EM 1 ◇		EM ◇	EM	EM 1 ◇ ⊠	XC 1 ◇	EM 1 ◇	EM 1 ◇ ⊠	XC 1 ◇		EM 1 ◇	EM ◇	EM	EM 1 ◇ ⊠	XC 1 ◇	EM 1 ◇	EM 1 ◇ ⊠		XC 1 ◇	EM 1 ◇	EM ◇	EM 1 ◇ ⊠	XC 1 ◇	EM
St Pancras International ⊖	d		08 00				08 25		08 30	08 55			09 00			09 25		09 30	09 55			10 00		10 25		
Gatwick Airport 10 ✈	d		06b24				06 46		07 01				07b01			07 37		08 01				08b22				
Luton Airport Parkway 7	d		08 22						08 36				09 22			09 25		09 40				10 22				
Luton 10	d		07 57				08 08		08 53				08 54			09 48		09 53				09 56				
Bedford 7	d		08 38				09 00		09 08				09 38					10 08				10 38				
Wellingborough	d		08 51						09 21				09 51					10 21				10 51				
Kettering	d		08 58						09 28				09 58					10 28				10 58				
Market Harborough	d		09 08						09 38				10 08					10 38				11 08				
Leicester	a		09 23				09 38		09 55	10 04			10 23			10 36		10 55	11 03			11 23		11 34		
	d		09 24			09 36	09 39		09 56	10 05			10 24		10 35	10 39		10 56	11 05			11 24		11 35		11 35
Syston	d					09 43									10 42											11 42
Sileby	d					09 48									10 47											11 47
Barrow Upon Soar	d					09 52									10 51											11 51
Loughborough	d		09 34			09 56			10 07				10 34		10 55			11 07	11 16			11 34				11 55
Beeston	a								10 19									11 20								
Nottingham 8	a					10 20			10 26	10 36					11 20			11 27	11 36							12 19
	d				09 40									10 42									11 42			
Langley Mill	d				09 57									10 58												
Alfreton	d				10 05									11 06									12 04			
Long Eaton	a		09 43										10 43									11 43				
Derby 10	a		09 56				10 05						10 56			11 04						11 56		12 05		
	d	09 42					10 07	10 14			10 42					11 06	11 14				11 42			12 07	12 14	
Burton-on-Trent	a		10 19				10 49						11 19			11 49						12 19		12 49		
Belper	a						10 38																	12 38		
Matlock	a						10 58																	12 58		
Chesterfield	d				10 18		10 27	10 33						11 18		11 27	11 33						12 18	12 27	12 33	
Dronfield	d																									
Sheffield 7	a	10 15			10 38		10 46	10 50			11 15			11 38		11 46	11 50				12 15		12 38	12 46	12 50	
Meadowhall	a	10 31			10 56		11 03	11 13			11 31			11 56			12 03				12 30		12 56	13 03	13 13	
Barnsley	a	11 00			11 11			11 34			12 00			12 11			12 34				13 00		13 11		13 34	
Doncaster 7	a	11 04						11 15			12 04						12 15				13 04				13 22	
Wakefield Westgate 7	a	10 46			11g29						11 46			12g29							12 46		13g29			
Leeds 10	a	11 02			11 50						12 02			12 50							13 02		13 50			
York 8	a	11 29					11 42	11 42			12 29					12 43	12 43				13 29			13 46	13 46	

For general notes see front of timetable
For details of catering facilities see Directory of Train Operators

b Change at Bedford
c Change at Derby
e Change at Sheffield
f Wakefield Kirkgate. Change at Sheffield
g Wakefield Kirkgate
h Change at Sheffield and Doncaster

London → East Midlands → Sheffield

Route Diagram - See first page of Table 53

		EM	EM	XC	EM	EM	EM	EM	XC	EM	EM	XC	EM	EM	EM	EM	XC	EM	EM	XC	EM	EM	EM
												R								R			
		1 ◇	1 ◇	1 ◇	1 ◇	◇		1 ◇	1 ◇	1 ◇	1 ◇	1	1 ◇	◇		1 ◇	1 ◇	1 ◇	1 ◇	1	1 ◇	◇	
		☕	☕	☕	☕			☕	☕	☕	☕	☕	☕			☕	☕	☕	☕	☕	☕		
St Pancras International ⊖	d	10 30	10 55		11 00			11 25		11 30	11 55		12 00			12 25		12 30	12 55		13 00		
Gatwick Airport 10 ✈	d	09 16			09b31					10 16			10b31					11 16			11b31		
Luton Airport Parkway 7	d	10 35			11 22					11 35			12 22					12 35			13 22		
Luton 10	d	10 53			10 54					11 53			11 54					12 53			12 54		
Bedford 7	d	11 08			11 38					12 08			12 38					13 08			13 38		
Wellingborough	d	11 21			11 51					12 21			12 51					13 21			13 51		
Kettering	d	11 28			11 58					12 28			12 58					13 28			13 58		
Market Harborough	d	11 38			12 08					12 38			13 08					13 38			14 08		
Leicester	a	11 55	12 04		12 23			12 34		12 55	13 04		13 23			13 34		13 55	14 04		14 23		
	d	11 56	12 05		12 24		12 35	12 36		12 56	13 05		13 24		13 35	13 36		13 56	14 05		14 24		14 35
Syston	d						12 42								13 42								14 42
Sileby	d						12 47								13 47								14 47
Barrow Upon Soar	d						12 51								13 51								14 51
Loughborough	d	12 07			12 34		12 55			13 07	13 15		13 34		13 55			14 07			14 34		14 55
Beeston	a	12 19								13 19								14 19					
Nottingham 8	a	12 26	12 35				13 18			13 26	13 36				14 21			14 26	14 36				15 18
	d					12 42								13 45								14 42	
Langley Mill	d					12 58																14 58	
Alfreton	d					13 06								14 07								15 06	
Long Eaton	a				12 43								13 43								14 43		
Derby 10	a				12 56			13 05					13 56			14 05					14 56		
	d			12 42				13 07	13 14			13 42				14 07	14 14			14 42			
Burton-on-Trent	a				13 19			13 49					14 19			14 49					15 19		
Belper	a															14 37							
Matlock	a															14 57							
Chesterfield	d					13 18		13 27	13 33					14 18		14 27	14 33					15 18	
Dronfield	d																						
Sheffield 7	a			13 15		13 38		13 46	13 50			14 15		14 38		14 46	14 50			15 15		15 38	
Meadowhall	a			13 30		13 57			14 03			14 31		14 56			15 03			15 30		15 56	
Barnsley	a			14 00		14 12			14 34			15 00		15 11			15 34			16 00		16 11	
Doncaster 7	a			14 04					14 18			15 04					15 15			16 04			
Wakefield Westgate 7	a			13 46		14c28			14e46			14 46		15c29			15e46			15 46		16c27	
Leeds 10	a			14 02		14 50			15e02			15 02		15 50			16e02			16 02		16 50	
York 8	a			14 29				14 45	14 45			15 29				15 40	15 40			16 29			

		EM	XC	EM	EM	XC	EM	EM	EM	EM	XC	EM	EM	XC	EM	EM	EM	EM	XC	EM	XC	EM	EM
						R								R					R		R		
		1 ◇	1 ◇	1 ◇	1 ◇	1	1 ◇	◇		1 ◇	1 ◇	1 ◇	1 ◇	1	1 ◇	◇		1 ◇	1	1 ◇	1	◇	1 ◇
		☕	☕	☕	☕	☕	☕			☕	☕	☕	☕	☕	☕			☕	☕	☕	☕	🛒	☕
St Pancras International ⊖	d	13 25		13 30	13 55		14 00			14 25		14 30	14 55		15 00			15 25		15 30			15 55
Gatwick Airport 10 ✈	d			12 16			12b31			13 01		13 16			13b31			14 16					14 46
Luton Airport Parkway 7	d			13 35			14 22					14 35			15 22			15 35					16 05
Luton 10	d			13 53			13 54			14 24		14 53			14 54			15 48		15 53			16 18
Bedford 7	d			14 08			14 38			15 00		15 08			15 38					16 08			
Wellingborough	d			14 21			14 51					15 21			15 51					16 21			16 43
Kettering	d			14 28			14 58					15 28			15 58			16 18		16 28			
Market Harborough	d			14 38			15 08					15 38			16 08					16 38			
Leicester	a	14 35		14 55	15 05		15 24			15 38		15 56	16 04		16 23			16 40		16 55			17 13
	d	14 36		14 56	15 05		15 24		15 35	15 39		15 56	16 05		16 24		16 35	16 44		16 56			17 13
Syston	d								15 42								16 42						
Sileby	d								15 47								16 47						
Barrow Upon Soar	d								15 51								16 51						
Loughborough	d			15 07	15 17		15 34		15 55			16 07	16 16		16 34		16 55			17 07			17 24
Beeston	a			15 19								16 19								17 19			17 38
Nottingham 8	a			15 26	15 36				16 18			16 26	16 35				17 18			17 26			17 50
	d							15 42								16 42						17 42	
Langley Mill	d															16 58						17 58	
Alfreton	d							16 06								17 06						18 06	
Long Eaton	a						15 44								16 43								
Derby 10	a	15 05					15 56			16 05					16 56			17 09					
	d	15 07	15 14			15 42				16 07	16 14			16 42				17 09	17 18		17 42		
Burton-on-Trent	a	15 49					16 19			16 49								17 49					
Belper	a									16 32								17 47					
Matlock	a									16 52								18 07					
Chesterfield	d	15 27	15 33					16 18		16 27	16 33					17 18		17 31	17 37			18 18	
Dronfield	d																					18 26	
Sheffield 7	a	15 46	15 50			16 15		16 38		16 46	16 50			17 15		17 34		17 48	17 50		18 15	18 38	
Meadowhall	a		16 03			16 30		16 56		17 03	17 13			17 31		17 46		18 03	18 03		18 29	18 56	
Barnsley	a		16 34			17 02		17 11			17 34			18 02		18 11		18 34	18 34		19 02	19 15	
Doncaster 7	a		16 15			17 07					17 15			18 07		18 13		18 35	18 16		18 53		
Wakefield Westgate 7	a		16e46			16 46		17c29			17e46			17 46		18c36		18 46			18 46	19c36	
Leeds 10	a		17e02			17 02		17 50			18e02			18 02		18 55		19 02			19 02	19 57	
York 8	a	16 40	16 40			17 29				17 40	17 40			18 29		18 41		19 29	18 41		19 29		

For general notes see front of timetable
For details of catering facilities see Directory of Train Operators

b Change at Bedford
c Wakefield Kirkgate
e Change at Sheffield

London → East Midlands → Sheffield

Route Diagram - See first page of Table 53

		EM	EM	EM	XC	EM	EM	EM	XC	EM	EM	EM	EM	XC		EM	XC	EM	EM	EM	EM	XC		EM	EM	EM
		1◇		1◇	R 1	1◇	1◇	1◇	R 1	◇	1◇		1◇	R 1		1◇	R 1	◇	1◇	1◇	1◇	1◇			1◇	1◇
								A			B															
		☕		☕	☕	☕	☕	☕	☕		☕		☕	☕		☕	☕		☕	☕	☕	☕			☕	☕
St Pancras International ⊖	d	16 00		16 25		16 30	16 08	16 55			17 00		17 15			17 30			17 45	17 55	18 00				18 15	18 25
Gatwick Airport 10 ✈	d					15 16										16 01			16 11		16b11				16 41	
Luton Airport Parkway 7	d	16 22				16 36							17 39			17 34			17 56	18 00	18 23					
Luton 10	d					16 53	16 53									17 36			18 10	18 20	18 04				18 13	
Bedford 7	d					17 08	16a56									18 10					18 38				18 54	
Wellingborough	d	16 49				17 21					17 44		18 03			18 23			18 34	18 44	18 51					19 12
Kettering	d	16 57		17 14		17 28					17 51		18 10			18 33			18 41	18 53	18 58				19 12	19 19
Market Harborough	d	17 07				17 38					18 01		18 20						18 53		19 09				19 23	19 31
Leicester	a	17 23		17 39		17 56		18 04			18 21		18 35			18 57			19 08	19 18	19 25				19 38	19 48
	d	17 24	17 35	17 40		17 57		18 06			18 21	18 33	18 36			18 57			19 09	19 19	19 26			19 36	19 42	19 48
Syston	d		17 42									18 42												19 44		
Sileby	d		17 47									18 47												19 49		
Barrow Upon Soar	d		17 51									18 51												19 53		
Loughborough	d	17 34	17 55	17 51		18 08						18 55	18 46							19 32	19 37			19 57		19 59
Beeston	a					18 19					18 42									19 45				20 16		
Nottingham 8 ⛴	a		18 18			18 26					18 48	19 20							19 35	19 53				20 22		
	d									18 40								19 27	19 42							
Langley Mill	d									18 56									19 59							
Alfreton	d									19 06								19 57	20 07							
Long Eaton	a	17 43											18 55								19 46				20 03	
Derby 10	a	17 56		18 10				18 31					19 10			19 25					19 59				20 15	20 22
	d			18 10	18 18			18 32	18 42					19 14		19 25	19 42				20 11	20 14			20 18	20 22
Burton-on-Trent	a			18 49				19 19								20 06					20 26					
Belper	a							19 07																	20 42	
Matlock	a							19 27																	21 02	
Chesterfield	d			18 31	18 37			18 57	19 03	19 18				19 33		19 46	20 03	20 08	20 18			20 33			20 39	20 44
Dronfield	d																									
Sheffield 7 ⛴	a			18 47	18 50			19 13	19 17	19 39				19 50		20 02	20 17	20 27	20 33			20 50			20 53	20 59
Meadowhall ⛴	a			19 03	19 03			19 35	19 35	19 56				20 03		20 16	20 34	20 44	20 47							21 13
Barnsley	a			19 34	19 34			20 04	20 04	20 12				20 34					21 06							21 34
Doncaster 7	a			19 17	19 17			20 08	20 08	20 20				20 20		20 41	21 18	21 18								21 26
Wakefield Westgate 7	a							19 44	19 49	20c28				20e51		20 53	20 53		21 01						21 44	21 44
Leeds 10	a							20 06	20 06	20 50						21 09	21 09		21 21							22 05
York 8	a			19 44	19 44			20f34	20 34	20 46				20 46		21 35	21 35					21 48			22g06	22h06

		EM	EM	XC	EM	EM	EM		EM	XC	EM	EM	EM	EM	EM		XC	EM	EM	XC	EM	EM	EM	EM		
		1◇	1◇	1◇	1◇		1◇		1◇	1◇	1◇	1◇	1◇	1◇	1◇		1◇	1◇	1◇	1◇	1◇	1◇	1◇	1◇		
		☕	☕		☕		☕		☕		☕	☕	☕	☕	☕		☕	☕	☕	☕	☕	☕	☕	☕		
St Pancras International ⊖	d	18 30	18 55		19 00		19 25		19 30		19 55	20 00	20 25	20 30	20 55			21 00	21 25		21 30	22 00	22 25	23 15		
Gatwick Airport 10 ✈	d	16 53	17 07				18 01		18 16			18b31		19 16				19b31			20 16	20 46	21 01	21 46		
Luton Airport Parkway 7	d	18 40	18 50		19 22		19 28		19 40			20 22		20 37				21 22			21 37	22 07	22 25	23 31		
Luton 10	d	18 54	18 53		19 04		19 51		19 53			19 57		20 53				20 54			21 53	22 22	22 48	23 45		
Bedford 7	d		19 30		19 38				20 08			20 38		21 08				21 38			22 07	22 38	23 05	00 09		
Wellingborough	d	19 18	19 42		19 51				20 21		20 39	20 51		21 21				21 51			22 20	22 51	23 18	00 22		
Kettering	d	19 26			19 58		20 19		20 28			20 58	21 15	21 28				21 58	22 14		22 27	22 59	23 27	00 29		
Market Harborough	d	19 38			20 08				20 38			21 08		21 38	21 51			22 08			22 37	23 09	23 39	00 39		
Leicester	a	19 55	20 10		20 23		20 44		20 56		21 06	21 23	21 39	21 55	22 06			22 23	22 38		22 55	23 29	23 56	01 01		
	d	19 56	20 10		20 24	20 34	20 44		20 56		21 07	21 24	21 39	21 56	22 06			22 24	22 39		22 56	23 30	23 57	01 02		
Syston	d					20 41																				
Sileby	d					20 45																				
Barrow Upon Soar	d					20 50																				
Loughborough	d	20 07	20 23		20 34	20 54			21 07		21 18	21 34		22 07	22 17			22 34	22 50		23 07	23 41	00 08	01 14		
Beeston	a	20 19				21 16			21 21					22 19				22 45			23 19	23 59				
Nottingham 8 ⛴	a	20 27	20 38			21 23			21 28		21 37			22 28	22 39			22 52			23 31	00 06		01 37		
	d										21 42							22 58						01 44		
Langley Mill	d										22 01															
Alfreton	d										22 10															
Long Eaton	a				20 43							21 43						23 13								
Derby 10	a				20 56		21 12					21 56	22 08					23 26	23 07				00 34	02 05		
	d			20 42	21 03		21 13			21 42			22 09						23 09	22 49			00 36			
Burton-on-Trent	a				21 16		21 37					22 19	22 37													
Belper	a												22 32													
Matlock	a												22 52													
Chesterfield	d			21 03			21 34			22 03	22 21		22 30				23 28		23 33	23 28			00 56			
Dronfield	d																									
Sheffield 7 ⛴	a			21 17			21 49			22 17	22 38		22 46				23 54		23 49	23 54			01 13			
Meadowhall ⛴	a			21 36			22 13			22 46			23 20													
Barnsley	a			22 05			22 34			23 06			23j50													
Doncaster 7	a						22 12						00 07													
Wakefield Westgate 7	a			21 49			22 30			22s46			00 09													
Leeds 10	a			22 05			22 50			23 05			00 30				01 01			01 01						
York 8	a			22 58			23h12																			

For general notes see front of timetable
For details of catering facilities see
Directory of Train Operators

A **The Master Cutler**
B **The Robin Hood**
b Change at Bedford
c Wakefield Kirkgate
e Wakefield Kirkgate. Change at Sheffield
f Change at Sheffield
g Change at Sheffield and Doncaster
h Change at Doncaster
j Mondays to Thursdays only

London → East Midlands → Sheffield

Route Diagram - See first page of Table 53

		EM	XC	EM	XC	XC	EM	XC	EM	XC	EM	EM	EM	XC	EM	EM	EM	EM	XC	EM	EM	XC	EM
		◇	1 ◇	◇		1 ◇		R 1	◇	1 ◇		1 ◇	1 ◇	R 1	1 ◇	◇		1 ◇ ⊠	1 ◇	1 ◇	1 ◇ ⊠	1 ◇	1 ◇
St Pancras International	d											06 10	06 35		07 00			07 25		07 30	07 55		08 00
Gatwick Airport 10	d											04 30			05b00			06 16					06b24
Luton Airport Parkway 7	d											06 05	06 57		07 22			07 35					08 22
Luton 10	d											06 33			07 04			07 50		07 53			07 57
Bedford 7	d											06 48			07 38					08 08			08 38
Wellingborough	d											07 01	07 21		07 51					08 21			08 51
Kettering	d											07 08	07 28		07 58					08 28			08 58
Market Harborough	d											07 18	07 38		08 08					08 38			09 08
Leicester	a											07 35	07 55		08 23			08 38		08 55	09 04		09 23
	d				06 30		06 40				07 24	07 35	07 56		08 24		08 35	08 39		08 56	09 05		09 24
Syston	d						06 47				07 31						08 42						
Sileby	d						06 52				07 38						08 47						
Barrow Upon Soar	d						06 56				07 43						08 51						
Loughborough	d				06 45		07 00				07 47	07 46	08 07		08 34		08 55	08 50		09 07	09 16		09 34
Beeston	a						07 21				08 10		08 19							09 19			
Nottingham 8	a						07 30				08 20		08 29				09 20			09 26	09 36		
	d	05 19		06 24					07 38							08 42							
Langley Mill	d			06 43					07 54							08 58							
Alfreton	d			06 51					08 02							09 06							
Long Eaton	a				06 56							07 59			08 43								09 43
Derby 10	a				07 10							08 12			08 56			09 09					09 56
	d		06 39			07 14		07 42		08 14		08 16		08 42				09 09	09 14			09 42	
Burton-on-Trent	a											08 37			09c19			09 49					10 19
Belper	a											08 25											
Matlock	a											08e59											
Chesterfield	d	05 56	06 58	07 05		07 41		08 04	08 14	08 33		08 40		09 04		09a18		09 30	09 41			10 09	
Dronfield	d																						
Sheffield 7	a	06 18	07 27	07 35		08 06		08 36	08 40	09 06		09 14		09 36				09 55	10 06			10 36	
Meadowhall	a	06 33	07 41	07 57		08 22		08 56	08 56	09 21		09 41		09 58				10 13				10 56	
Barnsley	a	07 00	08 00	08 11		09 00		09 11	09 11			10 00		10 13				10 34				11 11	
Doncaster 7	a	07 22	08 24	08 24		09 12		09 19	09 35			10 12		10 15				10 40				11 15	
Wakefield Westgate 7	a	07 19	08f28	08g28		08 46				09 46		09 46		10 51				10g51	10 46			11f29	
Leeds 10	a	07 44	08h51	08 51		09 02		09h50	09 50	10 02		10 02		10h50				11 27	11 02			11h50	
York 8	a	08j10	08 48	08 48		09 33		09 48		10 29		10 29		10 40				11j37	11 29			11 43	

		EM	EM	EM	XC	EM	EM	XC	EM	EM	EM	EM	XC	EM	EM	XC	EM	EM	EM	XC	EM	EM	EM
		◇		1 ◇ ⊠	1 ◇	1 ◇	1 ◇ ⊠	1 ◇	1 ◇	◇		1 ◇ ⊠	1 ◇	1 ◇	1 ◇ ⊠	1 ◇	1 ◇	◇	1 ◇ ⊠	1 ◇		1 ◇	1 ◇
St Pancras International	d			08 25		08 30	08 55		09 00			09 25		09 30	09 55		10 00		10 25			10 30	10 55
Gatwick Airport 10	d			06 46		07 01			07b01			07 37		08 01			08b22					09 16	
Luton Airport Parkway 7	d					08 36			09 22			09 25		09 40			10 22					10 35	
Luton 10	d			08 08		08 53			08 54			09 48		09 53			09 56					10 53	
Bedford 7	d			09 00		09 08			09 38					10 08			10 38					11 08	
Wellingborough	d					09 21			09 51					10 21			10 51					11 21	
Kettering	d					09 28			09 58					10 28			10 58					11 28	
Market Harborough	d					09 38			10 08					10 38			11 08					11 38	
Leicester	a			09 38		09 55	10 04		10 23			10 36		10 55	11 03		11 23		11 34			11 55	12 04
	d		09 36	09 39		09 56	10 05		10 24		10 35	10 39		10 56	11 05		11 24		11 35		11 35	11 56	12 05
Syston	d		09 43								10 42										11 42		
Sileby	d		09 48								10 47										11 47		
Barrow Upon Soar	d		09 52								10 51										11 51		
Loughborough	d		09 56			10 07			10 34		10 55			11 07	11 16		11 34				11 55	12 07	
Beeston	a					10 19								11 20								12 19	
Nottingham 8	a		10 20			10 26	10 36				11 20			11 27	11 36						12 19	12 26	12 35
	d	09 40								10 42								11 42					
Langley Mill	d	09 57								10 58													
Alfreton	d	10 05								11 06								12 04					
Long Eaton	a								10 43								11 43						
Derby 10	a			10 05					10 56			11 04					11 56		12 05				
	d			10 07	10 14			10 42				11 06	11 14			11 42			12 07	12 14			
Burton-on-Trent	a			10 49					11 19			11 49					12 19		12 49				
Belper	a			10 38															12 38				
Matlock	a			10 58															12 58				
Chesterfield	d	10a18		10 27	10 40			11 04		11a18		11 27	11 39			12 02		12a18	12 31	12 40			
Dronfield	d																						
Sheffield 7	a			10 55	11 06			11 36				11 55	12 06			12 36			12 55	13 06			
Meadowhall	a			11 13	11 20			11 56				12 13	12 20			12 56			13 13	13 20			
Barnsley	a			11 34	12 00			12 11				12 34	13 00			13 11			13 34	14 00			
Doncaster 7	a			11 40	12 11			12 15				12 38	13 11			13 22			13 38	14 14			
Wakefield Westgate 7	a				11 46			12f29					12 46			13f29				13 46			
Leeds 10	a				12 02			12h50					13 02			13h50				14 02			
York 8	a				12 34			12 43					13 29			13 46				14 29			

For general notes see front of timetable
For details of catering facilities see Directory of Train Operators

- b Change at Bedford
- c Mondays arr. 0917
- e Change at Derby
- f Wakefield Kirkgate. Change at Sheffield
- g Wakefield Kirkgate
- h Change at Sheffield
- j Change at Sheffield and Doncaster

London → East Midlands → Sheffield

Route Diagram - See first page of Table 53

		XC	EM		EM	XC	EM	EM	EM	EM		XC	EM	EM	EM	EM	XC		EM	EM	XC	EM	EM	EM		EM
		1 ◇ ☕	1 ◇ ☕		◇	1 ◇ ☕		1 ◇ ☕	1 ◇ ☕	1 ◇ ☕		R 1 ☕	1 ◇ ☕	◇		1 ◇ ☕	1 ◇ ☕		1 ◇ ☕	1 ◇ ☕	R 1 ☕	1 ◇ ☕	◇			1 ◇ ☕
St Pancras International ⊖	d		11 00					11 25	11 30	11 55			12 00			12 25			12 30	12 55		13 00				13 25
Gatwick Airport 10 ✈	d		09b31						10 16				10b31						11 16			11b31				
Luton Airport Parkway 7	d		11 22						11 35				12 22						12 35			13 22				
Luton 10	d		10 54						11 53				11 54						12 53			12 54				
Bedford 7	d		11 38						12 08				12 38						13 08			13 38				
Wellingborough	d		11 51						12 21				12 51						13 21			13 51				
Kettering	d		11 58						12 28				12 58						13 28			13 58				
Market Harborough	d		12 08						12 38				13 08						13 38			14 08				
Leicester	a		12 23					12 34	12 55	13 04			13 23			13 34			13 55	14 04		14 23				14 35
	d		12 24				12 35	12 36	12 56	13 05			13 24		13 35	13 36			13 56	14 05		14 24		14 35		14 36
Syston	d						12 42								13 42									14 42		
Sileby	d						12 47								13 47									14 47		
Barrow Upon Soar	d						12 51								13 51									14 51		
Loughborough	d		12 34				12 55		13 07	13 15			13 34		13 55				14 07			14 34		14 55		
Beeston	a								13 19										14 19							
Nottingham 8	a						13 18		13 26	13 36					14 21				14 26	14 36				15 18		
	d				12 42									13 45									14 42			
Langley Mill	d				12 58																		14 58			
Alfreton	d				13 06									14 07									15 06			
Long Eaton	a		12 43										13 43									14 43				
Derby 10	a		12 56					13 05					13 56			14 05						14 56				15 05
	d	12 42				13 14		13 07				13 42				14 07	14 14				14 42					15 07
Burton-on-Trent	a		13 19					13 49					14 19									15 19				15 49
Belper	a															14 37										
Matlock	a															14 57										
Chesterfield	d	13 03			13a18	13 40		13 27				14 04		14a19		14 30	14 41				15 01		15a17			15 31
Dronfield	d																									
Sheffield 7	a	13 36				14 06		13 55				14 36				14 55	15 06				15 36					15 55
Meadowhall	a	13 56						14 13				14 56				15 13	15 20				15 56					16 13
Barnsley	a	14 11						14 34				15 11				15 34	16 00				16 11					16 34
Doncaster 7	a	14 18						14 38				15 15				15 38	16 12				16 15					16 38
Wakefield Westgate 7	a	14c28				14 46		14e51				15c29					15 46				16c27					
Leeds 10	a	14f50				15 02		15 27				15f50					16 02				16f50					
York 8	a	14 45				15 29		15g26				15 40					16 29				16 40					

		XC	EM	EM	XC	EM	EM		EM	EM	XC	EM	EM	XC		EM	EM	EM	EM	XC	EM		XC	EM	EM	EM
		R 1 ☕	1 ◇ ☕	1 ◇ ☕	R 1 ☕	1 ◇ ☕	◇			1 ◇ ☕	R 1 ☕	1 ◇ ☕	1 ◇ ☕	R 1 ☕		1 ◇ ☕	◇		1 ◇ ☕	R 1 ☕	1 ◇ ☕		R 1 ☕	◇	1 ◇ ☕	1 ◇ ☕
St Pancras International ⊖	d		13 30	13 55		14 00				14 25		14 30	14 55			15 00			15 25		15 30				15 55	16 00
Gatwick Airport 10 ✈	d		12 16			12b31				13 01		13 16				13b31			14 16						14 46	
Luton Airport Parkway 7	d		13 35			14 22						14 35				15 22			15 35						16 05	16 22
Luton 10	d		13 53			13 54				14 24		14 53				14 54			15 48		15 53				16 18	
Bedford 7	d		14 08			14 38				15 00		15 08				15 38					16 08					
Wellingborough	d		14 21			14 51						15 21				15 51					16 21				16 43	16 49
Kettering	d		14 28			14 58						15 28				15 58			16 18		16 28					16 57
Market Harborough	d		14 38			15 08						15 38				16 08					16 38					17 07
Leicester	a		14 55	15 05		15 24				15 38		15 56	16 04			16 23			16 40		16 55				17 13	17 23
	d		14 56	15 05		15 24			15 35	15 39		15 56	16 05			16 24		16 35	16 42		16 56				17 13	17 24
Syston	d								15 42									16 42								
Sileby	d								15 47									16 47								
Barrow Upon Soar	d								15 51									16 51								
Loughborough	d		15 07	15 17		15 34			15 55			16 07	16 16			16 34		16 55			17 07				17 24	17 34
Beeston	a		15 19									16 19									17 19				17 38	
Nottingham 8	a		15 26	15 36					16 18			16 26	16 35					17 18			17 26				17 50	
	d						15 42										16 42							17 42		
Langley Mill	d																16 58							17 58		
Alfreton	d						16 06										17 06							18 06		
Long Eaton	a					15 44										16 43										17 43
Derby 10	a					15 56				16 05						16 56			17 05							17 56
	d	15 14			15 42					16 07	16 14			16 42					17 06	17 14			17 42			
Burton-on-Trent	a					16 19				16 49						17 19			17 49							18 19
Belper	a									16 32									17 47							
Matlock	a									16 52									18 07							
Chesterfield	d	15 40			16h08		16a18			16 27	16 39			17 02			17a18		17 30	17 40			18 11	18a18		
Dronfield	d																									
Sheffield 7	a	16 06			16 36					16 55	17 06			17 36					17 55	18 06			18 40			
Meadowhall	a	16 20			16 56					17 13	17 20			17 59					18 13	18 20			18 56			
Barnsley	a	17 02			17 11					17 34	18 02			18 14					18 34	19 02			19 15			
Doncaster 7	a	17 11			17 15					17 38	18 13			18 16					18 53	18 53			19 17			
Wakefield Westgate 7	a	16 46			17c29						17 46			18c36					18 46	18 46			19c36			
Leeds 10	a	17 02			17f50						18 02			18f55					19 02	19 02			19f56			
York 8	a	17 29			17 40						18 29			18 41					19 29	19 29			19 44			

For general notes see front of timetable
For details of catering facilities see Directory of Train Operators

b Change at Bedford
c Wakefield Kirkgate. Change at Sheffield
e Wakefield Kirkgate
f Change at Sheffield
g Change at Sheffield and Doncaster
h Arr. 1600

Table 53

Mondays to Fridays

from 8 September

London → East Midlands → Sheffield

Route Diagram - See first page of Table 53

	EM	EM	XC	EM	EM	EM	XC	EM	EM	EM	EM	XC	EM	XC	EM	EM	EM	EM	XC	EM	EM	EM	EM
		1 ◇	R 1	1 ◇	1 ◇	1 ◇	R 1	◇	1 ◇		1 ◇	R 1	1 ◇	R 1	◇	1 ◇	1 ◇	1 ◇	1 ◇		1 ◇	1 ◇	1 ◇
						A			B														
		☕	☕	☕	☕	☕	☕		☕		☕	☕	☕	☕		☕	☕	☕	☕		☕	☕	☕
St Pancras International ⊖ d		16 25		16 30	16 08	16 55			17 00		17 15		17 30			17 45	17 55	18 00			18 15	18 25	18 30
Gatwick Airport 10 ✈ d				15 16									16 01			16 11		16b11			16 41		16 53
Luton Airport Parkway 7 d				16 36							17 39		17 34			17 56	18 00	18 23					18 40
Luton 10 d				16 53	16 53								17 36			18 10	18 20	18 04			18 13		18 54
Bedford 7 d				17 08	16a56								18 10					18 38			18 54		
Wellingborough d				17 21					17 44		18 03		18 23			18 34	18 44	18 51				19 12	19 18
Kettering d		17 14		17 28					17 51		18 10		18 33			18 41	18 53	18 58			19 12	19 19	19 26
Market Harborough d				17 38					18 01		18 20					18 53		19 09			19 23	19 31	19 38
Leicester a		17 39		17 56		18 04			18 21		18 35		18 57			19 08	19 18	19 25			19 38	19 48	19 55
d	17 35	17 40		17 57		18 06			18 21	18 33	18 36		18 57			19 09	19 19	19 26		19 36	19 42	19 48	19 56
Syston d	17 42									18 42										19 44			
Sileby d	17 47									18 47										19 49			
Barrow Upon Soar d	17 51									18 51										19 53			
Loughborough d	17 55	17 51		18 08						18 55	18 46						19 32	19 37		19 57		19 59	20 07
Beeston a				18 19					18 42								19 45			20 16			20 19
Nottingham 8 a	18 18			18 26					18 48	19 20						19 35	19 53			20 22			20 27
d								18 40							19 27	19 42							
Langley Mill d								18 56								19 59							
Alfreton d								19 06							19 57	20 07							
Long Eaton a											18 55							19 46			20 03		
Derby 10 a		18 10				18 36					19 10		19 25					19 59			20 15	20 22	
d		18 10	18 14			18 36	18 42					19 20	19 25	19 42				20 11	20 14			20 25	
Burton-on-Trent a		18 49				19 19							20 06					20 26					
Belper a						19 07															20 42		
Matlock a						19 27															21 02		
Chesterfield d		18 31	18 41			19 00	19 06	19a22				19 41	19 50	20 07	20a11	20 20			20 38			20 57	
Dronfield d																							
Sheffield 7 a		18 54	19 12			19 24	19 36					20 06	20 17	20 36		20 49			21 11			21 25	
Meadowhall a		19 13	19 30			19 43							20 34			21 13			21 35			21 47	
Barnsley a		19 34				20 04										21 34						22 05	
Doncaster 7 a		19 41	20 04			20 11	20 20						21 18			21 40						21 57	
Wakefield Westgate 7 a		19 49	19 49			20 30						20 53	21 21			21 26			21 49			22 17	
Leeds 10 a		20 06	20 06			20 52						21 09	21 46			21 52			22 05			22 40	
York 8 a		20 34	20 34			21c01	20 46					21 35	21 48	21 48					22 58			23e12	

	EM	XC	EM	EM	EM	EM	XC	EM	EM	EM	EM	EM	XC	EM	EM	EM	EM	EM	EM
	1 ◇	1 ◇	1 ◇		1 ◇	1 ◇	1 ◇	1 ◇	1 ◇	1 ◇	1 ◇	1 ◇	1 ◇	1 ◇	1 ◇	1 ◇	1 ◇	1 ◇	1 ◇
	☕		☕		☕	☕		☕	☕	☕	☕	☕	☕	☕	☕	☕	☕	☕	☕
St Pancras International ⊖ d	18 55		19 00		19 25	19 30		19 55	20 00	20 25	20 30	20 55		21 00	21 25	21 30	22 00	22 25	23 15
Gatwick Airport 10 ✈ d	17 07				18 01	18 16			18b31		19 16			19b31		20 16	20 46	21 01	21 46
Luton Airport Parkway 7 d	18 50		19 22		19 28	19 40			20 22		20 37			21 22		21 37	22 07	22 25	23 31
Luton 10 d	18 53		19 04		19 51	19 53			19 57		20 53			20 54		21 53	22 22	22 48	23 45
Bedford 7 d	19 30		19 38			20 08			20 38		21 08			21 38		22 07	22 38	23 05	00 09
Wellingborough d	19 42		19 51			20 21		20 39	20 51		21 21			21 51		22 20	22 51	23 18	00 22
Kettering d			19 58		20 19	20 28			20 58	21 15	21 28			21 58	22 14	22 27	22 59	23 27	00 29
Market Harborough d			20 08			20 38			21 08		21 38	21 51		22 08		22 37	23 09	23 39	00 39
Leicester a	20 10		20 23		20 44	20 56		21 06	21 23	21 39	21 55	22 06		22 23	22 38	22 55	23 29	23 56	01 01
d	20 10		20 24	20 34	20 44	20 56		21 07	21 24	21 39	21 56	22 06		22 24	22 39	22 56	23 30	23 57	01 02
Syston d				20 41															
Sileby d				20 45															
Barrow Upon Soar d				20 50															
Loughborough d	20 23		20 34	20 54		21 07		21 18	21 34		22 07	22 17		22 34	22 50	23 07	23 41	00 08	01 14
Beeston a				21 16		21 21					22 19			22 45		23 19	23 59		
Nottingham 8 a	20 38			21 23		21 28		21 37			22 28	22 39		22 52		23 31	00 06		01 37
d								21 42						22 58					01 44
Langley Mill d								22 01											
Alfreton d								22 10											
Long Eaton a			20 43						21 43					23 13					
Derby 10 a			20 56		21 12				21 56	22 08				23 26	23 07			00 34	02 05
d		20 42	21 03		21 13		21 42			22 09			22 49		23 09			00 36	
Burton-on-Trent a			21 16		21 37				22 19	23 25									
Belper a										22 32									
Matlock a										22 52									
Chesterfield d		21 05			21 34		22 04	22 21		22 30			23 28		23 35			00 56	
Dronfield d																			
Sheffield 7 a		21 38			22 06		22 36	22 54		23 04			23 54		00 10			01 22	
Meadowhall a		22 13			22 21					23 20									
Barnsley a		22 34			23 06					23f50									
Doncaster 7 a		22 42			23 04					00 07									
Wakefield Westgate 7 a					22 46		23s17			00 09									
Leeds 10 a					23 07		23 39			00 30			01 01						
York 8 a		22 57			00c39														

For general notes see front of timetable
For details of catering facilities see Directory of Train Operators

A **The Master Cutler**
B **The Robin Hood**
b Change at Bedford
c Change at Sheffield and Doncaster
e Change at Doncaster
f Mondays to Thursdays only

until 6 September

London → East Midlands → Sheffield

Route Diagram - See first page of Table 53

	EM	EM	XC	EM	XC	EM	XC	EM	XC	EM	EM	XC	EM	EM	XC	EM	EM	EM	EM	XC	EM
	◇	1◇ ⊡	1◇ ⊡	◇	1◇ ⊡		1◇ ⊡	◇	1◇ ⊡		1◇ ⊡	1◇ ⊡	◇	1◇ ⊡	1◇ ⊡		1◇ ⊡	1◇ ⊡	1◇ ⊡	1◇ ⊡	1◇ ⊡
St Pancras International ⊖ d											06 20			07 00			07 25	07 30	07 55		08 00
Gatwick Airport 10 ✈ d											04 30			05b25			06 01				06b31
Luton Airport Parkway 7 d											06 05			07 25			07 20	07 36			08 22
Luton 10 d											06 44			06 56			07 49	07 53			07 56
Bedford 7 d											07 01			07 41				08 08			08 38
Wellingborough d											07 16			07 53				08 21			08 51
Kettering d											07 24			08 01				08 28			08 58
Market Harborough d											07 36			08 11				08 38			09 08
Leicester a											07 54			08 27			08 39	08 55	09 04		09 23
d						06 40				07 28	07 54			08 27		08 32	08 40	08 56	09 05		09 25
Syston d						06 47				07 39						08 39					
Sileby d						06 52				07 45						08 44					
Barrow Upon Soar d						06 56				07 49						08 48					
Loughborough d						07 00				07 53	08 06			08 38		08 52	08 51	09 07	09 16		09 34
Beeston a						07 20								08 48				09 19			
Nottingham 8 a						07 27				08 16				08 56		09 16		09 26	09 38		
d	05 23			06 34				07 42					08 42								
Langley Mill d				06 50				07 58					08 59								
Alfreton d				06 58				08 06					09 07								
Long Eaton a											08 21										09 43
Derby 10 a											08 34						09 15				09 56
d		06 30	06 39		07 14		07 42		08 14		08 34	08 42			09 14		09 18			09 42	
Burton-on-Trent a											09 19						09 49				10 21
Belper a																	10 01				
Matlock a																	10 21				
Chesterfield d	05 54	06 49		07 10	07 33		08 01	08 18	08 33		08 56	09 01	09 18		09 33		09 38				
Dronfield d				07 17	07 39			08 25													
Sheffield 7 a	06 10	07 05	07 09	07 31	07 50		08 17	08 38	08 50		09 13	09 17	09 38		09 50		09 56			10 15	
Meadowhall a	06 23	07 23	07 23	07 46	08 13		08 41	08 56	09 03		09 28	09 32	09 56				10 13			10 30	
Barnsley a	07 00	07 43	07 43	08 11	08 34		09 00	09 11	09 34			10 00	10 11				10 34			11 00	
Doncaster 7 a	06 57		08 02	08 20	08 23		09 09		09 21		09 52	10 05			10 18		10 40			11 04	
Wakefield Westgate 7 a	07 19		07 36	08c28			08 46	09c29				09 46	10c29							10 46	
Leeds 10 a	07 44		07 52	08 51			09 02	09 50				10 02	10 50							11 02	
York 8 a			08 24	08 50	08 50		09 30	09 45	09 45		10 16	10 29	10 45		10 45					11 31	

	EM	EM	EM	XC	EM	EM	XC	EM	EM	EM	EM	XC	EM	EM	XC	EM	EM	EM	EM	XC	EM
	◇		1◇ ⊡	1◇ ⊡	1◇ ⊡	1◇ ⊡	1◇ ⊡	1◇ ⊡	◇		1◇ ⊡	1◇ ⊡	1◇ ⊡	1◇ ⊠ ⫫	R 1 ⊡	1◇ ⊡	◇		1◇ ⊠ ⫫	1◇ ⊡	1◇ ⊡
St Pancras International ⊖ d			08 25		08 30	08 55		09 00			09 25		09 30	09 55		10 00			10 25		10 30
Gatwick Airport 10 ✈ d			07 01		07 16			07b31			08 16					08b31					09 16
Luton Airport Parkway 7 d					08 35			09 22			09 35					10 22					10 35
Luton 10 d			08 24		08 53			08 54			09 49		09 53			09 54					10 53
Bedford 7 d			09 00		09 08			09 38					10 08			10 38					11 08
Wellingborough d					09 21			09 51					10 21			10 51					11 21
Kettering d					09 28			09 58					10 28			10 58					11 28
Market Harborough d					09 38			10 08					10 38			11 08					11 38
Leicester a			09 38		09 55	10 04		10 23			10 38		10 55	11 04		11 23			11 34		11 56
d		09 30	09 39		09 56	10 05		10 25		10 30	10 39		10 56	11 05		11 24		11 30	11 36		11 57
Syston d		09 39								10 39								11 39			
Sileby d		09 44								10 44								11 44			
Barrow Upon Soar d		09 48								10 48								11 48			
Loughborough d		09 52			10 07			10 34		10 52			11 07	11 16		11 34		11 52			12 08
Beeston a					10 19								11 19								12 19
Nottingham 8 a		10 18			10 27	10 34				11 17			11 27	11 35				12 16			12 27
d	09 42								10 42								11 42				12 45 →
Langley Mill d	09 59																				
Alfreton d	10 07								11 04								12 04				
Long Eaton a								10 43								11 44					
Derby 10 a			10 05					10 56			11 05					11 56			12 05		
d			10 07	10 14			10 42				11 07	11 14			11 42				12 07	12 14	
Burton-on-Trent a			10 49					11 19			11 49					12 20			12 49		
Belper a											12 04										
Matlock a											12 24										
Chesterfield d	10 18		10 27	10 33					11 18		11 27	11 33					12 18		12 27	12 33	
Dronfield d																					
Sheffield 7 a	10 38		10 46	10 50			11 15		11 38		11 46	11 50			12 15		12 38		12 46	12 50	
Meadowhall a	10 56			11 03			11 30		11 56			12 03			12 30		12 56			13 03	
Barnsley a	11 11			11 34			12 00		12 11			12 34			13 00		13 11			13 34	
Doncaster 7 a				11 16			12 04					12 15			13 04					13 19	
Wakefield Westgate 7 a	11c29						11 46		12c29			12e46			12 46		13c29				
Leeds 10 a	11 50						12 02		12 50			13e03			13 02		13 50				
York 8 a			11 45	11 45			12 29				12 43	12 43			13 31				13 45	13 45	

For general notes see front of timetable
For details of catering facilities see Directory of Train Operators

b Change at Bedford
c Wakefield Kirkgate
e Change at Sheffield

Due to Engineering Operations, services from Saturday 13 September on this Table had not been confirmed at time of going to press. These services will be issued in a special Supplement as soon as exact timings have been confirmed

until 6 September

London → East Midlands → Sheffield

Route Diagram - See first page of Table 53

		EM 1 ◇	XC 1 ◇	EM 1 ◇	EM ◇	EM		EM 1 ◇	XC 1 ◇	EM 1 ◇	EM 1 ◇	EM 1 ◇		XC 1 ◇	EM 1 ◇	EM ◇	EM	EM 1 ◇		XC R 1	EM 1 ◇	EM 1 ◇	XC R 1	EM 1 ◇		EM ◇
St Pancras International ⊖	d	10 55		11 00				11 25		11 30		11 55			12 00			12 25			12 30	12 55		13 00		
Gatwick Airport 10 ✈	d			09b31						10 16					10b31						11 16			11b31		
Luton Airport Parkway 7	d			11 22						11 35					12 22						12 35			13 22		
Luton 10	d			10 54						11 53					11 54						12 53			12 54		
Bedford 7	d			11 38						12 08					12 38						13 08			13 38		
Wellingborough	d			11 51						12 21					12 51						13 21			13 51		
Kettering	d			11 58						12 28					12 58						13 28			13 58		
Market Harborough	d			12 08						12 38					13 08						13 38			14 08		
Leicester	a	12 03		12 23				12 34		12 56		13 06			13 23			13 34			13 55	14 04		14 23		
	d	12 05		12 24		12 30		12 36		12 57		13 07			13 24		13 30	13 36			13 56	14 05		14 24		
Syston	d					12 39											13 39									
Sileby	d					12 44											13 44									
Barrow Upon Soar	d					12 48											13 48									
Loughborough	d			12 34		12 52				13 08		13 19			13 34		13 52				14 07			14 34		
Beeston	a									13 19											14 19					
Nottingham 8	a	12 34				13 18				13 25	←	13 36					14 18				14 25	14 37				
	d				12 47						12 45					13 42										14 42
Langley Mill	d				13 03						13 22					13 59										14 59
Alfreton	d				13 11						13 30					14 07										15 07
Long Eaton	a			12 43											13 43									14 43		
Derby 10	a			12 56				13 05							13 56			14 05						14 56		
	d		12 42					13 07	13 14					13 42				14 07		14 14			14 42			
Burton-on-Trent	a			13 19				13 49							14 19			14 49						15 19		
Belper	a							13 42										15 00								
Matlock	a							14 02										15 20								
Chesterfield	d				13 22			13 28	13 33		13 41					14 18		14 27		14 33						15 18
Dronfield	d										13 49															
Sheffield 7	a		13 15		13 39			13 47	13 50		14 00			14 15		14 38		14 46		14 50			15 15			15 38
Meadowhall	a		13 30		13 57			14 03			14 13			14 30		14 56		15 03		15 03			15 30			15 56
Barnsley	a		14 00		14 12						14 34			15 00		15 11		15 34		15 34			16 00			16 11
Doncaster 7	a		14 04						14 15		14 38			15 04				15 15		15 15			16 04			
Wakefield Westgate 7	a		13 46		14c28									14 46		15c29		15 46					15 46			16c27
Leeds 10	a		14 02		14 50									15 02		15 50		16 02					16 02			16 50
York 8	a		14 29					14 46	14 46					15 29				15 43		15 43			16 29			

		EM	EM 1 ◇	XC 1 ◇	EM 1 ◇	EM 1 ◇		XC R 1	EM 1 ◇	EM ◇	EM	EM 1 ◇		XC 1 ◇	EM 1 ◇	EM 1 ◇	XC R 1	EM 1 ◇		EM ◇	EM	EM 1 ◇	XC 1 ◇	EM 1 ◇		EM 1 ◇
St Pancras International ⊖	d		13 25		13 30	13 55			14 00			14 25			14 30	14 55		15 00				15 25		15 30		15 55
Gatwick Airport 10 ✈	d				12 16				12b31			13 01			13 16			13b31				14 16				14 46
Luton Airport Parkway 7	d				13 35				14 22						14 35			15 22				15 35				16 05
Luton 10	d				13 53				13 54			14 24			14 53			14 54				15 48		15 53		16 18
Bedford 7	d				14 08				14 38			15 00			15 08			15 38						16 08		
Wellingborough	d				14 21				14 51						15 21			15 51						16 21		
Kettering	d				14 28				14 58						15 28			15 58						16 28		
Market Harborough	d				14 38				15 08						15 38			16 08						16 38		
Leicester	a		14 34		14 58	15 05			15 23			15 36			15 55	16 03		16 23				16 38		16 55		17 06
	d	14 30	14 36		14 58	15 05			15 24		15 30	15 39			15 56	16 05		16 24			16 30	16 39		16 56		17 10
Syston	d	14 39									15 39										16 39					
Sileby	d	14 44									15 44										16 44					
Barrow Upon Soar	d	14 48									15 48										16 48					
Loughborough	d	14 52			15 10	15 16			15 34		15 52				16 07			16 34			16 52			17 07		
Beeston	a				15 19										16 20									17 19		
Nottingham 8	a	15 18			15 26	15 34					16 16				16 26	16 36					17 16			17 28		17 34
	d									15 44										16 42						
Langley Mill	d																			16 58						
Alfreton	d									16 06										17 06						
Long Eaton	a								15 43									16 43								
Derby 10	a		15 05						15 56			16 05						16 56				17 05				
	d		15 07	15 14				15 42				16 07		16 14			16 42					17 07	17 14			
Burton-on-Trent	a		15 49						16 19			16 49						17 19				17 49				
Belper	a											16 34										18 00				
Matlock	a											16 54										18 20				
Chesterfield	d		15 27	15 33						16 18		16 27		16 33						17 18		17 27	17 33			
Dronfield	d																									
Sheffield 7	a		15 46	15 50				16 15		16 38		16 46		16 50			17 15			17 34		17 43	17 50			
Meadowhall	a			16 03				16 30		16 56				17 03			17 31			17 46		17 56	18 03			
Barnsley	a			16 34				17 02		17 11				17 34			18 02					18 11	18 34			
Doncaster 7	a			16 15				17 08						17 19			18 07			18 10			18 21			
Wakefield Westgate 7	a			16e46				16 46		17c29				17e46			17 46			18f35		18c36				
Leeds 10	a			17e02				17 02		17 50				18e02			18 02			18f53		18 55				
York 8	a		16 44	16 44				17 31				17 46		17 46			18 29					18 46	18 46			

For general notes see front of timetable
For details of catering facilities see Directory of Train Operators

b Change at Bedford
c Wakefield Kirkgate
e Change at Sheffield
f Change at Sheffield and Doncaster

Due to Engineering Operations, services from Saturday 13 September on this Table had not been confirmed at time of going to press. These services will be issued in a special Supplement as soon as exact timings have been confirmed

until 6 September

London → East Midlands → Sheffield

Route Diagram - See first page of Table 53

	XC	EM	EM	XC	EM	EM	EM	EM	XC	EM	EM	XC	EM	EM	EM	XC	EM	EM	EM	EM	EM
	1 ◇ ☕	1 ◇ ☕	◇	1 ◇ ☕		1 ◇ ☕	1 ◇ ☕	1 ◇ ☕	R 1 ☕	1 ◇ ☕	◇	1 ◇ ☕		1 ◇ ☕	1 ◇ ☕	1 ◇ ☕	◇	1 ◇ ☕	1 ◇ ☕	1 ◇ ☕	
St Pancras International ⊖ d		16 00				16 25	16 30	16 55		17 00				17 30	17 40			17 55		18 00	
Gatwick Airport 10 ✈ d		14b31					15 16			15b31				16 16	16 16			16 46		16b31	
Luton Airport Parkway 7 d		16 22					16 35			17 22				17 35	17 35			18 05		18 22	
Luton 10 d		15 54					16 53			16 54				17 53				18 19		17 54	
Bedford 7 d		16 38					17 08			17 38				18 08	18 19					18 38	
Wellingborough d		16 51					17 21	17 39		17 51				18 21	18 33					18 51	
Kettering d		16 58				17 15	17 28	17 47		17 58				18 28	18 41			18 49		18 58	
Market Harborough d		17 08					17 38	17 57		18 08				18 38				19 00		19 08	
Leicester a		17 23				17 39	17 56	18 17		18 24				18 55	19 05			19 21		19 26	
d		17 24			17 30	17 39	17 56	18 17		18 24			18 30	18 56	19 06			19 22		19 27	19 29
Syston d					17 39								18 39								19 39
Sileby d					17 44								18 44								19 44
Barrow Upon Soar d					17 48								18 48								19 48
Loughborough d		17 34			17 52	17 51	18 07			18 34			18 52	19 07				19 33		19 37	19 52
Beeston a							18 19							19 19							20 13
Nottingham 8 a					18 16		18 26	18 41					19 16	19 26				19 52	←		20 19
d			17 42								18 42			19 37 →			19 28		19 37		
Langley Mill d			17 58								18 59								19 53		
Alfreton d			18 06								19 07						19 52		20 02		
Long Eaton a		17 43								18 43										19 46	
Derby 10 a		17 54				18 16				18 56					19 31					19 57	
d	17 42	18 01		18 14		18 18			18 42			19 14			19 32	19 42				19 58	
Burton-on-Trent a		18 15				18 49				19 21					20 07					20 19	
Belper a										19 33										20 06	
Matlock a										19 53											
Chesterfield d			18 18	18 33		18 39			19 01		19 18	19 33			19 53	20 01	20 08		20 14	20 21	
Dronfield d			18 26																		
Sheffield 7 a	18 15		18 38	18 50		18 59			19 16		19 39	19 50			20 08	20 18	20 25		20 28	20 38	
Meadowhall a	18 29		18 56	19 06		19 13			19 35		19 56	20 03			20 20	20 36			20 43	20 53	
Barnsley a	19 02		19 15			19 34			20 04		20 12								21 06	21 14	
Doncaster 7 a	18 53			19 18		19 29			20 09			20 16			20 36						
Wakefield Westgate 7 a	18 46		19c36	19e46		19 59			19 46		20c28				20 53	20 48				21e34	
Leeds 10 a	19 02		19 57	20e02		20 22			20 02		20 50				21 15	21 05				21e54	
York 8 a	19 32		19 49	19 49		20e29			20 29		20 43	20 43				21 35					

	EM	XC	EM	EM	XC	EM	EM	EM	EM	XC	EM	EM	EM	EM	EM	EM	EM	EM	EM	EM
	1 ◇ ☕	1 ◇ ☕	1 ◇ ☕	1 ◇ ☕	R 1 ☕	1 ◇ ☕		1 ◇ ☕	1 ◇ ☕	1 ◇ ☕	1 ◇ ☕	1 ◇ ☕	1 ◇ ☕	1 ◇ ☕	1 ◇ ☕	1 ◇ ☕	1 ◇ ☕	🚌	1 ◇ ☕	1 ◇ ☕
St Pancras International ⊖ d	18 25		18 30	18 55		19 00		19 25	19 30		19 55	20 00	20 25	20 30	20 55	21 00	21 25		21 35	22 10
Gatwick Airport 10 ✈ d			17 16	17 46		17b31		18 16				18b31		19 16		19b31				21 01
Luton Airport Parkway 7 d			18 40	19 05		19 22		19 37	19 41			20 22		20 41		21 22				22 27
Luton 10 d			18 53	19 18		18 54		19 49	19 53			19 54		20 53		20 54				22 45
Bedford 7 d			19 08			19 38			20 08			20 38		21 08		21 38				23 08
Wellingborough d			19 21	19 42		19 51			20 21		20 39	20 51		21 21		21 51			22 20	23 21
Kettering d	19 15		19 28			19 58		20 19	20 28			20 58	21 14	21 28		21 58	22 15		22 27	23 30
Market Harborough d	19 26		19 38			20 08			20 38			21 08		21 38	21 51	22 08			22 37	23 40
Leicester a	19 42		19 55	20 13		20 23		20 43	20 55		21 06	21 23	21 36	21 55	22 07	22 23	22 39		22 52	23 55
d	19 43		19 56	20 14		20 24	20 30	20 43	20 56		21 07	21 24	21 39	21 57	22 09	22 24	22 40		22 57	23 56
Syston d							20 39													
Sileby d							20 44													
Barrow Upon Soar d							20 48													
Loughborough d			20 07	20 24		20 34	20 52		21 07		21 18	21 34		22 10	22 22	22 35	22 53		23 09	
Beeston a			20 22				21 11		21 19					22 19						
Nottingham 8 a			20 34	20 39			21 17		21 26		21 39			22 26	22 38				23 25	
d											21 47									
Langley Mill d											22 04									
Alfreton d											22 12									
Long Eaton a						20 43						21 43				22 43				00 13
Derby 10 a	20 09					20 56		21 10				21 56	22 05			22 55	23 12			00 26
d	20 11	20 14			20 42			21 11		21 45			22 07					23 22		
Burton-on-Trent a	20 49							21 37					22 29							
Belper a								22 03												
Matlock a								22 23												
Chesterfield d	20 31	20 37			21 01			21 31		22 04	22 24		22 30					00 07		
Dronfield d																				
Sheffield 7 a	20 47	20 50			21 18			21 47		22 19	22 40		22 44					00 38		
Meadowhall a		21 13			21 31			22 13		22 31			23 30							
Barnsley a		21 34			22 05			22 34		23 06										
Doncaster 7 a	21 13	21 40						22 21		23 04			00 03							
Wakefield Westgate 7 a	21 34	21 46			21 46			22 39		22s46										
Leeds 10 a	21 54	22 01			22 02			22 59		23 09										
York 8 a		21 49			22 36															

For general notes see front of timetable
For details of catering facilities see Directory of Train Operators

b Change at Bedford
c Wakefield Kirkgate
e Change at Sheffield

Due to Engineering Operations, services from Saturday 13 September on this Table had not been confirmed at time of going to press. These services will be issued in a special Supplement as soon as exact timings have been confirmed

Table 53

Sundays
until 13 July

London → East Midlands → Sheffield

Route Diagram - See first page of Table 53

		EM	EM	EM	EM	XC	EM	EM	EM	EM	XC	EM	EM		EM	EM	EM	EM	XC	EM	XC	EM	XC	EM	EM	EM
		🚌	◇	🚌	🚌	1 ◇ ☕	◇	🚌	1 ◇ ☕	🚌	1 ◇ ☕	1 ◇ ☕	◇		🚌	1 ◇ ☕	🚌	1 ◇ ☕	1 ◇ ☕	◇	1 ◇ ☕	1 ◇ ☕	R 1 ☕	🚌	1 ◇ ☕	◇
St Pancras International ⊖	d											09 00				09 30		10 00				10 30			11 00	
Gatwick Airport [10] ✈	d											*07 45*				*08 15*		*08 45*				*09 15*			*09b45*	
Luton Airport Parkway [7]	d											*09 15*				*09 45*		*10 15*				*10 45*			11 28	
Luton [10]	d											09 30				10 02		10 30				*10 49*			11 33	
Bedford [7]	d											09 50				10 22		10 50				11 24			11 55	
Wellingborough	d											10 03				10 35		11 04				11 35			12 08	
Kettering	d											10 14				10 43		11 12				11 43			12 16	
Market Harborough	d											10 24				10 53		11 22				11 53			12 26	
Leicester	a											10 37				11 12		11 42				12 12			12 45	
	d								10 07			10 37				11 13		11 43				12 12			12 49	
Syston	d																									
Sileby	d																									
Barrow Upon Soar	d																									
Loughborough	d								10 18			10 49				11 26		11 57				12 25			13 00	
Beeston	a											10 58													13 12	
Nottingham [8] 🚊	a			09 13								11 07						12 15							13 20	
	d		09 13				10 32						11 27							12 20						13 37
Langley Mill	d																			12 40						13 51
Alfreton	d						10 54	11 04					11 50		12 00					12 48						14 00
Long Eaton	a								10 26							11 33										
Derby [10]	a								10 37	10 47						11 45	11 55					12 44		12 54		
	d					10 25			11 02		11 25					11 55			12 25		12 53	13 07	13 39			
Burton-on-Trent	a															*12 29*										
Belper	a								*11 44*													*14 03*				
Matlock	a								*12 04*													*14 23*				
Chesterfield	d	09 40		09 58	10 10			11 34		11 32					12 30		12 40							13 39		
Dronfield	d																									
Sheffield [7] 🚊	a	10 10	10 20		10 40	11 17	11 32		11 47		12 11		12 32			12 41			13 11	13 26	13 46	13 58	14 25			14 40
Meadowhall 🚊	a		*10 44*			*11 37*	*11 44*		*12 13*		*12 29*		*12 44*						*13 29*	*13 41*		*14 13*				
Barnsley	a		*11 05*			*11 52*	*12 06*				*13 05*		*13 05*						*13 52*	*14 05*		*15 05*				
Doncaster [7]	a		*11 47*						12 17		*12 54*								*14 01*		14 15	*14 33*	15 15			
Wakefield Westgate [7]	a		*11c29*			11 47	*13e17*		*13 17*		12 41		*13c29*						13 42	*14 26*	14 33	*15e14*	15 43			
Leeds [10]	a		*12 07*			12 04	*13e36*		*13 36*		13 02		*14 04*						14 02	*14 52*	15 02	*15e33*	16 02			
York [8]	a		*12e34*			12 44	*12 40*		12 40		13 44					*14e33*			14 44		15 33	*15e05*	16 33			

		EM	EM		EM	EM	EM	EM	XC	EM	EM	EM	EM	EM	XC	EM		EM	EM	EM	EM	XC	EM	EM	EM	EM
		🚌	1 ◇ ☕		🚌	1 ◇ ☕	◇	🚌	R 1 ☕	1 ◇ ☕	🚌	1 ◇ ☕	◇	🚌	R 1 ☕	1 ◇ ☕		🚌	1 ◇ ☕	◇	🚌	R 1 ☕	1 ◇ ☕	🚌	◇	🚌
St Pancras International ⊖	d		11 30			12 00				12 30		13 00				13 30			14 00				14 30			
Gatwick Airport [10] ✈	d		*10 15*			*10 45*				*11 15*		*11b45*				*12 15*			*12 45*				*13 15*			
Luton Airport Parkway [7]	d		*11 35*			*12 05*				*12 48*		13 27				*13 48*			*14 18*				*14 35*			
Luton [10]	d		*11 39*			12 31				*12 52*		13 33				*13 52*			14 32				*14 39*			
Bedford [7]	d		12 23			12 55				13 24		13 54				14 23			14 46				15 16			
Wellingborough	d		12 36			13 08				13 36		14 06				14 36			15 01				15 28			
Kettering	d		12 44			13 16				13 45		14 13				14 44			15 12				15 40			
Market Harborough	d		12 55			13 26				13 56		14 23				14 55			15 23				15 51			
Leicester	a		13 17			13 45				14 20		14 43				15 19			15 42				16 09			
	d		13 17			13 45				14 20		14 44				15 19			15 43				16 10			
Syston	d																									
Sileby	d																									
Barrow Upon Soar	d																									
Loughborough	d		13 31			13 57				14 31		14 55				15 33			15 54				16 22			
Beeston	a											15 05														
Nottingham [8] 🚊	a					14 12						15 12							16 11							
	d						14 23						15 29							16 32					17 15	
Langley Mill	d						14 41													16 47					17 32	
Alfreton	d	14 10					14 49	14 59					15 48	15 58						16 55	17 05				17 40	17 50
Long Eaton	a		13 44													15 43										
Derby [10]	a		13 56		14 06					14 50	15 00					15 56		16 06					16 48	16 58		
	d		14 07						14 49	15 06					15 55	16 07						16 59	17 07			
Burton-on-Trent	a		*14 29*							*15 49*						*16 29*							*17 49*			
Belper	a									*15 56*																
Matlock	a									*16 18*																
Chesterfield	d	14 40			14 51			15 29			15 45			16 28				16 51			17 35			17 43		18 20
Dronfield	d																									
Sheffield [7] 🚊	a		14 54				15 26		15 46	15 54			16 26		16 44	16 57				17 32		17 47	18 02		18 17	
Meadowhall 🚊	a		*15 13*				*15 41*			*16 13*			*16 44*			*17 13*				*17 44*		*18 13*	*18 29*		*18 29*	
Barnsley	a		*15 52*				*16 06*			*17 05*			*17 05*			*18 05*				*18 05*			*19 05*		*19 05*	
Doncaster [7]	a		*15 33*				*16 15*		16 15	*16 33*			*17 15*		17 15	*17 33*				*18 15*		18 15	*18 54*		*18 54*	
Wakefield Westgate [7]	a		*16c11*				*16 27*		16 33	*17e14*			*17c29*		17 43	*18e12*				*19e06*		18 42	*19c29*		*19c29*	
Leeds [10]	a		*16 31*				*16 52*		17 02	*17e34*			*17 59*		18 02	*18e32*				*18 56*		19 02				
York [8]	a		*16e34*				*17 00*		17 33	*17e45*					18 33	*18e05*				*19e05*		19 33	*19e46*		*19e46*	

For general notes see front of timetable
For details of catering facilities see
Directory of Train Operators

b Change at Luton
c Wakefield Kirkgate
e Change at Sheffield and Doncaster

Sundays

until 13 July

London → East Midlands → Sheffield

Route Diagram - See first page of Table 53

		EM 1 ◇ ☕	XC R 1 ☕	EM 1 ◇ ☕	EM 🚌	EM 1 ◇ ☕		EM ◇	XC R 1 ☕	EM 🚌	EM 1 ◇ ☕	EM 🚌	EM 1 ◇ ☕	EM 1 ◇ ☕	EM 🚌	EM 1 ◇ ☕	EM ◇ trolley	EM 🚌	XC R 1 ☕		EM 1 ◇ ☕	EM 1 ◇ ☕	EM 🚌	EM 1 ◇ ☕	EM 1 ◇ ☕	EM 🚌
St Pancras International ⊖	d	15 00		15 30		16 00					16 30		17 00	17 25		17 30					18 00	18 25		18 30		
Gatwick Airport [10] ✈	d	13b45		14 15		14 45					15 15		15 45			16 15					16 45			17c15		
Luton Airport Parkway [7]	d	15 29		15 35		16 18					16 37		17 05			17 35					18 05			18 56		
Luton [10]	d	15 34		15 39		16 32					17 01		17 31			17 51					18 22			18 39		
Bedford [7]	d	15 51		16 16		16 48					17 15		17 47			18 15					18 46			19 17		
Wellingborough	d	16 04		16 28		17 01					17 28		18 01			18 28					18 59			19 29		
Kettering	d	16 12		16 35		17 09					17 36		18 08			18 35					19 06			19 37		
Market Harborough	d	16 22		16 48		17 20					17 49		18 18			18 45					19 17			19 51		
Leicester	a	16 42		17 04		17 36					18 04		18 37	18 46		19 05					19 36	19 51		20 07		
	d	16 42		17 05		17 36					18 04		18 38	18 50		19 06					19 37	19 51		20 07		
Syston	d																									
Sileby	d																									
Barrow Upon Soar	d																									
Loughborough	d	16 53		17 15							18 17		18 49			19 16					19 47			20 18		
Beeston	a	17 09											19 00								19 59					
Nottingham [8] ⛴	a	17 17				18 01							19 06								20 05					
	d							18 30									19 32				20 20 →				← 20 20	
Langley Mill	d							18 45																	20 37	
Alfreton	d							18 53		19 03							19 52	20 02							20 44	20 54
Long Eaton	a			17 24												19 25								20 26		
Derby [10]	a			17 35	17 45						18 42	18 52		19 19	19 29	19 36						20 19	20 29	20 39		
	d		17 47	17 51					18 44		18 55			19 19					19 59			20 19				
Burton-on-Trent	a			18 29										19 49		20 29						20 50		21 29		
Belper	a			18 08												20 01										
Matlock	a			18 28												20 21										
Chesterfield	d				18 30					19 33		19 37			20 14			20 32					21 14			21 24
Dronfield	d																									
Sheffield [7] ⛴	a		18 37	18 47				19 31	19 47		20 01			20 13			20 31		20 47			21 07			21 24	
Meadowhall ⛴	a			19 03				19 44			20 08			20 32			20 44		21 13			21 29			21 41	
Barnsley	a			20 05				20 05						21 06			21 06								22 09	
Doncaster [7]	a		19 15	19 15					20 15		20 30			20 45			21 15		21 15			21 37				
Wakefield Westgate [7]	a		19 34	19e57					20 45		21 03			21 03			21f29		21 34			22 01			22 26	
Leeds [10]	a		20 02	19 55					21 02		21 25			21 25			21 51		22 02			22 23			22 52	
York [8]	a		20 33	20e07					21 33		21e47			21g47			22e00		22 38			23g09			23e09	

		EM 1 ◇ ☕	EM 🚌	XC 1 ◇ ☕	EM 1 ◇ ☕		EM 1 ◇ ☕	EM 🚌	EM 🚌		XC 1 ◇ ☕	EM 1 ◇ ☕	EM 🚌	EM 🚌	EM 1 ◇ ☕	EM 1 ◇ ☕	EM 🚌	EM 🚌	EM ◇	EM 1 ◇ ☕	EM 🚌	EM 1 ◇ ☕	EM 1 ◇ ☕	EM 1 ◇ ☕		
St Pancras International ⊖	d	18 55			19 00		19 25					19 30			20 00	20 30				21 00		21 30	22 30	23 00		
Gatwick Airport [10] ✈	d				17 45							18 15			18 45	19 15				19 45		20 15	21 15	21c45		
Luton Airport Parkway [7]	d				19 05							19 35			20 05	20 35				21 05		21 35	22 35	23c15		
Luton [10]	d				19 27							19 55			20 26	20 39				21 23		21 39	22 55	23 26		
Bedford [7]	d				19 45							20 17			20 47	21 13				21 48		22 19	23 19	23 52		
Wellingborough	d				19 58							20 31			21 01	21 26				22 00		22 31	23 31	00 05		
Kettering	d				20 08							20 39			21 10	21 36				22 07		22 38	23 38	00 13		
Market Harborough	d				20 22							20 53			21 21	21 50				22 18		22 48	23 48	00 23		
Leicester	a	20 14			20 35		20 46					21 09			21 41	22 08				22 37		23 11	00 07	00 42		
	d	20 14			20 35		20 47					21 10			21 42	22 09				22 37		23 12	00 09	00 42		
Syston	d																									
Sileby	d																									
Barrow Upon Soar	d																									
Loughborough	d				20 46										21 53				22 10			23 23	00 19	00 55		
Beeston	a				20 56															23 05						
Nottingham [8] ⛴	a	20 38			21 03										22 11				22 31	23 11			00 47			
	d																									
Langley Mill	d																									
Alfreton	d																									
Long Eaton	a											21 28														
Derby [10]	a						21 12	21 22				21 46	21 56			22 35	22 45					23 49		01 21		
	d			20 48			21 13				21 42	21 47				22 36										
Burton-on-Trent	a											22 21				23 06										
Belper	a						22 05																			
Matlock	a						22 25																			
Chesterfield	d		20 55			21 25		22 07	21 55				22 41	22 25			23 30	22 55			23 25					
Dronfield	d																									
Sheffield [7] ⛴	a		21 25	21 37		21 55	22 00		22 25		22 40	22 47		22 55		23 22		23 25			00 05					
Meadowhall ⛴	a						22 31					23 25														
Barnsley	a						23 05																			
Doncaster [7]	a			22 15			22 55				23 15	23 15														
Wakefield Westgate [7]	a			22 45			23f28									23 53										
Leeds [10]	a			23 02			00 04				00 20	00 20				00 30										
York [8]	a			23 38							00g39	00e39														

For general notes see front of timetable
For details of catering facilities see Directory of Train Operators

b Change at Luton
c Change at Bedford
e Change at Sheffield and Doncaster
f Wakefield Kirkgate
g Change at Doncaster

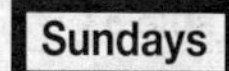

Sundays

20 July to 7 September

London → East Midlands → Sheffield

Route Diagram - See first page of Table 53

		EM	XC	EM	EM	XC	EM	EM	EM	EM	XC	EM	EM	XC	XC	EM	EM	EM	EM	XC	XC	EM	EM	EM
		◇	1◇ ☕	1◇ ☕	◇	1◇ ☕	1◇ ☕	1◇ ☕	◇	1◇ ☕	1◇ ☕	1◇ ☕	◇	1◇ ☕	1◇ ☕	1◇ ☕	◇	1◇ ☕	1◇ ☕	1◇ ☕	R 1 ☕	◇	1◇ ☕	1◇ ☕
St Pancras International ⊖	d						09 00	09 30		10 00		10 30				11 00		11 30	12 00				12 30	13 00
Gatwick Airport 10 ✈	d						07 45	08 15		08 45		09 15				09b45		10 15	10 45				11 15	11b45
Luton Airport Parkway 7	d						09 15	09 45		10 15		10 45				11 28		11 35	12 05				12 48	13 27
Luton 10	d						09 30	10 02		10 30		10 49				11 33		11 39	12 31				12 52	13 33
Bedford 7	d						09 50	10 22		10 50		11 24				11 55		12 23	12 55				13 24	13 54
Wellingborough	d						10 03	10 35		11 04		11 35				12 08		12 36	13 08				13 36	14 06
Kettering	d						10 14	10 43		11 12		11 43				12 16		12 44	13 16				13 45	14 13
Market Harborough	d						10 24	10 53		11 22		11 53				12 26		12 55	13 26				13 56	14 23
Leicester	a						10 37	11 12		11 42		12 12				12 45		13 17	13 45				14 20	14 43
	d			10 12			10 37	11 13		11 43		12 12				12 49		13 17	13 45				14 20	14 44
Syston	d																							
Sileby	d																							
Barrow Upon Soar	d																							
Loughborough	d			10 23			10 49	11 26		11 57		12 25				13 00		13 31	13 57				14 31	14 55
Beeston	a						10 58									13 12								15 05
Nottingham 8	a						11 07			12 15						13 20			14 12					15 12
	d	09 20			10 34				11 41				12 36				13 36					14 33		
Langley Mill	d												12 57				13 57					14 54		
Alfreton	d				10 58				12 09				13 05				14 06					15 02		
Long Eaton	a			10 31				11 33										13 44						
Derby 10	a			10 42				11 45				12 44						13 56					14 50	
	d		10 25	10 44		11 25		11 48			12 25	12 46		13 02	13 42			13 57		14 14	14 42		14 51	
Burton-on-Trent	a							12 29				14 07						14 49					15 49	
Belper	a			11 44								14 03											15 56	
Matlock	a			12 04								14 23											16 18	
Chesterfield	d	09 54	10 46	11 03	11 13			12 09	12 20			13 06	13 17	13 23	14 01		14 17	14 22		14 33		15 14	15 20	
Dronfield	d																							
Sheffield 7	a	10 15	10 59	11 17	11 32	11 58		12 25	12 36		12 57	13 20	13 34	13 41	14 14		14 33	14 40		14 48	15 13	15 31	15 39	
Meadowhall	a	10 31		11 37	11 44	12 13		12 44			13 29	13 37		14 13	14 27					15 13		15 44	15 51	
Barnsley	a	11 05		11 52	12 06			13 05				13 52			15 05					15 52		16 06		
Doncaster 7	a	10 51	11 23	11 54		12 33					14 02			14 16	14 56					15 16				
Wakefield Westgate 7	a	11c19	11 44	12e11		12 44		13f29			13 44	14f11			14 44					16e11	15 44		17c14	
Leeds 10	a	11c38	12 02	12g31		13 01					14 03	14 31			15 01					16g31	16 01		17c34	
York 8	a	11c29	12 44	12 19		13 45		14c33	14c33		14 47	14 39	14 39	14 39	15 45			15 40		15 40	16 45		16 44	

		XC	XC	EM	EM	EM	XC	XC	EM	EM	XC	EM	EM	XC	EM	EM	XC	XC	EM	EM	EM	XC	EM
		1◇ ☕	R 1 ☕	◇	1◇ ☕	1◇ ☕	R 1 ☕	1◇ ☕	1◇ ☕	◇	1◇ ☕	1◇ ☕	1◇ ☕	R 1 ☕	◇	1◇ ☕	R 1 ☕	R 1 ☕	1◇ ☕	◇	1◇ ☕	R 1 ☕	1◇ ☕
St Pancras International ⊖	d				13 30	14 00			14 30			15 00	15 30			16 00			16 30		17 00		17 25
Gatwick Airport 10 ✈	d				12 15	12 45			13 15			13b45	14 15			14 45			15 15		15 45		
Luton Airport Parkway 7	d				13 48	14 18			14 35			15 29	15 35			16 18			16 37		17 05		
Luton 10	d				13 52	14 32			14 39			15 34	15 39			16 32			17 01		17 31		
Bedford 7	d				14 23	14 46			15 16			15 51	16 16			16 48			17 15		17 47		
Wellingborough	d				14 36	15 01			15 28			16 04	16 28			17 01			17 28		18 01		
Kettering	d				14 44	15 12			15 40			16 12	16 35			17 09			17 36		18 08		
Market Harborough	d				14 55	15 23			15 51			16 22	16 48			17 20			17 49		18 18		
Leicester	a				15 19	15 42			16 09			16 42	17 04			17 36			18 04		18 37		18 46
	d				15 19	15 43			16 10			16 42	17 05			17 36			18 04		18 38		18 49
Syston	d																						
Sileby	d																						
Barrow Upon Soar	d																						
Loughborough	d				15 33	15 54			16 22			16 53	17 15						18 17		18 49		
Beeston	a											17 09									19 00		
Nottingham 8	a					16 11						17 17				18 01					19 06		
	d			15 30						16 45					17 35					18 34			
Langley Mill	d									17 01					17 52					18 52			
Alfreton	d			15 56						17 09					18 00					19 00			
Long Eaton	a				15 43								17 24										
Derby 10	a				15 56				16 46				17 35						18 43				19 18
	d	15 14	15 40		15 56		16 42	16 14	16 48		17 14		17 35	17 42			18 14	18 42	18 45			19 14	19 19
Burton-on-Trent	a				16 49				17 49				18 07						19 07				19 49
Belper	a												18 08										
Matlock	a												18 28										
Chesterfield	d	15 33		16 13	16 25			16 33	17 10	17 20	17 33		17 55		18 14		18 33	19 01	19 08	19 14		19 33	19 41
Dronfield	d																						
Sheffield 7	a	15 48	16 13	16 32	16 43		17 13	16 48	17 26	17 38	17 48		18 13	18 16	18 31		18 48	19 14	19 25	19 32		19 48	19 57
Meadowhall	a	16 13		16 44				17 13	17 41		18 13		18 29	18 29	18 44		19 03		19 41	19 44		20 08	20 13
Barnsley	a	17 05		17 05					18 05				19 05	19 05	19 05				20 05	20 05			21 05
Doncaster 7	a	16 16						17 14			18 16		18 54	18 54	19 16		19 16		20 16	20 16		20 16	20 22
Wakefield Westgate 7	a	17 14	16 44	17f29	18c12		17 44	18 12	18 27				18 44	18 44	19f29		19 57	19 44	20 26	20 44			20 49
Leeds 10	a	17 34	17 01	18 05	18c32		18 01	18 32	18 52				19 02	19 02	20 04		20 19	20 02	20 52	21 01			21 10
York 8	a	16 44	17 41		17 38		18 45	17 38	18 41	18 41	18 41		19 40	19 43	19 40		19 40	20 45	20 43	20 43		20 43	21h00

For general notes see front of timetable
For details of catering facilities see Directory of Train Operators

- b Change at Luton
- c Change at Sheffield and Doncaster
- e Wakefield Kirkgate. Change at Sheffield
- f Wakefield Kirkgate
- g Change at Sheffield
- h Change at Doncaster

Due to Engineering Operations, services from Sunday 14 September on this Table had not been confirmed at time of going to press. These services will be issued in a special Supplement as soon as exact timings have been confirmed

Table 53

Sundays

20 July to 7 September

London → East Midlands → Sheffield

Route Diagram - See first page of Table 53

		EM	XC	EM	EM	XC	EM	EM		EM	EM	XC	EM	EM	XC	EM	EM	EM	EM	XC	EM	EM	EM	EM		
		1 ◇	R 1	◇	1 ◇	1 ◇	1 ◇	1 ◇		1 ◇	1 ◇	R 1	1 ◇	1 ◇	1 ◇	1 ◇	1 ◇	1 ◇	◇	1 ◇	1 ◇	1 ◇	1 ◇	1 ◇		
St Pancras International ⊖	d	17 30			18 00		18 25	18 30			18 55		19 00	19 25		19 30	20 00	20 30			21 00	21 30	22 30	23 00		
Gatwick Airport 10 ✈	d	16 15			16 45			17b15					17 45			18 15	18 45	19 15			19 45	20 15	21 15	21b45		
Luton Airport Parkway 7	d	17 35			18 05			18 56					19 05			19 35	20 05	20 35			21 05	21 35	22 35	23b15		
Luton 10	d	17 51			18 22			18 39					19 27			19 55	20 26	20 39			21 23	21 39	22 55	23 26		
Bedford 7	d	18 15			18 46			19 17					19 45			20 17	20 47	21 13			21 48	22 19	23 19	23 52		
Wellingborough	d	18 28			18 59			19 29					19 58			20 31	21 01	21 26			22 00	22 31	23 31	00 05		
Kettering	d	18 35			19 06			19 37					20 08			20 39	21 10	21 36			22 07	22 38	23 38	00 13		
Market Harborough	d	18 45			19 17			19 51					20 22			20 53	21 21	21 50			22 18	22 48	23 48	00 23		
Leicester	a	19 05			19 36		19 51	20 07			20 14		20 35	20 46		21 09	21 41	22 08			22 37	23 11	00 07	00 42		
	d	19 06			19 37		19 51	20 07			20 14		20 35	20 47		21 10	21 42	22 09			22 37	23 12	00 09	00 42		
Syston	d																									
Sileby	d																									
Barrow Upon Soar	d																									
Loughborough	d	19 16			19 47			20 18					20 46				21 53		22 10			23 23	00 19	00 55		
Beeston	a				19 59								20 56								23 05					
Nottingham 8 🚌	a				20 05					←	20 38		21 03				22 11		22 31		23 11		00 47			
	d			19 40	20 12 →					20 12																
Langley Mill	d									20 30																
Alfreton	d			20 03						20 38																
Long Eaton	a	19 25						20 26								21 28										
Derby 10	a	19 36					20 19	20 39						21 12		21 45		22 35				23 49		01 21		
	d		19 42			20 14	20 19					20 42		21 13	21 42	21 45		22 36		22 53						
Burton-on-Trent	a	20 07					20 50	21 07						21 33		22 21		23 07								
Belper	a	20 01												22 05												
Matlock	a	20 21												22 25												
Chesterfield	d		20 01	20 14		20 33	20 40			20 49		21 01		21 34	22 03	22 10		22 59		23 12						
Dronfield	d																									
Sheffield 7 🚌	a		20 14	20 31		20 48	20 56			21 04		21 15		21 49	22 18	22 27		23 12		23 26						
Meadowhall 🚌	a		20 32	20 44			21 13			21 29		21 29			22 31	22 44		23 25								
Barnsley	a		21 05	21 05						22 09		22 09				23 05										
Doncaster 7	a		21 04			21 16	21 20			22 02		22 02			22 55			23 58								
Wakefield Westgate 7	a		20 44	21c29		21e39	21 39			21 44		21 44			22s45	23c28		23 39		23s52						
Leeds 10	a		21 01				22 02			22 01		22 01			23 09	00 04		00 16		00 34						
York 8	a		21 45	21 42		21 42	22f00			23g09		22 53			00g39											

For general notes see front of timetable
For details of catering facilities see Directory of Train Operators

b Change at Bedford
c Wakefield Kirkgate
e Change at Sheffield
f Change at Doncaster
g Change at Sheffield and Doncaster

Due to Engineering Operations, services from Sunday 14 September on this Table had not been confirmed at time of going to press. These services will be issued in a special Supplement as soon as exact timings have been confirmed

Sheffield → East Midlands → London

Route Diagram - See first page of Table 53

Miles	Miles			EM	EM	EM	EM	EM	EM	EM	EM	EM	EM	EM	EM	EM	EM	XC	EM	EM	EM	EM	EM	EM	XC	EM
				MO																						
					1◇	1◇		1◇		1◇	1◇	1◇		1◇	1◇	1◇	1◇	1◇	1◇	1◇	1◇		1◇	1◇	1◇	1◇
				A													B			C						D
				🚌	⊠	⊠		☕		⊠	⊠	☕		⊠	⊠	☕	⊠	☕	☕	⊠	⊠		☕	☕	☕	⊠
—	—	York 8	d																					05b50	06 16	
—	—	Leeds 10	d												05b05			06 00							06 14	06 14
—	—	Wakefield Westgate 7	d												05b17			06 12							06 26	06 26
—	—	Doncaster 7	d												05 42			06 00						06 40	06 45	06 45
—	—	Barnsley	d											05 18				05 53		06 27					06 46	
—	—	Meadowhall 🚊	d											05 39	06 00			06 27		06 49				06 59	07 04	
0	0	**Sheffield 7** 🚊	d	00 01		05 20								06 00	06 25		06 30	06 45		07 05				07 14	07 23	07 27
7	7	Dronfield	d																							
12¼	12¼	Chesterfield	d	00a31		05 33								06 14	06 38		06 45	06 57		07 19				07 27	07 35	07 40
—	—	Matlock	d												06 20											
—	28½	Belper	d												06 40											
—	—	Burton-on-Trent	d												06 25				07 10							
—	36½	**Derby 10**	a			05 54									07 00			07 16	07 25	07 46					07 55	
—	—		d		05 00	05 56			06 16		06 38				07 01				07 34	07 46						
—	44	Long Eaton	d			06 06			06 25										07 43							
22½	—	Alfreton	d														06 57							07 40		
34½	—	Langley Mill	d														07 05							07 50		
40¾	—	**Nottingham 8** 🚊	a											06 45			07 23							08 09		
—	—		d					06 07		06 25				06 53		07 07	07 30				05 30	07 38	08 07	08 26		
44	—	Beeston	d					06 13		06 31						07 13	07 36					07 44	08 13	08 34		
55½	53¼	Loughborough	d			06 15	06 08		06 39	06 41			←		07 18	07 22			07 52		05 45	08 01	08 22	08 43		
59½	57¼	Barrow Upon Soar	d				06 12		06 44				06 44									08 06				
61½	59¼	Sileby	d				06 17		→				06 48									08 10				
64¼	62	Syston	d				06 22						06 53									08 15				
68	65¾	**Leicester**	a		05 25	06 28	06 31	06 34		06 53	07 01		07 06	07 13	07 30	07 37	07 55		08 04	08 12	05 58	08 25	08 34	08 55		
—	—		d		05 25	06 30		06 35		06 55	07 04	05 00		07 15	07 30	07 37	07 57		08 05	08 14	06 00		08 35	08 56		
84½	82	Market Harborough	d		05 41	06 45		06 50		07 10				07 29	07 47	07 53			08 19		06 15		08 49			
95¼	93	Kettering	d		05 52	06 56		07 02		07 20	07 28	05 21		07 39	07 58	08 03	08 17		08 29		06 26		09 00	09 18		
102¼	100	Wellingborough	d		06 00	07 04		07 10		07 28	07 37	05 29		07 46	08 06	08 12			08 40		06 34		09 07			
117½	115½	Bedford 7	d		06 19						07 53	05 50				08 25			09 03		06 51		09 23			
137	134¾	**Luton 10**	d		06 35	07 29				07 52	08 27	06 23		08 10		08 53			09 33		07 08		09 38			
—	—	Luton Airport Parkway 7	d		06 52	07 42		07 38		08 04	08 30	06 08		08 30		09 06			09 21		07 35		09 51			
—	—	Gatwick Airport 10 ✈	a		08 40	09 22				09 40	09 55	07c43		09 55		10 25			10c55		08 56		11 10			
167¼	165	**St Pancras International** ⊖	a		07 05	07 59		08 06		08 24	08 38	06 41		08 42	08 55	09 06	09 12		09 45	09 29	07 36		10 04	10 19		09 33

		EM	EM	XC	EM	XC		EM	EM	EM	EM	EM	XC	EM	XC		EM	EM	EM	XC	EM	EM	EM	XC		EM
				R		R							R													
		◇	1◇	1		1		1◇	1◇	1◇	1◇	◇	1		1◇		1◇	1◇	◇	1◇	1◇	1◇		1◇		1◇
			☕	☕		☕		☕	☕	☕	☕	⚲	☕		☕		☕	☕	⚲	☕	☕	☕		☕		☕
York 8	d			06b30		07 27		07e27			07f27		07 44		08 27		08f27			08 44				09 27		09 27
Leeds 10	d			07 05		07f16		07 26			07f26		08 10		08f28		08 28			09 10				09f16		
Wakefield Westgate 7	d			07 19		07g32		07 38			07f38		08 23		08f39		08 39			09 23				09g32		
Doncaster 7	d			07 02		07 52		07 59							08 51				08 57	09 01				09 56		
Barnsley	d	06 58		06 58		07 48		07 48			08 06	07 58	08 14		08 48				08 58	08 58				09 48		
Meadowhall 🚊	d	07 19		07 33		08 07		08 07			08 24	08 22	08 34		09 03				09 21	09 33				10 03		10 07
Sheffield 7 🚊	d	07 40		07 53		08 23		08 27			08 36	08 38	08 53		09 23		09 27		09 38	09 53				10 23		10 27
Dronfield	d																									
Chesterfield	d	07 53		08 05		08 35		08 40			08 48	08 52			09 35		09 40		09 53					10 35		10 40
Matlock	d		07h38														09 04									
Belper	d		07h58								09 03						09 25									
Burton-on-Trent	d		08 10					08 29			08 58						09 18					09 47				10 18
Derby 10	a		08 25	08 26		08 55		09 02			09 13		09 22		09 55		10 02			10 22				10 55		11 02
	d		08 34					09 04			09 34						10 04					10 34				11 04
Long Eaton	d		08 43								09 43											10 43				
Alfreton	d	08 06										09 07							10 04							
Langley Mill	d	08 13										09 14														
Nottingham 8 🚊	a	08 29										09 30							10 25							
	d				08 36				09 07	09 30				09 38				10 07			10 30		10 38			
Beeston	d								09 13									10 13								
Loughborough	d		08 52		09 01				09 23	09 44	09 52			10 00				10 22				10 52	11 00			
Barrow Upon Soar	d				09 06									10 06									11 06			
Sileby	d				09 10									10 10									11 10			
Syston	d				09 15									10 15									11 15			
Leicester	a		09 04		09 25			09 28	09 35	09 57	10 04			10 25			10 28	10 34			10 57	11 04	11 25			11 28
	d		09 05					09 30	09 35	10 00	10 05						10 30	10 35			11 00	11 05				11 30
Market Harborough	d		09 19						09 49		10 19							10 49				11 19				
Kettering	d		09 29						09 59		10 29							10 59				11 29				
Wellingborough	d		09 36						10 06		10 36							11 06				11 36				
Bedford 7	d		09 53						10 21		10 51						11 12	11 21				11 51				
Luton 10	d		10 33						10 39		11 33							11 36				12 33				12 20
Luton Airport Parkway 7	d		10 09						10 51		11 07						11 51	11 51				12 07				12 36
Gatwick Airport 10 ✈	a		11c55						12 10		12c55						13 10	13 10				13c55				13 55
St Pancras International ⊖	a		10 34					10 48	11 04	11 18	11 34						11 51	12 04			12 16	12 34				12 51

For general notes see front of timetable
For details of catering facilities see Directory of Train Operators

A Until 14 July

B **The Robin Hood**
C **The Midland Express**
D **The Master Cutler**
b Change at Doncaster and Sheffield
c Change at Bedford

e Change at Doncaster
f Change at Sheffield
g Wakefield Kirkgate. Change at Sheffield
h Change at Derby

Sheffield → East Midlands → London

Route Diagram - See first page of Table 53

		EM	EM	EM	XC	EM	EM	XC	EM		EM	EM	XC	EM	EM	EM	XC	EM		EM	EM	XC	EM	EM	EM	XC
					R												R					R				
		1 ◇	1 ◇	◇	1	1 ◇		1 ◇	1 ◇		1 ◇	◇	1 ◇	1 ◇	1 ◇		1	1 ◇		1 ◇	◇	1	1 ◇	1 ◇		1 ◇
		☕	☕	🛒	☕	☕		☕	☕		☕	🛒	☕	☕	☕		☕	☕		☕	🛒	☕	☕	☕		☕
York 8	d				09 44			10 34	10 34				10 44				11 27	11 27				11 44				12 25
Leeds 10	d				10 10			10b16					11 10				11b16	11 16				12 10				12b16
Wakefield Westgate 7	d				10 23			10c32					11 23				11c32	11e32				12 23				12c32
Doncaster 7	d				10 02			10 58					11 02				11 54	11 54				11 58				12 55
Barnsley	d			10 01	10 01			10 48				11 01	11 01				11 48	11 48			12 01	12 01				12 48
Meadowhall	d			10 19	10 33			11 04	11 07			11 19	11 33				12 03	12 06			12 19	12 33				13 03
Sheffield 7	d			10 38	10 53			11 23	11 27			11 38	11 53				12 23	12 27			12 38	12 53				13 23
Dronfield	d																				12 49					
Chesterfield	d			10 53				11 35	11 40			11 53					12 35	12 40			12 53					13 35
Matlock	d								11 12																	
Belper	d								11 33																	
Burton-on-Trent	d					10 58			11 18						11 46			12 18						12 58		
Derby 10	a				11 22			11 55	12 02				12 22				12 55	13 02				13 22				13 55
	d					11 34			12 04						12 34			13 04						13 34		
Long Eaton	d					11 43									12 43									13 43		
Alfreton	d			11 04								12 04									13 04					
Langley Mill	d			11 11																	13 11					
Nottingham 8	a			11 30								12 29									13 29					
	d	11 07	11 30				11 38				12 07			12 30		12 38				13 07			13 30		13 38	
Beeston	d	11 13									12 13									13 13						
Loughborough	d	11 22	11 44			11 52	12 00				12 22				12 52	13 00				13 22			13 44	13 52	14 00	
Barrow Upon Soar	d						12 06									13 06									14 06	
Sileby	d						12 10									13 10									14 10	
Syston	d						12 15									13 15									14 15	
Leicester	a	11 34	11 57			12 04	12 25		12 28		12 34			12 57	13 04	13 25		13 26		13 34			13 57	14 04	14 25	
	d	11 35	12 00			12 05			12 30		12 35			13 00	13 05			13 30		13 35			14 00	14 05		
Market Harborough	d	11 49				12 19					12 49				13 19					13 49				14 19		
Kettering	d	11 59				12 29					12 59				13 29					13 59				14 29		
Wellingborough	d	12 06				12 36					13 06				13 36					14 06				14 36		
Bedford 7	d	12 21				12 51					13 21				13 51					14 21				14 51		
Luton 10	d	12 36				13 33					13 36				14 33					14 36				15 33		
Luton Airport Parkway 7	d	12 51				13 07					13 51				14 07					14 51				15 07		
Gatwick Airport 10	a	14 10				14f55					15 10				15f55					16 10				16f55		
St Pancras International ⊖	a	13 04	13 15			13 34			13 45		14 04			14 14	14 34			14 44		15 04			15 14	15 34		

		EM	EM	EM		XC	EM	EM	EM	XC	EM	EM	EM		XC	EM	EM	EM	XC	EM	EM	EM		EM	XC	EM
						R									R										R	
		1 ◇	1 ◇	◇		1	1 ◇	1 ◇		1 ◇	1 ◇	1 ◇	◇		1	1 ◇	1 ◇		1 ◇	1 ◇	1 ◇	1 ◇		◇	1	1 ◇
		☕	☕	🛒		☕	☕	☕		☕	☕	☕	🛒		☕	☕	☕		☕	☕	☕	☕		🛒	☕	☕
York 8	d	12 25				12 44				13 29	13 29				13 44				14 32	14 32					14 44	
Leeds 10	d					13 10				13b16					14 10				14b16						15 10	
Wakefield Westgate 7	d					13 23				13c32					14 23				14c32						15 23	
Doncaster 7	d					13 02				13 54					14 01				14 57						15 02	
Barnsley	d			13 01		13 01				13 48			14 01		14 01				14 48					15 01	15 01	
Meadowhall	d	13 07		13 21		13 33				14 03	14 06		14 19		14 33				15 03	15 06				15 19	15 33	
Sheffield 7	d	13 27		13 38		13 53				14 23	14 27		14 38		14 53				15 23	15 27				15 38	15 53	
Dronfield	d																							15 49		
Chesterfield	d	13 40		13 53						14 35	14 40		14 53						15 35	15 40				15 55		
Matlock	d	13 12																		15 17						
Belper	d	13 33																		15 38						
Burton-on-Trent	d	13 18						13 44			14 18						14 58			15 18						15 44
Derby 10	a	14 02				14 22				14 55	15 02				15 22				15 55	16 02					16 22	
	d	14 04						14 34			15 04						15 34			16 04						16 34
Long Eaton	d							14 43									15 43									16 43
Alfreton	d			14 04									15 04											16 06		
Langley Mill	d												15 11													
Nottingham 8	a			14 29									15 29											16 34		
	d		14 07				14 30		14 38			15 07				15 30		15 38			16 07	16 30				
Beeston	d		14 13									15 13									16 13					
Loughborough	d		14 22					14 52	15 00			15 22				15 44	15 52	16 00			16 22	16 44				16 52
Barrow Upon Soar	d								15 06									16 06								
Sileby	d								15 10									16 10								
Syston	d								15 15									16 15								
Leicester	a	14 28	14 34				14 57	15 04	15 25		15 28	15 34				15 58	16 04	16 25		16 28	16 34	16 58				17 04
	d	14 30	14 35				15 00	15 05			15 30	15 35				16 00	16 05			16 30	16 35	17 00				17 05
Market Harborough	d		14 49					15 19				15 49					16 19				16 49					17 19
Kettering	d		14 59					15 29				15 59					16 29				16 59	17 21				17 29
Wellingborough	d		15 06					15 36				16 06					16 36				17 06					17 36
Bedford 7	d		15 21					15 51				16 21					16 51			17 12	17 21					17 51
Luton 10	d	15 20	15 36					16 33				16 36					17 17				17 36					18 33
Luton Airport Parkway 7	d	15 36	15 51					16 07				16 51					17 07			17 46	17 50					18 07
Gatwick Airport 10	a	16 55	17 15					18f12				18 24					18f41			19 26	19 26					19f55
St Pancras International ⊖	a	15 50	16 04				16 15	16 34			16 45	17 04				17 13	17 34			17 53	18 04	18 19				18 34

For general notes see front of timetable
For details of catering facilities see Directory of Train Operators

b Change at Sheffield
c Wakefield Kirkgate. Change at Sheffield
e Wakefield Kirkgate
f Change at Bedford

Sheffield → East Midlands → London

Route Diagram - See first page of Table 53

		EM	XC R 1	EM 1◇	EM 1◇	EM ◇	XC R 1	EM 1◇		EM 1◇	EM	XC R 1	EM 1◇	EM 1◇	EM ◇	XC 1◇	EM 1◇		EM 1◇	EM	XC R 1	EM 1◇	EM 1◇	EM 1◇	EM ◇	XC R 1
York 8	d		15 29	15 29			15 44					16 25	16 25			16 44					17 34	17 34				17 44
Leeds 10	d		15b16	15 16			16 10						16 16			17 10					17b16	17 16				18 10
Wakefield Westgate 7	d		15c32	15e32			16 23						16e32			17 23					17c32	17e32				18 23
Doncaster 7	d		15 55	15 55			16 02					16 53	16 53			17 00					17 58	17 58				18 02
Barnsley	d		15 48	15 48		16 01	16 01					16 26	16 48		17 01	17 01					17 48	17 48			18 01	18 01
Meadowhall	d		16 06	16 09		16 19	16 33					17 00	17 07		17 19	17 33					18 04	18 07			18 19	18 33
Sheffield 7	d		16 23	16 27		16 38	16 53					17 20	17 27		17 41	17 53					18 23	18 27			18 45	18 53
Dronfield	d					16 49						17 28														
Chesterfield	d		16 35	16 40		16 55						17 35	17 40		17 55						18 35	18 40			19 01	
Matlock	d												16 58									18 13				
Belper	d												17 19									18 33				
Burton-on-Trent	d			16 22						16 48			17 20						17 40			18 22				
Derby 10	a		16 55	17 02			17 22					17 55	18 01			18 22					18 55	19 01				19 22
	d			17 04						17 34			18 02						18 34			19 02				
Long Eaton	d									17 43									18 43							
Alfreton	d					17 06									18 06										19 12	
Langley Mill	d					17 13									18 13											
Nottingham 8	a					17 29									18 29										19 37	
	d	16 38			17 07			17 30			17 38			18 07			18 30			18 38			19 07	19 30		
Beeston	d				17 13									18 13									19 13			
Loughborough	d	17 02			17 22			17 44		17 52	18 02		18 18	18 22			18 44		18 52	19 00		19 17	19 22	19 44		
Barrow Upon Soar	d	17 07									18 08									19 06						
Sileby	d	17 11									18 12									19 10						
Syston	d	17 16									18 17									19 15						
Leicester	a	17 25		17 30	17 33			17 58		18 04	18 26		18 30	18 35			18 57		19 04	19 25		19 28	19 35	19 55		
	d			17 30	17 35			18 00		18 05			18 30	18 35			19 00		19 05			19 30	19 35	20 00		
Market Harborough	d				17 49					18 19				18 51					19 19				19 51			
Kettering	d				17 59					18 29				19 01					19 29				20 01			
Wellingborough	d				18 06					18 36				19 09					19 36				20 09			
Bedford 7	d				18 23					18 53				19 23					19 51				20 23			
Luton 10	d			18 21	18 39								19 22	19 39									20 39			
Luton Airport Parkway 7	d			18 36	18 52					19 07			19 46	19 52					20 07				20 52			
Gatwick Airport 10 ✈	a			19 55	20 10					21f10			21 10	21 41					22f10				22 41			
St Pancras International ⊖	a			18 51	19 04			19 17		19 34			19 52	20 04			20 11		20 34			20 41	21 04	21 11		

		EM 1◇	EM		XC 1◇	EM 1◇	EM 1◇	EM ◇	XC 1◇	EM 1◇	EM	XC 1◇ A		EM 1◇	EM 1◇	EM ◇	XC 1◇ B	EM	EM ◇	XC 1◇ B	XC 1◇		EM 1◇	EM ◇
York 8	d				18 24	18 24			18 44			19 29		19 29			19 44		20 33	20 44	21 24		21g39	
Leeds 10	d				18b16				19 10			19b16					20 10		20 16	21 10			21 34	21 48
Wakefield Westgate 7	d				18c32				19 23			19c32					20 23		20e32	21 23			22e03	
Doncaster 7	d				18 52				18 55			19 57					20 03		20 56	21 07	21 48		22 13	
Barnsley	d				18 48			18 58	19 16			19 48					20 06		20 48	21 06	21 26		22 26	
Meadowhall	d				19 04	19 07		19 16	19 34			20 04		20 08			20 33		21 07	21 34	22 10		22 49	22 51
Sheffield 7	d				19 23	19 27		19 38	19 53			20 23		20 39		20 40	20 53		21 38	21 53	22 27		23 08	23 38
Dronfield	d							19 50																
Chesterfield	d				19 35	19 40		19 56	20 05			20 35		20 51		20 55	21 05		21 53	22 05	22 53		23 21	23 59
Matlock	d													19 38										
Belper	d													19 58										
Burton-on-Trent	d	18 58				19 20								20 29										
Derby 10	a				19 55	20 01			20 26			20 55		21 14			21 27			22 26	23 13		23 46	
	d	19 34				20 02								21 16										
Long Eaton	d	19 43																						
Alfreton	d							20 07								21 06			22 04					
Langley Mill	d							20 16								21 13			22 11					
Nottingham 8	a							20 31								21 38			22 36					00 46
	d		19 38				20 07			20 47	20 38				21 30			21 54						
Beeston	d		19 44				20 13																	
Loughborough	d	19 52	20 01			20 18	20 22			21 00	21 00			21 30	21 45			22 10						
Barrow Upon Soar	d		20 06								21 06													
Sileby	d		20 10								21 10													
Syston	d		20 15								21 15													
Leicester	a	20 04	20 25			20 29	20 35			21 12	21 25			21 43	21 56			22 23						
	d	20 05				20 30	20 35			21 15				21 45	22 00									
Market Harborough	d	20 19					20 51			21 28				21 59	22 13									
Kettering	d	20 29					21 01			21 38				22 09	22 23									
Wellingborough	d	20 36					21 09			21 45				22 16	22 30									
Bedford 7	d	20 51				21 11	21 23			22 00					22 45									
Luton 10	d						21 39			22 16					23 01									
Luton Airport Parkway 7	d	21 07				21 46	21 52			22 36					23 36									
Gatwick Airport 10 ✈	a					23 10	23 41			00 16					01 16									
St Pancras International ⊖	a	21 34				21 53	22 04			22 40				23 04	23 32									

For general notes see front of timetable
For details of catering facilities see Directory of Train Operators

A to Sheffield
B to Leeds
b Change at Sheffield
c Wakefield Kirkgate. Change at Sheffield
e Wakefield Kirkgate
f Change at Bedford
g Change at Doncaster and Sheffield

Sheffield → East Midlands → London

Route Diagram - See first page of Table 53

	EM	EM	EM	EM	EM	EM	EM	EM		EM	EM	EM	EM	EM	EM	XC	EM		EM	EM	XC	EM	EM	EM	EM
	1 ◇	1 ◇	1 ◇	1 ◇		1 ◇		1 ◇		1 ◇		1 ◇	1 ◇	1 ◇	1 ◇	1 ◇	1 ◇		1 ◇		1 ◇	1 ◇	1 ◇	1 ◇	◇
															A				B			C			
	☕	⊠ 🚲	⊠ 🚲	⊠ 🚲		☕		⊠ 🚲		⊠ 🚲		⊠ 🚲	⊠ 🚲	☕	⊠ 🚲	☕	☕		⊠ 🚲		☕	⊠ 🚲	☕	☕	
York 8 d																						*05b50*			
Leeds 10 d															*05c05*						06 00	05 54			
Wakefield Westgate 7 d															*05c17*						06 12	06 06			
Doncaster 7 d															*05 42*							06 34			
Barnsley d													*05 18*			*05 53*					*06 27*				
Meadowhall d													*05 39*		*06 00*	*06 13*					*06 49*	*07 00*			
Sheffield 7 d				05 13								05 32	06 10		06 25	06 31					07 07	07 19			
Dronfield d																									
Chesterfield d				05 33								05 57	06 39		06 45	06 57			07 20		07 35	07 40			07 53
Matlock d													*06 20*												
Belper d													*06 40*												
Burton-on-Trent d													*06 25*				07 10								
Derby 10 a				05 54									07 00			07 16	07 27		07 42		07 54				
d		05 00		05 56			06 16			06 38			07 01				07 34		07 46						
Long Eaton d				06 06			06 25										07 43								
Alfreton d															06 57										08 06
Langley Mill d															07 05										08 13
Nottingham 8 a												06 27			07 23										08 29
d			05 30			06 07		06 25				06 53		07 07	07 30					07 38			08 07	08 26	
Beeston d						06 13		06 31						07 13	07 36					07 44			08 13	08 34	
Loughborough d			05 45	06 15	06 08		06 39	06 41			←		07 18	07 22			07 52			08 01			08 22	08 43	
Barrow Upon Soar d					06 12		06 44 →				06 44									08 06					
Sileby d					06 17						06 48									08 10					
Syston d					06 22						06 53									08 15					
Leicester a		05 25	05 58	06 28	06 31	06 34		06 53		07 01	07 06	07 13	07 30	07 37	07 55		08 04		08 12	08 25			08 34	08 55	
d	05 00	05 25	06 00	06 30		06 35		06 55		07 04		07 15	07 30	07 37	07 57		08 05		08 14				08 35	08 56	
Market Harborough d		05 41	06 15	06 45		06 50		07 10				07 29	07 47	07 53			08 19						08 49		
Kettering d	05 21	05 52	06 26	06 56		07 02		07 20		07 28		07 39	07 58	08 03	08 17		08 29						09 00	09 18	
Wellingborough d	05 29	06 00	06 34	07 04		07 10		07 28		07 37		07 46	08 06	08 12			08 40						09 07		
Bedford 7 d	05 50	06 19	06 51							07 53				08 25			09 03						09 23		
Luton 10 d	*06 23*	06 35	07 08	07 29				07 52		*08 27*		08 10		*08 53*			*09 33*						09 38		
Luton Airport Parkway 7 d	06 08	*06 52*	*07 22*	*07 42*		07 38		*08 04*		*08 30*		*08 30*		*09 06*			09 21						*09 51*		
Gatwick Airport 10 a	*07h48*	*08 40*	*08 56*	*09 22*				*09 40*		*09 55*		*09 55*		*10 25*			*10h55*						*11 10*		
St Pancras International a	06 41	07 05	07 36	07 59		08 06		08 24		08 38		08 42	08 55	09 06	09 12		09 45		09 29			09 33	10 04	10 19	

	EM	XC	EM		XC	EM	EM	EM	EM	EM	XC	EM		EM	XC	EM	EM	EM	XC		EM		EM	EM	XC
								ThX	ThO																
	1 ◇	R 1			R 1	1 ◇	1 ◇	1 ◇	1 ◇	◇	R 1	1 ◇			1 ◇	1 ◇	1 ◇	◇	1 ◇		1 ◇		1 ◇		1 ◇
	☕	☕			☕	☕	☕	☕	☕	🚲	☕	☕			☕	☕	☕	🚲	☕		☕		☕		☕
York 8 d		06 16			*06c30*	*06c30*					07 27				07 44				08 27						08 44
Leeds 10 d		*06 05*			07 05	07 16									08 10	08 16									09 10
Wakefield Westgate 7 d		*06j22*			07 19	07 27					*07k32*				08 23										09 23
Doncaster 7 d		*06 40*			*07 02*	*07 35*					07 52				*07 52*	*08m42*			08 51						*09 01*
Barnsley d		*06 46*			*06 58*	*07 28*					*07 49*				*08 14*										*08 58*
Meadowhall d		*07 04*			*07 33*	*07 53*					*08 04*				*08 34*										*09 33*
Sheffield 7 d		07 33			07 59	08 18					08 31				08 57	09 18			09 31						10 00
Dronfield d																									
Chesterfield d		08 02			08 39	08 40				08 52	09 02				09 35	09 40		09 53	10 02						10 35
Matlock d	*07q38*															*09 04*									
Belper d	*07q58*															*09 25*									
Burton-on-Trent d	08 10					*08 29*						*08 50*				*09 18*							*09 47*		
Derby 10 a	08 25	08 26			08 55	09 02					09 22				09 55	10 02			10 22						10 55
d	08 34					09 04						09 34				10 04							10 34		
Long Eaton d	08 43											09 43											10 43		
Alfreton d										09 07								10 04							
Langley Mill d										09 14															
Nottingham 8 a										09 30								10 25							
d			08 36				09 07	09 30	09 30					09 38			10 07				10 30			10 38	
Beeston d							09 13										10 13								
Loughborough d	08 52		09 01				09 23	09 44	09 44			09 52		10 00			10 22						10 52	11 00	
Barrow Upon Soar d			09 06											10 06										11 06	
Sileby d			09 10											10 10										11 10	
Syston d			09 15											10 15										11 15	
Leicester a	09 04		09 25			09 28	09 35	09 57	09 57			10 04		10 25		10 28	10 34				10 57		11 04	11 25	
d	09 05					09 30	09 35	10 00	10 00			10 05				10 30	10 35				11 00		11 05		
Market Harborough d	09 19						09 49					10 19					10 49						11 19		
Kettering d	09 29						09 59					10 29					10 59						11 29		
Wellingborough d	09 36						10 06					10 36					11 06						11 36		
Bedford 7 d	09 53						10 21					10 51				11 12	11 21						11 51		
Luton 10 d	*10 33*						10 39					*11 33*					11 36						*12 33*		
Luton Airport Parkway 7 d	10 09						*10 51*					11 07				*11 51*	*11 51*						12 07		
Gatwick Airport 10 a	*11h55*						*12 10*					*12h55*				*13 10*	*13 10*						*13h55*		
St Pancras International a	10 34					10 48	11 04	11 17	11 18			11 34				11 51	12 04				12 16		12 34		

For general notes see front of timetable
For details of catering facilities see Directory of Train Operators

A The Robin Hood

B The Midland Express
C The Master Cutler
b Change at Doncaster
c Change at Doncaster and Sheffield
h Change at Bedford

j Wakefield Kirkgate
k Wakefield Kirkgate. Change at Sheffield
m Change at Sheffield
q Change at Derby

Sheffield → East Midlands → London

Route Diagram - See first page of Table 53

		EM	EM	EM	EM	XC	EM	EM		XC	EM	EM	EM	XC	EM	EM	EM		XC	EM	EM	EM	XC	EM	EM	EM
		1◇	1◇	1◇	◇	R 1	1◇			1◇	1◇	1◇	◇	1◇	1◇	1◇			R 1	1◇	1◇	◇	R 1	1◇	1◇	
York 8	d	08b51				09 27				09 44	10b06			10 34					10 44	10 44			11 27			
Leeds 10	d					09c16				10 10	10b05			10c16					11 10	11 10			11c16			
Wakefield Westgate 7	d					09e32				10 23	10b18			10e32					11 23	11 23			11e32			
Doncaster 7	d	09 42				09 56					10 42			10 58					11 02	11 42			11 54			
Barnsley	d	09 26				09 48					10 26			10 48					11 01	11 26			11 48			
Meadowhall	d	10 00				10 07					11 00			11 07					11 33	12 00			12 06			
Sheffield 7	d	10 18				10 31				11 00	11 18			11 31					12 01	12 18			12 31			
Dronfield	d																									
Chesterfield	d	10 40			10 53	11 02				11 35	11 40		11 53	12 02					12 34	12 40		12 53	13 01			
Matlock	d										11 12															
Belper	d										11 33															
Burton-on-Trent	d	10 18					10 58				11 18					11 44				12 18					12 46	
Derby 10	a	11 02				11 22				11 55	12 02			12 22					12 55	13 02			13 22			
	d	11 04					11 34				12 04					12 34				13 04					13 34	
Long Eaton	d						11 43									12 43									13 43	
Alfreton	d				11 04								12 04									13 04				
Langley Mill	d				11 11																	13 11				
Nottingham 8	a				11 30								12 29									13 29				
	d		11 07	11 30				11 38				12 07			12 30		12 38				13 07			13 30		13 38
Beeston	d		11 13									12 13									13 13					
Loughborough	d		11 22	11 44			11 52	12 00				12 22				12 52	13 00				13 22			13 44	13 52	14 00
Barrow Upon Soar	d							12 06									13 06									14 06
Sileby	d							12 10									13 10									14 10
Syston	d							12 15									13 15									14 15
Leicester	a	11 28	11 34	11 57			12 04	12 25			12 28	12 34			12 57	13 04	13 25			13 26	13 34			13 57	14 04	14 25
	d	11 30	11 35	12 00			12 05				12 30	12 35			13 00	13 05				13 30	13 35			14 00	14 05	
Market Harborough	d		11 49				12 19					12 49				13 19					13 49				14 19	
Kettering	d		11 59				12 29					12 59				13 29					13 59				14 29	
Wellingborough	d		12 06				12 36					13 06				13 36					14 06				14 36	
Bedford 7	d		12 21				12 51					13 21				13 51					14 21				14 51	
Luton 10	d	12 20	12 36				13 33					13 36				14 33					14 36				15 33	
Luton Airport Parkway 7	d	12 36	12 51				13 07					13 51				14 07					14 51				15 07	
Gatwick Airport 10	a	13 55	14 10				14f55					15 10				15f55					16 10				16f55	
St Pancras International	a	12 51	13 04	13 15			13 34				13 45	14 04			14 14	14 34				14 44	15 04			15 14	15 34	

		XC	EM		EM	EM	XC	EM	EM	XC	EM	EM		EM	EM	XC	EM	EM	EM	XC	EM		EM	EM	EM	XC
		1◇	1◇		1◇	◇	R 1	1◇	1◇	1◇		1◇		1◇	◇	R 1	1◇	1◇		1◇	1◇		1◇	1◇	◇	R 1
York 8	d	11 44					12 25			12 44		12b31				13 29				13 44	13b36					14 32
Leeds 10	d	12 10					12c16			13 10		12 48				13c16				14 10	13 48					14c16
Wakefield Westgate 7	d	12 23					12e32			13 23		13 03				13e32				14 23	14 03					14e32
Doncaster 7	d	11 58	12 42				12 55					13 42				13 54					14 42					14 57
Barnsley	d	12 01	12 26				12 48					13 26				13 48					14 26					14 48
Meadowhall	d	12 33	13 00				13 07					14 00				14 06					15 00					15 06
Sheffield 7	d	13 01	13 18				13 31			14 00		14 18				14 31				15 00	15 18					15 31
Dronfield	d																									
Chesterfield	d	13 35	13 40			13 53	14 02			14 33		14 40			14 53	15 03				15 35	15 40				15 55	16 02
Matlock	d		13 12																		15 17					
Belper	d		13 33																		15 38					
Burton-on-Trent	d								13 44									14 58			15 18					
Derby 10	a	13 55	14 01				14 22			14 55		15 02				15 22				15 55	16 02					16 22
	d		14 04						14 34			15 04						15 34			16 04					
Long Eaton	d								14 43									15 43								
Alfreton	d					14 04									15 04										16 06	
Langley Mill	d														15 11											
Nottingham 8	a					14 29									15 29										16 34	
	d				14 07			14 30			14 38			15 07			15 30		15 38				16 07	16 30		
Beeston	d				14 13									15 13									16 13			
Loughborough	d				14 22				14 52		15 00			15 22			15 44	15 52	16 00				16 22	16 44		
Barrow Upon Soar	d										15 06								16 06							
Sileby	d										15 10								16 10							
Syston	d										15 15								16 15							
Leicester	a		14 28		14 34			14 57	15 04		15 25	15 28		15 34			15 58	16 04	16 25		16 28		16 34	16 58		
	d		14 30		14 35			15 00	15 05			15 30		15 35			16 00	16 05			16 30		16 35	17 00		
Market Harborough	d				14 49				15 19					15 49				16 19					16 49			
Kettering	d				14 59				15 29					15 59				16 29					16 59	17 21		
Wellingborough	d				15 06				15 36					16 06				16 36					17 06			
Bedford 7	d				15 21				15 51					16 21				16 51			17 12		17 21			
Luton 10	d		15 20		15 36				16 33					16 36				17 17					17 36			
Luton Airport Parkway 7	d		15 36		15 51				16 07					16 51				17 07			17 46		17 50			
Gatwick Airport 10	a		16 55		17 15				18f12					18 24				18f41			19 26		19 26			
St Pancras International	a		15 50		16 04			16 15	16 34			16 45		17 04			17 13	17 34			17 53		18 04	18 19		

For general notes see front of timetable
For details of catering facilities see Directory of Train Operators

b Change at Doncaster and Sheffield
c Change at Sheffield
e Wakefield Kirkgate. Change at Sheffield
f Change at Bedford

Sheffield → East Midlands → London

Route Diagram - See first page of Table 53

	EM	EM	XC	EM	EM	EM		EM	XC	EM	EM	XC	EM	EM	EM		EM	XC	EM	EM	XC	EM	EM	EM	EM
			R						R			R									R				
	1 ◇		1	1 ◇	1 ◇	1 ◇		◇	1	1 ◇		1	1 ◇	1 ◇	1 ◇		◇	1 ◇	1 ◇		1	1 ◇	1 ◇	1 ◇	◇
	☕		☕	☕	☕	☕		🛒	☕	☕		☕	☕	☕	☕		🛒	☕	☕		☕	☕	☕	☕	🛒
York 8 d			14 44	15b11					15 29			15 44	15b35					16 25			16 44	16b56			
Leeds 10 d			15 10	14 48					15c16			16 10	15 48					16c16			17 10	16 48			
Wakefield Westgate 7 d			15 23	15 03					15e32			16 23	16 03					16e32			17 23	17 03			
Doncaster 7 d				15 42					15 55				16 42					16 53				17 42			
Barnsley d				15 26					15 48				16 26					16 48				17 26			
Meadowhall d				16 00					16 09				17 00					17 07				18 00			
Sheffield 7 d			16 00	16 18					16 31			17 00	17 18					17 31			18 00	18 18			
Dronfield d																									
Chesterfield d			16 35	16 40				16 57	17 02			17 35	17 40				17 57	18 02			18 35	18 40			18 57
Matlock d													16 58									18 13			
Belper d													17 19									18 33			
Burton-on-Trent d	15 44			16 22						16 48			17 20						17 40			18 22			
Derby 10 a			16 55	17 02					17 22			17 55	18 01					18 22			18 55	19 02			
d	16 34			17 04						17 34			18 02						18 34			19 03			
Long Eaton d	16 43									17 43									18 43						
Alfreton d								17 08									18 08								19 08
Langley Mill d								17 15									18 15								19 15
Nottingham 8 a								17 31									18 31								19 36
d		16 38			17 07	17 30					17 38			18 07	18 30					18 38			19 07	19 30	
Beeston d					17 13									18 13									19 13		
Loughborough d	16 52	17 02			17 22	17 44				17 52	18 02		18 18	18 22	18 44				18 52	19 00		19 17	19 22	19 44	
Barrow Upon Soar d		17 07									18 08									19 06					
Sileby d		17 11									18 12									19 10					
Syston d		17 16									18 17									19 15					
Leicester a	17 04	17 25		17 30	17 33	17 58				18 04	18 26		18 30	18 35	18 57				19 04	19 25		19 28	19 35	19 55	
d	17 05			17 30	17 35	18 00				18 05			18 30	18 35	19 00				19 05			19 30	19 35	20 00	
Market Harborough d	17 19				17 49					18 19				18 51					19 19				19 51		
Kettering d	17 29				17 59					18 29				19 01					19 29				20 01		
Wellingborough d	17 36				18 06					18 36				19 09					19 36				20 09		
Bedford 7 d	17 51				18 23					18 53				19 23					19 51				20 23		
Luton 10 d	18 33			18 21	18 39								19 22	19 39									20 39		
Luton Airport Parkway 7 d	18 07			18 36	18 52					19 07			19 46	19 52					20 07				20 52		
Gatwick Airport 10 a	19f55			19 55	20 10					21f10			21 10	21 41					22f10				22 41		
St Pancras International a	18 34			18 51	19 04	19 17				19 34			19 52	20 04	20 11				20 34			20 41	21 04	21 11	

	XC		EM	EM	XC	EM	EM	XC	EM	EM		EM	XC	EM	XC	EM	EM	EM	XC	EM	XC	EM	EM		
	R																								
	1		1 ◇		1 ◇	1 ◇	1 ◇	1 ◇	◇	1 ◇			1 ◇	1 ◇	1 ◇	1 ◇	◇		1 ◇	◇	1 ◇	1 ◇	◇		
								A											B						
	☕		☕		☕	☕	☕	☕	🛒	☕			☕	☕	☕	☕	🛒		☕	🛒		☕			
York 8 d	17 34				17 44	17b55		18 24	18 24				18 44		19 29		19 29		19 44	20b08	21 24	21b39			
Leeds 10 d	17c16				18 10			18c16					19 10		19c16				20 10	20 16	21 10	21 48			
Wakefield Westgate 7 d	17e32				18 23			18e32					19 23		19e32				20 23	20g32	21 23	22 03			
Doncaster 7 d	17 58				18 02	18 42		18 52						19 42	19 57				20 03	20 42	21 48	22 13			
Barnsley d	17 48				18 01	18 26		18 48	18 58				19 16	19 26	19 48					20 48	21 26	22 26			
Meadowhall d	18 07				18 33	19 00		19 08	19 16				19 34	20 00	20 08				20 33	21 07	22 10	22 51			
Sheffield 7 d	18 31				19 00	19 18		19 31	19 43				20 00	20 18	20 31		20 37		21 00	21 36	22 27	23 21	23 38		
Dronfield d																									
Chesterfield d	19 02				19 33	19 40		20 01	20 06				20 35	20 39	20 57		21 03		21 35	21 58	22 53	23 47	23 59		
Matlock d														19 38											
Belper d														19 58											
Burton-on-Trent d			18 58			19 24								20 29											
Derby 10 a	19 22				19 55	20 01		20 26					20 55	21 00	21 27				21 55		23 13	00 09			
d			19 34			20 02								21 16											
Long Eaton d			19 43																						
Alfreton d									20 17								21 14			22 10					
Langley Mill d									20 26								21 22			22 18					
Nottingham 8 a									20 41								21 45			22 41			00 46		
d				19 38			20 07			20 47		20 38				21 30		21 54							
Beeston d				19 44			20 13																		
Loughborough d			19 52	20 01		20 18	20 22			21 00		21 00		21 30		21 45		22 10							
Barrow Upon Soar d				20 06								21 06													
Sileby d				20 10								21 10													
Syston d				20 15								21 15													
Leicester a			20 04	20 25		20 29	20 35			21 12		21 25		21 43		21 56		22 23							
d			20 05			20 30	20 35			21 15				21 45		22 00									
Market Harborough d			20 19				20 51			21 28				21 59		22 13									
Kettering d			20 29				21 01			21 38				22 09		22 23									
Wellingborough d			20 36				21 09			21 45				22 16		22 30									
Bedford 7 d			20 51			21 11	21 23			22 00						22 45									
Luton 10 d							21 39			22 16						23 01									
Luton Airport Parkway 7 d			21 07			21 46	21 52			22 36						23 36									
Gatwick Airport 10 a						23 10	23 41			00 16						01 16									
St Pancras International a			21 34			21 53	22 04			22 40				23 04		23 32									

For general notes see front of timetable
For details of catering facilities see Directory of Train Operators

A ☕ to Chesterfield
B ☕ to Leeds
b Change at Doncaster and Sheffield
c Change at Sheffield
e Wakefield Kirkgate. Change at Sheffield
f Change at Bedford
g Wakefield Kirkgate

Sheffield → East Midlands → London

Route Diagram - See first page of Table 53

		EM	EM	EM	EM	XC	EM	EM	EM	EM	EM	XC	XC	EM	EM	EM	EM	EM	XC	EM	EM	XC	EM	EM	EM	EM
		1◇	1◇	1◇	1◇	1◇	1◇		1◇	1◇	1◇	1◇	1◇	1◇		1◇	1◇	1◇	1◇	1◇		R 1	1◇	1◇	1◇	◇
York 8	d															06b00			06 06			07 25	07c25			07 25
Leeds 10	d								05b05				06 00						06 48			07e16	07 19			07 19
Wakefield Westgate 7	d								05b17				06 11						06 32			07f32	07 32			07 32
Doncaster 7	d								05 42				06 00			06 40			07 26			07 52	07 59			
Barnsley	d					05 18					05 53					06 27			06 58			07 48	07 48			07 58
Meadowhall	d					05 39			06 00		06 13		06 27			07 00			07 33			08 06	08 06			08 22
Sheffield 7	d			05 00		06 01			06 16		06 34		06 52			07 27		07 32	07 53			08 23	08 27			08 38
Dronfield	d											←														
Chesterfield	d			05 13		06 24 →			06 29		06 46	06 24	07 04			07 40		07 45	08 05			08 35	08 39			08 54
Matlock	d													06 14						07g39						
Belper	d													06 34						07g59						
Burton-on-Trent	d								06 26					06 58		07 29				08 08			08 29			
Derby 10	a			05 53					06 51			07 08	07 25			08 01			08 25	08 25		08 55	09 01			
	d	05 00		06 00				06 26	06 53					07 33		08 03				08 33			09 03			
Long Eaton	d			06 10				06 36						07 43						08 43						
Alfreton	d										06 58							07 57								09 07
Langley Mill	d										07 07							08 06								09 14
Nottingham 8	a										07 23							08 26								09 30
	d		05 29		06 07		06 25			07 07	07 30				07 38		08 07	08 35			08 38			09 07	09 30	
Beeston	d				06 13					07 13					07 44		08 13							09 13		
Loughborough	d		05 44	06 20	06 26		06 40	06 55	07 10	07 23				07 52	08 01		08 22			08 52	09 01			09 22	09 45	
Barrow Upon Soar	d							06 59							08 06						09 06					
Sileby	d							07 05							08 10						09 10					
Syston	d							07 10							08 15						09 15					
Leicester	a	05 29	05 57	06 32	06 35		06 51	07 18	07 22	07 34	07 56			08 04	08 25	08 27	08 34	08 57		09 04	09 25		09 27	09 34	09 56	
	d	05 30	05 57	06 32	06 35		06 55		07 23	07 35	08 00			08 05		08 28	08 35	09 00		09 05			09 28	09 35	10 00	
Market Harborough	d		06 13		06 53		07 10			07 49				08 19		08 43	08 49			09 19				09 49	10 15	
Kettering	d	05 54	06 24	06 57	07 03		07 21		07 47	07 59	08 23			08 29		08 54	08 59	09 23		09 29			09 51	09 59		
Wellingborough	d	06 02	06 32	07 05	07 11		07 29		07 55	08 06				08 36			09 06	09 31		09 36				10 06		
Bedford 7	d	06 16	06 50		07 26					08 21				08 51			09 21	09 46		09 51				10 21		
Luton 10	d	06 37	07 08	07 30	08 03					08 36				09 33			09 36	10 18		10 33				10 36		
Luton Airport Parkway 7	d	06 51	07 21	07 46	07 42					08 51				09 07			09 51			10 07				10 51		
Gatwick Airport 10	a	08 10	08 40	09 10	09h25					10 10				10h55			11 10	11 40		11h55				12 10		
St Pancras International	a	07 05	07 38	08 05	08 09		08 21		08 45	09 04	09 17			09 34		09 49	10 04	10 29		10 36			10 46	11 04	11 17	

		XC	EM	EM	XC	EM	EM	EM	XC	EM	EM	EM	XC	EM	EM	EM	EM	XC	EM	EM	XC	EM	EM	EM	XC	EM
		R 1	1◇		1◇	1◇	1◇	◇	R 1	1◇	1◇		1◇	1◇	1◇	1◇	◇	1◇	1◇		1◇	1◇	1◇	◇	R 1	1◇
York 8	d	07 44	07e25		08 19				08 44				09 27	09 27				09 44			10 25	10 25			10 44	
Leeds 10	d	08 10	07e23		08 16	08 40			09 10				09e16					10 10			10e16				11 10	
Wakefield Westgate 7	d	08 23	07f55		08j32	08 52			09 23				09f32					10 23			10f32				11 23	
Doncaster 7	d				08 42			08 59	09 02				09 51					10 02			10 53				11 02	
Barnsley	d	07 58	08 30		08 48			08 58	08 58				09 48				10 01	10 01			10 48			11 01	11 01	
Meadowhall	d	08 22	08 47		09 03			09 22	09 33				10 03	10 07			10 19	10 33			11 04	11 06		11 19	11 33	
Sheffield 7	d	08 53	08 56		09 23	09 27		09 38	09 53				10 23	10 27			10 38	10 53			11 23	11 27		11 38	11 53	
Dronfield	d																									
Chesterfield	d		09 09		09 35	09 40		09 53					10 35	10 40			10 53				11 35	11 40		11 53		
Matlock	d					08 58													10 38							
Belper	d		09 26																10 58							
Burton-on-Trent	d		08 58			09 20					09 58			10 20					10 58			11 20				
Derby 10	a	09 22	09 33		09 55	10 01			10 22				10 55	11 01				11 22			11 55	12 01			12 28	
	d		09 33			10 03					10 33			11 03					11 33			12 03				
Long Eaton	d		09 43								10 43								11 43							
Alfreton	d							10 04									11 04							12 04		
Langley Mill	d																11 11									
Nottingham 8	a							10 24									11 30							12 29		
	d			09 38			10 07			10 30		10 38			11 07	11 30				11 38			12 07			12 30
Beeston	d						10 13								11 13								12 13			
Loughborough	d		09 52	10 01			10 22				10 52	11 01			11 22	11 45			11 52	12 01			12 22			
Barrow Upon Soar	d			10 06								11 06								12 06						
Sileby	d			10 10								11 10								12 10						
Syston	d			10 15								11 15								12 15						
Leicester	a		10 04	10 25		10 28	10 34			10 53	11 04	11 25		11 28	11 34	11 55			12 04	12 25		12 26	12 34			12 57
	d		10 05			10 30	10 35			11 00	11 05			11 30	11 35	12 00			12 05			12 30	12 35			13 00
Market Harborough	d		10 19				10 49				11 19				11 49				12 19				12 49			
Kettering	d		10 29			10 53	10 59				11 29				11 59				12 29				12 59			
Wellingborough	d		10 36			11 01	11 06				11 36				12 06				12 36				13 06			
Bedford 7	d		10 51			11 17	11 21				11 51				12 21				12 51				13 21			
Luton 10	d		11 33			11 48	11 36				12 33			12 21	12 36				13 33				13 36			
Luton Airport Parkway 7	d		11 07			11 51	11 51				12 07			12 36	12 51				13 07				13 51			
Gatwick Airport 10	a		12h56			13 10	13 10				13h55			13 55	14 10				14h55				15 10			
St Pancras International	a		11 34			11 59	12 04			12 15	12 34			12 51	13 04	13 15			13 34			13 44	14 04			14 15

For general notes see front of timetable
For details of catering facilities see Directory of Train Operators

- b Change at Doncaster and Sheffield
- c Change at Doncaster
- e Change at Sheffield
- f Wakefield Kirkgate. Change at Sheffield
- g Change at Derby
- h Change at Bedford
- j Wakefield Kirkgate

Due to Engineering Operations, services from Saturday 13 September on this Table had not been confirmed at time of going to press. These services will be issued in a special Supplement as soon as exact timings have been confirmed

Table 53

Saturdays
until 6 September

Sheffield → East Midlands → London

Route Diagram - See first page of Table 53

		EM	EM	XC	EM	EM	EM	XC	EM	EM	EM	XC	EM	EM	EM	EM	XC	EM	EM	XC	EM	EM	EM	EM	XC	EM
		1 ◇		R 1	1 ◇	1 ◇	◇	R 1	1 ◇	1 ◇		1 ◇	1 ◇	1 ◇	1 ◇	◇	R 1	1 ◇		1 ◇	1 ◇	1 ◇	1 ◇	◇	1 ◇	1 ◇
York 8	d			11 27	11 27			11 44				12 25	12 25				12 44			13 28	13 28				13 44	
Leeds 10	d			11b16	11 16			12 10				12b16					13 10			13b16					14 10	
Wakefield Westgate 7	d			11c32	11e32			12 23				12c32					13 23			13c32					14 23	
Doncaster 7	d			11 55	11 55			12 02				12 52					13 01			13 54					14 02	
Barnsley	d			11 48	11 48		12 01	12 01				12 48				13 01	13 01			13 48				14 01	14 01	
Meadowhall	d			12 03	12 06		12 19	12 33				13 03	13 06			13 21	13 33			14 03	14 07			14 19	14 33	
Sheffield 7	d			12 23	12 27		12 38	12 53				13 23	13 27			13 38	13 53			14 23	14 27			14 38	14 53	15 02
Dronfield	d						12 49																			
Chesterfield	d			12 35	12 40		12 53					13 35	13 40			13 53				14 35	14 40			14 53		15 14
Matlock	d									12 38											14 10					
Belper	d									12 58											14 30					
Burton-on-Trent	d	11 44			12 20					12 58			13 20					13 42			14 20					
Derby 10	a			12 55	13 01			13 22				13 55	14 01				14 22			14 55	15 01				15 22	
	d	12 33			13 03					13 33			14 03					14 33			15 03					
Long Eaton	d	12 43								13 43								14 43								
Alfreton	d						13 04									14 04								15 04		15 27
Langley Mill	d						13 11																	15 11		15 35
Nottingham 8	a						13 29									14 30								15 30		→
	d		12 38			13 07			13 30		13 38			14 07	14 30				14 38			15 07	15 30			
Beeston	d					13 13								14 13								15 13				
Loughborough	d	12 52	13 01			13 22			13 45	13 52	14 01			14 22				14 52	15 01			15 22	15 46			
Barrow Upon Soar	d		13 06								14 06								15 06							
Sileby	d		13 10								14 10								15 10							
Syston	d		13 15								14 15								15 15							
Leicester	a	13 04	13 25		13 28	13 34			13 55	14 04	14 25		14 28	14 34	14 54			15 04	15 25		15 28	15 34	15 58			
	d	13 05			13 30	13 35			14 00	14 05			14 30	14 35	15 00			15 05			15 30	15 35	16 00			
Market Harborough	d	13 19				13 49				14 19				14 49				15 19				15 49				
Kettering	d	13 29				13 59				14 29				14 59				15 29				15 59				
Wellingborough	d	13 36				14 06				14 36				15 06				15 36				16 06				
Bedford 7	d	13 51				14 21				14 51				15 21				15 51				16 21				
Luton 10	d	14 33				14 36				15 33			15 21	15 36				16 33				16 36				
Luton Airport Parkway 7	d	14 07				14 51				15 07			15 36	15 51				16 07				16 51				
Gatwick Airport 10	a	15f55				16 10				16f55			16 55	17 10				17f55				18 10				
St Pancras International	a	14 34			14 45	15 04			15 15	15 34			15 51	16 04	16 15			16 34			16 45	17 04	17 17			

		EM	EM	XC	EM	EM	EM	EM	XC	EM	EM	XC	EM	EM	EM	EM	XC	EM	EM	XC	EM	EM	EM	XC	EM	EM
		1 ◇		1 ◇	1 ◇	1 ◇	1 ◇	◇	1 ◇	1 ◇		1 ◇	1 ◇	1 ◇	1 ◇	◇	1 ◇	1 ◇		1 ◇	1 ◇	1 ◇	◇	1 ◇	1 ◇	1 ◇
York 8	d			14 30	14 30				14 44			15 27	15 27				15 44			16 25	16 25			16 44		
Leeds 10	d			14b16					15 10			15b16					16 10				16 16			17 10		
Wakefield Westgate 7	d			14c32					15 23			15c32					16 23				16e32			17 23		
Doncaster 7	d			14 56					15 02			15 55					16 02			16 53				17 02		
Barnsley	d			14 48				15 01	15 01			15 48				16 01	16 01			16 26	16 48		17 01	17 01		
Meadowhall	d			15 03	15 06			15 19	15 33			16 06	16 09			16 19	16 33			17 00	17 06		17 19	17 33		
Sheffield 7	d			15 23	15 27			15 38	15 53			16 23	16 27			16 38	16 53			17 20	17 27		17 41	17 53		
Dronfield	d															16 49				17 28						
Chesterfield	d			15 35	15 40			15 53				16 35	16 40			16 55				17 35	17 40		17 55			
Matlock	d									15 38											17 01					
Belper	d									15 58											17 21					
Burton-on-Trent	d	14 58			15 20					15 44			16 20					16 58			17 20					17 47
Derby 10	a			15 55	16 01				16 22			16 55	17 01				17 22			17 55	18 01			18 22		
	d	15 33			16 03					16 33			17 03					17 33			18 03					18 33
Long Eaton	d	15 43								16 43								17 43								18 43
Alfreton	d					←		16 04								17 06							18 06			
Langley Mill	d					15 35		16 11								17 13							18 13			
Nottingham 8	a					16 00		16 35								17 31							18 29			
	d		15 38			16 07	16 30				16 38			17 07	17 30				17 38			18 07			18 30	
Beeston	d					16 13								17 13								18 13				
Loughborough	d	15 52	16 01			16 22				16 52	17 03			17 22	17 45			17 52	18 03		18 20	18 25			18 45	18 52
Barrow Upon Soar	d		16 06								17 07								18 07							
Sileby	d		16 10								17 11								18 11							
Syston	d		16 15								17 16								18 16							
Leicester	a	16 04	16 25		16 28	16 34	16 55			17 04	17 25		17 28	17 34	17 56			18 04	18 25		18 33	18 39			18 56	19 04
	d	16 05			16 30	16 35	17 00			17 05			17 30	17 35	18 00			18 05			18 34	18 40			19 00	19 05
Market Harborough	d	16 19				16 49				17 19				17 49				18 19				18 51				19 19
Kettering	d	16 29				16 59				17 29				17 59				18 29				19 01				19 29
Wellingborough	d	16 36				17 06				17 36				18 06				18 36				19 11				19 36
Bedford 7	d	16 51			17 13	17 21				17 51				18 21				18 51				19 25				19 51
Luton 10	d	17 33				17 36				18 33			18 21	18 36								19 41				
Luton Airport Parkway 7	d	17 07			17 51	17 51				18 07			18 36	18 52				19 07								20 07
Gatwick Airport 10	a	18f55			19 10	19 10				19f56			19 56	20 25				21f10				21 40				22f10
St Pancras International	a	17 34			17 51	18 04	18 15			18 34			18 51	19 04	19 08			19 35			19 45	20 09			20 15	20 35

For general notes see front of timetable
For details of catering facilities see Directory of Train Operators

b Change at Sheffield
c Wakefield Kirkgate. Change at Sheffield
e Wakefield Kirkgate
f Change at Bedford

Due to Engineering Operations, services from Saturday 13 September on this Table had not been confirmed at time of going to press. These services will be issued in a special Supplement as soon as exact timings have been confirmed

Table 53

Saturdays
until 6 September

Sheffield → East Midlands → London

Route Diagram - See first page of Table 53

		EM	XC	EM	EM	EM	XC	EM	EM	EM	EM	XC	EM	EM	XC	EM	EM	EM	XC	EM	EM	XC	EM	EM
			1◇	1◇	1◇	◇	1◇	1◇	1◇		1◇	1◇	1◇	◇	1◇	1◇	◇	1◇	1◇		◇	1◇	1◇	◇
																			A			A		
			🍴	🍴	🍴		🍴	🍴	🍴		🍴	🍴	🍴		🍴	🍴			🍴			🍴	🍴	
York [8]	d		17 25	17 25			17 44				17 49	18 25		18 25	18 44				19 44		20c06	20 44		
Leeds [10]	d		17e16				18 10					18e16			19 10		19 16	19 16	20 10		20 16	21 10		
Wakefield Westgate [7]	d		17f32				18 23				18f03	18f32			19 23		19g32	19g32	20 23		20g32	21 23		
Doncaster [7]	d		17 55				18 15				18 15	18 51			19 03		19 49	19 49	20 03		20 42	21 07		21 49
Barnsley	d		17 48			18 01	18 01				18e26	18 48		19 01	19 01		19 48	20 06			20 48	21 06		21 26
Meadowhall	🚋 d		18 04	18 06		18 19	18 38				18 38	19 06		19 19	19 33		20 07	20 24	20 35		21 07	21 35		22 09
Sheffield [7]	🚋 d		18 23	18 27		18 38	18 53				19 07	19 23		19 38	19 53		20 40	20 47	20 53		21 37	21 53	22 00	22 36
Dronfield	d																							
Chesterfield	d		18 35	18 40		18 53					19 19	19 35		19 53	20 05		20 55	21 00	21 05		21 53	22 05	22 12	22 50
Matlock	d								18 38									20 20						
Belper	d								18 58									20 40						
Burton-on-Trent	d			18 29					18 58		19 20							20 29						
Derby [10]	a		18 55	19 01			19 22				19 40	19 55			20 26			21 22	21 26			22 26	22 35	
	d			19 03					19 33		19 51							21 22						
Long Eaton	d								19 43		20 02													
Alfreton	d					19 04								20 04			21 06				22 04			
Langley Mill	d																21 13				22 11			
Nottingham [8]	🚋 a					19 29								20 29			21 35				22 38			23 26
	d	18 38			19 07			19 30		19 33			20 07			20 30				21 30				
Beeston	d				19 13					19 39			20 13											
Loughborough	d	19 01		19 18	19 24			19 45	19 54	19 57	20 15					20 49		21 41		21 46				
Barrow Upon Soar	d	19 06								20 02														
Sileby	d	19 10								20 06														
Syston	d	19 15								20 12														
Leicester	a	19 25		19 30	19 38			19 56	20 04	20 22	20 26		20 34			21 02		21 56		22 00				
	d			19 30	19 39			20 00	20 05		20 27		20 35			21 03								
Market Harborough	d				19 53				20 19		20 41		20 49			21 18								
Kettering	d				20 03				20 29		20 51		20 59			21 28								
Wellingborough	d				20 11				20 36		20 59		21 07			21 36								
Bedford [7]	d				20 25				20 51		21 13		21 23			21 52								
Luton [10]	d				20 41						21 29		21 39			22 09								
Luton Airport Parkway [7]	d				20 52				21 09		21 46		21 52			22 22								
Gatwick Airport [10]	✈ a				22 40				23h10		23 10		23 40			00 17								
St Pancras International	⊖ a			20 48	21 08			21 12	21 35		21 52		22 04			22 43								

Sundays
until 13 July

		EM	EM	EM	EM	EM	EM	EM	EM	EM	XC	EM	EM	EM	EM	EM	EM	EM	EM	EM	EM	XC	EM	EM	EM	EM
		1◇	1◇	1◇	1◇	1◇	1◇	🚌	1◇	1◇	1◇	🚌	1◇	🚌	1◇	🚌	◇	🚌	1◇	🚌		R 1	1◇	🚌	1◇	1◇
		🍴	🍴	🍴	🍴	🍴	🍴		🍴	🍴	🍴		🍴		🍴		🛒		🍴			🍴	🍴		🍴	🍴
York [8]	d														09j00		09c00		09c00			09 27			10c23	
Leeds [10]	d										08 30				09 00		09 00		09c05			10 00			10 57	
Wakefield Westgate [7]	d										08 43				09 11		09 11		09c17			10 12			11 08	
Doncaster [7]	d										09 03				09 33		09 39		10 13			10 33			10 55	
Barnsley	d														09 21				10 12						10 49	
Meadowhall	🚋 d												09 00		09 41		10 00		10 42			11 00			11 13	
Sheffield [7]	🚋 d							08 25			09 32		09 50	10 15	10 04		10 36		11 02	11 15		11 21			11 44	
Dronfield	d																									
Chesterfield	d							08 56				09 49		10 45		10 30		10 54		11 45				11 38		
Matlock	d																		10 40		10 40					
Belper	d																		11 00		11 00					
Burton-on-Trent	d																									
Derby [10]	a							09 41			10 22	10 34	10 34		10 50			11 39	11 44		11 11	12 17		12 23	12 26	
	d	06 56		07 50		08 53			09 51				10 44		10 51				11 49		11 20				12 33	
Long Eaton	d			08 00					10 01				10 55						11 59		11 20					
Alfreton	d															11 00	11 10									
Langley Mill	d																									
Nottingham [8]	🚋 a														11 12		11 30				11 48					
	d		07 29		08 19		09 19			10 23					11 19								12 24			13 26
Beeston	d				08 27					10 29													12 30			
Loughborough	d			08 09		09 08	09 36		10 11	10 40			11 06		11 34				12 09				12 41		12 50	13 41
Barrow Upon Soar	d																									
Sileby	d																									
Syston	d																									
Leicester	a	07 19	07 50	08 20	08 47	09 19	09 48		10 22	10 51			11 19		11 47				12 20				12 52		13 03	13 51
	d	07 19	07 50	08 20	08 47	09 19	09 48		10 22	10 51			11 19		11 47				12 20				12 52		13 03	13 52
Market Harborough	d	07 39	08 09	08 39	09 06	09 39	10 08		10 41	11 10			11 38		12 07				12 39				13 11		13 23	14 06
Kettering	d	07 49	08 19	08 49	09 17	09 49	10 19		10 51	11 20			11 49		12 17				12 49				13 21		13 34	14 16
Wellingborough	d	08 01	08 31	09 01	09 29	10 01	10 30		10 58	11 27			11 57		12 28				12 58				13 28		13 44	14 23
Bedford [7]	d	08 16	08 46	09 15	09 45	10 15	10 46		11 16	11 46			12 16		12 45				13 16				13 45		14 07	14 44
Luton [10]	d	08 37	09 08	10 03	10 08	11 03	11 07		12 03	12 08			12 38		13 08				13 49				14 09		14 43	14 59
Luton Airport Parkway [7]	d	08 52	09 22	09 43	10 22	11 06	11 22		11 41	12 22			12 52		13 22				13 52				14h20		14 46	15 16
Gatwick Airport [10]	✈ a	10 48	11 18	11h48	12 18	12 48	13 18		13h48	14 18			14 48		15 18				15 48				16 18		16 18	16 48
St Pancras International	⊖ a	09 16	09 45	10 16	10 46	11 19	11 49		12 19	12 50			13 18		13 48				14 18				14 44		14 55	15 29

For general notes see front of timetable
For details of catering facilities see
Directory of Train Operators

A 🍴 to Leeds
c Change at Doncaster and Sheffield
e Change at Sheffield
f Wakefield Kirkgate. Change at Sheffield
g Wakefield Kirkgate
h Change at Bedford
j Change at Doncaster

Due to Engineering Operations, services from Saturday 13 September on this Table had not been confirmed at time of going to press. These services will be issued in a special Supplement as soon as exact timings have been confirmed

until 13 July

Sheffield → East Midlands → London

Route Diagram - See first page of Table 53

		EM	XC	EM	EM	EM	EM	XC	EM	EM	EM	EM	EM	EM	XC	EM	EM		EM	EM	EM	EM	EM	XC	EM	EM
			R 1 [catering]	[bus]	◇ [trolley]	[bus]	1 ◇ [catering]	R 1 [catering]	1 ◇ [catering]	[bus]	◇ [trolley]	[bus]	1 ◇ [catering]		R 1 [catering]	1 ◇ [catering]	1 ◇ [catering]		[bus]	◇	[bus]	1 ◇ [catering]	1 ◇ [catering]	R 1 [catering]	[bus]	◇
York 8	d		10 28		10 28		10 28	11 28			11b29		12b57		12 28							13b33		13 28		14b05
Leeds 10	d		11 00		11 14		11 14	12 00			11b40		12b40		13 00					13 14		13 14		14 00		13b40
Wakefield Westgate 7	d		11 12		11c30		11c30	12 12			11b52		12b52		13 12					13c30		13c30		14 12		13b52
Doncaster 7	d		11 38		11 42		11 42	12 33			12 42		13 38		13 38					13 42		14 13		14 39		14 42
Barnsley	d		11 49		11 49		12 12						13 12							13 49		14 12				
Meadowhall	d		12 05		12 10		12 33	13 00			13 00		13 51		14 00					14 11		14 42		15 00		15 00
Sheffield 7	d		12 21		12 43		13 01	13 21			13 41		14 14		14 21					14 44		15 02		15 21		15 36
Dronfield	d																									
Chesterfield	d			12 37		12 51				13 44		14 08							14 38		14 57				15 30	
Matlock	d	12 39					12 39							14 40		14 40										
Belper	d	13 00					13 00							15 01		15 01										
Burton-on-Trent	d	12 48					12 48						14 29													
Derby 10	a	13 12	13 17			13 36	13 43	14 14				14 53	14 56	15 12	15 18						15 42	15 51		16 17		
	d	13 16					13 46						15 03	15 14		15 30						15 52				
Long Eaton	d	13 26					13 56							15 24								16 02				
Alfreton	d			13 07	13 17					14 14	14 24								15 08	15 18					16 00	16 10
Langley Mill	d																			15 26						16 18
Nottingham 8	a	13 52			13 38						14 46			15 48						15 44						16 33
	d								14 18								15 39						16 03			
Beeston	d								14 24														16 08			
Loughborough	d						14 07		14 34				15 19				15 53					16 11	16 22			
Barrow Upon Soar	d																									
Sileby	d																									
Syston	d																									
Leicester	a						14 20		14 45				15 29			15 56	16 03					16 24	16 33			
	d						14 20		14 47				15 31			15 57	16 04					16 25	16 34			
Market Harborough	d						14 38		15 00				15 45				16 19						16 49			
Kettering	d						14 49		15 10				15 55				16 29						16 59			
Wellingborough	d						14 57		15 17				16 02				16 36						17 06			
Bedford 7	d						15 15		15 35								16 54					17 09	17 25			
Luton 10	d						15 49		15 55								17 11					17 43	18 13			
Luton Airport Parkway 7	d						15 52		16 16				16 35				17e22						17 42			
Gatwick Airport 10	a						17 48		17 48								19 18					19 18	19e48			
St Pancras International	a						16 06		16 27				17 06			17 24	17 41					17 55	18 11			

		EM	EM	EM	EM	EM	EM	XC	EM	EM	EM	EM	EM	XC		EM	EM	EM	EM	EM	EM	EM	XC	EM	EM	EM
		1 ◇ [catering]	[bus]	1 ◇ [catering]	1 ◇ [catering]	1 ◇ [catering]	1	R 1 [catering]	[bus]	◇	[bus]	1 ◇ [catering]	1 ◇ [catering]	R 1 [catering]		[bus]	◇	[bus]	1 ◇ [catering]	[bus]	1 ◇ [catering]		R 1 [catering]	[bus]	◇	[bus]
York 8	d			14b05				14 28		14b36		14b36		15 28			16b03		16b03		17 01		16 28		17b03	
Leeds 10	d			13b40				15 00		15 09		15 09		16 00			15b40		16 17		16 40		17 00		17 09	
Wakefield Westgate 7	d			13b52				15 12		15 24		15 24		16 12			15b52		16c46		16 52		17 12		17 24	
Doncaster 7	d			14 42				15 38		15 42		15 42		16 39			16 42		16 42		17 25		17 38		17 42	
Barnsley	d							15 12		15 12		15 12		16 12			16 12		17 12							
Meadowhall	d			15 00				16 00		16 11		16 11		17 00			17 00		17 33		17 52		18 00		18 11	
Sheffield 7	d			15 49				16 21		16 36		16 49		17 21			17 36		17 50		18 10		18 21		18 40	
Dronfield	d																									
Chesterfield	d		15 46						16 33		16 52					17 30		17 42		18 03				18 34		19 02
Matlock	d						16 40															18 40				
Belper	d						17 00															19 00				
Burton-on-Trent	d						16 29					17 20										18 20				
Derby 10	a		16 31	16 35			17 12	17 17			17 37	17 35		18 17				18 27	18 35			19 12	19 17			19 47
	d			16 41			17 22					17 47							18 37			19 14				
Long Eaton	d						17 32					17 59										19 26				
Alfreton	d								17 03	17 13						18 00	18 10			18 33	18 43			19 04	19 14	
Langley Mill	d									17 21							18 18				18 51				19 22	
Nottingham 8	a						17 57			17 36							18 36				19 10	19 43			19 43	
	d	16 39			17 02	17 06							18 17								19 36					
Beeston	d					17 16							18 22								19 43					
Loughborough	d			16 57	17 19							18 07	18 34						18 54							
Barrow Upon Soar	d																									
Sileby	d																									
Syston	d																									
Leicester	a	17 03		17 10	17 31	17 37						18 19	18 44						19 05		20 00					
	d	17 03		17 12	17 31	17 39						18 20	18 45						19 05		20 00					
Market Harborough	d			17 29		17 55						18 35	18 59						19 22		20 14					
Kettering	d			17 40		18 06						18 46	19 09						19 32		20 24					
Wellingborough	d			17 48		18 14						18 55	19 16						19 39		20 32					
Bedford 7	d			18 06		18 34						19 13	19 36						19 57		20 49					
Luton 10	d			18 27		18 55						19 43	19 52						20 33		21 08					
Luton Airport Parkway 7	d			18 46		19 16						19 46	20 16						20 36		21 36					
Gatwick Airport 10	a			20 18		20 48						21 18	21 48						22 18		23 18					
St Pancras International	a	18 28		18 57	19 04	19 24						19 59	20 21						20 49		21 37					

For general notes see front of timetable
For details of catering facilities see Directory of Train Operators

b Change at Doncaster and Sheffield
c Wakefield Kirkgate
e Change at Bedford

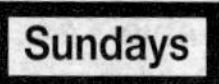

until 13 July

Sheffield → East Midlands → London

Route Diagram - See first page of Table 53

		EM 1 ◇ ☕	XC 1 ◇ ☕	EM 🚌	EM ◇	EM 1 ◇ ☕	EM	XC 1 ◇ ☕	EM ◇	EM 🚌	EM 🚌	XC 1 ◇ ☕	EM 🚌	EM 🚌	EM ◇	EM 🚌	XC 1 ◇ ☕	EM 1 ◇ ☕	EM 🚌	EM	EM 🚌	XC 1 ◇ ☕	EM ◇	EM 🚌		
York 8	d	17b35	17 28		18b05			18 28	19b05			19 28			20b02		20 28	20 44				21 25	21b28			
Leeds 10	d	17 09	18 00					19 00	19 09			20 00					21 00	20b20				22 00				
Wakefield Westgate 7	d	17 24	18 12					19 12	19 24			20 12					21 12					22 12				
Doncaster 7	d	18 13	18 38		18 42			19 34	19 42			20 34			20 42		21 33	21 42				22 33				
Barnsley	d	18 12						19 11				20 12					21 12					22 21				
Meadowhall	d	18 42	19 00					20 00	20 11			20 45			21 08		21 45	22 00				22 50				
Sheffield 7	d	19 01	19 21		19 37			20 21	20 37		21 00	21 21		21 30	21 40	22 00	22 04	22 18			23 00	23 10	23 26			
Dronfield	d																									
Chesterfield	d			19 31						20 33	21 30		21 35	22 00		22 30			22 18		23 30			23 20		
Matlock	d	18 40					20 40													22 41						
Belper	d	19 00					21 00													23 01						
Burton-on-Trent	d	19 20					20 29																			
Derby 10	a	19 43	20 17				21 12	21 17				22 12					22 54	23 02	23 03	23 14		23 59				
	d	19 57					21 14																			
Long Eaton	d	20 07					21 26																			
Alfreton	d			20 01	20 11				21 13	21 03			22 05		22 15								00 01	23 50		
Langley Mill	d								21 20						22 23								00 08			
Nottingham 8	a				20 32		21 45		21 41						22 44								00 30			
	d					21 14																				
Beeston	d																									
Loughborough	d	20 20				21 28																				
Barrow Upon Soar	d																									
Sileby	d																									
Syston	d																									
Leicester	a	20 36				21 40																				
	d	20 38				21 41																				
Market Harborough	d	20 54				21 55																				
Kettering	d	21 04				22 05																				
Wellingborough	d	21 11				22 13																				
Bedford 7	d	21 30				22 31																				
Luton 10	d	21 49				22 50																				
Luton Airport Parkway 7	d	22 06				23 06																				
Gatwick Airport 10 ✈	a	23 48				00 46																				
St Pancras International ⊖	a	22 18				23 22																				

Sundays

20 July to 7 September

		EM 1 ◇ ☕	EM 🚌	EM 1 ◇ ☕		EM 1 ◇ ☕	EM 🚌	EM 1 ◇ ☕		EM 1 ◇ ☕	EM 🚌	EM 1 ◇ ☕		EM 1 ◇ ☕	EM 1 ◇ ☕	XC 1 ◇ ☕		EM 1 ◇ ☕	EM	EM ◇		EM 1 ◇ ☕	EM	EM 1 ◇ ☕		XC R 1 ☕
York 8	d															09c00		09b00						09 13		09 13
Leeds 10	d															09 00		09 00				09 20		10 00		10 00
Wakefield Westgate 7	d															09 12		09 12				09 31		10 11		10 12
Doncaster 7	d															09 34				09 39		09 50		10 13		10 42
Barnsley	d															09 21								10 12		10 49
Meadowhall	d															09 41				10 00				10 42		11 05
Sheffield 7	d															10 00		10 08		10 34		10 14		11 13		11 23
Dronfield	d																									
Chesterfield	d															10 12		10 22		10 47		10 28		11 25		11 35
Matlock	d																		10 40					10 40		
Belper	d																		11 00					11 00		
Burton-on-Trent	d																									
Derby 10	a															10 38		10 44	11 11			10 50	←	11 46		11 57
	d	06 56				07 50				08 53				09 51				10 44	11 20			10 51	11 20	11 49		
Long Eaton	d					08 00								10 01				10 55	→				11 30	11 59		
Alfreton	d																									
Langley Mill	d																									
Nottingham 8	a																			11 18		11 12	11 48			
	d		06 50				07 26				08 46				10 16							11 19				
Beeston	d						07 47								10 22											
Loughborough	d					08 09				09 08		09 36		10 11	10 35			11 06				11 34		12 09		
Barrow Upon Soar	d																									
Sileby	d																									
Syston	d																									
Leicester	a	07 19	07 40			08 20	08 37			09 19	09 26	09 48		10 22	10 47			11 19				11 47		12 20		
	d	07 19		07 50		08 20		08 47		09 19		09 48		10 22	10 47			11 19				11 47		12 20		
Market Harborough	d	07 39		08 09		08 39		09 06		09 39		10 08		10 41	11 07			11 38				12 07		12 39		
Kettering	d	07 49		08 19		08 49		09 17		09 49		10 19		10 51	11 18			11 49				12 17		12 49		
Wellingborough	d	08 01		08 31		09 01		09 29		10 01		10 30		10 58	11 26			11 57				12 28		12 58		
Bedford 7	d	08 16		08 46		09 15		09 45		10 15		10 46		11 16	11 46			12 16				12 45		13 16		
Luton 10	d	08 37		09 08		10 03		10 08		11 03		11 07		12 03	12 08			12 38				13 08		13 49		
Luton Airport Parkway 7	d	08 52		09 22		09 43		10 22		11 06		11 22		11 41	12 22			12 52				13 22		13 52		
Gatwick Airport 10 ✈	a	10 48		11 18		11e48		12 18		12 48		13 18		13e48	14 18			14 48				15 18		15 48		
St Pancras International ⊖	a	09 16		09 45		10 16		10 46		11 19		11 49		12 19	12 50			13 18				13 48		14 18		

For general notes see front of timetable
For details of catering facilities see Directory of Train Operators

b Change at Doncaster and Sheffield
c Change at Doncaster
e Change at Bedford

Due to Engineering Operations, services from Sunday 14 September on this Table had not been confirmed at time of going to press. These services will be issued in a special Supplement as soon as exact timings have been confirmed

Table 53

Sundays

20 July to 7 September

Sheffield → East Midlands → London

Route Diagram - See first page of Table 53

		EM	EM	XC	XC	EM	EM	EM	EM	XC	EM	XC	EM	XC	EM	EM	EM	XC	EM	EM
		1 ◇	1 ◇	R 1	1 ◇	1 ◇	◇		1 ◇	1 ◇	1 ◇	R 1	◇	1 ◇	1 ◇	◇		R 1	1 ◇	1 ◇
York [8]	d		10b23	10 13	11 24		11 24		11b29	12 25		12 13	12 25	13 25	13 25			13 13		
Leeds [10]	d		11 06	11 00	11c14				11b40	11 40		13 00	13 00	13c14				14 00	14 00	
Wakefield Westgate [7]	d		11 17	11 12	11e30				11b52	11 52		13 12	13 11	13e30				14 12	14 11	
Doncaster [7]	d		10 55	11 37	11 50				12 16	12 50				13 50						
Barnsley	d		11 12		11 49		12 12		12 12				13 12	13 49					14 12	
Meadowhall	d		11 33	11 44	12 05		12 33		12 43	13 00			13 34	14 04		14 14		14 14	14 33	
Sheffield [7]	d		11 52	12 06	12 23		12 52		13 09	13 23		13 48	13 58	14 23	14 27	14 41		14 48	14 55	
Dronfield	d																			
Chesterfield	d		12 05		12 35		13 06		13 22	13 35			14 13	14 35	14 41	14 56			15 08	
Matlock	d							12 39	12 39								14 40		14 40	
Belper	d							13 00	13 00								15 01		15 01	
Burton-on-Trent	d							12 48	12 48						14 21				14 58	
Derby [10]	a		12 27	12 37	12 55			13 12	13 45	13 55		14 18		14 55	15 02		15 12	15 20	15 29	
	d		12 33					13 16	13 46						15 03		15 14		15 30	
Long Eaton	d							13 26	13 56								15 24			
Alfreton	d						13 18						14 24			15 07				
Langley Mill	d															15 15				
Nottingham [8]	a						13 40	13 52					14 47			15 36	15 48			
	d	12 24				13 26					14 18									15 39
Beeston	d	12 30									14 24									
Loughborough	d	12 41	12 50			13 41			14 07		14 34				15 19					15 53
Barrow Upon Soar	d																			
Sileby	d																			
Syston	d																			
Leicester	a	12 52	13 03			13 51			14 20		14 45				15 29				15 56	16 03
	d	12 52	13 03			13 52			14 20		14 47				15 31				15 57	16 04
Market Harborough	d	13 11	13 23			14 06			14 38		15 00				15 45					16 19
Kettering	d	13 21	13 34			14 16			14 49		15 10				15 55					16 29
Wellingborough	d	13 28	13 44			14 23			14 57		15 17				16 02					16 36
Bedford [7]	d	13 45	14 07			14 44			15 15		15 35									16 54
Luton [10]	d	14 09	14 43			14 59			15 49		15 55									17 11
Luton Airport Parkway [7]	d	14f20	14 46			15 16			15 52		16 16				16 35					17f22
Gatwick Airport [10]	a	16 18	16 18			16 48			17 48		17 48									19 18
St Pancras International	a	14 44	14 55			15 29			16 06		16 27				17 06				17 24	17 41

		EM	XC	EM	EM	XC	EM	EM	EM	EM	XC	EM	EM	XC	EM	XC	EM	EM	XC	EM
		1 ◇	1 ◇	1 ◇	◇	R 1	1 ◇	1 ◇	1 ◇	1 ◇	R 1	◇	1	R 1	1 ◇	1 ◇	1 ◇	◇	R 1	1 ◇
York [8]	d	13b33	14 25		14 25	14 14		14b36			15 25	15 25		15 13	15b34	16 25		16 25	16 13	16 25
Leeds [10]	d					15 00		14 59				15 09		16 00	16 00				17 00	17 00
Wakefield Westgate [7]	d					15 12		15 11				15 24		16 12	16 11				17 12	17 11
Doncaster [7]	d	14 13	14 50					15 13			15 48	15 48			16 13	16 50				
Barnsley	d							15 12							16 12					17 12
Meadowhall	d	14 43	15 00					15 43			16 00	16 11		16 11	16 42	17 00				17 34
Sheffield [7]	d	15 10	15 23		15 39	15 48		16 04		16 09	16 23	16 39		16 48	17 08	17 23		17 39	17 48	17 52
Dronfield	d																			
Chesterfield	d	15 25	15 35		15 54			16 18		16 24	16 35	16 54			17 22	17 35		17 53		18 04
Matlock	d												16 40							
Belper	d												17 00							
Burton-on-Trent	d												16 58							17 20
Derby [10]	a	15 51	15 55			16 19		16 40			16 55		17 12	17 20	17 43	17 55			18 17	18 27
	d	15 52						16 41					17 22		17 44					18 28
Long Eaton	d	16 02											17 32		17 56					
Alfreton	d				16 05					16 36		17 08						18 04		
Langley Mill	d				16 12					16 45		17 17						18 12		
Nottingham [8]	a				16 33					17 01		17 32	17 55					18 30		
	d			16 03			16 39		17 02	17 07							18 17			
Beeston	d			16 08						17 15							18 22			
Loughborough	d	16 11		16 22				16 57	17 19						18 04		18 34			18 46
Barrow Upon Soar	d																			
Sileby	d																			
Syston	d																			
Leicester	a	16 24		16 33			17 03	17 10	17 31	17 38					18 16		18 44			18 57
	d	16 25		16 34			17 03	17 12	17 31	17 39					18 17		18 45			18 57
Market Harborough	d			16 49				17 29		17 55					18 32		18 59			19 14
Kettering	d			16 59				17 40		18 06					18 43		19 09			19 24
Wellingborough	d			17 06				17 48		18 14					18 52		19 16			19 31
Bedford [7]	d	17 09		17 25				18 06		18 34					19 10		19 36			19 49
Luton [10]	d	17 43		18 13				18 27		18 55					19 43		19 52			20 19
Luton Airport Parkway [7]	d			17 42				18 46		19 16					19 46		20 16			20 22
Gatwick Airport [10]	a	19 18		19f48				20 18		20 48					21 18		21 48			22 18
St Pancras International	a	17 55		18 11			18 28	18 57	19 04	19 24					19 56		20 21			20 49

For general notes see front of timetable
For details of catering facilities see Directory of Train Operators

b Change at Doncaster and Sheffield
c Change at Sheffield
e Wakefield Kirkgate. Change at Sheffield
f Change at Bedford

Due to Engineering Operations, services from Sunday 14 September on this Table had not been confirmed at time of going to press. These services will be issued in a special Supplement as soon as exact timings have been confirmed

Table 53

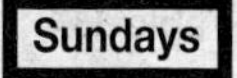

Sundays

20 July to 7 September

Sheffield → East Midlands → London

Route Diagram - See first page of Table 53

		XC	EM	EM		EM	XC	XC		EM	EM	XC		XC	EM	EM	EM	XC	EM	XC	EM	XC	EM	EM		
							R																			
		1 ◇	1 ◇	◇			1	1 ◇		1 ◇	◇	1 ◇		1 ◇	1 ◇	◇		1 ◇	◇	1 ◇	1 ◇	1 ◇		◇		
		🍴	🍴				🍴	🍴		🍴		🍴		🍴	🍴			🍴		🍴	🍴	🍴				
York 8	d	17 25	17 32	17 32			17 14	18 25		18 25		18 15		19 23		19 23		19 15	20b02	20 28	20b40	21 24		21b28		
Leeds 10	d	17 05	17c09				18 00	18c00				19 00				19 09		20 00		21 15				21 40		
Wakefield Westgate 7	d	17 18	17c24				18 12	18c11				19 12				19 24		20 12		21 26				21 55		
Doncaster 7	d	17 50	18 00					18 50						19 50					20 42	20 42	21 23	21 51		22 20		
Barnsley	d							18 12						19 12					20 12	21 12				22 21		
Meadowhall	d	18 00	18 11				18 26	19 00						20 00		20 11		20 11	21 08	21 32	21 45	22 00		22 50		
Sheffield 7	d	18 23	18 30	18 40			18 48	19 23		19 26	19 37	19 48		20 23		20 38		20 48	21 41	22 00	22 06	22 23		23 27		
Dronfield	d																									
Chesterfield	d	18 35	18 43	18 54				19 35		19 41	19 53	20 00		20 35		20 54		21 00	21 56	22 12	22 18	22 35		23 41		
Matlock	d					18 40				18 40							20 40						22 41			
Belper	d					19 00				19 00							21 00						23 01			
Burton-on-Trent	d					18 20				19 20							20 29									
Derby 10	a	18 55				19 12	19 20	19 55		20 01		20 20		20 55			21 12	21 20		22 34	22 43	22 55	23 14			
	d					19 14				20 02							21 14									
Long Eaton	d					19 26				20 12							21 26									
Alfreton	d		18 55	19 05							20 05					21 05			22 08					23 52		
Langley Mill	d		19 03	19 17												21 16			22 19					00 01		
Nottingham 8	a		19 23	19 39		19 43					20 29					21 38	21 45		22 41					00 23		
	d		19 36												21 14											
Beeston	d		19 43																							
Loughborough	d									20 25					21 28											
Barrow Upon Soar	d																									
Sileby	d																									
Syston	d																									
Leicester	a		20 00							20 36					21 40											
	d		20 00							20 38					21 41											
Market Harborough	d		20 14							20 54					21 55											
Kettering	d		20 24							21 04					22 05											
Wellingborough	d		20 32							21 11					22 13											
Bedford 7	d		20 49							21 30					22 31											
Luton 10	d		21 08							21 49					22 50											
Luton Airport Parkway 7	d		21 36							22 06					23 06											
Gatwick Airport 10 ✈	a		23 18							23 48					00 46											
St Pancras International ⊖	a		21 37							22 18					23 22											

For general notes see front of timetable
For details of catering facilities see
Directory of Train Operators

b Change at Doncaster and Sheffield
c Change at Sheffield

Due to Engineering Operations, services from Sunday 14 September on this Table had not been confirmed at time of going to press. These services will be issued in a special Supplement as soon as exact timings have been confirmed

Table 53A

Mondays to Fridays

Kettering → Corby
Bus Service

	EM MO	EM MX	EM	EM		EM	EM	EM	EM		EM	EM	EM	EM		EM	EM	EM	EM		EM	EM	EM	EM	EM
St Pancras International .. 53 d	23 00	23 15	.....	.....	.....	.....	.....	06 10	07 00	.....	07 30	08 00	08 30	09 00	.....	09 30	10 00	10 30	11 00	.....	11 30	12 00	12 30	13 00	13 30
Sheffield . . 53 d	.	.	.	.	.	.	.	.	.	.	.	.	.	.	.	.	.	.	.	.	.	.	.	.	.
Leicester .... 53 d	.....	.....	05 00	05 25	.....	06 00	06 30	06 55	07 30	.....	08 05	08 35	09 05	09 35	.....	10 05	10 35	11 05	11 35	.....	12 05	12 35	13 05	13 35	14 05
Kettering d	00 23	00 39	05 28	05 59	.	06 33	07 03	07 25	08 03	.	08 34	09 05	09 34	10 04	.	10 34	11 04	11 34	12 04	.	12 34	13 04	13 34	14 04	14 34
Corby Town Centre .... a	00 43	00 59	05 48	06 19	.....	06 53	07 23	07 45	08 23	.....	08 56	09 25	09 54	10 24	.....	10 54	11 24	11 54	12 24	.....	12 54	13 24	13 54	14 24	14 54

	EM		EM	EM	EM	EM		EM	EM	EM	EM		EM	EM	EM	EM		EM	EM	EM	EM		EM		
St Pancras International .. 53 d	14 00	.....	14 30	15 00	15 30	16 00	.....	16 30	17 00	17 30	18 00	.....	18 30	19 00	19 30	20 00	.....	20 30	21 00	21 30	22 00	.....	22 25	.....	.....
Sheffield . . 53 d	.	.	.	.	.	.	.	.	.	.	.	.	.	.	.	.	.	.	.	.	.	.	.	.	.
Leicester .... 53 d	14 35	.....	15 05	15 35	16 05	16 35	.....	17 05	17 35	18 05	18 35	.....	19 05	19 35	20 05	20 35	.....	.....	21 15	22 00	.....	.....	.....	.....	.....
Kettering d	15 04	.	15 34	16 04	16 34	17 04	.	17 34	18 04	18 38	19 06	.	19 34	20 06	20 36	21 06	.	21 33	22 04	22 32	23 06	.	23 34	.	.
Corby Town Centre .... a	15 24	.....	15 54	16 24	16 56	17 26	.....	17 56	18 24	18 58	19 26	.....	19 54	20 26	20 56	21 26	.....	21 53	22 24	22 52	23 26	.....	23 54	.....	.....

Saturdays

	EM	EM	EM		EM	EM	EM		EM		EM	EM	EM	EM	EM		EM	EM	EM		EM	EM	EM		EM
St Pancras International .. 53 d	.....	.....	.....	.....	.....	.....	.....	.....	.....	.....	.....	.....	.....	.....	.....	.....	.....	.....	.....	.....	.....	.....	.....	.....	.....
Sheffield . . 53 d	.	.	.	.	.	.	.	.	.	.	.	.	.	.	.	.	.	.	.	.	.	.	.	.	.
Leicester .... 53 d	.....	.....	.....	.....	.....	.....	.....	.....	.....	.....	.....	.....	.....	.....	.....	.....	.....	.....	.....	.....	.....	.....	.....	.....	.....
Kettering d	00 39	06 01	06 29	.	07 03	07 29	08 06	.	08 34	09 04	09 34	10 04	10 34	11 04	11 34	.	12 04	12 34	13 04	.	13 34	14 04	14 34	.	15 04
Corby Town Centre .... a	00 59	06 21	06 39	.....	07 23	07 49	08 26	.....	08 54	09 24	09 54	10 24	10 54	11 24	11 54	.....	12 24	12 54	13 24	.....	13 54	14 24	14 54	.....	15 24

	EM	EM	EM		EM	EM	EM		EM	EM	EM		EM	EM	EM		EM	EM	EM		EM				
St Pancras International .. 53 d	.....	.....	.....	.....	.....	.....	.....	.....	.....	.....	.....	.....	.....	.....	.....	.....	.....	.....	.....	.....	.....	.....	.....	.....	.....
Sheffield . . 53 d	.	.	.	.	.	.	.	.	.	.	.	.	.	.	.	.	.	.	.	.	.	.	.	.	.
Leicester .... 53 d	.....	.....	.....	.....	.....	.....	.....	.....	.....	.....	.....	.....	.....	.....	.....	.....	.....	.....	.....	.....	.....	.....	.....	.....	.....
Kettering d	15 34	16 04	16 34	.	17 04	17 34	18 04	.	18 34	19 04	19 34	.	20 08	20 34	21 04	.	21 33	22 22	22 34	.	23 40	.	.	.	.
Corby Town Centre .... a	15 54	16 24	16 54	.....	17 24	17 54	18 24	.....	18 54	19 24	19 54	.....	20 28	20 54	21 24	.....	21 53	22 42	22 54	.....	00 01	.....	.....	.....	.....

Sundays

	EM	EM		EM	EM		EM	EM		EM	EM		EM	EM		EM	EM		EM	EM		EM	EM		EM
St Pancras International .. 53 d	.....	.....	.....	.....	.....	.....	.....	.....	.....	.....	.....	.....	.....	.....	.....	.....	.....	.....	.....	.....	.....	.....	.....	.....	.....
Sheffield . . 53 d	.	.	.	.	.	.	.	.	.	.	.	.	.	.	.	.	.	.	.	.	.	.	.	.	.
Leicester .... 53 d	.....	.....	.....	.....	.....	.....	.....	.....	.....	.....	.....	.....	.....	.....	.....	.....	.....	.....	.....	.....	.....	.....	.....	.....	.....
Kettering d	23p40	07 56	.	08 24	08 56	.	09 22	09 55	.	10 21	10 56	.	11 24	11 26	.	11 56	12 24	.	12 54	13 23	.	13 52	14 18	.	14 51
Corby Town Centre .... a	00 01	08 16	.....	08 44	09 16	.....	09 42	10 15	.....	10 41	11 16	.....	11 44	11 46	.....	12 16	12 44	.....	13 14	13 43	.....	14 12	14 38	.....	15 11

	EM	EM		EM	EM		EM	EM		EM A	EM B		EM	EM		EM	EM		EM	EM	EM	EM	EM		
St Pancras International .. 53 d	.....	.....	.....	.....	.....	.....	.....	.....	.....	.....	.....	.....	.....	.....	.....	.....	.....	.....	.....	.....	.....	.....	.....	.....	.....
Sheffield . . 53 d	.	.	.	.	.	.	.	.	.	.	.	.	.	.	.	.	.	.	.	.	.	.	.	.	.
Leicester .... 53 d	.....	.....	.....	.....	.....	.....	.....	.....	.....	.....	.....	.....	.....	.....	.....	.....	.....	.....	.....	.....	.....	.....	.....	.....	.....
Kettering d	15 19	15 47	.	16 42	17 14	.	17 43	18 13	.	18 50	18 53	.	19 16	19 44	.	20 13	20 44	.	21 15	21 43	22 14	22 47	23 35	.	.
Corby Town Centre .... a	15 39	16 07	.....	17 02	17 34	.....	18 03	18 33	.....	19 10	19 13	.....	19 36	20 04	.....	20 33	21 04	.....	21 35	22 03	22 34	23 07	23 55	.....	.....

For general notes see front of timetable
For details of catering facilities see Directory of Train Operators

A From 20 July
B Until 13 July

Corby → Kettering
Bus Service

	EM MO 🚌	EM 🚌	EM 🚌	EM 🚌		EM 🚌	EM 🚌	EM 🚌	EM 🚌		EM 🚌	EM 🚌	EM 🚌	EM 🚌		EM 🚌	EM 🚌	EM 🚌	EM 🚌		EM 🚌	EM 🚌	EM 🚌	EM 🚌	EM 🚌
Corby Town Centre 🚌 d	23 43	04 49	05 20	05 54		06 24	06 56	07 26	07 47		08 23	08 56	09 26	09 56		10 26	10 56	11 26	11 56		12 26	12 56	13 26	13 56	14 26
Kettering 🚌 a	00 03	05 11	05 42	06 16		06 46	07 18	07 48	08 07		08 48	09 18	09 48	10 18		10 48	11 18	11 48	12 18		12 48	13 18	13 48	14 18	14 48
Leicester 53 a						07 35	07 55	08 23	08 55		09 23	09 55	10 23	10 55		11 23	11 55	12 23	12 55		13 23	13 55	14 23	14 55	15 24
Sheffield 53 a																									
St Pancras International 53 a		06 41	07 05	07 36		07 59	08 38	08 55	09 12		10 04	10 34	11 04	11 34		12 04	12 34	13 04	13 34		14 04	14 34	15 04	15 34	16 04

	EM 🚌		EM 🚌	EM 🚌	EM 🚌	EM 🚌		EM 🚌	EM 🚌	EM 🚌	EM 🚌		EM 🚌	EM 🚌	EM 🚌	EM 🚌		EM 🚌	EM 🚌	EM 🚌	EM 🚌		EM 🚌		
Corby Town Centre 🚌 d	14 56		15 26	15 56	16 26	16 58		17 28	17 58	18 26	18 58		19 26	19 56	20 26	21 06		21 37	21 53	22 27	22 55		23 54		
Kettering 🚌 a	15 18		15 48	16 18	16 48	17 20		17 50	18 20	18 48	19 18		19 48	20 18	20 48	21 28		21 59	22 13	22 49	23 17		00 16		
Leicester 53 a	15 56		16 23	16 55	17 23	17 56		18 35	18 57	19 18	19 55		20 23	20 56	21 23	22 23		22 38	22 55	23 29	23 56		01 01		
Sheffield 53 a																									
St Pancras International 53 a	16 34		17 04	17 34	18 04	18 34		19 04	19 34	20 04	20 34		21 04	21 34	22 04	22 40		23 04	23 32						

Saturdays

	EM 🚌	EM 🚌	EM 🚌		EM 🚌	EM 🚌	EM 🚌		EM 🚌	EM 🚌	EM 🚌		EM 🚌	EM 🚌	EM 🚌		EM 🚌	EM 🚌	EM 🚌		EM 🚌	EM 🚌	EM 🚌		EM 🚌
Corby Town Centre 🚌 d	05 22	05 52	06 25		06 51	07 26	07 51		08 28	08 56	09 26		09 56	10 26	10 56		11 26	11 56	12 26		12 56	13 26	13 56		14 26
Kettering 🚌 a	05 44	06 14	06 47		07 11	07 48	08 13		08 48	09 18	09 48		10 18	10 48	11 18		11 48	12 18	12 48		13 18	13 48	14 18		14 48
Leicester 53 a																									
Sheffield 53 a																									
St Pancras International 53 a																									

	EM 🚌	EM 🚌	EM 🚌		EM 🚌	EM 🚌	EM 🚌		EM 🚌	EM 🚌	EM 🚌		EM 🚌	EM 🚌	EM 🚌		EM 🚌	EM 🚌	EM 🚌		EM 🚌	EM 🚌			
Corby Town Centre 🚌 d	14 56	15 26	15 56		16 26	16 56	17 26		17 56	18 26	18 56		19 26	19 56	20 28		20 56	21 26	21 56		22 58	23 54			
Kettering 🚌 a	15 18	15 48	16 18		16 48	17 18	17 48		18 18	18 48	19 18		19 48	20 18	20 48		21 18	21 48	22 17		23 20	00 16			
Leicester 53 a																									
Sheffield 53 a																									
St Pancras International 53 a																									

Sundays

	EM 🚌	EM 🚌		EM 🚌	EM 🚌		EM 🚌	EM 🚌		EM 🚌	EM 🚌		EM 🚌	EM 🚌		EM 🚌	EM 🚌		EM 🚌	EM 🚌		EM 🚌	EM 🚌		EM 🚌
Corby Town Centre 🚌 d	07 19	07 49		08 19	08 47		09 19	09 44		10 21	10 48		11 19	11 47		12 19	12 51		13 15	13 46		14 19	14 40		15 25
Kettering 🚌 a	07 39	08 09		08 39	09 07		09 39	10 04		10 41	11 08		11 39	12 07		12 39	13 11		13 35	14 06		14 39	15 00		15 45
Leicester 53 a																									
Sheffield 53 a																									
St Pancras International 53 a																									

	EM 🚌	EM 🚌		EM 🚌	EM 🚌		EM 🚌	EM 🚌		EM 🚌	EM 🚌		EM 🚌	EM 🚌		EM 🚌	EM 🚌		EM 🚌	EM 🚌		EM 🚌			
Corby Town Centre 🚌 d	15 59	16 29		17 10	17 36		18 13	18 36		19 24	19 54		20 09	20 34		21 06	21 35		22 08	23 08		23 43			
Kettering 🚌 a	16 19	16 49		17 30	17 56		18 33	18 56		19 44	20 14		20 29	20 54		21 26	21 55		22 28	23 28		00 03			
Leicester 53 a																									
Sheffield 53 a																									
St Pancras International 53 a																									

For general notes see front of timetable
For details of catering facilities see Directory of Train Operators

Nottingham → Mansfield → Worksop

Network Diagram - see first page of Table 50

Mondays to Fridays

Miles			EM	EM	EM	EM	EM	EM	EM	EM	EM	EM	EM	EM	EM
0	**Nottingham** 3	d	05 44	06 10	07 03	08 23	08 47	09 26	09 56	10 26	10 56	11 26	11 56	12 26	12 56
5½	Bulwell	d	05 53		07 12	08 35	08 56		10 06		11 06		12 06		13 06
8¾	Hucknall	d	05 58		07 18	08 40	09 01	09 39	10 11	10 39	11 11	11 39	12 11	12 39	13 11
10¾	Newstead	d	06 03		07 24	08 45	09 06	09 44		10 44		11 44		12 44	
13¾	Kirkby In Ashfield	d	06 09	06 30	07 30	08 51	09 12	09 49	10 19	10 49	11 19	11 49	12 19	12 49	13 19
14½	Sutton Parkway	d	06 12	06 33	07 34	08 54	09 15	09 52	10 22	10 52	11 22	11 52	12 22	12 52	13 22
17¼	**Mansfield**	d	06 18	06 39	07 40	08 59	09 20	09 57	10 27	10 57	11 27	11 57	12 27	12 57	13 27
18¾	Mansfield Woodhouse	d	06 22	06 44	07 45	09 03	09a27	10 02	10a34	11 02	11a34	12 02	12a34	13 02	13a34
21½	Shirebrook	d	06 29	06 50	07 52	09 10		10 08		11 08		12 08		13 08	
22¼	Langwith - Whaley Thorns	d	06 33	06 54	07 56	09 14		10 12		11 12		12 12		13 12	
25½	Creswell (Derbys)	d	06 37	06 58	08 00	09 18		10 16		11 16		12 16		13 16	
26¾	Whitwell	d	06 40	07 02	08 03	09 21		10 20		11 20		12 20		13 20	
31½	**Worksop**	a	06 52	07 20	08 21	09 33		10 31		11 31		12 31		13 31	

		EM	EM	EM	EM	EM	EM	EM	EM	EM	EM	EM	EM	EM
Nottingham 8	d	13 26	13 56	14 26	14 56	15 26	15 56	16 26	16 56	17 26	17 55	18 56	19 56	21 05
Bulwell	d		14 06		15 06		16 06		17 06	17 39	18 11	19 05	20 05	21 14
Hucknall	d	13 39	14 11	14 39	15 11	15 39	16 11	16 38	17 12	17 44	18 16	19 10	20 11	21 19
Newstead	d	13 44		14 44		15 44		16 43	17 17	17 49	18 21	19 15	20 16	21 24
Kirkby In Ashfield	d	13 49	14 19	14 49	15 19	15 49	16 19	16 49	17 23	17 55	18 27	19 21	20 27	21 30
Sutton Parkway	d	13 52	14 22	14 52	15 22	15 52	16 22	16 52	17 27	17 58	18 30	19 24	20 30	21 33
Mansfield	d	13 57	14 27	14 57	15 27	15 57	16 27	16 57	17 32	18 03	18 35	19 29	20 35	21 38
Mansfield Woodhouse	d	14 02	14a34	15 02	15a34	16 02	16a34	17 02	17a39	18 08	18 39	19 33	20 39	21 43
Shirebrook	d	14 08		15 08		16 08		17 08		18 14	18 46	19 40	20 46	21 49
Langwith - Whaley Thorns	d	14 12		15 12		16 12		17 12		18 18	18 50	19 44	20 50	21 53
Creswell (Derbys)	d	14 16		15 16		16 16		17 16		18 22	18 54	19 48	20 54	21 57
Whitwell	d	14 20		15 20		16 20		17 20		18 26	18 57	19 51	20 57	22 01
Worksop	a	14 31		15 31		16 31		17 31		18 37	19 09	20 03	21 09	22 12

Saturdays

		EM	EM	EM	EM	EM	EM	EM	EM	EM	EM	EM	EM	EM
Nottingham 8	d	05 39	06 12	07 14	08 23	08 48	09 26	09 56	10 26	10 56	11 26	11 56	12 26	12 56
Bulwell	d	05 48	06 21	07 23	08 35	08 57		10 06		11 06		12 06		13 06
Hucknall	d	05 53	06 26	07 28	08 40	09 02	09 39	10 11	10 39	11 11	11 39	12 11	12 39	13 11
Newstead	d	05 58	06 31	07 33	08 45	09 07	09 44		10 44		11 44		12 44	
Kirkby In Ashfield	d	06 04	06 37	07 39	08 50	09 13	09 49	10 19	10 49	11 19	11 49	12 19	12 49	13 19
Sutton Parkway	d	06 07	06 40	07 42	08 53	09 16	09 52	10 22	10 52	11 22	11 52	12 22	12 52	13 22
Mansfield	d	06 13	06 45	07 47	08 59	09 21	09 57	10 27	10 57	11 27	11 57	12 27	12 57	13 27
Mansfield Woodhouse	d	06 17	06 50	07 52	09 03	09a28	10 02	10a34	11 02	11a34	12 02	12a34	13 02	13a34
Shirebrook	d	06 24	06 56	07 58	09 10		10 08		11 08		12 08		13 08	
Langwith - Whaley Thorns	d	06 28	07 00	08 02	09 14		10 12		11 12		12 12		13 12	
Creswell (Derbys)	d	06 32	07 04	08 06	09 18		10 16		11 16		12 16		13 16	
Whitwell	d	06 35	07 08	08 10	09 21		10 20		11 20		12 20		13 20	
Worksop	a	06 47	07 20	08 21	09 33		10 31		11 31		12 31		13 31	

		EM	EM	EM	EM	EM	EM	EM	EM	EM	EM	EM	EM	EM
Nottingham 8	d	13 26	13 56	14 26	14 56	15 26	15 56	16 26	16 56	17 26	17 56	18 56	19 56	21 05
Bulwell	d		14 06		15 06		16 06		17 06	17 40	18 12	19 05	20 05	21 14
Hucknall	d	13 39	14 11	14 39	15 11	15 39	16 11	16 39	17 11	17 45	18 17	19 10	20 11	21 19
Newstead	d	13 44		14 44		15 44		16 44	17 16	17 50	18 22	19 15	20 16	21 24
Kirkby In Ashfield	d	13 49	14 19	14 49	15 19	15 49	16 19	16 49	17 22	17 55	18 28	19 21	20 27	21 30
Sutton Parkway	d	13 52	14 22	14 52	15 22	15 52	16 22	16 52	17 26	17 58	18 31	19 24	20 30	21 33
Mansfield	d	13 57	14 27	14 57	15 27	15 57	16 27	16 57	17 31	18 03	18 36	19 29	20 35	21 38
Mansfield Woodhouse	d	14 02	14a34	15 02	15a34	16 02	16a34	17 02	17a38	18 08	18 39	19 33	20 39	21 43
Shirebrook	d	14 08		15 08		16 08		17 08		18 14	18 46	19 40	20 46	21 49
Langwith - Whaley Thorns	d	14 12		15 12		16 12		17 12		18 18	18 50	19 44	20 50	21 53
Creswell (Derbys)	d	14 16		15 16		16 16		17 16		18 22	18 54	19 48	20 54	21 57
Whitwell	d	14 20		15 20		16 20		17 20		18 26	18 57	19 51	20 57	22 01
Worksop	a	14 31		15 31		16 31		17 31		18 37	19 09	20 03	21 09	22 12

For general notes see front of timetable
For details of catering facilities see Directory of Train Operators

No Sunday Service

Worksop → Mansfield → Nottingham

Network Diagram - see first page of Table 50

Miles			EM	EM ◇ A	EM B	EM	EM		EM	EM	EM (bus)	EM	EM (bus)		EM	EM (bus)	EM	EM (bus)	EM		EM (bus)	EM	EM (bus)	EM	EM (bus)	EM
0	**Worksop**	d	05 50		06 56		07 37		08 38			09 40					10 40					11 40				12 40
4¾	Whitwell	d	05 59		07 06		07 46		08 47			09 49					10 49					11 49				12 49
6	Creswell (Derbys)	d	06 02		07 09		07 49		08 50			09 52					10 52					11 52				12 52
9¼	Langwith - Whaley Thorns	d	06 06		07 13		07 54		08 55			09 57					10 57					11 57				12 57
10	Shirebrook	d	06 10		07 17		07 57		08 58			10 00					11 00					12 00				13 00
12¾	Mansfield Woodhouse	d	06 18	07 06	07 25	07 39	08 05		09 06	09 37		10 08			10 37		11 08		11 37			12 08		12 37		13 08
14¼	**Mansfield**	d	06 21	07 10	07 29	07 43	08 09		09 10	09 40		10 12			10 40		11 12		11 40			12 12		12 40		13 12
17	Sutton Parkway	d	06 27	07 15	07 35	07 48	08 14		09 15	09 46		10 17			10 46		11 17		11 46			12 17		12 46		13 17
17¾	Kirkby In Ashfield	d	06 30	07 18	07 38	07 52	08 17		09 18	09 49		10 20			10 49		11 20		11 49			12 20		12 49		13 20
20¾	Newstead	d	06 35	07 29	07 43	07 57	08 22		09 23	09 54	09 50		10 25		10 54	10 50		11 25	11 54		11 50		12 25	12 54	12 50	
23¼	Hucknall (tram)	d	06 39	07 35	07 48	08 02	08 27		09 27	09 58	10a10	10 27	10a45		10 58	11a10	11 27	11a45	11 58		12a10	12 27	12a45	12 58	13a10	13 27
26	Bulwell (tram)	d	06 43	07 40	07 53	08 06	08 31		09 31			10 31					11 31					12 31				13 31
31½	**Nottingham** 8 (tram)	a	06 57	07 50	08 05	08 18	08 45		09 46	10 16		10 45			11 15		11 45		12 15			12 45		13 15		13 46

		EM (bus)		EM	EM (bus)	EM	EM (bus)	EM		EM (bus)	EM	EM (bus)	EM	EM		EM	EM (bus)	EM	EM	EM	EM	EM	EM	EM		
Worksop	d					13 40					14 40			15 40				16 42		17 45	18 52	19 21	20 15	21 21		
Whitwell	d					13 49					14 49			15 49				16 51		17 54	19 01	19 30	20 24	21 30		
Creswell (Derbys)	d					13 52					14 52			15 52				16 54		17 57	19 04	19 33	20 27	21 33		
Langwith - Whaley Thorns	d					13 57					14 57			15 57				16 59		18 01	19 09	19 37	20 31	21 38		
Shirebrook	d					14 00					15 00			16 00				17 02		18 07	19 12	19 41	20 35	21 41		
Mansfield Woodhouse	d			13 37		14 08		14 37			15 08		15 37	16 08		16 37		17 10	17 43	18 14	19 20	19 48	20 43	21 49		
Mansfield	d			13 40		14 12		14 40			15 12		15 40	16 11		16 41		17 14	17 46	18 18	19 24	19 52	20 47	21 53		
Sutton Parkway	d			13 46		14 17		14 46			15 17		15 46	16 17		16 46		17 19	17 52	18 24	19 29	19 57	20 52	21 58		
Kirkby In Ashfield	d			13 49		14 20		14 49			15 20		15 49	16 20		16 49		17 22	17 55	18 27	19 32	20 00	20 55	22 01		
Newstead	d	13 25		13 54	13 50		14 25	14 54		14 50		15 25	15 54			16 54	17 00		17 59	18 32	19 37	20 05	21 00	22 06		
Hucknall (tram)	d	13a45		13 58	14a10	14 27	14a45	14 58		15a10	15 27	15a45	15 58	16 27		16 58	17a20	17 30	18 04	18 36	19 41	20 09	21 04	22 10		
Bulwell (tram)	d					14 31					15 31			16 31				17 34		18 40	19 45	20 13	21 08	22 14		
Nottingham 8 (tram)	a			14 16		14 45		15 15			15 45		16 15	16 45		17 16		17 48	18 23	18 52	20 01	20 26	21 22	22 26		

Saturdays

		EM	EM	EM	EM		EM	EM (bus)	EM	EM (bus)		EM	EM (bus)	EM	EM (bus)		EM	EM (bus)	EM	EM (bus)		EM	EM (bus)	EM	EM (bus)	EM
Worksop	d	06 03	07 01	07 37	08 38				09 40					10 40					11 40					12 40		
Whitwell	d	06 12	07 10	07 46	08 47				09 49					10 49					11 49					12 49		
Creswell (Derbys)	d	06 15	07 13	07 49	08 50				09 52					10 52					11 52					12 52		
Langwith - Whaley Thorns	d	06 19	07 18	07 54	08 55				09 57					10 57					11 57					12 57		
Shirebrook	d	06 23	07 21	07 57	08 58				10 00					11 00					12 00					13 00		
Mansfield Woodhouse	d	06 31	07 29	08 05	09 06		09 37		10 08			10 37		11 08			11 37		12 08			12 37		13 08		13 37
Mansfield	d	06 34	07 33	08 08	09 09		09 40		10 11			10 40		11 11			11 40		12 11			12 40		13 11		13 40
Sutton Parkway	d	06 40	07 38	08 14	09 15		09 46		10 17			10 46		11 17			11 46		12 17			12 46		13 17		13 46
Kirkby In Ashfield	d	06 43	07 41	08 17	09 18		09 49		10 20			10 49		11 20			11 49		12 20			12 49		13 20		13 49
Newstead	d	06 48	07 46	08 22	09 23		09 54	09 50		10 25		10 54	10 50		11 25		11 54	11 50		12 25		12 54	12 50		13 25	13 54
Hucknall (tram)	d	06 52	07 51	08 26	09 27		09 58	10a10	10 27	10a45		10 58	11a10	11 27	11a45		11 58	12a10	12 27	12a45		12 58	13a10	13 27	13a45	13 58
Bulwell (tram)	d	06 56	07 55	08 30	09 31				10 31					11 31					12 31					13 31		
Nottingham 8 (tram)	a	07 10	08 08	08 45	09 45		10 15		10 45			11 15		11 46			12 15		12 45			13 16		13 45		14 15

		EM (bus)		EM	EM (bus)	EM	EM (bus)		EM	EM (bus)	EM	EM		EM	EM (bus)	EM	EM		EM	EM	EM	EM		EM		
Worksop	d			13 40					14 40			15 40				16 42			17 45	18 49	19 21	20 15		21 20		
Whitwell	d			13 49					14 49			15 49				16 51			17 54	18 58	19 30	20 24		21 29		
Creswell (Derbys)	d			13 52					14 52			15 52				16 54			17 57	19 01	19 33	20 27		21 32		
Langwith - Whaley Thorns	d			13 57					14 57			15 57				16 59			18 01	19 06	19 37	20 31		21 37		
Shirebrook	d			14 00					15 00			16 00				17 02			18 05	19 09	19 41	20 35		21 40		
Mansfield Woodhouse	d			14 08		14 37			15 08		15 37	16 08		16 37		17 10	17 43		18 12	19 17	19 48	20 43		21 48		
Mansfield	d			14 11		14 40			15 11		15 40	16 11		16 40		17 13	17 46		18 16	19 21	19 52	20 47		21 52		
Sutton Parkway	d			14 17		14 46			15 17		15 46	16 17		16 46		17 19	17 52		18 22	19 26	19 57	20 52		21 57		
Kirkby In Ashfield	d			14 20		14 49			15 20		15 49	16 20		16 49		17 22	17 55		18 25	19 29	20 00	20 55		22 00		
Newstead	d	13 50			14 25	14 54	14 50			15 25	15 54			16 54	17 00	17 27	18 00		18 31	19 36	20 05	21 02		22 07		
Hucknall (tram)	d	14a10		14 27	14a45	14 58	15a10		15 27	15a45	15 58	16 27		16 58	17a20	17 31	18 04		18 36	19 40	20 09	21 06		22 11		
Bulwell (tram)	d			14 31					15 31			16 31				17 35			18 40	19 44	20 13	21 10		22 15		
Nottingham 8 (tram)	a			14 45		15 15			15 46		16 15	16 45		17 15		17 49	18 19		18 55	20 01	20 29	21 26		22 31		

For general notes see front of timetable
For details of catering facilities see
Directory of Train Operators

A To Norwich (Table 49)
B To Lincoln (Table 27)

No Sunday Service

Derby → Matlock

Network Diagram - see first page of Table 50

Mondays to Fridays

Miles			EM	EM	EM 1 ◇ ☕	EM	EM	EM	EM	EM	EM	EM	EM	EM
0	**Derby** 10	d	05 42	06 57	08 16	08 27	10 26	12 26	14 25	16 20	17 35	18 55	20 30	22 20
5¼	Duffield	d	05 49	07 04	.	08 34	10 33	12 33	14 32	16 27	17 42	19 02	20 37	22 27
7¾	Belper	d	05 54	07 08	08a25	08 39	10 38	12 38	14 37	16 32	17 47	19 07	20 42	22 32
10½	Ambergate	d	06 00	07 14	.	08 45	10 44	12 44	14 43	16 38	17 52	19 13	20 48	22 38
12½	Whatstandwell	d	06 04	07 18	.	08 49	10 48	12 48	14 47	16 42	17 56	19 17	20 52	22 42
15½	Cromford	d	06 09	07 22	.	08 54	10 53	12 53	14 52	16 47	18 01	19 22	20 57	22 47
16¼	Matlock Bath	d	06 11	07 25	.	08 56	10 55	12 55	14 54	16 49	18 04	19 24	20 59	22 49
17¼	**Matlock**	a	06 14	07 27	.	08 59	10 58	12 58	14 57	16 52	18 07	19 27	21 02	22 52

Saturdays

		EM	EM	EM	EM A	EM B	EM	EM	EM	EM	85	EM	EM	EM 1 ◇ ☕	EM
Derby 10	d	05 37	07 02	08 21	09§49	09§51	11 52	13 30	14 48	16§22	16§24	17 48	19 21	19 58	21 51
Duffield	d	05 44	07 09	08 28	09§56	09§58	11 59	13 37	14 55	16§29	16§31	17 55	19 28	.	21 58
Belper	d	05 49	07 14	08 33	10§01	10§03	12 04	13 42	15 00	16§34	16§36	18 00	19 33	20a06	22 03
Ambergate	d	05 55	07 20	08 39	10§07	10§09	12 10	13 48	15 06	16§40	16§42	18 06	19 39	.	22 09
Whatstandwell	d	05 59	07 24	08 43	10§11	10§13	12 14	13 52	15 10	16§44	16§46	18 10	19 43	.	22 13
Cromford	d	06 04	07 29	08 48	10§16	10§18	12 19	13 57	15 15	16§49	16§51	18 15	19 48	.	22 18
Matlock Bath	d	06 06	07 31	08 50	10§18	10§20	12 21	13 59	15 17	16§51	16§53	18 17	19 50	.	22 20
Matlock	a	06 09	07 34	08 53	10§21	10§23	12 24	14 02	15 20	16§54	16§56	18 20	19 53	.	22 23

Sundays

		EM C	EM D	EM E	EM E	EM G	EM H	EM E	EM E	EM H	EM G
Derby 10	d	09§57	09§59	11 32	13 51	15§44	15§46	17 56	19 49	21§52	21§53
Duffield	d	10§04	10§06	11 39	13 58	15§51	15§53	18 03	19 56	21§59	22§00
Belper	d	10§09	10§11	11 44	14 03	15§56	15§58	18 08	20 01	22§04	22§05
Ambergate	d	10§15	10§17	11 50	14 09	16§02	16§04	18 14	20 07	22§10	22§11
Whatstandwell	d	10§19	10§21	11 54	14 13	16§08	16§08	18 18	20 11	22§14	22§15
Cromford	d	10§24	10§26	11 59	14 18	16§13	16§13	18 23	20 16	22§19	22§20
Matlock Bath	d	10§26	10§28	12 01	14 20	16§15	16§15	18 25	20 18	22§21	22§22
Matlock	a	10§29	10§31	12 04	14 23	16§18	16§18	18 28	20 21	22§24	22§25

For general notes see front of timetable
For details of catering facilities see Directory of Train Operators

A Until 6 September.

B From 13 September.

C 14 September to 2 November. From Nottingham

D Until 7 September and from 9 November. From 9 November from Nottingham. Until 7 September from Nottingham (Table 57)

E From 14 September from Nottingham. Until 7 September from Nottingham (Table 57)

G Until 7 September. From Nottingham (Table 57)

H From 14 September. From Nottingham

Matlock → Derby

Network Diagram - see first page of Table 50

Mondays to Fridays

Miles	Station		EM	EM	EM	EM	EM	EM	EM	EM	EM	EM	EM	EM
					1 ◇ A ⊏⊐									B
0	**Matlock**	d	06 20	07 38		09 04	11 12	13 12	15 17	16 58	18 13	19 38	21 10	22 59
1	Matlock Bath	d	06 22	07 40		09 06	11 14	13 14	15 19	17 00	18 15	19 40	21 12	23 01
1¾	Cromford	d	06 25	07 43		09 09	11 17	13 17	15 22	17 03	18 18	19 43	21 15	23 04
4¾	Whatstandwell	d	06 30	07 48		09 14	11 22	13 22	15 27	17 08	18 23	19 48	21 20	23 09
6¾	Ambergate	d	06 35	07 53		09 20	11 27	13 27	15 32	17 13	18 28	19 53	21 25	23 14
9½	Belper	d	06 40	07 58	09 03	09 25	11 33	13 33	15 38	17 19	18 33	19 58	21 30	23 19
12	Duffield	d	06 45	08 03		09 29	11 37	13 37	15 42	17 23	18 37	20 02	21 34	23 23
17¼	**Derby** 10	a	06 51	08 09	09 13	09 36	11 45	13 45	15 49	17 30	18 47	20 10	21 42	23 31

Saturdays

Station		EM	EM	EM	EM	EM	EM	EM	EM	EM	EM	EM	EM	EM	EM	EM
				C	D	1 ◇ C ⊏⊐					D	C	D	C		E
Matlock	d	06 14	07 39	08 58	09 00		10 38	12 38	14 10	15 38	17 01	17 01	18 38	18 38	20 20	22 28
Matlock Bath	d	06 16	07 41	09 00	09 02		10 40	12 40	14 12	15 40	17 03	17 03	18 40	18 40	20 22	22 30
Cromford	d	06 19	07 44	09 03	09 05		10 43	12 43	14 15	15 43	17 06	17 06	18 43	18 43	20 25	22 33
Whatstandwell	d	06 24	07 49	09 08	09 10		10 48	12 48	14 20	15 48	17 11	17 11	18 48	18 48	20 30	22 38
Ambergate	d	06 29	07 54	09 13	09 15		10 53	12 53	14 25	15 53	17 16	17 16	18 53	18 53	20 35	22 43
Belper	d	06 34	07 59	09 19	09 20	09 26	10 58	12 58	14 30	15 58	17 21	17 21	18 58	18 58	20 40	22 48
Duffield	d	06 38	08 03	09 23	09 24		11 02	13 02	14 34	16 02	17 25	17 25	19 02	19 02	20 44	22 53
Derby 10	a	06 46	08 11	09 30	09 32	09 33	11 10	13 10	14 42	16 10	17 33	17 34	19 10	19 11	20 52	23 00

Sundays

Station		EM	EM	EM	EM	EM	EM	EM	EM	EM	EM	EM
		G	H	J	J	H	1 K	J	H	G	L	N
Matlock	d	10 40	12 39	12 41	14 36	14 40	16 40	18 38	18 40	20 40	22 41	22 41
Matlock Bath	d	10 42	12 41	12 43	14 38	14 43	16 42	18 40	18 42	20 42	22 43	22 43
Cromford	d	10 44	12 44	12 46	14 41	14 45	16 45	18 43	18 45	20 45	22 46	22 46
Whatstandwell	d	10 49	12 49	12 51	14 46	14 50	16 50	18 48	18 50	20 50	22 51	22 51
Ambergate	d	10 55	12 54	12 56	14 51	14 56	16 55	18 53	18 55	20 55	22 56	22 56
Belper	d	11 00	13 00	13 02	14 58	15 01	17 00	19 00	19 00	21 00	23 01	23 01
Duffield	d	11 04	13 04	13 06	15 02	15 05	17 04	19 04	19 04	21 04	23 05	23 05
Derby 10	a	11 11	13 12	13 14	15 10	15 12	17 12	19 12	19 12	21 12	23 12	23 14

For general notes see front of timetable
For details of catering facilities see Directory of Train Operators

A Until 5 September
B To Nottingham (Table 57)
C Until 6 September
D From 13 September
E From 13 September to Nottingham. Until 6 September to Nottingham (Table 57)
G From 14 September to Nottingham. Until 7 September to Nottingham (Table 57)
H Until 7 September. To Nottingham (Table 57)
J From 14 September. To Nottingham
K From 14 September to Nottingham. Until 13 July to Nottingham (Table 57). 20 July to 7 September to Nottingham (Table 57)
L From 14 September
N Until 7 September

Nottingham, Derby and Leicester → Birmingham → Cardiff and Bristol

Network Diagram - see first page of Table 50

Miles	Miles	Miles			EM	AW	GW	XC	GW	XC	GW	GW	XC	GW		AW	XC	XC	EM	EM	EM	XC	XC	XC	XC
					MX 1 ◇		1 ◇		1 ◇			◇	1 ◇	1 ◇			1 ◇			1 ◇	1 ◇	◇	1 ◇		
						A						B	C			A	D		E						
					☕		☕		☕				☕	☕			☕			☕	⊠ 🍴	🍴	☕		
0	—	—	**Nottingham** 8	d	01 44														05 55	06 07	06 25				06 38
3¼	—	—	Beeston	d															06 00	06a12	06a30				
4¾	—	—	Attenborough	d															06 04						
7¾	—	—	Long Eaton	d															06 13						06 52
13½	—	—	Spondon	d															06 19						
16	—	—	**Derby** 10	a	02 05														06 26						07 05
—	—	—		d													06 10					06 35	06 55		07 08
22¼	—	—	Willington	d																		06 45			
27	—	—	Burton-on-Trent	d													06 20					06 51	07 07		07 19
40	—	—	Tamworth	d													06 31					07 03	07 18		07 31
41¾	—	—	Wilnecote	d																		07 06			07 35
—	0	—	**Leicester**	d														06 03						06 52	
—	1¾	—	South Wigston	d														06 11						06 57	
—	4¾	—	Narborough	d														06 16						07 02	
—	13¼	—	Hinckley	d														06 24						07 10	
—	18¾	—	Nuneaton	d														06 31						07 17	
—	29¼	—	Coleshill Parkway	d														06 47						07 33	
—	31	—	Water Orton	d																				07 36	
56¾	38¾	—	**Birmingham New Street** 12	a													06 51	07 05				07 27	07 36	07 50	07 57
—	—	0		d						05 30			06 10				07 10					07 30	07 40		
83¾	—	—	Worcester Shrub Hill 7	d				05 40		06 17		06 49													
98¼	—	39¼	Ashchurch for Tewkesbury	d				05 55		06 33		07 05													
105¾	—	46½	Cheltenham Spa	d		05 37	05 56	06 04	06 31	06 43	06 59	07 15	07 22	07 27		07 45	07 52					08 11	08 22		
112¼	—	—	Gloucester 7	a		05 48	06 06	06 14	06 41	06 52	07 09	07 25		07 36		07 56						08 23			
—	—	87	Bristol Parkway 7	a							07 47	08 24	07 54				08 24						08 54		
—	—	92¾	**Bristol Temple Meads** 10	a							08 02	08 36	08 11				08 41						09 11		
157	—	—	Newport (South Wales)	a		06 41		07 06		07 50						08 49						09 07			
168¾	—	—	**Cardiff Central** 7	a		07 00		07 27		08 12						09 10						09 29			

		XC	XC		GW	AW	XC	XC	XC	XC	EM	EM	XC	XC		XC	XC	EM	EM	GW	GW	XC	XC	XC	EM
			1 ◇		1 ◇		1 ◇	◇		◇	1 ◇	1 ◇	1 ◇	1 ◇		◇			1 ◇			R 1		◇	1 ◇
						A	D	G				H J	K			L			N	Q		U			
			☕		☕		☕			🍴	☕	⊠ 🍴	☕	☕		🍴			☕			☕		🍴	☕
Nottingham 8	d									07 00	07 07	07 30					07 34	07 38						08 00	08 07
Beeston	d									07 06	07a12	07a35					07 40	07a44						08 06	08a12
Attenborough	d									07 09														08 09	
Long Eaton	d	06 57								07 16							07 50		08 00					08 17	
Spondon	d	07 03																						08 24	
Derby 10	a	07 11								07 28							08 00		08 13					08 34	
	d		07 19				07 24			07 38			07 47	07 57			08 06					08 27		08 38	
Willington	d																08 13								
Burton-on-Trent	d						07 35			07 49			07 58				08 19					08 37		08 49	
Tamworth	d						07 46			08 01			08 10				08 31					08 48		09 01	
Wilnecote	d																08 35								
Leicester	d							07 09	07 24							07 52							08 09		
South Wigston	d															07 57									
Narborough	d							07 19								08 02							08 19		
Hinckley	d							07 27								08 10							08 28		
Nuneaton	d							07 35	07 43							08 18							08 35		
Coleshill Parkway	d							07 52	07 58							08 33							08 56		
Water Orton	d								08 02																
Birmingham New Street 12	a		07 58				08 07	08 09	08 15	08 25			08 36	08 36		08 51	08 54					09 06	09 09	09 27	
	d						08 10			08 30				08 40								09 10		09 30	
Worcester Shrub Hill 7	d																			09 05					
Ashchurch for Tewkesbury	d																			09 21					
Cheltenham Spa	d				08 31	08 45	08 52			09 11				09 22						09 31	09 38	09 52		10 11	
Gloucester 7	a				08 40	08 56				09 21										09 39	09 48			10 21	
Bristol Parkway 7	a						09 24							09 54						10 19		10 24			
Bristol Temple Meads 10	a						09 41							10 11						10 35		10 41			
Newport (South Wales)	a					09 50				10 09														11 10	
Cardiff Central 7	a					10 10				10 30														11 32	

For general notes see front of timetable
For details of catering facilities see Directory of Train Operators

A To Maesteg (Table 128)
B To Weymouth (Table 123)
C To Paignton (Table 51)
D To Plymouth (Table 51)
E To Crewe (Table 50)
G From Cambridge (Table 49)
H From Sheffield (Table 53)
J **The Robin Hood**
K To Manchester Piccadilly (Table 51)
L From Stansted Airport (Table 49)
N To Sheffield (Table 53)
Q From Great Malvern (Table 71) to Westbury (Table 123)
U From Leeds to Plymouth (Table 51)

Nottingham, Derby and Leicester → Birmingham → Cardiff and Bristol

Network Diagram - see first page of Table 50

		EM	EM	XC	XC	XC	XC	XC	GW	AW	XC	XC	EM	EM	XC	XC	XC	GW	GW	AW	XC	XC	XC
		1 ◇	1 ◇	R 1	◇		R 1		1 ◇		1 ◇	◇	1 ◇	1 ◇	1 ◇	◇		◇			1 ◇		◇
		A		B	C					D	E				G	H		J		D	E		
		🍴	🍴	🍴	🛒		🍴		🍴		🍴	🛒	🍴	🍴	🍴	🛒					🍴		🛒
Nottingham [8] 🚌	d	08 26				08 34						09 00	09 07				09 34						10 00
Beeston	d	08a33										09 06	09a12				09 41						10 06
Attenborough	d											09 09											
Long Eaton	d		08 44			08 50						09 18		09 44			09 50						10 18
Spondon	d											09 25											
Derby [10]	a		08 56			09 00						09 31		09 56			10 00						10 31
	d			08 57		09 04	09 24					09 38			09 57		10 08				10 24		10 38
Willington	d																10 15						
Burton-on-Trent	d					09 19						09 49			10 07		10 19						10 49
Tamworth	d					09 31						10 01			10 18		10 31						11 01
Wilnecote	d					09 35																	
Leicester	d				08 52			09 09								09 52						10 09	
South Wigston	d																					10 15	
Narborough	d							09 18														10 20	
Hinckley	d							09 27														10 28	
Nuneaton	d				09 13			09 34								10 14						10 35	
Coleshill Parkway	d				09 29			09 52								10 29						10 52	
Water Orton	d							09 56															
Birmingham New Street [12]	a			09 36	09 47	09 54	09 58	10 09				10 27			10 36	10 47	10 54				11 04	11 09	11 27
	d			09 40							10 10	10 30			10 40						11 10		11 30
Worcester Shrub Hill [7]	d																	11 05					
Ashchurch for Tewkesbury	d																	11 21					
Cheltenham Spa	d			10 22					10 31	10 45	10 52	11 11			11 22			11 31	11 38	11 45	11 52		12 11
Gloucester [7]	a								10 40	10 57		11 21						11 39	11 48	11 56			12 21
Bristol Parkway [7]	a			10 54							11 24				11 54			12 19			12 24		
Bristol Temple Meads [10]	a			11 11							11 41				12 11			12 35			12 41		
Newport (South Wales)	a									11 50		12 09								12 50			13 09
Cardiff Central [7]	a									12 10		12 32								13 10			13 32

		EM	EM	XC	XC	XC	XC	XC	GW	XC	XC	EM	EM	XC	XC	XC	GW	GW	AW	XC	XC	XC	EM
		1 ◇	1 ◇	1 ◇	◇		R 1		1 ◇	1 ◇	◇	1 ◇	1 ◇	1 ◇	◇		◇			1 ◇		◇	1 ◇
				B	H					E				G	H		K		D	E			
		🍴	🍴	🍴	🛒		🍴		🍴	🍴	🛒	🍴	🍴	🍴	🛒					🍴		🛒	🍴
Nottingham [8] 🚌	d	10 07				10 34					11 00	11 07				11 34						12 00	12 07
Beeston	d	10a12				10 40					11 06	11a12				11 40						12 06	12a12
Attenborough	d					10 43					11 09												
Long Eaton	d		10 44			10 49					11 18		11 44			11 50						12 18	
Spondon	d																					12 24	
Derby [10]	a		10 56			11 00					11 31		11 56			12 00						12 31	
	d			10 57		11 08	11 24				11 38			11 57		12 08				12 24		12 38	
Willington	d					11 15																12 45	
Burton-on-Trent	d					11 19					11 49			12 07		12 19						12 49	
Tamworth	d					11 31					12 01			12 18		12 31						13 01	
Wilnecote	d															12 35							
Leicester	d				10 52			11 09							11 52						12 09		
South Wigston	d																				12 15		
Narborough	d							11 19													12 20		
Hinckley	d							11 26													12 28		
Nuneaton	d				11 14			11 34							12 14						12 35		
Coleshill Parkway	d				11 29			11 50							12 29						12 52		
Water Orton	d							11 54															
Birmingham New Street [12]	a			11 36	11 47	11 54	11 58	12 09			12 27			12 36	12 47	12 54				13 04	13 09	13 27	
	d			11 40						12 10	12 30			12 40						13 10		13 30	
Worcester Shrub Hill [7]	d																13 05						
Ashchurch for Tewkesbury	d																13 21						
Cheltenham Spa	d			12 22					12 31	12 52	13 11			13 22			13 31	13 38	13 45	13 52		14 11	
Gloucester [7]	a								12 40		13 21						13 39	13 48	13 56			14 21	
Bristol Parkway [7]	a			12 54						13 24				13 54			14 19			14 24			
Bristol Temple Meads [10]	a			13 11						13 41				14 11			14 35			14 41			
Newport (South Wales)	a										14 09								14 50			15 09	
Cardiff Central [7]	a										14 32								15 10			15 32	

For general notes see front of timetable
For details of catering facilities see Directory of Train Operators

- **A** From Sheffield (Table 53)
- **B** To Paignton (Table 51)
- **C** From Cambridge (Table 49)
- **D** To Maesteg (Table 128)
- **E** To Plymouth (Table 51)
- **G** From Newcastle (Table 51)
- **H** From Stansted Airport (Table 49)
- **J** From Great Malvern (Table 71) to Brighton (Table 123)
- **K** From Great Malvern (Table 71) to Weymouth (Table 123)

Nottingham, Derby and Leicester → Birmingham → Cardiff and Bristol

Network Diagram - see first page of Table 50

		EM	XC		XC	XC	XC	XC	GW	AW	XC	XC	EM	EM		XC	XC	XC	GW	GW	XC	XC	XC	EM	EM
		1 ◇	R 1 A		◇ B		R 1		1 ◇ C	D	R 1 E	◇	1 ◇	1 ◇		1 ◇ G	◇ B		◇ H		R 1 J		◇	1 ◇	1 ◇
Nottingham 8	d					12 34						13 00	13 07					13 34					14 00	14 07	
Beeston	d					12 40						13 06	13a12					13 40					14 06	14a12	
Attenborough	d											13 09													
Long Eaton	d	12 44				12 50						13 18		13 44				13 50					14 18		14 44
Spondon	d																								
Derby 10	a	12 56				13 00						13 31		13 56				14 00					14 31		14 56
	d		12 57			13 08	13 24					13 38				13 57		14 08			14 24		14 38		
Willington	d																	14 15							
Burton-on-Trent	d					13 19						13 49				14 07		14 19					14 49		
Tamworth	d					13 31						14 01				14 18		14 31					15 01		
Wilnecote	d					13 35																	15 05		
Leicester	d				12 52			13 09									13 52					14 09			
South Wigston	d																					14 15			
Narborough	d							13 18														14 20			
Hinckley	d							13 26														14 28			
Nuneaton	d				13 14			13 35									14 14					14 35			
Coleshill Parkway	d				13 29			13 51									14 29					14 53			
Water Orton	d							13 54																	
Birmingham New Street 12	a		13 36		13 47	13 54	13 58	14 09				14 27				14 36	14 47	14 54			15 04	15 09	15 27		
	d		13 40								14 10	14 30				14 40					15 10		15 30		
Worcester Shrub Hill 7	d																		15 05						
Ashchurch for Tewkesbury	d																		15 21				16 06		
Cheltenham Spa	d		14 22						14 31	14 45	14 52	15 11				15 22			15 31	15 38	15 52		16 15		
Gloucester 7	a								14 40	14 56		15 21							15 39	15 48			16 24		
Bristol Parkway 7	a		14 54								15 24					15 54			16 19		16 24				
Bristol Temple Meads 10	a		15 11								15 41					16 11			16 35		16 41				
Newport (South Wales)	a									15 51		16 09											17 09		
Cardiff Central 7	a									16 09		16 32											17 32		

		XC	XC		XC	XC	XC	GW	AW	XC	XC	EM	EM	XC		XC	XC	GW	GW	AW	XC	XC	XC	EM	EM
		1 ◇ A	◇ B			R 1		1 ◇	D	R 1 E	◇	1 ◇	1 ◇	1 ◇ G		◇ B		K	L	D	R 1 A		◇	1 ◇	1 ◇
Nottingham 8	d				14 34						15 00	15 07					15 34						16 00	16 07	
Beeston	d				14 40						15 06	15a12					15 40						16 06	16a12	
Attenborough	d										15 09												16 09		
Long Eaton	d				14 50						15 17		15 45				15 50						16 17		16 44
Spondon	d																						16 24		
Derby 10	a				15 00						15 31		15 56				16 00						16 31		16 55
	d	14 57			15 08	15 24					15 38			15 57			16 08				16 24		16 38		
Willington	d																								
Burton-on-Trent	d				15 19						15 49			16 07			16 19						16 49		
Tamworth	d				15 31						16 01			16 18			16 31						17 01		
Wilnecote	d																16 35								
Leicester	d		14 52				15 09									15 52						16 09			
South Wigston	d																					16 15			
Narborough	d						15 21															16 20			
Hinckley	d						15 29															16 28			
Nuneaton	d		15 14				15 37									16 14						16 35			
Coleshill Parkway	d		15 29				15 53									16 29						16 52			
Water Orton	d						15 56																17 11		
Birmingham New Street 12	a	15 36	15 47		15 54	15 58	16 09				16 27			16 36		16 47	16 54				17 04	17 12	17 27		
	d	15 40								16 10	16 30			16 40							17 10		17 30		
Worcester Shrub Hill 7	d																		17 05						
Ashchurch for Tewkesbury	d																		17 21				18 09		
Cheltenham Spa	d	16 22						16 31	16 45	16 52	17 14			17 22				17 28	17 33	17 45	17 52		18 18		
Gloucester 7	a							16 40	16 56		17 23							17 36	17 43	17 56			18 29		
Bristol Parkway 7	a	16 54								17 24				17 54				18 18			18 24				
Bristol Temple Meads 10	a	17 11								17 41				18 11				18 37			18 41				
Newport (South Wales)	a								17 51		18 09									18 50			19 14		
Cardiff Central 7	a								18 10		18 32									19 09			19 32		

For general notes see front of timetable
For details of catering facilities see Directory of Train Operators

A To Plymouth (Table 51)

B From Stansted Airport (Table 49)

C **Cheltenham Spa Express**

D To Maesteg (Table 128)

E To Penzance (Table 51)

G From Newcastle (Table 51)

H From Great Malvern (Table 71) to Weymouth (Table 123)

J To Penzance (Table 135)

K To Westbury (Table 123)

L From Worcester Foregate Street (Table 71) to Southampton Central (Table 123)

Nottingham, Derby and Leicester → Birmingham → Cardiff and Bristol

Network Diagram - see first page of Table 50

		XC	XC	XC	EM	XC	XC	GW	AW	XC	XC	EM	EM	XC	XC	XC	EM	GW	AW	XC	XC	GW	XC
		R 1 ☕	◇ A 🛒		B	R 1 ☕		1 ◇ ☕	C	1 ◇ D ☕	◇	1 ◇ ☕	1 ◇ ☕	R 1 E ☕	◇ A		B	◇ G	C	1 ◇ D ☕			◇
Nottingham 8	d			16 34	16 38						17 00	17 07				17 34	17 38						18 00
Beeston	d			16 40							17 06	17a12				17 40							18 06
Attenborough	d				16a45						17 09						17a45						18 09
Long Eaton	d			16 50							17 18		17 44			17 50							18 18
Spondon	d										17 24												
Derby 10	a			17 00							17 31		17 55			18 00							18 30
	d	16 57		17 04		17 24					17 38			17 57		18 04				18 24			18 38
Willington	d										17 45												
Burton-on-Trent	d			17 19							17 49			18 07		18 19							18 49
Tamworth	d			17 31							18 01			18 18		18 31							19 01
Wilnecote	d																						19 05
Leicester	d		16 52				17 09								17 52						18 23		
South Wigston	d						17 16								17 58						18 29		
Narborough	d						17 21								18 02						18 33		
Hinckley	d						17 29								18 10						18 42		
Nuneaton	d		17 14				17 36								18 18						18 51		
Coleshill Parkway	d		17 29				17 52																
Water Orton	d															18 44							
Birmingham New Street 12	a	17 36	17 47	17 54		17 58	18 09				18 27			18 36	18 48	18 56				19 08	19 18		19 27
	d	17 40								18 10	18 30			18 40						19 10			19 30
Worcester Shrub Hill 7	d																	19 05					
Ashchurch for Tewkesbury	d																	19 21					20 06
Cheltenham Spa	d	18 22						18 31	18 45	18 52	19 14			19 22				19 31	19 45	19 52		20 00	20 15
Gloucester 7	a	18 34						18 40	18 56		19 23							19 39	19 56			20 10	20 24
Bristol Parkway 7	a	19 05								19 24				19 54				20 19		20 24			
Bristol Temple Meads 10	a	19 22								19 41				20 11				20 34		20 41			
Newport (South Wales)	a	19 59							19 51		20 09								20 50				21 09
Cardiff Central 7	a	20 19							20 11		20 32								21 10				21 32

		EM	XC	XC	XC	EM	EM	XC	XC	GW	XC	XC	XC	EM	XC	EM	EM	EM	EM	GW	GW	AW	XC
		1 ◇ ☕	R 1 ☕	◇ A		1 ◇ ☕	1 ◇ ☕	R 1 ☕		1 ☕	1 ◇ D	◇ A	1 ◇ H ☕	1 ◇ J ☕		B	1 ◇ J ☕	1 ◇ K ☕	1 ◇ ☕		L		1 ◇
Nottingham 8	d	18 07			18 34		19 07								19 34	19 38			20 07				
Beeston	d	18a12					19a12								19 40	19a44			20a12				
Attenborough	d																						
Long Eaton	d				18 46	18 56								19 47	19 50			20 03					
Spondon	d																						
Derby 10	a				18 56	19 10								19 59	20 00		⟵	20 15					
	d		18 57		19 06			19 24					19 57	20 11 ⟶	20 08		20 11						20 27
Willington	d				19 14												20 21						
Burton-on-Trent	d				19 20								20 07		20 19		20a26						
Tamworth	d				19 31								20 18		20 31								
Wilnecote	d																						
Leicester	d			18 52					19 09			19 41											
South Wigston	d								19 16														
Narborough	d								19 20														
Hinckley	d								19 30														
Nuneaton	d			19 14					19 38			20 01											
Coleshill Parkway	d			19 29					19 55			20 16											
Water Orton	d																						
Birmingham New Street 12	a		19 36	19 47	19 54			19 58	20 09			20 37	20 43		20 58								21 04
	d		19 40								20 10												21 10
Worcester Shrub Hill 7	d																				21 08		
Ashchurch for Tewkesbury	d																				21 24		
Cheltenham Spa	d		20 22							20 48	20 52									21 02	21 34	21 45	21 52
Gloucester 7	a									20 58										21 12	21 45	21 56	
Bristol Parkway 7	a		20 54								21 24									21 50			22 24
Bristol Temple Meads 10	a		21 11								21 41									22 02			22 41
Newport (South Wales)	a																					22 57	
Cardiff Central 7	a																					23 18	

For general notes see front of timetable
For details of catering facilities see Directory of Train Operators

A From Stansted Airport (Table 49)
B From Lincoln (Table 27)
C To Maesteg (Table 128)
D To Plymouth (Table 51)
E From Newcastle to Weston-super-Mare (Table 51)
G From Great Malvern (Table 71) to Weymouth (Table 123)
H From Newcastle (Table 51)
J From St Pancras International (Table 53)
K To Sheffield (Table 53)
L From Great Malvern (Table 71)

Table 57

Nottingham, Derby and Leicester → Birmingham → Cardiff and Bristol

Mondays to Fridays
until 5 September

Network Diagram - see first page of Table 50

		XC	XC		XC	EM	XC	GW	GW	AW	XC	XC	XC	EM		GW	XC	LM	XC	XC	XC	XC	EM		
																		FO							
			1 ◇		◇	1 ◇			◇		1 ◇		◇	1 ◇						1 ◇	◇	1 ◇	1 ◇		
					A	B					C		A							C	A	D	B		
						☕			☕					☕									☕		
Nottingham 8	d						20 34										21 34						22 58		
Beeston	d						20 40										21 40						23 04		
Attenborough	d																21 43								
Long Eaton	d					20 44	20 50							21 44			21 50						23 14		
Spondon	d																21 57								
Derby 10	a					20 56	21 00							21 56			22 04						23 26		
	d		20 57			21 03	21 08				21 27						22 08			22 27		23 15			
Willington	d					21 11																			
Burton-on-Trent	d					21a16	21 19				21 37						22 19			22 37		23 26			
Tamworth	d						21 31				21 48						22 31			22 48		23 37			
Wilnecote	d						21 35										22 34								
Leicester	d	20 09			20 52							21 09	21 41						22 27		22 49				
South Wigston	d	20 15										21 15							22 33						
Narborough	d	20 20										21 19							22 37						
Hinckley	d	20 28										21 28							22 46						
Nuneaton	d	20 37			21 14							21 37	22 01						22 54		23 08				
Coleshill Parkway	d	20 54			21 29								22 17						23 14		23 24				
Water Orton	d						21 44																		
Birmingham New Street 12	a	21 09	21 44		21 47		21 57				22 08	22 09	22 36				22 54		23 34	23 21	23 41	23 59			
	d										22 10							23 04							
Worcester Shrub Hill 7	d															22 32		23 44							
Ashchurch for Tewkesbury	d															22 51		23 58							
Cheltenham Spa	d							22 00	22 31	22 45	22 52					23 01		00 07							
Gloucester 7	a							22 10	22 41	22 56						23 13		00 16							
Bristol Parkway 7	a								23 16		23 24														
Bristol Temple Meads 10	a								23 37		23 41														
Newport (South Wales)	a									23 59															
Cardiff Central 7	a									00 24															

Mondays to Fridays
from 8 September

		EM	AW	GW	XC	GW	XC	GW	GW	XC		GW	AW	XC	XC	EM	EM	EM	XC	XC		XC	XC	XC	XC
		MX																							
		1 ◇		1 ◇		1 ◇			◇	1 ◇		1 ◇		1 ◇			1 ◇	1 ◇	◇	1 ◇					1 ◇
			E						G	H			E	J		K									
		☕		☕		☕				☕		☕		☕			☕	⊠ 🍴	🍴	☕					☕
Nottingham 8	d	01 44														05 55	06 07	06 25					06 38		
Beeston	d															06 00	06a12	06a30							
Attenborough	d															06 04									
Long Eaton	d															06 13							06 52	06 57	
Spondon	d															06 19								07 03	
Derby 10	a	02 05														06 26							07 03	07 10	
	d													06 10					06 35	06 55			07 08		07 20
Willington	d																		06 45						
Burton-on-Trent	d													06 20					06 51	07 07			07 19		
Tamworth	d													06 31					07 03	07 18			07 31		
Wilnecote	d																		07 06				07 35		
Leicester	d														06 03							06 52			
South Wigston	d														06 11							06 57			
Narborough	d														06 16							07 02			
Hinckley	d														06 24							07 10			
Nuneaton	d														06 31							07 17			
Coleshill Parkway	d														06 47							07 33			
Water Orton	d																					07 36			
Birmingham New Street 12	a													06 51	07 05				07 27	07 36		07 50	07 57		07 58
	d						05 30			06 10				07 10					07 30	07 40					
Worcester Shrub Hill 7	d				05 40		06 17		06 49																
Ashchurch for Tewkesbury	d				05 55		06 33		07 05																
Cheltenham Spa	d		05 37	05 56	06 04	06 31	06 43	06 59	07 15	07 22		07 27	07 45	07 52					08 11	08 22					
Gloucester 7	a		05 48	06 06	06 14	06 41	06 52	07 09	07 25			07 36	07 56						08 23						
Bristol Parkway 7	a							07 47	08 24	07 54				08 24						08 54					
Bristol Temple Meads 10	a							08 02	08 36	08 11				08 41						09 11					
Newport (South Wales)	a		06 41		07 06		07 50						08 49						09 07						
Cardiff Central 7	a		07 00		07 27		08 12						09 10						09 29						

For general notes see front of timetable
For details of catering facilities see Directory of Train Operators

- **A** From Stansted Airport (Table 49)
- **B** From St Pancras International (Table 53)
- **C** From Edinburgh (Table 51)
- **D** From Newcastle (Table 51)
- **E** To Maesteg (Table 128)
- **G** To Weymouth (Table 123)
- **H** To Paignton (Table 51)
- **J** To Plymouth (Table 51)
- **K** To Crewe (Table 50)

Table 57

Nottingham, Derby and Leicester → Birmingham → Cardiff and Bristol

Mondays to Fridays
from 8 September

Network Diagram - see first page of Table 50

Station		GW	AW	XC	XC	XC	XC	EM		EM	XC	XC	XC	XC	EM	EM	GW	GW		XC	XC	XC	EM	EM	EM
		1◇		1◇	◇		◇	1◇		1◇	1◇	1◇	◇			1◇				R 1		◇	1◇	1◇	1◇
			A	B	C					D E	G		H			J	K			L					
		☕		☕			🛒	☕		⊠ 🛒	☕	☕	🛒			☕				☕		🛒	☕	☕	☕
Nottingham 8	d						07 00	07 07		07 30				07 34	07 38							08 00	08 07	08 26	
Beeston	d						07 06	07a12		07a35				07 40	07a44							08 06	08a12	08a33	
Attenborough	d						07 09															08 09			
Long Eaton	d						07 16							07 50		08 00						08 17			08 44
Spondon	d																					08 24			
Derby 10	a						07 28							08 01		08 12						08 34			08 56
	d			07 24			07 38				07 47	07 57		08 06						08 27		08 38			
Willington	d													08 13											
Burton-on-Trent	d			07 35			07 49				07 58			08 19						08 37		08 49			
Tamworth	d			07 46			08 01				08 10			08 31						08 48		09 01			
Wilnecote	d													08 35											
Leicester	d				07 09	07 24							07 52								08 09				
South Wigston	d												07 57												
Narborough	d				07 19								08 02								08 19				
Hinckley	d				07 27								08 10								08 28				
Nuneaton	d				07 35	07 43							08 18								08 35				
Coleshill Parkway	d				07 52	07 58							08 33								08 56				
Water Orton	d					08 02																			
Birmingham New Street 12	a			08 07	08 09	08 15	08 25				08 36	08 36	08 51	08 54						09 06	09 09	09 27			
	d			08 10			08 30					08 40								09 10		09 30			
Worcester Shrub Hill 7	d																09 05								
Ashchurch for Tewkesbury	d																09 21								
Cheltenham Spa	d	08 31	08 45	08 52			09 11					09 22					09 31	09 38		09 52		10 11			
Gloucester 7	a	08 40	08 56				09 21										09 39	09 48				10 21			
Bristol Parkway 7	a			09 24								09 54					10 19			10 24					
Bristol Temple Meads 10	a			09 41								10 11					10 35			10 41					
Newport (South Wales)	a		09 50				10 09															11 10			
Cardiff Central 7	a		10 10				10 30															11 32			

Station		XC	XC	XC	XC	XC		GW	AW	XC	XC	EM	EM	XC	XC	XC		GW	GW	AW	XC	XC	XC	EM	EM
		R 1	◇		R 1			1◇		1◇	◇	1◇	1◇	1◇	◇			◇			1◇		◇	1◇	1◇
		N	C						A	B				Q	H			U		A	B				
		☕	🛒		☕			☕		☕	🛒	☕	☕	☕	🛒						☕		🛒	☕	☕
Nottingham 8	d			08 34							09 00	09 07				09 34							10 00	10 07	
Beeston	d										09 06	09a12				09 41							10 06	10a12	
Attenborough	d										09 09														
Long Eaton	d			08 50							09 18		09 44			09 50							10 18		10 44
Spondon	d										09 25														
Derby 10	a			09 00							09 31		09 56			10 00							10 31		10 56
	d	08 57		09 08	09 24						09 38			09 57		10 08					10 24		10 38		
Willington	d															10 15									
Burton-on-Trent	d			09 19							09 49			10 07		10 19							10 49		
Tamworth	d			09 31							10 01			10 18		10 31							11 01		
Wilnecote	d			09 35																					
Leicester	d		08 52			09 09									09 52							10 09			
South Wigston	d																					10 15			
Narborough	d					09 18																10 20			
Hinckley	d					09 27																10 28			
Nuneaton	d		09 13			09 34									10 14							10 35			
Coleshill Parkway	d		09 29			09 52									10 29							10 52			
Water Orton	d					09 56																			
Birmingham New Street 12	a	09 36	09 47	09 54	09 58	10 09					10 27			10 36	10 47	10 54					11 04	11 09	11 27		
	d	09 40								10 10	10 30			10 40							11 10		11 30		
Worcester Shrub Hill 7	d																	11 05							
Ashchurch for Tewkesbury	d																	11 21							
Cheltenham Spa	d	10 22						10 31	10 45	10 52	11 11			11 22				11 31	11 38	11 45	11 52		12 11		
Gloucester 7	a							10 40	10 57		11 21							11 39	11 48	11 56			12 21		
Bristol Parkway 7	a	10 54								11 24				11 54				12 19			12 24				
Bristol Temple Meads 10	a	11 11								11 41				12 11				12 35			12 41				
Newport (South Wales)	a								11 50		12 09									12 50			13 09		
Cardiff Central 7	a								12 10		12 32									13 10			13 32		

For general notes see front of timetable
For details of catering facilities see Directory of Train Operators

A To Maesteg (Table 128)
B To Plymouth (Table 51)
C From Cambridge (Table 49)
D From Sheffield (Table 53)
E **The Robin Hood**
G To Manchester Piccadilly (Table 51)
H From Stansted Airport (Table 49)
J To Sheffield (Table 53)
K From Great Malvern (Table 71) to Westbury (Table 123)
L From York to Plymouth (Table 51)
N To Paignton (Table 51)
Q From Newcastle (Table 51)
U From Great Malvern (Table 71) to Brighton (Table 123)

from 8 September

Nottingham, Derby and Leicester → Birmingham → Cardiff and Bristol

Network Diagram - see first page of Table 50

		XC	XC	XC		XC	XC	GW	XC	XC	XC	EM	XC	EM		XC	GW	GW	AW	XC	XC	XC	EM	EM	XC
		[1] ◊	◊			R [1]		[1] ◊	[1] ◊	◊	[1] ◊	[1] ◊	◊	[1] ◊			◊			[1] ◊		◊	[1] ◊	[1] ◊	R [1]
		A	B						C				B				D		E	C					C
		☕	🛒			☕		☕	☕	🛒	☕	☕	🛒	☕						☕		🛒	☕	☕	☕
Nottingham [8] 🚌	d			10 34						11 00		11 07				11 34						12 00	12 07		
Beeston	d			10 40						11 06		11a12				11 40						12 06	12a12		
Attenborough	d			10 43						11 09															
Long Eaton	d			10 49						11 18				11 44		11 50						12 18		12 44	
Spondon	d																					12 24			
Derby [10]	a			11 00						11 31				11 56		12 00						12 31		12 56	
	d	10 57		11 08		11 24				11 38	11 57					12 08				12 24		12 38			12 57
Willington	d			11 15																		12 45			
Burton-on-Trent	d			11 19						11 49	12 07					12 19						12 49			
Tamworth	d			11 31						12 01	12 18					12 31						13 01			
Wilnecote	d															12 35									
Leicester	d		10 52				11 09						11 52								12 09				
South Wigston	d																				12 15				
Narborough	d						11 19														12 20				
Hinckley	d						11 26														12 28				
Nuneaton	d		11 14				11 34						12 14								12 35				
Coleshill Parkway	d		11 29				11 50						12 29								12 52				
Water Orton	d						11 54																		
Birmingham New Street [12]	a	11 36	11 47	11 54		11 58	12 09			12 27	12 36		12 47			12 54				13 04	13 09	13 27			13 36
	d	11 40							12 10	12 30	12 40									13 10		13 30			13 40
Worcester Shrub Hill [7]	d																13 05								
Ashchurch for Tewkesbury	d																13 21								
Cheltenham Spa	d	12 22						12 31	12 52	13 11	13 22						13 31	13 38	13 45	13 52		14 11			14 22
Gloucester [7]	a							12 40		13 21							13 39	13 48	13 56			14 21			
Bristol Parkway [7]	a	12 54							13 24		13 54						14 19			14 24					14 54
Bristol Temple Meads [10]	a	13 11							13 41		14 11						14 35			14 41					15 11
Newport (South Wales)	a									14 09									14 50			15 09			
Cardiff Central [7]	a									14 32									15 10			15 32			

		XC		XC	XC	XC	GW	AW	XC	XC	EM	EM		XC	XC	XC	GW	GW	XC	XC	XC	XC		XC	EM
		◊			R [1]		[1] ◊		R [1]	◊	[1] ◊	[1] ◊		[1] ◊	◊		◊		R [1]		◊	[1] ◊		◊	[1] ◊
		B					G	E	H					J	B		D		K					B	
		🛒			☕		☕		☕	🛒	☕	☕		☕	🛒				☕			☕		🛒	☕
Nottingham [8] 🚌	d			12 34						13 00	13 07					13 34					14 00				14 07
Beeston	d			12 40						13 06	13a12					13 40					14 06				14a12
Attenborough	d									13 09															
Long Eaton	d			12 50						13 18		13 44				13 50					14 18				
Spondon	d																								
Derby [10]	a			13 00						13 31		13 56				14 00					14 31				
	d			13 08	13 24					13 38				13 57		14 08			14 24		14 38	14 57			
Willington	d															14 15									
Burton-on-Trent	d			13 19						13 49				14 07		14 19					14 49				
Tamworth	d			13 31						14 01				14 18		14 31					15 01				
Wilnecote	d			13 35																	15 05				
Leicester	d	12 52				13 09									13 52					14 09				14 52	
South Wigston	d																			14 15					
Narborough	d					13 18														14 20					
Hinckley	d					13 26														14 28					
Nuneaton	d	13 14				13 35									14 14					14 35				15 14	
Coleshill Parkway	d	13 29				13 51									14 29					14 53				15 29	
Water Orton	d					13 54																			
Birmingham New Street [12]	a	13 47		13 54	13 58	14 09				14 27				14 36	14 47	14 54			15 04	15 09	15 27	15 36		15 47	
	d								14 10	14 30				14 40					15 10		15 30	15 40			
Worcester Shrub Hill [7]	d																15 05								
Ashchurch for Tewkesbury	d																15 21				16 06				
Cheltenham Spa	d						14 31	14 45	14 52	15 11				15 22			15 31	15 38	15 52		16 15	16 22			
Gloucester [7]	a						14 40	14 56		15 21							15 39	15 48			16 24				
Bristol Parkway [7]	a								15 24					15 54			16 19		16 24			16 54			
Bristol Temple Meads [10]	a								15 41					16 11			16 35		16 41			17 11			
Newport (South Wales)	a							15 51		16 09											17 09				
Cardiff Central [7]	a							16 09		16 32											17 32				

For general notes see front of timetable
For details of catering facilities see Directory of Train Operators

- **A** To Paignton (Table 51)
- **B** From Stansted Airport (Table 49)
- **C** To Plymouth (Table 51)
- **D** From Great Malvern (Table 71) to Weymouth (Table 123)
- **E** To Maesteg (Table 128)
- **G** **Cheltenham Spa Express**
- **H** To Penzance (Table 51)
- **J** From Dundee (Table 51)
- **K** To Penzance (Table 135)

Table 57

Mondays to Fridays

from 8 September

Nottingham, Derby and Leicester → Birmingham → Cardiff and Bristol

Network Diagram - see first page of Table 50

		EM	XC	XC	XC	GW	AW	XC	XC	EM		XC	XC	EM	XC	GW	GW	AW	XC	XC		XC	EM	EM	XC
		1 ◇ ☕		R 1 ☕		1 ◇ ☕	A	R 1 B ☕	◇	1 ◇ ☕		1 ◇ ☕	◇ C 🍴	1 ◇ ☕		D	E	A	R 1 G ☕			◇	1 ◇ ☕	1 ◇ ☕	◇ C 🍴
Nottingham [8]	d		14 34						15 00	15 07					15 34							16 00	16 07		
Beeston	d		14 40						15 06	15a12					15 40							16 06	16a12		
Attenborough	d								15 09													16 09			
Long Eaton	d	14 44	14 50						15 17					15 45	15 50							16 17		16 44	
Spondon	d																					16 24			
Derby [10]	a	14 56	15 00						15 31					15 56	16 00							16 33		16 56	
	d		15 08	15 24					15 38			15 57			16 08				16 24			16 38			
Willington	d																								
Burton-on-Trent	d		15 19						15 49			16 07			16 19							16 49			
Tamworth	d		15 31						16 01			16 18			16 31							17 01			
Wilnecote	d														16 35										
Leicester	d				15 09								15 52							16 09					16 52
South Wigston	d																			16 15					
Narborough	d				15 21															16 20					
Hinckley	d				15 29															16 28					
Nuneaton	d				15 37								16 14							16 35					17 14
Coleshill Parkway	d				15 53								16 29							16 52					17 29
Water Orton	d				15 56																	17 11			
Birmingham New Street [12]	a		15 54	15 58	16 09				16 27			16 36	16 47		16 54				17 04	17 12		17 27			17 47
	d							16 10	16 30			16 40							17 10			17 30			
Worcester Shrub Hill [7]	d																17 05								
Ashchurch for Tewkesbury	d																17 21					18 09			
Cheltenham Spa	d					16 31	16 45	16 52	17 14			17 22				17 28	17 33	17 45	17 52			18 18			
Gloucester [7]	a					16 40	16 56		17 23							17 36	17 43	17 56				18 29			
Bristol Parkway [7]	a							17 24				17 54				18 18			18 24						
Bristol Temple Meads [10]	a							17 41				18 11				18 37			18 41						
Newport (South Wales)	a						17 51		18 09									18 50				19 14			
Cardiff Central [7]	a						18 10		18 32									19 09				19 32			

		XC	EM	XC	XC	XC	GW	AW		XC	XC	EM	XC	EM	XC	XC	EM	GW		AW	XC	XC	GW	XC	EM
			H	R 1 ☕		R 1 ☕	1 ◇ ☕	A		1 ◇ G ☕	◇	1 ◇ ☕	R 1 J ☕	1 ◇ ☕	◇ C		H	◇ K		A	1 ◇ G ☕			◇	1 ◇ ☕
Nottingham [8]	d	16 34	16 38								17 00	17 07				17 34	17 38							18 00	18 07
Beeston	d	16 40									17 06	17a12				17 40								18 06	18a12
Attenborough	d		16a45								17 09						17a45							18 09	
Long Eaton	d	16 50									17 18			17 44		17 50								18 18	
Spondon	d										17 24														
Derby [10]	a	17 00									17 31			17 56		18 00								18 33	
	d	17 08		17 24		16 57					17 38		17 57			18 08					18 24			18 38	
Willington	d										17 45														
Burton-on-Trent	d	17 19									17 49		18 07			18 19								18 49	
Tamworth	d	17 31									18 01		18 18			18 31								19 01	
Wilnecote	d																							19 05	
Leicester	d				17 09										17 52							18 23			
South Wigston	d				17 16										17 58							18 29			
Narborough	d				17 21										18 02							18 33			
Hinckley	d				17 29										18 10							18 42			
Nuneaton	d				17 36										18 18							18 51			
Coleshill Parkway	d				17 52																				
Water Orton	d															18 44									
Birmingham New Street [12]	a	17 54		17 58	18 09	17 36					18 27		18 36		18 48	18 56					19 08	19 18		19 27	
	d					17 40				18 10	18 30		18 40								19 10			19 30	
Worcester Shrub Hill [7]	d																	19 05							
Ashchurch for Tewkesbury	d																	19 21						20 06	
Cheltenham Spa	d					18 22	18 31	18 45		18 52	19 14		19 22					19 31		19 45	19 52		20 00	20 15	
Gloucester [7]	a					18 34	18 40	18 56			19 23							19 39		19 56			20 10	20 24	
Bristol Parkway [7]	a					19 05				19 24			19 54					20 19			20 24				
Bristol Temple Meads [10]	a					19 22				19 41			20 11					20 34			20 41				
Newport (South Wales)	a					19 59		19 51			20 09									20 50				21 09	
Cardiff Central [7]	a					20 19		20 11			20 32									21 10				21 32	

For general notes see front of timetable
For details of catering facilities see Directory of Train Operators

A To Maesteg (Table 128)
B To Penzance (Table 51)
C From Stansted Airport (Table 49)
D To Westbury (Table 123)
E From Worcester Foregate Street (Table 71) to Southampton Central (Table 123)
G To Plymouth (Table 51)
H From Lincoln (Table 27)
J From Newcastle to Weston-super-Mare (Table 51)
K From Great Malvern (Table 71) to Weymouth (Table 123)

from 8 September

Nottingham, Derby and Leicester → Birmingham → Cardiff and Bristol

Network Diagram - see first page of Table 50

		XC [R] [1] ☕	XC ◇ A	XC	EM [1] ◇ ☕	EM [1] ◇ ☕		XC [R] [1] ☕	XC	GW [1] ☕	XC [1] ◇ B	XC ◇ A	XC [1] ◇ C ☕	EM [1] ◇ D ☕	XC	EM E		EM [1] ◇ D ☕	EM [1] ◇ ☕	EM [1] ◇ ☕	GW	GW G	AW	XC [1] ◇	XC
Nottingham [8]	d			18 34		19 07									19 34	19 38				20 07					
Beeston	d					19a12									19 40	19a44				20a12					
Attenborough	d																								
Long Eaton	d			18 46	18 56									19 47	19 50				20 03						
Spondon	d																								
Derby [10]	a			18 56	19 10									19 59	20 00			←	20 15						
	d	18 57		19 06				19 24					19 57	20 11 →	20 08			20 11						20 27	
Willington	d			19 14														20 21							
Burton-on-Trent	d			19 20									20 07		20 19			20a26							
Tamworth	d			19 31									20 18		20 31										
Wilnecote	d																								
Leicester	d		18 52						19 09			19 41													20 09
South Wigston	d								19 16																20 15
Narborough	d								19 20																20 20
Hinckley	d								19 30																20 28
Nuneaton	d		19 14						19 38			20 01													20 37
Coleshill Parkway	d		19 29						19 55			20 16													20 54
Water Orton	d																								
Birmingham New Street [12]	a	19 36	19 47	19 54				19 58	20 09			20 37	20 43		20 58									21 04	21 09
	d	19 40									20 10													21 10	
Worcester Shrub Hill [7]	d																					21 08			
Ashchurch for Tewkesbury	d																					21 24			
Cheltenham Spa	d	20 22								20 48	20 52										21 02	21 34	21 45	21 52	
Gloucester [7]	a									20 58											21 12	21 45	21 56		
Bristol Parkway [7]	a	20 54									21 24										21 50			22 24	
Bristol Temple Meads [10]	a	21 11									21 41										22 02			22 41	
Newport (South Wales)	a																						22 57		
Cardiff Central [7]	a																						23 18		

		XC [1] ◇ ☕	XC ◇ A	EM [1] ◇ D ☕		XC	GW	GW ◇ ☕	AW	XC [1] ◇ H	XC	XC ◇ A	EM [1] ◇ ☕	GW		XC [1] ◇ C	XC	LM FO	XC	XC ◇ A	XC [1] ◇	EM [1] ◇ D ☕			
Nottingham [8]	d					20 34											21 34					22 58			
Beeston	d					20 40											21 40					23 04			
Attenborough	d																21 43								
Long Eaton	d			20 44		20 49							21 44				21 50					23 14			
Spondon	d																21 57								
Derby [10]	a			20 56		21 00							21 56				22 04					23 26			
	d	20 57		21 03		21 08				21 27						21 57	22 08				23 15				
Willington	d			21 11																					
Burton-on-Trent	d			21a16		21 19				21 37						22 07	22 19				23 26				
Tamworth	d					21 32				21 48						22 18	22 31				23 37				
Wilnecote	d					21 35											22 34								
Leicester	d		20 52								21 09	21 41							22 27	22 49					
South Wigston	d										21 15								22 33						
Narborough	d										21 19								22 37						
Hinckley	d										21 28								22 46						
Nuneaton	d		21 14								21 37	22 01							22 54	23 08					
Coleshill Parkway	d		21 29									22 17							23 14	23 24					
Water Orton	d					21 44																			
Birmingham New Street [12]	a	21 44	21 47			21 57				22 08	22 09	22 36				22 50	22 54		23 34	23 41	23 59				
	d									22 10								23 04							
Worcester Shrub Hill [7]	d													22 32				23 44							
Ashchurch for Tewkesbury	d													22 51				23 58							
Cheltenham Spa	d						22 00	22 31	22 45	22 52				23 01				00 07							
Gloucester [7]	a						22 10	22 41	22 56					23 13				00 16							
Bristol Parkway [7]	a							23 16		23 24															
Bristol Temple Meads [10]	a							23 37		23 41															
Newport (South Wales)	a								23 59																
Cardiff Central [7]	a								00 24																

For general notes see front of timetable
For details of catering facilities see Directory of Train Operators

A From Stansted Airport (Table 49)
B To Plymouth (Table 51)
C From Edinburgh (Table 51)
D From St Pancras International (Table 53)
E From Lincoln (Table 27)
G From Great Malvern (Table 71)
H From Newcastle (Table 51)

Table 57

Saturdays until 12 July

Nottingham, Derby and Leicester → Birmingham → Cardiff and Bristol

Network Diagram - see first page of Table 50

		LM	EM	GW	XC	XC	XC	GW	GW	GW	AW		XC	EM	EM	XC	XC	XC	XC	AW	XC	XC		GW	XC
			1 ◇							1 ◇			1 ◇		1 ◇	◇			1 ◇		1 ◇	◇		1 ◇	◇
									A		B		C	D					E	B	G	H			
Nottingham 8	d		01 44											05 52	06 07			06 31							06 58
Beeston	d													05 58	06a12			06 40							07 03
Attenborough	d													06 01											07 06
Long Eaton	d													06 11				06 50							07 14
Spondon	d													06 17											
Derby 10	a		02 05											06 23				07 01							07 32
	d												06 10			06 34		07 08	07 15		07 27				07 38
Willington	d															06 45									
Burton-on-Trent	d												06 20			06 51		07 19			07 37				07 49
Tamworth	d												06 31			07 03		07 31			07 48				08 01
Wilnecote	d															07 06									
Leicester	d						05 45										06 47					07 08			
South Wigston	d						05 50										06 53								
Narborough	d						05 55										06 58					07 17			
Hinckley	d						06 03										07 07					07 26			
Nuneaton	d						06 10										07 15					07 34			
Coleshill Parkway	d						06 32										07 31								
Water Orton	d																07 36					07 53			
Birmingham New Street 12	a						06 46						06 51			07 27	07 46	07 55	07 58		08 06	08 08			08 27
	d	23p04				05 30							07 10			07 30					08 10				08 30
Worcester Shrub Hill 7	d	23p44			05 40	06 17			06 56																
Ashchurch for Tewkesbury	d	23p58			05 56	06 33			07 12																
Cheltenham Spa	d	00 07		05 30	06 05	06 43		07 00	07 22	07 27	07 45		07 52			08 11				08 45	08 52			09 00	09 11
Gloucester 7	a	00 16		05 40	06 15	06 52		07 10	07 30	07 36	07 56					08 21				08 56				09 10	09 21
Bristol Parkway 7	a							07 51	08 15				08 24								09 24				
Bristol Temple Meads 10	a							08 05	08 34				08 41								09 41				
Newport (South Wales)	a				07 05	07 50					08 50					09 05				09 50					10 05
Cardiff Central 7	a				07 26	08 12					09 10					09 25				10 09					10 25

		EM	XC	XC	EM	XC	GW	XC	XC	GW	XC		EM	EM	XC	XC	XC	XC	XC	AW	XC	GW		XC	EM
		1 ◇	◇					R 1	1 ◇		◇		1 ◇	1 ◇	R 1	◇		R 1			R 1	1 ◇		◇	1 ◇
			J				K	L	N					Q	C	H				B	C				
Nottingham 8	d	07 07		07 34	07 38						08 00		08 07				08 32							09 00	09 07
Beeston	d	07a12		07 40	07a44						08 06		08a12											09 06	09a12
Attenborough	d										08 09													09 09	
Long Eaton	d			07 50							08 16			08 22			08 50							09 16	
Spondon	d										08 23													09 23	
Derby 10	a			08 01							08 29			08 34			09 01							09 31	
	d			08 08					08 27		08 38				08 57		09 08	09 24						09 38	
Willington	d			08 15																					
Burton-on-Trent	d			08 21					08 37		08 49						09 19							09 49	
Tamworth	d			08 33					08 48		09 01						09 33							10 01	
Wilnecote	d			08 37																					
Leicester	d		07 46			08 09										08 52			09 09						
South Wigston	d					08 16																			
Narborough	d		07 55			08 20													09 18						
Hinckley	d		08 04			08 29													09 26						
Nuneaton	d		08 11			08 41										09 14			09 33						
Coleshill Parkway	d		08 28			08 57										09 29			09 50						
Water Orton	d																		09 53						
Birmingham New Street 12	a		08 47	08 56		09 09			09 11		09 27				09 36	09 47	09 55	09 58	10 09					10 27	
	d							09 10			09 30				09 40						10 10			10 30	
Worcester Shrub Hill 7	d						09 05																		
Ashchurch for Tewkesbury	d						09 21																		
Cheltenham Spa	d						09 31	09 52		10 01	10 11				10 22					10 45	10 52	11 00		11 11	
Gloucester 7	a						09 39			10 11	10 21									10 56		11 10		11 21	
Bristol Parkway 7	a						10 19	10 24							10 54						11 24				
Bristol Temple Meads 10	a						10 35	10 41							11 11						11 41				
Newport (South Wales)	a										11 05									11 50				12 05	
Cardiff Central 7	a										11 25									12 10				12 25	

For general notes see front of timetable
For details of catering facilities see Directory of Train Operators

A To Weymouth (Table 123)
B To Maesteg (Table 128)
C To Paignton (Table 51)
D To Crewe (Table 50)
E From Sheffield to Bournemouth (Table 51)
G From Leeds to Plymouth (Table 51)
H From Cambridge (Table 49)
J From Stansted Airport (Table 49)
K From Great Malvern (Table 71) to Westbury (Table 123)
L To Newquay (Table 135)
N From York (Table 51)
Q To Scarborough (Table 26)

Table 57

Saturdays

until 12 July

Nottingham, Derby and Leicester → Birmingham → Cardiff and Bristol

Network Diagram - see first page of Table 50

		EM	XC	XC	XC	AW	GW	XC	XC	GW	XC		EM	EM	XC	XC	XC	XC	XC	XC	GW	XC		EM	EM
		1◇ ☕	1◇ A ☕	◇ B		C	◇ D	R 1 E ☕			◇		1◇ ☕	1◇ ☕	1◇ ☕	◇ B		1◇ ☕		R 1 G ☕	1◇ ☕	◇		1◇ ☕	1◇ ☕
Nottingham [8]	d				09 34						10 02		10 07				10 34					11 00		11 07	
Beeston	d				09 40						10 08		10a12				10 40					11 06		11a12	
Attenborough	d																					11 09			
Long Eaton	d	09 44			09 50						10 17			10 44			10 50					11 16			11 45
Spondon	d																								
Derby [10]	a	09 56			10 01						10 31			10 56			11 01					11 31			11 56
	d		09 57		10 08			10 24			10 39				10 57		11 08	11 24				11 38			
Willington	d				10 15																				
Burton-on-Trent	d		10 07		10 21						10 49						11 19					11 49			
Tamworth	d		10 18		10 33						11 01						11 31					12 01			
Wilnecote	d																11 35								
Leicester	d			09 52					10 09							10 52			11 09						
South Wigston	d								10 15																
Narborough	d								10 20										11 18						
Hinckley	d								10 28										11 26						
Nuneaton	d			10 14					10 35							11 14			11 35						
Coleshill Parkway	d			10 29					10 54							11 29			11 51						
Water Orton	d																		11 56						
Birmingham New Street [12]	a		10 36	10 47	10 55			11 04	11 09		11 27				11 36	11 47	11 55	11 58	12 09			12 27			
	d		10 40					11 10			11 30				11 40					12 10		12 30			
Worcester Shrub Hill [7]	d						11 05																		
Ashchurch for Tewkesbury	d						11 21																		
Cheltenham Spa	d		11 22			11 45	11 32	11 52		12 01	12 11				12 22					12 52	13 00	13 11			
Gloucester [7]	a					11 56	11 40			12 11	12 21										13 10	13 21			
Bristol Parkway [7]	a		11 54				12 23	12 24							12 54					13 24					
Bristol Temple Meads [10]	a		12 11				12 39	12 41							13 11					13 41					
Newport (South Wales)	a					12 50					13 05											14 05			
Cardiff Central [7]	a					13 10					13 25											14 25			

		XC	XC	XC	XC	GW	XC	AW	GW	XC	EM		EM	XC	XC	XC	XC	XC	AW	XC	GW	XC		EM	EM
		1◇ H ☕	◇ B			◇ J 🛒	R 1 ☕	C		◇	1◇ ☕		1◇ ☕	R 1 K ☕	◇ B		R 1 ☕		C	R 1 G ☕	1◇ ☕	◇		1◇ ☕	1◇ ☕
Nottingham [8]	d			11 34						12 00	12 07					12 34						13 00		13 07	
Beeston	d			11 40						12 06	12a12					12 40						13 06		13a12	
Attenborough	d																					13 09			
Long Eaton	d			11 50						12 16			12 44			12 50						13 16			13 44
Spondon	d									12 23															
Derby [10]	a			12 01						12 31			12 56			13 01						13 31			13 56
	d	11 57		12 08			12 30			12 38				12 57		13 08	13 24					13 38			
Willington	d																								
Burton-on-Trent	d	12 07		12 20						12 49						13 19						13 49			
Tamworth	d	12 18		12 31						13 01						13 31						14 01			
Wilnecote	d			12 35																					
Leicester	d		11 52		12 09										12 52			13 09							
South Wigston	d				12 15																				
Narborough	d				12 20													13 18							
Hinckley	d				12 28													13 26							
Nuneaton	d		12 14		12 35										13 14			13 35							
Coleshill Parkway	d		12 29		12 52										13 29			13 53							
Water Orton	d															13 44		13 56							
Birmingham New Street [12]	a	12 36	12 47	12 55	13 06		13 09			13 27				13 36	13 47	13 55	13 58	14 09				14 27			
	d	12 40					13 10			13 30				13 40						14 10		14 30			
Worcester Shrub Hill [7]	d					13 05																			
Ashchurch for Tewkesbury	d					13 21																			
Cheltenham Spa	d	13 22				13 32		13 45	14 01	14 11				14 22					14 45	14 52	15 00	15 11			
Gloucester [7]	a					13 40		13 56	14 11	14 21									14 56		15 10	15 21			
Bristol Parkway [7]	a	13 54				14 23								14 54						15 24					
Bristol Temple Meads [10]	a	14 11				14 39	14 41							15 11						15 41					
Newport (South Wales)	a							14 50		15 05									15 50			16 05			
Cardiff Central [7]	a							15 09		15 25									16 07			16 25			

For general notes see front of timetable
For details of catering facilities see Directory of Train Operators

A From Newcastle (Table 51)
B From Stansted Airport (Table 49)
C To Maesteg (Table 128)
D From Great Malvern (Table 71) to Brighton (Table 123)
E To Plymouth (Table 51)
G To Paignton (Table 51)
H From Edinburgh (Table 51)
J From Great Malvern (Table 71) to Weymouth (Table 123)
K To Penzance (Table 51)

Table 57

Saturdays

until 12 July

Nottingham, Derby and Leicester → Birmingham → Cardiff and Bristol

Network Diagram - see first page of Table 50

		XC	XC	XC	GW	XC	XC	GW	XC	EM	EM	XC	XC	XC	XC	XC	AW	XC	GW	XC	EM	EM	XC
		1◇ A ☕	◇ B		◇ C	R 1 D ☕			◇	1◇ ☕	1◇ ☕	1◇ ☕	◇ B		1◇ ☕		E	1◇ G ☕	1◇ ☕	◇	1◇ ☕	1◇ ☕	1◇ A ☕
Nottingham 8	d			13 34					14 00	14 07				14 34						15 00	15 07		
Beeston	d			13 40					14 06	14a12				14 40						15 06	15a12		
Attenborough	d																			15 09			
Long Eaton	d			13 50					14 16		14 44			14 50						15 16		15 44	
Spondon	d																						
Derby 10	a			14 01					14 31		14 56			15 01						15 31		15 56	
	d	13 57		14 08		14 24			14 38			14 57		15 08	15 24					15 38			15 57
Willington	d			14 15																			
Burton-on-Trent	d	14 07		14 19					14 49					15 19						15 49			16 07
Tamworth	d	14 18		14 31					15 01					15 31						16 01			16 18
Wilnecote	d													15 35									
Leicester	d		13 52				14 09						14 52			15 09							
South Wigston	d						14 15																
Narborough	d						14 20									15 18							
Hinckley	d						14 28									15 26							
Nuneaton	d		14 14				14 35						15 14			15 34							
Coleshill Parkway	d		14 29				14 54						15 29			15 50							
Water Orton	d															15 56							
Birmingham New Street 12	a	14 36	14 47	14 55		15 04	15 09		15 27			15 36	15 47	15 55	15 58	16 09				16 27			16 36
	d	14 40				15 10			15 30			15 40						16 10		16 30			16 40
Worcester Shrub Hill 7	d				15 05																		
Ashchurch for Tewkesbury	d				15 21				16 06														
Cheltenham Spa	d	15 22			15 31	15 52		16 01	16 15			16 22					16 45	16 52	17 00	17 14			17 22
Gloucester 7	a				15 40			16 11	16 24								16 56		17 10	17 23			
Bristol Parkway 7	a	15 54			16 19	16 24						16 54						17 24					17 54
Bristol Temple Meads 10	a	16 11			16 34	16 41						17 11						17 41					18 11
Newport (South Wales)	a								17 05								17 50			18 05			
Cardiff Central 7	a								17 25								18 10			18 25			

		XC	XC	GW	AW	XC	XC	GW	XC	EM	EM	XC	XC	XC	EM	XC	XC	AW	XC	GW	XC	EM	XC
		◇ B		H	E	1◇ G ☕			◇	1◇ J ☕	1◇ ☕	1◇ ☕	◇ B		K	1◇ ☕		E	1◇ L ☕	1◇ ☕	◇	1◇ ☕	1◇ A ☕
Nottingham 8	d		15 34						16 00	16 07				16 34	16 38						17 00	17 07	
Beeston	d		15 40						16 06	16a12				16 40							17 06	17a12	
Attenborough	d								16 09						16a47						17 09		
Long Eaton	d		15 50						16 16		16 44			16 48							17 16		
Spondon	d								16 23												17 23		
Derby 10	a		16 01						16 31		16 56			17 01							17 31		
	d		16 08			16 24			16 38			16 57		17 08		17 24					17 38		17 57
Willington	d													17 15									
Burton-on-Trent	d		16 19						16 49					17 19							17 49		18 07
Tamworth	d		16 31						17 01					17 31							18 01		18 18
Wilnecote	d		16 35																				
Leicester	d	15 52					16 09						16 52				17 09						
South Wigston	d						16 15										17 15						
Narborough	d						16 20										17 20						
Hinckley	d						16 28										17 28						
Nuneaton	d	16 14					16 35						17 14				17 35						
Coleshill Parkway	d	16 29					16 54						17 29				17 52						
Water Orton	d																						
Birmingham New Street 12	a	16 47	16 55			17 04	17 12		17 27			17 36	17 47	17 55		17 58	18 09				18 27		18 36
	d					17 10			17 30			17 40							18 10		18 30		18 40
Worcester Shrub Hill 7	d			17 05																			
Ashchurch for Tewkesbury	d			17 22					18 09														
Cheltenham Spa	d			17 32	17 45	17 52		18 01	18 18			18 21						18 45	18 52	19 00	19 14		19 22
Gloucester 7	a			17 41	17 56			18 11	18 28			18 33						18 56		19 10	19 23		
Bristol Parkway 7	a			18 23		18 24						19 09							19 24				19 54
Bristol Temple Meads 10	a			18 39		18 41						19 26							19 41				20 11
Newport (South Wales)	a				18 50				19 12			19 59						19 50			20 05		
Cardiff Central 7	a				19 10				19 33			20 19						20 10			20 25		

For general notes see front of timetable
For details of catering facilities see Directory of Train Operators

A From Newcastle (Table 51)
B From Stansted Airport (Table 49)
C From Worcester Foregate Street (Table 71) to Weymouth (Table 123)
D To Paignton (Table 51)
E To Maesteg (Table 128)
G To Penzance (Table 51)
H From Great Malvern (Table 71) to Westbury (Table 123)
J From Sheffield (Table 53)
K From Lincoln (Table 27)
L To Plymouth (Table 51)

Table 57

Saturdays

until 12 July

Nottingham, Derby and Leicester → Birmingham → Cardiff and Bristol

Network Diagram - see first page of Table 50

		XC	EM	XC	EM	GW	AW	XC	XC	XC	EM		EM	GW	XC	XC	XC	EM	XC	XC	EM	XC		XC	XC
		◇	**1** ◇			◇		**1** ◇			**1** ◇		**1** ◇		**1** ◇	◇		**1** ◇	**1** ◇			**1** ◇		**1** ◇	◇
		A	B		C	D	E	G						H		A						G		J	A
			☕					☕			☕		☕		☕			☕	☕			☕		☕	
Nottingham 8 🚌	d			17 34	17 38					18 00	18 07						18 34	19 07			19 33				
Beeston	d			17 40						18 06	18a12						18 40	19a12			19a39				
Attenborough	d				17a47					18 09															
Long Eaton	d		17 44	17 51						18 18			18 43				18 50								
Spondon	d																								
Derby 10	a		17 54	18 00						18 31			18 56				19 01								
	d		18 01	18 08				18 24		18 38					18 57		19 08		19 24					19 57	
Willington	d		18 10														19 15								
Burton-on-Trent	d		18a15	18 19						18 49							19 21							20 07	
Tamworth	d			18 31						19 01							19 33							20 18	
Wilnecote	d									19 05															
Leicester	d	17 52							18 09							18 52				19 09					19 52
South Wigston	d								18 16											19 15					
Narborough	d								18 21											19 20					
Hinckley	d								18 29											19 28					
Nuneaton	d	18 14							18 36							19 14				19 38					20 14
Coleshill Parkway	d	18 29							18 52							19 29				19 54					20 29
Water Orton	d																								
Birmingham New Street 12	a	18 47		18 55				19 04	19 08	19 27					19 36	19 47	19 55		19 58	20 09				20 43	20 47
	d							19 10							19 40		20 00					20 10			
Worcester Shrub Hill 7	d					19 10																			
Ashchurch for Tewkesbury	d					19 26											20 36								
Cheltenham Spa	d					19 36	19 45	19 52						20 01	20 22		20 49					20 52			
Gloucester 7	a					19 44	19 56							20 10			21 04								
Bristol Parkway 7	a					20 23		20 24							20 54							21 24			
Bristol Temple Meads 10	a					20 40		20 41							21 11							21 41			
Newport (South Wales)	a						20 50																		
Cardiff Central 7	a						21 10																		

		EM	XC	XC	EM	GW	GW	AW	XC	XC	EM		GW	XC	XC	XC	XC	EM	XC	XC	XC	EM			
		1 ◇			**1** ◇				**1** ◇		**1** ◇			◇		**1** ◇	◇	**1** ◇		**1** ◇		**1** ◇			
		K											L	A		J	A			N					
		☕			☕						☕							☕				☕			
Nottingham 8 🚌	d		19 40		20 07					20 11									21 45						
Beeston	d				20a12					20 17									21 51						
Attenborough	d		19 46																21 55						
Long Eaton	d	19 47	19 53							20 24	20 44							21 44	22 01			22 44			
Spondon	d									20 32									22 07						
Derby 10	a	19 57	20 03							20 37	20 56							21 56	22 13			22 55			
	d		20 07						20 27	20 38						21 27			22 17	22 27					
Willington	d																								
Burton-on-Trent	d		20 19							20 49						21 37			22 29	22 37					
Tamworth	d		20 31							21 01						21 48			22 42	22 48					
Wilnecote	d									21 05															
Leicester	d			20 09										20 52	21 10		21 39				22 26				
South Wigston	d			20 14											21 15						22 31				
Narborough	d			20 19											21 20						22 36				
Hinckley	d			20 27											21 28						22 44				
Nuneaton	d			20 34										21 14	21 35		22 01				22 51				
Coleshill Parkway	d			20 49										21 29	21 52		22 18				23 10				
Water Orton	d																								
Birmingham New Street 12	a		20 55	21 01					21 04	21 28				21 47	22 04	22 13	22 35		23 03	23 15	23 22				
	d								21 10																
Worcester Shrub Hill 7	d												21 34												
Ashchurch for Tewkesbury	d												21 52												
Cheltenham Spa	d					21 02	21 30	21 45	21 52				22 02												
Gloucester 7	a					21 12	21 40	21 56					22 11												
Bristol Parkway 7	a					21 51			22 24																
Bristol Temple Meads 10	a					22 04			22 41																
Newport (South Wales)	a							22 55																	
Cardiff Central 7	a							23 18																	

For general notes see front of timetable
For details of catering facilities see Directory of Train Operators

A From Stansted Airport (Table 49)
B From St Pancras International (Table 53)
C From Lincoln (Table 27)
D To Weymouth (Table 123)
E To Maesteg (Table 128)
G To Plymouth (Table 51)
H To Westbury (Table 123)
J From Newcastle (Table 51)
K To Barnsley (Table 53)
L From Great Malvern (Table 71)
N From Edinburgh (Table 51)

Table 57

Saturdays

Nottingham, Derby and Leicester → Birmingham → Cardiff and Bristol

19 July to 6 September

Network Diagram - see first page of Table 50

		AW	LM	EM	GW	XC	XC	XC	GW	GW	GW	AW		XC	EM	EM	XC	XC	XC	XC	AW	XC	XC	GW	XC
				1 ◇							1 ◇			1 ◇		1 ◇	◇			1 ◇		1 ◇	◇	1 ◇	◇
										A		B		C	D					E	B	G	H		
				☕							☕			☕		☕				☕		☕		☕	🍴
Nottingham 8	d			01 44											05 52	06 07			06 31						06 58
Beeston	d														05 58	06a12			06 40						07 03
Attenborough	d														06 01										07 06
Long Eaton	d														06 11				06 50						07 14
Spondon	d														06 17										
Derby 10	a			02 05											06 23				07 01						07 32
	d													06 10			06 34		07 08	07 15		07 27			07 38
Willington	d																06 45								
Burton-on-Trent	d													06 20			06 51		07 19			07 37			07 49
Tamworth	d													06 31			07 03		07 31			07 48			08 01
Wilnecote	d																07 06								
Leicester	d							05 45										06 47					07 08		
South Wigston	d							05 50										06 53							
Narborough	d							05 55										06 58					07 17		
Hinckley	d							06 03										07 07					07 26		
Nuneaton	d							06 10										07 15					07 34		
Coleshill Parkway	d							06 32										07 31							
Water Orton	d																	07 36					07 53		
Birmingham New Street 12	a							06 46						06 51			07 27	07 46	07 55	07 58		08 06	08 08		08 27
	d		23p04				05 30							07 10			07 30					08 10			08 30
Worcester Shrub Hill 7	d		23p44			05 40	06 17			06 56															
Ashchurch for Tewkesbury	d		23p58			05 56	06 33			07 12															
Cheltenham Spa	d	22 45	00 07		05 30	06 05	06 43		07 00	07 22	07 27	07 45		07 52			08 11				08 45	08 52		09 00	09 11
Gloucester 7	a	22 56	00 16		05 40	06 15	06 52		07 10	07 30	07 36	07 56					08 21				08 56			09 10	09 21
Bristol Parkway 7	a								07 53	08 15				08 24								09 24			
Bristol Temple Meads 10	a								08 05	08 34				08 41								09 41			
Newport (South Wales)	a	23 59				07 05	07 50					08 50					09 05				09 50				10 05
Cardiff Central 7	a	00 24				07 26	08 12					09 10					09 25				10 09				10 25

		EM		XC	EM	XC	EM	XC	GW	XC	XC	GW	XC	EM		EM	XC	XC	XC	XC	XC	AW	XC	GW	XC
										R							R			R			R		
		1 ◇		◇	1 ◇					1	1 ◇		◇	1 ◇		1 ◇	1	◇		1			1	1 ◇	◇
				J					K	L	N					Q	C	H				B	C		
		☕			☕					☕	☕			☕		☕	☕			☕			☕	☕	
Nottingham 8	d	07 07				07 34	07 38						08 00	08 07					08 32						09 00
Beeston	d	07a12				07 40	07a44						08 06	08a12											09 06
Attenborough	d												08 09												09 09
Long Eaton	d					07 50							08 16			08 22			08 50						09 16
Spondon	d												08 23												09 23
Derby 10	a					08 01							08 29			08 34			09 01						09 31
	d				07 33	08 08					08 27		08 38				08 57		09 08	09 24					09 38
Willington	d					08 15																			
Burton-on-Trent	d					08 21					08 37		08 49						09 19						09 49
Tamworth	d					08 33					08 48		09 01						09 33						10 01
Wilnecote	d					08 37																			
Leicester	d			07 46	08a04			08 09										08 52			09 09				
South Wigston	d							08 16																	
Narborough	d			07 55				08 20													09 18				
Hinckley	d			08 04				08 29													09 26				
Nuneaton	d			08 11				08 41										09 14			09 33				
Coleshill Parkway	d			08 28				08 57										09 29			09 50				
Water Orton	d																				09 53				
Birmingham New Street 12	a			08 47		08 56		09 09			09 11		09 27				09 36	09 47	09 55	09 58	10 09				10 27
	d									09 10			09 30				09 40						10 10		10 30
Worcester Shrub Hill 7	d								09 05																
Ashchurch for Tewkesbury	d								09 21																
Cheltenham Spa	d								09 31	09 52		10 01	10 11				10 22					10 45	10 52	11 00	11 11
Gloucester 7	a								09 39			10 11	10 21									10 56		11 10	11 21
Bristol Parkway 7	a								10 19	10 27							10 54						11 24		
Bristol Temple Meads 10	a								10 35	10 41							11 11						11 41		
Newport (South Wales)	a												11 05									11 50			12 05
Cardiff Central 7	a												11 25									12 10			12 25

For general notes see front of timetable
For details of catering facilities see Directory of Train Operators

A To Weymouth (Table 123)
B To Maesteg (Table 128)
C To Paignton (Table 51)
D To Crewe (Table 50)
E From Sheffield to Bournemouth (Table 51)
G From Leeds to Plymouth (Table 51)
H From Cambridge (Table 49)
J From Stansted Airport (Table 49)
K From Great Malvern (Table 71) to Westbury (Table 123)
L To Newquay (Table 135)
N From York (Table 51)
Q To Scarborough (Table 26)

Due to Engineering Operations, services from Saturday 13 September on this Table had not been confirmed at time of going to press. These services will be issued in a special Supplement as soon as exact timings have been confirmed

Table 57

Nottingham, Derby and Leicester → Birmingham → Cardiff and Bristol

19 July to 6 September

Network Diagram - see first page of Table 50

		EM	EM	XC		XC	XC	GW	AW	XC	XC	GW	XC	EM	EM	XC		XC	XC	XC	XC	XC	GW	XC	EM
		1◇	1◇	1◇		◇		◇		R 1			◇	1◇	1◇	1◇		◇		1◇		R 1	1◇	◇	1◇
				A		B		C	D	E								B				G			
		☕	☕	☕						☕				☕	☕	☕				☕		☕	☕		☕
Nottingham 8	d	09 07					09 34						10 02	10 07					10 34					11 00	11 07
Beeston	d	09a12					09 40						10 08	10a12					10 40					11 06	11a12
Attenborough	d																							11 09	
Long Eaton	d		09 44				09 50						10 17		10 44				10 50					11 16	
Spondon	d																								
Derby 10	a		09 56				10 01						10 31		10 56				11 01					11 31	
	d			09 57			10 08			10 24			10 39			10 57			11 08	11 24				11 38	
Willington	d						10 15																		
Burton-on-Trent	d			10 07			10 21						10 49						11 19					11 49	
Tamworth	d			10 18			10 33						11 01						11 31					12 01	
Wilnecote	d																		11 35						
Leicester	d					09 52					10 09							10 52			11 09				
South Wigston	d										10 15														
Narborough	d										10 20										11 18				
Hinckley	d										10 28										11 26				
Nuneaton	d					10 14					10 35							11 14			11 35				
Coleshill Parkway	d					10 29					10 54							11 29			11 51				
Water Orton	d																				11 56				
Birmingham New Street 12	a			10 36		10 47	10 55			11 04	11 09		11 27			11 36		11 47	11 55	11 58	12 09			12 27	
	d			10 40						11 10			11 30			11 40						12 10		12 30	
Worcester Shrub Hill 7	d							11 05																	
Ashchurch for Tewkesbury	d							11 21																	
Cheltenham Spa	d			11 22				11 32	11 45	11 52		12 01	12 11			12 22						12 52	13 00	13 11	
Gloucester 7	a							11 40	11 56			12 11	12 21										13 10	13 21	
Bristol Parkway 7	a			11 54				12 23		12 24						12 54						13 24			
Bristol Temple Meads 10	a			12 11				12 39		12 41						13 11						13 41			
Newport (South Wales)	a								12 50				13 05											14 05	
Cardiff Central 7	a								13 10				13 25											14 25	

		EM	XC	XC	XC	XC		GW	XC	AW	GW	XC	EM	EM	XC	XC	XC	XC		XC	AW	XC	GW	XC	EM
		1◇	1◇	◇				◇	R 1			◇	1◇	1◇	R 1	◇		R 1				R 1	1◇	◇	1◇
			H	B				J		D					K	B					D	G			
		☕	☕						☕				☕	☕	☕			☕				☕	☕		☕
Nottingham 8	d				11 34							12 00	12 07				12 34							13 00	13 07
Beeston	d				11 40							12 06	12a12				12 40							13 06	13a12
Attenborough	d																							13 09	
Long Eaton	d	11 45			11 50							12 16		12 44			12 50							13 16	
Spondon	d											12 23													
Derby 10	a	11 56			12 01							12 31		12 56			13 01							13 31	
	d		11 57		12 08				12 30			12 38			12 57		13 08	13 24						13 38	
Willington	d																								
Burton-on-Trent	d		12 07		12 20							12 49					13 19							13 49	
Tamworth	d		12 18		12 31							13 01					13 31							14 01	
Wilnecote	d				12 35																				
Leicester	d			11 52		12 09										12 52				13 09					
South Wigston	d					12 15																			
Narborough	d					12 20														13 18					
Hinckley	d					12 28														13 26					
Nuneaton	d			12 14		12 35										13 14				13 35					
Coleshill Parkway	d			12 29		12 52										13 29				13 53					
Water Orton	d																13 44			13 56					
Birmingham New Street 12	a		12 36	12 47	12 55	13 06			13 09			13 27			13 36	13 47	13 55	13 58		14 09				14 27	
	d		12 40						13 10			13 30			13 40							14 10		14 30	
Worcester Shrub Hill 7	d							13 05																	
Ashchurch for Tewkesbury	d							13 21																	
Cheltenham Spa	d		13 22					13 32		13 45	14 01	14 11			14 22						14 45	14 52	15 00	15 11	
Gloucester 7	a							13 40		13 56	14 11	14 21									14 56		15 10	15 21	
Bristol Parkway 7	a		13 54					14 23							14 54							15 24			
Bristol Temple Meads 10	a		14 11					14 39	14 41						15 11							15 41			
Newport (South Wales)	a									14 50		15 05									15 50			16 05	
Cardiff Central 7	a									15 09		15 25									16 07			16 25	

For general notes see front of timetable
For details of catering facilities see Directory of Train Operators

- A From Newcastle (Table 51)
- B From Stansted Airport (Table 49)
- C From Great Malvern (Table 71) to Brighton (Table 123)
- D To Maesteg (Table 128)
- E To Plymouth (Table 51)
- G To Paignton (Table 51)
- H From Edinburgh (Table 51)
- J From Great Malvern (Table 71) to Weymouth (Table 123)
- K To Penzance (Table 51)

Due to Engineering Operations, services from Saturday 13 September on this Table had not been confirmed at time of going to press. These services will be issued in a special Supplement as soon as exact timings have been confirmed

Table 57

Saturdays

Nottingham, Derby and Leicester → Birmingham → Cardiff and Bristol

19 July to 6 September

Network Diagram - see first page of Table 50

		EM 1◇ ☕	XC 1◇ A ☕	XC ◇ B	XC	GW ◇ C	XC R 1 D ☕	XC		GW	XC ◇	EM 1◇ ☕	EM 1◇ ☕	XC 1◇ ☕	XC ◇ B	XC	XC 1◇ ☕	XC	AW E	XC 1◇ G ☕		GW 1◇ ☕	XC ◇	EM 1◇ ☕	EM 1◇ ☕
Nottingham 8	d				13 34						14 00	14 07				14 34							15 00	15 07	
Beeston	d				13 40						14 06	14a12				14 40							15 06	15a12	
Attenborough	d																						15 09		
Long Eaton	d	13 44			13 50						14 16		14 44			14 50							15 16		15 44
Spondon	d																								
Derby 10	a	13 56			14 01						14 31		14 56			15 01							15 31		15 56
	d		13 57		14 08		14 24				14 38			14 57		15 08	15 24						15 38		
Willington	d				14 15																				
Burton-on-Trent	d		14 07		14 19						14 49					15 19							15 49		
Tamworth	d		14 18		14 31						15 01					15 31							16 01		
Wilnecote	d															15 35									
Leicester	d			13 52				14 09							14 52			15 09							
South Wigston	d							14 15																	
Narborough	d							14 20										15 18							
Hinckley	d							14 28										15 26							
Nuneaton	d			14 14				14 35							15 14			15 34							
Coleshill Parkway	d			14 29				14 54							15 29			15 50							
Water Orton	d																	15 56							
Birmingham New Street 12	a		14 36	14 47	14 55		15 04	15 09			15 27			15 36	15 47	15 55	15 58	16 09					16 27		
	d		14 40				15 10				15 30			15 40						16 10			16 30		
Worcester Shrub Hill 7	d					15 05																			
Ashchurch for Tewkesbury	d					15 21					16 06														
Cheltenham Spa	d		15 22			15 31	15 52			16 01	16 15			16 22					16 45	16 52		17 00	17 14		
Gloucester 7	a					15 40				16 11	16 24								16 56			17 10	17 23		
Bristol Parkway 7	a		15 54			16 19	16 24							16 54						17 24					
Bristol Temple Meads 10	a		16 11			16 34	16 41							17 11						17 41					
Newport (South Wales)	a										17 05								17 50				18 05		
Cardiff Central 7	a										17 25								18 10				18 25		

		XC 1◇ A ☕	XC ◇ B	XC	GW H	AW E	XC 1◇ G ☕	XC	GW	XC ◇		EM 1◇ J ☕	EM 1◇ ☕	XC 1◇ ☕	XC ◇ B	XC	EM K	XC 1◇ ☕	XC	AW E	XC 1◇ L ☕	GW 1◇ ☕		XC ◇	EM 1◇ ☕
Nottingham 8	d			15 34						16 00		16 07				16 34	16 38							17 00	17 07
Beeston	d			15 40						16 06		16a12				16 40								17 06	17a12
Attenborough	d									16 09							16a47							17 09	
Long Eaton	d			15 50						16 16			16 44			16 48								17 16	
Spondon	d									16 23														17 23	
Derby 10	a			16 01						16 31			16 56			17 01								17 31	
	d	15 57		16 08			16 24			16 38				16 57		17 08		17 24						17 38	
Willington	d															17 15									
Burton-on-Trent	d	16 07		16 19						16 49						17 19								17 49	
Tamworth	d	16 18		16 31						17 01						17 31								18 01	
Wilnecote	d			16 35																					
Leicester	d		15 52					16 09							16 52				17 09						
South Wigston	d							16 15											17 15						
Narborough	d							16 20											17 20						
Hinckley	d							16 28											17 28						
Nuneaton	d		16 14					16 35							17 14				17 35						
Coleshill Parkway	d		16 29					16 54							17 29				17 52						
Water Orton	d																								
Birmingham New Street 12	a	16 36	16 47	16 55			17 04	17 12		17 27				17 36	17 47	17 55		17 58	18 09					18 27	
	d	16 40					17 10			17 30				17 40							18 10			18 30	
Worcester Shrub Hill 7	d				17 05																				
Ashchurch for Tewkesbury	d				17 22					18 09															
Cheltenham Spa	d	17 22			17 32	17 45	17 52		18 01	18 18				18 21						18 45	18 52	19 00		19 14	
Gloucester 7	a				17 41	17 56			18 11	18 28				18 33						18 56		19 10		19 23	
Bristol Parkway 7	a	17 54			18 23		18 24							19 09							19 24				
Bristol Temple Meads 10	a	18 11			18 39		18 41							19 26							19 41				
Newport (South Wales)	a					18 50				19 12				19 59						19 50				20 05	
Cardiff Central 7	a					19 10				19 33				20 19						20 10				20 25	

For general notes see front of timetable
For details of catering facilities see Directory of Train Operators

A From Newcastle (Table 51)
B From Stansted Airport (Table 49)
C From Worcester Foregate Street (Table 71) to Weymouth (Table 123)
D To Paignton (Table 51)
E To Maesteg (Table 128)
G To Penzance (Table 51)
H From Great Malvern (Table 71) to Westbury (Table 123)
J From Sheffield (Table 53)
K From Lincoln (Table 27)
L To Plymouth (Table 51)

Due to Engineering Operations, services from Saturday 13 September on this Table had not been confirmed at time of going to press. These services will be issued in a special Supplement as soon as exact timings have been confirmed

Table 57

Saturdays

19 July to 6 September

Nottingham, Derby and Leicester → Birmingham → Cardiff and Bristol

Network Diagram - see first page of Table 50

		XC	XC	EM	XC	EM	GW	AW	XC	XC	XC	EM		EM	GW	XC	XC	XC	EM	XC	XC	EM	XC	XC	XC
		1◇	◇	1◇			◇		1◇			1◇		1◇		1◇	◇		1◇	1◇			1◇	1◇	◇
		A	B	C		D	E	G	H						J		B						H	A	B
		☕		☕					☕			☕		☕		☕			☕	☕			☕	☕	
Nottingham [8]	d				17 34	17 38					18 00	18 07						18 34	19 07			19 33			
Beeston	d				17 40						18 06	18a12						18 40	19a12			19a39			
Attenborough	d					17a47					18 09														
Long Eaton	d			17 44	17 51						18 18			18 43				18 50							
Spondon	d																								
Derby [10]	a			17 54	18 00						18 31			18 56				19 01							
	d	17 57		18 01	18 08				18 24		18 38					18 57		19 08		19 24				19 57	
Willington	d			18 10														19 15							
Burton-on-Trent	d	18 07		18a15	18 19						18 49							19 21						20 07	
Tamworth	d	18 18			18 31						19 01							19 33						20 18	
Wilnecote	d										19 05														
Leicester	d		17 52							18 09							18 52				19 09				19 52
South Wigston	d									18 16											19 15				
Narborough	d									18 21											19 20				
Hinckley	d									18 29											19 28				
Nuneaton	d		18 14							18 36							19 14				19 38				20 14
Coleshill Parkway	d		18 29							18 52							19 29				19 54				20 29
Water Orton	d																								
Birmingham New Street [12]	a	18 36	18 47		18 55				19 04	19 08	19 27					19 36	19 47	19 55		19 58	20 09			20 43	20 47
	d	18 40							19 10							19 40		20 00					20 10		
Worcester Shrub Hill [7]	d						19 10																		
Ashchurch for Tewkesbury	d						19 26											20 36							
Cheltenham Spa	d	19 22					19 36	19 45	19 52						20 01	20 22		20 49					20 52		
Gloucester [7]	a						19 44	19 56							20 10			21 04							
Bristol Parkway [7]	a	19 54					20 23		20 24							20 54							21 24		
Bristol Temple Meads [10]	a	20 11					20 40		20 41							21 11							21 41		
Newport (South Wales)	a							20 50																	
Cardiff Central [7]	a							21 10																	

		EM		XC	XC	EM	GW	GW	AW	XC	XC	EM	GW	XC		XC	XC	XC	EM	XC	XC	XC	EM		
		1◇				1◇				1◇		1◇		◇			1◇	◇	1◇		1◇		1◇		
		K											L	B			A	B			N				
		☕				☕						☕							☕				☕		
Nottingham [8]	d			19 40		20 07					20 11									21 45					
Beeston	d					20a12					20 17									21 51					
Attenborough	d			19 46																21 55					
Long Eaton	d	19 47		19 53							20 24	20 44							21 44	22 01			22 44		
Spondon	d										20 32									22 07					
Derby [10]	a	19 57		20 03							20 37	20 56							21 56	22 13			22 55		
	d			20 07						20 27	20 38						21 27			22 17	22 27				
Willington	d																								
Burton-on-Trent	d			20 19							20 49						21 37			22 29	22 37				
Tamworth	d			20 31							21 01						21 48			22 42	22 48				
Wilnecote	d										21 05														
Leicester	d				20 09									20 52		21 10		21 39				22 26			
South Wigston	d				20 14											21 15						22 31			
Narborough	d				20 19											21 20						22 36			
Hinckley	d				20 27											21 28						22 44			
Nuneaton	d				20 34									21 14		21 35		22 01				22 51			
Coleshill Parkway	d				20 49									21 29		21 52		22 18				23 10			
Water Orton	d																								
Birmingham New Street [12]	a			20 55	21 01					21 04	21 28			21 47		22 04	22 13	22 35		23 03	23 15	23 22			
	d									21 10															
Worcester Shrub Hill [7]	d												21 34												
Ashchurch for Tewkesbury	d												21 52												
Cheltenham Spa	d						21 02	21 30	21 45	21 52			22 02												
Gloucester [7]	a						21 12	21 40	21 56				22 11												
Bristol Parkway [7]	a						21 51			22 24															
Bristol Temple Meads [10]	a						22 04			22 41															
Newport (South Wales)	a								22 55																
Cardiff Central [7]	a								23 18																

For general notes see front of timetable
For details of catering facilities see Directory of Train Operators

A From Newcastle (Table 51)
B From Stansted Airport (Table 49)
C From St Pancras International (Table 53)
D From Lincoln (Table 27)
E To Weymouth (Table 123)
G To Maesteg (Table 128)
H To Plymouth (Table 51)
J To Westbury (Table 123)
K To Barnsley (Table 53)
L From Great Malvern (Table 71)
N From Edinburgh (Table 51)

Due to Engineering Operations, services from Saturday 13 September on this Table had not been confirmed at time of going to press. These services will be issued in a special Supplement as soon as exact timings have been confirmed

Table 57

Sundays

until 13 July

Nottingham, Derby and Leicester → Birmingham → Cardiff and Bristol

Network Diagram - see first page of Table 50

		EM	EM	XC	EM		GW	XC	EM	XC		EM	XC	GW	AW		XC	XC	XC	EM		XC	EM	XC	XC
		1 ◇	1 ◇					1 ◇	1 ◇	◇		1 ◇	1 ◇					1 ◇	1 ◇				1 ◇	◇	R 1
					A		B	C				D	E						E	A			G		H
		🛒	🛒					🛒	🛒			🛒	🛒					🛒	🛒				🛒		🛒
Nottingham [8]	d		08 19		09 25				10 23											11 03					
Beeston	d		08a26		09 31				10a28											11 09					
Attenborough	d				09 34															11 12					
Long Eaton	d	00 14			09 41							10 26								11 19			11 33		
Spondon	d																								
Derby [10]	a	00 26			09 55							10 37								11 30			11 45		
	d																	10 40							12 20
Willington	d																								
Burton-on-Trent	d																								12 30
Tamworth	d																								12 41
Wilnecote	d																								
Leicester	d																					11 15			
South Wigston	d																					11 21			
Narborough	d																					11 26			
Hinckley	d																					11 35			
Nuneaton	d																					11 46			
Coleshill Parkway	d																					12 03			
Water Orton	d																								
Birmingham New Street [12]	a																	11 53				12 17			13 03
	d							10 10		10 30			11 10				11 46		12 10					12 30	13 10
Worcester Shrub Hill [7]	d			09 35													12 24								
Ashchurch for Tewkesbury	d			09 49																					
Cheltenham Spa	d			09 58			10 05	10 52		11 11			11 52	12 00	12 16		12 45		12 52					13 11	13 52
Gloucester [7]	a			10 08			10 15			11 22				12 10	12 27		12 55							13 22	
Bristol Parkway [7]	a						10 55	11 25					12 25	12 52					13 25						14 25
Bristol Temple Meads [10]	a						11 07	11 38					12 38	13 06					13 38						14 38
Newport (South Wales)	a			10 51						12 05					13 25									14 05	
Cardiff Central [7]	a			11 12						12 25					13 45									14 25	

		XC	GW		XC	EM	XC	XC		EM	EM	AW	XC		XC	GW	XC	GW		XC	XC	GW	XC		EM
					◇	1 ◇	◇	R 1			1 ◇		R 1				◇	1 ◇		R 1			◇		1 ◇
							J			A	G		K			L				N					
						🛒		🛒			🛒		🛒					🛒		🛒					🛒
Nottingham [8]	d				12 09	12 24				13 16													14 08		14 18
Beeston	d					12a29				13 21													14 14		14a24
Attenborough	d									13 24													14 17		
Long Eaton	d				12 24					13 32	13 45												14 25		
Spondon	d																								
Derby [10]	a				12 34					13 43	13 56												14 35		
	d				12 38			13 20												14 20			14 38		
Willington	d																								
Burton-on-Trent	d				12 49															14 30			14 49		
Tamworth	d				13 02															14 41			15 01		
Wilnecote	d																						15 05		
Leicester	d	12 15					12 48								13 15						14 15				
South Wigston	d	12 22													13 22						14 21				
Narborough	d	12 27													13 27						14 26				
Hinckley	d	12 36													13 37						14 35				
Nuneaton	d	12 44					13 13								13 44						14 43				
Coleshill Parkway	d	13 02					13 29								14 00						15 00				
Water Orton	d																								
Birmingham New Street [12]	a	13 17			13 26		13 47	13 53							14 17					15 04	15 17		15 26		
	d				13 30								14 10				14 30			15 10			15 30		
Worcester Shrub Hill [7]	d															14 36									
Ashchurch for Tewkesbury	d															14 51	15 06								
Cheltenham Spa	d		14 02		14 11							14 16	14 52			15 01	15 15	15 31		15 52		16 02	16 11		
Gloucester [7]	a		14 12		14 22							14 27				15 11	15 24	15 41				16 12	16 22		
Bristol Parkway [7]	a												15 25			15 51				16 25					
Bristol Temple Meads [10]	a												15 38			16 06				16 38					
Newport (South Wales)	a				15 04							15 25					16 08						17 05		
Cardiff Central [7]	a				15 25							15 45					16 29						17 25		

For general notes see front of timetable
For details of catering facilities see Directory of Train Operators

- **A** To Matlock (Table 56)
- **B** To Taunton (Table 134)
- **C** To Paignton (Table 51)
- **D** To York (Table 53)
- **E** To Plymouth (Table 51)
- **G** To Sheffield (Table 53)
- **H** From York to Plymouth (Table 51)
- **J** From Cambridge (Table 49)
- **K** To Penzance (Table 51)
- **L** To Weston-super-Mare (Table 134)
- **N** From Edinburgh to Penzance (Table 51)

Sundays

until 13 July

Nottingham, Derby and Leicester → Birmingham → Cardiff and Bristol

Network Diagram - see first page of Table 50

		XC	XC	AW	XC		XC	GW	XC	EM		XC	EM	EM	GW		XC	XC	GW	XC		XC	EM	XC	AW
			R 1		R 1								1	1	1		R 1						1	R 1	
		◇ A			B				◇	C		◇ D	◇ E	◇	◇		G			◇		◇ A	◇		
			☕		☕								☕	☕	☕		☕						☕	☕	
Nottingham 8 🚌	d								15 02	15 14				16 03						16 09			17 06		
Beeston	d									15 19				16a08									17a16		
Attenborough	d									15 23															
Long Eaton	d								15 16	15 30			15 43							16 23					
Spondon	d																								
Derby 10	a								15 25	15 41			15 56							16 33					
	d		15 20						15 37								16 20			16 38				17 20	
Willington	d																								
Burton-on-Trent	d								15 49								16 30			16 49					
Tamworth	d								16 01								16 41			17 01					
Wilnecote	d																			17 05					
Leicester	d	14 40					15 15					15 44						16 15				16 30			
South Wigston	d						15 22											16 21							
Narborough	d						15 27											16 26							
Hinckley	d						15 36											16 35							
Nuneaton	d	15 01					15 44					16 12						16 43				16 57			
Coleshill Parkway	d	15 18					16 00					16 29						16 59				17 15			
Water Orton	d																								
Birmingham New Street 12	a	15 37	15 53				16 13		16 26			16 48					17 04	17 13		17 26		17 34		17 54	
	d				16 10				16 30								17 10			17 30					
Worcester Shrub Hill 7	d							16 40																	
Ashchurch for Tewkesbury	d							16 56																	
Cheltenham Spa	d			16 16	16 52			17 06	17 11						17 31		17 52		18 02	18 11					18 16
Gloucester 7	a			16 27				17 14	17 22						17 41				18 12	18 22					18 27
Bristol Parkway 7	a				17 25			17 55									18 25								
Bristol Temple Meads 10	a				17 38			18 09									18 38								
Newport (South Wales)	a			17 25					18 05											19 05					19 25
Cardiff Central 7	a			17 45					18 25											19 25					19 48

		XC	XC		GW	XC	EM	XC		EM	XC	XC	GW		XC	EM	XC	XC		AW	XC	XC	GW		XC
		R 1					1				R 1					1		R 1			R 1				
		H				◇	◇ E	◇ A		C	J				◇	◇	◇ A				H				
		☕					☕				☕					☕		☕			☕				
Nottingham 8 🚌	d					17 09				17 20					18 06	18 17									19 08
Beeston	d					17 16				17 26					18 11	18a22									
Attenborough	d									17 29					18 14										
Long Eaton	d					17 24	17 24			17 36					18 23										19 21
Spondon	d																								
Derby 10	a					17 33	17 35			17 51					18 32										19 30
	d					17 39					18 20				18 38			19 20							19 37
Willington	d																								
Burton-on-Trent	d					17 49					18 30				18 49										19 49
Tamworth	d					18 01					18 41				19 01										20 01
Wilnecote	d														19 05										
Leicester	d		17 15					17 43				18 13					18 38					19 15			
South Wigston	d		17 21									18 20										19 21			
Narborough	d		17 26									18 25										19 26			
Hinckley	d		17 35									18 34										19 34			
Nuneaton	d		17 43					18 04				18 42					18 59					19 42			
Coleshill Parkway	d		18 00					18 20				18 59					19 18					20 00			
Water Orton	d																								
Birmingham New Street 12	a		18 14			18 26		18 38			19 04	19 14			19 26		19 36	19 54				20 14			20 26
	d	18 10				18 30					19 10				19 30						20 10				20 30
Worcester Shrub Hill 7	d				18 39																		20 36		
Ashchurch for Tewkesbury	d				18 55																		20 53		21 05
Cheltenham Spa	d	18 52			19 06	19 11					19 52		20 02		20 11					20 16	20 52		21 03		21 14
Gloucester 7	a				19 15	19 22							20 12		20 22					20 27			21 13		21 29
Bristol Parkway 7	a	19 25			19 55						20 25										21 25		21 53		
Bristol Temple Meads 10	a	19 38			20 08						20 38										21 38		22 07		
Newport (South Wales)	a					20 05														21 25					
Cardiff Central 7	a					20 25														21 45					

For general notes see front of timetable
For details of catering facilities see Directory of Train Operators

A From Stansted Airport (Table 49)
B To Penzance (Table 51)
C To Matlock (Table 56)
D From Cambridge (Table 49)
E To Sheffield (Table 53)
G From Edinburgh to Plymouth (Table 51)
H To Plymouth (Table 51)
J From Glasgow Central to Plymouth (Table 51)

Table 57

Sundays

until 13 July

Nottingham, Derby and Leicester → Birmingham → Cardiff and Bristol

Network Diagram - see first page of Table 50

		EM	EM	EM	XC		GW	XC	XC	EM		XC	GW	XC	XC		EM	EM	XC	XC		XC	XC		
		1 ◇		1 ◇	◇			1 ◇		1 ◇		◇		1 ◇			1 ◇			1 ◇		1 ◇			
			A	B	C			D				C		E			G	A		H		E			
		☕		☕				☕		☕				☕			☕			☕		☕			
Nottingham 8	d		19 19	19 36					20 08									21 23	21 41						
Beeston	d		19 24	19a42					20 14									21 29	21 47						
Attenborough	d		19 28															21 32							
Long Eaton	d	19 26	19 34						20 21	20 26							21 28	21 39	21 55						
Spondon	d																								
Derby 10	a	19 36	19 48						20 33	20 39							21 46	21 50	22 05						
	d							20 20	20 38					21 20					22 09	22 15		22 57			
Willington	d																								
Burton-on-Trent	d							20 30	20 51					21 30					22 21	22 27		23 07			
Tamworth	d							20 41	21 04					21 41					22 34	22 38		23 18			
Wilnecote	d								21 07																
Leicester	d				20 09							21 02			21 15								23 15		
South Wigston	d														21 21								23 21		
Narborough	d														21 26								23 26		
Hinckley	d														21 35								23 35		
Nuneaton	d				20 30							21 22			21 43								23 43		
Coleshill Parkway	d				20 49							21 43			21 59										
Water Orton	d																								
Birmingham New Street 12	a				21 06			21 04	21 27			22 00		22 04	22 12				22 55	23 14		23 51	00 12		
	d							21 10						22 10											
Worcester Shrub Hill 7	d																								
Ashchurch for Tewkesbury	d																								
Cheltenham Spa	d						21 35	21 52					22 01	22 52											
Gloucester 7	a						21 45						22 11												
Bristol Parkway 7	a							22 25						23 25											
Bristol Temple Meads 10	a							22 41						23 41											
Newport (South Wales)	a																								
Cardiff Central 7	a																								

Sundays

20 July to 7 September

		EM	XC	EM	GW	XC	EM	XC		XC	GW	AW	XC	XC	EM	EM		EM	XC	XC	XC	XC	XC	XC	EM
		1 ◇				1 ◇	1 ◇	◇		1 ◇				1 ◇	1 ◇			1 ◇	1 ◇		◇	R 1		◇	1 ◇
				A	J	K				L					N	A		G	L			Q			
		☕				☕	☕			☕				☕	☕			☕	☕			☕			☕
Nottingham 8	d			09 25			10 16									11 03								12 09	12 24
Beeston	d			09 31			10a22									11 09									12a29
Attenborough	d			09 34												11 12									
Long Eaton	d	00 14		09 41											10 31	11 19		11 33						12 24	
Spondon	d																								
Derby 10	a	00 26		09 55											10 42	11 30		11 45						12 34	
	d													10 40								12 20		12 38	
Willington	d																								
Burton-on-Trent	d																					12 30		12 49	
Tamworth	d																					12 41		→	
Wilnecote	d																								
Leicester	d																			11 15			12 15		
South Wigston	d																			11 21			12 22		
Narborough	d																			11 26			12 27		
Hinckley	d																			11 35			12 36		
Nuneaton	d																			11 46			12 44		
Coleshill Parkway	d																			12 03			13 02		
Water Orton	d																								
Birmingham New Street 12	a													11 53						12 17		13 04	13 17		
	d					10 10		10 30		11 10			11 46						12 10		12 30	13 10			
Worcester Shrub Hill 7	d		09 35										12 24												
Ashchurch for Tewkesbury	d		09 49																						
Cheltenham Spa	d		09 58		10 06	10 52		11 11		11 52	12 00	12 16	12 45						12 52		13 11	13 52			
Gloucester 7	a		10 08		10 16			11 22			12 10	12 27	12 55								13 22				
Bristol Parkway 7	a				10 57	11 25				12 25	12 52								13 25			14 25			
Bristol Temple Meads 10	a				11 08	11 38				12 38	13 06								13 38			14 38			
Newport (South Wales)	a		10 51					12 05				13 25									14 05				
Cardiff Central 7	a		11 12					12 25				13 45									14 25				

For general notes see front of timetable
For details of catering facilities see Directory of Train Operators

- **A** To Matlock (Table 56)
- **B** From York (Table 53)
- **C** From Stansted Airport (Table 49)
- **D** From Aberdeen (Table 51)
- **E** From Edinburgh (Table 51)
- **G** To Sheffield (Table 53)
- **H** From Glasgow Central (Table 51)
- **J** To Taunton (Table 134)
- **K** To Paignton (Table 51)
- **L** To Plymouth (Table 51)
- **N** To York (Table 53)
- **Q** From York to Plymouth (Table 51)

Due to Engineering Operations, services from Sunday 14 September on this Table had not been confirmed at time of going to press. These services will be issued in a special Supplement as soon as exact timings have been confirmed

Nottingham, Derby and Leicester → Birmingham → Cardiff and Bristol

20 July to 7 September

Network Diagram - see first page of Table 50

		XC		GW	XC	AW	XC	XC	EM	EM		XC	XC	GW	XC	XC	GW	XC		XC	GW	XC	EM	AW	XC
		R 1			◇		1 ◇	◇		1 ◇		R 1			◇	1 ◇	1 ◇	R 1				◇	1 ◇		1 ◇
							A	B	C	D		E		G		H		E							
		☕					☕			☕		☕				☕	☕	☕					☕		☕
Nottingham 8	d								13 16													14 08	14 18		
Beeston	d								13 21													14 14	14a24		
Attenborough	d								13 24													14 17			
Long Eaton	d								13 32	13 45												14 25			
Spondon	d																								
Derby 10	a								13 43	13 56												14 35			
	d	12 39			←		12 57									13 57		14 20				14 38			14 57
Willington	d																								
Burton-on-Trent	d				12 49											14 07						14 49			
Tamworth	d				13 01											14 18						15 01			
Wilnecote	d																					15 05			
Leicester	d							12 48					13 15							14 15					
South Wigston	d												13 22							14 21					
Narborough	d												13 27							14 26					
Hinckley	d												13 37							14 35					
Nuneaton	d							13 13					13 44							14 43					
Coleshill Parkway	d							13 29					14 00							15 00					
Water Orton	d																								
Birmingham New Street 12	a	13 25			13 26		13 36	13 48					14 17			14 36		14 54		15 17		15 26			15 36
	d				13 30		13 40					14 10			14 30	14 40		15 10				15 30			15 40
Worcester Shrub Hill 7	d													14 36											
Ashchurch for Tewkesbury	d													14 51	15 06										
Cheltenham Spa	d			14 02	14 11	14 16	14 22					14 52		15 01	15 15	15 22	15 31	15 52			16 02	16 11		16 16	16 22
Gloucester 7	a			14 12	14 22	14 27								15 11	15 24		15 41				16 12	16 22		16 27	
Bristol Parkway 7	a						14 58					15 25		15 51		15 58		16 25							16 58
Bristol Temple Meads 10	a						15 11					15 38		16 06		16 14		16 38							17 13
Newport (South Wales)	a				15 05	15 25									16 08							17 05		17 25	
Cardiff Central 7	a				15 25	15 45									16 29							17 25		17 45	

		XC	XC	XC		XC	GW	XC	EM	EM	XC	XC		EM	GW	XC	XC	GW	XC	XC		EM	AW	XC	XC
		◇	R 1	R 1				◇		1 ◇	1 ◇	◇		1 ◇	1 ◇	R 1			◇	◇		1 ◇		R 1	R 1
		J		E					C	D	H	B				A				J		K			
			☕	☕						☕	☕			☕	☕	☕						☕		☕	☕
Nottingham 8	d							15 02	15 14					16 03					16 09			17 07			
Beeston	d								15 19					16a08								17a15			
Attenborough	d								15 23																
Long Eaton	d							15 16	15 30	15 43									16 23						
Spondon	d																								
Derby 10	a							15 25	15 41	15 56									16 32						
	d		15 20					15 37			15 57					16 20			16 38					16 57	17 20
Willington	d																								
Burton-on-Trent	d							15 49			16 07								16 49						
Tamworth	d							16 01			16 18								17 01						
Wilnecote	d																		17 05						
Leicester	d	14 40				15 15						15 44					16 15			16 30					
South Wigston	d					15 22											16 21								
Narborough	d					15 27											16 26								
Hinckley	d					15 36											16 35								
Nuneaton	d	15 01				15 44						16 12					16 43			16 57					
Coleshill Parkway	d	15 18				16 00						16 29					16 59			17 15					
Water Orton	d																								
Birmingham New Street 12	a	15 37	15 55			16 13		16 26			16 36	16 48				16 54	17 13		17 26	17 32				17 36	17 54
	d			16 10				16 30			16 40					17 10			17 30					17 40	
Worcester Shrub Hill 7	d						16 40																		
Ashchurch for Tewkesbury	d						16 56																		
Cheltenham Spa	d			16 52			17 06	17 11			17 22				17 31	17 52		18 02	18 11				18 16	18 22	
Gloucester 7	a						17 14	17 22							17 41			18 12	18 22				18 27	18 34	
Bristol Parkway 7	a			17 25			17 55				17 58					18 25								19 07	
Bristol Temple Meads 10	a			17 38			18 09				18 13					18 38								19 24	
Newport (South Wales)	a							18 05											19 05				19 25		
Cardiff Central 7	a							18 25											19 25				19 48		

For general notes see front of timetable
For details of catering facilities see Directory of Train Operators

A To Plymouth (Table 51)
B From Cambridge (Table 49)
C To Matlock (Table 56)
D To Sheffield (Table 53)
E To Penzance (Table 51)
G To Weston-super-Mare (Table 134)
H From Newcastle (Table 51)
J From Stansted Airport (Table 49)
K From Sheffield (Table 53)

Due to Engineering Operations, services from Sunday 14 September on this Table had not been confirmed at time of going to press. These services will be issued in a special Supplement as soon as exact timings have been confirmed

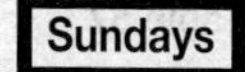

Nottingham, Derby and Leicester → Birmingham → Cardiff and Bristol

20 July to 7 September

Network Diagram - see first page of Table 50

		XC R 1 A ☕	XC	GW	XC ◇	EM 1◇ B ☕		EM C	XC 1◇ D ☕	XC ◇ E	XC R 1 A ☕	XC	GW	XC ◇		EM 1◇ ☕	XC ◇ E	AW	XC 1◇ D ☕	XC R 1 ☕	XC R 1 A ☕	XC		GW	XC
Nottingham [8]	d				17 09			17 20						18 06		18 17									19 08
Beeston	d				17 16			17 26						18 11		18a22									
Attenborough	d							17 29						18 14											
Long Eaton	d				17 24	17 24		17 36						18 23											19 21
Spondon	d																								
Derby [10]	a				17 33	17 35		17 51						18 32											19 30
	d				17 39				17 57		18 20			18 38					18 57	19 20					19 37
Willington	d																								
Burton-on-Trent	d				17 49				18 07					18 49					19 07						19 49
Tamworth	d				18 01				18 18					19 01					19 18						20 01
Wilnecote	d													19 05											
Leicester	d		17 15							17 43		18 13					18 38					19 15			
South Wigston	d		17 21									18 20										19 21			
Narborough	d		17 26									18 25										19 26			
Hinckley	d		17 35									18 34										19 34			
Nuneaton	d		17 43							18 04		18 42					18 59					19 42			
Coleshill Parkway	d		18 00							18 20		18 59					19 18					20 00			
Water Orton	d																								
Birmingham New Street [12]	a		18 14		18 26				18 36	18 38	18 54	19 14		19 26			19 36		19 36	19 54		20 14			20 26
	d	18 10			18 30				18 40		19 10			19 30					19 40		20 10				20 30
Worcester Shrub Hill [7]	d			18 39																				20 36	
Ashchurch for Tewkesbury	d			18 55																				20 53	21 05
Cheltenham Spa	d	18 52		19 06	19 11				19 22		19 52		20 02	20 11				20 16	20 22		20 52			21 03	21 14
Gloucester [7]	a			19 15	19 22								20 12	20 22				20 27						21 13	21 29
Bristol Parkway [7]	a	19 25		19 55					19 58		20 25								20 58		21 25			21 53	
Bristol Temple Meads [10]	a	19 38		20 08					20 13		20 38								21 13		21 38			22 07	
Newport (South Wales)	a				20 05													21 25							
Cardiff Central [7]	a				20 25													21 45							

		EM 1◇ ☕	EM C	EM 1◇ G ☕	GW	XC 1◇ D ☕	XC ◇ E	XC 1◇ ☕		XC	EM 1◇ ☕	GW	XC 1◇ D ☕	XC ◇ E	XC 1◇ H ☕	XC		EM 1◇ B ☕	EM C	XC	XC 1◇ J ☕	XC 1◇ D ☕	XC		
Nottingham [8]	d		19 19	19 36						20 08									21 23	21 41					
Beeston	d		19 24	19a42						20 14									21 29	21 47					
Attenborough	d		19 28																21 32						
Long Eaton	d	19 26	19 34							20 21	20 26							21 28	21 39	21 55					
Spondon	d																								
Derby [10]	a	19 36	19 48							20 33	20 39							21 45	21 50	22 05					
	d					19 57		20 24		20 38			20 57		21 24					22 09	22 36	22 57			
Willington	d																								
Burton-on-Trent	d					20 07		20 34		20 51			21 08		21 34					22 21	22 47	23 07			
Tamworth	d					20 18		20 45		21 04			21 19		21 45					22 34	22 58	23 19			
Wilnecote	d									21 07															
Leicester	d						20 09							21 02		21 15							23 15		
South Wigston	d															21 21							23 21		
Narborough	d															21 26							23 26		
Hinckley	d															21 35							23 35		
Nuneaton	d						20 30							21 22		21 43							23 43		
Coleshill Parkway	d						20 49							21 43		21 59									
Water Orton	d																								
Birmingham New Street [12]	a					20 36	21 06	21 11		21 27			21 45	22 00	22 11	22 12				22 55	23 22	23 45	00 12		
	d					21 10							22 10												
Worcester Shrub Hill [7]	d																								
Ashchurch for Tewkesbury	d																								
Cheltenham Spa	d				21 35	21 52						22 01	22 52												
Gloucester [7]	a				21 45							22 11													
Bristol Parkway [7]	a					22 25							23 25												
Bristol Temple Meads [10]	a					22 41							23 41												
Newport (South Wales)	a																								
Cardiff Central [7]	a																								

For general notes see front of timetable
For details of catering facilities see Directory of Train Operators

- **A** To Plymouth (Table 51)
- **B** To Sheffield (Table 53)
- **C** To Matlock (Table 56)
- **D** From Newcastle (Table 51)
- **E** From Stansted Airport (Table 49)
- **G** From York (Table 53)
- **H** From Glasgow Central (Table 51)
- **J** From Edinburgh (Table 51)

Due to Engineering Operations, services from Sunday 14 September on this Table had not been confirmed at time of going to press. These services will be issued in a special Supplement as soon as exact timings have been confirmed

Table 57

Mondays to Fridays
until 5 September

Bristol and Cardiff → Birmingham → Leicester, Derby and Nottingham

Network Diagram - see first page of Table 50

Miles	Miles	Miles			EM	AW	EM	XC	EM	XC	XC	XC	EM		XC	XC	GW	XC	EM	XC	XC	XC	EM		EM
					MX	MX																			
					■1 ◇		■1 ◇	◇				■1 ◇				■1 ◇			■1 ◇	◇		[R] ■1			■1 ◇
						A	B												C	D					
					☕		⊠ ⊥					☕				☕			☕	⊥		☕			☕
0	—	—	**Cardiff Central ■7**	d		23p20																			
11¾	—	—	Newport (South Wales)	d		23p39																			
—	—	0	**Bristol Temple Meads ■10**	d																					
—	—	5¾	Bristol Parkway ■7	d																					
56½	—	—	Gloucester ■7	d		00 39											06 02								
63	—	46¼	Cheltenham Spa	d		00a52											06 12								
70¼	—	53½	Ashchurch for Tewkesbury	d													06 20								
85	—	—	Worcester Shrub Hill ■7	a													06 40								
112	—	92¾	**Birmingham New Street ■12**	a																					
—	0	—		d				05 20			05 54	06 00			06 09	06 30				06 37	06 54	07 03			
119¾	7¾	—	Water Orton	d											06 19										
—	9½	—	Coleshill Parkway	d																06 49					
—	20	—	Nuneaton	d				05 48			06 21									07 05	07 22				
—	25¼	—	Hinckley	d							06 28										07 28				
—	34	—	Narborough	d							06 36										07 37				
—	37	—	South Wigston	d							06 40										07 42				
—	38¾	—	**Leicester**	a				06 08			06 46									07 28	07 48				
127	—	—	Wilnecote	d											06 27										
128¾	—	—	Tamworth	d								06 15			06 31	06 47						07 19			
141¾	—	—	Burton-on-Trent	d								06 25			06 42	06 58			07 10			07 29			
146¼	—	—	Willington	d															07 16						
152¾	—	—	**Derby ■10**	a								06 38			06 58	07 11			07 25			07 42			
—	—	—		d			05 56		06 16	06 28					07 11			07 22	07 34						
155¼	—	—	Spondon	d						06 33								07 27							
161	—	—	Long Eaton	d			06a05		06a25	06 40					07 20			07 35	07a43						
164	—	—	Attenborough	d						06 49			07 18					07 42					08 07		
165½	—	—	Beeston	d	00 01					06 52			07 21		07 28			07 45					08 10		08 20
168¾	—	—	**Nottingham ■8**	a	00 06					06 59			07 30		07 34			07 53					08 20		08 29

		XC	XC	XC	EM	EM	XC	XC	XC	EM		XC	GW	AW	XC	XC	EM	XC	GW	XC		XC	AW	XC	EM
			◇	■1 ◇		■1 ◇			[R] ■1	■1 ◇					◇	■1 ◇	■1 ◇		■1 ◇			■1 ◇		■1 ◇	■1 ◇
			D			C							E		D		G					H			
			⊥	☕		☕			☕	☕					⊥	☕	☕		☕			☕		☕	☕
Cardiff Central ■7	d													06 12									07 12		
Newport (South Wales)	d													06 27									07 27		
Bristol Temple Meads ■10	d								06 15							07 00						07 30			
Bristol Parkway ■7	d								06 25							07 10						07 40			
Gloucester ■7	d								07 02			07 09	07 15	07 21				07 46	07 54				08 21		
Cheltenham Spa	d								07 12			07 19	07 25	07a34		07 42		07 57	08a03			08 12	08a34		
Ashchurch for Tewkesbury	d											07 28	07 33					08 04							
Worcester Shrub Hill ■7	a												07 54												
Birmingham New Street ■12	a								07 57			08 16				08 26		08 46				09 00			
	d	07 10	07 21	07 30			07 49	07 54	08 03			08 19			08 24	08 30		08 49		08 54				09 03	
Water Orton	d	07 21																		09 06					
Coleshill Parkway	d							08 07							08 37										
Nuneaton	d		07 48					08 24							08 53					09 26					
Hinckley	d		07 55					08 31												09 33					
Narborough	d		08 03					08 39												09 41					
South Wigston	d		08 07					08 44																	
Leicester	a		08 13					08 50							09 13					09 51					
Wilnecote	d						08 05																		
Tamworth	d	07 30		07 47			08 09		08 19			08 37				08 47		09 06							
Burton-on-Trent	d	07 42		07 58		08 10	08 20		08 29			08 50				08 58		09 18							
Willington	d	07 47				08 16																			
Derby ■10	a	07 56		08 11		08 25	08 38		08 42			09 12				09 16		09 36						09 39	
	d	08 03			08 22	08 34	08 41					09 15					09 34	09 41							
Spondon	d	08 08										09 21													
Long Eaton	d	08 15			08 32	08a43	08 50					09 28					09a43	09 50							
Attenborough	d	08 23										09 35													
Beeston	d	08 26			08 39		08 57			09 20		09 39						09 57							10 20
Nottingham ■8	a	08 32			08 45		09 04			09 26		09 45						10 05							10 26

For general notes see front of timetable
For details of catering facilities see Directory of Train Operators

A From Maesteg (Table 128)
B From Sheffield (Table 53)
C To St Pancras International (Table 53)
D To Stansted Airport (Table 49)
E To Great Malvern (Table 71)
G From Barnsley (Table 53)
H From Exeter St Davids (Table 51)

Table 57

Mondays to Fridays
until 5 September

Bristol and Cardiff → Birmingham → Leicester, Derby and Nottingham

Network Diagram - see first page of Table 50

		XC	XC	XC	EM	XC	GW	XC	XC	EM	XC	XC	XC	GW	EM	XC	GW	XC	XC	AW	XC	EM	XC
			◇	[1] ◇	[1] ◇	◇			[1] ◇	[1] ◇		◇	[1] ◇		[1] ◇	◇	[1] ◇		[R] [1]		[1] ◇	[1] ◇	
			A				B		C			A	C	D					C				
			🛒	☕	☕	🛒			☕	☕	🛒	🛒	☕		☕	🛒	☕		☕		☕	☕	
Cardiff Central [7]	d	-	-	07 00	-	07 45	-	-	-	-	-	-	-	-	-	08 45	-	-	-	09 12	-	-	-
Newport (South Wales)	d	-	-	07 15	-	07 59	-	-	-	-	-	-	-	-	-	08 59	-	-	-	09 27	-	-	-
Bristol Temple Meads [10]	d	-	-	08 00	-	-	-	-	08 30	-	-	-	09 00	08 41	-	-	-	-	09 30	-	-	-	-
Bristol Parkway [7]	d	-	-	08 10	-	-	-	-	08 40	-	-	-	09 10	08 52	-	-	-	-	09 40	-	-	-	-
Gloucester [7]	d	-	-	-	-	08 46	08 50	-	-	-	-	-	-	09 38	-	09 46	09 50	-	-	10 21	-	-	-
Cheltenham Spa	d	-	-	08 42	-	08 57	09a03	-	09 12	-	-	-	09 42	09 48	-	09 57	10a03	-	10 12	10a34	-	-	-
Ashchurch for Tewkesbury	d	-	-	-	-	-	-	-	-	-	-	-	-	09 56	-	10 04	-	-	-	-	-	-	-
Worcester Shrub Hill [7]	a	-	-	-	-	-	-	-	-	-	-	-	-	10 13	-	-	-	-	-	-	-	-	-
Birmingham New Street [12]	a	-	-	09 26	-	09 45	-	-	09 57	-	-	-	10 26	-	-	10 45	-	-	10 57	-	-	-	-
	d	09 19	09 24	09 30	-	09 49	-	09 54	10 03	-	10 19	10 24	10 30	-	-	10 49	-	10 54	-	-	11 03	-	11 19
Water Orton	d	-	-	-	-	-	-	-	-	-	-	-	-	-	-	-	-	11 05	-	-	-	-	-
Coleshill Parkway	d	-	09 37	-	-	-	-	10 08	-	-	-	10 37	-	-	-	-	-	11 08	-	-	-	-	-
Nuneaton	d	-	09 53	-	-	-	-	10 25	-	-	-	10 53	-	-	-	-	-	11 25	-	-	-	-	-
Hinckley	d	-	-	-	-	-	-	10 32	-	-	-	-	-	-	-	-	-	11 32	-	-	-	-	-
Narborough	d	-	-	-	-	-	-	10 40	-	-	-	-	-	-	-	-	-	11 40	-	-	-	-	-
South Wigston	d	-	-	-	-	-	-	10 45	-	-	-	-	-	-	-	-	-	-	-	-	-	-	-
Leicester	a	-	10 13	-	-	-	-	10 50	-	-	-	11 13	-	-	-	-	-	11 50	-	-	-	-	-
Wilnecote	d	-	-	-	-	-	-	-	-	-	10 35	-	-	-	-	-	-	-	-	-	-	-	11 31
Tamworth	d	09 36	-	-	-	10 06	-	-	-	-	10 39	-	10 47	-	-	11 06	-	-	-	-	-	-	11 35
Burton-on-Trent	d	09 47	-	-	-	10 18	-	-	-	-	10 50	-	10 58	-	-	11 18	-	-	-	-	-	-	11 46
Willington	d	-	-	-	-	10 23	-	-	-	-	-	-	-	-	-	-	-	-	-	-	-	-	-
Derby [10]	a	10 08	-	10 11	-	10 36	-	-	10 39	-	11 08	-	11 11	-	-	11 36	-	-	-	-	11 39	-	12 08
	d	10 11	-	-	10 34	10 41	-	-	-	-	11 11	-	-	-	11 34	11 41	-	-	-	-	-	-	12 12
Spondon	d	-	-	-	-	-	-	-	-	-	-	-	-	-	-	-	-	-	-	-	-	-	12 17
Long Eaton	d	10 21	-	-	10a43	10 50	-	-	-	-	11 21	-	-	-	11a43	11 50	-	-	-	-	-	-	12 23
Attenborough	d	10 28	-	-	-	-	-	-	-	-	11 31	-	-	-	-	-	-	-	-	-	-	-	-
Beeston	d	10 31	-	-	-	10 57	-	-	-	11 21	11 34	-	-	-	-	11 57	-	-	-	-	-	12 20	12 32
Nottingham [8]	a	10 37	-	-	-	11 04	-	-	-	11 27	11 42	-	-	-	-	12 05	-	-	-	-	-	12 26	12 40

		XC	XC	EM	XC	GW	XC	XC	AW	EM	XC	XC	XC	GW	EM	XC	GW	XC	XC	XC	EM	XC	XC
		◇	[1] ◇	[1] ◇	◇			[1] ◇		[1] ◇		◇	[1] ◇	◇	[1] ◇	◇	[1] ◇		[R] [1]	[R] [1]	[1] ◇		◇
		A						C	E			A		G									A
		🛒	☕	☕	🛒			☕		☕		🛒	☕		☕	🛒	☕		☕	☕	☕		🛒
Cardiff Central [7]	d	-	-	-	09 45	-	-	-	10 12	-	-	-	-	-	-	10 45	-	-	-	-	-	-	-
Newport (South Wales)	d	-	-	-	09 59	-	-	-	10 27	-	-	-	-	-	-	10 59	-	-	-	-	-	-	-
Bristol Temple Meads [10]	d	-	10 00	-	-	-	-	10 30	-	-	-	-	11 00	10 41	-	-	-	-	11 30	-	-	-	-
Bristol Parkway [7]	d	-	10 10	-	-	-	-	10 40	-	-	-	-	11 10	10 52	-	-	-	-	11 40	-	-	-	-
Gloucester [7]	d	-	-	-	10 46	10 52	-	-	11 21	-	-	-	-	11 36	-	11 46	11 50	-	-	-	-	-	-
Cheltenham Spa	d	-	10 42	-	10 57	11a05	-	11 12	11a34	-	-	-	11 42	11 47	-	11 57	12a03	-	12 12	-	-	-	-
Ashchurch for Tewkesbury	d	-	-	-	-	-	-	-	-	-	-	-	-	11 55	-	-	-	-	-	-	-	-	-
Worcester Shrub Hill [7]	a	-	-	-	-	-	-	-	-	-	-	-	-	12 13	-	-	-	-	-	-	-	-	-
Birmingham New Street [12]	a	-	11 26	-	11 45	-	-	11 57	-	-	-	-	12 26	-	-	12 46	-	-	12 57	-	-	-	-
	d	11 24	11 30	-	11 49	-	11 54	12 03	-	-	12 13	12 24	12 30	-	-	12 49	-	12 54	-	13 03	-	13 13	13 24
Water Orton	d	-	-	-	-	-	-	-	-	-	-	-	-	-	-	-	-	13 06	-	-	-	-	-
Coleshill Parkway	d	11 37	-	-	-	-	12 08	-	-	-	-	12 37	-	-	-	-	-	13 10	-	-	-	-	13 37
Nuneaton	d	11 53	-	-	-	-	12 24	-	-	-	-	12 53	-	-	-	-	-	13 26	-	-	-	-	13 53
Hinckley	d	-	-	-	-	-	12 31	-	-	-	-	-	-	-	-	-	-	13 33	-	-	-	-	-
Narborough	d	-	-	-	-	-	12 39	-	-	-	-	-	-	-	-	-	-	13 41	-	-	-	-	-
South Wigston	d	-	-	-	-	-	12 44	-	-	-	-	-	-	-	-	-	-	-	-	-	-	-	-
Leicester	a	12 13	-	-	-	-	12 50	-	-	-	-	13 13	-	-	-	-	-	13 50	-	-	-	-	14 13
Wilnecote	d	-	-	-	-	-	-	-	-	-	12 28	-	-	-	-	-	-	-	-	-	-	13 29	-
Tamworth	d	-	-	-	12 06	-	-	-	-	-	12 32	-	12 47	-	-	13 06	-	-	-	-	-	13 33	-
Burton-on-Trent	d	-	-	-	12 18	-	-	-	-	-	12 46	-	12 58	-	-	13 18	-	-	-	-	-	13 44	-
Willington	d	-	-	-	-	-	-	-	-	-	12 56	-	-	-	-	-	-	-	-	-	-	-	-
Derby [10]	a	-	12 11	-	12 36	-	-	12 39	-	-	13 08	-	13 11	-	-	13 36	-	-	-	13 39	-	14 08	-
	d	-	-	12 34	12 41	-	-	-	-	-	13 12	-	-	-	13 34	13 41	-	-	-	-	-	14 12	-
Spondon	d	-	-	-	-	-	-	-	-	-	-	-	-	-	-	-	-	-	-	-	-	-	-
Long Eaton	d	-	-	12a43	12 50	-	-	-	-	-	13 21	-	-	-	13a43	13 50	-	-	-	-	-	14 21	-
Attenborough	d	-	-	-	-	-	-	-	-	-	13 31	-	-	-	-	-	-	-	-	-	-	-	-
Beeston	d	-	-	-	12 57	-	-	-	-	13 20	13 34	-	-	-	-	13 57	-	-	-	-	14 20	14 29	-
Nottingham [8]	a	-	-	-	13 04	-	-	-	-	13 26	13 41	-	-	-	-	14 05	-	-	-	-	14 26	14 39	-

For general notes see front of timetable
For details of catering facilities see Directory of Train Operators

A To Stansted Airport (Table 49)
B From Westbury (Table 123)
C From Plymouth (Table 51)
D From Warminster (Table 123) to Great Malvern (Table 71)
E From Maesteg (Table 128)
G From Westbury (Table 123) to Great Malvern (Table 71)

Bristol and Cardiff → Birmingham → Leicester, Derby and Nottingham

Network Diagram - see first page of Table 50

		XC	EM	XC		GW	XC	XC	AW	EM	XC	XC	XC	GW		EM	XC	GW	XC	XC	AW	XC	EM	XC	XC
		1 ◇	1 ◇	◇				R 1		1 ◇		◇	1 ◇	◇		1 ◇	◇	1 ◇		R 1		R 1	1 ◇		◇
		A						B	C			D		E				G		B	C				
Cardiff Central 7	d			11 45					12 12								12 45				13 12				
Newport (South Wales)	d			11 59					12 27								12 59				13 27				
Bristol Temple Meads 10	d	12 00						12 30					13 00	12 41						13 30					
Bristol Parkway 7	d	12 10						12 40					13 10	12 52						13 40					
Gloucester 7	d			12 46		12 50			13 21					13 38			13 46	13 50			14 21				
Cheltenham Spa	d	12 42		12 57		13a03		13 12	13a34				13 42	13 48			13 57	14a03		14 12	14a34				
Ashchurch for Tewkesbury	d													13 56											
Worcester Shrub Hill 7	a													14 20											
Birmingham New Street 12	a	13 26		13 45				13 57					14 26				14 45			14 57					
	d	13 30		13 49			13 54	14 03			14 13	14 24	14 30				14 49		14 54			15 03		15 13	15 24
Water Orton	d																		15 05						
Coleshill Parkway	d						14 08					14 37							15 09						
Nuneaton	d						14 24					14 53							15 25						15 53
Hinckley	d						14 31												15 32						
Narborough	d						14 39												15 40						
South Wigston	d						14 44																		
Leicester	a						14 50					15 13							15 50						16 13
Wilnecote	d																							15 29	
Tamworth	d			14 06							14 30		14 47				15 06							15 33	
Burton-on-Trent	d			14 18							14 42		14 58				15 18							15 44	
Willington	d										14 47														
Derby 10	a	14 11		14 36				14 39			15 08		15 11				15 36					15 39		16 08	
	d		14 34	14 41							15 12					15 34	15 41							16 12	
Spondon	d																								
Long Eaton	d		14a43	14 50							15 21					15a43	15 50							16 21	
Attenborough	d										15 31														
Beeston	d			14 57						15 20	15 34						15 57						16 20	16 31	
Nottingham 8	a			15 04						15 26	15 41						16 04						16 26	16 39	

		XC		EM	XC	GW	XC	XC	XC	EM	XC	XC		XC	GW	EM	EM	XC	GW	XC	XC	AW		XC	EM
		1 ◇		1 ◇	◇			R 1	◇	1 ◇		◇		R 1		1 ◇	1 ◇	◇	1 ◇		R 1			R 1	1 ◇
		H						H	J			D			K						H	C			
Cardiff Central 7	d				13 45													14 45				15 12			
Newport (South Wales)	d				13 59													14 59				15 27			
Bristol Temple Meads 10	d	14 00						14 30						15 00	14 41						15 30				
Bristol Parkway 7	d	14 10						14 40						15 10	14 52						15 40				
Gloucester 7	d				14 46	14 50									15 38			15 46	15 50			16 22			
Cheltenham Spa	d	14 42			14 56	15a03		15 12						15 42	15 48			15 57	16a03		16 12	16a34			
Ashchurch for Tewkesbury	d														15 57			16 04							
Worcester Shrub Hill 7	a														16 23										
Birmingham New Street 12	a	15 26			15 45			15 57						16 26				16 45			16 57				
	d	15 30			15 49		15 54	16 03	16 12		16 19	16 24		16 30				16 49		16 54				17 03	
Water Orton	d																			17 05					
Coleshill Parkway	d						16 08		16 26			16 40								17 08					
Nuneaton	d						16 24		16 41			16 56								17 25					
Hinckley	d						16 31													17 32					
Narborough	d						16 39													17 40					
South Wigston	d						16 44													17 44					
Leicester	a						16 50		17 01			17 27								17 50					
Wilnecote	d				16 05													17 05							
Tamworth	d				16 10						16 36							17 09							
Burton-on-Trent	d				16 22						16 48							17 20							
Willington	d																	17 26							
Derby 10	a	16 11			16 36			16 39			17 08			17 16				17 36						17 39	
	d			16 34	16 41						17 11					17 34		17 41							
Spondon	d										17 17														
Long Eaton	d			16a43	16 50						17 24					17a43		17 50							
Attenborough	d										17 30														
Beeston	d				16 57					17 20	17 34						17 39	17 57							18 20
Nottingham 8	a				17 04					17 26	17 40						17 50	18 04							18 26

For general notes see front of timetable
For details of catering facilities see Directory of Train Operators

A From Paignton (Table 51)
B From Penzance (Table 51)
C From Maesteg (Table 128)
D To Stansted Airport (Table 49)
E From Brighton (Table 123) to Great Malvern (Table 71)
G **Cheltenham Spa Express**
H From Plymouth (Table 51)
J To Cambridge (Table 49)
K From Westbury (Table 123) to Worcester Foregate Street (Table 71)

until 5 September

Bristol and Cardiff → Birmingham → Leicester, Derby and Nottingham

Network Diagram - see first page of Table 50

Station		XC	XC	XC ◇ A	XC R 1 B ☕	EM 1 ◇ ☕	XC R 1 C ☕	EM 1 ◇ D ☕	XC ◇	GW		XC	XC R 1 E ☕	AW G	XC	XC ◇ A	XC R 1 ☕	GW H	EM 1 ◇ ☕	EM 1 ◇ ☕		XC ◇	GW 1 ◇ ☕	XC	XC R 1 E ☕
Cardiff Central 7	d								15 45					16 12								16 45			
Newport (South Wales)	d								15 59					16 27								16 59			
Bristol Temple Meads 10	d				16 00								16 30				17 00	16 41							17 30
Bristol Parkway 7	d				16 10								16 40				17 10	16 52							17 40
Gloucester 7	d								16 46	16 50				17 22				17 38				17 46	17 54		
Cheltenham Spa	d				16 42				16 57	17a03			17 12	17a34			17 42	17 48				17 57	18a03		18 12
Ashchurch for Tewkesbury	d								17 04									17 56				18 04			
Worcester Shrub Hill 7	a																	18 17							
Birmingham New Street 12	a				17 26				17 45				17 57				18 26					18 45			18 57
	d	17 09	17 12	17 24	17 30		17 39		17 49			17 59	18 03		18 09	18 24	18 30					18 49		18 54	
Water Orton	d		17 25												18 21										
Coleshill Parkway	d		17 28	17 39			17 53								18 24	18 37								19 07	
Nuneaton	d		17 46	17 55								18 27				18 53								19 24	
Hinckley	d		17 53									18 34												19 31	
Narborough	d											18 42												19 39	
South Wigston	d											18 47												19 44	
Leicester	a		18 12	18 16								18 53				19 13								19 51	
Wilnecote	d								18 07																
Tamworth	d	17 29					18 06		18 11						18 36		18 47					19 08			
Burton-on-Trent	d	17 40					18 16		18 22						18 48		18 58					19 20			
Willington	d								18 27																
Derby 10	a	18 08			18 16		18 34		18 37				18 39		19 02		19 11					19 36			
	d	18 12				18 34			18 41						19 12				19 34			19 41			
Spondon	d														19 18										
Long Eaton	d	18 21				18a43			18 50						19 25				19a43			19 50			
Attenborough	d	18 29													19 32							19 57			
Beeston	d	18 32						18 43	18 57						19 36					19 46		20 00			
Nottingham 8	a	18 37						18 48	19 05						19 42					19 53		20 06			

Station		AW G	XC R 1 ☕	XC ◇	XC 1 ◇ B ☕	EM J	EM 1 ◇ ☕	XC ◇		GW	XC	XC 1 ◇ E ☕	AW G	XC ◇	XC 1 ◇ ☕	GW H	XC ◇	GW 1 ◇ ☕		EM	EM 1 ◇ ☕	XC	XC	XC 1 ◇ E ☕	XC 1 ◇
Cardiff Central 7	d	17 12						17 45					18 12				18 45								
Newport (South Wales)	d	17 27						17 59					18 27				18 59								
Bristol Temple Meads 10	d				18 00							18 30			19 00	18 41								19 30	
Bristol Parkway 7	d				18 10							18 40			19 10	18 52								19 40	
Gloucester 7	d	18 22						18 46		18 50			19 21			19 38	19 46	19 54							
Cheltenham Spa	d	18a34			18 42			18 57		19a03		19 12	19a34		19 42	19 48	19 57	20a03						20 12	
Ashchurch for Tewkesbury	d															19 56	20 04								
Worcester Shrub Hill 7	a															20 14									
Birmingham New Street 12	a				19 26			19 46				19 57			20 42		20 43							20 57	
	d		19 03	19 24	19 30			19 49			19 54	20 03		20 24								20 49	20 54		21 03
Water Orton	d										20 05														
Coleshill Parkway	d																						21 08		
Nuneaton	d			19 51							20 25			20 54									21 24		
Hinckley	d										20 32												21 31		
Narborough	d										20 40												21 39		
South Wigston	d										20 45												21 44		
Leicester	a			20 15							20 50			21 14									21 51		
Wilnecote	d							20 05														21 05			
Tamworth	d				19 47			20 10				20 19										21 09			21 19
Burton-on-Trent	d				19 58			20 22				20 29										21 20			21 29
Willington	d																								
Derby 10	a		19 39		20 11			20 36				20 42										21 36			21 42
	d							20 41														21 41			
Spondon	d							20 46																	
Long Eaton	d							20 52														21 50			
Attenborough	d							20 59																	
Beeston	d					20 16	20 20	21 02												21 16	21 22	21 57			
Nottingham 8	a					20 22	20 27	21 08												21 23	21 28	22 04			

For general notes see front of timetable
For details of catering facilities see Directory of Train Operators

A To Cambridge (Table 49)
B From Paignton (Table 51)
C From Reading (Table 51)
D **The Robin Hood**
E From Plymouth (Table 51)
G From Maesteg (Table 128)
H From Warminster (Table 123) to Great Malvern (Table 71)
J To Lincoln (Table 27)

Table 57

Bristol and Cardiff → Birmingham → Leicester, Derby and Nottingham

Mondays to Fridays
until 5 September

Network Diagram - see first page of Table 50

		GW ■1 ◇ ☕	EM ■1 ◇ ☕	EM ■1 ◇ A ☕	XC ◇	XC ■1 ◇ B		GW C	AW D	GW ◇ E	XC	XC ◇	GW ■1 ◇ ☕	AW D	EM ■1 ◇ ☕	EM G		XC	XC ■1 ◇	XC	GW	AW D			
Cardiff Central [7]	d				20 00				20 15			20 50		21 14								23 20			
Newport (South Wales)	d				20 15				20 30			21 04		21 29								23 39			
Bristol Temple Meads [10]	d					20 30				20 41									22 00						
Bristol Parkway [7]	d					20 40				20 52									22 10						
Gloucester [7]	d	20 50			20 57			21 16	21 23	21 34		21 46	21 54	22 23						22 41	22 51	00 39			
Cheltenham Spa	d	21a03			21 07	21 12		21a26	21a34	21 44		21 57	22a05	22a36					22 42	22 52	23a03	00a52			
Ashchurch for Tewkesbury	d									21 52															
Worcester Shrub Hill [7]	a									22 10										23 15					
Birmingham New Street [12]	a				21 52	21 57						22 48							23 43						
	d				21 54	22 03					22 15							23 10							
Water Orton	d																	23 21							
Coleshill Parkway	d																								
Nuneaton	d										22 45														
Hinckley	d										22 52														
Narborough	d										23 00														
South Wigston	d										23 04														
Leicester	a										23 10														
Wilnecote	d																	23 29							
Tamworth	d				22 12	22 19												23 33							
Burton-on-Trent	d				22 23	22 29												23 44							
Willington	d																	23 50							
Derby [10]	a				22 37	22 42												23s59							
	d				22 41											23 36									
Spondon	d																								
Long Eaton	d				22 50											23 46									
Attenborough	d																								
Beeston	d		22 20	22 46	22 57										23 19	23 54									
Nottingham [8]	🚌 a		22 28	22 52	23 05										23 31	00 01		00 23							

Mondays to Fridays
from 8 September

		EM MX ■1 ◇ ☕	AW MX D	EM ■1 ◇ H ⊠ 🍴	XC ◇	EM	XC	XC	XC ■1 ◇ ☕	EM	XC	XC ■1 ◇ ☕	GW	XC	EM ■1 ◇ J ☕	XC ◇ K 🍴	XC	XC R ■1 ☕	EM	EM ■1 ◇ ☕	XC	XC ◇ K 🍴	XC ■1 ◇ ☕	EM	EM ■1 ◇ J ☕
Cardiff Central [7]	d		23p20																						
Newport (South Wales)	d		23p39																						
Bristol Temple Meads [10]	d																								
Bristol Parkway [7]	d																								
Gloucester [7]	d		00 39										06 02												
Cheltenham Spa	d		00a52										06 12												
Ashchurch for Tewkesbury	d												06 20												
Worcester Shrub Hill [7]	a												06 40												
Birmingham New Street [12]	a																								
	d				05 20			05 54	06 00		06 09	06 30				06 37	06 54	07 03			07 10	07 21	07 30		
Water Orton	d										06 19										07 21				
Coleshill Parkway	d															06 49									
Nuneaton	d				05 48			06 21								07 05	07 22					07 48			
Hinckley	d							06 28									07 28					07 55			
Narborough	d							06 36									07 37					08 03			
South Wigston	d							06 40									07 42					08 07			
Leicester	a				06 08			06 46								07 28	07 48					08 13			
Wilnecote	d										06 27														
Tamworth	d								06 15		06 31	06 47						07 19			07 30		07 47		
Burton-on-Trent	d								06 25		06 42	06 58			07 10			07 29			07 42		07 58		08 10
Willington	d														07 16						07 47				08 16
Derby [10]	a								06 38		06 58	07 11			07 27			07 42			07 56		08 11		08 25
	d			05 56		06 16	06 28				07 11			07 22	07 34						08 03			08 22	08 34
Spondon	d						06 33							07 27							08 08				
Long Eaton	d			06a05		06a25	06 40				07 20			07 35	07a43						08 15			08 32	08a43
Attenborough	d						06 49			07 18				07 42					08 07		08 23				
Beeston	d	00 01					06 52			07 21	07 28			07 45					08 10	08 20	08 26			08 39	
Nottingham [8]	🚌 a	00 06					06 59			07 30	07 34			07 53					08 20	08 29	08 32			08 45	

For general notes see front of timetable
For details of catering facilities see Directory of Train Operators

- **A** To Derby
- **B** From Plymouth (Table 51)
- **C** From Westbury (Table 123)
- **D** From Maesteg (Table 128)
- **E** From Brighton (Table 123)
- **G** From Matlock (Table 56)
- **H** From Sheffield (Table 53)
- **J** To St Pancras International (Table 53)
- **K** To Stansted Airport (Table 49)

from 8 September

Bristol and Cardiff → Birmingham → Leicester, Derby and Nottingham

Network Diagram - see first page of Table 50

		XC	XC	XC	EM	XC	GW	AW	XC	XC	EM	XC	GW	XC	XC	AW	XC	EM	XC	XC	XC	EM	XC	GW	XC
				R 1 🍽	1◇ 🍽		A		◇ B 🛒	1◇ 🍽	1◇ 🍽		1◇ 🍽		1◇ C 🍽		1◇ 🍽	1◇ 🍽		◇ B 🛒	1◇ 🍽	1◇ 🍽	◇ 🛒	D	
Cardiff Central [7]	d							06 12								07 12					07 00		07 45		
Newport (South Wales)	d							06 27								07 27					07 15		07 59		
Bristol Temple Meads [10]	d			06 15						07 00					07 30						08 00				
Bristol Parkway [7]	d			06 25						07 10					07 40						08 10				
Gloucester [7]	d			07 02		07 09	07 15	07 21				07 46	07 54			08 21							08 46	08 50	
Cheltenham Spa	d			07 12		07 19	07 25	07a34		07 42		07 57	08a03		08 12	08a34					08 42		08 57	09a03	
Ashchurch for Tewkesbury	d					07 28	07 33					08 04													
Worcester Shrub Hill [7]	a						07 54																		
Birmingham New Street [12]	a			07 57		08 16				08 26		08 46			09 00						09 26		09 45		
	d	07 49	07 54	08 03		08 19			08 24	08 30		08 49		08 54			09 03		09 19	09 24	09 30		09 49		09 54
Water Orton	d													09 06											
Coleshill Parkway	d		08 07						08 37											09 37					10 08
Nuneaton	d		08 24						08 53					09 26						09 53					10 25
Hinckley	d		08 31											09 33											10 32
Narborough	d		08 39											09 41											10 40
South Wigston	d		08 44																						10 45
Leicester	a		08 50						09 13					09 51						10 13					10 50
Wilnecote	d	08 05																							
Tamworth	d	08 09		08 19		08 37				08 47		09 06							09 36				10 06		
Burton-on-Trent	d	08 20		08 29		08 50				08 58		09 18							09 47				10 18		
Willington	d																						10 23		
Derby [10]	a	08 38		08 42		09 12				09 11		09 38					09 39		10 08		10 11		10 36		
	d	08 41				09 15					09 34	09 41							10 11			10 34	10 41		
Spondon	d					09 21																			
Long Eaton	d	08 50				09 28					09a43	09 50							10 21			10a43	10 50		
Attenborough	d					09 35													10 28						
Beeston	d	08 57			09 20	09 39						09 57						10 20	10 31				10 57		
Nottingham [8]	a	09 05			09 26	09 45						10 05						10 26	10 37				11 04		

		XC	EM	XC	XC	XC	GW	EM	XC	GW	XC	XC	AW	XC	EM	XC	XC	XC	EM	XC	GW	XC	XC	AW	GW
		1◇ E 🍽	1◇ 🍽	🛒	◇ B 🛒	1◇ E 🍽	G	1◇ 🍽	◇ 🛒	1◇ 🍽		R 1 E 🍽		1◇ 🍽	1◇ 🍽		◇ B 🛒	1◇ 🍽	1◇ 🍽	◇ 🛒			1◇ E 🍽	H	◇ J
Cardiff Central [7]	d								08 45				09 12							09 45				10 12	
Newport (South Wales)	d								08 59				09 27							09 59				10 27	
Bristol Temple Meads [10]	d	08 30				09 00	08 41					09 30						10 00					10 30		10 41
Bristol Parkway [7]	d	08 40				09 10	08 52					09 40						10 10					10 40		10 52
Gloucester [7]	d						09 38		09 46	09 50			10 21							10 46	10 52			11 21	11 36
Cheltenham Spa	d	09 12				09 42	09 48		09 57	10a03		10 12	10a34					10 42		10 57	11a05		11 12	11a34	11 47
Ashchurch for Tewkesbury	d						09 56		10 04																11 55
Worcester Shrub Hill [7]	a						10 13																		12 13
Birmingham New Street [12]	a	09 57				10 26			10 45			10 57						11 26		11 45			11 57		
	d	10 03		10 13	10 24	10 30			10 49		10 54			11 03		11 13	11 24	11 30		11 49		11 54	12 03		
Water Orton	d										11 05														
Coleshill Parkway	d				10 37						11 08						11 37					12 08			
Nuneaton	d				10 53						11 25						11 53					12 24			
Hinckley	d										11 32											12 31			
Narborough	d										11 40											12 39			
South Wigston	d																					12 44			
Leicester	a				11 13						11 50						12 13					12 50			
Wilnecote	d			10 29												11 29									
Tamworth	d			10 33		10 47			11 06							11 33				12 06					
Burton-on-Trent	d			10 44		10 58			11 18							11 44				12 18					
Willington	d																								
Derby [10]	a	10 39		11 08		11 11			11 36					11 39		12 08		12 11		12 36			12 39		
	d			11 12				11 34	11 41							12 12			12 34	12 41					
Spondon	d															12 17									
Long Eaton	d			11 21				11a43	11 50							12 23			12a43	12 50					
Attenborough	d			11 31																					
Beeston	d		11 21	11 34					11 57						12 20	12 32				12 57					
Nottingham [8]	a		11 27	11 42					12 05						12 26	12 40				13 04					

For general notes see front of timetable
For details of catering facilities see Directory of Train Operators

A To Great Malvern (Table 71)
B To Stansted Airport (Table 49)
C From Exeter St Davids (Table 51)
D From Westbury (Table 123)
E From Plymouth (Table 51)
G From Warminster (Table 123) to Great Malvern (Table 71)
H From Maesteg (Table 128)
J From Westbury (Table 123) to Great Malvern (Table 71)

Bristol and Cardiff → Birmingham → Leicester, Derby and Nottingham

Network Diagram - see first page of Table 50

		GW	EM	XC	XC	XC	XC	EM	XC	XC	XC	EM	XC	XC	XC	GW	XC	EM	XC	XC	AW	EM	XC	XC	XC
		[1] ◇ ☕	[1] ◇ ☕		◇ A 🛒	[1] ◇ ☕		[1] ◇ ☕	◇ 🛒	[R] [1] ☕	[R] [1] ☕	[1] ◇ ☕		◇ A	[1] ◇ B ☕			[1] ◇ ☕	◇ 🛒	[R] [1] C ☕	D	[1] ◇ ☕		◇ A 🛒	[R] [1] ☕
Cardiff Central [7]	d								10 45										11 45		12 12				
Newport (South Wales)	d								10 59										11 59		12 27				
Bristol Temple Meads [10]	d					11 00					11 30				12 00					12 30					13 00
Bristol Parkway [7]	d					11 10					11 40				12 10					12 40					13 10
Gloucester [7]	d	11 50							11 46							12 50			12 46		13 21				
Cheltenham Spa	d	12a03				11 42			11 57		12 12				12 42	13a03			12 57	13 12	13a34				13 42
Ashchurch for Tewkesbury	d																								
Worcester Shrub Hill [7]	a																								
Birmingham New Street [12]	a					12 26			12 46		12 57				13 26				13 45	13 57					14 26
	d			12 13	12 24	12 30	12 54		12 49	13 03			13 13	13 24	13 30		13 54		13 49	14 03			14 13	14 24	14 30
Water Orton	d						13 06																		
Coleshill Parkway	d				12 37		13 10							13 37			14 08							14 37	
Nuneaton	d				12 53		13 26							13 53			14 24							14 53	
Hinckley	d						13 33										14 31								
Narborough	d						13 41										14 39								
South Wigston	d																14 44								
Leicester	a				13 13		13 50							14 13			14 50							15 13	
Wilnecote	d			12 28									13 29												
Tamworth	d			12 32		12 47			13 06				13 33						14 06				14 30		14 47
Burton-on-Trent	d			12 46		12 58			13 18				13 44						14 18				14 42		14 58
Willington	d			12 56																			14 47		
Derby [10]	a			13 08		13 11			13 36	13 39			14 08		14 11				14 36	14 39			15 08		15 11
	d			13 12				13 34	13 41				14 12					14 34	14 41				15 12		
Spondon	d																								
Long Eaton	d			13 21				13a43	13 50				14 21					14a43	14 50				15 21		
Attenborough	d			13 31																			15 31		
Beeston	d		13 20	13 34					13 57			14 20	14 29						14 57			15 20	15 34		
Nottingham [8]	a		13 26	13 41					14 05			14 26	14 39						15 04			15 26	15 41		

		GW	EM	XC	GW	XC	XC	AW	XC	EM	XC	XC	XC	EM	XC	GW	XC	XC	XC	EM	XC	XC	XC	GW	EM
		◇ E	[1] ◇ ☕	◇ 🛒	[1] ◇ G ☕		[R] [1] C ☕	D	[R] [1] ☕	[1] ◇ ☕		◇ 🛒	[R] [1] H ☕	[1] ◇ ☕	◇ 🛒			[R] [1] H ☕	◇ J 🛒	[1] ◇ ☕		◇ A	[R] [1] ☕	K	[1] ◇ ☕
Cardiff Central [7]	d			12 45				13 12							13 45										
Newport (South Wales)	d			12 59				13 27							13 59										
Bristol Temple Meads [10]	d	12 41					13 30						14 00					14 30					15 00	14 41	
Bristol Parkway [7]	d	12 52					13 40						14 10					14 40					15 10	14 53	
Gloucester [7]	d	13 38		13 46	13 50			14 21							14 46	14 50								15 37	
Cheltenham Spa	d	13 48		13 57	14a03		14 12	14a34					14 42		14 56	15a03		15 12					15 42	15 48	
Ashchurch for Tewkesbury	d	13 56																						15 56	
Worcester Shrub Hill [7]	a	14 20																						16 23	
Birmingham New Street [12]	a			14 45			14 57						15 26		15 45			15 57					16 26		
	d			14 49		14 54			15 03		15 13	15 24	15 30		15 49		15 54	16 03	16 12		16 19	16 24	16 30		
Water Orton	d					15 05																			
Coleshill Parkway	d					15 09											16 08		16 26			16 40			
Nuneaton	d					15 25						15 53					16 24		16 41			16 56			
Hinckley	d					15 32											16 31								
Narborough	d					15 40											16 39								
South Wigston	d																16 44								
Leicester	a					15 50						16 13					16 50		17 01			17 27			
Wilnecote	d										15 29				16 05										
Tamworth	d			15 06							15 33				16 10						16 36				
Burton-on-Trent	d			15 18							15 44				16 22						16 48				
Willington	d																								
Derby [10]	a			15 36					15 39		16 08		16 11		16 36			16 39			17 02		17 14		
	d		15 34	15 41							16 12			16 34	16 41						17 12				17 34
Spondon	d																				17 17				
Long Eaton	d		15a43	15 50							16 21			16a43	16 50						17 24				17a43
Attenborough	d																				17 30				
Beeston	d			15 57						16 20	16 31				16 57					17 20	17 34				
Nottingham [8]	a			16 04						16 26	16 39				17 04					17 26	17 40				

For general notes see front of timetable
For details of catering facilities see Directory of Train Operators

A To Stansted Airport (Table 49)
B From Paignton (Table 51)
C From Penzance (Table 51)
D From Maesteg (Table 128)
E From Brighton (Table 123) to Great Malvern (Table 71)
G **Cheltenham Spa Express**
H From Plymouth (Table 51)
J To Cambridge (Table 49)
K From Westbury (Table 123) to Worcester Foregate Street (Table 71)

Table 57

Bristol and Cardiff → Birmingham → Leicester, Derby and Nottingham

Mondays to Fridays
from 8 September

Network Diagram - see first page of Table 50

		EM	XC	GW	XC	XC	AW	XC	EM	XC	XC	XC	XC	EM	XC	EM	XC	GW	AW	XC	XC	XC	XC	XC	GW
		1 ◇	◇	1 ◇		R 1		R 1	1 ◇			◇	R 1	1 ◇	R 1	1 ◇	◇				R 1		◇	R 1	
						A	B					C	D		E	G			B		A		C		H
		☕	🛒	☕		☕		☕	☕				☕	☕	☕	☕					☕			☕	
Cardiff Central 7	d		14 45				15 12										15 45		16 12						
Newport (South Wales)	d		14 59				15 27										15 59		16 27						
Bristol Temple Meads 10	d					15 30							16 00								16 30			17 00	16 41
Bristol Parkway 7	d					15 40							16 10								16 40			17 10	16 52
Gloucester 7	d		15 46	15 50			16 22										16 46	16 50	17 22						17 38
Cheltenham Spa	d		15 57	16a03		16 12	16a34						16 42				16 57	17a03	17a34		17 12			17 42	17 48
Ashchurch for Tewkesbury	d		16 04														17 04								17 56
Worcester Shrub Hill 7	a																								18 17
Birmingham New Street 12	a		16 45			16 57							17 26				17 45				17 57			18 26	
	d		16 49		16 54			17 03		17 09	17 12	17 24	17 30		17 39		17 49			17 59	18 03	18 09	18 24	18 30	
Water Orton	d				17 05						17 25											18 21			
Coleshill Parkway	d				17 08						17 28	17 39			17 53							18 24	18 37		
Nuneaton	d				17 25						17 46	17 55								18 27			18 53		
Hinckley	d				17 32						17 53									18 34					
Narborough	d				17 40															18 42					
South Wigston	d				17 44															18 47					
Leicester	a				17 50						18 12	18 16								18 53			19 13		
Wilnecote	d		17 05														18 07								
Tamworth	d		17 09							17 29					18 06		18 11					18 36		18 47	
Burton-on-Trent	d		17 20							17 40					18 16		18 22					18 48		18 58	
Willington	d		17 26														18 27								
Derby 10	a		17 36					17 39		18 06			18 11		18 34		18 37				18 39	19 02		19 11	
	d		17 41							18 13				18 34			18 41					19 11			
Spondon	d																					19 18			
Long Eaton	d		17 50							18 22				18a43			18 50					19 25			
Attenborough	d									18 30												19 32			
Beeston	d	17 39	17 57						18 20	18 33						18 43	18 57					19 36			
Nottingham 8	a	17 50	18 04						18 26	18 38						18 48	19 05					19 42			

		EM	EM	XC	GW	XC	XC	AW	XC	XC	XC	EM	EM	XC	GW	XC	XC	AW	XC	XC	GW	XC	GW	EM	EM
		1 ◇	1 ◇	◇	1 ◇		R 1		R 1	◇	1 ◇		1 ◇	◇			1 ◇		◇	1 ◇		◇	1 ◇		1 ◇
							A	B			D	J					A	B			H				
		☕	☕		☕		☕		☕		☕		☕				☕			☕			☕		☕
Cardiff Central 7	d			16 45				17 12						17 45				18 12				18 45			
Newport (South Wales)	d			16 59				17 27						17 59				18 27				18 59			
Bristol Temple Meads 10	d						17 30				18 00						18 30			19 00	18 41				
Bristol Parkway 7	d						17 40				18 10						18 40			19 10	18 52				
Gloucester 7	d			17 46	17 54			18 22						18 46	18 50			19 21			19 38	19 46	19 54		
Cheltenham Spa	d			17 57	18a03		18 12	18a34			18 42			18 57	19a03		19 12	19a34		19 42	19 48	19 57	20a03		
Ashchurch for Tewkesbury	d			18 04																	19 56	20 04			
Worcester Shrub Hill 7	a																				20 14				
Birmingham New Street 12	a			18 45			18 57				19 26			19 46			19 57			20 42		20 43			
	d			18 49		18 54			19 03	19 24	19 30			19 49		19 54	20 03		20 24						
Water Orton	d															20 05									
Coleshill Parkway	d					19 07																			
Nuneaton	d					19 24				19 51						20 25			20 54						
Hinckley	d					19 31										20 32									
Narborough	d					19 39										20 40									
South Wigston	d					19 44										20 45									
Leicester	a					19 51				20 15						20 50			21 14						
Wilnecote	d													20 05											
Tamworth	d			19 08							19 47			20 10			20 19								
Burton-on-Trent	d			19 24							19 58			20 22			20 29								
Willington	d																								
Derby 10	a			19 36					19 39		20 11			20 36			20 42								
	d	19 34		19 41										20 41											
Spondon	d													20 46											
Long Eaton	d	19a43		19 50										20 52											
Attenborough	d			19 57										20 59											
Beeston	d		19 46	20 00								20 16	20 20	21 02										21 16	21 22
Nottingham 8	a		19 53	20 06								20 22	20 27	21 08										21 23	21 28

For general notes see front of timetable
For details of catering facilities see Directory of Train Operators

- **A** From Plymouth (Table 51)
- **B** From Maesteg (Table 128)
- **C** To Cambridge (Table 49)
- **D** From Paignton (Table 51)
- **E** From Reading (Table 51)
- **G** **The Robin Hood**
- **H** From Warminster (Table 123) to Great Malvern (Table 71)
- **J** To Lincoln (Table 27)

Bristol and Cardiff → Birmingham → Leicester, Derby and Nottingham

Network Diagram - see first page of Table 50

		XC	XC	XC 1◇ A ☕	XC 1◇	GW 1◇ ☕	EM 1◇ ☕	EM 1◇ B ☕	XC ◇	XC 1◇ A	GW C	AW D	GW ◇ E	XC	XC ◇	GW 1◇ ☕	AW D	EM 1◇ ☕	EM G	XC	XC 1◇	XC	GW	AW D
Cardiff Central 7	d								20 00			20 15			20 50		21 14							23 20
Newport (South Wales)	d								20 15			20 30			21 04		21 29							23 39
Bristol Temple Meads 10	d			19 30						20 30			20 41								22 00			
Bristol Parkway 7	d			19 40						20 40			20 52								22 10			
Gloucester 7	d					20 50			20 57		21 16	21 23	21 34		21 46	21 54	22 23					22 41	22 51	00 39
Cheltenham Spa	d			20 12		21a03			21 07	21 12	21a26	21a34	21 44		21 57	22a05	22a36				22 42	22 52	23a03	00a52
Ashchurch for Tewkesbury	d												21 52											
Worcester Shrub Hill 7	a												22 10									23 15		
Birmingham New Street 12	a			20 57					21 52	21 57					22 48						23 43			
	d	20 49	20 54		21 03				21 54	22 03				22 15						23 10				
Water Orton	d																			23 21				
Coleshill Parkway	d		21 08																					
Nuneaton	d		21 24											22 45										
Hinckley	d		21 31											22 52										
Narborough	d		21 39											23 00										
South Wigston	d		21 44											23 04										
Leicester	a		21 51											23 10										
Wilnecote	d	21 05																		23 29				
Tamworth	d	21 09			21 19				22 12	22 19										23 33				
Burton-on-Trent	d	21 20			21 29				22 23	22 29										23 44				
Willington	d																			23 50				
Derby 10	a	21 36			21 42				22 37	22 42										23s59				
	d	21 41							22 41										23 36					
Spondon	d																							
Long Eaton	d	21 50							22 50										23 46					
Attenborough	d																							
Beeston	d	21 57					22 20	22 46	22 57									23 19	23 54					
Nottingham 8	a	22 04					22 28	22 52	23 05									23 31	00 01	00 23				

Saturdays
until 12 July

		EM 1◇ ☕	AW D	EM 1◇ H ☕	XC ◇	EM	XC	XC	XC 1◇ ☕	GW	EM		XC	XC 1◇ ☕	XC ◇	EM 1◇ ☕	XC	XC 1◇ ☕	XC ◇	XC ◇ J	XC 1◇ ☕	EM 1◇ K ☕		EM 1◇ ☕	XC
Cardiff Central 7	d		23p20																						
Newport (South Wales)	d		23p39																						
Bristol Temple Meads 10	d																								
Bristol Parkway 7	d																								
Gloucester 7	d		00 39							05 50															06 46
Cheltenham Spa	d		00a52							06 00															06 57
Ashchurch for Tewkesbury	d									06 09															07 04
Worcester Shrub Hill 7	a									06 31															
Birmingham New Street 12	a																								07 45
	d				05 20			05 54	06 00				06 09	06 30	06 36		06 52	07 03	07 10	07 24	07 30				07 49
Water Orton	d												06 19												
Coleshill Parkway	d							06 07									07 06			07 37					
Nuneaton	d				05 46			06 24							07 04		07 24			07 53					
Hinckley	d							06 31									07 31								
Narborough	d							06 39									07 39								
South Wigston	d							06 44									07 44								
Leicester	a				06 06			06 51							07 25		07 50			08 13					
Wilnecote	d												06 27												08 05
Tamworth	d								06 16				06 31	06 47				07 19	07 28		07 47				08 09
Burton-on-Trent	d								06 26				06 42	06 58				07 29	07 39		07 58	08 08			08 20
Willington	d																		07 45			08 13			
Derby 10	a								06 39				06 57	07 11				07 42	07 58		08 11	08 25			08 36
	d			06 00		06 26	06 29						07 03			07 33			08 08			08 33			08 41
Spondon	d						06 34						07 09												08 46
Long Eaton	d			06a09		06a35	06 41						07 18			07a42			08 17			08a43			08 53
Attenborough	d						06 47				07 17		07 27						08 23						
Beeston	d	00 01					06 50				07 20		07 31						08 27					08 48	08 59
Nottingham 8	a	00 06					06 56				07 27		07 37						08 32					08 56	09 10

For general notes see front of timetable
For details of catering facilities see Directory of Train Operators

A From Plymouth (Table 51)
B To Derby
C From Westbury (Table 123)
D From Maesteg (Table 128)
E From Brighton (Table 123)
G From Matlock (Table 56)
H From Sheffield (Table 53)
J To Stansted Airport (Table 49)
K To St Pancras International (Table 53)

Saturdays

until 12 July

Bristol and Cardiff → Birmingham → Leicester, Derby and Nottingham

Network Diagram - see first page of Table 50

		XC	XC 1 ◇ ☕	GW A	AW	EM 1 ◇ ☕	XC	XC ◇ B	XC 1 ◇ ☕	EM 1 ◇ C ☕	XC	XC	XC 1 ◇ ☕	GW	AW	XC 1 ◇ ☕	EM 1 ◇ ☕	XC	XC ◇ B	XC 1 ◇ ☕	EM 1 ◇ ☕	XC ◇	XC
Cardiff Central 7	d				06 12										07 12							07 45	
Newport (South Wales)	d				06 27										07 27							07 59	
Bristol Temple Meads 10	d		06 15										07 30							08 00			
Bristol Parkway 7	d		06 25										07 40							08 10			
Gloucester 7	d		07 01	07 15	07 21						07 46			08 10	08 22							08 46	
Cheltenham Spa	d		07 12	07 25	07a34						07 57		08 12	08a23	08a32					08 42		08 57	
Ashchurch for Tewkesbury	d			07 34							08 04												
Worcester Shrub Hill 7	a			07 55																			
Birmingham New Street 12	a		07 57								08 45		08 57							09 26		09 45	
	d	07 54	08 03				08 13	08 24	08 30		08 49	08 54				09 03		09 13	09 24	09 30		09 49	09 54
Water Orton	d											09 07											
Coleshill Parkway	d	08 07						08 37				09 10							09 37				10 07
Nuneaton	d	08 24						08 53				09 25							09 53				10 23
Hinckley	d	08 31										09 32											10 30
Narborough	d	08 39										09 40											10 38
South Wigston	d	08 44																					10 43
Leicester	a	08 50						09 13				09 51							10 13				10 52
Wilnecote	d																						
Tamworth	d		08 19				08 34		08 47		09 08							09 30		09 47		10 08	
Burton-on-Trent	d		08 29				08 46		08 58		09 20							09 41		09 58		10 20	
Willington	d																	09 49					
Derby 10	a		08 42				09 07		09 11		09 38					09 39		10 08		10 11		10 36	
	d						09 11			09 33	09 41							10 11			10 33	10 41	
Spondon	d																						
Long Eaton	d						09 20			09a43	09 50							10 20			10a43	10 50	
Attenborough	d																	10 28					
Beeston	d					09 20	09 28				09 57						10 20	10 31				10 57	
Nottingham 8	a					09 26	09 35				10 05						10 27	10 37				11 04	

		XC 1 ◇ D ☕	EM 1 ◇ ☕	XC	XC ◇ B	XC 1 ◇ ☕	GW E	EM 1 ◇ ☕	XC ◇	XC	XC 1 ◇ D ☕	GW 1 ◇ ☕	AW	XC R 1 ☕	EM 1 ◇ G ☕	XC	XC ◇ B	XC 1 ◇ ☕	EM 1 ◇ ☕	XC ◇	XC	XC 1 ◇ D ☕	GW
Cardiff Central 7	d								08 45				09 12					09 00		09 45			
Newport (South Wales)	d								08 59				09 27					09 15		09 59			
Bristol Temple Meads 10	d	08 30				09 00	08 41				09 30							10 00				10 30	
Bristol Parkway 7	d	08 40				09 10	08 52				09 40							10 10				10 40	
Gloucester 7	d						09 40		09 46			10 11	10 21							10 46			11 08
Cheltenham Spa	d	09 12				09 42	09 51		09 57		10 12	10a23	10a34					10 42		10 56		11 12	11a20
Ashchurch for Tewkesbury	d						09 59		10 04														
Worcester Shrub Hill 7	a						10 17																
Birmingham New Street 12	a	09 57				10 26			10 45		10 57							11 26		11 45		11 57	
	d	10 03		10 13	10 24	10 30			10 49	10 54				11 03		11 13	11 24	11 30		11 49	11 54	12 03	
Water Orton	d									11 07													
Coleshill Parkway	d				10 37					11 10							11 37				12 07		
Nuneaton	d				10 53					11 27							11 53				12 24		
Hinckley	d									11 34											12 31		
Narborough	d									11 42											12 39		
South Wigston	d																				12 44		
Leicester	a				11 13					11 52							12 13				12 52		
Wilnecote	d			10 31												11 29							
Tamworth	d			10 35		10 47			11 08							11 33				12 08			
Burton-on-Trent	d			10 46		10 58			11 20							11 44				12 20			
Willington	d																						
Derby 10	a	10 39		11 08		11 11			11 36					11 39		12 08		12 11		12 36		12 39	
	d			11 11				11 33	11 41							12 11			12 33	12 41			
Spondon	d															12 16							
Long Eaton	d			11 20				11a43	11 50							12 20			12a43	12 50			
Attenborough	d			11 31																			
Beeston	d		11 19	11 34											12 19	12 27				12 57			
Nottingham 8	a		11 27	11 41					12 06						12 27	12 38				13 05			

For general notes see front of timetable
For details of catering facilities see Directory of Train Operators

- **A** To Great Malvern (Table 71)
- **B** To Stansted Airport (Table 49)
- **C** From Barnsley (Table 53)
- **D** From Plymouth (Table 51)
- **E** From Warminster (Table 123) to Great Malvern (Table 71)
- **G** To Sheffield (Table 53)

Table 57

Saturdays

until 12 July

Bristol and Cardiff → Birmingham → Leicester, Derby and Nottingham

Network Diagram - see first page of Table 50

		AW	EM	XC	XC	XC	GW	EM	XC	XC	XC		GW	XC	EM	XC	XC	XC	EM	XC	XC	XC		GW	AW
			1 ◇		◇	1 ◇	◇	1 ◇	◇		1 ◇		1 ◇	1 ◇	1 ◇		◇	R 1	1 ◇	◇		R 1			
		A			B	C	D				E							G				E			A
			☕			☕		☕			☕		☕	☕	☕			☕	☕			☕			
Cardiff Central 7	d	10 12							10 45											11 45					12 12
Newport (South Wales)	d	10 27							10 59											11 59					12 27
Bristol Temple Meads 10	d					11 00	10 41				11 30							12 00				12 30			
Bristol Parkway 7	d					11 10	10 52				11 40							12 10				12 40			
Gloucester 7	d	11 22					11 39		11 46				12 12							12 46				13 08	13 21
Cheltenham Spa	d	11a34				11 42	11 50		11 57		12 12		12a23					12 42		12 57		13 12		13a20	13a34
Ashchurch for Tewkesbury	d						11 59																		
Worcester Shrub Hill 7	a						12 18																		
Birmingham New Street 12	a					12 26			12 45		12 57							13 26		13 45		13 57			
	d			12 13	12 24	12 30			12 49	12 54				13 03		13 13	13 24	13 30		13 49	13 54	14 03			
Water Orton	d									13 05															
Coleshill Parkway	d				12 37					13 09											14 07				
Nuneaton	d				12 53					13 25							13 53				14 24				
Hinckley	d									13 32											14 31				
Narborough	d									13 40											14 39				
South Wigston	d																				14 44				
Leicester	a				13 13					13 51							14 13				14 53				
Wilnecote	d			12 29																					
Tamworth	d			12 33		12 47			13 08							13 30				14 08					
Burton-on-Trent	d			12 44		12 58			13 20							13 42				14 20					
Willington	d															13 48									
Derby 10	a			13 08		13 11			13 36					13 39		14 08		14 11		14 36		14 39			
	d			13 11				13 33	13 41							14 11			14 33	14 41					
Spondon	d																								
Long Eaton	d			13 20				13a43	13 50							14 20			14a43	14 50					
Attenborough	d			13 30																					
Beeston	d		13 20	13 33					13 57						14 19	14 27				14 57					
Nottingham 8	a		13 25	13 40					14 05						14 25	14 35				15 05					

		EM	XC	XC	XC	GW	EM	XC	GW	AW	XC		XC	EM	XC	XC	XC	EM	XC	XC	XC	GW		EM	XC
		1 ◇		◇	1 ◇	◇	1 ◇	◇	1 ◇				R 1	1 ◇		◇	1 ◇	1 ◇	◇		R 1			1 ◇	
				B		H				A						B					E				
		☕			☕		☕		☕				☕	☕			☕	☕			☕			☕	
Cardiff Central 7	d							12 45		13 12									13 45						
Newport (South Wales)	d							12 59		13 27									13 59						
Bristol Temple Meads 10	d				13 00	12 41							13 30				14 00				14 30				
Bristol Parkway 7	d				13 10	12 52											14 10				14 40				
Gloucester 7	d					13 40		13 46	14 11	14 21									14 46			15 08			
Cheltenham Spa	d				13 42	13 50		13 57	14a23	14a34							14 42		14 57		15 12	15a20			
Ashchurch for Tewkesbury	d					13 58																			
Worcester Shrub Hill 7	a					14 26																			
Birmingham New Street 12	a				14 26			14 45					14 57				15 26		15 45		15 57				
	d		14 13	14 24	14 30			14 49			14 54		15 03		15 13	15 24	15 30		15 49	15 54	16 03				16 13
Water Orton	d										15 06														
Coleshill Parkway	d			14 37							15 10					15 37				16 07					
Nuneaton	d			14 53							15 25					15 53				16 23					
Hinckley	d										15 32									16 30					
Narborough	d										15 40									16 38					
South Wigston	d																			16 42					
Leicester	a			15 13							15 50					16 13				16 50					
Wilnecote	d		14 29												15 29										16 31
Tamworth	d		14 33		14 47			15 08							15 33				16 08						16 35
Burton-on-Trent	d		14 46		14 58			15 20							15 44				16 20						16 46
Willington	d																								
Derby 10	a		15 08		15 11			15 36					15 39		16 08		16 11		16 36		16 39				17 08
	d		15 11				15 33	15 41							16 11			16 33	16 41						17 11
Spondon	d																								17 16
Long Eaton	d		15 20				15a43	15 50							16 20			16a43	16 50						17 20
Attenborough	d		15 30																						17 30
Beeston	d	15 20	15 33					15 57						16 21	16 27				16 57					17 20	17 33
Nottingham 8	a	15 26	15 41					16 05						16 26	16 33				17 06					17 28	17 40

For general notes see front of timetable
For details of catering facilities see Directory of Train Operators

A From Maesteg (Table 128)
B To Stansted Airport (Table 49)
C From Weston-super-Mare (Table 51)
D From Westbury (Table 123) to Great Malvern (Table 71)
E From Paignton (Table 51)
G From Penzance (Table 51)
H From Brighton (Table 123) to Worcester Foregate Street (Table 71)

Bristol and Cardiff → Birmingham → Leicester, Derby and Nottingham

until 12 July

Network Diagram - see first page of Table 50

		XC	XC	GW	EM	XC	XC	XC	GW	AW	XC		EM	XC	XC	XC	EM	XC	XC	GW	AW	XC		EM	XC
		◇	1 ◇		1 ◇	◇		R 1	1 ◇		1 ◇		1 ◇		◇	1 ◇	1 ◇	◇	R 1					1 ◇	
		A		B				C		D					E	G			H		D			J	
			🍴		🍴			🍴	🍴		🍴		🍴			🍴	🍴		🍴					🍴	
Cardiff Central 7	d					14 45				15 12								15 45			16 12				
Newport (South Wales)	d					14 59				15 27								15 59			16 26				
Bristol Temple Meads 10	d		15 00	14 41				15 30								16 00			16 30						
Bristol Parkway 7	d		15 10	14 52				15 40								16 10			16 40						
Gloucester 7	d			15 38		15 46			16 11	16 21								16 46		17 08	17 21				
Cheltenham Spa	d		15 42	15 48		15 57		16 12	16a23	16a34						16 42		16 57	17 12	17a20	17a34				
Ashchurch for Tewkesbury	d			15 56		16 04												17 04							
Worcester Shrub Hill 7	a			16 13																					
Birmingham New Street 12	a		16 26			16 45		16 57								17 26		17 45	17 57						
	d	16 24	16 30			16 49	16 54				17 03			17 13	17 24	17 30		17 49	18 03			18 05			18 13
Water Orton	d						17 05							17 23				17 59							18 26
Coleshill Parkway	d	16 37					17 08								17 37										
Nuneaton	d	16 53					17 25								17 53							18 33			
Hinckley	d						17 32															18 40			
Narborough	d						17 40															18 48			
South Wigston	d						17 44															18 53			
Leicester	a	17 13					17 50								18 13							18 59			
Wilnecote	d													17 31											18 34
Tamworth	d		16 47			17 08								17 35				18 08	18 19						18 38
Burton-on-Trent	d		16 58			17 20								17 47				18 20	18 29						18 50
Willington	d													17 53											18 56
Derby 10	a		17 11			17 36					17 39			18 08		18 11		18 36	18 42						19 08
	d				17 33	17 41								18 11			18 33	18 41							19 11
Spondon	d																								19 17
Long Eaton	d				17a43	17 50								18 20			18a43	18 50							19 23
Attenborough	d													18 26											19 29
Beeston	d					17 57							18 20	18 29				18 57						19 20	19 32
Nottingham 8 ⛴	a					18 06							18 26	18 39				19 05						19 26	19 40

		XC	XC	GW	EM	XC	XC	XC	GW	AW	XC		EM	XC	XC	EM	EM	XC	XC	XC	GW	AW		XC	GW
		◇	1 ◇		1 ◇	◇		R 1	1 ◇		1 ◇		1 ◇	◇	1 ◇		1 ◇	◇		R 1				1 ◇	
		A		K				G		D			L			N				G		D			Q
			🍴		🍴			🍴	🍴		🍴		🍴		🍴		🍴			🍴				🍴	
Cardiff Central 7	d					16 45				17 12								17 45				18 12			
Newport (South Wales)	d					16 59				17 27								17 59				18 27			
Bristol Temple Meads 10	d		17 00	16 41				17 30							18 00					18 30				19 00	18 41
Bristol Parkway 7	d		17 10	16 52				17 40							18 10					18 40				19 10	18 52
Gloucester 7	d			17 40		17 46			18 11	18 23								18 46			19 08	19 21			19 38
Cheltenham Spa	d		17 42	17 51		17 57		18 12	18a23	18a33					18 42			18 57		19 12	19a20	19a34		19 42	19 47
Ashchurch for Tewkesbury	d			17 59		18 04																			19 55
Worcester Shrub Hill 7	a			18 19																					20 14
Birmingham New Street 12	a		18 26			18 45		18 57							19 26			19 45		19 57				20 26	
	d	18 24	18 30			18 49	18 54				19 03			19 24	19 30			19 49	19 54	20 03					
Water Orton	d																		20 05						
Coleshill Parkway	d	18 37					19 07																		
Nuneaton	d	18 53					19 24							19b53					20 24						
Hinckley	d						19 31												20 31						
Narborough	d						19 39												20 39						
South Wigston	d						19 44												20 44						
Leicester	a	19 13					19 50							20 16					20 50						
Wilnecote	d					19 05												20 05							
Tamworth	d		18 47			19 08									19 47			20 08		20 19					
Burton-on-Trent	d		18 58			19 20									19 58			20 20		20 29					
Willington	d																								
Derby 10	a		19 11			19 36					19 39				20 11			20 36		20 42					
	d				19 33	19 41							19 51					20 41							
Spondon	d																	20 46							
Long Eaton	d				19a43	19 50							20a01					20 52							
Attenborough	d					19 55												20 59							
Beeston	d					19 59										20 13	20 22	21 02							
Nottingham 8 ⛴	a					20 10										20 19	20 34	21 11							

For general notes see front of timetable
For details of catering facilities see Directory of Train Operators

A To Cambridge (Table 49)
B From Southampton Central (Table 123) to Great Malvern (Table 71)
C From Penzance (Table 51)
D From Maesteg (Table 128)
E To Stansted Airport (Table 49)
G From Paignton (Table 51)
H From Plymouth (Table 51)
J To Sheffield (Table 53)
K From Warminster (Table 123) to Great Malvern (Table 71)
L From Scarborough (Table 26)
N To Lincoln (Table 27)
Q From Weymouth (Table 123) to Great Malvern (Table 71)
b Arr. 1950

Table 57

Saturdays

until 12 July

Bristol and Cardiff → Birmingham → Leicester, Derby and Nottingham

Network Diagram - see first page of Table 50

		XC	EM	EM	XC	XC	XC	GW	GW	XC	EM	XC	XC	GW	XC	AW	XC	EM	XC	GW	XC	GW
		◇		1 ◇	◇	1 ◇	R 1	1 ◇	◇		1 ◇	◇	1 ◇						1 ◇		◇	1 ◇
							A						B			C		D	E	G		
				🍴		🍴	🍴	🍴			🍴		🍴									🍴
Cardiff Central 7	d				18 45							20 00				20 15					20 50	
Newport (South Wales)	d				18 59							20 15				20 30					21 04	
Bristol Temple Meads 10	d						19 30		19 40				20 30						21 00	20 41		
Bristol Parkway 7	d						19 40		19 52				20 40						21 10	20 52		
Gloucester 7	d				19 46			20 11	20 40			20 57		21 05	21 17	21 23				21 37	21 48	22 11
Cheltenham Spa	d				19 57		20 12	20a23	20a48			21 07	21 12	21a16	21 27	21a34			21 42	21a46	21 59	22a23
Ashchurch for Tewkesbury	d				20 04																	
Worcester Shrub Hill 7	a														21 54						22 20	
Birmingham New Street 12	a				20 41		20 57					21 52	22 03						22 26		23 02	
	d	20 27			20 44	20 50				21 15		21 54					22 09		22 33			
Water Orton	d																					
Coleshill Parkway	d									21 28												
Nuneaton	d	20 54								21 44							22 36					
Hinckley	d									21 50							22 43					
Narborough	d									21 58							22 51					
South Wigston	d									22 03							22 56					
Leicester	a	21 14								22 11							23 02					
Wilnecote	d											22 09										
Tamworth	d				21 03	21 23						22 13							22 49			
Burton-on-Trent	d				21 14	21 33						22 25							22 59			
Willington	d																					
Derby 10	a				21 36	21 45						22 38							23 16			
	d				21 41							22 42						23 04				
Spondon	d																					
Long Eaton	d				21 50							22 51						23 14				
Attenborough	d																	23 22				
Beeston	d		21 11	21 20	21 57						22 20	22 57						23 26				
Nottingham 8	a		21 17	21 26	22 04						22 26	23 04						23 33				

Saturdays

19 July to 6 September

		EM	AW	EM	XC	EM	XC	XC	XC	GW	EM	XC	XC	XC	EM	XC	XC	XC	XC	XC	EM	EM	XC
		1 ◇		1 ◇	◇				1 ◇				1 ◇	◇	1 ◇		1 ◇	◇	◇	1 ◇	1 ◇	1 ◇	
			C	H															J		K		
		🍴		🍴					🍴				🍴		🍴		🍴			🍴	🍴	🍴	
Cardiff Central 7	d		23p20																				
Newport (South Wales)	d		23p39																				
Bristol Temple Meads 10	d																						
Bristol Parkway 7	d																						
Gloucester 7	d		00 39							05 50													06 46
Cheltenham Spa	d		00a52							06 00													06 57
Ashchurch for Tewkesbury	d									06 09													07 04
Worcester Shrub Hill 7	a									06 31													
Birmingham New Street 12	a																						07 45
	d				05 20			05 54	06 00			06 09	06 30	06 36		06 52	07 03	07 10	07 24	07 30			07 49
Water Orton	d											06 19											
Coleshill Parkway	d							06 07								07 06			07 37				
Nuneaton	d				05 46			06 24						07 04		07 24			07 53				
Hinckley	d							06 31								07 31							
Narborough	d							06 39								07 39							
South Wigston	d							06 44								07 44							
Leicester	a				06 06			06 51						07 25		07 50			08 13				
Wilnecote	d											06 27											08 05
Tamworth	d								06 16			06 31	06 47				07 19	07 28		07 47			08 09
Burton-on-Trent	d								06 26			06 42	06 58				07 29	07 39		07 58	08 08		08 20
Willington	d																	07 45			08 13		
Derby 10	a								06 39			06 57	07 11				07 42	07 58		08 11	08 25		08 36
	d			06 00		06 26	06 29					07 03			07 33			08 08			08 33		08 41
Spondon	d						06 34					07 09											08 46
Long Eaton	d			06a09		06a35	06 41					07 18			07a42			08 17			08a43		08 53
Attenborough	d						06 47				07 17	07 27						08 23					
Beeston	d	00 01					06 50				07 20	07 31						08 27				08 48	08 59
Nottingham 8	a	00 06					06 56				07 27	07 37						08 32				08 56	09 10

For general notes see front of timetable
For details of catering facilities see Directory of Train Operators

- **A** From Newquay (Table 135)
- **B** From Plymouth (Table 51)
- **C** From Maesteg (Table 128)
- **D** From Matlock (Table 56)
- **E** From Paignton (Table 51)
- **G** From Brighton (Table 123)
- **H** From Sheffield (Table 53)
- **J** To Stansted Airport (Table 49)
- **K** To St Pancras International (Table 53)

Due to Engineering Operations, services from Saturday 13 September on this Table had not been confirmed at time of going to press. These services will be issued in a special Supplement as soon as exact timings have been confirmed

Table 57

Bristol and Cardiff → Birmingham → Leicester, Derby and Nottingham

Saturdays

19 July to 6 September

Network Diagram - see first page of Table 50

	XC	XC	GW	AW	EM	XC	XC	XC	EM	XC	XC	XC	GW	AW	XC	EM	XC	XC	XC	EM	XC	XC
		1 ◇			**1** ◇		◇	**1** ◇	**1** ◇			**1** ◇			**1** ◇	**1** ◇		◇	**1** ◇	**1** ◇	◇	
			A				B		C									B				
		☕			☕			☕	☕			☕			☕	☕			☕	☕		
Cardiff Central 7 d				06 12										07 12							07 45	
Newport (South Wales) d				06 27										07 27							07 59	
Bristol Temple Meads 10 d		06 15										07 30							08 00			
Bristol Parkway 7 d		06 25										07 40							08 10			
Gloucester 7 d		07 01	07 15	07 21						07 46			08 10	08 22							08 46	
Cheltenham Spa d		07 12	07 25	07a34						07 57		08 12	08a23	08a32					08 42		08 57	
Ashchurch for Tewkesbury d			07 34							08 04												
Worcester Shrub Hill 7 a			07 55																			
Birmingham New Street 12 a		07 57								08 45		08 57							09 26		09 45	
d	07 54	08 03				08 13	08 24	08 30		08 49	08 54				09 03		09 13	09 24	09 30		09 49	09 54
Water Orton d											09 07											
Coleshill Parkway d	08 07						08 37				09 10							09 37				10 07
Nuneaton d	08 24						08 53				09 25							09 53				10 23
Hinckley d	08 31										09 32											10 30
Narborough d	08 39										09 40											10 38
South Wigston d	08 44																					10 43
Leicester a	08 50						09 13				09 51							10 13				10 52
Wilnecote d																						
Tamworth d		08 19				08 34		08 47		09 08							09 30		09 47		10 08	
Burton-on-Trent d		08 29				08 46		08 58		09 20							09 41		09 58		10 20	
Willington d																	09 49					
Derby 10 a		08 42				09 07		09 11		09 38					09 39		10 08		10 11		10 36	
d						09 11			09 33	09 41							10 11			10 33	10 41	
Spondon d																						
Long Eaton d						09 20			09a43	09 50							10 20			10a43	10 50	
Attenborough d																	10 28					
Beeston d					09 20	09 28				09 57						10 20	10 31				10 57	
Nottingham 8 a					09 26	09 35				10 05						10 27	10 37				11 04	

	XC	EM	XC	XC	XC	GW	EM	XC	XC	XC	GW	AW	XC	EM	XC	XC	XC	EM	XC	XC	XC	GW
													R									
	1 ◇	**1** ◇		◇	**1** ◇		**1** ◇	◇		**1** ◇	**1** ◇		**1**	**1** ◇		◇	**1** ◇	**1** ◇	◇		**1** ◇	
	D			B		E				D				G		B					D	
	☕	☕			☕		☕			☕	☕		☕	☕			☕	☕			☕	
Cardiff Central 7 d								08 45				09 12					09 00		09 45			
Newport (South Wales) d								08 59				09 27					09 15		09 59			
Bristol Temple Meads 10 d	08 30				09 00	08 41				09 30							10 00				10 30	
Bristol Parkway 7 d	08 40				09 10	08 52				09 40							10 10				10 40	
Gloucester 7 d						09 40		09 46			10 11	10 21							10 46			11 08
Cheltenham Spa d	09 12				09 42	09 51		09 57		10 12	10a23	10a34					10 42		10 56		11 12	11a20
Ashchurch for Tewkesbury d						09 59		10 04														
Worcester Shrub Hill 7 a						10 17																
Birmingham New Street 12 a	09 57				10 26			10 45		10 57							11 26		11 45		11 57	
d	10 03		10 13	10 24	10 30			10 49	10 54				11 03		11 13	11 24	11 30		11 49	11 54	12 03	
Water Orton d									11 07													
Coleshill Parkway d				10 37					11 10							11 37				12 07		
Nuneaton d				10 53					11 27							11 53				12 24		
Hinckley d									11 34											12 31		
Narborough d									11 42											12 39		
South Wigston d																				12 44		
Leicester a				11 13					11 52							12 13				12 52		
Wilnecote d			10 31												11 29							
Tamworth d			10 35		10 47			11 08							11 33				12 08			
Burton-on-Trent d			10 46		10 58			11 20							11 44				12 20			
Willington d																						
Derby 10 a	10 39		11 08		11 11			11 36					11 39		12 08		12 11		12 36		12 39	
d			11 11				11 33	11 41							12 11			12 33	12 41			
Spondon d															12 16							
Long Eaton d			11 20				11a43	11 50							12 20			12a43	12 50			
Attenborough d			11 31																			
Beeston d		11 19	11 34											12 19	12 27				12 57			
Nottingham 8 a		11 27	11 41					12 06						12 27	12 38				13 05			

For general notes see front of timetable
For details of catering facilities see Directory of Train Operators

- **A** To Great Malvern (Table 71)
- **B** To Stansted Airport (Table 49)
- **C** From Barnsley (Table 53)
- **D** From Plymouth (Table 51)
- **E** From Warminster (Table 123) to Great Malvern (Table 71)
- **G** To Sheffield (Table 53)

Due to Engineering Operations, services from Saturday 13 September on this Table had not been confirmed at time of going to press. These services will be issued in a special Supplement as soon as exact timings have been confirmed

Table 57

Saturdays

19 July to 6 September

Bristol and Cardiff → Birmingham → Leicester, Derby and Nottingham

Network Diagram - see first page of Table 50

		AW	EM	XC	XC	XC	GW	EM	XC	XC	XC		GW	XC	EM	XC	XC	XC	EM	XC	XC	XC		GW	AW
		A	1 ◇ ☕		◇ B	1 ◇ C ☕	◇ D	1 ◇ ☕	◇		1 ◇ E ☕		1 ◇ ☕	1 ◇ ☕	1 ◇ ☕		◇	R 1 G ☕	1 ◇ ☕	◇		R 1 E ☕			A
Cardiff Central 7	d	10 12							10 45											11 45					12 12
Newport (South Wales)	d	10 27							10 59											11 59					12 27
Bristol Temple Meads 10	d					11 00	10 41				11 30							12 00				12 30			
Bristol Parkway 7	d					11 10	10 52				11 40							12 10				12 40			
Gloucester 7	d	11 22					11 39		11 46				12 12							12 46				13 08	13 21
Cheltenham Spa	d	11a34				11 42	11 50		11 57		12 12		12a23					12 42		12 57		13 12		13a20	13a34
Ashchurch for Tewkesbury	d						11 59																		
Worcester Shrub Hill 7	a						12 18																		
Birmingham New Street 12	a					12 26			12 45		12 57							13 26		13 45		13 57			
	d			12 13	12 24	12 30			12 49	12 54				13 03		13 13	13 24	13 30		13 49	13 54	14 03			
Water Orton	d									13 05															
Coleshill Parkway	d				12 37					13 09											14 07				
Nuneaton	d				12 53					13 25							13 53				14 24				
Hinckley	d									13 32											14 31				
Narborough	d									13 40											14 39				
South Wigston	d																				14 44				
Leicester	a				13 13					13 51							14 13				14 53				
Wilnecote	d			12 29																					
Tamworth	d			12 33		12 47			13 08							13 30				14 08					
Burton-on-Trent	d			12 44		12 58			13 20							13 42				14 20					
Willington	d															13 48									
Derby 10	a			13 08		13 11			13 36					13 39		14 08		14 11		14 36		14 39			
	d			13 11				13 33	13 41							14 11			14 33	14 41					
Spondon	d																								
Long Eaton	d			13 20				13a43	13 50							14 20			14a43	14 50					
Attenborough	d			13 30																					
Beeston	d		13 20	13 33					13 57						14 19	14 27				14 57					
Nottingham 8	a		13 25	13 40					14 05						14 25	14 35				15 05					

		EM	XC	XC	XC	GW	EM	XC	GW	AW	XC		XC	EM	XC	XC	XC	EM	XC	XC	XC	GW		EM	XC
		1 ◇ ☕		◇ B	1 ◇ ☕	◇ H	1 ◇ ☕	◇	1 ◇ ☕	A			R 1 ☕	1 ◇ ☕		◇ B	1 ◇ ☕	1 ◇ ☕	◇		R 1 E ☕			1 ◇ ☕	
Cardiff Central 7	d							12 45		13 12									13 45						
Newport (South Wales)	d							12 59		13 27									13 59						
Bristol Temple Meads 10	d				13 00	12 41							13 30				14 00				14 30				
Bristol Parkway 7	d				13 10	12 52											14 10				14 40				
Gloucester 7	d					13 40		13 46	14 11	14 21									14 46			15 08			
Cheltenham Spa	d				13 42	13 50		13 57	14a23	14a34							14 42		14 57		15 12	15a20			
Ashchurch for Tewkesbury	d					13 58																			
Worcester Shrub Hill 7	a					14 26																			
Birmingham New Street 12	a				14 26			14 45					14 57				15 26		15 45		15 57				
	d		14 13	14 24	14 30			14 49			14 54		15 03		15 13	15 24	15 30		15 49	15 54	16 03				16 13
Water Orton	d										15 06														
Coleshill Parkway	d			14 37							15 10					15 37				16 07					
Nuneaton	d			14 53							15 25					15 53				16 23					
Hinckley	d										15 32									16 30					
Narborough	d										15 40									16 38					
South Wigston	d																			16 42					
Leicester	a			15 13							15 50					16 13				16 52					
Wilnecote	d		14 29												15 29										16 31
Tamworth	d		14 33		14 47			15 08							15 33				16 08						16 35
Burton-on-Trent	d		14 46		14 58			15 20							15 44				16 20						16 46
Willington	d																								
Derby 10	a		15 08		15 11			15 36					15 39		16 08		16 11		16 36		16 39				17 08
	d		15 11				15 33	15 41							16 11			16 33	16 41						17 11
Spondon	d																								17 16
Long Eaton	d		15 20				15a43	15 50							16 20			16a43	16 50						17 20
Attenborough	d		15 30																						17 30
Beeston	d	15 20	15 33					15 57						16 21	16 27				16 57					17 20	17 33
Nottingham 8	a	15 26	15 41					16 05						16 26	16 33				17 06					17 28	17 40

For general notes see front of timetable
For details of catering facilities see Directory of Train Operators

A From Maesteg (Table 128)
B To Stansted Airport (Table 49)
C From Weston-super-Mare (Table 51)
D From Westbury (Table 123) to Great Malvern (Table 71)
E From Paignton (Table 51)
G From Penzance (Table 51)
H From Brighton (Table 123) to Worcester Foregate Street (Table 71)

Due to Engineering Operations, services from Saturday 13 September on this Table had not been confirmed at time of going to press. These services will be issued in a special Supplement as soon as exact timings have been confirmed

Saturdays

Bristol and Cardiff → Birmingham → Leicester, Derby and Nottingham

19 July to 6 September

Network Diagram - see first page of Table 50

		XC	XC	GW	EM	XC	XC	XC	GW	AW	XC		EM	XC	XC	XC	EM	XC	XC	GW	AW	XC		EM	XC
		◇ A	1 ◇ 🍴	B	1 ◇ 🍴	◇		R 1 C 🍴	1 ◇ 🍴	D	1 ◇ 🍴		1 ◇ 🍴		◇ E	1 ◇ G 🍴	1 ◇ 🍴	◇	R 1 H 🍴		D			1 ◇ J 🍴	
Cardiff Central 7	d					14 45				15 12								15 45			16 12				
Newport (South Wales)	d					14 59				15 27								15 59			16 26				
Bristol Temple Meads 10	d		15 00	14 41				15 30								16 00			16 30						
Bristol Parkway 7	d		15 10	14 52				15 40								16 10			16 40						
Gloucester 7	d			15 38		15 46			16 11	16 21								16 46		17 08	17 21				
Cheltenham Spa	d		15 42	15 48		15 57		16 12	16a23	16a34						16 42		16 57	17 12	17a20	17a34				
Ashchurch for Tewkesbury	d			15 56		16 04												17 04							
Worcester Shrub Hill 7	a			16 13																					
Birmingham New Street 12	a		16 26			16 45		16 57								17 26		17 45	17 57						
	d	16 24	16 30			16 49	16 54				17 03			17 13	17 24	17 30		17 49	18 03			18 05			18 13
Water Orton	d						17 05							17 23				17 59							18 26
Coleshill Parkway	d	16 37					17 10								17 37										
Nuneaton	d	16 53					17 25								17 53							18 33			
Hinckley	d						17 32															18 40			
Narborough	d						17 40															18 48			
South Wigston	d						17 44															18 53			
Leicester	a	17 13					17 52								18 13							18 59			
Wilnecote	d													17 31											18 34
Tamworth	d		16 47			17 08								17 35				18 08	18 19						18 38
Burton-on-Trent	d		16 58			17 20								17 47				18 20	18 29						18 50
Willington	d													17 53											18 56
Derby 10	a		17 11			17 36					17 39			18 08		18 11		18 36	18 42						19 08
	d				17 33	17 41								18 11			18 33	18 41							19 11
Spondon	d																								19 17
Long Eaton	d				17a43	17 50								18 20			18a43	18 50							19 23
Attenborough	d													18 26											19 29
Beeston	d					17 57							18 20	18 29				18 57						19 20	19 32
Nottingham 8	a					18 06							18 26	18 39				19 05						19 26	19 40

		XC	XC	GW	EM	XC	XC	XC	GW	AW	XC		EM	XC	XC	EM	EM	XC	XC	XC	GW	AW		XC	GW
		◇ A	1 ◇ 🍴	K	1 ◇ 🍴	◇		R 1 G 🍴	1 ◇ 🍴	D	1 ◇ 🍴		1 ◇ L 🍴	◇	1 ◇ 🍴	N	1 ◇ 🍴	◇		R 1 G 🍴		D		1 ◇ 🍴	Q
Cardiff Central 7	d					16 45				17 12								17 45				18 12			
Newport (South Wales)	d					16 59				17 27								17 59				18 27			
Bristol Temple Meads 10	d		17 00	16 41				17 30							18 00					18 30				19 00	18 41
Bristol Parkway 7	d		17 10	16 52				17 40							18 10					18 40				19 10	18 52
Gloucester 7	d			17 40		17 46			18 11	18 23								18 46			19 08	19 21			19 38
Cheltenham Spa	d		17 42	17 51		17 57		18 12	18a23	18a33					18 42			18 57		19 12	19a20	19a34		19 42	19 47
Ashchurch for Tewkesbury	d			17 59		18 04																			19 55
Worcester Shrub Hill 7	a			18 19																					20 14
Birmingham New Street 12	a		18 26			18 45		18 57							19 26			19 45		19 57				20 26	
	d	18 24	18 30			18 49	18 54				19 03			19 24	19 30			19 49	19 54	20 03					
Water Orton	d																		20 05						
Coleshill Parkway	d	18 37					19 07																		
Nuneaton	d	18 53					19 24							19 53					20 24						
Hinckley	d						19 31												20 31						
Narborough	d						19 39												20 39						
South Wigston	d						19 44												20 44						
Leicester	a	19 13					19 51							20 16					20 50						
Wilnecote	d					19 05												20 05							
Tamworth	d		18 47			19 09									19 47			20 08		20 19					
Burton-on-Trent	d		18 58			19 20									19 58			20 20		20 29					
Willington	d																								
Derby 10	a		19 11			19 36					19 39				20 11			20 36		20 42					
	d				19 33	19 41							19 51					20 41							
Spondon	d																	20 46							
Long Eaton	d				19a43	19 50							20a01					20 52							
Attenborough	d					19 55												20 59							
Beeston	d					19 59										20 13	20 22	21 02							
Nottingham 8	a					20 10										20 19	20 34	21 11							

For general notes see front of timetable
For details of catering facilities see Directory of Train Operators

A To Cambridge (Table 49)
B From Southampton Central (Table 123) to Great Malvern (Table 71)
C From Penzance (Table 51)
D From Maesteg (Table 128)
E To Stansted Airport (Table 49)
G From Paignton (Table 51)
H From Plymouth (Table 51)
J To Sheffield (Table 53)
K From Warminster (Table 123) to Great Malvern (Table 71)
L From Scarborough (Table 26)
N To Lincoln (Table 27)
Q From Weymouth (Table 123) to Great Malvern (Table 71)

Due to Engineering Operations, services from Saturday 13 September on this Table had not been confirmed at time of going to press. These services will be issued in a special Supplement as soon as exact timings have been confirmed

Table 57

Bristol and Cardiff → Birmingham → Leicester, Derby and Nottingham

Saturdays

19 July to 6 September

Network Diagram - see first page of Table 50

		XC	EM	EM	XC	XC	XC	GW	GW	XC	EM		XC	XC	GW	XC	AW	XC	EM	XC	GW	XC	GW		
		◇		1 ◇	◇	1 ◇	R 1	1 ◇	◇		1 ◇		◇	1 ◇						1 ◇		◇	1 ◇		
							A							B			C		D	E	G				
				☕		☕	☕	☕			☕			☕									☕		
Cardiff Central [7]	d				18 45								20 00				20 15					20 50			
Newport (South Wales)	d				18 59								20 15				20 30					21 04			
Bristol Temple Meads [10]	d						19 30		19 40					20 30						21 00	20 41				
Bristol Parkway [7]	d						19 40		19 52					20 40						21 10	20 52				
Gloucester [7]	d				19 46			20 11	20 40				20 57		21 05	21 17	21 23				21 37	21 48	22 11		
Cheltenham Spa	d				19 57		20 12	20a23	20a48				21 07	21 12	21a16	21 27	21a34			21 42	21a46	21 59	22a23		
Ashchurch for Tewkesbury	d				20 04																				
Worcester Shrub Hill [7]	a															21 54						22 20			
Birmingham New Street [12]	a				20 41		20 57						21 52	22 03						22 26		23 02			
	d	20 27			20 44	20 50				21 15			21 54					22 09		22 33					
Water Orton	d																								
Coleshill Parkway	d									21 28															
Nuneaton	d	20 54								21 44								22 36							
Hinckley	d									21 50								22 43							
Narborough	d									21 58								22 51							
South Wigston	d									22 03								22 56							
Leicester	a	21 14								22 11								23 02							
Wilnecote	d												22 09												
Tamworth	d				21 03	21 23							22 13							22 49					
Burton-on-Trent	d				21 14	21 33							22 25							22 59					
Willington	d																								
Derby [10]	a				21 36	21 45							22 38							23 16					
	d				21 41								22 42						23 04						
Spondon	d																								
Long Eaton	d				21 50								22 51						23 14						
Attenborough	d																		23 22						
Beeston	d		21 11	21 20	21 57						22 20		22 57						23 26						
Nottingham [8]	a		21 17	21 26	22 04						22 26		23 04						23 33						

Sundays

until 13 July

		EM	EM	XC	EM	XC	EM	EM	EM	XC	XC	GW	EM	XC	XC	XC	XC	XC	AW	EM	XC	XC	GW	EM	EM
		1 ◇	1 ◇	1 ◇	1 ◇		1 ◇	1 ◇		1 ◇	1 ◇		1 ◇		1 ◇			1 ◇		1 ◇		1 ◇			1 ◇
					H				D				H			J						B		D	H
		☕	☕	☕	☕		☕	☕		☕	☕		☕		☕			☕		☕		☕			☕
Cardiff Central [7]	d																		10 30						
Newport (South Wales)	d																		10 45						
Bristol Temple Meads [10]	d										09 15	09 44						10 30				11 30			
Bristol Parkway [7]	d										09 25	09 55						10 40				11 40			
Gloucester [7]	d										10 00	10 37							11 44				12 40		
Cheltenham Spa	d										10 12	10a48						11 12	11a57			12 12	12a50		
Ashchurch for Tewkesbury	d																								
Worcester Shrub Hill [7]	a																								
Birmingham New Street [12]	a										10 51							11 51				12 51			
	d			09 03		09 53				10 03				10 55	11 03	11 26	11 55	12 03			12 18				
Water Orton	d																								
Coleshill Parkway	d					10 07								11 09		11 39	12 09								
Nuneaton	d					10 23								11 25		11 53	12 25								
Hinckley	d					10 31								11 32			12 32								
Narborough	d					10 40								11 41			12 41								
South Wigston	d					10 46								11 46			12 46								
Leicester	a					10 52								11 53		12 19	12 52								
Wilnecote	d																								
Tamworth	d																	12 19			12 36				
Burton-on-Trent	d																	12 29			12 48				
Willington	d																								
Derby [10]	a			10 24						11 22					12 22			12 46			13 00				
	d	07 50	09 51		10 44			10 51	11 20				11 49								13 06			13 16	13 46
Spondon	d																								
Long Eaton	d	07a59	10a01		10a55				11 30				11a59								13 18			13 26	13a56
Attenborough	d								11 38															13 42	
Beeston	d						10 59		11 41											13 12				13 46	
Nottingham [8]	a						11 07	11 12	11 48											13 20	13 30			13 52	

For general notes see front of timetable
For details of catering facilities see Directory of Train Operators

A From Newquay (Table 135)
B From Plymouth (Table 51)
C From Maesteg (Table 128)
D From Matlock (Table 56)
E From Paignton (Table 51)
G From Brighton (Table 123)
H From Sheffield (Table 53)
J To Stansted Airport (Table 49)

Due to Engineering Operations, services from Saturday 13 September on this Table had not been confirmed at time of going to press. These services will be issued in a special Supplement as soon as exact timings have been confirmed

Table 57

Sundays

until 13 July

Bristol and Cardiff → Birmingham → Leicester, Derby and Nottingham

Network Diagram - see first page of Table 50

		XC	XC	XC	XC	XC	XC	GW	AW	XC	EM	XC	XC	GW	EM	XC	XC	EM	XC	XC	XC	AW	XC	EM	EM
			R 1 ☕	◇ A	◇		R 1 B ☕			◇ A	1 ◇ ☕		R 1 C ☕		D	R 1 ☕	◇ E	1 ◇ G ☕	◇		R 1 C ☕		◇ A	1 ◇ ☕	1 D
Cardiff Central 7	d				11 50				12 30										13 50			14 30			
Newport (South Wales)	d				12 04				12 45										14 04			14 45			
Bristol Temple Meads 10	d						12 30	12 44					13 30								14 30				
Bristol Parkway 7	d						12 40	12 55					13 40								14 40				
Gloucester 7	d				12 46			13 38	13 44					14 39					14 46			15 38			
Cheltenham Spa	d				12 57		13 12	13 50	13a57				14 12	14a49					14 57		15 12	15a51			
Ashchurch for Tewkesbury	d							13 59											15 04						
Worcester Shrub Hill 7	a							14 28																	
Birmingham New Street 12	a				13 45		13 51						14 57						15 44		15 51				
	d	12 55	13 03	13 36	13 49	13 55	14 03			14 34		14 55				15 03	15 32		15 49	15 55	16 03		16 34		
Water Orton	d																								
Coleshill Parkway	d	13 10		13 49		14 08				14 47		15 08					15 47			16 09			16 48		
Nuneaton	d	13 26		14 04		14 25				15 02		15 25					16 01			16 25			17 03		
Hinckley	d	13 33				14 32						15 32								16 31					
Narborough	d	13 41				14 40						15 40								16 40					
South Wigston	d	13 47				14 46						15 46								16 45					
Leicester	a	13 53		14 26		14 52				15 23		15 51					16 25			16 52			17 25		
Wilnecote	d																		16 05						
Tamworth	d				14 09		14 19												16 09		16 19				
Burton-on-Trent	d				14 21		14 29												16 20		16 29				
Willington	d																								
Derby 10	a		13 39		14 32		14 42									15 39			16 32		16 46				
	d				14 37										15 14			15 52	16 45						17 22
Spondon	d																								
Long Eaton	d				14 47										15 24			16a02	16 54						17 32
Attenborough	d														15 37				17 01						17 48
Beeston	d										15 05				15 41				17 04					17 10	17 51
Nottingham 8	a				14 58						15 12				15 48				17 11					17 17	17 57

		XC	GW	XC	XC	GW	XC	EM	XC	EM	XC	XC	XC	XC	AW	EM	XC	GW	XC	XC	EM	EM	EM	XC	GW
		◇			R 1 H ☕		R 1 ☕	1 ◇ G ☕	◇ A	1 ◇ ☕	◇		R 1 B ☕	◇ A		D	◇		R 1 B ☕	R 1 ☕	1 ◇ J ☕	1 ◇ G ☕	1 ◇ ☕	◇	
Cardiff Central 7	d	14 50									15 50				16 30		16 50							17 50	
Newport (South Wales)	d	15 04									16 04				16 45		17 04							18 04	
Bristol Temple Meads 10	d		14 43		15 30								16 30					16 44	17 30						
Bristol Parkway 7	d		14 55		15 40								16 40					16 55	17 40						
Gloucester 7	d	15 46	15 51			16 39					16 46				17 38		17 46	17 52						18 46	18 52
Cheltenham Spa	d	15 57	16 02		16 12	16a49					16 57		17 12		17a51		17 57	18 02	18 12					18 57	19a02
Ashchurch for Tewkesbury	d		16 10															18 10							
Worcester Shrub Hill 7	a		16 30															18 30							
Birmingham New Street 12	a	16 45			16 57						17 45		17 51				18 45		18 57					19 45	
	d	16 49		16 55			17 03		17 34		17 49	17 55	18 03	18 34			18 49			19 03				19 49	
Water Orton	d																								
Coleshill Parkway	d			17 08					17 47			18 09		18 47											
Nuneaton	d			17 24					18 03			18 25		19 02											
Hinckley	d			17 31								18 32													
Narborough	d			17 40								18 41													
South Wigston	d			17 45								18 46													
Leicester	a			17 51					18 25			18 53		19 23											
Wilnecote	d	17 05																							
Tamworth	d	17 09									18 09		18 19				19 09							20 09	
Burton-on-Trent	d	17 20									18 20		18 29				19 20							20 21	
Willington	d																								
Derby 10	a	17 35					17 46				18 35		18 42				19 35			19 39				20 36	
	d	17 40						17 47			18 48					19 14	19 41					19 57		20 47	
Spondon	d																								
Long Eaton	d	17 50						17a58			18 57					19 26						20a07		20 57	
Attenborough	d										19 04					19 32								21 04	
Beeston	d									19 00	19 07					19 36					20 00		20 57	21 07	
Nottingham 8	a	18 04								19 06	19 13					19 43	20 00				20 05		21 03	21 12	

For general notes see front of timetable
For details of catering facilities see Directory of Train Operators

- **A** To Stansted Airport (Table 49)
- **B** From Plymouth (Table 51)
- **C** From Penzance (Table 51)
- **D** From Matlock (Table 56)
- **E** To Cambridge (Table 49)
- **G** From Sheffield (Table 53)
- **H** From Newquay (Table 135)
- **J** To Sheffield (Table 53)

Table 57

Sundays until 13 July

Bristol and Cardiff → Birmingham → Leicester, Derby and Nottingham

Network Diagram - see first page of Table 50

		XC	XC	GW	AW		XC	EM	XC	XC	GW	XC	XC	XC	GW	EM	XC	EM	XC	XC	XC	XC	XC		
			1 ◇				◇		◇	1 ◇		1 ◇	◇	1 ◇				1 ◇			1 ◇	1 ◇			
			A				B	C		A				A		D									
			☕							☕		☕		☕				☕				☕			
Cardiff Central 7	d				18 30				18 50				19 50										21 50		
Newport (South Wales)	d				18 45				19 04				20 04										22 09		
Bristol Temple Meads 10	d		18 30	18 44						19 30				20 30	20 43							22 10			
Bristol Parkway 7	d		18 40	18 55						19 40				20 40	20 55							22 20			
Gloucester 7	d			19 38	19 42				19 47		20 37		20 46		21 41					21 46			22 59		
Cheltenham Spa	d		19 12	19 49	19a55				19 57	20 12	20a47		20 57	21 12	21a49					21 57		22 52	23 12		
Ashchurch for Tewkesbury	d			19 57																			23 19		
Worcester Shrub Hill 7	a			20 15																			23 37		
Birmingham New Street 12	a		19 51						20 45	20 57			21 45	21 51						22 45		23 44			
	d	19 55	20 03				20 28		20 49			21 03		22 03			21 55		22 19		23 03				
Water Orton	d																								
Coleshill Parkway	d	20 08					20 42										22 08								
Nuneaton	d	20 25					20 58										22 25								
Hinckley	d	20 32															22 32								
Narborough	d	20 40															22 40								
South Wigston	d	20 45															22 45								
Leicester	a	20 54					21 19										22 52								
Wilnecote	d																		22 36						
Tamworth	d		20 19						21 09			21 19							22 40		23 19				
Burton-on-Trent	d		20 29						21 20			21 29		22 39					22 53		23 29				
Willington	d																								
Derby 10	a		20 42						21 35			21 42		22 55					23 08		23 50				
	d							21 14	21 40							22 39			23 15						
Spondon	d																								
Long Eaton	d							21 26	21 49							22 50			23 24						
Attenborough	d							21 34	21 56							22 57									
Beeston	d							21 38	22 00							23 00		23 06	23 32						
Nottingham 8	a							21 45	22 06							23 06		23 11	23 40						

Sundays 20 July to 7 September

		EM	EM	XC	EM	XC		EM	EM	XC	XC	GW		EM	XC	XC	XC	XC		XC	AW	EM	XC	XC	EM
		1 ◇	1 ◇	1 ◇	1 ◇			1 ◇		1 ◇	1 ◇			1 ◇		1 ◇				1 ◇		1 ◇		1 ◇	
					E				C					E			G							A	C
		☕	☕	☕	☕			☕		☕	☕			☕		☕				☕		☕		☕	
Cardiff Central 7	d																				10 30				
Newport (South Wales)	d																				10 45				
Bristol Temple Meads 10	d										09 15	09 44								10 30				11 30	
Bristol Parkway 7	d										09 25	09 55								10 40				11 40	
Gloucester 7	d										10 00	10 37									11 44				
Cheltenham Spa	d										10 12	10a48								11 12	11a57			12 12	
Ashchurch for Tewkesbury	d																								
Worcester Shrub Hill 7	a																								
Birmingham New Street 12	a										10 51									11 51				12 51	
	d			09 03		09 53				10 03					10 55	11 03	11 26	11 55		12 03			12 18		
Water Orton	d																								
Coleshill Parkway	d					10 07									11 09		11 39	12 09							
Nuneaton	d					10 23									11 25		11 53	12 25							
Hinckley	d					10 31									11 32			12 32							
Narborough	d					10 40									11 41			12 41							
South Wigston	d					10 46									11 46			12 46							
Leicester	a					10 52									11 53		12 19	12 52							
Wilnecote	d																								
Tamworth	d																			12 19			12 36		
Burton-on-Trent	d																			12 29			12 48		
Willington	d																								
Derby 10	a			10 24						11 22						12 22				12 42			13 00		
	d	07 50	09 51		10 44				11 20					11 49									13 06		13 16
Spondon	d																								
Long Eaton	d	07a59	10a01		10a55				11 30					11a59									13 18		13 26
Attenborough	d								11 38																13 42
Beeston	d							10 59	11 41													13 12			13 46
Nottingham 8	a							11 07	11 48													13 20	13 30		13 52

For general notes see front of timetable
For details of catering facilities see Directory of Train Operators

- **A** From Plymouth (Table 51)
- **B** To Cambridge (Table 49)
- **C** From Matlock (Table 56)
- **D** From Crewe (Table 50)
- **E** From Sheffield (Table 53)
- **G** To Stansted Airport (Table 49)

Due to Engineering Operations, services from Sunday 14 September on this Table had not been confirmed at time of going to press. These services will be issued in a special Supplement as soon as exact timings have been confirmed

Table 57

Sundays

Bristol and Cardiff → Birmingham → Leicester, Derby and Nottingham

20 July to 7 September

Network Diagram - see first page of Table 50

		XC		XC	EM	XC	GW	XC		XC	XC	XC	XC	GW	XC	AW	XC	EM	XC	XC		EM	XC	EM	XC
				1 ◇	1 ◇	1 ◇		◇		◇		R 1	1 ◇				◇	1 ◇		R 1			R 1	1 ◇	1 ◇
					A	B		C				D					C			E		G		A	
				🍴	🍴	🍴						🍴	🍴					🍴		🍴			🍴	🍴	🍴
Cardiff Central 7	d									11 50						12 30									
Newport (South Wales)	d									12 04						12 45									
Bristol Temple Meads 10	d					12 00						12 30	13 00	12 44						13 30					14 00
Bristol Parkway 7	d					12 10						12 40	13 10	12 55						13 40					14 10
Gloucester 7	d						12 40			12 46				13 38	13 16	13 44									
Cheltenham Spa	d					12 42	12a50			12 57		13 12	13 42	13 50	13 27	13a57				14 12					14 42
Ashchurch for Tewkesbury	d													13 59											
Worcester Shrub Hill 7	a													14 28											
Birmingham New Street 12	a					13 26				13 45		13 51	14 26		14 19					14 57					15 26
	d	12 55		13 03		13 30		13 36		13 49	13 55	14 03	14 30				14 34		14 55				15 03		15 30
Water Orton	d																								
Coleshill Parkway	d	13 10						13 49			14 08						14 47		15 08						
Nuneaton	d	13 26						14 04			14 25						15 02		15 25						
Hinckley	d	13 33									14 32								15 32						
Narborough	d	13 41									14 40								15 40						
South Wigston	d	13 47									14 46								15 46						
Leicester	a	13 53						14 26			14 52						15 23		15 51						
Wilnecote	d																								
Tamworth	d									14 09			14 47												
Burton-on-Trent	d									14 21			14 58												
Willington	d																								
Derby 10	a			13 39		14 11				14 32		14 39	15 11										15 39		16 11
	d				13 46					14 37												15 14		15 52	
Spondon	d																								
Long Eaton	d				13a56					14 47												15 24		16a02	
Attenborough	d																					15 37			
Beeston	d																	15 05				15 41			
Nottingham 8 ⛴	a									14 58								15 12				15 48			

		GW	XC	XC		XC	XC	XC	AW	XC		EM	EM	XC	GW	XC		XC	XC	EM	XC	GW		XC	EM
			◇	◇			R 1	1 ◇		◇		1 ◇	1	◇				R 1	R 1	1 ◇	R 1			◇	1 ◇
			H				E			C			G					J		A	K			C	
							🍴	🍴				🍴						🍴	🍴	🍴	🍴				🍴
Cardiff Central 7	d			13 50					14 30					14 50											
Newport (South Wales)	d			14 04					14 45					15 04											
Bristol Temple Meads 10	d						14 30	15 00							14 43			15 30			16 00				
Bristol Parkway 7	d						14 40	15 10							14 55			15 40			16 10				
Gloucester 7	d	14 39		14 46					15 38					15 46	15 51							16 39			
Cheltenham Spa	d	14a49		14 57			15 12	15 42	15a51					15 57	16 02			16 12			16 42	16a49			
Ashchurch for Tewkesbury	d			15 04											16 10										
Worcester Shrub Hill 7	a														16 30										
Birmingham New Street 12	a			15 44			15 51	16 26						16 45				16 57			17 26				
	d		15 32	15 49		15 55	16 03	16 30		16 34				16 49		16 55			17 03		17 30			17 34	
Water Orton	d																								
Coleshill Parkway	d		15 47			16 09				16 48						17 08								17 47	
Nuneaton	d		16 01			16 25				17 03						17 24								18 03	
Hinckley	d					16 31										17 31									
Narborough	d					16 40										17 40									
South Wigston	d					16 45										17 45									
Leicester	a		16 25			16 52				17 25						17 51								18 25	
Wilnecote	d			16 05										17 05											
Tamworth	d			16 09				16 47						17 09											
Burton-on-Trent	d			16 20				16 58						17 20											
Willington	d																								
Derby 10	a			16 32			16 39	17 11						17 35					17 39		18 11				
	d			16 45									17 22	17 40						17 44					
Spondon	d																								
Long Eaton	d			16 54									17 32	17 50						17a56					
Attenborough	d			17 01									17 46												
Beeston	d			17 04								17 10	17 49												19 00
Nottingham 8 ⛴	a			17 11								17 17	17 55	18 04											19 06

For general notes see front of timetable
For details of catering facilities see Directory of Train Operators

- **A** From Sheffield (Table 53)
- **B** From Exeter St Davids (Table 51)
- **C** To Stansted Airport (Table 49)
- **D** From Plymouth (Table 51)
- **E** From Penzance (Table 51)
- **G** From Matlock (Table 56)
- **H** To Cambridge (Table 49)
- **J** From Newquay (Table 135)
- **K** From Paignton (Table 51)

Due to Engineering Operations, services from Sunday 14 September on this Table had not been confirmed at time of going to press. These services will be issued in a special Supplement as soon as exact timings have been confirmed

Table 57

Sundays

20 July to 7 September

Bristol and Cardiff → Birmingham → Leicester, Derby and Nottingham

Network Diagram - see first page of Table 50

		XC	XC	XC	XC	AW		XC	EM	XC	GW	XC		XC	EM	EM	XC	EM		XC	GW	XC	XC	XC	GW
		◇		R 1	R 1			◇		◇		R 1		R 1	1 ◇	1 ◇	1 ◇	1 ◇		◇			R 1	1 ◇	
				A				B	C			A			D	E							A		
				☕	☕							☕		☕	☕	☕	☕	☕					☕	☕	
Cardiff Central 7	d	15 50				16 30				16 50										17 50					
Newport (South Wales)	d	16 04				16 45				17 04										18 04					
Bristol Temple Meads 10	d			16 30	17 00						16 44	17 30					18 00						18 30	19 00	18 44
Bristol Parkway 7	d			16 40	17 10						16 55	17 40					18 10						18 40	19 10	18 55
Gloucester 7	d	16 46				17 38				17 46	17 52									18 46	18 52				19 38
Cheltenham Spa	d	16 57		17 12	17 42	17a51				17 57	18 02	18 12					18 42			18 57	19a02		19 12	19 42	19 49
Ashchurch for Tewkesbury	d										18 10														19 57
Worcester Shrub Hill 7	a										18 30														20 15
Birmingham New Street 12	a	17 45		17 51	18 26					18 45		18 57					19 26			19 45			19 51	20 26	
	d	17 49	17 55	18 03	18 30			18 34		18 49				19 03			19 30			19 49		19 55	20 03		
Water Orton	d																								
Coleshill Parkway	d		18 09					18 47														20 08			
Nuneaton	d		18 25					19 02														20 25			
Hinckley	d		18 32																			20 32			
Narborough	d		18 41																			20 40			
South Wigston	d		18 46																			20 45			
Leicester	a		18 53					19 23														20 54			
Wilnecote	d																								
Tamworth	d	18 09			18 47					19 09							19 47			20 09			20 19		
Burton-on-Trent	d	18 20			18 58					19 20							19 58			20 21			20 29		
Willington	d																								
Derby 10	a	18 35		18 39	19 11					19 35				19 39			20 11			20 36			20 42		
	d	18 48							19 14	19 41						20 02				20 47					
Spondon	d																								
Long Eaton	d	18 57							19 26							20a12				20 57					
Attenborough	d	19 04							19 32											21 04					
Beeston	d	19 07							19 36						20 00			20 57		21 07					
Nottingham 8	a	19 13							19 43	20 00					20 05			21 03		21 12					

		AW		XC	EM	XC	XC	GW		XC	XC	EM	XC	XC		GW	EM	XC	XC	XC		XC	XC		
				◇		◇	1 ◇			1 ◇	◇			1 ◇			1 ◇			1 ◇		1 ◇			
				G	C		A					H		A											
							☕			☕				☕			☕					☕			
Cardiff Central 7	d	18 30				18 50					19 50												21 50		
Newport (South Wales)	d	18 45				19 04					20 04												22 09		
Bristol Temple Meads 10	d						19 30							20 30		20 43						22 10			
Bristol Parkway 7	d						19 40							20 40		20 55						22 20			
Gloucester 7	d	19 42				19 47		20 37			20 46					21 41			21 46				22 59		
Cheltenham Spa	d	19a55				19 57	20 12	20a47			20 57			21 12		21a49			21 57			22 52	23 12		
Ashchurch for Tewkesbury	d																						23 19		
Worcester Shrub Hill 7	a																						23 37		
Birmingham New Street 12	a					20 45	20 57				21 45			21 51					22 45			23 44			
	d			20 28		20 49				21 03			21 55	22 03				22 19		23 03					
Water Orton	d																								
Coleshill Parkway	d			20 42									22 08												
Nuneaton	d			20 58									22 25												
Hinckley	d												22 32												
Narborough	d												22 40												
South Wigston	d												22 45												
Leicester	a			21 19									22 52												
Wilnecote	d																	22 36							
Tamworth	d					21 09				21 19								22 40		23 20					
Burton-on-Trent	d					21 20				21 29				22 39				22 53		23 29					
Willington	d																								
Derby 10	a					21 35				21 43				22 50				23 08		23 50					
	d				21 14	21 40						22 39						23 15							
Spondon	d																								
Long Eaton	d				21 26	21 49						22 50						23 24							
Attenborough	d				21 34	21 56						22 57													
Beeston	d				21 38	22 00						23 00					23 06	23 32							
Nottingham 8	a				21 45	22 06						23 06					23 11	23 40							

For general notes see front of timetable
For details of catering facilities see Directory of Train Operators

- A From Plymouth (Table 51)
- B To Stansted Airport (Table 49)
- C From Matlock (Table 56)
- D To Sheffield (Table 53)
- E From Sheffield (Table 53)
- G To Cambridge (Table 49)
- H From Crewe (Table 50)

Due to Engineering Operations, services from Sunday 14 September on this Table had not been confirmed at time of going to press. These services will be issued in a special Supplement as soon as exact timings have been confirmed

Network Diagram for Tables 59, 60, 61, 62, 64, 66

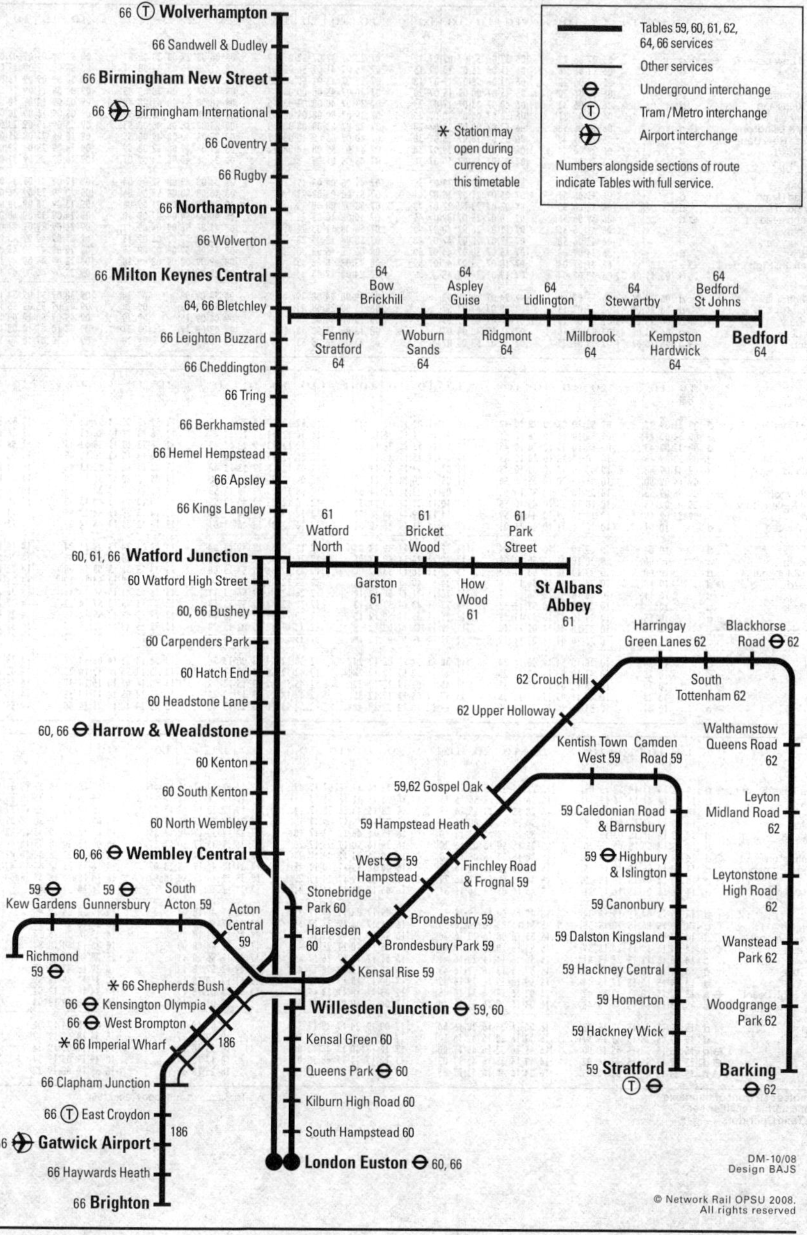

Tables 59, 60, 61, 62, 64, 66 services
Other services
Underground interchange
Tram / Metro interchange
Airport interchange
Numbers alongside sections of route indicate Tables with full service.
* Station may open during currency of this timetable
66 Wolverhampton
66 Sandwell & Dudley
66 Birmingham New Street
66 Birmingham International
66 Coventry
66 Rugby
66 Northampton
66 Wolverton
66 Milton Keynes Central
64, 66 Bletchley
66 Leighton Buzzard
66 Cheddington
66 Tring
66 Berkhamsted
66 Hemel Hempstead
66 Apsley
66 Kings Langley
60, 61, 66 Watford Junction
60 Watford High Street
60, 66 Bushey
60 Carpenders Park
60 Hatch End
60 Headstone Lane
60, 66 Harrow & Wealdstone
60 Kenton
60 South Kenton
60 North Wembley
60, 66 Wembley Central
Stonebridge Park 60
Harlesden 60
Willesden Junction 59, 60
Kensal Green 60
Queens Park 60
Kilburn High Road 60
South Hampstead 60
London Euston 60, 66
64 Bow Brickhill
64 Aspley Guise
64 Lidlington
64 Stewartby
64 Bedford St Johns
Fenny Stratford 64
Woburn Sands 64
Ridgmont 64
Millbrook 64
Kempston Hardwick 64
Bedford 64
61 Watford North
61 Bricket Wood
61 Park Street
Garston 61
How Wood 61
St Albans Abbey 61
59 Kew Gardens
59 Gunnersbury
South Acton 59
Acton Central 59
Richmond 59
* 66 Shepherds Bush
66 Kensington Olympia
66 West Brompton
* 66 Imperial Wharf
186
66 Clapham Junction
66 East Croydon
186
66 Gatwick Airport
66 Haywards Heath
66 Brighton
Kensal Rise 59
Brondesbury Park 59
Brondesbury 59
West Hampstead 59
Finchley Road & Frognal 59
59 Hampstead Heath
59,62 Gospel Oak
62 Upper Holloway
62 Crouch Hill
Harringay Green Lanes 62
South Tottenham 62
Blackhorse Road 62
Walthamstow Queens Road 62
Leyton Midland Road 62
Leytonstone High Road 62
Wanstead Park 62
Woodgrange Park 62
Barking 62
Kentish Town West 59
Camden Road 59
59 Caledonian Road & Barnsbury
59 Highbury & Islington
59 Canonbury
59 Dalston Kingsland
59 Hackney Central
59 Homerton
59 Hackney Wick
59 Stratford
DM-10/08
Design BAJS

Table 59

Mondays to Fridays

until 29 August and from 17 November

Stratford Low Level → Highbury and Islington West Hampstead, Willesden Junction and Richmond.

Network diagram - see first page of Table 59

Miles			LO	LO	LO	LO	LO	LO	LO	LO A	LO	LO	LO	LO	LO	LO	LO A	LO	LO	LO	LO	LO
0	**Stratford Low Level** 7 ⊖	d			06 07	06 22	06 37	06 52	07 07	07 12	07 22	07 37	07 52	07 59	08 06	08 22	08 30	08 37	08 52	09 03	09 07	09 22
1	Hackney Wick	d			06 11	06 26	06 41	06 56	07 10	07 16	07 26	07 41	07 56	08 03	08 11	08 26	08 34	08 41	08 56	09 07	09 11	09 26
1¾	Homerton	d			06 13	06 28	06 43	06 58	07 13	07 18	07 28	07 43	07 58	08 05	08 13	08 28	08 36	08 43	08 58	09 09	09 13	09 28
2½	Hackney Central	d			06 15	06 30	06 45	07 00	07 15	07 20	07 30	07 45	08 00	08 07	08 15	08 30	08 38	08 45	09 00	09 11	09 15	09 30
3¼	Dalston Kingsland	d			06 18	06 33	06 48	07 03	07 17	07 23	07 33	07 48	08 03	08 10	08 18	08 33	08 41	08 48	09 03	09 14	09 18	09 33
4¼	Canonbury	d			06 20	06 35	06 50	07 05	07 20	07 25	07 35	07 50	08 05	08 12	08 20	08 35	08 43	08 50	09 05	09 16	09 20	09 35
4¾	**Highbury & Islington** ⊖	d			06 23	06 38	06 53	07 08	07 23	07 28	07 38	07 53	08 08	08 15	08 23	08 38	08 46	08 53	09 08	09 19	09 23	09 38
5¼	Caledonian Rd & Barnsbury	d			06 25	06 40	06 55	07 10	07 25	07 30	07 40	07 55	08 10	08 17	08 25	08 40	08 49	08 55	09 10	09 22	09 25	09 40
6¼	Camden Road	d			06 29	06 44	06 59	07 14	07 28	07 34	07 44	07 59	08 14	08a22	08 29	08 44	08 52	08 59	09 14	09 25	09 29	09 44
6½	Kentish Town West	d			06 31	06 46	07 01	07 16	07 30	07 36	07 46	08 01	08 16		08 31	08 46	08 54	09 01	09 16	09 27	09 31	09 46
7½	**Gospel Oak**	d			06 34	06 49	07 04	07 19	07 33	07 39	07 49	08 04	08 19		08 34	08 49	08 57	09 04	09 19	09 31	09 34	09 49
8	Hampstead Heath	d			06 35	06 51	07 06	07 21	07 35	07 41	07 51	08 06	08 21		08 36	08 50	08 59	09 06	09 20	09 33	09 36	09 50
9	Finchley Road & Frognal	d			06 38	06 53	07 08	07 23	07 37	07 43	07 53	08 08	08 23		08 38	08 53	09 01	09 08	09 23	09 36	09 38	09 53
9½	West Hampstead ⊖	d			06 39	06 55	07 10	07 25	07 39	07 45	07 55	08 10	08 25		08 40	08 54	09 03	09 10	09 24	09 37	09 40	09 54
10	Brondesbury	d			06 41	06 56	07 11	07 26	07 40	07 46	07 56	08 11	08 26		08 41	08 56	09 04	09 11	09 26	09 39	09 41	09 56
10¼	Brondesbury Park	d			06 42	06 58	07 13	07 28	07 42	07 48	07 58	08 13	08 28		08 43	08 57	09 06	09 13	09 27	09 40	09 43	09 57
11	Kensal Rise	d			06 44	07 00	07 15	07 30	07 44	07 50	08 00	08 15	08 30		08 45	08 59	09 08	09 15	09 29	09 42	09 45	09 59
12	**Willesden Jn. High Level** ⊖	a			06 47	07 03	07 18	07 33	07 47	07 53	08 03	08 18	08 33		08 49	09 02	09 08	09 18	09 33	09 45	09 49	10 02
—		d	06 19	06 32	06 48	07 04	07 19	07 34	07 48		08 04	08 19	08 34		08 49	09 03		09 19	09 33	09 46	09 49	10 03
13½	Acton Central	d	06 24	06 37	06 53	07 09	07 24	07 39	07 53		08 09	08 24	08 39		08 54	09 08		09 24	09 38	09 51	09 54	10 08
14½	South Acton	d	06 28	06 41	06 57	07 13	07 28	07 43	07 57		08 13	08 28	08 43		08 58	09 12		09 28	09 42	09 55	09 58	10 12
15¼	Gunnersbury ⊖	d	06 30	06 43	07 00	07 15	07 30	07 45	07 59		08 15	08 30	08 45		09 00	09 15		09 30	09 45	09 58	10 00	10 15
16¼	Kew Gardens ⊖	d	06 33	06 46	07 02	07 18	07 33	07 48	08 02		08 18	08 33	08 48		09 03	09 17		09 33	09 47	10 01	10 03	10 17
17½	**Richmond** ⊖	a	06 38	06 51	07 08	07 23	07 38	07 53	08 07		08 23	08 38	08 53		09 10	09 23		09 38	09 54	10 07	10 12	10 23

		LO 1	LO	LO	LO	LO	LO	LO	LO	LO	LO	LO	LO	LO	LO	LO	LO	LO	LO	LO	LO
Stratford Low Level 7 ⊖	d	09 31	09 37	09 52	10 07	10 22	10 37	10 52	11 07	11 22	11 37	11 52	12 07	12 22	12 37	12 52	13 07	13 22	13 37	13 52	14 07
Hackney Wick	d	09 34	09 41	09 56	10 11	10 26	10 41	10 56	11 11	11 26	11 41	11 56	12 11	12 26	12 41	12 56	13 11	13 26	13 41	13 56	14 11
Homerton	d	09 37	09 43	09 58	10 13	10 28	10 43	10 58	11 13	11 28	11 43	11 58	12 13	12 28	12 43	12 58	13 13	13 28	13 43	13 58	14 13
Hackney Central	d	09 39	09 45	10 00	10 15	10 30	10 45	11 00	11 15	11 30	11 45	12 00	12 15	12 30	12 45	13 00	13 15	13 30	13 45	14 00	14 15
Dalston Kingsland	d	09 41	09 48	10 03	10 18	10 33	10 48	11 03	11 18	11 33	11 48	12 03	12 18	12 33	12 48	13 03	13 18	13 33	13 48	14 03	14 18
Canonbury	d	09 44	09 50	10 05	10 20	10 35	10 50	11 05	11 20	11 35	11 50	12 05	12 20	12 35	12 50	13 05	13 20	13 35	13 50	14 05	14 20
Highbury & Islington ⊖	d	09 46	09 53	10 08	10 23	10 38	10 53	11 08	11 23	11 38	11 53	12 08	12 23	12 38	12 53	13 08	13 23	13 38	13 53	14 08	14 23
Caledonian Rd & Barnsbury	d	09 48	09 55	10 10	10 25	10 40	10 55	11 10	11 25	11 40	11 55	12 10	12 25	12 40	12 55	13 10	13 25	13 40	13 55	14 10	14 25
Camden Road	d	09a53	09 59	10 14	10 29	10 44	10 59	11 14	11 29	11 44	11 59	12 14	12 29	12 44	12 59	13 14	13 29	13 44	13 59	14 14	14 29
Kentish Town West	d		10 01	10 16	10 31	10 46	11 01	11 16	11 31	11 46	12 01	12 16	12 31	12 46	13 01	13 16	13 31	13 46	14 01	14 16	14 31
Gospel Oak	d		10 04	10 19	10 34	10 49	11 04	11 19	11 34	11 49	12 04	12 19	12 34	12 49	13 04	13 19	13 34	13 49	14 04	14 19	14 34
Hampstead Heath	d		10 06	10 20	10 36	10 50	11 06	11 20	11 36	11 50	12 06	12 20	12 36	12 50	13 06	13 20	13 36	13 50	14 06	14 20	14 36
Finchley Road & Frognal	d		10 08	10 23	10 38	10 53	11 08	11 23	11 38	11 53	12 08	12 23	12 38	12 53	13 08	13 23	13 38	13 53	14 08	14 23	14 38
West Hampstead ⊖	d		10 10	10 24	10 40	10 54	11 10	11 24	11 40	11 54	12 10	12 24	12 40	12 54	13 10	13 24	13 40	13 54	14 10	14 24	14 40
Brondesbury	d		10 11	10 26	10 41	10 56	11 11	11 26	11 41	11 56	12 11	12 26	12 41	12 56	13 11	13 26	13 41	13 56	14 11	14 26	14 41
Brondesbury Park	d		10 13	10 27	10 43	10 57	11 13	11 27	11 43	11 57	12 13	12 27	12 43	12 57	13 13	13 27	13 43	13 57	14 13	14 27	14 43
Kensal Rise	d		10 15	10 29	10 45	10 59	11 15	11 29	11 45	11 59	12 15	12 29	12 45	12 59	13 15	13 29	13 45	13 59	14 15	14 29	14 45
Willesden Jn. High Level ⊖	a		10 19	10 32	10 48	11 02	11 18	11 32	11 48	12 02	12 18	12 33	12 48	13 02	13 18	13 32	13 48	14 02	14 18	14 32	14 49
	d		10 19	10 33	10 49	11 03	11 19	11 33	11 49	12 03	12 19	12 33	12 49	13 03	13 19	13 33	13 49	14 03	14 19	14 33	14 49
Acton Central	d		10 24	10 38	10 54	11 08	11 24	11 38	11 54	12 08	12 24	12 38	12 54	13 08	13 24	13 38	13 54	14 08	14 24	14 38	14 54
South Acton	d		10 28	10 42	10 58	11 12	11 28	11 42	11 58	12 12	12 28	12 42	12 58	13 12	13 28	13 42	13 58	14 12	14 28	14 42	14 58
Gunnersbury ⊖	d		10 30	10 45	11 02	11 15	11 32	11 45	12 02	12 15	12 32	12 45	13 02	13 15	13 32	13 45	14 02	14 15	14 32	14 45	15 00
Kew Gardens ⊖	d		10 33	10 47	11 05	11 17	11 35	11 47	12 05	12 17	12 35	12 47	13 05	13 17	13 35	13 47	14 05	14 17	14 35	14 47	15 03
Richmond ⊖	a		10 41	10 53	11 10	11 23	11 40	11 53	12 10	12 23	12 40	12 54	13 10	13 23	13 40	13 53	14 10	14 23	14 40	14 53	15 10

		LO	LO	LO	LO	LO	LO	LO	LO	LO	LO	LO	LO	LO A	LO	LO	LO	LO	LO	LO	LO	LO
Stratford Low Level 7 ⊖	d	14 22	14 37	14 52	15 07	15 22	15 37	15 52	16 07	16 22	16 37	16 52	17 07	17 13	17 22	17 37	17 44	17 52	18 07	18 22	18 31	18 36
Hackney Wick	d	14 26	14 41	14 56	15 11	15 26	15 41	15 56	16 11	16 26	16 41	16 56	17 11	17 17	17 26	17 41	17 48	17 56	18 11	18 26	18 35	18 41
Homerton	d	14 28	14 43	14 58	15 13	15 28	15 43	15 58	16 13	16 28	16 43	16 58	17 13	17 19	17 28	17 43	17 50	17 58	18 13	18 28	18 37	18 43
Hackney Central	d	14 30	14 45	15 00	15 15	15 30	15 45	16 00	16 15	16 30	16 45	17 00	17 15	17 21	17 30	17 45	17 52	18 00	18 15	18 30	18 39	18 45
Dalston Kingsland	d	14 33	14 48	15 03	15 18	15 33	15 48	16 03	16 18	16 33	16 48	17 03	17 18	17 24	17 33	17 48	17 55	18 03	18 18	18 33	18 42	18 48
Canonbury	d	14 35	14 50	15 05	15 20	15 35	15 50	16 05	16 20	16 35	16 50	17 05	17 20	17 26	17 35	17 50	17 57	18 05	18 20	18 35	18 44	18 50
Highbury & Islington ⊖	d	14 38	14 53	15 08	15 23	15 38	15 53	16 08	16 23	16 38	16 53	17 08	17 23	17 29	17 38	17 53	18 00	18 08	18 23	18 38	18 47	18 53
Caledonian Rd & Barnsbury	d	14 40	14 55	15 10	15 25	15 40	15 55	16 10	16 25	16 40	16 55	17 10	17 25	17 31	17 40	17 55	18 02	18 10	18 25	18 40	18 49	18 55
Camden Road	d	14 44	14 59	15 14	15 29	15 44	15 59	16 14	16 29	16 44	16 59	17 14	17 29	17 35	17 44	17 59	18a07	18 14	18 29	18 43	18a54	18 59
Kentish Town West	d	14 46	15 01	15 16	15 31	15 46	16 01	16 16	16 31	16 46	17 01	17 16	17 31	17 37	17 46	18 01		18 16	18 31	18 45		19 01
Gospel Oak	d	14 49	15 04	15 19	15 34	15 49	16 04	16 19	16 34	16 49	17 04	17 19	17 34	17 40	17 49	18 04		18 19	18 34	18 48		19 04
Hampstead Heath	d	14 50	15 06	15 20	15 35	15 51	16 06	16 20	16 36	16 51	17 06	17 21	17 36	17 42	17 50	18 05		18 22	18 36	18 50		19 06
Finchley Road & Frognal	d	14 53	15 08	15 23	15 38	15 53	16 08	16 22	16 38	16 54	17 08	17 23	17 38	17 45	17 53	18 08		18 25	18 38	18 52		19 08
West Hampstead ⊖	d	14 54	15 10	15 24	15 39	15 54	16 10	16 24	16 40	16 55	17 10	17 25	17 40	17 46	17 54	18 09		18 26	18 40	18 54		19 10
Brondesbury	d	14 56	15 11	15 26	15 41	15 56	16 11	16 25	16 41	16 57	17 11	17 26	17 41	17 48	17 56	18 11		18 28	18 41	18 55		19 11
Brondesbury Park	d	14 57	15 13	15 27	15 42	15 57	16 13	16 27	16 43	16 58	17 13	17 28	17 43	17 49	17 57	18 12		18 29	18 43	18 57		19 13
Kensal Rise	d	14 59	15 15	15 29	15 44	15 59	16 15	16 29	16 45	17 00	17 15	17 30	17 45	17 51	17 59	18 14		18 31	18 45	18 59		19 15
Willesden Jn. High Level ⊖	a	15 02	15 18	15 32	15 47	16 02	16 19	16 32	16 48	17 03	17 18	17 33	17 48	17 53	18 03	18 17		18 34	18 48	19 02		19 18
	d	15 03	15 19	15 33	15 48	16 03	16 19	16 33	16 49	17 04	17 19	17 34	17 49		18 03	18 18		18 35	18 49	19 03		19 19
Acton Central	d	15 08	15 24	15 38	15 53	16 08	16 24	16 38	16 54	17 09	17 24	17 39	17 54		18 08	18 23		18 40	18 54	19 08		19 24
South Acton	d	15 12	15 28	15 42	15 57	16 12	16 28	16 42	16 58	17 13	17 28	17 43	17 58		18 12	18 27		18 44	18 58	19 12		19 28
Gunnersbury ⊖	d	15 15	15 32	15 45	16 00	16 15	16 32	16 45	17 00	17 16	17 30	17 45	18 00		18 15	18 30		18 47	19 00	19 14		19 31
Kew Gardens ⊖	d	15 17	15 35	15 47	16 02	16 17	16 35	16 47	17 03	17 18	17 33	17 48	18 03		18 17	18 32		18 49	19 03	19 17		19 33
Richmond ⊖	a	15 23	15 40	15 53	16 08	16 24	16 40	16 53	17 08	17 24	17 38	17 53	18 08		18 25	18 38		18 55	19 08	19 22		19 39

For general notes see front of timetable
For details of catering facilities see Directory of Train Operators

A To Clapham Junction (Table 186)

Mondays to Fridays

until 29 August and from 17 November

Stratford Low Level → Highbury and Islington West Hampstead, Willesden Junction and Richmond.

Network diagram - see first page of Table 59

Station		LO		LO	LO	LO	LO		LO	LO	LO	LO		LO	LO	LO	LO		LO	LO	LO	LO				
Stratford Low Level 7 ⊖	d	18 52		19 01	19 06	19 23	19 33		19 52	20 12	20 32	20 52		21 12	21 32	21 52	22 12		22 32	22 52	23 12	23 32				
Hackney Wick	d	18 56		19 05	19 10	19 27	19 37		19 56	20 16	20 36	20 56		21 16	21 36	21 56	22 16		22 36	22 56	23 16	23 36				
Homerton	d	18 58		19 07	19 12	19 30	19 39		19 58	20 18	20 38	20 58		21 18	21 38	21 58	22 18		22 38	22 58	23 18	23 38				
Hackney Central	d	19 00		19 09	19 14	19 32	19 41		20 00	20 20	20 40	21 00		21 20	21 40	22 00	22 20		22 40	23 00	23 20	23 40				
Dalston Kingsland	d	19 03		19 12	19 17	19 34	19 44		20 03	20 23	20 43	21 03		21 23	21 43	22 03	22 23		22 43	23 03	23 23	23 43				
Canonbury	d	19 05		19 14	19 19	19 37	19 46		20 05	20 25	20 45	21 05		21 25	21 45	22 05	22 25		22 45	23 05	23 25	23 45				
Highbury & Islington ⊖	d	19 08		19 17	19 22	19 40	19 49		20 08	20 28	20 48	21 08		21 28	21 48	22 08	22 28		22 48	23 08	23 28	23 48				
Caledonian Rd & Barnsbury	d	19 10		19 19	19 24	19 42	19 51		20 10	20 30	20 50	21 10		21 30	21 50	22 10	22 30		22 50	23 10	23 30	23 50				
Camden Road	d	19 14		19a24	19 27	19 45	19 54		20 13	20 33	20 53	21 13		21 33	21 53	22 13	22 33		22 53	23 13	23 33	23a55				
Kentish Town West	d	19 16			19 29	19 47	19 56		20 15	20 35	20 55	21 15		21 35	21 55	22 15	22 35		22 55	23 15	23 35					
Gospel Oak	d	19 19			19 32	19 52	19 59		20 18	20 38	20 58	21 18		21 38	21 58	22 18	22 38		22 58	23 18	23 38					
Hampstead Heath	d	19 21			19 33	19 54	20 00		20 19	20 39	20 59	21 19		21 39	21 59	22 19	22 39		22 59	23 19	23 39					
Finchley Road & Frognal	d	19 23			19 36	19 56	20 03		20 22	20 42	21 02	21 22		21 42	22 02	22 22	22 42		23 02	23 22	23 42					
West Hampstead ⊖	d	19 25			19 37	19 58	20 04		20 23	20 43	21 03	21 23		21 43	22 03	22 23	22 43		23 03	23 23	23 43					
Brondesbury	d	19 26			19 39	19 59	20 06		20 25	20 45	21 05	21 25		21 45	22 05	22 25	22 45		23 05	23 25	23 45					
Brondesbury Park	d	19 28			19 40	20 01	20 07		20 26	20 46	21 06	21 26		21 46	22 06	22 26	22 46		23 06	23 26	23 46					
Kensal Rise	d	19 30			19 42	20 03	20 09		20 28	20 48	21 08	21 28		21 48	22 08	22 28	22 48		23 08	23 28	23 48					
Willesden Jn. High Level ⊖	a	19 33			19 44	20 06	20 13		20 32	20 52	21 12	21 32		21 52	22 12	22 32	22 52		23 12	23 32	23b53					
	d	19 34			19 44	20 07	20 13		20 32	20 52	21 12	21 32		21 52	22 12	22 32	22 52		23 12	23 32						
Acton Central	d	19 39			19 49	20 14	20 18		20 37	20 57	21 17	21 37		21 57	22 17	22 37	22 57		23 17	23 37						
South Acton	d	19 43			19 53	20 16	20 22		20 41	21 01	21 21	21 41		22 01	22 21	22 41	23 01		23 21	23 41						
Gunnersbury ⊖	d	19 45			19 57	20 18	20 25		20 44	21 04	21 24	21 44		22 04	22 24	22 44	23 04		23 24	23 44						
Kew Gardens ⊖	d	19 48			19 58	20 21	20 27		20 46	21 06	21 26	21 46		22 06	22 26	22 46	23 06		23 26	23 46						
Richmond ⊖	a	19 53			20 09	20 26	20 37		20 55	21 13	21 36	21 53		22 14	22 32	22 53	23 12		23 33	23 53						

Mondays to Fridays

1 September to 14 November

Station		LO	LO	LO A	LO	LO A	LO	LO	LO	LO A	LO	LO	LO A	LO	LO A		LO	LO	LO	LO A	LO	LO	LO	LO A	LO	LO
Stratford Low Level 7 ⊖	d			05 52		06 12		06 27		06 32	06 47		06 52		07 12			07 27		07 32		07 47		07 52		
Hackney Wick	d			05 56		06 16		06 31		06 36	06 51		06 56		07 16			07 31		07 36		07 51		07 56		
Homerton	d			05 58		06 18		06 33		06 38	06 53		06 58		07 18			07 33		07 38		07 53		07 58		
Hackney Central	d			06 00		06 20		06 35		06 40	06 55		07 00		07 20			07 35		07 40		07 55		08 00		
Dalston Kingsland	d			06 03		06 23		06 38		06 43	06 58		07 03		07 23			07 38		07 43		07 58		08 03		
Canonbury	d			06 05		06 25		06 40		06 45	07 00		07 05		07 25			07 40		07 45		08 00		08 05		
Highbury & Islington ⊖	d			06 08		06 28		06 43		06 48	07 03		07 08		07 28			07 43		07 48	07 55	08 03		08 08	08 25	
Caledonian Rd & Barnsbury	d			06 10		06 30		06 45		06 50	07 05		07 10		07 30			07 45		07 50		08 05		08 10		
Camden Road	d			06a13		06a33		06 49		06a53	07 09		07a13		07a33			07 49		07a53	08 00	08 09		08a13	08 30	
Kentish Town West	d							06 51			07 11							07 51			08 02	08 11			08 32	
Gospel Oak	d							06a54			07a14							07a54			08a05	08a14			08a35	
Hampstead Heath	d																									
Finchley Road & Frognal	d																									
West Hampstead ⊖	d																									
Brondesbury	d																									
Brondesbury Park	d																									
Kensal Rise	d																									
Willesden Jn. High Level ⊖	a																									
	d	06 19	06 32		06 48		07 03		07 19			07 34		07 48			08 04		08 21				08 34			08 49
Acton Central	d	06 24	06 37		06 53		07 08		07 24			07 39		07 53			08 09		08 26				08 39			08 54
South Acton	d	06 28	06 41		06 57		07 12		07 28			07 43		07 57			08 13		08 28				08 43			08 58
Gunnersbury ⊖	d	06 30	06 43		07 00		07 15		07 30			07 45		07 59			08 15		08 30				08 45			09 00
Kew Gardens ⊖	d	06 33	06 46		07 03		07 18		07 33			07 48		08 02			08 18		08 33				08 48			09 03
Richmond ⊖	a	06 38	06 51		07 08		07 23		07 38			07 53		08 07			08 23		08 38				08 53			09 10

Station		LO A	LO	LO	LO	LO A	LO		LO	LO	LO A	LO A	LO	LO	LO	LO A	LO	LO	LO	LO A	LO A	LO		LO	LO	LO A
Stratford Low Level 7 ⊖	d	08 12		08 27		08 32			08 47		08 52	09 12			09 27	09 32		09 47		09 52	10 12				10 27	10 32
Hackney Wick	d	08 16		08 31		08 36			08 51		08 56	09 16			09 31	09 36		09 51		09 56	10 16				10 31	10 36
Homerton	d	08 18		08 33		08 38			08 53		08 58	09 18			09 33	09 38		09 53		09 58	10 18				10 33	10 38
Hackney Central	d	08 20		08 35		08 40			08 55		09 00	09 20			09 35	09 40		09 55		10 00	10 20				10 35	10 40
Dalston Kingsland	d	08 23		08 38		08 43			08 58		09 03	09 23			09 38	09 43		09 58		10 03	10 23				10 38	10 43
Canonbury	d	08 25		08 40		08 45			09 00		09 05	09 25			09 40	09 45		10 00		10 05	10 25				10 40	10 45
Highbury & Islington ⊖	d	08 28		08 43		08 48	08 55		09 03		09 08	09 28			09 43	09 48		10 03		10 08	10 28				10 43	10 48
Caledonian Rd & Barnsbury	d	08 30		08 45		08 50			09 05		09 10	09 30			09 45	09 50		10 05		10 10	10 30				10 45	10 50
Camden Road	d	08a33		08 49		08a53	09 00		09 09		09a13	09a33			09 49	09a53		10 09		10a13	10a33				10 49	10a53
Kentish Town West	d			08 51			09 02		09 11						09 51			10 11							10 51	
Gospel Oak	d			08a54			09a05		09a14						09a54			10a14							10a54	
Hampstead Heath	d																									
Finchley Road & Frognal	d																									
West Hampstead ⊖	d																									
Brondesbury	d																									
Brondesbury Park	d																									
Kensal Rise	d																									
Willesden Jn. High Level ⊖	a																									
	d		09 03		09 19					09 34			09 49	10 04			10 19		10 34			10 49		11 04		
Acton Central	d		09 08		09 24					09 39			09 54	10 09			10 24		10 39			10 54		11 09		
South Acton	d		09 12		09 28					09 43			09 58	10 13			10 28		10 43			10 58		11 13		
Gunnersbury ⊖	d		09 15		09 30					09 45			10 02	10 15			10 32		10 45			11 02		11 15		
Kew Gardens ⊖	d		09 18		09 33					09 48			10 05	10 18			10 35		10 48			11 05		11 18		
Richmond ⊖	a		09 23		09 38					09 54			10 12	10 23			10 41		10 53			11 10		11 23		

For general notes see front of timetable
For details of catering facilities see Directory of Train Operators

A To Watford Junction Dc (Table 60)
b Willesden Jn Low Level

For passengers requiring stations between Hampstead Heath and Kensal Rise and connections to and from Willesden Junction High Level for services to and from Richmond, please use adjacent stations shown on Table 60, or local bus services. For further details please see local publicity or contact National Rail Enquiries on 08457-48-49-50.

1 September to 14 November

Stratford Low Level → Highbury and Islington West Hampstead, Willesden Junction and Richmond.

Network diagram - see first page of Table 59

Station		LO	LO	LO A	LO	LO A	LO	LO	LO	LO A	LO	LO	LO A	LO		LO A	LO	LO	LO	LO A	LO	LO	LO	LO A	LO A	LO
Stratford Low Level 7 ⊖	d		10 47	10 52		11 12			11 27	11 32		11 47	11 52			12 12			12 27	12 32		12 47		12 52	13 12	
Hackney Wick	d		10 51	10 56		11 16			11 31	11 36		11 51	11 56			12 16			12 31	12 36		12 51		12 56	13 16	
Homerton	d		10 53	10 58		11 18			11 33	11 38		11 53	11 58			12 18			12 33	12 38		12 53		12 58	13 18	
Hackney Central	d		10 55	11 00		11 20			11 35	11 40		11 55	12 00			12 20			12 35	12 40		12 55		13 00	13 20	
Dalston Kingsland	d		10 58	11 03		11 23			11 38	11 43		11 58	12 03			12 23			12 38	12 43		12 58		13 03	13 23	
Canonbury	d		11 00	11 05		11 25			11 40	11 45		12 00	12 05			12 25			12 40	12 45		13 00		13 05	13 25	
Highbury & Islington ⊖	d		11 03	11 08		11 28			11 43	11 48		12 03	12 08			12 28			12 43	12 48		13 03		13 08	13 28	
Caledonian Rd & Barnsbury	d		11 05	11 10		11 30			11 45	11 50		12 05	12 10			12 30			12 45	12 50		13 05		13 10	13 30	
Camden Road	d		11 09	11a13		11a33			11 49	11a53		12 09	12a13			12a33			12 49	12a53		13 09		13a13	13a33	
Kentish Town West	d		11 11						11 51			12 11							12 51			13 11				
Gospel Oak	d		11a14						11a54			12a14							12a54			13a14				
Hampstead Heath	d																									
Finchley Road & Frognal	d																									
West Hampstead ⊖	d																									
Brondesbury	d																									
Brondesbury Park	d																									
Kensal Rise	d																									
Willesden Jn. High Level ⊖	a																									
	d	11 19			11 34		11 49	12 04			12 19			12 34			12 49	13 04			13 19		13 34			13 49
Acton Central	d	11 24			11 39		11 54	12 09			12 24			12 39			12 54	13 09			13 24		13 39			13 54
South Acton	d	11 28			11 43		11 58	12 13			12 28			12 43			12 58	13 13			13 28		13 43			13 58
Gunnersbury ⊖	d	11 32			11 45		12 02	12 15			12 32			12 45			13 02	13 15			13 32		13 45			14 02
Kew Gardens ⊖	d	11 35			11 48		12 05	12 18			12 35			12 48			13 05	13 18			13 35		13 48			14 05
Richmond ⊖	a	11 40			11 53		12 10	12 23			12 40			12 54			13 10	13 23			13 40		13 53			14 10

Station		LO	LO	LO A	LO	LO		LO A	LO	LO A	LO	LO	LO	LO A	LO	LO	LO	LO A	LO A	LO	LO		LO	LO A	LO	LO
Stratford Low Level 7 ⊖	d		13 27	13 32		13 47		13 52		14 12			14 27	14 32		14 47		14 52	15 12				15 27	15 32		15 47
Hackney Wick	d		13 31	13 36		13 51		13 56		14 16			14 31	14 36		14 51		14 56	15 16				15 31	15 36		15 51
Homerton	d		13 33	13 38		13 53		13 58		14 18			14 33	14 38		14 53		14 58	15 18				15 33	15 38		15 53
Hackney Central	d		13 35	13 40		13 55		14 00		14 20			14 35	14 40		14 55		15 00	15 20				15 35	15 40		15 55
Dalston Kingsland	d		13 38	13 43		13 58		14 03		14 23			14 38	14 43		14 58		15 03	15 23				15 38	15 43		15 58
Canonbury	d		13 40	13 45		14 00		14 05		14 25			14 40	14 45		15 00		15 05	15 25				15 40	15 45		16 00
Highbury & Islington ⊖	d		13 43	13 48		14 03		14 08		14 28			14 43	14 48		15 03		15 08	15 28				15 43	15 48		16 03
Caledonian Rd & Barnsbury	d		13 45	13 50		14 05		14 10		14 30			14 45	14 50		15 05		15 10	15 30				15 45	15 50		16 05
Camden Road	d		13 49	13a53		14 09		14a13		14a33			14 49	14a53		15 09		15a13	15a33				15 49	15a53		16 09
Kentish Town West	d		13 51			14 11							14 51			15 11							15 51			16 11
Gospel Oak	d		13a54			14a14							14a54			15a14							15a54			16a14
Hampstead Heath	d																									
Finchley Road & Frognal	d																									
West Hampstead ⊖	d																									
Brondesbury	d																									
Brondesbury Park	d																									
Kensal Rise	d																									
Willesden Jn. High Level ⊖	a																									
	d	14 04			14 19				14 34		14 49	15 04			15 19		15 34			15 49	16 04				16 19	
Acton Central	d	14 09			14 24				14 39		14 54	15 09			15 24		15 39			15 54	16 09				16 24	
South Acton	d	14 13			14 28				14 43		14 58	15 13			15 28		15 43			15 58	16 13				16 28	
Gunnersbury ⊖	d	14 15			14 32				14 45		15 02	15 15			15 32		15 45			16 00	16 15				16 32	
Kew Gardens ⊖	d	14 18			14 35				14 48		15 05	15 18			15 35		15 48			16 03	16 18				16 35	
Richmond ⊖	a	14 23			14 40				14 53		15 10	15 23			15 40		15 53			16 08	16 24				16 40	

Station		LO A	LO	LO A	LO	LO	LO	LO A	LO	LO	LO	LO	LO A		LO	LO	LO A	LO	LO	LO	LO A	LO	LO	LO	LO A	LO
Stratford Low Level 7 ⊖	d	15 52		16 12			16 27	16 32			16 47		16 52				17 12		17 27		17 32		17 47		17 52	
Hackney Wick	d	15 56		16 16			16 31	16 36			16 51		16 56				17 16		17 31		17 36		17 51		17 56	
Homerton	d	15 58		16 18			16 33	16 38			16 53		16 58				17 18		17 33		17 38		17 53		17 58	
Hackney Central	d	16 00		16 20			16 35	16 40			16 55		17 00				17 20		17 35		17 40		17 55		18 00	
Dalston Kingsland	d	16 03		16 23			16 38	16 43			16 58		17 03				17 23		17 38		17 43		17 58		18 03	
Canonbury	d	16 05		16 25			16 40	16 45			17 00		17 05				17 25		17 40		17 45		18 00		18 05	
Highbury & Islington ⊖	d	16 08		16 28			16 43	16 48	16 55		17 03		17 08		17 25		17 28		17 43		17 48	17 55	18 03		18 08	18 25
Caledonian Rd & Barnsbury	d	16 10		16 30			16 45	16 50			17 05		17 10				17 30		17 45		17 50		18 05		18 10	
Camden Road	d	16a13		16a33			16 49	16a53	17 00		17 09		17a13		17 30		17a33		17 49		17a53	18 00	18 09		18a13	18 30
Kentish Town West	d						16 51		17 02		17 11				17 32				17 51			18 02	18 11			18 32
Gospel Oak	d						16a54		17a05		17a14				17a35				17a54			18a05	18a14			18a35
Hampstead Heath	d																									
Finchley Road & Frognal	d																									
West Hampstead ⊖	d																									
Brondesbury	d																									
Brondesbury Park	d																									
Kensal Rise	d																									
Willesden Jn. High Level ⊖	a																									
	d		16 34		16 49	17 04				17 19		17 34				17 49		18 04		18 19				18 34		
Acton Central	d		16 39		16 54	17 09				17 24		17 39				17 54		18 09		18 24				18 39		
South Acton	d		16 43		16 58	17 13				17 28		17 43				17 58		18 13		18 28				18 43		
Gunnersbury ⊖	d		16 45		17 00	17 15				17 30		17 45				18 00		18 15		18 30				18 45		
Kew Gardens ⊖	d		16 48		17 03	17 18				17 33		17 48				18 03		18 18		18 33				18 48		
Richmond ⊖	a		16 53		17 08	17 24				17 38		17 53				18 08		18 25		18 38				18 54		

For general notes see front of timetable
For details of catering facilities see Directory of Train Operators

A To Watford Junction Dc (Table 60)

For passengers requiring stations between Hampstead Heath and Kensal Rise and connections to and from Willesden Junction High Level for services to and from Richmond, please use adjacent stations shown on Table 60, or local bus services. For further details please see local publicity or contact National Rail Enquiries on 08457-48-49-50.

Table 59

Mondays to Fridays

1 September to 14 November

Stratford Low Level → Highbury and Islington West Hampstead, Willesden Junction and Richmond.

Network diagram - see first page of Table 59

	LO	LO	LO	LO		LO	LO	LO	LO	LO	LO	LO	LO	LO	LO	LO	LO	LO	LO		LO	LO	LO	LO	LO
		A					A			A	A				A			A			A			A	
Stratford Low Level 7 ⊖ d		18 12		18 27			18 32	18 47		18 52	19 12			19 27	19 32		19 47	19 52			20 12		20 27	20 32	
Hackney Wick d		18 16		18 31			18 36	18 51		18 56	19 16			19 31	19 36		19 51	19 56			20 16		20 31	20 36	
Homerton d		18 18		18 33			18 38	18 53		18 58	19 18			19 33	19 38		19 53	19 58			20 18		20 33	20 38	
Hackney Central d		18 20		18 35			18 40	18 55		19 00	19 20			19 35	19 40		19 55	20 00			20 20		20 35	20 40	
Dalston Kingsland d		18 23		18 38			18 43	18 58		19 03	19 23			19 38	19 43		19 58	20 03			20 23		20 38	20 43	
Canonbury d		18 25		18 40			18 45	19 00		19 05	19 25			19 40	19 45		20 00	20 05			20 25		20 40	20 45	
Highbury & Islington ⊖ d		18 28		18 43			18 48	19 03		19 08	19 28			19 43	19 48		20 03	20 08			20 28		20 43	20 48	
Caledonian Rd & Barnsbury d		18 30		18 45			18 50	19 05		19 10	19 30			19 45	19 50		20 05	20 10			20 30		20 45	20 50	
Camden Road d		18a33		18 49			18a53	19 09		19a13	19a33			19 49	19a53		20 09	20a13			20a33		20 49	20a53	
Kentish Town West d				18 51				19 11						19 51			20 11						20 51		
Gospel Oak d				18a54				19a14						19a54			20a14						20a54		
Hampstead Heath d																									
Finchley Road & Frognal d																									
West Hampstead ⊖ d																									
Brondesbury d																									
Brondesbury Park d																									
Kensal Rise d																									
Willesden Jn. High Level ⊖ a																									
d	18 49		19 03			19 20			19 34			19 50	20 06			20 20			20 32			20 53			21 13
Acton Central d	18 54		19 08			19 25			19 39			19 55	20 14			20 25			20 38			20 58			21 18
South Acton d	18 58		19 12			19 29			19 43			19 59	20 16			20 29			20 42			21 02			21 22
Gunnersbury ⊖ d	19 00		19 14			19 31			19 45			20 01	20 18			20 33			20 44			21 04			21 24
Kew Gardens ⊖ d	19 03		19 17			19 34			19 48			20 04	20 21			20 36			20 46			21 07			21 27
Richmond ⊖ a	19 08		19 22			19 39			19 53			20 09	20 26			20 39			20 55			21 13			21 36

	LO	LO	LO	LO	LO	LO	LO	LO	LO	LO	LO		LO	LO	LO	LO	LO	LO	LO	LO	LO	LO	LO		
		A		A			A			A			A			A			A		A		A		
Stratford Low Level 7 ⊖ d	20 47	20 52		21 12		21 27	21 32		21 47	21 52			22 12		22 27	22 32		22 47	22 52		23 13	23 27	23 33		
Hackney Wick d	20 51	20 56		21 16		21 31	21 36		21 51	21 56			22 16		22 31	22 36		22 51	22 56		23 17	23 31	23 37		
Homerton d	20 53	20 58		21 18		21 33	21 38		21 53	21 58			22 18		22 33	22 38		22 53	22 58		23 19	23 33	23 39		
Hackney Central d	20 55	21 00		21 20		21 35	21 40		21 55	22 00			22 20		22 35	22 40		22 55	23 00		23 21	23 35	23 41		
Dalston Kingsland d	20 58	21 03		21 23		21 38	21 43		21 58	22 03			22 23		22 38	22 43		22 58	23 03		23 24	23 38	23 44		
Canonbury d	21 00	21 05		21 25		21 40	21 45		22 00	22 05			22 25		22 40	22 45		23 00	23 05		23 26	23 40	23 46		
Highbury & Islington ⊖ d	21 03	21 08		21 28		21 43	21 48		22 03	22 08			22 28		22 43	22 48		23 03	23 08		23 29	23 43	23 49		
Caledonian Rd & Barnsbury d	21 05	21 10		21 30		21 45	21 50		22 05	22 10			22 30		22 45	22 50		23 05	23 10		23 31	23 45	23 51		
Camden Road d	21 09	21a13		21a33		21 49	21a53		22 09	22a13			22a33		22 49	22a53		23 09	23a13		23a34	23 49	23a54		
Kentish Town West d	21 11					21 51			22 11						22 51			23 11				23 51			
Gospel Oak d	21a14					21a54			22a14						22a54			23a14				23a54			
Hampstead Heath d																									
Finchley Road & Frognal d																									
West Hampstead ⊖ d																									
Brondesbury d																									
Brondesbury Park d																									
Kensal Rise d																									
Willesden Jn. High Level ⊖ a																									
d			21 33		21 53			22 13			22 33			22 53			23 13			23 33					
Acton Central d			21 38		21 58			22 18			22 38			22 58			23 18			23 38					
South Acton d			21 41		22 02			22 22			22 42			23 02			23 22			23 42					
Gunnersbury ⊖ d			21 44		22 04			22 24			22 44			23 04			23 24			23 44					
Kew Gardens ⊖ d			21 46		22 07			22 27			22 47			23 07			23 27			23 47					
Richmond ⊖ a			21 53		22 14			22 32			22 53			23 12			23 33			23 53					

Saturdays

until 30 August and from 22 November

	LO	LO	LO	LO	LO	LO	LO	LO	LO	LO	LO	LO		LO	LO	LO	LO	LO	LO	LO	LO	LO	LO	LO	LO
Stratford Low Level 7 ⊖ d			06 07	06 22	06 37	06 52	07 07	07 22	07 37	07 52	08 07	08 22		08 37	08 52	09 07	09 22	09 37	09 52	10 07	10 22	10 37	10 52	11 07	11 22
Hackney Wick d			06 11	06 26	06 41	06 56	07 11	07 26	07 41	07 56	08 11	08 26		08 41	08 56	09 11	09 26	09 41	09 56	10 11	10 26	10 41	10 56	11 11	11 26
Homerton d			06 13	06 28	06 43	06 58	07 13	07 28	07 43	07 58	08 13	08 28		08 43	08 58	09 13	09 28	09 43	09 58	10 13	10 28	10 43	10 58	11 13	11 28
Hackney Central d			06 15	06 30	06 45	07 00	07 15	07 30	07 45	08 00	08 15	08 30		08 45	09 00	09 15	09 30	09 45	10 00	10 15	10 30	10 45	11 00	11 15	11 30
Dalston Kingsland d			06 18	06 33	06 48	07 03	07 18	07 33	07 48	08 03	08 18	08 33		08 48	09 03	09 18	09 33	09 48	10 03	10 18	10 33	10 48	11 03	11 18	11 33
Canonbury d			06 20	06 35	06 50	07 05	07 20	07 35	07 50	08 05	08 20	08 35		08 50	09 05	09 20	09 35	09 50	10 05	10 20	10 35	10 50	11 05	11 20	11 35
Highbury & Islington ⊖ d			06 23	06 38	06 53	07 08	07 23	07 38	07 53	08 08	08 23	08 38		08 53	09 08	09 23	09 38	09 53	10 08	10 23	10 38	10 53	11 08	11 23	11 38
Caledonian Rd & Barnsbury d			06 25	06 40	06 55	07 10	07 25	07 40	07 55	08 10	08 25	08 40		08 55	09 10	09 25	09 40	09 55	10 10	10 25	10 40	10 55	11 10	11 25	11 40
Camden Road d			06 29	06 44	06 59	07 14	07 29	07 44	07 59	08 14	08 29	08 44		08 59	09 14	09 29	09 44	09 59	10 14	10 29	10 44	10 59	11 14	11 29	11 44
Kentish Town West d			06 31	06 46	07 01	07 16	07 31	07 46	08 01	08 16	08 31	08 46		09 01	09 16	09 31	09 46	10 01	10 16	10 31	10 46	11 01	11 16	11 31	11 46
Gospel Oak d			06 34	06 49	07 04	07 19	07 34	07 49	08 04	08 19	08 34	08 49		09 04	09 19	09 34	09 49	10 04	10 19	10 34	10 49	11 04	11 19	11 34	11 49
Hampstead Heath d			06 36	06 50	07 06	07 21	07 36	07 50	08 06	08 21	08 36	08 50		09 06	09 21	09 36	09 50	10 06	10 21	10 36	10 50	11 06	11 21	11 36	11 50
Finchley Road & Frognal d			06 38	06 53	07 08	07 23	07 38	07 53	08 08	08 23	08 38	08 53		09 08	09 23	09 38	09 53	10 08	10 23	10 38	10 53	11 08	11 23	11 38	11 53
West Hampstead ⊖ d			06 40	06 54	07 10	07 25	07 40	07 54	08 10	08 25	08 40	08 54		09 10	09 25	09 40	09 54	10 10	10 25	10 40	10 54	11 10	11 25	11 40	11 54
Brondesbury d			06 41	06 56	07 11	07 26	07 41	07 56	08 11	08 26	08 41	08 56		09 11	09 26	09 41	09 56	10 11	10 26	10 41	10 56	11 11	11 26	11 41	11 56
Brondesbury Park d			06 43	06 57	07 13	07 28	07 43	07 57	08 13	08 28	08 43	08 57		09 13	09 28	09 43	09 57	10 13	10 28	10 43	10 57	11 13	11 28	11 43	11 57
Kensal Rise d			06 45	06 59	07 15	07 30	07 45	07 59	08 15	08 30	08 45	08 59		09 15	09 30	09 45	09 59	10 15	10 30	10 45	10 59	11 15	11 30	11 45	11 59
Willesden Jn. High Level ⊖ a			06 48	07 02	07 18	07 33	07 48	08 03	08 18	08 33	08 49	09 02		09 18	09 33	09 48	10 02	10 18	10 33	10 48	11 02	11 18	11 33	11 48	12 02
d	06 17	06 33	06 49	07 03	07 19	07 34	07 49	08 03	08 19	08 34	08 49	09 03		09 19	09 34	09 49	10 03	10 19	10 34	10 49	11 03	11 19	11 34	11 49	12 03
Acton Central d	06 22	06 38	06 54	07 08	07 24	07 39	07 54	08 08	08 24	08 39	08 54	09 08		09 24	09 39	09 54	10 08	10 24	10 39	10 54	11 08	11 24	11 39	11 54	12 08
South Acton d	06 26	06 42	06 58	07 12	07 28	07 43	07 58	08 12	08 28	08 43	08 58	09 12		09 28	09 43	09 58	10 12	10 28	10 43	10 58	11 12	11 28	11 43	11 58	12 12
Gunnersbury ⊖ d	06 29	06 45	07 02	07 15	07 32	07 45	08 02	08 15	08 32	08 45	09 02	09 15		09 32	09 45	10 02	10 15	10 32	10 45	11 02	11 15	11 32	11 45	12 02	12 15
Kew Gardens ⊖ d	06 31	06 47	07 05	07 17	07 35	07 48	08 05	08 17	08 35	08 48	09 05	09 17		09 35	09 48	10 05	10 17	10 35	10 48	11 05	11 17	11 35	11 48	12 05	12 17
Richmond ⊖ a	06 37	06 53	07 10	07 23	07 40	07 53	08 10	08 24	08 40	08 53	09 10	09 23		09 40	09 53	10 10	10 23	10 40	10 53	11 10	11 23	11 40	11 53	12 10	12 23

For general notes see front of timetable
For details of catering facilities see Directory of Train Operators

A To Watford Junction Dc (Table 60)

For passengers requiring stations between Hampstead Heath and Kensal Rise and connections to and from Willesden Junction High Level for services to and from Richmond, please use adjacent stations shown on Table 60, or local bus services. For further details please see local publicity or contact National Rail Enquiries on 08457-48-49-50.

Table 59

Saturdays

Stratford Low Level → Highbury and Islington West Hampstead, Willesden Junction and Richmond.

until 30 August and from 22 November

Network diagram - see first page of Table 59

	LO	LO		LO	LO	LO	LO	LO	LO	LO	LO	LO	LO	LO	LO		LO	LO	LO	LO	LO	LO	LO	LO	LO
Stratford Low Level 7 ⊖ d	11 37	11 52		12 07	12 22	12 37	12 52	13 07	13 22	13 37	13 52	14 07	14 22	14 37	14 52		15 07	15 22	15 37	15 52	16 07	16 22	16 37	16 52	17 07
Hackney Wick d	11 41	11 56		12 11	12 26	12 41	12 56	13 11	13 26	13 41	13 56	14 11	14 26	14 41	14 56		15 11	15 26	15 41	15 56	16 11	16 26	16 41	16 56	17 11
Homerton d	11 43	11 58		12 13	12 28	12 43	12 58	13 13	13 28	13 43	13 58	14 13	14 28	14 43	14 58		15 13	15 28	15 43	15 58	16 13	16 28	16 43	16 58	17 13
Hackney Central d	11 45	12 00		12 15	12 30	12 45	13 00	13 15	13 30	13 45	14 00	14 15	14 30	14 45	15 00		15 15	15 30	15 45	16 00	16 15	16 30	16 45	17 00	17 15
Dalston Kingsland d	11 48	12 03		12 18	12 33	12 48	13 03	13 18	13 33	13 48	14 03	14 18	14 33	14 48	15 03		15 18	15 33	15 48	16 03	16 18	16 33	16 48	17 03	17 18
Canonbury d	11 50	12 05		12 20	12 35	12 50	13 05	13 20	13 35	13 50	14 05	14 20	14 35	14 50	15 05		15 20	15 35	15 50	16 05	16 20	16 35	16 50	17 05	17 20
Highbury & Islington ⊖ d	11 53	12 08		12 23	12 38	12 53	13 08	13 23	13 38	13 53	14 08	14 23	14 38	14 53	15 08		15 23	15 38	15 53	16 08	16 23	16 38	16 53	17 08	17 23
Caledonian Rd & Barnsbury d	11 55	12 10		12 25	12 40	12 55	13 10	13 25	13 40	13 55	14 10	14 25	14 40	14 55	15 10		15 25	15 40	15 55	16 10	16 25	16 40	16 55	17 10	17 25
Camden Road d	11 59	12 14		12 29	12 44	12 59	13 14	13 29	13 44	13 59	14 14	14 29	14 44	14 59	15 14		15 29	15 44	15 59	16 14	16 29	16 44	16 59	17 14	17 29
Kentish Town West d	12 01	12 16		12 31	12 46	13 01	13 16	13 31	13 46	14 01	14 16	14 31	14 46	15 01	15 16		15 31	15 46	16 01	16 16	16 31	16 46	17 01	17 16	17 31
Gospel Oak d	12 04	12 19		12 34	12 49	13 04	13 19	13 34	13 49	14 04	14 19	14 34	14 49	15 04	15 19		15 34	15 49	16 04	16 19	16 34	16 49	17 04	17 19	17 34
Hampstead Heath d	12 06	12 21		12 36	12 50	13 06	13 21	13 36	13 50	14 06	14 21	14 36	14 50	15 06	15 21		15 36	15 50	16 06	16 21	16 36	16 50	17 06	17 21	17 36
Finchley Road & Frognal d	12 08	12 23		12 38	12 53	13 08	13 23	13 38	13 53	14 08	14 23	14 38	14 53	15 08	15 23		15 38	15 53	16 08	16 23	16 38	16 53	17 08	17 23	17 38
West Hampstead ⊖ d	12 10	12 25		12 40	12 54	13 10	13 25	13 40	13 54	14 10	14 25	14 40	14 54	15 10	15 25		15 40	15 54	16 10	16 25	16 40	16 54	17 10	17 25	17 40
Brondesbury d	12 11	12 26		12 41	12 56	13 11	13 26	13 41	13 56	14 11	14 26	14 41	14 56	15 11	15 26		15 41	15 56	16 11	16 26	16 41	16 56	17 11	17 26	17 41
Brondesbury Park d	12 13	12 28		12 43	12 57	13 13	13 28	13 43	13 57	14 13	14 28	14 43	14 57	15 13	15 28		15 43	15 57	16 13	16 28	16 43	16 57	17 13	17 28	17 43
Kensal Rise d	12 15	12 30		12 45	12 59	13 15	13 30	13 45	13 59	14 15	14 30	14 45	14 59	15 15	15 30		15 45	15 59	16 15	16 30	16 45	16 59	17 15	17 30	17 45
Willesden Jn. High Level ⊖ a	12 18	12 33		12 48	13 02	13 18	13 33	13 48	14 02	14 18	14 33	14 48	15 02	15 18	15 33		15 48	16 02	16 18	16 33	16 48	17 02	17 18	17 33	17 48
d	12 19	12 34		12 49	13 03	13 19	13 34	13 49	14 03	14 19	14 34	14 49	15 03	15 19	15 34		15 49	16 03	16 19	16 34	16 49	17 03	17 19	17 34	17 49
Acton Central d	12 24	12 39		12 54	13 08	13 24	13 39	13 54	14 08	14 24	14 39	14 54	15 08	15 24	15 39		15 54	16 08	16 24	16 39	16 54	17 08	17 24	17 39	17 54
South Acton d	12 28	12 43		12 58	13 12	13 28	13 43	13 58	14 12	14 28	14 43	14 58	15 12	15 28	15 43		15 58	16 12	16 28	16 43	16 58	17 12	17 28	17 43	17 58
Gunnersbury ⊖ d	12 32	12 45		13 02	13 15	13 32	13 45	14 02	14 15	14 32	14 45	15 02	15 15	15 32	15 45		16 02	16 15	16 32	16 45	17 02	17 15	17 32	17 45	18 02
Kew Gardens ⊖ d	12 35	12 48		13 05	13 17	13 35	13 48	14 05	14 17	14 35	14 48	15 05	15 17	15 35	15 48		16 05	16 17	16 35	16 48	17 05	17 17	17 35	17 48	18 05
Richmond ⊖ a	12 40	12 53		13 10	13 23	13 40	13 53	14 10	14 23	14 40	14 53	15 10	15 23	15 40	15 53		16 10	16 23	16 40	16 53	17 10	17 23	17 40	17 53	18 10

	LO	LO	LO	LO	LO		LO	LO	LO	LO	LO	LO	LO	LO	LO	LO	LO	LO	LO	LO	LO	LO	LO		
Stratford Low Level 7 ⊖ d	17 22	17 37	17 52	18 12	18 22		18 35	18 52	19 07	19 22	19 37	19 52	20 12	20 32	20 52	21 12	21 32	21 52	22 12	22 32	22 52	23 12	23 32		
Hackney Wick d	17 26	17 41	17 56	18 16	18 26		18 38	18 56	19 11	19 26	19 41	19 56	20 16	20 36	20 56	21 16	21 36	21 56	22 16	22 36	22 56	23 16	23 36		
Homerton d	17 28	17 43	17 58	18 18	18 28		18 41	18 58	19 13	19 28	19 43	19 58	20 18	20 38	20 58	21 18	21 38	21 58	22 18	22 38	22 58	23 18	23 38		
Hackney Central d	17 30	17 45	18 00	18 20	18 30		18 43	19 00	19 15	19 30	19 45	20 00	20 20	20 40	21 00	21 20	21 40	22 00	22 20	22 40	23 00	23 20	23 40		
Dalston Kingsland d	17 33	17 48	18 03	18 23	18 33		18 45	19 03	19 18	19 33	19 48	20 03	20 23	20 43	21 03	21 23	21 43	22 03	22 23	22 43	23 03	23 23	23 43		
Canonbury d	17 35	17 50	18 05	18 25	18 35		18 48	19 05	19 20	19 35	19 50	20 05	20 25	20 45	21 05	21 25	21 45	22 05	22 25	22 45	23 05	23 25	23 45		
Highbury & Islington ⊖ d	17 38	17 53	18 08	18 28	18 38		18 51	19 08	19 23	19 38	19 53	20 08	20 28	20 48	21 08	21 28	21 48	22 08	22 28	22 48	23 08	23 28	23 48		
Caledonian Rd & Barnsbury d	17 40	17 55	18 10	18 30	18 40		18 53	19 10	19 25	19 40	19 55	20 10	20 30	20 50	21 10	21 30	21 50	22 10	22 30	22 50	23 10	23 30	23 50		
Camden Road d	17 44	17 59	18 14	18 34	18 44		18 56	19 14	19 29	19 44	19 59	20 14	20 34	20 54	21 14	21 34	21 54	22 14	22 34	22 54	23 14	23 34	23a55		
Kentish Town West d	17 46	18 01	18 16	18 36	18 46		18 58	19 16	19 31	19 46	20 01	20 16	20 36	20 56	21 16	21 36	21 56	22 16	22 36	22 56	23 16	23 36			
Gospel Oak d	17 49	18 04	18 19	18 39	18 49		19 01	19 19	19 34	19 49	20 04	20 18	20 39	20 59	21 19	21 39	21 59	22 19	22 39	22 59	23 19	23 39			
Hampstead Heath d	17 50	18 06	18 21	18 41	18 51		19 03	19 21	19 36	19 51	20 06	20 21	20 40	21 00	21 20	21 40	22 00	22 20	22 40	23 00	23 20	23 40			
Finchley Road & Frognal d	17 53	18 08	18 23	18 43	18 53		19 06	19 23	19 38	19 53	20 08	20 23	20 43	21 03	21 23	21 43	22 03	22 23	22 43	23 03	23 23	23 43			
West Hampstead ⊖ d	17 54	18 10	18 25	18 45	18 55		19 07	19 25	19 40	19 55	20 10	20 24	20 44	21 04	21 24	21 44	22 04	22 24	22 44	23 04	23 24	23 44			
Brondesbury d	17 56	18 11	18 26	18 46	18 56		19 09	19 26	19 41	19 56	20 11	20 25	20 46	21 06	21 26	21 46	22 06	22 26	22 46	23 06	23 26	23 46			
Brondesbury Park d	17 57	18 13	18 28	18 48	18 58		19 10	19 28	19 43	19 58	20 13	20 27	20 47	21 07	21 27	21 47	22 07	22 27	22 47	23 07	23 27	23 47			
Kensal Rise d	17 59	18 15	18 30	18 50	19 00		19 12	19 30	19 45	20 00	20 15	20 29	20 49	21 09	21 29	21 49	22 09	22 29	22 49	23 09	23 29	23 49			
Willesden Jn. High Level ⊖ a	18 02	18 18	18 33	18 53	19 05		19 15	19 33	19 48	20 03	20 18	20 32	20 52	21 13	21 33	21 52	22 12	22 33	22 52	23 13	23 33	23b53			
d	18 03	18 19	18 34	18 54			19 16	19 34	19 49	20 05	20 19	20 33	20 53	21 13	21 33	21 53	22 13	22 33	22 53	23 13	23 33				
Acton Central d	18 08	18 24	18 39	18 59			19 21	19 39	19 54	20 13	20 24	20 38	20 58	21 18	21 38	21 58	22 18	22 38	22 58	23 18	23 38				
South Acton d	18 12	18 28	18 43	19 03			19 25	19 43	19 58	20 17	20 28	20 42	21 02	21 22	21 42	22 02	22 22	22 42	23 02	23 22	23 42				
Gunnersbury ⊖ d	18 15	18 32	18 45	19 05			19 28	19 45	20 02	20 22	20 31	20 44	21 04	21 24	21 44	22 04	22 24	22 44	23 04	23 24	23 44				
Kew Gardens ⊖ d	18 17	18 35	18 48	19 08			19 31	19 48	20 05	20 25	20 33	20 47	21 07	21 27	21 47	22 07	22 27	22 47	23 07	23 27	23 47				
Richmond ⊖ a	18 23	18 41	18 53	19 13			19 36	19 53	20 10	20 30	20 40	20 53	21 13	21 36	21 53	22 12	22 32	22 53	23 13	23 33	23 53				

Saturdays

6 September to 15 November

	LO	LO A	LO	LO A	LO	LO	LO	LO A		LO	LO	LO A	LO	LO A	LO	LO	LO		LO A	LO	LO	LO	LO A	LO A	LO
Stratford Low Level 7 ⊖ d		05 52		06 12			06 27	06 32			06 47	06 52		07 12			07 27		07 32		07 47		07 52	08 12	
Hackney Wick d		05 56		06 16			06 31	06 36			06 51	06 56		07 16			07 31		07 36		07 51		07 56	08 16	
Homerton d		05 58		06 18			06 33	06 38			06 53	06 58		07 18			07 33		07 38		07 53		07 58	08 18	
Hackney Central d		06 00		06 20			06 35	06 40			06 55	07 00		07 20			07 35		07 40		07 55		08 00	08 20	
Dalston Kingsland d		06 03		06 23			06 38	06 43			06 58	07 03		07 23			07 38		07 43		07 58		08 03	08 23	
Canonbury d		06 05		06 25			06 40	06 45			07 00	07 05		07 25			07 40		07 45		08 00		08 05	08 25	
Highbury & Islington ⊖ d		06 08		06 28			06 43	06 48			07 03	07 08		07 28			07 43		07 48		08 03		08 08	08 28	
Caledonian Rd & Barnsbury d		06 10		06 30			06 45	06 50			07 05	07 10		07 30			07 45		07 50		08 05		08 10	08 30	
Camden Road d		06a13		06a33			06 49	06a53			07 09	07a13		07a33			07 49		07a53		08 09		08a13	08a33	
Kentish Town West d							06 51				07 11						07 51				08 11				
Gospel Oak d							06a54				07a14						07a54				08a14				
Hampstead Heath d																									
Finchley Road & Frognal d																									
West Hampstead ⊖ d																									
Brondesbury d																									
Brondesbury Park d																									
Kensal Rise d																									
Willesden Jn. High Level ⊖ a																									
d	06 17		06 33		06 49	07 04				07 19			07 34		07 49	08 04				08 19		08 34			08 49
Acton Central d	06 22		06 38		06 54	07 09				07 24			07 39		07 54	08 09				08 24		08 39			08 54
South Acton d	06 26		06 42		06 58	07 13				07 28			07 43		07 58	08 13				08 28		08 43			08 58
Gunnersbury ⊖ d	06 29		06 45		07 02	07 15				07 32			07 45		08 02	08 15				08 32		08 45			09 02
Kew Gardens ⊖ d	06 31		06 47		07 05	07 18				07 35			07 48		08 05	08 18				08 35		08 48			09 05
Richmond ⊖ a	06 37		06 53		07 10	07 23				07 40			07 53		08 10	08 23				08 40		08 53			09 10

For general notes see front of timetable
For details of catering facilities see Directory of Train Operators

A To Watford Junction Dc (Table 60)
b Willesden Jn Low Level

For passengers requiring stations between Hampstead Heath and Kensal Rise and connections to and from Willesden Junction High Level for services to and from Richmond, please use adjacent stations shown on Table 60, or local bus services. For further details please see local publicity or contact National Rail Enquiries on 08457-48-49-50.

Saturdays

Stratford Low Level → Highbury and Islington West Hampstead, Willesden Junction and Richmond.

6 September to 15 November

Network diagram - see first page of Table 59

Station		LO	LO	LO A		LO	LO	LO	LO A	LO A	LO	LO	LO		LO	LO A	LO	LO A	LO	LO A	LO	LO		LO	LO A	LO
Stratford Low Level 7 ⊖	d		08 27	08 32			08 47		08 52	09 12			09 27			09 32	09 47	09 52		10 12				10 27	10 32	
Hackney Wick	d		08 31	08 36			08 51		08 56	09 16			09 31			09 36	09 51	09 56		10 16				10 31	10 36	
Homerton	d		08 33	08 38			08 53		08 58	09 18			09 33			09 38	09 53	09 58		10 18				10 33	10 38	
Hackney Central	d		08 35	08 40			08 55		09 00	09 20			09 35			09 40	09 55	10 00		10 20				10 35	10 40	
Dalston Kingsland	d		08 38	08 43			08 58		09 03	09 23			09 38			09 43	09 58	10 03		10 23				10 38	10 43	
Canonbury	d		08 40	08 45			09 00		09 05	09 25			09 40			09 45	10 00	10 05		10 25				10 40	10 45	
Highbury & Islington ⊖	d		08 43	08 48			09 03		09 08	09 28			09 43			09 48	10 03	10 08		10 28				10 43	10 48	
Caledonian Rd & Barnsbury	d		08 45	08 50			09 05		09 10	09 30			09 45			09 50	10 05	10 10		10 30				10 45	10 50	
Camden Road	d		08 49	08a53			09 09		09a13	09a33			09 49			09a53	10 09	10a13		10a33				10 49	10a53	
Kentish Town West	d		08 51				09 11						09 51				10 11							10 51		
Gospel Oak	d		08a54				09a14						09a54				10a14							10a54		
Hampstead Heath	d																									
Finchley Road & Frognal	d																									
West Hampstead ⊖	d																									
Brondesbury	d																									
Brondesbury Park	d																									
Kensal Rise	d																									
Willesden Jn. High Level ⊖	a																									
	d	09 04				09 19		09 34			09 49	10 04			10 19				10 34		10 49	11 04				11 19
Acton Central	d	09 09				09 24		09 39			09 54	10 09			10 24				10 39		10 54	11 09				11 24
South Acton	d	09 13				09 28		09 43			09 58	10 13			10 28				10 43		10 58	11 13				11 28
Gunnersbury ⊖	d	09 15				09 32		09 45			10 02	10 15			10 32				10 45		11 02	11 15				11 32
Kew Gardens ⊖	d	09 18				09 35		09 48			10 05	10 18			10 35				10 48		11 05	11 18				11 35
Richmond ⊖	a	09 23				09 40		09 53			10 10	10 23			10 40				10 53		11 10	11 23				11 40

Station		LO	LO A	LO	LO	LO A	LO	LO		LO A	LO	LO	LO A	LO	LO A	LO	LO		LO	LO A	LO	LO	LO	LO A	LO A	LO
Stratford Low Level 7 ⊖	d	10 47	10 52			11 12		11 27		11 32		11 47	11 52		12 12				12 27	12 32		12 47		12 52	13 12	
Hackney Wick	d	10 51	10 56			11 16		11 31		11 36		11 51	11 56		12 16				12 31	12 36		12 51		12 56	13 16	
Homerton	d	10 53	10 58			11 18		11 33		11 38		11 53	11 58		12 18				12 33	12 38		12 53		12 58	13 18	
Hackney Central	d	10 55	11 00			11 20		11 35		11 40		11 55	12 00		12 20				12 35	12 40		12 55		13 00	13 20	
Dalston Kingsland	d	10 58	11 03			11 23		11 38		11 43		11 58	12 03		12 23				12 38	12 43		12 58		13 03	13 23	
Canonbury	d	11 00	11 05			11 25		11 40		11 45		12 00	12 05		12 25				12 40	12 45		13 00		13 05	13 25	
Highbury & Islington ⊖	d	11 03	11 08			11 28		11 43		11 48		12 03	12 08		12 28				12 43	12 48		13 03		13 08	13 28	
Caledonian Rd & Barnsbury	d	11 05	11 10			11 30		11 45		11 50		12 05	12 10		12 30				12 45	12 50		13 05		13 10	13 30	
Camden Road	d	11 09	11a13			11a33		11 49		11a53		12 09	12a13		12a33				12 49	12a53		13 09		13a13	13a33	
Kentish Town West	d	11 11						11 51				12 11							12 51			13 11				
Gospel Oak	d	11a14						11a54				12a14							12a54			13a14				
Hampstead Heath	d																									
Finchley Road & Frognal	d																									
West Hampstead ⊖	d																									
Brondesbury	d																									
Brondesbury Park	d																									
Kensal Rise	d																									
Willesden Jn. High Level ⊖	a																									
	d			11 34	11 49		12 04				12 19			12 34		12 49	13 04				13 19		13 34			13 49
Acton Central	d			11 39	11 54		12 09				12 24			12 39		12 54	13 09				13 24		13 39			13 54
South Acton	d			11 43	11 58		12 13				12 28			12 43		12 58	13 13				13 28		13 43			13 58
Gunnersbury ⊖	d			11 45	12 02		12 15				12 32			12 45		13 02	13 15				13 32		13 45			14 02
Kew Gardens ⊖	d			11 48	12 05		12 18				12 35			12 48		13 05	13 18				13 35		13 48			14 05
Richmond ⊖	a			11 53	12 10		12 23				12 40			12 53		13 10	13 23				13 40		13 53			14 10

Station		LO	LO		LO	LO A	LO	LO	LO A	LO A	LO	LO		LO	LO A	LO	LO	LO A	LO	LO A	LO		LO	LO	LO A	LO
Stratford Low Level 7 ⊖	d		13 27			13 32	13 47		13 52	14 12				14 27	14 32		14 47	14 52		15 12				15 27	15 32	
Hackney Wick	d		13 31			13 36	13 51		13 56	14 16				14 31	14 36		14 51	14 56		15 16				15 31	15 36	
Homerton	d		13 33			13 38	13 53		13 58	14 18				14 33	14 38		14 53	14 58		15 18				15 33	15 38	
Hackney Central	d		13 35			13 40	13 55		14 00	14 20				14 35	14 40		14 55	15 00		15 20				15 35	15 40	
Dalston Kingsland	d		13 38			13 43	13 58		14 03	14 23				14 38	14 43		14 58	15 03		15 23				15 38	15 43	
Canonbury	d		13 40			13 45	14 00		14 05	14 25				14 40	14 45		15 00	15 05		15 25				15 40	15 45	
Highbury & Islington ⊖	d		13 43			13 48	14 03		14 08	14 28				14 43	14 48		15 03	15 08		15 28				15 43	15 48	
Caledonian Rd & Barnsbury	d		13 45			13 50	14 05		14 10	14 30				14 45	14 50		15 05	15 10		15 30				15 45	15 50	
Camden Road	d		13 49			13a53	14 09		14a13	14a33				14 49	14a53		15 09	15a13		15a33				15 49	15a53	
Kentish Town West	d		13 51				14 11							14 51			15 11							15 51		
Gospel Oak	d		13a54				14a14							14a54			15a14							15a54		
Hampstead Heath	d																									
Finchley Road & Frognal	d																									
West Hampstead ⊖	d																									
Brondesbury	d																									
Brondesbury Park	d																									
Kensal Rise	d																									
Willesden Jn. High Level ⊖	a																									
	d	14 04			14 19			14 34			14 49	15 04				15 19			15 34		15 49		16 04			16 19
Acton Central	d	14 09			14 24			14 39			14 54	15 09				15 24			15 39		15 54		16 09			16 24
South Acton	d	14 13			14 28			14 43			14 58	15 13				15 28			15 43		15 58		16 13			16 28
Gunnersbury ⊖	d	14 15			14 32			14 45			15 02	15 15				15 32			15 45		16 02		16 15			16 32
Kew Gardens ⊖	d	14 18			14 35			14 48			15 05	15 18				15 35			15 48		16 05		16 18			16 35
Richmond ⊖	a	14 23			14 40			14 53			15 10	15 23				15 40			15 53		16 10		16 23			16 40

For general notes see front of timetable
For details of catering facilities see
Directory of Train Operators

A To Watford Junction Dc (Table 60)

For passengers requiring stations between Hampstead Heath and Kensal Rise and connections to and from Willesden Junction High Level for services to and from Richmond, please use adjacent stations shown on Table 60, or local bus services. For further details please see local publicity or contact National Rail Enquiries on 08457-48-49-50.

Table 59

Saturdays

Stratford Low Level → Highbury and Islington West Hampstead, Willesden Junction and Richmond.

6 September to 15 November

Network diagram - see first page of Table 59

	LO	LO	LO	LO	LO	LO		LO	LO	LO	LO	LO	LO	LO	LO		LO	LO	LO	LO	LO	LO	LO	LO	LO
			A	A						A			A	A					A			A		A	
Stratford Low Level 7 ⊖ d	15 47		15 52	16 12				16 27		16 32	16 47		16 52	17 12				17 27	17 32		17 47	17 52		18 12	
Hackney Wick d	15 51		15 56	16 16				16 31		16 36	16 51		16 56	17 16				17 31	17 36		17 51	17 56		18 16	
Homerton d	15 53		15 58	16 18				16 33		16 38	16 53		16 58	17 18				17 33	17 38		17 53	17 58		18 18	
Hackney Central d	15 55		16 00	16 20				16 35		16 40	16 55		17 00	17 20				17 35	17 40		17 55	18 00		18 20	
Dalston Kingsland d	15 58		16 03	16 23				16 38		16 43	16 58		17 03	17 23				17 38	17 43		17 58	18 03		18 23	
Canonbury d	16 00		16 05	16 25				16 40		16 45	17 00		17 05	17 25				17 40	17 45		18 00	18 05		18 25	
Highbury & Islington ⊖ d	16 03		16 08	16 28				16 43		16 48	17 03		17 08	17 28				17 43	17 48		18 03	18 08		18 28	
Caledonian Rd & Barnsbury d	16 05		16 10	16 30				16 45		16 50	17 05		17 10	17 30				17 45	17 50		18 05	18 10		18 30	
Camden Road d	16 09		16a13	16a33				16 49		16a53	17 09		17a13	17a33				17 49	17a53		18 09	18a13		18a33	
Kentish Town West d	16 11							16 51			17 11							17 51			18 11				
Gospel Oak d	16a14							16a54			17a14							17a54			18a14				
Hampstead Heath d																									
Finchley Road & Frognal d																									
West Hampstead ⊖ d																									
Brondesbury d																									
Brondesbury Park d																									
Kensal Rise d																									
Willesden Jn. High Level ⊖ a																									
d		16 34			16 49	17 04			17 19			17 34			17 49		18 04			18 19			18 34		18 54
Acton Central d		16 39			16 54	17 09			17 24			17 39			17 54		18 09			18 24			18 39		18 59
South Acton d		16 43			16 58	17 13			17 28			17 43			17 58		18 13			18 28			18 43		19 03
Gunnersbury ⊖ d		16 45			17 02	17 15			17 32			17 45			18 02		18 15			18 30			18 45		19 05
Kew Gardens ⊖ d		16 48			17 05	17 18			17 35			17 48			18 05		18 18			18 33			18 48		19 08
Richmond ⊖ a		16 53			17 10	17 23			17 40			17 53			18 10		18 23			18 38			18 53		19 13

	LO		LO	LO	LO	LO	LO	LO	LO	LO		LO	LO	LO	LO	LO	LO	LO	LO		LO	LO	LO	LO	LO
			A			A		A						A			A	A					A		
Stratford Low Level 7 ⊖ d	18 27		18 32		18 47	18 52		19 12				19 27		19 32	19 47		19 52	20 12			20 27		20 32	20 47	
Hackney Wick d	18 31		18 36		18 51	18 56		19 16				19 31		19 36	19 51		19 56	20 16			20 31		20 36	20 51	
Homerton d	18 33		18 38		18 53	18 58		19 18				19 33		19 38	19 53		19 58	20 18			20 33		20 38	20 53	
Hackney Central d	18 35		18 40		18 55	19 00		19 20				19 35		19 40	19 55		20 00	20 20			20 35		20 40	20 55	
Dalston Kingsland d	18 38		18 43		18 58	19 03		19 23				19 38		19 43	19 58		20 03	20 23			20 38		20 43	20 58	
Canonbury d	18 40		18 45		19 00	19 05		19 25				19 40		19 45	20 00		20 05	20 25			20 40		20 45	21 00	
Highbury & Islington ⊖ d	18 43		18 48		19 03	19 08		19 28				19 43		19 48	20 03		20 08	20 28			20 43		20 48	21 03	
Caledonian Rd & Barnsbury d	18 45		18 50		19 05	19 10		19 30				19 45		19 50	20 05		20 10	20 30			20 45		20 50	21 05	
Camden Road d	18 49		18a53		19 09	19a13		19a33				19 49		19a53	20 09		20a13	20a33			20 49		20a53	21 09	
Kentish Town West d	18 51				19 11							19 51			20 11						20 51			21 11	
Gospel Oak d	18a54				19a14							19a54			20a14						20a54			21a14	
Hampstead Heath d																									
Finchley Road & Frognal d																									
West Hampstead ⊖ d																									
Brondesbury d																									
Brondesbury Park d																									
Kensal Rise d																									
Willesden Jn. High Level ⊖ a																									
d				19 19			19 34		19 49	20 05			20 19			20 34			20 54			21 14			21 34
Acton Central d				19 24			19 39		19 54	20 13			20 24			20 39			20 59			21 20			21 39
South Acton d				19 28			19 43		19 58	20 17			20 28			20 43			21 02			21 22			21 42
Gunnersbury ⊖ d				19 30			19 45		20 02	20 22			20 31			20 44			21 04			21 24			21 44
Kew Gardens ⊖ d				19 33			19 48		20 05	20 25			20 33			20 47			21 07			21 27			21 47
Richmond ⊖ a				19 38			19 53		20 10	20 30			20 40			20 53			21 13			21 36			21 53

	LO	LO	LO	LO	LO		LO	LO	LO	LO	LO	LO	LO	LO		LO	LO	LO	LO	LO	LO	LO			
	A	A					A			A	A			A				A		A		A			
Stratford Low Level 7 ⊖ d	20 52	21 12		21 27			21 32	21 47		21 52	22 12		22 27	22 32			22 47	22 52		23 12	23 27	23 32			
Hackney Wick d	20 56	21 16		21 31			21 36	21 51		21 56	22 16		22 31	22 36			22 51	22 56		23 16	23 31	23 36			
Homerton d	20 58	21 18		21 33			21 38	21 53		21 58	22 18		22 33	22 38			22 53	22 58		23 18	23 33	23 38			
Hackney Central d	21 00	21 20		21 35			21 40	21 55		22 00	22 20		22 35	22 40			22 55	23 00		23 20	23 35	23 40			
Dalston Kingsland d	21 03	21 23		21 38			21 43	21 58		22 03	22 23		22 38	22 43			22 58	23 03		23 23	23 38	23 43			
Canonbury d	21 05	21 25		21 40			21 45	22 00		22 05	22 25		22 40	22 45			23 00	23 05		23 25	23 40	23 45			
Highbury & Islington ⊖ d	21 08	21 28		21 43			21 48	22 03		22 08	22 28		22 43	22 48			23 03	23 08		23 28	23 43	23 48			
Caledonian Rd & Barnsbury d	21 10	21 30		21 45			21 50	22 05		22 10	22 30		22 45	22 50			23 05	23 10		23 30	23 45	23 50			
Camden Road d	21a13	21a33		21 49			21a53	22 09		22a13	22a33		22 49	22a53			23 09	23a13		23a33	23 49	23a53			
Kentish Town West d				21 51				22 11					22 51				23 11				23 51				
Gospel Oak d				21a54				22a14					22a54				23a14				23a54				
Hampstead Heath d																									
Finchley Road & Frognal d																									
West Hampstead ⊖ d																									
Brondesbury d																									
Brondesbury Park d																									
Kensal Rise d																									
Willesden Jn. High Level ⊖ a																									
d			21 54		22 14				22 34			22 54				23 14			23 34						
Acton Central d			21 59		22 18				22 38			22 59				23 18			23 38						
South Acton d			22 02		22 22				22 42			23 02				23 22			23 42						
Gunnersbury ⊖ d			22 04		22 24				22 44			23 04				23 24			23 44						
Kew Gardens ⊖ d			22 07		22 27				22 47			23 07				23 27			23 47						
Richmond ⊖ a			22 12		22 32				22 53			23 13				23 33			23 53						

For general notes see front of timetable
For details of catering facilities see
Directory of Train Operators

A To Watford Junction Dc (Table 60)

For passengers requiring stations between Hampstead Heath and Kensal Rise and connections to and from Willesden Junction High Level for services to and from Richmond, please use adjacent stations shown on Table 60, or local bus services. For further details please see local publicity or contact National Rail Enquiries on 08457-48-49-50.

Table 59

Sundays

Stratford Low Level → Highbury and Islington West Hampstead, Willesden Junction and Richmond.

until 31 August and from 23 November

Network diagram - see first page of Table 59

		LO	LO	LO		LO	LO	LO
								A
Stratford Low Level 7 ⊖ ⛴	d		08 49	09 19		21 49	22 19	22 49
Hackney Wick	d		08 53	09 23		21 53	22 23	22 53
Homerton	d		08 55	09 25		21 55	22 25	22 55
Hackney Central	d		08 57	09 27		21 57	22 27	22 57
Dalston Kingsland	d		09 00	09 30		22 00	22 30	23 00
Canonbury	d		09 02	09 32		22 02	22 32	23 02
Highbury & Islington ⊖	d		09 05	09 35		22 05	22 35	23 05
Caledonian Rd & Barnsbury	d		09 07	09 37	and	22 07	22 37	23 07
Camden Road	d		09 11	09 41		22 11	22 41	23 11
Kentish Town West	d		09 13	09 43	every 30	22 13	22 43	23 13
Gospel Oak	d		09 16	09 46	minutes	22 16	22 46	23 16
Hampstead Heath	d		09 18	09 48		22 18	22 48	23 18
Finchley Road & Frognal	d		09 20	09 50	until	22 20	22 50	23 20
West Hampstead ⊖	d		09 22	09 52		22 22	22 52	23 22
Brondesbury	d		09 23	09 53		22 23	22 53	23 23
Brondesbury Park	d		09 25	09 55		22 25	22 55	23 25
Kensal Rise	d		09 27	09 57		22 27	22 57	23a27
Willesden Jn. High Level ⊖	a		09 30	10 00		22 30	23 00	
	d	09 01	09 31	10 01		22 31	23 01	
Acton Central	d	09 06	09 36	10 06		22 36	23 06	
South Acton	d	09 10	09 40	10 10		22 40	23 10	
Gunnersbury ⊖	d	09 12	09 42	10 12		22 42	23 12	
Kew Gardens ⊖	d	09 15	09 45	10 15		22 45	23 15	
Richmond ⊖	a	09 20	09 50	10 20		22 50	23 20	

Sundays

7 September to 16 November

		LO	LO	LO	LO	LO	LO	LO	LO	LO	LO	LO	LO	LO	LO	LO	LO	LO	LO	LO	LO	LO	LO
					B			B			B			B			B			B			B
Stratford Low Level 7 ⊖ ⛴	d				08 39			09 09			09 39			10 09			10 39			11 09			11 39
Hackney Wick	d				08 43			09 13			09 43			10 13			10 43			11 13			11 43
Homerton	d				08 45			09 15			09 45			10 15			10 45			11 15			11 45
Hackney Central	d				08 47			09 17			09 47			10 17			10 47			11 17			11 47
Dalston Kingsland	d				08 50			09 20			09 50			10 20			10 50			11 20			11 50
Canonbury	d				08 52			09 22			09 52			10 22			10 52			11 22			11 52
Highbury & Islington ⊖	d		08 42		08 55	09 12		09 25	09 42		09 55	10 12		10 25	10 42		10 55	11 12		11 25	11 42		11 55
Caledonian Rd & Barnsbury	d				08 57			09 27			09 57			10 27			10 57			11 27			11 57
Camden Road	d		08 46		09a00	09 16		09a30	09 46		10a00	10 16		10a30	10 46		11a00	11 16		11a30	11 46		12a00
Kentish Town West	d		08 48			09 18			09 48			10 18			10 48			11 18			11 48		
Gospel Oak	d		08a51			09a21			09a51			10a21			10a51			11a21			11a51		
Hampstead Heath	d																						
Finchley Road & Frognal	d																						
West Hampstead ⊖	d																						
Brondesbury	d																						
Brondesbury Park	d																						
Kensal Rise	d																						
Willesden Jn. High Level ⊖	a																						
	d	09 01		09 31			10 01			10 31			11 01			11 31			12 01			12 31	
Acton Central	d	09 06		09 36			10 06			10 36			11 06			11 36			12 06			12 36	
South Acton	d	09 10		09 40			10 10			10 40			11 10			11 40			12 10			12 40	
Gunnersbury ⊖	d	09 12		09 42			10 12			10 42			11 12			11 42			12 12			12 42	
Kew Gardens ⊖	d	09 15		09 45			10 15			10 45			11 15			11 45			12 15			12 45	
Richmond ⊖	a	09 20		09 50			10 20			10 50			11 20			11 50			12 20			12 50	

		LO	LO	LO	LO	LO	LO	LO	LO	LO	LO	LO	LO	LO	LO	LO	LO	LO	LO	LO	LO	LO	LO
				B			B			B			B			B			B			B	
Stratford Low Level 7 ⊖ ⛴	d			12 09			12 39			13 09			13 39			14 09			14 39			15 09	
Hackney Wick	d			12 13			12 43			13 13			13 43			14 13			14 43			15 13	
Homerton	d			12 15			12 45			13 15			13 45			14 15			14 45			15 15	
Hackney Central	d			12 17			12 47			13 17			13 47			14 17			14 47			15 17	
Dalston Kingsland	d			12 20			12 50			13 20			13 50			14 20			14 50			15 20	
Canonbury	d			12 22			12 52			13 22			13 52			14 22			14 52			15 22	
Highbury & Islington ⊖	d	12 12		12 25	12 42		12 55	13 12		13 25	13 42		13 55	14 12		14 25	14 42		14 55	15 12		15 25	15 42
Caledonian Rd & Barnsbury	d			12 27			12 57			13 27			13 57			14 27			14 57			15 27	
Camden Road	d	12 16		12a30	12 46		13a00	13 16		13a30	13 46		14a00	14 16		14a30	14 46		15a00	15 16		15a30	15 46
Kentish Town West	d	12 18			12 48			13 18			13 48			14 18			14 48			15 18			15 48
Gospel Oak	d	12a21			12a51			13a21			13a51			14a21			14a51			15a21			15a51
Hampstead Heath	d																						
Finchley Road & Frognal	d																						
West Hampstead ⊖	d																						
Brondesbury	d																						
Brondesbury Park	d																						
Kensal Rise	d																						
Willesden Jn. High Level ⊖	a																						
	d		13 01			13 31			14 01			14 31			15 01			15 31			16 01		
Acton Central	d		13 06			13 36			14 06			14 36			15 06			15 36			16 06		
South Acton	d		13 10			13 40			14 10			14 40			15 10			15 40			16 10		
Gunnersbury ⊖	d		13 12			13 42			14 12			14 42			15 12			15 42			16 12		
Kew Gardens ⊖	d		13 15			13 45			14 15			14 45			15 15			15 45			16 15		
Richmond ⊖	a		13 20			13 50			14 20			14 50			15 20			15 50			16 20		

For general notes see front of timetable
For details of catering facilities see Directory of Train Operators

A To Willesden Jn Low Level
B To Willesden Jn Low Level (Table 60)

For passengers requiring stations between Hampstead Heath and Kensal Rise and connections to and from Willesden Junction High Level for services to and from Richmond, please use adjacent stations shown on Table 60, or local bus services. For further details please see local publicity or contact National Rail Enquiries on 08457-48-49-50.

Table 59

Sundays

Stratford Low Level → Highbury and Islington West Hampstead, Willesden Junction and Richmond.

7 September to 16 November

Network diagram - see first page of Table 59

	LO	LO	LO	LO	LO	LO	LO		LO	LO	LO	LO	LO	LO	LO		LO	LO	LO	LO	LO	LO	LO		LO
		A			A				A			A			A				A			A			
Stratford Low Level 7 ⊖ d		15 39			16 09				16 39			17 09			17 39				18 09			18 39			
Hackney Wick d		15 43			16 13				16 43			17 13			17 43				18 13			18 43			
Homerton d		15 45			16 15				16 45			17 15			17 45				18 15			18 45			
Hackney Central d		15 47			16 17				16 47			17 17			17 47				18 17			18 47			
Dalston Kingsland d		15 50			16 20				16 50			17 20			17 50				18 20			18 50			
Canonbury d		15 52			16 22				16 52			17 22			17 52				18 22			18 52			
Highbury & Islington ⊖ d		15 55	16 12		16 25	16 42			16 55	17 12		17 25	17 42		17 55		18 12		18 25	18 42		18 55	19 12		
Caledonian Rd & Barnsbury d		15 57			16 27				16 57			17 27			17 57				18 27			18 57			
Camden Road d		16a00	16 16		16a30	16 46			17a00	17 16		17a30	17 46		18a00		18 16		18a30	18 46		19a00	19 16		
Kentish Town West d			16 18			16 48				17 18			17 48				18 18			18 48			19 18		
Gospel Oak d			16a21			16a51				17a21			17a51				18a21			18a51			19a21		
Hampstead Heath d																									
Finchley Road & Frognal d																									
West Hampstead ⊖ d																									
Brondesbury d																									
Brondesbury Park d																									
Kensal Rise d																									
Willesden Jn. High Level ⊖ a																									
d	16 31			17 01			17 31				18 01			18 31				19 01			19 31				20 01
Acton Central d	16 36			17 06			17 36				18 06			18 36				19 06			19 36				20 06
South Acton d	16 40			17 10			17 40				18 10			18 40				19 10			19 40				20 10
Gunnersbury ⊖ d	16 42			17 12			17 42				18 12			18 42				19 12			19 42				20 12
Kew Gardens ⊖ d	16 45			17 15			17 45				18 15			18 45				19 15			19 45				20 15
Richmond ⊖ a	16 50			17 20			17 50				18 20			18 50				19 20			19 50				20 20

	LO	LO	LO	LO	LO	LO	LO		LO	LO	LO	LO	LO	LO	LO	LO	LO	LO	LO	LO	LO	LO	LO		
	A			A			A				A			A			A			A		A			
Stratford Low Level 7 ⊖ d	19 09			19 39			20 09				20 39			21 09			21 39			22 11		22 49			
Hackney Wick d	19 13			19 43			20 13				20 43			21 13			21 43			22 15		22 53			
Homerton d	19 15			19 45			20 15				20 45			21 15			21 45			22 17		22 55			
Hackney Central d	19 17			19 47			20 17				20 47			21 17			21 47			22 19		22 57			
Dalston Kingsland d	19 20			19 50			20 20				20 50			21 20			21 50			22 22		23 00			
Canonbury d	19 22			19 52			20 22				20 52			21 22			21 52			22 24		23 02			
Highbury & Islington ⊖ d	19 25	19 42		19 55	20 12		20 25		20 42		20 55	21 12		21 25	21 42		21 55	22 12		22 27	22 42	23 05	23 12		
Caledonian Rd & Barnsbury d	19 27			19 57			20 27				20 57			21 27			21 57			22 29		23 07			
Camden Road d	19a30	19 46		20a00	20 16		20a30		20 46		21a00	21 16		21a30	21 46		22a00	22 16		22a32	22 46	23a10	23 16		
Kentish Town West d		19 48			20 18				20 48			21 18			21 48			22 18			22 48		23 18		
Gospel Oak d		19a51			20a21				20a51			21a21			21a51			22a21			22a51		23a21		
Hampstead Heath d																									
Finchley Road & Frognal d																									
West Hampstead ⊖ d																									
Brondesbury d																									
Brondesbury Park d																									
Kensal Rise d																									
Willesden Jn. High Level ⊖ a																									
d			20 31			21 01				21 31			22 01			22 31			23 01						
Acton Central d			20 36			21 06				21 36			22 06			22 36			23 06						
South Acton d			20 40			21 10				21 40			22 10			22 40			23 10						
Gunnersbury ⊖ d			20 42			21 12				21 42			22 12			22 42			23 12						
Kew Gardens ⊖ d			20 45			21 15				21 45			22 15			22 45			23 15						
Richmond ⊖ a			20 50			21 20				21 50			22 20			22 50			23 20						

For general notes see front of timetable
For details of catering facilities see
Directory of Train Operators

A To Willesden Jn Low Level (Table 60)

For passengers requiring stations between Hampstead Heath and Kensal Rise and connections to and from Willesden Junction High Level for services to and from Richmond, please use adjacent stations shown on Table 60, or local bus services. For further details please see local publicity or contact National Rail Enquiries on 08457-48-49-50.

Richmond → Willesden Junction, West Hampstead Highbury and Islington and Stratford Low Level

Network diagram - see first page of Table 59

Miles	Station		LO	LO	LO	LO		LO	LO	LO	LO		LO	LO A	LO	LO		LO	LO	LO	LO A		LO	LO	LO	LO
0	**Richmond**	⊖ d				06 12		06 27	06 42		06 58		07 13		07 29	07 46			07 59	08 13			08 29	08 42	08 59	09 14
1½	Kew Gardens	⊖ d				06 15		06 30	06 45		07 01		07 16		07 32	07 49			08 02	08 16			08 32	08 45	09 02	09 17
2½	Gunnersbury	⊖ d				06 18		06 33	06 48		07 04		07 19		07 35	07 52			08 05	08 19			08 35	08 48	09 05	09 20
3¼	South Acton	d				06 20		06 35	06 50		07 06		07 21		07 37	07 54			08 07	08 21			08 37	08 50	09 07	09 22
4	Acton Central	d				06b25		06 38	06 53		07 09		07 24		07 40	07 57			08 10	08 24			08 40	08 53	09 10	09 25
5¾	**Willesden Jn. High Level**	⊖ a				06 31		06 43	06 58		07 14		07 29		07 45	08 02			08 15	08 29			08 45	08 58	09 15	09 30
—		d	05c58	06c11		06 32		06 44	06 59		07 15		07 30	07 39	07 46	08 03			08 16	08 30	08 38		08 46	08 59	09 16	09 31
6¾	Kensal Rise	d	06 03	06 17		06 34		06 47	07 02		07 18		07 33	07 42	07 49	08 06			08 19	08 33	08 41		08 49	09 02	09 19	09 34
7½	Brondesbury Park	d	06 05	06 19		06 36		06 49	07 04		07 20		07 35	07 44	07 51	08 08			08 21	08 35	08 43		08 51	09 04	09 21	09 36
7¾	Brondesbury	d	06 07	06 21		06 38		06 51	07 06		07 22		07 37	07 46	07 53	08 10			08 23	08 37	08 45		08 53	09 06	09 23	09 38
8¼	West Hampstead	⊖ d	06 09	06 22		06 40		06 52	07 07		07 23		07 38	07 47	07 54	08 11			08 24	08 38	08 46		08 54	09 07	09 24	09 39
8¾	Finchley Road & Frognal	d	06 10	06 24		06 41		06 54	07 09		07 25		07 40	07 49	07 56	08 13			08 26	08 40	08 48		08 56	09 09	09 26	09 41
9¾	Hampstead Heath	d	06 13	06 27		06 44		06 57	07 12		07 28		07 43	07 52	07 59	08 16			08 29	08 43	08 51		08 59	09 12	09 29	09 44
10¼	**Gospel Oak**	d	06 15	06 29		06 46		06 59	07 14		07 30		07 45	07 54	08 01	08 18			08 31	08 45	08 53		09 01	09 14	09 31	09 46
11	Kentish Town West	d	06 17	06 31		06 48		07 01	07 16		07 32		07 47	07 56	08 03	08 20			08 33	08 47	08 55		09 03	09 16	09 33	09 48
11¼	Camden Road	d	06 20	06 33	06 39	06 51		07 03	07 18	07 27	07 34		07 49	07 58	08 05	08 22		08 30	08 35	08 49	08 57		09 05	09 18	09 35	09 50
12½	Caledonian Rd & Barnsbury	d	06 23	06 36	06 42	06 54		07 06	07 21	07 30	07 37		07 52	08 01	08 08	08 25		08 33	08 38	08 52	09 00		09 08	09 21	09 38	09 53
13	**Highbury & Islington**	⊖ d	06 25	06 39	06 45	06 56		07 09	07 24	07 32	07 40		07 55	08 04	08 11	08 27		08 35	08 41	08 54	09 03		09 11	09 24	09 40	09 56
13½	Canonbury	⊖ d	06 27	06 41	06 47	06 58		07 11	07 26	07 34	07 42		07 57	08 06	08 13	08 29		08 37	08 43	08 56	09 05		09 13	09 26	09 42	09 58
14½	Dalston Kingsland	d	06 30	06 44	06 50	07 01		07 14	07 29	07 37	07 45		08 00	08 09	08 16	08 32		08 40	08 46	08 59	09 08		09 16	09 29	09 45	10 01
15¼	Hackney Central	d	06 32	06 46	06 52	07 03		07 16	07 31	07 39	07 47		08 02	08 11	08 18	08 34		08 42	08 48	09 01	09 10		09 18	09 31	09 47	10 03
16	Homerton	d	06 34	06 48	06 54	07 05		07 18	07 33	07 41	07 49		08 04	08 13	08 20	08 36		08 44	08 50	09 03	09 12		09 20	09 33	09 49	10 05
16¾	Hackney Wick	d	06 37	06 51	06 57	07 08		07 21	07 36	07 44	07 52		08 07	08 16	08 23	08 38		08 47	08 53	09 06	09 15		09 23	09 36	09 52	10 08
17¾	**Stratford Low Level** 7	⊖ ⛴ a	06 44	06 58	07 04	07 15		07 28	07 43	07 51	07 59		08 14	08 23	08 30	08 45		08 54	09 00	09 13	09 22		09 30	09 43	09 59	10 15

Station		LO	LO		LO	LO	LO	LO		LO	LO	LO	LO		LO	LO	LO	LO		LO	LO	LO	LO		LO	LO
Richmond	⊖ d	09 27	09 41		09 57	10 11	10 27	10 41		10 57	11 11	11 27	11 41		11 57	12 11	12 27	12 41		12 57	13 11	13 27	13 41		13 57	14 11
Kew Gardens	⊖ d	09 30	09 44		10 00	10 14	10 30	10 44		11 00	11 14	11 30	11 44		12 00	12 14	12 30	12 44		13 00	13 14	13 30	13 44		14 00	14 14
Gunnersbury	⊖ d	09 33	09 47		10 03	10 17	10 33	10 47		11 03	11 17	11 33	11 47		12 03	12 17	12 33	12 47		13 03	13 17	13 33	13 47		14 03	14 17
South Acton	d	09 35	09 49		10 05	10 19	10 35	10 49		11 05	11 19	11 35	11 49		12 05	12 19	12 35	12 49		13 05	13 19	13 35	13 49		14 05	14 19
Acton Central	d	09 38	09 53		10 08	10 23	10 38	10 53		11 08	11 23	11 38	11 53		12 08	12 23	12 38	12 53		13 08	13 23	13 38	13 53		14 08	14 23
Willesden Jn. High Level	⊖ a	09 43	10 00		10 14	10 29	10 43	11 00		11 13	11 29	11 43	11 59		12 13	12 30	12 43	12 58		13 13	13 29	13 43	13 59		14 13	14 29
	d	09 44	10 00		10 14	10 30	10 44	11 00		11 14	11 30	11 44	12 00		12 14	12 30	12 44	13 00		13 14	13 30	13 44	14 00		14 14	14 30
Kensal Rise	d	09 47	10 03		10 17	10 33	10 47	11 03		11 17	11 33	11 47	12 03		12 17	12 33	12 47	13 03		13 17	13 33	13 47	14 03		14 17	14 33
Brondesbury Park	d	09 49	10 05		10 19	10 35	10 49	11 05		11 19	11 35	11 49	12 05		12 19	12 35	12 49	13 05		13 19	13 35	13 49	14 05		14 19	14 35
Brondesbury	d	09 51	10 07		10 21	10 37	10 51	11 07		11 21	11 37	11 51	12 07		12 21	12 37	12 51	13 07		13 21	13 37	13 51	14 07		14 21	14 37
West Hampstead	⊖ d	09 52	10 08		10 22	10 38	10 52	11 08		11 22	11 38	11 52	12 08		12 22	12 38	12 52	13 08		13 22	13 38	13 52	14 08		14 22	14 38
Finchley Road & Frognal	d	09 54	10 10		10 24	10 40	10 54	11 10		11 24	11 40	11 54	12 10		12 24	12 40	12 54	13 10		13 24	13 40	13 54	14 10		14 24	14 40
Hampstead Heath	d	09 57	10 13		10 27	10 43	10 57	11 13		11 27	11 43	11 57	12 13		12 27	12 43	12 57	13 13		13 27	13 43	13 57	14 13		14 27	14 43
Gospel Oak	d	09 59	10 15		10 29	10 45	10 59	11 15		11 29	11 45	11 59	12 15		12 29	12 45	12 59	13 15		13 29	13 45	13 59	14 15		14 29	14 45
Kentish Town West	d	10 01	10 17		10 31	10 47	11 01	11 17		11 31	11 47	12 01	12 17		12 31	12 47	13 01	13 17		13 31	13 47	14 01	14 17		14 31	14 47
Camden Road	d	10 03	10 19		10 33	10 49	11 03	11 19		11 33	11 49	12 03	12 19		12 33	12 49	13 03	13 19		13 33	13 49	14 03	14 19		14 33	14 49
Caledonian Rd & Barnsbury	d	10 06	10 22		10 36	10 52	11 06	11 22		11 36	11 52	12 06	12 22		12 36	12 52	13 06	13 22		13 36	13 52	14 06	14 22		14 36	14 52
Highbury & Islington	⊖ d	10 09	10 25		10 39	10 55	11 09	11 25		11 39	11 55	12 09	12 25		12 39	12 55	13 09	13 25		13 39	13 55	14 09	14 25		14 39	14 55
Canonbury	⊖ d	10 11	10 27		10 41	10 57	11 11	11 27		11 41	11 57	12 11	12 27		12 41	12 57	13 11	13 27		13 41	13 57	14 11	14 27		14 41	14 57
Dalston Kingsland	d	10 14	10 30		10 44	11 00	11 14	11 30		11 44	12 00	12 14	12 30		12 44	13 00	13 14	13 30		13 44	14 00	14 14	14 30		14 44	15 00
Hackney Central	d	10 16	10 32		10 46	11 02	11 16	11 32		11 46	12 02	12 16	12 32		12 46	13 02	13 16	13 32		13 46	14 02	14 16	14 32		14 46	15 02
Homerton	d	10 18	10 34		10 48	11 04	11 18	11 34		11 48	12 04	12 18	12 34		12 48	13 04	13 18	13 34		13 48	14 04	14 18	14 34		14 48	15 04
Hackney Wick	d	10 21	10 37		10 51	11 07	11 21	11 37		11 51	12 07	12 21	12 37		12 51	13 07	13 21	13 37		13 51	14 07	14 21	14 37		14 51	15 07
Stratford Low Level 7	⊖ ⛴ a	10 28	10 45		10 59	11 14	11 28	11 45		11 58	12 14	12 29	12 44		12 58	13 15	13 28	13 44		13 58	14 14	14 28	14 44		14 58	15 14

Station		LO	LO	LO	LO		LO	LO	LO	LO		LO	LO	LO	LO		LO	LO	LO A	LO		LO	LO	LO	LO	LO A
Richmond	⊖ d	14 27	14 41	14 57	15 11		15 27	15 41	15 57			16 15	16 27	16 35	16 44		16 59	17 12		17 29		17 44		18 00	18 15	
Kew Gardens	⊖ d	14 30	14 44	15 00	15 14		15 30	15 44	16 00			16 18	16 30	16 38	16 47		17 02	17 15		17 32		17 47		18 03	18 18	
Gunnersbury	⊖ d	14 33	14 47	15 03	15 17		15 33	15 47	16 03			16 21	16 33	16 41	16 50		17 05	17 18		17 35		17 50		18 06	18 21	
South Acton	d	14 35	14 49	15 05	15 19		15 35	15 49	16 05			16 23	16 35	16 43	16 52		17 07	17 20		17 37		17 52		18 08	18 23	
Acton Central	d	14 38	14 53	15 08	15 23		15 38	15 53	16 08			16 26	16 38	16 46	16 55		17 10	17 23		17 40		17 55		18 11	18 26	
Willesden Jn. High Level	⊖ a	14 44	14 59	15 13	15 30		15 43	15 59	16 13			16 31	16 43	16 51	17 00		17 15	17 30		17 45		18 00		18 16	18 32	
	d	14 44	15 00	15 14	15 30		15 44	16 00	16 14			16 32	16 44	16 52	17 01		17 16	17 31	17 39	17 46		18 01		18 17	18 32	18 39
Kensal Rise	d	14 47	15 03	15 17	15 33		15 47	16 03	16 17			16 35	16 47	16 55	17 04		17 19	17 34	17 42	17 49		18 04		18 20	18 35	18 42
Brondesbury Park	d	14 49	15 05	15 19	15 35		15 49	16 05	16 19			16 37	16 49	16 57	17 06		17 21	17 36	17 44	17 51		18 06		18 22	18 37	18 44
Brondesbury	d	14 51	15 07	15 21	15 37		15 51	16 07	16 21			16 39	16 51	16 59	17 08		17 23	17 38	17 46	17 53		18 08		18 24	18 39	18 46
West Hampstead	⊖ d	14 52	15 08	15 22	15 38		15 52	16 08	16 22			16 40	16 52	17 00	17 09		17 24	17 39	17 47	17 54		18 09		18 25	18 40	18 47
Finchley Road & Frognal	d	14 54	15 10	15 24	15 40		15 54	16 10	16 24			16 42	16 54	17 02	17 11		17 26	17 41	17 49	17 56		18 11		18 27	18 42	18 49
Hampstead Heath	d	14 57	15 13	15 27	15 43		15 57	16 13	16 27			16 45	16 57	17 05	17 14		17 29	17 44	17 52	17 59		18 14		18 30	18 45	18 52
Gospel Oak	d	14 59	15 15	15 29	15 45		15 59	16 15	16 29			16 47	16 59	17 07	17 16		17 31	17 46	17 54	18 01		18 16		18 32	18 47	18 54
Kentish Town West	d	15 01	15 17	15 31	15 47		16 01	16 17	16 31			16 49	17 01	17 09	17 18		17 33	17 48	17 56	18 03		18 18		18 34	18 49	18 56
Camden Road	d	15 03	15 19	15 33	15 49		16 03	16 19	16 33	16 40		16 51	17 03	17 12	17 21		17 35	17 51	17 58	18 05		18 20	18 27	18 37	18 51	18 58
Caledonian Rd & Barnsbury	d	15 06	15 22	15 36	15 52		16 06	16 22	16 36	16 43		16 54	17 06	17 15	17 24		17 39	17 54	18 01	18 08		18 23	18 30	18 40	18 54	19 01
Highbury & Islington	⊖ d	15 09	15 25	15 39	15 55		16 09	16 24	16 39	16 45		16 57	17 09	17 18	17 26		17 41	17 56	18 04	18 11		18 26	18 33	18 43	18 57	19 05
Canonbury	⊖ d	15 11	15 27	15 41	15 57		16 11	16 26	16 41	16 47		16 59	17 11	17 20	17 28		17 43	17 58	18 06	18 13		18 28	18 35	18 45	18 59	19 07
Dalston Kingsland	d	15 14	15 30	15 44	16 00		16 14	16 29	16 44	16 50		17 02	17 14	17 23	17 31		17 46	18 01	18 09	18 16		18 31	18 38	18 48	19 02	19 10
Hackney Central	d	15 16	15 32	15 46	16 02		16 16	16 31	16 46	16 52		17 04	17 16	17 25	17 33		17 48	18 03	18 11	18 18		18 33	18 41	18 50	19 04	19 12
Homerton	d	15 18	15 34	15 48	16 04		16 18	16 33	16 48	16 54		17 06	17 18	17 27	17 35		17 50	18 05	18 13	18 20		18 35	18 43	18 52	19 06	19 14
Hackney Wick	d	15 21	15 37	15 51	16 07		16 21	16 35	16 51	16 57		17 08	17 21	17 30	17 38		17 53	18 08	18 16	18 23		18 38	18 46	18 55	19 09	19 17
Stratford Low Level 7	⊖ ⛴ a	15 30	15 44	15 59	16 14		16 28	16 42	16 58	17 04		17 15	17 28	17 37	17 45		18 00	18 15	18 23	18 30		18 45	18 53	19 02	19 16	19 23

For general notes see front of timetable
For details of catering facilities see Directory of Train Operators

A From Clapham Junction (Table 186)
b Arr. 0622
c Willesden Jn Low Level

Mondays to Fridays

until 29 August and from 17 November

Richmond → Willesden Junction, West Hampstead Highbury and Islington and Stratford Low Level

Network diagram - see first page of Table 59

		LO	LO	LO	LO	LO	LO	LO	LO	LO	LO	LO	LO	LO	LO	LO	LO	LO
Richmond ⊖	d	18 31	18 44	18 55	19 15	19 26	19 41	19 59	20 15	20 35	20 55	21 15	21 35	21 55	22 15	22 35	22 55	23 15
Kew Gardens ⊖	d	18 34	18 47	18a58	19 18	19 29	19 44	20 02	20 18	20 38	20 58	21 18	21 38	21 58	22 18	22 38	22 58	23 18
Gunnersbury ⊖	d	18 37	18 50	19 01	19 21	19 32	19 47	20 05	20 21	20 41	21 01	21 21	21 41	22 01	22 21	22 41	23 01	23 21
South Acton	d	18 39	18 52	19 03	19 23	19 34	19 49	20 07	20 23	20 43	21 03	21 23	21 43	22 03	22 23	22 43	23 03	23 23
Acton Central	d	18 43	18 55	19 06	19 26	19 37	19 52	20 10	20 26	20 46	21 06	21 26	21 46	22 06	22 26	22 46	23 06	23 26
Willesden Jn. High Level ⊖	a	18 49	19 00	19 12	19 32	19 42	19 58	20 15	20 32	20 52	21 12	21 31	21 52	22 12	22 32	22 52	23 12	23 35
	d	18 50	19 01	19 12	19 32	19 43	19 58	20 16	20 32	20 52	21 12	21 32	21 52	22 12	22 32	22 52	23 12	
Kensal Rise	d	18 53	19 04	19 15	19 35	19 46	20 01	20 19	20 35	20 55	21 15	21 35	21 55	22 15	22 35	22 55	23 15	
Brondesbury Park	d	18 55	19 06	19 17	19 37	19 48	20 03	20 21	20 37	20 57	21 17	21 37	21 57	22 17	22 37	22 57	23 17	
Brondesbury	d	18 57	19 08	19 19	19 39	19 50	20 05	20 23	20 39	20 59	21 19	21 39	21 59	22 19	22 39	22 59	23 19	
West Hampstead ⊖	d	18 58	19 09	19 20	19 40	19 51	20 06	20 24	20 40	21 00	21 20	21 40	22 00	22 20	22 40	23 00	23 20	
Finchley Road & Frognal	d	19 00	19 11	19 22	19 42	19 53	20 08	20 26	20 42	21 02	21 22	21 42	22 02	22 22	22 42	23 02	23 22	
Hampstead Heath	d	19 03	19 14	19 25	19 45	19 56	20 11	20 29	20 45	21 05	21 25	21 45	22 05	22 25	22 45	23 05	23 25	
Gospel Oak	d	19 05	19 16	19 27	19 47	19 58	20 13	20 31	20 47	21 07	21 27	21 47	22 07	22 27	22 47	23 07	23 27	
Kentish Town West	d	19 07	19 18	19 29	19 49	20 00	20 15	20 33	20 49	21 09	21 29	21 49	22 09	22 29	22 49	23 09	23 29	
Camden Road	d	19 09	19 20	19 31	19 51	20 02	20 17	20 35	20 51	21 11	21 31	21 51	22 11	22 31	22 51	23 11	23 31	
Caledonian Rd & Barnsbury	d	19 12	19 23	19 34	19 54	20 05	20 20	20 38	20 54	21 14	21 34	21 54	22 14	22 34	22 54	23 14	23 34	
Highbury & Islington ⊖	d	19 15	19 26	19 37	19 57	20 08	20 23	20 41	20 57	21 17	21 37	21 57	22 17	22 37	22 57	23 17	23 37	
Canonbury ⊖	d	19 17	19 28	19 39	19 59	20 10	20 25	20 43	20 59	21 19	21 39	21 59	22 19	22 39	22 59	23 19	23 39	
Dalston Kingsland	d	19 20	19 31	19 42	20 02	20 13	20 28	20 46	21 02	21 22	21 42	22 02	22 22	22 42	23 02	23 22	23 42	
Hackney Central	d	19 23	19 33	19 44	20 04	20 15	20 30	20 48	21 04	21 24	21 44	22 04	22 24	22 44	23 04	23 24	23 44	
Homerton	d	19 25	19 35	19 46	20 06	20 17	20 32	20 50	21 06	21 26	21 46	22 06	22 26	22 46	23 06	23 26	23 46	
Hackney Wick	d	19 29	19 38	19 49	20 09	20 20	20 35	20 53	21 09	21 29	21 49	22 09	22 29	22 49	23 09	23 29	23 49	
Stratford Low Level 7 ⊖	a	19 36	19 45	20 00	20 17	20 27	20 44	21 01	21 16	21 38	21 58	22 16	22 37	22 57	23 17	23 37	23 59	

Mondays to Fridays

1 September to 14 November

		LO A	LO A	LO	LO A	LO	LO A	LO	LO	LO A	LO	LO	LO	LO A	LO	LO A	LO	LO	LO A	LO	LO	LO	LO	LO A	LO
Richmond ⊖	d					06 12			06 27			06 42	06 58		07 13			07 30				07 47	07 59		
Kew Gardens ⊖	d					06 15			06 30			06 45	07 01		07 16			07 33				07 50	08 02		
Gunnersbury ⊖	d					06 18			06 33			06 48	07 04		07 19			07 36				07 53	08 05		
South Acton	d					06 20			06 35			06 50	07 06		07 21			07 38				07 55	08 07		
Acton Central	d					06b25			06 38			06 53	07 09		07 25			07 41				07 58	08 10		
Willesden Jn. High Level ⊖	a					06 30			06 43			06 58	07 14		07 31			07 46				08 05	08 15		
	d																								
Kensal Rise	d																								
Brondesbury Park	d																								
Brondesbury	d																								
West Hampstead ⊖	d																								
Finchley Road & Frognal	d																								
Hampstead Heath	d																								
Gospel Oak	d			06 15				06 55			07 15						07 55			08 08	08 15				08 28
Kentish Town West	d			06 17				06 57			07 17						07 57			08 10	08 17				08 30
Camden Road	d	05 55	06 11	06 19	06 32		06 52	06 59		07 12	07 19			07 32		07 54	07 59		08 12	08 13	08 19			08 33	08 33
Caledonian Rd & Barnsbury	d	05 58	06 14	06 22	06 35		06 55	07 02		07 15	07 22			07 35		07 57	08 02		08 15		08 22			08 36	
Highbury & Islington ⊖	d	06 01	06 17	06 25	06 38		06 58	07 05		07 17	07 25			07 37		07 59	08 05		08 17	08a18	08 25			08 38	08a38
Canonbury ⊖	d	06 03	06 19	06 27	06 40		07 00	07 07		07 19	07 27			07 39		08 01	08 07		08 19		08 27			08 40	
Dalston Kingsland	d	06 06	06 22	06 30	06 43		07 03	07 10		07 22	07 30			07 42		08 04	08 10		08 22		08 30			08 43	
Hackney Central	d	06 08	06 24	06 32	06 45		07 05	07 12		07 24	07 32			07 44		08 06	08 12		08 24		08 32			08 45	
Homerton	d	06 10	06 26	06 34	06 47		07 07	07 14		07 26	07 34			07 46		08 08	08 14		08 26		08 34			08 47	
Hackney Wick	d	06 13	06 29	06 37	06 50		07 10	07 17		07 29	07 37			07 49		08 11	08 17		08 29		08 37			08 50	
Stratford Low Level 7 ⊖	a	06 20	06 36	06 44	06 57		07 17	07 24		07 36	07 44			07 56		08 16	08 24		08 36		08 44			08 57	

		LO	LO A	LO	LO	LO	LO	LO A	LO	LO	LO A	LO	LO A	LO	LO	LO A	LO	LO	LO	LO A	LO	LO A	LO	LO
Richmond ⊖	d	08 14			08 29		08 43			08 59		09 14			09 27		09 41		09 57		10 11			10 27
Kew Gardens ⊖	d	08 17			08 32		08 46			09 02		09 17			09 30		09 44		10 00		10 14			10 30
Gunnersbury ⊖	d	08 20			08 35		08 49			09 05		09 20			09 33		09 47		10 03		10 17			10 33
South Acton	d	08 22			08 37		08 51			09 07		09 22			09 35		09 49		10 05		10 19			10 35
Acton Central	d	08 25			08 40		08 54			09 10		09 25			09 38		09 53		10 08		10 23			10 38
Willesden Jn. High Level ⊖	a	08 31			08 47		09 01			09 15		09 30			09 43		10 00		10 14		10 29			10 43
	d																							
Kensal Rise	d																							
Brondesbury Park	d																							
Brondesbury	d																							
West Hampstead ⊖	d																							
Finchley Road & Frognal	d																							
Hampstead Heath	d																							
Gospel Oak	d			08 55		09 08			09 15					09 55				10 15					10 55	
Kentish Town West	d			08 57		09 10			09 17					09 57				10 17					10 57	
Camden Road	d		08 52	08 59		09 13		09 14	09 19		09 32		09 52	09 59		10 11		10 19		10 31		10 51	10 59	
Caledonian Rd & Barnsbury	d		08 55	09 02				09 17	09 22		09 35		09 55	10 02		10 14		10 22		10 34		10 54	11 02	
Highbury & Islington ⊖	d		08 57	09 05		09a18		09 20	09 25		09 37		09 57	10 05		10 17		10 25		10 37		10 57	11 05	
Canonbury ⊖	d		08 59	09 07				09 22	09 27		09 39		09 59	10 07		10 19		10 27		10 39		10 59	11 07	
Dalston Kingsland	d		09 02	09 10				09 25	09 30		09 42		10 02	10 10		10 22		10 30		10 42		11 02	11 10	
Hackney Central	d		09 04	09 12				09 27	09 32		09 44		10 04	10 12		10 24		10 32		10 44		11 04	11 12	
Homerton	d		09 06	09 14				09 29	09 34		09 46		10 06	10 14		10 26		10 34		10 46		11 06	11 14	
Hackney Wick	d		09 09	09 17				09 32	09 37		09 49		10 09	10 17		10 29		10 37		10 49		11 09	11 17	
Stratford Low Level 7 ⊖	a		09 16	09 24				09 39	09 44		09 56		10 16	10 24		10 36		10 44		10 56		11 16	11 24	

For general notes see front of timetable
For details of catering facilities see Directory of Train Operators

A From Watford Junction Dc (Table 60)
b Arr. 0622

For passengers requiring stations between Hampstead Heath and Kensal Rise and connections to and from Willesden Junction High Level for services to and from Richmond, please use adjacent stations shown on Table 60, or local bus services. For further details please see local publicity or contact National Rail Enquiries on 08457-48-49-50.

Richmond → Willesden Junction, West Hampstead Highbury and Islington and Stratford Low Level

Network diagram - see first page of Table 59

	LO A	LO	LO	LO	LO A		LO	LO A	LO	LO	LO A	LO	LO	LO	LO A	LO	LO A	LO		LO	LO A	LO	LO	LO	LO A
Richmond ⊖ d		10 41		10 57			11 11			11 27		11 41		11 57		12 11				12 27			12 41	12 57	
Kew Gardens ⊖ d		10 44		11 00			11 14			11 30		11 44		12 00		12 14				12 30			12 44	13 00	
Gunnersbury ⊖ d		10 47		11 03			11 17			11 33		11 47		12 03		12 17				12 33			12 47	13 03	
South Acton d		10 49		11 05			11 19			11 35		11 49		12 05		12 19				12 35			12 49	13 05	
Acton Central d		10 53		11 08			11 23			11 38		11 53		12 08		12 23				12 38			12 53	13 08	
Willesden Jn. High Level ⊖ a		10 59		11 13			11 29			11 43		11 59		12 13		12 30				12 43			12 58	13 13	
d																									
Kensal Rise d																									
Brondesbury Park d																									
Brondesbury d																									
West Hampstead ⊖ d																									
Finchley Road & Frognal d																									
Hampstead Heath d																									
Gospel Oak d			11 15						11 55				12 15					12 55				13 15			
Kentish Town West d			11 17						11 57				12 17					12 57				13 17			
Camden Road d	11 11		11 19		11 31			11 51	11 59		12 11		12 19		12 31		12 51	12 59			13 11	13 19			13 31
Caledonian Rd & Barnsbury d	11 14		11 22		11 34			11 54	12 02		12 14		12 22		12 34		12 54	13 02			13 14	13 22			13 34
Highbury & Islington ⊖ d	11 17		11 25		11 37			11 57	12 05		12 17		12 25		12 37		12 57	13 05			13 17	13 25			13 37
Canonbury ⊖ d	11 19		11 27		11 39			11 59	12 07		12 19		12 27		12 39		12 59	13 07			13 19	13 27			13 39
Dalston Kingsland d	11 22		11 30		11 42			12 02	12 10		12 22		12 30		12 42		13 02	13 10			13 22	13 30			13 42
Hackney Central d	11 24		11 32		11 44			12 04	12 12		12 24		12 32		12 44		13 04	13 12			13 24	13 32			13 44
Homerton d	11 26		11 34		11 46			12 06	12 14		12 26		12 34		12 46		13 06	13 14			13 26	13 34			13 46
Hackney Wick d	11 29		11 37		11 49			12 09	12 17		12 29		12 37		12 49		13 09	13 17			13 29	13 37			13 49
Stratford Low Level 7 ⊖ a	11 36		11 44		11 56			12 16	12 24		12 36		12 44		12 56		13 16	13 24			13 36	13 44			13 56

	LO A	LO	LO	LO	LO A	LO	LO	LO		LO A	LO	LO A	LO	LO	LO A	LO	LO	LO	LO A	LO	LO A		LO	LO	LO A
Richmond ⊖ d		13 11		13 27		13 41		13 57			14 11			14 27		14 41		14 57		15 11				15 27	
Kew Gardens ⊖ d		13 14		13 30		13 44		14 00			14 14			14 30		14 44		15 00		15 14				15 30	
Gunnersbury ⊖ d		13 17		13 33		13 47		14 03			14 17			14 33		14 47		15 03		15 17				15 33	
South Acton d		13 19		13 35		13 49		14 05			14 19			14 35		14 49		15 05		15 19				15 35	
Acton Central d		13 23		13 38		13 53		14 08			14 23			14 38		14 53		15 08		15 23				15 38	
Willesden Jn. High Level ⊖ a		13 29		13 43		14 00		14 13			14 29			14 44		14 59		15 13		15 30				15 43	
d																									
Kensal Rise d																									
Brondesbury Park d																									
Brondesbury d																									
West Hampstead ⊖ d																									
Finchley Road & Frognal d																									
Hampstead Heath d																									
Gospel Oak d			13 55				14 15						14 55				15 15						15 55		
Kentish Town West d			13 57				14 17						14 57				15 17						15 57		
Camden Road d	13 51		13 59		14 11		14 19			14 31		14 51	14 59		15 11		15 19		15 31		15 51		15 59		16 11
Caledonian Rd & Barnsbury d	13 54		14 02		14 14		14 22			14 34		14 54	15 02		15 14		15 22		15 34		15 54		16 02		16 14
Highbury & Islington ⊖ d	13 57		14 05		14 17		14 25			14 37		14 57	15 05		15 17		15 25		15 37		15 57		16 05		16 17
Canonbury ⊖ d	13 59		14 07		14 19		14 27			14 39		14 59	15 07		15 19		15 27		15 39		15 59		16 07		16 19
Dalston Kingsland d	14 02		14 10		14 22		14 30			14 42		15 02	15 10		15 22		15 30		15 42		16 02		16 10		16 22
Hackney Central d	14 04		14 12		14 24		14 32			14 44		15 04	15 12		15 24		15 32		15 44		16 04		16 12		16 24
Homerton d	14 06		14 14		14 26		14 34			14 46		15 06	15 14		15 26		15 34		15 46		16 06		16 14		16 26
Hackney Wick d	14 09		14 17		14 29		14 37			14 49		15 09	15 17		15 29		15 37		15 49		16 09		16 17		16 29
Stratford Low Level 7 ⊖ a	14 16		14 24		14 36		14 44			14 56		15 16	15 24		15 36		15 44		15 56		16 16		16 24		16 36

	LO	LO	LO	LO A	LO	LO A	LO	LO	LO A	LO	LO		LO	LO	LO A	LO	LO	LO A	LO	LO	LO A	LO	LO	LO	LO A
Richmond ⊖ d	15 41		15 57		16 15			16 27					16 44	16 59			17 12			17 29				17 44	
Kew Gardens ⊖ d	15 44		16 00		16 18			16 30					16 47	17 02			17 15			17 32				17 47	
Gunnersbury ⊖ d	15 47		16 03		16 21			16 33					16 50	17 05			17 18			17 35				17 50	
South Acton d	15 49		16 05		16 23			16 35					16 52	17 07			17 20			17 37				17 52	
Acton Central d	15 53		16 08		16 26			16 38					16 55	17 10			17 23			17 40				17 55	
Willesden Jn. High Level ⊖ a	15 59		16 13		16 31			16 43					17 02	17 15			17 30			17 45				18 00	
d																									
Kensal Rise d																									
Brondesbury Park d																									
Brondesbury d																									
West Hampstead ⊖ d																									
Finchley Road & Frognal d																									
Hampstead Heath d																									
Gospel Oak d		16 15					16 55			17 08	17 15					17 28			17 55			18 08	18 15		
Kentish Town West d		16 17					16 57			17 10	17 17					17 30			17 57			18 10	18 17		
Camden Road d		16 19		16 31		16 51	16 59		17 11	17 13	17 19				17 31	17 33		17 51	17 59		18 11	18 13	18 19		18 31
Caledonian Rd & Barnsbury d		16 22		16 34		16 54	17 02		17 14		17 22				17 34			17 54	18 02		18 14		18 22		18 34
Highbury & Islington ⊖ d		16 25		16 37		16 57	17 05		17 17	17a18	17 25				17 37	17a38		17 57	18 05		18 17	18a18	18 25		18 37
Canonbury ⊖ d		16 27		16 39		16 59	17 07		17 19		17 27				17 39			17 59	18 07		18 19		18 27		18 39
Dalston Kingsland d		16 30		16 42		17 02	17 10		17 22		17 30				17 42			18 02	18 10		18 22		18 30		18 42
Hackney Central d		16 32		16 44		17 04	17 12		17 24		17 32				17 44			18 04	18 12		18 24		18 32		18 44
Homerton d		16 34		16 46		17 06	17 14		17 26		17 34				17 46			18 06	18 14		18 26		18 34		18 46
Hackney Wick d		16 37		16 49		17 09	17 17		17 29		17 37				17 49			18 09	18 17		18 29		18 37		18 49
Stratford Low Level 7 ⊖ a		16 44		16 56		17 16	17 24		17 36		17 44				17 56			18 16	18 24		18 36		18 44		18 56

For general notes see front of timetable
For details of catering facilities see Directory of Train Operators

A From Watford Junction Dc (Table 60)

For passengers requiring stations between Hampstead Heath and Kensal Rise and connections to and from Willesden Junction High Level for services to and from Richmond, please use adjacent stations shown on Table 60, or local bus services. For further details please see local publicity or contact National Rail Enquiries on 08457-48-49-50.

1 September to 14 November

Richmond → Willesden Junction, West Hampstead Highbury and Islington and Stratford Low Level

Network diagram - see first page of Table 59

		LO		LO	LO	LO	LO	LO	LO	LO	LO	LO	LO	LO	LO		LO	LO	LO	LO	LO	LO	LO	LO	LO	LO
						A			A				A		A				A				A	A		
Richmond	⊖ d			18 00	18 15			18 31		18 44		18 55		19 15				19 26		19 41		19 59			20 15	
Kew Gardens	⊖ d			18 03	18 18			18 34		18 47		18a58		19 18				19 29		19 44		20 02			20 18	
Gunnersbury	⊖ d			18 06	18 21			18 37		18 50		19 01		19 21				19 32		19 47		20 05			20 21	
South Acton	d			18 08	18 23			18 39		18 52		19 03		19 23				19 34		19 49		20 07			20 23	
Acton Central	d			18 11	18 26			18 43		18 55		19 06		19 26				19 37		19 52		20 10			20 26	
Willesden Jn. High Level	⊖ a			18 16	18 32			18 49		19 00		19 12		19 32				19 42		19 58		20 15			20 32	
	d																									
Kensal Rise	d																									
Brondesbury Park	d																									
Brondesbury	d																									
West Hampstead	⊖ d																									
Finchley Road & Frognal	d																									
Hampstead Heath	d																									
Gospel Oak	d	18 28					18 55				19 15						19 55				20 15					20 55
Kentish Town West	d	18 30					18 57				19 17						19 57				20 17					20 57
Camden Road	d	18 33				18 51	18 59		19 11		19 19		19 31		19 51		19 59		20 11		20 19		20 31	20 51		20 59
Caledonian Rd & Barnsbury	d					18 54	19 02		19 14		19 22		19 34		19 54		20 02		20 14		20 22		20 34	20 54		21 02
Highbury & Islington	⊖ d	18a38				18 57	19 05		19 17		19 25		19 37		19 57		20 05		20 17		20 25		20 37	20 57		21 05
Canonbury	⊖ d					18 59	19 07		19 19		19 27		19 39		19 59		20 07		20 19		20 27		20 39	20 59		21 07
Dalston Kingsland	d					19 02	19 10		19 22		19 30		19 42		20 02		20 10		20 22		20 30		20 42	21 02		21 10
Hackney Central	d					19 04	19 12		19 24		19 32		19 44		20 04		20 12		20 24		20 32		20 44	21 04		21 12
Homerton	d					19 06	19 14		19 26		19 34		19 46		20 06		20 14		20 26		20 34		20 46	21 06		21 14
Hackney Wick	d					19 09	19 17		19 29		19 37		19 49		20 09		20 17		20 29		20 37		20 49	21 09		21 17
Stratford Low Level 7	⊖ ⛴ a					19 16	19 24		19 36		19 44		19 56		20 16		20 24		20 36		20 44		20 56	21 16		21 24

		LO	LO	LO	LO		LO	LO	LO	LO	LO	LO	LO	LO	LO	LO	LO	LO	LO	LO	LO	LO	LO	LO		
		A					A		A			A			A		A			A				A		
Richmond	⊖ d		20 35		20 55			21 15			21 35			21 55		22 15			22 35			22 55	23 15			
Kew Gardens	⊖ d		20 38		20 58			21 18			21 38			21 58		22 18			22 38			22 58	23 18			
Gunnersbury	⊖ d		20 41		21 01			21 21			21 41			22 01		22 21			22 41			23 01	23 21			
South Acton	d		20 43		21 03			21 23			21 43			22 03		22 23			22 43			23 03	23 23			
Acton Central	d		20 46		21 06			21 26			21 46			22 06		22 26			22 46			23 06	23 26			
Willesden Jn. High Level	⊖ a		20 52		21 12			21 31			21 52			22 12		22 32			22 52			23 12	23 35			
	d																									
Kensal Rise	d																									
Brondesbury Park	d																									
Brondesbury	d																									
West Hampstead	⊖ d																									
Finchley Road & Frognal	d																									
Hampstead Heath	d																									
Gospel Oak	d			21 15						21 55			22 15					22 55			23 15					
Kentish Town West	d			21 17						21 57			22 17					22 57			23 17					
Camden Road	d	21 11		21 19			21 31		21 51	21 59		22 11	22 19		22 31		22 51	22 59		23 11	23 19			23 31		
Caledonian Rd & Barnsbury	d	21 14		21 22			21 34		21 54	22 02		22 14	22 22		22 34		22 54	23 02		23 14	23 22			23 34		
Highbury & Islington	⊖ d	21 17		21 25			21 37		21 57	22 05		22 17	22 25		22 37		22 57	23 05		23 17	23 25			23 37		
Canonbury	⊖ d	21 19		21 27			21 39		21 59	22 07		22 19	22 27		22 39		22 59	23 07		23 19	23 27			23 39		
Dalston Kingsland	d	21 22		21 30			21 42		22 02	22 10		22 22	22 30		22 42		23 02	23 10		23 22	23 30			23 42		
Hackney Central	d	21 24		21 32			21 44		22 04	22 12		22 24	22 32		22 44		23 04	23 12		23 24	23 32			23 44		
Homerton	d	21 26		21 34			21 46		22 06	22 14		22 26	22 34		22 46		23 06	23 14		23 26	23 34			23 46		
Hackney Wick	d	21 29		21 37			21 49		22 09	22 17		22 29	22 37		22 49		23 09	23 17		23 29	23 37			23 49		
Stratford Low Level 7	⊖ ⛴ a	21 36		21 44			21 56		22 16	22 24		22 36	22 44		22 56		23 16	23 24		23 36	23 44			23 56		

Saturdays

until 30 August and from 22 November

		LO	LO	LO	LO	LO	LO	LO	LO	LO	LO		LO	LO	LO	LO	LO	LO	LO	LO	LO	LO		LO	LO	LO
Richmond	⊖ d			06 11	06 27	06 41	06 57	07 11	07 27	07 41	07 57		08 11	08 27	08 41	08 57	09 11	09 27	09 41	09 57	10 11	10 27		10 41	10 57	11 11
Kew Gardens	⊖ d			06 14	06 30	06 44	07 00	07 14	07 30	07 44	08 00		08 14	08 30	08 44	09 00	09 14	09 30	09 44	10 00	10 14	10 30		10 44	11 00	11 14
Gunnersbury	⊖ d			06 17	06 33	06 47	07 03	07 17	07 33	07 47	08 03		08 17	08 33	08 47	09 03	09 17	09 33	09 47	10 03	10 17	10 33		10 47	11 03	11 17
South Acton	d			06 19	06 35	06 49	07 05	07 19	07 35	07 49	08 05		08 19	08 35	08 49	09 05	09 19	09 35	09 49	10 05	10 19	10 35		10 49	11 05	11 19
Acton Central	d			06 23	06 38	06 53	07 08	07 23	07 38	07 53	08 08		08 23	08 38	08 53	09 08	09 23	09 38	09 53	10 08	10 23	10 38		10 53	11 08	11 23
Willesden Jn. High Level	⊖ a			06 29	06 43	06 58	07 14	07 29	07 43	07 58	08 13		08 29	08 43	08 58	09 13	09 29	09 43	09 58	10 13	10 29	10 43		10 59	11 13	11 29
	d	05b58	06b11	06 29	06 44	06 59	07 14	07 29	07 44	07 59	08 14		08 29	08 44	08 59	09 14	09 29	09 44	09 59	10 14	10 29	10 44		10 59	11 14	11 29
Kensal Rise	d	06 02	06 16	06 32	06 47	07 02	07 17	07 32	07 47	08 02	08 17		08 32	08 47	09 02	09 17	09 32	09 47	10 02	10 17	10 32	10 47		11 02	11 17	11 32
Brondesbury Park	d	06 04	06 18	06 34	06 49	07 04	07 19	07 34	07 49	08 04	08 19		08 34	08 49	09 04	09 19	09 34	09 49	10 04	10 19	10 34	10 49		11 04	11 19	11 34
Brondesbury	d	06 06	06 20	06 36	06 51	07 06	07 21	07 36	07 51	08 06	08 21		08 36	08 51	09 06	09 21	09 36	09 51	10 06	10 21	10 36	10 51		11 06	11 21	11 36
West Hampstead	⊖ d	06 07	06 21	06 37	06 52	07 07	07 22	07 37	07 52	08 07	08 22		08 37	08 52	09 07	09 22	09 37	09 52	10 07	10 22	10 37	10 52		11 07	11 22	11 37
Finchley Road & Frognal	d	06 09	06 23	06 39	06 54	07 09	07 24	07 39	07 54	08 09	08 24		08 39	08 54	09 09	09 24	09 39	09 54	10 09	10 24	10 39	10 54		11 09	11 24	11 39
Hampstead Heath	d	06 12	06 26	06 42	06 57	07 12	07 27	07 42	07 57	08 12	08 27		08 42	08 57	09 12	09 27	09 42	09 57	10 12	10 27	10 42	10 57		11 12	11 27	11 42
Gospel Oak	d	06 14	06 28	06 44	06 59	07 14	07 29	07 44	07 59	08 14	08 29		08 44	08 59	09 14	09 29	09 44	09 59	10 14	10 29	10 44	10 59		11 14	11 29	11 44
Kentish Town West	d	06 16	06 30	06 46	07 01	07 16	07 31	07 46	08 01	08 16	08 31		08 46	09 01	09 16	09 31	09 46	10 01	10 16	10 31	10 46	11 01		11 16	11 31	11 46
Camden Road	d	06 18	06 32	06 48	07 03	07 18	07 33	07 48	08 03	08 18	08 33		08 48	09 03	09 18	09 33	09 48	10 03	10 18	10 33	10 48	11 03		11 18	11 33	11 48
Caledonian Rd & Barnsbury	d	06 21	06 35	06 51	07 06	07 21	07 36	07 51	08 06	08 21	08 36		08 51	09 06	09 21	09 36	09 51	10 06	10 21	10 36	10 51	11 06		11 21	11 36	11 51
Highbury & Islington	⊖ d	06 24	06 38	06 54	07 09	07 24	07 39	07 54	08 09	08 24	08 39		08 54	09 09	09 24	09 39	09 54	10 09	10 24	10 39	10 54	11 09		11 24	11 39	11 54
Canonbury	⊖ d	06 26	06 40	06 56	07 11	07 26	07 41	07 56	08 11	08 26	08 41		08 56	09 11	09 26	09 41	09 56	10 11	10 26	10 41	10 56	11 11		11 26	11 41	11 56
Dalston Kingsland	d	06 29	06 43	06 59	07 14	07 29	07 44	07 59	08 14	08 29	08 44		08 59	09 14	09 29	09 44	09 59	10 14	10 29	10 44	10 59	11 14		11 29	11 44	11 59
Hackney Central	d	06 31	06 45	07 01	07 16	07 31	07 46	08 01	08 16	08 31	08 46		09 01	09 16	09 31	09 46	10 01	10 16	10 31	10 46	11 01	11 16		11 31	11 46	12 01
Homerton	d	06 33	06 47	07 03	07 18	07 33	07 48	08 03	08 18	08 33	08 48		09 03	09 18	09 33	09 48	10 03	10 18	10 33	10 48	11 03	11 18		11 33	11 48	12 03
Hackney Wick	d	06 36	06 50	07 06	07 21	07 36	07 51	08 06	08 21	08 36	08 51		09 06	09 21	09 36	09 51	10 06	10 21	10 36	10 51	11 06	11 21		11 36	11 51	12 06
Stratford Low Level 7	⊖ ⛴ a	06 44	06 57	07 14	07 28	07 43	08 01	08 15	08 28	08 43	08 58		09 15	09 28	09 43	09 58	10 13	10 28	10 43	10 58	11 13	11 28		11 43	11 59	12 13

For general notes see front of timetable
For details of catering facilities see
Directory of Train Operators

A From Watford Junction Dc (Table 60)
b Willesden Jn Low Level

For passengers requiring stations between Hampstead Heath and Kensal Rise and connections to and from Willesden Junction High Level for services to and from Richmond, please use adjacent stations shown on Table 60, or local bus services. For further details please see local publicity or contact National Rail Enquiries on 08457-48-49-50.

Saturdays

Richmond → Willesden Junction, West Hampstead Highbury and Islington and Stratford Low Level

until 30 August and from 22 November

Network diagram - see first page of Table 59

		LO	LO	LO	LO	LO	LO	LO	LO	LO		LO	LO	LO	LO	LO	LO	LO	LO	LO	LO		LO	LO	LO	LO
Richmond	⊖ d	11 27	11 41	11 57	12 11	12 27	12 41	12 57	13 11	13 27		13 41	13 57	14 11	14 27	14 41	14 57	15 11	15 27	15 41	15 57		16 11	16 27	16 41	16 57
Kew Gardens	⊖ d	11 30	11 44	12 00	12 14	12 30	12 44	13 00	13 14	13 30		13 44	14 00	14 14	14 30	14 44	15 00	15 14	15 30	15 44	16 00		16 14	16 30	16 44	17 00
Gunnersbury	⊖ d	11 33	11 47	12 03	12 17	12 33	12 47	13 03	13 17	13 33		13 47	14 03	14 17	14 33	14 47	15 03	15 17	15 33	15 47	16 03		16 17	16 33	16 47	17 03
South Acton	d	11 35	11 49	12 05	12 19	12 35	12 49	13 05	13 19	13 35		13 49	14 05	14 19	14 35	14 49	15 05	15 19	15 35	15 49	16 05		16 19	16 35	16 49	17 05
Acton Central	d	11 38	11 53	12 08	12 23	12 38	12 53	13 08	13 23	13 38		13 53	14 08	14 23	14 38	14 53	15 08	15 23	15 38	15 53	16 08		16 23	16 38	16 53	17 08
Willesden Jn. High Level	⊖ a	11 43	11 58	12 13	12 29	12 43	12 58	13 13	13 29	13 43		13 59	14 13	14 29	14 43	14 58	15 13	15 29	15 43	15 59	16 13		16 29	16 43	16 58	17 13
	d	11 44	11 59	12 14	12 29	12 44	12 59	13 14	13 29	13 44		13 59	14 14	14 29	14 44	14 59	15 14	15 29	15 44	15 59	16 14		16 29	16 44	16 59	17 14
Kensal Rise	d	11 47	12 02	12 17	12 32	12 47	13 02	13 17	13 32	13 47		14 02	14 17	14 32	14 47	15 02	15 17	15 32	15 47	16 02	16 17		16 32	16 47	17 02	17 17
Brondesbury Park	d	11 49	12 04	12 19	12 34	12 49	13 04	13 19	13 34	13 49		14 04	14 19	14 34	14 49	15 04	15 19	15 34	15 49	16 04	16 19		16 34	16 49	17 04	17 19
Brondesbury	d	11 51	12 06	12 21	12 36	12 51	13 06	13 21	13 36	13 51		14 06	14 21	14 36	14 51	15 06	15 21	15 36	15 51	16 06	16 21		16 36	16 51	17 06	17 21
West Hampstead	⊖ d	11 52	12 07	12 22	12 37	12 52	13 07	13 22	13 37	13 52		14 07	14 22	14 37	14 52	15 07	15 22	15 37	15 52	16 07	16 22		16 37	16 52	17 07	17 22
Finchley Road & Frognal	d	11 54	12 09	12 24	12 39	12 54	13 09	13 24	13 39	13 54		14 09	14 24	14 39	14 54	15 09	15 24	15 39	15 54	16 09	16 24		16 39	16 54	17 09	17 24
Hampstead Heath	d	11 57	12 12	12 27	12 42	12 57	13 12	13 27	13 42	13 57		14 12	14 27	14 42	14 57	15 12	15 27	15 42	15 57	16 12	16 27		16 42	16 57	17 12	17 27
Gospel Oak	d	11 59	12 14	12 29	12 44	12 59	13 14	13 29	13 44	13 59		14 14	14 29	14 44	14 59	15 14	15 29	15 44	15 59	16 14	16 29		16 44	16 59	17 14	17 29
Kentish Town West	d	12 01	12 16	12 31	12 46	13 01	13 16	13 31	13 46	14 01		14 16	14 31	14 46	15 01	15 16	15 31	15 46	16 01	16 16	16 31		16 46	17 01	17 16	17 31
Camden Road	d	12 03	12 18	12 33	12 48	13 03	13 18	13 33	13 48	14 03		14 18	14 33	14 48	15 03	15 18	15 33	15 48	16 03	16 18	16 33		16 48	17 03	17 18	17 33
Caledonian Rd & Barnsbury	d	12 06	12 21	12 36	12 51	13 06	13 21	13 36	13 51	14 06		14 21	14 36	14 51	15 06	15 21	15 36	15 51	16 06	16 21	16 36		16 51	17 06	17 21	17 36
Highbury & Islington	⊖ d	12 09	12 24	12 39	12 54	13 09	13 24	13 39	13 54	14 09		14 24	14 39	14 54	15 09	15 24	15 39	15 54	16 09	16 24	16 39		16 54	17 09	17 24	17 39
Canonbury	⊖ d	12 11	12 26	12 41	12 56	13 11	13 26	13 41	13 56	14 11		14 26	14 41	14 56	15 11	15 26	15 41	15 56	16 11	16 26	16 41		16 56	17 11	17 26	17 41
Dalston Kingsland	d	12 14	12 29	12 44	12 59	13 14	13 29	13 44	13 59	14 14		14 29	14 44	14 59	15 14	15 29	15 44	15 59	16 14	16 29	16 44		16 59	17 14	17 29	17 44
Hackney Central	d	12 16	12 31	12 46	13 01	13 16	13 31	13 46	14 01	14 16		14 31	14 46	15 01	15 16	15 31	15 46	16 01	16 16	16 31	16 46		17 01	17 16	17 31	17 46
Homerton	d	12 18	12 33	12 48	13 03	13 18	13 33	13 48	14 03	14 18		14 33	14 48	15 03	15 18	15 33	15 48	16 03	16 18	16 33	16 48		17 03	17 18	17 33	17 48
Hackney Wick	d	12 21	12 36	12 51	13 06	13 21	13 36	13 51	14 06	14 21		14 36	14 51	15 06	15 21	15 36	15 51	16 06	16 21	16 36	16 51		17 06	17 21	17 36	17 51
Stratford Low Level 7	⊖ ⛴ a	12 29	12 43	12 58	13 13	13 28	13 43	13 58	14 13	14 28		14 43	14 58	15 13	15 28	15 43	15 58	16 13	16 28	16 43	16 58		17 13	17 28	17 43	17 58

		LO	LO	LO	LO	LO	LO	LO	LO		LO	LO	LO	LO	LO	LO	LO	LO	LO	LO	LO	LO	LO	LO		
Richmond	⊖ d	17 11	17 27	17 41	17 57	18 11	18 26	18 41	18 56		19 16	19 26	19 40	19 56	20 16	20 36	20 56	21 16	21 36	21 56	22 16	22 36	22 56	23 16		
Kew Gardens	⊖ d	17 14	17 30	17 44	18 00	18 14	18 29	18 44	18 59		19 19	19 29	19 43	19 59	20 19	20 39	20 59	21 19	21 39	21 59	22 19	22 39	22 59	23 19		
Gunnersbury	⊖ d	17 17	17 33	17 47	18 03	18 17	18 32	18 47	19 02		19 22	19 32	19 46	20 02	20 22	20 42	21 02	21 22	21 42	22 02	22 22	22 42	23 02	23 22		
South Acton	d	17 19	17 35	17 49	18 05	18 19	18 34	18 49	19 04		19 24	19 34	19 48	20 04	20 24	20 44	21 04	21 24	21 44	22 04	22 24	22 44	23 04	23 24		
Acton Central	d	17 23	17 38	17 53	18 08	18 23	18 38	18 52	19 07		19 27	19 37	19 51	20 07	20 27	20 47	21 07	21 27	21 47	22 07	22 27	22 47	23 07	23 27		
Willesden Jn. High Level	⊖ a	17 29	17 43	17 58	18 13	18 29	18 43	18 57	19 12		19 32	19 43	19 59	20 13	20 32	20 52	21 12	21 32	21 52	22 12	22 32	22 52	23 13	23 35		
	d	17 29	17 44	17 59	18 14	18 29	18 44	18 58	19 13		19 33	19 43	20 00	20 13	20 33	20 53	21 13	21 33	21 53	22 13	22 33	22 53	23 13			
Kensal Rise	d	17 32	17 47	18 02	18 17	18 32	18 47	19 01	19 16		19 36	19 46	20 03	20 16	20 36	20 56	21 16	21 36	21 56	22 16	22 36	22 56	23 16			
Brondesbury Park	d	17 34	17 49	18 04	18 19	18 34	18 49	19 03	19 18		19 38	19 48	20 05	20 18	20 38	20 58	21 18	21 38	21 58	22 18	22 38	22 58	23 18			
Brondesbury	d	17 36	17 51	18 06	18 21	18 36	18 51	19 05	19 20		19 40	19 50	20 07	20 20	20 40	21 00	21 20	21 40	22 00	22 20	22 40	23 00	23 20			
West Hampstead	⊖ d	17 37	17 52	18 07	18 22	18 37	18 52	19 06	19 21		19 41	19 51	20 08	20 21	20 41	21 01	21 21	21 41	22 01	22 21	22 41	23 01	23 21			
Finchley Road & Frognal	d	17 39	17 54	18 09	18 24	18 39	18 54	19 08	19 23		19 43	19 53	20 10	20 23	20 43	21 03	21 23	21 43	22 03	22 23	22 43	23 03	23 23			
Hampstead Heath	d	17 42	17 57	18 12	18 27	18 42	18 57	19 11	19 26		19 46	19 56	20 13	20 26	20 46	21 06	21 26	21 46	22 06	22 26	22 46	23 06	23 26			
Gospel Oak	d	17 44	17 59	18 14	18 29	18 44	18 59	19 13	19 28		19 48	19 58	20 15	20 28	20 48	21 08	21 28	21 48	22 08	22 28	22 48	23 08	23 28			
Kentish Town West	d	17 46	18 01	18 16	18 31	18 46	19 01	19 15	19 30		19 50	20 00	20 17	20 30	20 50	21 10	21 30	21 50	22 10	22 30	22 50	23 10	23 30			
Camden Road	d	17 48	18 03	18 18	18 33	18 48	19 03	19 17	19 32		19 52	20 02	20 19	20 32	20 52	21 12	21 32	21 52	22 12	22 32	22 52	23 12	23 32			
Caledonian Rd & Barnsbury	d	17 51	18 06	18 21	18 36	18 51	19 06	19 20	19 35		19 55	20 05	20 22	20 35	20 55	21 15	21 35	21 55	22 15	22 35	22 55	23 15	23 35			
Highbury & Islington	⊖ d	17 54	18 09	18 24	18 39	18 54	19 09	19 23	19 37		19 57	20 07	20 24	20 37	20 57	21 17	21 37	21 57	22 17	22 37	22 57	23 17	23 37			
Canonbury	⊖ d	17 56	18 11	18 26	18 41	18 56	19 11	19 24	19 39		19 59	20 09	20 26	20 39	20 59	21 19	21 39	21 59	22 19	22 39	22 59	23 19	23 39			
Dalston Kingsland	d	17 59	18 14	18 29	18 44	18 59	19 14	19 27	19 42		20 02	20 12	20 29	20 42	21 02	21 22	21 42	22 02	22 22	22 42	23 02	23 22	23 42			
Hackney Central	d	18 01	18 16	18 31	18 46	19 01	19 16	19 29	19 44		20 04	20 14	20 31	20 44	21 04	21 24	21 44	22 04	22 24	22 44	23 04	23 24	23 44			
Homerton	d	18 03	18 18	18 33	18 48	19 03	19 18	19 31	19 46		20 06	20 16	20 33	20 46	21 06	21 26	21 46	22 06	22 26	22 46	23 06	23 26	23 46			
Hackney Wick	d	18 06	18 21	18 36	18 51	19 06	19 21	19 34	19 49		20 09	20 19	20 35	20 49	21 09	21 29	21 49	22 09	22 29	22 49	23 09	23 29	23 49			
Stratford Low Level 7	⊖ ⛴ a	18 13	18 28	18 43	18 59	19 13	19 28	19 44	19 59		20 16	20 28	20 42	20 57	21 19	21 39	21 59	22 16	22 36	22 56	23 16	23 36	23 59			

Saturdays

6 September to 15 November

		LO A	LO A	LO	LO A	LO	LO	LO		LO A	LO	LO	LO A	LO	LO A	LO		LO	LO	LO A	LO	LO	LO	LO A		LO
Richmond	⊖ d					06 11		06 27			06 41			06 57		07 11			07 27		07 41		07 57			08 11
Kew Gardens	⊖ d					06 14		06 30			06 44			07 00		07 14			07 30		07 44		08 00			08 14
Gunnersbury	⊖ d					06 17		06 33			06 47			07 03		07 17			07 33		07 47		08 03			08 17
South Acton	d					06 19		06 35			06 49			07 05		07 19			07 35		07 49		08 05			08 19
Acton Central	d					06 23		06 38			06 53			07 08		07 23			07 38		07 53		08 08			08 23
Willesden Jn. High Level	⊖ a					06 30		06 43			06 58			07 17		07 31			07 43		07 58		08 13			08 31
	d																									
Kensal Rise	d																									
Brondesbury Park	d																									
Brondesbury	d																									
West Hampstead	⊖ d																									
Finchley Road & Frognal	d																									
Hampstead Heath	d																									
Gospel Oak	d			06 15			06 55					07 15						07 55				08 15				
Kentish Town West	d			06 17			06 57					07 17						07 57				08 17				
Camden Road	d	05 55	06 11	06 19	06 32		06 59			07 11		07 19	07 31		07 51			07 59		08 11		08 19		08 31		
Caledonian Rd & Barnsbury	d	05 58	06 14	06 22	06 35		07 02			07 14		07 22	07 34		07 54			08 02		08 14		08 22		08 34		
Highbury & Islington	⊖ d	06 01	06 17	06 25	06 38		07 05			07 17		07 25	07 37		07 57			08 05		08 17		08 25		08 37		
Canonbury	⊖ d	06 03	06 19	06 27	06 40		07 07			07 19		07 27	07 39		07 59			08 07		08 19		08 27		08 39		
Dalston Kingsland	d	06 06	06 22	06 30	06 43		07 10			07 22		07 30	07 42		08 02			08 10		08 22		08 30		08 42		
Hackney Central	d	06 08	06 24	06 32	06 45		07 12			07 24		07 32	07 44		08 04			08 12		08 24		08 32		08 44		
Homerton	d	06 10	06 26	06 34	06 47		07 14			07 26		07 34	07 46		08 06			08 14		08 26		08 34		08 46		
Hackney Wick	d	06 13	06 29	06 37	06 50		07 17			07 29		07 37	07 49		08 09			08 17		08 29		08 37		08 49		
Stratford Low Level 7	⊖ ⛴ a	06 20	06 36	06 44	06 57		07 24			07 36		07 44	07 56		08 16			08 24		08 36		08 44		08 56		

For general notes see front of timetable
For details of catering facilities see Directory of Train Operators

A From Watford Junction Dc (Table 60)

For passengers requiring stations between Hampstead Heath and Kensal Rise and connections to and from Willesden Junction High Level for services to and from Richmond, please use adjacent stations shown on Table 60, or local bus services. For further details please see local publicity or contact National Rail Enquiries on 08457-48-49-50.

Table 59

Saturdays

Richmond → Willesden Junction, West Hampstead Highbury and Islington and Stratford Low Level

6 September to 15 November

Network diagram - see first page of Table 59

	LO A	LO	LO	LO A	LO	LO	LO	LO A	LO	LO A	LO	LO	LO A	LO	LO	LO	LO A	LO	LO A	LO	LO	LO A
Richmond ⊖ d			08 27		08 41		08 57		09 11			09 27		09 41		09 57		10 11			10 27	
Kew Gardens ⊖ d			08 30		08 44		09 00		09 14			09 30		09 44		10 00		10 14			10 30	
Gunnersbury ⊖ d			08 33		08 47		09 03		09 17			09 33		09 47		10 03		10 17			10 33	
South Acton d			08 35		08 49		09 05		09 19			09 35		09 49		10 05		10 19			10 35	
Acton Central d			08 38		08 53		09 08		09 23			09 38		09 53		10 08		10 23			10 38	
Willesden Jn. High Level ⊖ a			08 43		08 58		09 13		09 29			09 43		09 58		10 13		10 29			10 43	
d																						
Kensal Rise d																						
Brondesbury Park d																						
Brondesbury d																						
West Hampstead ⊖ d																						
Finchley Road & Frognal d																						
Hampstead Heath d																						
Gospel Oak d		08 55				09 15					09 55				10 15					10 55		
Kentish Town West d		08 57				09 17					09 57				10 17					10 57		
Camden Road d	08 51	08 59		09 11		09 19		09 31		09 51	09 59		10 11		10 19		10 31		10 51	10 59		11 11
Caledonian Rd & Barnsbury d	08 54	09 02		09 14		09 22		09 34		09 54	10 02		10 14		10 22		10 34		10 54	11 02		11 14
Highbury & Islington ⊖ d	08 57	09 05		09 17		09 25		09 37		09 57	10 05		10 17		10 25		10 37		10 57	11 05		11 17
Canonbury ⊖ d	08 59	09 07		09 19		09 27		09 39		09 59	10 07		10 19		10 27		10 39		10 59	11 07		11 19
Dalston Kingsland d	09 02	09 10		09 22		09 30		09 42		10 02	10 10		10 22		10 30		10 42		11 02	11 10		11 22
Hackney Central d	09 04	09 12		09 24		09 32		09 44		10 04	10 12		10 24		10 32		10 44		11 04	11 12		11 24
Homerton d	09 06	09 14		09 26		09 34		09 46		10 06	10 14		10 26		10 34		10 46		11 06	11 14		11 26
Hackney Wick d	09 09	09 17		09 29		09 37		09 49		10 09	10 17		10 29		10 37		10 49		11 09	11 17		11 29
Stratford Low Level 7 ⊖ a	09 16	09 24		09 36		09 44		09 56		10 16	10 24		10 36		10 44		10 56		11 16	11 24		11 36

	LO	LO	LO	LO A	LO	LO A	LO	LO	LO A	LO	LO	LO	LO A	LO	LO A	LO	LO	LO A	LO	LO	LO	LO A
Richmond ⊖ d	10 41		10 57		11 11			11 27			11 41	11 57		12 11			12 27		12 41		12 57	
Kew Gardens ⊖ d	10 44		11 00		11 14			11 30			11 44	12 00		12 14			12 30		12 44		13 00	
Gunnersbury ⊖ d	10 47		11 03		11 17			11 33			11 47	12 03		12 17			12 33		12 47		13 03	
South Acton d	10 49		11 05		11 19			11 35			11 49	12 05		12 19			12 35		12 49		13 05	
Acton Central d	10 53		11 08		11 23			11 38			11 53	12 08		12 23			12 38		12 53		13 08	
Willesden Jn. High Level ⊖ a	11 00		11 13		11 29			11 43			11 58	12 13		12 29			12 43		12 58		13 13	
d																						
Kensal Rise d																						
Brondesbury Park d																						
Brondesbury d																						
West Hampstead ⊖ d																						
Finchley Road & Frognal d																						
Hampstead Heath d																						
Gospel Oak d		11 15					11 55			12 15						12 55				13 15		
Kentish Town West d		11 17					11 57			12 17						12 57				13 17		
Camden Road d		11 19		11 31		11 51	11 59		12 11	12 19			12 31		12 51	12 59		13 11		13 19		13 31
Caledonian Rd & Barnsbury d		11 22		11 34		11 54	12 02		12 14	12 22			12 34		12 54	13 02		13 14		13 22		13 34
Highbury & Islington ⊖ d		11 25		11 37		11 57	12 05		12 17	12 25			12 37		12 57	13 05		13 17		13 25		13 37
Canonbury ⊖ d		11 27		11 39		11 59	12 07		12 19	12 27			12 39		12 59	13 07		13 19		13 27		13 39
Dalston Kingsland d		11 30		11 42		12 02	12 10		12 22	12 30			12 42		13 02	13 10		13 22		13 30		13 42
Hackney Central d		11 32		11 44		12 04	12 12		12 24	12 32			12 44		13 04	13 12		13 24		13 32		13 44
Homerton d		11 34		11 46		12 06	12 14		12 26	12 34			12 46		13 06	13 14		13 26		13 34		13 46
Hackney Wick d		11 37		11 49		12 09	12 17		12 29	12 37			12 49		13 09	13 17		13 29		13 37		13 49
Stratford Low Level 7 ⊖ a		11 44		11 56		12 16	12 24		12 36	12 44			12 56		13 16	13 24		13 36		13 44		13 56

	LO A	LO	LO	LO	LO A	LO	LO	LO	LO A	LO	LO A	LO	LO	LO A	LO	LO	LO	LO A	LO	LO A	LO	LO
Richmond ⊖ d		13 11		13 27			13 41	13 57		14 11			14 27		14 41		14 57		15 11			15 27
Kew Gardens ⊖ d		13 14		13 30			13 44	14 00		14 14			14 30		14 44		15 00		15 14			15 30
Gunnersbury ⊖ d		13 17		13 33			13 47	14 03		14 17			14 33		14 47		15 03		15 17			15 33
South Acton d		13 19		13 35			13 49	14 05		14 19			14 35		14 49		15 05		15 19			15 35
Acton Central d		13 23		13 38			13 53	14 08		14 23			14 38		14 53		15 08		15 23			15 38
Willesden Jn. High Level ⊖ a		13 29		13 43			14 00	14 13		14 29			14 43		14 58		15 13		15 29			15 43
d																						
Kensal Rise d																						
Brondesbury Park d																						
Brondesbury d																						
West Hampstead ⊖ d																						
Finchley Road & Frognal d																						
Hampstead Heath d																						
Gospel Oak d			13 55			14 15						14 55				15 15					15 55	
Kentish Town West d			13 57			14 17						14 57				15 17					15 57	
Camden Road d	13 51		13 59		14 11	14 19			14 31		14 51	14 59		15 11		15 19		15 31		15 51	15 59	
Caledonian Rd & Barnsbury d	13 54		14 02		14 14	14 22			14 34		14 54	15 02		15 14		15 22		15 34		15 54	16 02	
Highbury & Islington ⊖ d	13 57		14 05		14 17	14 25			14 37		14 57	15 05		15 17		15 25		15 37		15 57	16 05	
Canonbury ⊖ d	13 59		14 07		14 19	14 27			14 39		14 59	15 07		15 19		15 27		15 39		15 59	16 07	
Dalston Kingsland d	14 02		14 10		14 22	14 30			14 42		15 02	15 10		15 22		15 30		15 42		16 02	16 10	
Hackney Central d	14 04		14 12		14 24	14 32			14 44		15 04	15 12		15 24		15 32		15 44		16 04	16 12	
Homerton d	14 06		14 14		14 26	14 34			14 46		15 06	15 14		15 26		15 34		15 46		16 06	16 14	
Hackney Wick d	14 09		14 17		14 29	14 37			14 49		15 09	15 17		15 29		15 37		15 49		16 09	16 17	
Stratford Low Level 7 ⊖ a	14 16		14 24		14 36	14 44			14 56		15 16	15 24		15 36		15 44		15 56		16 16	16 24	

For general notes see front of timetable
For details of catering facilities see
Directory of Train Operators

A From Watford Junction Dc (Table 60)

For passengers requiring stations between Hampstead Heath and Kensal Rise and connections to and from Willesden Junction High Level for services to and from Richmond, please use adjacent stations shown on Table 60, or local bus services. For further details please see local publicity or contact National Rail Enquiries on 08457-48-49-50.

Table 59

Saturdays

Richmond → Willesden Junction, West Hampstead Highbury and Islington and Stratford Low Level

6 September to 15 November

Network diagram - see first page of Table 59

	LO	LO	LO	LO	LO	LO	LO		LO	LO	LO	LO	LO	LO	LO		LO	LO	LO	LO	LO	LO	LO		LO
	A				A		A			A					A			A			A				
Richmond ⊖ d			15 41	15 57		16 11					16 27		16 41	16 57			17 11			17 27			17 41		17 57
Kew Gardens ⊖ d			15 44	16 00		16 14					16 30		16 44	17 00			17 14			17 30			17 44		18 00
Gunnersbury ⊖ d			15 47	16 03		16 17					16 33		16 47	17 03			17 17			17 33			17 47		18 03
South Acton d			15 49	16 05		16 19					16 35		16 49	17 05			17 19			17 35			17 49		18 05
Acton Central d			15 53	16 08		16 23					16 38		16 53	17 08			17 23			17 38			17 53		18 08
Willesden Jn. High Level ⊖ a			15 59	16 13		16 29					16 43		16 58	17 13			17 29			17 43			17 58		18 13
d																									
Kensal Rise d																									
Brondesbury Park d																									
Brondesbury d																									
West Hampstead ⊖ d																									
Finchley Road & Frognal d																									
Hampstead Heath d																									
Gospel Oak d		16 15							16 55			17 15							17 55			18 15			
Kentish Town West d		16 17							16 57			17 17							17 57			18 17			
Camden Road d	16 11	16 19			16 31		16 51		16 59	17 11		17 19			17 31			17 51	17 59		18 11	18 19			
Caledonian Rd & Barnsbury d	16 14	16 22			16 34		16 54		17 02	17 14		17 22			17 34			17 54	18 02		18 14	18 22			
Highbury & Islington ⊖ d	16 17	16 25			16 37		16 57		17 05	17 17		17 25			17 37			17 57	18 05		18 17	18 25			
Canonbury ⊖ d	16 19	16 27			16 39		16 59		17 07	17 19		17 27			17 39			17 59	18 07		18 19	18 27			
Dalston Kingsland d	16 22	16 30			16 42		17 02		17 10	17 22		17 30			17 42			18 02	18 10		18 22	18 30			
Hackney Central d	16 24	16 32			16 44		17 04		17 12	17 24		17 32			17 44			18 04	18 12		18 24	18 32			
Homerton d	16 26	16 34			16 46		17 06		17 14	17 26		17 34			17 46			18 06	18 14		18 26	18 34			
Hackney Wick d	16 29	16 37			16 49		17 09		17 17	17 29		17 37			17 49			18 09	18 17		18 29	18 37			
Stratford Low Level 7 ⊖ a	16 36	16 44			16 56		17 16		17 24	17 36		17 44			17 56			18 16	18 24		18 36	18 44			

	LO	LO	LO	LO	LO	LO	LO		LO	LO	LO	LO	LO	LO	LO		LO	LO	LO	LO	LO	LO	LO		LO
	A		A			A					A		A				A				A		A		
Richmond ⊖ d		18 11			18 26		18 41			18 56		19 16			19 26			19 40		19 56		20 16			
Kew Gardens ⊖ d		18 14			18 29		18 44			18 59		19 19			19 29			19 43		19 59		20 19			
Gunnersbury ⊖ d		18 17			18 32		18 47			19 02		19 22			19 32			19 46		20 02		20 22			
South Acton d		18 19			18 34		18 49			19 04		19 24			19 34			19 48		20 04		20 24			
Acton Central d		18 23			18 38		18 52			19 07		19 27			19 37			19 51		20 07		20 27			
Willesden Jn. High Level ⊖ a		18 29			18 43		18 57			19 12		19 32			19 43			20 01		20 13		20 32			
d																									
Kensal Rise d																									
Brondesbury Park d																									
Brondesbury d																									
West Hampstead ⊖ d																									
Finchley Road & Frognal d																									
Hampstead Heath d																									
Gospel Oak d				18 55					19 15					19 55					20 15						20 55
Kentish Town West d				18 57					19 17					19 57					20 17						20 57
Camden Road d	18 31		18 51	18 59		19 11			19 19		19 31		19 51	19 59			20 11		20 19		20 31		20 51		20 59
Caledonian Rd & Barnsbury d	18 34		18 54	19 02		19 14			19 22		19 34		19 54	20 02			20 14		20 22		20 34		20 54		21 02
Highbury & Islington ⊖ d	18 37		18 57	19 05		19 17			19 25		19 37		19 57	20 05			20 17		20 25		20 37		20 57		21 05
Canonbury ⊖ d	18 39		18 59	19 07		19 19			19 27		19 39		19 59	20 07			20 19		20 27		20 39		20 59		21 07
Dalston Kingsland d	18 42		19 02	19 10		19 22			19 30		19 42		20 02	20 10			20 22		20 30		20 42		21 02		21 10
Hackney Central d	18 44		19 04	19 12		19 24			19 32		19 44		20 04	20 12			20 24		20 32		20 44		21 04		21 12
Homerton d	18 46		19 06	19 14		19 26			19 34		19 46		20 06	20 14			20 26		20 34		20 46		21 06		21 14
Hackney Wick d	18 49		19 09	19 17		19 29			19 37		19 49		20 09	20 17			20 29		20 37		20 49		21 09		21 17
Stratford Low Level 7 ⊖ a	18 56		19 16	19 24		19 36			19 44		19 56		20 16	20 24			20 36		20 44		20 56		21 16		21 24

	LO	LO	LO	LO	LO	LO	LO		LO	LO	LO	LO	LO	LO	LO	LO	LO	LO	LO	LO	LO	LO	LO		
		A			A		A				A			A		A			A				A		
Richmond ⊖ d	20 36			20 56		21 16				21 36			21 56		22 16			22 36			22 56	23 16			
Kew Gardens ⊖ d	20 39			20 59		21 19				21 39			21 59		22 19			22 39			22 59	23 19			
Gunnersbury ⊖ d	20 42			21 02		21 22				21 42			22 02		22 22			22 42			23 02	23 22			
South Acton d	20 44			21 04		21 24				21 44			22 04		22 24			22 44			23 04	23 24			
Acton Central d	20 47			21 07		21 27				21 47			22 07		22 27			22 47			23 07	23 27			
Willesden Jn. High Level ⊖ a	20 52			21 12		21 32				21 52			22 12		22 32			22 52			23 13	23 35			
d																									
Kensal Rise d																									
Brondesbury Park d																									
Brondesbury d																									
West Hampstead ⊖ d																									
Finchley Road & Frognal d																									
Hampstead Heath d																									
Gospel Oak d			21 15						21 55			22 15					22 55			23 15					
Kentish Town West d			21 17						21 57			22 17					22 57			23 17					
Camden Road d		21 11	21 19		21 31		21 51		21 59		22 11	22 19		22 31		22 51	22 59		23 11	23 19			23 31		
Caledonian Rd & Barnsbury d		21 14	21 22		21 34		21 54		22 02		22 14	22 22		22 34		22 54	23 02		23 14	23 22			23 34		
Highbury & Islington ⊖ d		21 17	21 25		21 37		21 57		22 05		22 17	22 25		22 37		22 57	23 05		23 17	23 25			23 37		
Canonbury ⊖ d		21 19	21 27		21 39		21 59		22 07		22 19	22 27		22 39		22 59	23 07		23 19	23 27			23 39		
Dalston Kingsland d		21 22	21 30		21 42		22 02		22 10		22 22	22 30		22 42		23 02	23 10		23 22	23 30			23 42		
Hackney Central d		21 24	21 32		21 44		22 04		22 12		22 24	22 32		22 44		23 04	23 12		23 24	23 32			23 44		
Homerton d		21 26	21 34		21 46		22 06		22 14		22 26	22 34		22 46		23 06	23 14		23 26	23 34			23 46		
Hackney Wick d		21 29	21 37		21 49		22 09		22 17		22 29	22 37		22 49		23 09	23 17		23 29	23 37			23 49		
Stratford Low Level 7 ⊖ a		21 36	21 44		21 56		22 16		22 24		22 36	22 44		22 56		23 16	23 24		23 36	23 44			23 56		

For general notes see front of timetable
For details of catering facilities see
Directory of Train Operators

A From Watford Junction Dc (Table 60)

For passengers requiring stations between Hampstead Heath and Kensal Rise and connections to and from Willesden Junction High Level for services to and from Richmond, please use adjacent stations shown on Table 60, or local bus services. For further details please see local publicity or contact National Rail Enquiries on 08457-48-49-50.

Table 59

Sundays

until 31 August and from 23 November

Richmond → Willesden Junction, West Hampstead Highbury and Islington and Stratford Low Level

Network diagram - see first page of Table 59

Station		LO A	LO	LO		LO	LO	LO
Richmond	⊖ d		09 08	09 38		22 08	22 38	23 08
Kew Gardens	⊖ d		09 11	09 41		22 11	22 41	23 11
Gunnersbury	⊖ d		09 14	09 44		22 14	22 44	23 14
South Acton	d		09 16	09 46		22 16	22 46	23 16
Acton Central	d		09 19	09 49		22 19	22 49	23 19
Willesden Jn. High Level	⊖ a		09 24	09 54		22 24	22 54	23 26
	d	08 55	09 25	09 55	and	22 25	22 55	
Kensal Rise	d	08 58	09 28	09 58		22 28	22 58	
Brondesbury Park	d	09 00	09 30	10 00	every 30	22 30	23 00	
Brondesbury	d	09 02	09 32	10 02		22 32	23 02	
West Hampstead	⊖ d	09 03	09 33	10 03	minutes	22 33	23 03	
Finchley Road & Frognal	d	09 05	09 35	10 05		22 35	23 05	
Hampstead Heath	d	09 08	09 38	10 08	until	22 38	23 08	
Gospel Oak	d	09 10	09 40	10 10		22 40	23 10	
Kentish Town West	d	09 12	09 42	10 12		22 42	23 12	
Camden Road	d	09 14	09 44	10 14		22 44	23 14	
Caledonian Rd & Barnsbury	d	09 17	09 47	10 17		22 47	23 17	
Highbury & Islington	⊖ d	09 20	09 50	10 20		22 50	23 20	
Canonbury	⊖ d	09 22	09 52	10 22		22 52	23 22	
Dalston Kingsland	d	09 25	09 55	10 25		22 55	23 25	
Hackney Central	d	09 27	09 57	10 27		22 57	23 27	
Homerton	d	09 29	09 59	10 29		22 59	23 29	
Hackney Wick	d	09 32	10 02	10 32		23 02	23 32	
Stratford Low Level 7	⊖ ⛴ a	09 39	10 09	10 39		23 09	23 39	

Sundays

7 September to 16 November

Station		LO B	LO	LO B	LO	LO	LO B	LO	LO	LO B	LO	LO	LO B	LO	LO	LO B	LO	LO	LO B	LO	LO	LO B	LO
Richmond	⊖ d				09 08			09 38			10 08			10 38			11 08			11 38			12 08
Kew Gardens	⊖ d				09 11			09 41			10 11			10 41			11 11			11 41			12 11
Gunnersbury	⊖ d				09 14			09 44			10 14			10 44			11 14			11 44			12 14
South Acton	d				09 16			09 46			10 16			10 46			11 16			11 46			12 16
Acton Central	d				09 19			09 49			10 19			10 49			11 19			11 49			12 19
Willesden Jn. High Level	⊖ a				09 24			09 54			10 24			10 54			11 24			11 54			12 24
	d																						
Kensal Rise	d																						
Brondesbury Park	d																						
Brondesbury	d																						
West Hampstead	⊖ d																						
Finchley Road & Frognal	d																						
Hampstead Heath	d																						
Gospel Oak	d		09 12			09 42			10 12			10 42			11 12			11 42			12 12		
Kentish Town West	d		09 14			09 44			10 14			10 44			11 14			11 44			12 14		
Camden Road	d	08 51	09 17	09 21		09 47	09 51		10 17	10 21		10 47	10 51		11 17	11 21		11 47	11 51		12 17	12 21	
Caledonian Rd & Barnsbury	d	08 54		09 24			09 54			10 24			10 54			11 24			11 54			12 24	
Highbury & Islington	⊖ d	08 56	09a22	09 26		09a52	09 56		10a22	10 26		10a52	10 56		11a22	11 26		11a52	11 56		12a22	12 26	
Canonbury	⊖ d	08 58		09 28			09 58			10 28			10 58			11 28			11 58			12 28	
Dalston Kingsland	d	09 01		09 31			10 01			10 31			11 01			11 31			12 01			12 31	
Hackney Central	d	09 03		09 33			10 03			10 33			11 03			11 33			12 03			12 33	
Homerton	d	09 05		09 35			10 05			10 35			11 05			11 35			12 05			12 35	
Hackney Wick	d	09 08		09 38			10 08			10 38			11 08			11 38			12 08			12 38	
Stratford Low Level 7	⊖ ⛴ a	09 15		09 45			10 15			10 45			11 15			11 45			12 15			12 45	

Station		LO	LO B	LO	LO	LO B	LO	LO	LO B	LO	LO	LO B	LO	LO	LO B	LO	LO	LO B	LO	LO	LO B	LO	LO
Richmond	⊖ d			12 38			13 08			13 38			14 08			14 38			15 08			15 38	
Kew Gardens	⊖ d			12 41			13 11			13 41			14 11			14 41			15 11			15 41	
Gunnersbury	⊖ d			12 44			13 14			13 44			14 14			14 44			15 14			15 44	
South Acton	d			12 46			13 16			13 46			14 16			14 46			15 16			15 46	
Acton Central	d			12 49			13 19			13 49			14 19			14 49			15 19			15 49	
Willesden Jn. High Level	⊖ a			12 54			13 24			13 54			14 24			14 54			15 24			15 54	
	d																						
Kensal Rise	d																						
Brondesbury Park	d																						
Brondesbury	d																						
West Hampstead	⊖ d																						
Finchley Road & Frognal	d																						
Hampstead Heath	d																						
Gospel Oak	d	12 42			13 12			13 42			14 12			14 42			15 12			15 42			16 12
Kentish Town West	d	12 44			13 14			13 44			14 14			14 44			15 14			15 44			16 14
Camden Road	d	12 47	12 51		13 17	13 21		13 47	13 51		14 17	14 21		14 47	14 51		15 17	15 21		15 47	15 51		16 17
Caledonian Rd & Barnsbury	d		12 54			13 24			13 54			14 24			14 54			15 24			15 54		
Highbury & Islington	⊖ d	12a52	12 56		13a22	13 26		13a52	13 56		14a22	14 26		14a52	14 56		15a22	15 26		15a52	15 56		16a22
Canonbury	⊖ d		12 58			13 28			13 58			14 28			14 58			15 28			15 58		
Dalston Kingsland	d		13 01			13 31			14 01			14 31			15 01			15 31			16 01		
Hackney Central	d		13 03			13 33			14 03			14 33			15 03			15 33			16 03		
Homerton	d		13 05			13 35			14 05			14 35			15 05			15 35			16 05		
Hackney Wick	d		13 08			13 38			14 08			14 38			15 08			15 38			16 08		
Stratford Low Level 7	⊖ ⛴ a		13 15			13 45			14 15			14 45			15 15			15 45			16 15		

For general notes see front of timetable
For details of catering facilities see Directory of Train Operators

A From Clapham Junction (Table 186)
B From Willesden Jn Low Level (Table 60)

For passengers requiring stations between Hampstead Heath and Kensal Rise and connections to and from Willesden Junction High Level for services to and from Richmond, please use adjacent stations shown on Table 60, or local bus services. For further details please see local publicity or contact National Rail Enquiries on 08457-48-49-50.

Sundays

Richmond → Willesden Junction, West Hampstead Highbury and Islington and Stratford Low Level

7 September to 16 November

Network diagram - see first page of Table 59

	LO A	LO	LO	LO A	LO	LO	LO A		LO	LO	LO A	LO	LO	LO A	LO		LO	LO A	LO	LO	LO A	LO	LO		LO A
Richmond ⊖ d		16 08			16 38				17 08			17 38			18 08				18 38			19 08			
Kew Gardens ⊖ d		16 11			16 41				17 11			17 41			18 11				18 41			19 11			
Gunnersbury ⊖ d		16 14			16 44				17 14			17 44			18 14				18 44			19 14			
South Acton d		16 16			16 46				17 16			17 46			18 16				18 46			19 16			
Acton Central d		16 19			16 49				17 19			17 49			18 19				18 49			19 19			
Willesden Jn. High Level ⊖ a		16 24			16 54				17 24			17 54			18 24				18 54			19 24			
d																									
Kensal Rise d																									
Brondesbury Park d																									
Brondesbury d																									
West Hampstead ⊖ d																									
Finchley Road & Frognal d																									
Hampstead Heath d																									
Gospel Oak d			16 42			17 12				17 42			18 12				18 42			19 12			19 42		
Kentish Town West d			16 44			17 14				17 44			18 14				18 44			19 14			19 44		
Camden Road d	16 21		16 47	16 51		17 17	17 21			17 47	17 51		18 17	18 21			18 47	18 51		19 17	19 21		19 47		19 51
Caledonian Rd & Barnsbury d	16 24			16 54			17 24				17 54			18 24				18 54			19 24				19 54
Highbury & Islington ⊖ d	16 26		16a52	16 56		17a22	17 26			17a52	17 56		18a22	18 26			18a52	18 56		19a22	19 26		19a52		19 56
Canonbury ⊖ d	16 28			16 58			17 28				17 58			18 28				18 58			19 28				19 58
Dalston Kingsland d	16 31			17 01			17 31				18 01			18 31				19 01			19 31				20 01
Hackney Central d	16 33			17 03			17 33				18 03			18 33				19 03			19 33				20 03
Homerton d	16 35			17 05			17 35				18 05			18 35				19 05			19 35				20 05
Hackney Wick d	16 38			17 08			17 38				18 08			18 38				19 08			19 38				20 08
Stratford Low Level 7 ⊖ ⛴ a	16 45			17 15			17 45				18 15			18 45				19 15			19 45				20 15

	LO	LO	LO A	LO	LO	LO A	LO		LO	LO A	LO	LO	LO A	LO	LO	LO A	LO	LO	LO A	LO	LO	LO	LO A		
Richmond ⊖ d	19 38			20 08			20 38				21 08			21 38			22 08			22 38		23 08			
Kew Gardens ⊖ d	19 41			20 11			20 41				21 11			21 41			22 11			22 41		23 11			
Gunnersbury ⊖ d	19 44			20 14			20 44				21 14			21 44			22 14			22 44		23 14			
South Acton d	19 46			20 16			20 46				21 16			21 46			22 16			22 46		23 16			
Acton Central d	19 49			20 19			20 49				21 19			21 49			22 19			22 49		23 19			
Willesden Jn. High Level ⊖ a	19 54			20 24			20 54				21 24			21 54			22 24			22 54		23 26			
d																									
Kensal Rise d																									
Brondesbury Park d																									
Brondesbury d																									
West Hampstead ⊖ d																									
Finchley Road & Frognal d																									
Hampstead Heath d																									
Gospel Oak d		20 12			20 42				21 12			21 42			22 12			22 42			23 12				
Kentish Town West d		20 14			20 44				21 14			21 44			22 14			22 44			23 14				
Camden Road d		20 17	20 21		20 47	20 51			21 17	21 21		21 47	21 51		22 17	22 21		22 47	22 51		23 17		23 21		
Caledonian Rd & Barnsbury d			20 24			20 54				21 24			21 54			22 24			22 54				23 24		
Highbury & Islington ⊖ d		20a22	20 26		20a52	20 56			21a22	21 26		21a52	21 56		22a22	22 26		22a52	22 56		23a22		23 26		
Canonbury ⊖ d			20 28			20 58				21 28			21 58			22 28			22 58				23 28		
Dalston Kingsland d			20 31			21 01				21 31			22 01			22 31			23 01				23 31		
Hackney Central d			20 33			21 03				21 33			22 03			22 33			23 03				23 33		
Homerton d			20 35			21 05				21 35			22 05			22 35			23 05				23 35		
Hackney Wick d			20 38			21 08				21 38			22 08			22 38			23 08				23 38		
Stratford Low Level 7 ⊖ ⛴ a			20 45			21 15				21 45			22 15			22 45			23 15				23 45		

For general notes see front of timetable
For details of catering facilities see
Directory of Train Operators

A From Willesden Jn Low Level (Table 60)

For passengers requiring stations between Hampstead Heath and Kensal Rise and connections to and from Willesden Junction High Level for services to and from Richmond, please use adjacent stations shown on Table 60, or local bus services. For further details please see local publicity or contact National Rail Enquiries on 08457-48-49-50.

Table 60

Mondays to Fridays

until 29 August and from 17 November

London, Queens Park and Harrow & Wealdstone → Watford Junction

Network Diagram - See first page of Table 59

Miles	Station		LO	LO MX	LO MO	LO MX	LO	LO	LO	LO	LO	LO	LO	LO	LO	LO	LO	LO	LO	LO	LO	LO
0	**London Euston** 15	⊖ d	23p17	23p37	23p47	23p57	05 27	05 57	06 17	06 37	06 57	07 17	07 37	07 57	08 17	08 37	08 57	09 17	09 37	09 57	10 17	10 37
2½	South Hampstead	d	23p23	23p43	23p53	00 03	05 33	06 03	06 23	06 43	07 03	07 23	07 43	08 03	08 23	08 43	09 03	09 23	09 43	10 03	10 23	10 43
3	Kilburn High Road	d	23p24	23p44	23p54	00 04	05 34	06 04	06 24	06 44	07 04	07 24	07 44	08 04	08 24	08 44	09 04	09 24	09 44	10 04	10 24	10 44
3¾	**Queens Park (Dc)**	⊖ d	23p26	23p46	23p56	00 06	05 36	06 06	06 26	06 46	07 06	07 26	07 46	08 06	08 26	08 46	09 06	09 26	09 46	10 06	10 26	10 46
4½	Kensal Green	d	23p28	23p48	23p58	00 08	05 38	06 08	06 28	06 48	07 08	07 28	07 48	08 08	08 28	08 48	09 08	09 28	09 48	10 08	10 28	10 48
5½	**Willesden Jn Low Level**	d	23p31	23p51	00 01	00 11	05 41	06 11	06 31	06 51	07 11	07 31	07 51	08 11	08 31	08 51	09 11	09 31	09 51	10 11	10 31	10 51
6	Harlesden	d	23p33	23p53	00 03	00 13	05 43	06 13	06 33	06 53	07 13	07 33	07 53	08 13	08 33	08 53	09 13	09 33	09 53	10 13	10 33	10 53
7	Stonebridge Park	d	23p35	23p55	00 05	00 15	05 45	06 15	06 35	06 55	07 15	07 35	07 55	08 15	08 35	08 55	09 15	09 35	09 55	10 15	10 35	10 55
8	Wembley Central Dc	d	23p38	23p58	00 08	00 18	05 48	06 18	06 38	06 58	07 18	07 38	07 58	08 18	08 38	08 58	09 18	09 38	09 58	10 18	10 38	10 58
9	North Wembley	d	23p40	00 01	00 10	00 20	05 50	06 20	06 40	07 00	07 20	07 40	08 00	08 20	08 40	09 00	09 20	09 40	10 00	10 20	10 40	11 00
9½	South Kenton	d	23p42	00 02	00 12	00 22	05 52	06 22	06 42	07 02	07 22	07 42	08 02	08 22	08 42	09 02	09 22	09 42	10 02	10 22	10 42	11 02
10¼	Kenton	d	23p44	00 04	00 14	00 24	05 54	06 24	06 44	07 04	07 24	07 44	08 04	08 24	08 44	09 04	09 24	09 44	10 04	10 24	10 44	11 04
11¼	**Harrow & Wealdstone D.C.**	d	23p46	00 06	00 16	00 26	05 56	06 26	06 46	07 06	07 26	07 46	08 06	08 26	08 46	09 06	09 26	09 46	10 06	10 26	10 46	11 06
12½	Headstone Lane	d	23p49	00 09	00 19	00 29	05 59	06 29	06 49	07 09	07 29	07 49	08 09	08 29	08 49	09 09	09 29	09 49	10 09	10 29	10 49	11 09
13¼	Hatch End	d	23p51	00 11	00 21	00 31	06 01	06 31	06 51	07 11	07 31	07 51	08 11	08 31	08 51	09 11	09 31	09 51	10 11	10 31	10 51	11 11
14¾	Carpenders Park	d	23p54	00 14	00 24	00 34	06 04	06 34	06 54	07 14	07 34	07 54	08 14	08 34	08 54	09 14	09 34	09 54	10 14	10 34	10 54	11 14
16	Bushey Dc	d	23p57	00 17	00 27	00 37	06 07	06 37	06 57	07 17	07 37	07 57	08 17	08 37	08 57	09 17	09 37	09 57	10 17	10 37	10 57	11 17
16¾	Watford High Street	d	00 01	00 20	00 30	00 40	06 10	06 40	07 00	07 20	07 40	08 00	08 20	08 40	09 00	09 20	09 40	10 00	10 20	10 40	11 00	11 20
17¾	**Watford Junction Dc**	a	00 04	00 24	00 34	00 44	06 14	06 44	07 05	07 24	07 44	08 04	08 24	08 44	09 04	09 24	09 44	10 04	10 24	10 45	11 04	11 24

Station		LO	LO	LO	LO	LO	LO	LO	LO	LO	LO	LO	LO	LO	LO	LO	LO	LO	LO	LO	LO
London Euston 15	⊖ d	10 57	11 17	11 37	11 57	12 17	12 37	12 57	13 17	13 37	13 57	14 17	14 37	14 57	15 17	15 37	15 57	16 17	16 37	16 57	17 17
South Hampstead	d	11 03	11 23	11 43	12 03	12 23	12 43	13 03	13 23	13 43	14 03	14 23	14 43	15 03	15 23	15 43	16 03	16 23	16 43	17 03	17 23
Kilburn High Road	d	11 04	11 24	11 44	12 04	12 24	12 44	13 04	13 24	13 44	14 04	14 24	14 44	15 04	15 24	15 44	16 04	16 24	16 44	17 04	17 24
Queens Park (Dc)	⊖ d	11 06	11 26	11 46	12 06	12 26	12 46	13 06	13 26	13 46	14 06	14 26	14 46	15 06	15 26	15 46	16 06	16 27	16 47	17 07	17 27
Kensal Green	d	11 08	11 28	11 48	12 08	12 28	12 48	13 08	13 28	13 48	14 08	14 28	14 48	15 08	15 28	15 48	16 08	16 29	16 49	17 09	17 29
Willesden Jn Low Level	d	11 11	11 31	11 51	12 11	12 31	12 51	13 11	13 31	13 51	14 11	14 31	14 51	15 11	15 31	15 51	16 11	16 32	16 52	17 12	17 32
Harlesden	d	11 13	11 33	11 53	12 13	12 33	12 53	13 13	13 33	13 53	14 13	14 33	14 53	15 13	15 33	15 53	16 13	16 34	16 54	17 14	17 34
Stonebridge Park	d	11 15	11 35	11 55	12 15	12 35	12 55	13 15	13 35	13 55	14 15	14 35	14 55	15 15	15 35	15 55	16 15	16 36	16 56	17 16	17 36
Wembley Central Dc	d	11 18	11 38	11 58	12 18	12 38	12 58	13 18	13 38	13 58	14 18	14 38	14 58	15 18	15 38	15 58	16 18	16 39	16 59	17 19	17 39
North Wembley	d	11 20	11 40	12 00	12 20	12 40	13 00	13 20	13 40	14 00	14 20	14 40	15 00	15 20	15 40	16 00	16 20	16 41	17 01	17 21	17 41
South Kenton	d	11 22	11 42	12 02	12 22	12 42	13 02	13 22	13 42	14 02	14 22	14 42	15 02	15 22	15 42	16 02	16 22	16 43	17 03	17 23	17 43
Kenton	d	11 24	11 44	12 04	12 24	12 44	13 04	13 24	13 44	14 04	14 24	14 44	15 04	15 24	15 44	16 04	16 24	16 45	17 05	17 25	17 45
Harrow & Wealdstone D.C.	d	11 26	11 46	12 06	12 26	12 46	13 06	13 26	13 46	14 06	14 26	14 46	15 06	15 26	15 46	16 06	16 26	16 48	17 08	17 28	17 48
Headstone Lane	d	11 29	11 49	12 09	12 29	12 49	13 09	13 29	13 49	14 09	14 29	14 49	15 09	15 29	15 49	16 09	16 29	16 51	17 11	17 31	17 51
Hatch End	d	11 31	11 51	12 11	12 31	12 51	13 11	13 31	13 51	14 11	14 31	14 51	15 11	15 31	15 51	16 11	16 31	16 53	17 13	17 33	17 53
Carpenders Park	d	11 34	11 54	12 14	12 34	12 54	13 14	13 34	13 54	14 14	14 34	14 54	15 14	15 34	15 54	16 14	16 34	16 56	17 16	17 36	17 56
Bushey Dc	d	11 37	11 57	12 17	12 37	12 57	13 17	13 37	13 57	14 17	14 37	14 57	15 17	15 37	15 57	16 17	16 37	16 59	17 19	17 39	17 59
Watford High Street	d	11 40	12 00	12 20	12 40	13 00	13 20	13 40	14 00	14 20	14 40	15 00	15 20	15 40	16 00	16 20	16 40	17 01	17 21	17 41	18 01
Watford Junction Dc	a	11 44	12 04	12 24	12 44	13 04	13 24	13 44	14 04	14 24	14 44	15 04	15 24	15 44	16 04	16 24	16 44	17 06	17 26	17 48	18 08

Station		LO	LO	LO	LO	LO	LO	LO	LO	LO	LO	LO	LO	LO	LO	LO	LO	LO	LO	LO	LO
London Euston 15	⊖ d	17 37	17 57	18 17	18 37	18 57	19 17	19 37	19 57	20 17	20 37	20 57	21 17	21 37	21 57	22 17	22 37	22 57	23 17	23 37	23 57
South Hampstead	d	17 43	18 03	18 23	18 43	19 03	19 23	19 43	20 03	20 23	20 43	21 03	21 23	21 43	22 03	22 23	22 43	23 03	23 23	23 43	00 03
Kilburn High Road	d	17 44	18 04	18 24	18 44	19 04	19 24	19 44	20 04	20 24	20 44	21 04	21 24	21 44	22 04	22 24	22 44	23 04	23 24	23 44	00 04
Queens Park (Dc)	⊖ d	17 47	18 07	18 27	18 47	19 07	19 26	19 46	20 06	20 26	20 46	21 06	21 26	21 46	22 06	22 26	22 46	23 06	23 26	23 46	00 06
Kensal Green	d	17 49	18 09	18 29	18 49	19 09	19 28	19 48	20 08	20 28	20 48	21 08	21 28	21 48	22 08	22 28	22 48	23 08	23 28	23 48	00 08
Willesden Jn Low Level	d	17 52	18 12	18 32	18 52	19 12	19 31	19 51	20 11	20 31	20 51	21 11	21 31	21 51	22 11	22 31	22 51	23 11	23 31	23 51	00 11
Harlesden	d	17 54	18 14	18 34	18 54	19 14	19 33	19 53	20 13	20 33	20 53	21 13	21 33	21 53	22 13	22 33	22 53	23 13	23 33	23 53	00 13
Stonebridge Park	d	17 56	18 16	18 36	18 56	19 16	19 35	19 55	20 15	20 35	20 55	21 15	21 35	21 55	22 15	22 35	22 55	23 15	23 35	23 55	00 15
Wembley Central Dc	d	17 59	18 19	18 39	18 59	19 19	19 38	19 58	20 18	20 38	20 58	21 18	21 38	21 58	22 18	22 38	22 58	23 18	23 38	23 58	00 18
North Wembley	d	18 01	18 21	18 41	19 01	19 21	19 40	20 00	20 20	20 40	21 00	21 20	21 40	22 00	22 20	22 40	23 00	23 20	23 40	00 01	00 20
South Kenton	d	18 03	18 23	18 43	19 03	19 23	19 42	20 02	20 22	20 42	21 02	21 22	21 42	22 02	22 22	22 42	23 02	23 22	23 42	00 02	00 22
Kenton	d	18 05	18 25	18 45	19 05	19 25	19 44	20 04	20 24	20 44	21 04	21 24	21 44	22 04	22 24	22 44	23 04	23 24	23 44	00 04	00 24
Harrow & Wealdstone D.C.	d	18 08	18 28	18 48	19 08	19 28	19 46	20 06	20 26	20 46	21 06	21 26	21 46	22 06	22 26	22 46	23 06	23 26	23 46	00 06	00 26
Headstone Lane	d	18 11	18 31	18 51	19 11	19 31	19 49	20 09	20 29	20 49	21 09	21 29	21 49	22 09	22 29	22 49	23 09	23 29	23 49	00 09	00 29
Hatch End	d	18 13	18 33	18 53	19 13	19 33	19 51	20 11	20 31	20 51	21 11	21 31	21 51	22 11	22 31	22 51	23 11	23 31	23 51	00 11	00 31
Carpenders Park	d	18 16	18 36	18 56	19 16	19 36	19 54	20 14	20 34	20 54	21 14	21 34	21 54	22 14	22 34	22 54	23 14	23 34	23 54	00 14	00 34
Bushey Dc	d	18 19	18 39	18 59	19 19	19 39	19 57	20 17	20 37	20 57	21 17	21 37	21 57	22 17	22 37	22 57	23 17	23 37	23 57	00 17	00 37
Watford High Street	d	18 21	18 41	19 01	19 21	19 41	20 00	20 20	20 40	21 00	21 20	21 40	22 00	22 20	22 40	23 00	23 20	23 40	00 01	00 20	00 40
Watford Junction Dc	a	18 28	18 48	19 08	19 28	19 48	20 04	20 24	20 44	21 04	21 24	21 44	22 04	22 24	22 44	23 04	23 24	23 44	00 04	00 24	00 44

For general notes see front of timetable
For details of catering facilities see Directory of Train Operators

Stations Queen's Park to Harrow & Wealdstone inclusive are also served by London Underground Bakerloo line services

Table 60

Mondays to Fridays

1 September to 14 November

London, Queens Park and Harrow & Wealdstone → Watford Junction

Network Diagram - See first page of Table 59

		LO MX A	LO MO	LO MX A	LO MO	LO MX A	LO	LO	LO A	LO A	LO A	LO A	LO A	LO A	LO A	LO A	LO A	LO A	LO A	LO A	LO A	LO A
London Euston 15	⊖ d		23p17		23p47																	
South Hampstead	d	23p21	23p23	23p41	23p53	00 01			06 21	06 41	07 01	07 21	07 41	08 01	08 21	08 41	09 01	09 21	09 41	10 01	10 21	10 41
Kilburn High Road	d	23p22	23p24	23p42	23p54	00 02			06 22	06 42	07 02	07 22	07 42	08 02	08 22	08 42	09 02	09 22	09 42	10 02	10 22	10 42
Queens Park (Dc)	⊖ d	23p26	23p26	23p46	23p56	00 05	05 36	06 06	06 26	06 46	07 06	07 26	07 46	08 06	08 26	08 46	09 06	09 26	09 46	10 06	10 26	10 46
Kensal Green	d	23p28	23p28	23p48	23p58	00 08	05 38	06 08	06 28	06 48	07 08	07 28	07 48	08 08	08 28	08 48	09 08	09 28	09 48	10 08	10 28	10 48
Willesden Jn Low Level	d	23p31	23p31	23p51	00 01	00 11	05 41	06 11	06 31	06 51	07 11	07 31	07 51	08 11	08 31	08 51	09 11	09 31	09 51	10 11	10 31	10 51
Harlesden	d	23p33	23p33	23p53	00 03	00 13	05 43	06 13	06 33	06 53	07 13	07 33	07 53	08 13	08 33	08 53	09 13	09 33	09 53	10 13	10 33	10 53
Stonebridge Park	d	23p35	23p35	23p55	00 05	00 15	05 45	06 15	06 35	06 55	07 15	07 35	07 55	08 15	08 35	08 55	09 15	09 35	09 55	10 15	10 35	10 55
Wembley Central Dc	d	23p38	23p38	23p58	00 08	00 18	05 48	06 18	06 38	06 58	07 18	07 38	07 58	08 18	08 38	08 58	09 18	09 38	09 58	10 18	10 38	10 58
North Wembley	d	23p40	23p40	00 01	00 10	00 20	05 50	06 20	06 40	07 00	07 20	07 40	08 00	08 20	08 40	09 00	09 20	09 40	10 00	10 20	10 40	11 00
South Kenton	d	23p42	23p42	00 02	00 12	00 22	05 52	06 22	06 42	07 02	07 22	07 42	08 02	08 22	08 42	09 02	09 22	09 42	10 02	10 22	10 42	11 02
Kenton	d	23p44	23p44	00 04	00 14	00 24	05 54	06 24	06 44	07 04	07 24	07 44	08 04	08 24	08 44	09 04	09 24	09 44	10 04	10 24	10 44	11 04
Harrow & Wealdstone D.C.	d	23p46	23p46	00 06	00 16	00 26	05 56	06 26	06 46	07 06	07 26	07 46	08 06	08 26	08 46	09 06	09 26	09 46	10 06	10 26	10 46	11 06
Headstone Lane	d	23p49	23p49	00 09	00 19	00 29	05 59	06 29	06 49	07 09	07 29	07 49	08 09	08 29	08 49	09 09	09 29	09 49	10 09	10 29	10 49	11 09
Hatch End	d	23p51	23p51	00 11	00 21	00 31	06 01	06 31	06 51	07 11	07 31	07 51	08 11	08 31	08 51	09 11	09 31	09 51	10 11	10 31	10 51	11 11
Carpenders Park	d	23p54	23p54	00 14	00 24	00 34	06 04	06 34	06 54	07 14	07 34	07 54	08 14	08 34	08 54	09 14	09 34	09 54	10 14	10 34	10 54	11 14
Bushey Dc	d	23p57	23p57	00 17	00 27	00 37	06 07	06 37	06 57	07 17	07 37	07 57	08 17	08 37	08 57	09 17	09 37	09 57	10 17	10 37	10 57	11 17
Watford High Street	d	00 01	00 01	00 20	00 30	00 40	06 10	06 40	07 00	07 20	07 40	08 00	08 20	08 40	09 00	09 20	09 40	10 00	10 20	10 40	11 00	11 20
Watford Junction Dc	a	00 04	00 04	00 24	00 34	00 44	06 14	06 44	07 05	07 24	07 44	08 04	08 24	08 44	09 04	09 24	09 44	10 04	10 24	10 45	11 04	11 24

		LO A	LO A	LO A	LO A	LO A	LO A	LO A	LO A	LO A	LO A	LO A	LO A	LO A	LO A	LO A	LO A	LO A	LO A	LO A	LO A
London Euston 15	⊖ d																				
South Hampstead	d	11 01	11 21	11 41	12 01	12 21	12 41	13 01	13 21	13 41	14 01	14 21	14 41	15 01	15 21	15 41	16 01	16 21	16 41	17 01	17 21
Kilburn High Road	d	11 02	11 22	11 42	12 02	12 22	12 42	13 02	13 22	13 42	14 02	14 22	14 42	15 02	15 22	15 42	16 02	16 22	16 42	17 02	17 22
Queens Park (Dc)	⊖ d	11 06	11 26	11 46	12 06	12 26	12 46	13 06	13 26	13 46	14 06	14 26	14 46	15 06	15 26	15 46	16 06	16 27	16 47	17 07	17 27
Kensal Green	d	11 08	11 28	11 48	12 08	12 28	12 48	13 08	13 28	13 48	14 08	14 28	14 48	15 08	15 28	15 48	16 08	16 29	16 49	17 09	17 29
Willesden Jn Low Level	d	11 11	11 31	11 51	12 11	12 31	12 51	13 11	13 31	13 51	14 11	14 31	14 51	15 11	15 31	15 51	16 11	16 32	16 52	17 12	17 32
Harlesden	d	11 13	11 33	11 53	12 13	12 33	12 53	13 13	13 33	13 53	14 13	14 33	14 53	15 13	15 33	15 53	16 13	16 34	16 54	17 14	17 34
Stonebridge Park	d	11 15	11 35	11 55	12 15	12 35	12 55	13 15	13 35	13 55	14 15	14 35	14 55	15 15	15 35	15 55	16 15	16 36	16 56	17 16	17 36
Wembley Central Dc	d	11 18	11 38	11 58	12 18	12 38	12 58	13 18	13 38	13 58	14 18	14 38	14 58	15 18	15 38	15 58	16 18	16 39	16 59	17 19	17 39
North Wembley	d	11 20	11 40	12 00	12 20	12 40	13 00	13 20	13 40	14 00	14 20	14 40	15 00	15 20	15 40	16 00	16 20	16 41	17 01	17 21	17 41
South Kenton	d	11 22	11 42	12 02	12 22	12 42	13 02	13 22	13 42	14 02	14 22	14 42	15 02	15 22	15 42	16 02	16 22	16 43	17 03	17 23	17 43
Kenton	d	11 24	11 44	12 04	12 24	12 44	13 04	13 24	13 44	14 04	14 24	14 44	15 04	15 24	15 44	16 04	16 24	16 45	17 05	17 25	17 45
Harrow & Wealdstone D.C.	d	11 26	11 46	12 06	12 26	12 46	13 06	13 26	13 46	14 06	14 26	14 46	15 06	15 26	15 46	16 06	16 26	16 48	17 08	17 28	17 48
Headstone Lane	d	11 29	11 49	12 09	12 29	12 49	13 09	13 29	13 49	14 09	14 29	14 49	15 09	15 29	15 49	16 09	16 29	16 51	17 11	17 31	17 51
Hatch End	d	11 31	11 51	12 11	12 31	12 51	13 11	13 31	13 51	14 11	14 31	14 51	15 11	15 31	15 51	16 11	16 31	16 53	17 13	17 33	17 53
Carpenders Park	d	11 34	11 54	12 14	12 34	12 54	13 14	13 34	13 54	14 14	14 34	14 54	15 14	15 34	15 54	16 14	16 34	16 56	17 16	17 36	17 56
Bushey Dc	d	11 37	11 57	12 17	12 37	12 57	13 17	13 37	13 57	14 17	14 37	14 57	15 17	15 37	15 57	16 17	16 37	16 59	17 19	17 39	17 59
Watford High Street	d	11 40	12 00	12 20	12 40	13 00	13 20	13 40	14 00	14 20	14 40	15 00	15 20	15 40	16 00	16 20	16 40	17 01	17 21	17 41	18 01
Watford Junction Dc	a	11 44	12 04	12 24	12 44	13 04	13 24	13 44	14 04	14 24	14 44	15 04	15 24	15 44	16 04	16 24	16 44	17 06	17 26	17 48	18 08

		LO A	LO A	LO A	LO A	LO A	LO A	LO A	LO A	LO A	LO A	LO A	LO A	LO A	LO A	LO A	LO A	LO A	LO A	LO A
London Euston 15	⊖ d																			
South Hampstead	d	17 41	18 01	18 21	18 41	19 01	19 21	19 41	20 01	20 21	20 41	21 01	21 21	21 41	22 01	22 21	22 41	23 01	23 21	23 41
Kilburn High Road	d	17 42	18 02	18 22	18 42	19 02	19 22	19 42	20 02	20 22	20 42	21 02	21 22	21 42	22 02	22 22	22 42	23 02	23 22	23 42
Queens Park (Dc)	⊖ d	17 47	18 07	18 27	18 47	19 07	19 26	19 46	20 06	20 26	20 46	21 06	21 26	21 46	22 06	22 26	22 46	23 06	23 26	23 46
Kensal Green	d	17 49	18 09	18 29	18 49	19 09	19 28	19 48	20 08	20 28	20 48	21 08	21 28	21 48	22 08	22 28	22 48	23 08	23 28	23 48
Willesden Jn Low Level	d	17 52	18 12	18 32	18 52	19 12	19 31	19 51	20 11	20 31	20 51	21 11	21 31	21 51	22 11	22 31	22 51	23 11	23 31	23 51
Harlesden	d	17 54	18 14	18 34	18 54	19 14	19 33	19 53	20 13	20 33	20 53	21 13	21 33	21 53	22 13	22 33	22 53	23 13	23 33	23 53
Stonebridge Park	d	17 56	18 16	18 36	18 56	19 16	19 35	19 55	20 15	20 35	20 55	21 15	21 35	21 55	22 15	22 35	22 55	23 15	23 35	23 55
Wembley Central Dc	d	17 59	18 19	18 39	18 59	19 19	19 38	19 58	20 18	20 38	20 58	21 18	21 38	21 58	22 18	22 38	22 58	23 18	23 38	23 58
North Wembley	d	18 01	18 21	18 41	19 01	19 21	19 40	20 00	20 20	20 40	21 00	21 20	21 40	22 00	22 20	22 40	23 00	23 20	23 40	00 01
South Kenton	d	18 03	18 23	18 43	19 03	19 23	19 42	20 02	20 22	20 42	21 02	21 22	21 42	22 02	22 22	22 42	23 02	23 22	23 42	00 02
Kenton	d	18 05	18 25	18 45	19 05	19 25	19 44	20 04	20 24	20 44	21 04	21 24	21 44	22 04	22 24	22 44	23 04	23 24	23 44	00 04
Harrow & Wealdstone D.C.	d	18 08	18 28	18 48	19 08	19 28	19 46	20 06	20 26	20 46	21 06	21 26	21 46	22 06	22 26	22 46	23 06	23 26	23 46	00 06
Headstone Lane	d	18 11	18 31	18 51	19 11	19 31	19 49	20 09	20 29	20 49	21 09	21 29	21 49	22 09	22 29	22 49	23 09	23 29	23 49	00 09
Hatch End	d	18 13	18 33	18 53	19 13	19 33	19 51	20 11	20 31	20 51	21 11	21 31	21 51	22 11	22 31	22 51	23 11	23 31	23 51	00 11
Carpenders Park	d	18 16	18 36	18 56	19 16	19 36	19 54	20 14	20 34	20 54	21 14	21 34	21 54	22 14	22 34	22 54	23 14	23 34	23 54	00 14
Bushey Dc	d	18 19	18 39	18 59	19 19	19 39	19 57	20 17	20 37	20 57	21 17	21 37	21 57	22 17	22 37	22 57	23 17	23 37	23 57	00 17
Watford High Street	d	18 21	18 41	19 01	19 21	19 41	20 00	20 20	20 40	21 00	21 20	21 40	22 00	22 20	22 40	23 00	23 20	23 40	00 01	00 20
Watford Junction Dc	a	18 28	18 48	19 08	19 28	19 48	20 04	20 24	20 44	21 04	21 24	21 44	22 04	22 24	22 44	23 04	23 24	23 44	00 04	00 24

For general notes see front of timetable
For details of catering facilities see
Directory of Train Operators

A From Stratford Low Level (Table 59)

Stations Queen's Park to Harrow & Wealdstone inclusive are also served by London Underground Bakerloo line services

Table 60

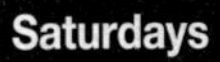

Saturdays

until 30 August and from 22 November

London, Queens Park and Harrow & Wealdstone → Watford Junction

Network Diagram - See first page of Table 59

		LO	LO	LO	LO	LO	LO	LO	LO	LO	LO	LO	LO	LO	LO	LO	LO	LO	LO	LO	LO
London Euston 15 ⊖	d	23p17	23p37	23p57	05 27	05 57	06 17	06 37	06 57	07 17	07 37	07 57	08 17	08 37	08 57	09 17	09 37	09 57	10 17	10 37	10 57	11 17
South Hampstead	d	23p23	23p43	00 03	05 33	06 03	06 23	06 43	07 03	07 23	07 43	08 03	08 23	08 43	09 03	09 23	09 43	10 03	10 23	10 43	11 03	11 23
Kilburn High Road	d	23p24	23p44	00 04	05 34	06 04	06 24	06 44	07 04	07 24	07 44	08 04	08 24	08 44	09 04	09 24	09 44	10 04	10 24	10 44	11 04	11 24
Queens Park (Dc) ⊖	d	23p26	23p46	00 06	05 36	06 06	06 26	06 46	07 06	07 26	07 46	08 06	08 26	08 46	09 06	09 26	09 46	10 06	10 26	10 46	11 06	11 26
Kensal Green	d	23p28	23p48	00 08	05 38	06 08	06 28	06 48	07 08	07 28	07 48	08 08	08 28	08 48	09 08	09 28	09 48	10 08	10 28	10 48	11 08	11 28
Willesden Jn Low Level	d	23p31	23p51	00 11	05 41	06 11	06 32	06 51	07 11	07 31	07 51	08 11	08 31	08 51	09 11	09 31	09 51	10 11	10 31	10 51	11 11	11 31
Harlesden	d	23p33	23p53	00 13	05 43	06 13	06 33	06 53	07 13	07 33	07 53	08 13	08 33	08 53	09 13	09 33	09 53	10 13	10 33	10 53	11 13	11 33
Stonebridge Park	d	23p35	23p55	00 15	05 45	06 15	06 35	06 55	07 15	07 35	07 55	08 15	08 35	08 55	09 15	09 35	09 55	10 15	10 35	10 55	11 15	11 35
Wembley Central Dc	d	23p38	23p58	00 18	05 48	06 18	06 38	06 58	07 18	07 38	07 58	08 18	08 38	08 58	09 18	09 38	09 58	10 18	10 38	10 58	11 18	11 38
North Wembley	d	23p40	00 01	00 20	05 50	06 20	06 40	07 00	07 20	07 40	08 00	08 20	08 40	09 00	09 20	09 40	10 00	10 20	10 40	11 00	11 20	11 40
South Kenton	d	23p42	00 02	00 22	05 52	06 22	06 42	07 02	07 22	07 42	08 02	08 22	08 42	09 02	09 22	09 42	10 02	10 22	10 42	11 02	11 22	11 42
Kenton	d	23p44	00 04	00 24	05 54	06 24	06 44	07 04	07 24	07 44	08 04	08 24	08 44	09 04	09 24	09 44	10 04	10 24	10 44	11 04	11 24	11 44
Harrow & Wealdstone D.C.	d	23p46	00 06	00 26	05 56	06 26	06 46	07 06	07 26	07 46	08 06	08 26	08 46	09 06	09 26	09 46	10 06	10 26	10 46	11 06	11 26	11 46
Headstone Lane	d	23p49	00 09	00 29	05 59	06 29	06 49	07 09	07 29	07 49	08 09	08 29	08 49	09 09	09 29	09 49	10 09	10 29	10 49	11 09	11 29	11 49
Hatch End	d	23p51	00 11	00 31	06 01	06 31	06 51	07 11	07 31	07 51	08 11	08 31	08 51	09 11	09 31	09 51	10 11	10 31	10 51	11 11	11 31	11 51
Carpenders Park	d	23p54	00 14	00 34	06 04	06 34	06 54	07 14	07 34	07 54	08 14	08 34	08 54	09 14	09 34	09 54	10 14	10 34	10 54	11 14	11 34	11 54
Bushey Dc	d	23p57	00 17	00 37	06 07	06 37	06 57	07 17	07 37	07 57	08 17	08 37	08 57	09 17	09 37	09 57	10 17	10 37	10 57	11 17	11 37	11 57
Watford High Street	d	00 01	00 20	00 40	06 10	06 40	07 00	07 20	07 40	08 00	08 20	08 40	09 00	09 20	09 40	10 00	10 20	10 40	11 00	11 20	11 40	12 00
Watford Junction Dc	a	00 04	00 24	00 44	06 14	06 44	07 05	07 24	07 44	08 04	08 24	08 44	09 04	09 24	09 44	10 04	10 24	10 44	11 04	11 24	11 44	12 04

		LO	LO	LO	LO	LO	LO	LO	LO	LO	LO	LO	LO	LO	LO	LO	LO	LO	LO	LO	LO
London Euston 15 ⊖	d	11 37	11 57	12 17	12 37	12 57	13 17	13 37	13 57	14 17	14 37	14 57	15 17	15 37	15 57	16 17	16 37	16 57	17 17	17 37	17 57
South Hampstead	d	11 43	12 03	12 23	12 43	13 03	13 23	13 43	14 03	14 23	14 43	15 03	15 23	15 43	16 03	16 23	16 43	17 03	17 23	17 43	18 03
Kilburn High Road	d	11 44	12 04	12 24	12 44	13 04	13 24	13 44	14 04	14 24	14 44	15 04	15 24	15 44	16 04	16 24	16 44	17 04	17 24	17 44	18 04
Queens Park (Dc) ⊖	d	11 46	12 06	12 26	12 46	13 06	13 26	13 46	14 06	14 26	14 46	15 06	15 26	15 46	16 06	16 26	16 46	17 06	17 26	17 46	18 06
Kensal Green	d	11 48	12 08	12 28	12 48	13 08	13 28	13 48	14 08	14 28	14 48	15 08	15 28	15 48	16 08	16 28	16 48	17 08	17 28	17 48	18 08
Willesden Jn Low Level	d	11 51	12 11	12 31	12 51	13 11	13 31	13 51	14 11	14 31	14 51	15 11	15 31	15 51	16 11	16 31	16 51	17 11	17 31	17 51	18 11
Harlesden	d	11 53	12 13	12 33	12 53	13 13	13 33	13 53	14 13	14 33	14 53	15 13	15 33	15 53	16 13	16 33	16 53	17 13	17 33	17 53	18 13
Stonebridge Park	d	11 55	12 15	12 35	12 55	13 15	13 35	13 55	14 15	14 35	14 55	15 15	15 35	15 55	16 15	16 35	16 55	17 15	17 35	17 55	18 15
Wembley Central Dc	d	11 58	12 18	12 38	12 58	13 18	13 38	13 58	14 18	14 38	14 58	15 18	15 38	15 58	16 18	16 38	16 58	17 18	17 38	17 58	18 18
North Wembley	d	12 00	12 20	12 40	13 00	13 20	13 40	14 00	14 20	14 40	15 00	15 20	15 40	16 00	16 20	16 40	17 00	17 20	17 40	18 00	18 20
South Kenton	d	12 02	12 22	12 42	13 02	13 22	13 42	14 02	14 22	14 42	15 02	15 22	15 42	16 02	16 22	16 42	17 02	17 22	17 42	18 02	18 22
Kenton	d	12 04	12 24	12 44	13 04	13 24	13 44	14 04	14 24	14 44	15 04	15 24	15 44	16 04	16 24	16 44	17 04	17 24	17 44	18 04	18 24
Harrow & Wealdstone D.C.	d	12 06	12 26	12 46	13 06	13 26	13 46	14 06	14 26	14 46	15 06	15 26	15 46	16 06	16 26	16 46	17 06	17 26	17 46	18 06	18 26
Headstone Lane	d	12 09	12 29	12 49	13 09	13 29	13 49	14 09	14 29	14 49	15 09	15 29	15 49	16 09	16 29	16 49	17 09	17 29	17 49	18 09	18 29
Hatch End	d	12 11	12 31	12 51	13 11	13 31	13 51	14 11	14 31	14 51	15 11	15 31	15 51	16 11	16 31	16 51	17 11	17 31	17 51	18 11	18 31
Carpenders Park	d	12 14	12 34	12 54	13 14	13 34	13 54	14 14	14 34	14 54	15 14	15 34	15 54	16 14	16 34	16 54	17 14	17 34	17 54	18 14	18 34
Bushey Dc	d	12 17	12 37	12 57	13 17	13 37	13 57	14 17	14 37	14 57	15 17	15 37	15 57	16 17	16 37	16 57	17 17	17 37	17 57	18 17	18 37
Watford High Street	d	12 20	12 40	13 00	13 20	13 40	14 00	14 20	14 40	15 00	15 20	15 40	16 00	16 20	16 40	17 00	17 20	17 40	18 00	18 20	18 40
Watford Junction Dc	a	12 24	12 44	13 04	13 24	13 44	14 04	14 24	14 44	15 04	15 24	15 44	16 04	16 24	16 44	17 04	17 24	17 44	18 04	18 24	18 44

		LO	LO	LO	LO	LO	LO	LO	LO	LO	LO	LO	LO	LO	LO	LO	LO	LO	LO
London Euston 15 ⊖	d	18 17	18 37	18 57	19 17	19 37	19 57	20 17	20 37	20 57	21 17	21 37	21 57	22 17	22 37	22 57	23 17	23 37	23 57
South Hampstead	d	18 23	18 43	19 03	19 23	19 43	20 03	20 23	20 43	21 03	21 23	21 43	22 03	22 23	22 43	23 03	23 23	23 43	00 03
Kilburn High Road	d	18 24	18 44	19 04	19 24	19 44	20 04	20 24	20 44	21 04	21 24	21 44	22 04	22 24	22 44	23 04	23 24	23 44	00 04
Queens Park (Dc) ⊖	d	18 26	18 46	19 06	19 26	19 46	20 06	20 26	20 46	21 06	21 26	21 46	22 06	22 26	22 46	23 06	23 26	23 46	00 06
Kensal Green	d	18 28	18 48	19 08	19 28	19 48	20 08	20 28	20 48	21 08	21 28	21 48	22 08	22 28	22 48	23 08	23 28	23 48	00 08
Willesden Jn Low Level	d	18 31	18 51	19 11	19 31	19 51	20 11	20 31	20 51	21 11	21 33	21 51	22 11	22 31	22 51	23 11	23 31	23 51	00 11
Harlesden	d	18 33	18 53	19 13	19 33	19 53	20 13	20 33	20 53	21 13	21 35	21 53	22 13	22 33	22 53	23 13	23 33	23 53	00 13
Stonebridge Park	d	18 35	18 55	19 15	19 35	19 55	20 15	20 35	20 55	21 15	21 37	21 55	22 15	22 35	22 55	23 15	23 35	23 55	00 15
Wembley Central Dc	d	18 38	18 58	19 18	19 38	19 58	20 18	20 38	20 58	21 18	21 40	21 58	22 18	22 38	22 58	23 18	23 38	23 58	00 18
North Wembley	d	18 40	19 00	19 20	19 40	20 00	20 20	20 40	21 00	21 20	21 42	22 00	22 20	22 40	23 00	23 20	23 40	00 01	00 20
South Kenton	d	18 42	19 02	19 22	19 42	20 02	20 22	20 42	21 02	21 22	21 44	22 02	22 22	22 42	23 02	23 22	23 42	00 02	00 22
Kenton	d	18 44	19 04	19 24	19 44	20 04	20 24	20 44	21 04	21 24	21 46	22 04	22 24	22 44	23 04	23 24	23 44	00 04	00 24
Harrow & Wealdstone D.C.	d	18 46	19 06	19 26	19 46	20 06	20 26	20 46	21 06	21 26	21 48	22 06	22 26	22 46	23 06	23 26	23 46	00 06	00 26
Headstone Lane	d	18 49	19 09	19 29	19 49	20 09	20 29	20 49	21 09	21 29	21 51	22 09	22 29	22 49	23 09	23 29	23 49	00 09	00 29
Hatch End	d	18 51	19 11	19 31	19 51	20 11	20 31	20 51	21 11	21 31	21 53	22 11	22 31	22 51	23 11	23 31	23 51	00 11	00 31
Carpenders Park	d	18 54	19 14	19 34	19 54	20 14	20 34	20 54	21 14	21 34	21 56	22 14	22 34	22 54	23 14	23 34	23 54	00 14	00 34
Bushey Dc	d	18 57	19 17	19 37	19 57	20 17	20 37	20 57	21 17	21 37	21 59	22 17	22 37	22 57	23 17	23 37	23 57	00 17	00 37
Watford High Street	d	19 00	19 20	19 40	20 00	20 20	20 40	21 00	21 20	21 40	22 02	22 20	22 40	23 00	23 20	23 40	00 01	00 20	00 40
Watford Junction Dc	a	19 04	19 24	19 44	20 04	20 24	20 44	21 04	21 24	21 44	22 06	22 24	22 44	23 04	23 24	23 44	00 04	00 24	00 44

For general notes see front of timetable
For details of catering facilities see Directory of Train Operators

Stations Queen's Park to Harrow & Wealdstone inclusive are also served by London Underground Bakerloo line services

Table 60

6 September to 15 November

London, Queens Park and Harrow & Wealdstone → Watford Junction

Network Diagram - See first page of Table 59

		LO A	LO A	LO A	LO	LO	LO A	LO A	LO A	LO A	LO A	LO A	LO A	LO A	LO A	LO A	LO A	LO A	LO A	LO A
London Euston [15] ⊖	d																			
South Hampstead	d	23p21	23p41	00 01			06 21	06 41	07 01	07 21	07 41	08 01	08 21	08 41	09 01	09 21	09 41	10 01	10 21	10 41
Kilburn High Road	d	23p22	23p42	00 02			06 22	06 42	07 02	07 22	07 42	08 02	08 22	08 42	09 02	09 22	09 42	10 02	10 22	10 42
Queens Park (Dc) ⊖	d	23p26	23p46	00 05	05 36	06 06	06 26	06 46	07 06	07 26	07 46	08 06	08 26	08 46	09 06	09 26	09 46	10 06	10 26	10 46
Kensal Green	d	23p28	23p48	00 08	05 38	06 08	06 28	06 48	07 08	07 28	07 48	08 08	08 28	08 48	09 08	09 28	09 48	10 08	10 28	10 48
Willesden Jn Low Level	d	23p31	23p51	00 11	05 41	06 11	06 32	06 51	07 11	07 31	07 51	08 11	08 31	08 51	09 11	09 31	09 51	10 11	10 31	10 51
Harlesden	d	23p33	23p53	00 13	05 43	06 13	06 33	06 53	07 13	07 33	07 53	08 13	08 33	08 53	09 13	09 33	09 53	10 13	10 33	10 53
Stonebridge Park	d	23p35	23p55	00 15	05 45	06 15	06 35	06 55	07 15	07 35	07 55	08 15	08 35	08 55	09 15	09 35	09 55	10 15	10 35	10 55
Wembley Central Dc	d	23p38	23p58	00 18	05 48	06 18	06 38	06 58	07 18	07 38	07 58	08 18	08 38	08 58	09 18	09 38	09 58	10 18	10 38	10 58
North Wembley	d	23p40	00 00	00 20	05 50	06 20	06 40	07 00	07 20	07 40	08 00	08 20	08 40	09 00	09 20	09 40	10 00	10 20	10 40	11 00
South Kenton	d	23p42	00 02	00 22	05 52	06 22	06 42	07 02	07 22	07 42	08 02	08 22	08 42	09 02	09 22	09 42	10 02	10 22	10 42	11 02
Kenton	d	23p44	00 04	00 24	05 54	06 24	06 44	07 04	07 24	07 44	08 04	08 24	08 44	09 04	09 24	09 44	10 04	10 24	10 44	11 04
Harrow & Wealdstone D.C.	d	23p46	00 06	00 26	05 56	06 26	06 46	07 06	07 26	07 46	08 06	08 26	08 46	09 06	09 26	09 46	10 06	10 26	10 46	11 06
Headstone Lane	d	23p49	00 09	00 29	05 59	06 29	06 49	07 09	07 29	07 49	08 09	08 29	08 49	09 09	09 29	09 49	10 09	10 29	10 49	11 09
Hatch End	d	23p51	00 11	00 31	06 01	06 31	06 51	07 11	07 31	07 51	08 11	08 31	08 51	09 11	09 31	09 51	10 11	10 31	10 51	11 11
Carpenders Park	d	23p54	00 14	00 34	06 04	06 34	06 54	07 14	07 34	07 54	08 14	08 34	08 54	09 14	09 34	09 54	10 14	10 34	10 54	11 14
Bushey Dc	d	23p57	00 17	00 37	06 07	06 37	06 57	07 17	07 37	07 57	08 17	08 37	08 57	09 17	09 37	09 57	10 17	10 37	10 57	11 17
Watford High Street	d	00 01	00 20	00 40	06 10	06 40	07 00	07 20	07 40	08 00	08 20	08 40	09 00	09 20	09 40	10 00	10 20	10 40	11 00	11 20
Watford Junction Dc	a	00 04	00 24	00 44	06 14	06 44	07 05	07 24	07 44	08 04	08 24	08 44	09 04	09 24	09 44	10 04	10 24	10 44	11 04	11 24

		LO A	LO A	LO A	LO A	LO A	LO A	LO A	LO A	LO A	LO A	LO A	LO A	LO A	LO A	LO A	LO A	LO A	LO A	LO A
London Euston [15] ⊖	d																			
South Hampstead	d	11 01	11 21	11 41	12 01	12 21	12 41	13 01	13 21	13 41	14 01	14 21	14 41	15 01	15 21	15 41	16 01	16 21	16 41	17 01
Kilburn High Road	d	11 02	11 22	11 42	12 02	12 22	12 42	13 02	13 22	13 42	14 02	14 22	14 42	15 02	15 22	15 42	16 02	16 22	16 42	17 02
Queens Park (Dc) ⊖	d	11 06	11 26	11 46	12 06	12 26	12 46	13 06	13 26	13 46	14 06	14 26	14 46	15 06	15 26	15 46	16 06	16 26	16 46	17 06
Kensal Green	d	11 08	11 28	11 48	12 08	12 28	12 48	13 08	13 28	13 48	14 08	14 28	14 48	15 08	15 28	15 48	16 08	16 28	16 48	17 08
Willesden Jn Low Level	d	11 11	11 31	11 51	12 11	12 31	12 51	13 11	13 31	13 51	14 11	14 31	14 51	15 11	15 31	15 51	16 11	16 31	16 51	17 11
Harlesden	d	11 13	11 33	11 53	12 13	12 33	12 53	13 13	13 33	13 53	14 13	14 33	14 53	15 13	15 33	15 53	16 13	16 33	16 53	17 13
Stonebridge Park	d	11 15	11 35	11 55	12 15	12 35	12 55	13 15	13 35	13 55	14 15	14 35	14 55	15 15	15 35	15 55	16 15	16 35	16 55	17 15
Wembley Central Dc	d	11 18	11 38	11 58	12 18	12 38	12 58	13 18	13 38	13 58	14 18	14 38	14 58	15 18	15 38	15 58	16 18	16 38	16 58	17 18
North Wembley	d	11 20	11 40	12 00	12 20	12 40	13 00	13 20	13 40	14 00	14 20	14 40	15 00	15 20	15 40	16 00	16 20	16 40	17 00	17 20
South Kenton	d	11 22	11 42	12 02	12 22	12 42	13 02	13 22	13 42	14 02	14 22	14 42	15 02	15 22	15 42	16 02	16 22	16 42	17 02	17 22
Kenton	d	11 24	11 44	12 04	12 24	12 44	13 04	13 24	13 44	14 04	14 24	14 44	15 04	15 24	15 44	16 04	16 24	16 44	17 04	17 24
Harrow & Wealdstone D.C.	d	11 26	11 46	12 06	12 26	12 46	13 06	13 26	13 46	14 06	14 26	14 46	15 06	15 26	15 46	16 06	16 26	16 46	17 06	17 26
Headstone Lane	d	11 29	11 49	12 09	12 29	12 49	13 09	13 29	13 49	14 09	14 29	14 49	15 09	15 29	15 49	16 09	16 29	16 49	17 09	17 29
Hatch End	d	11 31	11 51	12 11	12 31	12 51	13 11	13 31	13 51	14 11	14 31	14 51	15 11	15 31	15 51	16 11	16 31	16 51	17 11	17 31
Carpenders Park	d	11 34	11 54	12 14	12 34	12 54	13 14	13 34	13 54	14 14	14 34	14 54	15 14	15 34	15 54	16 14	16 34	16 54	17 14	17 34
Bushey Dc	d	11 37	11 57	12 17	12 37	12 57	13 17	13 37	13 57	14 17	14 37	14 57	15 17	15 37	15 57	16 17	16 37	16 57	17 17	17 37
Watford High Street	d	11 40	12 00	12 20	12 40	13 00	13 20	13 40	14 00	14 20	14 40	15 00	15 20	15 40	16 00	16 20	16 40	17 00	17 20	17 40
Watford Junction Dc	a	11 44	12 04	12 24	12 44	13 04	13 24	13 44	14 04	14 24	14 44	15 04	15 24	15 44	16 04	16 24	16 44	17 04	17 24	17 44

		LO A	LO A	LO A	LO A	LO A	LO A	LO A	LO A	LO A	LO A	LO A	LO A	LO A	LO A	LO A	LO A	LO A	LO A	LO A	LO A
London Euston [15] ⊖	d																				
South Hampstead	d	17 21	17 41	18 01	18 21	18 41	19 01	19 21	19 41	20 01	20 21	20 41	21 01	21 21	21 41	22 01	22 21	22 41	23 01	23 21	23 41
Kilburn High Road	d	17 22	17 42	18 02	18 22	18 42	19 02	19 22	19 42	20 02	20 22	20 42	21 02	21 22	21 42	22 02	22 22	22 42	23 02	23 22	23 42
Queens Park (Dc) ⊖	d	17 26	17 46	18 06	18 26	18 46	19 06	19 26	19 46	20 06	20 26	20 46	21 06	21 26	21 46	22 06	22 26	22 46	23 06	23 26	23 46
Kensal Green	d	17 28	17 48	18 08	18 28	18 48	19 08	19 28	19 48	20 08	20 28	20 48	21 08	21 28	21 48	22 08	22 28	22 48	23 08	23 28	23 48
Willesden Jn Low Level	d	17 31	17 51	18 11	18 31	18 51	19 11	19 31	19 51	20 11	20 31	20 51	21 11	21 33	21 51	22 11	22 31	22 51	23 11	23 31	23 51
Harlesden	d	17 33	17 53	18 13	18 33	18 53	19 13	19 33	19 53	20 13	20 33	20 53	21 13	21 35	21 53	22 13	22 33	22 53	23 13	23 33	23 53
Stonebridge Park	d	17 35	17 55	18 15	18 35	18 55	19 15	19 35	19 55	20 15	20 35	20 55	21 15	21 37	21 55	22 15	22 35	22 55	23 15	23 35	23 55
Wembley Central Dc	d	17 38	17 58	18 18	18 38	18 58	19 18	19 38	19 58	20 18	20 38	20 58	21 18	21 40	21 58	22 18	22 38	22 58	23 18	23 38	23 58
North Wembley	d	17 40	18 00	18 20	18 40	19 00	19 20	19 40	20 00	20 20	20 40	21 00	21 20	21 42	22 00	22 20	22 40	23 00	23 20	23 40	00 01
South Kenton	d	17 42	18 02	18 22	18 42	19 02	19 22	19 42	20 02	20 22	20 42	21 02	21 22	21 44	22 02	22 22	22 42	23 02	23 22	23 42	00 02
Kenton	d	17 44	18 04	18 24	18 44	19 04	19 24	19 44	20 04	20 24	20 44	21 04	21 24	21 46	22 04	22 24	22 44	23 04	23 24	23 44	00 04
Harrow & Wealdstone D.C.	d	17 46	18 06	18 26	18 46	19 06	19 26	19 46	20 06	20 26	20 46	21 06	21 26	21 48	22 06	22 26	22 46	23 06	23 26	23 46	00 06
Headstone Lane	d	17 49	18 09	18 29	18 49	19 09	19 29	19 49	20 09	20 29	20 49	21 09	21 29	21 51	22 09	22 29	22 49	23 09	23 29	23 49	00 09
Hatch End	d	17 51	18 11	18 31	18 51	19 11	19 31	19 51	20 11	20 31	20 51	21 11	21 31	21 53	22 11	22 31	22 51	23 11	23 31	23 51	00 11
Carpenders Park	d	17 54	18 14	18 34	18 54	19 14	19 34	19 54	20 14	20 34	20 54	21 14	21 34	21 56	22 14	22 34	22 54	23 14	23 34	23 54	00 14
Bushey Dc	d	17 57	18 17	18 37	18 57	19 17	19 37	19 57	20 17	20 37	20 57	21 17	21 37	21 59	22 17	22 37	22 57	23 17	23 37	23 57	00 17
Watford High Street	d	18 00	18 20	18 40	19 00	19 20	19 40	20 00	20 20	20 40	21 00	21 20	21 40	22 02	22 20	22 40	23 00	23 20	23 40	00 01	00 20
Watford Junction Dc	a	18 04	18 24	18 44	19 04	19 24	19 44	20 04	20 24	20 44	21 04	21 24	21 44	22 06	22 24	22 44	23 04	23 24	23 44	00 04	00 24

For general notes see front of timetable
For details of catering facilities see
Directory of Train Operators

A From Stratford Low Level (Table 59)

Stations Queen's Park to Harrow & Wealdstone inclusive are also served by London Underground Bakerloo line services

Table 60

Sundays

until 31 August and from 23 November

London, Queens Park and Harrow & Wealdstone → Watford Junction

Network Diagram - See first page of Table 59

		LO	LO	LO	LO		LO	LO	LO	LO		LO	LO	LO	LO		LO	LO	LO	LO		LO	LO	LO	LO	LO
London Euston 15 ⊖	d	23p17	23p37	23p57	00 22		02 00	06 47	07 17	07 47		08 17	08 47	09 17	09 47		10 17	10 47	11 17	11 47		12 17	12 47	13 17	13 47	14 17
South Hampstead	d	23p23	23p43	00 03				06 53	07 23	07 53		08 23	08 53	09 23	09 53		10 23	10 53	11 23	11 53		12 23	12 53	13 23	13 53	14 23
Kilburn High Road	d	23p24	23p44	00 04				06 54	07 24	07 54		08 24	08 54	09 24	09 54		10 24	10 54	11 24	11 54		12 24	12 54	13 24	13 54	14 24
Queens Park (Dc) ⊖	d	23p26	23p46	00 06	00 30			06 56	07 26	07 56		08 26	08 56	09 26	09 56		10 26	10 56	11 26	11 56		12 26	12 56	13 26	13 56	14 26
Kensal Green	d	23p28	23p48	00 08				06 58	07 28	07 58		08 28	08 58	09 28	09 58		10 28	10 58	11 28	11 58		12 28	12 58	13 28	13 58	14 28
Willesden Jn Low Level	d	23p31	23p51	00 11				07 01	07 31	08 01		08 31	09 01	09 31	10 01		10 31	11 01	11 31	12 01		12 31	13 01	13 31	14 01	14 31
Harlesden	d	23p33	23p53	00 13				07 03	07 33	08 03		08 33	09 03	09 33	10 03		10 33	11 03	11 33	12 03		12 33	13 03	13 33	14 03	14 33
Stonebridge Park	d	23p35	23p55	00 15				07 05	07 35	08 05		08 35	09 05	09 35	10 05		10 35	11 05	11 35	12 05		12 35	13 05	13 35	14 05	14 35
Wembley Central Dc	d	23p38	23p58	00 18	00 38		02 18	07 08	07 38	08 08		08 38	09 08	09 38	10 08		10 38	11 08	11 38	12 08		12 38	13 08	13 38	14 08	14 38
North Wembley	d	23p40	00 01	00 20				07 10	07 40	08 10		08 40	09 10	09 40	10 10		10 40	11 10	11 40	12 10		12 40	13 10	13 40	14 10	14 40
South Kenton	d	23p42	00 02	00 22				07 12	07 42	08 12		08 42	09 12	09 42	10 12		10 42	11 12	11 42	12 12		12 42	13 12	13 42	14 12	14 42
Kenton	d	23p44	00 04	00 24				07 14	07 44	08 14		08 44	09 14	09 44	10 14		10 44	11 14	11 44	12 14		12 44	13 14	13 44	14 14	14 44
Harrow & Wealdstone D.C.	d	23p46	00 06	00 26	00 45		02 27	07 16	07 46	08 16		08 46	09 16	09 46	10 16		10 46	11 16	11 46	12 16		12 46	13 16	13 46	14 16	14 46
Headstone Lane	d	23p49	00 09	00 29				07 19	07 49	08 19		08 49	09 19	09 49	10 19		10 49	11 19	11 49	12 19		12 49	13 19	13 49	14 19	14 49
Hatch End	d	23p51	00 11	00 31				07 21	07 51	08 21		08 51	09 21	09 51	10 21		10 51	11 21	11 51	12 21		12 51	13 21	13 51	14 21	14 51
Carpenders Park	d	23p54	00 14	00 34				07 24	07 54	08 24		08 54	09 24	09 54	10 24		10 54	11 24	11 54	12 24		12 54	13 24	13 54	14 24	14 54
Bushey Dc	d	23p57	00 17	00 37				07 27	07 57	08 27		08 57	09 27	09 57	10 27		10 57	11 27	11 57	12 27		12 57	13 27	13 57	14 27	14 57
Watford High Street	d	00 01	00 20	00 40				07 30	08 00	08 30		09 00	09 30	10 00	10 30		11 00	11 30	12 00	12 30		13 00	13 30	14 00	14 30	15 00
Watford Junction Dc	a	00 04	00 24	00 44	00 59		02 40	07 34	08 04	08 34		09 04	09 34	10 04	10 34		11 04	11 34	12 04	12 34		13 04	13 34	14 04	14 34	15 04

		LO		LO	LO	LO	LO		LO	LO	LO	LO		LO	LO	LO	LO		LO	LO	LO	LO	LO	LO		
London Euston 15 ⊖	d	14 47		15 17	15 47	16 17	16 47		17 17	17 47	18 17	18 47		19 17	19 47	20 17	20 47		21 17	21 47	22 17	22 47	23 17	23 47		
South Hampstead	d	14 53		15 23	15 53	16 23	16 53		17 23	17 53	18 23	18 53		19 23	19 53	20 23	20 53		21 23	21 53	22 23	22 53	23 23	23 53		
Kilburn High Road	d	14 54		15 24	15 54	16 24	16 54		17 24	17 54	18 24	18 54		19 24	19 54	20 24	20 54		21 24	21 54	22 24	22 54	23 24	23 54		
Queens Park (Dc) ⊖	d	14 56		15 26	15 56	16 26	16 56		17 26	17 56	18 26	18 56		19 26	19 56	20 26	20 56		21 26	21 56	22 26	22 56	23 26	23 56		
Kensal Green	d	14 58		15 28	15 58	16 28	16 58		17 28	17 58	18 28	18 58		19 28	19 58	20 28	20 58		21 28	21 58	22 28	22 58	23 28	23 58		
Willesden Jn Low Level	d	15 01		15 31	16 01	16 31	17 01		17 31	18 01	18 31	19 01		19 31	20 01	20 31	21 01		21 31	22 01	22 31	23 01	23 31	00 01		
Harlesden	d	15 03		15 33	16 03	16 33	17 03		17 33	18 03	18 33	19 03		19 33	20 03	20 33	21 03		21 33	22 03	22 33	23 03	23 33	00 03		
Stonebridge Park	d	15 05		15 35	16 05	16 35	17 05		17 35	18 05	18 35	19 05		19 35	20 05	20 35	21 05		21 35	22 05	22 35	23 05	23 35	00 05		
Wembley Central Dc	d	15 08		15 38	16 08	16 38	17 08		17 38	18 08	18 38	19 08		19 38	20 08	20 38	21 08		21 38	22 08	22 38	23 08	23 38	00 08		
North Wembley	d	15 10		15 40	16 10	16 40	17 10		17 40	18 10	18 40	19 10		19 40	20 10	20 40	21 10		21 40	22 10	22 40	23 10	23 40	00 10		
South Kenton	d	15 12		15 42	16 12	16 42	17 12		17 42	18 12	18 42	19 12		19 42	20 12	20 42	21 12		21 42	22 12	22 42	23 12	23 42	00 12		
Kenton	d	15 14		15 44	16 14	16 44	17 14		17 44	18 14	18 44	19 14		19 44	20 14	20 44	21 14		21 44	22 14	22 44	23 14	23 44	00 14		
Harrow & Wealdstone D.C.	d	15 16		15 46	16 16	16 46	17 16		17 46	18 16	18 46	19 16		19 46	20 16	20 46	21 16		21 46	22 16	22 46	23 16	23 46	00 16		
Headstone Lane	d	15 19		15 49	16 19	16 49	17 19		17 49	18 19	18 49	19 19		19 49	20 19	20 49	21 19		21 49	22 19	22 49	23 19	23 49	00 19		
Hatch End	d	15 21		15 51	16 21	16 51	17 21		17 51	18 21	18 51	19 21		19 51	20 21	20 51	21 21		21 51	22 21	22 51	23 21	23 51	00 21		
Carpenders Park	d	15 24		15 54	16 24	16 54	17 24		17 54	18 24	18 54	19 24		19 54	20 24	20 54	21 24		21 54	22 24	22 54	23 24	23 54	00 24		
Bushey Dc	d	15 27		15 57	16 27	16 57	17 27		17 57	18 27	18 57	19 27		19 57	20 27	20 57	21 27		21 57	22 27	22 57	23 27	23 57	00 27		
Watford High Street	d	15 30		16 00	16 30	17 00	17 30		18 00	18 30	19 00	19 30		20 00	20 30	21 00	21 30		22 00	22 30	23 00	23 30	00 01	00 30		
Watford Junction Dc	a	15 34		16 04	16 34	17 04	17 34		18 04	18 34	19 04	19 34		20 04	20 34	21 04	21 34		22 04	22 34	23 04	23 34	00 04	00 34		

Sundays

7 September to 16 November

		LO A	LO A	LO A	LO	LO	LO	LO	LO	LO	LO	LO A	LO		LO A	LO	LO A	LO	LO A	LO	LO A	LO	LO A	LO	LO A	LO
London Euston 15 ⊖	d				00 22	02 00	06 47	07 17	07 47	08 17	08 47		09 17			09 47		10 17		10 47		11 17		11 47		12 17
South Hampstead	d	23p21	23p41	00 01			06 53	07 23	07 53	08 23	08 53	09 08	09 23		09 38	09 53	10 08	10 23	10 38	10 53	11 08	11 23	11 38	11 53	12 08	12 23
Kilburn High Road	d	23p22	23p42	00 02			06 54	07 24	07 54	08 24	08 54	09 09	09 24		09 39	09 54	10 09	10 24	10 39	10 54	11 09	11 24	11 39	11 54	12 09	12 24
Queens Park (Dc) ⊖	d	23p26	23p46	00 06	00 30		06 56	07 26	07 56	08 26	08 56	09 15	09 26		09 46	09 56	10 17	10 26	10 45	10 56	11 17	11 26	11 45	11 56	12 18	12 26
Kensal Green	d	23p28	23p48	00 08			06 58	07 28	07 58	08 28	08 58	09 17	09 28		09 48	09 58	10 19	10 28	10 47	10 58	11 19	11 28	11 47	11 58	12 20	12 28
Willesden Jn Low Level	d	23p31	23p51	00 11			07 01	07 31	08 01	08 31	09 01	09a19	09 31		09a51	10 01	10a22	10 31	10a50	11 01	11a22	11 31	11a50	12 01	12a23	12 31
Harlesden	d	23p33	23p53	00 13			07 03	07 33	08 03	08 33	09 03		09 33			10 03		10 33		11 03		11 33		12 03		12 33
Stonebridge Park	d	23p35	23p55	00 15			07 05	07 35	08 05	08 35	09 05		09 35			10 05		10 35		11 05		11 35		12 05		12 35
Wembley Central Dc	d	23p38	23p58	00 18	00 38	02 18	07 08	07 38	08 08	08 38	09 08		09 38			10 08		10 38		11 08		11 38		12 08		12 38
North Wembley	d	23p40	00 01	00 20			07 10	07 40	08 10	08 40	09 10		09 40			10 10		10 40		11 10		11 40		12 10		12 40
South Kenton	d	23p42	00 02	00 22			07 12	07 42	08 12	08 42	09 12		09 42			10 12		10 42		11 12		11 42		12 12		12 42
Kenton	d	23p44	00 04	00 24			07 14	07 44	08 14	08 44	09 14		09 44			10 14		10 44		11 14		11 44		12 14		12 44
Harrow & Wealdstone D.C.	d	23p46	00 06	00 26	00 45	02 27	07 16	07 46	08 16	08 46	09 16		09 46			10 16		10 46		11 16		11 46		12 16		12 46
Headstone Lane	d	23p49	00 09	00 29			07 19	07 49	08 19	08 49	09 19		09 49			10 19		10 49		11 19		11 49		12 19		12 49
Hatch End	d	23p51	00 11	00 31			07 21	07 51	08 21	08 51	09 21		09 51			10 21		10 51		11 21		11 51		12 21		12 51
Carpenders Park	d	23p54	00 14	00 34			07 24	07 54	08 24	08 54	09 24		09 54			10 24		10 54		11 24		11 54		12 24		12 54
Bushey Dc	d	23p57	00 17	00 37			07 27	07 57	08 27	08 57	09 27		09 57			10 27		10 57		11 27		11 57		12 27		12 57
Watford High Street	d	00 01	00 20	00 40			07 30	08 00	08 30	09 00	09 30		10 00			10 30		11 00		11 30		12 00		12 30		13 00
Watford Junction Dc	a	00 04	00 24	00 44	00 59	02 40	07 34	08 04	08 34	09 04	09 34		10 04			10 34		11 04		11 34		12 04		12 34		13 04

For general notes see front of timetable
For details of catering facilities see Directory of Train Operators

A From Stratford Low Level (Table 59)

Stations Queen's Park to Harrow & Wealdstone inclusive are also served by London Underground Bakerloo line services

Table 60

Sundays

London, Queens Park and Harrow & Wealdstone → Watford Junction

7 September to 16 November

Network Diagram - See first page of Table 59

	LO A	LO		LO A	LO	LO A	LO	LO A	LO	LO A	LO	LO A	LO	LO A	LO		LO A	LO	LO A	LO	LO A	LO	LO A	LO	LO A
London Euston 15 ⊖ d		12 47			13 17		13 47		14 17		14 47		15 17		15 47			16 17		16 47		17 17		17 47	
South Hampstead d	12 38	12 53		13 08	13 23	13 38	13 53	14 08	14 23	14 38	14 53	15 08	15 23	15 38	15 53		16 08	16 23	16 38	16 53	17 08	17 23	17 38	17 53	18 08
Kilburn High Road d	12 39	12 54		13 09	13 24	13 39	13 54	14 09	14 24	14 39	14 54	15 09	15 24	15 39	15 54		16 09	16 24	16 39	16 54	17 09	17 24	17 39	17 54	18 09
Queens Park (Dc) ⊖ d	12 44	12 56		13 17	13 26	13 44	13 56	14 17	14 26	14 44	14 56	15 17	15 26	15 44	15 56		16 17	16 26	16 44	16 56	17 17	17 26	17 44	17 56	18 17
Kensal Green d	12 46	12 58		13 19	13 28	13 46	13 58	14 19	14 28	14 46	14 58	15 19	15 28	15 46	15 58		16 19	16 28	16 46	16 58	17 19	17 28	17 46	17 58	18 19
Willesden Jn Low Level d	12a49	13 01		13a22	13 31	13a49	14 01	14a22	14 31	14a49	15 01	15a22	15 31	15a49	16 01		16a22	16 31	16a49	17 01	17a22	17 31	17a49	18 01	18a22
Harlesden d		13 03			13 33		14 03		14 33		15 03		15 33		16 03			16 33		17 03		17 33		18 03	
Stonebridge Park d		13 05			13 35		14 05		14 35		15 05		15 35		16 05			16 35		17 05		17 35		18 05	
Wembley Central Dc d		13 08			13 38		14 08		14 38		15 08		15 38		16 08			16 38		17 08		17 38		18 08	
North Wembley d		13 10			13 40		14 10		14 40		15 10		15 40		16 10			16 40		17 10		17 40		18 10	
South Kenton d		13 12			13 42		14 12		14 42		15 12		15 42		16 12			16 42		17 12		17 42		18 12	
Kenton d		13 14			13 44		14 14		14 44		15 14		15 44		16 14			16 44		17 14		17 44		18 14	
Harrow & Wealdstone D.C. d		13 16			13 46		14 16		14 46		15 16		15 46		16 16			16 46		17 16		17 46		18 16	
Headstone Lane d		13 19			13 49		14 19		14 49		15 19		15 49		16 19			16 49		17 19		17 49		18 19	
Hatch End d		13 21			13 51		14 21		14 51		15 21		15 51		16 21			16 51		17 21		17 51		18 21	
Carpenders Park d		13 24			13 54		14 24		14 54		15 24		15 54		16 24			16 54		17 24		17 54		18 24	
Bushey Dc d		13 27			13 57		14 27		14 57		15 27		15 57		16 27			16 57		17 27		17 57		18 27	
Watford High Street d		13 30			14 00		14 30		15 00		15 30		16 00		16 30			17 00		17 30		18 00		18 30	
Watford Junction Dc a		13 34			14 04		14 34		15 04		15 34		16 04		16 34			17 04		17 34		18 04		18 34	

	LO	LO A	LO	LO A	LO		LO A	LO	LO A	LO	LO A	LO	LO A	LO	LO A	LO	LO A	LO	LO A	LO	LO A	LO	LO		
London Euston 15 ⊖ d	18 17		18 47		19 17			19 47		20 17		20 47		21 17		21 47		22 17		22 47		23 17	23 47		
South Hampstead d	18 23	18 38	18 53	19 08	19 23		19 38	19 53	20 08	20 23	20 38	20 53	21 08	21 23	21 38	21 53	22 08	22 23	22 40	22 53	23 18	23 23	23 53		
Kilburn High Road d	18 24	18 39	18 54	19 09	19 24		19 39	19 54	20 09	20 24	20 39	20 54	21 09	21 24	21 39	21 54	22 09	22 24	22 41	22 54	23 19	23 24	23 54		
Queens Park (Dc) ⊖ d	18 26	18 44	18 56	19 17	19 26		19 44	19 56	20 17	20 26	20 44	20 56	21 16	21 26	21 45	21 56	22 16	22 26	22 45	22 56	23 23	23 26	23 56		
Kensal Green d	18 28	18 46	18 58	19 19	19 28		19 46	19 58	20 19	20 28	20 47	20 58	21 19	21 28	21 47	21 58	22 18	22 28	22 47	22 58	23 25	23 28	23 58		
Willesden Jn Low Level d	18 31	18a49	19 01	19a22	19 31		19a49	20 01	20a22	20 31	20a50	21 01	21a22	21 31	21a50	22 01	22a21	22 31	22a51	23 01	23a27	23 31	00 01		
Harlesden d	18 33		19 03		19 33			20 03		20 33		21 03		21 33		22 03		22 33		23 03		23 33	00 03		
Stonebridge Park d	18 35		19 05		19 35			20 05		20 35		21 05		21 35		22 05		22 35		23 05		23 35	00 05		
Wembley Central Dc d	18 38		19 08		19 38			20 08		20 38		21 08		21 38		22 08		22 38		23 08		23 38	00 08		
North Wembley d	18 40		19 10		19 40			20 10		20 40		21 10		21 40		22 10		22 40		23 10		23 40	00 10		
South Kenton d	18 42		19 12		19 42			20 12		20 42		21 12		21 42		22 12		22 42		23 12		23 42	00 12		
Kenton d	18 44		19 14		19 44			20 14		20 44		21 14		21 44		22 14		22 44		23 14		23 44	00 14		
Harrow & Wealdstone D.C. d	18 46		19 16		19 46			20 16		20 46		21 16		21 46		22 16		22 46		23 16		23 46	00 16		
Headstone Lane d	18 49		19 19		19 49			20 19		20 49		21 19		21 49		22 19		22 49		23 19		23 49	00 19		
Hatch End d	18 51		19 21		19 51			20 21		20 51		21 21		21 51		22 21		22 51		23 21		23 51	00 21		
Carpenders Park d	18 54		19 24		19 54			20 24		20 54		21 24		21 54		22 24		22 54		23 24		23 54	00 24		
Bushey Dc d	18 57		19 27		19 57			20 27		20 57		21 27		21 57		22 27		22 57		23 27		23 57	00 27		
Watford High Street d	19 00		19 30		20 00			20 30		21 00		21 30		22 00		22 30		23 00		23 30		00 01	00 30		
Watford Junction Dc a	19 04		19 34		20 04			20 34		21 04		21 34		22 04		22 34		23 04		23 34		00 04	00 34		

For general notes see front of timetable
For details of catering facilities see
Directory of Train Operators

A From Stratford Low Level (Table 59)

Stations Queen's Park to Harrow & Wealdstone inclusive are also served by London Underground Bakerloo line services

Table 60

Watford Junction → Harrow & Wealdstone, Queens Park and London

Mondays to Fridays

until 29 August and from 17 November

Network Diagram - See first page of Table 59

Miles			LO	LO	LO		LO	LO	LO		LO	LO	LO		LO	LO	LO		LO	LO	LO		LO	LO	LO	LO
0	**Watford Junction Dc**	d	23p21	05 05	05 21	....	05 41	06 01	06 20	....	06 40	07 00	07 20	....	07 40	08 00	08 20	....	08 40	09 00	09 21	....	09 41	10 01	10 21	10 41
1	Watford High Street	d	23p24	05 08	05 24	.	05 44	06 04	06 23	....	06 43	07 03	07 23	.	07 43	08 03	08 23	.	08 43	09 03	09 24	....	09 44	10 04	10 24	10 44
1¾	Bushey Dc	d	23p26	05 10	05 26	.	05 46	06 06	06 25	....	06 45	07 05	07 25	.	07 45	08 05	08 25	....	08 45	09 05	09 26	....	09 46	10 06	10 26	10 46
3	Carpenders Park	d	23p29	05 13	05 29	.	05 49	06 09	06 28	.	06 48	07 08	07 28	.	07 48	08 08	08 28	.	08 48	09 08	09 29	.	09 49	10 09	10 29	10 49
4½	Hatch End	d	23p32	05 16	05 32	....	05 52	06 12	06 31	.	06 51	07 11	07 31	.	07 51	08 11	08 31	....	08 51	09 11	09 32	....	09 52	10 12	10 32	10 52
5½	Headstone Lane	d	23p34	05 18	05 34	.	05 54	06 14	06 33	.	06 53	07 13	07 33	.	07 53	08 13	08 33	.	08 53	09 13	09 34	.	09 54	10 14	10 34	10 54
6¼	**Harrow & Wealdstone D.C.**	d	23p37	05 21	05 37	....	05 57	06 17	06 36	....	06 56	07 16	07 36	....	07 56	08 16	08 36	....	08 56	09 16	09 37	....	09 57	10 17	10 37	10 57
7¼	Kenton	d	23p39	05 23	05 39	.	05 59	06 19	06 39	.	06 59	07 19	07 39	.	07 59	08 19	08 39	.	08 59	09 19	09 39	.	09 59	10 19	10 39	10 59
8¼	South Kenton	d	23p41	05 25	05 41	....	06 01	06 21	06 41	....	07 01	07 21	07 41	....	08 01	08 21	08 41	....	09 01	09 21	09 41	....	10 01	10 21	10 41	11 01
8¾	North Wembley	d	23p43	05 27	05 43	.	06 03	06 23	06 43	.	07 03	07 23	07 43	.	08 03	08 23	08 43	.	09 03	09 23	09 43	.	10 03	10 23	10 43	11 03
9½	Wembley Central Dc	d	23p45	05 29	05 45	....	06 05	06 25	06 45	....	07 05	07 25	07 45	....	08 05	08 25	08 45	....	09 05	09 25	09 45	....	10 05	10 25	10 45	11 05
10¾	Stonebridge Park	d	23p48	05 32	05 48	.	06 08	06 28	06 48	.	07 08	07 28	07 48	.	08 08	08 28	08 48	.	09 08	09 28	09 48	.	10 08	10 28	10 48	11 08
11½	Harlesden	d	23p50	05 34	05 50	....	06 10	06 30	06 50	....	07 10	07 30	07 50	....	08 10	08 30	08 50	....	09 10	09 30	09 50	....	10 10	10 30	10 50	11 10
12½	**Willesden Jn Low Level**	d	23p52	05 36	05 52	.	06 12	06 32	06 53	.	07 13	07 33	07 53	.	08 13	08 33	08 53	.	09 13	09 33	09 52	.	10 12	10 32	10 52	11 12
13¼	Kensal Green	d	23p55	05 39	05 55	....	06 15	06 35	06 55	....	07 15	07 35	07 55	....	08 15	08 35	08 55	....	09 15	09 35	09 55	....	10 15	10 35	10 55	11 15
14	**Queens Park (Dc)**	⊖ d	23p57	05 41	05 57	.	06 17	06 37	06 58	.	07 18	07 38	07 58	.	08 18	08 38	08 58	.	09 18	09 38	09 57	.	10 17	10 37	10 57	11 17
14¾	Kilburn High Road	d	23p59	05 43	05 59	....	06 19	06 39	07 00	....	07 20	07 40	08 00	....	08 20	08 40	09 00	....	09 20	09 40	09 59	....	10 19	10 39	10 59	11 19
15¾	South Hampstead	d	00 01	05 45	06 01	.	06 21	06 41	07 02	.	07 22	07 42	08 02	.	08 22	08 42	09 02	.	09 22	09 42	10 01	.	10 21	10 41	11 01	11 21
17¼	**London Euston 15**	⊖ a	00 08	05 52	06 11	....	06 29	06 50	07 12	....	07 32	07 52	08 12	....	08 32	08 52	09 12	....	09 32	09 52	10 10	....	10 30	10 50	11 11	11 30

		LO		LO	LO	LO		LO	LO	LO		LO	LO	LO		LO	LO	LO		LO	LO	LO		LO	LO	LO
Watford Junction Dc	d	11 01	....	11 21	11 41	12 01	....	12 21	12 41	13 01	....	13 21	13 41	14 01	....	14 21	14 41	15 01	....	15 21	15 41	16 01	....	16 21	16 41	17 01
Watford High Street	d	11 04	.	11 24	11 44	12 04	.	12 24	12 44	13 04	.	13 24	13 44	14 04	.	14 24	14 44	15 04	.	15 24	15 44	16 04	.	16 24	16 44	17 04
Bushey Dc	d	11 06	....	11 26	11 46	12 06	....	12 26	12 46	13 06	....	13 26	13 46	14 06	....	14 26	14 46	15 06	....	15 26	15 46	16 06	....	16 26	16 46	17 06
Carpenders Park	d	11 09	.	11 29	11 49	12 09	.	12 29	12 49	13 09	.	13 29	13 49	14 09	.	14 29	14 49	15 09	.	15 29	15 49	16 09	.	16 29	16 49	17 09
Hatch End	d	11 12	....	11 32	11 52	12 12	....	12 32	12 52	13 12	....	13 32	13 52	14 12	....	14 32	14 52	15 12	....	15 32	15 52	16 12	....	16 32	16 52	17 12
Headstone Lane	d	11 14	.	11 34	11 54	12 14	.	12 34	12 54	13 14	.	13 34	13 54	14 14	.	14 34	14 54	15 14	.	15 34	15 54	16 14	.	16 34	16 54	17 14
Harrow & Wealdstone D.C.	d	11 17	....	11 37	11 57	12 17	....	12 37	12 57	13 17	....	13 37	13 57	14 17	....	14 37	14 57	15 17	....	15 37	15 57	16 17	....	16 37	16 57	17 17
Kenton	d	11 19	.	11 39	11 59	12 19	.	12 39	12 59	13 19	.	13 39	13 59	14 19	.	14 39	14 59	15 19	.	15 39	15 59	16 19	.	16 39	16 59	17 19
South Kenton	d	11 21	....	11 41	12 01	12 21	....	12 41	13 01	13 21	....	13 41	14 01	14 21	....	14 41	15 01	15 21	....	15 41	16 01	16 21	....	16 41	17 01	17 21
North Wembley	d	11 23	.	11 43	12 03	12 23	.	12 43	13 03	13 23	.	13 43	14 03	14 23	.	14 43	15 03	15 23	.	15 43	16 03	16 23	.	16 43	17 03	17 23
Wembley Central Dc	d	11 25	....	11 45	12 05	12 25	....	12 45	13 05	13 25	....	13 45	14 05	14 25	....	14 45	15 05	15 25	....	15 45	16 05	16 25	....	16 45	17 05	17 25
Stonebridge Park	d	11 28	.	11 48	12 08	12 28	.	12 48	13 08	13 28	.	13 48	14 08	14 28	.	14 48	15 08	15 28	.	15 48	16 08	16 28	.	16 48	17 08	17 28
Harlesden	d	11 30	....	11 50	12 10	12 30	....	12 50	13 10	13 30	....	13 50	14 10	14 30	....	14 50	15 10	15 30	....	15 50	16 10	16 30	....	16 50	17 10	17 30
Willesden Jn Low Level	d	11 32	.	11 52	12 12	12 32	.	12 52	13 12	13 32	.	13 52	14 12	14 32	.	14 52	15 12	15 32	.	15 52	16 12	16 32	.	16 52	17 12	17 32
Kensal Green	d	11 35	....	11 55	12 15	12 35	....	12 55	13 15	13 35	....	13 55	14 15	14 35	....	14 55	15 15	15 35	....	15 55	16 15	16 35	....	16 55	17 15	17 35
Queens Park (Dc)	⊖ d	11 37	.	11 57	12 17	12 37	.	12 57	13 17	13 37	.	13 57	14 17	14 37	.	14 57	15 17	15 37	.	15 57	16 17	16 37	.	16 57	17 17	17 37
Kilburn High Road	d	11 39	....	11 59	12 19	12 39	....	12 59	13 19	13 39	....	13 59	14 19	14 39	....	14 59	15 19	15 39	....	15 59	16 19	16 39	....	16 59	17 19	17 39
South Hampstead	d	11 41	.	12 01	12 21	12 41	.	13 01	13 21	13 41	.	14 01	14 21	14 41	.	15 01	15 21	15 41	.	16 01	16 21	16 41	.	17 01	17 21	17 41
London Euston 15	⊖ a	11 50	....	12 11	12 30	12 50	....	13 11	13 30	13 50	....	14 11	14 30	14 50	....	15 11	15 30	15 50	....	16 11	16 30	16 50	....	17 11	17 30	17 50

		LO	LO		LO	LO	LO		LO	LO	LO		LO	LO	LO		LO	LO	LO		LO	LO	LO	LO		
Watford Junction Dc	d	17 21	17 41	....	18 01	18 21	18 41	....	19 01	19 21	19 41	....	20 01	20 21	20 41	....	21 01	21 21	21 41	....	22 01	22 21	22 41	23 01	....	....
Watford High Street	d	17 24	17 44	.	18 04	18 24	18 44	.	19 04	19 24	19 44	.	20 04	20 24	20 44	.	21 04	21 24	21 44	.	22 04	22 24	22 44	23 04	.	.
Bushey Dc	d	17 26	17 46	....	18 06	18 26	18 46	....	19 06	19 26	19 46	....	20 06	20 26	20 46	....	21 06	21 26	21 46	....	22 06	22 26	22 46	23 06	....	....
Carpenders Park	d	17 29	17 49	.	18 09	18 29	18 49	.	19 09	19 29	19 49	.	20 09	20 29	20 49	.	21 09	21 29	21 49	.	22 09	22 29	22 49	23 09	.	.
Hatch End	d	17 32	17 52	....	18 12	18 32	18 52	....	19 12	19 32	19 52	....	20 12	20 32	20 52	....	21 12	21 32	21 52	....	22 12	22 32	22 52	23 12	....	....
Headstone Lane	d	17 34	17 54	.	18 14	18 34	18 54	.	19 14	19 34	19 54	.	20 14	20 34	20 54	.	21 14	21 34	21 54	.	22 14	22 34	22 54	23 14	.	.
Harrow & Wealdstone D.C.	d	17 37	17 57	....	18 17	18 37	18 57	....	19 17	19 37	19 57	....	20 17	20 37	20 57	....	21 17	21 37	21 57	....	22 17	22 37	22 57	23 17	....	....
Kenton	d	17 39	17 59	.	18 19	18 39	18 59	.	19 19	19 39	19 59	.	20 19	20 39	20 59	.	21 19	21 39	21 59	.	22 19	22 39	22 59	23 19	.	.
South Kenton	d	17 41	18 01	....	18 21	18 41	19 01	....	19 21	19 41	20 01	....	20 21	20 41	21 01	....	21 21	21 41	22 01	....	22 21	22 41	23 01	23 21	....	....
North Wembley	d	17 43	18 03	.	18 23	18 43	19 03	.	19 23	19 43	20 03	.	20 23	20 43	21 03	.	21 23	21 43	22 03	.	22 23	22 43	23 03	23 23	.	.
Wembley Central Dc	d	17 45	18 05	....	18 25	18 45	19 05	....	19 25	19 45	20 05	....	20 25	20 45	21 05	....	21 25	21 45	22 05	....	22 25	22 45	23 05	23 25	....	....
Stonebridge Park	d	17 48	18 08	.	18 28	18 48	19 08	.	19 28	19 48	20 08	.	20 28	20 48	21 08	.	21 28	21 48	22 08	.	22 28	22 48	23 08	23 28	.	.
Harlesden	d	17 50	18 10	....	18 30	18 50	19 10	....	19 30	19 50	20 10	....	20 30	20 50	21 10	....	21 30	21 50	22 10	....	22 30	22 50	23 10	23 30	....	....
Willesden Jn Low Level	d	17 52	18 12	.	18 32	18 52	19 12	.	19 32	19 52	20 12	.	20 32	20 52	21 12	.	21 32	21 52	22 12	.	22 32	22 52	23 12	23 32	.	.
Kensal Green	d	17 55	18 15	....	18 35	18 55	19 15	....	19 35	19 55	20 15	....	20 35	20 55	21 15	....	21 35	21 55	22 15	....	22 35	22 55	23 15	23 35	....	....
Queens Park (Dc)	⊖ d	17 57	18 17	.	18 37	18 57	19 17	.	19 37	19 57	20 17	.	20 37	20 57	21 17	.	21 37	21 57	22 17	.	22 37	22 57	23 17	23 37	.	.
Kilburn High Road	d	17 59	18 19	....	18 39	18 59	19 19	....	19 39	19 59	20 19	....	20 39	20 59	21 19	....	21 39	21 59	22 19	....	22 39	22 59	23 19	23 39	....	....
South Hampstead	d	18 01	18 21	.	18 41	19 01	19 21	.	19 41	20 01	20 21	.	20 41	21 01	21 21	.	21 41	22 01	22 21	.	22 41	23 01	23 21	23 41	.	.
London Euston 15	⊖ a	18 10	18 30	....	18 50	19 10	19 30	....	19 50	20 10	20 30	....	20 51	21 10	21 30	....	21 51	22 10	22 30	....	22 50	23 10	23 30	23 50	....	....

Mondays to Fridays

1 September to 14 November

		LO MO	LO A	LO A		LO A	LO A	LO A		LO A	LO A	LO A		LO A	LO A	LO A		LO A	LO A	LO A		LO A	LO A	LO A		LO A
Watford Junction Dc	d	23p21	05 05	05 21	....	05 41	06 01	06 20	....	06 40	07 00	07 20	....	07 40	08 00	08 20	....	08 40	09 00	09 21	....	09 41	10 01	10 21	....	10 41
Watford High Street	d	23p24	05 08	05 24	.	05 44	06 04	06 23	.	06 43	07 03	07 23	.	07 43	08 03	08 23	.	08 43	09 03	09 24	.	09 44	10 04	10 24	.	10 44
Bushey Dc	d	23p26	05 10	05 26	....	05 46	06 06	06 25	....	06 45	07 05	07 25	....	07 45	08 05	08 25	....	08 45	09 05	09 26	....	09 46	10 06	10 26	....	10 46
Carpenders Park	d	23p29	05 13	05 29	.	05 49	06 09	06 28	.	06 48	07 08	07 28	.	07 48	08 08	08 28	.	08 48	09 08	09 29	.	09 49	10 09	10 29	.	10 49
Hatch End	d	23p32	05 16	05 32	....	05 52	06 12	06 31	....	06 51	07 11	07 31	....	07 51	08 11	08 31	....	08 51	09 11	09 32	....	09 52	10 12	10 32	....	10 52
Headstone Lane	d	23p34	05 18	05 34	.	05 54	06 14	06 33	.	06 53	07 13	07 33	.	07 53	08 13	08 33	.	08 53	09 13	09 34	.	09 54	10 14	10 34	.	10 54
Harrow & Wealdstone D.C.	d	23p37	05 21	05 37	....	05 57	06 17	06 36	....	06 56	07 16	07 36	....	07 56	08 16	08 36	....	08 56	09 16	09 37	....	09 57	10 17	10 37	....	10 57
Kenton	d	23p39	05 23	05 39	.	05 59	06 19	06 39	.	06 59	07 19	07 39	.	07 59	08 19	08 39	.	08 59	09 19	09 39	.	09 59	10 19	10 39	.	10 59
South Kenton	d	23p41	05 25	05 41	....	06 01	06 21	06 41	....	07 01	07 21	07 41	....	08 01	08 21	08 41	....	09 01	09 21	09 41	....	10 01	10 21	10 41	....	11 01
North Wembley	d	23p43	05 27	05 43	.	06 03	06 23	06 43	.	07 03	07 23	07 43	.	08 03	08 23	08 43	.	09 03	09 23	09 43	.	10 03	10 23	10 43	.	11 03
Wembley Central Dc	d	23p45	05 29	05 45	....	06 05	06 25	06 45	....	07 05	07 25	07 45	....	08 05	08 25	08 45	....	09 05	09 25	09 45	....	10 05	10 25	10 45	....	11 05
Stonebridge Park	d	23p48	05 32	05 48	.	06 08	06 28	06 48	.	07 08	07 28	07 48	.	08 08	08 28	08 48	.	09 08	09 28	09 48	.	10 08	10 28	10 48	.	11 08
Harlesden	d	23p50	05 34	05 50	....	06 10	06 30	06 50	....	07 10	07 30	07 50	....	08 10	08 30	08 50	....	09 10	09 30	09 50	....	10 10	10 30	10 50	....	11 10
Willesden Jn Low Level	d	23p52	05 36	05 52	.	06 12	06 32	06 53	.	07 13	07 33	07 53	.	08 13	08 33	08 53	.	09 13	09 33	09 52	.	10 12	10 32	10 52	.	11 12
Kensal Green	d	23p55	05 39	05 55	....	06 15	06 35	06 55	....	07 15	07 35	07 55	....	08 15	08 35	08 55	....	09 15	09 35	09 55	....	10 15	10 35	10 55	....	11 15
Queens Park (Dc)	⊖ d	23p57	05 44	06 00	.	06 20	06 40	07 00	.	07 20	07 40	08 00	.	08 20	08 40	09 00	.	09 20	09 40	10 00	.	10 20	10 40	11 00	.	11 20
Kilburn High Road	d	23p59	05 46	06 02	....	06 22	06 42	07 02	....	07 22	07 42	08 02	....	08 22	08 42	09 02	....	09 22	09 42	10 02	....	10 22	10 42	11 02	....	11 22
South Hampstead	d	00 01	05a48	06a04	.	06a24	06a44	07a04	.	07a24	07a44	08a04	.	08a24	08a44	09a04	.	09a24	09a44	10a04	.	10a24	10a44	11a04	.	11a24
London Euston 15	⊖ a	00 08	....	....	....	....	....	....	....	....	....	....	....	....	....	....	....	....	....	....	....	....	....	....	....	....

For general notes see front of timetable
For details of catering facilities see Directory of Train Operators

A To Stratford Low Level (Table 59)

Stations Harrow & Wealdstone to Queen's Park inclusive are also served by London Underground Bakerloo Line services

Table 60

Watford Junction → Harrow & Wealdstone, Queens Park and London

Mondays to Fridays

1 September to 14 November

Network Diagram - See first page of Table 59

Station		LO A	LO A	LO A	LO A	LO A	LO A	LO A	LO A	LO A	LO A	LO A	LO A	LO A	LO A	LO A	LO A	LO A	LO A	LO A
Watford Junction Dc	d	11 01	11 21	11 41	12 01	12 21	12 41	13 01	13 21	13 41	14 01	14 21	14 41	15 01	15 21	15 41	16 01	16 21	16 41	17 01
Watford High Street	d	11 04	11 24	11 44	12 04	12 24	12 44	13 04	13 24	13 44	14 04	14 24	14 44	15 04	15 24	15 44	16 04	16 24	16 44	17 04
Bushey Dc	d	11 06	11 26	11 46	12 06	12 26	12 46	13 06	13 26	13 46	14 06	14 26	14 46	15 06	15 26	15 46	16 06	16 26	16 46	17 06
Carpenders Park	d	11 09	11 29	11 49	12 09	12 29	12 49	13 09	13 29	13 49	14 09	14 29	14 49	15 09	15 29	15 49	16 09	16 29	16 49	17 09
Hatch End	d	11 12	11 32	11 52	12 12	12 32	12 52	13 12	13 32	13 52	14 12	14 32	14 52	15 12	15 32	15 52	16 12	16 32	16 52	17 12
Headstone Lane	d	11 14	11 34	11 54	12 14	12 34	12 54	13 14	13 34	13 54	14 14	14 34	14 54	15 14	15 34	15 54	16 14	16 34	16 54	17 14
Harrow & Wealdstone D.C.	d	11 17	11 37	11 57	12 17	12 37	12 57	13 17	13 37	13 57	14 17	14 37	14 57	15 17	15 37	15 57	16 17	16 37	16 57	17 17
Kenton	d	11 19	11 39	11 59	12 19	12 39	12 59	13 19	13 39	13 59	14 19	14 39	14 59	15 19	15 39	15 59	16 19	16 39	16 59	17 19
South Kenton	d	11 21	11 41	12 01	12 21	12 41	13 01	13 21	13 41	14 01	14 21	14 41	15 01	15 21	15 41	16 01	16 21	16 41	17 01	17 21
North Wembley	d	11 23	11 43	12 03	12 23	12 43	13 03	13 23	13 43	14 03	14 23	14 43	15 03	15 23	15 43	16 03	16 23	16 43	17 03	17 23
Wembley Central Dc	d	11 25	11 45	12 05	12 25	12 45	13 05	13 25	13 45	14 05	14 25	14 45	15 05	15 25	15 45	16 05	16 25	16 45	17 05	17 25
Stonebridge Park	d	11 28	11 48	12 08	12 28	12 48	13 08	13 28	13 48	14 08	14 28	14 48	15 08	15 28	15 48	16 08	16 28	16 48	17 08	17 28
Harlesden	d	11 30	11 50	12 10	12 30	12 50	13 10	13 30	13 50	14 10	14 30	14 50	15 10	15 30	15 50	16 10	16 30	16 50	17 10	17 30
Willesden Jn Low Level	d	11 32	11 52	12 12	12 32	12 52	13 12	13 32	13 52	14 12	14 32	14 52	15 12	15 32	15 52	16 12	16 32	16 52	17 12	17 32
Kensal Green	d	11 35	11 55	12 15	12 35	12 55	13 15	13 35	13 55	14 15	14 35	14 55	15 15	15 35	15 55	16 15	16 35	16 55	17 15	17 35
Queens Park (Dc) ⊖	d	11 40	12 00	12 20	12 40	13 00	13 20	13 40	14 00	14 20	14 40	15 00	15 20	15 40	16 00	16 20	16 40	17 00	17 20	17 40
Kilburn High Road	d	11 42	12 02	12 22	12 42	13 02	13 22	13 42	14 02	14 22	14 42	15 02	15 22	15 42	16 02	16 22	16 42	17 02	17 22	17 42
South Hampstead	d	11a44	12a04	12a24	12a44	13a04	13a24	13a44	14a04	14a24	14a44	15a04	15a24	15a44	16a04	16a24	16a44	17a04	17a24	17a44
London Euston 15 ⊖	a																			

Station		LO A	LO A	LO A	LO A	LO A	LO A	LO A	LO A	LO A	LO A	LO A	LO A	LO A	LO A	LO A	LO A	LO A	LO	
Watford Junction Dc	d	17 21	17 41	18 01	18 21	18 41	19 01	19 21	19 41	20 01	20 21	20 41	21 01	21 21	21 41	22 01	22 21	22 41	23 01	
Watford High Street	d	17 24	17 44	18 04	18 24	18 44	19 04	19 24	19 44	20 04	20 24	20 44	21 04	21 24	21 44	22 04	22 24	22 44	23 04	
Bushey Dc	d	17 26	17 46	18 06	18 26	18 46	19 06	19 26	19 46	20 06	20 26	20 46	21 06	21 26	21 46	22 06	22 26	22 46	23 06	
Carpenders Park	d	17 29	17 49	18 09	18 29	18 49	19 09	19 29	19 49	20 09	20 29	20 49	21 09	21 29	21 49	22 09	22 29	22 49	23 09	
Hatch End	d	17 32	17 52	18 12	18 32	18 52	19 12	19 32	19 52	20 12	20 32	20 52	21 12	21 32	21 52	22 12	22 32	22 52	23 12	
Headstone Lane	d	17 34	17 54	18 14	18 34	18 54	19 14	19 34	19 54	20 14	20 34	20 54	21 14	21 34	21 54	22 14	22 34	22 54	23 14	
Harrow & Wealdstone D.C.	d	17 37	17 57	18 17	18 37	18 57	19 17	19 37	19 57	20 17	20 37	20 57	21 17	21 37	21 57	22 17	22 37	22 57	23 17	
Kenton	d	17 39	17 59	18 19	18 39	18 59	19 19	19 39	19 59	20 19	20 39	20 59	21 19	21 39	21 59	22 19	22 39	22 59	23 19	
South Kenton	d	17 41	18 01	18 21	18 41	19 01	19 21	19 41	20 01	20 21	20 41	21 01	21 21	21 41	22 01	22 21	22 41	23 01	23 21	
North Wembley	d	17 43	18 03	18 23	18 43	19 03	19 23	19 43	20 03	20 23	20 43	21 03	21 23	21 43	22 03	22 23	22 43	23 03	23 23	
Wembley Central Dc	d	17 45	18 05	18 25	18 45	19 05	19 25	19 45	20 05	20 25	20 45	21 05	21 25	21 45	22 05	22 25	22 45	23 05	23 25	
Stonebridge Park	d	17 48	18 08	18 28	18 48	19 08	19 28	19 48	20 08	20 28	20 48	21 08	21 28	21 48	22 08	22 28	22 48	23 08	23 28	
Harlesden	d	17 50	18 10	18 30	18 50	19 10	19 30	19 50	20 10	20 30	20 50	21 10	21 30	21 50	22 10	22 30	22 50	23 10	23 30	
Willesden Jn Low Level	d	17 52	18 12	18 32	18 52	19 12	19 32	19 52	20 12	20 32	20 52	21 12	21 32	21 52	22 12	22 32	22 52	23 12	23 32	
Kensal Green	d	17 55	18 15	18 35	18 55	19 15	19 35	19 55	20 15	20 35	20 55	21 15	21 35	21 55	22 15	22 35	22 55	23 15	23 35	
Queens Park (Dc) ⊖	d	18 00	18 20	18 40	19 00	19 20	19 40	20 00	20 20	20 40	21 00	21 20	21 40	22 00	22 20	22 40	23 00	23 20	23a37	
Kilburn High Road	d	18 02	18 22	18 42	19 02	19 22	19 42	20 02	20 22	20 42	21 02	21 22	21 42	22 02	22 22	22 42	23 02	23 22		
South Hampstead	d	18a04	18a24	18a44	19a04	19a24	19a44	20a04	20a24	20a44	21a04	21a24	21a44	22a04	22a24	22a44	23a04	23a24		
London Euston 15 ⊖	a																			

Saturdays

until 30 August and from 22 November

Station		LO	LO	LO	LO	LO	LO	LO	LO	LO	LO	LO	LO	LO	LO	LO	LO	LO	LO	LO
Watford Junction Dc	d	05 05	05 21	05 41	06 01	06 21	06 41	07 01	07 21	07 41	08 01	08 21	08 41	09 01	09 21	09 41	10 01	10 21	10 41	11 01
Watford High Street	d	05 08	05 24	05 44	06 04	06 24	06 44	07 04	07 24	07 44	08 04	08 24	08 44	09 04	09 24	09 44	10 04	10 24	10 44	11 04
Bushey Dc	d	05 10	05 26	05 46	06 06	06 26	06 46	07 06	07 26	07 46	08 06	08 26	08 46	09 06	09 26	09 46	10 06	10 26	10 46	11 06
Carpenders Park	d	05 13	05 29	05 49	06 09	06 29	06 49	07 09	07 29	07 49	08 09	08 29	08 49	09 09	09 29	09 49	10 09	10 29	10 49	11 09
Hatch End	d	05 16	05 32	05 52	06 12	06 32	06 52	07 12	07 32	07 52	08 12	08 32	08 52	09 12	09 32	09 52	10 12	10 32	10 52	11 12
Headstone Lane	d	05 18	05 34	05 54	06 14	06 34	06 54	07 14	07 34	07 54	08 14	08 34	08 54	09 14	09 34	09 54	10 14	10 34	10 54	11 14
Harrow & Wealdstone D.C.	d	05 21	05 37	05 57	06 17	06 37	06 57	07 17	07 37	07 57	08 17	08 37	08 57	09 17	09 37	09 57	10 17	10 37	10 57	11 17
Kenton	d	05 23	05 39	05 59	06 19	06 39	06 59	07 19	07 39	07 59	08 19	08 39	08 59	09 19	09 39	09 59	10 19	10 39	10 59	11 19
South Kenton	d	05 25	05 41	06 01	06 21	06 41	07 01	07 21	07 41	08 01	08 21	08 41	09 01	09 21	09 41	10 01	10 21	10 41	11 01	11 21
North Wembley	d	05 27	05 43	06 03	06 23	06 43	07 03	07 23	07 43	08 03	08 23	08 43	09 03	09 23	09 43	10 03	10 23	10 43	11 03	11 23
Wembley Central Dc	d	05 29	05 45	06 05	06 25	06 45	07 05	07 25	07 45	08 05	08 25	08 45	09 05	09 25	09 45	10 05	10 25	10 45	11 05	11 25
Stonebridge Park	d	05 32	05 48	06 08	06 28	06 48	07 08	07 28	07 48	08 08	08 28	08 48	09 08	09 28	09 48	10 08	10 28	10 48	11 08	11 28
Harlesden	d	05 34	05 50	06 09	06 30	06 50	07 10	07 30	07 50	08 10	08 30	08 50	09 10	09 30	09 50	10 10	10 30	10 50	11 10	11 30
Willesden Jn Low Level	d	05 36	05 52	06 12	06 32	06 52	07 12	07 32	07 52	08 12	08 32	08 52	09 12	09 32	09 52	10 12	10 32	10 52	11 12	11 32
Kensal Green	d	05 39	05 55	06 15	06 35	06 55	07 15	07 35	07 55	08 15	08 35	08 55	09 15	09 35	09 55	10 15	10 35	10 55	11 15	11 35
Queens Park (Dc) ⊖	d	05 41	05 57	06 17	06 37	06 57	07 17	07 37	07 57	08 17	08 37	08 57	09 17	09 37	09 57	10 17	10 37	10 57	11 17	11 37
Kilburn High Road	d	05 43	05 59	06 19	06 39	06 59	07 19	07 39	07 59	08 19	08 39	08 59	09 19	09 39	09 59	10 19	10 39	10 59	11 19	11 39
South Hampstead	d	05 45	06 01	06 21	06 41	07 01	07 21	07 41	08 01	08 21	08 41	09 01	09 21	09 41	10 01	10 21	10 41	11 01	11 21	11 41
London Euston 15 ⊖	a	05 54	06 10	06 30	06 50	07 10	07 30	07 50	08 10	08 30	08 50	09 10	09 30	09 50	10 10	10 30	10 50	11 10	11 30	11 50

Station		LO	LO	LO	LO	LO	LO	LO	LO	LO	LO	LO	LO	LO	LO	LO	LO	LO	LO	LO
Watford Junction Dc	d	11 21	11 41	12 01	12 21	12 41	13 01	13 21	13 41	14 01	14 21	14 41	15 01	15 21	15 41	16 01	16 21	16 41	17 01	17 21
Watford High Street	d	11 24	11 44	12 04	12 24	12 44	13 04	13 24	13 44	14 04	14 24	14 44	15 04	15 24	15 44	16 04	16 24	16 44	17 04	17 24
Bushey Dc	d	11 26	11 46	12 06	12 26	12 46	13 06	13 26	13 46	14 06	14 26	14 46	15 06	15 26	15 46	16 06	16 26	16 46	17 06	17 26
Carpenders Park	d	11 29	11 49	12 09	12 29	12 49	13 09	13 29	13 49	14 09	14 29	14 49	15 09	15 29	15 49	16 09	16 29	16 49	17 09	17 29
Hatch End	d	11 32	11 52	12 12	12 32	12 52	13 12	13 32	13 52	14 12	14 32	14 52	15 12	15 32	15 52	16 12	16 32	16 52	17 12	17 32
Headstone Lane	d	11 34	11 54	12 14	12 34	12 54	13 14	13 34	13 54	14 14	14 34	14 54	15 14	15 34	15 54	16 14	16 34	16 54	17 14	17 34
Harrow & Wealdstone D.C.	d	11 37	11 57	12 17	12 37	12 57	13 17	13 37	13 57	14 17	14 37	14 57	15 17	15 37	15 57	16 17	16 37	16 57	17 17	17 37
Kenton	d	11 39	11 59	12 19	12 39	12 59	13 19	13 39	13 59	14 19	14 39	14 59	15 19	15 39	15 59	16 19	16 39	16 59	17 19	17 39
South Kenton	d	11 41	12 01	12 21	12 41	13 01	13 21	13 41	14 01	14 21	14 41	15 01	15 21	15 41	16 01	16 21	16 41	17 01	17 21	17 41
North Wembley	d	11 43	12 03	12 23	12 43	13 03	13 23	13 43	14 03	14 23	14 43	15 03	15 23	15 43	16 03	16 23	16 43	17 03	17 23	17 43
Wembley Central Dc	d	11 45	12 05	12 25	12 45	13 05	13 25	13 45	14 05	14 25	14 45	15 05	15 25	15 45	16 05	16 25	16 45	17 05	17 25	17 45
Stonebridge Park	d	11 48	12 08	12 28	12 48	13 08	13 28	13 48	14 08	14 28	14 48	15 08	15 28	15 48	16 08	16 28	16 48	17 08	17 28	17 48
Harlesden	d	11 50	12 10	12 30	12 50	13 10	13 30	13 50	14 10	14 30	14 50	15 10	15 30	15 50	16 10	16 30	16 50	17 10	17 30	17 50
Willesden Jn Low Level	d	11 52	12 12	12 32	12 52	13 12	13 32	13 52	14 12	14 32	14 52	15 12	15 32	15 52	16 12	16 32	16 52	17 12	17 32	17 52
Kensal Green	d	11 55	12 15	12 35	12 55	13 15	13 35	13 55	14 15	14 35	14 55	15 15	15 35	15 55	16 15	16 35	16 55	17 15	17 35	17 55
Queens Park (Dc) ⊖	d	11 57	12 17	12 37	12 57	13 17	13 37	13 57	14 17	14 37	14 57	15 17	15 37	15 57	16 17	16 37	16 57	17 17	17 37	17 57
Kilburn High Road	d	11 59	12 19	12 39	12 59	13 19	13 39	13 59	14 19	14 39	14 59	15 19	15 39	15 59	16 19	16 39	16 59	17 19	17 39	17 59
South Hampstead	d	12 01	12 21	12 41	13 01	13 21	13 41	14 01	14 21	14 41	15 01	15 21	15 41	16 01	16 21	16 41	17 01	17 21	17 41	18 01
London Euston 15 ⊖	a	12 10	12 30	12 50	13 10	13 30	13 50	14 10	14 30	14 50	15 10	15 30	15 50	16 10	16 30	16 50	17 10	17 30	17 50	18 10

For general notes see front of timetable
For details of catering facilities see
Directory of Train Operators

A To Stratford Low Level (Table 59)

Stations Harrow & Wealdstone to Queen's Park inclusive are also served by London Underground Bakerloo Line services

Table 60

Saturdays

Watford Junction → Harrow & Wealdstone, Queens Park and London

until 30 August and from 22 November

Network Diagram - See first page of Table 59

		LO	LO	LO	LO	LO	LO	LO	LO	LO	LO	LO	LO	LO	LO	LO	LO	LO
Watford Junction Dc	d	17 41	18 01	18 21	18 41	19 01	19 21	19 41	20 01	20 21	20 41	21 01	21 21	21 41	22 01	22 21	22 41	23 01
Watford High Street	d	17 44	18 04	18 24	18 44	19 04	19 24	19 44	20 04	20 24	20 44	21 04	21 24	21 44	22 04	22 24	22 44	23 04
Bushey Dc	d	17 46	18 06	18 26	18 46	19 06	19 26	19 46	20 06	20 26	20 46	21 06	21 26	21 46	22 06	22 26	22 46	23 06
Carpenders Park	d	17 49	18 09	18 29	18 49	19 09	19 29	19 49	20 09	20 29	20 49	21 09	21 29	21 49	22 09	22 29	22 49	23 09
Hatch End	d	17 52	18 12	18 32	18 52	19 12	19 32	19 52	20 12	20 32	20 52	21 12	21 32	21 52	22 12	22 32	22 52	23 12
Headstone Lane	d	17 54	18 14	18 34	18 54	19 14	19 34	19 54	20 14	20 34	20 54	21 14	21 34	21 54	22 14	22 34	22 54	23 14
Harrow & Wealdstone D.C.	d	17 57	18 17	18 37	18 57	19 17	19 37	19 57	20 17	20 37	20 57	21 17	21 37	21 57	22 17	22 37	22 57	23 17
Kenton	d	17 59	18 19	18 39	18 59	19 19	19 39	19 59	20 19	20 39	20 59	21 19	21 39	21 59	22 19	22 39	22 59	23 19
South Kenton	d	18 01	18 21	18 41	19 01	19 21	19 41	20 01	20 21	20 41	21 01	21 21	21 41	22 01	22 21	22 41	23 01	23 21
North Wembley	d	18 03	18 23	18 43	19 03	19 23	19 43	20 03	20 23	20 43	21 03	21 23	21 43	22 03	22 23	22 43	23 03	23 23
Wembley Central Dc	d	18 05	18 25	18 45	19 05	19 25	19 45	20 05	20 25	20 45	21 05	21 25	21 45	22 05	22 25	22 45	23 05	23 25
Stonebridge Park	d	18 08	18 28	18 48	19 08	19 28	19 48	20 08	20 28	20 48	21 08	21 28	21 48	22 08	22 28	22 48	23 08	23 28
Harlesden	d	18 10	18 30	18 50	19 10	19 30	19 50	20 10	20 30	20 50	21 10	21 30	21 50	22 10	22 30	22 50	23 10	23 30
Willesden Jn Low Level	d	18 12	18 32	18 52	19 12	19 32	19 52	20 12	20 32	20 52	21 12	21 32	21 52	22 12	22 32	22 52	23 12	23 32
Kensal Green	d	18 15	18 35	18 55	19 15	19 35	19 55	20 15	20 35	20 55	21 15	21 35	21 55	22 15	22 35	22 55	23 15	23 35
Queens Park (Dc) ⊖	d	18 17	18 37	18 57	19 17	19 37	19 57	20 17	20 37	20 57	21 17	21 37	21 57	22 17	22 37	22 57	23 17	23 37
Kilburn High Road	d	18 19	18 39	18 59	19 19	19 39	19 59	20 19	20 39	20 59	21 19	21 39	21 59	22 19	22 39	22 59	23 19	23 39
South Hampstead	d	18 21	18 41	19 01	19 21	19 41	20 01	20 21	20 41	21 01	21 21	21 41	22 01	22 21	22 41	23 01	23 21	23 41
London Euston 15 ⊖	a	18 30	18 50	19 10	19 30	19 50	20 10	20 30	20 50	21 10	21 30	21 50	22 10	22 30	22 50	23 10	23 30	23 50

Saturdays

6 September to 15 November

		LO A	LO A	LO A	LO	LO A	LO A	LO A	LO A	LO A	LO A	LO A	LO A	LO A	LO A	LO A	LO A	LO A	LO A	LO A
Watford Junction Dc	d	05 05	05 21	05 41	06 01	06 21	06 41	07 01	07 21	07 41	08 01	08 21	08 41	09 01	09 21	09 41	10 01	10 21	10 41	11 01
Watford High Street	d	05 08	05 24	05 44	06 04	06 24	06 44	07 04	07 24	07 44	08 04	08 24	08 44	09 04	09 24	09 44	10 04	10 24	10 44	11 04
Bushey Dc	d	05 10	05 26	05 46	06 06	06 26	06 46	07 06	07 26	07 46	08 06	08 26	08 46	09 06	09 26	09 46	10 06	10 26	10 46	11 06
Carpenders Park	d	05 13	05 29	05 49	06 09	06 29	06 49	07 09	07 29	07 49	08 09	08 29	08 49	09 09	09 29	09 49	10 09	10 29	10 49	11 09
Hatch End	d	05 16	05 32	05 52	06 12	06 32	06 52	07 12	07 32	07 52	08 12	08 32	08 52	09 12	09 32	09 52	10 12	10 32	10 52	11 12
Headstone Lane	d	05 18	05 34	05 54	06 14	06 34	06 54	07 14	07 34	07 54	08 14	08 34	08 54	09 14	09 34	09 54	10 14	10 34	10 54	11 14
Harrow & Wealdstone D.C.	d	05 21	05 37	05 57	06 17	06 37	06 57	07 17	07 37	07 57	08 17	08 37	08 57	09 17	09 37	09 57	10 17	10 37	10 57	11 17
Kenton	d	05 23	05 39	05 59	06 19	06 39	06 59	07 19	07 39	07 59	08 19	08 39	08 59	09 19	09 39	09 59	10 19	10 39	10 59	11 19
South Kenton	d	05 25	05 41	06 01	06 21	06 41	07 01	07 21	07 41	08 01	08 21	08 41	09 01	09 21	09 41	10 01	10 21	10 41	11 01	11 21
North Wembley	d	05 27	05 43	06 03	06 23	06 43	07 03	07 23	07 43	08 03	08 23	08 43	09 03	09 23	09 43	10 03	10 23	10 43	11 03	11 23
Wembley Central Dc	d	05 29	05 45	06 05	06 25	06 45	07 05	07 25	07 45	08 05	08 25	08 45	09 05	09 25	09 45	10 05	10 25	10 45	11 05	11 25
Stonebridge Park	d	05 32	05 48	06 08	06 28	06 48	07 08	07 28	07 48	08 08	08 28	08 48	09 08	09 28	09 48	10 08	10 28	10 48	11 08	11 28
Harlesden	d	05 34	05 50	06 09	06 30	06 50	07 10	07 30	07 50	08 10	08 30	08 50	09 10	09 30	09 50	10 10	10 30	10 50	11 10	11 30
Willesden Jn Low Level	d	05 36	05 52	06 13	06 32	06 52	07 12	07 32	07 52	08 12	08 32	08 52	09 12	09 32	09 52	10 12	10 32	10 52	11 12	11 32
Kensal Green	d	05 39	05 55	06 16	06 35	06 55	07 15	07 35	07 55	08 15	08 35	08 55	09 15	09 35	09 55	10 15	10 35	10 55	11 15	11 35
Queens Park (Dc) ⊖	d	05 44	06 00	06 21	06 40	07 00	07 20	07 40	08 00	08 20	08 40	09 00	09 20	09 40	10 00	10 20	10 40	11 00	11 20	11 40
Kilburn High Road	d	05 46	06 02	06 23	06 42	07 02	07 22	07 42	08 02	08 22	08 42	09 02	09 22	09 42	10 02	10 22	10 42	11 02	11 22	11 42
South Hampstead	d	05a48	06a04	06a24	06a44	07a04	07a24	07a44	08a04	08a24	08a44	09a04	09a24	09a44	10a04	10a24	10a44	11a04	11a24	11a44
London Euston 15 ⊖	a																			

		LO A	LO A	LO A	LO A	LO A	LO A	LO A	LO A	LO A	LO A	LO A	LO A	LO A	LO A	LO A	LO A	LO A	LO A	LO A
Watford Junction Dc	d	11 21	11 41	12 01	12 21	12 41	13 01	13 21	13 41	14 01	14 21	14 41	15 01	15 21	15 41	16 01	16 21	16 41	17 01	17 21
Watford High Street	d	11 24	11 44	12 04	12 24	12 44	13 04	13 24	13 44	14 04	14 24	14 44	15 04	15 24	15 44	16 04	16 24	16 44	17 04	17 24
Bushey Dc	d	11 26	11 46	12 06	12 26	12 46	13 06	13 26	13 46	14 06	14 26	14 46	15 06	15 26	15 46	16 06	16 26	16 46	17 06	17 26
Carpenders Park	d	11 29	11 49	12 09	12 29	12 49	13 09	13 29	13 49	14 09	14 29	14 49	15 09	15 29	15 49	16 09	16 29	16 49	17 09	17 29
Hatch End	d	11 32	11 52	12 12	12 32	12 52	13 12	13 32	13 52	14 12	14 32	14 52	15 12	15 32	15 52	16 12	16 32	16 52	17 12	17 32
Headstone Lane	d	11 34	11 54	12 14	12 34	12 54	13 14	13 34	13 54	14 14	14 34	14 54	15 14	15 34	15 54	16 14	16 34	16 54	17 14	17 34
Harrow & Wealdstone D.C.	d	11 37	11 57	12 17	12 37	12 57	13 17	13 37	13 57	14 17	14 37	14 57	15 17	15 37	15 57	16 17	16 37	16 57	17 17	17 37
Kenton	d	11 39	11 59	12 19	12 39	12 59	13 19	13 39	13 59	14 19	14 39	14 59	15 19	15 39	15 59	16 19	16 39	16 59	17 19	17 39
South Kenton	d	11 41	12 01	12 21	12 41	13 01	13 21	13 41	14 01	14 21	14 41	15 01	15 21	15 41	16 01	16 21	16 41	17 01	17 21	17 41
North Wembley	d	11 43	12 03	12 23	12 43	13 03	13 23	13 43	14 03	14 23	14 43	15 03	15 23	15 43	16 03	16 23	16 43	17 03	17 23	17 43
Wembley Central Dc	d	11 45	12 05	12 25	12 45	13 05	13 25	13 45	14 05	14 25	14 45	15 05	15 25	15 45	16 05	16 25	16 45	17 05	17 25	17 45
Stonebridge Park	d	11 48	12 08	12 28	12 48	13 08	13 28	13 48	14 08	14 28	14 48	15 08	15 28	15 48	16 08	16 28	16 48	17 08	17 28	17 48
Harlesden	d	11 50	12 10	12 30	12 50	13 10	13 30	13 50	14 10	14 30	14 50	15 10	15 30	15 50	16 10	16 30	16 50	17 10	17 30	17 50
Willesden Jn Low Level	d	11 52	12 12	12 32	12 52	13 12	13 32	13 52	14 12	14 32	14 52	15 12	15 32	15 52	16 12	16 32	16 52	17 12	17 32	17 52
Kensal Green	d	11 55	12 15	12 35	12 55	13 15	13 35	13 55	14 15	14 35	14 55	15 15	15 35	15 55	16 15	16 35	16 55	17 15	17 35	17 55
Queens Park (Dc) ⊖	d	12 00	12 20	12 40	13 00	13 20	13 40	14 00	14 20	14 40	15 00	15 20	15 40	16 00	16 20	16 40	17 00	17 20	17 40	18 00
Kilburn High Road	d	12 02	12 22	12 42	13 02	13 22	13 42	14 02	14 22	14 42	15 02	15 22	15 42	16 02	16 22	16 42	17 02	17 22	17 42	18 02
South Hampstead	d	12a04	12a24	12a44	13a04	13a24	13a44	14a04	14a24	14a44	15a04	15a24	15a44	16a04	16a24	16a44	17a04	17a24	17a44	18a04
London Euston 15 ⊖	a																			

For general notes see front of timetable
For details of catering facilities see
Directory of Train Operators

A To Stratford Low Level (Table 59)

Stations Harrow & Wealdstone to Queen's Park inclusive are also served by London Underground Bakerloo Line services

Table 60

6 September to 15 November

Watford Jn → Harrow & Wealdstone, Queens Park and London

Network Diagram - See first page of Table 59

		LO A	LO A	LO A	LO A	LO A	LO A	LO A	LO A	LO A	LO A	LO A	LO A	LO A	LO A	LO A	LO A	LO
Watford Junction Dc	d	17 41	18 01	18 21	18 41	19 01	19 21	19 41	20 01	20 21	20 41	21 01	21 21	21 41	22 01	22 21	22 41	23 01
Watford High Street	d	17 44	18 04	18 24	18 44	19 04	19 24	19 44	20 04	20 24	20 44	21 04	21 24	21 44	22 04	22 24	22 44	23 04
Bushey Dc	d	17 46	18 06	18 26	18 46	19 06	19 26	19 46	20 06	20 26	20 46	21 06	21 26	21 46	22 06	22 26	22 46	23 06
Carpenders Park	d	17 49	18 09	18 29	18 49	19 09	19 29	19 49	20 09	20 29	20 49	21 09	21 29	21 49	22 09	22 29	22 49	23 09
Hatch End	d	17 52	18 12	18 32	18 52	19 12	19 32	19 52	20 12	20 32	20 52	21 12	21 32	21 52	22 12	22 32	22 52	23 12
Headstone Lane	d	17 54	18 14	18 34	18 54	19 14	19 34	19 54	20 14	20 34	20 54	21 14	21 34	21 54	22 14	22 34	22 54	23 14
Harrow & Wealdstone D.C.	d	17 57	18 17	18 37	18 57	19 17	19 37	19 57	20 17	20 37	20 57	21 17	21 37	21 57	22 17	22 37	22 57	23 17
Kenton	d	17 59	18 19	18 39	18 59	19 19	19 39	19 59	20 19	20 39	20 59	21 19	21 39	21 59	22 19	22 39	22 59	23 19
South Kenton	d	18 01	18 21	18 41	19 01	19 21	19 41	20 01	20 21	20 41	21 01	21 21	21 41	22 01	22 21	22 41	23 01	23 21
North Wembley	d	18 03	18 23	18 43	19 03	19 23	19 43	20 03	20 23	20 43	21 03	21 23	21 43	22 03	22 23	22 43	23 03	23 23
Wembley Central Dc	d	18 05	18 25	18 45	19 05	19 25	19 45	20 05	20 25	20 45	21 05	21 25	21 45	22 05	22 25	22 45	23 05	23 25
Stonebridge Park	d	18 08	18 28	18 48	19 08	19 28	19 48	20 08	20 28	20 48	21 08	21 28	21 48	22 08	22 28	22 48	23 08	23 28
Harlesden	d	18 10	18 30	18 50	19 10	19 30	19 50	20 10	20 30	20 50	21 10	21 30	21 50	22 10	22 30	22 50	23 10	23 30
Willesden Jn Low Level	d	18 12	18 32	18 52	19 12	19 32	19 52	20 12	20 32	20 52	21 12	21 32	21 52	22 12	22 32	22 52	23 12	23 32
Kensal Green	d	18 15	18 35	18 55	19 15	19 35	19 55	20 15	20 35	20 55	21 15	21 35	21 55	22 15	22 35	22 55	23 15	23 35
Queens Park (Dc)	⊖ d	18 20	18 40	19 00	19 20	19 40	20 00	20 20	20 40	21 00	21 20	21 40	22 00	22 20	22 40	23 00	23 20	23a37
Kilburn High Road	d	18 22	18 42	19 02	19 22	19 42	20 02	20 22	20 42	21 02	21 22	21 42	22 02	22 22	22 42	23 02	23 22	
South Hampstead	d	18a24	18a44	19a04	19a24	19a44	20a04	20a24	20a44	21a04	21a24	21a44	22a04	22a24	22a44	23a04	23a24	
London Euston 15	⊖ a																	

Sundays

until 31 August and from 23 November

		LO	LO	LO	LO	LO	LO	LO	LO	LO	LO	LO	LO	LO	LO	LO	LO	LO	LO	LO
Watford Junction Dc	d	00 10	01 07	06 51	07 21	07 51	08 21	08 51	09 21	09 51	10 21	10 51	11 21	11 51	12 21	12 51	13 21	13 51	14 21	14 51
Watford High Street	d			06 54	07 24	07 54	08 24	08 54	09 24	09 54	10 24	10 54	11 24	11 54	12 24	12 54	13 24	13 54	14 24	14 54
Bushey Dc	d			06 56	07 26	07 56	08 26	08 56	09 26	09 56	10 26	10 56	11 26	11 56	12 26	12 56	13 26	13 56	14 26	14 56
Carpenders Park	d			06 59	07 29	07 59	08 29	08 59	09 29	09 59	10 29	10 59	11 29	11 59	12 29	12 59	13 29	13 59	14 29	14 59
Hatch End	d			07 02	07 32	08 02	08 32	09 02	09 32	10 02	10 32	11 02	11 32	12 02	12 32	13 02	13 32	14 02	14 32	15 02
Headstone Lane	d			07 04	07 34	08 04	08 34	09 04	09 34	10 04	10 34	11 04	11 34	12 04	12 34	13 04	13 34	14 04	14 34	15 04
Harrow & Wealdstone D.C.	d	00 22	01 19	07 07	07 37	08 07	08 37	09 07	09 37	10 07	10 37	11 07	11 37	12 07	12 37	13 07	13 37	14 07	14 37	15 07
Kenton	d			07 09	07 39	08 09	08 39	09 09	09 39	10 09	10 39	11 09	11 39	12 09	12 39	13 09	13 39	14 09	14 39	15 09
South Kenton	d			07 11	07 41	08 11	08 41	09 11	09 41	10 11	10 41	11 11	11 41	12 11	12 41	13 11	13 41	14 11	14 41	15 11
North Wembley	d			07 13	07 43	08 13	08 43	09 13	09 43	10 13	10 43	11 13	11 43	12 13	12 43	13 13	13 43	14 13	14 43	15 13
Wembley Central Dc	d	00 28	01 25	07 15	07 45	08 15	08 45	09 15	09 45	10 15	10 45	11 15	11 45	12 15	12 45	13 15	13 45	14 15	14 45	15 15
Stonebridge Park	d			07 18	07 48	08 18	08 48	09 18	09 48	10 18	10 48	11 18	11 48	12 18	12 48	13 18	13 48	14 18	14 48	15 18
Harlesden	d			07 20	07 50	08 20	08 50	09 20	09 50	10 20	10 50	11 20	11 50	12 20	12 50	13 20	13 50	14 20	14 50	15 20
Willesden Jn Low Level	d			07 22	07 52	08 22	08 52	09 22	09 52	10 22	10 52	11 22	11 52	12 22	12 52	13 22	13 52	14 22	14 52	15 22
Kensal Green	d			07 25	07 55	08 25	08 55	09 25	09 55	10 25	10 55	11 25	11 55	12 25	12 55	13 25	13 55	14 25	14 55	15 25
Queens Park (Dc)	⊖ d			07 27	07 57	08 27	08 57	09 27	09 57	10 27	10 57	11 27	11 57	12 27	12 57	13 27	13 57	14 27	14 57	15 27
Kilburn High Road	d			07 29	07 59	08 29	08 59	09 29	09 59	10 29	10 59	11 29	11 59	12 29	12 59	13 29	13 59	14 29	14 59	15 29
South Hampstead	d			07 31	08 01	08 31	09 01	09 31	10 01	10 31	11 01	11 31	12 01	12 31	13 01	13 31	14 01	14 31	15 01	15 31
London Euston 15	⊖ a	00 44	01 41	07 38	08 08	08 38	09 08	09 38	10 08	10 38	11 08	11 38	12 08	12 38	13 08	13 38	14 08	14 38	15 08	15 38

		LO	LO	LO	LO	LO	LO	LO	LO	LO	LO	LO	LO	LO	LO	LO	LO	LO
Watford Junction Dc	d	15 21	15 51	16 21	16 51	17 21	17 51	18 21	18 51	19 21	19 51	20 21	20 51	21 21	21 51	22 21	22 51	23 21
Watford High Street	d	15 24	15 54	16 24	16 54	17 24	17 54	18 24	18 54	19 24	19 54	20 24	20 54	21 24	21 54	22 24	22 54	23 24
Bushey Dc	d	15 26	15 56	16 26	16 56	17 26	17 56	18 26	18 56	19 26	19 56	20 26	20 56	21 26	21 56	22 26	22 56	23 26
Carpenders Park	d	15 29	15 59	16 29	16 59	17 29	17 59	18 29	18 59	19 29	19 59	20 29	20 59	21 29	21 59	22 29	22 59	23 29
Hatch End	d	15 32	16 02	16 32	17 02	17 32	18 02	18 32	19 02	19 32	20 02	20 32	21 02	21 32	22 02	22 32	23 02	23 32
Headstone Lane	d	15 34	16 04	16 34	17 04	17 34	18 04	18 34	19 04	19 34	20 04	20 34	21 04	21 34	22 04	22 34	23 04	23 34
Harrow & Wealdstone D.C.	d	15 37	16 07	16 37	17 07	17 37	18 07	18 37	19 07	19 37	20 07	20 37	21 07	21 37	22 07	22 37	23 07	23 37
Kenton	d	15 39	16 09	16 39	17 09	17 39	18 09	18 39	19 09	19 39	20 09	20 39	21 09	21 39	22 09	22 39	23 09	23 39
South Kenton	d	15 41	16 11	16 41	17 11	17 41	18 11	18 41	19 11	19 41	20 11	20 41	21 11	21 41	22 11	22 41	23 11	23 41
North Wembley	d	15 43	16 13	16 43	17 13	17 43	18 13	18 43	19 13	19 43	20 13	20 43	21 13	21 43	22 13	22 43	23 13	23 43
Wembley Central Dc	d	15 45	16 15	16 45	17 15	17 45	18 15	18 45	19 15	19 45	20 15	20 45	21 15	21 45	22 15	22 45	23 15	23 45
Stonebridge Park	d	15 48	16 18	16 48	17 18	17 48	18 18	18 48	19 18	19 48	20 18	20 48	21 18	21 48	22 18	22 48	23 18	23 48
Harlesden	d	15 50	16 20	16 50	17 20	17 50	18 20	18 50	19 20	19 50	20 20	20 50	21 20	21 50	22 20	22 50	23 20	23 50
Willesden Jn Low Level	d	15 52	16 22	16 52	17 22	17 52	18 22	18 52	19 22	19 52	20 22	20 52	21 22	21 52	22 22	22 52	23 22	23 52
Kensal Green	d	15 55	16 25	16 55	17 25	17 55	18 25	18 55	19 25	19 55	20 25	20 55	21 25	21 55	22 25	22 55	23 25	23 55
Queens Park (Dc)	⊖ d	15 57	16 27	16 57	17 27	17 57	18 27	18 57	19 27	19 57	20 27	20 57	21 27	21 57	22 27	22 57	23 27	23 57
Kilburn High Road	d	15 59	16 29	16 59	17 29	17 59	18 29	18 59	19 29	19 59	20 29	20 59	21 29	21 59	22 29	22 59	23 29	23 59
South Hampstead	d	16 01	16 31	17 01	17 31	18 01	18 31	19 01	19 31	20 01	20 31	21 01	21 31	22 01	22 31	23 01	23 31	00 01
London Euston 15	⊖ a	16 08	16 38	17 08	17 38	18 08	18 38	19 08	19 38	20 08	20 38	21 08	21 38	22 08	22 38	23 08	23 38	00 08

For general notes see front of timetable
For details of catering facilities see
Directory of Train Operators

A To Stratford Low Level (Table 59)

Stations Queen's Park to Harrow & Wealdstone inclusive are also served by London Underground Bakerloo line services

Table 60

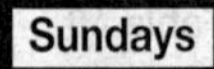

7 September to 16 November

Watford Junction → Harrow & Wealdstone, Queens Park and London

Network Diagram - See first page of Table 59

		LO	LO	LO	LO	LO	LO A	LO	LO A	LO	LO A	LO	LO A	LO	LO A	LO	LO A	LO	LO A	LO	LO A	LO	LO A
Watford Junction Dc	d	00 10	01 07	06 51	07 21	07 51		08 21		08 51		09 21		09 51		10 21		10 51		11 21		11 51	
Watford High Street	d			06 54	07 24	07 54		08 24		08 54		09 24		09 54		10 24		10 54		11 24		11 54	
Bushey Dc	d			06 56	07 26	07 56		08 26		08 56		09 26		09 56		10 26		10 56		11 26		11 56	
Carpenders Park	d			06 59	07 29	07 59		08 29		08 59		09 29		09 59		10 29		10 59		11 29		11 59	
Hatch End	d			07 02	07 32	08 02		08 32		09 02		09 32		10 02		10 32		11 02		11 32		12 02	
Headstone Lane	d			07 04	07 34	08 04		08 34		09 04		09 34		10 04		10 34		11 04		11 34		12 04	
Harrow & Wealdstone D.C.	d	00 22	01 19	07 07	07 37	08 07		08 37		09 07		09 37		10 07		10 37		11 07		11 37		12 07	
Kenton	d			07 09	07 39	08 09		08 39		09 09		09 39		10 09		10 39		11 09		11 39		12 09	
South Kenton	d			07 11	07 41	08 11		08 41		09 11		09 41		10 11		10 41		11 11		11 41		12 11	
North Wembley	d			07 13	07 43	08 13		08 43		09 13		09 43		10 13		10 43		11 13		11 43		12 13	
Wembley Central Dc	d	00 28	01 25	07 15	07 45	08 15		08 45		09 15		09 45		10 15		10 45		11 15		11 45		12 15	
Stonebridge Park	d			07 18	07 48	08 18		08 48		09 18		09 48		10 18		10 48		11 18		11 48		12 18	
Harlesden	d			07 20	07 50	08 20		08 50		09 20		09 50		10 20		10 50		11 20		11 50		12 20	
Willesden Jn Low Level	d			07 22	07 52	08 22	08 31	08 52	09 01	09 22	09 31	09 52	10 01	10 22	10 31	10 52	11 01	11 22	11 31	11 52	12 01	12 22	12 31
Kensal Green	d			07 25	07 55	08 25	08a33	08 55	09a03	09 25	09a33	09 55	10a03	10 25	10a33	10 55	11a03	11 25	11a33	11 55	12 03	12 25	12a33
Queens Park (Dc)	⊖ d			07 27	07 57	08 27	08 39	08 57	09 09	09 27	09 39	09 57	10 09	10 27	10 39	10 57	11 09	11 27	11 39	11 57	12 09	12 27	12 39
Kilburn High Road	d			07 29	07 59	08 29	08 41	08 59	09 11	09 29	09 41	09 59	10 11	10 29	10 41	10 59	11 11	11 29	11 41	11 59	12 11	12 29	12 41
South Hampstead	d			07 31	08 01	08 31	08a43	09 01	09a13	09 31	09a43	10 01	10a13	10 31	10a43	11 01	11a13	11 31	11a43	12 01	12a13	12 31	12a43
London Euston 15	⊖ a	00 44	01 41	07 38	08 08	08 38		09 08		09 38		10 08		10 38		11 08		11 38		12 08		12 38	

		LO	LO A	LO	LO A	LO	LO A	LO	LO A	LO	LO A	LO	LO A	LO	LO A	LO	LO A	LO	LO A	LO	LO A	LO	LO A
Watford Junction Dc	d	12 21		12 51		13 21		13 51		14 21		14 51		15 21		15 51		16 21		16 51		17 21	
Watford High Street	d	12 24		12 54		13 24		13 54		14 24		14 54		15 24		15 54		16 24		16 54		17 24	
Bushey Dc	d	12 26		12 56		13 26		13 56		14 26		14 56		15 26		15 56		16 26		16 56		17 26	
Carpenders Park	d	12 29		12 59		13 29		13 59		14 29		14 59		15 29		15 59		16 29		16 59		17 29	
Hatch End	d	12 32		13 02		13 32		14 02		14 32		15 02		15 32		16 02		16 32		17 02		17 32	
Headstone Lane	d	12 34		13 04		13 34		14 04		14 34		15 04		15 34		16 04		16 34		17 04		17 34	
Harrow & Wealdstone D.C.	d	12 37		13 07		13 37		14 07		14 37		15 07		15 37		16 07		16 37		17 07		17 37	
Kenton	d	12 39		13 09		13 39		14 09		14 39		15 09		15 39		16 09		16 39		17 09		17 39	
South Kenton	d	12 41		13 11		13 41		14 11		14 41		15 11		15 41		16 11		16 41		17 11		17 41	
North Wembley	d	12 43		13 13		13 43		14 13		14 43		15 13		15 43		16 13		16 43		17 13		17 43	
Wembley Central Dc	d	12 45		13 15		13 45		14 15		14 45		15 15		15 45		16 15		16 45		17 15		17 45	
Stonebridge Park	d	12 48		13 18		13 48		14 18		14 48		15 18		15 48		16 18		16 48		17 18		17 48	
Harlesden	d	12 50		13 20		13 50		14 20		14 50		15 20		15 50		16 20		16 50		17 20		17 50	
Willesden Jn Low Level	d	12 52	13 01	13 22	13 31	13 52	14 01	14 22	14 31	14 52	15 01	15 22	15 31	15 52	16 01	16 22	16 31	16 52	17 01	17 22	17 31	17 52	18 01
Kensal Green	d	12 55	13 04	13 25	13a33	13 55	14 04	14 25	14a33	14 55	15 04	15 25	15a33	15 55	16 04	16 25	16a33	16 55	17 04	17 25	17a33	17 55	18 04
Queens Park (Dc)	⊖ d	12 57	13 09	13 27	13 39	13 57	14 09	14 27	14 39	14 57	15 09	15 27	15b39	15 57	16 09	16 27	16 39	16 57	17 09	17 27	17 39	17 57	18 09
Kilburn High Road	d	12 59	13 11	13 29	13 41	13 59	14 11	14 29	14 41	14 59	15 11	15 29	15 41	15 59	16 11	16 29	16 41	16 59	17 11	17 29	17 41	17 59	18 11
South Hampstead	d	13 01	13a13	13 31	13a43	14 01	14a13	14 31	14a43	15 01	15a13	15 31	15a43	16 01	16a13	16 31	16a43	17 01	17a13	17 31	17a43	18 01	18a13
London Euston 15	⊖ a	13 08		13 38		14 08		14 38		15 08		15 38		16 08		16 38		17 08		17 38		18 08	

		LO	LO A	LO	LO A	LO	LO A	LO	LO A	LO	LO A	LO	LO A	LO	LO A	LO	LO A	LO	LO A	LO	LO A	LO	LO
Watford Junction Dc	d	17 51		18 21		18 51		19 21		19 51		20 21		20 51		21 21		21 51		22 21		22 51	23 21
Watford High Street	d	17 54		18 24		18 54		19 24		19 54		20 24		20 54		21 24		21 54		22 24		22 54	23 24
Bushey Dc	d	17 56		18 26		18 56		19 26		19 56		20 26		20 56		21 26		21 56		22 26		22 56	23 26
Carpenders Park	d	17 59		18 29		18 59		19 29		19 59		20 29		20 59		21 29		21 59		22 29		22 59	23 29
Hatch End	d	18 02		18 32		19 02		19 32		20 02		20 32		21 02		21 32		22 02		22 32		23 02	23 32
Headstone Lane	d	18 04		18 34		19 04		19 34		20 04		20 34		21 04		21 34		22 04		22 34		23 04	23 34
Harrow & Wealdstone D.C.	d	18 07		18 37		19 07		19 37		20 07		20 37		21 07		21 37		22 07		22 37		23 07	23 37
Kenton	d	18 09		18 39		19 09		19 39		20 09		20 39		21 09		21 39		22 09		22 39		23 09	23 39
South Kenton	d	18 11		18 41		19 11		19 41		20 11		20 41		21 11		21 41		22 11		22 41		23 11	23 41
North Wembley	d	18 13		18 43		19 13		19 43		20 13		20 43		21 13		21 43		22 13		22 43		23 13	23 43
Wembley Central Dc	d	18 15		18 45		19 15		19 45		20 15		20 45		21 15		21 45		22 15		22 45		23 15	23 45
Stonebridge Park	d	18 18		18 48		19 18		19 48		20 18		20 48		21 18		21 48		22 18		22 48		23 18	23 48
Harlesden	d	18 20		18 50		19 20		19 50		20 20		20 50		21 20		21 50		22 20		22 50		23 20	23 50
Willesden Jn Low Level	d	18 22	18 31	18 52	19 01	19 22	19 31	19 52	20 01	20 22	20 31	20 52	21 01	21 22	21 31	21 52	22 01	22 22	22 31	22 52	23 01	23 22	23 52
Kensal Green	d	18 25	18a33	18 55	19 03	19 25	19a33	19 55	20a03	20 25	20a33	20 55	21a03	21 25	21a33	21 55	22a03	22 25	22a33	22 55	23a03	23 25	23 55
Queens Park (Dc)	⊖ d	18 27	18 39	18 57	19 09	19 27	19 39	19 57	20 09	20 27	20 39	20 57	21 09	21 27	21 39	21 57	22 09	22 27	22 39	22 57	23 09	23 27	23 57
Kilburn High Road	d	18 29	18 41	18 59	19 11	19 29	19 41	19 59	20 11	20 29	20 41	20 59	21 11	21 29	21 41	21 59	22 11	22 29	22 41	22 59	23 11	23 29	23 59
South Hampstead	d	18 31	18a43	19 01	19a13	19 31	19a43	20 01	20a13	20 31	20a43	21 01	21a13	21 31	21a43	22 01	22a13	22 31	22a43	23 01	23a13	23 31	00 01
London Euston 15	⊖ a	18 38		19 08		19 38		20 08		20 38		21 08		21 38		22 08		22 38		23 08		23 38	00 08

For general notes see front of timetable
For details of catering facilities see Directory of Train Operators

A To Stratford Low Level (Table 59)
b Arr. 1536

Stations Queen's Park to Harrow & Wealdstone inclusive are also served by London Underground Bakerloo line services

Mondays to Fridays

Watford Junction — St. Albans

Network Diagram - See first page of Table 59

Miles			LM	LM	LM	LM	LM	LM	LM	LM	LM	LM	LM	LM	LM	LM	LM	LM	LM	LM	LM	LM	LM	LM
—	London Euston 15 ⊖	d	.....	05 55	06 37	07 34	08 34	09 24	10 04	10 54	11 34	12 24	13 04	13 54	14 34	15 24	16 04	16 54	17 40	18 24	19 04	20 04	21 04
0	**Watford Junction**	d	06 00	06 42	07 24	08 09	09 01	09 46	10 31	11 16	12 01	12 46	13 31	14 16	15 01	15 46	16 31	17 21	18 06	18 51	19 36	20 31	21 31
¾	Watford North	d	06 02	06 44	07 26	08 11	09 03	09 48	10 33	11 18	12 03	12 48	13 33	14 18	15 03	15 48	16 33	17 23	18 08	18 53	19 38	20 33	21 33
1¾	Garston (Hertfordshire)	d	06 05	06 47	07 29	08 14	09 06	09 51	10 36	11 21	12 06	12 51	13 36	14 21	15 06	15 51	16 36	17 26	18 11	18 56	19 41	20 36	21 36
3¼	Bricket Wood	d	06 08	06 50	07 32	08 17	09 09	09 54	10 39	11 24	12 09	12 54	13 39	14 24	15 09	15 54	16 39	17 29	18 14	18 59	19 44	20 39	21 39
4½	How Wood	d	06 10	06 52	07 34	08 19	09 11	09 56	10 41	11 26	12 11	12 56	13 41	14 26	15 11	15 56	16 41	17 31	18 16	19 01	19 46	20 41	21 41
5	Park Street	d	06 12	06 54	07 36	08 21	09 13	09 58	10 43	11 28	12 13	12 58	13 43	14 28	15 13	15 58	16 43	17 33	18 18	19 03	19 48	20 43	21 43
6½	**St Albans Abbey**	a	06 16	06 58	07 40	08 25	09 17	10 03	10 47	11 32	12 17	13 02	13 47	14 32	15 17	16 03	16 47	17 37	18 22	19 07	19 52	20 47	21 47

Saturdays

		LM	LM	LM	LM	LM	LM	LM	LM	LM	LM	LM	LM	LM	LM	LM	LM	LM	LM	LM	LM	LM
London Euston 15 ⊖	d	05 34																				
Watford Junction	d	06 01	06 46	07 31	08 16	09 01	09 46	10 31	11 16	12 01	12 46	13 31	14 16	15 01	15 46	16 31	17 16	18 01	18 46	19 31	20 31	21 31
Watford North	d	06 03	06 48	07 33	08 18	09 03	09 48	10 33	11 18	12 03	12 48	13 33	14 18	15 03	15 48	16 33	17 18	18 03	18 48	19 33	20 33	21 33
Garston (Hertfordshire)	d	06 06	06 51	07 36	08 21	09 06	09 51	10 36	11 21	12 06	12 51	13 36	14 21	15 06	15 51	16 36	17 21	18 06	18 51	19 36	20 36	21 36
Bricket Wood	d	06 09	06 54	07 39	08 24	09 09	09 54	10 39	11 24	12 09	12 54	13 39	14 24	15 09	15 54	16 39	17 24	18 09	18 54	19 39	20 39	21 39
How Wood	d	06 11	06 56	07 41	08 26	09 11	09 56	10 41	11 26	12 11	12 56	13 41	14 26	15 11	15 56	16 41	17 26	18 11	18 56	19 41	20 41	21 41
Park Street	d	06 13	06 58	07 43	08 28	09 13	09 58	10 43	11 28	12 13	12 58	13 43	14 28	15 13	15 58	16 43	17 28	18 13	18 58	19 43	20 43	21 43
St Albans Abbey	a	06 17	07 02	07 47	08 32	09 17	10 02	10 47	11 32	12 17	13 02	13 47	14 32	15 17	16 02	16 47	17 32	18 17	19 02	19 47	20 47	21 47

Sundays

		LM	LM	LM	LM	LM	LM	LM	LM	LM	LM	LM	LM	LM	LM	LM
London Euston 15 ⊖	d															
Watford Junction	d	08 07	09 07	10 07	11 07	12 07	13 07	14 07	15 07	16 07	17 07	18 07	19 07	20 07	21 07	22 07
Watford North	d	08 09	09 09	10 09	11 09	12 09	13 09	14 09	15 09	16 09	17 09	18 09	19 09	20 09	21 09	22 09
Garston (Hertfordshire)	d	08 12	09 12	10 12	11 12	12 12	13 12	14 12	15 12	16 12	17 12	18 12	19 12	20 12	21 12	22 12
Bricket Wood	d	08 15	09 15	10 15	11 15	12 15	13 15	14 15	15 15	16 15	17 15	18 15	19 15	20 15	21 15	22 15
How Wood	d	08 17	09 17	10 17	11 17	12 17	13 17	14 17	15 17	16 17	17 17	18 17	19 17	20 17	21 17	22 17
Park Street	d	08 19	09 19	10 19	11 19	12 19	13 19	14 19	15 19	16 19	17 19	18 19	19 19	20 19	21 19	22 19
St Albans Abbey	a	08 23	09 23	10 23	11 23	12 23	13 23	14 23	15 23	16 23	17 23	18 23	19 23	20 23	21 23	22 23

Mondays to Fridays

Miles			LM	LM	LM	LM	LM	LM	LM	LM	LM	LM	LM	LM	LM	LM	LM	LM	LM	LM	LM	LM	LM	LM
0	**St Albans Abbey**	d	06 21	07 03	07 45	08 30	09 22	10 07	10 52	11 37	12 22	13 07	13 52	14 37	15 22	16 07	16 52	17 42	18 27	19 12	19 57	20 52	21 52
1½	Park Street	d	06 24	07 06	07 48	08 33	09 25	10 10	10 55	11 40	12 25	13 10	13 55	14 40	15 25	16 10	16 55	17 45	18 30	19 15	20 00	20 55	21 55
2¼	How Wood	d	06 26	07 08	07 50	08 35	09 27	10 12	10 57	11 42	12 27	13 12	13 57	14 42	15 27	16 12	16 57	17 47	18 32	19 17	20 02	20 57	21 57
3	Bricket Wood	d	06 29	07 11	07 53	08 38	09 30	10 15	11 00	11 45	12 30	13 15	14 00	14 45	15 30	16 15	17 00	17 50	18 35	19 20	20 05	21 00	22 00
4¾	Garston (Hertfordshire)	d	06 32	07 14	07 56	08 41	09 33	10 18	11 03	11 48	12 33	13 18	14 03	14 48	15 33	16 18	17 03	17 53	18 38	19 23	20 08	21 03	22 03
5¾	Watford North	d	06 34	07 16	07 58	08 43	09 35	10 20	11 05	11 50	12 35	13 20	14 05	14 50	15 35	16 20	17 05	17 55	18 40	19 25	20 10	21 05	22 05
6½	**Watford Junction**	a	06 37	07 19	08 01	08 46	09 38	10 24	11 08	11 53	12 38	13 23	14 08	14 53	15 38	16 24	17 08	17 58	18 43	19 28	20 13	21 08	22 08
—	London Euston 15 ⊖	a	07 00	07 50	08 30	09 16	10 11	11 08	11 38	12 38	13 08	14 08	14 38	15 38	16 08	17 08	17 38	18 43	19 15	20 11	20 48	21 37	22 41

Saturdays

		LM	LM	LM	LM	LM	LM	LM	LM	LM	LM	LM	LM	LM	LM	LM	LM	LM	LM	LM	LM	LM
St Albans Abbey	d	06 22	07 07	07 52	08 37	09 22	10 07	10 52	11 37	12 22	13 07	13 52	14 37	15 22	16 07	16 52	17 37	18 22	19 07	19 52	20 52	21 52
Park Street	d	06 25	07 10	07 55	08 40	09 25	10 10	10 55	11 40	12 25	13 10	13 55	14 40	15 25	16 10	16 55	17 40	18 25	19 10	19 55	20 55	21 55
How Wood	d	06 27	07 12	07 57	08 42	09 27	10 12	10 57	11 42	12 27	13 12	13 57	14 42	15 27	16 12	16 57	17 42	18 27	19 12	19 57	20 57	21 57
Bricket Wood	d	06 30	07 15	08 00	08 45	09 30	10 15	11 00	11 45	12 30	13 15	14 00	14 45	15 30	16 15	17 00	17 45	18 30	19 15	20 00	21 00	22 00
Garston (Hertfordshire)	d	06 33	07 18	08 03	08 48	09 33	10 18	11 03	11 48	12 33	13 18	14 03	14 48	15 33	16 18	17 03	17 48	18 33	19 18	20 03	21 03	22 03
Watford North	d	06 35	07 20	08 05	08 50	09 35	10 20	11 05	11 50	12 35	13 20	14 05	14 50	15 35	16 20	17 05	17 50	18 35	19 20	20 05	21 05	22 05
Watford Junction	a	06 38	07 23	08 08	08 53	09 38	10 23	11 08	11 53	12 38	13 23	14 08	14 53	15 38	16 23	17 08	17 53	18 38	19 23	20 08	21 08	22 08
London Euston 15 ⊖	a	.	.	.	.	.	.	.	.	.	.	.	.	.	.	.	.	.	.	.	.	.

Sundays

		LM	LM	LM	LM	LM	LM	LM	LM	LM	LM	LM	LM	LM	LM	LM
St Albans Abbey	d	08 28	09 28	10 28	11 28	12 28	13 28	14 28	15 28	16 28	17 28	18 28	19 28	20 28	21 28	22 28
Park Street	d	08 31	09 31	10 31	11 31	12 31	13 31	14 31	15 31	16 31	17 31	18 31	19 31	20 31	21 31	22 31
How Wood	d	08 33	09 33	10 33	11 33	12 33	13 33	14 33	15 33	16 33	17 33	18 33	19 33	20 33	21 33	22 33
Bricket Wood	d	08 36	09 36	10 36	11 36	12 36	13 36	14 36	15 36	16 36	17 36	18 36	19 36	20 36	21 36	22 36
Garston (Hertfordshire)	d	08 39	09 39	10 39	11 39	12 39	13 39	14 39	15 39	16 39	17 39	18 39	19 39	20 39	21 39	22 39
Watford North	d	08 41	09 41	10 41	11 41	12 41	13 41	14 41	15 41	16 41	17 41	18 41	19 41	20 41	21 41	22 41
Watford Junction	a	08 44	09 44	10 44	11 44	12 44	13 44	14 44	15 44	16 44	17 44	18 44	19 44	20 44	21 44	22 44
London Euston 15 ⊖	a	.	.	.	.	.	.	.	.	.	.	.	.	.	.	.

For general notes see front of timetable
For details of catering facilities see Directory of Train Operators

Gospel Oak → Barking

Network diagram - see first page of Table 59

Miles			LO	LO	LO	LO	LO	LO	LO	LO	LO	LO	LO	LO	LO		LO	LO	LO	LO	LO
0	**Gospel Oak**	d	06 25	06 55	07 15	07 40	08 00	08 20	08 40	09 00	09 20	09 40	10 00	10 25	10 55		14 25	14 55	15 12	15 35	15 55
1¼	Upper Holloway	d	06 29	06 59	07 19	07 44	08 04	08 24	08 44	09 04	09 24	09 44	10 04	10 29	10 59	and	14 29	14 59	15b19	15 39	15 59
2	Crouch Hill	d	06 32	07 02	07 22	07 47	08 07	08 27	08 47	09 07	09 27	09 47	10 07	10 32	11 02		14 32	15 02	15 22	15 42	16 02
3	Harringay Green Lanes	d	06 35	07 05	07 25	07 50	08 10	08 30	08 50	09 10	09 30	09 50	10 10	10 35	11 05	every 30	14 35	15 05	15 25	15 45	16 05
4¼	South Tottenham	d	06 38	07 08	07 28	07 53	08 13	08 33	08 53	09 13	09 33	09 53	10 13	10 38	11 08		14 38	15 08	15 28	15 48	16 08
5¾	Blackhorse Road	⊖ d	06 41	07 11	07 31	07 56	08 16	08 36	08 56	09 16	09 36	09 56	10 16	10 41	11 11	minutes	14 41	15 11	15 31	15 51	16 11
6½	Walthamstow Queens Road	d	06 44	07 14	07 34	07 59	08 19	08 39	08 59	09 19	09 39	09 59	10 19	10 44	11 14		14 44	15 14	15 34	15 54	16 14
7½	Leyton Midland Road	d	06 47	07 17	07 37	08 02	08 22	08 42	09 02	09 22	09 42	10 02	10 22	10 47	11 17	until	14 47	15 17	15 37	15 57	16 17
8¼	Leytonstone High Road	d	06 50	07 20	07 40	08 05	08 25	08 45	09 05	09 25	09 45	10 05	10 25	10 50	11 20		14 50	15 20	15 40	16 00	16 20
9½	Wanstead Park	d	06 53	07 23	07 43	08 08	08 28	08 48	09 08	09 28	09 48	10 08	10 28	10 53	11 23		14 53	15 23	15 43	16 03	16 23
10½	Woodgrange Park	d	06 55	07 25	07 45	08 10	08 30	08 50	09 10	09 30	09 50	10 10	10 30	10 55	11 25		14 55	15 25	15 45	16 05	16 25
12¼	**Barking**	⊖ a	06 59	07 31	07 51	08 16	08 36	08 56	09 16	09 36	09 56	10 16	10 36	10 59	11 29		14 59	15 29	15 49	16 09	16 29

		LO	LO	LO	LO	LO	LO	LO	LO	LO	LO	LO	LO	LO	LO	LO	LO	LO	LO
Gospel Oak	d	16 15	16 35	16 55	17 15	17 35	17 55	18 15	18 35	18 55	19 25	19 55	20 25	20 55	21 25	21 55	22 25	22 55	23 25
Upper Holloway	d	16 19	16 39	16 59	17 19	17 39	17 59	18 19	18 39	18 59	19 29	19 59	20 29	20 59	21 29	21 59	22 29	22 59	23 29
Crouch Hill	d	16 22	16 42	17 02	17 22	17 42	18 02	18 22	18 42	19 02	19 32	20 02	20 32	21 02	21 32	22 02	22 32	23 02	23 32
Harringay Green Lanes	d	16 25	16 45	17 05	17 25	17 45	18 05	18 25	18 45	19 05	19 35	20 05	20 35	21 05	21 35	22 05	22 35	23 05	23 35
South Tottenham	d	16 28	16 48	17 08	17 28	17 48	18 08	18 28	18 48	19 08	19 38	20 08	20 38	21 08	21 38	22 08	22 38	23 08	23 38
Blackhorse Road	⊖ d	16 31	16 51	17 11	17 31	17 51	18 11	18 31	18 51	19 11	19 41	20 11	20 41	21 11	21 41	22 11	22 41	23 11	23 41
Walthamstow Queens Road	d	16 34	16 54	17 14	17 34	17 54	18 14	18 34	18 54	19 14	19 44	20 14	20 44	21 14	21 44	22 14	22 44	23 14	23 44
Leyton Midland Road	d	16 37	16 57	17 17	17 37	17 57	18 17	18 37	18 57	19 17	19 47	20 17	20 47	21 17	21 47	22 17	22 47	23 17	23 47
Leytonstone High Road	d	16 40	17 00	17 20	17 40	18 00	18 20	18 40	19 00	19 20	19 50	20 20	20 50	21 20	21 50	22 20	22 50	23 20	23 50
Wanstead Park	d	16 43	17 03	17 23	17 43	18 03	18 23	18 43	19 03	19 23	19 53	20 23	20 53	21 23	21 53	22 23	22 53	23 23	23 53
Woodgrange Park	d	16 45	17 05	17 25	17 45	18 05	18 25	18 45	19 05	19 25	19 55	20 25	20 55	21 25	21 55	22 25	22 55	23 25	23 55
Barking	⊖ a	16 51	17 11	17 31	17 51	18 11	18 31	18 51	19 11	19 31	19 59	20 32	20 59	21 29	21 59	22 29	22 59	23 29	23 59

Saturdays

		LO	LO	LO	LO	LO	LO	LO	LO	LO	LO	LO	LO	LO		LO	LO	LO	LO	LO
Gospel Oak	d	06 25	06 55	07 15	07 40	08 00	08 20	08 40	09 00	09 20	09 40	10 00	10 25	10 55		14 25	14 55	15 12	15 35	15 55
Upper Holloway	d	06 29	06 59	07 19	07 44	08 04	08 24	08 44	09 04	09 24	09 44	10 04	10 29	10 59	and	14 29	14 59	15b19	15 39	15 59
Crouch Hill	d	06 32	07 02	07 22	07 47	08 07	08 27	08 47	09 07	09 27	09 47	10 07	10 32	11 02		14 32	15 02	15 22	15 42	16 02
Harringay Green Lanes	d	06 35	07 05	07 25	07 50	08 10	08 30	08 50	09 10	09 30	09 50	10 10	10 35	11 05	every 30	14 35	15 05	15 25	15 45	16 05
South Tottenham	d	06 38	07 08	07 28	07 53	08 13	08 33	08 53	09 13	09 33	09 53	10 13	10 38	11 08		14 38	15 08	15 28	15 48	16 08
Blackhorse Road	⊖ d	06 41	07 11	07 31	07 56	08 16	08 36	08 56	09 16	09 36	09 56	10 16	10 41	11 11	minutes	14 41	15 11	15 31	15 51	16 11
Walthamstow Queens Road	d	06 44	07 14	07 34	07 59	08 19	08 39	08 59	09 19	09 39	09 59	10 19	10 44	11 14		14 44	15 14	15 34	15 54	16 14
Leyton Midland Road	d	06 47	07 17	07 37	08 02	08 22	08 42	09 02	09 22	09 42	10 02	10 22	10 47	11 17	until	14 47	15 17	15 37	15 57	16 17
Leytonstone High Road	d	06 50	07 20	07 40	08 05	08 25	08 45	09 05	09 25	09 45	10 05	10 25	10 50	11 20		14 50	15 20	15 40	16 00	16 20
Wanstead Park	d	06 53	07 23	07 43	08 08	08 28	08 48	09 08	09 28	09 48	10 08	10 28	10 53	11 23		14 53	15 23	15 43	16 03	16 23
Woodgrange Park	d	06 55	07 25	07 45	08 10	08 30	08 50	09 10	09 30	09 50	10 10	10 30	10 55	11 25		14 55	15 25	15 45	16 05	16 25
Barking	⊖ a	06 59	07 29	07 49	08 14	08 34	08 54	09 14	09 34	09 54	10 14	10 34	10 59	11 29		14 59	15 29	15 49	16 09	16 29

		LO	LO	LO	LO	LO	LO	LO	LO	LO	LO	LO	LO	LO	LO	LO	LO	LO	LO
Gospel Oak	d	16 15	16 35	16 55	17 15	17 35	17 55	18 15	18 35	18 55	19 25	19 55	20 25	20 55	21 25	21 55	22 25	22 55	23 25
Upper Holloway	d	16 19	16 39	16 59	17 19	17 39	17 59	18 19	18 39	18 59	19 29	19 59	20 29	20 59	21 29	21 59	22 29	22 59	23 29
Crouch Hill	d	16 22	16 42	17 02	17 22	17 42	18 02	18 22	18 42	19 02	19 32	20 02	20 32	21 02	21 32	22 02	22 32	23 02	23 32
Harringay Green Lanes	d	16 25	16 45	17 05	17 25	17 45	18 05	18 25	18 45	19 05	19 35	20 05	20 35	21 05	21 35	22 05	22 35	23 05	23 35
South Tottenham	d	16 28	16 48	17 08	17 28	17 48	18 08	18 28	18 48	19 08	19 38	20 08	20 38	21 08	21 38	22 08	22 38	23 08	23 38
Blackhorse Road	⊖ d	16 31	16 51	17 11	17 31	17 51	18 11	18 31	18 51	19 11	19 41	20 11	20 41	21 11	21 41	22 11	22 41	23 11	23 41
Walthamstow Queens Road	d	16 34	16 54	17 14	17 34	17 54	18 14	18 34	18 54	19 14	19 44	20 14	20 44	21 14	21 44	22 14	22 44	23 14	23 44
Leyton Midland Road	d	16 37	16 57	17 17	17 37	17 57	18 17	18 37	18 57	19 17	19 47	20 17	20 47	21 17	21 47	22 17	22 47	23 17	23 47
Leytonstone High Road	d	16 40	17 00	17 20	17 40	18 00	18 20	18 40	19 00	19 20	19 50	20 20	20 50	21 20	21 50	22 20	22 50	23 20	23 50
Wanstead Park	d	16 43	17 03	17 23	17 43	18 03	18 23	18 43	19 03	19 23	19 53	20 23	20 53	21 23	21 53	22 23	22 53	23 23	23 53
Woodgrange Park	d	16 45	17 05	17 25	17 45	18 05	18 25	18 45	19 05	19 25	19 55	20 25	20 55	21 25	21 55	22 25	22 55	23 25	23 55
Barking	⊖ a	16 49	17 09	17 29	17 49	18 09	18 29	18 50	19 09	19 29	19 59	20 32	20 59	21 29	21 59	22 29	22 59	23 29	23 59

Sundays

		LO	LO		LO	LO
Gospel Oak	d	08 50	09 20		22 50	23 20
Upper Holloway	d	08 54	09 24	and	22 54	23 24
Crouch Hill	d	08 57	09 27		22 57	23 27
Harringay Green Lanes	d	09 00	09 30	every 30	23 00	23 30
South Tottenham	d	09 03	09 33		23 03	23 33
Blackhorse Road	⊖ d	09 06	09 36	minutes	23 06	23 36
Walthamstow Queens Road	d	09 09	09 39		23 09	23 39
Leyton Midland Road	d	09 12	09 42	until	23 12	23 42
Leytonstone High Road	d	09 15	09 45		23 15	23 45
Wanstead Park	d	09 18	09 48		23 18	23 48
Woodgrange Park	d	09 20	09 50		23 20	23 50
Barking	⊖ a	09 24	09 54		23 24	23 54

For general notes see front of timetable
For details of catering facilities see Directory of Train Operators

b Arr. 1516

From 1 to 28 September,no trains will operate on this route, for details of replacement and alternative services, please see local publicity or contact National Rail Enquiries 08457-48-49-50.

Table 62 — Mondays to Fridays

Barking → Gospel Oak

Network diagram - see first page of Table 59

Miles			LO	LO	LO	LO	LO	LO	LO	LO	LO	LO	LO	LO	LO	LO	LO		LO	LO
0	**Barking**	⊖ d	06 32	06 54	07 20	07 40	08 00	08 20	08 40	09 00	09 20	09 40	10 00	10 20	10 40	11 08	11 38		15 08	15 34
1¾	Woodgrange Park	d	06 35	06 57	07 23	07 43	08 03	08 23	08 43	09 03	09 23	09 43	10 03	10 23	10 43	11 11	11 41	and	15 11	15 37
2¾	Wanstead Park	d	06 38	07 00	07 26	07 46	08 06	08 26	08 46	09 06	09 26	09 46	10 06	10 26	10 46	11 14	11 44		15 14	15 40
4	Leytonstone High Road	d	06 42	07 04	07 30	07 50	08 10	08 30	08 50	09 10	09 30	09 50	10 10	10 30	10 50	11 18	11 48	every 30	15 18	15 44
4¾	Leyton Midland Road	d	06 44	07 06	07 32	07 52	08 12	08 32	08 52	09 12	09 32	09 52	10 12	10 32	10 52	11 20	11 50		15 20	15 46
5¾	Walthamstow Queens Road	d	06 47	07 09	07 35	07 55	08 15	08 35	08 55	09 15	09 35	09 55	10 15	10 35	10 55	11 23	11 53	minutes	15 23	15 49
6¼	Blackhorse Road	⊖ d	06 50	07 12	07 38	07 58	08 18	08 38	08 58	09 18	09 38	09 58	10 18	10 38	10 58	11 26	11 56		15 26	15 52
8¼	South Tottenham	d	06 54	07 16	07 42	08 02	08 22	08 42	09 02	09 22	09 42	10 02	10 22	10 42	11 02	11 30	12 00	until	15 30	15 56
9¼	Harringay Green Lanes	d	06 57	07 19	07 45	08 05	08 25	08 45	09 05	09 25	09 45	10 05	10 25	10 45	11 05	11 33	12 03		15 33	15 59
10¼	Crouch Hill	d	07 00	07 22	07 48	08 08	08 28	08 48	09 08	09 28	09 48	10 08	10 28	10 48	11 08	11 36	12 06		15 36	16 02
11	Upper Holloway	d	07 02	07 24	07 50	08 10	08 30	08 50	09 10	09 30	09 50	10 10	10 30	10 50	11 10	11 38	12 08		15 38	16 04
12¼	**Gospel Oak**	a	07 07	07 29	07 57	08 17	08 37	08 57	09 17	09 37	09 57	10 17	10 37	10 58	11 15	11 44	12 13		15 43	16 11

		LO	LO	LO	LO	LO	LO	LO	LO	LO	LO	LO	LO	LO	LO	LO	LO	LO	LO	LO
Barking	⊖ d	15 54	16 14	16 34	16 54	17 14	17 34	17 54	18 14	18 34	18 54	19 18	19 43	20 08	20 38	21 08	21 38	22 08	22 38	23 08
Woodgrange Park	d	15 57	16 17	16 37	16 57	17 17	17 37	17 57	18 17	18 37	18 57	19 21	19 46	20 11	20 41	21 11	21 41	22 11	22 41	23 11
Wanstead Park	d	16 00	16 20	16 40	17 00	17 20	17 40	18 00	18 20	18 40	19 00	19 24	19 49	20 14	20 44	21 14	21 44	22 14	22 44	23 14
Leytonstone High Road	d	16 04	16 24	16 44	17 04	17 24	17 44	18 04	18 24	18 44	19 04	19 28	19 53	20 18	20 48	21 18	21 48	22 18	22 48	23 18
Leyton Midland Road	d	16 06	16 26	16 46	17 06	17 26	17 46	18 06	18 26	18 46	19 06	19 30	19 55	20 20	20 50	21 20	21 50	22 20	22 50	23 20
Walthamstow Queens Road	d	16 09	16 29	16 49	17 09	17 29	17 49	18 09	18 29	18 49	19 09	19 33	19 58	20 23	20 53	21 23	21 53	22 23	22 53	23 23
Blackhorse Road	⊖ d	16 12	16 32	16 52	17 12	17 32	17 52	18 12	18 32	18 52	19 12	19 36	20 01	20 26	20 56	21 26	21 56	22 26	22 56	23 26
South Tottenham	d	16 16	16 36	16 56	17 16	17 36	17 56	18 16	18 36	18 56	19 16	19 40	20 05	20 30	21 00	21 30	22 00	22 30	23 00	23 30
Harringay Green Lanes	d	16 19	16 39	16 59	17 19	17 39	17 59	18 19	18 39	18 59	19 19	19 43	20 08	20 33	21 03	21 33	22 03	22 33	23 03	23 33
Crouch Hill	d	16 22	16 42	17 02	17 22	17 42	18 02	18 22	18 42	19 02	19 22	19 46	20 11	20 36	21 06	21 36	22 06	22 36	23 06	23 36
Upper Holloway	d	16 24	16 44	17 04	17 24	17 44	18 04	18 24	18 44	19 04	19 24	19 48	20 13	20 38	21 08	21 38	22 08	22 38	23 08	23 38
Gospel Oak	a	16 31	16 51	17 11	17 31	17 51	18 11	18 31	18 51	19 11	19 31	19 53	20 18	20 43	21 13	21 43	22 13	22 43	23 13	23 43

Saturdays

		LO	LO	LO	LO	LO	LO	LO	LO	LO	LO	LO	LO	LO	LO	LO		LO	LO	LO
Barking	⊖ d	06 32	06 54	07 20	07 40	08 00	08 20	08 40	09 00	09 20	09 40	10 00	10 20	10 40	11 08	11 38		15 08	15 34	15 54
Woodgrange Park	d	06 35	06 57	07 23	07 43	08 03	08 23	08 43	09 03	09 23	09 43	10 03	10 23	10 43	11 11	11 41	and	15 11	15 37	15 57
Wanstead Park	d	06 38	07 00	07 26	07 46	08 06	08 26	08 46	09 06	09 26	09 46	10 06	10 26	10 46	11 14	11 44		15 14	15 40	16 00
Leytonstone High Road	d	06 42	07 04	07 30	07 50	08 10	08 30	08 50	09 10	09 30	09 50	10 10	10 30	10 50	11 18	11 48	every 30	15 18	15 44	16 04
Leyton Midland Road	d	06 44	07 06	07 32	07 52	08 12	08 32	08 52	09 12	09 32	09 52	10 12	10 32	10 52	11 20	11 50		15 20	15 46	16 06
Walthamstow Queens Road	d	06 47	07 09	07 35	07 55	08 15	08 35	08 55	09 15	09 35	09 55	10 15	10 35	10 55	11 23	11 53	minutes	15 23	15 49	16 09
Blackhorse Road	⊖ d	06 50	07 12	07 38	07 58	08 18	08 38	08 58	09 18	09 38	09 58	10 18	10 38	10 58	11 26	11 56		15 26	15 52	16 12
South Tottenham	d	06 54	07 16	07 42	08 02	08 22	08 42	09 02	09 22	09 42	10 02	10 22	10 42	11 02	11 30	12 00	until	15 30	15 56	16 16
Harringay Green Lanes	d	06 57	07 19	07 45	08 05	08 25	08 45	09 05	09 25	09 45	10 05	10 25	10 45	11 05	11 33	12 03		15 33	15 59	16 19
Crouch Hill	d	07 00	07 22	07 48	08 08	08 28	08 48	09 08	09 28	09 48	10 08	10 28	10 48	11 08	11 36	12 06		15 36	16 02	16 22
Upper Holloway	d	07 02	07 24	07 50	08 10	08 30	08 50	09 10	09 30	09 50	10 10	10 30	10 50	11 10	11 38	12 08		15 38	16 04	16 24
Gospel Oak	a	07 07	07 29	07 55	08 15	08 35	08 55	09 15	09 35	09 55	10 15	10 35	10 57	11 15	11 43	12 13		15 43	16 09	16 29

		LO	LO	LO	LO	LO	LO	LO	LO	LO	LO	LO	LO	LO	LO	LO	LO	LO	LO
Barking	⊖ d	16 14	16 34	16 54	17 14	17 34	17 54	18 14	18 34	18 55	19 18	19 43	20 08	20 38	21 08	21 38	22 08	22 38	23 08
Woodgrange Park	d	16 17	16 37	16 57	17 17	17 37	17 57	18 17	18 37	18 58	19 21	19 46	20 11	20 41	21 11	21 41	22 11	22 41	23 11
Wanstead Park	d	16 20	16 40	17 00	17 20	17 40	18 00	18 20	18 40	19 01	19 24	19 49	20 14	20 44	21 14	21 44	22 14	22 44	23 14
Leytonstone High Road	d	16 24	16 44	17 04	17 24	17 44	18 04	18 24	18 44	19 05	19 28	19 53	20 18	20 48	21 18	21 48	22 18	22 48	23 18
Leyton Midland Road	d	16 26	16 46	17 06	17 26	17 46	18 06	18 26	18 46	19 07	19 30	19 55	20 20	20 50	21 20	21 50	22 20	22 50	23 20
Walthamstow Queens Road	d	16 29	16 49	17 09	17 29	17 49	18 09	18 29	18 49	19 10	19 33	19 58	20 23	20 53	21 23	21 53	22 23	22 53	23 23
Blackhorse Road	⊖ d	16 32	16 52	17 12	17 32	17 52	18 12	18 32	18 52	19 13	19 36	20 01	20 26	20 56	21 26	21 56	22 26	22 56	23 26
South Tottenham	d	16 36	16 56	17 16	17 36	17 56	18 16	18 36	18 56	19 17	19 40	20 05	20 30	21 00	21 30	22 00	22 30	23 00	23 30
Harringay Green Lanes	d	16 39	16 59	17 19	17 39	17 59	18 19	18 39	18 59	19 20	19 43	20 08	20 33	21 03	21 33	22 03	22 33	23 03	23 33
Crouch Hill	d	16 42	17 02	17 22	17 42	18 02	18 22	18 42	19 02	19 23	19 46	20 11	20 36	21 06	21 36	22 06	22 36	23 06	23 36
Upper Holloway	d	16 44	17 04	17 24	17 44	18 04	18 24	18 44	19 04	19 25	19 48	20 13	20 38	21 08	21 38	22 08	22 38	23 08	23 38
Gospel Oak	a	16 49	17 09	17 29	17 49	18 11	18 29	18 49	19 09	19 30	19 53	20 18	20 43	21 13	21 43	22 13	22 43	23 13	23 43

Sundays

		LO	LO		LO	LO	LO
Barking	⊖ d	09 05	09 35		22 05	22 35	23 05
Woodgrange Park	d	09 08	09 38	and	22 08	22 38	23 08
Wanstead Park	d	09 11	09 41		22 11	22 41	23 11
Leytonstone High Road	d	09 15	09 45	every 30	22 15	22 45	23 15
Leyton Midland Road	d	09 17	09 47		22 17	22 47	23 17
Walthamstow Queens Road	d	09 20	09 50	minutes	22 20	22 50	23 20
Blackhorse Road	⊖ d	09 23	09 53		22 23	22 53	23 23
South Tottenham	d	09 27	09 57	until	22 27	22 57	23 27
Harringay Green Lanes	d	09 30	10 00		22 30	23 00	23 30
Crouch Hill	d	09 33	10 03		22 33	23 03	23 33
Upper Holloway	d	09 35	10 05		22 35	23 05	23 35
Gospel Oak	a	09 40	10 10		22 40	23 10	23 40

For general notes see front of timetable
For details of catering facilities see Directory of Train Operators

From 1 to 28 September,no trains will operate on this route, for details of replacement and alternative services, please see local publicity or contact National Rail Enquiries 08457-48-49-50.

Mondays to Fridays

Bletchley — Bedford

Network Diagram - See first page of Table 59

Miles			LM	LM	LM	LM	LM	LM	LM	LM	LM	LM	LM	LM	LM	LM	LM	LM
—	Milton Keynes Central 3	d	*05 24*	*06 25*	*07 22*	*08 25*	*09 49*	*10 49*	*11 49*	*12 49*	*13 49*	*14 49*	*15 25*	*16 25*	*17 19*	*18 15*	*19 19*	*20 19*
0	**Bletchley**	d	05 41	06 37	07 34	08 39	09 59	10 59	11 59	12 59	13 59	14 59	15 44	16 44	17 29	18 29	19 53	20 51
1	Fenny Stratford	d	05 44	06 40	07 37	08 42	10 02	11 02	12 02	13 02	14 02	15 02	15 47	16 47	17 32	18 32	19 56	20 54
2	Bow Brickhill	d	05 48	06 44	07 41	08 46	10 06	11 06	12 06	13 06	14 06	15 06	15 51	16 51	17 36	18 36	20 00	20 58
4	Woburn Sands	d	05 52	06 48	07 45	08 50	10 10	11 10	12 10	13 10	14 10	15 10	15 55	16 55	17 40	18 40	20 04	21 02
5	Aspley Guise	d	05 55	06 51	07 48	08 53	10 13	11 13	12 13	13 13	14 13	15 13	15 58	16 58	17 43	18 43	20 07	21 05
6¾	Ridgmont	d	05 58	06 54	07 51	08 56	10 16	11 16	12 16	13 16	14 16	15 16	16 01	17 01	17 46	18 46	20 10	21 08
8½	Lidlington	d	06 02	06 58	07 55	09 00	10 20	11 20	12 20	13 20	14 20	15 20	16 05	17 05	17 50	18 50	20 14	21 12
10	Millbrook (Bedfordshire)	d	06 05	07 01	07 58	09 03	10 23	11 23	12 23	13 23	14 23	15 23	16 08	17 08	17 53	18 53	20 17	21 15
11½	Stewartby	d	06 09	07 05	08 02	09 07	10 27	11 27	12 27	13 27	14 27	15 27	16 12	17 12	17 57	18 57	20 21	21 19
13	Kempston Hardwick	d	06 12	07 08	08 05	09 10	10 30	11 30	12 30	13 30	14 30	15 30	16 15	17 15	18 00	19 00	20 24	21 22
16	Bedford St Johns	d	06 19	07 15	08 12	09 17	10 37	11 37	12 37	13 37	14 37	15 37	16 22	17 22	18 07	19 07	20 31	21 29
16¾	**Bedford 7**	a	06 25	07 21	08 18	09 23	10 43	11 43	12 43	13 43	14 43	15 43	16 28	17 28	18 13	19 13	20 37	21 35

Saturdays

		LM	LM	LM	LM	LM	LM	LM	LM	LM	LM	LM	LM	LM	LM	LM	LM
Milton Keynes Central 5	d																
Bletchley	d	05 41	06 37	07 39	08 39	09 59	10 59	11 59	12 59	13 59	14 59	15 47	16 47	17 29	18 29	19 47	20 51
Fenny Stratford	d	05 44	06 40	07 42	08 42	10 02	11 02	12 02	13 02	14 02	15 02	15 50	16 50	17 32	18 32	19 50	20 54
Bow Brickhill	d	05 48	06 44	07 46	08 46	10 06	11 06	12 06	13 06	14 06	15 06	15 54	16 54	17 36	18 36	19 54	20 58
Woburn Sands	d	05 52	06 48	07 50	08 50	10 10	11 10	12 10	13 10	14 10	15 10	15 58	16 58	17 40	18 40	19 58	21 02
Aspley Guise	d	05 55	06 51	07 53	08 53	10 13	11 13	12 13	13 13	14 13	15 13	16 01	17 01	17 43	18 43	20 01	21 05
Ridgmont	d	05 58	06 54	07 56	08 56	10 16	11 16	12 16	13 16	14 16	15 16	16 04	17 04	17 46	18 46	20 04	21 08
Lidlington	d	06 02	06 58	08 00	09 00	10 20	11 20	12 20	13 20	14 20	15 20	16 08	17 08	17 50	18 50	20 08	21 12
Millbrook (Bedfordshire)	d	06 05	07 01	08 03	09 03	10 23	11 23	12 23	13 23	14 23	15 23	16 11	17 11	17 53	18 53	20 11	21 15
Stewartby	d	06 09	07 05	08 07	09 07	10 27	11 27	12 27	13 27	14 27	15 27	16 15	17 15	17 57	18 57	20 15	21 19
Kempston Hardwick	d	06 12	07 08	08 10	09 10	10 30	11 30	12 30	13 30	14 30	15 30	16 18	17 18	18 00	19 00	20 18	21 22
Bedford St Johns	d	06 19	07 15	08 17	09 17	10 37	11 37	12 37	13 37	14 37	15 37	16 25	17 25	18 07	19 07	20 25	21 29
Bedford 7	a	06 25	07 21	08 23	09 23	10 43	11 43	12 43	13 43	14 43	15 43	16 31	17 31	18 12	19 13	20 31	21 35

Mondays to Fridays

Miles			LM	LM	LM	LM	LM	LM	LM	LM	LM	LM	LM	LM	LM	LM	LM	LM
0	**Bedford 7**	d	06 31	07 31	08 31	09 31	10 51	11 51	12 51	13 51	14 51	15 51	16 36	17 36	18 21	19 25	20 42	21 41
¾	Bedford St Johns	d	06 34	07 34	08 34	09 34	10 54	11 54	12 54	13 54	14 54	15 54	16 39	17 39	18 24	19 28	20 45	21 44
3¾	Kempston Hardwick	d	06 41	07 41	08 41	09 41	11 01	12 01	13 01	14 01	15 01	16 01	16 46	17 46	18 31	19 35	20 52	21 51
5¼	Stewartby	d	06 44	07 44	08 44	09 44	11 04	12 04	13 04	14 04	15 04	16 04	16 49	17 49	18 34	19 38	20 55	21 54
6¾	Millbrook (Bedfordshire)	d	06 48	07 48	08 48	09 48	11 08	12 08	13 08	14 08	15 08	16 08	16 53	17 53	18 38	19 42	20 59	21 58
8¼	Lidlington	d	06 51	07 51	08 51	09 51	11 11	12 11	13 11	14 11	15 11	16 11	16 56	17 56	18 41	19 45	21 02	22 01
10	Ridgmont	d	06 56	07 56	08 56	09 56	11 16	12 16	13 16	14 16	15 16	16 16	17 01	18 01	18 46	19 50	21 07	22 06
11¾	Aspley Guise	d	06 59	07 59	08 59	09 59	11 19	12 19	13 19	14 19	15 19	16 19	17 04	18 04	18 49	19 53	21 10	22 09
12¾	Woburn Sands	d	07 02	08 02	09 02	10 02	11 22	12 22	13 22	14 22	15 22	16 22	17 07	18 07	18 52	19 56	21 13	22 12
14¾	Bow Brickhill	d	07 06	08 06	09 06	10 06	11 26	12 26	13 26	14 26	15 26	16 26	17 11	18 11	18 56	20 00	21 17	22 16
15¾	Fenny Stratford	d	07 09	08 09	09 09	10 09	11 29	12 29	13 29	14 29	15 29	16 29	17 14	18 14	18 59	20 03	21 20	22 19
16¾	**Bletchley**	a	07 14	08 14	09 14	10 14	11 34	12 34	13 34	14 34	15 34	16 34	17 19	18 19	19 03	20 08	21 25	22 24
—	Milton Keynes Central 3	a	*07 36*	*08 37*	*09 36*	*10 33*	*11 53*	*12 53*	*13 53*	*14 53*	*15 53*	*16 53*	*18 02*	*18 35*	*19 17*	*20 25*	*21 37*	*22 43*

Saturdays

		LM	LM	LM	LM	LM	LM	LM	LM	LM	LM	LM	LM	LM	LM	LM	LM
Bedford 7	d	06 31	07 31	08 31	09 31	10 51	11 51	12 51	13 51	14 51	15 51	16 36	17 36	18 21	19 25	20 42	21 41
Bedford St Johns	d	06 34	07 34	08 34	09 34	10 54	11 54	12 54	13 54	14 54	15 54	16 39	17 39	18 24	19 28	20 45	21 44
Kempston Hardwick	d	06 41	07 41	08 41	09 41	11 01	12 01	13 01	14 01	15 01	16 01	16 46	17 46	18 31	19 35	20 52	21 51
Stewartby	d	06 44	07 44	08 44	09 44	11 04	12 04	13 04	14 04	15 04	16 04	16 49	17 49	18 34	19 38	20 55	21 54
Millbrook (Bedfordshire)	d	06 48	07 48	08 48	09 48	11 08	12 08	13 08	14 08	15 08	16 08	16 53	17 53	18 38	19 42	20 59	21 58
Lidlington	d	06 51	07 51	08 51	09 51	11 11	12 11	13 11	14 11	15 11	16 11	16 56	17 56	18 41	19 45	21 02	22 01
Ridgmont	d	06 56	07 56	08 56	09 56	11 16	12 16	13 16	14 16	15 16	16 16	17 01	18 01	18 46	19 50	21 07	22 06
Aspley Guise	d	06 59	07 59	08 59	09 59	11 19	12 19	13 19	14 19	15 19	16 19	17 04	18 04	18 49	19 53	21 10	22 09
Woburn Sands	d	07 02	08 02	09 02	10 02	11 22	12 22	13 22	14 22	15 22	16 22	17 07	18 07	18 52	19 56	21 13	22 12
Bow Brickhill	d	07 06	08 06	09 06	10 06	11 26	12 26	13 26	14 26	15 26	16 26	17 11	18 11	18 56	20 00	21 17	22 16
Fenny Stratford	d	07 09	08 09	09 09	10 09	11 29	12 29	13 29	14 29	15 29	16 29	17 14	18 14	18 59	20 03	21 20	22 19
Bletchley	a	07 14	08 13	09 14	10 14	11 34	12 34	13 34	14 34	15 34	16 34	17 19	18 19	19 04	20 08	21 25	22 24
Milton Keynes Central 5	a																

For general notes see front of timetable
For details of catering facilities see
Directory of Train Operators

No Sunday Service

Route Diagram for Table 65

London-Scotland
See Tables 400-404 for Sleeper trains.

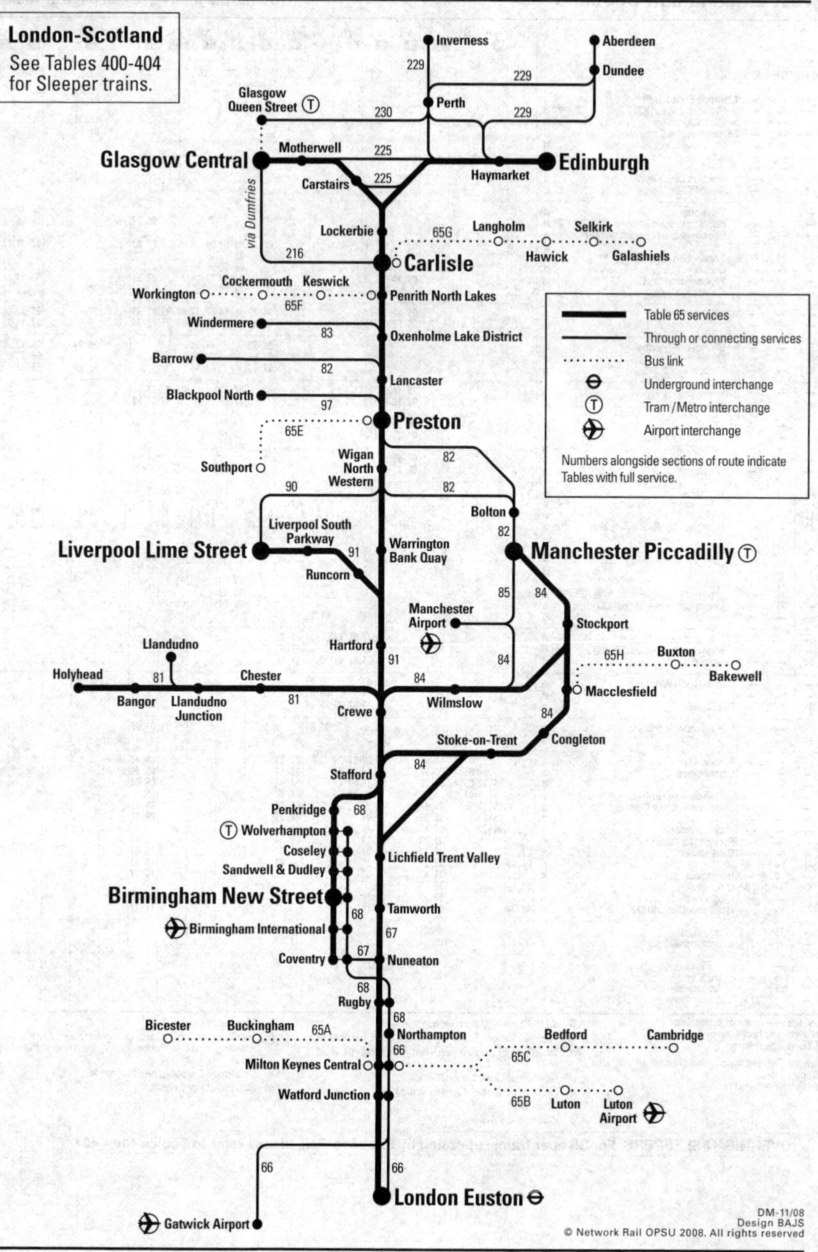

London and West Midlands → North West England and Scotland

Route Diagram - see first page of Table 65

Miles	Miles	Miles	Miles	Miles			SR	TP	NT	VT	VT	VT	TP	NT	TP	XC	LM	XC	LM	VT	NT	VT		XC	LM
								1 ◇ A		1 ◇	1 ◇	1 ◇ B	1 ◇		1 ◇	1 ◇	1 ◇	1 ◇	1	1 ◇	C	1 ◇		1 ◇	1 ◇
0	—	—	—	—	London Euston 15	d																06 20			
—	—	—	—	—	Gatwick Airport 10	d																			
17½	—	—	—	—	Watford Junction	d																06u36			
49¾	—	—	—	—	Milton Keynes Central	d																06 56			
—	—	—	—	—	Northampton	d													06b06						
82½	0	—	—	—	Rugby	d													06b29						
97	—	—	—	—	Nuneaton	d													06 43						
110	—	—	—	—	Tamworth Low Level	d													06 57			07 36			
116¼	—	0	—	—	Lichfield Trent Valley	d													07 04						
—	11½	—	—	—	Coventry	d																		06 27	
—	22	—	—	—	Birmingham International	d														06 23				06 45	
—	30½	—	—	—	Birmingham New Street 12	a																			
—	—	—	—	—		d					05 20	05 30				06 03	06 07	06 30		07 03				07 18	07 21
35¾	—	—	—	—	Sandwell & Dudley	d											06 18								
39	—	—	—	—	Coseley	d											06 27								07 34
—	43½	—	—	—	Wolverhampton 7	d					05 38	05 49				06 21	06 39	07 06		07 21				07 39	07 44
—	53¼	—	—	—	Penkridge	d											06 49								07 54
133½	59½	—	—	—	Stafford	a					05 51	06 04				06 33	06 56	07 17	07 23	07 33				07 53	08 01
—	—	—	—	—		d					05 52	06 05				06 34	07 00	07 18	07 25	07 34				07 54	08 01
—	75¾	30¼	—	—	Stoke-on-Trent	a										06 52		07 36				08 04		08 12	
—	87½	42	—	—	Congleton	a										07 04		07 48						08 24	
—	95¾	50¼	—	—	Macclesfield	a										07 13		07 56				08 20		08 32	
158	—	—	—	—	Crewe 10	a					06 16	06 25					07 22		07 45	07 53					08 22
—	—	—	0	—		d					06 18	06 26					07 23		07 47	07 56					08 24
—	—	—	—	—	Chester	a					06 37	07 00					07 59			08 27					08 57
—	—	—	—	—	Llandudno Junction	a					07 33	07c58					09c19			09c26					10c17
—	—	—	—	—	Llandudno	a						08c16					09c37			10e01					10c37
—	—	—	—	—	Bangor (Gwynedd)	a					07 49	08 43								09c43					
—	—	—	—	—	Holyhead	a					08 21	09 30								10c20					
—	—	—	—	—	Wilmslow	a						07 01					07 59		08 26	08 44					
—	—	—	—	—	Manchester Airport	a											08 14								
—	107¼	62½	—	—	Stockport	a					06f53	07 14				07 30		08 09	08 41			08s35		08 46	
—	113	68	—	—	Manchester Piccadilly 10	a					07f11	07 28				07 47		08 27	08 56			08 48		09 02	
169¾	—	—	11¾	—	Hartford	a											07 35		07 58						08 35
182	—	—	—	—	Warrington Bank Quay	a						06 44								08 12					
—	—	—	—	—		d						06 45								08 13					
—	—	—	22½	—	Runcorn	a						07f03					07 47		08 10						08 45
—	—	—	30	—	Liverpool South Parkway 7	a											07 53								08 53
—	—	—	35½	—	Liverpool Lime Street 10	a						07f27					08 11		08 35						09 09
—	—	—	—	—		d						06 04		07 30											
—	—	—	—	—	Manchester Airport	d			03 40	04 34		05g47	06 19		07 22										
—	—	—	—	—	Manchester Piccadilly 10	d			03 55	04 58		06g05	06 44		07 45										
—	—	79¼	—	—	Bolton	d						06g26	07 03		08 04										
193¾	—	—	—	—	Wigan North Western	a						07 03		08 01						08 23					
—	—	—	—	—		d						07 04		08 02						08 24					
209	—	99¼	—	—	Preston 8	a				05 54		07 17	07 26	08 24	08 27					08 41					
—	—	—	—	—	Blackpool North	a						07 56		08 51						09 32					
—	—	—	—	—		d			04 45	05 30		06 34			07 41						08 09				
—	—	—	—	—	Preston 8	d			05 24	06 04		07 20	07 29		08 28					08 43	08 46				
230	—	—	—	—	Lancaster 6	a			05 44	06 18		07 34	07 44		08 44					09 00	09 07				
—	—	—	—	—		d		05{22	05 45	06 20		07 35	07 45		08 44					09 02					
—	—	—	—	—	Barrow-in-Furness	a			07 05				08 49		09 57										
249	—	—	—	—	Oxenholme Lake District	a		05{53		06 34		07 47			08 58					09 17					
—	—	—	—	—		d		05{53		06 35		07 49			08 59					09 18					
—	—	—	—	—	Windermere	a		06{12		07 10		08 15			09 22										
281¼	—	—	—	—	Penrith North Lakes	d				07 00		08 13			09 24					09 43					
299	—	—	—	—	Carlisle 8	a				07 19		08 34			09 47					10 01					
—	—	—	—	—		d	06 09			07 21		08 35			09 47					10 03					
324¼	—	—	0	—	Lockerbie	d				07 43		08 55								10 22					
372½	—	—	—	0	Carstairs	a				08 17															
388½	—	—	—	—	Motherwell	a				08s35		09s50								11s04					
401¼	—	—	—	—	Glasgow Central 15	a	08 37			08 58		10 18								11 28					
—	—	—	75	26¼	Haymarket	a				09h05					11s03										
—	—	—	76¼	27½	Edinburgh 10	a				09h11					11 10										
—	—	—	—	97¼	Perth	a				10j37		12j37			12 56										
—	—	—	135½	—	Dundee	a				10k21					12m21										
—	—	—	206¾	—	Aberdeen	a				11k34					13m36										
—	—	—	—	215¼	Inverness	a				13j35					15 18										

For general notes see front of timetable
For details of catering facilities see Directory of Train Operators

A All Tuesdays to Fridays, also Mondays until 14 July and from 15 September. From Barrow-in-Furness (Table 82)

B to Crewe, from Crewe

C From Clitheroe (Table 94) to Morecambe (Table 98)

b 28 July to 22 August dep. Northampton 0603, Rugby 0627

c Change at Crewe and Chester

e Change at Crewe, Chester and Llandudno Junction

f Change at Crewe

g Change at Preston

h Change at Carstairs

j Via Glasgow Central and Glasgow Queen Street. Passengers make their own way from one station to the other

k Change at Carstairs and Haymarket

m Change at Haymarket

OVERNIGHT SLEEPERS. For Sleeper trains, operated by First ScotRail, please refer to Tables 400 - 404

London and West Midlands → North West England and Scotland

Route Diagram - see first page of Table 65

Station		XC	VT	VT	TP	VT	LM	NT	VT	NT	NT	TP	NT	VT	VT	XC	LM		XC	VT	TP	VT	LM	VT	NT
		1◇	1◇	1◇	1◇	1◇	1◇		1◇			1◇		1◇	1◇	1◇	1		1◇	1◇	1◇	1◇	1◇	1◇	
		A	B	C	D		E	G		G		D	H			J	K		L						
		⊏P	⊠	⊠	工	⊠	工		⊏P			工		⊠	⊠	⊏P	工		⊏P	⊠	工	⊠	工	⊏P	
London Euston 15 ⊖	d		06 44	06 46		07 03								07 13	07 35					07 46		08 05			
Gatwick Airport 10 ✈	d															05 15									
Watford Junction	d					07u18								07u28						08u01					
Milton Keynes Central	d		07 15	07 17										07 48								08 36			
Northampton	d																07 22			08b00					
Rugby	d		07 37	07 39													07c43			08 39					
Nuneaton	d													08 22											
Tamworth Low Level	d																		08e10						
Lichfield Trent Valley	d																								
Coventry	d	07 23							07 23								07 56		07 56				08 01	08 23	
Birmingham International ✈	d	07 34															08 09						08 19	08 34	
Birmingham New Street 12	a	07 45														08 18	08 25								
	d	07 48					07 51		08 03							08 18	08 26		08 48				08 51	09 03	
Sandwell & Dudley	d																						08 59		
Coseley	d																08 37								
Wolverhampton 7	d	08 06					08 09		08 21							08 39	08 44		09 06				09 10	09 21	
Penkridge	d						08 19										08 54								
Stafford	a	08 17					08 25							08 47		08 53	09 01		09 17				09 24		
	d	08 18					08 26							08 47		08 54	09 01		09 18				09 24		
Stoke-on-Trent	a	08 36				08 41									09 06	09 12			09 36			09 41			
Congleton	a																								
Macclesfield	a	08 52				08 57										09 31			09 52			09 57			
Crewe 10	a		08 30	08 30			08 51		08 54					09 07			09 22			09 30			09 46	09 53	
	d		08 31	08 31			08 52		08 56					09 08			09 24			09 31			09 47	09 56	
Chester	a						09 26										09 57							10 27	
Llandudno Junction	a						10 24										11f17							11f24	
Llandudno	a																11f35								
Bangor (Gwynedd)	a						10 46																	11f41	
Holyhead	a						11 30																	12f20	
Wilmslow	a		09 03	09 03										09 44			10 01						10 26		
Manchester Airport ✈	a		09 15	09 15													10 11								
Stockport	a	09 05	09 39	09 39		09s12									09s34	09 46			10 05			10s12	10 39		
Manchester Piccadilly 10	a	09 20	09 41	09 41		09 25									09 46	10 02			10 20			10 24	10 54		
Hartford	a																09 35								
Warrington Bank Quay	a		08 49	08 49					09 12											09 49				10 11	
	d		08 50	08 50					09 13											09 50				10 13	
Runcorn	a						09 08							09 25			09 45						10 03		
Liverpool South Parkway 7 ✈	a																09 53								
Liverpool Lime Street 10	a						09 31							09 47			10 09						10 26		
	d		08 04	08 04				08 28			08 57									09 04					09 57
Manchester Airport ✈	d		07g47	07g47	08 27							08 47									09 27				
Manchester Piccadilly 10	d		08g11	08g11	08 45							09 11									09 45				
Bolton	d		08g32	08g32	09 05							09 32									10 05				
Wigan North Western	a		09 00	09 00				09 12	09 23		09 30									10 00				10 22	10 31
	d		09 01	09 01				09 13	09 24	←	09 31									10 01				10 24	10 31
Preston 8	a		09 14	09 14	09 29			09 38	09 38	09 38	09 54	09 58								10 14	10 27			10 37	10 54
Blackpool North	a		09 57	09h57				→			10 21									10 57					11 21
	d		08 41	08 41								09 30								09 38					
Preston 8	d		09 18	09 18	09 32				09 40	09 44		10 06	10 10							10 18	10 29			10 40	
Lancaster 6	a		09 31	09 31	09 47				09 55	10 03		10 23	10 30							10 35	10 44				
	d		09 33	09 33	09 48				09 57			10 23	10 30								10 45				
Barrow-in-Furness	a				10 46								11 33								12 16				
Oxenholme Lake District	a		09 45	09 45					10 10			10 43									11 03			11 11	
	d		09 46	09 46					10 11			10 43									11 03			11 12	
Windermere	a		10 13	10 13								11 01													
Penrith North Lakes	d		10 12	10 12					10 35												11 30				
Carlisle 8	a		10 29	10 29					10 52												11 48			11 56	
	d		10 30	10 30					10 54												11 52			11 59	
Lockerbie	d								11 12												12 11				
Carstairs	a																								
Motherwell	a		11s27	11s27																	12s56				
Glasgow Central 15	a		11 50	11 50																	13 14			13 22	
Haymarket	a								12s08																
Edinburgh 10	a								12 19																
Perth	a		13j37	13j37					14 54																
Dundee	a								13k24																
Aberdeen	a								14k36																
Inverness	a								17 07																

For general notes see front of timetable
For details of catering facilities see Directory of Train Operators

- **A** From Southampton Central (Table 51)
- **B** 28 July to 22 August
- **C** Until 25 July and from 25 August
- **D** 工 to Preston
- **E** From Walsall (Table 70)
- **G** To Morecambe (Table 98)
- **H** To Carlisle via Whitehaven (Table 100)
- **J** ⊏P from Reading
- **K** 工 from Birmingham New Street
- **L** From Derby (Table 57)
- **b** 28 July to 22 August dep. 0758
- **c** 28 July to 22 August dep. 0641
- **e** Tamworth High Level
- **f** Change at Crewe and Chester
- **g** Change at Preston
- **h** From 6 October arr. 2 minutes later
- **j** Via Glasgow Central and Glasgow Queen Street. Passengers make their own way from one station to the other
- **k** Change at Haymarket

OVERNIGHT SLEEPERS. For Sleeper trains, operated by First ScotRail, please refer to Tables 400 - 404

London and West Midlands → North West England and Scotland

Route Diagram - see first page of Table 65

		XC 1◇	VT 1◇	LM 1◇	VT 1◇	NT	XC 1◇	VT 1◇	VT 1◇	TP 1◇	VT 1◇	LM 1◇		VT 1◇	NT	XC 1◇	VT 1◇	VT 1◇	LM 1◇	XC 1◇	VT 1◇	VT 1◇	TP 1◇	TP 1◇	LM 1◇
		A				B	C			D						E									
		🛒	⊠	☕	⊠		🛒	⊠	⊠	☕	⊠	☕		🛒		🛒	⊠	⊠	☕	🛒	⊠	⊠		☕	☕
London Euston 15 ⊖	d		08 17		08 35			08 46	09 00		09 05						09 17	09 35			09 38	09 46			
Gatwick Airport 10 ✈	d																								
Watford Junction	d		08u32					09u01			09u20														
Milton Keynes Central	d																09 48					10 17			
Northampton	d																				10 26 →				
Rugby	d								09 49													10 39			
Nuneaton	d		09 21														10 22								
Tamworth Low Level	d																								
Lichfield Trent Valley	d																								
Coventry	d						09 23									09 32									
Birmingham International ✈	d						09 34									09 50				10 18					10 20
Birmingham New Street 12	a						09 45													10 30					
	d	09 18		09 21			09 48					09 51		10 03		10 18			10 21	10 48					10 51
Sandwell & Dudley	d											09 59													10 59
Coseley	d			09 34															10 34						
Wolverhampton 7 🚌	d	09 39		09 44			10 06					10 10		10 21		10 39			10 44	11 06					11 10
Penkridge	d			09 54															10 54						
Stafford	a		09 47	10 01			10 17					10 24					10 47		11 01	11 17					11 24
	d		09 47	10 01			10 18					10 24					10 47		11 01	11 18					11 24
Stoke-on-Trent	a	10 12			10 06		10 36				10 41					11 12		11 06		11 36					
Congleton	a	10 24																							
Macclesfield	a	10 32					10 52				10 57					11 31				11 52					
Crewe 10	a		10 07	10 21				10 31	10 40			10 46		10 53			11 07		11 22			11 31			11 50
	d		10 08	10 24				10 32	10 49			10 47		10 56			11 08		11 24			11 32			
Chester	a			10 57					11 16					11 29					11 59						12 27
Llandudno Junction	a			11b55					12 06					12 25					13b17						13b24
Llandudno	a								12 35					13c01					13b35						
Bangor (Gwynedd)	a			12b12					12 26					12 48											13b48
Holyhead	a			12b47					13 03					13 30											14b30
Wilmslow	a		10 44	11 01								11 26					11 44		12 01						12 26
Manchester Airport ✈	a			11 11															12 11						
Stockport	a	10 46	10 53		10s34		11 05				11s12	11 39				11 46	11 53	11s34		12 05					12 39
Manchester Piccadilly 10 🚌	a	11 02	11 13		10 46		11 20				11 24	11 54				12 02	12 13	11 46		12 20					12 54
Hartford	a			10 33															11 35						
Warrington Bank Quay	a							10 50						11 11								11 50			
	d							10 51						11 13								11 51			
Runcorn	a		10 25	10 45								11 03					11 25		11 45						
Liverpool South Parkway 7 ✈	a			10 53															11 53						
Liverpool Lime Street 10	a		10 47	11 09								11 26					11 47		12 09						
	d							10 04							10 57							11 04			
Manchester Airport ✈	d							09e47		10 27												10e47		11 27	
Manchester Piccadilly 10 🚌	d					10f13		10e11		10 45												11e11		11 45	
Bolton	d							10e32		11 05												11e32		12 05	
Wigan North Western	a					10 48		11 01						11 22	11 30							12 01			
	d					10 49		11 02						11 24	11 30							12 02			
Preston 8	a					11 09		11 15		11 27				11 37	11 53							12 15		12 27	
Blackpool North	a					11 36		11g54						12h11	12 20							12g54			
	d							10 41														11 41			
Preston 8	d							11 19		11 29				11 40								12 19	12 23	12 29	
Lancaster 6	a							11 32		11 44				11 54								12 32	12 38	12 44	
	d							11 34		11 45				11 55								12 34	12 39	12 45	
Barrow-in-Furness	a									12 49															
Oxenholme Lake District	a							11 46														12 46	12 54	12 59	
	d							11 47														12 47	12 57	12 59	
Windermere	a							12 14															13 18	14 13	
Penrith North Lakes	d													12 33								13 12			
Carlisle 8	a							12 28						12 51								13 36		13 40	
	d							12 29						12 53										13 47 →	
Lockerbie	d													13 11											
Carstairs	a																								
Motherwell	a																								
Glasgow Central 15	a							13 46																	
Haymarket	a													14s08											
Edinburgh 10	a													14 19											
Perth	a							15j37																	
Dundee	a													15k21											
Aberdeen	a													16k37											
Inverness	a																								

For general notes see front of timetable
For details of catering facilities see Directory of Train Operators

- A From Exeter St Davids (Table 51)
- B Until 12 September
- C From Bournemouth (Table 51)
- D ☕ to Preston
- E From Reading (Table 51)
- b Change at Crewe and Chester
- c Change at Crewe and Llandudno Junction
- e Change at Preston
- f Manchester Victoria
- g From 6 October arr. 2 minutes later
- h Until 5 September only
- j Via Glasgow Central and Glasgow Queen Street. Passengers make their own way from one station to the other
- k Change at Haymarket

OVERNIGHT SLEEPERS. For Sleeper trains, operated by First ScotRail, please refer to Tables 400 - 404

London and West Midlands → North West England and Scotland

Route Diagram - see first page of Table 65

		VT	VT	XC	VT	VT	VT		TP	VT	NT	LM	VT	XC	VT	TP	LM	VT	NT	TP	VT	XC	VT	VT	LM
				R										R											
		1◇	1◇	1	1◇	1◇	1◇		1◇	1◇		1◇	1◇	1	1◇	1◇	1◇	1◇		1◇	1◇	1◇	1◇	1◇	1◇
				A										B		C				C		D			
		⊠	☕	☕	⊠	⊠	⊠		🛒	☕		🛒	⊠	☕	⊠	🛒	🛒	☕		🛒	☕	☕	☕	☕	🛒
London Euston 15 ⊖	d	10 05				10 15	10 29						10 35		10 46						11 05		11 17	11 28	
Gatwick Airport 10 ✈	d																								
Watford Junction	d	*09 41*				10u30									11u01						11u20				
Milton Keynes Central	d	10 36			←																				
Northampton	d				10 26																		11 48		
Rugby	d				10 47										11 39										
Nuneaton	d				11 00	11 20																	12 22		
Tamworth Low Level	d				11b16																				
Lichfield Trent Valley	d				11 23																				
Coventry	d		*10 23*	*10 32*								*10 45*		11 23								*11 32*			*11 44*
Birmingham International ✈	d		*10 34*	*10 50*								*10 58*		11 34								*11 50*			*11 58*
Birmingham New Street 12	a													11 45											
	d		11 03	11 18								11 21		11 48			11 51	12 03				12 18			12 21
Sandwell & Dudley	d																11 59								
Coseley	d											11 34													12 34
Wolverhampton 7	d		11 21	11 39								11 44					12 10	12 21				12 39			12 44
Penkridge	d											11 54													12 54
Stafford	a					11 45						12 01		12 17			12 24						12 48		13 01
	d					11 45						12 01		12 18			12 24						12 48		13 01
Stoke-on-Trent	a	11 41		12 12									12 06	12 36							12 41	13 12			
Congleton	a			12 24																					
Macclesfield	a	11 57		12 32										12 52							12 57	13 31			
Crewe 10	a		11 55		12 04	12 07						12 22			12 31		12 45	12 53					13 09	13 12	13 22
	d		11 56		12 08	12 08						12 24			12 32		12 48	12 56					13 10	13 12	13 24
Chester	a											*12 59*											*13 43*	13 32	*13 57*
Llandudno Junction	a											*14c09*											*14 38*	14 22	*15c18*
Llandudno	a											*14c27*												14 44	*15c36*
Bangor (Gwynedd)	a																							*14e55*	
Holyhead	a																							*15e30*	
Wilmslow	a				12 28	*12 44*						*13 01*					*13 26*							*13f44*	*14 01*
Manchester Airport ✈	a											*13 11*													*14 11*
Stockport	a	12s12		12 46	12s41	*12 52*							12s34	13 05			*13 39*				13s12	13 46			
Manchester Piccadilly 10	a	12 24		13 02	12 55	*13 13*							12 46	13 20			*13 54*				13 24	14 02			
Hartford	a											12 33													13 35
Warrington Bank Quay	a		12 13												12 50			13 11							
	d		12 14												12 51			13 13							
Runcorn	a					12 25						12 45					13 03						13 26		13 45
Liverpool South Parkway 7 ✈	a											12 53													13 53
Liverpool Lime Street 10	a					12 47						13 09					13 26						13 49		14 09
	d										11 57				*12 04*				12 57						
Manchester Airport ✈	d														*11g47*	12 27				12 47					
Manchester Piccadilly 10	d														*12g11*	12 45				13 11					
Bolton	d														*12g32*	13 05				13 32					
Wigan North Western	a		12 24							←	12 31				13 01			13 22	13 31						
	d		12 26 →							12 26	12 31				13 02			13 24	13 31						
Preston 8	a						12 43			12 47	12 56				13 15	13 27		13 37	13 54	14 04					
Blackpool North	a										13 21				*13h54*				14 21						
	d									*12 11*					*12 41*					*13 30*					
Preston 8	d						12 44			12 50					13 19	13 29		13 40		14 09					
Lancaster 6	a									13 04					13 38	13 44		13 54		14 24					
	d									13 06						13 45		13 55		14 26					
Barrow-in-Furness	a									*14 07*						14 41		*15 21*							
Oxenholme Lake District	a																	14 08		14 42					
	d																	14 10		14 51 →					
Windermere	a																								
Penrith North Lakes	d									13 44															
Carlisle 8	a						13 43		←	14 00								14 51							
	d						13 43		13 47	14 03								14 54							
Lockerbie	d									14 22								15 13							
Carstairs	a																								
Motherwell	a																								
Glasgow Central 15	a						14 54			15 25															
Haymarket	a								15s04									16s08							
Edinburgh 10	a								15 11									16 16							
Perth	a						*16j37*			*17j20*								*17 55*							
Dundee	a						*17j00*		*17 26*	*18j00*								*17 44*							
Aberdeen	a						*18j15*		*18 44*	*19j14*								*19 00*							
Inverness	a									*19j34*								*20 08*							

For general notes see front of timetable
For details of catering facilities see Directory of Train Operators

- **A** From Plymouth (Table 51)
- **B** From Bournemouth (Table 51)
- **C** 🛒 to Preston
- **D** From Reading (Table 51)
- **b** Arr. 1112
- **c** Change at Crewe and Chester
- **e** Change at Llandudno Junction
- **f** Change at Crewe
- **g** Change at Preston
- **h** From 6 October arr. 2 minutes later
- **j** Via Glasgow Central and Glasgow Queen Street. Passengers make their own way from one station to the other

OVERNIGHT SLEEPERS. For Sleeper trains, operated by First ScotRail, please refer to Tables 400 - 404

London and West Midlands → North West England and Scotland

Route Diagram - see first page of Table 65

		VT		XC	VT	TP	TP	LM	VT	VT	NT	VT	XC	LM	VT	XC	VT	TP	LM		VT	LM	VT	NT	XC
													Ⓡ			Ⓡ									
		■1 ◇		■1 ◇	■1 ◇	■1 ◇	■1 ◇	■1 ◇	■1 ◇	■1 ◇		■1 ◇	■1	■1 ◇	■1 ◇	■1	■1 ◇	■1 ◇	■1		■1 ◇	■1 ◇	■1 ◇		■1 ◇
						A							B			C		A	D						E
		🍽		🍽	🍽	🍴	🍴	🍴	🍽	🍽		🍽	🍽	🍴	🍽	🍽	🍽	🍴	🍴		🍽	🍴	🍽		🍽
London Euston 15 ⊖	d	11 35			11 46					12 05		12 17			12 35		12 46		12 49		13 05				
Gatwick Airport 10 ✈	d																								
Watford Junction	d											12u32									13u20				
Milton Keynes Central	d				12 17					12 36							13 17								
Northampton	d																								
Rugby	d				12 39												13 39		13 47						
Nuneaton	d											13 22							14 01						
Tamworth Low Level	d																		14 17						
Lichfield Trent Valley	d																		14 24						
Coventry	d								12 23					12 44		13 23			→						13 32
Birmingham International ✈	d			12 18				12 20	12 34					12 58		13 34									13 50
Birmingham New Street 12	a			12 30												13 45									
	d			12 48				12 51	13 03				13 18	13 21		13 48						13 51	14 03		14 18
Sandwell & Dudley	d							12 59														13 59			
Coseley	d													13 34											
Wolverhampton 7	d			13 06				13 10	13 21				13 39	13 44		14 06						14 10	14 21		14 39
Penkridge	d													13 54											
Stafford	a			13 17				13 24				13 47		14 01		14 17						14 24			
	d			13 18				13 24				13 47		14 01		14 18						14 24			
Stoke-on-Trent	a	13 06		13 36						13 41			14 12		14 06	14 36					14 41				15 12
Congleton	a												14 24												
Macclesfield	a			13 52						13 57			14 32			14 52					14 57				15 31
Crewe 10	a				13 31			13 50	13 53			14 07		14 22			14 31					14 45	14 53		
	d				13 32				13 56			14 08		14 24			14 32					14 47	14 56		
Chester	a								14 27					14 57									15 26		
Llandudno Junction	a								15b25					16b17									16 24		
Llandudno	a								16c01					16b35											
Bangor (Gwynedd)	a								15b47														16 46		
Holyhead	a								16b30														17 20		
Wilmslow	a							14 26				14 44		15 01								15 26			
Manchester Airport ✈	a													15 11											
Stockport	a	13s34		14 05				14 39		14s12		14 53	14 46		14s34	15 05					15s12	15 39			15 46
Manchester Piccadilly 10	a	13 46		14 20				14 54		14 24		15 13	15 02		14 46	15 20					15 24	15 54			16 02
Hartford	a													14 35											
Warrington Bank Quay	a				13 49				14 14								14 50						15 11		
	d				13 51				14 15								14 51						15 13		
Runcorn	a											14 25		14 45								15 03			
Liverpool South Parkway 7 ✈	a													14 53											
Liverpool Lime Street 10	a											14 47		15 09								15 26			
	d				13 04						13 57						14 04							14 57	
Manchester Airport ✈	d				12e47		13 27										13e47	14 27							
Manchester Piccadilly 10	d				13e11		13 45										14e11	14 45							
Bolton	d						14 05										14e32	15 05							
Wigan North Western	a				14 00				14 26		14 31						15 01						15 22	15 31	
	d				14 02				14 27		14 31						15 02						15 24	15 31	
Preston 8	a				14 15		14 27		14 41		14 54						15 15	15 27					15 37	15 54	
Blackpool North	a				14f54						15 21						15f54							16 21	
	d				13 41												14 41								
Preston 8	d				14 19		14 29		14 43								15 19	15 29					15 40		
Lancaster 6	a				14 32		14 44		14 57								15 38	15 44					15 56		
	d				14 34		14 45		14 59									15 52					15 58		
Barrow-in-Furness	a																	16 56							
Oxenholme Lake District	a				14 46	←	14 59		15 12																
	d				14 47	14 51	14 59		15 13																
Windermere	a					15 09			16 10																
Penrith North Lakes	d				15 12		15 25																16 33		
Carlisle 8	a				15 30		15 43		15 53														16 51		
	d				15 30		15 43		15 53														16 53		
Lockerbie	d						16 02																		
Carstairs	a																								
Motherwell	a				16s27																				
Glasgow Central 15	a				16 55				17 21																
Haymarket	a						17s08																18s09		
Edinburgh 10	a						17 14																18 19		
Perth	a				18g48		18 54		19g19																
Dundee	a						18h49																19h27		
Aberdeen	a						20j31																20h44		
Inverness	a						20 58																		

For general notes see front of timetable
For details of catering facilities see Directory of Train Operators

A 🍴 to Preston
B From Penzance (Table 135)
C From Bournemouth (Table 51)
D Also stops at Atherstone 1407, Polesworth 1412 and Rugeley Trent Valley 1432
E From Reading (Table 51)
b Change at Crewe and Chester
c Change at Crewe, Chester and Llandudno Junction
e Change at Preston
f From 6 October arr. 2 minutes later
g Via Glasgow Central and Glasgow Queen Street. Passengers make their own way from one station to the other
h Change at Haymarket
j Change at Haymarket and Dundee

OVERNIGHT SLEEPERS. For Sleeper trains, operated by First ScotRail, please refer to Tables 400 - 404

London and West Midlands → North West England and Scotland

Route Diagram - see first page of Table 65

		VT	LM	LM	VT	XC	VT	TP	VT	LM	VT	NT	XC	VT	LM	VT	XC	VT	TP	VT	LM	NT	VT	NT
		1 ◇	1	1 ◇	1 ◇	1 ◇	1 ◇	1 ◇	1 ◇	1 ◇	1 ◇		R 1	1 ◇	1 ◇	1 ◇	R 1	1 ◇	1 ◇	1 ◇	1 ◇		1 ◇	
			A										B				C		D					
		⊡	trolley	trolley	⊡	⊡	⊡	trolley	⊡	trolley	⊡		⊡	⊡	trolley	⊡	⊡	⊡	trolley	⊡	trolley		⊡	
London Euston 15 ⊖	d	13 17			13 35		13 46		14 05					14 17		14 35		14 46		15 05				
Gatwick Airport 10 ✈	d																							
Watford Junction	d						14u01							14u32						15u20				
Milton Keynes Central	d	13 48							14 36									15u17						
Northampton	d																							
Rugby	d						14 39											15 39						
Nuneaton	d	14 22												15 22										
Tamworth Low Level	d		←																					
Lichfield Trent Valley	d		14 24																					
Coventry	d			13 44							14 23		14 32		14 44		15 23							
Birmingham International ✈	d			13 58		14 18				14 20	14 34		14 50		14 58		15 34							
Birmingham New Street 12	a					14 30											15 45							
	d			14 21		14 48				14 51	15 03		15 18		15 21		15 48				15 51		16 03	
Sandwell & Dudley	d									14 59											15 59			
Coseley	d			14 34											15 34									
Wolverhampton 7	d			14 44		15 06				15 10	15 21		15 39		15 44						16 10		16 21	
Penkridge	d			14 54											15 54									
Stafford	a	14 47	14 43	15 01		15 17				15 24				15 47	16 01		16 17				16 24			
	d	14 47	14 44	15 01		15 18				15 24				15 47	16 01		16 18				16 24			
Stoke-on-Trent	a				15 06	15 36			15 41				16 12			16 06	16 36			16 41				
Congleton	a												16 24											
Macclesfield	a					15 52			15 57				16 32				16 52			16 57				
Crewe 10	a	15 07	15 10	15 22			15 31			15 50	15 55			16 07	16 22			16 31			16 45		16 53	
	d	15 08		15 24			15 32				15 57			16 08	16 24			16 32			16 47		16 56	
Chester	a			15 57						16 27					16 57								17 26	
Llandudno Junction	a			17b17						17b24					18b17								18 25	
Llandudno	a			17b35											18b35								18c46	
Bangor (Gwynedd)	a									17b47													18 47	
Holyhead	a									18b30													19 20	
Wilmslow	a		15 44	16 01						16 26				16 44				17 05			17 26			
Manchester Airport ✈	a			16 11														17 15						
Stockport	a		15 52		15s34	16 05			16s12	16 40			16 46	16 53		16s34	17 05			17s12	17 39			
Manchester Piccadilly 10	a		16 13		15 46	16 20			16 24	16 54			17 02	17 11		16 46	17 20	17 41		17 24	17 54			
Hartford	a			15 35											16 33									
Warrington Bank Quay	a						15 50				16 14							16 50					17 11	
	d						15 51				16 15							16 51					17 13	
Runcorn	a	15 25		15 45										16 25	16 45						17 03			
Liverpool South Parkway 7 ✈	a			15 53											16 53									
Liverpool Lime Street 10	a	15 48		16 09										16 48	17 09						17 26			
	d						15 04					15 57						16 04				16 30		
Manchester Airport ✈	d						14e47	15 27										15e47	16 27					
Manchester Piccadilly 10	d						15e11	15 45										16e11	16 44					
Bolton	d						15e32	16 05										16e32	17 05					
Wigan North Western	a						16 01				16 25	16 31						17 01				17 09	17 22	←
	d						16 02				16 27	16 31						17 02				17 10	17 24	17 10
Preston 8	a						16 15	16 27			16 40	16 54						17 15	17 27			→	17 37	17 40
Blackpool North	a						16f54					17 34						17 58						18 22
	d						15 41					16 25						16 38						
Preston 8	d						16 19	16 29			16 43	16 56						17 18	17 29				17 40	
Lancaster 6	a						16 32	16 44			16 59	17 16						17 32	17 44				17 54	
	d						16 34	16 45			17 00	17 16						17 34	17 45				17 55	
Barrow-in-Furness	a						17 44					18 23							18 50					
Oxenholme Lake District	a						16 46	16 59			17 15												18 11	
	d						16 47	16 59			17 17												18 12	
Windermere	a							17 23			18 04													
Penrith North Lakes	d						17 12	17 25															18 37	
Carlisle 8	a						17 29	17 43			17 57							18 26					18 55	
	d						17 29	17 44			17 59							18 27					18 58	
Lockerbie	d							18 04																
Carstairs	a																							
Motherwell	a										19s14													
Glasgow Central 15	a						18 46				19 37							19 47						
Haymarket	a							19s04															20s08	
Edinburgh 10	a							19 11															20 19	
Perth	a						20g37	20 53										21g42						
Dundee	a							20h26															21h41	
Aberdeen	a							21h39															23 12	
Inverness	a							23 10																

For general notes see front of timetable
For details of catering facilities see Directory of Train Operators

A Also stops at Atherstone 1407, Polesworth 1412 and Rugeley Trent Valley 1432

B From Penzance (Table 135)

C From Bournemouth (Table 51)

D trolley to Preston

b Change at Crewe and Chester

c Change at Crewe and Llandudno Junction

e Change at Preston

f From 6 October arr. 2 minutes later

g Via Glasgow Central and Glasgow Queen Street. Passengers make their own way from one station to the other

h Change at Haymarket

OVERNIGHT SLEEPERS. For Sleeper trains, operated by First ScotRail, please refer to Tables 400 - 404

London and West Midlands → North West England and Scotland

Route Diagram - see first page of Table 65

		TP	XC	VT	VT	LM	XC	TP	NT		VT	TP	NT	TP	VT	LM	VT	NT	VT	XC	VT	VT	LM	NT	VT
			R																	R					
		1 ◇	1	1 ◇	1 ◇	1 ◇	1 ◇	1 ◇			1 ◇	1 ◇		1 ◇	1 ◇	1 ◇	1 ◇		1 ◇	1	1 ◇	1 ◇	1 ◇		1 ◇
			A											B						C					
		⌶	▭	☒	☒	⌶	▭				☒			⌶	▭	⌶	▭		▭	▭	▭	▭	⌶		▭
London Euston [15] ⊖	d			15 17	15 35						15 46				15 49				16 05		16 17	16 35			16 46
Gatwick Airport [10] ✈	d																								
Watford Junction	d																				16u32				
Milton Keynes Central	d			15 48															16u36						
Northampton	d																								
Rugby	d														16 40										
Nuneaton	d			16 22																	17 22				
Tamworth Low Level	d										16 54														
Lichfield Trent Valley	d																								
Coventry	d		15 32			15 44											16 23			16 32			16 44		
Birmingham International ✈	d		15 50			15 58	16 18									16 20	16 34			16 50			16 58		
Birmingham New Street [12]	a						16 30																		
	d		16 18			16 21	16 48									16 51	17 03			17 18			17 21		
Sandwell & Dudley	d															16 59									
Coseley	d					16 34																	17 35		
Wolverhampton [7]	d		16 39			16 44	17 06									17 10				17 39			17 44		
Penkridge	d					16 54										17 20							17 54		
Stafford	a			16 47		17 01	17 17									17 26					17 47		18 01		18 11
	d			16 47		17 01	17 18									17 27					17 47		18 01		18 11
Stoke-on-Trent	a		17 12		17 06		17 36												17 41	18 12		18 06			
Congleton	a		17 24																	18 24					
Macclesfield	a		17 32		17 21		17 52												17 57	18 32		18 21			
Crewe [10]	a			17 07		17 22					17 30				17 34	17 48	17 53				18 07		18 22		18 31
	d			17 08		17 24					17 30				17 35	17 49	17 56				18 08		18 24		18 32
Chester	a			17 53											17 58		18 28						18 57		
Llandudno Junction	a														18 49		19b25						20b18		
Llandudno	a														19 36								20b35		
Bangor (Gwynedd)	a														19 05		19b48								
Holyhead	a														19 41		20b29								
Wilmslow	a			17 44		18 04										18 26					18 42				
Manchester Airport ✈	a					18 15															18 54				
Stockport	a		17 46	17 54	17s35		18 05									18 39			18s11	18 46	18 53	18s35			
Manchester Piccadilly [10]	a		18 02	18 12	17 49		18 20									18 56			18 25	19 02	19 13	18 49			
Hartford	a					17 35																	18 35		
Warrington Bank Quay	a										17 49					18 06									18 51
	d										17 51					18 07									18 52
Runcorn	a			17 25		17 45															18 25		18 45		
Liverpool South Parkway [7] ✈	a					17 53																	18 53		
Liverpool Lime Street [10]	a			17 47		18 09															18 47		19 09		
	d								17 20									17 45						18 04	
Manchester Airport ✈	d	16 47												17 32											17c47
Manchester Piccadilly [10]	d	17 11												17 50											18c11
Bolton	d	17 30												18 10											18c32
Wigan North Western	a								17 54		18 00		←			18 17		18 28						18 51	19 02
	d								17 54		18 02		17 54			18 17		18 28						18 51	19 03
Preston [8]	a	17 53							→		18 15		18 17	18 34		18 39	18 39	18 54						→	19 15
Blackpool North	a										19e00		18 48					19 23							
	d	17 19									17 38														18 38
Preston [8]	d	17 58									18 18			18 38			18 40								19 18
Lancaster [6]	a	18 13									18 31			18 54			18 58								19 33
	d	18 14						18 22			18 33			18 55			19 00								19 34
Barrow-in-Furness	a													19 59											20 44
Oxenholme Lake District	a	18 28						18 43			18 47	←					19 13								19 46
	d	18 28						18 52			18 49	18 52					19 14								19 48
Windermere	a							→				19 13													20 18
Penrith North Lakes	d	18 53									19 13														20 12
Carlisle [8]	a	19 11									19 31						19 54								20 29
	d	19 13									19 32						19 56								20 30
Lockerbie	d	19 32																							20 52
Carstairs	a																								
Motherwell	a										20s30														
Glasgow Central [15]	a	20 31									20 57						21 11								
Haymarket	a																								21s47
Edinburgh [10]	a																								21 56
Perth	a																22f37								
Dundee	a																23f00								
Aberdeen	a																00f16								
Inverness	a																								

For general notes see front of timetable
For details of catering facilities see Directory of Train Operators

A From Reading (Table 51)
B ⌶ to Preston
C From Plymouth (Table 51)
b Change at Crewe and Chester
c Change at Preston
e From 6 October arr. 2 minutes later
f Via Glasgow Central and Glasgow Queen Street. Passengers make their own way from one station to the other

OVERNIGHT SLEEPERS. For Sleeper trains, operated by First ScotRail, please refer to Tables 400 - 404

London and West Midlands → North West England and Scotland

Route Diagram - see first page of Table 65

	NT	XC	VT		LM	XC	VT	VT	VT	VT	VT	TP	VT	VT	LM	VT	NT	VT	NT	VT		TP	VT	LM
		R				R																		
		1	1 ◇		1 ◇	1	1 ◇	1 ◇	1 ◇	1 ◇	1 ◇	1 ◇	1 ◇	1 ◇	1 ◇	1 ◇		1 ◇		1 ◇		1 ◇	1 ◇	1 ◇
		A				B	C		D															
		🍴	🍴		⊤	🍴	🍴	🍴	🍴	⊠	🍴	⊤	⊠	⊠	⊤	⊠		⊠		🍴			⊠	⊤
London Euston 15 ⊖ d			16 49				17 02	17 05	17 10	17 15			17 17	17 21		17 35		17 45					17 48	
Gatwick Airport 10 ✈ d						14 51																		
Watford Junction d								17u20																
Milton Keynes Central d			17u20																				18u03	
Northampton d																								
Rugby d							17 55							18 10				18 34						
Nuneaton d														18 24										
Tamworth Low Level d													18 24											
Lichfield Trent Valley d			18 03																				19 01	
Coventry d		17 23					18 09		18 14						*17 44*									
Birmingham International ✈ d		17 34					18 21		18 28						*17 58*									
Birmingham New Street 12 a		17 45				18 18	18 32		18 39											←				
d		17 48			17 51	18 18	18 43		18 43		18 03				18 21					18 43				18 51
Sandwell & Dudley d					17 59		→		→											18 53				18 59
Coseley d															18 34									
Wolverhampton 7 d		18 06			18 10	18 39					18 21				18 44					19 06				19 10
Penkridge d					18 20										18 54									
Stafford a		18 17			18 26									18 50	19 01			19 10		19 21				19 24
d		18 18			18 27									18 50	19 03			19 10		19 27				19 25
Stoke-on-Trent a		18 36				19 12		18 41								19 06				→				
Congleton a																								
Macclesfield a		18 52				19 31		18 57								19 22								
Crewe 10 a			18 41		18 48						18 54		19 07	19 11	19 29								19 34	19 46
d			18 42		18 49						18 56		19 08	19 22	19 31								19 35	19 48
Chester a					*19 25*									19 49										
Llandudno Junction a														20 44										
Llandudno a														*21 12*										
Bangor (Gwynedd) a														21 03										
Holyhead a														21 40										
Wilmslow a			18 58		*19 26*									*19b44*									19 51	*20 26*
Manchester Airport ✈ a			*20 02*											*20c02*										
Stockport a		19 05	19s09		*19 39*	19 46		19s12						*19b53*		19s36							20s02	*20 39*
Manchester Piccadilly 10 a		19 20	19 21		*19 57*	20 02		19 24						*20b14*		19 50							20 14	*20 54*
Hartford a															19 44									
Warrington Bank Quay a										19 09	19 12							19 45						
d										19 09	19 13							19 47						
Runcorn a					19 05								19 25		19 53									20 05
Liverpool South Parkway 7 ✈ a															20 01									
Liverpool Lime Street 10 a					19 29								19 45		20 18									20 31
d																	19 04							
Manchester Airport ✈ d										*17e52*		18 27						*18f47*				19 27		
Manchester Piccadilly 10 d										*18f31*		18 45						*19f11*				19 44		
Bolton d										*18f51*		19 12						*19f32*				20 04		
Wigan North Western a	←									19 20	19 23						19 51	19 56	←					
d	18 51									19 20	19 24						19 51	19 58	19 51					
Preston 8 a	19 17									19 37	19 42	19 44					→	20 13	20 17			20 26		
Blackpool North a	*19 57*										*20 36*								*20 56*					
d											*19 10*	19g18						*19 25*				*19 42*		
Preston 8 d										19 40	19 45	19 50						20 16				20 27		
Lancaster 6 a											19 59	20 05						20 32				20 44		
d											20 00	20 06										20 51		
Barrow-in-Furness a																						21 56		
Oxenholme Lake District a											20 13	20 20												
d											20 15	20 21												
Windermere a																								
Penrith North Lakes d											20 40	20 46												
Carlisle 8 a										20 39	20 58	21 03												
d										20 40	20 59	21 05												
Lockerbie d												21 24												
Carstairs a																								
Motherwell a																								
Glasgow Central 15 a										21 55		22 31												
Haymarket a											22s13													
Edinburgh 10 a											22 24													
Perth a										*00h15*														
Dundee a											*00j05*													
Aberdeen a																								
Inverness a																								

For general notes see front of timetable
For details of catering facilities see Directory of Train Operators

- **A** From Bournemouth (Table 51)
- **B** From Brighton (Table 51)
- **C** 28 July to 22 August
- **D** Until 25 July and from 25 August
- **b** Change at Crewe
- **c** Change at Crewe and Wilmslow
- **e** Change at Manchester Piccadilly and Preston
- **f** Change at Preston
- **g** Until 12 September only
- **h** Via Glasgow Central and Glasgow Queen Street. Passengers make their own way from one station to the other
- **j** Change at Haymarket

OVERNIGHT SLEEPERS. For Sleeper trains, operated by First ScotRail, please refer to Tables 400 - 404

London and West Midlands → North West England and Scotland

Route Diagram - see first page of Table 65

		VT	VT	VT	VT	VT	XC	VT	VT	LM	VT	NT	XC	VT	VT	VT		XC	LM	VT	XC	VT	TP	NT	VT
								FO																	
				R			R				R		R												
		1 ◇	1 ◇	1	1 ◇	1 ◇	1	1 ◇	1 ◇	1 ◇	1		1	1 ◇	1 ◇	1 ◇		1 ◇	1 ◇	1 ◇	1 ◇	1 ◇	1 ◇		1 ◇
							A						B					C			D				
		⊏P	☒	☒	⊏P	☒	⊏P	⊏P	☒	⊤o	⊏P		⊏P	⊏P	⊏P	⊏P			⊤o	⊏P		⊏P			⊏P
London Euston 15 ⊖	d		18 05	18 08		18 17		18 20	18 35		18 45			19 05	19 17	19 35				19 38		19 46			20 05
Gatwick Airport 10 ✈	d																								
Watford Junction	d										19u00				19u32										
Milton Keynes Central	d					18u49																20 18			20 36
Northampton	d																								
Rugby	d			18 56																		20 41			
Nuneaton	d		19 05												20 21							21 00			
Tamworth Low Level	d										19 56														
Lichfield Trent Valley	d																			20 49					
Coventry	d				18 23		18 34						19 23					19 32	19 44		20 02				
Birmingham International ✈	d				18 34		18 46						19 34					19 50	19 58		20 20				
Birmingham New Street 12	a												19 45												
	d				19 03		19 18			19 21			20 03					20 18	20 21		20 48				
Sandwell & Dudley	d																								
Coseley	d									19 34									20 34						
Wolverhampton 7	d				19 21		19 39			19 44			20 21					20 39	20 44		21 11				
Penkridge	d									19 54									20 54						
Stafford	a	←			19 36	19 45		19 51		20 01			20 34			20 57			21 01		21 23				
	d	19 27			19 36	19 45		19 52		20 01			20 34			20 57			21 01		21 24				
Stoke-on-Trent	a	19 45	19 39				20 12		20 06					20 40				21 12			21 45				21 40
Congleton	a						20 24																		
Macclesfield	a	20 01	19 57				20 32		20 23					20 57				21 31			22 02				21 57
Crewe 10	a			19 52	19 58	20 07		20 14		20 22	20 32		20 54		21 03				21 23	21 29		21 37			
	d			19 54	19 59	20 08		20 16		20 24	20 32		20 56		21 04				21 24	21 29		21 38			
Chester	a			20 27						20 57	21 27									21 49		22 11			
Llandudno Junction	a			21b28											22 39					22 39					
Llandudno	a			21c43																					
Bangor (Gwynedd)	a			21b51											22 55					22 55					
Holyhead	a			22b35											23 30					23 30					
Wilmslow	a							20 32					21 15		21 44	21 31						22 26			
Manchester Airport ✈	a							21 02							22e07	22 07						23e02			
Stockport	a	20 16	20s12				20 46	20s44	20s36				21 25	21s12	21 53	21s42		21 46			22 15	22 39			22s12
Manchester Piccadilly 10	a	20 35	20 20				21 02	21 04	20 51				21 39	21 24	22 12	21 54		22 02			22 32	22 52			22 24
Hartford	a									20 35									21 36						
Warrington Bank Quay	a				20 16						20 50											21 56			
	d				20 17						20 51											21 57			
Runcorn	a					20 25				20 45					21 21				21 45						
Liverpool South Parkway 7 ✈	a									20 53									21 53						
Liverpool Lime Street 10	a					20 47				21 09					21 45				22 09						
	d										19 48											20 48		21 48	
Manchester Airport ✈	d										19f47											20f47	21 27		
Manchester Piccadilly 10	d										20f11											21f11	21 43		
Bolton	d										20f32											21f32	22 02		
Wigan North Western	a				20 27						21 01											22 07		22 37	
	d				20 29						21 02											22 08		22 38	
Preston 8	a			20 32	20 42						21 15											22 21	22 32	23 02	
Blackpool North	a				21 36						21 56													23 28	
	d										20 28	20 52											22 03		
Preston 8	d			20 35	20 45						21 19	21 29										22 24	22 34		
Lancaster 6	a				21 00						21 34	21 49										22 38	22 49		
	d				21 01						21 36	21 49										22 39	22 50		
Barrow-in-Furness	a											22 54											23 54		
Oxenholme Lake District	a			20 59	21 14						21 48											22 51			
	d			21 00	21 16						21 49											22 53			
Windermere	a			21 24							22 12														
Penrith North Lakes	d			21 25	21 42						22 14											23 22			
Carlisle 8	a			21 43	21 58						22 37											23 45			
	d			21 43	22 00																				
Lockerbie	d				22 18																				
Carstairs	a																								
Motherwell	a			22s49	23s04																				
Glasgow Central 15	a			23 04	23 33																				
Haymarket	a																								
Edinburgh 10	a																								
Perth	a			01g20																					
Dundee	a																								
Aberdeen	a																								
Inverness	a																								

For general notes see front of timetable
For details of catering facilities see Directory of Train Operators

A From Plymouth (Table 51)

B From Bournemouth (Table 51). ⊏P to Birmingham New Street

C From Guildford (Table 51)

D All Fridays, also Mondays to Thursdays until 4 September. From Bristol Temple Meads (Table 51)

b Change at Crewe and Chester

c Change at Crewe, Chester and Llandudno Junction

e Change at Crewe and Wilmslow

f Change at Preston

g Via Glasgow Central and Glasgow Queen Street. Passengers make their own way from one station to the other

OVERNIGHT SLEEPERS. For Sleeper trains, operated by First ScotRail, please refer to Tables 400 - 404

London and West Midlands → North West England and Scotland

Route Diagram - see first page of Table 65

		VT	VT	XC	LM	VT	NT	VT	VT	XC	SR		AW	LM	VT	SR	SR	SR	SR
																FO	FO	FO	FX
											R					R	R	R	R
		1 ◇	1 ◇	1 ◇	1 ◇	1 ◇		1 ◇	1 ◇	1 ◇			◇	1 ◇	1 ◇				
				A						B	C					D	E	G	
London Euston 15	d		20 17			20 46		21 05	21 10		21 15				22 05	23 00	23 20	23 45	23 45
Gatwick Airport 10	d																		
Watford Junction	d					21u01		21u20	21u25		21u33				22u20	23u19	23u39	00u04	00u04
Milton Keynes Central	d		20 48												22 40				
Northampton	d																		
Rugby	d					21 38									23 21				
Nuneaton	d		21 22						22 15						23 33				
Tamworth Low Level	d														23 44				
Lichfield Trent Valley	d					22 02													
Coventry	d	20 23			20 45					21 23			21 44	22 23					
Birmingham International	d	20 34			20 58					21 34			21 58	22 34					
Birmingham New Street 12	a									21 45									
	d	21 03		21 18	21 21					22 18			22 33	23 07					
Sandwell & Dudley	d													23 18					
Coseley	d				21 34									23 27					
Wolverhampton 7	d	21 21		21 39	21 44					22 39			22 48	23 34					
Penkridge	d				21 54									23 43					
Stafford	a	21 36	21 47	21 53	22 01				22 41	22 53				23 50	00s04				
	d	21 36	21 47	21 54	22 01				22 41	22 54				23 51					
Stoke-on-Trent	a			22 12				22 44		23s12									
Congleton	a			22 24															
Macclesfield	a			22 32				23 00											
Crewe 10	a	21 58	22 07		22 22	22 35			23 01				00 01	00 21	00s32				
	d	21 59	22 08		22 24	22 36			23 02		23u45		00 02						
Chester	a		22 40			23 09			23 35				00 26						
Llandudno Junction	a		23b38										01 25						
Llandudno	a																		
Bangor (Gwynedd)	a		00b01										01 42						
Holyhead	a		00b47										02 15						
Wilmslow	a					23 23													
Manchester Airport	a														01 21				
Stockport	a			22 46		23 33		23s15							00s58				
Manchester Piccadilly 10	a			23 02		23 49		23 29		00 07					01 10				
Hartford	a				22 35														
Warrington Bank Quay	a	22 17				22 53													
	d	22 17				22 54													
Runcorn	a		22 25		22 45				23 19										
Liverpool South Parkway 7	a				22 54														
Liverpool Lime Street 10	a		22 47		23 12				23 47										
	d						23 05												
Manchester Airport	d										22 47								
Manchester Piccadilly 10	d										23 11								
Bolton	d										23 32								
Wigan North Western	a	22 43				23 04	23 51												
	d	22 44				23 04	23 51												
Preston 8	a	23 04				23 24	00 15												
Blackpool North	a																		
	d										23 13								
Preston 8	d										00u44								
Lancaster 6	a																		
	d																		
Barrow-in-Furness	a																		
Oxenholme Lake District	a																		
	d																		
Windermere	a																		
Penrith North Lakes	d																		
Carlisle 8	a															04s27	04s36	04s36	05s03
	d																		
Lockerbie	d																		
Carstairs	a															05s32	05s43	05s43	06s24
Motherwell	a															06s10	06s24	06s24	06s58
Glasgow Central 15	a															06 30	06 43	06 43	07 17
Haymarket	a																		
Edinburgh 10	a															06 40	06 40	06 40	07 16
Perth	a										05s44					08c05	08c37	08c37	09c36
Dundee	a										06s08					08 25	08 25	08 25	09 22
Aberdeen	a										07 37					09 40	09 40	09 40	10 35
Inverness	a										08 30					10c26	11 59	11 59	11 59

For general notes see front of timetable
For details of catering facilities see Directory of Train Operators

A From Plymouth (Table 51)
B From Bournemouth (Table 51)
C Also conveys portion to Fort William (Table 227)
D From 12 September
E Until 11 July
G 18 July to 5 September
b Change at Crewe and Chester
c Via Glasgow Central and Glasgow Queen Street. Passengers make their own way from one station to the other

OVERNIGHT SLEEPERS. For Sleeper trains, operated by First ScotRail, please refer to Tables 400 - 404

Table 65

Saturdays

until 12 July

London and West Midlands → North West England and Scotland

Route Diagram - see first page of Table 65

		SR	TP	VT	VT	VT	TP	LM	NT	TP	XC	LM	VT	NT	VT	XC	LM	XC	VT	TP	VT	NT	TP	VT	VT
			1 ◇	1 ◇	1 ◇	1 ◇	1 ◇	1 ◇		1 ◇	1 ◇	1 ◇	1 ◇		1 ◇	1 ◇	1 ◇	1 ◇	1 ◇	1 ◇	1 ◇		1 ◇	1 ◇	1 ◇
			A											B						C			C		
				☕		☕				🛒	☕		☕		☕	☕		☕	☕	🛒	☕		🛒	☕	☕
London Euston 15 ⊖	d														06 00				06 16					06 20	06 40
Gatwick Airport 10 ✈	d																								
Watford Junction	d																							06u35	07u01
Milton Keynes Central	d														06 46				07 00						07 32
Northampton	d																								
Rugby	d																		07 41						
Nuneaton	d																								08 23
Tamworth Low Level	d																								
Lichfield Trent Valley	d																								
Coventry	d												06 04			06 32		07 04							
Birmingham International ✈	d												06 20			06 50		07 20							
Birmingham New Street 12	a																								
	d				05 20	05 30		06 07			06 20		07 03			07 20	07 21	07 48			08 03				
Sandwell & Dudley	d							06 18																	
Coseley	d							06 27									07 34								
Wolverhampton 7	d				05 38	05 49		06 33			06 40		07 21			07 40	07 44	08 06			08 21				
Penkridge	d							06 43									07 53								
Stafford	a				05 51	06 04		06 50			06 52	←	07 33			07 52	08 01	08 17							08 48
	d				05 52	06 05		07 00			06 54	07 00	07 33			07 54	08 02	08 18							08 48
Stoke-on-Trent	a							↦			07 12				08 06	08 12		08 41						08 33	
Congleton	a										07 24					08 24									
Macclesfield	a										07 33				08 22	08 33		08 58						08 49	
Crewe 10	a				06 16	06 25						07 22	07 54				08 23		08 32		08 54				09 10
	d				06 18	06 28						07 22	07 55				08 24		08 35		08 55				09 11
Chester	a				06 37	07 03						07 57					08 57		09 26						
Llandudno Junction	a				07 33	08 20						09b19					10b17		10 24						
Llandudno	a				08 16							09b37					10b37								
Bangor (Gwynedd)	a				07 49	08 43						09b43							10 46						
Holyhead	a				08 21	09 30						10b20							11 30						
Wilmslow	a					07 01						07 59	08 48				09 01		09 26						09 48
Manchester Airport ✈	a											08 14					09 12								
Stockport	a				06c53	07 14					07 46	08 13			08s36	08 46		09 11	09 39					09s04	
Manchester Piccadilly 10	a				07c11	07 28					08 02	08e29			08 50	09 02		09 27	09 54					09 17	
Hartford	a											07 34					08 36								
Warrington Bank Quay	a					06 43							08 12						08 50		09 11				
	d					06 45							08 13						08 52		09 12				
Runcorn	a											07 46					08 46								09 27
Liverpool South Parkway 7 ✈	a											07 54					08 56								
Liverpool Lime Street 10	a											08 10					09 10								09 50
	d					06 04			07 30										08 04			08 57			
Manchester Airport ✈	d			04 34		05f47	06 19			07 22									07f47	08 27			08 47		
Manchester Piccadilly 10	d			05 10		06f05	06 44			07 45									08f11	08 45			09 11		
Bolton	d					06f26	07 03			08 04									08f32	09 05			09 32		
Wigan North Western	a					07 02			08 01				08 23						09 01		09 22	09 30			
	d					07 04			08 02				08 24						09 03		09 23	09 31			
Preston 8	a			06 01		07 17	07 26		08 24	08 27			08 39						09 16	09 29	09 38	09 54	10 01		
Blackpool North	a					07 56			08 51				09 32						09 57			10 21			
	d			05 30		06 34				07 41				08 09					08 41				09 30		
Preston 8	d			06 03		07 20	07 29			08 28			08 40	08 46					09 19	09 32	09 39		10 06		
Lancaster 6	a			06 17		07 33	07 44			08 44			08 59	09 07					09 32	09 48	09 53		10 23		
	d		05 50	06 18		07 35	07 45			08 44			09 01						09 34	09 48	09 55		10 23		
Barrow-in-Furness	a						08 49			09 54										10 53					
Oxenholme Lake District	a		06 04	06 32		07 47				08 58			09 16						09 46		10 08		10 43		
	d		06 04	06 33		07 49				08 59			09 17						09 47		10 09		10 43		
Windermere	a		06 25	07 19		08 15				09 22									10 13				11 01		
Penrith North Lakes	d			06 58		08 13				09 24			09 42						10 12		10 34				
Carlisle 8	a			07 18		08 31				09 41			10 00						10 30		10 52				
	d	06 09		07 21		08 34				09 43			10 03						10 30		10 53				
Lockerbie	d			07 41		08 52							10 21								11 12				
Carstairs	a			08 15																					
Motherwell	a			08s30		09s33							11s03						11s30						
Glasgow Central 15	a	08 37		09 00		09 59							11 27						12 00						
Haymarket	a									11s04											12s08				
Edinburgh 10	a									11 11											12 19				
Perth	a			10g37		11g37				12 56									13g37		14 54				
Dundee	a			11g00		12g00				12h21											13h24				
Aberdeen	a			12g18		13g14				13h36											14h36				
Inverness	a			13g35						15 18											17 07				

For general notes see front of timetable
For details of catering facilities see Directory of Train Operators

A From Barrow-in-Furness (Table 82)
B From Clitheroe (Table 94) to Morecambe (Table 98)
C 🛒 to Preston
b Change at Crewe and Chester
c Change at Crewe
e Change at Crewe and Stockport
f Change at Preston
g Via Glasgow Central and Glasgow Queen Street. Passengers make their own way from one station to the other
h Change at Haymarket

Table 65

Saturdays

London and West Midlands → North West England and Scotland

until 12 July

Route Diagram - see first page of Table 65

		VT	XC	LM	VT	TP	VT	XC	VT	VT		NT	VT	VT	TP	NT	XC	LM	VT	TP	XC	VT	NT	TP	VT
		1◇	1◇	1◇	1◇	1◇	1◇	1◇	1◇	1◇			1◇	1◇	1◇		1◇	1◇	1◇	1◇	1◇	1◇		1◇	1◇
			A														B			C	D				
		🛒	🛒		🛒	☕	🛒	🛒	🛒	🛒			🛒	🛒	☕		🛒		🛒	☕	🛒	🛒			🛒
London Euston 15 ⊖	d	07 04			07 24		07 36			07 42			07 55	08 03											08 28
Gatwick Airport 10 ✈	d		05 15																						
Watford Junction	d				07u40								08u11												08u43
Milton Keynes Central	d						08 14			08 19															
Northampton	d																								
Rugby	d				08 43					08 58															
Nuneaton	d												09 24												
Tamworth Low Level	d																								
Lichfield Trent Valley	d																		←						
Coventry	d		07 32	07 44				08 00	08 23	09 10								08 44	09 10		09 23				
Birmingham International ✈	d		07 50	07 58				08 16	08 34	→							08 50	08 58	09 22		09 34				
Birmingham New Street 12	a		08 18																09 36		09 45				
	d		08 20	08 21				08 48	09 03								09 20	09 21	09 40		09 48	10 03			
Sandwell & Dudley	d																		09 52						
Coseley	d			08 34														09 34							
Wolverhampton 7	d		08 40	08 44				09 08	09 21								09 40	09 44			10 08	10 21			
Penkridge	d			08 53														09 53							
Stafford	a		08 52	09 01	09 19			09 22					09 49				09 52	10 01	10 17		10 22				
	d		08 54	09 02	09 20			09 22					09 49				09 54	10 02	10 19		10 23				
Stoke-on-Trent	a	09 05	09 12				09 34	09 41						10 03			10 12				10 41				11 05
Congleton	a		09 24																						
Macclesfield	a		09 33				09 50	09 57									10 32				10 57				11 21
Crewe 10	a			09 23	09 40				09 54				10 10					10 22	10 38			10 54			
	d			09 24	09 40				09 55				10 11					10 24	10 41			10 55			
Chester	a			09 57	10 27													10 57	11 07						
Llandudno Junction	a			11b17	11b26														11 51						
Llandudno	a			11b35															12c35						
Bangor (Gwynedd)	a				11b43														12 08						
Holyhead	a				12b20														12 45						
Wilmslow	a			10 01	10 26								10 48					11 01	11 26			11 48			
Manchester Airport ✈	a			10 11														11 11							
Stockport	a	09s33	09 46				10s05	10 11						10s33			10 46				11 11				11s34
Manchester Piccadilly 10	a	09 46	10 02				10 18	10 27						10 44			11 02				11 27				11 48
Hartford	a			09 36														10 33							
Warrington Bank Quay	a				09 58				10 12										10 57			11 11			
	d				09 59				10 13										10 58			11 13			
Runcorn	a			09 45									10 28					10 45							
Liverpool South Parkway 7 ✈	a			09 54														10 54							
Liverpool Lime Street 10	a			10 09									10 50					11 09							
	d				09 04							09 57							10 04				10 57		
Manchester Airport ✈	d					09 27													10e07	10 27				10 47	
Manchester Piccadilly 10	d					09 45										10f13			10e23	10 45				11 11	
Bolton	d					10 05													10g51	11 05				11 32	
Wigan North Western	a				10 09				10 23			10 31				10 48			11 08			11 22	11 30		
	d				10 10				10 24			10 31				10 48			11 09			11 24	11 30		
Preston 8	a				10 23	10 27			10 38			10 55				11 14			11 22	11 27		11 37	11 53		
Blackpool North	a				11 03							11 22				11 44			12 01			12 14	12 20		
	d				09 40														10 41					11 41	
Preston 8	d				10 26	10 29			10 40										11 25	11 29		11 40		12 19	
Lancaster 6	a				10 42	10 47													11 40	11 44		11 54		12 34	
	d					10 48													11 41	11 45		11 55		12 35	
Barrow-in-Furness	a					11 56														12 49					
Oxenholme Lake District	a					11 06			11 11										11 53					12 50	
	d					11 06			11 12										11 55					12 59	
Windermere	a														←				12 17					→	
Penrith North Lakes	d					11 34									11 34				12 19			12 33			
Carlisle 8	a					→			11 50						11 52				12 37			12 49			
	d								11 52						11 54				12 40			12 50			
Lockerbie	d														12 14							13 09			
Carstairs	a																								
Motherwell	a														13s00										
Glasgow Central 15	a								13 16						13 18				13 59						
Haymarket	a																					14s04			
Edinburgh 10	a																					14 14			
Perth	a																		15h37						
Dundee	a																					15j21			
Aberdeen	a																					16j37			
Inverness	a																								

For general notes see front of timetable
For details of catering facilities see Directory of Train Operators

A 🛒 from Reading
B From Bristol Temple Meads (Table 51)
C ☕ to Preston
D From Bournemouth (Table 51)
b Change at Crewe and Chester
c Change at Crewe and Llandudno Junction
e Change at Bolton and Preston
f Manchester Victoria
g Change at Preston
h Via Glasgow Central and Glasgow Queen Street. Passengers make their own way from one station to the other
j Change at Haymarket

Table 65

Saturdays

until 12 July

London and West Midlands → North West England and Scotland

Route Diagram - see first page of Table 65

Station		XC	LM	XC	VT	TP	TP	XC	VT	VT	NT	VT	VT	XC	LM	VT	TP	VT	XC	VT		VT	NT	VT	TP
		1 ◇	1 ◇	1 ◇	1 ◇	1 ◇	1 ◇	1 ◇	1 ◇	R 1		1 ◇	1 ◇	1 ◇	1 ◇	1 ◇	1 ◇	1 ◇	R 1	1 ◇		1 ◇		1 ◇	1 ◇
		A												B			C		D						C
		☕		☕	☕		🛒	☕	☕	☕		☕	☕	☕		☕	🛒	☕	☕	☕		☕		☕	🛒
London Euston 15 ⊖	d				08 32				08 37			08 57	09 31			09 34		09 37						09 55	
Gatwick Airport 10 ✈	d																								
Watford Junction	d				08u48				08u52									09u52						10u10	
Milton Keynes Central	d											09 31	10 07			10 14									
Northampton	d																								
Rugby	d				09 58							10 12				10 57								11 12	
Nuneaton	d																								
Tamworth Low Level	d																								
Lichfield Trent Valley	d																								
Coventry	d	09 32			10 10				10 16	10 23		10 27		10 32	10 44	11 10		11 16	11 23					11 27	
Birmingham International ✈	d	09 50		10 12	10 22				10 28	10 34		10 39		10 50	10 58	11 22		11 28	11 34	←				11 39	
Birmingham New Street 12	a			10 30	10 36			←	10s39							11 36		11s39	11 45	11s39					
	d	10 20	10 21	10 48	10 40			10 48		11 03				11 20	11 21	11 40		→	11 48			12 03			
Sandwell & Dudley	d			→	10 52											11 52									
Coseley	d		10 34												11 34										
Wolverhampton 7	d	10 40	10 44					11 08		11 21				11 40	11 44				12 08			12 21			
Penkridge	d		10 53												11 53										
Stafford	a	10 52	11 01		11 17			11 22						11 52	12 01	12 17			12 22						
	d	10 54	11 02		11 19			11 23						11 54	12 02	12 19			12 23						
Stoke-on-Trent	a	11 12						11 41	11 48				12 05	12 12					12 41	12 48					
Congleton	a	11 24																							
Macclesfield	a	11 33						11 57					12 21	12 32					12 57						
Crewe 10	a		11 23		11 38					11 54		11 59			12 23	12 38						12 54		12 58	
	d		11 24		11 41					11 55		12 01			12 24	12 41						12 55		13 01	
Chester	a		11 59		12 27										12 59	13 27								13 45	
Llandudno Junction	a		13b17		13b24										14b09	14 28								14 36	
Llandudno	a		13b35												14b27									14 47	
Bangor (Gwynedd)	a				13b48											14 45									
Holyhead	a				14b30											15 19									
Wilmslow	a		12 01		12 26							12 48			13 01	13 26								13 48	
Manchester Airport ✈	a		12 11												13 11										
Stockport	a	11 46						12 11	12s20			12 58	12s34	12 46					13 11	13s20					
Manchester Piccadilly 10	a	12 02						12 27	12 34			13 13	12 48	13 02					13 27	13 34					
Hartford	a		11 36												12 34										
Warrington Bank Quay	a				11 57					12 13						12 56						13 11			
	d				11 58					12 13						12 58						13 12			
Runcorn	a		11 45									12 17			12 46									13 17	
Liverpool South Parkway 7 ✈	a		11 54												12 54										
Liverpool Lime Street 10	a		12 09									12 40			13 09									13 40	
	d				11 04						11 57					12 04							12 57		
Manchester Airport ✈	d						11 27									11c47	12 27								12 47
Manchester Piccadilly 10	d						11 45									12c11	12 45								13 11
Bolton	d						12 05									12c32	13 05								13 32
Wigan North Western	a				12 08					12 24	12 31					13 07						13 22	13 31		
	d				12 09					12 25	12 31					13 09						13 23	13 31		
Preston 8	a				12 22		12 27			12 39	12 56					13 24	13 27					13 36	13 54		14 04
Blackpool North	a				13 01						13 21					14 00							14 21		
	d															12 41									13 30
Preston 8	d				12 25		12 29			12 41						13 25	13 29					13 38			14 09
Lancaster 6	a				12 39		12 44			12 55						13 39	13 49					13 55			14 24
	d				12 40		12 45			12 56							13 49					13 56			14 25
Barrow-in-Furness	a																14 47					15 23			
Oxenholme Lake District	a				12 54	←	12 59															14 10			14 42
	d				12 56	12 59	12 59															14 11			14 43
Windermere	a					13 20	14 14																		15 01
Penrith North Lakes	d				13 20					13 34															
Carlisle 8	a				13 38		13 43			13 52												14 50			
	d				13 41		13 45			13 55												14 52			
Lockerbie	d						14 05			14 13												15 10			
Carstairs	a																								
Motherwell	a																								
Glasgow Central 15	a				14 58					15 17															
Haymarket	a						15s04															16s09			
Edinburgh 10	a						15 11															16 19			
Perth	a				16e37					17e20												17 55			
Dundee	a				17e00		17 26															17 44			
Aberdeen	a				18e15		18 44															19 00			
Inverness	a									19e34												20 08			

For general notes see front of timetable
For details of catering facilities see Directory of Train Operators

A From Reading (Table 51)
B From Plymouth (Table 51)
C 🛒 to Preston
D From Bournemouth (Table 51)
b Change at Crewe and Chester
c Change at Preston
e Via Glasgow Central and Glasgow Queen Street. Passengers make their own way from one station to the other

Saturdays

until 12 July

London and West Midlands → North West England and Scotland

Route Diagram - see first page of Table 65

		VT	XC	LM	XC	VT	TP	XC	VT	VT	NT	VT	VT	XC	LM	VT	TP	XC	VT	VT	NT	VT	VT	XC	LM
										R										R					
		1 ◇	1 ◇	1 ◇	1 ◇	1 ◇	1 ◇	1 ◇	1 ◇	1		1 ◇	1 ◇	1 ◇	1 ◇	1 ◇	1 ◇	1 ◇	1 ◇	1		1 ◇	1 ◇	1 ◇	1 ◇
			A											B			C	D						A	
		☕	☕		☕	☕	🛒	☕	☕	☕		☕	☕	☕		☕	🛒	☕	☕	☕		☕	☕	☕	
London Euston 15 ⊖	d	10 29				10 33			10 38			10 57	11 29			11 33			11 38			11 55	12 29		
Gatwick Airport 10 ✈	d																								
Watford Junction	d	10u44				10u48			10u53										11u53			12u10	12u44		
Milton Keynes Central	d											11 32	12 10			12 16									
Northampton	d																								
Rugby	d					11 58						12 12				12 57						13 12			
Nuneaton	d																								
Tamworth Low Level	d																								
Lichfield Trent Valley	d																								
Coventry	d		*11 32*			12 10			12 16			12u27		*12 32*	*12 46*	13 10			13 16			13 27		*13 32*	*13 42*
Birmingham International ✈	d		*11 50*		12 12	12 22			12 28			12 39		*12 50*	*12 58*	13 22			13 28			13 39		*13 50*	*13 57*
Birmingham New Street 12	a				12 30	12 36		←	12s39							13 36			13s39						
	d		12 20	12 21	12 48	12 40		12 48		13 03				13 20	13 21	13 40		13 48		14 03				14 20	14 21
Sandwell & Dudley	d				→	12 52										13 52									
Coseley	d			12 34											13 34										14 34
Wolverhampton 7	d		12 40	12 44				13 08		13 21				13 40	13 44			14 08		14 21				14 40	14 44
Penkridge	d			12 53											13 53										14 53
Stafford	a		12 52	13 01		13 17		13 22						13 52	14 01	14 18		14 22						14 52	15 01
	d		12 54	13 02		13 19		13 23						13 54	14 02	14 19		14 23						14 54	15 02
Stoke-on-Trent	a	13 05	13 12					13 41	13 48				14 05	14 12				14 41	14 48				15 05	15 12	
Congleton	a		13 24																					15 24	
Macclesfield	a	13 21	13 33					13 57					14 21	14 32				14 57					15 21	15 33	
Crewe 10	a			13 23		13 38				13 54		13 58			14 23	14 39				14 54		14 58			15 23
	d			13 24		13 41				13 55		14 01			14 24	14 41				14 55		15 01			15 24
Chester	a			*13 59*		*14 27*									*14 57*	*15 26*									*15 57*
Llandudno Junction	a			*15b18*		*15b25*									*16b17*	*16 24*									*17b17*
Llandudno	a			*15b36*		*16c01*									*16b35*										*17b35*
Bangor (Gwynedd)	a					*15b47*										*16 46*									
Holyhead	a					*16b30*										*17 20*									
Wilmslow	a			*14 01*		*14 26*						*14 48*			*15 01*	*15 26*						*15 48*			*16 01*
Manchester Airport ✈	a			*14 11*											*15 11*										*16 11*
Stockport	a	13s34	13 46					14 11	14s20				14s34	14 46				15 11	15s20				15s34	15 46	
Manchester Piccadilly 10	a	13 48	14 02					14 27	14 34				14 48	15 02				15 27	15 34				15 48	16 02	
Hartford	a			13 36											14 36										15 36
Warrington Bank Quay	a					13 57				14 12						14 57				15 12					
	d					13 58				14 13						14 58				15 13					
Runcorn	a			13 45								14 17			14 45							15 17			15 46
Liverpool South Parkway 7 ✈	a			13 54											14 54										15 54
Liverpool Lime Street 10	a			14 09								14 37			15 09							15 37			16 09
	d					*13 04*					13 57					*14 04*					14 57				
Manchester Airport ✈	d						13 27									*13e47*	14 27								
Manchester Piccadilly 10	d						13 45									*14e11*	14 45								
Bolton	d						14 05									*14e32*	15 05								
Wigan North Western	a					14 08				14 23	14 31					15 08				15 23	15 31				
	d					14 09				14 24	14 31					15 09				15 24	15 31				
Preston 8	a					14 23	14 27			14 39	14 54					15 22	15 27			15 39	15 54				
Blackpool North	a					*15 01*					15 21					*16 01*					16 21				
	d					*13 41*										*14 41*									
Preston 8	d					14 26	14 29			14 40						15 25	15 30			15 40					
Lancaster 6	a					14 39	14 44			14 54						15 39	15 45			15 54					
	d					14 41	14 45			14 56						15 40	15 50			15 56					
Barrow-in-Furness	a																16 53			*17 17*					
Oxenholme Lake District	a					14 53	14 59			15 09						15 52									
	d					14 54	14 59			15 10						15 54									
Windermere	a															*16 17*									
Penrith North Lakes	d					15 19	15 25			15 37						16 18				16 33					
Carlisle 8	a					15 37	15 43			15 54						16 36				16 49					
	d					15 39	15 43			15 55						16 39				16 53					
Lockerbie	d						16 02																		
Carstairs	a																								
Motherwell	a					16s34				16s53						17s34									
Glasgow Central 15	a					16 58				17 18						17 57									
Haymarket	a						17s08													18s05					
Edinburgh 10	a						17 14													18 15					
Perth	a					*18f41*	*18 54*			*19f19*						*19f43*									
Dundee	a						*18g49*													*19g27*					
Aberdeen	a						*20h27*													*20g41*					
Inverness	a						*20 58*																		

For general notes see front of timetable
For details of catering facilities see Directory of Train Operators

A From Reading (Table 51)
B From Paignton (Table 51)
C 🛒 to Preston
D From Bournemouth (Table 51)
b Change at Crewe and Chester
c Change at Crewe, Chester and Llandudno Junction
e Change at Preston
f Via Glasgow Central and Glasgow Queen Street. Passengers make their own way from one station to the other
g Change at Haymarket
h Change at Haymarket and Dundee

Table 65

Saturdays

until 12 July

London and West Midlands → North West England and Scotland

Route Diagram - see first page of Table 65

		XC	VT	TP	XC	VT	XC	VT	NT	VT	VT	XC	LM	VT	TP	VT	XC	VT	NT	VT	NT	TP	NT	VT
								[R]									[R]							
		[1]◇	[1]◇	[1]◇	[1]◇	[1]◇	[1]◇	[1]		[1]◇	[1]◇	[1]◇	[1]◇	[1]◇	[1]◇	[1]◇	[1]	[1]◇		[1]◇		[1]◇		[1]◇
							A		B			A			C		A							
		☕	☕	🛒	☕	☕	☕	☕		☕	☕	☕		☕	🛒	☕	☕	☕		☕		🛒		☕
London Euston [15]	d		12 33			12 38				12 56	13 29			13 33		13 38								13 56
Gatwick Airport [10]	d																							
Watford Junction	d		12u48			12u53										13u53								14u11
Milton Keynes Central	d									13 30	14 09			14 14										
Northampton	d		12 58																					
Rugby	d		13 58							14 11				14 57										15 12
Nuneaton	d																							
Tamworth Low Level	d																							
Lichfield Trent Valley	d																							
Coventry	d		14 10			14 16	14 23			14u27			14 32	15 10		15 16	15 23							15 27
Birmingham International	d	14 12	14 22			14 28	14 34			14 39			14 50	15 22		15 28	15 34	←						15 39
Birmingham New Street [12]	a	14 30	14 36		←	14s39	14 45					←		15 36		15s39	15 45	15s39						
	d	14 48 →	14 40		14 48		15 20 →	15 03				15 20	15 21	15 40		→	15 48			16 03				
Sandwell & Dudley	d		14 52											15 52										
Coseley	d												15 34											
Wolverhampton [7]	d				15 10			15 21				15 40	15 44				16 08			16 21				
Penkridge	d												15 53											
Stafford	a		15 17		15 22							15 52	16 01	16 17			16 22							
	d		15 19		15 23							15 54	16 02	16 19			16 23							
Stoke-on-Trent	a				15 41	15 48					16 05	16 12					16 41	16 48						
Congleton	a																							
Macclesfield	a				15 57						16 21	16 32					16 57							
Crewe [10]	a		15 38					15 54		15 59			16 23	16 38						16 54				16 59
	d		15 41					15 55		16 01			16 24	16 41						16 55				17 01
Chester	a		16 27										16 56	17 26										17 54
Llandudno Junction	a		17b24										18b17	18 25										19b17
Llandudno	a												18b35	18c46										19b37
Bangor (Gwynedd)	a		17b47											18 47										
Holyhead	a		18b30											19 20										
Wilmslow	a		16 26							16 48			17 05	17 26										17 48
Manchester Airport	a												17 15											
Stockport	a				16 11	16s20					16s34	16 46					17 11	17s20						
Manchester Piccadilly [10]	a				16 27	16 34					16 48	17 02					17 27	17 34						
Hartford	a												16 34											
Warrington Bank Quay	a		15 56					16 12						16 57						17 12				
	d		15 58					16 13						16 58						17 13				
Runcorn	a									16 17			16 46											17 17
Liverpool South Parkway [7]	a												16 54											
Liverpool Lime Street [10]	a									16 37			17 09											17 37
	d		15 04						15 57					16 04					16 30				17 20	
Manchester Airport	d		14e47	15 27										15e47	16 27							16 47		
Manchester Piccadilly [10]	d		15e11	15 45										16e11	16 44							17 11		
Bolton	d		15e32	16 05										16e32	17 05							17 30		
Wigan North Western	a		16 07					16 23	16 31					17 08					17 11	17 23	←		17 54	
	d		16 09					16 24	16 31					17 09					17 12 →	17 24	17 12		17 54	
Preston [8]	a		16 22	16 27				16 39	16 54					17 23	17 27					17 39	17 40	17 53	18 17	
Blackpool North	a		17 01						17 34					18 03							18 30		18 48	
	d		15 41						16 25					16 38								17 19		
Preston [8]	d		16 25	16 29				16 40	16 56					17 26	17 29					17 40		17 58		
Lancaster [6]	a		16 38	16 44				16 57	17 16					17 40	17 44					17 55		18 13		
	d		16 40	16 45				16 59	17 17					17 41	17 45					17 56		18 14		
Barrow-in-Furness	a								18 21						18 50									
Oxenholme Lake District	a		16 52	16 59				17 12												18 09		18 28		
	d		16 53	16 59				17 13												18 11		18 28		
Windermere	a			17 23				18 04																
Penrith North Lakes	d		17 18	17 25				17 38																
Carlisle [8]	a		17 36	17 43				17 56						18 29						18 55		19 09		
	d		17 39	17 44				18 00						18 32						18 58		19 10		
Lockerbie	d			18 04				18 18												19 16		19 29		
Carstairs	a																							
Motherwell	a							19s00																
Glasgow Central [15]	a		18 58					19 27						19 57								20 31		
Haymarket	a			19s04																20s12				
Edinburgh [10]	a			19 11																20 22				
Perth	a		20f37	20 53										21f42										
Dundee	a			20g26										22f08						22 26				
Aberdeen	a			21g39										23f21						23 40				
Inverness	a			23 10																				

For general notes see front of timetable
For details of catering facilities see Directory of Train Operators

A From Bournemouth (Table 51)

B To Millom (Table 100)

C 🛒 to Preston

b Change at Crewe and Chester

c Change at Crewe and Llandudno Junction

e Change at Preston

f Via Glasgow Central and Glasgow Queen Street. Passengers make their own way from one station to the other

g Change at Haymarket

Table 65

Saturdays

until 12 July

London and West Midlands → North West England and Scotland

Route Diagram - see first page of Table 65

		TP	VT	XC	LM	XC	VT	TP	XC	VT	VT	NT	NT	VT	SR	VT	XC	LM		VT	TP	VT	XC	VT	VT
		1 ◇	1 ◇	1 ◇	1 ◇	1 ◇	1 ◇	1 ◇	1 ◇	1 ◇	R 1			1 ◇		1 ◇	R 1	1 ◇		1 ◇	1 ◇	1 ◇	1 ◇	R 1	
				A				B									C						D		
London Euston 15 ⊖	d		14 29				14 33			14 38				14 56		15 29				15 33		15 38			
Gatwick Airport 10 ✈	d																								
Watford Junction	d		14u44				14u48			14u53												15u53			
Milton Keynes Central	d													15 31		16 07				16 13					
Northampton	d																								
Rugby	d						15 58							16 12						16 57					
Nuneaton	d																								
Tamworth Low Level	d																								
Lichfield Trent Valley	d																								
Coventry	d			15 32	15 44		16 10			16 16	16 23			16u27			16 32			17 10		17 16	17 23	17 23	
Birmingham International ✈	d			15 50	15 58	16 12	16 22			16 28	16 34			16 39			16 50			17 22		17 28	17 34		
Birmingham New Street 12	a					16 30	16 36		←	16s39										17 36		17s39	17 45		
	d			16 20	16 21	16 48 →	16 40		16 48		17 03						17 20	17 21		17 40			17 48	18 03	
Sandwell & Dudley	d						16 52													17 52					
Coseley	d				16 34													17 34							
Wolverhampton 7	d			16 40	16 44				17 08		17 21						17 40	17 44					18 08	18 20	
Penkridge	d				16 53													17 53							
Stafford	a			16 52	17 01		17 17		17 22								17 52	18 01		18 17			18 22		
	d			16 54	17 02		17 19		17 23								17 54	18 02		18 19			18 23		
Stoke-on-Trent	a		17 05	17 12					17 41	17 48						18 05	18 12					18 48	18 41		
Congleton	a			17 24																					
Macclesfield	a		17 21	17 33					17 57							18 21	18 32						18 57		
Crewe 10	a				17 23		17 38				17 54			17 59				18 23		18 38				18 54	
	d				17 24		17 41				17 55			18 01				18 24		18 41				18 55	
Chester	a						18 29											18 57		19 25					
Llandudno Junction	a						19b26											19 54							
Llandudno	a																	20c35							
Bangor (Gwynedd)	a						19b49											20 11							
Holyhead	a						20b30											20 55							
Wilmslow	a				18 04		18 26							18 48				19 05		19 26					
Manchester Airport ✈	a				18 15													19 16		20e02					
Stockport	a		17s34	17 46					18 11	18s22						18s34	18 46					19s19	19 11		
Manchester Piccadilly 10	a		17 48	18 02					18 27	18 35						18 48	19 02					19 34	19 27		
Hartford	a				17 36													18 34							
Warrington Bank Quay	a						17 57				18 12									18 57				19 12	
	d						17 58				18 13									18 58				19 13	
Runcorn	a				17 45									18 17				18 43							
Liverpool South Parkway 7 ✈	a				17 53													18 54							
Liverpool Lime Street 10	a				18 09									18 37				19 09							
	d										17 25	17 45	18 04												
Manchester Airport ✈	d							17 32			17f04									17g47	18 27				
Manchester Piccadilly 10	d						17g15	17 50			17g30									18g11	18 45				
Bolton	d						17g37	18 10			17g53									18g32	19 12				
Wigan North Western	a						18 08				18 23	18 28	18 51							19 08				19 24	
	d						18 09				18 24	18 28	18 51							19 09				19 24	
Preston 8	a						18 22	18 34			18 39	18 52	19 17							19 25	19 36			19 43	
Blackpool North	a						18 59					19 21								20 01				20 36	
	d						17 38													18 42					19 25
Preston 8	d						18 25	18 38			18 40									19 25	19 38				20 00
Lancaster 6	a						18 39	18 54			18 59									19 39	19 54				
	d	18 21					18 40	18 55			19 01									19 40	19 55				
Barrow-in-Furness	a							19 59													21 00				
Oxenholme Lake District	a	18 40					18 52				19 14									19 52					
	d	18 41					18 54				19 15									19 54					
Windermere	a	19 02																		20 19					
Penrith North Lakes	d						19 19													20 18					
Carlisle 8	a						19 36				19 55									20 41					22 00
	d						19 41				19 56				20 08										
Lockerbie	d																								
Carstairs	a																								
Motherwell	a						20s39																		
Glasgow Central 15	a						21 00				21 13				22 27										
Haymarket	a																								
Edinburgh 10	a																								
Perth	a						22h37				00h15				01h19										
Dundee	a						23h00																		
Aberdeen	a						00h16																		
Inverness	a																								

For general notes see front of timetable
For details of catering facilities see Directory of Train Operators

A From Reading (Table 51)

B to Preston

C From Penzance (Table 135)

D From Bournemouth (Table 51)

b Change at Crewe and Chester

c Change at Crewe and Llandudno Junction

e Change at Crewe and Wilmslow

f Change at Manchester Piccadilly and Preston

g Change at Preston

h Via Glasgow Central and Glasgow Queen Street. Passengers make their own way from one station to the other

Saturdays

until 12 July

London and West Midlands → North West England and Scotland

Route Diagram - see first page of Table 65

		VT	NT	VT	VT	XC	LM	XC	VT	TP	XC	VT	VT	VT	VT	XC	LM	VT	VT	VT	VT	VT	VT	XC	NT
				1 ◇	1 ◇	1 ◇	1 ◇	1 ◇	1 ◇	1 ◇	1 ◇	1 ◇	R 1	1 ◇	1 ◇	R 1	1 ◇				1 ◇	1 ◇	1 ◇	1 ◇	
						A										B								C	
		🚌		☕	☕	☕		☕	☕		☕	☕	☕	☕	☕	☕		🚌	🚌	🚌	☕	☕	☕	☕	🚌
London Euston 15 ⊖	d			15 56	16 29				16 33			16 38		16 56	17 29						17 32	17 37	17 56		
Gatwick Airport 10 ✈	d					14 52																			
Watford Junction	d			16u11	16u44				16u49			16u53										17u52	18u11		
Milton Keynes Central	d													17 32	18 07						18 13				
Northampton	d																								
Rugby	d			17 12					17 58					18 12									19 13		
Nuneaton	d																								
Tamworth Low Level	d																								
Lichfield Trent Valley	d																								
Coventry	d			17 27		*17 32*			18 10			18 16	*18 23*	18u27		*18 32*					19 07	19 16		19 23	
Birmingham International ✈	d			17 39		*17 50*		18 12	18 22			18 28	*18 34*	18 41		*18 50*						19 28		19 34	
Birmingham New Street 12	a					18 18		18 30	18 36		←	18s39										19 39		19 45	
	d					18 20	18 21	18 48 →	18 40		18 48		19 03			19 20	19 21					19 48		20 03	
Sandwell & Dudley	d								18 52																
Coseley	d						18 34										19 34								
Wolverhampton 7	d					18 40	18 44				19 08		19 21			19 40	19 44					20 09		20 21	
Penkridge	d						18 53										19 53								
Stafford	a					18 52	19 01		19 17		19 22		19 33			19 52	20 01				20 13	20 23		20 33	
	d					18 54	19 02		19 19		19 23		19 33			19 54	20 02				20 15	20 25		20 34	
Stoke-on-Trent	a				19 05	19 12					19 41	19 48			20 05	20 12						20 43			
Congleton	a					19 24																			
Macclesfield	a				19 21	19 33					19 57				20 21	20 32						20 59			
Crewe 10	a			18 58			19 23		19 38				19 54	20 00			20 23				20 34		20 50	20 55	
	d			19 01			19 24		19 41				19 55	20 03			20 24				20 37		20 52	20 56	
Chester	a						*20 02*		*20 07*								*20 57*						*21 27*	*21 53*	
Llandudno Junction	a								*20 54*														*22 25*	*22 48*	
Llandudno	a								*21b12*																
Bangor (Gwynedd)	a								*21 11*														*22 42*	*23 07*	
Holyhead	a								*21 46*														*23 30*	*23 44*	
Wilmslow	a			*19 48*					*20 26*					*20 45*									*21 26*	21 12	
Manchester Airport ✈	a													*21c02*										22 05	
Stockport	a				19s34	19 46					20 11	20s19			20s34	20 46						21s13		21 22	
Manchester Piccadilly 10	a				19 48	20 02					20 27	20 37			20 48	21 02						21 26		21 36	
Hartford	a						19 36										20 36								
Warrington Bank Quay	a								19 57				20 12								20 52				
	d								19 58				20 13								20 54				
Runcorn	a			19 17			19 45							20 18			20 45						21 08		
Liverpool South Parkway 7 ✈	a						19 54										20 54								
Liverpool Lime Street 10	a			19 37			20 09							20 38			21 09						21 27		
	d		19 04																		*19 48*				
Manchester Airport ✈	d									19 27															*19 47*
Manchester Piccadilly 10	d									19 44															*20 11*
Bolton	d									20 05															*20 32*
Wigan North Western	a		19 51						20 08				20 23								21 03				
	d		19 51						20 09				20 24								21 05				
Preston 8	a		20 17						20 26	20 27			20 43								21 24				
Blackpool North	a		*20 56*										*21 36*								*21 56*				
	d									*19 42*															*20 52*
Preston 8	d	20 00								20 29								20 55	21 00						21 35
Lancaster 6	a	20 50								20 47								21 45							22 20
	d	20 50								20 47								21 45 →							
Barrow-in-Furness	a	*22 50*								21 54															
Oxenholme Lake District	a	21 35																		←					
	d	21 35 →																		21 35					
Windermere	a																								
Penrith North Lakes	d																			22 30					
Carlisle 8	a																		23 00	23 05					
	d																								
Lockerbie	d																								
Carstairs	a																								
Motherwell	a																								
Glasgow Central 15	a																								
Haymarket	a																								
Edinburgh 10	a																								
Perth	a																								
Dundee	a																								
Aberdeen	a																								
Inverness	a																								

For general notes see front of timetable
For details of catering facilities see Directory of Train Operators

A From Brighton (Table 51)
B From Paignton (Table 51)
C From Bournemouth (Table 51). ☕ to Birmingham New Street
b Change at Crewe and Llandudno Junction
c Change at Crewe and Wilmslow

Table 65

Saturdays

until 12 July

London and West Midlands → North West England and Scotland

Route Diagram - see first page of Table 65

		VT	XC	LM	VT	VT	XC	VT	VT	VT	NT	VT	VT	VT	XC	LM	NT	VT	VT	VT	XC	AW	VT
		1 ◇	1 ◇	1 ◇		1 ◇	1 ◇		1 ◇			1 ◇	1 ◇		R 1	1 ◇		1 ◇		1 ◇	1 ◇	◇	
			A				B								C						D		
					(bus)			(bus)		(bus)				(bus)					(bus)				(bus)
		(catering)				(catering)			(catering)			(catering)	(catering)					(catering)		(catering)			
London Euston 15 ⊖	d	18 26				18 33			18 38			18 56	19 21					19 34		20 00			
Gatwick Airport 10 ✈	d																						
Watford Junction	d	18u41				18u48			18u53			19u11						19u52		20u16			
Milton Keynes Central	d					19 11			19 19			19 38	19 56					20 36		21 01			
Northampton	d																						
Rugby	d											20 17						21 16		21 41			
Nuneaton	d																						
Tamworth Low Level	d																						
Lichfield Trent Valley	d																						
Coventry	d		*19 32*			20 10			20 16			20 29			*20 32*			21 28			21b23	*21 32*	
Birmingham International ✈	d		*19 50*				*20 16*		20 28						*20 50*						21b34	*21 50*	
Birmingham New Street 12	a								20s39												21 45		
	d		20 20	20 21			20 48								21 20	21 21					22 20	22 33	
Sandwell & Dudley	d																						
Coseley	d			20 34												21 34							
Wolverhampton 7	d		20 40	20 44			21 08								21 40	21 44					22 40	22 48	
Penkridge	d			20 53												21 54							
Stafford	a		20 52	21 01		21 13	21 22		21 33				21 42		21 52	22 01		22 16		22 47	22 52		
	d		20 54	21 02		21 15	21 22		21 35				21 43	21 50	21 54	22 02		22 18		22 49	22 54		22 55
Stoke-on-Trent	a	21 05	21 12											22 20									23 25
Congleton	a		21 24																←				
Macclesfield	a	21 21	21 33											23 10					23 10				00 15
Crewe 10	a			21 27		21 34						21 46		→	22 20	22 30		22 42		23 14		00 01	
	d					21 37						21 49			22 22			22 45		23 17		00 02	
Chester	a					*22 09*						*22 30*				*23 10*		*23 34*		*00 10*		00 24	
Llandudno Junction	a											23c30											
Llandudno	a																						
Bangor (Gwynedd)	a											23c52											
Holyhead	a											00c31											
Wilmslow	a						21 57		22 08			*22 26*	22 29		22 40			*23 22*		23 34	23 39		
Manchester Airport ✈	a														*23 05*								
Stockport	a	21s34	21 46				22 11		22s18			*22 39*	22s41		22 50			*23 33*	23 40	23s44	23s49		00 45
Manchester Piccadilly 10	a	21 51	22 02				22 27		22 36			*22 52*	23 01		23 07			*23 50*		23 57	00 06		
Hartford	a																						
Warrington Bank Quay	a					21 53																	
	d					21 54																	
Runcorn	a											22 05						23 00					
Liverpool South Parkway 7 ✈	a																						
Liverpool Lime Street 10	a											22 24						23 22					
	d					*20 48*					21 48						23 05						
Manchester Airport ✈	d									*21 27*													
Manchester Piccadilly 10	d									*21 45*													
Bolton	d									*22 05*													
Wigan North Western	a					22 04					22 37						23 51						
	d					22 05					22 38						23 51						
Preston 8	a					22 24					23 02						00 15						
Blackpool North	a					*23 28*					23 28												
	d									*22 03*													
Preston 8	d				21 40					22 40													
Lancaster 6	a				22 30			←		23 30													
	d							21 45															
Barrow-in-Furness	a				*23 50*																		
Oxenholme Lake District	a							22 30															
	d							22 30															
Windermere	a																						
Penrith North Lakes	d							23s25															
Carlisle 8	a							23 59															
	d																						
Lockerbie	d																						
Carstairs	a																						
Motherwell	a																						
Glasgow Central 15	a																						
Haymarket	a																						
Edinburgh 10	a																						
Perth	a																						
Dundee	a																						
Aberdeen	a																						
Inverness	a																						

For general notes see front of timetable
For details of catering facilities see Directory of Train Operators

A From Guildford (Table 51)
B From Bristol Temple Meads (Table 51)
C From Newquay (Table 135)
D From Bournemouth (Table 51)
b By changing at Birmingham New Street, passengers may depart Coventry at 2132, Birmingham International at 2150
c Change at Crewe and Chester

Saturdays

19 July to 6 September

London and West Midlands → North West England and Scotland

Route Diagram - see first page of Table 65

		SR	TP 1◇ A	VT 1◇	VT 1◇	VT 1◇	TP 1◇	LM 1◇	NT	TP 1◇	XC 1◇	LM 1◇	VT 1◇	NT B	VT 1◇	XC 1◇		LM 1◇	XC 1◇	VT 1◇	TP 1◇ C	VT 1◇	NT	TP 1◇ C	VT 1◇
London Euston 15 ⊖	d														06 00					06 21					06 57
Gatwick Airport 10 ✈	d																								
Watford Junction	d																								07u14
Milton Keynes Central	d														06 46					07 04					
Northampton	d																								
Rugby	d																			07u41					
Nuneaton	d																								
Tamworth Low Level	d																								
Lichfield Trent Valley	d																								
Coventry	d												06 04			06 32			07 04						
Birmingham International ✈	d												06 20			06 50			07 20						
Birmingham New Street 12	a																								
	d				05 20	05 30		06 07			06 20		07 03			07 20		07 21	07 48			08 03			
Sandwell & Dudley	d							06 18																	
Coseley	d							06 27										07 34							
Wolverhampton 7	d				05 38	05 49		06 33			06 40		07 21			07 40		07 44	08 06			08 21			
Penkridge	d							06 43										07 53							
Stafford	a				05 51	06 04		06 50			06 52	←	07 33			07 52		08 01	08 17						
	d				05 52	06 05		07 00			06 54	07 00	07 33			07 54		08 02	08 18						
Stoke-on-Trent	a							→			07 12				08 06	08 12			08 36						08 40
Congleton	a										07 24					08 24									
Macclesfield	a										07 33				08 22	08 33			08 52						08 56
Crewe 10	a				06 16	06 25						07 22	07 54					08 23		08 32		08 54			
	d				06 18	06 28						07 22	07 55					08 24		08 35		08 55			
Chester	a				06 37	07 03						07 57						08 57		09 26					
Llandudno Junction	a				07 33	08 20						09b19						10b17		10 24					
Llandudno	a				08 16							09b37						10b37							
Bangor (Gwynedd)	a				07 49	08 43						09b43								10 46					
Holyhead	a				08 21	09 30						10b20								11 30					
Wilmslow	a					07 01						07 59	08 48					09 03		09 26					
Manchester Airport ✈	a											08 14						09 15							
Stockport	a				06c53	07 14					07 46	08 13			08s36	08 46			09 05	09 39					09s12
Manchester Piccadilly 10	a				07c11	07 28					08 02	08e29			08 50	09 02			09 20	09 54					09 24
Hartford	a											07 34						08 36							
Warrington Bank Quay	a					06 43							08 12							08 50		09 11			
	d					06 45							08 13							08 52		09 12			
Runcorn	a											07 46						08 46							
Liverpool South Parkway 7 ✈	a											07 54						08 56							
Liverpool Lime Street 10	a											08 10						09 10							
	d					06 04			07 30											08 04			08 57		
Manchester Airport ✈	d			04 34		05f47	06 19			07 22										07f47	08 27			08 47	
Manchester Piccadilly 10	d			05 10		06f05	06 44			07 45										08f11	08 45			09 11	
Bolton	d					06f26	07 03			08 04										08f32	09 05			09 32	
Wigan North Western	a					07 02			08 01				08 23							09 01		09 22	09 30		
	d					07 04			08 02				08 24							09 03		09 23	09 31		
Preston 8	a			06 01		07 17	07 26		08 24	08 27			08 39							09 16	09 29	09 38	09 54	10 01	
Blackpool North	a			07 31		07 56			08 51				09 32							09 57			10 21		
	d			05 30		06 34				07 41				08 09						08 41				09 30	
Preston 8	d			06 03		07 20	07 29			08 28			08 40	08 46						09 19	09 32	09 39		10 06	
Lancaster 6	a			06 17		07 33	07 44			08 44			08 59	09 07						09 32	09 48	09 53		10 23	
	d		05 50	06 18		07 35	07 45			08 44			09 01							09 34	09 48	09 55		10 23	
Barrow-in-Furness	a						08 49			09 54											10 53				
Oxenholme Lake District	a		06 04	06 32		07 47				08 58			09 16							09 46		10 08		10 43	
	d		06 04	06 33		07 49				08 59			09 17							09 47		10 09		10 43	
Windermere	a		06 25	07 19		08 15				09 22										10 13				11 01	
Penrith North Lakes	d			06 58		08 13				09 24			09 42							10 12		10 34			
Carlisle 8	a			07 18		08 31				09 41			10 00							10 30		10 52			
	d	06 09		07 21		08 34				09 43			10 03							10 30		10 53			
Lockerbie	d			07 41		08 52							10 21									11 12			
Carstairs	a			08 15																					
Motherwell	a			08s30		09s33							11s03							11s30					
Glasgow Central 15	a	08 37		09 00		09 59							11 27							12 01					
Haymarket	a									11s04												12s08			
Edinburgh 10	a									11 11												12 19			
Perth	a			10g37		11g37				12 56										13g37		14 54			
Dundee	a			11g00		12g00				12h21												13h24			
Aberdeen	a			12g18		13g14				13h36												14h36			
Inverness	a			13g35						15 18												17 07			

For general notes see front of timetable
For details of catering facilities see Directory of Train Operators

A From Barrow-in-Furness (Table 82)

B From Clitheroe (Table 94) to Morecambe (Table 98)
C to Preston
b Change at Crewe and Chester
c Change at Crewe
e Change at Crewe and Stockport

f Change at Preston
g Via Glasgow Central and Glasgow Queen Street. Passengers make their own way from one station to the other
h Change at Haymarket

Due to ongoing Engineering Operations, some services from Saturday 13 September on this Table had not been confirmed at time of going to press. These services will be issued in a special Supplement as soon as exact timings have been confirmed.

Table 65

Saturdays

London and West Midlands → North West England and Scotland

19 July to 6 September

Route Diagram - see first page of Table 65

		VT	VT	XC	LM	VT	TP	VT	XC	VT		TP	NT	NT	VT	VT	XC	LM	VT	TP	VT	VT	XC	VT	NT
		1◇	1◇	1◇	1◇	1◇	1◇	1◇	1◇	1◇		1◇			1◇	1◇	1◇	1◇	1◇	1◇	1◇	1◇	1◇	1◇	
				A													B			C			D		
		🍴	🍴	🍴		🍴	🛒	🍴	🍴	🍴		🛒			🍴	🍴	🍴		🍴	🛒	🍴	🍴	🍴	🍴	
London Euston 15 ⊖	d	07 09	07 25			07 45		07 54							08 12	08 17			08 42		08 45	08 55			
Gatwick Airport 10 ✈	d			05 15																					
Watford Junction	d	07u28				08u04									08u34							09u13			
Milton Keynes Central	d	07 49						08 31											09 21						
Northampton	d																								
Rugby	d					08u43													09u45						
Nuneaton	d	08 23													09 24										
Tamworth Low Level	d																								
Lichfield Trent Valley	d																								
Coventry	d			07 32					08 00	08 23							08 32						09 23		
Birmingham International ✈	d			07 50					08 16	08 34							08 50						09 34		
Birmingham New Street 12	a			08 18																			09 45		
	d			08 20	08 21				08 48	09 03							09 20	09 21					09 48	10 03	
Sandwell & Dudley	d																								
Coseley	d				08 34													09 34							
Wolverhampton 7	d			08 40	08 44				09 08	09 21							09 40	09 44					10 08	10 21	
Penkridge	d				08 53													09 53							
Stafford	a	08 48		08 52	09 01				09 22						09 49		09 52	10 01					10 22		
	d	08 48		08 54	09 02				09 22						09 49		09 54	10 02					10 23		
Stoke-on-Trent	a		09 05	09 12				09 35	09 41							10 03	10 12					10 34	10 41		
Congleton	a			09 24																					
Macclesfield	a			09 33				09 51	09 57								10 32					10 50	10 57		
Crewe 10	a	09 10			09 23	09 36				09 54					10 10			10 22	10 36		10 39			10 54	
	d	09 11			09 24	09 37				09 55					10 11			10 24	10 37		10 49			10 55	
Chester	a				09 57	10 27												10 57			11 15				
Llandudno Junction	a				11b17	11b26															12 07				
Llandudno	a				11b35																12 35				
Bangor (Gwynedd)	a					11b43															12 26				
Holyhead	a					12b20															13 02				
Wilmslow	a	09 48				10 26									10 48			11 01			11c26				
Manchester Airport ✈	a																	11 11							
Stockport	a		09s33	09 46		10 39		10s05	10 11							10s33	10 46					11s05	11 11		
Manchester Piccadilly 10	a		09 46	10 02		10 54		10 19	10 27							10 46	11 02					11 18	11 27		
Hartford	a				09 36													10 33							
Warrington Bank Quay	a					09 54				10 12									10 54					11 11	
	d					09 56				10 13									10 56					11 13	
Runcorn	a	09 27			09 45										10 28			10 45							
Liverpool South Parkway 7 ✈	a				09 54													10 54							
Liverpool Lime Street 10	a	09 50			10 09										10 50			11 09							
	d					09 04							09 57						10 04						10 57
Manchester Airport ✈	d						09 27												10e07	10 27					
Manchester Piccadilly 10	d						09 45							10f13					10e23	10 45					
Bolton	d						10 05												10g51	11 05					
Wigan North Western	a					10 05				10 23			10 31	10 48					11 05					11 22	11 30
	d					10 07				10 24			10 31	10 48					11 07					11 24	11 30
Preston 8	a					10 20	10 27			10 38			10 55	11 14					11 20	11 27				11 37	11 53
Blackpool North	a					10 57							11 22	11 44						12 01				12 14	12 20
	d					09 40													10 41						
Preston 8	d					10 23	10 29			10 40									11 23	11 29				11 40	
Lancaster 6	a					10 39	10 44												11 37	11 44				11 54	
	d						10 45												11 39	11 45				11 55	
Barrow-in-Furness	a						11 56													12 49					
Oxenholme Lake District	a						11 03			11 11									11 51						
	d						11 03			11 12									11 52						
Windermere	a																		12 17						
Penrith North Lakes	d						11 30																	12 33	
Carlisle 8	a						11 48			11 50		←							12 31					12 49	
	d						11 54 →			11 52		11 54							12 32					12 50	
Lockerbie	d											12 14												13 09	
Carstairs	a																								
Motherwell	a											13s00													
Glasgow Central 15	a									13 16		13 18							13 53						
Haymarket	a																							14s04	
Edinburgh 10	a																							14 14	
Perth	a																		15h37						
Dundee	a																							15j21	
Aberdeen	a																							16j37	
Inverness	a																								

For general notes see front of timetable
For details of catering facilities see Directory of Train Operators

A 🍴 from Reading
B From Bristol Temple Meads (Table 51)
C 🛒 to Preston
D From Bournemouth (Table 51)
b Change at Crewe and Chester
c Change at Crewe
e Change at Bolton and Preston
f Manchester Victoria
g Change at Preston
h Via Glasgow Central and Glasgow Queen Street. Passengers make their own way from one station to the other
j Change at Haymarket

Due to ongoing Engineering Operations, some services from Saturday 13 September on this Table had not been confirmed at time of going to press. These services will be issued in a special Supplement as soon as exact timings have been confirmed.

Table 65

Saturdays

19 July to 6 September

London and West Midlands → North West England and Scotland

Route Diagram - see first page of Table 65

		VT	TP	VT		XC	LM	VT	TP	TP	VT	XC	VT	NT	VT	VT	XC	LM	VT	TP		VT	XC	VT	NT
		1◇	1◇	1◇		1◇ A	1◇	1◇	1◇	1◇	1◇	1◇	R 1		1◇	1◇	1◇ B	1◇	1◇	1◇ C		1◇	R 1 D	1◇	
		☕		☕		☕		☕		🛒	☕	☕	☕		☕	☕	☕		☕	🛒		☕	☕	☕	
London Euston 15 ⊖	d	09 15		09 25				09 45			09 55				10 12	10 25			10 45			10 55			
Gatwick Airport 10 ✈	d																								
Watford Junction	d							10u04							10u32							11u14			
Milton Keynes Central	d	09 50									10 31								11 22						
Northampton	d																								
Rugby	d							10u45											11u46						
Nuneaton	d	10 24													11 24										
Tamworth Low Level	d			10 39																					
Lichfield Trent Valley	d							11 08																	
Coventry	d					09 32							10 23				10 32						11 23		
Birmingham International ✈	d					09 50						10 09	10 34				10 50						11 34		
Birmingham New Street 12	a											10 20											11 45		
	d					10 20	10 21					10 48	11 03				11 20	11 21					11 48	12 03	
Sandwell & Dudley	d																								
Coseley	d						10 34											11 34							
Wolverhampton 7	d					10 40	10 44					11 08	11 21				11 40	11 44					12 08	12 21	
Penkridge	d						10 53											11 53							
Stafford	a	10 49				10 52	11 01					11 22			11 49		11 52	12 01					12 22		
	d	10 49				10 54	11 02					11 23			11 49		11 54	12 02					12 23		
Stoke-on-Trent	a			11 05		11 12					11 34	11 41				12 01	12 12					12 33	12 41		
Congleton	a					11 24																			
Macclesfield	a					11 33					11 50	11 57					12 32					12 49	12 57		
Crewe 10	a	11 10					11 23	11 40					11 54		12 10			12 23	12 37					12 54	
	d	11 11					11 24	11 42					11 55		12 11			12 24	12 40					12 55	
Chester	a						11 59	12 27										12 59	13 27						
Llandudno Junction	a						13b17	13b24										14b09	14 28						
Llandudno	a						13b35											14b27							
Bangor (Gwynedd)	a							13b48											14 45						
Holyhead	a							14b30											15 19						
Wilmslow	a	11 48					12 01	12 26							12 48			13 01	13 26						
Manchester Airport ✈	a																	13 11							
Stockport	a			11s34		11 46		12 39			12s05	12 11				12s30	12 46		13 39			13s05	13 11		
Manchester Piccadilly 10	a			11 48		12 02		12 54			12 18	12 27				12 45	13 02		13 54			13 17	13 27		
Hartford	a						11 36											12 34							
Warrington Bank Quay	a							11 58					12 13						12 55					13 11	
	d							11 59					12 13						12 57					13 12	
Runcorn	a	11 28					11 45								12 29			12 46							
Liverpool South Parkway 7 ✈	a						11 54											12 54							
Liverpool Lime Street 10	a	11 50					12 09								12 50			13 09							
	d							11 04						11 57					12 04						12 57
Manchester Airport ✈	d		10 47							11 27									11c47	12 27					
Manchester Piccadilly 10	d		11 11							11 45									12c11	12 45					
Bolton	d		11 32							12 05									12c32	13 05					
Wigan North Western	a							12 09					12 24	12 31					13 06					13 22	13 31
	d							12 10					12 25	12 31					13 08					13 23	13 31
Preston 8	a							12 24		12 27			12 39	12 56					13 21	13 27				13 36	13 54
Blackpool North	a							13 01						13 21					14 00						14 21
	d		11 41																12 41						
Preston 8	d		12 19					12 27		12 29			12 41						13 24	13 29				13 38	
Lancaster 6	a		12 34					12 41		12 44			12 55						13 43	13 49				13 55	
	d		12 35					12 42		12 45			12 56							13 49				13 56	
Barrow-in-Furness	a																			14 47				15 23	
Oxenholme Lake District	a		12 50					12 54	←	12 59														14 10	
	d		12 59					12 56	12 59	12 59														14 11	
Windermere	a		→						13 20	14 14															
Penrith North Lakes	d							13 20					13 34												
Carlisle 8	a							13 38		13 43			13 52											14 50	
	d							13 41		13 45			13 55											14 52	
Lockerbie	d									14 05			14 13											15 10	
Carstairs	a																								
Motherwell	a																								
Glasgow Central 15	a							14 58					15 17												
Haymarket	a									15s04														16s09	
Edinburgh 10	a									15 11														16 19	
Perth	a							16e37					17e20											17 55	
Dundee	a							17e00		17 26			18e00											17 44	
Aberdeen	a							18e15		18 44			19e14											19 00	
Inverness	a												19e34											20 08	

For general notes see front of timetable
For details of catering facilities see Directory of Train Operators

A From Reading (Table 51)
B From Plymouth (Table 51)
C 🛒 to Preston
D From Bournemouth (Table 51)
b Change at Crewe and Chester
c Change at Preston
e Via Glasgow Central and Glasgow Queen Street. Passengers make their own way from one station to the other

Due to ongoing Engineering Operations, some services from Saturday 13 September on this Table had not been confirmed at time of going to press. These services will be issued in a special Supplement as soon as exact timings have been confirmed.

Saturdays

London and West Midlands → North West England and Scotland

19 July to 6 September

Route Diagram - see first page of Table 65

	TP	VT	VT	XC	LM	VT	VT	TP	VT	XC	VT	NT	VT	VT	XC	LM	VT	TP	VT	XC	VT	NT	VT
	1 ◇	1 ◇	1 ◇	1 ◇	1 ◇	1 ◇	1 ◇	1 ◇	1 ◇	1 ◇	R 1		1 ◇	1 ◇	1 ◇	1 ◇	1 ◇	1 ◇	1 ◇	1 ◇	R 1		1 ◇
	A			B											C			A		D			
	🛒	☕	☕	☕		☕	☕	🛒	☕	☕	☕		☕	☕	☕		☕	🛒	☕	☕	☕		☕
London Euston 15 ⊖ d		11 12	11 25			11 39	11 45		11 55				12 12	12 25			12 45		12 55				13 12
Gatwick Airport 10 ✈ d																							
Watford Junction d							12u04						12u31						13u13				
Milton Keynes Central d		11 50							12 31								13 21						13 50
Northampton d																							
Rugby d							12u43										13u45						
Nuneaton d		12 24											13 24										14 24
Tamworth Low Level d																							
Lichfield Trent Valley d																							
Coventry d				11 32											12 32					13 00			
Birmingham International ✈ d				11 50						12 09					12 50					13 16			
Birmingham New Street 12 a										12 20													
d				12 20	12 21					12 48	13 03				13 20	13 21				13 48	14 03		
Sandwell & Dudley d																							
Coseley d					12 34											13 34							
Wolverhampton 7 🚢 d				12 40	12 44					13 08	13 21				13 40	13 44				14 08	14 21		
Penkridge d					12 53											13 53							
Stafford a		12 49		12 52	13 01					13 22			13 49		13 52	14 01				14 22			14 49
d		12 49		12 54	13 02					13 23			13 49		13 54	14 02				14 23			14 49
Stoke-on-Trent a			13 01	13 12					13 34	13 41				14 01	14 12				14 34	14 41			
Congleton a				13 24																			
Macclesfield a				13 33					13 50	13 57					14 32				14 50	14 57			
Crewe 10 a		13 10			13 23	13 34	13 35				13 54		14 10			14 23	14 36				14 54		15 10
d		13 11			13 24	13 43	13 36				13 55		14 11			14 24	14 39				14 55		15 11
Chester a					13 57	14 01	14 27									14 57	15 26						
Llandudno Junction a						14 53	15b25									16b17	16 24						
Llandudno a						15 36	16c01									16b35							
Bangor (Gwynedd) a							15b47										16 46						
Holyhead a							16b30										17 20						
Wilmslow a		13 48			14 01		14 26						14 48			15 01	15 26						15 48
Manchester Airport ✈ a					14 11											15 11							
Stockport a			13s30	13 46			14 39		14s04	14 11				14s30	14 46		15 39		15s04	15 11			
Manchester Piccadilly 10 🚢 a			13 45	14 02			14 54		14 18	14 27				14 45	15 02		15 54		15 18	15 32			
Hartford a					13 36											14 36							
Warrington Bank Quay a							13 54				14 12						14 54				15 12		
d							13 55				14 13						14 56				15 13		
Runcorn a		13 28			13 45								14 28			14 45							15 28
Liverpool South Parkway 7 ✈ a					13 54											14 54							
Liverpool Lime Street 10 a		13 50			14 09								14 50			15 09							15 50
d							13 04					13 57					14 04					14 57	
Manchester Airport ✈ d	12 47							13 27									13e47	14 27					
Manchester Piccadilly 10 🚢 d	13 11							13 45									14e11	14 45					
Bolton d	13 32							14 05									14e32	15 05					
Wigan North Western a							14 05				14 23	14 31					15 05				15 23	15 31	
d							14 07				14 24	14 31					15 07				15 24	15 31	
Preston 8 a	14 04						14 20	14 27			14 39	14 54					15 20	15 27			15 39	15 54	
Blackpool North a							15 01					15 21					16 01					16 21	
d	13 30						13 41										14 41						
Preston 8 d	14 09						14 23	14 29			14 40						15 23	15 30			15 40		
Lancaster 6 a	14 24						14 39	14 44			14 54						15 39	15 45			15 54		
d	14 25						14 41	14 45			14 56						15 40	15 50			15 56		
Barrow-in-Furness a																		16 53			17 17		
Oxenholme Lake District a	14 42						14 53	14 59			15 09						15 52						
d	14 43						14 54	14 59			15 10						15 54						
Windermere a	15 01																16 17						
Penrith North Lakes d							15 19	15 25			15 37						16 20				16 33		
Carlisle 8 a							15 37	15 43			15 54						16 36				16 49		
d							15 39	15 43			15 55										16 53		
Lockerbie d								16 02															
Carstairs a																							
Motherwell a							16s34				16s53												
Glasgow Central 15 a							16 58				17 18												
Haymarket a								17s08													18s05		
Edinburgh 10 a								17 14													18 15		
Perth a							18f41	18 54			19f19												
Dundee a								18g49													19g27		
Aberdeen a								20h27													20g41		
Inverness a								20 58															

For general notes see front of timetable
For details of catering facilities see Directory of Train Operators

A 🛒 to Preston

B From Reading (Table 51)
C From Paignton (Table 51)
D From Bournemouth (Table 51)
b Change at Crewe and Chester
c Change at Crewe, Chester and Llandudno Junction
e Change at Preston

f Via Glasgow Central and Glasgow Queen Street. Passengers make their own way from one station to the other
g Change at Haymarket
h Change at Haymarket and Dundee

Due to ongoing Engineering Operations, some services from Saturday 13 September on this Table had not been confirmed at time of going to press. These services will be issued in a special Supplement as soon as exact timings have been confirmed.

Table 65

Saturdays

London and West Midlands → North West England and Scotland

19 July to 6 September

Route Diagram - see first page of Table 65

		VT	XC	LM	VT	TP	VT	XC		XC	VT	NT	VT	VT	XC	LM	VT	TP	VT	XC	NT	VT	NT	TP	NT
		1◇	1◇	1◇	1◇	1◇	1◇	1◇		1◇	R 1		1◇	1◇	1◇	1◇	1◇	1◇	1◇	R 1		1◇		1◇	
			A							B		C			B			D		B					
		⊡	⊡		⊡	✠	⊡	⊡		⊡	⊡		⊡	⊡	⊡		⊡	✠	⊡	⊡		⊡		✠	
London Euston 15 ⊖	d	13 25			13 45		13 55						14 12	14 25			14 45		14 55						
Gatwick Airport 10 ✈	d																								
Watford Junction	d				14u04								14u31						15u14						
Milton Keynes Central	d						14 31										15 21								
Northampton	d																								
Rugby	d				14u45												15u45								
Nuneaton	d												15 24												
Tamworth Low Level	d																								
Lichfield Trent Valley	d																								
Coventry	d		13 32							14b23						15 32				15 23					
Birmingham International ✈	d		13 50					14 09		14b34						15 50				15 34					
Birmingham New Street 12	a							14 20		14 45					←					15 45					
	d		14 20	14 21				14 48		15 20 →	15 03				15 20	15 21				15 48		16 03			
Sandwell & Dudley	d																								
Coseley	d			14 34												15 34									
Wolverhampton 7	d		14 40	14 44				15 08			15 21				15 40	15 44				16 08		16 21			
Penkridge	d			14 53												15 53									
Stafford	a		14 52	15 01				15 22					15 49		15 52	16 01				16 22					
	d		14 54	15 02				15 23					15 49		15 54	16 02				16 23					
Stoke-on-Trent	a	15 01	15 12				15 34	15 41						16 01	16 12				16 34	16 41					
Congleton	a		15 24																						
Macclesfield	a		15 33				15 50	15 57							16 32				16 50	16 57					
Crewe 10	a			15 23	15 36						15 54		16 10			16 23	16 36					16 54			
	d			15 24	15 39						15 55		16 11			16 24	16 39					16 55			
Chester	a			15 57	16 27											16 56	17 26								
Llandudno Junction	a			17c17	17c24											18c17	18 25								
Llandudno	a			17c35												18c35	18e46								
Bangor (Gwynedd)	a				17c47												18 47								
Holyhead	a				18c30												19 20								
Wilmslow	a			16 01	16 26								16 48			17 05	17 26								
Manchester Airport ✈	a			16 11												17 15									
Stockport	a	15s30	15 46		16 40		16s05	16 11						16s33	16 46		17 39		17s04	17 11					
Manchester Piccadilly 10	a	15 45	16 02		16 54		16 18	16 27						16 45	17 02		17 54		17 18	17 27					
Hartford	a			15 36												16 34									
Warrington Bank Quay	a				15 54						16 12						16 54					17 12			
	d				15 56						16 13						16 56					17 13			
Runcorn	a			15 46									16 28			16 46									
Liverpool South Parkway 7 ✈	a			15 54												16 54									
Liverpool Lime Street 10	a			16 09									16 50			17 09									
	d				15 04							15 57					16 04				16 30				17 20
Manchester Airport ✈	d				14f47	15 27											15f47	16 27						16 47	
Manchester Piccadilly 10	d				15f11	15 45											16f11	16 44						17 11	
Bolton	d				15f32	16 05											16f32	17 05						17 30	
Wigan North Western	a				16 05						16 23	16 31					17 05				17 11	17 23	←		17 54
	d				16 07						16 24	16 31					17 07				17 12	17 24	17 12		17 54
Preston 8	a				16 20	16 27					16 39	16 54					17 20	17 27			→	17 39	17 40	17 53	18 17
Blackpool North	a				17 01	17 34						17 34					17 58						18 30		18 48
	d				15 41							16 25					16 38							17 19	
Preston 8	d				16 23	16 29					16 40	16 56					17 23	17 29				17 40		17 58	
Lancaster 6	a				16 37	16 44					16 57	17 16					17 36	17 44				17 55		18 13	
	d				16 38	16 45					16 59	17 17					17 38	17 45				17 56		18 14	
Barrow-in-Furness	a					18 21						18 21						18 50							
Oxenholme Lake District	a				16 50	16 59					17 12											18 09		18 28	
	d				16 52	16 59					17 13											18 11		18 28	
Windermere	a					17 23					18 04														
Penrith North Lakes	d				17 16	17 25					17 38														
Carlisle 8	a				17 36	17 43					17 56						18 26					18 55		19 09	
	d				17 37	17 44					18 00						18 30					18 58		19 10	
Lockerbie	d					18 04					18 18											19 16		19 29	
Carstairs	a																								
Motherwell	a										19s00														
Glasgow Central 15	a				18 58						19 27						19 57							20 31	
Haymarket	a					19s04																20s12			
Edinburgh 10	a					19 11																20 22			
Perth	a				20g37	20 53											21g42								
Dundee	a					20h26											22g08					22 26			
Aberdeen	a					21h39											23g21					23 40			
Inverness	a					23 10																			

For general notes see front of timetable
For details of catering facilities see Directory of Train Operators

A From Reading (Table 51)
B From Bournemouth (Table 51)
C To Millom (Table 100)
D ✠ to Preston
b By changing at Birmingham New Street, passengers may depart Coventry at 1432, Birmingham International at 1450
c Change at Crewe and Chester
e Change at Crewe and Llandudno Junction
f Change at Preston
g Via Glasgow Central and Glasgow Queen Street. Passengers make their own way from one station to the other
h Change at Haymarket

Due to ongoing Engineering Operations, some services from Saturday 13 September on this Table had not been confirmed at time of going to press. These services will be issued in a special Supplement as soon as exact timings have been confirmed.

Saturdays

London and West Midlands → North West England and Scotland

19 July to 6 September

Route Diagram - see first page of Table 65

		VT		VT	XC	TP	LM	VT	VT	XC	TP	VT	NT	VT	VT	XC	LM	NT		VT	VT	TP	VT	XC	VT
		1 ◇		1 ◇	1 ◇	1 ◇	1 ◇	1 ◇	1 ◇	1 ◇	1 ◇	R 1		1 ◇	1 ◇	R 1	1 ◇			1 ◇	1 ◇	1 ◇	1 ◇	1 ◇	R 1
					A						B					C								D	
		🍴		🍴	🍴			🍴	🍴	🍴	🛒	🍴		🍴	🍴	🍴				🍴	🍴		🍴	🍴	🍴
London Euston 15 ⊖	d	15 12		15 25				15 45	15 55					16 12	16 25					16 35	16 45		16 55		
Gatwick Airport 10 ✈	d																								
Watford Junction	d							16u04						16u31									17u14		
Milton Keynes Central	d	15 50							16 31												17 21				
Northampton	d																								
Rugby	d																				17u45				
Nuneaton	d	16 24												17 24											
Tamworth Low Level	d								17 12																
Lichfield Trent Valley	d																								
Coventry	d				15 32							16 23				16 32								17 23	
Birmingham International ✈	d				15 50					16 09		16 34				16 50								17 34	
Birmingham New Street 12	a									16 20														17 45	
	d				16 20		16 21			16 48		17 03				17 20	17 21							17 48	18 03
Sandwell & Dudley	d																								
Coseley	d						16 34										17 34								
Wolverhampton 7	d				16 40		16 44			17 08		17 21				17 40	17 44							18 08	18 20
Penkridge	d						16 53										17 53								
Stafford	a	16 49			16 52		17 01			17 22				17 49		17 52	18 01							18 22	
	d	16 49			16 54		17 02			17 23				17 49		17 54	18 02							18 23	
Stoke-on-Trent	a			17 01	17 12				17 38	17 41					18 01	18 12							18 34	18 41	
Congleton	a				17 24																				
Macclesfield	a			17 17	17 33				17 54	17 57					18 17	18 32							18 50	18 57	
Crewe 10	a	17 10					17 23	17 34				17 54		18 10			18 23			18 31	18 36				18 54
	d	17 11					17 24	17 36				17 55		18 11			18 24			18 43	18 37				18 55
Chester	a	17 54						18 29									18 57			19 04	19 25				
Llandudno Junction	a	19b17						19b26												19 54					
Llandudno	a	19b37																		20 35					
Bangor (Gwynedd)	a							19b49												20 11					
Holyhead	a							20b30												20 55					
Wilmslow	a	17 48					18 04	18 26						18 48						19 05	19 26				
Manchester Airport ✈	a						18 15													19 16	20c02				
Stockport	a			17s32	17 46			18 39	18s11	18 11					18s32	18 46					19 39		19s05	19 11	
Manchester Piccadilly 10	a			17 49	18 02			18 54	18 25	18 27					18 49	19 02					19 57		19 22	19 27	
Hartford	a						17 36										18 34								
Warrington Bank Quay	a							17 53				18 12									18 54				19 12
	d							17 54				18 13									18 56				19 13
Runcorn	a	17 28					17 45							18 30			18 43								
Liverpool South Parkway 7 ✈	a						17 53										18 54								
Liverpool Lime Street 10	a	17 50					18 09							18 52			19 09								
	d											17 25	17 45					18 04			18 04				
Manchester Airport ✈	d										17 32	17e04									17f47	18 27			
Manchester Piccadilly 10	d							17f15			17 50	17f30									18f11	18 45			
Bolton	d							17f37			18 10	17f53									18f32	19 12			
Wigan North Western	a							18 04				18 23	18 28					18 51			19 05				19 24
	d							18 05				18 24	18 28					18 51			19 07				19 24
Preston 8	a							18 18			18 34	18 39	18 52					19 17			19 20	19 36			19 43
Blackpool North	a							18 59					19 21								20 01				20 36
	d							17 38													18 42				
Preston 8	d							18 22			18 38	18 40									19 23	19 38			
Lancaster 6	a							18 37			18 54	18 59									19 36	19 54			
	d					18 21		18 39			18 55	19 01									19 38	19 55			
Barrow-in-Furness	a										19 59											21 00			
Oxenholme Lake District	a					18 40		18 51				19 14									19 50				
	d					18 41		18 52				19 15									19 51				
Windermere	a					19 02															20 19				
Penrith North Lakes	d							19 17													20 16				
Carlisle 8	a							19 36				19 55									20 34				
	d							19 39				19 56									20 36				
Lockerbie	d																				20 55				
Carstairs	a																								
Motherwell	a							20s39													21s34				
Glasgow Central 15	a							21 00				21 13									21 57				
Haymarket	a																								
Edinburgh 10	a																								
Perth	a							22g37													00g15				
Dundee	a							23g00																	
Aberdeen	a							00g16																	
Inverness	a																								

For general notes see front of timetable
For details of catering facilities see Directory of Train Operators

A From Reading (Table 51)
B 🛒 to Preston
C From Penzance (Table 135)
D From Bournemouth (Table 51)
b Change at Crewe and Chester
c Change at Crewe and Wilmslow
e Change at Manchester Piccadilly and Preston
f Change at Preston
g Via Glasgow Central and Glasgow Queen Street. Passengers make their own way from one station to the other

Due to ongoing Engineering Operations, some services from Saturday 13 September on this Table had not been confirmed at time of going to press. These services will be issued in a special Supplement as soon as exact timings have been confirmed.

Table 65

Saturdays

London and West Midlands → North West England and Scotland

19 July to 6 September

Route Diagram - see first page of Table 65

		VT	NT	VT	VT	XC	LM	VT	VT	XC	TP	VT		VT	VT	XC	LM	VT	VT	VT	VT	VT	VT	NT	XC
												R				R									
				1 ◇	1 ◇	1 ◇	1 ◇	1 ◇	1 ◇	1 ◇	1 ◇	1		1 ◇	1 ◇	1	1 ◇					1 ◇	1 ◇		1 ◇
						A										B									C
		[bus]																[bus]	[bus]	[bus]	[bus]			[bus]	
				[catering]	[catering]	[catering]		[catering]	[catering]	[catering]		[catering]		[catering]	[catering]	[catering]						[catering]	[catering]		[catering]
London Euston 15 ⊖	d			17 12	17 25			17 45	17 55					18 12	18 25							18 45	18 55		
Gatwick Airport 10 ✈	d					14 52																			
Watford Junction	d							18u04															19u14		
Milton Keynes Central	d			17 50					18 31					18 50								19 21			
Northampton	d																								
Rugby	d							18u45														19u45			
Nuneaton	d													19 26											
Tamworth Low Level	d																					20 03			
Lichfield Trent Valley	d			18 35																					
Coventry	d					17 32				18b00		18 23				18 32									19 23
Birmingham International ✈	d					17 50				18 09		18 34				18 50									19 34
Birmingham New Street 12	a					18 18				18 20															19 45
	d					18 20	18 21			18 48		19 03				19 20	19 21								20 03
Sandwell & Dudley	d																								
Coseley	d						18 34										19 34								
Wolverhampton 7	d					18 40	18 44			19 08		19 21				19 40	19 44								20 21
Penkridge	d						18 53										19 53								
Stafford	a					18 52	19 01	19 22		19 22		19 33		19 49		19 52	20 01								20 33
	d					18 54	19 02	19 23		19 23		19 33		19 49		19 54	20 02								20 34
Stoke-on-Trent	a				19 04	19 12			19 34	19 41					20 01	20 12							20 42		
Congleton	a					19 24																			
Macclesfield	a				19 20	19 33			19 50	19 57					20 17	20 32							20 58		
Crewe 10	a			19 07			19 23					19 54		20 10			20 23					20 40			20 55
	d			19 08			19 24					19 55		20 11			20 24					20 41			20 56
Chester	a						20 02										20 57					21 27			
Llandudno Junction	a						21c28										22 25					22 25			
Llandudno	a						21e43																		
Bangor (Gwynedd)	a						21c51										22 42					22 42			
Holyhead	a						22c35										23 30					23 30			
Wilmslow	a			19 48			20 26							20 45											21 12
Manchester Airport ✈	a													21f02											
Stockport	a			19 59	19s35	19 46			20s07	20 11					20s33	20 46							21s13		21 22
Manchester Piccadilly 10	a			20 13	19 48	20 02			20 22	20 27					20 50	21 02							21 26		21 36
Hartford	a						19 36										20 36								
Warrington Bank Quay	a							19 55				20 12										20 58			
	d							19 56				20 13										21 00			
Runcorn	a			19 25			19 45							20 29			20 45								
Liverpool South Parkway 7 ✈	a						19 54										20 54								
Liverpool Lime Street 10	a			19 45			20 09							20 52			21 09								
	d		19 04																			19 48			
Manchester Airport ✈	d							18g47			19 27													19 47	
Manchester Piccadilly 10	d							19g11			19 44													20 11	
Bolton	d							19g32			20 05													20 32	
Wigan North Western	a		19 51					20 06				20 23										21 09			
	d		19 51					20 07				20 24										21 11			
Preston 8	a		20 17					20 20			20 27	20 43										21 29			
Blackpool North	a							20 56				21 36										22 36			
	d	19 25						19 42																20 52	
Preston 8	d	20 00						20 23			20 29							20 55	21 00					21 35	
Lancaster 6	a							20 39			20 47							21 45			←			22 20	
	d										20 47							21 45 →		20 50	21 45				
Barrow-in-Furness	a										21 54														
Oxenholme Lake District	a																			21 35	22 30				
	d																			21 35	22 30				
Windermere	a																								
Penrith North Lakes	d																			22 30	23s25				
Carlisle 8	a	22 00																	23 00	23 05	23 59				
	d																								
Lockerbie	d																								
Carstairs	a																								
Motherwell	a																								
Glasgow Central 15	a																								
Haymarket	a																								
Edinburgh 10	a																								
Perth	a																								
Dundee	a																								
Aberdeen	a																								
Inverness	a																								

For general notes see front of timetable
For details of catering facilities see Directory of Train Operators

A From Brighton (Table 51)
B From Paignton (Table 51)
C From Bournemouth (Table 51). [catering] to Birmingham New Street
b Change at Birmingham New Street
c Change at Crewe and Chester
e Change at Crewe, Chester and Llandudno Junction
f Change at Crewe and Wilmslow
g Change at Preston

Due to ongoing Engineering Operations, some services from Saturday 13 September on this Table had not been confirmed at time of going to press. These services will be issued in a special Supplement as soon as exact timings have been confirmed.

Table 65

London and West Midlands → North West England and Scotland

19 July to 6 September

Route Diagram - see first page of Table 65

Station		VT	VT	VT	XC	LM		VT	XC	VT	NT	VT	VT	XC	LM	VT	NT	VT	VT	XC	VT	VT	AW
			1 ◇	1 ◇	1 ◇	1 ◇		1 ◇	1 ◇			1 ◇		R 1	1 ◇	1 ◇		1 ◇		1 ◇	1 ◇	1 ◇	◇
					A				B					C						D			
		bus								bus			bus						bus				
			catering	catering				catering				catering				catering		catering			catering	catering	
London Euston 15	⊖ d		19 09	19 13				19 17				19 27				19 56		20 23			20 36	20 40	
Gatwick Airport 10	✈ d																						
Watford Junction	d		19u31					19u38				19u52				20u19		20u47			20u58	21u04	
Milton Keynes Central	d							20 05				20 30						21 32			21 47	21 53	
Northampton	d																						
Rugby	d							20u31															
Nuneaton	d		20 23																			22 31	
Tamworth Low Level	d							20 52													22 35		
Lichfield Trent Valley	d																						
Coventry	d				*19 32*				*20 00*					*20 32*						21b23			*21 32*
Birmingham International	✈ d				*19 50*				*20 16*					*20 50*						21b34			*21 50*
Birmingham New Street 12	a																			21 45			
	d				20 20	20 21			20 48					21 20	21 21					22 20			22 33
Sandwell & Dudley	d																						
Coseley	d					20 34									21 34								
Wolverhampton 7	🚢 d				20 40	20 44			21 08					21 40	21 44					22 40			22 48
Penkridge	d					20 53									21 54								
Stafford	a				20 52	21 01			21 22			21 27		21 52	22 01			22 37		22 52	22 58	23 04	
	d				20 54	21 02			21 22			21 29	21 40	21 54	22 02			22 38	22 50	22 54	23 00	23 04	
Stoke-on-Trent	a			21 07	21 12				21 41				22 10						23 20	23s12			
Congleton	a				21 24																		
Macclesfield	a			21 23	21 33				21 57			22c50	23 00						00 10	23s29			
Crewe 10	a		21 06			21 27		21 37						22 20	22 30	22 34						23 43	00 01
	d		21 07					21 40						22 22		22 35						23 45	00 02
Chester	a		*21 51*			*22 09*		*22 30*								*23 10*							00 24
Llandudno Junction	a		*22 43*					*23e30*															
Llandudno	a																						
Bangor (Gwynedd)	a		*22 59*					*23e52*															
Holyhead	a		*23 39*					*00e31*															
Wilmslow	a		*21 46*					*22 26*				22 07		22 40				23 16					
Manchester Airport	✈ a		*22f05*											*23 05*									
Stockport	a		*21 57*	21s41	21 46			*22 39*	22 11			22s18	23 30	22 50				23s28	00 40	23s44	23s50		
Manchester Piccadilly 10	🚢 a		*22 13*	21 54	22 02			*22 52*	22 27			22 36		23 07				23 41		00 04	00 04		
Hartford	a																						
Warrington Bank Quay	a							21 55								22 53							
	d							21 57								22 53							
Runcorn	a		21 24																			23 59	
Liverpool South Parkway 7	✈ a																						
Liverpool Lime Street 10	a		21 48																			00 22	
	d							*20 48*			21 48						23 05						
Manchester Airport	✈ d									*21 27*													
Manchester Piccadilly 10	🚢 d									*21 45*													
Bolton	d									*22 05*													
Wigan North Western	a							22 06			22 37					23 03	23 51						
	d							22 08			22 38					23 03	23 51						
Preston 8	a							22 27			23 02					23 23	00 15						
Blackpool North	a										23 28					*00 38*							
	d									*22 03*													
Preston 8	d	21 40								22 40													
Lancaster 6	a	22 30								23 30													
	d																						
Barrow-in-Furness	a	*23 50*																					
Oxenholme Lake District	a																						
	d																						
Windermere	a																						
Penrith North Lakes	d																						
Carlisle 8	a																						
	d																						
Lockerbie	d																						
Carstairs	a																						
Motherwell	a																						
Glasgow Central 15	a																						
Haymarket	a																						
Edinburgh 10	a																						
Perth	a																						
Dundee	a																						
Aberdeen	a																						
Inverness	a																						

For general notes see front of timetable
For details of catering facilities see Directory of Train Operators

A From Guildford (Table 51)

B From Bristol Temple Meads (Table 51)

C From Newquay (Table 135)

D From Bournemouth (Table 51)

b By changing at Birmingham New Street, passengers may depart Coventry at 2132, Birmingham International at 2150

c Change at Wilmslow. By bus

e Change at Crewe and Chester

f Change at Crewe and Wilmslow

Due to ongoing Engineering Operations, some services from Saturday 13 September on this Table had not been confirmed at time of going to press. These services will be issued in a special Supplement as soon as exact timings have been confirmed.

Table 65

Sundays

until 13 July

London and West Midlands → North West England and Scotland

Route Diagram - see first page of Table 65

		NT	TP		TP	VT	NT	XC	LM	VT	XC	VT	VT	VT	TP	VT	VT	NT	VT	XC	TP	VT	LM	VT
			1◇		1◇	1◇		1◇	1◇	1◇	1◇	1◇		1◇	1◇	1◇	1◇		1◇	1◇	1◇		1◇	1◇
																				A				
													🚌									🚌		
						☕		☕		☕	☕	☕		☕	🛒	☕	☕		☕	☕				☕
London Euston 15 ⊖	d											08 35		08 55		09 02			09 35					10 01
Gatwick Airport 10 ✈	d																							
Watford Junction	d											08u51		09u17		09u23								10u18
Milton Keynes Central	d											09 37		09 57		10 03			10 27					
Northampton	d																							
Rugby	d													10u37										11u40
Nuneaton	d															10 54								
Tamworth Low Level	d																							
Lichfield Trent Valley	d																							
Coventry	d																							
Birmingham International ✈	d																							
Birmingham New Street 12	a																							
	d					08 52		09 03	09 22	09 52	10 03						10 52			11 03			11 24	
Sandwell & Dudley	d																							
Coseley	d																							
Wolverhampton 7	d					09 21		09 32	09 46	10 21	10 32						11 21			11 32			11 48	
Penkridge	d								09 55															
Stafford	a					09 33		09 44	10 02		10 44	10 51		11 12		11 20			11 37	11 44			12 03	
	d					09 35		09 45	10 03		10 45	10 53	11 05	11 13		11 22			11 39	11 45		11 50	12 03	
Stoke-on-Trent	a												11 35									12 20		
Congleton	a																							
Macclesfield	a											12b10	12 25						12b55			13 10		
Crewe 10	a					10 01			10 28	10 59				11 38		11 46	11 59						12 26	12 40
	d					10 02			10 29	11 00				11 40		11 49	12 01						12 29	12 43
Chester	a					10 33				11 43						12 30								13 27
Llandudno Junction	a					11 28				12 34						13c28								
Llandudno	a					11 41				12e51						13f42								
Bangor (Gwynedd)	a					12e13				12 51						13c59								
Holyhead	a					12e44				13 25														
Wilmslow	a							10 25			11 25	11 30					12 50		12 17	12 24				
Manchester Airport ✈	a							10 59									13 02			13 02				
Stockport	a							10 35			11 35	11s41	12 55						12s30	12 34		13 40		
Manchester Piccadilly 10	a							10 52			11 52	11 56							12 43	12 49				
Hartford	a								10 41															
Warrington Bank Quay	a					10 18				11 17				11 56			12 15							12 58
	d					10 19				11 17				11 57			12 17							13 00
Runcorn	a								10 50							12 04							12 46	
Liverpool South Parkway 7 ✈	a								10 58														12 55	
Liverpool Lime Street 10	a								11 13							12 25							13 12	
	d	08 00	09g00				10 00			10 00				11 00				12 00						
Manchester Airport ✈	d		08 51		09 36					09h47				10h47	11 27						11 47			
Manchester Piccadilly 10	d		09 21		09 51					10h25				11h03	11 42						12n43			
Bolton	d		09 38		10 09					10h45				11h22	11 59						13 00			
Wigan North Western	a	08 41	09 50			10 29	10 41			11 28				12 07			12 27	12 42						13 09
	d	08 42	09 53			10 30	10 42			11 28				12 08			12 28	12 42						13 11
Preston 8	a	09 05	10 09		10 30	10 44	11 05			11 42				12 21	12 25		12 44	13 06			13 20			13 25
Blackpool North	a	09 34	10 47		11 16		11 34			12 47					13 16			13 34						14 16
	d		09 28							11 12				11 28			12 02				12 28			
Preston 8	d		10 13	10 25	10 35					11 44				12 24	12 27		12 46				13 22			13 28
Lancaster 6	a		10 30	10 40	10 50					11 58				12 38	12 43		13 01				13 37			13 47
	d		10 31	10 41	10 51					12 00				12 39	12 43		13 01				13 38			
Barrow-in-Furness	a			11 49																	14 41			
Oxenholme Lake District	a		10 46		11 06					12 13				12 51	12 57									
	d		10 47		11 07					12 15				12 53	12 58									
Windermere	a		11 10							12 34					13 18									
Penrith North Lakes	d				11 33					12 40				13 17	13 25		13 39							
Carlisle 8	a				11 50					12 58				13 35	13 42		13 56							
	d				11 53					13 03				13 38	13 42		13 57							
Lockerbie	d				12 12					13 21					14 03									
Carstairs	a																							
Motherwell	a				12s57																			
Glasgow Central 15	a				13 19									15 00			15 16							
Haymarket	a														15s01									
Edinburgh 10	a									14 29					15 08									
Perth	a				15j45									16j45										
Dundee	a														16k48									
Aberdeen	a														18m23									
Inverness	a				17j50																			

For general notes see front of timetable
For details of catering facilities see Directory of Train Operators

A From Bristol Temple Meads (Table 51)
b Change at Wilmslow. By bus
c Change at Crewe and Chester
e Change at Crewe and Llandudno Junction
f Change at Crewe, Chester and Llandudno Junction
g Change at Wigan North Western
h Change at Preston
j Via Glasgow Central and Glasgow Queen Street. Passengers make their own way from one station to the other
k Change at Haymarket
m Change at Haymarket and Dundee
n Manchester Oxford Road

OVERNIGHT SLEEPERS. For Sleeper trains, operated by First ScotRail, please refer to Tables 400 - 404

Table 65

Sundays

until 13 July

London and West Midlands → North West England and Scotland

Route Diagram - see first page of Table 65

Station		VT	TP	VT	XC	VT	VT	VT	NT	VT	VT	XC	VT	TP	VT	LM	VT	VT	VT	XC	VT	TP	VT
																	R			R			
					A							B								C			
London Euston 15	d			10 35		10 50	11 17			11 29	11 46		12 01		12 05			12 35	12 51		13 01		13 05
Gatwick Airport 10	d																						
Watford Junction	d			10u50		11u08							12u18		12u23			12u50	13u06				13u23
Milton Keynes Central	d					11 55	12 19			12 25	12 48				13 03						14 00		14 04
Northampton	d																						
Rugby	d						12u46						13u30								14u26		
Nuneaton	d					12 36									13 46								14 43
Tamworth Low Level	d																						
Lichfield Trent Valley	d																						
Coventry	d																						
Birmingham International	d																						
Birmingham New Street 12	a																						
	d	11 40			12 03			12 52				13 03				13 30	13 52			14 03			
Sandwell & Dudley	d																						
Coseley	d																						
Wolverhampton 7	d	12 15			12 32			13 21				13 38				13 54	14 21			14 38			
Penkridge	d															14 03							
Stafford	a			12 37	12 44	13 02	13 22					13 51			14 10	14 10				14 51			15 07
	d			12 39	12 45	13 04	13 23					13 53			14 11	14 11				14 53			15 09
Stoke-on-Trent	a									13 45	13 57	14 12						14 27	14 56	15 12			
Congleton	a																						
Macclesfield	a			13b55						14 01	14 13	14 27						14 43	15 12	15 27			
Crewe 10	a	12 59				13 28	13 47	13 54					14 24		14 29	14 37	14 52				15 19		15 27
	d	13 00				13 31	13 50	13 55					14 26		14 32	14 37	14 55				15 21		15 30
Chester	a					14 13										15 13							16 18
Llandudno Junction	a					15 08										16 08							17 08
Llandudno	a					15c22										16 22							17c26
Bangor (Gwynedd)	a					15 29																	17 25
Holyhead	a					16e38																	17 55
Wilmslow	a			13 17	13 25			14 42									15 44						
Manchester Airport	a				15 04			15 04															
Stockport	a			13s30	13 35					14s15	14s30	14 41						14s58	15s30	15 41			
Manchester Piccadilly 10	a			13 43	13 56					14 28	14 44	14 56						15 15	15 43	15 56			
Hartford	a															14 49							
Warrington Bank Quay	a	13 16					14 05	14 11					14 42				15 11				15 37		
	d	13 17					14 07	14 11					14 43				15 11				15 38		
Runcorn	a					13 46									14 48	14 58							15 46
Liverpool South Parkway 7	a															15 06							
Liverpool Lime Street 10	a					14 09									15 10	15 23							16 08
	d						13 00		14 00												15 00		
Manchester Airport	d		13 27										13f47	14 27							14f47	15 27	
Manchester Piccadilly 10	d		13 42										14f03	14 42							15f03	15 42	
Bolton	d		14 00										14f22	15 00							15f22	16 00	
Wigan North Western	a	13 27					14 16	14 22	14 42				14 55				15 22				15 48		
	d	13 28					14 18	14 22	14 42				14 56				15 22				15 49		
Preston 8	a	13 42	14 22				14 31	14 38	15 07				15 09	15 22			15 38				16 02	16 22	
Blackpool North	a	14 47						15 16	15 34				15 47				16 16				16 47		
	d	13 12	13 28				13 57						14 28				15 02				15 28		
Preston 8	d	13 44	14 24				14 34	14 42					15 12	15 25			15 39				16 05	16 25	
Lancaster 6	a	13 58	14 39				14 47	14 57					15 32	15 40			15 55				16 19	16 40	
	d	14 00	14 40				14 49	14 58						15 41			15 56				16 20	16 41	
Barrow-in-Furness	a													16 44									
Oxenholme Lake District	a	14 13	14 54				15 02	15 11													16 32	16 55	
	d	14 15	14 54				15 03	15 13													16 34	16 55	
Windermere	a							15 36														17 16	
Penrith North Lakes	d		15 21				15 28	15 41									16 32				16 58	17 22	
Carlisle 8	a	14 54	15 37				15 46	15 56									16 48				17 16	17 38	
	d	14 57	15 37				15 48	15 58									16 51				17 19	17 42	
Lockerbie	d	15 16	15 58																			18 03	
Carstairs	a																						
Motherwell	a						16s45																
Glasgow Central 15	a						17 10	17 19													18 39		
Haymarket	a	16s12	16s55														18s03					19s01	
Edinburgh 10	a	16 19	17 03														18 14					19 08	
Perth	a		18g27				18h44	19h15													20h46		
Dundee	a	17 49	18g14				19h08										20 01					20g46	
Aberdeen	a	19 05	19g30				20h26										21 21					22j24	
Inverness	a		20g44					21h34															

For general notes see front of timetable
For details of catering facilities see Directory of Train Operators

- **A** From Southampton Central (Table 51)
- **B** From Plymouth (Table 51)
- **C** From Bournemouth (Table 51)
- **b** Change at Wilmslow. By bus
- **c** Change at Crewe and Llandudno Junction
- **e** Change at Crewe and Bangor (Gwynedd)
- **f** Change at Preston
- **g** Change at Haymarket
- **h** Via Glasgow Central and Glasgow Queen Street. Passengers make their own way from one station to the other
- **j** Change at Haymarket and Dundee

OVERNIGHT SLEEPERS. For Sleeper trains, operated by First ScotRail, please refer to Tables 400 - 404

Table 65

Sundays

until 13 July

London and West Midlands → North West England and Scotland

Route Diagram - see first page of Table 65

		VT	VT	VT	XC	NT	VT	NT	TP	TP	LM	VT	VT	NT	VT		VT	XC	VT	TP	VT	VT	VT	VT	XC
		R			R								R					R				R			R
		1	1 ◇	1 ◇	1		1 ◇		1 ◇	1 ◇	1 ◇	1 ◇	1		1 ◇		1 ◇	1	1 ◇	1 ◇	1 ◇	1	1 ◇	1 ◇	1
					A													B							C
		☕	☕	☕	☕		☕					☕	☕		☕		☕	☕	☕	🛒	☕	☕	☕	☕	☕
London Euston 15 ⊖	d		13 35	13 51			14 01					14 05			14 35		14 51		15 01		15 05		15 35	15 51	
Gatwick Airport 10 ✈	d																								
Watford Junction	d						14u17								14u50		15u07				15u22				
Milton Keynes Central	d		14 25	14 50								15 06							16 00				16 25	16 50	
Northampton	d																								
Rugby	d						15u27																		
Nuneaton	d											15 44									16 44				
Tamworth Low Level	d		15 05												16 08										
Lichfield Trent Valley	d																		16 51						
Coventry	d																								
Birmingham International ✈	d																								
Birmingham New Street 12	a																								
	d	14 52			15 03						15 27		15 40					16 03				16 40			17 03
Sandwell & Dudley	d																								
Coseley	d																								
Wolverhampton 7 ⛴	d	15 21			15 38						15 50		16 15					16 38				17 15			17 38
Penkridge	d																								
Stafford	a				15 51						16 05	16 08						16 51			17 11				17 51
	d				15 53						16 05	16 09						16 53			17 12				17 53
Stoke-on-Trent	a		15 36	15 58	16 12										16 36		16 58	17 12					17 35	17 58	18 12
Congleton	a																								
Macclesfield	a		15 54	16 14	16 27										16 53		17 14	17 27					17 53	18 14	18 27
Crewe 10	a	15 53					16 17				16 26	16 30	16 54						17 26		17 31	17 53			
	d	15 55					16 20				16 28	16 33	16 55						17 27		17 33	17 55			
Chester	a											17 20	17 53									18 25			
Llandudno Junction	a											18 15	18 48									19b34			
Llandudno	a											18c40													
Bangor (Gwynedd)	a											18 36	19 05									20b05			
Holyhead	a												19 45												
Wilmslow	a						16 50												17 58			18 50			
Manchester Airport ✈	a						16 59															19 00			
Stockport	a		16s12	16s30	16 41										17s07		17s30	17 41	18 13				18s07	18s30	18 41
Manchester Piccadilly 10 ⛴	a		16 24	16 44	16 56										17 24		17 44	17 56	18 28				18 23	18 45	18 56
Hartford	a																								
Warrington Bank Quay	a	16 11					16 35						17 10						17 43			18 12			
	d	16 11					16 37						17 11						17 44			18 12			
Runcorn	a										16 44	16 49									17 49				
Liverpool South Parkway 7 ✈	a										16 52														
Liverpool Lime Street 10	a										17 08	17 12									18 11				
	d					16 00								17 00											
Manchester Airport ✈	d						15e47			16 27									16e47	17 27					
Manchester Piccadilly 10 ⛴	d						16e03			16 42									17e03	17 42					
Bolton	d						16e22			17 00									17e22	18 00					
Wigan North Western	a	16 22				16 41	16 46	←					17 21	17 41					17 54			18 23			
	d	16 23				16 42	16 48	16 42					17 22	17 42					17 55			18 23			
Preston 8	a	16 37				→	17 01	17 04		17 23			17 37	18 05					18 08	18 23		18 37			
Blackpool North	a	17 16					17 40	17 37					18 16	18 34					18 47			19 16			
	d	16 02					16 28						17 02						17 28			17 58			
Preston 8	d	16 39					17 04			17 25			17 39						18 11	18 25		18 39			
Lancaster 6	a	16 53					17 18			17 42			17 53						18 25	18 40		18 53			
	d	16 55					17 19		17 38	17 43			17 55						18 26	18 41		18 55			
Barrow-in-Furness	a									18 46			19 22												
Oxenholme Lake District	a	17 08							17 53										18 40	18 55		19 08			
	d	17 09							17 54										18 42	18 55		19 09			
Windermere	a								18 15											19 16					
Penrith North Lakes	d												18 30						19 06	19 22		19 36			
Carlisle 8	a	17 49					18 07						18 48						19 24	19 39		19 52			
	d	17 51					18 10						18 51						19 27	19 42		19 55			
Lockerbie	d																			20 03					
Carstairs	a																								
Motherwell	a	18s52																	20s25	20s47					
Glasgow Central 15	a	19 16					19 32												20 51	21 07		21 18			
Haymarket	a												20s04												
Edinburgh 10	a												20 14												
Perth	a																			22f46					
Dundee	a												22 17							23f09					
Aberdeen	a												23 33							00f25					
Inverness	a																								

For general notes see front of timetable
For details of catering facilities see Directory of Train Operators

- **A** From Penzance (Table 135)
- **B** From Bournemouth (Table 51)
- **C** From Newquay (Table 135)
- **b** Change at Crewe and Chester
- **c** Change at Crewe and Llandudno Junction
- **e** Change at Preston
- **f** Via Glasgow Central and Glasgow Queen Street. Passengers make their own way from one station to the other

OVERNIGHT SLEEPERS. For Sleeper trains, operated by First ScotRail, please refer to Tables 400 - 404

London and West Midlands → North West England and Scotland

Route Diagram - see first page of Table 65

		NT	VT	NT	TP	VT	LM	VT		VT	VT	VT	XC	VT	VT	VT	VT	NT	VT	XC	VT	TP	VT		LM
										R			R				R			R					
			1◇		1◇	1◇	1◇	1◇		1	1◇	1◇	1	1◇	1◇	1◇	1		1◇	1	1◇	1◇	1◇		1◇
													A							B					
			⊡			⊡		⊡		⊡	⊡	⊡	⊡	⊡	⊡	⊡	⊡		⊡	⊡	⊡		⊡		
London Euston 15 ⊖	d		16 01			16 05		16 25			16 35	16 51		17 01	17 05	17 35			17 51		18 01		18 05		
Gatwick Airport 10 ✈	d																								
Watford Junction	d		16u17					16u44			16u50	17u06			17u22						18u17				
Milton Keynes Central	d					17 06		17 19						18 00		18 22			18 50				19 06		
Northampton	d																								
Rugby	d		17u27					17 45						18u26											
Nuneaton	d					17 44									18 43								19 44		
Tamworth Low Level	d										18 09										19 48				
Lichfield Trent Valley	d																								
Coventry	d																								
Birmingham International ✈	d																								
Birmingham New Street 12	a																								
	d						17 26			17 52			18 03				18 41			19 03					19 26
Sandwell & Dudley	d																								
Coseley	d																								
Wolverhampton 7	d						17 50			18 21			18 38				19 15			19 38					19 50
Penkridge	d						17 59																		19 59
Stafford	a					18 08	18 06	18 19					18 51	18 59	19 09		19 33			19 51			20 10		20 06
	d					18 09	18 07	18 20					18 53	18 59	19 10		19 34			19 53			20 12		20 07
Stoke-on-Trent	a										18 37	18 57	19 12			19 27			19 58	20 12					
Congleton	a																								
Macclesfield	a										18 56	19 13	19 27			19 46			20 14	20 27					
Crewe 10	a		18 19			18 28	18 32	18 41		18 52				19 24	19 29		19 54				20 23		20 30		20 31
	d		18 22			18 31	18 33	18 52		18 54				19 26	19 32		19 55				20 26		20 33		20 37
Chester	a						*19 08*	19 18									*20 33*						*21 00*		
Llandudno Junction	a							20 15									*21 28*								
Llandudno	a																								
Bangor (Gwynedd)	a							20 34									*21 51*								
Holyhead	a							21 06									*22 21*								
Wilmslow	a									*19 48*							*20 50*								*21 46*
Manchester Airport ✈	a																*20 59*								
Stockport	a										19s11	19s30	19 41			20s06			20s30	20 41					
Manchester Piccadilly 10	a										19 27	19 44	19 56			20 18			20 44	20 56					
Hartford	a						18 46																		20 48
Warrington Bank Quay	a		18 37							19 10				19 41			20 12				20 41				
	d		18 39							19 10				19 43			20 12				20 43				
Runcorn	a					18 46	18 56								19 47								20 49		20 58
Liverpool South Parkway 7 ✈	a						19 04																		21 08
Liverpool Lime Street 10	a					19 09	19 18								20 10								21 11		21 24
	d	18 00												*19 00*				20 00							
Manchester Airport ✈	d		*17b47*		18 27									*18b47*			*19c01*				*19b47*	20 27			
Manchester Piccadilly 10	d		*18b03*		18 42									*19b03*			*19b25*				*20b03*	20 42			
Bolton	d		*18b22*		19 00									*19b22*			*19b45*				*20b22*	21 00			
Wigan North Western	a	18 41	18 48	←						19 21				19 52			20 23	20 41			20 52				
	d	18 42	18 50	18 42						19 21				19 54			20 23	20 42			20 54				
Preston 8	a	→	19 04	19 05	19 21					19 41				20 07			20 38	21 05			21 08	21 21			
Blackpool North	a		*19 38*	19 32	*20 16*									*20 47*			*21 16*	21 34			*21 47*				
	d		*18 28*							*19 02*				*19 28*			*20 02*				*20 28*				
Preston 8	d		19 07		19 25					19 41				20 10			20 40				21 11	21 25			
Lancaster 6	a		19 21		19 40					19 55				20 23			20 54				21 24	21 40			
	d		19 22		19 41					19 57				20 25			20 56				21 26	21 41			
Barrow-in-Furness	a				20 44																	22 44			
Oxenholme Lake District	a		19 34							20 10				20 37			21 09				21 38				
	d		19 36							20 11				20 38			21 10				21 39				
Windermere	a		*20 09*											*21 04*											
Penrith North Lakes	d		20 00							20 36				21 03			21 35				22 04				
Carlisle 8	a		20 18							20 52				21 41			22 13				22 41				
	d		20 21							20 54				21 43			22 16				22 43				
Lockerbie	d		20 40														22 34								
Carstairs	a																								
Motherwell	a		21s22											22s38			23s16								
Glasgow Central 15	a		21 46											23 08			23 38				23 59				
Haymarket	a									22s08															
Edinburgh 10	a									22 19															
Perth	a									*00 06*															
Dundee	a									*23e56*															
Aberdeen	a																								
Inverness	a																								

For general notes see front of timetable
For details of catering facilities see Directory of Train Operators

A From Bournemouth (Table 51)
B From Plymouth (Table 51)
b Change at Preston
c Change at Manchester Piccadilly and Preston
e Change at Haymarket

OVERNIGHT SLEEPERS. For Sleeper trains, operated by First ScotRail, please refer to Tables 400 - 404

Sundays

until 13 July

London and West Midlands → North West England and Scotland

Route Diagram - see first page of Table 65

		VT	VT	XC	VT	VT	VT	NT	VT	VT	XC	SR	VT	LM	VT	VT	SR	XC	VT	VT	AW	SR		
		1◇	1◇	R 1	1◇	1◇	1◇		1◇	1◇	1◇	R	1◇	1◇	1◇	1◇	R	1◇	1◇	1◇	◇	R		
				A							B	C					C	A						
		☕	☕		☕	☕	☕		☕	☕		☕	☕		☕	☕	☕		☕	☕		☕		
London Euston 15 ⊖	d	18 35	18 51		19 01	19 05	19 25		19 35	19 51		20 00	20 05		20 31	20 35			21 00	21 50		23 00		
Gatwick Airport 10 ✈	d																							
Watford Junction	d	18u50	19u07		19u18							20u21	20u23		20u46	20u52			21u17	22u05		23u23		
Milton Keynes Central	d				19 59	20 05	20 19		20 25	20 50			21 06		21 22				21 56	22 50				
Northampton	d																							
Rugby	d				20u26		20u46								21 50					23 29				
Nuneaton	d					20 44							21 46						22 48					
Tamworth Low Level	d	20 05					21 04																	
Lichfield Trent Valley	d														22 12									
Coventry	d																							
Birmingham International ✈	d																							
Birmingham New Street 12	a																							
	d			20 03							21 03			21 34				22 03			22 54			
Sandwell & Dudley	d																							
Coseley	d																							
Wolverhampton 7	d			20 38							21 38			21 57				22 38			23 24			
Penkridge	d													22 07										
Stafford	a			20 51	21 01	21 09					21 51		22 14	22 16		22 31		22 51	23 14	00 05				
	d			20 53	21 03	21 10					21 53		22 16	22 19		22 32		22 53	23 15	00 07				
Stoke-on-Trent	a	20 36	20 56	21 12					21 39	21 57	22 12					22 49		23 12						
Congleton	a																							
Macclesfield	a	20 55	21 12	21 27					21 57	22 13	22 27					23 05		23 27						
Crewe 10	a				21 22	21 29	21 40						22 35	22 44	22 46		←		23 39	00 30	00 33			
	d				21 24	21 32	21 42					23u20	22 38		22 47		23u20		23 42	00 33	00 35			
Chester	a				21 43		22 38					↦		23 19							00 53			
Llandudno Junction	a				22 28		23 44														01 40			
Llandudno	a																							
Bangor (Gwynedd)	a				22 44		00 01														01 57			
Holyhead	a				23 14		00 31														02 28			
Wilmslow	a						22 51													00 49				
Manchester Airport ✈	a						22 59																	
Stockport	a	21s11	21s30	21 41					22s11	22s30	22 41					23s19		23 41		00s58				
Manchester Piccadilly 10	a	21 26	21 44	21 56			23 22		22 26	22 42	22 56					23 32		23 56		01 11				
Hartford	a																							
Warrington Bank Quay	a						21 58								23 07									
	d						21 59								23 07									
Runcorn	a					21 47							23 00						00 14					
Liverpool South Parkway 7 ✈	a																							
Liverpool Lime Street 10	a					22 10							23 28						00 39					
	d						21 00	22 00																
Manchester Airport ✈	d						20b52										22 47							
Manchester Piccadilly 10	d						21c25										23 03							
Bolton	d						21c45										23 22							
Wigan North Western	a						22 09	22 41							23 18									
	d						22 11	22 42							23 18									
Preston 8	a						22 35	23 15							23 50									
Blackpool North	a						23 16	23 43																
	d						22 02										23 02							
Preston 8	d						22 38										00u37							
Lancaster 6	a						22 52																	
	d						22 53																	
Barrow-in-Furness	a						00 13																	
Oxenholme Lake District	a						23 05																	
	d						23 07																	
Windermere	a																							
Penrith North Lakes	d						23 41																	
Carlisle 8	a						00 09															04s58		
	d																							
Lockerbie	d																							
Carstairs	a																					06s28		
Motherwell	a																					06s58		
Glasgow Central 15	a																					07 17		
Haymarket	a																							
Edinburgh 10	a																						07 16	
Perth	a																05s44					09e36		
Dundee	a																06s08						09 22	
Aberdeen	a																07 37						10 35	
Inverness	a																08 30						11 59	

For general notes see front of timetable
For details of catering facilities see Directory of Train Operators

A From Bournemouth (Table 51)
B From Plymouth (Table 51)
C Also conveys portion to Fort William (Table 227)
b Change at Manchester Piccadilly and Preston
c Change at Preston
e Via Glasgow Central and Glasgow Queen Street. Passengers make their own way from one station to the other

OVERNIGHT SLEEPERS. For Sleeper trains, operated by First ScotRail, please refer to Tables 400 - 404

Sundays

London and West Midlands → North West England and Scotland

20 July to 7 September

Route Diagram - see first page of Table 65

	NT	TP		TP	VT	NT	XC	XC	VT	TP	XC	VT	VT	XC	NT	VT	VT	VT	XC	TP	XC	VT	VT
		1 ◇		1 ◇	1 ◇		1 ◇	1 ◇	1 ◇	1 ◇	1 ◇	1 ◇	1 ◇	1 ◇		1 ◇	1 ◇	1 ◇	1 ◇	1 ◇	1 ◇	1 ◇	1 ◇
																			A				
London Euston 15 d												08 56	09 01			09 25	09 31					10 01	10 30
Gatwick Airport 10 d																							
Watford Junction d												09u18	09u23			09u47						10u23	10u53
Milton Keynes Central d												09 53	10 06			10 21	10 37						
Northampton d																							
Rugby d													10u34									11u37	
Nuneaton d																10 59							
Tamworth Low Level d																							
Lichfield Trent Valley d																							
Coventry d																							
Birmingham International d																							
Birmingham New Street 12 a																							
d					09 03		09 18	09 48	10 03		10 18			10 48				11 03	11 18		11 48		
Sandwell & Dudley d																							
Coseley d																							
Wolverhampton 7 d					09 21		09 38	10 08	10 21		10 38			11 08				11 21	11 38		12 08		
Penkridge d																							
Stafford a					09 33		09 50	10 23	10 33		10 50			11 20		11 26		11 33	11 50		12 20		
d					09 35		09 52	10 25	10 34		10 51			11 21		11 28		11 34	11 52		12 21		
Stoke-on-Trent a							10 09	10 42			11 09	11 01		11 39			11 55		12 09		12 39		12 55
Congleton a																							
Macclesfield a							10 27	11 00			11 27	11 17		11 57			12 11		12 27		12 57		13 11
Crewe 10 a					10 12				11 12				11 39			12 11		12 17				12 40	
d					10 14				11 13				11 42			12 13		12 19				12 43	
Chester a									11 43				12 30									13 27	
Llandudno Junction a									12 34				13b28										
Llandudno a									12c51				13e42										
Bangor (Gwynedd) a									12 51				13b59										
Holyhead a									13 25														
Wilmslow a					10 51				11 50									12 59					
Manchester Airport a																							
Stockport a							10 41	11 14			11 41	11s32		12 11			12s26		12 40		13 11		13s26
Manchester Piccadilly 10 a							10 56	11 32			11 56	11 47		12 26			12 44		13 02		13 26		13 43
Hartford a					10 41																		
Warrington Bank Quay a					10 29				11 30				11 57					12 35				12 58	
d					10 31				11 30				11 59					12 36				13 00	
Runcorn a					10f50											12 30		12f46					
Liverpool South Parkway 7 a					10f57													12f55					
Liverpool Lime Street 10 a					11f13											12 49		13f12					
d	08 00	09g00				10 00							11 00		12 00								
Manchester Airport d		08 47		09 36					10h46	10 58								11h46					
Manchester Piccadilly 10 d		09 21		09 51					11h03	11j45								12h03		12j43			
Bolton d		09 38		10 09					11h22	11 59								12h22		13 00			
Wigan North Western a	08 41	09 50			10 40	10 41			11 41				12 08		12 42			12 47				13 09	
d	08 42	09 53			10 42	10 42			11 41				12 10		12 42			12 47				13 11	
Preston 8 a	09 05	10 09		10 30	10 57	11 06			11 55	12 20			12 25		13 06			13 06		13 20		13 25	
Blackpool North a	09 34	10 47		11 16		11 34			12 47				13 16		13 34			13 39				14 16	
d		09 28							11 12	11 28								12 28					
Preston 8 d		10 13	10 25	10 35					11 57	12 22			12 28					13 08		13 22		13 28	
Lancaster 6 a		10 30	10 40	10 50					12 11	12 37			12 42					13 23		13 37		13 47	
d		10 31	10 41	10 51					12 13	12 38			12 43					13 24		13 38			
Barrow-in-Furness a			11 49																	14 41			
Oxenholme Lake District a		10 46		11 06					12 26	12 52			12 57										
d		10 47		11 07					12 28	12 52			12 58										
Windermere a		11 10		12 26									13 18										
Penrith North Lakes d				11 33					12 53	13 19			13 23					14 01					
Carlisle 8 a				11 50					13 11	13 35			13 41					14 18					
d				11 53					13 14	13 36			13 43					14 19					
Lockerbie d				12 12					13 33	13 56													
Carstairs a																							
Motherwell a				12s57																			
Glasgow Central 15 a				13 19					14 34				15 10										
Haymarket a										15s01								15s31					
Edinburgh 10 a										15 08								15 41					
Perth a				15k45									16k45										
Dundee a										16m48			17k09					17 24					
Aberdeen a													18k23					18 46					
Inverness a				17k50																			

For general notes see front of timetable
For details of catering facilities see Directory of Train Operators

A From Bristol Temple Meads (Table 51)

b Change at Crewe and Chester
c Change at Crewe and Llandudno Junction
e Change at Crewe, Chester and Llandudno Junction
f Change at Crewe
g Change at Wigan North Western
h Change at Preston
j Manchester Oxford Road
k Via Glasgow Central and Glasgow Queen Street. Passengers make their own way from one station to the other
m Change at Haymarket

OVERNIGHT SLEEPERS. For Sleeper trains, operated by First ScotRail, please refer to Tables 400 - 404

Due to ongoing Engineering Operations, some services from Sunday 14 September on this Table had not been confirmed at time of going to press. These services will be issued in a special Supplement as soon as exact timings have been confirmed.

Table 65

Sundays

20 July to 7 September

London and West Midlands → North West England and Scotland

Route Diagram - see first page of Table 65

		VT	XC	TP	VT	VT	VT	VT	XC	NT	VT	NT	TP	VT	XC	VT	VT	VT	XC	VT	VT	XC	VT
																			R	R			
		1◇	1◇	1◇	1◇	1◇	1◇	1◇	1◇		1◇		1◇	1◇	1◇	1◇	1◇	1◇	1	1	1◇	1◇	1◇
			A												B				C			D	
		🍴	🍴	🛒	🍴	🍴	🍴	🍴	🍴		🍴			🍴	🍴	🍴	🍴	🍴	🍴	🍴	🍴	🍴	🍴
London Euston 15 ⊖	d				10 56	11 13	11 29							11 46		11 56	12 01	12 29			12 45		12 58
Gatwick Airport 10 ✈	d																						
Watford Junction	d				11u18											12u18	12u24	12u50			13u06		
Milton Keynes Central	d				12 00	12 19	12 25							12 48			13 05						13 59
Northampton	d																						
Rugby	d					12u46										13u28							14u26
Nuneaton	d				12 45												13 48						
Tamworth Low Level	d																						
Lichfield Trent Valley	d																						
Coventry	d																						
Birmingham International ✈	d																						
Birmingham New Street 12	a																						
	d	12 03	12 18						12 48		13 03				13 18				13 48	14 03		14 18	
Sandwell & Dudley	d																						
Coseley	d																						
Wolverhampton 7	d	12 21	12 38						13 08		13 21				13 38				14 08	14 21		14 38	
Penkridge	d																						
Stafford	a	12 33	12 51		13 12				13 20		13 36				13 50		14 13		14 20	14 33		14 51	
	d	12 34	12 53		13 13				13 21		13 37				13 53		14 14		14 22	14 34		14 53	
Stoke-on-Trent	a		13 12				13 37		13 43					13 58	14 12			14 27	14 39		14 56	15 12	
Congleton	a																						
Macclesfield	a		13 30				13 53	⟵	14 01					14 16	14 28			14 43	14 57		15 12	15 30	
Crewe 10	a	13 13			13 54	13 48		13 54			14 15					14 45	14 51			15 15			15 29
	d	13 14				13 51		13 56			14 16					14 48	14 54			15 15			15 32
Chester	a	14 13														15 13							
Llandudno Junction	a	15 08														16 08							
Llandudno	a	15b22														16 22							
Bangor (Gwynedd)	a	15 29																					
Holyhead	a	16c38																					
Wilmslow	a	13 55			14 42 ⟶						15 02									15 44			
Manchester Airport ✈	a																						
Stockport	a		13 41				14s12		14 16					14s30	14 41			14s57	15 12		15s30	15 43	
Manchester Piccadilly 10	a		13 59				14 24		14 30					14 44	14 56			15 10	15 32		15 43	15 59	
Hartford	a										14 43												
Warrington Bank Quay	a	13 30				14 07					14 32					15 03				15 32			15 54
	d	13 31				14 08					14 32					15 05				15 32			15 56
Runcorn	a							14 12			14e53						15 10						
Liverpool South Parkway 7 ✈	a										15e02												
Liverpool Lime Street 10	a							14 33			15e22						15 28						
	d					13 00				14 00													15 00
Manchester Airport ✈	d	12f46				12g49					13f46		13 58							14f46			
Manchester Piccadilly 10	d	13f02		13h45		13f25					14f03		14 42							15f03			
Bolton	d	13f22		14 00							14f22		15 00							15f22			
Wigan North Western	a	13 41				14 18				14 41	14 47	⟵				15 16				15 43			16 05
	d	13 42				14 19				14 42	14 47	14 42				15 18				15 43			16 07
Preston 8	a	13 56		14 26		14 32				⟶	15 02	15 04	15 22			15 31				15 59			16 20
Blackpool North	a	14 47				15 16					15 40	15 34				16 16				16 47			17 16
	d	13 12		13 28		13 57					14 28									15 28			
Preston 8	d	13 59		14 29		14 35					15 04		15 25			15 34				16 00			16 23
Lancaster 6	a	14 13		14 44		14 49					15 17		15 40			15 53				16 16			16 36
	d	14 14		14 45		14 50					15 18		15 41							16 17			16 38
Barrow-in-Furness	a												16 44										
Oxenholme Lake District	a	14 27		14 59		15 07					15 31												16 50
	d	14 29		14 59		15 08					15 33												16 51
Windermere	a					15 36					16 19												
Penrith North Lakes	d			15 26		15 33					16 01									16 53			17 16
Carlisle 8	a	15 08		15 46		15 57					16 16									17 09			17 34
	d	15 11		15 46		16 00					16 18									17 12			17 36
Lockerbie	d	15 30		16 07																			
Carstairs	a																						
Motherwell	a					16s55																	
Glasgow Central 15	a	16 33				17 18														18 22			19 11
Haymarket	a			17s05							17s29												
Edinburgh 10	a			17 12							17 36												
Perth	a			18j27		19k15																	20k46
Dundee	a			18j46							20 01												
Aberdeen	a			20m26							21 21												
Inverness	a			20j44		21k34																	

For general notes see front of timetable
For details of catering facilities see Directory of Train Operators

A From Southampton Central (Table 51)
B From Plymouth (Table 51)
C From Bournemouth (Table 51)
D From Reading (Table 51)
b Change at Crewe and Llandudno Junction
c Change at Crewe and Bangor (Gwynedd)
e Change at Crewe
f Change at Preston
g Change at Manchester Piccadilly and Preston
h Manchester Oxford Road
j Change at Haymarket
k Via Glasgow Central and Glasgow Queen Street. Passengers make their own way from one station to the other
m Change at Haymarket and Dundee

OVERNIGHT SLEEPERS. For Sleeper trains, operated by First ScotRail, please refer to Tables 400 - 404

Due to ongoing Engineering Operations, some services from Sunday 14 September on this Table had not been confirmed at time of going to press. These services will be issued in a special Supplement as soon as exact timings have been confirmed.

Table 65

London and West Midlands → North West England and Scotland

Sundays

20 July to 7 September

Route Diagram - see first page of Table 65

		TP	VT	VT	XC	VT	VT	NT	XC	VT	TP	TP	NT	VT	VT	XC	VT	XC	VT	TP	VT	VT	XC
		1◇	1◇	1◇	1◇	1◇	R 1		R 1	1◇	1◇	1◇		1◇	1◇	R 1	1◇	1◇	1◇	1◇	1◇	1◇	1◇
									A							B		C					
London Euston 15	d		13 01	13 29		13 46				13 57				14 01	14 29		14 45		14 58		15 01	15 29	
Gatwick Airport 10	d																						
Watford Junction	d		13u23							14u18					14u50		15u07				15u24		
Milton Keynes Central	d		14 06	14 22		14 50								15 08					16 00			16 25	
Northampton	d																						
Rugby	d									15u26													
Nuneaton	d		14 43											15 47							16 45		
Tamworth Low Level	d			15 05											16 08								
Lichfield Trent Valley	d																		16 46				
Coventry	d																						
Birmingham International	d																						
Birmingham New Street 12	a																						
	d				14 48		15 03		15 18							15 48		16 18					16 48
Sandwell & Dudley	d																						
Coseley	d																						
Wolverhampton 7	d				15 08		15 21		15 38							16 08		16 38					17 08
Penkridge	d																						
Stafford	a		15 07		15 20		15 33		15 50					16 12		16 21		16 51			17 11		17 20
	d		15 09		15 21		15 34		15 52					16 13		16 22		16 53			17 12		17 21
Stoke-on-Trent	a			15 36	15 42	15 59			16 13						16 39	16 45	17 00	17 15				17 39	17 45
Congleton	a																						
Macclesfield	a			15 54	16 00	16 16			16 34						16 56	17 03	17 16	17 34				17 58	18 04
Crewe 10	a		15 46				16 12			16 31				17 01					17 33		17 49		
	d		15 48				16 13			16 33				17 04					17 36		17 52		
Chester	a		16 18							17 20				17 53							18 25		
Llandudno Junction	a		17 08							18 15				18 48							19b34		
Llandudno	a		17c26							18c40													
Bangor (Gwynedd)	a		17 25							18 36				19 05							20b05		
Holyhead	a		17 55											19 45									
Wilmslow	a						16 59							17 58									
Manchester Airport	a																						
Stockport	a			16s11	16 15	16s30			16 48						17s12	17 17	17s30	17 48				18s15	18 19
Manchester Piccadilly 10	a			16 24	16 30	16 44			17 05						17 24	17 32	17 44	18 03				18 27	18 34
Hartford	a																						
Warrington Bank Quay	a						16 29			16 49									17 51				
	d						16 29			16 51									17 53				
Runcorn	a		16 07				16e44							17 19							18 08		
Liverpool South Parkway 7	a						16e52																
Liverpool Lime Street 10	a		16 30				17e09							17 41							18 30		
	d							16 00					17 00										
Manchester Airport	d	14 58					15f46					15 58							16f46	16 58			
Manchester Piccadilly 10	d	15 42					16f03					16 42							17f03	17 42			
Bolton	d	16 00					16f22					17 00							17f22	18 00			
Wigan North Western	a						16 40	16 42		17 00			17 41						18 02				
	d						16 41	16 42		17 02			17 42						18 04				
Preston 8	a	16 22					16 55	17 07		17 16		17 22	18 07						18 17	18 23			
Blackpool North	a							17 37		18 16			18 34							19 16			
	d						16 17			16 28									17 28				
Preston 8	d	16 25					16 57			17 19		17 25							18 20	18 25			
Lancaster 6	a	16 42					17 11			17 32		17 42							18 33	18 40			
	d	16 43					17 13			17 34	17 38	17 43							18 35	18 41			
Barrow-in-Furness	a											18 46											
Oxenholme Lake District	a	16 55					17 26				17 53								18 47	18 55			
	d	16 55					17 27				17 54								18 48	18 55			
Windermere	a	17 16									18 15									19 16			
Penrith North Lakes	d	17 22																	19 13	19 22			
Carlisle 8	a	17 38					18 07			18 26									19 31	19 39			
	d	17 42					18 09			18 28									19 39	19 42			
Lockerbie	d	18 03																		20 03			
Carstairs	a																						
Motherwell	a						19s10													20s48			
Glasgow Central 15	a						19 32			19 51									20 56	21 07			
Haymarket	a	19s01																					
Edinburgh 10	a	19 08																					
Perth	a																			22g46			
Dundee	a	20h46																		23g09			
Aberdeen	a	22j24																		00g25			
Inverness	a																						

For general notes see front of timetable
For details of catering facilities see Directory of Train Operators

A From Penzance (Table 135)
B From Bournemouth (Table 51)
C From Reading (Table 51)
b Change at Crewe and Chester
c Change at Crewe and Llandudno Junction
e Change at Crewe
f Change at Preston
g Via Glasgow Central and Glasgow Queen Street. Passengers make their own way from one station to the other
h Change at Haymarket
j Change at Haymarket and Dundee

OVERNIGHT SLEEPERS. For Sleeper trains, operated by First ScotRail, please refer to Tables 400 - 404

Due to ongoing Engineering Operations, some services from Sunday 14 September on this Table had not been confirmed at time of going to press. These services will be issued in a special Supplement as soon as exact timings have been confirmed.

Table 65

Sundays

20 July to 7 September

London and West Midlands → North West England and Scotland

Route Diagram - see first page of Table 65

		NT	VT	NT	TP	VT	XC	VT	VT	VT	XC	VT		VT	XC	VT	VT	VT	XC	NT	VT	NT	TP	VT	XC
			R 1		1 ◇	1 ◇	R 1	1 ◇	1 ◇	1 ◇	R 1	1 ◇		R 1	1 ◇	1 ◇	1 ◇	1 ◇	1 ◇		R 1		1 ◇	1 ◇	R 1
							A				B				C										D
London Euston 15	d					15 46		15 56	16 13	16 29		16 45				16 58	17 01	17 29						17 45	
Gatwick Airport 10	d																								
Watford Junction	d					15 58		16u18		16u50		17u06					17u23								
Milton Keynes Central	d					16 50			17 05							17 59		18 22						18 50	
Northampton	d																								
Rugby	d							17u26								18u26									
Nuneaton	d								17 44								18 45								
Tamworth Low Level	d									18 09															
Lichfield Trent Valley	d																								
Coventry	d																								
Birmingham International	d																								
Birmingham New Street 12	a																								
	d		17 03				17 18				17 48			18 03	18 18				18 48		19 03				19 18
Sandwell & Dudley	d																								
Coseley	d																								
Wolverhampton 7	d		17 21				17 38				18 06			18 21	18 38				19 08		19 21				19 36
Penkridge	d																								
Stafford	a		17 33				17 50		18 08		18 19			18 33	18 51		19 11		19 20		19 33				19 49
	d		17 34				17 53		18 10		18 20			18 34	18 53		19 12		19 22		19 34				19 50
Stoke-on-Trent	a					17 58	18 14			18 37	18 43	18 57			19 13			19 27	19 40					19 58	20 07
Congleton	a																								
Macclesfield	a					18 14	18 31			18 56	19 01	19 13			19 31			19 46	20 01					20 14	20 25
Crewe 10	a		18 15					18 34	18 49					19 12		19 31	19 51				20 15				
	d		18 16					18 37	18 52					19 14		19 34	19 54				20 16				
Chester	a							19 08	19 20								20 33				21 00				
Llandudno Junction	a								20 15								21 28								
Llandudno	a																								
Bangor (Gwynedd)	a								20 34								21 51								
Holyhead	a								21 06								22 21								
Wilmslow	a		18 59											19 49							20 59				
Manchester Airport	a																								
Stockport	a					18s30	18 50			19s11	19 15	19s30			19 46			20s06	20 15					20s30	20 41
Manchester Piccadilly 10	a					18 45	19 04			19 24	19 30	19 44			20 01			20 23	20 32					20 44	20 56
Hartford	a		18 41																		20 45				
Warrington Bank Quay	a		18 33					18 55						19 30		19 49					20 32				
	d		18 33					18 57						19 30		19 51					20 32				
Runcorn	a		18b51						19 07								20 10				20b54				
Liverpool South Parkway 7	a		18b59																		21b05				
Liverpool Lime Street 10	a		19b13						19 31								20 32				21b22				
	d	18 00														19 00				20 00					
Manchester Airport	d		17c46		17 58									18c46							19c46		19 58		
Manchester Piccadilly 10	d		18c03		18 42									19c03							20c03		20 42		
Bolton	d		18c22		19 00									19c22							20c22		21 00		
Wigan North Western	a	18 41	18 47	←				19 11						19 41		20 00				20 41	20 46	←			
	d	18 42	18 47	18 42				19 12						19 41		20 02				20 42	20 47	20 42			
Preston 8	a	→	19 01	19 05	19 21			19 28						19 57		20 15				→	21 01	21 05	21 22		
Blackpool North	a		19 38	19 32				20 16						20 47		21 03					21 38	21 34	22 16		
	d		18 28											19 12		19 28					20 28				
Preston 8	d		19 04		19 25			19 31						19 58		20 18					21 04		21 25		
Lancaster 6	a		19 18		19 40			19 45						20 12		20 31					21 18		21 40		
	d		19 19		19 41			19 46						20 13		20 33					21 19		21 41		
Barrow-in-Furness	a				20 44																		22 44		
Oxenholme Lake District	a		19 32					19 59						20 26		20 45					21 32				
	d		19 34					20 01						20 28		20 46					21 34				
Windermere	a							20 23								21 09									
Penrith North Lakes	d		20 01					20 25						20 52		21 18					21 59				
Carlisle 8	a		20 17					20 42						21 08		21 56					22 17				
	d		20 19					20 45						21 15		21 59					22 18				
Lockerbie	d							21 03													22 37				
Carstairs	a																								
Motherwell	a							21s45								22s54					23s19				
Glasgow Central 15	a		21 34					22 09								23 23					23 41				
Haymarket	a													22s30											
Edinburgh 10	a													22 41											
Perth	a													00e06											
Dundee	a																								
Aberdeen	a																								
Inverness	a																								

For general notes see front of timetable
For details of catering facilities see Directory of Train Operators

A From Newquay (Table 135)
B From Bournemouth (Table 51)
C From Reading (Table 51)
D From Plymouth (Table 51)

b Change at Crewe
c Change at Preston
e Change at Haymarket

OVERNIGHT SLEEPERS. For Sleeper trains, operated by First ScotRail, please refer to Tables 400 - 404

Due to ongoing Engineering Operations, some services from Sunday 14 September on this Table had not been confirmed at time of going to press. These services will be issued in a special Supplement as soon as exact timings have been confirmed.

Table 65

London and West Midlands → North West England and Scotland

20 July to 7 September

Route Diagram - see first page of Table 65

		VT	VT		XC	VT	XC	VT	VT	NT	XC	VT	VT	XC	VT	SR	VT	VT	XC	VT	VT	SR	AW		
		1 ◇	1 ◇		R 1	1 ◇	1 ◇	1 ◇	1 ◇		1 ◇	1 ◇	1 ◇	1 ◇	1 ◇	R	1 ◇	1 ◇	1 ◇	1 ◇	1 ◇	R	◇		
					A		B				C			D		E			A			G			
London Euston 15	d	18 01	18 29			18 45		19 01	19 24			19 31	19 46		20 01	20 17	20 31	20 51		21 01	21 56	22 40			
Gatwick Airport 10	d																								
Watford Junction	d		18u50			19u07									20u20		20u53	21u12		21u23	22u18				
Milton Keynes Central	d	19 08						20 08	20 19			20 34	20 50		21 01		21 39			22 08	22 59				
Northampton	d																								
Rugby	d								20u46								22 12				23 27				
Nuneaton	d	19 43						20 46							21 41					22 54					
Tamworth Low Level	d		20 05						21 04																
Lichfield Trent Valley	d																22 36								
Coventry	d																								
Birmingham International	d																								
Birmingham New Street 12	a																								
	d				19 48		20 18				20 48			21 18					22 18				22 54		
Sandwell & Dudley	d																								
Coseley	d																								
Wolverhampton 7	d				20 08		20 38				21 06			21 38					22 38				23 11		
Penkridge	d																								
Stafford	a	20 08			20 20		20 51	21 11			21 19			21 50	22 07				22 50	23 20	00 03				
	d	20 10			20 22		20 53	21 13			21 20			21 52	22 09				22 52	23 21	00 05				
Stoke-on-Trent	a		20 36		20 42	20 57	21 12				21 43	21 48	21 57	22 09				23 04	23s09						
Congleton	a																								
Macclesfield	a		20 56		21 01	21 17	21 30				22 04	22 09	22 14	22 27				23 20	23s27						
Crewe 10	a	20 47						21 53	22 08						22 46		23 19			23 58	00 42		00 20		
	d	20 50						21 56	22 10						22 49		23 21			00 01	00 44		00 23		
Chester	a	21 43							22 38														00 41		
Llandudno Junction	a	22 28							23 44														01 28		
Llandudno	a																								
Bangor (Gwynedd)	a	22 44							00 01														01 45		
Holyhead	a	23 14							00 31														02 16		
Wilmslow	a	21 46							23 00												01 00				
Manchester Airport	a																								
Stockport	a		21s11		21 16	21s31	21 42				22 18	22s23	22s31	22 40				23s34	23s41		01s09				
Manchester Piccadilly 10	a		21 26		21 31	21 44	21 56		23 22		22 32	22 36	22 43	22 56				23 46	23 56		01 22				
Hartford	a																								
Warrington Bank Quay	a								22 26								23 37								
	d								22 27								23 37								
Runcorn	a	21 05						22 11							23 08					00 21					
Liverpool South Parkway 7	a																								
Liverpool Lime Street 10	a	21 30						22 34							23 36					00 46					
	d								21 00	22 00							22 00								
Manchester Airport	d																								
Manchester Piccadilly 10	d																								
Bolton	d																								
Wigan North Western	a								22 37	22 42							23 47								
	d								22 38	22 42							23 47								
Preston 8	a								23 06	23 15							00 19								
Blackpool North	a									23 43															
	d																								
Preston 8	d																								
Lancaster 6	a																								
	d																								
Barrow-in-Furness	a																								
Oxenholme Lake District	a																								
	d																								
Windermere	a																								
Penrith North Lakes	d																								
Carlisle 8	a																								
	d																								
Lockerbie	d																								
Carstairs	a																					07s13			
Motherwell	a																					07s39			
Glasgow Central 15	a																					07 58			
Haymarket	a																								
Edinburgh 10	a																					06s27			
Perth	a															05s44						07 54			
Dundee	a															06s08						08 21			
Aberdeen	a															07 37						09 40			
Inverness	a															08 30						10b26			

For general notes see front of timetable
For details of catering facilities see Directory of Train Operators

A From Bournemouth (Table 51)
B From Reading (Table 51)
C From Bristol Temple Meads (Table 51)
D From Plymouth (Table 51)
E Also conveys portion to Fort William (Table 227)
G Stops at Edinburgh before Carstairs, Motherwell and Glasgow Central
b Change at Edinburgh and Perth

OVERNIGHT SLEEPERS. For Sleeper trains, operated by First ScotRail, please refer to Tables 400 - 404

Due to ongoing Engineering Operations, some services from Sunday 14 September on this Table had not been confirmed at time of going to press. These services will be issued in a special Supplement as soon as exact timings have been confirmed.

Scotland and North West England → West Midlands and London

Route Diagram - see first page of Table 65

Miles	Miles	Miles	Miles	Miles			VT	XC	VT	XC	LM	VT	VT	VT	TP	LM	VT	TP	LM	VT	VT	VT	VT	VT	LM
														MO	MO										
							1◇	1◇	1◇	1◇	1◇	1◇	1◇		1◇	1	1◇	1◇	1	1◇	1◇	1◇	1◇	1◇	1◇
								A		A				B	B	C			C	D					
														🚌											
								🛒	⊠	🛒	☕	⊠	⊠				⊠			⊠	⊠	🛒	⊠	⊠	☕
—	0	—	—	—	Inverness	d																			
—	—	0	—	—	Aberdeen	d																			
—	—	71¼	—	—	Dundee	d																			
—	118	—	—	—	Perth	d																			
—	130¼	187¼	—	—	**Edinburgh** [10]	d																			
—	131½	188½	—	—	Haymarket	d																			
0	—	—	—	—	**Glasgow Central** [15]	d																			
12¾	—	—	—	—	Motherwell	d																			
28¾	158	—	—	—	Carstairs	d																			
77	—	263½	—	—	Lockerbie	d																			
102¼	—	—	—	—	**Carlisle** [8]	a																			
—	—	—	—	—		d																			
120	—	—	—	—	Penrith North Lakes	d																			
—	—	—	—	—	Windermere	d																			
152¼	—	—	—	—	Oxenholme Lake District	a																			
—	—	—	—	—		d																			
—	—	—	—	—	Barrow-in-Furness	d									04 20		*04b20*								
171¼	—	—	—	—	Lancaster [6]	a									05 22										
—	—	—	—	—		d								04 50	05 22		05b36								
192¼	—	—	—	—	**Preston** [8]	a								05 40	05 42		05b51								
—	—	—	—	—	Blackpool North	a																			
—	—	—	—	—		d											*05 19*	05 19				*05 30*			
—	—	—	0	—	**Preston** [8]	d											05 54	05 58				06 15			
207½	—	—	—	—	Wigan North Western	a											06 04	06 14				06 26			
—	—	—	—	—		d											06 06	06 15				06 27			
—	—	—	20	—	Bolton	a												06 31							
—	—	—	31¼	—	**Manchester Piccadilly** [10]	a												06 56							
—	—	—	—	—	Manchester Airport	a												07 15							
—	—	—	—	—	**Liverpool Lime Street** [10]	a																*07 29*			
—	0	—	—	—		d						05 44									06 27				06 35
—	5½	—	—	—	Liverpool South Parkway [7]	d																			06 45
—	13	—	—	—	Runcorn	d						06 00									06 43				06 53
219¼	—	—	—	—	Warrington Bank Quay	a											06 25					06 44			
—	—	—	—	—		d											06 27					06 45			
231½	23¾	—	—	—	Hartford	d																			07 05
—	—	—	—	0	**Manchester Piccadilly** [10]	d			05 20				06 02							06 17			06 35	06 45	
—	—	—	37	5¾	Stockport	d			05u31				06u11							06 25			06u44	06u53	
—	—	—	—	—	Manchester Airport	d															*05c53*				
—	—	—	—	—	Wilmslow	d			05 39												*06 05*		06 51		
—	—	—	—	—	Holyhead	d	02 15														*04e27*				
—	—	—	—	—	Bangor (Gwynedd)	d	02 42														*05e00*				
—	—	—	—	—	Llandudno	d																			
—	—	—	—	—	Llandudno Junction	d	03 00					*04 55*									*05e18*				
—	—	—	—	—	Chester	d	03 40	*04 55*				*05 51*									*06 30*				
243¼	35½	—	—	—	**Crewe** [10]	a	03 59		05 56			06 20					06 46				07 02	07 08	07 10		07 20
—	—	—	—	—		d	04 02	05 45	05 59		06 09	06 24				06 36	06 49				07 05	07 10	07 13		07 23
—	—	—	49	17¾	Macclesfield	d							06 24							06 38				07 09	
—	—	—	57	25¾	Congleton	d				←															
—	—	—	68¾	37¼	**Stoke-on-Trent**	d		06 04		06 04			06 40							06 54				07 24	
267¾	—	—	—	53½	**Stafford**	a	04 29	→	06 16	06 22	06 29	06 42				06 56				07 13	07 24				07 43
—	—	—	—	—		d	04 30		06 18	06 24	06 30	06 43				06 57				07 15	07 25				07 46
—	—	—	—	59¼	Penkridge	a					06 35														07 51
—	—	—	—	69¾	Wolverhampton [7]	a	04 44			06 41	06 47									07 32		07 48			08 05
74	—	—	—	—	Coseley	a																			
77¼	—	—	—	—	Sandwell & Dudley	a														07 44					
—	—	—	—	82½	**Birmingham New Street** [12]	a	05 12			06 58	07 08									07 55		08 11			08 29
—	—	—	—	—		d				07 03										08 00					
—	—	—	—	91	Birmingham International	a	*05 39*			07 14	*07 40*									08 09		*08 39*			
—	—	—	—	101½	Coventry	a	*05 49*			07 23	*07 54*									08 20		*08 49*			
285	—	—	99¼	—	Lichfield Trent Valley	a			06 32							07 15	07 19			→					
291½	—	—	—	—	Tamworth Low Level	a			06 39				07 05			07 22			←						
304¼	—	—	—	—	Nuneaton	a			06 50			07 05				07f37			07f37		07 47				
318¾	—	—	—	113	Rugby	a	*06 02*		07 04				07 27			→	07 45		07 54						
—	—	—	—	—	Northampton	a													08g29						
351½	—	—	—	—	Milton Keynes Central	a																			
383½	—	—	—	—	Watford Junction	a			07s44			07s57													
—	—	—	—	—	Gatwick Airport [10]	a																			
401¼	—	—	—	—	**London Euston** [15]	a			08 04			08 19	08 27				08 40				08 58		09 01	09 07	

For general notes see front of timetable
For details of catering facilities see Directory of Train Operators

A To Bournemouth (Table 51)

B 21 July to 8 September

C Also stops at Rugeley Trent Valley 0707 and Atherstone 0731

D 🛒 to Wolverhampton, ⊠ from Wolverhampton

b Not Mondays 21 July to 8 September

c Change at Wilmslow and Crewe

e Change at Chester and Crewe

f From 25 August arr. 0738

g 28 July to 22 August arr. 0831

OVERNIGHT SLEEPERS. For Sleeper trains, operated by First ScotRail, please refer to Tables 400 - 404

Scotland and North West England → West Midlands and London

Route Diagram - see first page of Table 65

		XC	TP	VT	VT	VT	VT	VT	XC	VT		VT MO	VT	VT MO	LM	XC	VT	NT	VT	NT	LM	TP	VT	VT MO	XC
		1 ◇	1 ◇	1 ◇	1 ◇	1 ◇	1 ◇	1 ◇	1 ◇	1 ◇			1 ◇	1 ◇	1 ◇	R 1	1 ◇		1 ◇		1 ◇	1 ◇	1 ◇	1 ◇	1 ◇
		A							A			B 🚌	C	B		D						E	C	B	G
		☕		⊠	⊠	⊠	⊠	⊠	☕	⊠			⊠	⊠	🛒	☕	⊠		☕		🛒	🛒	⊠	⊠	☕
Inverness	d																								
Aberdeen	d																								
Dundee	d																								
Perth	d																								
Edinburgh 10	d																								
Haymarket	d																								
Glasgow Central 15	d																								
Motherwell	d																								
Carstairs	d																								
Lockerbie	d																								
Carlisle 8	a																								
	d											04 35	05 44										06 09	06 30	
Penrith North Lakes	d											05 10	05 58										06 23	06 44	
Windermere	d																						06 20	06b20	
Oxenholme Lake District	a											06 05	06 21										06 46	07 07	
	d											06 05	06 22										06 47	07 08	
Barrow-in-Furness	d		05c00																			06 15			
Lancaster 6	a		05c53									06 50	06 37									07 15	07 22	07 22	
	d		05c53		06 33								06 38	06 58								07 16	07 23	07 23	
Preston 8	a		06 27		06 48								07 15	07 15								07 35	07 40	07 40	
Blackpool North	a				07 31								07 56	07 56									08 12	08 12	
	d				06 09								06 34	06 34				06 57					07 03	07 03	
Preston 8	d		06 28		06 51								07 18	07 18				07 25	07 29	←		07 40	07 43	07 43	
Wigan North Western	a				07 01								07 29	07 29				07 44	07 40	07 44			07 55	07 55	
	d				07 03								07 30	07 30				→	07 41	07 45			07 55	07 55	
Bolton	a		06 52		07e33																	08 02	08e24	08e24	
Manchester Piccadilly 10	a		07 15		07e54																	08 25	08e47	08e47	
Manchester Airport	a		07 40		08e19																	08 42	09e06	09e06	
Liverpool Lime Street 10	a				07 59															08 27			09 19	09 19	
	d					07 07									07 18						07 40				
Liverpool South Parkway 7	d																				07 50				
Runcorn	d					07u22									07 35						07 58				
Warrington Bank Quay	a				07 12								07 40	07 40					07 51				08 07	08 07	
	d				07 14								07 41	07 41					07 53				08 07	08 07	
Hartford	d																				08 08				
Manchester Piccadilly 10	d	06 54		07 05			06f38			07 15						07 24	07 45				07 28				07 54
Stockport	d			07u14			06f48			07u23						07 33	07u55				07 37				08 03
Manchester Airport	d						06f57																		
Wilmslow	d						07f04												07 27		07 46				
Holyhead	d						05 32																06g00	06g00	
Bangor (Gwynedd)	d						06 01																06g28	06g28	
Llandudno	d																						06h39	06h39	
Llandudno Junction	d						06 21																06g53	06g53	
Chester	d						07 15												07 30				08 00	08 00	
Crewe 10	a						07 38								07 54				08 12		08 23		08 31	08 31	
	d						07 48								07 56				08 15		08 25		08 34	08 34	
Macclesfield	d									07 37						07 47	08 07								08 16
Congleton	d	07 21							←							07 55									08 24
Stoke-on-Trent	d	07 33							07 33	07 53						08 08	08 22								08 39
Stafford	a	→			07 46				07 53				08 14	08 14	08 20	08 25					08 45				08 55
	d				07 48				07 54				08 16	08 16	08 21	08 26					08 46				08 57
Penkridge	a																				08 51				
Wolverhampton 7	a								08 12						08 37	08 41			08 48		09 06				09 12
Coseley	a																				09 12				
Sandwell & Dudley	a														08 46										
Birmingham New Street 12	a								08 30						08 58	08 58			09 11		09 30				09 30
	d															09 03									09 33
Birmingham International	a							←	08 57							09 14			09 39						09 57
Coventry	a							08 20	09 15							09 23			09 49						10 15
Lichfield Trent Valley	a																								
Tamworth Low Level	a																								
Nuneaton	a									08 29															
Rugby	a												08 49	08 49									09 23	09 23	
Northampton	a																								
Milton Keynes Central	a									09 04							09 31						09 46	09 46	
Watford Junction	a						09j14	09k20					09s28	09s28											
Gatwick Airport 10	a																								12 33
London Euston 15	⊖ a			09 11	09 14	09 17	09m36	09n44		09 45			09 53	09 53			10 09						10 27	10 27	

For general notes see front of timetable
For details of catering facilities see Directory of Train Operators

- **A** To Reading (Table 51)
- **B** 21 July to 8 September
- **C** Not Mondays 21 July to 8 September
- **D** To Bournemouth (Table 51)
- **E** 🛒 from Preston
- **G** To Brighton (Table 51)
- **b** By bus
- **c** 15 minutes later on Mondays
- **e** Change at Preston
- **f** Change at Crewe
- **g** Change at Chester and Crewe
- **h** Change at Llandudno Junction, Chester and Crewe
- **j** Stops to set down only. 28 July to 22 August arr. 0919
- **k** Stops to set down only. 28 July to 22 August arr. 0914
- **m** 28 July to 22 August arr. 0941
- **n** 28 July to 22 August arr. 0939

OVERNIGHT SLEEPERS. For Sleeper trains, operated by First ScotRail, please refer to Tables 400 - 404

Scotland and North West England → West Midlands and London

Route Diagram - see first page of Table 65

		VT	VT	VT	LM	XC	VT	LM	VT	TP	NT	VT	NT	XC	VT		VT	LM	XC	VT	NT	VT	LM	TP	VT
																			R						
		1◇	1◇	1◇	1◇	1◇	1◇	1◇	1◇	1◇		1◇		1◇	1◇		1◇	1◇	1	1◇		1◇	1◇	1◇	1◇
						A				B				C					D		E				
		⊠	☕	⊠	🛒	☕	☕	🛒	⊠	🛒		⊠		☕	⊠		⊠	🛒	☕	⊠		☕	🛒	🛒	⊠
Inverness	d																								
Aberdeen	d																								
Dundee	d																								
Perth	d																								05b15
Edinburgh 10	d																					06 36			
Haymarket	d																					06u40			
Glasgow Central 15	d											05 55												06 40	07 10
Motherwell	d											06u10													
Carstairs	d																								
Lockerbie	d																							07 40	
Carlisle 8	a											07 10										07 51		08 02	08 19
	d											07 14										07 53		08 04	08 21
Penrith North Lakes	d											07 29										08 09		08 19	
Windermere	d											07 24												08 20	
Oxenholme Lake District	a											07 51										08 32		08 59	
	d											07 53										08 33		08 59	
Barrow-in-Furness	d									07 01	07 17										07 58				
Lancaster 6	a									07 58	08 19	08 27									08 59	09 08		09 14	09 27
	d									07 59	08 19	08 29									09 00	09 09		09 14	09 29
Preston 8	a									08 17	08 42	08 46									09 25	09 26		09 33	09 47
Blackpool North	a									08 51		09 32										10 02			10 21
	d						07 41					08 09	←									08 41			09 11
Preston 8	d						08 29			08 34	08 50	08 49	08 50									09 29		09 38	09 49
Wigan North Western	a						08 39				→	08 59	09 10									09 40			10 00
	d						08 41					09 01	09 11									09 41			10 02
Bolton	a									08 58		09c34												09 58	10c34
Manchester Piccadilly 10	a									09 20		09c57												10 20	10c57
Manchester Airport ✈	a									09 40		10c19												10 40	11c19
Liverpool Lime Street 10	a						09 49						09 53									10 49			
	d	08 15			08 19			08 40									09 15	09 19					09 40		
Liverpool South Parkway 7 ✈	d							08 50															09 50		
Runcorn	d	08 31			08 35			08 58									09 31	09 35					09 58		
Warrington Bank Quay	a						08 51					09 10										09 51			10 11
	d						08 52					09 12										09 53			10 13
Hartford	d							09 10															10 08		
Manchester Piccadilly 10	d		07e34	08 15		08 24			08 45			08 34		08 54	09 15				09 24	09 45			09 34		
Stockport	d		07f43	08u24		08 33			08u55			08 44		09 03	09u23				09 33	09u54			09 42		
Manchester Airport ✈	d		08e00	08 00													09 00								
Wilmslow	d		08e07	08 33								08 52					09 07					09 24	09 54		
Holyhead	d		06 45														07 15								
Bangor (Gwynedd)	d		07 12														08 01								
Llandudno	d		07 03									07g47													08g47
Llandudno Junction	d		07 31									07g56					08 27								08g56
Chester	d		08 22				08 30					09 00					09 19								10 00
Crewe 10	a		08 45	08 51	08 59		09 13	09 23				09 31					09 50	09 58				10 12	10 23		10 32
	d		08 50	08 54	09 00		09 15	09 25				09 34					09 53	10 00				10 15	10 25		10 34
Macclesfield	d					08 47			09 08					09 16					09 47	10 07					
Congleton	d													09 24											
Stoke-on-Trent	d					09 04			09 24					09 39	09 50				10 04	10 23					
Stafford	a			09 12	09 21	09 25		09 45									10 10	10 20	10 25				10 45		
	d			09 13	09 21	09 26		09 46									10 12	10 21	10 26				10 46		
Penkridge	a							09 51															10 52		
Wolverhampton 7	a				09 36	09 41	09 48	10 06						10 12				10 36	10 41			10 47	11 07		
Coseley	a							10 12															11 12		
Sandwell & Dudley	a				09 46													10 46							
Birmingham New Street 12	a				09 58	09 58	10 11	10 30						10 30				10 58	10 58			11 11	11 30		
	d																		11 03						
Birmingham International ✈	a					10 27	10 39							10 57					11 14			11 39			
Coventry	a					10 45	10 49							11 15					11 23			11 49			
Lichfield Trent Valley	a			09 26																					
Tamworth Low Level	a		09 22																						
Nuneaton	a	09 24															10 34								
Rugby	a											10 23													11 23
Northampton	a																								
Milton Keynes Central	a			10 11																11 28					11 46
Watford Junction	a		10s21						10s46			11s02					11s25								
Gatwick Airport 10 ✈	a																								
London Euston 15 ⊖	a	10 35	10 46	10 50					11 09			11 27			11 28		11 48			12 07					12 26

For general notes see front of timetable
For details of catering facilities see Directory of Train Operators

A To Plymouth (Table 51)
B 🛒 from Preston
C To Reading (Table 51)
D To Bournemouth (Table 51)
E From Maryport (Table 100)
b Via Glasgow Queen Street and Glasgow Central. Passengers make their own way from one station to the other
c Change at Preston
e Change at Crewe
f Change at Wilmslow and Crewe
g Change at Chester and Crewe

OVERNIGHT SLEEPERS. For Sleeper trains, operated by First ScotRail, please refer to Tables 400 - 404

Scotland and North West England → West Midlands and London

Route Diagram - see first page of Table 65

		NT	XC	VT	VT	LM	XC	VT	LM	NT	VT	LM	TP	VT	XC	VT	VT	VT	LM	XC		VT	NT	TP
			1 ◇	1 ◇	1 ◇	1	1 ◇	1 ◇	1		1 ◇	1 ◇	1 ◇	1 ◇	1 ◇	1 ◇	1 ◇	1 ◇	1 ◇	R 1		1 ◇		1 ◇
			A			B	C		B	D			E		A					G				
			◫	⊠	⊠	⊤	◫	⊠	⊤		◫	⊤	⊤	⊠	◫	◫	◫	◫	⊤	◫		◫		
Inverness	d																							
Aberdeen	d																							
Dundee	d																							
Perth	d													06b09										
Edinburgh 10	d																							
Haymarket	d																							
Glasgow Central 15	d										07 45			08 10										
Motherwell	d													08u28										
Carstairs	d																							
Lockerbie	d																							
Carlisle 8	a										09 11			09 30										
	d										09 13			09 34										
Penrith North Lakes	d										09 29			09 49										
Windermere	d										09 28													10 18
Oxenholme Lake District	a										09 52			10 11										10 35
	d										09 54			10 13										10 37
Barrow-in-Furness	d												09 15											
Lancaster 6	a										10 08		10 15	10 27										10 52
	d									09 35	10 09		10 16	10 29										10 53
Preston 8	a									10 01	10 27		10 34	10 49										11 13
Blackpool North	a									10 57			11 21	11 32										11c54
	d	09 25									09 38			10 11									10 25	
Preston 8	d	09 50									10 28		10 38	10 49									10 50	
Wigan North Western	a	10 10									10 40			10 59									11 11	
	d	10 11									10 42			11 01									11 11	
Bolton	a												10 58	11e34										
Manchester Piccadilly 10	a												11 20	11e57										
Manchester Airport	a												11 40	12e19										
Liverpool Lime Street 10	a	10 52									11 49												11 52	
	d				10 15	10 19						10 40						11 15	11 19					
Liverpool South Parkway 7	d											10 50												
Runcorn	d				10 31	10 35						10 58						11 31	11 35					
Warrington Bank Quay	a										10 52			11 10										
	d										10 53			11 12										
Hartford	d					10 46						11 09												
Manchester Piccadilly 10	d		09 54	10 15			10 24	10 45						10 34	10 54	11 15				11 24		11 45		
Stockport	d		10 03	10u24			10 33	10u54						10 42	11 03	11u23				11 33		11u54		
Manchester Airport	d				10 00												11f00							
Wilmslow	d				10 06						10 24			10 54			11f06							
Holyhead	d					08g10											09 50	09 28						
Bangor (Gwynedd)	d					09g04											10 18	10 07						
Llandudno	d													09g47			10 14	10h14						
Llandudno Junction	d					09g27								09g56			10 36	10 30						
Chester	d					10 29								11 00			11 28	11 14						
Crewe 10	a				10 50	10 58					11 13	11 23		11 31			11 47	11 50	11 58					
	d				10 53	11 00					11 14	11 25		11 34			11 49	11 53	12 00					
Macclesfield	d		10 16				10 47	11 07							11 16					11 47		12 07		
Congleton	d														11 24									
Stoke-on-Trent	d		10 39	10 50			11 04	11 23							11 39	11 50				12 04		12 23		
Stafford	a				11 10	11 19	11 25					11 45						12 10	12 20	12 25				
	d				11 12	11 21	11 26					11 46						12 12	12 21	12 26				
Penkridge	a											11 51												
Wolverhampton 7	a		11 12				11 41				11 48	12 06			12 12				12 36	12 41				
Coseley	a											12 12												
Sandwell & Dudley	a																		12 47					
Birmingham New Street 12	a		11 30				11 58				12 11	12 30			12 30				12 58	12 58				
	d																			13 03				
Birmingham International	a		11 57				12 27				12 39				12 57					13 14				
Coventry	a		12 15				12 45				12 49				13 15					13 24				
Lichfield Trent Valley	a					11 40																		
Tamworth Low Level	a					11 47			←															
Nuneaton	a				11 34	12 02 →			12 02									12 34						
Rugby	a								12 16					12 23										
Northampton	a																							
Milton Keynes Central	a				12 09																			
Watford Junction	a							12s46						13s03				13s24						
Gatwick Airport 10	a																							
London Euston 15 ⊖	a			12 26	12 48			13 09	13 18					13 27		13 28	13 40	13 47				14 04		

For general notes see front of timetable
For details of catering facilities see Directory of Train Operators

A To Reading (Table 51)
B Also stops at Rugeley Trent Valley 1132 and Atherstone 1156
C To Plymouth (Table 51)
D From Morecambe (Table 98)
E ⊤ from Preston
G To Bournemouth (Table 51)
b Via Glasgow Queen Street and Glasgow Central. Passengers make their own way from one station to the other
c From 6 October arr. 2 minutes later
e Change at Preston
f Change at Crewe
g Change at Chester and Crewe
h Change at Llandudno Junction and Crewe

OVERNIGHT SLEEPERS. For Sleeper trains, operated by First ScotRail, please refer to Tables 400 - 404

Scotland and North West England → West Midlands and London

Route Diagram - see first page of Table 65

		TP	TP	VT	TP	LM	NT	VT	VT	XC	VT	VT	NT	VT	LM	XC	LM	VT	XC	VT	TP	VT	NT	VT	VT
				R												R				R					
		1◇	1◇	1	1◇	1◇		1◇	1◇	1◇	1◇	1◇		1◇	1◇	1	1◇	1◇	1◇	1	1◇	1◇		1◇	1◇
										A						B			C		D				
		⊼	⊼	☕	⊼	⊼		☕	⊠	☕	☕	☕		☕	⊼	☕	⊼	☕	☕	☕	⊼	☕		☕	☕
Inverness	d																					06b45			
Aberdeen	d			06 00																06c34		07 20			
Dundee	d	06 38		07b16																07c52		08 31			
Perth	d	06 14		07b03					07c14											08c13		08b47			
Edinburgh 10	d	08 21		08 51																		10 10			
Haymarket	d			08u56																		10u16			
Glasgow Central 15	d		08 40						09 39											10 10					
Motherwell	d																								
Carstairs	d																								
Lockerbie	d		09 40																			11 14			
Carlisle 8	a	09 54	10 02	10 16					10 47											11 22		11 32			
	d		10 06	10 17					10 50											11 22		11 34			
Penrith North Lakes	d		10 22																			11 49			
Windermere	d																					11 30			
Oxenholme Lake District	a		10 46	10 52																		12 11			
	d		10 46	10 53																		12 13			
Barrow-in-Furness	d			09 57																	11 18				
Lancaster 6	a		11 04	11 09																12 12	12 16	12 27			
	d		11 05	11 10				11 29												12 12	12 16	12 29			
Preston 8	a		11 23	11 27				11 46	11 50											12 31	12 36	12 46			
Blackpool North	a			12 01				12 20	12 32			←										13 21			
	d			10 41	←		11 25		11 11			11 25								11 41		12 11	12 25		
Preston 8	d		11 38 →	11 29	11 38		11 50	11 56 →	11 52			11 56	←							12 32	12 38	12 49	12 50		
Wigan North Western	a			11 40			12 10 →					12 07	12 10							12 44		12 59	13 10		
	d			11 41								12 08	12 11							12 45		13 01	13 11		
Bolton	a				11 58				12 34											13e12	12 58	13e34			
Manchester Piccadilly 10	a				12 20				12 57											13e35	13 20	13e57			
Manchester Airport ✈	a				12 40				13 19											14f01	13 40	14e19			
Liverpool Lime Street 10	a			12 49								13 19	12 52							13 49			13 52		
	d					11 40								12 15			12 40								13 15
Liverpool South Parkway 7 ✈	d					11 50											12 50								
Runcorn	d					11 58								12 31			12 58								13 31
Warrington Bank Quay	a			11 51								12 18								12 57		13 10			
	d			11 52								12 20								12 59		13 12			
Hartford	d					12 08											13 10								
Manchester Piccadilly 10	d									11 54	12 15	11 34				12 24	12 34	12 45	12 54					13 15	
Stockport	d									12 03	12u24	11 42				12 33	12 42	12u54	13 03					13u24	
Manchester Airport ✈	d											12 00													13 00
Wilmslow	d			11 24								12 06					12 54								13 06
Holyhead	d														10g30										
Bangor (Gwynedd)	d														11g03										
Llandudno	d											10g44										11g47			
Llandudno Junction	d											10g53			11g26							11g56			
Chester	d											12 00			12 29							13 00			
Crewe 10	a			12 12		12 24						12 41		12 50			13 23			13 27		13 32			13 50
	d			12 13		12 24						12 44		12 53	13 00		13 25			13 33		13 34			13 53
Macclesfield	d									12 16						12 47		13 07	13 16						
Congleton	d																		13 24						
Stoke-on-Trent	d									12 39	12 50					13 04		13 23	13 39					13 49	
Stafford	a					12 46								13 10	13 19	13 25	13 45								14 10
	d					12 46								13 12	13 21	13 26	13 46								14 12
Penkridge	a					12 52											13 51								
Wolverhampton 7	a			12 48		13 06				13 12					13 37	13 41	14 06		14 12	14 17					
Coseley	a					13 12											14 12								
Sandwell & Dudley	a														13 46										
Birmingham New Street 12	a			13 11		13 30				13 30					13 58	13 58	14 30		14 30	14 41					
	d																								
Birmingham International ✈	a			13 39						13 57						14 27			14 57	15 09					
Coventry	a			13 49						14 15						14 45			15 15	15 19					
Lichfield Trent Valley	a																								
Tamworth Low Level	a																								
Nuneaton	a													13 34											14 34
Rugby	a											13 38										14 23			
Northampton	a																								
Milton Keynes Central	a											14 01		14 09											
Watford Junction	a																	14s46				15s02			15s25
Gatwick Airport 10 ✈	a																								
London Euston 15 ⊖	a								14 05		14 26	14 40		14 49				15 08				15 26		15 28	15 48

For general notes see front of timetable
For details of catering facilities see Directory of Train Operators

A To Reading (Table 51)
B To Penzance (Table 135)
C To Guildford (Table 51)
D ⊼ from Preston
b Change at Haymarket
c Via Glasgow Queen Street and Glasgow Central. Passengers make their own way from one station to the other
e Change at Preston
f Change at Preston and Manchester Piccadilly
g Change at Chester and Crewe

OVERNIGHT SLEEPERS. For Sleeper trains, operated by First ScotRail, please refer to Tables 400 - 404

Scotland and North West England → West Midlands and London

Route Diagram - see first page of Table 65

		LM	XC		VT	TP	VT	TP	LM	VT	XC	VT	VT	VT	LM	XC	VT	NT	TP	VT	TP	LM	NT	VT	NT
		1◇	1◇		1◇	1◇	1◇	1◇	1◇	1◇	1◇	1◇	1◇	1◇	1◇	R 1	1◇		1	R 1	1◇	1◇		1◇	
			A			B		B			C					D									
Inverness	d																		07 55						
Aberdeen	d						08b20												08 51						
Dundee	d						09b32												09 59						
Perth	d									09c08									09 55	10c13					
Edinburgh 10	d						10 51												11 52						
Haymarket	d						10u57																		
Glasgow Central 15	d									11 10										12 10					
Motherwell	d									11u26															
Carstairs	d																								
Lockerbie	d																								
Carlisle 8	a						12 11			12 32									13 09	13 21					
	d						12 13			12 34									13 11	13 21					
Penrith North Lakes	d						12 29			12 49									13 25						
Windermere	d					12 21													13 24						
Oxenholme Lake District	a					12 38	12 52			13 11									13 49	13 57					
	d					12 40	12 53			13 13									13 49	13 59					
Barrow-in-Furness	d									12 06									12 57						
Lancaster 6	a					12 58	13 08			13 28									14 05						
	d					12 59	13 09			13 29									14 06					14 29	
Preston 8	a					13 17	13 26			13 46									14 24	14 28				14 46	
Blackpool North	a					13e54	13 59			14 21									15 00					15 21	
	d						12 41	←		13 11								13 25		13 41	←		14 21	14 11	
Preston 8	d					13 38	13 29	13 38		13 49								13 50	14 38	14 30	14 38		14 46	14 49	←
Wigan North Western	a					→	13 40			14 00								14 11	→	14 41			15 09	14 59	15 09
	d						13 41			14 01								14 11		14 42			→	15 01	15 11
Bolton	a							13 58		14f34											14 58				
Manchester Piccadilly 10	a							14 20		14f57											15 20				
Manchester Airport	a							14 40		15f19											15 40				
Liverpool Lime Street 10	a						14 49											14 52		15 49					15 52
	d	13 19							13 40					14 15								14 40			
Liverpool South Parkway 7	d								13 50													14 50			
Runcorn	d	13 35							13 58					14 31								14 58			
Warrington Bank Quay	a						13 51			14 11										14 52				15 10	
	d						13 53			14 12										14 54				15 12	
Hartford	d								14 08													15 08		→	
Manchester Piccadilly 10	d		13 24		13 45				13 34		13 54	14 05	14 15			14 24	14 45								
Stockport	d		13 33		13u54				13 42		14 03	14 15	14u24			14 33	14u54								
Manchester Airport	d											14 00													
Wilmslow	d						13 24		13 54			14 25								14 26					
Holyhead	d						11 40													12g35					
Bangor (Gwynedd)	d						12 19													13g04					
Llandudno	d									12g47										13h14					
Llandudno Junction	d						12 42			12g56										13g27					
Chester	d						13 33			14 00										14 30					
Crewe 10	a	13 58					14 12		14 23	14 32		14 42		14 50						15 12		15 23			
	d	14 00					14 14		14 25	14 34		14 49		14 53	15 00					15 15		15 25			
Macclesfield	d		13 47		14 07						14 16					14 47	15 07								
Congleton	d																								
Stoke-on-Trent	d		14 04		14 23						14 39		14 50			15 04	15 23								
Stafford	a	14 20	14 25						14 45					15 10	15 20	15 25						15 45			
	d	14 21	14 26						14 46					15 12	15 21	15 26						15 46			
Penkridge	a								14 51													15 51			
Wolverhampton 7	a	14 36	14 41				14 47		15 06		15 12				15 36	15 41				15 48		16 06			
Coseley	a								15 12													16 12			
Sandwell & Dudley	a	14 46													15 46										
Birmingham New Street 12	a	14 58	14 58				15 11		15 30		15 30				15 58	15 58				16 11		16 30			
	d		15 03																						
Birmingham International	a		15 14				15 39				15 57					16 27				16 39					
Coventry	a		15 23				15 49				16 15					16 45				16 49					
Lichfield Trent Valley	a											15 17													
Tamworth Low Level	a											15 24													
Nuneaton	a											→		15 34											
Rugby	a									15 23															
Northampton	a																								
Milton Keynes Central	a				15 28					15 46				16 09											
Watford Junction	a																16s46								
Gatwick Airport 10	a																								
London Euston 15	⊖ a				16 07					16 27			16 28	16 48			17 08								

For general notes see front of timetable
For details of catering facilities see Directory of Train Operators

A To Bournemouth (Table 51)
B ⚲ from Preston
C To Reading (Table 51)
D To Penzance (Table 135)
b Change at Haymarket
c Via Glasgow Queen Street and Glasgow Central. Passengers make their own way from one station to the other
e From 6 October arr. 2 minutes later
f Change at Preston
g Change at Chester and Crewe
h Change at Llandudno Junction, Chester and Crewe

OVERNIGHT SLEEPERS. For Sleeper trains, operated by First ScotRail, please refer to Tables 400 - 404

Scotland and North West England → West Midlands and London

Route Diagram - see first page of Table 65

		VT	XC	VT	VT	VT	VT	LM		XC	TP	TP	VT	TP	VT	LM	VT	VT	VT	NT	XC	VT	VT	VT	LM
		1 ◇	R 1	1 ◇	1 ◇	1 ◇	1 ◇	1 ◇		R 1	1 ◇	1 ◇	R 1	1 ◇	1 ◇	1 ◇	1 ◇	1 ◇	1 ◇		R 1	1 ◇	1 ◇	1 ◇	1
			A							B				C							D				E
		🍴	🍴	🍴	🍴	🍴	🍴	🛒		🍴			🍴	🛒	🍴	🛒	🍴	🍴	🍴		🍴	🍴	🍴	🍴	🛒
Inverness	d																								
Aberdeen	d	09b32											10c22												
Dundee	d	10b52											11c30												
Perth	d	11b14																							
Edinburgh 10	d												12 52												
Haymarket	d												12u56												
Glasgow Central 15	d	12 49																							
Motherwell	d																								
Carstairs	d																								
Lockerbie	d												13 53												
Carlisle 8	a	13 57											14 12												
	d	14 00											14 14						14 34						
Penrith North Lakes	d												14 29						14 48						
Windermere	d										14 18														
Oxenholme Lake District	a										14 35		14 52						15 11						
	d										14 37		14 53						15 12						
Barrow-in-Furness	d											14 10													
Lancaster 6	a										14 54	15 02	15 07	←					15 27						
	d										15 15		15 08	15 15					15 28						
Preston 8	a	14 59										→	15 25	15 34					15 45						
Blackpool North	a	15e54											16 00						16 21						
	d	14 30											14 41						15 11	15 25					
Preston 8	d	15 02											15 29	15 38					15 48	15 50					
Wigan North Western	a												15 40						15 59	16 10					
	d												15 41						16 00	16 11					
Bolton	a	15 34												15 58					16f34						
Manchester Piccadilly 10	a	15 57												16 20					16f57						
Manchester Airport	a	16 19												16 40					17f19						
Liverpool Lime Street 10	a												16 49							16 53					
	d						15 15	15 19								15 40								16 15	
Liverpool South Parkway 7	d															15 50									
Runcorn	d						15 31	15 35								15 58								16 31	
Warrington Bank Quay	a					←							15 51						16 10						
	d					15 12							15 52						16 11						
Hartford	d															16 08									
Manchester Piccadilly 10	d		14 54		15 15	14 34				15 24						15 34	15 45				15 54	16 15			
Stockport	d		15 03		15u24	14 42				15 33						15 42	15u54				16 03	16u24			
Manchester Airport	d						15 00																16g00		
Wilmslow	d					14 54	15 06						15 24			15 54							16g06		
Holyhead	d					13h20							13 35		14 14										
Bangor (Gwynedd)	d					13h49							14 14		14 43										
Llandudno	d					13h47									14 35								15 08		
Llandudno Junction	d					14h07							14 37		15 03								15 17		
Chester	d					15 03							15 30		15 48				16 00				16 08		
Crewe 10	a					15 35	15 50	15 58					16 11		16 14	16 23		←	16 31				16 38	16 50	
	d					15 38	15 53	16 00					16 11		16 28	16 25		16 28	16 34				16 49	16 53	17 00
Macclesfield	d		15 16							15 47					→		16 07				16 16				
Congleton	d		15 24																						
Stoke-on-Trent	d		15 39		15 50					16 04							16 23				16 39	16 50			
Stafford	a						16 10	16 20		16 25						16 46								17 10	17 19
	d						16 12	16 21		16 26						16 46								17 12	17 20
Penkridge	a															16 52									
Wolverhampton 7	a		16 12					16 36		16 41			16 48			17 05					17 12				
Coseley	a															17 12									
Sandwell & Dudley	a							16 47																	
Birmingham New Street 12	a		16 30					16 58		16 58			17 11			17 30					17 30				
	d		16 33							17 03															
Birmingham International	a									17 14			17 39								17 55				
Coventry	a									17 24			17 52								18 04				
Lichfield Trent Valley	a			←																					17 37
Tamworth Low Level	a			15 24																					17 44
Nuneaton	a			15 38			16 34																	17 34	17 59
Rugby	a			15 53		16 38													17 23					17 49	18 14
Northampton	a			16 16																					→
Milton Keynes Central	a			16 35													17 28	17 40	17 46					18 11	
Watford Junction	a					17s17	17s25																18s17		
Gatwick Airport 10	a		19 52																						
London Euston 15	a	17 17		17 22	17 27	17 40	17 47										18 07	18 21	18 27			18 28	18 42	18 50	

For general notes see front of timetable
For details of catering facilities see Directory of Train Operators

A To Brighton (Table 51)
B To Bournemouth (Table 51)
C 🛒 from Preston
D To Reading (Table 51)
E Also stops at Rugeley Trent Valley 1729 and Atherstone 1753
b Via Glasgow Queen Street and Glasgow Central. Passengers make their own way from one station to the other
c Change at Haymarket
e From 6 October arr. 2 minutes later
f Change at Preston
g Change at Crewe
h Change at Chester and Crewe

OVERNIGHT SLEEPERS. For Sleeper trains, operated by First ScotRail, please refer to Tables 400 - 404

Scotland and North West England → West Midlands and London

Route Diagram - see first page of Table 65

		XC	TP	VT	TP	VT	LM	LM	VT	XC	VT	VT	LM		NT	XC	VT	VT	LM	TP	VT	XC	NT	VT	VT
		1 ◇	1 ◇	1 ◇	1 ◇	1 ◇	1 ◇	1 ◇	1 ◇	R 1	1 ◇	1 ◇	1 ◇			R 1	1 ◇	1 ◇	1 ◇	1 ◇	1 ◇	R 1		1 ◇	1 ◇
		A					B			C						D				E		C			
		⊡	⊼	⊡	⊼	⊡	⊼	⊼	⊡	⊡	⊡	⊡	⊼			⊡	⊡	⊡	⊼	⊼	⊡	⊡		⊡	⊡
Inverness	d		09b19															10 53							
Aberdeen	d			10b42														12c24							
Dundee	d			11b52														13c33							
Perth	d		11b38	12b14														13 04			13b14				
Edinburgh 10	d																	14 52							
Haymarket	d																	14u57							
Glasgow Central 15	d		13 40	14 10																	15 10				
Motherwell	d																				15u29				
Carstairs	d																								
Lockerbie	d		14 38															15 53							
Carlisle 8	a		14 58	15 21														16 12			16 32				
	d		15 08	15 21														16 14			16 34				
Penrith North Lakes	d		15 23															16 29			16 49				
Windermere	d		15 21															16 28							
Oxenholme Lake District	a		15 46															16 52			17 11				
	d		15 47															16 53			17 13				
Barrow-in-Furness	d																	15 28		16 21					
Lancaster 6	a		16 02	16 09														17 08		17 15	17 27				
	d		16 03	16 09					16 29									17 09		17 16	17 29				
Preston 8	a		16 22	16 27					16 46									17 26		17 35	17 46				
Blackpool North	a		17 00						17 34									18 03			18 22				
	d			15 41	←				16 10						16 25			16 38			17 10				
Preston 8	d		16 38	16 29	16 38				16 49						16 50			17 29		17 35	17 49		17 50		
Wigan North Western	a		→	16 40					16 59						17 09			17 40			17 59		18 11		
	d			16 41					17 01						17 11			17 41			18 00		18 11		
Bolton	a				16 58				17e36											17 59	18e34				
Manchester Piccadilly 10	a				17 20				17e57											18 20	18e57				
Manchester Airport	a				17 40				18e19											18 42	19e19				
Liverpool Lime Street 10	a			17 49											17 53			18 49					18 55		
	d							16 40				17 15	17 18						17 37						18 15
Liverpool South Parkway 7	d							16 50					17 28						17 47						
Runcorn	d							16 58				17 31	17 36						17 56						18 31
Warrington Bank Quay	a			16 51					17 10									17 51			18 10				
	d			16 53					17 12									17 53			18 12				
Hartford	d							17 09											18 08						
Manchester Piccadilly 10	d	16 24				16 45			16 34	16 54	17 15					17 24	17 45		17 34			17 54		18 15	17f39
Stockport	d	16 33				16u54			16 42	17 03	17u23					17 33	17u55		17 42			18 03		18u24	17f51
Manchester Airport	d											17 00													18 00
Wilmslow	d			16 24					16 54			17 06						17 26	17 51						18 11
Holyhead	d			14g35														15 39							
Bangor (Gwynedd)	d			15g04														16 17							
Llandudno	d								15g47									16h14			16g47				
Llandudno Junction	d			15g27					15g56									16 40			16g56				
Chester	d			16 31					17 00									17 31			17 59				
Crewe 10	a			17 13				17 23	17 32			17 51	17 58					18 12	18 23		18 31				18 50
	d			17 15				17 24	17 34			17 54	18 00					18 15	18 25		18 34				18 53
Macclesfield	d	16 47				17 08				17 16						17 47	18 08					18 16			
Congleton	d									17 24												18 24			
Stoke-on-Trent	d	17 04				17 24				17 39	17 50					18 04	18 24					18 39		18 51	
Stafford	a	17 25						17 45				18 11	18 20			18 25			18 45						19 10
	d	17 26						17 46				18 13	18 21			18 26			18 46						19 12
Penkridge	a							17 51											18 51						
Wolverhampton 7	a	17 41		17 48				18 06		18 12			18 36			18 41		18 48	19 05			19 12			
Coseley	a							18 12											19 12						
Sandwell & Dudley	a												18 46												
Birmingham New Street 12	a	17 58		18 11				18 30		18 30			18 58			18 58		19 11	19 30			19 30			
	d									18 33						19 03						19 33			
Birmingham International	a	18 29		18 39						18 57			19 27			19 14		19 39	19 57						
Coventry	a	18 46		18 49						19 15			19 45			19 24		19 49							
Lichfield Trent Valley	a																								
Tamworth Low Level	a																								
Nuneaton	a						←					18 35													19 34
Rugby	a						18 14		18 23												19 24				
Northampton	a																								
Milton Keynes Central	a																19 28				19 47				20 09
Watford Junction	a					18s50			19s02			19s28												20s10	
Gatwick Airport 10	a									21 47												22 37			
London Euston 15	⊖ a					19 11	19 18		19 25		19 28	19 50					20 07				20 26			20 33	20 48

For general notes see front of timetable
For details of catering facilities see Directory of Train Operators

A To Plymouth (Table 51)

B Also stops at Rugeley Trent Valley 1729 and Atherstone 1753

C ⊡ to Reading

D To Bournemouth (Table 51)

E ⊼ from Preston

b Via Glasgow Queen Street and Glasgow Central. Passengers make their own way from one station to the other

c Change at Haymarket

e Change at Preston

f Change at Wilmslow and Crewe

g Change at Chester and Crewe

h Change at Llandudno Junction and Crewe

OVERNIGHT SLEEPERS. For Sleeper trains, operated by First ScotRail, please refer to Tables 400 - 404

Scotland and North West England → West Midlands and London

Route Diagram - see first page of Table 65

		XC	TP	VT	TP	LM	VT	XC	NT	VT	TP	VT	TP	LM	XC	VT	LM	XC	NT	NT	VT	VT	XC	VT
		1 ◇	1 ◇	1 ◇	1 ◇	1 ◇	1 ◇	1 ◇		1 ◇	1 ◇	1 ◇	1 ◇	1 ◇	1 ◇	1 ◇	1 ◇	1 ◇			1 ◇	1 ◇	1 ◇	1 ◇
		A													B				C					
		☕	🛒	☕	🛒	🛒	☕	☕		☕		☕		🛒		☕	🛒				☕	☕		☕
Inverness	d											12b40												
Aberdeen	d		13c21									13e42				14c25								
Dundee	d		14c30									14e52				15c32								
Perth	d			14e14								15e14												
Edinburgh 10	d		15 52													16 51								
Haymarket	d		15u56													16u56								
Glasgow Central 15	d			16 10								16 46												17 40
Motherwell	d																							
Carstairs	d																							
Lockerbie	d		16 52													17 49								18 47
Carlisle 8	a		17 13	17 21								17 56				18 11								19 03
	d		17 15	17 21								17 59				18 11								19 06
Penrith North Lakes	d		17 29	17 36												18 27								19 20
Windermere	d		17 27								18 09													19 18
Oxenholme Lake District	a		17 53	17 59							18 29	18 32	←			18 51								19 43
	d		17 53	18 00							18 38	18 34	18 38			18 51								19 44
Barrow-in-Furness	d		17 06								→	17 43												
Lancaster 6	a		18 09		←							18 49	18 55			19 08								19 59
	d		18 16		18 16							18 51	18 55			19 08								20 01
Preston 8	a		→	18 28	18 36							19 08	19 14			19 27								20 18
Blackpool North	a			19 11	19 23								19 57			20 03								20 56
	d			17 38					18 25			18 38							19 18	19 25				19 42
Preston 8	d			18 29	18 38				18 50			19 10	19 14			19 29			19 43	19 50				20 21
Wigan North Western	a			18 41					19 10			19 21				19 40			20 00	20 11				20 31
	d			18 42					19 11			19 22				19 41			20 01	20 11				20 33
Bolton	a				18 58								19 45			20f12								
Manchester Piccadilly 10	a				19 20								20 04			20f34			20g36					
Manchester Airport ✈	a				19 40								20 26			21h06								
Liverpool Lime Street 10	a								19 52			20 19								20 52				
	d					18 40								19 19			19 40					19 49		
Liverpool South Parkway 7 ✈	d					18 50											19 50							
Runcorn	d					18 58								19 35			19 58					20 05		
Warrington Bank Quay	a			18 52								19 32				19 51								20 42
	d			18 53								19 33				19 53								20 44
Hartford	d					19 12											20 08							
Manchester Piccadilly 10	d	18 24				18 34	18 45	18 54		19 15					19 24	19 03		19 54			20 15		20 24	
Stockport	d	18 33				18 42	18u54	19 03		19u24					19 33	19 15		20 03			20u24		20 33	
Manchester Airport ✈	d															19j01								
Wilmslow	d			18 24		18 54										19 26						19 54		
Holyhead	d			16k35								17 27												18k35
Bangor (Gwynedd)	d			17k04								18 06												19k14
Llandudno	d											17m47										18k47		18n53
Llandudno Junction	d			17k27								18 29										18k56		19k32
Chester	d			18 30								19 22										20 05		20 30
Crewe 10	a			19 12		19 25						19 52		19 58		20 13	20 22					20 31		21 03
	d			19 15		19 27						19 54		20 00		20 15	20 24					20 39		21 05
Macclesfield	d	18 47					19 07	19 16		19 37					19 47			20 16			20 37		20 47	
Congleton	d							19 24										20 24						
Stoke-on-Trent	d	19 04					19 24	19 39		19 53					20 04			20 39			20 53		21 04	
Stafford	a	19 24				19 47		19 57				20 12		20 20	20 25		20 44	20 56				20 59	21 25	
	d	19 25				19 48		19 58				20 14		20 21	20 26		20 46	20 57				21 04	21 26	
Penkridge	a					19 53											20 51							
Wolverhampton 7	a	19 41		19 48		20 06		20 12						20 36	20 41	20 48	21 05	21 12					21 41	
Coseley	a					20 12											21 12							
Sandwell & Dudley	a													20 46										
Birmingham New Street 12	a	19 58		20 11		20 30		20 35						20 58	20 58	21 11	21 30	21 35					22 04	
	d														21 03									
Birmingham International ✈	a			20 39											21 14	21 39		22 20					22 52	
Coventry	a			20 49											21 23	21 49		22 39					23 12	
Lichfield Trent Valley	a																							
Tamworth Low Level	a																							
Nuneaton	a																					21 27		
Rugby	a											20 47										21 42		
Northampton	a																							
Milton Keynes Central	a						20 28														21 55	22 05		22 16
Watford Junction	a									21s13		21s26										22s25		
Gatwick Airport 10 ✈	a																							
London Euston 15 ⊖	a						21 07			21 36		21 51									22 52	23 05		23 14

For general notes see front of timetable
For details of catering facilities see Directory of Train Operators

A To Plymouth (Table 51)
B To Southampton Central (Table 51)
C Until 12 September
b Change at Perth, Glasgow Queen Street and Glasgow Central. Passengers make their own way from Glasgow Queen Street to Glasgow Central
c Change at Haymarket
e Via Glasgow Queen Street and Glasgow Central. Passengers make their own way from one station to the other
f Change at Preston
g Manchester Victoria
h Change at Preston and Manchester Piccadilly
j Change at Wilmslow and Crewe
k Change at Chester and Crewe
m Change at Llandudno Junction and Crewe
n Change at Llandudno Junction, Chester and Crewe

OVERNIGHT SLEEPERS. For Sleeper trains, operated by First ScotRail, please refer to Tables 400 - 404

Scotland and North West England → West Midlands and London

Route Diagram - see first page of Table 65

		LM	VT	NT	TP	TP	VT	VT	LM	XC	NT	VT	NT	TP	NT	SR	SR FO	SR FO	SR FX	SR FX	SR FO	SR FO	SR FX	SR FO
		1 ◇	1 ◇		1 ◇	1 ◇	1 ◇	1 ◇	1 ◇	1 ◇		1 ◇		1 ◇			R	R	R	R	R	R	R	R
														A			B	B			C	C	D	D
Inverness	d							14 41								16b56		18 27		18 27		18 27	20 38	20 38
Aberdeen	d				15c20			16c21				17e21				18b40	19b41		19b41		19b41		21 40	21 40
Dundee	d				16c31			17c31				18e35				19b52		21 28		21 28		21 28	23u06	23u06
Perth	d						16b14	16 48				18b14				20b14	21b14		21b14		21b14		23u14	23u14
Edinburgh 10	d				17 52			18 52				20f15						23 40		23 40		23 40		
Haymarket	d				17u56			18u56				20f19												
Glasgow Central 15	d						18 10					20 10				22 03	23 41		23 41		23 41			
Motherwell	d						18u27										23u56		23u56		23u56			
Carstairs	d											20u51					00u16		00u16		00u16			
Lockerbie	d				18 53			19 49				21 26												
Carlisle 8	a				19 15		19 30	20 11				21 45				00 34								
	d				19 16		19 32	20 11				21 47					01u39		01u39		01u39			
Penrith North Lakes	d				19 31			20 27				22 02												
Windermere	d							20 27				21 28		22 16										
Oxenholme Lake District	a				19 54		20 06	20 52				22 26		22 36										
	d				19 55		20 07	20 52				22 27		22 36										
Barrow-in-Furness	d					19 10							21 45											
Lancaster 6	a				20 10	20 15	20 22	21 07				22 42	22 49	22 53	←									
	d				20 11	20 17	20 23	21 07				22 44	23 01 →		23 01									
Preston 8	a				20 29	20 35	20 42	21 26				23 02			23 25								04s29	04s05
Blackpool North	a						21 36	22 12																
	d							20 52			22 03													
Preston 8	d			20 27	20 32	20 38	20 49	21 29			22 27	23 23			23 29									
Wigan North Western	a			20 46			21 00	21 41			22 47	23s39												
	d			20 47			21 01	21 42			22 47													
Bolton	a				20 53	21 08	21g52	22g52							23 51									
Manchester Piccadilly 10	a				21 14	21 30	22g18	23g30				00 16			00h09									
Manchester Airport ✈	a				21 37	21 51	22g39	23g56							00j45									
Liverpool Lime Street 10	a			21 38				22 38			23 38													
	d	20 40							21 40															
Liverpool South Parkway 7 ✈	d	20 50							21 51															
Runcorn	d	20 58							21 59															
Warrington Bank Quay	a						21 11	21 52																
	d						21 13	21 54																
Hartford	d	21 08							22 09															
Manchester Piccadilly 10	d	20 34	20 45					21 03		21 54														
Stockport	d	20 46	20u54					21 15		22 03														
Manchester Airport ✈	d	19k56						21k10																
Wilmslow	d	20 54	21 05					21 26																
Holyhead	d							19 35																
Bangor (Gwynedd)	d							20 14																
Llandudno	d		19m47																					
Llandudno Junction	d		19m56					20 37																
Chester	d		21 00					21 33																
Crewe 10	a	21 23	21 28				21 32	22 13	22 24														05s30	05s02
	d	21 25	21 34				21 35	22 16	22 24															
Macclesfield	d									22 16														
Congleton	d									22 24														
Stoke-on-Trent	d		21 52							22 39														
Stafford	a	21 45					21 55	22 35	22 47	22 56														
	d	21 46					21 55	22 36	22 47	22 57														
Penkridge	a	21 51							22 52															
Wolverhampton 7	a	22 08					22 16	22 48	23 06	23 12														
Coseley	a																							
Sandwell & Dudley	a																							
Birmingham New Street 12	a	22 30					22 38	23 11	23 30	23 47														
	d																							
Birmingham International ✈	a						23 09																	
Coventry	a						23 19																	
Lichfield Trent Valley	a		22 16																					
Tamworth Low Level	a		22 23																					
Nuneaton	a		22 34																					
Rugby	a		22 49																					
Northampton	a																							
Milton Keynes Central	a		23 11																					
Watford Junction	a		23s31														06n28		06s34		06s50			
Gatwick Airport 10 ✈	a																							
London Euston 15 ⊖	a		00 09														07 00		07 00		07 15		07 43	07q56

For general notes see front of timetable
For details of catering facilities see Directory of Train Operators

- **A** To Windermere (Table 83). Also stops at Bare Lane 2302 and Morecambe 2306 (Table 98)
- **B** Until 5 September
- **C** From 12 September
- **D** Also conveys portion from Fort William (Table 227)
- **b** Via Glasgow Queen Street and Glasgow Central. Passengers make their own way from one station to the other
- **c** Change at Haymarket
- **e** Change at Edinburgh and Carstairs
- **f** Change at Carstairs
- **g** Change at Preston
- **h** Manchester Victoria. Also connection applies. Manchester Piccadilly. Arr. 0029. Change at Bolton
- **j** Change at Bolton
- **k** Change at Wilmslow and Crewe
- **m** Change at Chester and Crewe
- **n** Stops to set down only. From 18 July arr. 0632
- **q** From 12 September arr. 0804

OVERNIGHT SLEEPERS. For Sleeper trains, operated by First ScotRail, please refer to Tables 400 - 404

Table 65

Saturdays

until 12 July

Scotland and North West England → West Midlands and London

Route Diagram - see first page of Table 65

Station		VT	XC	VT	VT	XC	LM	VT	VT	VT	TP	VT	LM	TP	VT	XC	VT	VT	VT	XC	VT	LM	NT	TP
																			R	R				
		1 ◇	1 ◇	1 ◇	1 ◇	1 ◇	1 ◇	1 ◇	1 ◇	1 ◇	1 ◇	1 ◇	1 ◇	1 ◇	1 ◇	1 ◇	1 ◇	1 ◇	1	1	1 ◇	1 ◇		1 ◇
			A			A										B				C				D
			☕	☕	☕	☕		☕	☕	☕		☕			☕	☕	☕	☕	☕	☕	☕			🛒
Inverness	d																							
Aberdeen	d																							
Dundee	d																							
Perth	d																							
Edinburgh 10	d																							
Haymarket	d																							
Glasgow Central 15	d																							
Motherwell	d																							
Carstairs	d																							
Lockerbie	d																							
Carlisle 8	a																							
	d																							
Penrith North Lakes	d																							
Windermere	d																							
Oxenholme Lake District	a																							
	d																							
Barrow-in-Furness	d							04 15						05 15										06 15
Lancaster 6	a													06 08										07 15
	d							05 33						06 08	06 31									07 16
Preston 8	a							05 50						06 27	06 48									07 35
Blackpool North	a														07 31									08 12
	d							05 19			05 19	05 30			06 08				06 34				06 57	
Preston 8	d							05 53			05 58	06 15		06 28	06 51				07 20				07 25	07 40
Wigan North Western	a							06 03			06 14	06 26			07 01				07 31				07 44	
	d							06 05			06 15	06 27			07 03				07 32				07 45	
Bolton	a										06 31			06 52	07b32									08 02
Manchester Piccadilly 10	a										06 56			07 15	07b54									08 25
Manchester Airport	a										07 15			07 40	08b19									08 42
Liverpool Lime Street 10	a							06 59				07 29			07 59								08 27	
	d								06 15				06 33					07 15				07 39		
Liverpool South Parkway 7	d												06 45									07 49		
Runcorn	d								06 31				06 53					07 30				07 57		
Warrington Bank Quay	a							06 14				06 46			07 12				07 42					
	d							06 16				06 47			07 14				07 44					
Hartford	d												07 07									08 06		
Manchester Piccadilly 10	d			05 10	06 09					06 43			06 13		06 38	06 54	07 15			07 24	07 45	07 28		
Stockport	d			05u19	06u16					06u50			06 25		06 48	07 03	07u23			07 33	07u54	07 37		
Manchester Airport	d												05c53					06 57						
Wilmslow	d			05 27									06 36		06 55			07 04		07 42		07 46		
Holyhead	d	02 15										04e27						05 30						
Bangor (Gwynedd)	d	02 42										05e00						05 59						
Llandudno	d																							
Llandudno Junction	d	03 00						05 00				05e18			05 45			06 19						
Chester	d	03 40	04 55					06 00				06 30			06 56			07 15	07 30			07 30		
Crewe 10	a	03 59		05 45				06 46	06 50			07 08	07 23		07 33			07 50	08 03	08 05		08 21		
	d	04 02	05 45	05 48			06 09	06 49	06 53			07 10	07 23		07 35			07 53	08 06	08 10		08 22		
Macclesfield	d				06 29					07 03						07 16	07 35				08 07			
Congleton	d					←										07 24								
Stoke-on-Trent	d		06 06		06 45	06 06				07 21						07 39	07 50				08 23			
Stafford	a	04 29	→	06 12		06 24	06 29		07 11				07 44			07 56		08 10		08 32		08 43		
	d	04 30		06 14		06 26	06 30		07 12				07 44			07 58		08 12		08 33		08 44		
Penkridge	a						06 35						07 50									08 50		
Wolverhampton 7	a	04 45				06 40	06 47					07 47	08 07			08 12			08 42	08 47		09 05		
Coseley	a												08 14									09 14		
Sandwell & Dudley	a																							
Birmingham New Street 12	a	05 08				06 58	07 08					08 10	08 27			08 30			09 05	09 06		09 27		
	d					07 03																		
Birmingham International	a	06 09				07 14	07 40					08 40				09 09				09 39				
Coventry	a	06 19				07 24	07 52					08 54				09 19				09 49				
Lichfield Trent Valley	a			06 27				07 18																
Tamworth Low Level	a			06 34					07 29															
Nuneaton	a			06 45					07 40									08 34						
Rugby	a			07 00	07 33			07 44							08 28									
Northampton	a																							
Milton Keynes Central	a				08 07			08 25	08 34								09 12				09 48			
Watford Junction	a			08s01	08s36			08s54		09s17					09s33			09s50						
Gatwick Airport 10	a																							
London Euston 15	⊖ a			08 19	08 57			09 17	09 19	09 38					09 56		10 03	10 12			10 27			

For general notes see front of timetable
For details of catering facilities see Directory of Train Operators

A To Bournemouth (Table 51)
B To Reading (Table 51)
C To Newquay (Table 135)
D 🛒 from Preston

b Change at Preston
c Change at Wilmslow and Crewe
e Change at Chester and Crewe

Table 65

Saturdays

Scotland and North West England → West Midlands and London

until 12 July

Route Diagram - see first page of Table 65

		VT	XC	VT	VT	XC	VT	VT	TP	LM	VT	LM	XC	VT	VT	NT	XC	VT	VT	TP	LM	VT	LM
						R																	
		1◇	1◇	1◇	1◇	1	1◇	1◇	1◇	1◇	1◇	1◇	1◇	1◇	1◇		1◇	1◇	1◇	1◇	1◇	1◇	1◇
			A			B			C				D				E						
		☕	☕	☕	☕	☕	☕	☕	🛒		☕		☕	☕	☕		☕	☕	☕	🛒		☕	
Inverness	d																						
Aberdeen	d																						
Dundee	d																						
Perth	d																					*05b15*	
Edinburgh 10	d																		06 51				
Haymarket	d																		06u55				
Glasgow Central 15	d										06 10									06 58		07 10	
Motherwell	d										06u25												
Carstairs	d																						
Lockerbie	d																		07 52	07 57			
Carlisle 8	a										07 26								08 11	08 19		08 32	
	d	06 30									07 28								08 13	08 20		08 39	
Penrith North Lakes	d	06 44									07 43								08 29	08 35			
Windermere	d	*06 35*									*07 24*								*08 28*				
Oxenholme Lake District	a	07 07									08 05								08 52	08 59			
	d	07 08									08 07								08 53	08 59			
Barrow-in-Furness	d								07 05										*07 58*				
Lancaster 6	a	07 23							08 02		08 21								09 08	09 14		09 25	
	d	07 24							08 03		08 23								09 09	09 14		09 27	
Preston 8	a	07 41							08 21		08 44								09 26	09 35		09 44	
Blackpool North	a	*08 36*							*09 00*		*09 32*								*10 02*			*10 21*	
	d	*07 03*					*07 41*				*08 09*								*08 41*			*09 11*	
Preston 8	d	07 44					08 29		08 34		08 47					08 50			09 29	09 38		09 47	
Wigan North Western	a	07 55					08 39				08 57					09 10			09 40			09 57	
	d	07 56					08 40				08 59					09 11			09 41			09 59	
Bolton	a	*08c24*							08 58		*09c34*									09 58		*10c34*	
Manchester Piccadilly 10	a	*08c47*							09 20		*09c57*									10 20		*10c57*	
Manchester Airport ✈	a	*09c06*							09 40		*10c19*									10 40		*11c19*	
Liverpool Lime Street 10	a	*09 19*					*09 49*									09 52			*10 49*				
	d				08 15					08 38					09 15						09 37		
Liverpool South Parkway 7 ✈	d									08 47											09 47		
Runcorn	d				08 30					08 55					09 31						09 55		
Warrington Bank Quay	a	08 06					08 50				09 08								09 51			10 08	
	d	08 07					08 52				09 10								09 53			10 10	
Hartford	d									09 07											10 05		
Manchester Piccadilly 10	d		07 54	08 15		08 24		08 40			*08 34*		08 54	09 15			09 24	09 40				*09 34*	
Stockport	d		08 03	08u23		08 33		08u49			*08 44*		09 03	09u24			09 33	09u49				*09 42*	
Manchester Airport ✈	d				*08 00*										*09 00*								
Wilmslow	d				*08 07*		*08 21*				*08 52*				*09 07*				*09 24*			*09 52*	
Holyhead	d				*06 45*										*07 15*								
Bangor (Gwynedd)	d				*07 12*										*08 01*								
Llandudno	d				*07e03*										*07e47*								
Llandudno Junction	d				*07 30*										*08 27*								
Chester	d				*08 22*		*08 30*								*09 19*								
Crewe 10	a	08 29			08 50		09 12			09 21	09 29				09 50				10 12		10 21	10 29	
	d	08 32			08 53		09 14			09 22	09 31				09 53				10 15		10 22	10 31	
Macclesfield	d		08 16	08 36		08 46		09 05					09 16				09 46	10 05					
Congleton	d		08 24										09 24										
Stoke-on-Trent	d		08 39	08 55		09 06		09 21					09 39	09 50			10 06	10 21					
Stafford	a		08 56		09 11	09 25				09 43			09 56		10 11		10 25				10 43		
	d		08 58		09 12	09 26				09 44		←	09 58		10 13		10 26				10 44		←
Penkridge	a									09 50		09 50									10 50		10 50
Wolverhampton 7	a		09 11			09 41	09 48			→		10 05	10 12		10 35		10 41		10 48		→		11 05
Coseley	a											10 14											11 14
Sandwell & Dudley	a														10 47								
Birmingham New Street 12	a		09 30			09 58	10 11				10 24	10 27	10 30	10 47	10 56		10 58		11 11			11 24	11 27
	d		09 33								10 30			10 51	11 00		11 03					11 30	
Birmingham International ✈	a		*10 09*								10 39			11 03	11 09		11 14					11 39	
Coventry	a		*10 19*								10 49			11 13	11 19		11 23					11 49	
Lichfield Trent Valley	a			09 19																			
Tamworth Low Level	a																						
Nuneaton	a				09 34																		
Rugby	a	09 26			09 54										11 33								
Northampton	a																						
Milton Keynes Central	a	10 05			10 29													12 13				12 37	
Watford Junction	a			10s51				11s38			12s00			12s33	12s38								
Gatwick Airport 10 ✈	a		12 53																				
London Euston 15 ⊖	a	10 58		11 13	11 16			12 00			12 21			12 54	13 01			13 04				13 22	

For general notes see front of timetable
For details of catering facilities see Directory of Train Operators

A To Brighton (Table 51)

B To Paignton (Table 51)

C 🛒 from Preston

D To Reading (Table 51)

E To Bournemouth (Table 51)

b Via Glasgow Queen Street and Glasgow Central. Passengers make their own way from one station to the other

c Change at Preston

e Change at Llandudno Junction and Crewe

Scotland and North West England → West Midlands and London

Route Diagram - see first page of Table 65

		NT	XC	VT	VT	XC	VT	VT	TP	LM	VT	LM	NT	XC	VT	VT	XC	VT	TP	TP	TP	VT	TP
			1 ◇	1 ◇	1 ◇	R 1	1 ◇	R 1	1 ◇	1 ◇	1 ◇	1 ◇		1 ◇	1 ◇	1 ◇	1 ◇	1 ◇	1 ◇	1 ◇	1 ◇	R 1	1 ◇
			A			B			C					A			D						
			☕	☕	☕	☕	☕	☕	✕		☕			☕	☕	☕	☕	☕		✕	✕	☕	✕
Inverness	d																						
Aberdeen	d																				06 00		
Dundee	d																				07 11	07b16	
Perth	d																				07 03		
Edinburgh 10	d																				08 41	08 52	
Haymarket	d																				08 45	08u56	
Glasgow Central 15	d							07 40			08 07									08 40			
Motherwell	d										08u26												
Carstairs	d																						
Lockerbie	d																			09 36			
Carlisle 8	a							09 08			09 21									09 58	10 06	10 08	←
	d							09 11			09 32										10 15 →	10 10	10 15
Penrith North Lakes	d							09 26			09 47												10 30
Windermere	d							09 26			09 26								10 18				
Oxenholme Lake District	a							09 49			10 09								10 35			10 45	10 53
	d							09 51			10 11								10 37			10 47	10 54
Barrow-in-Furness	d								09 15														09 58
Lancaster 6	a							10 08	10 15		10 25								10 52			11 04	11 11
	d							10 09	10 16		10 27								10 53			11 06	11 12
Preston 8	a							10 27	10 34		10 44								11 13			11 23	11 32
Blackpool North	a										11 22								11 56			12 01	12 14
	d	09 25						09 40			10 11		10 25									10 41	
Preston 8	d	09 50						10 29	10 38		10 47		10 50									11 28	11 38
Wigan North Western	a	10 09						10 40			10 57		11 11									11 39	
	d	10 11						10 41			10 59		11 11									11 40	
Bolton	a								10 58		11c34												11 58
Manchester Piccadilly 10	a								11 20		11c57												12 20
Manchester Airport	a								11 40		12c19												12 40
Liverpool Lime Street 10	a	10 52						11 49					11 52									12 49	
	d				10 15					10 37						11 15							
Liverpool South Parkway 7	d									10 47													
Runcorn	d				10 31					10 55						11 31							
Warrington Bank Quay	a							10 51			11 08											11 51	
	d							10 53			11 10											11 53	
Hartford	d									11 05													
Manchester Piccadilly 10	d		09 54	10 15		10 24	10 40				10 34			10 54	11 15		11 24	11 40					
Stockport	d		10 03	10u24		10 33	10u49				10 43			11 03	11u24		11 33	11u49					
Manchester Airport	d				10 00											11 00							
Wilmslow	d				10 06			10 24			10 51					11 06						11 24	
Holyhead	d							08e25								09 28						09 50	
Bangor (Gwynedd)	d							09e04								10 07						10 18	
Llandudno	d				08e47											10f14							
Llandudno Junction	d				08e56			09e27								10 30						10 36	
Chester	d				10 00			10 29								11 14						11 28	
Crewe 10	a				10 50			11 13		11 21	11 29					11 50						12 13	
	d				10 53			11 15		11 22	11 31					11 53						12 13	
Macclesfield	d		10 16			10 46	11 05							11 16			11 46	12 05					
Congleton	d													11 24									
Stoke-on-Trent	d		10 39	10 50		11 06	11 21							11 39	11 50		12 06	12 21					
Stafford	a		10 56		11 11	11 24				11 43				11 56		12 16	12 24						
	d		10 58		11 13	11 26				11 44		←		11 58		12 18	12 26						
Penkridge	a									11 50 →		11 50											
Wolverhampton 7	a		11 12		11 35	11 41		11 48				12 06		12 12		12 35	12 41					12 49	
Coseley	a											12 14											
Sandwell & Dudley	a				11 47											12 47							
Birmingham New Street 12	a		11 30	11 47	11 56	11 58		12 11			12 24	12 27		12 30	12 47	12 56	12 58					13 11	
	d			11 51	12 00						12 30				12 51	13 00	13 03						
Birmingham International	a			12 03	12 09						12 39				13 03	13 09	13 14						
Coventry	a			12 13	12 19						12 49				13 13	13 19	13 23						
Lichfield Trent Valley	a																						
Tamworth Low Level	a																						
Nuneaton	a																						
Rugby	a				12 33											13 33							
Northampton	a																						
Milton Keynes Central	a				13 09													14 12					
Watford Junction	a			13s33			13s43				14 02				14s33	14s38							
Gatwick Airport 10	a																						
London Euston 15	⊖ a			13 54	13 58		14 04				14 23				14 54	15 01		15 04					

For general notes see front of timetable
For details of catering facilities see Directory of Train Operators

A To Reading (Table 51)
B To Paignton (Table 51)
C ✕ from Preston
D To Bournemouth (Table 51)

b Change at Haymarket
c Change at Preston
e Change at Chester and Crewe
f Change at Llandudno Junction and Crewe

Table 65

Saturdays

Scotland and North West England → West Midlands and London

until 12 July

Route Diagram - see first page of Table 65

		LM	VT	LM	XC	VT	VT	XC	VT	NT	VT	TP	LM		VT	LM	NT	XC	VT	VT	XC	VT	TP	VT	TP
		1◇	1◇	1◇	1◇	1◇	1◇	R 1	1◇		R 1	1◇	1◇		1◇	1◇		1◇	1◇	1◇	1◇	1◇	1◇	1◇	1◇
					A			B				C						D			E		C		C
			🍴		🍴	🍴	🍴	🍴	🍴		🍴	🛒			🍴			🍴	🍴	🍴	🍴	🍴	🛒	🍴	🛒
Inverness	d																							06 45	
Aberdeen	d										06b34				07b07									08c20	
Dundee	d										07b52				08b21									09c32	
Perth	d										08b13				08b43									08 47	
Edinburgh 10	d																							10 52	
Haymarket	d																							10u56	
Glasgow Central 15	d										10 10				10 20										
Motherwell	d																								
Carstairs	d																								
Lockerbie	d																								
Carlisle 8	a										11 20				11 30									12 11	
	d										11 22				11 32									12 13	
Penrith North Lakes	d														11 47									12 29	
Windermere	d														11 27								12 23		
Oxenholme Lake District	a														12 09								12 40	12 52	
	d														12 11								12 42	12 53	
Barrow-in-Furness	d											11 18													
Lancaster 6	a										12 09	12 16			12 25								13 02	13 08	
	d		11 24								12 11	12 16			12 27								13 04	13 09	
Preston 8	a		11 44								12 28	12 36			12 44								13 22	13 26	
Blackpool North	a		12 20												13 21									14 00	
	d		11 11							11 25	11 41				12 11		12 25							12 41	←
Preston 8	d		11 47							11 50	12 29	12 38			12 47		12 50						13 38 →	13 29	13 38
Wigan North Western	a		11 57							12 09	12 40				12 57		13 09							13 40	
	d		11 59							12 11	12 41				12 59		13 11							13 41	
Bolton	a		12e34									12 58			13e34									13e58	13 58
Manchester Piccadilly 10	a		12e57									13 20			13e57									14e20	14 20
Manchester Airport ✈	a		13e19									13 40			14e19									14e40	14 40
Liverpool Lime Street 10	a									12 52	13 49						13 52							14 49	
	d	11 37					12 15						12 37							13 15					
Liverpool South Parkway 7 ✈	d	11 47											12 47												
Runcorn	d	11 55					12 31						12 55							13 31					
Warrington Bank Quay	a		12 08								12 51				13 08									13 51	
	d		12 10								12 53				13 10									13 53	
Hartford	d	12 05											13 07												
Manchester Piccadilly 10	d		11 34		11 54	12 15		12 24	12 40						12 34			12 54	13 15		13 24	13 40			
Stockport	d		11 42		12 03	12u24		12 33	12u49						12 42			13 03	13u24		13 33	13u49			
Manchester Airport ✈	d						12 00													13 00					
Wilmslow	d		11 51				12 06				12 24				12 51					13 06				13 24	
Holyhead	d										10f30													11 40	
Bangor (Gwynedd)	d										11f03													12 19	
Llandudno	d						10f47													11f47					
Llandudno Junction	d						10f56				11f26									11f56				12 42	
Chester	d						12 00				12 29									13 00				13 33	
Crewe 10	a	12 21	12 29				12 50				13 12		13 21		13 29					13 50				14 12	
	d	12 22	12 31				12 53				13 15		13 22		13 31					13 53				14 15	
Macclesfield	d				12 16			12 46	13 05									13 16			13 46	14 05			
Congleton	d																	13 24							
Stoke-on-Trent	d				12 39	12 50		13 06	13 21									13 39	13 50		14 06	14 21			
Stafford	a	12 43			12 56		13 11	13 24					13 43					13 56		14 11	14 24				
	d	12 44		←	12 58		13 13	13 26					13 44			←		13 58		14 13	14 26				
Penkridge	a	12 50 →		12 50									13 50 →			13 50									
Wolverhampton 7	a			13 05	13 12		13 35	13 40			13 48					14 05		14 12		14 35	14 41			14 48	
Coseley	a			13 14												14 14									
Sandwell & Dudley	a						13 47													14 47					
Birmingham New Street 12	a		13 24	13 27	13 30	13 47	13 56	13 58			14 11				14 24	14 27		14 30	14 47	14 56	14 58			15 11	
	d		13 30			13 51	14 00								14 30				14 51	15 00	15 03				
Birmingham International ✈	a		13 39			14 03	14 09								14 39				15 00	15 09	15 14				
Coventry	a		13 49			14 13	14 19								14 49				15 13	15 19	15 23				
Lichfield Trent Valley	a																								
Tamworth Low Level	a																								
Nuneaton	a																								
Rugby	a																			15 33					
Northampton	a																								
Milton Keynes Central	a		14 39				15 09															16 13			
Watford Junction	a					15s33			15s43						16s02				16s34	16s38					
Gatwick Airport 10 ✈	a																								
London Euston 15 ⊖	a		15 24			15 54	15 59		16 04						16 25				16 54	17 01		17 04			

For general notes see front of timetable
For details of catering facilities see Directory of Train Operators

A To Reading (Table 51)

B To Paignton (Table 51)

C 🛒 from Preston

D To Guildford (Table 51)

E To Bournemouth (Table 51)

b Via Glasgow Queen Street and Glasgow Central. Passengers make their own way from one station to the other

c Change at Haymarket

e Change at Preston

f Change at Chester and Crewe

Table 65

Saturdays

until 12 July

Scotland and North West England → West Midlands and London

Route Diagram - see first page of Table 65

		LM	VT	LM		NT	XC	VT	VT	XC	TP	VT	VT	TP	LM	VT	LM		NT	XC	VT	VT	XC	VT	
													R												
		1 ◇	1 ◇	1 ◇			1 ◇	1 ◇	1 ◇	1 ◇	1 ◇	1 ◇	1	1 ◇	1 ◇	1 ◇	1 ◇			1 ◇	1 ◇	1 ◇	1 ◇	1 ◇	
							A			B										C			D		
			🍴				🍴	🍴	🍴	🍴	🛒	🍴	🍴	🛒		🍴				🍴	🍴	🍴	🍴	🍴	
Inverness	d										07 55														
Aberdeen	d										08 51														
Dundee	d										09 59														
Perth	d		09b08								09 55		10b13												
Edinburgh 10	d										11 52														
Haymarket	d																								
Glasgow Central 15	d		11 10										12 10												
Motherwell	d		11u23																						
Carstairs	d																								
Lockerbie	d																								
Carlisle 8	a		12 30								13 09		13 20												
	d		12 32								13 11		13 21												
Penrith North Lakes	d		12 47								13 25														
Windermere	d										13 25														
Oxenholme Lake District	a		13 09								13 49		13 57												
	d		13 11								13 50		13 58												
Barrow-in-Furness	d										12 56														
Lancaster 6	a		13 25								14 07			←											
	d		13 27								14 17			14 17		14 27									
Preston 8	a		13 44								→		14 26	14 36		14 44									
Blackpool North	a		14 21										15 01			15 21									
	d		13 11			13 25							13 41	13 41		14 11			14 25						
Preston 8	d		13 47			13 50							14 29	14 38		14 47			14 50						
Wigan North Western	a		13 57			14 11							14 40			14 57			15 10						
	d		13 59			14 11							14 41			14 59			15 11						
Bolton	a		14c34											14 58		15c34									
Manchester Piccadilly 10	a		14c57											15 20		15c57									
Manchester Airport	a		15c19											15 40		16c19									
Liverpool Lime Street 10	a					14 52							15 49						15 52						
	d	13 37							14 15						14 37							15 15			
Liverpool South Parkway 7	d	13 47													14 47										
Runcorn	d	13 55							14 31						14 55							15 31			
Warrington Bank Quay	a		14 08										14 50			15 08									
	d		14 10										14 52			15 10									
Hartford	d	14 05													15 05										
Manchester Piccadilly 10	d		13 34				13 54	14 15		14 24		14 40				14 34				14 54	15 15		15 24	15 40	
Stockport	d		13 42				14 03	14u24		14 33		14u49				14 42				15 03	15u24		15 33	15u49	
Manchester Airport	d								14 00													15 00			
Wilmslow	d		13 54						14 06				14 24			14 51						15 06			
Holyhead	d												12e35												
Bangor (Gwynedd)	d												13e04												
Llandudno	d								12e47				13f14									13e47			
Llandudno Junction	d								12e56				13e27									13e56			
Chester	d								14 03				14 30									15 03			
Crewe 10	a	14 21	14 28						14 50				15 10		15 21	15 28						15 50			
	d	14 22	14 31						14 53				15 13		15 22	15 31						15 53			
Macclesfield	d						14 16			14 46		15 05								15 16			15 46	16 05	
Congleton	d																			15 24					
Stoke-on-Trent	d						14 39	14 50		15 06		15 21								15 39	15 50		16 06	16 21	
Stafford	a	14 43					14 56		15 11	15 24					15 43					15 56		16 11	16 24		
	d	14 44		←			14 58		15 13	15 26					15 44		←			15 58		16 13	16 26		
Penkridge	a	14 50		14 50											15 50		15 50								
Wolverhampton 7	a	→		15 05			15 12		15 35	15 41			15 46		→		16 05			16 12		16 35	16 41		
Coseley	a			15 14													16 14								
Sandwell & Dudley	a								15 47													16 47			
Birmingham New Street 12	a		15 24	15 27			15 30	15 47	15 56	15 58			16 11			16 24	16 27			16 30	16 47	16 56	16 58		
	d		15 30					15 51	16 00							16 30				16 33	16 51	17 00	17 03		
Birmingham International	a		15 39					16 03	16 09							16 39					17 03	17 09	17 14		
Coventry	a		15 49					16 13	16 19							16 49					17 13	17 19	17 23		
Lichfield Trent Valley	a																								
Tamworth Low Level	a																								
Nuneaton	a																								
Rugby	a								16 33													17 33			
Northampton	a																								
Milton Keynes Central	a		16 36						17 08															18 13	
Watford Junction	a							17s33				17s42				18s01					18s34	18s39			
Gatwick Airport 10	a																			19 52					
London Euston 15	⊖ a		17 23					17 54	17 58			18 04				18 23					18 55	19 02		19 05	

For general notes see front of timetable
For details of catering facilities see Directory of Train Operators

A To Reading (Table 51)

B To Penzance (Table 135)

C To Brighton (Table 51)

D To Bournemouth (Table 51)

b Via Glasgow Queen Street and Glasgow Central. Passengers make their own way from one station to the other

c Change at Preston

e Change at Chester and Crewe

f Change at Llandudno Junction, Chester and Crewe

Scotland and North West England → West Midlands and London

Route Diagram - see first page of Table 65

		TP	TP	VT	TP	LM	VT	LM	NT	XC	VT	VT	XC	VT	TP	VT	TP	LM	VT	LM	NT	XC	VT
		1◇	1◇	R 1	1◇	1◇	1◇	1◇		1◇	1◇	1◇	1◇	1◇	1◇	1◇	1◇	1◇	1◇	1◇		1◇	1◇
					A					B			C									D	
				☕	🛒		☕			☕	☕	☕	☕	☕	🛒	☕	🛒		☕			☕	☕
Inverness	d														09b19								
Aberdeen	d			10c22												10b42							
Dundee	d			11c30												11b52							
Perth	d			11 08			11b14								11b38	12b14							
Edinburgh 10	d			12 52																			
Haymarket	d			12u56																			
Glasgow Central 15	d						13 10								13 40	14 10							
Motherwell	d						13u25																
Carstairs	d																						
Lockerbie	d			13 52											14 38								
Carlisle 8	a			14 11			14 30								14 58	15 20							
	d			14 13			14 32								15 08	15 21			15 27				
Penrith North Lakes	d			14 28			14 47								15 23				15 41				
Windermere	d	14 18													15 22								
Oxenholme Lake District	a	14 35		14 51			15 09								15 46				16 04				
	d	14 37		14 53			15 11								15 47				16 05				
Barrow-in-Furness	d		14 10																				
Lancaster 6	a	14 54	15 02	15 07	←		15 25								16 02	16 09			16 24				
	d	15 15 →		15 09	15 15		15 27								16 03	16 10			16 27				
Preston 8	a			15 26	15 34		15 44								16 22	16 27			16 44				
Blackpool North	a			16 01			16 21								17 01				17 34				
	d			14 41			15 11		15 25							15 41	←		16 10		16 25		
Preston 8	d			15 29	15 38		15 47		15 50						16 38 →	16 29	16 38		16 47		16 50		
Wigan North Western	a			15 40			15 57		16 10							16 40			16 57		17 09		
	d			15 41			15 59		16 11							16 41			16 59		17 11		
Bolton	a				15 58		16e34										16 58		17e36				
Manchester Piccadilly 10	a				16 20		16e57										17 20		17e57				
Manchester Airport ✈	a				16 40		17e19										17 40		18e19				
Liverpool Lime Street 10	a			16 49					16 53							17 49					17 53		
	d					15 37						16 15						16 37					
Liverpool South Parkway 7 ✈	d					15 47												16 47					
Runcorn	d					15 55						16 31						16 55					
Warrington Bank Quay	a			15 51			16 08									16 51			17 08				
	d			15 52			16 10									16 52			17 10				
Hartford	d					16 05												17 07					
Manchester Piccadilly 10	d						15 34			15 54	16 15		16 24	16 40					16 34			16 54	17 15
Stockport	d						15 42			16 03	16u24		16 33	16u49					16 43			17 03	17u24
Manchester Airport ✈	d											16 00											
Wilmslow	d			15 24			15 51					16 06				16 24			16 51				
Holyhead	d			13 35		14 15										14f35							
Bangor (Gwynedd)	d			14 14		14 43										15f04							
Llandudno	d					14g35						15 08											
Llandudno Junction	d			14 37		15 01						15 16				15f27							
Chester	d			15 30		15 46						16 12				16 31							
Crewe 10	a			16 11		16 21	16 29					16 50				17 13		17 21	17 29				
	d			16 12		16 22	16 31					16 53				17 15		17 22	17 31				
Macclesfield	d									16 16			16 46	17 05								17 16	
Congleton	d																					17 24	
Stoke-on-Trent	d									16 39	16 50		17 06	17 21								17 39	17 50
Stafford	a					16 44				16 56		17 11	17 24					17 43				17 56	
	d					16 44		←		16 58		17 13	17 26					17 44		←		17 58	
Penkridge	a					16 50 →		16 50										17 50 →		17 50			
Wolverhampton 7	a			16 48				17 05		17 12		17 35	17 41			17 48				18 07		18 12	
Coseley	a							17 14												18 14			
Sandwell & Dudley	a											17 47											
Birmingham New Street 12	a			17 11			17 24	17 27		17 30	17 47	17 56	17 58			18 11			18 24	18 27		18 30	18 47
	d						17 30				17 51	18 00							18 30			18 33	18 51
Birmingham International ✈	a						17 39				18 03	18 09							18 39				19 03
Coventry	a						17 49				18 13	18 19							18 49				19 13
Lichfield Trent Valley	a																						
Tamworth Low Level	a																						
Nuneaton	a																						
Rugby	a											18 33											
Northampton	a																						
Milton Keynes Central	a						18 36					19 09											
Watford Junction	a										19s29			19s40					20s04				20s56
Gatwick Airport 10 ✈	a																					21 47	
London Euston 15 ⊖	a						19 21				19 48	19 55		20 01					20 28				21 22

For general notes see front of timetable
For details of catering facilities see Directory of Train Operators

A 🛒 from Preston

B To Reading (Table 51)

C To Plymouth (Table 51)

D ☕ to Reading

b Via Glasgow Queen Street and Glasgow Central. Passengers make their own way from one station to the other

c Change at Haymarket

e Change at Preston

f Change at Chester and Crewe

g Change at Llandudno Junction and Crewe

Scotland and North West England → West Midlands and London

Route Diagram - see first page of Table 65

		VT	XC	VT	VT	LM	TP	VT	NT	XC	VT	VT		TP	XC	VT	VT	LM	TP	VT	XC	VT	XC	NT	TP
		1 ◇	1 ◇	1 ◇	1 ◇	1 ◇	1 ◇	1 ◇		1 ◇	1 ◇	1 ◇		1 ◇	1 ◇	1 ◇	1 ◇	1 ◇	1 ◇	1 ◇	1 ◇	1 ◇	1 ◇		1 ◇
			A				B								C								D		
		⊡	⊡	⊡	⊡		⊼	⊡		⊡	⊡	⊡		⊼	⊡	⊡	⊡		⊼	⊡	⊡	⊡	⊡		
Inverness	d				10 53																				
Aberdeen	d				12b24									13b21											
Dundee	d				13b33									14b30											
Perth	d				13 04			13c14									14c14								
Edinburgh 10	d				14 52									15 52											
Haymarket	d				14u56									15u56											
Glasgow Central 15	d							15 10									16 03			16 10					
Motherwell	d							15u27																	
Carstairs	d																								
Lockerbie	d													16 52											
Carlisle 8	a				16 07			16 30						17 13			17 20			17 30					
	d				16 09			16 32						17 15			17 21			17 33					
Penrith North Lakes	d				16 24			16 47						17 29			17 36			17 47					
Windermere	d				16 22									17 27											18 10
Oxenholme Lake District	a				16 47			17 09						17 53			17 59			18 10					18 30
	d				16 48			17 11						17 53			18 00			18 11					18 33
Barrow-in-Furness	d				15 28		16 21							17 06											
Lancaster 6	a				17 03		17 15	17 25						18 09					⟵	18 26					18 49
	d				17 04		17 16	17 27						18 16					18 16	18 27					18 51
Preston 8	a				17 21		17 34	17 44						⟶			18 29		18 36	18 44					19 09
Blackpool North	a				18 03			18 30												19 21					20 01
	d				16 38			17 10									17 38			18 11				18 25	
Preston 8	d				17 24		17 35	17 47	17 50								18 30		18 38	18 47				18 50	19 14
Wigan North Western	a				17 35			17 57	18 11								18 41			18 58				19 10	
	d				17 36			17 58	18 11								18 42			18 59				19 11	
Bolton	a						17 59	18e34											18 58	19e33					19 38
Manchester Piccadilly 10	a						18 20	18e57											19 20	19e57					20 04
Manchester Airport	a						18 42	19e19											19 40	20e19					20 26
Liverpool Lime Street 10	a				18 34				18 55															19 52	
	d	17 15				17 37						18 15						18 40							
Liverpool South Parkway 7	d					17 47												18 50							
Runcorn	d	17 31				17 55						18 31						18 58							
Warrington Bank Quay	a				17 46			18 08									18 52			19 09					
	d				17 48			18 10									18 53			19 10					
Hartford	d					18 05												19 09							
Manchester Piccadilly 10	d		17 24	17 40				17 34		17 54	18 15				18 24	18 40				18 34	18 54	19 15	19 24		
Stockport	d		17 33	17u49				17 42		18 03	18u24				18 33	18u49				18 43	19 03	19u24	19 33		
Manchester Airport	d	17 00										18 00													
Wilmslow	d	17 06			17 26			17 51				18 11					18 25			18 53					
Holyhead	d				15 39												16f35								
Bangor (Gwynedd)	d				16 17												17f04								
Llandudno	d	15f47			16g14							16f47													
Llandudno Junction	d	15f56			16 40							16f56					17f27								
Chester	d	17 00			17 31							18 04					18 30								
Crewe 10	a	17 50			18 07	18 21		18 29				18 50					19 13	19 22		19 29					
	d	17 53			18 13	18 21		18 32				18 53					19 15	19 23		19 31					
Macclesfield	d		17 46	18 05						18 16					18 46	19 05					19 16		19 46		
Congleton	d									18 24											19 24				
Stoke-on-Trent	d		18 06	18 21						18 39	18 50				19 06	19 21					19 39	19 50	20 06		
Stafford	a	18 11	18 24			18 44				18 56		19 11			19 24			19 44		19 50	19 56		20 24		
	d	18 13	18 25			18 44				18 58		19 13			19 25			19 44		19 52	19 58		20 26		
Penkridge	a					18 50												19 50							
Wolverhampton 7	a	18 35	18 41		18 48	19 06				19 12		19 35			19 40		19 48	20 07			20 12		20 40		
Coseley	a					19 14																			
Sandwell & Dudley	a	18 47										19 47													
Birmingham New Street 12	a	18 56	18 58		19 11	19 27				19 35	19 47	19 56			19 58		20 11	20 30			20 35	20 49	20 58		
	d	19 00	19 03								19 51	20 00										20 53	21 03		
Birmingham International	a	19 09	19 14		19 42						20 03	20 09					20 51					21 03	21 14		
Coventry	a	19 19	19 23		19 52						20 13	20 19					21 09					21 13	21 23		
Lichfield Trent Valley	a																								
Tamworth Low Level	a																								
Nuneaton	a																								
Rugby	a	19 33						20 00				20 33								21 00		21 27			
Northampton	a																								
Milton Keynes Central	a			20 14				20 35				21 15										22 08			
Watford Junction	a	21s02									22s02					22s16				22s21		22s58			
Gatwick Airport 10	a																								
London Euston 15	⊖ a	21 27		21 28				21 37			22 28	22 33				22 40				22 46		23 24			

For general notes see front of timetable
For details of catering facilities see Directory of Train Operators

A To Bournemouth (Table 51)

B ⊼ from Preston

C To Plymouth (Table 51)

D To Southampton Central (Table 51). ⊡ to Birmingham New Street

b Change at Haymarket

c Via Glasgow Queen Street and Glasgow Central. Passengers make their own way from one station to the other

e Change at Preston

f Change at Chester and Crewe

g Change at Llandudno Junction and Crewe

Table 65

Saturdays

Scotland and North West England → West Midlands and London

until 12 July

Route Diagram - see first page of Table 65

Station		VT	LM		XC	NT	NT	VT	VT	NT	VT	NT	TP	TP	VT	XC		LM	VT	TP	NT	NT	SR	SR	
		1 ◇	1 ◇		1 ◇			1 ◇	1 ◇		1 ◇		1 ◇	1 ◇	1 ◇	1 ◇		1 ◇	1 ◇	1					
						A															B				
Inverness	d	12 40																					14b41	16c56	
Aberdeen	d	14e25											15e20										16c41	18c40	
Dundee	d	15e32											16e31										17c52	19c52	
Perth	d	14 49						15c14							16c14								18c14	20c14	
Edinburgh 10	d	16 52											17 52												
Haymarket	d	16u56											17u56												
Glasgow Central 15	d							17 07							18 10								20 03	22 03	
Motherwell	d														18u27										
Carstairs	d																								
Lockerbie	d	17 50											18 53		19 12										
Carlisle 8	a	18 11						18 31					19 15		19 31								22 24	00 34	
	d	18 11						18 33					19 16		19 32										
Penrith North Lakes	d	18 27						18 48					19 31												
Windermere	d												19 22							20 24					
Oxenholme Lake District	a	18 51						19 10					19 54		20 07					20 44					
	d	18 51						19 12					19 55		20 08					20 46					
Barrow-in-Furness	d					18 14								19 15											
Lancaster 6	a	19 07				19 17		19 26					20 10	20 16	20 20					21 03					
	d	19 07				19 18		19 28					20 11	20 17	20 21						21 20				
Preston 8	a	19 26				19 43		19 45					20 29	20 35	20 41						21 45				
Blackpool North	a	20 07						20 36							21 36						22 36				
	d						19 19	19 10		19 25		19 42							20 30			22 03			
Preston 8	d	19 29					19 46	19 48		19 50		20 27	20 32	20 37	20 43				21 22			22 28			
Wigan North Western	a	19 40					20 06	19 59		20 10		20 47			20 54				21 33			22 47			
	d	19 41					20 09	20 00		20 11		20 48			20 55				21 34			22 47			
Bolton	a	20f11						20f32					20 53	21 07	21f52						22 52				
Manchester Piccadilly 10	a	20f34					20g44	20f58					21 14	21 29	22f18						23 30				
Manchester Airport ✈	a	21h06						21f19					21 37	21 51	22f39						23 56				
Liverpool Lime Street 10	a									20 52		21 39							22 38			23 38			
	d		19 37						20 10									21 16							
Liverpool South Parkway 7 ✈	d		19 47															21 26							
Runcorn	d		19 55						20 26									21 34							
Warrington Bank Quay	a	19 51						20 10							21 05				21 44						
	d	19 53						20 11							21 06				21 46						
Hartford	d		20 05															21 44							
Manchester Piccadilly 10	d				19 54			19 34			20 15				20 34	20 54			20 58						
Stockport	d				20 03			19 42			20u24				20 46	21 03			21 15						
Manchester Airport ✈	d	19j01													19j56				21j10						
Wilmslow	d	19 26						19 54							20 54				21 26						
Holyhead	d	17 35													18k35				19 35						
Bangor (Gwynedd)	d	18 14													19k14				20 14						
Llandudno	d	17m47							18k47						18n53			19k47							
Llandudno Junction	d	18 37							18k56						19k32			19k56	20 37						
Chester	d	19 34							20 05						20 30			21 00	21 33						
Crewe 10	a	20 13	20 21					20 29	20 45						21 26			21 58	22 05						
	d	20 15	20 22					20 32	20 48						21 28			22 00	22 08						
Macclesfield	d				20 16						20 38					21 16									
Congleton	d				20 24											21 24									
Stoke-on-Trent	d				20 39						20 56					21 39									
Stafford	a		20 43		20 57						21 17				21 51	21 58		22 24	22 32						
	d		20 44		20 58						21 18				21 51	21 58		22 25	22 33						
Penkridge	a		20 50															22 30							
Wolverhampton 7	a	20 48	21 08		21 12						21 35				22 06	22 12		22 43	22 48						
Coseley	a																								
Sandwell & Dudley	a										21 46														
Birmingham New Street 12	a	21 11	21 27		21 35						21 56				22 30	22 35		23 04	23 10						
	d										22 00														
Birmingham International ✈	a	21 52									22 09					23 04		23 33	00 21						
Coventry	a	22 10									22 19					23 22		23 49	00 37						
Lichfield Trent Valley	a																								
Tamworth Low Level	a																								
Nuneaton	a																								
Rugby	a							22 00	22 09		22 33														
Northampton	a																								
Milton Keynes Central	a							22 35	22 44		23 08														
Watford Junction	a							23s10	23s19		23s52														
Gatwick Airport 10 ✈	a																								
London Euston 15 ⊖	a							23 36	23 43		00 16														

For general notes see front of timetable
For details of catering facilities see Directory of Train Operators

A From Carlisle via Whitehaven (Table 100)
B From Morecambe (Table 98)

b Change at Perth, Glasgow Queen Street and Glasgow Central. Passengers make their own way between Glasgow Queen Street and Glasgow Central
c Via Glasgow Queen Street and Glasgow Central. Passengers make their own way from one station to the other
e Change at Haymarket

f Change at Preston
g Manchester Victoria
h Change at Preston and Manchester Piccadilly
j Change at Wilmslow and Crewe
k Change at Chester and Crewe
m Change at Llandudno Junction and Crewe
n Change at Llandudno Junction, Chester and Crewe

Table 65

Saturdays

19 July to 6 September

Scotland and North West England → West Midlands and London

Route Diagram - see first page of Table 65

Station		VT	XC	VT	VT	XC	LM	VT	VT	VT	TP		VT	LM	XC	TP	VT	VT	VT	VT	VT	VT		XC	VT
		1◇	1◇	1◇	1◇	1◇	1◇	1◇	1◇	1◇	1◇		1◇	1◇	1◇	1◇	1◇	1◇	1◇	1◇	1◇	Ⓡ 1		Ⓡ 1	1◇
			A			A									B									C	
			🍴	🍴	🍴	🍴		🍴	🍴	🍴			🍴		🍴		🍴	🍴	🍴	🍴	🍴	🍴		🍴	🍴
Inverness	d																								
Aberdeen	d																								
Dundee	d																								
Perth	d																								
Edinburgh 10	d																								
Haymarket	d																								
Glasgow Central 15	d																								
Motherwell	d																								
Carstairs	d																								
Lockerbie	d																								
Carlisle 8	a																								
	d																								
Penrith North Lakes	d																								
Windermere	d																								
Oxenholme Lake District	a																								
	d																								
Barrow-in-Furness	d							04 15								05 15									
Lancaster 6	a															06 08									
	d							05 33								06 08	06 31								
Preston 8	a							05 50								06 27	06 48								
Blackpool North	a																07 31								
	d							05 19			05 19		05 30				06 08					06 34			
Preston 8	d							05 53			05 58		06 15			06 28	06 51					07 20			
Wigan North Western	a							06 03			06 14		06 26				07 01					07 31			
	d							06 05			06 15		06 27				07 03					07 32			
Bolton	a										06 31					06 52	07b32								
Manchester Piccadilly 10	a										06 56					07 15	07b54								
Manchester Airport	a										07 15					07 40	08b19								
Liverpool Lime Street 10	a							06 59					07 29				07 59								
	d								06 15					06 33						07 15					
Liverpool South Parkway 7	d													06 45											
Runcorn	d								06 31					06 53						07 30					
Warrington Bank Quay	a							06 14					06 46				07 12					07 42			
	d							06 16					06 47				07 14					07 44			
Hartford	d													07 07											
Manchester Piccadilly 10	d			05 10	06 09					06 43				06 13	06 54			07 15						07 24	07 45
Stockport	d			05u19	06u16					06u50				06 25	07 03			07u23						07 33	07u54
Manchester Airport	d													05c53						06 57					
Wilmslow	d			05 27										06 36			06 55			07 04				07 42	
Holyhead	d	02 15											04e27						05 30						
Bangor (Gwynedd)	d	02 42											05e00						05 59						
Llandudno	d																								
Llandudno Junction	d	03 00						05 00					05e18				05 45		06 19						
Chester	d	03 40	04 55					06 00					06 30				06 56		07 18			07 30			
Crewe 10	a	03 59		05 45				06 46	06 50				07 08	07 23			07 33		07 43	07 50	←	08 03		08 05	
	d	04 02	05 45	05 48			06 09	06 49	06 53				07 10	07 23			07 35		07 57	07 53	07 57	08 06		08 10	
Macclesfield	d				06 29					07 03					07 16			07 35	→						08 07
Congleton	d					←									07 24										
Stoke-on-Trent	d		06 06		06 45	06 06				07 21					07 39			07 50							08 23
Stafford	a	04 29	→	06 12		06 24	06 29		07 10					07 44	07 56					08 10				08 32	
	d	04 30		06 14		06 26	06 30		07 12					07 44	07 58					08 12				08 33	
Penkridge	a						06 35							07 50											
Wolverhampton 7	a	04 45				06 40	06 47						07 47	08 03	08 12							08 42		08 47	
Coseley	a													08 12											
Sandwell & Dudley	a																								
Birmingham New Street 12	a	05 08				06 58	07 08						08 10	08 27	08 30							09 05		09 06	
	d					07 03																			
Birmingham International	a	06 14				07 14	07 51						08 51		09 14									09 52	
Coventry	a	06 23				07 24	08 09						09 09											10 10	
Lichfield Trent Valley	a			06 27				07 18																	
Tamworth Low Level	a			06 34					07 29																
Nuneaton	a			06 45					07 40											08 34					
Rugby	a			07 00	07 33			07 46																	
Northampton	a																								
Milton Keynes Central	a				07 55			08 07	08 17									08 55							09 28
Watford Junction	a			07s50	08s16			08s30		08s45							09s01			09s34					
Gatwick Airport 10	a																								
London Euston 15	a			08 14	08 42			08 59	09 00	09 10							09 27	09 38		09 59	10 03				10 15

For general notes see front of timetable
For details of catering facilities see Directory of Train Operators

- **A** To Bournemouth (Table 51)
- **B** To Reading (Table 51)
- **C** To Newquay (Table 135)
- **b** Change at Preston
- **c** Change at Wilmslow and Crewe
- **e** Change at Chester and Crewe

Due to ongoing Engineering Operations, some services from Saturday 13 September on this Table had not been confirmed at time of going to press. These services will be issued in a special Supplement as soon as exact timings have been confirmed.

Saturdays

Scotland and North West England → West Midlands and London

19 July to 6 September

Route Diagram - see first page of Table 65

		LM	XC	NT	TP	VT	VT	VT	VT	XC	VT		VT	LM	XC	TP	VT	VT	NT	VT	XC	VT		VT	LM
		1 ◊	1 ◊		1 ◊	1 ◊	1 ◊	1 ◊	1 ◊	R 1	1 ◊		1 ◊	1 ◊	1 ◊	1 ◊	1 ◊	1 ◊		1 ◊	1 ◊	1 ◊		1 ◊	1 ◊
			A		B					C					D	B					E				
			⊡		⊼	⊡	⊡	⊡	⊡	⊡	⊡		⊡		⊡	⊼	⊡	⊡		⊡	⊡	⊡		⊡	
Inverness	d																								
Aberdeen	d																								
Dundee	d																								
Perth	d																								
Edinburgh 10	d																							06 51	
Haymarket	d																							06u55	
Glasgow Central 15	d																06 10								
Motherwell	d																06u25								
Carstairs	d																								
Lockerbie	d																							07 52	
Carlisle 8	a																07 26							08 11	
	d					06 30											07 28							08 13	
Penrith North Lakes	d					06 44											07 43							08 29	
Windermere	d					*06 35*											*07 24*							*08 28*	
Oxenholme Lake District	a					07 07											08 05							08 52	
	d					07 08											08 07							08 53	
Barrow-in-Furness	d				06 15											07 05								*07 58*	
Lancaster 6	a				07 15	07 23										08 02	08 21							09 08	
	d				07 16	07 24										08 03	08 23							09 09	
Preston 8	a				07 35	07 41										08 21	08 44							09 26	
Blackpool North	a				*08 12*	*08 36*										*09 00*	*09 32*							*10 02*	
	d			06 57		*07 03*							*07 41*				*08 09*							*08 41*	
Preston 8	d			07 25	07 40	07 44							08 29			08 34	08 47		08 50					09 29	
Wigan North Western	a			07 44		07 55							08 39				08 57		09 10					09 40	
	d			07 45		07 56							08 40				08 59		09 11					09 41	
Bolton	a				08 02	*08b24*										08 58	*09b34*								
Manchester Piccadilly 10	a				08 25	*08b47*										09 20	*09b57*								
Manchester Airport	a				08 42	*09b06*										09 40	*10b19*								
Liverpool Lime Street 10	a			08 27		*09 19*							*09 49*						09 52					*10 49*	
	d	07 39							08 15					08 38						09 15					09 37
Liverpool South Parkway 7	d	07 49												08 47											09 47
Runcorn	d	07 57							08 30					08 55						09 31					09 55
Warrington Bank Quay	a					08 06							08 50				09 08							09 51	
	d					08 07							08 52				09 10							09 53	
Hartford	d	08 06												09 07											10 05
Manchester Piccadilly 10	d	*07 28*	07 54				08 15	*07c34*		08 24	08 45				08 54		*08 34*	09 15			09 24	09 45			
Stockport	d	*07 37*	08 03				08u23	*07e43*		08 33	08u55				09 03		*08 44*	09u22			09 33	09u54			
Manchester Airport	d							*08c00*												*09 00*					
Wilmslow	d	*07 46*						*08c07*					*08 21*				*08 52*			*09 07*				*09 24*	
Holyhead	d							06 45	*06f00*											*07 15*					
Bangor (Gwynedd)	d							07 12	*06f30*											*08 01*					
Llandudno	d							*07 03*	*06g39*											*07h47*					
Llandudno Junction	d							07 31	*06f54*											*08 27*					
Chester	d							08 22	*08 00*											*09 19*					
Crewe 10	a	08 21				08 29		08 45	08 50				09 12	09 22			09 29			09 50				10 12	10 21
	d	08 22				08 32		08 50	08 53				09 14	09 23			09 32			09 53				10 15	10 22
Macclesfield	d		08 16				08 36			08 46	09 08				09 16						09 46	10 07			
Congleton	d		08 24												09 24										
Stoke-on-Trent	d		08 39				08 55			09 06	09 24				09 39			09 48			10 06	10 23			
Stafford	a	08 43	08 56						09 11	09 25				09 44	09 56					10 11	10 25				10 43
	d	08 44	08 58						09 12	09 26				09 44	09 58					10 12	10 26				10 44
Penkridge	a	08 50												09 50											10 50
Wolverhampton 7	a	09 03	09 11							09 41			09 48	10 03	10 12						10 41			10 48	11 03
Coseley	a	09 12												10 12											11 12
Sandwell & Dudley	a																								
Birmingham New Street 12	a	09 27	09 30							09 58			10 11	10 27	10 30						10 58			11 11	11 27
	d		09 33																		11 03				
Birmingham International	a		*10 14*										*10 52*								11 14			*11 51*	
Coventry	a		*10 23*										*11 10*								11 23			*12 09*	
Lichfield Trent Valley	a						09 17																		
Tamworth Low Level	a							09 27			09 50														
Nuneaton	a								09 38											10 34					
Rugby	a					09 22											10 21								
Northampton	a																								
Milton Keynes Central	a					09 44			10 15													11 28			
Watford Junction	a						10s19	10s36			10s52						11s00			11s34					
Gatwick Airport 10	a		12 53																						
London Euston 15	⊖ a					10 29	10 48	11 04	11 05		11 16						11 27	11 31		12 00		12 19			

For general notes see front of timetable
For details of catering facilities see Directory of Train Operators

A To Brighton (Table 51)
B ⊼ from Preston
C To Paignton (Table 51)
D To Reading (Table 51)
E To Bournemouth (Table 51)
b Change at Preston
c Change at Crewe
e Change at Wilmslow and Crewe
f Change at Chester and Crewe
g Change at Llandudno Junction, Chester and Crewe
h Change at Llandudno Junction and Crewe

Due to ongoing Engineering Operations, some services from Saturday 13 September on this Table had not been confirmed at time of going to press. These services will be issued in a special Supplement as soon as exact timings have been confirmed.

Table 65

Saturdays

19 July to 6 September

Scotland and North West England → West Midlands and London

Route Diagram - see first page of Table 65

		XC	TP	VT	VT	NT	VT	XC	VT	VT	LM	XC	TP	VT	NT	VT	VT	VT	TP	XC	VT	TP	TP
		1 ◇	1 ◇	1 ◇	1 ◇		1 ◇	R 1	1 ◇	R 1	1 ◇	1 ◇	1 ◇	1 ◇		1 ◇	1 ◇	1 ◇	1 ◇	1 ◇	1 ◇	1 ◇	1 ◇
		A						B				A	C							D			
		🍴	🛒	🍴	🍴		🍴	🍴	🍴	🍴		🍴	🛒	🍴		🍴	🍴	🍴		🍴	🍴	🛒	🛒
Inverness	d																						*06 00*
Aberdeen	d																						*07 11*
Dundee	d																						*07 03*
Perth	d			*05b15*																			
Edinburgh 10	d																						08 41
Haymarket	d																						08 45
Glasgow Central 15	d		06 58	07 10						07 40				08 07								08 40	
Motherwell	d													08u26									
Carstairs	d																						
Lockerbie	d		07 57																			09 36	
Carlisle 8	a		08 19	08 32						09 08				09 21								09 58	10 06
	d		08 20	08 39						09 11				09 32									10 15 →
Penrith North Lakes	d		08 35							09 26				09 47									
Windermere	d									*09 26*				*09 26*					10 18				
Oxenholme Lake District	a		08 59							09 49				10 09					10 35				
	d		08 59							09 51				10 11					10 37				
Barrow-in-Furness	d												09 15										
Lancaster 6	a		09 14	09 25						10 08			10 15	10 25					10 52				
	d		09 14	09 27						10 09			10 16	10 27					10 53				
Preston 8	a		09 35	09 44						10 27			10 34	10 44					11 13				
Blackpool North	a			*10 21*										*11 22*					*11 56*				
	d			*09 11*		09 25				*09 40*				*10 11*	10 25								
Preston 8	d		09 38	09 47		09 50				10 29			10 38	10 47	10 50								
Wigan North Western	a			09 57		10 09				10 40				10 57	11 11								
	d			09 59		10 11				10 41				10 59	11 11								
Bolton	a		09 58	*10c34*									10 58	*11c34*									
Manchester Piccadilly 10	a		10 20	*10c57*									11 20	*11c57*									
Manchester Airport	a		10 40	*11c19*									11 40	*12c19*									
Liverpool Lime Street 10	a					10 52				*11 49*					11 52								
	d						10 15				10 37							11 15					
Liverpool South Parkway 7	d										10 47												
Runcorn	d						10 31				10 55							11 30					
Warrington Bank Quay	a			10 08						10 51				11 08									
	d			10 10						10 53				11 10									
Hartford	d										11 05												
Manchester Piccadilly 10	d	09 54		*09 34*	10 15			10 24	10 45			10 54		*10 34*		11 15				11 24	11 45		
Stockport	d	10 03		*09 42*	10u24			10 33	10u54			11 03		*10 43*		11u24				11 33	11u54		
Manchester Airport	d						*10 00*										*11e00*						
Wilmslow	d			*09 52*			*10 06*			*10 24*				*10 51*			*11e06*						
Holyhead	d									*08f25*							09 50	*09 28*					
Bangor (Gwynedd)	d									*09f04*							10 18	*10 07*					
Llandudno	d						*08f47*										*10 14*	10g14					
Llandudno Junction	d						*08f56*			*09f27*							10 36	*10 30*					
Chester	d						*10 00*			*10 29*							11 28	*11 14*					
Crewe 10	a			10 28			10 50			11 13	11 21			11 29			11 47	11 50					
	d			10 31			10 53			11 15	11 22			11 32			11 49	11 53					
Macclesfield	d	10 16						10 46	11 07			11 16								11 46	12 07		
Congleton	d											11 24											
Stoke-on-Trent	d	10 39			10 50			11 06	11 23			11 39				11 50				12 06	12 23		
Stafford	a	10 56					11 11	11 24			11 43	11 56						12 10		12 24			
	d	10 58					11 12	11 26			11 44	11 58						12 12		12 26			
Penkridge	a										11 50												
Wolverhampton 7	a	11 12						11 41		11 48	12 03	12 12								12 41			
Coseley	a										12 12												
Sandwell & Dudley	a																						
Birmingham New Street 12	a	11 30						11 58		12 11	12 27	12 30								12 58			
	d																			13 03			
Birmingham International	a									*12 51*										13 14			
Coventry	a									*13 09*										13 23			
Lichfield Trent Valley	a																						
Tamworth Low Level	a								11 50														
Nuneaton	a						11 34											12 35					
Rugby	a			11 19										12 20									
Northampton	a																						
Milton Keynes Central	a			11 40			12 09														13 27		
Watford Junction	a								12s53					12s59				13s36					
Gatwick Airport 10	a																						
London Euston 15	⊖ a			12 27	12 31		12 54		13 20					13 28		13 31	13 40	14 03			14 19		

For general notes see front of timetable
For details of catering facilities see Directory of Train Operators

A To Reading (Table 51)
B To Paignton (Table 51)
C 🛒 from Preston
D To Bournemouth (Table 51)
b Via Glasgow Queen Street and Glasgow Central. Passengers make their own way from one station to the other
c Change at Preston
e Change at Crewe
f Change at Chester and Crewe
g Change at Llandudno Junction and Crewe

Due to ongoing Engineering Operations, some services from Saturday 13 September on this Table had not been confirmed at time of going to press. These services will be issued in a special Supplement as soon as exact timings have been confirmed.

Scotland and North West England → West Midlands and London

19 July to 6 September

Route Diagram - see first page of Table 65

		VT	LM	TP	XC	VT	VT	NT	VT	XC	VT	VT	LM	XC	TP	VT	VT	NT	VT	XC	VT	TP	VT
		R 1	1◇	1◇	1◇	1◇	1◇		1◇	R 1	1◇	R 1	1◇	1◇	1◇	1◇	1◇		1◇	1◇	1◇	1◇	1◇
					A					B				C	D					E		D	
		🍽		🛒	🍽	🍽	🍽		🍽	🍽	🍽	🍽		🍽	🛒	🍽	🍽		🍽	🍽	🍽	🛒	🍽
Inverness	d																						06 45
Aberdeen	d											06b34				07b07							08c20
Dundee	d	07c16										07b52				08b21							09c32
Perth	d											08b13				08b43							08 47
Edinburgh 10	d	08 52																					10 52
Haymarket	d	08u56																					10u56
Glasgow Central 15	d											10 10				10 20							
Motherwell	d																						
Carstairs	d																						
Lockerbie	d																						
Carlisle 8	a	10 08		←								11 20				11 30							12 11
	d	10 10		10 15								11 22				11 32							12 13
Penrith North Lakes	d			10 30												11 47							12 29
Windermere	d															11 27						12 23	
Oxenholme Lake District	a	10 45		10 53												12 09						12 40	12 52
	d	10 47		10 54												12 11						12 42	12 53
Barrow-in-Furness	d			09 58											11 18								
Lancaster 6	a	11 04		11 10								12 09			12 16	12 25						13 02	13 08
	d	11 06		11 10		11 24						12 11			12 16	12 27						13 04	13 09
Preston 8	a	11 23		11 32		11 44						12 28			12 36	12 44						13 22	13 26
Blackpool North	a	12 01		12 14		12 20										13 21							14 00
	d	10 41				11 11		11 25				11 41				12 11		12 25					12 41
Preston 8	d	11 28		11 38		11 47		11 50				12 29			12 38	12 47		12 50				13 38 →	13 29
Wigan North Western	a	11 39				11 57		12 09				12 40				12 57		13 09					13 40
	d	11 40				11 59		12 11				12 41				12 59		13 11					13 41
Bolton	a			11 58		12e34									12 58	13e34							
Manchester Piccadilly 10	a			12 20		12e57									13 20	13e57							
Manchester Airport	a			12 40		13e19									13 40	14e19							
Liverpool Lime Street 10	a	12 49						12 52				13 49						13 52					14 49
	d		11 37						12 15				12 37						13 15				
Liverpool South Parkway 7	d		11 47										12 47										
Runcorn	d		11 55						12 31				12 55						13 31				
Warrington Bank Quay	a	11 51				12 08						12 51				13 08							13 51
	d	11 53				12 10						12 53				13 10							13 53
Hartford	d		12 05										13 07										
Manchester Piccadilly 10	d				11 54	11 34	12 15			12 24	12 45			12 54		12 34	13 15			13 24	13 45		
Stockport	d				12 03	11 42	12u24			12 33	12u54			13 03		12 42	13u22			13 33	13u54		
Manchester Airport	d								12 00										13 00				
Wilmslow	d	11 24				11 51			12 06			12 24				12 51			13 06				13 24
Holyhead	d											10f30											11 40
Bangor (Gwynedd)	d											11f03											12 19
Llandudno	d								10f47										11f47				
Llandudno Junction	d								10f56			11f26							11f56				12 42
Chester	d								12 00			12 29							13 00				13 33
Crewe 10	a	12 13	12 21			12 29			12 50			13 12	13 21			13 29			13 50				14 12
	d	12 13	12 22			12 32			12 53			13 15	13 22			13 32			13 53				14 15
Macclesfield	d				12 16					12 46	13 07			13 16						13 46	14 07		
Congleton	d													13 24									
Stoke-on-Trent	d				12 39		12 50			13 06	13 23			13 39			13 48			14 06	14 23		
Stafford	a		12 43		12 56				13 11	13 24			13 43	13 56					14 11	14 24			
	d		12 44		12 58				13 12	13 26			13 44	13 58					14 12	14 26			
Penkridge	a		12 50										13 50										
Wolverhampton 7	a	12 48	13 03		13 12					13 40		13 48	14 03	14 12						14 41			14 48
Coseley	a		13 12										14 12										
Sandwell & Dudley	a																						
Birmingham New Street 12	a	13 11	13 27		13 30					13 58		14 11	14 27	14 30						14 58			15 11
	d																			15 03			
Birmingham International	a	13 52			14 25							14 51								15 14			15 51
Coventry	a	14 10										15 09								15 23			16 09
Lichfield Trent Valley	a																						
Tamworth Low Level	a																						
Nuneaton	a								13 34										14 34				
Rugby	a					13 20										14 20							
Northampton	a																						
Milton Keynes Central	a					13 41			14 09												15 27		
Watford Junction	a										14s44					14s58			15s36				
Gatwick Airport 10	a																						
London Euston 15	a					14 25	14 31		15 00		15 10					15 26	15 31		16 03		16 16		

For general notes see front of timetable
For details of catering facilities see Directory of Train Operators

A To Reading (Table 51)
B To Paignton (Table 51)
C To Guildford (Table 51)
D 🛒 from Preston
E To Bournemouth (Table 51)
b Via Glasgow Queen Street and Glasgow Central. Passengers make their own way from one station to the other
c Change at Haymarket
e Change at Preston
f Change at Chester and Crewe

Due to ongoing Engineering Operations, some services from Saturday 13 September on this Table had not been confirmed at time of going to press. These services will be issued in a special Supplement as soon as exact timings have been confirmed.

Scotland and North West England → West Midlands and London

19 July to 6 September

Route Diagram - see first page of Table 65

		TP	LM	XC	VT	VT	NT	VT	TP	XC	VT	VT	LM	XC	TP	VT	VT	NT	VT	XC	VT	TP	TP
		1 ◇	1 ◇	1 ◇	1 ◇	1 ◇		1 ◇	1 ◇	1 ◇	1 ◇	R 1	1 ◇	1 ◇	1 ◇	1 ◇	1 ◇		1 ◇	1 ◇	1 ◇	1 ◇	1 ◇
		A		B						C				D						E			
		⊼		☕	☕	☕		☕	⊼	☕	☕	☕		☕	⊼	☕	☕		☕	☕	☕		
Inverness	d								07 55														
Aberdeen	d								08 51														
Dundee	d								09 59														
Perth	d				09b08				09 55			10b13											
Edinburgh 10	d								11 52														
Haymarket	d																						
Glasgow Central 15	d				11 10							12 10											
Motherwell	d				11u23																		
Carstairs	d																						
Lockerbie	d																						
Carlisle 8	a				12 30				13 09			13 20											
	d				12 32				13 11			13 21											
Penrith North Lakes	d				12 47				13 25														
Windermere	d								13 25													14 18	
Oxenholme Lake District	a				13 09				13 49			13 57										14 35	
	d				13 11				13 50			13 58										14 37	
Barrow-in-Furness	d								12 56														14 10
Lancaster 6	a				13 25				14 07						←							14 54	15 02
	d				13 27				14 17 →						14 17	14 27						15 15 →	
Preston 8	a				13 44							14 26			14 36	14 44							
Blackpool North	a				14 21							15 01				15 21							
	d	←			13 11		13 25					13 41				14 11		14 25					
Preston 8	d	13 38			13 47		13 50					14 29			14 38	14 47		14 50					
Wigan North Western	a				13 57		14 11					14 40				14 57		15 10					
	d				13 59		14 11					14 41				14 59		15 11					
Bolton	a	13 58			14c34										14 58	15c34							
Manchester Piccadilly 10	a	14 20			14c57										15 20	15c57							
Manchester Airport	a	14 40			15c19										15 40	16c19							
Liverpool Lime Street 10	a						14 52					15 49						15 52					
	d		13 37					14 15					14 37						15 15				
Liverpool South Parkway 7	d		13 47										14 47										
Runcorn	d		13 55					14 31					14 55						15 31				
Warrington Bank Quay	a				14 08							14 50				15 08							
	d				14 10							14 52				15 10							
Hartford	d		14 05										15 05										
Manchester Piccadilly 10	d			13 54	13 34	14 15				14 24	14 45			14 54		14 34	15 15			15 24	15 45		
Stockport	d			14 03	13 42	14u24				14 33	14u54			15 03		14 42	15u24			15 33	15u54		
Manchester Airport	d							14 00											15 00				
Wilmslow	d				13 54			14 06				14 24	14 24			14 51			15 06				
Holyhead	d											12e35											
Bangor (Gwynedd)	d											13e04											
Llandudno	d							12e47				13f14							13e47				
Llandudno Junction	d							12e56				13e27							13e56				
Chester	d							14 03				14 30							15 03				
Crewe 10	a		14 21		14 29			14 50				15 10	15 21			15 29			15 50				
	d		14 22		14 32			14 53				15 13	15 22			15 32			15 53				
Macclesfield	d			14 16						14 46	15 07			15 16						15 46	16 07		
Congleton	d													15 24									
Stoke-on-Trent	d			14 39		14 50				15 06	15 23			15 39			15 50			16 06	16 23		
Stafford	a		14 43	14 56				15 10		15 24			15 43	15 56					16 11	16 24			
	d		14 44	14 58				15 12		15 26			15 44	15 58					16 12	16 26			
Penkridge	a		14 50										15 50										
Wolverhampton 7	a		15 03	15 12						15 41		15 46	16 03	16 12						16 41			
Coseley	a		15 12										16 12										
Sandwell & Dudley	a																						
Birmingham New Street 12	a		15 27	15 30						15 58		16 11	16 27	16 30						16 58			
	d													16 33						17 03			
Birmingham International	a											16 51								17 14			
Coventry	a											17 09								17 23			
Lichfield Trent Valley	a															16 00							
Tamworth Low Level	a							15 27															
Nuneaton	a																		16 34				
Rugby	a				15 20											16 25				18g30			
Northampton	a																						
Milton Keynes Central	a				15 42			16 08													17 27		
Watford Junction	a					16s10					16s44					17s03			17s33		18 24		
Gatwick Airport 10	a													19 52									
London Euston 15	⊖ a				16 28	16 36		17 00			17 10					17 28	17 31		18 00		18 19		

For general notes see front of timetable
For details of catering facilities see Directory of Train Operators

A ⊼ from Preston
B To Reading (Table 51)
C To Penzance (Table 135)
D To Brighton (Table 51)
E To Bournemouth (Table 51)

b Via Glasgow Queen Street and Glasgow Central. Passengers make their own way from one station to the other
c Change at Preston
e Change at Chester and Crewe
f Change at Llandudno Junction, Chester and Crewe
g By bus

Due to ongoing Engineering Operations, some services from Saturday 13 September on this Table had not been confirmed at time of going to press. These services will be issued in a special Supplement as soon as exact timings have been confirmed.

Table 65

Saturdays

Scotland and North West England → West Midlands and London

19 July to 6 September

Route Diagram - see first page of Table 65

		VT	TP	VT	LM	XC	VT	VT	NT	VT	XC		TP	VT	VT	TP	LM	XC	VT	VT	NT	VT		XC	VT
		R																							
		1	1 ◇	1 ◇	1 ◇	1 ◇	1 ◇	1 ◇		1 ◇	1 ◇		1 ◇	1 ◇	1 ◇	1 ◇	1 ◇	1 ◇	1 ◇	1 ◇		1 ◇		1 ◇	1 ◇
			A			B					C							D						E	
		⊐P	⌶	⊐P		⊐P	⊐P	⊐P		⊐P	⊐P		⌶	⊐P	⊐P	⌶		⊐P	⊐P	⊐P		⊐P		⊐P	⊐P
Inverness	d												*09b19*												
Aberdeen	d	*10c22*													*10b42*										
Dundee	d	*11c30*													*11b52*										
Perth	d	*11 08*					*11b14*						*11b38*		*12b14*										
Edinburgh 10	d	12 52																							
Haymarket	d	12u56																							
Glasgow Central 15	d						13 10						13 40		14 10										
Motherwell	d						13u25																		
Carstairs	d																								
Lockerbie	d	13 52											14 38												
Carlisle 8	a	14 11					14 30						14 58		15 20										
	d	14 13					14 32						15 08		15 21				15 30						
Penrith North Lakes	d	14 28					14 47						15 23						15 44						
Windermere	d												*15 22*												
Oxenholme Lake District	a	14 51					15 09						15 46						16 07						
	d	14 53					15 11						15 47						16 08						
Barrow-in-Furness	d																								
Lancaster 6	a	15 07	←				15 25						16 02		16 09				16 23						
	d	15 09	15 15				15 27						16 03		16 10				16 24						
Preston 8	a	15 26	15 34				15 44						16 22		16 27				16 41						
Blackpool North	a	*16 01*					*16 21*						*17 01*						*17 34*						
	d	*14 41*					*15 11*		15 25						*15 41*	←			*16 10*		16 25				
Preston 8	d	15 29	15 38				15 47		15 50				16 38 →		16 29	16 38			16 46		16 50				
Wigan North Western	a	15 40					15 57		16 10						16 40				16 56		17 09				
	d	15 41					15 59		16 11						16 41				16 58		17 11				
Bolton	a		15 58				*16e34*									16 58			*17e36*						
Manchester Piccadilly 10 🚊	a		16 20				*16e57*									17 20			*17e57*						
Manchester Airport ✈	a		16 40				*17e19*									17 40			*18e19*						
Liverpool Lime Street 10	a	*16 49*							16 53						*17 49*						17 53				
	d				15 37					16 15							16 37					17 15			
Liverpool South Parkway 7 ✈	d				15 47												16 47								
Runcorn	d				15 55					16 31							16 55					17 31			
Warrington Bank Quay	a	15 51					16 08								16 51				17 07						
	d	15 52					16 10								16 52				17 09						
Hartford	d				16 05												17 07								
Manchester Piccadilly 10 🚊	d					15 54	*15 34*	16 15			16 24			16 45				16 54	*16 34*	17 15				17 24	17 45
Stockport	d					16 03	*15 42*	16u24			16 33			16u54				17 03	*16 43*	17u23				17 33	17u54
Manchester Airport ✈	d									*16 00*												*17 00*			
Wilmslow	d			*15f24*			*15 51*			*16 06*					*16 24*				*16 51*			*17 06*			
Holyhead	d	*13 35*		14 15											*14g35*										
Bangor (Gwynedd)	d	*14 14*		14 44											*15g04*										
Llandudno	d			*14 35*																		*15g47*			
Llandudno Junction	d	*14 37*		15 03						*15 17*					*15g27*							*15g56*			
Chester	d	*15 30*		15 49						*16 12*					*16 31*							*17 00*			
Crewe 10	a	16 11		16 14	16 21		16 29			16 50					17 13		17 21		17 28			17 50			
	d	16 12		16 17	16 22		16 32			16 53					17 15		17 22		17 31			17 53			
Macclesfield	d					16 16					16 46			17 07				17 16						17 46	18 07
Congleton	d																	17 24							
Stoke-on-Trent	d					16 39		16 50			17 06			17 23				17 39		17 50				18 06	18 23
Stafford	a				16 44	16 56				17 11	17 24						17 43	17 56				18 11		18 24	
	d				16 44	16 58				17 12	17 26						17 44	17 58				18 12		18 26	
Penkridge	a				16 50												17 50								
Wolverhampton 7 🚊	a	16 48			17 03	17 12					17 41				17 48		18 03	18 12						18 41	
Coseley	a				17 12												18 12								
Sandwell & Dudley	a																								
Birmingham New Street 12	a	17 11			17 27	17 30					17 58				18 11		18 27	18 30						18 58	
	d																	18 33						19 03	
Birmingham International ✈	a	*17 52*													*18 52*									19 14	
Coventry	a	*18 10*													*19 10*									19 23	
Lichfield Trent Valley	a																								
Tamworth Low Level	a																								
Nuneaton	a									17 34												18 34			
Rugby	a						17 23			17 49									18 20						
Northampton	a																								
Milton Keynes Central	a						17 44			18 10															19 28
Watford Junction	a													18s44					18s58			19s31			20 03
Gatwick Airport 10 ✈	a																	21 47							
London Euston 15 ⊖	a			18 27			18 30	18 31		19 00				19 10					19 24	19 31		19 57			20 35

For general notes see front of timetable
For details of catering facilities see Directory of Train Operators

A ⌶ from Preston
B To Reading (Table 51)
C To Plymouth (Table 51)
D ⊐P to Reading
E To Bournemouth (Table 51)

b Via Glasgow Queen Street and Glasgow Central. Passengers make their own way from one station to the other
c Change at Haymarket
e Change at Preston
f Change at Crewe
g Change at Chester and Crewe

Due to ongoing Engineering Operations, some services from Saturday 13 September on this Table had not been confirmed at time of going to press. These services will be issued in a special Supplement as soon as exact timings have been confirmed.

Scotland and North West England → West Midlands and London

19 July to 6 September

Route Diagram - see first page of Table 65

		VT	LM	XC	TP	VT	VT	NT	VT	XC	VT	TP	VT	TP	LM	XC	VT	VT	NT	TP	VT	XC	VT
		1◇	1◇	1◇	1◇	1◇	1◇		1◇	1◇	1◇	1◇	1◇	1◇	1◇	1◇	1◇	1◇		1◇	1◇	1◇	1◇
					A					B												C	
		☕		☕	🛒	☕	☕		☕	☕	☕	🛒	☕	🛒		☕	☕	☕			☕	☕	☕
Inverness	d	10 53																					12 40
Aberdeen	d	12b24										13b21											14b25
Dundee	d	13b33										14b30											15b32
Perth	d	13 04				13c14							14c14										14 49
Edinburgh 10	d	14 52										15 52											16 52
Haymarket	d	14u56										15u56											16u56
Glasgow Central 15	d					15 10							16 03								16 37		
Motherwell	d					15u27																	
Carstairs	d																						
Lockerbie	d											16 52											17 50
Carlisle 8	a	16 07				16 30						17 13	17 20								17 57		18 11
	d	16 09				16 32						17 15	17 21								18 00		18 11
Penrith North Lakes	d	16 24				16 47						17 29	17 36										18 27
Windermere	d	16 22										17 27								18 10			
Oxenholme Lake District	a	16 47				17 09						17 53	17 59							18 30	18 36		18 51
	d	16 48				17 11						17 53	18 00							18 33	18 38		18 51
Barrow-in-Furness	d	15 28			16 21							17 06											
Lancaster 6	a	17 03			17 15	17 25						18 09		←						18 49	18 55		19 07
	d	17 04			17 16	17 27						18 16		18 16						18 51	18 56		19 07
Preston 8	a	17 21			17 34	17 44						→	18 29	18 36						19 09	19 14		19 26
Blackpool North	a	18 03				18 30								19 21							20 01		20 07
	d	16 38				17 10							17 38						18 25				
Preston 8	d	17 24			17 35	17 47		17 50					18 30	18 38					18 50	19 14	19 21		19 29
Wigan North Western	a	17 35				17 57		18 11					18 41						19 10		19 31		19 40
	d	17 36				17 58		18 11					18 42						19 11		19 33		19 41
Bolton	a				17 59	18e34								18 58						19 38			20e11
Manchester Piccadilly 10 🚋	a				18 20	18e57								19 20						20 04			20e34
Manchester Airport ✈	a				18 42	19e19								19 40						20 26			21f06
Liverpool Lime Street 10	a	18 34						18 55											19 52				
	d		17 37						18 15						18 40			19 15					
Liverpool South Parkway 7 ✈	d		17 47												18 50								
Runcorn	d		17 55						18 31						18 58			19 31					
Warrington Bank Quay	a	17 46				18 08							18 52								19 42		19 51
	d	17 48				18 10							18 53								19 44		19 53
Hartford	d		18 05												19 09								
Manchester Piccadilly 10 🚋	d			17 54		17 34	18 15			18 24	18 45					18 54	19 15					19 24	
Stockport	d			18 03		17 42	18u24			18 33	18u56					19 03	19u24					19 33	
Manchester Airport ✈	d								18 00														19g01
Wilmslow	d	17 26				17 51			18 11				18 24					18 53					19 26
Holyhead	d	15 39											16h35										17 35
Bangor (Gwynedd)	d	16 17											17h04										18 14
Llandudno	d	16j14							16h47									17h47					
Llandudno Junction	d	16 40							16h56				17h27					17h56					18 37
Chester	d	17 31							18 04				18 30					19 00					19 34
Crewe 10	a	18 07	18 21			18 29			18 50				19 13		19 22			19 50			20 03		20 13
	d	18 13	18 21			18 32			18 53				19 15		19 23			19 53			20 05		20 15
Macclesfield	d			18 16						18 46	19 09					19 16	19 37					19 46	
Congleton	d			18 24												19 24							
Stoke-on-Trent	d			18 39			18 51			19 06	19 25					19 39	19 53					20 06	
Stafford	a		18 44	18 56					19 11	19 24					19 44	19 56		20 13				20 24	
	d		18 44	18 58					19 12	19 25					19 44	19 58		20 15				20 26	
Penkridge	a		18 50												19 50								
Wolverhampton 7 🚋	a	18 48	19 03	19 12						19 40			19 48		20 03	20 12						20 40	20 48
Coseley	a		19 12																				
Sandwell & Dudley	a																						
Birmingham New Street 12	a	19 11	19 27	19 35						19 58			20 11		20 30	20 35						20 58	21 11
	d																					21 03	
Birmingham International ✈	a	19 51											20 51									21 14	21 52
Coventry	a	20 09											21 09									21 23	22 10
Lichfield Trent Valley	a																						
Tamworth Low Level	a																						
Nuneaton	a								19 34									20 37					
Rugby	a					19 22															21 02		
Northampton	a																						
Milton Keynes Central	a					19 44			20 12								21 15						
Watford Junction	a					20 21	20s35		21 02		21s07							22s09			22s16		
Gatwick Airport 10 ✈	a										22 23												
London Euston 15 ⊖	a					20 58	21 05		21 34		21 41						22 35	22 45			22 52		

For general notes see front of timetable
For details of catering facilities see Directory of Train Operators

A 🛒 from Preston
B To Plymouth (Table 51)
C To Southampton Central (Table 51). ☕ to Birmingham New Street
b Change at Haymarket
c Via Glasgow Queen Street and Glasgow Central. Passengers make their own way from one station to the other
e Change at Preston
f Change at Preston and Manchester Piccadilly
g Change at Wilmslow and Crewe
h Change at Chester and Crewe
j Change at Llandudno Junction and Crewe

Due to ongoing Engineering Operations, some services from Saturday 13 September on this Table had not been confirmed at time of going to press. These services will be issued in a special Supplement as soon as exact timings have been confirmed.

Table 65

Scotland and North West England → West Midlands and London

19 July to 6 September

Route Diagram - see first page of Table 65

Station		LM	XC	VT	NT	NT	VT	NT	VT	VT	NT	TP	TP	VT	XC	LM	VT	TP	NT	NT	SR	SR
		1 ◇	1 ◇	1 ◇			1 ◇		1 ◇	1 ◇		1 ◇	1 ◇	1 ◇	1 ◇	1 ◇	1 ◇	1				
					A														B			
				🍴			🍴		🍴	🍴		🛒		🍴			🍴					
Inverness	d																				14b41	16c56
Aberdeen	d											15e20									16c41	18c40
Dundee	d											16e31									17c52	19c52
Perth	d								15c14					16c14							18c14	20c14
Edinburgh [10]	d											17 52										
Haymarket	d											17u56										
Glasgow Central [15]	d								17 40					18 10							20 03	22 03
Motherwell	d													18u27								
Carstairs	d																					
Lockerbie	d											18 53		19 12								
Carlisle [8]	a								18 49			19 15		19 31							22 24	00 34
	d								18 59			19 16		19 32								
Penrith North Lakes	d								19 19			19 31										
Windermere	d											19 22						20 24				
Oxenholme Lake District	a								19 41			19 54		20 07				20 44				
	d								19 43			19 55		20 08				20 46				
Barrow-in-Furness	d				18 14				18 14				19 15									
Lancaster [6]	a				19 17				19 57			20 10	20 16	20 20				21 03				
	d				19 18				19 59			20 11	20 17	20 21					21 20			
Preston [8]	a				19 43				20 16			20 29	20 35	20 41					21 45			
Blackpool North	a								20 56					21 36					22 36			
	d					19 19		19 25	19 42								20 30			22 03		
Preston [8]	d					19 46		19 50	20 19		20 27	20 32	20 37	20 43			21 22			22 28		
Wigan North Western	a					20 06		20 10	20 29		20 47			20 54			21 33			22 47		
	d					20 09		20 11	20 31		20 48			20 55			21 34			22 47		
Bolton	a											20 53	21 07	21f52					22 52			
Manchester Piccadilly [10]	a					20g44						21 14	21 29	22f18					23 30			
Manchester Airport	a											21 37	21 51	22f39					23 56			
Liverpool Lime Street [10]	a							20 52			21 39						22 38			23 38		
	d	19 37					20 13									21 16						
Liverpool South Parkway [7]	d	19 47														21 26						
Runcorn	d	19 55					20 29									21 34						
Warrington Bank Quay	a								20 40					21 05			21 44					
	d								20 42					21 06			21 46					
Hartford	d	20 05														21 44						
Manchester Piccadilly [10]	d		19 54	20 15						20 45				20 34	20 54		20 58					
Stockport	d		20 03	20u24						20u56				20 46	21 03		21 15					
Manchester Airport	d													19h56			21h10					
Wilmslow	d						19 54							20 54			21 26					
Holyhead	d													18j35			19 35					
Bangor (Gwynedd)	d													19j14			20 14					
Llandudno	d						18j47							18k53		19j47						
Llandudno Junction	d						18j56							19j32		19j56	20 37					
Chester	d						20 05							20 30		21 00	21 33					
Crewe [10]	a	20 21					20 48		21 01					21 26		21 58	22 05					
	d	20 22					20 51		21 04					21 28		22 00	22 08					
Macclesfield	d		20 16	20 37						21 09					21 16							
Congleton	d		20 24												21 24							
Stoke-on-Trent	d		20 39	20 53						21 25					21 39							
Stafford	a	20 43	20 57				21 16							21 51	21 58	22 24	22 32					
	d	20 44	20 58				21 18							21 51	21 58	22 25	22 33					
Penkridge	a	20 50														22 30						
Wolverhampton [7]	a	21 03	21 12											22 06	22 12	22 43	22 48					
Coseley	a																					
Sandwell & Dudley	a																					
Birmingham New Street [12]	a	21 27	21 35											22 30	22 35	23 04	23 10					
	d																					
Birmingham International	a		22 34												23 04	23 33	00 21					
Coventry	a		22 50												23 22	23 49	00 37					
Lichfield Trent Valley	a			21 24																		
Tamworth Low Level	a			21 31																		
Nuneaton	a						21 45															
Rugby	a			21 54			22 00															
Northampton	a																					
Milton Keynes Central	a			22 18			22 24		22 31	22 39												
Watford Junction	a			23s04			23s10		23s18	23s23												
Gatwick Airport [10]	a																					
London Euston [15]	a			23 37			23 45		23 53	23 56												

For general notes see front of timetable
For details of catering facilities see Directory of Train Operators

A From Carlisle via Whitehaven (Table 100)
B From Morecambe (Table 98)
b Change at Perth, Glasgow Queen Street and Glasgow Central. Passengers make their own way between Glasgow Queen Street and Glasgow Central
c Via Glasgow Queen Street and Glasgow Central. Passengers make their own way from one station to the other
e Change at Haymarket
f Change at Preston
g Manchester Victoria
h Change at Wilmslow and Crewe
j Change at Chester and Crewe
k Change at Llandudno Junction, Chester and Crewe

Due to ongoing Engineering Operations, some services from Saturday 13 September on this Table had not been confirmed at time of going to press. These services will be issued in a special Supplement as soon as exact timings have been confirmed.

Table 65

Sundays

until 13 July

Scotland and North West England → West Midlands and London

Route Diagram - see first page of Table 65

		NT	XC 1◇ A	VT	VT	VT 1◇	VT		LM 1◇	VT 1◇	VT	XC 1◇ B	VT 1◇	VT 1◇		VT	VT	VT 1◇	XC 1◇ C	VT	VT 1◇		VT 1◇	VT	VT
Inverness	d																								
Aberdeen	d																								
Dundee	d																								
Perth	d																								
Edinburgh 10	d																								
Haymarket	d																								
Glasgow Central 15	d																								
Motherwell	d																								
Carstairs	d																								
Lockerbie	d																								
Carlisle 8	a																								
	d																								
Penrith North Lakes	d																								
Windermere	d																								
Oxenholme Lake District	a																								
	d																								
Barrow-in-Furness	d																								
Lancaster 6	a																								
	d																08 40								09 25
Preston 8	a																09 30								10 15
Blackpool North	a																*10 16*								*10 54*
	d	08 17																*09 02*							
Preston 8	d	08 42																09 41							
Wigan North Western	a	09 01																09 51							
	d	09 01																09 53							
Bolton	a																*10 26*								*10 51*
Manchester Piccadilly 10	a																*10 49*								*11 15*
Manchester Airport	a																*11b20*								*11 33*
Liverpool Lime Street 10	a	09 49																*10 49*							
	d												09 15										10 15		
Liverpool South Parkway 7	d																								
Runcorn	d												09 32										10 32		
Warrington Bank Quay	a																	10 02							
	d																	10 04							
Hartford	d																								
Manchester Piccadilly 10	d		08 10			08 41				09 05		09 08	*09 05*					*09 14*	10 04		10 15				
Stockport	d				08 10	08u50				09u14	09 15	09 18	*09 14*					*09 18*	10 13	10 15	10u24				
Manchester Airport	d																	*09 33*							
Wilmslow	d		08 24			08 59				09 23		09 27						*09 41*	10 20		10 32				
Holyhead	d																								
Bangor (Gwynedd)	d								*07 42*																
Llandudno	d																								
Llandudno Junction	d								*08 00*																
Chester	d					*08 25*			*08 57*																
Crewe 10	a		08 43			09 17				09 41		09 46	09 52					10 25	10 40				10 52		
	d		08 48			09 17	←		09 37	09 44		09 48	09 54	10 08		←		10 25	10 42				10 54	←	
Macclesfield	d			08 15	08 40 →	*08c20*	08 40			*08c45*	09 45 →					09 45				10 45 →	*09c50*			10 45	
Congleton	d																								
Stoke-on-Trent	d			09 05			09 30									10 35								11 35	
Stafford	a		09 15	09 35		09 48	10 00		10 01	10 08		10 14	10 20	10 31		11 05			11 08		11 14		11 20	12 05	
	d		09 15			09 49			10 01	10 10		10 15	10 21	10 32					11 09		11 15		11 21		
Penkridge	a								10 07																
Wolverhampton 7	a		09 29						10 18			10 29		10 48					11 29						
Coseley	a																								
Sandwell & Dudley	a																								
Birmingham New Street 12	a		09 58						10 42			10 58		11 17					11 58						
	d																								
Birmingham International	a																								
Coventry	a																								
Lichfield Trent Valley	a																								
Tamworth Low Level	a																								
Nuneaton	a												10 42										11 43		
Rugby	a																	11 22							
Northampton	a																								
Milton Keynes Central	a					10 52				11 24			11 30					11 56							
Watford Junction	a					11s33												12s33			13s06		13s11		
Gatwick Airport 10	a																								
London Euston 15	a					11 55				12 29			12 33					13 00			13 30		13 35		

For general notes see front of timetable
For details of catering facilities see Directory of Train Operators

A To Paignton (Table 51)
B To Bournemouth (Table 51)
C To Plymouth (Table 51)
b Change at Preston and Manchester Piccadilly
c Change at Wilmslow. By bus

OVERNIGHT SLEEPERS. For Sleeper trains, operated by First ScotRail, please refer to Tables 400 - 404

Table 65

Sundays

until 13 July

Scotland and North West England → West Midlands and London

Route Diagram - see first page of Table 65

		VT	VT	NT	TP	XC	VT	VT	VT	VT	LM	VT	VT	XC	VT	VT	VT	VT	XC	VT	NT
		1◇	1◇		1◇	1◇		1◇	1◇	1◇	1◇		1◇	R 1◇	1◇	1◇	1◇	1◇	R 1◇	1◇	
						A								B					A		
		🍴	🍴		🍴	🍴	🚌	🍴	🍴	🍴		🚌	🍴	🍴	🍴	🍴	🍴	🍴	🍴	🍴	
Inverness	d																				
Aberdeen	d																				
Dundee	d																				
Perth	d																				
Edinburgh 10	d																				
Haymarket	d																				
Glasgow Central 15	d																				
Motherwell	d																				
Carstairs	d																				
Lockerbie	d																				
Carlisle 8	a																				
	d												10 46								
Penrith North Lakes	d												11 01								
Windermere	d																				
Oxenholme Lake District	a												11 23								
	d												11 25								
Barrow-in-Furness	d				09 55																
Lancaster 6	a				10 55								11 39								
	d				10 56								11 41								
Preston 8	a				11 14								11 58								
Blackpool North	a				12 16								12 47								
	d	09 28	10 02	10 17									11 28								12 17
Preston 8	d	10 24	10 40	10 42	11 20					11 24			12 02				12 23				12 42
Wigan North Western	a	10 36	10 51	10 59						11 35			12 12				12 34				13 02
	d	10 36	10 52	11 01						11 36			12 14				12 35				13 02
Bolton	a				11 39								12b51								
Manchester Piccadilly 10	a				11 58								13b15								
Manchester Airport	a				12 18								13b33								
Liverpool Lime Street 10	a			11 49						12 49											13 50
	d								11 18		11 35					12 18					
Liverpool South Parkway 7	d										11 45										
Runcorn	d								11 35		11 53					12 34					
Warrington Bank Quay	a	10 47	11 02							11 46			12 23				12 45				
	d	10 47	11 03							11 48			12 25				12 47				
Hartford	d										12 03										
Manchester Piccadilly 10	d					11 06		11 15						12 06	12 10			12 52	13 06	13 15	
Stockport	d					11 15	11 15	11u24						12 15	12u22			13u00	13 16	13u26	
Manchester Airport	d										11 32										
Wilmslow	d					11 22		11 32			11 40			12 23	12 30			13 10			
Holyhead	d	08c24									09 35										
Bangor (Gwynedd)	d	08c51									10 12										
Llandudno	d										10e22										
Llandudno Junction	d	09c09									10 36										
Chester	d	10 27									11 41										
Crewe 10	a	11 08	11 22			11 41			11 55	12 07	12 17	←	12 45	12 41		12 53	13 06				
	d	11 09	11 25			11 42			11 56	12 10	12 19		12 48	12 43		12 57	13 08				
Macclesfield	d						11 45 ↳	10f50				11 45			11f50			12f30	13 31	13 39	
Congleton	d																				
Stoke-on-Trent	d											12 35							13 50	13 57	
Stafford	a					12 08		12 14	12 20		12 42	13 05		13 07	13 16	13 22		13 48	14 13		
	d					12 09		12 15	12 22		12 43			13 08	13 18	13 24		13 50	14 14		
Penkridge	a										12 48										
Wolverhampton 7	a	11 48				12 29				12 48	12 59			13 29			13 48		14 29		
Coseley	a																				
Sandwell & Dudley	a																				
Birmingham New Street 12	a	12 17				12 58				13 17	13 27			13 58			14 17		14 58		
	d																				
Birmingham International	a																				
Coventry	a																				
Lichfield Trent Valley	a																				
Tamworth Low Level	a																				
Nuneaton	a								12 44							13 46					
Rugby	a		12 22										13 46								
Northampton	a																				
Milton Keynes Central	a							13 16	13 29				14 16							15 00	
Watford Junction	a		13s31												15s04	15s10		15s31			
Gatwick Airport 10	a																				
London Euston 15	⊖ a		13 57					14 24	14 30				15 24		15 25	15 34		15 54		16 03	

For general notes see front of timetable
For details of catering facilities see Directory of Train Operators

A To Bournemouth (Table 51)
B To Penzance (Table 135)
b Change at Preston
c Change at Chester and Crewe
e Change at Llandudno Junction and Crewe
f Change at Wilmslow. By bus

OVERNIGHT SLEEPERS. For Sleeper trains, operated by First ScotRail, please refer to Tables 400 - 404

Table 65

Sundays

until 13 July

Scotland and North West England → West Midlands and London

Route Diagram - see first page of Table 65

		VT	TP	VT	LM	VT	VT	VT	TP	XC	VT	VT	VT	VT	NT	VT	NT	XC	VT	TP	VT	LM
										R			R					R				
		1◇	1◇	1◇	1◇	1◇	1◇	1◇	1◇	1	1◇	1◇	1	1◇		1◇		1	1◇	1◇	1◇	1◇
										A								B				
		☕		☕		☕	☕	☕	🍴	☕	☕	☕	☕	☕		☕		☕	☕		☕	
Inverness	d																					
Aberdeen	d																					
Dundee	d							08b43	09 25													
Perth	d							09b05	09 27													
Edinburgh [10]	d								11 26													
Haymarket	d								11u30													
Glasgow Central [15]	d	10 07						11 06					11 55									
Motherwell	d	10u25						11u23					12u11									
Carstairs	d																					
Lockerbie	d								12 44													
Carlisle [8]	a	11 28						12 29	13 05				13 12									
	d	11 35						12 35	13 07				13 16									
Penrith North Lakes	d	11 50						12 50	13 21				13 32									
Windermere	d	*11 40*						*12 38*	*13 23*													
Oxenholme Lake District	a	12 12						13 12	13 45													
	d	12 14						13 14	13 45													
Barrow-in-Furness	d		12 00																	13 55		
Lancaster [6]	a	12 28	13 00					13 26	14 01				14 07							14 56		
	d	12 30	13 02					13 28	14 01				14 09			14 25				14 58		
Preston [8]	a	12 47	13 20					13 45	14 20				14 26			14 42				15 16		
Blackpool North	a	*13 34*	*14 16*					*14 47*					*15 16*			*15 34*						
	d							*13 12*					*13 28*		14 17	*13 57*						
Preston [8]	d	12 50	13 22					13 47	14 22				14 27		14 42	14 45	←			15 22		
Wigan North Western	a	13 08						13 58					14 40		15 00	14 55	15 00					
	d	13 10						13 59					14 41		→	14 57	15 01					
Bolton	a		13 41					*14c26*	14 41							*15c26*				15 41		
Manchester Piccadilly [10]	a		14 00					*14c49*	15 00							*15c49*				16 00		
Manchester Airport	a		14 18						15 18											16 18		
Liverpool Lime Street [10]	a	*14 49*															15 50					
	d			13 18	13 26						14 18										15 18	15 31
Liverpool South Parkway [7]	d				13 36																	15 41
Runcorn	d			13 34	13 44						14 34										15 34	15 49
Warrington Bank Quay	a	13 19						14 09					14 52			15 06						
	d	13 21						14 10					14 52			15 08						
Hartford	d				13 54																	
Manchester Piccadilly [10]	d	*12 29*				13 49	14 10			14 08		14 45				*14 34*		15 06	15 08			
Stockport	d	*12 40*				13u57	14u23			14 18		14u55				*14 42*		15 16	15u18			
Manchester Airport	d				*13 26*																	*15 25*
Wilmslow	d	*12 55*			*13 33*											*14 54*						*15 33*
Holyhead	d	*10e35*												13 15							*13e30*	
Bangor (Gwynedd)	d	*11e04*		*12 10*										13 42							*13e58*	
Llandudno	d	*11f08*		*12g15*							*13 10*			*13 45*								
Llandudno Junction	d	*11e22*		*12 28*							*13 19*			14 00							*14e16*	
Chester	d	*12 43*		*13 22*							*14 17*			14 46							*15 15*	
Crewe [10]	a	13 40		13 53	14 08			14 29			14 53		15 13	15 06		15 28					15 53	16 08
	d	13 40		13 55	14 10			14 32			14 55		15 13	15 15		15 31					15 56	16 11
Macclesfield	d					14 10	14 36			14 32		15 08						15 31	15 35			
Congleton	d																					
Stoke-on-Trent	d					14 26	14 56			14 50		15 24						15 49	15 54			
Stafford	a			14 18	14 31					15 13	15 16			15 39				16 06			16 13	16 36
	d			14 20	14 31					15 14	15 18			15 40				16 08			16 15	16 36
Penkridge	a				14 37																	16 42 →
Wolverhampton [7]	a				14 49					15 29			15 48					16 29				
Coseley	a																					
Sandwell & Dudley	a																					
Birmingham New Street [12]	a				15 13					15 58			16 17					16 58				
	d																					
Birmingham International	a																					
Coventry	a																					
Lichfield Trent Valley	a																					
Tamworth Low Level	a																					
Nuneaton	a			14 41							15 39										16 41	
Rugby	a	14 32						15 24								16 20						
Northampton	a																					
Milton Keynes Central	a			15 18		15 33		15 49													17 19	
Watford Junction	a	15s36					16s35				17s00	17s06		17s11		17s31			17s42			
Gatwick Airport [10]	a																					
London Euston [15]	⊖ a	16 03		16 24		16 25	16 56	16 57			17 26	17 27		17 37		17 55			18 03		18 24	

For general notes see front of timetable
For details of catering facilities see Directory of Train Operators

A To Penzance (Table 135)
B To Bournemouth (Table 51)
b Via Glasgow Queen Street and Glasgow Central. Passengers make their own way from one station to the other
c Change at Preston
e Change at Chester and Crewe
f Change at Llandudno Junction, Chester and Crewe
g Change at Llandudno Junction and Crewe

OVERNIGHT SLEEPERS. For Sleeper trains, operated by First ScotRail, please refer to Tables 400 - 404

Table 65

Sundays

until 13 July

Scotland and North West England → West Midlands and London

Route Diagram - see first page of Table 65

Station		VT	LM	VT	VT	XC	TP	VT	VT	VT	VT	NT	VT	XC	TP	VT	LM	VT	LM	VT	VT	VT
		R 1	1 ◊	1 ◊	1 ◊	R 1	1 ◊	1 ◊	1 ◊	R 1	1 ◊		1 ◊	R 1	1 ◊	1 ◊	1 ◊	1 ◊	1 ◊	1 ◊	R 1	1 ◊
						A								B								
		☕		☕	☕	☕	🛒	☕	☕	☕	☕		☕	☕		☕		☕		☕	☕	☕
Inverness	d																				09 38	
Aberdeen	d	09 48																			11 58	
Dundee	d	11 02																			13 12	
Perth	d				11b05																11 55	
Edinburgh 10	d	12 52																			14 53	
Haymarket	d	12u57																			14u58	
Glasgow Central 15	d				13 06		13 35			14 03												
Motherwell	d				13u23																	
Carstairs	d																					
Lockerbie	d	13 51					14 34														15 53	
Carlisle 8	a	14 11			14 20		14 56			15 14											16 12	
	d	14 13			14 35		15 03			15 20											16 14	
Penrith North Lakes	d	14 28			14 50		15 17														16 29	
Windermere	d	14 28																			16 26	
Oxenholme Lake District	a	14 51			15 12		15 41														16 52	
	d	14 53			15 14		15 41														16 53	
Barrow-in-Furness	d														16 00							
Lancaster 6	a	15 07			15 28		15 57			16 07					17 00						17 08	
	d	15 09			15 30		15 57			16 08			16 41		17 02						17 09	
Preston 8	a	15 26			15 47		16 16			16 25			16 58		17 20						17 26	
Blackpool North	a	16 16			16 47					17 16			17 37								18 16	
	d	14 28			15 12					15 28		16 17	16 28									
Preston 8	d	15 28			15 50		16 22			16 27		16 42	17 01		17 22						17 29	
Wigan North Western	a	15 39			16 00					16 38		17 01	17 10								17 40	
	d	15 41			16 02					16 40		17 01	17 12								17 41	
Bolton	a	16c26					16 41			17c26					17 41							
Manchester Piccadilly 10	a	16c49					17 00			17c49					18 00							
Manchester Airport	a						17 18								18 18							
Liverpool Lime Street 10	a	16 49										17 49										
	d								16 18								17 14	17 18	←			
Liverpool South Parkway 7	d																17 26		17 26			
Runcorn	d								16 34								→	17 34	17 38			
Warrington Bank Quay	a	15 51			16 11					16 50			17 21								17 51	
	d	15 52			16 13					16 51			17 23								17 53	
Hartford	d																		17 47			
Manchester Piccadilly 10	d			15 45	15 39	16 08		16 10			16 45		16 36	17 06		17 10						17 45
Stockport	d			15u55	15 47	16 18		16u22			16u56		16 44	17 16		17u22						17u55
Manchester Airport	d																				17 25	
Wilmslow	d				15 57								16 54								17 32	
Holyhead	d																			15 50		
Bangor (Gwynedd)	d				14 41														15e45	16 20		
Llandudno	d				14f50														15g50	15 50		
Llandudno Junction	d				15 04														16e03	16 40		
Chester	d				16 00								16 48						17 28	17 34		
Crewe 10	a	16 13			16 32				16 53	17 11			17 43					17 53	18 02	17 57	18 12	
	d	16 14			16 35				16 55	17 13			17 45					17 56	18 03	18 10	18 15	
Macclesfield	d			16 08		16 31		16 36			17 09			17 31		17 35						18 08
Congleton	d																					
Stoke-on-Trent	d			16 24		16 49		16 55			17 25			17 49		17 55						18 24
Stafford	a					17 07			17 18					18 14				18 16	18 29	18 28		
	d		←			17 09			17 20					18 15				18 17	18 30	18 29		
Penkridge	a		16 42																18 35			
Wolverhampton 7	a	16 48	16 54			17 29				17 48				18 29					18 48		18 51	
Coseley	a																					
Sandwell & Dudley	a																					
Birmingham New Street 12	a	17 17	17 20			17 58				18 17				18 58					19 11		19 20	
	d																					
Birmingham International	a																					
Coventry	a																					
Lichfield Trent Valley	a								17 32													
Tamworth Low Level	a								17 39											18 45		
Nuneaton	a								17 50									18 42				
Rugby	a				17 23								18 35									
Northampton	a																					
Milton Keynes Central	a			17 29	17 49			18 00										19 20		19 29		19 35
Watford Junction	a								19s06		19s11		19s31			19s42						
Gatwick Airport 10	a																					
London Euston 15	⊖ a			18 25	18 57			18 59	19 29		19 33		19 55			20 03		20 24		20 25		20 32

For general notes see front of timetable
For details of catering facilities see Directory of Train Operators

A To Plymouth (Table 51)
B To Bournemouth (Table 51)
b Via Glasgow Queen Street and Glasgow Central. Passengers make their own way from one station to the other
c Change at Preston
e Change at Chester and Crewe
f Change at Llandudno Junction and Crewe
g Change at Llandudno Junction, Chester and Crewe

OVERNIGHT SLEEPERS. For Sleeper trains, operated by First ScotRail, please refer to Tables 400 - 404

Table 65

Sundays

until 13 July

Scotland and North West England → West Midlands and London

Route Diagram - see first page of Table 65

Station		NT	VT		NT	XC	TP	TP	VT	VT		VT	TP	VT	VT	NT	VT		NT	TP	XC	VT	LM	VT	VT
			1◇			R 1 A	1◇	1◇	1◇	1◇		R 1	1◇	1◇	1◇		1◇			1◇	1◇ B	1◇	1◇	1◇	1◇
Inverness	d																								13 25
Aberdeen	d																								13 50
Dundee	d							13 25																	15b25
Perth	d		13c05																						15 25
Edinburgh 10	d							15 43																	16 56
Haymarket	d							15u47																	17u01
Glasgow Central 15	d		15 06									15 54					16 15								
Motherwell	d		15u23																						
Carstairs	d																								
Lockerbie	d							16 44																	17 58
Carlisle 8	a		16 20					17 05				17 10					17 28								18 18
	d		16 30					17 07				17 17					17 30								18 21
Penrith North Lakes	d		16 45					17 21									17 45								18 36
Windermere	d						17 21																		18 30
Oxenholme Lake District	a		17 07				17 38	17 45				17 53					18 07								18 59
	d		17 09				17 40	17 45				17 53					18 09								19 00
Barrow-in-Furness	d																			18 00					
Lancaster 6	a		17 23				17 55	18 01				18 09					18 23			19 00					19 14
	d		17 25				17 55	18 01				18 10					18 25			19 02					19 15
Preston 8	a		17 42				18 15	18 20				18 28					18 42			19 20					19 32
Blackpool North	a		18 34									19 16					19 32								20 16
	d	17 17	17 10									17 28	←			18 17	18 10								18 28
Preston 8	d	17 42	17 45		←		18 30	18 22				18 29	18 30			18 42	18 45		←	19 22					19 35
Wigan North Western	a	18 01	17 55		18 01		→					18 40				19 00	18 55		19 00						19 46
	d	→	17 56		18 01							18 41				→	18 57		19 01						19 47
Bolton	a		18e26					18 41					18 52				19e26			19 41					
Manchester Piccadilly 10	a		18e49					19 00					19 15				19e49			20 00					
Manchester Airport	a							19 18					19 33							20 18					
Liverpool Lime Street 10	a				18 49														19 49						
	d									18 18												19 18	19 30		
Liverpool South Parkway 7	d																						19 39		
Runcorn	d									18 34												19 34	19 47		
Warrington Bank Quay	a		18 06									18 51					19 06								19 57
	d		18 08									18 52					19 08								19 58
Hartford	d																								
Manchester Piccadilly 10	d					18 08			18 10					18 45	19 05		18 40				19 10			19 47	19 06
Stockport	d					18 18			18u22					18u55	19u13		18 48				19 18			19u55	
Manchester Airport	d																								19 25
Wilmslow	d																18 56								19 32
Holyhead	d									16 32							17 00					17f23			
Bangor (Gwynedd)	d									16 59							17 27					17f51			
Llandudno	d									17g04							17g30					18f10			
Llandudno Junction	d									17 22							17 45					18f20			
Chester	d									18 21							18 41					19 23			
Crewe 10	a		18 27							18 53		19 12					19 27					19 53	20 07		20 17
	d		18 30							18 55		19 13					19 30					19 55	20 08		20 19
Macclesfield	d					18 31			18 38					19 10	19 25						19 34			20 08	
Congleton	d																								
Stoke-on-Trent	d					18 49			18 55					19 26	19 47						19 53			20 22	
Stafford	a					19 14				19 16											20 11	20 16	20 29		
	d					19 15				19 17											20 13	20 17	20 31		
Penkridge	a																								
Wolverhampton 7	a					19 29						19 48									20 29		20 46		20 52
Coseley	a																								
Sandwell & Dudley	a																								
Birmingham New Street 12	a					19 58						20 17									20 58		21 10		21 21
	d																								
Birmingham International	a																								
Coventry	a																								
Lichfield Trent Valley	a																							20 49	
Tamworth Low Level	a																							20 56	
Nuneaton	a									19 39												20 39			
Rugby	a		19 19														20 19								
Northampton	a																								
Milton Keynes Central	a		19 46						20 00													21 17		21 46	
Watford Junction	a								20s35	21s00				21s06	21s36		21s31							22s31	
Gatwick Airport 10	a																								
London Euston 15	⊖ a		20 57						20 59	21 24				21 27	21 57		21 57					22 24		22 52	

For general notes see front of timetable
For details of catering facilities see Directory of Train Operators

A To Plymouth (Table 51)
B To Southampton Central (Table 51)
b Change at Haymarket
c Via Glasgow Queen Street and Glasgow Central. Passengers make their own way from one station to the other
e Change at Preston
f Change at Chester and Crewe
g Change at Llandudno Junction and Crewe

OVERNIGHT SLEEPERS. For Sleeper trains, operated by First ScotRail, please refer to Tables 400 - 404

Sundays

until 13 July

Scotland and North West England → West Midlands and London

Route Diagram - see first page of Table 65

		VT		VT	VT	TP	VT	XC	NT		VT	XC	LM	TP	TP	NT		VT	SR	SR	SR	SR			
		1 ◇		1 ◇	1 ◇	1 ◇	1 ◇	1 ◇			1 ◇	1 ◇	1 ◇	1 ◇	1 ◇			1 ◇		R	R	R			
																						A			
		☕		☕	☕	🛒	☕				☕							☕		☕	☕	☕			
Inverness	d																		16b15		18 30	20 25			
Aberdeen	d					15c10					15e30								17f50		20 10	21 40			
Dundee	d					16c25					17c25								19f02		21 21	23u04			
Perth	d																	17f05	19f24	21f08		22u59			
Edinburgh 10	d					17 35					18 52										23 15				
Haymarket	d					17u39					18u57														
Glasgow Central 15	d	17 05					18 04											20 04	22 28	23 15					
Motherwell	d																	20u18		23u30					
Carstairs	d																			23u50					
Lockerbie	d					18 44					19 58							21 02							
Carlisle 8	a	18 26				19 05	19 13				20 16							21 23	00 49						
	d	18 32				19 07	19 15				20 18							21 30		01u24					
Penrith North Lakes	d	18 46				19 21					20 34							21 45							
Windermere	d					19 20					20 23				21 20										
Oxenholme Lake District	a	19 09				19 45	19 51				20 57				21 40			22 08							
	d	19 10				19 45	19 52				20 58				21 40			22 09							
Barrow-in-Furness	d										19 57			20 50											
Lancaster 6	a	19 25				20 01	20 07				21 13			21 52	21 56			22 25							
	d	19 26				20 01	20 08				21 14			22 02				22 26							
Preston 8	a	19 43				20 20	20 25				21 31			22 20				22 58				04s22			
Blackpool North	a	20 47					21 03				22 16			23 16				23 43							
	d	19 12					19 28		20 17		20 28					22 17									
Preston 8	d	19 46				20 22	20 28		20 42		21 34			22 22		22 42		23 01							
Wigan North Western	a	19 56					20 39		21 01		21 46					23 10		23s23							
	d	19 58					20 40		21 01		21 46					23 10									
Bolton	a	20g26				20 41	21g26				22g26			22 41				23s37							
Manchester Piccadilly 10	a	20g49				21 00	21g49				22g49			23 00				23 59							
Manchester Airport ✈	a					21 18	22g33							23 18				00 33							
Liverpool Lime Street 10	a	20 49							21 49		22 49					23 59									
	d				20 18								21 47												
Liverpool South Parkway 7 ✈	d												21 57												
Runcorn	d				20 34								22 05												
Warrington Bank Quay	a	20 07					20 50				21 56														
	d	20 09					20 52				21 58														
Hartford	d												22 15												
Manchester Piccadilly 10	d			20 23				20 55			21 06	21 55													
Stockport	d			20u32				21 04			20 54	22 04													
Manchester Airport ✈	d										21 25														
Wilmslow	d										21 32														
Holyhead	d						18h40																		
Bangor (Gwynedd)	d						19h09				20 11														
Llandudno	d						18j45																		
Llandudno Junction	d						19h27				20 34														
Chester	d						20 23				21 33														
Crewe 10	a	20 28			20 53		21 11				22 17		22 33									05s29			
	d	20 31			20 55		21 13				22 20		22 35												
Macclesfield	d			20 45				21 16				22 16													
Congleton	d																								
Stoke-on-Trent	d			21 01				21 35				22 35													
Stafford	a				21 16		21 32	21 53			22 39	22 53	22 58												
	d				21 17		21 33	21 53			22 40	22 53	22 59												
Penkridge	a												23 04												
Wolverhampton 7	a						21 47	22 09			22 54	23 09	23 19												
Coseley	a																								
Sandwell & Dudley	a																								
Birmingham New Street 12	a						22 17	22 41			23 23	23 42	23 53												
	d																								
Birmingham International ✈	a																								
Coventry	a																								
Lichfield Trent Valley	a																								
Tamworth Low Level	a																								
Nuneaton	a			21 32	21 40																				
Rugby	a	21 21		21 48																					
Northampton	a																								
Milton Keynes Central	a	21 52		22 22	22 28																				
Watford Junction	a	22s36		23s00	23s06															06s03					
Gatwick Airport 10 ✈	a																								
London Euston 15 ⊖	a	23 02		23 21	23 30															06 28		07 43			

For general notes see front of timetable
For details of catering facilities see Directory of Train Operators

A Also conveys portion from Fort William (Table 227)

b Change at Perth, Glasgow Queen Street and Glasgow Central. Passengers make their own way between Glasgow Queen Street and Glasgow Central

c Change at Haymarket

e Change at Dundee and Haymarket

f Via Glasgow Queen Street and Glasgow Central. Passengers make their own way from one station to the other

g Change at Preston

h Change at Chester and Crewe

j Change at Llandudno Junction, Chester and Crewe

OVERNIGHT SLEEPERS. For Sleeper trains, operated by First ScotRail, please refer to Tables 400 - 404

Sundays

Scotland and North West England → West Midlands and London

20 July to 7 September

Route Diagram - see first page of Table 65

		XC	VT	VT	LM	XC	NT	XC	VT	VT	XC	VT	VT	VT	XC		VT	VT	VT	XC	VT	VT	NT	TP	XC
		1◇	1◇	1◇		1◇		1◇	1◇	1◇	1◇	1◇		1◇	1◇		1◇		1◇	1◇	1◇	1◇		1◇	1◇
		A				B		C			B				D					B					C
					bus								bus					bus							
Inverness	d																								
Aberdeen	d																								
Dundee	d																								
Perth	d																								
Edinburgh 10	d																								
Haymarket	d																								
Glasgow Central 15	d																								
Motherwell	d																								
Carstairs	d																								
Lockerbie	d																								
Carlisle 8	a																								
	d																								
Penrith North Lakes	d																								
Windermere	d																								
Oxenholme Lake District	a																								
	d																								
Barrow-in-Furness	d																							09 55	
Lancaster 6	a																							10 55	
	d												08 40					09 25						10 56	
Preston 8	a												09 30					10 15						11 14	
Blackpool North	a												10 16					10 54						12 16	
	d						08 17							09 02					09 28			10 02	10 17		
Preston 8	d						08 42							09 40					10 24			10 38	10 42	11 20	
Wigan North Western	a						09 01							09 50					10 36			10 48	10 59		
	d						09 01							09 52					10 36			10 50	11 01		
Bolton	a												10 26					10 51						11 39	
Manchester Piccadilly 10	a												10 49					11 15						11b54	
Manchester Airport	a																	11 36						12 36	
Liverpool Lime Street 10	a						09 49							10 49									11 49		
	d								09 15								10 15								
Liverpool South Parkway 7	d																								
Runcorn	d								09 32								10 33								
Warrington Bank Quay	a													10 01					10 47			10 59			
	d													10 03					10 47			11 01			
Hartford	d																								
Manchester Piccadilly 10	d	08 10	08 44	09 08				09 24			09 53	10 15			10 24					10 53	11 15				11 23
Stockport	d		08u53	09u17				09 33			10 04	10u24			10 33					11 04	11u24				11 33
Manchester Airport	d													09 33											
Wilmslow	d	08 24												09 41											
Holyhead	d																		08c24						
Bangor (Gwynedd)	d								07 42										08c51						
Llandudno	d																								
Llandudno Junction	d								08 00										09c09						
Chester	d				08 25				08 57										10 27						
Crewe 10	a	08 43							09 51					10 23			10 52		11 07			11 20			
	d	08 46			09 15	09 17			09 52	10 08				10 24			10 54		11 09			11 21			
Macclesfield	d		09 06	09 30				09 46			10 16	10 37			10 46					11 16	11 37				11 47
Congleton	d																								
Stoke-on-Trent	d	09 05	09 22	09 46				10 05			10 35	10 53			11 03					11 35	11 53				12 05
Stafford	a	09 24			10 00	09 52		10 26	10 31	10 45	10 53			11 02	11 21		11 33			11 53		12 03			12 26
	d	09 26				09 53		10 26	10 32	10 46	10 53			11 04	11 21		11 35			11 53		12 05			12 26
Penkridge	a																								
Wolverhampton 7	a	09 41				10 09		10 41		11 01	11 09				11 36				12 00	12 09					12 41
Coseley	a																								
Sandwell & Dudley	a																								
Birmingham New Street 12	a	09 58				10 31		10 58		11 24	11 28				11 58				12 17	12 31					12 58
	d																								
Birmingham International	a																								
Coventry	a																								
Lichfield Trent Valley	a																								
Tamworth Low Level	a																								
Nuneaton	a								10 54								11 57								
Rugby	a													11 38								12 38			
Northampton	a																								
Milton Keynes Central	a		10 24	10 52					11 29					12 01							12 55				
Watford Junction	a		11s06									12s31		12s36			13s02					13s36			
Gatwick Airport 10	a																								
London Euston 15	a		11 36	12 06					12 39			13 05		13 17			13 36				14 05	14 12			

For general notes see front of timetable
For details of catering facilities see Directory of Train Operators

A To Paignton (Table 51)
B To Reading (Table 51)
C To Bournemouth (Table 51)
D To Plymouth (Table 51)

b Manchester Oxford Road
c Change at Chester and Crewe

OVERNIGHT SLEEPERS. For Sleeper trains, operated by First ScotRail, please refer to Tables 400 - 404

Due to ongoing Engineering Operations, some services from Sunday 14 September on this Table had not been confirmed at time of going to press. These services will be issued in a special Supplement as soon as exact timings have been confirmed.

Table 65

Sundays

Scotland and North West England → West Midlands and London

20 July to 7 September

Route Diagram - see first page of Table 65

Station		VT	XC	VT	VT	XC	VT	VT	VT	VT	XC	VT	VT	NT	TP	XC	VT	VT	XC	VT	VT	TP	XC
		1◇	1◇	1◇	1◇	R 1	1◇	1◇	1◇	1◇	1◇	1◇	1◇		1◇	R 1	1◇	1◇	1◇	1◇	1◇	1◇	R 1
			A			B					A					C			A				B
Inverness	d																						
Aberdeen	d																						
Dundee	d																				08b43	09 25	
Perth	d																				09b05	09 27	
Edinburgh 10	d																					11 26	
Haymarket	d																					11u30	
Glasgow Central 15	d												10 07								11 06		
Motherwell	d												10u25								11u23		
Carstairs	d																						
Lockerbie	d																					12 44	
Carlisle 8	a												11 24								12 23	13 05	
	d						10 46						11 27								12 29	13 07	
Penrith North Lakes	d						11 01						11 41								12 43	13 21	
Windermere	d												11 40								12 30	13 23	
Oxenholme Lake District	a						11 23						12 04								13 06	13 45	
	d						11 25						12 05								13 07	13 45	
Barrow-in-Furness	d														12 00								
Lancaster 6	a						11 39						12 20		13 00						13 20	14 01	
	d						11 41						12 21		13 02						13 21	14 01	
Preston 8	a						11 58						12 39		13 20						13 38	14 20	
Blackpool North	a						12 47						13 16								14 16		
	d						11 28						12 02	12 17							13 02		
Preston 8	d				11 22		12 02			12 23			12 42	12 42	13 22						13 41	14 22	
Wigan North Western	a				11 35		12 12			12 34			12 54	13 00							13 51		
	d				11 36		12 14			12 35			12 55	13 01							13 53		
Bolton	a						12c52						13c26		13 41						14c26	14 41	
Manchester Piccadilly 10	a						13c18						13c49		14 00						14c49	15 00	
Manchester Airport	a						13c36						14e33		14 33						15c36	15 36	
Liverpool Lime Street 10	a				12 49									13 50							14 49		
	d	11 15					11f35		12 15								13 15				13f26		
Liverpool South Parkway 7	d						11f45														13f36		
Runcorn	d	11 32					11f53		12 32								13 31				13f44		
Warrington Bank Quay	a				11 46		12 23			12 45			13 05								14 02		
	d				11 48		12 25			12 47			13 06								14 04		
Hartford	d						12 03														13 54		
Manchester Piccadilly 10	d		11 53	12 10		12 24		12 45			12 53	13 09				13 17		13 45	13 53	14 10			14 24
Stockport	d		12 04	12u22		12 33		12u55			13 04	13u20				13 33		13u54	14 04	14u19			14 33
Manchester Airport	d																						
Wilmslow	d				11 28												12 56				13 28		
Holyhead	d				09 35								10g35										
Bangor (Gwynedd)	d				10 12								11g04								12 10		
Llandudno	d				10h22								11j08								12h15		
Llandudno Junction	d				10 36								11g22								12 28		
Chester	d				11 41								12 43								13 22		
Crewe 10	a	11 52			12 08		12 45		12 53	13 07			13 26				13 51				14 26		
	d	11 53			12 16		12 47		12 54	13 09			13 27				13 53				14 27		
Macclesfield	d		12 16	12 35		12 47		13 09			13 16	13 33				13 47		14 07	14 16	14 31			14 46
Congleton	d																						
Stoke-on-Trent	d		12 35	12 51		13 05		13 25			13 35	13 52				14 05		14 26	14 35	14 52			15 05
Stafford	a	12 31	12 53			13 23	13 28		13 34		13 53		14 05			14 24	14 30		14 53		15 05		15 24
	d	12 33	12 53			13 24	13 30		13 36		13 53		14 06			14 26	14 32		14 53		15 06		15 26
Penkridge	a																						
Wolverhampton 7	a		13 09		13 17	13 41				14 01	14 09					14 40			15 09				15 41
Coseley	a																						
Sandwell & Dudley	a																						
Birmingham New Street 12	a		13 31		13 55	13 58				14 24	14 31					14 58			15 31				15 58
	d																						
Birmingham International	a																						
Coventry	a																						
Lichfield Trent Valley	a																						
Tamworth Low Level	a																						
Nuneaton	a	12 55							14 01								14 54						
Rugby	a						14 03						14 40								15 40		
Northampton	a																						
Milton Keynes Central	a	13 32					14 27					14 56					15 30	15 36			16 03		
Watford Junction	a			14s31				15s07	15s12				15s36							16s31			
Gatwick Airport 10	a																						
London Euston 15	a	14 42		15 02			15 34	15 36	15 53			16 03	16 13				16 37	16 49		17 02	17 13		

For general notes see front of timetable
For details of catering facilities see Directory of Train Operators

A To Reading (Table 51)
B To Penzance (Table 135)
C To Bournemouth (Table 51)
b Via Glasgow Queen Street and Glasgow Central. Passengers make their own way from one station to the other
c Change at Preston
e Change at Preston and Manchester Piccadilly
f Change at Crewe
g Change at Chester and Crewe
h Change at Llandudno Junction and Crewe
j Change at Llandudno Junction, Chester and Crewe

OVERNIGHT SLEEPERS. For Sleeper trains, operated by First ScotRail, please refer to Tables 400 - 404

Due to ongoing Engineering Operations, some services from Sunday 14 September on this Table had not been confirmed at time of going to press. These services will be issued in a special Supplement as soon as exact timings have been confirmed.

Table 65

Sundays

20 July to 7 September

Scotland and North West England → West Midlands and London

Route Diagram - see first page of Table 65

		VT	VT	VT	XC	VT	VT	NT	XC	VT	VT	VT	XC	TP	VT	VT	XC	VT	TP	VT	VT	XC	VT	NT
		1 ◇	1 ◇	R 1	1 ◇	1 ◇	1 ◇		R 1	1 ◇	R 1	1 ◇	1 ◇	1 ◇	1 ◇	1 ◇	R 1	1 ◇	1 ◇	1 ◇	R 1	1 ◇	1 ◇	
					A				B				C				D					E		
		□	□	□	□	□	□		□	□	□	□	□		□	□	□	□	⊼	□	□	□	□	
Inverness	d																							
Aberdeen	d										09 48													
Dundee	d										11 02													
Perth	d															11b05								
Edinburgh 10	d										12 39													
Haymarket	d										12u44													
Glasgow Central 15	d			11 55												13 06			13 35		14 03			
Motherwell	d			12u10												13u23								
Carstairs	d																							
Lockerbie	d										13 40								14 34					
Carlisle 8	a			13 12							14 00					14 20			14 56		15 14			
	d			13 16							14 01					14 26			15 03		15 15			
Penrith North Lakes	d			13 31							14 17					14 41			15 17					
Windermere	d															14 34								
Oxenholme Lake District	a										14 40					15 03			15 41					
	d										14 41					15 05			15 41					
Barrow-in-Furness	d													14 00										
Lancaster 6	a			14 07							14 56			15 01		15 19			15 57		16 02			
	d			14 08			14 20				14 57			15 03		15 21			15 57		16 04			
Preston 8	a			14 25			14 37				15 14			15 21		15 38			16 16		16 22			
Blackpool North	a						15 16									16 16					17 16			
	d			13 28			13 57	14 17			14 28					15 02					15 28			16 17
Preston 8	d			14 27			14 40	14 42			15 18			15 22		15 41			16 22		16 26			16 42
Wigan North Western	a			14 40			14 50	15 01			15 29					15 51					16 37			17 00
	d			14 40			14 52	15 01			15 30					15 53					16 38			17 01
Bolton	a						15c26							15 41		16c26			16 41		16c51			
Manchester Piccadilly 10	a						15c49							16 00		16c49			17 00		17c15			
Manchester Airport	a													16 33					17 32		17c36			
Liverpool Lime Street 10	a							15 50								16 49								17 49
	d	14 15								15 15						15e31				16 15				
Liverpool South Parkway 7	d															15e41								
Runcorn	d	14 31								15 31						15e49				16 31				
Warrington Bank Quay	a			14 51			15 01				15 40					16 02					16 48			
	d			14 52			15 03				15 42					16 04					16 49			
Hartford	d																							
Manchester Piccadilly 10	d		14 45		14 51	15 10			15 24			15 45	15 55		16 10		16 24	16 45				16 55	17 10	
Stockport	d		14u55		15 04	15u20			15 33			15u55	16 04		16u18		16 33	16u56				17 04	17u19	
Manchester Airport	d																							
Wilmslow	d									14 54	15 28									15 57				
Holyhead	d						13 15			13f30														
Bangor (Gwynedd)	d						13 42			13f58										14 41				
Llandudno	d	13 10					13g45													14g50				
Llandudno Junction	d	13 19					14 00			14f16										15 04				
Chester	d	14 17					14 46			15 15										16 00				
Crewe 10	a	14 50		15 12			15 23			15 52	16 03					16 24				16 51	17 10			
	d	14 52		15 13			15 24			15 53	16 07					16 26				16 56	17 10			
Macclesfield	d		15 08		15 16	15 36			15 46			16 08	16 16		16 31		16 46	17 09				17 16	17 31	
Congleton	d																							
Stoke-on-Trent	d		15 29		15 36	15 52			16 07			16 24	16 35		16 51		17 05	17 25				17 35	17 48	
Stafford	a	15 30			15 53		16 02		16 25	16 31			16 53			17 04	17 24			17 34		17 53		
	d	15 32			15 53		16 03		16 26	16 32			16 53			17 05	17 26			17 35		17 53		
Penkridge	a																							
Wolverhampton 7	a			16 06	16 09				16 41		17 01		17 09				17 41				18 01	18 09		
Coseley	a																							
Sandwell & Dudley	a																							
Birmingham New Street 12	a			16 28	16 31				16 58		17 23		17 31				17 58				18 23	18 31		
	d												17 33									18 33		
Birmingham International	a																							
Coventry	a																							
Lichfield Trent Valley	a																			17 50				
Tamworth Low Level	a																			17 57				
Nuneaton	a	15 54								16 54										18 08				
Rugby	a						16 38									17 39								
Northampton	a																							
Milton Keynes Central	a									17 31		17 37			17 56	18 02								
Watford Junction	a	17s03	17s09			17s30	17s36											19s02		19s31			19s35	
Gatwick Airport 10	a												20 44									21 47		
London Euston 15	a	17 39	17 49			18 02	18 10			18 38		18 49			19 05	19 13		19 35		20 04			20 08	

For general notes see front of timetable
For details of catering facilities see Directory of Train Operators

A To Reading (Table 51)
B To Bournemouth (Table 51)
C To Brighton (Table 51)
D To Plymouth (Table 51)
E □ to Reading

b Via Glasgow Queen Street and Glasgow Central. Passengers make their own way from one station to the other
c Change at Preston
e Change at Crewe
f Change at Chester and Crewe
g Change at Llandudno Junction and Crewe

OVERNIGHT SLEEPERS. For Sleeper trains, operated by First ScotRail, please refer to Tables 400 - 404

Due to ongoing Engineering Operations, some services from Sunday 14 September on this Table had not been confirmed at time of going to press. These services will be issued in a special Supplement as soon as exact timings have been confirmed.

Table 65

Sundays

Scotland and North West England → West Midlands and London

20 July to 7 September

Route Diagram - see first page of Table 65

		XC	VT	VT	VT	XC	TP	VT		NT	VT	NT	XC	VT	TP	TP	VT	VT	XC	VT	NT	VT	NT		TP
		R 1	1◇	1◇	1◇	1◇	1◇	1◇			1◇		R 1	1◇	1◇	1◇	1◇	R 1	1◇	1◇		1◇			1◇
		A											B												
Inverness	d										09b38														
Aberdeen	d										11c28					11 58									
Dundee	d										12c43					13e25									
Perth	d										13c05														
Edinburgh 10	d															15 43									
Haymarket	d															15u47									
Glasgow Central 15	d										15 06							15 54				16 15			
Motherwell	d										15u23														
Carstairs	d																								
Lockerbie	d															16 44									
Carlisle 8	a										16 20					17 05		17 11				17 28			
	d										16 31					17 07		17 15				17 31			
Penrith North Lakes	d										16 46					17 21						17 45			
Windermere	d										16 26				17 21										
Oxenholme Lake District	a										17 08				17 38	17 45		17 51				18 08			
	d										17 10				17 40	17 45		17 51				18 09			
Barrow-in-Furness	d						16 00																		18 00
Lancaster 6	a						17 00				17 24				17 55	18 01		18 09				18 24			19 00
	d		16 31				17 02				17 26				17 55	18 01		18 10				18 25			19 02
Preston 8	a		16 48				17 20				17 43				18 15	18 20		18 28				18 42			19 20
Blackpool North	a		17 37				18 16				18 34							19 16				19 32			
	d		16 17							17 17	17 10							17 28			18 17	18 10			
Preston 8	d		16 51				17 22			17 42	17 46	←			18 30	18 22		18 29			18 42	18 45	←		19 22
Wigan North Western	a		17 04							18 01	17 56	18 01						18 40			19 00	18 56	19 00		
	d		17 06							→	17 57	18 01						18 41			→	18 57	19 01		
Bolton	a						17 41				18f26					18 41						19f26			19 41
Manchester Piccadilly 10	a						18 00				18f49					19 00						19f49			20 00
Manchester Airport ✈	a						18 33									19 32									20 32
Liverpool Lime Street 10	a											18 49											19 49		
	d				17 15						17g25						18 15								
Liverpool South Parkway 7 ✈	d										17g35														
Runcorn	d				17 31						17g43						18 31								
Warrington Bank Quay	a		17 15								18 07							18 51				19 07			
	d		17 17								18 09							18 52				19 08			
Hartford	d										17 52														
Manchester Piccadilly 10	d	17 24		17 45		17 55		18 10					18 24	18 45					18 55	19 10					
Stockport	d	17 33		17u55		18 04		18u19					18 33	18u55					19 04	19u19					
Manchester Airport ✈	d																								
Wilmslow	d		16 54								17 28											18 56			
Holyhead	d										15 57							16 32				17 00			
Bangor (Gwynedd)	d										16 24							16 59				17 27			
Llandudno	d										15h50							17h04				17h30			
Llandudno Junction	d										16 42							17 22				17 45			
Chester	d		16 48								17 35							18 21				18 41			
Crewe 10	a		17 43		17 50						18 29						18 51	19 11				19 28			
	d		17 45		17 52						18 31						18 53	19 11				19 34			
Macclesfield	d	17 46		18 08		18 16		18 33					18 47	19 10					19 16	19 31					
Congleton	d																								
Stoke-on-Trent	d	18 03		18 24		18 35		18 55					19 05	19 26					19 35	19 48					
Stafford	a	18 21	18 27		18 35	18 53					19 09		19 24				19 36		19 53			20 11			
	d	18 22	18 28		18 36	18 53					19 10		19 26				19 38		19 53			20 13			
Penkridge	a																								
Wolverhampton 7	a	18 41				19 09							19 41					20 04	20 09						
Coseley	a																								
Sandwell & Dudley	a																								
Birmingham New Street 12	a	18 58				19 34							19 58					20 26	20 31						
	d																								
Birmingham International ✈	a																								
Coventry	a																								
Lichfield Trent Valley	a																								
Tamworth Low Level	a																								
Nuneaton	a				18 59												20 03								
Rugby	a		19 02								19 46											20 49			
Northampton	a																								
Milton Keynes Central	a			19 31	19 36			19 59			20 16														
Watford Junction	a		20s00					20s33						21s06			21s12			21s37		22s00			
Gatwick Airport 10 ✈	a																								
London Euston 15 ⊖	a		20 35	20 38	20 52			21 06			21 36			21 36			21 52			22 06		22 36			

For general notes see front of timetable
For details of catering facilities see Directory of Train Operators

A To Bournemouth (Table 51)

B To Plymouth (Table 51)

b Change at Perth, Glasgow Queen Street and Glasgow Central. Passengers make their own way between Glasgow Queen Street and Glasgow Central

c Via Glasgow Queen Street and Glasgow Central. Passengers make their own way from one station to the other

e Change at Haymarket

f Change at Preston

g Change at Crewe

h Change at Llandudno Junction and Crewe

OVERNIGHT SLEEPERS. For Sleeper trains, operated by First ScotRail, please refer to Tables 400 - 404

Due to ongoing Engineering Operations, some services from Sunday 14 September on this Table had not been confirmed at time of going to press. These services will be issued in a special Supplement as soon as exact timings have been confirmed.

Table 65

Sundays

20 July to 7 September

Scotland and North West England → West Midlands and London

Route Diagram - see first page of Table 65

		XC	VT	VT	VT	XC	VT	VT	VT	TP	VT	XC	NT	XC	VT	LM	TP	TP	NT	VT	SR	SR	SR
		1 ◇	1 ◇	1 ◇	1 ◇	1 ◇	1 ◇	1 ◇	1 ◇	1 ◇	1 ◇	1 ◇		1 ◇	1 ◇		1 ◇	1 ◇		1 ◇		R	R
		A																				B	C
		🍽	🍽	🍽	🍽	🍽	🍽	🍽	🍽	trolley	🍽				🍽	🚌				🍽		🍽	🍽
Inverness	d				13b25																16c15	18 30	20 25
Aberdeen	d				13 50					15b10					15e30						17f50	20 10	21 40
Dundee	d				15b25					16b25					17b25						19f02	21 21	23u04
Perth	d				15b25															17f05	19f24	20 46	22u59
Edinburgh 10	d				16 49					17 37					18 56							23u15	
Haymarket	d				16u54					17u41					19u01								
Glasgow Central 15	d						17 05				18 04									20 04	22 28	21 42	
Motherwell	d																			20u18		22u01	
Carstairs	d																					22u22	
Lockerbie	d				17 48					18 44					19 58					21 02			
Carlisle 8	a				18 08		18 22			19 05	19 13				20 16					21 23	00 49		
	d				18 11		18 28			19 07	19 15				20 18					21 30			
Penrith North Lakes	d				18 26		18 42			19 21					20 34					21 45			
Windermere	d				18 25					19 20					20 28			21 20					
Oxenholme Lake District	a				18 49		19 05			19 45	19 51				20 57			21 40		22 08			
	d				18 50		19 06			19 45	19 52				20 58			21 40		22 09			
Barrow-in-Furness	d														19 57		20 50						
Lancaster 6	a				19 06		19 21			20 01	20 07				21 13		21 52	21 56		22 25			
	d				19 07		19 22			20 01	20 08				21 14			22 02		22 26			
Preston 8	a				19 24		19 39			20 20	20 25				21 31			22 20		22 58			
Blackpool North	a						20 16				21 03				22 16					23 43			
	d				18 28		19 02			19 28			20 17		20 28			21 28	22 17				
Preston 8	d				19 27		19 42			20 22	20 28		20 42		21 35			22 22	22 42	23 01			
Wigan North Western	a				19 38		19 52				20 39		21 01		21 46				23 10	23s23			
	d				19 39		19 54				20 40		21 01		21 46				23 10				
Bolton	a						20g26			20 41	21g26				22g26			22 41		23s37			
Manchester Piccadilly 10	a						20g49			21 00	21g49				22g49			23 00		23 59			
Manchester Airport ✈	a									21 32	22h34				23h27			23 33		00 33			
Liverpool Lime Street 10	a						20 49						21 49		22 49				23 59				
	d		19 15				19j26		20 15							21 47							
Liverpool South Parkway 7 ✈	d						19j35									21 57							
Runcorn	d		19 31				19j43		20 31							22 05							
Warrington Bank Quay	a				19 49		20 03				20 50				21 56								
	d				19 50		20 05				20 52				21 59								
Hartford	d															22 15							
Manchester Piccadilly 10	d	19 24		19 47		19 55		20 23				20 55		21 55									
Stockport	d	19 33		19u55		20 04		20u32				21 04		22 04									
Manchester Airport ✈	d																						
Wilmslow	d				19 28										21 28								
Holyhead	d		17k23								18k40												
Bangor (Gwynedd)	d		17k51								19k09				20 11								
Llandudno	d		18k10								18m45												
Llandudno Junction	d		18k20								19k27				20 34								
Chester	d		19 23								20 23				21 33								
Crewe 10	a		19 51		20 10		20 25		20 50		21 12				22 18								
	d		19 57		20 10		20 27		20 53		21 13				22 19	22 50							
Macclesfield	d	19 46		20 08		20 16		20 45				21 16		22 16									
Congleton	d																						
Stoke-on-Trent	d	20 05		20 22		20 35		21 03				21 35		22 35									
Stafford	a	20 24	20 34			20 53	21 05		21 30		21 49	21 53		22 53	22 58	23 35							
	d	20 26	20 36			20 53	21 07		21 32		21 50	21 53		22 53	23 00	23 36							
Penkridge	a															00 01							
Wolverhampton 7	a	20 41			21 02	21 09					22 04	22 16		23 09	23 18	00 32							
Coseley	a																						
Sandwell & Dudley	a																						
Birmingham New Street 12	a	20 58			21 25	21 31					22 27	22 41		23 30	23 41	01 08							
	d																						
Birmingham International ✈	a																						
Coventry	a																						
Lichfield Trent Valley	a			20 53																			
Tamworth Low Level	a			21 00																			
Nuneaton	a		20 58					21 35	21 54														
Rugby	a						21 45	21 51															
Northampton	a																						
Milton Keynes Central	a		21 35	21 47			22 08	22 18	22 29														
Watford Junction	a			22s31			22s44	23s02	23s08														
Gatwick Airport 10 ✈	a																						
London Euston 15 ⊖	a		22 52	23 02			23 19	23 33	23 52													07 11	09 21

For general notes see front of timetable
For details of catering facilities see Directory of Train Operators

A To Southampton Central (Table 51)
B Stops at Edinburgh after Glasgow Central, Motherwell and Carstairs
C Also conveys portion from Fort William (Table 227)
b Change at Haymarket
c Change at Perth, Glasgow Queen Street and Glasgow Central. Passengers make their own way between Glasgow Queen Street and Glasgow Central
e Change at Dundee and Haymarket
f Via Glasgow Queen Street and Glasgow Central. Passengers make their own way from one station to the other
g Change at Preston
h Change at Preston and Manchester Piccadilly
j Change at Crewe
k Change at Chester and Crewe
m Change at Llandudno Junction, Chester and Crewe

OVERNIGHT SLEEPERS. For Sleeper trains, operated by First ScotRail, please refer to Tables 400 - 404

Due to ongoing Engineering Operations, some services from Sunday 14 September on this Table had not been confirmed at time of going to press. These services will be issued in a special Supplement as soon as exact timings have been confirmed.

Table 65A

Mondays to Fridays

Milton Keynes Central → Buckingham and Bicester

Bus Service

		VT	VT	VT	VT	VT	VT	VT	VT	VT	VT	VT	VT	VT
Milton Keynes Central	d	05 50	06 20	06 50	07 20	07 40	08 20	08 45	09 15	09 45	10 15	10 45	11 15	11 45
Buckingham Tesco	d	06 10	06 40	07 10	07 40	08 00	08 40	09 05	09 35	10 05	10 35	11 05	11 35	12 05
Bicester Bure Place	a	06 30	07 00	07 30	08 00	08 25	09 00	09 25	09 55	10 25	10 55	11 25	11 55	12 25

		VT	VT	VT	VT	VT	VT	VT	VT	VT	VT	VT	VT	VT	VT	VT	VT
Milton Keynes Central	d	12 15	12 45	13 15	13 45	14 15	14 45	15 15	15 45	16 15	16 45	17 15	17 45	18 15	18 45	19 45	20 45
Buckingham Tesco	d	12 35	13 05	13 35	14 05	14 35	15 05	15 35	16 05	16 35	17 05	17 35	18 05	18 35	19 05	20 05	21 05
Bicester Bure Place	a	12 55	13 25	13 55	14 25	14 55	15 25	15 55	16 25	16 55	17 25	17 55	18 25	18 55	19 25	20 25	21 25

Saturdays

		VT	VT	VT	VT	VT	VT	VT	VT	VT	VT	VT	VT	VT
Milton Keynes Central	d	05 50	06 20	06 50	07 20	07 40	08 20	08 45	09 15	09 45	10 15	10 45	11 15	11 45
Buckingham Tesco	d	06 10	06 40	07 10	07 40	08 00	08 40	09 05	09 35	10 05	10 35	11 05	11 35	12 05
Bicester Bure Place	a	06 30	07 00	07 30	08 00	08 25	09 00	09 25	09 55	10 25	10 55	11 25	11 55	12 25

		VT	VT	VT	VT	VT	VT	VT	VT	VT	VT	VT	VT	VT	VT	VT	VT
Milton Keynes Central	d	12 15	12 45	13 15	13 45	14 15	14 45	15 15	15 45	16 15	16 45	17 15	17 45	18 15	18 45	19 45	20 45
Buckingham Tesco	d	12 35	13 05	13 35	14 05	14 35	15 05	15 35	16 05	16 35	17 05	17 35	18 05	18 35	19 05	20 05	21 05
Bicester Bure Place	a	12 55	13 25	13 55	14 25	14 55	15 25	15 55	16 25	16 55	17 25	17 55	18 25	18 55	19 25	20 25	21 25

Sundays

		VT	VT	VT	VT	VT	VT	VT	VT	VT	VT	VT	VT	VT	VT	VT	VT	VT	VT	VT	VT	VT	VT	VT	VT	VT
Milton Keynes Central	d	06 45	07 45	08 45	09 45	10 15	10 45	11 15	11 45	12 15	12 45	13 15	13 45	14 15	14 45	15 15	15 45	16 15	16 45	17 15	17 45	18 15	18 45	19 45	20 40	21 53
Buckingham Tesco	d	07 05	08 05	09 05	10 05	10 35	11 05	11 35	12 05	12 35	13 05	13 35	14 05	14 35	15 05	15 35	16 05	16 35	17 05	17 35	18 05	18 35	19 05	20 05	21 00	22 13
Bicester Bure Place	a	07 25	08 25	09 25	10 25	10 55	11 25	11 55	12 25	12 55	13 25	13 55	14 25	14 55	15 25	15 55	16 25	16 55	17 25	17 55	18 25	18 55	19 25	20 25	21 20	22 33

For general notes see front of timetable
For details of catering facilities see
Directory of Train Operators

This is the X5 service operated by Stagecoach East

Bicester and Buckingham → Milton Keynes Central

Bus Service

Mondays to Fridays

		VT	VT	VT	VT	VT	VT	VT	VT	VT	VT	VT	VT	VT
Bicester Bure Place	d	07 35	08 05	08 35	09 05	09 35	10 05	10 35	11 05	11 35	12 05	12 35	13 05	13 35
Buckingham Tesco	d	07 55	08 25	08 55	09 25	09 55	10 25	10 55	11 25	11 55	12 25	12 55	13 25	13 55
Milton Keynes Central	a	08 15	08 45	09 15	09 45	10 15	10 45	11 15	11 45	12 15	12 45	13 15	13 45	14 15

		VT	VT	VT	VT	VT	VT	VT	VT	VT	VT	VT	VT	VT	VT	VT	VT
Bicester Bure Place	d	14 05	14 35	15 05	15 35	16 05	16 35	17 05	17 35	18 05	18 35	19 05	19 30	20 00	20 25	21 25	22 25
Buckingham Tesco	d	14 25	14 55	15 25	15 55	16 25	16 55	17 25	17 55	18 25	18 55	19 25	19 50	20 20	20 45	21 45	22 45
Milton Keynes Central	a	14 45	15 15	15 45	16 15	16 45	17 15	17 45	18 15	18 45	19 15	19 45	20 10	20 40	21 05	22 05	23 05

Saturdays

		VT	VT	VT	VT	VT	VT	VT	VT	VT	VT	VT	VT	VT
Bicester Bure Place	d	07 35	08 05	08 35	09 05	09 35	10 05	10 35	11 05	11 35	12 05	12 35	13 05	13 35
Buckingham Tesco	d	07 55	08 25	08 55	09 25	09 55	10 25	10 55	11 25	11 55	12 25	12 55	13 25	13 55
Milton Keynes Central	a	08 15	08 45	09 15	09 45	10 15	10 45	11 15	11 45	12 15	12 45	13 15	13 45	14 15

		VT	VT	VT	VT	VT	VT	VT	VT	VT	VT	VT	VT	VT	VT	VT	VT
Bicester Bure Place	d	14 05	14 35	15 05	15 35	16 05	16 35	17 05	17 35	18 05	18 35	19 05	19 30	20 00	20 25	21 25	22 25
Buckingham Tesco	d	14 25	14 55	15 25	15 55	16 25	16 55	17 25	17 55	18 25	18 55	19 25	19 50	20 20	20 45	21 45	22 45
Milton Keynes Central	a	14 45	15 15	15 45	16 15	16 45	17 15	17 45	18 15	18 45	19 15	19 45	20 10	20 40	21 05	22 05	23 05

Sundays

		VT	VT	VT	VT	VT	VT	VT	VT	VT	VT	VT	VT	VT	VT	VT	VT	VT
Bicester Bure Place	d	08 35	09 35	10 35	11 35	12 05	12 35	13 05	13 35	14 05	14 35	15 05	17 35	18 05	18 35	19 30	20 30	22 30
Buckingham Tesco	d	08 55	09 55	10 55	11 55	12 25	12 55	13 25	13 55	14 25	14 55	15 25	17 55	18 25	18 55	19 50	20 50	22 50
Milton Keynes Central	a	09 15	10 15	11 15	12 15	12 45	13 15	13 45	14 15	14 45	15 15	15 45	18 15	18 45	19 15	20 10	21 10	23 10

For general notes see front of timetable
For details of catering facilities see
Directory of Train Operators

This is the X5 service operated by Stagecoach East

Milton Keynes Central — London Luton Airport

Bus Service

Mondays to Fridays

		VT	VT	VT	VT	VT	VT	VT	VT	VT	VT	VT
Milton Keynes Central	d	06 40	07 10	07 55	08 55	09 55	10 55	11 55	12 55	13 25	13 55	14 25
Milton Keynes The Point	d	06 45	07 15	08 00	09 00	10 00	11 00	12 00	13 00	13 30	14 00	14 30
Luton	d	07 25	08 05	08 45	09 40	10 40	11 40	12 40	13 40	14 10	14 40	15 10
London Luton Airport	a	07 35	08 15	08 55	09 50	10 50	11 50	12 50	13 50	14 20	14 50	15 20

		VT	VT	VT	VT	VT	VT	VT	VT	VT	VT
Milton Keynes Central	d	14 55	15 25	15 55	16 55	17 25	17 55	18 55	19 55	20 55	21 55
Milton Keynes The Point	d	15 00	15 30	16 00	17 00	17 30	18 00	19 00	20 00	21 00	22 00
Luton	d	15 40	16 10	16 40	17 40	18 10	18 40	19 40	20 40	21 40	22 40
London Luton Airport	a	15 50	16 20	16 50	17 50	18 20	18 50	19 50	20 50	21 50	22 50

Saturdays

		VT	VT	VT	VT	VT	VT	VT	VT	VT	VT	VT	VT	VT	VT	VT
Milton Keynes Central	d	06 40	07 55	08 55	09 55	10 55	11 55	12 55	13 55	14 55	15 55	16 55	17 55	18 55	19 55	20 55
Milton Keynes The Point	d	06 45	08 00	09 00	10 00	11 00	12 00	13 00	14 00	15 00	16 00	17 00	18 00	19 00	20 00	21 00
Luton	d	07 25	08 40	09 40	10 40	11 40	12 40	13 40	14 40	15 40	16 40	17 40	18 40	19 40	20 40	21 40
London Luton Airport	a	07 35	08 50	09 50	10 50	11 50	12 50	13 50	14 50	15 50	16 50	17 50	18 50	19 50	20 50	21 50

Sundays

Network diagram - see first page of Table 1

		VT
Milton Keynes Central	d	11 20
Milton Keynes The Point	d	11 25
Luton	d	12 05
London Luton Airport	a	12 15

Mondays to Fridays

		VT	VT	VT	VT	VT	VT	VT	VT	VT	VT	VT	VT
London Luton Airport	d	05 50	06 50	07 20	07 50	08 35	09 05	10 05	11 05	12 05	13 05	13 35	14 05
Luton	d	06 00	07 00	07 30	08 00	08 45	09 15	10 15	11 15	12 15	13 15	13 45	14 15
Luton Galaxy Centre	d	06 02	07 02	07 32	08 02	08 47	09 17	10 17	11 17	12 17	13 17	13 47	14 17
Milton Keynes The Point	d	06 40	07 45	08 18	08 48	09 25	09 55	10 55	11 55	12 55	13 55	14 25	14 55
Milton Keynes Central	a	06 45	07 50	08 30	09 00	09 30	10 00	11 00	12 00	13 00	14 00	14 30	15 00

		VT	VT	VT	VT	VT	VT	VT	VT	VT	VT A	VT A
London Luton Airport	d	14 35	15 05	15 35	16 05	16 35	17 05	17 35	18 05	19 05	20 05	21 05
Luton	d	14 45	15 15	15 45	16 15	16 45	17 15	17 45	18 15	19 15	20 15	21 15
Luton Galaxy Centre	d	14 47	15 17	15 47	16 17	16 47	17 17	17 47	18 17	19 17	20 17	21 17
Milton Keynes The Point	d	15 25	15 55	16 25	16 55	17 25	17 55	18 25	18 55	19 55	.	.
Milton Keynes Central	a	15 30	16 00	16 30	17 00	17 30	18 00	18 30	19 00	20 00	20 55	21 55

Saturdays

		VT A	VT	VT	VT	VT	VT	VT	VT	VT	VT	VT	VT	VT	VT A	VT A
London Luton Airport	d	05 50	06 50	07 50	09 05	10 05	11 05	12 05	13 05	14 05	15 05	16 05	17 05	18 05	19 05	20 05
Luton	d	06 00	07 00	08 00	09 15	10 15	11 15	12 15	13 15	14 15	15 15	16 15	17 15	18 15	19 15	20 15
Luton Galaxy Centre	d	06 02	07 02	08 02	09 17	10 17	11 17	12 17	13 17	14 17	15 17	16 17	17 17	18 17	19 17	20 17
Milton Keynes The Point	d	.	07 40	08 40	09 55	10 55	11 55	12 55	13 55	14 55	15 55	16 55	17 55	18 55	.	.
Milton Keynes Central	a	06 40	07 45	08 45	10 00	11 00	12 00	13 00	14 00	15 00	16 00	17 00	18 00	19 00	19 50	20 50

Sundays

London Luton Airport	d
Luton	d
Luton Galaxy Centre	d
Milton Keynes The Point	d
Milton Keynes Central	a

For general notes see front of timetable
For details of catering facilities see
Directory of Train Operators

A To Milton Keynes The Point

Milton Keynes Central → Bedford and Cambridge

Bus Service

		VT	VT	VT	VT	VT	VT	VT	VT	VT	VT	VT	VT	VT	VT	VT	VT	VT
Milton Keynes Central	d	07 15	07 50	08 15	08 45	09 15	09 45	10 15	10 45	11 15	11 45	12 15	12 45	13 15	13 45	14 15	14 45	15 15
Bedford Bus Station	a	08 00	08 35	09 05	09 35	10 05	10 35	11 05	11 35	12 05	12 35	13 05	13 35	14 05	14 35	15 05	15 35	16 05
St Neots Cross Keys	a	08 42	09 17	09 47	10 17	10 47	11 17	11 47	12 17	12 47	13 17	13 47	14 17	14 47	15 17	15 47	16 17	16 47
Cambridge Bus Station	a	09 20	09 55	10 25	10 55	11 25	11 55	12 25	12 55	13 25	13 55	14 25	14 55	15 25	15 55	16 25	16 55	17 25

		VT	VT	VT	VT	VT	VT	VT	VT	VT	VT	VT	VT	VT	VT
Milton Keynes Central	d	15 45	16 15	16 45	17 15	17 45	18 15	18 45	19 15	19 45	20 10	20 40	21 05	22 05	23 05
Bedford Bus Station	a	16 35	17 05	17 35	18 05	18 35	19 05	19 35	20 05	20 35	20 55	21 25	21 50	22 50	23 50
St Neots Cross Keys	a	17 17	17 47	18 17	18 47	19 17	.	20 10	.	21 10	.	22 10	.	.	.
Cambridge Bus Station	a	17 55	18 25	18 55	19 25	19 48	.	20 43	.	21 43	.	22 43	.	.	.

Saturdays

		VT	VT	VT	VT	VT	VT	VT	VT	VT	VT	VT	VT	VT	VT	VT	VT	VT
Milton Keynes Central	d	07 15	07 50	08 15	08 45	09 15	09 45	10 15	10 45	11 15	11 45	12 15	12 45	13 15	13 45	14 15	14 45	15 15
Bedford Bus Station	a	08 00	08 35	09 05	09 35	10 05	10 35	11 05	11 35	12 05	12 35	13 05	13 35	14 05	14 35	15 05	15 35	16 05
St Neots Cross Keys	a	08 42	09 17	09 47	10 17	10 47	11 17	11 47	12 17	12 47	13 17	13 47	14 17	14 47	15 17	15 47	16 17	16 47
Cambridge Bus Station	a	09 20	09 55	10 25	10 55	11 25	11 55	12 25	12 55	13 25	13 55	14 25	14 55	15 25	15 55	16 25	16 55	17 25

		VT	VT	VT	VT	VT	VT	VT	VT	VT	VT	VT	VT	VT	VT
Milton Keynes Central	d	15 45	16 15	16 45	17 15	17 45	18 15	18 45	19 15	19 45	20 10	20 40	21 05	22 05	23 05
Bedford Bus Station	a	16 35	17 05	17 35	18 05	18 35	19 05	19 35	20 05	20 30	20 55	21 25	21 50	22 50	23 50
St Neots Cross Keys	a	17 17	17 47	18 17	18 47	19 15	.	20 10	.	21 10	.	22 10	.	.	.
Cambridge Bus Station	a	17 55	18 25	18 55	19 25	19 48	.	20 43	.	21 43	.	22 43	.	.	.

Sundays

		VT	VT	VT	VT	VT	VT	VT	VT	VT	VT	VT	VT	VT	VT	VT	VT	VT	VT	VT	VT	VT
Milton Keynes Central	d	09 15	10 15	11 15	12 15	12 45	13 15	13 45	14 15	14 45	15 15	15 45	16 15	16 45	17 15	17 45	18 45	19 45	20 45	21 10	22 10	23 10
Bedford Bus Station	a	10 05	11 05	12 05	13 05	13 35	14 05	14 35	15 05	15 35	16 05	16 35	17 05	17 35	18 05	18 35	19 35	20 35	21 35	21 55	22 55	23 55
St Neots Cross Keys	a	10 47	11 47	12 47	13 47	14 17	14 47	15 17	15 47	16 17	16 45	17 15	17 40	18 10	18 40	19 10	20 10	21 10	22 10	.	.	.
Cambridge Bus Station	a	11 25	12 25	13 25	14 25	14 55	15 25	15 55	16 25	16 55	17 18	17 48	18 13	18 43	19 13	19 43	20 43	21 43	22 43	.	.	.

For general notes see front of timetable
For details of catering facilities see Directory of Train Operators

This is the X5 service operated by Stagecoach East

Cambridge and Bedford → Milton Keynes Central

Bus Service

Mondays to Fridays

		VT	VT	VT	VT	VT	VT	VT	VT	VT	VT	VT	VT	VT	VT	VT	VT	VT
Cambridge Bus Station	d					05 40		06 30	07 00	07 30	08 10	08 40	09 10	09 40	10 10	10 40	11 10	11 40
St Neots Sq (Bus)	d					06 15		07 05	07 35	08 05	08 45	09 15	09 45	10 15	10 45	11 15	11 45	12 15
Bedford Bus Station	d	05 05	05 35	06 05	06 35	06 55	07 30	07 55	08 25	09 00	09 30	10 00	10 30	11 00	11 30	12 00	12 30	13 00
Milton Keynes Central	a	05 50	06 20	06 50	07 20	07 40	08 20	08 45	09 15	09 45	10 15	10 45	11 15	11 45	12 15	12 45	13 15	13 45

		VT	VT	VT	VT	VT	VT	VT	VT	VT	VT	VT	VT	VT	VT
Cambridge Bus Station	d	12 10	12 40	13 10	13 40	14 10	14 40	15 10	15 40	16 10	16 40	17 10	17 40	18 10	18 40
St Neots Sq (Bus)	d	12 45	13 15	13 45	14 15	14 45	15 15	15 45	16 15	16 45	17 15	17 45	18 15	18 45	19 15
Bedford Bus Station	d	13 30	14 00	14 30	15 00	15 30	16 00	16 30	17 00	17 30	18 00	18 30	19 00	19 30	20 00
Milton Keynes Central	a	14 15	14 45	15 15	15 45	16 15	16 45	17 15	17 45	18 15	18 45	19 15	19 45	20 10	20 45

Saturdays

		VT	VT	VT	VT	VT	VT	VT	VT	VT	VT	VT	VT	VT	VT	VT	VT	VT
Cambridge Bus Station	d							06 30	07 00	07 30	08 10	08 40	09 10	09 40	10 10	10 40	11 10	11 40
St Neots Sq (Bus)	d							07 05	07 35	08 05	08 45	09 15	09 45	10 15	10 45	11 15	11 45	12 15
Bedford Bus Station	d	05 05	05 35	06 05	06 35	07 00	07 30	08 00	08 30	09 00	09 30	10 00	10 30	11 00	11 30	12 00	12 30	13 00
Milton Keynes Central	a	05 50	06 20	06 50	07 20	07 45	08 15	08 45	09 15	09 45	10 15	10 45	11 15	11 45	12 15	12 45	13 15	13 45

		VT	VT	VT	VT	VT	VT	VT	VT	VT	VT	VT	VT	VT	VT
Cambridge Bus Station	d	12 10	12 40	13 10	13 40	14 10	14 40	15 10	15 40	16 10	16 40	17 10	17 40	18 10	18 40
St Neots Sq (Bus)	d	12 45	13 15	13 45	14 15	14 45	15 15	15 45	16 15	16 45	17 15	17 45	18 15	18 45	19 15
Bedford Bus Station	d	13 30	14 00	14 30	15 00	15 30	16 00	16 30	17 00	17 30	18 00	18 30	19 00	19 30	20 00
Milton Keynes Central	a	14 15	14 45	15 15	15 45	16 15	16 45	17 15	17 45	18 15	18 45	19 15	19 45	20 10	20 45

Sundays

		VT	VT	VT	VT	VT	VT	VT	VT	VT	VT	VT	VT	VT	VT	VT	VT	VT	VT	VT	VT	VT	VT	VT	VT	VT
Cambridge Bus Station	d					08 10		09 10		10 10		11 10	11 40	12 10	12 40	13 10	13 40	14 10	14 40	15 10	15 40	16 10	16 40	17 10	17 40	18 40
St Neots Sq (Bus)	d					08 45		09 45		10 45		11 45	12 15	12 45	13 15	13 45	14 15	14 45	15 15	15 45	16 15	16 45	17 15	17 45	18 15	19 15
Bedford Bus Station	d	06 00	07 00	08 00	09 00	09 30	10 00	10 30	11 00	11 30	12 00	12 30	13 00	13 30	14 00	14 30	15 00	15 30	16 00	16 30	17 00	17 30	18 00	18 30	19 00	20 00
Milton Keynes Central	a	06 45	07 45	08 45	09 45	10 15	10 45	11 15	11 45	12 15	12 45	13 15	13 45	14 15	14 45	15 15	15 45	16 15	16 45	17 15	17 45	18 15	18 45	19 15	19 45	20 45

For general notes see front of timetable
For details of catering facilities see
Directory of Train Operators

This is the X5 service operated by Stagecoach East

Table 65E

Mondays to Saturdays

Preston — Southport

Bus Service

		VT 🚌	VT 🚌		VT 🚌	VT 🚌		VT 🚌	VT 🚌		VT 🚌	VT 🚌		VT 🚌	VT 🚌		VT 🚌	VT 🚌		VT 🚌	VT 🚌		VT 🚌			
Preston 8	d	06 13	07 00		08 09	09 09		10 09	11 09		12 09	13 09		14 09	15 09		16 09	17 19		18 19	19 34		20 19			
Southport (Lord Street)	a	06 45	07 33		08 46	09 46		10 46	11 46		12 46	13 46		14 46	15 46		16 46	17 56		18 56	20 11		20 46			

Sundays

		VT 🚌				VT 🚌				VT 🚌				VT 🚌				VT 🚌				VT 🚌				
Preston 8	d	08 09				10 09				12 09				14 09				16 09				18 09				
Southport (Lord Street)	a	08 46				10 46				12 46				14 46				16 46				18 46				

Mondays to Saturdays

		VT SX 🚌	VT SO 🚌	VT SO 🚌		VT SX 🚌	VT 🚌	VT 🚌		VT 🚌	VT 🚌	VT 🚌		VT 🚌	VT 🚌	VT 🚌		VT SO 🚌	VT SX 🚌	VT 🚌		VT 🚌	VT 🚌	VT 🚌		
Southport (Lord Street)	d	06 55	06 57	07 48		07 41	09 08	10 08		11 08	12 08	13 08		14 08	15 08	16 08		17 11	17 23	18 20		19 20	20 20	21 20		
Preston (Fishergate)	a	07 31	07 31	08 28		08 41	09 55	10 55		11 55	12 55	13 55		14 55	15 55	16 55		17 58	18 10	18 57		19 57	20 57	21 57		

Sundays

		VT 🚌			VT 🚌			VT 🚌			VT 🚌			VT 🚌			VT 🚌			VT 🚌						
Southport (Lord Street)	d	09 05			11 05			13 05			15 05			17 05			19 05			21 05						
Preston (Fishergate)	a	09 45			11 45			13 45			15 45			17 45			19 45			21 45						

For general notes see front of timetable
For details of catering facilities see Directory of Train Operators

This is the X2 service operated jointly by Stagecoach in Lancashire and Stagecoach in Merseyside

Table 65F

Mondays to Saturdays

Penrith — Keswick, Cockermouth and Workington

Bus Service

		VT	VT	VT	VT	VT	VT	VT	VT	VT	VT	VT	VT	VT	VT	VT SX	VT SO	VT
Penrith North Lakes	d	07 20	08 30	09 30	10 30	11 30	12 30	13 30	14 30	15 30	16 30	17 30	18 30	19 30	20 34	21 35	21 35	22 40
Keswick (Bus Station)	a	07 55	09 05	10 05	11 05	12 05	13 05	14 05	15 05	16 05	17 05	18 05	19 05	20 05	21 03	22 10	22 10	23 15
Cockermouth (Main Street)	a	08 31	09 41	10 41	11 41	12 41	13 41	14 41	15 41	16 41	17 41	18 41	19 41	20 41	21 36	22 44	22 46	23 45
Workington (Bus Station)	a	08 52	10 02	11 02	12 02	13 02	14 02	15 02	16 02	17 02	18 02	19 02	20 02	21 02	21 53	23 07	23 07	00 07

Sundays

		VT	VT	VT	VT	VT	VT	VT
Penrith North Lakes	d	08 45	09 20	11 20	13 20	15 20	17 20	19 20
Keswick (Bus Station)	a	09 20	09 55	11 55	13 55	15 55	17 55	19 55
Cockermouth (Main Street)	a		10 31	12 31	14 31	16 31	18 31	20 31
Workington (Bus Station)	a		10 52	12 52	14 52	16 52	18 52	20 52

Mondays to Saturdays

		VT	VT	VT	VT	VT	VT	VT	VT	VT	VT	VT	VT	VT	VT	VT	VT	VT
Workington (Bus Station)	d	05 15	06 15	07 15	08 15	09 15	10 15	11 15	12 15	13 15	14 15	15 15	16 15	17 15		18 15	19 15	
Cockermouth (Main Street)	d	05 36	06 36	07 36	08 36	09 36	10 36	11 36	12 36	13 36	14 36	15 36	16 36	17 36		18 36	19 36	
Keswick (Bus Station)	d	06 15	07 15	08 15	09 15	10 15	11 15	12 15	13 15	14 15	15 15	16 15	17 15	18 15	18 40	19 15	20 15	21 50
Penrith North Lakes	a	06 50	07 50	08 50	09 50	10 50	11 50	12 50	13 50	14 50	15 50	16 50	17 50	18 50	19 17	19 50	20 50	22 25

Sundays

		VT	VT	VT	VT	VT	VT	VT
Workington (Bus Station)	d	07 15	09 15	11 15	13 15	15 15	17 15	
Cockermouth (Main Street)	d	07 36	09 36	11 36	13 36	15 36	17 36	
Keswick (Bus Station)	d	08 15	10 15	12 15	14 15	16 15	18 15	18 40
Penrith North Lakes	a	08 50	10 50	12 50	14 50	16 50	18 50	19 15

For general notes see front of timetable
For details of catering facilities see
Directory of Train Operators

This is an amalgamation of the X4/X5/X50 services operated by Stagecoach in Cumbria

Table 65G

Mondays to Saturdays

Carlisle — Scottish Border Towns

Bus Service

		VT SO 🚌	VT 🚌	VT 🚌	VT 🚌	VT 🚌	VT 🚌	VT 🚌	VT 🚌	VT 🚌	VT 🚌	VT 🚌	VT 🚌	VT FSO 🚌
Carlisle	d	22p50	09 10	10 10	11 10	12 10	13 10	14 10	15 10	16 10	17 10	18 50	20 50	22 50
Langholm	a	23p32	09 57	10 57	11 57	12 57	13 57	14 57	15 57	16 57	17 57	19 37	21 37	23 32
Hawick	a	00 07	10 32	11 32	12 32	13 32	14 32	15 32	16 32	17 32	18 32	20 12	22 12	00 07
Selkirk	a	00 30	10 55	11 55	12 55	13 55	14 55	15 55	16 55	17 55	18 55	20 35	22 35	00 30
Galashiels	a	00 45	11 15	12 15	13 15	14 15	15 15	16 15	17 15	18 15	19 15	20 50	22 50	00 45

Sundays

		VT 🚌	VT 🚌	VT 🚌	VT 🚌
Carlisle	d	22p50	14 05	18 05	21 20
Langholm	a	23p32	14 50	18 50	22 05
Hawick	a	00 07	15 25	19 25	22 40
Selkirk	a	00 30	15 45	19 45	23 00
Galashiels	a	00 45	16 00	20 00	23 15

Mondays to Saturdays

		VT 🚌	VT 🚌	VT 🚌	VT 🚌	VT 🚌	VT 🚌	VT 🚌	VT 🚌	VT 🚌	VT SX 🚌	VT SX 🚌	VT FSO 🚌
Galashiels	d	06 20	07 15	08 10	09 25	10 25	11 25	12 25	13 25	14 25	16 30	17 35	19 25
Selkirk	d	06 35	07 30	08 25	09 40	10 40	11 40	12 40	13 40	14 40	16 45	17 50	19 40
Hawick	d	06 55	07 50	08 45	10 00	11 00	12 00	13 00	14 00	15 00	17 05	18 10	19 58
Langholm	d	07 35	08 30	09 25	10 40	11 40	12 40	13 40	14 40	15 40	17 45	18 50	20 38
Carlisle	a	08 27	09 17	10 12	11 27	12 27	13 27	14 27	15 27	16 27	18 32	19 37	21 25

Sundays

		VT 🚌	VT 🚌	VT 🚌	VT 🚌
Galashiels	d	09 30	11 30	15 30	17 30
Selkirk	d	09 45	11 45	15 45	17 45
Hawick	d	10 05	12 05	16 05	18 05
Langholm	d	10 38	12 38	16 38	18 38
Carlisle	a	11 27	13 27	17 27	19 27

For general notes see front of timetable
For details of catering facilities see Directory of Train Operators

Table 65H

Mondays to Saturdays

Macclesfield — Buxton and Bakewell

Bus Service

		VT bus	VT bus	VT bus	VT bus	VT bus	VT bus	VT bus	VT bus
Macclesfield	d	07 25	08 30	10 55	12 30	14 50	16 30	17 30	18 35
Buxton (Market Place)	a	07 54	08 59	11 25	12 59	15 20	16 59	17 59	19 04
Bakewell Square	a		09 24						

Sundays

		VT bus	VT bus	VT bus	VT bus	VT bus	VT bus
Macclesfield	d	09 42	11 00	12 35	13 35	16 15	18 15
Buxton (Market Place)	a	10 12	11 30	13 00	14 00	16 40	18 45
Bakewell Square	a			13 30	14 30	17 10	

Mondays to Saturdays

		VT bus	VT bus	VT bus	VT bus	VT bus	VT bus	VT bus	VT bus
Bakewell Square	d					13 50			
Buxton (Market Place)	d	06 55	07 55	10 20	12 00	14 15	15 55	17 00	18 05
Macclesfield	a	07 24	08 24	10 50	12 29	14 44	16 25	17 29	18 34

Sundays

		VT bus	VT bus	VT bus
Bakewell Square	d	12 35	15 15	17 15
Buxton (Market Place)	d	13 00	15 40	17 40
Macclesfield	a	13 30	16 10	18 10

For general notes see front of timetable
For details of catering facilities see Directory of Train Operators

London → Watford Junction, Milton Keynes, Northampton and West Midlands

Network Diagram - See first page of Table 59

Miles	Miles	Miles			VT	LM	LM	LM	VT	VT	VT	LM	LM	LM	LM	LM	LM	LM		LM	LM	LM	SN	LM	VT	LM
					MO	MO	MO	MO	MO	MO	MO	MX	MO	MO	MO	MX	MO	MX								
					1 ◇	1	1	1	1 ◇	1 ◇	1 ◇	1	1	1	1	1	1	1		1	1	1	1	1	1 ◇	1
							A	B	B	C	A		C	A	B											
					☕				☕	☕	☕														⊠	
0	0	—	**London Euston 15** ⊖	d	23p01	23p04	23p09	23p13	23p35	23p31	23p30	23p34	23p34	23p39	23p43	00 04	00 34	00 34		01 34		05 24		05 55	06 20	
—	—	0	**Brighton 10**	d																						
—	—	13	Haywards Heath 3	d																						
—	—	24¼	Gatwick Airport 10 ✈	d																						
—	—	40½	East Croydon 🚌	d																						
—	—	48¼	Clapham Junction 10	d																						
—	—	49¼	Imperial Wharf §	d																						
—	—	49¾	West Brompton ⊖	d																			05 31			
—	—	51¾	Kensington Olympia ⊖	d																			05 34			
—	—	53	Shepherds Bush §	d																						
8	—	57¼	Wembley Central	d													00 45	00 45		01 45						
11½	11½	—	Harrow & Wealdstone ⊖	d		23p20	23p21	23p25				23p46	23p50	23p51	23p55	00 16	00 50	00 50		01 50		05 36	05 51	06 09		
16	—	—	Bushey	d								23p51						00 55								
—	—	—	**Watford Junction**	a		23p28	23p28	23p32				23p54	23p58	23p58	00 02	00 23	00 56	00 58		01 59		05 43	05 58	06 15		
17½	17½	—		d	23b23	23p28	23p28	23p32	23b52			23p55	23p58	23p58	00 02	00 23	00 58	00 58		02 00		05 43		06 16	06u36	
21	—	—	Kings Langley	d		23p33	23p33	23p37				23p59					01 03	01 03				05 48		06 20		
23	—	—	Apsley	d		23p36	23p36	23p40				00 03					01 06	01 06				05 51		06 24		
—	—	—	Hemel Hempstead	a		23p39	23p39	23p43				00 06	00 06	00 06	00 10	00 31	01 09	01 09		02 07		05 54		06 27		
24½	—	—		d		23p39	23p39	23p43				00 06	00 06	00 06	00 10	00 31	01 09	01 09		02 07		05 54		06 27		←
28	—	—	Berkhamsted	d		23p44	23p44	23p48				00 10	00 10	00 10	00 14	00 35	01 14	01 14		02 12		05 59		06 32 →		06 32
31¾	—	—	Tring	d								00 15	00 15	00 15	00 19	00 40	01 19	01 19		02 17		06 06				06 40
36	—	—	Cheddington	d								00 20	00 20	00 20	00 24		01 24	01 24				06 11				
40¼	—	—	Leighton Buzzard	d		23p57	23p57	00 01				00 25	00 27	00 27	00 31	00 48	01 31	01 29		02 25		06 16				06 48
46¾	—	—	Bletchley	d		00 04	00 04	00 08				00 33	00 35	00 35	00 39	00 56	01 38	01 36		02 32	05 25	06 25				06 56
—	—	—	**Milton Keynes Central 10**	a	00 03	00 13	00 13	00 17	00 28	00 37	00 37	00 43	00 43	00 43	00 47	01 07	01 47	01 45		02 45	05 29	06 32			06 55	07 02
49¾	49¾	—		d	00 05	00 13	00 13	00 17	00 29	00 39	00 39		00 44	00 44	00 48	01 07	01 47	01 45			05 30	06 32				07 02
52½	52½	—	Wolverton	d		00 17	00 17	00 21					00 47	00 47	00 51	01 10	01 51	01 49			05 33	06 36				07 06
65¾	—	—	**Northampton**	a		00 35	00 35	00 39					01 06	01 06	01 10	01 28	02 10	02 07			05 47	06 49				07 19
—	—	—	**Rugby**	a	00s31				00 58	01s07	01s08															
84½	82½	—		d					01 00																	
—	—	—	Nuneaton	a																						
96	—	—	Coventry	a					01 11																	
106¾	—	—	Birmingham International ✈	a					01 23																	
115¼	—	—	**Birmingham New Street 12**	a	01 39				01 35	02 11	02 11															
120½	—	—	Sandwell & Dudley	a																						
128	—	—	Wolverhampton 7 🚌	a	02 02				01 57	02 34	02 47															

		LM	VT	VT	VT	LM	SN	LM	VT	VT	SN	LM	VT	VT	LM	LM		VT	VT	LM	LM	LM	VT	VT	SN	LM
		1	1 ◇	1 ◇	1 ◇	1	1	1	1 ◇	1 ◇	1	1	1 ◇	1 ◇	1	1		1 ◇	1 ◇	1	1	1	1 ◇	1 ◇	1	1
				E	G		H						G	E												
			⊠	⊠	⊠				⊠	⊠			⊠	⊠				⊠	⊠				⊠	⊠		
London Euston 15 ⊖	d	06 24	06 35	06 44	06 46	06 37		07 04	07 08	07 13		07 21	07 40	07 40	07 14	07 34		07 46	08 05	07 49	07 54	08 04	08 10	08 17		08 25
Brighton 10	d						05 22																			
Haywards Heath 3	d						05 36																			
Gatwick Airport 10 ✈	d						05 53																			
East Croydon 🚌	d						06 10																			
Clapham Junction 10	d						06 30				06 49														07 57	
Imperial Wharf §	d																									
West Brompton ⊖	d						06 35				06 54														08 02	
Kensington Olympia ⊖	d						06 39				06 57														08 05	
Shepherds Bush §	d																									
Wembley Central	d						06 57				07 17														08 21	
Harrow & Wealdstone ⊖	d	06 36					07 02	07 16			07 22					07 46						08 16			08 26	
Bushey	d																					08 21				
Watford Junction	a	06 43				06 53	07 09	07 23			07 30				07 31	07 53				08 05	08 10	08 24			08 33	
	d	06 43	06u50			06 54		07 23	07u23	07u28					07 31	07 53		08u01		08 06	08 11	08 25	08u25	08u32		
Kings Langley	d	06 48						07 28								07 58						08 29				
Apsley	d	06 51						07 31								08 01						08 33				
Hemel Hempstead	a	06 54				07 01		07 34							07 39	08 04					08 18	08 36				
	d	06 54				07 01		07 34							07 39	08 04					08 18	08 36				
Berkhamsted	d	06 59				07 06		07 39							07 43	08 09					08 23	08 40				
Tring	d	07a07				07 13		07a47							07 50	08a17					08 30	08a47				
Cheddington	d					07 18															08 35					
Leighton Buzzard	d					07 23									07 58					08 23	08 40					
Bletchley	d					07 30									08 06					08 32	08 47					
Milton Keynes Central 10	a		07 10	07 14	07 16	07 36				07 47		08 01	08 10	08 10	08 11				08 35	08 37	08 53					09 05
	d		07 10	07 15	07 17	07 36				07 48			08 10	08 10	08 12					08 37	08 53					09 06
Wolverton	d					07 40									08 15					08 41	08 57					
Northampton	a					07 53									08 30					08 55	09 10					09 21
Rugby	a			07 37	07 39													08 39								
	d																									
Nuneaton	a									08 22														09 21		
Coventry	a		07 44						08 12				08 45	08 45									09 13			
Birmingham International ✈	a		07 57						08 27				08 57	08 57									09 26			
Birmingham New Street 12	a		08 09						08 41				09 09	09 10									09 41			
Sandwell & Dudley	a		08 22										09 22	09 22												
Wolverhampton 7 🚌	a		08 36										09 36	09 36												

For general notes see front of timetable
For details of catering facilities see Directory of Train Operators

§ It is unknown, at the time of going to press, when this station will open. For further details contact National Rail Enquiries 08457 484950 or see local publicity.

A Until 14 July
B From 15 September
C 21 July to 8 September
E 28 July to 22 August

G Until 25 July and from 25 August
H Also stops at Selhurst 0613
b Previous night.
Stops to pick up only

London → Watford Junction, Milton Keynes, Northampton and West Midlands

Network Diagram - See first page of Table 59

		VT	LM	LM	SN	LM	VT	VT	LM	LM	VT	LM	VT	VT	VT	LM	LM	SN	LM	VT	LM	LM	VT	VT	LM	VT
		1◇	1	1	1	1	1◇	1◇	1	1	1◇	1	1◇	1◇	1◇	1	1	1	1	1◇	1	1	1◇	1◇	1	1◇
		⊠					⊠	⊠			⊠		⊠	⊠	⊠					⊠			⊠	⊠		☕
London Euston 15 ⊖	d	08 40	08 24	08 34		08 50	09 00	09 17	08 54	09 04	09 10	09 22	09 38	09 40	09 46	09 24	09 34		09 51	10 05	09 54	10 04	10 10	10 15	10 22	10 40
Brighton 10	d																									
Haywards Heath 3	d																									
Gatwick Airport 10 ✈	d																									
East Croydon	d																									
Clapham Junction 10	d				08 24													09 27								
Imperial Wharf §	d																									
West Brompton ⊖	d				08 29													09 32								
Kensington Olympia ⊖	d				08 32													09 35								
Shepherds Bush §	d																									
Wembley Central	d				08 48													09 53								
Harrow & Wealdstone ⊖	d			08 46	08 53					09 16							09 46	09 58				10 16				
Bushey	d			08 51						09 21							09 51					10 21				
Watford Junction	a		08 40	08 54	09 00				09 10	09 24						09 40	09 54	10 05			10 10	10 24				
	d		08 41	08 55					09 11	09 25	09u25					09 41	09 55				10 11	10 25	10u25	10u30		
Kings Langley	d			08 59						09 29							09 59					10 29				
Apsley	d			09 03						09 33							10 03					10 33				
Hemel Hempstead	a		08 48	09 06					09 18	09 36						09 48	10 06				10 18	10 36				
	d		08 48	09 06					09 18	09 36						09 48	10 06				10 18	10 36				
Berkhamsted	d		08 53	09 10					09 23	09 40						09 53	10 10				10 23	10 40				
Tring	d			09a18					09 30	09a48							10a17				10 30	10a48				
Cheddington	d								09 35												10 35					
Leighton Buzzard	d		09 06			09 23			09 40							10 06			10 20		10 40					
Bletchley	d		09 13			09 31			09 47							10 13			10 28		10 47					
Milton Keynes Central 10	a	09 10	09 19			09 36		09 47	09 53			10 00		10 11	10 16	10 19			10 33	10 35	10 53				10 59	11 10
	d	09 10	09 19			09 37		09 48				10 00		10 12	10 17	10 19			10 33						10 59	11 10
Wolverton	d		09 23			09 40										10 23			10 37							
Northampton	a		09 36			09 55						10 16	10 24			10 36			10 51						11 15	
Rugby	a						09 49						10 46		10 39											
	d												10 47													
Nuneaton	a							10 22					10 58											11 20		
Coventry	a	09 44									10 13			10 45									11 13			11 44
Birmingham International ✈	a	09 57									10 26			10 57									11 26			11 57
Birmingham New Street 12	a	10 09									10 41			11 09									11 41			12 09
Sandwell & Dudley	a	10 22												11 22												12 22
Wolverhampton 7	a	10 36												11 36												12 36

		LM	SN	LM	VT	LM		LM	VT	LM	LM	VT	LM	VT	VT	LM	SN	LM	VT	LM	LM	LM	VT	VT	LM	VT
		1	1	1	1◇	1		1	1◇	1	1	1◇	1	1◇	1◇	1	1	1	1◇	1	1	1	1◇	1◇	1	1◇
						A		B																		
					⊠				☕			☕		☕	☕				☕				☕	☕		☕
London Euston 15 ⊖	d	10 24		10 34	10 46	10 53		10 53	11 17	10 54	11 04	11 10	11 22	11 40	11 46	11 24		11 34	12 05	11 53	11 54	12 04	12 10	12 17	12 22	12 40
Brighton 10	d																09 55									
Haywards Heath 3	d																10 16									
Gatwick Airport 10 ✈	d		09 37														10 37									
East Croydon	d		09 52														10 52									
Clapham Junction 10	d		10 03														11 03									
Imperial Wharf §	d																									
West Brompton ⊖	d		10 09														11 09									
Kensington Olympia ⊖	d		10 12														11 12									
Shepherds Bush §	d																									
Wembley Central	d																									
Harrow & Wealdstone ⊖	d		10 29	10 46							11 16						11 29	11 46				12 16				
Bushey	d			10 51							11 21							11 51				12 21				
Watford Junction	a	10 40	10 45	10 54						11 10	11 24					11 40	11 45	11 54			12 10	12 24				
	d	10 41		10 55	11u01					11 11	11 25	11u25				11 41		11 55			12 11	12 25	12u25	12u32		
Kings Langley	d			10 59							11 29							11 59				12 29				
Apsley	d			11 03							11 33							12 03				12 33				
Hemel Hempstead	a	10 48		11 06						11 18	11 36					11 48		12 06			12 18	12 36				
	d	10 48		11 06						11 18	11 36					11 48		12 06			12 18	12 36				
Berkhamsted	d	10 53		11 10						11 23	11 40					11 53		12 10			12 23	12 40				
Tring	d			11a18						11 30	11a48							12a18			12 30	12a48				
Cheddington	d									11 35											12 35					
Leighton Buzzard	d	11 06				11 22		11 22		11 40						12 06				12 24	12 40					
Bletchley	d	11 13				11 30		11 30		11 47						12 13				12 32	12 47					
Milton Keynes Central 10	a	11 19				11 35		11 35	11 47	11 53			12 01	12 10	12 16	12 19			12 35	12 37	12 53				13 00	13 10
	d	11 19				11 35		11 35	11 48				12 02	12 10	12 17	12 19				12 37					13 00	13 10
Wolverton	d	11 23				11 39		11 39								12 23				12 41						
Northampton	a	11 36				11 53		11 53					12 17			12 36				12 55					13 16	
Rugby	a				11 39	12 18		12 20							12 39											
	d					12 18		12 20																		
Nuneaton	a								12 22															13 22		
Coventry	a					12 32		12 32				12 14		12 44									13 13			13 44
Birmingham International ✈	a					12 50		12 50				12 26		12 57									13 26			13 57
Birmingham New Street 12	a					13 06		13 06				12 41		13 09									13 41			14 09
Sandwell & Dudley	a													13 22												14 22
Wolverhampton 7	a													13 36												14 36

For general notes see front of timetable
For details of catering facilities see Directory of Train Operators

§ It is unknown, at the time of going to press, when this station will open. For further details contact National Rail Enquiries 08457 484950 or see local publicity.

A 28 July to 22 August
B Until 25 July and from 25 August

London → Watford Junction, Milton Keynes, Northampton and West Midlands

Network Diagram - See first page of Table 59

	VT	LM	SN	LM	LM	LM	LM	VT	LM	LM	VT	LM	VT	LM	SN	LM	VT	VT		LM	LM	LM	VT FX	VT	VT FO
	1 ◇	1	1	1	1	1	1	1 ◇	1	1	1 ◇	1	1 ◇	1	1	1	1 ◇	1 ◇		1	1	1	1 ◇	1 ◇	1 ◇
						A	B																C	A	D
	☕				🛒			☕			☕		☕				☕	☕					☕	☕	☕
London Euston 15 ⊖ d	12 46	12 24		12 34	12 49	12 53	12 53	13 17	12 54	13 04	13 10	13 22	13 40	13 24		13 34	13 46	14 05		13 53	13 54	14 04	14 10	14 10	14 10
Brighton 10 d			10 55												11 55										
Haywards Heath 3 d			11 16												12 16										
Gatwick Airport 10 ✈ d			11 37												12 37										
East Croydon d			11 52												12 52										
Clapham Junction 10 d			12 03												13 03										
Imperial Wharf § d																									
West Brompton ⊖ d			12 09												13 09										
Kensington Olympia ⊖ d			12 12												13 12										
Shepherds Bush § d																									
Wembley Central d																									
Harrow & Wealdstone ⊖ d			12 29	12 46						13 16					13 29	13 46						14 16			
Bushey d				12 51						13 21						13 51						14 21			
Watford Junction a		12 40	12 45	12 54					13 10	13 24				13 40	13 45	13 54					14 10	14 24			
d		12 41		12 55					13 11	13 25	13u25			13 41		13 55	14u01				14 11	14 25	14u25	14u25	14u25
Kings Langley d				12 59						13 29						13 59						14 29			
Apsley d				13 03						13 33						14 03						14 33			
Hemel Hempstead a		12 48		13 06					13 18	13 36				13 48		14 06					14 18	14 36			
d		12 48		13 06					13 18	13 36				13 48		14 06					14 18	14 36			
Berkhamsted d		12 53		13 10					13 23	13 40				13 53		14 10					14 23	14 40			
Tring d				13a18					13 30	13a48						14a18					14 30	14a48			
Cheddington d									13 35												14 35				
Leighton Buzzard d		13 06				13 22	13 22		13 40					14 06						14 24	14 40				
Bletchley d		13 13				13 30	13 30		13 47					14 13						14 32	14 47				
Milton Keynes Central 10 a	13 16	13 19				13 35	13 35	13 47	13 53			14 01	14 10	14 19				14 35		14 37	14 53				
d	13 17	13 19				13 35	13 35	13 48				14 02	14 10	14 19						14 37					
Wolverton d		13 23				13 39	13 39							14 23						14 41					
Northampton a		13 36				13 53	13 53					14 18		14 36						14 57					
Rugby a	13 39				13 46	14 18	14 20										14 39								15 03
d					13 47	14 18	14 20																		15 04
Nuneaton a					14 01			14 22																	
Coventry a						14 32	14 32				14 13		14 44										15 13	15 13	15 14
Birmingham International ✈ a						14 50	14 50				14 27		14 57										15 26	15 27	15 27
Birmingham New Street 12 a						15 06	15 06				14 41		15 09										15 41	15 41	15 41
Sandwell & Dudley a													15 22												
Wolverhampton 7 a													15 36												

	VT	LM	VT	VT	LM	SN	LM	LM	VT	LM	LM	VT	VT FO	LM	VT	LM	SN	LM	VT	LM	LM	LM	VT	VT	LM
	1 ◇	1	1 ◇	1 ◇	1	1	1	1	1 ◇	1	1	1 ◇	1 ◇	1	1 ◇	1	1	1	1 ◇	1	1	1	1 ◇	1 ◇	1
												E	D												
	☕		☕	☕					⊠			☕	☕		☕				☕				☕	☕	
London Euston 15 ⊖ d	14 17	14 22	14 40	14 46	14 24		14 34	14 53	15 17	14 54	15 04	15 10	15 10	15 26	15 40	15 24		15 34	15 49	15 53	15 54	16 04	16 10	16 17	16 22
Brighton 10 d						12 55											13 55								
Haywards Heath 3 d						13 16											14 16								
Gatwick Airport 10 ✈ d						13 37											14 37								
East Croydon d						13 52											14 52								
Clapham Junction 10 d						14 03											15 03								
Imperial Wharf § d																									
West Brompton ⊖ d						14 09											15 09								
Kensington Olympia ⊖ d						14 12											15 12								
Shepherds Bush § d																									
Wembley Central d																									
Harrow & Wealdstone ⊖ d						14 29	14 46				15 16						15 29	15 46				16 16			
Bushey d							14 51				15 21							15 51				16 21			
Watford Junction a					14 40	14 45	14 54			15 10	15 24					15 40	15 45	15 54			16 10	16 24			
d	14u32				14 41		14 55			15 11	15 25	15u25	15u25			15 41		15 55			16 11	16 25	16u25	16u32	
Kings Langley d							14 59				15 29							15 59				16 29			
Apsley d							15 03				15 33							16 03				16 33			
Hemel Hempstead a					14 48		15 06			15 18	15 36					15 48		16 06			16 18	16 36			
d					14 48		15 06			15 18	15 36					15 48		16 06			16 18	16 36			
Berkhamsted d					14 53		15 10			15 23	15 40					15 53		16 10			16 23	16 40			
Tring d							15a18			15 30	15a48							16a18			16 30	16a50			
Cheddington d										15 35											16 35				
Leighton Buzzard d					15 06			15 22		15 40						16 06				16 24	16 40				16 55
Bletchley d					15 13			15 30		15 47						16 13				16 32	16 47				17 04
Milton Keynes Central 10 a		15 01	15 10		15 19			15 35	15 47	15 53				16 03	16 10	16 19				16 37	16 53				17 09
d		15 02	15 10	15u17	15 19			15 35	15 48					16 03	16 10	16 19				16 37					17 09
Wolverton d					15 23			15 39								16 23				16 41					17 13
Northampton a		15 18			15 36			15 53						16 19		16 36				16 55					17 27
Rugby a				15 39				16 20					16 03						16 40						
d								16 20					16 04												
Nuneaton a	15 22								16 22															17 22	
Coventry a			15 44					16 32				16 13	16 14		16 44								17 13		
Birmingham International ✈ a			15 57					16 50				16 26	16 27		16 57								17 26		
Birmingham New Street 12 a			16 09					17 06				16 41	16 41		17 09								17 41		
Sandwell & Dudley a			16 22												17 22										
Wolverhampton 7 a			16 36												17 36										

For general notes see front of timetable
For details of catering facilities see Directory of Train Operators

§ It is unknown, at the time of going to press, when this station will open. For further details contact National Rail Enquiries 08457 484950 or see local publicity.

A 28 July to 22 August
B Until 25 July and from 25 August
C Until 24 July and from 25 August
D Until 25 July and from 29 August
E All Mondays to Thursdays, also Fridays 1 to 22 August

London → Watford Junction, Milton Keynes, Northampton and West Midlands

Network Diagram - See first page of Table 59

	VT	LM	SN	LM	VT	LM	VT	LM		LM	LM	LM	VT	VT	LM	LM	SN	VT	VT	VT	LM	LM	LM	LM	LM
	1 ◇	1	1	1	1 ◇	1	1 ◇	1		1	1	1	1 ◇	1 ◇	1	1	1	1 ◇	1 ◇	1 ◇	1	1	1	1	1
					A		B	A		B			A	C											
	☕				☕		☕						☕	⊠				☕	⊠	☕					
London Euston 15 ⊖ d	16 40	16 24		16 34	16 51	16 54	17 02	16 55		16 55	17 04	17 09	17 10	17 21	17 23	17 24		17 30	17 45	17 50	17 34	17 40	17 55	17 54	18 04
Brighton 10 d			14 55														15 55								
Haywards Heath 3 d			15 16														16 16								
Gatwick Airport 10 ✈ d			15 37														16 37								
East Croydon d			15 52														16 52								
Clapham Junction 10 d			16 03														17 03								
Imperial Wharf § d																									
West Brompton ⊖ d			16 09														17 09								
Kensington Olympia ⊖ d			16 12														17 12								
Shepherds Bush § d																									
Wembley Central d			16 26														17 26								
Harrow & Wealdstone ⊖ d			16 31	16 46							17 16					17 36	17 31					17 52			18 16
Bushey d				16 51								17 25										17 57			
Watford Junction a		16 41	16 45	16 54		17 10					17 23	17 28				17 43	17 45				17 50	18 00		18 10	18 23
d		16 42		16 55		17 11					17 23	17 28				17 43					17 51	18 01		18 11	18 23
Kings Langley d				16 59								17 33									17 55				
Apsley d				17 03								17 36									17 59				
Hemel Hempstead a		16 49		17 06		17 18						17 39				17 51					18 02			18 18	
d		16 49		17 06		17 18						17 39				17 51					18 02			18 18	
Berkhamsted d		16 54		17 10		17 23						17 44				17 55						18 11		18 23	
Tring d		17 01		17a20		17a33					17 38	17a54									18 11	18a21			18 38
Cheddington d		17 06									17 43										18 16				18 43
Leighton Buzzard d		17 11						17 27		17 27	17 48				17 57						18 21		18 28		18 48
Bletchley d		17 18									17 55					18 14					18 28			18 41	18 56
Milton Keynes Central 10 a		17 25						17 38		17 38	18 02				18 08	18 20					18 35		18 39	18 46	19 02
d	17u10							17 39		17 39					18 09	18 20				18u25			18 40	18 47	
Wolverton d								17 42		17 42					18 14								18 45	18 50	
Northampton a								17 57		17 57					18 28	18 36							18 59	19 04	
Rugby a					17 47		17 53	18 26		18 26				18 10					18 34						
d					17 47		17 55	18 26		18 26				18 10											
Nuneaton a														18 24											
Coventry a	17 44				18 01		18 08	18 41		18 44			18 14					18 32		18 58					
Birmingham International ✈ a	17 56				18 12		18 20						18 26					18 44		19 10					
Birmingham New Street 12 a	18 09				18 29		18 32						18 39					18 57		19 27					
Sandwell & Dudley a	18 22						18 53						18 53					19 22							
Wolverhampton 7 a	18 36						19 06						19 06					19 36							

	VT	VT	VT	VT	LM	LM	VT	LM	SN	LM	LM	VT	LM	LM	LM	LM	VT	VT	LM	VT	VT		LM	SN	LM
		R																							
	1 ◇	1	1 ◇	1 ◇	1	1	1 ◇	1	1	1	1	1 ◇	1	1	1	1	1 ◇	1 ◇	1	1 ◇	1 ◇		1	1	1
			A	B									B	A											
	⊠	⊠	☕	☕			☕					☕					☕	☕		☕	☕				
London Euston 15 ⊖ d	18 05	18 08	18 10	18 10	18 09	18 23	18 40	18 24		18 34	18 40	18 57	18 48	18 49	18 54	19 04	19 10	19 17	19 22	19 40	19 46		19 24		19 34
Brighton 10 d									16 55															17 55	
Haywards Heath 3 d									17 21															18 22	
Gatwick Airport 10 ✈ d									17 37															18 37	
East Croydon d									17 52															18 52	
Clapham Junction 10 d									18 04															19 03	
Imperial Wharf § d																									
West Brompton ⊖ d									18 09															19 08	
Kensington Olympia ⊖ d									18 12															19 11	
Shepherds Bush § d																									
Wembley Central d									18 28															19 26	
Harrow & Wealdstone ⊖ d								18 37	18 33	18 47					19 06	19 16								19 31	19 46
Bushey d					18 25						18 56					19 21									19 51
Watford Junction a					18 28			18 44	18 45	18 54	18 59				19 13	19 24							19 42	19 45	19 54
d			18u25	18u25	18 28			18 44		18 54	18 59				19 13	19 25	19u25	19u32					19 43		19 55
Kings Langley d					18 33						19 04					19 29									19 59
Apsley d					18 36						19 07					19 33									20 03
Hemel Hempstead a					18 39			18 52			19 10				19 21	19 36							19 50		20 06
d					18 39			18 52			19 10				19 21	19 36							19 50		20 06
Berkhamsted d					18 44					19 03	19 15				19 25	19 40							19 55		20 10
Tring d					18a54					19 11	19a25				19 32	19 47							20 02		20a18
Cheddington d										19 17						19 52							20 07		
Leighton Buzzard d						18 58				19 25			19 21	19 21	19 40	20 00			19 55				20 12		
Bletchley d								19 12		19a34					19 48	20a08			20 03				20 20		
Milton Keynes Central 10 a						19 08		19 17					19 32	19 32	19 54				20 08	20 11	20 18		20 25		
d						19 09	19u10	19 18					19 33	19 33					20 09	20 12	20 18				
Wolverton d						19 13		19 21					19 36	19 36					20 12						
Northampton a						19 28		19 35					19 51	19 51					20 27						
Rugby a		18 56										19 47	20 17	20 20							20 41				
d												19 47	20 17	20 20											
Nuneaton a	19 05																	20 21							
Coventry a			19 14	19 18			19 44					20 00	20 32	20 32			20 14			20 45					
Birmingham International ✈ a			19 26	19 30			19 57					20 12	20 50	20 50			20 26			20 57					
Birmingham New Street 12 a			19 39	19 43			20 09					20 26	21 08	21 08			20 39			21 09					
Sandwell & Dudley a			19 59	19 59			20 22										20 52			21 22					
Wolverhampton 7 a			20 13	20 13			20 36										21 06			21 36					

For general notes see front of timetable
For details of catering facilities see Directory of Train Operators

§ It is unknown, at the time of going to press, when this station will open. For further details contact National Rail Enquiries 08457 484950 or see local publicity.

A Until 25 July and from 25 August
B 28 July to 22 August
C To Holyhead (Table 81)

London → Watford Junction, Milton Keynes, Northampton and West Midlands

Network Diagram - See first page of Table 59

		LM	VT	VT	LM	LM	VT	LM	VT	LM	SN	LM	VT	LM	LM	LM	LM	VT	LM	SN	LM	VT	LM	LM	LM	VT
		1	1◇	1◇	1	1	1◇	1	1◇	1	1	1	1◇	1	1	1	1	1◇	1	1	1	1◇	1	1	1	1◇
														A	B											
			☕	☕			☕		☕				☕					☕				☕				☕
London Euston 15 ⊖	d	19 52	20 05	20 17	19 54	20 04	20 10	20 22	20 40	20 24		20 34	20 46	20 58	20 58	20 54	21 04	21 10	21 24		21 25	21 40		21 34	21 54	22 05
Brighton 10	d																									
Haywards Heath 3	d																									
Gatwick Airport 10 ✈	d										19 37									20 37						
East Croydon 🚊	d										19 52									20 52						
Clapham Junction 10	d										20 03									21 03						
Imperial Wharf §	d																									
West Brompton ⊖	d										20 09									21 09						
Kensington Olympia ⊖	d										20 12									21 12						
Shepherds Bush §	d																									
Wembley Central	d																									
Harrow & Wealdstone ⊖	d					20 16					20 30	20 46					21 16			21 29				21 46		
Bushey	d					20 21						20 51					21 21							21 51		
Watford Junction	a				20 12	20 24				20 40	20 45	20 54				21 10	21 24		21 42	21 45				21 54	22 10	
	d				20 12	20 25	20u25			20 41		20 55	21u01			21 11	21 25	21u25	21 43			21u54		21 55	22 11	22u20
Kings Langley	d					20 29						20 59					21 29							21 59		
Apsley	d					20 33						21 03					21 33							22 03		
Hemel Hempstead	a				20 20	20 36				20 48		21 06				21 18	21 36		21 50					22 06	22 18	
	d				20 20	20 36				20 48		21 06				21 18	21 36		21 50				←	22 06	22 18	
Berkhamsted	d				20 24	20 40				20 53		21 10				21 23	21 40		21 55				21 55	22 10	22 23	
Tring	d					20a48				21 00		21a18					21 46		→					→	22 28	
Cheddington	d									21 05															→	
Leighton Buzzard	d				20 38			20 50		21 10						21 37					21 59		22 06			
Bletchley	d				20 46			20 58		21 17				21 32	21 32	21 44	22a00				22 08		22 13			
Milton Keynes Central 10	a	20 31	20 35	20 47	20 52			21 03	21 10	21 23				21 37	21 37	21 50					22 13	22 14	22 22			22 39
	d	20 31		20 48				21 04	21 10					21 38	21 38	21 50					22 14	22 14	22 22			22 40
Wolverton	d	20 35						21 07						21 42	21 42	21 54					22 18		22 26			
Northampton	a	20 50						21 21						21 55	21 55	22 08					22 37		22 44			
Rugby	a												21 38	22 18	22 22							22 57				23 19
	d													22 18	22 22							22 58				23 21
Nuneaton	a			21 22														22 15								23 33
Coventry	a						21 13		21 44					22 32	22 32							23 10				
Birmingham International ✈	a						21 26		21 57					22 50	22 50							23 27				
Birmingham New Street 12	a						21 39		22 09					23 08	23 08							23 39				
Sandwell & Dudley	a						21 59		22 22													23 52				
Wolverhampton 7 🚊	a						22 13		22 36													00 05				

		LM	LM	LM	LM	SN	LM	VT	VT	VT	VT	VT	VT	LM	LM	LM	VT	VT	LM	SN	VT	VT	VT	LM
								FO	FX	FX	FO	FO	FX				FO	FO			FX	FX	FO	
		1	1	1	1	1	1	1◇	1◇	1◇	1◇	1◇	1◇	1	1	1	1◇	1◇	1	1	1◇	1◇	1◇	1
								C	D	E	G	H	J				K	L			D	N	Q	
								☕	☕	☕	☕	☕	☕				☕	☕			☕	☕	☕	
London Euston 15 ⊖	d		22 04		22 24		22 34	22 40	22 40	22 40	22 40	22 40	22 40			22 54	23 40	23 40	23 24		23 40	23 40	23 40	23 34
Brighton 10	d																							
Haywards Heath 3	d																							
Gatwick Airport 10 ✈	d					21 37														22 37				
East Croydon 🚊	d					21 52														22 52				
Clapham Junction 10	d					22 03														23 03				
Imperial Wharf §	d																							
West Brompton ⊖	d					22 09														23 09				
Kensington Olympia ⊖	d					22 12														23 12				
Shepherds Bush §	d																							
Wembley Central	d																							
Harrow & Wealdstone ⊖	d		22 16			22 29	22 46													23 28				23 46
Bushey	d		22 21				22 51																	23 51
Watford Junction	a		22 27		22 42	22 45	22 54									23 10			23 41	23 45				23 54
	d				22 43		22 55	22u56	22u57	22u57	22u57	22u57	22u57			23 11			23 42					23 55
Kings Langley	d						22 59																	23 59
Apsley	d						23 03																	00 03
Hemel Hempstead	a				22 50		23 06									23 18			23 49					00 06
	d	←			22 50		23 06							←	←	23 18			23 49					00 06
Berkhamsted	d	22 10		←	22 55		23 10							22 55	23 10	23 23			23 54					00 10
Tring	d	22 15		22 28	→		→								23 15	23 28								00 15
Cheddington	d	22 20													23 20									00 20
Leighton Buzzard	d	22 25		22 36										23 06	23 25	23 36			00 05					00 25
Bletchley	d	22 33		22 43										23 13	23 33	23 43			00 12					00 33
Milton Keynes Central 10	a	22 43		22 54				23 19	23 20	23 20	23 20	23 20	23 23	23 24	23 43	23 54	00 16	00 16	00 20		00 23	00 23	00 25	00 43
	d			22 54				23 20	23 20	23 20	23 21	23 21	23 24	23 24		23 54	00 18	00 18	00 20		00 24	00 24	00 26	
Wolverton	d			22 58										23 28		23 58			00 24					
Northampton	a			23 15				23s33	23s34	23s34	23s34	23s34	23s38	23 44		00 14	00s33	00s33	00 42		00s50	00s50	00s46	
Rugby	a							00s18	00s17	00s18	00s17	00s19	00s23				01s20	01s20			01s19	01s20	01s23	
	d																							
Nuneaton	a																	01s37						
Coventry	a							00s32	00s31	00s30	00s32	00s32	00s35				01s33				01s33	01s33	01s35	
Birmingham International ✈	a							00s47	00s42	00s42	00s47	00s47	00s47				01s46				01s46	01s46	01s48	
Birmingham New Street 12	a							01s01	00s59	00s59	01s01	01s01	01s01				01s57	02s25			01s58	01s58	02s00	
Sandwell & Dudley	a																							
Wolverhampton 7 🚊	a							01 33	01 33	01 33	01 33	01 33	01 34				02 31	03 00			02 32	02 32	02 34	

For general notes see front of timetable
For details of catering facilities see Directory of Train Operators

§ It is unknown, at the time of going to press, when this station will open. For further details contact National Rail Enquiries 08457 484950 or see local publicity.

A 28 July to 22 August
B Until 25 July and from 25 August
C 1 to 22 August
D 28 July to 21 August
E Until 24 July
G Until 25 July
H From 29 August
J From 25 August
K From 12 September
L 18 July to 5 September
N Until 24 July and from 25 August
Q Until 11 July

Table 66

Saturdays

until 12 July

London → Watford Junction, Milton Keynes, Northampton and West Midlands

Network Diagram - See first page of Table 59

	LM 1	VT 1◇ ☕	LM 1	LM 1	LM 1	LM 1	LM 1	LM 1	VT 1◇ ☕	VT 1◇ ⊠	VT 1◇ ☕	LM 1	VT 1◇ ⊠	VT 1◇ ☕	SN 1	LM 1	VT 1◇ ⊠		LM 1	SN 1	VT 1◇ ☕	VT 1◇ ☕	VT 1◇ ☕	LM 1	LM 1
London Euston 15 ⊖ d	23p24	23p40	23p34	00 04	00 34	02 00		05 34	06 00	06 05	06 16	06 30	06 37	06 40			07 19		07 04		07 24	07 36	07 42	07 24	07 34
Brighton 10 d															05 21					05 56					
Haywards Heath 3 d															05 34					06 22					
Gatwick Airport 10 ✈ d															05 52					06 37					
East Croydon 🚌 d															06 10					06 53					
Clapham Junction 10 d															06 23					07 03					
Imperial Wharf § d																									
West Brompton ⊖ d															06 29					07 09					
Kensington Olympia ⊖ d															06 32					07 12					
Shepherds Bush § d																									
Wembley Central d					00 45	02 11																			
Harrow & Wealdstone ⊖ d			23p46	00 16	00 50	02 16		05 46				06 42			06 56				07 16	07 29					07 46
Bushey d			23p51		00 55							06 47							07 21						07 51
Watford Junction a	23p41		23p54	00 23	00 58	02 22		05 53				06 50			07 04				07 24	07 36				07 40	07 54
d	23p42		23p55	00 23	00 58	02 23		05 53		06u26		06 51	06u55	07u01					07 25		07u40			07 41	07 55
Kings Langley d			23p59		01 03			05 58				06 55							07 29						07 59
Apsley d			00 03		01 06			06 01				06 59							07 33						08 03
Hemel Hempstead a	23p49		00 06	00 31	01 09	02 30		06 04				07 02							07 36					07 48	08 06
d	23p49		00 06	00 31	01 09	02 30		06 04				07 02				←			07 36					07 48	08 06
Berkhamsted d	23p54		00 10	00 35	01 14	02 35		06 09				07 06 →				07 06			07 40					07 53	08 10
Tring d			00 15	00 40	01 19	02 40		06 14								07 13			07 47					08 00	08a18
Cheddington d			00 20		01 24			06 19								07 18								08 05	
Leighton Buzzard d	00 05		00 25	00 48	01 29	02 48		06 24								07 23			07 55					08 10	
Bletchley d	00 12		00 33	00 56	01 36	02 55	05 25	06 31								07 31			08 04					08 18	
Milton Keynes Central 10 a	00 20	00 25	00 43	01 04	01 45	03 06	05 29	06 40	06 44	06 53	06 59			07 30		07 36	07 52		08 08			08 13	08 18	08 23	
d	00 20	00 26		01 05	01 45		05 30	06 40		06 54	07 00			07 32		07 37	07 54		08 09				08 19		
Wolverton d	00 24			01 08	01 49		05 33	06 44								07 40			08 12						
Northampton a	00 42	00s46		01 27	02 09		05 49	07 03								07 58			08 30						
Rugby a		01s23									07 40										08 43		08 56		
d																							08 58		
Nuneaton a														08 23											
Coventry a		01s35								07 44			08 11				08 44						09 09		
Birmingham International ✈ a		01s48								07 57			08 27				08 57						09 21		
Birmingham New Street 12 a		02s00								08 09			08 40				09 09						09 36		
Sandwell & Dudley a										08 21													09 51		
Wolverhampton 7 🚌 a		02 34								08 35															

	VT 1◇ ☕	VT 1◇ ⊠	LM 1	LM 1	SN 1	LM 1	VT 1◇ ☕	VT 1◇ ☕	LM 1	VT 1◇ ☕	LM 1	LM 1		SN 1	VT 1◇ ⊠	VT 1◇ ☕	VT 1◇ ☕	LM 1	VT 1◇ ⊠	LM 1	VT 1◇ ☕	VT 1◇ ☕	LM 1	LM 1	SN 1
London Euston 15 ⊖ d	07 55	08 07	07 54	08 04		08 24	08 32	08 37	08 34	08 57	08 54	09 04			09 19	09 31	09 34	09 24	09 37	09 34	09 55	10 06	09 54	10 04	
Brighton 10 d					06 55									07 55											08 55
Haywards Heath 3 d					07 16									08 16											09 16
Gatwick Airport 10 ✈ d					07 37									08 37											09 37
East Croydon 🚌 d					07 52									08 52											09 52
Clapham Junction 10 d					08 03									09 03											10 03
Imperial Wharf § d																									
West Brompton ⊖ d					08 09									09 09											10 09
Kensington Olympia ⊖ d					08 12									09 12											10 12
Shepherds Bush § d																									
Wembley Central d																									
Harrow & Wealdstone ⊖ d				08 16	08 29				08 46			09 16		09 29						09 46				10 16	10 29
Bushey d				08 21					08 51			09 21								09 51				10 21	
Watford Junction a			08 10	08 24	08 37	08 40			08 54		09 10	09 24		09 36				09 40		09 54			10 10	10 24	10 35
d	08u11		08 11	08 25		08 41	08u48	08u52	08 55		09 11	09 25						09 41	09u52	09 55	10u10		10 11	10 25	
Kings Langley d				08 29					08 59			09 29								09 59				10 29	
Apsley d				08 33					09 03			09 33								10 03				10 33	
Hemel Hempstead a			08 18	08 36		08 48			09 06		09 18	09 36						09 48		10 06			10 18	10 36	
d			08 18	08 36		08 48			09 06		09 18	09 36						09 48		10 06			10 18	10 36	
Berkhamsted d			08 23	08 40		08 53			09 10		09 23	09 40						09 53		10 10			10 23	10 40	
Tring d				08a48		09 00			09a18			09a48						10 00		10a18				10a48	
Cheddington d						09 05												10 05							
Leighton Buzzard d			08 35			09 10					09 36							10 10					10 36		
Bletchley d			08 45			09 17					09 43							10 17					10 43		
Milton Keynes Central 10 a		08 42	08 51			09 23				09 29	09 49				09 53	10 05	10 13	10 23				10 41	10 49		
d		08 44	08 51			09 23				09 31	09 49				09 55		10 14	10 23				10 43	10 49		
Wolverton d			08 55			09 27					09 53							10 27					10 53		
Northampton a			09 10			09 44					10 10							10 44					11 10		
Rugby a							09 56			10 10							10 56				11 10				
d							09 58			10 12							10 57				11 12				
Nuneaton a	09 24																								
Coventry a		09 40					10 09	10 15		10 23					10 44		11 09		11 15		11 23	11 40			
Birmingham International ✈ a		09 55					10 21	10 27		10 38					10 57		11 21		11 27		11 38	11 55			
Birmingham New Street 12 a		10 11					10 36	10s39							11 09		11 36		11s39			12 11			
Sandwell & Dudley a							10 51										11 51								
Wolverhampton 7 🚌 a																									

For general notes see front of timetable
For details of catering facilities see
Directory of Train Operators

§ It is unknown, at the time of going to press, when this station will open. For further details contact National Rail Enquiries 08457 484950 or see local publicity.

Saturdays

until 12 July

London → Watford Junction, Milton Keynes, Northampton and West Midlands

Network Diagram - See first page of Table 59

		LM	LM	VT	VT	LM	VT	LM		LM	SN	VT	LM	VT	VT	LM	VT	LM	VT	LM	LM	SN	VT	LM	LM	VT
		1	1	1 ◇ ☕	1 ◇ ☕	1	1 ◇ ☕	1		1	1	1 ◇ ☕	1	1 ◇ ☕	1 ◇ ☕	1	1 ◇ ☕	1	1 ◇ ☕	1	1	1	1 ◇ ☕	1	1	1 ◇ ☕
London Euston [15] ⊖	d	10 20	10 24	10 33	10 38	10 34	10 57	10 54		11 04		11 17	11 20	11 29	11 33	11 24	11 38	11 34	11 55	11 54	12 04		12 17	12 20	12 24	12 33
Brighton [10]	d										09 55											10 55				
Haywards Heath [3]	d										10 16											11 16				
Gatwick Airport [10] ✈	d										10 37											11 37				
East Croydon 🚌	d										10 52											11 52				
Clapham Junction [10]	d										11 03											12 03				
Imperial Wharf §	d																									
West Brompton ⊖	d										11 09											12 09				
Kensington Olympia ⊖	d										11 12											12 12				
Shepherds Bush §	d																									
Wembley Central	d																									
Harrow & Wealdstone ⊖	d					10 46				11 16	11 29							11 46			12 16	12 29				
Bushey	d					10 51				11 21								11 51			12 21					
Watford Junction	a		10 40			10 54		11 10		11 24	11 36					11 40		11 54		12 10	12 24	12 36			12 40	
	d		10 41	10u48	10u53	10 55		11 11		11 25						11 41	11u53	11 55	12u10	12 11	12 25				12 41	12u48
Kings Langley	d					10 59				11 29								11 59			12 29					
Apsley	d					11 03				11 33								12 03			12 33					
Hemel Hempstead	a		10 48			11 06		11 18		11 36						11 48		12 06		12 18	12 36				12 48	
	d		10 48			11 06		11 18		11 36						11 48		12 06		12 18	12 36				12 48	
Berkhamsted	d		10 53			11 10		11 23		11 40						11 53		12 10		12 23	12 40				12 53	
Tring	d		11 00			11a18				11a48						12 00		12a18			12a48				13 00	
Cheddington	d		11 05													12 05									13 05	
Leighton Buzzard	d	10 51	11 10					11 36					11 51			12 10				12 36				12 49	13 10	
Bletchley	d	10 58	11 17					11 43					11 58			12 20				12 43				12 56	13 20	
Milton Keynes Central [10]	a	11 04	11 23				11 30	11 49				11 54	12 04	12 08	12 14	12 24				12 49			12 56	13 01	13 24	
	d	11 04					11 32	11 49				11 56	12 04		12 16					12 49			12 58	13 01		
Wolverton	d	11 08						11 53					12 08							12 53				13 05		
Northampton	a	11 25						12 10					12 25							13 10				13 22		
Rugby	a			11 56			12 10								12 56				13 10							13 56
	d			11 58			12 12								12 57				13 12							13 58
Nuneaton	a																									
Coventry	a			12 09	12 15							12 44			13 09		13 15		13 23				13 40			14 09
Birmingham International ✈	a			12 21	12 27		12 38					12 57			13 21		13 27		13 38				13 55			14 21
Birmingham New Street [12]	a			12 36	12s39							13 09			13 36		13s39						14 09			14 36
Sandwell & Dudley	a			12 51											13 51											14 51
Wolverhampton [7] 🚌	a																									

		VT	LM		VT	LM	LM	SN	VT	LM	VT	VT	LM	VT	LM	LM	VT	LM	SN	VT	LM		LM	VT	VT	LM
		1 ◇ ☕	1		1 ◇ ☕	1	1	1	1 ◇ ☕	1	1 ◇ ☕	1 ◇ ☕	1	1 ◇ ☕	1	1	1 ◇ ☕	1	1	1 ◇ ☕	1		1	1 ◇ ☕	1 ◇ ☕	1
London Euston [15] ⊖	d	12 38	12 34		12 56	12 54	13 04		13 17	13 20	13 29	13 33	13 24	13 38	13 34	13 54	13 56	14 04		14 17	14 20		14 24	14 33	14 38	14 34
Brighton [10]	d							11 55											12 55							
Haywards Heath [3]	d							12 16											13 16							
Gatwick Airport [10] ✈	d							12 37											13 37							
East Croydon 🚌	d							12 52											13 52							
Clapham Junction [10]	d							13 03											14 03							
Imperial Wharf §	d																									
West Brompton ⊖	d							13 09											14 09							
Kensington Olympia ⊖	d							13 12											14 12							
Shepherds Bush §	d																									
Wembley Central	d																									
Harrow & Wealdstone ⊖	d		12 46				13 16	13 29							13 46			14 16	14 29							14 46
Bushey	d		12 51				13 21								13 51			14 21								14 51
Watford Junction	a		12 54			13 10	13 24	13 37					13 40		13 54	14 10		14 24	14 37				14 40			14 54
	d	12u53	12 55			13 11	13 25						13 41	13u53	13 55	14 11	14u11	14 25					14 41	14u48	14u53	14 55
Kings Langley	d		12 59				13 29								13 59			14 29								14 59
Apsley	d		13 03				13 33								14 03			14 33								15 03
Hemel Hempstead	a		13 06			13 18	13 36						13 48		14 06	14 18		14 36					14 48			15 06
	d		13 06			13 18	13 36						13 48		14 06	14 18		14 36					14 48			15 06
Berkhamsted	d		13 10			13 23	13 40						13 53		14 10	14 23		14 40					14 53			15 10
Tring	d		13a18				13a48						14 00		14a18			14a48					15 00			15a18
Cheddington	d												14 05										15 05			
Leighton Buzzard	d					13 36				13 49			14 10			14 36					14 49		15 10			
Bletchley	d					13 43				13 56			14 20			14 43					14 56		15 20			
Milton Keynes Central [10]	a				13 29	13 49			13 54	14 01	14 07	14 12	14 24			14 49				14 53	15 01		15 24			
	d				13 30	13 49			13 55	14 01		14 14				14 49				14 55	15 01					
Wolverton	d					13 53				14 05						14 53					15 05					
Northampton	a					14 10				14 22						15 10					15 22					
Rugby	a				14 10							14 56					15 10							15 56		
	d				14 11							14 57					15 12							15 58		
Nuneaton	a																									
Coventry	a	14 15							14 41			15 09		15 15			15 23			15 44				16 09	16 15	
Birmingham International ✈	a	14 27			14 38				14 55			15 21		15 27			15 38			15 57				16 21	16 27	
Birmingham New Street [12]	a	14s39							15 11			15 36		15s39						16 09				16 36	16s39	
Sandwell & Dudley	a											15 51												16 51		
Wolverhampton [7] 🚌	a																									

For general notes see front of timetable
For details of catering facilities see
Directory of Train Operators

§ It is unknown, at the time of going to press, when this station will open. For further details contact National Rail Enquiries 08457 484950 or see local publicity.

Saturdays

until 12 July

London → Watford Junction, Milton Keynes, Northampton and West Midlands

Network Diagram - See first page of Table 59

		VT 1◇ ☕	LM 1	LM 1	SN 1	VT 1◇ ☕	LM 1	VT 1◇ ☕	VT 1◇ ☕	LM 1	VT 1◇ ☕	LM 1	LM 1	VT 1◇ ☕	LM 1	SN 1		VT 1◇ ☕	LM 1	LM 1	VT 1◇ ☕	VT 1◇ ☕	LM 1	VT 1◇ ☕	LM 1	LM 1
London Euston 15 ⊖	d	14 56	14 54	15 04		15 17	15 20	15 29	15 33	15 24	15 38	15 34	15 54	15 56	16 04			16 17	16 20	16 24	16 33	16 38	16 34	16 56	16 54	17 04
Brighton 10	d				13 55											14 55										
Haywards Heath 3	d				14 16											15 16										
Gatwick Airport 10 ✈	d				14 37											15 37										
East Croydon 🚢	d				14 52											15 52										
Clapham Junction 10	d				15 03											16 03										
Imperial Wharf §	d																									
West Brompton ⊖	d				15 09											16 09										
Kensington Olympia ⊖	d				15 12											16 12										
Shepherds Bush §	d																									
Wembley Central	d																									
Harrow & Wealdstone ⊖	d			15 16	15 29							15 46			16 16	16 29							16 46			17 16
Bushey	d			15 21								15 51			16 21								16 51			17 21
Watford Junction	a		15 10	15 24	15 37					15 40		15 54	16 10		16 24	16 37				16 40			16 54		17 10	17 24
	d		15 11	15 25						15 41	15u53	15 55	16 11	16u11	16 25					16 41	16u49	16u53	16 55		17 11	17 25
Kings Langley	d			15 29								15 59			16 29								16 59			17 29
Apsley	d			15 33								16 03			16 33								17 03			17 33
Hemel Hempstead	a		15 18	15 36						15 48		16 06	16 18		16 36					16 48			17 06		17 18	17 36
	d		15 18	15 36						15 48		16 06	16 18		16 36					16 48			17 06		17 18	17 36
Berkhamsted	d		15 23	15 40						15 53		16 10	16 23		16 40					16 53			17 10		17 23	17 40
Tring	d			15a48						16 00		16a18			16a48					17 00			17a18			17a48
Cheddington	d									16 05										17 05						
Leighton Buzzard	d		15 36				15 49			16 10			16 36						16 49	17 10					17 36	
Bletchley	d		15 43				15 56			16 17			16 43						16 56	17 20					17 43	
Milton Keynes Central 10	a	15 29	15 49			15 54	16 01	16 05	16 11	16 23			16 49					16 55	17 01	17 24				17 30	17 49	
	d	15 31	15 49			15 56	16 01		16 13				16 49					16 56	17 01					17 32	17 49	
Wolverton	d		15 53				16 05						16 53						17 05						17 53	
Northampton	a		16 10				16 22						17 10						17 22						18 10	
Rugby	a	16 10							16 56					17 10							17 56			18 10		
	d	16 12							16 57					17 12							17 58			18 12		
Nuneaton	a																									
Coventry	a					16 41			17 09		17 15			17 23				17 41			18 09	18 15				
Birmingham International ✈	a	16 38				16 55			17 21		17 27			17 38				17 55			18 21	18 27		18 39		
Birmingham New Street 12	a					17 11			17 36		17s39							18 11			18 36	18s39				
Sandwell & Dudley	a								17 51												18 51					
Wolverhampton 7 🚢	a																									

		SN 1	VT 1◇ ☕	LM 1	VT 1◇ ☕	VT 1◇ ☕	LM 1	VT 1◇ ☕	LM 1	LM 1	VT 1◇ ☕		LM 1	SN 1	VT 1◇ ☕	LM 1	LM 1	VT 1◇ ☕	VT 1◇ ☕	LM 1	LM 1	LM 1	VT 1◇ ☕	LM 1	LM 1	SN 1
London Euston 15 ⊖	d		17 17	17 20	17 29	17 32	17 24	17 37	17 34	17 54	17 56		18 04		18 17	18 20	18 24	18 33	18 38		18 34	18 50	18 56	18 54	19 04	
Brighton 10	d	15 55												16 55												17 55
Haywards Heath 3	d	16 16												17 16												18 16
Gatwick Airport 10 ✈	d	16 37												17 37												18 37
East Croydon 🚢	d	16 52												17 52												18 52
Clapham Junction 10	d	17 03												18 03												19 03
Imperial Wharf §	d																									
West Brompton ⊖	d	17 09												18 09												19 09
Kensington Olympia ⊖	d	17 12												18 12												19 12
Shepherds Bush §	d																									
Wembley Central	d																									
Harrow & Wealdstone ⊖	d	17 29							17 46				18 16	18 29							18 46				19 16	19 29
Bushey	d								17 51				18 21								18 51				19 21	
Watford Junction	a	17 36					17 40		17 54	18 10			18 24	18 37			18 40				18 54			19 10	19 24	19 37
	d						17 41	17u52	17 55	18 11	18u11		18 25				18 41	18u48	18u53		18 55		19u11	19 11	19 25	
Kings Langley	d								17 59				18 29								18 59				19 29	
Apsley	d								18 03				18 33								19 03				19 33	
Hemel Hempstead	a						17 48		18 06	18 18			18 36				18 48				19 06			19 18	19 36	
	d						17 48		18 06	18 18			18 36				18 48				19 06			19 18	19 36	
Berkhamsted	d						17 53		18 10	18 23			18 40				18 53			←	19 10			19 23	19 40	
Tring	d						18 00		18a18				18a48				19 00 →			19 00	19a18				19a48	
Cheddington	d						18 05													19 05						
Leighton Buzzard	d			17 49			18 10			18 36						18 49				19 10		19 19		19 36		
Bletchley	d			17 56			18 18			18 43						18 56				19 20		19 26		19 43		
Milton Keynes Central 10	a		17 54	18 01	18 06	18 12	18 24			18 49					18 56	19 01		19 10	19 17	19 24		19 31	19 36	19 49		
	d		17 56	18 01		18 13				18 49					18 57	19 01		19 11	19 19			19 31	19 38	19 49		
Wolverton	d			18 05						18 53						19 05						19 35		19 53		
Northampton	a			18 22						19 10						19 22						19 48		20 10		
Rugby	a										19 11												20 15			
	d																						20 17			
Nuneaton	a																									
Coventry	a		18 41			19 06		19 15							19 41			20 09	20 15				20 28			
Birmingham International ✈	a		18 55					19 27							19 55				20 27							
Birmingham New Street 12	a		19 11					19 39							20 11				20s39							
Sandwell & Dudley	a																									
Wolverhampton 7 🚢	a							20 07																		

For general notes see front of timetable
For details of catering facilities see Directory of Train Operators

§ It is unknown, at the time of going to press, when this station will open. For further details contact National Rail Enquiries 08457 484950 or see local publicity.

Table 66

Saturdays

until 12 July

London → Watford Junction, Milton Keynes, Northampton and West Midlands

Network Diagram - See first page of Table 59

		VT	VT	LM	VT	LM		LM	VT	LM	VT	SN	LM	LM	LM	VT	SN	LM	VT	LM	SN	LM	LM	LM
		1 ◇	1 ◇	1	1 ◇	1		1	1 ◇	1	1 ◇	1	1	1	1	1 ◇	1	1	1 ◇	1	1	1	1	1
		🍴	🍴		🍴				🍴		🍴					🍴			🍴					
London Euston 15 ⊖	d	19 21	19 26	19 24	19 34	19 34		19 54	20 00	20 04	20 14		20 24	20 48	21 04	21 25		21 34	21 50	21 54		22 34	23 04	23 45
Brighton 10	d											18 55												
Haywards Heath 3	d											19 16												
Gatwick Airport 10 ✈	d											19 37					20 37				21 37			
East Croydon	d											19 52					20 52				21 52			
Clapham Junction 10	d											20 03					21 03				22 03			
Imperial Wharf §	d																							
West Brompton ⊖	d											20 09					21 09				22 09			
Kensington Olympia ⊖	d											20 12					21 12				22 12			
Shepherds Bush §	d																							
Wembley Central	d																							
Harrow & Wealdstone ⊖	d					19 46				20 16		20 29		21 00			21 29			22 06	22 29		23 16	23 57
Bushey	d					19 51																		
Watford Junction	a			19 40		19 56		20 10		20 23		20 37	20 40	21 07	21 20		21 46	21 50		22 13	22 46	22 50	23 23	00 04
	d		19u41	19 41	19u52	19 57		20 11	20u16	20 23	20u31		20 41	21 07	21 21	21u39		21 51	22u07	22 13		22 51	23 25	00 04
Kings Langley	d					20 01				20 28				21 12						22 18			23 29	00 09
Apsley	d					20 05				20 31				21 15						22 21			23 33	00 12
Hemel Hempstead	a			19 48		20 08		20 18		20 34			20 48	21 18	21 28			21 58		22 24		22 58	23 36	00 15
	d			19 48		20 08		20 18		20 34			20 48	21 18	21 28			21 58		22 24		22 58	23 36	00 15
Berkhamsted	d			19 53		20 12		20 23		20 39			20 53	21 23	21 33			22 03		22 29		23 03	23 40	00 20
Tring	d					20 17				20 44				21 28						22 34			23 47	00 27
Cheddington	d					20 22				20 53				21 37						22 39			23 52	00 32
Leighton Buzzard	d			20 06		20 29		20 38		20 58			21 08	21 42				22 18		22 48		23 18	23 57	00 37
Bletchley	d			20 13		20a37		20 45		21a05			21 16	21 49	21a56			22 25		22a55		23 25	00 05	00 44
Milton Keynes Central 10	a	19 54	20 13	20 22	20 34			20 54	21 00		21 15		21 24	21 58		22 13		22 34	22 55			23 34	00 10	00 50
	d		20 15	20 22	20 36			20 54	21 01		21 16		21 25	21 58		22 14		22 34	22 57			23 34	00 11	00 50
Wolverton	d			20 26				20 58					21 28	22 02				22 38				23 38	00 14	00 54
Northampton	a			20 42				21 14					21 45	22 18				22 54				23 54	00 28	01 07
Rugby	a				21 14				21 40		21 55					22 54								
	d				21 16						21 56					22 55								
Nuneaton	a																							
Coventry	a		21 13		21 27						22 07					23 06			23s47					
Birmingham International ✈	a		21 26								22 25					23 18			23s59					
Birmingham New Street 12	a		21 39								22 39					23 33			00s13					
Sandwell & Dudley	a		21 59								22 56													
Wolverhampton 7	a		22 13								23 11					23 58			00 47					

Saturdays

19 July to 6 September

		VT	VT	VT	VT	LM	LM	LM	LM	LM	LM	LM	VT	VT	VT		LM	SN	LM	VT	SN	LM	LM	VT	LM	LM
		1 ◇	1 ◇	1 ◇	1 ◇	1	1	1	1	1	1	1	1 ◇	1 ◇	1 ◇		1	1	1	1 ◇	1	1	1	1 ◇	1	1
		A	B	C																						
		🍴	🍴	🍴	🍴								🍴	🍴	🍴					🍴				🍴		
London Euston 15 ⊖	d	22p40	22p40	22p40	23p40	23p24	23p34	00 04	00 34	02 00		05 34	06 00	06 05	06 21		06 34		07 00	07 09			07 20	07 28		07 30
Brighton 10	d	≀	≀	≀														05 21			05 56					
Haywards Heath 3	d	≀	≀	≀														05 34			06 22					
Gatwick Airport 10 ✈	d	≀	≀	≀														05 52			06 37					
East Croydon	d	≀	≀	≀														06 10			06 53					
Clapham Junction 10	d	≀	≀	≀														06 23			07 03					
Imperial Wharf §	d	≀	≀	≀																						
West Brompton ⊖	d	≀	≀	≀														06 29			07 09					
Kensington Olympia ⊖	d	≀	≀	≀														06 32			07 12					
Shepherds Bush §	d	≀	≀	≀																						
Wembley Central	d	≀	≀	≀					00 45	02 11																
Harrow & Wealdstone ⊖	d	≀	≀	≀			23p46	00 16	00 50	02 16		05 46					06 46	06 56	07 17		07 29					07 47
Bushey	d	≀	≀	≀			23p51		00 55								06 51									
Watford Junction	a	≀	≀	≀		23p41	23p54	00 23	00 58	02 22		05 53					06 54	07 04	07 24		07 36		07 42			07 54
	d	22b56	22b57	22b57		23p42	23p55	00 23	00 58	02 23		05 53		06u20			06 55		07 25	07u28			07 42	07u49		07 55
Kings Langley	d	≀	≀	≀			23p59		01 03			05 58					06 59		07 29							07 59
Apsley	d	≀	≀	≀			00 03		01 06			06 01					07 03		07 33							08 03
Hemel Hempstead	a	≀	≀	≀		23p49	00 06	00 31	01 09	02 30		06 04					07 06		07 36				07 50			08 06
	d	≀	≀	≀		23p49	00 06	00 31	01 09	02 30		06 04					07 06		07 36			←	07 50			08 06
Berkhamsted	d	≀	≀	≀		23p54	00 10	00 35	01 14	02 35		06 09					07 10		07 40			07 40	07 54		←	08 10
Tring	d	≀	≀	≀			00 15	00 40	01 19	02 40		06 14					07 17		→			07 47	08 01		08 01	08a18
Cheddington	d	≀	≀	≀			00 20		01 24			06 19					07 22						→		08 06	
Leighton Buzzard	d	≀	≀	≀		00 05	00 25	00 48	01 29	02 48		06 24					07 27					07 55			08 11	
Bletchley	d	≀	≀	≀		00 12	00 33	00 56	01 36	02 55	05 25	06 31					07 35					08 03			08 19	
Milton Keynes Central 10	a	23p19	23p20	23p20	00 16	00 20	00 43	01 04	01 45	03 06	05 29	06 40	06 44	06 50	07 03		07 40			07 47		08 08		08 08	08 24	
	d	23p20	23p21	23p21	00 18	00 20		01 05	01 45		05 30	06 40		06 52			07 41			07 49		08 09		08 09		
Wolverton	d	≀	≀	≀		00 24		01 08	01 49		05 33	06 44					07 44					08 12				
Northampton	a	23c33	23c34	23c34	00s33	00 42		01 27	02 09		05 49	07 03					08 00					08 26				
Rugby	a	00s18	00s17	00s19	01s20									07 33										08 33		
	d	≀	≀	≀										07 35										08 35		
Nuneaton	a	≀	≀	≀	01s37									07s48						08 23				08s50		
Coventry	a	00s32	00s32	00s32																						
Birmingham International ✈	a	00s47	00s47	00s47																						
Birmingham New Street 12	a	01s01	01s01	01s01	02s25									08 38										09 38		
Sandwell & Dudley	a	≀	≀	≀										08 51										09 51		
Wolverhampton 7	a	01 33	01 33	01 33	03 00									09 07										10 07		

For general notes see front of timetable
For details of catering facilities see Directory of Train Operators

§ It is unknown, at the time of going to press, when this station will open. For further details contact National Rail Enquiries 08457 484950 or see local publicity.

A 2 to 23 August
B 19 and 26 July
C 30 August and 6 September

b Previous night. Stops to pick up only
c Previous night. Stops to set down only

Due to Engineering Operations, services from Saturday 13 September on this Table had not been confirmed at time of going to press. These services will be issued in a special Supplement as soon as exact timings have been confirmed

Saturdays

London → Watford Junction, Milton Keynes Northampton and West Midlands

19 July to 6 September

Network Diagram - See first page of Table 59

		VT 1◇ ☕	LM 1	LM 1	VT 1◇ ☕	SN 1	LM 1		VT 1◇ ☕	LM 1	VT 1◇ ☕	LM 1	LM 1	LM 1	SN 1	VT 1◇ ☕	LM 1	VT 1◇ ☕	LM 1	LM 1	VT 1◇ ☕	LM 1		LM 1	VT 1◇ ☕	SN 1
London Euston 15 ⊖	d	07 54	07 48	08 00	08 12		08 20		08 27	08 30	08 42		08 48	09 00		09 15	09 20	09 28		09 30	09 55	09 48		10 00	10 12	
Brighton 10	d					06 55									07 55											08 55
Haywards Heath 3	d					07 16									08 16											09 16
Gatwick Airport 10 ✈	d					07 37									08 37											09 37
East Croydon	d					07 52									08 52											09 52
Clapham Junction 10	d					08 03									09 03											10 03
Imperial Wharf §	d																									
West Brompton ⊖	d					08 09									09 09											10 09
Kensington Olympia ⊖	d					08 12									09 12											10 12
Shepherds Bush §	d																									
Wembley Central	d																									
Harrow & Wealdstone ⊖	d			08 17		08 29				08 47				09 17	09 29					09 47				10 17		10 29
Bushey	d																									
Watford Junction	a		08 10	08 24		08 37	08 42			08 54			09 10	09 24	09 36		09 42			09 54		10 10		10 24		10 35
	d		08 11	08 25	08u34		08 42		08u50	08 55			09 11	09 25			09 42	09u50		09 55		10 10		10 25	10u32	
Kings Langley	d			08 29						08 59				09 29						09 59				10 29		
Apsley	d			08 33						09 03				09 33						10 03				10 33		
Hemel Hempstead	a		08 18	08 36			08 50			09 06			09 18	09 36			09 50			10 06		10 18		10 36		
	d		08 18	08 36			08 50			09 06			09 18	09 36			09 50			10 06		10 18		10 36		
Berkhamsted	d		08 23	08 40			08 54			09 10		←	09 23	09 40			09 54		←	10 10		10 22		10 40		
Tring	d			08a48			09 01 →			09a18		09 01		09a48			10 01 →		10 01	10a18				10a48		
Cheddington	d											09 06							10 06							
Leighton Buzzard	d		08 36									09 11	09 36						10 11			10 35				
Bletchley	d		08 43									09 19	09 43						10 19			10 43				
Milton Keynes Central 10	a	08 30	08 49						09 09		09 19	09 24	09 49			09 49		10 09	10 24		10 30	10 48				
	d		08 49						09 10		09 21	09 25	09 49			09 50		10 10	10 25			10 49				
Wolverton	d		08 53									09 28	09 53						10 28			10 52				
Northampton	a		09 07									09 42	10 07						10 42			11 07				
Rugby	a								09 33		09 44							10 34								
	d								09 35									10 36								
Nuneaton	a				09 24				09s50							10 24		10s48							11 24	
Coventry	a																									
Birmingham International ✈	a																									
Birmingham New Street 12	a								10 38									11 38								
Sandwell & Dudley	a								10 51									11 50								
Wolverhampton 7	a								11 07									12 07								

		LM 1	LM 1	VT 1◇ ☕	LM 1	VT 1◇ ☕	LM 1	LM 1	LM 1	SN 1	VT 1◇ ☕	LM 1	LM 1	VT 1◇ ☕		LM 1	LM 1	VT 1◇ ☕	LM 1	LM 1	VT 1◇ ☕	SN 1	LM 1	LM 1	VT 1◇ ☕	LM 1
London Euston 15 ⊖	d	10 16	10 20	10 28	10 30	10 45		10 48	11 00		11 12	11 16	11 20	11 28			11 30	11 55	11 48	12 00	12 12		12 16	12 20	12 28	12 30
Brighton 10	d									09 55												10 55				
Haywards Heath 3	d									10 16												11 16				
Gatwick Airport 10 ✈	d									10 37												11 37				
East Croydon	d									10 52												11 52				
Clapham Junction 10	d									11 03												12 03				
Imperial Wharf §	d																									
West Brompton ⊖	d									11 09												12 09				
Kensington Olympia ⊖	d									11 12												12 12				
Shepherds Bush §	d																									
Wembley Central	d																									
Harrow & Wealdstone ⊖	d				10 46				11 16	11 29							11 47			12 16		12 29				12 47
Bushey	d																									
Watford Junction	a		10 42		10 54			11 10	11 24	11 36			11 42				11 54		12 10	12 24		12 36		12 42		12 54
	d		10 42	10u50	10 55			11 10	11 25				11 42	11u50			11 55		12 10	12 25	12u31			12 42	12u50	12 55
Kings Langley	d				10 59				11 29								11 59			12 29						12 59
Apsley	d				11 03				11 33								12 03			12 33						13 03
Hemel Hempstead	a		10 50		11 06			11 18	11 36				11 50				12 06		12 18	12 36				12 50		13 06
	d		10 50		11 06			11 18	11 36				11 50				12 06		12 18	12 36				12 50		13 06
Berkhamsted	d		10 54		11 10		←	11 22	11 40				11 54			←	12 10		12 22	12 40				12 54		13 10
Tring	d		11 01 →		11a18		11 01		11a48				12 01 →			12 01	12a18			12a48				13 01 →		13a18
Cheddington	d						11 06									12 06										
Leighton Buzzard	d	10 51					11 11	11 35				11 51				12 11			12 35				12 51			
Bletchley	d	10 58					11 19	11 43				11 58				12 19			12 43				12 58			
Milton Keynes Central 10	a	11 04		11 09		11 20	11 24	11 48			11 49	12 04		12 09		12 24		12 29	12 48				13 03		13 09	
	d	11 04		11 10		11 22		11 49			11 50	12 04		12 10					12 49				13 04		13 10	
Wolverton	d	11 08						11 52				12 08							12 52				13 08			
Northampton	a	11 21						12 07				12 21							13 07				13 20			
Rugby	a			11 33		11 45								12 32											13 32	
	d			11 35										12 33											13 33	
Nuneaton	a			11s50							12 24			12s48							13 24				13s48	
Coventry	a																									
Birmingham International ✈	a																									
Birmingham New Street 12	a			12 38										13 38											14 38	
Sandwell & Dudley	a			12 50										13 51											14 51	
Wolverhampton 7	a			13 07										14 07											15 07	

For general notes see front of timetable
For details of catering facilities see
Directory of Train Operators

§ It is unknown, at the time of going to press, when this station will open. For further details contact National Rail Enquiries 08457 484950 or see local publicity.

Due to Engineering Operations, services from Saturday 13 September on this Table had not been confirmed at time of going to press. These services will be issued in a special Supplement as soon as exact timings have been confirmed

Table 66

Saturdays

19 July to 6 September

London → Watford Junction, Milton Keynes Northampton and West Midlands

Network Diagram - See first page of Table 59

		VT	LM	LM	LM	SN	VT	LM	LM	VT	LM	LM	VT	LM	LM	VT	SN	LM	LM	VT	LM	VT	LM	LM
London Euston 15 ⊖	d	12 45		12 48	13 00		13 12	13 16	13 20	13 28		13 30	13 55	13 48	14 00	14 12		14 16	14 20	14 28	14 30	14 45		14 48
Brighton 10	d					11 55											12 55							
Haywards Heath 3	d					12 16											13 16							
Gatwick Airport 10 ✈	d					12 37											13 37							
East Croydon	d					12 52											13 52							
Clapham Junction 10	d					13 03											14 03							
Imperial Wharf §	d																							
West Brompton ⊖	d					13 09											14 09							
Kensington Olympia ⊖	d					13 12											14 12							
Shepherds Bush §	d																							
Wembley Central	d																							
Harrow & Wealdstone ⊖	d				13 17	13 29						13 47			14 17		14 29				14 47			
Bushey	d																							
Watford Junction	a			13 10	13 24	13 37			13 42			13 54		14 10	14 24		14 37		14 42		14 54			15 10
	d			13 10	13 25				13 42	13u50		13 55		14 10	14 25	14u31			14 42	14u50	14 55			15 11
Kings Langley	d				13 29							13 59			14 29						14 59			
Apsley	d				13 33							14 03			14 33						15 03			
Hemel Hempstead	a			13 18	13 36				13 50			14 06		14 18	14 36				14 50		15 06			15 18
	d			13 18	13 36				13 50			14 06		14 18	14 36				14 50		15 06			15 18
Berkhamsted	d		←	13 22	13 40				13 54		←	14 10		14 22	14 40				14 54		15 10		←	15 23
Tring	d		13 01		13a48				14 01		14 01	14a18			14a48				15 01		15a18		15 01	
Cheddington	d		13 06						→		14 06								→				15 06	
Leighton Buzzard	d		13 11	13 35				13 51			14 11			14 35				14 51					15 11	15 36
Bletchley	d		13 19	13 43				13 58			14 19			14 43				14 58					15 19	15 43
Milton Keynes Central 10	a	13 19	13 24	13 48			13 49	14 03		14 09	14 24		14 29	14 48				15 03		15 09		15 19	15 24	15 49
	d			13 49			13 50	14 04		14 10				14 49				15 04		15 10				15 49
Wolverton	d			13 52				14 08						14 52				15 08						15 53
Northampton	a			14 07				14 20						15 07				15 20						16 07
Rugby	a									14 33										15 33				
	d									14 35										15 35				
Nuneaton	a						14 24			14s50						15 24				15s49				
Coventry	a																							
Birmingham International ✈	a																							
Birmingham New Street 12	a									15 38										16 38				
Sandwell & Dudley	a									15 50										16 51				
Wolverhampton 7	a									16 07										17 07				

		LM	SN	VT	LM	LM	VT	LM	LM	VT	LM	LM	VT	SN	LM	LM	VT	LM	VT	LM	LM	LM	SN	VT	LM
London Euston 15 ⊖	d	15 00		15 12	15 16	15 20	15 28		15 30	15 55	15 48	16 00	16 12		16 16	16 20	16 28	16 30	16 45		16 48	17 00		17 12	17 16
Brighton 10	d		13 55											14 55									15 55		
Haywards Heath 3	d		14 16											15 16									16 16		
Gatwick Airport 10 ✈	d		14 37											15 37									16 37		
East Croydon	d		14 52											15 52									16 52		
Clapham Junction 10	d		15 03											16 03									17 03		
Imperial Wharf §	d																								
West Brompton ⊖	d		15 09											16 09									17 09		
Kensington Olympia ⊖	d		15 12											16 12									17 12		
Shepherds Bush §	d																								
Wembley Central	d																								
Harrow & Wealdstone ⊖	d	15 17	15 29						15 47			16 17		16 29				16 47				17 17	17 29		
Bushey	d																								
Watford Junction	a	15 24	15 37			15 42			15 54		16 10	16 24		16 37		16 42		16 54			17 10	17 24	17 36		
	d	15 25				15 42	15u50		15 55		16 10	16 25	16u31			16 42	16u50	16 55			17 10	17 25			
Kings Langley	d	15 29							15 59			16 29						16 59				17 29			
Apsley	d	15 33							16 03			16 33						17 03				17 33			
Hemel Hempstead	a	15 36				15 50			16 06		16 18	16 36				16 50		17 06			17 18	17 36			
	d	15 36				15 50			16 06		16 18	16 36				16 50		17 06			17 18	17 36			
Berkhamsted	d	15 40				15 54		←	16 10		16 22	16 40				16 54		17 10		←	17 22	17 40			
Tring	d	15a48				16 01		16 01	16a18			16a48				17 01		17a18		17 01		17a48			
Cheddington	d					→		16 06								→				17 06					
Leighton Buzzard	d				15 51			16 11			16 35				16 51					17 11	17 35				17 51
Bletchley	d				15 58			16 19			16 43				16 58					17 19	17 43				17 58
Milton Keynes Central 10	a			15 49	16 03		16 09	16 24		16 29	16 48				17 03		17 09		17 19	17 24	17 48			17 49	18 03
	d			15 50	16 04		16 10				16 49				17 04		17 10		17 21		17 49				18 04
Wolverton	d				16 08						16 52				17 08						17 52				18 08
Northampton	a				16 20						17 07				17 20						18 06				18 20
Rugby	a						16 33										17 33		17 44						
	d						16 35										17 35								
Nuneaton	a			16 24			16s48						17 24				17s50								
Coventry	a																								
Birmingham International ✈	a																								
Birmingham New Street 12	a						17 38										18 38								
Sandwell & Dudley	a						17 51										18 51								
Wolverhampton 7	a						18 07										19 07								

For general notes see front of timetable
For details of catering facilities see
Directory of Train Operators

§ It is unknown, at the time of going to press, when this station will open. For further details contact National Rail Enquiries 08457 484950 or see local publicity.

Due to Engineering Operations, services from Saturday 13 September on this Table had not been confirmed at time of going to press. These services will be issued in a special Supplement as soon as exact timings have been confirmed

Table 66

London → Watford Junction, Milton Keynes Northampton and West Midlands

Saturdays

19 July to 6 September

Network Diagram - See first page of Table 59

Station		LM	VT ◇	LM	LM		VT ◇	LM	LM	SN	VT ◇	LM	LM	VT ◇	LM	VT R	LM	LM	LM	LM		VT ◇	SN	VT ◇	LM	VT ◇
London Euston ⊖	d	17 20	17 28		17 30		17 55	17 48	18 00		18 12	18 16	18 20	18 28	18 30	18 45		18 40	18 48	19 00		19 09		19 17	19 20	19 24
Brighton	d									16 55													17 55			
Haywards Heath	d									17 16													18 16			
Gatwick Airport	d									17 37													18 37			
East Croydon	d									17 52													18 52			
Clapham Junction	d									18 03													19 03			
Imperial Wharf §	d																									
West Brompton ⊖	d									18 09													19 09			
Kensington Olympia ⊖	d									18 12													19 12			
Shepherds Bush §	d																									
Wembley Central	d																									
Harrow & Wealdstone ⊖	d				17 47				18 17	18 29					18 47					19 16			19 29			
Bushey	d																									
Watford Junction	a	17 42			17 54			18 10	18 24	18 37			18 42		18 54				19 10	19 24			19 37		19 42	
	d	17 42	17u50		17 55			18 10	18 25				18 42	18u50	18 55				19 10	19 24		19u31		19u38	19 42	19u45
Kings Langley	d				17 59				18 29						18 59					19 29						
Apsley	d				18 03				18 33						19 03					19 32						
Hemel Hempstead	a	17 50			18 06			18 18	18 36				18 50		19 06				19 18	19 35					19 50	
	d	17 50			18 06			18 18	18 36				18 50		19 06				19 18	19 35					19 50	
Berkhamsted	d	17 54		←	18 10			18 22	18 40				18 54		19 10		←		19 22	19 40					19 54	
Tring	d	18 01		18 01	18a18				18a48				19 01		19a18		19 01			19a48					→	
Cheddington	d	→		18 06									→				19 06									
Leighton Buzzard	d			18 11				18 35				18 51					19 11	19 16	19 35							
Bletchley	d			18 19				18 43				18 58					19 19	19 24	19 43							
Milton Keynes Central	a		18 09	18 24			18 29	18 48			18 49	19 03		19 09		19 19	19 24	19 28	19 48					20 03		20 09
	d		18 10					18 49			18 50	19 04		19 10		19 21		19 29	19 49					20 05		20 11
Wolverton	d							18 52				19 08						19 33	19 52							
Northampton	a							19 07				19 20						19 45	20 07							
Rugby	a		18 33											19 33		19 44								20 30		20 35
	d		18 35											19 35												20 36
Nuneaton	a		18s50								19 24			19s50								20 23				20s49
Coventry	a																									
Birmingham International	a																									
Birmingham New Street	a		19 38											20 39												21 37
Sandwell & Dudley	a		19 50											20 51												21 51
Wolverhampton	a		20 07											21 07												22 07

Station		LM	VT ◇	LM	LM	LM	SN	LM	VT ◇	VT ◇	VT ◇	VT ◇		LM	LM	VT ◇	SN	LM	VT ◇	LM	SN	LM	LM	LM		
London Euston ⊖	d		19 27	19 30	19 48	20 00		20 20	20 23	20 30	20 36	20 40		20 43	21 00	21 04		21 30	21 36	21 49		22 28	23 00	23 40		
Brighton	d						18 55																			
Haywards Heath	d						19 16																			
Gatwick Airport	d						19 37										20 37				21 37					
East Croydon	d						19 52										20 52				21 52					
Clapham Junction	d						20 03										21 03				22 03					
Imperial Wharf §	d																									
West Brompton ⊖	d						20 09										21 09				22 09					
Kensington Olympia ⊖	d						20 12										21 12				22 12					
Shepherds Bush §	d																									
Wembley Central	d																									
Harrow & Wealdstone ⊖	d			19 47		20 16	20 29							20 59			21 29			22 05	22 29		23 17	23 56		
Bushey	d																									
Watford Junction	a			19 56	20 10	20 24	20 37	20 42						21 08	21 22		21 46	21 52		22 13	22 46	22 50	23 24	00 04		
	d		19u52	19 57	20 11	20 24		20 42	20u47	20u53	20u58	21u04		21 09	21 22	21u28		21 52	21u58	22 13		22 51	23 25	00 04		
Kings Langley	d			20 01		20 29								21 13						22 18			23 29	00 09		
Apsley	d			20 05		20 32								21 17						22 21			23 33	00 12		
Hemel Hempstead	a			20 08	20 18	20 35		20 50						21 20	21 30			22 00		22 24		22 58	23 36	00 15		
	d	←		20 08	20 18	20 35		20 50						21 20	21 30			22 00		22 24		22 58	23 36	00 15		
Berkhamsted	d	19 54		20 12	20 23	20 40		20 54						21 24	21 34			22 04		22 29		23 03	23 40	00 20		
Tring	d			20 17		20 45								21 29						22 34			23 47	00 27		
Cheddington	d			20 22		20 54								21 38						22 39			23 52	00 32		
Leighton Buzzard	d	20 07		20 29	20 38	20 59		21 09						21 43				22 19		22 48		23 18	23 57	00 37		
Bletchley	d	20 15		20a37	20 45	21a06		21 17						21 51	21a56			22 27		22a55		23 25	00 05	00 44		
Milton Keynes Central	a	20 23	20 28		20 54			21 25	21 31	21 39	21 45	21 52		21 59		22 07		22 35	22 43			23 34	00 10	00 50		
	d	20 24			20 54			21 26		21 41		21 53		22 00		22 08		22 36	22 44			23 34	00 11	00 50		
Wolverton	d	20 27			20 58			21 29						22 03				22 39				23 38	00 14	00 54		
Northampton	a	20 44			21 14			21 46						22 20				22 56				23 54	00 28	01 07		
Rugby	a									22 11						22 37			23 12							
	d									22 12						22 38			23 14							
Nuneaton	a									22s24		22 31				22s51			23s32							
Coventry	a																									
Birmingham International	a																									
Birmingham New Street	a									23 13						23 41			00 21							
Sandwell & Dudley	a									23 29																
Wolverhampton	a									23 45						00 07			00 47							

For general notes see front of timetable
For details of catering facilities see Directory of Train Operators

§ It is unknown, at the time of going to press, when this station will open. For further details contact National Rail Enquiries 08457 484950 or see local publicity.

Due to Engineering Operations, services from Saturday 13 September on this Table had not been confirmed at time of going to press. These services will be issued in a special Supplement as soon as exact timings have been confirmed

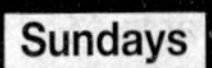

Sundays

until 13 July

London → Watford Junction, Milton Keynes Northampton and West Midlands

Network Diagram - See first page of Table 59

		LM ■1	LM ■1	LM 🚌	LM 🚌	LM 🚌	LM 🚌	LM 🚌	LM 🚌		LM 🚌	LM 🚌	LM 🚌	LM 🚌	LM 🚌	LM 🚌	VT ■1◇ ☕	VT ■1◇ ☕		LM 🚌	LM ■1	SN ■1	VT ■1◇ ☕	VT ■1◇ ☕	LM ■1	SN ■1
London Euston 15 ⊖	d	23p04	23p45			00 34			02 00					05 24	06 24	07 24	08 30	08 35			08 39		08 55	09 02	09 09	
Brighton 10	d																									
Haywards Heath 3	d																									
Gatwick Airport 10 ✈	d																									
East Croydon 🚋	d																									
Clapham Junction 10	d																					08 35				09 05
Imperial Wharf §	d																									
West Brompton ⊖	d																					08 40				09 10
Kensington Olympia ⊖	d																					08 43				09 13
Shepherds Bush §	d																									
Wembley Central	d																									
Harrow & Wealdstone ⊖	d	23p16	23p57											06 00	07 00	08 00					08 51	09 06			09 21	09 32
Bushey	d																									
Watford Junction	a	23p23	00 04			01 19			02 45					06 20	07 20	08 20					08 58	09 14			09 28	09 42
	d	23p25	00 04	01 06	01 06	01 20		02 43	02 46					06 21	07 21		08u45	08u51			08 58		09u17	09u23	09 28	
Kings Langley	d	23p29	00 09		01 22			02 59						06 37	07 37						09 03				09 33	
Apsley	d	23p33	00 12		01 33			03 10						06 48	07 48						09 06				09 36	
Hemel Hempstead	a	23p36	00 15		01 38		←	03 15			←			06 53	07 53						09 09				09 39	
	d	23p36	00 15		01 39		01 39	03 16			03 16			06 54	07 54					←	09 09				09 39	
Berkhamsted	d	23p40	00 20		→		01 50	→			03 27			07 05	08 05					08 05	09 14				09 44	
Tring	d	23p47	00 27				02 06				03 43			07 21	→					08 21	09 19					
Cheddington	d	23p52	00 32				02 27				04 04			07 42						08 42	09 24					
Leighton Buzzard	d	23p57	00 37	01 52		02 06	02 48		03 32		04 25			08 03						09 03	09 31				09 57	
Bletchley	d	00 05	00 44	02 18		02 32	03 14		03 58		04 51	06 55	07 55	08 29						09 29	09 38				10 04	
Milton Keynes Central 10	a	00 10	00 50	02 33		02 47	03 29		04 13		05 06	07 10	08 10	08 44			09 28	09 35		09 44	09 47		09 56	10 02	10 13	
	d	00 11	00 50									07 11	08 11				09 30				09 47			10 03	10 13	
Wolverton	d	00 14	00 54									07 22	08 22								09 50				10 17	
Northampton	a	00 28	01 07									07 57	08 57								10 09				10 35	
Rugby	a																10 08									
	d																10 10									
Nuneaton	a																10s23							10 53		
Coventry	a																									
Birmingham International ✈	a																									
Birmingham New Street 12	a																11 14									
Sandwell & Dudley	a																									
Wolverhampton 7 🚋	a																11 56									

		VT ■1◇ ☕	LM ■1	VT ■1◇ ☕		LM ■1	SN ■1	LM ■1	VT ■1◇ ☕	VT ■1◇ ☕	LM ■1	SN ■1	VT ■1◇ ☕		VT ■1◇ ☕	LM ■1	VT ■1◇ ☕	VT ■1◇ ☕	VT ■1◇ ☕	LM ■1	SN ■1	LM ■1		VT ■1◇ ☕	VT ■1◇ ☕	VT ■1◇ ☕
London Euston 15 ⊖	d	09 35	09 39	09 56		10 09		10 39	10 50	10 56	11 09		11 17		11 29	11 39	11 46	11 56	12 05	12 09		12 39		12 56	13 01	13 05
Brighton 10	d																									
Haywards Heath 3	d																									
Gatwick Airport 10 ✈	d																									
East Croydon 🚋	d																									
Clapham Junction 10	d						10 05					11 05									12 05					
Imperial Wharf §	d																									
West Brompton ⊖	d						10 10					11 10									12 10					
Kensington Olympia ⊖	d						10 13					11 13									12 13					
Shepherds Bush §	d																									
Wembley Central	d																									
Harrow & Wealdstone ⊖	d		09 51			10 21	10 35	10 51			11 21	11 32				11 51				12 21	12 32	12 51				
Bushey	d																									
Watford Junction	a		09 58			10 28	10 42	10 58			11 28	11 42				11 58				12 28	12 41	12 58				
	d		09 58	10u12		10 28		10 58	11u08	11u13	11 28					11 58		12u12	12u23	12 28		12 58		13u13		13u23
Kings Langley	d					10 33					11 33									12 33						
Apsley	d					10 36					11 36									12 36						
Hemel Hempstead	a		10 06			10 39		11 06			11 39					12 06				12 39		13 06				
	d		10 06			10 39		11 06			11 39					12 06				12 39		13 06				
Berkhamsted	d		10 10			10 44		11 10			11 44					12 10				12 44		13 10				
Tring	d		10 15					11 15								12 15						13 15				
Cheddington	d		10 20					11 20								12 20						13 20				
Leighton Buzzard	d		10 27			10 57		11 27			11 57					12 27				12 57		13 27				
Bletchley	d		10 35			11 04		11 35			12 04					12 35				13 04		13 35				
Milton Keynes Central 10	a	10 25	10 43	10 52		11 13		11 43	11 54	12 00	12 13		12 18		12 24	12 43	12 46	12 54	13 02	13 13		13 43		13 52	13 58	14 02
	d		10 44	10 54		11 13		11 44	11 55	12 01	12 13					12 44		12 56	13 03	13 13		13 44		13 54	14 00	14 04
Wolverton	d		10 47			11 17		11 47			12 17					12 47				13 17		13 47				
Northampton	a		11 06			11 35		12 06			12 35					13 06				13 35		14 06				
Rugby	a			11 32						12 27								13 23						14 19	14 25	
	d			11 34						12 29								13 25						14 20		
Nuneaton	a			11s46					12 34	12s42								13s38	13 45					14s31		14 42
Coventry	a																									
Birmingham International ✈	a																									
Birmingham New Street 12	a			12 35						13 36								14 23						15 23		
Sandwell & Dudley	a																									
Wolverhampton 7 🚋	a			13 11						14 12								15 01						16 03		

For general notes see front of timetable
For details of catering facilities see
Directory of Train Operators

§ It is unknown, at the time of going to press, when this station will open. For further details contact National Rail Enquiries 08457 484950 or see local publicity.

Table 66

Sundays

until 13 July

London → Watford Junction, Milton Keynes Northampton and West Midlands

Network Diagram - See first page of Table 59

	LM 1	SN 1	VT 1 ◇	LM 1	VT 1 ◇	VT 1 ◇	VT 1 ◇		LM 1	SN 1	LM 1	VT 1 ◇	VT 1 ◇	VT 1 ◇	LM 1	SN 1		VT 1 ◇	LM 1	VT 1 ◇	VT 1 ◇	VT 1 ◇	LM 1	SN 1	VT 1 ◇ A
London Euston 15 ⊖ d	13 09		13 35	13 39	13 51	13 56	14 05		14 09		14 39	14 56	15 01	15 05	15 09			15 35	15 39	15 51	15 56	16 05	16 09		16 25
Brighton 10 d																									
Haywards Heath 3 d																									
Gatwick Airport 10 ✈ d																									
East Croydon d																									
Clapham Junction 10 d		13 05								14 05						15 05								16 05	
Imperial Wharf § d																									
West Brompton ⊖ d		13 10								14 10						15 10								16 10	
Kensington Olympia ⊖ d		13 13								14 13						15 13								16 13	
Shepherds Bush § d																									
Wembley Central d																									
Harrow & Wealdstone ⊖ d	13 21	13 32		13 51					14 21	14 32	14 51				15 21	15 32			15 51				16 21	16 32	
Bushey d																									
Watford Junction a	13 28	13 42		13 58					14 28	14 42	14 58				15 28	15 42			15 58				16 28	16 42	
d	13 28			13 58		14u11			14 28		14 58	15u12		15u22	15 28				15 58		16u11		16 28		16u44
Kings Langley d	13 33								14 33						15 33								16 33		
Apsley d	13 36								14 36						15 36								16 36		
Hemel Hempstead a	13 39			14 06					14 39		15 06				15 39				16 06				16 39		
d	13 39			14 06					14 39		15 06				15 39				16 06				16 39		
Berkhamsted d	13 44			14 10					14 44		15 10				15 44				16 10				16 44		
Tring d				14 15							15 15								16 15						
Cheddington d				14 20							15 20								16 20						
Leighton Buzzard d	13 57			14 28					14 57		15 27				15 57				16 27				16 57		
Bletchley d	14 04			14 36					15 04		15 35				16 04				16 35				17 04		
Milton Keynes Central 10 a	14 13		14 23	14 43	14 48	14 54	15 04		15 13		15 43	15 52	15 58		16 13			16 23	16 43	16 48	16 54	17 04	17 13		17 18
d	14 13			14 44		14 56	15 06		15 13		15 44	15 54			16 13				16 44		16 56	17 06	17 13		17 19
Wolverton d	14 17			14 47					15 17		15 47				16 17				16 47				17 17		
Northampton a	14 35			15 06					15 35		16 06				16 35				17 06				17 35		
Rugby a						15 21						16 20									17 21				17 44
d						15 22						16 21									17 22				
Nuneaton a						15s33	15 42					16s33		16 43							17s33	17 42			
Coventry a																									
Birmingham International ✈ a																									
Birmingham New Street 12 a						16 25						17 25									18 25				
Sandwell & Dudley a																									
Wolverhampton 7 a						17 04						18 03									19 01				

	LM 1	VT 1 ◇		VT 1 ◇	VT 1 ◇	LM 1	SN 1	VT 1 ◇	LM 1	VT 1 ◇	VT 1 ◇		VT 1 ◇	LM 1	SN 1	LM 1	VT 1 ◇	VT 1 ◇ A	VT 1 ◇	LM 1		SN 1	VT 1 ◇	VT 1 ◇	LM 1
London Euston 15 ⊖ d	16 39	16 56		17 01	17 05	17 09		17 35	17 39	17 51	17 56		18 05	18 09		18 39	18 56	19 01	19 05	19 09			19 25	19 35	19 39
Brighton 10 d																									
Haywards Heath 3 d																									
Gatwick Airport 10 ✈ d																									
East Croydon d																									
Clapham Junction 10 d							17 05								18 05							19 05			
Imperial Wharf § d																									
West Brompton ⊖ d							17 10								18 10							19 10			
Kensington Olympia ⊖ d							17 13								18 13							19 13			
Shepherds Bush § d																									
Wembley Central d																									
Harrow & Wealdstone ⊖ d	16 51					17 21	17 32		17 51					18 21	18 32	18 51				19 21		19 32			19 51
Bushey d																									
Watford Junction a	16 58					17 28	17 42		17 58					18 28	18 42	18 58				19 28		19 41			19 58
d	16 58	17u12			17u22	17 28			17 58		18u11			18 28		18 58	19u12	19u18		19 28					19 58
Kings Langley d						17 33								18 33						19 33					
Apsley d						17 36								18 36						19 36					
Hemel Hempstead a	17 06					17 39			18 06					18 39		19 06				19 39					20 06
d	17 06					17 39			18 06					18 39		19 06				19 39					20 06
Berkhamsted d	17 10					17 44			18 10					18 44		19 10				19 44					20 10
Tring d	17 15								18 15							19 15									20 15
Cheddington d	17 20								18 20							19 20									20 20
Leighton Buzzard d	17 27					17 57			18 27					18 57		19 27				19 57					20 27
Bletchley d	17 35					18 04			18 35					19 04		19 35				20 04					20 35
Milton Keynes Central 10 a	17 43	17 52		17 58		18 13		18 20	18 43	18 48	18 54		19 04	19 13		19 43	19 52	19 58	20 04	20 13			20 18	20 24	20 43
d	17 44	17 54		18 00		18 13			18 44		18 56		19 06	19 13		19 44	19 54		20 05	20 13			20 19		20 44
Wolverton d	17 47					18 17			18 47					19 17		19 47				20 17					20 47
Northampton a	18 06					18 35			19 06					19 35		20 06				20 35					21 06
Rugby a		18 19		18 25							19 21						20 19						20 44		
d		18 20									19 22						20 20								
Nuneaton a		18s33			18 41						19s34		19 42				20s33		20 42						
Coventry a																									
Birmingham International ✈ a																									
Birmingham New Street 12 a		19 23									20 27						21 23								
Sandwell & Dudley a																									
Wolverhampton 7 a		20 00									21 03						22 06								

For general notes see front of timetable
For details of catering facilities see Directory of Train Operators

§ It is unknown, at the time of going to press, when this station will open. For further details contact National Rail Enquiries 08457 484950 or see local publicity.

A To Holyhead (Table 81)

Sundays until 13 July

London → Watford Junction, Milton Keynes Northampton and West Midlands

Network Diagram - See first page of Table 59

Station		VT 1 ◇	VT 1 ◇	VT 1 ◇	LM 1	SN 1	VT 1 ◇	LM 1	VT 1 ◇	VT 1 ◇	LM 1	SN 1	LM 1	VT 1 ◇	VT 1 ◇	LM 1	SN 1	LM 1	VT 1 ◇	LM 1	VT 1 ◇	LM 1
London Euston 15 ⊖	d	19 51	19 56	20 05	20 09		20 31	20 39	20 56	21 00	21 09		21 39	21 50	21 56	22 09		22 39	22 56	23 09	23 30	23 39
Brighton 10	d																					
Haywards Heath 3	d																					
Gatwick Airport 10 ✈	d																					
East Croydon	d																					
Clapham Junction 10	d					20 05						21 05					22 05					
Imperial Wharf §	d																					
West Brompton ⊖	d					20 10						21 10					22 10					
Kensington Olympia ⊖	d					20 13						21 13					22 13					
Shepherds Bush §	d																					
Wembley Central	d																					
Harrow & Wealdstone ⊖	d				20 21	20 32		20 51			21 21	21 32	21 51			22 21	22 32	22 51		23 21		23 51
Bushey	d																					
Watford Junction	a				20 28	20 42		20 58			21 28	21 42	21 58			22 28	22 42	22 58		23 28		23 58
	d		20u11	20u23	20 28		20u46	20 58	21u11	21u17	21 28		21 58	22u05	22u11	22 28		22 58	23u11	23 28		23 58
Kings Langley	d				20 33						21 33					22 33				23 33		
Apsley	d				20 36						21 36					22 36				23 36		
Hemel Hempstead	a				20 39			21 06			21 39		22 06			22 39		23 06		23 39		00 06
	d				20 39			21 06			21 39		22 06			22 39		23 06		23 39		00 06
Berkhamsted	d				20 44			21 10			21 44		22 10			22 44		23 10		23 44		00 10
Tring	d							21 15					22 15					23 15				00 15
Cheddington	d							21 20					22 20					23 20				00 20
Leighton Buzzard	d				20 57			21 27			21 57		22 27			22 57		23 27		23 57		00 27
Bletchley	d				21 04			21 35			22 04		22 35			23 04		23 35		00 04		00 35
Milton Keynes Central 10	a	20 48	20 54	21 04	21 13		21 21	21 43	21 48	21 54	22 13		22 43	22 48	22 54	23 13		23 43	23 48	00 13	00 29	00 43
	d		20 56	21 06	21 13		21 22	21 44	21 50	21 56	22 13		22 44	22 50	22 56	23 13		23 44	23 50	00 13	00 31	00 44
Wolverton	d				21 17			21 47			22 17		22 47			23 17		23 47		00 17		00 47
Northampton	a				21 38			22 06			22 35		23 06			23 35		00 06		00 35		01 06
Rugby	a		21 21				21 48		22 28					23 27	23 35				00s31		01s08	
	d		21 22						22 30						23 37							
Nuneaton	a		21s35	21 45					22s43	22 46					23s50							
Coventry	a																					
Birmingham International ✈	a																					
Birmingham New Street 12	a		22 25						23 32						00 43				01 39		02 11	
Sandwell & Dudley	a																					
Wolverhampton 7	a		23 03						00 08						01 19				02 15		02 47	

Sundays 20 July to 7 September

Station		LM 1	LM 1	LM (bus)	LM (bus)	LM (bus)	LM (bus)	LM (bus)	LM (bus)	LM (bus)	LM (bus)	LM (bus)	LM (bus)	LM (bus)	LM (bus)	VT 1 ◇	LM (bus)	LM 1	SN 1	VT 1 ◇	VT 1 ◇	LM 1	SN 1
London Euston 15 ⊖	d	23p00	23p40			00 34			02 00				05 24	06 24	07 24	08 31		08 34		08 56	09 01	09 04	
Brighton 10	d																						
Haywards Heath 3	d																						
Gatwick Airport 10 ✈	d																						
East Croydon	d																						
Clapham Junction 10	d																		08 35				09 05
Imperial Wharf §	d																						
West Brompton ⊖	d																		08 40				09 10
Kensington Olympia ⊖	d																		08 43				09 13
Shepherds Bush §	d																						
Wembley Central	d																						
Harrow & Wealdstone ⊖	d	23p17	23p56										06 00	07 00	08 00			08 50	09 06			09 20	09 32
Bushey	d																						
Watford Junction	a	23p24	00 04			01 19			02 45				06 20	07 20	08 20			08 58	09 14			09 28	09 42
	d	23p25	00 04	01 06	01 06	01 20		02 43	02 46				06 21	07 21		08u53		08 58		09u18	09u23	09 28	
Kings Langley	d	23p29	00 09		01 22			02 59					06 37	07 37				09 03				09 33	
Apsley	d	23p33	00 12		01 33			03 10					06 48	07 48				09 06				09 36	
Hemel Hempstead	a	23p36	00 15		01 38		←	03 15		←			06 53	07 53			←	09 09				09 39	
	d	23p36	00 15		01 39 →		01 39	03 16 →		03 16			06 54	07 54				09 09				09 39	
Berkhamsted	d	23p40	00 20				01 50			03 27			07 05	08 05 →			08 05	09 14				09 44	
Tring	d	23p47	00 27				02 06			03 43			07 21				08 21	09 19					
Cheddington	d	23p52	00 32				02 27			04 04			07 42				08 42	09 24					
Leighton Buzzard	d	23p57	00 37	01 52		02 06	02 48		03 32	04 25			08 03				09 03	09 31				09 57	
Bletchley	d	00 05	00 44	02 18		02 32	03 14		03 58	04 51	06 55	07 55	08 29				09 29	09 38				10 04	
Milton Keynes Central 10	a	00 10	00 50	02 33		02 47	03 29		04 13	05 06	07 10	08 10	08 44			09 41	09 44	09 47		09 52	10 05	10 13	
	d	00 11	00 50								07 11	08 11				09 42		09 47			10 06	10 13	
Wolverton	d	00 14	00 54								07 22	08 22						09 50				10 17	
Northampton	a	00 28	01 07								07 57	08 57						10 09				10 35	
Rugby	a															10 10					10 32		
	d															10 12							
Nuneaton	a															10s24							
Coventry	a																						
Birmingham International ✈	a																						
Birmingham New Street 12	a															11 13							
Sandwell & Dudley	a															11 31							
Wolverhampton 7	a															11 44							

For general notes see front of timetable
For details of catering facilities see Directory of Train Operators

§ It is unknown, at the time of going to press, when this station will open. For further details contact National Rail Enquiries 08457 484950 or see local publicity.

Due to Engineering Operations, services from Sunday 14 September on this Table had not been confirmed at time of going to press. These services will be issued in a special Supplement as soon as exact timings have been confirmed

London → Watford Junction, Milton Keynes Northampton and West Midlands

20 July to 7 September

Network Diagram - See first page of Table 59

		VT	VT	LM	VT	LM	SN	LM		VT	VT	LM	SN	VT	VT	LM		VT	VT	VT	LM	SN	LM	VT		VT
		1 ◇ ☕	1 ◇ ☕	1	1 ◇ ☕	1	1	1		1 ◇ ☕	1 ◇ ☕	1	1	1 ◇ ☕	1 ◇ ☕	1		1 ◇ ☕	1 ◇ ☕	1 ◇ ☕	1	1	1	1 ◇ ☕		1 ◇ ☕
London Euston 15 ⊖	d	09 25	09 31	09 34	09 56	10 04		10 34		10 56	11 01	11 04		11 13	11 29	11 34		11 46	11 50	12 01	12 04		12 34	12 51		12 58
Brighton 10	d																									
Haywards Heath 3	d																									
Gatwick Airport 10 ✈	d																									
East Croydon 🚌	d																									
Clapham Junction 10	d						10 05						11 05									12 05				
Imperial Wharf §	d																									
West Brompton ⊖	d						10 10						11 10									12 10				
Kensington Olympia ⊖	d						10 13						11 13									12 13				
Shepherds Bush §	d																									
Wembley Central	d																									
Harrow & Wealdstone ⊖	d			09 50		10 20	10 35	10 50				11 20	11 32			11 50					12 20	12 32	12 50			
Bushey	d																									
Watford Junction	a			09 58		10 28	10 42	10 58				11 28	11 42			11 58					12 28	12 41	12 58			
	d	09u47		09 58	10u18	10 28		10 58		11u18	11u23	11 28				11 58			12u12	12u24	12 28		12 58	13u12		
Kings Langley	d					10 33						11 33									12 33					
Apsley	d					10 36						11 36									12 36					
Hemel Hempstead	a			10 06		10 39		11 06				11 39				12 06					12 39		13 06			
	d			10 06		10 39		11 06				11 39				12 06					12 39		13 06			
Berkhamsted	d			10 10		10 44		11 10				11 44				12 10					12 44		13 10			
Tring	d			10 15				11 15								12 15							13 15			
Cheddington	d			10 20				11 20								12 20							13 20			
Leighton Buzzard	d			10 27		10 57		11 27				11 57				12 27					12 57		13 27			
Bletchley	d			10 35		11 04		11 35				12 04				12 35					13 04		13 35			
Milton Keynes Central 10	a	10 19	10 36	10 43	11 03	11 13		11 43		11 59	12 07	12 13		12 18	12 24	12 43		12 46	12 54	13 04	13 13		13 43	13 52		13 58
	d	10 21		10 44	11 04	11 13		11 44		12 00	12 08	12 13		12 19		12 44			12 56	13 05	13 13		13 44	13 53		13 59
Wolverton	d			10 47		11 17		11 47				12 17				12 47					13 17		13 47			
Northampton	a			11 06		11 35		12 06				12 35				13 06					13 35		14 06			
Rugby	a				11 31						12 35			12 44					13 21					14 18		14 24
	d				11 32						12 36								13 23					14 20		
Nuneaton	a	10 58			11s43					12 44	12s48								13s35	13 47				14s32		
Coventry	a																									
Birmingham International ✈	a																									
Birmingham New Street 12	a				12 34						13 42								14 24					15 23		
Sandwell & Dudley	a				13 01						14 01								14 50					15 50		
Wolverhampton 7 🚌	a				13 14						14 14								15 03					16 03		

		VT	LM	SN	VT	LM	VT	VT		VT	LM	SN	LM	VT	VT	VT		LM	SN	VT	LM	VT	VT	VT		LM
		1 ◇ ☕	1	1	1 ◇ ☕	1	1 ◇ ☕	1 ◇ ☕		1 ◇ ☕	1	1	1	1 ◇ ☕	1 ◇ ☕	1 ◇ ☕		1	1	1 ◇ ☕	1	1 ◇ ☕	1 ◇ ☕	1 ◇ ☕		1
London Euston 15 ⊖	d	13 01	13 04		13 29	13 34	13 46	13 51		14 01	14 04		14 34	14 51	14 58	15 01		15 04		15 29	15 34	15 46	15 51	16 13		16 04
Brighton 10	d																									
Haywards Heath 3	d																									
Gatwick Airport 10 ✈	d																									
East Croydon 🚌	d																									
Clapham Junction 10	d			13 05								14 05							15 05							
Imperial Wharf §	d																									
West Brompton ⊖	d			13 10								14 10							15 10							
Kensington Olympia ⊖	d			13 13								14 13							15 13							
Shepherds Bush §	d																									
Wembley Central	d																									
Harrow & Wealdstone ⊖	d		13 20	13 32		13 50					14 20	14 32	14 50					15 20	15 32		15 50					16 20
Bushey	d																									
Watford Junction	a		13 28	13 42		13 58					14 28	14 42	14 58					15 28	15 42		15 58					16 28
	d	13u23	13 28			13 58		14u12			14 28		14 58	15u12		15u24		15 28			15 58		16u12			16 28
Kings Langley	d		13 33								14 33							15 33								16 33
Apsley	d		13 36								14 36							15 36								16 36
Hemel Hempstead	a		13 39			14 06					14 39		15 06					15 39			16 06					16 39
	d		13 39			14 06					14 39		15 06					15 39			16 06					16 39
Berkhamsted	d		13 44			14 10					14 44		15 10					15 44			16 10					16 44
Tring	d					14 15							15 15								16 15					
Cheddington	d					14 20							15 20								16 20					
Leighton Buzzard	d		13 57			14 28					14 57		15 27					15 57			16 27					16 57
Bletchley	d		14 04			14 36					15 04		15 35					16 04			16 35					17 04
Milton Keynes Central 10	a	14 04	14 13		14 20	14 43	14 48	14 54		15 07	15 13		15 43	15 52	15 58			16 13		16 23	16 43	16 48	16 54	17 04		17 13
	d	14 06	14 13			14 44		14 55		15 08	15 13		15 44	15 54				16 13			16 44		16 55	17 05		17 13
Wolverton	d		14 17			14 47					15 17		15 47					16 17			16 47					17 17
Northampton	a		14 35			15 06					15 35		16 06					16 35			17 06					17 35
Rugby	a							15 18						16 19									17 18			
	d							15 20						16 21									17 20			
Nuneaton	a	14 42						15s32		15 46				16s32		16 44							17s32	17 43		
Coventry	a																									
Birmingham International ✈	a																									
Birmingham New Street 12	a							16 23						17 23									18 23			
Sandwell & Dudley	a							16 37						17 37									18 37			
Wolverhampton 7 🚌	a							16 50						17 50									18 50			

For general notes see front of timetable
For details of catering facilities see Directory of Train Operators

§ It is unknown, at the time of going to press, when this station will open. For further details contact National Rail Enquiries 08457 484950 or see local publicity.

Due to Engineering Operations, services from Sunday 14 September on this Table had not been confirmed at time of going to press. These services will be issued in a special Supplement as soon as exact timings have been confirmed

Table 66

Sundays

20 July to 7 September

London → Watford Junction, Milton Keynes Northampton and West Midlands

Network Diagram - See first page of Table 59

	SN	LM	VT	VT	VT	LM	SN		VT	LM	VT	VT	VT	LM	SN		LM	VT	VT	LM	SN	VT	VT		LM
	1	1	1 ◇	1 ◇	1 ◇	1	1		1 ◇	1	1 ◇	1 ◇	1 ◇	1	1		1	1 ◇	1 ◇	1	1	1 ◇	1 ◇		1
			☕	☕	☕				☕		☕	☕	☕					☕	☕			☕	☕		
London Euston 15 ⊖ d		16 34	16 51	16 58	17 01	17 04			17 29	17 34	17 45	17 51	18 01	18 04			18 34	18 51	19 01	19 04		19 24	19 31		19 34
Brighton 10 d																									
Haywards Heath 3 d																									
Gatwick Airport 10 ✈ d																									
East Croydon d																									
Clapham Junction 10 d	16 05						17 05								18 05						19 05				
Imperial Wharf § d																									
West Brompton ⊖ d	16 10						17 10								18 10						19 10				
Kensington Olympia ⊖ d	16 13						17 13								18 13						19 13				
Shepherds Bush § d																									
Wembley Central d																									
Harrow & Wealdstone ⊖ d	16 32	16 50				17 20	17 32			17 50				18 20	18 32		18 50			19 20	19 32				19 50
Bushey d																									
Watford Junction a	16 42	16 58				17 28	17 42			17 58				18 28	18 42		18 58			19 28	19 41				19 58
d		16 58	17u12		17u23	17 28				17 58		18u12		18 28			18 58	19u12		19 28					19 58
Kings Langley d						17 33								18 33						19 33					
Apsley d						17 36								18 36						19 36					
Hemel Hempstead a		17 06				17 39				18 06				18 39			19 06			19 39					20 06
d		17 06				17 39				18 06				18 39			19 06			19 39					20 06
Berkhamsted d		17 10				17 44				18 10				18 44			19 10			19 44					20 10
Tring d		17 15								18 15							19 15								20 15
Cheddington d		17 20								18 20							19 20								20 20
Leighton Buzzard d		17 27				17 57				18 27				18 57			19 27			19 57					20 27
Bletchley d		17 35				18 04				18 35				19 04			19 35			20 04					20 35
Milton Keynes Central 10 a		17 43	17 52	17 58		18 13			18 20	18 43	18 48	18 54	19 07	19 13			19 43	19 52	20 06	20 13		20 18	20 33		20 43
d		17 44	17 53	17 59		18 13				18 44		18 55	19 08	19 13			19 44	19 54	20 08	20 13		20 19			20 44
Wolverton d		17 47				18 17				18 47				19 17			19 47			20 17					20 47
Northampton a		18 06				18 35				19 06				19 35			20 06			20 35					21 06
Rugby a			18 18	18 24								19 18						20 18				20 44			
d			18 20									19 20						20 19							
Nuneaton a			18s32		18 44							19s32	19 41					20s31	20 44						
Coventry a																									
Birmingham International ✈ a																									
Birmingham New Street 12 a			19 21									20 23						21 21							
Sandwell & Dudley a			19 37									20 37						21 37							
Wolverhampton 7 a			19 50									20 50						21 50							

	VT	VT	VT	LM	SN	VT	LM		VT	VT	LM	SN	LM	VT	VT	LM	SN	LM	VT	VT	LM	VT	LM		
	1 ◇	1 ◇	1 ◇	1	1	1 ◇	1		1 ◇	1 ◇	1	1	1	1 ◇	1 ◇	1	1	1	1 ◇	1 ◇	1	1 ◇	1		
																			A	B					
	☕	☕	☕			☕			☕	☕				☕	☕				☕	☕		☕			
London Euston 15 ⊖ d	19 46	19 51	20 01	20 04		20 31	20 34		20 56	21 01	21 04		21 34	21 56	22 00	22 04		22 34	23 01	23 01	23 04	23 31	23 34		
Brighton 10 d																									
Haywards Heath 3 d																									
Gatwick Airport 10 ✈ d																									
East Croydon d																									
Clapham Junction 10 d					20 05							21 05					22 05								
Imperial Wharf § d																									
West Brompton ⊖ d					20 10							21 10					22 10								
Kensington Olympia ⊖ d					20 13							21 13					22 13								
Shepherds Bush § d																									
Wembley Central d																									
Harrow & Wealdstone ⊖ d				20 20	20 32		20 50				21 20	21 32	21 50			22 20	22 32	22 50			23 20		23 50		
Bushey d																									
Watford Junction a				20 28	20 42		20 58				21 28	21 42	21 58			22 28	22 42	22 58			23 28		23 58		
d		20u12	20u20	20 28		20u53	20 58		21u18	21u23	21 28		21 58	22u18	22u23	22 28		22 58	23u23	23u23	23 28		23 58		
Kings Langley d				20 33							21 33					22 33					23 33				
Apsley d				20 36							21 36					22 36					23 36				
Hemel Hempstead a				20 39			21 06				21 39		22 06			22 39		23 06			23 39		00 06		
d				20 39			21 06				21 39		22 06			22 39		23 06			23 39		00 06		
Berkhamsted d				20 44			21 10				21 44		22 10			22 44		23 10			23 44		00 10		
Tring d							21 15						22 15					23 15					00 15		
Cheddington d							21 20						22 20					23 20					00 20		
Leighton Buzzard d				20 57			21 27				21 57		22 27			22 57		23 27			23 57		00 27		
Bletchley d				21 04			21 35				22 04		22 35			23 04		23 35			00 04		00 35		
Milton Keynes Central 10 a	20 48	20 54	21 00	21 13		21 37	21 43		21 59	22 07	22 13		22 43	22 58	23 07	23 13		23 43	00 03	00 03	00 13	00 37	00 43		
d		20 55	21 01	21 13		21 39	21 44		22 00	22 08	22 13		22 44	22 59	23 08	23 13		23 44	00 05	00 05	00 13	00 39	00 44		
Wolverton d				21 17			21 47				22 17		22 47			23 17		23 47			00 17		00 47		
Northampton a				21 33			22 06				22 35		23 06			23 35		00 06			00 35		01 06		
Rugby a		21 18				22 10			22 35					23 25	23 35				00s30	00s31		01s07			
d		21 20							22 37						23 37										
Nuneaton a		21s32	21 39						22s49	22 52					23s50										
Coventry a																									
Birmingham International ✈ a																									
Birmingham New Street 12 a		22 22							23 38						00 43				01 39	01 39		02 11			
Sandwell & Dudley a		22 37							23 54																
Wolverhampton 7 a		22 50							00 07						01 06				02 02	02 02		02 34			

For general notes see front of timetable
For details of catering facilities see Directory of Train Operators

§ It is unknown, at the time of going to press, when this station will open. For further details contact National Rail Enquiries 08457 484950 or see local publicity.

A 27 July to 17 August

B 20 July, 24, 31 August and 7 September

Due to Engineering Operations, services from Sunday 14 September on this Table had not been confirmed at time of going to press. These services will be issued in a special Supplement as soon as exact timings have been confirmed

West Midlands, Northampton, Milton Keynes and Watford Junction → London

Network Diagram - See first page of Table 59

Miles	Miles	Miles	Station		LM	LM	LM	LM	LM	LM	LM	LM	LM	SN	LM	LM	LM	LM	LM	VT	LM	LM	LM	SN	LM
					MO	MO	MX	MO	MO			MO													
					1	1	1	1	1	1	1	1	1	1	1	1	1	1	1	1 ◇	1	1	1	1	1
					A	B		A	B		A	B													
																				☒					
0	—	—	Wolverhampton 7	d																05 05					
7½	—	—	Sandwell & Dudley	d																05 15					
12¾	—	—	**Birmingham New Street 12**	d																05 30					
21¼	—	—	Birmingham International	d																05 40					
32	—	—	Coventry	d																05 50					
—	—	—	Nuneaton	d																					
43½	0	—	**Rugby**	a																06 02					
—	—	—		d																06 04					
62¼	—	—	**Northampton**	d	22p56	22p56	23p46	23p56	23p56		04 15	04 15	04 43			05 35		05 58				06 27			
75¼	30	—	Wolverton	d	23p08	23p08	23p58	00 08	00 08		04 27	04 27	04 55			05 47		06 10				06 39			
—	—	—	**Milton Keynes Central 10**	a	23p11	23p11	00 01	00 11	00 11		04 30	04 30	04 58			05 50		06 14		06 25		06 43			
78¼	32¾	—		d	23p12	23p12	00 02	00 12	00 12	03 31	04 31	04 31	04 59		05 24	05 51		06 14	06 25	06 27		06 43			06 48
81¼	—	—	Bletchley	d	23p17	23p17	00 09	00 17	00 17	03 36	04 36	04 36	05 04		05 29	05 56	06 01		06 30				06 34		06 53
87¾	—	—	Leighton Buzzard	d	23p23	23p23	00 17	00 23	00 23	03 42	04 42	04 42	05 10		05 35	06 02	06 07	06 23				06 53	06 40		06 59
92	—	—	Cheddington	d	23p28	23p28	00 22	00 28	00 28				05 19		05 41		06 13						06 46		
96¼	—	—	Tring	d	23p37	23p37	00 27	00 37	00 37	03 54	04 54	04 54	05 24		05 47		06 19				←		06 52		07 10
100	—	—	Berkhamsted	d	23p42	23p42	00 32	00 42	00 42	03 59	04 59	04 59	05 29		05 52	06 15	06 24		06 49		06 49		06 57		07 15
—	—	—	Hemel Hempstead	a	23p46	23p46	00 36	00 46	00 46	04 03	05 03	05 03	05 33		05 56	06 20	06 28		→		06 53		07 01		07 19
103½	—	—		d	23p46	23p46	00 36	00 46	00 46	04 03	05 03	05 03	05 33		05 57	06 20	06 28				06 53		07 01		07 20
105	—	—	Apsley	d	23p49	23p49		00 49	00 49				05 36		06 00		06 31						07 04		
107	—	—	Kings Langley	d	23p53	23p53		00 53	00 53				05 40		06 04		06 35						07 08		
—	—	—	**Watford Junction**	a	23p58	23p58	00 43	00 59	00 59	04 10	05 10	05 10	05 44		06 09	06 27	06 39	06 41		06s47	07 00		07 12		07 27
110½	65	—		d	23p59	23p59	00 44	01 00	01 00	04 11	05 11	05 11	05 45	06 05	06 09	06 27	06 40	06 42			07 01		07 13	07 18	07 27
112	—	—	Bushey	d													06 43						07 16		
116½	71	—	Harrow & Wealdstone ⊖	d	00 05	00 07	00 50	01 06	01 08	04 17	05 22	05 22	05 51	06 11	06 16		06 48				07 07		07 21	07 25	07 34
119¾	—	0	Wembley Central	d			00 54			04 21														07 29	
—	—	4¼	Shepherds Bush §	a																					
—	—	5½	Kensington Olympia ⊖	a										06 30										07 43	
—	—	7½	West Brompton ⊖	a										06 33										07 45	
—	—	8	Imperial Wharf §	a																					
—	—	9	Clapham Junction 10	a										06 42										07 52	
—	—	16¾	East Croydon	a																					
—	—	33	Gatwick Airport 10	a																					
—	—	44¼	Haywards Heath 3	a																					
—	—	57¼	**Brighton 10**	a																					
128	82½	—	**London Euston 15** ⊖	a	00 24	00 32	01 09	01 24	01 33	04 43	05 38	05 46	06 08	.	06 29	06 46	07 04	07 00	.	07 09	07 23	07 28	07 37	.	07 50

Station		VT	VT	LM	VT	LM	SN	VT	LM	VT	VT	LM	LM	LM	VT	VT	LM	VT	LM	LM	LM	LM	VT	VT	LM
		1 ◇	1 ◇	1	1 ◇	1	1	1 ◇	1	1	1 ◇	1	1	1	1 ◇	1 ◇	1	1 ◇	1	1	1	1	1 ◇	1 ◇	1
		C	D								C		C	D	D										
		🍴	🍴		☒			☒			☒				☒	☒		☒					☒	☒	
Wolverhampton 7	d				05 45						06 12				06 15								06 35		
Sandwell & Dudley	d				05 55						06 22				06 25								06 45		
Birmingham New Street 12	d				06 10						06 35				06 40								07 00		
Birmingham International	d				06 21						06 45				06 50								07 10		
Coventry	d				06 32						06 55		06 18	06 18	07 00								07 20		
Nuneaton	d							06 51								07 07									
Rugby	a							07 04			07 07		06 29	06 32	07 13										
	d	06 17	06 20					07 04			07 09		06 29	06 32	07 14			07 28						07 46	
Northampton	d	06 41	06 41	06 49						07 12			07 06	07 06			07 21					07 31			
Wolverton	d			07 01									07 18	07 18								07 44			
Milton Keynes Central 10	a	06 55	06 55	07 05	07 07								07 22	07 22			07 35					07 48	07s56		
	d	06 56	06 56	07 06	07 08	←						07 15	07 22	07 22			07 36				07 42	07 49			
Bletchley	d			07 11		07 11						07 20	07 27	07 27					07 34		07 47				07 56
Leighton Buzzard	d			→		07 19						07 27					07 47		07 42		07 53	07 58			08 03
Cheddington	d											07 33									07 59				
Tring	d								07 24			07 39								07 55	08 05				
Berkhamsted	d								07 29				07 47	07 47						07 59	08 10				
Hemel Hempstead	a								07 33										07 58	08 04					08 18
	d								07 34										07 58	08 04					08 19
Apsley	d								07 37											08 07					
Kings Langley	d								07 40											08 11					
Watford Junction	a				07s28	07 36		07s44	07 45			07 51	07 57	07 57		07s57			08 05	08 15	08 20				08 26
	d					07 37	07 40		07 46			07 52	07 57	07 57					08 06	08 16	08 21				08 26
Bushey	d								07 49										08 09						
Harrow & Wealdstone ⊖	d						07 46					07 58							08 14		08 27				08 32
Wembley Central	d						07 51																		
Shepherds Bush §	a																								
Kensington Olympia ⊖	a						08 07																		
West Brompton ⊖	a						08 10																		
Imperial Wharf §	a																								
Clapham Junction 10	a						08 16																		
East Croydon	a																								
Gatwick Airport 10	a																								
Haywards Heath 3	a																								
Brighton 10	a																								
London Euston 15 ⊖	a	07 36	07 36	.	07 50	07 55	.	08 04	08 08	08 00	08 09	08 14	08 17	08 17	08 09	08 19	08 21	08 27	08 30	08 36	08 43	08 34	08 39	08 40	08 48

For general notes see front of timetable
For details of catering facilities see Directory of Train Operators

§ It is unknown, at the time of going to press, when this station will open. For further details contact National Rail Enquiries 08457 484950 or see local publicity.

A Until 14 July and from 15 September
B 21 July to 8 September
C 28 July to 22 August
D Until 25 July and from 25 August

Table 66

Mondays to Fridays

West Midlands, Northampton, Milton Keynes and Watford Junction → London

Network Diagram - See first page of Table 59

		VT 1◇ A ⊠	LM 1	SN 1	VT 1◇ ⊠	VT 1◇ B ⊠	VT 1◇ A ⊠		VT 1◇ B ⊠	LM 1	LM 1	LM 1 B	LM 1 A	VT 1◇ A ⊠	LM 1	SN 1	VT 1◇ B ⊠	LM 1	VT 1◇ A ⊠	VT 1◇ ⊠	LM 1	VT 1◇ ⊠	LM 1	LM 1	VT 1◇ ⊠
Wolverhampton 7	d						07 05		07 05								07 35		07 35						08 05
Sandwell & Dudley	d						07 15		07 15								07 45		07 45						08 15
Birmingham New Street 12	d	07 15				07 15	07 30		07 30			06 43	06 43	07 45			08 00		08 00						08 30
Birmingham International	d	07 28				07 28	07 40		07 40			06 59	06 59	07 56			08 10		08 10						08 40
Coventry	d	07 38				07 40	07 56		07 58			07 17	07 27				08 20		08 24						08 50
Nuneaton	d				07 49																	08 31			
Rugby	a											07 29	07 40												
	d											07 30	07 41							08 51					
Northampton	d		07 47									08 10	08 10		08 24						08 42				
Wolverton	d		07 59												08 36						08 54				
Milton Keynes Central 10	a		08 03									08 24	08 24		08 39						08 57	09 04			09 25
	d		08 03								08 21	08 25	08 25		08 40						08 58	09 05		09 15	09 26
Bletchley	d		08 08									08 30	08 30								09 03			09 20	
Leighton Buzzard	d										08 30	08 36	08 36		08 49						09 09			09 26	
Cheddington	d											08 42	08 42											09 32	
Tring	d									08 26		08 48	08 48					08 57					09 27	09 38	
Berkhamsted	d									08 31	08 43							09 01			09 22		09 31	09 43	
Hemel Hempstead	a									08 35		08 55	08 55					09 06			09 27		09 36	09 47	
	d									08 36		08 56	08 56					09 06			09 27		09 36	09 47	
Apsley	d									08 39								09 09					09 39		
Kings Langley	d									08 42								09 12					09 42		
Watford Junction	a		08 34							08 47	08 53	09 03	09 03				09s14	09 17	09s20	09s28	09 34		09 47	09 54	
	d		08 34	08 42						08 47	08 54	09 03	09 03			09 11		09 17			09 34		09 47	09 55	
Bushey	d									08 50								09 20					09 50		
Harrow & Wealdstone	⊖ d			08 48							09 00	09 09	09 09			09 17		09 25					09 55		
Wembley Central	d			08 53												09 22									
Shepherds Bush §	a																								
Kensington Olympia	⊖ a			09 08												09 37									
West Brompton	⊖ a			09 11												09 40									
Imperial Wharf §	a																								
Clapham Junction 10	a			09 18												09 50									
East Croydon	a															10 07									
Gatwick Airport 10	a															10 22									
Haywards Heath 3	a															10 42									
Brighton 10	a															11 07									
London Euston 15	⊖ a	08 43	08 57	.	08 58	08 48	09 01	.	09 04	09 10	09 16	09 25	09 25	09 07	09 25	.	09 39	09 41	09 44	09 53	09 55	09 45	10 11	10 14	10 03

		LM 1	VT 1◇ ⊠	VT 1◇ ⊠	VT 1◇ ⊠	VT 1◇ ⊠	SN 1	LM 1	LM 1	LM 1	VT 1◇ ⊠	LM 1	LM 1	VT 1◇ ⊠	LM 1 A	LM 1 B	VT 1◇ ⊠	SN 1	VT 1◇ ⊠	LM 1	LM 1	LM 1	VT 1◇ ⊠	LM 1	LM 1
Wolverhampton 7	d													09 05											
Sandwell & Dudley	d													09 15											
Birmingham New Street 12	d					09 00								09 30	08 48	08 48			10 00						
Birmingham International	d					09 10								09 40	08 57	08 57			10 10						
Coventry	d					09 20								09 50	09 15	09 18			10 20						
Nuneaton	d				09 26																		10 35		
Rugby	a														09 27	09 28									
	d			09 25											09 27	09 28	10 25								
Northampton	d	09 11							09 33	09 45					10 09	10 09					10 33	10 43			
Wolverton	d	09 23							09 45						10 21	10 21					10 45				
Milton Keynes Central 10	a	09 27		09 46					09 48	09 59				10 22	10 25	10 25					10 48	10 57			
	d	09 27	09 31	09 47					09 49	10 00	10 12		10 15	10 23	10 25	10 25					10 49	10 57			11 15
Bletchley	d	09 32							09 54				10 20		10 30	10 30					10 54				11 20
Leighton Buzzard	d	09 40							10 00				10 26		10 38	10 38					11 00				11 26
Cheddington	d												10 32												11 32
Tring	d							09 56				10 26	10 38							10 56				11 26	11 38
Berkhamsted	d							10 00	10 13			10 30	10 43							11 00	11 13			11 30	11 43
Hemel Hempstead	a							10 05	10 18			10 35	10 47							11 05	11 18			11 35	11 47
	d							10 05	10 18			10 35	10 47							11 05	11 18			11 35	11 47
Apsley	d							10 08				10 38								11 08				11 38	
Kings Langley	d							10 11				10 41								11 11				11 41	
Watford Junction	a					10s10		10 16	10 25			10 46	10 54				11s02		11s13	11 16	11 25		11s25	11 46	11 54
	d						10 11	10 16	10 25			10 46	10 55					11 11		11 16	11 25			11 46	11 55
Bushey	d							10 19				10 49								11 19				11 49	
Harrow & Wealdstone	⊖ d						10 17	10 24				10 54						11 17		11 24				11 54	
Wembley Central	d																								
Shepherds Bush §	a																								
Kensington Olympia	⊖ a						10 37											11 37							
West Brompton	⊖ a						10 39											11 39							
Imperial Wharf §	a																								
Clapham Junction 10	a						10 50											11 50							
East Croydon	a						11 07											12 07							
Gatwick Airport 10	a						11 22											12 22							
Haywards Heath 3	a						11 42											12 42							
Brighton 10	a						12 07											13 07							
London Euston 15	⊖ a	10 14	10 09	10 27	10 35	10 31	.	10 38	10 44	10 44	10 50	11 08	11 14	11 00	11 11	11 11	11 27	.	11 35	11 38	11 44	11 38	11 48	12 08	12 14

For general notes see front of timetable
For details of catering facilities see
Directory of Train Operators

§ It is unknown, at the time of going to press, when this station will open. For further details contact National Rail Enquiries 08457 484950 or see local publicity.

A Until 25 July and from 25 August
B 28 July to 22 August

West Midlands, Northampton, Milton Keynes and Watford Junction → London

Network Diagram - See first page of Table 59

		VT	LM	VT	VT	SN	VT	LM	LM	LM	VT		LM	LM	VT	LM	LM	VT	SN	VT	LM	VT	LM	LM	LM
		1 ◇	1	1 ◇	1 ◇	1	1 ◇	1	1	1	1 ◇		1	1	1 ◇	1	1	1 ◇	1	1 ◇	1	1 ◇	1	1	1
		⊠		⊠	⊠		☕				⊠				☕		🍽	⊠		☕		☕			
Wolverhampton 7	d	10 05													11 05										
Sandwell & Dudley	d	10 15													11 15										
Birmingham New Street 12	d	10 30					11 00								11 30					12 00					
Birmingham International	d	10 40					11 10								11 40					12 10					
Coventry	d	10 50					11 20								11 50					12 20					
Nuneaton	d										11 35						12 02					12 35			
Rugby	a																12 17								
	d				11 25												12 17	12 25							
Northampton	d		11 09						11 33	11 43						12 09							12 33	12 43	
Wolverton	d		11 21						11 45							12 21							12 45		
Milton Keynes Central 10	a	11 22	11 25		11 46				11 48	11 57	12 09				12 22	12 25							12 48	12 57	
	d	11 23	11 25	11 29	11 46				11 49	11 57	12 10			12 15	12 23	12 25							12 49	12 57	
Bletchley	d		11 30						11 54					12 20		12 30							12 54		
Leighton Buzzard	d		11 38						12 00					12 26		12 38							13 00		
Cheddington	d													12 32											
Tring	d							11 56					12 26	12 38							12 56				13 26
Berkhamsted	d							12 00	12 13				12 30	12 43							13 00		13 13		13 30
Hemel Hempstead	a							12 05	12 18				12 35	12 47							13 05		13 18		13 35
	d							12 05	12 18				12 35	12 47							13 05		13 18		13 35
Apsley	d							12 08					12 38								13 08				13 38
Kings Langley	d							12 11					12 41								13 11				13 41
Watford Junction	a						12s12	12 16	12 25				12 46	12 56				13s03		13s13	13 16	13s24	13 25		13 46
	d					12 11		12 16	12 25				12 46	12 57					13 11		13 16		13 25		13 46
Bushey	d							12 19					12 49								13 19				13 49
Harrow & Wealdstone ⊖	d					12 17		12 24					12 54						13 17		13 24				13 54
Wembley Central	d																								
Shepherds Bush §	a																								
Kensington Olympia ⊖	a					12 37													13 37						
West Brompton ⊖	a					12 39													13 39						
Imperial Wharf §	a																								
Clapham Junction 10	a					12 50													13 50						
East Croydon	a					13 07													14 07						
Gatwick Airport 10	a					13 22													14 22						
Haywards Heath 3	a					13 42													14 42						
Brighton 10	a					14 07													15 07						
London Euston 15 ⊖	a	12 00	12 11	12 07	12 26		12 33	12 38	12 44	12 38	12 48		13 08	13 14	13 00	13 12	13 18	13 27		13 34	13 38	13 47	13 44	13 39	14 08

		LM	VT	LM	LM	SN	VT	LM	LM	LM	VT	VT	LM	LM	VT	LM	LM	VT	SN	VT	LM	LM	LM	VT	LM
		1	1 ◇	1	1	1	1 ◇	1	1	1	1 ◇	1 ◇	1	1	1 ◇	1	1	1 ◇	1	1 ◇	1	1	1	1 ◇	1
				A	B											A	B								
			☕				☕				☕	☕			☕			☕		☕				☕	
Wolverhampton 7	d		12 05												13 05										
Sandwell & Dudley	d		12 15												13 15										
Birmingham New Street 12	d		12 30				13 00								13 30	12 48	12 48			14 00					
Birmingham International	d		12 40				13 10								13 40	12 57	12 57			14 10					
Coventry	d		12 50				13 20								13 50	13 15	13 15			14 20					
Nuneaton	d											13 35												14 35	
Rugby	a															13 27	13 29								
	d										13 40					13 27	13 29	14 25							
Northampton	d			13 09	13 09				13 33	13 43						14 09	14 09					14 33	14 43		
Wolverton	d			13 21	13 21				13 45							14 22	14 22					14 45			
Milton Keynes Central 10	a		13 22	13 25	13 25				13 48	13 57	14 01	14 09			14 22	14 25	14 25					14 48	14 57		
	d	13 15	13 23	13 25	13 25				13 49	13 57	14 02	14 10		14 15	14 23	14 26	14 26					14 49	14 57		
Bletchley	d	13 20		13 30	13 30				13 54					14 20		14 31	14 31					14 54			
Leighton Buzzard	d	13 26		13 38	13 38				14 00					14 26		14 39	14 39					15 00			
Cheddington	d	13 32												14 32											
Tring	d	13 38						13 56					14 26	14 38							14 56				15 26
Berkhamsted	d	13 43						14 00	14 13				14 30	14 43							15 00	15 13			15 30
Hemel Hempstead	a	13 47						14 05	14 18				14 35	14 47							15 05	15 18			15 35
	d	13 47						14 05	14 18				14 35	14 47							15 05	15 18			15 35
Apsley	d							14 08					14 38								15 08				15 38
Kings Langley	d							14 11					14 41								15 11				15 41
Watford Junction	a	13 54					14s12	14 16	14 25				14 46	14 54				15s02		15s13	15 16	15 25		15s25	15 46
	d	13 55				14 11		14 16	14 25				14 46	14 55					15 11		15 16	15 25			15 46
Bushey	d							14 19					14 49								15 19				15 49
Harrow & Wealdstone ⊖	d					14 17		14 24					14 54						15 17		15 24				15 54
Wembley Central	d																								
Shepherds Bush §	a																								
Kensington Olympia ⊖	a					14 37													15 39						
West Brompton ⊖	a					14 39													15 41						
Imperial Wharf §	a																								
Clapham Junction 10	a					14 50													15 47						
East Croydon	a					15 07													16 07						
Gatwick Airport 10	a					15 22													16 22						
Haywards Heath 3	a					15 42													16 39						
Brighton 10	a					16 07													17 07						
London Euston 15 ⊖	a	14 14	14 00	14 11	14 13		14 33	14 38	14 44	14 43	14 40	14 49	15 08	15 14	15 00	15 11	15 11	15 26		15 34	15 38	15 46	15 38	15 48	16 08

For general notes see front of timetable
For details of catering facilities see Directory of Train Operators

§ It is unknown, at the time of going to press, when this station will open. For further details contact National Rail Enquiries 08457 484950 or see local publicity.

A Until 25 July and from 25 August
B 28 July to 22 August

West Midlands, Northampton, Milton Keynes and Watford Junction → London

Network Diagram - See first page of Table 59

		LM 1	VT 1 ◇ ☕	LM 1	VT 1 ◇ ☕	VT 1 ◇ ☕	VT 1 ◇ ☕	LM 1	LM 1	LM 1	VT 1 ◇ ☕	SN 1	LM 1	LM 1	VT 1 ◇ ☕		LM 1	VT 1 ◇ ☕	VT 1 ◇ ☕	LM 1	VT 1 ◇ ☕	LM 1	LM 1	VT 1 ◇ ☕	SN 1
Wolverhampton 7	d		14 05												15 05										
Sandwell & Dudley	d		14 15												15 15										
Birmingham New Street 12	d		14 30				15 00								15 30				16 00						
Birmingham International	d		14 40				15 10								15 40				16 10						
Coventry	d		14 50				15 20								15 50				16 20						
Nuneaton	d										15 35							15 40						16 35	
Rugby	a																	15 53							
	d					15 25												15 55			16 40				
Northampton	d			15 09					15 33	15 43							16 09	16 17				16 33	16 43		
Wolverton	d			15 21					15 45								16 21					16 45			
Milton Keynes Central 10	a		15 22	15 25		15 46			15 48	15 57	16 09				16 22		16 25	16 35				16 48	16 57		
	d	15 15	15 23	15 25	15 29	15 47			15 49	15 57	16 10			16 15	16 23		16 25	16 36				16 49	16 57		
Bletchley	d	15 20		15 31					15 54					16 20			16 30					16 54			
Leighton Buzzard	d	15 26		15 37					16 00					16 26			16 38					17 00			
Cheddington	d	15 32												16 32											
Tring	d	15 38						15 56					16 26	16 38						16 56					
Berkhamsted	d	15 43						16 00	16 13				16 30	16 43						17 00		17 13			
Hemel Hempstead	a	15 47						16 05	16 18				16 35	16 47						17 05		17 18			
	d	15 47						16 05	16 18				16 35	16 47						17 05		17 18			
Apsley	d							16 08					16 38							17 08					
Kings Langley	d							16 11					16 41							17 11					
Watford Junction	a	15 54					16s12	16 16	16 25				16 46	16 54					17s12	17 16	17s17	17 25		17s25	
	d	15 55						16 16	16 25			16 29	16 46	16 55						17 16		17 25			17 29
Bushey	d							16 19					16 49							17 19					
Harrow & Wealdstone	⊖ d							16 24				16 35	16 54							17 24					17 35
Wembley Central	d											16 40													17 40
Shepherds Bush §	a																								
Kensington Olympia	⊖ a											16 53													17 55
West Brompton	⊖ a											16 56													17 58
Imperial Wharf §	a																								
Clapham Junction 10	a											17 02													18 04
East Croydon	a																								18 28
Gatwick Airport 10	a																								
Haywards Heath 3	a																								
Brighton 10	a																								
London Euston 15	⊖ a	16 14	16 00	16 13	16 07	16 27	16 34	16 38	16 44	16 38	16 48	.	17 08	17 15	17 00	.	17 11	17 22	17 33	17 38	17 40	17 44	17 41	17 47	.

		LM 1	LM 1	VT 1 ◇ ☕	VT 1 ◇ ☕	SN 1	VT 1 ◇ ☕	LM 1	VT 1 ◇ ☕	VT 1 ◇ ☕	LM 1	LM 1	VT 1 ◇ ☕	LM 1	LM 1	LM 1	VT 1 ◇ ☕	LM 1 🛒	VT 1 ◇ ☕	SN 1	VT 1 ◇ A ☕	VT 1 ◇ B ☕	LM 1	LM 1	LM 1
Wolverhampton 7	d			16 05													17 05								
Sandwell & Dudley	d			16 15													17 15								
Birmingham New Street 12	d			16 30			17 00										17 30				18 00	18 00			
Birmingham International	d			16 40			17 10										17 40				18 10	18 10			
Coventry	d			16 50			17 20										17 52				18 20	18 23			
Nuneaton	d												17 35					18 00							
Rugby	a												17 49					18 14							
	d									17 24			17 50					18 14	18 25						
Northampton	d		17 03								17 33	17 43				18 09								18 33	18 43
Wolverton	d		17 15								17 45					18 21								18 45	
Milton Keynes Central 10	a		17 18	17 22						17 46	17 48	17 57	18 11			18 24	18 26							18 48	18 57
	d	17 04	17 19	17 23	17 29			17 37	17 41	17 47	17 49	17 58	18 12		18 15	18 25	18 27							18 49	18 58
Bletchley	d	17 09	17 24					17 42			17 54				18 20	18 30								18 54	
Leighton Buzzard	d	17 15	17 30					17 48			18 00				18 26	18 37								19 00	
Cheddington	d	17 21						17 54							18 32										
Tring	d	17 27						18 00						18 26	18 38								18 59		
Berkhamsted	d	17 32	17 43					18 05			18 13			18 30	18 43								19 03	19 13	
Hemel Hempstead	a	17 36	17 48					18 09			18 18			18 36	18 47								19 08	19 18	
	d	17 36	17 48					18 09			18 18			18 36	18 47								19 08	19 18	
Apsley	d	17 39						18 12						18 39									19 11		
Kings Langley	d	17 43						18 16						18 42									19 14		
Watford Junction	a	17 47	17 55				18s13	18 21			18 26			18 47	18 55				19s02		19s12	19s16	19 19	19 25	
	d	17 48	17 55			18 12		18 21			18 26			18 47	18 55					19 11			19 19	19 25	
Bushey	d	17 51						18 24						18 51									19 22		
Harrow & Wealdstone	⊖ d	17 56				18 18		18 29						18 56						19 18			19 27		
Wembley Central	d					18 23														19 23					
Shepherds Bush §	a																								
Kensington Olympia	⊖ a					18 38														19 39					
West Brompton	⊖ a					18 41														19 41					
Imperial Wharf §	a																								
Clapham Junction 10	a					18 48														19 48					
East Croydon	a					19 07														20 07					
Gatwick Airport 10	a					19 23														20 23					
Haywards Heath 3	a																								
Brighton 10	a																								
London Euston 15	⊖ a	18 11	18 14	18 00	18 07	.	18 34	18 43	18 21	18 27	18 47	18 42	18 50	19 11	19 15	19 14	19 03	19 18	19 25	.	19 34	19 38	19 41	19 45	19 41

For general notes see front of timetable
For details of catering facilities see Directory of Train Operators

§ It is unknown, at the time of going to press, when this station will open. For further details contact National Rail Enquiries 08457 484950 or see local publicity.

A Until 25 July and from 25 August
B 28 July to 22 August

West Midlands, Northampton, Milton Keynes and Watford Junction → London

Network Diagram - See first page of Table 59

		VT	LM	LM	VT	VT	VT	SN	LM	VT	LM	VT	LM	VT	VT	LM	LM	SN	LM	VT	LM	LM	VT	LM	LM
		1◇	1	1	1◇	1◇	1◇	1	1	1◇	1	1◇	1	1◇	1◇	1	1	1	1	1◇	1	1	1◇	1	1
										A															
		🍴			🍴	🍴	🍴			🍴		🍴		🍴	🍴					🍴			🍴		
Wolverhampton 7	d				18 05									19 05									20 05		
Sandwell & Dudley	d				18 15									19 15									20 15		
Birmingham New Street 12	d				18 30					19 00				19 30									20 30		
Birmingham International ✈	d				18 40					19 10				19 40									20 40		
Coventry	d				18 50					19 20				19 50									20 50		
Nuneaton	d	18 36								≀		19 35													
Rugby	a									≀															
	d						19 25			≀										20 49					
Northampton	d			19 01						≀	19 33		20 03								20 33	21 03			
Wolverton	d			19 15						≀	19 45		20 15								20 45	21 15			
Milton Keynes Central 10	a			19 18	19 22		19 47			≀	19 48	20 09	20 18	20 22							20 48	21 18	21 22		
	d		19 03	19 19	19 23	19 29	19 47			≀	19 49	20 10	20 19	20 23	20 29						20 49	21 19	21 23		
Bletchley	d		19 08	19 24						≀	19 54		20 24				←				20 54	21 24			←
Leighton Buzzard	d		19 14	19 30						≀	20 00		20 30				20 30				21 00	21 30			21 30
Cheddington	d		19 20							≀	20 07		→								21 07	→			
Tring	d		19 26						19 55	≀	20 12					20 26			20 55		21 12			21 26	
Berkhamsted	d		19 31	19 43					19 59	≀	20 17					20 30	20 43		20 59		21 17			21 30	21 43
Hemel Hempstead	a		19 35	19 48					20 04	≀	20 21					20 35	20 48		21 04		21 21			21 35	21 48
	d		19 35	19 48					20 04	≀	20 21					20 35	20 48		21 04		21 21			21 35	21 48
Apsley	d		19 38						20 07	≀						20 38			21 07					21 38	
Kings Langley	d		19 42						20 10	≀						20 41			21 10					21 41	
Watford Junction	a	19s28	19 46	19 55					20 15	20s19	20 28			20s43		20 46	20 55		21 15	21s26	21 28		21s43	21 46	21 55
	d		19 47	19 55				20 11	20 15	≀	20 29					20 46	20 55	21 11	21 15		21 29			21 46	21 55
Bushey	d		19 50						20 18	≀						20 49			21 18					21 49	
Harrow & Wealdstone ⊖	d		19 55					20 17	20 23	≀						20 54		21 17	21 23					21 54	
Wembley Central	d									≀															
Shepherds Bush §	a									≀															
Kensington Olympia ⊖	a							20 38		≀								21 36							
West Brompton ⊖	a							20 41		≀								21 39							
Imperial Wharf §	a									≀															
Clapham Junction 10	a							20 48		≀								21 47							
East Croydon	a							21 07		≀								22 07							
Gatwick Airport 10 ✈	a							21 23		≀								22 23							
Haywards Heath 3	a									≀															
Brighton 10	a									≀															
London Euston 15 ⊖	a	19 50	20 11	20 14	20 00	20 07	20 26	.	20 37	20 41	20 48	20 48	.	21 04	21 07	21 08	21 14	.	21 37	21 51	21 48	.	22 04	22 08	22 18

		SN	LM	VT	LM	VT	VT	VT	LM	LM	SN	LM	VT	LM	LM	LM	VT	VT	VT	VT	VT	LM	LM
																FO	FX	FO	FX	FO	FO		FO
		1	1	1◇	1	1◇	1◇	1◇	1	1	1	1	1◇	1	1	1	1	1	1	1	1	1	1
															B	C	D	B	E	G	H	B	C
				🍴		🍴	🍴	🍴					🍴										
Wolverhampton 7	d							21 05									22 39	22 39	22 39	22 39	22 39		
Sandwell & Dudley	d							21 15									≀	≀	≀	≀	≀		
Birmingham New Street 12	d							21 30									23 00	23 00	23 00	23 00	23 00		
Birmingham International ✈	d							21 40									23 10	23 10	23 10	23 10	23 10		
Coventry	d							21 50									23 20	23 20	23 23	23 23	23 23		
Nuneaton	d					21 29							22 35				≀	≀	≀	≀	≀		
Rugby	a					21 42							22 49				23 32	23 32	23 36	23 34	23 36		
	d					21 44							22 50				23 34	23 34	23 37	23 35	23 37		
Northampton	d				21 46					22 16		22 47			23 46	23 46	≀	≀	≀	≀	≀		
Wolverton	d				21 58					22 28		22 59			23 58	23 58	≀	≀	≀	≀	≀		
Milton Keynes Central 10	a				22 01	22 05		22 23		22 31		23 02	23 11		00 01	00 01	00s14	00s15	00s15	00s16	00s16		
	d		21 32	21 57	22 02	22 06	22 17	22 23		22 32		23 03	23 11		00 02	00 02	≀	≀	≀	≀	≀		
Bletchley	d		21 37		22 07					22 37		23 08			00 09	00 09	≀	≀	≀	≀	≀		
Leighton Buzzard	d		21 43		22 13					22 43		23 14			00 17	00 17	≀	≀	≀	≀	≀	←	←
Cheddington	d				22 22				←			23 23		←	00 22	00 22	≀	≀	≀	≀	≀	00 22	00 22
Tring	d		21 55		22 27				22 27			23 28		23 28	→	→	≀	≀	≀	≀	≀	00 27	00 27
Berkhamsted	d		21 59		→				22 32	22 58		→		23 33			≀	≀	≀	≀	≀	00 32	00 32
Hemel Hempstead	a		22 04						22 36	23 03				23 37			≀	≀	≀	≀	≀	00 36	00 36
	d		22 04						22 36	23 03				23 37			≀	≀	≀	≀	≀	00 36	00 36
Apsley	d		22 07						22 39					23 40			≀	≀	≀	≀	≀	≀	≀
Kings Langley	d		22 10						22 43					23 44			≀	≀	≀	≀	≀	≀	≀
Watford Junction	a		22 15			22s25		22s43	22 47	23 10			23s31	23 48			00s37	00s38	00s39	00s39	00s39	00 43	00 43
	d	22 12	22 15						22 48	23 10	23 18			23 49			≀	≀	≀	≀	≀	00 44	00 44
Bushey	d								22 51					23 52			≀	≀	≀	≀	≀	≀	≀
Harrow & Wealdstone ⊖	d	22 18	22 21						22 56		23 24			23 57			≀	≀	≀	≀	≀	00 50	00 50
Wembley Central	d																≀	≀	≀	≀	≀	00 54	00 59
Shepherds Bush §	a																≀	≀	≀	≀	≀	≀	≀
Kensington Olympia ⊖	a	22 41									23 44						≀	≀	≀	≀	≀	≀	≀
West Brompton ⊖	a	22 43									23 47						≀	≀	≀	≀	≀	≀	≀
Imperial Wharf §	a																≀	≀	≀	≀	≀	≀	≀
Clapham Junction 10	a	22 51									23 54						≀	≀	≀	≀	≀	≀	≀
East Croydon	a																≀	≀	≀	≀	≀	≀	≀
Gatwick Airport 10 ✈	a																≀	≀	≀	≀	≀	≀	≀
Haywards Heath 3	a																≀	≀	≀	≀	≀	≀	≀
Brighton 10	a																≀	≀	≀	≀	≀	≀	≀
London Euston 15 ⊖	a	.	22 41	22 52	.	23 05	23 14	23 20	23 13	23 32	.	.	00 09	00 14	.	.	01 02	01 02	01 03	01 04	01 04	01 09	01 09

For general notes see front of timetable
For details of catering facilities see Directory of Train Operators

§ It is unknown, at the time of going to press, when this station will open. For further details contact National Rail Enquiries 08457 484950 or see local publicity.

A Until 25 July and from 25 August
B Until 11 July
C From 18 July
D Until 24 July and from 25 August
E 28 July to 21 August
G 18 and 25 July and from 29 August
H 1 to 22 August

West Midlands, Northampton, Milton Keynes and Watford Junction → London

Network Diagram - See first page of Table 59

		LM 1	VT 1	LM 1	LM 1	LM 1	SN 1	LM 1	LM 1	LM 1	SN 1	LM 1	LM 1	LM 1		LM 1	VT 1◇ ☒	LM 1	VT 1◇ ☕	SN 1	LM 1	VT 1◇ ☒	LM 1	VT 1◇ ☕	VT 1◇ ☕
Wolverhampton 7	d		22p39														05 37					06 05			06 35
Sandwell & Dudley	d																05 47					06 15			06 48
Birmingham New Street 12	d		23p00														06 00					06 30			07 00
Birmingham International	d		23p10														06 10					06 41			07 10
Coventry	d		23p20														06 21					06 55			07 22
Nuneaton	d																		06 46						
Rugby	a		23p32														06 33		07 00						07 38
	d		23p34														06 35		07 01					07 35	07 40
Northampton	d	23p46						05 15		06 02			06 32			07 02							07 32		
Wolverton	d	23p58						05 29		06 14			06 44			07 14							07 44		
Milton Keynes Central 10	a	00 01	00s15					05 32		06 17			06 47			07 17	07 24					07 43	07 49	08 07	
	d	00 02			03 40	04 35		05 33		06 18		06 34	06 48			07 18	07 26				07 33	07 45	07 50	08 09	
Bletchley	d	00 09			03 45	04 40		05 38	06 05	06 23		06 39	06 53	07 09		07 27		←			07 38		07 57		
Leighton Buzzard	d	00 17		←	03 51	04 46		05 44	06 11	06 29		06 45	06 59	07 15		07 33		07 33			07 44		08 03		
Cheddington	d	00 22		00 22				05 53				06 54				→					07 51				
Tring	d	→		00 27	04 03	04 58		05 58	06 23			06 59		07 24							07 56				
Berkhamsted	d			00 32	04 08	05 03		06 03	06 28	06 44		07 04	07 12	07 29				07 46			08 01		08 16		
Hemel Hempstead	a			00 36	04 12	05 07		06 07	06 32	06 49		07 08	07 17	07 33				07 51			08 05		08 21		
	d			00 36	04 12	05 07		06 07	06 32	06 49		07 08	07 17	07 33				07 51			08 05		08 21		
Apsley	d							06 10	06 35			07 11		07 36							08 08				
Kings Langley	d							06 14	06 39			07 15		07 40							08 12				
Watford Junction	a		00s38	00 43	04 19	05 14		06 18	06 43	06 56		07 19	07 24	07 44			07s50	07 58	08s01		08 16		08 28	08s36	08s40
	d			00 44	04 20	05 15	06 11	06 19	06 44	06 56	07 13	07 20	07 25	07 45				07 58		08 11	08 17		08 28		
Bushey	d							06 22	06 47			07 23		07 48							08 20				
Harrow & Wealdstone ⊖	d			00 50	04 26	05 21	06 17	06 27	06 52		07 19	07 28		07 53						08 17	08 25				
Wembley Central	d			00 54	04 35	05 30																			
Shepherds Bush §	a																								
Kensington Olympia ⊖	a						06 42				07 42									08 42					
West Brompton ⊖	a						06 45				07 45									08 45					
Imperial Wharf §	a																								
Clapham Junction 10	a						06 53				07 53									08 53					
East Croydon	a						07 07				08 07									09 07					
Gatwick Airport 10	a						07 22				08 22									09 22					
Haywards Heath 3	a						07 42				08 42									09 42					
Brighton 10	a						08 08				09 09									10 07					
London Euston 15 ⊖	a		01 02	01 09	04 47	05 42		06 44	07 11	07 18		07 42	07 51	08 11			08 10	08 18	08 19		08 39	08 29	08 51	08 57	09 01

		LM 1	LM 1	VT 1◇ ☕	LM 1	VT 1◇ ☕		VT 1◇ ☕	SN 1	LM 1	LM 1	LM 1	VT 1◇ ☕	VT 1◇ ☕	VT 1◇ ☕	LM 1	VT 1◇ ☕	LM 1	VT 1◇ ☕	SN 1		LM 1	LM 1	VT 1◇ ☕	LM 1
Wolverhampton 7	d							07 05						07 35					08 05						
Sandwell & Dudley	d							07 16						07 48					08 16						
Birmingham New Street 12	d							07 30						08 00					08 30						
Birmingham International	d							07 41						08 10					08 41						
Coventry	d							07 54						08 21					08 56						
Nuneaton	d					07 42											08 35								
Rugby	a																								
	d			07 46									08 29												
Northampton	d		08 02									08 42						09 02							09 42
Wolverton	d		08 15									08 54						09 14							09 54
Milton Keynes Central 10	a		08 18	08 25		08 34		08 40				08 57						09 17	09 40						09 57
	d		08 19	08 27		08 36		08 41			08 45	08 58			09 13			09 18	09 42				09 45	09 49	09 58
Bletchley	d		08 26		←						08 50	09 07						09 27					09 50		10 07
Leighton Buzzard	d		08 33		08 33						08 56	09 14						09 33					09 56		10 15
Cheddington	d		→								09 03												10 03		
Tring	d	08 26								08 56	09 08					09 26						09 56	10 08		
Berkhamsted	d	08 30			08 46					09 00	09 13					09 30		09 46				10 00	10 13		
Hemel Hempstead	a	08 35			08 51					09 05	09 17					09 35		09 51				10 05	10 17		
	d	08 35			08 51					09 05	09 17					09 35		09 51				10 05	10 17		
Apsley	d	08 38								09 08						09 38						10 08			
Kings Langley	d	08 41								09 11						09 41						10 11			
Watford Junction	a	08 46		08s54	08 59					09 16	09 24		09s33	09s38		09 46	09s50	09 58				10 16	10 24		
	d	08 46			08 59				09 11	09 16	09 25					09 46		09 58		10 11		10 16	10 25		
Bushey	d	08 49								09 19						09 49						10 19			
Harrow & Wealdstone ⊖	d	08 54							09 17	09 24						09 54				10 17		10 24			
Wembley Central	d																								
Shepherds Bush §	a																								
Kensington Olympia ⊖	a								09 42											10 42					
West Brompton ⊖	a								09 45											10 45					
Imperial Wharf §	a																								
Clapham Junction 10	a								09 53											10 53					
East Croydon	a								10 07											11 07					
Gatwick Airport 10	a								10 22											11 22					
Haywards Heath 3	a								10 42											11 42					
Brighton 10	a								11 07											12 07					
London Euston 15 ⊖	a	09 11		09 17	09 17	09 19		09 25		09 37	09 44	09 50	09 56	10 00	10 03	10 11	10 12	10 17	10 24			10 37	10 44	10 27	10 50

For general notes see front of timetable
For details of catering facilities see Directory of Train Operators

§ It is unknown, at the time of going to press, when this station will open. For further details contact National Rail Enquiries 08457 484950 or see local publicity.

Table 66

Saturdays

until 12 July

West Midlands, Northampton, Milton Keynes and Watford Junction → London

Network Diagram - See first page of Table 59

		VT	VT	LM	LM	VT	VT	SN	LM	LM	LM	VT		LM	LM	VT	SN	LM	LM	VT	LM	LM	VT	VT	VT
		1 ◇	1 ◇	1	1	1 ◇	1 ◇	1	1	1	1	1 ◇		1	1	1 ◇	1	1	1	1 ◇	1	1	1 ◇	1 ◇	1 ◇
		☕	⊠			☕	⊠					⊠				☕				☕			☕	☕	☕
Wolverhampton 7	d						09 05																	10 37	
Sandwell & Dudley	d						09 15																	10 48	
Birmingham New Street 12	d		09 00				09 30					10 00				10 30				10 33			10 51	11 00	
Birmingham International	d		09 10				09 40					10 10				10 40				10 45			11 04	11 10	
Coventry	d		09 20				09 50					10 20				10 51				10 56			11 15	11 21	
Nuneaton	d					09 36																			
Rugby	a					09 54														11 08				11 33	
	d	09 28				09 56														11 10				11 35	
Northampton	d				10 02						10 42				11 02							11 42			
Wolverton	d				10 14						10 54				11 15							11 54			
Milton Keynes Central 10	a	10 05			10 17	10 29	10 36				10 57				11 18					11 49		11 57			
	d	10 07			10 18	10 31	10 37			10 45	10 58				11 19				11 45	11 51		11 58			12 14
Bletchley	d				10 26					10 50	11 07				11 28				11 50			12 04			
Leighton Buzzard	d				10 33					10 56	11 15				11 34				11 56		←	12 15			
Cheddington	d									11 03									12 03		12 03				
Tring	d			10 26					10 56	11 08				11 26				11 56	→		12 08				
Berkhamsted	d			10 30	10 46				11 00	11 13				11 30	11 47			12 00			12 13				
Hemel Hempstead	a			10 35	10 51				11 05	11 17				11 35	11 52			12 05			12 17				
	d			10 35	10 51				11 05	11 17				11 35	11 52			12 05			12 17				
Apsley	d			10 38					11 08					11 38				12 08							
Kings Langley	d			10 41					11 11					11 41				12 11							
Watford Junction	a		10s40	10 46	10 58				11 16	11 24		11s33		11 46	11 59	12s00		12 16		12s16	12 24		12s33	12s38	
	d			10 46	10 58			11 11	11 16	11 25				11 46	11 59		12 11	12 16			12 25				
Bushey	d			10 49					11 19					11 49				12 19							
Harrow & Wealdstone ⊖	d			10 54				11 17	11 24					11 54			12 17	12 24							
Wembley Central	d																								
Shepherds Bush §	a																								
Kensington Olympia ⊖	a							11 42									12 42								
West Brompton ⊖	a							11 45									12 45								
Imperial Wharf §	a																								
Clapham Junction 10	a							11 53									12 52								
East Croydon	a							12 07									13 07								
Gatwick Airport 10	a							12 22									13 22								
Haywards Heath 3	a							12 42									13 42								
Brighton 10	a							13 07									14 07								
London Euston 15 ⊖	a	10 58	11 00	11 11	11 19	11 16	11 21		11 38	11 44	11 50	11 55		12 11	12 18	12 21		12 37		12 38	12 44	12 47	12 54	13 01	13 04

		LM	LM	VT		SN	LM	LM	VT	LM	LM	VT	VT	LM	LM	VT	SN	LM		LM	VT	LM	LM	VT	VT
		1	1	1 ◇		1	1	1	1 ◇	1	1	1 ◇	1 ◇	1	1	1 ◇	1	1		1	1 ◇	1	1	1 ◇	1 ◇
				☕					☕			☕	☕			☕					☕			☕	☕
Wolverhampton 7	d												11 37												12 37
Sandwell & Dudley	d												11 48												12 48
Birmingham New Street 12	d			11 30					11 33			11 51	12 00			12 30					12 33			12 51	13 00
Birmingham International	d			11 40					11 45			12 04	12 10			12 40					12 46			13 04	13 10
Coventry	d			11 51					11 56			12 15	12 21			12 51					12 57			13 15	13 21
Nuneaton	d																								
Rugby	a								12 08				12 33								13 09				13 33
	d								12 10				12 35								13 11				13 35
Northampton	d		12 02								12 42				13 02								13 42		
Wolverton	d		12 14								12 54				13 15								13 54		
Milton Keynes Central 10	a		12 18	12 37					12 49		12 57		13 09		13 18						13 49		13 57		
	d		12 19	12 38				12 45	12 51		12 58		13 11		13 19					13 45	13 51		13 58		
Bletchley	d		12 28					12 50			13 07				13 28					13 50			14 07		
Leighton Buzzard	d		12 34					12 56		←	13 15				13 34					13 56		←	14 15		
Cheddington	d							13 03		13 03										14 03		14 03			
Tring	d	12 26					12 56	→		13 08				13 26				13 56		→		14 08			
Berkhamsted	d	12 30	12 47				13 00			13 13				13 30	13 47			14 00				14 13			
Hemel Hempstead	a	12 35	12 52				13 05			13 17				13 35	13 52			14 05				14 17			
	d	12 35	12 52				13 05			13 17				13 35	13 52			14 05				14 17			
Apsley	d	12 38					13 08							13 38				14 08							
Kings Langley	d	12 41					13 11							13 41				14 11							
Watford Junction	a	12 46	12 59				13 16		13s17	13 24		13s33		13 46	13 59	14 02		14 16			14s17	14 24		14s33	14s38
	d	12 46	12 59			13 11	13 16			13 25				13 46	13 59	14 03	14 11	14 16				14 25			
Bushey	d	12 49					13 19							13 49				14 19							
Harrow & Wealdstone ⊖	d	12 54				13 17	13 24							13 54			14 17	14 24							
Wembley Central	d																								
Shepherds Bush §	a																								
Kensington Olympia ⊖	a					13 42											14 42								
West Brompton ⊖	a					13 45											14 45								
Imperial Wharf §	a																								
Clapham Junction 10	a					13 53											14 53								
East Croydon	a					14 07											15 07								
Gatwick Airport 10	a					14 22											15 22								
Haywards Heath 3	a					14 42											15 42								
Brighton 10	a					15 07											16 07								
London Euston 15 ⊖	a	13 11	13 18	13 22			13 38		13 38	13 44	13 47	13 54	13 58	14 11	14 18	14 23		14 37			14 38	14 44	14 47	14 54	15 01

For general notes see front of timetable
For details of catering facilities see Directory of Train Operators

§ It is unknown, at the time of going to press, when this station will open. For further details contact National Rail Enquiries 08457 484950 or see local publicity.

Table 66

Saturdays

until 12 July

West Midlands, Northampton, Milton Keynes and Watford Junction → London

Network Diagram - See first page of Table 59

		VT 1◇ ☕	LM 1	LM 1	VT 1◇ ☕	SN 1	LM 1	LM 1	VT 1◇ ☕	LM 1		LM 1	VT 1◇ ☕	VT 1◇ ☕	LM 1	LM 1	VT 1◇ ☕	SN 1	LM 1	LM 1	VT 1◇ ☕	LM 1	LM 1	VT 1◇ ☕	VT 1◇ ☕
Wolverhampton 7	d													13 37											14 37
Sandwell & Dudley	d													13 48											14 48
Birmingham New Street 12	d				13 30				13 33				13 51	14 00			14 30				14 33			14 51	15 00
Birmingham International	d				13 40				13 45				14 04	14 10			14 40				14 46			15 01	15 10
Coventry	d				13 51				13 57				14 15	14 21			14 51				14 57			15 15	15 21
Nuneaton	d																								
Rugby	a								14 09												15 09				15 33
	d								14 11												15 11				15 35
Northampton	d			14 02								14 42				15 02							15 42		
Wolverton	d			14 15								14 54				15 15							15 54		
Milton Keynes Central 10	a			14 18	14 39				14 49			14 57		15 09		15 18					15 49		15 57		
	d	14 14		14 19	14 40			14 45	14 51			14 58		15 11		15 19				15 45	15 51		15 58		
Bletchley	d			14 28				14 50				15 07				15 28				15 50			16 07		
Leighton Buzzard	d			14 34				14 56		⟵		15 15				15 34				15 56		⟵	16 15		
Cheddington	d							15 03 ⟶		15 03										16 03 ⟶		16 03			
Tring	d		14 26				14 56			15 08					15 26				15 56			16 08			
Berkhamsted	d		14 30	14 47			15 00			15 13					15 30	15 47			16 00			16 13			
Hemel Hempstead	a		14 35	14 52			15 05			15 17					15 35	15 52			16 05			16 17			
	d		14 35	14 52			15 05			15 17					15 35	15 52			16 05			16 17			
Apsley	d		14 38				15 08								15 38				16 08						
Kings Langley	d		14 41				15 11								15 41				16 11						
Watford Junction	a		14 46	14 59			15 16		15s17	15 24			15s33		15 46	15 59	16s02		16 16		16s17	16 24		16s34	16s38
	d		14 46	14 59		15 11	15 16			15 25					15 46	15 59		16 11	16 16			16 25			
Bushey	d		14 49				15 19								15 49				16 19						
Harrow & Wealdstone ⊖	d		14 54			15 17	15 24								15 54			16 17	16 24						
Wembley Central	d																								
Shepherds Bush §	a																								
Kensington Olympia ⊖	a					15 42												16 42							
West Brompton ⊖	a					15 45												16 45							
Imperial Wharf §	a																								
Clapham Junction 10	a					15 53												16 53							
East Croydon	a					16 07												17 07							
Gatwick Airport 10 ✈	a					16 22												17 22							
Haywards Heath 3	a					16 42												17 42							
Brighton 10	a					17 07												18 07							
London Euston 15 ⊖	a	15 04	15 11	15 18	15 24		15 37		15 38	15 44		15 47	15 54	15 59	16 11	16 18	16 25		16 37		16 38	16 44	16 47	16 54	17 01

		VT 1◇ ☕		LM 1	LM 1	VT 1◇ ☕	LM 1	SN 1	LM 1	VT 1◇ ☕	LM 1	LM 1	VT 1◇ ☕	VT 1◇ ☕	LM 1	LM 1		VT 1◇ ☕	SN 1	LM 1	LM 1	VT 1◇ ☕	LM 1	LM 1	VT 1◇ ☕
Wolverhampton 7	d													15 37											
Sandwell & Dudley	d													15 48											
Birmingham New Street 12	d					15 30				15 33			15 51	16 00				16 30				16 33			16 51
Birmingham International	d					15 40				15 46			16 04	16 10				16 40				16 46			17 04
Coventry	d					15 51				15 57			16 15	16 21				16 51				16 57			17 15
Nuneaton	d																								
Rugby	a									16 09				16 33								17 09			
	d									16 11				16 35								17 11			
Northampton	d				16 02							16 42				17 02								17 42	
Wolverton	d				16 15							16 54				17 15								17 54	
Milton Keynes Central 10	a				16 18	16 36				16 49		16 57		17 08		17 18						17 49		17 57	
	d	16 15			16 19	16 37	16 45			16 51		16 58		17 10		17 19					17 45	17 51		17 58	
Bletchley	d				16 28		16 50					17 07				17 28					17 50			18 07	
Leighton Buzzard	d				16 34		16 56				⟵	17 15				17 34					17 56		⟵	18 15	
Cheddington	d						17 03 ⟶				17 03										18 03 ⟶		18 03		
Tring	d			16 26					16 56		17 08				17 26					17 56			18 08		
Berkhamsted	d			16 30	16 47				17 00		17 13				17 30	17 47				18 00			18 13		
Hemel Hempstead	a			16 35	16 52				17 05		17 17				17 35	17 52				18 05			18 17		
	d			16 35	16 52				17 05		17 17				17 35	17 52				18 05			18 17		
Apsley	d			16 38					17 08						17 38					18 08					
Kings Langley	d			16 41					17 11						17 41					18 11					
Watford Junction	a			16 46	16 59				17 16	17s17	17 24		17s33		17 46	17 59		18s01		18 16		18s17	18 24		18s34
	d			16 46	16 59			17 11	17 16		17 25				17 46	17 59			18 11	18 16			18 25		
Bushey	d			16 49					17 19						17 49					18 19					
Harrow & Wealdstone ⊖	d			16 54				17 17	17 24						17 54				18 17	18 24					
Wembley Central	d																								
Shepherds Bush §	a																								
Kensington Olympia ⊖	a							17 42											18 42						
West Brompton ⊖	a							17 45											18 45						
Imperial Wharf §	a																								
Clapham Junction 10	a							17 53											18 53						
East Croydon	a							18 07											19 07						
Gatwick Airport 10 ✈	a							18 22											19 22						
Haywards Heath 3	a							18 42											19 42						
Brighton 10	a							19 07											20 07						
London Euston 15 ⊖	a	17 04		17 11	17 18	17 23			17 37	17 37	17 44	17 47	17 54	17 58	18 11	18 18		18 23		18 37		18 38	18 44	18 47	18 55

For general notes see front of timetable
For details of catering facilities see Directory of Train Operators

§ It is unknown, at the time of going to press, when this station will open. For further details contact National Rail Enquiries 08457 484950 or see local publicity.

West Midlands, Northampton, Milton Keynes and Watford Junction → London

until 12 July

Network Diagram - See first page of Table 59

		VT	VT	LM	LM	VT	SN	LM		LM	VT	VT	LM	VT	LM	LM	VT	SN	LM	LM	VT	LM		VT	VT
		1 ◇ ☕	1 ◇ ☕	1	1	1 ◇ ☕	1	1		1	1 ◇ ☕	1 ◇ ☕	1	1 ◇ ☕	1	1	1 ◇ ☕	1	1	1	1 ◇ ☕	1		1 ◇ ☕	1 ◇ ☕
Wolverhampton 7 🚆	d	16 37												17 37											18 37
Sandwell & Dudley	d	16 48												17 48											18 48
Birmingham New Street 12	d	17 00				17 30					17 33	17 51		18 00			18 30				18 33			18 51	19 00
Birmingham International ✈	d	17 10				17 40					17 45	18 04		18 10			18 40				18 45			19 04	19 10
Coventry	d	17 21				17 51					17 57	18 15		18 21			18 51				18 57			19 15	19 21
Nuneaton	d																								
Rugby	a	17 33									18 09			18 33							19 09				19 33
	d	17 35									18 11			18 35							19 11				19 35
Northampton	d				18 02					18 32						19 02				19 32		19 47			
Wolverton	d				18 15					18 44						19 15				19 44					
Milton Keynes Central 10	a				18 18	18 36				18 47	18 52			19 09		19 18				19 47	19 54	20 01			
	d		18 15		18 19	18 37				18 48	18 54			19 11		19 19				19 48	19 56	20 02			
Bletchley	d				18 28					18 57						19 28				19 53		20 07			
Leighton Buzzard	d				18 34					19 03			←			19 34				19 59		20 13			
Cheddington	d									19 10 →			19 10									20 18			
Tring	d			18 26				18 56					19 15		19 26				19 53			20 27			
Berkhamsted	d			18 30	18 47			19 00					19 20		19 30	19 47			19 57	20 14		20 32			
Hemel Hempstead	a			18 35	18 52			19 05					19 24		19 35	19 52			20 02	20 19		20 36			
	d			18 35	18 52			19 05					19 24		19 35	19 52			20 02	20 19		20 36			
Apsley	d			18 38				19 08							19 38				20 05			20 39			
Kings Langley	d			18 41				19 11							19 41				20 08			20 43			
Watford Junction	a	18s39		18 46	18 59			19 16			19s20	19s29	19 31		19 46	19 59	20s04		20 17	20 30	20s35	20 51		20s56	21s02
	d			18 46	18 59		19 11	19 16					19 32		19 46	19 59		20 13	20 17	20 30		20 52			
Bushey	d			18 49				19 19							19 49				20 20			20 55			
Harrow & Wealdstone ⊖	d			18 54			19 17	19 24							19 54			20 19	20 25			21 00			
Wembley Central	d																								
Shepherds Bush §	a																								
Kensington Olympia ⊖	a						19 42											20 42							
West Brompton ⊖	a						19 45											20 45							
Imperial Wharf §	a																								
Clapham Junction 10	a						19 53											20 53							
East Croydon 🚆	a						20 07											21 07							
Gatwick Airport 10 ✈	a						20 22											21 22							
Haywards Heath 3	a						20 42																		
Brighton 10	a						21 07																		
London Euston 15 ⊖	a	19 02	19 05	19 11	19 18	19 21		19 37			19 43	19 48	19 51	19 55	20 11	20 21	20 28		20 42	20 52	20 59	21 17		21 22	21 27

		VT	VT	SN	VT	LM	LM	VT	VT	SN	VT	LM	LM	VT		VT	SN	VT	LM	VT	LM	LM	LM		
		1 ◇ ☕	1 ◇ ☕	1	1 ◇ ☕	1	1	1 ◇ ☕	1 ◇ ☕	1	1 ◇ ☕	1	1	1 ◇ ☕		1 ◇ ☕	1	1 ◇ ☕	1	1 ◇ ☕	1	🚌	🚌		
Wolverhampton 7 🚆	d								19 37											21 35					
Sandwell & Dudley	d								19 48											21 47					
Birmingham New Street 12	d				19 33			19 51	20 00					20 53						22 00					
Birmingham International ✈	d				19 43			20 04	20 10					21 04						22 10					
Coventry	d				19 54			20 15	20 21					21 15						22 21					
Nuneaton	d																								
Rugby	a								20 33					21 27						22 33					
	d		20 01						20 35		21 01			21 29		22 01		22 11		22 35					
Northampton	d					20 32	20 50					21 32	21 47						22 42		23 35				
Wolverton	d					20 44						21 44							22 54		23 47				
Milton Keynes Central 10	a		20 35		20 41	20 48	21 05		21 15			21 47	22 03	22 08		22 35		22 44	22 57	23 08	23 50				
	d	20 16	20 36		20 42	20 49	21 06		21 17			21 48	22 04	22 10		22 36		22 46	22 58	23 10	23 51	23 58	23 58		
Bletchley	d					20 54	21 12					21 53	22 09						23 03		23a55	00 13	00 13		
Leighton Buzzard	d					21 00	21 19					21 59	22 15						23 09			00 38	00 38		
Cheddington	d						21 24						22 20						23 18				00 58		
Tring	d						21 33						22 29						23 23				01 18		
Berkhamsted	d					21 14	21 37					22 14	22 34						23 28				01 33		
Hemel Hempstead	a					21 19	21 42					22 19	22 38						23 32				01 43		
	d					21 19	21 42					22 19	22 38						23 32				01 43		
Apsley	d						21 45						22 41						23 39						
Kings Langley	d						21 48						22 45						23 43						
Watford Junction	a				21s18	21 30	21 57	22s02			22s21	22 32	22 53	22s58		23s10		23s19	23 47	23s52		01 23	02 08		
	d			21 13		21 30	21 57			22 11		22 32	22 54				23 13		23 48			01 23	02 08		
Bushey	d						22 00						22 57						23 51						
Harrow & Wealdstone ⊖	d			21 19			22 05			22 17			23 02				23 19		23 56				02 28		
Wembley Central	d																						02 43		
Shepherds Bush §	a																								
Kensington Olympia ⊖	a			21 42						22 42							23 42								
West Brompton ⊖	a			21 45						22 45							23 45								
Imperial Wharf §	a																								
Clapham Junction 10	a			21 53						22 52							23 53								
East Croydon 🚆	a			22 07																					
Gatwick Airport 10 ✈	a			22 23																					
Haywards Heath 3	a																								
Brighton 10	a																								
London Euston 15 ⊖	a	21 28	21 37		21 42	21 52	22 22	22 28	22 33		22 46	22 52	23 19	23 24		23 36		23 43	00 13	00 16		02 08	03 13		

For general notes see front of timetable
For details of catering facilities see Directory of Train Operators

§ It is unknown, at the time of going to press, when this station will open. For further details contact National Rail Enquiries 08457 484950 or see local publicity.

Table 66

19 July to 6 September

West Midlands, Northampton, Milton Keynes and Watford Junction → London

Network Diagram - See first page of Table 59

	LM	VT	VT	LM	LM	LM	SN		LM	LM	LM	SN	LM	LM	LM		VT	LM	VT	LM	LM	LM	SN	VT
	1	1	1	1	1	1	1		1	1	1	1	1	1	1		1 ◇	1	1 ◇	1	1	1	1	1 ◇
		A	B														□P		□P					□P
Wolverhampton 7 d		22p39	22p39														05 18							
Sandwell & Dudley d																	05 29							
Birmingham New Street 12 d		23p00	23p00														05 43							
Birmingham International d		23p10	23p10																					
Coventry d		23p23	23p23																					
Nuneaton d																	06u20		06 46					
Rugby a		23p34	23p36														06 38		07 00					
d		23p35	23p37														06 40		07 01					07 35
Northampton d	23p46								05 15		06 02			06 32	07 02							07 32		
Wolverton d	23p58								05 29		06 14			06 44	07 14							07 44		
Milton Keynes Central 10 a	00 01	00s16	00s16						05 32		06 17			06 47	07 17		07 20					07 47		07 55
d	00 02				03 40	04 35			05 33		06 18		06 34	06 48	07 18		07 21				07 33	07 48		07 57
Bletchley d	00 09				03 45	04 40			05 38	06 05	06 23		06 39	06 53	07 23			07 09		←	07 38	07 53		
Leighton Buzzard d	00 17			←	03 51	04 46			05 44	06 11	06 29		06 45	06 59	07 29			07 15		07 29	07 44	07 59		
Cheddington d	00 22			00 22					05 53				06 54		→						07 51	→		
Tring d	→			00 27	04 03	04 58			05 58	06 23			06 59					07 24			07 56			
Berkhamsted d				00 32	04 08	05 03			06 03	06 28	06 44		07 04	07 12				07 29		07 42	→			
Hemel Hempstead a				00 36	04 12	05 07			06 07	06 32	06 49		07 08	07 17				07 33		07 47				
d				00 36	04 12	05 07			06 07	06 32	06 49		07 08	07 17				07 33		07 47				
Apsley d									06 10	06 35			07 11					07 36						
Kings Langley d									06 14	06 39			07 15					07 40						
Watford Junction a		00s39	00s39	00 43	04 19	05 14			06 18	06 43	06 56		07 19	07 24			07s41	07 46	07s50	07 54				08s16
d				00 44	04 20	05 15	06 11		06 19	06 44	06 56	07 13	07 20	07 25				07 47		07 54			08 11	
Bushey d									06 22	06 47														
Harrow & Wealdstone ⊖ d				00 50	04 26	05 21	06 17		06 27	06 52		07 19	07 28					07 55					08 17	
Wembley Central d				00 59	04 35	05 30																		
Shepherds Bush § a																								
Kensington Olympia ⊖ a							06 42					07 42											08 42	
West Brompton ⊖ a							06 45					07 45											08 45	
Imperial Wharf § a																								
Clapham Junction 10 a							06 53					07 53											08 53	
East Croydon a							07 07					08 07											09 07	
Gatwick Airport 10 a							07 22					08 22											09 22	
Haywards Heath 3 a							07 42					08 42											09 42	
Brighton 10 a							08 08					09 09											10 07	
London Euston 15 ⊖ a		01 04	01 04	01 09	04 47	05 42			06 44	07 11	07 22		07 45	07 51			08 05	08 12	08 14	08 18				08 42

	LM		VT	LM	VT	VT	LM	LM	LM		VT	SN	LM	LM	VT	LM	VT		LM	LM	VT	SN	LM	LM
	1		1 ◇	1	1 ◇	1 ◇	1	1	1		1 ◇	1	1	1	1 ◇	1	1 ◇		1	1	1 ◇	1	1	1
			□P		□P	□P					□P				□P		□P				□P			
Wolverhampton 7 d			06 18												07 18									
Sandwell & Dudley d			06 30												07 29									
Birmingham New Street 12 d			06 46												07 44									
Birmingham International d																								
Coventry d																								
Nuneaton d			07u23			07 42									08u20		08 35							
Rugby a			07 41												08 40									
d			07 43		07 48										08 42									
Northampton d								08 02						08 42						09 02				
Wolverton d								08 14						08 54						09 14				
Milton Keynes Central 10 a			08 02		08 07	08 17		08 17						08 57	09 02					09 17				
d			08 04		08 09	08 18		08 18	08 45		08 57			08 58	09 04					09 18	09 30			09 45
Bletchley d				←				08 23	08 50					09 03						09 23				09 50
Leighton Buzzard d				07 59				08 29	08 56					09 10		←				09 29				09 56
Cheddington d	←								09 03							09 03								10 03
Tring d	07 56						08 26		→				08 56			09 08			09 26				09 56	10 08
Berkhamsted d	08 01			08 12			08 30	08 42					09 00			09 13			09 30	09 42			10 00	10 13
Hemel Hempstead a	08 05			08 17			08 35	08 47					09 05			09 17			09 35	09 47			10 05	10 17
d	08 05			08 17			08 35	08 47					09 05			09 17			09 35	09 47			10 05	10 17
Apsley d	08 08						08 38						09 08						09 38				10 08	
Kings Langley d	08 12						08 41						09 11						09 41				10 11	
Watford Junction a	08 20		08s24	08 28	08s30		08 48	08 55					09 18		09s23	09 27	09s34		09 47	09 54			10 16	10 24
d	08 21			08 29			08 49	08 55				09 11	09 18			09 28			09 47	09 54		10 11	10 16	10 25
Bushey d																								
Harrow & Wealdstone ⊖ d	08 29						08 57					09 17	09 27						09 56			10 17	10 25	
Wembley Central d																								
Shepherds Bush § a																								
Kensington Olympia ⊖ a												09 42										10 42		
West Brompton ⊖ a												09 45										10 45		
Imperial Wharf § a																								
Clapham Junction 10 a												09 53										10 53		
East Croydon a												10 07										11 07		
Gatwick Airport 10 a												10 22										11 22		
Haywards Heath 3 a												10 42										11 42		
Brighton 10 a												11 07										12 07		
London Euston 15 ⊖ a	08 46		08 50	08 52	08 59	09 00	09 14	09 18			09 38		09 43	09 53	09 48	09 50	09 59		10 13	10 20	10 15		10 42	10 48

For general notes see front of timetable
For details of catering facilities see Directory of Train Operators

§ It is unknown, at the time of going to press, when this station will open. For further details contact National Rail Enquiries 08457 484950 or see local publicity.

A 19 and 26 July, 30 August and 6 September

B 2 to 23 August

Due to Engineering Operations, services from Saturday 13 September on this Table had not been confirmed at time of going to press. These services will be issued in a special Supplement as soon as exact timings have been confirmed

Table 66

Saturdays

West Midlands, Northampton, Milton Keynes and Watford Junction → London

19 July to 6 September

Network Diagram - See first page of Table 59

		VT 1 ◇ ☕	LM 1	VT 1 ◇ ☕		VT 1 ◇ ☕	LM 1	LM 1	VT 1 ◇ ☕	SN 1	LM 1	LM 1		LM 1	VT 1 ◇ ☕	LM 1	VT 1 ◇ ☕	LM 1	LM 1	VT 1 ◇ ☕		VT 1 ◇ ☕	LM 1	SN 1	LM 1
Wolverhampton 7	d			08 18											09 18										
Sandwell & Dudley	d			08 29											09 29										
Birmingham New Street 12	d			08 44											09 44										
Birmingham International	d																								
Coventry	d																								
Nuneaton	d			09u28		09 40									10u21		10 36								
Rugby	a			09 46											10 40										
	d	09 24		09 48					10 23						10 41							11 21			
Northampton	d		09 42					10 02						10 42					11 02						
Wolverton	d		09 54					10 14						10 54					11 14						
Milton Keynes Central 10	a	09 44	09 57	10 07		10 15		10 17						10 57	11 01				11 17			11 40			
	d	09 46	09 58	10 09		10 17		10 18				10 45		10 58	11 02				11 18	11 30		11 42	11 45		
Bletchley	d		10 03					10 23				10 50		11 03					11 23				11 50		
Leighton Buzzard	d		10 11					10 29				10 56		11 11		←			11 29				11 56		
Cheddington	d											11 03 →				11 03							12 03 →		
Tring	d						10 26				10 56					11 08		11 26							11 56
Berkhamsted	d						10 30	10 42			11 00					11 13		11 30	11 42						12 00
Hemel Hempstead	a						10 35	10 47			11 05					11 17		11 35	11 47						12 05
	d						10 35	10 47			11 05					11 17		11 35	11 47						12 05
Apsley	d						10 38				11 08							11 38							12 08
Kings Langley	d						10 41				11 11							11 41							12 11
Watford Junction	a			10s31			10 46	10 54	11s00		11 16				11s23	11 26	11s34	11 46	11 54						12 16
	d						10 46	10 54		11 11	11 16					11 27		11 46	11 54					12 11	12 16
Bushey	d																								
Harrow & Wealdstone	⊖ d						10 55			11 17	11 25							11 55						12 17	12 25
Wembley Central	d																								
Shepherds Bush §	a																								
Kensington Olympia	⊖ a									11 42														12 42	
West Brompton	⊖ a									11 45														12 45	
Imperial Wharf §	a																								
Clapham Junction 10	a									11 53														12 52	
East Croydon	a									12 07														13 07	
Gatwick Airport 10	a									12 22														13 22	
Haywards Heath 3	a									12 42														13 42	
Brighton 10	a									13 07														14 07	
London Euston 15	⊖ a	10 29	10 52	10 57		11 05	11 13	11 20	11 27		11 43			11 54	11 48	11 51	12 00	12 13	12 19	12 19		12 27			12 42

		LM 1	VT 1 ◇ ☕	LM 1	VT 1 ◇ ☕	LM 1		LM 1	VT 1 ◇ ☕	SN 1	LM 1	LM 1	LM 1	VT 1 ◇ ☕		VT 1 ◇ ☕	LM 1	LM 1	VT 1 ◇ ☕	VT 1 ◇ ☕	LM 1	SN 1		LM 1	LM 1
Wolverhampton 7	d		10 18											11 18											
Sandwell & Dudley	d		10 29											11 29											
Birmingham New Street 12	d		10 44											11 44											
Birmingham International	d																								
Coventry	d																								
Nuneaton	d		11u21		11 36									12u24		12 37									
Rugby	a		11 40											12 43											
	d		11 41						12 22					12 44						13 22					
Northampton	d	11 42						12 02					12 42					13 02							13 42
Wolverton	d	11 54						12 14					12 54					13 14							13 54
Milton Keynes Central 10	a	11 57	12 01		12 09			12 17					12 57	13 04				13 17		13 41					13 57
	d	11 58	12 02		12 10			12 18				12 45	12 58	13 05				13 18	13 29	13 43	13 45				13 58
Bletchley	d	12 03						12 23				12 50	13 03					13 23			13 50				14 03
Leighton Buzzard	d	12 11		←				12 29				12 56	13 11					13 29			13 56				14 11
Cheddington	d			12 03								13 03									14 03 →				
Tring	d			12 08		12 26					12 56	13 08					13 26							13 56	
Berkhamsted	d			12 13		12 30		12 42			13 00	13 13					13 30	13 42						14 00	
Hemel Hempstead	a			12 17		12 35		12 47			13 05	13 17					13 35	13 47						14 05	
	d			12 17		12 35		12 47			13 05	13 17					13 35	13 47						14 05	
Apsley	d					12 38					13 08						13 38							14 08	
Kings Langley	d					12 41					13 11						13 41							14 11	
Watford Junction	a		12s23	12 26		12 46		12 56	12s59		13 18	13 24		13s31		13s36	13 46	13 56						14 16	
	d			12 27		12 46		12 56		13 11	13 18	13 25					13 46	13 56				14 11		14 16	
Bushey	d																								
Harrow & Wealdstone	⊖ d					12 55				13 17	13 27						13 55					14 17		14 25	
Wembley Central	d																								
Shepherds Bush §	a																								
Kensington Olympia	⊖ a									13 42												14 42			
West Brompton	⊖ a									13 45												14 45			
Imperial Wharf §	a																								
Clapham Junction 10	a									13 53												14 53			
East Croydon	a									14 07												15 07			
Gatwick Airport 10	a									14 22												15 22			
Haywards Heath 3	a									14 42												15 42			
Brighton 10	a									15 07												16 07			
London Euston 15	⊖ a	12 51	12 47	12 48	12 54	13 14		13 20	13 28		13 43	13 51	13 54	13 59		14 03	14 13	14 19	14 19	14 25				14 42	14 55

For general notes see front of timetable
For details of catering facilities see
Directory of Train Operators

§ It is unknown, at the time of going to press, when this station will open. For further details contact National Rail Enquiries 08457 484950 or see local publicity.

Due to Engineering Operations, services from Saturday 13 September on this Table had not been confirmed at time of going to press. These services will be issued in a special Supplement as soon as exact timings have been confirmed

West Midlands, Northampton, Milton Keynes and Watford Junction → London

19 July to 6 September

Network Diagram - See first page of Table 59

		VT	LM	VT	LM	LM	VT	SN		LM	LM	LM	VT	VT	LM	LM		VT	VT	LM	SN	LM	LM	VT	LM
		1◇ 🛒	1	1◇ 🛒	1	1	1◇ 🛒	1		1	1	1	1◇ 🛒	1◇ 🛒	1	1		1◇ 🛒	1◇ 🛒	1	1	1	1	1◇ 🛒	1
Wolverhampton 7	d	12 18											13 18											14 18	
Sandwell & Dudley	d	12 29											13 29											14 29	
Birmingham New Street 12	d	12 44											13 44											14 44	
Birmingham International	d																								
Coventry	d																								
Nuneaton	d	13u21		13 36									14u24	14 36										15u21	
Rugby	a	13 40											14 43											15 40	
	d	13 41					14 22						14 44						15 22					15 41	
Northampton	d					14 02						14 42				15 02							15 42		
Wolverton	d					14 14						14 54				15 14							15 54		
Milton Keynes Central 10	a	14 01		14 09		14 17						14 57	15 04			15 17			15 42				15 57	16 01	
	d	14 02		14 10		14 18					14 45	14 58	15 05			15 18		15 29	15 44	15 45			15 58	16 02	
Bletchley	d					14 23					14 50	15 03				15 23				15 50			16 03		
Leighton Buzzard	d		←			14 29					14 56	15 11				15 29				15 56			16 11		←
Cheddington	d		14 03								15 03									16 03 →					16 03
Tring	d		14 08		14 26					14 56	15 08				15 26							15 56			16 08
Berkhamsted	d		14 13		14 30	14 42				15 00	15 13				15 30	15 42						16 00			16 13
Hemel Hempstead	a		14 17		14 35	14 47				15 05	15 17				15 35	15 47						16 05			16 17
	d		14 17		14 35	14 47				15 05	15 17				15 35	15 47						16 05			16 17
Apsley	d				14 38					15 08					15 38							16 08			
Kings Langley	d				14 41					15 11					15 41							16 11			
Watford Junction	a	14s23	14 26		14 48	14 54	14s58			15 16	15 24		15s31	15s36	15 46	15 54						16 16		16s23	16 26
	d		14 27		14 48	14 54		15 11		15 16	15 25				15 46	15 54					16 11	16 16			16 27
Bushey	d																								
Harrow & Wealdstone	⊖ d				14 57			15 17		15 25					15 55						16 17	16 25			
Wembley Central	d																								
Shepherds Bush §	a																								
Kensington Olympia	⊖ a							15 42													16 42				
West Brompton	⊖ a							15 45													16 45				
Imperial Wharf §	a																								
Clapham Junction 10	a							15 53													16 53				
East Croydon	a							16 07													17 07				
Gatwick Airport 10	✈ a							16 22													17 22				
Haywards Heath 3	a							16 42													17 42				
Brighton 10	a							17 07													18 07				
London Euston 15	⊖ a	14 47	14 51	15 00	15 13	15 18	15 26			15 42	15 51	15 54	15 59	16 03	16 13	16 20		16 16	16 28			16 42	16 54	16 47	16 51

		VT		LM	LM	VT	SN	LM	LM	LM		VT	LM	VT	LM	LM	VT	SN		LM	LM	VT	LM	VT	VT
		1◇ 🛒		1	1	1◇ 🛒	1	1	1	1		1◇ 🛒	1	1◇ 🛒	1	1	1◇ 🛒	1		1	1	1◇ 🛒	1	1◇ 🛒	1◇ 🛒
Wolverhampton 7	d											15 18												16 18	
Sandwell & Dudley	d											15 29												16 29	
Birmingham New Street 12	d											15 44												16 44	
Birmingham International	d																								
Coventry	d																								
Nuneaton	d											16u21		16 36										17u24	17 36
Rugby	a											16 40												17 43	17 49
	d					16 26						16 41										17 25		17 44	17 51
Northampton	d				16 02					16 42						17 02							17 42		
Wolverton	d				16 14					16 54						17 14							17 54		
Milton Keynes Central 10	a				16 17					16 57		17 01				17 17						17 44	17 57	18 04	18 10
	d	16 10			16 18				16 45	16 58		17 02				17 18	17 29				17 45	17 46	17 58	18 05	18 12
Bletchley	d				16 23				16 50	17 03						17 23					17 50		18 03		
Leighton Buzzard	d				16 29				16 56	17 11			←			17 29					17 56		18 11		
Cheddington	d								17 03 →				17 03								18 03				
Tring	d			16 26				16 56					17 08		17 26					17 56	18 08				
Berkhamsted	d			16 30	16 42			17 00					17 13		17 30	17 42				18 00	18 13				
Hemel Hempstead	a			16 35	16 47			17 05					17 17		17 35	17 47				18 05	18 17				
	d			16 35	16 47			17 05					17 17		17 35	17 47				18 05	18 17				
Apsley	d			16 38				17 08							17 38					18 08					
Kings Langley	d			16 41				17 11							17 41					18 11					
Watford Junction	a			16 48	16 54	17s03		17 16				17s23	17 26	17s33	17 46	17 54				18 16	18 24			18s31	
	d			16 48	16 54		17 11	17 16					17 27		17 46	17 54		18 11		18 16	18 25				
Bushey	d																								
Harrow & Wealdstone	⊖ d			16 57			17 17	17 25							17 55			18 17		18 25					
Wembley Central	d																								
Shepherds Bush §	a																								
Kensington Olympia	⊖ a						17 42											18 42							
West Brompton	⊖ a						17 45											18 45							
Imperial Wharf §	a																								
Clapham Junction 10	a						17 53											18 53							
East Croydon	a						18 07											19 07							
Gatwick Airport 10	✈ a						18 22											19 22							
Haywards Heath 3	a						18 42											19 42							
Brighton 10	a						19 07											20 07							
London Euston 15	⊖ a	17 00		17 13	17 18	17 28		17 42		17 54		17 46	17 51	18 00	18 13	18 20	18 19			18 42	18 48	18 30	18 51	18 56	19 00

For general notes see front of timetable
For details of catering facilities see Directory of Train Operators

§ It is unknown, at the time of going to press, when this station will open. For further details contact National Rail Enquiries 08457 484950 or see local publicity.

Due to Engineering Operations, services from Saturday 13 September on this Table had not been confirmed at time of going to press. These services will be issued in a special Supplement as soon as exact timings have been confirmed

Saturdays

West Midlands, Northampton, Milton Keynes and Watford Junction → London

19 July to 6 September

Network Diagram - See first page of Table 59

		LM	LM	VT		LM	SN	LM	VT	LM	VT	LM		LM	VT	SN	LM	VT	LM	LM		VT	VT	SN	LM
		1	1	1 ◇		1	1	1	1 ◇	1	1 ◇	1		1	1 ◇	1	1	1 ◇	1	1		1 ◇	1 ◇	1	1
				☕					☕		☕				☕			☕				☕	☕		
Wolverhampton 7	d								17 18													18 18			
Sandwell & Dudley	d								17 29													18 29			
Birmingham New Street 12	d								17 44													18 44			
Birmingham International	d																								
Coventry	d																								
Nuneaton	d								18u21		18 36											19u21	19 36		
Rugby	a								18 40													19 40			
	d			18 22					18 41									19 23				19 41			
Northampton	d		18 02			18 32								19 02					19 32	19 47					20 32
Wolverton	d		18 14			18 44								19 14					19 44						20 44
Milton Keynes Central 10	a		18 17			18 47			19 02					19 17				19 44	19 47	20 01		20 06	20 12		20 48
	d		18 18			18 48			19 03					19 18	19 30			19 45	19 48	20 02		20 08	20 14		20 49
Bletchley	d		18 23			18 53								19 23					19 53	20 07					20 54
Leighton Buzzard	d		18 29			18 59				←				19 29					19 59	20 13					21 00
Cheddington	d					19 06				19 06										20 18					
Tring	d	18 26				→		18 56		19 11		19 26					19 53			20 27					
Berkhamsted	d	18 30	18 42					19 00		19 16		19 30					19 57		20 14	20 32					
Hemel Hempstead	a	18 35	18 47					19 05		19 20		19 35		19 42			20 02		20 19	20 36					21 14
	d	18 35	18 47					19 05		19 20		19 35		19 47			20 02		20 19	20 36					21 19
Apsley	d	18 38						19 08				19 38					20 05			20 39					
Kings Langley	d	18 41						19 11				19 41					20 08			20 43					
Watford Junction	a	18 48	18 54	18s58				19 16	19s22	19 27	19s31	19 46		19 54	20 03		20 17	20 21	20 30	20 51		20s56	21 02		21 30
	d	18 48	18 54				19 11	19 16		19 28		19 46		19 54	20 04	20 13	20 17	20 22	20 30	20 52			21 03	21 13	21 30
Bushey	d																								
Harrow & Wealdstone ⊖	d	18 57					19 17	19 25				19 55				20 19	20 25		20 39	21 00				21 19	
Wembley Central	d																								
Shepherds Bush §	a																								
Kensington Olympia ⊖	a						19 42									20 42								21 42	
West Brompton ⊖	a						19 45									20 45								21 45	
Imperial Wharf §	a																								
Clapham Junction 10	a						19 53									20 53								21 53	
East Croydon	a						20 07									21 07								22 07	
Gatwick Airport 10	a						20 22									21 22								22 23	
Haywards Heath 3	a						20 42																		
Brighton 10	a						21 07																		
London Euston 15 ⊖	a	19 13	19 18	19 24				19 42	19 47	19 51	19 57	20 13		20 21	20 35		20 47	20 58	21 01	21 22		21 26	21 34		21 59

		LM	VT	VT	VT	SN		VT	LM	LM	VT	VT	VT	SN		VT	VT	LM	VT	LM	LM	LM			
		1	1 ◇	1 ◇	1 ◇	1		1 ◇	1	1	1 ◇	1 ◇	1 ◇	1		1 ◇	1 ◇	1	1 ◇	1	🚌	🚌			
			☕	☕	☕			☕			☕	☕	☕			☕	☕		☕						
Wolverhampton 7	d		19 18								20 18								21 18						
Sandwell & Dudley	d		19 29								20 29								21 29						
Birmingham New Street 12	d		19 44								20 44								21 44						
Birmingham International	d																								
Coventry	d																								
Nuneaton	d		20u21		20 38						21u24		21 46						22u24						
Rugby	a		20 40								21 43		22 00						22 43						
	d		20 41					21 03			21 44	21 55	22 01						22 44						
Northampton	d	20 50							21 32	21 47								22 42		23 35					
Wolverton	d								21 44									22 54		23 47					
Milton Keynes Central 10	a	21 03	21 09						21 47	22 03	22 08	22 18	22 24					22 57	23 07	23 50					
	d	21 04	21 10	21 17					21 48	22 04	22 10	22 20	22 26			22 32	22 40	22 58	23 09	23 51	23 58	23 58			
Bletchley	d	21 10							21 53	22 09								23 03		23a55	00 13	00 13			
Leighton Buzzard	d	21 16							21 59	22 15								23 09			00 38	00 38			
Cheddington	d	21 21								22 20								23 18				00 58			
Tring	d	21 30								22 29								23 23				01 18			
Berkhamsted	d	21 35							22 14	22 34								23 28				01 33			
Hemel Hempstead	a	21 39							22 19	22 38								23 32				01 43			
	d	21 39							22 19	22 38								23 32				01 43			
Apsley	d	21 42								22 41								23 39							
Kings Langley	d	21 46								22 45								23 43							
Watford Junction	a	21 52	21s57		22s09			22s16	22 30	22 53	22s58	23s04	23s10			23s18	23s23	23 47			01 23	02 08			
	d	21 53				22 11			22 30	22 54				23 13				23 48			01 23	02 08			
Bushey	d																								
Harrow & Wealdstone ⊖	d	22 01				22 17				23 02				23 19				23 57				02 28			
Wembley Central	d																					02 43			
Shepherds Bush §	a																								
Kensington Olympia ⊖	a					22 42								23 42											
West Brompton ⊖	a					22 45								23 45											
Imperial Wharf §	a																								
Clapham Junction 10	a					22 52								23 53											
East Croydon	a																								
Gatwick Airport 10	a																								
Haywards Heath 3	a																								
Brighton 10	a																								
London Euston 15 ⊖	a	22 25	22 31	22 35	22 45			22 52	23 01	23 24	23 31	23 37	23 45			23 53	23 56	00 19	00 26		02 08	03 13			

For general notes see front of timetable
For details of catering facilities see Directory of Train Operators

§ It is unknown, at the time of going to press, when this station will open. For further details contact National Rail Enquiries 08457 484950 or see local publicity.

Due to Engineering Operations, services from Saturday 13 September on this Table had not been confirmed at time of going to press. These services will be issued in a special Supplement as soon as exact timings have been confirmed

Table 66

Sundays

until 13 July

West Midlands, Northampton, Milton Keynes and Watford Junction → London

Network Diagram - See first page of Table 59

		LM 🚌	LM 🚌	LM 🚌	LM 🚌	LM 🚌	LM 🚌	LM 🚌		LM 🚌	LM 🚌	LM 🚌	SN 1	LM 1	LM 1	SN 1		LM 1	LM 1	VT 1 ◇ ☕	SN 1	LM 1	VT 1 ◇ ☕	LM 1	VT 1 ◇ ☕
Wolverhampton 7	d																			08 26					09 10
Sandwell & Dudley	d																								
Birmingham New Street 12	d																			08 59					09 45
Birmingham International	d																								
Coventry	d																								
Nuneaton	d																			09u43					10u26
Rugby	a																			09 57					10 40
	d																			09 58					10 41
Northampton	d										06 40	08 10						09 30	09 56			10 26		10 56	
Wolverton	d										07 14	08 44						09 43	10 08			10 38		11 08	
Milton Keynes Central 10	a										07 29	08 59						09 46	10 11	10 30		10 41		11 11	11 16
	d	23p58	23p58		04 50	05 50	06 40			07 15	07 30	09 00						09 47	10 12	10 31		10 42	10 54	11 12	11 18
Bletchley	d	00 13	00 13		05 06	06 06	06 56			07 31	07 46	09a15			09 30			09 52	10 17			10 47		11 17	
Leighton Buzzard	d	00 38	00 38		05 32	06 32				07 57					09 36			09 58	10 23			10 53		11 23	
Cheddington	d		00 58		05 53	06 53				08 18					09 41				10 28					11 28	
Tring	d		01 18	05 14	06 14	07 14		←		08 39					09 50				10 37					11 37	
Berkhamsted	d		01 33	05 30	06 30	07 30		07 30		08 55					09 55			10 13	10 42			11 08		11 42	
Hemel Hempstead	a		01 43	05 40	06 40	→		07 40		09 05					09 59			10 18	10 46			11 13		11 46	
	d		01 43	05 41	06 41			07 41						09 27	09 59			10 18	10 46			11 13		11 46	
Apsley	d			05 47	06 47			07 47						09 30				10 21				11 16			
Kings Langley	d			05 58	06 58			07 58						09 33				10 24				11 19			
Watford Junction	a	01 23	02 08	06 13	07 13		07 56	08 13			08 46			09 38	10 06			10 31	10 55	11s04		11 26	11s33	11 55	12s00
	d	01 23	02 08	06 14	07 14		07 57	08 14			08 47		09 22	09 38	10 07	10 22		10 31	10 56		11 22	11 26		11 56	
Bushey	d																								
Harrow & Wealdstone ⊖	d		02 28	06 35	07 35		08 18	08 35			09 08		09 28	09 48	10 13	10 27		10 37	11 02		11 28	11 32		12 02	
Wembley Central	d		02 43																						
Shepherds Bush §	a																								
Kensington Olympia ⊖	a												09 47			10 47					11 47				
West Brompton ⊖	a												09 49			10 49					11 49				
Imperial Wharf §	a																								
Clapham Junction 10	a												10 00			11 00					12 00				
East Croydon	a																								
Gatwick Airport 10	a																								
Haywards Heath 3	a																								
Brighton 10	a																								
London Euston 15 ⊖	a	02 08	03 13	07 10	08 10		08 53	09 10			09 43			10 08	10 33			10 55	11 20	11 25		11 50	11 55	12 20	12 22

		VT 1 ◇ ☕		VT 1 ◇ ☕	SN 1	LM 1	VT 1 ◇ ☕	LM 1	VT 1 ◇ ☕	VT 1 ◇ ☕		SN 1	LM 1	VT 1 ◇ ☕	VT 1 ◇ ☕	LM 1	VT 1 ◇ ☕	VT 1 ◇ ☕		SN 1	LM 1	VT 1 ◇ ☕	LM 1	VT 1 ◇ ☕	VT 1 ◇ ☕
Wolverhampton 7	d								10 12						11 12							12 12			
Sandwell & Dudley	d																								
Birmingham New Street 12	d								10 45						11 45							12 45			
Birmingham International	d																								
Coventry	d																								
Nuneaton	d			10 44					11u26	11 45					12u26			12 45				13u26			13 47
Rugby	a								11 40						12 40							13 40			
	d						11 23		11 41					12 23	12 41							13 41		13 47	
Northampton	d					11 26		11 56					12 26			12 56					13 26		13 56		
Wolverton	d					11 38		12 08					12 38			13 08					13 38		14 08		
Milton Keynes Central 10	a			11 30		11 41	11 56	12 11	12 16				12 41		13 02	13 11		13 29			13 41	14 02	14 11	14 16	
	d	11 25		11 31		11 42	11 57	12 12	12 18				12 42		13 04	13 12	13 18	13 30			13 42	14 04	14 12	14 18	
Bletchley	d					11 47		12 17					12 47			13 17					13 47		14 17		
Leighton Buzzard	d					11 53		12 23					12 53			13 23					13 53		14 23		
Cheddington	d							12 28								13 28							14 28		
Tring	d							12 37								13 37							14 37		
Berkhamsted	d					12 08		12 42					13 08			13 42					14 08		14 42		
Hemel Hempstead	a					12 13		12 46					13 13			13 46					14 13		14 46		
	d					12 13		12 46					13 13			13 46					14 13		14 46		
Apsley	d					12 16							13 16								14 16				
Kings Langley	d					12 19							13 19								14 19				
Watford Junction	a					12 26	12s33	12 55	13s00	13s11			13 26	13s31	13s36	13 55					14 26	14s36	14 55		15s10
	d				12 22	12 26		12 56				13 22	13 26			13 56				14 22	14 26		14 56		
Bushey	d																								
Harrow & Wealdstone ⊖	d				12 28	12 32		13 02				13 28	13 32			14 02				14 28	14 32		15 02		
Wembley Central	d																								
Shepherds Bush §	a																								
Kensington Olympia ⊖	a				12 47							13 47								14 47					
West Brompton ⊖	a				12 49							13 48								14 49					
Imperial Wharf §	a																								
Clapham Junction 10	a				13 00							14 00								15 00					
East Croydon	a																								
Gatwick Airport 10	a																								
Haywards Heath 3	a																								
Brighton 10	a																								
London Euston 15 ⊖	a	12 29		12 33		12 50	13 00	13 20	13 22	13 35			13 50	13 57	13 57	14 20	14 24	14 30			14 50	14 57	15 20	15 24	15 34

For general notes see front of timetable
For details of catering facilities see Directory of Train Operators

§ It is unknown, at the time of going to press, when this station will open. For further details contact National Rail Enquiries 08457 484950 or see local publicity.

Table 66

Sundays

until 13 July

West Midlands, Northampton, Milton Keynes and Watford Junction → London

Network Diagram - See first page of Table 59

Station		SN 1	LM 1	VT 1◇		VT 1◇	VT 1◇	LM 1	VT 1◇	VT 1◇	SN 1	LM 1		VT 1◇	VT 1◇	LM 1	VT 1◇	SN 1	LM 1	VT 1◇		VT 1◇	LM 1	VT 1◇	VT 1◇
Wolverhampton 7	d						13 12								14 12							15 12			
Sandwell & Dudley	d																								
Birmingham New Street 12	d						13 45								14 45							15 45			
Birmingham International	d																								
Coventry	d																								
Nuneaton	d						14u30		14 43						15u29		15 41					16u27		16 42	
Rugby	a						14 43								15 42							16 41			
	d			14 34			14 45							15 25	15 44					16 22		16 42			
Northampton	d		14 26					14 56				15 26				15 56			16 26				16 56		
Wolverton	d		14 38					15 08				15 38				16 08			16 38				17 08		
Milton Keynes Central 10	a		14 41				15 06	15 11	15 18			15 41		15 49	16 06	16 11			16 41			17 04	17 11	17 19	
	d		14 42			15 02	15 08	15 12	15 20	15 34		15 42		15 51	16 07	16 12			16 42			17 06	17 12	17 20	17 31
Bletchley	d		14 47					15 17				15 47				16 17			16 47				17 17		
Leighton Buzzard	d		14 53					15 23				15 53				16 23			16 53				17 23		
Cheddington	d							15 28								16 28							17 28		
Tring	d							15 37								16 37							17 37		
Berkhamsted	d		15 08					15 42				16 08				16 42			17 08				17 42		
Hemel Hempstead	a		15 13					15 46				16 13				16 46			17 13				17 46		
	d		15 13					15 46				16 13				16 46			17 13				17 46		
Apsley	d		15 16									16 16							17 16						
Kings Langley	d		15 19									16 19							17 19						
Watford Junction	a		15 26	15s36			15s47	15 55				16 26			16s42	16 55	17s00		17 26	17s31		17s48	17 55		
	d	15 22	15 26					15 56			16 22	16 26				16 56		17 22	17 26				17 56		
Bushey	d																								
Harrow & Wealdstone ⊖	d	15 28	15 32					16 02			16 28	16 32				17 02		17 28	17 32				18 02		
Wembley Central	d																								
Shepherds Bush §	a																								
Kensington Olympia ⊖	a	15 47									16 47							17 47							
West Brompton ⊖	a	15 50									16 50							17 50							
Imperial Wharf §	a																								
Clapham Junction 10	a	16 00									17 00							18 00							
East Croydon	a																								
Gatwick Airport 10	a																								
Haywards Heath 3	a																								
Brighton 10	a																								
London Euston 15 ⊖	a	.	15 50	16 03	.	16 03	16 11	16 20	16 24	16 25	.	16 50	.	16 57	17 03	17 20	17 26	.	17 50	17 55	.	18 10	18 20	18 24	18 25

Station		SN 1	LM 1	VT 1◇	VT 1◇	LM 1		VT 1◇	VT 1◇	SN 1	LM 1	VT 1◇	VT 1◇	LM 1		VT 1◇	VT 1◇	VT 1◇	SN 1	LM 1	VT 1◇	VT 1◇		VT 1◇	LM 1
Wolverhampton 7	d							16 12					17 12											18 10	
Sandwell & Dudley	d																								
Birmingham New Street 12	d							16 45					17 45											18 45	
Birmingham International	d																								
Coventry	d																								
Nuneaton	d							17u31	17 52				18u29			18 43								19u27	
Rugby	a							17 46					18 43											19 40	
	d			17 24				17 47				18 36	18 45								19 21			19 42	
Northampton	d		17 26			17 56					18 26			18 56						19 26					19 56
Wolverton	d		17 38			18 08					18 38			19 08						19 38					20 08
Milton Keynes Central 10	a		17 41	17 49		18 11		18 16			18 41		19 07	19 11		19 20				19 41	19 46			20 06	20 11
	d		17 42	17 50	18 02	18 12		18 18			18 42		19 08	19 12		19 21	19 31	19 37		19 42	19 48	20 01		20 07	20 12
Bletchley	d		17 47			18 17					18 47			19 17						19 47					20 17
Leighton Buzzard	d		17 53			18 23					18 53			19 23						19 53					20 23
Cheddington	d					18 28								19 28											20 28
Tring	d					18 37								19 37											20 37
Berkhamsted	d		18 08			18 42					19 08			19 42						20 08					20 42
Hemel Hempstead	a		18 13			18 46					19 13			19 46						20 13					20 46
	d		18 13			18 46					19 13			19 46						20 13					20 46
Apsley	d		18 16								19 16									20 16					
Kings Langley	d		18 19								19 19									20 19					
Watford Junction	a		18 26			18 55		19s00	19s06		19 26	19s31	19s48	19 55						20 26		20s35		20s42	20 55
	d	18 22	18 26			18 56				19 22	19 26			19 56					20 22	20 26					20 56
Bushey	d																								
Harrow & Wealdstone ⊖	d	18 28	18 32			19 02				19 28	19 32			20 02					20 28	20 32					21 02
Wembley Central	d																								
Shepherds Bush §	a																								
Kensington Olympia ⊖	a	18 47								19 47									20 47						
West Brompton ⊖	a	18 50								19 50									20 50						
Imperial Wharf §	a																								
Clapham Junction 10	a	19 00								20 00									21 00						
East Croydon	a																								
Gatwick Airport 10	a																								
Haywards Heath 3	a																								
Brighton 10	a																								
London Euston 15 ⊖	a	.	18 50	18 57	18 59	19 20	.	19 23	19 29	.	19 50	19 55	20 11	20 20	.	20 24	20 25	20 32	.	20 50	20 57	20 59	.	21 07	21 20

For general notes see front of timetable
For details of catering facilities see Directory of Train Operators

§ It is unknown, at the time of going to press, when this station will open. For further details contact National Rail Enquiries 08457 484950 or see local publicity.

Table 66

Sundays

until 13 July

West Midlands, Northampton, Milton Keynes and Watford Junction → London

Network Diagram - See first page of Table 59

		VT	SN	LM	VT	VT	LM	VT		SN	LM	VT	VT	VT	LM	VT		VT	SN	LM	VT	LM			
		1◇	1	1	1◇	1◇	1	1◇		1	1	1◇	1◇	1◇	1	1◇		1◇	1	1	1◇	1			
		☕			☕	☕		☕				☕	☕	☕		☕		☕			☕				
Wolverhampton 7	d					19 12								20 04							21 12				
Sandwell & Dudley	d																								
Birmingham New Street 12	d					19 45								20 45							21 45				
Birmingham International	d																								
Coventry	d																								
Nuneaton	d	19 40				20u26		20 40						21u26		21 34		21 41			22u26				
Rugby	a					20 40								21 40		21 48					22 39				
	d				20 21	20 41							21 23	21 41		21 50					22 40				
Northampton	d			20 26			20 56				21 26				21 56					22 56		23 56			
Wolverton	d			20 38			21 08				21 38				22 08					23 08		00 08			
Milton Keynes Central 10	a			20 41		21 03	21 11	21 17			21 41		21 52	22 03	22 11	22 22		22 28		23 11	23 16	00 11			
	d			20 42		21 05	21 12	21 18			21 42	21 48	21 54	22 05	22 12	22 24		22 30		23 12	23 18	00 12			
Bletchley	d			20 47			21 17				21 47				22 17					23 17		00 17			
Leighton Buzzard	d			20 53			21 23				21 53				22 23					23 23		00 23			
Cheddington	d						21 28								22 28					23 28		00 28			
Tring	d						21 37								22 37					23 37		00 37			
Berkhamsted	d			21 08			21 42				22 08				22 42					23 42		00 42			
Hemel Hempstead	a			21 13			21 46				22 13				22 46					23 46		00 46			
	d			21 13			21 46				22 13				22 46					23 46		00 46			
Apsley	d			21 16							22 16									23 49		00 49			
Kings Langley	d			21 19							22 19									23 53		00 53			
Watford Junction	a	21s00		21 26	21s31	21s44	21 55				22 26	22s31	22s36	22s44	22 55	23s00		23s06		23 58	00s03	00 59			
	d		21 22	21 26			21 56			22 22	22 26				22 56				23 22	23 59		01 00			
Bushey	d																								
Harrow & Wealdstone ⊖	d		21 28	21 32			22 02			22 28	22 32				23 02				23 28	00 05		01 06			
Wembley Central	d																								
Shepherds Bush §	a																								
Kensington Olympia ⊖	a		21 47							22 47									23 47						
West Brompton ⊖	a		21 50							22 50									23 50						
Imperial Wharf §	a																								
Clapham Junction 10	a		22 00							23 00									00 01						
East Croydon	a																		00 20						
Gatwick Airport 10	a																								
Haywards Heath 3	a																								
Brighton 10	a																								
London Euston 15 ⊖	a	21 24		21 50	21 57	22 04	22 20	22 24			22 50	22 52	23 02	23 05	23 20	23 21		23 30		00 24	00 25	01 24			

Sundays

20 July to 7 September

		LM	LM	LM	LM	LM	LM		LM	LM	LM	LM	SN	LM		LM	SN	LM	LM	VT	VT		SN	LM	VT
		🚌	🚌	🚌	🚌	🚌	🚌		🚌	🚌	🚌	🚌	1	1		1	1	1	1	1◇	1◇		1	1	1◇
																				☕	☕				☕
Wolverhampton 7	d																			08 33					
Sandwell & Dudley	d																			08 44					
Birmingham New Street 12	d																			08 59					
Birmingham International	d																								
Coventry	d																								
Nuneaton	d																			09u40					
Rugby	a																			09 54					
	d																			09 55					
Northampton	d										06 40	08 10						09 30	09 56					10 26	
Wolverton	d										07 14	08 44						09 43	10 08					10 38	
Milton Keynes Central 10	a										07 29	08 59						09 46	10 11	10 16				10 41	
	d	23p58	23p58		04 50	05 50	06 40			07 15	07 30	09 00						09 47	10 12	10 18	10 25			10 42	10 53
Bletchley	d	00 13	00 13		05 06	06 06	06 56			07 31	07 46	09a15				09 30		09 52	10 17					10 47	
Leighton Buzzard	d	00 38	00 38		05 32	06 32				07 57						09 36		09 58	10 23					10 53	
Cheddington	d		00 58		05 53	06 53				08 18						09 41			10 28						
Tring	d		01 18	05 14	06 14	07 14			←	08 39						09 50			10 37						
Berkhamsted	d		01 33	05 30	06 30	07 30			07 30	08 55						09 55		10 13	10 42					11 08	
Hemel Hempstead	a		01 43	05 40	06 40	→			07 40	09 05						09 59		10 18	10 46					11 13	
	d		01 43	05 41	06 41				07 41					09 27		09 59		10 18	10 46					11 13	
Apsley	d			05 47	06 47				07 47					09 30				10 21						11 16	
Kings Langley	d			05 58	06 58				07 58					09 33				10 24						11 19	
Watford Junction	a	01 23	02 08	06 13	07 13		07 56		08 13		08 46			09 38		10 06		10 31	10 55	11s00	11s06			11 26	
	d	01 23	02 08	06 14	07 14		07 57		08 14		08 47		09 22	09 38		10 07	10 22	10 31	10 56				11 22	11 26	
Bushey	d																								
Harrow & Wealdstone ⊖	d		02 28	06 35	07 35		08 18		08 35		09 08		09 28	09 51		10 15	10 27	10 40	11 04				11 28	11 35	
Wembley Central	d		02 43																						
Shepherds Bush §	a																								
Kensington Olympia ⊖	a												09 47				10 47						11 47		
West Brompton ⊖	a												09 49				10 49						11 49		
Imperial Wharf §	a																								
Clapham Junction 10	a												10 00				11 00						12 00		
East Croydon	a																								
Gatwick Airport 10	a																								
Haywards Heath 3	a																								
Brighton 10	a																								
London Euston 15 ⊖	a	02 08	03 13	07 10	08 10		08 53		09 10		09 43			10 16		10 40		11 05	11 29	11 31	11 36			12 00	12 06

For general notes see front of timetable
For details of catering facilities see Directory of Train Operators

§ It is unknown, at the time of going to press, when this station will open. For further details contact National Rail Enquiries 08457 484950 or see local publicity.

Due to Engineering Operations, services from Sunday 14 September on this Table had not been confirmed at time of going to press. These services will be issued in a special Supplement as soon as exact timings have been confirmed

Table 66

Sundays

West Midlands, Northampton, Milton Keynes and Watford Junction → London

20 July to 7 September

Network Diagram - See first page of Table 59

Station		VT	LM	VT	SN	LM	VT	VT	LM	VT	SN	LM	VT	VT	VT	LM	VT	SN	LM	VT	LM	VT
		1 ◇ ☕	1	1 ◇ ☕	1	1	1 ◇ ☕	1 ◇ ☕	1	1 ◇ ☕	1	1	1 ◇ ☕	1 ◇ ☕	1 ◇ ☕	1	1 ◇ ☕	1	1	1 ◇ ☕	1	1 ◇ ☕
Wolverhampton 7	d	09 18						10 18							11 18					12 18		
Sandwell & Dudley	d	09 29						10 29							11 29					12 29		
Birmingham New Street 12	d	09 45						10 45							11 45					12 45		
Birmingham International	d																					
Coventry	d																					
Nuneaton	d	10u26		10 56				11u29		11 58					12u29		12 56			13u26		
Rugby	a	10 40						11 43							12 43					13 40		
	d	10 41					11 40	11 45						12 40	12 45					13 41		14 05
Northampton	d		10 56			11 26			11 56			12 26				12 56			13 26		13 56	
Wolverton	d		11 08			11 38			12 08			12 38				13 08			13 38		14 08	
Milton Keynes Central 10	a	11 04	11 11	11 29		11 41	12 01	12 06	12 12			12 41			13 06	13 12	13 32		13 41	14 02	14 11	14 27
	d	11 06	11 12	11 31		11 42	12 02	12 08	12 13			12 42	12 57		13 07	13 13	13 33		13 42	14 04	14 12	14 28
Bletchley	d		11 17			11 47			12 18			12 47				13 18			13 47		14 17	
Leighton Buzzard	d		11 23			11 53			12 24			12 53				13 24			13 53		14 23	
Cheddington	d		11 28						12 29							13 29					14 28	
Tring	d		11 37						12 38							13 38					14 37	
Berkhamsted	d		11 42			12 08			12 43			13 08				13 43			14 08		14 42	
Hemel Hempstead	a		11 46			12 13			12 47			13 13				13 47			14 13		14 46	
	d		11 46			12 13			12 47			13 13				13 47			14 13		14 46	
Apsley	d					12 16						13 16							14 16			
Kings Langley	d					12 19						13 19							14 19			
Watford Junction	a	11s44	11 55			12 26	12s36	12s43	12 56	13s02		13 26		13s36	13s43	13 56			14 26	14s42	14 55	
	d		11 56		12 22	12 26			12 57		13 22	13 26				13 57		14 22	14 26		14 56	
Bushey	d																					
Harrow & Wealdstone	⊖ d		12 04		12 28	12 35			13 05		13 28	13 35				14 05		14 28	14 35		15 04	
Wembley Central	d																					
Shepherds Bush §	a																					
Kensington Olympia	⊖ a				12 47						13 47							14 47				
West Brompton	⊖ a				12 49						13 48							14 49				
Imperial Wharf §	a																					
Clapham Junction 10	a				13 00						14 00							15 00				
East Croydon	a																					
Gatwick Airport 10	a																					
Haywards Heath 3	a																					
Brighton 10	a																					
London Euston 15	⊖ a	12 14	12 29	12 39		13 00	13 17	13 17	13 30	13 36		14 00	14 05	14 12	14 13	14 30	14 42		15 00	15 12	15 29	15 34

Station		VT	SN	LM	VT	VT	VT	LM	VT	VT	SN	LM	VT	VT	LM	VT	SN	LM	VT	VT	LM	VT
		1 ◇ ☕	1	1	1 ◇ ☕	1 ◇ ☕	1 ◇ ☕	1	1 ◇ ☕	1 ◇ ☕	1	1	1 ◇ ☕	1 ◇ ☕	1	1 ◇ ☕	1	1	1 ◇ ☕	1 ◇ ☕	1	1 ◇ ☕
Wolverhampton 7	d						13 18							14 18						15 18		
Sandwell & Dudley	d						13 29							14 29						15 29		
Birmingham New Street 12	d						13 45							14 45						15 45		
Birmingham International	d																					
Coventry	d																					
Nuneaton	d	14 03					14u30		14 55					15u31		15 55				16u29		16 56
Rugby	a						14 45							15 45						16 43		
	d					14 41	14 46						15 41	15 46					16 40	16 45		
Northampton	d			14 26				14 56				15 26			15 56			16 26			16 56	
Wolverton	d			14 39				15 09				15 38			16 10			16 38			17 09	
Milton Keynes Central 10	a			14 42			15 07	15 12	15 30			15 41	16 03	16 08	16 14			16 41		17 07	17 12	17 31
	d			14 43	14 58		15 09	15 13	15 31	15 37		15 42	16 05	16 10	16 15			16 42		17 08	17 13	17 33
Bletchley	d			14 48				15 18				15 47			16 20			16 47			17 18	
Leighton Buzzard	d			14 54				15 24				15 53			16 26			16 53			17 24	
Cheddington	d							15 29							16 31						17 29	
Tring	d							15 38							16 40						17 38	
Berkhamsted	d			15 09				15 43				16 08			16 45			17 08			17 43	
Hemel Hempstead	a			15 14				15 47				16 13			16 49			17 13			17 47	
	d			15 14				15 47				16 13			16 49			17 13			17 47	
Apsley	d			15 17								16 16						17 16				
Kings Langley	d			15 20								16 19						17 19				
Watford Junction	a	15s12		15 27		15s36	15s43	15 56				16 26		16s42	16 58	17s03		17 26	17s36	17s43	17 56	
	d		15 22	15 27				15 57			16 22	16 26			16 59		17 22	17 26			17 57	
Bushey	d																					
Harrow & Wealdstone	⊖ d		15 28	15 36				16 05			16 28	16 35			17 07		17 28	17 35			18 05	
Wembley Central	d																					
Shepherds Bush §	a																					
Kensington Olympia	⊖ a		15 47								16 47						17 47					
West Brompton	⊖ a		15 50								16 50						17 50					
Imperial Wharf §	a																					
Clapham Junction 10	a		16 00								17 00						18 00					
East Croydon	a																					
Gatwick Airport 10	a																					
Haywards Heath 3	a																					
Brighton 10	a																					
London Euston 15	⊖ a	15 53		16 01	16 03	16 13	16 13	16 30	16 37	16 49		17 00	17 13	17 13	17 32	17 39		18 00	18 10	18 13	18 30	18 38

For general notes see front of timetable
For details of catering facilities see
Directory of Train Operators

§ It is unknown, at the time of going to press, when this station will open. For further details contact National Rail Enquiries 08457 484950 or see local publicity.

Due to Engineering Operations, services from Sunday 14 September on this Table had not been confirmed at time of going to press. These services will be issued in a special Supplement as soon as exact timings have been confirmed

Table 66

Sundays

20 July to 7 September

West Midlands, Northampton, Milton Keynes and Watford Junction → London

Network Diagram - See first page of Table 59

		VT	SN	LM	VT	VT	VT	LM	SN	LM	VT	VT	LM	VT	VT	VT	SN	LM	VT	VT	LM	VT
		1 ◇	1	1	1 ◇	1 ◇	1 ◇	1	1	1	1 ◇	1 ◇	1	1 ◇	1 ◇	1 ◇	1	1	1 ◇	1 ◇	1	1 ◇
Wolverhampton 7	d						16 18					17 18								18 19		
Sandwell & Dudley	d						16 29					17 29								18 31		
Birmingham New Street 12	d						16 45					17 45								18 45		
Birmingham International	d																					
Coventry	d																					
Nuneaton	d						17u29				18 10	18u26				19 01				19u28		
Rugby	a						17 43					18 40								19 41		
	d					17 39	17 45					18 41		19 03						19 43		19 48
Northampton	d			17 26				17 56		18 26			18 56					19 26			19 56	
Wolverton	d			17 39				18 10		18 38			19 08					19 39			20 08	
Milton Keynes Central 10	a			17 42		18 02	18 08	18 13		18 41		19 03	19 11			19 36		19 42		20 06	20 11	20 16
	d	17 38		17 43	17 58	18 04	18 10	18 14		18 42		19 05	19 12		19 32	19 38		19 43	20 01	20 07	20 12	20 18
Bletchley	d			17 48				18 19		18 47			19 17					19 48			20 17	
Leighton Buzzard	d			17 54				18 25		18 53			19 23					19 54			20 23	
Cheddington	d							18 30					19 28								20 28	
Tring	d							18 39					19 37								20 37	
Berkhamsted	d			18 09				18 44		19 08			19 42					20 09			20 42	
Hemel Hempstead	a			18 14				18 48		19 13			19 46					20 14			20 46	
	d			18 14				18 48		19 13			19 46					20 14			20 46	
Apsley	d			18 17						19 16								20 17				
Kings Langley	d			18 20						19 19								20 20				
Watford Junction	a			18 27			18s43	18 57		19 26	19s31	19s42	19 55	20s00				20 27	20s33	20s42	20 55	
	d		18 22	18 27				18 58	19 22	19 26			19 56				20 22	20 27			20 56	
Bushey	d																					
Harrow & Wealdstone ⊖	d		18 28	18 36				19 06	19 28	19 35			20 04				20 28	20 36			21 04	
Wembley Central	d																					
Shepherds Bush §	a																					
Kensington Olympia ⊖	a		18 47						19 47								20 47					
West Brompton ⊖	a		18 50						19 50								20 50					
Imperial Wharf §	a																					
Clapham Junction 10	a		19 00						20 00								21 00					
East Croydon	a																					
Gatwick Airport 10	a																					
Haywards Heath 3	a																					
Brighton 10	a																					
London Euston 15 ⊖	a	18 49		19 01	19 05	19 13	19 13	19 31		20 00	20 04	20 11	20 29	20 35	20 38	20 52		21 01	21 06	21 14	21 29	21 36

		VT	SN	LM	VT	LM	VT	VT	SN	LM	VT	VT	VT	LM	VT	VT	SN	VT	LM	LM
		1 ◇	1	1	1 ◇	1	1 ◇	1 ◇	1	1	1 ◇	1 ◇	1 ◇	1	1 ◇	1 ◇	1	1 ◇	1	1
Wolverhampton 7	d				19 18							20 18						21 18		
Sandwell & Dudley	d				19 29							20 29						21 29		
Birmingham New Street 12	d				19 45							20 45						21 45		
Birmingham International	d																			
Coventry	d																			
Nuneaton	d	20 04			20u26			20 59				21u26			21 36	21 55		22u26		
Rugby	a				20 40							21 40			21 51			22 39		
	d				20 41		20 50					21 41	21 46		21 52			22 40		
Northampton	d			20 26		20 56				21 26				21 56					22 56	23 56
Wolverton	d			20 40		21 08				21 38				22 10					23 08	00 08
Milton Keynes Central 10	a			20 43	21 03	21 11		21 35		21 41		22 02	22 08	22 13	22 18	22 29		23 02	23 11	00 11
	d			20 44	21 05	21 12		21 36		21 42	21 48	22 04	22 10	22 14	22 20	22 30		23 04	23 12	00 12
Bletchley	d			20 49		21 17				21 47				22 19					23 17	00 17
Leighton Buzzard	d			20 55		21 23				21 53				22 25					23 23	00 23
Cheddington	d					21 28								22 30					23 28	00 28
Tring	d					21 37								22 39					23 37	00 37
Berkhamsted	d			21 10		21 42				22 08				22 44					23 42	00 42
Hemel Hempstead	a			21 15		21 46				22 13				22 48					23 46	00 46
	d			21 15		21 46				22 13				22 48					23 46	00 46
Apsley	d			21 18						22 16									23 49	00 49
Kings Langley	d			21 21						22 19									23 53	00 53
Watford Junction	a	21s12		21 28	21s44	21 55	22s00			22 26	22s31	22s36	22s44	22 57	23s02	23s08		23s36	23 58	00 59
	d		21 22	21 28		21 56			22 22	22 26				22 58			23 22		23 59	01 00
Bushey	d																			
Harrow & Wealdstone ⊖	d		21 28	21 37		22 04			22 28	22 35				23 06			23 28		00 07	01 08
Wembley Central	d																			
Shepherds Bush §	a																			
Kensington Olympia ⊖	a		21 47						22 47								23 47			
West Brompton ⊖	a		21 50						22 50								23 50			
Imperial Wharf §	a																			
Clapham Junction 10	a		22 00						23 00								00 01			
East Croydon	a																00 20			
Gatwick Airport 10	a																			
Haywards Heath 3	a																			
Brighton 10	a																			
London Euston 15 ⊖	a	21 52		22 02	22 15	22 29	22 36	22 52		23 00	23 02	23 06	23 19	23 31	23 33	23 52		00 06	00 32	01 33

For general notes see front of timetable
For details of catering facilities see
Directory of Train Operators

§ It is unknown, at the time of going to press, when this station will open. For further details contact National Rail Enquiries 08457 484950 or see local publicity.

Due to Engineering Operations, services from Sunday 14 September on this Table had not been confirmed at time of going to press. These services will be issued in a special Supplement as soon as exact timings have been confirmed

Network Diagram for Tables 67, 68, 69, 70

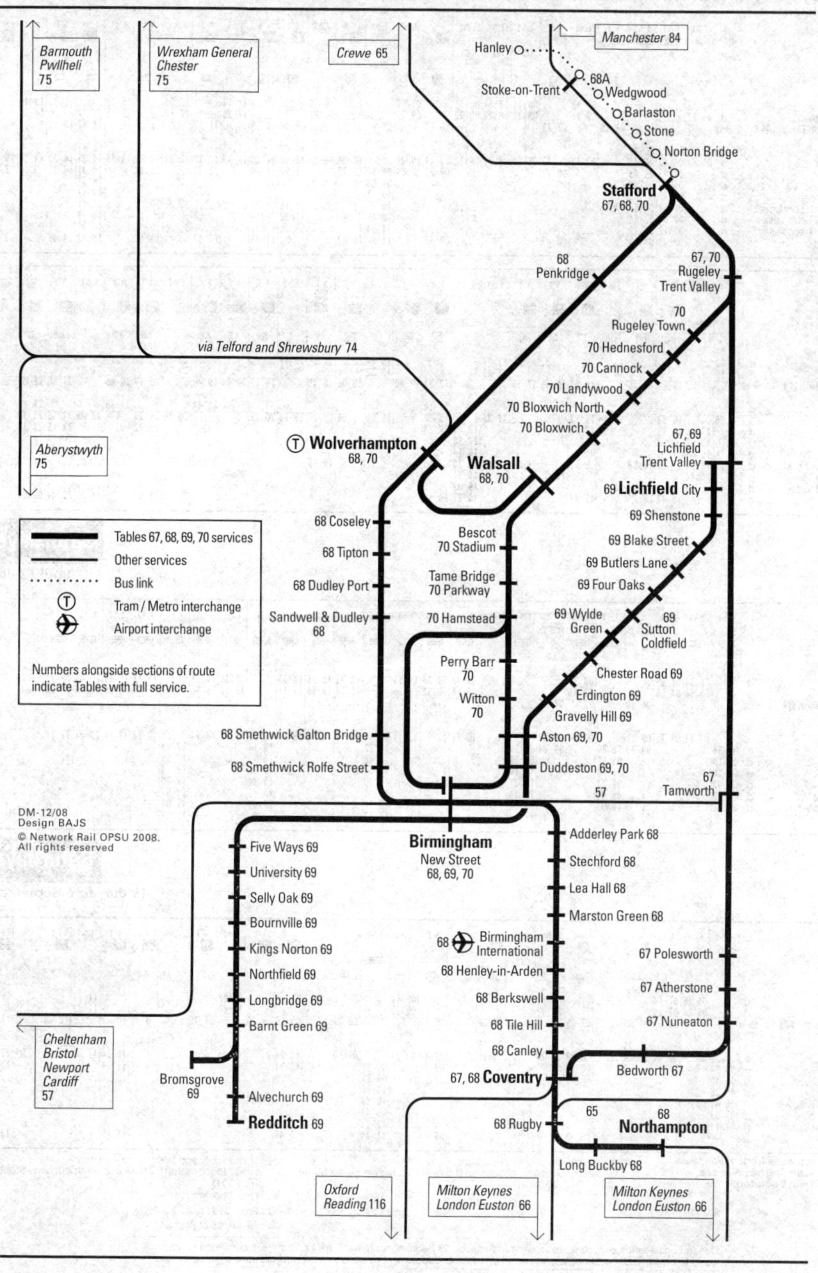

Barmouth
Pwllheli
75
Wrexham General
Chester
75
Crewe 65
Manchester 84
Hanley
Stoke-on-Trent
68A
Wedgwood
Barlaston
Stone
Norton Bridge
Stafford
67, 68, 70
68
Penkridge
67, 70
Rugeley
Trent Valley
70
Rugeley Town
70 Hednesford
70 Cannock
70 Landywood
70 Bloxwich North
70 Bloxwich
via Telford and Shrewsbury 74
Wolverhampton
68, 70
Walsall
68, 70
67, 69
Lichfield
Trent Valley
69 Lichfield City
69 Shenstone
Aberystwyth
75
Tables 67, 68, 69, 70 services
Other services
Bus link
Tram / Metro interchange
Airport interchange
Numbers alongside sections of route indicate Tables with full service.
68 Coseley
68 Tipton
68 Dudley Port
Sandwell & Dudley
68
Bescot
70 Stadium
Tame Bridge
70 Parkway
70 Hamstead
Perry Barr
70
Witton
70
69 Blake Street
69 Butlers Lane
69 Four Oaks
69 Wylde
Green
69
Sutton
Coldfield
Chester Road 69
Erdington 69
Gravelly Hill 69
68 Smethwick Galton Bridge
68 Smethwick Rolfe Street
Aston 69, 70
Duddeston 69, 70
67
Tamworth
57
DM-12/08
Design BAJS
© Network Rail OPSU 2008.
All rights reserved
Birmingham
New Street
68, 69, 70
Five Ways 69
University 69
Selly Oak 69
Bournville 69
Kings Norton 69
Northfield 69
Longbridge 69
Barnt Green 69
Adderley Park 68
Stechford 68
Lea Hall 68
Marston Green 68
68
Birmingham
International
68 Henley-in-Arden
68 Berkswell
68 Tile Hill
68 Canley
67, 68 Coventry
67 Polesworth
67 Atherstone
67 Nuneaton
Bedworth 67
Cheltenham
Bristol
Newport
Cardiff
57
Bromsgrove
69
Alvechurch 69
Redditch 69
68 Rugby
65
68
Northampton
Long Buckby 68
Oxford
Reading 116
Milton Keynes
London Euston 66
Milton Keynes
London Euston 66

Coventry → Nuneaton → Stafford

Network Diagram - see first page of Table 67

Miles			LM	LM	LM	VT	LM	VT	LM	LM	LM	VT	LM	LM	VT	LM	VT	VT	LM	VT	LM	VT	LM	LM	VT	LM	VT
				[1] A	[1] B	[1] ◇ ⊠		[1] ◇ ⊠	C	D	E	[1] ◇ ⊠		🚌	[1] ◇ ⊠		[1] ◇ ⊠	[1] ◇ ⊠		[1] ◇ ☕		[1] ◇ ☕		[1] 🛒	[1] ◇ ☕		[1] ◇ ☕
0	**Coventry**	d	06 15				07 13		08 11	08 11	08 11		09 10			10 10			11 12		12 06		13 06			14 10	
6¼	Bedworth	d	06 27				07 25		08 22	08 22	08 22		09 21			10 21			11 26		12 17		13 17			14 21	
—	London Euston 15	⊖ d				06 20		07 13				08 17			09 17		09 38	10 15		11 17		12 17		12 49	13 17		14 17
—	Rugby	d		06 27	06 29												10 47							13 47			
10	**Nuneaton**	a	06 34	06 42	06 42		07 32	08 22	08 29	08 31	08 32	09 21	09 28		10 22	10 28	10 58	11 20	11 33	12 22	12 24	13 22	13 24	14 01	14 22	14 28	15 22
—		d		06 43	06 43			08 22				09 21		09 39	10 22		11 00	11 20		12 22		13 22		14 01	14 22		15 22
15	Atherstone	d		06 49	06 49									09 55										14 07			
19	Polesworth	d												10 11										14 12			
22¼	Tamworth Low Level	d		06 57	06 57	07a36								10 27			11 16							14 17			
28¾	Lichfield Trent Valley	d		07 04	07 04									10 48			11a22							14 23			
36¼	Rugeley Trent Valley	d		07 12	07 12									11 04										14 31			
46	**Stafford**	a		07 23	07 23			08 47				09 47		11 24	10 47			11 45		12 48		13 47		14 43	14 47		15 47

		LM	LM	VT	VT	LM	VT	VT	VT	LM	LM	VT	VT	LM	VT	VT	LM	VT	VT	VT	LM	VT	VT	LM	VT	VT
			🚌	[1] ◇ ⊠	[1] ◇ ⊠		[1] ◇ ☕	[1] ◇ ☕	[1] ◇ ⊠		🚌	[1] ◇ ⊠	[1] ◇ ⊠		[1] ◇ ⊠	R [1] ☕		[1] ◇ ☕	[1] ◇ ☕	[1] ◇ ☕		[1] ◇ ☕	[1] ◇ ☕		[1] ◇ ☕	[1] ◇ ☕
Coventry	d	15 08				16 17				17 17				18 17			19 17				20 18			21 50		
Bedworth	d	15 19				16 29				17 29				18 32			19 29				20 29			22 01		
London Euston 15	⊖ d			15 17	15 46		16 17	16 49	17 17			17 21	17 48		18 05	18 45		19 17	19 38	19 46		20 17	20 46		21 10	22 05
Rugby	d											18 10								20 41			21 38			23 21
Nuneaton	a	15 26		16 22		16 38	17 22			17 36		18 24		18 39	19 05		19 36	20 21			20 36	21 22		22 08	22 15	23 33
	d		15 36	16 22			17 22				17 42	18 24										21 22			22 15	23 33
Atherstone	d		15 52								17 58															
Polesworth	d		16 08								18 14															
Tamworth Low Level	d		16 24		16a54				18a24		18 30					19a56				21a00						23 44
Lichfield Trent Valley	d		16a44					18a03			18 51		19a01						20a49				22a02			
Rugeley Trent Valley	d										19 07															
Stafford	a			16 47			17 47				19 27	18 50										21 47			22 41	00s04

Saturdays
until 12 July

		LM	LM	LM	VT	LM	LM	VT	LM	LM	LM	LM	LM	LM	LM	LM	LM	LM	LM	LM	LM	LM	LM	LM	LM
		🚌	🚌	🚌	[1] ◇ ☕	🚌	🚌	[1] ◇ ☕	🚌	🚌	🚌	🚌	🚌	🚌	🚌	🚌	🚌	🚌	🚌	🚌	🚌	🚌	🚌	🚌	🚌
Coventry	d		06 35	07 35			08 35			09 35	10 35	11 35		12 35	13 35	14 35		15 35	16 35		17 15	18 35	20 05	21 35	
Bedworth	d		06 56	07 56			08 56			09 56	10 56	11 56		12 56	13 56	14 56		15 56	16 56		17 36	18 56	20 26	21 56	
London Euston 15	⊖ d				06 40			07 55																	
Rugby	d																								
Nuneaton	a		07 11	08 11	08 23		09 11	09 24		10 11	11 11	12 11		13 11	14 11	15 11		16 11	17 11		17 51	19 11	20 41	22 11	
	d	05 54			08 23	08 39		09 24	09 39				12 32				15 36			17 42					
Atherstone	d	06 10				08 55			09 55				12 48				15 52			17 58					
Polesworth	d	06 26				09 11			10 11				13 04				16 08			18 14					
Tamworth Low Level	d	06 42				09 27			10 27				13 20				16 24			18 30					
Lichfield Trent Valley	d	07 03				09 48			10 48				13 41				16 45			18 51					
Rugeley Trent Valley	d	07a18				10a03			11 04				13 57				17a00			19 07					
Stafford	a				08 48			09 49	11 24				14 17							19 27					

Saturdays
19 July to 6 September

		LM	LM	LM	VT	VT	LM	LM	VT	VT	LM	LM	VT	VT	VT	LM	VT	VT	VT	LM	VT	VT
		🚌			[1] ◇ ☕	[1] ◇ ☕		🚌	[1] ◇ ☕	[1] ◇ ☕		🚌	[1] ◇ ☕	[1] ◇ ☕	[1] ◇ ☕		[1] ◇ ☕	[1] ◇ ☕	[1] ◇ ☕		[1] ◇ ☕	[1] ◇ ☕
Coventry	d		06 15	07 14			08 11				09 11					10 06				11 12		
Bedworth	d		06 26	07 25			08 22				09 22					10 17				11 23		
London Euston 15	⊖ d				06 05	07 09			07 28	08 12			08 27	09 15	09 25		09 28	09 45	10 12		10 28	11 12
Rugby	d				07 35				08 35				09 35				10 36	10u45			11 35	
Nuneaton	a		06 34	07 32	07s48	08 23	08 29		08s50	09 24	09 29		09s50	10 24		10 24	10s48		11 24	11 30	11s50	12 24
	d	05 54				08 23		08 39		09 24		09 39		10 24					11 24			12 24
Atherstone	d	06 10						08 55				09 55										
Polesworth	d	06 26						09 11				10 11										
Tamworth Low Level	d	06 42						09 27				10 27			10a38							
Lichfield Trent Valley	d	07 03						09 48				10 48						11a07				
Rugeley Trent Valley	d	07a18						10a03				11 04										
Stafford	a					08 48				09 49		11 24		10 49					11 49			12 49

For general notes see front of timetable
For details of catering facilities see Directory of Train Operators

A 28 July to 22 August. From Northampton (Table 68) to Liverpool Lime Street (Table 91)

B Until 25 July and from 25 August. From Northampton (Table 68) to Liverpool Lime Street (Table 91)

C Until 25 July

D From 25 August

E 28 July to 22 August

Due to Engineering Operations, services from Saturday 13 September on this Table had not been confirmed at time of going to press. These services will be issued in a special Supplement as soon as exact timings have been confirmed

Table 67

Coventry → Nuneaton → Stafford

Saturdays

19 July to 6 September

Network Diagram - see first page of Table 67

		LM	LM	VT	VT	LM	VT	LM	VT	VT	VT	LM	LM	VT	VT	LM	VT	VT	VT	LM	VT	LM
				1 ◇	1 ◇		1 ◇		1 ◇	1 ◇	1 ◇			1 ◇	1 ◇		1 ◇	1 ◇	1 ◇		1 ◇	
			🚌	☕	☕		☕		☕	☕	☕		🚌	☕	☕		☕	☕	☕		☕	🚌
Coventry	d	12 06				13 06		14 05				15 06				16 06				17 06		
Bedworth	d	12 17				13 17		14 16				15 17				16 17				17 17		
London Euston 15 ⊖	d			11 28	12 12		12 28		13 12	13 28	14 12			14 28	15 12		15 28	15 55	16 12		17 12	
Rugby	d			12 33			13 33			14 35				15 35			16 35					
Nuneaton	a	12 24		12s48	13 24	13 24	13s48	14 23	14 24	14s50	15 24	15 24		15s49	16 24	16 24	16s48		17 24	17 24		
	d		12 32		13 24				14 24		15 24		15 36		16 24				17 24			17 42
Atherstone	d		12 48										15 52									17 58
Polesworth	d		13 04										16 08									18 14
Tamworth Low Level	d		13 20										16 24					17a11				18 30
Lichfield Trent Valley	d		13 41										16 45								18a34	18 51
Rugeley Trent Valley	d		13 57										17a00									19 07
Stafford	a		14 17		13 49				14 49		15 49				16 49				17 49			19 27

		VT	LM	VT	VT	VT	LM	VT	VT	VT	VT	LM	VT	LM	VT	VT	LM	VT	VT	VT
		1 ◇		1 ◇	1 ◇	1 ◇		1 ◇	R 1	1 ◇	1 ◇		1 ◇		1 ◇	1 ◇		1 ◇	1 ◇	1 ◇
		☕		☕	☕	☕		☕	☕	☕	☕		☕		☕	☕		☕	☕	☕
Coventry	d		18 06				19 06					20 06		21 06			22 06			
Bedworth	d		18 17				19 17					20 17		21 17			22 17			
London Euston 15 ⊖	d	16 28		17 28	17 35	18 12		18 28	18 45	19 09	19 17		19 24		20 30	20 36		20 40	21 04	21 36
Rugby	d	17 35		18 35	18 40			19 35	19u45		20u31		20 36		22 12				22 38	23 14
Nuneaton	a	17s50	18 24	18s50	18 52	19 24	19 24	19s50		20 23		20 24	20s49	21 24	22s24		22 28	22 31	22s51	23s32
	d				18 53	19 26												22 31		
Atherstone	d																			
Polesworth	d																			
Tamworth Low Level	d								20a03		20a51					22 35				
Lichfield Trent Valley	d																			
Rugeley Trent Valley	d																			
Stafford	a				19 17	19 49										22 58		23 04		

Sundays

until 13 July

		VT	VT	VT	LM	VT	VT	VT	VT	LM	VT	VT	VT	LM	VT	VT	VT	LM	VT	VT	VT	LM
		1 ◇	1 ◇	1 ◇		1 ◇	1 ◇	1 ◇	1 ◇		1 ◇	1 ◇	1 ◇		1 ◇	1 ◇	1 ◇		1 ◇	1 ◇	1 ◇	
		☕	☕	☕	🚌	☕	☕	☕	☕	🚌	☕	☕	☕	🚌	☕	☕	☕	🚌	☕	☕	☕	🚌
Coventry	d				11 35					13 35				14 35				15 35				16 35
Bedworth	d				11 56					13 56				14 56				15 56				16 56
London Euston 15 ⊖	d	08 30	09 02	09 56		10 50	10 56	11 56	12 05		12 56	13 05	13 35		13 56	14 05	14 35		14 56	15 01	15 05	
Rugby	d	10 10		11 34			12 29	13 25			14 20				15 22				16 21			
Nuneaton	a	10s23	10 53	11s46	12 11	12 34	12s42	13s38	13 45	14 11	14s31	14 42		15 11	15s33	15 42		16 11	16s33		16 43	17 11
	d		10 54			12 36			13 46			14 43				15 44					16 44	
Atherstone	d																					
Polesworth	d																					
Tamworth Low Level	d												15a04				16a07					
Lichfield Trent Valley	d																			16a50		
Rugeley Trent Valley	d																					
Stafford	a		11 20			13 02			14 10			15 07				16 08					17 11	

		VT	VT	VT	LM	VT	VT	VT	VT	VT	VT	LM	VT	VT	VT	VT	VT	VT	LM	VT	VT	VT
		1 ◇	1 ◇	1 ◇		1 ◇	1 ◇	1 ◇	1 ◇	1 ◇	1 ◇		1 ◇	1 ◇	1 ◇	1 ◇	1 ◇	1 ◇		1 ◇	1 ◇	1 ◇
		☕	☕	☕	🚌	☕	☕	☕	☕	☕	☕	🚌	☕	☕	☕	☕	☕	☕	🚌	☕	☕	☕
Coventry	d				17 35							19 35							21 35			
Bedworth	d				17 56							19 56							21 56			
London Euston 15 ⊖	d	15 56	16 05	16 35		16 56	17 05	17 56	18 01	18 05	18 35		18 56	19 05	19 25	19 56	20 05	20 31		20 56	21 00	21 56
Rugby	d	17 22				18 20		19 22					20 20		20u46	21 22		21 50		22 30		23 37
Nuneaton	a	17s33	17 42		18 11	18s33	18 41	19s34		19 42		20 11	20s33	20 42		21s35	21 45		22 11	22s43	22 46	23s50
	d		17 44				18 43			19 44				20 44			21 46				22 48	
Atherstone	d																					
Polesworth	d																					
Tamworth Low Level	d			18a08					19a47		20a04				21a03							
Lichfield Trent Valley	d																	22a11				
Rugeley Trent Valley	d																					
Stafford	a		18 08				19 09			20 10				21 09			22 14				23 14	

For general notes see front of timetable
For details of catering facilities see
Directory of Train Operators

Due to Engineering Operations, services from Saturday 13 September on this Table had not been confirmed at time of going to press. These services will be issued in a special Supplement as soon as exact timings have been confirmed

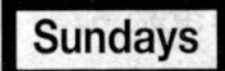

Sundays

20 July to 7 September

Coventry → Nuneaton → Stafford

Network Diagram - see first page of Table 67

		VT 1 ◇ ☕	VT 1 ◇ ☕	VT 1 ◇ ☕	LM 🚌		VT 1 ◇ ☕	VT 1 ◇ ☕	VT 1 ◇ ☕	VT 1 ◇ ☕		LM 🚌	VT 1 ◇ ☕	VT 1 ◇ ☕	VT 1 ◇ ☕		LM 🚌	VT 1 ◇ ☕	VT 1 ◇ ☕	VT 1 ◇ ☕		LM 🚌	VT 1 ◇ ☕	VT 1 ◇ ☕	VT 1 ◇ ☕		LM 🚌
Coventry	d				11 35							13 35					14 35					15 35					16 35
Bedworth	d				11 56							13 56					14 56					15 56					16 56
London Euston 15	⊖ d	08 31	09 25	09 56			10 56	11 01	11 50	12 01			12 51	13 01	13 29			13 51	14 01	14 29			14 51	14 58	15 01		
Rugby	d	10 12		11 32				12 36	13 23				14 20					15 20					16 21				
Nuneaton	a	10s24	10 58	11s43	12 11		12 44	12s48	13s35	13 47		14 11	14s32	14 42			15 11	15s32	15 46			16 11	16s32		16 44		17 11
	d		10 59				12 45			13 48				14 43					15 47						16 45		
Atherstone	d																										
Polesworth	d																										
Tamworth Low Level	d														15a04					16a07							
Lichfield Trent Valley	d																							16a45			
Rugeley Trent Valley	d																										
Stafford	a		11 26				13 12			14 13				15 07					16 12						17 11		

		VT 1 ◇ ☕	VT 1 ◇ ☕	VT 1 ◇ ☕	LM 🚌		VT 1 ◇ ☕	VT 1 ◇ ☕	VT 1 ◇ ☕	VT 1 ◇ ☕		VT 1 ◇ ☕	LM 🚌	VT 1 ◇ ☕	VT 1 ◇ ☕		VT 1 ◇ ☕	VT 1 ◇ ☕	VT 1 ◇ ☕	VT 1 ◇ ☕		LM 🚌	VT 1 ◇ ☕	VT 1 ◇ ☕	VT 1 ◇ ☕		
Coventry	d				17 35								19 35									21 35					
Bedworth	d				17 56								19 56									21 56					
London Euston 15	⊖ d	15 51	16 13	16 29			16 51	17 01	17 51	18 01		18 29		18 51	19 01		19 24	19 51	20 01	20 31			20 56	21 01	22 00		
Rugby	d	17 20					18 20		19 20					20 19			20u46	21 20		22 12			22 37		23 37		
Nuneaton	a	17s32	17 43		18 11		18s32	18 44	19s32	19 41			20 11	20s31	20 44			21s32	21 39			22 11	22s49	22 52	23s50		
	d		17 44					18 45		19 43					20 46				21 41					22 54			
Atherstone	d																										
Polesworth	d																										
Tamworth Low Level	d			18a08								20a04					21a03										
Lichfield Trent Valley	d																			22a35							
Rugeley Trent Valley	d																										
Stafford	a		18 08					19 11		20 08					21 11				22 07					23 20			

For general notes see front of timetable
For details of catering facilities see
Directory of Train Operators

Due to Engineering Operations, services from Sunday 14 September on this Table had not been confirmed at time of going to press. These services will be issued in a special Supplement as soon as exact timings have been confirmed

Stafford → Nuneaton → Coventry

Network Diagram - see first page of Table 67

Miles			LM	VT	VT	VT	LM	LM	VT	VT	VT	LM	VT	LM	VT	VT	VT	LM	VT	LM	LM	VT	LM	VT
				[1] ◇	[1] ◇	[1] ◇	[1]		[1] ◇	[1] ◇	[1] ◇		[1] ◇		[1] ◇	[1] ◇	[1] ◇		[1] ◇		[1] A	[1] ◇		[1] ◇
				⊠	⊠	⊠			⊠	⊠	⊠		⊠		☕	⊠	⊠		⊠		trolley	☕		☕
0	**Stafford**	d		06 18	06 43		06 57			07 25						09 13	10 12		11 12		11 21	12 12		13 12
9¼	Rugeley Trent Valley	d					07 07														11 32			
17¼	Lichfield Trent Valley	d		06 33			07 15		07 21							09 27					11 41			
23½	Tamworth Low Level	d		06 40		07 06	07 22								09 23						11 48			
27	Polesworth	d																						
31	Atherstone	d					07 31														11 56			
—	**Nuneaton**	a		06 50	07 05		07 37			07 47							10 34		11 34		12 02	12 34		13 34
36		d	06 46	06 51	07 07		07 37	07 42		07 49	08 31	08 42	09 26	09 42			10 35	10 40	11 35	11 38	12 02	12 35	12 38	13 35
—	Rugby	a		07 04		07 27	07 54		07 45												12 17			
—	London Euston [15]	⊖ a		08 04	08 19	08 27			08 40	08 58	09 45		10 35		10 46	10 50	11 48		12 48		13 18	13 47		14 49
39½	Bedworth	d	06 52					07 49				08 48		09 48				10 46		11 44			12 44	
46	**Coventry**	a	07 04					08 01				09 00		10 00				10 58		11 56			12 59	

		LM	LM	VT	LM	VT	VT	LM	VT	LM	VT	LM	LM	VT	LM	VT	LM	LM	VT	LM	LM	VT
				[1] ◇		[1] ◇	[1] ◇		[1] ◇		[1] ◇		[1] B	[1] ◇		[1] ◇			[1] ◇			[1] ◇
			🚌	☕		☕	☕		☕		☕		trolley	☕		☕			☕	🚌		☕
Stafford	d		12 40	14 12		15 12			16 12		17 12		17 20	18 13		19 12			21 04	20 20		
Rugeley Trent Valley	d		13 05										17 29							20 45		
Lichfield Trent Valley	d		13 26				15 18						17 38							21 06		22 17
Tamworth Low Level	d		13 47				15 25						17 45							21 27		22 24
Polesworth	d		14 02																	21 42		
Atherstone	d		14 18										17 53							21 58		
Nuneaton	a		14 33	14 34		15 34	15 38		16 34		17 34		17 59	18 35		19 34			21 27	22 13		22 34
	d	13 42		14 35	14 38	15 35	15 40	15 53	16 35	16 50	17 35	17 48	18 00	18 36	18 47	19 35	19 48	21 17	21 29		22 30	22 35
Rugby	a						15 53				17 49		18 14						21 42			22 49
London Euston [15]	⊖ a			15 48		16 48	17 22		17 47		18 50		19 18	19 50		20 48			23 05			00 09
Bedworth	d	13 48			14 44			15 59		16 56		17 54			18 54		19 54	21 23			22 36	
Coventry	a	14 00			14 56			16 11		17 08		18 07			19 06		20 08	21 35			22 48	

Saturdays

until 12 July

		VT	LM	LM	VT	VT	LM	LM	VT	LM	LM	VT	VT	LM	LM
		[1] ◇			[1] ◇	[1] ◇			[1] ◇			[1] ◇	[1] ◇		
		☕	🚌	🚌	☕	☕	🚌	🚌	☕	🚌	🚌	☕	☕	🚌	🚌
Stafford	d	06 14		05 54		07 12			08 12				09 12		
Rugeley Trent Valley	d			06 20							07 57				
Lichfield Trent Valley	d	06 28		06 41	07 20						08 18	09 20			
Tamworth Low Level	d	06 35		07 02		07 30		←			08 39				
Polesworth	d			07 18 →				07 18			08 55				
Atherstone	d							07 34			09 11				
Nuneaton	a	06 45				07 40		07 49	08 34		09 26		09 34		
	d	06 46	06 48			07 42	07 48		08 35	08 48			09 36	09 48	10 48
Rugby	a	07 00			07 44								09 54		
London Euston [15]	⊖ a	08 19			09 17	09 19			10 12			11 13	11 16		
Bedworth	d		07 04				08 04			09 04				10 04	11 04
Coventry	a		07 24				08 24			09 24				10 24	11 24

		LM	LM	LM	LM	LM	LM	LM	LM	LM	LM	LM	LM	LM	LM	LM
		🚌	🚌	🚌	🚌	🚌	🚌	🚌	🚌	🚌	🚌	🚌	🚌	🚌	🚌	🚌
Stafford	d					12 45				15 30					19 52	
Rugeley Trent Valley	d		10 55			13 11				15 56			18 06		20 18	
Lichfield Trent Valley	d		11 16			13 32				16 17			18 27		20 39	
Tamworth Low Level	d		11 37			13 53				16 38			18 48		21 00	
Polesworth	d		11 53			14 09				16 54			19 04		21 16	
Atherstone	d		12 09			14 25				17 10			19 20		21 32	
Nuneaton	a		12 24			14 40				17 25			19 35		21 47	
	d	11 48		12 48	13 48		14 48	15 48	16 48		17 48	19 24		20 48		22 48
Rugby	a															
London Euston [15]	⊖ a															
Bedworth	d	12 04		13 04	14 04		15 04	16 04	17 04		18 04	19 40		21 04		23 04
Coventry	a	12 24		13 24	14 24		15 24	16 24	17 24		18 24	20 00		21 24		23 24

For general notes see front of timetable
For details of catering facilities see Directory of Train Operators

A From Liverpool Lime Street (Table 65)
B From Crewe (Table 65)

Table 67

Saturdays

19 July to 6 September

Stafford → Nuneaton → Coventry

Network Diagram - see first page of Table 67

		VT 1◇ ☕	LM	VT 1◇ ☕	LM 🚌	VT 1◇ ☕	VT 1◇ ☕	VT 1◇ ☕	LM	LM 🚌	VT 1◇ ☕	VT 1◇ ☕	LM	LM 🚌	VT 1◇ ☕	VT 1◇ ☕	VT 1◇ ☕	VT 1◇ ☕	LM	VT 1◇ ☕	VT 1◇ ☕	VT 1◇ ☕	LM
Stafford	d			06 14	05 54			07 12				08 12						09 12				10 12	
Rugeley Trent Valley	d				06 20									07 57									
Lichfield Trent Valley	d			06 28	06 41		07 19							08 18	09 18								
Tamworth Low Level	d			06 35	07 02			07 30		←				08 39			09 28			09 52			
Polesworth	d				07 18					07 18				08 55									
Atherstone	d				↪					07 34				09 11									
Nuneaton	a			06 45				07 40		07 49		08 34		09 26				09 38				10 34	
	d	06u20	06 42	06 46		07u23		07 42	07 42		08u20	08 35	08 42			09u28		09 40	09 42		10u21	10 36	10 42
Rugby	a	06 38		07 00		07 41	07 46				08 40					09 46					10 40		
London Euston 15 ⊖	a	08 05		08 14		08 50	08 59	09 00			09 48	09 59			10 48	10 57	11 04	11 05		11 16	11 48	12 00	
Bedworth	d		06 48						07 49				08 48						09 48				10 48
Coventry	a		07 00						08 01				09 00						10 00				11 00

		VT 1◇ ☕	VT 1◇ ☕	LM	VT 1◇ ☕	LM 🚌	VT 1◇ ☕	VT 1◇ ☕	LM	VT 1◇ ☕	VT 1◇ ☕	LM	VT 1◇ ☕	VT 1◇ ☕	LM 🚌	LM	VT 1◇ ☕	LM	VT 1◇ ☕	VT 1◇ ☕	VT 1◇ ☕	VT 1◇ ☕	LM
Stafford	d		11 12					12 12			13 12			14 12	12 45				15 12			16 12	
Rugeley Trent Valley	d					10 55									13 11								
Lichfield Trent Valley	d					11 16									13 32					16 01			
Tamworth Low Level	d					11 37	11 51								13 53				15 28				
Polesworth	d					11 53									14 09								
Atherstone	d					12 09									14 25								
Nuneaton	a		11 34			12 24		12 35			13 34			14 34	14 40							16 34	
	d	11u21	11 36	11 42	12u24			12 37	12 42	13u21	13 36	13 42	14u24	14 36		14 42	15u21	15 42			16u21	16 36	16 42
Rugby	a	11 40			12 43					13 40			14 43				15 40			16 25	16 40		
London Euston 15 ⊖	a	12 47	12 54		13 59		13 20	14 03		14 47	15 00		15 59	16 03			16 47		17 00	17 28	17 46	18 00	
Bedworth	d			11 48					12 48			13 48				14 48		15 48					16 48
Coventry	a			12 00					13 00			14 00				15 00		16 00					17 00

		VT 1◇ ☕	LM 🚌	VT 1◇ ☕	LM	VT 1◇ ☕	VT 1◇ ☕	LM	VT 1◇ ☕	VT 1◇ ☕	LM 🚌	LM	VT 1◇ ☕	VT 1◇ ☕	LM	VT 1◇ ☕	LM	VT 1◇ ☕	LM 🚌	VT 1◇ ☕	VT 1◇ ☕	LM
Stafford	d		15 30	17 12			18 12			19 12				20 15				21 18	19 52			
Rugeley Trent Valley	d		15 56								18 06								20 18			
Lichfield Trent Valley	d		16 17								18 27								20 39	21 25		
Tamworth Low Level	d		16 38								18 48								21 00	21 33		
Polesworth	d		16 54								19 04								21 16			
Atherstone	d		17 10								19 20								21 32			
Nuneaton	a		17 25	17 34			18 34			19 34	19 35			20 37				21 45	21 47			
	d	17u24		17 36	17 42	18u21	18 36	18 42	19u21	19 36		19 42	20u21	20 38	20 42	21u24	21 42	21 46			22u24	22 42
Rugby	a	17 43		17 49		18 40			19 40				20 40			21 43		22 00		21 54	22 43	
London Euston 15 ⊖	a	18 56		19 00		19 47	19 57		21 26	21 34			22 31	22 45		23 31		23 45		23 37	00 26	
Bedworth	d				17 48			18 48				19 48			20 48		21 48					22 48
Coventry	a				18 00			19 00				20 00			21 00		22 00					23 05

Sundays

until 13 July

		VT 1◇ ☕	VT 1◇ ☕	VT 1◇ ☕	VT 1◇ ☕	VT 1◇ ☕	LM 🚌	VT 1◇ ☕	VT 1◇ ☕	VT 1◇ ☕	VT 1◇ ☕	LM 🚌	VT 1◇ ☕	VT 1◇ ☕	LM 🚌	VT 1◇ ☕	VT 1◇ ☕	LM 🚌	VT 1◇ ☕
Stafford	d			10 21		11 21			12 22		13 24			14 20			15 18		
Rugeley Trent Valley	d																		
Lichfield Trent Valley	d																		
Tamworth Low Level	d																		
Polesworth	d																		
Atherstone	d																		
Nuneaton	a			10 42		11 43			12 44		13 46			14 41			15 39		
	d	09u43	10u26	10 44	11u26	11 45	11 48	12u26	12 45	13u26	13 47	13 48	14u30	14 43	14 48	15u29	15 41	15 48	16u27
Rugby	a	09 57	10 40		11 40			12 40		13 40			14 43			15 42			16 41
London Euston 15 ⊖	a	11 25	12 22	12 33	13 22	13 35		13 57	14 30	14 57	15 34		16 11	16 24		17 03	17 26		18 10
Bedworth	d						12 04					14 04			15 04			16 04	
Coventry	a						12 24					14 24			15 24			16 24	

For general notes see front of timetable
For details of catering facilities see
Directory of Train Operators

Due to Engineering Operations, services from Saturday 13 September on this Table had not been confirmed at time of going to press. These services will be issued in a special Supplement as soon as exact timings have been confirmed

Stafford → Nuneaton → Coventry

Sundays

until 13 July

Network Diagram - see first page of Table 67

		VT	LM	VT	LM	VT	VT	VT	VT	VT	VT	LM	VT	VT	VT	VT	VT	VT	LM	VT
		1 ◇		1 ◇		1 ◇	1 ◇	1 ◇	1 ◇	1 ◇	1 ◇		1 ◇	1 ◇	1 ◇	1 ◇	1 ◇	1 ◇		1 ◇
									A											
Stafford	d	16 15				17 20		18 17	18 29		19 17			20 17				21 17		
Rugeley Trent Valley	d																			
Lichfield Trent Valley	d					17 33									20 50					
Tamworth Low Level	d					17 40			18 46						20 57					
Polesworth	d																			
Atherstone	d																			
Nuneaton	a	16 41				17 50		18 42			19 39			20 39				21 40		
	d	16 42	16 48	17u31	17 48	17 52	18u29	18 43		19u27	19 40	19 48	20u26	20 40		21u26	21 34	21 41	21 48	22u26
Rugby	a			17 46			18 43			19 40			20 40			21 40	21 48			22 39
London Euston 15 ⊖	a	18 24		19 23		19 29	20 11	20 24	20 25	21 07	21 24		22 04	22 24	22 52	23 05	23 21	23 30		00 25
Bedworth	d		17 04		18 04							20 04							22 04	
Coventry	a		17 24		18 24							20 24							22 24	

Sundays

20 July to 7 September

		VT	VT	VT	VT	LM	VT	VT	VT	VT	LM	VT	VT	LM	VT	VT	LM	VT	VT
		1 ◇	1 ◇	1 ◇	1 ◇		1 ◇	1 ◇	1 ◇	1 ◇		1 ◇	1 ◇		1 ◇	1 ◇		1 ◇	1 ◇
Stafford	d			10 32			11 35		12 33			13 36			14 32			15 32	
Rugeley Trent Valley	d																		
Lichfield Trent Valley	d																		
Tamworth Low Level	d																		
Polesworth	d																		
Atherstone	d																		
Nuneaton	a			10 54			11 57		12 55			14 01			14 54			15 54	
	d	09u40	10u26	10 56	11u29	11 48	11 58	12u29	12 56	13u26	13 48	14 03	14u30	14 48	14 55	15u31	15 48	15 55	16u29
Rugby	a	09 54	10 40		11 43			12 43		13 40			14 45			15 45			16 43
London Euston 15 ⊖	a	11 31	12 14	12 39	13 17		13 36	14 13	14 42	15 12		15 53	16 13		16 37	17 13		17 39	18 13
Bedworth	d					12 04					14 04			15 04			16 04		
Coventry	a					12 24					14 24			15 24			16 24		

		LM	VT	VT	LM	VT	VT	VT	VT	LM	VT	VT	VT	VT	VT	VT	LM	VT	VT
			1 ◇	1 ◇		1 ◇	1 ◇	1 ◇	1 ◇		1 ◇	1 ◇	1 ◇	1 ◇	1 ◇	1 ◇		1 ◇	1 ◇
Stafford	d		16 32			17 35		18 36			19 38		20 36					21 32	
Rugeley Trent Valley	d																		
Lichfield Trent Valley	d					17 51								20 54					
Tamworth Low Level	d					17 58								21 01					
Polesworth	d																		
Atherstone	d																		
Nuneaton	a		16 54			18 08		18 59			20 03		20 58					21 54	
	d	16 48	16 56	17u29	17 48	18 10	18u26	19 01	19u28	19 48	20 04	20u26	20 59		21u26	21 36	21 48	21 55	22u26
Rugby	a			17 43			18 40		19 41			20 40			21 40	21 51			22 39
London Euston 15 ⊖	a		18 38	19 13		20 04	20 11	20 52	21 14		21 52	22 15	22 52	23 02	23 06	23 33		23 52	00 06
Bedworth	d	17 04			18 04					20 04							22 04		
Coventry	a	17 24			18 24					20 24							22 24		

For general notes see front of timetable
For details of catering facilities see Directory of Train Operators

A From Holyhead (Table 81)

Due to Engineering Operations, services from Sunday 14 September on this Table had not been confirmed at time of going to press. These services will be issued in a special Supplement as soon as exact timings have been confirmed

Northampton → Coventry → Birmingham → Wolverhampton → Stafford

Network Diagram - see first page of Table 67

Miles			VT MO A	VT MO 1 ◇ B	VT MO 1 ◇ C	VT MO 1 ◇ A	VT MO D	VT MX 1 ◇ E	VT MX 1 ◇ G	VT MX 1 ◇ H	VT MO 1 ◇ B	VT MO 1 ◇ J	VT MO 1 ◇ K	VT MO 1 ◇ A	VT MO D	VT MX 1 ◇ G	VT MX 1 ◇ L	VT MO 1 ◇ C	VT MO 1 ◇ A	VT MO D	VT 1 ◇ N	VT 1 ◇	XC 1 ◇	LM 1 ◇ Q	LM MO 1
—	London Euston 15 ⊖	d		22p35	22p00	21p56		22p40	22p40	22p40	23p35	23p01	23p01	22p56		23p40	23p40	23p31	23p30						
0	**Northampton**	d																							05 19
9½	Long Buckby	d																							05 29
18¾	Rugby	d		23p54	23p37	23p37	23p45	00s18	00s17	00s23	01 00	00s30	00s31	00s31	00 40	01s19	01s20	01s07	01s08	01 15					05 40
32¼	**Coventry**	a		00 05			00s25	00s30	00s31	00s35	01 11				01s20	01s33	01s33			01s55					05 54
—		d		00 06							01 12														05 55
34	Canley	d																							
36	Tile Hill	d																							
38	Berkswell	d																							
41¼	Hampton-in-Arden	d																							
43	**Birmingham International** ✈	a		00 17			00 50	00s42	00s42	00s47	01 23				01 45	01s46	01s46			02 20					06 04
—		d		00 18							01 24														06 05
45	Marston Green	d																							
46½	Lea Hall	d																							
47¾	Stechford	d																							
49½	Adderley Park	d																							
51½	**Birmingham New Street 12**	a		00 29	00 43	00 43		00s59	00s59	01s01	01 35	01 39	01 39	01 39		01s58	01s58	02 11	02 11						06 22
—		d	23p45	00 33	00 47	00 47					01 39	01 43	01 43	01 43				02 15	02 15		05 20	05 30	06 03	06 07	
54¾	Smethwick Rolfe Street	d																						06 13	
55½	Smethwick Galton Bdg L.L. 7	d																						06 15	
56¾	Sandwell & Dudley	d	00s10																					06 18	
57¾	Dudley Port	d																						06 22	
58½	Tipton	d																						06 24	
60	Coseley	d																						06 27	
—	Walsall	d																							
64¼	**Wolverhampton 7**	a	00 45	00 51	01 06	01 19		01 33	01 33	01 34	01 57	02 02	02 02	02 15		02 32	02 32	02 34	02 47		05 37	05 48	06 20	06 32	
—		d																			05 38	05 49	06 21	06 39	
74¼	Penkridge	d																						06 49	
79½	**Stafford**	a																			05 51	06 04	06 33	06 56	

		LM MX 1		AW ◇	XC 1 ◇	LM 1 U	LM	LM	LM	LM 1 V	VT 1 ◇	LM	LM 1 X	LM 1 Y	AW ◇	XC 1 ◇	LM 1 ◇	LM 1	LM Z	LM 1 Y	LM 1 X	LM	XC 1 ◇ AA	LM 1 ◇ BB	LM CC
London Euston 15 ⊖	d																								
Northampton	d	05 19				06 03				06 06			06 11	06 15						06 35	06 34				
Long Buckby	d	05 29				06 14				06 17			06 21	06 25						06 45	06 44				
Rugby	d	05 43				06 27				06 29			06 33	06 36						06 56	06 56				
Coventry	a	05 54											06 47	06 48						07 08	07 10				
	d	05 55						06 05	06 27				06 48	06 48				06 53		07 10	07 10		07 23		
Canley	d							06 08	06 30									06 56							
Tile Hill	d							06 12	06 34									07 00							
Berkswell	d							06 15	06 37									07 03							
Hampton-in-Arden	d							06 19	06 41									07 07							
Birmingham International ✈	a	06 04						06 23	06 45				06 58	06 58				07 11		07 19	07 19		07 33		
	d	06 05						06 23	06 45				06 58	06 58				07 11		07 20	07 20		07 34		07 37
Marston Green	d							06 26	06 48									07 14							07 40
Lea Hall	d							06 30	06 52									07 18							07 43
Stechford	d							06 32	06 54									07 20							07 45
Adderley Park	d							06 36										07 24							
Birmingham New Street 12	a	06 22						06 42	07 01				07 15	07 15				07 28		07 35	07 35		07 45		07 53
	d			06 33	06 30		06 37				07 03	07 07			07 17	07 18	07 21					07 37	07 48	07 51	
Smethwick Rolfe Street	d						06 43					07 13										07 43			
Smethwick Galton Bdg L.L. 7	d						06 45					07 15										07 45			
Sandwell & Dudley	d						06 47					07 17										07 47			
Dudley Port	d						06 50					07 20										07 50			
Tipton	d						06 52					07 22										07 52			
Coseley	d						06 55					07 25					07 34								
Walsall	d																		07 30						
Wolverhampton 7	a			06 48	07 00		07 01				07 20	07 31			07 33	07 39	07 43		07 45			08 00	08 05	08 09	
	d				07 06						07 21					07 39	07 44						08 06	08 09	
Penkridge	d																07 54							08 19	
Stafford	a				07 17	07 23				07 23	07 33					07 53	08 01						08 17	08 25	

For general notes see front of timetable
For details of catering facilities see Directory of Train Operators

- **A** Until 14 July
- **B** From 15 September
- **C** 21 July to 8 September
- **D** Until 8 September
- **E** Until 25 July
- **G** 29 July to 22 August
- **H** From 26 August
- **J** 28 July to 18 August
- **K** 21 July, 25 August, 1 and 8 September
- **L** Until 25 July and from 26 August
- **N** To Holyhead (Table 81)
- **Q** To Liverpool Lime Street (Table 91)
- **U** 28 July to 22 August. To Liverpool Lime Street (Table 91)
- **V** Until 25 July and from 25 August. To Liverpool Lime Street (Table 91)
- **X** 28 July to 22 August
- **Y** Until 25 July and from 25 August
- **Z** To Shrewsbury (Table 74)
- **AA** From Southampton Central (Table 51)
- **BB** From Walsall (Table 70) to Liverpool Lime Street (Table 65). Trolley from Birmingham New Street
- **CC** To Walsall (Table 70)

Northampton → Coventry → Birmingham → Wolverhampton → Stafford

Network Diagram - see first page of Table 67

		LM	LM		VT	LM	LM	LM	VT	XC	LM	LM	LM	AW	LM	LM	LM	VT	XC	XC	LM	LM	LM	VT	LM
					1 ◇	1	1		1 ◇	1 ◇		1	1	◇			1	1 ◇	1 ◇	1 ◇	1 ◇			1 ◇	1
						A	B				C	D	E			G				H		C			A
					☕				⊠	☕		🛒	🛒	🛒				⊠	☕	☕	🛒			☕	
London Euston [15] ⊖	d								06 35									07 08							
Northampton	d					07 00	06 57					07 22	07 22												08 00
Long Buckby	d					07 10	07 07					07 32	07 32												08 10
Rugby	d					07 20	07 17					07 41	07 43												08 20
Coventry	a					07 32	07 34		07 44			07 56	07 56					08 12							08 32
	d					07 32	07 34		07 44			07 56	07 56				08 01	08 14		08 23					08 32
Canley	d					07 35	07 37										08 04								08 35
Tile Hill	d					07 39	07 41					08 01	08 01				08 08								08 39
Berkswell	d					07 42	07 44										08 11								08 42
Hampton-in-Arden	d					07 47	07 49										08 15								08 46
Birmingham International ✈	a					07 50	07 52		07 57			08 09	08 09				08 19	08 27		08 33					08 50
	d					07 51	07 53		07 58		08 04	08 09	08 09				08 19	08 28		08 34		08 37			08 50
Marston Green	d										08 07	08 12	08 12				08 22					08 40			
Lea Hall	d										08 10						08 26					08 43			
Stechford	d										08 13						08 28					08 45			
Adderley Park	d										08 16						08 32								
Birmingham New Street [12]	a					08 04	08 06		08 09		08 21	08 25	08 25				08 37	08 41		08 48		08 52			09 06
	d	07 57			08 03			08 07	08 13	08 18		08 26	08 26	08 33		08 37			08 48		08 51		08 57	09 03	
Smethwick Rolfe Street	d							08 13								08 43									
Smethwick Galton Bdg L.L. [7]	d							08 15								08 45									
Sandwell & Dudley	d							08 17	08 23							08 47					08 59				
Dudley Port	d							08 20								08 50									
Tipton	d							08 22								08 52									
Coseley	d	08 09						08 25				08 37	08 37										09 09		
Walsall	d		08 03												08 44										
Wolverhampton [7]	a	08 15	08 20		08 20			08 31	08 36	08 38		08 44	08 44	08 48	08 59	09 01			09 05		09 09		09 15	09 20	
	d									08 39		08 44	08 44						09 06		09 10				
Penkridge	d											08 54	08 54												
Stafford	a									08 53		09 01	09 01						09 17		09 24				

		LM	LM	VT		VT	XC	LM	LM	AW	LM	LM	LM	VT	XC	LM	LM	LM	VT	LM	LM	LM	VT	XC	LM
		1		1 ◇		1 ◇	1 ◇	1 ◇		◇	1			1 ◇	1 ◇	1 ◇			1 ◇	1	1		1 ◇	1 ◇	1 ◇
		B		A		B			C						J		C			B	A				
				⊠		⊠	☕	🛒		🛒				⊠	☕	🛒			☕				⊠	☕	🛒
London Euston [15] ⊖	d			07 40		07 40								08 10									08 40		
Northampton	d	07 58																		08 58	09 00				
Long Buckby	d	08 08																		09 08	09 10				
Rugby	d	08 18																		09 18	09 20				
Coventry	a	08 33		08 45		08 45								09 13						09 31	09 31		09 44		
	d	08 33		08 45		08 45					09 02			09 14	09 23					09 32	09 32		09 44		
Canley	d	08 36									09 05									09 35	09 35				
Tile Hill	d	08 40									09 09									09 39	09 39				
Berkswell	d	08 43									09 12									09 42	09 42				
Hampton-in-Arden	d	08 46									09 16									09 46	09 46				
Birmingham International ✈	a	08 50		08 57		08 57					09 19			09 26	09 33					09 50	09 50		09 57		
	d	08 50		08 58		08 58			09 05		09 20			09 28	09 34		09 37			09 50	09 50		09 58		
Marston Green	d								09 08								09 40								
Lea Hall	d								09 11								09 43								
Stechford	d								09 13								09 45								
Adderley Park	d								09 16																
Birmingham New Street [12]	a	09 06		09 09		09 10			09 21		09 34			09 41	09 45		09 52			10 06	10 06		10 09		
	d		09 07	09 13		09 13	09 18	09 21		09 33			09 37		09 48	09 51		09 57	10 03			10 07	10 13	10 18	10 21
Smethwick Rolfe Street	d		09 13										09 43									10 13			
Smethwick Galton Bdg L.L. [7]	d		09 15										09 45									10 15			
Sandwell & Dudley	d			09 23		09 23							09 47			09 59							10 23		
Dudley Port	d		09 20										09 50									10 19			
Tipton	d		09 22										09 52									10 21			
Coseley	d		09 25					09 34										10 09				10 23			10 34
Walsall	d											09 44													
Wolverhampton [7]	a		09 31	09 36		09 36	09 38	09 44		09 48		09 59	10 00		10 05	10 09		10 15	10 20			10 30	10 36	10 38	10 44
	d							09 44							10 06	10 10									10 44
Penkridge	d							09 54																	10 54
Stafford	a							10 01							10 17	10 24									11 01

For general notes see front of timetable
For details of catering facilities see Directory of Train Operators

A Until 25 July and from 25 August
B 28 July to 22 August
C To Walsall (Table 70)
D 28 July to 22 August. To Liverpool Lime Street (Table 65). 🛒 from Birmingham New Street
E Until 25 July and from 25 August. To Liverpool Lime Street (Table 65). 🛒 from Birmingham New Street
G From Four Oaks (Table 69)
H From Southampton Central (Table 51)
J From Bournemouth (Table 51)

Northampton → Coventry → Birmingham → Wolverhampton → Stafford

Network Diagram - see first page of Table 67

		LM	AW	LM	VT		XC	LM	LM	VT	XC	XC	LM	LM	LM	VT	LM	LM	LM	VT	XC	LM	LM	AW	LM
			◇		1 ◇		1 ◇	1		1 ◇	1 ◇	1 ◇	1 ◇			1 ◇	1	1		1 ◇	R 1	1 ◇		◇	1
		A									B			A			C	D					A		
			🛒		⊠		☕			⊠	☕	☕	🛒			☕				⊠	☕	🛒		🛒	
London Euston 15 ⊖	d				09 38					09 10										09 40					
Northampton	d				10 26												09 58	10 00							
Long Buckby	d																10 08	10 10							
Rugby	d				10a46												10 18	10 20							
Coventry	a									10 13							10 32	10 32		10 45					
	d							10 02		10 14	10 23						10 32	10 32		10 45					11 02
Canley	d							10 05									10 35	10 35							11 05
Tile Hill	d							10 09									10 39	10 39							11 09
Berkswell	d							10 12									10 42	10 42							11 12
Hampton-in-Arden	d							10 16									10 46	10 46							11 16
Birmingham International ✈	a							10 20		10 26	10 33						10 50	10 50		10 57					11 20
	d	10 05					10 18	10 20		10 28	10 34			10 37			10 50	10 50		10 58			11 05		11 20
Marston Green	d	10 08												10 40									11 08		
Lea Hall	d	10 11												10 43									11 11		
Stechford	d	10 13												10 45									11 13		
Adderley Park	d	10 16																					11 16		
Birmingham New Street 12	a	10 21					10 30	10 34		10 41	10 45	←		10 53			11 06	11 06		11 09			11 21		11 34
	d		10 33				10 48 →		10 37			10 48	10 51		10 57	11 03			11 07	11 13	11 18	11 21		11 33	
Smethwick Rolfe Street	d								10 43										11 13						
Smethwick Galton Bdg L.L. 7	d								10 45										11 15						
Sandwell & Dudley	d								10 47				10 59							11 23					
Dudley Port	d								10 50										11 19						
Tipton	d								10 52										11 21						
Coseley	d														11 09				11 23			11 34			
Walsall	d			10 44																					
Wolverhampton 7 🚌	a		10 48	10 59					11 00			11 05	11 09		11 15	11 20			11 30	11 36	11 38	11 44		11 48	
	d											11 06	11 10									11 44			
Penkridge	d																					11 54			
Stafford	a											11 17	11 24									12 01			

		LM	LM	VT	XC	LM		LM	LM	VT	LM	LM	LM	VT	XC	LM	LM	AW	LM	XC	LM	LM	VT	XC	XC
				1 ◇	R 1	1 ◇				1 ◇	1	1		1 ◇	1 ◇	1 ◇		◇		1 ◇	1		1 ◇	R 1	1 ◇
					B			A			C	D					A							B	
				⊠	☕	🛒				☕				☕	☕	🛒		🛒		☕			☕	☕	☕
London Euston 15 ⊖	d			10 10										10 40									11 10		
Northampton	d										10 58	11 00													
Long Buckby	d										11 08	11 10													
Rugby	d										11 18	11 20													
Coventry	a			11 13							11 32	11 32		11 44									12 14		
	d			11 14	11 23						11 32	11 32		11 44							12 02		12 16	12 23	
Canley	d										11 35	11 35									12 05				
Tile Hill	d										11 39	11 39									12 09				
Berkswell	d										11 42	11 42									12 12				
Hampton-in-Arden	d										11 46	11 46									12 16				
Birmingham International ✈	a			11 26	11 33						11 50	11 50		11 57							12 20		12 26	12 33	
	d			11 28	11 34			11 37			11 50	11 50		11 58			12 05			12 18	12 20		12 28	12 34	
Marston Green	d							11 40									12 08								
Lea Hall	d							11 43									12 11								
Stechford	d							11 45									12 13								
Adderley Park	d																12 16								
Birmingham New Street 12	a			11 41	11 45			11 53			12 06	12 06		12 09			12 21			12 30	12 34		12 41	12 45	←
	d		11 37		11 48	11 51			11 57	12 03			12 07	12 13	12 18	12 21		12 33		12 48 →		12 37			12 48
Smethwick Rolfe Street	d		11 43										12 13									12 43			
Smethwick Galton Bdg L.L. 7	d		11 45										12 15									12 45			
Sandwell & Dudley	d		11 47			11 59								12 23								12 47			
Dudley Port	d		11 50										12 19									12 50			
Tipton	d		11 52										12 21									12 52			
Coseley	d								12 09				12 23			12 34									
Walsall	d	11 44																	12 44						
Wolverhampton 7 🚌	a	11 59	12 00			12 09			12 15	12 20			12 30	12 36	12 38	12 44		12 48	12 59			13 00			13 05
	d					12 10										12 44									13 06
Penkridge	d															12 54									
Stafford	a				12 17	12 24										13 01									13 17

For general notes see front of timetable
For details of catering facilities see Directory of Train Operators

A To Walsall (Table 70)
B From Bournemouth (Table 51)
C 28 July to 22 August
D Until 25 July and from 25 August

Northampton → Coventry → Birmingham → Wolverhampton → Stafford

Network Diagram - see first page of Table 67

		LM	LM	LM	VT	LM	LM		LM	VT	XC	LM	LM	AW	LM	LM	LM	VT	XC	LM	LM	LM	VT	LM	LM
		1 ◇			1 ◇	1	1			1 ◇	R 1	1 ◇		◇	1			1 ◇	R 1	1 ◇			1 ◇	1	1
			A			B	C						A						D		A			B	C
London Euston 15 ⊖	d					10 53	10 53			11 40								12 10							
Northampton	d					11 58	12 00																	12 58	13 00
Long Buckby	d					12 08	12 10																	13 08	13 10
Rugby	d					12 18	12 20																	13 18	13 20
Coventry	a					12 32	12 32			12 44								13 13						13 32	13 32
	d					12 32	12 32			12 44					13 02			13 14	13 23					13 32	13 32
Canley	d					12 35	12 35								13 05									13 35	13 35
Tile Hill	d					12 39	12 39								13 09									13 39	13 39
Berkswell	d					12 42	12 42								13 12									13 42	13 42
Hampton-in-Arden	d					12 46	12 46								13 16									13 46	13 46
Birmingham International ✈	a					12 50	12 50			12 57					13 20			13 26	13 33					13 50	13 50
	d		12 37			12 50	12 50			12 58			13 05		13 20			13 28	13 34		13 37			13 50	13 50
Marston Green	d		12 40										13 08								13 40				
Lea Hall	d		12 43										13 11								13 43				
Stechford	d		12 45										13 13								13 45				
Adderley Park	d												13 16												
Birmingham New Street 12	a		12 53			13 06	13 06			13 09			13 21		13 34			13 41	13 45		13 53			14 06	14 06
	d	12 51		12 57	13 03				13 07	13 13	13 18	13 21		13 33			13 37		13 48	13 51		13 57	14 03		
Smethwick Rolfe Street	d								13 13								13 43								
Smethwick Galton Bdg L.L. 7	d								13 15								13 45								
Sandwell & Dudley	d	12 59								13 23							13 47			13 59					
Dudley Port	d								13 19								13 50								
Tipton	d								13 21								13 52								
Coseley	d			13 09					13 23			13 34										14 09			
Walsall	d															13 44									
Wolverhampton 7	a	13 09		13 15	13 20				13 30	13 36	13 38	13 44		13 48		13 59	14 00		14 05	14 09		14 15	14 20		
	d	13 10										13 44							14 06	14 10					
Penkridge	d											13 54													
Stafford	a	13 24										14 01							14 17	14 24					

		LM	VT	LM	XC	LM	LM	AW		LM	XC	LM	LM	VT	XC	XC	LM	LM	LM	VT	LM	LM	LM	VT	XC
			1 ◇	1	1 ◇	1 ◇		◇			1 ◇	1		1 ◇	R 1	1 ◇	1 ◇			1 ◇	1	1		1 ◇	R 1
							A								D			A			B	C			
London Euston 15 ⊖	d		12 40	12 49										13 10							12 53	12 53		13 40	
Northampton	d																				13 58	14 00			
Long Buckby	d																				14 08	14 10			
Rugby	d			13 47																	14 18	14 20			
Coventry	a		13 44											14 13							14 32	14 32		14 44	
	d		13 44									14 02		14 14	14 23						14 32	14 32		14 44	
Canley	d											14 05									14 35	14 35			
Tile Hill	d											14 09									14 39	14 39			
Berkswell	d											14 12									14 42	14 42			
Hampton-in-Arden	d											14 16									14 46	14 46			
Birmingham International ✈	a		13 57									14 20		14 27	14 33						14 50	14 50		14 57	
	d		13 58				14 05				14 18	14 20		14 28	14 34			14 37			14 50	14 50		14 58	
Marston Green	d						14 08											14 40							
Lea Hall	d						14 11											14 43							
Stechford	d						14 13											14 45							
Adderley Park	d						14 16																		
Birmingham New Street 12	a		14 09				14 21				14 30	14 34		14 41	14 45	←		14 53			15 06	15 06		15 09	
	d	14 07	14 13		14 18	14 21		14 33			14 48 →		14 37			14 48	14 51		14 57	15 03			15 07	15 13	15 18
Smethwick Rolfe Street	d	14 13											14 43										15 13		
Smethwick Galton Bdg L.L. 7	d	14 15											14 45										15 15		
Sandwell & Dudley	d		14 23										14 47				14 59							15 23	
Dudley Port	d	14 19											14 50										15 19		
Tipton	d	14 21											14 52										15 21		
Coseley	d	14 23				14 34													15 09				15 23		
Walsall	d									14 44															
Wolverhampton 7	a	14 30	14 36		14 38	14 44		14 48		14 59			15 00			15 05	15 09		15 15	15 20			15 30	15 36	15 38
	d					14 44										15 06	15 10								
Penkridge	d					14 54																			
Stafford	a			14 43		15 01										15 17	15 24								

For general notes see front of timetable
For details of catering facilities see Directory of Train Operators

A To Walsall (Table 70)
B 28 July to 22 August
C Until 25 July and from 25 August
D From Bournemouth (Table 51)

Northampton → Coventry → Birmingham → Wolverhampton → Stafford

Network Diagram - see first page of Table 67

		LM	LM	AW	LM	LM	LM	VT	VT		VT	XC	LM	LM	LM	VT	LM	LM	LM	VT	XC	LM	LM	AW	LM
								FX			FO	R									R			R	
		1◇		◇	1			1◇	1◇		1◇	1	1◇			1◇	1	1		1◇	1	1◇			
			A					B	C		D	E		A			C	G					A		
		⌶		⌶				⊏P	⊏P		⊏P	⊏P	⌶			⊏P				⊏P	⊏P	⌶		⌶	
London Euston 15 ⊖	d							14 10	14 10		14 10									14 40					
Northampton	d																14 58	15 00							
Long Buckby	d																15 08	15 10							
Rugby	d										15 04						15 18	15 20							
Coventry	a							15 13	15 13		15 14						15 32	15 32		15 44					
	d				15 02			15 14	15 15		15 16	15 23					15 32	15 32		15 44					
Canley	d				15 05												15 35	15 35							
Tile Hill	d				15 09												15 39	15 39							
Berkswell	d				15 12												15 42	15 42							
Hampton-in-Arden	d				15 16												15 46	15 46							
Birmingham International ✈	a				15 20			15 26	15 27		15 27	15 33					15 50	15 50		15 57					
	d		15 05		15 20			15 28	15 28		15 28	15 34		15 37			15 50	15 50		15 58			16 05		
Marston Green	d		15 08											15 40									16 08		
Lea Hall	d		15 11											15 43									16 11		
Stechford	d		15 13											15 45									16 13		
Adderley Park	d		15 16																				16 16		
Birmingham New Street 12	a		15 21		15 34			15 41	15 41		15 41	15 45		15 53			16 06	16 06		16 09			16 21		
	d	15 21		15 33			15 37					15 48	15 51		15 57	16 03			16 07	16 13	16 18	16 21		16 33	
Smethwick Rolfe Street	d						15 43												16 13						
Smethwick Galton Bdg L.L. 7	d						15 45												16 15						
Sandwell & Dudley	d						15 47						15 59							16 23					
Dudley Port	d						15 50												16 19						
Tipton	d						15 52												16 21						
Coseley	d	15 34													16 09				16 23			16 34			
Walsall	d					15 44																			16 44
Wolverhampton 7	a	15 44		15 48		15 59	16 00						16 09		16 15	16 20			16 30	16 36	16 38	16 43		16 48	16 59
	d	15 44											16 10									16 44			
Penkridge	d	15 54																				16 54			
Stafford	a	16 01										16 17	16 24									17 01			

		XC	LM	LM	LM	VT	VT	XC	XC	LM		LM	LM	LM	LM	VT	XC	LM	LM	LM	AW	LM	LM	LM	LM
							FO	R									R								
		1◇	1	1		1◇	1◇	1	1◇	1◇				1		1◇	1	1◇			◇				
			H	J		K	D	E				A						L	A	N		Q	U		
		⊏P				⊏P	⊏P	⊏P	⊏P	⌶						⊏P	⊏P	⌶			⌶				
London Euston 15 ⊖	d					15 10	15 10							14 53		15 40									
Northampton	d													16 00								16 29	16 30		
Long Buckby	d													16 10								16 39	16 40		
Rugby	d						16 04							16 20								16 48	16 50		
Coventry	a					16 13	16 14							16 32		16 44						17 01	17 01		
	d		16 00	16 02		16 14	16 16	16 23						16 32		16 44						17 02	17 02		
Canley	d		16 03	16 05										16 35								17 05	17 05		
Tile Hill	d		16 07	16 09										16 39								17 09	17 09		
Berkswell	d		16 11	16 12										16 42								17 12	17 12		
Hampton-in-Arden	d		16 15	16 16										16 46								17 16	17 16		
Birmingham International ✈	a		16 19	16 20		16 26	16 27	16 33						16 50		16 57						17 20	17 20		
	d	16 18	16 20	16 20		16 28	16 28	16 34				16 37		16 50		16 58			17 05			17 20	17 20		
Marston Green	d											16 40							17 08						
Lea Hall	d											16 43							17 11						
Stechford	d											16 45							17 13						
Adderley Park	d																		17 16						
Birmingham New Street 12	a	16 30	16 34	16 34		16 41	16 41	16 45	←			16 53		17 06		17 09			17 21			17 36	17 36		
	d	16 48			16 37				16 48	16 51			16 57		17 07	17 13	17 18	17 21		17 24	17 33				17 37
Smethwick Rolfe Street	d	→			16 43										17 13										17 43
Smethwick Galton Bdg L.L. 7	d				16 45										17 15					17 31					17 45
Sandwell & Dudley	d				16 47					16 59						17 23				17 34					17 47
Dudley Port	d				16 50										17 19					17 37					17 50
Tipton	d				16 52										17 21			17 32							17 52
Coseley	d												17 09		17 23			17 35							17 55
Walsall	d																							17 44	
Wolverhampton 7	a				17 00				17 05	17 09			17 15		17 30	17 36	17 38	17 43		17 48	17 48			17 59	18 01
	d								17 06	17 10								17 44							
Penkridge	d									17 20								17 54							
Stafford	a								17 17	17 26								18 01							

For general notes see front of timetable
For details of catering facilities see Directory of Train Operators

- **A** To Walsall (Table 70)
- **B** Until 24 July and from 25 August
- **C** 28 July to 22 August
- **D** Until 25 July and from 29 August
- **E** From Bournemouth (Table 51)
- **G** Until 25 July and from 25 August
- **H** From 27 October
- **J** Until 24 October
- **K** All Mondays to Thursdays, also Fridays 1 to 22 August
- **L** To Liverpool Lime Street (Table 65)
- **N** To Shrewsbury (Table 74)
- **Q** 28 July to 22 August. First Class accommodation available to Coventry, First Class accommodation available from Coventry
- **U** Until 25 July and from 25 August. First Class accommodation available to Coventry, First Class accommodation available from Coventry

Northampton → Coventry → Birmingham → Wolverhampton → Stafford

Network Diagram - see first page of Table 67

	VT	XC	LM	LM	LM	VT	LM	LM	LM	VT		XC	LM	VT	LM	LM	VT	LM	AW	LM	VT	VT	LM	LM
	1 ◇	R 1	1 ◇			1 ◇	1	1		1 ◇		R 1	1	1 ◇	1 ◇		1 ◇	1	◇		1 ◇	1 ◇	1	
		A		B			C	D					C	E		B	C	D				D	C	
	☕	☕	🛒			☕				☕		☕		⊠	🛒		☕		🛒		⊠	☕		
London Euston 15 ⊖ d	16 10									16 40				17 21			16 51				17 45	17 02		
Northampton d							17 00	17 02																
Long Buckby d							17 10	17 12																
Rugby d							17 20	17 23						18 10			17 47				18 34	17 55		
Coventry a	17 13						17 32	17 35		17 44							18 01					18 08		
d	17 14	17 23					17 32	17 36		17 44			18 02				18 02	18 09				18 09		
Canley d							17 35	17 39					18 05					18 12						
Tile Hill d							17 39	17 43					18 09					18 16						
Berkswell d							17 42	17 46					18 12					18 19						
Hampton-in-Arden d							17 46	17 50					18 16					→						
Birmingham International ✈ a	17 26	17 33					17 50	17 54		17 56			18 20				18 12					18 20	←	
d	17 28	17 34		17 37			17 50	17 54		17 58			18 20			18 05	18 14					18 21	18 20	
Marston Green d				17 40									→			18 08								
Lea Hall d				17 43												18 11								
Stechford d				17 45												18 13								
Adderley Park d																18 16								
Birmingham New Street 12 a	17 41	17 45		17 53			18 06	18 06		18 09						18 21	18 29					18 32	18 34	
d		17 48	17 51		17 57	18 03			18 07	18 13		18 18			18 21				18 33			18 43		18 37
Smethwick Rolfe Street d									18 13													→		18 43
Smethwick Galton Bdg L.L. 7 d									18 15															18 45
Sandwell & Dudley d			17 59							18 23														18 47
Dudley Port d									18 19															18 50
Tipton d									18 21															18 52
Coseley d					18 09				18 23						18 34									
Walsall d																				18 44				
Wolverhampton 7 🚌 a		18 05	18 09		18 15	18 20			18 30	18 36		18 38			18 43				18 48	18 59				19 00
d		18 06	18 10												18 44									
Penkridge d			18 20												18 54									
Stafford a		18 17	18 26											18 50	19 01						19 10			

	VT	LM	VT	XC	LM	LM	LM	VT	LM	VT	LM		LM	LM	LM	XC	LM	LM	VT	AW	LM	LM	LM	VT
	1 ◇	1	1 ◇	R 1	1 ◇	1		1 ◇		1 ◇	1		1	1	1	R 1	1 ◇	1	1 ◇	◇	1			1 ◇
	C	D	D	A							C		D	C	D									C
	☕		☕	☕	🛒			☕		☕						☕	🛒		☕					☕
London Euston 15 ⊖ d	17 10									17 30				16 55	16 55				17 50					18 10
Northampton d														18 05	18 05									
Long Buckby d														18 15	18 15									
Rugby d														18 26	18 26									
Coventry a	18 14									18 32				18 41	18 44				18 58					19 14
d	18 14			18 23						18 34	18 36		18 39						18 58		19 02			19 14
Canley d											18 39		18 42								19 05			
Tile Hill d		←									18 43		18 46								19 09			
Berkswell d		18 19									18 46		18 49								19 12			
Hampton-in-Arden d		18 23									18 50		18 53								19 16			
Birmingham International ✈ a	18 26	18 27		18 33						18 44	18 54		18 57						19 10		19 19			19 26
d	18 28	18 27		18 34		18 37				18 46	18 54		18 57					19 05	19 11		19 20			19 28
Marston Green d						18 40												19 08						
Lea Hall d						18 43												19 11						
Stechford d						18 45												19 13						
Adderley Park d																		19 16						
Birmingham New Street 12 a	18 39	18 41	←	18 45		18 53				18 57	19 08		19 11					19 21	19 27		19 34			19 39
d	18 43		18 43		18 51		18 57	19 03	19 07	19 13						19 18	19 21			19 33			19 37	19 51
Smethwick Rolfe Street d									19 13														19 43	
Smethwick Galton Bdg L.L. 7 d									19 15														19 45	
Sandwell & Dudley d	18 53		18 53		18 59					19 23													19 47	20 00
Dudley Port d									19 19														19 50	
Tipton d									19 21														19 52	
Coseley d							19 09		19 23								19 34							
Walsall d																						19 44		
Wolverhampton 7 🚌 a	19 06		19 06		19 09		19 15	19 20	19 30	19 36						19 38	19 42			19 48		19 59	20 00	20 13
d	19 06		19 06		19 10			19 21									19 44							
Penkridge d																	19 54							
Stafford a	19 21		19 21		19 24			19 36									20 01							

For general notes see front of timetable
For details of catering facilities see Directory of Train Operators

A From Bournemouth (Table 51)
B To Walsall (Table 70)
C Until 25 July and from 25 August
D 28 July to 22 August
E To Holyhead (Table 81)

Table 68

Northampton → Coventry → Birmingham → Wolverhampton → Stafford

Network Diagram - see first page of Table 67

		VT	XC	LM	LM	LM	XC	LM	LM	LM	VT	LM	LM		XC	LM	LM	VT	AW	LM	LM	VT	XC	XC	LM
		1 ◇	R 1	1	1		R 1	1	1		1 ◇				1 ◇	1 ◇	1	1 ◇	◇	1		1 ◇	1 ◇	1 ◇	
		A		B	A			A	B			B	A										C	D	
		🍽									🍽					🛒		🍽	🛒			🍽		🍽	
London Euston 15 ⊖	d	18 10									18 40							18 57				19 10			
Northampton	d							18 58	19 00			19 14	19 14												
Long Buckby	d							19 08	19 10			19 24	19 24												
Rugby	d							19 18	19 20									19 47							
Coventry	a	19 18						19 32	19 32		19 44	19 55	19 56					20 00				20 14			
	d	19 18	19 23					19 32	19 32		19 44							20 00		20 02		20 14		20 23	
Canley	d							19 35	19 35											20 04					
Tile Hill	d							19 39	19 39											20 08					
Berkswell	d							19 42	19 42											20 11					
Hampton-in-Arden	d							19 46	19 46											20 15					
Birmingham International ✈	a	19 30	19 33					19 50	19 50		19 57							20 12		20 20		20 26		20 33	
	d	19 32	19 34	19 37	19 40			19 50	19 50		19 58						20 05	20 12		20 20		20 28		20 34	
Marston Green	d			19 40	19 43												20 08			20 23					
Lea Hall	d			19 43	19 46												20 11			20 26					
Stechford	d			19 45	19 48												20 13			20 28					
Adderley Park	d																20 16								
Birmingham New Street 12	a	19 43	19 45	19 53	19 56		←	20 06	20 06		20 09						20 21	20 26		20 36		20 39		20 48	
	d	19 51	20 03			19 57	20 03			20 07	20 13				20 18	20 21			20 33		20 37	20 43	20 48		
Smethwick Rolfe Street	d		→							20 13											20 43				
Smethwick Galton Bdg L.L. 7	d									20 15											20 45				
Sandwell & Dudley	d	20 00									20 23										20 47	20 53			
Dudley Port	d									20 19											20 50				
Tipton	d									20 21											20 52				
Coseley	d					20 09				20 23						20 34									
Walsall	d																								21 00
Wolverhampton 7 🚌	a	20 13				20 15	20 20			20 30	20 36				20 38	20 43			20 49		21 00	21 06	21 08		21 13
	d						20 21									20 44							21 11		
Penkridge	d															20 54									
Stafford	a						20 34									21 01							21 23		

		LM	VT	LM	LM	LM	VT	XC	LM	LM	LM	VT	XC	LM		LM	LM	LM	LM	VT	XC	AW	LM	LM	XC
			1 ◇		1	1	1 ◇	1 ◇	1 ◇		1	1 ◇	1 ◇				1	1		1 ◇	1 ◇	◇		1	1 ◇
					B	A							E				A	B			E				E
			🍽				🍽		🛒			🍽	🍽							🍽	🍽				🍽
London Euston 15 ⊖	d				18 49	18 48	19 40					20 10								20 40					
Northampton	d				20 00	19 57											20 58	21 00							
Long Buckby	d				20 10	20 07											21 08	21 10							
Rugby	d				20 20	20 17											21 18	21 20							
Coventry	a				20 32	20 32	20 45					21 13					21 32	21 32		21 44					
	d				20 32	20 32	20 45				21 02	21 14	21 23				21 32	21 32		21 44				22 02	22 23
Canley	d				20 34	20 34					21 04						21 34	21 34						22 04	
Tile Hill	d				20 38	20 39					21 08						21 38	21 38						22 08	
Berkswell	d				20 41	20 42					21 11						21 41	21 41						22 11	
Hampton-in-Arden	d				20 45	20 45					21 15						21 45	21 45						22 15	
Birmingham International ✈	a				20 50	20 50	20 57				21 18	21 26	21 33				21 50	21 50		21 57				22 18	22 33
	d				20 50	20 51	20 58				21 19	21 28	21 34				21 50	21 50		21 58				22 19	22 34
Marston Green	d				20 53	20 54					21 22						21 53	21 53						22 22	
Lea Hall	d				20 56	20 57					21 25						21 56	21 56						22 25	
Stechford	d				20 58	20 58					21 27						21 58	21 58						22 27	
Adderley Park	d										21 30													22 30	
Birmingham New Street 12	a				21 08	21 08	21 09				21 38	21 39	21 45				22 08	22 08		22 09	←			22 38	22 52
	d	20 57	21 03	21 07			21 13	21 18	21 21	21 37		21 51	22 18	21 57		22 07				22 13	22 18	22 33	22 37		
Smethwick Rolfe Street	d			21 13						21 43			→			22 13							22 43		
Smethwick Galton Bdg L.L. 7	d			21 15						21 45						22 15							22 45		
Sandwell & Dudley	d						21 23			21 47		22 00				22 17				22 23			22 47		
Dudley Port	d			21 19						21 50						22 20							22 50		
Tipton	d			21 21						21 52						22 22							22 52		
Coseley	d	21 09		21 23					21 34					22 09		22 25							22 55		
Walsall	d																		22 15						
Wolverhampton 7 🚌	a	21 16	21 20	21 30			21 36	21 38	21 43	22 00		22 13		22 16		22 31			22 32	22 36	22 38	22 48	23 01		
	d		21 21					21 39	21 44												22 39				
Penkridge	d								21 54																
Stafford	a		21 36					21 53	22 01												22 53				

For general notes see front of timetable
For details of catering facilities see Directory of Train Operators

A 28 July to 22 August
B Until 25 July and from 25 August
C All Fridays, also Mondays to Thursdays until 4 September
D From Bournemouth (Table 51)
E From Bournemouth (Table 51). 🍽 to Reading

Northampton → Coventry → Birmingham → Wolverhampton → Stafford

Network Diagram - see first page of Table 67

	LM	LM	LM	LM	LM	AW	VT	VT	LM	LM	VT	VT	VT	VT	VT	VT	VT	VT	VT	VT	VT
											FX	FX	FO	FO	FO	FX	FO	FX	FX	FO	FO
	1 ◇	1	1		1		1 ◇	1 ◇	1	1	1 ◇	1 ◇	1 ◇	1 ◇	1 ◇	1 ◇	1 ◇	1 ◇	1 ◇	1 ◇	1 ◇
	A	B	C						C	B	D	E	G	H	J	K	L	E	N	Q	U
							☕	☕			☕	☕	☕	☕	☕	☕	☕	☕	☕	☕	☕
London Euston 15 ⊖ d		20 58	20 58				21 40	22 05			22 40	22 40	22 40	22 40	22 40	22 40	23 40	23 40	23 40	23 40	23 40
Northampton d		21 58	22 00						23 00	23 00											
Long Buckby d		22 08	22 10						23 10	23 10											
Rugby d		22 18	22 22				22 58	23 21	23 20	23 20	00s18	00s17	00s17	00s18	00s19	00s23	01s20	01s19	01s20	01s23	01s20
Coventry a		22 32	22 32				23 10		23 36	23 38	00s30	00s31	00s32	00s32	00s32	00s35	01s33	01s33	01s33	01s35	
d		22 32	22 32		23 02		23 10														
Canley d		22 34	22 34		23 04																
Tile Hill d		22 38	22 38		23 08																
Berkswell d		22 41	22 41		23 11																
Hampton-in-Arden d		22 45	22 45		23 15																
Birmingham International ✈ a		22 50	22 50		23 18		23 27				00s42	00s42	00s47	00s47	00s47	00s47	01s46	01s46	01s46	01s48	
d		22 50	22 50		23 19		23 27														
Marston Green d		22 53	22 53		23 22																
Lea Hall d		22 56	22 56		23 25																
Stechford d		22 58	22 58		23 27																
Adderley Park d					23 30																
Birmingham New Street 12 a		23 08	23 08		23 39		23 39				00s59	00s59	01s01	01s01	01s01	01s01	01s57	01s58	01s58	02s00	02s25
d	23 07					23 40	23 43														
Smethwick Rolfe Street d	23 13																				
Smethwick Galton Bdg L.L. 7 d	23 15																				
Sandwell & Dudley d	23 18						23 53														
Dudley Port d	23 22																				
Tipton d	23 24																				
Coseley d	23 27																				
Walsall d				23 20																	
Wolverhampton 7 a	23 33			23 34		00 10	00 05				01 33	01 33	01 33	01 33	01 33	01 34	02 31	02 32	02 32	02 34	03 00
d	23 34																				
Penkridge d	23 43																				
Stafford a	23 50							00s04													

Saturdays

until 12 July

	VT	VT	VT	VT	LM	XC	AW	LM	LM	LM	VT	LM	LM	XC	LM	AW	LM		LM	LM	XC	LM	VT	LM
	1 ◇	1 ◇	1 ◇	1 ◇	1 ◇	1 ◇	◇				1 ◇		1	1 ◇	1 ◇	◇					1 ◇		1 ◇	
			V		X																			
	☕	☕		☕		☕					☕			☕							☕		☕	
London Euston 15 ⊖ d	22p40	23p40																						
Northampton d													05 58											
Long Buckby d													06 08											
Rugby d	00s17	01s23											06 20											
Coventry a	00s32	01s35											06 31											
d								06 04					06 32				07 04							
Canley d								06 06					06 35				07 06							
Tile Hill d								06 10					06 39				07 10							
Berkswell d								06 13					06 42				07 13							
Hampton-in-Arden d								06 17					06 46				07 17							
Birmingham International ✈ a	00s47	01s48						06 20					06 49				07 20							
d								06 20					06 50				07 20							
Marston Green d								06 23					06 53				07 23							
Lea Hall d								06 26					06 56				07 26							
Stechford d								06 29					06 59				07 29							
Adderley Park d								06 32									07 32							
Birmingham New Street 12 a	01s01	02s00						06 36					07 08				07 36							
d			05 20	05 30	06 07	06 20	06 33			06 37	07 03	07 07		07 20	07 21	07 33				07 37	07 48	07 57	08 03	08 07
Smethwick Rolfe Street d					06 13					06 43		07 13								07 43				08 13
Smethwick Galton Bdg L.L. 7 d					06 15					06 45		07 15								07 45				08 15
Sandwell & Dudley d					06 18					06 47		07 17								07 47				08 17
Dudley Port d					06 22					06 50		07 20								07 50				08 20
Tipton d					06 24					06 52		07 22								07 52				08 22
Coseley d					06 27					06 55		07 25			07 34							08 09		08 25
Walsall d									06 42										07 44					
Wolverhampton 7 a	01 33	02 34	05 37	05 48	06 32	06 38	06 48		06 57	07 01	07 20	07 31		07 38	07 42	07 48			07 59	08 00	08 05	08 14	08 20	08 31
d			05 38	05 49	06 33	06 40					07 21			07 40	07 44						08 06			
Penkridge d					06 43										07 53									
Stafford a			05 51	06 04	06 50	06 52					07 33			07 52	08 01						08 17			

For general notes see front of timetable
For details of catering facilities see Directory of Train Operators

- **A** To Crewe (Table 65)
- **B** 28 July to 22 August
- **C** Until 25 July and from 25 August
- **D** Until 24 July
- **E** 28 July to 21 August
- **G** Until 25 July
- **H** 1 to 22 August
- **J** From 29 August
- **K** From 25 August
- **L** From 12 September
- **N** Until 24 July and from 25 August
- **Q** Until 11 July
- **U** 18 July to 5 September
- **V** To Holyhead (Table 81)
- **X** To Liverpool Lime Street (Table 91)

Table 68

Saturdays

until 12 July

Northampton → Coventry → Birmingham → Wolverhampton → Stafford

Network Diagram - see first page of Table 67

		LM	VT	XC	LM	AW	LM	LM	LM	VT	XC	VT	XC	LM		VT	LM	LM	VT	XC	LM	AW	LM	LM	LM
		1	1 ◇	1 ◇	1 ◇	◇				1 ◇	1 ◇	1 ◇	1 ◇			1 ◇		1	1 ◇	1 ◇	1 ◇	◇			
											A														
			⊠	☕		🛒				⊠	☕	☕	☕			☕			⊠	☕		🛒			
London Euston 15 ⊖	d		06 05							06 37		07 24							07 19						
Northampton	d	06 58																07 58							
Long Buckby	d	07 08																08 08							
Rugby	d	07 20										08 43						08 20							
Coventry	a	07 31	07 44							08 11								08 31	08 44						
	d	07 32	07 44				08 00			08 14	08 23							08 32	08 44				09 00		
Canley	d	07 35					08 02											08 35					09 02		
Tile Hill	d	07 39					08 06											08 39					09 06		
Berkswell	d	07 42					08 09											08 42					09 09		
Hampton-in-Arden	d	07 46					08 13											08 46					09 13		
Birmingham International ✈	a	07 49	07 57				08 16			08 27	08 33							08 49	08 57				09 16		
	d	07 50	07 58				08 16			08 28	08 34							08 50	08 58				09 16		
Marston Green	d	07 53					08 19											08 53					09 19		
Lea Hall	d	07 56					08 22											08 56					09 22		
Stechford	d	07 59					08 25											08 59					09 25		
Adderley Park	d						08 28																09 28		
Birmingham New Street 12	a	08 08	08 09				08 35			08 40	08 45							09 08	09 09				09 33		
	d		08 13	08 20	08 21	08 33			08 37				08 48	08 57		09 03	09 07			09 20	09 21	09 33			09 37
Smethwick Rolfe Street	d								08 43								09 13								09 43
Smethwick Galton Bdg L.L. 7	d								08 45								09 15								09 45
Sandwell & Dudley	d		08 22						08 47								09 17								09 47
Dudley Port	d								08 50								09 20								09 50
Tipton	d								08 52								09 22								09 52
Coseley	d				08 34									09 09			09 25				09 34				
Walsall	d							08 44																09 44	
Wolverhampton 7 🚌	a		08 35	08 38	08 42	08 48		08 59	09 01				09 08	09 15		09 20	09 30			09 38	09 42	09 48		09 59	10 00
	d			08 40	08 44								09 08							09 40	09 44				
Penkridge	d				08 53																09 53				
Stafford	a			08 52	09 01							09 19	09 22							09 52	10 01				

		VT	XC	LM	VT	LM	LM	VT	XC	LM		XC	AW	LM	LM	LM	VT	VT	XC	VT	XC	LM	VT	LM	LM
																			R				R		
		1 ◇	1 ◇		1 ◇		1	1 ◇	1 ◇	1 ◇		1 ◇	◇				1 ◇	1 ◇	1	1 ◇	1 ◇		1		1
			B																B						
		☕	☕		☕			⊠	☕			☕	🛒				☕	☕	☕	☕	☕		☕		
London Euston 15 ⊖	d	07 42						08 07									08 32	08 37		08 57					
Northampton	d						08 58																		09 58
Long Buckby	d						09 08																		10 08
Rugby	d	08 58					09 20										09 58			10 12					10 20
Coventry	a	09 09					09 31	09 40									10 09	10 15		10 23					10 31
	d	09 10	09 23				09 32	09 42						10 00			10 10	10 16	10 23	10 27					10 32
Canley	d						09 35							10 02											10 35
Tile Hill	d						09 39							10 06											10 39
Berkswell	d						09 42							10 09											10 42
Hampton-in-Arden	d						09 46							10 13											10 46
Birmingham International ✈	a	09 21	09 33				09 49	09 55						10 16			10 21	10 27	10 33	10 38					10 49
	d	09 22	09 34				09 50	09 57				10 12		10 17			10 22	10 28	10 34						10 50
Marston Green	d						09 53							10 20											10 53
Lea Hall	d						09 56							10 23											10 56
Stechford	d						09 59							10 25											10 59
Adderley Park	d													10 28											
Birmingham New Street 12	a	09 36	09 45				10 08	10 11				10 30		10 33			10 36	10s39	10 45		←				11 08
	d	09 40	09 48	09 57	10 03	10 07			10 20	10 21		10 48 →	10 33			10 37	10 40				10 48	10 57	11 03	11 07	
Smethwick Rolfe Street	d					10 13										10 43								11 13	
Smethwick Galton Bdg L.L. 7	d					10 15										10 45								11 15	
Sandwell & Dudley	d	09 52				10 17										10 47	10 52							11 17	
Dudley Port	d					10 20										10 50								11 20	
Tipton	d					10 22										10 52								11 22	
Coseley	d			10 09		10 25				10 34												11 09		11 25	
Walsall	d														10 44										
Wolverhampton 7 🚌	a		10 08	10 15	10 21	10 30			10 38	10 42			10 48		10 59	11 00					11 08	11 15	11 20	11 30	
	d		10 08						10 40	10 44											11 08				
Penkridge	d									10 53															
Stafford	a	10 17	10 22						10 52	11 01							11 17				11 22				

For general notes see front of timetable
For details of catering facilities see Directory of Train Operators

A From Southampton Central (Table 51)
B From Bournemouth (Table 51)

Table 68

Saturdays

until 12 July

Northampton → Coventry → Birmingham → Wolverhampton → Stafford

Network Diagram - see first page of Table 67

		VT	XC	LM	AW	LM		LM	LM	VT	VT	XC	VT	LM	VT	LM	LM	VT	XC	LM	XC	AW	LM	LM	LM
		1 ◇ ⊠	1 ◇ ☕	1 ◇	◇ 🛒					1 ◇ ☕	1 ◇ ⊠	R 1 A ☕	1 ◇ ☕		1 ◇ ☕		1	1 ◇ ☕	1 ◇ ☕	1 ◇	1 ◇ ☕	◇ 🛒			
London Euston 15 ⊖	d	09 19								09 34	09 37		09 55					10 06							
Northampton	d																10 58								
Long Buckby	d																11 08								
Rugby	d									10 57			11 12				11 20								
Coventry	a	10 44								11 09	11 15		11 23				11 31	11 40							
	d	10 44				11 00				11 10	11 16	11 23	11 27				11 32	11 42					12 00		
Canley	d					11 02											11 35						12 02		
Tile Hill	d					11 06											11 39						12 06		
Berkswell	d					11 09											11 42						12 09		
Hampton-in-Arden	d					11 13											11 46						12 13		
Birmingham International ✈	a	10 57				11 16				11 21	11 27	11 33	11 38				11 49	11 55					12 16		
	d	10 58				11 16				11 22	11 28	11 34					11 50	11 57			12 12		12 16		
Marston Green	d					11 19											11 53						12 19		
Lea Hall	d					11 22											11 56						12 22		
Stechford	d					11 25											11 59						12 25		
Adderley Park	d					11 28																	12 28		
Birmingham New Street 12	a	11 09				11 33				11 36	11s39	11 45					12 08	12 11			12 30		12 33		
	d		11 20	11 21	11 33				11 37	11 40		11 48		11 57	12 03	12 07			12 20	12 21	12 48 →	12 33			12 37
Smethwick Rolfe Street	d								11 43							12 13									12 43
Smethwick Galton Bdg L.L. 7	d								11 45							12 15									12 45
Sandwell & Dudley	d								11 47	11 52						12 17									12 47
Dudley Port	d								11 50							12 20									12 50
Tipton	d								11 52							12 22									12 52
Coseley	d			11 34												12 25				12 34					
Walsall	d							11 44																12 44	
Wolverhampton 7	a		11 38	11 42	11 48			11 59	12 00			12 08		12 15	12 20	12 30			12 38	12 42		12 48		12 59	13 00
	d		11 40	11 44								12 08							12 40	12 44					
Penkridge	d			11 53																12 53					
Stafford	a		11 52	12 01						12 17		12 22							12 52	13 01					

		VT		VT	VT	XC	LM	VT	LM	LM	VT	XC	LM	AW	LM	LM	LM	VT	VT	VT		XC	LM	VT	LM
		1 ◇ ☕		1 ◇ ☕	1 ◇ ☕	1 ◇ ☕		R 1 ☕		1	1 ◇ ☕	1 ◇ ☕	1 ◇	◇ 🛒				1 ◇ ☕	1 ◇ ☕	1 ◇ ☕		1 ◇ ☕		R 1 ☕	
London Euston 15 ⊖	d	10 33		10 38	10 57						11 17							11 33	11 38	11 55					
Northampton	d									11 58															
Long Buckby	d									12 08															
Rugby	d	11 58			12 12					12 20								12 57		13 12					
Coventry	a	12 09		12 15						12 31	12 44							13 09	13 15	13 23					
	d	12 10		12 16	12u27					12 32	12 46				13 00			13 10	13 16	13 27					
Canley	d									12 35					13 02										
Tile Hill	d									12 39					13 06										
Berkswell	d									12 42					13 09										
Hampton-in-Arden	d									12 46					13 13										
Birmingham International ✈	a	12 21		12 27	12 38					12 49	12 57				13 16			13 21	13 27	13 38					
	d	12 22		12 28						12 50	12 58				13 16			13 22	13 28						
Marston Green	d									12 53					13 19										
Lea Hall	d									12 56					13 22										
Stechford	d									12 59					13 25										
Adderley Park	d														13 28										
Birmingham New Street 12	a	12 36		12s39		←				13 08	13 09				13 33			13 36	13s39						
	d	12 40				12 48	12 57	13 03	13 07			13 20	13 21	13 33			13 37	13 40				13 48	13 57	14 03	14 07
Smethwick Rolfe Street	d								13 13								13 43								14 13
Smethwick Galton Bdg L.L. 7	d								13 15								13 45								14 15
Sandwell & Dudley	d	12 52							13 17								13 47	13 52							14 17
Dudley Port	d								13 20								13 50								14 20
Tipton	d								13 22								13 52								14 22
Coseley	d						13 09		13 25				13 34										14 09		14 25
Walsall	d															13 44									
Wolverhampton 7	a					13 08	13 15	13 20	13 30			13 38	13 42	13 48		13 59	14 00					14 08	14 15	14 20	14 30
	d					13 08						13 40	13 44									14 08			
Penkridge	d												13 53												
Stafford	a	13 17				13 22						13 52	14 01					14 18				14 22			

For general notes see front of timetable
For details of catering facilities see Directory of Train Operators

A From Bournemouth (Table 51)

Table 68 | **Saturdays** until 12 July

Northampton → Coventry → Birmingham → Wolverhampton → Stafford

Network Diagram - see first page of Table 67

	LM	VT	XC	LM	XC	AW	LM	LM	LM	VT	VT	XC	LM	VT	LM		XC	VT	LM	VT	LM	AW	LM	LM
	[1]	[1] ◇	[1] ◇	[1] ◇	[1] ◇	◇				[1] ◇	[1] ◇	[1] ◇		[R] [1]			[1] ◇ A	[1] ◇	[1]	[1] ◇	[1] ◇	◇		
		☕	☕		☕	🍴				☕	☕	☕		☕			☕	☕		☕		🍴		
London Euston [15] ⊖ d		12 17								12 33	12 38							12 56		13 17				
Northampton d	12 58																		13 58					
Long Buckby d	13 08																		14 08					
Rugby d	13 20									13 58								14 11	14 20					
Coventry a	13 31	13 40								14 09	14 15								14 31	14 41				
d	13 32	13 42					14 00			14 10	14 16						14 23	14u27	14 32	14 43			15 00	
Canley d	13 35						14 02												14 35				15 02	
Tile Hill d	13 39						14 06												14 39				15 06	
Berkswell d	13 42						14 09												14 42				15 09	
Hampton-in-Arden d	13 46						14 13												14 46				15 13	
Birmingham International ✈ a	13 49	13 55					14 16			14 21	14 27						14 33	14 38	14 49	14 55			15 16	
d	13 50	13 57			14 12		14 17			14 22	14 28						14 34		14 50	14 57			15 16	
Marston Green d	13 53						14 20												14 53				15 19	
Lea Hall d	13 56						14 23												14 56				15 22	
Stechford d	13 59						14 25												14 59				15 25	
Adderley Park d							14 28																15 28	
Birmingham New Street [12] a	14 08	14 09			14 30		14 33			14 36	14s39	←					14 45		15 08	15 11			15 33	
d			14 20	14 21	14 48 →	14 33			14 37	14 40		14 48	14 57	15 03	15 07		15 20				15 21	15 33		
Smethwick Rolfe Street d									14 43						15 13									
Smethwick Galton Bdg L.L. [7] d									14 45						15 15									
Sandwell & Dudley d									14 47	14 52					15 17									
Dudley Port d									14 50						15 20									
Tipton d									14 52						15 22									
Coseley d				14 34									15 09		15 25						15 34			
Walsall d								14 44																15 44
Wolverhampton [7] a			14 38	14 42		14 48		14 59	15 00			15 08	15 15	15 20	15 30		15 38				15 42	15 48		15 59
d			14 40	14 44								15 08					15 40				15 44			
Penkridge d				14 53																	15 53			
Stafford a			14 52	15 01						15 17		15 22					15 52				16 01			

	LM	VT	VT	XC	VT	LM	VT	LM	LM	VT	XC		LM	XC	AW	LM	LM	LM	VT	VT	XC	VT	XC	LM
		[1] ◇	[1] ◇	[R] [1] A	[1] ◇		[1] ◇		[1]	[1] ◇	[1] ◇		[1] ◇	[1] ◇	[R]				[1] ◇	[1] ◇	[1] ◇ A	[1] ◇	[1] ◇	
		☕	☕	☕	☕		☕			☕	☕			☕	🍴				☕	☕	☕	☕	☕	
London Euston [15] ⊖ d		13 33	13 38		13 56					14 17									14 33	14 38		14 56		
Northampton d									14 58															
Long Buckby d									15 08															
Rugby d		14 57			15 12				15 20										15 58			16 12		
Coventry a		15 09	15 15		15 23				15 31	15 44									16 09	16 15				
d		15 10	15 16	15 23	15 27				15 32	15 44						16 00			16 10	16 16	16 23	16u27		
Canley d									15 35							16 02								
Tile Hill d									15 39							16 06								
Berkswell d									15 42							16 09								
Hampton-in-Arden d									15 46							16 13								
Birmingham International ✈ a		15 21	15 27	15 33	15 38				15 49	15 57						16 16			16 21	16 27	16 33	16 38		
d		15 22	15 28	15 34					15 50	15 58				16 12		16 17			16 22	16 28	16 34			
Marston Green d									15 53							16 20								
Lea Hall d									15 56							16 23								
Stechford d									15 59							16 25								
Adderley Park d																16 28								
Birmingham New Street [12] a		15 36	15s39	15 45					16 08	16 09				16 30		16 33			16 36	16s39	16 45		←	
d	15 37	15 40		15 48		15 57	16 03	16 07			16 20		16 21	16 48 →	16 33			16 37	16 40				16 48	16 57
Smethwick Rolfe Street d	15 43							16 13										16 43						
Smethwick Galton Bdg L.L. [7] d	15 45							16 15										16 45						
Sandwell & Dudley d	15 47	15 52						16 17										16 47	16 52					
Dudley Port d	15 50							16 20										16 50						
Tipton d	15 52							16 22										16 52						
Coseley d								16 25					16 34											17 09
Walsall d																	16 44							
Wolverhampton [7] a	16 00			16 08		16 15	16 20	16 30			16 38		16 42		16 48		16 59	17 00					17 08	17 15
d				16 08							16 40		16 44										17 08	
Penkridge d													16 53											
Stafford a		16 17		16 22							16 52		17 01						17 17				17 22	

For general notes see front of timetable
For details of catering facilities see Directory of Train Operators

A From Bournemouth (Table 51)

Table 68

Northampton → Coventry → Birmingham → Wolverhampton → Stafford

Saturdays

until 12 July

Network Diagram - see first page of Table 67

		VT [R] [1]	LM	LM [1]	VT [1] ◇	XC [R] [1]	LM [1] ◇	AW ◇		LM	LM	LM	VT [1] ◇	VT [1] ◇	XC [1] ◇ A	VT [1] ◇	LM	VT [R] [1]	LM	LM [1]	VT [1] ◇	XC [1] ◇	LM [1] ◇	XC [1] ◇	AW ◇
London Euston [15] ⊖	d				15 17								15 33	15 38		15 56					16 17				
Northampton	d			15 58																16 58					
Long Buckby	d			16 08																17 08					
Rugby	d			16 20									16 57			17 12				17 20					
Coventry	a			16 31	16 41								17 09	17 15		17 23				17 31	17 41				
	d			16 32	16 43					17 00			17 10	17 16	17 23	17 27				17 32	17 43				
Canley	d			16 35						17 02										17 35					
Tile Hill	d			16 39						17 06										17 39					
Berkswell	d			16 42						17 09										17 42					
Hampton-in-Arden	d			16 46						17 13										17 46					
Birmingham International ✈	a			16 49	16 55					17 16			17 21	17 27	17 33	17 38				17 49	17 55				
	d			16 50	16 57					17 16			17 22	17 28	17 34					17 50	17 57			18 12	
Marston Green	d			16 53						17 19										17 53					
Lea Hall	d			16 56						17 22										17 56					
Stechford	d			16 59						17 25										17 59					
Adderley Park	d									17 28															
Birmingham New Street [12]	a			17 08	17 11					17 33			17 36	17s39	17 45					18 08	18 11			18 30	
	d	17 03	17 07			17 20	17 21	17 33				17 37	17 40		17 48		17 57	18 03	18 07			18 20	18 21	18 48 →	18 33
Smethwick Rolfe Street	d		17 13									17 43							18 13						
Smethwick Galton Bdg L.L. [7]	d		17 15									17 45							18 15						
Sandwell & Dudley	d		17 17									17 47	17 52						18 17						
Dudley Port	d		17 20									17 50							18 20						
Tipton	d		17 22									17 52							18 22						
Coseley	d		17 25				17 34										18 09		18 25				18 34		
Walsall	d										17 44														
Wolverhampton [7] ⛴	a	17 20	17 30			17 38	17 42	17 48			17 59	18 00			18 08		18 15	18 20	18 30			18 38	18 42		18 48
	d					17 40	17 44								18 08							18 40	18 44		
Penkridge	d						17 53																18 53		
Stafford	a					17 52	18 01						18 17		18 22							18 52	19 01		

		LM	LM	LM		VT [1] ◇	VT [1] ◇	XC [1] ◇ A	VT [1] ◇	XC [1] ◇	LM	VT [R] [1]	LM	LM [1]	VT [1] ◇	XC [R] [1]	LM [1] ◇	AW ◇	LM	VT [1] ◇	LM	LM		VT [1] ◇	LM
London Euston [15] ⊖	d					16 33	16 38		16 56						17 17					17 32				17 37	
Northampton	d													17 58											
Long Buckby	d													18 08											
Rugby	d					17 58			18 12					18 20											
Coventry	a					18 09	18 15							18 31	18 41					19 06				19 15	
	d	18 00				18 10	18 16	18 23	18u27					18 32	18 43				19 00	19 07				19 16	
Canley	d	18 02												18 35					19 02						
Tile Hill	d	18 06												18 39					19 06						
Berkswell	d	18 09												18 42					19 09						
Hampton-in-Arden	d	18 13												18 46					19 13						
Birmingham International ✈	a	18 16				18 21	18 27	18 33	18 39					18 49	18 55				19 16					19 27	
	d	18 17				18 22	18 28	18 34						18 50	18 57				19 16					19 28	
Marston Green	d	18 20												18 53					19 19						
Lea Hall	d	18 23												18 56					19 22						
Stechford	d	18 25												18 59					19 25						
Adderley Park	d	18 28																	19 28						
Birmingham New Street [12]	a	18 33				18 36	18s39	18 45		←				19 08	19 11				19 36					19 39	
	d			18 37		18 40				18 48	18 57	19 03	19 07			19 20	19 21	19 33				19 37		19 48	19 57
Smethwick Rolfe Street	d			18 43									19 13									19 43			
Smethwick Galton Bdg L.L. [7]	d			18 45									19 15									19 45			
Sandwell & Dudley	d			18 47		18 52							19 17									19 47			
Dudley Port	d			18 50									19 20									19 50			
Tipton	d			18 52									19 22									19 52			
Coseley	d										19 09		19 25				19 34								
Walsall	d		18 44																		19 44				20 09
Wolverhampton [7] ⛴	a		18 59	19 00						19 08	19 15	19 20	19 30			19 38	19 42	19 48			19 59	20 00		20 07	20 15
	d									19 08		19 21				19 40	19 44							20 09	
Penkridge	d																19 53								
Stafford	a					19 17				19 22		19 33				19 52	20 01			20 13				20 23	

For general notes see front of timetable
For details of catering facilities see Directory of Train Operators

A From Bournemouth (Table 51)

Table 68

Saturdays

until 12 July

Northampton → Coventry → Birmingham → Wolverhampton → Stafford

Network Diagram - see first page of Table 67

		XC	LM	LM	VT	XC	LM	AW	LM	VT	LM	LM	VT	XC	VT	XC	LM	LM		LM	VT	XC	LM	AW	LM
		1 ◇		1	1 ◇	1 ◇	1 ◇	◇		1 ◇			1 ◇	1 ◇	1 ◇	1 ◇				1	1 ◇	R 1	1 ◇	◇	
		A												A											
		☕			☕	☕		🛒		☕			☕	☕	☕	☕					☕				
London Euston 15 ⊖	d				18 17					18 33			18 38		18 56										
Northampton	d			18 58																19 58					
Long Buckby	d			19 08																20 08					
Rugby	d			19 20											20 17					20 20					
Coventry	a			19 31	19 41					20 09			20 15		20 28					20 32					
	d	19 23		19 32	19 43				20 00	20 10			20 16	20 23						20 32					21 00
Canley	d			19 35					20 02											20 35					21 02
Tile Hill	d			19 39					20 06											20 39					21 06
Berkswell	d			19 42					20 09											20 42					21 09
Hampton-in-Arden	d			19 46					20 13											20 45					21 13
Birmingham International ✈	a	19 33		19 49	19 55				20 16				20 27	20 33						20 50					21 16
	d	19 34		19 50	19 57				20 16				20 28	20 34						20 50					21 16
Marston Green	d			19 53					20 19											20 53					21 19
Lea Hall	d			19 56					20 22											20 55					21 22
Stechford	d			19 59					20 25											20 59					21 25
Adderley Park	d								20 28												←				21 28
Birmingham New Street 12	a	19 45		20 08	20 11				20 35				20s39	20 45						21 08	20s39				21 33
	d	20 03	20 07			20 20	20 21	20 33				20 37	→			20 48	20 57	21 07				21 20	21 21	21 33	
Smethwick Rolfe Street	d		20 13									20 43						21 13							
Smethwick Galton Bdg L.L. 7	d		20 15									20 45						21 15							
Sandwell & Dudley	d		20 17									20 47						21 17							
Dudley Port	d		20 20									20 50						21 20							
Tipton	d		20 22									20 52						21 22							
Coseley	d		20 25				20 34										21 09	21 25					21 34		
Walsall	d										20 44														
Wolverhampton 7	a	20 20	20 30			20 38	20 42	20 48			20 59	21 00				21 08	21 15	21 30				21 38	21 42	21 48	
	d	20 21				20 40	20 44									21 08						21 40	21 44		
Penkridge	d						20 53																21 54		
Stafford	a	20 33				20 52	21 01			21 13						21 22					21 33	21 52	22 01		

		LM	VT	LM	LM	XC	VT	LM	VT	LM	XC	AW	LM	VT		XC	LM	LM	LM	LM	AW	VT	VT		
			1 ◇			1 ◇	1 ◇	1	1 ◇		1 ◇	◇		1 ◇		1 ◇						1 ◇	1 ◇		
						A					A					A									
			☕			☕	☕		☕		☕			☕								☕	☕		
London Euston 15 ⊖	d		19 26				19 34		20 00					20 14								21 25	21 50		
Northampton	d							20 58																	
Long Buckby	d							21 08																	
Rugby	d						21 16	21 20	21 41					21 56								22 55			
Coventry	a		21 13				21 27	21 32						22 07								23 06	23s47		
	d		21 14			21 23	21 28	21 32					22 03	22 09		22 23		22 32		22 56		23 08			
Canley	d							21 35					22 05					22 35		22 59					
Tile Hill	d							21 39					22 09					22 39		23 02					
Berkswell	d							21 42					22 12					22 42		23 06					
Hampton-in-Arden	d							21 45					22 16					22 46		23 10					
Birmingham International ✈	a		21 26			21 33		21 50					22 19	22 25		22 33		22 49		23 13		23 18	23s59		
	d		21 28			21 34		21 50					22 19	22 26		22 34		22 50		23 13		23 20			
Marston Green	d							21 53					22 22					22 53		23 16					
Lea Hall	d							21 55					22 25					22 56		23 19					
Stechford	d							21 59					22 28					22 59		23 22					
Adderley Park	d												22 31							23 25					
Birmingham New Street 12	a		21 39			21 45		22 08			←		22 36	22 39		22 50		23 08		23 30		23 33	00s13		
	d	21 37	21 51	21 57	22 07	22 20					22 20	22 33	22 37	22 48			23 07				23 33	23 37			
Smethwick Rolfe Street	d	21 43			22 13	→							22 43				23 13								
Smethwick Galton Bdg L.L. 7	d	21 45			22 15								22 45				23 15								
Sandwell & Dudley	d	21 47	22 00		22 17								22 47	22 57			23 17								
Dudley Port	d	21 50			22 20								22 50				23 20								
Tipton	d	21 52			22 22								22 52				23 22								
Coseley	d			22 09	22 25								22 55				23 25								
Walsall	d									22 15									23 20						
Wolverhampton 7	a	22 00	22 13	22 15	22 30					22 32	22 38	22 48	23 01	23 11			23 30		23 39		23 49	23 58	00 47		
	d										22 40														
Penkridge	d																								
Stafford	a						22 16		22 47		22 52														

For general notes see front of timetable
For details of catering facilities see
Directory of Train Operators

A From Bournemouth (Table 51)

Table 68

Saturdays

Northampton → Coventry → Birmingham → Wolverhampton → Stafford

19 July to 6 September

Network Diagram - see first page of Table 67

	VT	VT	VT	VT	VT	VT	LM	XC	AW	LM	LM	LM	LM	LM	VT		LM	LM	XC	LM	AW	LM	LM	LM
	1 ◇	1 ◇	1 ◇	1 ◇	1 ◇	1 ◇	1 ◇	1 ◇	◇						1 ◇			1	1 ◇	1 ◇	◇			
	A	B	C		D		E																	
	☕	☕	☕	☕		☕		☕			🚌	🚌			☕				☕					
London Euston 15 ⊖ d	22p40	22p40	22p40	23p40																				
Northampton d											04 50	05 35												
Long Buckby d											05 11	05 56												
Rugby d	00s17	00s18	00s19	01s20							05 42	06a26												
Coventry a	00s32	00s32	00s32								06 22													
d										06 04								06 32				07 04		
Canley d										06 06								06 35				07 06		
Tile Hill d										06 10								06 39				07 10		
Berkswell d										06 13								06 42				07 13		
Hampton-in-Arden d										06 17								06 46				07 17		
Birmingham International ✈ a	00s47	00s47	00s47							06 20								06 49				07 20		
d										06 20								06 50				07 20		
Marston Green d										06 23								06 53				07 23		
Lea Hall d										06 26								06 56				07 26		
Stechford d										06 29								06 59				07 29		
Adderley Park d										06 32												07 32		
Birmingham New Street 12 a	01s01	01s01	01s01	02s25						06 36								07 08				07 36		
d					05 20	05 30	06 07	06 20	06 33					06 37	07 03		07 07		07 20	07 21	07 33			07 37
Smethwick Rolfe Street d							06 13							06 43			07 13							07 43
Smethwick Galton Bdg L.L. 7 d							06 15							06 45			07 15							07 45
Sandwell & Dudley d							06 18							06 47			07 17							07 47
Dudley Port d							06 22							06 50			07 20							07 50
Tipton d							06 24							06 52			07 22							07 52
Coseley d							06 27							06 55			07 25			07 34				
Walsall d													06 42										07 44	
Wolverhampton 7 ⛴ a	01 33	01 33	01 33	03 00	05 37	05 48	06 32	06 38	06 48				06 57	07 01	07 20		07 31		07 38	07 42	07 48		07 59	08 00
d					05 38	05 49	06 33	06 40							07 21				07 40	07 44				
Penkridge d							06 43													07 53				
Stafford a					05 51	06 04	06 50	06 52							07 33				07 52	08 01				

	VT	LM	XC	LM	VT	LM	LM	XC	LM		AW	LM	LM	LM	VT	XC	VT	LM	XC	LM	VT	LM	LM	XC
			1 ◇		1 ◇		1	1 ◇	1 ◇		◇				1 ◇	1 ◇			1 ◇		1 ◇		1	1 ◇
																G								
	🚌	🚌	☕		☕			☕			trolley				☕	☕	🚌	🚌	☕		☕			☕
London Euston 15 ⊖ d															06 05									
Northampton d		06 35																07 35						
Long Buckby d		06 56																07 56						
Rugby d	06 45	07a26													07 35		07 45	08a26						
Coventry a	07s25																08s25							
d							07 32					08 00				08 23							08 32	
Canley d							07 35					08 02											08 35	
Tile Hill d							07 39					08 06											08 39	
Berkswell d							07 42					08 09											08 42	
Hampton-in-Arden d							07 46					08 13											08 46	
Birmingham International ✈ a	07 50						07 49					08 16				08 33	08 50						08 49	
d							07 50					08 16				08 34							08 50	
Marston Green d							07 53					08 19											08 53	
Lea Hall d							07 56					08 22											08 56	
Stechford d							07 59					08 25											08 59	
Adderley Park d												08 28												
Birmingham New Street 12 a							08 08					08 35			08 38	08 45							09 08	
d			07 48	07 57	08 03	08 07		08 20	08 21		08 33			08 37	08 41				08 48	08 57	09 03	09 07		09 20
Smethwick Rolfe Street d						08 13								08 43								09 13		
Smethwick Galton Bdg L.L. 7 d						08 15								08 45								09 15		
Sandwell & Dudley d						08 17								08 47	08 52							09 17		
Dudley Port d						08 20								08 50								09 20		
Tipton d						08 22								08 52								09 22		
Coseley d				08 09		08 25			08 34											09 09		09 25		
Walsall d													08 44											
Wolverhampton 7 ⛴ a			08 05	08 14	08 20	08 31		08 38	08 42		08 48		08 59	09 01	09 07				09 08	09 15	09 20	09 30		09 38
d			08 06					08 40	08 44										09 08					09 40
Penkridge d									08 53															
Stafford a			08 17					08 52	09 01										09 22					09 52

For general notes see front of timetable
For details of catering facilities see Directory of Train Operators

A 19 and 26 July
B 2 to 23 August
C 30 August and 6 September
D To Holyhead (Table 81)
E To Liverpool Lime Street (Table 91)
G From Southampton Central (Table 51)

Due to Engineering Operations, services from Saturday 13 September on this Table had not been confirmed at time of going to press. These services will be issued in a special Supplement as soon as exact timings have been confirmed

Table 68

Saturdays

19 July to 6 September

Northampton → Coventry → Birmingham → Wolverhampton → Stafford

Network Diagram - see first page of Table 67

		LM	AW	LM		LM	LM	VT	XC	VT	LM	LM	VT	LM	LM	XC	XC	LM	AW	LM		LM	LM	VT	XC
		1 ◇	◇ 🛒					1 ◇ ☕	1 ◇ A ☕	🚌	🚌		1 ◇ ☕		1	1 ◇ ☕	1 ◇ ☕	1 ◇	◇ 🛒					1 ◇ ☕	R 1 A ☕
London Euston 15 ⊖	d							07 28																08 27	
Northampton	d										08 35														
Long Buckby	d										08 56														
Rugby	d							08 35		08 45	09a26													09 35	
Coventry	a									09s25															
	d			09 00					09 23						09 32					10 00					10 23
Canley	d			09 02											09 35					10 02					
Tile Hill	d			09 06											09 39					10 06					
Berkswell	d			09 09											09 42					10 09					
Hampton-in-Arden	d			09 13											09 46					10 13					
Birmingham International ✈	a			09 16					09 33	09 50					09 49					10 16					10 33
	d			09 16					09 34						09 50		10 09			10 16					10 34
Marston Green	d			09 19											09 53					10 19					
Lea Hall	d			09 22											09 56					10 22					
Stechford	d			09 25											09 59					10 25					
Adderley Park	d			09 28																10 28					
Birmingham New Street 12	a			09 33				09 38	09 45						10 08		10 20			10 33				10 38	10 45
	d	09 21	09 33				09 37	09 41	09 48			09 57	10 03	10 07		10 20	10 48 →	10 21	10 33				10 37	10 41	
Smethwick Rolfe Street	d						09 43							10 13									10 43		
Smethwick Galton Bdg L.L. 7	d						09 45							10 15									10 45		
Sandwell & Dudley	d						09 47	09 51						10 17									10 47	10 51	
Dudley Port	d						09 50							10 20									10 50		
Tipton	d						09 52							10 22									10 52		
Coseley	d	09 34										10 09		10 25				10 34							
Walsall	d					09 44																10 44			
Wolverhampton 7 🚉	a	09 42	09 48			09 59	10 00	10 07	10 08			10 15	10 21	10 30		10 38		10 42	10 48			10 59	11 00	11 07	
	d	09 44							10 08							10 40		10 44							
Penkridge	d	09 53																10 53							
Stafford	a	10 01							10 22							10 52		11 01							

		VT	LM	XC	LM	VT	LM	LM	XC	LM	AW	LM	LM	LM		VT	XC	VT	LM	LM	VT	LM	LM	XC	XC
		🚌	🚌	1 ◇ ☕		R 1 ☕		1	1 ◇ ☕	1 ◇	◇ 🛒					1 ◇ ☕	R 1 A ☕	🚌	🚌		1 ◇ ☕		1	1 ◇ ☕	1 ◇ ☕
London Euston 15 ⊖	d															09 28									
Northampton	d		09 35																10 35						
Long Buckby	d		09 56																10 56						
Rugby	d	09 45	10a26													10 36		10 45	11a26						
Coventry	a	10s25																11s25							
	d							10 32				11 00					11 23						11 32		
Canley	d							10 35				11 02											11 35		
Tile Hill	d							10 39				11 06											11 39		
Berkswell	d							10 42				11 09											11 42		
Hampton-in-Arden	d							10 46				11 13											11 46		
Birmingham International ✈	a	10 50						10 49				11 16					11 33	11 50					11 49		
	d							10 50				11 16					11 34						11 50		12 09
Marston Green	d							10 53				11 19											11 53		
Lea Hall	d							10 56				11 22											11 56		
Stechford	d							10 59				11 25											11 59		
Adderley Park	d											11 28													
Birmingham New Street 12	a			←				11 08				11 33				11 38	11 45						12 08		12 20
	d			10 48	10 57	11 03	11 07		11 20	11 21	11 33			11 37		11 41	11 48			11 57	12 03	12 07		12 20	12 48 →
Smethwick Rolfe Street	d						11 13							11 43								12 13			
Smethwick Galton Bdg L.L. 7	d						11 15							11 45								12 15			
Sandwell & Dudley	d						11 17							11 47		11 50						12 17			
Dudley Port	d						11 20							11 50								12 20			
Tipton	d						11 22							11 52								12 22			
Coseley	d				11 09		11 25			11 34												12 25			
Walsall	d												11 44												
Wolverhampton 7 🚉	a			11 08	11 15	11 20	11 30		11 38	11 42	11 48		11 59	12 00		12 07	12 08			12 15	12 20	12 30		12 38	
	d			11 08					11 40	11 44							12 08							12 40	
Penkridge	d									11 53															
Stafford	a			11 22					11 52	12 01							12 22							12 52	

For general notes see front of timetable
For details of catering facilities see Directory of Train Operators

A From Bournemouth (Table 51)

Due to Engineering Operations, services from Saturday 13 September on this Table had not been confirmed at time of going to press. These services will be issued in a special Supplement as soon as exact timings have been confirmed

Table 68

Saturdays

Northampton → Coventry → Birmingham → Wolverhampton → Stafford

19 July to 6 September

Network Diagram - see first page of Table 67

		LM	AW	LM	LM	LM	VT	VT		LM	XC	LM	VT	LM	LM	XC	LM	AW	LM	LM	LM	VT	VT	LM	XC
		1 ◇	◇ 🛒				1 ◇ ☕	🚌		🚌	1 ◇ ☕		R 1 ☕		1	1 ◇ ☕	1 ◇	◇ 🛒				1 ◇ ☕	🚌	🚌	1 ◇ ☕
London Euston 15 ⊖	d						10 28															11 28			
Northampton	d									11 35														12 35	
Long Buckby	d									11 56														12 56	
Rugby	d						11 35	11 45		12a26												12 33	12 45	13a26	
Coventry	a							12s25															13s25		
	d			12 00											12 32				13 00						
Canley	d			12 02											12 35				13 02						
Tile Hill	d			12 06											12 39				13 06						
Berkswell	d			12 09											12 42				13 09						
Hampton-in-Arden	d			12 13											12 46				13 13						
Birmingham International ✈	a			12 16				12 50							12 49				13 16				13 50		
	d			12 16											12 50				13 16						
Marston Green	d			12 19											12 53				13 19						
Lea Hall	d			12 22											12 56				13 22						
Stechford	d			12 25											12 59				13 25						
Adderley Park	d			12 28															13 28						
Birmingham New Street 12	a			12 33			12 38				←				13 08				13 33			13 38			
	d	12 21	12 33			12 37	12 41				12 48	12 57	13 03	13 07		13 20	13 21	13 33			13 37	13 41			13 48
Smethwick Rolfe Street	d					12 43								13 13							13 43				
Smethwick Galton Bdg L.L. 7	d					12 45								13 15							13 45				
Sandwell & Dudley	d					12 47	12 50							13 17							13 47	13 51			
Dudley Port	d					12 50								13 20							13 50				
Tipton	d					12 52								13 22							13 52				
Coseley	d	12 34										13 09		13 25			13 34								
Walsall	d				12 44															13 44					
Wolverhampton 7 🚋	a	12 42	12 48		12 59	13 00	13 07				13 08	13 15	13 20	13 30		13 38	13 42	13 48		13 59	14 00	14 07			14 08
	d	12 44									13 08					13 40	13 44								14 08
Penkridge	d	12 53															13 53								
Stafford	a	13 01									13 22					13 52	14 01								14 22

		LM		VT	LM	LM	XC	XC	LM	AW	LM	LM	LM	VT	XC	LM	VT	LM		XC	VT	LM	LM	LM	AW
				R 1 ☕		1	1 ◇ ☕	1 ◇ ☕	1 ◇	◇ 🛒				1 ◇ ☕	1 ◇ ☕		R 1 ☕			1 ◇ A ☕	🚌	🚌	1	1 ◇	◇ 🛒
London Euston 15 ⊖	d													12 28											
Northampton	d																					13 35			
Long Buckby	d																					13 56			
Rugby	d													13 33							13 45	14a26			
Coventry	a																				14s25				
	d					13 32					14 00									14 23			14 32		
Canley	d					13 35					14 02												14 35		
Tile Hill	d					13 39					14 06												14 39		
Berkswell	d					13 42					14 09												14 42		
Hampton-in-Arden	d					13 46					14 13												14 46		
Birmingham International ✈	a					13 49					14 16									14 33	14 50		14 49		
	d					13 50		14 09			14 16									14 34			14 50		
Marston Green	d					13 53					14 19												14 53		
Lea Hall	d					13 56					14 22												14 56		
Stechford	d					13 59					14 25												14 59		
Adderley Park	d										14 28														
Birmingham New Street 12	a					14 08		14 20			14 33			14 38	←					14 45			15 08		
	d	13 57		14 03	14 07		14 20	14 48 →	14 21	14 33			14 37	14 41	14 48	14 57	15 03	15 07		15 20				15 21	15 33
Smethwick Rolfe Street	d				14 13								14 43					15 13							
Smethwick Galton Bdg L.L. 7	d				14 15								14 45					15 15							
Sandwell & Dudley	d				14 17								14 47	14 51				15 17							
Dudley Port	d				14 20								14 50					15 20							
Tipton	d				14 22								14 52					15 22							
Coseley	d	14 09			14 25				14 34							15 09		15 25						15 34	
Walsall	d											14 44													
Wolverhampton 7 🚋	a	14 15		14 20	14 30		14 38		14 42	14 48		14 59	15 00	15 07	15 08	15 15	15 20	15 30		15 38				15 42	15 48
	d						14 40		14 44						15 08					15 40				15 44	
Penkridge	d								14 53															15 53	
Stafford	a						14 52		15 01						15 22					15 52				16 01	

For general notes see front of timetable
For details of catering facilities see Directory of Train Operators

A From Bournemouth (Table 51)

Due to Engineering Operations, services from Saturday 13 September on this Table had not been confirmed at time of going to press. These services will be issued in a special Supplement as soon as exact timings have been confirmed

Table 68

19 July to 6 September

Northampton → Coventry → Birmingham → Wolverhampton → Stafford

Network Diagram - see first page of Table 67

Station		LM	LM	LM	VT	XC	VT	LM	LM	VT	LM	LM		XC	XC	LM	AW	LM	LM	LM	VT	XC	VT	LM	XC
					1 ◇	R 1 A				1 ◇		1		1 ◇	1 ◇	1 ◇	R				1 ◇	1 ◇ A			1 ◇
					☕	☕	🚌	🚌		☕				☕	☕		🛒				☕	☕	🚌	🚌	☕
London Euston 15 ⊖	d				13 28																14 28				
Northampton	d							14 35																15 35	
Long Buckby	d							14 56																15 56	
Rugby	d				14 35		14 45	15a26													15 35		15 45	16a26	
Coventry	a						15s25																16s25		
	d	15 00				15 23						15 32						16 00				16 23			
Canley	d	15 02										15 35						16 02							
Tile Hill	d	15 06										15 39						16 06							
Berkswell	d	15 09										15 42						16 09							
Hampton-in-Arden	d	15 13										15 46						16 13							
Birmingham International ✈	a	15 16				15 33	15 50					15 49						16 16				16 33	16 50		
	d	15 16				15 34						15 50			16 09			16 16				16 34			
Marston Green	d	15 19										15 53						16 19							
Lea Hall	d	15 22										15 56						16 22							
Stechford	d	15 25										15 59						16 25							
Adderley Park	d	15 28																16 28							
Birmingham New Street 12	a	15 33			15 38	15 45						16 08			16 20			16 33			16 38	16 45			←
	d			15 37	15 41	15 48			15 57	16 03	16 07			16 20	16 48 →	16 21	16 33			16 37	16 41				16 48
Smethwick Rolfe Street	d			15 43							16 13									16 43					
Smethwick Galton Bdg L.L. 7	d			15 45							16 15									16 45					
Sandwell & Dudley	d			15 47	15 50						16 17									16 47	16 51				
Dudley Port	d			15 50							16 20									16 50					
Tipton	d			15 52							16 22									16 52					
Coseley	d										16 25					16 34									
Walsall	d		15 44																16 44						
Wolverhampton 7 🚢	a		15 59	16 00	16 07	16 08			16 15	16 20	16 30			16 38		16 42	16 48		16 59	17 00	17 07				17 08
	d					16 08								16 40		16 44									17 08
Penkridge	d															16 53									
Stafford	a					16 22								16 52		17 01									17 22

Station		LM	VT	LM	LM	XC		LM	AW	LM	LM	LM	VT	XC	VT	LM	LM	VT	LM	LM	XC	XC		LM	AW
			R 1		1	R 1		1 ◇	◇				1 ◇	1 ◇ A				R 1		1	1 ◇	1 ◇		1 ◇	◇
			☕			☕			🛒				☕	☕	🚌	🚌		☕			☕	☕			🛒
London Euston 15 ⊖	d												15 28												
Northampton	d															16 35									
Long Buckby	d															16 56									
Rugby	d												16 35		16 45	17a26									
Coventry	a														17s25										
	d				16 32					17 00				17 23						17 32					
Canley	d				16 35					17 02										17 35					
Tile Hill	d				16 39					17 06										17 39					
Berkswell	d				16 42					17 09										17 42					
Hampton-in-Arden	d				16 46					17 13										17 46					
Birmingham International ✈	a				16 49					17 16				17 33	17 50					17 49					
	d				16 50					17 16				17 34						17 50		18 09			
Marston Green	d				16 53					17 19										17 53					
Lea Hall	d				16 56					17 22										17 56					
Stechford	d				16 59					17 25										17 59					
Adderley Park	d									17 28															
Birmingham New Street 12	a				17 08					17 33			17 38	17 45						18 08		18 20			
	d	16 57	17 03	17 07		17 20		17 21	17 33			17 37	17 41	17 48			17 57	18 03	18 07		18 20	18 48 →		18 21	18 33
Smethwick Rolfe Street	d			17 13								17 43							18 13						
Smethwick Galton Bdg L.L. 7	d			17 15								17 45							18 15						
Sandwell & Dudley	d			17 17								17 47	17 51						18 17						
Dudley Port	d			17 20								17 50							18 20						
Tipton	d			17 22								17 52							18 22						
Coseley	d	17 09		17 25				17 34									18 09		18 25					18 34	
Walsall	d										17 44														
Wolverhampton 7 🚢	a	17 15	17 20	17 30		17 38		17 42	17 48		17 59	18 00	18 07	18 08			18 15	18 20	18 30		18 38			18 42	18 48
	d					17 40		17 44						18 08							18 40			18 44	
Penkridge	d							17 53																18 53	
Stafford	a					17 52		18 01						18 22							18 52			19 01	

For general notes see front of timetable
For details of catering facilities see Directory of Train Operators

A From Bournemouth (Table 51)

Due to Engineering Operations, services from Saturday 13 September on this Table had not been confirmed at time of going to press. These services will be issued in a special Supplement as soon as exact timings have been confirmed

Northampton → Coventry → Birmingham → Wolverhampton → Stafford

Saturdays

19 July to 6 September

Network Diagram - see first page of Table 67

Station		LM	LM	LM	VT	XC	VT	LM	XC	LM	VT	LM	LM	XC	LM	AW		LM	LM	LM	VT	LM	XC	VT	LM
Symbols					1 ◇ ☕	1 ◇ A ☕	🚌	🚌	1 ◇ ☕		R 1 ☕		1	R 1 ☕	1 ◇	◇					1 ◇ ☕		1 ◇ A ☕	🚌	🚌
London Euston 15 ⊖	d				16 28																17 28				
Northampton	d							17 35																	18 35
Long Buckby	d							17 56																	18 56
Rugby	d				17 35		17 45	18a26													18 35			18 45	19a26
Coventry	a						18s25																	19s25	
	d	18 00				18 23							18 32					19 00					19 23		
Canley	d	18 02											18 35					19 02							
Tile Hill	d	18 06											18 39					19 06							
Berkswell	d	18 09											18 42					19 09							
Hampton-in-Arden	d	18 13											18 46					19 13							
Birmingham International ✈	a	18 16				18 33	18 50						18 49					19 16					19 33	19 50	
	d	18 16				18 34							18 50					19 16					19 34		
Marston Green	d	18 19											18 53					19 19							
Lea Hall	d	18 22											18 56					19 22							
Stechford	d	18 25											18 59					19 25							
Adderley Park	d	18 28																19 28							
Birmingham New Street 12	a	18 33			18 38	18 45			←				19 08					19 36			19 38		19 45		
	d			18 37	18 41				18 48	18 57	19 03	19 07		19 20	19 21	19 33				19 37	19 41	19 57	20 03		
Smethwick Rolfe Street	d			18 43								19 13								19 43					
Smethwick Galton Bdg L.L. 7	d			18 45								19 15								19 45					
Sandwell & Dudley	d			18 47	18 51							19 17								19 47	19 50				
Dudley Port	d			18 50								19 20								19 50					
Tipton	d			18 52								19 22								19 52					
Coseley	d									19 09		19 25			19 34							20 09			
Walsall	d		18 44																19 44						
Wolverhampton 7	a		18 59	19 00	19 07				19 08	19 15	19 20	19 30		19 38	19 42	19 48			19 59	20 00	20 07	20 15	20 20		
	d								19 08		19 21			19 40	19 44								20 21		
Penkridge	d														19 53										
Stafford	a								19 22		19 33			19 52	20 01								20 33		

Station		LM	LM	XC	LM	AW	LM	LM	LM	VT		XC	VT	LM	XC	LM	LM	LM	XC	LM	AW	LM	LM	VT	LM
Symbols			1	1 ◇ ☕	1 ◇	◇ trolley				1 ◇ ☕		1 ◇ A ☕	🚌	🚌	1 ◇ ☕			1	R 1	1 ◇	◇			1 ◇ ☕	
London Euston 15 ⊖	d									18 28														19 24	
Northampton	d													19 35											
Long Buckby	d													19 56											
Rugby	d									19 35			19 45	20a26										20 36	
Coventry	a												20s25												
	d		19 32				20 00					20 23						20 32				21 00			
Canley	d		19 35				20 02											20 35				21 02			
Tile Hill	d		19 39				20 06											20 39				21 06			
Berkswell	d		19 42				20 09											20 42				21 09			
Hampton-in-Arden	d		19 46				20 13											20 46				21 13			
Birmingham International ✈	a		19 49				20 16					20 33	20 50					20 50				21 16			
	d		19 50				20 16					20 34						20 50				21 16			
Marston Green	d		19 53				20 19											20 53				21 19			
Lea Hall	d		19 56				20 22											20 56				21 22			
Stechford	d		19 59				20 25											20 59				21 25			
Adderley Park	d						20 28															21 28			
Birmingham New Street 12	a		20 08				20 35			20 39		20 45						21 08				21 33		21 37	
	d	20 07		20 20	20 21	20 33			20 37	20 41					20 48	20 57	21 07		21 20	21 21	21 33		21 37	21 41	21 57
Smethwick Rolfe Street	d	20 13							20 43								21 13						21 43		
Smethwick Galton Bdg L.L. 7	d	20 15							20 45								21 15						21 45		
Sandwell & Dudley	d	20 17							20 47	20 51							21 17						21 47	21 51	
Dudley Port	d	20 20							20 50								21 20						21 50		
Tipton	d	20 22							20 52								21 22						21 52		
Coseley	d	20 25			20 34											21 09	21 25			21 34					22 09
Walsall	d							20 44																	
Wolverhampton 7	a	20 30		20 38	20 42	20 48		20 59	21 00	21 07					21 08	21 18	21 30		21 38	21 42	21 48		22 00	22 07	22 15
	d			20 40	20 44										21 08				21 40	21 44					
Penkridge	d				20 53															21 54					
Stafford	a			20 52	21 01										21 22				21 52	22 01					

For general notes see front of timetable
For details of catering facilities see Directory of Train Operators

A From Bournemouth (Table 51)

Due to Engineering Operations, services from Saturday 13 September on this Table had not been confirmed at time of going to press. These services will be issued in a special Supplement as soon as exact timings have been confirmed

Table 68

Saturdays

19 July to 6 September

Northampton → Coventry → Birmingham → Wolverhampton → Stafford

Network Diagram - see first page of Table 67

		LM	LM	XC 1 ◇ A ☕		VT 🚌	LM 1	AW ◇	LM	LM 🚌	XC 1 ◇ A	LM	LM	LM	VT 1 ◇ ☕	LM	VT 🚌	AW	VT 1 ◇ ☕	VT 🚌		VT 1 ◇ ☕	VT 🚌		
London Euston 15 ⊖	d														20 30				21 04			21 36			
Northampton	d									20 50															
Long Buckby	d									21 11															
Rugby	d					20 45				21 42					22 12		22 20		22 38	22 50		23 14	23 20		
Coventry	a					21s25				22 22							23s00			23s30			00s01		
	d			21 23			21 32		22 03		22 23		22 32			22 56									
Canley	d						21 35		22 05				22 35			22 59									
Tile Hill	d						21 39		22 09				22 39			23 02									
Berkswell	d						21 42		22 12				22 42			23 06									
Hampton-in-Arden	d						21 46		22 16				22 46			23 10									
Birmingham International ✈	a			21 33		21 50	21 50		22 19		22 33		22 49			23 13	23 25			23 55			00 25		
	d			21 34			21 50		22 19		22 34		22 50			23 13									
Marston Green	d						21 53		22 22				22 53			23 16									
Lea Hall	d						21 56		22 25				22 56			23 19									
Stechford	d						21 59		22 28				22 59			23 22									
Adderley Park	d								22 31							23 25									
Birmingham New Street 12	a			21 45			22 08		22 36		22 50		23 08		23 13	23 30			23 41			00 21			
	d	22 07		22 20				22 33	22 37			23 07			23 19			23 33	23 45			00 25			
Smethwick Rolfe Street	d	22 13							22 43			23 13													
Smethwick Galton Bdg L.L. 7	d	22 15							22 45			23 15													
Sandwell & Dudley	d	22 17							22 47			23 17			23 29										
Dudley Port	d	22 20							22 50			23 20													
Tipton	d	22 22							22 52			23 22													
Coseley	d	22 25							22 55			23 25													
Walsall	d		22 15											23 20											
Wolverhampton 7 🚢	a	22 30	22 32	22 38				22 48	23 01			23 30		23 39	23 45			23 49	00 07			00 47			
	d			22 40																					
Penkridge	d																								
Stafford	a			22 52																					

Sundays

until 13 July

		VT 1 ◇ ☕	XC 1 ◇ ☕	LM 🚌	LM	LM 1 ◇	AW ◇	VT 1 ◇ ☕	XC 1 ◇ ☕	LM 🚌	LM 🚌	LM	AW	LM 🚌	VT 1 ◇ ☕	VT 🚌	LM 🚌		XC 1 ◇ ☕	VT 1 ◇ ☕	LM	LM 1 ◇	VT 🚌	LM 🚌	VT 1 ◇ ☕
London Euston 15 ⊖	d																			08 30					
Northampton	d										09 10														
Long Buckby	d										09 31														
Rugby	d										10a01									10 10					
Coventry	a																								
	d			07 30						08 30				09 30		10 05								10 30	
Canley	d			07 39						08 39				09 39										10 39	
Tile Hill	d			07 48						08 48				09 48										10 48	
Berkswell	d			07 58						08 58				09 58										10 58	
Hampton-in-Arden	d			08 08						09 08				10 08										11 08	
Birmingham International ✈	a			08 17						09 17				10 17		10 30								11 17	
	d			08 20						09 20				10 20		10 30	←							11 20	
Marston Green	d			08 25						09 25				10 25										11 25	
Lea Hall	d			08 35						09 35				10 35 →			10 35							11 35 →	
Stechford	d			08 45						09 45							10 45								
Adderley Park	d			08 55						09 55							10 55								←
Birmingham New Street 12	a			09 05						10 05						10 55	11 05			11 14					
	d	08 52	09 03			09 22	09 36	09 52	10 03				10 28		10 52				11 03	11 18 →		11 24	11 30		11 18
Smethwick Rolfe Street	d																								
Smethwick Galton Bdg L.L. 7	d																						11 55		
Sandwell & Dudley	d																						→		
Dudley Port	d																								
Tipton	d																								
Coseley	d																								
Walsall	d				09 20							10 20									11 20				
Wolverhampton 7 🚢	a	09 19	09 30		09 37	09 45	10 04	10 19	10 30			10 37	10 56		11 19				11 30		11 37	11 47			11 56
	d	09 21	09 32			09 46			10 32										11 32			11 48			
Penkridge	d					09 55																			
Stafford	a	09 33	09 44			10 02			10 44										11 44			12 03			

For general notes see front of timetable
For details of catering facilities see Directory of Train Operators

A From Bournemouth (Table 51)

Due to Engineering Operations, services from Saturday 13 September on this Table had not been confirmed at time of going to press. These services will be issued in a special Supplement as soon as exact timings have been confirmed

Table 68

until 13 July

Northampton → Coventry → Birmingham → Wolverhampton → Stafford

Network Diagram - see first page of Table 67

		AW ◇	VT 1 ◇	VT	LM	LM	XC 1 ◇	LM	VT	LM	AW ◇	VT 1 ◇	
London Euston 15 ⊖	d											09 56	
Northampton	d				10 35								
Long Buckby	d				10 56								
Rugby	d			10 20	11a26							11 34	
Coventry	a			11 00									
	d			11 05		11 30							
Canley	d					11 39							
Tile Hill	d					11 48							
Berkswell	d					→							
Hampton-in-Arden	d												
Birmingham International ✈	a			11 30									
	d			11 30									
Marston Green	d							←					
Lea Hall	d							11 35					
Stechford	d							11 45					
Adderley Park	d							11 55					
Birmingham New Street 12	a			11 55				12 05				12 35	
	d	11 32	11 40				12 03				12 27	12 39	
Smethwick Rolfe Street	d												
Smethwick Galton Bdg L.L. 7	d								←				
Sandwell & Dudley	d								11 55				
Dudley Port	d												
Tipton	d												
Coseley	d												
Walsall	d									12 20			
Wolverhampton 7	a	11 58	12 13				12 30		12 30	12 37	12 55	13 11	
	d						12 32						
Penkridge	d												
Stafford	a						12 44						

		VT	VT	VT 1 ◇	LM	XC	LM	XC 1 ◇	LM	AW	VT	LM	VT
London Euston 15 ⊖	d												
Northampton	d											11 30	
Long Buckby	d											11 51	
Rugby	d										11 45	12a21	
Coventry	a										12 25		
	d	11 45				11 55	12 30				12 30		
Canley	d				←		12 39						
Tile Hill	d				11 48		12 48						
Berkswell	d				11 58		→						
Hampton-in-Arden	d				12 08								
Birmingham International ✈	a	12 10			12 17	12 25					12 55		
	d	12 10			12 20						12 55		
Marston Green	d				12 25								
Lea Hall	d				12 35								
Stechford	d				12 45								
Adderley Park	d				12 55								
Birmingham New Street 12	a	12 35			13 05						13 20		
	d		12 50	12 52				13 03		13 19			
Smethwick Rolfe Street	d												
Smethwick Galton Bdg L.L. 7	d												←
Sandwell & Dudley	d		13 15										13 15
Dudley Port	d		→										
Tipton	d												
Coseley	d												
Walsall	d								13 20				
Wolverhampton 7	a			13 19				13 33	13 37	13 47			13 50
	d							13 38					
Penkridge	d												
Stafford	a							13 51					

		LM 1 ◇	VT	VT 1 ◇	VT	VT R 1	XC R 1		LM	XC	VT	LM	LM
London Euston 15 ⊖	d			10 56									
Northampton	d											12 20	
Long Buckby	d											12 41	
Rugby	d			12 29							12 40	13a11	
Coventry	a										13 20		
	d		12 45							12 55	13 25		13 30
Canley	d								←				13 39
Tile Hill	d								12 48				13 48
Berkswell	d								12 58				→
Hampton-in-Arden	d								13 08				
Birmingham International ✈	a		13 10						13 17	13 25	13 50		
	d		13 10						13 20		13 50		
Marston Green	d								13 25				
Lea Hall	d								13 35				
Stechford	d								13 45				
Adderley Park	d								13 55				
Birmingham New Street 12	a		13 35	13 36					14 05		14 15		
	d	13 30		13 40	13 50	13 52	14 03						
Smethwick Rolfe Street	d												
Smethwick Galton Bdg L.L. 7	d												
Sandwell & Dudley	d				14 15								
Dudley Port	d				→								
Tipton	d												
Coseley	d												
Walsall	d												
Wolverhampton 7	a	13 53		14 12		14 19	14 33						
	d	13 54					14 38						
Penkridge	d	14 03											
Stafford	a	14 10					14 51						

		LM	VT	AW ◇	VT 1 ◇	VT	VT	VT R 1	XC R 1	LM	XC	VT	LM
London Euston 15 ⊖	d				11 56								
Northampton	d												13 20
Long Buckby	d												13 41
Rugby	d				13 25							13 30	14a11
Coventry	a											14 10	
	d						13 45				13 55	14 15	
Canley	d									←			
Tile Hill	d									13 48			
Berkswell	d									13 58			
Hampton-in-Arden	d									14 08			
Birmingham International ✈	a						14 10			14 17	14 25	14 40	
	d						14 10			14 20		14 40	
Marston Green	d									14 25			
Lea Hall	d									14 35			
Stechford	d									14 45			
Adderley Park	d									14 55			
Birmingham New Street 12	a				14 23		14 35			15 05		15 05	
	d			14 26	14 27	14 35		14 52	15 03				
Smethwick Rolfe Street	d												
Smethwick Galton Bdg L.L. 7	d		←										
Sandwell & Dudley	d		14 15			15 00							
Dudley Port	d					→							
Tipton	d												
Coseley	d												
Walsall	d	14 20											
Wolverhampton 7	a	14 37	14 50	14 54	15 01			15 19	15 33				
	d								15 38				
Penkridge	d												
Stafford	a								15 51				

For general notes see front of timetable
For details of catering facilities see Directory of Train Operators

Table 68

Sundays

until 13 July

Northampton → Coventry → Birmingham → Wolverhampton → Stafford

Network Diagram - see first page of Table 67

Station		LM		VT	LM	LM	VT	VT	VT	VT	AW	XC	LM	XC	VT	LM	LM	VT	LM		VT	VT	VT	VT	AW
		bus		bus		1 ◇	1 ◇ catering	bus	bus	R 1 catering	◇	R 1 catering	bus	bus	bus	bus	bus	bus			1 ◇ catering	bus	bus	R 1 catering	◇
London Euston 15 ⊖	d						12 56														13 56				
Northampton	d															14 20									
Long Buckby	d															14 41									
Rugby	d						14 20								14 30	15a11					15 22				
Coventry	a														15 10										
	d	14 30							14 45					14 55	15 15		15 30					15 45			
Canley	d	14 39											←				15 39								
Tile Hill	d	14 48											14 48				15 48								
Berkswell	d	→											14 58				→								
Hampton-in-Arden	d												15 08												
Birmingham International ✈	a								15 10				15 17	15 25	15 40							16 10			
	d								15 10				15 20		15 40							16 10			
Marston Green	d												15 25												
Lea Hall	d												15 35												
Stechford	d												15 45												
Adderley Park	d												15 55												
Birmingham New Street 12	a						15 23		15 35				16 05		16 05						16 25	16 35			
	d					15 27	15 27	15 35		15 40	15 48	16 03									16 29		16 40	16 40	16 48
Smethwick Rolfe Street	d																								
Smethwick Galton Bdg L.L. 7	d			←														←							
Sandwell & Dudley	d			15 00				16 00										16 00					17 05		
Dudley Port	d							→															→		
Tipton	d																								
Coseley	d																								
Walsall	d				15 20														16 20						
Wolverhampton 7	a			15 35	15 37	15 50	16 03			16 13	16 20	16 33						16 35	16 37		17 04			17 13	17 22
	d					15 50						16 38													
Penkridge	d																								
Stafford	a					16 05						16 51													

Station		XC	LM	XC	VT	LM	LM	LM	VT	LM	VT	VT	VT	VT		AW	XC	LM		XC	LM	VT	LM	LM	VT
		R 1 catering	bus	bus	bus	bus	bus		bus	1 ◇	1 ◇ catering	bus	bus	R 1 catering		◇	bus	bus		R 1 catering	bus	bus	bus		bus
London Euston 15 ⊖	d										14 56														
Northampton	d					15 20												16 20							
Long Buckby	d					15 41												16 41							
Rugby	d				15 30	16a11					16 21							17a11				16 30			
Coventry	a				16 10																	17 10			
	d			15 55	16 15		16 30					16 45					16 55					17 15	17 30		
Canley	d		←				16 39														←		17 39		
Tile Hill	d		15 48				16 48														16 48		17 48		
Berkswell	d		15 58				→														16 58		→		
Hampton-in-Arden	d		16 08																		17 08				
Birmingham International ✈	a		16 17	16 25	16 40							17 10					17 25				17 17	17 40			
	d		16 20		16 40							17 10									17 20	17 40			
Marston Green	d		16 25																		17 25				
Lea Hall	d		16 35																		17 35				
Stechford	d		16 45																		17 45				
Adderley Park	d		16 55																		17 55				
Birmingham New Street 12	a		17 05		17 05						17 25	17 35									18 05	18 05			
	d	17 03								17 26	17 29		17 40	17 52		17 58				18 03					
Smethwick Rolfe Street	d																								
Smethwick Galton Bdg L.L. 7	d								←																←
Sandwell & Dudley	d								17 05				18 05												18 05
Dudley Port	d												→												
Tipton	d																								
Coseley	d																								
Walsall	d							17 20																18 20	
Wolverhampton 7	a	17 33						17 37	17 40	17 49	18 03			18 19		18 26				18 33				18 37	18 40
	d	17 38								17 50										18 38					
Penkridge	d									17 59															
Stafford	a	17 51								18 06										18 51					

For general notes see front of timetable
For details of catering facilities see Directory of Train Operators

Table 68

until 13 July

Northampton → Coventry → Birmingham → Wolverhampton → Stafford

Network Diagram - see first page of Table 67

		VT	VT	VT	VT	AW	XC	LM	XC		VT	LM	LM	LM	VT	LM	VT	VT	VT	AW	XC	LM	XC	VT	LM
		1 ◇ ☕	🚌	🚌	R 1 ☕	◇	R 1 ☕	🚌	🚌		🚌	🚌	🚌		🚌	1 ◇	1 ◇ ☕	🚌	🚌	◇	R 1 ☕	🚌	🚌	🚌	🚌
London Euston 15 ⊖	d	15 56															16 56								
Northampton	d											17 20													18 20
Long Buckby	d											17 41													18 41
Rugby	d	17 22									17 30	18a11					18 20							18 30	19a11
Coventry	a										18 10													19 10	
	d		17 45						17 55		18 15		18 30						18 45				18 55	19 15	
Canley	d							←					18 39									←			
Tile Hill	d							17 48					18 48 →									18 48			
Berkswell	d							17 58														18 58			
Hampton-in-Arden	d							18 08														19 08			
Birmingham International ✈	a		18 10					18 17	18 25		18 40								19 10			19 17	19 25	19 40	
	d		18 10					18 20			18 40								19 10			19 20		19 40	
Marston Green	d							18 25														19 25			
Lea Hall	d							18 35														19 35			
Stechford	d							18 45														19 45			
Adderley Park	d							18 55														19 55			
Birmingham New Street 12	a	18 25	18 35					19 05			19 05						19 23		19 35			20 05		20 05	
	d	18 29		18 40	18 41	18 56	19 03									19 26	19 27	19 35		19 48	20 03				
Smethwick Rolfe Street	d																								
Smethwick Galton Bdg L.L. 7	d														←										
Sandwell & Dudley	d			19 05 →											19 05			20 00 →							
Dudley Port	d																								
Tipton	d																								
Coseley	d																								
Walsall	d													19 20											
Wolverhampton 7	a	19 01			19 13	19 19	19 33							19 37	19 40	19 49	20 00			20 22	20 33				
	d				19 15		19 38									19 50					20 38				
Penkridge	d															19 59									
Stafford	a				19 33		19 51									20 06					20 51				

		VT	LM	VT		VT	AW	XC	LM	XC	VT	LM	VT	LM	VT	LM	VT	VT	AW	XC	LM		XC	VT	LM
		🚌		1 ◇ ☕		🚌		1 ◇ ☕	🚌	🚌	🚌	🚌	1 ◇ ☕		🚌	1 ◇	🚌	1 ◇ ☕		1 ◇ ☕	🚌		🚌	🚌	🚌
London Euston 15 ⊖	d			17 56									18 56												
Northampton	d											19 20													20 20
Long Buckby	d											19 41													20 41
Rugby	d			19 22							19 30	20a11	20 20											20 30	21a11
Coventry	a										20 10													21 10	
	d								19 30	19 55	20 15										20 30		20 55	21 15	
Canley	d								19 39												20 39				
Tile Hill	d								19 48												20 48				
Berkswell	d								19 58												20 58				
Hampton-in-Arden	d								20 08												21 08				
Birmingham International ✈	a								20 17	20 25	20 40										21 17		21 25	21 40	
	d								20 20		20 40										21 20			21 40	
Marston Green	d								20 25												21 25				
Lea Hall	d								20 35												21 35				
Stechford	d								20 45												21 45				
Adderley Park	d								20 55												21 55				
Birmingham New Street 12	a			20 27					21 05		21 05		21 23					←			22 05			22 05	
	d			20 31		20 40	21 00	21 03					21 27 →			21 34	21 35	21 27	21 49	22 03					
Smethwick Rolfe Street	d																								
Smethwick Galton Bdg L.L. 7	d	←													←										
Sandwell & Dudley	d	20 00				21 05 →									21 05		22 00 →								
Dudley Port	d																								
Tipton	d																								
Coseley	d																								
Walsall	d		20 20											21 20											
Wolverhampton 7	a	20 35	20 37	21 03			21 26	21 33						21 37	21 40	21 56		22 06	22 20	22 33					
	d							21 38								21 57				22 38					
Penkridge	d															22 07									
Stafford	a							21 51								22 16				22 51					

For general notes see front of timetable
For details of catering facilities see Directory of Train Operators

until 13 July

Northampton → Coventry → Birmingham → Wolverhampton → Stafford

Network Diagram - see first page of Table 67

		VT	LM	VT 1 ◇	LM	VT	AW	LM	XC	VT	LM	VT 1 ◇	VT	LM	XC	VT	LM	VT 1 ◇	VT 1 ◇	VT	LM	VT 1 ◇	VT 1 ◇		
London Euston 15 ⊖	d			19 56								20 56						21 50	21 56			22 56	23 30		
Northampton	d										21 30						22 35				23 35				
Long Buckby	d										21 51						22 56				23 56				
Rugby	d			21 22						21 30	22a21	22 30				22 40	23a26	23 29	23 37	23 45	00a26	00s31	01s08		
Coventry	a									22 10						23 20				00s25					
	d							21 30	21 55	22 15				22 30	22 55	23 20									
Canley	d							21 39						22 39											
Tile Hill	d							21 48						22 48											
Berkswell	d							21 58						22 58											
Hampton-in-Arden	d							22 08						23 08											
Birmingham International ✈	a							22 17	22 25	22 40				23 17	23 25	23 45				00 50					
	d							22 20		22 40				23 20		23 45									
Marston Green	d							22 25						23 25											
Lea Hall	d							22 35						23 35											
Stechford	d							22 45						23 45											
Adderley Park	d							22 55						23 55											
Birmingham New Street 12	a			22 25				23 05		23 05		23 32		00 05		00 10			00 43			01 39	02 11		
	d			22 30		22 40	22 54					23 36	23 45						00 47			01 43	02 15		
Smethwick Rolfe Street	d																								
Smethwick Galton Bdg L.L. 7	d	←																							
Sandwell & Dudley	d	22 00				23 05							00s10												
Dudley Port	d																								
Tipton	d																								
Coseley	d																								
Walsall	d		22 20		23 20																				
Wolverhampton 7	a	22 35	22 37	23 03	23 37	23 40	23 24					00 08	00 45						01 19			02 15	02 47		
	d																								
Penkridge	d																								
Stafford	a																	00 05							

Sundays

20 July to 7 September

		VT 1 ◇	VT 1 ◇	LM	LM	XC 1 ◇	LM 1 ◇	AW ◇	LM	XC 1 ◇	VT 1 ◇	LM	LM	LM	XC 1 ◇	LM	AW	LM	XC 1 ◇	VT	VT 1 ◇	LM	LM	XC 1 ◇	VT 1 ◇
London Euston 15 ⊖	d	21p36																							08 31
Northampton	d												09 10												
Long Buckby	d												09 31												
Rugby	d	23p14											10a01												10 12
Coventry	a																								
	d			07 30								08 30				09 30				10 05					
Canley	d			07 39								08 39				09 39									
Tile Hill	d			07 48								08 48				09 48									
Berkswell	d			07 58								08 58				09 58									
Hampton-in-Arden	d			08 08								09 08				10 08									
Birmingham International ✈	a			08 17								09 17				10 17				10 30					
	d			08 20								09 20				10 20				10 30					
Marston Green	d			08 25								09 25				10 25						←			
Lea Hall	d			08 35								09 35				10 35						10 35			
Stechford	d			08 45								09 45				→						10 45			
Adderley Park	d			08 55								09 55										10 55			
Birmingham New Street 12	a	00 21		09 05								10 05								10 55		11 05			11 13
	d	00 25	09 03			09 18	09 30	09 37	09 40	09 48	10 03				10 18		10 37	10 40	10 48		11 03			11 18	11 21
Smethwick Rolfe Street	d								09 46									10 46							
Smethwick Galton Bdg L.L. 7	d								09 48									10 48							11 32
Sandwell & Dudley	d								09 50									10 50							
Dudley Port	d								09 53									10 53							
Tipton	d								09 55									10 55							
Coseley	d								09 58									10 58							
Walsall	d				09 15									10 15									11 15		
Wolverhampton 7	a	00 47	09 20		09 35	09 36	09 45	09 56	10 03	10 06	10 20			10 35	10 36		10 56	11 03	11 06		11 20		11 35	11 36	11 44
	d		09 21			09 38	09 46			10 08	10 21				10 38				11 08		11 21			11 38	
Penkridge	d						09 55																		
Stafford	a		09 33			09 50	10 02			10 23	10 33				10 50				11 20		11 33			11 50	

For general notes see front of timetable
For details of catering facilities see Directory of Train Operators

Due to Engineering Operations, services from Sunday 14 September on this Table had not been confirmed at time of going to press. These services will be issued in a special Supplement as soon as exact timings have been confirmed

Table 68

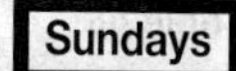

Sundays

Northampton → Coventry → Birmingham → Wolverhampton → Stafford

20 July to 7 September

Network Diagram - see first page of Table 67

		LM		LM	AW	LM	XC	VT	LM	LM	VT	LM	LM	XC	LM	VT	VT	AW	LM	XC	VT	VT	LM	XC	LM
		🚌		1 ◇	◇		1 ◇ ☕	🚌	🚌	🚌	1 ◇ ☕	🚌	🚌	1 ◇ ☕	🚌	1 ◇ ☕	🚌	◇		1 ◇ ☕	1 ◇ ☕	1 ◇ ☕	🚌	🚌	🚌
London Euston 15	⊖ d															09 56									
Northampton	d								10 35						11 30										
Long Buckby	d								10 56						11 51										
Rugby	d							10 20	11a26						12a21	11 32									
Coventry	a							11 00																	
	d	10 30						11 05		11 30							11 45							11 55	12 30
Canley	d	10 39								11 39													←		12 39
Tile Hill	d	10 48								11 48 →													11 48		12 48 →
Berkswell	d	10 58																					11 58		
Hampton-in-Arden	d	11 08																					12 08		
Birmingham International ✈	a	11 17						11 30									12 10						12 17	12 25	
	d	11 20						11 30									12 10						12 20		
Marston Green	d	11 25										←											12 25		
Lea Hall	d	11 35 →										11 35											12 35		
Stechford	d											11 45											12 45		
Adderley Park	d											11 55											12 55		
Birmingham New Street 12	a							11 55				12 05				12 34	12 35				←		13 05		
	d			11 30	11 37	11 40	11 48				12 03			12 18		12 51 →		12 37	12 40	12 48	12 51	13 03			
Smethwick Rolfe Street	d					11 46													12 46						
Smethwick Galton Bdg L.L. 7	d					11 48													12 48						
Sandwell & Dudley	d					11 50													12 50		13 02				
Dudley Port	d					11 53													12 53						
Tipton	d					11 55													12 55						
Coseley	d					11 58													12 58						
Walsall	d												12 15												
Wolverhampton 7 🚢	a			11 48	11 56	12 04	12 06				12 20		12 35	12 37				12 55	13 02	13 06	13 14	13 20			
	d			11 49			12 08				12 21			12 38						13 08		13 21			
Penkridge	d																								
Stafford	a			12 03			12 20				12 33			12 51						13 20		13 36			

		LM	XC	VT		LM	AW	LM	VT	XC	VT	VT	LM	XC	VT	LM	LM	LM	XC	LM	VT	VT	AW	VT	XC
		🚌	1 ◇ ☕	🚌				1 ◇	🚌	R 1 ☕	1 ◇ ☕	R 1 ☕	🚌	🚌	🚌	🚌	🚌	🚌	1 ◇ ☕		1 ◇ ☕	🚌	◇	1 ◇ ☕	1 ◇ ☕
London Euston 15	⊖ d										11 01										11 50				
Northampton	d																12 20								
Long Buckby	d																12 41								
Rugby	d			11 45							12 36				12 40		13a11				13 23				
Coventry	a			12 25											13 20										
	d			12 30					12 45					12 55	13 25	13 30						13 45			
Canley	d												←			13 39									
Tile Hill	d												12 48			13 48 →									
Berkswell	d												12 58												
Hampton-in-Arden	d												13 08												
Birmingham International ✈	a			12 55					13 10				13 17	13 25	13 50							14 10			
	d			12 55					13 10				13 20		13 50							14 10			
Marston Green	d												13 25												
Lea Hall	d												13 35												
Stechford	d												13 45												
Adderley Park	d												13 55												
Birmingham New Street 12	a			13 20					13 35		13 42		14 05		14 15						14 24	14 35		←	
	d		13 18			13 21	13 27	13 30		13 48	13 51	14 03							14 18	14 21	14 40 →		14 37	14 40	14 48
Smethwick Rolfe Street	d					13 27														14 27					
Smethwick Galton Bdg L.L. 7	d					13 29														14 29					
Sandwell & Dudley	d					13 31					14 02									14 31				14 51	
Dudley Port	d					13 34														14 34					
Tipton	d					13 36														14 36					
Coseley	d					13 39														14 39					
Walsall	d	13 15																14 15							
Wolverhampton 7 🚢	a	13 35	13 36			13 44	13 47	13 51		14 06	14 14	14 20						14 35	14 37	14 44			14 54	15 03	15 06
	d		13 38					13 52		14 08		14 21							14 38						15 08
Penkridge	d							14 01																	
Stafford	a		13 50					14 08		14 20		14 33							14 51						15 20

For general notes see front of timetable
For details of catering facilities see Directory of Train Operators

Due to Engineering Operations, services from Sunday 14 September on this Table had not been confirmed at time of going to press. These services will be issued in a special Supplement as soon as exact timings have been confirmed

Table 68

20 July to 7 September

Northampton → Coventry → Birmingham → Wolverhampton → Stafford

Network Diagram - see first page of Table 67

		VT	LM	XC	VT	LM		LM	LM	XC	LM	LM	VT	VT	AW	VT	XC	LM	XC	VT	LM	LM	LM	XC	LM
		R 1 ☕	🚌	🚌	🚌	🚌		🚌	🚌	R 1 ☕		1 ◇	1 ◇ ☕	🚌	◇	1 ◇ ☕	R 1 ☕	🚌	🚌	🚌	🚌	🚌	🚌	1 ◇ ☕	
London Euston 15 ⊖	d												12 51												
Northampton	d							13 20															14 20		
Long Buckby	d							13 41															14 41		
Rugby	d				13 30			14a11					14 20							14 30			15a11		
Coventry	a				14 10															15 10					
	d			13 55	14 15	14 30								14 45					14 55	15 15	15 30				
Canley	d		←			14 39												←			15 39				
Tile Hill	d		13 48			14 48 →												14 48			15 48 →				
Berkswell	d		13 58															14 58							
Hampton-in-Arden	d		14 08															15 08							
Birmingham International ✈	a		14 17	14 25	14 40									15 10				15 17	15 25	15 40					
	d		14 20		14 40									15 10				15 20		15 40					
Marston Green	d		14 25															15 25							
Lea Hall	d		14 35															15 35							
Stechford	d		14 45															15 45							
Adderley Park	d		14 55															15 55							
Birmingham New Street 12	a		15 05		15 05								15 23	15 35		←		16 05		16 05					
	d	15 03								15 18	15 21	15 30	15 40 →		15 37	15 40	15 48							16 18	16 21
Smethwick Rolfe Street	d										15 27														16 27
Smethwick Galton Bdg L.L. 7	d										15 29														16 29
Sandwell & Dudley	d										15 31					15 51									16 31
Dudley Port	d										15 34														16 34
Tipton	d										15 36														16 36
Coseley	d										15 39														16 39
Walsall	d								15 15													16 15			
Wolverhampton 7 🚢	a	15 20							15 35	15 36	15 44	15 50			15 54	16 03	16 07					16 35		16 37	16 45
	d	15 21								15 38		15 50					16 08							16 38	
Penkridge	d																								
Stafford	a	15 33								15 50		16 05					16 21							16 51	

		VT	VT	AW	XC	VT	LM	XC		VT	LM	LM	XC	LM	LM	VT	LM	VT	XC	VT	LM	XC	VT	LM	AW
		1 ◇ ☕	🚌	◇	1 ◇ ☕	R 1 ☕	🚌	🚌		🚌	🚌	🚌	R 1 ☕	🚌		1 ◇ ☕	1 ◇	🚌	R 1 ☕	R 1 ☕	🚌	🚌	🚌	🚌	◇
London Euston 15 ⊖	d	13 51														14 51									
Northampton	d													15 20											
Long Buckby	d													15 41											
Rugby	d	15 20								15 30				16a11		16 21							16 30		
Coventry	a									16 10													17 10		
	d		15 45					15 55		16 15	16 30							16 45				16 55	17 15	17 30	
Canley	d						←				16 39										←			17 39	
Tile Hill	d						15 48				16 48 →										16 48			17 48 →	
Berkswell	d						15 58														16 58				
Hampton-in-Arden	d						16 08														17 08				
Birmingham International ✈	a		16 10				16 17	16 25		16 40								17 10			17 17	17 25	17 40		
	d		16 10				16 20			16 40								17 10			17 20		17 40		
Marston Green	d						16 25														17 25				
Lea Hall	d						16 35														17 35				
Stechford	d						16 45														17 45				
Adderley Park	d						16 55														17 55				
Birmingham New Street 12	a	16 23	16 35				17 05			17 05						17 23		17 35			18 05		18 05		
	d	16 27		16 37	16 48	17 03							17 18		17 21	17 27	17 30		17 48	18 03					18 07
Smethwick Rolfe Street	d														17 27										
Smethwick Galton Bdg L.L. 7	d														17 29										
Sandwell & Dudley	d	16 38													17 31	17 38									
Dudley Port	d														17 34										
Tipton	d														17 36										
Coseley	d														17 39										
Walsall	d											17 15													
Wolverhampton 7 🚢	a	16 50		16 57	17 06	17 20						17 35	17 36		17 45	17 50	17 54		18 05	18 20					18 26
	d				17 08	17 21							17 38				17 55		18 06	18 21					
Penkridge	d																18 04								
Stafford	a				17 20	17 33							17 50				18 13		18 19	18 33					

For general notes see front of timetable
For details of catering facilities see Directory of Train Operators

Due to Engineering Operations, services from Sunday 14 September on this Table had not been confirmed at time of going to press. These services will be issued in a special Supplement as soon as exact timings have been confirmed

Table 68

Sundays

Northampton → Coventry → Birmingham → Wolverhampton → Stafford

20 July to 7 September

Network Diagram - see first page of Table 67

		LM	LM	XC	LM	VT	VT	XC	AW	VT	LM	XC	VT	LM	LM	XC	LM	LM	LM	VT	VT	AW	XC	LM
		🚌	🚌	1 ◇ ☕		1 ◇ ☕	🚌	1 ◇ ☕	◇	R 1 ☕	🚌	🚌	🚌	🚌	🚌	R 1 ☕	1 ◇	🚌		1 ◇ ☕	🚌	◇	R 1 ☕	🚌
London Euston 15 ⊖	d					15 51														16 51				
Northampton	d		16 20															17 20						
Long Buckby	d		16 41															17 41						
Rugby	d		17a11			17 20							17 30					18a11		18 20				
Coventry	a												18 10											
	d						17 45					17 55	18 15	18 30							18 45			
Canley	d										←			18 39										←
Tile Hill	d										17 48			18 48										18 48
Berkswell	d										17 58			→										18 58
Hampton-in-Arden	d										18 08													19 08
Birmingham International ✈	a						18 10				18 17	18 25	18 40								19 10			19 17
	d						18 10				18 20		18 40								19 10			19 20
Marston Green	d										18 25													19 25
Lea Hall	d										18 35													19 35
Stechford	d										18 45													19 45
Adderley Park	d										18 55													19 55
Birmingham New Street 12	a					18 23	18 35				19 05		19 05							19 21	19 35			20 05
	d			18 18	18 21	18 27		18 48	18 57	19 03						19 18	19 21		19 24	19 27		19 37	19 48	
Smethwick Rolfe Street	d				18 27														19 30					
Smethwick Galton Bdg L.L. 7	d				18 29														19 32					
Sandwell & Dudley	d				18 31	18 38													19 34	19 38				
Dudley Port	d				18 34														19 37					
Tipton	d				18 36														19 39					
Coseley	d				18 39														19 42					
Walsall	d	18 15													19 15									
Wolverhampton 7 ⛴	a	18 35		18 37	18 45	18 50		19 06	19 14	19 20					19 35	19 35	19 39		19 48	19 50		19 59	20 06	
	d			18 38				19 08		19 21						19 36	19 40						20 08	
Penkridge	d																19 50							
Stafford	a			18 51				19 20		19 33						19 49	19 57						20 20	

		XC	VT	LM	XC	LM	LM	VT	XC	LM	XC	VT	AW	LM	XC	LM	LM	LM	VT	AW	LM	XC	VT	LM
		🚌	🚌	🚌	1 ◇ ☕	🚌		1 ◇ ☕	1 ◇ ☕	🚌	🚌	🚌		🚌	1 ◇ ☕	1 ◇		🚌	1 ◇ ☕		🚌	🚌	🚌	🚌
London Euston 15 ⊖	d							17 51											18 51					
Northampton	d					18 20												19 20						
Long Buckby	d					18 41												19 41						
Rugby	d		18 30			19a11		19 20				19 30						20a11	20 19				20 30	
Coventry	a		19 10									20 10											21 10	
	d	18 55	19 15							19 30	19 55	20 15									20 30	20 55	21 15	
Canley	d									19 39											20 39			
Tile Hill	d									19 48											20 48			
Berkswell	d									19 58											20 58			
Hampton-in-Arden	d									20 08											21 08			
Birmingham International ✈	a	19 25	19 40							20 17	20 25	20 40									21 17	21 25	21 40	
	d		19 40							20 20		20 40									21 20		21 40	
Marston Green	d									20 25											21 25			
Lea Hall	d									20 35											21 35			
Stechford	d									20 45											21 45			
Adderley Park	d									20 55											21 55			
Birmingham New Street 12	a		20 05					20 23		21 05		21 05							21 21		22 05		22 05	
	d				20 18		20 21	20 27	20 48				21 07		21 18	21 21	21 24		21 27	21 55				
Smethwick Rolfe Street	d						20 27										21 30							
Smethwick Galton Bdg L.L. 7	d						20 29										21 32							
Sandwell & Dudley	d						20 31	20 38									21 34		21 38					
Dudley Port	d						20 34										21 37							
Tipton	d						20 36										21 39							
Coseley	d						20 39										21 42							
Walsall	d			20 15										21 15										22 15
Wolverhampton 7 ⛴	a			20 35	20 37		20 45	20 50	21 05				21 26	21 35	21 36	21 39	21 48		21 50	22 12				22 35
	d				20 38				21 06						21 38	21 40								
Penkridge	d															21 50								
Stafford	a				20 51				21 19						21 50	21 58								

For general notes see front of timetable
For details of catering facilities see Directory of Train Operators

Due to Engineering Operations, services from Sunday 14 September on this Table had not been confirmed at time of going to press. These services will be issued in a special Supplement as soon as exact timings have been confirmed

Table 68

Sundays

20 July to 7 September

Northampton → Coventry → Birmingham → Wolverhampton → Stafford

Network Diagram - see first page of Table 67

		XC	LM	LM	VT	LM	XC	VT	LM	LM	LM	VT	LM	XC	VT		LM	VT	VT	LM	VT	VT	VT		
		1 ◇			1 ◇							1 ◇						1 ◇			1 ◇	1 ◇	1 ◇		
																					A	B			
			bus			bus	bus	bus		bus	bus		bus	bus	bus		bus		bus	bus					
		catering			catering							catering						catering			catering	catering	catering		
London Euston 15	⊖ d				19 51							20 56						22 00			23 01	23 01	23 31		
Northampton	d		20 20								21 30						22 35			23 35					
Long Buckby	d		20 41								21 51						22 56			23 56					
Rugby	d		21a11		21 20			21 30			22a21	22 37			22 40		23a26	23 37	23 45	00a26	00s30	00s31	01s07		
Coventry	a							22 10							23 20				00s25						
	d					21 30	21 55	22 15					22 30	22 55	23 20										
Canley	d					21 39							22 39												
Tile Hill	d					21 48							22 48												
Berkswell	d					21 58							22 58												
Hampton-in-Arden	d					22 08							23 08												
Birmingham International ✈	a					22 17	22 25	22 40					23 17	23 25	23 45				00 50						
	d					22 20		22 40					23 20		23 45										
Marston Green	d					22 25							23 25												
Lea Hall	d					22 35							23 35												
Stechford	d					22 45							23 45												
Adderley Park	d					22 55							23 55												
Birmingham New Street 12	a				22 22	23 05		23 05				23 38	00 05		00 10			00 43			01 39	01 39	02 11		
	d	22 18		22 21	22 27				23 10			23 44						00 47			01 43	01 43	02 15		
Smethwick Rolfe Street	d			22 27					23 16																
Smethwick Galton Bdg L.L. 7	d			22 29					23 18																
Sandwell & Dudley	d			22 31	22 38				23 20			23 55													
Dudley Port	d			22 34					23 23																
Tipton	d			22 36					23 25																
Coseley	d			22 39					23 28																
Walsall	d									23 15															
Wolverhampton 7	a	22 36		22 45	22 50				23 33	23 35		00 07						01 06			02 02	02 02	02 34		
	d	22 38																							
Penkridge	d																								
Stafford	a	22 50																							

For general notes see front of timetable
For details of catering facilities see Directory of Train Operators

A 27 July to 17 August
B 20 July, 24, 31 August and 7 September

Due to Engineering Operations, services from Sunday 14 September on this Table had not been confirmed at time of going to press. These services will be issued in a special Supplement as soon as exact timings have been confirmed

Table 68

Mondays to Fridays

Stafford → Wolverhampton → Birmingham → Coventry → Northampton

Network Diagram - see first page of Table 67

Miles	Station		LM	LM	VT	LM	VT	VT	VT	LM	LM	XC	VT	LM	AW			VT	VT	LM	LM	LM	AW	VT	LM
			MX	MO	1 ◇	1	1 ◇	1 ◇	1 ◇	1	1	1 ◇	1 ◇					1 ◇	1 ◇	1	1			1 ◇	
				A				B	C	B	C							B	C	C	B				
				🚌			⊠	☕	☕			☕	⊠					⊠	⊠					⊠	
0	**Stafford**	d		23p36	04 30																				
5¾	Penkridge	d		00 02																					
10¼	**Wolverhampton** 7	a		00 32	04 44																				
—		d		00 33	04 45		05 05						05 45		06 01			06 12	06 15			06 22	06 31	06 35	06 38
—	Walsall	a																							06 50
18½	Coseley	d																				06 27			
20	Tipton	d																				06 29			
20¾	Dudley Port	d																				06 31			
22¾	Sandwell & Dudley	d					05 15						05 55					06 22	06 25			06 35		06 45	
24	Smethwick Galton Bdg L.L. 7	d																				06 37			
24¾	Smethwick Rolfe Street	d																				06 39			
28	**Birmingham New Street** 12	a		01 08	05 12		05 26						06 05		06 18			06 31	06 34			06 45	06 48	06 56	
—		d	00 10				05 30					06 03	06 10	06 13				06 35	06 40	06 43	06 43			07 00	
30	Adderley Park	d												06 17											
32	Stechford	d												06 21						06 49	06 49				
33	Lea Hall	d												06 23						06 52	06 52				
34½	Marston Green	d	00 18											06 27						06 55	06 55				
36¼	**Birmingham International** ✈	a	00 21				05 39					06 14	06 21	06 30				06 44	06 49	06 58	06 58			07 09	
—		d	00 22				05 40					06 15	06 21	06 30				06 45	06 50	06 59	06 59			07 10	
38½	Hampton-in-Arden	d												06 33						07 02	07 02				
41¼	Berkswell	d												06 38						07 07	07 07				
43¼	Tile Hill	d												06 41						07 10	07 10				
45½	Canley	d												06 45						07 13	07 13				
47¼	**Coventry**	a	00 37				05 49					06 23	06 32	06 48				06 54	06 59	07 16	07 16			07 19	
—		d				05 15	05 50			06 18	06 18		06 32					06 55	07 00	07 27	07 17			07 20	
60¾	Rugby	d				05 25	06 04	06 17	06 20	06 29	06 32							07 09	07 14	⟶	07 30				
70	Long Buckby	d				05 37				06 42	06 43										07 42				
79½	**Northampton**	a				05 51		06 39	06 39	06 59	07 00										07 57				
—	London Euston 15	⊖ a					07 09	07 36	07 36	08 17	08 17		07 50					08 09	08 09		09 25			08 39	

Station		XC	LM	LM	LM	LM	LM	VT	VT		LM	LM	LM	VT	VT	LM	VT	LM	LM	LM	LM	VT	VT	LM	XC
		1 ◇		1 ◇	1	1	1	1 ◇	1 ◇					1 ◇	1 ◇		1 ◇		1	1		1 ◇	1 ◇		1 ◇
					D	E	C	C	B			G		C	B		C		C	B		B	C		H
		☕		🛒				⊠	⊠					⊠	⊠		⊠					⊠	⊠		☕
Stafford	d	06 24		06 30	06 57	06 57																07 15	07 15	07 20	
Penkridge	d			06 36																				07 26	
Wolverhampton 7	a	06 41		06 47																		07 32	07 32	07 37	
	d	06 41		06 47							06 52	06 56		07 05	07 05			07 22			07 29	07 35	07 35	07 38	
Walsall	a											07 12													
Coseley	d										06 57							07 27						07 43	
Tipton	d										06 59							07 29						07 45	
Dudley Port	d										07 01							07 31						07 47	
Sandwell & Dudley	d										07 05			07 15	07 15			07 35				07 45	07 45		
Smethwick Galton Bdg L.L. 7	d										07 07							07 37						07 51	
Smethwick Rolfe Street	d										07 09							07 39						07 53	
Birmingham New Street 12	a	06 58		07 08							07 15			07 24	07 24			07 45			07 48	07 55	07 55	08 00	
	d	07 03	07 06					07 15	07 15				07 18	07 30	07 30	07 33	07 45		07 48	07 48		08 00	08 00		08 03
Adderley Park	d															07 37									
Stechford	d		07 13													07 40									
Lea Hall	d		07 15													07 43									
Marston Green	d		07 18													07 46									
Birmingham International ✈	a	07 14	07 23					07 27	07 27				07 30	07 40	07 40	07 51	07 54		07 59	07 59		08 09	08 09		08 14
	d	07 15						07 28	07 28				07 31	07 40	07 40		07 56		07 59	07 59		08 10	08 10		08 15
Hampton-in-Arden	d												07 34						08 02	08 02					
Berkswell	d												07 39						08 07	08 07					
Tile Hill	d												07 42						08 10	08 10					
Canley	d												07 45						08 14	08 14					
Coventry	a	07 23					⟵	07 38	07 38				07 50	07 54	07 54				08 17	08 17		08 20	08 20		08 23
	d						07 27	07 38	07 40					07 56	07 58				08 17	08 18		08 20	08 24		
Rugby	d				07 55	07b57	07 41												08 28	08 29					
Long Buckby	d				08 05	08 07	07 51												08 39	08 40					
Northampton	a				08 29	08 31	08 05												08 59	09 01					
London Euston 15	⊖ a						09 25	08 43	08 48					09 01	09 04		09 07					09 39	09 44		

For general notes see front of timetable
For details of catering facilities see Directory of Train Operators

A 21 July to 8 September

B 28 July to 22 August

C Until 25 July and from 25 August

D Until 25 July and from 25 August. From Crewe (Table 65)

E 28 July to 22 August. From Crewe (Table 65)

G From Shrewsbury (Table 74)

H Until 5 September from Leeds (Table 51). From 8 September from Sheffield (Table 51).

b Arr. 0754

Table 68

Stafford → Wolverhampton → Birmingham → Coventry → Northampton

Network Diagram - see first page of Table 67

Station		LM	VT 1 ◇ ☕	LM	LM	AW ◇ 🛒	VT 1 ◇ ⊠	LM 1 ◇ A 🛒	XC 1 ◇ ☕	LM B	LM	LM	LM	LM 1 C	LM 1 D	LM	LM 1 ◇ 🛒	VT 1 ◇ ⊠	XC R 1 ☕	LM B	VT 1 ◇ ☕	LM
Stafford	d							07 46	07 54								08 21		08 26			
Penkridge	d							07 52														
Wolverhampton 7	a							08 05	08 12								08 37		08 41			
	d		07 49	07 52		07 59	08 05	08 08	08 13		08 19	08 22	08 23			08 35	08 37		08 41		08 49	08 52
Walsall	a												08 38									
Coseley	d			07 57								08 27										08 57
Tipton	d			07 59								08 29										08 59
Dudley Port	d			08 01								08 31										09 01
Sandwell & Dudley	d			08 05			08 15					08 35					08 46					
Smethwick Galton Bdg L.L. 7	d			08 07								08 37										09 06
Smethwick Rolfe Street	d			08 09								08 39										09 08
Birmingham New Street 12	a		08 11	08 15		08 18	08 24	08 29	08 30		08 36	08 46				08 55	08 58		08 58		09 11	09 15
	d	08 06			08 18		08 30			08 33				08 48	08 48			09 00	09 03	09 06		
Adderley Park	d									08 37												
Stechford	d	08 13								08 40										09 13		
Lea Hall	d	08 15								08 43										09 15		
Marston Green	d	08 18								08 46										09 18		
Birmingham International ✈	a	08 23			08 27		08 39			08 51				08 57	08 57			09 09	09 14	09 23		
	d				08 27		08 40							08 57	08 57			09 10	09 15			
Hampton-in-Arden	d				08 30									09 00	09 00							
Berkswell	d				08 35									09 05	09 05							
Tile Hill	d				08 38									09 08	09 08							
Canley	d				08 41									09 12	09 12							
Coventry	a				08 45		08 49							09 15	09 15			09 19	09 23			
	d						08 50							09 15	09 18			09 20				
Rugby	d													09 27	09 28							
Long Buckby	d													09 37	09 39							
Northampton	a													09 58	09 58							
London Euston 15 ⊖	a						10 03							11 11	11 11			10 31				

Station		LM	AW ◇ 🛒	VT 1 ◇ ⊠	LM 1 ◇ 🛒	XC 1 ◇ ☕	LM	LM 1 C	LM 1 D	LM	LM	LM	LM 1 ◇ E 🛒	LM 1 ◇ G 🛒	XC 1 ◇ ☕	VT 1 ◇ ⊠	XC R 1 H ☕	LM	VT 1 ◇ ☕	LM	LM	AW ◇ 🛒	VT 1 ◇ ⊠	LM 1 ◇ 🛒
Stafford	d				08 46	08 57							09 21	09 21	09 26									09 46
Penkridge	d				08 52																			09 52
Wolverhampton 7	a				09 06	09 12							09 36	09 36	09 41									10 06
	d		08 59	09 05	09 08	09 13				09 22	09 25	09 30	09 37	09 37	09 41				09 49	09 52		09 59	10 05	10 08
Walsall	a										09 38													
Coseley	d				09 12							09 35								09 57				10 12
Tipton	d									09 28										10 00				
Dudley Port	d									09 30										10 02				
Sandwell & Dudley	d			09 15						09 33			09 46	09 46									10 15	
Smethwick Galton Bdg L.L. 7	d									09 36										10 07				
Smethwick Rolfe Street	d									09 38										10 09				
Birmingham New Street 12	a		09 18	09 24	09 30	09 30				09 48		09 51	09 58	10 00	09 58				10 11	10 16		10 18	10 24	10 30
	d	09 18		09 30			09 34	09 48	09 48							10 00	10 03	10 06			10 18		10 30	
Adderley Park	d						09 39																	
Stechford	d						09 42											10 13						
Lea Hall	d						09 44											10 15						
Marston Green	d						09 47											10 18						
Birmingham International ✈	a	09 27		09 39			09 52	09 57	09 57							10 09	10 14	10 23			10 27		10 39	
	d	09 27		09 40				09 57	09 57							10 10	10 15				10 27		10 40	
Hampton-in-Arden	d	09 30						10 00	10 00												10 30			
Berkswell	d	09 35						10 05	10 05												10 35			
Tile Hill	d	09 38						10 08	10 08												10 38			
Canley	d	09 42						10 12	10 12												10 42			
Coventry	a	09 45		09 49				10 15	10 15							10 19	10 23				10 45		10 49	
	d			09 50				10 15	10 17							10 20							10 50	
Rugby	d							10 27	10 28															
Long Buckby	d							10 37	10 39															
Northampton	a							10 58	11 01															
London Euston 15 ⊖	a			11 00												11 35							12 00	

For general notes see front of timetable
For details of catering facilities see Directory of Train Operators

A From Liverpool Lime Street (Table 91)
B From Walsall (Table 70)
C Until 25 July and from 25 August
D 28 July to 22 August
E Until 24 October
G From 27 October
H Until 5 September from Newcastle (Table 51). From 8 September from Newcastle (Table 51)

Stafford → Wolverhampton → Birmingham → Coventry → Northampton

Network Diagram - see first page of Table 67

		XC	LM		LM	LM	LM	LM	LM	LM	VT	XC	LM	VT	LM	LM	AW	VT		LM	XC		LM	LM	LM
		1 ◇					1	1		1 ◇	1 ◇	R 1		1 ◇			◇	1 ◇		1 ◇	1 ◇				
							A	B					C										C		
		☕								🍴	☕	☕		☕			🍴	☕		🍴	☕				
Stafford	d									10 21		10 26								10 46					
Penkridge	d																			10 52					
Wolverhampton 7	a									10 36		10 41								11 07					
	d	10 13			10 22	10 25			10 28	10 37		10 41		10 49	10 52		10 59	11 05		11 08	11 13			11 22	11 25
Walsall	a					10 38																			11 38
Coseley	d								10 33						10 57					11 12					
Tipton	d				10 28										10 59									11 28	
Dudley Port	d				10 30										11 01									11 30	
Sandwell & Dudley	d				10 33					10 46								11 15						11 33	
Smethwick Galton Bdg L.L. 7	d				10 36										11 06									11 36	
Smethwick Rolfe Street	d				10 38										11 08									11 38	
Birmingham New Street 12	a	10 30			10 45				10 48	10 58		10 58		11 11	11 15		11 18	11 24		11 30	11 30			11 45	
	d		10 34				10 48	10 48			11 00	11 03	11 06			11 18		11 30					11 34		
Adderley Park	d		10 39																				11 39		
Stechford	d		10 42										11 13										11 42		
Lea Hall	d		10 44										11 15										11 44		
Marston Green	d		10 47										11 18										11 47		
Birmingham International ✈	a		10 52				10 57	10 57			11 09	11 14	11 23			11 27		11 39					11 52		
	d						10 57	10 57			11 10	11 15				11 27		11 40							
Hampton-in-Arden	d						11 00	11 00								11 30									
Berkswell	d						11 05	11 05								11 35									
Tile Hill	d						11 08	11 08								11 38									
Canley	d						11 12	11 12								11 42									
Coventry	a						11 15	11 15			11 19	11 23				11 45		11 49							
	d						11 15	11 15			11 20							11 50							
Rugby	d						11 27	11 28																	
Long Buckby	d						11 37	11 38																	
Northampton	a						11 58	12 00																	
London Euston 15 ⊖	a										12 33							13 00							

		LM	LM	LM	XC	VT	XC	LM	VT	LM	LM		AW	VT	LM	XC	LM	LM	LM	LM	LM	LM	LM	VT	XC
		1	1		1 ◇	1 ◇	R 1		1 ◇				◇	1 ◇	1 ◇	1 ◇				1	1		1 ◇	1 ◇	R 1
		A	B				D	C									C			A	B				
					☕	☕	☕		☕				🍴	☕	🍴	☕							🍴	☕	☕
Stafford	d				11 26										11 46								12 21		12 26
Penkridge	d														11 52										
Wolverhampton 7	a				11 41										12 06								12 36		12 41
	d			11 28	11 41				11 49	11 52			11 59	12 05	12 08	12 13		12 22	12 25			12 28	12 38		12 41
Walsall	a																		12 39						
Coseley	d			11 33						11 57					12 12							12 33			
Tipton	d									11 59								12 28							
Dudley Port	d									12 01								12 30							
Sandwell & Dudley	d									12 05				12 15				12 33					12 47		
Smethwick Galton Bdg L.L. 7	d									12 07								12 36							
Smethwick Rolfe Street	d									12 09								12 38							
Birmingham New Street 12	a			11 48	11 58				12 11	12 15			12 18	12 24	12 30	12 30		12 45				12 48	12 58		12 58
	d	11 48	11 48			12 00	12 03	12 06			12 18			12 30			12 34			12 48	12 48			13 00	13 03
Adderley Park	d																12 39								
Stechford	d							12 13									12 42								
Lea Hall	d							12 15									12 44								
Marston Green	d							12 18									12 47								
Birmingham International ✈	a	11 57	11 57			12 09	12 14	12 23			12 27			12 39			12 52			12 57	12 57			13 09	13 14
	d	11 57	11 57			12 10	12 15				12 27			12 40						12 57	12 57			13 10	13 15
Hampton-in-Arden	d	12 00	12 00								12 30									13 00	13 00				
Berkswell	d	12 05	12 05								12 35									13 05	13 05				
Tile Hill	d	12 08	12 08								12 38									13 08	13 08				
Canley	d	12 12	12 12								12 42									13 12	13 12				
Coventry	a	12 15	12 15			12 19	12 23				12 45			12 49						13 15	13 15			13 19	13 24
	d	12 15	12 15			12 20								12 50						13 15	13 15			13 20	
Rugby	d	12 27	12 28																	13 27	13 29				
Long Buckby	d	12 37	12 40																	13 37	13 40				
Northampton	a	12 56	12 59																	13 57	14 00				
London Euston 15 ⊖	a					13 34								14 00						15 11	15 11			14 33	

For general notes see front of timetable
For details of catering facilities see Directory of Train Operators

A Until 25 July and from 25 August
B 28 July to 22 August
C From Walsall (Table 70)
D Until 5 September from Glasgow Central (Table 51). From 8 September from Newcastle (Table 51).

Stafford → Wolverhampton → Birmingham → Coventry → Northampton

Network Diagram - see first page of Table 67

		LM	VT	LM		LM	AW	VT	LM	XC	LM	LM	LM	LM	LM	LM	LM	XC	VT		XC	LM	LM	LM	AW
			R 1				◇	1 ◇	1 ◇	1 ◇				1	1		1 ◇	R 1	1 ◇		R 1				◇
		A									A			B	C						D	A			
			☕				🛒	☕	🛒	☕							🛒	☕	☕		☕				🛒
Stafford	d								12 46								13 21	13 26							
Penkridge	d								12 52																
Wolverhampton 7	a								13 06								13 36	13 41							
	d		12 49	12 52			12 59	13 05	13 08	13 13		13 22	13 25			13 28	13 37	13 41						13 52	13 59
Walsall	a												13 38												
Coseley	d			12 57					13 12							13 33								13 57	
Tipton	d			12 59								13 28												13 59	
Dudley Port	d			13 01								13 30												14 01	
Sandwell & Dudley	d							13 15				13 33					13 46								
Smethwick Galton Bdg L.L. 7	d			13 06								13 36												14 06	
Smethwick Rolfe Street	d			13 08								13 38												14 08	
Birmingham New Street 12	a		13 11	13 15			13 18	13 24	13 30	13 30		13 45				13 48	13 58	13 58						14 15	14 18
	d	13 06				13 18		13 30			13 34			13 48	13 48				14 00		14 03	14 06	14 18		
Adderley Park	d										13 39														
Stechford	d	13 13									13 42											14 13			
Lea Hall	d	13 15									13 44											14 15			
Marston Green	d	13 18									13 47											14 18			
Birmingham International ✈	a	13 23				13 27		13 39			13 52			13 57	13 57				14 09		14 14	14 23	14 27		
	d					13 27		13 40						13 57	13 57				14 10		14 15		14 27		
Hampton-in-Arden	d					13 30								14 00	14 00								14 30		
Berkswell	d					13 35								14 05	14 05								14 35		
Tile Hill	d					13 38								14 08	14 08								14 38		
Canley	d					13 42								14 12	14 12								14 42		
Coventry	a					13 45		13 49						14 15	14 15				14 19		14 23		14 45		
	d							13 50						14 15	14 15				14 20						
Rugby	d													14 27	14 28										
Long Buckby	d													14 37	14 39										
Northampton	a													14 57	14 58										
London Euston 15	⊖ a							15 00											15 34						

		VT	LM	XC	LM	VT	LM	LM	LM	LM	LM	LM		VT	XC	LM	VT	LM	LM	AW	VT	LM	XC	LM	LM
		1 ◇	1 ◇	1 ◇		R 1			1	1		1 ◇		1 ◇	1 ◇		1 ◇			◇	1 ◇	1 ◇	1 ◇		
					A				B	C						A								A	
		☕	🛒	☕		☕						🛒		☕	☕		☕			🛒	☕	🛒	☕		
Stafford	d		13 46									14 21			14 26							14 46			
Penkridge	d		13 52																			14 52			
Wolverhampton 7	a		14 06									14 37			14 41							15 06			
	d	14 05	14 08	14 13		14 18	14 22	14 25			14 28	14 37			14 41		14 49	14 52		14 59	15 05	15 08	15 13		15 22
Walsall	a							14 38																	
Coseley	d		14 12								14 33							14 57				15 12			
Tipton	d						14 28											14 59							15 28
Dudley Port	d						14 30											15 01							15 30
Sandwell & Dudley	d	14 15					14 33					14 46									15 15				15 33
Smethwick Galton Bdg L.L. 7	d						14 36											15 06							15 36
Smethwick Rolfe Street	d						14 38											15 08							15 38
Birmingham New Street 12	a	14 24	14 30	14 30		14 41	14 45				14 48	14 58			14 58		15 11	15 15		15 18	15 24	15 30	15 30		15 45
	d	14 30			14 34				14 48	14 48				15 00	15 03	15 06			15 18		15 30			15 34	
Adderley Park	d				14 39																			15 39	
Stechford	d				14 42											15 13								15 42	
Lea Hall	d				14 44											15 15								15 44	
Marston Green	d				14 47											15 18								15 47	
Birmingham International ✈	a	14 39			14 52				14 57	14 57				15 09	15 14	15 23			15 27		15 39			15 52	
	d	14 40							14 57	14 57				15 10	15 15				15 27		15 40				
Hampton-in-Arden	d								15 00	15 00									15 30						
Berkswell	d								15 05	15 05									15 35						
Tile Hill	d								15 08	15 08									15 38						
Canley	d								15 12	15 12									15 42						
Coventry	a	14 49							15 15	15 15				15 19	15 23				15 45		15 49				
	d	14 50							15 15	15 15				15 20							15 50				
Rugby	d								15 27	15 28															
Long Buckby	d								15 37	15 40															
Northampton	a								15 57	15 59															
London Euston 15	⊖ a	16 00												16 34							17 00				

For general notes see front of timetable
For details of catering facilities see Directory of Train Operators

A From Walsall (Table 70)
B Until 25 July and from 25 August
C 28 July to 22 August
D Until 5 September from Dundee (Table 51). From 8 September from Newcastle (Table 51).

Stafford → Wolverhampton → Birmingham → Coventry → Northampton

Network Diagram - see first page of Table 67

		LM	VT	LM	LM	LM	LM	XC	VT	XC	LM	VT	LM	LM	AW	VT	LM	XC	LM	LM	LM	LM	LM
			1 ◇	1	1		1 ◇	R 1	1 ◇	R 1		R 1			◇	1 ◇	1 ◇	R 1					
				A	B					C	D								D	B	A		
			☕				⚲	☕	☕	☕		☕			⚲	☕	⚲	☕					
Stafford	d						15 21	15 26									15 46						
Penkridge	d																15 52						
Wolverhampton 7	a						15 36	15 41									16 06						
	d	15 25				15 28	15 37	15 41				15 49	15 52		15 59	16 05	16 08	16 13				16 22	16 25
Walsall	a	15 38																					16 40
Coseley	d					15 33							15 57				16 12						
Tipton	d												15 59									16 28	
Dudley Port	d												16 01									16 30	
Sandwell & Dudley	d						15 46									16 15						16 33	
Smethwick Galton Bdg L.L. 7	d												16 06									16 36	
Smethwick Rolfe Street	d												16 08									16 38	
Birmingham New Street 12	a					15 48	15 58	15 58				16 11	16 15		16 18	16 24	16 30	16 30				16 45	
	d			15 48	15 48				16 00	16 03	16 06			16 18		16 30			16 34	16 45	16 45		
Adderley Park	d																		16 39				
Stechford	d										16 13								16 42				
Lea Hall	d										16 15								16 44				
Marston Green	d										16 18								16 47				
Birmingham International ✈	a			15 57	15 57				16 09	16 14	16 23			16 27		16 39			16 52		16 55		
	d			15 57	15 57				16 10	16 15				16 27		16 40					16 56		
Hampton-in-Arden	d			16 00	16 00									16 30									
Berkswell	d			16 05	16 05									16 35									
Tile Hill	d			16 08	16 08									16 38									
Canley	d			16 12	16 12									16 42									
Coventry	a			16 15	16 15				16 19	16 23				16 45		16 49				17 02	17 04		
	d			16 15	16 15				16 20							16 50				17 02	17 05		
Rugby	d		15 55	16 27	16 29															17 15	17 17		
Long Buckby	d			16 38	16 40															17 25	17 28		
Northampton	a		16 16	16 57	16 59															17 43	17 46		
London Euston 15	⊖ a		17 22						17 33							18 00							

		LM	LM	LM	VT	LM	XC	LM	VT	LM	LM	LM	LM	AW	VT	LM	XC	LM	LM	LM	LM	LM
		1		1 ◇	1 ◇	1	R 1		R 1	1	1			◇	1 ◇	1 ◇	R 1		1	1		
										B	A							D	B	A		
				⚲	☕		☕		☕					⚲	☕	⚲	☕					
Stafford	d			16 21			16 26									16 46						
Penkridge	d															16 52						
Wolverhampton 7	a			16 36			16 41									17 05						
	d		16 28	16 38			16 41		16 49			16 52		16 59	17 05	17 08	17 13				17 22	17 25
Walsall	a																					17 40
Coseley	d		16 33									16 57				17 12						
Tipton	d											16 59									17 28	
Dudley Port	d											17 01									17 30	
Sandwell & Dudley	d			16 47											17 15						17 33	
Smethwick Galton Bdg L.L. 7	d											17 06									17 36	
Smethwick Rolfe Street	d											17 08									17 38	
Birmingham New Street 12	a		16 48	16 58			16 58		17 11			17 15		17 18	17 24	17 30	17 30				17 45	
	d	16 48			17 00		17 03	17 06		17 15	17 15		17 18		17 30			17 34	17 45	17 45		
Adderley Park	d																	17 39				
Stechford	d							17 13										17 42				
Lea Hall	d							17 15					17 25					17 44				
Marston Green	d	16 56						17 18					17 28					17 47				
Birmingham International ✈	a	16 59			17 09		17 14	17 23		17 26	17 26		17 31		17 39			17 52	17 55	17 55		
	d	17 00			17 10		17 15			17 27	17 27		17 32		17 40				17 56	17 56		
Hampton-in-Arden	d	17 03				←							17 35									
Berkswell	d	17 08				17 08							17 40									
Tile Hill	d	→				17 11							17 43									
Canley	d					17 14							17 46									
Coventry	a				17 19	17 20	17 24			17 35	17 35		17 52		17 52				18 04	18 04		
	d				17 20					17 36	17 37				17 52				18 05	18 05		
Rugby	d									17 47	17 54								18 15	18 17		
Long Buckby	d									17 58	18 04								18 27	18 27		
Northampton	a									18 22	18 23								18 52	18 53		
London Euston 15	⊖ a				18 34										19 03							

For general notes see front of timetable
For details of catering facilities see Directory of Train Operators

A Until 25 July and from 25 August
B 28 July to 22 August
C Until 5 September from Aberdeen (Table 51). From 8 September from Newcastle (Table 51).
D From Walsall (Table 70)

Stafford → Wolverhampton → Birmingham → Coventry → Northampton

Network Diagram - see first page of Table 67

	LM	LM	XC	VT	VT		XC	LM	VT	LM	LM	LM	AW	VT	LM	XC	LM	LM	LM	LM		LM	LM	LM
							R									R								
			1 ◇	1 ◇	1 ◇		1		1 ◇		1	1	◇	1 ◇	1 ◇	1				1		1	1	
				A	B		C	D			A	B					D			B		A	B	
			☕	☕	☕		☕		☕				🛒	☕	🛒	☕								
Stafford d			17 26												17 46									
Penkridge d															17 52									
Wolverhampton 7 a			17 41												18 06									
d		17 28	17 41						17 49	17 52			17 59	18 05	18 08	18 13		18 22	18 25					18 28
Walsall a																			18 40					
Coseley d		17 33								17 57					18 12									18 33
Tipton d										17 59								18 28						
Dudley Port d										18 01								18 30						
Sandwell & Dudley d										18 05				18 15				18 33						
Smethwick Galton Bdg L.L. 7 d										18 07								18 36						
Smethwick Rolfe Street d										18 09								18 38						
Birmingham New Street 12 a		17 48	17 58						18 11	18 15			18 18	18 24	18 30	18 30		18 45						18 48
d	17 48			18 00	18 00		18 03	18 06			18 18	18 18		18 30			18 34					18 48	18 48	
Adderley Park d																	18 39							
Stechford d								18 13									18 42							
Lea Hall d								18 15									18 44							
Marston Green d	17 56							18 18			18 26	18 26					18 47							
Birmingham International ✈ a	17 59			18 09	18 09		18 14	18 23			18 29	18 29		18 39			18 52					18 57	18 57	
d	18 00			18 10	18 10		18 15				18 30	18 30		18 40								18 57	18 57	
Hampton-in-Arden d	18 03										18 33	18 33										19 00	19 00	
Berkswell d	18 07										18 37	18 37										19 05	19 05	
Tile Hill d	18 10										18 40	18 40										19 08	19 08	
Canley d	18 14										18 44	18 44										19 12	19 12	
Coventry a	18 20			18 20	18 20		18 24				18 46	18 46		18 49						←		19 15	19 15	
d				18 20	18 23						18 47	18 54 →		18 50						18 54		19 15	19 15	
Rugby d											18 58									19 05		19 27	19 28	
Long Buckby d											19 08									19 17		19 37	19 40	
Northampton a											19 29									19 31		19 56	19 59	
London Euston 15 ⊖ a				19 34	19 38									20 00										

	LM	VT	XC	LM	VT	LM	LM	AW	VT	LM	LM	XC	LM		LM	LM	LM	LM	XC	XC	LM	VT	LM	AW
			R																	R				
	1 ◇	1 ◇	1		1 ◇			◇	1 ◇	1 ◇		1 ◇				1	1		1 ◇	1		1 ◇		◇
		A		D						E	D					A	B			C				
	🛒	☕	☕		☕			🛒	☕	🛒		☕							☕	☕		☕		🛒
Stafford d	18 21		18 26							18 46									19 25					
Penkridge d										18 52														
Wolverhampton 7 a	18 36		18 41							19 05									19 41					
d	18 37		18 41		18 49	18 52		18 59	19 05	19 08		19 13	19 22		19 25			19 30	19 41			19 49	19 52	19 59
Walsall a															19 40									
Coseley d						18 57				19 12								19 35					19 57	
Tipton d						18 59							19 28										19 59	
Dudley Port d						19 01							19 30										20 01	
Sandwell & Dudley d	18 46								19 15				19 33										20 05	
Smethwick Galton Bdg L.L. 7 d						19 06							19 36										20 07	
Smethwick Rolfe Street d						19 08							19 38										20 09	
Birmingham New Street 12 a	18 58		18 58		19 11	19 15		19 18	19 24	19 30		19 30	19 45					19 48	19 58			20 11	20 15	20 18
d		19 00	19 03	19 06			19 18		19 30		19 34					19 48	19 48			20 03	20 06			
Adderley Park d											19 39													
Stechford d				19 13							19 42										20 12			
Lea Hall d				19 15							19 44										20 15			
Marston Green d				19 18							19 47										20 17			
Birmingham International ✈ a		19 09	19 14	19 24			19 27		19 39		19 52					19 57	19 57			20 14	20 21			
d		19 10	19 15				19 27		19 40							19 57	19 57			20 15	20 21			
Hampton-in-Arden d							19 30									20 00	20 00				20 24			
Berkswell d							19 35									20 05	20 05				20 28			
Tile Hill d							19 38									20 08	20 08				20 31			
Canley d							19 42									20 12	20 12				20 34			
Coventry a		19 19	19 24				19 45		19 49							20 15	20 15			20 23	20 39			
d		19 20							19 50							20 15	20 17							
Rugby d																20 27	20 29							
Long Buckby d																20 37	20 40							
Northampton a																20 57	20 59							
London Euston 15 ⊖ a		20 41							21 04															

For general notes see front of timetable
For details of catering facilities see Directory of Train Operators

A Until 25 July and from 25 August
B 28 July to 22 August
C Until 5 September from Edinburgh (Table 51). From 8 September from Newcastle (Table 51).
D From Walsall (Table 70)
E From Liverpool Lime Street (Table 91)

Stafford → Wolverhampton → Birmingham → Coventry → Northampton

Network Diagram - see first page of Table 67

		VT	LM	LM	XC	VT	LM		LM	LM	LM	LM	XC	LM	VT	LM	VT	LM	XC		LM	LM		LM	LM
		1 ◇	1 ◇	1 ◇	1 ◇	1 ◇	1		1			1 ◇	1 ◇		1 ◇		1 ◇	1 ◇	1 ◇			1		1	
			A	B			C		D				E									C		D	
		[buffet]	[trolley]	[trolley]	[buffet]	[buffet]						[trolley]	[buffet]		[buffet]		[buffet]	[trolley]							
Stafford	d	.	19 46	19 48	19 58	20 14	.	.	.	.	.	20 21	20 26	.	.	.	.	20 46	20 57	.	.	.	.	.	.
Penkridge	d	.	19 52	19 54	.	.	.	.	.	.	.	.	.	.	.	.	.	20 52	.	.	.	.	.	.	.
Wolverhampton 7	a	.	20 05	20 06	20 12	.	.	.	.	.	.	20 36	20 41	.	.	.	.	21 05	21 12	.	.	.	.	.	.
	d	20 05	20 08	20 08	20 13	.	.	.	.	20 22	20 34	20 37	20 41	.	20 49	20 52	21 05	21 08	21 13	.	21 19	.	.	.	21 22
Walsall	a	.	.	.	.	.	.	.	.	.	20 49	.	.	.	.	.	.	.	.	.	21 32	.	.	.	.
Coseley	d	.	20 12	20 12	.	.	.	.	.	.	.	.	.	.	.	20 57	.	21 12	.	.	.	.	.	.	.
Tipton	d	.	.	.	.	.	.	.	.	20 28	.	.	.	.	.	20 59	.	.	.	.	.	.	.	.	.
Dudley Port	d	.	.	.	.	.	.	.	.	20 30	.	.	.	.	.	21 01	.	.	.	.	.	.	.	.	.
Sandwell & Dudley	d	20 15	.	.	.	.	.	.	.	20 33	.	20 46	.	.	.	21 05	21 15	.	.	.	.	.	.	.	.
Smethwick Galton Bdg L.L. 7	d	.	.	.	.	.	.	.	.	20 36	.	.	.	.	.	21 07	.	.	.	.	.	.	.	.	.
Smethwick Rolfe Street	d	.	.	.	.	.	.	.	.	20 38	.	.	.	.	.	21 09	.	.	.	.	.	.	.	.	.
Birmingham New Street 12	a	20 24	20 30	20 30	20 35	.	.	.	.	20 45	.	20 58	20 58	.	21 11	21 16	21 24	21 30	21 35	.	.	.	.	.	21 44
	d	20 30	.	.	.	.	20 36	.	20 36	.	.	.	21 03	21 06	.	.	21 30	.	.	.	.	21 36	.	21 36	.
Adderley Park	d	.	.	.	.	.	20 40	.	20 40	.	.	.	.	.	.	.	.	.	.	.	.	21 40	.	21 40	.
Stechford	d	.	.	.	.	.	20 44	.	20 44	.	.	.	.	21 12	.	.	.	.	.	.	.	21 44	.	21 44	.
Lea Hall	d	.	.	.	.	.	20 46	.	20 46	.	.	.	.	21 15	.	.	.	.	.	.	.	21 46	.	21 46	.
Marston Green	d	.	.	.	.	.	20 50	.	20 50	.	.	.	.	21 17	.	.	.	.	.	.	.	21 50	.	21 50	.
Birmingham International ✈	a	20 39	.	.	.	.	20 53	.	20 53	.	.	.	21 14	21 20	.	.	21 39	.	.	.	.	21 53	.	21 53	.
	d	20 40	.	.	.	.	20 53	.	20 53	.	.	.	21 15	21 21	.	.	21 40	.	.	.	.	21 53	.	21 53	.
Hampton-in-Arden	d	.	.	.	.	.	20 56	.	20 56	.	.	.	.	21 24	.	.	.	.	.	.	.	21 56	.	21 56	.
Berkswell	d	.	.	.	.	.	21 01	.	21 01	.	.	.	.	21 28	.	.	.	.	.	.	.	22 01	.	22 01	.
Tile Hill	d	.	.	.	.	.	21 04	.	21 04	.	.	.	.	21 31	.	.	.	.	.	.	.	22 04	.	22 04	.
Canley	d	.	.	.	.	.	21 08	.	21 08	.	.	.	.	21 34	.	.	.	.	.	.	.	22 08	.	22 08	.
Coventry	a	20 49	.	.	.	.	21 11	.	21 11	.	.	.	21 23	21 39	.	.	21 49	.	.	.	.	22 11	.	22 11	.
	d	20 50	.	.	.	.	21 11	.	21 18	.	.	.	.	.	.	.	21 50	.	.	.	.	22 11	.	22 18	.
Rugby	d	.	.	.	.	20 49	21 22	.	21 28	.	.	.	.	.	.	.	.	.	.	.	.	22 22	.	22 28	.
Long Buckby	d	.	.	.	.	.	21 33	.	21 40	.	.	.	.	.	.	.	.	.	.	.	.	22 34	.	22 38	.
Northampton	a	.	.	.	.	.	21 47	.	21 54	.	.	.	.	.	.	.	.	.	.	.	.	22 54	.	22 59	.
London Euston 15	⊖ a	22 04	.	.	.	21 51	.	.	.	.	.	.	.	.	.	.	23 20	.	.	.	.	.	.	.	.

		LM	XC	LM	LM	AW	LM	LM	VT	LM	VT	VT	VT	VT	VT		LM	LM	LM		AW	LM	XC		
												FO	FO	FX											
			1 ◇			◇	1 ◇	1	1 ◇		1	1	1	1	1 ◇							1 ◇	1 ◇		
											G	H	J	K					L			N			
						[trolley]	[trolley]		[buffet]						[buffet]							[trolley]			
Stafford	d	.	21 26	.	.	.	21 46	.	21 55	.	.	.	.	.	22 36	.	.	.	.	.	.	22 46	22 57	.	.
Penkridge	d	.	.	.	.	.	21 52	.	.	.	.	.	.	.	.	.	.	.	.	.	.	22 52	.	.	.
Wolverhampton 7	a	.	21 41	.	.	.	22 08	.	22 16	.	.	.	.	.	22 48	.	.	.	.	.	.	23 06	23 12	.	.
	d	21 25	21 41	.	21 52	22 03	22 08	.	22 16	22 22	22 39	22 39	22 39	22 39	22 49	.	.	22 52	22 55	.	22 59	23 08	23 13	.	.
Walsall	a	.	.	.	.	.	.	.	.	.	.	.	.	.	.	.	.	.	23 12	.	.	.	.	.	.
Coseley	d	21 30	.	.	21 57	.	.	.	.	22 27	.	.	.	.	.	.	.	22 57	.	.	.	.	.	.	.
Tipton	d	21 32	.	.	21 59	.	.	.	.	22 29	.	.	.	.	.	.	.	22 59	.	.	.	.	.	.	.
Dudley Port	d	21 34	.	.	22 01	.	.	.	.	22 31	.	.	.	.	.	.	.	23 01	.	.	.	.	.	.	.
Sandwell & Dudley	d	21 38	.	.	22 05	.	.	.	.	22 35	.	.	.	.	.	.	.	23 05	.	.	.	.	.	.	.
Smethwick Galton Bdg L.L. 7	d	21 40	.	.	22 07	.	.	.	.	22 37	.	.	.	.	.	.	.	23 07	.	.	.	.	.	.	.
Smethwick Rolfe Street	d	21 42	.	.	22 09	.	.	.	.	22 39	.	.	.	.	.	.	.	23 09	.	.	.	.	.	.	.
Birmingham New Street 12	a	21 48	22 04	.	22 15	22 18	22 30	.	22 38	22 45	22 56	22 56	22 56	22 56	23 11	.	.	23 15	.	.	23 33	23 30	23 47	.	.
	d	.	.	22 06	.	.	.	22 36	.	.	23 00	23 00	23 00	23 00	.	.	23 15	.	.	.	.	.	.	.	.
Adderley Park	d	.	.	.	.	.	.	22 41	.	.	.	.	.	.	.	.	23 19	.	.	.	.	.	.	.	.
Stechford	d	.	.	22 12	.	.	.	22 44	.	.	.	.	.	.	.	.	23 23	.	.	.	.	.	.	.	.
Lea Hall	d	.	.	22 15	.	.	.	22 46	.	.	.	.	.	.	.	.	23 25	.	.	.	.	.	.	.	.
Marston Green	d	.	.	22 17	.	.	.	22 49	.	.	.	.	.	.	.	.	23 29	.	.	.	.	.	.	.	.
Birmingham International ✈	a	.	.	22 20	.	.	.	22 52	.	.	23 09	23 09	23 09	23 09	.	.	23 32	.	.	.	.	.	.	.	.
	d	.	.	22 21	.	.	.	22 52	.	.	23 10	23 10	23 10	23 10	.	.	23 32	.	.	.	.	.	.	.	.
Hampton-in-Arden	d	.	.	22 24	.	.	.	22 55	.	.	.	.	.	.	.	.	23 35	.	.	.	.	.	.	.	.
Berkswell	d	.	.	22 28	.	.	.	22 59	.	.	.	.	.	.	.	.	23 40	.	.	.	.	.	.	.	.
Tile Hill	d	.	.	22 31	.	.	.	23 02	.	.	.	.	.	.	.	.	23 43	.	.	.	.	.	.	.	.
Canley	d	.	.	22 34	.	.	.	23 05	.	.	.	.	.	.	.	.	23 47	.	.	.	.	.	.	.	.
Coventry	a	.	.	22 39	.	.	.	23 12	.	.	23 19	23 19	23 19	23 19	.	.	23 52	.	.	.	.	.	.	.	.
	d	.	.	.	.	.	.	.	.	.	23 20	23 23	23 23	23 23	.	.	.	.	.	.	.	.	.	.	.
Rugby	d	.	.	.	.	.	.	.	.	.	23 34	23 35	23 37	23 37	.	.	.	.	.	.	.	.	.	.	.
Long Buckby	d	.	.	.	.	.	.	.	.	.	.	.	.	.	.	.	.	.	.	.	.	.	.	.	.
Northampton	a	.	.	.	.	.	.	.	.	.	23s56	23s57	23s58	23s59	.	.	.	.	.	.	.	.	.	.	.
London Euston 15	⊖ a	.	.	.	.	.	.	.	.	.	01 02	01 04	01 04	01 03	.	.	.	.	.	.	.	.	.	.	.

For general notes see front of timetable
For details of catering facilities see Directory of Train Operators

- **A** From 27 October
- **B** Until 24 October
- **C** Until 25 July and from 25 August
- **D** 28 July to 22 August
- **E** [buffet] to Birmingham New Street
- **G** Mondays to Thursdays until 24 July and from 25 August, and Fridays until 11 July
- **H** 18 and 25 July and from 29 August
- **J** 1 to 22 August
- **K** 28 July to 21 August
- **L** From Shrewsbury (Table 74)
- **N** From Liverpool Lime Street (Table 91)

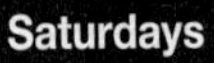

until 12 July

Stafford → Wolverhampton → Birmingham → Coventry → Northampton

Network Diagram - see first page of Table 67

		LM	VT 1◇	VT 1◇ ⊠	XC 1◇ ☕	LM	AW	VT 1◇ ☕	VT 1◇ ⊠	LM	LM 1	LM		VT 1◇ ☕	XC 1◇ ☕	LM 1◇	LM	LM	AW	VT 1◇ ☕	LM 1	LM	LM	LM	VT 1◇ ☕
Stafford	d		04 30					06 14							06 26	06 30									
Penkridge	d															06 36									
Wolverhampton 7	a		04 45												06 40	06 47									
	d		04 46	05 37			06 01		06 05	06 08		06 22		06 35	06 41	06 47		06 52	06 59	07 05		07 22	07 25	07 31	07 35
Walsall	a									06 22													07 38		
Coseley	d											06 27						06 57				07 27			
Tipton	d											06 29						06 59				07 29			
Dudley Port	d											06 31						07 01				07 31			
Sandwell & Dudley	d			05 47					06 15			06 35		06 48				07 05		07 16		07 35			07 48
Smethwick Galton Bdg L.L. 7	d											06 37						07 07				07 37			
Smethwick Rolfe Street	d											06 39						07 09				07 39			
Birmingham New Street 12	a		05 08	05 56			06 18		06 24			06 45		06 56	06 58	07 08		07 15	07 18	07 24		07 47		07 51	07 56
	d	00 10		06 00	06 03	06 13			06 30		06 43			07 00	07 03		07 09			07 30	07 36				08 00
Adderley Park	d					06 18											07 14								
Stechford	d					06 21					06 48						07 17				07 42				
Lea Hall	d					06 24					06 51						07 20				07 45				
Marston Green	d	00 18				06 26					06 54						07 22				07 48				
Birmingham International ✈	a	00 22		06 09	06 14	06 29			06 39		06 58			07 09	07 14		07 25			07 40	07 51				08 09
	d	00 22		06 10	06 15	06 30			06 41		06 58			07 10	07 15		07 26			07 41	07 52				08 10
Hampton-in-Arden	d					06 33					07 01						07 29				07 55				
Berkswell	d					06 37					07 06						07 33				08 00				
Tile Hill	d					06 40					07 09						07 36				08 03				
Canley	d					06 43					07 12						07 39				08 06				
Coventry	a	00 37		06 19	06 23	06 45			06 54		07 16			07 20	07 24		07 41			07 52	08 09				08 19
	d			06 21					06 55		07 16			07 22						07 54	08 10				08 21
Rugby	d			06 35				07 01			07 30			07 40							08 21				
Long Buckby	d										07 40										08 31				
Northampton	a										07 53										08 46				
London Euston 15 ⊖	a			08 10				08 19	08 29					09 01						09 25					10 00

		XC 1◇ A ☕		LM	VT 1◇ ☕	LM	AW ◇ ⊤	VT 1◇ ☕	LM 1◇ B	XC 1◇ ☕	LM 1	LM	LM	LM		VT 1◇ ⊠	XC R 1 ☕	VT R 1 ☕	XC R 1 C ☕	LM	LM	AW ◇ ⊤	VT 1◇ ⊠	LM 1◇	XC 1◇ ☕
Stafford	d								07 44	07 58									08 33					08 44	08 58
Penkridge	d								07 50															08 50	
Wolverhampton 7	a								08 07	08 12									08 47					09 05	09 11
	d				07 48	07 52	07 59	08 05	08 09	08 13		08 22	08 25	08 31				08 43	08 49		08 52	08 59	09 05	09 09	09 13
Walsall	a												08 40												
Coseley	d					07 57			08 14					08 37							08 57			09 14	
Tipton	d					07 59						08 28									08 59				
Dudley Port	d					08 01						08 30									09 01				
Sandwell & Dudley	d					08 05		08 16				08 33									09 05		09 15		
Smethwick Galton Bdg L.L. 7	d					08 07						08 36									09 07				
Smethwick Rolfe Street	d					08 09						08 38									09 09				
Birmingham New Street 12	a				08 10	08 15	08 18	08 24	08 27	08 30		08 46		08 51				09 05	09 06		09 15	09 18	09 24	09 27	09 30
	d	08 03		08 09				08 30			08 36					09 00	09 03			09 09			09 30		
Adderley Park	d			08 14																09 14					
Stechford	d			08 17							08 42									09 17					
Lea Hall	d			08 20							08 45									09 20					
Marston Green	d			08 22							08 48									09 22					
Birmingham International ✈	a	08 14		08 25				08 40			08 51					09 09	09 14			09 25			09 39		
	d	08 15		08 26				08 41			08 52					09 10	09 15			09 26			09 40		
Hampton-in-Arden	d			08 29							08 55									09 29					
Berkswell	d			08 33							09 00									09 33					
Tile Hill	d			08 36							09 03									09 36					
Canley	d			08 39							09 06									09 39					
Coventry	a	08 23		08 42				08 54			09 09					09 19	09 23			09 41			09 49		
	d							08 56			09 10					09 20							09 50		
Rugby	d										09 21														
Long Buckby	d										09 31														
Northampton	a										09 48														
London Euston 15 ⊖	a							10 24								11 00							11 21		

For general notes see front of timetable
For details of catering facilities see Directory of Train Operators

A From Sheffield (Table 51)
B From Liverpool Lime Street (Table 91)
C To Newquay (Table 135)

until 12 July

Stafford → Wolverhampton → Birmingham → Coventry → Northampton

Network Diagram - see first page of Table 67

		VT	LM	LM		LM	LM	XC	VT	XC	LM	VT	LM	AW	LM	VT		XC	VT	LM	LM	LM	VT	LM	VT
		1 ◇	1					R 1	1 ◇	R 1		1 ◇		◇	1 ◇	1 ◇		1 ◇	1 ◇	1			1 ◇		1 ◇
										A															
		☕						☕	⊠	☕		☕		🛒		☕		☕	☕				☕		☕
Stafford	d	09 12						09 26							09 44			09 58							10 13
Penkridge	d														09 50										
Wolverhampton 7	a							09 41							10 05			10 12							10 35
	d			09 22		09 25	09 31	09 41				09 49	09 52	09 59	10 09			10 13			10 22	10 25		10 31	10 37
Walsall	a					09 40																10 40			
Coseley	d						09 37						09 57		10 14									10 37	
Tipton	d			09 28									09 59								10 28				
Dudley Port	d			09 30									10 01								10 30				
Sandwell & Dudley	d			09 33									10 05								10 33				
Smethwick Galton Bdg L.L. 7	d			09 36									10 07								10 36				10 48
Smethwick Rolfe Street	d			09 38									10 09								10 38				
Birmingham New Street 12	a			09 45			09 51	09 58				10 11	10 15	10 18	10 27			10 30			10 45			10 51	10 56
	d		09 36						10 00	10 03	10 09					10 30			10 33	10 36			10 51		11 00
Adderley Park	d										10 14														
Stechford	d		09 42								10 17									10 42					
Lea Hall	d		09 45								10 20									10 45					
Marston Green	d		09 48								10 22									10 48					
Birmingham International ✈	a		09 52						10 09	10 14	10 25					10 39			10 44	10 52			11 03		11 09
	d		09 52						10 10	10 15	10 26					10 40			10 45	10 52			11 04		11 10
Hampton-in-Arden	d		09 55								10 29									10 55					
Berkswell	d		10 00								10 33									11 00					
Tile Hill	d		10 03								10 36									11 03					
Canley	d		10 06								10 39									11 06					
Coventry	a		10 10						10 19	10 23	10 41					10 49			10 54	11 10			11 13		11 19
	d		10 10						10 20							10 51			10 56	11 10			11 15		11 21
Rugby	d	09 56	10 21																11 10	11 21					11 35
Long Buckby	d		10 31																	11 31					
Northampton	a		10 46																	11 46					
London Euston 15	⊖ a	11 16							11 55							12 21			12 38				12 54		13 01

		XC	LM	VT	LM	AW		LM	VT	XC	VT	LM	LM	LM	VT	LM	VT	XC		XC	LM	VT	LM	AW	LM
		1 ◇		1 ◇		◇		1 ◇	1 ◇	1 ◇	1 ◇	1			1 ◇		1 ◇	R 1		1 ◇		R 1		◇	1 ◇
																				B					
		☕		☕		🛒			☕	☕	☕				☕		☕	☕		☕		☕		🛒	
Stafford	d	10 26						10 44		10 58							11 13	11 26							11 44
Penkridge	d							10 50																	11 50
Wolverhampton 7	a	10 41						11 05		11 12							11 35	11 41							12 06
	d	10 41		10 49	10 52	10 59		11 09		11 13			11 22	11 25		11 31	11 37	11 41				11 49	11 52	11 59	12 09
Walsall	a													11 40											
Coseley	d				10 57			11 14								11 37							11 57		12 14
Tipton	d				10 59								11 28										11 59		
Dudley Port	d				11 01								11 30										12 01		
Sandwell & Dudley	d				11 05								11 33										12 05		
Smethwick Galton Bdg L.L. 7	d				11 07								11 36				11 48						12 07		
Smethwick Rolfe Street	d				11 09								11 38										12 09		
Birmingham New Street 12	a	10 58		11 11	11 15	11 18		11 27		11 30			11 45			11 51	11 56	11 58				12 11	12 15	12 18	12 27
	d	11 03	11 09						11 30		11 33	11 36			11 51		12 00			12 03	12 09				
Adderley Park	d		11 14																		12 14				
Stechford	d		11 17									11 42									12 17				
Lea Hall	d		11 20									11 45									12 20				
Marston Green	d		11 22									11 48									12 22				
Birmingham International ✈	a	11 14	11 25						11 39		11 44	11 51			12 03		12 09			12 14	12 25				
	d	11 15	11 26						11 40		11 45	11 52			12 04		12 10			12 15	12 26				
Hampton-in-Arden	d		11 29									11 55									12 29				
Berkswell	d		11 33									12 00									12 33				
Tile Hill	d		11 36									12 03									12 36				
Canley	d		11 39									12 06									12 39				
Coventry	a	11 23	11 41						11 49		11 54	12 09			12 13		12 19			12 23	12 41				
	d								11 51		11 56	12 10			12 15		12 21								
Rugby	d										12 10	12 21					12 35								
Long Buckby	d											12 31													
Northampton	a											12 46													
London Euston 15	⊖ a								13 22		13 38				13 54		13 58								

For general notes see front of timetable
For details of catering facilities see Directory of Train Operators

A From Newcastle (Table 51)
B From Glasgow Central (Table 51)

Stafford → Wolverhampton → Birmingham → Coventry → Northampton

Network Diagram - see first page of Table 67

	VT	XC	VT	LM	LM	LM	VT		LM	VT	XC	LM	VT	LM	AW	LM	VT	XC	VT		LM	LM	LM	VT
	1 ◇ ☕	1 ◇ ☕	1 ◇ ☕	1			1 ◇ ☕			1 ◇ ☕	1 ◇ ☕		R 1 ☕		◇ 🛒	1 ◇	1 ◇ ☕	1 ◇ ☕	1 ◇ ☕		1			1 ◇ ☕
Stafford d		11 58								12 18	12 26					12 44		12 58						
Penkridge d																12 50								
Wolverhampton 7 a		12 12								12 35	12 41					13 05		13 12						
d		12 13			12 22	12 25			12 31	12 37	12 41		12 49	12 52	12 59	13 09		13 13				13 22	13 25	
Walsall a						12 40																	13 40	
Coseley d									12 37					12 57		13 14								
Tipton d					12 28									12 59								13 28		
Dudley Port d					12 30									13 01								13 30		
Sandwell & Dudley d					12 33					12 48				13 05								13 33		
Smethwick Galton Bdg L.L. 7 d					12 36									13 07								13 36		
Smethwick Rolfe Street d					12 38									13 09								13 38		
Birmingham New Street 12 a		12 30			12 45				12 51	12 56	12 58		13 11	13 15	13 18	13 27		13 30				13 45		
d	12 30		12 33	12 36			12 51			13 00	13 03	13 09					13 30		13 33		13 36			13 51
Adderley Park d												13 14												
Stechford d				12 42								13 17									13 42			
Lea Hall d				12 45								13 20									13 45			
Marston Green d				12 48								13 22									13 48			
Birmingham International ✈ a	12 39		12 45	12 51			13 03			13 09	13 14	13 25					13 39		13 44		13 52			14 03
d	12 40		12 46	12 52			13 04			13 10	13 15	13 26					13 40		13 45		13 52			14 04
Hampton-in-Arden d				12 55								13 29									13 55			
Berkswell d				13 00								13 33									14 00			
Tile Hill d				13 03								13 36									14 03			
Canley d				13 06								13 39									14 06			
Coventry a	12 49		12 55	13 09			13 13			13 19	13 23	13 41					13 49		13 55		14 10			14 13
d	12 51		12 57	13 10			13 15			13 21							13 51		13 57		14 10			14 15
Rugby d			13 11	13 21						13 35									14 11		14 21			
Long Buckby d				13 31																	14 31			
Northampton a				13 47																	14 46			
London Euston 15 ⊖ a	14 23		14 38				14 54			15 01							15 24		15 38					15 54

	LM	VT	XC	LM	VT	LM	AW	LM	VT		XC	VT	LM	LM	LM	VT	LM	VT	XC	LM	VT		LM	AW
		1 ◇ ☕	R 1 ☕		R 1 ☕		◇ 🛒	1 ◇	1 ◇ ☕		1 ◇ ☕	1 ◇ ☕	1			1 ◇ ☕		1 ◇ ☕	1 ◇ ☕		1 ◇ ☕			◇ 🛒
Stafford d		13 13	13 26					13 44			13 58							14 13	14 26					
Penkridge d								13 50																
Wolverhampton 7 a		13 35	13 40					14 05			14 12							14 35	14 41					
d	13 31	13 37	13 41		13 49	13 52	13 59	14 09			14 13			14 22	14 25		14 31	14 37	14 41		14 49		14 52	14 59
Walsall a															14 40									
Coseley d	13 37					13 57		14 14									14 37						14 57	
Tipton d						13 59								14 28									14 59	
Dudley Port d						14 01								14 30									15 01	
Sandwell & Dudley d		13 48				14 05								14 33				14 48					15 05	
Smethwick Galton Bdg L.L. 7 d						14 07								14 36									15 07	
Smethwick Rolfe Street d						14 09								14 38									15 09	
Birmingham New Street 12 a	13 51	13 56	13 58		14 11	14 15	14 18	14 27			14 30			14 45			14 51	14 56	14 58		15 11		15 15	15 18
d		14 00		14 09					14 30			14 33	14 36			14 51		15 00	15 03	15 09				
Adderley Park d				14 14																15 14				
Stechford d				14 17									14 42							15 17				
Lea Hall d				14 20									14 45							15 20				
Marston Green d				14 22									14 48							15 22				
Birmingham International ✈ a		14 09		14 25					14 39			14 45	14 51			15 00		15 09	15 14	15 25				
d		14 10		14 26					14 40			14 46	14 52			15 01		15 10	15 15	15 26				
Hampton-in-Arden d				14 29									14 55							15 29				
Berkswell d				14 33									15 00							15 33				
Tile Hill d				14 36									15 03							15 36				
Canley d				14 39									15 06							15 39				
Coventry a		14 19		14 41					14 49			14 55	15 09			15 13		15 19	15 23	15 41				
d		14 21							14 51			14 57	15 10			15 15		15 21						
Rugby d												15 11	15 21					15 35						
Long Buckby d													15 31											
Northampton a													15 46											
London Euston 15 ⊖ a		15 59							16 25			16 38				16 54		17 01						

For general notes see front of timetable
For details of catering facilities see Directory of Train Operators

Table 68

Saturdays

until 12 July

Stafford → Wolverhampton → Birmingham → Coventry → Northampton

Network Diagram - see first page of Table 67

		LM	VT	XC	VT	LM	LM	LM	VT	LM	VT	XC		XC	LM	VT	LM	AW	LM	VT	XC	VT	LM	LM	LM
		1 ◇	1 ◇	1 ◇	1 ◇	1			1 ◇		1 ◇	1 ◇		1 ◇		R 1		◇	1 ◇	1 ◇	1 ◇	1 ◇	1		
														A											
			☕	☕	☕				☕		☕	☕		☕		☕		🛒		☕	☕	☕			
Stafford	d	14 44		14 58							15 13	15 26							15 44		15 58				
Penkridge	d	14 50																	15 50						
Wolverhampton 7	a	15 05		15 12							15 35	15 41							16 05		16 12				
	d	15 09		15 13			15 22	15 25		15 31	15 37	15 41				15 47	15 52	15 59	16 09		16 13			16 22	16 25
Walsall	a							15 40																	16 40
Coseley	d	15 14								15 37							15 57		16 14						
Tipton	d						15 28										15 59							16 28	
Dudley Port	d						15 30										16 01							16 30	
Sandwell & Dudley	d						15 33				15 48						16 05							16 33	
Smethwick Galton Bdg L.L. 7	d						15 36										16 07							16 36	
Smethwick Rolfe Street	d						15 38										16 09							16 38	
Birmingham New Street 12	a	15 27		15 30			15 45			15 51	15 56	15 58				16 11	16 15	16 18	16 27		16 30			16 45	
	d		15 30		15 33	15 36			15 51		16 00			16 03	16 09					16 30		16 33	16 36		
Adderley Park	d														16 14										
Stechford	d					15 42									16 17								16 42		
Lea Hall	d					15 45									16 20								16 45		
Marston Green	d					15 48									16 22								16 48		
Birmingham International ✈	a		15 39		15 45	15 51			16 03		16 09			16 14	16 25					16 39		16 45	16 51		
	d		15 40		15 46	15 52			16 04		16 10			16 15	16 26					16 40		16 46	16 52		
Hampton-in-Arden	d					15 55									16 29								16 55		
Berkswell	d					16 00									16 33								17 00		
Tile Hill	d					16 03									16 36								17 03		
Canley	d					16 06									16 39								17 06		
Coventry	a		15 49		15 55	16 09			16 13		16 19			16 23	16 41					16 49		16 55	17 09		
	d		15 51		15 57	16 10			16 15		16 21									16 51		16 57	17 10		
Rugby	d				16 11	16 21					16 35											17 11	17 21		
Long Buckby	d					16 31																	17 31		
Northampton	a					16 46																	17 46		
London Euston 15	⊖ a		17 23		17 37				17 54		17 58									18 23		18 38			

		VT		LM	VT	XC	LM	VT	LM	AW	LM	VT	XC	VT		LM	LM	LM	VT	LM	VT	XC	XC	LM	VT
		1 ◇			1 ◇	1 ◇		R 1		◇	1 ◇	1 ◇	1 ◇	1 ◇		1			1 ◇		1 ◇	1 ◇	1 ◇		1 ◇
																							B		
		☕			☕	☕		☕		🛒		☕	☕	☕					☕		☕	☕	☕		☕
Stafford	d				16 13	16 26					16 44		16 58								17 13	17 26			
Penkridge	d										16 50														
Wolverhampton 7	a				16 35	16 41					17 05		17 12								17 35	17 41			
	d			16 31	16 37	16 41		16 49	16 52	16 59	17 09		17 13				17 22	17 25		17 31	17 37	17 41			17 49
Walsall	a																	17 40							
Coseley	d			16 37					16 57		17 14									17 37					
Tipton	d								16 59								17 28								
Dudley Port	d								17 01								17 30								
Sandwell & Dudley	d				16 48				17 05								17 33				17 48				
Smethwick Galton Bdg L.L. 7	d								17 07								17 36								
Smethwick Rolfe Street	d								17 09								17 38								
Birmingham New Street 12	a			16 51	16 56	16 58		17 11	17 15	17 18	17 27		17 30				17 45			17 51	17 56	17 58			18 11
	d	16 51			17 00	17 03	17 09					17 30		17 33		17 36			17 51		18 00		18 03	18 09	
Adderley Park	d						17 14																	18 14	
Stechford	d						17 17									17 42								18 17	
Lea Hall	d						17 20									17 45								18 20	
Marston Green	d						17 22									17 48								18 22	
Birmingham International ✈	a	17 03			17 09	17 14	17 25					17 39		17 44		17 52			18 03		18 09		18 14	18 25	
	d	17 04			17 10	17 15	17 26					17 40		17 45		17 52			18 04		18 10		18 15	18 26	
Hampton-in-Arden	d						17 29									17 55								18 29	
Berkswell	d						17 33									18 00								18 33	
Tile Hill	d						17 36									18 03								18 36	
Canley	d						17 39									18 06								18 39	
Coventry	a	17 13			17 19	17 23	17 41					17 49		17 55		18 10			18 13		18 19		18 23	18 41	
	d	17 15			17 21							17 51		17 57		18 10			18 15		18 21				
Rugby	d				17 35									18 11		18 21					18 35				
Long Buckby	d															18 31									
Northampton	a															18 46									
London Euston 15	⊖ a	18 55			19 02							19 21		19 43					19 48		19 55				

For general notes see front of timetable
For details of catering facilities see Directory of Train Operators

A From Aberdeen (Table 51)
B From Edinburgh (Table 51)

Table 68

Saturdays

until 12 July

Stafford → Wolverhampton → Birmingham → Coventry → Northampton

Network Diagram - see first page of Table 67

		LM	AW	LM		VT	XC	VT	LM	LM	LM	VT	LM	VT	XC	LM		VT	LM	AW	LM	VT	XC	LM	LM
			◇	1 ◇		1 ◇	1 ◇	1 ◇	1			1 ◇		1 ◇	1 ◇			1 ◇		◇	1 ◇	1 ◇	1 ◇	1	
																					A				
			🛒			☕	☕	☕				☕		☕	☕			☕				☕	☕		
Stafford	d			17 44			17 58							18 13	18 26						18 44		18 58		
Penkridge	d			17 50																	18 50				
Wolverhampton 7	a			18 07			18 12							18 35	18 41						19 06		19 12		
	d	17 52	17 59	18 09			18 13			18 22	18 25		18 31	18 37	18 41			18 49	18 52	18 59	19 09		19 13		19 22
Walsall	a										18 40														
Coseley	d	17 57		18 14									18 37						18 57		19 14				
Tipton	d	17 59								18 28									18 59						19 28
Dudley Port	d	18 01								18 30									19 01						19 30
Sandwell & Dudley	d	18 05								18 33				18 48					19 05						19 33
Smethwick Galton Bdg L.L. 7	d	18 07								18 36									19 07						19 36
Smethwick Rolfe Street	d	18 09								18 38									19 09						19 38
Birmingham New Street 12	a	18 16	18 19	18 27			18 30			18 45			18 51	18 56	18 58			19 11	19 15	19 18	19 27		19 35		19 45
	d					18 30		18 33	18 36			18 51		19 00	19 03	19 09						19 33		19 36	
Adderley Park	d															19 14									
Stechford	d								18 42							19 17								19 42	
Lea Hall	d								18 45							19 20								19 45	
Marston Green	d								18 48							19 22								19 48	
Birmingham International ✈	a					18 39		18 44	18 52			19 03		19 09	19 14	19 25						19 42		19 51	
	d					18 40		18 45	18 52			19 04		19 10	19 15	19 26						19 43		19 52	
Hampton-in-Arden	d								18 55							19 29								19 55	
Berkswell	d								19 00							19 33								20 00	
Tile Hill	d								19 03							19 36								20 03	
Canley	d								19 06							19 39								20 06	
Coventry	a					18 49		18 55	19 10			19 13		19 19	19 23	19 41						19 52		20 09	
	d					18 51		18 57	19 10			19 15		19 21								19 54		20 10	
Rugby	d							19 11	19 21					19 35										20 21	
Long Buckby	d								19 31															20 31	
Northampton	a								19 46															20 46	
London Euston 15 ⊖	a					20 28		20 59				21 22		21 27								21 42			

		LM	VT	LM	VT	XC		XC	LM	VT	LM	AW	LM	VT	XC	LM	LM	LM		VT	XC	LM	VT	LM	AW
			1 ◇		1 ◇	1 ◇		1 ◇		1 ◇		◇	1 ◇	1 ◇	1 ◇	1				1 ◇	1 ◇		1 ◇		
								B													C				
			☕		☕	☕		☕		☕		🛒		☕	☕					☕	☕		☕		
Stafford	d				19 13	19 25							19 44	19 52	19 58						20 26				
Penkridge	d												19 50												
Wolverhampton 7	a				19 35	19 40							20 07		20 12						20 40				
	d	19 25		19 31	19 37	19 41				19 49	19 52	19 59	20 09		20 13		20 22	20 25			20 41		20 49	20 52	20 59
Walsall	a	19 39																20 39							
Coseley	d			19 37							19 57						20 27							20 57	
Tipton	d										19 59						20 29							20 59	
Dudley Port	d										20 01						20 31							21 01	
Sandwell & Dudley	d				19 48						20 05						20 35							21 05	
Smethwick Galton Bdg L.L. 7	d										20 07						20 37							21 07	
Smethwick Rolfe Street	d										20 09						20 39							21 09	
Birmingham New Street 12	a			19 51	19 56	19 58				20 11	20 15	20 18	20 30		20 35		20 45				20 58		21 11	21 15	21 18
	d		19 51		20 00			20 03	20 09							20 36				20 53	21 03	21 09			
Adderley Park	d								20 14													21 14			
Stechford	d								20 17							20 42						21 17			
Lea Hall	d								20 20							20 45						21 20			
Marston Green	d								20 22							20 48						21 22			
Birmingham International ✈	a		20 03		20 09			20 14	20 25							20 51				21 03	21 14	21 25			
	d		20 04		20 10			20 15	20 26							20 52				21 04	21 15	21 26			
Hampton-in-Arden	d								20 29							20 55						21 29			
Berkswell	d								20 33							21 00						21 33			
Tile Hill	d								20 36							21 03						21 36			
Canley	d								20 39							21 06						21 39			
Coventry	a		20 13		20 19			20 24	20 41							21 09				21 13	21 23	21 41			
	d		20 15		20 21											21 10				21 15					
Rugby	d				20 35									21 01		21 21				21 29					
Long Buckby	d															21 31									
Northampton	a															21 49									
London Euston 15 ⊖	a		22 28		22 33									22 46						23 24					

For general notes see front of timetable
For details of catering facilities see Directory of Train Operators

A From Liverpool Lime Street (Table 91)
B From Edinburgh (Table 51)
C ☕ to Birmingham New Street

Table 68

Saturdays until 12 July

Stafford → Wolverhampton → Birmingham → Coventry → Northampton

Network Diagram - see first page of Table 67

		LM	LM	XC	LM	LM	LM	VT		LM	LM	AW	VT	XC	LM	LM	LM	VT	LM	LM		LM	AW	
			1 ◇	1 ◇	1			1 ◇				◇	1 ◇	1 ◇		1	1 ◇	1 ◇		A				
								☕				trolley	☕					☕						
Stafford	d		20 44	20 58				21 18					21 51	21 58			22 25	22 33						
Penkridge	d		20 50														22 31							
Wolverhampton 7	a		21 08	21 12				21 35					22 06	22 12			22 43	22 48						
	d	21 03	21 09	21 13		21 22	21 31	21 35		21 52		22 03	22 09	22 13	22 22		22 43	22 49	22 52	22 55			22 59	
Walsall	a	21 18																		23 12				
Coseley	d					21 27				21 57					22 27				22 57					
Tipton	d					21 29				21 59					22 29				22 59					
Dudley Port	d					21 31				22 01					22 31				23 01					
Sandwell & Dudley	d					21 35		21 47		22 05					22 35				23 05					
Smethwick Galton Bdg L.L. 7	d					21 37				22 07					22 37				23 07					
Smethwick Rolfe Street	d					21 39				22 09					22 39				23 09					
Birmingham New Street 12	a		21 27	21 35		21 45	21 53	21 56		22 15		22 18	22 30	22 35	22 45		23 04	23 10	23 15				23 18	
	d				21 36			22 00			22 18					22 48						23 17		
Adderley Park	d										22 23											23 22		
Stechford	d				21 42						22 26					22 55						23 25		
Lea Hall	d				21 45						22 29					22 58						23 28		
Marston Green	d				21 48						22 31					23 01						23 30		
Birmingham International ✈	a				21 52			22 09			22 34					23 04						23 33		
	d				21 52			22 10			22 35					23 04						23 34		
Hampton-in-Arden	d				21 55						22 38					23 07						23 37		
Berkswell	d				22 00						22 42					23 12						23 41		
Tile Hill	d				22 03						22 45					23 15						23 44		
Canley	d				22 06						22 48					23 19						23 47		
Coventry	a				22 10			22 19			22 50					23 22						23 49		
	d				22 10			22 21								23 22								
Rugby	d				22 21			22 35								23 34								
Long Buckby	d				22 31											23 44								
Northampton	a				22 49											23 58								
London Euston 15 ⊖	a							00 16																

Saturdays 19 July to 6 September

		LM	VT	VT	XC	LM	AW	LM	LM	VT	VT	LM	VT		LM	XC	LM	LM	LM	AW	LM	VT	LM	VT	LM
			1 ◇	1 ◇	1 ◇				🚌	1 ◇	🚌	1	1 ◇			1 ◇	1 ◇				🚌	🚌	1	1 ◇	
				☕	☕					☕			☕			☕								☕	
Stafford	d		04 30							06 14						06 26	06 30								
Penkridge	d																06 36								
Wolverhampton 7	a		04 45													06 40	06 47								
	d		04 46	05 18			06 01	06 08					06 18		06 22	06 41	06 47		06 52	06 59				07 18	07 22
Walsall	a							06 22																	
Coseley	d														06 27				06 57						07 27
Tipton	d														06 29				06 59						07 29
Dudley Port	d														06 31				07 01						07 31
Sandwell & Dudley	d			05 29									06 30		06 35				07 05					07 29	07 35
Smethwick Galton Bdg L.L. 7	d														06 37				07 07						07 37
Smethwick Rolfe Street	d														06 39				07 09						07 39
Birmingham New Street 12	a		05 08	05 40			06 18						06 40		06 45	06 58	07 08		07 15	07 18				07 40	07 47
	d	00 10		05 43	06 03	06 13						06 43	06 46			07 03		07 09					07 36	07 44	
Adderley Park	d					06 18												07 14							
Stechford	d					06 21						06 49						07 17					07 42		
Lea Hall	d					06 24						06 52						07 20					07 45		
Marston Green	d	00 18				06 26						06 55						07 22					07 48		
Birmingham International ✈	a	00 22			06 14	06 29						06 59				07 14		07 25					07 51		
	d	00 22			06 15	06 30					06 20	06 59				07 15		07 26				07 20	07 52		
Hampton-in-Arden	d					06 33						07 02						07 29					07 55		
Berkswell	d					06 37						07 07						07 33					08 00		
Tile Hill	d					06 40						07 10						07 36					08 03		
Canley	d					06 43						07 13						07 39					08 06		
Coventry	a	00 37			06 23	06 45						07 17				07 24		07 41					08 09		
	d										06u50											07u50			
Rugby	d			06 40					06 50	07 01	07a30		07 43								07 50	08a30		08 42	
Long Buckby	d								07 16												08 16				
Northampton	a								07 41												08 41				
London Euston 15 ⊖	a			08 05						08 14			08 50											09 48	

For general notes see front of timetable
For details of catering facilities see Directory of Train Operators

A From Shrewsbury (Table 74)

Due to Engineering Operations, services from Saturday 13 September on this Table had not been confirmed at time of going to press. These services will be issued in a special Supplement as soon as exact timings have been confirmed

19 July to 6 September

Stafford → Wolverhampton → Birmingham → Coventry → Northampton

Network Diagram - see first page of Table 67

		LM	LM	XC		LM	VT	LM	AW	LM	XC	LM	VT	LM	VT	LM	LM		LM	XC	VT	XC	LM	LM	AW
				[1] ◇ A			[1] ◇		◇	[1] ◇ B	[1] ◇			[1]	[1] ◇					[R] [1]	[R] [1]	[R] [1] C			◇
				[catering]			[catering]		[trolley]		[catering]	[bus]	[bus]		[catering]					[catering]	[catering]	[catering]			[trolley]
Stafford	d									07 44	07 58											08 33			
Penkridge	d									07 50															
Wolverhampton [7]	a									08 03	08 12											08 47			
	d	07 25	07 31				07 48	07 52	07 59	08 07	08 13				08 18	08 22	08 25		08 31		08 43	08 49		08 52	08 59
Walsall	a	07 38															08 40								
Coseley	d							07 57		08 12									08 37					08 57	
Tipton	d							07 59								08 28								08 59	
Dudley Port	d							08 01								08 30								09 01	
Sandwell & Dudley	d							08 05							08 29	08 33								09 05	
Smethwick Galton Bdg L.L. [7]	d							08 07								08 36								09 07	
Smethwick Rolfe Street	d							08 09								08 38								09 09	
Birmingham New Street [12]	a		07 51				08 10	08 15	08 18	08 27	08 30				08 42	08 46			08 51		09 05	09 06		09 15	09 18
	d			08 03		08 09								08 36	08 44					09 03			09 09		
Adderley Park	d					08 14																	09 14		
Stechford	d					08 17								08 42									09 17		
Lea Hall	d					08 20								08 45									09 20		
Marston Green	d					08 22								08 48									09 22		
Birmingham International ✈	a			08 14		08 25								08 51						09 14			09 25		
	d			08 15		08 26							08 20	08 52						09 15			09 26		
Hampton-in-Arden	d					08 29								08 55									09 29		
Berkswell	d					08 33								09 00									09 33		
Tile Hill	d					08 36								09 03									09 36		
Canley	d					08 39								09 06									09 39		
Coventry	a			08 23		08 42								09 09						09 23			09 41		
	d												08u50												
Rugby	d											08 50	09a30		09 48										
Long Buckby	d											09 16													
Northampton	a											09 41													
London Euston [15] ⊖	a														10 57										

		LM	XC	LM	VT	LM	VT	LM		LM	LM	XC	XC	LM	VT	LM	AW	LM	XC	LM	VT		LM	VT	LM
		[1] ◇	[1] ◇			[1]	[1] ◇					[R] [1]	[R] [1] D		[1] ◇		◇	[1] ◇	[1] ◇				[1]	[1] ◇	
			[catering]	[bus]	[bus]		[catering]					[catering]	[catering]		[catering]		[trolley]		[catering]	[bus]	[bus]			[catering]	
Stafford	d	08 44	08 58									09 26						09 44	09 58						
Penkridge	d	08 50																09 50							
Wolverhampton [7]	a	09 03	09 11									09 41						10 03	10 12						
	d	09 07	09 13				09 18	09 22		09 25	09 31	09 41			09 49	09 52	09 59	10 07	10 13					10 18	10 22
Walsall	a									09 40															
Coseley	d	09 12									09 37					09 57		10 12							
Tipton	d							09 28								09 59									10 28
Dudley Port	d							09 30								10 01									10 30
Sandwell & Dudley	d						09 29	09 33								10 05								10 29	10 33
Smethwick Galton Bdg L.L. [7]	d							09 36								10 07									10 36
Smethwick Rolfe Street	d							09 38								10 09									10 38
Birmingham New Street [12]	a	09 27	09 30				09 42	09 45			09 51	09 58			10 11	10 15	10 18	10 27	10 30					10 42	10 45
	d					09 36	09 44						10 03	10 09									10 36	10 44	
Adderley Park	d													10 14											
Stechford	d					09 42								10 17									10 42		
Lea Hall	d					09 45								10 20									10 45		
Marston Green	d					09 48								10 22									10 48		
Birmingham International ✈	a					09 52							10 14	10 25									10 52		
	d				09 20	09 52							10 15	10 26							10 20		10 52		
Hampton-in-Arden	d					09 55								10 29									10 55		
Berkswell	d					10 00								10 33									11 00		
Tile Hill	d					10 03								10 36									11 03		
Canley	d					10 06								10 39									11 06		
Coventry	a					10 10							10 23	10 41									11 10		
	d				09u50																10u50				
Rugby	d			09 50	10a30		10 41													10 50	11a30			11 41	
Long Buckby	d			10 16																11 16					
Northampton	a			10 41																11 41					
London Euston [15] ⊖	a						11 48																	12 47	

For general notes see front of timetable
For details of catering facilities see Directory of Train Operators

A From Sheffield (Table 51)
B From Liverpool Lime Street (Table 91)
C To Newquay (Table 135)
D From Newcastle (Table 51)

Due to Engineering Operations, services from Saturday 13 September on this Table had not been confirmed at time of going to press. These services will be issued in a special Supplement as soon as exact timings have been confirmed

Table 68

Saturdays

Stafford → Wolverhampton → Birmingham → Coventry → Northampton

19 July to 6 September

Network Diagram - see first page of Table 67

		LM	LM	XC	LM	VT	LM	AW	LM	XC	LM	VT	LM	VT	LM	LM	LM	XC	XC	LM	VT	LM	AW	LM
				1 ◇ ☕		1 ◇ ☕		◇ 🛒	1 ◇	1 ◇ ☕	🚌	🚌	1	1 ◇ ☕				R 1 ☕	1 ◇ A ☕		R 1 ☕		◇ 🛒	1 ◇
Stafford	d			10 26					10 44	10 58								11 26						11 44
Penkridge	d								10 50															11 50
Wolverhampton 7	a			10 41					11 03	11 12								11 41						12 03
	d	10 25	10 31	10 41		10 49	10 52	10 59	11 07	11 13				11 18	11 22	11 25	11 31	11 41			11 49	11 52	11 59	12 07
Walsall	a	10 40														11 40								
Coseley	d		10 37				10 57		11 12								11 37					11 57		12 12
Tipton	d						10 59								11 28							11 59		
Dudley Port	d						11 01								11 30							12 01		
Sandwell & Dudley	d						11 05							11 29	11 33							12 05		
Smethwick Galton Bdg L.L. 7	d						11 07								11 36							12 07		
Smethwick Rolfe Street	d						11 09								11 38							12 09		
Birmingham New Street 12	a		10 51	10 58		11 11	11 15	11 18	11 27	11 30				11 42	11 45		11 51	11 58			12 11	12 15	12 18	12 27
	d			11 03	11 09								11 36	11 44					12 03	12 09				
Adderley Park	d				11 14															12 14				
Stechford	d				11 17								11 42							12 17				
Lea Hall	d				11 20								11 45							12 20				
Marston Green	d				11 22								11 48							12 22				
Birmingham International ✈	a			11 14	11 25								11 51						12 14	12 25				
	d			11 15	11 26							11 20	11 52						12 15	12 26				
Hampton-in-Arden	d				11 29								11 55							12 29				
Berkswell	d				11 33								12 00							12 33				
Tile Hill	d				11 36								12 03							12 36				
Canley	d				11 39								12 06							12 39				
Coventry	a			11 23	11 41								12 09						12 23	12 41				
	d											11u50												
Rugby	d										11 50	12a30		12 44										
Long Buckby	d										12 16													
Northampton	a										12 41													
London Euston 15 ⊖	a													13 59										

		XC	LM	VT	LM	VT	LM	LM	LM	XC	LM	VT	LM	AW	LM	XC	LM	VT	LM	VT	LM	LM	LM
		1 ◇ ☕	🚌	🚌	1	1 ◇ ☕				1 ◇ ☕		R 1 ☕		◇ 🛒	1 ◇	1 ◇ ☕	🚌	🚌	1	1 ◇ ☕			
Stafford	d	11 58								12 26					12 44	12 58							
Penkridge	d														12 50								
Wolverhampton 7	a	12 12								12 41					13 03	13 12							
	d	12 13				12 18	12 22	12 25	12 31	12 41		12 49	12 52	12 59	13 07	13 13				13 18	13 22	13 25	13 31
Walsall	a							12 40														13 40	
Coseley	d								12 37				12 57		13 12								13 37
Tipton	d						12 28						12 59								13 28		
Dudley Port	d						12 30						13 01								13 30		
Sandwell & Dudley	d					12 29	12 33						13 05							13 29	13 33		
Smethwick Galton Bdg L.L. 7	d						12 36						13 07								13 36		
Smethwick Rolfe Street	d						12 38						13 09								13 38		
Birmingham New Street 12	a	12 30				12 42	12 45		12 51	12 58		13 11	13 15	13 18	13 27	13 30				13 42	13 45		13 51
	d				12 36	12 44				13 03	13 09								13 36	13 44			
Adderley Park	d										13 14												
Stechford	d				12 42						13 17								13 42				
Lea Hall	d				12 45						13 20								13 45				
Marston Green	d				12 48						13 22								13 48				
Birmingham International ✈	a				12 51					13 14	13 25								13 52				
	d			12 20	12 52					13 15	13 26							13 20	13 52				
Hampton-in-Arden	d				12 55						13 29								13 55				
Berkswell	d				13 00						13 33								14 00				
Tile Hill	d				13 03						13 36								14 03				
Canley	d				13 06						13 39								14 06				
Coventry	a				13 09					13 23	13 41								14 10				
	d			12u50														13u50					
Rugby	d		12 50	13a30		13 41											13 50	14a30		14 44			
Long Buckby	d		13 16														14 16						
Northampton	a		13 41														14 41						
London Euston 15 ⊖	a					14 47														15 59			

For general notes see front of timetable
For details of catering facilities see Directory of Train Operators

A From Glasgow Central (Table 51)

Due to Engineering Operations, services from Saturday 13 September on this Table had not been confirmed at time of going to press. These services will be issued in a special Supplement as soon as exact timings have been confirmed

Stafford → Wolverhampton → Birmingham → Coventry → Northampton

Network Diagram - see first page of Table 67

		XC R 1 ☕	LM	VT R 1 ☕	LM	AW ◇ 🛒	LM 1 ◇		XC 1 ◇ ☕	LM 🚌	VT 🚌	LM 1	VT 1 ◇ ☕	LM	LM	LM	XC 1 ◇ ☕	LM	VT 1 ◇ ☕	LM		AW ◇ 🛒	LM 1 ◇	XC 1 ◇ ☕	LM 🚌
Stafford	d	13 26					13 44		13 58								14 26						14 44	14 58	
Penkridge	d						13 50																14 50		
Wolverhampton 7	a	13 40					14 03		14 12								14 41						15 03	15 12	
	d	13 41		13 49	13 52	13 59	14 07		14 13				14 18	14 22	14 25	14 31	14 41		14 49	14 52		14 59	15 07	15 13	
Walsall	a														14 40										
Coseley	d				13 57		14 12									14 37				14 57			15 12		
Tipton	d				13 59									14 28						14 59					
Dudley Port	d				14 01									14 30						15 01					
Sandwell & Dudley	d				14 05								14 29	14 33						15 05					
Smethwick Galton Bdg L.L. 7	d				14 07									14 36						15 07					
Smethwick Rolfe Street	d				14 09									14 38						15 09					
Birmingham New Street 12	a	13 58		14 11	14 15	14 18	14 27		14 30				14 42	14 45		14 51	14 58		15 11	15 15		15 18	15 27	15 30	
	d		14 09									14 36	14 44				15 03	15 09							
Adderley Park	d		14 14															15 14							
Stechford	d		14 17									14 42						15 17							
Lea Hall	d		14 20									14 45						15 20							
Marston Green	d		14 22									14 48						15 22							
Birmingham International ✈	a		14 25									14 51					15 14	15 25							
	d		14 26								14 20	14 52					15 15	15 26							
Hampton-in-Arden	d		14 29									14 55						15 29							
Berkswell	d		14 33									15 00						15 33							
Tile Hill	d		14 36									15 03						15 36							
Canley	d		14 39									15 06						15 39							
Coventry	a		14 41									15 09					15 23	15 41							
	d										14u50														
Rugby	d									14 50	15a30		15 41												15 50
Long Buckby	d									15 16															16 16
Northampton	a									15 41															16 41
London Euston 15	⊖ a												16 47												

		VT 🚌	LM 1	VT 1 ◇ ☕	LM	LM	LM	XC 1 ◇ ☕	XC 1 ◇ A ☕	LM	VT R 1 ☕		LM	AW ◇ 🛒	LM 1 ◇	XC 1 ◇ ☕	LM 🚌	VT 🚌	LM 1	VT 1 ◇ ☕	LM	LM	LM	XC 1 ◇ ☕	LM
Stafford	d							15 26							15 44	15 58								16 26	
Penkridge	d														15 50										
Wolverhampton 7	a							15 41							16 03	16 12								16 41	
	d			15 18	15 22	15 25	15 31	15 41			15 47		15 52	15 59	16 07	16 13				16 18	16 22	16 25	16 31	16 41	
Walsall	a					15 40																16 40			
Coseley	d						15 37						15 57		16 12								16 37		
Tipton	d				15 28								15 59								16 28				
Dudley Port	d				15 30								16 01								16 30				
Sandwell & Dudley	d			15 29	15 33								16 05							16 29	16 33				
Smethwick Galton Bdg L.L. 7	d				15 36								16 07								16 36				
Smethwick Rolfe Street	d				15 38								16 09								16 38				
Birmingham New Street 12	a			15 42	15 45		15 51	15 58			16 11		16 15	16 18	16 27	16 30				16 42	16 45		16 51	16 58	
	d		15 36	15 44					16 03	16 09									16 36	16 44				17 03	17 09
Adderley Park	d									16 14															17 14
Stechford	d		15 42							16 17									16 42						17 17
Lea Hall	d		15 45							16 20									16 45						17 20
Marston Green	d		15 48							16 22									16 48						17 22
Birmingham International ✈	a		15 51						16 14	16 25									16 51					17 14	17 25
	d	15 20	15 52						16 15	16 26								16 20	16 52					17 15	17 26
Hampton-in-Arden	d		15 55							16 29									16 55						17 29
Berkswell	d		16 00							16 33									17 00						17 33
Tile Hill	d		16 03							16 36									17 03						17 36
Canley	d		16 06							16 39									17 06						17 39
Coventry	a		16 09						16 23	16 41									17 09					17 23	17 41
	d	15u50																16u50							
Rugby	d	16a30		16 41													16 50	17a30		17 44					
Long Buckby	d																17 16								
Northampton	a																17 41								
London Euston 15	⊖ a			17 46																18 56					

For general notes see front of timetable
For details of catering facilities see
Directory of Train Operators

A From Aberdeen (Table 51)

Due to Engineering Operations, services from Saturday 13 September on this Table had not been confirmed at time of going to press. These services will be issued in a special Supplement as soon as exact timings have been confirmed

Saturdays

Stafford → Wolverhampton → Birmingham → Coventry → Northampton

19 July to 6 September

Network Diagram - see first page of Table 67

		VT		LM	AW	LM	XC	LM	VT	VT	LM	VT	LM	LM	LM		XC	XC	LM	VT	LM	AW	LM	XC	LM
		R 1			◇	1 ◇	1 ◇		1 ◇		1	1 ◇					1 ◇	1 ◇ A		1 ◇		◇	1 ◇	1 ◇	
		☕			🛒		☕	🚌	☕	🚌		☕					☕	☕		☕		🛒		☕	🚌
Stafford	d					16 44	16 58		17 12								17 26						17 44	17 58	
Penkridge	d					16 50																	17 50		
Wolverhampton 7	a					17 03	17 12										17 41						18 03	18 12	
	d	16 49		16 52	16 59	17 07	17 13					17 18	17 22	17 25	17 31		17 41			17 49	17 52	17 59	18 07	18 13	
Walsall	a													17 40											
Coseley	d			16 57		17 12									17 37						17 57		18 12		
Tipton	d			16 59									17 28								17 59				
Dudley Port	d			17 01									17 30								18 01				
Sandwell & Dudley	d			17 05								17 29	17 33								18 05				
Smethwick Galton Bdg L.L. 7	d			17 07									17 36								18 07				
Smethwick Rolfe Street	d			17 09									17 38								18 09				
Birmingham New Street 12	a	17 11		17 15	17 18	17 27	17 30					17 42	17 45		17 51		17 58			18 11	18 16	18 19	18 27	18 30	
	d										17 36	17 44						18 03	18 09						
Adderley Park	d																		18 14						
Stechford	d										17 42								18 17						
Lea Hall	d										17 45								18 20						
Marston Green	d										17 48								18 22						
Birmingham International ✈	a										17 52							18 14	18 25						
	d									17 20	17 52							18 15	18 26						
Hampton-in-Arden	d										17 55								18 29						
Berkswell	d										18 00								18 33						
Tile Hill	d										18 03								18 36						
Canley	d										18 06								18 39						
Coventry	a										18 10							18 23	18 41						
	d									17u50															
Rugby	d							17 50	17 51	18a30		18 41													18 50
Long Buckby	d							18 16																	19 16
Northampton	a							18 41																	19 41
London Euston 15 ⊖	a								19 00			19 47													

		VT	LM	VT	LM	LM		LM	XC	LM	VT	LM	AW	LM	XC	LM	VT	LM	VT		LM	LM	LM	XC	XC
			1	1 ◇					1 ◇		1 ◇		◇	1 ◇ B	1 ◇			1	1 ◇					1 ◇	1 ◇ A
		🚌		☕					☕		☕				☕	🚌	🚌		☕					☕	☕
Stafford	d								18 26					18 44	18 58									19 25	
Penkridge	d													18 50											
Wolverhampton 7	a								18 41					19 03	19 12									19 40	
	d			18 18	18 22	18 25		18 31	18 41		18 49	18 52	18 59	19 07	19 13				19 18		19 22	19 25	19 31	19 41	
Walsall	a					18 40																19 39			
Coseley	d							18 37				18 57		19 12									19 37		
Tipton	d				18 28							18 59									19 28				
Dudley Port	d				18 30							19 01									19 30				
Sandwell & Dudley	d			18 29	18 33							19 05							19 29		19 33				
Smethwick Galton Bdg L.L. 7	d				18 36							19 07									19 36				
Smethwick Rolfe Street	d				18 38							19 09									19 38				
Birmingham New Street 12	a			18 41	18 45			18 51	18 58		19 11	19 15	19 18	19 27	19 35				19 41		19 45		19 51	19 58	
	d		18 36	18 44					19 03	19 09								19 36	19 44						20 03
Adderley Park	d									19 14															
Stechford	d		18 42							19 17								19 42							
Lea Hall	d		18 45							19 20								19 45							
Marston Green	d		18 48							19 22								19 48							
Birmingham International ✈	a		18 52						19 14	19 25								19 51							20 14
	d	18 20	18 52						19 15	19 26							19 20	19 52							20 15
Hampton-in-Arden	d		18 55							19 29								19 55							
Berkswell	d		19 00							19 33								20 00							
Tile Hill	d		19 03							19 36								20 03							
Canley	d		19 06							19 39								20 06							
Coventry	a	18 45	19 10						19 23	19 41								20 09							20 23
	d	18u50															19u50								
Rugby	d	19a30		19 41												19 50	20a30		20 41						
Long Buckby	d															20 16									
Northampton	a															20 41									
London Euston 15 ⊖	a			21 26															22 31						

For general notes see front of timetable
For details of catering facilities see Directory of Train Operators

A From Edinburgh (Table 51)
B From Liverpool Lime Street (Table 91)

Due to Engineering Operations, services from Saturday 13 September on this Table had not been confirmed at time of going to press. These services will be issued in a special Supplement as soon as exact timings have been confirmed

Table 68

Saturdays

19 July to 6 September

Stafford → Wolverhampton → Birmingham → Coventry → Northampton

Network Diagram - see first page of Table 67

		LM	VT	LM	AW	LM	XC	LM	VT	LM		VT	LM	LM	XC	LM	VT	LM	AW	LM	LM	XC	LM		
			1 ◇		◇	1 ◇	1 ◇	🚌	🚌	1		1 ◇			1 ◇ A		1 ◇				1 ◇	1 ◇	🚌		
			☕		trolley		☕					☕			☕		☕								
Stafford	d					19 44	19 58								20 26						20 44	20 58			
Penkridge	d					19 50															20 50				
Wolverhampton 7	a					20 03	20 12								20 40						21 03	21 12			
	d		19 49	19 52	19 59	20 07	20 13					20 18	20 22	20 25	20 41		20 49	20 52	20 59	21 03	21 07	21 13			
Walsall	a													20 39						21 18					
Coseley	d			19 57									20 27					20 57							
Tipton	d			19 59									20 29					20 59							
Dudley Port	d			20 01									20 31					21 01							
Sandwell & Dudley	d			20 05								20 29	20 35					21 05							
Smethwick Galton Bdg L.L. 7	d			20 07									20 37					21 07							
Smethwick Rolfe Street	d			20 09									20 39					21 09							
Birmingham New Street 12	a		20 11	20 15	20 18	20 30	20 35					20 41	20 45		20 58		21 11	21 15	21 18		21 27	21 35			
	d	20 09								20 36		20 44			21 03	21 09									
Adderley Park	d	20 14														21 14									
Stechford	d	20 17								20 42						21 17									
Lea Hall	d	20 20								20 45						21 20									
Marston Green	d	20 22								20 48						21 22									
Birmingham International ✈	a	20 25								20 51					21 14	21 25									
	d	20 26							20 20	20 52					21 15	21 26									
Hampton-in-Arden	d	20 29								20 55						21 29									
Berkswell	d	20 33								21 00						21 33									
Tile Hill	d	20 36								21 03						21 36									
Canley	d	20 39								21 06						21 39									
Coventry	a	20 41								21 09					21 23	21 41									
	d								20u50														21 50		
Rugby	d							20 50	21a30			21 44											22 16		
Long Buckby	d							21 16															22 41		
Northampton	a							21 41																	
London Euston 15	⊖ a											23 31													

		VT	LM	VT	LM	LM	LM	LM	VT	LM	AW	VT	XC		LM	LM	LM	VT	LM	LM	LM	AW	LM		
		🚌	1	1 ◇				🚌	🚌		◇	1 ◇	1 ◇			1	1 ◇	1 ◇		B			🚌		
				☕							trolley	☕						☕							
Stafford	d											21 51	21 58				22 25	22 33							
Penkridge	d																22 31								
Wolverhampton 7	a											22 06	22 12				22 43	22 48							
	d			21 18	21 22	21 31	21 52				22 03	22 09	22 13		22 22		22 43	22 49	22 52	22 55		22 59			
Walsall	a																			23 12					
Coseley	d				21 27		21 57								22 27				22 57						
Tipton	d				21 29		21 59								22 29				22 59						
Dudley Port	d				21 31		22 01								22 31				23 01						
Sandwell & Dudley	d			21 29	21 35		22 05								22 35				23 05						
Smethwick Galton Bdg L.L. 7	d				21 37		22 07								22 37				23 07						
Smethwick Rolfe Street	d				21 39		22 09								22 39				23 09						
Birmingham New Street 12	a			21 41	21 45	21 53	22 15				22 18	22 30	22 35		22 45		23 04	23 10	23 15			23 18			
	d		21 36	21 44						22 18						22 48					23 17				
Adderley Park	d									22 23											23 22				
Stechford	d		21 42							22 26						22 55					23 25				
Lea Hall	d		21 45							22 29						22 58					23 28				
Marston Green	d		21 48							22 31						23 01					23 30				
Birmingham International ✈	a		21 52							22 34						23 04					23 33				
	d	21 20	21 52						22 20	22 35						23 04					23 34				
Hampton-in-Arden	d		21 55							22 38						23 07					23 37				
Berkswell	d		22 00							22 42						23 12					23 41				
Tile Hill	d		22 03							22 45						23 15					23 44				
Canley	d		22 06							22 48						23 19					23 47				
Coventry	a		22 10							22 50						23 22					23 49				
	d	21u45							22u45														23 35		
Rugby	d	22a25		22 44				22 50	23a25														00 01		
Long Buckby	d							23 16															00 26		
Northampton	a							23 41																	
London Euston 15	⊖ a			00 26																					

For general notes see front of timetable
For details of catering facilities see Directory of Train Operators

A ☕ to Birmingham New Street
B From Shrewsbury (Table 74)

Due to Engineering Operations, services from Saturday 13 September on this Table had not been confirmed at time of going to press. These services will be issued in a special Supplement as soon as exact timings have been confirmed

Table 68

Stafford → Wolverhampton → Birmingham → Coventry → Northampton

Sundays

until 13 July

Network Diagram - see first page of Table 67

		LM	XC	VT	LM	VT	VT	VT	XC	LM	VT	LM	LM	LM		VT	VT	LM	VT	XC	LM	AW	XC	LM	VT
			🚌	🚌	🚌	🚌	🚌	1 ◇ ☕	🚌	🚌	🚌		🚌	🚌		1 ◇ ☕	🚌	🚌	🚌	1 ◇ ☕			🚌	🚌	🚌
Stafford	d																			09 15					
Penkridge	d																								
Wolverhampton 7	a																			09 29					
	d					07 45		08 26			08 30	08 54				09 10	09 30			09 31	09 41	09 45			
Walsall	a											09 15									09 56				
Coseley	d																								
Tipton	d																								
Dudley Port	d																								
Sandwell & Dudley	d					08 20					09 05						10 05 →								← 10 05
Smethwick Galton Bdg L.L. 7	d																								
Smethwick Rolfe Street	d																								
Birmingham New Street 12	a					08 45		08 55			09 30					09 41				09 58		10 10			10 30
	d	00 10			08 30		08 55	08 59		09 30						09 45			09 55					10 30	
Adderley Park	d				08 41					09 41														10 41	
Stechford	d				08 51					09 51														10 51	
Lea Hall	d				09 01					10 01														11 01	
Marston Green	d	00 18			09 11					10 11														11 11	
Birmingham International ✈	a	00 21			09 15		09 20			10 15									10 20					11 15	
	d	00 22	08 30	08 35	09 16		09 20		09 30	10 16									10 20				10 30	11 16	
Hampton-in-Arden	d				09 26					10 26														11 26	
Berkswell	d				09 36 →					10 36 →			← 09 36											11 36 →	
Tile Hill	d												09 46												
Canley	d												09 55												
Coventry	a	00 37	08 55	09 00			09 45		09 55				10 03						10 45				10 55		
	d			09 05			09 50												10 50						
Rugby	d			09a45			10a30	09 58						10 05		10 41		10 55	11a30						
Long Buckby	d													10 31				11 21							
Northampton	a													10 56				11 46							
London Euston 15 ⊖	a							11 25								12 22									

		VT	LM	LM	VT	LM		VT	XC	LM	VT	AW	XC	LM	VT	AW	VT	LM	VT	LM		VT	XC	LM	VT
		1 ◇ ☕	1 ◇	🚌	🚌	🚌		🚌	1 ◇ ☕		1 ◇ ☕		🚌	🚌	🚌	◇	1 ◇ ☕	🚌	🚌	🚌		🚌	1 ◇ ☕		1 ◇ ☕
Stafford	d		10 01						10 15		10 32												11 09		
Penkridge	d		10 07																						
Wolverhampton 7	a		10 18						10 29		10 48												11 29		
	d	10 12	10 19		10 30				10 31	10 41	10 49	10 54				11 06	11 12		11 30				11 31	11 41	11 49
Walsall	a									10 56														11 56	
Coseley	d																								
Tipton	d																								
Dudley Port	d																								
Sandwell & Dudley	d				11 05 →										← 11 05				12 05 →						
Smethwick Galton Bdg L.L. 7	d																								
Smethwick Rolfe Street	d																								
Birmingham New Street 12	a	10 41	10 42						10 58		11 17	11 20			11 30	11 32	11 41						11 58		12 17
	d	10 45						10 55						11 30			11 45					11 55			
Adderley Park	d													11 41											
Stechford	d													11 51											
Lea Hall	d													12 01											
Marston Green	d													12 11											
Birmingham International ✈	a							11 20						12 15								12 20			
	d							11 20					11 30	12 16								12 20			
Hampton-in-Arden	d													12 26											
Berkswell	d			← 10 36										12 36 →				← 11 36							
Tile Hill	d			10 46														11 46							
Canley	d			10 55														11 55							
Coventry	a			11 03				11 45					11 55					12 03				12 45			
	d							11 50														12 50			
Rugby	d	11 41				11 55		12a30									12 41			12 55		13a30			
Long Buckby	d					12 21														13 21					
Northampton	a					12 46														13 46					
London Euston 15 ⊖	a	13 22															13 57								

For general notes see front of timetable
For details of catering facilities see Directory of Train Operators

Table 68

Sundays

until 13 July

Stafford → Wolverhampton → Birmingham → Coventry → Northampton

Network Diagram - see first page of Table 67

		AW	XC	LM	VT	VT	LM	VT	LM	VT	XC	LM		VT	LM	XC	LM	VT	AW	VT	LM	VT	LM	VT	XC
			🚌	🚌	🚌	[1] ◇ ☕	🚌	🚌	🚌	🚌	[1] ◇ ☕			[1] ◇ ☕	[1] ◇	🚌	🚌	🚌	◇	[1] ◇ ☕	🚌	🚌	🚌	🚌	[R] [1] ☕
Stafford	d										12 09				12 43										13 08
Penkridge	d														12 48										
Wolverhampton [7]	a										12 29				12 59										13 29
	d	11 54				12 12		12 30			12 31	12 41		12 49	13 00				13 06	13 12		13 30			13 31
Walsall	a											12 56													
Coseley	d																								
Tipton	d																								
Dudley Port	d				←													←							
Sandwell & Dudley	d				12 05			13 05 →										13 05				14 05 →			
Smethwick Galton Bdg L.L. [7]	d																								
Smethwick Rolfe Street	d																								
Birmingham New Street [12]	a	12 20			12 30	12 41					12 58			13 17	13 27			13 30	13 39	13 41					13 58
	d			12 30		12 45				12 55							13 30			13 45				13 55	
Adderley Park	d			12 41													13 41								
Stechford	d			12 51													13 51								
Lea Hall	d			13 01													14 01								
Marston Green	d			13 11													14 11								
Birmingham International ✈	a			13 15						13 20							14 15							14 20	
	d		12 30	13 16						13 20						13 30	14 16							14 20	
Hampton-in-Arden	d			13 26			←										14 26				←				
Berkswell	d			13 36 →			12 36										14 36 →				13 36				
Tile Hill	d						12 46														13 46				
Canley	d						12 55														13 55				
Coventry	a		12 55				13 03			13 45						13 55					14 03			14 45	
	d									13 50														14 50	
Rugby	d					13 41			13 55	14a30										14 45			14 55	15a30	
Long Buckby	d								14 21														15 21		
Northampton	a								14 46														15 46		
London Euston [15] ⊖	a					14 57														16 11					

		LM	VT	XC		LM	VT	VT	LM	VT	LM	VT	XC	LM	LM	XC	LM	VT		AW	VT	LM	VT	LM	VT
			[1] ◇ ☕	🚌		🚌	🚌	[1] ◇ ☕	🚌	🚌	🚌	🚌	[R] [1] ☕		[1] ◇	🚌	🚌	🚌			[1] ◇ ☕	🚌	🚌	🚌	🚌
Stafford	d												14 14		14 31										
Penkridge	d														14 37										
Wolverhampton [7]	a												14 29		14 49										
	d	13 41	13 49					14 12		14 30			14 31	14 41	14 49					15 02	15 12		15 30		
Walsall	a	13 56												14 56											
Coseley	d																								
Tipton	d																								
Dudley Port	d						←											←							
Sandwell & Dudley	d						14 05			15 05 →								15 05					16 05 →		
Smethwick Galton Bdg L.L. [7]	d																								
Smethwick Rolfe Street	d																								
Birmingham New Street [12]	a		14 17				14 30	14 41					14 58		15 13			15 30		15 32	15 41				
	d					14 30		14 45				14 55					15 30				15 45				15 55
Adderley Park	d					14 41											15 41								
Stechford	d					14 51											15 51								
Lea Hall	d					15 01											16 01								
Marston Green	d					15 11											16 11								
Birmingham International ✈	a					15 15						15 20					16 15								16 20
	d			14 30		15 16						15 20				15 30	16 16								16 20
Hampton-in-Arden	d					15 26			←								16 26					←			
Berkswell	d					15 36 →			14 36								16 36 →					15 36			
Tile Hill	d								14 46													15 46			
Canley	d								14 55													15 55			
Coventry	a			14 55					15 03			15 45				15 55						16 03			16 45
	d											15 50													16 50
Rugby	d							15 44			15 55	16a30									16 42			16 55	17a30
Long Buckby	d										16 21													17 21	
Northampton	a										16 46													17 46	
London Euston [15] ⊖	a							17 03													18 10				

For general notes see front of timetable
For details of catering facilities see
Directory of Train Operators

Table 68

Sundays

until 13 July

Stafford → Wolverhampton → Birmingham → Coventry → Northampton

Network Diagram - see first page of Table 67

		XC	LM	VT	XC	LM	VT	AW	VT	LM		VT	LM	VT	XC	LM	VT	LM	XC	LM	VT	AW	VT	LM	VT
		R 1 ☕		R 1 ☕	🚌	🚌	🚌	◇	1 ◇ ☕	🚌		🚌	🚌	🚌	R 1 ☕		R 1 ☕	1 ◇	🚌	🚌	🚌		1 ◇ ☕	🚌	🚌
Stafford	d	15 14													16 08			16 36							
Penkridge	d																	16 42							
Wolverhampton 7	a	15 29													16 29			16 54							
	d	15 31	15 41	15 49				16 03	16 12			16 30			16 31	16 41	16 49	16 54				17 07	17 12		17 30
Walsall	a		15 56													16 56									
Coseley	d																								
Tipton	d																								
Dudley Port	d						←														←				
Sandwell & Dudley	d						16 05					17 05									17 05				18 05
Smethwick Galton Bdg L.L. 7	d											→													→
Smethwick Rolfe Street	d																								
Birmingham New Street 12	a	15 58		16 17			16 30	16 32	16 41						16 58		17 17	17 20			17 30	17 32	17 41		
	d					16 30			16 45					16 55						17 30			17 45		
Adderley Park	d					16 41														17 41					
Stechford	d					16 51														17 51					
Lea Hall	d					17 01														18 01					
Marston Green	d					17 11														18 11					
Birmingham International ✈	a					17 15								17 20						18 15					
	d				16 30	17 16								17 20					17 30	18 16					
Hampton-in-Arden	d					17 26				←										18 26				←	
Berkswell	d					17 36				16 36										18 36				17 36	
Tile Hill	d					→				16 46										→				17 46	
Canley	d									16 55														17 55	
Coventry	a				16 55					17 03				17 45					17 55					18 03	
	d													17 50											
Rugby	d								17 47				17 55	18a30									18 45		
Long Buckby	d												18 21												
Northampton	a												18 46												
London Euston 15	⊖ a								19 23														20 11		

		LM		VT	XC	LM	VT	XC	LM	VT	VT	AW	LM	VT	LM	VT		XC	LM	LM	VT	XC	LM	VT	AW
		🚌		🚌	R 1 ☕		R 1 ☕	🚌	🚌	🚌	1 ◇ ☕	◇	🚌	🚌	🚌	🚌		R 1 ☕		1 ◇	R 1 ☕	🚌	🚌	🚌	
Stafford	d				17 09													18 15		18 30					
Penkridge	d																			18 35					
Wolverhampton 7	a				17 29													18 29		18 48					
	d				17 31	17 41	17 49				18 10	18 16		18 30				18 31	18 41	18 48	18 52				19 07
Walsall	a					17 56													18 56						
Coseley	d																								
Tipton	d																								
Dudley Port	d									←														←	
Sandwell & Dudley	d									18 05				19 05										19 05	
Smethwick Galton Bdg L.L. 7	d													→											
Smethwick Rolfe Street	d																								
Birmingham New Street 12	a				17 58		18 17			18 30	18 41	18 41						18 58		19 11	19 20			19 30	19 33
	d			17 55					18 30		18 45					18 55							19 30		
Adderley Park	d								18 41														19 41		
Stechford	d								18 51														19 51		
Lea Hall	d								19 01														20 01		
Marston Green	d								19 11														20 11		
Birmingham International ✈	a			18 20					19 15							19 20							20 15		
	d			18 20				18 30	19 16							19 20						19 30	20 16		
Hampton-in-Arden	d								19 26				←										20 26		
Berkswell	d								19 36				18 36										20 36		
Tile Hill	d								→				18 46										→		
Canley	d												18 55												
Coventry	a			18 45				18 55					19 03			19 45						19 55			
	d			18 50												19 50									
Rugby	d	18 55		19a30							19 42				19 55	20a30									
Long Buckby	d	19 21													20 21										
Northampton	a	19 46													20 46										
London Euston 15	⊖ a										21 07														

For general notes see front of timetable
For details of catering facilities see Directory of Train Operators

Table 68

Sundays

until 13 July

Stafford → Wolverhampton → Birmingham → Coventry → Northampton

Network Diagram - see first page of Table 67

		VT	LM	VT	LM	VT	XC	LM		VT	VT	XC	LM	VT	AW	VT	LM	VT	LM	VT	XC	LM		LM	VT
		1 ◇ ☕	🚌	🚌	🚌	🚌	R 1 ☕			R 1 ☕	1 ◇ ☕	🚌	🚌	🚌	◇	1 ◇ ☕	🚌	🚌	🚌	🚌	1 ◇ ☕			1 ◇	1 ◇ ☕
Stafford	d						19 15														20 13			20 31	
Penkridge	d																								
Wolverhampton 7	a						19 29									←					20 29			20 46	
	d	19 12		19 30			19 31	19 41		19 49	20 04 →				20 14	20 04		20 30			20 31	20 41		20 46	20 52
Walsall	a							19 56														20 56			
Coseley	d																								
Tipton	d																								
Dudley Port	d													←											
Sandwell & Dudley	d			20 05 →										20 05				21 05 →							
Smethwick Galton Bdg L.L. 7	d																								
Smethwick Rolfe Street	d																								
Birmingham New Street 12	a	19 41					19 58			20 17				20 30	20 39	20 41					20 58			21 10	21 21
	d	19 45				19 55							20 30			20 45				20 55					
Adderley Park	d												20 41												
Stechford	d												20 51												
Lea Hall	d												21 01												
Marston Green	d												21 11												
Birmingham International ✈	a					20 20							21 15							21 20					
	d					20 20						20 30	21 16							21 20					
Hampton-in-Arden	d		←										21 26				←								
Berkswell	d		19 36										21 36 →				20 36								
Tile Hill	d		19 46														20 46								
Canley	d		19 55														20 55								
Coventry	a		20 03			20 45						20 55					21 03			21 45					
	d					20 50														21 50					
Rugby	d	20 41			20 55	21a30										21 41			21 55	22a30					
Long Buckby	d				21 21														22 21						
Northampton	a				21 46														22 46						
London Euston 15	⊖ a	22 04														23 05									

		LM	VT	AW	VT	LM	LM	LM	VT	VT	XC	LM	AW	XC		LM	LM	VT	VT	LM	XC	LM	LM		
		🚌	🚌	◇	1 ◇ ☕	🚌		🚌	🚌	1 ◇ ☕	1 ◇	🚌	◇	1 ◇		🚌		🚌	1 ◇ ☕	🚌	1 ◇	🚌	1 ◇		
Stafford	d									21 33	21 53								22 40		22 53		22 59		
Penkridge	d																						23 04		
Wolverhampton 7	a									21 47	22 09			←					22 54		23 09		23 19		
	d			21 05	21 12		21 41			21 49	22 09 →		22 14	22 09			22 41		22 55		23 09		23 20		
Walsall	a						21 56										22 56								
Coseley	d																								
Tipton	d																								
Dudley Port	d		←																						
Sandwell & Dudley	d		21 05																						
Smethwick Galton Bdg L.L. 7	d																								
Smethwick Rolfe Street	d																								
Birmingham New Street 12	a		21 30	21 32	21 41					22 17			22 40	22 41					23 23		23 42		23 53		
	d	21 30			21 45				21 55			22 30						22 55							
Adderley Park	d	21 41										22 41													
Stechford	d	21 51										22 51													
Lea Hall	d	22 01										23 01													
Marston Green	d	22 11										23 11													
Birmingham International ✈	a	22 15							22 20			23 15						23 20							
	d	22 16							22 20			23 16						23 20							
Hampton-in-Arden	d	22 26				←						23 26				←						←			
Berkswell	d	22 36 →				21 36						23 36 →				22 36						23 36			
Tile Hill	d					21 46										22 46						23 46			
Canley	d					21 55										22 55						23 55			
Coventry	a					22 03			22 45							23 03		23 45				00 03			
	d								22 45																
Rugby	d				22 40			22 55	23a25											23 30					
Long Buckby	d							23 21												23 56					
Northampton	a							23 46												00 21					
London Euston 15	⊖ a				00 25																				

For general notes see front of timetable
For details of catering facilities see Directory of Train Operators

Table 68

Sundays

Stafford → Wolverhampton → Birmingham → Coventry → Northampton

20 July to 7 September

Network Diagram - see first page of Table 67

		LM	LM	XC	VT	LM	VT	VT	LM	LM	XC	LM	LM	LM	VT	LM	LM	VT	XC	AW	LM	XC	LM	XC	LM
								1 ◇							1 ◇				1 ◇					1 ◇	
		🚌		🚌	🚌	🚌	🚌			🚌	🚌	🚌	🚌	🚌		🚌	🚌	🚌				🚌	🚌		🚌
								☕							☕				☕					☕	
Stafford	d																		09 26					09 53	
Penkridge	d																								
Wolverhampton 7	a																		09 41					10 09	
	d							08 33	08 52	09 01					09 18	09 40			09 41	09 47	09 52			10 09	
Walsall	a									09 21						10 00									
Coseley	d								08 57												09 57				
Tipton	d								08 59												09 59				
Dudley Port	d								09 01												10 01				
Sandwell & Dudley	d							08 44	09 05						09 29						10 05				
Smethwick Galton Bdg L.L. 7	d								09 07												10 07				
Smethwick Rolfe Street	d								09 09												10 09				
Birmingham New Street 12	a							08 55	09 16						09 41				09 58	10 04	10 16			10 31	
	d		00 10			08 30	08 55	08 59					09 30		09 45			09 55					10 30		
Adderley Park	d					08 41							09 41										10 41		
Stechford	d					08 51							09 51										10 51		
Lea Hall	d					09 01							10 01										11 01		
Marston Green	d		00 18			09 11							10 11										11 11		
Birmingham International ✈	a		00 21			09 15	09 20						10 15					10 20					11 15		
	d		00 22	08 30	08 35	09 16	09 20				09 30		10 16					10 20				10 30	11 16		
Hampton-in-Arden	d					09 26						←	10 26										11 26		←
Berkswell	d					09 36 →						09 36	10 36 →										11 36 →		10 36
Tile Hill	d											09 46													10 46
Canley	d											09 55													10 55
Coventry	a		00 37	08 55	09 00		09 45				09 55	10 03						10 45				10 55			11 03
	d				09 05		09 50											10 50							
Rugby	d	23p35			09a45		10a30	09 55						10 05	10 41		10 55	11a30							
Long Buckby	d	00 01												10 31			11 21								
Northampton	a	00 26												10 56			11 46								
London Euston 15 ⊖	a							11 31							12 14										

		VT	LM	LM	LM	VT	XC	AW	LM	VT	AW	VT	XC	LM	XC		LM	VT	LM	LM	VT	XC	LM	AW	VT
		1 ◇	1 ◇				1 ◇			1 ◇	◇	1 ◇			1 ◇			1 ◇				1 ◇			1 ◇
				🚌	🚌	🚌							🚌	🚌			🚌			🚌	🚌		🚌		
		☕					☕			☕		☕			☕			☕				☕			☕
Stafford	d		10 10				10 26			10 46					10 53							11 21			
Penkridge	d		10 15																						
Wolverhampton 7	a		10 27				10 41			11 01		←			11 09							11 36			
	d	10 18	10 27	10 40			10 41	10 49	10 52	11 02 →	11 07	11 02			11 09			11 18	11 22			11 36	11 40	11 55	12 01
Walsall	a			11 00																			12 00		
Coseley	d								10 57										11 27						
Tipton	d								10 59										11 29						
Dudley Port	d								11 01										11 31						
Sandwell & Dudley	d	10 29							11 05									11 29	11 35						
Smethwick Galton Bdg L.L. 7	d								11 07										11 37						
Smethwick Rolfe Street	d								11 09										11 39						
Birmingham New Street 12	a	10 40	10 43				10 58	11 05	11 16		11 22	11 24			11 28			11 40	11 46			11 58		12 11	12 17
	d	10 45				10 55								11 30				11 45			11 55				
Adderley Park	d													11 41											
Stechford	d													11 51											
Lea Hall	d													12 01											
Marston Green	d													12 11											
Birmingham International ✈	a					11 20								12 15							12 20				
	d					11 20							11 30	12 16							12 20				
Hampton-in-Arden	d													12 26			←								
Berkswell	d													12 36 →			11 36								
Tile Hill	d																11 46								
Canley	d																11 55								
Coventry	a					11 45							11 55				12 03				12 45				
	d					11 50															12 50				
Rugby	d	11 45			11 55	12a30												12 45		12 55	13a30				
Long Buckby	d				12 21															13 21					
Northampton	a				12 46															13 46					
London Euston 15 ⊖	a	13 17																14 13							

For general notes see front of timetable
For details of catering facilities see Directory of Train Operators

Due to Engineering Operations, services from Sunday 14 September on this Table had not been confirmed at time of going to press. These services will be issued in a special Supplement as soon as exact timings have been confirmed

Table 68

Sundays

20 July to 7 September

Stafford → Wolverhampton → Birmingham → Coventry → Northampton

Network Diagram - see first page of Table 67

		XC	LM	XC		VT	LM	LM	LM	LM	VT	XC	LM	AW	XC	LM	XC	LM	VT	LM	LM	VT	VT	LM	XC
		🚌	🚌	1 ◇ ☕		1 ◇ ☕	🚌		🚌	🚌	🚌	1 ◇ ☕	1 ◇	◇	🚌	🚌	1 ◇ ☕	🚌	1 ◇ ☕		🚌	🚌	1 ◇ ☕	🚌	R 1 ☕
Stafford	d			11 53								12 26	12 43				12 53								13 24
Penkridge	d												12 49												
Wolverhampton 7	a			12 09								12 41	13 00				13 09								13 41
	d			12 09		12 18		12 22	12 40			12 41	13 01	13 06			13 09		13 18	13 22			13 26	13 40	13 41
Walsall	a								13 00															14 00	
Coseley	d							12 27												13 27					
Tipton	d							12 29												13 29					
Dudley Port	d							12 31												13 31					
Sandwell & Dudley	d					12 29		12 35											13 29	13 35					
Smethwick Galton Bdg L.L. 7	d							12 37												13 37					
Smethwick Rolfe Street	d							12 39												13 39					
Birmingham New Street 12	a			12 31		12 40		12 46				12 58	13 20	13 23			13 31		13 40	13 46			13 55		13 58
	d		12 30			12 45					12 55					13 30			13 45			13 55			
Adderley Park	d		12 41													13 41									
Stechford	d		12 51													13 51									
Lea Hall	d		13 01													14 01									
Marston Green	d		13 11													14 11									
Birmingham International ✈	a		13 15								13 20					14 15						14 20			
	d	12 30	13 16								13 20				13 30	14 16						14 20			
Hampton-in-Arden	d		13 26				←									14 26		←							
Berkswell	d		13 36				12 36									14 36		13 36							
Tile Hill	d		→				12 46									→		13 46							
Canley	d						12 55											13 55							
Coventry	a	12 55					13 03				13 45				13 55			14 03				14 45			
	d										13 50											14 50			
Rugby	d					13 41				13 55	14a30								14 46		14 55	15a30			
Long Buckby	d									14 21											15 21				
Northampton	a									14 46											15 46				
London Euston 15 ⊖	a					15 12													16 13						

			VT	XC	LM	XC		LM	VT	LM	LM	LM	VT	XC	LM	AW	XC	LM	XC		LM	VT	LM	LM	LM
			1 ◇ ☕	🚌	🚌	1 ◇ ☕		🚌	1 ◇ ☕		🚌	🚌	🚌	R 1 ☕	1 ◇		🚌	🚌	1 ◇ ☕		🚌	1 ◇ ☕		🚌	🚌
Stafford	d					13 53								14 26	14 36				14 53						
Penkridge	d														14 42										
Wolverhampton 7	a					14 09								14 40	14 54				15 09						
	d		14 02			14 09			14 18	14 22	14 40			14 41	14 54	15 02			15 09			15 18	15 22	15 40	
Walsall	a										15 00													16 00	
Coseley	d									14 27													15 27		
Tipton	d									14 29													15 29		
Dudley Port	d									14 31													15 31		
Sandwell & Dudley	d								14 29	14 35												15 29	15 35		
Smethwick Galton Bdg L.L. 7	d									14 37													15 37		
Smethwick Rolfe Street	d									14 39													15 39		
Birmingham New Street 12	a		14 24			14 31			14 40	14 46				14 58	15 12	15 18			15 31			15 40	15 46		
	d				14 30				14 45				14 55					15 30				15 45			
Adderley Park	d				14 41													15 41							
Stechford	d				14 51													15 51							
Lea Hall	d				15 01													16 01							
Marston Green	d				15 11													16 11							
Birmingham International ✈	a				15 15								15 20					16 15							
	d			14 30	15 16								15 20				15 30	16 16							
Hampton-in-Arden	d				15 26			←										16 26			←				
Berkswell	d				15 36			14 36										16 36			15 36				
Tile Hill	d				→			14 46										→			15 46				
Canley	d							14 55													15 55				
Coventry	a			14 55				15 03					15 45				15 55				16 03				
	d												15 50												
Rugby	d								15 46			15 55	16a30									16 45			16 55
Long Buckby	d											16 21													17 21
Northampton	a											16 46													17 46
London Euston 15 ⊖	a								17 13													18 13			

For general notes see front of timetable
For details of catering facilities see Directory of Train Operators

Due to Engineering Operations, services from Sunday 14 September on this Table had not been confirmed at time of going to press. These services will be issued in a special Supplement as soon as exact timings have been confirmed

Sundays

Stafford → Wolverhampton → Birmingham → Coventry → Northampton

20 July to 7 September

Network Diagram - see first page of Table 67

	VT	XC	AW	VT	XC	LM	XC		LM	VT	LM	LM	LM	VT	XC	LM	VT	AW	XC	LM	XC		VT	LM
	🚌	R 1 ☕	◇	R 1 ☕	🚌	🚌	1 ◇ ☕		🚌	1 ◇ ☕		🚌	🚌	🚌	R 1 ☕	1 ◇	R 1 ☕		🚌	🚌	1 ◇ ☕		1 ◇ ☕	🚌
Stafford d		15 26					15 53								16 26	16 36					16 53			
Penkridge d																16 41								
Wolverhampton 7 a		15 41					16 09								16 41	16 53					17 09			
d		15 41	16 03	16 07			16 09			16 18	16 22	16 40			16 41	16 54	17 02	17 07			17 09		17 18	
Walsall a												17 00												
Coseley d											16 27													
Tipton d											16 29													
Dudley Port d											16 31													
Sandwell & Dudley d										16 29	16 35												17 29	
Smethwick Galton Bdg L.L. 7 d											16 37													
Smethwick Rolfe Street d											16 39													
Birmingham New Street 12 a		15 58	16 20	16 28			16 31			16 40	16 46				16 58	17 10	17 23	17 23			17 31		17 40	
d	15 55					16 30				16 45				16 55						17 30			17 45	
Adderley Park d						16 41														17 41				
Stechford d						16 51														17 51				
Lea Hall d						17 01														18 01				
Marston Green d						17 11														18 11				
Birmingham International ✈ a	16 20					17 15								17 20						18 15				
d	16 20				16 30	17 16								17 20					17 30	18 16				
Hampton-in-Arden d						17 26			←											18 26				←
Berkswell d						17 36 →			16 36											18 36 →				17 36
Tile Hill d									16 46															17 46
Canley d									16 55															17 55
Coventry a	16 45				16 55				17 03					17 45					17 55					18 03
d	16 50													17 50										
Rugby d	17a30									17 45			17 55	18a30									18 41	
Long Buckby d													18 21											
Northampton a													18 46											
London Euston 15 ⊖ a										19 13													20 11	

	LM	LM	LM	VT	XC	VT	XC	LM	XC	AW	LM	VT	LM	LM	LM	VT	XC		LM	AW	XC	LM	XC	
		🚌	🚌	🚌	R 1 ☕	R 1 ☕	🚌	🚌	1 ◇ ☕	◇	🚌	1 ◇ ☕		🚌	🚌	🚌	R 1 ☕		1 ◇		🚌	🚌	1 ◇ ☕	
Stafford d					17 26				17 53								18 22		18 36				18 53	
Penkridge d																			18 41					
Wolverhampton 7 a					17 41				18 09								18 41		18 53				19 09	
d	17 22	17 40			17 41	18 02			18 09	18 15		18 19	18 22	18 40			18 41		18 54	19 08			19 09	
Walsall a		18 00												19 00										
Coseley d	17 27												18 27											
Tipton d	17 29												18 29											
Dudley Port d	17 31												18 31											
Sandwell & Dudley d	17 35											18 31	18 35											
Smethwick Galton Bdg L.L. 7 d	17 37												18 37											
Smethwick Rolfe Street d	17 39												18 39											
Birmingham New Street 12 a	17 46				17 58	18 23			18 31	18 32		18 41	18 46				18 58		19 10	19 25			19 34	
d				17 55				18 30				18 45				18 55						19 30		
Adderley Park d								18 41														19 41		
Stechford d								18 51														19 51		
Lea Hall d								19 01														20 01		
Marston Green d								19 11														20 11		
Birmingham International ✈ a				18 20				19 15								19 20						20 15		
d				18 20			18 30	19 16								19 20					19 30	20 16		
Hampton-in-Arden d								19 26			←											20 26		
Berkswell d								19 36 →			18 36											20 36 →		
Tile Hill d											18 46													
Canley d											18 55													
Coventry a				18 45			18 55				19 03					19 45					19 55			
d				18 50												19 50								
Rugby d			18 55	19a30								19 43			19 55	20a30								
Long Buckby d			19 21												20 21									
Northampton a			19 46												20 46									
London Euston 15 ⊖ a												21 14												

For general notes see front of timetable
For details of catering facilities see Directory of Train Operators

Due to Engineering Operations, services from Sunday 14 September on this Table had not been confirmed at time of going to press. These services will be issued in a special Supplement as soon as exact timings have been confirmed

Table 68

Sundays

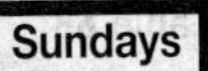

20 July to 7 September

Stafford → Wolverhampton → Birmingham → Coventry → Northampton

Network Diagram - see first page of Table 67

	VT	LM	LM	LM	LM	VT	XC	VT	XC	VT	XC	LM	AW	VT	LM	LM	LM	LM	VT	XC	LM	VT	AW	VT
	1 ◇ ☕	🚌		🚌	🚌	🚌	R 1 ☕	R 1 ☕	1 ◇ ☕	1 ◇ ☕	🚌	🚌	◇	1 ◇ ☕	🚌		🚌	🚌	🚌	1 ◇ ☕	1 ◇	1 ◇ ☕	◇	1 ◇ ☕
Stafford d							19 26		19 53	20 13										20 26	20 36			
Penkridge d																								
Wolverhampton 7 a							19 41		20 09											20 41	20 51			←
d	19 18		19 22	19 40			19 41	20 04	20 09				20 14	20 18		20 22	20 40			20 41	20 51	21 02 →	21 07	21 02
Walsall a				20 00													21 00							
Coseley d			19 27													20 27								
Tipton d			19 29													20 29								
Dudley Port d			19 31													20 31								
Sandwell & Dudley d	19 29		19 35											20 29		20 35								
Smethwick Galton Bdg L.L. 7 d			19 37													20 37								
Smethwick Rolfe Street d			19 39													20 39								
Birmingham New Street 12 a	19 40		19 46				19 58	20 26	20 31				20 30	20 40		20 46				20 58	21 12		21 24	21 25
d	19 45					19 55						20 30		20 45					20 55					
Adderley Park d												20 41												
Stechford d												20 51												
Lea Hall d												21 01												
Marston Green d												21 11												
Birmingham International ✈ a						20 20						21 15							21 20					
d						20 20					20 30	21 16							21 20					
Hampton-in-Arden d		←										21 26			←									
Berkswell d		19 36										21 36 →			20 36									
Tile Hill d		19 46													20 46									
Canley d		19 55													20 55									
Coventry a		20 03				20 45					20 55				21 03				21 45					
d						20 50													21 50					
Rugby d	20 41				20 55	21a30				20 50				21 41				21 55	22a30					
Long Buckby d					21 21													22 21						
Northampton a					21 46													22 46						
London Euston 15 ⊖ a	22 15									22 36				23 06										

	LM	XC	VT	VT	LM	LM	LM	LM	VT	VT	LM	AW	XC	LM	LM	LM	LM	VT	XC	VT	LM	LM	LM	
	🚌	1 ◇ ☕	1 ◇ ☕	1 ◇ ☕	🚌		🚌	🚌	🚌	1 ◇ ☕	🚌	◇	1 ◇	🚌		🚌	🚌	🚌	1 ◇	1 ◇ ☕	1 ◇	🚌	🚌	
Stafford d		20 53	21 07							21 50			21 53						22 53	23 00	23 07		23 36	
Penkridge d																					23 12		00 02	
Wolverhampton 7 a		21 09								22 04			22 16						23 09	23 18	23 25		00 32	
d		21 09		21 18		21 22	21 40			22 06		22 13	22 17		22 22	22 40			23 09	23 19	23 25		00 33	
Walsall a							22 00									23 00								
Coseley d						21 27									22 27									
Tipton d						21 29									22 29									
Dudley Port d						21 31									22 31									
Sandwell & Dudley d				21 29		21 35									22 35									
Smethwick Galton Bdg L.L. 7 d						21 37									22 37									
Smethwick Rolfe Street d						21 39									22 39									
Birmingham New Street 12 a		21 31		21 40		21 46				22 27		22 30	22 41		22 46				23 30	23 41	23 45		01 08	
d	21 30			21 45					21 55		22 30							22 55						
Adderley Park d	21 41										22 41													
Stechford d	21 51										22 51													
Lea Hall d	22 01										23 01													
Marston Green d	22 11										23 11													
Birmingham International ✈ a	22 15								22 20		23 15							23 20						
d	22 16								22 20		23 16							23 20						
Hampton-in-Arden d	22 26				←						23 26			←								←		
Berkswell d	22 36 →				21 36						23 36 →			22 36								23 36		
Tile Hill d					21 46									22 46								23 46		
Canley d					21 55									22 55								23 55		
Coventry a					22 03				22 45					23 03				23 45				00 03		
d									22 45															
Rugby d			21 46	22 40				22 55	23a25								23 30							
Long Buckby d								23 21									23 56							
Northampton a								23 46									00 21							
London Euston 15 ⊖ a			23 19	00 06																				

For general notes see front of timetable
For details of catering facilities see Directory of Train Operators

Due to Engineering Operations, services from Sunday 14 September on this Table had not been confirmed at time of going to press. These services will be issued in a special Supplement as soon as exact timings have been confirmed

Table 68A

Mondays to Fridays

Stafford — Stoke-on-Trent

Bus Service

Network Diagram - see first page of Table 67

		LM	LM	LM	LM	LM		LM	LM	LM	LM	LM		LM	LM	LM	LM	LM	LM	LM	LM	LM	LM		
Stafford	d		07 20	08 15	08 35	09 35		10 05	10 35	11 35	12 25	12 35		13 35	14 15	14 35	15 35	16 30	16 35	17 25	17 35	18 35	19 25		
Norton Bridge Station Drv	d			08 37				10 27			12 47				14 37			16a52		18a02					
Stone Granville Square	d	07 00	08 10	09a00	09 20	10 20		10a52	11 20	12 20	13a29	13 20		14 20	14a52	15 20	16 20		17 20		18 20	19 20	20 05		
Barlaston Orchard Place	d	07 10	08 20		09 30	10 30			11 30	12 30		13 30		14 30		15 30	16 30		17 30		18 30	19 30	20 15		
Wedgwood Old Road Bridge	d	07 12	08 22		09 32	10 32			11 32	12 32		13 32		14 32		15 32	16 32		17 32		18 32	19 32	20 17		
Stoke-on-Trent	a	07 35	08 48		09 48	10 48			11 48	12 48		13 48		14 48		15 48	16 48		17 48		18 48	19 48	20 33		
Hanley Bus Station	a	07 44	08 57		09 57	10 57			11 57	12 57		13 57		14 57		15 57	16 57		17 57		18 57	19 55	20 45		

Saturdays

until 6 September

		LM		LM		LM		LM		LM		LM		LM		LM		LM	LM	LM	LM	LM	LM		
Stafford	d			08 15		08 35		09 35		10 05		11 35		12 25		13 35		14 15	15 35	16 30	17 25	17 35	19 35		
Norton Bridge Station Drv	d			08 37						10 27				12 47				14 37		16a52	18a02				
Stone Granville Square	d	07 00		09a00		09 20		10 20		10a52		12 20		13a29		14 20		14a52	16 20			18 20	19 55		
Barlaston Orchard Place	d	07 10				09 30		10 30				12 30				14 30			16 30			18 30	20 05		
Wedgwood Old Road Bridge	d	07 12				09 32		10 32				12 32				14 32			16 32			18 32	20 07		
Stoke-on-Trent	a	07 35				09 48		10 48				12 48				14 48			16 48			18 48	20 23		
Hanley Bus Station	a	07 44				09 57		10 57				12 57				14 57			16 57			18 57	20 30		

Mondays to Fridays

		LM	LM	LM	LM	LM		LM	LM	LM	LM	LM		LM	LM	LM	LM	LM	LM	LM	LM	LM	LM		
Hanley Bus Station	d		06 55		07 50			09 00	10 00	11 00		12 00			13 00	14 00	15 00		16 00		17 00	18 00	19 00		
Stoke-on-Trent	d		07 01		08 01			09 11	10 11	11 11		12 11			13 11	14 11	15 11		16 11		17 11	18 11	19 11		
Wedgwood Old Road Bridge	d		07 10		08 10			09 22	10 22	11 22		12 22			13 22	14 22	15 22		16 22		17 22	18 22	19 22		
Barlaston Orchard Place	d		07 12		08 12			09 25	10 25	11 25		12 25			13 25	14 25	15 25		16 25		17 25	18 25	19 25		
Stone Granville Square	d	06 40	07 25		08 25	08 56		09 35	10 35	11 35	11 39	12 35		13 39	13 35	14 35	15 35	15 41	16 35		17 35	18 35	19a32		
Norton Bridge Station Drv	d			07 56		09 46					12 06			13 56				16 11		17 06					
Stafford	a	06 58	08 03	08 15	09 08	10 05		10 18	11 18	12 18	12 25	13 18		14 15	14 18	15 18	16 18	16 30	17 18	17 25	18 18	19 18			

Saturdays

until 6 September

		LM		LM		LM		LM		LM		LM		LM		LM		LM	LM	LM	LM	LM	LM		
Hanley Bus Station	d	06 55				07 50				10 00				12 00				14 00		16 00		18 00	19 00		
Stoke-on-Trent	d	07 01				08 01				10 11				12 11				14 11		16 11		18 11	19 11		
Wedgwood Old Road Bridge	d	07 10				08 10				10 22				12 22				14 22		16 22		18 22	19 22		
Barlaston Orchard Place	d	07 12				08 12				10 25				12 25				14 25		16 25		18 25	19 25		
Stone Granville Square	d	07 25				08 25		08 56		10 35		11 39		12 35		13 39		14 35	15 41	16 35		18 35	19a32		
Norton Bridge Station Drv	d			07 56				09 46				12 06				13 56			16 11		17 06				
Stafford	a	08 05		08 15		09 10		10 05		11 18		12 25		13 18		14 15		15 18	16 30	17 18	17 25	19 18			

For general notes see front of timetable
For details of catering facilities see Directory of Train Operators

No Sunday Service

Mondays to Fridays
until 24 October

Lichfield → Birmingham → Longbridge and Redditch

Network Diagram - see first page of Table 67

Miles	Miles			LM	LM	LM	LM	LM	LM	LM	LM	LM	LM	LM	LM	LM	LM	LM	LM	LM	LM	LM	XC ◇ A ⚒	LM
0	—	**Lichfield Trent Valley**	d							06 09		06 23				06 52		07 10		07 22		07 40		07 54
1¼	—	**Lichfield City**	d							06 12		06 26			06 43	06 55		07 14		07 25		07 45		07 57
4¼	—	Shenstone	d							06 17					06 48			07 19				07 50		
6¾	—	Blake Street	d					06 04		06 21		06 34			06 51	07 03		07 23		07 33		07 54		08 05
8½	—	Butlers Lane	d					06 06		06 23		06 36			06 53	07 05		07 25		07 35		07 56		08 07
9½	—	Four Oaks	d					06 09	06 18	06 25		06 39	06 48		06 56	07 08	07 18	07 28		07 38	07 48	07 59		08 10
11	—	Sutton Coldfield	d					06 12	06 21	06 29		06 42	06 51		07 00	07 11	07 21	07 31		07 41	07 51	08 02		08 13
12	—	Wylde Green	d					06 15	06 24	06 31		06 45	06 54		07 02	07 14	07 24	07 34		07 44	07 54	08 05		08 16
12¾	—	Chester Road	d					06 17	06 26	06 34		06 47	06 56		07 04	07 16	07 26	07 36		07 46	07 56	08 07		08 18
13¼	—	Erdington	d					06 18	06 27	06 35		06 48	06 57		07 06	07 17	07 27	07 37		07 47	07 57	08 08		08 19
14½	—	Gravelly Hill	d					06 21	06 30	06 38		06 51	07 00		07 08	07 20	07 30	07 40		07 50	08 00	08 11		08 22
15¾	—	Aston	d					06 24	06 33	06 41		06 54	07 03		07 11	07 23	07 33	07 43		07 53	08 03	08 14		08 25
17	—	Duddeston	d					06 26	06 36	06 44			07 06				07 36	07 45			08 06	08 17		
18½	—	**Birmingham New Street** 12	a					06 31	06 42	06 48		07 00	07 11		07 19	07 30	07 42	07 51		08 01	08 11	08 21		08 31
—	0		d	05 54	06 04	06 14	06 24	06 34	06 44	06 54	06 59	07 04	07 14	07 20	07 24	07 34	07 44	07 54	07 59	08 04	08 14	08 24	08 30	08 34
19½	—	Five Ways	d	05 57	06 07	06 17	06 27	06 37	06 47	06 57		07 07	07 17		07 27	07 37	07 47	07 57		08 07	08 17	08 27		08 37
20	1½	University	d	06 01	06 11	06 21	06 31	06 41	06 51	07 01	07 05	07 11	07 21	07 26	07 31	07 41	07 51	08 01	08 05	08 11	08 21	08 31	08a36	08 41
20¾	—	Selly Oak	d	06 03	06 13	06 23	06 33	06 43	06 53	07 03		07 13	07 23		07 33	07 43	07 53	08 03		08 13	08 23	08 33		08 43
21¾	—	Bournville	d	06 05	06 15	06 25	06 35	06 45	06 55	07 05		07 15	07 25		07 35	07 45	07 55	08 05		08 15	08 25	08 35		08 45
22¾	—	Kings Norton	d	06 07	06 17	06 27	06 37	06 47	06 57	07 07		07 17	07 27		07 37	07 47	07 57	08 07		08 17	08 27	08 37		08 47
24¼	—	Northfield	d	06 10	06 20	06 30	06 40	06 50	07 00	07 10		07 20	07 30		07 40	07 50	08 00	08 10		08 20	08 30	08 40		08 50
25¼	—	Longbridge	d	06a14	06a24	06 34	06a44	06a54	07 04	07a14		07a24	07 34		07a44	07a54	08 04	08a14		08a24	08 34	08a44		08a54
28	9½	Barnt Green	d			06 39			07 09				07 39	07 42			08 09				08 39			
29¾	—	Alvechurch	d			06 43			07 13				07 43				08 13				08 43			
33	—	**Redditch**	a			06 53			07 23				07 53				08 23				08 53			
—	13	Bromsgrove	a								07 23			07 47					08 21					

		LM B	LM	LM	LM	LM	LM	LM	LM	LM	LM	LM	LM	LM	LM	XC ◇ A ⚒	LM	LM	LM	LM	LM	LM	LM
Lichfield Trent Valley	d			08 12				08 40	08 52				09 22				09 52				10 22		
Lichfield City	d		08 09	08 15		08 26		08 45	08 55		09 16		09 25		09 46		09 55		10 16		10 25		10 46
Shenstone	d			08 20				08 50			09 21				09 51				10 21				10 51
Blake Street	d			08 24		08 33		08 54	09 03		09 24		09 33		09 54		10 03		10 24		10 33		10 54
Butlers Lane	d			08 26		08 35		08 56	09 05		09 26		09 35		09 56		10 05		10 26		10 35		10 56
Four Oaks	d	08 15	08 19	08 29		08 38	08 48	08 59	09 08	09 18	09 29		09 38	09 48	09 59		10 08	10 18	10 29		10 38	10 48	10 59
Sutton Coldfield	d	08 18	08 22	08 32		08 42	08 51	09 02	09 11	09 21	09 33		09 41	09 51	10 03		10 11	10 21	10 33		10 41	10 51	11 03
Wylde Green	d	08 21	08 25	08 35		08 45	08 54	09 05	09 14	09 24	09 35		09 44	09 54	10 05		10 14	10 24	10 35		10 44	10 54	11 05
Chester Road	d	08 23	08 27	08 37		08 47	08 56	09 07	09 16	09 26	09 37		09 46	09 56	10 06		10 16	10 26	10 36		10 46	10 56	11 07
Erdington	d	08 25	08 28	08 38		08 48	08 57	09 08	09 17	09 27	09 38		09 47	09 57	10 08		10 17	10 27	10 38		10 47	10 57	11 09
Gravelly Hill	d		08 31	08 41		08 51	09 00	09 11	09 20	09 30	09 41		09 50	10 00	10 10		10 20	10 30	10 40		10 50	11 00	11 11
Aston	d		08 34	08 44		08 54	09 03	09 14	09 24	09 33	09 45		09 54	10 03	10 15		10 24	10 33	10 45		10 54	11 03	11 15
Duddeston	d		08 36	08 46			09 06			09 36				10 06				10 36				11 06	
Birmingham New Street 12	a	08 34	08 41	08 51		09 02	09 12	09 21	09 31	09 41	09 51		10 01	10 12	10 21		10 30	10 41	10 51		11 01	11 12	11 21
	d		08 44	08 54	08 59	09 04	09 14	09 24	09 34	09 44	09 54	09 59	10 04	10 14	10 24	10 30	10 34	10 44	10 54	10 59	11 04	11 14	11 24
Five Ways	d		08 47	08 57		09 07	09 17	09 27	09 37	09 47	09 57		10 07	10 17	10 27		10 37	10 47	10 57		11 07	11 17	11 27
University	d		08 51	09 01	09 05	09 11	09 21	09 31	09 41	09 51	10 01	10 05	10 11	10 21	10 31	10a36	10 41	10 51	11 01	11 05	11 11	11 21	11 31
Selly Oak	d		08 53	09 03		09 13	09 23	09 33	09 43	09 53	10 03		10 13	10 23	10 33		10 43	10 53	11 03		11 13	11 23	11 33
Bournville	d		08 55	09 05		09 15	09 25	09 35	09 45	09 55	10 05		10 15	10 25	10 35		10 45	10 55	11 05		11 15	11 25	11 35
Kings Norton	d		08 57	09 07		09 17	09 27	09 37	09 47	09 57	10 07		10 17	10 27	10 37		10 47	10 57	11 07		11 17	11 27	11 37
Northfield	d		09 00	09 10		09 20	09 30	09 40	09 50	10 00	10 10		10 20	10 30	10 40		10 50	11 00	11 10		11 20	11 30	11 40
Longbridge	d		09 04	09a14		09a24	09 34	09a44	09a54	10 04	10a14		10a24	10 34	10a44		10a54	11 04	11a14		11a24	11 34	11a44
Barnt Green	d		09 09				09 39			10 09				10 39				11 09				11 39	
Alvechurch	d		09 13				09 43			10 13				10 43				11 13				11 43	
Redditch	a		09 23				09 53			10 23				10 53				11 23				11 53	
Bromsgrove	a				09 21							10 21								11 21			

		LM	LM	LM	LM	LM	LM	LM	XC ◇ A ⚒	LM	LM	LM	LM	LM	LM	LM	LM	LM	LM	LM	LM	LM	LM
Lichfield Trent Valley	d	10 52				11 22				11 52				12 22			12 52				13 22		
Lichfield City	d	10 55		11 16		11 25		11 46		11 55		12 16		12 25		12 46	12 55		13 16		13 25		13 46
Shenstone	d			11 21				11 51				12 21				12 51			13 21				13 51
Blake Street	d	11 03		11 24		11 33		11 54		12 03		12 24		12 33		12 54	13 03		13 24		13 33		13 54
Butlers Lane	d	11 05		11 26		11 35		11 56		12 05		12 26		12 35		12 56	13 05		13 26		13 35		13 56
Four Oaks	d	11 08	11 18	11 29		11 38	11 48	11 59		12 08	12 18	12 29		12 38	12 48	12 59	13 08	13 18	13 29		13 38	13 48	13 59
Sutton Coldfield	d	11 11	11 21	11 33		11 41	11 51	12 03		12 11	12 21	12 33		12 41	12 51	13 03	13 11	13 21	13 33		13 41	13 51	14 03
Wylde Green	d	11 14	11 24	11 35		11 44	11 54	12 05		12 14	12 24	12 35		12 44	12 54	13 05	13 14	13 24	13 35		13 44	13 54	14 05
Chester Road	d	11 16	11 26	11 37		11 46	11 56	12 07		12 16	12 26	12 37		12 46	12 56	13 07	13 16	13 26	13 37		13 46	13 56	14 07
Erdington	d	11 17	11 27	11 39		11 47	11 57	12 09		12 17	12 27	12 39		12 47	12 57	13 09	13 17	13 27	13 39		13 47	13 57	14 09
Gravelly Hill	d	11 20	11 30	11 41		11 50	12 00	12 11		12 20	12 30	12 41		12 50	13 00	13 11	13 20	13 30	13 41		13 50	14 00	14 11
Aston	d	11 24	11 33	11 45		11 54	12 03	12 15		12 24	12 33	12 45		12 53	13 03	13 15	13 24	13 33	13 45		13 54	14 03	14 15
Duddeston	d		11 36				12 06				12 36				13 06			13 36				14 06	
Birmingham New Street 12	a	11 30	11 41	11 51		12 01	12 12	12 21		12 30	12 41	12 51		13 01	13 12	13 21	13 30	13 41	13 51		14 01	14 12	14 21
	d	11 34	11 44	11 54	11 59	12 04	12 14	12 24	12 30	12 34	12 44	12 54	12 59	13 04	13 14	13 24	13 34	13 44	13 54	13 59	14 04	14 14	14 24
Five Ways	d	11 37	11 47	11 57		12 07	12 17	12 27		12 37	12 47	12 57		13 07	13 17	13 27	13 37	13 47	13 57		14 07	14 17	14 27
University	d	11 41	11 51	12 01	12 05	12 11	12 21	12 31	12a36	12 41	12 51	13 01	13 05	13 11	13 21	13 31	13 41	13 51	14 01	14 05	14 11	14 21	14 31
Selly Oak	d	11 43	11 53	12 03		12 13	12 23	12 33		12 43	12 53	13 03		13 13	13 23	13 33	13 43	13 53	14 03		14 13	14 23	14 33
Bournville	d	11 45	11 55	12 05		12 15	12 25	12 35		12 45	12 55	13 05		13 15	13 25	13 35	13 45	13 55	14 05		14 15	14 25	14 35
Kings Norton	d	11 47	11 57	12 07		12 17	12 27	12 37		12 47	12 57	13 07		13 17	13 27	13 37	13 47	13 57	14 07		14 17	14 27	14 37
Northfield	d	11 50	12 00	12 10		12 20	12 30	12 40		12 50	13 00	13 10		13 20	13 30	13 40	13 50	14 00	14 10		14 20	14 30	14 40
Longbridge	d	11a54	12 04	12a14		12a24	12 34	12a44		12a54	13 04	13a14		13a24	13 34	13a44	13a54	14 04	14a14		14a24	14 34	14a44
Barnt Green	d		12 09				12 39				13 09				13 39			14 09				14 39	
Alvechurch	d		12 13				12 43				13 13				13 43			14 13				14 43	
Redditch	a		12 23				12 53				13 23				13 53			14 23				14 53	
Bromsgrove	a				12 21								13 21							14 21			

For general notes see front of timetable
For details of catering facilities see
Directory of Train Operators

A From Nottingham (Table 57)
B To Wolverhampton (Table 68)

Lichfield → Birmingham → Longbridge and Redditch

Network Diagram - see first page of Table 67

		XC ◇ A	LM	LM	LM	LM	LM	LM	LM	LM	LM	LM	LM	LM	LM	LM	LM	XC ◇ B	LM	LM	LM	LM	LM
Lichfield Trent Valley	d		13 52				14 22			14 52				15 22					15 51				16 22
Lichfield City	d		13 55		14 16		14 25		14 46	14 55		15 16		15 25			15 46		15 54		16 16		16 25
Shenstone	d				14 21				14 51			15 21					15 51		15 59		16 21		
Blake Street	d		14 03		14 24		14 33		14 54	15 03		15 24		15 33			15 54		16 03		16 24		16 33
Butlers Lane	d		14 05		14 26		14 35		14 56	15 05		15 27		15 35			15 56		16 05		16 26		16 35
Four Oaks	d		14 08	14 18	14 29		14 38	14 48	14 59	15 08	15 18	15 29		15 38	15 48		15 59		16 08	16 18	16 29		16 38
Sutton Coldfield	d		14 11	14 21	14 33		14 41	14 51	15 03	15 11	15 21	15 33		15 41	15 51		16 03		16 11	16 21	16 33		16 41
Wylde Green	d		14 14	14 24	14 35		14 44	14 54	15 05	15 14	15 24	15 35		15 44	15 54		16 05		16 14	16 24	16 35		16 44
Chester Road	d		14 16	14 26	14 37		14 46	14 56	15 07	15 16	15 26	15 37		15 46	15 56		16 07		16 16	16 26	16 37		16 46
Erdington	d		14 17	14 27	14 39		14 48	14 57	15 09	15 17	15 27	15 39		15 48	15 57		16 09		16 17	16 27	16 39		16 47
Gravelly Hill	d		14 20	14 30	14 41		14 50	15 00	15 11	15 20	15 30	15 41		15 50	16 00		16 11		16 20	16 30	16 41		16 50
Aston	d		14 24	14 33	14 45		14 54	15 03	15 15	15 24	15 33	15 45		15 54	16 03		16 15		16 24	16 33	16 45		16 54
Duddeston	d			14 36				15 06			15 36				16 06					16 36			
Birmingham New Street 12	a		14 30	14 41	14 51		15 03	15 12	15 21	15 30	15 41	15 51		16 01	16 12		16 21		16 30	16 42	16 51		17 02
	d	14 30	14 34	14 44	14 54	14 59	15 04	15 14	15 24	15 34	15 44	15 54	15 59	16 04	16 14	16 19	16 24	16 30	16 34	16 44	16 54	16 59	17 04
Five Ways	d		14 37	14 47	14 57		15 07	15 17	15 27	15 37	15 47	15 57		16 07	16 17		16 27		16 37	16 47	16 57		17 07
University	d	14a36	14 41	14 51	15 01	15 05	15 11	15 21	15 31	15 41	15 51	16 01	16 05	16 11	16 21	16a25	16 31	16 36	16 41	16 51	17 01	17 05	17 11
Selly Oak	d		14 43	14 53	15 03		15 13	15 23	15 33	15 43	15 53	16 04		16 14	16 23		16 34		16 44	16 53	17 04		17 14
Bournville	d		14 45	14 55	15 05		15 15	15 25	15 35	15 45	15 55	16 06		16 16	16 25		16 36		16 46	16 55	17 06		17 16
Kings Norton	d		14 47	14 57	15 07		15 17	15 27	15 37	15 47	15 57	16 09		16 19	16 27		16 39		16 49	16 57	17 09		17 19
Northfield	d		14 50	15 00	15 10		15 20	15 30	15 40	15 50	16 00	16 11		16 21	16 30		16 41		16 51	17 00	17 11		17 21
Longbridge	d		14a54	15 04	15a14		15a24	15 34	15a44	15a54	16 04	16a14		16a24	16 36		16a44		16a54	17 04	17a14		17a24
Barnt Green	d			15 09				15 39			16 09				16 40					17 09			
Alvechurch	d			15 13				15 43			16 13				16 45					17 13			
Redditch	a			15 23				15 53			16 23				16 55					17 23			
Bromsgrove	a					15 21							16 21					16 50				17 21	

		LM	LM	LM	XC ◇ B	LM	LM	LM	LM	LM	LM	LM	LM	XC ◇ A	LM	LM	LM	LM	LM	LM	LM	LM	LM
Lichfield Trent Valley	d					16 52				17 21			17 40		17 52		18 10	18 22				18 52	
Lichfield City	d			16 46		16 55	17 05			17 24			17 45		17 55		18 15	18 25			18 46	18 55	
Shenstone	d			16 51						17 29			17 50				18 20				18 51		
Blake Street	d			16 54		17 03	17 12			17 33			17 54		18 03		18 24	18 33			18 54	19 03	
Butlers Lane	d			16 56		17 05	17 14			17 35			17 56		18 05		18 26	18 35			18 56	19 05	
Four Oaks	d	16 48		16 59		17 08	17 18	17 29		17 38	17 48		17 59		18 08	18 18	18 29	18 38	18 48		18 59	19 08	19 18
Sutton Coldfield	d	16 51		17 03		17 11	17 21	17 33		17 41	17 51		18 02		18 11	18 21	18 32	18 41	18 51		19 03	19 11	19 21
Wylde Green	d	16 54		17 05		17 14	17 24	17 35		17 44	17 54		18 05		18 14	18 24	18 35	18 44	18 54		19 05	19 14	19 24
Chester Road	d	16 56		17 07		17 16	17 26	17 37		17 46	17 56		18 07		18 16	18 26	18 37	18 46	18 56		19 07	19 16	19 26
Erdington	d	16 57		17 09		17 17	17 27	17 39		17 47	17 57		18 09		18 17	18 27	18 39	18 47	18 57		19 09	19 17	19 27
Gravelly Hill	d	17 00		17 11		17 20	17 30	17 41		17 50	18 00		18 11		18 20	18 30	18 41	18 50	19 00		19 11	19 20	19 30
Aston	d	17 03		17 14		17 24	17 33	17 44		17 54	18 03		18 15		18 24	18 33	18 45	18 54	19 03		19 15	19 24	19 33
Duddeston	d	17 06					17 36				18 06					18 36			19 06				19 36
Birmingham New Street 12	a	17 11		17 21		17 30	17 41	17 51		18 01	18 11		18 21		18 30	18 41	18 51	19 01	19 11		19 21	19 31	19 41
	d	17 14	17 19	17 24	17 30	17 34	17 44	17 54	17 59	18 04	18 14	18 19	18 24	18 30	18 34	18 44	18 54	19 04	19 14	19 19	19 24	19 34	19 44
Five Ways	d	17 17		17 27		17 37	17 47	17 57		18 07	18 17		18 27		18 37	18 47	18 57	19 07	19 17		19 27	19 37	19 47
University	d	17 21	17 25	17 31	17 36	17 41	17 51	18 01	18 05	18 11	18 21		18 31		18 41	18 51	19 01	19 11	19 21	19 25	19 31	19 41	19 51
Selly Oak	d	17 23		17 34		17 44	17 53	18 04		18 14	18 23		18 33		18 43	18 53	19 03	19 13	19 23		19 33	19 43	19 53
Bournville	d	17 25		17 36		17 46	17 55	18 06		18 16	18 25		18 35		18 45	18 55	19 05	19 15	19 25		19 35	19 45	19 55
Kings Norton	d	17 27		17 39		17 49	17 57	18 08		18 18	18 27		18 37		18 47	18 57	19 07	19 17	19 27		19 37	19 47	19 57
Northfield	d	17 30		17 41		17 51	18 00	18 11		18 21	18 30		18 40		18 50	19 00	19 10	19 20	19 30		19 40	19 50	20 00
Longbridge	d	17 34		17a45		17a54	18 06	18a15		18a24	18 34		18a44		18a54	19 04	19a14	19a24	19 35		19a44	19a54	20 04
Barnt Green	d	17 39					18 10				18 39					19 09			19 40				20 09
Alvechurch	d	17 43					18 15				18 43					19 13			19 44				20 13
Redditch	a	17 55					18 25				18 53					19 23			19 54				20 23
Bromsgrove	a		17 45		17 51				18 21			18 46		18 50						19 40			

		LM	LM	LM	LM	LM	LM	LM	LM	LM	LM	LM	LM	LM	LM	LM	LM	LM	LM	LM	LM
Lichfield Trent Valley	d		19 22			20 00			20 30		21 00			21 30		22 00			22 30	22 56	
Lichfield City	d	19 16	19 25		19 46	20 03			20 33		21 03			21 33		22 03			22 33	22 59	
Shenstone	d	19 21			19 51	20 08			20 38		21 08			21 38		22 08			22 38	23 04	
Blake Street	d	19 24	19 33		19 54	20 12			20 42		21 12			21 42		22 12			22 42	23 08	23 36
Butlers Lane	d	19 26	19 35		19 56	20 14			20 44		21 14			21 44		22 14			22 44	23 10	23 38
Four Oaks	d	19 29	19 38	19 48	19 59	20 17			20 47		21 17			21 47		22 17			22 47	23 13	23 41
Sutton Coldfield	d	19 33	19 41	19 51	20 03	20 20			20 50		21 20			21 50		22 20			22 50	23 16	23 44
Wylde Green	d	19 35	19 44	19 54	20 05	20 23			20 53		21 23			21 53		22 23			22 53	23 19	
Chester Road	d	19 37	19 46	19 56	20 07	20 25			20 55		21 25			21 55		22 25			22 55		
Erdington	d	19 39	19 48	19 57	20 09	20 26			20 56		21 26			21 56		22 26			22 56		
Gravelly Hill	d	19 41	19 50	20 00	20 11	20 29			20 59		21 29			21 59		22 29			22 59		
Aston	d	19 45	19 54	20 03	20 15	20 32			21 02		21 32			22 02		22 32			23 02		
Duddeston	d			20 06		20 35			21 05		21 35			22 05		22 35			23 05		
Birmingham New Street 12	a	19 51	20 03	20 12	20 21	20 41			21 12		21 41			22 12		22 41			23 11	23 30	23 58
	d	19 54		20 14	20 24	20 44	20 54	20 59	21 14	21 24	21 44	21 54	21 59	22 14	22 24	22 44	22 55	23 04	23 14	23 35	
Five Ways	d	19 57		20 17	20 27	20 47	20 57		21 17	21 27	21 47	21 57		22 17	22 27	22 47	22 58		23 17	23 38	
University	d	20 01		20 21	20 31	20 51	21 01	21 05	21 21	21 31	21 51	22 01	22 05	22 21	22 31	22 51	23 02	23 10	23 21	23 42	
Selly Oak	d	20 03		20 23	20 33	20 53	21 03		21 23	21 33	21 53	22 03		22 23	22 33	22 53	23 04		23 23	23 45	
Bournville	d	20 05		20 25	20 35	20 55	21 05		21 25	21 35	21 55	22 05		22 25	22 35	22 55	23 06		23 25	23 47	
Kings Norton	d	20 07		20 27	20 37	20 57	21 07		21 27	21 37	21 57	22 07		22 27	22 37	22 57	23 08		23 27	23 49	
Northfield	d	20 10		20 30	20 40	21 00	21 10		21 30	21 40	22 00	22 10		22 30	22 40	23 00	23 11		23 30	23 52	
Longbridge	d	20a14		20 34	20a44	21 04	21a14		21 34	21a44	22 04	22a14		22 34	22a44	23 04	23a15		23 34	23a55	
Barnt Green	d			20 39		21 09			21 39		22 09			22 39		23 09			23 39		
Alvechurch	d			20 43		21 13			21 43		22 13			22 43		23 13			23 43		
Redditch	a			20 53		21 23			21 53		22 23			22 53		23 23			23 53		
Bromsgrove	a							21 21					22 21					23 23			

For general notes see front of timetable
For details of catering facilities see
Directory of Train Operators

A From Nottingham (Table 57)
B From Nottingham to Cardiff Central (Table 57)

Mondays to Fridays

from 27 October

Lichfield → Birmingham → Longbridge and Redditch

Network Diagram - see first page of Table 67

		LM	LM	LM	LM	LM	LM	LM	LM		LM	LM	LM	LM	LM	LM	LM	LM		XC ◇ A	LM	LM	LM	LM	LM	LM
Lichfield Trent Valley	d							06 17				06 47				07 17					07 47				08 17	
Lichfield City	d					06 09		06 20				06 50	07 03			07 20	07 33				07 50	08 03			08 20	08 32
Shenstone	d					06 14		06 26				06 56				07 26					07 56				08 26	08 37
Blake Street	d				06 00	06 18		06 30				07 00	07 11			07 30	07 41				08 00	08 11			08 30	08 41
Butlers Lane	d				06 02	06 21		06 32				07 02	07 13			07 32	07 43				08 02	08 13			08 32	08 44
Four Oaks	d				06 05	06 24		06 35			06 54	07 05	07 16	07 24		07 35	07 46	07 54			08 05	08 16	08 24		08 35	08 47
Sutton Coldfield	d				06 09	06 27		06 39			06 57	07 09	07 20	07 27		07 39	07 50	07 57			08 09	08 20	08 27		08 39	08 50
Wylde Green	d				06 12	06 30		06 42			07 00	07 12	07 23	07 30		07 42	07 53	08 00			08 12	08 23	08 30		08 42	08 53
Chester Road	d				06 14	06 33		06 44			07 03	07 14	07 25	07 33		07 45	07 55	08 03			08 14	08 25	08 33		08 44	08 56
Erdington	d				06 16	06 35		06 46			07 05	07 16	07 27	07 35		07 47	07 57	08 05			08 16	08 27	08 35		08 46	08 58
Gravelly Hill	d				06 19	06 38		06 49			07 08	07 19	07 30	07 38		07 50	08 00	08 08			08 19	08 30	08 38		08 49	09 01
Aston	d				06 23	06 41		06 53			07 11	07 23	07 34	07 43		07 53	08 04	08 11			08 23	08 34	08 41		08 53	09 04
Duddeston	d				06 25	06 44					07 14		07 36	07 46			08 06	08 14				08 37	08 44			
Birmingham New Street 12	a				06 31	06 48		07 00			07 19	07 30	07 42	07 51		08 01	08 12	08 21			08 31	08 42	08 51		09 02	09 12
	d	05 54	06 04	06 24	06 34	06 54	06 59	07 04	07 20		07 24	07 34	07 44	07 54	07 59	08 04	08 14	08 24		08 30	08 34	08 44	08 54	08 59	09 04	09 14
Five Ways	d	05 57	06 07	06 27	06 37	06 57		07 07			07 27	07 37	07 47	07 57		08 07	08 17	08 27			08 37	08 46	08 57		09 07	09 17
University	d	06 01	06 11	06 31	06 41	07 01	07 05	07 11	07 26		07 31	07 41	07 51	08 01	08 05	08 11	08 21	08 31		08a36	08 41	08 50	09 01	09 05	09 11	09 21
Selly Oak	d	06 04	06 14	06 34	06 43	07 04		07 14			07 34	07 44	07 53	08 04		08 14	08 23	08 34			08 44	08 52	09 04		09 13	09 23
Bournville	d	06 06	06 16	06 36	06 45	07 06		07 16			07 36	07 46	07 55	08 06		08 16	08 25	08 36			08 46	08 54	09 06		09 15	09 25
Kings Norton	d	06 10	06 19	06 39	06 47	07 09		07 19			07 39	07 48	07 57	08 09		08 19	08 27	08 39			08 49	08 56	09 09		09 17	09 27
Northfield	d	06 13	06 22	06 42	06 51	07 12		07 22			07 42	07 52	08 00	08 12		08 22	08 30	08 42			08 52	08 59	09 12		09 20	09 30
Longbridge	d	06a19	06 26	06a46	06 56	07a16		07 26			07a46	07 56	08a06	08a16		08 26	08a36	08a46			08 56	09a05	09a16		09 25	09a36
Barnt Green	d		06b39		07b09			07b39	07 42			08b09				08b39					09b09				09b39	
Alvechurch	d		06 44		07 14			07 44				08 14				08 44					09 14				09 43	
Redditch	a		06 53		07 23			07 53				08 23				08 53					09 23				09 53	
Bromsgrove	a						07 23		07 47						08 21									09 21		

		LM	LM	LM		LM	LM	LM	LM	LM	XC ◇ A	LM	LM		LM	LM	LM	LM	LM	LM	LM	LM		XC ◇ A	LM	LM
Lichfield Trent Valley	d		08 47	08 58				09 17	09 28			09 47				10 17		10 47			11 17				11 47	
Lichfield City	d		08 50	09 01				09 20	09 31			09 50				10 20		10 50			11 20				11 50	
Shenstone	d		08 56	09 07				09 26	09 37			09 56				10 26		10 56			11 26				11 56	
Blake Street	d		09 00	09 11				09 30	09 41			10 00				10 30		11 00			11 30				12 00	
Butlers Lane	d		09 02	09 13				09 32	09 43			10 02				10 32		11 02			11 32				12 02	
Four Oaks	d	08 54	09 05	09 16		09 24		09 35	09 46	09 54		10 05	10 24			10 35	10 54	11 05	11 24		11 35	11 54			12 05	12 24
Sutton Coldfield	d	08 57	09 09	09 20		09 27		09 39	09 50	09 57		10 09	10 27			10 39	10 57	11 09	11 27		11 39	11 57			12 09	12 27
Wylde Green	d	09 00	09 12	09 23		09 30		09 42	09 53	10 00		10 12	10 30			10 42	11 00	11 12	11 30		11 42	12 00			12 12	12 30
Chester Road	d	09 03	09 14	09 25		09 32		09 44	09 55	10 03		10 14	10 32			10 44	11 03	11 14	11 33		11 44	12 03			12 14	12 33
Erdington	d	09 05	09 16	09 27		09 34		09 46	09 57	10 05		10 16	10 34			10 46	11 05	11 16	11 35		11 46	12 05			12 16	12 35
Gravelly Hill	d	09 08	09 19	09 30		09 37		09 49	10 00	10 08		10 19	10 37			10 49	11 08	11 19	11 38		11 49	12 08			12 19	12 38
Aston	d	09 11	09 23	09 34		09 41		09 53	10 04	10 11		10 23	10 41			10 53	11 11	11 23	11 41		11 53	12 11			12 23	12 41
Duddeston	d	09 14				09 44				10 14			10 44				11 14		11 44			12 14				12 44
Birmingham New Street 12	a	09 21	09 30	09 42		09 51		10 01	10 12	10 21		10 30	10 51			11 01	11 21	11 31	11 51		12 01	12 21			12 31	12 51
	d	09 24	09 34			09 54	09 59	10 04	10 14	10 24	10 30	10 34	10 54		10 59	11 04	11 24	11 34	11 54	11 59	12 04	12 24		12 30	12 34	12 54
Five Ways	d	09 27	09 37			09 57		10 07	10 17	10 27		10 37	10 57			11 07	11 27	11 37	11 57		12 07	12 27			12 37	12 57
University	d	09 31	09 41			10 01	10 05	10 11	10 21	10 31	10a36	10 41	11 01		11 05	11 11	11 31	11 41	12 01	12 05	12 11	12 31		12a36	12 41	13 01
Selly Oak	d	09 34	09 44			10 04		10 14	10 23	10 34		10 44	11 04			11 14	11 34	11 44	12 04		12 14	12 34			12 44	13 04
Bournville	d	09 36	09 46			10 06		10 16	10 25	10 36		10 46	11 06			11 16	11 36	11 46	12 06		12 16	12 36			12 46	13 06
Kings Norton	d	09 39	09 49			10 09		10 19	10 27	10 39		10 49	11 09			11 19	11 39	11 49	12 09		12 19	12 39			12 49	13 09
Northfield	d	09 42	09 52			10 12		10 22	10 30	10 42		10 52	11 12			11 22	11 42	11 52	12 12		12 22	12 42			12 52	13 12
Longbridge	d	09a46	09 56			10a15		10 26	10a36	10a46		10 56	11a16			11c35	11a46	11 56	12a16		12 26	12a46			12 56	13a16
Barnt Green	d		10b09					10b39				11b09				11 39		12b09			12b39				13b09	
Alvechurch	d		10 14					10 44				11 14				11 44		12 14			12 44				13 14	
Redditch	a		10 23					10 53				11 23				11 53		12 23			12 53				13 23	
Bromsgrove	a						10 21								11 21					12 21						

		LM	LM	LM	LM	LM	LM	LM		LM	XC ◇ A	LM	LM	LM	LM	LM	LM		LM	LM	LM	LM	LM	LM	LM	XC ◇ B
Lichfield Trent Valley	d		12 17		12 47			13 17				13 47			14 17		14 47					15 17				
Lichfield City	d		12 20		12 50			13 20				13 50			14 20		14 50					15 20				
Shenstone	d		12 26		12 56			13 26				13 56			14 26		14 56					15 26				
Blake Street	d		12 30		13 00			13 30				14 00			14 30		15 00					15 30				
Butlers Lane	d		12 32		13 02			13 32				14 02			14 32		15 02					15 32				
Four Oaks	d		12 35	12 54	13 05	13 24		13 35		13 54		14 05	14 24		14 35	14 54	15 05			15 24		15 35	15 40		15 54	
Sutton Coldfield	d		12 39	12 57	13 09	13 27		13 39		13 57		14 09	14 27		14 39	14 57	15 09			15 27		15 39	15 47		15 57	
Wylde Green	d		12 42	13 00	13 12	13 30		13 42		14 00		14 12	14 30		14 42	15 00	15 12			15 30		15 42	15 50		16 00	
Chester Road	d		12 44	13 03	13 14	13 33		13 44		14 03		14 14	14 33		14 44	15 03	15 14			15 33		15 44	15 53		16 03	
Erdington	d		12 46	13 05	13 16	13 35		13 46		14 05		14 16	14 35		14 46	15 05	15 16			15 35		15 46	15 55		16 05	
Gravelly Hill	d		12 49	13 08	13 19	13 38		13 49		14 08		14 19	14 38		14 49	15 08	15 19			15 38		15 49	15 58		16 08	
Aston	d		12 53	13 11	13 23	13 41		13 53		14 11		14 23	14 41		14 53	15 11	15 23			15 41		15 53	16 01		16 11	
Duddeston	d			13 14		13 44				14 14			14 44			15 14				15 44			16 04		16 14	
Birmingham New Street 12	a		13 01	13 21	13 31	13 51		14 01		14 21		14 31	14 51		15 01	15 21	15 31			15 51		16 01	16 12		16 21	
	d	12 59	13 04	13 24	13 34	13 54	13 59	14 04		14 24	14 30	14 34	14 54	14 59	15 04	15 24	15 34		15 44	15 54	15 59	16 04	16 14	16 19	16 24	16 30
Five Ways	d		13 07	13 27	13 37	13 57		14 07		14 27		14 37	14 57		15 07	15 27	15 37		15 47	15 57		16 07	16 17		16 27	
University	d	13 05	13 11	13 31	13 41	14 01	14 05	14 11		14 31	14a36	14 41	15 01	15 05	15 11	15 31	15 41		15 51	16 01	16 05	16 11	16 21	16a25	16 31	16 36
Selly Oak	d		13 14	13 34	13 43	14 04		14 14		14 34		14 44	15 04		15 14	15 34	15 44		15 53	16 04		16 14	16 23		16 34	
Bournville	d		13 16	13 36	13 45	14 06		14 16		14 36		14 46	15 06		15 16	15 36	15 46		15 55	16 06		16 16	16 25		16 36	
Kings Norton	d		13 19	13 39	13 47	14 09		14 19		14 39		14 49	15 09		15 19	15 39	15 49		15 57	16 09		16 19	16 27		16 39	
Northfield	d		13 22	13 42	13 51	14 12		14 22		14 42		14 52	15 12		15 22	15 42	15 52		16 00	16 12		16 22	16 30		16 42	
Longbridge	d		13 26	13a46	13 56	14a16		14 26		14a46		14 56	15a14		15 26	15a46	15 56		16a06	16a16		16 30	16a36		16a46	
Barnt Green	d		13b39		14b09			14b39				15b09			15b39		16b09					16 39				
Alvechurch	d		13 44		14 14			14 44				15 14			15 44		16 14					16 44				
Redditch	a		13 53		14 23			14 53				15 23			15 53		16 23					16 53				
Bromsgrove	a	13 21					14 21							15 21							16 21					16 50

For general notes see front of timetable
For details of catering facilities see Directory of Train Operators

A From Nottingham (Table 57)
B From Nottingham to Cardiff Central (Table 57)
b Arives 9 minutes earlier
c Arr. 1124

Mondays to Fridays
from 27 October

Lichfield → Birmingham → Longbridge and Redditch

Network Diagram - see first page of Table 67

		LM	LM	LM	LM	LM	LM	LM	LM	XC ◇ A	LM	LM	LM	LM	LM	LM	LM	XC ◇ B	LM	LM	LM	LM	LM
Lichfield Trent Valley	d	15 47				16 17					16 47				17 17				17 47		18 17		
Lichfield City	d	15 50				16 20					16 50				17 20				17 50		18 20		
Shenstone	d	15 56				16 26					16 56				17 26				17 56		18 26		
Blake Street	d	16 00				16 30					17 00				17 30				18 00		18 30		
Butlers Lane	d	16 02				16 32					17 02				17 32				18 02		18 32		
Four Oaks	d	16 05		16 24		16 35			16 54		17 05		17 24		17 35		17 54		18 05	18 24	18 35		18 54
Sutton Coldfield	d	16 09		16 27		16 39			16 57		17 09		17 27		17 39		17 57		18 09	18 27	18 39		18 57
Wylde Green	d	16 12		16 30		16 42			17 00		17 12		17 30		17 42		18 00		18 12	18 30	18 42		19 00
Chester Road	d	16 14		16 33		16 44			17 03		17 14		17 33		17 44		18 03		18 14	18 33	18 44		19 03
Erdington	d	16 16		16 35		16 46			17 05		17 16		17 35		17 46		18 05		18 16	18 35	18 46		19 05
Gravelly Hill	d	16 19		16 38		16 49			17 08		17 19		17 38		17 49		18 08		18 19	18 38	18 49		19 08
Aston	d	16 23		16 41		16 53			17 11		17 23		17 41		17 53		18 11		18 23	18 41	18 53		19 11
Duddeston	d			16 44					17 14				17 44				18 17			18 44			19 14
Birmingham New Street 12	a	16 30		16 51		17 01			17 21		17 30		17 51		18 01		18 21		18 30	18 51	19 01		19 22
	d	16 34	16 44	16 54	16 59	17 04	17 14	17 19	17 24	17 30	17 34	17 44	17 54	17 59	18 04	18 19	18 24	18 30	18 34	18 54	19 04	19 19	19 24
Five Ways	d	16 37	16 47	16 57		17 07	17 17		17 27		17 37	17 47	17 57		18 07		18 27		18 37	18 57	19 07		19 27
University	d	16 41	16 51	17 01	17 05	17 11	17 21	17 25	17 31	17 36	17 41	17 51	18 01	18 05	18 11		18 31		18 41	19 01	19 11	19 25	19 31
Selly Oak	d	16 44	16 54	17 04		17 14	17 23		17 34		17 44	17 54	18 04		18 14		18 34		18 44	19 04	19 14		19 34
Bournville	d	16 46	16 56	17 06		17 16	17 25		17 36		17 46	17 56	18 06		18 16		18 36		18 46	19 06	19 16		19 36
Kings Norton	d	16 49	16 59	17 09		17 19	17 27		17 39		17 49	17 59	18 09		18 19		18 39		18 49	19 09	19 19		19 39
Northfield	d	16 52	17 02	17 12		17 22	17 30		17 42		17 52	18 02	18 12		18 22		18 42		18 52	19 12	19 22		19 42
Longbridge	d	16 56	17a06	17a16		17 30	17a36		17a46		17 56	18a06	18a15		18 28		18a46		18 56	19a16	19 26		19a46
Barnt Green	d	17b09				17 39					18b09				18 39				19b09		19b39		
Alvechurch	d	17 14				17 44					18 14				18 44				19 14		19 44		
Redditch	a	17 23				17 53					18 23				18 53				19 23		19 53		
Bromsgrove	a				17 21			17 45		17 51				18 21		18 46		18 50				19 40	

		LM	LM	LM	LM	LM	LM	LM	LM	LM	LM	LM	LM	LM	LM	LM	LM	LM	LM	LM	LM	LM
Lichfield Trent Valley	d	18 47				19 17		19 57			20 27		20 57			21 27		21 57			22 27	22 55
Lichfield City	d	18 50				19 20		20 00			20 30		21 00			21 30		22 00			22 30	22 58
Shenstone	d	18 56				19 26		20 06			20 36		21 06			21 36		22 06			22 36	23 04
Blake Street	d	19 00				19 30		20 10			20 40		21 10			21 40		22 10			22 40	23 08
Butlers Lane	d	19 02				19 32		20 12			20 42		21 12			21 42		22 12			22 42	23 10
Four Oaks	d	19 05	19 16		19 46	19 35		20 15			20 45		21 15			21 45		22 15			22 45	23 13
Sutton Coldfield	d	19 09	19 19		19 49	19 39		20 19			20 49		21 19			21 49		22 19			22 49	23 17
Wylde Green	d	19 12	19 22		19 52	19 42		20 22			20 52		21 22			21 52		22 22			22 52	23 20
Chester Road	d	19 14	19 25		19 55	19 44		20 24			20 54		21 24			21 54		22 24			22 54	
Erdington	d	19 16	19 27		19 57	19 46		20 26			20 56		21 26			21 56		22 26			22 56	
Gravelly Hill	d	19 19	19 30		20 00	19 49		20 29			20 59		21 29			21 59		22 29			22 59	
Aston	d	19 23	19 33		20 03	19 53		20 33			21 03		21 33			22 03		22 33			23 03	
Duddeston	d		19 36		20 06			20 36			21 06		21 36			22 06		22 36			23 06	
Birmingham New Street 12	a	19 31	19 42		20 12	20 01		20 42			21 12		21 42			22 12		22 42			23 12	23 30
	d		19 44	19 54		20 14	20 24	20 44	20 54	20 59	21 14	21 24	21 44	21 54	21 59	22 15	22 24	22 44	22 54	23 04	23 14	23 34
Five Ways	d		19 47	19 57		20 17	20 27	20 47	20 57		21 17	21 27	21 47	21 57		22 18	22 27	22 47	22 57		23 17	23 38
University	d		19 51	20 01		20 21	20 31	20 51	21 01	21 05	21 21	21 31	21 51	22 01	22 05	22 22	22 31	22 51	23 01	23 10	23 21	23 42
Selly Oak	d		19 53	20 04		20 23	20 34	20 53	21 03		21 24	21 34	21 53	22 04		22 25	22 33	22 53	23 03		23 23	23 45
Bournville	d		19 55	20 06		20 25	20 36	20 55	21 05		21 26	21 36	21 55	22 06		22 27	22 35	22 55	23 05		23 25	23 47
Kings Norton	d		19 57	20 09		20 27	20 40	20 57	21 07		21 29	21 39	21 57	22 09		22 30	22 37	22 57	23 07		23 27	23 50
Northfield	d		20 00	20 12		20 30	20 43	21 00	21 10		21 32	21 42	22 00	22 12		22 33	22 40	23 00	23 10		23 30	23 53
Longbridge	d		20 04	20a16		20 34	20a47	21 04	21a16		21 35	21a46	22 04	22a15		22 36	22a44	23 04	23a16		23 34	23a57
Barnt Green	d		20 09			20 39		21 09			21 40		22 09			22 41		23 09			23 39	
Alvechurch	d		20 13			20 43		21 13			21 45		22 13			22 46		23 13			23 43	
Redditch	a		20 22			20 52		21 22			21 52		22 22			22 53		23 23			23 52	
Bromsgrove	a									21 21					22 21					23 23		

Saturdays
until 25 October

		LM	LM	LM	LM	LM	LM	LM	LM	LM	LM	LM	LM	LM	LM	LM	LM	LM	LM	XC ◇ B	LM	LM	LM	LM	LM	LM
Lichfield Trent Valley	d									06 21			06 50				07 22				07 52				08 22	
Lichfield City	d									06 24	06 40		06 54	07 11			07 25	07 36			07 55	08 06			08 25	08 36
Shenstone	d									06 29			06 59				07 30	07 41			08 00	08 11			08 30	08 41
Blake Street	d					06 04				06 33			07 03				07 34	07 44			08 04	08 14			08 34	08 44
Butlers Lane	d					06 06				06 35			07 05				07 36	07 46			08 06	08 16			08 36	08 46
Four Oaks	d					06 09				06 38	06 50		07 08	07 21			07 39	07 50			08 09	08 20			08 39	08 49
Sutton Coldfield	d					06 12				06 41	06 53		07 11	07 24			07 42	07 53			08 12	08 23			08 42	08 53
Wylde Green	d					06 15				06 44	06 56		07 14	07 27			07 45	07 56			08 15	08 26			08 45	08 56
Chester Road	d					06 17				06 46	06 58		07 16	07 29			07 47	07 58			08 17	08 28			08 47	08 58
Erdington	d					06 18				06 47	06 59		07 17	07 30			07 48	07 59			08 18	08 29			08 48	08 59
Gravelly Hill	d					06 21				06 50	07 02		07 20	07 33			07 51	08 02			08 21	08 32			08 51	09 02
Aston	d					06 24				06 53	07 05		07 23	07 35			07 54	08 05			08 24	08 35			08 54	09 05
Duddeston	d					06 26				06 56	07 08		07 26	07 38				08 08				08 38				09 08
Birmingham New Street 12	a					06 31				07 01	07 13		07 30	07 43			08 00	08 12			08 30	08 43			09 00	09 12
	d	05 54	06 04	06 14	06 24	06 34	06 44	06 54	06 59	07 04	07 14	07 24	07 34	07 44	07 54	07 59	08 04	08 14	08 24	08 30	08 34	08 44	08 54	08 59	09 04	09 14
Five Ways	d	05 57	06 07	06 17	06 27	06 37	06 47	06 57		07 07	07 17	07 27	07 37	07 47	07 57		08 07	08 17	08 27		08 37	08 47	08 57		09 07	09 17
University	d	06 01	06 11	06 21	06 31	06 41	06 51	07 01	07 05	07 11	07 21	07 31	07 41	07 51	08 01	08 05	08 11	08 21	08 31	08a36	08 41	08 51	09 01	09 05	09 11	09 21
Selly Oak	d	06 03	06 13	06 23	06 33	06 43	06 53	07 03		07 13	07 23	07 33	07 43	07 53	08 03		08 13	08 23	08 33		08 43	08 53	09 03		09 13	09 23
Bournville	d	06 05	06 15	06 25	06 35	06 45	06 55	07 05		07 15	07 25	07 35	07 45	07 55	08 05		08 15	08 25	08 35		08 45	08 55	09 05		09 15	09 25
Kings Norton	d	06 07	06 17	06 27	06 37	06 47	06 57	07 07		07 17	07 27	07 37	07 47	07 57	08 07		08 17	08 27	08 37		08 47	08 57	09 07		09 17	09 27
Northfield	d	06 10	06 20	06 30	06 40	06 50	07 00	07 10		07 20	07 30	07 40	07 50	08 00	08 10		08 20	08 30	08 40		08 50	09 00	09 10		09 20	09 30
Longbridge	d	06a14	06a24	06 34	06a44	06a54	07 04	07a14		07a24	07 34	07a44	07a54	08 04	08a14		08a24	08 34	08a44		08a54	09 04	09a14		09a24	09 34
Barnt Green	d			06 39			07 09				07 39			08 09				08 39				09 09				09 39
Alvechurch	d			06 43			07 13				07 43			08 13				08 43				09 13				09 43
Redditch	a			06 53			07 23				07 53			08 23				08 53				09 23				09 53
Bromsgrove	a								07 22							08 21								09 21		

For general notes see front of timetable
For details of catering facilities see
Directory of Train Operators

A From Nottingham to Cardiff Central (Table 57)
B From Nottingham (Table 57)
b Arives 9 minutes earlier

Table 69

Saturdays
until 25 October

Lichfield → Birmingham → Longbridge and Redditch

Network Diagram - see first page of Table 67

		LM	LM	LM	LM	LM	LM	LM		LM	XC	LM	LM	LM	LM	LM	LM	LM	LM	LM	LM	LM	LM	LM	LM	LM
											◇ A															
Lichfield Trent Valley	d		08 52				09 22					09 52				10 22			10 52				11 22			11 52
Lichfield City	d		08 55	09 06			09 25	09 36				09 55	10 06			10 25	10 36		10 55	11 06			11 25	11 36		11 55
Shenstone	d		09 00	09 11			09 30	09 41				10 00	10 11			10 30	10 41		11 00	11 11			11 30	11 41		12 00
Blake Street	d		09 04	09 14			09 34	09 44				10 04	10 14			10 34	10 44		11 04	11 14			11 34	11 44		12 04
Butlers Lane	d		09 06	09 16			09 36	09 46				10 06	10 16			10 36	10 46		11 06	11 16			11 36	11 46		12 06
Four Oaks	d		09 09	09 20			09 39	09 50				10 09	10 20			10 39	10 50		11 09	11 20			11 39	11 50		12 09
Sutton Coldfield	d		09 12	09 23			09 42	09 53				10 12	10 23			10 42	10 53		11 12	11 23			11 42	11 53		12 12
Wylde Green	d		09 15	09 26			09 45	09 56				10 15	10 26			10 45	10 56		11 15	11 26			11 45	11 56		12 15
Chester Road	d		09 17	09 28			09 47	09 58				10 17	10 28			10 47	10 58		11 17	11 28			11 47	11 58		12 17
Erdington	d		09 18	09 29			09 48	09 59				10 18	10 29			10 48	10 59		11 18	11 29			11 48	11 59		12 18
Gravelly Hill	d		09 21	09 32			09 51	10 02				10 21	10 32			10 51	11 02		11 21	11 32			11 51	12 02		12 21
Aston	d		09 24	09 35			09 54	10 05				10 24	10 35			10 54	11 05		11 24	11 35			11 54	12 05		12 24
Duddeston	d			09 38				10 08					10 38				11 08			11 38				12 08		
Birmingham New Street 12	a		09 30	09 43			10 01	10 12				10 30	10 42			11 01	11 12		11 30	11 43			12 01	12 12		12 30
	d	09 24	09 34	09 44	09 54	09 59	10 04	10 14		10 24	10 30	10 34	10 44	10 54	10 59	11 04	11 14	11 24	11 34	11 44	11 54	11 59	12 04	12 14	12 24	12 34
Five Ways	d	09 27	09 37	09 47	09 57		10 07	10 17		10 27		10 37	10 47	10 57		11 07	11 17	11 27	11 37	11 47	11 57		12 07	12 17	12 27	12 37
University	d	09 31	09 41	09 51	10 01	10 05	10 11	10 21		10 31	10a36	10 41	10 51	11 01	11 05	11 11	11 21	11 31	11 41	11 51	12 01	12 05	12 11	12 21	12 31	12 41
Selly Oak	d	09 33	09 43	09 53	10 03		10 13	10 23		10 33		10 43	10 53	11 03		11 13	11 23	11 33	11 43	11 53	12 03		12 13	12 23	12 33	12 43
Bournville	d	09 35	09 45	09 55	10 05		10 15	10 25		10 35		10 45	10 55	11 05		11 15	11 25	11 35	11 45	11 55	12 05		12 15	12 25	12 35	12 45
Kings Norton	d	09 37	09 47	09 57	10 07		10 17	10 27		10 37		10 47	10 57	11 07		11 17	11 27	11 37	11 47	11 57	12 07		12 17	12 27	12 37	12 47
Northfield	d	09 40	09 50	10 00	10 10		10 20	10 30		10 40		10 50	11 00	11 10		11 20	11 30	11 40	11 50	12 00	12 10		12 20	12 30	12 40	12 50
Longbridge	d	09a44	09a54	10 04	10a14		10a24	10 34		10a44		10a54	11 04	11a14		11a24	11 34	11a44	11a54	12 04	12a14		12a24	12 34	12a44	12a54
Barnt Green	d			10 09				10 39					11 09				11 39			12 09				12 39		
Alvechurch	d			10 13				10 43					11 13				11 43			12 13				12 43		
Redditch	a			10 23				10 53					11 23				11 53			12 23				12 53		
Bromsgrove	a					10 21									11 21							12 21				

		LM	LM	LM	LM	LM	LM	LM	LM	LM	LM	LM	LM	LM	XC	LM		LM	LM	LM	LM	LM	LM	LM	LM	LM
															◇ A											
Lichfield Trent Valley	d				12 22			12 52				13 22				13 52					14 22			14 52		
Lichfield City	d	12 06			12 25	12 36		12 55	13 06			13 25	13 36			13 55		14 06			14 25	14 36		14 55	15 06	
Shenstone	d	12 11			12 30	12 41		13 00	13 11			13 30	13 41			14 00		14 11			14 30	14 41		15 00	15 11	
Blake Street	d	12 14			12 34	12 44		13 04	13 14			13 34	13 44			14 04		14 14			14 34	14 44		15 04	15 14	
Butlers Lane	d	12 16			12 36	12 46		13 06	13 16			13 36	13 46			14 06		14 16			14 36	14 46		15 06	15 16	
Four Oaks	d	12 20			12 39	12 50		13 09	13 20			13 39	13 50			14 09		14 20			14 39	14 50		15 09	15 20	
Sutton Coldfield	d	12 23			12 42	12 53		13 12	13 23			13 42	13 53			14 12		14 23			14 42	14 53		15 12	15 23	
Wylde Green	d	12 26			12 45	12 56		13 15	13 26			13 45	13 56			14 15		14 26			14 45	14 56		15 15	15 26	
Chester Road	d	12 28			12 47	12 58		13 17	13 28			13 47	13 58			14 17		14 28			14 47	14 58		15 17	15 28	
Erdington	d	12 29			12 48	12 59		13 18	13 29			13 48	13 59			14 18		14 29			14 48	14 59		15 18	15 29	
Gravelly Hill	d	12 32			12 51	13 02		13 21	13 32			13 51	14 02			14 21		14 32			14 51	15 02		15 21	15 32	
Aston	d	12 35			12 54	13 05		13 24	13 35			13 54	14 05			14 24		14 35			14 54	15 05		15 24	15 35	
Duddeston	d	12 38				13 08			13 38				14 08					14 38				15 08			15 38	
Birmingham New Street 12	a	12 42			13 01	13 12		13 30	13 43			14 01	14 12			14 31		14 43			15 01	15 12		15 30	15 43	
	d	12 44	12 54	12 59	13 04	13 14	13 24	13 34	13 44	13 54	13 59	14 04	14 14	14 24	14 30	14 34		14 44	14 54	14 59	15 04	15 14	15 24	15 34	15 44	15 54
Five Ways	d	12 47	12 57		13 07	13 17	13 27	13 37	13 47	13 57		14 07	14 17	14 27		14 37		14 47	14 57		15 07	15 17	15 27	15 37	15 47	15 57
University	d	12 51	13 01	13 05	13 11	13 21	13 31	13 41	13 51	14 01	14 05	14 11	14 21	14 31	14a36	14 41		14 51	15 01	15 05	15 11	15 21	15 31	15 41	15 51	16 01
Selly Oak	d	12 53	13 03		13 13	13 23	13 33	13 43	13 53	14 03		14 13	14 23	14 33		14 43		14 53	15 03		15 13	15 23	15 33	15 43	15 53	16 03
Bournville	d	12 55	13 05		13 15	13 25	13 35	13 45	13 55	14 05		14 15	14 25	14 35		14 45		14 55	15 05		15 15	15 25	15 35	15 45	15 55	16 05
Kings Norton	d	12 57	13 07		13 17	13 27	13 37	13 47	13 57	14 07		14 17	14 27	14 37		14 47		14 57	15 07		15 17	15 27	15 37	15 47	15 57	16 07
Northfield	d	13 00	13 10		13 20	13 30	13 40	13 50	14 00	14 10		14 20	14 30	14 40		14 50		15 00	15 10		15 20	15 30	15 40	15 50	16 00	16 10
Longbridge	d	13 04	13a14		13a24	13 34	13a44	13a54	14 04	14a14		14a24	14 34	14a44		14a54		15 04	15a14		15a24	15 34	15a44	15a54	16 04	16a14
Barnt Green	d	13 09				13 39			14 09				14 39					15 09				15 39			16 09	
Alvechurch	d	13 13				13 43			14 13				14 43					15 13				15 43			16 13	
Redditch	a	13 23				13 53			14 23				14 53					15 23				15 53			16 23	
Bromsgrove	a			13 21							14 21									15 21						

		LM	LM	LM	LM	XC	LM	LM	LM	LM	LM	LM	LM	XC	LM	LM	LM	LM	LM	LM	LM	XC	LM	LM	LM	LM
						◇ B								◇ B								◇ A				
Lichfield Trent Valley	d		15 22				15 52				16 22				16 52				17 22				17 52			18 22
Lichfield City	d		15 25	15 36			15 55	16 06			16 25	16 36			16 55	17 06			17 25	17 36			17 55	18 06		18 25
Shenstone	d		15 30	15 41			16 00	16 11			16 30	16 41			17 00	17 11			17 30	17 41			18 00	18 11		18 30
Blake Street	d		15 34	15 44			16 04	16 14			16 34	16 44			17 04	17 14			17 34	17 44			18 04	18 14		18 34
Butlers Lane	d		15 36	15 46			16 06	16 16			16 36	16 46			17 06	17 16			17 36	17 46			18 06	18 16		18 36
Four Oaks	d		15 39	15 50			16 09	16 20			16 39	16 50			17 09	17 20			17 39	17 50			18 09	18 20		18 39
Sutton Coldfield	d		15 42	15 53			16 12	16 23			16 42	16 53			17 12	17 23			17 42	17 53			18 12	18 23		18 42
Wylde Green	d		15 45	15 56			16 15	16 26			16 45	16 56			17 15	17 26			17 45	17 56			18 15	18 26		18 45
Chester Road	d		15 47	15 58			16 17	16 28			16 47	16 58			17 17	17 28			17 47	17 58			18 17	18 28		18 47
Erdington	d		15 48	15 59			16 18	16 29			16 48	16 59			17 18	17 29			17 48	17 59			18 18	18 29		18 48
Gravelly Hill	d		15 51	16 02			16 21	16 32			16 51	17 02			17 21	17 32			17 51	18 02			18 21	18 32		18 51
Aston	d		15 54	16 05			16 24	16 35			16 54	17 05			17 24	17 35			17 54	18 05			18 24	18 35		18 54
Duddeston	d			16 08				16 38				17 08				17 38				18 08				18 38		
Birmingham New Street 12	a		16 01	16 12			16 30	16 43			17 01	17 12			17 30	17 42			18 01	18 12			18 30	18 43		19 00
	d	15 59	16 04	16 14	16 24	16 30	16 34	16 44	16 54	16 59	17 04	17 14	17 24	17 30	17 34	17 44	17 54	17 59	18 04	18 14	18 24	18 30	18 34	18 44	18 54	19 04
Five Ways	d		16 07	16 17	16 27		16 37	16 47	16 57		17 07	17 17	17 27		17 37	17 47	17 57		18 07	18 17	18 27		18 37	18 47	18 57	19 07
University	d	16 05	16 11	16 21	16 31	16 36	16 41	16 51	17 01	17 05	17 11	17 21	17 31	17 36	17 41	17 51	18 01	18 05	18 11	18 21	18 31		18 41	18 51	19 01	19 11
Selly Oak	d		16 13	16 23	16 33		16 43	16 53	17 03		17 13	17 23	17 33		17 43	17 53	18 03		18 13	18 23	18 33		18 43	18 53	19 03	19 13
Bournville	d		16 15	16 25	16 35		16 45	16 55	17 05		17 15	17 25	17 35		17 45	17 55	18 05		18 15	18 25	18 35		18 45	18 55	19 05	19 15
Kings Norton	d		16 17	16 27	16 37		16 47	16 57	17 07		17 17	17 27	17 37		17 47	17 57	18 07		18 17	18 27	18 37		18 47	18 57	19 07	19 17
Northfield	d		16 20	16 30	16 40		16 50	17 00	17 10		17 20	17 30	17 40		17 50	18 00	18 10		18 20	18 30	18 40		18 50	19 00	19 10	19 20
Longbridge	d		16a24	16 34	16a44		16a54	17 04	17a14		17a24	17 34	17a44		17a54	18 04	18a14		18a24	18 34	18a44		18a54	19 04	19a14	19a24
Barnt Green	d			16 39				17 09				17 39				18 09				18 39				19 09		
Alvechurch	d			16 43				17 13				17 43				18 13				18 43				19 13		
Redditch	a			16 53				17 23				17 53				18 23				18 53				19 23		
Bromsgrove	a	16 21				16 50				17 21				17 51				18 20				18 50				

For general notes see front of timetable
For details of catering facilities see Directory of Train Operators

A From Nottingham (Table 57)
B From Nottingham to Cardiff Central (Table 57)

Table 69

until 25 October

Lichfield → Birmingham → Longbridge and Redditch

Network Diagram - see first page of Table 67

		LM	LM	LM	LM	LM	LM	LM	LM	LM	LM	LM	LM	LM	LM	LM	LM	LM	LM	LM	LM	LM	LM	LM		
Lichfield Trent Valley	d				18 52			19 22			20 00			20 30		21 00		21 30		22 00		22 30	22 57			
Lichfield City	d	18 36			18 55	19 06		19 25	19 36		20 03			20 33		21 03		21 33		22 03		22 33	23 00			
Shenstone	d	18 41			19 00	19 11		19 30	19 41		20 08			20 38		21 08		21 38		22 08		22 38	23 05			
Blake Street	d	18 44			19 04	19 14		19 34	19 44		20 12			20 42		21 12		21 42		22 12		22 42	23 09	23 36		
Butlers Lane	d	18 46			19 06	19 16		19 36	19 46		20 14			20 44		21 14		21 44		22 14		22 44	23 11	23 38		
Four Oaks	d	18 50			19 09	19 20		19 39	19 50		20 17			20 47		21 17		21 47		22 17		22 47	23 14	23 41		
Sutton Coldfield	d	18 53			19 12	19 23		19 42	19 53		20 20			20 50		21 20		21 50		22 20		22 50	23 17	23 44		
Wylde Green	d	18 56			19 15	19 26		19 45	19 56		20 23			20 53		21 23		21 53		22 23		22 53	23 20			
Chester Road	d	18 58			19 17	19 28		19 47	19 58		20 25			20 55		21 25		21 55		22 25		22 55				
Erdington	d	18 59			19 18	19 29		19 48	19 59		20 26			20 56		21 26		21 56		22 26		22 56				
Gravelly Hill	d	19 02			19 21	19 32		19 51	20 02		20 29			20 59		21 29		21 59		22 29		22 59				
Aston	d	19 05			19 24	19 35		19 54	20 05		20 32			21 02		21 32		22 02		22 32		23 02				
Duddeston	d	19 08				19 38			20 08		20 35			21 05		21 35		22 05		22 35		23 05				
Birmingham New Street 12	a	19 12			19 30	19 42		20 03	20 12		20 41			21 11		21 42		22 13		22 41		23 12	23 31	23 58		
	d	19 14	19 24	19 30	19 34	19 44	19 54		20 14	20 24	20 44	20 54	20 59	21 14	21 24	21 44	21 54	22 14	22 24	22 44	22 55	23 14	23 35			
Five Ways	d	19 17	19 27		19 37	19 47	19 57		20 17	20 27	20 47	20 57		21 17	21 27	21 47	21 57	22 17	22 27	22 47	22 58	23 17	23 38			
University	d	19 21	19 31	19 36	19 41	19 51	20 01		20 21	20 31	20 51	21 01	21 05	21 21	21 31	21 51	22 01	22 21	22 31	22 51	23 02	23 21	23 42			
Selly Oak	d	19 23	19 33		19 43	19 53	20 03		20 23	20 33	20 53	21 03		21 23	21 33	21 53	22 03	22 23	22 33	22 53	23 04	23 23	23 45			
Bournville	d	19 25	19 35		19 45	19 55	20 05		20 25	20 35	20 55	21 05		21 25	21 35	21 55	22 05	22 25	22 35	22 55	23 06	23 25	23 47			
Kings Norton	d	19 27	19 37		19 47	19 57	20 07		20 27	20 37	20 57	21 07		21 27	21 37	21 57	22 07	22 27	22 37	22 57	23 08	23 27	23 49			
Northfield	d	19 30	19 40		19 50	20 00	20 10		20 30	20 40	21 00	21 10		21 30	21 40	22 00	22 10	22 30	22 40	23 00	23 11	23 30	23 52			
Longbridge	d	19 34	19a44		19a54	20 04	20a14		20 34	20a44	21 04	21a14		21 34	21a44	22 04	22a14	22 34	22a44	23 04	23a15	23 34	23a55			
Barnt Green	d	19 39				20 09			20 39		21 09			21 39		22 09		22 39		23 09		23 39				
Alvechurch	d	19 43				20 13			20 43		21 13			21 43		22 13		22 43		23 13		23 43				
Redditch	a	19 53				20 23			20 53		21 23			21 53		22 23		22 53		23 23		23 53				
Bromsgrove	a			19 50									21 21													

Saturdays

from 1 November

		LM	LM	LM	LM	LM	LM	LM	LM	LM	LM	LM	LM		LM	XC ◇	LM	LM	LM	LM	LM	LM	LM	LM	LM	LM
Lichfield Trent Valley	d							06 17		06 47			07 17				07 47			08 17		08 47			09 17	
Lichfield City	d							06 20		06 50			07 20				07 50			08 20		08 50			09 20	
Shenstone	d							06 26		06 56			07 26				07 56			08 26		08 56			09 26	
Blake Street	d				06 00			06 30		07 00			07 30				08 00			08 30		09 00			09 30	
Butlers Lane	d				06 02			06 32		07 02			07 32				08 02			08 32		09 02			09 32	
Four Oaks	d				06 05	06 24		06 35	06 58	07 05	07 24		07 35		07 54		08 05	08 24		08 35	08 54	09 05	09 24		09 35	09 54
Sutton Coldfield	d				06 09	06 28		06 39	07 01	07 09	07 27		07 39		07 57		08 09	08 27		08 39	08 57	09 09	09 27		09 39	09 57
Wylde Green	d				06 12	06 31		06 42	07 04	07 12	07 30		07 42		08 00		08 12	08 30		08 42	09 00	09 12	09 30		09 42	10 00
Chester Road	d				06 14	06 33		06 44	07 07	07 14	07 33		07 44		08 03		08 14	08 33		08 44	09 03	09 14	09 33		09 44	10 03
Erdington	d				06 16	06 35		06 46	07 09	07 16	07 35		07 46		08 05		08 16	08 35		08 46	09 05	09 16	09 35		09 46	10 05
Gravelly Hill	d				06 19	06 38		06 49	07 12	07 19	07 38		07 49		08 08		08 19	08 38		08 49	09 08	09 19	09 38		09 49	10 08
Aston	d				06 23	06 42		06 53	07 15	07 23	07 41		07 53		08 11		08 23	08 41		08 53	09 11	09 23	09 41		09 53	10 11
Duddeston	d				06 25	06 44		06 55	07 17		07 44				08 14			08 44			09 14		09 44			10 14
Birmingham New Street 12	a				06 31	06 52		07 00	07 23	07 30	07 50		08 00		08 20		08 30	08 51		09 00	09 21	09 30	09 50		10 01	10 20
	d	05 54	06 04	06 24	06 34	06 54	06 59	07 04	07 24	07 34	07 54	07 59	08 04		08 24	08 30	08 34	08 54	08 59	09 04	09 24	09 34	09 54	09 59	10 04	10 24
Five Ways	d	05 57	06 07	06 27	06 37	06 57		07 07	07 27	07 37	07 57		08 07		08 27		08 37	08 57		09 07	09 27	09 37	09 57		10 07	10 27
University	d	06 01	06 11	06 31	06 41	07 01	07 05	07 11	07 31	07 41	08 01	08 05	08 11		08 31	08a36	08 41	09 01	09 05	09 11	09 31	09 41	10 01	10 05	10 11	10 31
Selly Oak	d	06 04	06 14	06 34	06 44	07 04		07 14	07 34	07 44	08 04		08 14		08 34		08 44	09 04		09 14	09 34	09 44	10 04		10 14	10 34
Bournville	d	06 06	06 16	06 36	06 46	07 06		07 16	07 36	07 46	08 06		08 16		08 36		08 46	09 06		09 16	09 36	09 46	10 06		10 16	10 36
Kings Norton	d	06 09	06 19	06 39	06 49	07 09		07 19	07 39	07 49	08 09		08 19		08 39		08 49	09 09		09 19	09 39	09 49	10 09		10 19	10 39
Northfield	d	06 12	06 22	06 42	06 52	07 12		07 22	07 42	07 52	08 12		08 22		08 42		08 52	09 12		09 22	09 42	09 52	10 12		10 22	10 42
Longbridge	d	06a16	06 26	06a46	06 56	07a16		07 26	07a46	07 56	08a16		08 26		08a46		08 56	09a16		09 26	09a46	09 56	10a16		10 26	10a46
Barnt Green	d		06b39		07b09			07 39		08b09			08b39				09c09			09c39		10c09			10b39	
Alvechurch	d		06 44		07 14			07 44		08 14			08 44				09 14			09 44		10 14			10 44	
Redditch	a		06 53		07 21			07 51		08 23			08 53				09 23			09 53		10 23			10 53	
Bromsgrove	a						07 22					08 21							09 21					10 21		

		XC ◇	LM		LM	LM	LM	LM	LM	LM	LM	LM	LM	LM	LM	LM		LM	LM	LM	LM	LM	LM	LM	XC ◇	LM
Lichfield Trent Valley	d		09 47				10 17		10 47			11 17		11 47				12 17		12 47			13 17			13 47
Lichfield City	d		09 50				10 20		10 50			11 20		11 50				12 20		12 50			13 20			13 50
Shenstone	d		09 56				10 26		10 56			11 26		11 56				12 26		12 56			13 26			13 56
Blake Street	d		10 00				10 30		11 00			11 30		12 00				12 30		13 00			13 30			14 00
Butlers Lane	d		10 02				10 32		11 02			11 32		12 02				12 32		13 02			13 32			14 02
Four Oaks	d		10 05		10 24		10 35	10 54	11 05	11 24		11 35	11 54	12 05	12 24			12 35	12 54	13 05	13 24		13 35	13 54		14 05
Sutton Coldfield	d		10 09		10 27		10 39	10 57	11 09	11 27		11 39	11 57	12 09	12 27			12 39	12 57	13 09	13 27		13 39	13 57		14 09
Wylde Green	d		10 12		10 30		10 42	11 00	11 12	11 30		11 42	12 00	12 12	12 30			12 42	13 00	13 12	13 30		13 42	14 00		14 12
Chester Road	d		10 14		10 33		10 44	11 03	11 14	11 33		11 44	12 03	12 14	12 33			12 44	13 03	13 14	13 33		13 44	14 03		14 14
Erdington	d		10 16		10 35		10 46	11 05	11 16	11 35		11 46	12 05	12 16	12 35			12 46	13 05	13 16	13 35		13 46	14 05		14 16
Gravelly Hill	d		10 19		10 38		10 49	11 08	11 19	11 38		11 49	12 08	12 19	12 38			12 49	13 08	13 19	13 38		13 49	14 08		14 19
Aston	d		10 23		10 41		10 53	11 11	11 23	11 41		11 53	12 11	12 23	12 41			12 53	13 11	13 23	13 41		13 53	14 11		14 23
Duddeston	d				10 44			11 14		11 44			12 14		12 44				13 14		13 44			14 14		
Birmingham New Street 12	a		10 30		10 50		11 01	11 20	11 30	11 50		12 01	12 20	12 30	12 50			13 01	13 20	13 30	13 52		14 01	14 20		14 31
	d	10 30	10 34		10 54	10 59	11 04	11 24	11 34	11 54	11 59	12 04	12 24	12 34	12 54	12 59		13 04	13 24	13 34	13 54	13 59	14 04	14 24	14 30	14 34
Five Ways	d		10 37		10 57		11 07	11 27	11 37	11 57		12 07	12 27	12 37	12 57			13 07	13 27	13 37	13 57		14 07	14 27		14 37
University	d	10a36	10 41		11 01	11 05	11 11	11 31	11 41	12 01	12 05	12 11	12 31	12 41	13 01	13 05		13 11	13 31	13 41	14 01	14 05	14 11	14 31	14a36	14 41
Selly Oak	d		10 44		11 04		11 14	11 34	11 44	12 04		12 14	12 34	12 44	13 04			13 14	13 34	13 44	14 04		14 14	14 34		14 44
Bournville	d		10 46		11 06		11 16	11 36	11 46	12 06		12 16	12 36	12 46	13 06			13 16	13 36	13 46	14 06		14 16	14 36		14 46
Kings Norton	d		10 49		11 09		11 19	11 39	11 49	12 09		12 19	12 39	12 49	13 09			13 19	13 39	13 49	14 09		14 19	14 39		14 49
Northfield	d		10 52		11 12		11 22	11 42	11 52	12 12		12 22	12 42	12 52	13 12			13 22	13 42	13 52	14 12		14 22	14 42		14 52
Longbridge	d		10 56		11a16		11 26	11a46	11 56	12a16		12 26	12a46	12 56	13a16			13 26	13a46	13 56	14a16		14 26	14a46		14 56
Barnt Green	d		11c09				11c39		12c09			12b39		13c09				13c39		14c09			14b39			15c09
Alvechurch	d		11 14				11 44		12 14			12 44		13 14				13 44		14 14			14 44			15 14
Redditch	a		11 23				11 53		12 23			12 53		13 23				13 53		14 23			14 53			15 23
Bromsgrove	a					11 21					12 21					13 21						14 21				

For general notes see front of timetable
For details of catering facilities see
Directory of Train Operators

b Arrives 9 minutes earlier
c Arrives 8 minutes earlier

Table 69

Saturdays
from 1 November

Lichfield → Birmingham → Longbridge and Redditch

Network Diagram - see first page of Table 67

		LM	LM	LM	LM	LM		LM	LM	LM	LM	XC ◇	LM	LM	LM	LM	LM	XC ◇	LM		LM	LM	LM	LM	XC ◇	LM
Lichfield Trent Valley	d			14 17		14 47				15 17			15 47			16 17			16 47				17 17			17 47
Lichfield City	d			14 20		14 50				15 20			15 50			16 20			16 50				17 20			17 50
Shenstone	d			14 26		14 56				15 26			15 56			16 26			16 56				17 26			17 56
Blake Street	d			14 30		15 00				15 30			16 00			16 30			17 00				17 30			18 00
Butlers Lane	d			14 32		15 02				15 32			16 02			16 32			17 02				17 32			18 02
Four Oaks	d	14 24		14 35	14 54	15 05		15 24		15 35	15 54		16 05	16 24		16 35	16 54		17 05		17 24		17 35	17 54		18 05
Sutton Coldfield	d	14 27		14 39	14 57	15 09		15 27		15 39	15 57		16 09	16 27		16 39	16 57		17 09		17 27		17 39	17 57		18 09
Wylde Green	d	14 30		14 42	15 00	15 12		15 30		15 42	16 00		16 12	16 30		16 42	17 00		17 12		17 30		17 42	18 00		18 12
Chester Road	d	14 33		14 44	15 03	15 14		15 33		15 44	16 03		16 14	16 33		16 44	17 03		17 14		17 33		17 44	18 03		18 14
Erdington	d	14 35		14 46	15 05	15 16		15 35		15 46	16 05		16 16	16 35		16 46	17 05		17 16		17 35		17 46	18 05		18 16
Gravelly Hill	d	14 38		14 49	15 08	15 19		15 38		15 49	16 08		16 19	16 38		16 49	17 08		17 19		17 38		17 49	18 08		18 19
Aston	d	14 41		14 53	15 11	15 23		15 41		15 53	16 11		16 23	16 41		16 53	17 11		17 23		17 41		17 53	18 11		18 23
Duddeston	d	14 44			15 14			15 44			16 14			16 44			17 14				17 44			18 14		
Birmingham New Street 12	a	14 50		15 01	15 20	15 30		15 50		16 01	16 20		16 30	16 50		17 01	17 20		17 30		17 50		18 01	18 20		18 30
	d	14 54	14 59	15 04	15 24	15 34		15 54	15 59	16 04	16 24	16 30	16 34	16 54	16 59	17 04	17 24	17 30	17 34		17 54	17 59	18 04	18 24	18 30	18 34
Five Ways	d	14 57		15 07	15 27	15 37		15 57		16 07	16 27		16 37	16 57		17 07	17 27		17 37		17 57		18 07	18 27		18 37
University	d	15 01	15 05	15 11	15 31	15 41		16 01	16 05	16 11	16 31	16 36	16 41	17 01	17 05	17 11	17 31	17 36	17 41		18 01	18 05	18 11	18 31		18 41
Selly Oak	d	15 04		15 14	15 34	15 44		16 04		16 14	16 34		16 44	17 04		17 14	17 34		17 44		18 04		18 14	18 34		18 44
Bournville	d	15 06		15 16	15 36	15 46		16 06		16 16	16 36		16 46	17 06		17 16	17 36		17 46		18 06		18 16	18 36		18 46
Kings Norton	d	15 09		15 19	15 39	15 49		16 09		16 19	16 39		16 49	17 09		17 19	17 39		17 49		18 09		18 19	18 39		18 49
Northfield	d	15 12		15 22	15 42	15 52		16 12		16 22	16 42		16 52	17 12		17 22	17 42		17 52		18 12		18 22	18 42		18 52
Longbridge	d	15a16		15 26	15a46	15 56		16a16		16 26	16a46		16 56	17a16		17 26	17a46		17 56		18a16		18 26	18a46		18 56
Barnt Green	d			15b39		16b09				16c39			17b09			17b39			18e09				18c39			19b09
Alvechurch	d			15 44		16 14				16 44			17 14			17 44			18 14				18 44			19 14
Redditch	a			15 51		16 23				16 53			17 23			17 53			18 23				18 53			19 23
Bromsgrove	a		15 21						16 21			16 50			17 21			17 51				18 20			18 50	

		LM	LM	LM	LM 🚲	LM	LM	LM	LM		LM	LM	LM	LM	LM	LM	LM	LM	LM	LM	LM	LM	LM	LM		
Lichfield Trent Valley	d		18 17			18 47		19 17				19 57			20 27		20 57		21 27		21 57		22 27	22 55		
Lichfield City	d		18 20			18 50		19 20				20 00			20 30		21 00		21 30		22 00		22 30	22 58		
Shenstone	d		18 26			18 56		19 26				20 06			20 36		21 06		21 36		22 06		22 36	23 04		
Blake Street	d		18 30			19 00		19 30				20 10			20 40		21 10		21 40		22 10		22 40	23 08		
Butlers Lane	d		18 32			19 02		19 32				20 12			20 42		21 12		21 42		22 12		22 42	23 10		
Four Oaks	d	18 24	18 35	18 54		19 05	19 24	19 35	19 45			20 15			20 45		21 15		21 45		22 15		22 45	23 13		
Sutton Coldfield	d	18 27	18 39	18 57		19 09	19 27	19 39	19 49			20 19			20 49		21 19		21 49		22 19		22 49	23 17		
Wylde Green	d	18 30	18 42	19 00		19 12	19 30	19 42	19 52			20 22			20 52		21 22		21 52		22 22		22 52	23 20		
Chester Road	d	18 33	18 44	19 03		19 14	19 33	19 44	19 54			20 24			20 54		21 24		21 54		22 24		22 54			
Erdington	d	18 35	18 46	19 05		19 16	19 35	19 46	19 56			20 26			20 56		21 26		21 56		22 26		22 56			
Gravelly Hill	d	18 38	18 49	19 08		19 19	19 38	19 49	19 59			20 29			20 59		21 29		21 59		22 29		22 59			
Aston	d	18 41	18 53	19 11		19 23	19 41	19 53	20 03			20 33			21 03		21 33		22 03		22 33		23 03			
Duddeston	d	18 44		19 14			19 44		20 06			20 36			21 06		21 36		22 06		22 36		23 06			
Birmingham New Street 12	a	18 50	19 00	19 20		19 30	19 50	20 04	20 12			20 41			21 12		21 42		22 13		22 42		23 12	23 31		
	d	18 54	19 04	19 24	19 30	19 34	19 54		20 14		20 24	20 44	20 54	20 59	21 14	21 24	21 44	21 54	22 14	22 24	22 44	22 54	23 14	23 34		
Five Ways	d	18 57	19 07	19 27		19 37	19 57		20 17		20 27	20 47	20 57		21 17	21 27	21 47	21 57	22 17	22 27	22 47	22 57	23 17	23 37		
University	d	19 01	19 11	19 31	19 36	19 41	20 01		20 21		20 31	20 51	21 01	21 05	21 21	21 31	21 51	22 01	22 21	22 31	22 51	23 01	23 21	23 41		
Selly Oak	d	19 04	19 14	19 34		19 44	20 04		20 24		20 34	20 54	21 04		21 24	21 34	21 54	22 04	22 24	22 34	22 54	23 04	23 24	23 44		
Bournville	d	19 06	19 16	19 36		19 46	20 06		20 26		20 36	20 56	21 06		21 26	21 36	21 56	22 06	22 27	22 36	22 56	23 06	23 26	23 46		
Kings Norton	d	19 09	19 19	19 39		19 49	20 09		20 29		20 39	20 59	21 09		21 29	21 39	21 59	22 09	22 29	22 39	22 59	23 09	23 29	23 49		
Northfield	d	19 12	19 22	19 42		19 52	20 12		20 32		20 42	21 02	21 12		21 32	21 42	22 02	22 12	22 32	22 42	23 02	23 12	23 32	23 52		
Longbridge	d	19a16	19 26	19a46		19 56	20a16		20 35		20a46	21 05	21a16		21 35	21a46	22 05	22a16	22 35	22a46	23 05	23a16	23 35	23a56		
Barnt Green	d		19b39			20c09			20 39			21 09			21 39		22 09		22 39		23 09		23 39			
Alvechurch	d		19 44			20 14			20 44			21 14			21 44		22 14		22 44		23 14		23 44			
Redditch	a		19 53			20 23			20 56			21 26			21 56		22 26		22 56		23 26		23 56			
Bromsgrove	a				19 50									21 21												

Sundays

		LM	LM	LM		LM	LM	XC		LM	LM	LM		LM	LM	LM		LM	LM	LM		LM	LM	LM		LM
Lichfield Trent Valley	d			09 37		10 07	10 37			11 07	11 37	12 07		12 37		13 07		13 37	14 07	14 37		15 07		15 37		16 07
Lichfield City	d			09 40		10 10	10 40			11 10	11 40	12 10		12 40		13 10		13 40	14 10	14 40		15 10		15 40		16 10
Shenstone	d			09 45		10 15	10 45			11 15	11 45	12 15		12 45		13 15		13 45	14 15	14 45		15 15		15 45		16 15
Blake Street	d			09 49		10 19	10 49			11 19	11 49	12 19		12 49		13 19		13 49	14 19	14 49		15 19		15 49		16 19
Butlers Lane	d			09 51		10 21	10 51			11 21	11 51	12 21		12 51		13 21		13 51	14 21	14 51		15 21		15 51		16 21
Four Oaks	d		09 24	09 54		10 24	10 54			11 24	11 54	12 24		12 54		13 24		13 54	14 24	14 54		15 24		15 54		16 24
Sutton Coldfield	d		09 27	09 57		10 27	10 57			11 27	11 57	12 27		12 57		13 27		13 57	14 27	14 57		15 27		15 57		16 27
Wylde Green	d		09 30	10 00		10 30	11 00			11 30	12 00	12 30		13 00		13 30		14 00	14 30	15 00		15 30		16 00		16 30
Chester Road	d		09 32	10 02		10 32	11 02			11 32	12 02	12 32		13 02		13 32		14 02	14 32	15 02		15 32		16 02		16 32
Erdington	d		09 33	10 03		10 33	11 03			11 33	12 03	12 33		13 03		13 33		14 03	14 33	15 03		15 33		16 03		16 33
Gravelly Hill	d		09 36	10 06		10 36	11 06			11 36	12 06	12 36		13 06		13 36		14 06	14 36	15 06		15 36		16 06		16 36
Aston	d		09 39	10 09		10 39	11 09			11 39	12 09	12 39		13 09		13 39		14 09	14 39	15 09		15 39		16 09		16 39
Duddeston	d		09 41	10 11		10 41	11 11			11 41	12 11	12 41		13 11		13 41		14 11	14 41	15 11		15 41		16 11		16 41
Birmingham New Street 12	a		09 47	10 17		10 47	11 18			11 47	12 17	12 47		13 17		13 47		14 17	14 47	15 17		15 47		16 17		16 47
	d	09 20	09 50	10 20		10 50	11 20	11 46		11 50	12 20	12 50		13 20	13 45	13 50		14 20	14 50	15 20		15 50	16 00	16 20		16 50
Five Ways	d	09 23	09 53	10 23		10 53	11 23			11 53	12 23	12 53		13 23		13 53		14 23	14 53	15 23		15 53		16 23		16 53
University	d	09 27	09 57	10 27		10 57	11 27			11 57	12 27	12 57		13 27		13 57		14 27	14 57	15 27		15 57		16 27		16 57
Selly Oak	d	09 29	09 59	10 29		10 59	11 29			11 59	12 29	12 59		13 29		13 59		14 29	14 59	15 29		15 59		16 29		16 59
Bournville	d	09 31	10 01	10 31		11 01	11 31			12 01	12 31	13 01		13 31		14 01		14 31	15 01	15 31		16 01		16 31		17 01
Kings Norton	d	09 33	10 03	10 33		11 03	11 33			12 03	12 33	13 03		13 33		14 03		14 33	15 03	15 33		16 03		16 33		17 03
Northfield	d	09 36	10 06	10 36		11 06	11 36			12 06	12 36	13 06		13 36		14 06		14 36	15 06	15 36		16 06		16 36		17 06
Longbridge	d	09 39	10 09	10 39		11 09	11 39			12 09	12 39	13 09		13 39		14 09		14 39	15 09	15 39		16 09		16 39		17 09
Barnt Green	d	09 43	10 13	10 43		11 13	11 43			12 13	12 43	13 13		13 43		14 13		14 43	15 13	15 43		16 13		16 43		17 13
Alvechurch	d	09 48	10 18	10 48		11 18	11 48			12 18	12 48	13 18		13 48		14 18		14 48	15 18	15 48		16 18		16 48		17 18
Redditch	a	09 57	10 27	10 57		11 27	11 57			12 27	12 57	13 27		13 57		14 27		14 57	15 27	15 57		16 27		16 57		17 27
Bromsgrove	a							12 04							14 05								16 20			

For general notes see front of timetable
For details of catering facilities see Directory of Train Operators

b Arrives 8 minutes earlier
c Arrives 9 minutes earlier
e Arr. 1802

Lichfield → Birmingham → Longbridge and Redditch

Network Diagram - see first page of Table 67

		LM	LM	LM		LM	LM	LM		LM	LM	LM		LM	LM	LM		LM	LM	LM		LM	LM			
Lichfield Trent Valley	d	16 37	17 07			17 37	18 07			18 37	19 07	19 37		20 07		20 37		21 07	21 37	22 07		22 37	23 07			
Lichfield City	d	16 40	17 10			17 40	18 10			18 40	19 10	19 40		20 10		20 40		21 10	21 40	22 10		22 40	23 10			
Shenstone	d	16 45	17 15			17 45	18 15			18 45	19 15	19 45		20 15		20 45		21 15	21 45	22 15		22 45	23 15			
Blake Street	d	16 49	17 19			17 49	18 19			18 49	19 19	19 49		20 19		20 49		21 19	21 49	22 19		22 49	23 19			
Butlers Lane	d	16 51	17 21			17 51	18 21			18 51	19 21	19 51		20 21		20 51		21 21	21 51	22 21		22 51	23 21			
Four Oaks	d	16 54	17 24			17 54	18 24			18 54	19 24	19 54		20 24		20 54		21 24	21 54	22 24		22 54	23 24			
Sutton Coldfield	d	16 57	17 27			17 57	18 27			18 57	19 27	19 57		20 27		20 57		21 27	21 57	22 27		22 57	23 27			
Wylde Green	d	17 00	17 30			18 00	18 30			19 00	19 30	20 00		20 30		21 00		21 30	22 00	22 30		23 00	23 30			
Chester Road	d	17 02	17 32			18 02	18 32			19 02	19 32	20 02		20 32		21 02		21 32	22 02	22 32		23 02				
Erdington	d	17 03	17 33			18 03	18 33			19 03	19 33	20 03		20 33		21 03		21 33	22 03	22 33		23 03				
Gravelly Hill	d	17 06	17 36			18 06	18 36			19 06	19 36	20 06		20 36		21 06		21 36	22 06	22 36		23 06				
Aston	d	17 09	17 39			18 09	18 39			19 09	19 39	20 09		20 39		21 09		21 39	22 09	22 39		23 09				
Duddeston	d	17 11	17 41			18 11	18 41			19 11	19 41	20 11		20 41		21 11		21 41	22 11	22 41		23 11				
Birmingham New Street 12	a	17 17	17 47			18 17	18 47			19 17	19 47	20 18		20 47		21 17		21 47	22 17	22 47		23 17	23 44			
	d	17 20	17 50	18 00		18 20	18 50	19 00		19 20	19 50	20 20		20 50	21 00	21 20		21 50	22 20	22 50		23 20				
Five Ways	d	17 23	17 53			18 23	18 53			19 23	19 53	20 23		20 53		21 23		21 53	22 23	22 53		23 23				
University	d	17 27	17 57			18 27	18 57			19 27	19 57	20 27		20 57		21 27		21 57	22 27	22 57		23 27				
Selly Oak	d	17 29	17 59			18 29	18 59			19 29	19 59	20 29		20 59		21 29		21 59	22 29	22 59		23 29				
Bournville	d	17 31	18 01			18 31	19 01			19 31	20 01	20 31		21 01		21 31		22 01	22 31	23 01		23 31				
Kings Norton	d	17 33	18 03			18 33	19 03			19 33	20 03	20 33		21 03		21 33		22 03	22 33	23 03		23 33				
Northfield	d	17 36	18 06			18 36	19 06			19 36	20 06	20 36		21 06		21 36		22 06	22 36	23 06		23 36				
Longbridge	d	17 39	18 09			18 39	19 09			19 39	20 09	20 39		21 09		21 39		22 09	22 39	23 09		23 39				
Barnt Green	d	17 43	18 13			18 43	19 13			19 43	20 13	20 43		21 13		21 43		22 13	22 43	23 13		23 43				
Alvechurch	d	17 48	18 18			18 48	19 18			19 48	20 18	20 48		21 18		21 48		22 18	22 48	23 18		23 48				
Redditch	a	17 57	18 27			18 57	19 27			19 57	20 27	20 57		21 27		21 57		22 27	22 57	23 27		23 57				
Bromsgrove	a			18 20				19 21							21 20											

For general notes see front of timetable
For details of catering facilities see
Directory of Train Operators

Redditch and Longbridge → Birmingham → Lichfield

Network Diagram - see first page of Table 67

Miles	Miles			LM	LM	LM	LM	LM	LM	LM	LM	LM	LM	LM	LM	LM	LM	LM	LM	LM	LM	XC A	LM
—	0	Bromsgrove	d					06 21			06 42					07 23						07 50	
0	—	**Redditch**	d							06 27				06 57					07 27				
3¼	—	Alvechurch	d							06 32				07 02					07 32				
5	3½	Barnt Green	d							06 38				07 08					07 38				
7¾	—	Longbridge	d			06 13	06 23		06 33	06 43		06 53	07 03	07 13	07 23			07 33	07 43		07 53		08 03
8¾	—	Northfield	d			06 15	06 25		06 35	06 45		06 55	07 05	07 15	07 25			07 35	07 45		07 55		08 05
10¼	—	Kings Norton	d			06 17	06 27		06 37	06 47		06 57	07 07	07 17	07 27			07 37	07 47		07 57		08 07
11¼	—	Bournville	d			06 20	06 30		06 40	06 50		07 00	07 10	07 20	07 30			07 40	07 50		08 00		08 10
12¼	—	Selly Oak	d			06 22	06 32		06 42	06 52		07 02	07 12	07 22	07 32			07 42	07 52		08 02		08 12
13	11½	University	d			06 25	06 35	06 39	06 45	06 55	06 59	07 05	07 15	07 25	07 35			07 45	07 55	07 59	08 05	08 09	08 15
13½	—	Five Ways	d			06 28	06 38		06 48	06 58		07 08	07 18	07 28	07 38			07 48	07 58		08 08		08 18
14½	13	**Birmingham New Street 12**	a			06 33	06 43	06 45	06 53	07 03	07 07	07 14	07 23	07 33	07 43	07 45		07 53	08 03	08 09	08 13	08 16	08 23
—	—		d	06 03	06 24	06 35	06 45		06 55	07 05		07 15	07 25	07 35	07 45		07 51	07 55	08 05		08 15		08 25
16	—	Duddeston	d	06 07	06 28		06 49					07 19			07 49						08 19		
17¼	—	Aston	d	06 10	06 31	06 41	06 52		07 01	07 12		07 22	07 31	07 41	07 52		07 57	08 00	08 12		08 22		08 30
18½	—	Gravelly Hill	d	06 13	06 34	06 45	06 56		07 04	07 15		07 25	07 34	07 44	07 55		08 00	08 04	08 15		08 25		08 33
19¼	—	Erdington	d	06 15	06 36	06 47	06 58		07 06	07 17		07 28	07 37	07 47	07 58		08 02	08 07	08 17		08 28		08 36
20¼	—	Chester Road	d	06 17	06 38	06 49	07 00		07 08	07 19		07 30	07 39	07 48	07 59		08 04	08 09	08 19		08 30		08 38
21	—	Wylde Green	d	06 19	06 40	06 51	07 02		07 10	07 21		07 32	07 41	07 50	08 01		08 06	08 11	08 21		08 32		08 40
22	—	Sutton Coldfield	d	06 22	06 43	06 54	07 05		07 13	07 24		07 35	07 44	07 53	08 03		08 09	08 14	08 24		08 35		08 43
23½	—	Four Oaks	d	06 25	06 46	06 58	07a11		07 16	07 27		07a42	07 47		08a08		08 12	08 17	08 28		08a41		08 46
24½	—	Butlers Lane	d	06 27	06 48	07 00			07 18	07 29			07 49					08 19	08 30				08 49
26¼	—	Blake Street	d	06 29	06 50	07 02			07 20	07 31			07 51					08 21	08 32				08 51
28¾	—	Shenstone	d	06 33	06 54				07 24				07 55					08 25	08 36				08 55
31¾	—	**Lichfield City**	d	06a41	06 59	07 12			07 29	07 42			08 00	08a07			08a24	08 30	08 42				09a03
33	—	**Lichfield Trent Valley**	a		07 05	07 16			07 35	07 47			08 05					08 35	08 46				

		LM	LM	LM	XC A	LM	LM	LM	LM	LM	LM	LM	XC ◇ B ⚲	LM	LM	LM	LM	LM	LM	LM	LM	LM	LM
Bromsgrove	d				08 23			08 41					09 21				09 50						
Redditch	d	07 57					08 27				08 57				09 27				09 57			10 27	
Alvechurch	d	08 02					08 32				09 02				09 32				10 02			10 32	
Barnt Green	d	08 08					08 38				09 08				09 38				10 08			10 38	
Longbridge	d	08 13		08 23		08 33	08 43		08 53	09 03	09 13	09 23		09 33	09 43	09 53		10 03	10 13	10 23	10 33	10 43	10 53
Northfield	d	08 15		08 25		08 35	08 45		08 55	09 05	09 15	09 25		09 35	09 45	09 55		10 05	10 15	10 25	10 35	10 45	10 55
Kings Norton	d	08 17		08 27		08 37	08 48		08 57	09 07	09 17	09 27		09 37	09 47	09 57		10 07	10 17	10 27	10 37	10 47	10 57
Bournville	d	08 20		08 30		08 40	08 50		09 00	09 10	09 20	09 30		09 40	09 50	10 00		10 10	10 20	10 30	10 40	10 50	11 00
Selly Oak	d	08 22		08 32		08 42	08 52		09 02	09 12	09 22	09 32		09 42	09 52	10 02		10 12	10 22	10 32	10 42	10 52	11 02
University	d	08 25	08 29	08 35	08 39	08 45	08 55	08 59	09 05	09 15	09 25	09 35		09 45	09 55	10 05	10 09	10 15	10 25	10 35	10 44	10 55	11 05
Five Ways	d	08 28		08 38		08 48	08 58		09 08	09 18	09 28	09 38		09 48	09 58	10 08		10 18	10 28	10 38	10 47	10 58	11 08
Birmingham New Street 12	a	08 34	08 37	08 43	08 46	08 53	09 03	09 07	09 13	09 23	09 34	09 43	09 45	09 53	10 03	10 13	10 24	10 23	10 33	10 43	10 53	11 03	11 13
	d	08 35		08 45		08 55	09 05		09 15	09 25	09 35	09 45		09 55	10 05	10 15		10 25	10 35	10 45	10 55	11 05	11 15
Duddeston	d			08 49					09 19			09 49				10 19				10 49			11 19
Aston	d	08 41		08 52		09 00	09 11		09 23	09 31	09 41	09 52		10 00	10 11	10 22		10 30	10 41	10 52	11 00	11 11	11 22
Gravelly Hill	d	08 44		08 55		09 04	09 15		09 26	09 34	09 45	09 55		10 03	10 15	10 25		10 34	10 45	10 55	11 04	11 15	11 25
Erdington	d	08 47		08 58		09 06	09 17		09 29	09 36	09 47	09 58		10 06	10 17	10 28		10 36	10 47	10 58	11 06	11 17	11 28
Chester Road	d	08 49		09 00		09 08	09 19		09 31	09 38	09 49	10 00		10 08	10 19	10 30		10 38	10 49	11 00	11 08	11 19	11 30
Wylde Green	d	08 51		09 02		09 10	09 21		09 33	09 40	09 51	10 02		10 10	10 21	10 32		10 40	10 51	11 02	11 10	11 21	11 32
Sutton Coldfield	d	08 54		09 05		09 13	09 24		09 36	09 43	09 54	10 05		10 13	10 24	10 35		10 43	10 54	11 05	11 13	11 24	11 35
Four Oaks	d	08 57		09a11		09 17	09 27		09a41	09 46	09 57	10a11		10 17	10 27	10a41		10 47	10 57	11a11	11 17	11 27	11a41
Butlers Lane	d	08 59				09 19	09 29			09 48	09 59			10 19	10 29			10 49	10 59		11 19	11 29	
Blake Street	d	09 01				09 21	09 31			09 50	10 01			10 21	10 31			10 51	11 01		11 21	11 31	
Shenstone	d					09 25				09 54				10 25				10 55			11 25		
Lichfield City	d	09 09				09a34	09 39			10a03	10 09			10a33	10 39			11a03	11 09		11a33	11 39	
Lichfield Trent Valley	a	09 15					09 45				10 15				10 45				11 15			11 45	

		LM	LM	LM	LM	LM	LM	LM	LM	LM	LM	LM	XC ◇ C ⚲	LM	LM	LM	LM	LM	LM	LM	LM	LM	LM
Bromsgrove	d	10 50							11 50								12 50						
Redditch	d			10 57			11 27				11 57				12 27				12 57			13 27	
Alvechurch	d			11 02			11 32				12 02				12 32				13 02			13 32	
Barnt Green	d			11 08			11 38				12 08				12 38				13 08			13 38	
Longbridge	d		11 03	11 13	11 23	11 33	11 43	11 53		12 03	12 13	12 23		12 33	12 43	12 53		13 03	13 13	13 23	13 33	13 43	13 53
Northfield	d		11 05	11 15	11 25	11 35	11 45	11 55		12 05	12 15	12 25		12 35	12 45	12 55		13 05	13 15	13 25	13 35	13 45	13 55
Kings Norton	d		11 07	11 17	11 27	11 37	11 47	11 57		12 07	12 17	12 27		12 37	12 47	12 57		13 07	13 17	13 27	13 37	13 47	13 57
Bournville	d		11 10	11 20	11 30	11 40	11 50	12 00		12 10	12 20	12 30		12 40	12 50	13 00		13 10	13 20	13 30	13 40	13 50	14 00
Selly Oak	d		11 12	11 22	11 32	11 42	11 52	12 02		12 12	12 22	12 32		12 42	12 52	13 02		13 12	13 22	13 32	13 42	13 52	14 02
University	d	11 09	11 15	11 25	11 35	11 45	11 55	12 05	12 09	12 15	12 25	12 35	12 39	12 44	12 55	13 05	13 09	13 15	13 25	13 35	13 44	13 55	14 05
Five Ways	d		11 18	11 28	11 38	11 48	11 58	12 08		12 18	12 28	12 38		12 47	12 58	13 08		13 18	13 28	13 38	13 47	13 58	14 08
Birmingham New Street 12	a	11 23	11 23	11 33	11 43	11 53	12 03	12 13	12 23	12 23	12 34	12 43	12 46	12 53	13 03	13 13	13 18	13 23	13 33	13 43	13 53	14 03	14 13
	d		11 25	11 35	11 45	11 55	12 05	12 15		12 25	12 35	12 45		12 55	13 05	13 15		13 25	13 35	13 45	13 55	14 05	14 15
Duddeston	d				11 49			12 19				12 49				13 19				13 49			14 19
Aston	d		11 30	11 42	11 52	12 00	12 11	12 22		12 30	12 41	12 52		13 00	13 11	13 22		13 30	13 42	13 52	14 00	14 11	14 22
Gravelly Hill	d		11 34	11 45	11 55	12 04	12 15	12 26		12 34	12 45	12 55		13 04	13 15	13 25		13 34	13 46	13 55	14 04	14 15	14 25
Erdington	d		11 36	11 47	11 58	12 06	12 17	12 28		12 36	12 47	12 58		13 06	13 17	13 28		13 36	13 48	13 58	14 06	14 17	14 28
Chester Road	d		11 38	11 49	12 00	12 08	12 19	12 30		12 38	12 49	13 00		13 08	13 19	13 30		13 38	13 50	14 00	14 08	14 19	14 30
Wylde Green	d		11 40	11 51	12 02	12 10	12 21	12 32		12 40	12 51	13 02		13 10	13 21	13 32		13 40	13 52	14 02	14 10	14 21	14 32
Sutton Coldfield	d		11 43	11 54	12 05	12 13	12 24	12 35		12 43	12 54	13 05		13 13	13 24	13 35		13 43	13 55	14 05	14 13	14 24	14 35
Four Oaks	d		11 47	11 57	12a11	12 17	12 27	12a41		12 47	12 57	13a11		13 17	13 27	13a41		13 47	13 58	14a11	14 17	14 27	14a41
Butlers Lane	d		11 49	11 59		12 19	12 29			12 49	12 59			13 19	13 29			13 49	14 00		14 19	14 29	
Blake Street	d		11 51	12 01		12 21	12 31			12 51	13 01			13 21	13 31			13 51	14 02		14 21	14 31	
Shenstone	d		11 55			12 25				12 55				13 25				13 55			14 25		
Lichfield City	d		12a03	12 09		12a33	12 39			13a03	13 09			13a33	13 39			14a03	14 10		14a33	14 39	
Lichfield Trent Valley	a			12 15			12 45				13 15				13 45				14 15			14 45	

For general notes see front of timetable
For details of catering facilities see Directory of Train Operators

A From Gloucester to Nottingham (Table 57)
B To Nottingham (Table 57)
C Until 5 September.
To Nottingham (Table 57)

Redditch and Longbridge → Birmingham → Lichfield

Network Diagram - see first page of Table 67

		LM	LM	LM	LM	LM	LM	LM	LM	LM	LM	LM	LM	LM	LM	LM	LM	LM	LM	LM	LM	LM
Bromsgrove	d	13 50							14 50						15 44							16 44
Redditch	d			13 57			14 27				14 57			15 27				15 57			16 27	
Alvechurch	d			14 02			14 32				15 02			15 32				16 02			16 32	
Barnt Green	d			14 08			14 38				15 08			15 38				16 08			16 38	16 50
Longbridge	d		14 03	14 13	14 23	14 33	14 43	14 53		15 03	15 13	15 23	15 33	15 43		15 53	16 03	16 13	16 23	16 33	16 43	
Northfield	d		14 05	14 15	14 25	14 35	14 45	14 55		15 05	15 15	15 25	15 35	15 45		15 55	16 05	16 15	16 25	16 35	16 45	
Kings Norton	d		14 07	14 17	14 27	14 37	14 47	14 57		15 07	15 17	15 27	15 37	15 47		15 57	16 07	16 17	16 27	16 37	16 47	
Bournville	d		14 10	14 20	14 30	14 40	14 50	15 00		15 10	15 20	15 30	15 40	15 50		16 00	16 10	16 20	16 30	16 40	16 50	
Selly Oak	d		14 12	14 22	14 32	14 42	14 52	15 02		15 12	15 22	15 32	15 42	15 52		16 02	16 12	16 22	16 32	16 42	16 52	
University	d	14 09	14 15	14 25	14 35	14 44	14 55	15 05	15 09	15 15	15 25	15 35	15 45	15 55	15 59	16 05	16 15	16 25	16 35	16 45	16 55	17 00
Five Ways	d		14 18	14 28	14 38	14 47	14 58	15 08		15 18	15 28	15 38	15 48	15 58		16 08	16 18	16 28	16 38	16 48	16 58	
Birmingham New Street 12	a	14 23	14 23	14 33	14 43	14 53	15 03	15 13	15 21	15 23	15 33	15 43	15 53	16 03	16 09	16 13	16 23	16 33	16 43	16 53	17 03	17 14
	d		14 25	14 35	14 45	14 55	15 05	15 15		15 25	15 35	15 45	15 55	16 05		16 15	16 25	16 35	16 45	16 55	17 05	
Duddeston	d				14 49			15 19				15 49				16 19			16 49			
Aston	d		14 30	14 41	14 52	15 00	15 11	15 22		15 30	15 41	15 52	16 00	16 11		16 22	16 31	16 41	16 52	17 01	17 12	
Gravelly Hill	d		14 34	14 45	14 55	15 04	15 15	15 25		15 34	15 45	15 55	16 04	16 15		16 25	16 34	16 45	16 55	17 04	17 15	
Erdington	d		14 36	14 47	14 58	15 06	15 17	15 28		15 36	15 47	15 58	16 06	16 17		16 28	16 36	16 47	16 58	17 07	17 17	
Chester Road	d		14 38	14 49	15 00	15 08	15 19	15 30		15 38	15 49	16 00	16 08	16 19		16 30	16 38	16 49	17 00	17 09	17 19	
Wylde Green	d		14 40	14 51	15 02	15 10	15 21	15 32		15 40	15 51	16 02	16 10	16 21		16 33	16 40	16 51	17 02	17 11	17 21	
Sutton Coldfield	d		14 43	14 54	15 05	15 13	15 24	15 35		15 43	15 54	16 05	16 13	16 24		16 35	16 43	16 54	17 05	17 14	17 24	
Four Oaks	d		14 47	14 57	15a11	15 17	15 27	15a41		15 47	15 57	16a11	16 17	16 27		16a41	16 46	16 57	17a11	17 17	17 28	
Butlers Lane	d		14 49	14 59		15 19	15 29			15 49	15 59		16 19	16 29			16 48	16 59		17 19	17 30	
Blake Street	d		14 51	15 01		15 21	15 31			15 51	16 01		16 21	16 31			16 51	17 01		17 21	17 32	
Shenstone	d		14 55			15 25				15 55			16 25				16 55			17 25	17 36	
Lichfield City	d		15a03	15 09		15a33	15 39			16a03	16 09		16a33	16 39			17a03	17 09		17 30	17 41	
Lichfield Trent Valley	a			15 15			15 45				16 15			16 45				17 15		17 35	17 46	

		LM	LM	LM	LM	LM	LM	LM	LM	LM	LM	LM	XC ◇ A	LM	LM	LM	LM	LM	LM	LM	LM	LM	LM
Bromsgrove	d								17 49							18 42							
Redditch	d			16 57			17 27				17 57				18 27				18 57			19 27	
Alvechurch	d			17 02			17 32				18 02				18 32				19 02			19 32	
Barnt Green	d			17 08			17 38				18 08				18 38	18 49			19 08			19 38	
Longbridge	d	16 53	17 03	17 13	17 23	17 33	17 43	17 53		18 03	18 13	18 23		18 33	18 43		18 53	19 03	19 13	19 23	19 33	19 43	19 53
Northfield	d	16 55	17 05	17 15	17 25	17 35	17 45	17 55		18 05	18 15	18 25		18 35	18 45		18 55	19 05	19 15	19 25	19 35	19 45	19 55
Kings Norton	d	16 57	17 07	17 17	17 27	17 37	17 47	17 57		18 07	18 17	18 27		18 37	18 47		18 57	19 07	19 17	19 27	19 37	19 47	19 57
Bournville	d	17 00	17 10	17 20	17 30	17 40	17 50	18 00		18 10	18 20	18 30		18 40	18 50		19 00	19 10	19 20	19 30	19 40	19 50	20 00
Selly Oak	d	17 02	17 12	17 22	17 32	17 42	17 52	18 02		18 12	18 22	18 32		18 42	18 52		19 02	19 12	19 22	19 32	19 42	19 52	20 02
University	d	17 05	17 15	17 25	17 35	17 45	17 55	18 04	18 09	18 15	18 25	18 34	18 39	18 44	18 55	18 59	19 05	19 15	19 25	19 35	19 45	19 55	20 05
Five Ways	d	17 08	17 18	17 28	17 38	17 48	17 58	18 07		18 18	18 28	18 37		18 47	18 58		19 08	19 18	19 28	19 38	19 48	19 58	20 08
Birmingham New Street 12	a	17 13	17 23	17 34	17 43	17 53	18 03	18 13	18 21	18 23	18 33	18 43	18 45	18 53	19 03	19 12	19 13	19 23	19 33	19 43	19 53	20 03	20 13
	d	17 15	17 25	17 35	17 45	17 55	18 05	18 15		18 25	18 35	18 45		18 55	19 05		19 15		19 35			20 05	
Duddeston	d	17 19			17 49			18 19		18 29		18 49		18 59			19 19		19 39			20 09	
Aston	d	17 22	17 31	17 42	17 52	18 01	18 11	18 22		18 32	18 41	18 52		19 02	19 11		19 22		19 42			20 12	
Gravelly Hill	d	17 25	17 34	17 45	17 55	18 04	18 14	18 25		18 35	18 45	18 55		19 05	19 15		19 25		19 45			20 15	
Erdington	d	17 28	17 36	17 47	17 58	18 06	18 17	18 28		18 38	18 47	18 58		19 08	19 17		19 28		19 47			20 17	
Chester Road	d	17 30	17 38	17 49	18 00	18 08	18 19	18 30		18 40	18 49	19 00		19 10	19 19		19 30		19 49			20 19	
Wylde Green	d	17 32	17 40	17 51	18 02	18 10	18 21	18 32		18 42	18 51	19 02		19 12	19 21		19 32		19 51			20 21	
Sutton Coldfield	d	17 35	17 43	17 54	18 05	18 14	18 24	18 35		18 45	18 54	19 05		19 15	19 24		19 35		19 54			20 24	
Four Oaks	d	17a41	17 47	17 58	18a11	18 17	18 27	18a41		18 48	18 57	19a11		19 18	19 27		19a41		19 57			20 27	
Butlers Lane	d		17 49	18 00		18 19	18 29			18 50	18 59			19 20	19 29				19 59			20 29	
Blake Street	d		17 51	18 02		18 21	18 31			18 53	19 01			19 22	19 31				20 01			20 31	
Shenstone	d		17 55	18 06		18 25				18 57				19 26					20 05			20 35	
Lichfield City	d		18 00	18 11		18a33	18 39			19a03	19 09			19a33	19 39				20 10			20 40	
Lichfield Trent Valley	a		18 05	18 16			18 45				19 15				19 45				20 15			20 45	

		LM	LM	LM	LM	LM	LM	LM	LM	LM	LM	LM	LM	XC ◇	LM	LM	LM	LM	LM	LM
Bromsgrove	d			20 10				20 59						22 20		22 28				
Redditch	d		19 57			20 27			20 57		21 27		21 57				22 27		22 57	
Alvechurch	d		20 02			20 32			21 02		21 32		22 02				22 32		23 02	
Barnt Green	d		20 08			20 38			21 08		21 38		22 08				22 38		23 08	
Longbridge	d	20 03	20 13		20 30	20 43	21 00		21 13	21 30	21 43	22 00	22 13		22 30		22 43	22 52	23 13	23 27
Northfield	d	20 05	20 15		20 32	20 45	21 02		21 15	21 32	21 45	22 02	22 15		22 32		22 45	22 54	23 15	23 29
Kings Norton	d	20 07	20 17		20 34	20 47	21 04		21 17	21 34	21 47	22 04	22 17		22 34		22 47	22 56	23 17	23 31
Bournville	d	20 10	20 20		20 37	20 50	21 07		21 20	21 37	21 50	22 07	22 20		22 37		22 50	22 59	23 20	23 34
Selly Oak	d	20 12	20 22		20 39	20 52	21 09		21 22	21 39	21 52	22 09	22 22		22 39		22 52	23 01	23 22	23 36
University	d	20 15	20 25	20 29	20 41	20 55	21 12	21 16	21 25	21 42	21 55	22 12	22 25		22 42	22 46	22 55	23 04	23 25	23 39
Five Ways	d	20 18	20 28		20 44	20 58	21 15		21 28	21 45	21 58	22 15	22 28		22 45		22 58	23 07	23 28	23 42
Birmingham New Street 12	a	20 23	20 33	20 44	20 50	21 03	21 20	21 27	21 33	21 50	22 04	22 20	22 33	22 48	22 50	22 57	23 03	23 12	23 34	23 47
	d		20 35			21 05			21 35		22 05		22 35		22 55			23 14		
Duddeston	d		20 39			21 09			21 39		22 09		22 39		22 59			23 18		
Aston	d		20 42			21 12			21 42		22 12		22 42		23 02			23 21		
Gravelly Hill	d		20 45			21 15			21 45		22 15		22 45		23 05			23 24		
Erdington	d		20 47			21 17			21 47		22 17		22 47		23 07			23 26		
Chester Road	d		20 49			21 19			21 49		22 19		22 49		23 09			23 28		
Wylde Green	d		20 51			21 21			21 51		22 21		22 51		23 11			23 30		
Sutton Coldfield	d		20 54			21 24			21 54		22 24		22 54		23 14			23 33		
Four Oaks	d		20 57			21 27			21 57		22 27		22 57		23 17			23 36		
Butlers Lane	d		20 59			21 29			21 59		22 29		22 59		23 19			23 38		
Blake Street	d		21 01			21 31			22 01		22 31		23 01		23a24			23 40		
Shenstone	d		21 05			21 35			22 05		22 35		23 05					23 44		
Lichfield City	d		21 10			21 40			22 10		22 40		23 10					23a53		
Lichfield Trent Valley	a		21 15			21 45			22 15		22 45		23 15							

For general notes see front of timetable
For details of catering facilities see
Directory of Train Operators

A To Nottingham (Table 57)

Redditch and Longbridge → Birmingham → Lichfield

Network Diagram - see first page of Table 67

		LM	LM	LM	LM	LM	LM		LM	LM	LM	LM	LM	LM		LM	LM	LM	XC A	LM	LM		LM	LM	XC A	LM
Bromsgrove	d				06 21		06 42					07 23							07 50						08 23	
Redditch	d			05 57					06 27		06 57							07 27						07 57		
Alvechurch	d			06 03					06 33		07 03							07 33						08 03		
Barnt Green	d			06 11					06 43		07 13							07 39						08 09		
Longbridge	d		06 03	06b23		06 33			06 53	07 03	07 23			07 33		07 43		07 53		08 03	08 13			08 23		08 33
Northfield	d		06 05	06 25		06 35			06 55	07 05	07 25			07 35		07 45		07 55		08 05	08 15			08 25		08 35
Kings Norton	d		06 08	06 28		06 38			06 58	07 08	07 28			07 38		07 47		07 58		08 08	08 17			08 28		08 38
Bournville	d		06 10	06 30		06 40			07 00	07 10	07 30			07 40		07 50		08 00		08 10	08 20			08 30		08 40
Selly Oak	d		06 13	06 33		06 43			07 03	07 13	07 33			07 43		07 52		08 03		08 13	08 22			08 33		08 43
University	d		06 15	06 35	06 39	06 45	06 59		07 05	07 15	07 35			07 45		07 55	07 59	08 05	08 09	08 15	08 25		08 29	08 35	08 39	08 45
Five Ways	d		06 19	06 39		06 49			07 09	07 19	07 39			07 49		07 58		08 09		08 19	08 28			08 39		08 49
Birmingham New Street 12	a		06 22	06 42	06 45	06 53	07 07		07 12	07 23	07 42	07 45		07 52		08 03	08 09	08 12	08 16	08 22	08 33		08 37	08 42	08 46	08 53
	d	06 03	06 24	06 45		06 55			07 15	07 25	07 45		07 51	07 55		08 05		08 15		08 25	08 36			08 45		08 55
Duddeston	d	06 07		06 49					07 19		07 49							08 19						08 49		
Aston	d	06 10	06 30	06 52		07 01			07 22	07 31	07 52		07 57	08 01		08 11		08 22		08 31	08 42			08 52		09 01
Gravelly Hill	d	06 13	06 33	06 56		07 04			07 26	07 34	07 56		08 00	08 05		08 14		08 26		08 34	08 45			08 56		09 04
Erdington	d	06 15	06 36	06 59		07 07			07 29	07 37	07 59		08 03	08 08		08 17		08 29		08 37	08 48			08 59		09 07
Chester Road	d	06 17	06 38	07 01		07 09			07 31	07 39	08 01		08 05	08 10		08 19		08 31		08 39	08 50			09 01		09 09
Wylde Green	d	06 19	06 41	07 03		07 12			07 33	07 42	08 03		08 08	08 13		08 22		08 33		08 42	08 53			09 03		09 12
Sutton Coldfield	d	06 22	06 44	07 06		07 15			07 36	07 45	08 06		08 11	08 16		08 25		08 36		08 45	08 56			09 06		09 15
Four Oaks	d	06 25	06 47	07a13		07 18			07a43	07 48	08a13		08 14	08 19		08 28		08a43		08 48	08 59			09a13		09 18
Butlers Lane	d	06 27	06 50			07 21				07 51			08 16	08 22		08 31				08 51	09 02					09 21
Blake Street	d	06 29	06 52			07 23				07 53			08 19	08 24		08 33				08 53	09 04					09 23
Shenstone	d	06 33	06 57			07 28				07 58			08 23	08 29						08 58						09 28
Lichfield City	d	06 38	07 02			07 33				08 03			08a29	08 34		08 47				09 03	09 17					09 33
Lichfield Trent Valley	a	06 44	07 10			07 40				08 10				08 40		08 55				09 10	09 25					09 40

		LM	LM	LM	LM		LM	LM	XC ◇ B ✠	LM	LM	LM		LM	LM	LM	LM	LM	LM		LM	LM	LM	LM	LM	LM
Bromsgrove	d		08 41						09 21					09 50					10 50						11 50	
Redditch	d			08 27				08 57				09 27				09 57		10 27				10 57		11 27		
Alvechurch	d			08 33				09 03				09 33				10 03		10 33				11 03		11 33		
Barnt Green	d			08 39				09 10				09 42				10 14		10 44				11 14		11 44		
Longbridge	d	08 43		08 53	09 03		09 13	09 23		09 33	09 43	09 53			10 03	10 23	10 33	10 53			11 03	11 23	11 33	11 53		12 03
Northfield	d	08 45		08 55	09 05		09 15	09 25		09 35	09 45	09 55			10 05	10 25	10 35	10 55			11 05	11 25	11 35	11 55		12 05
Kings Norton	d	08 48		08 58	09 08		09 18	09 28		09 38	09 48	09 58			10 08	10 28	10 38	10 58			11 08	11 28	11 38	11 58		12 08
Bournville	d	08 50		09 00	09 10		09 20	09 30		09 40	09 50	10 00			10 10	10 30	10 40	11 00			11 10	11 30	11 40	12 00		12 10
Selly Oak	d	08 53		09 03	09 13		09 23	09 33		09 43	09 53	10 03			10 13	10 33	10 43	11 03			11 13	11 33	11 43	12 03		12 13
University	d	08 55	08 59	09 05	09 15		09 25	09 35		09 45	09 55	10 05		10 09	10 15	10 35	10 45	11 05	11 09		11 15	11 35	11 45	12 05	12 09	12 15
Five Ways	d	08 59		09 09	09 19		09 29	09 39		09 49	09 59	10 09			10 19	10 39	10 49	11 09			11 19	11 39	11 49	12 09		12 19
Birmingham New Street 12	a	09 02	09 07	09 12	09 23		09 33	09 42	09 45	09 53	10 02	10 13		10 24	10 22	10 42	10 53	11 12	11 23		11 23	11 42	11 53	12 12	12 23	12 24
	d	09 05		09 15	09 27		09 36	09 45		09 55	10 05	10 15			10 25	10 45	10 55	11 15			11 25	11 45	11 55	12 15		12 25
Duddeston	d			09 19				09 49				10 19				10 49		11 19				11 49		12 19		
Aston	d	09 11		09 22	09 33		09 42	09 52		10 01	10 11	10 22			10 31	10 52	11 01	11 22			11 31	11 52	12 01	12 22		12 31
Gravelly Hill	d	09 14		09 26	09 36		09 45	09 56		10 04	10 14	10 26			10 34	10 56	11 04	11 26			11 34	11 56	12 04	12 26		12 34
Erdington	d	09 17		09 29	09 39		09 48	09 59		10 07	10 17	10 29			10 37	10 59	11 07	11 29			11 37	11 59	12 07	12 29		12 37
Chester Road	d	09 19		09 31	09 40		09 50	10 01		10 09	10 19	10 31			10 39	11 01	11 09	11 31			11 39	12 01	12 09	12 31		12 39
Wylde Green	d	09 22		09 33	09 43		09 53	10 03		10 12	10 22	10 33			10 42	11 03	11 12	11 33			11 42	12 03	12 12	12 33		12 42
Sutton Coldfield	d	09 25		09 36	09 45		09 56	10 06		10 15	10 25	10 36			10 45	11 06	11 15	11 36			11 45	12 06	12 15	12 36		12 45
Four Oaks	d	09 28		09a43	09 49		09 59	10a13		10 18	10 28	10 40			10a48	11a13	11 18	11a43			11 48	12a13	12 18	12a43		12 48
Butlers Lane	d	09 31			09 51		10 02			10 21	10 31	10 42					11 21				11 51		12 21			12 51
Blake Street	d	09 34			09 53		10 04			10 23	10 34	10 45					11 23				11 53		12 23			12 53
Shenstone	d				09 57					10 28		10 49					11 28				11 58		12 28			12 58
Lichfield City	d	09a45			10 03		10a15			10 33	10a45	10 54					11 35				12 03		12 33			13 03
Lichfield Trent Valley	a				10 08					10 38		11 01					11 38				12 08		12 38			13 08

		LM	LM		LM	LM	LM	LM	LM	LM		LM	LM	LM	LM	LM	LM		LM	LM	LM	LM	LM	LM		LM
Bromsgrove	d					12 50						13 50					14 50						15 44			
Redditch	d	11 57			12 27			12 57		13 27				13 57		14 27					14 57			15 27		
Alvechurch	d	12 03			12 33			13 03		13 33				14 03		14 33					15 03			15 33		
Barnt Green	d	12 14			12 44			13 14		13 42				14 14		14 44					15 14			15 44		
Longbridge	d	12 23	12 33		12 53		13 03	13 23	13 33	13 53			14 03	14 23	14 33	14 53			15 03	15 13	15 23	15 33		15 53		16 03
Northfield	d	12 25	12 35		12 55		13 05	13 25	13 35	13 55			14 05	14 25	14 35	14 55			15 05	15 15	15 25	15 35		15 55		16 05
Kings Norton	d	12 28	12 38		12 58		13 08	13 28	13 38	13 58			14 08	14 28	14 38	14 58			15 08	15 18	15 28	15 38		15 58		16 08
Bournville	d	12 30	12 40		13 00		13 11	13 30	13 41	14 00			14 10	14 30	14 40	15 00			15 10	15 20	15 30	15 40		16 00		16 10
Selly Oak	d	12 33	12 43		13 03		13 13	13 33	13 43	14 03			14 13	14 33	14 43	15 03			15 13	15 23	15 33	15 43		16 03		16 13
University	d	12 35	12 45		13 05	13 09	13 15	13 35	13 46	14 05		14 09	14 15	14 35	14 45	15 05	15 09		15 15	15 25	15 35	15 45	15 59	16 05		16 15
Five Ways	d	12 39	12 49		13 09		13 19	13 39	13 49	14 09			14 19	14 39	14 49	15 09			15 19	15 29	15 39	15 49		16 09		16 19
Birmingham New Street 12	a	12 42	12 53		13 12	13 18	13 23	13 42	13 54	14 12		14 23	14 23	14 42	14 53	15 13	15 21		15 23	15 34	15 42	15 53	16 09	16 13		16 23
	d	12 45	12 55		13 15		13 25	13 45	13 55	14 15			14 25	14 45	14 55	15 15			15 25	15 36	15 45	15 55		16 15		16 25
Duddeston	d	12 49			13 19			13 49		14 19				14 49		15 19					15 49			16 19		
Aston	d	12 52	13 01		13 22		13 31	13 52	14 01	14 22			14 31	14 52	15 01	15 22			15 31	15 42	15 52	16 01		16 22		16 31
Gravelly Hill	d	12 56	13 04		13 26		13 34	13 56	14 04	14 26			14 34	14 56	15 04	15 26			15 34	15 45	15 56	16 04		16 26		16 34
Erdington	d	12 59	13 07		13 29		13 37	13 59	14 07	14 29			14 37	14 59	15 07	15 29			15 37	15 48	15 59	16 07		16 29		16 37
Chester Road	d	13 01	13 09		13 31		13 39	14 01	14 09	14 31			14 39	15 01	15 09	15 31			15 39	15 50	16 01	16 09		16 31		16 39
Wylde Green	d	13 03	13 12		13 33		13 42	14 03	14 12	14 33			14 42	15 03	15 12	15 33			15 42	15 53	16 03	16 12		16 33		16 42
Sutton Coldfield	d	13 06	13 15		13 36		13 45	14 06	14 15	14 36			14 45	15 06	15 15	15 36			15 45	15 56	16 06	16 15		16 36		16 45
Four Oaks	d	13a13	13 18		13a43		13 48	14a13	14 18	14a43			14 48	15a13	15 18	15a45			15 48	15 59	16a13	16 18		16a43		16 48
Butlers Lane	d		13 21				13 51		14 21				14 51		15 21				15 51	16 02		16 21				16 51
Blake Street	d		13 23				13 53		14 23				14 53		15 23				15 53	16 04		16 23				16 53
Shenstone	d		13 28				13 58		14 28				14 58		15 28				15 58	16 09		16 28				16 58
Lichfield City	d		13 33				14 03		14 33				15 03		15 33				16 03	16a15		16 33				17 03
Lichfield Trent Valley	a		13 38				14 10		14 40				15 08		15 40				16 10			16 40				17 08

For general notes see front of timetable
For details of catering facilities see Directory of Train Operators

A From Gloucester to Nottingham (Table 57)
B To Nottingham (Table 57)
b Arr. 0615

Mondays to Fridays
from 27 October

Redditch and Longbridge → Birmingham → Lichfield

Network Diagram - see first page of Table 67

		LM	LM	LM	LM	LM	LM		LM	LM	LM	LM	LM	LM		LM	LM	XC ◇ A	LM	LM	LM		LM	LM	LM	LM
Bromsgrove	d					16 44								17 49						18 42						
Redditch	d		15 57				16 27				16 57		17 27				17 57				18 27			18 57		19 27
Alvechurch	d		16 03				16 33				17 03		17 33				18 03				18 33			19 03		19 33
Barnt Green	d		16 14			16 50	16 44				17 14		17 44				18 14			18 49	18 44			19 09		19 39
Longbridge	d	16 13	16 23	16 33			16 53		17 03		17 23	17 33	17 53			18 03	18 23		18 33		18 53		19 03	19 14	19 33	19 44
Northfield	d	16 15	16 25	16 35			16 55		17 05		17 25	17 35	17 55			18 05	18 25		18 35		18 55		19 05	19 16	19 35	19 46
Kings Norton	d	16 18	16 28	16 38			16 58		17 08		17 28	17 38	17 58			18 08	18 28		18 38		18 58		19 07	19 19	19 38	19 49
Bournville	d	16 20	16 30	16 40			17 00		17 10		17 30	17 40	18 00			18 10	18 30		18 40		19 00		19 10	19 21	19 40	19 51
Selly Oak	d	16 23	16 33	16 43			17 03		17 13		17 33	17 43	18 03			18 13	18 33		18 43		19 03		19 12	19 24	19 43	19 54
University	d	16 25	16 35	16 45	16 55	17 00	17 05		17 15	17 25	17 35	17 45	18 05	18 09		18 15	18 35	18 39	18 45	18 59	19 05		19 15	19 26	19 45	19 56
Five Ways	d	16 29	16 39	16 49	16 59		17 09		17 19	17 29	17 39	17 49	18 09			18 19	18 39		18 49		19 09		19 18	19 30	19 49	20 00
Birmingham New Street 12	a	16 33	16 42	16 53	17 02	17 14	17 12		17 23	17 34	17 42	17 53	18 12	18 21		18 23	18 42	18 45	18 53	19 12	19 12		19 24	19 34	19 53	20 03
	d	16 36	16 45	16 55	17 06		17 15		17 25	17 36	17 45	17 55	18 15			18 25	18 45		18 55		19 15		19 25	19 35		20 06
Duddeston	d		16 49				17 19				17 49		18 19				18 49				19 19			19 39		20 09
Aston	d	16 42	16 52	17 01	17 12		17 22		17 31	17 42	17 52	18 01	18 22			18 31	18 52		19 01		19 22		19 31	19 42		20 12
Gravelly Hill	d	16 45	16 56	17 04	17 15		17 26		17 34	17 45	17 56	18 04	18 26			18 34	18 56		19 04		19 26		19 34	19 46		20 16
Erdington	d	16 48	16 59	17 07	17 18		17 29		17 37	17 48	17 59	18 07	18 29			18 37	18 59		19 07		19 29		19 37	19 49		20 19
Chester Road	d	16 50	17 01	17 09	17 20		17 31		17 39	17 50	18 01	18 09	18 31			18 39	19 01		19 09		19 31		19 39	19 51		20 21
Wylde Green	d	16 53	17 03	17 12	17 23		17 33		17 42	17 53	18 03	18 12	18 33			18 42	19 03		19 12		19 33		19 42	19 53		20 23
Sutton Coldfield	d	16 56	17 06	17 15	17 26		17 36		17 45	17 56	18 06	18 15	18 36			18 45	19 06		19 15		19 36		19 45	19 56		20 26
Four Oaks	d	16 59	17a13	17 18	17 29		17a43		17 48	17 59	18a13	18 18	18a43			18 48	19a13		19 18		19a43		19 48	20 00		20 30
Butlers Lane	d	17 02		17 21	17 32				17 51	18 02		18 21				18 51			19 21				19 51	20 02		20 32
Blake Street	d	17a10		17 23	17 34				17 53	18 04		18 23				18 53			19 23				19 53	20 05		20 35
Shenstone	d			17 28	17 39				17 58	18 09		18 28				18 58			19 28				19 58	20 09		20 39
Lichfield City	d			17 33	17a45				18 03	18a15		18 33				19 03			19 33				20 03	20 14		20 44
Lichfield Trent Valley	a			17 40					18 10			18 40				19 10			19 40				20 10	20 22		20 52

		LM	LM	LM	LM		LM	LM	LM	LM	LM	LM		LM	LM	XC ◇	LM	LM	LM		LM	LM	LM			
Bromsgrove	d			20 10					20 59							22 20		22 28								
Redditch	d		19 57				20 27			20 57		21 27			21 57				22 27			22 57				
Alvechurch	d		20 03				20 33			21 03		21 33			22 03				22 33			23 03				
Barnt Green	d		20 09				20 39			21 09		21 39			22 09				22 39			23 09				
Longbridge	d	20 03	20 14		20 30		20 44	21 00		21 14	21 30	21 44		22 00	22 14		22 30		22 44		22 52	23 14	23 27			
Northfield	d	20 05	20 16		20 32		20 46	21 02		21 16	21 32	21 46		22 02	22 16		22 32		22 46		22 54	23 16	23 29			
Kings Norton	d	20 08	20 19		20 35		20 49	21 05		21 18	21 35	21 49		22 05	22 19		22 34		22 49		22 57	23 19	23 32			
Bournville	d	20 10	20 21		20 37		20 51	21 07		21 21	21 37	21 51		22 07	22 21		22 37		22 51		22 59	23 21	23 34			
Selly Oak	d	20 13	20 24		20 40		20 54	21 10		21 24	21 40	21 54		22 10	22 24		22 39		22 54		23 02	23 24	23 37			
University	d	20 15	20 26	20 29	20 42		20 56	21 12	21 16	21 26	21 42	21 56		22 12	22 26		22 42	22 46	22 56		23 04	23 26	23 39			
Five Ways	d	20 19	20 30		20 46		21 00	21 16		21 30	21 46	22 00		22 16	22 30		22 45		23 00		23 08	23 30	23 43			
Birmingham New Street 12	a	20 23	20 34	20 44	20 50		21 03	21 20	21 27	21 34	21 50	22 03		22 20	22 34	22 48	22 50	22 57	23 04		23 12	23 34	23 47			
	d		20 35				21 05			21 35		22 06			22 35		22 55				23 14					
Duddeston	d		20 39				21 09			21 39		22 09			22 39		22 59				23 18					
Aston	d		20 42				21 12			21 42		22 12			22 42		23 02				23 21					
Gravelly Hill	d		20 46				21 16			21 46		22 16			22 46		23 05				23 25					
Erdington	d		20 49				21 19			21 49		22 19			22 49		23 07				23 28					
Chester Road	d		20 51				21 21			21 51		22 21			22 51		23 09				23 30					
Wylde Green	d		20 53				21 23			21 53		22 23			22 53		23 11				23 32					
Sutton Coldfield	d		20 56				21 26			21 56		22 26			22 56		23 14				23 35					
Four Oaks	d		21 00				21 30			22 00		22 30			23 00		23 17				23 39					
Butlers Lane	d		21 02				21 32			22 02		22 32			23 02		23 19				23 41					
Blake Street	d		21 05				21 35			22 05		22 35			23 05		23a24				23 44					
Shenstone	d		21 09				21 39			22 09		22 39			23 09						23 48					
Lichfield City	d		21 14				21 44			22 14		22 44			23 14						23a56					
Lichfield Trent Valley	a		21 22				21 52			22 22		22 52			23 22											

Saturdays
until 25 October

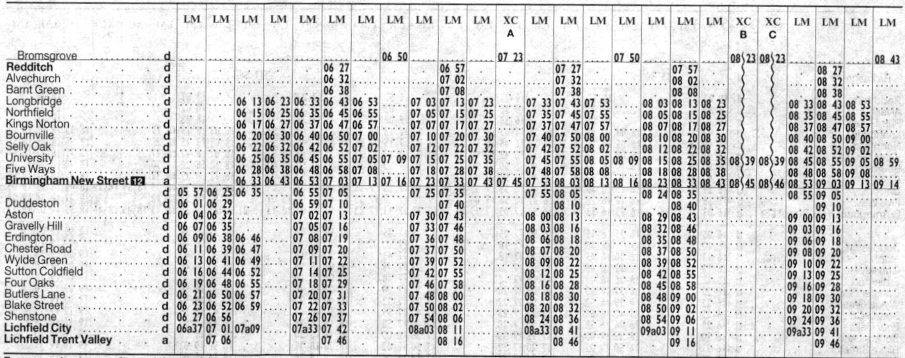

		LM	LM	LM	LM	LM	LM	LM	LM	LM	LM	LM	XC A	LM	LM	LM	LM	LM	LM	LM	XC B	XC C	LM	LM	LM	LM
Bromsgrove	d								06 50				07 23				07 50				08 23	08 23				08 43
Redditch	d						06 27				06 57				07 27				07 57					08 27		
Alvechurch	d						06 32				07 02				07 32				08 02					08 32		
Barnt Green	d						06 38				07 08				07 38				08 08					08 38		
Longbridge	d			06 13	06 23	06 33	06 43	06 53		07 03	07 13	07 23		07 33	07 43	07 53		08 03	08 13	08 23			08 33	08 43	08 53	
Northfield	d			06 15	06 25	06 35	06 45	06 55		07 05	07 15	07 25		07 35	07 45	07 55		08 05	08 15	08 25			08 35	08 45	08 55	
Kings Norton	d			06 17	06 27	06 37	06 47	06 57		07 07	07 17	07 27		07 37	07 47	07 57		08 07	08 17	08 27			08 37	08 47	08 57	
Bournville	d			06 20	06 30	06 40	06 50	07 00		07 10	07 20	07 30		07 40	07 50	08 00		08 10	08 20	08 30			08 40	08 50	09 00	
Selly Oak	d			06 22	06 32	06 42	06 52	07 02		07 12	07 22	07 32		07 42	07 52	08 02		08 12	08 22	08 32			08 42	08 52	09 02	
University	d			06 25	06 35	06 45	06 55	07 05	07 09	07 15	07 25	07 35		07 45	07 55	08 05	08 09	08 15	08 25	08 35	08 39	08 39	08 45	08 55	09 05	08 59
Five Ways	d			06 28	06 38	06 48	06 58	07 08		07 18	07 28	07 38		07 48	07 58	08 08		08 18	08 28	08 38			08 48	08 58	09 08	
Birmingham New Street 12	a			06 33	06 43	06 53	07 03	07 13	07 16	07 23	07 33	07 43	07 45	07 53	08 03	08 13	08 16	08 23	08 33	08 43	08 45	08 46	08 53	09 03	09 13	09 14
	d	05 57	06 25	06 35		06 55	07 05			07 25	07 35			07 55	08 05			08 24	08 35				08 55	09 05		
Duddeston	d	06 01	06 29			06 59	07 10				07 40				08 10				08 40					09 10		
Aston	d	06 04	06 32			07 02	07 13			07 30	07 43			08 00	08 13			08 29	08 43				09 00	09 13		
Gravelly Hill	d	06 07	06 35			07 05	07 16			07 33	07 46			08 03	08 16			08 32	08 46				09 03	09 16		
Erdington	d	06 09	06 38	06 46		07 08	07 19			07 36	07 48			08 06	08 18			08 35	08 48				09 06	09 18		
Chester Road	d	06 11	06 39	06 47		07 09	07 20			07 37	07 50			08 07	08 20			08 37	08 50				09 08	09 20		
Wylde Green	d	06 13	06 41	06 49		07 11	07 22			07 39	07 52			08 09	08 22			08 39	08 52				09 10	09 22		
Sutton Coldfield	d	06 16	06 44	06 52		07 14	07 25			07 42	07 55			08 12	08 25			08 42	08 55				09 13	09 25		
Four Oaks	d	06 19	06 48	06 55		07 18	07 29			07 46	07 58			08 16	08 28			08 45	08 58				09 16	09 28		
Butlers Lane	d	06 21	06 50	06 57		07 20	07 31			07 48	08 00			08 18	08 30			08 48	09 00				09 18	09 30		
Blake Street	d	06 23	06 52	06 59		07 22	07 33			07 50	08 02			08 20	08 32			08 50	09 02				09 20	09 32		
Shenstone	d	06 27	06 56			07 26	07 37			07 54	08 06			08 24	08 36			08 54	09 06				09 24	09 36		
Lichfield City	d	06a37	07 01	07a09		07a33	07 42			08a03	08 11			08a33	08 41			09a03	09 11				09a33	09 41		
Lichfield Trent Valley	a		07 06				07 46				08 16				08 46				09 16					09 46		

For general notes see front of timetable
For details of catering facilities see Directory of Train Operators

A To Nottingham (Table 57)

B Until 6 September.
From Gloucester to Nottingham (Table 57)

C From 13 September.
From Gloucester to Nottingham (Table 57)

Saturdays
until 25 October

Redditch and Longbridge → Birmingham → Lichfield

Network Diagram - see first page of Table 67

		LM	LM	LM	XC ◇ A	LM	LM	LM		LM	LM	LM	LM	LM	LM	LM	LM	LM	LM	LM	LM	LM	LM	LM	LM	LM
Bromsgrove	d				09 23					09 50							10 50						11 50			
Redditch	d		08 57				09 27					09 57			10 27			10 57			11 27				11 57	
Alvechurch	d		09 02				09 32					10 02			10 32			11 02			11 32				12 02	
Barnt Green	d		09 08				09 38					10 08			10 38			11 08			11 38				12 08	
Longbridge	d	09 03	09 13	09 23		09 33	09 43	09 53			10 03	10 13	10 23	10 33	10 43	10 53		11 13	11 23	11 33	11 43	11 53		12 03	12 13	12 23
Northfield	d	09 05	09 15	09 25		09 35	09 45	09 55			10 05	10 15	10 25	10 35	10 45	10 55		11 15	11 25	11 35	11 45	11 55		12 05	12 15	12 25
Kings Norton	d	09 07	09 17	09 27		09 37	09 47	09 57			10 07	10 17	10 27	10 37	10 47	10 57		11 17	11 27	11 37	11 47	11 57		12 07	12 17	12 27
Bournville	d	09 10	09 20	09 30		09 40	09 50	10 00			10 10	10 20	10 30	10 40	10 50	11 00		11 20	11 30	11 40	11 50	12 00		12 10	12 20	12 30
Selly Oak	d	09 12	09 22	09 32		09 42	09 52	10 02			10 12	10 22	10 32	10 42	10 52	11 02		11 22	11 32	11 42	11 52	12 02		12 12	12 22	12 32
University	d	09 15	09 25	09 35		09 45	09 55	10 05		10 09	10 15	10 25	10 35	10 44	10 55	11 05	11 09	11 25	11 35	11 45	11 55	12 05	12 09	12 15	12 25	12 35
Five Ways	d	09 18	09 28	09 38		09 48	09 58	10 08			10 18	10 28	10 38	10 47	10 58	11 08		11 28	11 38	11 48	11 58	12 08		12 18	12 28	12 38
Birmingham New Street 12	a	09 23	09 33	09 43	09 45	09 53	10 03	10 13		10 21	10 23	10 33	10 43	10 53	11 02	11 13	11 21	11 33	11 43	11 53	12 03	12 13	12 21	12 23	12 33	12 43
	d	09 25	09 35			09 55	10 05				10 25	10 35		10 55	11 05			11 35		11 55	12 05			12 25	12 35	
Duddeston	d		09 40				10 10					10 40			11 10			11 40			12 10				12 40	
Aston	d	09 30	09 43			10 00	10 13				10 30	10 43		11 00	11 13			11 43		12 00	12 13			12 30	12 43	
Gravelly Hill	d	09 33	09 46			10 03	10 16				10 33	10 46		11 03	11 16			11 46		12 03	12 16			12 33	12 46	
Erdington	d	09 36	09 48			10 06	10 18				10 36	10 48		11 06	11 18			11 48		12 06	12 18			12 36	12 48	
Chester Road	d	09 37	09 50			10 07	10 20				10 37	10 50		11 07	11 20			11 50		12 07	12 20			12 37	12 50	
Wylde Green	d	09 39	09 52			10 09	10 22				10 39	10 52		11 09	11 22			11 52		12 09	12 22			12 39	12 52	
Sutton Coldfield	d	09 42	09 55			10 12	10 25				10 42	10 55		11 12	11 25			11 55		12 12	12 25			12 42	12 55	
Four Oaks	d	09 46	09 58			10 16	10 28				10 46	10 58		11 16	11 28			11 58		12 16	12 28			12 46	12 58	
Butlers Lane	d	09 48	10 00			10 18	10 30				10 48	11 00		11 18	11 30			12 00		12 18	12 30			12 48	13 00	
Blake Street	d	09 50	10 02			10 20	10 32				10 50	11 02		11 20	11 32			12 02		12 20	12 32			12 50	13 02	
Shenstone	d	09 54	10 06			10 24	10 36				10 54	11 06		11 24	11 36			12 06		12 24	12 36			12 54	13 06	
Lichfield City	d	10a03	10 11			10a33	10 41				11a03	11 11		11a33	11 41			12 11		12a33	12 41			13a03	13 11	
Lichfield Trent Valley	a		10 16				10 46					11 16			11 46			12 16			12 46				13 16	

		XC ◇ B	XC ◇ C	LM	LM	LM	LM	LM	LM	LM	LM	LM	LM	LM	LM	LM		LM	LM	LM	LM	LM	LM	LM	LM	LM
Bromsgrove	d						12 50							13 50								14 50				
Redditch	d				12 27				12 57			13 27				13 57				14 27				14 57		
Alvechurch	d				12 32				13 02			13 32				14 02				14 32				15 02		
Barnt Green	d				12 38				13 08			13 38				14 08				14 38				15 08		
Longbridge	d			12 33	12 43	12 53		13 03	13 13	13 23	13 33	13 43	13 53		14 03	14 13		14 23	14 33	14 43	14 53		15 03	15 13	15 23	15 33
Northfield	d			12 35	12 45	12 55		13 05	13 15	13 25	13 35	13 45	13 55		14 05	14 15		14 25	14 35	14 45	14 55		15 05	15 15	15 25	15 35
Kings Norton	d			12 37	12 47	12 57		13 07	13 17	13 27	13 37	13 47	13 57		14 07	14 17		14 27	14 37	14 47	14 57		15 07	15 17	15 27	15 37
Bournville	d			12 40	12 50	13 00		13 10	13 20	13 30	13 40	13 50	14 00		14 10	14 20		14 30	14 40	14 50	15 00		15 10	15 20	15 30	15 40
Selly Oak	d			12 42	12 52	13 02		13 12	13 22	13 32	13 42	13 52	14 02		14 12	14 22		14 32	14 42	14 52	15 02		15 12	15 22	15 32	15 42
University	d	12 39	12 39	12 44	12 55	13 05	13 09	13 15	13 25	13 35	13 45	13 55	14 05	14 09	14 15	14 25		14 35	14 44	14 55	15 05	15 09	15 15	15 25	15 35	15 45
Five Ways	d			12 47	12 58	13 08		13 18	13 28	13 38	13 48	13 58	14 08		14 18	14 28		14 38	14 47	14 58	15 08		15 18	15 28	15 38	15 48
Birmingham New Street 12	a	12 45	12 46	12 53	13 03	13 13	13 21	13 23	13 33	13 43	13 53	14 03	14 13	14 21	14 23	14 33		14 43	14 53	15 03	15 13	15 21	15 23	15 33	15 43	15 53
	d			12 55	13 05			13 25	13 35		13 55	14 05			14 25	14 35			14 55	15 05			15 25	15 35		15 55
Duddeston	d				13 10				13 40			14 10				14 40				15 10				15 40		
Aston	d			13 00	13 13			13 30	13 43		14 00	14 13			14 30	14 43			15 00	15 13			15 30	15 43		16 00
Gravelly Hill	d			13 03	13 16			13 33	13 46		14 03	14 16			14 33	14 46			15 03	15 16			15 33	15 46		16 03
Erdington	d			13 06	13 18			13 36	13 48		14 06	14 18			14 36	14 48			15 06	15 18			15 36	15 48		16 06
Chester Road	d			13 07	13 20			13 37	13 50		14 07	14 20			14 37	14 50			15 07	15 20			15 37	15 50		16 07
Wylde Green	d			13 09	13 22			13 39	13 52		14 09	14 22			14 39	14 52			15 09	15 22			15 39	15 52		16 09
Sutton Coldfield	d			13 12	13 25			13 42	13 55		14 12	14 25			14 42	14 55			15 12	15 25			15 42	15 55		16 12
Four Oaks	d			13 16	13 28			13 46	13 58		14 16	14 28			14 46	14 58			15 16	15 28			15 46	15 58		16 16
Butlers Lane	d			13 18	13 30			13 48	14 00		14 18	14 30			14 48	15 00			15 18	15 30			15 48	16 00		16 18
Blake Street	d			13 20	13 32			13 50	14 02		14 20	14 32			14 50	15 02			15 20	15 32			15 50	16 02		16 20
Shenstone	d			13 24	13 36			13 54	14 06		14 24	14 36			14 54	15 06			15 24	15 36			15 54	16 06		16 24
Lichfield City	d			13a33	13 41			14a03	14 11		14a33	14 41			15a03	15 11			15a33	15 41			16a03	16 11		16a33
Lichfield Trent Valley	a				13 46				14 16			14 46				15 16				15 46				16 16		

		LM	LM	LM	LM	LM	LM	LM	LM	LM	LM	LM	LM	LM	LM	LM	LM	LM	LM	LM	LM	XC ◇ B	XC ◇ C	LM	LM	LM
Bromsgrove	d			15 50							16 50							17 50								
Redditch	d	15 27				15 57			16 27				16 57			17 27				17 57					18 27	
Alvechurch	d	15 32				16 02			16 32				17 02			17 32				18 02					18 32	
Barnt Green	d	15 38				16 08			16 38				17 08			17 38				18 08					18 38	
Longbridge	d	15 43	15 53		16 03	16 13	16 23	16 33	16 43	16 53		17 03	17 13	17 23	17 33	17 43	17 53		18 03	18 13	18 23			18 33	18 43	18 53
Northfield	d	15 45	15 55		16 05	16 15	16 25	16 35	16 45	16 55		17 05	17 15	17 25	17 35	17 45	17 55		18 05	18 15	18 25			18 35	18 45	18 55
Kings Norton	d	15 47	15 57		16 07	16 17	16 27	16 37	16 47	16 57		17 07	17 17	17 27	17 37	17 47	17 57		18 07	18 17	18 27			18 37	18 47	18 57
Bournville	d	15 50	16 00		16 10	16 20	16 30	16 40	16 50	17 00		17 10	17 20	17 30	17 40	17 50	18 00		18 10	18 20	18 30			18 40	18 50	19 00
Selly Oak	d	15 52	16 02		16 12	16 22	16 32	16 42	16 52	17 02		17 12	17 22	17 32	17 42	17 52	18 02		18 12	18 22	18 32			18 42	18 52	19 02
University	d	15 55	16 05	16 09	16 15	16 25	16 35	16 44	16 55	17 05	17 09	17 15	17 25	17 35	17 45	17 55	18 04	18 09	18 14	18 25	18 35	18 39	18 39	18 44	18 55	19 05
Five Ways	d	15 58	16 08		16 18	16 28	16 38	16 47	16 58	17 08		17 18	17 28	17 38	17 48	17 58	18 07		18 17	18 28	18 38			18 47	18 58	19 08
Birmingham New Street 12	a	16 03	16 13	16 21	16 23	16 33	16 43	16 53	17 03	17 13	17 21	17 23	17 33	17 43	17 53	18 03	18 13	18 21	18 23	18 33	18 43	18 45	18 46	18 53	19 03	19 13
	d	16 05			16 25	16 35		16 55	17 05			17 25	17 35		17 55	18 05			18 25	18 35				18 55	19 05	
Duddeston	d	16 10				16 40			17 10				17 40			18 10				18 40					19 10	
Aston	d	16 13			16 30	16 43		17 00	17 13			17 30	17 43		18 00	18 13			18 30	18 43				19 00	19 13	
Gravelly Hill	d	16 16			16 33	16 46		17 03	17 16			17 33	17 46		18 03	18 16			18 33	18 46				19 03	19 16	
Erdington	d	16 18			16 36	16 48		17 06	17 18			17 36	17 48		18 06	18 18			18 36	18 48				19 06	19 18	
Chester Road	d	16 20			16 37	16 50		17 07	17 20			17 37	17 50		18 07	18 20			18 37	18 50				19 07	19 20	
Wylde Green	d	16 22			16 39	16 52		17 09	17 22			17 39	17 52		18 09	18 22			18 39	18 52				19 09	19 22	
Sutton Coldfield	d	16 25			16 42	16 55		17 12	17 25			17 42	17 55		18 12	18 25			18 42	18 55				19 12	19 25	
Four Oaks	d	16 28			16 46	16 58		17 16	17 28			17 46	17 58		18 16	18 28			18 46	18 58				19 16	19 28	
Butlers Lane	d	16 30			16 48	17 00		17 18	17 30			17 48	18 00		18 18	18 30			18 48	19 00				19 18	19 30	
Blake Street	d	16 32			16 50	17 02		17 20	17 32			17 50	18 02		18 20	18 32			18 50	19 02				19 20	19 32	
Shenstone	d	16 36			16 54	17 06		17 24	17 36			17 54	18 06		18 24	18 36			18 54	19 06				19 24	19 36	
Lichfield City	d	16 41			17a03	17 11		17a33	17 41			18a03	18 11		18a33	18 41			19a03	19 11				19a33	19 41	
Lichfield Trent Valley	a	16 46				17 16			17 46				18 16			18 46				19 16					19 46	

For general notes see front of timetable
For details of catering facilities see Directory of Train Operators

A To Nottingham (Table 57)

B Until 6 September. To Nottingham (Table 57)

C From 13 September. From Cardiff Central to Nottingham (Table 57)

Saturdays

until 25 October

Redditch and Longbridge → Birmingham → Lichfield

Network Diagram - see first page of Table 67

		LM	LM	LM	LM	LM	LM	LM	LM	LM	LM	LM	LM	LM	LM	LM	LM	LM	LM	LM	LM	LM	LM	LM
Bromsgrove	d	18 50												21 00										
Redditch	d			18 57			19 27			19 57		20 27			20 57		21 27		21 57		22 27		22 57	
Alvechurch	d			19 02			19 32			20 02		20 32			21 02		21 32		22 02		22 32		23 02	
Barnt Green	d			19 08			19 38			20 08		20 38			21 08		21 38		22 08		22 38		23 08	
Longbridge	d		19 03	19 13	19 23	19 33	19 43	19 53	20 03	20 13	20 30	20 43	21 00		21 13	21 30	21 43	22 00	22 13	22 30	22 43	22 52	23 13	23 24
Northfield	d		19 05	19 15	19 25	19 35	19 45	19 55	20 05	20 15	20 32	20 45	21 02		21 15	21 32	21 45	22 02	22 15	22 32	22 45	22 54	23 15	23 26
Kings Norton	d		19 07	19 17	19 27	19 37	19 47	19 57	20 07	20 17	20 34	20 47	21 04		21 17	21 34	21 47	22 04	22 17	22 34	22 47	22 56	23 17	23 28
Bournville	d		19 10	19 20	19 30	19 40	19 50	20 00	20 10	20 20	20 37	20 50	21 07		21 20	21 37	21 50	22 07	22 20	22 37	22 50	22 59	23 20	23 31
Selly Oak	d		19 12	19 22	19 32	19 42	19 52	20 02	20 12	20 22	20 39	20 52	21 09		21 22	21 39	21 52	22 09	22 22	22 39	22 52	23 01	23 22	23 33
University	d	19 09	19 15	19 25	19 35	19 45	19 55	20 05	20 15	20 25	20 42	20 55	21 12	21 16	21 25	21 42	21 55	22 12	22 25	22 42	22 55	23 04	23 25	23 36
Five Ways	d		19 18	19 28	19 38	19 48	19 58	20 08	20 18	20 28	20 45	20 58	21 15		21 28	21 45	21 58	22 15	22 28	22 45	22 58	23 07	23 28	23 39
Birmingham New Street 12	a	19 21	19 23	19 33	19 43	19 53	20 03	20 13	20 23	20 33	20 50	21 03	21 20	21 28	21 33	21 50	22 03	22 20	22 33	22 50	23 03	23 12	23 33	23 44
	d			19 35			20 05			20 35		21 05			21 35		22 05		22 35		23 05	23 14		
Duddeston	d			19 39			20 09			20 39		21 09			21 39		22 09		22 39		23 09	23 18		
Aston	d			19 42			20 12			20 42		21 12			21 42		22 12		22 42		23 12	23 21		
Gravelly Hill	d			19 45			20 15			20 45		21 15			21 45		22 15		22 45		23 15	23 24		
Erdington	d			19 47			20 17			20 47		21 17			21 47		22 17		22 47		23 17	23 26		
Chester Road	d			19 49			20 19			20 49		21 19			21 49		22 19		22 49		23 19	23 28		
Wylde Green	d			19 51			20 21			20 51		21 21			21 51		22 21		22 51		23 21	23 30		
Sutton Coldfield	d			19 54			20 24			20 54		21 24			21 54		22 24		22 54		23 24	23 33		
Four Oaks	d			19 57			20 27			20 57		21 27			21 57		22 27		22 57		23 27	23 36		
Butlers Lane	d			19 59			20 29			20 59		21 29			21 59		22 29		22 59		23 29	23 38		
Blake Street	d			20 01			20 31			21 01		21 31			22 01		22 31		23 01		23a34	23 40		
Shenstone	d			20 05			20 35			21 05		21 35			22 05		22 35		23 05			23 44		
Lichfield City	d			20 10			20 40			21 10		21 40			22 10		22 40		23 10			23a53		
Lichfield Trent Valley	a			20 16			20 46			21 16		21 46			22 16		22 46		23 16					

Saturdays

from 1 November

		LM	LM	LM	LM	LM	LM	LM	LM	XC	LM	LM	LM	LM	LM	XC	LM	LM	LM	LM	LM	XC ◇	LM	LM	LM
Bromsgrove	d						06 50			07 23			07 50			08 23		08 43				09 23			09 50
Redditch	d			05 57		06 27			06 57			07 27			07 57				08 27		08 57			09 27	
Alvechurch	d			06 02		06 32			07 02			07 32			08 02				08 32		09 02			09 32	
Barnt Green	d			06 15		06 45			07 15			07 41			08 13				08 43		09 09			09 43	
Longbridge	d		06 03	06 23	06 33	06 53		07 03	07 23		07 33	07 53		08 03	08 23		08 33		08 53	09 03	09 23		09 33	09 53	
Northfield	d		06 05	06 25	06 35	06 55		07 05	07 25		07 35	07 55		08 05	08 25		08 35		08 55	09 05	09 25		09 35	09 55	
Kings Norton	d		06 08	06 28	06 38	06 58		07 08	07 28		07 38	07 58		08 08	08 28		08 38		08 58	09 08	09 28		09 38	09 58	
Bournville	d		06 10	06 30	06 40	07 00		07 10	07 30		07 40	08 00		08 10	08 30		08 40		09 00	09 10	09 30		09 40	10 00	
Selly Oak	d		06 13	06 33	06 43	07 03		07 13	07 33		07 43	08 03		08 13	08 33		08 43		09 03	09 13	09 33		09 43	10 03	
University	d		06 15	06 35	06 45	07 05	07 09	07 15	07 35		07 45	08 05	08 09	08 15	08 35	08 39	08 45	08 59	09 05	09 15	09 35		09 45	10 05	10 09
Five Ways	d		06 19	06 39	06 49	07 09		07 19	07 39		07 49	08 09		08 19	08 39		08 49		09 09	09 19	09 39		09 49	10 09	
Birmingham New Street 12	a		06 23	06 43	06 53	07 13	07 16	07 23	07 43	07 45	07 53	08 13	08 16	08 23	08 43	08 46	08 53	09 14	09 15	09 22	09 43	09 45	09 53	10 13	10 21
	d	05 57	06 25	06 45	06 55	07 15		07 25	07 45		07 55	08 15		08 25	08 45		08 55		09 15	09 25	09 45		09 55	10 15	
Duddeston	d	06 01		06 49		07 19			07 49			08 19			08 49				09 19		09 49			10 19	
Aston	d	06 04	06 31	06 52	07 01	07 22		07 31	07 52		08 01	08 22		08 31	08 52		09 00		09 22	09 30	09 52		10 00	10 22	
Gravelly Hill	d	06 08	06 34	06 56	07 04	07 26		07 34	07 56		08 04	08 26		08 34	08 56		09 04		09 26	09 34	09 56		10 04	10 26	
Erdington	d	06 11	06 37	06 59	07 07	07 29		07 37	07 59		08 07	08 29		08 37	08 59		09 07		09 29	09 37	09 59		10 07	10 29	
Chester Road	d	06 13	06 39	07 01	07 09	07 31		07 39	08 01		08 09	08 31		08 39	09 01		09 09		09 31	09 39	10 01		10 09	10 31	
Wylde Green	d	06 15	06 42	07 03	07 12	07 33		07 42	08 03		08 12	08 33		08 42	09 03		09 12		09 33	09 42	10 03		10 12	10 33	
Sutton Coldfield	d	06 18	06 45	07 06	07 15	07 36		07 45	08 06		08 15	08 36		08 45	09 06		09 15		09 36	09 45	10 06		10 15	10 36	
Four Oaks	d	06 22	06 48	07a13	07 18	07a43		07 48	08a13		08 18	08a43		08 48	09a13		09 18		09a43	09 48	10a13		10 18	10a43	
Butlers Lane	d	06 24	06 51		07 21			07 51			08 21			08 51			09 21			09 51			10 21		
Blake Street	d	06 27	06 53		07 23			07 53			08 23			08 53			09 23			09 53			10 23		
Shenstone	d	06 31	06 58		07 28			07 58			08 28			08 58			09 28			09 58			10 28		
Lichfield City	d	06 36	07 03		07 33			08 03			08 33			09 03			09 33			10 03			10 33		
Lichfield Trent Valley	a	06 44	07 08		07 38			08 08			08 38			09 08			09 38			10 08			10 38		

		LM	LM	LM	LM	LM	LM	LM	LM	LM	LM	LM	LM	XC ◇	LM	LM	LM	LM	LM	LM	LM	LM	LM	LM
Bromsgrove	d					10 50					11 50						12 50					13 50		
Redditch	d		09 57		10 27			10 57		11 27			11 57			12 27			12 57		13 27			13 57
Alvechurch	d		10 02		10 32			11 02		11 32			12 02			12 32			13 02		13 32			14 02
Barnt Green	d		10 13		10 43			11 13		11 43			12 13			12 43			13 13		13 43			14 13
Longbridge	d	10 03	10 23	10 33	10 53		11 03	11 23	11 33	11 53		12 03	12 23		12 33	12 53		13 03	13 23	13 33	13 53		14 03	14 23
Northfield	d	10 05	10 25	10 35	10 55		11 05	11 25	11 35	11 55		12 05	12 25		12 35	12 55		13 05	13 25	13 35	13 55		14 05	14 25
Kings Norton	d	10 08	10 28	10 38	10 58		11 08	11 28	11 38	11 58		12 08	12 28		12 38	12 58		13 08	13 28	13 38	13 58		14 08	14 28
Bournville	d	10 10	10 30	10 40	11 00		11 10	11 30	11 40	12 00		12 10	12 30		12 40	13 00		13 10	13 30	13 40	14 00		14 10	14 30
Selly Oak	d	10 13	10 33	10 43	11 03		11 13	11 33	11 43	12 03		12 13	12 33		12 43	13 03		13 13	13 33	13 43	14 03		14 13	14 33
University	d	10 15	10 35	10 45	11 05	11 09	11 15	11 35	11 45	12 05	12 09	12 15	12 35	12 39	12 45	13 05	13 09	13 15	13 35	13 45	14 05	14 09	14 15	14 35
Five Ways	d	10 19	10 39	10 49	11 09		11 19	11 39	11 49	12 09		12 19	12 39		12 49	13 09		13 19	13 39	13 49	14 09		14 19	14 39
Birmingham New Street 12	a	10 23	10 43	10 53	11 13	11 21	11 23	11 43	11 53	12 13	12 21	12 23	12 43	12 46	12 52	13 13	13 21	13 23	13 43	13 53	14 13	14 21	14 23	14 43
	d	10 25	10 45	10 55	11 15		11 25	11 45	11 55	12 15		12 25	12 45		12 55	13 15		13 25	13 45	13 55	14 15		14 25	14 45
Duddeston	d		10 49		11 19			11 49		12 19			12 49			13 19			13 49		14 19			14 48
Aston	d	10 30	10 52	11 00	11 22		11 30	11 52	12 00	12 22		12 30	12 52		13 00	13 22		13 30	13 52	14 00	14 22		14 30	14 52
Gravelly Hill	d	10 34	10 56	11 04	11 26		11 34	11 56	12 04	12 26		12 34	12 56		13 04	13 26		13 34	13 56	14 04	14 26		14 34	14 56
Erdington	d	10 37	10 59	11 07	11 29		11 37	11 59	12 07	12 29		12 37	12 59		13 07	13 29		13 37	13 59	14 07	14 29		14 37	14 59
Chester Road	d	10 39	11 01	11 09	11 31		11 39	12 01	12 09	12 31		12 39	13 01		13 09	13 31		13 39	14 01	14 09	14 31		14 39	15 01
Wylde Green	d	10 42	11 03	11 12	11 33		11 42	12 03	12 12	12 33		12 42	13 03		13 12	13 33		13 42	14 03	14 12	14 33		14 42	15 03
Sutton Coldfield	d	10 45	11 06	11 15	11 36		11 45	12 06	12 15	12 36		12 45	13 06		13 15	13 36		13 45	14 06	14 15	14 36		14 45	15 06
Four Oaks	d	10 48	11a13	11 18	11a43		11 48	12a13	12 18	12a43		12 48	13a13		13 18	13a43		13 48	14a13	14 18	14a43		14 48	15a13
Butlers Lane	d	10 51		11 21			11 51		12 21			12 51			13 21			13 51		14 21			14 51	
Blake Street	d	10 53		11 23			11 53		12 23			12 53			13 23			13 53		14 23			14 53	
Shenstone	d	10 58		11 28			11 58		12 28			12 58			13 28			13 58		14 28			14 58	
Lichfield City	d	11 03		11 33			12 03		12 33			13 03			13 33			14 03		14 33			15 03	
Lichfield Trent Valley	a	11 08		11 38			12 08		12 38			13 08			13 38			14 08		14 38			15 08	

For general notes see front of timetable
For details of catering facilities see
Directory of Train Operators

Table 69

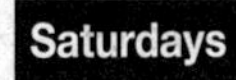

from 1 November

Redditch and Longbridge → Birmingham → Lichfield

Network Diagram - see first page of Table 67

		LM	LM	LM	LM	LM		LM	LM	LM	LM	LM	LM	LM	LM	LM	LM	LM	LM		LM	LM	LM	LM	XC ◇	LM
Bromsgrove	d			14 50						15 50					16 50							17 50				
Redditch	d		14 27			14 57			15 27			15 57		16 27			16 57				17 27			17 57		
Alvechurch	d		14 32			15 02			15 32			16 02		16 32			17 02				17 32			18 02		
Barnt Green	d		14 43			15 13			15 43			16 13		16 43			17 13				17 43			18 13		
Longbridge	d	14 33	14 53		15 03	15 23		15 33	15 53		16 03	16 23	16 33	16 53		17 03	17 23	17 33			17 53		18 03	18 23		18 33
Northfield	d	14 35	14 55		15 05	15 25		15 35	15 55		16 05	16 25	16 35	16 55		17 05	17 25	17 35			17 55		18 05	18 25		18 35
Kings Norton	d	14 38	14 58		15 08	15 28		15 38	15 58		16 08	16 28	16 38	16 58		17 08	17 28	17 38			17 58		18 08	18 28		18 38
Bournville	d	14 40	15 00		15 10	15 30		15 40	16 00		16 10	16 30	16 40	17 00		17 10	17 30	17 40			18 00		18 10	18 30		18 40
Selly Oak	d	14 43	15 03		15 13	15 33		15 43	16 03		16 13	16 33	16 43	17 03		17 13	17 33	17 43			18 03		18 13	18 33		18 43
University	d	14 45	15 05	15 09	15 15	15 35		15 45	16 05	16 09	16 15	16 35	16 45	17 05	17 09	17 15	17 35	17 45	17 55		18 05	18 09	18 15	18 35	18 39	18 45
Five Ways	d	14 49	15 09		15 19	15 39		15 49	16 09		16 19	16 39	16 49	17 09		17 19	17 39	17 49	17 58		18 09		18 19	18 39		18 49
Birmingham New Street 12	a	14 53	15 13	15 21	15 23	15 43		15 53	16 13	16 21	16 24	16 43	16 54	17 13	17 21	17 24	17 43	17 53	18 02		18 13	18 21	18 23	18 43	18 46	18 54
	d	14 55	15 15		15 25	15 45		15 55	16 15		16 25	16 45	16 55	17 15		17 25	17 45	17 55	18 06		18 15		18 25	18 45		18 55
Duddeston	d		15 19			15 49			16 19			16 49		17 19			17 49				18 19			18 49		
Aston	d	15 00	15 22		15 30	15 52		16 00	16 22		16 30	16 52	17 00	17 22		17 30	17 52	18 00	18 11		18 22		18 30	18 52		19 00
Gravelly Hill	d	15 04	15 26		15 34	15 56		16 04	16 26		16 34	16 56	17 04	17 26		17 34	17 56	18 04	18 14		18 26		18 34	18 56		19 04
Erdington	d	15 07	15 29		15 37	15 59		16 07	16 29		16 37	16 59	17 07	17 29		17 37	17 59	18 07	18 17		18 29		18 37	18 59		19 07
Chester Road	d	15 09	15 31		15 39	16 01		16 09	16 31		16 39	17 01	17 09	17 31		17 39	18 01	18 09	18 19		18 31		18 39	19 01		19 09
Wylde Green	d	15 12	15 33		15 42	16 03		16 12	16 33		16 42	17 03	17 12	17 33		17 42	18 03	18 12	18 22		18 33		18 42	19 03		19 12
Sutton Coldfield	d	15 15	15 36		15 45	16 06		16 15	16 36		16 45	17 06	17 15	17 36		17 45	18 06	18 15	18 25		18 36		18 45	19 06		19 15
Four Oaks	d	15 18	15a43		15 48	16a13		16 18	16a43		16 48	17a13	17 18	17a43		17 48	18a13	18 18	18 28		18a43		18 48	19a13		19 18
Butlers Lane	d	15 21			15 51			16 21			16 51		17 21			17 51		18 21	18 31				18 51			19 21
Blake Street	d	15 23			15 53			16 23			16 53		17 23			17 53		18 23	18 33				18 53			19 23
Shenstone	d	15 28			15 58			16 28			16 58		17 28			17 58		18 28	18 38				18 58			19 28
Lichfield City	d	15 33			16 03			16 33			17 03		17 33			18 03		18 33	18a46				19 03			19 33
Lichfield Trent Valley	a	15 38			16 08			16 38			17 08		17 38			18 08		18 38					19 08			19 38

		LM	LM	LM	LM	LM	LM	LM	LM		LM	LM	LM	LM	LM	LM	LM	LM	LM	LM	LM	LM	LM	LM		
Bromsgrove	d		18 50											21 00												
Redditch	d	18 27			18 57		19 27		19 57			20 27			20 57		21 27		21 57		22 27		22 57			
Alvechurch	d	18 32			19 02		19 32		20 02			20 32			21 02		21 32		22 02		22 32		23 02			
Barnt Green	d	18b43			19 08		19 38		20 08			20 38			21 08		21 38		22 08		22 38		23 08			
Longbridge	d	18 53		19 03	19 13	19 33	19 43	20 03	20 13		20 30	20 43	21 00		21 13	21 30	21 43	22 00	22 13	22 30	22 43	22 55	23 13	23 25		
Northfield	d	18 55		19 05	19 15	19 35	19 45	20 05	20 15		20 32	20 45	21 02		21 15	21 32	21 45	22 02	22 15	22 32	22 45	22 57	23 15	23 27		
Kings Norton	d	18 58		19 08	19 18	19 38	19 48	20 08	20 18		20 35	20 48	21 05		21 18	21 35	21 48	22 05	22 18	22 35	22 48	23 00	23 18	23 30		
Bournville	d	19 00		19 10	19 20	19 40	19 50	20 10	20 20		20 37	20 50	21 07		21 20	21 37	21 50	22 07	22 20	22 37	22 50	23 02	23 20	23 32		
Selly Oak	d	19 03		19 13	19 23	19 43	19 53	20 13	20 23		20 40	20 53	21 10		21 23	21 40	21 53	22 10	22 23	22 40	22 53	23 05	23 23	23 35		
University	d	19 05	19 09	19 15	19 25	19 45	19 55	20 15	20 25		20 42	20 55	21 12	21 16	21 25	21 42	21 55	22 12	22 25	22 42	22 55	23 07	23 25	23 37		
Five Ways	d	19 09		19 19	19 29	19 49	19 59	20 19	20 29		20 46	20 59	21 16		21 29	21 46	21 59	22 16	22 29	22 46	22 59	23 11	23 29	23 41		
Birmingham New Street 12	a	19 13	19 21	19 23	19 34	19 53	20 03	20 23	20 33		20 50	21 03	21 20	21 28	21 33	21 50	22 03	22 20	22 33	22 50	23 04	23 15	23 34	23 45		
	d	19 15		19 25	19 35		20 05		20 35			21 05			21 35		22 05		22 35		23 05	23 15				
Duddeston	d	19 19			19 39		20 09		20 39			21 09			21 39		22 09		22 39		23 09	23 19				
Aston	d	19 22		19 30	19 42		20 12		20 42			21 12			21 42		22 12		22 42		23 12	23 22				
Gravelly Hill	d	19 26		19 34	19 46		20 16		20 46			21 16			21 46		22 16		22 46		23 16	23 26				
Erdington	d	19 29		19 37	19 49		20 19		20 49			21 19			21 49		22 19		22 49		23 19	23 29				
Chester Road	d	19 31		19 39	19 51		20 21		20 51			21 21			21 51		22 21		22 51		23 21	23 31				
Wylde Green	d	19 33		19 42	19 53		20 23		20 53			21 23			21 53		22 23		22 53		23 23	23 33				
Sutton Coldfield	d	19 36		19 45	19 56		20 26		20 56			21 26			21 56		22 26		22 56		23 26	23 36				
Four Oaks	d	19a43		19 48	20 00		20 30		21 00			21 30			22 00		22 30		23 00		23 30	23 40				
Butlers Lane	d			19 51	20 02		20 32		21 02			21 32			22 02		22 32		23 02		23 32	23 42				
Blake Street	d			19 53	20 05		20 35		21 05			21 35			22 05		22 35		23 05		23a38	23 43				
Shenstone	d			19 58	20 09		20 39		21 09			21 39			22 09		22 39		23 09			23 47				
Lichfield City	d			20 03	20 14		20 44		21 14			21 44			22 14		22 44		23 14			23a57				
Lichfield Trent Valley	a			20 08	20 22		20 52		21 22			21 52			22 22		22 52		23 22							

Sundays

		LM	LM	LM		LM	LM	LM		LM	LM	LM		LM	LM	LM		LM	LM	LM		LM	LM	LM		LM
Bromsgrove	d																			15 09						16 51
Redditch	d			09 31		10 01	10 31	11 01		11 31	12 01	12 31		13 01	13 31	14 01		14 31	15 01			15 31	16 01	16 31		
Alvechurch	d			09 36		10 06	10 36	11 06		11 36	12 06	12 36		13 06	13 36	14 06		14 36	15 06			15 36	16 06	16 36		
Barnt Green	d			09 41		10 11	10 41	11 11		11 41	12 11	12 41		13 11	13 41	14 11		14 41	15 11			15 41	16 11	16 41		
Longbridge	d			09 46		10 16	10 46	11 16		11 46	12 16	12 46		13 16	13 46	14 16		14 46	15 16			15 46	16 16	16 46		
Northfield	d			09 48		10 18	10 48	11 18		11 48	12 18	12 48		13 18	13 48	14 18		14 48	15 18			15 48	16 18	16 48		
Kings Norton	d			09 51		10 21	10 51	11 21		11 51	12 21	12 51		13 21	13 51	14 21		14 51	15 21			15 51	16 21	16 51		
Bournville	d			09 53		10 23	10 53	11 23		11 53	12 23	12 53		13 23	13 53	14 23		14 53	15 23			15 53	16 23	16 53		
Selly Oak	d			09 55		10 25	10 55	11 25		11 55	12 25	12 55		13 25	13 55	14 25		14 55	15 25			15 55	16 25	16 55		
University	d			09 57		10 27	10 57	11 27		11 57	12 27	12 57		13 27	13 57	14 27		14 57	15 27			15 57	16 27	16 57		
Five Ways	d			10 01		10 31	11 01	11 31		12 01	12 31	13 01		13 31	14 01	14 31		15 01	15 31			16 01	16 31	17 01		
Birmingham New Street 12	a			10 06		10 36	11 06	11 36		12 06	12 36	13 06		13 36	14 06	14 36		15 06	15 36	15 40		16 06	16 36	17 06		17 17
	d	09 12	09 39	10 09		10 39	11 09	11 39		12 09	12 39	13 09		13 39	14 09	14 39		15 09	15 39			16 09	16 39	17 09		
Duddeston	d		09 43	10 13		10 43	11 13	11 43		12 13	12 43	13 13		13 43	14 13	14 43		15 13	15 43			16 13	16 43	17 13		
Aston	d		09 46	10 16		10 46	11 16	11 46		12 16	12 46	13 16		13 46	14 16	14 46		15 16	15 46			16 16	16 46	17 16		
Gravelly Hill	d		09 49	10 19		10 49	11 19	11 49		12 19	12 49	13 19		13 49	14 19	14 49		15 19	15 49			16 19	16 49	17 19		
Erdington	d		09 51	10 21		10 51	11 21	11 51		12 21	12 51	13 21		13 51	14 21	14 51		15 21	15 51			16 21	16 51	17 21		
Chester Road	d		09 53	10 23		10 53	11 23	11 53		12 23	12 53	13 23		13 53	14 23	14 53		15 23	15 53			16 23	16 53	17 23		
Wylde Green	d		09 55	10 25		10 55	11 25	11 55		12 25	12 55	13 25		13 55	14 25	14 55		15 25	15 55			16 25	16 55	17 25		
Sutton Coldfield	d	09 24	09 58	10 28		10 58	11 28	11 58		12 28	12 58	13 28		13 58	14 28	14 58		15 28	15 58			16 28	16 58	17 28		
Four Oaks	d	09 28	10 01	10 31		11 01	11 31	12 01		12 31	13 01	13 31		14 01	14 31	15 01		15 31	16 01			16 31	17 01	17 31		
Butlers Lane	d	09 30	10 03	10 33		11 03	11 33	12 03		12 33	13 03	13 33		14 03	14 33	15 03		15 33	16 03			16 33	17 03	17 33		
Blake Street	d	09 32	10 05	10 35		11 05	11 35	12 05		12 35	13 05	13 35		14 05	14 35	15 05		15 35	16 05			16 35	17 05	17 35		
Shenstone	d	09 36	10 09	10 39		11 09	11 39	12 09		12 39	13 09	13 39		14 09	14 39	15 09		15 39	16 09			16 39	17 09	17 39		
Lichfield City	d	09 41	10 14	10 44		11 14	11 44	12 14		12 44	13 14	13 44		14 14	14 44	15 14		15 44	16 14			16 44	17 14	17 44		
Lichfield Trent Valley	a	09 46	10 19	10 49		11 19	11 49	12 19		12 49	13 19	13 49		14 19	14 49	15 19		15 49	16 19			16 49	17 19	17 49		

For general notes see front of timetable
For details of catering facilities see Directory of Train Operators

b Arr. 1837

Table 69

Sundays

Redditch and Longbridge → Birmingham → Lichfield

Network Diagram - see first page of Table 67

		LM	LM	LM	LM	LM	LM	LM	LM	LM	LM	LM	LM	LM	LM	XC	LM	LM
Bromsgrove	d			17 51						20 13			21 08			22 20		
Redditch	d	17 01	17 31		18 01	18 31	19 01	19 31	20 01		20 31	21 01		21 31	22 01		22 31	23 01
Alvechurch	d	17 06	17 36		18 06	18 36	19 06	19 36	20 06		20 36	21 06		21 36	22 06		22 36	23 06
Barnt Green	d	17 11	17 41		18 11	18 41	19 11	19 41	20 11		20 41	21 11		21 41	22 11		22 41	23 11
Longbridge	d	17 16	17 46		18 16	18 46	19 16	19 46	20 16		20 46	21 16		21 46	22 16		22 46	23 16
Northfield	d	17 18	17 48		18 18	18 48	19 18	19 48	20 18		20 48	21 18		21 48	22 18		22 48	23 18
Kings Norton	d	17 21	17 51		18 21	18 51	19 21	19 51	20 21		20 51	21 21		21 51	22 21		22 51	23 21
Bournville	d	17 23	17 53		18 23	18 53	19 23	19 53	20 23		20 53	21 23		21 53	22 23		22 53	23 23
Selly Oak	d	17 25	17 55		18 25	18 55	19 25	19 55	20 25		20 55	21 25		21 55	22 25		22 55	23 25
University	d	17 27	17 57		18 27	18 57	19 27	19 57	20 27		20 57	21 27		21 57	22 27		22 57	23 27
Five Ways	d	17 31	18 01		18 31	19 01	19 31	20 01	20 31		21 01	21 31		22 01	22 31		23 01	23 31
Birmingham New Street 12	a	17 36	18 07	18 12	18 36	19 06	19 36	20 07	20 36	20 40	21 07	21 36	21 45	22 07	22 36	22 45	23 06	23 36
	d	17 39	18 09		18 39	19 09	19 39	20 09	20 39		21 09	21 39		22 09	22 39		23 09	
Duddeston	d	17 43	18 13		18 43	19 13	19 43	20 13	20 43		21 13	21 43		22 13	22 43		23 13	
Aston	d	17 46	18 16		18 46	19 16	19 46	20 16	20 46		21 16	21 46		22 16	22 46		23 16	
Gravelly Hill	d	17 49	18 19		18 49	19 19	19 49	20 19	20 49		21 19	21 49		22 19	22 49		23 19	
Erdington	d	17 51	18 21		18 51	19 21	19 51	20 21	20 51		21 21	21 51		22 21	22 51		23 21	
Chester Road	d	17 53	18 23		18 53	19 23	19 53	20 23	20 53		21 23	21 53		22 23	22 53		23 23	
Wylde Green	d	17 55	18 25		18 55	19 25	19 55	20 25	20 55		21 25	21 55		22 25	22 55		23 25	
Sutton Coldfield	d	17 58	18 28		18 58	19 28	19 58	20 28	20 58		21 28	21 58		22 28	22 58		23 28	
Four Oaks	d	18 01	18 31		19 01	19 31	20 01	20 31	21 01		21 31	22 01		22 31	23 01		23 31	
Butlers Lane	d	18 03	18 33		19 03	19 33	20 03	20 33	21 03		21 33	22 03		22 33	23 03		23 33	
Blake Street	d	18 05	18 35		19 05	19 35	20 05	20 35	21 05		21 35	22 05		22 35	23 05		23 35	
Shenstone	d	18 09	18 39		19 09	19 39	20 09	20 39	21 09		21 39	22 09		22 39	23 09		23 39	
Lichfield City	d	18 14	18 44		19 14	19 44	20 14	20 44	21 14		21 44	22 14		22 44	23 14		23 44	
Lichfield Trent Valley	a	18 19	18 49		19 19	19 49	20 19	20 49	21 19		21 49	22 19		22 49	23 19		23 49	

For general notes see front of timetable
For details of catering facilities see
Directory of Train Operators

Birmingham → Walsall, Rugeley and Stafford

Network Diagram - see first page of Table 67

Miles	Miles			LM MO A 🚌	LM MX	LM	LM [1]	LM	LM	LM		LM	LM	LM	LM	LM B	LM	LM		LM	LM C	LM	LM	LM C	LM
0	—	**Birmingham New Street** [12]	d	22p12	23p20	05 33		06 07	06 27			06 49	07 12	07 27	07 42						07 57	08 12		08 27	08 42
1½	—	Duddeston	d	⌇	23p24			06 11	06 32			06 53		07 31							08 01			08 31	
2¾	—	Aston	d	⌇	23p26			06 14	06 35			06 56		07 34							08 04			08 34	
3½	—	Witton	d	⌇	23p28			06 16	06 37			06 58		07 36				←			08 06			08 36	
4¼	—	Perry Barr	d	⌇	23p31			06 18	06 40			07 01		07 38				07 38			08 08			08 38	
5¾	—	Hamstead	d	⌇	23p34	05 41		06 21	06 43			07 04		→			←	07 41			08 11			08 41	
8½	—	Tame Bridge Parkway	d	22p38	23p38	05 45		06 26	06 47			07 09	07 23		07 54		07 23	07 45			08 15	08 23		08 45	08 53
9½	—	Bescot Stadium	d	⌇	23p41	05 48		06 29	06 49			07 11	→					07 47			08 17			08 47	
10¾	—	**Walsall**	a	22p53	23p45	05 55		06 33	06 55			07 17			08 05		07 30	07 55			08 25	08 30		08 55	09 05
—	0		d	22p54	23p46			06 34		07 04						07 30	07 30			08 03		08 30	08 44		
—	6¾	**Wolverhampton** [7] 🚢	a	⌇												07 45				08 20			08 59		
14	—	Bloxwich	d	23p03	23p53			06 41		07 12							07 37					08 37			
14½	—	Bloxwich North	d	23p12	23p55			06 43		07 14							07 39					08 39			
16¾	—	Landywood	d	23p24	23p59			06 47		07 18							07 43					08 43			
18¾	—	Cannock	d	23p32	00 03			06 51		07 23							07 48					08 48			
20¾	—	Hednesford	d	23p40	00a09			06 56		07a30							07 53					08 53			
24¾	—	Rugeley Town	a	00⌇01				07 05									08 01					09 01			
—	—		d	00⌇01				07 10									08 02					09 02			
26¼	—	Rugeley Trent Valley	d	00a11			07 12	07 15									08 09					09 09			
35½	—	**Stafford**	a				07 23	07 31									08 25					09 25			

		LM C	LM	LM		LM C	LM	LM	LM 🚌	LM	LM	LM C		LM	LM C	LM	LM	LM C	LM	LM C		LM	LM	LM C	LM
Birmingham New Street [12]	d	08 57	09 12			09 27	09 42	09 57		10 12		10 27		10 42	10 57	11 12		11 27	11 42	11 57		12 12		12 27	12 42
Duddeston	d	09 01				09 31		10 01				10 31			11 01			11 31		12 01				12 31	
Aston	d	09 04				09 34		10 04				10 34			11 04			11 34		12 04				12 34	
Witton	d	09 06				09 36		10 06				10 36			11 06			11 36		12 06				12 36	
Perry Barr	d	09 08				09 38		10 08				10 38			11 08			11 38		12 08				12 38	
Hamstead	d	09 11				09 41		10 11				10 41			11 11			11 41		12 11				12 41	
Tame Bridge Parkway	d	09 15	09 23			09 45	09 53	10 15		10 23		10 45		10 53	11 15	11 23		11 45	11 53	12 15		12 23		12 45	12 53
Bescot Stadium	d	09 17				09 47		10 17				10 47			11 17			11 47		12 17				12 47	
Walsall	a	09 25	09 30			09 55	10 05	10 26		10 30		10 55		11 05	11 25	11 30		11 55	12 05	12 25		12 30		12 55	13 05
	d		09 30	09 44						10 30	10 44					11 30	11 44					12 30	12 44		
Wolverhampton [7] 🚢	a			09 59							10 59						11 59						12 59		
Bloxwich	d		09 37							10 37						11 37						12 37			
Bloxwich North	d		09 39							10 39						11 39						12 39			
Landywood	d		09 43							10 43						11 43						12 43			
Cannock	d		09 48							10 48						11 48						12 48			
Hednesford	d		09 53							10 53						11 53						12 53			
Rugeley Town	a		10 01							11 01						12 01						13 01			
	d		10 02							11 02						12 02						13 02			
Rugeley Trent Valley	d		10 09						11 04	11 09						12a10						13 09			
Stafford	a		10 26						11 24	11 25												13 25			

		LM C	LM	LM	LM C	LM		LM C	LM [1] ⚮	LM	LM	LM C	LM	LM C		LM	LM	LM C	LM	LM C	LM	LM		LM C	LM
Birmingham New Street [12]	d	12 57	13 12		13 27	13 42		13 57		14 12		14 27	14 42	14 57		15 12		15 27	15 42	15 57	16 12			16 27	16 42
Duddeston	d	13 01			13 31			14 01				14 31		15 01				15 31		16 01				16 31	
Aston	d	13 04			13 34			14 04				14 34		15 04				15 34		16 04				16 34	
Witton	d	13 06			13 36			14 06				14 36		15 06				15 36		16 06				16 36	
Perry Barr	d	13 08			13 38			14 08				14 38		15 08				15 38		16 08				16 38	
Hamstead	d	13 11			13 41			14 11				14 41		15 11				15 41		16 11				16 41	
Tame Bridge Parkway	d	13 15	13 23		13 45	13 53		14 15		14 23		14 45	14 53	15 15		15 23		15 45	15 53	16 15	16 23			16 45	16 53
Bescot Stadium	d	13 17			13 47			14 17				14 47		15 17				15 47		16 17				16 47	
Walsall	a	13 25	13 30		13 55	14 05		14 25		14 30		14 55	15 05	15 25		15 30		15 55	16 05	16 25	16 30			16 55	17 00
	d		13 30	13 44						14 30	14 44					15 30	15 44				16 30	16 44			17 01
Wolverhampton [7] 🚢	a			13 59							14 59						15 59					16 59			
Bloxwich	d		13 37							14 37						15 37					16 37				17 08
Bloxwich North	d		13 39							14 39						15 39					16 40				17 10
Landywood	d		13 43							14 43						15 43					16 44				17 14
Cannock	d		13 48							14 48						15 48					16 48				17 19
Hednesford	d		13 53							14 53						15 53					16 54				17a28
Rugeley Town	a		14 01							15 01						16 01					17 03				
	d		14 02							15 02						16 02					17 05				
Rugeley Trent Valley	d		14 09						14 31	15 09						16 09					17 09				
Stafford	a		14 25						14 43	15 25						16 25					17 25				

For general notes see front of timetable
For details of catering facilities see Directory of Train Operators

A 21 July to 8 September
B To Shrewsbury (Table 74)
C From Birmingham International (Table 68)

Birmingham → Walsall, Rugeley and Stafford

Network Diagram - see first page of Table 67

		LM A	LM	LM	LM A	LM	LM A	LM		LM	LM A	LM (bus)	LM	LM	LM	LM		LM	LM	LM	LM	LM	LM		
Birmingham New Street 12	d	16 57	17 12		17 27	17 42	17 57	18 12			18 27		19 09		19 42	20 12			21 12		22 12		23 20		
Duddeston	d	17 01			17 31		18 01				18 31		19 13		19 46	20 16			21 16		22 16		23 24		
Aston	d	17 04			17 34		18 04				18 34		19 15		19 49	20 18			21 18		22 18		23 26		
Witton	d	17 06			17 36		18 06				18 36		19 17		19 51	20 20			21 20		22 20		23 28		
Perry Barr	d	17 08			17 38		18 08				18 38		19 20		19 53	20 23			21 23		22 23		23 31		
Hamstead	d	17 11			17 41		18 11				18 41		19 23		19 56	20 26			21 26		22 26		23 34		
Tame Bridge Parkway	d	17 15	17 23		17 45	17 53	18 15	18 23			18 45		19 27		20 00	20 30			21 30		22 30		23 38		
Bescot Stadium	d	17 17			17 47		18 17				18 47		19 30		20 02	20 33			21 33		22 33		23 41		
Walsall	a	17 25	17 30		17 55	18 00	18 25	18 30			18 55		19 34		20 10	20 37			21 37		22 37		23 45		
Walsall	d		17 30	17 44		18 02		18 32		18 44			19 35	19 44		20 38		21 00	21 38	22 15	22 38	23 20	23 46		
Wolverhampton 7	a			17 59						18 59				19 59				21 13		22 32		23 34			
Bloxwich	d		17 37			18 10		18 40					19 42			20 45			21 45		22 45		23 53		
Bloxwich North	d		17 40			18 12		18 42					19 44			20 47			21 47		22 47		23 55		
Landywood	d		17 44			18 16		18 46					19 48			20 51			21 51		22 51		23 59		
Cannock	d		17 48			18 21		18 51					19 52			20 55			21 55		22 55		00 03		
Hednesford	d		17 54			18 26		18 56					20a02			21a01			22a01		23a03		00a09		
Rugeley Town	a		18 02			18 34		19 04																	
	d		18 03			18 35		19 05																	
Rugeley Trent Valley	d		18 07			18a43		19a13				19 07													
Stafford	a		18 25									19 27													

Saturdays

until 6 September

		LM	LM	LM	LM		LM	LM	LM	LM		LM	LM	LM	LM		LM	LM	LM	LM		LM	LM	LM (bus)	LM
Birmingham New Street 12	d	23p20	06 06		06 40		07 12		07 27	07 57		08 12		08 27	08 42		08 57	09 12		09 27		09 42	09 57		10 12
Duddeston	d	23p24	06 10		06 44		07 16			08 01				08 31			09 01			09 31			10 01		
Aston	d	23p26	06 12		06 47		07 19		07 33	08 04				08 34			09 04			09 34			10 04		
Witton	d	23p28	06 14		06 49		07 21			08 06				08 36			09 06			09 36			10 06		
Perry Barr	d	23p31	06 17		06 51		07 23		07 36	08 08				08 38			09 08			09 38			10 08		
Hamstead	d	23p34	06 20		06 54		07 26		07 39	08 11				08 41			09 11			09 41			10 11		
Tame Bridge Parkway	d	23p38	06 24		06 59		07 30		07 43	08 15		08 23		08 45	08 53		09 15	09 23		09 45		09 53	10 15		10 23
Bescot Stadium	d	23p41	06 27		07 02		07 32			08 17				08 47			09 17			09 47			10 17		
Walsall	a	23p45	06 31		07 08		07 39		07 50	08 25		08 34		08 55	09 05		09 25	09 34		09 55		10 05	10 25		10 34
Walsall	d	23p46	06 32	06 42	07 09			07 44	07 51			08 34	08 44					09 34	09 44						10 34
Wolverhampton 7	a			06 57				07 59					08 59						09 59						
Bloxwich	d	23p53	06 39		07 16				07 58			08 41						09 41							10 41
Bloxwich North	d	23p55	06 41		07 18				08 00			08 43						09 43							10 43
Landywood	d	23p59	06 45		07 22				08 04			08 47						09 47							10 47
Cannock	d	00 03	06 50		07 26				08 09			08 51						09 51							10 51
Hednesford	d	00a09	06a56		07 31				08a15			08 56						09 56							10 56
Rugeley Town	a				07 38							09 04						10 04							11 04
	d				07 40							09 07						10 09							11 09
Rugeley Trent Valley	d				07 46							09 13						10 19						11 04	11 22
Stafford	a				08 02							09 30						10 35						11 24	11 37

		LM	LM		LM	LM	LM	LM		LM	LM	LM	LM		LM	LM	LM	LM		LM (bus)	LM	LM	LM		LM
Birmingham New Street 12	d		10 27		10 42	10 57	11 12			11 27	11 42	11 57	12 12			12 27	12 42	12 57			13 12		13 27		13 42
Duddeston	d		10 31			11 01				11 31		12 01				12 31		13 01					13 31		
Aston	d		10 34			11 04				11 34		12 04				12 34		13 04					13 34		
Witton	d		10 36			11 06				11 36		12 06				12 36		13 06					13 36		
Perry Barr	d		10 38			11 08				11 38		12 08				12 38		13 08					13 38		
Hamstead	d		10 41			11 11				11 41		12 11				12 41		13 11					13 41		
Tame Bridge Parkway	d		10 45		10 53	11 15	11 23			11 45	11 53	12 15	12 23			12 45	12 53	13 15			13 23		13 45		13 53
Bescot Stadium	d		10 47			11 17				11 47		12 17				12 47		13 17					13 47		
Walsall	a		10 55		11 05	11 25	11 34			11 55	12 05	12 25	12 34			12 55	13 05	13 25			13 34		13 55		14 05
Walsall	d	10 44					11 34	11 44					12 34		12 44						13 34	13 44			
Wolverhampton 7	a	10 59						11 59							12 59							13 59			
Bloxwich	d						11 41						12 41								13 41				
Bloxwich North	d						11 43						12 43								13 43				
Landywood	d						11 47						12 47								13 47				
Cannock	d						11 51						12 51								13 51				
Hednesford	d						11 56						12 56								13 56				
Rugeley Town	a						12 04						13 04								14 04				
	d						12 08						13 08								14 16				
Rugeley Trent Valley	d						12 14						13 13							13 57	14 22				
Stafford	a						12 37						13 37							14 17	14 37				

For general notes see front of timetable
For details of catering facilities see Directory of Train Operators

A From Birmingham International (Table 68)

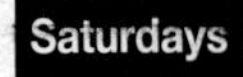

until 6 September

Birmingham → Walsall, Rugeley and Stafford

Network Diagram - see first page of Table 67

		LM	LM	LM	LM		LM	LM	LM	LM		LM	LM	LM	LM		LM	LM	LM	LM		LM	LM	LM	LM
Birmingham New Street 12	d	13 57	14 12		14 27		14 42	14 57	15 12			15 27	15 42	15 57	16 12			16 27	16 42	16 57		17 12		17 27	17 42
Duddeston	d	14 01			14 31			15 01				15 31		16 01				16 31		17 01				17 31	
Aston	d	14 04			14 34			15 04				15 34		16 04				16 34		17 04				17 34	
Witton	d	14 06			14 36			15 06				15 36		16 06				16 36		17 06				17 36	
Perry Barr	d	14 08			14 38			15 08				15 38		16 08				16 38		17 08				17 38	
Hamstead	d	14 11			14 41			15 11				15 41		16 11				16 41		17 11				17 41	
Tame Bridge Parkway	d	14 15	14 23		14 45		14 53	15 15	15 23			15 45	15 53	16 15	16 23			16 45	16 53	17 15		17 23		17 45	17 53
Bescot Stadium	d	14 17			14 47			15 17				15 47		16 17				16 47		17 17				17 47	
Walsall	a	14 25	14 34		14 55		15 05	15 25	15 34			15 55	16 05	16 25	16 34			16 55	17 05	17 25		17 34		17 55	18 00
	d		14 34	14 44					15 34	15 44					16 34		16 44					17 34	17 44		18 00
Wolverhampton 7	a			14 59						15 59							16 59						17 59		
Bloxwich	d		14 41						15 41						16 41							17 41			18 07
Bloxwich North	d		14 43						15 43						16 43							17 43			18 09
Landywood	d		14 47						15 47						16 47							17 47			18 13
Cannock	d		14 51						15 51						16 51							17 51			18 18
Hednesford	d		14 56						15 56						16 56							17 56			18a25
Rugeley Town	a		15 04						16 04						17 04							18 02			
	d		15 08						16 08						17 09							18 07			
Rugeley Trent Valley	d		15 13						16 13						17 13							18 13			
Stafford	a		15 37						16 30						17 30							18 37			

		LM	LM		LM	LM	LM bus	LM		LM	LM	LM	LM		LM	LM	LM	LM		LM	LM				
Birmingham New Street 12	d	17 57	18 12			18 27		18 57		19 12		19 42	20 12			21 12		22 12			23 20				
Duddeston	d	18 01				18 31		19 01		19 16		19 46	20 16			21 16		22 16			23 24				
Aston	d	18 04				18 34		19 04		19 18		19 48	20 18			21 18		22 18			23 26				
Witton	d	18 06				18 36		19 06		19 20		19 50	20 20			21 20		22 20			23 28				
Perry Barr	d	18 08				18 38		19 08		19 23		19 53	20 23			21 23		22 23			23 31				
Hamstead	d	18 11				18 41		19 11		19 26		19 56	20 26			21 26		22 26			23 34				
Tame Bridge Parkway	d	18 15	18 23			18 45		19 15		19 30		20 00	20 30			21 30		22 30			23 38				
Bescot Stadium	d	18 17				18 47		19 17		19 33		20 03	20 33			21 33		22 33			23 41				
Walsall	a	18 25	18 34			18 55		19 25		19 37		20 10	20 37			21 37		22 37			23 45				
	d		18 34		18 44					19 38	19 44		20 38		20 44	21 38	22 15	22 38		23 20	23 46				
Wolverhampton 7	a				18 59						19 59				20 59		22 32			23 39					
Bloxwich	d		18 41							19 45			20 45			21 45		22 45			23 53				
Bloxwich North	d		18 43							19 47			20 47			21 47		22 47			23 55				
Landywood	d		18 47							19 51			20 51			21 51		22 51			23 59				
Cannock	d		18 51							19 55			20 55			21 55		22 55			00 03				
Hednesford	d		18 56							20 00			21a01			22a01		23a01			00a09				
Rugeley Town	a		19 05							20 07															
	d		19 06							20 08															
Rugeley Trent Valley	d		19a14				19 07			20a14															
Stafford	a						19 27																		

Saturdays

from 13 September

		LM	LM	LM	LM bus	LM	LM	LM bus	LM	LM	LM		LM	LM	LM	LM	LM bus	LM	LM	LM	LM	LM		LM bus	LM
Birmingham New Street 12	d	23p20	06 06			06 40	07 12			07 27	07 57		08 12		08 27	08 42		08 57	09 12		09 27	09 42			09 57
Duddeston	d	23p24	06 10			06 44	07 16				08 01				08 31			09 01			09 31				10 01
Aston	d	23p26	06 12			06 47	07 19			07 33	08 04				08 34			09 04			09 34				10 04
Witton	d	23p28	06 14			06 49	07 21				08 06				08 36			09 06			09 36				10 06
Perry Barr	d	23p31	06 17			06 51	07 23			07 36	08 08				08 38			09 08			09 38				10 08
Hamstead	d	23p34	06 20			06 54	07 26			07 39	08 11				08 41			09 11			09 41				10 11
Tame Bridge Parkway	d	23p38	06 24			06 59	07 30			07 43	08 15		08 23		08 45	08 53		09 15	09 23		09 45	09 53			10 15
Bescot Stadium	d	23p41	06 27			07 02	07 32				08 17				08 47			09 17			09 47				10 17
Walsall	a	23p45	06 31			07 08	07 39			07 50	08 25		08 34		08 55	09 05		09 25	09 34		09 55	10 05			10 25
	d	23p46	06 32	06 42		07 09			07 44	07 51			08 34	08 44					09 34	09 44					
Wolverhampton 7	a			06 57					07 59					08 59						09 59					
Bloxwich	d	23p53	06 39			07 16				07 58			08 41						09 41						
Bloxwich North	d	23p55	06 41			07 18				08 00			08 43						09 43						
Landywood	d	23p59	06 45			07 22				08 04			08 47						09 47						
Cannock	d	00 03	06 50			07 26				08 09			08 51						09 51						
Hednesford	d	00a09	06a56		07 01	07 31				08a15			08 56						09 56						
Rugeley Town	a				07 21	07 38							09 03						10 03						
	d				07 22	07 39		07 45					09 03				09 10		10 03					10 10	
Rugeley Trent Valley	d				07 33	07a45		07 56					09a12				09 21		10a12					10 21	
Stafford	a				07 53			08 16									09 41							10 41	

For general notes see front of timetable
For details of catering facilities see
Directory of Train Operators

Table 70

Saturdays

from 13 September

Birmingham → Walsall, Rugeley and Stafford

Network Diagram - see first page of Table 67

		LM 🚌	LM	LM	LM	LM	LM 🚌	LM	LM	LM	LM	LM	LM 🚌	LM	LM	LM	LM	LM	LM 🚌	LM	LM 🚌	LM	LM
Birmingham New Street 12	d		10 12		10 27	10 42		10 57	11 12		11 27	11 42		11 57	12 12		12 27	12 42		12 57		13 12	
Duddeston	d				10 31			11 01			11 31			12 01			12 31			13 01			
Aston	d				10 34			11 04			11 34			12 04			12 34			13 04			
Witton	d				10 36			11 06			11 36			12 06			12 36			13 06			
Perry Barr	d				10 38			11 08			11 38			12 08			12 38			13 08			
Hamstead	d				10 41			11 11			11 41			12 11			12 41			13 11			
Tame Bridge Parkway	d		10 23		10 45	10 53		11 15	11 23		11 45	11 53		12 15	12 23		12 45	12 53		13 15		13 23	
Bescot Stadium	d				10 47			11 17			11 47			12 17			12 47			13 17			
Walsall	a		10 34		10 55	11 05		11 25	11 34		11 55	12 05		12 25	12 34		12 55	13 05		13 25		13 34	
	d		10 34	10 44					11 34	11 44					12 34	12 44						13 34	13 44
Wolverhampton 7	a			10 59						11 59						12 59							13 59
Bloxwich	d		10 41						11 41						12 41							13 41	
Bloxwich North	d		10 43						11 43						12 43							13 43	
Landywood	d		10 47						11 47						12 47							13 47	
Cannock	d		10 51						11 51						12 51							13 51	
Hednesford	d		10 56						11 56						12 56							13 56	
Rugeley Town	a		11 03						12 03						13 03							14 03	
	d		11 03				11 10		12 03				12 10		13 03				13 10			14 03	
Rugeley Trent Valley	d	11 04	11a12				11 21		12a12				12 21		13a12				13 21		13 57	14a12	
Stafford	a	11 24					11 41						12 41						13 41		14 17		

		LM	LM	LM 🚌	LM	LM	LM	LM	LM	LM 🚌	LM	LM	LM	LM	LM	LM 🚌	LM	LM	LM	LM	LM	LM 🚌	LM
Birmingham New Street 12	d	13 27	13 42		13 57	14 12		14 27	14 42		14 57	15 12		15 27	15 42		15 57	16 12		16 27	16 42		16 57
Duddeston	d	13 31			14 01			14 31			15 01			15 31			16 01			16 31			17 01
Aston	d	13 34			14 04			14 34			15 04			15 34			16 04			16 34			17 04
Witton	d	13 36			14 06			14 36			15 06			15 36			16 06			16 36			17 06
Perry Barr	d	13 38			14 08			14 38			15 08			15 38			16 08			16 38			17 08
Hamstead	d	13 41			14 11			14 41			15 11			15 41			16 11			16 41			17 11
Tame Bridge Parkway	d	13 45	13 53		14 15	14 23		14 45	14 53		15 15	15 23		15 45	15 53		16 15	16 23		16 45	16 53		17 15
Bescot Stadium	d	13 47			14 17			14 47			15 17			15 47			16 17			16 47			17 17
Walsall	a	13 55	14 05		14 25	14 34		14 55	15 05		15 25	15 34		15 55	16 05		16 25	16 34		16 55	17 05		17 25
	d					14 34	14 44					15 34	15 44					16 34	16 44				
Wolverhampton 7	a						14 59						15 59						16 59				
Bloxwich	d					14 41						15 41						16 41					
Bloxwich North	d					14 43						15 43						16 43					
Landywood	d					14 47						15 47						16 47					
Cannock	d					14 51						15 51						16 51					
Hednesford	d					14 56						15 56						16 56					
Rugeley Town	a					15 03						16 03						17 02					
	d			14 10		15 03				15 10		16 03				16 10		17 03				17 10	
Rugeley Trent Valley	d			14 21		15a12				15 21		16a12				16 21		17a12				17 21	
Stafford	a			14 41						15 41						16 41						17 41	

		LM	LM	LM	LM 🚌	LM	LM	LM	LM	LM	LM 🚌	LM	LM	LM	LM	LM	LM	LM	LM	LM	LM	LM
Birmingham New Street 12	d	17 12		17 27		17 42	17 57	18 12		18 27		18 57	19 12		19 42	20 12		21 12		22 12		23 20
Duddeston	d			17 31			18 01			18 31		19 01	19 16		19 46	20 16		21 16		22 16		23 24
Aston	d			17 34			18 04			18 34		19 04	19 18		19 48	20 18		21 18		22 18		23 26
Witton	d			17 36			18 06			18 36		19 06	19 20		19 50	20 20		21 20		22 20		23 28
Perry Barr	d			17 38			18 08			18 38		19 08	19 23		19 53	20 23		21 23		22 23		23 31
Hamstead	d			17 41			18 11			18 41		19 11	19 26		19 56	20 26		21 26		22 26		23 34
Tame Bridge Parkway	d	17 23		17 45		17 53	18 15	18 23		18 45		19 15	19 30		20 00	20 30		21 30		22 30		23 38
Bescot Stadium	d			17 47			18 17			18 47		19 17	19 33		20 03	20 33		21 33		22 33		23 41
Walsall	a	17 34		17 55		18 00	18 25	18 34		18 55		19 25	19 37		20 10	20 37		21 37		22 37		23 45
	d	17 34	17 44			18 00		18 34	18 44				19 38	19 44		20 38	20 44	21 38	22 15	22 38	23 20	23 46
Wolverhampton 7	a		17 59						18 59					19 59			20 59		22 32		23 39	
Bloxwich	d	17 41				18 07		18 41					19 45			20 45		21 45		22 45		23 53
Bloxwich North	d	17 43				18 09		18 43					19 47			20 47		21 47		22 47		23 55
Landywood	d	17 47				18 13		18 47					19 51			20 51		21 51		22 51		23 59
Cannock	d	17 51				18 18		18 51					19 55			20 55		21 55		22 55		00 03
Hednesford	d	17 56				18a25		18 56					20 00			21a01		22a01		23a01		00a09
Rugeley Town	a	18 02						19 05					20 07									
	d	18 03			18 10			19 06					20 08									
Rugeley Trent Valley	d	18a12			18 21			19a14			19 07		20a14									
Stafford	a				18 41						19 27											

Sundays

Until 13 July

		LM	LM	LM	LM	LM	LM	LM	LM	LM	LM	LM	LM	LM	LM	LM	LM	LM	LM	LM	LM	LM	LM
Birmingham New Street 12	d	23p20		09 42		10 12	10 42		11 12	11 42		12 12	12 42		13 12	13 42		14 12	14 42		15 12	15 42	
Duddeston	d	23p24		09 46			10 46			11 46			12 46			13 46			14 46			15 46	
Aston	d	23p26		09 49			10 49			11 49			12 49			13 49			14 49			15 49	
Witton	d	23p28		09 51			10 51			11 51			12 51			13 51			14 51			15 51	
Perry Barr	d	23p31		09 53			10 53			11 53			12 53			13 53			14 53			15 53	
Hamstead	d	23p34		09 56			10 56			11 56			12 56			13 56			14 56			15 56	
Tame Bridge Parkway	d	23p38		10 01		10 24	11 01		11 24	12 01		12 24	13 01		13 24	14 01		14 24	15 01		15 24	16 01	
Bescot Stadium	d	23p41		10 03			11 03			12 03			13 03			14 03			15 03			16 03	
Walsall	a	23p45		10 10		10 33	11 10		11 33	12 10		12 33	13 10		13 33	14 11		14 33	15 10		15 33	16 10	
	d	23p46	09 20		10 20	10 34		11 20	11 34		12 20	12 34		13 20	13 34		14 20	14 34		15 20	15 34		16 20
Wolverhampton 7	a		09 37		10 37			11 37			12 37			13 37			14 37			15 37			16 37
Bloxwich	d	23p53				10 41			11 41			12 41			13 41			14 41			15 41		
Bloxwich North	d	23p55				10 43			11 43			12 43			13 43			14 43			15 43		
Landywood	d	23p59				10 47			11 47			12 47			13 47			14 47			15 47		
Cannock	d	00 03				10 51			11 51			12 51			13 51			14 51			15 51		
Hednesford	d	00a09				10 56			11 56			12 56			13 56			14 56			15 56		
Rugeley Town	a					11 03			12 03			13 03			14 03			15 03			16 03		
	d					11 04			12 04			13 04			14 04			15 04			16 04		
Rugeley Trent Valley	d					11a07			12a07			13a07			14a07			15a07			16a07		
Stafford	a																						

For general notes see front of timetable
For details of catering facilities see
Directory of Train Operators

Table 70

Sundays

Until 13 July

Birmingham → Walsall, Rugeley and Stafford

Network Diagram - see first page of Table 67

		LM	LM	LM	LM	LM	LM	LM		LM	LM	LM	LM	LM	LM	LM	LM	LM	LM	LM	LM	LM	LM		
Birmingham New Street 12	d	16 12	16 42		17 12	17 42		18 12		18 42		19 12	19 42		20 12	20 42		21 12	21 42		22 12	22 42			
Duddeston	d		16 46			17 46				18 46			19 46			20 46			21 46			22 46			
Aston	d		16 49			17 49				18 49			19 49			20 49			21 49			22 49			
Witton	d		16 51			17 51				18 51			19 51			20 51			21 51			22 51			
Perry Barr	d		16 53			17 53				18 53			19 53			20 53			21 53			22 53			
Hamstead	d		16 56			17 56				18 56			19 56			20 56			21 56			22 56			
Tame Bridge Parkway	d	16 24	17 01		17 24	18 01		18 24		19 01		19 24	20 01		20 24	21 01		21 24	22 01		22 24	23 01			
Bescot Stadium	d		17 03			18 03				19 03			20 03			21 03			22 03			23 03			
Walsall	a	16 33	17 10		17 33	18 10		18 33		19 10		19 33	20 10		20 33	21 10		21 33	22 10		22 33	23 11			
	d	16 34		17 20	17 34		18 20	18 34			19 20	19 34		20 20	20 34		21 20	21 34		22 20	22 34		23 20		
Wolverhampton 7	a			17 37			18 37				19 37			20 37			21 37			22 37			23 37		
Bloxwich	d	16 41			17 41			18 41				19 41			20 41			21 41			22 41				
Bloxwich North	d	16 43			17 43			18 43				19 43			20 43			21 43			22 43				
Landywood	d	16 47			17 47			18 47				19 47			20 47			21 47			22 47				
Cannock	d	16 51			17 51			18 51				19 51			20 51			21 51			22 51				
Hednesford	d	16 56			17 56			18 56				19 56			20 56			21 56			22 56				
Rugeley Town	a	17 03			18 03			19 03				20 03			21 03			22 03			23 03				
	d	17 04			18 04			19 04				20 04			21 04			22 04			23 04				
Rugeley Trent Valley	d	17a07			18a07			19a07				20a07			21a07			22a07			23a07				
Stafford	a																								

Sundays

20 July to 7 September

		LM 🚌	LM 🚌	LM 🚌	LM 🚌	LM 🚌	LM 🚌	LM 🚌	LM 🚌	LM 🚌	LM 🚌	LM 🚌		LM 🚌	LM 🚌	LM 🚌	LM 🚌	LM 🚌	LM 🚌	LM 🚌	LM 🚌	LM 🚌	LM 🚌	LM 🚌	LM 🚌
Birmingham New Street 12	d		09 05	09 12		10 12	09 42		10 42	11 12		11 42		12 12		12 42	13 12		13 42	14 12		14 42	15 12		15 42
Duddeston	d		09 15				09 52		10 52			11 52				12 52			13 52			14 52			15 52
Aston	d		09 20				09 57		10 57			11 57				12 57			13 57			14 57			15 57
Witton	d		09 27				10 04		11 04			12 04				13 04			14 04			15 04			16 04
Perry Barr	d		09 35				10 12		11 12			12 12				13 12			14 12			15 12			16 12
Hamstead	d		09 44				10 21		11 21			12 21				13 21			14 21			15 21			16 21
Tame Bridge Parkway	d		09 55	09 38		10 38	10 32		11 32	11 38		12 32		12 38		13 32	13 38		14 32	14 38		15 32	15 38		16 32
Bescot Stadium	d		10 04				10 41		11 41			12 41				13 41			14 41			15 41			16 41
Walsall	a		10 12	09 53		10 53	10 49		11 49	11 53		12 49		12 53		13 49	13 53		14 49	14 53		15 49	15 53		16 49
	d	09 15		09 54	10 15	10 54		11 15		11 54	12 15			12 54	13 15		13 54	14 15		14 54	15 15		15 54	16 15	
Wolverhampton 7	a	09 35			10 35			11 35			12 35				13 35			14 35			15 35			16 35	
Bloxwich	d			10 03		11 03				12 03				13 03			14 03			15 03			16 03		
Bloxwich North	d			10 12		11 12				12 12				13 12			14 12			15 12			16 12		
Landywood	d			10 24		11 24				12 24				13 24			14 24			15 24			16 24		
Cannock	d			10 32		11 32				12 32				13 32			14 32			15 32			16 32		
Hednesford	d			10 40		11 40				12 40				13 40			14 40			15 40			16 40		
Rugeley Town	a			11 00		12 00				13 00				14 00			15 00			16 00			17 00		
	d			11 01		12 01				13 01				14 01			15 01			16 01			17 01		
Rugeley Trent Valley	d			11a11		12a11				13a11				14a11			15a11			16a11			17a11		
Stafford	a																								

		LM 🚌		LM 🚌	LM 🚌	LM 🚌	LM 🚌	LM 🚌	LM 🚌	LM 🚌	LM 🚌	LM 🚌	LM 🚌	LM 🚌	LM 🚌	LM 🚌	LM 🚌	LM 🚌	LM 🚌	LM 🚌	LM 🚌	LM 🚌	LM 🚌		
Birmingham New Street 12	d	16 12			16 42	17 12		17 42	18 12		18 42	19 12		19 42	20 12		20 42	21 12		21 42	22 12		22 42		
Duddeston	d				16 52			17 52			18 52			19 52			20 52			21 52			22 52		
Aston	d				16 57			17 57			18 57			19 57			20 57			21 57			22 57		
Witton	d				17 04			18 04			19 04			20 04			21 04			22 04			23 04		
Perry Barr	d				17 12			18 12			19 12			20 12			21 12			22 12			23 12		
Hamstead	d				17 21			18 21			19 21			20 21			21 21			22 21			23 21		
Tame Bridge Parkway	d	16 38			17 32	17 38		18 32	18 38		19 32	19 38		20 32	20 38		21 32	21 38		22 32	22 38		23 32		
Bescot Stadium	d				17 41			18 41			19 41			20 41			21 41			22 41			23 41		
Walsall	a	16 53			17 49	17 53		18 49	18 53		19 49	19 53		20 49	20 53		21 49	21 53		22 49	22 53		23 49		
	d	16 54		17 15		17 54	18 15		18 54	19 15		19 54	20 15		20 54	21 15		21 54	22 15		22 54	23 15			
Wolverhampton 7	a			17 35			18 35			19 35			20 35			21 35			22 35			23 35			
Bloxwich	d	17 03				18 03			19 03			20 03			21 03			22 03			23 03				
Bloxwich North	d	17 12				18 12			19 12			20 12			21 12			22 12			23 12				
Landywood	d	17 24				18 24			19 24			20 24			21 24			22 24			23 24				
Cannock	d	17 32				18 32			19 32			20 32			21 32			22 32			23 32				
Hednesford	d	17 40				18 40			19 40			20 40			21 40			22 40			23 40				
Rugeley Town	a	18 00				19 00			20 00			21 00			22 00			23 00			00 01				
	d	18 01				19 01			20 01			21 01			22 01			23 01			00 01				
Rugeley Trent Valley	d	18a11				19a11			20a11			21a11			22a11			23a11			00a11				
Stafford	a																								

For general notes see front of timetable
For details of catering facilities see
Directory of Train Operators

From 14 September

Birmingham → Walsall, Rugeley and Stafford

Network Diagram - see first page of Table 67

		LM	LM	LM	LM	LM	LM	LM		LM	LM	LM	LM	LM	LM	LM		LM	LM	LM	LM	LM	LM	LM	LM
Birmingham New Street 12	d		09 42		10 12	10 42		11 12		11 42		12 12	12 42		13 12	13 42			14 12	14 42		15 12	15 42		16 12
Duddeston	d		09 46			10 46				11 46			12 46			13 46				14 46			15 46		
Aston	d		09 49			10 49				11 49			12 49			13 49				14 49			15 49		
Witton	d		09 51			10 51				11 51			12 51			13 51				14 51			15 51		
Perry Barr	d		09 53			10 53				11 53			12 53			13 53				14 53			15 53		
Hamstead	d		09 56			10 56				11 56			12 56			13 56				14 56			15 56		
Tame Bridge Parkway	d		10 01		10 24	11 01		11 24		12 01		12 24	13 01		13 24	14 01			14 24	15 01		15 24	16 01		16 24
Bescot Stadium	d		10 03			11 03				12 03			13 03			14 03				15 03			16 03		
Walsall	a		10 10		10 33	11 10		11 33		12 10		12 33	13 10		13 33	14 11			14 33	15 10		15 33	16 10		16 33
	d	09 20		10 20	10 34		11 20	11 34			12 20	12 34		13 20	13 34			14 20	14 34		15 20	15 34		16 20	16 34
Wolverhampton 7	a	09 35		10 36			11 36				12 36			13 37				14 36			15 36			16 36	
Bloxwich	d				10 41			11 41				12 41			13 41				14 41			15 41			16 41
Bloxwich North	d				10 43			11 43				12 43			13 43				14 43			15 43			16 43
Landywood	d				10 47			11 47				12 47			13 47				14 47			15 47			16 47
Cannock	d				10 51			11 51				12 51			13 51				14 51			15 51			16 51
Hednesford	d				10 56			11 56				12 56			13 56				14 56			15 56			16 56
Rugeley Town	a				11 03			12 03				13 03			14 03				15 03			16 03			17 03
	d				11 04			12 04				13 04			14 04				15 04			16 04			17 04
Rugeley Trent Valley	d				11a07			12a07				13a07			14a07				15a07			16a07			17a07
Stafford	a																								

		LM		LM	LM	LM	LM	LM	LM	LM		LM	LM	LM	LM	LM	LM	LM	LM	LM	LM	LM	LM		
Birmingham New Street 12	d	16 42			17 12	17 42		18 12	18 42			19 12	19 42		20 12	20 42		21 12	21 42		22 12	22 42			
Duddeston	d	16 46				17 46			18 46				19 46			20 46			21 46			22 46			
Aston	d	16 49				17 49			18 49				19 49			20 49			21 49			22 49			
Witton	d	16 51				17 51			18 51				19 51			20 51			21 51			22 51			
Perry Barr	d	16 53				17 53			18 53				19 53			20 53			21 53			22 53			
Hamstead	d	16 56				17 56			18 56				19 56			20 56			21 56			22 56			
Tame Bridge Parkway	d	17 01			17 24	18 01		18 24	19 01			19 24	20 01		20 24	21 01		21 24	22 01		22 24	23 01			
Bescot Stadium	d	17 03				18 03			19 03				20 03			21 03			22 03			23 03			
Walsall	a	17 10			17 33	18 10		18 33	19 10			19 33	20 10		20 33	21 10		21 33	22 10		22 33	23 10			
	d			17 20	17 34		18 20	18 34		19 20		19 34		20 20	20 34		21 30	21 34		22 20	22 34		23 20		
Wolverhampton 7	a			17 36			18 36			19 36				20 36			21 36			22 36			23 37		
Bloxwich	d				17 41			18 41				19 41			20 41			21 41			22 41				
Bloxwich North	d				17 43			18 43				19 43			20 43			21 43			22 43				
Landywood	d				17 47			18 47				19 47			20 47			21 47			22 47				
Cannock	d				17 51			18 51				19 51			20 51			21 51			22 51				
Hednesford	d				17 56			18 56				19 56			20 56			21 56			22 56				
Rugeley Town	a				18 03			19 03				20 03			21 03			22 03			23 03				
	d				18 04			19 04				20 04			21 04			22 04			23 04				
Rugeley Trent Valley	d				18a07			19a07				20a07			21a07			22a07			23a07				
Stafford	a																								

For general notes see front of timetable
For details of catering facilities see
Directory of Train Operators

Stafford, Rugeley and Walsall → Birmingham

Network Diagram - see first page of Table 67

Miles	Miles			LM	LM	LM	LM	LM	LM	LM	LM	LM	LM	LM	LM	LM	LM	LM	LM	LM	LM	LM	LM
									A		1 ◇ B			C	1		C						
0	—	**Stafford**	d												06 57	07 35					08 35		
9¼	—	Rugeley Trent Valley	d				06 18			06 37					07a06	07 45					08 46		
10¾	—	Rugeley Town	a				06 22			06 40						07 49					08 50		
—	—		d				06 23			06 45						07 49					08 51		
14¾	—	Hednesford	d		06 03		06 31			06 53		07 16	07 35			07 58			08 27		08 59		
16¾	—	Cannock	d		06 07		06 35			06 57		07 20	07 39			08 02			08 31		09 03		
18¾	—	Landywood	d		06 11		06 39			07 01		07 24				08 06			08 34		09 07		
21	—	Bloxwich North	d		06 15		06 44			07 05		07 28				08 10			08 39		09 11		
21½	—	Bloxwich	d		06 17		06 46			07 07		07 30				08 12			08 41		09 13		
—	0	**Wolverhampton 7** 🚌	d			06 38			06 56									08 23					09 25
24¾	6¾	**Walsall**	a		06 24	06 50	06 55		07 12	07 14		07 38	07 53			08 20		08 38	08 47		09 20		09 38
—	—		d	06 00	06 25			07 00		07 15	07 20	07 42	07 54	08 00		08 20	08 30		08 48	09 00	09 20	09 30	
26	—	Bescot Stadium	d	06 03	06 29			07 03			07 24			08 03			08 33			09 03		09 33	
27	—	Tame Bridge Parkway	d	06 06	06 32			07 06		07 21	07 27	07 47	08 00	08 06		08 26	08 36		08 54	09 06	09 26	09 36	
29¾	—	Hamstead	d	06 10	06 36			07 10			07 30			08 10			08 40			09 10		09 40	
31¼	—	Perry Barr	d	06 12	06 39			07 13			07 34			08 13			08 43			09 13		09 43	
32	—	Witton	d	06 14	06 42			07 15			07 36			08 15			08 45			09 16		09 45	
32¾	—	Aston	d	06 17	06 45			07 18			07 39			08 18			08 48			09 18		09 48	
34	—	Duddeston	d	06 19	06 48			07 20			07 42			08 20			08 50			09 21		09 50	
35½	—	**Birmingham New Street 12**	a	06 28	06 53			07 28		07 39	07 48	08 05	08 23	08 28		08 44	08 58		09 11	09 28	09 45	09 58	

		LM	LM	LM	LM	LM	LM	LM	LM	LM	LM	LM	LM	LM	LM	LM	LM	LM	LM	LM	LM	LM
					C			C		C			C	1 🛒		C			C		C	
Stafford	d			09 35					10 35					11 21	11 35							
Rugeley Trent Valley	d			09 46					10 46					11a32	11 46					12 46		
Rugeley Town	a			09 50					10 50						11 50					12 50		
	d			09 51					10 51						11 51					12 51		
Hednesford	d			09 59					10 59						11 59					12 59		
Cannock	d			10 03					11 03						12 03					13 03		
Landywood	d			10 07					11 07						12 07					13 07		
Bloxwich North	d			10 11					11 11						12 11					13 11		
Bloxwich	d			10 13					11 13						12 13					13 13		
Wolverhampton 7 🚌	d					10 25					11 25						12 25					13 25
Walsall	a			10 19		10 38			11 20		11 38				12 20		12 39			13 20		13 38
	d	09 42	10 00	10 20	10 30		10 42	11 00	11 20	11 30		11 42	12 00		12 20	12 30		12 42	13 00	13 20	13 30	
Bescot Stadium	d		10 03		10 33			11 03		11 33			12 03			12 33			13 03		13 33	
Tame Bridge Parkway	d	09 47	10 06	10 26	10 36		10 47	11 06	11 26	11 36		11 47	12 06		12 26	12 36		12 47	13 06	13 26	13 36	
Hamstead	d		10 10		10 40			11 10		11 40			12 10			12 40			13 10		13 40	
Perry Barr	d		10 13		10 43			11 13		11 43			12 13			12 43			13 13		13 43	
Witton	d		10 15		10 45			11 15		11 45			12 15			12 45			13 15		13 45	
Aston	d		10 18		10 48			11 18		11 48			12 18			12 48			13 18		13 48	
Duddeston	d		10 20		10 50			11 20		11 50			12 20			12 50			13 20		13 50	
Birmingham New Street 12	a	10 05	10 28	10 43	10 58		11 05	11 28	11 43	11 58		12 05	12 28		12 43	12 58		13 05	13 28	13 43	13 58	

		LM	LM	LM	LM	LM	LM	LM	LM	LM	LM	LM	LM	LM	LM	LM	LM	LM	LM	LM	LM	LM
			C	🚌		C			C		C			C					C		C	
Stafford	d			12 40	13 35					14 35					15 35					16 35		
Rugeley Trent Valley	d			13a05	13 46					14 46					15 46					16 46		
Rugeley Town	a				13 50					14 50					15 50					16 50		
	d				13 51					14 51					15 51					16 51		
Hednesford	d				13 59					14 59					15 59					16 59		
Cannock	d				14 03					15 03					16 03					17 03		
Landywood	d				14 07					15 07					16 07					17 07		
Bloxwich North	d				14 11					15 11					16 11					17 11		
Bloxwich	d				14 13					15 13					16 13					17 13		
Wolverhampton 7 🚌	d						14 25					15 25					16 25					17 25
Walsall	a				14 20		14 38			15 20		15 38			16 20		16 40			17 20		17 40
	d	13 42	14 00		14 20	14 30		14 42	15 00	15 20	15 30		15 42	16 00	16 20	16 30		16 42	17 00	17 20	17 30	
Bescot Stadium	d		14 03			14 33			15 03		15 33			16 03		16 33			17 03		17 33	
Tame Bridge Parkway	d	13 47	14 06		14 26	14 36		14 47	15 06	15 26	15 36		15 47	16 06	16 26	16 36		16 47	17 06	17 26	17 36	
Hamstead	d		14 10			14 40			15 10		15 40			16 10		16 40			17 10		17 40	
Perry Barr	d		14 13			14 43			15 13		15 43			16 13		16 43			17 13		17 43	
Witton	d		14 15			14 45			15 15		15 45			16 15		16 45			17 15		17 45	
Aston	d		14 18			14 48			15 18		15 48			16 18		16 48			17 18		17 48	
Duddeston	d		14 20			14 50			15 20		15 50			16 20		16 50			17 20		17 50	
Birmingham New Street 12	a	14 05	14 28		14 43	14 58		15 05	15 28	15 43	15 58		16 05	16 28	16 43	16 58		17 05	17 28	17 43	17 58	

For general notes see front of timetable
For details of catering facilities see Directory of Train Operators

A From Shrewsbury (Table 74)
B To Liverpool Lime Street (Table 65).
C To Birmingham International (Table 68)

Stafford, Rugeley and Walsall → Birmingham

Network Diagram - see first page of Table 67

		LM	LM	LM	LM	LM	LM	LM	LM	LM	LM	LM	LM	LM	LM	LM	LM	LM	LM
			A	1 ✠		A		A									B		🚌
Stafford	d			17 20	17 35														20 20
Rugeley Trent Valley	d			17a29	17 46				18 52		19 22								20a45
Rugeley Town	a				17 50				18 56		19 26								
	d				17 51				18 57		19 27								
Hednesford	d	17 27			17 59				19 05		19 35	20 09		21 09		22 09		23 09	
Cannock	d	17 30			18 03				19 09		19 39	20 13		21 13		22 13		23 13	
Landywood	d	17 34			18 07				19 13		19 43	20 17		21 17		22 17		23 17	
Bloxwich North	d	17 38			18 11				19 17		19 47	20 21		21 21		22 21		23 21	
Bloxwich	d	17 40			18 13				19 19		19 49	20 23		21 23		22 23		23 23	
Wolverhampton 7 🚢	d						18 25			19 25			20 34		21 19		22 55		
Walsall	a	17 47			18 20		18 40		19 26	19 40	19 56	20 30	20 49	21 30	21 32	22 30	23 12	23 30	
	d	17 48	18 00		18 20	18 30		19 00	19 28		19 58	20 31		21 31		22 31		23 31	
Bescot Stadium	d		18 03			18 33		19 03	19 32		20 02	20 36		21 36		22 36			
Tame Bridge Parkway	d	17 53	18 06		18 26	18 36		19 06	19 35		20 05	20 39		21 39		22 39			
Hamstead	d		18 10			18 40		19 10	19 39		20 09	20 43		21 43		22 43			
Perry Barr	d		18 13			18 43		19 13	19 42		20 12	20 46		21 46		22 46			
Witton	d		18 15			18 45		19 15	19 44		20 14	20 48		21 48		22 48			
Aston	d		18 18			18 48		19 18	19 47		20 17	20 51		21 51		22 51			
Duddeston	d		18 20			18 50		19 20	19 50		20 20	20 54		21 54		22 54			
Birmingham New Street 12	a	18 11	18 30		18 43	18 58		19 28	19 56		20 28	21 02		21 59		22 59		23 55	

Saturdays
until 6 September

		LM	LM	LM	LM	LM	LM	LM	LM	LM	LM	LM	LM	LM	LM	LM	LM	LM	LM	LM	LM	LM	LM	LM	LM	LM
									🚌																	
Stafford	d								05 54	07 27								08 48					09 54			
Rugeley Trent Valley	d				06 18				06a19	07 38								09 03					10 05			
Rugeley Town	a				06 22					07 42								09 07					10 09			
	d				06 23					07 48								09 17					10 17			
Hednesford	d				06 31	07 05				07 56			08 21					09 25					10 25			
Cannock	d				06 35	07 09				08 00			08 25					09 29					10 29			
Landywood	d				06 39	07 12				08 04			08 28					09 33					10 33			
Bloxwich North	d				06 43	07 17				08 08			08 32					09 37					10 37			
Bloxwich	d				06 45	07 19				08 10			08 34					09 39					10 39			
Wolverhampton 7 🚢	d		06 08				07 25					08 25					09 25					10 25				
Walsall	a		06 22		06 52	07 25	07 38			08 17		08 40	08 41				09 40	09 46				10 40	10 46			
	d	05 58		06 32	06 53	07 31		08 02		08 18	08 30		08 47	09 00	09 15	09 30		09 47	10 00	10 16	10 30		10 47	11 00	11 18	11 30
Bescot Stadium	d	06 02		06 35	06 57	07 35		08 05			08 33			09 03		09 33			10 03		10 33			11 03		11 33
Tame Bridge Parkway	d	06 04		06 38	07 00	07 37		08 08		08 24	08 36		08 52	09 06	09 20	09 36		09 52	10 06	10 21	10 36		10 52	11 06	11 23	11 36
Hamstead	d	06 08		06 41	07 04	07 41		08 11			08 40			09 10		09 40			10 10		10 40			11 10		11 40
Perry Barr	d	06 11		06 44	07 07	07 44		08 14			08 43			09 13		09 43			10 13		10 43			11 13		11 43
Witton	d	06 14		06 46	07 09	07 47		08 16			08 45			09 15		09 45			10 15		10 45			11 15		11 45
Aston	d	06 16		06 48	07 12	07 50		08 19			08 48			09 18		09 48			10 18		10 48			11 18		11 48
Duddeston	d	06 19		06 50	07 15	07 53		08 21			08 50			09 20		09 50			10 20		10 50			11 20		11 50
Birmingham New Street 12	a	06 26		06 58	07 20	08 01		08 30		08 42	08 58		09 10	09 28	09 41	09 58		10 10	10 28	10 41	10 58		11 10	11 28	11 41	11 58

		LM	LM	LM	LM	LM	LM	LM	LM	LM	LM	LM	LM	LM	LM	LM	LM	LM	LM	LM	LM	LM	LM	LM	LM	LM
													🚌													
Stafford	d		10 53					11 53					12 45	12 53					13 53					14 53		
Rugeley Trent Valley	d		11 04					12 04					13a10	13 04					14 08					15 04		
Rugeley Town	a		11 08					12 08						13 08					14 11					15 08		
	d		11 17					12 17						13 17					14 17					15 17		
Hednesford	d		11 25					12 25						13 25					14 25					15 25		
Cannock	d		11 29					12 29						13 29					14 29					15 29		
Landywood	d		11 33					12 33						13 33					14 33					15 33		
Bloxwich North	d		11 37					12 37						13 37					14 37					15 37		
Bloxwich	d		11 39					12 39						13 39					14 39					15 39		
Wolverhampton 7 🚢	d	11 25					12 25					13 25						14 25					15 25			
Walsall	a	11 40	11 46				12 40	12 46				13 40		13 46				14 40	14 46				15 40	15 46		
	d		11 47	12 00	12 18	12 30		12 47	13 00	13 18	13 30			13 47	14 00	14 18	14 30		14 47	15 00	15 18	15 30		15 47	16 00	16 18
Bescot Stadium	d			12 03		12 33			13 03		13 33				14 03		14 33			15 03		15 33			16 03	
Tame Bridge Parkway	d		11 52	12 06	12 23	12 36		12 52	13 06	13 23	13 36			13 52	14 06	14 23	14 36		14 52	15 06	15 23	15 36		15 52	16 06	16 23
Hamstead	d			12 10		12 40			13 10		13 40				14 10		14 40			15 10		15 40			16 10	
Perry Barr	d			12 13		12 43			13 13		13 43				14 13		14 43			15 13		15 43			16 13	
Witton	d			12 15		12 45			13 15		13 45				14 15		14 45			15 15		15 45			16 15	
Aston	d			12 18		12 48			13 18		13 48				14 18		14 48			15 18		15 48			16 18	
Duddeston	d			12 20		12 50			13 20		13 50				14 20		14 50			15 20		15 50			16 20	
Birmingham New Street 12	a		12 10	12 28	12 41	12 58		13 10	13 28	13 41	13 58			14 10	14 28	14 41	14 58		15 10	15 28	15 41	15 58		16 10	16 28	16 41

For general notes see front of timetable
For details of catering facilities see
Directory of Train Operators

A To Birmingham International (Table 68)
B From Shrewsbury (Table 74)

Saturdays

until 6 September

Stafford, Rugeley and Walsall → Birmingham

Network Diagram - see first page of Table 67

		LM	LM	LM [bus]	LM	LM	LM	LM	LM	LM	LM	LM	LM	LM	LM	LM	LM	LM	LM	LM	LM	LM	LM A	LM	LM [bus]
Stafford	d			15 30	15 53					16 53				17 53											19 52
Rugeley Trent Valley	d			15a55	16 04					17 04				18 04			19 25		20 16						20a17
Rugeley Town	a				16 08					17 08				18 08			19 29		20 19						
	d				16 17					17 17				18 17			19 30		20 20						
Hednesford	d				16 25					17 25				18 25			19 38		20 28		21 09	22 09		23 09	
Cannock	d				16 29					17 29				18 29			19 42		20 32		21 13	22 13		23 13	
Landywood	d				16 33					17 33				18 33			19 46		20 36		21 17	22 17		23 17	
Bloxwich North	d				16 37					17 37				18 37			19 50		20 40		21 21	22 21		23 21	
Bloxwich	d				16 39					17 39				18 39			19 52		20 42		21 23	22 23		23 23	
Wolverhampton 7	d		16 25						17 25				18 25			19 25		20 25		21 03			22 55		
Walsall	a		16 40		16 46				17 40	17 46			18 40	18 46		19 39	19 59	20 39	20 49	21 18	21 30	22 30	23 12	23 30	
	d	16 30			16 47	17 00	17 18	17 30		17 47	18 00	18 30		18 47	19 00		20 00		20 50		21 31	22 31		23 31	
Bescot Stadium	d	16 33				17 03		17 33			18 03	18 33			19 03		20 04		20 54		21 36	22 36			
Tame Bridge Parkway	d	16 36			16 52	17 06	17 23	17 36		17 52	18 06	18 36		18 52	19 06		20 07		20 57		21 39	22 39			
Hamstead	d	16 40				17 10		17 40			18 10	18 40			19 10		20 11		21 01		21 43	22 43			
Perry Barr	d	16 43				17 13		17 43			18 13	18 43			19 13		20 14		21 04		21 46	22 46			
Witton	d	16 45				17 15		17 45			18 15	18 45			19 15		20 17		21 07		21 48	22 48			
Aston	d	16 48				17 18		17 48			18 18	18 48			19 18		20 20		21 10		21 51	22 51			
Duddeston	d	16 50				17 20		17 50			18 20	18 50			19 20		20 23		21 13		21 54	22 54			
Birmingham New Street 12	a	16 58			17 10	17 28	17 41	17 58		18 10	18 28	18 58		19 10	19 28		20 28		21 18		21 59	22 59		23 55	

Saturdays

from 13 September

		LM	LM	LM	LM	LM	LM		LM	LM [bus]	LM [bus]	LM	LM	LM		LM	LM	LM	LM	LM	LM [bus]		LM	LM	LM	LM
Stafford	d									05 54	07 05										08 35					
Rugeley Trent Valley	d				06 18					06a19	07 31	07 47									09 01		09 13			
Rugeley Town	a				06 22						07 41	07 50									09 11		09 16			
	d				06 23							07 51											09 17			
Hednesford	d				06 31	07 05						07 59				08 20							09 25			
Cannock	d				06 35	07 09						08 02				08 24							09 29			
Landywood	d				06 39	07 12						08 06				08 28							09 33			
Bloxwich North	d				06 43	07 17						08 10				08 32							09 37			
Bloxwich	d				06 45	07 19						08 12				08 34							09 39			
Wolverhampton 7	d		06 08				07 25							08 25						09 25						
Walsall	a		06 22		06 52	07 25	07 38					08 18		08 40		08 41				09 40			09 46			
	d	05 58		06 32	06 53	07 31			08 02			08 19	08 30			08 47	09 00	09 15	09 30				09 47	10 00	10 16	10 30
Bescot Stadium	d	06 02		06 35	06 57	07 35			08 05				08 33				09 03		09 33					10 03		10 33
Tame Bridge Parkway	d	06 04		06 38	07 00	07 37			08 08			08 24	08 36			08 52	09 06	09 20	09 36				09 52	10 06	10 21	10 36
Hamstead	d	06 08		06 41	07 04	07 41			08 11				08 40				09 10		09 40					10 10		10 40
Perry Barr	d	06 11		06 44	07 07	07 44			08 14				08 43				09 13		09 43					10 13		10 43
Witton	d	06 14		06 46	07 09	07 47			08 16				08 45				09 15		09 45					10 15		10 45
Aston	d	06 16		06 48	07 12	07 50			08 19				08 48				09 18		09 48					10 18		10 48
Duddeston	d	06 19		06 50	07 15	07 53			08 21				08 50				09 20		09 50					10 20		10 50
Birmingham New Street 12	a	06 26		06 58	07 20	08 01			08 30			08 42	08 58			09 10	09 28	09 41	09 58				10 10	10 28	10 41	10 58

		LM	LM [bus]	LM	LM		LM	LM	LM	LM [bus]	LM	LM		LM	LM	LM	LM [bus]	LM	LM		LM	LM	LM	LM [bus]	LM [bus]	LM
Stafford	d		09 35							10 35							11 35							12 35	12 45	
Rugeley Trent Valley	d		10 01	10 13						11 01	11 13						12 01	12 13						13 01	13a10	13 13
Rugeley Town	a		10 11	10 16						11 11	11 16						12 11	12 16						13 11		13 16
	d			10 17							11 17							12 17								13 17
Hednesford	d			10 25							11 25							12 25								13 25
Cannock	d			10 29							11 29							12 29								13 29
Landywood	d			10 33							11 33							12 33								13 33
Bloxwich North	d			10 37							11 37							12 37								13 37
Bloxwich	d			10 39							11 39							12 39								13 39
Wolverhampton 7	d	10 25							11 25							12 25							13 25			
Walsall	a	10 40		10 46					11 40		11 46					12 40		12 46					13 40			13 46
	d			10 47	11 00		11 18	11 30			11 47	12 00		12 18	12 30			12 47	13 00		13 18	13 30				13 47
Bescot Stadium	d				11 03			11 33				12 03			12 33				13 03			13 33				
Tame Bridge Parkway	d			10 52	11 06		11 23	11 36			11 52	12 06		12 23	12 36			12 52	13 06		13 23	13 36				13 52
Hamstead	d				11 10			11 40				12 10			12 40				13 10			13 40				
Perry Barr	d				11 13			11 43				12 13			12 43				13 13			13 43				
Witton	d				11 15			11 45				12 15			12 45				13 15			13 45				
Aston	d				11 18			11 48				12 18			12 48				13 18			13 48				
Duddeston	d				11 20			11 50				12 20			12 50				13 20			13 50				
Birmingham New Street 12	a			11 10	11 28		11 41	11 58			12 10	12 28		12 41	12 58			13 10	13 28		13 41	13 58				14 10

For general notes see front of timetable
For details of catering facilities see
Directory of Train Operators

A From Shrewsbury (Table 74)

Table 70

Saturdays

from 13 September

Stafford, Rugeley and Walsall → Birmingham

Network Diagram - see first page of Table 67

Station		LM	LM		LM	LM	LM	LM	LM	LM		LM	LM	LM	LM	LM	LM		LM	LM	LM	LM	LM	LM		LM
							Bus							Bus							Bus	Bus				
Stafford	d						13 35							14 35							15 30	15 35				
Rugeley Trent Valley	d						14 01	14 13						15 01	15 13						15a55	16 01	16 13			
Rugeley Town	a						14 11	14 16						15 11	15 16							16 11	16 16			
	d							14 17							15 17								16 17			
Hednesford	d							14 25							15 25								16 25			
Cannock	d							14 29							15 29								16 29			
Landywood	d							14 33							15 33								16 33			
Bloxwich North	d							14 37							15 37								16 37			
Bloxwich	d							14 39							15 39								16 39			
Wolverhampton 7	d					14 25							15 25							16 25						
Walsall	a					14 40		14 46					15 40		15 46					16 40			16 46			
	d	14 00	14 18		14 30			14 47	15 00	15 18		15 30			15 47	16 00	16 18		16 30				16 47	17 00		17 18
Bescot Stadium	d	14 03			14 33				15 03			15 33				16 03			16 33					17 03		
Tame Bridge Parkway	d	14 06	14 23		14 36			14 52	15 06	15 23		15 36			15 52	16 06	16 23		16 36				16 52	17 06		17 23
Hamstead	d	14 10			14 40				15 10			15 40				16 10			16 40					17 10		
Perry Barr	d	14 13			14 43				15 13			15 43				16 13			16 43					17 13		
Witton	d	14 15			14 45				15 15			15 45				16 15			16 45					17 15		
Aston	d	14 18			14 48				15 18			15 48				16 18			16 48					17 18		
Duddeston	d	14 20			14 50				15 20			15 50				16 20			16 50					17 20		
Birmingham New Street 12	a	14 28	14 41		14 58			15 10	15 28	15 41		15 58			16 10	16 28	16 41		16 58				17 10	17 28		17 41

Station		LM	LM	LM	LM	LM	LM		LM	LM	LM	LM	LM	LM		LM	LM	LM	LM	LM	LM		LM	LM		
																					A					
				Bus						Bus														Bus		
Stafford	d			16 35						17 35														19 52		
Rugeley Trent Valley	d			17 01	17 13					18 01	18 13			19 25			20 16							20a17		
Rugeley Town	a			17 11	17 16					18 11	18 16			19 29			20 19									
	d				17 17						18 17			19 30			20 20									
Hednesford	d				17 25						18 25			19 38			20 28		21 09	22 09			23 09			
Cannock	d				17 29						18 29			19 42			20 32		21 13	22 13			23 13			
Landywood	d				17 33						18 33			19 46			20 36		21 17	22 17			23 17			
Bloxwich North	d				17 37						18 37			19 50			20 40		21 21	22 21			23 21			
Bloxwich	d				17 39						18 39			19 52			20 42		21 23	22 23			23 23			
Wolverhampton 7	d		17 25						18 25				19 25			20 25		21 03			22 55					
Walsall	a		17 40		17 46				18 40		18 46		19 39	19 59		20 39	20 49	21 18	21 30	22 30	23 12		23 30			
	d	17 30			17 47	18 00	18 30				18 47	19 00		20 00			20 50		21 31	22 31			23 31			
Bescot Stadium	d	17 33				18 03	18 33					19 03		20 04			20 54		21 36	22 36						
Tame Bridge Parkway	d	17 36			17 52	18 06	18 36				18 52	19 06		20 07			20 57		21 39	22 39						
Hamstead	d	17 40				18 10	18 40					19 10		20 11			21 01		21 43	22 43						
Perry Barr	d	17 43				18 13	18 43					19 13		20 14			21 04		21 46	22 46						
Witton	d	17 45				18 15	18 45					19 15		20 17			21 07		21 48	22 48						
Aston	d	17 48				18 18	18 48					19 18		20 20			21 10		21 51	22 51						
Duddeston	d	17 50				18 20	18 50					19 20		20 23			21 13		21 54	22 54						
Birmingham New Street 12	a	17 58			18 10	18 28	18 58				19 10	19 28		20 28			21 18		21 59	22 59			23 55			

Sundays

Until 13 July

Station		LM	LM	LM	LM	LM		LM	LM	LM	LM	LM		LM	LM	LM	LM	LM		LM	LM	LM	LM	LM		LM
Stafford	d																									
Rugeley Trent Valley	d				10 13				11 13			12 13				13 13				14 13			15 13			
Rugeley Town	a				10 16				11 16			12 16				13 16				14 16			15 16			
	d				10 17				11 17			12 17				13 17				14 17			15 17			
Hednesford	d				10 25				11 25			12 25				13 25				14 25			15 25			
Cannock	d				10 28				11 28			12 28				13 28				14 28			15 28			
Landywood	d				10 32				11 32			12 32				13 32				14 32			15 32			
Bloxwich North	d				10 36				11 36			12 36				13 36				14 36			15 36			
Bloxwich	d				10 38				11 38			12 38				13 38				14 38			15 38			
Wolverhampton 7	d	08 54	09 41			10 41				11 41				12 41			13 41				14 41			15 41		
Walsall	a	09 15	09 56		10 44	10 56			11 44	11 56		12 44		12 56		13 44	13 56			14 44	14 56		15 44	15 56		
	d			10 02	10 45			11 02	11 45		12 02	12 45			13 00	13 45		14 02		14 45		15 02	15 45			16 02
Bescot Stadium	d			10 06				11 06			12 06				13 04			14 06				15 06				16 06
Tame Bridge Parkway	d			10 08	10 51			11 08	11 51		12 08	12 51			13 06	13 51		14 08		14 51		15 08	15 51			16 08
Hamstead	d			10 12				11 12			12 12				13 10			14 12				15 12				16 12
Perry Barr	d			10 15				11 15			12 15				13 14			14 15				15 15				16 15
Witton	d			10 18				11 18			12 18				13 16			14 18				15 18				16 18
Aston	d			10 20				11 20			12 20				13 19			14 20				15 20				16 20
Duddeston	d			10 23				11 23			12 23				13 22			14 23				15 23				16 23
Birmingham New Street 12	a			10 30	11 06			11 30	12 06		12 30	13 06			13 28	14 06		14 30		15 07		15 30	16 06			16 30

For general notes see front of timetable
For details of catering facilities see
Directory of Train Operators

A From Shrewsbury (Table 74)

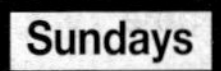

Until 13 July

Stafford, Rugeley and Walsall → Birmingham

Network Diagram - see first page of Table 67

		LM	LM	LM	LM	LM		LM	LM	LM	LM	LM		LM	LM	LM	LM	LM	LM	LM	LM	LM	LM	LM		
Stafford	d																									
Rugeley Trent Valley	d	16 13			17 13				18 13			19 13				20 13			21 13			22 13				
Rugeley Town	a	16 16			17 16				18 16			19 16				20 16			21 16			22 16				
	d	16 17			17 17				18 17			19 17				20 17			21 17			22 17				
Hednesford	d	16 25			17 25				18 25			19 25				20 25			21 25			22 25				
Cannock	d	16 28			17 28				18 28			19 28				20 28			21 28			22 28				
Landywood	d	16 32			17 32				18 32			19 32				20 32			21 32			22 32				
Bloxwich North	d	16 36			17 36				18 36			19 36				20 36			21 36			22 36				
Bloxwich	d	16 38			17 38				18 38			19 38				20 38			21 38			22 38				
Wolverhampton 7 🚌	d		16 41			17 41				18 41				19 41			20 41			21 41			22 41			
Walsall	a	16 44	16 56		17 44	17 56			18 44	18 56		19 44		19 56		20 44	20 56		21 44	21 56		22 44	22 56			
	d	16 45		17 02	17 45			18 02	18 45		19 02	19 45			20 02	20 45		21 02	21 45		22 02	22 45		23 07		
Bescot Stadium	d			17 06				18 06			19 06				20 06			21 06			22 06			23 11		
Tame Bridge Parkway	d	16 51		17 08	17 51			18 08	18 51		19 08	19 51			20 08	20 51		21 08	21 51		22 08	22 51		23 13		
Hamstead	d			17 12				18 12			19 12				20 12			21 12			22 12			23 17		
Perry Barr	d			17 15				18 15			19 15				20 15			21 15			22 15					
Witton	d			17 18				18 18			19 18				20 18			21 18			22 18					
Aston	d			17 20				18 20			19 20				20 20			21 20			22 20					
Duddeston	d			17 23				18 23			19 23				20 23			21 23			22 23					
Birmingham New Street 12	a	17 06		17 30	18 06			18 30	19 06		19 30	20 06			20 30	21 06		21 30	22 07		22 30	23 06		23 33		

Sundays

20 July to 7 September

		LM 🚌	LM 🚌	LM 🚌	LM 🚌	LM 🚌	LM 🚌		LM 🚌	LM 🚌	LM 🚌	LM 🚌	LM 🚌	LM 🚌		LM 🚌	LM 🚌	LM 🚌	LM 🚌	LM 🚌	LM 🚌		LM 🚌	LM 🚌	LM 🚌	LM 🚌
Stafford	d																									
Rugeley Trent Valley	d				08 50				09 50			10 50				11 50			12 50				13 50			14 50
Rugeley Town	a				09 00				10 00			11 00				12 00			13 00				14 00			15 00
	d				09 01				10 01			11 01				12 01			13 01				14 01			15 01
Hednesford	d				09 22				10 22			11 22				12 22			13 22				14 22			15 22
Cannock	d				09 30				10 30			11 30				12 30			13 30				14 30			15 30
Landywood	d				09 38				10 38			11 38				12 38			13 38				14 38			15 38
Bloxwich North	d				09 50				10 50			11 50				12 50			13 50				14 50			15 50
Bloxwich	d				09 59				10 59			11 59				12 59			13 59				14 59			15 59
Wolverhampton 7 🚌	d	09 01		09 40			10 40				11 40			12 40				13 40			14 40				15 40	
Walsall	a	09 21		10 00	10 07		11 00		11 07		12 00	12 07		13 00		13 07		14 00	14 07		15 00		15 07		16 00	16 07
	d		09 30		10 10	10 30			11 10	11 30		12 10	12 30			13 10	13 30		14 10	14 30			15 10	15 30		16 10
Bescot Stadium	d		09 39			10 39				11 39			12 39				13 39			14 39				15 39		
Tame Bridge Parkway	d		09 48		10 26	10 48			11 26	11 48		12 26	12 48			13 26	13 48		14 26	14 48			15 26	15 48		16 26
Hamstead	d		09 58			10 58				11 58			12 58				13 58			14 58				15 58		
Perry Barr	d		10 08			11 08				12 08			13 08				14 08			15 08				16 08		
Witton	d		10 15			11 15				12 15			13 15				14 15			15 15				16 15		
Aston	d		10 19			11 19				12 19			13 19				14 19			15 19				16 19		
Duddeston	d		10 24			11 24				12 24			13 24				14 24			15 24				16 24		
Birmingham New Street 12	a		10 33		10 51	11 33			11 51	12 33		12 51	13 33			13 51	14 33		14 51	15 33			15 51	16 33		16 51

		LM 🚌	LM 🚌	LM 🚌	LM 🚌		LM 🚌	LM 🚌	LM 🚌	LM 🚌	LM 🚌	LM 🚌		LM 🚌	LM 🚌	LM 🚌	LM 🚌	LM 🚌	LM 🚌	LM 🚌	LM 🚌	LM 🚌	LM 🚌	LM 🚌		
Stafford	d																									
Rugeley Trent Valley	d			15 50				16 50			17 50				18 50			19 50			20 50			21 50		
Rugeley Town	a			16 00				17 00			18 00				19 00			20 00			21 00			22 00		
	d			16 01				17 01			18 01				19 01			20 01			21 01			22 01		
Hednesford	d			16 22				17 22			18 22				19 22			20 22			21 22			22 22		
Cannock	d			16 30				17 30			18 30				19 30			20 30			21 30			22 30		
Landywood	d			16 38				17 38			18 38				19 38			20 38			21 38			22 38		
Bloxwich North	d			16 50				17 50			18 50				19 50			20 50			21 50			22 50		
Bloxwich	d			16 59				17 59			18 59				19 59			20 59			21 59			22 59		
Wolverhampton 7 🚌	d		16 40				17 40			18 40				19 40			20 40			21 40			22 40			
Walsall	a		17 00	17 07			18 00	18 07		19 00	19 07			20 00	20 07		21 00	21 07		22 00	22 07		23 00	23 07		
	d	16 30		17 10	17 30			18 10	18 30		19 10	19 30			20 10	20 30		21 10	21 30		22 10	22 30		23 10		
Bescot Stadium	d	16 39			17 39				18 39			19 39				20 39			21 39			22 39				
Tame Bridge Parkway	d	16 48		17 26	17 48			18 26	18 48		19 26	19 48			20 26	20 48		21 26	21 48		22 26	22 48		23 26		
Hamstead	d	16 58			17 58				18 58			19 58				20 58			21 58			22 58				
Perry Barr	d	17 08			18 08				19 08			20 08				21 08			22 08			23 08				
Witton	d	17 15			18 15				19 15			20 15				21 15			22 15			23 15				
Aston	d	17 19			18 19				19 19			20 19				21 19			22 19			23 19				
Duddeston	d	17 24			18 24				19 24			20 24				21 24			22 24			23 24				
Birmingham New Street 12	a	17 33		17 51	18 33			18 51	19 33		19 51	20 33			20 51	21 33		21 51	22 33		22 51	23 33		23 51		

For general notes see front of timetable
For details of catering facilities see Directory of Train Operators

From 14 September

Stafford, Rugeley and Walsall → Birmingham

Network Diagram - see first page of Table 67

		LM	LM	LM	LM	LM	LM	LM	LM	LM	LM	LM	LM	LM	LM	LM	LM	LM	LM	LM	LM	LM
Stafford	d																					
Rugeley Trent Valley	d				10 13			11 13			12 13			13 13			14 13			15 13		
Rugeley Town	a				10 16			11 16			12 16			13 16			14 16			15 16		
	d				10 17			11 17			12 17			13 17			14 17			15 17		
Hednesford	d				10 25			11 25			12 25			13 25			14 25			15 25		
Cannock	d				10 28			11 28			12 28			13 28			14 28			15 28		
Landywood	d				10 32			11 32			12 32			13 32			14 32			15 32		
Bloxwich North	d				10 36			11 36			12 36			13 36			14 36			15 36		
Bloxwich	d				10 38			11 38			12 38			13 38			14 38			15 38		
Wolverhampton 7	d	08 54	09 41			10 40			11 40			12 40			13 40			14 40			15 40	
Walsall	a	09 15	09 56		10 44	10 56		11 44	11 56		12 44	12 56		13 44	13 56		14 44	14 56		15 44	15 56	
	d			10 02	10 45		11 02	11 45		12 02	12 45		13 02	13 45		14 02	14 45		15 02	15 45		16 02
Bescot Stadium	d			10 06			11 06			12 06			13 06			14 06			15 06			16 06
Tame Bridge Parkway	d			10 08	10 51		11 08	11 51		12 08	12 51		13 08	13 51		14 08	14 51		15 08	15 51		16 08
Hamstead	d			10 12			11 12			12 12			13 12			14 12			15 12			16 12
Perry Barr	d			10 15			11 15			12 15			13 15			14 15			15 15			16 15
Witton	d			10 18			11 18			12 18			13 18			14 18			15 18			16 18
Aston	d			10 20			11 20			12 20			13 20			14 20			15 20			16 20
Duddeston	d			10 23			11 23			12 23			13 23			14 23			15 23			16 23
Birmingham New Street 12	a			10 30	11 06		11 30	12 06		12 30	13 06		13 30	14 06		14 30	15 06		15 30	16 06		16 30

		LM	LM	LM	LM	LM	LM	LM	LM	LM	LM	LM	LM	LM	LM	LM	LM	LM	LM	LM	LM	LM
Stafford	d																					
Rugeley Trent Valley	d	16 13			17 13			18 13			19 13			20 13			21 13			22 13		
Rugeley Town	a	16 16			17 16			18 16			19 16			20 16			21 16			22 16		
	d	16 17			17 17			18 17			19 17			20 17			21 17			22 17		
Hednesford	d	16 25			17 25			18 25			19 25			20 25			21 25			22 25		
Cannock	d	16 28			17 28			18 28			19 28			20 28			21 28			22 28		
Landywood	d	16 32			17 32			18 32			19 32			20 32			21 32			22 32		
Bloxwich North	d	16 36			17 36			18 36			19 36			20 36			21 36			22 36		
Bloxwich	d	16 38			17 38			18 38			19 38			20 38			21 38			22 38		
Wolverhampton 7	d		16 40			17 40			18 40			19 40			20 40			21 40				22 41
Walsall	a	16 44	16 56		17 44	17 56		18 44	18 56		19 44	19 56		20 44	20 56		21 44	21 56		22 44		22 56
	d	16 45		17 02	17 45		18 02	18 45		19 02	19 45		20 02	20 45		21 02	21 45		22 02	22 45	23 02	
Bescot Stadium	d			17 06			18 06			19 06			20 06			21 06			22 06		23 06	
Tame Bridge Parkway	d	16 51		17 08	17 51		18 08	18 51		19 08	19 51		20 08	20 51		21 08	21 51		22 08	22 51	23 08	
Hamstead	d			17 12			18 12			19 12			20 12			21 12			22 12		23 12	
Perry Barr	d			17 15			18 15			19 15			20 15			21 15			22 15		23 15	
Witton	d			17 18			18 18			19 18			20 18			21 18			22 18		23 18	
Aston	d			17 20			18 20			19 20			20 20			21 20			22 20		23 20	
Duddeston	d			17 23			18 23			19 23			20 23			21 23			22 23		23 23	
Birmingham New Street 12	a	17 06		17 30	18 06		18 30	19 06		19 30	20 06		20 30	21 06		21 30	22 07		22 30	23 06	23 30	

For general notes see front of timetable
For details of catering facilities see
Directory of Train Operators

Network Diagram for Tables 71, 72

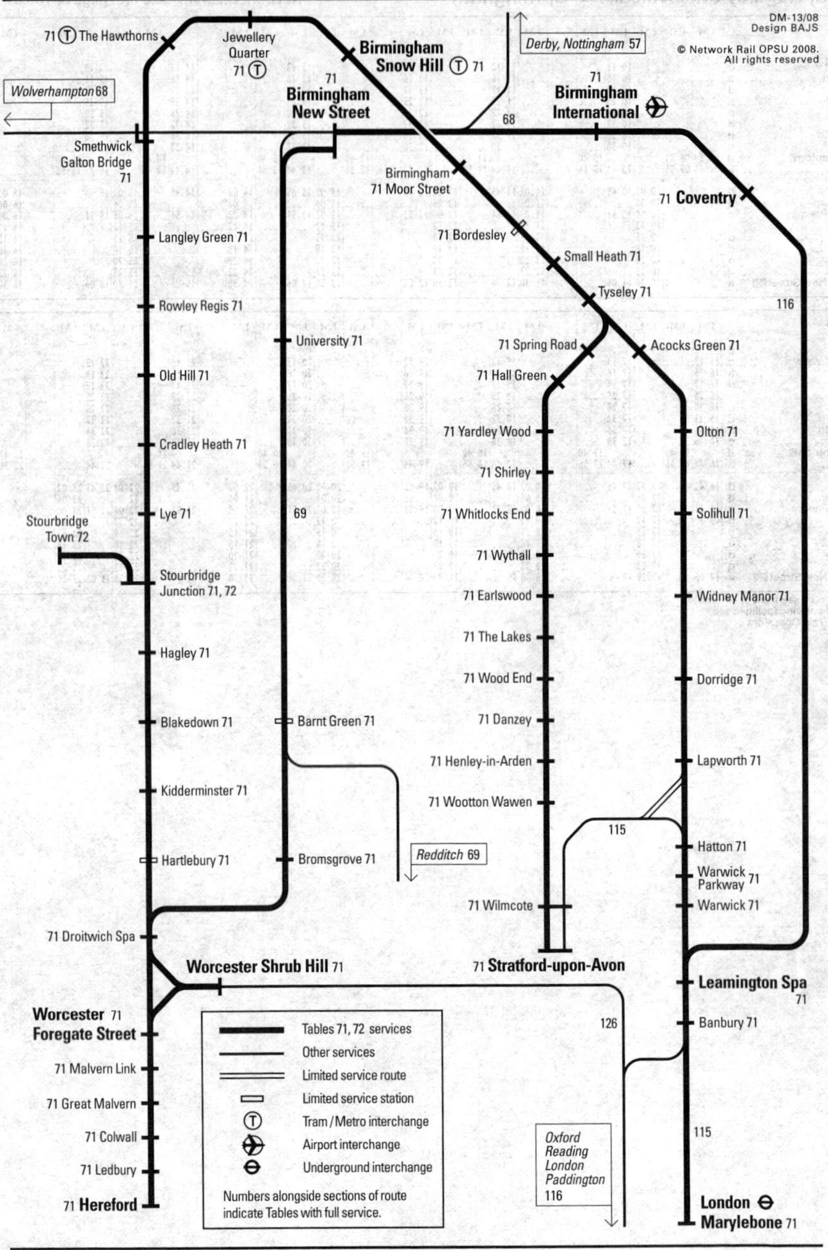

DM-13/08
Design BAJS
© Network Rail OPSU 2008.
All rights reserved
71 The Hawthorns
Jewellery Quarter 71
Birmingham Snow Hill 71
Derby, Nottingham 57
Wolverhampton 68
71 Birmingham New Street
71 Birmingham International
68
Smethwick Galton Bridge 71
Birmingham 71 Moor Street
71 Coventry
71 Bordesley
Small Heath 71
Tyseley 71
116
Langley Green 71
Rowley Regis 71
University 71
71 Spring Road
Acocks Green 71
71 Hall Green
Old Hill 71
71 Yardley Wood
Olton 71
Cradley Heath 71
71 Shirley
Stourbridge Town 72
Lye 71
69
71 Whitlocks End
Solihull 71
71 Wythall
Stourbridge Junction 71, 72
71 Earlswood
Widney Manor 71
71 The Lakes
Hagley 71
71 Wood End
Dorridge 71
Blakedown 71
Barnt Green 71
71 Danzey
71 Henley-in-Arden
Lapworth 71
Kidderminster 71
71 Wootton Wawen
115
Hatton 71
Hartlebury 71
Bromsgrove 71
Redditch 69
Warwick Parkway 71
71 Wilmcote
Warwick 71
71 Droitwich Spa
Worcester Shrub Hill 71
71 Stratford-upon-Avon
Leamington Spa 71
Worcester Foregate Street 71
126
Banbury 71
71 Malvern Link
71 Great Malvern
71 Colwall
71 Ledbury
71 Hereford
115
Oxford
Reading
London
Paddington
116
London Marylebone 71
Tables 71, 72 services
Other services
Limited service route
Limited service station
Tram / Metro interchange
Airport interchange
Underground interchange
Numbers alongside sections of route indicate Tables with full service.

Hereford, Worcester and Stourbridge → Birmingham → Leamington Spa, Marylebone and Stratford-upon-Avon

Network Diagram - See first page of Table 71

Miles	Miles	Miles			CH	CH	CH	LM	XC	CH	CH	LM	GW	LM	LM	XC	LM	CH	CH	XC	LM	CH	LM	LM	LM
					MX				[1] ◇				[1] ◇			[1] ◇			A	[1] ◇		A			
						⌶	⌶		☕		⌶		☕			☕			⌶	☕		⌶			
0	—	—	**Hereford [7]**	d																					
13¾	—	—	Ledbury	a																					
—	—	—		d																					
18	—	—	Colwall	d																					
20¾	—	—	**Great Malvern**	a																					
—	—	—		d									05 30				05 50								
22	—	—	Malvern Link	d									05 34				05 53								
28¾	0	—	**Worcester Foregate Street [7]**	a													06 01								
—	—	—		d													06 03								
29½	—	—	**Worcester Shrub Hill [7]**	a									05 44												
—	—	—		d								05 30												06 15	06 25
34¼	5½	—	Droitwich Spa	d								05 38					06 12							06 23	06 33
40½	—	—	Bromsgrove	d													06 21								06 42
44	—	—	Barnt Green	d																					
52	—	—	University	d													06 39								06 59
—	11	—	Hartlebury	d																				06 30	
—	14¾	—	**Kidderminster**	d								05 48							06 09			06 30		06 37	
—	17¾	—	Blakedown	d																				06 42	
—	19½	—	Hagley	d																				06 45	
—	21½	—	**Stourbridge Junction [2]**	d								05 57							06 17		06 24	06 39		06 50	
—	22¾	—	Lye	d								06 01									06 27			06 53	
—	24	—	Cradley Heath	d								06 04							06 24		06 31	06 44		06 57	
—	25½	—	Old Hill	d								06 08									06 35			07 01	
—	26¾	—	Rowley Regis	d								06 12							06 30		06 38	06 50		07 04	
—	28½	0	Langley Green	d								06 15									06 41			07 07	
—	29½	—	Smethwick Galton Bdg H.L. [7]	d								06 18							06 35		06 45	06 56		07 11	
54½	—	6¼	**Birmingham New Street [12]**	a													06 45								07 07
—	—	—		d					06 03							06 33				07 03					
—	—	—	**Birmingham International** ✈	d					06 15											07 15					
—	—	—	**Coventry**	d					06 25											07 25					
—	30¼	—	The Hawthorns	d								06 21							06 38		06 47	06 58		07 13	
—	32¾	—	Jewellery Quarter	d								06 24									06 51			07 17	
—	33½	—	**Birmingham Snow Hill**	a								06 28							06 46		06 54	07 04		07 20	
—	—	—		d	23p30		05 43	05 58			06 14	06 29		06 33	06 43				06 50		06 56	07 13	07 19	07 25	
—	34	—	**Birmingham Moor Street**	d	23p33		05 46	06 01			06 17	06 32		06 36	06 46				06 53		06 59	07 16	07 22	07 28	
—	34¾	—	Bordesley	d																					
—	35¾	9¼	Small Heath	d				06 05						06 41	06 50						07 03			07 32	
—	36¾	10¼	Tyseley	d	23p37			06 07				06 36		06 42	06 52						07 05			07 34	
—	—	11¼	Acocks Green	d	23p40			06 10						06 45							07 08		07 28		
—	—	12¼	Olton	d	23p43			06 13						06 48							07 11		07 30		
—	—	14	Solihull	d	23p47		05 56	06 16			06 27			06 50					07 04		07 14	07 26	07 34		
—	—	15½	Widney Manor	d	23p50			06 20						06 55							07 17		07 37		
—	—	17½	Dorridge	d	23p54		06 01	06 24			06 32			07a02					07 09		07 21	07 31	07a42		
—	—	20	Lapworth	d	23p58			06 28													07 25				
—	—	24¼	Hatton	d	00 03					06 31								07 03			07 31				
—	—	27	Warwick Parkway	d	00 08	05 40	06 12				06 44							07 09	07 21			07 43			
—	—	28¼	Warwick	d	00 11		06 15			06 38								07 13			07 37	07 46			
—	—	30¼	**Leamington Spa [8]**	a	00 14	05 45	06 20		06 37	06 45	06 49					06 59		07 17	07 26	07 37	07 44	07 50			
—	—	—		d	00 15	05 45	06 20		06 38		06 49					07 00		07 18	07 26	07 38		07 50			
—	—	—	Banbury	d	00a38	06 03	06 38		06a54		07 07					07a18		07 36	07 44	07a54		08 08			
—	—	—	**London Marylebone [10]** ⊖	a		07 18	07 52				08 16							08 50	08 53			09 23			
—	37¾	—	Spring Road	d								06 39			06 55									07 37	
—	38½	—	Hall Green	d								06 42			06 58									07 40	
—	39½	—	Yardley Wood	d								06 45			07 01									07 43	
—	40¾	—	Shirley	d								06 48			07 06									07 46	
—	41¾	—	Whitlocks End	d								06 51			07 09									07 49	
—	42¾	—	Wythall	d								06 53			07 11									07 51	
—	43¾	—	Earlswood (West Midlands)	d											07 14									07 54	
—	44½	—	The Lakes	d											07x16									07x56	
—	45¾	—	Wood End	d											07x18									07x58	
—	47½	—	Danzey	d											07x21									08x01	
—	50¼	—	Henley-in-Arden	d								07 03			07 26									08 06	
—	52¼	—	Wootton Wawen	d											07x28									08x09	
—	56	—	Wilmcote	d				06 44							07 34									08 14	
—	58¾	—	**Stratford-upon-Avon**	a				06 48				07 15			07 39									08 20	

For general notes see front of timetable
For details of catering facilities see Directory of Train Operators

A ⌶ from Birmingham Snow Hill

Hereford, Worcester and Stourbridge → Birmingham → Leamington Spa, Marylebone and Stratford-upon-Avon

Network Diagram - See first page of Table 71

		GW	LM	XC	CH	CH	LM	GW	LM	LM	XC	CH	LM	LM	GW	LM	LM	XC	XC	LM	LM	XC	CH	LM	LM
		1 ◇		1 ◇				1			1 ◇				1 ◇				1 ◇						
		A				B									C D			E				E			
		⊠		☕		trolley					☕				⊠				☕						
Hereford 7	d	05 41													06 43						07 09				
Ledbury	a	05 58													06 59						07 25				
	d	05 59													07 00						07 26				
Colwall	d	06 07													07 08						07 32				
Great Malvern	a	06 11													07 14						07 37				
	d	06 12								06 49				07 05	07 15						07 37				
Malvern Link	d	06 16								06 51				07 08	07 19						07 40				
Worcester Foregate Street 7	a	06 26								06 59				07 15	07 28						07 49				
	d	06 27					06 45	06 52		06 59				07 16	07 29		07 33				07 49				08 03
Worcester Shrub Hill 7	a	06 30						06 54		07 03				07 18	07 32						07 52				
	d									07 06			07 15	07 24							07 56				
Droitwich Spa	d						06 54			07 14			07 23	07 34			07 42				08 05				08 11
Bromsgrove	d									07 23								07 50				08 23			
Barnt Green	d																								
University	d													07 59				08 09			08 29	08 39			
Hartlebury	d						07 01						07 31												
Kidderminster	d					06 56	07 09		07 18			07 30	07 37				07 53						08 10		08 22
Blakedown	d						07 14		07 24				07 42				07 58						08 15		08 27
Hagley	d						07 18		07 28				07 46				08 02						08 18		08 30
Stourbridge Junction 2	d					07 07	07 23		07 32			07 40	07 50			07 56	08 08			08 14			08 23		08 35
Lye	d					07 11			07 35							07 59				08 17					08 38
Cradley Heath	d					07 14	07 29		07 39			07 45	07 56			08 02	08 14			08 21			08 28		08 41
Old Hill	d					07 18			07 43							08 06				08 25					08 45
Rowley Regis	d					07 22	07 35		07 47			07 53	08 01			08 10	08 20			08 29			08 34		08 49
Langley Green	d					07 25			07 50							08 13				08 32					08 52
Smethwick Galton Bdg H.L. 7	d					07 29	07 40		07 53			07 59	08 06			08 16	08 25			08 35			08 40		08 55
Birmingham New Street 12	a									07 45				08 09				08 16			08 37	08 46			
	d			07 33							08 03								08 33						
Birmingham International ✈	d										08 15														
Coventry	d										08 25														
The Hawthorns 🚊	d					07 32	07 42		07 56			08 02	08 09			08 19	08 28			08 38			08 42		08 58
Jewellery Quarter 🚊	d					07 36	07 46		07 59			08 06	08 12			08 22	08 31			08 41			08 47		09 01
Birmingham Snow Hill 🚊	a					07 40	07 49		08 03			08 11	08 16			08 25	08 35			08 45			08 51		09 05
	d		07 39			07 45	07 50		08 05			08 12	08 17			08 27	08 37			08 47			08 52	08 57	09 07
Birmingham Moor Street	d		07 42			07 48	07 53		08 08			08 15	08 20			08 30	08 40			08 50			08 55	09 00	09 10
Bordesley	d																								
Small Heath	d		07 46						08 12								08 44								09 14
Tyseley	d		07 48				07 58		08 14								08 46								09 16
Acocks Green	d						08 01						08 26				08 49							09 06	
Olton	d						08 03						08 28				08 52							09 08	
Solihull	d					07 58	08 07					08 25	08 32				08 55						09 05	09 12	
Widney Manor	d						08 10						08 35				08 58							09 15	
Dorridge	d					08 03	08a16					08 30	08a41				09a03						09 10	09a22	
Lapworth	d					08 07																			
Hatton	d				07 56	08 13																			
Warwick Parkway	d					08 19						08 41											09 21		
Warwick	d				08 05	08 23						08 44											09 24		
Leamington Spa 8	a			07 59	08 09	08 26					08 37	08 49							08 59				09 29		
	d			08 00	08 09	08 27					08 38	08 49							09 00				09 29		
Banbury	d			08a18	08 28	08 45					08a54	09 09							09a18				09 47		
London Marylebone 10 ⊖	a				09 53	09 59						10 25											10 59		
Spring Road	d		07 51						08 17							08 36				08 56					09 19
Hall Green	d		07 54						08 20							08 39				08 59					09 22
Yardley Wood	d		07 57						08 23							08 42				09 02					09 25
Shirley	d		08a00						08a26							08 45				09a05					09a28
Whitlocks End	d															08 48									
Wythall	d															08 50									
Earlswood (West Midlands)	d															08 53									
The Lakes	d															08x55									
Wood End	d															08x57									
Danzey	d															09x00									
Henley-in-Arden	d															09 05									
Wootton Wawen	d															09x08									
Wilmcote	d															09 13									
Stratford-upon-Avon	a															09 19									

For general notes see front of timetable
For details of catering facilities see Directory of Train Operators

A From Abergavenny (Table 131)
B trolley from Birmingham Snow Hill
C All Tuesdays to Frodays, also Mondays from 15 September from Abergavenny (Table 131)
D **Cathedrals Express**
E From Gloucester to Nottingham (Table 57)

Hereford, Worcester and Stourbridge → Birmingham → Leamington Spa, Marylebone and Stratford-upon-Avon

Network Diagram - See first page of Table 71

		XC	LM	GW	CH	LM	LM	LM	LM	XC	LM	GW	XC	CH	CH	LM	LM	XC	CH	LM	LM	LM	GW	LM	XC
		R 1		1 ◇						1 ◇		A	◇ B					R 1					1 ◇		1 ◇
		☕		☕						☕			🍴					☕							☕
Hereford 7	d		07 35																			08 50			
Ledbury	a		07 50																			09 06			
	d		07 51																			09 07			
Colwall	d		07 57																			09 13			
Great Malvern	a		08 01																			09 18			
	d		08 03								08 35	08 51										09 18			
Malvern Link	d		08 06								08 37	08 54										09 21			
Worcester Foregate Street 7	a		08 14								08 46	09 01										09 30			
	d		08 19	08 37							08 46	09 02								09 15		09 31	09 37		
Worcester Shrub Hill 7	a			08 40								09 04											09 39		
	d																								
Droitwich Spa	d		08 32								08 55									09 24		09 40			
Bromsgrove	d		08 41										09 21									09 50			
Barnt Green	d																								
University	d		08 59																			10 09			
Hartlebury	d																								
Kidderminster	d							08 56									09 30			09 36				09 56	
Blakedown	d							09 01												09 41					
Hagley	d							09 04												09 44					
Stourbridge Junction 2	d					08 45	08 55	09 09	09 19							09 25	09 39			09 49	09 55			10 09	
Lye	d						08 58									09 28					09 58				
Cradley Heath	d					08 51	09 01	09 14	09 24							09 31	09 44			09 54	10 01			10 14	
Old Hill	d						09 05									09 35					10 05				
Rowley Regis	d					08 57	09 09	09 20	09 30							09 39	09 50			10 00	10 09			10 20	
Langley Green	d						09 12									09 42					10 12				
Smethwick Galton Bdg H.L. 7	d					09 02	09 15	09 25	09 35							09 45	09 55			10 05	10 15			10 25	
Birmingham New Street 12	a		09 07								09 43		09 45									10 24			
	d	09 03								09 33								10 03							10 33
Birmingham International ✈	d	09 15																10 15							
Coventry	d	09 25																10 25							
The Hawthorns	d					09 05	09 18	09 28	09 38							09 48	09 58			10 08	10 18			10 28	
Jewellery Quarter	d					09 09	09 21	09 31	09 41							09 51	10 01			10 11	10 21			10 31	
Birmingham Snow Hill	a					09 15	09 25	09 36	09 45							09 55	10 05			10 15	10 25			10 35	
	d				09 12	09 17	09 27	09 37	09 47						09 52	09 57	10 07		10 12	10 17	10 27			10 37	
Birmingham Moor Street	d				09 15	09 20	09 30	09 40	09 50						09 55	10 00	10 10		10 15	10 20	10 30			10 40	
Bordesley	d																								
Small Heath	d							09 44									10 14							10 44	
Tyseley	d							09 46									10 16							10 46	
Acocks Green	d					09 26		09 49								10 06				10 26				10 49	
Olton	d					09 28		09 52								10 08				10 28				10 52	
Solihull	d				09 25	09 32		09 55							10 05	10 12			10 25	10 32				10 55	
Widney Manor	d					09 35		09 58								10 15				10 35				10 58	
Dorridge	d				09 30	09a41		10a04							10 11	10a22			10 30	10a41				11a04	
Lapworth	d				09 34														10 34						
Hatton	d				09 40									10 00					10 40						
Warwick Parkway	d				09 45										10 22				10 45						
Warwick	d				09 49									10 06	10 25				10 49						
Leamington Spa 8	a	09 37			09 53					09 59				10 10	10 29			10 37	10 53						10 59
	d	09 38			09 54					10 00				10 11	10 29			10 38	10 54						11 00
Banbury	d	09a54			10 12					10a18				10 29	10 47			10a54	11 13						11a18
London Marylebone 10 ⊖	a				11 30									11 56	12 00				12 30						
Spring Road	d						09 36		09 56								10 19				10 36				
Hall Green	d						09 39		09 59								10 22				10 39				
Yardley Wood	d						09 42		10 02								10 25				10 42				
Shirley	d						09 45		10a05								10a28				10 45				
Whitlocks End	d						09 48														10 48				
Wythall	d						09 50														10 50				
Earlswood (West Midlands)	d						09 53														10 53				
The Lakes	d						09x55														10x55				
Wood End	d						09x57														10x57				
Danzey	d						10x00														11x00				
Henley-in-Arden	d						10 05														11 05				
Wootton Wawen	d						10x08														11x08				
Wilmcote	d						10 13														11 13				
Stratford-upon-Avon	a						10 21														11 21				

For general notes see front of timetable
For details of catering facilities see Directory of Train Operators

A To Westbury (Table 123)
B To Nottingham (Table 57)

Hereford, Worcester and Stourbridge → Birmingham → Leamington Spa, Marylebone and Stratford-upon-Avon

Network Diagram - See first page of Table 71

Station		LM	CH	LM	LM	XC	CH	LM	LM	LM	LM	LM	GW	XC	CH	CH	LM	LM	XC	CH	LM	GW	LM	LM
						R 1 ☕							◇ A	1 ◇ ☕					R 1 ☕			1 ◇ ☕		
Hereford 7	d									09 50														
Ledbury	a									10 06														
	d									10 07														
Colwall	d									10 13														
Great Malvern	a									10 18														
	d	09 35								10 18			10 43									11 06		
Malvern Link	d	09 37								10 21			10 46									11 10		
Worcester Foregate Street 7	a	09 46								10 30			11 01									11 25		
	d	09 46						10 15		10 31			11 02								11 15	11 26		
Worcester Shrub Hill 7	a												11 04									11 29		
	d											10 47												
Droitwich Spa	d	09 55						10 24		10 40		10 55									11 24			
Bromsgrove	d									10 50														
Barnt Green	d																							
University	d									11 09														
Hartlebury	d																							
Kidderminster	d	10 06			10 26			10 36			10 56	11 06						11 26			11 36			11 56
Blakedown	d	10 11			10 31							11 11						11 31						
Hagley	d	10 14			10 34							11 14						11 34						
Stourbridge Junction 2	d	10 19		10 25	10 39			10 49	10 55		11 09	11 19					11 25	11 39			11 49		11 55	12 09
Lye	d			10 28					10 58								11 28						11 58	
Cradley Heath	d	10 24		10 31	10 44			10 54	11 01		11 14	11 24					11 31	11 44			11 54		12 01	12 14
Old Hill	d			10 35					11 05								11 35						12 05	
Rowley Regis	d	10 30		10 39	10 50			11 00	11 09		11 20	11 30					11 39	11 50			12 00		12 09	12 20
Langley Green	d			10 42					11 12								11 42						12 12	
Smethwick Galton Bdg H.L. 7	d	10 35		10 45	10 55			11 05	11 15		11 25	11 35					11 45	11 55			12 05		12 15	12 25
Birmingham New Street 12	a									11 23														
	d					11 03								11 33					12 03					
Birmingham International ✈	d					11 15													12 15					
Coventry	d					11 25													12 25					
The Hawthorns 🚋	d	10 38		10 48	10 58			11 08	11 18		11 28	11 38					11 48	11 58			12 08		12 18	12 28
Jewellery Quarter 🚋	d	10 41		10 51	11 01			11 11	11 21		11 31	11 41					11 51	12 01			12 11		12 21	12 31
Birmingham Snow Hill 🚋	a	10 45		10 55	11 05			11 15	11 25		11 35	11 45					11 55	12 05			12 15		12 25	12 35
	d	10 47	10 52	10 57	11 07		11 12	11 17	11 27		11 37	11 47				11 52	11 57	12 07		12 12	12 17		12 27	12 37
Birmingham Moor Street	d	10 50	10 55	11 00	11 10		11 15	11 20	11 30		11 40	11 50				11 55	12 00	12 10		12 15	12 20		12 30	12 40
Bordesley	d																							
Small Heath	d				11 14						11 44							12 14						12 44
Tyseley	d				11 16						11 46							12 16						12 46
Acocks Green	d			11 06				11 26			11 49						12 06				12 26			12 49
Olton	d			11 08				11 28			11 52						12 08				12 28			12 52
Solihull	d		11 05	11 12			11 25	11 32			11 55					12 05	12 12			12 25	12 32			12 55
Widney Manor	d			11 15				11 35			11 58						12 15				12 35			12 58
Dorridge	d		11 10	11a21			11 31	11a41			12a04					12 10	12a22			12 31	12a41			13a04
Lapworth	d																			12 35				
Hatton	d														11 59					12 41				
Warwick Parkway	d		11 21				11 41									12 21				12 46				
Warwick	d		11 24				11 45								12 05	12 24				12 49				
Leamington Spa 8	a		11 29			11 37	11 51							11 59	12 07	12 29			12 37	12 53				
	d		11 29			11 38	11 52							12 00	12 08	12 29			12 38	12 54				
Banbury	d		11 47			11a54	12 09							12a18	12 28	12 47			12a54	13 12				
London Marylebone 10 ⊖	a		12 59				13 29								13 55	13 59				14 30				
Spring Road	d	10 56			11 19				11 36			11 56						12 19					12 36	
Hall Green	d	10 59			11 22				11 39			11 59						12 22					12 39	
Yardley Wood	d	11 02			11 25				11 42			12 02						12 25					12 42	
Shirley	d	11a05			11a28				11 45			12a05						12a28					12 45	
Whitlocks End	d								11 48														12 48	
Wythall	d								11 50														12 50	
Earlswood (West Midlands)	d								11 53														12 53	
The Lakes	d								11x55														12x55	
Wood End	d								11x57														12x57	
Danzey	d								12x00														13x00	
Henley-in-Arden	d								12 05														13 05	
Wootton Wawen	d								12x08														13x08	
Wilmcote	d								12 13														13 13	
Stratford-upon-Avon	a								12 21														13 21	

For general notes see front of timetable
For details of catering facilities see Directory of Train Operators

A To Brighton (Table 123)

Table 71

Mondays to Fridays

Hereford, Worcester and Stourbridge → Birmingham → Leamington Spa, Marylebone and Stratford-upon-Avon

Network Diagram - See first page of Table 71

		LM	XC	LM	CH	LM	LM	XC	CH	LM	LM	LM	GW	LM	LM	GW	XC	CH	CH	LM	LM	XC	CH	LM	LM
								R														R			
			1 ◇					1					1 ◇			◇	1 ◇					1			
																A									
			🛒					🛒					🛒				🛒					🛒			
Hereford 7	d	10 50																							
Ledbury	a	11 06																							
	d	11 07																							
Colwall	d	11 13																							
Great Malvern	a	11 18																							
	d	11 18		11 30								12 18				12 51									
Malvern Link	d	11 21		11 32								12 21				12 54									
Worcester Foregate Street 7	a	11 30		11 40								12 29				13 01									
	d	11 31		11 41						12 15		12 31	12 40			13 02								13 15	
Worcester Shrub Hill 7	a			11 43									12 43			13 04									
	d			11 47											12 47										
Droitwich Spa	d	11 40		11 55						12 24		12 40			12 55									13 24	
Bromsgrove	d	11 50										12 50													
Barnt Green	d																								
University	d	12 09										13 09													
Hartlebury	d																								
Kidderminster	d			12 06			12 26			12 36				12 56	13 06									13 36	
Blakedown	d			12 11			12 31								13 11										
Hagley	d			12 14			12 34								13 14										
Stourbridge Junction 2	d			12 19		12 25	12 39			12 49	12 55			13 09	13 19					13 25	13 37			13 49	13 55
Lye	d					12 28					12 58									13 28					13 58
Cradley Heath	d			12 24		12 31	12 44			12 54	13 01			13 14	13 24					13 31	13 43			13 54	14 01
Old Hill	d					12 35					13 05									13 35					14 05
Rowley Regis	d			12 30		12 39	12 50			13 00	13 09			13 20	13 30					13 39	13 49			14 00	14 09
Langley Green	d					12 42					13 12									13 42					14 12
Smethwick Galton Bdg H.L. 7	d			12 35		12 45	12 55			13 05	13 15			13 25	13 35					13 45	13 53			14 05	14 15
Birmingham New Street 12	a	12 23										13 18													
	d		12 33					13 03									13 33					14 03			
Birmingham International ✈	d							13 15														14 15			
Coventry	d							13 25														14 25			
The Hawthorns 🚊	d			12 38		12 48	12 58			13 08	13 18			13 28	13 38					13 48	13 56			14 08	14 18
Jewellery Quarter 🚊	d			12 41		12 51	13 01			13 11	13 21			13 31	13 41					13 51	13 59			14 11	14 21
Birmingham Snow Hill 🚊	a			12 45		12 55	13 05			13 15	13 25			13 35	13 45					13 55	14 03			14 15	14 25
	d			12 47	12 52	12 57	13 07		13 12	13 17	13 27			13 37	13 47				13 52	13 57	14 07		14 12	14 17	14 27
Birmingham Moor Street	d			12 50	12 55	13 00	13 10		13 15	13 20	13 30			13 40	13 50				13 55	14 00	14 10		14 15	14 20	14 30
Bordesley	d																								
Small Heath	d						13 14							13 44							14 14				
Tyseley	d						13 16							13 46							14 16				
Acocks Green	d					13 06				13 26				13 49						14 06				14 26	
Olton	d					13 08				13 28				13 52						14 08				14 28	
Solihull	d				13 05	13 12			13 25	13 32				13 55					14 05	14 12			14 25	14 32	
Widney Manor	d					13 15				13 35				13 58						14 15				14 35	
Dorridge	d				13 10	13a21			13 31	13a41				14a04					14 10	14a22			14 31	14a41	
Lapworth	d																						14 35		
Hatton	d																	13 57					14 41		
Warwick Parkway	d				13 21				13 41										14 21				14 46		
Warwick	d				13 24				13 45									14 03	14 24				14 49		
Leamington Spa 8	a		12 59		13 29			13 37	13 50								13 59	14 07	14 29			14 37	14 53		
	d		13 00		13 29			13 38	13 50								14 00	14 08	14 29			14 38	14 54		
Banbury	d		13a18		13 47			13a54	14 08								14a18	14 27	14 47			14a54	15 12		
London Marylebone 10 ⊖	a				14 59				15 28									15 53	16 00				16 31		
Spring Road	d			12 56			13 19				13 36				13 56						14 19				14 36
Hall Green	d			12 59			13 22				13 39				13 59						14 22				14 39
Yardley Wood	d			13 02			13 25				13 42				14 02						14 25				14 42
Shirley	d			13a05			13a28				13 45				14a05						14a28				14 45
Whitlocks End	d										13 48														14 48
Wythall	d										13 50														14 50
Earlswood (West Midlands)	d										13 53														14 53
The Lakes	d										13x55														14x55
Wood End	d										13x57														14x57
Danzey	d										14x00														15x00
Henley-in-Arden	d										14 05														15 05
Wootton Wawen	d										14x08														15x08
Wilmcote	d										14 13														15 13
Stratford-upon-Avon	a										14 21														15 21

For general notes see front of timetable
For details of catering facilities see Directory of Train Operators

A To Weymouth (Table 123)

Hereford, Worcester and Stourbridge → Birmingham → Leamington Spa, Marylebone and Stratford-upon-Avon

Network Diagram - See first page of Table 71

Station		LM	LM	LM	XC	CH	LM	LM	GW	XC	CH	LM	LM	LM	LM	LM	GW	XC	CH	CH	LM	LM	XC	CH	LM
					1 ◇ ☕				1 ◇ ☕	1 ◇ ☕							◇ A	1 ◇ ☕					R 1 ☕		
Hereford 7	d		12 50						13 23					13 50											
Ledbury	a		13 06						13 39					14 06											
	d		13 07						13 41					14 07											
Colwall	d		13 13						13 48					14 13											
Great Malvern	a		13 18						13 53					14 18											
	d		13 18					13 38	13 54					14 18			14 51								
Malvern Link	d		13 21					13 40	13 58					14 21			14 54								
Worcester Foregate Street 7	a		13 30					13 48	14 07					14 30			15 01								
	d		13 31					13 49	14 09			14 15		14 31			15 02								15 15
Worcester Shrub Hill 7	a							13 51	14 12								15 04								
	d			13 47				13 57								14 43									
Droitwich Spa	d		13 40	13 55				14b07				14 24		14 40		14 55									15 24
Bromsgrove	d		13 50											14 50											
Barnt Green	d																								
University	d		14 09											15 09											
Hartlebury	d																								
Kidderminster	d	13 56		14 06				14c26				14 36			14 56	15 06						15 26			15 36
Blakedown	d			14 11				14 31								15 11						15 31			15 41
Hagley	d			14 14				14 34								15 14						15 34			15 44
Stourbridge Junction 2	d	14 09		14 19			14 25	14 39				14 49	14 55		15 09	15 19					15 25	15 39			15 49
Lye	d						14 28						14 58								15 28				
Cradley Heath	d	14 14		14 24			14 31	14 44				14 54	15 01		15 14	15 24					15 31	15 44			15 54
Old Hill	d						14 35						15 05								15 35				
Rowley Regis	d	14 20		14 30			14 39	14 50				15 00	15 09		15 20	15 30					15 39	15 50			16 00
Langley Green	d						14 42						15 12								15 42				
Smethwick Galton Bdg H.L. 7	d	14 25		14 35			14 45	14 55				15 05	15 15		15 25	15 35					15 45	15 55			16 05
Birmingham New Street 12	a		14 23											15 21											
	d				14 33					15 03								15 33					16 03		
Birmingham International ✈	d									15 15													16 15		
Coventry	d									15 25													16 25		
The Hawthorns 🚊	d	14 28		14 38			14 48	14 58				15 08	15 18		15 28	15 38					15 48	15 58			16 08
Jewellery Quarter 🚊	d	14 31		14 41			14 51	15 01				15 11	15 21		15 31	15 41					15 51	16 01			16 11
Birmingham Snow Hill 🚊	a	14 35		14 45			14 55	15 05				15 15	15 25		15 35	15 45					15 55	16 05			16 15
	d	14 37		14 47		14 52	14 57	15 07			15 12	15 17	15 27		15 37	15 47				15 52	15 57	16 07		16 12	16 17
Birmingham Moor Street	d	14 40		14 50		14 55	15 00	15 10			15 15	15 20	15 30		15 40	15 50				15 55	16 00	16 10		16 15	16 20
Bordesley	d																								
Small Heath	d	14 44						15 14							15 44							16 14			
Tyseley	d	14 46						15 16							15 46							16 16			
Acocks Green	d	14 49					15 06					15 26			15 49						16 06				16 26
Olton	d	14 52					15 08					15 28			15 52						16 08				16 28
Solihull	d	14 55				15 05	15 12				15 25	15 32			15 55					16 05	16 12			16 25	16 32
Widney Manor	d	14 58					15 15					15 35			15 58						16 15				16 35
Dorridge	d	15a04				15 10	15a21				15 30	15a41			16a04					16 10	16a22			16 30	16a41
Lapworth	d																							16 34	
Hatton	d																		15 58					16 40	
Warwick Parkway	d					15 21					15 41									16 21				16 45	
Warwick	d					15 24					15 44								16 04	16 24				16 49	
Leamington Spa 8	a				14 59	15 29				15 37	15 49							15 59	16 07	16 29			16 37	16 53	
	d				15 00	15 29				15 38	15 49							16 00	16 08	16 29			16 38	16 54	
Banbury	d				15a18	15 47				15a54	16 07							16a18	16 27	16 47			16a54	17 12	
London Marylebone 10 ⊖	a					17 01					17 31								17 55	18 04				18 33	
Spring Road	d			14 56				15 19					15 36			15 56						16 19			
Hall Green	d			14 59				15 22					15 39			15 59						16 22			
Yardley Wood	d			15 02				15 25					15 42			16 02						16 25			
Shirley	d			15a05				15a28					15 45			16a05						16a28			
Whitlocks End	d												15 48												
Wythall	d												15 50												
Earlswood (West Midlands)	d												15 53												
The Lakes	d												15x55												
Wood End	d												15x57												
Danzey	d												16x00												
Henley-in-Arden	d												16 05												
Wootton Wawen	d												16x08												
Wilmcote	d												16 13												
Stratford-upon-Avon	a												16 21												

For general notes see front of timetable
For details of catering facilities see Directory of Train Operators

A To Weymouth (Table 123)
b Arr. 1404
c Arr. 1417

Table 71

Mondays to Fridays

Hereford, Worcester and Stourbridge → Birmingham → Leamington Spa, Marylebone and Stratford-upon-Avon

Network Diagram - See first page of Table 71

Station		LM	LM	LM	LM	GW	XC	CH	LM	LM	XC	CH	LM	LM	LM	LM	XC	CH	LM	LM	GW	LM	CH	XC	LM
						1 ◇	R 1				R 1						R 1							R 1	
							🍴				🍴						🍴				A			🍴	
Hereford 7	d					15 19										15 38									
Ledbury	a					15 35										15 53									
	d					15 36										15 55									
Colwall	d					15 44										16 01									
Great Malvern	a					15 48										16 06									
	d	15 14				15 51										16 10									
Malvern Link	d	15 17				15 55										16 13									
Worcester Foregate Street 7	a	15 24				16 04										16 22									
	d	15 25			15 38	16 06							16 07			16 24				16 34	17 02				
Worcester Shrub Hill 7	a				15 40	16 09														16 36	17 04				
	d				15 44									16 17						16 40					
Droitwich Spa	d	15 34			15 55								16 16	16 25		16 34				16 48					
Bromsgrove	d	15 44														16 44									
Barnt Green	d															16 50									
University	d	15 59														17 00									
Hartlebury	d												16 23												
Kidderminster	d			15 56	16 06					16 23			16 30	16 37					16 52	16 59					
Blakedown	d				16 11					16 28			16 35	16 43						17 04					
Hagley	d				16 14					16 31			16 39	16 47						17 08					
Stourbridge Junction 2	d		15 55	16 09	16 19				16 25	16 35			16 44	16 51	16 55				17 02	17 13					17 25
Lye	d		15 58						16 28						16 58										17 28
Cradley Heath	d		16 01	16 14	16 24				16 31	16 41			16 50	16 57	17 01				17 12	17 19					17 31
Old Hill	d		16 05						16 35						17 05										17 35
Rowley Regis	d		16 09	16 20	16 30				16 39	16 47			16 55	17 03	17 09				17 17	17 24					17 39
Langley Green	d		16 12						16 42						17 12										17 42
Smethwick Galton Bdg H.L. 7	d		16 15	16 25	16 35				16 45	16 52			17 00	17 08	17 15				17 22	17 29					17 45
Birmingham New Street 12	a	16 09														17 14									
	d						16 33				17 03						17 33							18 03	
Birmingham International ✈	d										17 15													18 15	
Coventry	d										17 25													18 25	
The Hawthorns 🚊	d		16 18	16 28	16 38				16 48	16 54			17 03	17 10	17 18				17 25	17 32					17 48
Jewellery Quarter 🚊	d		16 21	16 31	16 41				16 51	16 58			17 06	17 14	17 21				17 28	17 35					17 51
Birmingham Snow Hill 🚊	a		16 25	16 35	16 45				16 55	17 01			17 09	17 17	17 25				17 32	17 38					17 55
	d		16 27	16 37	16 47			16 52	16 57	17 02		17 10	17 15	17 22	17 27				17 34	17 42		17 47	17 52		17 57
Birmingham Moor Street	d		16 30	16 40	16 50			16 55	17 00	17 05		17 13	17 18	17 25	17 30				17 37	17 45		17 50	17 55		18 00
Bordesley	d																								
Small Heath	d			16 44	16 54								17 22						17 41	17 49		17 54			18 04
Tyseley	d		16 34	16 46	16 56				17 04				17 24		17 34				17 45	17 51		17 56			18 06
Acocks Green	d			16 49					17 07					17 31					17 48	17 54					18 09
Olton	d			16 52					17 10					17 33					17 50	17 57					18 12
Solihull	d			16 55				17 05	17 12			17 23		17 37					17 54	18 00			18 05		18 15
Widney Manor	d			16 58					17 16			17 26		17 40					17 57	18 03					18 19
Dorridge	d			17a04				17 10	17a22			17 30		17a46					18 01	18a08			18 12		18 23
Lapworth	d											17 34							18 05						18 27
Hatton	d											17 40						18 02	18 11						18 33
Warwick Parkway	d							17 20				17 45							18 15				18 23		18 37
Warwick	d							17 23				17 48						18 08	18 19				18 26		18 40
Leamington Spa 8	a						16 59	17 28			17 37	17 53					17 59	18 12	18 24				18 30	18 37	18 47
	d						17 00	17 28			17 38	17 53					18 00	18 12					18 30	18 38	
Banbury	d						17a18	17 46			17a54	18 11					18a18	18 32					18 48	18a54	
London Marylebone 10 ⊖	a							19 08				19 33						19 57					20 06		
Spring Road	d		16 37		16 59					17 11			17 27		17 37							17 59			
Hall Green	d		16 40		17 02					17 14			17 30		17 40							18 02			
Yardley Wood	d		16 43		17 05					17 17			17 33		17 43							18 05			
Shirley	d		16 46		17a08					17 20			17a37		17 46							18 08			
Whitlocks End	d		16 49							17 23					17 49							18 11			
Wythall	d		16 51							17 25					17 51							18 13			
Earlswood (West Midlands)	d		16 54												17 54							18 16			
The Lakes	d		16x56												17x56							18x18			
Wood End	d		16x58												17x58							18x20			
Danzey	d		17x01												18x01							18x23			
Henley-in-Arden	d		17 06							17 35					18 06							18 28			
Wootton Wawen	d		17x09												18x09							18x30			
Wilmcote	d		17 14												18 14							18 38			
Stratford-upon-Avon	a		17 22							17 49					18 22							18 45			

For general notes see front of timetable
For details of catering facilities see Directory of Train Operators

A To Southampton Central (Table 123)

Hereford, Worcester and Stourbridge → Birmingham → Leamington Spa, Marylebone and Stratford-upon-Avon

Network Diagram - See first page of Table 71

		LM	CH	LM	GW	LM	LM	LM	LM	XC	LM	XC	LM	CH	LM	LM	LM	LM	GW	GW	GW	LM	XC	CH	CH
					1 ◇			1		R 1		R 1							1 ◇	◇ A	1		1 ◇		
					☕					☕		☕							☕				☕		
Hereford 7	d						16 50						17 38									18 52			
Ledbury	a						17 06						17 53									19 06			
	d						17 07						17 54									19 11			
Colwall	d						17 13						18 00									19 17			
Great Malvern	a						17 18						18 05									19 21			
	d				17 06		17 18	17 42					18 05							18 54		19 22			
Malvern Link	d				17 10		17 21	17 45					18 08									19 25			
Worcester Foregate Street 7	a				17 19		17 30	17 53					18 17							19 02		19 33			
	d			17 14	17 21		17 31	17 54			17 55		18 18				18 34		18 49	19 02	19 27	19 34			
Worcester Shrub Hill 7	a				17 24			17 56					18 20						18 52	19 04	19 29	19 36			
	d												18 24					18 48				19 54			
Droitwich Spa	d			17 23			17 40				18 04		18 34				18 43	18 56				→			
Bromsgrove	d						17 49						18 42												
Barnt Green	d												18 49												
University	d						18 09						18 59												
Hartlebury	d			17 30														19 03							
Kidderminster	d	17 26		17 36					18 00		18 16				18 37		18 53	19 10							
Blakedown	d	17 31		17 41					18 05						18 42		18 58	19 15							
Hagley	d	17 34		17 44					18 09						18 46		19 02	19 19							
Stourbridge Junction 2	d	17 39		17 48		17 57			18 13		18 25				18 51		19 09	19 24							
Lye	d					18 00					18 28				18 54			19 27							
Cradley Heath	d	17 44		17 54		18 03			18 19		18 31				18 57		19 15	19 30							
Old Hill	d					18 07					18 35				19 01			19 34							
Rowley Regis	d	17 50		18 00		18 11			18 25		18 39				19 05		19 21	19 38							
Langley Green	d					18 14					18 42				19 08			19 41							
Smethwick Galton Bdg H.L. 7	d	17 55		18 05		18 17			18 30		18 45				19 11		19 26	19 44							
Birmingham New Street 12	a						18 21						19 12												
	d									18 33		19 03											19 33		
Birmingham International ✈	d											19 15													
Coventry	d											19 25													
The Hawthorns	d	17 58		18 08		18 20			18 33		18 48				19 14		19 29	19 47							
Jewellery Quarter	d	18 01		18 11		18 23			18 36		18 51				19 17		19 32	19 50							
Birmingham Snow Hill	a	18 05		18 15		18 26			18 41		18 55				19 20		19 35	19 53							
	d	18 07	18 12	18 22		18 27			18 45		18 57			19 12	19 22	19 27	19 37	19 55							
Birmingham Moor Street	d	18 10	18 15	18 25		18 30			18 48		19 00			19 15	19 25	19 30	19a39	19 58							
Bordesley	d																								
Small Heath	d	18 14				18 34			18 52		19 04					19 34		20 02							
Tyseley	d	18 16				18 36			18 54		19 06					19 36		20 04							
Acocks Green	d			18 31					18 57						19 31			20 07							
Olton	d			18 33					19 00						19 33			20 10							
Solihull	d		18 25	18 37					19 03					19 25	19 37			20 13							
Widney Manor	d			18 40					19 07					19 28	19 40			20 17							
Dorridge	d		18 30	18a47					19 11					19 32	19a47			20a22							
Lapworth	d		18 34						19 15					19 36											
Hatton	d		18 40						19 21					19 42										19 59	20 17
Warwick Parkway	d		18 45											19 47										20 06	
Warwick	d		18 49						19 27					19 50										20 09	20 23
Leamington Spa 8	a		18 53						19 32	18 59		19 37		19 54									19 59	20 15	20 33
	d		18 54							19 00		19 38		19 54									20 00	20 15	
Banbury	d		19 12							19a18		19a54		20 11									20a18	20 33	
London Marylebone 10 ⊖	a		20 35											21 38										21 57	
Spring Road	d	18 19				18 39					19 09					19 39									
Hall Green	d	18 22				18 42					19 12					19 42									
Yardley Wood	d	18 25				18 45					19 15					19 45									
Shirley	d	18a28				18 48					19a18					19 48									
Whitlocks End	d					18 51										19 51									
Wythall	d					18 53										19 53									
Earlswood (West Midlands)	d					18 56										19 56									
The Lakes	d					18x58										19x58									
Wood End	d					19x00										20x00									
Danzey	d					19x03										20x03									
Henley-in-Arden	d					19 08										20 08									
Wootton Wawen	d					19x10										20x10									
Wilmcote	d					19 16										20 16									
Stratford-upon-Avon	a					19 23										20 23									

For general notes see front of timetable
For details of catering facilities see Directory of Train Operators

A To Weymouth (Table 123)

Hereford, Worcester and Stourbridge → Birmingham → Leamington Spa, Marylebone and Stratford-upon-Avon

Network Diagram - See first page of Table 71

		XC	CH	LM	LM	LM	XC	LM	CH	LM	LM	GW	GW	CH	LM	LM	XC	LM	LM	GW	CH	LM	CH
		R 1					1 ◇					1 ◇ A (restaurant / trolley)	B				◇			1 ◇ A (restaurant / trolley)			
Hereford 7	d							19 50										21 30				22 43	
Ledbury	a							20 08										21 46				22 58	
	d							20 17										21 47				22 59	
Colwall	d							20 23										21 53				23 05	
Great Malvern	a							20 28										21 58				23 10	
	d							20 28					20 51					21 58		22 33		23 10	
Malvern Link	d							20 31					20 54					22 01				23 13	
Worcester Foregate Street 7	a							20 40					21 04					22 10		22 43		23 20	
	d				19 44			20 42				20 58	21 05					22 10	22 17	22 44		23 20	
Worcester Shrub Hill 7	a					←						21 01	21 07						22 19	22 47		23 25	
	d					19 54					20 53					21 52			22 27				
Droitwich Spa	d				19 53	20 02		20 51			21 01					22 00		22 19	22 35				
Bromsgrove	d					20 10		20 59									22 20	22 28					
Barnt Green	d																						
University	d					20 29		21 16										22 46					
Hartlebury	d																						
Kidderminster	d				20b10						21 11					22 10			22 45				
Blakedown	d				20 15						21 16					22 15							
Hagley	d				20 19						21 20					22 19							
Stourbridge Junction 2	d			19 54	20 24					20 54	21 24				21 54	22 24			22 54				
Lye	d			19 57	20 27					20 57	21 27				21 57	22 27			22 57				
Cradley Heath	d			20 00	20 30					21 00	21 30				22 00	22 30			23 00				
Old Hill	d			20 04	20 34					21 04	21 34				22 04	22 34			23 04				
Rowley Regis	d			20 08	20 38					21 08	21 38				22 08	22 38			23 08				
Langley Green	d			20 11	20 41					21 11	21 41				22 11	22 41			23 11				
Smethwick Galton Bdg H.L. 7	d			20 14	20 44					21 14	21 44				22 14	22 44			23 14				
Birmingham New Street 12	a					20 44		21 27									22 48	22 57					
	d	20 03					21 03																
Birmingham International ✈	d	20 15					21 15																
Coventry	d	20 25					21 25																
The Hawthorns (tram)	d			20 17	20 47					21 17	21 47				22 17	22 47			23 17				
Jewellery Quarter (tram)	d			20 20	20 50					21 20	21 50				22 20	22 50			23 20				
Birmingham Snow Hill (tram)	a			20 23	20 53					21 23	21 53				22 23	22 53			23 24				
	d		20 12	20 27	20 55				21 15	21 25	21 55			22 15	22 25	22 57			23 25				23 30
Birmingham Moor Street	d		20 15	20 30	20 58				21 18	21 28	21 58			22 18	22 28	23 00			23 28				23 33
Bordesley	d																						
Small Heath	d			20 34	21 02					21 32	22 02				22 32	23 04			23 32				
Tyseley	d			20 36	21 04					21 34	22 04			22 22	22 34	23 06			23 34				23 37
Acocks Green	d				21 07						22 07			22 25		23 09							23 40
Olton	d				21 10						22 10			22 28		23 11							23 43
Solihull	d		20 25		21 13				21 27		22 13			22 32		23 15							23 47
Widney Manor	d		20 28		21 17						22 17			22 35		23 18							23 50
Dorridge	d		20 32		21a22				21 33		22a22			22 39		23a24							23 54
Lapworth	d		20 36						21 37					22 43									23 58
Hatton	d		20 42						21 42					22 48									00 03
Warwick Parkway	d		20 47						21 47					22 53									00 08
Warwick	d		20 50						21 50					22 56							23 21		00 11
Leamington Spa 8	a	20 37	20 54				21 37		21 54					23 00							23 24		00 14
	d	20 38	20 54				21 38		21 55					23 01							23 25		00 15
Banbury	d	20a54	21 12				21a54		22 14					23a23							23a43		00a38
London Marylebone 10 ⊖	a		22 32						23 53														
Spring Road	d			20 39						21 37					22 37				23 37				
Hall Green	d			20 42						21 40					22 40				23 40				
Yardley Wood	d			20 45						21 43					22 43				23 43				
Shirley	d			20 48						21a46					22a46				23a46				
Whitlocks End	d			20 51																			
Wythall	d			20 53																			
Earlswood (West Midlands)	d			20 56																			
The Lakes	d			20x58																			
Wood End	d			21x00																			
Danzey	d			21x03																			
Henley-in-Arden	d			21 08																			
Wootton Wawen	d			21x10																			
Wilmcote	d			21 16																			
Stratford-upon-Avon	a			21 23																			

For general notes see front of timetable
For details of catering facilities see Directory of Train Operators

A (restaurant) Mondays to Thursdays. (trolley) Fridays

B To Gloucester (Table 57)

b Arr. 2003

Table 71

Saturdays
until 6 September

Hereford, Worcester and Stourbridge → Birmingham → Leamington Spa, Marylebone and Stratford-upon-Avon

Network Diagram - See first page of Table 71

		CH	XC	CH	CH	LM	GW	XC	CH	LM	LM	LM	XC	XC	CH	CH	LM	GW	XC	CH	LM	LM	LM	LM	LM
			1 ◇				1 ◇	1 ◇					1 ◇					1 ◇	1 ◇						
														A											
			☕					☕					☕					☕	☕						
Hereford 7	d																								
Ledbury	a																								
	d																								
Colwall	d																								
Great Malvern	a																								
	d						06 07					06 20						07 07							07 30
Malvern Link	d						06 10					06 23						07 11							07 32
Worcester Foregate Street 7	a						06 17					06 30						07 20							07 40
	d						06 19					06 31						07 22							07 43
Worcester Shrub Hill 7	a						06 21											07 25							
	d					05 44					06 24						06 58				07 33				
Droitwich Spa	d					05 52					06 32	06 40					07 06				07 40				07 52
Bromsgrove	d											06 50		07 23							07 50				
Barnt Green	d																								
University	d											07 09									08 09				
Hartlebury	d										06 39						07 13								
Kidderminster	d					06 02			06 37		06 45					07 11	07 22						07 46		08 06
Blakedown	d					06 07					06 50						07 27						07 51		08 11
Hagley	d					06 11					06 54						07 30						07 54		08 14
Stourbridge Junction 2	d					06 15			06 45		07 02					07 20	07 35						07 59	08 05	08 19
Lye	d					06 18					07 05						07 38							08 08	
Cradley Heath	d					06 22			06 50		07 09					07 27	07 41						08 04	08 11	08 24
Old Hill	d					06 26					07 13						07 45							08 15	
Rowley Regis	d					06 29			06 56		07 16					07 33	07 49						08 10	08 19	08 30
Langley Green	d					06 32					07 19						07 52							08 22	
Smethwick Galton Bdg H.L. 7	d					06 36			07 02		07 23					07 39	07 55						08 15	08 25	08 35
Birmingham New Street 12	a											07 16		07 45							08 16				
	d		06 03					07 03					07 33						08 03						
Birmingham International ✈	d		06 15					07 15											08 15						
Coventry	d		06 25					07 25											08 25						
The Hawthorns 🚊	d					06 38			07 04		07 25					07 41	07 58						08 18	08 28	08 38
Jewellery Quarter 🚊	d					06 42					07 29						08 01						08 21	08 31	08 41
Birmingham Snow Hill 🚊	a					06 46			07 10		07 32					07 47	08 05						08 25	08 35	08 45
	d	23p30		06 12	06 37	06 51			07 12	07 20	07 35					07 52	08 07			08 12		08 17	08 27	08 37	08 47
Birmingham Moor Street	d	23p33		06 15	06 40	06 54			07 15	07 23	07 38					07 55	08 10			08 15		08 20	08 30	08 40	08 50
Bordesley	d																								
Small Heath	d					06 58				07 27							08 14							08 44	
Tyseley	d	23p37				07 00				07 29							08 16							08 46	
Acocks Green	d	23p40				07 03					07 46											08 26		08 49	
Olton	d	23p43				07 06					07 49											08 28		08 52	
Solihull	d	23p47		06 25	06 50	07 09			07 25		07 52					08 04				08 25		08 32		08 55	
Widney Manor	d	23p50				07 12					07 56											08 35		08 58	
Dorridge	d	23p54		06 30	06 55	07a17			07 30		08a01					08 10				08 31		08a41		09a03	
Lapworth	d	23p58							07 34											08 35					
Hatton	d	00 03							07 40						07 56					08 40					
Warwick Parkway	d	00 08		06 41	07 06				07 45							08 20				08 45					
Warwick	d	00 11		06 44	07 09				07 50						08 03	08 23				08 48					
Leamington Spa 8	a	00 14	06 37	06 49	07 14			07 37	07 53				07 58		08 06	08 28			08 37	08 51					
	d	00 15	06 38	06 49	07 14			07 38	07 54				08 00		08 08	08 29			08 38	08 52					
Banbury	d	00a38	06a54	07 08	07 33			07a54	08 12				08a17		08 27	08 47			08a54	09 12					
London Marylebone 10 ⊖	a			08 29	08 47				09 30						09 55	10 01				10 32					
Spring Road	d									07 32							08 19						08 36		08 56
Hall Green	d									07 35							08 22						08 39		08 59
Yardley Wood	d									07 38							08 25						08 42		09 02
Shirley	d									07 41							08a28						08 45		09a05
Whitlocks End	d									07 44													08 48		
Wythall	d									07 46													08 50		
Earlswood (West Midlands)	d									07 49													08 53		
The Lakes	d									07x51													08x55		
Wood End	d									07x53													08x57		
Danzey	d									07x56													09x00		
Henley-in-Arden	d									08 01													09 05		
Wootton Wawen	d									08x04													09x08		
Wilmcote	d									08 09													09 13		
Stratford-upon-Avon	a									08 16													09 21		

For general notes see front of timetable
For details of catering facilities see Directory of Train Operators

A To Nottingham (Table 57)

Due to Engineering Operations, services from Saturday 13 September on this Table had not been confirmed at time of going to press. These services will be issued in a special Supplement as soon as exact timings have been confirmed

Table 71

until 6 September

Hereford, Worcester and Stourbridge → Birmingham → Leamington Spa, Marylebone and Stratford-upon-Avon

Network Diagram - See first page of Table 71

		GW	XC	CH	XC		LM	LM	XC	CH	LM	LM	GW	LM	LM	LM	XC	XC	CH	CH	LM	LM	XC	CH	LM
		1 ◇	1 ◇						R 1								1 ◇	◇					R 1		
					A								B					C							
		☕	☕						☕								☕	🍴					☕		
Hereford 7	d	07 22										07 37													
Ledbury	a	07 38										07 53													
	d	07 40										07 54													
Colwall	d	07 47										08 00													
Great Malvern	a	07 51										08 04													
	d	07 52										08 06	08 25								08 35				
Malvern Link	d	07 56										08 09	08 28								08 37				
Worcester Foregate Street 7	a	08 06										08 17	08 35								08 46				
	d	08 07										08 19	08 36								08 46				09 15
Worcester Shrub Hill 7	a	08 10										08 21	08 38								08 49				
	d										08 14	08 26									08 53				
Droitwich Spa	d										08 22	08 34									09 01				09 24
Bromsgrove	d				08 23							08 43						09 23							
Barnt Green	d																								
University	d				08 39							08 59													
Hartlebury	d										08 29														
Kidderminster	d			08 13							08 36									09 03	09 16	09 26			09 36
Blakedown	d										08 41									09 08		09 31			09 41
Hagley	d										08 44									09 12		09 34			09 44
Stourbridge Junction 2	d			08 26				08 35			08 49			08 55	09 09					09 15	09 25	09 39			09 49
Lye	d							08 38						08 58							09 28				
Cradley Heath	d			08 31				08 41			08 54			09 01	09 14					09 21	09 31	09 44			09 54
Old Hill	d							08 45						09 05							09 35				
Rowley Regis	d			08 37				08 49			09 00			09 09	09 20					09 26	09 39	09 50			10 00
Langley Green	d							08 52						09 12							09 42				
Smethwick Galton Bdg H.L. 7	d			08 42				08 55			09 05			09 15	09 25					09 33	09 45	09 55			10 05
Birmingham New Street 12	a				08 45							09 14						09 45							
	d		08 33						09 03								09 33						10 03		
Birmingham International ✈	d								09 15														10 15		
Coventry	d								09 25														10 25		
The Hawthorns 🚊	d			08 44				08 58			09 08			09 18	09 28					09 34	09 48	09 58			10 08
Jewellery Quarter 🚊	d							09 01			09 11			09 21	09 31						09 51	10 01			10 11
Birmingham Snow Hill 🚊	a			08 51				09 05			09 16			09 25	09 35					09 42	09 55	10 05			10 17
	d			08 52			08 57	09 07		09 12	09 17			09 27	09 37	09 47				09 52	09 57	10 07		10 12	10 17
Birmingham Moor Street	d			08 55			09 00	09 10		09 15	09 20			09 30	09 40	09 50				09 55	10 00	10 10		10 15	10 20
Bordesley	d																								
Small Heath	d							09 14							09 44							10 14			
Tyseley	d							09 16							09 46							10 16			
Acocks Green	d						09 06				09 26				09 49						10 06				10 26
Olton	d						09 08				09 28				09 52						10 08				10 28
Solihull	d			09 06			09 12			09 25	09 32				09 55					10 05	10 12			10 25	10 32
Widney Manor	d			09 09			09 15				09 35				09 58						10 15				10 35
Dorridge	d			09 13			09a21			09 31	09a41				10a04					10 12	10a22			10 31	10a41
Lapworth	d									09 35														10 35	
Hatton	d																		09 56					10 41	
Warwick Parkway	d			09 23						09 43										10 22				10 46	
Warwick	d			09 27						09 46									10 04	10 26				10 49	
Leamington Spa 8	a		08 58	09 31					09 37	09 50							09 58		10 07	10 29			10 37	10 53	
	d		09 00	09 32					09 38	09 50							10 00		10 08	10 30			10 38	10 54	
Banbury	d		09a17	09 50					09a54	10 10							10a17		10 28	10 48			10a54	11 12	
London Marylebone 10 ⊖	a			11 01						11 31									11 56	11 59				12 30	
Spring Road	d							09 19						09 36		09 56						10 19			
Hall Green	d							09 22						09 39		09 59						10 22			
Yardley Wood	d							09 25						09 42		10 02						10 25			
Shirley	d							09a28						09 45		10a05						10a28			
Whitlocks End	d													09 48											
Wythall	d													09 50											
Earlswood (West Midlands)	d													09 53											
The Lakes	d													09x55											
Wood End	d													09x57											
Danzey	d													10x00											
Henley-in-Arden	d													10 05											
Wootton Wawen	d													10x08											
Wilmcote	d													10 13											
Stratford-upon-Avon	a													10 21											

For general notes see front of timetable
For details of catering facilities see Directory of Train Operators

A From Gloucester to Nottingham (Table 57)
B To Westbury (Table 123)
C To Nottingham (Table 57)

Due to Engineering Operations, services from Saturday 13 September on this Table had not been confirmed at time of going to press. These services will be issued in a special Supplement as soon as exact timings have been confirmed

Table 71

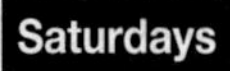

until 6 September

Hereford, Worcester and Stourbridge → Birmingham → Leamington Spa, Marylebone and Stratford-upon-Avon

Network Diagram - See first page of Table 71

		GW	LM	LM	LM	LM	GW	XC	CH	LM	LM	XC	CH	LM	LM	LM	LM	LM	GW	XC	CH	CH	LM	LM
		1 ◇					1 ◇	1 ◇				1 ◇							◇ A	1 ◇				
		☕					☕	☕				☕								☕				
Hereford 7	d				08 50											09 50								
Ledbury	a				09 06											10 06								
	d				09 07											10 07								
Colwall	d				09 13											10 13								
Great Malvern	a				09 18											10 18								
	d	09 07			09 18		09 55									10 18			10 43					
Malvern Link	d	09 11			09 21		09 59									10 21			10 46					
Worcester Foregate Street 7	a	09 20			09 30		10 08									10 30			11 01					
	d	09 20			09 31		10 10							10 15		10 31			11 02					
Worcester Shrub Hill 7	a	09 25					10 13												11 04					
	d					09 47												10 47						
Droitwich Spa	d				09 40	09 55								10 24		10 40		10 55						
Bromsgrove	d				09 50											10 50								
Barnt Green	d																							
University	d				10 09											11 09								
Hartlebury	d																							
Kidderminster	d			09 56		10 06					10 26			10 36			10 56	11 06						11 26
Blakedown	d					10 11					10 31							11 11						11 31
Hagley	d					10 14					10 34							11 14						11 34
Stourbridge Junction 2	d		09 55	10 09		10 19				10 25	10 39			10 49	10 55		11 09	11 19					11 25	11 39
Lye	d		09 58							10 28					10 58								11 28	
Cradley Heath	d		10 01	10 14		10 24				10 31	10 44			10 54	11 01		11 14	11 24					11 31	11 44
Old Hill	d		10 05							10 35					11 05								11 35	
Rowley Regis	d		10 09	10 20		10 30				10 39	10 50			11 00	11 09		11 20	11 30					11 39	11 50
Langley Green	d		10 12							10 42					11 12								11 42	
Smethwick Galton Bdg H.L. 7	d		10 15	10 25		10 35				10 45	10 55			11 05	11 15		11 25	11 35					11 45	11 55
Birmingham New Street 12	a				10 21											11 21								
	d							10 33				11 03								11 33				
Birmingham International ✈	d											11 15												
Coventry	d											11 25												
The Hawthorns 🚋	d		10 18	10 28		10 38				10 48	10 58			11 08	11 18		11 28	11 38					11 48	11 58
Jewellery Quarter 🚋	d		10 21	10 31		10 41				10 51	11 01			11 11	11 21		11 31	11 41					11 51	12 01
Birmingham Snow Hill 🚋	a		10 25	10 35		10 45				10 56	11 05			11 17	11 25		11 35	11 45					11 56	12 05
	d		10 27	10 37		10 47			10 52	10 57	11 07		11 12	11 17	11 27		11 37	11 47				11 52	11 57	12 07
Birmingham Moor Street	d		10 30	10 40		10 50			10 55	11 00	11 10		11 15	11 20	11 30		11 40	11 50				11 55	12 00	12 10
Bordesley	d																							
Small Heath	d			10 44							11 14						11 44							12 14
Tyseley	d			10 46							11 16						11 46							12 16
Acocks Green	d			10 49						11 06				11 26			11 49						12 06	
Olton	d			10 52						11 08				11 28			11 52						12 08	
Solihull	d			10 55					11 05	11 12			11 25	11 32			11 55					12 05	12 12	
Widney Manor	d			10 58						11 15				11 35			11 58						12 15	
Dorridge	d			11a04					11 12	11a22			11 31	11a41			12a04					12 12	12a22	
Lapworth	d																							
Hatton	d																				11 57			
Warwick Parkway	d								11 22				11 41									12 22		
Warwick	d								11 26				11 45								12 03	12 26		
Leamington Spa 8	a							10 58	11 30			11 37	11 49							11 58	12 07	12 29		
	d							11 00	11 31			11 38	11 49							12 00	12 07	12 30		
Banbury	d							11a17	11 49			11a54	12 07							12a17	12 27	12 49		
London Marylebone 10 ⊖	a								13 01				13 31								13 58	14 01		
Spring Road	d		10 36			10 56					11 19				11 36			11 56						12 19
Hall Green	d		10 39			10 59					11 22				11 39			11 59						12 22
Yardley Wood	d		10 42			11 02					11 25				11 42			12 02						12 25
Shirley	d		10 45			11a05					11a28				11 45			12a05						12a28
Whitlocks End	d		10 48												11 48									
Wythall	d		10 50												11 50									
Earlswood (West Midlands)	d		10 53												11 53									
The Lakes	d		10x55												11x55									
Wood End	d		10x57												11x57									
Danzey	d		11x00												12x00									
Henley-in-Arden	d		11 05												12 05									
Wootton Wawen	d		11x08												12x08									
Wilmcote	d		11 13												12 13									
Stratford-upon-Avon	a		11 21												12 21									

For general notes see front of timetable
For details of catering facilities see Directory of Train Operators

A To Brighton (Table 123)

Due to Engineering Operations, services from Saturday 13 September on this Table had not been confirmed at time of going to press. These services will be issued in a special Supplement as soon as exact timings have been confirmed

Saturdays
until 6 September

Hereford, Worcester and Stourbridge → Birmingham → Leamington Spa, Marylebone and Stratford-upon-Avon

Network Diagram - See first page of Table 71

Station		XC	CH	LM	GW	LM	LM	LM	LM	GW	XC	CH	LM	LM	XC		CH	LM	LM	LM	LM	LM	GW	XC	CH
		1 ◇			1 ◇					1 ◇	1 ◇				1 ◇								◇ A	1 ◇	
Hereford 7	d							10 50												11 50					
Ledbury	a							11 05												12 06					
	d							11 07												12 07					
Colwall	d							11 13												12 13					
Great Malvern	a							11 18												12 18					
	d				11 07			11 18	11 30	11 45										12 18			12 51		
Malvern Link	d				11 11			11 21	11 32	11 49										12 21			12 54		
Worcester Foregate Street 7	a				11 20			11 31	11 40	11 58										12 30			13 01		
	d			11 15	11 22			11 31	11 41	12 00								12 15		12 31			13 02		
Worcester Shrub Hill 7	a				11 25				11 43	12 03													13 04		
	d								11 47													12 47			
Droitwich Spa	d			11 24				11 40	11 55									12 24		12 40		12 55			
Bromsgrove	d							11 50												12 50					
Barnt Green	d																								
University	d							12 09												13 09					
Hartlebury	d																								
Kidderminster	d			11 36			11 56		12 06					12 26				12 36			12 56	13 06			
Blakedown	d								12 11					12 31								13 11			
Hagley	d								12 14					12 34								13 14			
Stourbridge Junction 2	d			11 49		11 55	12 09		12 19				12 25	12 39				12 49	12 55		13 09	13 19			
Lye	d					11 58							12 28						12 58						
Cradley Heath	d			11 54		12 01	12 14		12 24				12 31	12 44				12 54	13 01		13 14	13 24			
Old Hill	d					12 05							12 35						13 05						
Rowley Regis	d			12 00		12 09	12 20		12 30				12 39	12 50				13 00	13 09		13 20	13 30			
Langley Green	d					12 12							12 42						13 12						
Smethwick Galton Bdg H.L. 7	d			12 05		12 15	12 25		12 35				12 45	12 55				13 05	13 15		13 25	13 35			
Birmingham New Street 12	a							12 21												13 21					
	d	12 03									12 33				13 03									13 33	
Birmingham International ✈	d	12 15													13 15										
Coventry	d	12 25													13 25										
The Hawthorns 🚊	d			12 08		12 18	12 28		12 38				12 48	12 58				13 08	13 18		13 28	13 38			
Jewellery Quarter 🚊	d			12 11		12 21	12 31		12 41				12 51	13 01				13 11	13 21		13 31	13 41			
Birmingham Snow Hill 🚊	a			12 16		12 25	12 35		12 45				12 56	13 05				13 16	13 25		13 35	13 45			
	d		12 12	12 17		12 27	12 37		12 47			12 52	12 57	13 07			13 12	13 17	13 27		13 37	13 47			
Birmingham Moor Street	d		12 15	12 20		12 30	12 40		12 50			12 55	13 00	13 10			13 15	13 20	13 30		13 40	13 50			
Bordesley	d																								
Small Heath	d						12 44							13 14							13 44				
Tyseley	d						12 46							13 16							13 46				
Acocks Green	d			12 26			12 49						13 06					13 26			13 49				
Olton	d			12 28			12 52						13 08					13 28			13 52				
Solihull	d		12 25	12 32			12 55					13 05	13 12				13 25	13 32			13 55				
Widney Manor	d			12 35			12 58						13 15					13 35			13 58				
Dorridge	d		12 31	12a41			13a04					13 10	13a21				13 31	13a41			14a04				
Lapworth	d		12 35																						
Hatton	d		12 40																						13 59
Warwick Parkway	d		12 45									13 21					13 41								
Warwick	d		12 48									13 24					13 45								14 06
Leamington Spa 8	a	12 37	12 51								12 58	13 29			13 37		13 49							13 58	14 09
	d	12 38	12 52								13 00	13 29			13 38		13 49							14 00	14 11
Banbury	d	12a54	13 11								13a17	13 47			13a54		14 07							14a17	14 30
London Marylebone 10 ⊖	a		14 33									15 01					15 30								15 58
Spring Road	d					12 36			12 56					13 19					13 36			13 56			
Hall Green	d					12 39			12 59					13 22					13 39			13 59			
Yardley Wood	d					12 42			13 02					13 25					13 42			14 02			
Shirley	d					12 45			13a05					13a28					13 45			14a05			
Whitlocks End	d					12 48													13 48						
Wythall	d					12 50													13 50						
Earlswood (West Midlands)	d					12 53													13 53						
The Lakes	d					12x55													13x55						
Wood End	d					12x57													13x57						
Danzey	d					13x00													14x00						
Henley-in-Arden	d					13 05													14 05						
Wootton Wawen	d					13x08													14x08						
Wilmcote	d					13 13													14 13						
Stratford-upon-Avon	a					13 21													14 21						

For general notes see front of timetable
For details of catering facilities see Directory of Train Operators

A To Weymouth (Table 123)

Due to Engineering Operations, services from Saturday 13 September on this Table had not been confirmed at time of going to press. These services will be issued in a special Supplement as soon as exact timings have been confirmed

Table 71

Saturdays
until 6 September

Hereford, Worcester and Stourbridge → Birmingham → Leamington Spa, Marylebone and Stratford-upon-Avon

Network Diagram - See first page of Table 71

		CH	LM	LM	CH	LM	GW	LM	LM	LM	LM	XC	CH	LM	LM	XC	CH	LM	GW	LM		LM	GW	LM	XC
							1 ◇					1 ◇				1 ◇			1 ◇				◇ A		1 ◇
							☕					☕				☕			☕						☕
Hereford 7	d									12 50									13 20			13 50			
Ledbury	a									13 06									13 37			14 06			
	d									13 07									13 39			14 07			
Colwall	d									13 13									13 46			14 13			
Great Malvern	a									13 18									13 51			14 18			
	d									13 18	13 30								14 05			14 18			
Malvern Link	d									13 21	13 32								14 09			14 21			
Worcester Foregate Street 7	a									13 30	13 40								14 19			14 30			
	d					13 15	13 22			13 31	13 41							14 15	14 21			14 31	14 42		
Worcester Shrub Hill 7	a						13 25				13 43								14 24				14 44		
	d										13 47														
Droitwich Spa	d					13 24				13 40	13 55							14 24				14 40			
Bromsgrove	d									13 50												14 50			
Barnt Green	d																								
University	d									14 09												15 09			
Hartlebury	d																								
Kidderminster	d			13 26		13 36			13 56		14 06				14 26			14 36						14 56	
Blakedown	d			13 31							14 11				14 31										
Hagley	d			13 34							14 14				14 34										
Stourbridge Junction 2	d		13 25	13 39		13 49		13 55	14 09		14 19			14 25	14 39			14 49		14 55				15 09	
Lye	d		13 28					13 58						14 28						14 58					
Cradley Heath	d		13 31	13 44		13 54		14 01	14 14		14 24			14 31	14 44			14 54		15 01				15 14	
Old Hill	d		13 35					14 05						14 35						15 05					
Rowley Regis	d		13 39	13 50		14 00		14 09	14 20		14 30			14 39	14 50			15 00		15 09				15 20	
Langley Green	d		13 42					14 12						14 42						15 12					
Smethwick Galton Bdg H.L. 7	d		13 45	13 55		14 05		14 15	14 25		14 35			14 45	14 55			15 05		15 15				15 25	
Birmingham New Street 12	a									14 21												15 21			
	d											14 33				15 03									15 33
Birmingham International ✈	d															15 15									
Coventry	d															15 25									
The Hawthorns 🚊	d		13 48	13 58		14 08		14 18	14 28		14 38			14 48	14 58			15 08		15 18				15 28	
Jewellery Quarter 🚊	d		13 51	14 01		14 11		14 21	14 31		14 41			14 51	15 01			15 11		15 21				15 31	
Birmingham Snow Hill 🚊	a		13 56	14 05		14 16		14 25	14 35		14 45			14 56	15 05			15 16		15 25				15 35	
	d	13 52	13 57	14 07	14 12	14 17		14 27	14 37		14 47		14 52	14 57	15 07		15 12	15 17		15 27				15 37	
Birmingham Moor Street	d	13 55	14 00	14 10	14 15	14 20		14 30	14 40		14 50		14 55	15 00	15 10		15 15	15 20		15 30				15 40	
Bordesley	d																								
Small Heath	d			14 14					14 44						15 14									15 44	
Tyseley	d			14 16					14 46						15 16									15 46	
Acocks Green	d		14 06			14 26			14 49					15 06				15 26						15 49	
Olton	d		14 08			14 28			14 52					15 08				15 28						15 52	
Solihull	d	14 05	14 12		14 25	14 32			14 55				15 05	15 12			15 25	15 32						15 55	
Widney Manor	d		14 15			14 35			14 58					15 15				15 35						15 58	
Dorridge	d	14 10	14a23		14 31	14a41			15a04				15 10	15a21			15 31	15a41						16a04	
Lapworth	d				14 35																				
Hatton	d				14 40																				
Warwick Parkway	d	14 21			14 45								15 21				15 41								
Warwick	d	14 24			14 48								15 24				15 45								
Leamington Spa 8	a	14 29			14 51							14 58	15 29			15 37	15 49								15 58
	d	14 29			14 52							15 00	15 29			15 38	15 49								16 00
Banbury	d	14 47			15 11							15a17	15 47			15a54	16 07								16a17
London Marylebone 10	⊖ a	16 01			16 33								16 59				17 29								
Spring Road	d			14 19				14 36			14 56				15 19					15 36					
Hall Green	d			14 22				14 39			14 59				15 22					15 39					
Yardley Wood	d			14 25				14 42			15 02				15 25					15 42					
Shirley	d			14a28				14 45			15a05				15a28					15 45					
Whitlocks End	d							14 48												15 48					
Wythall	d							14 50												15 50					
Earlswood (West Midlands)	d							14 53												15 53					
The Lakes	d							14x55												15x55					
Wood End	d							14x57												15x57					
Danzey	d							15x00												16x00					
Henley-in-Arden	d							15 05												16 05					
Wootton Wawen	d							15x08												16x08					
Wilmcote	d							15 13												16 13					
Stratford-upon-Avon	a							15 21												16 21					

For general notes see front of timetable
For details of catering facilities see Directory of Train Operators

A To Weymouth (Table 123)

Due to Engineering Operations, services from Saturday 13 September on this Table had not been confirmed at time of going to press. These services will be issued in a special Supplement as soon as exact timings have been confirmed

Table 71

Hereford, Worcester and Stourbridge → Birmingham → Leamington Spa, Marylebone and Stratford-upon-Avon

Saturdays

until 6 September

Network Diagram - See first page of Table 71

		LM	CH	CH	LM	LM	XC	CH	LM	LM	LM	LM	LM	GW	XC	CH	LM	LM	XC	CH	LM	LM	LM	LM	LM
							1 ◇							1 ◇	1 ◇				1 ◇						
Hereford 7	d											14 50		15 23									15 50		
Ledbury	a											15 06		15 39									16 06		
	d											15 07		15 40									16 07		
Colwall	d											15 13		15 47									16 13		
Great Malvern	a											15 18		15 52									16 18		
	d											15 18	15 30	15 53									16 18		
Malvern Link	d											15 21	15 32	15 57									16 21		
Worcester Foregate Street 7	a											15 30	15 40	16 05									16 31		
	d								15 15			15 31	15 41	16 06							16 13		16 31		
Worcester Shrub Hill 7	a												15 43	16 11											
	d	14 47											15 47												16 47
Droitwich Spa	d	14 55							15 24			15 40	15 55								16 22		16 40		16 55
Bromsgrove	d											15 50											16 50		
Barnt Green	d																								
University	d											16 09											17 09		
Hartlebury	d																				16 29				
Kidderminster	d	15 06				15 26			15 36		15 56		16 06					16 26			16 36			16 56	17 06
Blakedown	d	15 11				15 31			15 41				16 11					16 31			16 41				17 11
Hagley	d	15 14				15 34			15 44				16 14					16 34			16 44				17 14
Stourbridge Junction 2	d	15 19			15 25	15 39			15 49	15 55	16 09		16 19				16 25	16 39			16 49	16 55		17 09	17 19
Lye	d				15 28					15 58							16 28					16 58			
Cradley Heath	d	15 24			15 31	15 44			15 54	16 01	16 14		16 24				16 31	16 44			16 54	17 01		17 14	17 24
Old Hill	d				15 35					16 05							16 35					17 05			
Rowley Regis	d	15 30			15 39	15 50			16 00	16 09	16 20		16 30				16 39	16 50			17 00	17 09		17 20	17 30
Langley Green	d				15 42					16 12							16 42					17 12			
Smethwick Galton Bdg H.L. 7	d	15 35			15 45	15 55			16 05	16 15	16 25		16 35				16 45	16 55			17 05	17 15		17 25	17 35
Birmingham New Street 12	a											16 21											17 21		
	d						16 03								16 33				17 03						
Birmingham International ✈	d						16 15												17 15						
Coventry	d						16 25												17 25						
The Hawthorns	d	15 38			15 48	15 58			16 08	16 18	16 28		16 38				16 48	16 58			17 08	17 18		17 28	17 38
Jewellery Quarter	d	15 41			15 51	16 01			16 11	16 21	16 31		16 41				16 51	17 01			17 11	17 21		17 31	17 41
Birmingham Snow Hill	a	15 45			15 56	16 05			16 16	16 25	16 35		16 45				16 56	17 05			17 16	17 25		17 35	17 45
	d	15 47		15 52	15 57	16 05		16 12	16 17	16 27	16 37		16 47			16 52	16 57	17 07		17 12	17 17	17 27		17 37	17 47
Birmingham Moor Street	d	15 50		15 55	16 00	16 08		16 15	16 20	16 30	16 40		16 50			16 55	17 00	17 10		17 15	17 20	17 30		17 40	17 50
Bordesley	d																								
Small Heath	d					16 12					16 44		16 54					17 14						17 44	17 54
Tyseley	d					16 14				16 34	16 46		16 56				17 04	17 16				17 34		17 46	17 56
Acocks Green	d				16 06				16 26		16 49						17 07				17 26			17 49	
Olton	d				16 08				16 28		16 52						17 10				17 28			17 52	
Solihull	d			16 05	16 12			16 25	16 32		16 55					17 06	17 13			17 25	17 32			17 55	
Widney Manor	d				16 15				16 35		16 58						17 16				17 35			17 58	
Dorridge	d			16 10	16a22			16 30	16a42		17a04					17 12	17a22			17 31	17a42			18a04	
Lapworth	d							16 34												17 35					
Hatton	d		15 58					16 40												17 41					
Warwick Parkway	d			16 21				16 45								17 22				17 46					
Warwick	d		16 04	16 24				16 49								17 26				17 49					
Leamington Spa 8	a		16 08	16 29			16 37	16 53							16 58	17 29			17 37	17 53					
	d		16 09	16 29			16 38	16 54							17 00	17 30			17 38	17 54					
Banbury	d		16 28	16 47			16a54	17 12							17a17	17 49			17a54	18 12					
London Marylebone 10 ⊖	a		17 57	18 00				18 32								19 02				19 30					
Spring Road	d	15 56				16 17				16 37			16 59					17 19				17 37			17 59
Hall Green	d	15 59				16 20				16 40			17 02					17 22				17 40			18 02
Yardley Wood	d	16 02				16 23				16 43			17 05					17 25				17 43			18 05
Shirley	d	16a05				16a26				16 46			17a08					17 28				17a46			18 08
Whitlocks End	d									16 49								17 31							18 11
Wythall	d									16 51								17 33							18 13
Earlswood (West Midlands)	d									16 54								17 36							18 16
The Lakes	d									16x56								17x38							18x18
Wood End	d									16x58								17x40							18x20
Danzey	d									17x01								17x43							18x23
Henley-in-Arden	d									17 06								17 48							18 28
Wootton Wawen	d									17x09								17x51							18x30
Wilmcote	d									17 14								17 56							18 36
Stratford-upon-Avon	a									17 22								18 03							18 43

For general notes see front of timetable
For details of catering facilities see Directory of Train Operators

Due to Engineering Operations, services from Saturday 13 September on this Table had not been confirmed at time of going to press. These services will be issued in a special Supplement as soon as exact timings have been confirmed

until 6 September

Hereford, Worcester and Stourbridge → Birmingham → Leamington Spa, Marylebone and Stratford-upon-Avon

Network Diagram - See first page of Table 71

		GW	XC 1 ◇		CH	CH	LM	LM	XC 1 ◇	CH	LM	GW 1 ◇	LM	LM	LM	LM	XC 1 ◇	XC 1 ◇	CH	LM	GW 1 ◇	LM	LM	LM	GW 1 ◇
		A																							
Hereford [7]	d													16 50									17 50		
Ledbury	a													17 06									18 06		
	d													17 07									18 07		
Colwall	d													17 13									18 13		
Great Malvern	a													17 18									18 18		
	d	16 43										17 07		17 18	17 30						18 07		18 18	18 30	19 20
Malvern Link	d	16 46										17 11		17 21	17 32						18 11		18 21	18 32	19 23
Worcester Foregate Street [7]	a	17 01										17 20		17 30	17 40						18 20		18 30	18 40	19 34
	d	17 02									17 14	17 22		17 31	17 41						18 22		18 31	18 41	19 35
Worcester Shrub Hill [7]	a	17 04										17 25			17 43						18 25			18 43	19 38
	d														17 47					18 18				18 47	
Droitwich Spa	d										17 23			17 40	17 55					18 26			18 40	18 55	
Bromsgrove	d													17 50									18 50		
Barnt Green	d																								
University	d													18 09									19 09		
Hartlebury	d										17 30													19 02	
Kidderminster	d							17 26			17 36				18 06					18 36				19 10	
Blakedown	d							17 31			17 41				18 11									19 15	
Hagley	d							17 34			17 44				18 14									19 18	
Stourbridge Junction [2]	d						17 25	17 39			17 49		17 55		18 19	18 25				18 49		18 55		19 24	
Lye	d						17 28						17 58			18 28						18 58		19 27	
Cradley Heath	d						17 31	17 44			17 54		18 01		18 24	18 31				18 54		19 01		19 30	
Old Hill	d						17 35						18 05			18 35						19 05		19 34	
Rowley Regis	d						17 39	17 50			18 00		18 09		18 30	18 39				19 00		19 09		19 38	
Langley Green	d						17 42						18 12			18 42						19 12		19 41	
Smethwick Galton Bdg H.L. [7]	d						17 45	17 55			18 05		18 15		18 35	18 45				19 05		19 15		19 44	
Birmingham New Street [12]	a													18 21									19 21		
	d		17 33						18 03								18 33	19 03							
Birmingham International ✈	d								18 15									19 15							
Coventry	d								18 25									19 25							
The Hawthorns (tram)	d						17 48	17 58			18 08		18 18		18 38	18 48				19 08		19 18		19 47	
Jewellery Quarter (tram)	d						17 51	18 01			18 11		18 21		18 41	18 51				19 11		19 21		19 50	
Birmingham Snow Hill (tram)	a						17 56	18 05			18 16		18 25		18 45	18 56				19 15		19 25		19 55	
	d					17 52	17 57	18 07		18 12	18 17		18 27		18 47	18 57			19 10	19 17		19 27		19 55	
Birmingham Moor Street	d					17 55	18 00	18 10		18 15	18 20		18 30		18 50	19 00			19 13	19 20		19 30		19 58	
Bordesley	d																								
Small Heath	d							18 14			18 24				18 54	19 04				19 24		19 34		20 02	
Tyseley	d							18 16			18 26				18 56	19 06				19 26		19 36		20 04	
Acocks Green	d						18 06				18 29				18 59					19 29				20 07	
Olton	d						18 08				18 32				19 02					19 32				20 10	
Solihull	d					18 06	18 12			18 25	18 35				19 05				19 23	19 35				20 13	
Widney Manor	d						18 15			18 28	18 38				19 08				19 26	19 39				20 17	
Dorridge	d					18 11	18a22			18 32	18a43				19a13				19 30	19a42				20a22	
Lapworth	d									18 36									19 34						
Hatton	d				17 56					18 42									19 40						
Warwick Parkway	d					18 22				18 46									19 44						
Warwick	d				18 04	18 25				18 48									19 47						
Leamington Spa [8]	a		17 58		18 07	18 29			18 37	18 52							18 58	19 37	19 50						
	d		18 00		18 08	18 29			18 38	18 52							19 00	19 38	19 51						
Banbury	d		18a17		18 28	18 47			18a54	19 12							19a17	19a54	20 10						
London Marylebone [10]	⊖ a				19 56	20 01				20 37									21 36						
Spring Road	d							18 19					18 36			19 09						19 39			
Hall Green	d							18 22					18 39			19 12						19 42			
Yardley Wood	d							18 25					18 42			19 15						19 45			
Shirley	d							18a28					18 45			19a18						19 48			
Whitlocks End	d												18 48									19 51			
Wythall	d												18 50									19 53			
Earlswood (West Midlands)	d												18 53									19 56			
The Lakes	d												18x55									19x58			
Wood End	d												18x57									20x00			
Danzey	d												19x00									20x03			
Henley-in-Arden	d												19 05									20 08			
Wootton Wawen	d												19x08									20x10			
Wilmcote	d												19 13									20 16			
Stratford-upon-Avon	a												19 21									20 23			

For general notes see front of timetable
For details of catering facilities see Directory of Train Operators

A To Westbury (Table 123)

Due to Engineering Operations, services from Saturday 13 September on this Table had not been confirmed at time of going to press. These services will be issued in a special Supplement as soon as exact timings have been confirmed

Table 71

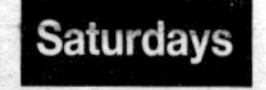

Saturdays

until 6 September

Hereford, Worcester and Stourbridge → Birmingham → Leamington Spa, Marylebone and Stratford-upon-Avon

Network Diagram - See first page of Table 71

		LM	CH	XC	CH	LM	LM	XC	CH	LM	LM	LM	GW	GW	CH	LM	LM	LM	XC	LM	LM	GW	LM
				1 ◇				1 ◇					1 ◇	A					◇			1	
Hereford 7	d	19 04									19 59		20 22					21 33					22 45
Ledbury	a	19 19									20 14		20 38					21 48					23 02
	d	19 20									20 15		20 45					21 49					23 02
Colwall	d	19 26									20 21		20 52					21 55					23 09
Great Malvern	a	19 31									20 25		20 57					22 00					23 13
	d	19 31									20 26		20 58	21 18			21 30	22 00				22 40	23 14
Malvern Link	d	19 34									20 29		21 02	21 21			21 32	22 03				22 43	23 16
Worcester Foregate Street 7	a	19 41									20 37		21 11	21 28			21 41	22 12				22 50	23 24
	d	19 42					19 50				20 38		21 19	21 29			21 42	22 13				22 51	23 25
Worcester Shrub Hill 7	a	19 49									20 40		21 22	21 31			21 44	22 17				22 53	23 31
	d										20 44	20 52					21 52		22 22		22 48		
Droitwich Spa	d						19 59				20 52	21 00					22 00				22 56		
Bromsgrove	d										21 00												
Barnt Green	d																						
University	d										21 16												
Hartlebury	d																						
Kidderminster	d					19 40	20 10					21 11					22 10				23 06		
Blakedown	d					19 45	20 15					21 16					22 15				23 11		
Hagley	d					19 49	20 19					21 20					22 19				23 15		
Stourbridge Junction 2	d					19 54	20 24			20 54		21 24				21 54	22 24			22 54	23 19		
Lye	d					19 57	20 27			20 57		21 27				21 57	22 27			22 57			
Cradley Heath	d					20 00	20 30			21 00		21 30				22 00	22 30			23 00			
Old Hill	d					20 04	20 34			21 04		21 34				22 04	22 34			23 04			
Rowley Regis	d					20 08	20 38			21 08		21 38				22 08	22 38			23 08			
Langley Green	d					20 11	20 41			21 11		21 41				22 11	22 41			23 11			
Smethwick Galton Bdg H.L. 7	d					20 14	20 44			21 14		21 44				22 14	22 44			23 14			
Birmingham New Street 12	a										21 28								23 02				
	d			20 03				21 03															
Birmingham International ✈	d			20 15				21 15															
Coventry	d			20 25				21 25															
The Hawthorns 🚊	d					20 17	20 47			21 17		21 47				22 17	22 47			23 17			
Jewellery Quarter 🚊	d					20 20	20 50			21 20		21 50				22 20	22 50			23 20			
Birmingham Snow Hill 🚊	a					20 23	20 54			21 23		21 53				22 23	22 53			23 24	23 37		
	d				20 10	20 27	20 55		21 11	21 25		21 55			22 15	22 25	22 55			23 25	23 38		
Birmingham Moor Street	d				20 13	20 30	20 58		21 14	21 28		21 58			22 18	22 28	22 58			23 28	23 41		
Bordesley	d																						
Small Heath	d					20 34	21 02			21 32		22 02				22 32	23 02			23 32	23 45		
Tyseley	d					20 36	21 04			21 34		22 04			22 22	22 34	23 04			23 34	23 47		
Acocks Green	d						21 07					22 07			22 25		23 07				23 50		
Olton	d						21 10					22 10			22 28		23 10				23 53		
Solihull	d				20 23		21 13		21 23			22 13			22 32		23 13				23 56		
Widney Manor	d				20 26		21 17		21 26			22 17			22 35		23 17				23 59		
Dorridge	d				20 30		21a23		21 30			22a22			22 39		23a22				00 04		
Lapworth	d				20 34				21 34						22 43						00 08		
Hatton	d		20 10		20 40				21 40						22 48						00 14		
Warwick Parkway	d		20 16		20 45				21 44						22 53								
Warwick	d		20 19		20 48				21 47						22 56						00 19		
Leamington Spa 8	a		20 22	20 37	20 53			21 37	21 51						23 00						00 24		
	d		20 23	20 38	20 53			21 38	21 52						23 01								
Banbury	d		20 42	20a54	21 15			21a54	22 15						23a22								
London Marylebone 10	⊖ a		22 21		22 40				23 46														
Spring Road	d					20 39				21 37						22 37				23 37			
Hall Green	d					20 42				21 40						22 40				23 40			
Yardley Wood	d					20 45				21 43						22 43				23 43			
Shirley	d					20 48				21a46						22a46				23a46			
Whitlocks End	d					20 51																	
Wythall	d					20 53																	
Earlswood (West Midlands)	d					20 56																	
The Lakes	d					20x58																	
Wood End	d					21x00																	
Danzey	d					21x03																	
Henley-in-Arden	d					21 08																	
Wootton Wawen	d					21x10																	
Wilmcote	d					21 16																	
Stratford-upon-Avon	a					21 23																	

For general notes see front of timetable
For details of catering facilities see Directory of Train Operators

A To Gloucester (Table 57)

Due to Engineering Operations, services from Saturday 13 September on this Table had not been confirmed at time of going to press. These services will be issued in a special Supplement as soon as exact timings have been confirmed

Table 71

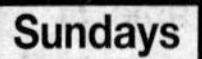

until 13 July

Hereford, Worcester and Stourbridge → Birmingham → Leamington Spa, Marylebone and Stratford-upon-Avon

Network Diagram - See first page of Table 71

		LM	XC	XC	CH		GW	LM	CH	XC		CH	XC	CH	LM		CH	XC	LM	XC		CH	LM	LM	GW
				1 ◇			1 ◇						1 ◇							1 ◇					1 ◇
Hereford 7	d																								
Ledbury	a																								
	d																								
Colwall	d																								
Great Malvern	a																								
	d						09 01																10 02	10 56	11 08
Malvern Link	d						09 04																10 04	10 58	11 11
Worcester Foregate Street 7	a						09 11																10 12	11 06	11 18
	d						09 13																10 13	11 20	11 19
Worcester Shrub Hill 7	a						09 17																10 15	→	11 22
	d	22p48													09 21								10 21		
Droitwich Spa	d	22p56													09 32								10 29		
Bromsgrove	d																								
Barnt Green	d																								
University	d																								
Hartlebury	d																								
Kidderminster	d	23p06													09 42				10 08				10 39		
Blakedown	d	23p11													09 47				10 13						
Hagley	d	23p15													09 51				10 17				10 46		
Stourbridge Junction 2	d	23p19													09 55				10 22				10 52		
Lye	d																		10 25						
Cradley Heath	d														10 01				10 29				10 58		
Old Hill	d																		10 33						
Rowley Regis	d														10 06				10 36				11 03		
Langley Green	d																		10 39						
Smethwick Galton Bdg H.L. 7	d														10 12				10 43				11 09		
Birmingham New Street 12	a																								
	d			09 03									10 03							11 03					
Birmingham International ✈	d		08 30							09 30								10 30							
Coventry	d		08 55							09 55								10 55							
The Hawthorns 🚊	d														10 15				10 45				11 12		
Jewellery Quarter 🚊	d														10 18				10 49				11 15		
Birmingham Snow Hill 🚊	a	23p37													10 20				10 52				11 17		
	d	23p38			09 10			09 19	09 40					10 10	10 22		10 40		10 53			11 10	11 19		
Birmingham Moor Street	d	23p41			09 13			09 22	09 43					10 13	10 25		10 43		10 56			11 13	11 22		
Bordesley	d																								
Small Heath	d	23p45																							
Tyseley	d	23p47						09 26							10 29								11 26		
Acocks Green	d	23p50																	11 02						
Olton	d	23p53																	11 04						
Solihull	d	23p56			09 22				09 52					10 22			10 52		11 08			11 22			
Widney Manor	d	23p59																	11 11						
Dorridge	d	00 04			09 28				09 58					10 28			10 58		11a16			11 28			
Lapworth	d	00 08							10 02																
Hatton	d	00 14										10 17					11 05								
Warwick Parkway	d				09 39				10 10					10 38			11 10					11 38			
Warwick	d	00 19			09 42							10 24		10 41								11 41			
Leamington Spa 8	a	00 24	09 25	09 36	09 46				10 16	10 25		10 27	10 36	10 46			11 16	11 25		11 36		11 46			
	d			09 38	09 47				10 16			10 29	10 38	10 47			11 16			11 38		11 47			
Banbury	d			09a54	10 06				10 36			10 48	10a54	11 06			11 36			11a54		12 06			
London Marylebone 10 ⊖	a				11 23				12 00			12 16		12 22			13 00					13 22			
Spring Road	d							09 29							10 32								11 29		
Hall Green	d							09 32							10 35								11 32		
Yardley Wood	d							09 35							10 38								11 35		
Shirley	d							09 38							10 41								11 38		
Whitlocks End	d																								
Wythall	d							09 42							10 45								11 42		
Earlswood (West Midlands)	d																								
The Lakes	d							09x45							10x48								11x45		
Wood End	d																								
Danzey	d																								
Henley-in-Arden	d							09 53							10 56								11 53		
Wootton Wawen	d																								
Wilmcote	d							10 03							11 04								12 01		
Stratford-upon-Avon	a							10 08							11 11								12 08		

For general notes see front of timetable
For details of catering facilities see
Directory of Train Operators

Table 71

Sundays

until 13 July

Hereford, Worcester and Stourbridge → Birmingham → Leamington Spa, Marylebone and Stratford-upon-Avon

Network Diagram - See first page of Table 71

Station		CH	XC	LM	CH	XC	CH	LM	CH	XC	LM	XC	CH	LM	GW	CH	XC	LM	CH	XC
			🚌			1 ◇ ☕				🚌		1 ◇ ☕			1 ◇		🚌			R 1 ☕
Hereford 7	d																			
Ledbury	a																			
	d																			
Colwall	d																			
Great Malvern	a																			
	d													12 04	13 06					
Malvern Link	d													12 06	13 09					
Worcester Foregate Street 7	a							⟵						12 15	13 19					
	d							11 20						12 16	13 20					
Worcester Shrub Hill 7	a													12 18	13 24					
	d													12 21						
Droitwich Spa	d							11 29						12 29						
Bromsgrove	d																			
Barnt Green	d																			
University	d																			
Hartlebury	d																			
Kidderminster	d							11 39						12 39						
Blakedown	d													12 44						
Hagley	d							11 46						12 48						
Stourbridge Junction 2	d			11 22				11 52			12 22			12 52				13 22		
Lye	d			11 25							12 25							13 25		
Cradley Heath	d			11 29				11 58			12 29			12 58				13 29		
Old Hill	d			11 33							12 33							13 33		
Rowley Regis	d			11 36				12 03			12 36			13 03				13 36		
Langley Green	d			11 39							12 39							13 39		
Smethwick Galton Bdg H.L. 7	d			11 43				12 08			12 43			13 08				13 43		
Birmingham New Street 12	a																			
	d					12 03						13 03								14 03
Birmingham International ✈	d		11 30							12 30							13 30			
Coventry	d		11 55							12 55							13 55			
The Hawthorns 🚊	d			11 45				12 11			12 45			13 11				13 45		
Jewellery Quarter 🚊	d			11 49				12 14			12 49			13 14				13 49		
Birmingham Snow Hill 🚊	a			11 52				12 17			12 52			13 17				13 52		
	d	11 40		11 53			12 10	12 19	12 40		12 53		13 10	13 19		13 40		13 53		
Birmingham Moor Street	d	11 43		11 56			12 13	12 22	12 43		12 56		13 13	13 22		13 43		13 56		
Bordesley	d																			
Small Heath	d																			
Tyseley	d							12 26						13 26						
Acocks Green	d			12 02							13 02							14 02		
Olton	d			12 04							13 04							14 04		
Solihull	d	11 52		12 08			12 22		12 52		13 08		13 23			13 52		14 08		
Widney Manor	d			12 11							13 11							14 11		
Dorridge	d	11 58		12a16			12 28		12 58		13a16		13 29			13 58		14a17		
Lapworth	d	12 02														14 02				
Hatton	d				12 19				13 05										14 19	
Warwick Parkway	d	12 10					12 38		13 10				13 39			14 10				
Warwick	d				12 24		12 41						13 42						14 24	
Leamington Spa 8	a	12 16	12 25		12 27	12 36	12 45		13 16	13 25		13 36	13 46			14 16	14 25		14 27	14 36
	d	12 16			12 29	12 38	12 46		13 16			13 38	13 47			14 16			14 29	14 38
Banbury	d	12 36			12 48	12a54	13 06		13 36			13a54	14 06			14 36			14 48	14a54
London Marylebone 10 ⊖	a	14 00			14 16		14 22		15 00				15 22			16 00			16 16	
Spring Road	d							12 29						13 29						
Hall Green	d							12 32						13 32						
Yardley Wood	d							12 35						13 35						
Shirley	d							12 38						13 38						
Whitlocks End	d																			
Wythall	d							12 42						13 42						
Earlswood (West Midlands)	d																			
The Lakes	d							12x45						13x45						
Wood End	d																			
Danzey	d																			
Henley-in-Arden	d							12 53						13 53						
Wootton Wawen	d																			
Wilmcote	d							13 01						14 01						
Stratford-upon-Avon	a							13 08						14 08						

For general notes see front of timetable
For details of catering facilities see Directory of Train Operators

Table 71

Sundays

until 13 July

Hereford, Worcester and Stourbridge → Birmingham → Leamington Spa, Marylebone and Stratford-upon-Avon

Network Diagram - See first page of Table 71

		CH	LM	GW	CH	XC	LM	XC	CH	LM	CH	LM	LM	XC	CH	XC	CH	LM	GW	CH	LM
				1 ◇ ☕		🚌		R 1 ☕						🚌		R 1 ☕			1 ◇ ☕		
Hereford 7	d			13 30															14 30		
Ledbury	a			13 46															14 46		
	d			13 48															14 57		
Colwall	d			13 55															15 04		
Great Malvern	a			13 59															15 08		
	d			14 01								14 35							15 09		
Malvern Link	d			14 05								14 37							15 13		
Worcester Foregate Street 7	a			14 14								14 45							15 23		
	d		13 20	14 16						14 20		14 45						15 20	15 24		
Worcester Shrub Hill 7	a			14 19								14 48							15 27		
	d											14 51									15 46
Droitwich Spa	d		13 29							14 29		14 59						15 29			15 54
Bromsgrove	d											15 09									
Barnt Green	d																				
University	d																				
Hartlebury	d																				
Kidderminster	d		13 39							14 39								15 39			16 04
Blakedown	d									14 44											
Hagley	d		13 46							14 48								15 46			16 11
Stourbridge Junction 2	d		13 52				14 22			14 52			15 22					15 52			16 16
Lye	d						14 25						15 25								
Cradley Heath	d		13 58				14 29			14 58			15 29					15 58			
Old Hill	d						14 33						15 33								
Rowley Regis	d		14 03				14 36			15 03			15 36					16 03			
Langley Green	d						14 39						15 39								
Smethwick Galton Bdg H.L. 7	d		14 08				14 43			15 08			15 43					16 08			16 29
Birmingham New Street 12	a											15 40									
	d							15 03								16 03					
Birmingham International ✈	d					14 30								15 30							
Coventry	d					14 55								15 55							
The Hawthorns 🚊	d		14 11				14 45			15 11			15 45					16 11			
Jewellery Quarter 🚊	d		14 14				14 49			15 14			15 49					16 14			
Birmingham Snow Hill 🚊	a		14 17				14 52			15 17			15 52					16 17			16 35
	d	14 10	14 19		14 40		14 53		15 10	15 19	15 40		15 53				16 10	16 19		16 40	16 45
Birmingham Moor Street	d	14 13	14 22		14 43		14 56		15 13	15 22	15 43		15 56				16 13	16 22		16 43	16a47
Bordesley	d																				
Small Heath	d																				
Tyseley	d		14 26							15 26								16 26			
Acocks Green	d						15 02						16 02								
Olton	d						15 04						16 04								
Solihull	d	14 22			14 52		15 08		15 22		15 52		16 08				16 22			16 52	
Widney Manor	d						15 11						16 11								
Dorridge	d	14 28			14 58		15a17		15 28		15 58		16a16				16 28			16 58	
Lapworth	d										16 02										
Hatton	d				15 05										16 17					17 05	
Warwick Parkway	d	14 38			15 10				15 38		16 10						16 38			17 10	
Warwick	d	14 41							15 41						16 24		16 41				
Leamington Spa 8	a	14 46			15 16	15 25		15 36	15 46		16 16			16 25	16 27	16 36	16 46			17 16	
	d	14 47			15 16			15 38	15 47		16 16				16 29	16 38	16 47			17 16	
Banbury	d	15 06			15 36			15a54	16 06		16 36				16 48	16a54	17 06			17 36	
London Marylebone 10	⊖ a	16 22			17 00				17 22		18 00				18 17		18 21			19 00	
Spring Road	d		14 29							15 29								16 29			
Hall Green	d		14 32							15 32								16 32			
Yardley Wood	d		14 35							15 35								16 35			
Shirley	d		14b53							15 38								16 38			
Whitlocks End	d																				
Wythall	d		14 57							15 42								16 42			
Earlswood (West Midlands)	d																				
The Lakes	d		15x00							15x45								16x45			
Wood End	d																				
Danzey	d																				
Henley-in-Arden	d		15 08							15 53								16 53			
Wootton Wawen	d																				
Wilmcote	d		15 16							16 01								17 01			
Stratford-upon-Avon	a		15 24							16 08								17 08			

For general notes see front of timetable
For details of catering facilities see
Directory of Train Operators

b Arr. 1437

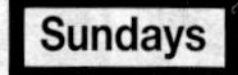

until 13 July

Hereford, Worcester and Stourbridge → Birmingham → Leamington Spa, Marylebone and Stratford-upon-Avon

Network Diagram - See first page of Table 71

		XC	LM	XC	CH	LM	LM	XC	CH	XC	LM	CH	XC	CH	LM	GW	LM	CH	XC	XC
		🚌		R 1 ☕				1 ◇ ☕		🚌			R 1 ☕			1 ◇ ☕			🚌	R 1 ☕
Hereford 7	d						15 47									16 30				
Ledbury	a						16 03									16 46				
	d						16 03									16 47				
Colwall	d						16 10									16 55				
Great Malvern	a						16 15									17 00				
	d						16 15									17 00	17 16			
Malvern Link	d						16 18									17 04	17 19			
Worcester Foregate Street 7	a						16 26									17 20	17 27			
	d					16 20	16 27								17 20	17 21	17 27			
Worcester Shrub Hill 7	a						16 29									17 24	17 30			
	d						16 33										17 33			
Droitwich Spa	d					16 29	16 41								17 29		17 41			
Bromsgrove	d						16 51										17 51			
Barnt Green	d																			
University	d																			
Hartlebury	d																			
Kidderminster	d					16 39									17 39					
Blakedown	d														17 44					
Hagley	d					16 46									17 48					
Stourbridge Junction 2	d		16 22			16 52					17 22				17 52					
Lye	d		16 25								17 25									
Cradley Heath	d		16 29			16 58					17 29				17 58					
Old Hill	d		16 33								17 33									
Rowley Regis	d		16 36			17 03					17 36				18 03					
Langley Green	d		16 39								17 39									
Smethwick Galton Bdg H.L. 7	d		16 43			17 08					17 43				18 08					
Birmingham New Street 12	a						17 17										18 12			
	d			17 03				17 33					18 03							19 03
Birmingham International ✈	d	16 30								17 30									18 30	
Coventry	d	16 55								17 55									18 55	
The Hawthorns 🚊	d		16 45			17 11					17 45				18 11					
Jewellery Quarter 🚊	d		16 49			17 14					17 49				18 14					
Birmingham Snow Hill 🚊	a		16 52			17 17					17 53				18 17					
	d		16 53		17 10	17 19			17 40		17 53			18 10	18 19			18 40		
Birmingham Moor Street	d		16 56		17 13	17 22			17 43		17 56			18 13	18 22			18 43		
Bordesley	d																			
Small Heath	d																			
Tyseley	d					17 26									18 26					
Acocks Green	d		17 02								18 02									
Olton	d		17 04								18 04									
Solihull	d		17 08		17 22				17 52		18 08			18 22				18 52		
Widney Manor	d		17 11								18 11									
Dorridge	d		17a17		17 28				17 58		18a17			18 28				18 58		
Lapworth	d								18 02											
Hatton	d											18 17						19 05		
Warwick Parkway	d				17 38				18 10					18 38				19 10		
Warwick	d				17 41							18 24		18 41						
Leamington Spa 8	a	17 25		17 36	17 46			17 59	18 16	18 25		18 27	18 36	18 46				19 15	19 25	19 36
	d			17 38	17 47			18 00	18 16			18 29	18 38	18 47				19 16		19 38
Banbury	d			17a54	18 06			18a18	18 36			18 48	18a54	19 06				19 35		19a54
London Marylebone 10 ⊖	a				19 22				20 00			20 16		20 21				21 00		
Spring Road	d					17 29									18 29					
Hall Green	d					17 32									18 32					
Yardley Wood	d					17 35									18 35					
Shirley	d					17 38									18 38					
Whitlocks End	d																			
Wythall	d					17 42									18 42					
Earlswood (West Midlands)	d																			
The Lakes	d					17x45									18x45					
Wood End	d																			
Danzey	d																			
Henley-in-Arden	d					17 53									18 53					
Wootton Wawen	d																			
Wilmcote	d					18 01									19 01					
Stratford-upon-Avon	a					18 08									19 08					

For general notes see front of timetable
For details of catering facilities see Directory of Train Operators

Sundays

until 13 July

Hereford, Worcester and Stourbridge → Birmingham → Leamington Spa, Marylebone and Stratford-upon-Avon

Network Diagram - See first page of Table 71

		CH	LM	GW	XC		CH	XC	CH	LM		LM	GW	XC	XC	CH	LM	LM	LM	GW	XC	LM	LM		
				1 ◇ ☕	🚌			R 1 ☕					1 ◇ ☕	🚌	1 ◇ ☕					1 ◇ ☕					
Hereford 7	d			18 30														20 05					22 40		
Ledbury	a			18 46														20 20					22 56		
	d			18 48														20 21					22 56		
Colwall	d			18 55														20 27					23 03		
Great Malvern	a			18 59														20 32					23 07		
	d			19 08									20 08					20 32		21 05		22 02	23 08		
Malvern Link	d			19 12									20 12					20 35		21 09		22 05	23 10		
Worcester Foregate Street 7	a			19 21									20 21					20 44		21 21		22 16	23 19		
	d		18 20	19 23									20 23					20 44		21 23		22 20	23 22		
Worcester Shrub Hill 7	a			19 26									20 26					20 47		21 26		22 22	23 24		
	d									19 31		19 56					20 33	20 50	21 17			22 26			
Droitwich Spa	d		18 29							19 39		20 04					20 41	20 58	21 25			22 34			
Bromsgrove	d											20 13						21 08			22 20				
Barnt Green	d																								
University	d																								
Hartlebury	d																								
Kidderminster	d		18 39							19 49							20 51		21 41			22 44			
Blakedown	d																								
Hagley	d		18 46							19 56							20 58		21 48			22 51			
Stourbridge Junction 2	d		18 52							20 01							21 02		21 52			22 55			
Lye	d																								
Cradley Heath	d		18 58							20 07							21 07		21 58			23 01			
Old Hill	d																								
Rowley Regis	d		19 03							20 12							21 13		22 03			23 06			
Langley Green	d																								
Smethwick Galton Bdg H.L. 7	d		19 08							20 17							21 18		22 08			23 11			
Birmingham New Street 12	a											20 40						21 45			22 45				
	d							20 03							21 03										
Birmingham International ✈	d				19 30									20 30											
Coventry	d				19 55									20 55											
The Hawthorns 🚋	d		19 11							20 20							21 20		22 11			23 14			
Jewellery Quarter 🚋	d		19 14							20 23							21 24		22 14			23 17			
Birmingham Snow Hill 🚋	a		19 18							20 26							21 27		22 18			23 21			
	d	19 15	19 20						20 15	20 27						21 15	21 27		22 18						
Birmingham Moor Street	d	19 18	19a22						20 18	20a30						21 18	21a30		22a21						
Bordesley	d																								
Small Heath	d																								
Tyseley	d																								
Acocks Green	d																								
Olton	d																								
Solihull	d	19 27							20 27							21 27									
Widney Manor	d	19 30							20 30							21 30									
Dorridge	d	19 34							20 34							21 34									
Lapworth	d																								
Hatton	d						20 17																		
Warwick Parkway	d	19 45							20 45							21 45									
Warwick	d	19 48					20 24		20 48							21 48									
Leamington Spa 8	a	19 53			20 25		20 28	20 36	20 53					21 25	21 36	21 53									
	d	19 53					20 29	20 38	20 53						21 38	21 53									
Banbury	d	20 13					20 48	20a54	21 13						21a54	22 15									
London Marylebone 10 ⊖	a	21 50					22 16		22 50							23 53									
Spring Road	d																								
Hall Green	d																								
Yardley Wood	d																								
Shirley	d																								
Whitlocks End	d																								
Wythall	d																								
Earlswood (West Midlands)	d																								
The Lakes	d																								
Wood End	d																								
Danzey	d																								
Henley-in-Arden	d																								
Wootton Wawen	d																								
Wilmcote	d																								
Stratford-upon-Avon	a																								

For general notes see front of timetable
For details of catering facilities see Directory of Train Operators

Table 71

Sundays

Hereford, Worcester and Stourbridge → Birmingham → Leamington Spa, Marylebone and Stratford-upon-Avon

20 July to 7 September

Network Diagram - See first page of Table 71

		LM	XC	XC 1◇	CH	GW 1◇	LM	CH	XC		CH	XC 1◇	CH	LM	XC 1◇	CH	XC	LM		XC 1◇	CH	LM	LM	GW 1◇	XC 1◇
Hereford 7	d																								
Ledbury	a																								
	d																								
Colwall	d																								
Great Malvern	a																								
	d					09 01																10 02	10 56	11 08	
Malvern Link	d					09 04																10 04	10 58	11 11	
Worcester Foregate Street 7	a					09 11																10 12	11 06	11 18	
	d					09 13																10 13	11 20	11 19	
Worcester Shrub Hill 7	a					09 17																10 15	→	11 22	
	d	22p48												09 21								10 21			
Droitwich Spa	d	22p56												09 32								10 29			
Bromsgrove	d																								
Barnt Green	d																								
University	d																								
Hartlebury	d																								
Kidderminster	d	23p06												09 42				10 08				10 39			
Blakedown	d	23p11												09 47				10 13							
Hagley	d	23p15												09 51				10 17				10 46			
Stourbridge Junction 2	d	23p19												09 55				10 22				10 52			
Lye	d																	10 25							
Cradley Heath	d													10 01				10 29				10 58			
Old Hill	d																	10 33							
Rowley Regis	d													10 06				10 36				11 03			
Langley Green	d																	10 39							
Smethwick Galton Bdg H.L. 7	d													10 12				10 43				11 09			
Birmingham New Street 12	a																								
	d			09 03								10 03			10 33					11 03					11 33
Birmingham International ✈	d		08 30						09 30								10 30								
Coventry	d		08 55						09 55								10 55								
The Hawthorns 🚊	d													10 15				10 45				11 12			
Jewellery Quarter 🚊	d													10 18				10 49				11 15			
Birmingham Snow Hill 🚊	a	23p37												10 20				10 52				11 17			
	d	23p38			09 10		09 19	09 40					10 10	10 22		10 40		10 53			11 10	11 19			
Birmingham Moor Street	d	23p41			09 13		09 22	09 43					10 13	10 25		10 43		10 56			11 13	11 22			
Bordesley	d																								
Small Heath	d	23p45																							
Tyseley	d	23p47					09 26							10 29								11 26			
Acocks Green	d	23p50																11 02							
Olton	d	23p53																11 04							
Solihull	d	23p56			09 22			09 52					10 22			10 52		11 08			11 22				
Widney Manor	d	23p59																11 11							
Dorridge	d	00 04			09 28			09 58					10 28			10 58		11a16			11 28				
Lapworth	d	00 08						10 02																	
Hatton	d	00 14									10 17					11 05									
Warwick Parkway	d				09 39			10 10					10 38			11 10					11 38				
Warwick	d	00 19			09 42						10 24		10 41								11 41				
Leamington Spa 8	a	00 24	09 25	09 36	09 46			10 16	10 25		10 27	10 36	10 46		10 59	11 16	11 25			11 36	11 46				11 59
	d			09 38	09 47			10 16			10 29	10 38	10 47		11 00	11 16				11 38	11 47				12 00
Banbury	d			09a54	10 06			10 36			10 48	10a54	11 06		11a18	11 36				11a54	12 06				12a18
London Marylebone 10 ⊖	a				11 23			12 00			12 16		12 22			13 00					13 22				
Spring Road	d						09 29							10 32								11 29			
Hall Green	d						09 32							10 35								11 32			
Yardley Wood	d						09 35							10 38								11 35			
Shirley	d						09 38							10 41								11 38			
Whitlocks End	d																								
Wythall	d						09 42							10 45								11 42			
Earlswood (West Midlands)	d																								
The Lakes	d						09x45							10x48								11x45			
Wood End	d																								
Danzey	d																								
Henley-in-Arden	d						09 53							10 56								11 53			
Wootton Wawen	d																								
Wilmcote	d						10 03							11 04								12 01			
Stratford-upon-Avon	a						10 08							11 11								12 08			

For general notes see front of timetable
For details of catering facilities see
Directory of Train Operators

Due to Engineering Operations, services from Sunday 14 September on this Table had not been confirmed at time of going to press. These services will be issued in a special Supplement as soon as exact timings have been confirmed

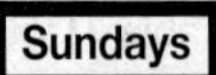

20 July to 7 September

Hereford, Worcester and Stourbridge → Birmingham → Leamington Spa, Marylebone and Stratford-upon-Avon

Network Diagram - See first page of Table 71

		CH	XC	LM	CH	XC	CH	LM	XC	CH	XC	LM	XC	CH	LM	GW	XC	CH	XC	LM	CH	XC
						1 ◇			1 ◇				1 ◇			1 ◇	1 ◇					R 1
			🚌			☕			☕		🚌		☕				☕		🚌			☕
Hereford 7	d																					
Ledbury	a																					
	d																					
Colwall	d																					
Great Malvern	a																					
	d														12 04	13 06						
Malvern Link	d														12 06	13 09						
Worcester Foregate Street 7	a							←							12 15	13 19						
	d							11 20							12 16	13 20						
Worcester Shrub Hill 7	a														12 18	13 24						
	d														12 21							
Droitwich Spa	d							11 29							12 29							
Bromsgrove	d																					
Barnt Green	d																					
University	d																					
Hartlebury	d																					
Kidderminster	d							11 39							12 39							
Blakedown	d														12 44							
Hagley	d							11 46							12 48							
Stourbridge Junction 2	d			11 22				11 52				12 22			12 52					13 22		
Lye	d			11 25								12 25								13 25		
Cradley Heath	d			11 29				11 58				12 29			12 58					13 29		
Old Hill	d			11 33								12 33								13 33		
Rowley Regis	d			11 36				12 03				12 36			13 03					13 36		
Langley Green	d			11 39								12 39								13 39		
Smethwick Galton Bdg H.L. 7	d			11 43				12 08				12 43			13 08					13 43		
Birmingham New Street 12	a																					
	d					12 03			12 33				13 03				13 33					14 03
Birmingham International ✈	d		11 30								12 30								13 30			
Coventry	d		11 55								12 55								13 55			
The Hawthorns 🚋	d			11 45				12 11				12 45			13 11					13 45		
Jewellery Quarter 🚋	d			11 49				12 14				12 49			13 14					13 49		
Birmingham Snow Hill 🚋	a			11 52				12 17				12 52			13 17					13 52		
	d	11 40		11 53			12 10	12 19		12 40		12 53		13 10	13 19			13 40		13 53		
Birmingham Moor Street	d	11 43		11 56			12 13	12 22		12 43		12 56		13 13	13 22			13 43		13 56		
Bordesley	d																					
Small Heath	d																					
Tyseley	d							12 26							13 26							
Acocks Green	d			12 02								13 02								14 02		
Olton	d			12 04								13 04								14 04		
Solihull	d	11 52		12 08			12 22			12 52		13 08		13 23				13 52		14 08		
Widney Manor	d			12 11								13 11								14 11		
Dorridge	d	11 58		12a16			12 28			12 58		13a16		13 29				13 58		14a17		
Lapworth	d	12 02																14 02				
Hatton	d				12 19					13 05											14 19	
Warwick Parkway	d	12 10					12 38			13 10				13 39				14 10				
Warwick	d				12 24		12 41							13 42							14 24	
Leamington Spa 8	a	12 16	12 25		12 27	12 36	12 45		12 59	13 16	13 25		13 36	13 46			13 59	14 16	14 25		14 27	14 36
	d	12 16			12 29	12 38	12 46		13 00	13 16			13 38	13 47			14 00	14 16			14 29	14 38
Banbury	d	12 36			12 48	12a54	13 06		13a18	13 36			13a54	14 06			14a18	14 36			14 48	14a54
London Marylebone 10	⊖ a	14 00			14 16		14 22			15 00				15 22				16 00			16 16	
Spring Road	d							12 29							13 29							
Hall Green	d							12 32							13 32							
Yardley Wood	d							12 35							13 35							
Shirley	d							12 38							13 38							
Whitlocks End	d																					
Wythall	d							12 42							13 42							
Earlswood (West Midlands)	d																					
The Lakes	d							12x45							13x45							
Wood End	d																					
Danzey	d																					
Henley-in-Arden	d							12 53							13 53							
Wootton Wawen	d																					
Wilmcote	d							13 01							14 01							
Stratford-upon-Avon	a							13 08							14 08							

For general notes see front of timetable
For details of catering facilities see Directory of Train Operators

Due to Engineering Operations, services from Sunday 14 September on this Table had not been confirmed at time of going to press. These services will be issued in a special Supplement as soon as exact timings have been confirmed

Sundays

Hereford, Worcester and Stourbridge → Birmingham → Leamington Spa, Marylebone and Stratford-upon-Avon

20 July to 7 September

Network Diagram - See first page of Table 71

		CH	LM	GW	XC	CH	XC	LM	XC		CH	LM	XC	CH	LM	LM	XC	CH		XC	CH	LM	GW	CH	LM
				1 ◇	1 ◇		🚌		R 1				1 ◇				🚌			R 1			1 ◇		
				☕	☕				☕				☕							☕			☕		
Hereford 7	d			13 30																			14 30		
Ledbury	a			13 46																			14 46		
	d			13 48																			14 57		
Colwall	d			13 55																			15 04		
Great Malvern	a			13 59																			15 08		
	d			14 01											14 35								15 09		
Malvern Link	d			14 05											14 37								15 13		
Worcester Foregate Street 7	a			14 14											14 45								15 23		
	d		13 20	14 16								14 20			14 45							15 20	15 24		
Worcester Shrub Hill 7	a			14 19											14 48								15 27		
	d														14 51										15 46
Droitwich Spa	d		13 29									14 29			14 59							15 29			15 54
Bromsgrove	d														15 09										
Barnt Green	d																								
University	d																								
Hartlebury	d																								
Kidderminster	d		13 39									14 39										15 39			16 04
Blakedown	d											14 44													
Hagley	d		13 46									14 48										15 46			16 11
Stourbridge Junction 2	d		13 52					14 22				14 52				15 22						15 52			16 16
Lye	d							14 25								15 25									
Cradley Heath	d		13 58					14 29				14 58				15 29						15 58			
Old Hill	d							14 33								15 33									
Rowley Regis	d		14 03					14 36				15 03				15 36						16 03			
Langley Green	d							14 39								15 39									
Smethwick Galton Bdg H.L. 7	d		14 08					14 43				15 08				15 43						16 08			16 29
Birmingham New Street 12	a														15 40										
	d				14 33				15 03				15 33							16 03					
Birmingham International ✈	d						14 30										15 30								
Coventry	d						14 55										15 55								
The Hawthorns 🚊	d		14 11					14 45				15 11				15 45						16 11			
Jewellery Quarter 🚊	d		14 14					14 49				15 14				15 49						16 14			
Birmingham Snow Hill 🚊	a		14 17					14 52				15 17				15 52						16 17			16 35
	d	14 10	14 19			14 40		14 53			15 10	15 19		15 40		15 53					16 10	16 19		16 40	16 45
Birmingham Moor Street	d	14 13	14 22			14 43		14 56			15 13	15 22		15 43		15 56					16 13	16 22		16 43	16a47
Bordesley	d																								
Small Heath	d																								
Tyseley	d		14 26									15 26										16 26			
Acocks Green	d							15 02								16 02									
Olton	d							15 04								16 04									
Solihull	d	14 22				14 52		15 08			15 22			15 52		16 08					16 22			16 52	
Widney Manor	d							15 11								16 11									
Dorridge	d	14 28				14 58		15a17			15 28			15 58		16a16					16 28			16 58	
Lapworth	d													16 02											
Hatton	d					15 05												16 17						17 05	
Warwick Parkway	d	14 38				15 10					15 38			16 10							16 38			17 10	
Warwick	d	14 41									15 41							16 24			16 41				
Leamington Spa 8	a	14 46			14 59	15 16	15 25		15 36		15 46		15 59	16 16			16 25	16 27		16 36	16 46			17 16	
	d	14 47			15 00	15 16			15 38		15 47		16 00	16 16				16 29		16 38	16 47			17 16	
Banbury	d	15 06			15a18	15 36			15a54		16 06		16a18	16 36				16 48		16a54	17 06			17 36	
London Marylebone 10 ⊖	a	16 22				17 00					17 22			18 00				18 17			18 21			19 00	
Spring Road	d		14 29									15 29										16 29			
Hall Green	d		14 32									15 32										16 32			
Yardley Wood	d		14 35									15 35										16 35			
Shirley	d		14b53									15 38										16 38			
Whitlocks End	d																								
Wythall	d		14 57									15 42										16 42			
Earlswood (West Midlands)	d																								
The Lakes	d		15x00									15x45										16x45			
Wood End	d																								
Danzey	d																								
Henley-in-Arden	d		15 08									15 53										16 53			
Wootton Wawen	d																								
Wilmcote	d		15 16									16 01										17 01			
Stratford-upon-Avon	a		15 24									16 08										17 08			

For general notes see front of timetable
For details of catering facilities see
Directory of Train Operators

b Arr. 1437

Due to Engineering Operations, services from Sunday 14 September on this Table had not been confirmed at time of going to press. These services will be issued in a special Supplement as soon as exact timings have been confirmed

Table 71

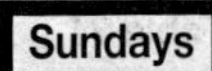
Sundays

20 July to 7 September

Hereford, Worcester and Stourbridge → Birmingham → Leamington Spa, Marylebone and Stratford-upon-Avon

Network Diagram - See first page of Table 71

		XC	XC	LM	XC		CH	LM	LM	XC	CH	XC	LM	CH		XC	CH	LM	GW	LM	XC	CH	XC		XC
		1 ◇			R 1					1 ◇						R 1			1 ◇		1 ◇				R 1
			🚌									🚌											🚌		
		☕			☕					☕						☕			☕		☕				☕
Hereford 7	d								15 47										16 30						
Ledbury	a								16 03										16 46						
	d								16 03										16 47						
Colwall	d								16 10										16 55						
Great Malvern	a								16 15										17 00						
	d								16 15										17 00	17 16					
Malvern Link	d								16 18										17 04	17 19					
Worcester Foregate Street 7	a								16 26										17 20	17 27					
	d							16 20	16 27									17 20	17 21	17 27					
Worcester Shrub Hill 7	a								16 29										17 24	17 30					
	d								16 33											17 33					
Droitwich Spa	d							16 29	16 41									17 29		17 41					
Bromsgrove	d								16 51											17 51					
Barnt Green	d																								
University	d																								
Hartlebury	d																								
Kidderminster	d							16 39										17 39							
Blakedown	d																	17 44							
Hagley	d							16 46										17 48							
Stourbridge Junction 2	d			16 22				16 52					17 22					17 52							
Lye	d			16 25									17 25												
Cradley Heath	d			16 29				16 58					17 29					17 58							
Old Hill	d			16 33									17 33												
Rowley Regis	d			16 36				17 03					17 36					18 03							
Langley Green	d			16 39									17 39												
Smethwick Galton Bdg H.L. 7	d			16 43				17 08					17 43					18 08							
Birmingham New Street 12	a								17 17											18 12					
	d	16 33			17 03					17 33						18 03					18 33				19 03
Birmingham International ✈	d		16 30									17 30											18 30		
Coventry	d		16 55									17 55											18 55		
The Hawthorns 🚊	d			16 45				17 11					17 45					18 11							
Jewellery Quarter 🚊	d			16 49				17 14					17 49					18 14							
Birmingham Snow Hill 🚊	a			16 52				17 17					17 53					18 17							
	d			16 53			17 10	17 19			17 40		17 53				18 10	18 19				18 40			
Birmingham Moor Street	d			16 56			17 13	17 22			17 43		17 56				18 13	18 22				18 43			
Bordesley	d																								
Small Heath	d																								
Tyseley	d							17 26										18 26							
Acocks Green	d			17 02									18 02												
Olton	d			17 04									18 04												
Solihull	d			17 08			17 22				17 52		18 08				18 22					18 52			
Widney Manor	d			17 11									18 11												
Dorridge	d			17a17			17 28				17 58		18a17				18 28					18 58			
Lapworth	d										18 02														
Hatton	d													18 17								19 05			
Warwick Parkway	d						17 38				18 10						18 38					19 10			
Warwick	d						17 41							18 24			18 41								
Leamington Spa 8	a	16 59	17 25		17 36		17 46			17 59	18 16	18 25		18 27		18 36	18 46				18 59	19 15	19 25		19 36
	d	17 00			17 38		17 47			18 00	18 16			18 29		18 38	18 47				19 00	19 16			19 38
Banbury	d	17a18			17a54		18 06			18a18	18 36			18 48		18a54	19 06				19a18	19 35			19a54
London Marylebone 10 ⊖	a						19 22				20 00			20 16			20 21					21 00			
Spring Road	d							17 29										18 29							
Hall Green	d							17 32										18 32							
Yardley Wood	d							17 35										18 35							
Shirley	d							17 38										18 38							
Whitlocks End	d																								
Wythall	d							17 42										18 42							
Earlswood (West Midlands)	d																								
The Lakes	d							17x45										18x45							
Wood End	d																								
Danzey	d																								
Henley-in-Arden	d							17 53										18 53							
Wootton Wawen	d																								
Wilmcote	d							18 01										19 01							
Stratford-upon-Avon	a							18 08										19 08							

For general notes see front of timetable
For details of catering facilities see Directory of Train Operators

Due to Engineering Operations, services from Sunday 14 September on this Table had not been confirmed at time of going to press. These services will be issued in a special Supplement as soon as exact timings have been confirmed

Table 71

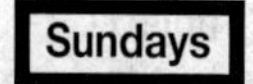

Sundays

20 July to 7 September

Hereford, Worcester and Stourbridge → Birmingham → Leamington Spa, Marylebone and Stratford-upon-Avon

Network Diagram - See first page of Table 71

		CH	LM	GW	XC	CH	XC	CH	LM	LM	GW	XC	XC	CH	LM	LM	LM	GW	XC	LM	LM
				1 ◇	bus		R 1				1 ◇	bus	1 ◇					1 ◇			
				catering			catering				catering		catering					trolley			
Hereford 7	d			18 30												20 05					22 40
Ledbury	a			18 46												20 20					22 56
	d			18 48												20 21					22 56
Colwall	d			18 55												20 27					23 03
Great Malvern	a			18 59												20 32					23 07
	d			19 08							20 08					20 32		21 05		22 02	23 08
Malvern Link	d			19 12							20 12					20 35		21 09		22 05	23 10
Worcester Foregate Street 7	a			19 21							20 21					20 44		21 21		22 16	23 19
	d		18 20	19 23							20 23					20 44		21 23		22 20	23 22
Worcester Shrub Hill 7	a			19 26							20 26					20 47		21 26		22 22	23 24
	d								19 31	19 56					20 33	20 50	21 17			22 26	
Droitwich Spa	d		18 29						19 39	20 04					20 41	20 58	21 25			22 34	
Bromsgrove	d									20 13						21 08			22 20		
Barnt Green	d																				
University	d																				
Hartlebury	d																				
Kidderminster	d		18 39						19 49						20 51		21 41			22 44	
Blakedown	d																				
Hagley	d		18 46						19 56						20 58		21 48			22 51	
Stourbridge Junction 2	d		18 52						20 01						21 02		21 52			22 55	
Lye	d																				
Cradley Heath	d		18 58						20 07						21 07		21 58			23 01	
Old Hill	d																				
Rowley Regis	d		19 03						20 12						21 13		22 03			23 06	
Langley Green	d																				
Smethwick Galton Bdg H.L. 7	d		19 08						20 17						21 18		22 08			23 11	
Birmingham New Street 12	a									20 40						21 45			22 45		
	d						20 03						21 03								
Birmingham International ✈	d				19 30							20 30									
Coventry	d				19 55							20 55									
The Hawthorns 🚋	d		19 11						20 20						21 20		22 11			23 14	
Jewellery Quarter 🚋	d		19 14						20 23						21 24		22 14			23 17	
Birmingham Snow Hill 🚋	a		19 18						20 26						21 27		22 18			23 21	
	d	19 15	19 20					20 15	20 27					21 15	21 27		22 18				
Birmingham Moor Street	d	19 18	19a22					20 18	20a30					21 18	21a30		22a21				
Bordesley	d																				
Small Heath	d																				
Tyseley	d																				
Acocks Green	d																				
Olton	d																				
Solihull	d	19 27						20 27						21 27							
Widney Manor	d	19 30						20 30						21 30							
Dorridge	d	19 34						20 34						21 34							
Lapworth	d																				
Hatton	d					20 17															
Warwick Parkway	d	19 45						20 45						21 45							
Warwick	d	19 48				20 24		20 48						21 48							
Leamington Spa 8	a	19 53			20 25	20 28	20 36	20 53				21 25	21 36	21 53							
	d	19 53				20 29	20 38	20 53					21 38	21 53							
Banbury	d	20 13				20 48	20a54	21 13					21a54	22 15							
London Marylebone 10 ⊖	a	21 50				22 16		22 50						23 53							
Spring Road	d																				
Hall Green	d																				
Yardley Wood	d																				
Shirley	d																				
Whitlocks End	d																				
Wythall	d																				
Earlswood (West Midlands)	d																				
The Lakes	d																				
Wood End	d																				
Danzey	d																				
Henley-in-Arden	d																				
Wootton Wawen	d																				
Wilmcote	d																				
Stratford-upon-Avon	a																				

For general notes see front of timetable
For details of catering facilities see Directory of Train Operators

Due to Engineering Operations, services from Sunday 14 September on this Table had not been confirmed at time of going to press. These services will be issued in a special Supplement as soon as exact timings have been confirmed

Stratford -upon-Avon, Marylebone and Leamington Spa → Birmingham → Stourbridge, Worcester and Hereford

Network Diagram - See first page of Table 71

Miles	Miles	Miles	Station		CH	LM	LM	GW	LM	LM	LM	GW	LM	LM	LM	GW	LM	LM	LM	CH	XC	LM	LM	LM	CH
					MX			[1]				A				[1] ◇ catering					[1] ◇ B catering				C
—	0	—	**Stratford-upon-Avon**	d														06 31					06 54		
—	2¾	—	Wilmcote	d														06 36					06 59		
—	6½	—	Wootton Wawen	d														06x41					07x04		
—	8¾	—	Henley-in-Arden	d														06 45					07 09		
—	11¼	—	Danzey	d														06x49					07x13		
—	13	—	Wood End	d														06x53					07x17		
—	14¼	—	The Lakes	d														06x55					07x19		
—	15	—	Earlswood (West Midlands)	d														06 57					07 22		
—	16	—	Wythall	d														07 00					07 24		
—	17	—	Whitlocks End	d														07 02					07 27		
—	18	—	Shirley	d									06 35		06 52			07 05					07 30		
—	19¼	—	Yardley Wood	d									06 38		06 55			07 08					07 33		
—	20½	—	Hall Green	d									06 41		06 58			07 11					07 36		
—	21	—	Spring Road	d									06 43		07 00			07 13					07 38		
—	—	—	**London Marylebone [10]** ⊖	d	22p10																				
—	—	—	Banbury	d	23p29																06 53				07 02
—	—	—	**Leamington Spa [8]**	a	23p48																07 10				07 22
—	—	0		d	23p48					05 48							06 30			06 55	07 11			07 07	07 22
—	—	2	Warwick	d	23p53					05 52							06 34			06 58				07 11	07 26
—	—	3¼	Warwick Parkway	d	23p56					05 55							06 37			07 01				07 15	07 30
—	—	6	Hatton	d						06 00							06 42			07a07				07 20	07 34
—	—	10½	Lapworth	d						06 06							06 48							07 27	
—	—	12¾	Dorridge	d	00 07				05 53	06 11							06 53		07 12					07 33	07 43
—	—	14¾	Widney Manor	d					05 57	06 15							06 57		07 16					07 37	07 47
—	—	16¼	Solihull	d	00 13				06 01	06 18							07 00		07 20					07 41	07 51
—	—	18	Olton	d					06 04	06 22							07 04		07 23					07 44	07 55
—	—	19	Acocks Green	d					06 07	06 24							07 06		07 26					07 47	
—	22	20	Tyseley	d					06 10	06 27			06 46		07 03		07 10	07 17	07 29				07 42	07 50	
—	23	21	Small Heath	d					06 12	06 30			06 47		07 05		07 13	07 19	07 32				07 44	07 53	
—	24	—	Bordesley	d																					
—	24¾	—	**Birmingham Moor Street**	d	00 24				06 16	06 35			06 51		07 09		07 19	07 23	07 36				07 48	07 57	08 04
—	25¼	—	**Birmingham Snow Hill** ⇌	a	00 31				06 19	06 37			06 54		07 12		07 21	07 27	07 38				07 52	07 59	08 11
—	—	—		d					06 20				06 55		07 15		07 23		07 39				07 53	08 03	
—	26	—	Jewellery Quarter ⇌	d					06 22				06 58		07 17		07 25		07 42				07 55	08 05	
—	28½	—	The Hawthorns ⇌	d					06 27				07 02		07 22		07 30		07 46				08 00	08 10	
—	—	—	**Coventry**	a																	07 22				
—	—	—	**Birmingham International** ✈	a																	07 33				
—	—	24	**Birmingham New Street [12]**	a																	07 45				
0	—	—		d							06 59			07 20								07 59			
—	29¼	29	Smethwick Galton Bdg H.L. [7]	d					06 29				07 05		07 24		07 32		07 49				08 02	08 12	
—	30½	30¼	Langley Green	d					06 32				07 08				07 35		07 52					08 15	
—	32¼	—	Rowley Regis	d					06 36				07 11		07 29		07 39		07 56				08 07	08 19	
—	33½	—	Old Hill	d					06 39				07 14				07 42		07 59					08 22	
—	34¾	—	Cradley Heath	d					06 42				07 17		07 33		07 45		08 02				08 12	08 25	
—	36¼	—	Lye	d					06 45				07 20				07 48		08 05					08 28	
—	37¼	—	**Stourbridge Junction [2]**	d					06 49				07 24		07a39		07 52		08a09				08 17	08 32	
—	39¼	—	Hagley	d					06 52				07 28				07 55						08 21	08 36	
—	41	—	Blakedown	d					06 55				07 31				07 58						08 24	08 39	
—	44¼	—	**Kidderminster**	d			06 00		07 00				07 36				08 03						08 29	08a45	
—	47¾	—	Hartlebury	d									07 41				08 08								
2½	—	—	University	d							07 05			07 26								08 05			
10½	—	—	Barnt Green	d										07 42											
13	—	—	Bromsgrove	d							07 23			07 47								08 21			
19¼	53½	—	Droitwich Spa	d			06 10		07 12		07 33		07 49	07 57			08 17					08 31	08 40		
25	—	—	**Worcester Shrub Hill [7]**	a										08 05											
—	—	—		d		06 00		06 34				07 55		08 08		08 17									
25¾	58¾	—	**Worcester Foregate Street [7]**	a		06 02	06 21	06 38	07 20		07 41	07 57	07 58	08 11		08 20	08 25					08 39	08 53		
—	—	—		d		06 03					07 42	07 58		08 11			08 26					08 40			
32½	—	—	Malvern Link	d		06 12					07 52	08 09		08 20			08 36					08 50			
33¾	—	—	**Great Malvern**	a		06 15					07 54	08 13		08 23			08 39					08 52			
—	—	—		d		06 15					07 59											08 53			
36½	—	—	Colwall	d		06 20					08 05											08 58			
40¾	—	—	Ledbury	a		06 27					08 12											09 06			
—	—	—		d		06 28					08 12											09 08			
54½	—	—	**Hereford [7]**	a		06 50					08 33											09 28			

For general notes see front of timetable
For details of catering facilities see Directory of Train Operators

A From Gloucester (Table 57)
B From Southampton Central (Table 51)
C From High Wycombe (Table 115)

Stratford -upon-Avon, Marylebone and Leamington Spa → Birmingham → Stourbridge, Worcester and Hereford

Network Diagram - See first page of Table 71

		XC 1 ◇ A ⊡	LM	LM	LM	GW 1	LM	XC 1 ◇ B ⊡	LM	LM	LM	LM	LM	CH	XC 1 ◇ C ⊡	LM	LM	LM	CH	CH	XC 1 ◇ D ⊡	LM	GW E	GW 1 ◇ ⊡	LM
Stratford-upon-Avon	d		07 23							07 45							08 27								
Wilmcote	d									07 50							08 32								
Wootton Wawen	d									07x55							08x37								
Henley-in-Arden	d		07 34							07 59							08 41								
Danzey	d									08x04							08x45								
Wood End	d									08x08							08x49								
The Lakes	d									08x10							08x51								
Earlswood (West Midlands)	d		07 43							08 13							08 54								
Wythall	d		07 45							08 15							08 56								
Whitlocks End	d		07 48							08 18							08 59								
Shirley	d		07 52		08 09					08 21			08 38				09 02					09 22			
Yardley Wood	d		07 55		08 12					08 24			08 41				09 05					09 25			
Hall Green	d		07 58		08 15					08 27			08 44				09 08					09 28			
Spring Road	d		08 00		08 17					08 29			08 46				09 10					09 30			
London Marylebone 10 ⊖	d													06 50					07 20						
Banbury	d	07 25						07 53						08 05	08 25				08 35		08 53				
Leamington Spa 8	a	07 41						08 10						08 23	08 41				08 53		09 10				
	d	07 43					07 47	08 11				08 03		08 24	08 43				08 53	09 04	09 11				
Warwick	d						07 51					08 07		08 28					08 57	09 07					
Warwick Parkway	d						07 55					08 11		08 32					09 01	09 10					
Hatton	d						08 00					08 16							09 07	09a16					
Lapworth	d						08 06					08 22							09 12						
Dorridge	d			07 58			08 11				08 20	08 29		08 43		08 46		09 09	09 16						
Widney Manor	d			08 01			08 14				08 24	08 32				08 50		09 13							
Solihull	d			08 05			08 18				08 28	08 36		08 48		08 53		09 16	09 21						
Olton	d			08 08			08 21				08 31	08 39				08 57		09 20							
Acocks Green	d			08 11			08 24				08 34	08 42				08 59		09 22							
Tyseley	d			08 14	08 20		08 28			08 32	08 37		08 49			09 02						09 33			
Small Heath	d				08 23		08 31			08 34	08 40		08 51			09 05						09 35			
Bordesley	d																								
Birmingham Moor Street	d		08 07	08 19	08 27		08 35			08 38	08 44	08 48	08 55	09 00		09 09	09 17	09 29	09 33			09 39			
Birmingham Snow Hill 🚋	a		08 11	08 21	08 29		08 37			08 42	08 46	08 51	08 58	09 07		09 11	09 20	09 31	09 41			09 42			
	d		08 13	08 23	08 33					08 43	08 53		09 03			09 13	09 23	09 33				09 43			
Jewellery Quarter 🚋	d		08 15	08 25	08 35					08 45	08 55		09 05			09 15	09 25	09 35				09 45			
The Hawthorns 🚋	d		08 20	08 30	08 40					08 50	09 00		09 10			09 20	09 30	09 40				09 50			
Coventry	a							08 22													09 22				
Birmingham International ✈	a							08 33													09 33				
Birmingham New Street 12	a	08 18						08 48							09 18						09 45				
	d								08 59																09 59
Smethwick Galton Bdg H.L. 7	d		08 22	08 32	08 42					08 52	09 02		09 12			09 22	09 32	09 42				09 52			
Langley Green	d				08 45								09 15					09 45							
Rowley Regis	d		08 27	08 37	08 49					08 57	09 07		09 19			09 27	09 37	09 49				09 57			
Old Hill	d				08 52								09 22					09 52							
Cradley Heath	d		08 32	08 42	08 55					09 02	09 12		09 25			09 32	09 42	09 55				10 02			
Lye	d				08 58								09 28					09 58							
Stourbridge Junction 2	d		08a38	08a49	09 02					09a08	09 17		09 32			09 39	09a48	10 02				10a08			
Hagley	d				09 06						09 21							10 06							
Blakedown	d				09 09						09 24							10 09							
Kidderminster	d				09a15						09 29		09a42			09 48		10a15							
Hartlebury	d															09 53									
University	d								09 05																10 05
Barnt Green	d																								
Bromsgrove	d								09 21																10 21
Droitwich Spa	d								09 31		09 40					10 01									10 31
Worcester Shrub Hill 7	a															10 10									
	d					09 22																	10 14	10 23	
Worcester Foregate Street 7	a					09 26			09 39		09 54												10 16	10 26	10 39
	d								09 40														10 17	10 27	10 40
Malvern Link	d								09 50														10 26	10 36	10 50
Great Malvern	a								09 52														10 30	10 43	10 52
	d								09 53																10 53
Colwall	d								09 58																10 58
Ledbury	a								10 06																11 06
	d								10 08																11 08
Hereford 7	a								10 28																11 28

For general notes see front of timetable
For details of catering facilities see Directory of Train Operators

A From Gatwick Airport (Table 51). ⊡ from Reading
B From Southampton Central (Table 51)
C From Gatwick Airport (Table 51)
D From Bournemouth (Table 51)
E From Warminster (Table 123)

Stratford -upon-Avon, Marylebone and Leamington Spa → Birmingham → Stourbridge, Worcester and Hereford

Network Diagram - See first page of Table 71

		LM	CH	XC	LM	LM	LM	LM	CH	XC	LM	GW	LM	LM	CH	CH	XC	LM	LM	LM	LM	CH	XC	GW
				1 ◇						1 ◇		1 ◇					1 ◇						R 1	◇
										A													A	B
				☕						☕		☕					☕						☕	
Stratford-upon-Avon	d						09 27													10 27				
Wilmcote	d						09 32													10 32				
Wootton Wawen	d						09x37													10x37				
Henley-in-Arden	d						09 41													10 41				
Danzey	d						09x45													10x45				
Wood End	d						09x49													10x49				
The Lakes	d						09x51													10x51				
Earlswood (West Midlands)	d						09 54													10 54				
Wythall	d						09 56													10 56				
Whitlocks End	d						09 59													10 59				
Shirley	d				09 42		10 02				10 22							10 42		11 02				
Yardley Wood	d				09 45		10 05				10 25							10 45		11 05				
Hall Green	d				09 48		10 08				10 28							10 48		11 08				
Spring Road	d				09 50		10 10				10 30							10 50		11 10				
London Marylebone 10 ⊖	d		07 50						08 20						08 50	08 54						09 20		
Banbury	d		08 56	09 25					09 35	09 53					09 56	10 14	10 25					10 35	10 53	
Leamington Spa 8	a		09 14	09 41					09 53	10 10					10 14	10 33	10 41					10 54	11 10	
	d		09 14	09 43					09 54	10 11					10 14	10 34	10 43					10 54	11 11	
Warwick	d		09 19						09 58						10 19	10 38						10 59		
Warwick Parkway	d		09 22						10 02						10 22							11 02		
Hatton	d								10 07							10a45								
Lapworth	d								10 12															
Dorridge	d	09 28	09 33			09 46		10 09	10 17					10 28	10 33				10 46		11 09	11 13		
Widney Manor	d	09 32				09 50		10 13						10 32					10 50		11 13			
Solihull	d	09 35	09 39			09 53		10 16	10 23					10 35	10 39				10 53		11 16	11 19		
Olton	d	09 39				09 57		10 20						10 39					10 57		11 20			
Acocks Green	d	09 41				09 59		10 22						10 41					10 59		11 22			
Tyseley	d					10 02					10 33								11 02					
Small Heath	d					10 05					10 35								11 05					
Bordesley	d																							
Birmingham Moor Street	d	09 48	09 51		09 58	10 09	10 17	10 29	10 34		10 39			10 48	10 51			10 57	11 09	11 17	11 29	11 31		
Birmingham Snow Hill 🚊	a	09 50	10 01		10 01	10 11	10 20	10 31	10 41		10 42			10 50	11 01			11 01	11 11	11 20	11 31	11 41		
	d	09 53			10 03	10 13	10 23	10 33			10 43			10 53				11 03	11 13	11 23	11 33			
Jewellery Quarter 🚊	d	09 55			10 05	10 15	10 25	10 35			10 45			10 55				11 05	11 15	11 25	11 35			
The Hawthorns 🚊	d	10 00			10 10	10 20	10 30	10 40			10 50			11 00				11 10	11 20	11 30	11 40			
Coventry	a									10 22													11 22	
Birmingham International ✈	a									10 33													11 33	
Birmingham New Street 12	a			10 18						10 45							11 18						11 45	
	d												10 59											
Smethwick Galton Bdg H.L. 7	d	10 02			10 12	10 22	10 32	10 42			10 52			11 02				11 12	11 22	11 32	11 42			
Langley Green	d				10 15			10 45										11 15			11 45			
Rowley Regis	d	10 07			10 19	10 27	10 37	10 49			10 57			11 07				11 19	11 27	11 37	11 49			
Old Hill	d				10 22			10 52										11 22			11 52			
Cradley Heath	d	10 12			10 25	10 32	10 42	10 55			11 02			11 12				11 25	11 32	11 42	11 55			
Lye	d				10 28			10 58										11 28			11 58			
Stourbridge Junction 2	d	10 17			10 32	10 37	10a48	11 02			11a08			11 17				11 32	11 37	11a48	12 02			
Hagley	d	10 21						11 06						11 21							12 06			
Blakedown	d	10 24						11 09						11 24							12 09			
Kidderminster	d	10 29			10a42	10 48		11a15						11 29				11a42	11 48		12a15			
Hartlebury	d																							
University	d												11 05											
Barnt Green	d																							
Bromsgrove	d												11 21											
Droitwich Spa	d	10 40				11 00							11 31	11 40					12 00					
Worcester Shrub Hill 7	a	10 48																	12 09					
	d	10 52										11 12												12 15
Worcester Foregate Street 7	a	10 54				11 08						11 16	11 39	11 49										12 17
	d	10 55										11 16	11 40											12 18
Malvern Link	d	11 03										11 26	11 50											12 27
Great Malvern	a	11 06										11 30	11 55											12 30
	d											11 30												
Colwall	d											11 35												
Ledbury	a											11 43												
	d											11 45												
Hereford 7	a											12 03												

For general notes see front of timetable
For details of catering facilities see Directory of Train Operators

A From Bournemouth (Table 51)
B From Westbury (Table 123)

Stratford -upon-Avon, Marylebone and Leamington Spa → Birmingham → Stourbridge, Worcester and Hereford

Network Diagram - See first page of Table 71

		GW	LM	LM	CH	XC	LM	LM	LM	LM	CH	XC	LM	LM	LM	CH	CH	XC	LM	GW	LM	LM	LM	CH	XC
		1 ◇				1 ◇						R 1						1 ◇		1 ◇					R 1
												A						B							A
		🍽				🍽						🍽						🍽		🍽					🍽
Stratford-upon-Avon	d								11 27													12 27			
Wilmcote	d								11 32													12 32			
Wootton Wawen	d								11x37													12x37			
Henley-in-Arden	d								11 41													12 41			
Danzey	d								11x45													12x45			
Wood End	d								11x49													12x49			
The Lakes	d								11x51													12x51			
Earlswood (West Midlands)	d								11 54													12 54			
Wythall	d								11 56													12 56			
Whitlocks End	d								11 59													12 59			
Shirley	d						11 42		12 02				12 22						12 42			13 02			
Yardley Wood	d						11 45		12 05				12 25						12 45			13 05			
Hall Green	d						11 48		12 08				12 28						12 48			13 08			
Spring Road	d						11 50		12 10				12 30						12 50			13 10			
London Marylebone 10 ⊖	d				09 50						10 20					10 50	10 54							11 20	
Banbury	d				10 56	11 25					11 35	11 53				11 56	12 17	12 25						12 35	12 53
Leamington Spa 8	a				11 14	11 41					11 54	12 10				12 14	12 37	12 41						12 54	13 10
	d				11 14	11 43					11 54	12 11				12 15	12 38	12 43						12 54	13 11
Warwick	d				11 19						11 59					12 19	12 42							12 59	
Warwick Parkway	d				11 22						12 02					12 23								13 02	
Hatton	d										12 07						12a49								
Lapworth	d										12 13														
Dorridge	d			11 28	11 33			11 46		12 09	12 17				12 28	12 34					12 46		13 09	13 13	
Widney Manor	d			11 32				11 50		12 13					12 32						12 50		13 13		
Solihull	d			11 35	11 39			11 53		12 16	12 23				12 35	12 39					12 53		13 16	13 21	
Olton	d			11 39				11 57		12 20					12 39						12 57		13 20		
Acocks Green	d			11 41				11 59		12 22					12 41						12 59		13 22		
Tyseley	d							12 02					12 33								13 02				
Small Heath	d							12 05					12 35								13 05				
Bordesley	d																								
Birmingham Moor Street	d			11 48	11 51		11 58	12 10	12 17	12 29	12 35		12 39		12 48	12 51			12 58		13 09	13 17	13 29	13 32	
Birmingham Snow Hill 🚋	a			11 50	12 01		12 00	12 12	12 20	12 31	12 42		12 42		12 51	13 02			13 01		13 11	13 20	13 31	13 41	
	d			11 53			12 03	12 13	12 23	12 33			12 43		12 53				13 03		13 13	13 23	13 33		
Jewellery Quarter 🚋	d			11 55			12 05	12 15	12 25	12 35			12 45		12 55				13 05		13 15	13 25	13 35		
The Hawthorns 🚋	d			12 00			12 10	12 20	12 30	12 40			12 50		13 00				13 10		13 20	13 30	13 40		
Coventry	a											12 22													13 21
Birmingham International ✈	a											12 33													13 33
Birmingham New Street 12	a					12 18						12 45						13 18							13 45
	d		11 59											12 59											
Smethwick Galton Bdg H.L. 7	d			12 02			12 12	12 22	12 32	12 42			12 52		13 02				13 12		13 22	13 32	13 42		
Langley Green	d						12 15			12 45									13 15				13 45		
Rowley Regis	d			12 07			12 19	12 27	12 37	12 49			12 57		13 07				13 19		13 27	13 37	13 49		
Old Hill	d						12 22			12 52									13 22				13 52		
Cradley Heath	d			12 12			12 25	12 32	12 42	12 55			13 02		13 12				13 25		13 32	13 42	13 55		
Lye	d						12 28			12 58									13 28				13 58		
Stourbridge Junction 2	d			12 17			12 32	12 37	12a48	13 02			13a08		13 17				13a32		13 40	13a50	14 02		
Hagley	d			12 21						13 06					13 21										
Blakedown	d			12 24						13 09					13 24										
Kidderminster	d			12 29			12a42	12 48		13a15					13 29						13 48		14a12		
Hartlebury	d																								
University	d		12 05											13 05											
Barnt Green	d																								
Bromsgrove	d		12 21											13 21											
Droitwich Spa	d		12 31	12 40				13 00						13 31	13 40						14 00				
Worcester Shrub Hill 7	a			12 48																	14 18				
	d	12 21		12 52																14 13					
Worcester Foregate Street 7	a	12 26	12 39	12 54				13 08						13 39	13 49					14 15					
	d		12 40	12 55										13 40						14 17					
Malvern Link	d		12 50	13 03										13 50						14 25					
Great Malvern	a		12 52	13 06										13 52						14 28					
	d		12 53											13 53						14 29					
Colwall	d		12 58											13 58						14 35					
Ledbury	a		13 06											14 06						14 42					
	d		13 08											14 08						14 44					
Hereford 7	a		13 28											14 28						15 03					

For general notes see front of timetable
For details of catering facilities see Directory of Train Operators

A From Bournemouth (Table 51)
B From Brighton (Table 51)

Stratford -upon-Avon, Marylebone and Leamington Spa → Birmingham → Stourbridge, Worcester and Hereford

Network Diagram - See first page of Table 71

		LM	GW	LM	LM	CH	XC	LM	LM	LM	LM	CH	XC	LM	LM	LM	CH	CH	XC	LM	LM	LM	LM		CH
			◇				1 ◇						R 1						1 ◇						
			A										B												
							☕						☕						☕						
Stratford-upon-Avon	d									13 27												14 27			
Wilmcote	d									13 32												14 32			
Wootton Wawen	d									13x37												14x37			
Henley-in-Arden	d									13 41												14 41			
Danzey	d									13x45												14x45			
Wood End	d									13x49												14x49			
The Lakes	d									13x51												14x51			
Earlswood (West Midlands)	d									13 54												14 54			
Wythall	d									13 56												14 56			
Whitlocks End	d									13 59												14 59			
Shirley	d	13 22						13 42		14 02				14 22						14 42		15 02			
Yardley Wood	d	13 25						13 45		14 05				14 25						14 45		15 05			
Hall Green	d	13 28						13 48		14 08				14 28						14 48		15 08			
Spring Road	d	13 30						13 50		14 10				14 30						14 50		15 10			
London Marylebone 10 ⊖	d					11 50						12 20					12 50	12 54							13 20
Banbury	d					12 56	13 25					13 35	13 53				13 56	14 17	14 25						14 35
Leamington Spa 8	a					13 14	13 41					13 54	14 10				14 14	14 37	14 41						14 54
	d					13 14	13 43					13 54	14 11				14 15	14 38	14 43						14 54
Warwick	d					13 19						13 59					14 19	14 42							14 59
Warwick Parkway	d					13 22						14 02					14 23								15 02
Hatton	d											14 07						14a49							
Lapworth	d											14 13													
Dorridge	d				13 28	13 33			13 46		14 09	14 17				14 28	14 34				14 46		15 09		15 13
Widney Manor	d				13 32				13 50		14 13					14 32					14 50		15 13		
Solihull	d				13 35	13 39			13 53		14 16	14 23				14 35	14 39				14 53		15 16		15 21
Olton	d				13 39				13 57		14 20					14 39					14 57		15 20		
Acocks Green	d				13 41				13 59		14 22					14 41					14 59		15 22		
Tyseley	d	13 33							14 02					14 33							15 02				
Small Heath	d	13 35							14 05					14 35							15 05				
Bordesley	d																								
Birmingham Moor Street	d	13 39			13 48	13 51		13 59	14 09	14 17	14 29	14 35		14 39		14 48	14 51			14 58	15 09	15 17	15 29		15 33
Birmingham Snow Hill 🚋	a	13 42			13 51	14 01		14 01	14 11	14 21	14 31	14 42		14 42		14 51	15 02			15 01	15 11	15 21	15 31		15 41
	d	13 43			13 53			14 03	14 13	14 23	14 33			14 43		14 53				15 03	15 13	15 23	15 33		
Jewellery Quarter 🚋	d	13 45			13 55			14 05	14 15	14 25	14 35			14 45		14 55				15 05	15 15	15 25	15 35		
The Hawthorns 🚋	d	13 50			14 00			14 10	14 20	14 30	14 40			14 50		15 00				15 10	15 20	15 30	15 40		
Coventry	a												14 22												
Birmingham International ✈	a												14 33												
Birmingham New Street 12	a						14 18						14 45						15 18						
	d			13 59											14 59										
Smethwick Galton Bdg H.L. 7	d	13 52			14 02			14 12	14 22	14 32	14 42			14 52		15 02				15 12	15 22	15 32	15 42		
Langley Green	d							14 15			14 45									15 15			15 45		
Rowley Regis	d	13 57			14 07			14 19	14 27	14 37	14 49			14 57		15 07				15 19	15 27	15 37	15 49		
Old Hill	d							14 22			14 52									15 22			15 52		
Cradley Heath	d	14 02			14 12			14 25	14 32	14 42	14 55			15 02		15 12				15 25	15 32	15 42	15 55		
Lye	d							14 28			14 58									15 28			15 58		
Stourbridge Junction 2	d	14a08			14 17			14 32	14 39	14a49	15 02			15a08		15 17				15 32	15 37	15a48	16 02		
Hagley	d				14 21						15 06					15 21					15 41				
Blakedown	d				14 24						15 09					15 24					15 44				
Kidderminster	d				14 29			14a42	14 48		15a15					15 29				15a42	15 49		16a12		
Hartlebury	d																								
University	d			14 05											15 05										
Barnt Green	d																								
Bromsgrove	d			14 21											15 21										
Droitwich Spa	d			14 31	14 40				15 00						15 31	15 41					16 00				
Worcester Shrub Hill 7	a				14 48																16 08				
	d		14 21																						
Worcester Foregate Street 7	a		14 24	14 39					15 08						15 39	15 51									
	d		14 24	14 40											15 45										
Malvern Link	d			14 50											15 55										
Great Malvern	a		14 38	14 55											15 57										
	d														16 05										
Colwall	d														16 10										
Ledbury	a														16 17										
	d														16 18										
Hereford 7	a														16 38										

For general notes see front of timetable
For details of catering facilities see Directory of Train Operators

A From Brighton (Table 123)
B From Bournemouth (Table 51)

Stratford -upon-Avon, Marylebone and Leamington Spa → Birmingham → Stourbridge, Worcester and Hereford

Network Diagram - See first page of Table 71

		XC	LM	GW	LM	GW	LM	CH	XC	LM	LM	LM	XC	LM	LM	CH	XC	LM	LM	LM	LM	CH	CH	XC	LM
		R 1 A		1 ◇		B			R 1				◇ C				R 1 A							R 1 D	
Stratford-upon-Avon	d													15 27											
Wilmcote	d													15 32											
Wootton Wawen	d													15x37											
Henley-in-Arden	d													15 41											
Danzey	d													15x45											
Wood End	d													15x49											
The Lakes	d													15x51											
Earlswood (West Midlands)	d													15 54											
Wythall	d													15 56											
Whitlocks End	d													15 59											
Shirley	d		15 22							15 42				16 02						16 22					16 42
Yardley Wood	d		15 25							15 45				16 05						16 25					16 45
Hall Green	d		15 28							15 48				16 08						16 28					16 48
Spring Road	d		15 30							15 50				16 10						16 30					16 50
London Marylebone 10 ⊖	d							13 50								14 20						14 50	14 54		
Banbury	d	14 53						14 56	15 25							15 35	15 53					15 56	16 17	16 25	
Leamington Spa 8	a	15 10						15 14	15 41							15 54	16 10					16 14	16 37	16 41	
	d	15 11						15 15	15 43							15 54	16 11					16 14	16 38	16 43	
Warwick	d							15 19								15 59						16 19	16 42		
Warwick Parkway	d							15 23								16 02						16 22			
Hatton	d															16 07							16a49		
Lapworth	d															16 13									
Dorridge	d						15 28	15 34				15 46			16 09	16 17					16 27	16 33			
Widney Manor	d						15 32					15 50			16 13						16 31				
Solihull	d						15 35	15 39				15 53			16 16	16 23					16 34	16 39			
Olton	d						15 39					15 57			16 20						16 38				
Acocks Green	d						15 41					15 59			16 22						16 40				
Tyseley	d		15 33									16 02								16 33	16 43				16 53
Small Heath	d		15 35									16 05								16 35					
Bordesley	d																								
Birmingham Moor Street	d		15 39				15 48	15 51		15 58		16 09		16 17	16 29	16 35				16 39	16 48	16 51			16 58
Birmingham Snow Hill	a		15 42				15 51	16 01		16 01		16 11		16 21	16 31	16 42				16 42	16 51	17 01			17 01
	d		15 43				15 53			16 03		16 13		16 23	16 33					16 43	16 53				17 03
Jewellery Quarter	d		15 45				15 55			16 05		16 15		16 25	16 35					16 45	16 55				17 05
The Hawthorns	d		15 50				16 00			16 10		16 20		16 30	16 40					16 50	17 00				17 10
Coventry	a	15 22															16 22								
Birmingham International ✈	a	15 33															16 33								
Birmingham New Street 12	a	15 45							16 18								16 45							17 18	
	d				15 59						16 19		16 30						16 59						
Smethwick Galton Bdg H.L. 7	d		15 52				16 02			16 12		16 22		16 32	16 43					16 52	17 02				17 13
Langley Green	d									16 15					16 46										17 16
Rowley Regis	d		15 57				16 07			16 19		16 28		16 38	16 49					16 58	17 07				17 19
Old Hill	d									16 22					16 52										17 22
Cradley Heath	d		16 02				16 12			16 25		16 33		16 43	16 56					17 03	17 12				17 26
Lye	d									16 28					16 59										17 29
Stourbridge Junction 2	d		16a08				16 17			16 32		16 39		16a49	17 02					17 10	17a18				17 33
Hagley	d						16 21								17 06					17 14					17 37
Blakedown	d						16 24								17 09					17 17					17 40
Kidderminster	d						16 29			16a42		16 48			17a15					17 22					17a45
Hartlebury	d																			17 27					
University	d				16 05						16 25		16 36						17 05						
Barnt Green	d																								
Bromsgrove	d				16 21								16a50						17 21						
Droitwich Spa	d				16 31		16 40				16 49	17 00							17 31	17 38					
Worcester Shrub Hill 7	a										17 00							⟵	17 38						
	d			16 14		16 40					17 08							17 08	17 42						
Worcester Foregate Street 7	a			16 18	16 39	16 42	16 49				⟶	17 09						17 10	17 44	17 47					
	d			16 18	16 40													17 12	17 46						
Malvern Link	d			16 27	16 50													17 21	17 56						
Great Malvern	a			16 34	16 52													17 24	17 58						
	d				16 53														18 08						
Colwall	d				16 58														18 13						
Ledbury	a				17 06														18 20						
	d				17 08														18 21						
Hereford 7	a				17 28														18 41						

For general notes see front of timetable
For details of catering facilities see Directory of Train Operators

A From Bournemouth (Table 51)
B From Westbury (Table 123)
C From Nottingham to Cardiff Central (Table 57)
D To Derby (Table 57)

Stratford -upon-Avon, Marylebone and Leamington Spa → Birmingham → Stourbridge, Worcester and Hereford

Network Diagram - See first page of Table 71

		LM	LM	XC ◇ A 🛒	LM	GW B	CH	XC [R] [1] C ⊡	LM	LM	LM	LM	LM	CH 🛒	XC [R] [1] D ⊡	LM	LM	LM	CH 🛒	CH	GW [1]	LM	XC ◇ E	XC [R] [1] C ⊡	XC [R] [1] ⊡
Stratford-upon-Avon	d				16 27												17 27								
Wilmcote	d				16 32												17 32								
Wootton Wawen	d				16x37												17x37								
Henley-in-Arden	d				16 41												17 41								
Danzey	d				16x45												17x45								
Wood End	d				16x49												17x49								
The Lakes	d				16x51												17x51								
Earlswood (West Midlands)	d				16 54												17 54								
Wythall	d				16 56												17 56								
Whitlocks End	d				16 59												17 59								
Shirley	d				17 02							17 22				17 45	18 02								
Yardley Wood	d				17 05							17 25				17 48	18 05								
Hall Green	d				17 08							17 28				17 51	18 08								
Spring Road	d				17 10							17 30				17 53	18 10								
London Marylebone [10] ⊖	d						15 20							16 00					16 30	16 34					
Banbury	d						16 35	16 53						17 03	17 25				17 34	17 49				17 53	18 25
Leamington Spa [8]	a						16 53	17 10						17 22	17 41				17 52	18 06				18 10	18 41
	d						16 54	17 11						17 22	17 43				17 52	18 07				18 11	18 43
Warwick	d						16 58												17 57						
Warwick Parkway	d						17 02							17 28					18 00	18 13					
Hatton	d																			18a19					
Lapworth	d																		18 09						
Dorridge	d		16 46				17 13			17 09			17 27	17 39				18 02	18 13						
Widney Manor	d		16 50							17 13			17 31					18 06							
Solihull	d		16 53				17 21			17 16			17 34	17 44				18 09	18 19						
Olton	d		16 57							17 20			17 38					18 13							
Acocks Green	d		16 59							17 22			17 40					18 15							
Tyseley	d		17 02									17 33	17 43					18 20							
Small Heath	d		17 05									17 35	17 46					18 22							
Bordesley	d																								
Birmingham Moor Street	d		17 09		17 17		17 33			17 29		17 39	17 50	17 59		18 00	18 17	18 26	18 30						
Birmingham Snow Hill ⇌	a		17 12		17 21		17 41			17 31		17 42	17 52	18 12		18 02	18 20	18 29	18 40						
	d		17 13		17 23					17 33		17 43	17 53			18 03	18 23								
Jewellery Quarter ⇌	d		17 15		17 25					17 35		17 45	17 55			18 05	18 25								
The Hawthorns ⇌	d		17 20		17 30					17 40		17 50	18 00			18 10	18 30								
Coventry	a							17 22																18 22	
Birmingham International ✈	a							17 33																18 33	
Birmingham New Street [12]	a							17 45							18 18									18 45	19 18
	d	17 19		17 30					17 50		17 59											18 19	18 30		
Smethwick Galton Bdg H.L. [7]	d		17 22		17 32					17 42		17 53	18 02			18 13	18 33								
Langley Green	d				17 35							17 56				18 16	18 36								
Rowley Regis	d		17 28		17 39					17 48		17 59	18 08			18 19	18 39								
Old Hill	d				17 42							18 02				18 22	18 42								
Cradley Heath	d		17 33		17 45					17 53		18 06	18 13			18 26	18 46								
Lye	d				17 48							18 09				18 29	18 49								
Stourbridge Junction [2]	d		17 42		17a53					18 03		18 13	18 23			18 33	18 54								
Hagley	d		17 46							18 07		18 17	18 27			18 37	18 58								
Blakedown	d		17 49							18 10		18 20	18 30			18 40	19 01								
Kidderminster	d		17 54							18 15		18a26	18 35			18a46	19a06								
Hartlebury	d									18 20			18 40												
University	d	17 25		17 36							18 05														
Barnt Green	d																								
Bromsgrove	d	17 45		17a51							18 22											18 47	18a50		
Droitwich Spa	d	17 54	18 06						18 19	18 28	18 35		18 49									18 56			
Worcester Shrub Hill [7]	a	18 05							18 29	18 38			18 57									19 11			
	d	18 08				18 26															19 11				
Worcester Foregate Street [7]	a	18 11	18 14			18 28					18 44										19 15				
	d	18 11				18 29					18 44														
Malvern Link	d	18 20				18 38					18 54														
Great Malvern	a	18 23				18 40					18 57														
	d	18 23									18 57														
Colwall	d	18 29									19 02														
Ledbury	a	18 36									19 10														
	d	18 36									19 13														
Hereford [7]	a	18 57									19 33														

For general notes see front of timetable
For details of catering facilities see Directory of Train Operators

A From Nottingham to Cardiff Central (Table 57). 🛒 to Newport (South Wales)
B From Warminster (Table 123)
C From Bournemouth (Table 51)
D From Brighton (Table 51)
E From Nottingham (Table 57)

Stratford -upon-Avon, Marylebone and Leamington Spa → Birmingham → Stourbridge, Worcester and Hereford

Network Diagram - See first page of Table 71

Station		LM	LM	LM	CH	GW	LM	LM	GW	LM	LM	CH	XC	CH	LM	GW	LM	CH	XC	LM	CH	XC	LM	GW
					A ⌶	[1] ◇ ⊏P			B				[R] [1] C ⊏P			[1] ◇ D ⊏P		A ⌶	[1] ◇ E ⊏P			[1] ◇ C ⊏P		[1] ◇ ⊏P
Stratford-upon-Avon	d	17 58						18 26			18 50									19 27				
Wilmcote	d							18 31			18 55									19 32				
Wootton Wawen	d							18x36			19x00									19x37				
Henley-in-Arden	d	18 08						18 40			19 04									19 41				
Danzey	d							18x44												19x45				
Wood End	d							18x48												19x49				
The Lakes	d							18x50												19x51				
Earlswood (West Midlands)	d							18 53												19 54				
Wythall	d							18 55												19 56				
Whitlocks End	d							18 58												19 59				
Shirley	d	18 22		18 37				19 02			19 16				19 30					20 02				
Yardley Wood	d	18 25		18 40				19 05			19 19				19 33					20 05				
Hall Green	d	18 28		18 43				19 08			19 22				19 36					20 08				
Spring Road	d	18 30		18 45				19 10			19 24				19 38					20 10				
London Marylebone [10] ⊖	d				17 00							17 30		17 41				18 00			18 30			
Banbury	d				18 03							18 39	18 53	18 58				19 03	19 25		19 36	19 53		
Leamington Spa [8]	a				18 23							18 58	19 10	19 15				19 22	19 41		19 54	20 10		
	d				18 23							18 58	19 11	19 16				19 22	19 43		19 54	20 11		
Warwick	d											19 03		19 20							19 59			
Warwick Parkway	d				18 29							19 06						19 28			20 02			
Hatton	d											19 11		19a27							20 07			
Lapworth	d											19 17									20 13			
Dorridge	d		18 23		18 40					18 58		19 21					19 31	19 39			20 17			
Widney Manor	d		18 27							19 02							19 35							
Solihull	d		18 30		18 45					19 06		19 27					19 38	19 44			20 23			
Olton	d		18 34							19 09							19 41							
Acocks Green	d		18 36							19 12							19 44							
Tyseley	d	18 33	18 39	18 48						19 16					19 41		19 47							
Small Heath	d	18 35	18 42							19 19					19 43		19 49							
Bordesley	d																							
Birmingham Moor Street	d	18 39	18 46	18 53	18 56			19 17		19 23	19 32	19 38			19 48		19 53	19 57		20 17	20 34			
Birmingham Snow Hill 🚋	a	18 42	18 48	18 55	19 01			19 19		19 25	19 35	19 47			19 50		19 56	20 01		20 20	20 44			
	d	18 43		18 57	19 10					19 27	19 36						19 57	20 10		20 21				
Jewellery Quarter 🚋	d	18 45		18 59						19 29	19 38						19 59			20 24				
The Hawthorns 🚋	d	18 50		19 04	19 16					19 34	19 43						20 04	20 16		20 28				
Coventry	a												19 22									20 22		
Birmingham International ✈	a												19 33									20 33		
Birmingham New Street [12]	a												19 45						20 18			20 48		
	d						19 19																20 59	
Smethwick Galton Bdg H.L. [7]	d	18 53		19 07	19 19					19 36	19 45						20 06	20 19		20 31				
Langley Green	d			19 10						19 39							20 09			20 34				
Rowley Regis	d	18 58		19 13	19 24					19 43	19 50						20 13	20 24		20 37				
Old Hill	d			19 16						19 46							20 16			20 40				
Cradley Heath	d	19 03		19 20	19 29					19 49	19 55						20 19	20 29		20 43				
Lye	d			19 23						19 52							20 22			20 46				
Stourbridge Junction [2]	d	19 08		19a27	19 36					19 56	20a01						20 26	20 36		20a51				
Hagley	d	19 12								19 59							20 29							
Blakedown	d	19 15								20 02							20 32							
Kidderminster	d	19 20			19a48					20 07							20 37	20a50						
Hartlebury	d																							
University	d						19 25																21 05	
Barnt Green	d																							
Bromsgrove	d						19 40																21 21	
Droitwich Spa	d	19 31					19 50			20 19							20 50						21 31	
Worcester Shrub Hill [7]	a						20 01			20 26							20 58						21 41	
	d					19 44	20 12		20 18							20 41							21 48	21 54
Worcester Foregate Street [7]	a	19 40				19 48	20 14		20 20							20 44							21 50	21 57
	d					19 48	20 15		20 25							20 44							21 51	21 58
Malvern Link	d					19 57	20 24		20 34							20 54							22 00	22 10
Great Malvern	a					20 01	20 26		20 37							20 58							22 02	22 13
	d					20 01	20 27									20 58							22 03	
Colwall	d					20 07	20 32									21 04							22 08	
Ledbury	a					20 15	20 39									21 12							22 15	
	d					20 16	20 40									21 13							22 16	
Hereford [7]	a					20 36	21 00									21 33							22 36	

For general notes see front of timetable
For details of catering facilities see Directory of Train Operators

A ⌶ to Birmingham Snow Hill
B From Warminster (Table 123)
C From Bournemouth (Table 51)
D **Cathedrals Express**
E From Guildford (Table 51)

Stratford -upon-Avon, Marylebone and Leamington Spa → Birmingham → Stourbridge, Worcester and Hereford

Network Diagram - See first page of Table 71

		LM	CH	GW	XC	LM	CH	CH	XC	LM	LM	CH	LM	CH	XC	LM	LM	LM	CH	LM	CH	CH	CH
																FO	FX						FO
				1 ◇	1 ◇				1 ◇						1 ◇								
			A						B						B	C							
			🛒	☕	☕				☕						☕								
Stratford-upon-Avon	d					20 27																	
Wilmcote	d					20 32																	
Wootton Wawen	d					20x37																	
Henley-in-Arden	d					20 41																	
Danzey	d					20x45																	
Wood End	d					20x49																	
The Lakes	d					20x51																	
Earlswood (West Midlands)	d					20 54																	
Wythall	d					20 56																	
Whitlocks End	d					20 59																	
Shirley	d					21 02							21 56							22 54			
Yardley Wood	d					21 05							21 59							22 57			
Hall Green	d					21 08							22 02							23 00			
Spring Road	d					21 10							22 04							23 02			
London Marylebone 10 ⊖	d		19 00				19 30	19 33				20 00		20 30					21 00		21 30	22 10	23 54
Banbury	d		20 03		20 25		20 38	20 49	20 53			21 06		21 47	21 53				22 08		22 47	23 29	01 17
Leamington Spa 8	a		20 23		20 41		20 55	21 06	21 10			21 25		22 04	22 10				22 27		23 05	23 48	01 39
	d		20 23		20 43		20 56	21 07	21 11			21 25		22 05	22 11				22 27		23 06	23 48	
Warwick	d						21 00	21 12						22 10							23 10	23 53	
Warwick Parkway	d		20 29				21 04					21 31		22 14					22 32		23 14	23 56	
Hatton	d						21 09	21a19						22 19									
Lapworth	d						21 14							22 24									
Dorridge	d	20 28	20 40				21 19				21 31	21 42		22 29				22 30	22 43		23 25	00 07	
Widney Manor	d	20 32									21 35			22 32				22 37					
Solihull	d	20 35	20 45				21 25				21 38	21 47		22 36				22 40	22 49		23 30	00 13	
Olton	d	20 39									21 42			22 40				22 43					
Acocks Green	d	20 41									21 44			22 43				22 46					
Tyseley	d	20 44									21 47		22 07					22 50		23 05			
Small Heath	d	20 47									21 50		22 09					22 52		23 07			
Bordesley	d																						
Birmingham Moor Street	d	20 51	20 57			21 17	21 37				21 54	21 59	22 13	22 51				22 56	23 00	23 12	23 42	00 24	
Birmingham Snow Hill 🚋	a	20 54	21 03			21 20	21 47				21 56	22 04	22 16	22 58				22 59	23 05	23 15	23 51	00 31	
	d	20 55	21 05			21 21					21 57	22 10	22 17					23 00	23 15				
Jewellery Quarter 🚋	d	20 57				21 23					22 00		22 19					23 03	23 17				
The Hawthorns 🚋	d	21 02	21 11			21 28					22 04	22 16	22 24					23 07	23 22				
Coventry	a								21 22						22 22								
Birmingham International ✈	a								21 33						22 33								
Birmingham New Street 12	a				21 18				21 45						22 52								
	d									21 59						23 04	23 04						
Smethwick Galton Bdg H.L. 7	d	21 05	21 14			21 30					22 07	22 19	22 27					23 10	23 25				
Langley Green	d	21 08				21 33					22 10		22 30					23 13	23 28				
Rowley Regis	d	21 11	21 20			21 36					22 13	22 24	22 33					23 16	23 31				
Old Hill	d	21 14				21 39					22 16		22 36					23 19	23 34				
Cradley Heath	d	21 17	21 25			21 42					22 19	22 29	22 40					23 22	23 38				
Lye	d	21 20				21 45					22 22		22 43					23 25	23 41				
Stourbridge Junction 2	d	21 24	21 33			21a50					22 26	22 36	22a47					23 27	23a50				
Hagley	d	21 28									22 30							23 32					
Blakedown	d	21 31									22 33							23 35					
Kidderminster	d	21 36	21a49								22 38	22a50						23 40					
Hartlebury	d																						
University	d									22 05						23 10	23 10						
Barnt Green	d																						
Bromsgrove	d									22 21						23 23	23 23						
Droitwich Spa	d	21 47								22 31	22 49					23 32	23 32	23 52					
Worcester Shrub Hill 7	a	21 58								22 45	22 56					23 42	23 45	00 01					
	d	22 02		22 33							23 05												
Worcester Foregate Street 7	a	22 04		22 37							23 07												
	d			22 37							23 08												
Malvern Link	d			22 47							23 16												
Great Malvern	a			22 53							23 19												
	d																						
Colwall	d																						
Ledbury	a																						
	d																						
Hereford 7	a																						

For general notes see front of timetable
For details of catering facilities see Directory of Train Operators

A 🛒 to Birmingham Snow Hill

B From Bournemouth (Table 51). ☕ to Reading

C To Gloucester (Table 57)

Table 71

until 6 September

Stratford -upon-Avon, Marylebone and Leamington Spa → Birmingham → Stourbridge, Worcester and Hereford

Network Diagram - See first page of Table 71

		CH	CH	XC	LM	LM	LM	GW	LM	LM	LM	GW	LM	LM	LM	CH	XC	LM	GW	XC	LM	LM	LM	LM	CH
				A				B				1 ◇					1 ◇ C		1 ◇	1 ◇ D					
Stratford-upon-Avon	d														07 00							07 45			
Wilmcote	d														07 05							07 50			
Wootton Wawen	d														07x10							07x55			
Henley-in-Arden	d														07 14							07 59			
Danzey	d														07x19							08x04			
Wood End	d														07x22							08x08			
The Lakes	d														07x24							08x10			
Earlswood (West Midlands)	d														07 27							08 13			
Wythall	d														07 29							08 15			
Whitlocks End	d														07 32							08 18			
Shirley	d										07 05				07 35							08 21		08 38	
Yardley Wood	d										07 08				07 38							08 24		08 41	
Hall Green	d										07 11				07 41							08 27		08 44	
Spring Road	d										07 13				07 43							08 29		08 46	
London Marylebone 10 ⊖	d	22p10	23p54																						06 27
Banbury	d	23p29	01 17													07 00	07 25			07 53					08 01
Leamington Spa 8	a	23p48	01 39													07 19	07 42			08 10					08 19
	d	23p48								06 28						07 19	07 43			08 11			07 56		08 20
Warwick	d	23p53								06 32						07 24							08 00		08 24
Warwick Parkway	d	23p56														07 27							08 04		08 28
Hatton	d									06 39													08 09		08 33
Lapworth	d									06 45													08 15		08 38
Dorridge	d	00 07								06 50				07 27		07 38		08 05					08 21		08 43
Widney Manor	d									06 53				07 31				08 08					08 25		08 47
Solihull	d	00 13								06 56				07 34		07 44		08 12					08 28		08 51
Olton	d									07 00				07 38				08 15					08 31		
Acocks Green	d									07 02				07 40				08 18					08 34		
Tyseley	d									07 05	07 17			07 43	07 46			08 21				08 32	08 37	08 49	
Small Heath	d									07 08	07 20			07 46	07 49							08 34	08 40	08 51	
Bordesley	d																								
Birmingham Moor Street	d	00 24				06 26			07 01	07 12	07 24			07 50	07 55	07 59		08 26				08 38	08 44	08 55	09 01
Birmingham Snow Hill	a	00 31				06 28			07 03	07 15	07 26			07 52	07 57	08 07		08 29				08 42	08 48	08 58	09 11
	d					06 29			07 05		07 30			07 53	08 03			08 30				08 43	08 53	09 03	
Jewellery Quarter	d								07 07		07 32			07 55	08 05			08 32				08 45	08 55	09 05	
The Hawthorns	d					06 34			07 12		07 37			08 00	08 10			08 37				08 50	09 00	09 10	
Coventry	a																			08 22					
Birmingham International ✈	a																			08 33					
Birmingham New Street 12	a																08 18			08 45					
	d			05 30			06 59						07 59								08 59				
Smethwick Galton Bdg H.L. 7	d					06 37			07 15		07 39			08 02	08 12			08 39				08 52	09 02	09 12	
Langley Green	d					06 40			07 18		07 42				08 15			08 42						09 15	
Rowley Regis	d					06 43			07 21		07 46			08 07	08 19			08 46				08 57	09 07	09 19	
Old Hill	d					06 46			07 24		07 49				08 22			08 49						09 22	
Cradley Heath	d					06 50			07 27		07 52			08 12	08 25			08 52				09 02	09 12	09 25	
Lye	d					06 53			07 30		07 55				08 28			08 55						09 28	
Stourbridge Junction 2	d					06 57			07 35		07a59			08 17	08a32			08a59				09a08	09 17	09 32	
Hagley	d					07 00			07 38					08 21									09 21		
Blakedown	d					07 03			07 41					08 24									09 24		
Kidderminster	d					07 08			07 46					08 29									09 29	09a42	
Hartlebury	d					07 13																			
University	d						07 05						08 05								09 05				
Barnt Green	d																								
Bromsgrove	d						07 23						08 21								09 21				
Droitwich Spa	d					07 22	07 32		07 58				08 31	08 40							09 31		09 40		
Worcester Shrub Hill 7	a			06 11		07 32	07 40																09 52		
	d				06 38		07 44	07 55				08 24							09 08						
Worcester Foregate Street 7	a				06 40		07 46	07 57	08 06			08 26	08 39	08 49					09 11		09 39				
	d				06 41		07 47	07 58	08 08			08 28	08 40						09 12		09 40				
Malvern Link	d				06 49		07 56	08 09	08 18				08 50						09 21		09 50				
Great Malvern	a				06 52		07 58	08 11	08 21			08 37	08 52						09 25		09 52				
	d				06 53		08 01						08 53								09 53				
Colwall	d				07 00		08 08						08 58								09 58				
Ledbury	a				07 07		08 14						09 06								10 06				
	d				07 07		08 14						09 08								10 08				
Hereford 7	a				07 28		08 35						09 28								10 28				

For general notes see front of timetable
For details of catering facilities see Directory of Train Operators

A To Cardiff Central (Table 132)
B From Gloucester (Table 57)
C From Gatwick Airport (Table 51)
D From Southampton Central (Table 51)

Due to Engineering Operations, services from Saturday 13 September on this Table had not been confirmed at time of going to press. These services will be issued in a special Supplement as soon as exact timings have been confirmed

Table 71

Saturdays

until 6 September

Stratford -upon-Avon, Marylebone and Leamington Spa → Birmingham → Stourbridge, Worcester and Hereford

Network Diagram - See first page of Table 71

		XC		LM	CH	XC	LM	LM	LM	GW	GW	LM	LM	CH	XC	LM	LM	LM	LM	CH	XC	GW	LM	LM	LM
		1 ◇				1 ◇					1 ◇				1 ◇						R 1	1 ◇			
		A				B				C											B				
		☕				☕					☕				☕						☕	☕			
Stratford-upon-Avon	d						08 27											09 27							
Wilmcote	d						08 32											09 32							
Wootton Wawen	d						08x37											09x37							
Henley-in-Arden	d						08 41											09 41							
Danzey	d						08x45											09x45							
Wood End	d						08x49											09x49							
The Lakes	d						08x51											09x51							
Earlswood (West Midlands)	d						08 54											09 54							
Wythall	d						08 56											09 56							
Whitlocks End	d						08 59											09 59							
Shirley	d						09 02		09 22							09 42		10 02					10 22		
Yardley Wood	d						09 05		09 25							09 45		10 05					10 25		
Hall Green	d						09 08		09 28							09 48		10 08					10 28		
Spring Road	d						09 10		09 30							09 50		10 10					10 30		
London Marylebone 10	⊖ d													07 23						08 20					
Banbury	d	08 25			08 40	08 53								08 55	09 25					09 39	09 53				
Leamington Spa 8	a	08 42			08 59	09 10								09 14	09 42					09 57	10 10				
	d	08 43			09 00	09 11								09 14	09 43					09 58	10 11				
Warwick	d				09 04									09 20						10 02					
Warwick Parkway	d				09 08									09 23						10 06					
Hatton	d				09a12																				
Lapworth	d																								
Dorridge	d			08 46				09 09					09 28	09 34			09 46		10 09	10 17					10 28
Widney Manor	d			08 50				09 13					09 32				09 50		10 13						10 32
Solihull	d			08 53				09 16					09 35	09 44			09 53		10 16	10 22					10 35
Olton	d			08 57				09 20					09 39				09 57		10 20						10 39
Acocks Green	d			08 59				09 22					09 41				09 59		10 22						10 41
Tyseley	d			09 02					09 33								10 02						10 33		
Small Heath	d			09 05					09 35								10 05						10 35		
Bordesley	d																								
Birmingham Moor Street	d			09 09			09 17	09 29	09 39				09 48	09 55		10 01	10 09	10 17	10 29	10 34			10 39		10 49
Birmingham Snow Hill	🚊 a			09 11			09 20	09 31	09 42				09 50	10 04		10 03	10 11	10 20	10 31	10 41			10 42		10 51
	d			09 13			09 23	09 33	09 43				09 53			10 03	10 13	10 23	10 33				10 43		10 53
Jewellery Quarter	🚊 d			09 15			09 25	09 35	09 45				09 55			10 05	10 15	10 25	10 35				10 45		10 55
The Hawthorns	🚊 d			09 20			09 30	09 40	09 50				10 00			10 10	10 20	10 30	10 40				10 50		11 00
Coventry	a					09 22															10 22				
Birmingham International	✈ a					09 33															10 33				
Birmingham New Street 12	a	09 18				09 45									10 18						10 45				
	d											09 59												10 59	
Smethwick Galton Bdg H.L. 7	d			09 22			09 32	09 42	09 52				10 02			10 12	10 22	10 32	10 42				10 52		11 02
Langley Green	d							09 45								10 15			10 45						
Rowley Regis	d			09 27			09 37	09 49	09 57				10 07			10 19	10 27	10 37	10 49				10 57		11 07
Old Hill	d							09 52								10 22			10 52						
Cradley Heath	d			09 32			09 42	09 55	10 02				10 12			10 25	10 32	10 42	10 55				11 02		11 12
Lye	d							09 58								10 28			10 58						
Stourbridge Junction 2	d			09 39			09a48	10 02	10a08				10 17			10 32	10 37	10a48	11 02				11a08		11 17
Hagley	d							10 06					10 21						11 06						11 21
Blakedown	d							10 09					10 24						11 09						11 24
Kidderminster	d			09 48				10a15					10 29			10a42	10 48		11a15						11 29
Hartlebury	d																								
University	d											10 05												11 05	
Barnt Green	d																								
Bromsgrove	d											10 21												11 21	
Droitwich Spa	d			10 00								10 31	10 40				11 00							11 31	11 40
Worcester Shrub Hill 7	a												10 48												11 48
	d									10 17	10 22		10 52									11 08			
Worcester Foregate Street 7	a			10 08						10 20	10 24	10 39	10 54				11 11					11 11		11 39	
	d									10 20	10 28	10 40	10 55									11 12		11 40	
Malvern Link	d									10 29	10 36	10 50	11 03									11 21		11 50	
Great Malvern	a									10 32	10 39	10 52	11 06									11 24		11 52	
	d											10 53												11 53	
Colwall	d											10 58												11 58	
Ledbury	a											11 06												12 06	
	d											11 08												12 08	
Hereford 7	a											11 28												12 28	

For general notes see front of timetable
For details of catering facilities see Directory of Train Operators

A From Gatwick Airport (Table 51)
B From Bournemouth (Table 51)
C From Warminster (Table 123)

Due to Engineering Operations, services from Saturday 13 September on this Table had not been confirmed at time of going to press. These services will be issued in a special Supplement as soon as exact timings have been confirmed

Table 71

Stratford -upon-Avon, Marylebone and Leamington Spa → Birmingham → Stourbridge, Worcester and Hereford

until 6 September

Network Diagram - See first page of Table 71

		CH	CH	XC		LM	LM	LM	LM	CH	XC	GW	LM	GW	LM	LM	CH	XC	LM	LM	LM	LM	CH	GW	LM
				1 ◇							R 1 A	1 ◇		◇ B				1 ◇						1 ◇	
Stratford-upon-Avon	d							10 27													11 27				
Wilmcote	d							10 32													11 32				
Wootton Wawen	d							10x37													11x37				
Henley-in-Arden	d							10 41													11 41				
Danzey	d							10x45													11x45				
Wood End	d							10x49													11x49				
The Lakes	d							10x51													11x51				
Earlswood (West Midlands)	d							10 54													11 54				
Wythall	d							10 56													11 56				
Whitlocks End	d							10 59													11 59				
Shirley	d					10 42		11 02					11 22						11 42		12 02				12 22
Yardley Wood	d					10 45		11 05					11 25						11 45		12 05				12 25
Hall Green	d					10 48		11 08					11 28						11 48		12 08				12 28
Spring Road	d					10 50		11 10					11 30						11 50		12 10				12 30
London Marylebone 10 ⊖	d	08 23	08 54							09 18							09 45						10 18		
Banbury	d	09 56	10 17	10 25						10 39	10 53						10 58	11 25					11 35		
Leamington Spa 8	a	10 12	10 37	10 42						10 57	11 10						11 16	11 42					11 54		
	d	10 14	10 38	10 43						10 58	11 11						11 16	11 43					11 54		
Warwick	d	10 18	10 42							11 02							11 20						11 59		
Warwick Parkway	d	10 22								11 06							11 24						12 02		
Hatton	d	10 27	10a49																				12 07		
Lapworth	d	10 32																					12 13		
Dorridge	d	10 38					10 46		11 09	11 17						11 28	11 35			11 46		12 09	12 17		
Widney Manor	d						10 50		11 13							11 32				11 50		12 13			
Solihull	d	10 44					10 53		11 16	11 22						11 35	11 41			11 53		12 16	12 23		
Olton	d						10 57		11 20							11 39				11 57		12 20			
Acocks Green	d						10 59		11 22							11 41				11 59		12 22			
Tyseley	d						11 02						11 33							12 02					12 33
Small Heath	d						11 05						11 35							12 05					12 35
Bordesley	d																								
Birmingham Moor Street	d	10 55				10 58	11 09	11 17	11 29	11 34			11 39			11 48	11 52		11 57	12 09	12 17	12 29	12 35		12 39
Birmingham Snow Hill 🚊	a	11 03				11 01	11 11	11 20	11 31	11 41			11 42			11 50	12 01		12 01	12 11	12 20	12 31	12 42		12 42
	d					11 03	11 13	11 23	11 33				11 43			11 53			12 03	12 13	12 23	12 33			12 43
Jewellery Quarter 🚊	d					11 05	11 15	11 25	11 35				11 45			11 55			12 05	12 15	12 25	12 35			12 45
The Hawthorns 🚊	d					11 10	11 20	11 30	11 40				11 50			12 00			12 10	12 20	12 30	12 40			12 50
Coventry	a										11 22														
Birmingham International ✈	a										11 33														
Birmingham New Street 12	a			11 18							11 45							12 18							
	d														11 59										
Smethwick Galton Bdg H.L. 7	d					11 12	11 22	11 32	11 42				11 52			12 02			12 12	12 22	12 32	12 42			12 52
Langley Green	d					11 15			11 45										12 15			12 45			
Rowley Regis	d					11 19	11 27	11 37	11 49				11 57			12 07			12 19	12 27	12 37	12 49			12 57
Old Hill	d					11 22			11 52										12 22			12 52			
Cradley Heath	d					11 25	11 32	11 42	11 55				12 02			12 12			12 25	12 32	12 42	12 55			13 02
Lye	d					11 28			11 58										12 28			12 58			
Stourbridge Junction 2	d					11 32	11 41	11a48	12 02				12a08			12 17			12 32	12 37	12a48	13 02			13a08
Hagley	d								12 06							12 21						13 06			
Blakedown	d								12 09							12 24						13 09			
Kidderminster	d					11a43	11 50		12a15							12 29			12a42	12 48		13a15			
Hartlebury	d																								
University	d														12 05										
Barnt Green	d																								
Bromsgrove	d														12 21										
Droitwich Spa	d						12 02								12 31	12 40				13 00					
Worcester Shrub Hill 7	a															12 48									
	d											12 08		12 16		12 52								13 08	
Worcester Foregate Street 7	a						12 10					12 10		12 18	12 39	12 54				13 08				13 11	
	d											12 12		12 19	12 40	12 55									
Malvern Link	d													12 29	12 50	13 03									
Great Malvern	a											12 21		12 31	12 52	13 06									
	d											12 22			12 53										
Colwall	d											12 27			12 58										
Ledbury	a											12 34			13 06										
	d											12 37			13 08										
Hereford 7	a											12 53			13 28										

For general notes see front of timetable
For details of catering facilities see Directory of Train Operators

A From Bournemouth (Table 51)
B From Westbury (Table 123)

Due to Engineering Operations, services from Saturday 13 September on this Table had not been confirmed at time of going to press. These services will be issued in a special Supplement as soon as exact timings have been confirmed

Saturdays

until 6 September

Stratford -upon-Avon, Marylebone and Leamington Spa → Birmingham → Stourbridge, Worcester and Hereford

Network Diagram - See first page of Table 71

		LM	LM	CH	CH	XC		LM	LM	LM	LM	CH	GW	LM	GW	LM	LM	CH	XC	LM	LM	LM	LM	CH	XC
						1 ◇ A ☕							1 ◇ ☕		◇ B				1 ◇ ☕						1 ◇ C ☕
Stratford-upon-Avon	d									12 27												13 27			
Wilmcote	d									12 32												13 32			
Wootton Wawen	d									12x37												13x37			
Henley-in-Arden	d									12 41												13 41			
Danzey	d									12x45												13x45			
Wood End	d									12x49												13x49			
The Lakes	d									12x51												13x51			
Earlswood (West Midlands)	d									12 54												13 54			
Wythall	d									12 56												13 56			
Whitlocks End	d									12 59												13 59			
Shirley	d							12 42		13 02				13 22						13 42		14 02			
Yardley Wood	d							12 45		13 05				13 25						13 45		14 05			
Hall Green	d							12 48		13 08				13 28						13 48		14 08			
Spring Road	d							12 50		13 10				13 30						13 50		14 10			
London Marylebone 10 ⊖	d			10 50	10 53							11 20						11 50						12 20	
Banbury	d			11 58	12 19	12 25						12 35						12 58	13 25					13 35	13 53
Leamington Spa 8	a			12 17	12 38	12 42						12 54						13 17	13 42					13 54	14 10
	d			12 17	12 39	12 43						12 54						13 17	13 43					13 54	14 11
Warwick	d			12 22	12 43							12 59						13 22						13 59	
Warwick Parkway	d			12 25								13 02						13 25						14 02	
Hatton	d				12a49																			14 07	
Lapworth	d																							14 13	
Dorridge	d		12 28	12 36					12 46		13 09	13 13					13 28	13 36			13 46		14 09	14 17	
Widney Manor	d		12 32						12 50		13 13						13 32				13 50		14 13		
Solihull	d		12 35	12 42					12 53		13 16	13 20					13 35	13 42			13 53		14 16	14 23	
Olton	d		12 39						12 57		13 20						13 39				13 57		14 20		
Acocks Green	d		12 41						12 59		13 22						13 41				13 59		14 22		
Tyseley	d								13 02					13 33							14 02				
Small Heath	d								13 05					13 35							14 05				
Bordesley	d													13 38											
Birmingham Moor Street	d		12 48	12 53				12 57	13 09	13 17	13 29	13 32		13 41			13 48	13 53		13 58	14 09	14 17	14 29	14 34	
Birmingham Snow Hill 🚋	a		12 50	13 01				13 01	13 11	13 20	13 31	13 41		13 43			13 50	14 01		14 01	14 11	14 21	14 31	14 42	
	d		12 53					13 03	13 13	13 23	13 33			13 43			13 53			14 03	14 13	14 23	14 33		
Jewellery Quarter 🚋	d		12 55					13 05	13 15	13 25	13 35			13 45			13 55			14 05	14 15	14 25	14 35		
The Hawthorns 🚋	d		13 00					13 10	13 20	13 30	13 40			13 50			14 00			14 10	14 20	14 30	14 40		
Coventry	a																								14 22
Birmingham International ✈	a																								14 33
Birmingham New Street 12	a					13 18													14 18						14 45
	d	12 59														13 59									
Smethwick Galton Bdg H.L. 7	d		13 02					13 12	13 22	13 32	13 42			13 52			14 02			14 12	14 22	14 32	14 42		
Langley Green	d							13 15			13 45									14 15			14 45		
Rowley Regis	d		13 07					13 19	13 27	13 37	13 49			13 57			14 07			14 19	14 27	14 37	14 49		
Old Hill	d							13 22			13 52									14 22			14 52		
Cradley Heath	d		13 12					13 25	13 32	13 42	13 55			14 02			14 12			14 25	14 32	14 42	14 55		
Lye	d							13 28			13 58									14 28			14 58		
Stourbridge Junction 2	d		13 17					13 32	13 39	13a48	14 02			14a09			14 17			14 32	14 39	14a48	15 02		
Hagley	d		13 21								14 06						14 21						15 06		
Blakedown	d		13 24								14 09						14 24						15 09		
Kidderminster	d		13 29					13a42	13 48		14a15						14 29			14a42	14 48		15a15		
Hartlebury	d																								
University	d	13 05														14 05									
Barnt Green	d																								
Bromsgrove	d	13 21														14 21									
Droitwich Spa	d	13 31	13 40						14 00							14 31	14 40				15 00				
Worcester Shrub Hill 7	a		13 48														14 48								
	d												14 08		14 27		14 52								
Worcester Foregate Street 7	a	13 39							14 08				14 10		14 29	14 39	14 54				15 08				
	d	13 40											14 12			14 40	14 55								
Malvern Link	d	13 50														14 50	15 03								
Great Malvern	a	13 52											14 21			14 52	15 06								
	d	13 53											14 22			14 53									
Colwall	d	13 58											14 27			14 58									
Ledbury	a	14 06											14 34			15 06									
	d	14 08											14 37			15 08									
Hereford 7	a	14 28											14 53			15 28									

For general notes see front of timetable
For details of catering facilities see Directory of Train Operators

A From Brighton (Table 51)
B From Brighton (Table 123)
C From Bournemouth (Table 51)

Due to Engineering Operations, services from Saturday 13 September on this Table had not been confirmed at time of going to press. These services will be issued in a special Supplement as soon as exact timings have been confirmed

Table 71

Saturdays

until 6 September

Stratford -upon-Avon, Marylebone and Leamington Spa → Birmingham → Stourbridge, Worcester and Hereford

Network Diagram - See first page of Table 71

		LM	LM	LM	CH	CH	XC	LM	LM	LM	LM	CH	XC	LM	GW	GW	LM	LM	CH	XC	LM	LM	XC	LM
							[1] ◇						[R] [1]			[1] ◇				[1] ◇			◇	
													A		B								C	
							🍽						🍽			🍽				🍽				
Stratford-upon-Avon	d									14 27														15 27
Wilmcote	d									14 32														15 32
Wootton Wawen	d									14x37														15x37
Henley-in-Arden	d									14 41														15 41
Danzey	d									14x45														15x45
Wood End	d									14x49														15x49
The Lakes	d									14x51														15x51
Earlswood (West Midlands)	d									14 54														15 54
Wythall	d									14 56														15 56
Whitlocks End	d									14 59														15 59
Shirley	d	14 22						14 42		15 02				15 22							15 42			16 02
Yardley Wood	d	14 25						14 45		15 05				15 25							15 45			16 05
Hall Green	d	14 28						14 48		15 08				15 28							15 48			16 08
Spring Road	d	14 30						14 50		15 10				15 30							15 50			16 10
London Marylebone [10] ⊖	d				12 50	12 53						13 20							13 50					
Banbury	d				13 58	14 19	14 25					14 35	14 53						14 58	15 25				
Leamington Spa [8]	a				14 17	14 38	14 42					14 54	15 10						15 17	15 42				
	d				14 17	14 39	14 43					14 54	15 11						15 17	15 43				
Warwick	d				14 22	14 43						14 59							15 22					
Warwick Parkway	d				14 25							15 02							15 25					
Hatton	d					14a49																		
Lapworth	d																							
Dorridge	d			14 28	14 36				14 46		15 09	15 13						15 28	15 36			15 46		
Widney Manor	d			14 32					14 50		15 13							15 32				15 50		
Solihull	d			14 35	14 42				14 53		15 16	15 20						15 35	15 42			15 53		
Olton	d			14 39					14 57		15 20							15 39				15 57		
Acocks Green	d			14 41					14 59		15 22							15 41				15 59		
Tyseley	d	14 33							15 02					15 33								16 02		
Small Heath	d	14 35							15 05					15 35								16 05		
Bordesley	d																							
Birmingham Moor Street	d	14 40		14 48	14 54			14 57	15 09	15 17	15 29	15 33		15 39				15 48	15 54		15 57	16 09		16 17
Birmingham Snow Hill 🚋	a	14 42		14 50	15 01			15 01	15 11	15 21	15 31	15 41		15 42				15 51	16 01		16 01	16 12		16 21
	d	14 43		14 53				15 03	15 13	15 23	15 33			15 43				15 53			16 03	16 13		16 23
Jewellery Quarter 🚋	d	14 45		14 55				15 05	15 15	15 25	15 35			15 45				15 55			16 05	16 15		16 25
The Hawthorns 🚋	d	14 50		15 00				15 10	15 20	15 30	15 40			15 50				16 00			16 10	16 20		16 30
Coventry	a												15 22											
Birmingham International ✈	a												15 33											
Birmingham New Street [12]	a						15 18						15 45							16 18				
	d		14 59														15 59						16 30	
Smethwick Galton Bdg H.L. [7]	d	14 52		15 02				15 12	15 22	15 32	15 42			15 52				16 02			16 12	16 22		16 32
Langley Green	d							15 15			15 45										16 15			
Rowley Regis	d	14 57		15 07				15 19	15 27	15 37	15 49			15 57				16 07			16 19	16 27		16 37
Old Hill	d							15 22			15 52										16 22			
Cradley Heath	d	15 02		15 12				15 25	15 32	15 42	15 55			16 02				16 12			16 25	16 32		16 42
Lye	d							15 28			15 58										16 28			
Stourbridge Junction [2]	d	15a08		15 17				15 32	15 39	15a48	16 02			16a08				16 17			16 32	16 39		16a48
Hagley	d			15 21							16 06							16 21						
Blakedown	d			15 24							16 09							16 24						
Kidderminster	d			15 29				15a42	15 48		16a15							16 29			16a42	16 48		
Hartlebury	d																							
University	d		15 05														16 05						16 36	
Barnt Green	d																							
Bromsgrove	d		15 21														16 21						16a50	
Droitwich Spa	d		15 31	15 40					16 00								16 31	16 40				17 00		
Worcester Shrub Hill [7]	a			15 48														16 48						
	d														16 14	16 23		16 52						
Worcester Foregate Street [7]	a		15 39						16 08						16 16	16 26	16 39	16 54				17 08		
	d		15 40												16 17	16 27	16 40	16 55						
Malvern Link	d		15 50												16 26	16 36	16 50	17 03						
Great Malvern	a		15 52												16 28	16 39	16 52	17 06						
	d		15 53														16 53							
Colwall	d		15 58														16 58							
Ledbury	a		16 06														17 06							
	d		16 08														17 08							
Hereford [7]	a		16 28														17 28							

For general notes see front of timetable
For details of catering facilities see Directory of Train Operators

A From Bournemouth (Table 51)
B From Southampton Central (Table 123)
C From Nottingham to Cardiff Central (Table 57)

Due to Engineering Operations, services from Saturday 13 September on this Table had not been confirmed at time of going to press. These services will be issued in a special Supplement as soon as exact timings have been confirmed

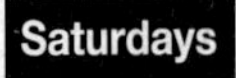

Saturdays

until 6 September

Stratford -upon-Avon, Marylebone and Leamington Spa → Birmingham → Stourbridge, Worcester and Hereford

Network Diagram - See first page of Table 71

		LM	CH	XC	GW	LM	LM	LM	CH	CH		XC	LM	XC	GW	LM	LM	LM	CH	XC	LM	GW	LM	LM	CH
				1 ◇ A ☕	1 ◇ ☕							1 ◇ ☕		◇ B	1 ◇ ☕					1 ◇ A ☕		C			
Stratford-upon-Avon	d																16 27								
Wilmcote	d																16 32								
Wootton Wawen	d																16x37								
Henley-in-Arden	d																16 41								
Danzey	d																16x45								
Wood End	d																16x49								
The Lakes	d																16x51								
Earlswood (West Midlands)	d																16 54								
Wythall	d																16 56								
Whitlocks End	d																16 59								
Shirley	d					16 22							16 42				17 02				17 22				
Yardley Wood	d					16 25							16 45				17 05				17 25				
Hall Green	d					16 28							16 48				17 08				17 28				
Spring Road	d					16 30							16 50				17 10				17 30				
London Marylebone 10 ⊖	d		14 20						14 50	14 53									15 20						15 50
Banbury	d		15 35	15 53					15 58	16 19		16 25							16 35	16 53					16 57
Leamington Spa 8	a		15 54	16 10					16 16	16 38		16 42							16 53	17 10					17 16
	d		15 54	16 11					16 17	16 39		16 43							16 53	17 11					17 16
Warwick	d		15 59						16 21	16 43									16 58						17 21
Warwick Parkway	d		16 02						16 25										17 01						17 24
Hatton	d		16 07							16a49									17 06						
Lapworth	d		16 13																17 12						
Dorridge	d	16 09	16 17					16 27	16 36							16 46		17 09	17 16					17 27	17 35
Widney Manor	d	16 13						16 31								16 50		17 13						17 31	
Solihull	d	16 16	16 23					16 34	16 41							16 53		17 16	17 23					17 34	17 41
Olton	d	16 20						16 38								16 57		17 20						17 38	
Acocks Green	d	16 22						16 40								16 59		17 22						17 40	
Tyseley	d					16 33		16 43					16 53			17 02					17 33			17 43	
Small Heath	d					16 35										17 05					17 35				
Bordesley	d																								
Birmingham Moor Street	d	16 29	16 34			16 39		16 48	16 53				16 57			17 09	17 17	17 29	17 34		17 39			17 48	17 53
Birmingham Snow Hill	a	16 32	16 41			16 42		16 51	17 02				17 01			17 12	17 21	17 31	17 41		17 42			17 51	18 01
	d	16 33				16 43		16 53					17 03			17 13	17 23	17 33			17 43			17 53	
Jewellery Quarter	d	16 35				16 45		16 55					17 05			17 15	17 25	17 35			17 45			17 55	
The Hawthorns	d	16 40				16 50		17 00					17 10			17 20	17 30	17 40			17 50			18 00	
Coventry	a			16 22																17 22					
Birmingham International ✈	a			16 33																17 33					
Birmingham New Street 12	a			16 45								17 18								17 45					
	d						16 59							17 30									17 59		
Smethwick Galton Bdg H.L. 7	d	16 42				16 52		17 02					17 12			17 22	17 32	17 42			17 52			18 02	
Langley Green	d	16 45											17 15					17 45						18 05	
Rowley Regis	d	16 49				16 57		17 07					17 19			17 27	17 37	17 49			17 57			18 09	
Old Hill	d	16 52											17 22					17 52						18 12	
Cradley Heath	d	16 55				17 02		17 12					17 25			17 32	17 42	17 55			18 02			18 15	
Lye	d	16 58											17 28					17 58						18 18	
Stourbridge Junction 2	d	17 02				17a08		17 17					17 32			17 37	17a48	18 02			18a08			18 22	
Hagley	d	17 06						17 21								17 41		18 06						18 25	
Blakedown	d	17 09						17 24								17 44		18 09						18 28	
Kidderminster	d	17a15						17 29					17a42			17 49		18a15						18 33	
Hartlebury	d							17 34								17 54								18 38	
University	d						17 05							17 36									18 05		
Barnt Green	d																								
Bromsgrove	d						17 21							17a51									18 21		
Droitwich Spa	d						17 31	17 42								18 02							18 31	18 47	
Worcester Shrub Hill 7	a															18 14							18 40	18 54	
	d				17 08										18 08							18 26	18 50		
Worcester Foregate Street 7	a				17 11		17 39	17 54							18 11							18 29	18 52		
	d				17 12		17 40	17 54							18 12							18 29	18 53		
Malvern Link	d				17 21		17 50	18 04							18 21							18 38	19 02		
Great Malvern	a				17 25		17 52	18 07							18 25							18 41	19 04		
	d						17 53																19 05		
Colwall	d						17 58																19 10		
Ledbury	a						18 06																19 17		
	d						18 08																19 22		
Hereford 7	a						18 28																19 42		

For general notes see front of timetable
For details of catering facilities see Directory of Train Operators

A From Bournemouth (Table 51)
B From Nottingham to Cardiff Central (Table 57)
C From Warminster (Table 123)

Due to Engineering Operations, services from Saturday 13 September on this Table had not been confirmed at time of going to press. These services will be issued in a special Supplement as soon as exact timings have been confirmed

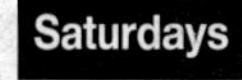

until 6 September

Stratford -upon-Avon, Marylebone and Leamington Spa → Birmingham → Stourbridge, Worcester and Hereford

Network Diagram - See first page of Table 71

		XC	LM	XC	GW	LM	LM	CH	XC	LM	LM	CH	CH	XC	LM	LM	GW	LM	CH	XC	LM	GW	LM	CH
		■1 ◇		◇	■1 ◇				■1 ◇					■1 ◇						■1 ◇		■1 ◇		
		A		B					C								D			C				
		☕			☕				☕					☕		🛒				☕		☕		
Stratford-upon-Avon	d					17 27									18 07						18 46			
Wilmcote	d					17 32									18 12						18 51			
Wootton Wawen	d					17x37									18x17						18x56			
Henley-in-Arden	d					17 41									18 21						19 00			
Danzey	d					17x45									18x25						19x04			
Wood End	d					17x49									18x29						19x08			
The Lakes	d					17x51									18x31						19x10			
Earlswood (West Midlands)	d					17 54									18 34						19 12			
Wythall	d					17 56									18 36						19 15			
Whitlocks End	d					17 59									18 39						19 17			
Shirley	d					18 02				18 22					18 42						19 22			
Yardley Wood	d					18 05				18 25					18 45						19 25			
Hall Green	d					18 08				18 28					18 48						19 28			
Spring Road	d					18 10				18 30					18 50						19 30			
London Marylebone ■10 ⊖	d							16 20				16 50	16 53						17 20					17 50
Banbury	d	17 25						17 35	17 53			17 59	18 19	18 25					18 35	18 53				19 03
Leamington Spa ■8	a	17 42						17 54	18 10			18 18	18 38	18 42					18 54	19 10				19 23
	d	17 43						17 54	18 11			18 18	18 39	18 43					18 54	19 11				19 23
Warwick	d							17 59				18 23	18 43						18 59					19 27
Warwick Parkway	d							18 02				18 26							19 02					19 31
Hatton	d							18 07					18a49						19 07					
Lapworth	d							18 13											19 14					
Dorridge	d		17 46				18 09	18 17			18 28	18 37						19 00	19 18				19 28	19 42
Widney Manor	d		17 50				18 13				18 32							19 06					19 32	
Solihull	d		17 53				18 16	18 23			18 35	18 43						19 09	19 24				19 35	19 48
Olton	d		17 57				18 20				18 39							19 12					19 39	
Acocks Green	d		17 59				18 22				18 41							19 15					19 41	
Tyseley	d		18 02							18 33	18 44				18 54			19 18			19 33		19 44	
Small Heath	d		18 04							18 35	18 46				18 56			19 20			19 35		19 47	
Bordesley	d																							
Birmingham Moor Street	d		18 08			18 17	18 28	18 34		18 40	18 50	18 55			19 00			19 24	19 34		19 39		19 51	19 59
Birmingham Snow Hill 🚋	a		18 11			18 20	18 31	18 41		18 43	18 53	19 03			19 03			19 27	19 41		19 42		19 53	20 06
	d		18 13			18 23	18 33				18 57							19 28					19 55	
Jewellery Quarter 🚋	d		18 15			18 25	18 35				18 59							19 30					19 57	
The Hawthorns 🚋	d		18 20			18 30	18 40				19 04							19 35					20 02	
Coventry	a								18 22											19 22				
Birmingham International ✈	a								18 33											19 33				
Birmingham New Street ■12	a	18 18							18 45					19 18						19 45				
	d			18 30												19 30								
Smethwick Galton Bdg H.L. ■7	d		18 22			18 32	18 42				19 06							19 37					20 04	
Langley Green	d		18 25				18 45				19 09							19 40					20 07	
Rowley Regis	d		18 29			18 37	18 49				19 13							19 44					20 11	
Old Hill	d		18 32				18 52				19 16							19 47					20 14	
Cradley Heath	d		18 35			18 42	18 55				19 19							19 50					20 17	
Lye	d		18 38				18 58				19 22							19 53					20 20	
Stourbridge Junction ■2	d		18a42			18 48	19 02				19 26							19 57					20 24	
Hagley	d					18 51	19 06				19 29							20 00					20 27	
Blakedown	d					18 54	19 09				19 32							20 03					20 30	
Kidderminster	d					18 59	19a15				19 37							20 08					20 35	
Hartlebury	d					19 04																		
University	d															19 36								
Barnt Green	d																							
Bromsgrove	d			18a50												19 51								
Droitwich Spa	d					19 13					19 52					20 00		20 20					20 47	
Worcester Shrub Hill ■7	a										20 00					20 07		20 30					20 54	
	d				19 16											20 11	20 23					20 43	20 58	
Worcester Foregate Street ■7	a				19 18	19 21										20 14	20 25					20 46	21 00	
	d				19 20											20 14	20 26					20 47	21 01	
Malvern Link	d				19 29											20 23	20 35					20 56	21 09	
Great Malvern	a				19 32											20 26	20 38					20 59	21 12	
	d				19 33											20 26						21 00		
Colwall	d				19 38											20 32						21 06		
Ledbury	a				19 45											20 40						21 13		
	d				19 46											20 40						21 15		
Hereford ■7	a				20 02											21 00						21 32		

For general notes see front of timetable
For details of catering facilities see Directory of Train Operators

A From Brighton (Table 51)
B From Nottingham (Table 57)
C From Bournemouth (Table 51)
D From Weymouth (Table 123)

Due to Engineering Operations, services from Saturday 13 September on this Table had not been confirmed at time of going to press. These services will be issued in a special Supplement as soon as exact timings have been confirmed

Table 71

until 6 September

Stratford -upon-Avon, Marylebone and Leamington Spa → Birmingham → Stourbridge, Worcester and Hereford

Network Diagram - See first page of Table 71

		XC	LM	CH	XC	LM	LM	CH	CH	XC	GW	CH	XC	LM	LM	CH	LM	CH	XC	LM	CH	LM	CH
		1 ◇			1 ◇					1 ◇	1 ◇		1 ◇						1 ◇				
		A			B								B						B				
		[catering]			[catering]					[catering]			[catering]										
Stratford-upon-Avon	d		19 27											20 27		21 15							
Wilmcote	d		19 32											20 32									
Wootton Wawen	d		19x37											20x37									
Henley-in-Arden	d		19 41											20 41									
Danzey	d		19x45											20x45									
Wood End	d		19x49											20x49									
The Lakes	d		19x51											20x51									
Earlswood (West Midlands)	d		19 54											20 54									
Wythall	d		19 56											20 56									
Whitlocks End	d		19 59											20 59									
Shirley	d		20 02											21 02			21 56					22 54	
Yardley Wood	d		20 05											21 05			21 59					22 57	
Hall Green	d		20 08											21 08			22 02					23 00	
Spring Road	d		20 10											21 10			22 04					23 02	
London Marylebone 10 ⊖	d			18 20				18 50	18 53			19 20						20 00			20 50		21 40
Banbury	d	19 25		19 35	19 53			20 03	20 19	20 25		20 37	20 53					21 19	21 53		22 07		23 03
Leamington Spa 8	a	19 42		19 54	20 10			20 23	20 38	20 42		20 55	21 10					21 39	22 10		22 27		23 23
	d	19 43		19 54	20 11			20 23	20 39	20 43		20 55	21 11					21 39	22 11		22 28		23 24
Warwick	d			19 59				20 27	20 43			21 00						21 43			22 32		23 28
Warwick Parkway	d			20 02				20 31				21 03						21 47			22 35		23 31
Hatton	d			20 07					20a49			21 08				21a33							
Lapworth	d			20 13								21 14											
Dorridge	d			20 17			20 28	20 42				21 18			21 28			21 58		22 28	22 47		23 43
Widney Manor	d						20 32								21 32					22 32			23 46
Solihull	d			20 23			20 35	20 48				21 25			21 35			22 04		22 35	22 52		23 50
Olton	d						20 39								21 39					22 39			
Acocks Green	d						20 41								21 41					22 41			
Tyseley	d						20 44								21 44		22 07			22 44		23 05	
Small Heath	d						20 47								21 47		22 09			22 47		23 07	
Bordesley	d																						
Birmingham Moor Street	d		20 17	20 35			20 51	20 58				21 36		21 17	21 51		22 13	22 17		22 51	23 03	23 11	00 02
Birmingham Snow Hill 🚋	a		20 20	20 42			20 53	21 06				21 43		21 20	21 53		22 16	22 26		22 53	23 10	23 14	00 09
	d		20 21				20 55							21 21	21 55		22 18			22 56		23 15	
Jewellery Quarter 🚋	d		20 24				20 57							21 23	21 57		22 20			22 59		23 17	
The Hawthorns 🚋	d		20 28				21 02							21 28	22 02		22 25			23 03		23 22	
Coventry	a				20 21								21 22						22 22				
Birmingham International ✈	a				20 33								21 33						22 33				
Birmingham New Street 12	a	20 18			20 45					21 22			21 45						22 50				
	d					20 59																	
Smethwick Galton Bdg H.L. 7	d		20 31				21 05							21 30	22 04		22 27			23 06		23 24	
Langley Green	d		20 34				21 08							21 33	22 07		22 30			23 09		23 27	
Rowley Regis	d		20 37				21 11							21 36	22 11		22 34			23 12		23 31	
Old Hill	d		20 40				21 14							21 39	22 14		22 37			23 15		23 34	
Cradley Heath	d		20 43				21 17							21 42	22 17		22 40			23 18		23 37	
Lye	d		20 46				21 20							21 45	22 20		22 43			23 21		23 40	
Stourbridge Junction 2	d		20a50				21 24							21a50	22 24		22a47			23 26		23a44	
Hagley	d						21 28								22 27					23 29			
Blakedown	d						21 31								22 30					23 32			
Kidderminster	d						21 36								22 35					23 37			
Hartlebury	d																						
University	d					21 05																	
Barnt Green	d																						
Bromsgrove	d					21 21																	
Droitwich Spa	d					21 31	21 47								22 46					23 48			
Worcester Shrub Hill 7	a					21 38	21 55								22 55					23 56			
	d					21 46					22 05				22 57								
Worcester Foregate Street 7	a					21 49					22 08				23 00								
	d					21 49					22 08				23 00								
Malvern Link	d					21 58					22 17				23 09								
Great Malvern	a					22 01					22 21				23 12								
	d					22 01																	
Colwall	d					22 07																	
Ledbury	a					22 14																	
	d					22 14																	
Hereford 7	a					22 35																	

For general notes see front of timetable
For details of catering facilities see Directory of Train Operators

A From Guildford (Table 51)
B From Bournemouth (Table 51)

Due to Engineering Operations, services from Saturday 13 September on this Table had not been confirmed at time of going to press. These services will be issued in a special Supplement as soon as exact timings have been confirmed

Table 71

Sundays

until 13 July

Stratford -upon-Avon, Marylebone and Leamington Spa → Birmingham → Stourbridge, Worcester and Hereford

Network Diagram - See first page of Table 71

Station		CH	LM	GW	LM	CH	LM	GW	CH	LM	XC	XC	LM	CH	XC	GW	LM	CH	LM	XC	CH	XC	XC	LM	CH
				1 ◇				1 ◇ ☕			A	1 ◇ B ☕			🚌	1 ◇ ☕				R 1 C ☕		🚌	1 ◇ D ☕		
Stratford-upon-Avon	d				09 28					10 28							11 28							12 30	
Wilmcote	d				09 33					10 33							11 33							12 35	
Wootton Wawen	d																								
Henley-in-Arden	d				09 40					10 40							11 40							12 42	
Danzey	d																								
Wood End	d																								
The Lakes	d				09x48					10x48							11x48							12x50	
Earlswood (West Midlands)	d																								
Wythall	d				09 52					10 52							11 52							12 54	
Whitlocks End	d																								
Shirley	d				09 57					10 57							11 57							12 59	
Yardley Wood	d				10 00					11 00							12 00							13 02	
Hall Green	d				10 03					11 03							12 03							13 05	
Spring Road	d				10 05					11 05							12 05							13 07	
London Marylebone 10 ⊖	d	21p40				08 00			09 15					09 33				10 15			10 50				11 20
Banbury	d	23p03				09 34			10 36			10 53		11 01				11 38		11 53	12 02		12 25		12 41
Leamington Spa 8	a	23p23				09 54			10 56			11 10		11 21				11 58		12 10	12 22		12 41		13 01
	d	23p24				09 54			10 57			11 11		11 21	11 25			11 59		12 11	12 22	12 25	12 43		13 02
Warwick	d	23p28				09 59			11 01					11 25				12 03							13 06
Warwick Parkway	d	23p31				10 02			11 04									12 06			12 28				13 09
Hatton	d					10 07								11a33				12 11							
Lapworth	d					10 11			11 13																13 18
Dorridge	d	23p43				10 16	10 25		11 19				11 25					12 19	12 25		12 39				13 23
Widney Manor	d	23p46					10 29						11 29						12 29						
Solihull	d	23p50				10 21	10 32		11 24				11 32					12 24	12 32		12 45				13 28
Olton	d						10 36						11 36						12 36						
Acocks Green	d						10 38						11 38						12 38						
Tyseley	d				10 08					11 08							12 08							13 10	
Small Heath	d																								
Bordesley	d																								
Birmingham Moor Street	d	00 02	09 26		10 13	10 33	10 45		11 34	11 13			11 45				12 13	12 35	12 45		12 56			13 15	13 36
Birmingham Snow Hill 🚋	a	00 09	09 28		10 15	10 40	10 47		11 41	11 15			11 47				12 15	12 43	12 47		13 03			13 17	13 46
	d		09 30		10 18		10 48			11 18			11 48				12 18		12 48					13 20	
Jewellery Quarter 🚋	d		09 32		10 20		10 51			11 20			11 51				12 20		12 51					13 22	
The Hawthorns 🚋	d		09 37		10 25		10 55			11 25			11 55				12 25		12 55					13 27	
Coventry	a														11 50							12 50			
Birmingham International ✈	a														12 25							13 25			
Birmingham New Street 12	a											11 51								12 46			13 15		
	d										11 46														
Smethwick Galton Bdg H.L. 7	d		09 39		10 27		10 58			11 27			11 58				12 27		12 58					13 29	
Langley Green	d						11 01						12 01						13 01						
Rowley Regis	d		09 44		10 32		11 04			11 32			12 04				12 32		13 04					13 34	
Old Hill	d						11 07						12 07						13 07						
Cradley Heath	d		09 49		10 37		11 10			11 37			12 10				12 37		13 10					13 39	
Lye	d						11 13						12 13						13 13						
Stourbridge Junction 2	d		09 54		10 43		11a17			11 43			12a17				12 43		13a17					13 46	
Hagley	d		09 58		10 46					11 47							12 46							13 49	
Blakedown	d									11 50							12 49								
Kidderminster	d		10 04		10 52					11 55							12 54							13 55	
Hartlebury	d																								
University	d																								
Barnt Green	d																								
Bromsgrove	d										12 05														
Droitwich Spa	d		10 15		11 04					12 06	12 13						13 06							14 07	
Worcester Shrub Hill 7	a		10 23		11 11					12 14	12 22						13 13								
	d		10 26	10 35	11 24			12 04								13 09	13 25								
Worcester Foregate Street 7	a		10 29	10 37	11 27			12 07								13 11	13 27							14 20	
	d		10 29	10 39	11 27			12 08								13 13	13 28								
Malvern Link	d		10 38	10 48	11 36			12 17								13 22	13 36								
Great Malvern	a		10 41	10 50	11 39			12 20								13 25	13 39								
	d							12 22								13 26									
Colwall	d							12 27								13 32									
Ledbury	a							12 34								13 39									
	d							12 37								13 48									
Hereford 7	a							12 54								14 04									

For general notes see front of timetable
For details of catering facilities see Directory of Train Operators

A To Gloucester (Table 57)
B From Southampton Central (Table 51)
C From Bournemouth (Table 51)
D From Brighton (Table 51)

Table 71

Sundays

until 13 July

Stratford -upon-Avon, Marylebone and Leamington Spa → Birmingham → Stourbridge, Worcester and Hereford

Network Diagram - See first page of Table 71

		LM	XC	LM	CH	XC	CH	GW	LM	CH	XC	LM	CH	XC	CH	XC	CH	LM	LM	LM	XC	CH	LM	CH	XC
			R 1					1 ◇			R 1					R 1									R 1
			A								A					A									A
						🚌								🚌							🚌				
			☕					☕			☕					☕									☕
Stratford-upon-Avon	d								13 28									14 28					15 28		
Wilmcote	d								13 33									14 33					15 33		
Wootton Wawen	d																								
Henley-in-Arden	d								13 40									14 40					15 40		
Danzey	d																								
Wood End	d																								
The Lakes	d								13x48									14x48					15x48		
Earlswood (West Midlands)	d																								
Wythall	d								13 52									14 52					15 52		
Whitlocks End	d																								
Shirley	d								13 57									14 57					15 57		
Yardley Wood	d								14 00									15 00					16 00		
Hall Green	d								14 03									15 03					16 03		
Spring Road	d								14 05									15 05					16 05		
London Marylebone 10	⊖ d				11 33		11 50			12 20			12 50		13 20		13 33					13 50		14 20	
Banbury	d		12 53		13 01		13 05			13 43	13 53		14 02		14 41	14 53	15 01					15 05		15 41	15 53
Leamington Spa 8	a		13 10		13 21		13 25			14 02	14 10		14 22		15 01	15 10	15 21					15 25		16 01	16 10
	d		13 11		13 21	13 25	13 26			14 03	14 11		14 22	14 25	15 02	15 11	15 21				15 25	15 26		16 02	16 11
Warwick	d				13 25					14 07					15 06		15 25							16 06	
Warwick Parkway	d						13 31			14 10			14 28		15 09							15 31		16 09	
Hatton	d				13a33												15a33							16 14	
Lapworth	d														15 18										
Dorridge	d			13 25			13 43			14 22		14 25	14 39		15 23				15 25			15 43		16 22	
Widney Manor	d			13 29								14 29							15 29						
Solihull	d			13 32			13 48			14 28		14 32	14 45		15 28				15 32			15 48		16 28	
Olton	d			13 36								14 36							15 36						
Acocks Green	d			13 38								14 38							15 38						
Tyseley	d								14 08									15 08					16 08		
Small Heath	d																								
Bordesley	d																								
Birmingham Moor Street	d			13 45			14 01		14 13	14 39		14 45	14 56		15 39			15 13	15 45			15 59	16 13	16 39	
Birmingham Snow Hill	🚊 a			13 48			14 08		14 15	14 47		14 47	15 03		15 46			15 15	15 48			16 06	16 15	16 46	
	d			13 48					14 18			14 48						15 18	15 48				16 18		
Jewellery Quarter	🚊 d			13 51					14 20			14 51						15 20	15 51				16 20		
The Hawthorns	🚊 d			13 55					14 25			14 55						15 25	15 55				16 25		
Coventry	a					13 50								14 50							15 50				
Birmingham International	✈ a					14 25								15 25							16 25				
Birmingham New Street 12	a		13 57								14 57					15 57									16 56
	d	13 45																		16 00					
Smethwick Galton Bdg H.L. 7	d			13 58					14 27			14 58						15 27	15 58				16 27		
Langley Green	d			14 01								15 01							16 01						
Rowley Regis	d			14 04					14 32			15 04						15 32	16 04				16 32		
Old Hill	d			14 07								15 07							16 07						
Cradley Heath	d			14 10					14 37			15 10						15 37	16 10				16 37		
Lye	d			14 13								15 13							16 13						
Stourbridge Junction 2	d			14a18					14 43			15a17						15 43	16a18				16 43		
Hagley	d								14 46									15 46					16 46		
Blakedown	d								14 49																
Kidderminster	d								14 54									15 52					16 52		
Hartlebury	d																								
University	d																								
Barnt Green	d																								
Bromsgrove	d	14 05																		16 21					
Droitwich Spa	d	14 15							15 06									16 04		16 30			17 04		
Worcester Shrub Hill 7	a	14 22																		16 41					
	d	14 28						15 08												16 45					
Worcester Foregate Street 7	a	14 30						15 10	15 14									16 12		16 47			17 12		
	d	14 31						15 12												16 48					
Malvern Link	d	14 39																		16 57					
Great Malvern	a	14 42						15 21												17 02					
	d	14 43						15 22																	
Colwall	d	14 48																							
Ledbury	a	14 55						15 32																	
	d	14 58						15 34																	
Hereford 7	a	15 19						15 51																	

For general notes see front of timetable
For details of catering facilities see
Directory of Train Operators

A From Bournemouth (Table 51)

Table 71

Sundays

until 13 July

Stratford -upon-Avon, Marylebone and Leamington Spa → Birmingham → Stourbridge, Worcester and Hereford

Network Diagram - See first page of Table 71

		LM	CH	XC	GW	LM	CH	XC	CH	LM	LM	LM	XC	CH	GW	LM	CH	XC	XC	CH	LM	GW	CH	XC	CH
					1 ◇			R 1							1 ◇			R 1				1 ◇		R 1	
								A										A						A	
				🚌									🚌						🚌						
					☕			☕							☕			☕				☕		☕	
Stratford-upon-Avon	d									16 28						17 28									
Wilmcote	d									16 33						17 33									
Wootton Wawen	d																								
Henley-in-Arden	d									16 40						17 40									
Danzey	d									16x45															
Wood End	d																								
The Lakes	d									16x48						17x48									
Earlswood (West Midlands)	d																								
Wythall	d									16 52						17 52									
Whitlocks End	d																								
Shirley	d									16 57						17 57									
Yardley Wood	d									17 00						18 00									
Hall Green	d									17 03						18 03									
Spring Road	d									17 05						18 05									
London Marylebone 10 ⊖	d		14 50				15 20		15 33					15 50			16 20			16 57			17 20		17 35
Banbury	d		16 02				16 40	16 53	17 01					17 05			17 41	17 53		18 09			18 41	18 53	19 01
Leamington Spa 8	a		16 22				17 01	17 10	17 20					17 25			18 01	18 10		18 29			19 01	19 10	19 21
	d		16 22	16 25			17 01	17 11	17 21				17 25	17 26			18 02	18 11	18 25	18 29			19 02	19 11	19 21
Warwick	d						17 06		17 26								18 06						19 06		19 25
Warwick Parkway	d		16 28				17 09							17 31			18 09			18 35			19 09		
Hatton	d								17a33								18 14								19a32
Lapworth	d						17 18																19 18		
Dorridge	d	16 25	16 39				17 22				17 25			17 43			18 22			18 46			19 23		
Widney Manor	d	16 29									17 29						18 26						19 26		
Solihull	d	16 32	16 45				17 27				17 32			17 48			18 29			18 52			19 30		
Olton	d	16 36									17 36														
Acocks Green	d	16 38									17 38														
Tyseley	d									17 09						18 08									
Small Heath	d																								
Bordesley	d																								
Birmingham Moor Street	d	16 45	16 56			17 02	17 39			17 13	17 45			17 59		18 13	18 41			19 02			19 41		
Birmingham Snow Hill 🚋	a	16 48	17 03			17 04	17 46			17 18	17 48			18 07		18 15	18 49			19 10			19 48		
	d	16 48				17 06				17 20	17 48					18 18									
Jewellery Quarter 🚋	d	16 51								17 22	17 51					18 20									
The Hawthorns 🚋	d	16 55								17 27	17 55					18 25									
Coventry	a			16 50									17 50						18 50						
Birmingham International ✈	a			17 25									18 25						19 25						
Birmingham New Street 12	a							17 57										18 51						19 51	
	d											18 00									19 00				
Smethwick Galton Bdg H.L. 7	d	16 58								17 29	17 58					18 27									
Langley Green	d	17 01									18 01														
Rowley Regis	d	17 04								17 34	18 04					18 32									
Old Hill	d	17 07									18 07														
Cradley Heath	d	17 10								17 39	18 10					18 37									
Lye	d	17 13									18 13														
Stourbridge Junction 2	d	17a18				17 27				17 45	18a19					18 43									
Hagley	d					17 30				17 48						18 47									
Blakedown	d															18 50									
Kidderminster	d					17 36				17 54						18 55									
Hartlebury	d																								
University	d																								
Barnt Green	d																								
Bromsgrove	d											18 21									19 21				
Droitwich Spa	d					17 48				18 06		18 30				19 06					19 31				
Worcester Shrub Hill 7	a									18 13		18 38				19 14					19 41				
	d				17 09							18 41			19 10							20 10			
Worcester Foregate Street 7	a				17 12	18 01						18 44			19 12							20 12			
	d				17 13							18 44			19 14							20 14			
Malvern Link	d				17 22							18 53			19 22							20 22			
Great Malvern	a				17 25							18 56			19 26							20 26			
	d				17 27							18 57													
Colwall	d				17 32							19 02													
Ledbury	a				17 39							19 09													
	d				17 42							19 09													
Hereford 7	a				17 58							19 30													

For general notes see front of timetable
For details of catering facilities see Directory of Train Operators

A From Bournemouth (Table 51)

Table 71

Sundays

until 13 July

Stratford -upon-Avon, Marylebone and Leamington Spa → Birmingham → Stourbridge, Worcester and Hereford

Network Diagram - See first page of Table 71

		LM	XC	CH	GW	LM	CH	XC	XC	CH	LM	GW	LM	CH	XC	XC	CH	CH	XC	XC	LM	CH	XC	CH
					1◇			1◇				1◇			1◇				1◇				1◇	
								A							A				A				A	
			🚌						🚌							🚌				🚌				
					☕			☕							☕									
Stratford-upon-Avon	d	18 28				19 28																		
Wilmcote	d	18 33				19 33																		
Wootton Wawen	d																							
Henley-in-Arden	d	18 40				19 40																		
Danzey	d																							
Wood End	d																							
The Lakes	d	18x48				19x48																		
Earlswood (West Midlands)	d																							
Wythall	d	18 52				19 52																		
Whitlocks End	d																							
Shirley	d	18 57				19 57																		
Yardley Wood	d	19 00				20 00																		
Hall Green	d	19 03				20 03																		
Spring Road	d	19 05				20 05																		
London Marylebone 10 ⊖	d			17 57			18 20			18 57				19 22			19 57	20 20				20 50		21 40
Banbury	d			19 09			19 41	19 53		20 09				20 44	20 53		21 09	21 41	21 53			22 10	22 53	23 01
Leamington Spa 8	a			19 29			20 01	20 10		20 29				21 04	21 10		21 29	22 01	22 10			22 30	23 10	23 21
	d		19 25	19 29			20 02	20 11	20 25	20 29				21 04	21 11	21 25	21 29	22 02	22 11	22 25		22 31	23 11	23 22
Warwick	d						20 06							21 09				22 06				22 35		23 26
Warwick Parkway	d			19 35			20 09			20 35				21 12			21 35	22 09				22 38		23 29
Hatton	d																					22 43		
Lapworth	d																					22 48		
Dorridge	d			19 46			20 21			20 46				21 23			21 46	22 21				22 52		23 41
Widney Manor	d						20 24							21 27								22 56		
Solihull	d			19 52			20 28			20 52				21 30			21 52	22 26				22 59		23 46
Olton	d																							
Acocks Green	d																							
Tyseley	d	19 08				20 08																		
Small Heath	d																							
Bordesley	d																							
Birmingham Moor Street	d	19 13		20 02		20 13	20 39			21 02			21 35	21 41			22 02	22 38			22 55	23 11		23 57
Birmingham Snow Hill 🚋	a	19 15		20 10		20 15	20 46			21 10			21 37	21 48			22 10	22 45			22 57	23 18		00 04
	d	19 18				20 18							21 45								23 00			
Jewellery Quarter 🚋	d	19 20				20 20							21 47								23 02			
The Hawthorns 🚋	d	19 25				20 25							21 52								23 07			
Coventry	a		19 50						20 50							21 50				22 50				
Birmingham International ✈	a		20 25						21 25							22 25				23 25				
Birmingham New Street 12	a							20 51							21 51				22 51				23 43	
	d										21 00													
Smethwick Galton Bdg H.L. 7	d	19 27				20 27							21 54								23 09			
Langley Green	d																							
Rowley Regis	d	19 32				20 32							21 59								23 14			
Old Hill	d																							
Cradley Heath	d	19 37				20 37							22 03								23 19			
Lye	d																							
Stourbridge Junction 2	d	19 43				20 43							22 09								23 24			
Hagley	d	19 46				20 46							22 12								23 28			
Blakedown	d																							
Kidderminster	d	19 52				20 53							22 18								23 34			
Hartlebury	d																							
University	d																							
Barnt Green	d																							
Bromsgrove	d										21 21													
Droitwich Spa	d	20 08				21 05					21 30		22 30								23 45			
Worcester Shrub Hill 7	a	20 15				21 15					21 37		22 37								23 53			
	d				21 11	21 28					21 40	22 22	22 41											
Worcester Foregate Street 7	a				21 13	21 31					21 42	22 24	22 43											
	d				21 15	21 31					21 43	22 25	22 44											
Malvern Link	d				21 24	21 40					21 52	22 33	22 52											
Great Malvern	a				21 27	21 43					21 54	22 40	22 55											
	d				21 28						21 55													
Colwall	d				21 33						22 00													
Ledbury	a				21 40						22 07													
	d				21 43						22 08													
Hereford 7	a				22 02						22 28													

For general notes see front of timetable
For details of catering facilities see Directory of Train Operators

A From Bournemouth (Table 51)

Table 71

Sundays

Stratford -upon-Avon, Marylebone and Leamington Spa → Birmingham → Stourbridge, Worcester and Hereford

20 July to 7 September

Network Diagram - See first page of Table 71

		CH	LM	GW	LM	CH	LM	GW	CH	LM	XC	XC	LM	CH	XC	GW	LM	CH	XC	LM	CH	XC
				1 ◇				1 ◇				1 ◇				1 ◇			1 ◇			
											A	B							C			
															(bus)							(bus)
								(catering)				(catering)				(catering)			(catering)			
Stratford-upon-Avon	d				09 28					10 28							11 28					
Wilmcote	d				09 33					10 33							11 33					
Wootton Wawen	d																					
Henley-in-Arden	d				09 40					10 40							11 40					
Danzey	d																					
Wood End	d																					
The Lakes	d				09x48					10x48							11x48					
Earlswood (West Midlands)	d																					
Wythall	d				09 52					10 52							11 52					
Whitlocks End	d																					
Shirley	d				09 57					10 57							11 57					
Yardley Wood	d				10 00					11 00							12 00					
Hall Green	d				10 03					11 03							12 03					
Spring Road	d				10 05					11 05							12 05					
London Marylebone 10 ⊖	d	21p40				08 00			09 15					09 33				10 15			10 50	
Banbury	d	23p03				09 34			10 36			10 53		11 01				11 38	11 53		12 02	
Leamington Spa 8	a	23p23				09 54			10 56			11 10		11 21				11 58	12 10		12 22	
	d	23p24				09 54			10 57			11 11		11 21	11 25			11 59	12 11		12 22	12 25
Warwick	d	23p28				09 59			11 01					11 25				12 03				
Warwick Parkway	d	23p31				10 02			11 04									12 06			12 28	
Hatton	d					10 07								11a33				12 11				
Lapworth	d					10 11			11 13													
Dorridge	d	23p43				10 16	10 25		11 19				11 25					12 19		12 25	12 39	
Widney Manor	d	23p46					10 29						11 29							12 29		
Solihull	d	23p50				10 21	10 32		11 24				11 32					12 24		12 32	12 45	
Olton	d						10 36						11 36							12 36		
Acocks Green	d						10 38						11 38							12 38		
Tyseley	d				10 08					11 08							12 08					
Small Heath	d																					
Bordesley	d																					
Birmingham Moor Street	d	00 02	09 26		10 13	10 33	10 45		11 34	11 13			11 45				12 13	12 35		12 45	12 56	
Birmingham Snow Hill (tram)	a	00 09	09 28		10 15	10 40	10 47		11 41	11 15			11 47				12 15	12 43		12 47	13 03	
	d		09 30		10 18		10 48			11 18			11 48				12 18			12 48		
Jewellery Quarter (tram)	d		09 32		10 20		10 51			11 20			11 51				12 20			12 51		
The Hawthorns (tram)	d		09 37		10 25		10 55			11 25			11 55				12 25			12 55		
Coventry	a														11 50							12 50
Birmingham International ✈	a														12 25							13 25
Birmingham New Street 12	a											11 51							12 46			
	d										11 46											
Smethwick Galton Bdg H.L. 7	d		09 39		10 27		10 58			11 27			11 58				12 27			12 58		
Langley Green	d						11 01						12 01							13 01		
Rowley Regis	d		09 44		10 32		11 04			11 32			12 04				12 32			13 04		
Old Hill	d						11 07						12 07							13 07		
Cradley Heath	d		09 49		10 37		11 10			11 37			12 10				12 37			13 10		
Lye	d						11 13						12 13							13 13		
Stourbridge Junction 2	d		09 54		10 43		11a17			11 43			12a17				12 43			13a17		
Hagley	d		09 58		10 46					11 47							12 46					
Blakedown	d									11 50							12 49					
Kidderminster	d		10 04		10 52					11 55							12 54					
Hartlebury	d																					
University	d																					
Barnt Green	d																					
Bromsgrove	d										12 05											
Droitwich Spa	d		10 15		11 04					12 06	12 13						13 06					
Worcester Shrub Hill 7	a		10 23		11 11					12 14	12 22						13 13					
	d		10 26	10 35	11 24			12 04								13 09	13 25					
Worcester Foregate Street 7	a		10 29	10 37	11 27			12 07								13 11	13 27					
	d		10 29	10 39	11 27			12 08								13 13	13 28					
Malvern Link	d		10 38	10 48	11 36			12 17								13 22	13 36					
Great Malvern	a		10 41	10 50	11 39			12 20								13 25	13 39					
	d							12 22								13 26						
Colwall	d							12 27								13 32						
Ledbury	a							12 34								13 39						
	d							12 37								13 48						
Hereford 7	a							12 54								14 04						

For general notes see front of timetable
For details of catering facilities see Directory of Train Operators

A To Gloucester (Table 57)
B From Southampton Central (Table 51)
C From Bournemouth (Table 51)

Due to Engineering Operations, services from Sunday 14 September on this Table had not been confirmed at time of going to press. These services will be issued in a special Supplement as soon as exact timings have been confirmed

Sundays

20 July to 7 September

Stratford -upon-Avon, Marylebone and Leamington Spa → Birmingham → Stourbridge, Worcester and Hereford

Network Diagram - See first page of Table 71

Station		XC	CH	LM	LM	XC	LM	CH	XC	CH	XC	GW	LM	CH	XC	LM	CH	XC	XC	CH	XC	CH
		1 ◇				R 1					1 ◇	1 ◇			R 1				1 ◇		R 1	
		A				B									B						B	
									🚌									🚌				
		☕				☕					☕	☕			☕				☕		☕	
Stratford-upon-Avon	d			12 30									13 28									
Wilmcote	d			12 35									13 33									
Wootton Wawen	d																					
Henley-in-Arden	d			12 42									13 40									
Danzey	d																					
Wood End	d																					
The Lakes	d			12x50									13x48									
Earlswood (West Midlands)	d																					
Wythall	d			12 54									13 52									
Whitlocks End	d																					
Shirley	d			12 59									13 57									
Yardley Wood	d			13 02									14 00									
Hall Green	d			13 05									14 03									
Spring Road	d			13 07									14 05									
London Marylebone 10 ⊖	d		11 15					11 33		11 50				12 20			12 50			13 15		13 33
Banbury	d	12 25	12 36			12 53		13 01		13 05	13 25			13 43	13 53		14 02		14 25	14 36	14 53	15 01
Leamington Spa 8	a	12 41	12 56			13 10		13 21		13 25	13 41			14 02	14 10		14 22		14 41	14 56	15 10	15 21
	d	12 43	12 57			13 11		13 21	13 25	13 26	13 43			14 03	14 11		14 22	14 25	14 43	14 57	15 11	15 21
Warwick	d		13 01					13 25						14 07						15 01		15 25
Warwick Parkway	d		13 04							13 31				14 10			14 28			15 04		
Hatton	d							13a33														15a33
Lapworth	d		13 13																	15 13		
Dorridge	d		13 18				13 25			13 43				14 22		14 25	14 39			15 18		
Widney Manor	d						13 29									14 29						
Solihull	d		13 23				13 32			13 48				14 28		14 32	14 45			15 23		
Olton	d						13 36									14 36						
Acocks Green	d						13 38									14 38						
Tyseley	d			13 10									14 08									
Small Heath	d																					
Bordesley	d																					
Birmingham Moor Street	d		13 31	13 15			13 45			14 01			14 13	14 39		14 45	14 56			15 31		
Birmingham Snow Hill ⛴	a		13 41	13 17			13 48			14 08			14 15	14 47		14 47	15 03			15 41		
	d			13 20			13 48						14 18			14 48						
Jewellery Quarter ⛴	d			13 22			13 51						14 20			14 51						
The Hawthorns ⛴	d			13 27			13 55						14 25			14 55						
Coventry	a								13 50									14 50				
Birmingham International ✈	a								14 25									15 25				
Birmingham New Street 12	a	13 15				13 45					14 15				14 54				15 15		15 46	
	d				13 45																	
Smethwick Galton Bdg H.L. 7	d			13 29			13 58						14 27			14 58						
Langley Green	d						14 01									15 01						
Rowley Regis	d			13 34			14 04						14 32			15 04						
Old Hill	d						14 07									15 07						
Cradley Heath	d			13 39			14 10						14 37			15 10						
Lye	d						14 13									15 13						
Stourbridge Junction 2	d			13 46			14a18						14 43			15a17						
Hagley	d			13 49									14 46									
Blakedown	d												14 49									
Kidderminster	d			13 55									14 54									
Hartlebury	d																					
University	d																					
Barnt Green	d																					
Bromsgrove	d				14 05																	
Droitwich Spa	d			14 07	14 15								15 06									
Worcester Shrub Hill 7	a				14 22																	
	d				14 28							15 08										
Worcester Foregate Street 7	a			14 20	14 30							15 10	15 14									
	d				14 31							15 12										
Malvern Link	d				14 39																	
Great Malvern	a				14 42							15 21										
	d				14 43							15 22										
Colwall	d				14 48																	
Ledbury	a				14 55							15 32										
	d				14 58							15 34										
Hereford 7	a				15 19							15 51										

For general notes see front of timetable
For details of catering facilities see Directory of Train Operators

A From Brighton (Table 51)
B From Bournemouth (Table 51)

Due to Engineering Operations, services from Sunday 14 September on this Table had not been confirmed at time of going to press. These services will be issued in a special Supplement as soon as exact timings have been confirmed

Table 71

Sundays

20 July to 7 September

Stratford -upon-Avon, Marylebone and Leamington Spa → Birmingham → Stourbridge, Worcester and Hereford

Network Diagram - See first page of Table 71

		LM	LM	LM	XC		CH	XC	LM	CH	XC	LM		CH	XC	XC	GW	LM	CH		XC	CH	LM	LM	LM
								1 ◇			R 1					1 ◇	1 ◇				R 1				
											A										A				
					🚌										🚌										
								☕			☕					☕	☕				☕				
Stratford-upon-Avon	d	14 28							15 28														16 28		
Wilmcote	d	14 33							15 33														16 33		
Wootton Wawen	d																								
Henley-in-Arden	d	14 40							15 40														16 40		
Danzey	d																								
Wood End	d																						16x45		
The Lakes	d	14x48							15x48														16x48		
Earlswood (West Midlands)	d																								
Wythall	d	14 52							15 52														16 52		
Whitlocks End	d																								
Shirley	d	14 57							15 57														16 57		
Yardley Wood	d	15 00							16 00														17 00		
Hall Green	d	15 03							16 03														17 03		
Spring Road	d	15 05							16 05														17 05		
London Marylebone 10 ⊖	d						13 50			14 20				14 50					15 15			15 33			
Banbury	d						15 05	15 25		15 41	15 53			16 02		16 25			16 35		16 53	17 01			
Leamington Spa 8	a						15 25	15 41		16 01	16 10			16 22		16 41			16 56		17 10	17 20			
	d				15 25		15 26	15 43		16 02	16 11			16 22	16 25	16 43			16 56		17 11	17 21			
Warwick	d									16 06									17 01			17 26			
Warwick Parkway	d						15 31			16 09				16 28					17 04						
Hatton	d									16 14												17a33			
Lapworth	d																		17 13						
Dorridge	d		15 25				15 43			16 22		16 25		16 39					17 17					17 25	
Widney Manor	d		15 29									16 29												17 29	
Solihull	d		15 32				15 48			16 28		16 32		16 45					17 22					17 32	
Olton	d		15 36									16 36												17 36	
Acocks Green	d		15 38									16 38												17 38	
Tyseley	d	15 08							16 08														17 09		
Small Heath	d																								
Bordesley	d																								
Birmingham Moor Street	d	15 13	15 45				15 59		16 13	16 39		16 45		16 56				17 02	17 34				17 13	17 45	
Birmingham Snow Hill 🚋	a	15 15	15 48				16 06		16 15	16 46		16 48		17 03				17 04	17 41				17 18	17 48	
	d	15 18	15 48						16 18			16 48						17 06					17 20	17 48	
Jewellery Quarter 🚋	d	15 20	15 51						16 20			16 51											17 22	17 51	
The Hawthorns 🚋	d	15 25	15 55						16 25			16 55											17 27	17 55	
Coventry	a				15 50										16 50										
Birmingham International ✈	a				16 25										17 25										
Birmingham New Street 12	a							16 15			16 57					17 15					17 46				
	d			16 00																					18 00
Smethwick Galton Bdg H.L. 7	d	15 27	15 58						16 27			16 58											17 29	17 58	
Langley Green	d		16 01									17 01												18 01	
Rowley Regis	d	15 32	16 04						16 32			17 04											17 34	18 04	
Old Hill	d		16 07									17 07												18 07	
Cradley Heath	d	15 37	16 10						16 37			17 10											17 39	18 10	
Lye	d		16 13									17 13												18 13	
Stourbridge Junction 2	d	15 43	16a18						16 43			17a18						17 27					17 45	18a19	
Hagley	d	15 46							16 46									17 30					17 48		
Blakedown	d																								
Kidderminster	d	15 52							16 52									17 36					17 54		
Hartlebury	d																								
University	d																								
Barnt Green	d																								
Bromsgrove	d			16 21																					18 21
Droitwich Spa	d	16 04		16 30					17 04									17 48					18 06		18 30
Worcester Shrub Hill 7	a			16 41																			18 13		18 38
	d			16 45													17 09								18 41
Worcester Foregate Street 7	a	16 12		16 47					17 12								17 12	18 01							18 44
	d			16 48													17 13								18 44
Malvern Link	d			16 57													17 22								18 53
Great Malvern	a			17 02													17 25								18 56
	d																17 27								18 57
Colwall	d																17 32								19 02
Ledbury	a																17 39								19 09
	d																17 42								19 09
Hereford 7	a																17 58								19 30

For general notes see front of timetable
For details of catering facilities see Directory of Train Operators

A From Bournemouth (Table 51)

Due to Engineering Operations, services from Sunday 14 September on this Table had not been confirmed at time of going to press. These services will be issued in a special Supplement as soon as exact timings have been confirmed

Table 71

Sundays

20 July to 7 September

Stratford -upon-Avon, Marylebone and Leamington Spa → Birmingham → Stourbridge, Worcester and Hereford

Network Diagram - See first page of Table 71

		XC	CH	XC	GW	LM	CH	XC	XC	CH	LM	XC	GW	CH	XC	CH	LM	XC	CH	XC	GW	LM
				1 ◇	1 ◇			R 1				1 ◇	1 ◇		R 1					1 ◇	1 ◇	
								A							A							
		🚌							🚌									🚌				
				🍴	🍴			🍴				🍴	🍴		🍴					🍴	🍴	
Stratford-upon-Avon	d					17 28											18 28					19 28
Wilmcote	d					17 33											18 33					19 33
Wootton Wawen	d																					
Henley-in-Arden	d					17 40											18 40					19 40
Danzey	d																					
Wood End	d																					
The Lakes	d					17x48											18x48					19x48
Earlswood (West Midlands)	d																					
Wythall	d					17 52											18 52					19 52
Whitlocks End	d																					
Shirley	d					17 57											18 57					19 57
Yardley Wood	d					18 00											19 00					20 00
Hall Green	d					18 03											19 03					20 03
Spring Road	d					18 05											19 05					20 05
London Marylebone 10 ⊖	d		15 50				16 20			16 57				17 20		17 35			17 57			
Banbury	d		17 05	17 25			17 41	17 53		18 09		18 25		18 41	18 53	19 01			19 09	19 25		
Leamington Spa 8	a		17 25	17 41			18 01	18 10		18 29		18 41		19 01	19 10	19 21			19 29	19 41		
	d	17 25	17 26	17 43			18 02	18 11	18 25	18 29		18 43		19 02	19 11	19 21		19 25	19 29	19 43		
Warwick	d						18 06							19 06		19 25						
Warwick Parkway	d		17 31				18 09			18 35				19 09					19 35			
Hatton	d						18 14									19a32						
Lapworth	d													19 18								
Dorridge	d		17 43				18 22			18 46				19 23					19 46			
Widney Manor	d						18 26							19 26								
Solihull	d		17 48				18 29			18 52				19 30					19 52			
Olton	d																					
Acocks Green	d																					
Tyseley	d					18 08											19 08					20 08
Small Heath	d																					
Bordesley	d																					
Birmingham Moor Street	d		17 59			18 13	18 41			19 02				19 41			19 13		20 02			20 13
Birmingham Snow Hill 🚋	a		18 07			18 15	18 49			19 10				19 48			19 15		20 10			20 15
	d					18 18											19 18					20 18
Jewellery Quarter 🚋	d					18 20											19 20					20 20
The Hawthorns 🚋	d					18 25											19 25					20 25
Coventry	a	17 50							18 50									19 50				
Birmingham International ✈	a	18 25							19 25									20 25				
Birmingham New Street 12	a			18 15				18 51				19 15			19 46					20 15		
	d										19 00											
Smethwick Galton Bdg H.L. 7	d					18 27											19 27					20 27
Langley Green	d																					
Rowley Regis	d					18 32											19 32					20 32
Old Hill	d																					
Cradley Heath	d					18 37											19 37					20 37
Lye	d																					
Stourbridge Junction 2	d					18 43											19 43					20 43
Hagley	d					18 47											19 46					20 46
Blakedown	d					18 50																
Kidderminster	d					18 55											19 52					20 53
Hartlebury	d																					
University	d																					
Barnt Green	d																					
Bromsgrove	d										19 21											
Droitwich Spa	d					19 06					19 31						20 08					21 05
Worcester Shrub Hill 7	a					19 14					19 41						20 15					21 15
	d				19 10								20 10								21 11	21 28
Worcester Foregate Street 7	a				19 12								20 12								21 13	21 31
	d				19 14								20 14								21 15	21 31
Malvern Link	d				19 22								20 22								21 24	21 40
Great Malvern	a				19 26								20 26								21 27	21 43
	d																				21 28	
Colwall	d																				21 33	
Ledbury	a																				21 40	
	d																				21 43	
Hereford 7	a																				22 02	

For general notes see front of timetable
For details of catering facilities see
Directory of Train Operators

A From Bournemouth (Table 51)

Due to Engineering Operations, services from Sunday 14 September on this Table had not been confirmed at time of going to press. These services will be issued in a special Supplement as soon as exact timings have been confirmed

Sundays

20 July to 7 September

Stratford -upon-Avon, Marylebone and Leamington Spa → Birmingham → Stourbridge, Worcester and Hereford

Network Diagram - See first page of Table 71

Station		CH	XC	XC	CH	LM	GW	LM	CH	XC	XC	CH	CH	XC	XC	LM	CH	XC	CH
			1 ◇				1 ◇			1 ◇				1 ◇				1 ◇	
			A							A				A				A	
			🍴	🚌						🍴	🚌				🚌				
Stratford-upon-Avon	d																		
Wilmcote	d																		
Wootton Wawen	d																		
Henley-in-Arden	d																		
Danzey	d																		
Wood End	d																		
The Lakes	d																		
Earlswood (West Midlands)	d																		
Wythall	d																		
Whitlocks End	d																		
Shirley	d																		
Yardley Wood	d																		
Hall Green	d																		
Spring Road	d																		
London Marylebone 10 ⊖	d	18 20			18 57				19 22			19 57	20 20				20 50		21 40
Banbury	d	19 41	19 53		20 09				20 44	20 53		21 09	21 41	21 53			22 10	22 53	23 01
Leamington Spa 8	a	20 01	20 10		20 29				21 04	21 10		21 29	22 01	22 10			22 30	23 10	23 21
	d	20 02	20 11	20 25	20 29				21 04	21 11	21 25	21 29	22 02	22 11	22 25		22 31	23 11	23 22
Warwick	d	20 06							21 09				22 06				22 35		23 26
Warwick Parkway	d	20 09			20 35				21 12			21 35	22 09				22 38		23 29
Hatton	d																22 43		
Lapworth	d																22 48		
Dorridge	d	20 21			20 46				21 23			21 46	22 21				22 52		23 41
Widney Manor	d	20 24							21 27								22 56		
Solihull	d	20 28			20 52				21 30			21 52	22 26				22 59		23 46
Olton	d																		
Acocks Green	d																		
Tyseley	d																		
Small Heath	d																		
Bordesley	d																		
Birmingham Moor Street	d	20 39			21 02			21 35	21 41			22 02	22 38			22 55	23 11		23 57
Birmingham Snow Hill 🚊	a	20 46			21 10			21 37	21 48			22 10	22 45			22 57	23 18		00 04
	d							21 45								23 00			
Jewellery Quarter 🚊	d							21 47								23 02			
The Hawthorns 🚊	d							21 52								23 07			
Coventry	a			20 50							21 50				22 50				
Birmingham International ✈	a			21 25							22 25				23 25				
Birmingham New Street 12	a		20 51							21 51				22 51				23 43	
	d					21 00													
Smethwick Galton Bdg H.L. 7	d							21 54								23 09			
Langley Green	d																		
Rowley Regis	d							21 59								23 14			
Old Hill	d																		
Cradley Heath	d							22 03								23 19			
Lye	d																		
Stourbridge Junction 2	d							22 09								23 24			
Hagley	d							22 12								23 28			
Blakedown	d																		
Kidderminster	d							22 18								23 34			
Hartlebury	d																		
University	d																		
Barnt Green	d																		
Bromsgrove	d					21 21													
Droitwich Spa	d					21 30		22 30								23 45			
Worcester Shrub Hill 7	a					21 37		22 37								23 53			
	d					21 40	22 22	22 41											
Worcester Foregate Street 7	a					21 42	22 24	22 43											
	d					21 43	22 25	22 44											
Malvern Link	d					21 52	22 33	22 52											
Great Malvern	a					21 54	22 40	22 55											
	d					21 55													
Colwall	d					22 00													
Ledbury	a					22 07													
	d					22 08													
Hereford 7	a					22 28													

For general notes see front of timetable
For details of catering facilities see Directory of Train Operators

A From Bournemouth (Table 51)

Due to Engineering Operations, services from Sunday 14 September on this Table had not been confirmed at time of going to press. These services will be issued in a special Supplement as soon as exact timings have been confirmed

Stourbridge Junction — Stourbridge Town

Network Diagram - See first page of Table 71

Miles			LM	LM	LM	LM	LM	LM	LM	LM	LM	LM	LM	LM	LM	LM	LM	LM	LM	LM	LM	LM	LM	LM	LM	LM
0	Stourbridge Junction 2	d	06 07	06 37	06 50	07 03	07 16	07 29	07 42	07 56	08 09	08 24	08 37	08 50	09 07	09 24	09 37	09 54	10 07	10 24	10 37	10 54	11 07	11 24	11 37	11 54
¾	Stourbridge Town	a	06 10	06 40	06 53	07 06	07 19	07 32	07 45	07 59	08 12	08 27	08 40	08 53	09 10	09 27	09 40	09 57	10 10	10 27	10 40	10 57	11 10	11 27	11 40	11 57

		LM	LM	LM	LM	LM	LM	LM	LM	LM	LM	LM	LM	LM	LM	LM	LM	LM	LM	LM	LM	LM	LM	LM	LM	LM
Stourbridge Junction 2	d	12 07	12 24	12 37	12 54	13 07	13 24	13 37	13 54	14 07	14 24	14 37	14 54	15 11	15 24	15 37	15 52	16 05	16 18	16 31	16 44	16 57	17 10	17 23	17 35	17 48
Stourbridge Town	a	12 10	12 27	12 40	12 57	13 10	13 27	13 40	13 57	14 10	14 27	14 40	14 58	15 14	15 27	15 40	15 55	16 08	16 21	16 34	16 47	17 00	17 13	17 26	17 38	17 51

		LM	LM	LM	LM	LM	LM	LM	LM	LM	LM	LM	LM	LM	LM	LM	LM	LM	LM	LM	LM	LM	LM	LM	LM	
																	SO	SO								
Stourbridge Junction 2	d	18 01	18 16	18 30	18 44	18 57	19 10	19 23	19 36	19 55	20 08	20 28	20 41	20 54	21 07	21 20	21 33	21 46	21 59	22 30	22 51	23 03	23 15	23 34	23 47	.....
Stourbridge Town	a	18 04	18 19	18 33	18 47	19 00	19 13	19 26	19 39	19 58	20 11	20 31	20 44	20 57	21 10	21 23	21 36	21 49	22 02	22 33	22 54	23 06	23 18	23 37	23 50	.

Mondays to Saturdays

Miles			LM	LM	LM	LM	LM	LM	LM	LM	LM	LM	LM	LM	LM	LM	LM	LM	LM	LM	LM	LM	LM	LM	LM	LM
0	Stourbridge Town	d	05 50	06 13	06 43	06 56	07 09	07 22	07 35	07 48	08 02	08 17	08 30	08 43	09 00	09 13	09 30	09 43	10 00	10 13	10 30	10 43	11 00	11 13	11 30	11 43
¾	Stourbridge Junction 2	a	05 53	06 16	06 46	06 59	07 12	07 25	07 38	07 51	08 05	08 20	08 33	08 46	09 03	09 16	09 33	09 46	10 03	10 16	10 33	10 46	11 03	11 16	11 33	11 46

		LM	LM	LM	LM	LM	LM	LM	LM	LM	LM	LM	LM	LM	LM	LM	LM	LM	LM	LM	LM	LM	LM	LM	LM	LM
Stourbridge Town	d	12 00	12 13	12 30	12 43	13 00	13 13	13 30	13 43	14 00	14 13	14 30	14 43	15 00	15 17	15 30	15 43	15 58	16 11	16 24	16 37	16 50	17 03	17 16	17 28	17 41
Stourbridge Junction 2	a	12 03	12 16	12 33	12 46	13 03	13 16	13 33	13 46	14 03	14 16	14 33	14 46	15 04	15 20	15 33	15 46	16 01	16 14	16 27	16 40	16 53	17 06	17 19	17 31	17 44

		LM	LM	LM	LM	LM	LM	LM	LM	LM	LM	LM	LM	LM	LM	LM	LM	LM	LM	LM	LM	LM	LM	LM	LM	
																	SO	SO								
Stourbridge Town	d	17 54	18 07	18 22	18 36	18 50	19 03	19 16	19 29	19 42	20 01	20 15	20 34	20 47	21 00	21 13	21 26	21 39	21 52	22 16	22 44	22 57	23 09	23 21	23 40	.....
Stourbridge Junction 2	a	17 57	18 10	18 25	18 39	18 53	19 06	19 19	19 32	19 45	20 04	20 18	20 37	20 50	21 03	21 16	21 29	21 42	21 55	22 19	22 47	23 00	23 12	23 24	23 43	.

For general notes see front of timetable
For details of catering facilities see
Directory of Train Operators

No Sunday Service

Network Diagram for Tables 74, 75

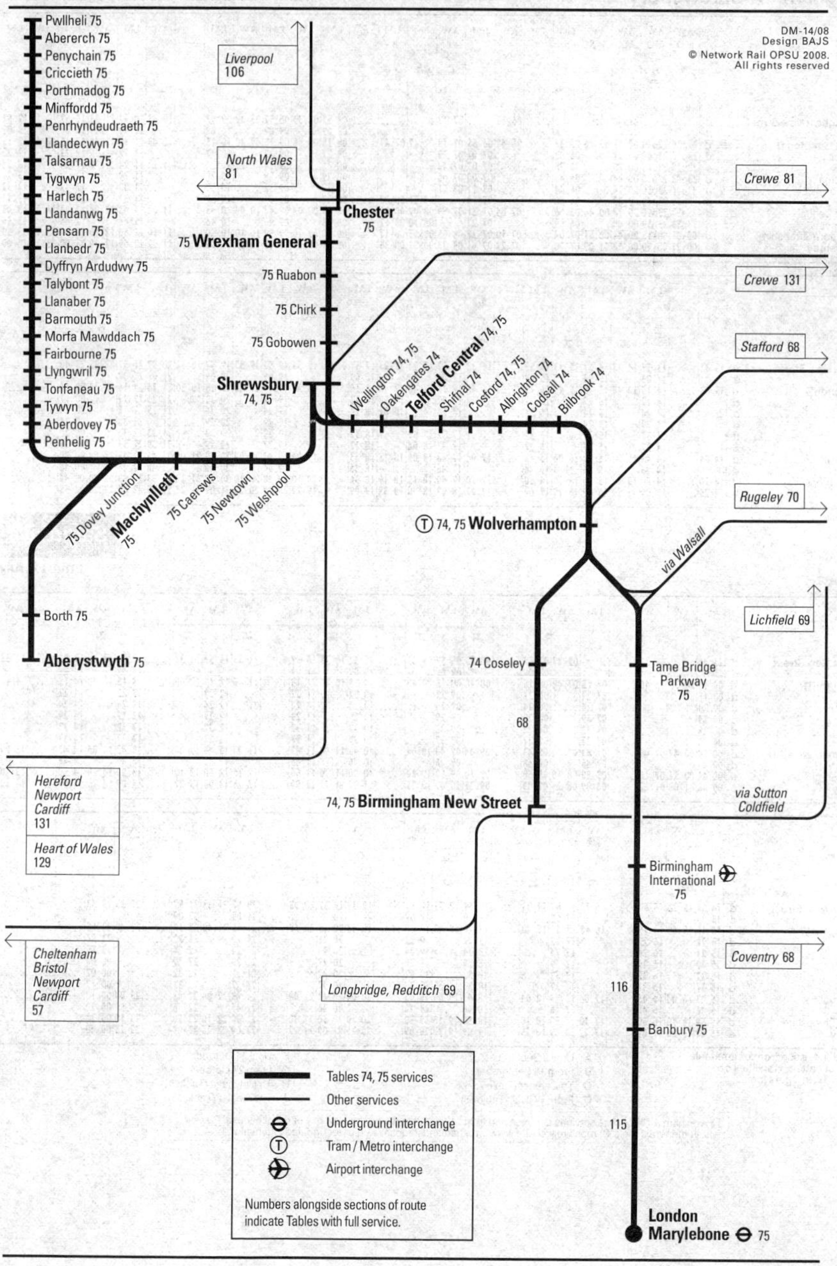

DM-14/08
Design BAJS
© Network Rail OPSU 2008.
All rights reserved
Pwllheli 75
Abererch 75
Penychain 75
Criccieth 75
Porthmadog 75
Minffordd 75
Penrhyndeudraeth 75
Llandecwyn 75
Talsarnau 75
Tygwyn 75
Harlech 75
Llandanwg 75
Pensarn 75
Llanbedr 75
Dyffryn Ardudwy 75
Talybont 75
Llanaber 75
Barmouth 75
Morfa Mawddach 75
Fairbourne 75
Llyngwril 75
Tonfaneau 75
Tywyn 75
Aberdovey 75
Penhelig 75
Liverpool 106
North Wales 81
Chester 75
75 Wrexham General
75 Ruabon
75 Chirk
75 Gobowen
Shrewsbury 74, 75
Wellington 74, 75
Oakengates 74
Telford Central 74, 75
Shifnal 74
Cosford 74, 75
Albrighton 74
Codsall 74
Bilbrook 74
Crewe 81
Crewe 131
Stafford 68
Rugeley 70
75 Dovey Junction
Machynlleth 75
75 Caersws
75 Newtown
75 Welshpool
74, 75 Wolverhampton
via Walsall
Lichfield 69
Borth 75
Aberystwyth 75
74 Coseley
Tame Bridge Parkway 75
68
Hereford
Newport
Cardiff
131
Heart of Wales
129
74, 75 Birmingham New Street
via Sutton Coldfield
Birmingham International 75
Cheltenham
Bristol
Newport
Cardiff
57
Coventry 68
Longbridge, Redditch 69
116
Banbury 75
Tables 74, 75 services
Other services
Underground interchange
Tram / Metro interchange
Airport interchange
Numbers alongside sections of route indicate Tables with full service.
115
London Marylebone 75

Birmingham → Shrewsbury

Network Diagram - see first page of Table 67

Mondays to Fridays

Miles	Station		AW	AW	AW	AW	LM	AW	LM	AW	LM	LM	LM	AW	LM	AW	LM	AW	LM	AW	LM	AW	LM
			MO	MO	MX	MX		◇		◇				◇		◇		◇		◇		◇	
			A	B 🚌						C	D E	D G		🍴		🍴		🍴		🍴		🍴	
0	**Birmingham New Street**	d			23p40			06 33		07 17			07 57	08 33	08 57	09 33	09 57	10 33	10 57	11 33	11 57	12 33	12 57
8½	Coseley	d											08 09		09 09		10 09		11 09		12 09		13 09
13	**Wolverhampton** 7	d	23p30	22p40	00 11	00 26	06 27	06 48	06 55	07 33	07 47	07 47	08 15	08 48	09 15	09 48	10 15	10 48	11 15	11 48	12 15	12 48	13 15
17	Bilbrook	d	23p36	23p00	00 17		06 33		07 01	07 39			08 22		09 22		10 22		11 22		12 22		13 22
17¾	Codsall	d	23p38	23p05	00 20		06 36		07 03	07 42			08 24		09 24		10 24		11 24		12 24		13 24
20¾	Albrighton	d	23p43	23p20	00 24		06 41		07 08	07 46			08 29		09 29		10 29		11 29		12 29		13 29
22¼	Cosford	d	23p46	23p30	00 28		06 44		07 11	07 51			08 32		09 32		10 32		11 32		12 32		13 32
25¼	Shifnal	d	23p51	23p40	00 33		06 50		07 16		08 01	08 03	08 37		09 37		10 37		11 37		12 37		13 37
28¼	Telford Central	d	23p57	23p50	00 38	00 44	06 56	07 04	07 21	07 59	08 07	08 09	08 43	09 04	09 43	10 04	10 43	11 04	11 43	12 04	12 43	13 04	13 43
29¾	Oakengates	d	23p59	23p59	00 40		06 59		07 23		08 10	08 12	08 46		09 46		10 46		11 46		12 46		13 46
32¼	Wellington (Shropshire)	d	00 05	00 15	00 44	00 51	07 04	07 10	07 27	08 05	08 15	08 17	08 50	09 10	09 50	10 10	10 50	11 10	11 50	12 10	12 50	13 10	13 50
43	**Shrewsbury**	a	00 21	00 40	00 58	01 05	07 20	07 22	07 41	08 22	08 37	08 35	09 09	09 22	10 09	10 25	11 09	11 22	12 09	12 25	13 09	13 22	14 09

Station		AW	LM	AW	LM	AW	LM	AW	LM	LM	AW	LM	AW	LM	AW	LM	AW	LM	LM	AW	AW
		◇		◇		◇		R			◇		◇		◇		◇			◇	
		🍴		🍴		🍴		🍴			C 🍴		🍴				🍴			H	
Birmingham New Street	d	13 33	13 57	14 33	14 57	15 33	15 57	16 33	16 57	17 24	17 33	17 57	18 33	18 57	19 33	19 57	20 33	20 57	21 57	22 33	23 40
Coseley	d		14 09		15 09		16 09		17 09			18 09		19 09		20 09		21 09	22 09		
Wolverhampton 7	d	13 48	14 15	14 48	15 15	15 48	16 15	16 48	17 15	17 48	17 48	18 15	18 48	19 15	19 48	20 15	20 50	21 16	22 16	22 48	00 11
Bilbrook	d		14 22		15 22		16 22		17 22		17 58	18 22		19 22		20 22		21 23	22 23		00 17
Codsall	d		14 24		15 24		16 24		17 24		18 01	18 24		19 24		20 24		21 25	22 25		00 20
Albrighton	d		14 29		15 29		16 29		17 29		18 05	18 29		19 29		20 29		21 30	22 30		00 24
Cosford	d		14 32		15 32		16 32		17 32	17 59		18 32		19 32		20 32		21 33	22 33		00 28
Shifnal	d		14 37		15 37		16 37		17 37	18 04		18 37		19 37		20 37		21 39	22 39		00 33
Telford Central	d	14 04	14 43	15 04	15 43	16 04	16 43	17 04	17 43	18 09	18 13	18 43	19 04	19 43	20 04	20 43	21 06	21 45	22 45	23 04	00 38
Oakengates	d		14 46		15 46		16 46		17 46			18 46		19 46		20 46		21 48	22 48		00 40
Wellington (Shropshire)	d	14 10	14 50	15 10	15 50	16 10	16 50	17 10	17 50	18 15	18 19	18 50	19 10	19 50	20 10	20 50	21 12	21 53	22 53	23 10	00 44
Shrewsbury	a	14 25	15 09	15 22	16 09	16 25	17 09	17 22	18 09	18 30	18 35	19 09	19 22	20 09	20 25	21 09	21 27	22 09	23 06	23 26	00 58

Saturdays

until 12 July

Station		AW	AW	AW	LM	AW	LM	AW	LM	AW	LM	AW	LM	AW	LM	AW	LM	AW	LM	AW
				◇		◇		◇ 🍴		◇ 🍴		◇ 🍴		◇ 🍴		◇ 🍴		◇ 🍴		◇ 🍴
Birmingham New Street	d	23p40		06 33		07 33	07 57	08 33	08 57	09 33	09 57	10 33	10 57	11 33	11 57	12 33	12 57	13 33	13 57	14 33
Coseley	d						08 09		09 09		10 09		11 09				13 09		14 09	
Wolverhampton 7	d	00 11	00 26	06 48	07 15	07 48	08 15	08 48	09 15	09 48	10 15	10 48	11 15	11 48	12 15	12 48	13 15	13 48	14 15	14 48
Bilbrook	d	00 17			07 22		08 22		09 22		10 22		11 22		12 22		13 22		14 22	
Codsall	d	00 20			07 24		08 24		09 24		10 24		11 24		12 24		13 24		14 24	
Albrighton	d	00 24			07 29		08 29		09 29		10 29		11 29		12 29		13 29		14 29	
Cosford	d	00 28			07 32		08 32		09 32		10 32		11 32		12 32		13 32		14 32	
Shifnal	d	00 33			07 37		08 37		09 37		10 37		11 37		12 37		13 37		14 37	
Telford Central	d	00 38	00 44	07 04	07 43	08 04	08 43	09 04	09 43	10 04	10 43	11 04	11 43	12 04	12 43	13 04	13 43	14 04	14 43	15 04
Oakengates	d	00 40			07 46		08 46		09 46		10 46		11 46		12 46		13 46		14 46	
Wellington (Shropshire)	d	00 44	00 51	07 10	07 50	08 10	08 50	09 10	09 50	10 10	10 50	11 10	11 50	12 10	12 50	13 10	13 50	14 10	14 50	15 10
Shrewsbury	a	00 58	01 05	07 22	08 09	08 25	09 09	09 22	10 09	10 25	11 09	11 22	12 09	12 25	13 09	13 22	14 09	14 25	15 09	15 22

Station		LM	AW	LM	AW	LM	AW	LM	AW	LM	AW	LM	AW	LM	AW	LM	AW	AW
			◇		R		◇		◇		◇		◇		◇		◇	
			🍴		🍴		🍴		🍴				🍴				J	
Birmingham New Street	d	14 57	15 33	15 57	16 33	16 57	17 33	17 57	18 33	18 57	19 33	19 57	20 33	20 57	21 33	21 57	22 33	23 33
Coseley	d	15 09				17 09		18 09		19 09		20 09		21 09		22 09		
Wolverhampton 7	d	15 15	15 48	16 15	16 48	17 15	17 48	18 15	18 48	19 15	19 48	20 15	20 48	21 15	21 48	22 15	22 48	23 50
Bilbrook	d	15 22		16 22		17 22		18 22		19 22		20 22		21 22		22 22		23 57
Codsall	d	15 24		16 24		17 24		18 24		19 24		20 24		21 24		22 24		23 59
Albrighton	d	15 29		16 29		17 29		18 29		19 29		20 29		21 29		22 29		00 04
Cosford	d	15 32		16 32		17 32		18 32		19 32		20 32		21 32		22 32		00 07
Shifnal	d	15 37		16 37		17 37		18 37		19 37		20 37		21 37		22 37		00 12
Telford Central	d	15 43	16 04	16 43	17 04	17 43	18 04	18 43	19 04	19 43	20 04	20 43	21 04	21 43	22 04	22 43	23 04	00 18
Oakengates	d	15 46		16 46		17 46		18 46		19 46		20 46		21 46		22 46		00 20
Wellington (Shropshire)	d	15 50	16 10	16 50	17 10	17 50	18 10	18 50	19 10	19 50	20 10	20 50	21 10	21 50	22 10	22 50	23 10	00 26
Shrewsbury	a	16 09	16 25	17 09	17 22	18 09	18 25	19 09	19 22	20 09	20 25	21 09	21 22	22 09	22 25	23 09	23 25	00 40

For general notes see front of timetable
For details of catering facilities see Directory of Train Operators

A Until 8 September
B From 15 September
C To Chester (Table 75)
D From Walsall (Table 68)
E Until 24 October.
G From 27 October.
H To Holyhead (Table 81)
J To Chester (Table 65)

Wrexham & Shropshire services are expected to start operating during the currency of this timetable. Please visit the Wrexham & Shropshire website www.wrexhamandshropshire.co.uk for updated information

Table 74

Saturdays

19 July to 6 September

Birmingham → Shrewsbury

Network Diagram - see first page of Table 67

		AW	AW	AW	LM	AW	LM	AW	LM	AW	LM	AW	LM	AW	LM	AW	LM	AW	LM	AW
				◇		◇		◇ 🛒		◇ 🛒		◇ 🛒		◇ 🛒		◇ 🛒		◇ 🛒		◇ 🛒
Birmingham New Street	d	23p40		06 33		07 33	07 57	08 33	08 57	09 33	09 57	10 33	10 57	11 33	11 57	12 33	12 57	13 33	13 57	14 33
Coseley	d						08 09		09 09		10 09		11 09				13 09		14 09	
Wolverhampton 7 🚌	d	00 11	00 26	06 48	07 15	07 48	08 15	08 48	09 15	09 48	10 15	10 48	11 15	11 48	12 15	12 48	13 15	13 48	14 15	14 48
Bilbrook	d	00 17			07 22		08 22		09 22		10 22		11 22		12 22		13 22		14 22	
Codsall	d	00 20			07 24		08 24		09 24		10 24		11 24		12 24		13 24		14 24	
Albrighton	d	00 24			07 29		08 29		09 29		10 29		11 29		12 29		13 29		14 29	
Cosford	d	00 28			07 32		08 32		09 32		10 32		11 32		12 32		13 32		14 32	
Shifnal	d	00 33			07 37		08 37		09 37		10 37		11 37		12 37		13 37		14 37	
Telford Central	d	00 38	00 44	07 04	07 43	08 04	08 43	09 04	09 43	10 04	10 43	11 04	11 43	12 04	12 43	13 04	13 43	14 04	14 43	15 04
Oakengates	d	00 40			07 46		08 46		09 46		10 46		11 46		12 46		13 46		14 46	
Wellington (Shropshire)	d	00 44	00 51	07 10	07 50	08 10	08 50	09 10	09 50	10 10	10 50	11 10	11 50	12 10	12 50	13 10	13 50	14 10	14 50	15 10
Shrewsbury	a	00 58	01 05	07 22	08 09	08 25	09 09	09 22	10 09	10 25	11 09	11 22	12 09	12 25	13 09	13 22	14 09	14 25	15 09	15 22

		LM	AW	LM	AW	LM	AW	LM	AW	LM	AW	LM	AW	LM	AW	LM	AW	AW
					R													
			◇				◇		◇		◇		◇		◇		◇ A	
			🛒		🛒		🛒		🛒				🛒					
Birmingham New Street	d	14 57	15 33	15 57	16 33	16 57	17 33	17 57	18 33	18 57	19 33	19 57	20 33	20 57	21 33	21 57	22 33	23 33
Coseley	d	15 09				17 09		18 09		19 09		20 09		21 09		22 09		
Wolverhampton 7 🚌	d	15 15	15 48	16 15	16 48	17 15	17 48	18 15	18 48	19 15	19 48	20 15	20 48	21 19	21 48	22 15	22 48	23 50
Bilbrook	d	15 22		16 22		17 22		18 22		19 22		20 22		21 28		22 22		23 57
Codsall	d	15 24		16 24		17 24		18 24		19 24		20 24		21 31		22 24		23 59
Albrighton	d	15 29		16 29		17 29		18 29		19 29		20 29		21 35		22 29		00 04
Cosford	d	15 32		16 32		17 32		18 32		19 32		20 32		21 39		22 32		00 07
Shifnal	d	15 37		16 37		17 37		18 37		19 37		20 37		21 44		22 37		00 12
Telford Central	d	15 43	16 04	16 43	17 04	17 43	18 04	18 43	19 04	19 43	20 04	20 43	21 04	21 50	22 04	22 43	23 04	00 18
Oakengates	d	15 46		16 46		17 46		18 46		19 46		20 46		21 52		22 46		00 20
Wellington (Shropshire)	d	15 50	16 10	16 50	17 10	17 50	18 10	18 50	19 10	19 50	20 10	20 50	21 10	21 57	22 10	22 50	23 10	00 26
Shrewsbury	a	16 09	16 25	17 09	17 22	18 09	18 25	19 09	19 22	20 09	20 25	21 09	21 22	22 14	22 25	23 09	23 25	00 40

Saturdays

from 13 September

		AW	AW	AW	LM	AW	LM	AW	LM	AW	LM	AW	LM	AW	LM	AW	LM	AW	LM	AW
				◇		◇		◇ 🛒		◇ 🛒		◇ 🛒		◇ 🛒		◇ 🛒		◇ 🛒		◇ 🛒
Birmingham New Street	d	23p40		06 33		07 33	07 57	08 33	08 57	09 33	09 57	10 33	10 57	11 33	11 57	12 33	12 57	13 33	13 57	14 33
Coseley	d						08 09		09 09		10 09		11 09				13 09		14 09	
Wolverhampton 7 🚌	d	00 11	00 26	06 48	07 15	07 48	08 15	08 48	09 15	09 48	10 15	10 48	11 15	11 48	12 15	12 48	13 15	13 48	14 15	14 48
Bilbrook	d	00 17			07 22		08 22		09 22		10 22		11 22		12 22		13 22		14 22	
Codsall	d	00 20			07 24		08 24		09 24		10 24		11 24		12 24		13 24		14 24	
Albrighton	d	00 24			07 29		08 29		09 29		10 29		11 29		12 29		13 29		14 29	
Cosford	d	00 28			07 32		08 32		09 32		10 32		11 32		12 32		13 32		14 32	
Shifnal	d	00 33			07 37		08 37		09 37		10 37		11 37		12 37		13 37		14 37	
Telford Central	d	00 38	00 44	07 04	07 43	08 04	08 43	09 04	09 43	10 04	10 43	11 04	11 43	12 04	12 43	13 04	13 43	14 04	14 43	15 04
Oakengates	d	00 40			07 46		08 46		09 46		10 46		11 46		12 46		13 46		14 46	
Wellington (Shropshire)	d	00 44	00 51	07 10	07 50	08 10	08 50	09 10	09 50	10 10	10 50	11 10	11 50	12 10	12 50	13 10	13 50	14 10	14 50	15 10
Shrewsbury	a	00 58	01 05	07 22	08 09	08 25	09 09	09 22	10 09	10 25	11 09	11 22	12 09	12 25	13 09	13 22	14 09	14 25	15 09	15 22

		LM	AW	LM	AW	LM	AW	LM	AW	LM	AW	LM	AW	LM	AW	LM	AW	AW
					R													
			◇				◇		◇		◇		◇		◇		◇ A	
			🛒		🛒		🛒		🛒				🛒					
Birmingham New Street	d	14 57	15 33	15 57	16 33	16 57	17 33	17 57	18 33	18 57	19 33	19 57	20 33	20 57	21 33	21 57	22 33	23 33
Coseley	d	15 09				17 09		18 09		19 09		20 09		21 10		22 09		
Wolverhampton 7 🚌	d	15 15	15 48	16 15	16 48	17 15	17 48	18 15	18 48	19 15	19 48	20 15	20 48	21 17	21 48	22 15	22 48	23 50
Bilbrook	d	15 22		16 22		17 22		18 22		19 22		20 22		21 23		22 22		23 57
Codsall	d	15 24		16 24		17 24		18 24		19 24		20 24		21 25		22 24		23 59
Albrighton	d	15 29		16 29		17 29		18 29		19 29		20 29		21 29		22 29		00 04
Cosford	d	15 32		16 32		17 32		18 32		19 32		20 32		21 33		22 32		00 07
Shifnal	d	15 37		16 37		17 37		18 37		19 37		20 37		21 38		22 37		00 12
Telford Central	d	15 43	16 04	16 43	17 04	17 43	18 04	18 43	19 04	19 43	20 04	20 43	21 04	21 44	22 04	22 43	23 04	00 18
Oakengates	d	15 46		16 46		17 46		18 46		19 46		20 46		21 46		22 46		00 20
Wellington (Shropshire)	d	15 50	16 10	16 50	17 10	17 50	18 10	18 50	19 10	19 50	20 10	20 50	21 10	21 51	22 10	22 50	23 10	00 26
Shrewsbury	a	16 09	16 25	17 09	17 22	18 09	18 25	19 09	19 22	20 09	20 25	21 09	21 22	22 09	22 25	23 09	23 25	00 40

For general notes see front of timetable
For details of catering facilities see Directory of Train Operators

A To Chester (Table 65)

Wrexham & Shropshire services are expected to start operating during the currency of this timetable. Please visit the Wrexham & Shropshire website www.wrexhamandshropshire.co.uk for updated information

Table 74

Sundays

until 13 July

Birmingham → Shrewsbury

Network Diagram - see first page of Table 67

		AW	AW	AW ◇ A	AW	AW ◇	AW ◇ B	AW	AW ◇	AW ◇ A	AW ◇ B	AW ◇ A	AW ◇ B	AW ◇	AW	AW	AW ◇	AW
Birmingham New Street	d	23p33		09 36	10 28	11 32	12 27	13 19	14 26	15 48	16 48	17 58	18 56	19 48	21 00	21 49	22 54	
Coseley	d																	
Wolverhampton 7	d	23p50	00 26	10 04	10 56	11 59	12 56	13 48	14 55	16 20	17 23	18 26	19 20	20 22	21 27	22 20	23 24	23 29
Bilbrook	d	23p57		10 11	11 03		13 02			16 27		18 33	19 26		21 33	22 28		23 35
Codsall	d	23p59		10 13	11 05		13 04			16 29		18 36	19 29		21 36	22 30		23 37
Albrighton	d	00 04		10 18	11 10		13 09			16 34		18 40	19 33		21 40	22 35		23 42
Cosford	d	00 07		10 22	11 13		13 13			16 37		18 44	19 37		21 44	22 38		23 45
Shifnal	d	00 12		10 27	11 18		13 18			16 42		18 49	19 42		21 49	22 43		23 50
Telford Central	d	00 18	00 44	10 32	11 23	12 16	13 23	14 04	15 11	16 48	17 39	18 55	19 48	20 39	21 55	22 49	23 41	23 56
Oakengates	d	00 20		10 35	11 26		13 26	14 07		16 51	17 42	18 57	19 51		21 58	22 52		23 58
Wellington (Shropshire)	d	00 26	00 50	10 42	11 32	12 23	13 33	14 13	15 18	16 58	17 49	19 04	19 58	20 45	22 05	22 59	23 47	00 04
Shrewsbury	a	00 40	01 05	10 55	11 47	12 36	13 46	14 27	15 34	17 12	18 02	19 23	20 11	20 59	22 18	23 13	00 01	00 21

Sundays

20 July to 7 September

		AW	AW	AW ◇ A	AW	AW ◇	AW ◇ B	AW	AW ◇	AW ◇ A	AW ◇ B	AW ◇ A	AW ◇ B	AW ◇	AW	AW	AW
Birmingham New Street	d	23p33		09 37	10 37	11 37	12 37	13 27	14 37	15 37	16 37	18 07	18 57	19 37	21 07	21 55	
Coseley	d																
Wolverhampton 7	d	23p50	00 26	09 57	10 56	11 57	12 56	13 48	14 55	15 55	16 58	18 26	19 15	20 00	21 27	22 13	23 29
Bilbrook	d	23p57		10 03	11 03		13 02			16 01		18 33	19 21		21 33	22 20	23 35
Codsall	d	23p59		10 06	11 05		13 04			16 04		18 36	19 24		21 36	22 23	23 37
Albrighton	d	00 04		10 11	11 10		13 09			16 08		18 40	19 28		21 40	22 27	23 42
Cosford	d	00 07		10 14	11 13		13 13			16 12		18 44	19 32		21 44	22 31	23 45
Shifnal	d	00 12		10 19	11 18		13 18			16 17		18 49	19 37		21 49	22 35	23 50
Telford Central	d	00 18	00 44	10 25	11 23	12 19	13 23	14 04	15 11	16 23	17 14	18 55	19 43	20 16	21 55	22 41	23 56
Oakengates	d	00 20		10 28	11 26		13 26	14 07		16 26	17 17	18 57	19 46		21 58	22 44	23 58
Wellington (Shropshire)	d	00 26	00 50	10 34	11 32	12 26	13 33	14 13	15 18	16 33	17 24	19 04	19 53	20 23	22 05	22 51	00 04
Shrewsbury	a	00 40	01 05	10 47	11 47	12 39	13 46	14 27	15 34	16 46	17 40	19 23	20 06	20 36	22 18	23 05	00 21

Sundays

from 14 September

		AW	AW	AW 🚌	AW 🚌	AW 🚌	AW 🚌	AW 🚌	AW 🚌	AW 🚌	AW 🚌	AW 🚌	AW 🚌
Birmingham New Street	d	23p33											
Coseley	d												
Wolverhampton 7	d	23p50	00 26	10 25	11 25	12 25	13 56	14 45	15 40	17 45	19 45	21 40	22 40
Bilbrook	d	23p57		10 45	11 45	12 45		15 05	16 00	18 05	20 05	22 00	23 00
Codsall	d	23p59		10 50	11 50	12 50		15 10	16 05	18 10	20 10	22 05	23 05
Albrighton	d	00 04		11 05	12 05	13 05		15 25	16 20	18 25	20 25	22 20	23 20
Cosford	d	00 07		11 15	12 15	13 15		15 35	16 30	18 35	20 35	22 30	23 30
Shifnal	d	00 12		11 25	12 25	13 25		15 45	16 40	18 45	20 45	22 40	23 40
Telford Central	d	00 18	00 44	11 35	12 35	13 35	14 36	15 55	16 50	18 55	20 55	22 50	23 50
Oakengates	d	00 20		11 45	12 45	13 45	14 46	16 05	17 00	19 05	21 05	23 00	23 59
Wellington (Shropshire)	d	00 26	00 50	12 00	13 00	14 00	15 01	16 20	17 15	19 20	21 20	23 15	00 15
Shrewsbury	a	00 40	01 05	12 25	13 25	14 25	15 26	16 45	17 40	19 45	21 45	23 40	00 40

For general notes see front of timetable
For details of catering facilities see
Directory of Train Operators

A To Aberystwyth (Table 75)
B To Chester (Table 75)

Wrexham & Shropshire services are expected to start operating during the currency of this timetable. Please visit the Wrexham & Shropshire website www.wrexhamandshropshire.co.uk for updated information

Shrewsbury → Birmingham

Network Diagram - see first page of Table 67

Miles			AW MO ◇ A	AW MX	AW	LM	AW	LM B	LM	AW ◇ C	LM	LM	AW ◇	LM	AW ◇	LM	AW ◇	LM	AW ◇	LM	AW ◇	LM
0	**Shrewsbury**	d	22p40	23p31	05 24	05 30	05 54	06 05	06 48	07 12	07 37	07 47	08 22	08 42	09 22	09 35	10 22	10 35	11 22	11 35	12 22	12 35
10½	Wellington (Shropshire)	d	23p05	23p43	05 37	05 43	06 07	06 18	07 02	07 22	07 50	08 00	08 35	08 55	09 35	09 48	10 35	10 48	11 35	11 48	12 35	12 48
13¾	Oakengates	d	23p15	23p49		05 49		06 23		07 26		08 04		08 59		09 54		10 54		11 54		12 54
14¾	Telford Central	d	23p25	23p52	05 43	05 52	06 13	06 26	07 09	07 29	07 57	08 07	08 41	09 02	09 41	09 57	10 41	10 57	11 41	11 57	12 41	12 57
17¾	Shifnal	d	23p35	23p57		05 57		06 32		07 34		08 12		09 07		10 02		11 02		12 02		13 02
20¾	Cosford	d	23p45	00 03		06 03		06 37		07 39		08 17		09 12		10 07		11 07		12 07		13 07
22¼	Albrighton	d	23p50	00 06		06 06		06 40		07 43		08 20		09 15		10 10		11 10		12 10		13 10
25½	Codsall	d	23p59	00 12		06 12		06 45		07 48		08 26		09 21		10 16		11 16		12 16		13 16
26	Bilbrook	d	00 05	00 14		06 14		06 47		07 51		08 28		09 23		10 18		11 18		12 18		13 18
30	**Wolverhampton** 7	a	00 25	00 27	06 00	06 22	06 30	06 55	07 27	07 58	08 19	08 35	08 58	09 30	09 58	10 27	10 58	11 27	11 58	12 27	12 58	13 27
34½	Coseley	a												09 35		10 33		11 33		12 33		13 33
43	**Birmingham New Street** 12	a			06 18		06 48		07 48	08 18	08 36	08 55	09 18	09 51	10 18	10 48	11 18	11 48	12 18	12 48	13 18	13 48

		AW ◇	LM	AW ◇	LM	AW ◇	LM	AW ◇	LM	AW ◇	LM	AW ◇	LM	AW ◇	LM	AW ◇	LM B	AW TThX	AW
Shrewsbury	d	13 22	13 35	14 22	14 35	15 22	15 35	16 22	16 35	17 22	17 35	18 22	18 38	19 22	20 31	21 26	22 04	22 22	23 31
Wellington (Shropshire)	d	13 35	13 48	14 35	14 48	15 35	15 48	16 35	16 48	17 35	17 48	18 35	18 51	19 35	20 44	21 39	22 17	22 35	23 43
Oakengates	d		13 54		14 54		15 54		16 54		17 54		18 57		20 49		22 22		23 49
Telford Central	d	13 41	13 57	14 41	14 57	15 41	15 57	16 41	16 57	17 41	17 57	18 41	19 00	19 41	20 52	21 45	22 25	22 41	23 52
Shifnal	d		14 02		15 02		16 02		17 02		18 02		19 05		20 58		22 31		23 57
Cosford	d		14 07		15 07		16 07		17 07		18 07		19 10		21 03		22 36		00 03
Albrighton	d		14 10		15 10		16 10		17 10		18 10		19 13		21 06		22 39		00 06
Codsall	d		14 16		15 16		16 16		17 16		18 16		19 19		21 11		22 44		00 12
Bilbrook	d		14 18		15 18		16 18		17 18		18 18		19 21		21 13		22 46		00 14
Wolverhampton 7	a	13 58	14 27	14 58	15 27	15 58	16 27	16 58	17 27	17 58	18 27	18 58	19 29	19 58	21 21	22 02	22 54	22 58	00 27
Coseley	a		14 33		15 33		16 33		17 33		18 33		19 35						
Birmingham New Street 12	a	14 18	14 48	15 18	15 48	16 18	16 48	17 18	17 48	18 18	18 48	19 18	19 48	20 18	21 44	22 18		23 33	

Saturdays

until 12 July

		AW	AW	AW	LM	AW ◇ C	LM	AW ◇	LM	AW ◇	LM	AW ◇	LM	AW ◇	LM	AW ◇	LM	AW ◇
Shrewsbury	d	23p31	05 24	06 22	06 40	07 12	07 40	08 22	08 40	09 22	09 40	10 22	10 40	11 22	11 40	12 22	12 40	13 22
Wellington (Shropshire)	d	23p43	05 37	06 35	06 53	07 22	07 53	08 35	08 53	09 35	09 53	10 35	10 53	11 35	11 53	12 35	12 53	13 35
Oakengates	d	23p49			06 59	07 26	07 59		08 59		09 59		10 59		11 59		12 59	
Telford Central	d	23p52	05 43	06 41	07 02	07 29	08 02	08 41	09 02	09 41	10 02	10 41	11 02	11 41	12 02	12 41	13 02	13 41
Shifnal	d	23p57			07 07	07 34	08 07		09 07		10 07		11 07		12 07		13 07	
Cosford	d	00 03			07 12	07 39	08 12		09 12		10 12		11 12		12 12		13 12	
Albrighton	d	00 06			07 15	07 43	08 15		09 15		10 15		11 15		12 15		13 15	
Codsall	d	00 12			07 21	07 48	08 21		09 21		10 21		11 21		12 21		13 21	
Bilbrook	d	00 14			07 23	07 51	08 23		09 23		10 23		11 23		12 23		13 23	
Wolverhampton 7	a	00 27	06 00	06 58	07 31	07 58	08 31	08 58	09 31	09 58	10 31	10 58	11 31	11 58	12 31	12 58	13 31	13 58
Coseley	a						08 37		09 37		10 37		11 37		12 37		13 37	
Birmingham New Street 12	a		06 18	07 18	07 51	08 18	08 51	09 18	09 51	10 18	10 51	11 18	11 51	12 18	12 51	13 18	13 51	14 18

		LM	AW ◇	LM	AW ◇	LM	AW ◇	LM	AW ◇	LM	AW ◇	LM	AW ◇	AW	LM	AW ◇	LM B	AW	AW
Shrewsbury	d	13 40	14 22	14 40	15 22	15 40	16 22	16 40	17 22	17 40	18 22	18 40	19 22	20 22	20 40	21 26	22 04	22 22	23 31
Wellington (Shropshire)	d	13 53	14 35	14 53	15 35	15 53	16 35	16 53	17 35	17 53	18 35	18 53	19 35	20 35	20 53	21 39	22 17	22 35	23 43
Oakengates	d	13 59		14 59		15 59		16 59		17 59		18 59			20 59		22 22		23 49
Telford Central	d	14 02	14 41	15 02	15 41	16 02	16 41	17 02	17 41	18 02	18 41	19 02	19 41	20 41	21 02	21 45	22 25	22 41	23 52
Shifnal	d	14 07		15 07		16 07		17 07		18 07		19 07			21 07		22 31		23 57
Cosford	d	14 12		15 12		16 12		17 12		18 12		19 12			21 12		22 36		00 03
Albrighton	d	14 15		15 15		16 15		17 15		18 15		19 15			21 15		22 39		00 06
Codsall	d	14 21		15 21		16 21		17 21		18 21		19 21			21 21		22 44		00 12
Bilbrook	d	14 23		15 23		16 23		17 23		18 23		19 23			21 23		22 46		00 14
Wolverhampton 7	a	14 31	14 58	15 31	15 58	16 31	16 58	17 31	17 58	18 31	18 58	19 31	19 58	20 58	21 31	22 02	22 54	22 58	00 24
Coseley	a	14 37		15 37		16 37		17 37		18 37		19 37							
Birmingham New Street 12	a	14 51	15 18	15 51	16 18	16 51	17 18	17 51	18 19	18 51	19 18	19 51	20 18	21 18	21 53	22 18		23 18	

For general notes see front of timetable
For details of catering facilities see Directory of Train Operators

A From 15 September
B To Walsall (Table 68)
C From Aberystwyth (Table 75)

Wrexham & Shropshire services are expected to start operating during the currency of this timetable. Please visit the Wrexham & Shropshire website www.wrexhamandshropshire.co.uk for updated information

Table 74

Shrewsbury → Birmingham

Saturdays

19 July to 6 September

Network Diagram - see first page of Table 67

		AW	AW	AW	LM	AW ◇ A ⊥	LM	AW ◇ ⊥	LM	AW ◇ ⊥	LM	AW ◇ ⊥	LM	AW ◇ ⊥	LM	AW ◇ ⊥	LM	AW ◇ ⊥
Shrewsbury	d	23p31	05 24	06 22	06 40	07 12	07 40	08 22	08 40	09 22	09 40	10 22	10 40	11 22	11 40	12 22	12 40	13 22
Wellington (Shropshire)	d	23p43	05 37	06 35	06 53	07 22	07 53	08 35	08 53	09 35	09 53	10 35	10 53	11 35	11 53	12 35	12 53	13 35
Oakengates	d	23p49	.	.	06 59	07 26	07 59	.	08 59	.	09 59	.	10 59	.	11 59	.	12 59	.
Telford Central	d	23p52	05 43	06 41	07 02	07 29	08 02	08 41	09 02	09 41	10 02	10 41	11 02	11 41	12 02	12 41	13 02	13 41
Shifnal	d	23p57	.	.	07 07	07 34	08 07	.	09 07	.	10 07	.	11 07	.	12 07	.	13 07	.
Cosford	d	00 03	.	.	07 12	07 39	08 12	.	09 12	.	10 12	.	11 12	.	12 12	.	13 12	.
Albrighton	d	00 06	.	.	07 15	07 43	08 15	.	09 15	.	10 15	.	11 15	.	12 15	.	13 15	.
Codsall	d	00 12	.	.	07 21	07 48	08 21	.	09 21	.	10 21	.	11 21	.	12 21	.	13 21	.
Bilbrook	d	00 14	.	.	07 23	07 51	08 23	.	09 23	.	10 23	.	11 23	.	12 23	.	13 23	.
Wolverhampton 7	a	00 27	06 00	06 58	07 31	07 58	08 31	08 58	09 31	09 58	10 31	10 58	11 31	11 58	12 31	12 58	13 31	13 58
Coseley	a	.	.	.	.	.	08 37	.	09 37	.	10 37	.	11 37	.	12 37	.	13 37	.
Birmingham New Street 12	a	.	06 18	07 18	07 51	08 18	08 51	09 18	09 51	10 18	10 51	11 18	11 51	12 18	12 51	13 18	13 51	14 18

		LM	AW ◇ ⊥	LM	AW ◇ ⊥	LM	AW ◇ ⊥	LM	AW ◇ ⊥	LM	AW ◇	LM	AW ◇ ⊥	AW	LM	AW ◇ ⊥	LM B	AW	AW
Shrewsbury	d	13 40	14 22	14 40	15 22	15 40	16 22	16 40	17 22	17 40	18 22	18 40	19 22	20 22	20 40	21 26	22 04	22 22	23 31
Wellington (Shropshire)	d	13 53	14 35	14 53	15 35	15 53	16 35	16 53	17 35	17 53	18 35	18 53	19 35	20 35	20 53	21 39	22 17	22 35	23 43
Oakengates	d	13 59	.	14 59	.	15 59	.	16 59	.	17 59	.	18 59	.	.	20 59	.	22 22	.	23 49
Telford Central	d	14 02	14 41	15 02	15 41	16 02	16 41	17 02	17 41	18 02	18 41	19 02	19 41	20 41	21 02	21 45	22 25	22 41	23 52
Shifnal	d	14 07	.	15 07	.	16 07	.	17 07	.	18 07	.	19 07	.	.	21 07	.	22 31	.	23 57
Cosford	d	14 12	.	15 12	.	16 12	.	17 12	.	18 12	.	19 12	.	.	21 12	.	22 36	.	00 03
Albrighton	d	14 15	.	15 15	.	16 15	.	17 15	.	18 15	.	19 15	.	.	21 15	.	22 39	.	00 06
Codsall	d	14 21	.	15 21	.	16 21	.	17 21	.	18 21	.	19 21	.	.	21 21	.	22 44	.	00 12
Bilbrook	d	14 23	.	15 23	.	16 23	.	17 23	.	18 23	.	19 23	.	.	21 23	.	22 46	.	00 14
Wolverhampton 7	a	14 31	14 58	15 31	15 58	16 31	16 58	17 31	17 58	18 31	18 58	19 31	19 58	20 58	21 31	22 02	22 54	22 58	00 24
Coseley	a	14 37	.	15 37	.	16 37	.	17 37	.	18 37	.	19 37	.	.	.	.	.	.	.
Birmingham New Street 12	a	14 51	15 18	15 51	16 18	16 51	17 18	17 51	18 19	18 51	19 18	19 51	20 18	21 18	21 53	22 18	.	23 18	.

Saturdays

from 13 September

		AW	AW	AW	LM	AW ◇ A ⊥	LM	AW ◇ ⊥	LM	AW ◇ ⊥	LM	AW ◇ ⊥	LM	AW ◇ ⊥	LM	AW ◇ ⊥	LM	AW ◇ ⊥
Shrewsbury	d	23p31	05 24	06 22	06 40	07 12	07 40	08 22	08 40	09 22	09 40	10 22	10 40	11 22	11 40	12 22	12 40	13 22
Wellington (Shropshire)	d	23p43	05 37	06 35	06 53	07 22	07 53	08 35	08 53	09 35	09 53	10 35	10 53	11 35	11 53	12 35	12 53	13 35
Oakengates	d	23p49	.	.	06 59	07 26	07 59	.	08 59	.	09 59	.	10 59	.	11 59	.	12 59	.
Telford Central	d	23p52	05 43	06 41	07 02	07 29	08 02	08 41	09 02	09 41	10 02	10 41	11 02	11 41	12 02	12 41	13 02	13 41
Shifnal	d	23p57	.	.	07 07	07 34	08 07	.	09 07	.	10 07	.	11 07	.	12 07	.	13 07	.
Cosford	d	00 03	.	.	07 12	07 39	08 12	.	09 12	.	10 12	.	11 12	.	12 12	.	13 12	.
Albrighton	d	00 06	.	.	07 15	07 43	08 15	.	09 15	.	10 15	.	11 15	.	12 15	.	13 15	.
Codsall	d	00 12	.	.	07 21	07 48	08 21	.	09 21	.	10 21	.	11 21	.	12 21	.	13 21	.
Bilbrook	d	00 14	.	.	07 23	07 51	08 23	.	09 23	.	10 23	.	11 23	.	12 23	.	13 23	.
Wolverhampton 7	a	00 27	06 00	06 58	07 31	07 58	08 31	08 58	09 31	09 58	10 31	10 58	11 31	11 58	12 31	12 58	13 31	13 58
Coseley	a	.	.	.	.	.	08 37	.	09 37	.	10 37	.	11 37	.	12 37	.	13 37	.
Birmingham New Street 12	a	.	06 18	07 18	07 51	08 18	08 51	09 18	09 51	10 18	10 51	11 18	11 51	12 18	12 51	13 18	13 51	14 18

		LM	AW ◇ ⊥	LM	AW ◇ ⊥	LM	AW ◇ ⊥	LM	AW ◇ ⊥	LM	AW ◇	LM	AW ◇ ⊥	AW	LM	AW ◇ ⊥	LM B	AW	AW
Shrewsbury	d	13 40	14 22	14 40	15 22	15 40	16 22	16 40	17 22	17 40	18 22	18 40	19 22	20 22	20 40	21 26	22 04	22 22	23 31
Wellington (Shropshire)	d	13 53	14 35	14 53	15 35	15 53	16 35	16 53	17 35	17 53	18 35	18 53	19 35	20 35	20 53	21 39	22 17	22 35	23 43
Oakengates	d	13 59	.	14 59	.	15 59	.	16 59	.	17 59	.	18 59	.	.	20 59	.	22 22	.	23 49
Telford Central	d	14 02	14 41	15 02	15 41	16 02	16 41	17 02	17 41	18 02	18 41	19 02	19 41	20 41	21 02	21 45	22 25	22 41	23 52
Shifnal	d	14 07	.	15 07	.	16 07	.	17 07	.	18 07	.	19 07	.	.	21 07	.	22 31	.	23 57
Cosford	d	14 12	.	15 12	.	16 12	.	17 12	.	18 12	.	19 12	.	.	21 12	.	22 36	.	00 03
Albrighton	d	14 15	.	15 15	.	16 15	.	17 15	.	18 15	.	19 15	.	.	21 15	.	22 39	.	00 06
Codsall	d	14 21	.	15 21	.	16 21	.	17 21	.	18 21	.	19 21	.	.	21 21	.	22 44	.	00 12
Bilbrook	d	14 23	.	15 23	.	16 23	.	17 23	.	18 23	.	19 23	.	.	21 23	.	22 46	.	00 14
Wolverhampton 7	a	14 31	14 58	15 31	15 58	16 31	16 58	17 31	17 58	18 31	18 58	19 31	19 58	20 58	21 31	22 02	22 54	22 58	00 24
Coseley	a	14 37	.	15 37	.	16 37	.	17 37	.	18 37	.	19 37	.	.	.	.	.	.	.
Birmingham New Street 12	a	14 51	15 18	15 51	16 18	16 51	17 18	17 51	18 19	18 51	19 18	19 51	20 18	21 18	21 53	22 18	.	23 18	.

For general notes see front of timetable
For details of catering facilities see Directory of Train Operators

A From Aberystwyth (Table 75)
B To Walsall (Table 68)

Wrexham & Shropshire services are expected to start operating during the currency of this timetable. Please visit the Wrexham & Shropshire website www.wrexhamandshropshire.co.uk for updated information

Table 74

Shrewsbury → Birmingham

Sundays

until 13 July

Network Diagram - see first page of Table 67

		AW	AW	AW	AW ◇	AW	AW ◇ A	AW	AW ◇	AW B	AW ◇ A	AW B	AW ◇ A	AW ◇	AW ◇ C	AW ◇ A
Shrewsbury	d	23p31	08 54	09 58	10 27	10 59	12 26	14 12	15 26	16 16	17 26	18 27	19 23	20 27	21 20	22 24
Wellington (Shropshire)	d	23p43	09 08	10 12	10 41	11 12	12 40	14 25	15 40	16 30	17 39	18 41	19 37	20 41	21 34	22 38
Oakengates	d	23p49	09 14	10 18		11 18	12 46	14 31		16 36	17 45	18 46	19 42		21 40	22 43
Telford Central	d	23p52	09 17	10 21	10 47	11 21	12 49	14 34	15 46	16 39	17 48	18 49	19 45	20 47	21 43	22 46
Shifnal	d	23p57	09 22	10 26		11 26		14 39		16 44	17 53		19 50		21 48	22 51
Cosford	d	00 03	09 27	10 30		11 31		14 44		16 49	17 58		19 55		21 53	22 56
Albrighton	d	00 06	09 30	10 34		11 34		14 47		16 52	18 01		19 58		21 56	22 59
Codsall	d	00 12	09 35	10 39		11 39		14 52		16 57	18 06		20 04		22 01	23 05
Bilbrook	d	00 14	09 37	10 41		11 41		14 54		16 59	18 08		20 06		22 03	23 07
Wolverhampton 7	a	00 24	09 44	10 50	11 04	11 53	13 06	15 01	16 03	17 06	18 15	19 06	20 13	21 05	22 10	23 17
Coseley	a															
Birmingham New Street 12	a	.	10 10	11 20	11 32	12 20	13 39	15 32	16 32	17 32	18 41	19 33	20 39	21 32	22 40	.

Sundays

20 July to 7 September

		AW	AW	AW	AW ◇	AW	AW ◇ A	AW	AW ◇	AW B	AW ◇ A	AW B	AW ◇ A	AW ◇	AW ◇ C	AW ◇ A
Shrewsbury	d	23p31	08 54	09 58	10 27	10 59	12 26	14 12	15 26	16 16	17 26	18 28	19 23	20 27	21 20	22 24
Wellington (Shropshire)	d	23p43	09 08	10 12	10 41	11 12	12 40	14 25	15 40	16 30	17 39	18 42	19 37	20 41	21 34	22 38
Oakengates	d	23p49	09 14	10 18		11 18	12 46	14 31		16 36	17 45	18 47	19 42		21 40	22 43
Telford Central	d	23p52	09 17	10 21	10 47	11 21	12 49	14 34	15 46	16 39	17 48	18 50	19 45	20 47	21 43	22 46
Shifnal	d	23p57	09 22	10 26		11 26		14 39		16 44	17 53		19 50		21 48	22 51
Cosford	d	00 03	09 27	10 30		11 31		14 44		16 49	17 58		19 55		21 53	22 56
Albrighton	d	00 06	09 30	10 34		11 34		14 47		16 52	18 01		19 58		21 56	22 59
Codsall	d	00 12	09 35	10 39		11 39		14 52		16 57	18 06		20 04		22 01	23 05
Bilbrook	d	00 14	09 37	10 41		11 41		14 54		16 59	18 08		20 06		22 03	23 07
Wolverhampton 7	a	00 24	09 44	10 48	11 04	11 54	13 06	15 01	16 02	17 06	18 14	19 08	20 13	21 05	22 11	23 17
Coseley	a															
Birmingham New Street 12	a	.	10 04	11 05	11 22	12 11	13 23	15 18	16 20	17 23	18 32	19 25	20 30	21 24	22 30	.

Sundays

from 14 September

		AW	AW 🚌	AW 🚌	AW 🚌	AW 🚌	AW 🚌	AW 🚌	AW 🚌	AW 🚌	AW 🚌	AW 🚌	AW 🚌	AW 🚌	AW 🚌
Shrewsbury	d	23p31	08 15	10 15	11 00	12 30	13 30	14 35	15 35	17 35	18 35	19 35	20 35	21 30	22 40
Wellington (Shropshire)	d	23p43	08 40	10 40	11 25	12 55	13 55	15 00	16 00	18 00	19 00	20 00	21 00	21 55	23 05
Oakengates	d	23p49	08 50	10 50	11 35	13 05	14 05	15 10	16 10	18 10	19 10	20 10	21 10	22 05	23 15
Telford Central	d	23p52	09 00	11 00	11 45	13 15	14 15	15 20	16 20	18 20	19 20	20 20	21 20	22 15	23 25
Shifnal	d	23p57	09 10	11 10	11 55	13 25	14 25	15 30	16 30	18 30	19 30	20 30	21 30	22 25	23 35
Cosford	d	00 03	09 20	11 20	12 05	13 35	14 35	15 40	16 40	18 40	19 40	20 40	21 40	22 35	23 45
Albrighton	d	00 06	09 25	11 25	12 10	13 40	14 40	15 45	16 45	18 45	19 45	20 45	21 45	22 40	23 50
Codsall	d	00 12	09 35	11 35	12 20	13 50	14 50	15 55	16 55	18 55	19 55	20 55	21 55	22 50	23 59
Bilbrook	d	00 14	09 40	11 40	12 25	13 55	14 55	16 00	17 00	19 00	20 00	21 00	22 00	22 55	00 05
Wolverhampton 7	a	00 24	10 00	12 00	12 45	14 15	15 15	16 20	17 20	19 20	20 20	21 20	22 20	23 15	00 25
Coseley	a														
Birmingham New Street 12	a	.	.	.	.	.	.	.	.	.	.	.	.	.	.

For general notes see front of timetable
For details of catering facilities see
Directory of Train Operators

A From Aberystwyth (Table 75)
B From Chester (Table 75)
C From Holyhead (Table 81)

Wrexham & Shropshire services are expected to start operating during the currency of this timetable. Please visit the Wrexham & Shropshire website www.wrexhamandshropshire.co.uk for updated information

Birmingham and Shrewsbury → Chester, Aberystwyth, Barmouth and Pwllheli

Network Diagram - see first page of Table 67

Miles	Miles	Miles			AW MX	AW	AW ◇	AW	AW	AW ◇	AW	AW	AW ◇	AW ◇ A ⚲	AW ◇	AW ◇	AW ◇ B ⚲	
—	—	—	London Euston 15 ⊖	d													06 35	
—	—	—	London Marylebone 10 ⊖	d														
—	—	—	Banbury	d														
—	—	—	Birmingham International ✈	d												06 45	08 04	
0	—	—	**Birmingham New Street 12**	d									06 33			07 17	08 33	
—	—	—	Tame Bridge Parkway	d														
12¾	—	—	**Wolverhampton 7**	d									06 48			07 33	08 48	
22	—	—	Cosford	d												07 51		
28¼	—	—	Telford Central	d									07 04			07 59	09 04	
32¼	—	—	Wellington (Shropshire)	d									07 10			08 05	09 10	
42¾	—	—	**Shrewsbury**	a									07 22			08 22	09 22	
—	—	—	Cardiff Central 7	d									05 10	05 10		05 35	07 20	
—	—	—	Manchester Piccadilly 10	d													07 28	
—	—	—	Crewe 10	d									05 55				08 08	
—	—	0	**Shrewsbury**	d	23p39			05 20			06 10		07 28	07 30		08 28	09 28	
—	—	17¾	Gobowen	d	23p58			05 39			06 29			07 49		08 47		
—	—	20¾	Chirk	d	00 03			05 44			06 34			07 54		08 52		
—	—	25	Ruabon	d	00 09			05 50			06 40			08 00		08 58		
—	—	30	Wrexham General	d	00 17			05 57			06 47			08 07		09 05		
—	—	42	**Chester**	a	00 35			06 16			07 09			08 28		09 27		
62½	—	—	Welshpool	d									07 51				09 51	
76½	—	—	Newtown (Powys)	d									08 07				10 07	
82	—	—	Caersws	d									08 13				10 13	
103¾	—	—	**Machynlleth 4**	a									08 42				10 42	
—	0	—		d		04 35	05 15		06 30	06 49		08 10	08 45		09 05		10 45	11 00
107¾	4	—	Dovey Junction 4	d		04 41	05 21		06 36	06 55		08 16	08 51		09 11		10 51	11 06
116	—	—	Borth	d		04 52			06 47			08 27	09 02				11 02	
124¼	—	—	**Aberystwyth**	a		05 05			07 00			08 40	09 22				11 22	
—	9	—	Penhelig	d			05x30			07x04					09x20			11x15
—	10	—	Aberdovey	d			05 33			07 07					09 23			11 18
—	13½	—	Tywyn	d			05 39			07 15					09 30			11 26
—	16	—	Tonfanau	d			05x43			07x19					09x34			11x30
—	20	—	Llwyngwril	d			05x49			07x25					09x40			11x36
—	22¾	—	Fairbourne	d			05 57			07 33					09 48			11 44
—	23¾	—	Morfa Mawddach	d			05x59			07x35					09x50			11x46
—	25½	—	**Barmouth**	a			06 05			07 40					09 56			11 52
—	—	—		d			06 08			07 50					09 57			11 56
—	26¾	—	Llanaber	d			06x12			07x53					10x00			11x59
—	29¼	—	Talybont	d						07x57					10x04			12x03
—	30¼	—	Dyffryn Ardudwy	d						07x59					10x06			12x05
—	32½	—	Llanbedr	d						08x02					10x09			12x08
—	33¼	—	Pensarn	d						08x04					10x11			12x10
—	34	—	Llandanwg	d						08x05					10x12			12x11
—	35¾	—	Harlech	d			06 29			08b32					10 21			12c24
—	38½	—	Tygwyn	d						08x36					10x25			12x28
—	39¼	—	Talsarnau	d						08x37					10x27			12x30
—	40½	—	Llandecwyn	d						08x40					10x29			12x32
—	41½	—	Penrhyndeudraeth	d						08 43					10 32			12 35
—	42½	—	Minffordd	d						08 46					10 36			12 39
—	44½	—	Porthmadog	d			06 45			08 52					10 42			12 47
—	49½	—	Criccieth	d						08 59					10 50			12 55
—	54	—	Penychain	d			06x58			09x05					10x55			13x00
—	55½	—	Abererch	d						09x08					10x58			13x03
—	57½	—	**Pwllheli**	a			07 05			09 13					11 09			13 14

For general notes see front of timetable
For details of catering facilities see Directory of Train Operators

A To Holyhead (Table 81)
B From 8 September
b Arr. 0811
c Arr. 1217

Wrexham & Shropshire services are expected to start operating during the currency of this timetable. Please visit the Wrexham & Shropshire website www.wrexhamandshropshire.co.uk for updated information

Birmingham and Shrewsbury → Chester, Aberystwyth, Barmouth and Pwllheli

Network Diagram - see first page of Table 67

		AW ◇ A		AW ◇ B	AW ◇	AW ◇		AW ◇ B	AW ◇	AW ◇		AW ◇ B	AW ◇	AW ◇ C		AW ◇ A		AW ◇ B
London Euston 15	⊖ d	06 35			07 40	08 40			09 40	10 40			11 40	12 40		12 40		
London Marylebone 10	⊖ d																	
Banbury	d																	
Birmingham International	d	08 04			09 05	10 05			11 05	12 05			13 05	14 05		14 05		
Birmingham New Street 12	d	08 33			09 33	10 33			11 33	12 33			13 33	14 33		14 33		
Tame Bridge Parkway	d																	
Wolverhampton 7	d	08 48			09 48	10 48			11 48	12 48			13 48	14 48		14 48		
Cosford	d																	
Telford Central	d	09 04			10 04	11 04			12 04	13 04			14 04	15 04		15 04		
Wellington (Shropshire)	d	09 10			10 10	11 10			12 10	13 10			14 10	15 10		15 10		
Shrewsbury	a	09 22			10 25	11 22			12 25	13 22			14 25	15 22		15 22		
Cardiff Central 7	d	07 20		07 20		09 20		09 20	09 50	11 20		11 20	11 50	13 20		13 20		13 20
Manchester Piccadilly 10	d	07 28				09 34				11 34				13 34		13 34		
Crewe 10	d	08 08				10 17				12 18				14 18		14 18		
Shrewsbury	d	09 28		09 30	10 26	11 28		11 30	12 26	13 28		13 30	14 26	15 28		15 28		15 30
Gobowen	d			09 49	10 46			11 49	12 46			13 49	14 46					15 49
Chirk	d			09 54	10 51			11 54	12 51			13 54	14 51					15 54
Ruabon	d			10 00	10 57			12 00	12 57			14 00	14 57					16 00
Wrexham General	d			10 07	11 03			12 07	13 03			14 07	15 03					16 07
Chester	a			10 28	11 22			12 28	13 26			14 28	15 22					16 28
Welshpool	d	09 51				11 51				13 51				15 51		15 51		
Newtown (Powys)	d	10 07				12 07				14 07				16 07		16 07		
Caersws	d	10 13				12 13				14 13				16 13		16 13		
Machynlleth 4	a	10 42				12 42				14 42				16 42		16 42		
	d	10 45	11 00			12 45	12 56			14 45	14 56			16 45	17 00	16 45	17 05	
Dovey Junction 4	d	10 51	11 06			12 51	13 02			14 51	15 02			16 51	17 06	16 51	17 11	
Borth	d	11 02				13 02				15 02				17 02		17 02		
Aberystwyth	a	11 22				13 22				15 22				17 22		17 22		
Penhelig	d		11x15				13x11				15x11				17x15		17x20	
Aberdovey	d		11 18				13 14				15 14				17 18		17 23	
Tywyn	d		11b31				13 22				15 22				17 26		17 29	
Tonfanau	d		11x35				13x26				15x26				17x30		17x33	
Llwyngwril	d		11x41				13x32				15x32				17x36		17x39	
Fairbourne	d		11 49				13 40				15 40				17 44		17 47	
Morfa Mawddach	d		11x51				13x42				15x42				17x46		17x49	
Barmouth	a		11 56				13 48				15 47				17 52		17 55	
	d		11 56				13 52				15 52				17 56		17 56	
Llanaber	d		11x59				13x55				15x55				17x59		17x59	
Talybont	d		12x03				13x59				15x58				18x03		18x03	
Dyffryn Ardudwy	d		12x05				14x01				16x00				18x05		18x05	
Llanbedr	d		12x08				14x04				16x04				18x08		18x08	
Pensarn	d		12x10				14x06				16x05				18x10		18x10	
Llandanwg	d		12x11				14x07				16x07				18x11		18x11	
Harlech	d		12c24				14e30				16f20				18g24		18g24	
Tygwyn	d		12x28				14x34				16x24				18x28		18x28	
Talsarnau	d		12x30				14x36				16x26				18x30		18x30	
Llandecwyn	d		12x32				14x38				16x28				18x32		18x32	
Penrhyndeudraeth	d		12 35				14 41				16 31				18 35		18 35	
Minffordd	d		12 39				14 45				16 35				18 39		18 39	
Porthmadog	d		12 47				14 53				16 42				18 46		18 46	
Criccieth	d		12 55				15 01				16 50				18 54		18 54	
Penychain	d		13x00				15x06				16x55				18x59		18x59	
Abererch	d		13x03				15x09				16x58				19x03		19x03	
Pwllheli	a		13 14				15 18				17 09				19 13		19 13	

For general notes see front of timetable
For details of catering facilities see Directory of Train Operators

A Until 5 September
B To Holyhead (Table 81)
C From 8 September
b Arr. 1124
c Arr. 1217
e Arr. 1413
f Arr. 1612
g Arr. 1817

Wrexham & Shropshire services are expected to start operating during the currency of this timetable. Please visit the Wrexham & Shropshire website www.wrexhamandshropshire.co.uk for updated information

Birmingham and Shrewsbury → Chester, Aberystwyth, Barmouth and Pwllheli

Network Diagram - see first page of Table 67

	AW	AW	AW	AW	AW	AW		AW	AW	AW	AW	AW	AW	AW	AW
				FO										FO	FX
		R							R						
	◇		◇		◇	◇				◇	◇	◇			
			A						A		A				
	(trolley)	(trolley)	(trolley)		(trolley)	(trolley)			(trolley)		(trolley)	(trolley)			
London Euston 15 ⊖ d	13 40	14 40			15 40	16 40				17 30		18 40			
London Marylebone 10 ⊖ d															
Banbury d															
Birmingham International ✈ d	15 05	16 05			17 05	18 05				19 05		20 05			
Birmingham New Street 12 d	15 33	16 33			17 33	18 33				19 33		20 33			
Tame Bridge Parkway d															
Wolverhampton 7 ⛴ d	15 48	16 48			17 48	18 48				19 48		20 50			
Cosford d															
Telford Central d	16 04	17 04			18 13	19 04				20 04		21 06			
Wellington (Shropshire) d	16 10	17 10			18 19	19 10				20 10		21 12			
Shrewsbury a	16 25	17 22			18 35	19 22				20 25		21 27			
Cardiff Central 7 d	13 50	15 20	15 20		15 50	17 20			17 20	17 50	19 34		20 10		
Manchester Piccadilly 10 ⛴ d		15 34				17 34						19 34			
Crewe 10 d		16 18				18 18						20 18			
Shrewsbury d	16 26	17 28	17 30		18 36	19 28			19 30	20 26	21 38	21 47	22 26	23 39	23 39
Gobowen d	16 46		17 49		18 55				19 49	20 47	21 57		22 46	23 58	23 58
Chirk d	16 51		17 54		19 01				19 54	20 52	22 02		22 51	00 03	00 03
Ruabon d	16 57		18 00		19 07				20 00	20 58	22 08		22 57	00 09	00 09
Wrexham General d	17 03		18 07		19 13			19 38	20b13	21 04	22 15		23c06	00 16	00 17
Chester a	17 22		18 25		19 34			19 55	20 31	21 23	22 32		23 26	00 35	00 35
Welshpool d		17 51				19 51						22 10			
Newtown (Powys) d		18 07				20 07						22 26			
Caersws d		18 13				20 13						22 33			
Machynlleth 4 a		18 42				20 42						23 06			
d		18 45		19 00		20 45	21 17					23 08			
Dovey Junction 4 d		18 51		19 06		20 51	21 23					23 15			
Borth d		19 02				21 02						23 25			
Aberystwyth a		19 22				21 22						23 43			
Penhelig d				19x15			21x32								
Aberdovey d				19 18			21 35								
Tywyn d				19 26			21 41								
Tonfanau d				19x30			21x45								
Llwyngwril d				19x37			21x51								
Fairbourne d				19 44			21 59								
Morfa Mawddach d				19x47			22x01								
Barmouth a				19 56			22 07								
d							22 08								
Llanaber d							22x11								
Talybont d							22x14								
Dyffryn Ardudwy d							22x16								
Llanbedr d							22x20								
Pensarn d							22x21								
Llandanwg d							22x23								
Harlech d							22 29								
Tygwyn d							22x33								
Talsarnau d							22x34								
Llandecwyn d							22x37								
Penrhyndeudraeth d							22 40								
Minffordd d							22 43								
Porthmadog d							22 48								
Criccieth d							22 55								
Penychain d							23x01								
Abererch d							23x03								
Pwllheli a							23 13								

For general notes see front of timetable
For details of catering facilities see Directory of Train Operators

A To Holyhead (Table 81)
b Arr. 2006
c Arr. 2303

Wrexham & Shropshire services are expected to start operating during the currency of this timetable. Please visit the Wrexham & Shropshire website www.wrexhamandshropshire.co.uk for updated information

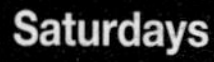

Birmingham and Shrewsbury → Chester, Aberystwyth, Barmouth and Pwllheli

Network Diagram - see first page of Table 67

	AW	AW	AW	AW	AW	AW		AW	AW	AW	AW	AW	AW			AW	AW	AW			AW		AW	
			◇			◇			◇	◇	◇	◇	◇			◇	◇	◇			◇		◇	
										A						A				A				
										🛒			🛒			🛒	🛒	🛒			🛒		🛒	
London Euston 15 ⊖ d													06b05				07c19	08e07			09f19		10g06	
London Marylebone 10 ⊖ d																								
Banbury d																								
Birmingham International ✈ d												06h50	07j58				08k58	09m57			10n58		11q57	
Birmingham New Street 12 d									06 33			07 33	08 33				09 33	10 33			11 33		12 33	
Tame Bridge Parkway d																								
Wolverhampton 7 🚌 d									06 48			07 48	08 48				09 48	10 48			11 48		12 48	
Cosford d																								
Telford Central d									07 04			08 04	09 04				10 04	11 04			12 04		13 04	
Wellington (Shropshire) d									07 10			08 10	09 10				10 10	11 10			12 10		13 10	
Shrewsbury a									07 22			08 25	09 22				10 25	11 22			12 25		13 22	
Cardiff Central 7 d									*05 10*	05 10		*05 35*	*07 20*			07 20	*07 50*	*09 20*		09 20	*09 50*		*11 20*	
Manchester Piccadilly 10 🚌 d													*07 28*					*09 34*					*11 34*	
Crewe 10 d									*05 55*				*08 08*					*10 17*					*12 18*	
Shrewsbury d	23p39			05 20				06 10	07 28	07 30		08 28	09 28			09 30	10 26	11 28		11 30	12 26		13 28	
Gobowen d	23p58			05 39				06 29		07 49		08 47				09 49	10 46			11 49	12 46			
Chirk d	00 03			05 44				06 34		07 54		08 52				09 54	10 51			11 54	12 51			
Ruabon d	00 09			05 50				06 40		08 00		08 58				10 00	10 57			12 00	12 57			
Wrexham General d	00 16			05 57				06 47		08 07		09 05				10 07	11 03			12 07	13 03			
Chester a	00 35			06 16				07 09		08 28		09 27				10 28	11 27			12 25	13 26			
Welshpool d									07 51				09 51					11 51					13 51	
Newtown (Powys) d									08 07				10 07					12 07					14 07	
Caersws d									08 13				10 13					12 13					14 13	
Machynlleth 4 a									08 42				10 42					12 42					14 42	
d		04 35	05 15		06 30	06 49			08 45		09 05		10 45	11 00				12 45	12 56				14 45	14 56
Dovey Junction 4 d		04 41	05 21		06 36	06 55			08 51		09 11		10 51	11 06				12 51	13 02				14 51	15 02
Borth d		04 52			06 47				09 02				11 02					13 02					15 02	
Aberystwyth a		05 05			07 00				09 22				11 22					13 22					15 22	
Penhelig d			05x30			07x04					09x20			11x15					13x11					15x11
Aberdovey d			05 33			07 07					09 23			11 18					13 14					15 14
Tywyn d			05 39			07 15					09 30			11 26					13 22					15 22
Tonfanau d			05x43			07x19					09x34			11x30					13x26					15x26
Llwyngwril d			05x49			07x25					09x40			11x36					13x32					15x32
Fairbourne d			05 57			07 33					09 48			11 44					13 40					15 40
Morfa Mawddach d			05x59			07x35					09x50			11x46					13x42					15x42
Barmouth a			06 05			07 40					09 56			11 52					13 48					15 47
d			06 08			07 50					09 57			11 56					13 52					15 52
Llanaber d			06x12			07x53					10x00			11x59					13x55					15x55
Talybont d						07x57					10x04			12x03					13x59					15x58
Dyffryn Ardudwy d						07x59					10x06			12x05					14x01					16x00
Llanbedr d						08x02					10x09			12x08					14x04					16x04
Pensarn d						08x04					10x11			12x10					14x06					16x05
Llandanwg d						08x05					10x12			12x11					14x07					16x07
Harlech d			06 29			08r32					10 21			12t24					14v30					16w20
Tygwyn d						08x36					10x25			12x28					14x34					16x24
Talsarnau d						08x37					10x27			12x30					14x36					16x26
Llandecwyn d						08x40					10x29			12x32					14x38					16x28
Penrhyndeudraeth d						08 43					10 32			12 35					14 41					16 31
Minffordd d						08 46					10 36			12 39					14 45					16 35
Porthmadog d			06 45			08 52					10 42			12y47					14 53					16 42
Criccieth d						08 59					10 50			12 55					15 01					16 50
Penychain d			06x58			09x05					10x55			13x00					15x06					16x55
Abererch d						09x08					10x58			13x03					15x09					16x58
Pwllheli a			07 05			09 13					11 09			13 14					15 18					17 09

For general notes see front of timetable
For details of catering facilities see Directory of Train Operators

- **A** To Holyhead (Table 81)
- **b** Until 12 July only
- **c** Until 6 September only. 19 July to 6 September dep. 0605
- **e** Until 6 September only. 19 July to 6 September dep. 0728
- **f** Until 6 September only. 19 July to 6 September dep. 0827
- **g** Until 6 September only. 19 July to 6 September dep. 0928
- **h** Until 6 September only
- **j** Until 6 September only. 19 July to 6 September dep. 0750
- **k** Until 6 September only. 19 July to 6 September dep. 0850
- **m** Until 6 September only. 19 July to 6 September dep. 1009
- **n** Until 6 September only. 19 July to 6 September dep. 1050
- **q** Until 6 September only. 19 July to 6 September dep. 1209
- **r** Arr. 0811
- **t** Arr. 1217
- **v** Arr. 1413
- **w** Arr. 1612
- **y** Arr. 1244

Wrexham & Shropshire services are expected to start operating during the currency of this timetable. Please visit the Wrexham & Shropshire website www.wrexhamandshropshire.co.ukfor updated information

Birmingham and Shrewsbury → Chester, Aberystwyth, Barmouth and Pwllheli

Network Diagram - see first page of Table 67

	AW	AW	AW		AW		AW	AW	AW	AW	AW	AW		AW	AW	AW	AW	AW	AW	AW
									R											
	◇	◇	◇		◇		◇	◇		◇	◇	◇			◇	◇	◇	◇	◇	
	A		B		C		A			A					A			D		
	🛒	🛒	🛒		🛒		🛒	🛒	🛒	🛒	🛒	🛒			🛒		🛒	🛒		
London Euston 15 ⊖ d		11b17			12c17			13e17	14f17		15g17	16h17				17j17	18k17		18m38	
London Marylebone 10 ⊖ d																				
Banbury d																				
Birmingham International ✈ d		12n58			13q57			14r57	15t58		16v57	17w57				18y57	19z57		20E50	
Birmingham New Street 12 d		13 33	14 33		14 33			15 33	16 33		17 33	18 33				19 33	20 33		21 33	
Tame Bridge Parkway d																				
Wolverhampton 7 ⛴ d		13 48	14 48		14 48			15 48	16 48		17 48	18 48				19 48	20 48		21 48	
Cosford d																				
Telford Central d		14 04	15 04		15 04			16 04	17 04		18 04	19 04				20 04	21 04		22 04	
Wellington (Shropshire) d		14 10	15 10		15 10			16 10	17 10		18 10	19 10				20 10	21 10		22 10	
Shrewsbury a		14 25	15 22		15 22			16 25	17 22		18 25	19 22				20 25	21 22		22 25	
Cardiff Central 7 d	11 20	11 50	13 20		13 20		13 20	13 50	15 20	15 20	15 50	17 20			17 20	17 50	18 50	19 34	20 10	
Manchester Piccadilly 10 ⛴ d			13 34		13 34				15 34			17 34					19 34			
Crewe 10 d			14 18		14 18				16 15			18 18					20 18			
Shrewsbury d	13 30	14 26	15 28		15 28		15 30	16 26	17 28	17 30	18 26	19 28			19 30	20 26	21 28	21 38	22 26	23 31
Gobowen d	13 49	14 46					15 49	16 46		17 49	18 46				19 49	20 46		21 57	22 46	23 50
Chirk d	13 54	14 51					15 54	16 51		17 54	18 51				19 54	20 51		22 02	22 51	23 55
Ruabon d	14 00	14 57					16 00	16 57		18 00	18 57				20 00	20 57		22 08	22 57	00 01
Wrexham General d	14 07	15 03					16 07	17 03		18 07	19 03			19 46	20 07	21 03		22 15	23 06	00H12
Chester a	14 28	15 26					16 28	17 26		18 25	19 22			20 05	20 26	21 26		22 32	23 26	00 30
Welshpool d			15 51		15 51				17 51			19 51					21 51			
Newtown (Powys) d			16 07		16 07				18 07			20 07					22 07			
Caersws d			16 13		16 13				18 13			20 13					22 17			
Machynlleth 4 a			16 42		16 42				18 42			20 42					22 45			
d			16 45	17 00	16 45	17 05			18 45			20 45	21 17				22 52			
Dovey Junction 4 d			16 51	17 06	16 51	17 11			18 51			20 51	21 23				22 59			
Borth d			17 02		17 02				19 02			21 02					23 09			
Aberystwyth a			17 22		17 22				19 22			21 22					23 30			
Penhelig d				17x15		17x20							21x32							
Aberdovey d				17 18		17 23							21 35							
Tywyn d				17 26		17 29							21 41							
Tonfanau d				17x30		17x33							21x45							
Llwyngwril d				17x36		17x39							21x51							
Fairbourne d				17 44		17 47							21 59							
Morfa Mawddach d				17x46		17x49							22x01							
Barmouth a				17 52		17 55							22 07							
d				17 56		17 56							22 08							
Llanaber d				17x59		17x59							22x11							
Talybont d				18x03		18x03							22x14							
Dyffryn Ardudwy d				18x05		18x05							22x16							
Llanbedr d				18x08		18x08							22x20							
Pensarn d				18x10		18x10							22x21							
Llandanwg d				18x11		18x11							22x23							
Harlech d				18J24		18J24							22 29							
Tygwyn d				18x28		18x28							22x33							
Talsarnau d				18x30		18x30							22x34							
Llandecwyn d				18x32		18x32							22x37							
Penrhyndeudraeth d				18 35		18 35							22 40							
Minffordd d				18 39		18 39							22 43							
Porthmadog d				18 46		18 46							22 48							
Criccieth d				18 54		18 54							22 55							
Penychain d				18x59		18x59							23x01							
Abererch d				19x03		19x03							23x03							
Pwllheli a				19 13		19 13							23 13							

For general notes see front of timetable
For details of catering facilities see Directory of Train Operators

- A To Holyhead (Table 81)
- B From 13 September
- C Until 6 September
- D Until 6 September to Holyhead, from 13 September to Llandudno Junction (Table 81)
- E Until 6 September only
- H Arr. 0007
- J Arr. 1817
- b Until 6 September only. 19 July to 6 September dep. 1028
- c 19 July to 6 September dep. 1128
- e Until 6 September only. 19 July to 6 September dep. 1228
- f Until 6 September only. 19 July to 6 September dep. 1328
- g Until 6 September only. 19 July to 6 September dep. 1428
- h Until 6 September only. 19 July to 6 September dep. 1528
- j Until 6 September only. 19 July to 6 September dep. 1628
- k Until 6 September only. 19 July to 6 September dep. 1728
- m Until 6 September only. 19 July to 6 September dep. 1828
- n Until 6 September only. 19 July to 6 September dep. 1250
- q Until 6 September only. 19 July to 6 September dep. 1409
- r Until 6 September only. 19 July to 6 September dep. 1450
- t Until 6 September only. 19 July to 6 September dep. 1609
- v Until 6 September only. 19 July to 6 September dep. 1650
- w Until 6 September only. 19 July to 6 September dep. 1809
- y Until 6 September only. 19 July to 6 September dep. 1850
- z Until 6 September only. 19 July to 6 September dep. 1950

Wrexham & Shropshire services are expected to start operating during the currency of this timetable. Please visit the Wrexham & Shropshire website www.wrexhamandshropshire.co.uk for updated information

Table 75

Birmingham and Shrewsbury → Chester, Aberystwyth, Barmouth and Pwllheli

until 13 July

Network Diagram - see first page of Table 67

		AW	AW	AW	AW ◇	AW	AW ◇	AW ◇	AW	AW ◇ A	AW ◇	AW	AW ◇	AW ◇		AW ◇	AW ◇	AW ◇	AW R A	AW ◇	AW
London Euston 15 ⊖	d							08 30					10 56	12 56		13 56	14 56	15 56		16 56	
London Marylebone 10 ⊖	d																				
Banbury	d																				
Birmingham International ✈	d						08b20	10b30			11b30		13b20	15b10		16b10	17b10	18b10		18b40	
Birmingham New Street 12	d						09 36	11 32			12 27		14 26	15 48		16 48	17 58	18 56		19 48	
Tame Bridge Parkway	d																				
Wolverhampton 7	d						10 04	11 59			12 56		14 55	16 20		17 23	18 26	19 20		20 22	
Cosford	d						10 22				13 13			16 37			18 44	19 37			
Telford Central	d						10 32	12 16			13 23		15 11	16 48		17 39	18 55	19 48		20 39	
Wellington (Shropshire)	d						10 42	12 23			13 33		15 18	16 58		17 49	19 04	19 58		20 45	
Shrewsbury	a						10 55	12 36			13 46		15 34	17 12		18 02	19 23	20 11		20 59	
Cardiff Central 7	d									11 35	11 35		12 39	14 35		15 35	16 35		18 35		
Manchester Piccadilly 10	d													15 39							
Crewe 10	d													16 21			19 00				
Shrewsbury	d	23p31		08 33		10 16	11 01	12 46		13 50	14 05		15 38	17 18		18 04	19 55	20 16	20 48	21 06	
Gobowen	d	23p50				10 35					14 25		15 57			18 23		20 36			
Chirk	d	23p55				10 40					14 30		16 02			18 28		20 41			
Ruabon	d	00 01				10 46					14 36		16 08			18 34		20 47			
Wrexham General	d	00c12				10 53					14 42		16 15			18 41		20 54	21 18		22 35
Chester	a	00 30				11 11				14 39	15 01		16 36			18 59		21 14	21 36		22 53
Welshpool	d			08 55			11 24	13 09						17 41			20 17			21 28	
Newtown (Powys)	d			09 11			11e45	13 25						17 57			20 33			21 44	
Caersws	d			09 18			11 52	13 32						18 04			20 41			21 51	
Machynlleth 4	a			09 48			12 20	14 00						18 32			21 13			22 19	
	d		08 00	09 49	09 53		12 22	14 04	14 08			16 30		18 36	18 40		21 14			22 23	
Dovey Junction 4	d		08 07	09 56	10 00		12 29	14 11	14 15			16 37		18 43	18 47		21 21			22 29	
Borth	d		08 17	10 06			12 39		14 25			16 47		18 54			21 31			22 40	
Aberystwyth	a		08 31	10 21			12 53		14 39			17 01		19 07			21 45			22 53	
Penhelig	d				10x08			14x19							18x55						
Aberdovey	d				10 11			14 22							18 58						
Tywyn	d				10 18			14 29							19 05						
Tonfanau	d				10x22			14x33							19x09						
Llwyngwril	d				10x28			14x39							19x15						
Fairbourne	d				10 36			14 47							19 23						
Morfa Mawddach	d				10x38			14x49							19x25						
Barmouth	a				10 43			14 54							19 31						
	d				10 44			15 02							19 31						
Llanaber	d				10x47			15x05							19x34						
Talybont	d				10x51			15x09							19x38						
Dyffryn Ardudwy	d				10x53			15x11							19x41						
Llanbedr	d				10x57			15x15							19x44						
Pensarn	d				10x59			15x17							19x46						
Llandanwg	d				11x00			15x18							19x48						
Harlech	d				11 07			15 25							19 55						
Tygwyn	d				11x11			15x29							19x59						
Talsarnau	d				11x13			15x31							20x01						
Llandecwyn	d				11x16			15x34							20x03						
Penrhyndeudraeth	d				11 19			15 37							20 06						
Minffordd	d				11 21			15 40							20 10						
Porthmadog	d				11 27			15 45							20 14						
Criccieth	d				11 34			15 52							20 22						
Penychain	d				11x39			15x58							20x27						
Abererch	d				11x43			16x01							20x30						
Pwllheli	a				11 49			16 07							20 40						

For general notes see front of timetable
For details of catering facilities see Directory of Train Operators

A To Holyhead (Table 81)
b By bus
c Arr. 0007
e Arr. 1139

Wrexham & Shropshire services are expected to start operating during the currency of this timetable. Please visit the Wrexham & Shropshire website www.wrexhamandshropshire.co.uk for updated information

Table 75

Sundays

Birmingham and Shrewsbury → Chester, Aberystwyth, Barmouth and Pwllheli

20 July to 7 September

Network Diagram - see first page of Table 67

		AW	AW	AW	AW	AW	AW	AW	AW	AW	AW	AW	AW	AW	AW	AW	AW	AW	AW R	AW	AW
					◇		◇	◇		◇ A	◇		◇	◇	◇	◇	◇	◇	A	◇	
London Euston 15	⊖ d							08 31					11 50	12 51		13 51	14 51	15 51		16 51	
London Marylebone 10	⊖ d																				
Banbury	d																				
Birmingham International	d						08b20	10b30			11b30		13b50	14b40		15b40	17b10	18b10		18b40	
Birmingham New Street 12	d						09 37	11 37			12 37		14 37	15 37		16 37	18 07	18 57		19 37	
Tame Bridge Parkway	d																				
Wolverhampton 7	d						09 57	11 57			12 56		14 55	15 55		16 58	18 26	19 15		20 00	
Cosford	d						10 14				13 13			16 12			18 44	19 32			
Telford Central	d						10 25	12 19			13 23		15 11	16 23		17 14	18 55	19 43		20 16	
Wellington (Shropshire)	d						10 34	12 26			13 33		15 18	16 33		17 24	19 04	19 53		20 23	
Shrewsbury	a						10 47	12 39			13 46		15 34	16 46		17 40	19 23	20 06		20 36	
Cardiff Central 7	d									11 35	11 35		12 39	14 35		15 35	16 35		18 35		
Manchester Piccadilly 10	d													15 39						18 40	
Crewe 10	d													16 21			19 00			19 21	
Shrewsbury	d	23p31		08 33		10 16	11 01	12 46		13 50	14 05		15 38	17 18		17 50	19 55	20 16	20 48	21 00	
Gobowen	d	23p50				10 35					14 25		15 57			18 09		20 36			
Chirk	d	23p55				10 40					14 30		16 02			18 14		20 41			
Ruabon	d	00 01				10 46					14 36		16 08			18 20		20 47			
Wrexham General	d	00c12				10 53					14 42		16 15			18 27		20 54	21 18		22 35
Chester	a	00 30				11 11				14 39	15 01		16 36			18 46		21 14	21 36		22 53
Welshpool	d			08 55			11 24	13 09						17 41			20 17			21e28	
Newtown (Powys)	d			09 11			11f45	13 25						17 57			20 33			21 44	
Caersws	d			09 18			11 52	13 32						18 04			20 41			21 51	
Machynlleth 4	a			09 48			12 20	14 00						18 32			21 13			22 19	
	d		08 00	09 49	09 53		12 22	14 04	14 08			16 30		18 36	18 40		21 14			22 23	
Dovey Junction 4	d		08 07	09 56	10 00		12 29	14 11	14 15			16 37		18 43	18 47		21 21			22 29	
Borth	d		08 17	10 06			12 39		14 25			16 47		18 54			21 31			22 40	
Aberystwyth	a		08 31	10 21			12 53		14 39			17 01		19 07			21 45			22 53	
Penhelig	d				10x08			14x19							18x55						
Aberdovey	d				10 11			14 22							18 58						
Tywyn	d				10 18			14 29							19 05						
Tonfanau	d				10x22			14x33							19x09						
Llwyngwril	d				10x28			14x39							19x15						
Fairbourne	d				10 36			14 47							19 23						
Morfa Mawddach	d				10x38			14x49							19x25						
Barmouth	a				10 43			14 54							19 31						
	d				10 44			15 02							19 31						
Llanaber	d				10x47			15x05							19x34						
Talybont	d				10x51			15x09							19x38						
Dyffryn Ardudwy	d				10x53			15x11							19x41						
Llanbedr	d				10x57			15x15							19x44						
Pensarn	d				10x59			15x17							19x46						
Llandanwg	d				11x00			15x18							19x48						
Harlech	d				11 07			15 25							19 55						
Tygwyn	d				11x11			15x29							19x59						
Talsarnau	d				11x13			15x31							20x01						
Llandecwyn	d				11x16			15x34							20x03						
Penrhyndeudraeth	d				11 19			15 37							20 06						
Minffordd	d				11 21			15 40							20 10						
Porthmadog	d				11 27			15 45							20 14						
Criccieth	d				11 34			15 52							20 22						
Penychain	d				11x39			15x58							20x27						
Abererch	d				11x43			16x01							20x30						
Pwllheli	a				11 49			16 07							20 40						

For general notes see front of timetable
For details of catering facilities see Directory of Train Operators

A To Holyhead (Table 81)
b By bus
c Arr. 0007
e Arr. 2122
f Arr. 1139

Wrexham & Shropshire services are expected to start operating during the currency of this timetable. Please visit the Wrexham & Shropshire website www.wrexhamandshropshire.co.uk for updated information

Table 75

Sundays

Birmingham and Shrewsbury → Chester, Aberystwyth, Barmouth and Pwllheli

from 14 September

Network Diagram - see first page of Table 67

	AW	AW	AW	AW	AW	AW	AW	AW	AW	AW	AW	AW	AW	AW	AW
						◇ A				◇			R A		
London Euston 15 ⊖ d															
London Marylebone 10 ⊖ d															
Banbury d															
Birmingham International ✈ d															
Birmingham New Street 12 d															
Tame Bridge Parkway d															
Wolverhampton 7 d															
Cosford d															
Telford Central d															
Wellington (Shropshire) d															
Shrewsbury a															
Cardiff Central 7 d						11 35		12 35	14b35		15 35	16 35	18 35		
Manchester Piccadilly 10 d							12 33		15 48						
Crewe 10 d							14 05		16 44					20 25	
Shrewsbury d	23p31	10 16		12 34		13 50	14 40	15 38	17 18		17 50	20 14	20 48	21 00	
Gobowen d	23p50	10 35		12 53		14 08		15 58			18 09	20 34			
Chirk d	23p55	10 40		12 58		14 14		16 03			18 14	20 39			
Ruabon d	00 01	10 46		13 04		14 20		16 09			18 20	20 45			
Wrexham General d	00c12	10 53		13 11		14e40		16 14			18 27	20 52	21 18		22 35
Chester a	00 30	11 11		13 29		14 58		16 35			18 45	21 11	21 36		22 53
Welshpool d							15 02		17 43					21 22	
Newtown (Powys) d							15 18		17 59					21 38	
Caersws d							15 25		18 06					21 46	
Machynlleth 4 a							15 53		18 34					22 15	
d			11 30		14 30		16 10		18 36	18 40				22 19	
Dovey Junction 4 d			11 36		14 36		16 16		18 43	18 47				22 25	
Borth d			11 47		14 47		16 27		18 54					22 36	
Aberystwyth a			12 00		15 00		16 40		19 07					22 49	
Penhelig d										18x55					
Aberdovey d										18 58					
Tywyn d										19 05					
Tonfanau d										19x09					
Llwyngwril d										19x15					
Fairbourne d										19 23					
Morfa Mawddach d										19x25					
Barmouth a										19 31					
d										19 31					
Llanaber d										19x34					
Talybont d										19x38					
Dyffryn Ardudwy d										19x41					
Llanbedr d										19x44					
Pensarn d										19x46					
Llandanwg d										19x48					
Harlech d										19 55					
Tygwyn d										19x59					
Talsarnau d										20x01					
Llandecwyn d										20x03					
Penrhyndeudraeth d										20 06					
Minffordd d										20 10					
Porthmadog d										20 14					
Criccieth d										20 22					
Penychain d										20x27					
Abererch d										20x30					
Pwllheli a										20 40					

For general notes see front of timetable
For details of catering facilities see Directory of Train Operators

A To Holyhead (Table 81)
b Change at Shrewsbury
c Arr. 0007
e Arr. 1428

Wrexham & Shropshire services are expected to start operating during the currency of this timetable. Please visit the Wrexham & Shropshire website www.wrexhamandshropshire.co.uk for updated information

Pwllheli, Barmouth, Aberystwyth and Chester → Shrewsbury and Birmingham

Network Diagram - see first page of Table 67

Miles	Miles	Miles			AW	AW	AW	AW	AW	AW	AW	AW	AW	AW	AW	AW	AW	AW	AW	AW	AW	AW	AW	AW	AW
					MX	◇		◇	◇	◇		◇	◇	◇	◇	◇	◇	◇	◇	◇	◇	◇	◇	◇	◇
									A			A				A				A	B	B	C	C	
								🍴	🍴	🍴		🍴	🍴		🍴	🍴	🍴	🍴	🍴	🍴	🍴	🍴	🍴	🍴	🍴
—	0	—	**Pwllheli**	d										06 21				07 31			09 36		09 36		
—	1¾	—	Abererch	d										06x25				07x35			09x40		09x40		
—	3¼	—	Penychain	d										06x27				07x37			09x42		09x42		
—	7¾	—	Criccieth	d										06 35				07 45			09 49		09 49		
—	12¾	—	Porthmadog	d										06b47				07 54			09 58		09 58		
—	15	—	Minffordd	d										06 51				07 58			10 02		10 02		
—	16½	—	Penrhyndeudraeth	d										06 54				08 01			10 05		10 05		
—	17	—	Llandecwyn	d										06x57				08 04			10x08		10x08		
—	18¾	—	Talsarnau	d										06x59				08x06			10x10		10x10		
—	19	—	Tygwyn	d										07x01				08 08			10x12		10x12		
—	21½	—	Harlech	d										07c20				08e32			10f22		10f22		
—	23¼	—	Llandanwg	d										07x25				08x37			10x27		10x27		
—	24¼	—	Pensarn	d										07x26				08x38			10x28		10x28		
—	25	—	Llanbedr	d										07x28				08x40			10x30		10x30		
—	27	—	Dyffryn Ardudwy	d										07x32				08x44			10x34		10x34		
—	28½	—	Talybont	d										07x34				08x46			10x36		10x36		
—	30½	—	Llanaber	d										07x37				08x49			10x39		10x39		
—	32	—	**Barmouth**	a										07 41				08 53			10 43		10 43		
—	—	—		d							06 46			07 49				08 59			10 49		11 05		
—	33¾	—	Morfa Mawddach	d							06x50			07x54				09x04			10x54		11x10		
—	34¾	—	Fairbourne	d							06 53			07 56				09 06			10 56		11 12		
—	37¼	—	Llwyngwril	d							07x00			08x03				09x13			11x03		11x19		
—	41½	—	Tonfanau	d							07x06			08x09				09x19			11x09		11x25		
—	44¼	—	Tywyn	d							07g16			08 15				09h31			11j27		11 30		
—	47½	—	Aberdovey	d							07 22			08 21				09 37			11 33		11 36		
—	48¼	—	Penhelig	d							07x24			08x24				09x40			11x35		11x39		
0	—	—	**Aberystwyth**	d	23p53			05 12					07 27				09 27					11 27		11 27	
8¼	—	—	Borth	d	00 05			05 25					07 39				09 39					11 39		11 39	
16½	53½	—	Dovey Junction 4	d	00 16			05 37			07 35		07 50	08 35			09 50	09 51			11 47	11 50	11 49	11 50	
20½	57½	—	**Machynlleth 4**	a	00 26			05 44			07 44		07 59	08 44			09 59	09 58			11 57	11 59	11 57	11 59	
—	—	—		d				05 45					08 02				10 02					12 02		12 02	
42¼	—	—	Caersws	d				06 17					08 33				10 33					12 33		12 33	
47¾	—	—	Newtown (Powys)	d				06 24					08 40				10 40					12 40		12 40	
61¾	—	—	Welshpool	d				06 39					08 55				10 55					12 55		12 55	
—	—	0	**Chester**	d		05 07	05 37		06 12	07 28		08 20			09 28	10 20			11 28	12 20					13 28
—	—	12	Wrexham General	d		05 24	05a57		06 28	07 44		08 37			09 44	10 37			11 44	12 37					13 44
—	—	17	Ruabon	d		05 30			06 35	07 51		08 44			09 51	10 43			11 51	12 43					13 51
—	—	21½	Chirk	d		05 36			06 41	07 57		08 50			09 57	10 49			11 57	12 49					13 57
—	—	24¼	Gobowen	d		05 42			06 46	08 02		08 55			10 02	10 55			12 02	12 55					14 02
81½	—	42	**Shrewsbury**	a		06 07		07 05	07 07	08 22		09 15	09 21		10 22	11 15	11 21		12 22	13 15		13 21		13 21	14 22
—	—	—	Crewe 10	a				08 25					10 25				12 25					14 24		14 24	
—	—	—	Manchester Piccadilly 10	⛴ a				09 13					11 13				13 13					15 13		15 13	
—	—	—	Cardiff Central 7	a		08 29			09 18	10 54		11 20	11 54		12 54	13 20	13 54		14 54	15 20		15 54		15 54	16 54
—	—	—	**Shrewsbury**	d				07 12		08 22			09 22		10 22		11 22		12 22			13 22		13 22	14 22
92	—	—	Wellington (Shropshire)	d				07 22		08 35			09 35		10 35		11 35		12 35			13 35		13 35	14 35
96	—	—	Telford Central	d				07 29		08 41			09 41		10 41		11 41		12 41			13 41		13 41	14 41
122¾	—	—	Cosford	d				07 39																	
111½	—	—	**Wolverhampton 7**	⛴ a				07 58		08 58			09 58		10 58		11 58		12 58			13 58		13 58	14 58
—	—	—	Tame Bridge Parkway	d																					
124¾	—	—	**Birmingham New Street 12**	a				08 18		09 18			10 18		11 18		12 18		13 18			14 18		14 18	15 18
—	—	—	Birmingham International	✈ a				08 39		09 39			10 39		11 39		12 39		13 39			14 39		14 39	15 39
—	—	—	Banbury	a																					
—	—	—	London Marylebone 10	⊖ a																					
—	—	—	London Euston 15	⊖ a				10 03		11 00			12 00		13 00		14 00		15 00			16 00		16 00	17 00

For general notes see front of timetable
For details of catering facilities see Directory of Train Operators

A From Holyhead (Table 81)

B From 8 September
C Until 5 September
b Arr. 0642
c Arr. 0705
e Arr. 0812

f Arr. 1016
g Arr. 0710
h Arr. 0925
j Arr. 1114

Wrexham & Shropshire services are expected to start operating during the currency of this timetable. Please visit the Wrexham & Shropshire website www.wrexhamandshropshire.co.uk for updated information

Pwllheli, Barmouth, Aberystwyth and Chester → Shrewsbury and Birmingham

Network Diagram - see first page of Table 67

		AW	AW	AW	AW	AW	AW	AW	AW	AW	AW	AW	AW	AW	AW	AW	AW	AW	AW	AW	AW	AW	AW	AW
		◇ A ✠	◇ ✠	◇ ✠	◇ ✠	◇ A ✠	◇ ✠	◇ ✠	◇ ✠	◇ A ✠	◇ B ✠	◇ B ✠	◇ C ✠	◇ C ✠		◇		◇ A ✠			◇	◇ A	FO	
Pwllheli	d		11 32				13 32				15∫32		15∫32			17 32					20 00			
Abererch	d		11x36				13x36				15x36		15x36			17x36					20x04			
Penychain	d		11x38				13x38				15x38		15x38			17x38					20x06			
Criccieth	d		11 45				13 45				15∫45		15∫45			17 45					20 13			
Porthmadog	d		11 56				13 56				15∫56		15∫56			17 56					20 23			
Minffordd	d		12 00				14 00				16∫00		16∫00			18 00					20 27			
Penrhyndeudraeth	d		12 03				14 03				16∫03		16∫03			18 03					20 30			
Llandecwyn	d		12x06				14x06				16x06		16x06			18x06					20x33			
Talsarnau	d		12x08				14x08				16x08		16x08			18x08					20x35			
Tygwyn	d		12x10				14x10				16x11		16x11			18x10					20x37			
Harlech	d		12b25				14c30				16e20		16e20			18f25					20g46			
Llandanwg	d		12x30				14x35				16x25		16x25			18x30					20x51			
Pensarn	d		12x31				14x36				16x26		16x26			18x31					20x52			
Llanbedr	d		12x33				14x38				16x28		16x28			18x33					20x54			
Dyffryn Ardudwy	d		12x37				14x42				16x32		16x32			18x37					20x58			
Talybont	d		12x39				14x44				16x34		16x34			18x39					21x00			
Llanaber	d		12x42				14x47				16x37		16x37			18x42					21x03			
Barmouth	a		12 46				14 51				16∫41		16∫41			18 46					21 07			
	d		12 49				14 52				16∫50		16∫50			18 49					21 14		22 12	
Morfa Mawddach	d		12x54				14x57				16x55		16x55			18x54					21x19		22x17	
Fairbourne	d		12 56				14 59				16∫57		16∫57			18 56					21 21		22 19	
Llwyngwril	d		13x03				15x06				17x04		17x04			19x03					21x28		22x27	
Tonfanau	d		13x09				15x12				17x10		17x10			19x09					21x34		22x33	
Tywyn	d		13h23				15j23				17k27		17k30			19m26					21n46		22 38	
Aberdovey	d		13 29				15 29				17∫33		17∫36			19 32					21 52		22 44	
Penhelig	d		13x32				15x32				17x36		17x39			19x35					21x55		22x46	
Aberystwyth	d			13 27				15 27				17∫27		17∫27			19 27			21 36				23 53
Borth	d			13 39				15 39				17∫39		17∫39			19 39			21 48				00 05
Dovey Junction 4	d		13 41	13 50			15 41	15 50			17∫46	17∫50	17∫49	17∫50		19 46	19 50			21 59	22 07		22 58	00 16
Machynlleth 4	a		13 52	13 59			15 48	15 59			17∫57	17∫59	17∫57	17∫59		19 57	19 59			22 11	22 16		23 07	00 26
	d		14 02				16 02				18∫02		18∫02				20 02							
Caersws	d		14 33				16 33				18∫33		18∫33				20 33							
Newtown (Powys)	d		14 40				16 40				18∫40		18∫40				20 40							
Welshpool	d		14 55				16 55				18∫55		18∫55				20 55							
Chester	d	14 20			15 28	16 20			17 28	18 20					19 56			20 28	21 28			22 29		
Wrexham General	d	14 37			15 44	16 36			17 44	18 36					20 12			20 44	21 44			22 46		
Ruabon	d	14 43			15 51	16 43			17 51	18 43					20 19			20 51	21 51			22 52		
Chirk	d	14 49			15 57	16 49			17 57	18 49					20 25			20 57	21 57			22 58		
Gobowen	d	14 55			16 02	16 54			18 02	18 54					20 30			21 02	22 02			23 04		
Shrewsbury	a	15 15	15 21		16 22	17 15	17 21		18 22	19 15	19∫21		19∫21		20 55		21 21	21 23	22 22			23 26		
Crewe 10	a		16 25				18 24				20∫26		20∫26				23 03					00 01		
Manchester Piccadilly 10 ⛴	a		17 11				19 13				21∫13		21∫13				23 49							
Cardiff Central 7	a	17 15	17 54		19 01	19 20	19 54			21 19	21∫57		21∫57					00 17	01 22					
Shrewsbury	d		15 22		16 22		17 22		18 22		19∫22		19∫22					21 26	22 22					
Wellington (Shropshire)	d		15 35		16 35		17 35		18 35		19∫35		19∫35					21 39	22 35					
Telford Central	d		15 41		16 41		17 41		18 41		19∫41		19∫41					21 45	22 41					
Cosford	d																							
Wolverhampton 7 ⛴	a		15 58		16 58		17 58		18 58		19∫51		19∫51					22 02	22 58					
Tame Bridge Parkway	d																							
Birmingham New Street 12	a		16 18		17 18		18 18		19 18		20∫18		20∫18					22 18	23 33					
Birmingham International ✈	a		16 39		17 39		18 39		19 39		20∫39		20∫39					22 52	00 21					
Banbury	a																							
London Marylebone 10 ⊖	a																							
London Euston 15 ⊖	a		18 00		19 03		20 00		21 04		22∫04		22∫04											

For general notes see front of timetable
For details of catering facilities see Directory of Train Operators

A From Holyhead (Table 81)
B From 8 September
C Until 5 September
b Arr. 1214
c Arr. 1414
e Arr. 1615
f Arr. 1814
g Arr. 2041
h Arr. 1316
j Arr. 1517
k Arr. 1715
m Arr. 1914
n Arr. 2139

Wrexham & Shropshire services are expected to start operating during the currency of this timetable. Please visit the Wrexham & Shropshire website www.wrexhamandshropshire.co.uk for updated information

Table 75

Saturdays

Pwllheli, Barmouth, Aberystwyth and Chester → Shrewsbury and Birmingham

Network Diagram - see first page of Table 67

		AW	AW	AW	AW	AW	AW	AW	AW	AW	AW	AW	AW	AW	AW	AW	AW	AW	AW	AW	AW
					◇	◇	◇		◇	◇	◇	◇	◇	◇	◇	◇	◇	◇	◇	◇	◇
						A			A				A				A				A
					🛒	🛒	🛒		🛒	🛒		🛒	🛒	🛒	🛒	🛒	🛒	🛒	🛒	🛒	🛒
Pwllheli	d										06 21				07 31			09 36			
Abererch	d										06x25				07x35			09x40			
Penychain	d										06x27				07x37			09x42			
Criccieth	d										06 35				07 45			09 49			
Porthmadog	d										06b47				07 54			09 58			
Minffordd	d										06 51				07 58			10 02			
Penrhyndeudraeth	d										06 54				08 01			10 05			
Llandecwyn	d										06x57				08 04			10x08			
Talsarnau	d										06x59				08x06			10x10			
Tygwyn	d										07x01				08 08			10x12			
Harlech	d										07c20				08e32			10f22			
Llandanwg	d										07x25				08x37			10x27			
Pensarn	d										07x26				08x38			10x28			
Llanbedr	d										07x28				08x40			10x30			
Dyffryn Ardudwy	d										07x32				08x44			10x34			
Talybont	d										07x34				08x46			10x36			
Llanaber	d										07x37				08x49			10x39			
Barmouth	a										07 41				08 53			10 43			
	d							06 46			07 49				08 59			10 49			
Morfa Mawddach	d							06x50			07x54				09x04			10x54			
Fairbourne	d							06 53			07 56				09 06			10 56			
Llwyngwril	d							07x00			08x03				09x13			11x03			
Tonfanau	d							07x06			08x09				09x19			11x09			
Tywyn	d							07g16			08 15				09h31			11j27			
Aberdovey	d							07 22			08 21				09 37			11 33			
Penhelig	d							07x24			08x24				09x40			11x35			
Aberystwyth	d	23p53			05 12					07 27				09 27					11 27		
Borth	d	00 05			05 25					07 39				09 39					11 39		
Dovey Junction 4	d	00 16			05 37			07 35		07 50	08 35			09 50	09 51			11 47	11 50		
Machynlleth 4	a	00 26			05 44			07 44		07 59	08 44			09 59	09 58			11 57	11 59		
	d				05 45					08 02				10 02				12 02			
Caersws	d				06 17					08 33				10 33				12 33			
Newtown (Powys)	d				06 24					08 40				10 40				12 40			
Welshpool	d				06 39					08 55				10 55				12 55			
Chester	d		05 16	05 37		06 12	07 28		08 20			09 28	10 20			11 28	12 20			13 28	14 20
Wrexham General	d		05 32	05a55		06 29	07 44		08 37			09 44	10 37			11 44	12 37			13 44	14 37
Ruabon	d		05 39			06 35	07 51		08 43			09 51	10 43			11 51	12 43			13 51	14 43
Chirk	d		05 45			06 41	07 57		08 49			09 57	10 49			11 57	12 49			13 57	14 49
Gobowen	d		05 50			06 47	08 02		08 55			10 02	10 55			12 02	12 55			14 02	14 55
Shrewsbury	a		06 11		07 05	07 07	08 22		09 16	09 21		10 22	11 15	11 21		12 22	13 15	13 21		14 22	15 15
Crewe 10	a				*08 28*					*10 28*				*12 28*				*14 28*			
Manchester Piccadilly 10	a				*09 12*					*11 13*				*13 13*				*15 13*			
Cardiff Central 7	a		*08 25*			09 18	*10 54*		11 20	*11 54*		*12 54*	13 20	*13 53*		*14 54*	15 20	*15 53*		*16 54*	17 20
Shrewsbury	d		06 22		07 12		08 22			09 22		10 22		11 22		12 22		13 22		14 22	
Wellington (Shropshire)	d		06 35		07 22		08 35			09 35		10 35		11 35		12 35		13 35		14 35	
Telford Central	d		06 41		07 29		08 41			09 41		10 41		11 41		12 41		13 41		14 41	
Cosford	d				07 39																
Wolverhampton 7	a		06 58		07 58		08 58			09 58		10 58		11 58		12 58		13 58		14 58	
Tame Bridge Parkway	d																				
Birmingham New Street 12	a		07 18		08 18		09 18			10 18		11 18		12 18		13 18		14 18		15 18	
Birmingham International ✈	a		*07k40*		*08m40*		*09n39*			*10q39*		*11r39*		*12t39*		*13v39*		*14w39*		*15y39*	
Banbury	a																				
London Marylebone 10 ⊖	a																				
London Euston 15 ⊖	a		*09z25*		*10B24*		*11C21*			*12D21*		*13E22*		*14G23*		*15H24*		*16J25*		*17K23*	

For general notes see front of timetable
For details of catering facilities see Directory of Train Operators

- **A** From Holyhead (Table 81)
- **B** Until 6 September only. 19 July to 6 September arr. 1057
- **C** Until 6 September only. 19 July to 6 September arr. 1148
- **D** Until 6 September only. 19 July to 6 September arr. 1247
- **E** Until 6 September only. 19 July to 6 September arr. 1359
- **G** Until 6 September only. 19 July to 6 September arr. 1447
- **H** Until 6 September only. 19 July to 6 September arr. 1559
- **J** Until 6 September only. 19 July to 6 September arr. 1647
- **K** Until 6 September only. 19 July to 6 September arr. 1746
- **b** Arr. 0642
- **c** Arr. 0705
- **e** Arr. 0812
- **f** Arr. 1016
- **g** Arr. 0710
- **h** Arr. 0925
- **j** Arr. 1114
- **k** Until 6 September only. 19 July to 6 September arr. 0751
- **m** Until 6 September only. 19 July to 6 September arr. 0851
- **n** Until 6 September only. 19 July to 6 September arr. 0952
- **q** Until 6 September only. 19 July to 6 September arr. 1052
- **r** Until 6 September only. 19 July to 6 September arr. 1151
- **t** Until 6 September only. 19 July to 6 September arr. 1251
- **v** Until 6 September only. 19 July to 6 September arr. 1352
- **w** Until 6 September only. 19 July to 6 September arr. 1451
- **y** Until 6 September only. 19 July to 6 September arr. 1551
- **z** Until 6 September only. 19 July to 6 September arr. 0948

Wrexham & Shropshire services are expected to start operating during the currency of this timetable. Please visit the Wrexham & Shropshire website www.wrexhamandshropshire.co.uk for updated information

Saturdays

Pwllheli, Barmouth, Aberystwyth and Chester → Shrewsbury and Birmingham

Network Diagram - see first page of Table 67

		AW	AW	AW		AW	AW	AW	AW		AW	AW	AW	AW		AW	AW	AW	AW	AW	AW	AW	AW		
		◇	◇	◇		◇	◇	◇	◇		◇	◇	◇			◇		◇			◇	◇			
						A					A							A				A			
		⚒	⚒	⚒		⚒	⚒	⚒			⚒	⚒	⚒					⚒							
Pwllheli	d	11 32					13 32					15 32				17 32					20 00				
Abererch	d	11x36					13x36					15x36				17x36					20x04				
Penychain	d	11x38					13x38					15x38				17x38					20x06				
Criccieth	d	11 45					13 45					15 45				17 45					20 13				
Porthmadog	d	11 56					13 56					15 56				17 56					20 23				
Minffordd	d	12 00					14 00					16 00				18 00					20 27				
Penrhyndeudraeth	d	12 03					14 03					16 03				18 03					20 30				
Llandecwyn	d	12x06					14x06					16x06				18x06					20x33				
Talsarnau	d	12x08					14x08					16x08				18x08					20x35				
Tygwyn	d	12x10					14x10					16x11				18x10					20x37				
Harlech	d	12b25					14c30					16e20				18f25					20g46				
Llandanwg	d	12x30					14x35					16x25				18x30					20x51				
Pensarn	d	12x31					14x36					16x26				18x31					20x52				
Llanbedr	d	12x33					14x38					16x28				18x33					20x54				
Dyffryn Ardudwy	d	12x37					14x42					16x32				18x37					20x58				
Talybont	d	12x39					14x44					16x34				18x39					21x00				
Llanaber	d	12x42					14x47					16x37				18x42					21x03				
Barmouth	a	12 46					14 51					16 41				18 46					21 07				
	d	12 49					14 52					16 50				18 49					21 14				
Morfa Mawddach	d	12x54					14x57					16x55				18x54					21x19				
Fairbourne	d	12 56					14 59					16 57				18 56					21 21				
Llwyngwril	d	13x03					15x06					17x04				19x03					21x28				
Tonfanau	d	13x09					15x12					17x10				19x09					21x34				
Tywyn	d	13h23					15j23					17k27				19m26					21n46				
Aberdovey	d	13 29					15 29					17 33				19 32					21 52				
Penhelig	d	13x32					15x32					17x36				19x35					21x55				
Aberystwyth	d		13 27					15 27					17 27				19 27			21 36			23 40		
Borth	d		13 39					15 39					17 39				19 39			21 48			23 52		
Dovey Junction 4	d	13 41	13 50				15 41	15 50				17 46	17 50			19 46	19 50			21 59	22 07		00 03		
Machynlleth 4	a	13 52	13 59				15 48	15 59				17 57	17 59			19 57	19 59			22 11	22 16		00 13		
	d	14 02					16 02					18 02					20 02								
Caersws	d	14 33					16 33					18 33					20 33								
Newtown (Powys)	d	14 40					16 40					18 40					20 40								
Welshpool	d	14 55					16 55					18 55					20 55								
Chester	d			15 28		16 20			17 28		18 20			19 28				20 28	21 28			22 29			
Wrexham General	d			15 44		16 36			17 44		18 36			19 44				20 44	21 44			22 46			
Ruabon	d			15 51		16 43			17 51		18 43			19 51				20 51	21 51			22 52			
Chirk	d			15 57		16 49			17 57		18 49			19 57				20 57	21 57			22 58			
Gobowen	d			16 02		16 54			18 02		18 54			20 02				21 02	22 02			23 04			
Shrewsbury	a	15 21		16 22		17 15	17 21		18 22		19 15	19 21		20 22			21 21	21 23	22 22			23 26			
Crewe 10	a	*16 28*					*18 28*					*20 26*					*23 03*								
Manchester Piccadilly 10	a	*17 13*					*19 16*					*21 13*					*23 50*								
Cardiff Central 7	a	*17q54*		*18 54*		*19 22*	*19 58*		*21 01*		*21 20*	*22 00*		*23 01*				*00 17*	*01 19*						
Shrewsbury	d	15 22		16 22			17 22		18 22			19 22		20 22				21 26	22 22						
Wellington (Shropshire)	d	15 35		16 35			17 35		18 35			19 35		20 35				21 39	22 35						
Telford Central	d	15 41		16 41			17 41		18 41			19 41		20 41				21 45	22 41						
Cosford	d																								
Wolverhampton 7	a	15 58		16 58			17 58		18 58			19 58		20 58				22 02	22 58						
Tame Bridge Parkway	d																								
Birmingham New Street 12	a	16 18		17 18			18 19		19 18			20 18		21 18				22 18	23 18						
Birmingham International ✈	a	*16r39*		*17t39*			*18v44*		*19w42*			*20y51*		*21y52*				*23 04*	*00 21*						
Banbury	a																								
London Marylebone 10 ⊖	a																								
London Euston 15 ⊖	a	*18z23*		*19B21*			*20C59*		*21D42*			*23E24*													

For general notes see front of timetable
For details of catering facilities see Directory of Train Operators

- **A** From Holyhead (Table 81)
- **B** Until 6 September only. 19 July to 6 September arr. 1947
- **C** Until 6 September only. 19 July to 6 September arr. 2126
- **D** Until 6 September only. 19 July to 6 September arr. 2231
- **E** Until 6 September only. 19 July to 6 September arr. 2331
- **b** Arr. 1214
- **c** Arr. 1414
- **e** Arr. 1615
- **f** Arr. 1814
- **g** Arr. 2041
- **h** Arr. 1316
- **j** Arr. 1517
- **k** Arr. 1715
- **m** Arr. 1914
- **n** Arr. 2139
- **q** From 13 September arr. 1755
- **r** Until 6 September only. 19 July to 6 September arr. 1651
- **t** Until 6 September only. 19 July to 6 September arr. 1752
- **v** Until 6 September only. 19 July to 6 September arr. 1852
- **w** Until 6 September only. 19 July to 6 September arr. 1951
- **y** Until 6 September only
- **z** Until 6 September only. 19 July to 6 September arr. 1856

Wrexham & Shropshire services are expected to start operating during the currency of this timetable. Please visit the Wrexham & Shropshire website www.wrexhamandshropshire.co.uk for updated information

Table 75

Sundays

until 13 July

Pwllheli, Barmouth, Aberystwyth and Chester → Shrewsbury and Birmingham

Network Diagram - see first page of Table 67

		AW	AW	AW	AW	AW	AW	AW		AW	AW	AW	AW	AW	AW	AW	AW	AW	AW	AW	AW	AW	AW		
																R									
				◇		◇	◇	◇		◇		◇	◇		◇		◇	◇	◇	◇					
							A									A		A							
							🚲									🚲									
Pwllheli	d							11 55				13 55							18 23						
Abererch	d							11x59				13x59							18x27						
Penychain	d							12x01				14x01							18x30						
Criccieth	d							12 08				14 08							18 36						
Porthmadog	d							12 18				14 17							18 47						
Minffordd	d							12 23				14 22							18 51						
Penrhyndeudraeth	d							12 26				14 25							18 55						
Llandecwyn	d							12x29				14x28							18x57						
Talsarnau	d							12x31				14x30							19x00						
Tygwyn	d							12x33				14x32							19x02						
Harlech	d							12 38				14 37							19 07						
Llandanwg	d							12x43				14x42							19x12						
Pensarn	d							12x44				14x43							19x13						
Llanbedr	d							12x46				14x45							19x15						
Dyffryn Ardudwy	d							12x50				14x49							19x19						
Talybont	d							12x52				14x51							19x21						
Llanaber	d							12x56				14x55							19x25						
Barmouth	a							13 00				14 58							19 30						
	d							13 02				15 00							19 32						
Morfa Mawddach	d							13x07				15x05							19x37						
Fairbourne	d							13 09				15 07							19 40						
Llwyngwril	d							13x17				15x15							19x47						
Tonfanau	d							13x23				15x21							19x54						
Tywyn	d							13 28				15 26							19 59						
Aberdovey	d							13 34				15 32							20 05						
Penhelig	d							13x37				15x35							20x08						
Aberystwyth	d	23p40		08 37		10 35				13 29			15 31		17 15					20 03			23 04		
Borth	d	23p52		08 49		10 47				13 41			15 43		17 27					20 15			23 16		
Dovey Junction 4	d	00 03		09 00		10 58		13 47		13 52		15 45	15 54		17 38				20 18	20 26			23 27		
Machynlleth 4	a	00 13		09 07		11 05		13 54		14 00		15 52	16 03		17 46				20 25	20 33			23 37		
	d			09 09		11 08				14 05		16 06			17 52					20 35					
Caersws	d			09 37		11 36				14 34		16 34			18 25					21 03					
Newtown (Powys)	d			09 44		11 44				14 41		16 41			18 33					21 10					
Welshpool	d			10 00		12 00				14 57		16 57			18 49					21 29					
Chester	d		08 08		11 15		12 20				15 20			17 30		19 07	19 28	20 24			21 31	22 03			
Wrexham General	d		08a26		11 32		12 37				15 36			17 46		19 24	19 44	20 40			21 47	22a21			
Ruabon	d				11 38		12 44				15 43			17 53		19 31	19 51	20 47			21 54				
Chirk	d				11 44		12 49				15 49			17 59		19 36	19 57	20 53			22 00				
Gobowen	d				11 50		12 55				15 54			18 04		19 42	20 02	20 58			22 05				
Shrewsbury	a			10 23	12 10	12 23	13 13			15 20	16 15	17 22		18 25	19 12	19 56	20 23	21 19		21 52	22 27				
Crewe 10	a			*11 41*		*13 35*						*18 12*			*20 15*										
Manchester Piccadilly 10	🚢 a			*12 26*		*14 21*																			
Cardiff Central 7	a			*13 53*			15 35			*18 13*	*18 55*	*20 15*			*21 37*	22 27				*00 25*					
Shrewsbury	d			10 27		12 26				15 26	16 16	17 26		18 27	19 23		20 27	21 20		22 24					
Wellington (Shropshire)	d			10 41		12 40				15 40	16 30	17 39		18 41	19 37		20 41	21 34		22 38					
Telford Central	d			10 47		12 49				15 46	16 39	17 48		18 49	19 45		20 47	21 43		22 46					
Cosford	d										16 49	17 58			19 55			21 53		22 56					
Wolverhampton 7	🚢 a			11 04		13 06				16 03	17 06	18 15		19 06	20 13		21 05	22 10		23 17					
Tame Bridge Parkway	d																								
Birmingham New Street 12	a			11 32		13 39				16 32	17 32	18 41		19 33	20 39		21 32	22 40							
Birmingham International	✈ a			*12b20*		*14b20*				*17b20*	*18b20*	*19b20*		*20b20*	*21b20*		*22b20*	*23b20*							
Banbury	a																								
London Marylebone 10	⊖ a																								
London Euston 15	⊖ a			*13 57*		*17 03*				*19 23*	*20 11*			*22 04*			*00 25*								

For general notes see front of timetable
For details of catering facilities see Directory of Train Operators

A From Holyhead (Table 81)
b By bus

Wrexham & Shropshire services are expected to start operating during the currency of this timetable. Please visit the Wrexham & Shropshire website www.wrexhamandshropshire.co.uk for updated information

Table 75

Pwllheli, Barmouth, Aberystwyth and Chester → Shrewsbury and Birmingham

20 July to 7 September

Network Diagram - see first page of Table 67

		AW	AW	AW	AW	AW	AW	AW		AW	AW	AW	AW	AW	AW	AW	AW	AW	AW	AW	AW	AW	AW
				◇		◇	◇ A 🛒	◇		◇		◇	◇		◇	R A 🛒	◇	◇ A	◇	◇			
Pwllheli	d							11 55				13 55							18 23				
Abererch	d							11x59				13x59							18x27				
Penychain	d							12x01				14x01							18x30				
Criccieth	d							12 08				14 08							18 36				
Porthmadog	d							12 18				14 17							18 47				
Minffordd	d							12 23				14 22							18 51				
Penrhyndeudraeth	d							12 26				14 25							18 55				
Llandecwyn	d							12x29				14x28							18x57				
Talsarnau	d							12x31				14x30							19x00				
Tygwyn	d							12x33				14x32							19x02				
Harlech	d							12 38				14 37							19 07				
Llandanwg	d							12x43				14x42							19x12				
Pensarn	d							12x44				14x43							19x13				
Llanbedr	d							12x46				14x45							19x15				
Dyffryn Ardudwy	d							12x50				14x49							19x19				
Talybont	d							12x52				14x51							19x21				
Llanaber	d							12x56				14x55							19x25				
Barmouth	a							13 00				14 58							19 30				
	d							13 02				15 00							19 32				
Morfa Mawddach	d							13x07				15x05							19x37				
Fairbourne	d							13 09				15 07							19 40				
Llwyngwril	d							13x17				15x15							19x47				
Tonfanau	d							13x23				15x21							19x54				
Tywyn	d							13 28				15 26							19 59				
Aberdovey	d							13 34				15 32							20 05				
Penhelig	d							13x37				15x35							20x08				
Aberystwyth	d	23p40		08 37		10 35				13 29			15 31		17 15					20 03			23 04
Borth	d	23p52		08 49		10 47				13 41			15 43		17 27					20 15			23 16
Dovey Junction 4	d	00 03		09 00		10 58		13 47		13 52		15 45	15 54		17 38				20 18	20 26			23 27
Machynlleth 4	a	00 13		09 07		11 05		13 54		14 00		15 52	16 03		17 46				20 25	20 33			23 37
	d			09 09		11 08				14 05		16 06			17 52					20 35			
Caersws	d			09 37		11 36				14 34		16 34			18 25					21 03			
Newtown (Powys)	d			09 44		11 44				14 41		16 41			18 33					21 10			
Welshpool	d			10 00		12 00				14 57		16 57			18 49					21 27			
Chester	d		08 08		11 15		12 20				15 20			17 30		19 06	19 28	20 24			21 31	22 03	
Wrexham General	d		08a26		11 32		12 37				15 36			17 47		19 22	19 44	20 40			21 47	22a21	
Ruabon	d				11 38		12 44				15 43			17 54		19 29	19 51	20 47			21 54		
Chirk	d				11 44		12 49				15 49			18 00		19 35	19 57	20 53			22 00		
Gobowen	d				11 50		12 55				15 54			18 05		19 40	20 02	20 58			22 05		
Shrewsbury	a			10 23	12 10	12 23	13 13			15 20	16 15	17 22		18 26	19 12	19 56	20 23	21 19		21 50	22 27		
Crewe 10	a			*11 30*		*13 35*						*18 12*			*20 15*								
Manchester Piccadilly 10	a			*12 16*		*14 21*																	
Cardiff Central 7	a			*13 53*			15 31			*18 13*	*18 55*	*20 15*			*21 37*	22 27				*00 25*			
Shrewsbury	d			10 27		12 26				15 26	16 16	17 26		18 28	19 23		20 27	21 20		22 24			
Wellington (Shropshire)	d			10 41		12 40				15 40	16 30	17 39		18 42	19 37		20 41	21 34		22 38			
Telford Central	d			10 47		12 49				15 46	16 39	17 48		18 50	19 45		20 47	21 43		22 46			
Cosford	d										16 49	17 58			19 55			21 53		22 56			
Wolverhampton 7	a			11 04		13 06				16 02	17 06	18 14		19 08	20 13		21 05	22 11		23 17			
Tame Bridge Parkway	d																						
Birmingham New Street 12	a			11 22		13 23				16 20	17 23	18 32		19 25	20 30		21 24	22 30					
Birmingham International ✈	a			*12b20*		*14b20*				*17b20*	*18b20*	*19b20*		*20b20*	*21b20*		*22b20*	*23b20*					
Banbury	a																						
London Marylebone 10 ⊖	a																						
London Euston 15 ⊖	a			*14 13*		*16 13*				*19 13*	*20 11*	*21 14*		*22 15*	*23 06*		*00 06*						

For general notes see front of timetable
For details of catering facilities see Directory of Train Operators

A From Holyhead (Table 81)
b By bus

Wrexham & Shropshire services are expected to start operating during the currency of this timetable. Please visit the Wrexham & Shropshire website www.wrexhamandshropshire.co.uk for updated information

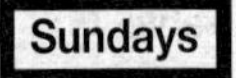

from 14 September

Pwllheli, Barmouth, Aberystwyth and Chester → Shrewsbury and Birmingham

Network Diagram - see first page of Table 67

		AW	AW	AW	AW	AW	AW	AW	AW	AW	AW	AW	AW	AW	AW	AW	AW	AW	AW
						◇ A ✕			◇				R B ✕			◇ B			
Pwllheli	d								13 55										
Abererch	d								13x59										
Penychain	d								14x01										
Criccieth	d								14 08										
Porthmadog	d								14 19										
Minffordd	d								14 23										
Penrhyndeudraeth	d								14 26										
Llandecwyn	d								14x29										
Talsarnau	d								14x31										
Tygwyn	d								14x33										
Harlech	d								14 38										
Llandanwg	d								14x43										
Pensarn	d								14x44										
Llanbedr	d								14x46										
Dyffryn Ardudwy	d								14x50										
Talybont	d								14x52										
Llanaber	d								14x56										
Barmouth	a								15 00										
	d								15 01										
Morfa Mawddach	d								15x06										
Fairbourne	d								15 08										
Llwyngwril	d								15x15										
Tonfanau	d								15x21										
Tywyn	d								15 26										
Aberdovey	d								15 32										
Penhelig	d								15x35										
Aberystwyth	d	23p40					12 34			15 34		17 15			19 25				23 15
Borth	d	23p52					12 46			15 46		17 27			19 37				23 27
Dovey Junction 4	d	00 03					12 57		15 45	15 57		17 38			19 48				23 38
Machynlleth 4	a	00 13					13 04		15 52	16 06		17 45			19 56				23 46
	d						13 07			16 09		17 49							
Caersws	d						13 35			16 37		18 26							
Newtown (Powys)	d						13 42			16 44		18 33							
Welshpool	d						13 58			17 00		18 49							
Chester	d		08 08	10 00	11 15	12 20		14 23			17 30		19 06	19 28		20 24	21 31	22 03	
Wrexham General	d		08a26	10 17	11 32	12 37		14b44			17 47		19 22	19 44		20 40	21 47	22a21	
Ruabon	d			10 23	11 38	12 44		14 51			17 54		19 29	19 51		20 47	21 54		
Chirk	d			10 29	11 44	12 49		14 57			18 00		19 35	19 57		20 53	22 00		
Gobowen	d			10 35	11 50	12 55		15 02			18 05		19 40	20 02		20 58	22 05		
Shrewsbury	a			10 55	12 10	13 13	14 21	15 23		17 23	18 26	19 12	19 56	20 23		21 19	22 26		
Crewe 10	a						14 54			17 58		19 45							
Manchester Piccadilly 10	a						16 10												
Cardiff Central 7	a			13 53		15 31		18 13		20c15		21c37	22 27			00 25			
Shrewsbury	d																		
Wellington (Shropshire)	d																		
Telford Central	d																		
Cosford	d																		
Wolverhampton 7	a																		
Tame Bridge Parkway	d																		
Birmingham New Street 12	a																		
Birmingham International	a																		
Banbury	a																		
London Marylebone 10	⊖ a																		
London Euston 15	⊖ a																		

For general notes see front of timetable
For details of catering facilities see Directory of Train Operators

A From Llandudno Junction (Table 81)
B From Holyhead (Table 81)
b Arr. 1439
c Change at Shrewsbury

Wrexham & Shropshire services are expected to start operating during the currency of this timetable. Please visit the Wrexham & Shropshire website www.wrexhamandshropshire.co.uk for updated information

Network Diagram for Tables 78, 79, 84, 85, 86

DM-11/06(2)
Design BAJS

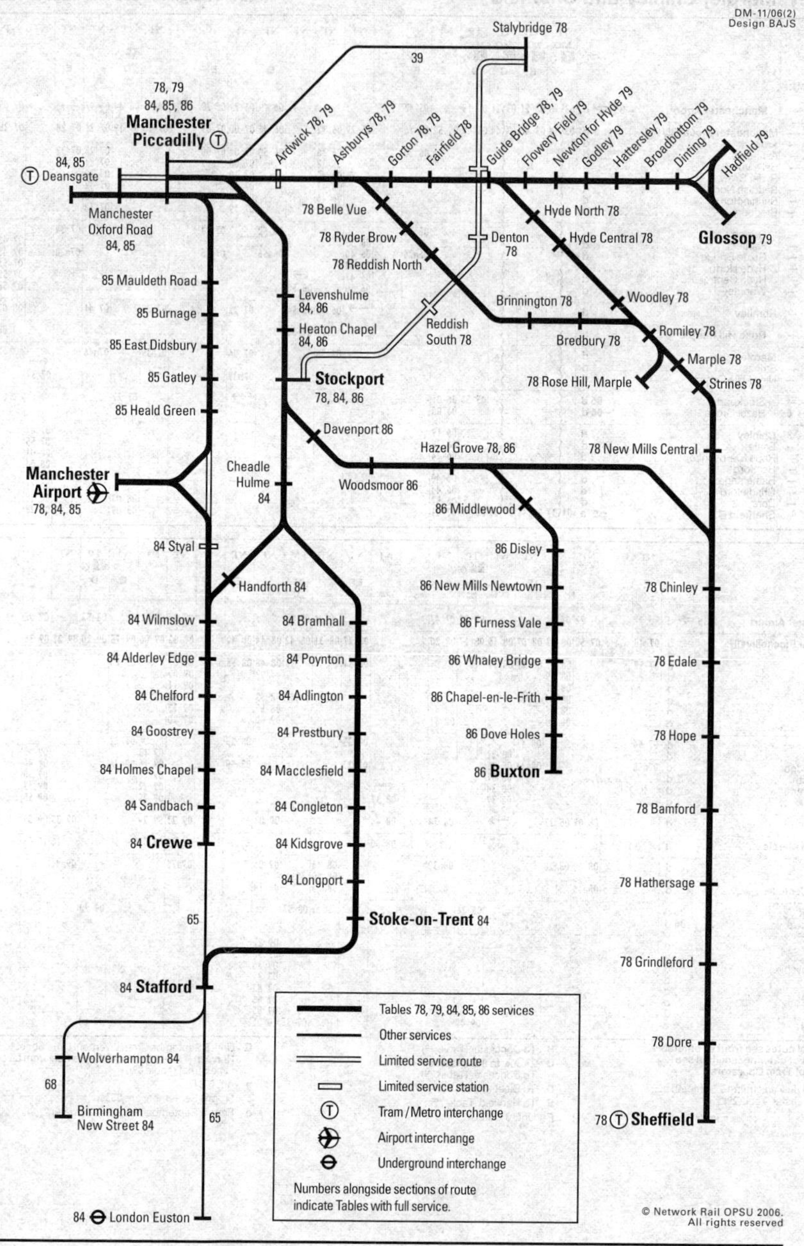

Stalybridge 78
39
78, 79
84, 85, 86
Manchester Piccadilly
84, 85
Deansgate
Manchester Oxford Road 84, 85
Ardwick 78, 79
Ashburys 78, 79
Gorton 78, 79
Fairfield 78
Guide Bridge 78, 79
Flowery Field 79
Newton for Hyde 79
Godley 79
Hattersley 79
Broadbottom 79
Dinting 79
Hadfield 79
Glossop 79
78 Belle Vue
78 Ryder Brow
78 Reddish North
Denton 78
Hyde North 78
Hyde Central 78
Woodley 78
Brinnington 78
Bredbury 78
Romiley 78
Marple 78
78 Rose Hill, Marple
Strines 78
85 Mauldeth Road
85 Burnage
85 East Didsbury
85 Gatley
85 Heald Green
Levenshulme 84, 86
Heaton Chapel 84, 86
Reddish South 78
Stockport 78, 84, 86
Davenport 86
Hazel Grove 78, 86
78 New Mills Central
Manchester Airport 78, 84, 85
Cheadle Hulme 84
Woodsmoor 86
86 Middlewood
86 Disley
86 New Mills Newtown
86 Furness Vale
86 Whaley Bridge
86 Chapel-en-le-Frith
86 Dove Holes
86 Buxton
84 Styal
Handforth 84
84 Wilmslow
84 Alderley Edge
84 Chelford
84 Goostrey
84 Holmes Chapel
84 Sandbach
84 Crewe
84 Bramhall
84 Poynton
84 Adlington
84 Prestbury
84 Macclesfield
84 Congleton
84 Kidsgrove
84 Longport
Stoke-on-Trent 84
65
84 Stafford
78 Chinley
78 Edale
78 Hope
78 Bamford
78 Hathersage
78 Grindleford
78 Dore
78 Sheffield
Wolverhampton 84
68
Birmingham New Street 84
65
84 London Euston
Tables 78, 79, 84, 85, 86 services
Other services
Limited service route
Limited service station
Tram / Metro interchange
Airport interchange
Underground interchange
Numbers alongside sections of route indicate Tables with full service.

Manchester Airport and Manchester → Romiley, Marple, Chinley and Sheffield

Network Diagram - see first page of Table 78

Miles	Miles	Miles			TP MO 1 ◇ A	TP MX 1 ◇ B	TP MO 1 ◇ C	TP 1 ◇ D	NT	NT E	NT	NT	NT	NT E	NT	NT E	NT	TP 1 ◇ D ⚲	NT	NT E	NT	NT	EM ◇ G ⚲
—	—	—	**Manchester Airport**	85 ✈ d	03 18	03 21	03 21	05 15	.	05 47	.	.	.	06 19	06 23	06 28	06 44	06 44	06 47	.	.	07 05	.
0	0	—	**Manchester Piccadilly** 10	⇌ d	03 37	03 40	03 44	05 49	05 52	06 16	06 29	06 32	.	06 46	07 00	07 03	07 18	07 19	07 21	07 28	.	07 38	07 43
½	½	—	Ardwick	d		.		.	.	.	.	.	.	.	.	.	.	.	.	.	.	.	.
1½	1½	—	Ashburys	d		.		.	.	06 20	.	06 36	.	06 50	07 04	07 08	.	.	07 25	07 32	.	.	.
2¼	—	—	Belle Vue	d		.		.	.	.	.	06 38	.	.	07 08	.	.	.	07 27	.	.	.	.
2¾	—	—	Ryder Brow	d		.		.	.	.	.	06 40	.	.	07 10	.	.	.	07 29	.	.	.	.
3¾	—	—	Reddish North	d		.		.	.	.	.	06 43	.	.	07 13	.	.	.	07 32	.	.	.	.
5½	—	—	Brinnington	d		.		.	.	.	.	06 46	.	.	07 16	.	.	.	07 35	.	.	.	.
6½	—	—	Bredbury	d		.		.	.	.	.	06 49	.	.	07 19	.	.	.	07 38	.	.	.	.
—	2½	—	Gorton	d		.		.	.	06 22	.	.	.	06 52	.	07 11	.	.	.	07 34	.	.	.
—	3½	—	Fairfield	d		.		.	.	.	06 36	.	.	.	.	.	.	.	.	.	.	07 46	.
—	4¾	—	Guide Bridge	d		.		.	.	06a26	06 40	.	.	06a56	.	07a15	.	.	.	07a38	.	07 49	.
—	6½	—	Hyde North	d		.		.	.	.	06 44	.	.	.	.	.	.	.	.	.	.	07 53	.
—	7¾	—	Hyde Central	d		.		.	.	.	06 47	.	←	.	.	.	.	.	.	.	.	07 55	.
—	9¼	—	Woodley	d		.		.	.	.	06 50	.	06 50	.	.	.	.	.	.	.	.	07 58	.
7½	10½	—	**Romiley**	d		.		.	.	.	→	06 52	06 54	.	07 22	.	07 30	.	07 41	.	.	08 02	.
—	12½	—	**Rose Hill Marple**	a		.		.	.	.	.	.	07 00	.	.	.	.	.	.	.	.	08 08	.
9	—	—	**Marple**	d		.		.	.	.	.	06 56	.	.	07 26	.	07a35	.	07a46	.	←	.	.
11½	—	—	Strines	d		.		.	.	.	.	.	.	.	.	.	.	.	.	.	.	.	.
12¾	—	—	New Mills Central	d		.		.	.	.	.	07a03	.	.	07b39	.	.	.	.	.	07 39	.	.
—	—	—	Stockport	86 d		.		05 58	06 01	.	.	.	.	.	→	.	.	07 27	.	.	.	.	07 54
—	—	0	Hazel Grove	86 d		.		.	06 08	.	.	.	.	.	.	.	.	.	.	.	.	.	.
16½	—	8½	**Chinley**	d		.		.	06 19	.	.	.	.	.	.	.	.	.	.	.	07 47	.	.
22	—	—	Edale	d		.		.	06 28	.	.	.	.	.	.	.	.	.	.	.	07 55	.	.
27¼	—	—	Hope (Derbyshire)	d		.		.	06 34	.	.	.	.	.	.	.	.	.	.	.	08 01	.	.
29	—	—	Bamford	d		.		.	06 37	.	.	.	.	.	.	.	.	.	.	.	08 04	.	.
30¾	—	—	Hathersage	d		.		.	06 40	.	.	.	.	.	.	.	.	.	.	.	08 09	.	.
32¼	—	—	Grindleford	d		.		.	06 44	.	.	.	.	.	.	.	.	.	.	.	08 11	.	.
37¾	—	—	Dore	d		.		.	06 52	.	.	.	.	.	.	.	.	08 03	.	.	08 20	.	08 28
42	—	—	**Sheffield** 7	⇌ a	04 37	04 31	04 37	06 48	07 01	.	.	.	.	.	.	.	.	08 09	.	.	08 28	.	08c34

		NT E	NT	NT	NT E	NT	TP 1 ◇ D ⚲	NT	NT	NT EF	NT	EM ◇ G ⚲	NT	NT E	NT	NT	NT E	TP 1 ◇ D ⚲	NT	NT	EM ◇ G ⚲
Manchester Airport	85 ✈ d	.	07 22	07 34	.	.	07 52	07 47	.	.	08 04	08 07	.	.	08 33	.	.	08 52	.	09 07	.
Manchester Piccadilly 10	⇌ d	07 48	07 52	08 03	08 07	08 15	08 17	08 20	.	08 27	08 31	08 42	08 44	08 49	09 03	09 06	09 15	09 20	09 22	09 36	09 42
Ardwick	d	.	.	.	.	.	.	.	.	.	.	.	.	.	.	.	.	.	.	.	.
Ashburys	d	07 52	.	08 07	08 11	08 19	.	.	.	08 31	.	.	08 48	08 53	09 07	.	09 20	.	.	.	.
Belle Vue	d	.	.	08 09	.	.	.	.	.		.	.	.	.	09 09	.	.	.	.	.	.
Ryder Brow	d	.	.	08 11	.	.	.	.	.		.	.	.	.	09 11	.	.	.	.	.	.
Reddish North	d	.	.	08 14	.	.	.	.	.		.	.	08 53	.	09 14	.	.	.	.	.	.
Brinnington	d	.	.	08 17	.	.	.	.	.		.	.	08 57	.	09 17	.	.	.	.	.	.
Bredbury	d	.	.	08 20	.	.	.	08 31	.		.	.	09 00	.	09 20	.	.	.	.	.	.
Gorton	d	07 54	.	.	08 13	.	.	.	.	08 33	.	.	.	08 55	.	.	09 22	.	.	.	.
Fairfield	d	.	.	.	.	08 22	.	.	.	.	.	.	.	.	.	09 13	.	.	.	09 43	.
Guide Bridge	d	07a58	.	.	08a17	08 25	.	.	.	08a37	.	.	.	08a59	.	09 16	09a26	.	.	09 46	.
Hyde North	d	.	.	.	.	08 31	.	.	.	.	.	.	.	.	.	09 20	.	.	.	09 50	.
Hyde Central	d	.	.	.	.	08 34	.	.	←	.	.	.	.	.	.	09 22	.	.	.	09 52	.
Woodley	d	.	.	.	.	08 37	.	.	08 37	.	.	.	.	.	.	09 25	.	.	.	09 55	.
Romiley	d	.	08 05	08 23	.	→	.	08 34	08 44	.	.	.	09 03	.	09 23	09 29	.	.	09 35	09 59	.
Rose Hill Marple	a	.	.	.	.	.	.	.	08 50	.	.	.	.	.	.	09 35	.	.	.	10 05	.
Marple	d	.	08 09	08a28	.	.	.	08a39	.	.	08 46	.	09 06	.	09a28	.	.	.	09a41	.	.
Strines	d	.	.	.	.	.	.	.	.	.	08 50	.	.	.	.	.	.	.	.	.	.
New Mills Central	d	.	08a15	.	.	.	.	.	.	.	08a54	.	09 14	.	.	.	.	.	.	.	.
Stockport	86 d	.	.	.	.	.	08 26	.	.	.	.	08 53	.	.	.	.	.	09 28	.	.	09 55
Hazel Grove	86 d	.	.	.	.	.	.	.	.	.	.	.	.	.	.	.	.	.	.	.	.
Chinley	d	.	.	.	.	.	.	.	.	.	.	.	09 22	.	.	.	.	.	.	.	.
Edale	d	.	.	.	.	.	.	.	.	.	.	.	09 30	.	.	.	.	.	.	.	.
Hope (Derbyshire)	d	.	.	.	.	.	.	.	.	.	.	.	09 36	.	.	.	.	.	.	.	.
Bamford	d	.	.	.	.	.	.	.	.	.	.	.	09 39	.	.	.	.	.	.	.	.
Hathersage	d	.	.	.	.	.	.	.	.	.	.	.	09 43	.	.	.	.	.	.	.	.
Grindleford	d	.	.	.	.	.	.	.	.	.	.	.	09 46	.	.	.	.	.	.	.	.
Dore	d	.	.	.	.	.	.	.	.	.	.	.	09 55	.	.	.	.	.	.	.	.
Sheffield 7	⇌ a	.	.	.	.	.	09 09	.	.	.	.	09e35	10 05	.	.	.	.	10 08	.	.	10e35

For general notes see front of timetable
For details of catering facilities see Directory of Train Operators

A Until 14 July and from 15 September. To Doncaster (Table 29)
B To Doncaster (Table 29)
C 21 July to 8 September. To Doncaster (Table 29)
D To Cleethorpes (Table 29)
E To Hadfield (Table 79)
F Until 3 October
G Until 5 September from Liverpool Lime Street to Norwich (Table 49). From 8 September from Liverpool Lime Street (Table 89)
b Arr. 0731
c From 8 September arr. 0836
e From 8 September arr. 3 minutes later

Manchester Airport and Manchester → Romiley, Marple, Chinley and Sheffield

Network Diagram - see first page of Table 78

Station		NT	NT A	NT	NT A	TP 1 ◇ B	NT	NT	EM ◇ C	NT	NT A	NT	NT A	TP 1 ◇ B	NT	NT	EM ◇ C	NT	NT A	NT	NT A	TP 1 ◇ B
Manchester Airport 85	d			*09 34*		09 52		*10 07*			*10 15*	*10 34*	*10 47*	10 52		*11 07*			*11 15*	*11 34*	*11 47*	11 52
Manchester Piccadilly 10	d	09 46	09 49	10 03	10 19	10 20	10 22	10 36	10 42	10 46	10 49	11 03	11 19	11 20	11 22	11 36	11 42	11 46	11 49	12 03	12 19	12 20
Ardwick	d																					
Ashburys	d		09 53	10 07	10 23						10 53	11 07	11 23						11 53	12 07	12 23	
Belle Vue	d			10 09								11 09								12 09		
Ryder Brow	d			10 11								11 11								12 11		
Reddish North	d	09 53		10 14						10 53		11 14						11 53		12 14		
Brinnington	d	09 57		10 17						10 57		11 17						11 57		12 17		
Bredbury	d	10 00		10 20						11 00		11 20						12 00		12 20		
Gorton	d		09 55		10 25						10 55		11 25						11 55		12 25	
Fairfield	d							10 43								11 43						
Guide Bridge	d		09a59		10a29			10 46			10a59		11a29			11 46			11a59		12a29	
Hyde North	d							10 50								11 50						
Hyde Central	d							10 52								11 52						
Woodley	d							10 55								11 55						
Romiley	d	10 03		10 23			10 37	10 59		11 03		11 23			11 37	11 59		12 03		12 23		
Rose Hill Marple	a							11 05								12 05						
Marple	d	10 06		10a28			10a43			11 06		11a28			11a43			12 06		12a28		
Strines	d	10 10																12 10				
New Mills Central	d	10a15								11 12								12a15				
Stockport 86	d					10 28			10 55					11 27			11 55					12 28
Hazel Grove 86	d																					
Chinley	d									11 19												
Edale	d									11 28												
Hope (Derbyshire)	d									11 34												
Bamford	d									11 38												
Hathersage	d									11 42												
Grindleford	d									11 46												
Dore	d									11 55												
Sheffield 7	a					11 08			11b35	12 04				12 08			12b35					13 08

Station		NT	NT	EM ◇ C	NT	NT A	NT	NT A	TP 1 ◇ B	NT	NT	EM ◇ C	NT	NT A	NT	NT A	TP 1 ◇ B	NT	NT	EM ◇ D	NT	NT A
Manchester Airport 85	d		*12 07*			*12 15*	*12 34*	*12 47*	12 52		*13 07*			*13 15*	*13 34*	*13 47*	13 52		*14 07*			*14 15*
Manchester Piccadilly 10	d	12 22	12 36	12 42	12 46	12 49	13 03	13 19	13 20	13 22	13 36	13 42	13 46	13 49	14 03	14 19	14 20	14 22	14 36	14 42	14 46	14 49
Ardwick	d																					
Ashburys	d					12 53	13 07	13 23						13 53	14 07	14 23						14 53
Belle Vue	d						13 09								14 09							
Ryder Brow	d						13 11								14 11							
Reddish North	d				12 53		13 14						13 53		14 14						14 53	
Brinnington	d				12 57		13 17						13 57		14 17						14 57	
Bredbury	d				13 00		13 20						14 00		14 20						15 00	
Gorton	d					12 55		13 25						13 55		14 25						14 55
Fairfield	d		12 43								13 43								14 43			
Guide Bridge	d		12 46			12a59		13a29			13 46			13a59		14a29			14 46			14a59
Hyde North	d		12 50								13 50								14 50			
Hyde Central	d		12 52								13 52								14 52			
Woodley	d		12 55								13 55								14 55			
Romiley	d	12 37	12 59		13 03		13 23			13 37	13 59		14 03		14 23			14 37	14 59		15 03	
Rose Hill Marple	a		13 05								14 05								15 05			
Marple	d	12a43			13 06		13a28			13a43			14 06		14a28			14a43			15 06	
Strines	d												14 10									
New Mills Central	d				13 12								14a15								15 12	
Stockport 86	d			12 55					13 28			13 55					14 28			14 55		
Hazel Grove 86	d																					
Chinley	d				13 19																15 19	
Edale	d				13 28																15 28	
Hope (Derbyshire)	d				13 34																15 34	
Bamford	d				13 38																15 38	
Hathersage	d				13 42																15 42	
Grindleford	d				13 46																15 46	
Dore	d				13 55																15 55	
Sheffield 7	a			13b35	14 04				14 08			14c35					15 08			15c35	16 04	

For general notes see front of timetable
For details of catering facilities see Directory of Train Operators

A To Hadfield (Table 79)

B To Cleethorpes (Table 29)

C Until 5 September from Liverpool Lime Street to Norwich (Table 49). From 8 September from Liverpool Lime Street (Table 89)

D Until 5 September from Liverpool Lime Street to Nottingham (Table 49). From 8 September from Liverpool Lime Street (Table 89)

b From 8 September arr. 3 minutes later

c From 8 September arr. 0836

Manchester Airport and Manchester → Romiley, Marple, Chinley and Sheffield

Network Diagram - see first page of Table 78

	NT	NT	TP	NT	NT	EM	NT	NT	NT	NT	NT	TP	NT	NT	EM	NT	NT	NT	NT	NT	NT
			1 ◇			◇						1 ◇			◇						
		A	B			C		A			A	B		A	C			A			A
			trolley			trolley						trolley			trolley						
Manchester Airport 85 ✈ d	14 34	14 47	14 52		15 07			15 15	15 34			15 52		16 07				16 34			
Manchester Piccadilly 10 d	15 03	15 19	15 20	15 22	15 36	15 42	15 46	15 49	16 02	16 05	16 17	16 20	16 22	16 36	16 42	16 46	16 49	16 58	17 03	17 14	17 17
Ardwick d																			17 06		
Ashburys d	15 07	15 23						15 53	16 07	16 09	16 21			16 40		16 50	16 53	17 02	17 08		17 21
Belle Vue d	15 09								16 09							16 52			17 11		
Ryder Brow d	15 11								16 11							16 54			17 13		
Reddish North d	15 14						15 53		16 14							16 57				17 22	
Brinnington d	15 17						15 57		16 17							17 00				17 25	
Bredbury d	15 20						16 00		16 20							17 03			17 19	17 28	
Gorton d		15 25						15 55			16 23			16 42				17 04			17 23
Fairfield d					15 43					16 13							16 57				
Guide Bridge d		15a29			15 46			15a59		16 16	16a26			16a46			17 00	17a08			17a27
Hyde North d					15 50					16 20							17 04				
Hyde Central d					15 52					16 22							17 06				
Woodley d					15 55					16 25							17 09				
Romiley d	15 23			15 35	15 59		16 03		16 23	16 29			16 34			17 06	17 13		17 22	17 31	
Rose Hill Marple a					16 05					16 35							17 18				
Marple d	15a28			15a40			16 06		16a28				16a39			17 10			17a27	17 35	
Strines d							16 10													17 39	
New Mills Central d							16 14									17a15				17 44	
Stockport 86 d			15 28			15 51						16 28			16 53					↪	
Hazel Grove 86 d																					
Chinley d							16 21								17 10						
Edale d							16 30														
Hope (Derbyshire) d							16 36														
Bamford d							16 39														
Hathersage d							16 42														
Grindleford d							16 46														
Dore d							16 55								17 30						
Sheffield 7 a			16 08			16b35	17 04					17 08			17 38						

	TP	NT	NT	NT	NT	EM	NT	NT	NT	NT	TP	NT	NT	NT	EM	NT	NT	NT	TP	NT	NT
	1 ◇					◇					1 ◇				◇				1 ◇		
	B				A	G			A		B	A			H		A		B	A	
	trolley					trolley					trolley				trolley						
Manchester Airport 85 ✈ d	16 52			17 04				17 19	17 34		17 52			18 10				18 34	18 52	18 47	
Manchester Piccadilly 10 d	17 20		17 28	17 31	17 36	17 42	17 45	17 51	18 00	18 05	18 18	18 18	18 22	18 36	18 44	18 46	18 49	19 02	19 18	19 19	19 22
Ardwick d										18 08											
Ashburys d			17 32	17 35	17 40			17 56	18 04	18 10		18 22	18 26				18 53	19 08		19 23	
Belle Vue d								17 58										19 10			
Ryder Brow d								18 00										19 12			
Reddish North d			17 37					18 03					18 31			18 53		19 15			
Brinnington d			17 40					18 06					18 34			18 57		19 18			
Bredbury d			17 43					18 09					18 37			19 00		19 21			
Gorton d					17 42				18 06			18 25					18 55			19 25	
Fairfield d				17 39						18 14				18 43							
Guide Bridge d				17 42	17a46				18a10	18 17		18a29		18 46			18a59			19a29	
Hyde North d				17 46						18 21				18 50							
Hyde Central d				17 48						18 24				18 52							
Woodley d				17 51						18 27				18 55							
Romiley d			17 46	17 55			17 59	18 12		18 30			18 40	18 59		19 03		19 24			19 34
Rose Hill Marple a				18 00						18 35				19 06							
Marple d			17a51				18 04	18a16					18 44			19 06		19a29			19a39
Strines d		↤					18 08						18 48								
New Mills Central d		17 44					18 12						18a51			19 12					
Stockport 86 d	17 28					17 53					18 26				18 55				19 26		
Hazel Grove 86 d																					
Chinley d	17 43	17 53					18a20									19 19					
Edale d		18 02														19 28					
Hope (Derbyshire) d		18 08														19 34					
Bamford d		18 11														19 38					
Hathersage d		18 14														19 42					
Grindleford d		18 18														19 46					
Dore d	18 06	18 25				18 32					19 02					19c55					
Sheffield 7 a	18 15	18 37				18 43					19 08				19e36	20 07			20 08		

For general notes see front of timetable
For details of catering facilities see Directory of Train Operators

A To Hadfield (Table 79)
B To Cleethorpes (Table 29)
C Until 5 September from Liverpool Lime Street to Norwich (Table 49). From 8 September from Liverpool Lime Street (Table 89)
G Until 5 September from Liverpool Lime Street to Nottingham (Table 49). From 8 September from Liverpool Lime Street (Table 89)
H From Liverpool Lime Street to Norwich (from 8 September to Nottingham) (Table 49)
b From 8 September arr. 0836
c Arr. 1952
e From 8 September arr. 1941

Manchester Airport and Manchester → Romiley, Marple, Chinley and Sheffield

Network Diagram - see first page of Table 78

	EM	NT		NT	TP	NT	EM	NT	NT		TP	NT	NT	TP	EM	NT		NT	NT	NT	TP		
	◇				1 ◇		◇				1 ◇			1 ◇	◇						1 ◇		
	A			B	C		A		B		C	B			A			B		D			
	⚲						⚲																
Manchester Airport 85 ✈ d	19 12			19 22	19 52		20 15		20 22		20 52	21 22	21 27	21 52				22 22	22 47		23 52		
Manchester Piccadilly 10 d	19 42	19 46		19 49	20 18	20 27	20 42	20 46	20 49		21 18	21 49	21 52	22 18	22 27	22 38		22 49	23 23	23 26	00 15		
Ardwick d																							
Ashburys d		19 50		19 53					20 53			21 53	21 56			22 42		22 53	23 27	23 30			
Belle Vue d		19 52											21 58			22 44			23 29				
Ryder Brow d		19 54											22 00			22 46			23 31				
Reddish North d		19 57						20 53					22 03			22 49			23 34				
Brinnington d		20 00						20 57					22 06			22 52			23 37				
Bredbury d		20 03						21 00					22 09			22 55			23 40				
Gorton d				19 55					20 55			21 55						22 55		23 32			
Fairfield d						20 34																	
Guide Bridge d				19a59		20 39			20a59			21a59						22a59		23a36			
Hyde North d						20 43																	
Hyde Central d						20 45																	
Woodley d						20 48																	
Romiley d		20 06				20 52		21 03					22 12			22 58			23 43				
Rose Hill Marple a						20 57																	
Marple d		20 11						21 06					22 16			23 02			23 47				
Strines d		20 15											22 20			23 06			23 51				
New Mills Central d		20a20						21 12					22a26			23a10			23a56				
Stockport 86 d	19 55				20 26		20 55				21 26			22 26	22 38								
Hazel Grove 86 d																							
Chinley d								21 19							22 53								
Edale d								21 28							23 02								
Hope (Derbyshire) d								21 34							23 08								
Bamford d								21 38							23 11								
Hathersage d								21 42							23 15								
Grindleford d								21 46							23 22								
Dore d								21 54							23 29								
Sheffield 7 a	20b39				21 08		21 34	22 03			22 09			23 13	23 35						01 13		

Saturdays

	TP	TP	NT	NT	NT	NT	NT	TP	NT	NT	EM		NT	NT	NT	TP	TP	NT	NT	NT	EM	NT	NT	NT
	1 ◇	1 ◇						1 ◇			◇					1 ◇	1 ◇				◇			
	E	C		B		B		C	B		H			B		J	K	B			H		B	
								⚲								⚲	⚲							
Manchester Airport 85 ✈ d	03 21	05 15		05 47		06 19	06 28	06 44	06 47		07 05				07 34	07 52	07 52			08 04	08 07			08 33
Manchester Piccadilly 10 d	03 40	05 49	05 52	06 16	06 32	06 46	07 05	07 19	07 19	07 28	07 43		07 46	07 49	08 03	08 17	08 18	08 19	08 22	08 36	08 42	08 46	08 49	09 03
Ardwick d																								
Ashburys d				06 20	06 36	06 50	07 09		07 23					07 53	08 07			08 23					08 53	09 07
Belle Vue d					06 38		07 11								08 09									09 09
Ryder Brow d					06 40		07 13								08 11									09 11
Reddish North d					06 43		07 16						07 53		08 14							08 53		09 14
Brinnington d					06 46		07 19						07 57		08 17							08 57		09 17
Bredbury d					06 49		07 22						08 00		08 20							09 00		09 20
Gorton d				06 22		06 52			07 25					07 55				08 25					08 55	
Fairfield d										07 35										08 43				
Guide Bridge d				06a26		06a56			07a29	07 38				07a59				08a29		08 46			08a59	
Hyde North d										07 42										08 50				
Hyde Central d										07 44										08 52				
Woodley d										07 47										08 55				
Romiley d					06 52		07 25			07 51			08 03		08 23				08 37	08 59		09 03		09 23
Rose Hill Marple a										07 57										09 05				
Marple d					06 56		07a30						08 06		08a28				08a43			09 06		09a28
Strines d																						09 10		
New Mills Central d					07 01								08 12									09 14		
Stockport 86 d		05 58	06 01					07 27			07 54					08 26	08 26				08 55			
Hazel Grove 86 d			06 08																					
Chinley d			06 19		07 09								08 20									09 22		
Edale d			06 28		07 19								08 29									09 30		
Hope (Derbyshire) d			06 34		07 25								08 35									09 36		
Bamford d			06 37		07 29								08 39									09 39		
Hathersage d			06 40		07 33								08 41									09 43		
Grindleford d			06 44		07 37								08 46									09 46		
Dore d			06 52		07 48			08 03					08 55									09 55		
Sheffield 7 a	04 31	06 48	07 01		07 57			08 09			08 35		09 04			09 09	09 09				09c35	10 05		

For general notes see front of timetable
For details of catering facilities see Directory of Train Operators

A From Liverpool Lime Street to Nottingham (Table 49)
B To Hadfield (Table 79)
C To Cleethorpes (Table 29)
D To Glossop (Table 79)
E To Doncaster (Table 29)
H Until 6 September from Liverpool Lime Street to Norwich (Table 49). From 13 September from Liverpool Lime Street (Table 89)
J Until 6 September. To Cleethorpes (Table 29)
K From 13 September. To Cleethorpes (Table 29)
b From 8 September arr. 2035
c From 13 September arr. 3 minutes later

Manchester Airport and Manchester → Romiley, Marple, Chinley and Sheffield

Network Diagram - see first page of Table 78

	NT A		TP 1 ◇ B	TP 1 ◇ C	NT	NT	EM ◇ D	NT	NT A	NT	TP 1 ◇ B	NT A	TP 1 ◇ C		NT	NT	EM ◇ D	NT	NT A	NT	TP 1 ◇ B	NT A	TP 1 ◇ C	NT
Manchester Airport 85 ✈ d			08 52	08 52		09 07				09 34	09 52		09 52			10 07			10 15	10 34	10 52	10 47	10 52	
Manchester Piccadilly 10 d	09 16		09 18	09 20	09 22	09 36	09 42	09 46	09 49	10 03	10 18	10 19	10 20		10 22	10 36	10 42	10 46	10 49	11 03	11 18	11 19	11 20	11 22
Ardwick d																								
Ashburys d	09 20								09 53	10 07		10 23							10 53	11 07		11 23		
Belle Vue d										10 09										11 09				
Ryder Brow d										10 11										11 11				
Reddish North d								09 53		10 14								10 53		11 14				
Brinnington d								09 57		10 17								10 57		11 17				
Bredbury d								10 00		10 20								11 00		11 20				
Gorton d	09 22								09 55			10 25							10 55			11 25		
Fairfield d						09 43										10 43								
Guide Bridge d	09a26					09 46			09a59			10a29				10 46			10a59			11a29		
Hyde North d						09 50										10 50								
Hyde Central d						09 52										10 52								
Woodley d						09 55										10 55								
Romiley d					09 37	09 59		10 03		10 23					10 37	10 59		11 03		11 23				11 37
Rose Hill Marple a						10 05										11 05								
Marple d					09a43			10 06		10a28					10a43			11 06		11a28				11a43
Strines d								10 10																
New Mills Central d								10 14										11 12						
Stockport 86 d			09 26	09 28			09 55				10 26		10 28				10 55				11 26		11 28	
Hazel Grove 86 d																								
Chinley d								10 21										11 19						
Edale d								10 30										11 29						
Hope (Derbyshire) d								10 36										11 34						
Bamford d								10 39										11 38						
Hathersage d								10 42										11 42						
Grindleford d								10 46										11 46						
Dore d								10 54										11 55						
Sheffield 7 a			10 08	10 08			10b35	11 03			11 08		11 08				11b35	12 04			12 08		12 08	

	NT	EM ◇ D	NT		NT A	NT	TP 1 ◇ B	NT A	TP 1 ◇ C	NT	NT	EM ◇ D	NT	NT A	NT		TP 1 ◇ B	NT A	TP 1 ◇ C	NT	NT	EM ◇ D	NT	NT A
Manchester Airport 85 ✈ d	11 07				11 15	11 34	11 52	11 47	11 52		12 07			12 15	12 34		12 52	12 47	12 52		13 07			13 15
Manchester Piccadilly 10 d	11 36	11 42	11 46		11 49	12 03	12 18	12 19	12 20	12 22	12 36	12 42	12 46	12 49	13 03		13 18	13 19	13 20	13 22	13 36	13 42	13 46	13 49
Ardwick d																								
Ashburys d					11 53	12 07		12 23						12 53	13 07			13 23						13 53
Belle Vue d						12 09									13 09									
Ryder Brow d						12 11									13 11									
Reddish North d			11 53			12 14							12 53		13 14								13 53	
Brinnington d			11 57			12 17							12 57		13 17								13 57	
Bredbury d			12 00			12 20							13 00		13 20								14 00	
Gorton d					11 55			12 25						12 55				13 25						13 55
Fairfield d	11 43										12 43										13 43			
Guide Bridge d	11 46				11a59			12a29			12 46			12a59				13a29			13 46			13a59
Hyde North d	11 50										12 50										13 50			
Hyde Central d	11 52										12 52										13 52			
Woodley d	11 55										12 55										13 55			
Romiley d	11 59		12 03			12 23				12 37	12 59		13 03		13 23					13 37	13 59		14 03	
Rose Hill Marple a	12 05										13 05										14 05			
Marple d			12 06			12a28				12a43			13 06		13a28					13a43			14 06	
Strines d			12 10																				14 10	
New Mills Central d			12 14										13 12										14 14	
Stockport 86 d		11 55					12 26		12 28			12 55					13 26		13 28			13 55		
Hazel Grove 86 d																								
Chinley d			12 21										13 19										14 21	
Edale d			12 30										13 28										14 30	
Hope (Derbyshire) d			12 36										13 34										14 36	
Bamford d			12 39										13 38										14 39	
Hathersage d			12 42										13 42										14 42	
Grindleford d			12 46										13 46										14 46	
Dore d			12 55										13 55										14 55	
Sheffield 7 a		12b35	13 04				13 08		13 08			13b35	14 04				14 08		14 08			14b35	15 03	

For general notes see front of timetable
For details of catering facilities see Directory of Train Operators

A To Hadfield (Table 79)
B From 13 September. To Cleethorpes (Table 29)
C Until 6 September. To Cleethorpes (Table 29)
D Until 6 September from Liverpool Lime Street to Norwich (Table 49). From 13 September from Liverpool Lime Street (Table 89)
b From 13 September arr. 3 minutes later

Table 78

Saturdays

Manchester Airport and Manchester → Romiley, Marple, Chinley and Sheffield

Network Diagram - see first page of Table 78

		NT	TP 1◇ A	NT B	TP 1◇ C	NT		NT	EM ◇ D	NT	NT B	NT	TP 1◇ E	NT B	NT	NT	EM ◇ G	NT		NT B	NT	NT B	TP 1◇ A	TP 1◇ C	NT
Manchester Airport	85 d	13 34	13 52	13 47	13 52			14 07			14 15	14 34	14 52	14 47		15 07				15 15	15 34		15 52	15 52	
Manchester Piccadilly 10	d	14 03	14 18	14 19	14 20	14 22		14 36	14 42	14 46	14 49	15 03	15 18	15 19	15 22	15 36	15 42	15 46		15 49	16 03	16 17	16 18	16 20	16 22
Ardwick	d																								
Ashburys	d	14 07		14 23							14 53	15 07		15 23						15 53	16 07	16 23			
Belle Vue	d	14 09										15 09									16 09				
Ryder Brow	d	14 11										15 11									16 11				
Reddish North	d	14 14								14 53		15 14						15 53			16 14				
Brinnington	d	14 17								14 57		15 17						15 57			16 17				
Bredbury	d	14 20								15 00		15 20						16 00			16 20				
Gorton	d			14 25							14 55			15 25						15 55		16 25			
Fairfield	d							14 43								15 43									
Guide Bridge	d			14a29				14 46			14a59			15a29		15 46				15a59		16a29			
Hyde North	d							14 50								15 50									
Hyde Central	d							14 52								15 52									
Woodley	d							14 55								15 55									
Romiley	d	14 23				14 37		14 59		15 03		15 23			15 37	15 59		16 03			16 23				16 37
Rose Hill Marple	a							15 05								16 05									
Marple	d	14a28				14a43				15 06		15a28			15a43			16 06			16a28				16a43
Strines	d																	16 10							
New Mills Central	d									15 12								16 14							
Stockport	86 d		14 26		14 28				14 55				15 26				15 55						16 26	16 28	
Hazel Grove	86 d																								
Chinley	d									15 20								16 21							
Edale	d									15 28								16 30							
Hope (Derbyshire)	d									15 34								16 36							
Bamford	d									15 38								16 39							
Hathersage	d									15 42								16 42							
Grindleford	d									15 46								16 47							
Dore	d									15 55								16 55							
Sheffield 7	a		15 08		15 08				15b35	16 04			16 08				16b35	17 03					17 08	17 08	

		NT	EM ◇ G	NT	NT B	NT	NT B	TP 1◇ A		TP 1◇ C	NT	NT	EM ◇ D	NT	NT B	NT	TP 1◇ C	NT B	TP 1◇ A	NT		NT	EM ◇ H	NT	NT B
Manchester Airport	85 d	16 07				16 34		16 52		16 52		17 04				17 34	17 52		17 52			18 10			
Manchester Piccadilly 10	d	16 36	16 42	16 46	16 49	17 03	17 17	17 18		17 20	17 28	17 36	17 42	17 46	17 49	18 03	18 17	18 18	18 18	18 22		18 36	18 44	18 46	18 49
Ardwick	d																								
Ashburys	d				16 53	17 07	17 21								17 53	18 07		18 22							18 53
Belle Vue	d					17 09										18 09									
Ryder Brow	d					17 11										18 11									
Reddish North	d			16 53		17 14								17 53		18 14								18 53	
Brinnington	d			16 57		17 17								17 57		18 17								18 57	
Bredbury	d			17 00		17 20								18 00		18 20								19 00	
Gorton	d				16 55		17 23								17 55			18 25							18 55
Fairfield	d	16 43										17 43										18 43			
Guide Bridge	d	16 46			16a59		17a27					17 46			17a59			18a29				18 46			18a59
Hyde North	d	16 50										17 50										18 50			
Hyde Central	d	16 52										17 52										18 52			
Woodley	d	16 55										17 55										18 55			
Romiley	d	16 59		17 03		17 23					17 41	17 59		18 03		18 23				18 37		18 59		19 03	
Rose Hill Marple	a	17 05										18 05										19 05			
Marple	d			17 06		17a28					17a45			18 06		18a28				18a43				19 06	
Strines	d													18 10											
New Mills Central	d			17 12										18 14										19 13	
Stockport	86 d		16 53					17 26		17 28			17 55				18 26		18 26				18 55		
Hazel Grove	86 d																								
Chinley	d			17 19				17 43		17 43				18 21										19 19	
Edale	d			17 28										18 30										19 28	
Hope (Derbyshire)	d			17 34										18 36										19 34	
Bamford	d			17 38										18 39										19 38	
Hathersage	d			17 42										18 42										19 42	
Grindleford	d			17 46										18 46										19 46	
Dore	d		17 28	17 55				18 06		18 06				18 55			19 02		19 02					19 55	
Sheffield 7	a		17 38	18 04				18 12		18 12			18b35	19 04			19 08		19 08				19 35	20 04	

For general notes see front of timetable
For details of catering facilities see Directory of Train Operators

- **A** From 13 September. To Cleethorpes (Table 29)
- **B** To Hadfield (Table 79)
- **C** Until 6 September. To Cleethorpes (Table 29)
- **D** Until 6 September from Liverpool Lime Street to Nottingham (Table 49). From 13 September from Liverpool Lime Street (Table 89)
- **E** To Cleethorpes (Table 29)
- **G** Until 6 September from Liverpool Lime Street to Norwich (Table 49). From 13 September from Liverpool Lime Street (Table 89)
- **H** From Liverpool Lime Street to Norwich (from 13 September to Nottingham) (Table 49)
- **b** From 13 September arr. 3 minutes later

Table 78

Saturdays

Manchester Airport and Manchester → Romiley, Marple, Chinley and Sheffield

Network Diagram - see first page of Table 78

		TP ■1 ◇ A	NT	EM ◇ B	NT	NT C	TP ■1 ◇ D	TP ■1 ◇ E	NT	EM ◇ B		NT	NT C	TP ■1 ◇ A	EM ◇ G	NT	NT C	TP ■1 ◇ H	TP ■1 ◇ J	NT	NT C	NT K	NT L		
Manchester Airport	85 ✈ d	18 52		19 12		19 15	19 52	19 52		20 15			20 22	20 52	21 04	21 16	21 22	21 52	21 52		22 22	22 47			
Manchester Piccadilly 10	d	19 18	19 22	19 42	19 46	19 49	20 18	20 20	20 27	20 42		20 46	20 49	21 18	21 42	21 46	21 49	22 18	22 18	22 38	22 49	23 23	23 26		
Ardwick	d																								
Ashburys	d		19 26		19 51	19 53						20 50	20 53			21 50	21 53			22 42	22 53	23 27	23 30		
Belle Vue	d		19 28		19 53							20 52				21 52				22 44		23 29			
Ryder Brow	d		19 30		19 55							20 54				21 54				22 46		23 31			
Reddish North	d		19 33		19 58							20 57				21 57				22 49		23 34			
Brinnington	d		19 36		20 01							21 00				22 00				22 52		23 37			
Bredbury	d		19 39		20 04							21 03				22 03				22 55		23 40			
Gorton	d					19 55							20 55				21 55				22 55		23 32		
Fairfield	d								20 34																
Guide Bridge	d					19a59			20 39				20a59				21a59				22a59		23a36		
Hyde North	d								20 43																
Hyde Central	d								20 45																
Woodley	d								20 48																
Romiley	d		19 42		20 07				20 52			21 06				22 06				22 58		23 43			
Rose Hill Marple	a								20 57																
Marple	d		19a47		20 11							21 10				22 10				23 02		23 47			
Strines	d				20 15											22 14				23 06		23 51			
New Mills Central	d				20a21							21 14				22a20				23a10		23a56			
Stockport	86 d	19 26		19 55			20 26	20 28		20 55				21 26	21 52			22 26	22 26						
Hazel Grove	86 d																								
Chinley	d											21 21							22 41						
Edale	d											21 30							22 49						
Hope (Derbyshire)	d											21 36							22 56						
Bamford	d											21 39							22 59						
Hathersage	d											21 42							23 03						
Grindleford	d											21 46							23 06						
Dore	d											21 55							23 16						
Sheffield 7	a	20 08		20 34			21 08	21 08		21 34		22 04		22 09	22 31			23 13	23 26						

Sundays

until 13 July

		NT	NT 🚌	NT	TP ■1 ◇ A	NT C	NT 🚌	NT	NT C	NT C	NT	NT 🚌	NT C	TP ■1 ◇ A	NT C	NT C	NT	NT C	EM ◇ N	NT 🚌	NT C	TP ■1 ◇ A	NT C	EM ◇ Q	NT C
Manchester Airport	85 ✈ d				08 40									10 52								12 52			
Manchester Piccadilly 10	d	08 12	08 25	08 43	09 00	09 23		09 43	09 53	10 23	10 30	10 50	10 53	11 12	11 23	11 53	12 09	12 23	12 43	12 50	12 53	13 12	13 23	13 46	13 53
Ashburys	d		08 33			09 27			09 57	10 27		10 58	10 57		11 27	11 57		12 27		12 58	12 57		13 27		13 57
Belle Vue	d		08 38									11 03								13 03					
Ryder Brow	d		08 42									11 07								13 07					
Reddish North	d		08 50									11 15								13 15					
Brinnington	d		09 10									11 35								13 35					
Bredbury	d		09 18									11 43								13 43					
Gorton	d					09 29			09 59	10 29			10 59		11 29	11 59		12 29			12 59		13 29		13 59
Guide Bridge	d					09a33			10a03	10a33			11a03		11a33	12a03		12a33			13a03		13a33		14a03
Romiley	d		09 26									11 51								13 51					
Marple	d		09 35									12 00								14 00					
Strines	d		09 41				←					12 06								14 06					
New Mills Central	d		09 47				09 47					12 12								14 12					
Stockport	86 d	08 22	→	08 53	09 09			09 56			10 46			11 21			12 23		12 53			13 21		13 57	
Hazel Grove	86 d			09 00							10 53														
Chinley	d	08 38		09 10			10 07	10 14			11 06	12a32					12 42			14a32					
Edale	d	08 47		09 19				10 23			11 14						12 51								
Hope (Derbyshire)	d	08 53		09 25				10 29			11 20						12 57								
Bamford	d	08 56		09 28				10 32			11 23						13 00								
Hathersage	d	08 59		09 31				10 35			11 27						13 03								
Grindleford	d	09 03		09 35				10 39			11 30						13 07								
Dore	d	09 11		09 44				10 48			11 38						13 18								
Sheffield 7	a	09 20		09 53	09 55			10 58			11 47			12 03			13 27		13 38			14 06		14 36	

For general notes see front of timetable
For details of catering facilities see
Directory of Train Operators

- **A** To Cleethorpes (Table 29)
- **B** From Liverpool Lime Street to Nottingham (Table 49)
- **C** To Hadfield (Table 79)
- **D** From 13 September. To Cleethorpes (Table 29)
- **E** Until 6 September. To Cleethorpes (Table 29)
- **G** To Nottingham (Table 49)
- **H** From 13 September
- **J** Until 6 september
- **K** From Manchester Oxford Road dep. 2319 (Table 84)
- **L** To Glossop (Table 79)
- **N** To Norwich (Table 49)
- **Q** From Liverpool Lime Street to Norwich (Table 49)

Table 78

Sundays

until 13 July

Manchester Airport and Manchester → Romiley, Marple, Chinley and Sheffield

Network Diagram - see first page of Table 78

	TP 1◇ A	NT	NT B	EM ◇ C	NT 🚌	NT B	NT	TP 1◇ A	NT	NT B	EM ◇ C	NT B
Manchester Airport 85 ✈ d	13 52							14 52				
Manchester Piccadilly 10 d	14 15	14 19	14 23	14 43	14 50	14 53	15 05	15 15		15 23	15 43	15 53
Ashburys d			14 27		14 58	14 57				15 27		15 57
Belle Vue d					15 03							
Ryder Brow d					15 07							
Reddish North d					15 15							
Brinnington d					15 35							
Bredbury d					15 43							
Gorton d			14 29			14 59				15 29		15 59
Guide Bridge d			14a33			15a03				15a33		16a03
Romiley d					15 51							
Marple d					16 00							
Strines d					16 06							
New Mills Central d					16 12				⟵			
Stockport 86 d	14 23	14 28		14 54	⟶		15 27	15 23	15 27		15 54	
Hazel Grove 86 d							⟶		15 34			
Chinley d		14 42							15 45			
Edale d		14 51							15 54			
Hope (Derbyshire) d		14 57							16 00			
Bamford d		15 00							16 03			
Hathersage d		15 03							16 06			
Grindleford d		15 07							16 10			
Dore d		15 15							16 20			
Sheffield 7 a	15 05	15 25		15 34				16 04	16 29		16 34	

	TP 1◇ A	NT 🚌	NT	NT B	EM ◇ C	NT 🚌	NT B	TP 1◇ A	NT	NT B	EM ◇ D	NT B
Manchester Airport 85 ✈ d	15 52							16 52				
Manchester Piccadilly 10 d	16 15		16 19	16 23	16 43	16 50	16 53	17 15	17 19	17 23	17 43	17 53
Ashburys d				16 27		16 58	16 57			17 27		17 57
Belle Vue d						17 03						
Ryder Brow d						17 07						
Reddish North d						17 15						
Brinnington d						17 35						
Bredbury d						17 43						
Gorton d				16 29			16 59			17 29		17 59
Guide Bridge d				16a33			17a03			17a33		18a03
Romiley d						17 51						
Marple d						18 00						
Strines d		⟵				18 06						
New Mills Central d		16 12				18 12						
Stockport 86 d	16 23		16 29		16 54	⟶		17 23	17 28		17 54	
Hazel Grove 86 d									17 35			
Chinley d		16a32	16 50						17 47			
Edale d			16 59						17 56			
Hope (Derbyshire) d			17 05						18 02			
Bamford d			17 08						18 05			
Hathersage d			17 12						18 08			
Grindleford d			17 15						18 12			
Dore d			17 24						18 23			
Sheffield 7 a	17 05		17 33		17 34			18 04	18 34		18 36	

	NT	TP 1◇ A	NT 🚌	NT	NT B	EM ◇ C	NT 🚌	NT B	TP 1◇ A	NT B	EM ◇ D
Manchester Airport 85 ✈ d		17 52							18 52		
Manchester Piccadilly 10 d	18 07	18 15			18 23	18 42	18 50	18 53	19 15	19 23	19 42
Ashburys d					18 27		18 58	18 57		19 27	
Belle Vue d							19 03				
Ryder Brow d							19 07				
Reddish North d							19 15				
Brinnington d							19 35				
Bredbury d							19 43				
Gorton d					18 29			18 59		19 29	
Guide Bridge d					18a33			19a03		19a33	
Romiley d							19 51				
Marple d							20 00				
Strines d			⟵				20 06				
New Mills Central d			18 12	⟵			20 12				
Stockport 86 d	18 27	18 23		18 27		18 56			19 22		19 54
Hazel Grove 86 d	⟶										
Chinley d			18a32	18 42			20a32				
Edale d				18 50							
Hope (Derbyshire) d				18 56							
Bamford d				18 59							
Hathersage d				19 03							
Grindleford d				19 06							
Dore d				19 12							
Sheffield 7 a		19 05		19 23		19 35			20 04		20 35

	NT B	TP 1◇ A	NT	EM ◇ D	NT B	TP 1◇ A	EM ◇ D	TP 1◇ A	EM ◇ D	NT 🚌	TP 1◇
Manchester Airport 85 ✈ d		19 52				20 52		21 52			22 52
Manchester Piccadilly 10 d	19 53	20 15	20 19	20 43	20 53	21 15	22 12	22 15		22 20	23 15
Ashburys d	19 57				20 57					22 28	
Belle Vue d										22 33	
Ryder Brow d										22 37	
Reddish North d										22 45	
Brinnington d										23 05	
Bredbury d										23 13	
Gorton d	19 59				20 59						
Guide Bridge d	20a03				21a03						
Romiley d										23 21	
Marple d										23 30	
Strines d										23 36	
New Mills Central d									⟵	23a42	
Stockport 86 d		20 23	20 29	20 53		21 22	22 26	22 22	22 26		23 23
Hazel Grove 86 d							⟶				
Chinley d			20 44						22 43		
Edale d			20 53						22 51		
Hope (Derbyshire) d			20 59						22 57		
Bamford d			21 02						23 00		
Hathersage d			21 05						23 03		
Grindleford d			21 09						23 07		
Dore d			21 15						23 17		
Sheffield 7 a		21 06	21 24	21 38		22 06		23 06	23 23		00 09

Sundays

20 July to 7 September

	NT	TP 1◇ A	NT	NT B	NT	NT B	NT B	NT	NT B	TP 1◇ A	NT B
Manchester Airport 85 ✈ d		08 40								10 49	
Manchester Piccadilly 10 d	07 39	09 00	09 04	09 23	09 35	09 53	10 23	10 30	10 53	11 12	11 23
Ashburys d	07 43			09 27	09 39	09 57	10 27		10 57		11 27
Belle Vue d	07 45				09 42						
Ryder Brow d	07 47				09 44						
Reddish North d	07 50				09 46						
Brinnington d	07 53				09 50						
Bredbury d	07 56				09 53						
Gorton d				09 29		09 59	10 29		10 59		11 29
Guide Bridge d				09a33		10a03	10a33		11a03		11a33
Romiley d	07 59				09 56						
Marple d	08 03				09 59						
Strines d	08 07				10 03						
New Mills Central d	08 11				10 07						
Stockport 86 d		09 09	09 17					10 46		11 21	
Hazel Grove 86 d			09 24					10 53			
Chinley d	08 18		09 34		10 14			11 06			
Edale d	08 27		09 43		10 23			11 14			
Hope (Derbyshire) d	08 33		09 49		10 29			11 20			
Bamford d	08 36		09 52		10 32			11 23			
Hathersage d	08 40		09 55		10 35			11 27			
Grindleford d	08 43		09 59		10 39			11 30			
Dore d	08 52		10 08		10 48			11 38			
Sheffield 7 a	09 01	09 55	10 17		10 56			11 47		12 03	

	NT B	NT	NT B	EM ◇ E	NT B	TP 1◇ A	NT B	EM ◇ C	NT B	NT	TP 1◇ A
Manchester Airport 85 ✈ d						12 49					13 49
Manchester Piccadilly 10 d	11 53	12 01	12 23	12 43	12 53	13 12	13 23	13 48	13 53	14 01	14 15
Ashburys d	11 57	12 05	12 27		12 57		13 27		13 57	14 05	
Belle Vue d		12 07								14 07	
Ryder Brow d		12 09								14 09	
Reddish North d		12 12								14 12	
Brinnington d		12 15								14 15	
Bredbury d		12 18								14 18	
Gorton d	11 59		12 29		12 59		13 29		13 59		
Guide Bridge d	12a03		12a33		13a03		13a33		14a03		
Romiley d		12 21								14 21	
Marple d		12 25								14 25	
Strines d		12 29								14 29	
New Mills Central d		12 34								14 34	
Stockport 86 d				12 53		13 21		13 58		⟶	14 23
Hazel Grove 86 d											
Chinley d		12 42									
Edale d		12 51									
Hope (Derbyshire) d		12 57									
Bamford d		13 00									
Hathersage d		13 03									
Grindleford d		13 07									
Dore d		13 18									
Sheffield 7 a		13 27		13 38		14 06		14 38			15 05

For general notes see front of timetable
For details of catering facilities see Directory of Train Operators

A To Cleethorpes (Table 29)
B To Hadfield (Table 79)
C From Liverpool Lime Street to Norwich (Table 49)
D From Liverpool Lime Street to Nottingham (Table 49)
E To Norwich (Table 49)

Table 78

Manchester Airport and Manchester → Romiley, Marple, Chinley and Sheffield

Sundays

20 July to 7 September

Network Diagram - see first page of Table 78

	NT	NT	EM	NT		NT	TP	NT	NT	EM	NT	NT	TP		NT	NT	EM	NT	TP	NT	NT	EM		NT
			◇				[1] ◇			◇			[1] ◇				◇		[1] ◇			◇		
	A		B	A			C		A	B	A		C		A		B	A	C		A	D		A
Manchester Airport 85 ✈ d							14 49						15 49						16 49					
Manchester Piccadilly [10] d	14 23		14 43	14 53		15 08	15 15		15 23	15 43	15 53	16 07	16 15		16 23		16 43	16 53	17 15	17 19	17 23	17 43		17 53
Ashburys d	14 27			14 57					15 27		15 57	16 11			16 27			16 57			17 27			17 57
Belle Vue d												16 13												
Ryder Brow d												16 15												
Reddish North d												16 18												
Brinnington d												16 21												
Bredbury d												16 24												
Gorton d	14 29			14 59					15 29		15 59				16 29			16 59			17 29			17 59
Guide Bridge d	14a33			15a03					15a33		16a03				16a33			17a03			17a33			18a03
Romiley d												16 27												
Marple d												16 31												
Strines d		←										16 35				←								
New Mills Central d		14 34						←				16 38				16 38								
Stockport 86 d			14 54			15 27 →	15 23	15 27		15 54		→	16 23				16 54		17 23	17 28		17 54		
Hazel Grove 86 d								15 34												17 35				
Chinley d		14 42						15 45								16 46				17 47				
Edale d		14 51						15 54								16 55				17 56				
Hope (Derbyshire) d		14 57						16 00								17 01				18 02				
Bamford d		15 00						16 03								17 04				18 05				
Hathersage d		15 03						16 06								17 07				18 08				
Grindleford d		15 07						16 10								17 11				18 12				
Dore d		15 15						16 20								17 22				18 24				
Sheffield [7] a		15 25	15 34				16 04	16 29		16 34			17 05			17 32	17 34		18 04	18 33		18 36		

	NT	TP	NT	NT	EM	NT	TP	NT		EM	NT	NT	TP	NT	EM	NT	TP	EM	TP	EM	NT	TP		
		[1] ◇			◇		[1] ◇			◇			[1] ◇		◇		[1] ◇	◇	[1] ◇	◇		[1] ◇		
		C	A		B	A	C	A		D	A		C		D	A		D		D				
Manchester Airport 85 ✈ d		17 49					18 49						19 49				20 49		21 49			22 49		
Manchester Piccadilly [10] d	18 01	18 15	18 23		18 42	18 53	19 15	19 23		19 42	19 53	20 01	20 15		20 43	20 53	21 15	22 12	22 15		22 20	23 15		
Ashburys d	18 05		18 27			18 57		19 27			19 57	20 05				20 57					22 24			
Belle Vue d	18 07											20 07									22 26			
Ryder Brow d	18 09											20 09									22 28			
Reddish North d	18 12											20 12									22 31			
Brinnington d	18 15											20 15									22 34			
Bredbury d	18 18											20 18									22 37			
Gorton d			18 29			18 59		19 29			19 59					20 59								
Guide Bridge d			18a33			19a03		19a33			20a03					21a03								
Romiley d	18 21											20 21									22 40			
Marple d	18 25											20 25									22 44			
Strines d	18 29			←								20 29		←							22 48			
New Mills Central d	18 34			18 34								20 32		20 32						←	22a53			
Stockport 86 d	→	18 23			18 56		19 22			19 54		→	20 23		20 53		21 22	22 26 →	22 22	22 26		23 23		
Hazel Grove 86 d																								
Chinley d				18 42										20 42						22 43				
Edale d				18 50										20 51						22 51				
Hope (Derbyshire) d				18 56										20 57						22 57				
Bamford d				18 59										21 00						23 00				
Hathersage d				19 03										21 04						23 03				
Grindleford d				19 06										21 07						23 07				
Dore d				19 12										21 16						23 17				
Sheffield [7] a		19 05		19 22	19 35		20 04			20 35			21 06	21 23	21 38		22 06		23 06	23 23		00 09		

Sundays

14 September to 2 November

	NT	NT	TP	NT	NT	NT	NT	NT		TP	NT	NT	NT	NT	NT	EM	NT		TP	NT	EM	NT	NT	TP
																◇			[1] ◇		◇			[1] ◇
					A		A	A			A	A	A		A	E	A		C	A	B	A		C
	Bus		Bus	Bus						Bus														
Manchester Airport 85 ✈ d			08 00							10 05									12 52					13 52
Manchester Piccadilly [10] d	07 05	08 12	08 25		09 23	09 35	09 53	10 23		10 30	10 53	11 23	11 53	12 01	12 23	12 43	12 53		13 12	13 23	13 48	13 53	14 01	14 15
Ashburys d	07 13				09 27	09 39	09 57	10 27			10 57	11 27	11 57	12 05	12 27		12 57			13 27		13 57	14 05	
Belle Vue d	07 18					09 42								12 07									14 07	
Ryder Brow d	07 22					09 44								12 09									14 09	
Reddish North d	07 30					09 46								12 12									14 12	
Brinnington d	07 50					09 50								12 15									14 15	
Bredbury d	07 58					09 53								12 18									14 18	
Gorton d					09 29		09 59	10 29			10 59	11 29	11 59		12 29		12 59			13 29		13 59		
Guide Bridge d					09a33		10a03	10a33			11a03	11a33	12a03		12a33		13a03			13a33		14a03		
Romiley d	08 06					09 56								12 21									14 21	
Marple d	08 15					09 59								12 25									14 25	
Strines d	08 21			←		10 03								12 29									14 29	
New Mills Central d	08 27			08 27		10 07								12 34									14 34	
Stockport 86 d	→	08 22														12 53			13 21		13 58		→	14 23
Hazel Grove 86 d																								
Chinley d		08a38		08 47		10 14								12 42										
Edale d				09 07		10 23								12 51										
Hope (Derbyshire) d				09 21		10 29								12 57										
Bamford d				09 27		10 32								13 00										
Hathersage d				09 32		10 35								13 03										
Grindleford d				09 42		10 39								13 07										
Dore d				10 05		10 48								13 18										
Sheffield [7] a			09 45	10 17		10 58				12 00				13 27		13 37			14 06		14 38			15 05

For general notes see front of timetable
For details of catering facilities see Directory of Train Operators

A To Hadfield (Table 79)
B From Liverpool Lime Street to Norwich (Table 49)
C To Cleethorpes (Table 29)
D From Liverpool Lime Street to Nottingham (Table 49)
E To Norwich (Table 49)

Manchester Airport and Manchester → Romiley, Marple, Chinley and Sheffield

Network Diagram - see first page of Table 78

	NT	NT	EM	NT		NT	TP	NT	NT	EM	NT	NT	TP		NT	NT	EM	NT	TP	NT	NT	EM		NT
			◇				1 ◇			◇			1 ◇				◇		1 ◇			◇		
	A		B	A		C	D	C	A	B	A		D		A		B	A	D	C	A	E		A
Manchester Airport 85 ✈ d							14 52						15 52						16 52					
Manchester Piccadilly 10 d	14 23		14 43	14 53		15 08	15 15		15 23	15 43	15 53	16 07	16 15		16 23		16 43	16 53	17 15	17 19	17 23	17 43		17 53
Ashburys d	14 27			14 57					15 27		15 57	16 11			16 27			16 57			17 27			17 57
Belle Vue d												16 13												
Ryder Brow d												16 15												
Reddish North d												16 18												
Brinnington d												16 21												
Bredbury d												16 24												
Gorton d	14 29			14 59					15 29		15 59				16 29			16 59			17 29			17 59
Guide Bridge d	14a33			15a03					15a33		16a03				16a33			17a03			17a33			18a03
Romiley d												16 27												
Marple d												16 31												
Strines d		←										16 35				←								
New Mills Central d		14 34						←				16 38				16 38								
Stockport 86 d			14 54			15 27 →	15 23	15 27		15 54		→	16 23				16 54		17 23	17 28		17 54		
Hazel Grove 86 d								15 34												17 35				
Chinley d		14 42						15 45								16 46				17 47				
Edale d		14 51						15 54								16 55				17 56				
Hope (Derbyshire) d		14 57						16 00								17 01				18 02				
Bamford d		15 00						16 03								17 04				18 05				
Hathersage d		15 03						16 06								17 07				18 08				
Grindleford d		15 07						16 10								17 11				18 12				
Dore d		15 15						16 20								17 22				18 24				
Sheffield 7 a		15 25	15 34				16 05	16 29		16 34			17 05			17 32	17 34		18 04	18 33		18 36		

	NT	TP	NT	NT	EM	NT	TP	NT		EM	NT	NT	TP	NT	EM	NT	TP	EM	TP	EM	NT	TP		
		1 ◇			◇		1 ◇			◇			1 ◇		◇		1 ◇	◇	1 ◇	◇		1 ◇		
		D	A		B	A	D	A		E	A		D		E	A		E		E				
Manchester Airport 85 ✈ d		17 52					18 52						19 50				20 52		21 52			22 52		
Manchester Piccadilly 10 d	18 01	18 15	18 23		18 42	18 53	19 15	19 23		19 42	19 53	20 01	20 15		20 43	20 53	21 15	22 12	22 15		22 20	23 15		
Ashburys d	18 05		18 27			18 57		19 27			19 57	20 05				20 57					22 24			
Belle Vue d	18 07											20 07									22 26			
Ryder Brow d	18 09											20 09									22 28			
Reddish North d	18 12											20 12									22 31			
Brinnington d	18 15											20 15									22 34			
Bredbury d	18 18											20 18									22 37			
Gorton d			18 29			18 59		19 29			19 59					20 59								
Guide Bridge d			18a33			19a03		19a33			20a03					21a03								
Romiley d	18 21											20 21									22 40			
Marple d	18 25											20 25									22 44			
Strines d	18 29			←								20 29		←							22 48			
New Mills Central d	18 34			18 34								20 32		20 32						←	22a53			
Stockport 86 d	→	18 23			18 56		19 22			19 54		→	20 23		20 53		21 22	22 26 →	22 22	22 26		23 23		
Hazel Grove 86 d																								
Chinley d				18 42										20 42						22 43				
Edale d				18 50										20 51						22 51				
Hope (Derbyshire) d				18 56										20 57						22 57				
Bamford d				18 59										21 00						23 00				
Hathersage d				19 03										21 04						23 03				
Grindleford d				19 06										21 07						23 07				
Dore d				19 12										21 16						23 17				
Sheffield 7 a		19 05		19 22	19 35		20 04			20 35			21 06	21 23	21 38		22 06		23 06	23 23		00 09		

Sundays
from 9 November

	NT	NT		TP	NT		NT	NT		NT	TP		NT	NT		NT	EM		TP	NT		EM	NT	TP
																	◇		1 ◇			◇		1 ◇
							A			A			A			A	G		D	A		B		D
	Bus			Bus	Bus		Bus			Bus	Bus		Bus			Bus				Bus				
Manchester Airport 85 ✈ d				08 00							10 05								12 52					13 52
Manchester Piccadilly 10 d	07 05	08 12		08 25			09 22	09 35		10 22	10 30		11 22	12 01		12 22	12 43		13 12	13 22		13 48	14 01	14 15
Ashburys d	07 13						09 30	09 39		10 30			11 30	12 05		12 30				13 30			14 05	
Belle Vue d	07 18							09 42						12 07									14 07	
Ryder Brow d	07 22							09 44						12 09									14 09	
Reddish North d	07 30							09 46						12 12									14 12	
Brinnington d	07 50							09 50						12 15									14 15	
Bredbury d	07 58							09 53						12 18									14 18	
Gorton d							09 36			10 36			11 36			12 36				13 36				
Guide Bridge d							09a46			10a46			11a46			12a46				13a46				
Romiley d	08 06							09 56						12 21									14 21	
Marple d	08 15							09 59						12 25									14 25	
Strines d	08 21				←			10 03						12 29									14 29	
New Mills Central d	08 27				08 27			10 07						12 34									14 34	
Stockport 86 d	→	08 22															12 53		13 21			13 58	→	14 23
Hazel Grove 86 d																								
Chinley d		08a38			08 47			10 14						12 42										
Edale d					09 07			10 23						12 51										
Hope (Derbyshire) d					09 21			10 29						12 57										
Bamford d					09 27			10 32						13 00										
Hathersage d					09 32			10 35						13 03										
Grindleford d					09 42			10 39						13 07										
Dore d					10 05			10 48						13 18										
Sheffield 7 a				09 45	10 17			10 58			12 00			13 27			13 38		14 06			14 38		15 05

For general notes see front of timetable
For details of catering facilities see Directory of Train Operators

A To Hadfield (Table 79)
B From Liverpool Lime Street to Norwich (Table 49)
C 14 September
D To Cleethorpes (Table 29)
E From Liverpool Lime Street to Nottingham (Table 49)
G To Norwich (Table 49)

Table 78

Sundays

from 9 November

Manchester Airport and Manchester → Romiley, Marple, Chinley and Sheffield

Network Diagram - see first page of Table 78

	NT	NT	EM	TP	NT	EM	NT	TP	NT	NT	EM	TP	NT	EM	NT	TP
			◇	1 ◇		◇		1 ◇			◇	1 ◇		◇		1 ◇
		A 🚌	B	C	A 🚌	B		C		A 🚌	B	C	A 🚌	D		C
Manchester Airport 85 ✈ d				14 52				15 52				16 52				17 52
Manchester Piccadilly 10 d		14 22	14 43	15 15	15 22	15 43	16 07	16 15		16 22	16 43	17 15	17 22	17 43	18 01	18 15
Ashburys d		14 30			15 30		16 11			16 30			17 30		18 05	
Belle Vue d							16 13								18 07	
Ryder Brow d							16 15								18 09	
Reddish North d							16 18								18 12	
Brinnington d							16 21								18 15	
Bredbury d							16 24								18 18	
Gorton d		14 36			15 36					16 36			17 36			
Guide Bridge d		14a46			15a46					16a46			17a46			
Romiley d							16 27								18 21	
Marple d							16 31								18 25	
Strines d	←						16 35		←						18 29	
New Mills Central d	14 34						16 38		16 38						18 34	
Stockport 86 d			14 54	15 23		15 54	→	16 23			16 54	17 23		17 54	→	18 23
Hazel Grove 86 d																
Chinley d	14 42								16 46							
Edale d	14 51								16 55							
Hope (Derbyshire) d	14 57								17 01							
Bamford d	15 00								17 04							
Hathersage d	15 03								17 07							
Grindleford d	15 07								17 11							
Dore d	15 15								17 22							
Sheffield 7 a	15 25		15 34	16 04		16 34		17 05	17 32		17 34	18 03		18 36		19 03

	NT	NT	EM	TP	NT	EM	NT	TP	NT	NT	EM	TP	EM	TP	EM	NT	TP
			◇	1 ◇		◇		1 ◇			◇	1 ◇	◇	1 ◇	◇		1 ◇
		A 🚌	B	C	A 🚌	D		C		A 🚌	D		D		D		
Manchester Airport 85 ✈ d				18 52				19 50				20 52		21 52			22 50
Manchester Piccadilly 10 d		18 22	18 42	19 15	19 22	19 42	20 01	20 15		20 22	20 43	21 15	22 12	22 15		22 20	23 15
Ashburys d		18 30			19 30		20 05			20 30						22 24	
Belle Vue d							20 07									22 26	
Ryder Brow d							20 09									22 28	
Reddish North d							20 12									22 31	
Brinnington d							20 15									22 34	
Bredbury d							20 18									22 37	
Gorton d		18 36			19 36					20 36							
Guide Bridge d		18a46			19a46					20a46							
Romiley d							20 21									22 40	
Marple d							20 25									22 44	
Strines d	←						20 29		←						←	22 48	
New Mills Central d	18 34						20 32		20 32							22a53	
Stockport 86 d			18 56	19 22		19 54	→	20 23			20 53	21 22	22 26 →	22 22	22 26		23 23
Hazel Grove 86 d																	
Chinley d	18 42								20 42						22 43		
Edale d	18 50								20 51						22 51		
Hope (Derbyshire) d	18 56								20 57						22 57		
Bamford d	18 59								21 00						23 00		
Hathersage d	19 03								21 04						23 03		
Grindleford d	19 06								21 07						23 07		
Dore d	19 12								21 16						23 17		
Sheffield 7 a	19 22		19 35	20 03		20 35		21 06	21 23		21 38	22 08		23 06	23 23		00 09

For general notes see front of timetable
For details of catering facilities see Directory of Train Operators

A To Hadfield (Table 79)
B From Liverpool Lime Street to Norwich (Table 49)
C To Cleethorpes (Table 29)
D From Liverpool Lime Street to Nottingham (Table 49)

Sheffield, Chinley, Marple and Romiley → Manchester and Manchester Airport

Network Diagram - see first page of Table 78

Miles	Miles	Miles		TP 1 ◇	TP 1 ◇	TP 1 ◇	NT A	NT	TP 1 ◇ B	NT	NT A	NT C	EM ◇ D	NT	NT A	NT	NT	NT A	TP 1 ◇ E	NT	NT	NT A
0	—	—	**Sheffield 7** d	01 50	03 45	05 11			06 11				06 20						07 10			
4¾	—	—	Dore d										06 27						07 16			
9¾	—	—	Grindleford d										06 35									
11¼	—	—	Hathersage d										06 39									
13	—	—	Bamford d										06 43									
14¾	—	—	Hope (Derbyshire) d										06 47									
20	—	—	Edale d										06 55									
25½	—	0	**Chinley** d										07 03									
—	—	8½	Hazel Grove 86 a																			
—	—	—	Stockport 86 a			05 53			06 53				07 23						07 55			
29¼	—	—	New Mills Central d					06b21				06b42				07b14	07b29					
30¾	—	—	Strines d					06b24				06b45				07b17	07b32					
33	—	—	**Marple** d					06b28				06b49				07b21	07b35				07 49	
—	0	—	**Rose Hill Marple** d							06c33				07 04						07 40		
34¼	2	—	**Romiley** d					06 31		06 38		06 52		07 09		07 24	07 39			07 45	07 52	
—	3¼	—	Woodley d							06 41				07 12						07 48		
—	4¾	—	Hyde Central d							06 44				07 15						07 51		
—	6	—	Hyde North d							06 47				07 18						07 55		
—	7¾	—	Guide Bridge d				06 27			06 50	06 57			07 22	07 28			07 47		07 59		08 07
—	9	—	Fairfield d							06 53				07 25						08 02		
—	10	—	Gorton d				06 30				07 00				07 31			07 50				08 10
35½	—	—	Bredbury d					06 34				06 55				07 27	07 42				07 55	
36½	—	—	Brinnington d					06 37				06 58				07 30	07 44				07 58	
38¼	—	—	Reddish North d					06 40				07 01				07 33	07 47				08 01	
39¼	—	—	Ryder Brow d					06 42				07 03				07 35					08 03	
39½	—	—	Belle Vue d					06 44				07 05				07 37					08 05	
40½	11	—	Ashburys d				06 33	06 47		06 56	07 03	07 08		07 28	07 34	07 40		07 54		08 06	08 09	08 13
41½	12	—	Ardwick d												07 37							
42	12½	8¾	**Manchester Piccadilly 10** a	02 42	04 40	06 04	06 42	06 53	07 05	07 06	07 12	07 15	07 35	07 36	07 42	07 47	08 00	08 03	08 08	08 13	08 16	08 19
—	—	—	**Manchester Airport** 85 ✈ a	03 06	05 01	06 34	*07 12*	*07 20*	07 35	*07 40*		*07 48*		*08 02*	*08 19*	*08 22*			08 33	*08 42*		*08 51*

	NT	NT	EM ◇ D	NT A	NT	NT	NT	TP 1 ◇ E	NT A	NT	NT A	NT	NT	EM ◇ D	NT A	NT	TP 1 ◇ E	NT A	NT	NT	NT
Sheffield 7 d		07 14	07 37					08 05						08 42			09 11				09 14
Dore d		07 21	07 45					08 11													09 21
Grindleford d		07 29																			09 29
Hathersage d		07 32																			09 32
Bamford d		07 36																			09 36
Hope (Derbyshire) d		07 39																			09 39
Edale d		07 47																			09 47
Chinley d		07 55	08 06					08 32													09 55
Hazel Grove 86 a			08 19																		
Stockport 86 a			08 26					08 50						09 24			09 53				
New Mills Central d		08 04				08 19							09 03								10 01
Strines d		08 07											09 06								10 04
Marple d	07 57	08 11				08 24	08 35			08 50			09 10			09 35			09 52		10 07
Rose Hill Marple d					08 13							08 59								09 54	
Romiley d	08 01	08 14			08 18	08 27	08 38			08 53		09 04	09 14			09 38			09 55	09 59	10 11
Woodley d					08 21							09 09								10 03	
Hyde Central d					08 24							09 12								10 06	
Hyde North d					08 27							09 14								10 09	
Guide Bridge d				08 27	08 31				08 47		09 07	09 18			09 28			09 58		10 15	
Fairfield d					08 34							09 21								10 18	
Gorton d				08 30					08 50		09 10				09 31			10 01			
Bredbury d	08 04					08 30	08 41			08 56			09 17			09 41					10 14
Brinnington d	08 06					08 33	08 44			08 59			09 20			09 44					10 16
Reddish North d	08 09					08 36	08 47			09 02			09 23			09 47					10 19
Ryder Brow d	08 12									09 04									10 03		
Belle Vue d	08 14									09 06									10 04		
Ashburys d	08 17			08 33	08 37	08 41			08 53	09 09	09 13				09 34			10 04	10 07		
Ardwick d	08 20					08 44															
Manchester Piccadilly 10 a	08 26	08 34	08 36	08 42	08 45	08 49	08 57	09 01	09 02	09 15	09 21	09 31	09 34	09 36	09 42	09 57	10 03	10 12	10 15	10 28	10 31
Manchester Airport 85 ✈ a			*09 06*	*09 13*	*09 18*	*09 25*		09 33	*09 40*	*09 44*	*09 56*			*10 01*	*10 14*		10 33	*10 40*	*10 44*		

For general notes see front of timetable
For details of catering facilities see Directory of Train Operators

A From Hadfield (Table 79)
B From Doncaster (Table 29)
C Until 3 October
D From Nottingham to Liverpool Lime Street (Table 49)
E From Cleethorpes (Table 29)
b From 6 October dep. 3 minutes earlier
c From 6 October dep. 0631

Sheffield, Chinley, Marple and Romiley → Manchester and Manchester Airport

Network Diagram - see first page of Table 78

	EM ◇ A	NT B	NT	NT	NT	TP 1 ◇ C		NT B	NT	NT	EM ◇ D	NT B	NT	NT		NT	TP 1 ◇ C	NT B	NT	NT	EM ◇ A	NT B		NT
Sheffield 7 d	09 42					10 11				10 14	10 42						11 11				11 42			
Dore d										10 21														
Grindleford d										10 29														
Hathersage d										10 32														
Bamford d										10 36														
Hope (Derbyshire) d										10 39														
Edale d										10 47														
Chinley d										10 55														
Hazel Grove 86 a																								
Stockport 86 a	10 24					10 53					11 24						11 53				12 24			
New Mills Central d										11 01										12 01				
Strines d																				12 04				
Marple d				10 35					10 52	11 07				11 35					11 52	12 07				
Rose Hill Marple d			10 30										11 30											12 30
Romiley d			10 35	10 38	←				10 55	11 11			11 35	11 38		←			11 55	12 11				12 35
Woodley d			10 38 →		10 38								11 38 →			11 38								12 38 →
Hyde Central d					10 41											11 41								
Hyde North d					10 44											11 44								
Guide Bridge d		10 28			10 48			10 58				11 28				11 48		11 58				12 28		
Fairfield d					10 51											11 51								
Gorton d		10 31						11 01				11 31						12 01				12 31		
Bredbury d				10 41						11 14				11 41						12 14				
Brinnington d				10 44						11 16				11 44						12 16				
Reddish North d				10 47						11 19				11 47						12 19				
Ryder Brow d									11 03										12 03					
Belle Vue d									11 04										12 04					
Ashburys d		10 34						11 04	11 07			11 34						12 04	12 07			12 34		
Ardwick d																								
Manchester Piccadilly 10 a	10 36	10 42		10 57	11 02	11 03		11 12	11 15	11 31	11 36	11 42		11 57		12 02	12 03	12 12	12 15	12 31	12 36	12 42		
Manchester Airport 85 a	11 01	11 14				11 33		11 40	11 44		12 01	12 14					12 33	12 40	12 51		13 01	13 14		

	NT	NT	TP 1 ◇ C	NT B	NT	NT	EM ◇ A		NT B	NT	NT	NT	TP 1 ◇ C	NT B	NT		NT	EM ◇ A	NT B	NT	NT	NT	TP 1 ◇ C	NT B
Sheffield 7 d			12 11			12 14	12 42						13 11					13 42					14 11	
Dore d						12 21																		
Grindleford d						12 29																		
Hathersage d						12 32																		
Bamford d						12 36																		
Hope (Derbyshire) d						12 39																		
Edale d						12 47																		
Chinley d						12 55																		
Hazel Grove 86 a																								
Stockport 86 a			12 53				13 24						13 53					14 24					14 53	
New Mills Central d						13 01											14 01							
Strines d																	14 04							
Marple d	12 35				12 52	13 07					13 35				13 52		14 07				14 35			
Rose Hill Marple d										13 30										14 30				
Romiley d	12 38	←			12 55	13 11				13 35	13 38	←			13 55		14 11			14 35	14 38	←		
Woodley d		12 38								13 38 →		13 38								14 38 →		14 38		
Hyde Central d		12 41										13 41										14 41		
Hyde North d		12 44										13 44										14 44		
Guide Bridge d		12 48		12 58					13 28			13 48		13 58					14 28			14 48		14 58
Fairfield d		12 51										13 51										14 51		
Gorton d				13 01					13 31					14 01					14 31					15 01
Bredbury d	12 41					13 14					13 41						14 14				14 41			
Brinnington d	12 44					13 16					13 44						14 16				14 44			
Reddish North d	12 47					13 19					13 47						14 19				14 47			
Ryder Brow d					13 03										14 03									
Belle Vue d					13 04										14 04									
Ashburys d				13 04	13 07				13 34					14 04	14 07				14 34					15 04
Ardwick d																								
Manchester Piccadilly 10 a	12 57	13 02	13 03	13 12	13 15	13 31	13 36		13 42		13 57	14 02	14 03	14 12	14 15		14 31	14 36	14 42		14 57	15 02	15 03	15 12
Manchester Airport 85 a			13 33	13 40	13 44		14 01		14 14				14 33	14 40	14 44			15 01	15 14				15 33	15 40

For general notes see front of timetable
For details of catering facilities see Directory of Train Operators

A Until 5 September from Norwich to Liverpool Lime Street (Table 49). From 8 September to Liverpool Lime Street (Table 89)

B From Hadfield (Table 79)

C From Cleethorpes (Table 29)

D Until 5 September from Cambridge to Liverpool Lime Street (Table 49). From 8 September to Liverpool Lime Street (Table 89)

Sheffield, Chinley, Marple and Romiley → Manchester and Manchester Airport

Network Diagram - see first page of Table 78

		NT	NT	EM ◇ A	NT B	NT	NT	NT	TP [1] ◇ C	NT	NT B	NT	NT	EM ◇ A	NT B	NT	TP [1] ◇ C	NT D	NT	NT	NT	NT
Sheffield [7]	d		14 14	14 42					15 11					15 42			16 11					16 14
Dore	d		14 21																			16 21
Grindleford	d		14 29																			16 29
Hathersage	d		14 32																			16 32
Bamford	d		14 36																			16 36
Hope (Derbyshire)	d		14 39																			16 39
Edale	d		14 47																			16 47
Chinley	d		14 55																			16 55
Hazel Grove	86 a																					
Stockport	86 a			15 24					15 53					16 24			16 53					
New Mills Central	d		15 01									15 47										17 01
Strines	d											15 50										
Marple	d	14 52	15 07				15 35			15 47		15 53				16 36				16 46		17 06
Rose Hill Marple	d					15 27							16 10						16 39			
Romiley	d	14 55	15 11			15 32	15 38	←		15 50		15 57	16 15			16 39			16 44	16 49	←	17 10
Woodley	d					15 38 →		15 38											16 47 →		16 47	
Hyde Central	d							15 41													16 50	
Hyde North	d							15 44													16 53	
Guide Bridge	d				15 28			15 48			15 58				16 28			16 40			16 57	
Fairfield	d							15 51													17 00	
Gorton	d				15 31						16 01				16 31			16 52				
Bredbury	d		15 14				15 41					16 00	16 18							16 52		
Brinnington	d		15 16				15 44					16 02										
Reddish North	d		15 19				15 47					16 05	16 22							16 57		
Ryder Brow	d	15 03								15 58										16 59		
Belle Vue	d	15 04								15 59										17 01		
Ashburys	d	15 07			15 34					16 02	16 04				16 34			16 56		17 04	17 06	
Ardwick	d																					
Manchester Piccadilly [10]	a	15 15	15 31	15 36	15 42		15 57	16 01	16 03	16 10	16 12	16 16	16 32	16 35	16 42	16 54	17 03	17 04		17 10	17 14	17 28
Manchester Airport	85 a	15 44		16 01	16 14				16 33		16 40	16 51			17 14		17 39	17 39		17 40	17 56	

		NT B	EM ◇ E	NT	NT	NT B	NT	TP [1] ◇ C	NT B	NT	NT	NT B	EM ◇ A	NT	NT	NT D	NT G	TP [1] ◇ C	NT	NT B	NT	EM ◇ A
Sheffield [7]	d		16 42					17 11			17 14		17 42					18 11				18 42
Dore	d										17 21											
Grindleford	d										17 29											
Hathersage	d										17 32											
Bamford	d										17 36											
Hope (Derbyshire)	d										17 39											
Edale	d										17 47											
Chinley	d										17 55							18 35			18 55	
Hazel Grove	86 a																					
Stockport	86 a		17 25					17 53					18 26					18 53				19 24
New Mills Central	d				17 21						18 01										19 01	
Strines	d										18 04										19 04	
Marple	d				17 26		17 34			17 58	18 07				18 25						19 07	
Rose Hill Marple	d			17 21										18 11					18 44			
Romiley	d				17 30		17 37				18 11			18 16	18 28				18 49		19 11	
Woodley	d													18 19								
Hyde Central	d													18 22								
Hyde North	d													18 25								
Guide Bridge	d	17 16				17 41			17 58			18 16		18 29		18 46	18 48			19 00		
Fairfield	d													18 32								
Gorton	d	17 19				17 44			18 02			18 20				18 49	18 52			19 03		
Bredbury	d						17 40				18 14				18 31				18 52		19 14	
Brinnington	d						17 43												18 54		19 16	
Reddish North	d						17 46												18 57		19 19	
Ryder Brow	d																		19 00			
Belle Vue	d																		19 01			
Ashburys	d	17 22				17 47	17 51		18 04			18 24				18 53	18 54			19 06		
Ardwick	d																					
Manchester Piccadilly [10]	a	17 31	17 36	17 42	17 45	17 56	18 00	18 03	18 12	18 16	18 31	18 32	18 36	18 41	18 45	19 01	19 01	19 03	19 10	19 13	19 31	19 36
Manchester Airport	85 a		18 05		18 14			18 38	18 42	18 46				19 09	19 14			19 34	19 40	19 52		20 05

For general notes see front of timetable
For details of catering facilities see Directory of Train Operators

A Until 5 September from Norwich to Liverpool Lime Street (Table 49). From 8 September to Liverpool Lime Street (Table 89)
B From Hadfield (Table 79)
C From Cleethorpes (Table 29)
D Until 3 October. From Hadfield (Table 79)
G From 6 October. From Hadfield (Table 79)

Sheffield, Chinley, Marple and Romiley → Manchester and Manchester Airport

Network Diagram - see first page of Table 78

		NT	NT	NT	TP	NT	NT	EM	NT	TP	NT	NT	EM	NT	NT	NT	TP	NT	NT	NT	NT
					1 ◇			◇		1 ◇			◇				1 ◇				
		A			B	A		C	A	B		A	D			A	B		A		
Sheffield 7	d				19 11		19 14	19 42		20 11			20 31		20 34		22 11			22 47	
Dore	d						19 22								20 42					22 54	
Grindleford	d						19 29								20 50					23 01	
Hathersage	d						19 32								20 54					23 05	
Bamford	d						19 36								20 57					23 08	
Hope (Derbyshire)	d						19 39								21 01					23 12	
Edale	d						19 47								21 08					23 19	
Chinley	d						19 55								21 16					23 27	
Hazel Grove	86 a																				
Stockport	86 a				19 52			20 26		20 53			21 17				22 53			23 46	
New Mills Central	d						20 01				20 30				21 30			22 30			23 30
Strines	d										20 33							22 33			23 33
Marple	d			19 36			20 07				20 36				21 36			22 36			23 36
Rose Hill Marple	d		19 15											21 10							
Romiley	d		19 20	19 39			20 11				20 40			21 15	21 40			22 40			23 40
Woodley	d		19 23											21 18							
Hyde Central	d		19 26											21 21							
Hyde North	d		19 29											21 24							
Guide Bridge	d	19 28	19 33			19 58			20 28			20 58		21 28		21 58			22 58		
Fairfield	d		19 36											21 31							
Gorton	d	19 31				20 01			20 31			21 01				22 01			23 01		
Bredbury	d			19 42			20 14				20 43				21 43			22 43			23 43
Brinnington	d			19 45			20 16				20 45				21 45			22 45			23 45
Reddish North	d			19 48			20 19				20 48				21 48			22 48			23 48
Ryder Brow	d			19 50							20 51				21 51			22 51			23 51
Belle Vue	d			19 52							20 52				21 52			22 52			23 52
Ashburys	d	19 34		19 55		20 04			20 34		20 55	21 04			21 55	22 04		22 55	23 04		23 55
Ardwick	d																				
Manchester Piccadilly 10	a	19 43	19 47	20 02	20 03	20 12	20 31	20 36	20 42	21 03	21 03	21 12	21 30	21 41	22 03	22 12	23 03	23 03	23 12	23 59	00 03
Manchester Airport	85 a	20 12	20 19		20 34	20 58	21 06	21 09	21 19	21 34	21 37	21 51		22 15	22 39	22 58	23 28		23 56	00 45	00 45

Saturdays

		TP	TP	TP	TP	NT	EM	NT	NT	NT	NT	NT	TP	NT	NT	EM	NT	NT	NT	TP	NT	NT	NT	NT
		1 ◇	1 ◇	1 ◇	1 ◇		◇						1 ◇			◇				1 ◇				
					E	A	G	A					B	A		G	A			B		A		
Sheffield 7	d	01 50	03 45	05 11	06 11		06 20						07 10		07 14	07 36				08 05				08 14
Dore	d						06 27						07 16		07 21					08 11				08 21
Grindleford	d						06 35								07 29									08 29
Hathersage	d						06 39								07 32									08 32
Bamford	d						06 43								07 36									08 36
Hope (Derbyshire)	d						06 47								07 39									08 39
Edale	d						06 55								07 47									08 47
Chinley	d						07 03								07 55	08 03				08 32				08 55
Hazel Grove	86 a																							
Stockport	86 a			05 53	06 53		07 23						07 55			08 25				08 50				
New Mills Central	d								07b10						08 04									09 01
Strines	d								07b13						08 07									09 04
Marple	d								07b17		07 37				08 10				08 35				08 52	09 07
Rose Hill Marple	d									07 30								08 30						
Romiley	d								07 20	07 35	07 40	←			08 14			08 35	08 38		←		08 55	09 11
Woodley	d									07 38 →		07 38						08 38 →			08 38			
Hyde Central	d											07 41									08 41			
Hyde North	d											07 44									08 44			
Guide Bridge	d					06 58		07 28				07 48		07 58			08 28				08 48	08 58		
Fairfield	d											07 51									08 51			
Gorton	d					07 01		07 31						08 01			08 31					09 01		
Bredbury	d								07 23		07 43								08 41					09 14
Brinnington	d								07 26		07 46								08 44					09 16
Reddish North	d								07 29		07 49								08 47					09 19
Ryder Brow	d								07 31														09 03	
Belle Vue	d								07 33														09 04	
Ashburys	d					07 04		07 34	07 37					08 04			08 34					09 04	09 07	
Ardwick	d																							
Manchester Piccadilly 10	a	02 43	04 40	06 04	07 05	07 12	07 35	07 42	07 45		08 01	08 02	08 08	08 12	08 31	08 36	08 42		08 57	09 01	09 02	09 12	09 15	09 31
Manchester Airport	85 a	03 06	05 01	06 34	07 35	07 48	08 02		08 19				08 33	08 42		09 06	09 13			09 33	09 40		09 44	

For general notes see front of timetable
For details of catering facilities see Directory of Train Operators

A From Hadfield (Table 79)

B From Cleethorpes (Table 29)

C Until 5 September from Norwich to Liverpool Lime Street (Table 49). From 8 September to Liverpool Lime Street (Table 89)

D Until 5 September. From Norwich (Table 49)

E From Doncaster (Table 29)

G From Nottingham to Liverpool Lime Street (Table 49)

b Until 11 October dep. 3 minutes earlier

Sheffield, Chinley, Marple and Romiley → Manchester and Manchester Airport

Network Diagram - see first page of Table 78

	EM ◇ A	NT B	NT	NT	NT		TP 1 ◇ C	NT B	NT	NT	NT	EM ◇ D	NT B	NT	NT	NT	TP 1 ◇ C	NT B	NT		NT	EM ◇ E	NT B	NT G
Sheffield 7 d	08 42						09 11			09 14		09 42					10 11				10 14	10 42		
Dore d										09 21											10 21			
Grindleford d										09 29											10 29			
Hathersage d										09 32											10 32			
Bamford d										09 36											10 36			
Hope (Derbyshire) d										09 39											10 39			
Edale d										09 47											10 47			
Chinley d										09 55											10 55			
Hazel Grove 86 a																								
Stockport 86 a	09 25						09 53					10 24					10 53					11 24		11d28
New Mills Central d										10 01											11 01			
Strines d										10 04														
Marple d				09 35					09 52	10 07					10 35				10 52		11 07			
Rose Hill Marple d			09 30								10 30			10 30										
Romiley d			09 35	09 38	←				09 55	10 11	10 35			10 35	10 38	←			10 55		11 11			
Woodley d			09 38 →		09 38						→			10 38 →		10 38								
Hyde Central d					09 41											10 41								
Hyde North d					09 44											10 44								
Guide Bridge d		09 28			09 48			09 58					10 28			10 48		10 58					11 28	11a42
Fairfield d					09 51											10 51								
Gorton d		09 31						10 01					10 31					11 01					11 31	
Bredbury d				09 41						10 14					10 41						11 14			
Brinnington d				09 44						10 16					10 44						11 16			
Reddish North d				09 47						10 19					10 47						11 19			
Ryder Brow d									10 03										11 03					
Belle Vue d									10 04										11 04					
Ashburys d		09 34						10 04	10 07				10 34					11 04	11 07				11 34	
Ardwick d																								
Manchester Piccadilly 10 a	09 36	09 42		09 57	10 02		10 03	10 12	10 15	10 31		10 36	10 42		10 57	11 02	11 03	11 12	11 15		11 31	11 36	11 42	
Manchester Airport 85 a	*10 02*	*10 14*					10 33	*10 40*	*10 44*			*11 01*	*11 14*				11 33	*11 40*	*11 44*			*12 01*	*12 14*	

	NT	NT	NT	TP 1 ◇ C	NT B	NT	NT	EM ◇ D	NT B	NT	NT		NT	TP 1 ◇ C	NT B	NT	NT	EM ◇ D	NT B	NT	NT	NT	TP 1 ◇ C	NT B
Sheffield 7 d				11 11			11 14	11 42						12 11			12 14	12 42					13 11	
Dore d							11 21										12 21							
Grindleford d							11 29										12 29							
Hathersage d							11 32										12 32							
Bamford d							11 36										12 36							
Hope (Derbyshire) d							11 39										12 39							
Edale d							11 47										12 47							
Chinley d							11 55										12 55							
Hazel Grove 86 a																								
Stockport 86 a				11 53				12 24						12 53				13 24					13 53	
New Mills Central d							12 01										13 01							
Strines d							12 04																	
Marple d		11 35				11 52	12 07				12 35					12 52	13 07				13 35			
Rose Hill Marple d	11 30									12 30										13 30				
Romiley d	11 35	11 38	←			11 55	12 11			12 35	12 38		←			12 55	13 11			13 35	13 38	←		
Woodley d	11 38 →		11 38							12 38 →			12 38							13 38 →		13 38		
Hyde Central d			11 41										12 41									13 41		
Hyde North d			11 44										12 44									13 44		
Guide Bridge d			11 48		11 58				12 28				12 48		12 58				13 28			13 48		13 58
Fairfield d			11 51										12 51									13 51		
Gorton d					12 01				12 31						13 01				13 31					14 01
Bredbury d		11 41					12 14				12 41						13 14				13 41			
Brinnington d		11 44					12 16				12 44						13 16				13 44			
Reddish North d		11 47					12 19				12 47						13 19				13 47			
Ryder Brow d						12 03										13 03								
Belle Vue d						12 04										13 04								
Ashburys d					12 04	12 07			12 34						13 04	13 07			13 34					14 04
Ardwick d																								
Manchester Piccadilly 10 a		11 57	12 02	12 03	12 12	12 15	12 31	12 36	12 42		12 57		13 02	13 03	13 12	13 15	13 31	13 36	13 42		13 57	14 02	14 03	14 12
Manchester Airport 85 a				12 33	*12 40*	*12 51*		*13 01*	*13 14*					13 33	*13 40*	*13 44*		*14 01*	*14 14*				14 33	*14 40*

For general notes see front of timetable
For details of catering facilities see Directory of Train Operators

A From Nottingham to Liverpool Lime Street (Table 49)

B From Hadfield (Table 79)

C From Cleethorpes (Table 29)

D Until 6 September from Norwich to Liverpool Lime Street (Table 49). From 13 September to Liverpool Lime Street (Table 89)

E Until 6 September from Cambridge to Liverpool Lime Street (Table 49). From 13 September to Liverpool Lime Street (Table 89)

G To Stalybridge arr. 1149. Also stops at Reddish South 11x33 and Denton 11x37

Table 78

Saturdays

Sheffield, Chinley, Marple and Romiley → Manchester and Manchester Airport

Network Diagram - see first page of Table 78

		NT	NT	EM ◇ A		NT B	NT	NT	NT	TP 1 ◇ C	NT B	NT	NT	EM ◇ A	NT B	NT	NT	NT		TP 1 ◇ C	NT B	NT	NT	EM ◇ A	NT B
Sheffield 7	d		13 14	13 42						14 11			14 14	14 42						15 11			15 14	15 42	
Dore	d		13 21										14 21										15 21		
Grindleford	d		13 29										14 29										15 29		
Hathersage	d		13 32										14 32										15 32		
Bamford	d		13 36										14 36										15 36		
Hope (Derbyshire)	d		13 39										14 39										15 39		
Edale	d		13 47										14 47										15 47		
Chinley	d		13 55										14 55										15 55		
Hazel Grove	86 a																								
Stockport	86 a			14 25						14 53				15 24						15 53				16 24	
New Mills Central	d		14 04										15 01										16 01		
Strines	d		14 07																				16 04		
Marple	d	13 52	14 09					14 35				14 52	15 07				15 35					15 52	16 07		
Rose Hill Marple	d						14 30									15 30									
Romiley	d	13 55	14 14				14 35	14 38	←			14 55	15 11			15 35	15 38	←				15 55	16 11		
Woodley	d						14 38 →		14 38							15 38 →		15 38							
Hyde Central	d								14 41									15 41							
Hyde North	d								14 44									15 44							
Guide Bridge	d					14 28			14 48		14 58				15 28			15 48			15 58				16 28
Fairfield	d								14 51									15 51							
Gorton	d					14 31					15 01				15 31						16 01				16 31
Bredbury	d		14 17					14 41					15 14				15 41						16 14		
Brinnington	d		14 19					14 44					15 16				15 44						16 16		
Reddish North	d		14 22					14 47					15 19				15 47						16 19		
Ryder Brow	d	14 03										15 03										16 03			
Belle Vue	d	14 04										15 04										16 04			
Ashburys	d	14 07				14 34					15 04	15 07			15 34						16 04	16 07			16 34
Ardwick	d																								
Manchester Piccadilly 10	a	14 15	14 34	14 36		14 42		14 57	15 02	15 03	15 12	15 15	15 31	15 36	15 42		15 57	16 02		16 03	16 12	16 15	16 32	16 36	16 42
Manchester Airport	85 ✈ a	14 44		15 01		15 14				15 33	15 40	15 44		16 01	16 14					16 33	16 40	16 51			17 11

		NT	NT	NT	TP 1 ◇ C	NT B	NT	NT	EM ◇ A	NT B		NT	NT	NT	TP 1 ◇ C	NT B	NT	NT	EM ◇ D	NT B	NT	NT	NT	TP 1 ◇ C	NT B
Sheffield 7	d				16 11			16 14	16 42						17 11			17 14	17 42					18 11	
Dore	d							16 21										17 21							
Grindleford	d							16 29										17 29							
Hathersage	d							16 32										17 32							
Bamford	d							16 36										17 36							
Hope (Derbyshire)	d							16 39										17 39							
Edale	d							16 47										17 47							
Chinley	d							16 55										17 55						18 35	
Hazel Grove	86 a																								
Stockport	86 a				16 53				17 24						17 53				18 26					18 52	
New Mills Central	d							17 01										18 01							
Strines	d																	18 04							
Marple	d		16 36				16 50	17 07					17 35				17 52	18 07				18 35			
Rose Hill Marple	d	16 30										17 30									18 30				
Romiley	d	16 35	16 39	←			16 53	17 11				17 35	17 38	←			17 55	18 11			18 35	18 38	←		
Woodley	d	16 38 →		16 38								17 38 →		17 38							18 38 →		18 38		
Hyde Central	d			16 41										17 41									18 41		
Hyde North	d			16 44										17 44									18 44		
Guide Bridge	d			16 48		16 58				17 28				17 48		17 58				18 28			18 48		18 58
Fairfield	d			16 51										17 51									18 51		
Gorton	d					17 01				17 31						18 01				18 31					19 01
Bredbury	d						16 56	17 14					17 41					18 14				18 41			
Brinnington	d						16 59	17 16									18 00	18 16				18 44			
Reddish North	d						17 02	17 19									18 03	18 19				18 47			
Ryder Brow	d						17 04										18 05								
Belle Vue	d						17 06										18 07								
Ashburys	d					17 04	17 09			17 34						18 04	18 10			18 34					19 04
Ardwick	d																								
Manchester Piccadilly 10	a		16 54	17 02	17 03	17 12	17 16	17 32	17 35	17 42			17 54	17b59	18 03	18 12	18 17	18 31	18 35	18 42		18 57	19 02	19 03	19 12
Manchester Airport	85 ✈ a				17 39	17 40	17 56		18c05	18 14			18 27		18 38	18 42	18 46			19 08			19 40	19 34	

For general notes see front of timetable
For details of catering facilities see Directory of Train Operators

A Until 6 September from Norwich to Liverpool Lime Street (Table 49). From 13 September to Liverpool Lime Street (Table 89)

B From Hadfield (Table 79)

C From Cleethorpes (Table 29)

b From 13 September arr. 1803

c From 13 September arr. 1801

Table 78

Saturdays

Sheffield, Chinley, Marple and Romiley → Manchester and Manchester Airport

Network Diagram - see first page of Table 78

	NT		NT	EM ◇ A	NT B	NT	TP [1] ◇ C 🍴	NT B	NT	NT	EM ◇ D	TP [1] ◇ C 🍴	NT	NT B	EM ◇ E	NT	NT	NT B	NT	NT B	NT	NT		
Sheffield [7] d			18 14	18 42			19 11			19 14	19 42	20 11			20 29		20 32				22 24			
Dore d			18 21							19 21							20 41				22 31			
Grindleford d			18 29							19 28							20 50				22 38			
Hathersage d			18 32							19 32							20 54				22 41			
Bamford d			18 36							19 35							20 57				22 45			
Hope (Derbyshire) d			18 39							19 39							21 01				22 48			
Edale d			18 47							19 46							21 08				22 56			
Chinley d			18 55							19 54							21 16				23 04			
Hazel Grove 86 a																								
Stockport 86 a				19 24			19 53				20 25	20 53			21 16						23 21			
New Mills Central d			19 01							20 01			20 30				21b30		22 30			23 23		
Strines d			19 04										20 33						22 33			23 26		
Marple d	18 52		19 07						19 59	20 06			20 36				21 36		22 36			23 29		
Rose Hill Marple d						19 15										21 10								
Romiley d	18 55		19 11			19 20			20 02	20 09			20 40			21 15	21 40		22 40			23 33		
Woodley d						19 23										21 18								
Hyde Central d						19 26										21 21								
Hyde North d						19 29										21 24								
Guide Bridge d					19 28	19 33		19 58						20 58		21 28		21 58		22 58				
Fairfield d						19 36										21 31								
Gorton d					19 31			20 01						21 01				22 01		23 01				
Bredbury d			19 14						20 05	20 12			20 43				21 43		22 43			23 36		
Brinnington d			19 16						20 08	20 15			20 45				21 45		22 45			23 38		
Reddish North d			19 19						20 11	20 18			20 48				21 48		22 48			23 41		
Ryder Brow d	19 03								20 13				20 51				21 51		22 51			23 44		
Belle Vue d	19 04								20 15				20 52				21 52		22 52			23 45		
Ashburys d	19 07				19 34			20 04	20 18				20 55	21 04			21 55	22 04	22 55	23 04		23 48		
Ardwick d																								
Manchester Piccadilly [10] a	19 15		19 33	19 35	19 42	19 47	20 03	20 12	20c28	20 31	20 36	21 03	21 03	21 12	21 26	21 40	22 03	22 12	23 03	23 12	23 37	00 03		
Manchester Airport 85 ✈ a	*19 52*			*20 05*	*20 12*	*20 19*	**20 34**		*20 58*	*21 06*	*21 09*	**21 34**	*21 37*	*21 51*	*21 58*	*22 16*	*22 39*	*22 58*		*23 56*		*00 45*		

Sundays

until 13 July

	TP [1] ◇	TP [1] ◇ G	NT 🚌	NT	NT 🚌	NT B	NT B	EM ◇ H	NT B	NT	NT 🚌	TP [1] ◇ J	NT B	EM ◇ H	NT B	NT	NT 🚌	TP [1] ◇ C	NT B	EM ◇ H	NT B	NT	TP [1] ◇ J	NT B
Sheffield [7] d	07 55	09 13		09 30				10 26		10 35		11 13		11 40		11 43		12 13		12 39		12 56	13 13	
Dore d				09 37				10 33		10 42						11 50						13 03		
Grindleford d				09 45						10 51						11 59						13 10		
Hathersage d				09 49						10 54						12 03						13 14		
Bamford d				09 52						10 58						12 06						13 18		
Hope (Derbyshire) d				09 56						11 02						12 10						13 21		
Edale d				10 03						11 10						12 18						13 29		
Chinley d				10 11	10 20					11 18						12 26	12 35					13 37		
Hazel Grove 86 a										11 32												13 50		
Stockport 86 a	08 39	09 58		10 30				11 18		11 38	←	11 58		12 23		12 45		12 56		13 23		13 57	14 01	
New Mills Central d			09 10		10 40 →						10 40						12 55 →							
Strines d			09 17								10 47													
Marple d			09 24								10 54													
Romiley d			09 33								11 03													
Guide Bridge d						10 32	11 02		11 32				12 02		12 32				13 02		13 32			14 02
Gorton d						10 35	11 05		11 35				12 05		12 35				13 05		13 35			14 05
Bredbury d			09 43								11 13													
Brinnington d			09 51								11 21													
Reddish North d			10 09								11 39													
Ryder Brow d			10 17								11 47													
Belle Vue d			10 21								11 51													
Ashburys d			10 26			10 38	11 08		11 38		11 56		12 08		12 38				13 08		13 38			14 08
Manchester Piccadilly [10] a	08 48	10 08	10 35	10 41		10 47	11 17	11 32	11 47	11 56	12 05	12 08	12 17	12 36	12 47	12 56		13 10	13 17	13 36	13 47	14 10	14 11	14 17
Manchester Airport 85 ✈ a	09 12	10 36										12 37						13 39					14 36	

For general notes see front of timetable
For details of catering facilities see Directory of Train Operators

- **A** Until 6 September from Norwich (Table 49)
- **B** From Hadfield (Table 79)
- **C** From Cleethorpes (Table 29)
- **D** Until 6 September from Norwich to Manchester Oxford Road (Table 49). From 13 September to Manchester Oxford Road arr. 2039 (Table 84)
- **E** Until 6 September. From Norwich (Table 49)
- **G** From Meadowhall (Table 29)
- **H** From Nottingham to Liverpool Lime Street (Table 49)
- **J** From Doncaster (Table 29)
- **b** Arr. 2125
- **c** From 13 September arr. 2025

Sheffield, Chinley, Marple and Romiley → Manchester and Manchester Airport

Sundays
until 13 July

Network Diagram - see first page of Table 78

Station		NT Bus	EM ◇ A	NT B	NT	NT Bus	TP 1◇ C	NT B	EM ◇ D	NT B	TP 1◇ C	NT B	NT Bus	EM ◇ A	NT B	NT	NT Bus	TP 1◇ C	NT B	EM ◇ A	NT B	NT	TP 1◇ C	NT B	NT Bus
Sheffield 7	d		13 37		13 41		14 12		14 43		15 13			15 34		15 43		16 13		16 36		16 44	17 13		
Dore	d				13 48											15 50						16 51			
Grindleford	d				13 56											15 58						16 57			
Hathersage	d				14 00											16 01						17 00			
Bamford	d				14 03											16 05						17 04			
Hope (Derbyshire)	d				14 07											16 09						17 08			
Edale	d				14 15											16 17						17 16			
Chinley	d				14 23	14 35										16 25	16 35					17 24			
Hazel Grove	86 a															16 36						17 36			
Stockport	86 a	←	14 20		14 49		15 01		15 24		16 03		←	16 20		16 45		16 56		17 21		17 44	17 55		←
New Mills Central	d	12 55				14 55 →							14 55				16 55 →								16 55
Strines	d	13 02											15 02												17 02
Marple	d	13 09											15 09												17 09
Romiley	d	13 18											15 18												17 18
Guide Bridge	d			14 32				15 02		15 32		16 02			16 32				17 02		17 32			18 02	
Gorton	d			14 35				15 05		15 35		16 05			16 35				17 05		17 35			18 05	
Bredbury	d	13 28											15 28												17 28
Brinnington	d	13 36											15 36												17 36
Reddish North	d	13 54											15 54												17 54
Ryder Brow	d	14 02											16 02												18 02
Belle Vue	d	14 06											16 06												18 06
Ashburys	d	14 11		14 38				15 08		15 38		16 08	16 11		16 38				17 08		17 38			18 08	18 11
Manchester Piccadilly 10	a	14 20	14 33	14 47	15 02		15 13	15 17	15 34	15 47	16 13	16 17	16 20	16 33	16 47	16 56		17 11	17 17	17 36	17 47	17 57	18 12	18 17	18 20
Manchester Airport	85 a						15 37				16 36							17 36					18 36		

Station		EM ◇ D	NT B	NT	NT Bus	TP 1◇ C	NT B	EM ◇ A	NT B	NT	TP 1◇ C	NT B	NT Bus	EM ◇ E	NT B	NT	TP 1◇ C	NT B	EM ◇ E	TP 1◇ C	NT B	NT Bus	NT	NT Bus	
Sheffield 7	d	17 42		17 53		18 13		18 35		18 43	19 13			19 35		19 42	20 13		20 35	21 19			21 56		
Dore	d			18 03						18 51						19 49							22 03		
Grindleford	d			18 11						18 58						19 55							22 12		
Hathersage	d			18 14						19 02						19 59							22 15		
Bamford	d			18 18						19 06						20 02							22 19		
Hope (Derbyshire)	d			18 22						19 09						20 07							22 23		
Edale	d			18 30						19 17						20 15							22 31		
Chinley	d			18 38	18 45					19 25						20 23						20 35	22 39		
Hazel Grove	86 a									19 38															
Stockport	86 a	18 24		18 56		19 00		19 20		19 46	20 00		←	20 24		20 45	20 54		21 16	22 00			23 00		
New Mills Central	d				19 05 →								19 05									20 55		23 45	
Strines	d												19 12									21 02			
Marple	d												19 19									21 09		23 55	
Romiley	d												19 28									21 18		00 04	
Guide Bridge	d		18 32				19 02		19 32			20 02			20 32			21 02			22 02				
Gorton	d		18 35				19 05		19 35			20 05			20 35			21 05			22 05				
Bredbury	d												19 38									21 28		00 14	
Brinnington	d												19 46									21 36			
Reddish North	d												20 04									21 54		00 30	
Ryder Brow	d												20 12									22 02			
Belle Vue	d												20 16									22 06		00 36	
Ashburys	d		18 38				19 08		19 38			20 08	20 21		20 38			21 08			22 08	22 11			
Manchester Piccadilly 10	a	18 35	18 47	19 10		19 12	19 17	19 32	19 47	19 59	20 09	20 17	20 30	20 35	20 47	20 55	21 04	21 17	21 31	22 14	22 17	22 20	23 13	00 45	
Manchester Airport	85 a					19 36					20 36						21 36			22 36					

Sundays
20 July to 7 September

Station		TP 1◇	TP 1◇ G	NT B	NT	NT B	EM ◇ A		NT B	NT	TP 1◇ H	NT B	EM ◇ A	NT B		NT	TP 1◇ C	NT	NT B	EM ◇ A	NT B		NT	TP 1◇ H	NT B
Sheffield 7	d	07 55	09 13		09 30		10 26			10 30	11 13		11 40			11 43	12 13			12 39			12 56	13 13	
Dore	d				09 37		10 33			10 37						11 50							13 03		
Grindleford	d				09 45					10 47						11 59							13 10		
Hathersage	d				09 49					10 50						12 03							13 14		
Bamford	d				09 52					10 54						12 06							13 18		
Hope (Derbyshire)	d				09 56					10 58						12 10							13 21		
Edale	d				10 03					11 06						12 18							13 29		
Chinley	d				10 11					11 14						12 26							13 37		
Hazel Grove	86 a									11 25													13 50		
Stockport	86 a	08 39	09 58				11 18			11 32	11 58		12 23				12 56	←		13 23			13 57	14 01	
New Mills Central	d				10 18											12 33 →		12 33							
Strines	d				10 21													12 36							
Marple	d				10 24													12 39							
Romiley	d				10 28													12 43							
Guide Bridge	d			10 32		11 02			11 32			12 02		12 32					13 02		13 32				14 02
Gorton	d			10 35		11 05			11 35			12 05		12 35					13 05		13 35				14 05
Bredbury	d				10 31													12 46							
Brinnington	d				10 33													12 48							
Reddish North	d				10 36													12 51							
Ryder Brow	d				10 39													12 54							
Belle Vue	d				10 40													12 55							
Ashburys	d			10 38	10 45	11 08			11 38			12 08		12 38				13 02	13 08		13 38				14 08
Manchester Piccadilly 10	a	08 48	10 08	10 47	10 54	11 17	11 32		11 47	11 49	12 08	12 17	12 36	12 47			13 10	13 12	13 17	13 36	13 47		14 10	14 11	14 17
Manchester Airport	85 a	09 12	10 33								12 33						13 39							14 33	

For general notes see front of timetable
For details of catering facilities see Directory of Train Operators

- A From Nottingham to Liverpool Lime Street (Table 49)
- B From Hadfield (Table 79)
- C From Cleethorpes (Table 29)
- D From Norwich to Liverpool Lime Street (Table 49)
- E From Norwich (Table 49)
- G From Meadowhall (Table 29)
- H From Doncaster (Table 29)

Sheffield, Chinley, Marple and Romiley → Manchester and Manchester Airport

Sundays

20 July to 7 September

Network Diagram - see first page of Table 78

	EM	NT	NT	TP	NT	EM	NT	TP	NT	EM	NT	NT	TP	NT	EM	NT	NT	TP	NT	EM	NT
	◇			1 ◇		◇		1 ◇		◇			1 ◇		◇			1 ◇		◇	
	A	B		C	B	A	B	C	B	D	B		C	B	D	B		C	B	A	B
Sheffield 7 d	13 37		13 41	14 12		14 37		15 13		15 34		15 43	16 13		16 36		16 44	17 13		17 42	
Dore d			13 48									15 50					16 51				
Grindleford d			13 56									15 58					16 57				
Hathersage d			14 00									16 01					17 00				
Bamford d			14 03									16 05					17 04				
Hope (Derbyshire) d			14 07									16 09					17 08				
Edale d			14 15									16 17					17 16				
Chinley d			14 23									16 25					17 24				
Hazel Grove 86 a																	17 36				
Stockport 86 a	14 20			15 01		15 20		16 03		16 20			16 56		17 21		17 44	17 55		18 24	
New Mills Central d			14 30									16 32									
Strines d			14 33									16 35									
Marple d			14 36									16 38									
Romiley d			14 40									16 42									
Guide Bridge d		14 32			15 02		15 32		16 02		16 32			17 02		17 32			18 02		18 32
Gorton d		14 35			15 05		15 35		16 05		16 35			17 05		17 35			18 05		18 35
Bredbury d			14 43									16 45									
Brinnington d			14 45									16 47									
Reddish North d			14 48									16 50									
Ryder Brow d			14 51									16 53									
Belle Vue d			14 52									16 54									
Ashburys d		14 38	14 59		15 08		15 38		16 08		16 38	17 02		17 08		17 38			18 08		18 38
Manchester Piccadilly 10 a	14 33	14 47	15 12	15 13	15 17	15 34	15 47	16 13	16 17	16 33	16 47	17 10	17 11	17 17	17 36	17 47	17 57	18 12	18 17	18 35	18 47
Manchester Airport 85 a				15 37				16 33					17 32					18 33			

	NT	TP	NT	NT	EM	NT	NT	TP	NT	EM	NT	NT	TP	NT	NT	EM	TP	NT	NT	NT
		1 ◇			◇			1 ◇		◇			1 ◇			◇	1 ◇			
		C	B		A	B		C	B	E	B		C		B	E	C	B		
Sheffield 7 d	17 53	18 13			18 35		18 43	19 13		19 35		19 42	20 13			20 35	21 19		21 56	
Dore d	18 03						18 51					19 49							22 03	
Grindleford d	18 11						18 58					19 55							22 12	
Hathersage d	18 14						19 02					19 58							22 15	
Bamford d	18 18						19 06					20 02							22 19	
Hope (Derbyshire) d	18 22						19 09					20 07							22 23	
Edale d	18 30						19 17					20 15							22 31	
Chinley d	18 38						19 25					20 23							22 39	
Hazel Grove 86 a							19 38													
Stockport 86 a		19 01		←	19 20		19 46	20 00		20 24			20 54	←		21 16	22 00		23 00	
New Mills Central d	18 45 →			18 45								20 32 →		20 32						23 02
Strines d				18 48										20 35						23 05
Marple d				18 51										20 38						23 09
Romiley d				18 55										20 42						23 12
Guide Bridge d			19 02			19 32			20 02		20 32				21 02			22 02		
Gorton d			19 05			19 35			20 05		20 35				21 05			22 05		
Bredbury d				18 58										20 45						23 15
Brinnington d				19 00										20 47						23 18
Reddish North d				19 03										20 50						23 21
Ryder Brow d				19 06										20 53						23 23
Belle Vue d				19 07										20 54						23 25
Ashburys d			19 08	19 10		19 38			20 08		20 38			21 02	21 08			22 08		23 28
Manchester Piccadilly 10 a		19 12	19 17	19 21	19 32	19 47	19 59	20 09	20 17	20 35	20 47		21 04	21 11	21 17	21 31	22 14	22 17	23 13	23 35
Manchester Airport 85 a		19 32						20 32					21 32				22 34			

Sundays

14 September to 2 November

	TP	NT	TP	NT	NT	NT	EM	NT	TP	NT	EM	NT	NT	TP	NT	NT	EM	NT	NT	TP	NT
							◇		1 ◇		◇			1 ◇			◇			1 ◇	
				B		B	D	B	G	B	D	B		C		B	D	B	H	G	B
	🚌	🚌	🚌																		
Sheffield 7 d	07 40	08 30	09 13				10 26		11 13		11 40		11 43	12 13			12 39		12 56	13 13	
Dore d		08 42					10 33						11 50						13 03		
Grindleford d		09 05											11 59						13 10		
Hathersage d		09 15											12 03						13 14		
Bamford d		09 20											12 06						13 18		
Hope (Derbyshire) d		09 26											12 10						13 21		
Edale d		09 40											12 18						13 29		
Chinley d		10a00			10 11								12 26						13 37		
Hazel Grove 86 a																			13 50		
Stockport 86 a							11 18		12 00		12 23			12 56	←		13 23		13 57	14 01	
New Mills Central d					10 18								12 33 →		12 33						
Strines d					10 21										12 36						
Marple d					10 24										12 39						
Romiley d					10 28										12 43						
Guide Bridge d				10 32		11 02		11 32		12 02		12 32				13 02		13 32			14 02
Gorton d				10 35		11 05		11 35		12 05		12 35				13 05		13 35			14 05
Bredbury d					10 31										12 46						
Brinnington d					10 33										12 48						
Reddish North d					10 36										12 51						
Ryder Brow d					10 39										12 54						
Belle Vue d					10 40										12 55						
Ashburys d				10 38	10 45	11 08		11 38		12 08		12 38			13 02	13 08		13 38			14 08
Manchester Piccadilly 10 a	09 00		10 33	10 47	10 54	11 17	11 32	11 47	12 12	12 17	12 36	12 47		13 10	13 12	13 17	13 36	13 47	14 10	14 11	14 17
Manchester Airport 85 a	09 25		10 58						12 37					13 39						14 36	

For general notes see front of timetable
For details of catering facilities see Directory of Train Operators

- A From Norwich to Liverpool Lime Street (Table 49)
- B From Hadfield (Table 79)
- C From Cleethorpes (Table 29)
- D From Nottingham to Liverpool Lime Street (Table 49)
- E From Norwich (Table 49)
- G From Doncaster (Table 29)
- H 14 September

Table 78

Sundays

14 September to 2 November

Sheffield, Chinley, Marple and Romiley → Manchester and Manchester Airport

Network Diagram - see first page of Table 78

		EM	NT	NT	TP	NT	EM	NT	TP	NT	EM	NT	NT	TP	NT	EM	NT	NT	TP	NT	EM	NT
		◇			1 ◇		◇		1 ◇		◇			1 ◇		◇			1 ◇		◇	
		A	B		C	B	D	B	C	B	A	B		C	B	A	B	E	C	B	D	B
Sheffield 7	(train) d	13 37		13 41	14 12		14 43		15 13		15 34		15 43	16 13		16 36		16 44	17 13		17 42	
Dore	d			13 48									15 50					16 51				
Grindleford	d			13 56									15 58					16 57				
Hathersage	d			14 00									16 01					17 00				
Bamford	d			14 03									16 05					17 04				
Hope (Derbyshire)	d			14 07									16 09					17 08				
Edale	d			14 15									16 17					17 16				
Chinley	d			14 23									16 25					17 24				
Hazel Grove	86 a																	17 36				
Stockport	86 a	14 20			15 01		15 24		16 03		16 20			16 56		17 21		17 44	17 55		18 24	
New Mills Central	d			14 30									16 32									
Strines	d			14 33									16 35									
Marple	d			14 36									16 38									
Romiley	d			14 40									16 42									
Guide Bridge	d		14 32			15 02		15 32		16 02		16 32			17 02		17 32			18 02		18 32
Gorton	d		14 35			15 05		15 35		16 05		16 35			17 05		17 35			18 05		18 35
Bredbury	d			14 43									16 45									
Brinnington	d			14 45									16 47									
Reddish North	d			14 48									16 50									
Ryder Brow	d			14 51									16 53									
Belle Vue	d			14 52									16 54									
Ashburys	d		14 38	14 59		15 08		15 38		16 08		16 38	17 02		17 08		17 38			18 08		18 38
Manchester Piccadilly 10	(train) a	14 33	14 47	15 12	15 13	15 17	15 34	15 47	16 13	16 17	16 33	16 47	17 10	17 11	17 17	17 36	17 47	17 57	18 12	18 17	18 35	18 47
Manchester Airport	85 (plane) a				15 37				16 36					17 36					18 36			

		NT	TP	NT	NT	EM	NT	NT	TP	NT	EM	NT	NT	TP	NT	NT	EM	TP	NT	NT	NT
			1 ◇			◇			1 ◇		◇			1 ◇			◇	1 ◇			
			C	B		A	B	E	C	B	G	B		C		B	G	C	B		
Sheffield 7	(train) d	17 53	18 13			18 35		18 43	19 13		19 35		19 42	20 13			20 35	21 19		21 56	
Dore	d	18 03						18 51					19 49							22 03	
Grindleford	d	18 11						18 58					19 55							22 12	
Hathersage	d	18 14						19 02					19 59							22 15	
Bamford	d	18 18						19 06					20 02							22 19	
Hope (Derbyshire)	d	18 22						19 09					20 07							22 23	
Edale	d	18 30						19 17					20 15							22 31	
Chinley	d	18 38						19 25					20 23							22 39	
Hazel Grove	86 a							19 38													
Stockport	86 a		19 00		←	19 20		19 46	20 00		20 24			20 54	←		21 16	22 00		23 00	
New Mills Central	d	18 45 →			18 45								20 32 →		20 32						23 02
Strines	d				18 48										20 35						23 05
Marple	d				18 51										20 38						23 09
Romiley	d				18 55										20 42						23 12
Guide Bridge	d			19 02			19 32			20 02		20 32				21 02			22 02		
Gorton	d			19 05			19 35			20 05		20 35				21 05			22 05		
Bredbury	d				18 58										20 45						23 15
Brinnington	d				19 00										20 47						23 18
Reddish North	d				19 03										20 50						23 21
Ryder Brow	d				19 06										20 53						23 23
Belle Vue	d				19 07										20 54						23 25
Ashburys	d			19 08	19 10		19 38			20 08		20 38			21 02	21 08			22 08		23 28
Manchester Piccadilly 10	(train) a		19 12	19 17	19 21	19 32	19 47	19 59	20 13	20 17	20 35	20 47		21 04	21 11	21 17	21 31	22 14	22 17	23 13	23 36
Manchester Airport	85 (plane) a		19 36						20 36					21 36				22 36			

Sundays

from 9 November

		TP	NT	TP	NT	NT	EM	TP	NT	EM	NT	TP	NT	NT	EM	TP	NT	EM
							◇	1 ◇		◇		1 ◇			◇	1 ◇		◇
						B	A	H	B	A		C		B	A	H	B	A
		(bus)	(bus)	(bus)		(bus)			(bus)					(bus)			(bus)	
Sheffield 7	(train) d	07 40	08 30	09 13			10 26	11 13		11 40	11 43	12 13			12 39	13 13		13 37
Dore	d		08 42				10 33				11 50							
Grindleford	d		09 05								11 59							
Hathersage	d		09 15								12 03							
Bamford	d		09 20								12 06							
Hope (Derbyshire)	d		09 26								12 10							
Edale	d		09 40								12 18							
Chinley	d		10a00		10 11						12 26							
Hazel Grove	86 a																	
Stockport	86 a						11 18	12 00		12 23		12 56	←		13 23	14 01		14 20
New Mills Central	d				10 18						12 33 →		12 33					
Strines	d				10 21								12 36					
Marple	d				10 24								12 39					
Romiley	d				10 28								12 43					
Guide Bridge	d					10 55			11 55					12 55			13 55	
Gorton	d					11 04			12 04					13 04			14 04	
Bredbury	d				10 31								12 46					
Brinnington	d				10 33								12 48					
Reddish North	d				10 36								12 51					
Ryder Brow	d				10 39								12 54					
Belle Vue	d				10 40								12 55					
Ashburys	d				10 45	11 09			12 09				13 02	13 09			14 09	
Manchester Piccadilly 10	(train) a	09 00		10 33	10 54	11 17	11 32	12 12	12 17	12 36		13 10	13 12	13 17	13 36	14 11	14 17	14 33
Manchester Airport	85 (plane) a	09 25		10 58				12 37				13 39				14 36		

For general notes see front of timetable
For details of catering facilities see Directory of Train Operators

A From Nottingham to Liverpool Lime Street (Table 49)
B From Hadfield (Table 79)
C From Cleethorpes (Table 29)
D From Norwich to Liverpool Lime Street (Table 49)
E 14 September
G From Norwich (Table 49)
H From Doncaster (Table 29)

Table 78

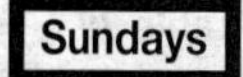

Sheffield, Chinley, Marple and Romiley → Manchester and Manchester Airport

from 9 November

Network Diagram - see first page of Table 78

		NT	TP 1 ◇ A	NT B 🚌	EM ◇ C	TP 1 ◇ A	NT B 🚌	EM ◇ D	NT	TP 1 ◇ A	NT B 🚌	EM ◇ D	TP 1 ◇ A	NT B 🚌	EM ◇ C	NT	TP 1 ◇ A
Sheffield 7	d	13 41	14 12		14 43	15 13		15 34	15 43	16 13		16 36	17 13		17 42	17 53	18 13
Dore	d	13 48							15 50							18 03	
Grindleford	d	13 56							15 58							18 11	
Hathersage	d	14 00							16 01							18 14	
Bamford	d	14 03							16 05							18 18	
Hope (Derbyshire)	d	14 07							16 09							18 22	
Edale	d	14 15							16 17							18 30	
Chinley	d	14 23							16 25							18 38	
Hazel Grove	86 a																
Stockport	86 a		15 01		15 24	16 03		16 20		16 56		17 21	17 55		18 24		19 00
New Mills Central	d	14 30							16 32							18 45 →	
Strines	d	14 33							16 35								
Marple	d	14 36							16 38								
Romiley	d	14 40							16 42								
Guide Bridge	d			14 55			15 55				16 55			17 55			
Gorton	d			15 04			16 04				17 04			18 04			
Bredbury	d	14 43							16 45								
Brinnington	d	14 45							16 47								
Reddish North	d	14 48							16 50								
Ryder Brow	d	14 51							16 53								
Belle Vue	d	14 52							16 54								
Ashburys	d	14 59		15 09			16 09		17 02		17 09			18 09			
Manchester Piccadilly 10	a	15 12	15 13	15 17	15 34	16 13	16 17	16 33	17 10	17 11	17 17	17 36	18 12	18 17	18 35		19 12
Manchester Airport	85 ✈ a		15 37			16 36				17 36			18 36				19 36

		NT B 🚌	NT	EM ◇ D	TP 1 ◇ A	NT B 🚌	EM ◇ E	NT	TP 1 ◇ A	NT	NT B 🚌	EM ◇ E	TP 1 ◇ A	NT B 🚌	NT	NT
Sheffield 7	d			18 35	19 13		19 35	19 42	20 13			20 35	21 19		21 56	
Dore	d							19 49							22 03	
Grindleford	d							19 55							22 12	
Hathersage	d							19 59							22 15	
Bamford	d							20 02							22 19	
Hope (Derbyshire)	d							20 07							22 23	
Edale	d							20 15							22 31	
Chinley	d							20 23							22 39	
Hazel Grove	86 a															
Stockport	86 a		←	19 20	20 00		20 24		20 54	←		21 23	22 00		23 00	
New Mills Central	d		18 45					20 32 →		20 32						23 02
Strines	d		18 48							20 35						23 05
Marple	d		18 51							20 38						23 09
Romiley	d		18 55							20 42						23 12
Guide Bridge	d	18 55				19 55					20 55			21 55		
Gorton	d	19 04				20 04					21 04			22 04		
Bredbury	d		18 58							20 45						23 15
Brinnington	d		19 00							20 47						23 18
Reddish North	d		19 03							20 50						23 21
Ryder Brow	d		19 06							20 53						23 23
Belle Vue	d		19 07							20 54						23 25
Ashburys	d	19 09	19 10			20 09				21 02	21 09			22 09		23 28
Manchester Piccadilly 10	a	19 17	19 21	19 32	20 13	20 17	20 35		21 04	21 11	21 17	21 33	22 14	22 17	23 13	23 36
Manchester Airport	85 ✈ a				20 36				21 36				22 36			

For general notes see front of timetable
For details of catering facilities see Directory of Train Operators

A From Cleethorpes (Table 29)
B From Hadfield (Table 79)
C From Norwich to Liverpool Lime Street (Table 49)
D From Nottingham to Liverpool Lime Street (Table 49)
E From Norwich (Table 49)

Table 79

Mondays to Fridays

until 3 October

Manchester → Glossop and Hadfield

Network Diagram - see first page of Table 78

Miles	Miles			NT	NT	NT	NT	NT	NT	NT	NT	NT	NT	NT		NT	NT	NT
0	—	**Manchester Piccadilly** 10	78 ⛴ d	06 16	06 46	07 03	07 28	07 48	08 07	08 27	08 49	09 15	09 49	10 19	and at	15 19	15 49	16 17
½	—	Ardwick	78 d															
1½	—	Ashburys	78 d	06 20	06 50	07 08	07 32	07 52	08 11	08 31	08 53	09 20	09 53	10 23	the same	15 23	15 53	16 21
2½	—	Gorton	78 d	06 22	06 52	07 11	07 34	07 54	08 13	08 33	08 55	09 22	09 55	10 25		15 25	15 55	16 23
4¾	—	Guide Bridge	78 d	06 26	06 56	07 15	07 38	07 58	08 17	08 37	08 59	09 27	09 59	10 29	minutes	15 29	15 59	16 26
6¾	—	Flowery Field	d	06 29	06 59	07 18	07 41	08 01	08 20	08 40	09 02	09 30	10 02	10 32		15 32	16 02	16 29
7½	—	Newton for Hyde	d	06 31	07 01	07 20	07 43	08 03	08 22	08 42	09 04	09 32	10 04	10 34	past	15 34	16 04	16 31
8½	—	Godley	d	06 33	07 03	07 22	07 45	08 05	08 24	08 44	09 06	09 34	10 06	10 36		15 36	16 06	16 33
9	—	Hattersley	d	06 35	07 05	07 24	07 47	08 07	08 26	08 46	09 08	09 36	10 08	10 38	each	15 38	16 08	16 35
10	—	Broadbottom	d	06 37	07 07	07 26	07 49	08 09	08 28	08 48	09 10	09 38	10 10	10 40		15 40	16 10	16 37
12¼	0	Dinting 3	d	06 45	07 15	07 34	07 55	08 15	08 34	08 54	09 16	09 45	10 16	10 46	hour until	15 46	16 16	16 42
13¼	—	**Glossop**	a	06 48	07b25	07b45	08b05	08b25	08b44	09b06	09 19	09 49	10 19	10 49		15 49	16 19	16 45
—	—		d	06 51							09 22	09 51	10 22	10 52		15 52	16 22	16 48
15	¾	**Hadfield**	a	06 57	07 17	07 36	07 57	08 18	08 38	08 57	09 28	09 57	10 28	10 58		15 58	16 28	16 56

		NT	NT	NT	NT	NT	NT	NT	NT	NT	NT	NT	NT	NT
Manchester Piccadilly 10	78 ⛴ d	16 36	16 58	17 17	17 36	18 00	18 18	18 49	19 19	19 49	20 49	21 49	22 49	23 26
Ardwick	78 d													
Ashburys	78 d	16 40	17 02	17 21	17 40	18 04	18 22	18 53	19 23	19 53	20 53	21 53	22 53	23 30
Gorton	78 d	16 42	17 04	17 23	17 42	18 06	18 25	18 55	19 25	19 55	20 55	21 55	22 55	23 32
Guide Bridge	78 d	16 46	17 08	17 27	17 46	18 10	18 29	18 59	19 29	19 59	20 59	21 59	22 59	23 36
Flowery Field	d	16 49	17 11	17 30	17 49	18 13	18 32	19 02	19 32	20 02	21 02	22 02	23 02	23 39
Newton for Hyde	d	16 51	17 13	17 32	17 51	18 15	18 34	19 04	19 34	20 04	21 04	22 04	23 04	23 41
Godley	d	16 53	17 14	17 34	17 53	18 17	18 36	19 06	19 36	20 06	21 06	22 06	23 06	23 43
Hattersley	d	16 55	17 17	17 36	17 55	18 19	18 38	19 08	19 38	20 08	21 08	22 08	23 08	23 45
Broadbottom	d	16 57	17 19	17 38	17 57	18 21	18 40	19 10	19 40	20 10	21 10	22 10	23 10	23 47
Dinting 3	d	17 04	17 26	17 44	18 04	18 26	18 46	19 16	19 46	20 16	21 16	22 16	23 16	23 53
Glossop	a	17 08	17 29	17 47	18 08	18 29	18 48	19 19	19 49	20 19	21 19	22 19	23 19	00b05
	d	17 10	17 32	17 50	18 10	18 32	18 52	19 22	19 52	20 22	21 22	22 22	23 22	
Hadfield	a	17 17	17 38	17 57	18 17	18 39	19 00	19 29	19 58	20 30	21 28	22 28	23 28	23 56

Mondays to Fridays

from 6 October

		NT	NT	NT	NT	NT	NT	NT	NT	NT	NT	NT	NT	NT	NT	NT	NT	NT	NT	NT
Manchester Piccadilly 10	78 ⛴ d	06 16	06 46	07 03	07 28	07 48	08 07	08 49	09 15	09 49	10 19	10 49	11 19	11 49	12 19	12 49	13 19	13 49	14 19	14 49
Ardwick	78 d																			
Ashburys	78 d	06 20	06 50	07 08	07 32	07 52	08 11	08 53	09 20	09 53	10 23	10 53	11 23	11 53	12 23	12 53	13 23	13 53	14 23	14 53
Gorton	78 d	06 22	06 52	07 11	07 34	07 54	08 13	08 55	09 22	09 55	10 25	10 55	11 25	11 55	12 25	12 55	13 25	13 55	14 25	14 55
Guide Bridge	78 d	06 26	06 56	07 15	07 38	07 58	08 17	08 59	09 27	09 59	10 29	10 59	11 29	11 59	12 29	12 59	13 29	13 59	14 29	14 59
Flowery Field	d	06 29	06 59	07 18	07 41	08 01	08 20	09 02	09 30	10 02	10 32	11 02	11 32	12 02	12 32	13 02	13 32	14 02	14 32	15 02
Newton for Hyde	d	06 31	07 01	07 20	07 43	08 03	08 22	09 04	09 32	10 04	10 34	11 04	11 34	12 04	12 34	13 04	13 34	14 04	14 34	15 04
Godley	d	06 33	07 03	07 22	07 45	08 05	08 24	09 06	09 34	10 06	10 36	11 06	11 36	12 06	12 36	13 06	13 36	14 06	14 36	15 06
Hattersley	d	06 35	07 05	07 24	07 47	08 07	08 26	09 08	09 36	10 08	10 38	11 08	11 38	12 08	12 38	13 08	13 38	14 08	14 38	15 08
Broadbottom	d	06 37	07 07	07 26	07 49	08 09	08 28	09 10	09 38	10 10	10 40	11 10	11 40	12 10	12 40	13 10	13 40	14 10	14 40	15 10
Dinting 3	d	06 46	07c19	07c39	07 59	08 20	08 39	09 16	09 44	10 16	10 46	11 16	11 46	12 16	12 46	13 16	13 46	14 16	14 46	15 16
Glossop	a	06b59	07b38	07b58	08b20	08b38	08b59	09b29	09b59	10b29	10b59	11b29	11b59	12b29	12 49	13 19	13 49	14 19	14 49	15 19
	d														12 54	13 24	13 54	14 24	14 54	15 24
Hadfield	a	06 48	07 21	07 41	08 01	08 23	08 43	09 18	09 46	10 18	10 48	11 18	11 48	12 18	13 00	13 30	14 00	14 30	15 00	15 30

		NT	NT	NT	NT	NT	NT	NT	NT	NT	NT	NT	NT	NT	NT	NT	NT
Manchester Piccadilly 10	78 ⛴ d	15 19	15 49	16 17	16 36	16 58	17 17	17 36	18 00	18 18	18 49	19 19	19 49	20 49	21 49	22 49	23 26
Ardwick	78 d																
Ashburys	78 d	15 23	15 53	16 21	16 40	17 02	17 21	17 40	18 04	18 22	18 53	19 23	19 53	20 53	21 53	22 53	23 30
Gorton	78 d	15 25	15 55	16 23	16 42	17 04	17 23	17 42	18 06	18 25	18 55	19 25	19 55	20 55	21 55	22 55	23 32
Guide Bridge	78 d	15 29	15 59	16 26	16 46	17 08	17 27	17 46	18 10	18 29	18 59	19 29	19 59	20 59	21 59	22 59	23 36
Flowery Field	d	15 32	16 02	16 29	16 49	17 11	17 30	17 49	18 13	18 32	19 02	19 32	20 02	21 02	22 02	23 02	23 39
Newton for Hyde	d	15 34	16 04	16 31	16 51	17 13	17 32	17 51	18 15	18 34	19 04	19 34	20 04	21 04	22 04	23 04	23 41
Godley	d	15 36	16 06	16 33	16 53	17 15	17 34	17 53	18 17	18 36	19 06	19 36	20 06	21 06	22 06	23 06	23 43
Hattersley	d	15 38	16 08	16 35	16 55	17 17	17 36	17 55	18 19	18 38	19 08	19 38	20 08	21 08	22 08	23 08	23 45
Broadbottom	d	15 40	16 10	16 37	16 57	17 19	17 38	17 57	18 21	18 40	19 10	19 40	20 10	21 10	22 10	23 10	23 47
Dinting 3	d	15 46	16 16	16 42	17 04	17 26	17 44	18 04	18 26	18 46	19 16	19 46	20 16	21 16	22 16	23 16	23 53
Glossop	a	15 49	16 19	16 45	17 08	17 29	17 47	18 08	18 29	18 48	19 19	19 49	20 19	21 19	22 19	23 19	00b05
	d	15 54	16 24	16 50	17 12	17 34	17 52	18 12	18 32	18 52	19 22	19 52	20 22	21 22	22 22	23 22	
Hadfield	a	16 00	16 30	16 58	17 19	17 41	17 59	18 19	18 39	19 00	19 29	19 58	20 30	21 28	22 28	23 28	23 56

Saturdays

		NT	NT	NT	NT	NT	NT	NT	NT	NT		NT	NT	NT	NT	NT	NT	NT	NT	NT	NT	NT	NT
Manchester Piccadilly 10	78 ⛴ d	06 16	06 46	07 19	07 49	08 19	08 49	09 16	09 49	10 19	and at	15 49	16 17	16 49	17 17	17 49	18 18	18 49	19 49	20 49	21 49	22 49	23 26
Ashburys	78 d	06 20	06 50	07 23	07 53	08 23	08 53	09 20	09 53	10 23	the same	15 53	16 23	16 53	17 21	17 53	18 22	18 53	19 53	20 53	21 53	22 53	23 30
Gorton	78 d	06 22	06 52	07 25	07 55	08 25	08 55	09 22	09 55	10 25		15 55	16 25	16 55	17 23	17 55	18 25	18 55	19 55	20 55	21 55	22 55	23 32
Guide Bridge	78 d	06 26	06 56	07 29	07 59	08 29	08 59	09 27	09 59	10 29	minutes	15 59	16 29	16 59	17 27	17 59	18 29	18 59	19 59	20 59	21 59	22 59	23 36
Flowery Field	d	06 29	06 59	07 32	08 02	08 32	09 02	09 30	10 02	10 32		16 02	16 32	17 02	17 30	18 02	18 32	19 02	20 02	21 02	22 02	23 02	23 39
Newton for Hyde	d	06 31	07 01	07 34	08 04	08 34	09 04	09 32	10 04	10 34	past	16 04	16 34	17 04	17 32	18 04	18 34	19 04	20 04	21 04	22 04	23 04	23 41
Godley	d	06 33	07 03	07 36	08 06	08 36	09 06	09 34	10 06	10 36		16 06	16 36	17 06	17 34	18 06	18 36	19 06	20 06	21 06	22 06	23 06	23 43
Hattersley	d	06 35	07 05	07 38	08 08	08 38	09 08	09 36	10 08	10 38	each	16 08	16 38	17 08	17 36	18 08	18 38	19 08	20 08	21 08	22 08	23 08	23 45
Broadbottom	d	06 37	07 07	07 40	08 10	08 40	09 10	09 38	10 10	10 40		16 10	16 40	17 10	17 38	18 10	18 40	19 10	20 10	21 10	22 10	23 10	23 47
Dinting 3	d	06 45	07 15	07 46	08 16	08 46	09 16	09 45	10 16	10 46	hour until	16 16	16 46	17 16	17 45	18 16	18 46	19 16	20 16	21 16	22 16	23 16	23 53
Glossop	a	06 48	07 18	07 49	08 19	08 49	09 19	09 49	10 19	10 49		16 19	16 49	17 19	17 48	18 19	18 49	19 19	20 19	21 19	22 19	23 19	00b05
	d	06 51	07 21	07 52	08 22	08 52	09 22	09 51	10 22	10 52		16 22	16 52	17 22	17 51	18 22	18 52	19 22	20 22	21 22	22 22	23 22	
Hadfield	a	06 57	07 27	07 58	08 28	08 58	09 28	09 57	10 28	10 58		16 28	16 58	17 28	17 57	18 28	18 58	19 28	20 30	21 28	22 28	23 28	23 56

For general notes see front of timetable
For details of catering facilities see Directory of Train Operators

b Via Hadfield
c Arr. 3 minutes earlier

Table 79

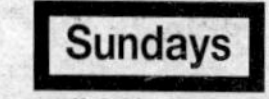

until 2 November

Manchester → Glossop and Hadfield

Network Diagram - see first page of Table 78

Station		NT	NT		NT	NT
Manchester Piccadilly 10	78 ⛴ d	09 23	09 53	and at	19 53	20 53
Ashburys	78 d	09 27	09 57	the same	19 57	20 57
Gorton	78 d	09 29	09 59	minutes	19 59	20 59
Guide Bridge	78 d	09 33	10 03	past	20 03	21 03
Flowery Field	d	09 36	10 06	each	20 06	21 06
Newton for Hyde	d	09 38	10 08	hour until	20 08	21 08
Godley	d	09 40	10 10		20 10	21 10
Hattersley	d	09 42	10 12		20 12	21 12
Broadbottom	d	09 44	10 14		20 14	21 14
Dinting 3	d	09 49	10 19		20 19	21 19
Glossop	a	09 53	10 23		20 23	21 23
	d	09 55	10 25		20 25	21 25
Hadfield	a	10 03	10 33		20 33	21 33

from 9 November

Station		NT 🚌	NT 🚌		NT 🚌	NT 🚌	NT 🚌
Manchester Piccadilly 10	78 d	09 22		and at		20 22	
Ashburys	78 d	09 30		the same		20 30	
Gorton	78 d	09 36		minutes		20 36	
Guide Bridge	78 d	09 46		past		20 46	
Flowery Field	d	09 55		each		20 55	
Newton for Hyde	d	10 00		hour until		21 00	
Godley	d	10 05	10 10		20 10	21 05	21 10
Hattersley	d		10 15		20 15		21 15
Broadbottom	d		10 27		20 27		21 27
Glossop	d	10 30	10 52		20 52	21 30	21 52
Dinting 3	d	10 34	10 56		20 56	21 34	21 56
Hadfield	a	10 38	11 00		21 00	21 38	22 00

For general notes see front of timetable
For details of catering facilities see Directory of Train Operators

Mondays to Fridays

until 3 October

Hadfield and Glossop → Manchester

Network Diagram - see first page of Table 78

Miles	Miles			NT	NT	NT	NT	NT	NT	NT	NT	NT	NT		NT	NT	NT
0	0	**Hadfield**	d	06 00	06 30	07 01	07 20	07 40	08 00	08 20	08 39	09 01	09 31	and at	15 31	16 01	16 31
1¾	—	**Glossop**	a	06 05	06 35	07 06	07 25	07 45	08 05	08 25	08 44	09 06	09 36		15 36	16 06	
—	—		d	06 08	06 38	07 09	07 28	07 48	08 08	08 28	08 48	09 09	09 39	the same	15 39	16 09	16b22
2¾	¾	Dinting 3	d	06 11	06 41	07 12	07 31	07 51	08 11	08 31	08 51	09 12	09 42		15 42	16 12	16 33
5	—	Broadbottom	d	06 15	06 45	07 16	07 35	07 55	08 15	08 35	08 55	09 16	09 46	minutes	15 46	16 16	16 37
6	—	Hattersley	d	06 18	06 48	07 19	07 38	07 58	08 18	08 38	08 58	09 19	09 49		15 49	16 19	16 40
6½	—	Godley	d	06 20	06 50	07 21	07 40	08 00	08 20	08 40	09 00	09 21	09 51	past	15 51	16 21	16 42
7½	—	Newton for Hyde	d	06 22	06 52	07 23	07 42	08 02	08 22	08 42	09 02	09 23	09 53		15 53	16 23	16 44
8¼	—	Flowery Field	d	06 24	06 54	07 25	07 44	08 04	08 24	08 44	09 04	09 25	09 55	each	15 55	16 25	16 46
10¼	—	Guide Bridge	78 a	06 27	06 57	07 28	07 47	08 07	08 27	08 47	09 07	09 28	09 58		15 58	16 28	16 49
12½	—	Gorton	78 a	06 30	07 00	07 31	07 50	08 10	08 30	08 50	09 10	09 31	10 01	hour until	16 01	16 31	16 52
13½	—	Ashburys	78 a	06 33	07 03	07 34	07 54	08 13	08 33	08 53	09 13	09 34	10 04		16 04	16 34	16 56
14½	—	Ardwick	78 a			07 37											
15	—	**Manchester Piccadilly 10**	78 ⛴ a	06 42	07 12	07 42	08 03	08 19	08 42	09 02	09 21	09 42	10 12		16 12	16 42	17 04

		NT	NT	NT	NT	NT	NT	NT	NT	NT	NT	NT	NT	NT A
Hadfield	d	16 59	17 20	17 45	17 59	18 28	18 42	19 01	19 31	20 01	20 31	21 31	22 31	23 59
Glossop	a							19 07	19 36	20 06	20 36	21 36	22 36	00 05
	d	16b48	17b10	17b32	17b50	18b10	18b32	19 09	19 39	20 09	20 39	21 39	22 39	
Dinting 3	d	17 01	17 22	17 47	18 01	18 30	18 44	19 12	19 42	20 12	20 42	21 42	22 42	
Broadbottom	d	17 05	17 26	17 50	18 05	18 34	18 48	19 16	19 46	20 16	20 46	21 46	22 46	
Hattersley	d	17 08	17 29		18 08	18 37	18 51	19 19	19 49	20 19	20 49	21 49	22 49	
Godley	d	17 10	17 31		18 10	18 39	18 53	19 21	19 51	20 21	20 51	21 51	22 51	
Newton for Hyde	d	17 12	17 33	17 55	18 12	18 41	18 55	19 23	19 53	20 23	20 53	21 53	22 53	
Flowery Field	d	17 14	17 35		18 14	18 43	18 57	19 25	19 55	20 25	20 55	21 55	22 55	
Guide Bridge	78 a	17 16	17 41	17 58	18 16	18 46	19 00	19 28	19 58	20 28	20 58	21 58	22 58	
Gorton	78 a	17 19	17 44	18 02	18 20	18 49	19 03	19 31	20 01	20 31	21 01	22 01	23 01	
Ashburys	78 a	17 22	17 47	18 04	18 24	18 53	19 06	19 34	20 04	20 34	21 04	22 04	23 04	
Ardwick	78 a													
Manchester Piccadilly 10	78 ⛴ a	17 31	17 56	18 12	18 32	19 01	19 13	19 43	20 12	20 42	21 12	22 12	23 12	

Mondays to Fridays

from 6 October

		NT	NT	NT	NT	NT	NT	NT	NT	NT	NT	NT	NT	NT	NT	NT	NT	NT	NT	NT
Hadfield	d	05 53	06 25	06 54	07 13	07 33	07 53	08 15	08 33	08 54	09 24	09 54	10 24	10 54	11 24	11 54	12 24	13 05	13 35	14 05
Glossop	a	05 58	06 30	06 59	07 18	07 38	07 58	08 20	08 38	08 59	09 29	09 59	10 29	10 59	11 29	11 59	12 29			
	d	06 03	06 33	07 05	07 23	07 43	08 03	08 25	08 43	09 04	09 34	10 04	10 34	11 04	11 34	12 04	12 34	12b54	13b24	13b54
Dinting 3	d	06 06	06 36	07 08	07 26	07 46	08 06	08 28	08 46	09 07	09 37	10 07	10 37	11 07	11 37	12 07	12 37	13 07	13 37	14 07
Broadbottom	d	06 10	06 40	07 12	07 30	07 50	08 10	08 32	08 50	09 11	09 41	10 11	10 41	11 11	11 41	12 11	12 41	13 11	13 41	14 11
Hattersley	d	06 13	06 43	07 15	07 33	07 53	08 13	08 35	08 53	09 14	09 44	10 14	10 44	11 14	11 44	12 14	12 44	13 14	13 44	14 14
Godley	d	06 15	06 45	07 17	07 35	07 55	08 15	08 37	08 55	09 16	09 46	10 16	10 46	11 16	11 46	12 16	12 46	13 16	13 46	14 16
Newton for Hyde	d	06 17	06 47	07 19	07 37	07 57	08 17	08 39	08 57	09 18	09 48	10 18	10 48	11 18	11 48	12 18	12 48	13 18	13 48	14 18
Flowery Field	d	06 19	06 49	07 21	07 39	07 59	08 19	08 41	08 59	09 20	09 50	10 20	10 50	11 20	11 50	12 20	12 50	13 20	13 50	14 20
Guide Bridge	78 a	06 27	06 57	07 28	07 47	08 07	08 27	08 47	09 07	09 28	09 58	10 28	10 58	11 28	11 58	12 28	12 58	13 28	13 58	14 28
Gorton	78 a	06 30	07 00	07 31	07 50	08 10	08 30	08 50	09 10	09 31	10 01	10 31	11 01	11 31	12 01	12 31	13 01	13 31	14 01	14 31
Ashburys	78 a	06 33	07 03	07 34	07 54	08 13	08 33	08 53	09 13	09 34	10 04	10 34	11 04	11 34	12 04	12 34	13 04	13 34	14 04	14 34
Ardwick	78 a			07 37																
Manchester Piccadilly 10	78 ⛴ a	06 42	07 12	07 42	08 03	08 19	08 42	09 02	09 21	09 42	10 12	10 42	11 12	11 42	12 12	12 42	13 12	13 42	14 12	14 42

		NT	NT	NT	NT	NT	NT	NT	NT	NT	NT	NT	NT	NT	NT	NT	NT	NT A
Hadfield	d	14 35	15 05	15 35	16 05	16 49	17 10	17 31	17 49	18 22	18 42	19 01	19 31	20 01	20 31	21 31	22 31	23 59
Glossop	a											19 07	19 36	20 06	20 36	21 36	22 36	00 05
	d	14b24	14b54	15b24	15b54	16b24	16b50	17b12	17b34	18b12	18b32	19 09	19 39	20 09	20 39	21 39	22 39	
Dinting 3	d	14 37	15 07	15 37	16 07	16c56	17c17	17c38	17c56	18 24	18 44	19 12	19 42	20 12	20 42	21 42	22 42	
Broadbottom	d	14 41	15 11	15 41	16 11	17 00	17 21	17 42	18 00	18 29	18 48	19 16	19 46	20 16	20 46	21 46	22 46	
Hattersley	d	14 44	15 14	15 44	16 14	17 03	17 24	17 44	18 03	18 32	18 51	19 19	19 49	20 19	20 49	21 49	22 49	
Godley	d	14 46	15 16	15 46	16 16	17 05	17 26	17 46	18 05	18 34	18 53	19 21	19 51	20 21	20 51	21 51	22 51	
Newton for Hyde	d	14 48	15 18	15 48	16 18	17 07	17 28	17 48	18 07	18 36	18 55	19 23	19 53	20 23	20 53	21 53	22 53	
Flowery Field	d	14 50	15 20	15 50	16 20	17 09	17 30	17 50	18 09	18 38	18 57	19 25	19 55	20 25	20 55	21 55	22 55	
Guide Bridge	78 a	14 58	15 28	15 58	16 28	17 16	17 41	17 58	18 16	18 48	19 00	19 28	19 58	20 28	20 58	21 58	22 58	
Gorton	78 a	15 01	15 31	16 01	16 31	17 19	17 44	18 02	18 20	18 52	19 03	19 31	20 01	20 31	21 01	22 01	23 01	
Ashburys	78 a	15 04	15 34	16 04	16 34	17 22	17 47	18 04	18 24	18 54	19 06	19 34	20 04	20 34	21 04	22 04	23 04	
Ardwick	78 a																	
Manchester Piccadilly 10	78 ⛴ a	15 12	15 42	16 12	16 42	17 31	17 56	18 12	18 32	19 01	19 13	19 43	20 12	20 42	21 12	22 12	23 12	

For general notes see front of timetable
For details of catering facilities see Directory of Train Operators

A From Manchester Piccadilly dep. 2326
b Via Hadfield
c Arr. 5 minutes earlier

Table 79

Saturdays

Hadfield and Glossop → Manchester

Network Diagram - see first page of Table 78

		NT	NT		NT	NT	NT	NT	NT	NT A
Hadfield	d	06 31	07 01	and at	19 01	19 31	20 31	21 31	22 31	23 59
Glossop	a	06 36	07 06	the same	19 06	19 36	20 36	21 36	22 36	00 05
	d	06 39	07 09		19 09	19 39	20 39	21 39	22 39	
Dinting [3]	d	06 42	07 12	minutes	19 12	19 42	20 42	21 42	22 42	
Broadbottom	d	06 46	07 16		19 16	19 46	20 46	21 46	22 46	
Hattersley	d	06 49	07 19	past	19 19	19 49	20 49	21 49	22 49	
Godley	d	06 51	07 21		19 21	19 51	20 51	21 51	22 51	
Newton for Hyde	d	06 53	07 23	each	19 23	19 53	20 53	21 53	22 53	
Flowery Field	d	06 55	07 25		19 25	19 55	20 55	21 55	22 55	
Guide Bridge	78 a	06 58	07 28	hour until	19 28	19 58	20 58	21 58	22 58	
Gorton	78 a	07 01	07 31		19 31	20 01	21 01	22 01	23 01	
Ashburys	78 a	07 04	07 34		19 34	20 04	21 04	22 04	23 04	
Manchester Piccadilly [10]	78 ⛴ a	07 12	07 42		19 42	20 12	21 12	22 12	23 12	

Sundays
until 2 November

		NT	NT		NT	NT
Hadfield	d	10 05	10 35	and at	20 35	21 35
Glossop	a	10 10	10 40		20 40	21 40
	d	10 13	10 43	the same	20 43	21 43
Dinting [3]	d	10 16	10 46		20 46	21 46
Broadbottom	d	10 20	10 50	minutes	20 50	21 50
Hattersley	d	10 23	10 53		20 53	21 53
Godley	d	10 25	10 55	past	20 55	21 55
Newton for Hyde	d	10 27	10 57		20 57	21 57
Flowery Field	d	10 29	10 59	each	20 59	21 59
Guide Bridge	78 a	10 32	11 02		21 02	22 02
Gorton	78 a	10 35	11 05	hour until	21 05	22 05
Ashburys	78 a	10 38	11 08		21 08	22 08
Manchester Piccadilly [10]	78 ⛴ a	10 47	11 17		21 17	22 17

Sundays
from 9 November

		NT 🚌	NT 🚌		NT 🚌	NT 🚌	NT 🚌
Hadfield	d	09 40	10 05	and at	20 05	20 40	21 05
Dinting [3]	d	09 44	10 09	the same	20 09	20 44	21 09
Glossop	d	09 49	10 13		20 13	20 49	21 13
Broadbottom	d	10 14		minutes		21 14	
Hattersley	d	10 26				21 26	
Godley	d	10a31	10 36	past	20 36	21a31	21 36
Newton for Hyde	d		10 41		20 41		21 41
Flowery Field	d		10 46	each	20 46		21 46
Guide Bridge	78 a		10 55		20 55		21 55
Gorton	78 a		11 04	hour until	21 04		22 04
Ashburys	78 a		11 09		21 09		22 09
Manchester Piccadilly [10]	78 a		11 17		21 17		22 17

For general notes see front of timetable
For details of catering facilities see
Directory of Train Operators

A From Manchester Piccadilly dep. 2326

Network Diagram for Tables 81, 102

DM-21/04
Design BAJS

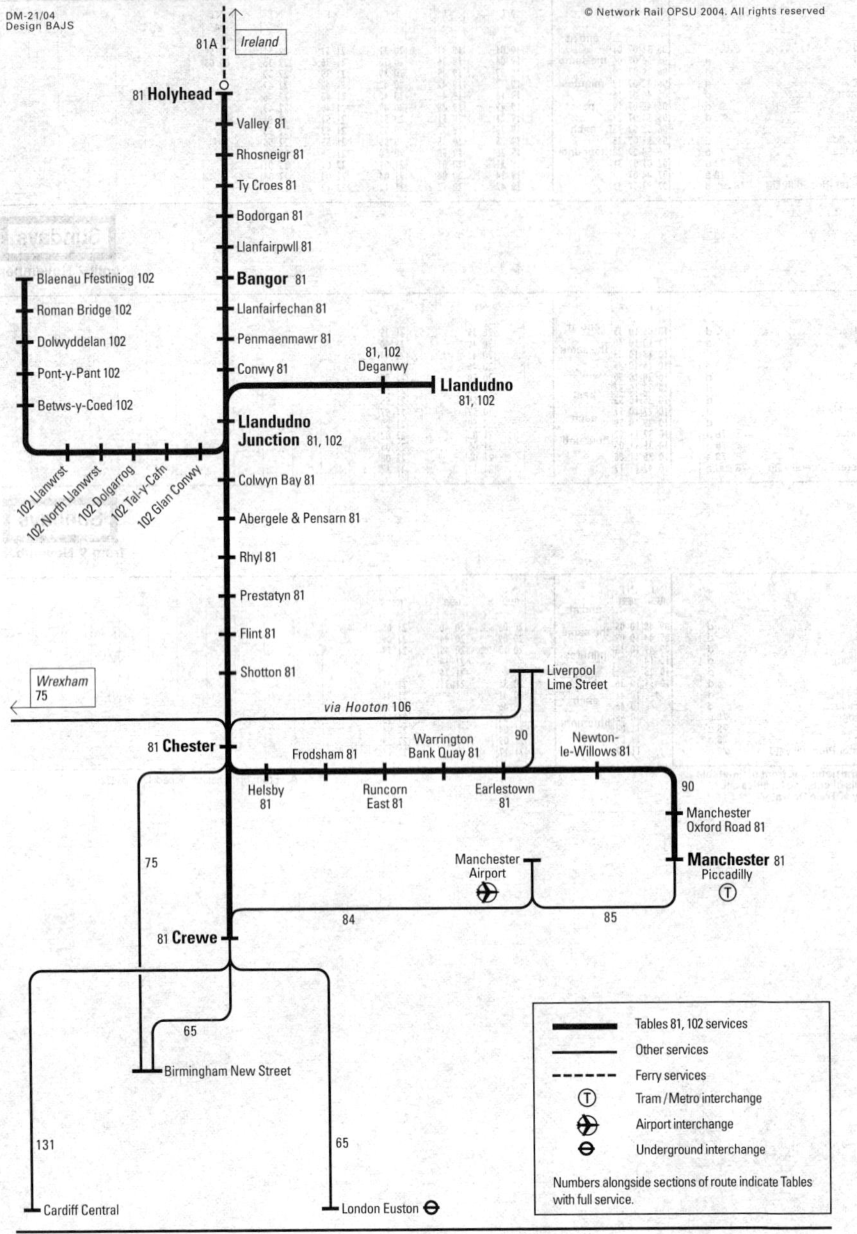

81A
Ireland
81 Holyhead
Valley 81
Rhosneigr 81
Ty Croes 81
Bodorgan 81
Llanfairpwll 81
Bangor 81
Llanfairfechan 81
Penmaenmawr 81
Conwy 81
81, 102
Deganwy
Llandudno
81, 102
Llandudno Junction 81, 102
Blaenau Ffestiniog 102
Roman Bridge 102
Dolwyddelan 102
Pont-y-Pant 102
Betws-y-Coed 102
102 Llanrwst
102 North Llanrwst
102 Dolgarrog
102 Tal-y-Cafn
102 Glan Conwy
Colwyn Bay 81
Abergele & Pensarn 81
Rhyl 81
Prestatyn 81
Flint 81
Shotton 81
Wrexham
75
Liverpool
Lime Street
via Hooton 106
90
81 Chester
Frodsham 81
Warrington
Bank Quay 81
Newton-
le-Willows 81
Helsby
81
Runcorn
East 81
Earlestown
81
90
Manchester
Oxford Road 81
Manchester
Airport
Manchester 81
Piccadilly
75
84
85
81 Crewe
65
Birmingham New Street
131
65
Cardiff Central
London Euston
Tables 81, 102 services
Other services
Ferry services
Tram / Metro interchange
Airport interchange
Underground interchange
Numbers alongside sections of route indicate Tables with full service.

Crewe and Manchester → Chester and North Wales

Network Diagram - see first page of Table 81

Miles	Miles		AW	AW	NT	AW	VT	AW	AW	AW	AW	AW	AW	AW	AW	AW	AW	AW	AW	AW	AW
							1 ◇		◇	◇		◇		◇		◇	◇	◇		◇	
					A											B					
									⊼	⊼		⊼		⊼			⊼	⊼		⊼	
—	—	London Euston 15 ⊖ 65 d																06b46	07 13		07 46
—	—	Birmingham New Street 12 65 d					05 20	05 30			06 07		07 03		07 21			07 51	08 26		09 03
—	—	Manchester Airport 84, 85 ✈ d							05 34			06 44	06 57				07c47	08 00		08c47	09 00
—	—	Cardiff Central 7 131 d									04 00			05 10				05 35			06 50
0	—	**Crewe 10** d					06 18	06 35		07 03	07 33		08 03		08 33			09 03	09 33		10 03
—	0	**Manchester Piccadilly 10** 90 d							06 00			07 16					08 16			09 16	
—	½	**Manchester Oxford Road** 90 d							06 03			07 19					08 19			09 19	
—	16¼	Newton-le-Willows 90 d							06 21			07 37					08 37			09 38	
—	18	Earlestown 8 90 d							06 24			07 40					08 40			09 41	
—	22	Warrington Bank Quay 90 d			06 00				06 33			07 48					08 49			09 50	
—	27	Runcorn East d							06 40			07 55					08 56			09 57	
—	30¼	Frodsham d							06 44			08 00					09 00			10 01	
—	32¾	Helsby d			06a13				06 48			08 04					09 04			10 05	
—	—	Liverpool Lime Street 10 106 d					05 43		06 13	06 43		07 13		07 43			08 13	08 43		09 13	
21	40¼	**Chester** a					06 37	07 00	07 03	07 24	07 59	08 19	08 27	08 28	08 57		09 17	09 26	09 57	10 19	10 27
—	—	d					06 45		07 05	07 32		08 24		08 35			09 24	09 35		10 24	
29	—	Shotton d							07 14			08 35					09 33			10 33	
33½	—	Flint d					06 57		07 20	07 45		08 41		08 51			09 39	09 49		10 39	
47½	—	Prestatyn d					07 10		07 33	07 58		08 54		09 04			09 52	10 02		10 52	
51	—	Rhyl d					07 17		07 39	08 04		09 00		09 10			09 58	10 08		10 58	
55¼	—	Abergele & Pensarn d							07 45			09 06					10 04			11 04	
61½	—	Colwyn Bay d					07 28		07 53	08 15		09 14		09 21			10 12	10 19		11 12	
65½	—	**Llandudno Junction** a					07 33		07 58	08 20		09 19		09 26			10 17	10 24		11 17	
—	0	d	06 25	06 51		07 33	07 34		08 00	08 22		09 21		09 27		09 52	10 19	10 25		11 19	
—	1¼	Deganwy d	06x28	06x54		07x36			08x04			09x25				09x55	10x23			11x23	
—	3	**Llandudno** a	06 35	07 01		07 43			08 16			09 37				10 01	10 37			11 35	
66½	—	Conwy d								08x25								10x28			
70¾	—	Penmaenmawr d								08x31								10x34			
73¼	—	Llanfairfechan d								08x35								10x38			
80¾	—	**Bangor (Gwynedd)** a					07 49			08 43				09 43				10 46			
—	—	d					07 51			08 43				09 43				10 47			
84½	—	Llanfairpwll d								08x49								10x53			
93½	—	Bodorgan d								08x59								11x03			
96¼	—	Ty Croes d								09x04								11x07			
98	—	Rhosneigr d								09x07								11x10			
102	—	Valley d								09x12								11x16			
105½	—	**Holyhead** a					08 21			09 30				10 20				11 30			

	AW	AW	AW	VT	AW	AW	AW	AW	AW	AW	AW	AW	AW	VT	AW	AW	AW	AW	AW	AW	AW
	◇		◇	1 ◇	◇	◇		◇	◇		◇		◇	1 ◇	◇		◇		◇		◇
								B													B
			⊼	⊠	⊼	⊼			⊼		⊼		⊼	⊡	⊼		⊼		⊼		
London Euston 15 ⊖ 65 d		08 17		09 00			09 17			09 46		10 15		11 28				11 46		12 17	
Birmingham New Street 12 65 d		09 21				10 03	10 21			10 51		11 21		12 03		12 21		13 03		13 21	
Manchester Airport 84, 85 ✈ d			09 34	10 00	09c47				10c47	11 00			11c47	12 00			12c47	13 00			
Cardiff Central 7 131 d	07 20			07 50						08 50	09 20			09 50				10 50	11 20		
Crewe 10 d		10 33		10 49		11 03	11 33			12 03		12 33		13 12	13 19	13 33		14 03		14 33	
Manchester Piccadilly 10 90 d			10 03		10 16				11 16				12 16				13 16				
Manchester Oxford Road 90 d			10 06		10 19				11 19				12 19				13 19				
Newton-le-Willows 90 d			10 30		10 38				11 38				12 39				13 38				
Earlestown 8 90 d					10 41				11 41				12 41				13 41				
Warrington Bank Quay 90 d			10 40		10 50				11 50				12 50				13 50				
Runcorn East d					10 57				11 57				12 57				13 57				
Frodsham d					11 01				12 01				13 01				14 01				
Helsby d					11 05				12 05				13 05				14 05				
Liverpool Lime Street 10 106 d	09 43		10 13			10 43			11 13		11 43		12 13	12 43			13 13		13 43		
Chester a	10 28	10 57	11 05	11 16	11 22	11 29	11 59		12 19	12 27	12 28	12 59	13 20	13 32	13 43	13 57	14 20	14 27	14 28	14 57	
d	10 35		11 07	11 18	11 24	11 35			12 24		12 35		13 22	13 34	13 44		14 25		14 35		
Shotton d					11 33				12 33						13 53		14 34				
Flint d	10 49		11 20		11 40	11 50			12 39		12 49			13 47	13 59		14 40		14 50		
Prestatyn d	11 02		11 33		11 54	12 04			12 52		13 02		13 47	14 00	14 13		14 53		15 03		
Rhyl d	11 08		11 39	11 47	12 00	12 10			12 58		13 08		13 53	14 06	14 19		14 59		15 09		
Abergele & Pensarn d					12 06				13 04						14 25		15 05				
Colwyn Bay d	11 19		11 50	12 00	12 14	12 20			13 12		13 19		14 04	14 17	14 33		15 13		15 20		
Llandudno Junction a	11 24		11 55	12 06	12 19	12 25			13 17		13 24		14 09	14 22	14 38		15 18		15 25		
d	11 25		11 56	12 08	12 20	12 27		12 52	13 19		13 25		14 11	14 24	14 39		15 20		15 26		15 52
Deganwy d					12x24			12x55	13x23				14x14				15x24				15x55
Llandudno a					12 35			13 01	13 35				14 27	14 44			15 36				16 01
Conwy d						12x30					13x29								15x29		
Penmaenmawr d						12x36					13x35								15x35		
Llanfairfechan d						12x40					13x40								15x39		
Bangor (Gwynedd) a	11 41		12 12	12 26		12 48					13 48				14 55				15 47		
d	11 41		12 12	12 28		12 48					13 48				14 55				15 48		
Llanfairpwll d						12x54					13x54								15x55		
Bodorgan d						13x04					14x04								16x05		
Ty Croes d						13x09					14x09								16x09		
Rhosneigr d						13x12					14x12								16x12		
Valley d						13x17					14x17								16x18		
Holyhead a	12 20		12 47	13 03		13 30					14 30				15 30				16 30		

For general notes see front of timetable
For details of catering facilities see Directory of Train Operators

A To Ellesmere Port (Table 109)
B From Blaenau Ffestiniog (Table 102)
b 28 July to 22 August dep. 0644
c Change at Manchester Oxford Road

Crewe and Manchester → Chester and North Wales

Network Diagram - see first page of Table 81

Station			AW	AW	NT	AW	AW	AW	AW	AW		AW	AW	AW	AW	VT	AW	AW	AW	AW		AW	AW	AW	VT
			◇	◇	A		◇		◇			◇	◇		◇ B	1 ◇	◇	◇		◇			◇		1 ◇
			🚲	🚲			🚲		🚲			🚲	🚲			(catering)	🚲	🚲							⊠
London Euston 15	⊖ 65	d		12 46		13 17		13 46		14 17			14 46	15 17		15 49						16 17		16 49	17 21
Birmingham New Street 12	65	d		14 03		14 21		14 51		15 21			16 03			16 21			17 03			17 21		17 51	18 03
Manchester Airport	84, 85 ✈	d	13b47	14 00			14b47	15 00				15b47	16 00				16 47		17 00	17 04			17b47	18 00	
Cardiff Central 7	131	d		11 50				12 50	13 20				13 50					15 20						15 50	
Crewe 10		d		15 03		15 33		16 03		16 33			17 03	17 29		17 35			18 03			18 33		19 03	19 22
Manchester Piccadilly 10	90	d	14 16				15 16					16 16					17 20			17 41			18 16		
Manchester Oxford Road	90	d	14 19				15 19					16 19					17 23			17 47			18 19		
Newton-le-Willows	90	d	14 38				15 38					16 37					17 42			18 05			18 37		
Earlestown 8	90	d	14 41		14 51		15 41					16 40					17 45			18 08			18 40		
Warrington Bank Quay	90	d	14 50		15 02		15 50					16 48					17 56			18 18			18 49		
Runcorn East		d	14 57		15 10		15 56					16 55					18 03			18 25			18 56		
Frodsham		d	15 01		15 15		16 01					17 00					18 07			18 30			19 00		
Helsby		d	15 05		15a21		16 07					17 04					18 11			18 36			19 04		
Liverpool Lime Street 10	106	d	14 13	14 43			15 13		15 43			16 35				17 05	17 35			17 50			18 13		18 43
Chester		a	15 19	15 26		15 57	16 19	16 27	16 28	16 57		17 19	17 26	17 53		17 58	18 23	18 25	18 28	18 48		18 57	19 17	19 25	19 49
		d	15 24	15 35			16 24		16 35			17 24	17 35			18 00	18 23	18 35		18 50			19 24		19 51
Shotton		d	15 33				16 33					17 33	17 44				18 32						19 33		
Flint		d	15 39	15 49			16 39		16 49			17 39	17 50			18 13	18 38	18 50		19 03			19 39		
Prestatyn		d	15 52	16 02			16 52		17 03			17 52	18 03			18 26	18 51	19 03		19 16			19 52		20 18
Rhyl		d	15 58	16 08			16 58		17 09			17 58	18 09			18 33	18 57	19 09		19 22			19 58		20 25
Abergele & Pensarn		d	16 04				17 04					18 04					19 03						20 04		
Colwyn Bay		d	16 12	16 19			17 12		17 19			18 12	18 20			18 44	19 11	19 20		19 33			20 12		20 38
Llandudno Junction		a	16 17	16 24			17 17		17 24			18 17	18 25			18 49	19 16	19 25		19 38			20 18		20 44
		d	16 19	16 25			17 19		17 26			18 19	18 26		18 37	18 50	19 18	19 26		19 40			20 19		20 46
Deganwy		d	16x23				17x23					18x23			18x40		19x22						20x23		
Llandudno		a	16 35				17 35					18 35			18 46		19 36						20 35		
Conwy		d		16x28					17x29				18x29					19x30							
Penmaenmawr		d		16x34					17x35				18x35					19x36							
Llanfairfechan		d		16x38					17x39				18x39					19x40							
Bangor (Gwynedd)		a		16 46					17 47				18 47			19 05		19 48		19 56					21 03
		d		16 47					17 48				18 48			19 07		19 48		20 00					21 05
Llanfairpwll		d							17x54									19x54							
Bodorgan		d							18x04									20x04							
Ty Croes		d							18x08									20x09							
Rhosneigr		d							18x11									20x12							
Valley		d							18x17									20x17							
Holyhead		a		17 20					18 30				19 20			19 41		20 29		20 45					21 40

Station			AW	AW	AW	AW	AW	AW	AW		AW	AW	VT	AW	AW	AW	AW	AW	AW	AW	AW	AW	AW		
						◇ B	R						1 ◇			◇					◇ C		◇		
							🚲						(catering)												
London Euston 15	⊖ 65	d			18 08			18c17			18 45		19 38	19 46			20 17	20 46		21 10					
Birmingham New Street 12	65	d			18 51			19 21					20 03	20 21			21 03	21 21					22 33		
Manchester Airport	84, 85 ✈	d		18b47					19b47						20b47				21b47			22 47			
Cardiff Central 7	131	d	16 50				17 20				17 50			18 50		19 34					20 53				
Crewe 10		d	19 38		20 03			20 33			21 03		21 29	21 47			22 17	22 45		23 11	23 51		00 02		
Manchester Piccadilly 10	90	d		19 16					20 16						21 16				22 16			23 20			
Manchester Oxford Road	90	d		19 19					20 19						21 19				22 19			23 23			
Newton-le-Willows	90	d		19 37					20 37						21 37				22 37			23 41			
Earlestown 8	90	d		19 40					20 40						21 40				22 40			23 44			
Warrington Bank Quay	90	d		19 48					20 48						21 49				22 48			23 52			
Runcorn East		d		19 55					20 55						21 56				22 55			23 59			
Frodsham		d		20 00					21 00						22 01				23 01			00 04			
Helsby		d		20 04					21 04						22 05				23 04			00 08			
Liverpool Lime Street 10	106	d					19 43						20 43			21 43							23 43		
Chester		a	20 02	20 22	20 27		20 31	20 57	21 23		21 27		21 49	22 11	22 17	22 32	22 40	23 09	23 23	23 35	00 16	00 21	00 26		
		d					20 35						21 50			22 45							00 40		
Shotton		d					20 44									22 54									
Flint		d					20 50						22 03			23 00							00 53		
Prestatyn		d					21 03						22 16			23 13									
Rhyl		d					21 09						22 23			23 19							01 09		
Abergele & Pensarn		d					21 15									23 25									
Colwyn Bay		d					21 23						22 34			23 33							01 20		
Llandudno Junction		a					21 28						22 39			23 38							01 25		
		d				21 02	21 30					21 33	22 40			23 40							01 26		
Deganwy		d				21x05						21x36													
Llandudno		a				21 12						21 43													
Conwy		d					21x33									23x43									
Penmaenmawr		d					21x39									23x49									
Llanfairfechan		d					21x43									23x53									
Bangor (Gwynedd)		a					21 51						22 55			00 01							01 42		
		d					21 52						22 57			00 02							01 42		
Llanfairpwll		d					21x58									00x08									
Bodorgan		d					22x08									00x18									
Ty Croes		d					22x12									00x22									
Rhosneigr		d					22x15									00x25									
Valley		d					22x21									00x31									
Holyhead		a					22 35						23 30			00 47							02 15		

For general notes see front of timetable
For details of catering facilities see Directory of Train Operators

A From Liverpool Lime Street (Table 90) to Ellesmere Port (Table 109)
B From Blaenau Ffestiniog (Table 102)
C From Carmarthen (Table 128)
b Change at Manchester Oxford Road
c Fridays dep. 1820

until 6 September

Crewe and Manchester → Chester and North Wales

Network Diagram - see first page of Table 81

		AW	AW	NT	AW	VT	AW	AW	AW	AW	AW	AW	AW	AW	NT	AW	AW	AW		AW	AW	AW	AW	AW
				A		1 ◇	◇ 🛒		◇		◇ 🛒		◇ 🛒		B	◇ C	◇ 🛒	◇ 🛒			◇ 🛒		◇ 🛒	
London Euston 15	⊖ 65 d																							
Birmingham New Street 12	65 d					05 20																		
Manchester Airport	84, 85 ✈ d						05 34				06 44	06 57			07 05		07b47	08 00			08b47	09 00		
Cardiff Central 7	131 d									04 00			05 10					05 35				06 50	07 20	
Crewe 10	d					06 18		06 37	07 03	07 33		08 03		08 33				09 03		09 33		10 03		10 33
Manchester Piccadilly 10	90 ⛴ d						06 00				07 16				07 39		08 16				09 16			
Manchester Oxford Road	90 d						06 03				07 19				07 33		08 19				09 19			
Newton-le-Willows	90 d						06 21				07 37						08 37				09 38			
Earlestown 8	90 d						06 24				07 40						08 40				09 41			
Warrington Bank Quay	90 d			06 00			06 33				07 48						08 49				09 50			
Runcorn East	d						06 40				07 55						08 56				09 57			
Frodsham	d						06 44				08 00						09 00				10 01			
Helsby	d			06a13			06 48				08 04						09 04				10 05			
Liverpool Lime Street 10	106 d					05 43	06 13		06 43		07 13		07 43				08 13	08 43			09 13		09 43	
Chester	a					06 37	07 03	07 03	07 24	07 57	08 18	08 27	08 28	08 57	09 06		09 17	09 26		09 57	10 19	10 27	10 28	10 57
	d					06 45	07 05		07 32		08 24		08 35				09 21	09 35			10 24		10 35	
Shotton	d						07 14				08 35						09 33				10 33			
Flint	d					06 57	07 20		07 45		08 41		08 51				09 39	09 49			10 39		10 51	
Prestatyn	d					07 10	07 33		07 58		08 54		09 04				09 52	10 02			10 52		11 04	
Rhyl	d					07 17	07 39		08 04		09 00		09 10				09 58	10 08			10 58		11 10	
Abergele & Pensarn	d						07 45				09 06						10 04				11 04			
Colwyn Bay	d					07 28	07 53		08 15		09 14		09 21				10 12	10 19			11 12		11 21	
Llandudno Junction	a					07 33	07 58		08 20		09 19		09 26				10 17	10 24			11 17		11 26	
	d	06 25	06 51		07 33	07 34	08 00		08 22		09 21		09 27			09 52	10 19	10 25			11 19		11 27	
Deganwy	d	06x28	06x54		07x36		08x04				09x25					09x55	10x23				11x23			
Llandudno	a	06 35	07 01		07 43		08 16				09 37					10 01	10 37				11 35			
Conwy	d								08x25									10x28						
Penmaenmawr	d								08x31									10x34						
Llanfairfechan	d								08x35									10x38						
Bangor (Gwynedd)	a					07 49			08 43				09 43					10 46					11 43	
	d					07 51			08 43				09 43					10 47					11 43	
Llanfairpwll	d								08x49									10x53						
Bodorgan	d								08x59									11x03						
Ty Croes	d								09x04									11x07						
Rhosneigr	d								09x07									11x10						
Valley	d								09x12									11x16						
Holyhead	a					08 21			09 30				10 20					11 30					12 20	

		VT	AW	VT	AW	AW	AW	AW	AW	AW	AW	AW	AW	AW	VT		AW	AW	VT	AW	AW	AW	AW	AW
		1 ◇ D 🍽		1 ◇ E 🍽	◇ 🛒	◇ 🛒		◇ C	◇ 🛒	◇ 🛒			◇ 🛒	◇ 🛒	1 ◇ D 🍽		E	D	1 ◇ E 🍽	◇ 🛒		◇ 🛒		◇ C
London Euston 15	⊖ 65 d			08 45															11 39					
Birmingham New Street 12	65 d																							
Manchester Airport	84, 85 ✈ d	10 00	09 34	10 00					10b47		11 00		11b47	12 00	12 00				13 00	12b47	13 00			
Cardiff Central 7	131 d	07 50		07 50						09 20				09 50	09 50				10 50		10 50	11 20		
Crewe 10	d	10 49		10 49		11 03	11 33				12 03	12 33		13 03	13 27		13 33	13 33	13 43		14 03		14 33	
Manchester Piccadilly 10	90 ⛴ d		10 03		10 16				11 16				12 16							13 16				
Manchester Oxford Road	90 d		10 06		10 18				11 19				12 19							13 19				
Newton-le-Willows	90 d		10 30		10 38				11 38				12 39							13 38				
Earlestown 8	90 d				10 41				11 41				12 41							13 41				
Warrington Bank Quay	90 d		10 40		10 50				11 50				12 50							13 50				
Runcorn East	d				10 57				11 57				12 57							13 57				
Frodsham	d				11 01				12 01				13 01							14 01				
Helsby	d				11 05				12 05				13 05							14 05				
Liverpool Lime Street 10	106 d	10 13		10 13		10 43			11 13	11 43			12 13	12 43					13 13	13 13		13 43		
Chester	a	11 07	11 10	11 15	11 22	11 29	11 59		12 19	12 25	12 27	12 59	13 20	13 27	13 45		13 57	13 59	14 01	14 20	14 27	14 28	14 57	
	d	11 08		11 18	11 24	11 35			12 24	12 35			13 24	13 35	13 47				14 03	14 25		14 35		
Shotton	d				11 33				12 33					13 44						14 34				
Flint	d				11 40	11 50			12 39	12 49				13 50	14 00				14 15	14 40		14 50		
Prestatyn	d				11 54	12 04			12 52	13 02			13 47	14 03	14 13				14 28	14 53		15 03		
Rhyl	d	11 35		11 47	12 00	12 10			12 58	13 08			13 53	14 09	14 20				14 34	14 59		15 09		
Abergele & Pensarn	d				12 06				13 04					14 15						15 05				
Colwyn Bay	d	11 46		12 00	12 14	12 20			13 12	13 19			14 04	14 23	14 31				14 45	15 13		15 20		
Llandudno Junction	a	11 51		12 07	12 19	12 25			13 17	13 24			14 09	14 28	14 36				14 53	15 18		15 25		
	d	11 53		12 07	12 20	12 27		12 52	13 19	13 25			14 11	14 30	14 37					15 20		15 26		15 52
Deganwy	d				12x24			12x55	13x23				14x14							15x24				15x55
Llandudno	a				12 35			13 01	13 35				14 27		14 47					15 36				16 01
Conwy	d					12x30				13x29												15x29		
Penmaenmawr	d					12x36				13x35												15x35		
Llanfairfechan	d					12x40				13x40												15x39		
Bangor (Gwynedd)	a	12 08		12 26		12 48				13 48				14 45								15 47		
	d	12 09		12 27		12 48				13 48				14 46								15 48		
Llanfairpwll	d					12x54				13x54												15x54		
Bodorgan	d					13x04				14x04												16x04		
Ty Croes	d					13x09				14x09												16x08		
Rhosneigr	d					13x12				14x12												16x11		
Valley	d					13x17				14x17												16x17		
Holyhead	a	12 45		13 02		13 30				14 30				15 19								16 30		

For general notes see front of timetable
For details of catering facilities see Directory of Train Operators

A To Ellesmere Port (Table 109)
B From Blackpool North (Table 82)
C From Blaenau Ffestiniog (Table 102)
D Until 12 July
E From 19 July
b Change at Manchester Oxford Road

For connections from London Euston and Birmingham New Street, please see Table 65.

Crewe and Manchester → Chester and North Wales

Network Diagram - see first page of Table 81

		AW ◇ ⊼	AW ◇ ⊼	NT A	AW	AW ◇ ⊼	AW	AW ◇ ⊼	AW	AW ◇ ⊼	AW ◇ ⊼	AW		AW ◇ B	AW ◇ ⊼	AW ◇ ⊼	AW	AW ◇	AW	VT 1 ◇ C ⊡	VT 1 ◇ D ⊡	AW ◇ ⊼	AW	AW
London Euston 15	⊖ 65 d																				16 35			
Birmingham New Street 12	65 d																							
Manchester Airport	84, 85 ✈ d	13b47	14 00			14b47	15 00			15b47	16 00				16 47		17 00	17 04		17 00	17 00	17b47	18 00	
Cardiff Central 7	131 d		11 50				12 50	13 20			13 50					15 20				15 50	15 50			16 50
Crewe 10	d		15 03		15 33		16 03		16 33		17 03	17 30					18 03		18 33	18 43	18 43		19 03	19 38
Manchester Piccadilly 10	90 ⛴ d	14 16				15 16				16 16					17 20			17 41				18 16		
Manchester Oxford Road	90 d	14 19				15 19				16 19					17 26			17 47				18 19		
Newton-le-Willows	90 d	14 38				15 38				16 38					17 45			18 04				18 37		
Earlestown 8	90 d	14 41		14 51		15 41				16 41					17 47			18 07				18 40		
Warrington Bank Quay	90 d	14 50		15 02		15 49				16 50					17 56			18 18				18 49		
Runcorn East	d	14 57		15 10		15 56				16 57					18 03			18 25				18 56		
Frodsham	d	15 01		15 15		16 00				17 01					18 07			18 29				19 00		
Helsby	d	15 05		15a21		16 04				17 05					18 11			18 33				19 04		
Liverpool Lime Street 10	106 d	14 13	14 43			15 13		15 43		16 13	16 43				17 13	17 43				18 13	18 13			
Chester	a	15 19	15 26		15 57	16 17	16 27	16 28	16 56	17 19	17 26	17 54			18 24	18 25	18 29	18 45	18 57	19 04	19 04	19 17	19 25	20 02
	d	15 24	15 35			16 24		16 35		17 24	17 35				18 24	18 35		18 50		19 06	19 06	19 24		
Shotton	d	15 33				16 33				17 33	17 44				18 33							19 33		
Flint	d	15 39	15 49			16 39		16 49		17 39	17 50				18 39	18 51		19 03		19 19	19 19	19 39		
Prestatyn	d	15 52	16 02			16 52		17 03		17 52	18 03				18 52	19 04		19 16		19 32	19 32	19 52		
Rhyl	d	15 58	16 08			16 58		17 09		17 58	18 09				18 58	19 10		19 22		19 38	19 38	19 58		
Abergele & Pensarn	d	16 04				17 04				18 04					19 04							20 04		
Colwyn Bay	d	16 12	16 19			17 12		17 19		18 12	18 20				19 12	19 21		19 33		19 49	19 49	20 12		
Llandudno Junction	a	16 17	16 24			17 17		17 24		18 17	18 25				19 17	19 26		19 38		19 54	19 54	20 18		
	d	16 19	16 25			17 19		17 26		18 19	18 26			18 37	19 19	19 27		19 40		19 56	19 56	20 19		
Deganwy	d	16x23				17x23				18x23				18x40	19x23							20x23		
Llandudno	a	16 35				17 35				18 35				18 46	19 37							20 35		
Conwy	d		16x28					17x29			18x29					19x31								
Penmaenmawr	d		16x34					17x35			18x35					19x37								
Llanfairfechan	d		16x38					17x39			18x39					19x41								
Bangor (Gwynedd)	a		16 46					17 47			18 47					19 49		19 56		20 11	20 11			
	d		16 47					17 48			18 48					19 49		20 00		20 14	20 14			
Llanfairpwll	d							17x54								19x55								
Bodorgan	d							18x04								20x05								
Ty Croes	d							18x08								20x10								
Rhosneigr	d							18x11								20x13								
Valley	d							18x17								20x18								
Holyhead	a		17 20					18 30			19 20					20 30		20 46		20 55	20 55			

		VT 1 ◇ C ⊡	AW	AW ◇ B	AW ◇ ⊼	AW	AW	AW	AW	AW ◇	VT 1 ◇ D ⊡	VT 1 ◇ C ⊡	AW	AW	AW	AW ◇ ⊼	AW	AW	AW	AW ◇ E ⊼	AW	AW ◇		
London Euston 15	⊖ 65 d																							
Birmingham New Street 12	65 d																					22 33		
Manchester Airport	84, 85 ✈ d	18 00	18b47					19b47						20b47				21b47			22 47			
Cardiff Central 7	131 d	16 50			17 20					17 50			18 50			19 34				20 53				
Crewe 10	d	19 49				20 03	20 33			21 03	21 32	21 27	21 45		22 06		22 46		23 11	23 45		00 02		
Manchester Piccadilly 10	90 ⛴ d		19 16					20 16						21 16				22 16			23 20			
Manchester Oxford Road	90 d		19 19					20 20						21 19				22 19			23 23			
Newton-le-Willows	90 d		19 37					20 37						21 37				22 37			23 41			
Earlestown 8	90 d		19 40					20 40						21 40				22 40			23 44			
Warrington Bank Quay	90 d		19 48					20 48						21 49				22 48			23 52			
Runcorn East	d		19 55					20 55						21 56				22 55			23 59			
Frodsham	d		20 00					21 00						22 00				23 00			00 04			
Helsby	d		20 04					21 04						22 04				23 04			00 08			
Liverpool Lime Street 10	106 d	19 13			19 43					20 43	20 43	20 43				21 43								
Chester	a	20 07	20 22		20 26	20 27	20 57	21 23		21 27	21 51	21 53	22 09	22 17	22 30	22 32	23 10	23 23	23 34	00 10	00 21	00 24		
	d	20 08			20 35					21 35	21 53	21 56				22 35								
Shotton	d				20 44					21 44						22 45								
Flint	d				20 50					21 50						22 51								
Prestatyn	d	20 32			21 03					22 03	22 20	22 21				23 05								
Rhyl	d	20 38			21 09					22 09	22 27	22 29				23 11								
Abergele & Pensarn	d				21 15											23 17								
Colwyn Bay	d	20 49			21 23					22 20	22 38	22 42				23 25								
Llandudno Junction	a	20 54			21 28					22 25	22 43	22 48				23 30								
	d	20 56		21 02	21 30				21 33	22 26	22 44	22 49				23 31								
Deganwy	d			21x05					21x36															
Llandudno	a			21 12					21 43															
Conwy	d				21x33											23x34								
Penmaenmawr	d				21x39											23x40								
Llanfairfechan	d				21x43											23x44								
Bangor (Gwynedd)	a	21 11			21 51					22 42	22 59	23 07				23 52								
	d	21 12			21 52					22 42	23 01	23 08				23 53								
Llanfairpwll	d				21x58					22x48						23x59								
Bodorgan	d				22x08					22x58						00x09								
Ty Croes	d				22x12					23x03						00x13								
Rhosneigr	d				22x15					23x06						00x16								
Valley	d				22x21					23x11						00x22								
Holyhead	a	21 46			22 35					23 30	23 39	23 44				00 31								

For general notes see front of timetable
For details of catering facilities see Directory of Train Operators

A From Liverpool Lime Street (Table 90) to Ellesmere Port (Table 109)
B From Blaenau Ffestiniog (Table 102)
C Until 12 July
D From 19 July
E From Carmarthen (Table 128)
b Change at Manchester Oxford Road

For connections from London Euston and Birmingham New Street, please see Table 65.

Saturdays
from 13 September

Crewe and Manchester → Chester and North Wales

Network Diagram - see first page of Table 81

Station		AW	AW	NT	AW		VT	AW	AW	AW		AW
				A			[1] ◇ B	◇ ⊥		◇		
London Euston [15] ⊖ 65	d											
Birmingham New Street [12] 65	d						05 10					
Manchester Airport 84, 85 ✈	d							05 34				
Cardiff Central [7] 131	d											04 00
Crewe [10]	d						06 27		06 37	07 03		07 33
Manchester Piccadilly [10] 90	d							06 00				
Manchester Oxford Road 90	d							06 03				
Newton-le-Willows 90	d							06 21				
Earlestown [8] 90	d							06 24				
Warrington Bank Quay 90	d			06 00				06 33				
Runcorn East	d							06 40				
Frodsham	d							06 44				
Helsby	d			06a13				06 48				
Liverpool Lime Street [10] 106	d						05 43	06 13		06 43		
Chester	a						06 48	07 03	07 03	07 24		07 57
	d						06 51	07 05		07 32		
Shotton	d							07 14				
Flint	d						07 05	07 20		07 45		
Prestatyn	d						07 20	07 33		07 58		
Rhyl	d						07 28	07 39		08 04		
Abergele & Pensarn	d							07 45				
Colwyn Bay	d						07 41	07 53		08 15		
Llandudno Junction	a						07 47	07 58		08 20		
	d	06 25	06 51		07 33		07 48	08 00		08 22		
Deganwy	d	06x28	06x54		07x36			08x04				
Llandudno	a	06 35	07 01		07 43			08 16				
Conwy	d									08x25		
Penmaenmawr	d									08x31		
Llanfairfechan	d									08x35		
Bangor (Gwynedd)	a						08 06			08 43		
	d						08 07			08 43		
Llanfairpwll	d									08x49		
Bodorgan	d									08x59		
Ty Croes	d									09x04		
Rhosneigr	d									09x07		
Valley	d									09x12		
Holyhead	a						08 40			09 30		

Station		AW	AW	AW		AW	AW	AW	AW		AW	AW	AW
		◇ ⊥		◇ ⊥			◇ C	◇ ⊥	◇ ⊥			◇ ⊥	
London Euston [15] ⊖ 65	d												
Birmingham New Street [12] 65	d												
Manchester Airport 84, 85 ✈	d	06 44						07b47				08b47	
Cardiff Central [7] 131	d			05 10					05 35				06 50
Crewe [10]	d		08 03			08 33			09 03		09 33		10 03
Manchester Piccadilly [10] 90	d	07 16						08 16				09 16	
Manchester Oxford Road 90	d	07 19						08 19				09 19	
Newton-le-Willows 90	d	07 37						08 37				09 38	
Earlestown [8] 90	d	07 40						08 40				09 41	
Warrington Bank Quay 90	d	07 48						08 49				09 50	
Runcorn East	d	07 55						08 56				09 57	
Frodsham	d	08 00						09 00				10 01	
Helsby	d	08 04						09 04				10 05	
Liverpool Lime Street [10] 106	d	07 13		07 43				08 13	08 43			09 13	
Chester	a	08 18	08 27	08 28		08 57		09 17	09 26		09 57	10 19	10 27
	d	08 24		08 35				09 21	09 35			10 24	
Shotton	d	08 35						09 33				10 33	
Flint	d	08 41		08 51				09 39	09 49			10 39	
Prestatyn	d	08 54		09 04				09 52	10 02			10 52	
Rhyl	d	09 00		09 10				09 58	10 08			10 58	
Abergele & Pensarn	d	09 06						10 04				11 04	
Colwyn Bay	d	09 14		09 21				10 12	10 19			11 12	
Llandudno Junction	a	09 19		09 26				10 17	10 24			11 17	
	d	09 21		09 27			09 52	10 19	10 25			11 19	
Deganwy	d	09x25					09x55	10x23				11x23	
Llandudno	a	09 37					10 01	10 37				11 35	
Conwy	d								10x28				
Penmaenmawr	d								10x34				
Llanfairfechan	d								10x38				
Bangor (Gwynedd)	a			09 43					10 46				
	d			09 43					10 47				
Llanfairpwll	d								10x53				
Bodorgan	d								11x03				
Ty Croes	d								11x07				
Rhosneigr	d								11x10				
Valley	d								11x16				
Holyhead	a			10 20					11 30				

Station		AW	AW	AW		VT	AW	AW	VT		AW	AW
		◇ ⊥				[1] ◇ ⊐	◇ ⊥	◇ ⊥	[1] ◇ D ⊐			◇ C
London Euston [15] ⊖ 65	d											
Birmingham New Street [12] 65	d											
Manchester Airport 84, 85 ✈	d			09 34								
Cardiff Central [7] 131	d	07 20				07 50						
Crewe [10]	d		10 33			10 54		11 03			11 33	
Manchester Piccadilly [10] 90	d			10 03			10 16					
Manchester Oxford Road 90	d			10 06			10 18					
Newton-le-Willows 90	d			10 30			10 38					
Earlestown [8] 90	d						10 41					
Warrington Bank Quay 90	d			10 40			10 50		10 55			
Runcorn East	d						10 57					
Frodsham	d						11 01					
Helsby	d						11 05					
Liverpool Lime Street [10] 106	d	09 43				10 13		10 43				
Chester	a	10 28	10 57	11 10		11 15	11 22	11 29	11 34		11 59	
	d	10 35				11 18	11 24	11 35				
Shotton	d						11 33					
Flint	d	10 51					11 40	11 50				
Prestatyn	d	11 04					11 54	12 04				
Rhyl	d	11 10				11 47	12 00	12 10				
Abergele & Pensarn	d						12 06					
Colwyn Bay	d	11 21				12 00	12 14	12 20				
Llandudno Junction	a	11 26				12 07	12 19	12 25				
	d	11 27				12 07	12 20	12 27				12 52
Deganwy	d						12x24					12x55
Llandudno	a						12 35					13 01
Conwy	d							12x30				
Penmaenmawr	d							12x36				
Llanfairfechan	d							12x40				
Bangor (Gwynedd)	a	11 43				12 26		12 48				
	d	11 43				12 27		12 48				
Llanfairpwll	d							12x54				
Bodorgan	d							13x04				
Ty Croes	d							13x09				
Rhosneigr	d							13x12				
Valley	d							13x17				
Holyhead	a	12 20				13 02		13 30				

Station		AW	AW		AW	VT	VT	AW		VT	AW	AW	AW
		◇ ⊥	◇ ⊥			[1] ◇ E ⊐	[1] ◇ G ⊐			[1] ◇ H ⊐	◇ ⊥	◇ ⊥	
London Euston [15] ⊖ 65	d									10 17			
Birmingham New Street [12] 65	d					11 03				11 54			
Manchester Airport 84, 85 ✈	d	10b47									11b47		
Cardiff Central [7] 131	d		09 20							09 50			
Crewe [10]	d				12 03	12 13		12 33		12 54		13 03	13 33
Manchester Piccadilly [10] 90	d	11 16									12 16		
Manchester Oxford Road 90	d	11 19									12 19		
Newton-le-Willows 90	d	11 38									12 39		
Earlestown [8] 90	d	11 41									12 41		
Warrington Bank Quay 90	d	11 50					12 20				12 50		
Runcorn East	d	11 57									12 57		
Frodsham	d	12 01									13 01		
Helsby	d	12 05									13 05		
Liverpool Lime Street [10] 106	d	11 13	11 43								12 13	12 43	
Chester	a	12 19	12 25		12 27	12 32	12 44	12 59		13 13	13 20	13 27	13 57
	d	12 24	12 35								13 24	13 35	
Shotton	d	12 33										13 44	
Flint	d	12 39	12 49									13 50	
Prestatyn	d	12 52	13 02								13 47	14 03	
Rhyl	d	12 58	13 08								13 53	14 09	
Abergele & Pensarn	d	13 04										14 15	
Colwyn Bay	d	13 12	13 19								14 04	14 23	
Llandudno Junction	a	13 17	13 24								14 09	14 28	
	d	13 19	13 25								14 11	14 30	
Deganwy	d	13x23									14x14		
Llandudno	a	13 35									14 27		
Conwy	d		13x29										
Penmaenmawr	d		13x35										
Llanfairfechan	d		13x40										
Bangor (Gwynedd)	a		13 48									14 45	
	d		13 48									14 46	
Llanfairpwll	d		13x54										
Bodorgan	d		14x04										
Ty Croes	d		14x09										
Rhosneigr	d		14x12										
Valley	d		14x17										
Holyhead	a		14 30									15 19	

For general notes see front of timetable
For details of catering facilities see Directory of Train Operators

A To Ellesmere Port (Table 109)
B Also stops at Wolverhampton 0529 and Stafford 0546
C From Blaenau Ffestiniog (Table 102)
D From Glasgow Central to Birmingham New Street (Table 65)
E To Edinburgh (Table 65)
G From Glasgow Central to London Euston (Table 65)
H To Glasgow Central (Table 65)
b Change at Manchester Oxford Road

For connections from London Euston and Birmingham New Street, please refer to the re-issued Table 65 contained in the September supplement.

Table 81

Saturdays

from 13 September

Crewe and Manchester → Chester and North Wales

Network Diagram - see first page of Table 81

	AW ◇ ⊼	AW		AW ◇ ⊼	VT 1 ◇ A ⊡	VT 1 ◇ B ⊡	AW		VT 1 ◇ C ⊡	AW ◇ D	AW ◇ ⊼	AW ◇ ⊼		VT 1 ◇ A ⊡	NT E	AW	AW ◇ ⊼		VT 1 ◇ G ⊡	AW	AW ◇ ⊼	AW	AW ◇ ⊼
London Euston 15 ⊖ 65 d									12 17														
Birmingham New Street 12 65 d					13 03				13 54					14 03									
Manchester Airport 84, 85 ✈ d	12b47										13b47						14b47						15b47
Cardiff Central 7 131 d		10 50		11 20					11 50											12 50	13 20		
Crewe 10 d		14 03			14 13		14 33		14 54			15 03		15 13		15 33				16 03		16 33	
Manchester Piccadilly 10 90 ⇌ d	13 16										14 16						15 16						16 16
Manchester Oxford Road 90 d	13 19										14 19						15 19						16 19
Newton-le-Willows 90 d	13 38										14 38						15 38						16 38
Earlestown 8 90 d	13 41										14 41				14 51		15 41						16 41
Warrington Bank Quay 90 d	13 50					14 20					14 50				15 02		15 49		15 59				16 50
Runcorn East d	13 57										14 57				15 10		15 56						16 57
Frodsham d	14 01										15 01				15 15		16 00						17 01
Helsby d	14 05										15 05				15a21		16 04						17 05
Liverpool Lime Street 10 106 d	13 13			13 43							14 13	14 43					15 13				15 43		16 13
Chester a	14 20	14 27		14 28	14 35	14 41	14 57		15 13		15 19	15 26		15 33		15 57	16 17		16 27	16 27	16 28	16 56	17 19
d	14 25			14 35							15 24	15 35					16 24				16 35		17 24
Shotton d	14 34										15 33						16 33						17 33
Flint d	14 40			14 50							15 39	15 49					16 39				16 49		17 39
Prestatyn d	14 53			15 03							15 52	16 02					16 52				17 03		17 52
Rhyl d	14 59			15 09							15 58	16 08					16 58				17 09		17 58
Abergele & Pensarn d	15 05										16 04						17 04						18 04
Colwyn Bay d	15 13			15 20							16 12	16 19					17 12				17 19		18 12
Llandudno Junction a	15 18			15 25							16 17	16 24					17 17				17 24		18 17
d	15 20			15 26						15 52	16 19	16 25					17 19				17 26		18 19
Deganwy d	15x24									15x55	16x23						17x23						18x23
Llandudno a	15 36									16 01	16 35						17 35						18 35
Conwy d				15x29								16x28									17x29		
Penmaenmawr d				15x35								16x34									17x35		
Llanfairfechan d				15x39								16x38									17x39		
Bangor (Gwynedd) a				15 47								16 46									17 47		
d				15 48								16 47									17 48		
Llanfairpwll d				15x54																	17x54		
Bodorgan d				16x04																	18x04		
Ty Croes d				16x08																	18x08		
Rhosneigr d				16x11																	18x11		
Valley d				16x17																	18x17		
Holyhead a				16 30								17 20									18 30		

	AW ◇ ⊼		AW	AW ◇ D	AW ◇ ⊼	AW ◇ ⊼		AW	AW ◇	AW	VT 1 ◇ ⊡		AW ◇ ⊼	AW	AW	AW ◇ D		VT 1 ◇ ⊡	VT 1 ◇ H ⊡	AW	VT 1 ◇ G ⊡		AW ◇ ⊼
London Euston 15 ⊖ 65 d																			17 17				
Birmingham New Street 12 65 d																							
Manchester Airport 84, 85 ✈ d					16 47				17 04				17b47							18b47			
Cardiff Central 7 131 d	13 50					15 20					15 50								16 50				17 20
Crewe 10 d	17 03		17 30					18 03		18 33	18 43			19 03	19 30			19 37	19 53				
Manchester Piccadilly 10 90 ⇌ d					17 20				17 41				18 16							19 16			
Manchester Oxford Road 90 d					17 26				17 47				18 19							19 19			
Newton-le-Willows 90 d					17 45				18 04				18 37							19 37			
Earlestown 8 90 d					17 47				18 07				18 40							19 40			
Warrington Bank Quay 90 d					17 56				18 18				18 49							19 48	20 00		
Runcorn East d					18 03				18 25				18 56							19 55			
Frodsham d					18 07				18 29				19 00							20 00			
Helsby d					18 11				18 33				19 04							20 04			
Liverpool Lime Street 10 106 d	16 43				17 13	17 43					18 13							19 13					19 43
Chester a	17 26		17 54		18 24	18 25		18 29	18 45	18 57	19 04		19 17	19 25	19 54			20 04	20 12	20 22	20 24		20 26
d	17 35				18 24	18 35			18 50		19 06		19 24					20 17					20 35
Shotton d	17 44				18 33								19 33										20 44
Flint d	17 50				18 39	18 51			19 03		19 19		19 39										20 50
Prestatyn d	18 03				18 52	19 04			19 16		19 32		19 52					20 43					21 03
Rhyl d	18 09				18 58	19 10			19 22		19 38		19 58					20 50					21 09
Abergele & Pensarn d					19 04								20 04										21 15
Colwyn Bay d	18 20				19 12	19 21			19 33		19 49		20 12					21 03					21 23
Llandudno Junction a	18 25				19 17	19 26			19 38		19 54		20 18					21 09					21 28
d	18 26			18 37	19 19	19 27			19 40		19 56		20 19			21 02		21 11					21 30
Deganwy d				18x40	19x23								20x23			21x05							
Llandudno a				18 46	19 37								20 35			21 12							
Conwy d	18x29					19x31																	21x33
Penmaenmawr d	18x35					19x37																	21x39
Llanfairfechan d	18x39					19x41																	21x43
Bangor (Gwynedd) a	18 47					19 49			19 56		20 11							21 28					21 51
d	18 48					19 49			20 00		20 14							21 30					21 52
Llanfairpwll d						19x55																	21x58
Bodorgan d						20x05																	22x08
Ty Croes d						20x10																	22x12
Rhosneigr d						20x13																	22x15
Valley d						20x18																	22x21
Holyhead a	19 20					20 30			20 46		20 55							22 05					22 35

For general notes see front of timetable
For details of catering facilities see Directory of Train Operators

- **A** To Edinburgh (Table 65)
- **B** From Glasgow Central to London Euston (Table 65)
- **C** To Glasgow Central (Table 65)
- **D** From Blaenau Ffestiniog (Table 102)
- **E** From Liverpool Lime Street (Table 90) to Ellesmere Port (Table 109)
- **G** From Edinburgh to Birmingham New Street (Table 65)
- **H** To Liverpool Lime Street (Table 65)
- **b** Change at Manchester Oxford Road

For connections from London Euston and Birmingham New Street, please refer to the re-issued Table 65 contained in the September supplement.

Table 81

Saturdays

from 13 September

Crewe and Manchester → Chester and North Wales

Network Diagram - see first page of Table 81

		AW	AW	AW	AW		AW ◇	VT 1 ◇	AW	AW		AW	AW ◇	AW	AW		AW	AW	AW ◇ A	AW		AW ◇	
London Euston 15	⊖ 65 d																						
Birmingham New Street 12	65 d																					22 33	
Manchester Airport	84, 85 ✈ d			19b47																			
Cardiff Central 7	131 d						17 50		18 50				19 34						20 53				
Crewe 10	d	20 03	20 33				21 03	21 32	21 45			22 06		22 46			23 11		23 45			00 02	
Manchester Piccadilly 10	90 ⛴ d			20 16						21 17					22 16					23 10			
Manchester Oxford Road	90 d			20 20																			
Newton-le-Willows	90 d			20 37																			
Earlestown 8	90 d			20 40																			
Warrington Bank Quay	90 d			20 48																			
Runcorn East	d			20 55																			
Frodsham	d			21 00																			
Helsby	d			21 04																			
Liverpool Lime Street 10	106 d						20 43	20 43					21 43										
Chester	a	20 27	20 57	21 23			21 27	21 51	22 09	22 22		22 30	22 32	23 10	23 25		23 34		00 10	00 13		00 24	
	d						21 35	21 53					22 35										
Shotton	d						21 44						22 45										
Flint	d						21 50						22 51										
Prestatyn	d						22 03	22 20					23 05										
Rhyl	d						22 09	22 27					23 11										
Abergele & Pensarn	d												23 17										
Colwyn Bay	d						22 20	22 38					23 25										
Llandudno Junction	a						22 25	22 43					23 33										
	d				21 33		22 26	22 44										23 43					
Deganwy	d				21x36																		
Llandudno	a				21 43																		
Conwy	d																	23 48					
Penmaenmawr	d																	23 58					
Llanfairfechan	d																	00 04					
Bangor (Gwynedd)	a						22 42	22 59										00 25					
	d						22 42	23 01										00 25					
Llanfairpwll	d						22x48											00 40					
Bodorgan	d						22x58											01 00					
Ty Croes	d						23x03											01 10					
Rhosneigr	d						23x06											01 20					
Valley	d						23x11											01 35					
Holyhead	a						23 30	23 39										01 45					

Sundays

until 7 September

		AW	AW		AW ◇	AW		AW	AW		AW ◇	AW		AW	AW ◇		AW	AW ◇ B		AW ◇	AW		AW	AW
London Euston 15	⊖ 65 d																							
Birmingham New Street 12	65 d																							
Manchester Airport	84, 85 ✈ d					07b36					09b36				09 33									
Cardiff Central 7	131 d																							
Crewe 10	d				09 00				10 15						11 25		12 06				13 07			
Manchester Piccadilly 10	90 ⛴ d					07 52					09 58									11 25				
Manchester Oxford Road	90 d					08 02					10 01									11 33				
Newton-le-Willows	90 d					08 27					10 19									11 51				
Earlestown 8	90 d					08 35					10 22									11 54				
Warrington Bank Quay	90 d					08 50					10 30									12 02				
Runcorn East	d					09 05					10 37									12 09				
Frodsham	d					09 23					10 42									12 14				
Helsby	d					09 31					10 46									12 18				
Liverpool Lime Street 10	106 d				08 13			08 43	09 43		10 13				10 43					11 43				
Chester	a				09 18	09 46			10 33		10 58				11 43		12 30			12 30	13 27			
	d	06 20			09 20			09 56	10 35		11 08				11 49					12 35				
Shotton	d				09 29			10 05	10 44											12 44				
Flint	d	06 33			09 35			10 11	10 50		11 21				12 02					12 50				
Prestatyn	d	06 46			09 48			10 25	11 03		11 34									13 03				
Rhyl	d	06 52			09 54			10 31	11 09		11 40				12 18					13 09				
Abergele & Pensarn	d							10 37	11 15											13 15				
Colwyn Bay	d	07 03			10 05			10 45	11 23		11 51				12 29					13 23				
Llandudno Junction	a	07 08			10 10			10 50	11 28		11 56				12 34					13 28				
	d	07 09	10 10		10 11			10 51	11 30		11 57	12 15		12 31	12 35			12 42		13 30			13 33	14 06
Deganwy	d		10x13											12x34				12x45					13x36	14x09
Llandudno	a		10 19					11 02	11 41			12 23		12 40				12 51					13 42	14 15
Conwy	d				10x14															13x33				
Penmaenmawr	d				10x20															13x39				
Llanfairfechan	d				10x24															13x43				
Bangor (Gwynedd)	a	07 25			10 36						12 13				12 51					13 59				
	d	07 30									12 13				12 51									
Llanfairpwll	d																							
Bodorgan	d																							
Ty Croes	d																							
Rhosneigr	d																							
Valley	d																							
Holyhead	a	08 00									12 44				13 25									

For general notes see front of timetable
For details of catering facilities see Directory of Train Operators

A From Carmarthen (Table 128)
B From Blaenau Ffestiniog (Table 102)
b Change at Manchester Oxford Road

For connections from London Euston and Birmingham New Street, please see Table 65.

For connections from London Euston and Birmingham New Street, please refer to the re-issued Table 65 contained in the September supplement.

Table 81

Sundays

until 7 September

Crewe and Manchester → Chester and North Wales

Network Diagram - see first page of Table 81

		AW	AW	AW	AW	AW	AW	AW	AW	AW	AW	AW	AW	AW	AW	AW	AW
			◇				◇				◇			◇		◇	◇
							A									B	
			⊤	⊤			⊤			⊤	⊤			⊤			⊤
London Euston 15	⊖ 65 d																
Birmingham New Street 12	65 d																
Manchester Airport	84, 85 ✈ d																
Cardiff Central 7	131 d								*11 35*		*12 39*						
Crewe 10	d		13 55						14 55		16 00			17 02			17 35
Manchester Piccadilly 10	90 ⛴ d			13 15						14 57					16 29		
Manchester Oxford Road	90 d			13 18						15 00					16 32		
Newton-le-Willows	90 d			13 36						15 18					16 50		
Earlestown 8	90 d			13 39						15 21					16 53		
Warrington Bank Quay	90 d			13 48						15 29					17 01		
Runcorn East	d			13 55						15 36					17 08		
Frodsham	d			13 59						15 41					17 13		
Helsby	d			14 03						15 45					17 17		
Liverpool Lime Street 10	106 d		*13 13*				*13 43*		*14 13*		*15 13*			*16 13*			*16 43*
Chester	a		14 13	14 16					15 13	16 01	16 18			17 20	17 31		17 53
	d		14 15				14 44		15 15		16 20			17 25			17 55
Shotton	d		14 24				14 53		15 24					17 34			18 03
Flint	d		14 30				14 59		15 30		16 33			17 40			18 09
Prestatyn	d		14 43				15 13		15 43		16 46			17 53			18 22
Rhyl	d		14 49				15 19		15 49		16 52			17 59			18 29
Abergele & Pensarn	d		14 55				15 26		15 55								18 35
Colwyn Bay	d		15 03				15 34		16 03		17 03			18 10			18 43
Llandudno Junction	a		15 08				15 40		16 08		17 08			18 15			18 48
	d	14 37	15 10		15 13	15 38	15 41	16 06	16 11		17 09	17 17	17 49	18 16		18 30	18 49
Deganwy	d				15x16	15x41			16x14			17x20	17x52			18x34	
Llandudno	a	14 45			15 22	15 47		16 14	16 22			17 26	17 58			18 40	
Conwy	d						15x44										
Penmaenmawr	d						15x50										
Llanfairfechan	d						15x54										
Bangor (Gwynedd)	a		15 29				16 03				17 25			18 36			19 05
	d						16 03				17 25						19 05
Llanfairpwll	d																19x12
Bodorgan	d																19x22
Ty Croes	d																19x26
Rhosneigr	d																19x29
Valley	d																19x34
Holyhead	a						16 38				17 55						19 45

		AW	AW	AW	VT	VT	AW	AW	AW	AW	VT	AW	AW	AW	AW	AW	AW	AW
												R						
			◇		1 ◇	1 ◇					1 ◇			◇			◇	◇
					C	D						E					D	C
			⊤		⊏⊐	⊏⊐					⊏⊐	⊤						
London Euston 15	⊖ 65 d				16 25						19b01							
Birmingham New Street 12	65 d																22 54	22 54
Manchester Airport	84, 85 ✈ d																	
Cardiff Central 7	131 d	*14 35*		*15 35*				*16 35*						*18 35*				
Crewe 10	d	18 05		18 48	18 52	18 59		20 15	20 40		21 24			22 20	22 55		00 23	00 35
Manchester Piccadilly 10	90 ⛴ d		17 32				18 32			20 14			21 14			23 17		
Manchester Oxford Road	90 d		17 35				18 35			20 18			21 18			23 20		
Newton-le-Willows	90 d		17 53				18 53			20 36			21 36			23 38		
Earlestown 8	90 d		17 55				18 56			20 39			21 39			23 41		
Warrington Bank Quay	90 d		18 05				19 04			20 48			21 47			23 49		
Runcorn East	d		18 12				19 11			20 55			21 54			23 56		
Frodsham	d		18 16				19 16			20 59			21 59			00 01		
Helsby	d		18 20				19 20			21 03			22 03			00 05		
Liverpool Lime Street 10	106 d		*17 43*		*18 13*	*18 13*		*19 43*			*20 43*			*21 43*				
Chester	a	18 25	18 32	19 08	19 18	19 20	19 34	20 33	21 00	21 17	21 43		22 17	22 38	23 19	00 18	00 41	00 53
	d		18 41		19 23	19 23		20 35			21 45	21 50		22 54			00 43	00 55
Shotton	d		18 50					20 44				21 59		23 03				
Flint	d		18 56					20 50				22 05		23 09			00 56	01 08
Prestatyn	d		19 09		19 49	19 49		21 03				22 22		23 22				
Rhyl	d		19 15		19 56	19 56		21 09			22 12	22 28		23 28			01 12	01 24
Abergele & Pensarn	d		19 21					21 15				22 35						
Colwyn Bay	d		19 29		20 09	20 09		21 23			22 23	22 43		23 39			01 23	01 35
Llandudno Junction	a		19 34		20 15	20 15		21 28			22 28	22 49		23 44			01 28	01 40
	d		19 36		20 17	20 17		21 30			22 29	22 50		23 45			01 29	01 41
Deganwy	d																	
Llandudno	a																	
Conwy	d		19x39					21x33				22x53						
Penmaenmawr	d		19x45					21x39				22x59						
Llanfairfechan	d		19x49					21x43				23x03						
Bangor (Gwynedd)	a		20 05		20 34	20 34		21 51			22 44	23 12		00 01			01 45	01 57
	d				20 36	20 36		21 51			22 46	23 12		00 01			01 45	01 57
Llanfairpwll	d											23x18						
Bodorgan	d											23x28						
Ty Croes	d											23x33						
Rhosneigr	d											23x36						
Valley	d											23x41						
Holyhead	a				21 06	21 06		22 21			23 14	23 57		00 31			02 16	02 28

For general notes see front of timetable
For details of catering facilities see Directory of Train Operators

- **A** From Shrewsbury
- **B** From Blaenau Ffestiniog (Table 102)
- **C** Until 13 July
- **D** From 20 July
- **E** From Shrewsbury (Table 75)
- **b** Until 13 July only

For connections from London Euston and Birmingham New Street, please see Table 65.

Table 81

from 14 September

Crewe and Manchester → Chester and North Wales

Network Diagram - see first page of Table 81

	AW	AW	AW ◇	AW	AW	AW	AW ◇	AW	AW A	AW ◇	AW	AW	AW	AW	AW ◇	AW
London Euston 15 ⊖ 65 d																
Birmingham New Street 12 65 d																
Manchester Airport 84, 85 d																
Cardiff Central 7 131 d																
Crewe 10 d	08 55	09 25	10 00	10 25	10 55		11 15	11 55			12 25	12 55	13 25		13 55	14 25
Manchester Piccadilly 10 90 d										11 29				13 04		
Manchester Oxford Road 90 d																
Newton-le-Willows 90 d																
Earlestown 8 90 d																
Warrington Bank Quay 90 d																
Runcorn East d																
Frodsham d																
Helsby d																
Liverpool Lime Street 10 106 d			*09 43*				*10 43*			*11 43*					*13 13*	
Chester a	09 20	09 50	10 21	10 50	11 20		11 36	12 20		12 32	12 50	13 20	13 50	14 09	14 15	14 50
d			10 32				11 38			12 40					14 19	
Shotton d			10 41				11 47			12 49					14 28	
Flint d			10 47				11 53			12 55					14 34	
Prestatyn d			11 00				12 06			13 09					14 47	
Rhyl d			11 06				12 12			13 15					14 53	
Abergele & Pensarn d			11 12				12 18			13 21						
Colwyn Bay d			11 20				12 26			13 29					15 04	
Llandudno Junction a			11 25				12 31			13 34					15 09	
d			11 27			11 45	12 33		13 00	13 35					15 10	
Deganwy d									13 05							
Llandudno a									13 20							
Conwy d						11x48				13x38						
Penmaenmawr d						11x55				13x44						
Llanfairfechan d						11x59				13x48						
Bangor (Gwynedd) a			11 46			12 13	12 48			14 04					15 33	
d							12 49									
Llanfairpwll d																
Bodorgan d																
Ty Croes d																
Rhosneigr d																
Valley d																
Holyhead a							13 24									

	AW ◇	VT 1 ◇ B	AW	AW	VT 1 ◇ C	AW A	AW ◇	VT 1 ◇ B	AW	AW ◇	AW	AW ◇	VT 1 ◇ C	VT 1 ◇ D	AW	AW A
London Euston 15 ⊖ 65 d					12 35								14 35			
Birmingham New Street 12 65 d																
Manchester Airport 84, 85 d																
Cardiff Central 7 131 d	*11 35*				*12 35*								*14 35*			
Crewe 10 d			14 55		15 47		16 00		16 30	17 05		17 40	17 50		17 58	
Manchester Piccadilly 10 90 d				14 57							16 29					
Manchester Oxford Road 90 d				15 00							16 32					
Newton-le-Willows 90 d				15 18							16 50					
Earlestown 8 90 d				15 21							16 53					
Warrington Bank Quay 90 d		14 45		15 29				16 28			17 01			17 54		
Runcorn East d				15 36							17 08					
Frodsham d				15 41							17 13					
Helsby d				15 45							17 17					
Liverpool Lime Street 10 106 d	*14 13*						*15 13*			*16 43*		*17 13*				
Chester a	14 58	15 09	15 20	16 01	16 06		16 22	16 49	16 54	17 29	17 31	18 01	18 09	18 15	18 23	
d	15 02						16 24			17 36		18 03				
Shotton d	15 11									17 45						
Flint d	15 17						16 37			17 51		18 16				
Prestatyn d	15 31						16 50			18 04		18 29				
Rhyl d	15 37						16 56			18 10		18 35				
Abergele & Pensarn d	15 43									18 16		18 41				
Colwyn Bay d	15 51						17 07			18 24		18 49				
Llandudno Junction a	15 56						17 12			18 29		18 54				
d	15 57					16 10	17 14			18 31		18 59				19 00
Deganwy d						16 15										19 05
Llandudno a						16 30										19 20
Conwy d	16x00															
Penmaenmawr d	16x06															
Llanfairfechan d	16x10															
Bangor (Gwynedd) a	16 18						17 29			18 51		19 14				
d	16 20						17 30					19 15				
Llanfairpwll d												19x21				
Bodorgan d												19x31				
Ty Croes d												19x35				
Rhosneigr d												19x38				
Valley d												19x44				
Holyhead a	16 55						18 05					20 00				

For general notes see front of timetable
For details of catering facilities see Directory of Train Operators

A From Blaenau Ffestiniog (Table 102)
B From Glasgow Central to London Euston (Table 65)
C To Glasgow Central (Table 65)
D From Edinburgh to Birmingham New Street (Table 65)

For connections from London Euston and Birmingham New Street, please refer to the re-issued Table 65 contained in the September supplement.

Table 81

Sundays

from 14 September

Crewe and Manchester → Chester and North Wales

Network Diagram - see first page of Table 81

		AW	AW		AW	AW		VT	AW		VT	AW		AW	AW	AW	AW	AW	VT	AW	AW	AW		
		◇						1 ◇			1 ◇	◇				R			1 ◇	◇				
											A					B								
		trolley						buffet			buffet					trolley			buffet					
London Euston 15 ⊖ 65	d							16 14			17 14													
Birmingham New Street 12 65	d																		20 48					
Manchester Airport 84, 85 ✈	d																							
Cardiff Central 7 131	d		15 35					15 35	16 35							18 35								
Crewe 10	d		18 25		18 55			19 30	19 55		20 23	20 35			20 55			21 55	22 00	22 20	22 55			
Manchester Piccadilly 10 90 ⛴	d	17 32				18 32								20 14			21 14					23 21		
Manchester Oxford Road 90	d	17 35				18 35								20 18			21 18					23 24		
Newton-le-Willows 90	d	17 53				18 53								20 36			21 36					23 42		
Earlestown 8 90	d	17 56				18 56								20 39			21 39					23 44		
Warrington Bank Quay 90	d	18 05				19 04								20 48			21 47					23 53		
Runcorn East	d	18 12				19 11								20 55			21 54					23 59		
Frodsham	d	18 16				19 16								20 59			21 59					00 04		
Helsby	d	18 20				19 20								21 03			22 03					00 08		
Liverpool Lime Street 10 106	d	17 43						18 43				19 43				20 43			21 13	21 43				
Chester	a	18 32	18 50		19 20	19 34		19 56	20 20		20 42	20 56		21 17	21 20	21 36	22 17	22 20	22 24	22 41	23 20	00 21		
	d	18 36						19 59				20 58				21 50			22 26	22 43				
Shotton	d	18 45										21 07				21 59				22 52				
Flint	d	18 51										21 13				22 05				22 58				
Prestatyn	d	19 04						20 24				21 26				22 19				23 11				
Rhyl	d	19 10						20 32				21 32				22 25			22 53	23 17				
Abergele & Pensarn	d	19 16										21 38				22 32								
Colwyn Bay	d	19 24						20 45				21 46				22 40			23 04	23 28				
Llandudno Junction	a	19 29						20 51				21 51				22 46			23 09	23 33				
	d	19 31						20 52				21 53				22 47			23 12	23 34				
Deganwy	d																							
Llandudno	a																							
Conwy	d	19x34										21x56				22x50								
Penmaenmawr	d	19x40										22x02				22x56								
Llanfairfechan	d	19x44										22x06				23x00								
Bangor (Gwynedd)	a	19 52						21 10				22 14				23 09			23 27	23 50				
	d	19 52						21 11				22 14				23 09			23 28	23 50				
Llanfairpwll	d															23x15								
Bodorgan	d															23x25								
Ty Croes	d															23x30								
Rhosneigr	d															23x33								
Valley	d															23x38								
Holyhead	a	20 30						21 42				22 50				23 54			00 01	00 26				

For general notes see front of timetable
For details of catering facilities see Directory of Train Operators

A To Liverpool Lime Street (Table 65)
B From Milford Haven (Table 128)

For connections from London Euston and Birmingham New Street, please refer to the re-issued Table 65 contained in the September supplement.

North Wales and Chester → Manchester and Crewe

Network Diagram - see first page of Table 81

Miles	Miles			VT	AW	AW	AW	AW	AW	AW	AW	VT	AW	NT	AW	AW	AW		AW	AW	AW	VT	AW	AW
				1 ◇				◇				1 ◇		A			◇				◇ B	1 ◇		◇
						⊤		⊤		⊤		⊠			⊤		⊤				⊤	ⓡ		⊤
0	—	**Holyhead**	d	02 15				04 27				05 32					06 00				06 15	06 45		
3½	—	Valley	d					04x33													06x21			
7½	—	Rhosneigr	d																		06x26			
9¼	—	Ty Croes	d																		06x30			
12	—	Bodorgan	d																		06x34			
21	—	Llanfairpwll	d					04x51													06x44			
24¾	—	**Bangor (Gwynedd)**	a	02 41				04 59				06 00					06 27				06 53	07 11		
—	—		d	02 42				05 00				06 01					06 28				06 59	07 12		
32¼	—	Llanfairfechan	d														06x37							
34¾	—	Penmaenmawr	d														06x41							
39	—	Conwy	d														06x48							
—	0	**Llandudno**	d										06 39						07 03					07 47
—	1¾	Deganwy	d										06x43						07x07					07x51
40	3	**Llandudno Junction**	a	02 59				05 17				06 19	06 48				06 51		07 12		07 16	07 29		07 55
—	—		d	03 00			04 55	05 18			05 45	06 21					06 53				07 17	07 31		07 56
44	—	Colwyn Bay	d				05 01	05 24			05 51	06 29					06 59				07 23	07 37		08 02
50¼	—	Abergele & Pensarn	d				05 08				05 59						07 06				07 30			08 09
54½	—	Rhyl	d				05 14	05 35			06 06	06 42					07 12				07 36	07 48		08 15
58	—	Prestatyn	d				05 19	05 40			06 12						07 17				07 42	07 54		08 21
72	—	Flint	d				05 33	05 54			06 27						07 31				07 55	08 07		08 34
76¼	—	Shotton	d				05 39				06 34						07 37				08 01			08 40
84¼	—	**Chester**	a	03 38			05 50	06 08			06 45	07 12					07 48				08 12	08 21		08 51
—	0		d	03 40	04 55	05 27	05 51	06 12	06 30	06 50	07 00	07 15			07 27	07 30	07 53			08 00	08 20	08 22	08 30	08 54
—	—	Liverpool Lime Street 10	106 a				06 43	07 13			07 43	08 05					08 50					09 13		09 43
—	7½	Helsby	d			05 36				06 59				07 12	07 36		08 03							09 03
—	10	Frodsham	d			05 40				07 03					07 40		08 07							09 07
—	13¼	Runcorn East	d			05 45				07 08					07 45		08 13							09 12
—	18¼	Warrington Bank Quay	90 a			05 52				07 15				07 27	07 52		08 20							09 19
—	22¼	Earlestown 8	90 a			06 00				07 23					08 01		08 28							09 27
—	24	Newton-le-Willows	90 a			06 03				07 26					08 04		08 31							09 30
—	39¾	**Manchester Oxford Road**	90 a			06 22				07 45					08 31		08 52							09 50
—	40¼	**Manchester Piccadilly 10**	90 ⇌ a			06 32				07 54					08 40		09 02							09 58
105½	—	**Crewe 10**	a	03 59	05 19		06 14		06 55		07 24	07 38				07 55				08 24		08 45	08 55	
—	—	Cardiff Central 7	131 a	07 50	08 53			09 18	09 53							10 54					11 20		11 54	
—	—	Manchester Airport	84, 85 ✈ a			07 12				08b19	08 14				09b06		09b25			09 15		10 11		10b19
—	—	Birmingham New Street 12	65 a	05 12	06 58		07c55		08 11			08 58				09 11						09 58	10 11	
—	—	London Euston 15	⊖ 65 a		08 04		08 19		08 58			09e36								10 27		10 46		

		AW	AW	AW	AW	AW	AW	AW	AW	AW	AW		VT	AW	AW	AW	AW	AW	AW	AW	AW	AW	AW	AW
			◇	◇		◇		◇	◇ C		◇		1 ◇	◇		◇		◇		◇	◇	◇ C		◇
				⊤		⊤		⊤			⊤		ⓡ	⊤		⊤		⊤		⊤	⊤			⊤
Holyhead	d		07 15			08 10					09 28		09 50			10 30				11 40				12 35
Valley	d		07x21			08x16					09x34					10x36				11x46				
Rhosneigr	d		07x26			08x21					09x39									11x51				
Ty Croes	d		07x30			08x25					09x43									11x55				
Bodorgan	d		07x34			08x29					09x47									11x59				
Llanfairpwll	d		07x44			08x39					09x57					10x54				12x09				
Bangor (Gwynedd)	a		07 52			08 47					10 05		10 16			11 03				12 17				13 04
	d		08 01			09 04					10 07		10 18			11 03				12 19				13 04
Llanfairfechan	d		08x09			09x12					10x15					11x11				12x27				13x12
Penmaenmawr	d		08x13			09x16					10x19					11x15				12x31				13x16
Conwy	d		08x19			09x22					10x25					11x21				12x37				13x22
Llandudno	d			08 47				09 47	10 14					10 44				11 47			12 47	13 14		
Deganwy	d			08x51				09x51	10x18					10x48				11x51			12x51	13x18		
Llandudno Junction	a		08 22	08 55		09 25		09 55	10 22		10 28		10 34	10 52		11 25		11 55		12 40	12 55	13 22		13 26
	d		08 27	08 56		09 27		09 56			10 30		10 36	10 53		11 26		11 56		12 42	12 56			13 27
Colwyn Bay	d		08 33	09 02		09 33		10 02					10 42	10 59		11 32		12 02		12 48	13 02			13 33
Abergele & Pensarn	d			09 09				10 09						11 06				12 09			13 09			
Rhyl	d		08 43	09 15		09 43		10 15					10 53	11 12		11 43		12 15		12 58	13 15			13 44
Prestatyn	d		08 49	09 21		09 49		10 21					10 59	11 18		11 48		12 21		13 04	13 21			13 49
Flint	d		09 02	09 34		10 02		10 34					11 12	11 31		12 02		12 34		13 17	13 34			14 03
Shotton	d			09 40				10 40						11 37				12 40			13 40			
Chester	a		09 17	09 51		10 16		10 51			11 09		11 26	11 48		12 16		12 51		13 31	13 51			14 17
	d	09 00	09 19	09 54	10 00	10 20	10 29	10 54		11 00	11 14		11 28	11 50	12 00	12 20	12 29	12 54	13 00	13 33	13 54		14 00	14 20
Liverpool Lime Street 10	106 a		10 13	10 43		11 13		11 43			12 13			12 43		13 13		13 43			14 43			15 13
Helsby	d			10 03				11 03						11 59				13 03			14 03			
Frodsham	d			10 07				11 07						12 03				13 07			14 07			
Runcorn East	d			10 12				11 12						12 08				13 12			14 12			
Warrington Bank Quay	90 a			10 19				11 19						12 17				13 19			14 20			
Earlestown 8	90 a			10 27				11 27						12 28				13 28			14 27			
Newton-le-Willows	90 a			10 30				11 30						12 30				13 30			14 29			
Manchester Oxford Road	90 a			10 50				11 50						12 50				13 50			14 50			
Manchester Piccadilly 10	90 ⇌ a			10 58				11 58						12 58				13 58			14 58			
Crewe 10	a	09 24	09 43		10 24		10 50			11 24	11 41		11 47		12 27		12 50		13 24	14 00			14 24	
Cardiff Central 7	131 a		12 54			13 20	13 54						14 54			15 20	15 54			16 54				17 15
Manchester Airport	84, 85 ✈ a	10 11		11b19	11 11			12b19		12 11			13 11	13b19	13 11			14b19	14 11		15b19		15 11	
Birmingham New Street 12	65 a		10 58				11c58						12 58				13 58		14 58	15 11			15 58	
London Euston 15	⊖ 65 a	11 27	11 48		12 26		13 18			13 27			13 40		14 40				15 26				16 27	

For general notes see front of timetable
For details of catering facilities see Directory of Train Operators

A From Ellesmere Port (Table 109)
B ⊤ Shrewsbury to Newport (South Wales)
C To Blaenau Ffestiniog (Table 102)
b Change at Manchester Oxford Road
c Change at Crewe and Stafford
e 28 July to 22 August arr. 0941

North Wales and Chester → Manchester and Crewe

Network Diagram - see first page of Table 81

Station		AW	AW	AW	AW		NT	AW	AW	VT	AW	AW	VT	AW	NT	AW	AW	AW	AW	AW		AW	AW	AW
			◇		◇			◇	◇	1 ◇	◇		1 ◇	◇			◇	◇		◇		◇		◇
							A								B			C						
			🛒		🛒			🛒	🛒	🍴	🛒		🍴	🛒			🛒			🛒		🛒		🛒
Holyhead	d				13 20			13 35		14 14				14 35						15 39				16 35
Valley	d							13x41												15x45				
Rhosneigr	d							13x46												15x50				
Ty Croes	d							13x50												15x54				
Bodorgan	d							13x54												15x58				
Llanfairpwll	d							14x04												16x08				
Bangor (Gwynedd)	a				13 47			14 12		14 42				15 02						16 16				17 02
	d				13 49			14 14		14 43				15 04						16 17				17 04
Llanfairfechan	d							14x22						15x12						16x25				17x12
Penmaenmawr	d							14x26						15x16						16x29				17x16
Conwy	d							14x32						15x22						16x35				17x22
Llandudno	d		13 47						14 35				15 08				15 47	16 14				16 47		
Deganwy	d		13x51						14x39								15x51	16x18				16x51		
Llandudno Junction	a		13 55		14 05			14 35	14 43	15 01			15 15	15 25			15 55	16 22		16 38		16 55		17 25
	d		13 56		14 07			14 37	14 44	15 03			15 17	15 27			15 56			16 40		16 56		17 27
Colwyn Bay	d		14 02		14 13			14 43	14 50				15 23	15 33			16 02			16 46		17 02		17 33
Abergele & Pensarn	d		14 09						14 57								16 09					17 09		
Rhyl	d		14 15		14 23			14 53	15 03				15 34	15 43			16 15			16 56		17 15		17 43
Prestatyn	d		14 21		14 29			14 59	15 09				15 40	15 49			16 21			17 02		17 21		17 49
Flint	d		14 34					15 12	15 22				15 53	16 02			16 34			17 15		17 34		18 02
Shotton	d		14 40						15 28								16 40					17 40		
Chester	a		14 51		14 57			15 27	15 39	15 45	←		16 06	16 16			16 51			17 29		17 51		18 16
	d	14 30	14 54	15 03	15 09			15 30	15 54	15 48	15 54	16 00	16 08	16 20		16 31	16 54		17 00	17 31		17 53	18 00	18 20
Liverpool Lime Street [10] 106	a		*15 43*		*16 13*				→	*16 43*				*17 13*			*17 43*					*18 43*		*19 13*
Helsby	d		15 03				15 29				16 03				16 27		17 03					18 02		
Frodsham	d		15 07				15 34				16 07				16 32		17 07					18 06		
Runcorn East	d		15 12				15 39				16 12				16 37		17 12					18 11		
Warrington Bank Quay 90	a		15 19		15 31		15 47				16 19				16 45		17 20					18 19		
Earlestown [8] 90	a		15 27		15 43		15 56				16 27				16 56		17 28					18 27		
Newton-le-Willows 90	a		15 30		15 46						16 30						17 30					18 30		
Manchester Oxford Road 90	a		15 50		16 13						16 50						17 51					18 51		
Manchester Piccadilly [10] 90	a		15 58		16 21						16 58						17 59					19 01		
Crewe [10]	a	14 55		15 28				15 55		16 14		16 24	16 38			16 59			17 24	17 56			18 24	
Cardiff Central [7] 131	a	*17 54*						*19 01*						19 20		*19 54*				*21 01*				21 19
Manchester Airport 84, 85 ✈	a		*16b19*	*16 11*	*16b40*					*17 15*	*17b19*	*17 15*	*18 15*				*18b27*		*18 15*	*18 54*		*19b26*		
Birmingham New Street [12] 65	a	*16 11*		*16 58*				*17 11*		*17 30*			*17c58*			*18 11*			*18 58*	*19 11*			*19c58*	
London Euston [15] ⊖ 65	a			*17 40*						18 21		*18 27*	18 42						*19 25*				*20 26*	

Station		AW	AW	AW	AW	AW	AW	AW	AW	AW	AW	AW	AW	AW	AW	AW	AW	AW	AW	AW	AW	AW		
			◇		◇	◇	◇		◇					◇	◇			◇						
							C											D						
			🛒		🛒				🛒															
Holyhead	d				17 27				18 35					19 35				20 35						
Valley	d				17x33				18x41					19x41										
Rhosneigr	d				17x38				18x46					19x46										
Ty Croes	d				17x42				18x50					19x50										
Bodorgan	d				17x46				18x54					19x54										
Llanfairpwll	d				17x56				19x04					20x04										
Bangor (Gwynedd)	a				18 04				19 12					20 12				21 02						
	d				18 06				19 14					20 14				21 03						
Llanfairfechan	d				18x14									20x22				21x11						
Penmaenmawr	d				18x18									20x26				21x15						
Conwy	d				18x24									20x32				21x21						
Llandudno	d		17 47			18 47	18 53				19 47				20 47	21 15			21 47					
Deganwy	d		17x51			18x51	18x57				19x51				20x51	21x19			21x51					
Llandudno Junction	a		17 55		18 27	18 55	19 01		19 30		19 55			20 35	20 55	21 23		21 24	21 57					
	d		17 56		18 29	18 56			19 32		19 56			20 37	20 56			21 28						
Colwyn Bay	d		18 02		18 35	19 02			19 38		20 02			20 43	21 02			21 34						
Abergele & Pensarn	d		18 09			19 09					20 09				21 09			21 41						
Rhyl	d		18 15		18 45	19 15			19 48		20 15			20 53	21 15			21 47						
Prestatyn	d		18 21		18 51	19 21			19 54		20 21			20 59	21 21			21 52						
Flint	d		18 34		19 04	19 34			20 07		20 34			21 12	21 34			22 06						
Shotton	d		18 40			19 40					20 40				21 40			22 12						
Chester	a		18 51		19 20	19 51			20 22		20 51			21 26	21 51			22 23						
	d	18 30	18 53	19 00	19 22	19 53		20 05	20 28	20 30		20 56	21 00	21 33	21 54		22 14			22 44	23 12	23 22		
Liverpool Lime Street [10] 106	a		*19 43*		*20 13*	*20 43*			*21 13*		*21 43*				*22 43*			*23 13*						
Helsby	d		19 02			20 02						21 05			22 03							23 31		
Frodsham	d		19 06			20 06						21 09			22 07							23 35		
Runcorn East	d		19 11			20 11						21 14			22 12							23 40		
Warrington Bank Quay 90	a		19 19			20 20						21 23			22 21							23 50		
Earlestown [8] 90	a		19 27			20 27						21 30			22 32							23 57		
Newton-le-Willows 90	a		19 30			20 30						21 33			22 34							23 59		
Manchester Oxford Road 90	a		19 50			20 51						21 54			22 55									
Manchester Piccadilly [10] 90	a		19 59			21 00						22 01			23 05							00 27		
Crewe [10]	a	18 56		19 24	19 44			20 29		20 55			21 24	21 57			22 38			23 07	23 39			
Cardiff Central [7] 131	a	*21 57*			*23 04*					*00 17*				*01e22*										
Manchester Airport 84, 85 ✈	a		*20b19*			*21b28*						*22 39*			*23 56*						*01 21*	*01f11*		
Birmingham New Street [12] 65	a	*20 11*			*20 58*			*22c04*	22 18	*22 30*			*22 38*	*23 11*										
London Euston [15] ⊖ 65	a				*21 51*			*23 05*		*23 14*			*00 09*											

For general notes see front of timetable
For details of catering facilities see Directory of Train Operators

- A To Liverpool Lime Street (Table 90)
- B From Ellesmere Port (Table 109) to Liverpool Lime Street (Table 90)
- C To Blaenau Ffestiniog (Table 102)
- D To Shrewsbury (Table 75)
- b Change at Manchester Oxford Road
- c Change at Crewe and Stafford
- e Fridays arr. 0114
- f Fridays arr. 0112

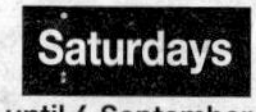

until 6 September

North Wales and Chester → Manchester and Crewe

Network Diagram - see first page of Table 81

	VT	AW	AW	AW	AW	AW	AW	AW	VT	VT	AW	AW	AW	AW	AW	AW	AW	VT	VT	NT	AW	AW	AW
	1 ◇				◇				1 ◇	1 ◇				◇			◇	1 ◇	1 ◇			◇	
									A	B								A	B				
Holyhead d	02 15				04 27				05 30	05 30				06 00			06 15	06 45	06 45				
Valley d					04x33												06x21						
Rhosneigr d																	06x26						
Ty Croes d																	06x30						
Bodorgan d																	06x34						
Llanfairpwll d					04x51												06x44						
Bangor (Gwynedd) a	02 41				04 59				05 58	05 58				06 27			06 53	07 11	07 11				
d	02 42				05 00				05 59	05 59				06 30			06 59	07 12	07 12				
Llanfairfechan d														06x38									
Penmaenmawr d														06x43									
Conwy d														06x49									
Llandudno d											06 39				07 03							07 47	
Deganwy d											06x43				07x07							07x51	
Llandudno Junction a	02 59				05 17				06 17	06 17	06 48			06 53	07 12		07 16	07 29	07 29			07 55	
d	03 00			05 00	05 18			05 45	06 19	06 19				06 54			07 17	07 30	07 31			07 56	
Colwyn Bay d				05 06	05 24			05 51	06 27	06 27				07 00			07 23	07 37	07 37			08 02	
Abergele & Pensarn d				05 13				05 59						07 07			07 30					08 09	
Rhyl d				05 19	05 35			06 06	06 40	06 40				07 13			07 36	07 48	07 48			08 15	
Prestatyn d				05 24	05 40			06 12		06 47				07 19			07 42	07 53	07 54			08 21	
Flint d				05 38	05 54			06 27						07 32			07 55	08 06	08 07			08 34	
Shotton d				05 44				06 34						07 38			08 01					08 40	
Chester a	03 38			05 55	06 08			06 45	07 12	07 14				07 49			08 12	08 20	08 21			08 51	
d	03 40	04 55	05 35	06 00	06 12	06 30	06 50	06 56	07 15	07 18		07 27	07 30	07 53		08 00	08 20	08 22	08 22	08 25	08 30	08 54	09 00
Liverpool Lime Street 10 106 a				06 43	07 13			07 43	08 13	08 13				08 43				09 13	09 13			09 43	
Helsby d			05 44				06 59					07 36		08 03								09 03	
Frodsham d			05 48				07 03					07 40		08 07								09 07	
Runcorn East d			05 53				07 08					07 45		08 13						08b51		09 12	
Warrington Bank Quay 90 a			06 00				07 15					07 52		08 20								09 19	
Earlestown 8 90 a			06 08				07 23					08 01		08 28								09 27	
Newton-le-Willows 90 a			06 11				07 26					08 04		08 31								09 30	
Manchester Oxford Road 90 a			06 31				07 45					08 31		08 52								09 50	
Manchester Piccadilly 10 90 a			06 40				07 54					08 40		09 02								09 58	
Crewe 10 a	03 59	05 19		06 23		06 55		07 20	07 38	07 43			07 55			08 24		08 42	08 45		08 56		09 24
Cardiff Central 7 131 a	07 57	08 51			09 18	09 53							10 54				11 20				11 54		
Manchester Airport 84, 85 a			07 12				08c19	08 14	09 12	09 15		09c06		09c25		09e12						10c19	10 11
Birmingham New Street 12 65 a	05 08																						
London Euston 15 ⊖ 65 a										10 03									11 04				

	AW	AW	AW	AW	AW	AW	AW	AW	AW		VT	AW	AW	AW	AW	AW	AW	AW	AW	AW	AW	AW	AW
	◇	◇		◇		◇	◇		◇		1 ◇	◇		◇		◇		◇	◇	◇		◇	
							C													C			
Holyhead d	07 15			08 25					09 28		09 50			10 30				11 40				12 35	
Valley d	07x21			08x31					09x34					10x36				11x46					
Rhosneigr d	07x26			08x36					09x39									11x51					
Ty Croes d	07x30			08x40					09x43									11x55					
Bodorgan d	07x34			08x44					09x47									11x59					
Llanfairpwll d	07x44			08x54					09x57					10x54				12x09					
Bangor (Gwynedd) a	07 52			09 02					10 05		10 16			11 03				12 17				13 04	
d	08 01			09 04					10 07		10 18			11 03				12 19				13 04	
Llanfairfechan d	08x09			09x12					10x15					11x11				12x27				13x12	
Penmaenmawr d	08x13			09x16					10x19					11x15				12x31				13x16	
Conwy d	08x19			09x22					10x25					11x21				12x37				13x22	
Llandudno d		08 47				09 47	10 14					10 47				11 47			12 47	13 14			
Deganwy d		08x51				09x51	10x18					10x51				11x51			12x51	13x18			
Llandudno Junction a	08 22	08 55		09 25		09 55	10 22		10 28		10 34	10 55		11 25		11 55		12 40	12 55	13 22		13 26	
d	08 27	08 56		09 27		09 56			10 30		10 36	10 56		11 26		11 56		12 42	12 56			13 27	
Colwyn Bay d	08 33	09 02		09 33		10 02					10 42	11 02		11 32		12 02		12 48	13 02			13 33	
Abergele & Pensarn d		09 09				10 09						11 09				12 09			13 09				
Rhyl d	08 43	09 15		09 43		10 15					10 53	11 15		11 43		12 15		12 58	13 15			13 44	
Prestatyn d	08 49	09 21		09 49		10 21					10 59	11 21		11 48		12 21		13 04	13 21			13 49	
Flint d	09 02	09 34		10 02		10 34					11 12	11 34		12 02		12 34		13 17	13 34			14 03	
Shotton d		09 40				10 40						11 40				12 40			13 40				
Chester a	09 17	09 51		10 16		10 51			11 09		11 26	11 51		12 16		12 51		13 32	13 51			14 17	
d	09 19	09 54	10 00	10 20	10 29	10 54		11 00	11 14		11 28	11 54	12 00	12 20	12 29	12 54	13 00	13 33	13 54		14 03	14 20	14 30
Liverpool Lime Street 10 106 a	10 13	10 43		11 13		11 43			12 13			12 43		13 13		13 43			14 43			15 13	
Helsby d		10 03				11 03						12 03				13 03			14 03				
Frodsham d		10 07				11 07						12 07				13 07			14 07				
Runcorn East d		10 12				11 12						12 12				13 12			14 12				
Warrington Bank Quay 90 a		10 19				11 19						12 19				13 19			14 19				
Earlestown 8 90 a		10 27				11 27						12 28				13 28			14 28				
Newton-le-Willows 90 a		10 30				11 30						12 30				13 30			14 30				
Manchester Oxford Road 90 a		10 50				11 50						12 50				13 50			14 50				
Manchester Piccadilly 10 90 a		10 58				11 58						12 58				13 58			14 58				
Crewe 10 a	09 43		10 24		10 50			11 24	11 41		11 47		12 24		12 50		13 24	14 00			14 27		14 55
Cardiff Central 7 131 a	12 54			13 20	13 53						14 54			15 20	15 53			16 54				17 20	17 54
Manchester Airport 84, 85 a		11c19	11 11			12c19		12 11				13c19	13 11			14c19	14 11		15c19		15 11		16 11
Birmingham New Street 12 65 a																							
London Euston 15 ⊖ 65 a											13f40												

For general notes see front of timetable
For details of catering facilities see Directory of Train Operators

A Until 12 July
B From 19 July
C To Blaenau Ffestiniog (Table 102)
b Runcorn (Mainline). Arrival time
c Change at Manchester Oxford Road
e From 19 July arr. 0915
f From 19 July only

For connections to Birmingham New Street and London Euston, please see Table 65.

North Wales and Chester → Manchester and Crewe

Network Diagram - see first page of Table 81

		AW ◇	AW	AW A	NT B	AW ◇	AW ◇	VT 1 ◇ A	VT 1 ◇ C	AW ◇	AW	VT 1 ◇ A	VT 1 ◇ C	AW ◇	AW C	NT D	AW	AW ◇	AW ◇ E	AW	AW ◇	AW ◇	AW	AW ◇
Holyhead	d					13 35		14 15	14 15					14 35							15 39			16 35
Valley	d					13x41															15x45			
Rhosneigr	d					13x46															15x50			
Ty Croes	d					13x50															15x54			
Bodorgan	d					13x54															15x58			
Llanfairpwll	d					14x04															16x08			
Bangor (Gwynedd)	a					14 12		14 41	14 42					15 02							16 16			17 02
	d					14 14		14 43	14 44					15 04							16 17			17 04
Llanfairfechan	d					14x22								15x12							16x25			17x12
Penmaenmawr	d					14x26								15x16							16x29			17x16
Conwy	d					14x32								15x22							16x35			17x22
Llandudno	d	13 47					14 35					15 08						15 47	16 14			16 47		
Deganwy	d	13x51					14x39											15x51	16x18			16x51		
Llandudno Junction	a	13 55				14 35	14 43	14 59	15 02			15 15		15 25				15 55	16 22		16 38	16 55		17 25
	d	13 56				14 37	14 44	15 01	15 03			15 16	15 17	15 27				15 56			16 40	16 56		17 27
Colwyn Bay	d	14 02				14 43	14 50					15 23	15 23	15 33				16 02			16 46	17 02		17 33
Abergele & Pensarn	d	14 09					14 57											16 09				17 09		
Rhyl	d	14 15				14 53	15 03					15 34	15 34	15 43				16 15			16 56	17 15		17 43
Prestatyn	d	14 21				14 59	15 09					15 39	15 39	15 49				16 21			17 02	17 21		17 49
Flint	d	14 34				15 12	15 22					15 52	15 52	16 02				16 34			17 15	17 34		18 02
Shotton	d	14 40					15 28											16 40				17 40		
Chester	a	14 51				15 27	15 39	15 44	15 45	←		16 07	16 07	16 16				16 51			17 29	17 51		18 16
	d	14 53	15 03	15 14		15 30	15 54	15 46	15 49	15 54	16 00	16 12	16 12	16 20	16 22		16 31	16 54		17 00	17 31	17 53	18 04	18 20
Liverpool Lime Street 10	106 a	15 43					→	16 43	16 43					17 13				17 43				18 43		19 13
Helsby	d	15 02			15 29					16 03						16 27		17 03				18 02		
Frodsham	d	15 06			15 34					16 07						16 32		17 07				18 06		
Runcorn East	d	15 11			15 39					16 12						16 37		17 12				18 11		
Warrington Bank Quay	90 a	15 18		15 36	15 47					16 19						16 45		17 19				18 21		
Earlestown 8	90 a	15 28		15 44	15 56					16 28						16 56		17 27				18 27		
Newton-le-Willows	90 a	15 30		15 47						16 30								17 30				18 30		
Manchester Oxford Road	90 a	15 50		16 10						16 50								17 51				18 50		
Manchester Piccadilly 10	90 ⛴ a	15 58		16 19						16 58					17 39			17 59				18 59		
Crewe 10	a		15 30			15 55		16 10	16 14		16 24	16 38	16 38				16 59			17 26	17 56		18 28	
Cardiff Central 7	131 a					18 54								19 22			19 58				21 01			21 20
Manchester Airport	84, 85 ✈ a	16b19		16b40						17b19	17 15							18b27		18 15		19b19	19 16	
Birmingham New Street 12	65 a																							
London Euston 15	⊖ 65 a								18 27															

		AW	AW ◇	AW	AW ◇	AW ◇	AW ◇ E	AW G	AW ◇	AW	AW	AW	AW	AW ◇	AW ◇	AW	AW	AW ◇ H	AW	AW	AW	AW
Holyhead	d				17 35				18 35					19 35				20 35				
Valley	d				17x41				18x41					19x41								
Rhosneigr	d				17x46				18x46					19x46								
Ty Croes	d				17x50				18x50					19x50								
Bodorgan	d				17x54				18x54					19x54								
Llanfairpwll	d				18x04				19x04					20x04								
Bangor (Gwynedd)	a				18 12				19 12					20 12				21 02				
	d				18 14				19 14					20 14				21 03				
Llanfairfechan	d				18x22									20x22				21x11				
Penmaenmawr	d				18x26									20x26				21x15				
Conwy	d				18x32									20x32				21x21				
Llandudno	d		17 47			18 47	18 53				19 47				20 47	21 15			21 47			
Deganwy	d		17x51			18x51	18x57				19x51				20x51	21x19			21x51			
Llandudno Junction	a		17 55		18 35	18 55	19 01		19 30		19 55			20 35	20 55	21 23		21 24	21 57			
	d		17 56		18 37	18 56			19 32		19 56			20 37	20 56			21 28				
Colwyn Bay	d		18 02		18 43	19 02			19 38		20 02			20 43	21 02			21 34				
Abergele & Pensarn	d		18 09			19 09					20 09				21 09			21 41				
Rhyl	d		18 15		18 53	19 15			19 48		20 15			20 53	21 15			21 47				
Prestatyn	d		18 21		18 59	19 21			19 54		20 21			20 59	21 21			21 52				
Flint	d		18 34		19 12	19 34			20 07		20 34			21 12	21 34			22 06				
Shotton	d		18 40			19 40					20 40				21 40			22 12				
Chester	a		18 51		19 30	19 51			20 22		20 51			21 26	21 51			22 23				
	d	18 30	18 53	19 00	19 34	19 53		20 05	20 28	20 30		20 56	21 00	21 33	21 54		22 12			22 33	23 13	23 22
Liverpool Lime Street 10	106 a		19 43			20 43			21 13		21 43				22 43			23 13				
Helsby	d		19 02			20 02						21 05			22 03							23 31
Frodsham	d		19 06			20 06						21 09			22 07							23 35
Runcorn East	d		19 11			20 11						21 14			22 12							23 40
Warrington Bank Quay	90 a		19 19			20 18						21 23			22 19							23 50
Earlestown 8	90 a		19 28			20 27						21 30			22 27							23 57
Newton-le-Willows	90 a		19 30			20 30						21 33			22 30							23 59
Manchester Oxford Road	90 a		19 50			20 50						21 54			22 55							
Manchester Piccadilly 10	90 ⛴ a		19 59			20 59						22 01			23 05							00 27
Crewe 10	a	18 56		19 24	19 59			20 29		20 55			21 24	21 57			22 36			22 56	23 40	
Cardiff Central 7	131 a	22 00			23 01					00 17				01 19								
Manchester Airport	84, 85 ✈ a		20b19			21b19						22 39			23 56							00 57
Birmingham New Street 12	65 a								22 18													
London Euston 15	⊖ 65 a																					

For general notes see front of timetable
For details of catering facilities see Directory of Train Operators

- **A** Until 12 July
- **B** To Liverpool Lime Street (Table 90)
- **C** From 19 July
- **D** From Ellesmere Port (Table 109) to Liverpool Lime Street (Table 90)
- **E** To Blaenau Ffestiniog (Table 102)
- **G** From Wrexham General (Table 75)
- **H** To Shrewsbury (Table 75)
- **b** Change at Manchester Oxford Road

For connections to Birmingham New Street and London Euston, please see Table 65.

Saturdays

from 13 September

North Wales and Chester → Manchester and Crewe

Network Diagram - see first page of Table 81

		VT **1** ◇	AW	AW	AW		AW ◇	AW	AW	AW		VT **1** ◇	AW	AW	AW		AW ◇	AW	AW	AW ◇		VT **1** ◇	NT A	AW
Holyhead	d	02 15					04 27					05 30					06 00			06 15		06 45		
Valley	d						04x33													06x21				
Rhosneigr	d																			06x26				
Ty Croes	d																			06x30				
Bodorgan	d																			06x34				
Llanfairpwll	d						04x51													06x44				
Bangor (Gwynedd)	a	02 41					04 59					05 58					06 27			06 53		07 11		
	d	02 43					05 00					05 59					06 30			06 59		07 12		
Llanfairfechan	d																06x38							
Penmaenmawr	d																06x43							
Conwy	d																06x49							
Llandudno	d												06 39					07 03						
Deganwy	d												06x43					07x07						
Llandudno Junction	a	02 59					05 17					06 17	06 48				06 53	07 12		07 16		07 29		
	d	03 01			05 00		05 18			05 45		06 19					06 54			07 17		07 30		
Colwyn Bay	d				05 06		05 24			05 51		06 27					07 00			07 23		07 37		
Abergele & Pensarn	d				05 13					05 59							07 07			07 30				
Rhyl	d				05 19		05 35			06 06		06 40					07 13			07 36		07 48		
Prestatyn	d				05 24		05 40			06 12							07 19			07 42		07 53		
Flint	d				05 38		05 54			06 27							07 32			07 55		08 06		
Shotton	d				05 44					06 34							07 38			08 01				
Chester	a	03 39			05 55		06 08			06 45		07 12					07 49			08 12		08 20		
	d	03 41	04 55	05 35	06 00		06 12	06 30	06 50	06 56		07 15		07 27	07 30		07 53		08 00	08 20		08 22	08 25	08 30
Liverpool Lime Street **10**	106 a				*06 43*		*07 13*			*07 43*		*08 13*					*08 43*					*09 13*		
Helsby	d			05 44					06 59					07 36			08 03							
Frodsham	d			05 48					07 03					07 40			08 07							
Runcorn East	d			05 53					07 08					07 45			08 13						08b51	
Warrington Bank Quay	90 a			06 00					07 15					07 52			08 20							
Earlestown **8**	90 a			06 08					07 23					08 01			08 28							
Newton-le-Willows	90 a			06 11					07 26					08 04			08 31							
Manchester Oxford Road	90 a			06 31					07 45					08 31			08 52							
Manchester Piccadilly 10	90 a			06 40					07 54					08 40			09 02							
Crewe 10	a	04 00	05 19		06 23			06 55		07 20		07 38			07 55				08 24			08 42		08 56
Cardiff Central **7**	131 a	*07 57*	*08 51*				09 18	*09 53*				*10 54*			*10 54*					11 20		*11 54*		*11 54*
Manchester Airport	84, 85 a			*07 12*					08c19					09c06			09c25							
Birmingham New Street **12**	65 a	05 08																						
London Euston **15**	⊖ 65 a																							

		AW ◇	AW	AW ◇		AW ◇	AW	AW ◇	AW		AW ◇	AW ◇ B	AW	AW ◇		VT **1** ◇	VT **1** ◇ C	AW ◇	AW		AW ◇	AW	VT **1** ◇ D	VT **1** ◇ C
Holyhead	d			07 15				08 25						09 28		09 50					10 30			
Valley	d			07x21				08x31						09x34							10x36			
Rhosneigr	d			07x26				08x36						09x39										
Ty Croes	d			07x30				08x40						09x43										
Bodorgan	d			07x34				08x44						09x47										
Llanfairpwll	d			07x44				08x54						09x57							10x54			
Bangor (Gwynedd)	a			07 52				09 02						10 05		10 16					11 03			
	d			08 01				09 04						10 07		10 18					11 03			
Llanfairfechan	d			08x09				09x12						10x15							11x11			
Penmaenmawr	d			08x13				09x16						10x19							11x15			
Conwy	d			08x19				09x22						10x25							11x21			
Llandudno	d	07 47				08 47					09 47	10 14						10 47						
Deganwy	d	07x51				08x51					09x51	10x18						10x51						
Llandudno Junction	a	07 55		08 22		08 55		09 25			09 55	10 22		10 28		10 34		10 55			11 25			
	d	07 56		08 27		08 56		09 27			09 56			10 30		10 36		10 56			11 26			
Colwyn Bay	d	08 02		08 33		09 02		09 33			10 02					10 42		11 02			11 32			
Abergele & Pensarn	d	08 09				09 09					10 09							11 09						
Rhyl	d	08 15		08 43		09 15		09 43			10 15					10 53		11 15			11 43			
Prestatyn	d	08 21		08 49		09 21		09 49			10 21					10 59		11 21			11 48			
Flint	d	08 34		09 02		09 34		10 02			10 34					11 12		11 34			12 02			
Shotton	d	08 40				09 40					10 40							11 40						
Chester	a	08 51		09 17		09 51		10 16			10 51			11 09		11 26		11 51			12 16			
	d	08 54	09 00	09 19		09 54	10 00	10 20	10 29		10 54		11 00	11 14		11 28	11 42	11 54	12 00		12 20	12 29	12 40	12 52
Liverpool Lime Street **10**	106 a	*09 43*		*10 13*		*10 43*		*11 13*			*11 43*			*12 13*		*12 43*		*12 43*			*13 13*			
Helsby	d	09 03				10 03					11 03							12 03						
Frodsham	d	09 07				10 07					11 07							12 07						
Runcorn East	d	09 12				10 12					11 12							12 12						
Warrington Bank Quay	90 a	09 19				10 19					11 19							12 19					13 02	
Earlestown **8**	90 a	09 27				10 27					11 27							12 28						
Newton-le-Willows	90 a	09 30				10 30					11 30							12 30						
Manchester Oxford Road	90 a	09 50				10 50					11 50							12 50						
Manchester Piccadilly 10	90 a	09 58				10 58					11 58							12 58						
Crewe 10	a		09 24	09 43			10 24		10 50				11 24	11 41		11 47	12 01		12 24			12 50		13 12
Cardiff Central **7**	131 a			*12 54*				13 20	*13 53*								*14 54*				15 20	*15 53*		*16 54*
Manchester Airport	84, 85 a	10c19				11c19					12c19							13c19						
Birmingham New Street **12**	65 a																13 01							14 24
London Euston **15**	⊖ 65 a																							16 03

For general notes see front of timetable
For details of catering facilities see Directory of Train Operators

A 13 September only
B To Blaenau Ffestiniog (Table 102)
C From Glasgow Central (Table 65)
D From Birmingham New Street to Edinburgh (Table 65)
b Runcorn (Mainline). Arrival time
c Change at Manchester Oxford Road

For connections to Birmingham New Street and London Euston, please refer to the re-issued Table 65 contained in the September supplement.

Table 81

Saturdays

from 13 September

North Wales and Chester → Manchester and Crewe

Network Diagram - see first page of Table 81

		AW ◇	AW		VT 1 ◇ A	AW ◇	AW ◇	AW ◇ B		AW	AW ◇	AW	VT 1 ◇ C		VT 1 ◇ D	AW ◇	AW	AW		VT 1 ◇ A	AW ◇	AW ◇	VT 1 ◇ E	VT 1 ◇
Holyhead	d					11 40					12 35										13 35			14 15
Valley	d					11x46															13x41			
Rhosneigr	d					11x51															13x46			
Ty Croes	d					11x55															13x50			
Bodorgan	d					11x59															13x54			
Llanfairpwll	d					12x09															14x04			
Bangor (Gwynedd)	a					12 17					13 04										14 12			14 42
	d					12 19					13 04										14 14			14 44
Llanfairfechan	d					12x27					13x12										14x22			
Penmaenmawr	d					12x31					13x16										14x26			
Conwy	d					12x37					13x22										14x32			
Llandudno	d	11 47					12 47	13 14								13 47						14 35		
Deganwy	d	11x51					12x51	13x18								13x51						14x39		
Llandudno Junction	a	11 55				12 40	12 55	13 22			13 26					13 55					14 35	14 43		15 02
	d	11 56				12 42	12 56				13 27					13 56					14 37	14 44		15 03
Colwyn Bay	d	12 02				12 48	13 02				13 33					14 02					14 43	14 50		
Abergele & Pensarn	d	12 09					13 09									14 09						14 57		
Rhyl	d	12 15				12 58	13 15				13 44					14 15					14 53	15 03		
Prestatyn	d	12 21				13 04	13 21				13 49					14 21					14 59	15 09		
Flint	d	12 34				13 17	13 34				14 03					14 34					15 12	15 22		
Shotton	d	12 40					13 40									14 40						15 28		
Chester	a	12 51				13 32	13 51				14 17					14 51					15 27	15 39		15 45
	d	12 54	13 00		13 21	13 33	13 54			14 00	14 20	14 30	14 43		14 49	14 53	15 03	15 09		15 21	15 30	15 54	15 41	15 49
Liverpool Lime Street 10	106 a	*13 43*					*14 43*				*15 13*					*15 43*						→		*16 43*
Helsby	d	13 03					14 03									15 02								
Frodsham	d	13 07					14 07									15 06								
Runcorn East	d	13 12					14 12									15 11								
Warrington Bank Quay	90 a	13 19			13 42		14 19						15 05			15 18		15 31		15 42			16 03	
Earlestown 8	90 a	13 28					14 28									15 28		15 44						
Newton-le-Willows	90 a	13 30					14 30									15 30		15 47						
Manchester Oxford Road	90 a	13 50					14 50									15 50		16 10						
Manchester Piccadilly 10	90 a	13 58					14 58									15 58		16 19						
Crewe 10	a		13 24			14 00				14 24		14 55			15 08		15 30				15 55			16 14
Cardiff Central 7	131 a					*16 54*					17 20				*17 55*						*18 54*			
Manchester Airport	84, 85 ✈ a	*14b19*					*15b19*									*16b19*		*16b40*						
Birmingham New Street 12	65 a														16 24									17 24
London Euston 15	⊖ 65 a														18 03									18 59

		AW ◇		AW	AW ◇	NT G	AW		VT 1 ◇ H	AW ◇	AW ◇ B	AW		AW ◇	AW ◇	AW	AW ◇		AW	AW ◇	AW	AW ◇		AW ◇
Holyhead	d				14 35									15 39			16 35					17 35		
Valley	d													15x45								17x41		
Rhosneigr	d													15x50								17x46		
Ty Croes	d													15x54								17x50		
Bodorgan	d													15x58								17x54		
Llanfairpwll	d													16x08								18x04		
Bangor (Gwynedd)	a				15 02									16 16			17 02					18 12		
	d				15 04									16 17			17 04					18 14		
Llanfairfechan	d				15x12									16x25			17x12					18x22		
Penmaenmawr	d				15x16									16x29			17x16					18x26		
Conwy	d				15x22									16x35			17x22					18x32		
Llandudno	d									15 47	16 14				16 47					17 47				18 47
Deganwy	d									15x51	16x18				16x51					17x51				18x51
Llandudno Junction	a				15 25					15 55	16 22			16 38	16 55		17 25			17 55		18 35		18 55
	d				15 27					15 56				16 40	16 56		17 27			17 56		18 37		18 56
Colwyn Bay	d				15 33					16 02				16 46	17 02		17 33			18 02		18 43		19 02
Abergele & Pensarn	d									16 09					17 09					18 09				19 09
Rhyl	d				15 43					16 15				16 56	17 15		17 43			18 15		18 53		19 15
Prestatyn	d				15 49					16 21				17 02	17 21		17 49			18 21		18 59		19 21
Flint	d				16 02					16 34				17 15	17 34		18 02			18 34		19 12		19 34
Shotton	d									16 40					17 40					18 40				19 40
Chester	a	←			16 16					16 51				17 29	17 51		18 16			18 51		19 30		19 51
	d	15 54		16 00	16 20		16 31		16 40	16 54		17 00		17 31	17 53	18 04	18 20		18 30	18 53	19 00	19 34		19 53
Liverpool Lime Street 10	106 a				*17 13*					*17 43*					*18 43*		*19 13*			*19 43*				*20 43*
Helsby	d	16 03				16 27				17 03					18 02					19 02				20 02
Frodsham	d	16 07				16 32				17 07					18 06					19 06				20 06
Runcorn East	d	16 12				16 37				17 12					18 11					19 11				20 11
Warrington Bank Quay	90 a	16 19				16 45				17 19					18 21					19 19				20 18
Earlestown 8	90 a	16 28				16 56				17 27					18 27					19 28				20 27
Newton-le-Willows	90 a	16 30								17 30					18 30					19 30				20 30
Manchester Oxford Road	90 a	16 50								17 51					18 50					19 50				20 50
Manchester Piccadilly 10	90 a	16 58								17 59					18 59					19 59				20 59
Crewe 10	a			16 24			16 59		17 04			17 26		17 56		18 28			18 56		19 24	19 59		
Cardiff Central 7	131 a				19 22				*19 58*					*21 01*			21 20		*22 00*			*23 01*		
Manchester Airport	84, 85 ✈ a	*17b19*								*18b27*					*19b19*					*20b19*				*21b19*
Birmingham New Street 12	65 a								18 11															
London Euston 15	⊖ 65 a																							

For general notes see front of timetable
For details of catering facilities see Directory of Train Operators

A From London Euston to Glasgow Central (Table 65)
B To Blaenau Ffestiniog (Table 102)
C From Birmingham New Street to Edinburgh (Table 65)
D From Glasgow Central (Table 65)
E From Birmingham New Street to Edinburgh
G From Ellesmere Port (Table 109) to Liverpool Lime Street (Table 90)
H From Edinburgh (Table 65)
b Change at Manchester Oxford Road

For connections to Birmingham New Street and London Euston, please refer to the re-issued Table 65 contained in the September supplement.

Table 81

Saturdays

from 13 September

North Wales and Chester → Manchester and Crewe

Network Diagram - see first page of Table 81

		AW ◇ A	AW B	VT [1] ◇ C ☕	AW ◇ 🛒		AW	VT [1] ◇ D ☕	AW	AW		AW	AW ◇ 🛒	AW ◇	AW		AW	AW ◇ E	AW	AW		AW		
Holyhead	d				18 35								19 35					20 35						
Valley	d				18x41								19x41											
Rhosneigr	d				18x46								19x46											
Ty Croes	d				18x50								19x50											
Bodorgan	d				18x54								19x54											
Llanfairpwll	d				19x04								20x04											
Bangor (Gwynedd)	a				19 12								20 12					21 02						
	d				19 14								20 14					21 03						
Llanfairfechan	d												20x22					21x11						
Penmaenmawr	d												20x26					21x15						
Conwy	d												20x32					21x21						
Llandudno	d	18 53							19 47					20 47	21 15				21 47					
Deganwy	d	18x57							19x51					20x51	21x19				21x51					
Llandudno Junction	a	19 01			19 30				19 55				20 35	20 55	21 23			21 24	21 57					
	d				19 32				19 56				20 37	20 56				21 28						
Colwyn Bay	d				19 38				20 02				20 43	21 02				21 34						
Abergele & Pensarn	d								20 09					21 09				21 41						
Rhyl	d				19 48				20 15				20 53	21 15				21 47						
Prestatyn	d				19 54				20 21				20 59	21 21				21 52						
Flint	d				20 07				20 34				21 12	21 34				22 06						
Shotton	d								20 40					21 40				22 12						
Chester	a				20 22				20 51				21 26	21 51				22 23						
	d		20 05	20 20	20 28		20 30	20 40		20 56		21 00	21 33	21 54			22 12			22 33		23 13		
Liverpool Lime Street [10]	106 a				*21 13*				*21 43*					*22 43*				*23 13*						
Helsby	d																							
Frodsham	d																							
Runcorn East	d																							
Warrington Bank Quay	90 a			20 41																				
Earlestown [8]	90 a																							
Newton-le-Willows	90 a																							
Manchester Oxford Road	90 a																							
Manchester Piccadilly [10]	90 ⛴ a									22 06				23 02										
Crewe [10]	a		20 29				20 55	20 59				21 24	21 57				22 36			22 56		23 40		
Cardiff Central [7]	131 a							*00 17*					*01 19*											
Manchester Airport	84, 85 ✈ a													*23 56*										
Birmingham New Street [12]	65 a				22 18			22 11																
London Euston [15]	⊖ 65 a																							

Sundays

until 7 September

		AW	AW		AW ◇	AW		AW ◇ A	AW ◇		AW	AW 🛒		AW ◇ 🛒	AW		AW	AW ◇		AW	AW 🛒		AW	AW ◇ A
Holyhead	d				08 24				09 35					10 35										
Valley	d								09x41															
Rhosneigr	d								09x47															
Ty Croes	d								09x50															
Bodorgan	d								09x55															
Llanfairpwll	d								10x04															
Bangor (Gwynedd)	a				08 50				10 12					11 02										
	d		07 42		08 51				10 12					11 04				12 10						
Llanfairfechan	d								10x20															
Penmaenmawr	d								10x24															
Conwy	d								10x32															
Llandudno	d							10 22			11 08				12 15					12 41			13 10	13 30
Deganwy	d							10x26			11x12				12x19					12x45			13x14	13x34
Llandudno Junction	a		07 58		09 08			10 30	10 34		11 17			11 21	12 23			12 26		12 50			13 18	13 38
	d		08 00		09 09				10 36					11 22				12 28					13 19	
Colwyn Bay	d		08 06		09 15				10 42					11 28				12 34					13 25	
Abergele & Pensarn	d		08 13						10 49														13 32	
Rhyl	d		08 19		09 26				10 55					11 39				12 44					13 38	
Prestatyn	d		08 24		09 31				11 00					11 45				12 50					13 44	
Flint	d		08 38		09 45				11 14					11 59				13 03					13 57	
Shotton	d		08 44						11 20					12 05				13 09					14 03	
Chester	a		08 55		09 58				11 31					12 17				13 20					14 14	
	d	08 25	08 57		10 00	10 27			11 41			11 55		12 20			12 43	13 22			13 30		14 17	
Liverpool Lime Street [10]	106 a		*09 43*		*11 13*				*12 43*					*13 13*				*14 13*					*15 13*	
Helsby	d				10 09							12 04									13 39			
Frodsham	d				10 13							12 08									13 43			
Runcorn East	d				10 18							12 13									13 48			
Warrington Bank Quay	90 a				10 28							12 21									13b57			
Earlestown [8]	90 a				10 37							12 30									14b08			
Newton-le-Willows	90 a				10 40							12 33									14 11			
Manchester Oxford Road	90 a				11c00							12 52									14 31			
Manchester Piccadilly [10]	90 ⛴ a				11c04							13e02									14 41			
Crewe [10]	a	08 50	09 17			10 52			12 02								13 08	13 44					14 37	
Cardiff Central [7]	131 a		*13 53*											*15 31*			*16 15*							
Manchester Airport	84, 85 ✈ a																							
Birmingham New Street [12]	65 a					*12 17*																		
London Euston [15]	⊖ 65 a																							

For general notes see front of timetable
For details of catering facilities see Directory of Train Operators

A To Blaenau Ffestiniog (Table 102)

B From Wrexham General (Table 75)

C From London Euston to Liverpool Lime Street (Table 65)

D From Edinburgh (Table 65)

E To Shrewsbury (Table 75)

b From 20 July arr. Warrington Bank Quay 1354, Earlestown 1407

c From 20 July arr. Manchester Oxford Road 1103, Manchester Piccadilly 1106

e From 20 July arr. 1304

For connections to Birmingham New Street and London Euston, please see Table 65.

For connections to Birmingham New Street and London Euston, please refer to the re-issued Table 65 contained in the September supplement.

Table 81

Sundays
until 7 September

North Wales and Chester → Manchester and Crewe

Network Diagram - see first page of Table 81

		AW	VT	VT	AW	AW	AW	AW	AW	AW	AW	AW	AW	AW	AW	VT	VT
			1 ◇	1 ◇	◇					◇				◇		1 ◇	1 ◇
				A										B		C	A
			₽	₽	🍴									🍴		₽	₽
Holyhead	d		13 15	13 15	13 30											15 50	15 57
Valley	d																
Rhosneigr	d																
Ty Croes	d																
Bodorgan	d																
Llanfairpwll	d																
Bangor (Gwynedd)	a		13 41	13 41	13 56											16 19	16 23
	d		13 42	13 42	13 58					14 41				15 45		16 20	16 24
Llanfairfechan	d									14x49							
Penmaenmawr	d									14x53							
Conwy	d									14x59							
Llandudno	d	13 45				14 20	14 50				15 25	15 50					
Deganwy	d	13x49					14x54				15x29	15x54					
Llandudno Junction	a	13 54	13 59	13 59	14 14	14 28	14 59			15 02	15 35	15 58		16 01		16 38	16 41
	d		14 00	14 00	14 16					15 04				16 03		16 40	16 42
Colwyn Bay	d		14 07	14 07	14 22					15 10				16 09		16 48	16 49
Abergele & Pensarn	d									15 17							
Rhyl	d		14 18	14 18	14 32					15 23				16 19		17 01	17 00
Prestatyn	d				14 38					15 28				16 25			
Flint	d				14 51					15 42				16 38			
Shotton	d									15 50							
Chester	a		14 45	14 45	15 05					15 59				16 52		17 31	17 27
	d		14 46	14 46	15 08			15 15	15 54	16 00			16 48	16 54	17 28	17 34	17 35
Liverpool Lime Street [10]	106 a		*15 43*	*15 43*	*16 13*					*17 13*				*17 43*			
Helsby	d								16 03								
Frodsham	d								16 07								
Runcorn East	d								16 12								
Warrington Bank Quay	90 a				15b31				16 21					17 14			
Earlestown [8]	90 a				15 39				16 29					17 22			
Newton-le-Willows	90 a				15 42				16 31					17 25			
Manchester Oxford Road	90 a				16 03				16 51					17 50			
Manchester Piccadilly [10]	90 a				16 12				17 00					17 59			
Crewe [10]	a		15 06	15 06				15 36		16 20			17 09		17 49	17 57	17 56
Cardiff Central [7]	131 a		*18 13*	*18 13*				*18 55*					*20 15*				
Manchester Airport	84, 85 ✈ a																
Birmingham New Street [12]	65 a																
London Euston [15]	⊖ 65 a		17c37													20 25	

		AW	AW	AW	AW	AW	AW	AW	AW	AW	AW	AW	AW	AW	AW	AW	AW
							R										
		◇		◇		◇		◇			◇		◇		◇		◇
							🍴										
Holyhead	d			16 32		17 00	17 23						18 40				20 40
Valley	d																20x46
Rhosneigr	d																20x51
Ty Croes	d																20x55
Bodorgan	d																20x59
Llanfairpwll	d																21x09
Bangor (Gwynedd)	a			16 58		17 26	17 50						19 07				21 17
	d			16 59		17 27	17 51				18 46		19 09		20 11		21 19
Llanfairfechan	d			17x07											20x19		
Penmaenmawr	d			17x11											20x23		
Conwy	d			17x17											20x29		
Llandudno	d	16 41	17 04		17 30			18 10	18 45								
Deganwy	d	16x45	17x08		17x34			18x14	18x49								
Llandudno Junction	a	16 49	17 13	17 21	17 39	17 43	18 08	18 18	18 54		19 02		19 25		20 32		21 36
	d	16 51		17 22		17 45	18 09	18 20			19 04		19 27		20 34		21 37
Colwyn Bay	d	16 57		17 28		17 51	18 15	18 26			19 10		19 33		20 40		21 43
Abergele & Pensarn	d			17 35				18 32			19 17				20 47		21 50
Rhyl	d	17 07		17 41		18 01	18 26	18 38			19 23		19 43		20 53		21 56
Prestatyn	d	17 13		17 47		18 07	18 32	18 44			19 28		19 49		20 58		22 02
Flint	d	17 26		18 00		18 20	18 46	18 57			19 42		20 02		21 12		22 15
Shotton	d			18 08		18 26		19 03			19 48				21 18		22 21
Chester	a	17 40		18 20		18 37	19e03	19 14			19 59		20 16		21 29		22 32
	d	17 41		18 21		18 41	19e07	19 16		19 23	20 21	20 23	20 24	21 20	21 33	22 25	22 35
Liverpool Lime Street [10]	106 a	*18 43*		*19 13*		*19 43*		*20 13*					*21 13*		*22 43*		*23 43*
Helsby	d	17 50						19 25			20 30			21 29			22 44
Frodsham	d	17 54						19 29			20 34			21 33			22 48
Runcorn East	d	18 00						19 34			20 39			21 38			22 53
Warrington Bank Quay	90 a	18 07						19 41			20 48			21 48			23 02
Earlestown [8]	90 a	18 15						19 52			20 56			21 56			23 10
Newton-le-Willows	90 a	18 18						19 55			20 59			21 58			23 12
Manchester Oxford Road	90 a	18 43						20 15			21 24			22 18			23 37
Manchester Piccadilly [10]	90 a	18 50						20f24			21 34			22g27			23 44
Crewe [10]	a			18 44		19 04				19 44		20 50			21 54	22 50	
Cardiff Central [7]	131 a			*21 37*			*22 27*					*00 25*					
Manchester Airport	84, 85 ✈ a																
Birmingham New Street [12]	65 a												22h40				
London Euston [15]	⊖ 65 a																

For general notes see front of timetable
For details of catering facilities see Directory of Train Operators

- A From 20 July
- B 🍴 from Chester
- C Until 13 July
- b From 20 July arr. 1529
- c Until 13 July only
- e From 20 July Chester arr. 1901, dep. 1906
- f From 20 July arr. 2027
- g From 20 July arr. 2228
- h From 20 July arr. 2230

For connections to Birmingham New Street and London Euston, please see Table 65.

Sundays

from 14 September

North Wales and Chester → Manchester and Crewe

Network Diagram - see first page of Table 81

		AW	AW	AW	AW		AW	AW	AW	AW		AW	AW	AW	AW		AW	AW	AW	AW		AW	AW	AW
									A				◇				◇		◇					◇
Holyhead	d												09 56		10 17									
Valley	d												10x02											
Rhosneigr	d												10x07											
Ty Croes	d												10x11											
Bodorgan	d												10x15											
Llanfairpwll	d												10x25											
Bangor (Gwynedd)	a												10 33		10 47									
	d												10 34		10 47				11 56					13 00
Llanfairfechan	d												10x42											13x08
Penmaenmawr	d												10x46											13x12
Conwy	d												10x52											13x18
Llandudno	d								10 15															
Deganwy	d								10 30															
Llandudno Junction	a								10 35				10 56		11 12				12 12					13 21
	d												10 57				11 22		12 14					13 23
Colwyn Bay	d												11 03				11 28		12 20					13 29
Abergele & Pensarn	d																							13 36
Rhyl	d												11 14				11 39		12 30					13 42
Prestatyn	d												11 19				11 45		12 36					13 47
Flint	d												11 33				11 59		12 49					14 01
Shotton	d																12 05		12 55					14 07
Chester	a												11 47				12 17		13 06					14 18
	d	08 25	08 55	09 25	09 55		10 00	10 25		10 55		11 25	11 48	11 54			12 20	12 25	13 08	13 25		13 30	13 55	14 19
Liverpool Lime Street 10	106 a												*12 43*				*13 13*		*14 13*					*15 13*
Helsby	d																					13 39		
Frodsham	d																					13 43		
Runcorn East	d																					13 48		
Warrington Bank Quay	90 a																					13 57		
Earlestown 8	90 a																					14 08		
Newton-le-Willows	90 a																					14 11		
Manchester Oxford Road	90 a																					14 32		
Manchester Piccadilly 10	90 a						11 11							13 00								14 41		
Crewe 10	a	08 50	09 20	09 50	10 20			10 50		11 19		11 49	12 11					12 49	13 31	13 49			14 20	14 45
Cardiff Central 7	131 a				*13 53*												15 31	*16 15*						*18 13*
Manchester Airport	84, 85 a																					*15 21*		
Birmingham New Street 12	65 a																							
London Euston 15	⊖ 65 a																							

		AW	AW	VT		AW	VT	AW	AW		AW	VT	AW	AW		AW	AW	VT	AW		AW	AW	VT	VT
		A		1 ◇		◇	1 ◇ B					1 ◇ C				◇	A	1 ◇ B				◇	1 ◇	1 ◇ C
Holyhead	d			13 14		13 30																	16 21	
Valley	d																							
Rhosneigr	d																							
Ty Croes	d																							
Bodorgan	d																							
Llanfairpwll	d																							
Bangor (Gwynedd)	a			13 42		13 56																	16 49	
	d			13 43		13 58										15 42						16 38	16 50	
Llanfairfechan	d																					16x46		
Penmaenmawr	d																					16x50		
Conwy	d																					16x56		
Llandudno	d	13 15															16 00							
Deganwy	d	13 30															16 15							
Llandudno Junction	a	13 35		14 01		14 14										15 58	16 20					16 58	17 08	
	d			14 03		14 16										16 00						17 00	17 10	
Colwyn Bay	d			14 11		14 22										16 06						17 06	17 18	
Abergele & Pensarn	d																					17 13		
Rhyl	d			14 24		14 32										16 16						17 19	17 31	
Prestatyn	d					14 38										16 22						17 24		
Flint	d					14 51										16 35						17 38		
Shotton	d																							
Chester	a			14 54		15 05										16 50						17 51	18 01	
	d		14 55	15 04		15 08	15 18	15 25	15 54		16 00	16 14	16 25	16 48		16 51		17 01	17 25		17 52	17 53	18 04	18 17
Liverpool Lime Street 10	106 a			*15 43*		*16 13*										*17 43*						*18 43*	*19 13*	
Helsby	d								16 03													18 02		
Frodsham	d								16 07													18 06		
Runcorn East	d								16 12													18 12		
Warrington Bank Quay	90 a					15 31			16 21			16 35				17 12						18 18		18 36
Earlestown 8	90 a					15 39			16 29							17 19						18 27		
Newton-le-Willows	90 a					15 42			16 31							17 22						18 30		
Manchester Oxford Road	90 a					16 03			16 51							17 43						18 51		
Manchester Piccadilly 10	90 a					16 12			17 00							17 51						18 56		
Crewe 10	a		15 20	15 27			15 41	15 49			16 24		16 49	17 13				17 20	17 50		18 16		18 27	
Cardiff Central 7	131 a							*19 08*					*20 15*											
Manchester Airport	84, 85 a																							
Birmingham New Street 12	65 a																							
London Euston 15	⊖ 65 a			18 22			19 00											20 24					21 22	

For general notes see front of timetable
For details of catering facilities see Directory of Train Operators

A To Blaenau Ffestiniog (Table 102)
B From Glasgow Central (Table 65)
C From London Euston to Glasgow Central (Table 65)

For connections to Birmingham New Street and London Euston, please refer to the re-issued Table 65 contained in the September supplement.

from 14 September

North Wales and Chester → Manchester and Crewe

Network Diagram - see first page of Table 81

		AW	VT	AW	AW	AW	AW	AW	AW	AW	VT	AW	AW	AW	AW	AW	AW	AW
			1 ◇	◇	R			◇			1 ◇		◇					◇
			A					B			C							
Holyhead	d			16 48	17 23			18 40										20 35
Valley	d			16x54														20x41
Rhosneigr	d			16x59														20x47
Ty Croes	d			17x03														20x50
Bodorgan	d			17x07														20x55
Llanfairpwll	d			17x17														21x04
Bangor (Gwynedd)	a			17 25	17 50			19 07										21 13
	d			17 27	17 51			19 09					19 55					21 15
Llanfairfechan	d												20x03					
Penmaenmawr	d												20x07					
Conwy	d												20x13					
Llandudno	d																	
Deganwy	d																	
Llandudno Junction	a			17 43	18 08			19 25					20 16					21 32
	d			17 46	18 09			19 27					20 18					21 33
Colwyn Bay	d			17 52	18 15			19 33					20 24					21 39
Abergele & Pensarn	d			17 59									20 31					21 46
Rhyl	d			18 05	18 26			19 43					20 37					21 52
Prestatyn	d			18 10	18 32			19 49					20 42					21 58
Flint	d			18 24	18 46			20 02					20 56					22 11
Shotton	d			18 30									21 02					22 17
Chester	a			18 41	19 01			20 17					21 13					22 28
	d	18 25	18 35	18 46	19 06	19 25	19 55		20 22	20 25	20 50	20 55	21 14	21 19	21 25	21 55	22 25	22 35
Liverpool Lime Street 10	106 a			*19 43*	*20 13*			*21 13*					*22 13*					*23 43*
Helsby	d								20 31					21 28				22 44
Frodsham	d								20 35					21 32				22 48
Runcorn East	d								20 40					21 37				22 53
Warrington Bank Quay	90 a								20 50		21 10			21 46				23 01
Earlestown 8	90 a								20 57					21 54				23 10
Newton-le-Willows	90 a								21 00					21 56				23 12
Manchester Oxford Road	90 a								21 24					22 16				23 35
Manchester Piccadilly 10	90 a								21 33					22 25				23 41
Crewe 10	a	18 49	19 01	19 09		19 49	20 20			20 49		21 19	21 37		21 49	22 19	22 49	
Cardiff Central 7	131 a	*21 37*			22 27							*00 25*						
Manchester Airport	84, 85 a																	
Birmingham New Street 12	65 a		20 10															
London Euston 15	⊖ 65 a																	

For general notes see front of timetable
For details of catering facilities see Directory of Train Operators

A From Edinburgh (Table 65)
B To Shrewsbury (Table 75)
C From London Euston to Liverpool Lime Street (Table 65)

For connections to Birmingham New Street and London Euston, please refer to the re-issued Table 65 contained in the September supplement.

Holyhead — Dublin

Daily

		AW R A	AW R B	AW R C	AW R A	AW R B	AW R C
Holyhead	⛴ d	02 40	08 55	12 00	14 10	15 30	17 15
Dun Laoghaire	⛴ a		10 34			17 09	
Dublin Ferryport §	⛴ a	05 55		13 49	17 25		19 15

Daily

		AW R C	AW R A	AW R B	AW R C	AW R B	AW R A
Dublin Ferryport §	⛴ d	08 45	08 05		14 30		20 55
Dun Laoghaire	⛴ d			11 10		18 00	
Holyhead	⛴ a	10 45	11 30	12 49	16 30	19 39	00 20

For general notes see front of timetable
For details of catering facilities see Directory of Train Operators

§ Bus connections to/from city centre and railway stations

A **Irish Ferries** Cruise Ferry
B **Stena Line** High-Speed Sea Service
C **Irish Ferries** Fast Ferry

Network Diagram for Tables 82, 83

DM-14/07
Design BAJS

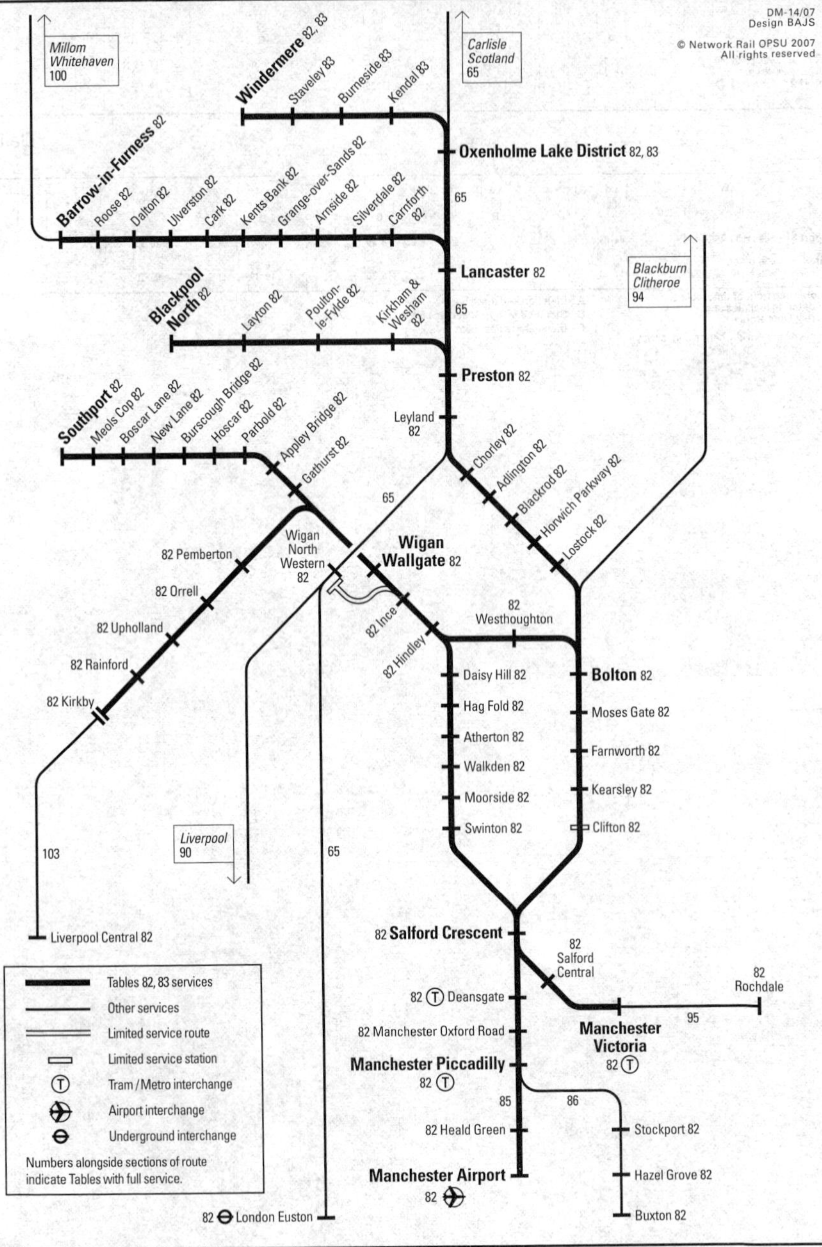

Table 82

Manchester → Bolton → Wigan, Kirkby, Southport, Preston, Blackpool North and Barrow-in-Furness

Mondays to Fridays
until 3 October

Network Diagram - see first page of Table 82

Miles	Miles	Miles	Miles	Miles	Station		NT	TP	TP	NT	VT	NT	NT	TP	NT	NT		NT	NT	TP	NT	NT	NT	NT	TP
							MX A	1 ◇	1 ◇		1 ◇ B (reservations)		C	1 ◇	D					1 ◇		D			1 ◇
0	0	0	—	—	**Manchester Airport**	85 ✈ d		01 06	03 40		*04 34*			05 47						06 19					06 47
1½	1½	1½	—	—	Heald Green	85 d								05 51						06 23					06 51
—	—	—	—	—	Buxton	86 d																			*05 54*
—	—	—	—	—	Hazel Grove	86 d																			*06 27*
—	—	—	—	—	Stockport	84 d												06 17							*06 42*
9¾	9¾	9¾	—	—	**Manchester Piccadilly 10**	d		01 25	03 55		04 58			06 05				06 29		06 44					07 11
10¼	10¼	10¼	—	—	**Manchester Oxford Road**	d								06 10				06 32		06 48					07 15
10½	10½	10½	—	—	Deansgate	d												06 34							
—	—	—	—	—	Rochdale	95 d															*06 24*				
—	—	—	0	—	**Manchester Victoria**	d						06 00			06 26				06 35		06 51	07 00		07 05	
—	—	—	¾	—	Salford Central	d													06 38		06 54	07 03		07 08	
12	12	12	1¾	—	**Salford Crescent**	a						06 05		06 15	06 31			06 38	06 41	06 52	06 57	07 06		07 11	07 21
—	—	—	—	—		d						06 06		06 15	06 31			06 38	06 42	06 53	06 57	07 06		07 11	07 21
—	—	—	5¾	—	Swinton	d																		07 18	
—	—	—	6½	—	Moorside	d																		07 20	
—	—	—	8¼	—	Walkden	d																		07 24	
—	—	—	11¾	—	Atherton	d																		07 29	
—	—	—	13	—	Hag Fold	d																		07 32	
—	—	—	13¼	—	Daisy Hill	d																		07 35	
18	18	18	—	—	Kearsley	d													06 49						
18¾	18	18¾	—	—	Farnworth	d													06 51						
19¾	19¾	19¾	—	—	Moses Gate	d													06 54						
21	21	21	—	—	**Bolton**	a		01s39	04s09			06 16		06 25	06 44			06 48	06 57	07 03	07 07	07 18			07 31
—	—	—	—	—		d						06 17		06 26				06 49	06 58	07 03	07 08				07 32
—	—	25½	—	—	Westhoughton	d						06 24							07 05		07 15				
—	—	28	15¾	—	Hindley	d						06 28							07 09		07 19			07 39	
—	—	29½	17¼	0	Ince	d													07 12					07 42	
—	—	—	—	¾	Wigan North Western	a													07 19						
—	—	30½	18¼	—	**Wigan Wallgate**	a						06 33									07 24			07 45	
—	—	—	—	—		d						06 35				06 40					07 26		07 40	07 47	
—	—	—	20	—	Pemberton	d						06 39											07 44		
—	—	—	22	—	Orrell	d						06 43											07 48		
—	—	—	23¼	—	Upholland	d						06 46											07 51		
—	—	—	25¼	—	Rainford	d						06 50											07 55		
—	—	—	30½	—	**Kirkby**	a						07 00											08 05		
—	—	—	—	—	Liverpool Central 10	103 a						*07 31*											*08 31*		
—	—	33¼	—	—	Gathurst	d										06 44					07 30			07 51	
—	—	35	—	—	Appley Bridge	d										06 48					07 34			07 55	
—	—	37¼	—	—	Parbold	d										06 52					07 38			07 59	
—	—	38¾	—	—	Hoscar	d										06 55								08 02	
—	—	40¼	—	—	Burscough Bridge	d										06 58					07 42			08 05	
—	—	41½	—	—	New Lane	d										07 00								08 07	
—	—	43½	—	—	Bescar Lane	d										07 04								08 11	
—	—	46¾	—	—	Meols Cop	d										07 09					07 50			08 16	
—	—	48	—	—	**Southport**	a										07 16					07 57			08 23	
24	24	—	—	—	Lostock	d								06 30				06 54							07 36
26	26	—	—	—	Horwich Parkway	d								06 34				06 58							07 40
27½	27½	—	—	—	Blackrod	d								06 37				07 01							07 43
29½	29½	—	—	—	Adlington (Lancashire)	d								06 41				07 05							07 46
33½	33½	—	—	—	Chorley	d								06 45				07 09		07 15					07 50
37	37	—	—	—	Leyland	d	00 06							06 51				07 19							07 58
41	41	—	—	—	**Preston 8**	a	00 15	02s10	04s41		05 54			07 00				07 26		07 26					08 06
48¾	—	—	—	—	Kirkham & Wesham	97 a					*06 54*			07 11				07 37		*07 47*					08 15
55¼	—	—	—	—	Poulton-le-Fylde	97 a								07 21				07 46		*08 04*					08 27
57¼	—	—	—	—	Layton	97 a								07 24				07 50							08 30
58½	—	—	—	—	**Blackpool North**	97 a		02 34	05 05					07 31				07 56		*08 12*					08 36
—	—	—	—	—	**Preston 8**	65 d				05 24	06 04									07 29					
—	62	—	—	—	**Lancaster 6**	65 a				05 44	06 18			*07b34*						07 44					
—	—	—	—	—		d				05 45	06 20		07 15							07 45					
—	81	—	—	—	Oxenholme Lake District	65 a					06 34			*07b47*											
—	91	—	—	—	Windermere	83 a					*07 10*			*08c15*											
—	68	—	—	—	Carnforth	d				06 10			07a24							07 53					
—	71¾	—	—	—	Silverdale	d				06 15										08 00					
—	74	—	—	—	Arnside	d				06 20										08 04					
—	77¼	—	—	—	Grange-over-Sands	d				06 26										08 09					
—	79½	—	—	—	Kents Bank	d				06 29										08 13					
—	81½	—	—	—	Cark	d				06 33										08 17					
—	87½	—	—	—	Ulverston	d				06 42										08 25					
—	90¾	—	—	—	Dalton	d				06 50										08 34					
—	95	—	—	—	Roose	d				06 56										08 39					
—	96¾	—	—	—	**Barrow-in-Furness**	a				07 05										08 49					

For general notes see front of timetable
For details of catering facilities see
Directory of Train Operators

A From Liverpool Lime Street (Table 90)
B To Glasgow Central (Table 65)
C To Leeds (Table 36)
D To Clitheroe (Table 94)

b Change at Preston
c Change at Preston and Oxenholme Lake District

Mondays to Fridays
until 3 October

Manchester → Bolton → Wigan, Kirkby, Southport, Preston, Blackpool North and Barrow-in-Furness

Network Diagram - see first page of Table 82

		NT	NT	NT	NT	NT	NT	TP	NT	NT	NT	NT	TP	NT	NT	NT	NT	NT	NT	NT	TP	NT	NT
								1◇					1◇								1◇		
			A		B			C 🍴	D	E	G			D	A	H			H		J 🍴	K	
Manchester Airport 85 ✈	d					07b02		07 22					07 47				08 07				08 27		
Heald Green 85	d							07 26					07 51				08 11				08 31		
Buxton 86	d					06 34							07 04					07 40					
Hazel Grove 86	d					07 10							07 40					08 14					
Stockport 84	d					07 19		07 24					07 49				08 03	08 21			08c27		
Manchester Piccadilly 10	d					07 30		07 45					08 11				08 28	08 32			08 45		
Manchester Oxford Road	d					07 33		07 48					08 15				08 31	08 35			08 48		
Deansgate	d					07 35											08 33	08 37			08 50		
Rochdale 95	d						07 06							07 35	07 52	08 05							08 33
Manchester Victoria	d	07 18	07 23	07 28			07 38		07 49		08 00			08 20	08 23	08 27				08 42			08 57
Salford Central	d	07 21	07 26	07 31			07 40		07 52		08 03			08 23	08 26	08 30				08 45			09 00
Salford Crescent	a	07 25	07 31	07 34		07 40	07 44	07 53	07 56		08 06		08 21	08 26	08 29	08 33	08 37	08 43		08 47	08 54		09 03
	d	07 25	07 31	07 35		07 40	07 44	07 54	07 57		08 07		08 21	08 26	08 29	08 33	08 37	08 43		08 47	08 54		09 04
Swinton	d								08 03							08 42							09 10
Moorside	d								08 06							08 44							
Walkden	d			07 43					08 09							08 48							09 15
Atherton	d			07 49					08 15							08 53							09 20
Hag Fold	d								08 17							08 56			←				
Daisy Hill	d			07 52					08 20							08 59			08 59				09 24
Kearsley	d						07 52									→				08 55			
Farnworth	d						07 54													08 57			
Moses Gate	d						07 56								08 37								
Bolton	a	07 35	07 44			07 51	08 00	08 04			08 18		08 31	08 36	08 42		08 48	08 53		09 01	09 04		
	d	07 36				07 51	08 00	08 04					08 32	08 37			08 49	08 54		09 02	09 05		
Westhoughton	d	07 43					08 08										08 56			09 09			
Hindley	d	07 47					08 12		08 25					08 47					09 03	09 13			09 28
Ince	d	07 50							08 28										09 06				
Wigan North Western	a	07 55																					
Wigan Wallgate	a			08 02			08 19		08 31					08 56			09 04		09 09	09 22			09 33
	d								08 32								09 05		09 11				09 35
Pemberton	d																		09 15				
Orrell	d																		09 19				
Upholland	d																		09 22				
Rainford	d																		09 26				
Kirkby	a																		09 34				
Liverpool Central 10 103	a	08e50																	10 01				
Gathurst	d								08 37														09 39
Appley Bridge	d								08 40														09 43
Parbold	d								08 44														09 47
Hoscar	d																						
Burscough Bridge	d								08 49								09 17						09 51
New Lane	d																						
Bescar Lane	d																						
Meols Cop	d								08 56														09 59
Southport	a								09 06								09 33						10 08
Lostock	d					07 56							08 36					08 59					
Horwich Parkway	d					08 00							08 40					09 03					
Blackrod	d					08 03												09 06					
Adlington (Lancashire)	d					08 07												09 10					
Chorley	d					08 12		08 16				←	08 47					09 15			09 17		
Leyland	d				08 17	08 20						08 20	08 56									09 28	
Preston 8	a				08 24	→		08 27				08 28	09 03					09 27			09 29	09 38	
Kirkham & Wesham 97	a											08 38	09 22					09 38					
Poulton-le-Fylde 97	a											08 48	09 23					09 46					
Layton 97	a											08 52						09 50					
Blackpool North 97	a				08 51							08 59	09 32					09 57					
Preston 8 65	d							08 28													09 32	09 44	
Lancaster 6 65	a							08 44				09f00	09f31					09f55			09 47	10 03	
	d							08 44		08 54											09 48		
Oxenholme Lake District 65	a							08 58				09f17	09f45								10 10		
Windermere 83	a							09 22					10g13										
Carnforth	d									09 03											09 57		
Silverdale	d									09 09													
Arnside	d									09 13											10 06		
Grange-over-Sands	d									09 19											10 11		
Kents Bank	d									09 23													
Cark	d									09 27													
Ulverston	d									09 35											10 24		
Dalton	d									09 43													
Roose	d									09 49													
Barrow-in-Furness	a									09 57											10 46		

For general notes see front of timetable
For details of catering facilities see Directory of Train Operators

- **A** To Blackburn (Table 94)
- **B** From Liverpool Lime Street (Table 90)
- **C** To Edinburgh (Table 65)
- **D** From Huddersfield (Table 39)
- **E** To Carlisle via Whitehaven (Table 100)
- **G** To Clitheroe (Table 94)
- **H** From Todmorden (Table 41)
- **J** 🍴 to Preston
- **K** From Liverpool Lime Street (Table 90) to Morecambe (Table 98)
- **b** Change at Manchester Piccadilly
- **c** Change at Manchester Oxford Road
- **e** Liverpool Lime Street (Table 90)
- **f** Change at Preston
- **g** Change at Preston and Oxenholme Lake District

Table 82

Manchester → Bolton → Wigan, Kirkby, Southport, Preston, Blackpool North and Barrow-in-Furness

Mondays to Fridays until 3 October

Network Diagram - see first page of Table 82

	NT A	NT B	TP [1]◇ C (bicycle)		NT	NT D	NT	NT	NT	NT	TP [1]◇ E (bicycle)	NT G	NT	NT A		NT	NT B	TP [1]◇ (bicycle)	NT H	NT	NT	NT	NT J
Manchester Airport 85 d			08 47				09 07				09 27							09 47			10 07		
Heald Green 85 d			*08 37*				*08 56*				09 31										*09 56*		
Buxton 86 d			*07 57*						08 36														
Hazel Grove 86 d			*08 33*						09 10									*09 41*					
Stockport 84 d			*08 51*				*09b02*		09 19		*09b24*							*09 49*			*10b02*		10 18
Manchester Piccadilly [10] d			09 11				09 23		09 33		09 45							10 11			10 23		10 30
Manchester Oxford Road d			09 15				09 26		09 36		09 48							10 15			10 26		10 33
Deansgate d							09 28		09 38														10 35
Rochdale 95 d					*08 52*			09 03					09 33							*09 53*		10 03	
Manchester Victoria d	09 00				09 18			09 29		09 41			09 57	10 00					10 13	10 18		10 29	
Salford Central d	09 03				09 21			09 32		09 44			10 00	10 03						10 21		10 32	
Salford Crescent a	09 06		09 21		09 24		09 32	09 35	09 43	09 47	09 53		10 03	10 06				10 21		10 24	10 32	10 35	10 40
d	09 07		09 21		09 24		09 32	09 35	09 43	09 47	09 54		10 04	10 07				10 21		10 24	10 32	10 35	10 40
Swinton d								09 42					10 10									10 42	
Moorside d								09 44														10 44	
Walkden d								09 48					10 15						10 28			10 48	
Atherton d								09 53					10 20						10 33			10 53	
Hag Fold d								09 56														10 56	
Daisy Hill d								09 59					10 24						10 37			10 59	
Kearsley d										09 55													
Farnworth d										09 57													
Moses Gate d					09 32															10 32			
Bolton a	09 18		09 31		09 36		09 42		09 53	10 01	10 04			10 18				10 31		10 36	10 42		10 50
d			09 32		09 36		09 43		09 54	10 02	10 05							10 32		10 36	10 43		10 51
Westhoughton d							09 50			10 09											10 50		
Hindley d								10 03		10 13			10 28						10 41			11 03	
Ince d								10 06														11 06	
Wigan North Western a																			10 48				
Wigan Wallgate a					09 54		10 01	10 09		10 20			10 33							10 54	11 01	11 09	
d							10 02	10 11					10 35								11 02	11 11	
Pemberton d								10 15														11 15	
Orrell d								10 19														11 19	
Upholland d								10 22														11 22	
Rainford d								10 26														11 26	
Kirkby a								10 35														11 35	
Liverpool Central [10] 103 a								*11 01*														*12 01*	
Gathurst d													10 39										
Appley Bridge d							10 09						10 43								11 09		
Parbold d							10 13						10 47								11 13		
Hoscar d													10 50										
Burscough Bridge d							10 17						10 53								11 17		
New Lane d													10 55										
Bescar Lane d													10 59										
Meols Cop d													11 04										
Southport a							10 34						11 13								11 34		
Lostock d									09 59									10 36					10 56
Horwich Parkway d			09 39						10 03									10 40					11 00
Blackrod d									10 06														11 03
Adlington (Lancashire) d									10 10														11 07
Chorley d			09 46						10 15		10 17							10 47					11 12
Leyland d		09 47	09 53														10 47	10 56					
Preston [8] a		09 54	09 58						10 27		10 27						10 54	11 03	11 09				11 26
Kirkham & Wesham 97 a			*10 21*						10 38									*11 21*					11 35
Poulton-le-Fylde 97 a			10 18						10 46									11 23					11 43
Layton 97 a									10 50														11 47
Blackpool North 97 a		10 21	10 28						10 57								11 21	11 32	11 36				11 54
Preston [8] 65 d			10 06			10 10					10 29												
Lancaster [6] 65 a			10 23			10 30					10 44							*11c32*	*11c32*				
d			10 23			10 30					10 45	11 02				11 11							
Oxenholme Lake District 65 a			10 43						*11c11*		11 03							*11c46*	*11c46*				
Windermere 83 a			11 01															*12e14*	*12e14*				
Carnforth d						10 40						11a11				11 20							
Silverdale d						10 45										11 26							
Arnside d						10 50										11 30							
Grange-over-Sands d						10 56										11 36							
Kents Bank d						10 59										11 40							
Cark d						11 03										11 44							
Ulverston d						11 12										11 52							
Dalton d						11 20										12 00							
Roose d						11 26										12 06							
Barrow-in-Furness a						11 33										12 16							

For general notes see front of timetable
For details of catering facilities see Directory of Train Operators

A To Clitheroe (Table 94)
B From Liverpool Lime Street (Table 90)
C (bicycle) to Blackpool North
D To Carlisle via Whitehaven (Table 100)
E To Glasgow Central (Table 65)
G From Morecambe to Leeds (Table 36)
H Until 12 September
J From Northwich (Table 88)
b Change at Manchester Oxford Road
c Change at Preston
e Change at Preston and Oxenholme Lake District

Manchester → Bolton → Wigan, Kirkby, Southport, Preston, Blackpool North and Barrow-in-Furness

Network Diagram - see first page of Table 82

Station		NT	TP	NT	NT	NT	NT	TP	NT	NT	NT	NT	NT	TP	NT	NT	NT	NT	NT	TP	NT	NT	NT
			1 ◇					1 ◇						1 ◇						1 ◇			
			A		B	C	D							E		B	G	D	H				
			(trolley)					(trolley)						(trolley)						(trolley)			
Manchester Airport	85 ✈ d		10 27					10 47		11 07				11 27						11 47		12 07	
Heald Green	85 d		10 31							*10 56*				11 31								*11 56*	
Buxton	86 d		*09 36*									10 37											
Hazel Grove	86 d		*10 12*					*10 41*				11 10								*11 41*			
Stockport	84 d		*10b25*					*10 49*		*11b02*		11 19		*11b25*						*11 49*		*12b02*	
Manchester Piccadilly 10	⛴ d		10 45			10 55		11 11		11 23		11 30		11 45						12 11		12 23	
Manchester Oxford Road	d		10 48			11 00		11 15		11 26		11 33		11 48						12 15		12 26	
Deansgate	⛴ d		10 50									11 35											
Rochdale	95 d			10 33					*10 50*		11 03				11 33						*11 50*		12 03
Manchester Victoria	⛴ d	10 41		10 57	11 00				11 18		11 29		11 41		11 57	12 00					12 18		12 29
Salford Central	d	10 44		11 00	11 03				11 21		11 32		11 44		12 00	12 03					12 21		12 32
Salford Crescent	a	10 47	10 53	11 03	11 06	11 09		11 21	11 24	11 32	11 35	11 40	11 47	11 53	12 03	12 06				12 21	12 24	12 32	12 35
	d	10 47	10 54	11 04	11 07	11 10		11 21	11 24	11 32	11 35	11 40	11 47	11 54	12 04	12 07				12 21	12 24	12 32	12 35
Swinton	d			11 10							11 42				12 10								12 42
Moorside	d										11 44												12 44
Walkden	d			11 15							11 48				12 15								12 48
Atherton	d			11 20							11 53				12 20								12 53
Hag Fold	d										11 56												12 56
Daisy Hill	d			11 24							11 59				12 24								12 59
Kearsley	d	10 55											11 55										
Farnworth	d	10 57											11 57										
Moses Gate	d								11 32												12 32		
Bolton	a	11 01	11 05		11 18	11 22		11 31	11 36	11 42		11 50	12 01	12 05		12 18				12 31	12 36	12 42	
	d	11 02	11 05			11 22		11 32	11 36	11 43		11 51	12 02	12 05						12 32	12 36	12 43	
Westhoughton	d	11 09								11 50			12 09									12 50	
Hindley	d	11 13		11 28							12 03		12 13		12 28								13 03
Ince	d										12 06												13 06
Wigan North Western	a																						
Wigan Wallgate	a	11 20		11 33					11 54	12 01	12 09		12 20		12 33						12 54	13 01	13 09
	d			11 35						12 02	12 11				12 35							13 02	13 11
Pemberton	d										12 15												13 15
Orrell	d										12 19												13 19
Upholland	d										12 22												13 22
Rainford	d										12 26												13 26
Kirkby	a										12 35												13 35
Liverpool Central 10	103 a										*13 01*												*14 01*
Gathurst	d			11 39											12 39								
Appley Bridge	d			11 43						12 09					12 43							13 09	
Parbold	d			11 47						12 13					12 47							13 13	
Hoscar	d			11 50																			
Burscough Bridge	d			11 53						12 17					12 51							13 17	
New Lane	d			11 55																			
Bescar Lane	d			11 59																			
Meols Cop	d			12 04											12 59								
Southport	a			12 14						12 34					13 08							13 34	
Lostock	d							11 36				11 56								12 36			
Horwich Parkway	d							11 40				12 00								12 40			
Blackrod	d											12 03											
Adlington (Lancashire)	d											12 07											
Chorley	d		11 17					11 47				12 12		12 17						12 47			
Leyland	d						11 46	11 56										12 47		12 56			
Preston 8	a		11 27			11 46	11 53	12 04				12 24		12 27				12 56		13 04			
Kirkham & Wesham	97 a							*12 23*				12 35								*13 21*			
Poulton-le-Fylde	97 a		*11 52*					12 23				12 43								13 23			
Layton	97 a											12 47											
Blackpool North	97 a		*12 01*			12 11	12 20	12 32				12 54						13 21		13 32			
Preston 8	65 d		11 29											12 29									
Lancaster 6	65 a		11 44					*12c32*						12 44						*13c38*			
	d		11 45											12 45			13 12		13 15				
Oxenholme Lake District	65 a							*12c46*						12 59									
Windermere	83 a							*13c18*						*14 13*									
Carnforth	d		11 53														13 21		13a25				
Silverdale	d		12 00																				
Arnside	d		12 04																				
Grange-over-Sands	d		12 09														13 36						
Kents Bank	d		12 13																				
Cark	d		12 17																				
Ulverston	d		12 25														13 49						
Dalton	d		12 34																				
Roose	d		12 39																				
Barrow-in-Furness	a		12 49														14 07						

For general notes see front of timetable
For details of catering facilities see Directory of Train Operators

- **A** (trolley) to Preston
- **B** To Clitheroe (Table 94)
- **C** Until 5 September
- **D** From Liverpool Lime Street (Table 90)
- **E** To Edinburgh (Table 65)
- **G** To Carlisle via Whitehaven (Table 100)
- **H** From Morecambe to Leeds (Table 36)
- **b** Change at Manchester Oxford Road
- **c** Change at Preston

Table 82

Mondays to Fridays

until 3 October

Manchester → Bolton → Wigan, Kirkby, Southport, Preston, Blackpool North and Barrow-in-Furness

Network Diagram - see first page of Table 82

Station		NT	NT	TP 1◇ A 🛒	NT	NT B	NT C	NT D	TP 1◇ E 🛒	NT	NT	NT	NT	NT	TP 1◇ G 🛒	NT	NT B	NT C	TP 1◇ 🛒	NT	NT	NT
Manchester Airport	85 ✈ d			12 27					12 47		13 07				13 27				13 47		14 07	
Heald Green	85 d			12 31							*12 56*				13 31						*13 56*	
Buxton	86 d	11 34											12 37									
Hazel Grove	86 d	12 10							*12 41*				13 10						*13 41*			
Stockport	84 d	12 19		*12b25*					*12 49*		*13b02*		13 19		*13b25*				*13 49*		*14b02*	
Manchester Piccadilly 10	🚇 d	12 30		12 45					13 11		13 23		13 30		13 45				14 11		14 23	
Manchester Oxford Road	d	12 33		12 48					13 15		13 26		13 33		13 48				14 15		14 26	
Deansgate	🚇 d	12 35		12 50									13 35									
Rochdale	95 d				12 33					*12 52*		13 03				13 33				*13 50*		14 03
Manchester Victoria	🚇 d		12 41		12 57	13 00				13 18		13 29		13 41		13 57	14 00			14 18		14 29
Salford Central	d		12 44		13 00	13 03				13 21		13 32		13 44		14 00	14 03			14 21		14 32
Salford Crescent	a	12 40	12 47	12 53	13 03	13 06			13 21	13 24	13 32	13 35	13 40	13 47	13 53	14 03	14 06		14 21	14 24	14 32	14 35
	d	12 40	12 47	12 54	13 04	13 07			13 21	13 24	13 32	13 35	13 40	13 47	13 54	14 04	14 07		14 21	14 24	14 32	14 35
Swinton	d				13 10							13 42				14 10						14 42
Moorside	d											13 44										14 44
Walkden	d				13 15							13 48				14 15						14 48
Atherton	d				13 20							13 53				14 20						14 53
Hag Fold	d											13 56										14 56
Daisy Hill	d				13 24							13 59				14 24						14 59
Kearsley	d		12 55											13 55								
Farnworth	d		12 57											13 57								
Moses Gate	d									13 32										14 32		
Bolton	a	12 50	13 01	13 05		13 18			13 31	13 36	13 42		13 50	14 01	14 05		14 18		14 31	14 36	14 42	
	d	12 51	13 02	13 05					13 32	13 36	13 43		13 51	14 02	14 05				14 32	14 36	14 43	
Westhoughton	d		13 09								13 50			14 09							14 50	
Hindley	d		13 13		13 28							14 03		14 13		14 28						15 03
Ince	d											14 06										15 06
Wigan North Western	a																					
Wigan Wallgate	a		13 20		13 33					13 54	14 01	14 09		14 20		14 33				14 54	15 01	15 09
	d				13 35						14 02	14 11				14 35					15 02	15 11
Pemberton	d											14 15										15 15
Orrell	d											14 19										15 19
Upholland	d											14 22										15 22
Rainford	d											14 26										15 26
Kirkby	a											14 35										15 35
Liverpool Central 10	103 a											*15 01*										*16 01*
Gathurst	d				13 39											14 39						
Appley Bridge	d				13 43						14 09					14 43					15 09	
Parbold	d				13 47						14 13					14 47					15 13	
Hoscar	d				13 50																	
Burscough Bridge	d				13 53						14 17					14 51					15 17	
New Lane	d				13 55																	
Bescar Lane	d				13 59																	
Meols Cop	d				14 04											14 59						
Southport	a				14 13						14 34					15 08					15 34	
Lostock	d	12 56							13 36				13 56						14 36			
Horwich Parkway	d	13 00							13 40				14 00						14 40			
Blackrod	d	13 03											14 03									
Adlington (Lancashire)	d	13 07											14 07									
Chorley	d	13 12		13 17					13 47				14 12		14 17				14 47			
Leyland	d						13 47		13 56									14 47	14 56			
Preston 8	a	13 24		13 27			13 54		14 04				14 24		14 27			14 54	15 04			
Kirkham & Wesham	97 a	13 35							*14 21*				14 35						*15 21*			
Poulton-le-Fylde	97 a	13 43							14 23				14 43						15 23			
Layton	97 a	13 47											14 47									
Blackpool North	97 a	13 54					14 21		14 32				14 54					15 21	15 32			
Preston 8	65 d			13 29					14 09						14 29							
Lancaster 6	65 a			13 44					14 24						14 44				*15c38*			
	d			13 45				14 17	14 26						14 45							
Oxenholme Lake District	65 a			*14 08*					14 42						14 59							
Windermere	83 a								15 09						*16 10*							
Carnforth	d			13 53				14 27														
Silverdale	d							14 33														
Arnside	d			14 02				14 37														
Grange-over-Sands	d			14 07				14 43														
Kents Bank	d							14 47														
Cark	d							14 51														
Ulverston	d			14 20				14 59														
Dalton	d							15 07														
Roose	d							15 13														
Barrow-in-Furness	a			14 41				15 21														

For general notes see front of timetable
For details of catering facilities see Directory of Train Operators

- **A** 🛒 to Preston
- **B** To Clitheroe (Table 94)
- **C** From Liverpool Lime Street (Table 90)
- **D** To Sellafield (Table 100)
- **E** 🛒 to Blackpool North
- **G** To Edinburgh (Table 65)
- **b** Change at Manchester Oxford Road
- **c** Change at Preston

Manchester → Bolton → Wigan, Kirkby, Southport, Preston, Blackpool North and Barrow-in-Furness

Network Diagram - see first page of Table 82

Station	NT	NT	TP	NT		NT	NT	TP	NT	NT	NT	NT	NT	NT	TP		NT	NT	NT	NT	NT	TP	NT	NT
			1 ◇					1 ◇							1 ◇							1 ◇		
			A			B	C							D	E		B	G			C		B	
			🛒					🛒							🛒							🛒		
Manchester Airport 85 ✈ d			14 27					14 47		15 07					15 27							15 47		16 07
Heald Green 85 d			14 31							*14 56*					15 31									*15 56*
Buxton 86 d	13 34											14 37												
Hazel Grove 86 d	14 09							*14 41*				15 10										*15 41*		
Stockport 84 d	14 19		*14b25*					*14 49*		*15b02*		15 19			*15b25*							*15 49*		*16b02*
Manchester Piccadilly 10 d	14 30		14 45					15 11		15 23		15 30			15 45							16 11		16 23
Manchester Oxford Road d	14 33		14 48					15 15		15 26		15 33			15 48							16 15		16 26
Deansgate d	14 35		14 50									15 35												16 28
Rochdale 95 d				14 33					*14 52*		15 03						*15 23*		15 33				*15 54*	
Manchester Victoria d		14 41		14 57		15 00			15 18		15 29		15 41				15 50		15 57	16 10			16 23	
Salford Central d		14 44		15 00		15 03			15 21		15 32		15 44				15 53		16 00	16 13			16 26	
Salford Crescent a	14 40	14 47	14 53	15 03		15 06		15 21	15 24	15 32	15 35	15 40	15 47		15 53		15 56		16 03	16 16		16 21	16 29	16 32
d	14 40	14 47	14 54	15 04		15 07		15 21	15 24	15 32	15 35	15 40	15 47		15 54		15 57		16 04	16 16		16 21	16 30	16 32
Swinton d				15 10							15 42								16 10					
Moorside d											15 44													
Walkden d				15 15							15 48								16 15					
Atherton d				15 20							15 53								16 20					
Hag Fold d											15 56													
Daisy Hill d				15 24							15 59								16 24					
Kearsley d		14 55											15 55											
Farnworth d		14 57											15 57											
Moses Gate d									15 32											16 24				
Bolton a	14 50	15 01	15 05			15 18		15 31	15 36	15 42		15 50	16 01		16 05		16 08			16 28		16 31	16 42	16 43
d	14 51	15 02	15 05					15 32	15 36	15 43		15 51	16 02		16 05					16 28		16 32		16 43
Westhoughton d		15 09								15 50			16 09							16 36				16 50
Hindley d		15 13		15 28							16 03		16 13						16 28	16 40				
Ince d											16 06									16 43				
Wigan North Western a																								
Wigan Wallgate a		15 20		15 33					15 54	16 01	16 09		16 20						16 33	16 50				17 01
d				15 35						16 02	16 11								16 35					17 02
Pemberton d											16 15													
Orrell d											16 19													
Upholland d											16 22													
Rainford d											16 26													
Kirkby a											16 35													
Liverpool Central 10 103 a											*17 01*													
Gathurst d				15 39						16 07									16 39					17 06
Appley Bridge d				15 43						16 10									16 43					17 10
Parbold d				15 47						16 14									16 47					17 14
Hoscar d										16 17														
Burscough Bridge d				15 51						16 20									16 51					17 18
New Lane d										16 23														
Bescar Lane d										16 26														
Meols Cop d				15 59						16 31									16 59					17 26
Southport a				16 08						16 41									17 08					17 35
Lostock d	14 56							15 36				15 56										16 36		
Horwich Parkway d	15 00							15 40				16 00										16 40		
Blackrod d	15 03											16 03												
Adlington (Lancashire) d	15 07											16 07												
Chorley d	15 12		15 17					15 47				16 12			16 17							16 47		
Leyland d							15 47	15 56													16 47	16 56		
Preston 8 a	15 24		15 27				15 54	16 04				16 24			16 27						16 54	17 04		
Kirkham & Wesham 97 a	15 35							*16 23*				16 35										17 15		
Poulton-le-Fylde 97 a	15 43							16 23				16 43										17 25		
Layton 97 a	15 47											16 47										17 28		
Blackpool North 97 a	15 54						16 21	16 32				16 54										17 34		
Preston 8 65 d			15 29												16 29						16 56			
Lancaster 6 65 a			15 44					*16c32*							16 44						17 16	*17c32*		
d			15 52											16 39	16 45			16 54			17 16			
Oxenholme Lake District 65 a								*16c46*							16 59									
Windermere 83 a															*17 23*									
Carnforth d			16 01											16 49				17a03			17 26			
Silverdale d			16 07											16 55							17 31			
Arnside d			16 11											16 59							17 36			
Grange-over-Sands d			16 16											17 05							17 44			
Kents Bank d			16 20											17 09							17 47			
Cark d			16 25											17 13							17 51			
Ulverston d			16 33											17 22							18 00			
Dalton d			16 41											17 30							18 08			
Roose d			16 47											17 36							18 14			
Barrow-in-Furness a			16 56											17 44							18 23			

For general notes see front of timetable
For details of catering facilities see Directory of Train Operators

A 🛒 to Preston
B To Clitheroe (Table 94)
C From Liverpool Lime Street (Table 90)
D To Millom (Table 100)
E To Edinburgh (Table 65)
G From Morecambe to Skipton (Table 36)
b Change at Manchester Oxford Road
c Change at Preston

Manchester → Bolton → Wigan, Kirkby, Southport, Preston, Blackpool North and Barrow-in-Furness

Network Diagram - see first page of Table 82

Station		NT	NT	NT	TP	NT	NT	NT	NT	NT	NT	TP	NT	NT	NT	NT	NT	NT	NT	NT	TP
					1 ◇					BHX		1 ◇									1 ◇
					A 🛒		B		C	D		E 🛒			G	H	B			J	K 🛒
Manchester Airport	85 ✈ d				16 27							16 47						17b04			17 32
Heald Green	85 d				16 31													16b56			
Buxton	86 d							15 47										16 36			
Hazel Grove	86 d		16 10					16 28				16 41						17 09			
Stockport	84 d		16 19		16c25			16 41				16 49		16 59				17 18			17 26
Manchester Piccadilly 10	🚋 d		16 30		16 44			16 52				17 11		17 15				17 32			17 50
Manchester Oxford Road	d		16 33		16 48			16 56				17 15		17 19				17 35			17 53
Deansgate	🚋 d		16 35					16 59						17 21				17 38			
Rochdale	95 d	16 03				16 23				16 33			16 52			17 03					
Manchester Victoria	🚋 d	16 29		16 41		16 48			17 00	17 05	17 10		17 15		17 23	17 29			17 38	17 42	
Salford Central	d	16 32		16 44		16 51			17 03	17 08	17 13		17 18		17 26	17 32			17 41	17 45	
Salford Crescent	a	16 35	16 40	16 47		16 54		17 02	17 06		17 16		17 22	17 26	17 29	17 35		17 42	17 45	17 48	17 59
	d	16 35	16 40	16 47		16 54		17 03	17 06		17 16		17 23	17 26	17 30	17 36		17 42	17 46	17 49	18 00
Swinton	d	16 42				17 01							17 29								
Moorside	d	16 44				17 03							17 32								
Walkden	d	16 47				17 09							17 36								
Atherton	d	16 54				17 14					17 29		17 42						17 55		
Hag Fold	d	16 56				17 17							17 44						18 01		
Daisy Hill	d	16 59				17 20					17 33		17 47						18 05		
Kearsley	d			16 55												17 43				17 59	
Farnworth	d			16 57											17 38					18 01	
Moses Gate	d			16 59											17 41					18 03	
Bolton	a		16 50	17 02	17 05			17 13	17 18	17 22		17 30		17 36	17 44	17 49		17 53		18 07	18 10
	d		16 51	17 02	17 05			17 13		17 22		17 30		17 37	17 45			17 53		18 07	18 10
Westhoughton	d			17 10											17 52					18 15	
Hindley	d	17 03		17 17		17 24							17 52		17 56					18 19	
Ince	d	17 06				17 27							17 55		17 59						
Wigan North Western	a			17 26		17 36									18 07					18 27	
Wigan Wallgate	a	17 10									17 43		17 58						18 14		
	d	17 11									17 43		17 59						18 14		
Pemberton	d	17 15											18 03								
Orrell	d	17 19											18 07								
Upholland	d	17 22											18 11								
Rainford	d	17 26											18 14								
Kirkby	a	17 35											18 23								
Liverpool Central 10	103 a	18 01											18 46								
Gathurst	d										17 47								18 19		
Appley Bridge	d										17 51								18 23		
Parbold	d										17 56								18 27		
Hoscar	d																				
Burscough Bridge	d										18 01								18 32		
New Lane	d																				
Bescar Lane	d																				
Meols Cop	d										18 09								18 40		
Southport	a										18 18								18 49		
Lostock	d		16 56					17 18		17 27				17 42				17 58			18 15
Horwich Parkway	d		17 00					17 22						17 46				18 02			
Blackrod	d		17 03					17 25						17 49				18 05			
Adlington (Lancashire)	d		17 07					17 29						17 53				18 09			
Chorley	d		17 12		17 17			17 34		17 39		17 42		17 57				18 14			
Leyland	d		17 19				17 25	17 40						18 04			18 09	18 20			18 24
Preston 8	a		17 27		17 27		17 40	17 50		17 53		17 53		18 12			18 17	18 28			18 34
Kirkham & Wesham	97 a		17 38		18 04					18 04		18 10		18 22				18 40			18 51
Poulton-le-Fylde	97 a		17 47		17 53					18 13		18 20		18 32				18 49			19 01
Layton	97 a		17 51									18 24		18 36				18 53			19 05
Blackpool North	97 a		17 58		18 03					18 22		18 30		18 43			18 48	19 00			19 11
Preston 8	65 d				17 29							17 58									18 38
Lancaster 6	65 a				17 44					18e31		18 13									18 54
	d				17 45							18 14									18 55
Oxenholme Lake District	65 a				18 11					18e47		18 28						19e13			
Windermere	83 a											19 18									
Carnforth	d				17 53																19 03
Silverdale	d				18 00																19 09
Arnside	d				18 04																19 14
Grange-over-Sands	d				18 09																19 19
Kents Bank	d				18 13																19 23
Cark	d				18 17																19 28
Ulverston	d				18 25																19 36
Dalton	d				18 34																19 44
Roose	d				18 39																19 50
Barrow-in-Furness	a				18 50																19 59

For general notes see front of timetable
For details of catering facilities see Directory of Train Operators

A 🛒 to Preston
B From Liverpool Lime Street (Table 90)
C To Clitheroe (Table 94)
D From Stalybridge (Table 39)
E Oxenholme Lake District portion continues to Glasgow Central (Table 65)
G From Huddersfield (Table 39)
H To Colne (Table 97)
J Also stops at Clifton 1754
K 🛒 to Blackpool North
b Change at Manchester Piccadilly
c Change at Manchester Oxford Road
e Change at Preston

Table 82

Mondays to Fridays

until 3 October

Manchester → Bolton → Wigan, Kirkby, Southport, Preston, Blackpool North and Barrow-in-Furness

Network Diagram - see first page of Table 82

	NT	NT	NT	TP		NT	NT	NT	NT	NT	NT	NT	NT	NT	TP		NT	TP	NT	NT	NT	NT	TP	NT
	A		B	1 ◇		C		A			D				1 ◇ E		B	1 ◇			A		1 ◇	B
				🍴											🍴			🍴						
Manchester Airport 85 ✈ d				17 47					18 10						18 27			18 47		18b52		19 12	19 27	
Heald Green 85 d				17 22					17 56						18 31					18b56			19 31	
Buxton 86 d									17 06				17 34							18 22				
Hazel Grove 86 d									17 40				18 10					18 22		18 55				
Stockport 84 d				17 39					17 56				18 19		18c26			18 39		19 05		19 06	19c24	
Manchester Piccadilly 10 d				18 11					18 26				18 31		18 45			19 11		19 26		19 33	19 44	
Manchester Oxford Road d				18 15					18 29				18 34		18 48			19 15		19 29		19 37	19 47	
Deansgate d				18 17					18 31				18 36		18 50			19 17		19 33			19 49	
Rochdale 95 d		17 33				17 52	18 03										18 23		18 32					19 23
Manchester Victoria d		17 57	18 00			18 21	18 29							18 41			18 58		19 18					19 58
Salford Central d		18 00	18 03			18 24	18 32							18 44			19 01		19 21					20 01
Salford Crescent a		18 03	18 07	18 19		18 27	18 35		18 38				18 42	18 47	18 59		19 04	19 21	19 24	19 38		19 42	19 52	20 04
d		18 04	18 07	18 21		18 28	18 35		18 39				18 42	18 47	19 01		19 05	19 21	19 25			19 42	19 53	20 05
Swinton d		18 10					18 42												19 31					
Moorside d		18 13					18 44												19 34					
Walkden d		18 16					18 48												19 37					
Atherton d		18 22					18 53												19 43					
Hag Fold d		18 24					18 56			←									19 45					
Daisy Hill d		18 27					18 59			18 59									19 48					
Kearsley d							→							18 55										
Farnworth d														18 57										
Moses Gate d														19 00										
Bolton a			18 19	18 32		18 44			18 49				18 50	19 03	19 11		19 17	19 31				19 52	20 03	20 17
d				18 32					18 50				18 51	19 04	19 12			19 32				19 53	20 04	
Westhoughton d									18 57					19 11								20 00		
Hindley d		18 32								19 05				19 15					19 53			20 04		
Ince d		18 35								19 08									19 56					
Wigan North Western a																								
Wigan Wallgate a		18 39							19 05	19 13				19 23					20 01			20 09		
d		18 39							19 06													20 11		
Pemberton d																								
Orrell d																								
Upholland d																								
Rainford d																								
Kirkby a																								
Liverpool Central 10 103 a																								
Gathurst d		18 44							19 11													20 15		
Appley Bridge d		18 47							19 14													20 19		
Parbold d		18 51							19 18													20 23		
Hoscar d									19 21															
Burscough Bridge d		18 56							19 24													20 27		
New Lane d									19 27															
Bescar Lane d									19 30															
Meols Cop d		19 03							19 35													20 35		
Southport a		19 13							19 45													20 44		
Lostock d				18 36									18 56		19 17			19 36						
Horwich Parkway d				18 40									19 00					19 40						
Blackrod d				18 43									19 03					19 43						
Adlington (Lancashire) d													19 07					19 47						
Chorley d				18 51									19 12		19 26			19 51					20 15	
Leyland d	18 44			18 58				19 07					19 20					19 58			20 07			
Preston 8 a	18 54			19 05				19 17					19 27		19 44			20 05			20 17		20 26	
Kirkham & Wesham 97 a				19 16									19 37					20 15						
Poulton-le-Fylde 97 a	19 14			19 26									19 45					20 26			20 49			
Layton 97 a													19 49					20 30						
Blackpool North 97 a	19 23			19 35									19 57					20 36			20 56			
Preston 8 65 d															19 50								20 27	
Lancaster 6 65 a				19e33									19e59		20 05			20e32					20 44	
d											19 24	19 39			20 06								20 51	
Oxenholme Lake District 65 a				19e46									20e13		20 20								20e59	
Windermere 83 a				20f18																			21f24	
Carnforth d											19a33	19 49											21 00	
Silverdale d												19 54											21 06	
Arnside d												19 59											21 10	
Grange-over-Sands d												20 05											21 16	
Kents Bank d												20 08											21 20	
Cark d												20 12											21 24	
Ulverston d												20 21											21 32	
Dalton d												20 29											21 41	
Roose d												20 35											21 46	
Barrow-in-Furness a												20 44											21 56	

For general notes see front of timetable
For details of catering facilities see Directory of Train Operators

- **A** From Liverpool Lime Street (Table 90)
- **B** To Clitheroe (Table 94)
- **C** To Blackburn (Table 94)
- **D** From Morecambe to Leeds (Table 36)
- **E** To Glasgow Central (Table 65)
- **b** Change at Manchester Piccadilly
- **c** Change at Manchester Oxford Road
- **e** Change at Preston
- **f** Change at Preston and Oxenholme Lake District

Table 82

Mondays to Fridays

until 3 October

Manchester → Bolton → Wigan, Kirkby, Southport, Preston, Blackpool North and Barrow-in-Furness

Network Diagram - see first page of Table 82

	TP 1 ◇	NT	NT	NT	NT A	NT	TP 1 ◇	NT	NT	TP 1 ◇	NT B	TP 1 ◇ C	NT D	TP 1 ◇	NT	NT	NT	NT	NT B	TP 1 ◇	NT
Manchester Airport 85 d	19 47		20 15	20b22			20 47		21 16	21 27				21 47		21b52		22b22		22 47	
Heald Green 85 d			19 56	20b07					20 56	21 08						21b56		22b12		22 52	
Buxton 86 d	18 55			19 55												21 38					
Hazel Grove 86 d	19 31			20 31												22 14					
Stockport 84 d	19 40		19 57	20 40					21 10	21c17				21 39		22 23		22 38		22 39	
Manchester Piccadilly [10] d	20 11		20 32	20 52			21 11		21 35	21 43				22 11		22 35		22 49		23 11	
Manchester Oxford Road d	20 15		20 35	20 54			21 15		21 38	21 46				22 15		22 38		22 52		23 15	
Deansgate d	20 17		20 37	20 56			21 17		21 40	21 48				22 17		22 40		22 54		23 17	
Rochdale 95 d		19 52			20 02			20 52			21 02				21 52				22 02		
Manchester Victoria d		20 21			20 58			21 21			21 58				22 34				23 08		23 18
Salford Central d		20 24			21 01			21 24			22e01				22e37				23e11		23e21
Salford Crescent a	20 20	20 28	20 41	21 00	21 04		21 20	21 27	21 44	21 51	22 04			22 21	22 40	22 44		23 00	23 14	23 21	23 25
d	20 21	20 28	20 41	21 00	21 05		21 21	21 28	21 44	21 51	22 05			22 21	22 41	22 44		23 00	23 14	23 21	23 25
Swinton d		20 34						21 34							22 47						23 32
Moorside d		20 37						21 37							22 50						23 34
Walkden d		20 40						21 40							22 53						23 38
Atherton d		20 46						21 46							22 59						23 43
Hag Fold d		20 48						21 48							23 01		←				23 46
Daisy Hill d		20 51						21 51							23 04		23 04				23 49
Kearsley d															→			23 08			
Farnworth d																		23 10			
Moses Gate d																		23 12			
Bolton a	20 31		20 51	21 16	21 17		21 31		21 54	22 02	22 16			22 31		22 54		23 16	23 26	23 31	
d	20 32		20 52				21 32		21 55	22 02				22 32		22 55		23 16		23 32	
Westhoughton d			20 59						22 02							23 02		23 24			
Hindley d		20 56	21 03					21 56	22 06							23 06	23 10	23 28			23 53
Ince d		20 59						21 59									23 13	23 31			23 56
Wigan North Western a																					
Wigan Wallgate a		21 05	21 10					22 05	22 11							23 11	23 18	23 36			00 03
d			21 12						22 13							23 13					
Pemberton d																					
Orrell d																					
Upholland d																					
Rainford d																					
Kirkby a																					
Liverpool Central [10] 103 a																					
Gathurst d			21 16						22 17							23 17					
Appley Bridge d			21 20						22 21							23 21					
Parbold d			21 24						22 25							23 25					
Hoscar d			21 27																		
Burscough Bridge d			21 30						22 29							23 29					
New Lane d			21 32																		
Bescar Lane d			21 36																		
Meols Cop d			21 41						22 37							23 37					
Southport a			21 49						22 45							23 46					
Lostock d	20 36						21 36							22 36						23 36	
Horwich Parkway d	20 40						21 40							22 40						23 40	
Blackrod d	20 43						21 43							22 43						23 43	
Adlington (Lancashire) d	20 47						21 47							22 47						23 47	
Chorley d	20 51						21 51							22 51						23 51	
Leyland d	20 58						21 58						22 54	22 58						23 58	
Preston [8] a	21 05						22 05			22 32			23 02	23 05						00 05	
Kirkham & Wesham 97 a	21 15						22 15			23 00				23 15						00 15	
Poulton-le-Fylde 97 a	21 26						22 26							23 26						00 26	
Layton 97 a	21 30						22 30							23 30						00 30	
Blackpool North 97 a	21 36						22 36						23 28	23 36						00 38	
Preston [8] 65 d						21 29				22 34											
Lancaster [6] 65 a	21f34					21 49	22f38			22 49											
d						21 49				22 50		22 57									
Oxenholme Lake District 65 a	21f48						22f51														
Windermere 83 a	22g12																				
Carnforth d						21 59				22 58		23 25									
Silverdale d						22 04				23 04											
Arnside d						22 09				23 09		23 34									
Grange-over-Sands d						22 15				23 14		23 40									
Kents Bank d						22 18				23 18											
Cark d						22 22				23 22											
Ulverston d						22 31				23 30		23 53									
Dalton d						22 39				23 39											
Roose d						22 45				23 44											
Barrow-in-Furness a						22 54				23 54		00 14									

For general notes see front of timetable
For details of catering facilities see Directory of Train Operators

A To Clitheroe (Table 94)
B To Blackburn (Table 94)
C From Windermere (Table 83). Also stops at Bare Lane 2302 and Morecambe 2306
D From Liverpool Lime Street (Table 90)
b Change at Manchester Piccadilly
c Until 5 September only
e Fridays only
f Change at Preston
g Change at Preston and Oxenholme Lake District

Table 82

Mondays to Fridays
from 6 October

Manchester → Bolton → Wigan, Kirkby, Southport, Preston, Blackpool North and Barrow-in-Furness

Network Diagram - see first page of Table 82

		NT	TP	TP	NT	VT	NT	NT	TP	NT	NT	NT	NT	TP	NT	NT	NT	NT	TP	NT	NT	NT	NT	NT	NT
		MX																							
			1 ◇	1 ◇		1 ◇			1 ◇					1 ◇					1 ◇						
		A				B		C		D						D					E		A		
Manchester Airport	85 ✈ d		01 06	03 40		*04 34*			05 47					06 19					06 47					07b02	
Heald Green	85 d								05 51					06 23					06 51						
Buxton	86 d																		*05 49*					06 29	
Hazel Grove	86 d																		*06 27*					07 10	
Stockport	84 d											06 17							*06 42*					07 19	
Manchester Piccadilly 10	d		01 25	03 55		04 58			06 05			06 29		06 44					07 11					07 30	
Manchester Oxford Road	d								06 10			06 32		06 48					07 15					07 33	
Deansgate	d											06 34												07 35	
Rochdale	95 d														*06 24*										*07 06*
Manchester Victoria	d						06 00			06 26			06 35		06 51	07 00		07 05		07 18	07 23	07 28			07 38
Salford Central	d												06 38		06 54	07 03		07 08		07 21	07 26	07 31			07 40
Salford Crescent	a						06 05		06 15	06 31		06 38	06 41	06 52	06 57	07 06		07 11	07 21	07 25	07 31	07 34		07 40	07 44
	d						06 06		06 15	06 31		06 38	06 42	06 53	06 57	07 06		07 11	07 21	07 25	07 31	07 35		07 40	07 44
Swinton	d																	07 18							
Moorside	d																	07 20							
Walkden	d																	07 24				07 43			
Atherton	d																	07 29				07 49			
Hag Fold	d																	07 32							
Daisy Hill	d																	07 35				07 52			
Kearsley	d												06 49												07 52
Farnworth	d												06 51												07 54
Moses Gate	d												06 54												07 56
Bolton	a		01s39	04s09			06 16		06 25	06 44		06 48	06 57	07 03	07 07	07 18			07 31	07 35	07 44			07 51	08 00
	d						06 17		06 26			06 49	06 58	07 03	07 08				07 32	07 36				07 51	08 00
Westhoughton	d						06 24						07 05		07 15					07 43					08 08
Hindley	d						06 28						07 09		07 19			07 39		07 47					08 12
Ince	d												07 12					07 42		07 50					
Wigan North Western	a												07 19							07 55					
Wigan Wallgate	a						06 33								07 24			07 45				08 04			08 21
	d						06 35				06 40				07 26		07 40	07 47							
Pemberton	d						06 39										07 44								
Orrell	d						06 43										07 48								
Upholland	d						06 46										07 51								
Rainford	d						06 50										07 55								
Kirkby	a						07 00										08 07								
Liverpool Central 10	103 a						*07 31*										*08 31*			08c50					
Gathurst	d										06 44				07 30			07 51							
Appley Bridge	d										06 48				07 34			07 55							
Parbold	d										06 52				07 38			07 59							
Hoscar	d										06 55							08 02							
Burscough Bridge	d										06 58				07 42			08 05							
New Lane	d										07 00							08 07							
Bescar Lane	d										07 04							08 11							
Meols Cop	d										07 09				07 50			08 16							
Southport	a										07 16				07 59			08 25							
Lostock	d								06 30			06 54							07 36					07 56	
Horwich Parkway	d								06 34			06 58							07 40					08 00	
Blackrod	d								06 37			07 01							07 43					08 03	
Adlington (Lancashire)	d								06 41			07 05							07 46					08 07	
Chorley	d								06 45			07 09		07 15					07 50					08 12	
Leyland	d	00 06							06 51			07 19							07 58				08 17	08 20	
Preston 8	a	00 15	02s10	04s41		05 54			07 00			07 26		07 26					08 06				08 24	→	
Kirkham & Wesham	97 a					*06 54*			07 11			07 37		*07 47*					08 15						
Poulton-le-Fylde	97 a								07 21			07 46		*08 04*					08 27						
Layton	97 a								07 24			07 50							08 30						
Blackpool North	97 a		02 34	05 05					07 31			07 56		*08 12*					08 36				08 51		
Preston 8	65 d				05 24	06 04								07 29											
Lancaster 6	65 a				05 44	06 18			*07e34*					07 44											
	d				05 45	06 20		07 15						07 45											
Oxenholme Lake District	65 a					06 34			*07e47*																
Windermere	83 a					*07 10*			*08f15*																
Carnforth	d				06 10			07a24						07 53											
Silverdale	d				06 15									08 00											
Arnside	d				06 20									08 04											
Grange-over-Sands	d				06 26									08 09											
Kents Bank	d				06 29									08 13											
Cark	d				06 33									08 17											
Ulverston	d				06 42									08 25											
Dalton	d				06 50									08 34											
Roose	d				06 56									08 39											
Barrow-in-Furness	a				07 05									08 49											

For general notes see front of timetable
For details of catering facilities see Directory of Train Operators

A From Liverpool Lime Street (Table 90)
B To Glasgow Central (Table 65)
C To Leeds (Table 36)
D To Clitheroe (Table 94)
E To Blackburn (Table 94)

b Change at Manchester Piccadilly
c Liverpool Lime Street (Table 90)
e Change at Preston
f Change at Preston and Oxenholme Lake District

Manchester → Bolton → Wigan, Kirkby, Southport, Preston, Blackpool North and Barrow-in-Furness

Network Diagram - see first page of Table 82

	TP	NT	NT	NT	NT	TP	NT	NT	NT	NT	NT	NT	NT	TP	NT	NT	NT	NT	TP	NT	NT	NT	NT
	1 ◇					1 ◇								1 ◇					1 ◇				
	A	B	C	D			B	E	G			G		H	J	K		D	L		C		
	⊼													⊼					⊼				
Manchester Airport 85 ✈ d	07 22					07 47				08 07				08 27					08 47			09 07	
Heald Green 85 d	07 26					07 51				08 11				08 31					*08 37*			*08 56*	
Buxton 86 d						*06 59*					07 35								*07 52*				
Hazel Grove 86 d						*07 40*					08 14								*08 33*				
Stockport 84 d	*07 24*					*07 49*				*08 03*	08 21			08b27					*08 51*			09b02	
Manchester Piccadilly 10 ⇌ d	07 45					08 11				08 28	08 31			08 45					09 11			09 23	
Manchester Oxford Road d	07 48					08 15				08 31	08 35			08 48					09 15			09 26	
Deansgate ⇌ d										08 33	08 37			08 50								09 28	
Rochdale 95 d				*07 31*				*07 52*	08 05								08 33			*08 52*			
Manchester Victoria ⇌ d		07 49		08 00			08 20	08 23	08 27				08 42				08 57	09 00		09 18			09 03
Salford Central d		07 52		08 03			08 23	08 26	08 30				08 45				09 00	09 03		09 21			09 32
Salford Crescent a	07 53	07 56		08 06		08 21	08 26	08 29	08 33	08 37	08 43		08 47	08 54			09 03	09 06	09 21	09 24		09 32	09 35
d	07 54	07 57		08 07		08 21	08 26	08 29	08 33	08 37	08 43		08 47	08 54			09 04	09 07	09 21	09 24		09 32	09 35
Swinton d		08 03							08 42								09 10						09 42
Moorside d		08 06							08 44														09 44
Walkden d		08 09							08 48														09 48
Atherton d		08 15							08 53								09 15						09 53
Hag Fold d		08 17							08 56			←					09 20						09 56
Daisy Hill d		08 20							08 59			08 59					09 24						09 59
Kearsley d									↦				08 55										
Farnworth d													08 57										
Moses Gate d								08 37												09 32			
Bolton a	08 04			08 18		08 31	08 36	08 42		08 48	08 53		09 01	09 04				09 18	09 31	09 36		09 42	
d	08 04					08 32	08 37			08 49	08 54		09 02	09 05					09 32	09 36		09 43	
Westhoughton d										08 56			09 09									09 50	
Hindley d		08 25					08 47					09 03	09 13				09 28						10 03
Ince d		08 28										09 06											10 06
Wigan North Western a																							
Wigan Wallgate a		08 31					08 58			09 04		09 09	09 24				09 33			09 56		10 01	10 09
d		08 32								09 05		09 11					09 35					10 02	10 11
Pemberton d												09 15											10 15
Orrell d												09 19											10 19
Upholland d												09 22											10 22
Rainford d												09 26											10 26
Kirkby a												09 36											10 37
Liverpool Central 10 103 a												*10 01*											*11 01*
Gathurst d		08 37															09 39						
Appley Bridge d		08 40															09 43						
Parbold d		08 44															09 47					10 09	
Hoscar d																						10 13	
Burscough Bridge d		08 49								09 17							09 51					10 17	
New Lane d																							
Bescar Lane d																							
Meols Cop d		08 56															09 59						
Southport a		09 08								09 35							10 10					10 36	
Lostock d						08 36					08 59												
Horwich Parkway d						08 40					09 03								09 39				
Blackrod d											09 06												
Adlington (Lancashire) d											09 10												
Chorley d	08 16				←	08 47					09 15			09 17					09 46				
Leyland d					08 20	08 56									09 28	09 47			09 53				
Preston 8 a	08 27				08 28	09 03					09 27			09 29	09 38	09 54			09 58				
Kirkham & Wesham 97 a					08 38	*09 22*					09 38								*10 21*				
Poulton-le-Fylde 97 a					08 48	09 23					09 46								10 18				
Layton 97 a					08 52						09 50												
Blackpool North 97 a					09 01	09 32					09 59					10 21			10 28				
Preston 8 65 d	08 28													09 32	09 44				10 06		10 10		
Lancaster 6 65 a	08 44				*09c00*	*09c31*					*09c55*			09 47	10 03				10 23		10 30		
d	08 44		08 54											09 48					10 23		10 30		
Oxenholme Lake District 65 a	08 58				*09c17*	*09c45*								*10 10*					10 43				
Windermere 83 a	*09 22*					*10e13*													11 01				
Carnforth d			09 03											09 57							10 40		
Silverdale d			09 09																		10 45		
Arnside d			09 13											10 06							10 50		
Grange-over-Sands d			09 19											10 11							10 56		
Kents Bank d			09 23																		10 59		
Cark d			09 27																		11 03		
Ulverston d			09 35											10 24							11 12		
Dalton d			09 43																		11 20		
Roose d			09 49																		11 26		
Barrow-in-Furness a			09 57											10 46							11 33		

For general notes see front of timetable
For details of catering facilities see Directory of Train Operators

- **A** To Edinburgh (Table 65)
- **B** From Huddersfield (Table 39)
- **C** To Carlisle via Whitehaven (Table 100)
- **D** To Clitheroe (Table 94)
- **E** To Blackburn (Table 94)
- **G** From Todmorden (Table 41)
- **H** ⊼ to Preston
- **J** From Liverpool Lime Street (Table 90) to Morecambe (Table 98)
- **K** From Liverpool Lime Street (Table 90)
- **L** ⊼ to Blackpool North
- **b** Change at Manchester Oxford Road
- **c** Change at Preston
- **e** Change at Preston and Oxenholme Lake District

Manchester → Bolton → Wigan, Kirkby, Southport, Preston, Blackpool North and Barrow-in-Furness

Network Diagram - see first page of Table 82

Station	NT	NT	TP	NT	NT	NT	NT	NT	TP	NT	NT	NT	NT	NT	TP	NT	NT	NT	TP	NT	NT	NT	NT	NT
			[1] ◇						[1] ◇						[1] ◇				[1] ◇					
			A	B		C		D					E		G		C	D						
			✠						✠						✠				✠					
Manchester Airport 85 ✈ d			09 27						09 47		10 07				10 27				10 47		11 07			
Heald Green 85 d			09 31								*09 56*				10 31						*10 56*			
Buxton 86 d	08 36														*09 31*								10 32	
Hazel Grove 86 d	09 10								*09 41*						*10 12*				*10 41*				11 10	
Stockport 84 d	09 19		*09b24*						*09 49*		*10b02*		10 18		*10b25*				*10 49*		*11b02*		11 19	
Manchester Piccadilly [10] ⇌ d	09 33		09 45						10 11		10 23		10 30		10 45				11 11		11 23		11 30	
Manchester Oxford Road d	09 36		09 48						10 15		10 26		10 33		10 48				11 15		11 26		11 33	
Deansgate ⇌ d	09 38												10 35		10 50								11 35	
Rochdale 95 d					09 33					*09 53*		10 03				10 33				*10 50*		11 03		
Manchester Victoria ⇌ d		09 41			09 57	10 00				10 18		10 29		10 41		10 57	11 00			11 18		11 29		11 41
Salford Central d		09 44			10 00	10 03				10 21		10 32		10 44		11 00	11 03			11 21		11 32		11 44
Salford Crescent a	09 43	09 47	09 53		10 03	10 06			10 21	10 24	10 32	10 35	10 40	10 47	10 53	11 03	11 06		11 21	11 24	11 32	11 35	11 40	11 47
d	09 43	09 47	09 54		10 04	10 07			10 21	10 24	10 32	10 35	10 40	10 47	10 54	11 04	11 07		11 21	11 24	11 32	11 35	11 40	11 47
Swinton d					10 10							10 42				11 10						11 42		
Moorside d												10 44										11 44		
Walkden d					10 15							10 48				11 15						11 48		
Atherton d					10 20							10 53				11 20						11 53		
Hag Fold d												10 56										11 56		
Daisy Hill d					10 24							10 59				11 24						11 59		
Kearsley d		09 55												10 55										11 55
Farnworth d		09 57												10 57										11 57
Moses Gate d										10 32										11 32				
Bolton a	09 53	10 01	10 04			10 18			10 31	10 36	10 42		10 50	11 01	11 05		11 18		11 31	11 36	11 42		11 50	12 01
d	09 54	10 02	10 05						10 32	10 36	10 43		10 51	11 02	11 05				11 32	11 36	11 43		11 51	12 02
Westhoughton d		10 09									10 50			11 09							11 50			12 09
Hindley d		10 13			10 28							11 03		11 13		11 28						12 03		12 13
Ince d												11 06										12 06		
Wigan North Western a																								
Wigan Wallgate a		10 22			10 33					10 56	11 01	11 09		11 22		11 33				11 56	12 01	12 09		12 22
d					10 35						11 02	11 11				11 35					12 02	12 11		
Pemberton d												11 15										12 15		
Orrell d												11 19										12 19		
Upholland d												11 22										12 22		
Rainford d												11 26										12 26		
Kirkby a												11 37										12 37		
Liverpool Central [10] 103 a												*12 01*										*13 01*		
Gathurst d					10 39											11 39								
Appley Bridge d					10 43						11 09					11 43					12 09			
Parbold d					10 47						11 13					11 47					12 13			
Hoscar d					10 50											11 50								
Burscough Bridge d					10 53						11 17					11 53					12 17			
New Lane d					10 55											11 55								
Bescar Lane d					10 59											11 59								
Meols Cop d					11 04											12 04								
Southport a					11 15						11 36					12 16					12 36			
Lostock d	09 59								10 36				10 56						11 36				11 56	
Horwich Parkway d	10 03								10 40				11 00						11 40				12 00	
Blackrod d	10 06												11 03										12 03	
Adlington (Lancashire) d	10 10												11 07										12 07	
Chorley d	10 15		10 17						10 47				11 12		11 17				11 47				12 12	
Leyland d								10 47	10 56									11 46	11 56					
Preston [8] a	10 27		10 27					10 54	11 03				11 26		11 27			11 53	12 04				12 24	
Kirkham & Wesham 97 a	10 38								*11 21*				11 35						*12 23*				12 35	
Poulton-le-Fylde 97 a	10 46								11 23				11 43		*11 52*				12 23				12 43	
Layton 97 a	10 50												11 47										12 47	
Blackpool North 97 a	10 57							11 21	11 32				11 56		*12 01*			12 20	12 32				12 56	
Preston [8] 65 d			10 29												11 29									
Lancaster [6] 65 a			10 44						*11c32*						11 44				*12c32*					
d			10 45	11 02			11 11								11 45									
Oxenholme Lake District 65 a	*11c11*		11 03						*11c46*										*12c46*					
Windermere 83 a									*12e14*										*13c18*					
Carnforth d				11a11			11 20								11 53									
Silverdale d							11 26								12 00									
Arnside d							11 30								12 04									
Grange-over-Sands d							11 36								12 09									
Kents Bank d							11 40								12 13									
Cark d							11 44								12 17									
Ulverston d							11 52								12 25									
Dalton d							12 00								12 34									
Roose d							12 06								12 39									
Barrow-in-Furness a							12 16								12 49									

For general notes see front of timetable
For details of catering facilities see Directory of Train Operators

A To Glasgow Central (Table 65)
B From Morecambe to Leeds (Table 36)
C To Clitheroe (Table 94)
D From Liverpool Lime Street (Table 90)
E From Northwich (Table 88)
G ✠ to Preston
b Change at Manchester Oxford Road
c Change at Preston
e Change at Preston and Oxenholme Lake District

from 6 October

Manchester → Bolton → Wigan, Kirkby, Southport, Preston, Blackpool North and Barrow-in-Furness

Network Diagram - see first page of Table 82

		TP	NT	NT	NT	NT	NT	TP	NT	NT	NT	NT	NT	TP	NT	NT	NT	NT	TP	NT	NT	NT	NT	NT
		1 ◇						1 ◇						1 ◇					1 ◇					
		A		B	C	D	E							G		B	D	H	J					
		⚒						⚒						⚒					⚒					
Manchester Airport	85 ✈ d	11 27						11 47		12 07				12 27					12 47		13 07			
Heald Green	85 d	11 31								11 56				12 31							12 56			
Buxton	86 d											11 29											12 32	
Hazel Grove	86 d							11 41				12 10							12 41				13 10	
Stockport	84 d	11b25						11 49		12b02		12 19		12b25					12 49		13b02		13 19	
Manchester Piccadilly 10	d	11 45						12 11		12 23		12 30		12 45					13 11		13 23		13 30	
Manchester Oxford Road	d	11 48						12 15		12 26		12 33		12 48					13 15		13 26		13 33	
Deansgate	d											12 35		12 50									13 35	
Rochdale	95 d		11 33						11 50		12 03				12 33					12 52		13 03		
Manchester Victoria	d		11 57	12 00					12 18		12 29		12 41		12 57	13 00				13 18		13 29		13 41
Salford Central	d		12 00	12 03					12 21		12 32		12 44		13 00	13 03				13 21		13 32		13 44
Salford Crescent	a	11 53	12 03	12 06				12 21	12 24	12 32	12 35	12 40	12 47	12 53	13 03	13 06			13 21	13 24	13 32	13 35	13 40	13 47
	d	11 54	12 04	12 07				12 21	12 24	12 32	12 35	12 40	12 47	12 54	13 04	13 07			13 21	13 24	13 32	13 35	13 40	13 47
Swinton	d		12 10								12 42				13 10							13 42		
Moorside	d										12 44											13 44		
Walkden	d		12 15								12 48				13 15							13 48		
Atherton	d		12 20								12 53				13 20							13 53		
Hag Fold	d										12 56											13 56		
Daisy Hill	d		12 24								12 59				13 24							13 59		
Kearsley	d												12 55											13 55
Farnworth	d												12 57											13 57
Moses Gate	d								12 32											13 32				
Bolton	a	12 05		12 18				12 31	12 36	12 42		12 50	13 01	13 05		13 18			13 31	13 36	13 42		13 50	14 01
	d	12 05						12 32	12 36	12 43		12 51	13 02	13 05					13 32	13 36	13 43		13 51	14 02
Westhoughton	d									12 50			13 09								13 50			14 09
Hindley	d		12 28								13 03		13 13		13 28							14 03		14 13
Ince	d										13 06											14 06		
Wigan North Western	a																							
Wigan Wallgate	a		12 33						12 56	13 01	13 09		13 22		13 33					13 56	14 01	14 09		14 22
	d		12 35							13 02	13 11				13 35						14 02	14 11		
Pemberton	d										13 15											14 15		
Orrell	d										13 19											14 19		
Upholland	d										13 22											14 22		
Rainford	d										13 26											14 26		
Kirkby	a										13 37											14 37		
Liverpool Central 10	103 a										14 01											15 01		
Gathurst	d		12 39												13 39									
Appley Bridge	d		12 43							13 09					13 43						14 09			
Parbold	d		12 47							13 13					13 47						14 13			
Hoscar	d														13 50									
Burscough Bridge	d		12 51							13 17					13 53						14 17			
New Lane	d														13 55									
Bescar Lane	d														13 59									
Meols Cop	d		12 59												14 04									
Southport	a		13 10							13 36					14 15						14 36			
Lostock	d							12 36				12 56							13 36				13 56	
Horwich Parkway	d							12 40				13 00							13 40				14 00	
Blackrod	d											13 03											14 03	
Adlington (Lancashire)	d											13 07											14 07	
Chorley	d	12 17						12 47				13 12		13 17					13 47				14 12	
Leyland	d					12 47		12 56									13 47		13 56					
Preston 8	a	12 27				12 56		13 04				13 24		13 27			13 54		14 04				14 24	
Kirkham & Wesham	97 a							13 21				13 35							14 21				14 35	
Poulton-le-Fylde	97 a							13 23				13 43							14 23				14 43	
Layton	97 a											13 47											14 47	
Blackpool North	97 a					13 21		13 32				13 56					14 21		14 32				14 56	
Preston 8	65 d	12 29												13 29					14 09					
Lancaster 6	65 a	12 44						13c38						13 44					14 24					
	d	12 45			13 12		13 15							13 45				14 17	14 26					
Oxenholme Lake District	65 a	12 59												14 08					14 42					
Windermere	83 a	14 13																	15 09					
Carnforth	d				13 21		13a25							13 53				14 27						
Silverdale	d																	14 33						
Arnside	d													14 02				14 37						
Grange-over-Sands	d				13 36									14 07				14 43						
Kents Bank	d																	14 47						
Cark	d																	14 51						
Ulverston	d				13 49									14 20				14 59						
Dalton	d																	15 07						
Roose	d																	15 13						
Barrow-in-Furness	a				14 07									14 41				15 21						

For general notes see front of timetable
For details of catering facilities see Directory of Train Operators

A To Edinburgh (Table 65)
B To Clitheroe (Table 94)
C To Carlisle via Whitehaven (Table 100)
D From Liverpool Lime Street (Table 90)
E From Morecambe to Leeds (Table 36)
G ⚒ to Preston
H To Sellafield (Table 100)
J ⚒ to Blackpool North
b Change at Manchester Oxford Road
c Change at Preston

Table 82

Mondays to Fridays
from 6 October

Manchester → Bolton → Wigan, Kirkby, Southport, Preston, Blackpool North and Barrow-in-Furness

Network Diagram - see first page of Table 82

Station		TP	NT	NT	NT	TP	NT	NT	NT	NT	NT	TP	NT	NT	NT	TP	NT	NT	NT	NT	NT	NT	TP	NT	NT
		1 ◇				1 ◇						1 ◇				1 ◇							1 ◇		
		A		B	C							D		B	C							E	A	B	G
		🛒				🛒						🛒				🛒							🛒		
Manchester Airport	85 ✈ d	13 27				13 47		14 07				14 27				14 47		15 07					15 27		
Heald Green	85 d	13 31						*13 56*				14 31						*14 56*					15 31		
Buxton	86 d									13 29										14 32					
Hazel Grove	86 d					*13 41*				14 09						*14 41*				15 10					
Stockport	84 d	*13b25*				*13 49*		*14b02*		14 19		*14b25*				*14 49*		*15b02*		15 19			*15b25*		
Manchester Piccadilly 10	🚢 d	13 45				14 11		14 23		14 30		14 45				15 11		15 23		15 30			15 45		
Manchester Oxford Road	d	13 48				14 15		14 26		14 33		14 48				15 15		15 26		15 33			15 48		
Deansgate	🚢 d									14 35		14 50								15 35					
Rochdale	95 d		13 33				*13 50*		14 03				14 33				*14 52*		15 03					*15 23*	
Manchester Victoria	🚢 d		13 57	14 00			14 18		14 29		14 41		14 57	15 00			15 18		15 29		15 41			15 50	
Salford Central	d		14 00	14 03			14 21		14 32		14 44		15 00	15 03			15 21		15 32		15 44			15 53	
Salford Crescent	a	13 53	14 03	14 06		14 21	14 24	14 32	14 35	14 40	14 47	14 53	15 03	15 06		15 21	15 24	15 32	15 35	15 40	15 47		15 53	15 56	
	d	13 54	14 04	14 07		14 21	14 24	14 32	14 35	14 40	14 47	14 54	15 04	15 07		15 21	15 24	15 32	15 35	15 40	15 47		15 54	15 57	
Swinton	d		14 10						14 42				15 10						15 42						
Moorside	d								14 44										15 44						
Walkden	d		14 15						14 48				15 15						15 48						
Atherton	d		14 20						14 53				15 20						15 53						
Hag Fold	d								14 56										15 56						
Daisy Hill	d		14 24						14 59				15 24						15 59						
Kearsley	d										14 55										15 55				
Farnworth	d										14 57										15 57				
Moses Gate	d						14 32										15 32								
Bolton	a	14 05		14 18		14 31	14 36	14 42		14 50	15 01	15 05		15 18		15 31	15 36	15 42		15 50	16 01		16 05	16 08	
	d	14 05				14 32	14 36	14 43		14 51	15 02	15 05				15 32	15 36	15 43		15 51	16 02		16 05		
Westhoughton	d							14 50			15 09							15 50			16 09				
Hindley	d		14 28						15 03		15 13		15 28						16 03		16 13				
Ince	d								15 06										16 06						
Wigan North Western	a																								
Wigan Wallgate	a		14 33				14 56	15 01	15 09		15 22		15 33				15 56	16 01	16 09		16 22				
	d		14 35					15 02	15 11				15 35					16 02	16 11						
Pemberton	d								15 15										16 15						
Orrell	d								15 19										16 19						
Upholland	d								15 22										16 22						
Rainford	d								15 26										16 26						
Kirkby	a								15 37										16 37						
Liverpool Central 10	103 a								*16 01*										*17 01*						
Gathurst	d		14 39										15 39					16 07							
Appley Bridge	d		14 43					15 09					15 43					16 10							
Parbold	d		14 47					15 13					15 47					16 14							
Hoscar	d																	16 17							
Burscough Bridge	d		14 51					15 17					15 51					16 20							
New Lane	d																	16 23							
Bescar Lane	d																	16 26							
Meols Cop	d		14 59										15 59					16 31							
Southport	a		15 10					15 36					16 10					16 43							
Lostock	d					14 36				14 56						15 36				15 56					
Horwich Parkway	d					14 40				15 00						15 40				16 00					
Blackrod	d									15 03										16 03					
Adlington (Lancashire)	d									15 07										16 07					
Chorley	d	14 17				14 47				15 12		15 17				15 47				16 12			16 17		
Leyland	d				14 47	14 56									15 47	15 56									
Preston 8	a	14 27			14 54	15 04				15 24		15 27			15 54	16 04				16 24			16 27		
Kirkham & Wesham	97 a					*15 21*				15 35						*16 23*				16 35					
Poulton-le-Fylde	97 a					15 23				15 43						16 23				16 43					
Layton	97 a									15 47										16 47					
Blackpool North	97 a				15 21	15 32				15 56					16 21	16 32				16 56					
Preston 8	65 d	14 29										15 29											16 29		
Lancaster 6	65 a	14 44				*15c38*						15 44				*16c32*							16 44		
	d	14 45										15 52										16 39	16 45		16 54
Oxenholme Lake District	65 a	14 59														*16c46*							16 59		
Windermere	83 a	*16 10*																					*17 23*		
Carnforth	d											16 01										16 49			17a03
Silverdale	d											16 07										16 55			
Arnside	d											16 11										16 59			
Grange-over-Sands	d											16 16										17 05			
Kents Bank	d											16 20										17 09			
Cark	d											16 25										17 13			
Ulverston	d											16 33										17 22			
Dalton	d											16 41										17 30			
Roose	d											16 47										17 36			
Barrow-in-Furness	a											16 56										17 44			

For general notes see front of timetable
For details of catering facilities see Directory of Train Operators

- **A** To Edinburgh (Table 65)
- **B** To Clitheroe (Table 94)
- **C** From Liverpool Lime Street (Table 90)
- **D** 🛒 to Preston
- **E** To Millom (Table 100)
- **G** From Morecambe to Skipton (Table 36)
- **b** Change at Manchester Oxford Road
- **c** Change at Preston

Table 82

Mondays to Fridays

from 6 October

Manchester → Bolton → Wigan, Kirkby, Southport, Preston, Blackpool North and Barrow-in-Furness

Network Diagram - see first page of Table 82

	NT	NT	NT	TP	NT	NT	NT	NT	NT	TP	NT	NT	NT	NT	NT	NT	TP	NT	NT	NT	NT	NT	NT
				1 ◇						1 ◇					BHX		1 ◇						
			A		B					C		A		B	D		E			G	H	A	
				🛒						🛒							🛒						
Manchester Airport 85 ✈ d				15 47		16 07				16 27							16 47						17b04
Heald Green 85 d						15 56				16 31													16b56
Buxton 86 d													15 42										16 31
Hazel Grove 86 d				15 41				16 10					16 28				16 41						17 09
Stockport 84 d				15 49		16c02		16 19		16c25			16 41				16 49		16 59				17 18
Manchester Piccadilly 10 🚆 d				16 11		16 23		16 30		16 44			16 52				17 11		17 15				17 32
Manchester Oxford Road d				16 15		16 26		16 33		16 48			16 56				17 15		17 19				17 35
Deansgate 🚆 d						16 28		16 35					16 59						17 21				17 38
Rochdale 95 d	15 33				15 54		16 03				16 23				16 33			16 52			17 03		
Manchester Victoria 🚆 d	15 57	16 10			16 23		16 29		16 41		16 48			17 00	17 05	17 10		17 15		17 23	17 29		
Salford Central d	16 00	16 13			16 26		16 32		16 44		16 51			17 03	17 08	17 13		17 18		17 26	17 32		
Salford Crescent a	16 03	16 16		16 21	16 29	16 32	16 35	16 40	16 47		16 54		17 02	17 06		17 16		17 22	17 26	17 29	17 35		17 42
d	16 04	16 16		16 21	16 29	16 32	16 35	16 40	16 47		16 54		17 03	17 06		17 16		17 23	17 26	17 30	17 36		17 42
Swinton d	16 10						16 42				17 01							17 29					
Moorside d							16 44				17 03							17 32					
Walkden d	16 15						16 47				17 09							17 36					
Atherton d	16 20						16 54				17 14					17 29		17 42					
Hag Fold d							16 56				17 17							17 44					
Daisy Hill d	16 24						16 59				17 20					17 33		17 47					
Kearsley d									16 55												17 43		
Farnworth d									16 57											17 38			
Moses Gate d		16 24							16 59											17 41			
Bolton a		16 28		16 31	16 42	16 43		16 50	17 02	17 05			17 13	17 18	17 22		17 30		17 36	17 44	17 49		17 53
d		16 28		16 32		16 43		16 51	17 02	17 05			17 13		17 22		17 30		17 37	17 45			17 53
Westhoughton d		16 36				16 50			17 10											17 52			
Hindley d	16 28	16 40					17 03		17 17		17 24							17 52		17 56			
Ince d		16 43					17 06				17 27							17 55		17 59			
Wigan North Western a									17 26		17 36									18 07			
Wigan Wallgate a	16 33	16 52				17 01	17 10									17 43		17 58					
d	16 35					17 02	17 11									17 43		17 59					
Pemberton d							17 15											18 03					
Orrell d							17 19											18 07					
Upholland d							17 22											18 11					
Rainford d							17 26											18 14					
Kirkby a							17 37											18 25					
Liverpool Central 10 103 a							18 01											19 01					
Gathurst d	16 39					17 06										17 47							
Appley Bridge d	16 43					17 10										17 51							
Parbold d	16 47					17 14										17 56							
Hoscar d																							
Burscough Bridge d	16 51					17 18										18 01							
New Lane d																							
Bescar Lane d																							
Meols Cop d	16 59					17 26										18 09							
Southport a	17 10					17 37										18 20							
Lostock d				16 36				16 56					17 18		17 27				17 42				17 58
Horwich Parkway d				16 40				17 00					17 22						17 46				18 02
Blackrod d								17 03					17 25						17 49				18 05
Adlington (Lancashire) d								17 07					17 29						17 53				18 09
Chorley d				16 47				17 12		17 17			17 34		17 39		17 42		17 57				18 14
Leyland d			16 47	16 56				17 19				17 25	17 40						18 04			18 09	18 20
Preston 8 a			16 54	17 04				17 27		17 27		17 40	17 50		17 53		17 53		18 12			18 17	18 28
Kirkham & Wesham 97 a				17 15				17 38							18 04		18 10		18 22				18 40
Poulton-le-Fylde 97 a				17 25				17 47		17 53					18 13		18 20		18 32				18 49
Layton 97 a				17 28				17 51									18 24		18 36				18 53
Blackpool North 97 a				17 34				17 58		18 03					18 22		18 30		18 43			18 48	19 02
Preston 8 65 d			16 56							17 29							17 58						
Lancaster 6 65 a			17 16	17e32						17 44			18 13		18e31		18 13						
d			17 16							17 45							18 14						
Oxenholme Lake District 65 a										18 11			18 28		18e47		18 28						19e13
Windermere 83 a																	19 13						
Carnforth d			17 26							17 53													
Silverdale d			17 31							18 00													
Arnside d			17 36							18 04													
Grange-over-Sands d			17 44							18 09													
Kents Bank d			17 47							18 13													
Cark d			17 51							18 17													
Ulverston d			18 00							18 25													
Dalton d			18 08							18 34													
Roose d			18 14							18 39													
Barrow-in-Furness a			18 23							18 50													

For general notes see front of timetable
For details of catering facilities see Directory of Train Operators

A From Liverpool Lime Street (Table 90)
B To Clitheroe (Table 94)
C 🛒 to Preston
D From Stalybridge (Table 39)
E Oxenholme Lake District portion continues to Glasgow Central (Table 65)
G From Huddersfield (Table 39)
H To Colne (Table 97)
b Change at Manchester Piccadilly
c Change at Manchester Oxford Road
e Change at Preston

Manchester → Bolton → Wigan, Kirkby, Southport, Preston, Blackpool North and Barrow-in-Furness

Network Diagram - see first page of Table 82

Station		NT	NT A	TP 1 ◇ B ⊼	NT C	NT	NT D	TP 1 ◇ ⊼	NT E	NT	NT C	NT	NT	NT G	NT	NT	NT	TP 1 ◇ H ⊼	NT D	TP 1 ◇ ⊼	NT	NT	NT C	NT
Manchester Airport	85 ✈ d			17 32				17 47				18 10						18 27		18 47		18b52		19 12
Heald Green	85 d							17 22				17 56						18 31				18b56		
Buxton	86 d											17 01				17 34						18 17		
Hazel Grove	86 d											17 40				18 10				18 22		18 55		
Stockport	84 d			17 26				17 39				17 56				18 19		18c26		18 39		19 05		19 06
Manchester Piccadilly 10	🚊 d			17 50				18 11				18 26				18 31		18 45		19 11		19 26		19 33
Manchester Oxford Road	d			17 53				18 15				18 29				18 34		18 48		19 15		19 29		19 37
Deansgate	🚊 d							18 17				18 31				18 36		18 50		19 17		19 33		
Rochdale	95 d					17 33			17 52	18 03									18 23		18 32			
Manchester Victoria	🚊 d	17 38	17 42			17 57	18 00		18 21	18 29							18 41		18 58		19 18			
Salford Central	d	17 41	17 45			18 00	18 03		18 24	18 32							18 44		19 01		19 21			
Salford Crescent	a	17 45	17 48	17 59		18 03	18 07	18 19	18 27	18 35		18 38				18 42	18 47	18 59	19 04	19 21	19 24	19 38		19 42
	d	17 46	17 49	18 00		18 04	18 07	18 21	18 28	18 35		18 39				18 42	18 47	19 01	19 05	19 21	19 25			19 42
Swinton	d					18 10				18 42											19 31			
Moorside	d					18 13				18 44											19 34			
Walkden	d	17 55				18 16				18 48											19 37			
Atherton	d	18 01				18 22				18 53											19 43			
Hag Fold	d					18 24				18 56			←								19 45			
Daisy Hill	d	18 05				18 27				18 59			18 59								19 48			
Kearsley	d		17 59							→							18 55							
Farnworth	d		18 01														18 57							
Moses Gate	d		18 03														19 00							
Bolton	a		18 07	18 10			18 19	18 32	18 44			18 49				18 50	19 03	19 11	19 17	19 31				19 52
	d		18 07	18 10				18 32				18 50				18 51	19 04	19 12		19 32				19 53
Westhoughton	d		18 15									18 57					19 11							20 00
Hindley	d		18 19			18 32							19 05				19 15				19 53			20 04
Ince	d					18 35							19 08								19 56			
Wigan North Western	a		18 27																					
Wigan Wallgate	a	18 14				18 39						19 05	19 15				19 25				20 03			20 09
	d	18 14				18 39						19 06												20 11
Pemberton	d																							
Orrell	d																							
Upholland	d																							
Rainford	d																							
Kirkby	a																							
Liverpool Central 10	103 a																							
Gathurst	d	18 19				18 44						19 11												20 15
Appley Bridge	d	18 23				18 47						19 14												20 19
Parbold	d	18 27				18 51						19 18												20 23
Hoscar	d											19 21												
Burscough Bridge	d	18 32				18 56						19 24												20 27
New Lane	d											19 27												
Bescar Lane	d											19 30												
Meols Cop	d	18 40				19 03						19 35												20 35
Southport	a	18 51				19 15						19 47												20 46
Lostock	d			18 15				18 36								18 56		19 17		19 36				
Horwich Parkway	d							18 40								19 00				19 40				
Blackrod	d							18 43								19 03				19 43				
Adlington (Lancashire)	d															19 07				19 47				
Chorley	d			18 24				18 51								19 12		19 26		19 51				
Leyland	d				18 44			18 58			19 07					19 20				19 58			20 07	
Preston 8	a			18 34	18 54			19 05			19 17					19 27		19 44		20 05			20 17	
Kirkham & Wesham	97 a			18 51				19 16								19 37				20 15				
Poulton-le-Fylde	97 a			19 01	19 14			19 26								19 45				20 26			20 49	
Layton	97 a			19 05												19 49				20 30				
Blackpool North	97 a			19 11	19 23			19 35								19 57				20 36			20 56	
Preston 8	65 d			18 38														19 50						
Lancaster 6	65 a			18 54				19e33								19e59		20 05		20e32				
	d			18 55										19 24	19 39			20 06						
Oxenholme Lake District	65 a							19e46								20e13		20 20						
Windermere	83 a							20f18																
Carnforth	d			19 03										19a33	19 49									
Silverdale	d			19 09											19 54									
Arnside	d			19 14											19 59									
Grange-over-Sands	d			19 19											20 05									
Kents Bank	d			19 23											20 08									
Cark	d			19 28											20 12									
Ulverston	d			19 36											20 21									
Dalton	d			19 44											20 29									
Roose	d			19 50											20 35									
Barrow-in-Furness	a			19 59											20 44									

For general notes see front of timetable
For details of catering facilities see Directory of Train Operators

A Also stops at Clifton 1754

B ⊼ to Blackpool North
C From Liverpool Lime Street (Table 90)
D To Clitheroe (Table 94)
E To Blackburn (Table 94)
G From Morecambe to Leeds (Table 36)

H To Glasgow Central (Table 65)
b Change at Manchester Piccadilly
c Change at Manchester Oxford Road
e Change at Preston
f Change at Preston and Oxenholme Lake District

Table 82

Mondays to Fridays

from 6 October

Manchester → Bolton → Wigan, Kirkby, Southport, Preston, Blackpool North and Barrow-in-Furness

Network Diagram - see first page of Table 82

	TP	NT	TP	NT	NT	NT	NT	NT	TP	NT	NT	TP	NT	TP	NT	TP	NT	NT	NT	NT	NT	TP	NT
	1 ◇		1 ◇						1 ◇			1 ◇		1 ◇		1 ◇						1 ◇	
		A					A						B	C	D						B		
Manchester Airport 85 ✈ d	19 27		19 47		20 15	20b22			20 47		21 16	21 27				21 47		21b52		22b22		22 47	
Heald Green 85 d	19 31				*19 56*	20b07					*20 56*	*21 08*						21b56		22b12		22 52	
Buxton 86 d			*18 50*			19 50												21 33					
Hazel Grove 86 d			*19 31*			20 31												22 14					
Stockport 84 d	*19c24*		*19 40*		*19 57*	20 40					*21 10*					*21 39*		22 23		22 38		*22 39*	
Manchester Piccadilly 10 d	19 44		20 11		20 32	20 52			21 11		21 35	21 43				22 11		22 35		22 49		23 11	
Manchester Oxford Road d	19 47		20 15		20 35	20 54			21 15		21 38	21 46				22 15		22 38		22 52		23 15	
Deansgate d	19 49		20 17		20 37	20 56			21 17		21 40	21 48				22 17		22 40		22 54		23 17	
Rochdale 95 d		*19 23*		*19 52*			*20 02*			*20 52*			*21 02*				*21 52*				*22 02*		
Manchester Victoria d		19 58		20 21			20 58			21 21			21 58				22 34				23 08		23 18
Salford Central d		20 01		20 24			21 01			21 24			22e01				22e37				23e11		23e21
Salford Crescent a	19 52	20 04	20 20	20 28	20 41	21 00	21 04		21 20	21 27	21 44	21 51	22 04			22 21	22 40	22 44		23 00	23 14	23 21	23 25
d	19 53	20 05	20 21	20 28	20 41	21 00	21 05		21 21	21 28	21 44	21 51	22 05			22 21	22 41	22 44		23 00	23 14	23 21	23 25
Swinton d				20 34						21 34							22 47						23 32
Moorside d				20 37						21 37							22 50						23 34
Walkden d				20 40						21 40							22 53						23 38
Atherton d				20 46						21 46							22 59						23 43
Hag Fold d				20 48						21 48							23 01		←				23 46
Daisy Hill d				20 51						21 51							23 04		23 04				23 49
Kearsley d																	→			23 08			
Farnworth d																				23 10			
Moses Gate d																				23 12			
Bolton a	20 03	20 17	20 31		20 51	21 16	21 17		21 31		21 54	22 02	22 16			22 31		22 54		23 16	23 26	23 31	
d	20 04		20 32		20 52				21 32		21 55	22 02				22 32		22 55		23 16		23 32	
Westhoughton d					20 59						22 02							23 02		23 24			
Hindley d				20 56	21 03					21 56	22 06							23 06	23 10	23 28			23 53
Ince d				20 59						21 59									23 13	23 31			23 56
Wigan North Western a																							
Wigan Wallgate a				21 07	21 10					22 07	22 11							23 11	23 18	23 38			00 03
d					21 12						22 13							23 13					
Pemberton d																							
Orrell d																							
Upholland d																							
Rainford d																							
Kirkby a																							
Liverpool Central 10 103 a																							
Gathurst d					21 16						22 17							23 17					
Appley Bridge d					21 20						22 21							23 21					
Parbold d					21 24						22 25							23 25					
Hoscar d					21 27																		
Burscough Bridge d					21 30						22 29							23 29					
New Lane d					21 32																		
Bescar Lane d					21 36																		
Meols Cop d					21 41						22 37							23 37					
Southport a					21 51						22 47							23 48					
Lostock d			20 36						21 36							22 36						23 36	
Horwich Parkway d			20 40						21 40							22 40						23 40	
Blackrod d			20 43						21 43							22 43						23 43	
Adlington (Lancashire) d			20 47						21 47							22 47						23 47	
Chorley d	20 15		20 51						21 51							22 51						23 51	
Leyland d			20 58						21 58						22 54	22 58						23 58	
Preston 8 a	20 26		21 05						22 05			22 32			23 02	23 05						00 05	
Kirkham & Wesham 97 a			21 15						22 15			*23 00*				23 15						00 15	
Poulton-le-Fylde 97 a			21 26						22 26							23 26						00 26	
Layton 97 a			21 30						22 30							23 30						00 30	
Blackpool North 97 a			21 36						22 36						23 28	23 36						00 38	
Preston 8 65 d	20 27							21 29				22 34											
Lancaster 6 65 a	20 44		*21f34*					21 49	*22f38*			22 49											
d	20 51							21 49				22 50		22 57									
Oxenholme Lake District 65 a	*20f59*		*21f48*						*22f51*														
Windermere 83 a	*21g24*		*22g12*																				
Carnforth d	21 00							21 59				22 58		23 25									
Silverdale d	21 06							22 04				23 04											
Arnside d	21 10							22 09				23 09		23 34									
Grange-over-Sands d	21 16							22 15				23 14		23 40									
Kents Bank d	21 20							22 18				23 18											
Cark d	21 24							22 22				23 22											
Ulverston d	21 32							22 31				23 30		23 53									
Dalton d	21 41							22 39				23 39											
Roose d	21 46							22 45				23 44											
Barrow-in-Furness a	21 56							22 54				23 54		00 14									

For general notes see front of timetable
For details of catering facilities see Directory of Train Operators

A To Clitheroe (Table 94)

B To Blackburn (Table 94)

C From Windermere (Table 83). Also stops at Bare Lane 2302 and Morecambe 2306

D From Liverpool Lime Street (Table 90)

b Change at Manchester Piccadilly

c Change at Manchester Oxford Road

e Fridays only

f Change at Preston

g Change at Preston and Oxenholme Lake District

Table 82

until 12 July

Manchester → Bolton → Wigan, Kirkby, Southport, Preston, Blackpool North and Barrow-in-Furness

Network Diagram - see first page of Table 82

		NT	TP	TP	VT	NT	TP	NT	NT	NT	NT	TP	NT	NT	NT	NT	TP	NT	NT	NT	NT	NT	NT	TP	NT
			1 ◇	1 ◇	1 ◇		1 ◇					1 ◇					1 ◇							1 ◇	
		A			B				C					C					D	E	A			G	
Manchester Airport	85 d		01 06	03 40	*04 34*		05 47					06 19					06 47					07b02		07 22	
Heald Green	85 d						05 51					06 23					06 51							07 26	
Buxton	86 d																*05 54*					06 34			
Hazel Grove	86 d																*06 27*					07 10			
Stockport	84 d									06 17							*06 41*					07 19		*07 23*	
Manchester Piccadilly 10	d		01 25	03 55	05 10		06 05			06 29		06 44					07 11					07 30		07 45	
Manchester Oxford Road	d						06 10			06 32		06 48					07 15					07 33		07 48	
Deansgate	d									06 34												07 35			
Rochdale	95 d													*06 18*									*07 06*		
Manchester Victoria	d					06 00			06 26		06 35		06 51	07 00		07 05		07 18	07 23				07 37		07 49
Salford Central	d										06 38		06 54	07 03		07 08		07 21	07 26				07 40		07 52
Salford Crescent	a					06 05	06 15		06 31	06 38	06 41	06 52	06 57	07 06		07 11	07 21	07 25	07 31			07 40	07 44	07 53	07 56
	d					06 06	06 15		06 31	06 38	06 42	06 53	06 57	07 06		07 11	07 21	07 25	07 31			07 40	07 44	07 54	07 57
Swinton	d															07 18									08 03
Moorside	d															07 20									08 06
Walkden	d															07 24									08 09
Atherton	d															07 29									08 15
Hag Fold	d															07 32									08 17
Daisy Hill	d															07 35									08 20
Kearsley	d										06 49												07 52		
Farnworth	d										06 51												07 54		
Moses Gate	d										06 54												07 56		
Bolton	a		01s39	04s09		06 16	06 25		06 44	06 48	06 57	07 03	07 07	07 18			07 31	07 35	07 43			07 51	08 00	08 04	
	d					06 17	06 26			06 49	06 58	07 03	07 08				07 32	07 36				07 51	08 00	08 04	
Westhoughton	d					06 24					07 05		07 15					07 43					08 08		
Hindley	d					06 28					07 09		07 19			07 39		07 47					08 12		08 25
Ince	d										07 12					07 42		07 50							08 28
Wigan North Western	a																	07 54							
Wigan Wallgate	a					06 33					07 17		07 24			07 45							08 19		08 31
	d					06 35		06 40					07 26		07 40	07 47									08 32
Pemberton	d					06 39									07 44										
Orrell	d					06 43									07 48										
Upholland	d					06 46									07 51										
Rainford	d					06 50									07 55										
Kirkby	a					07 00									08 05										
Liverpool Central 10	103 a					*07 31*									*08 31*			08c50							
Gathurst	d							06 44					07 30			07 51									08 37
Appley Bridge	d							06 48					07 34			07 55									08 40
Parbold	d							06 52					07 38			07 59									08 44
Hoscar	d							06 55								08 02									
Burscough Bridge	d							06 58					07 42			08 05									08 49
New Lane	d							07 00								08 07									
Bescar Lane	d							07 04								08 11									
Meols Cop	d							07 09					07 50			08 16									08 56
Southport	a							07 16					07 57			08 23									09 06
Lostock	d						06 30			06 54							07 36					07 56			
Horwich Parkway	d						06 34			06 58							07 40					08 00			
Blackrod	d						06 37			07 01							07 43					08 03			
Adlington (Lancashire)	d						06 41			07 05							07 46					08 07			
Chorley	d						06 45			07 09		07 15					07 50					08 12		08 16	
Leyland	d	00 06					06 51			07 19							07 58				08 17	08 20			
Preston 8	a	00 15	02s18	04s41	06 01		07 00			07 26		07 26					08 06				08 24	→		08 27	
Kirkham & Wesham	97 a				*06 54*		07 11			07 37		*07 49*					08 15								
Poulton-le-Fylde	97 a						07 21			07 46		*08 04*					08 26								
Layton	97 a						07 24			07 50							08 30								
Blackpool North	97 a		02 46	05 05			07 31			07 56		*08 12*					08 36				08 51				
Preston 8	65 d				06 03							07 29												08 28	
Lancaster 6	65 a				06 17		07e33					07 44												08 44	
	d				06 18							07 45								08 12				08 44	
Oxenholme Lake District	65 a				06 32		07e47																	08 58	
Windermere	83 a				*07 19*		08f15																	*09 22*	
Carnforth	d											07 53								08a21					
Silverdale	d											08 00													
Arnside	d											08 04													
Grange-over-Sands	d											08 09													
Kents Bank	d											08 13													
Cark	d											08 17													
Ulverston	d											08 25													
Dalton	d											08 34													
Roose	d											08 39													
Barrow-in-Furness	a											08 49													

For general notes see front of timetable
For details of catering facilities see Directory of Train Operators

A From Liverpool Lime Street (Table 90)
B To Glasgow Central (Table 65)
C To Clitheroe (Table 94)
D To Blackburn (Table 94)
E To Leeds (Table 36)
G To Edinburgh (Table 65)
b Change at Manchester Piccadilly
c Liverpool Lime Street (Table 90)
e Change at Preston
f Change at Preston and Oxenholme Lake District

Table 82

Saturdays

until 12 July

Manchester → Bolton → Wigan, Kirkby, Southport, Preston, Blackpool North and Barrow-in-Furness

Network Diagram - see first page of Table 82

	NT	NT	NT	TP		NT	NT	NT	NT	NT	NT	NT	TP	NT	NT	NT	TP	NT	NT	NT	NT	NT	TP
	A	B		1 ◇		C	D	E			E		1 ◇ G ⊼		A	H	1 ◇ J ⊼						1 ◇ K ⊼
Manchester Airport 85 ✈ d				07 47					08 07				08 27				08 47		09 07				09 27
Heald Green 85 d				07 51					08 11				08 31				08 37		08 56				09 31
Buxton 86 d										07 36							07 57				08 37		
Hazel Grove 86 d				07 24					07 53	08 14							08 33				09 12		
Stockport 84 d				07 42					08 00	08 20			08b27				08 51		09b02		09 21		09b25
Manchester Piccadilly 10 ⇌ d				08 11					08 28	08 31			08 45				09 11		09 23		09 33		09 45
Manchester Oxford Road d				08 15					08 31	08 35			08 48				09 15		09 26		09 36		09 48
Deansgate ⇌ d									08 33	08 37			08 50						09 28		09 38		
Rochdale 95 d						07 35	07 52	08 05						08 33				08 52		09 03			
Manchester Victoria ⇌ d	08 00					08 20	08 23	08 27				08 42		08 57	09 00			09 18		09 29		09 41	
Salford Central d	08 03					08 23	08 26	08 30				08 45		09 00	09 03			09 21		09 32		09 44	
Salford Crescent a	08 06			08 21		08 26	08 29	08 33	08 37	08 42		08 47	08 54	09 03	09 06		09 21	09 24	09 32	09 35	09 43	09 47	09 53
d	08 07			08 21		08 26	08 29	08 33	08 37	08 43		08 47	08 54	09 04	09 07		09 21	09 24	09 32	09 35	09 43	09 47	09 54
Swinton d								08 42						09 10						09 42			
Moorside d								08 44												09 44			
Walkden d								08 48						09 15						09 48			
Atherton d								08 53						09 20						09 53			
Hag Fold d								08 56			←									09 56			
Daisy Hill d								08 59			08 59			09 24						09 59			
Kearsley d								→				08 55										09 55	
Farnworth d												08 57										09 57	
Moses Gate d							08 37											09 32					
Bolton a	08 18			08 31		08 36	08 42		08 48	08 53		09 01	09 04		09 18		09 31	09 36	09 42		09 53	10 01	10 04
d				08 32		08 37			08 49	08 54		09 02	09 05				09 32	09 36	09 43		09 54	10 02	10 05
Westhoughton d									08 56			09 09							09 50			10 09	
Hindley d						08 47					09 03	09 13		09 28						10 03		10 13	
Ince d											09 06									10 06			
Wigan North Western a																							
Wigan Wallgate a						08 56			09 04		09 09	09 22		09 33				09 54	10 01	10 09		10 20	
d									09 05		09 11			09 35					10 02	10 11			
Pemberton d											09 15									10 15			
Orrell d											09 19									10 19			
Upholland d											09 22									10 22			
Rainford d											09 26									10 26			
Kirkby a											09 34									10 35			
Liverpool Central 10 103 a											10 01									11 01			
Gathurst d														09 39									
Appley Bridge d														09 43					10 09				
Parbold d														09 47					10 13				
Hoscar d																							
Burscough Bridge d									09 17					09 51					10 17				
New Lane d																							
Bescar Lane d																							
Meols Cop d														09 59									
Southport a									09 33					10 08					10 34				
Lostock d				08 36						08 59							09 36				09 59		
Horwich Parkway d				08 40						09 03							09 40				10 03		
Blackrod d										09 06											10 06		
Adlington (Lancashire) d										09 10											10 10		
Chorley d			←	08 47						09 15			09 17				09 47				10 15		10 17
Leyland d			08 20	08 56												09 47	09 56						
Preston 8 a			08 28	09 04						09 28			09 29			09 54	10 01				10 27		10 27
Kirkham & Wesham 97 a			08 39	09 22						09 38							10 21				10 38		
Poulton-le-Fylde 97 a			08 48	09 23						09 46							10 20				10 46		
Layton 97 a			08 52							09 50											10 50		
Blackpool North 97 a			09 00	09 32						09 57						10 21	10 29				10 57		
Preston 8 65 d													09 32				10 06						10 29
Lancaster 6 65 a			08c59	09c32						09c53			09 48				10 23						10 47
d		08 50											09 48				10 23						10 48
Oxenholme Lake District 65 a			09c16	09c46									10 08				10 43				11c11		11 06
Windermere 83 a				10e13													11 01						
Carnforth d		08 59											09 57										
Silverdale d		09 05											10 03										
Arnside d		09 09											10 07										
Grange-over-Sands d		09 15											10 12										
Kents Bank d		09 19											10 16										
Cark d		09 23											10 21										
Ulverston d		09 31											10 29										
Dalton d		09 39											10 37										
Roose d		09 45											10 45										
Barrow-in-Furness a		09 54											10 53										

For general notes see front of timetable
For details of catering facilities see Directory of Train Operators

A To Clitheroe (Table 94)
B To Carlisle via Whitehaven (Table 100)
C From Huddersfield (Table 39)
D To Blackburn (Table 94)
E From Todmorden (Table 41)
G ⊼ to Preston
H From Liverpool Lime Street (Table 90)
J ⊼ to Blackpool North
K To Glasgow Central (Table 65)
b Change at Manchester Oxford Road
c Change at Preston
e Change at Preston and Oxenholme Lake District

Table 82

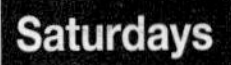

until 12 July

Manchester → Bolton → Wigan, Kirkby, Southport, Preston, Blackpool North and Barrow-in-Furness

Network Diagram - see first page of Table 82

		NT	NT	NT	NT	TP	NT	NT	NT	NT	NT	NT	NT	NT	TP	NT	NT	NT	NT	TP	NT	NT	NT	NT
						1 ◇									1 ◇					1 ◇				
		A		B	C		D						E		G		B		C					
						🍴									🍴					🍴				
Manchester Airport	85 ✈ d					09 47				10 07					10 27			*10 34*		10 47		11 07		
Heald Green	85 d									*09 56*					10 31							*10 56*		
Buxton	86 d														*09 36*									10 37
Hazel Grove	86 d					*09 37*									*10 12*					*10 41*				11 10
Stockport	84 d					*09 40*				10b02			10 18		10b25			*10 25*		*10 49*		11b02		11 19
Manchester Piccadilly 10	🚇 d					10 11				10 23			10 30		10 45			11 03		11 11		11 23		11 30
Manchester Oxford Road	d					10 15				10 26		10 34	10 36		10 48			11 06		11 15		11 26		11 33
Deansgate	🚇 d												10 38		10 50									11 35
Rochdale	95 d		09 33						*09 50*		10 03					10 33					*10 50*		11 03	
Manchester Victoria	🚇 d		09 57	10 00				10 13	10 18		10 29			10 41		10 57	11 00				11 18		11 29	
Salford Central	d		10 00	10 03					10 21		10 32			10 44		11 00	11 03				11 21		11 32	
Salford Crescent	a		10 03	10 06		10 21			10 24	10 32	10 35	10 40	10 43	10 47	10 53	11 03	11 06			11 21	11 24	11 32	11 35	11 40
	d		10 04	10 07		10 21			10 24	10 32	10 35	10 40	10 43	10 47	10 54	11 04	11 07			11 21	11 24	11 32	11 35	11 40
Swinton	d		10 10								10 42					11 10							11 42	
Moorside	d										10 44												11 44	
Walkden	d		10 15					10c28			10 48					11 15							11 48	
Atherton	d		10 20					10 33			10 53					11 20							11 53	
Hag Fold	d										10 56												11 56	
Daisy Hill	d		10 24					10 37			10 59					11 24							11 59	
Kearsley	d													10 55										
Farnworth	d													10 57										
Moses Gate	d								10 32												11 32			
Bolton	a			10 18		10 31			10 36	10 42		10 50	10 53	11 01	11 05		11 18	11 21		11 31	11 36	11 42		11 50
	d					10 32			10 36	10 43		10 51	10 54	11 02	11 05			11 22		11 32	11 36	11 43		11 51
Westhoughton	d									10 50				11 09								11 50		
Hindley	d		10 28					10 41			11 03			11 13		11 28							12 03	
Ince	d										11 06												12 06	
Wigan North Western	a							10 48																
Wigan Wallgate	a		10 33						10 54	11 01	11 09			11 20		11 33					11 54	12 01	12 09	
	d		10 35							11 02	11 11					11 35						12 02	12 11	
Pemberton	d										11 15												12 15	
Orrell	d										11 19												12 19	
Upholland	d										11 22												12 22	
Rainford	d										11 26												12 26	
Kirkby	a										11 35												12 35	
Liverpool Central 10	103 a										*12 01*												*13 01*	
Gathurst	d		10 39													11 39								
Appley Bridge	d		10 43							11 09						11 43						12 09		
Parbold	d		10 47							11 13						11 47						12 13		
Hoscar	d		10 50													11 50								
Burscough Bridge	d		10 53							11 17						11 53						12 17		
New Lane	d		10 55													11 55								
Bescar Lane	d		10 59													11 59								
Meols Cop	d		11 04													12 04								
Southport	a		11 13							11 34						12 14						12 34		
Lostock	d					10 36							10 59							11 36				11 56
Horwich Parkway	d					10 40							11 03							11 40				12 00
Blackrod	d												11 06											12 03
Adlington (Lancashire)	d												11 10											12 07
Chorley	d					10 47							11 15		11 17			11 34		11 47				12 12
Leyland	d				10 47	10 56													11 46	11 56				
Preston 8	a				10 55	11 03		11 14				11 14	11 27		11 27			11 46	11 53	12 04				12 24
Kirkham & Wesham	97 a				*11 18*								11 37							*12 23*				12 35
Poulton-le-Fylde	97 a					11 23							11 45		*11 52*					12 23				12 43
Layton	97 a												11 49											12 47
Blackpool North	97 a				11 22	11 32		11 44				11 40	11 56		*12 01*			12 14	12 20	12 32				12 54
Preston 8	65 d														11 29									
Lancaster 6	65 a											*11e40*	*11e54*		11 44					*12e34*				
	d	10 56					11 01								11 45									
Oxenholme Lake District	65 a											*11e53*								*12e50*				
Windermere	83 a											*12f17*								*13e20*				
Carnforth	d	11a05					11 10								11 53									
Silverdale	d														12 00									
Arnside	d						11 19								12 04									
Grange-over-Sands	d						11 25								12 09									
Kents Bank	d														12 13									
Cark	d														12 17									
Ulverston	d						11 38								12 25									
Dalton	d														12 34									
Roose	d														12 39									
Barrow-in-Furness	a						11 56								12 49									

For general notes see front of timetable
For details of catering facilities see Directory of Train Operators

A From Morecambe to Leeds (Table 36)
B To Clitheroe (Table 94)
C From Liverpool Lime Street (Table 90)
D To Carlisle via Whitehaven (Table 100)
E From Northwich (Table 88)
G 🍴 to Preston
b Change at Manchester Oxford Road
c Arr. 1024
e Change at Preston
f Change at Preston and Oxenholme Lake District

Saturdays until 12 July

Manchester → Bolton → Wigan, Kirkby, Southport, Preston, Blackpool North and Barrow-in-Furness

Network Diagram - see first page of Table 82

Station		NT	TP	NT	NT	NT	NT	TP	NT	NT	NT	NT	NT	TP	NT	NT	NT	NT	TP	NT	NT	NT	NT
			1 ◇					1 ◇						1 ◇					1 ◇				
			A		B	C	D							E		B	C	G	H				
			🍴					🍴						🍴					🍴				
Manchester Airport	85 ✈ d		11 27					11 47		12 07				12 27					12 47		13 07		
Heald Green	85 d		11 31							11 56				12 31							12 56		
Buxton	86 d											11 33											12 36
Hazel Grove	86 d							11 41				12 09							12 41				13 09
Stockport	84 d		11b25					11 49		12b02		12 19		12b25					12 49		13b02		13 19
Manchester Piccadilly 10	🚊 d		11 45					12 11		12 23		12 30		12 45					13 11		13 23		13 30
Manchester Oxford Road	d		11 48					12 15		12 26		12 33		12 48					13 15		13 26		13 33
Deansgate	🚊 d											12 35		12 50									13 35
Rochdale	95 d			11 33					11 50		12 03				12 33					12 52		13 03	
Manchester Victoria	🚊 d	11 41		11 57	12 00				12 18		12 29		12 41		12 57	13 00				13 18		13 29	
Salford Central	d	11 44		12 00	12 03				12 21		12 32		12 44		13 00	13 03				13 21		13 32	
Salford Crescent	a	11 47	11 53	12 03	12 06			12 21	12 24	12 32	12 35	12 40	12 47	12 53	13 03	13 06			13 21	13 24	13 32	13 35	13 40
	d	11 47	11 54	12 04	12 07			12 21	12 24	12 32	12 35	12 40	12 47	12 54	13 04	13 07			13 21	13 24	13 32	13 35	13 40
Swinton	d			12 10							12 42				13 10							13 42	
Moorside	d										12 44											13 44	
Walkden	d			12 15							12 48				13 15							13 48	
Atherton	d			12 20							12 53				13 20							13 53	
Hag Fold	d										12 56											13 56	
Daisy Hill	d			12 24							12 59				13 24							13 59	
Kearsley	d	11 55											12 55										
Farnworth	d	11 57											12 57										
Moses Gate	d								12 32											13 32			
Bolton	a	12 01	12 05		12 18			12 31	12 36	12 42		12 50	13 01	13 05		13 18			13 31	13 36	13 42		13 50
	d	12 02	12 05					12 32	12 36	12 43		12 51	13 02	13 05					13 32	13 36	13 43		13 51
Westhoughton	d	12 09								12 50			13 09								13 50		
Hindley	d	12 13		12 28							13 03		13 13		13 28							14 03	
Ince	d										13 06											14 06	
Wigan North Western	a																						
Wigan Wallgate	a	12 20		12 33					12 54	13 01	13 09		13 20		13 33					13 54	14 01	14 09	
	d			12 35						13 02	13 11				13 35						14 02	14 11	
Pemberton	d										13 15											14 15	
Orrell	d										13 19											14 19	
Upholland	d										13 22											14 22	
Rainford	d										13 26											14 26	
Kirkby	a										13 35											14 35	
Liverpool Central 10	103 a										14 01											15 01	
Gathurst	d			12 39											13 39								
Appley Bridge	d			12 43						13 09					13 43						14 09		
Parbold	d			12 47						13 13					13 47						14 13		
Hoscar	d														13 50								
Burscough Bridge	d			12 51						13 17					13 53						14 17		
New Lane	d														13 55								
Bescar Lane	d														13 59								
Meols Cop	d			12 59											14 04								
Southport	a			13 08						13 34					14 13						14 34		
Lostock	d							12 36				12 56							13 36				13 56
Horwich Parkway	d							12 40				13 00							13 40				14 00
Blackrod	d											13 03											14 03
Adlington (Lancashire)	d											13 07											14 07
Chorley	d		12 17					12 47				13 12		13 17					13 47				14 12
Leyland	d					12 47		12 56									13 47		13 56				
Preston 8	a		12 27			12 56		13 04				13 25		13 27			13 54		14 04				14 24
Kirkham & Wesham	97 a							13 21				13 35							14 21				14 35
Poulton-le-Fylde	97 a							13 23				13 43							14 23				14 43
Layton	97 a											13 47											14 47
Blackpool North	97 a					13 21		13 32				13 54					14 21		14 32				14 54
Preston 8	65 d		12 29											13 29					14 09				
Lancaster 6	65 a		12 44					13c39						13 49					14 24				
	d		12 45				13 13							13 49				14 18	14 25				
Oxenholme Lake District	65 a		12 59											14 10					14 42				
Windermere	83 a		14 14																15 01				
Carnforth	d						13a23							13 59				14 28					
Silverdale	d																	14 34					
Arnside	d													14 07				14 38					
Grange-over-Sands	d													14 13				14 44					
Kents Bank	d																	14 48					
Cark	d																	14 52					
Ulverston	d													14 25				15 01					
Dalton	d																	15 09					
Roose	d																	15 15					
Barrow-in-Furness	a													14 47				15 23					

For general notes see front of timetable
For details of catering facilities see Directory of Train Operators

A To Edinburgh (Table 65)
B To Clitheroe (Table 94)
C From Liverpool Lime Street (Table 90)
D From Morecambe to Leeds (Table 36)
E 🍴 to Preston
G To Carlisle via Whitehaven (Table 100)
H 🍴 to Blackpool North
b Change at Manchester Oxford Road
c Change at Preston

Table 82

Saturdays

until 12 July

Manchester → Bolton → Wigan, Kirkby, Southport, Preston, Blackpool North and Barrow-in-Furness

Network Diagram - see first page of Table 82

	NT	TP	NT	NT	NT	TP	NT	NT	NT	NT	NT	TP	NT	NT	NT	NT	TP	NT	NT		NT	NT	NT	TP
		1 ◇				1 ◇						1 ◇					1 ◇							1 ◇
		A		B	C							D		B	E	C								A
Manchester Airport 85 d		13 27				13 47		14 07				14 27					14 47		15 07					15 27
Heald Green 85 d		13 31						13 56				14 31							14 56					15 31
Buxton 86 d										13 33												14 36		
Hazel Grove 86 d						13 41				14 09							14 41					15 09		
Stockport 84 d		13b25				13 49		14b02		14 19		14b25					14 49		15b02			15 19		15b24
Manchester Piccadilly 10 d		13 45				14 11		14 23		14 30		14 45					15 11		15 23			15 30		15 45
Manchester Oxford Road d		13 48				14 15		14 26		14 33		14 48					15 15		15 26			15 33		15 48
Deansgate d										14 35		14 50										15 35		
Rochdale 95 d			13 33				13 50		14 03				14 33					14 52			15 03			
Manchester Victoria d	13 41		13 57	14 00			14 18		14 29		14 41		14 57	15 00				15 18			15 29		15 41	
Salford Central d	13 44		14 00	14 03			14 21		14 32		14 44		15 00	15 03				15 21			15 32		15 44	
Salford Crescent a	13 47	13 53	14 03	14 06		14 21	14 24	14 32	14 35	14 40	14 47	14 53	15 03	15 06			15 21	15 24	15 32		15 35	15 40	15 47	15 53
d	13 47	13 54	14 04	14 07		14 21	14 24	14 32	14 35	14 40	14 47	14 54	15 04	15 07			15 21	15 24	15 32		15 35	15 40	15 47	15 54
Swinton d			14 10						14 42				15 10								15 42			
Moorside d									14 44												15 44			
Walkden d			14 15						14 48				15 15								15 48			
Atherton d			14 20						14 53				15 20								15 53			
Hag Fold d									14 56												15 56			
Daisy Hill d			14 24						14 59				15 24								15 59			
Kearsley d	13 55										14 55												15 55	
Farnworth d	13 57										14 57												15 57	
Moses Gate d							14 32											15 32						
Bolton a	14 01	14 05		14 18		14 31	14 36	14 42		14 50	15 01	15 05		15 18			15 31	15 36	15 42			15 50	16 01	16 05
d	14 02	14 05				14 32	14 36	14 43		14 51	15 02	15 05					15 32	15 36	15 43			15 51	16 02	16 05
Westhoughton d	14 09							14 50			15 09								15 50				16 09	
Hindley d	14 13		14 28						15 03		15 13		15 28								16 03		16 13	
Ince d									15 06												16 06			
Wigan North Western a																								
Wigan Wallgate a	14 20		14 33				14 54	15 01	15 09		15 20		15 33					15 54	16 01		16 09		16 20	
d			14 35					15 02	15 11				15 35						16 02		16 11			
Pemberton d									15 15												16 15			
Orrell d									15 19												16 19			
Upholland d									15 22												16 22			
Rainford d									15 26												16 26			
Kirkby a									15 35												16 35			
Liverpool Central 10 103 a									16 01												17 01			
Gathurst d			14 39										15 39						16 07					
Appley Bridge d			14 43					15 09					15 43						16 10					
Parbold d			14 47					15 13					15 47						16 14					
Hoscar d																			16 17					
Burscough Bridge d			14 51					15 17					15 51						16 20					
New Lane d																			16 23					
Bescar Lane d																			16 26					
Meols Cop d			14 59										15 59						16 31					
Southport a			15 08					15 34					16 08						16 41					
Lostock d						14 36				14 56							15 36					15 56		
Horwich Parkway d						14 40				15 00							15 40					16 00		
Blackrod d										15 03												16 03		
Adlington (Lancashire) d										15 07												16 07		
Chorley d		14 17				14 47				15 12		15 17					15 47					16 12		16 17
Leyland d					14 47	14 56										15 47	15 56							
Preston 8 a		14 27			14 54	15 04				15 25		15 27				15 54	16 04					16 25		16 27
Kirkham & Wesham 97 a						15 21				15 35							16 23					16 35		
Poulton-le-Fylde 97 a						15 23				15 43							16 23					16 43		
Layton 97 a										15 47												16 47		
Blackpool North 97 a					15 21	15 32				15 54						16 21	16 32					16 54		
Preston 8 65 d		14 29										15 30												16 29
Lancaster 6 65 a		14 44				15c39						15 45					16c38							16 44
d		14 45										15 50			16 14									16 45
Oxenholme Lake District 65 a		14 59				15c52											16c52							16 59
Windermere 83 a						16e17																		17 23
Carnforth d												15 58			16 23									
Silverdale d												16 04			16 29									
Arnside d												16 08			16 33									
Grange-over-Sands d												16 13			16 39									
Kents Bank d												16 17			16 43									
Cark d												16 22			16 47									
Ulverston d												16 30			16 55									
Dalton d												16 38			17 03									
Roose d												16 44			17 09									
Barrow-in-Furness a												16 53			17 17									

For general notes see front of timetable
For details of catering facilities see
Directory of Train Operators

- **A** To Edinburgh (Table 65)
- **B** To Clitheroe (Table 94)
- **C** From Liverpool Lime Street (Table 90)
- **D** to Preston
- **E** To Carlisle via Whitehaven (Table 100)
- **b** Change at Manchester Oxford Road
- **c** Change at Preston
- **e** Change at Preston and Oxenholme Lake District

Table 82

Saturdays

Manchester → Bolton → Wigan, Kirkby, Southport, Preston, Blackpool North and Barrow-in-Furness

until 12 July

Network Diagram - see first page of Table 82

	NT	NT	NT	NT	NT	TP	NT	NT	NT	NT	NT	TP	NT	NT	NT	NT	TP	NT	NT	NT	NT	NT	NT
						1 ◇						**1** ◇					**1** ◇						
	A			B	C		A					D	E	G		A	H			J	K	E	
						🛒						🛒					🛒						
Manchester Airport 85 ✈ d						15 47		16 07				16 27					16 47						*17b04*
Heald Green 85 d								*15 56*				16 31											*16b56*
Buxton 86 d										15 33													16 33
Hazel Grove 86 d						*15 41*				16 09							*16 41*						17 06
Stockport 84 d						*15 49*		*15 59*		16 19		*16c25*			16 40		*16 49*		17 01				17 15
Manchester Piccadilly [10] 🚇 d						16 11		16 23		16 30		16 44			16 52		17 11		17 15				17 30
Manchester Oxford Road d						16 15		16 26		16 33		16 48			16 56		17 15		17 19				17 33
Deansgate 🚇 d								16 28		16 35					16 59				17 21				17 35
Rochdale 95 d	*15 23*	15 33					*15 54*		16 03					*16 23*				*16 52*			17 03		
Manchester Victoria 🚇 d	15 50	15 57	16 10				16 23		16 29		16 41			16 48		17 00		17 15		17 23	17 29		
Salford Central d	15 53	16 00	16 13				16 26		16 32		16 44			16 51		17 03		17 18		17 26	17 32		
Salford Crescent a	15 56	16 03	16 16			16 21	16 29	16 32	16 35	16 40	16 47			16 54	17 03	17 06		17 22	17 26	17 29	17 35		17 40
d	15 57	16 04	16 16			16 21	16 29	16 32	16 35	16 40	16 47			16 54	17 03	17 07		17 23	17 26	17 29	17 36		17 40
Swinton d		16 10							16 42					17 01				17 29					
Moorside d									16 44					17 03				17 32					
Walkden d		16 15							16 47					17 09				17 36					
Atherton d		16 20							16 54					17 14				17 42					
Hag Fold d									16 56					17 17				17 44					
Daisy Hill d		16 24							16 59					17 20				17 47					
Kearsley d											16 55										17 43		
Farnworth d											16 57									17 38			
Moses Gate d			16 24								16 59									17 40			
Bolton a	16 08		16 28			16 31	16 42	16 43		16 51	17 02	17 05			17 13	17 18	17 30		17 36	17 44	17 49		17 53
d			16 28			16 32		16 43		16 51	17 02	17 05			17 13		17 30		17 37	17 45			17 53
Westhoughton d			16 36					16 50			17 10									17 52			
Hindley d		16 28	16 40						17 03		17 17			17 24				17 52		17 56			
Ince d			16 43						17 06					17 27				17 55		17 59			
Wigan North Western a											17 26												
Wigan Wallgate a		16 33	16 50					17 01	17 10					17 36				17 58		18 06			
d		16 35						17 02	17 11					17 38				17 59					
Pemberton d									17 15									18 03					
Orrell d									17 19									18 07					
Upholland d									17 22									18 11					
Rainford d									17 26									18 14					
Kirkby a									17 35									18 23					
Liverpool Central [10] 103 a									*18 01*									*18 46*					
Gathurst d		16 39						17 06						17 42									
Appley Bridge d		16 43						17 10						17 46									
Parbold d		16 47						17 14						17 50									
Hoscar d																							
Burscough Bridge d		16 51						17 18						17 54									
New Lane d																							
Bescar Lane d																							
Meols Cop d		16 59						17 26						18 02									
Southport a		17 08						17 35						18 09									
Lostock d						16 36				16 56					17 18				17 42				17 58
Horwich Parkway d						16 40				17 00					17 22				17 46				18 02
Blackrod d										17 03					17 25				17 49				18 05
Adlington (Lancashire) d										17 07					17 29				17 53				18 09
Chorley d						16 47				17 12		17 17			17 34		17 42		17 57				18 14
Leyland d					16 47	16 56				17 19			17 29		17 40				18 04			18 09	18 20
Preston [8] a					16 54	17 04				17 27		17 27	17 40		17 50		17 53		18 12			18 17	18 29
Kirkham & Wesham 97 a						17 15				17 38							18 10		18 22				18 39
Poulton-le-Fylde 97 a						17 25				17 47		*17 53*					18 20		18 32				18 48
Layton 97 a						17 28				17 51							18 24		18 36				18 52
Blackpool North 97 a						17 34				17 58		*18 03*					18 30		18 43			18 48	18 59
Preston [8] 65 d					16 56							17 29					17 58						
Lancaster [6] 65 a					17 16	*17e40*						17 44					18 13					*18e39*	
d				16 53	17 17							17 45					18 14						
Oxenholme Lake District 65 a												*18 09*					18 28					*18e52*	
Windermere 83 a																	*19 02*						
Carnforth d				17a02	17 26							17 53											
Silverdale d					17 32							18 00											
Arnside d					17 37							18 04											
Grange-over-Sands d					17 43							18 09											
Kents Bank d					17 46							18 13											
Cark d					17 51							18 17											
Ulverston d					17 59							18 25											
Dalton d					18 07							18 34											
Roose d					18 13							18 39											
Barrow-in-Furness a					18 21							18 50											

For general notes see front of timetable
For details of catering facilities see Directory of Train Operators

A To Clitheroe (Table 94)
B From Morecambe to Skipton (Table 36)
C From Liverpool Lime Street (Table 90) to Millom (Table 100)
D 🛒 to Preston
E From Liverpool Lime Street (Table 90)
G From Stalybridge (Table 39)
H Oxenholme Lake District portion continues to Glasgow Central (Table 65)
J From Huddersfield (Table 39)
K To Blackburn (Table 94)
b Change at Manchester Piccadilly
c Change at Manchester Oxford Road
e Change at Preston

Table 82

Saturdays

until 12 July

Manchester → Bolton → Wigan, Kirkby, Southport, Preston, Blackpool North and Barrow-in-Furness

Network Diagram - see first page of Table 82

		NT	NT		TP	NT	NT	NT	TP	NT	NT	NT	NT	NT	NT	NT	NT	TP	NT	TP	NT	NT	NT	NT	TP
					1 ◇				1 ◇									1 ◇		1 ◇					1 ◇
			A		B		C	D		E		D					G		C				D		
					🍴																				
Manchester Airport	85 ✈ d				17 32				17 47				18 10					18 27		18 47				19 12	19 27
Heald Green	85 d								17 22				17 56					18 31						18 56	19 31
Buxton	86 d													17 31								18 22			
Hazel Grove	86 d												17 41	18 07						18 41		18 55			
Stockport	84 d				17 25				17 39				17 59	18 16				18 26		18 50		19 05			19 12
Manchester Piccadilly 10	🚇 d				17 50				18 11				18 26	18 31				18 45		19 11		19 20		19 33	19 44
Manchester Oxford Road	d				17 54				18 15				18 29	18 36				18 47		19 15		19 23		19 37	19 48
Deansgate	🚇 d				17 56				18 17				18 31	18 38				18 50		19 17		19 26			19 50
Rochdale	95 d					17 33				17 52	18 03								18 23		18 32				
Manchester Victoria	🚇 d	17 38	17 42			17 57	18 00			18 21	18 29					18 41			18 58		19 18				
Salford Central	d	17 41	17 45			18 00	18 03			18 24	18 32					18 44			19 01		19 21				
Salford Crescent	a	17 45	17 48		17 59	18 03	18 07		18 19	18 28	18 35		18 38	18 46		18 47		18 59	19 04	19 21	19 24	19 31		19 42	19 54
	d	17 46	17 49		18 00	18 04	18 07		18 21	18 28	18 35		18 39	18 46		18 47		19 01	19 05	19 21	19 25			19 42	19 54
Swinton	d					18 10					18 42										19 31				
Moorside	d					18 13					18 44										19 34				
Walkden	d	17 55				18 16					18 48										19 37				
Atherton	d	18 01				18 22					18 53										19 43				
Hag Fold	d					18 24					18 56				←						19 45				
Daisy Hill	d	18 05				18 27					18 59				18 59						19 48				
Kearsley	d		17 59								→					18 55									
Farnworth	d		18 01													18 57									
Moses Gate	d		18 03													19 00									
Bolton	a		18 07		18 10		18 19		18 32	18 44			18 49	18 56		19 04		19 11	19 17	19 31				19 52	20 04
	d		18 07		18 10				18 32				18 50	18 57		19 04		19 12		19 32				19 53	20 05
Westhoughton	d		18 15										18 57			19 11								20 00	
Hindley	d		18 19			18 32									19 05	19 15					19 53			20 04	
Ince	d					18 35									19 08						19 56				
Wigan North Western	a																								
Wigan Wallgate	a	18 14	18 26			18 42							19 05		19 13	19 24					20 01			20 09	
	d	18 14											19 06											20 11	
Pemberton	d																								
Orrell	d																								
Upholland	d																								
Rainford	d																								
Kirkby	a																								
Liverpool Central 10	103 a																								
Gathurst	d	18 19											19 11											20 15	
Appley Bridge	d	18 23											19 14											20 19	
Parbold	d	18 27											19 18											20 23	
Hoscar	d												19 21												
Burscough Bridge	d	18 32											19 24											20 27	
New Lane	d												19 27												
Bescar Lane	d												19 30												
Meols Cop	d	18 40											19 35											20 35	
Southport	a	18 49											19 45											20 44	
Lostock	d				18 15				18 36					19 02						19 36					
Horwich Parkway	d								18 40					19 06						19 40					
Blackrod	d								18 43					19 09						19 43					
Adlington (Lancashire)	d													19 12						19 47					
Chorley	d				18 24				18 51					19 17				19 24		19 51					20 16
Leyland	d							18 44	18 58			19 07		19 23						19 58			20 07		
Preston 8	a				18 34			18 52	19 05			19 17		19 31				19 36		20 05			20 17		20 27
Kirkham & Wesham	97 a								19 16					19 42						20 15					
Poulton-le-Fylde	97 a							19 10	19 26					19 51						20 26			20 49		
Layton	97 a													19 55						20 30					
Blackpool North	97 a							19 21	19 35					20 01						20 36			20 56		
Preston 8	65 d				18 38													19 38							20 29
Lancaster 6	65 a				18 54							19 39						19 54							20 47
	d				18 55												19 19	19 55							20 47
Oxenholme Lake District	65 a				19 14							19 52						21b35							22b30
Windermere	83 a											20c19													
Carnforth	d				19 03												19a31	20 03							20 58
Silverdale	d				19 09													20 09							21 04
Arnside	d				19 14													20 14							21 08
Grange-over-Sands	d				19 19													20 19							21 14
Kents Bank	d				19 23													20 23							21 18
Cark	d				19 28													20 28							21 22
Ulverston	d				19 36													20 36							21 30
Dalton	d				19 44													20 44							21 39
Roose	d				19 50													20 50							21 44
Barrow-in-Furness	a				19 59													21 00							21 54

For general notes see front of timetable
For details of catering facilities see Directory of Train Operators

- **A** Also stops at Clifton 1754
- **B** 🍴 to Preston
- **C** To Clitheroe (Table 94)
- **D** From Liverpool Lime Street (Table 90)
- **E** To Blackburn (Table 94)
- **G** From Morecambe to Leeds (Table 36)
- **b** By bus
- **c** Change at Preston and Oxenholme Lake District

Table 82

Saturdays

until 12 July

Manchester → Bolton → Wigan, Kirkby, Southport, Preston, Blackpool North and Barrow-in-Furness

Network Diagram - see first page of Table 82

	NT A	TP 1 ◇	TP 1 ◇	NT	NT	NT	NT A	NT	TP 1 ◇	NT	NT	TP 1 ◇	NT B	NT C	TP 1 ◇	NT	NT	NT	NT	NT B	TP 1 ◇	NT		
Manchester Airport 85 ✈ d			19 47		20 15	20b22			20 47		21 16	21 27			21 47		21b52		22b22		22 47			
Heald Green 85 d					19 56	20b07					20 56	21 08					21b56		22b12		22 51			
Buxton 86 d			18 55			19 55											21 38							
Hazel Grove 86 d			19 31			20 31											22 14							
Stockport 84 d			19 40		20 03	20 40					21 10	21 17			21 39		22 23		22 38		22 39			
Manchester Piccadilly 10 d			20 11		20 32	20 52			21 11		21 35	21 45			22 11		22 35		22 49		23 11			
Manchester Oxford Road d			20 15		20 35	20 54			21 15		21 38	21 48			22 15		22 38		22 52		23 15			
Deansgate d			20 17		20 37	20 56			21 17		21 40	21 50			22 17		22 40		22 54		23 17			
Rochdale 95 d	19 24			19 52			20 02			20 52			21 02			21 52				22 02				
Manchester Victoria d	19 58			20 21			20 58			21 21			21 58			22 34				23 08		23 18		
Salford Central d	20 01			20 24			21 01			21 24			22 01			22 37				23 11		23 21		
Salford Crescent a	20 04		20 20	20 28	20 41	21 00	21 04		21 20	21 27	21 44	21 53	22 04		22 20	22 40	22 44		23 00	23 13	23 20	23 25		
d	20 05		20 21	20 28	20 41	21 00	21 05		21 21	21 28	21 44	21 54	22 05		22 21	22 41	22 44		23 00	23 14	23 21	23 25		
Swinton d				20 34						21 34						22 47						23 32		
Moorside d				20 37						21 37						22 50						23 34		
Walkden d				20 40						21 40						22 53						23 38		
Atherton d				20 46						21 46						22 59						23 43		
Hag Fold d				20 48						21 48						23 01		←				23 46		
Daisy Hill d				20 51						21 51						23 04		23 04				23 49		
Kearsley d																→			23 08					
Farnworth d																			23 10					
Moses Gate d																			23 12					
Bolton a	20 16		20 31		20 51	21 16	21 17		21 31		21 54	22 05	22 16		22 31		22 54		23 16	23 27	23 31			
d			20 32		20 52				21 32		21 55	22 05			22 32		22 55		23 16		23 32			
Westhoughton d					20 59						22 02						23 02		23 24					
Hindley d				20 56	21 03					21 56	22 06						23 06	23 13	23 28			23 53		
Ince d				20 59						21 59								23 16	23 31			23 56		
Wigan North Western a																								
Wigan Wallgate a				21 05	21 10					22 05	22 11						23 11	23 21	23 36			00 03		
d					21 12						22 13						23 13							
Pemberton d																								
Orrell d																								
Upholland d																								
Rainford d																								
Kirkby a																								
Liverpool Central 10 103 a																								
Gathurst d					21 16						22 17						23 17							
Appley Bridge d					21 20						22 21						23 21							
Parbold d					21 24						22 25						23 25							
Hoscar d					21 27																			
Burscough Bridge d					21 30						22 29						23 29							
New Lane d					21 32																			
Bescar Lane d					21 36																			
Meols Cop d					21 41						22 37						23 37							
Southport a					21 49						22 47						23 46							
Lostock d			20 36						21 36						22 36						23 36			
Horwich Parkway d			20 40						21 40						22 40						23 40			
Blackrod d			20 43						21 43						22 43						23 43			
Adlington (Lancashire) d			20 47						21 47						22 47						23 47			
Chorley d			20 51						21 51			22 17			22 51						23 51			
Leyland d			20 58						21 58					22 54	22 58						23 58			
Preston 8 a			21 05						22 04			22 32		23 02	23 05						00 06			
Kirkham & Wesham 97 a			21 15						22 15			23 00			23 15						00 15			
Poulton-le-Fylde 97 a			21 26						22 26						23 26						00 26			
Layton 97 a			21 30						22 30						23 30						00 30			
Blackpool North 97 a			21 36						22 36					23 28	23 36						00 38			
Preston 8 65 d																								
Lancaster 6 65 a			22c20									23e30												
d		21 45						22 45																
Oxenholme Lake District 65 a																								
Windermere 83 a																								
Carnforth d		21 53						22 54																
Silverdale d		22 00						23 00																
Arnside d		22 04						23 04																
Grange-over-Sands d		22 09						23 10																
Kents Bank d		22 13						23 14																
Cark d		22 17						23 18																
Ulverston d		22 25						23 26																
Dalton d		22 34						23 34																
Roose d		22 39						23 40																
Barrow-in-Furness a		22 50						23 50																

For general notes see front of timetable
For details of catering facilities see Directory of Train Operators

A To Clitheroe (Table 94)
B To Blackburn (Table 94)
C From Liverpool Lime Street (Table 90)
b Change at Manchester Piccadilly
c Change at Preston. By bus
e By bus

19 July to 4 October

Manchester → Bolton → Wigan, Kirkby, Southport, Preston, Blackpool North and Barrow-in-Furness

Network Diagram - see first page of Table 82

		NT	TP	TP	VT	NT	TP	NT	NT	NT	NT	TP	NT	NT	NT	NT	TP	NT	NT	NT	NT	NT	NT	TP	NT
			1 ◇	1 ◇	1 ◇		1 ◇					1 ◇					1 ◇							1 ◇	
		A			B				C					C					D	E	A			G	
Manchester Airport	85 ✈ d		01 06	03 40	*04 34*		05 47					06 19					06 47					*07b02*		07 22	
Heald Green	85 d						05 51					06 23					06 51							07 26	
Buxton	86 d																					06 34			
Hazel Grove	86 d																					07 10			
Stockport	84 d									06 17												07 19			
Manchester Piccadilly 10	d		01 25	03 55	05 10		06 05			06 29		06 44					07 11					07 30		07 45	
Manchester Oxford Road	d						06 10			06 32		06 48					07 15					07 33		07 48	
Deansgate	d									06 34												07 35			
Rochdale	95 d													*06 18*									*07 06*		
Manchester Victoria	d					06 00			06 26		06 35		06 51	07 00		07 05		07 18	07 23				07 37		07 49
Salford Central	d										06 38		06 54	07 03		07 08		07 21	07 26				07 40		07 52
Salford Crescent	a					06 05	06 15		06 31	06 38	06 41	06 52	06 57	07 06		07 11	07 21	07 25	07 31			07 40	07 44	07 53	07 56
	d					06 06	06 15		06 31	06 38	06 42	06 53	06 57	07 06		07 11	07 21	07 25	07 31			07 40	07 44	07 54	07 57
Swinton	d															07 18									08 03
Moorside	d															07 20									08 06
Walkden	d															07 24									08 09
Atherton	d															07 29									08 15
Hag Fold	d															07 32									08 17
Daisy Hill	d															07 35									08 20
Kearsley	d										06 49												07 52		
Farnworth	d										06 51												07 54		
Moses Gate	d										06 54												07 56		
Bolton	a		01s39	04s09		06 16	06 25		06 44	06 48	06 57	07 03	07 07	07 18			07 31	07 35	07 43			07 51	08 00	08 04	
	d					06 17	06 26			06 49	06 58	07 03	07 08				07 32	07 36				07 51	08 00	08 04	
Westhoughton	d					06 24					07 05		07 15					07 43					08 08		
Hindley	d					06 28					07 09		07 19			07 39		07 47					08 12		08 25
Ince	d										07 12					07 42		07 50							08 28
Wigan North Western	a																	07 54							
Wigan Wallgate	a					06 33					07 17		07 24			07 45							08 19		08 31
	d					06 35		06 40					07 26		07 40	07 47									08 32
Pemberton	d					06 39									07 44										
Orrell	d					06 43									07 48										
Upholland	d					06 46									07 51										
Rainford	d					06 50									07 55										
Kirkby	a					07 00									08 05										
Liverpool Central 10	103 a					*07 31*									*08 31*			08c50							
Gathurst	d							06 44					07 30			07 51									08 37
Appley Bridge	d							06 48					07 34			07 55									08 40
Parbold	d							06 52					07 38			07 59									08 44
Hoscar	d							06 55								08 02									
Burscough Bridge	d							06 58					07 42			08 05									08 49
New Lane	d							07 00								08 07									
Bescar Lane	d							07 04								08 11									
Meols Cop	d							07 09					07 50			08 16									08 56
Southport	a							07 16					07 57			08 23									09 06
Lostock	d						06 30			06 54							07 36					07 56			
Horwich Parkway	d						06 34			06 58							07 40					08 00			
Blackrod	d						06 37			07 01							07 43					08 03			
Adlington (Lancashire)	d						06 41			07 05							07 46					08 07			
Chorley	d						06 45			07 09		07 15					07 50					08 12		08 16	
Leyland	d	00 06					06 51			07 19							07 58				08 17	08 20			
Preston 8	a	00 15	02s18	04s41	06 01		07 00			07 26		07 26					08 06				08 24	⟶		08 27	
Kirkham & Wesham	97 a				*06 54*		07 11			07 37		*07 49*					08 15								
Poulton-le-Fylde	97 a						07 21			07 46		*08 04*					08 26								
Layton	97 a						07 24			07 50							08 30								
Blackpool North	97 a		02 46	05 05			07 31			07 56		*08 12*					08 36				08 51				
Preston 8	65 d				06 03							07 29												08 28	
Lancaster 6	65 a				06 18		*07e33*					07 44												08 44	
	d				06 19							07 45								08 12				08 44	
Oxenholme Lake District	65 a				06 33		*07e47*																	08 58	
Windermere	83 a				*07 19*		*08h15*																	*09 22*	
Carnforth	d											07 53								08a21					
Silverdale	d											08 00													
Arnside	d											08 04													
Grange-over-Sands	d											08 09													
Kents Bank	d											08 13													
Cark	d											08 17													
Ulverston	d											08 25													
Dalton	d											08 34													
Roose	d											08 39													
Barrow-in-Furness	a											08 49													

For general notes see front of timetable
For details of catering facilities see Directory of Train Operators

A From Liverpool Lime Street (Table 90)
B To Glasgow Central (Table 65)
C To Clitheroe (Table 94)
D To Blackburn (Table 94)
E To Leeds (Table 36)
G To Edinburgh (Table 65)
b Change at Manchester Piccadilly
c Liverpool Lime Street (Table 90)
e Change at Preston
h Change at Preston and Oxenholme Lake District

Manchester → Bolton → Wigan, Kirkby, Southport, Preston, Blackpool North and Barrow-in-Furness

19 July to 4 October

Network Diagram - see first page of Table 82

	NT	NT	NT	TP	NT	NT	NT	NT	NT	NT	NT	TP	NT	NT	NT	TP	NT	NT	NT	NT	NT	TP	NT
				1 ◇								1 ◇				1 ◇						1 ◇	
	A	B			C	D	E			E		G		A	H	J						K	L
												[trolley]				[trolley]						[trolley]	
Manchester Airport 85 ✈ d				07 47				08 07				08 27				08 47		09 07				09 27	
Heald Green 85 d				07 51				08 11				08 31				*08 37*		*08 56*				09 31	
Buxton 86 d									07 36											08 37			
Hazel Grove 86 d									08 14											09 12			
Stockport 84 d									08 20											09 21			
Manchester Piccadilly 10 d				08 11				08 28	08 31			08 45				09 11		09 23		09 33		09 45	
Manchester Oxford Road d				08 15				08 31	08 35			08 48				09 15		09 26		09 36		09 48	
Deansgate d								08 33	08 37			08 50						09 28		09 38			
Rochdale 95 d					*07 35*	*07 52*	08 05						08 33				*08 52*		09 03				
Manchester Victoria d	08 00				08 20	08 23	08 27				08 42		08 57	09 00			09 18		09 29		09 41		
Salford Central d	08 03				08 23	08 26	08 30				08 45		09 00	09 03			09 21		09 32		09 44		
Salford Crescent a	08 06			08 21	08 26	08 29	08 33	08 37	08 42		08 47	08 54	09 03	09 06		09 21	09 24	09 32	09 35	09 43	09 47	09 53	
d	08 07			08 21	08 26	08 29	08 33	08 37	08 43		08 47	08 54	09 04	09 07		09 21	09 24	09 32	09 35	09 43	09 47	09 54	
Swinton d							08 42						09 10						09 42				
Moorside d							08 44												09 44				
Walkden d							08 48						09 15						09 48				
Atherton d							08 53						09 20						09 53				
Hag Fold d							08 56			←									09 56				
Daisy Hill d							08 59			08 59			09 24						09 59				
Kearsley d							→				08 55										09 55		
Farnworth d											08 57										09 57		
Moses Gate d						08 37											09 32						
Bolton a	08 18			08 31	08 36	08 42		08 48	08 53		09 01	09 04		09 18		09 31	09 36	09 42		09 53	10 01	10 04	
d				08 32	08 37			08 49	08 54		09 02	09 05				09 32	09 36	09 43		09 54	10 02	10 05	
Westhoughton d								08 56			09 09							09 50			10 09		
Hindley d					08 47					09 03	09 13		09 28						10 03		10 13		
Ince d										09 06									10 06				
Wigan North Western a																							
Wigan Wallgate a					08 56			09 04		09 09	09 22		09 33				09 54	10 01	10 09		10 20		
d								09 05		09 11			09 35					10 02	10 11				
Pemberton d										09 15									10 15				
Orrell d										09 19									10 19				
Upholland d										09 22									10 22				
Rainford d										09 26									10 26				
Kirkby a										09 34									10 35				
Liverpool Central 10 103 a										*10 01*									*11 01*				
Gathurst d													09 39										
Appley Bridge d													09 43					10 09					
Parbold d													09 47					10 13					
Hoscar d																							
Burscough Bridge d								09 17					09 51					10 17					
New Lane d																							
Bescar Lane d																							
Meols Cop d													09 59										
Southport a								09 33					10 08					10 34					
Lostock d				08 36					08 59							09 36				09 59			
Horwich Parkway d				08 40					09 03							09 40				10 03			
Blackrod d									09 06											10 06			
Adlington (Lancashire) d									09 10											10 10			
Chorley d			←	08 47					09 15			09 17				09 47				10 15		10 17	
Leyland d			08 20	08 56											09 47	09 56							
Preston 8 a			08 28	09 04					09 28			09 29			09 54	10 01				10 27		10 27	
Kirkham & Wesham 97 a			08 39	*09 22*					09 38							*10 21*				10 38			
Poulton-le-Fylde 97 a			08 48	09 23					09 46							10 20				10 46			
Layton 97 a			08 52						09 50											10 50			
Blackpool North 97 a			09 00	09 32					09 57						10 21	10 29				10 57			
Preston 8 65 d												09 32				10 06						10 29	
Lancaster 6 65 a				*09b32*								09 48				10 23						10 44	
d		08 50										09 48				10 23						10 45	10 56
Oxenholme Lake District 65 a				*09b46*												10 43						11 03	
Windermere 83 a				*10c13*												11 01							
Carnforth d		08 59										09 57											11a05
Silverdale d		09 05										10 03											
Arnside d		09 09										10 07											
Grange-over-Sands d		09 15										10 12											
Kents Bank d		09 19										10 16											
Cark d		09 23										10 21											
Ulverston d		09 31										10 29											
Dalton d		09 39										10 37											
Roose d		09 45										10 45											
Barrow-in-Furness a		09 54										10 53											

For general notes see front of timetable
For details of catering facilities see Directory of Train Operators

- **A** To Clitheroe (Table 94)
- **B** To Carlisle via Whitehaven (Table 100)
- **C** From Huddersfield (Table 39)
- **D** To Blackburn (Table 94)
- **E** From Todmorden (Table 41)
- **G** [trolley] to Preston
- **H** From Liverpool Lime Street (Table 90)
- **J** [trolley] to Blackpool North
- **K** To Glasgow Central (Table 65)
- **L** From Morecambe to Leeds (Table 36)
- **b** Change at Preston. From 13 September arr. Lancaster 0837, Oxenholme Lake District 0948
- **c** Change at Preston and Oxenholme Lake District

19 July to 4 October

Manchester → Bolton → Wigan, Kirkby, Southport, Preston, Blackpool North and Barrow-in-Furness

Network Diagram - see first page of Table 82

	NT	NT	NT	NT	TP	NT	NT	NT	NT	NT	NT	NT	NT	TP	NT	NT	NT	NT	TP	NT	NT	NT	NT
					1 ◇									1 ◇					1 ◇				
	A		B	C		D				E	G	H		J		B	E	C					
					trolley									trolley					trolley				
Manchester Airport 85 ✈ d					09 47			10 07						10 27			10 34		10 47		11 07		
Heald Green 85 d								09 56						10 31							10 56		
Buxton 86 d																							10 37
Hazel Grove 86 d																							11 10
Stockport 84 d											10 18	10 18											11 19
Manchester Piccadilly 10 d					10 11			10 23			10 30	10 30		10 45			11 03		11 11		11 23		11 30
Manchester Oxford Road d					10 15			10 26		10 34	10 33	10 36		10 48			11 06		11 15		11 26		11 33
Deansgate d											10 35	10 38		10 50									11 35
Rochdale 95 d		09 33					09 50		10 03						10 33					10 50		11 03	
Manchester Victoria d		09 57	10 00			10 13	10 18		10 29				10 41		10 57	11 00				11 18		11 29	
Salford Central d		10 00	10 03				10 21		10 32				10 44		11 00	11 03				11 21		11 32	
Salford Crescent a		10 03	10 06		10 21		10 24	10 32	10 35	10 40	10 40	10 43	10 47	10 53	11 03	11 06			11 21	11 24	11 32	11 35	11 40
d		10 04	10 07		10 21		10 24	10 32	10 35	10 40	10 40	10 43	10 47	10 54	11 04	11 07			11 21	11 24	11 32	11 35	11 40
Swinton d		10 10							10 42						11 10							11 42	
Moorside d									10 44													11 44	
Walkden d		10 15				10b28			10 48						11 15							11 48	
Atherton d		10 20				10 33			10 53						11 20							11 53	
Hag Fold d									10 56													11 56	
Daisy Hill d		10 24				10 37			10 59						11 24							11 59	
Kearsley d													10 55										
Farnworth d													10 57										
Moses Gate d							10 32													11 32			
Bolton a			10 18		10 31		10 36	10 42		10 50	10 51	10 53	11 01	11 05		11 18	11 21		11 31	11 36	11 42		11 50
d					10 32		10 36	10 43		10 51	10 51	10 54	11 02	11 05			11 22		11 32	11 36	11 43		11 51
Westhoughton d								10 50					11 09								11 50		
Hindley d		10 28				10 41			11 03				11 13		11 28							12 03	
Ince d									11 06													12 06	
Wigan North Western a						10 48																	
Wigan Wallgate a		10 33					10 54	11 01	11 09				11 20		11 33					11 54	12 01	12 09	
d		10 35						11 02	11 11						11 35						12 02	12 11	
Pemberton d									11 15													12 15	
Orrell d									11 19													12 19	
Upholland d									11 22													12 22	
Rainford d									11 26													12 26	
Kirkby a									11 35													12 35	
Liverpool Central 10 103 a									12 01													13 01	
Gathurst d		10 39													11 39								
Appley Bridge d		10 43						11 09							11 43						12 09		
Parbold d		10 47						11 13							11 47						12 13		
Hoscar d		10 50													11 50								
Burscough Bridge d		10 53						11 17							11 53						12 17		
New Lane d		10 55													11 55								
Bescar Lane d		10 59													11 59								
Meols Cop d		11 04													12 04								
Southport a		11 13						11 34							12 14						12 34		
Lostock d					10 36						10 56	10 59							11 36				11 56
Horwich Parkway d					10 40						11 00	11 03							11 40				12 00
Blackrod d											11 03	11 06											12 03
Adlington (Lancashire) d											11 07	11 10											12 07
Chorley d					10 47						11 12	11 15		11 17			11 34		11 47				12 12
Leyland d				10 47	10 56													11 46	11 56				
Preston 8 a				10 55	11 03	11 14				11 14	11 27	11 27		11 27			11 46	11 53	12 04				12 24
Kirkham & Wesham 97 a				11 18							11 37	11 37							12 23				12 35
Poulton-le-Fylde 97 a					11 23						11 45	11 45		11 52					12 23				12 43
Layton 97 a											11 49	11 49											12 47
Blackpool North 97 a				11 22	11 32	11 44				11 40	11 56	11 56		12 01			12 14	12 20	12 32				12 54
Preston 8 65 d														11 29									
Lancaster 6 65 a					11c37					11e37				11 44					12e34				
d	11 01													11 45									
Oxenholme Lake District 65 a					11c51					11e51									12e50				
Windermere 83 a					12f17					12f17									13g20				
Carnforth d	11 10													11 53									
Silverdale d														12 00									
Arnside d	11 19													12 04									
Grange-over-Sands d	11 25													12 09									
Kents Bank d														12 13									
Cark d														12 17									
Ulverston d	11 38													12 25									
Dalton d														12 34									
Roose d														12 39									
Barrow-in-Furness a	11 56													12 49									

For general notes see front of timetable
For details of catering facilities see Directory of Train Operators

- **A** To Carlisle via Whitehaven (Table 100)
- **B** To Clitheroe (Table 94)
- **C** From Liverpool Lime Street (Table 90)
- **D** Until 13 September
- **E** Until 6 September
- **G** From 13 September. From Northwich (Table 88)
- **H** Until 6 September. From Northwich (Table 88)
- **J** trolley to Preston
- **b** Arr. 1024
- **c** Change at Preston. From 13 September arr. 1 minute later
- **e** Change at Preston
- **f** Change at Preston and Oxenholme Lake District
- **g** Change at Preston. From 13 September arr. 1312

Table 82

Saturdays

Manchester → Bolton → Wigan, Kirkby, Southport, Preston, Blackpool North and Barrow-in-Furness

19 July to 4 October

Network Diagram - see first page of Table 82

	NT	TP 1◇ A	NT	NT B	NT C	TP 1◇	NT	NT D	NT	NT	NT	NT	TP 1◇ E	TP 1◇ G	NT	NT B	NT C	NT H	TP 1◇ J	NT	NT	NT	NT
Manchester Airport 85 ✈ d		11 27				11 47			12 07				12 27	12 27					12 47		13 07		
Heald Green 85 d		11 31							*11 56*				12 31	12 31							*12 56*		
Buxton 86 d											11 34												12 37
Hazel Grove 86 d											12 10												13 10
Stockport 84 d											12 19												13 19
Manchester Piccadilly 10 d		11 45				12 11			12 23		12 30		12 45	12 45					13 11		13 23		13 30
Manchester Oxford Road d		11 48				12 15			12 26		12 33		12 48	12 48					13 15		13 26		13 33
Deansgate d											12 35		12 50	12 50									13 35
Rochdale 95 d			11 33				*11 50*			12 03					12 33					*12 52*		13 03	
Manchester Victoria d	11 41		11 57	12 00			12 18			12 29		12 41			12 57	13 00				13 18		13 29	
Salford Central d	11 44		12 00	12 03			12 21			12 32		12 44			13 00	13 03				13 21		13 32	
Salford Crescent a	11 47	11 53	12 03	12 06		12 21	12 24		12 32	12 35	12 40	12 47	12 53	12 53	13 03	13 06			13 21	13 24	13 32	13 35	13 40
d	11 47	11 54	12 04	12 07		12 21	12 24		12 32	12 35	12 40	12 47	12 54	12 54	13 04	13 07			13 21	13 24	13 32	13 35	13 40
Swinton d			12 10							12 42					13 10							13 42	
Moorside d										12 44												13 44	
Walkden d			12 15							12 48					13 15							13 48	
Atherton d			12 20							12 53					13 20							13 53	
Hag Fold d										12 56												13 56	
Daisy Hill d			12 24							12 59					13 24							13 59	
Kearsley d	11 55											12 55											
Farnworth d	11 57											12 57											
Moses Gate d							12 32													13 32			
Bolton a	12 01	12 05		12 18		12 31	12 36		12 42		12 50	13 01	13 05	13 05		13 18			13 31	13 36	13 42		13 50
d	12 02	12 05				12 32	12 36		12 43		12 51	13 02	13 05	13 05					13 32	13 36	13 43		13 51
Westhoughton d	12 09								12 50			13 09									13 50		
Hindley d	12 13		12 28							13 03		13 13			13 28							14 03	
Ince d										13 06												14 06	
Wigan North Western a																							
Wigan Wallgate a	12 20		12 33				12 54		13 01	13 09		13 20			13 33					13 54	14 01	14 09	
d			12 35						13 02	13 11					13 35						14 02	14 11	
Pemberton d										13 15												14 15	
Orrell d										13 19												14 19	
Upholland d										13 22												14 22	
Rainford d										13 26												14 26	
Kirkby a										13 35												14 35	
Liverpool Central 10 103 a										*14 01*												*15 01*	
Gathurst d			12 39												13 39								
Appley Bridge d			12 43						13 09						13 43						14 09		
Parbold d			12 47						13 13						13 47						14 13		
Hoscar d															13 50								
Burscough Bridge d			12 51						13 17						13 53						14 17		
New Lane d															13 55								
Bescar Lane d															13 59								
Meols Cop d			12 59												14 04								
Southport a			13 08						13 34						14 13						14 34		
Lostock d						12 36					12 56								13 36				13 56
Horwich Parkway d						12 40					13 00								13 40				14 00
Blackrod d											13 03												14 03
Adlington (Lancashire) d											13 07												14 07
Chorley d		12 17				12 47					13 12		13 17	13 17					13 47				14 12
Leyland d					12 47	12 56											13 47		13 56				
Preston 8 a		12 27			12 56	13 04					13 25		13 27	13 27			13 54		14 04				14 24
Kirkham & Wesham 97 a						*13 21*					13 35								*14 21*				14 35
Poulton-le-Fylde 97 a						13 23					13 43								14 23				14 43
Layton 97 a											13 47												14 47
Blackpool North 97 a					13 21	13 32					13 54						14 21		14 32				14 54
Preston 8 65 d		12 29											13 29	13 29					14 09				
Lancaster 6 65 a		12 44											13 44	13 49					14 24				
d		12 45						13 13					13 45	13 49				14 18	14 25				
Oxenholme Lake District 65 a		12 59																	14 42				
Windermere 83 a		*14 14*																	15 01				
Carnforth d								13a23					13 53	13 59				14 28					
Silverdale d																		14 34					
Arnside d													14 02	14 07				14 38					
Grange-over-Sands d													14 07	14 13				14 44					
Kents Bank d																		14 48					
Cark d																		14 52					
Ulverston d													14 20	14 25				15 01					
Dalton d																		15 09					
Roose d																		15 15					
Barrow-in-Furness a													14 41	14 47				15 23					

For general notes see front of timetable
For details of catering facilities see Directory of Train Operators

A To Edinburgh (Table 65)
B To Clitheroe (Table 94)
C From Liverpool Lime Street (Table 90)
D From Morecambe to Leeds (Table 36)
E From 13 September. Trolley service to Preston
G Until 6 September. Trolley service to Preston
H To Carlisle via Whitehaven (Table 100)
J Trolley service to Blackpool North

Saturdays

19 July to 4 October

Manchester → Bolton → Wigan, Kirkby, Southport, Preston, Blackpool North and Barrow-in-Furness

Network Diagram - see first page of Table 82

	NT	TP 1 ◇ A 🛒	NT	NT B	NT C	TP 1 ◇	NT		NT	NT	NT	NT	TP 1 ◇ D 🛒	NT	NT B	NT C	TP 1 ◇	NT	NT	NT	NT E	NT	NT	TP 1 ◇ A 🛒
Manchester Airport 85 ✈ d		13 27				13 47			14 07				14 27				14 47		15 07					15 27
Heald Green 85 d		13 31							*13 56*				14 31						*14 56*					15 31
Buxton 86 d											13 34											14 37		
Hazel Grove 86 d											14 10											15 10		
Stockport 84 d											14 19											15 19		
Manchester Piccadilly 10 d		13 45				14 11			14 23		14 30		14 45				15 11		15 23			15 30		15 45
Manchester Oxford Road d		13 48				14 15			14 26		14 33		14 48				15 15		15 26			15 33		15 48
Deansgate d											14 35		14 50									15 35		
Rochdale 95 d			13 33				*13 50*			14 03				14 33				*14 52*		15 03				
Manchester Victoria d	13 41		13 57	14 00			14 18			14 29		14 41		14 57	15 00			15 18		15 29			15 41	
Salford Central d	13 44		14 00	14 03			14 21			14 32		14 44		15 00	15 03			15 21		15 32			15 44	
Salford Crescent a	13 47	13 53	14 03	14 06		14 21	14 24		14 32	14 35	14 40	14 47	14 53	15 03	15 06		15 21	15 24	15 32	15 35		15 40	15 47	15 53
d	13 47	13 54	14 04	14 07		14 21	14 24		14 32	14 35	14 40	14 47	14 54	15 04	15 07		15 21	15 24	15 32	15 35		15 40	15 47	15 54
Swinton d			14 10							14 42				15 10						15 42				
Moorside d										14 44										15 44				
Walkden d			14 15							14 48				15 15						15 48				
Atherton d			14 20							14 53				15 20						15 53				
Hag Fold d										14 56										15 56				
Daisy Hill d			14 24							14 59				15 24						15 59				
Kearsley d	13 55											14 55											15 55	
Farnworth d	13 57											14 57											15 57	
Moses Gate d							14 32											15 32						
Bolton a	14 01	14 05		14 18		14 31	14 36		14 42		14 50	15 01	15 05		15 18		15 31	15 36	15 42			15 50	16 01	16 05
d	14 02	14 05				14 32	14 36		14 43		14 51	15 02	15 05				15 32	15 36	15 43			15 51	16 02	16 05
Westhoughton d	14 09								14 50			15 09							15 50				16 09	
Hindley d	14 13		14 28							15 03		15 13		15 28						16 03			16 13	
Ince d										15 06										16 06				
Wigan North Western a																								
Wigan Wallgate a	14b20		14 33				14 54		15 01	15 09		15 20		15 33				15 54	16 01	16 09			16 20	
d			14 35						15 02	15 11				15 35					16 02	16 11				
Pemberton d										15 15										16 15				
Orrell d										15 19										16 19				
Upholland d										15 22										16 22				
Rainford d										15 26										16 26				
Kirkby a										15 35										16 35				
Liverpool Central 10 103 a										*16 01*										*17 01*				
Gathurst d			14 39											15 39					16 07					
Appley Bridge d			14 43						15 09					15 43					16 10					
Parbold d			14 47						15 13					15 47					16 14					
Hoscar d																			16 17					
Burscough Bridge d			14 51						15 17					15 51					16 20					
New Lane d																			16 23					
Bescar Lane d																			16 26					
Meols Cop d			14 59											15 59					16 31					
Southport a			15 08						15 34					16 08					16 41					
Lostock d						14 36					14 56						15 36					15 56		
Horwich Parkway d						14 40					15 00						15 40					16 00		
Blackrod d											15 03											16 03		
Adlington (Lancashire) d											15 07											16 07		
Chorley d		14 17				14 47					15 12		15 17				15 47					16 12		16 17
Leyland d					14 47	14 56										15 47	15 56							
Preston 8 a		14 27			14 54	15 04					15 25		15 27			15 54	16 04					16 25		16 27
Kirkham & Wesham 97 a						*15 21*					15 35						*16 23*					16 35		
Poulton-le-Fylde 97 a						15 23					15 43						16 23					16 43		
Layton 97 a											15 47											16 47		
Blackpool North 97 a					15 21	15 32					15 54					16 21	16 32					16 54		
Preston 8 65 d		14 29											15 30											16 29
Lancaster 6 65 a		14 44				*15c39*							15 45											16 44
d		14 45											15 50								16 14			16 45
Oxenholme Lake District 65 a		14 59				*15c52*																		16 59
Windermere 83 a		*16e17*				*16f17*																		*17 23*
Carnforth d													15 58								16 23			
Silverdale d													16 04								16 29			
Arnside d													16 08								16 33			
Grange-over-Sands d													16 13								16 39			
Kents Bank d													16 17								16 43			
Cark d													16 22								16 47			
Ulverston d													16 30								16 55			
Dalton d													16 38								17 03			
Roose d													16 44								17 09			
Barrow-in-Furness a													16 53								17 17			

For general notes see front of timetable
For details of catering facilities see Directory of Train Operators

A To Edinburgh (Table 65)

B To Clitheroe (Table 94)
C From Liverpool Lime Street (Table 90)
D 🛒 to Preston
E To Carlisle via Whitehaven (Table 100)
b From 13 September arr. 1422

c Until 6 September only. Change at Preston
e See following column for later connections available from certain stations until 6 September only
f Until 6 September only. Change at Preston and Oxenholme Lake District

Table 82

Saturdays

Manchester → Bolton → Wigan, Kirkby, Southport, Preston, Blackpool North and Barrow-in-Furness

19 July to 4 October

Network Diagram - see first page of Table 82

		NT	NT	NT	NT	NT	TP	NT	NT	NT	NT	NT	TP	NT	NT	NT	NT	TP	NT	NT	NT	NT	NT	NT
							1 ◇						1 ◇					1 ◇						
		A			B	C		A					D	E	G		A	H			J	K	E	
							✈						✈					✈						
Manchester Airport	85 ✈ d						15 47		16 07				16 27					16 47						*17b04*
Heald Green	85 d								*15 56*				16 31											*16b56*
Buxton	86 d										15 34													16 36
Hazel Grove	86 d										16 10													17 09
Stockport	84 d										16 19					16 40				17 01				17 18
Manchester Piccadilly 10	d						16 11		16 23		16 30		16 44			16 52		17 11		17 15				17 30
Manchester Oxford Road	d						16 15		16 26		16 33		16 48			16 56		17 15		17 19				17 33
Deansgate	d								16 28		16 35					16 59				17 21				17 35
Rochdale	95 d	*15 23*	15 33					*15 54*		16 03					*16 23*				*16 52*			17 03		
Manchester Victoria	d	15 50	15 57	16 10				16 23		16 29		16 41			16 48		17 00		17 15		17 23	17 29		
Salford Central	d	15 53	16 00	16 13				16 26		16 32		16 44			16 51		17 03		17 18		17 26	17 32		
Salford Crescent	a	15 56	16 03	16 16			16 21	16 29	16 32	16 35	16 40	16 47			16 54	17 03	17 06		17 22	17 26	17 29	17 35		17 40
	d	15 57	16 04	16 16			16 21	16 29	16 32	16 35	16 40	16 47			16 54	17 03	17 07		17 23	17 26	17 29	17 36		17 40
Swinton	d		16 10							16 42					17 01				17 29					
Moorside	d									16 44					17 03				17 32					
Walkden	d		16 15							16 47					17 09				17 36					
Atherton	d		16 20							16 54					17 14				17 42					
Hag Fold	d									16 56					17 17				17 44					
Daisy Hill	d		16 24							16 59					17 20				17 47					
Kearsley	d											16 55										17 43		
Farnworth	d											16 57									17 38			
Moses Gate	d			16 24								16 59									17 40			
Bolton	a	16 08		16 28			16 31	16 42	16 43		16 51	17 02	17 05			17 13	17 18	17 30		17 36	17 44	17 49		17 53
	d			16 28			16 32		16 43		16 51	17 02	17 05			17 13		17 30		17 37	17 45			17 53
Westhoughton	d			16 36					16 50			17 10									17 52			
Hindley	d		16 28	16 40						17 03		17 17			17 24				17 52		17 56			
Ince	d			16 43						17 06					17 27				17 55		17 59			
Wigan North Western	a											17 26												
Wigan Wallgate	a		16 33	16 50					17 01	17 10					17 36				17 58		18 06			
	d		16 35						17 02	17 11					17 38				17 59					
Pemberton	d									17 15									18 03					
Orrell	d									17 19									18 07					
Upholland	d									17 22									18 11					
Rainford	d									17 26									18 14					
Kirkby	a									17 35									18 23					
Liverpool Central 10	103 a									*18 01*									*18 46*					
Gathurst	d		16 39						17 06						17 42									
Appley Bridge	d		16 43						17 10						17 46									
Parbold	d		16 47						17 14						17 50									
Hoscar	d																							
Burscough Bridge	d		16 51						17 18						17 54									
New Lane	d																							
Bescar Lane	d																							
Meols Cop	d		16 59						17 26						18 02									
Southport	a		17 08						17 35						18 09									
Lostock	d						16 36				16 56					17 18				17 42				17 58
Horwich Parkway	d						16 40				17 00					17 22				17 46				18 02
Blackrod	d										17 03					17 25				17 49				18 05
Adlington (Lancashire)	d										17 07					17 29				17 53				18 09
Chorley	d						16 47				17 12		17 17			17 34		17 42		17 57				18 14
Leyland	d					16 47	16 56				17 19			17 29		17 40				18 04			18 09	18 20
Preston 8	a					16 54	17 04				17 27		17 27	17 40		17 50		17 53		18 12			18 17	18 29
Kirkham & Wesham	97 a						17 15				17 38							18 10		18 22				18 39
Poulton-le-Fylde	97 a						17 25				17 47		*17 53*					18 20		18 32				18 48
Layton	97 a						17 28				17 51							18 24		18 36				18 52
Blackpool North	97 a						17 34				17 58		*18 03*					18 30		18 43			18 48	18 59
Preston 8	65 d					16 56							17 29					17 58						
Lancaster 6	65 a					17 16							17 44					18 13						
	d				16 53	17 17							17 45					18 14						
Oxenholme Lake District	65 a																	18 28						
Windermere	83 a																	*19 02*						
Carnforth	d				17a02	17 26							17 53											
Silverdale	d					17 32							18 00											
Arnside	d					17 37							18 04											
Grange-over-Sands	d					17 43							18 09											
Kents Bank	d					17 46							18 13											
Cark	d					17 51							18 17											
Ulverston	d					17 59							18 25											
Dalton	d					18 07							18 34											
Roose	d					18 13							18 39											
Barrow-in-Furness	a					18 21							18 50											

For general notes see front of timetable
For details of catering facilities see Directory of Train Operators

A To Clitheroe (Table 94)
B From Morecambe to Skipton (Table 36)
C From Liverpool Lime Street (Table 90) to Millom (Table 100)
D ✈ to Preston
E From Liverpool Lime Street (Table 90)
G From Stalybridge (Table 39)
H Oxenholme Lake District portion continues to Glasgow Central (Table 65)
J From Huddersfield (Table 39)
K To Blackburn (Table 94)
b Change at Manchester Piccadilly

Manchester → Bolton → Wigan, Kirkby, Southport, Preston, Blackpool North and Barrow-in-Furness

19 July to 4 October

Network Diagram - see first page of Table 82

		NT	NT	TP	NT	NT	NT	NT	TP	NT	NT	NT	NT	NT	NT	NT	NT	TP	NT	TP	NT	NT	NT	NT	TP
				1 ◇					1 ◇									1 ◇		1 ◇					1 ◇
			A	B 🍴		C	D	E		G		E		H	J				C				E		
Manchester Airport	85 ✈ d			17 32					17 47				18 10					18 27		18 47				19 12	19 27
Heald Green	85 d								*17 22*				*17 56*					18 31						*18 56*	19 31
Buxton	86 d													17 34	17 34							18 22			
Hazel Grove	86 d													18 10	18 10							18 55			
Stockport	84 d													18 19	18 19							19 05			
Manchester Piccadilly 10	d			17 50					18 11				18 26	18 31	18 31			18 45		19 11		19 20		19 33	19 44
Manchester Oxford Road	d			17 54					18 15				18 29	18 36	18 36			18 47		19 15		19 23		19 37	19 48
Deansgate	d			17 56					18 17				18 31	18 38	18 38			18 50		19 17		19 26			19 50
Rochdale	95 d				17 33					*17 52*	18 03								*18 23*		*18 32*				
Manchester Victoria	d	17 38	17 42		17 57	18 00				18 21	18 29						18 41		18 58		19 18				
Salford Central	d	17 41	17 45		18 00	18 03				18 24	18 32						18 44		19 01		19 21				
Salford Crescent	a	17 45	17 48	17 59	18 03	18 07			18 19	18 28	18 35		18 38	18 41	18 46		18 47	18 59	19 04	19 21	19 24	19 31		19 42	19 54
	d	17 46	17 49	18 00	18 04	18 07			18 21	18 28	18 35		18 39	18 42	18 46		18 47	19 01	19 05	19 21	19 25			19 42	19 54
Swinton	d				18 10						18 42										19 31				
Moorside	d				18 13						18 44										19 34				
Walkden	d	17 55			18 16						18 48										19 37				
Atherton	d	18 01			18 22						18 53										19 43				
Hag Fold	d				18 24						18 56					←					19 45				
Daisy Hill	d	18 05			18 27						18 59					18 59					19 48				
Kearsley	d		17 59								→						18 55								
Farnworth	d		18 01														18 57								
Moses Gate	d		18 03														19 00								
Bolton	a		18 07	18 10		18 19			18 32	18 44			18 49	18 52	18 56		19 04	19 11	19 17	19 31				19 52	20 04
	d		18 07	18 10					18 32				18 50	18 53	18 57		19 04	19 12		19 32				19 53	20 05
Westhoughton	d		18 15										18 57				19 11							20 00	
Hindley	d		18 19		18 32											19 05	19 15				19 53			20 04	
Ince	d				18 35											19 08					19 56				
Wigan North Western	a																								
Wigan Wallgate	a	18 14	18 26		18 42								19 05			19 13	19 24				20 01			20 09	
	d	18 14											19 06											20 11	
Pemberton	d																								
Orrell	d																								
Upholland	d																								
Rainford	d																								
Kirkby	a																								
Liverpool Central 10	103 a																								
Gathurst	d	18 19											19 11											20 15	
Appley Bridge	d	18 23											19 14											20 19	
Parbold	d	18 27											19 18											20 23	
Hoscar	d												19 21												
Burscough Bridge	d	18 32											19 24											20 27	
New Lane	d												19 27												
Bescar Lane	d												19 30												
Meols Cop	d	18 40											19 35											20 35	
Southport	a	18 49											19 45											20 44	
Lostock	d			18 15					18 36					18 58	19 02					19 36					
Horwich Parkway	d								18 40					19 02	19 06					19 40					
Blackrod	d								18 43					19 05	19 09					19 43					
Adlington (Lancashire)	d													19 08	19 12					19 47					
Chorley	d			18 24					18 51					19 13	19 17			19 24		19 51					20 16
Leyland	d							18 44	18 58			19 07		19 19	19 23					19 58			20 07		
Preston 8	a			18 34				18 52	19 05			19 17		19 27	19 31			19 36		20 05			20 17		20 27
Kirkham & Wesham	97 a								19 16					19 38	19 42					20 15					
Poulton-le-Fylde	97 a							19 10	19 26					19 47	19 51					20 26			*20 49*		
Layton	97 a													19 51	19 55					20 30					
Blackpool North	97 a							19 21	19 35					19 57	20 01					20 36			*20 56*		
Preston 8	65 d			18 38														19 38							20 29
Lancaster 6	65 a			18 54					*19b36*									19 54							20 47
	d			18 55			19 19											19 55							20 47
Oxenholme Lake District	65 a			*19c15*					*19b50*																
Windermere	83 a			*20e19*					*20f19*																
Carnforth	d			19 03			19a31											20 03							20 58
Silverdale	d			19 09														20 09							21 04
Arnside	d			19 14														20 14							21 08
Grange-over-Sands	d			19 19														20 19							21 14
Kents Bank	d			19 23														20 23							21 18
Cark	d			19 28														20 28							21 22
Ulverston	d			19 36														20 36							21 30
Dalton	d			19 44														20 44							21 39
Roose	d			19 50														20 50							21 44
Barrow-in-Furness	a			19 59														21 00							21 54

For general notes see front of timetable
For details of catering facilities see Directory of Train Operators

A Also stops at Clifton 1754
B 🍴 to Preston
C To Clitheroe (Table 94)
D From Morecambe to Leeds (Table 36)
E From Liverpool Lime Street (Table 90)
G To Blackburn (Table 94)
H From 13 September
J Until 6 September
b Until 6 September only. Change at Preston
c From 13 September only
e From 13 September only. Change at Lancaster and Oxenholme Lake District
f Until 6 September only. Change at Preston and Oxenholme Lake District

Table 82

Saturdays

Manchester → Bolton → Wigan, Kirkby, Southport, Preston, Blackpool North and Barrow-in-Furness

19 July to 4 October

Network Diagram - see first page of Table 82

	NT A	TP 1◇	NT	NT	NT	NT A	TP 1◇	TP 1◇	NT	NT	TP 1◇	NT B	NT	NT C	TP 1◇	NT	NT	NT	NT	NT B	TP 1◇	NT
Manchester Airport 85 ✈ d		19 47		20 15	20b22			20 47		21 16	21 27				21 47		21b52		22b22		22 47	
Heald Green 85 d				19 56	20b07					20 56	21 08						21b56		22b12		22 51	
Buxton 86 d					19 55												21 38					
Hazel Grove 86 d					20 31												22 14					
Stockport 84 d					20 40												22 23		22 38			
Manchester Piccadilly 10 d		20 11		20 32	20 52			21 11		21 35	21 45				22 11		22 35		22 49		23 11	
Manchester Oxford Road d		20 15		20 35	20 54			21 15		21 38	21 48				22 15		22 38		22 52		23 15	
Deansgate d		20 17		20 37	20 56			21 17		21 40	21 50				22 17		22 40		22 54		23 17	
Rochdale 95 d	19 24		19 52			20 02			20 52			21 02				21 52				22 02		
Manchester Victoria d	19 58		20 21			20 58			21 21			21 58				22 34				23 08		23 18
Salford Central d	20 01		20 24			21 01			21 24			22 01				22 37				23 11		23 21
Salford Crescent a	20 04	20 20	20 28	20 41	21 00	21 04		21 20	21 27	21 44	21 53	22 04			22 20	22 40	22 44		23 00	23 13	23 20	23 25
d	20 05	20 21	20 28	20 41	21 00	21 05		21 21	21 28	21 44	21 54	22 05			22 21	22 41	22 44		23 00	23 14	23 21	23 25
Swinton d			20 34						21 34							22 47						23 32
Moorside d			20 37						21 37							22 50						23 34
Walkden d			20 40						21 40							22 53						23 38
Atherton d			20 46						21 46							22 59						23 43
Hag Fold d			20 48						21 48							23 01						23 46
Daisy Hill d			20 51						21 51							23 04		← 23 04				23 49
Kearsley d																→			23 08			
Farnworth d																			23 10			
Moses Gate d																			23 12			
Bolton a	20 16	20 31		20 51	21 16	21 17		21 31		21 54	22 05	22 16			22 31		22 54		23 16	23 27	23 31	
d		20 32		20 52				21 32		21 55	22 05				22 32		22 55		23 16		23 32	
Westhoughton d				20 59						22 02							23 02		23 24			
Hindley d			20 56	21 03					21 56	22 06							23 06	23 13	23 28			23 53
Ince d			20 59						21 59									23 16	23 31			23 56
Wigan North Western a																						
Wigan Wallgate a			21 05	21 10					22 05	22 11							23 11	23 21	23 36			00 03
d				21 12						22 13							23 13					
Pemberton d																						
Orrell d																						
Upholland d																						
Rainford d																						
Kirkby a																						
Liverpool Central 10 103 a																						
Gathurst d				21 16						22 17							23 17					
Appley Bridge d				21 20						22 21							23 21					
Parbold d				21 24						22 25							23 25					
Hoscar d				21 27																		
Burscough Bridge d				21 30						22 29							23 29					
New Lane d				21 32																		
Bescar Lane d				21 36																		
Meols Cop d				21 41						22 37							23 37					
Southport a				21 49						22 47							23 46					
Lostock d		20 36						21 36							22 36						23 36	
Horwich Parkway d		20 40						21 40							22 40						23 40	
Blackrod d		20 43						21 43							22 43						23 43	
Adlington (Lancashire) d		20 47						21 47							22 47						23 47	
Chorley d		20 51						21 51			22 17				22 51						23 51	
Leyland d		20 58						21 58						22 54	22 58						23 58	
Preston 8 a		21 05						22 04			22 32			23 02	23 05						00 06	
Kirkham & Wesham 97 a		21 15						22 15			23 00				23 15						00 15	
Poulton-le-Fylde 97 a		21 26						22 26							23 26						00 26	
Layton 97 a		21 30						22 30							23 30						00 30	
Blackpool North 97 a		21 36						22 36						23 28	23 36						00 38	
Preston 8 65 d																						
Lancaster 6 65 a																						
d							21 45						22 45									
Oxenholme Lake District 65 a																						
Windermere 83 a																						
Carnforth d							21 53						22 54									
Silverdale d							22 00						23 00									
Arnside d							22 04						23 04									
Grange-over-Sands d							22 09						23 10									
Kents Bank d							22 13						23 14									
Cark d							22 17						23 18									
Ulverston d							22 25						23 26									
Dalton d							22 34						23 34									
Roose d							22 39						23 40									
Barrow-in-Furness a							22 50						23 50									

For general notes see front of timetable
For details of catering facilities see Directory of Train Operators

A To Clitheroe (Table 94)
B To Blackburn (Table 94)
C From Liverpool Lime Street (Table 90)

b Change at Manchester Piccadilly

Table 82

from 11 October

Manchester → Bolton → Wigan, Kirkby, Southport, Preston, Blackpool North and Barrow-in-Furness

Network Diagram - see first page of Table 82

		NT	TP	TP	VT	NT	TP	NT	NT	NT	NT	TP	NT	NT	NT	NT	TP	NT	NT		NT	NT	NT	NT	TP
			1 ◇	1 ◇	1 ◇		1 ◇					1 ◇					1 ◇								1 ◇
		A			B				C					C					D		E	A			G
Manchester Airport	85 ✈ d		01 06	03 40	*04 34*		05 47					06 19					06 47						*07b02*		07 22
Heald Green	85 d						05 51					06 23					06 51								07 26
Buxton	86 d																						06 29		
Hazel Grove	86 d																						07 10		
Stockport	84 d									06 17													07 19		
Manchester Piccadilly 10	d		01 25	03 55	05 10		06 05			06 29		06 44					07 11						07 30		07 45
Manchester Oxford Road	d						06 10			06 32		06 48					07 15						07 33		07 48
Deansgate	d									06 34													07 35		
Rochdale	95 d													*06 18*										*07 06*	
Manchester Victoria	d					06 00			06 26		06 35		06 51	07 00		07 05		07 18	07 23					07 37	
Salford Central	d										06 38		06 54	07 03		07 08		07 21	07 26					07 40	
Salford Crescent	a					06 05	06 15		06 31	06 38	06 41	06 52	06 57	07 06		07 11	07 21	07 25	07 31				07 40	07 44	07 53
	d					06 06	06 15		06 31	06 38	06 42	06 53	06 57	07 06		07 11	07 21	07 25	07 31				07 40	07 44	07 54
Swinton	d															07 18									
Moorside	d															07 20									
Walkden	d															07 24									
Atherton	d															07 29									
Hag Fold	d															07 32									
Daisy Hill	d															07 35									
Kearsley	d										06 49													07 52	
Farnworth	d										06 51													07 54	
Moses Gate	d										06 54													07 56	
Bolton	a		01s39	04s09		06 16	06 25		06 44	06 48	06 57	07 03	07 07	07 18			07 31	07 35	07 43				07 51	08 00	08 04
	d					06 17	06 26			06 49	06 58	07 03	07 08				07 32	07 36					07 51	08 00	08 04
Westhoughton	d					06 24					07 05		07 15					07 43						08 08	
Hindley	d					06 28					07 09		07 19			07 39		07 47						08 12	
Ince	d										07 12					07 42		07 50							
Wigan North Western	a																	07 54							
Wigan Wallgate	a					06 33					07 19		07 24			07 45								08 21	
	d					06 35		06 40					07 26		07 40	07 47									
Pemberton	d					06 39									07 44										
Orrell	d					06 43									07 48										
Upholland	d					06 46									07 51										
Rainford	d					06 50									07 55										
Kirkby	a					07 02									08 07										
Liverpool Central 10	103 a					*07 31*									*08 31*			08c50							
Gathurst	d							06 44					07 30			07 51									
Appley Bridge	d							06 48					07 34			07 55									
Parbold	d							06 52					07 38			07 59									
Hoscar	d							06 55								08 02									
Burscough Bridge	d							06 58					07 42			08 05									
New Lane	d							07 00								08 07									
Bescar Lane	d							07 04								08 11									
Meols Cop	d							07 09					07 50			08 16									
Southport	a							07 18					07 59			08 25									
Lostock	d						06 30			06 54							07 36						07 56		
Horwich Parkway	d						06 34			06 58							07 40						08 00		
Blackrod	d						06 37			07 01							07 43						08 03		
Adlington (Lancashire)	d						06 41			07 05							07 46						08 07		
Chorley	d						06 45			07 09		07 15					07 50						08 12		08 16
Leyland	d	00 06					06 51			07 19							07 58					08 17	08 20		
Preston 8	a	00 15	02s18	04s41	06 01		07 00			07 26		07 26					08 06					08 24	⟶		08 27
Kirkham & Wesham	97 a				*06 54*		07 11			07 37		*07 49*					08 15								
Poulton-le-Fylde	97 a						07 21			07 46		*08 04*					08 26								
Layton	97 a						07 24			07 50							08 30								
Blackpool North	97 a		02 46	05 05			07 31			07 56		*08 12*					08 36					08 51			
Preston 8	65 d				06 03							07 29													08 28
Lancaster 6	65 a				06 18		*07e33*					07 44													08 44
	d				06 19							07 45									08 12				08 44
Oxenholme Lake District	65 a				06 33		*07e47*																		08 58
Windermere	83 a				*07 19*		*08f15*																		*09 22*
Carnforth	d											07 53									08a21				
Silverdale	d											08 00													
Arnside	d											08 04													
Grange-over-Sands	d											08 09													
Kents Bank	d											08 13													
Cark	d											08 17													
Ulverston	d											08 25													
Dalton	d											08 34													
Roose	d											08 39													
Barrow-in-Furness	a											08 49													

For general notes see front of timetable
For details of catering facilities see Directory of Train Operators

A From Liverpool Lime Street (Table 90)
B To Glasgow Central (Table 65)
C To Clitheroe (Table 94)
D To Blackburn (Table 94)
E To Leeds (Table 36)
G To Edinburgh (Table 65)
b Change at Manchester Piccadilly
c Liverpool Lime Street (Table 90)
e Change at Preston
f Change at Preston and Oxenholme Lake District

Table 82

Saturdays

from 11 October

Manchester → Bolton → Wigan, Kirkby, Southport, Preston, Blackpool North and Barrow-in-Furness

Network Diagram - see first page of Table 82

		NT	NT	NT	NT	TP	NT	NT	NT	NT	NT	NT	NT	TP	NT	NT		NT	TP		NT	NT	NT	NT	NT
			A	B		1 ◇	C	D	E			E		1 ◇ G [trolley]		A		H	1 ◇ J [trolley]						
Manchester Airport	85 ✈ d					07 47				08 07				08 27					08 47			09 07			
Heald Green	85 d					07 51				08 11				08 31					*08 37*			*08 56*			
Buxton	86 d										07 31													08 37	
Hazel Grove	86 d										08 14													09 12	
Stockport	84 d										08 20													09 21	
Manchester Piccadilly 10	🚇 d					08 11				08 28	08 31			08 45					09 11			09 23		09 33	
Manchester Oxford Road	d					08 15				08 31	08 35			08 48					09 15			09 26		09 36	
Deansgate	🚇 d									08 33	08 37			08 50								09 28		09 38	
Rochdale	95 d		*07 31*					*07 52*	08 05						08 33						*08 52*		09 03		
Manchester Victoria	🚇 d	07 49	08 00				08 20	08 23	08 27				08 42		08 57	09 00					09 18		09 29		09 41
Salford Central	d	07 52	08 03				08 23	08 26	08 30				08 45		09 00	09 03					09 21		09 32		09 44
Salford Crescent	a	07 56	08 06			08 21	08 26	08 29	08 33	08 37	08 42		08 47	08 54	09 03	09 06			09 21		09 24	09 32	09 35	09 43	09 47
	d	07 57	08 07			08 21	08 26	08 29	08 33	08 37	08 43		08 47	08 54	09 04	09 07			09 21		09 24	09 32	09 35	09 43	09 47
Swinton	d	08 03							08 42						09 10								09 42		
Moorside	d	08 06							08 44														09 44		
Walkden	d	08 09							08 48						09 15								09 48		
Atherton	d	08 15							08 53						09 20								09 53		
Hag Fold	d	08 17							08 56			←											09 56		
Daisy Hill	d	08 20							08 59			08 59			09 24								09 59		
Kearsley	d								→				08 55												09 55
Farnworth	d												08 57												09 57
Moses Gate	d							08 37													09 32				
Bolton	a		08 18			08 31	08 36	08 42		08 48	08 53		09 01	09 04		09 18			09 31		09 36	09 42		09 53	10 01
	d					08 32	08 37			08 49	08 54		09 02	09 05					09 32		09 36	09 43		09 54	10 02
Westhoughton	d									08 56			09 09									09 50			10 09
Hindley	d	08 25					08 47					09 03	09 13		09 28								10 03		10 13
Ince	d	08 28										09 06											10 06		
Wigan North Western	a																								
Wigan Wallgate	a	08 31					08 58			09 04		09 09	09 24		09 33						09 56	10 01	10 09		10 22
	d	08 32								09 05		09 11			09 35							10 02	10 11		
Pemberton	d											09 15											10 15		
Orrell	d											09 19											10 19		
Upholland	d											09 22											10 22		
Rainford	d											09 26											10 26		
Kirkby	a											09 36											10 37		
Liverpool Central 10	103 a											*10 01*											*11 01*		
Gathurst	d	08 37													09 39										
Appley Bridge	d	08 40													09 43							10 09			
Parbold	d	08 44													09 47							10 13			
Hoscar	d																								
Burscough Bridge	d	08 49								09 17					09 51							10 17			
New Lane	d																								
Bescar Lane	d																								
Meols Cop	d	08 56													09 59										
Southport	a	09 08								09 35					10 10							10 36			
Lostock	d					08 36					08 59								09 36					09 59	
Horwich Parkway	d					08 40					09 03								09 40					10 03	
Blackrod	d										09 06													10 06	
Adlington (Lancashire)	d										09 10													10 10	
Chorley	d				←	08 47					09 15			09 17					09 47					10 15	
Leyland	d				08 20	08 56													09 56						
Preston 8	a				08 28	09 04					09 28			09 29				09 47	10 01					10 27	
Kirkham & Wesham	97 a				08 39	*09 22*					09 38							09 54	*10 21*					10 38	
Poulton-le-Fylde	97 a				08 48	09 23					09 46								10 20					10 46	
Layton	97 a				08 52						09 50													10 50	
Blackpool North	97 a				09 02	09 32					09 59							10 21	10 29					10 57	
Preston 8	65 d													09 32						10 06					
Lancaster 6	65 a					*09b37*								09 48						10 23					
	d			08 50										09 48						10 23					
Oxenholme Lake District	65 a					*09b48*														10 43					
Windermere	83 a					*10c13*														11 01					
Carnforth	d			08 59										09 57											
Silverdale	d			09 05										10 03											
Arnside	d			09 09										10 07											
Grange-over-Sands	d			09 15										10 12											
Kents Bank	d			09 19										10 16											
Cark	d			09 23										10 21											
Ulverston	d			09 31										10 29											
Dalton	d			09 39										10 37											
Roose	d			09 45										10 45											
Barrow-in-Furness	a			09 54										10 53											

For general notes see front of timetable
For details of catering facilities see Directory of Train Operators

A To Clitheroe (Table 94)
B To Carlisle via Whitehaven (Table 100)
C From Huddersfield (Table 39)
D To Blackburn (Table 94)
E From Todmorden (Table 41)
G [trolley] to Preston
H From Liverpool Lime Street (Table 90)
J [trolley] to Blackpool North
b Change at Preston
c Change at Preston and Oxenholme Lake District

Table 82

from 11 October

Manchester → Bolton → Wigan, Kirkby, Southport, Preston, Blackpool North and Barrow-in-Furness

Network Diagram - see first page of Table 82

Station		TP	NT	NT	NT	NT	NT	TP	NT	NT	NT	NT	NT		TP	NT	NT	NT	TP	NT	NT	NT	NT	NT	TP
		1 ◇ A	B		C	D	E	1 ◇				G			1 ◇ H		C	E	1 ◇						1 ◇ J
Manchester Airport	85 ✈ d	09 27						09 47		10 07					10 27				10 47		11 07				11 27
Heald Green	85 d	09 31								*09 56*					10 31						*10 56*				11 31
Buxton	86 d																						10 32		
Hazel Grove	86 d																						11 10		
Stockport	84 d											10 18											11 19		
Manchester Piccadilly 10	d	09 45						10 11		10 23		10 30			10 45				11 11		11 23		11 30		11 45
Manchester Oxford Road	d	09 48						10 15		10 26		10 33			10 48				11 15		11 26		11 33		11 48
Deansgate	d											10 35			10 50								11 35		
Rochdale	95 d			09 33					*09 50*		10 03					10 33				*10 50*		11 03			
Manchester Victoria	d			09 57	10 00				10 18		10 29		10 41			10 57	11 00			11 18		11 29		11 41	
Salford Central	d			10 00	10 03				10 21		10 32		10 44			11 00	11 03			11 21		11 32		11 44	
Salford Crescent	a	09 53		10 03	10 06			10 21	10 24	10 32	10 35	10 40	10 47		10 53	11 03	11 06		11 21	11 24	11 32	11 35	11 40	11 47	11 53
	d	09 54		10 04	10 07			10 21	10 24	10 32	10 35	10 40	10 47		10 54	11 04	11 07		11 21	11 24	11 32	11 35	11 40	11 47	11 54
Swinton	d			10 10							10 42					11 10						11 42			
Moorside	d										10 44											11 44			
Walkden	d			10 15							10 48					11 15						11 48			
Atherton	d			10 20							10 53					11 20						11 53			
Hag Fold	d										10 56											11 56			
Daisy Hill	d			10 24							10 59					11 24						11 59			
Kearsley	d												10 55											11 55	
Farnworth	d												10 57											11 57	
Moses Gate	d								10 32											11 32					
Bolton	a	10 04			10 18			10 31	10 36	10 42		10 51	11 01		11 05		11 18		11 31	11 36	11 42		11 50	12 01	12 05
	d	10 05						10 32	10 36	10 43		10 51	11 02		11 05				11 32	11 36	11 43		11 51	12 02	12 05
Westhoughton	d									10 50			11 09								11 50			12 09	
Hindley	d			10 28							11 03		11 13			11 28						12 03		12 13	
Ince	d										11 06											12 06			
Wigan North Western	a																								
Wigan Wallgate	a			10 33					10 56	11 01	11 09		11 22			11 33				11 56	12 01	12 09		12 22	
	d			10 35						11 02	11 11					11 35					12 02	12 11			
Pemberton	d										11 15											12 15			
Orrell	d										11 19											12 19			
Upholland	d										11 22											12 22			
Rainford	d										11 26											12 26			
Kirkby	a										11 37											12 37			
Liverpool Central 10	103 a										*12 01*											*13 01*			
Gathurst	d			10 39												11 39									
Appley Bridge	d			10 43						11 09						11 43					12 09				
Parbold	d			10 47						11 13						11 47					12 13				
Hoscar	d			10 50												11 50									
Burscough Bridge	d			10 53						11 17						11 53					12 17				
New Lane	d			10 55												11 55									
Bescar Lane	d			10 59												11 59									
Meols Cop	d			11 04												12 04									
Southport	a			11 15						11 36						12 16					12 36				
Lostock	d							10 36				10 56							11 36				11 56		
Horwich Parkway	d							10 40				11 00							11 40				12 00		
Blackrod	d											11 03											12 03		
Adlington (Lancashire)	d											11 07											12 07		
Chorley	d	10 17						10 47				11 12			11 17				11 47				12 12		12 17
Leyland	d						10 47	10 56										11 46	11 56						
Preston 8	a	10 27					10 55	11 03				11 27			11 27			11 53	12 04				12 24		12 27
Kirkham & Wesham	97 a						*11 18*					11 37							*12 23*				12 35		
Poulton-le-Fylde	97 a							11 23				11 45			*11 52*				12 23				12 43		
Layton	97 a											11 49											12 47		
Blackpool North	97 a						11 22	11 32				11 58			*12 01*			12 20	12 32				12 56		
Preston 8	65 d	10 29													11 29										12 29
Lancaster 6	65 a	10 44						*11b38*							11 44				*12b34*						12 44
	d	10 45	10 56			11 01									11 45										12 45
Oxenholme Lake District	65 a	11 03						*11b52*											*12b50*						12 59
Windermere	83 a							*12c17*											*13b12*						*14 14*
Carnforth	d		11a05			11 10									11 53										
Silverdale	d														12 00										
Arnside	d					11 19									12 04										
Grange-over-Sands	d					11 25									12 09										
Kents Bank	d														12 13										
Cark	d														12 17										
Ulverston	d					11 38									12 25										
Dalton	d														12 34										
Roose	d														12 39										
Barrow-in-Furness	a					11 56									12 49										

For general notes see front of timetable
For details of catering facilities see Directory of Train Operators

A To Glasgow Central (Table 65)
B From Morecambe to Leeds (Table 36)
C To Clitheroe (Table 94)
D To Carlisle via Whitehaven (Table 100)
E From Liverpool Lime Street (Table 90)
G From Northwich (Table 88)
H to Preston
J To Edinburgh (Table 65)
b Change at Preston
c Change at Preston and Oxenholme Lake District

Table 82

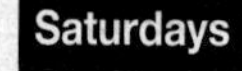

Manchester → Bolton → Wigan, Kirkby, Southport, Preston, Blackpool North and Barrow-in-Furness

Saturdays from 11 October

Network Diagram - see first page of Table 82

	NT	NT A	NT B	TP 1 ◇ 🍴	NT	NT C	NT	NT	NT	NT	TP 1 ◇ D 🍴	NT	NT A	NT B	NT E	TP 1 ◇ G 🍴	NT	NT	NT	NT	NT	TP 1 ◇ H 🍴
Manchester Airport 85 ✈ d				11 47			12 07				12 27					12 47		13 07				13 27
Heald Green 85 d							*11 56*				12 31							*12 56*				13 31
Buxton 86 d									11 29											12 32		
Hazel Grove 86 d									12 10											13 10		
Stockport 84 d									12 19											13 19		
Manchester Piccadilly 10 🚇 d				12 11			12 23		12 30		12 45					13 11		13 23		13 30		13 45
Manchester Oxford Road d				12 15			12 26		12 33		12 48					13 15		13 26		13 33		13 48
Deansgate 🚇 d									12 35		12 50									13 35		
Rochdale 95 d	11 33				*11 50*			12 03				12 33					*12 52*		13 03			
Manchester Victoria 🚇 d	11 57	12 00			12 18			12 29		12 41		12 57	13 00				13 18		13 29		13 41	
Salford Central d	12 00	12 03			12 21			12 32		12 44		13 00	13 03				13 21		13 32		13 44	
Salford Crescent a	12 03	12 06		12 21	12 24		12 32	12 35	12 40	12 47	12 53	13 03	13 06			13 21	13 24	13 32	13 35	13 40	13 47	13 53
d	12 04	12 07		12 21	12 24		12 32	12 35	12 40	12 47	12 54	13 04	13 07			13 21	13 24	13 32	13 35	13 40	13 47	13 54
Swinton d	12 10							12 42				13 10							13 42			
Moorside d								12 44											13 44			
Walkden d	12 15							12 48				13 15							13 48			
Atherton d	12 20							12 53				13 20							13 53			
Hag Fold d								12 56											13 56			
Daisy Hill d	12 24							12 59				13 24							13 59			
Kearsley d										12 55											13 55	
Farnworth d										12 57											13 57	
Moses Gate d					12 32												13 32					
Bolton a		12 18		12 31	12 36		12 42		12 50	13 01	13 05		13 18			13 31	13 36	13 42		13 50	14 01	14 05
d				12 32	12 36		12 43		12 51	13 02	13 05					13 32	13 36	13 43		13 51	14 02	14 05
Westhoughton d							12 50			13 09								13 50			14 09	
Hindley d	12 28							13 03		13 13		13 28							14 03		14 13	
Ince d								13 06											14 06			
Wigan North Western a																						
Wigan Wallgate a	12 33				12 56		13 01	13 09		13 22		13 33					13 56	14 01	14 09		14 24	
d	12 35						13 02	13 11				13 35						14 02	14 11			
Pemberton d								13 15											14 15			
Orrell d								13 19											14 19			
Upholland d								13 22											14 22			
Rainford d								13 26											14 26			
Kirkby a								13 37											14 37			
Liverpool Central 10 103 a								*14 01*											*15 01*			
Gathurst d	12 39											13 39										
Appley Bridge d	12 43						13 09					13 43						14 09				
Parbold d	12 47						13 13					13 47						14 13				
Hoscar d												13 50										
Burscough Bridge d	12 51						13 17					13 53						14 17				
New Lane d												13 55										
Bescar Lane d												13 59										
Meols Cop d	12 59											14 04										
Southport a	13 10						13 36					14 15						14 36				
Lostock d				12 36					12 56							13 36				13 56		
Horwich Parkway d				12 40					13 00							13 40				14 00		
Blackrod d									13 03											14 03		
Adlington (Lancashire) d									13 07											14 07		
Chorley d				12 47					13 12		13 17					13 47				14 12		14 17
Leyland d			12 47	12 56										13 47		13 56						
Preston 8 a			12 56	13 04					13 25		13 27			13 54		14 04				14 24		14 27
Kirkham & Wesham 97 a				*13 21*					13 35							*14 21*				14 35		
Poulton-le-Fylde 97 a				13 23					13 43							14 23				14 43		
Layton 97 a									13 47											14 47		
Blackpool North 97 a			13 21	13 32					13 56					14 21		14 32				14 56		
Preston 8 65 d											13 29					14 09						14 29
Lancaster 6 65 a											13 44					14 24						14 44
d						13 13					13 45				14 18	14 25						14 45
Oxenholme Lake District 65 a																14 42						14 59
Windermere 83 a																15 01						*16 17*
Carnforth d						13a23					13 53				14 28							
Silverdale d															14 34							
Arnside d											14 02				14 38							
Grange-over-Sands d											14 07				14 44							
Kents Bank d															14 48							
Cark d															14 52							
Ulverston d											14 20				15 01							
Dalton d															15 09							
Roose d															15 15							
Barrow-in-Furness a											14 41				15 23							

For general notes see front of timetable
For details of catering facilities see Directory of Train Operators

A To Clitheroe (Table 94)
B From Liverpool Lime Street (Table 90)
C From Morecambe to Leeds (Table 36)
D 🍴 to Preston
E To Carlisle via Whitehaven (Table 100)
G 🍴 to Blackpool North
H To Edinburgh (Table 65)

Table 82

from 11 October

Manchester → Bolton → Wigan, Kirkby, Southport, Preston, Blackpool North and Barrow-in-Furness

Network Diagram - see first page of Table 82

	NT	NT	NT	TP	NT	NT	NT	NT	NT	TP	NT	NT	NT	TP	NT	NT	NT	NT	NT	NT	TP	NT	NT
				1 ◇						1 ◇				1 ◇							1 ◇		
		A	B							C ⊼		A	B					D			E ⊼	A	G
Manchester Airport 85 ✈ d				13 47		14 07				14 27				14 47		15 07					15 27		
Heald Green 85 d						*13 56*				14 31						*14 56*					15 31		
Buxton 86 d								13 29											14 32				
Hazel Grove 86 d								14 10											15 10				
Stockport 84 d								14 19											15 19				
Manchester Piccadilly 10 d				14 11		14 23		14 30		14 45				15 11		15 23			15 30		15 45		
Manchester Oxford Road d				14 15		14 26		14 33		14 48				15 15		15 26			15 33		15 48		
Deansgate d								14 35		14 50									15 35				
Rochdale 95 d	13 33				*13 50*		14 03				14 33				*14 52*		15 03					*15 23*	
Manchester Victoria d	13 57	14 00			14 18		14 29		14 41		14 57	15 00			15 18		15 29			15 41		15 50	
Salford Central d	14 00	14 03			14 21		14 32		14 44		15 00	15 03			15 21		15 32			15 44		15 53	
Salford Crescent a	14 03	14 06		14 21	14 24	14 32	14 35	14 40	14 47	14 53	15 03	15 06		15 21	15 24	15 32	15 35		15 40	15 47	15 53	15 56	
d	14 04	14 07		14 21	14 24	14 32	14 35	14 40	14 47	14 54	15 04	15 07		15 21	15 24	15 32	15 35		15 40	15 47	15 54	15 57	
Swinton d	14 10						14 42				15 10						15 42						
Moorside d							14 44										15 44						
Walkden d	14 15						14 48				15 15						15 48						
Atherton d	14 20						14 53				15 20						15 53						
Hag Fold d							14 56										15 56						
Daisy Hill d	14 24						14 59				15 24						15 59						
Kearsley d									14 55											15 55			
Farnworth d									14 57											15 57			
Moses Gate d					14 32										15 32								
Bolton a		14 18		14 31	14 36	14 42		14 50	15 01	15 05		15 18		15 31	15 36	15 42			15 50	16 01	16 05	16 08	
d				14 32	14 36	14 43		14 51	15 02	15 05				15 32	15 36	15 43			15 51	16 02	16 05		
Westhoughton d						14 50			15 09							15 50				16 09			
Hindley d	14 28						15 03		15 13		15 28						16 03			16 13			
Ince d							15 06										16 06						
Wigan North Western a																							
Wigan Wallgate a	14 33				14 56	15 01	15 09		15 22		15 33				15 56	16 01	16 09			16 22			
d	14 35					15 02	15 11				15 35					16 02	16 11						
Pemberton d							15 15										16 15						
Orrell d							15 19										16 19						
Upholland d							15 22										16 22						
Rainford d							15 26										16 26						
Kirkby a							15 37										16 37						
Liverpool Central 10 103 a							*16 01*										*17 01*						
Gathurst d	14 39										15 39					16 07							
Appley Bridge d	14 43					15 09					15 43					16 10							
Parbold d	14 47					15 13					15 47					16 14							
Hoscar d																16 17							
Burscough Bridge d	14 51					15 17					15 51					16 20							
New Lane d																16 23							
Bescar Lane d																16 26							
Meols Cop d	14 59										15 59					16 31							
Southport a	15 10					15 36					16 10					16 43							
Lostock d				14 36				14 56						15 36					15 56				
Horwich Parkway d				14 40				15 00						15 40					16 00				
Blackrod d								15 03											16 03				
Adlington (Lancashire) d								15 07											16 07				
Chorley d				14 47				15 12		15 17				15 47					16 12		16 17		
Leyland d			14 47	14 56									15 47	15 56									
Preston 8 a			14 54	15 04				15 25		15 27			15 54	16 04					16 25		16 27		
Kirkham & Wesham 97 a				*15 21*				15 35						*16 23*					16 35				
Poulton-le-Fylde 97 a				15 23				15 43						16 23					16 43				
Layton 97 a								15 47											16 47				
Blackpool North 97 a			15 21	15 32				15 56					16 21	16 32					16 56				
Preston 8 65 d										15 30											16 29		
Lancaster 6 65 a										15 45											16 44		
d										15 50								16 14			16 45		16 53
Oxenholme Lake District 65 a																					16 59		
Windermere 83 a																					*17 23*		
Carnforth d										15 58								16 23					17a02
Silverdale d										16 04								16 29					
Arnside d										16 08								16 33					
Grange-over-Sands d										16 13								16 39					
Kents Bank d										16 17								16 43					
Cark d										16 22								16 47					
Ulverston d										16 30								16 55					
Dalton d										16 38								17 03					
Roose d										16 44								17 09					
Barrow-in-Furness a										16 53								17 17					

For general notes see front of timetable
For details of catering facilities see Directory of Train Operators

A To Clitheroe (Table 94)
B From Liverpool Lime Street (Table 90)
C ⊼ to Preston
D To Carlisle via Whitehaven (Table 100)
E To Edinburgh (Table 65)
G From Morecambe to Skipton (Table 36)

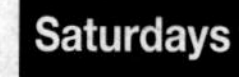

Manchester → Bolton → Wigan, Kirkby, Southport, Preston, Blackpool North and Barrow-in-Furness

Saturdays from 11 October

Network Diagram - see first page of Table 82

		NT	NT	NT	TP	NT	NT	NT	NT	NT	TP	NT	NT	NT	NT	TP	NT	NT	NT	NT	NT	NT
				A	1 ◇ 🛒	B					1 ◇ C 🛒	D	E		B	1 ◇ G 🛒			H	J	D	
Manchester Airport	85 ✈ d				15 47		16 07				16 27					16 47						*17b04*
Heald Green	85 d						*15 56*				16 31											*16b56*
Buxton	86 d								15 29													16 31
Hazel Grove	86 d								16 10													17 09
Stockport	84 d								16 19					16 40				17 01				17 18
Manchester Piccadilly 10	🚊 d				16 11		16 23		16 30		16 44			16 52		17 11		17 15				17 30
Manchester Oxford Road	d				16 15		16 26		16 33		16 48			16 56		17 15		17 19				17 33
Deansgate	🚊 d						16 28		16 35					16 59				17 21				17 35
Rochdale	95 d	15 33				*15 54*		16 03					*16 23*				*16 52*			17 03		
Manchester Victoria	🚊 d	15 57	16 10			16 23		16 29		16 41			16 48		17 00		17 15		17 23	17 29		
Salford Central	d	16 00	16 13			16 26		16 32		16 44			16 51		17 03		17 18		17 26	17 32		
Salford Crescent	a	16 03	16 16		16 21	16 29	16 32	16 35	16 40	16 47			16 54	17 03	17 06		17 22	17 26	17 29	17 35		17 40
	d	16 04	16 16		16 21	16 29	16 32	16 35	16 40	16 47			16 54	17 03	17 07		17 23	17 26	17 29	17 36		17 40
Swinton	d	16 10						16 42					17 01				17 29					
Moorside	d							16 44					17 03				17 32					
Walkden	d	16 15						16 47					17 09				17 36					
Atherton	d	16 20						16 54					17 14				17 42					
Hag Fold	d							16 56					17 17				17 44					
Daisy Hill	d	16 24						16 59					17 20				17 47					
Kearsley	d									16 55										17 43		
Farnworth	d									16 57									17 38			
Moses Gate	d		16 24							16 59									17 40			
Bolton	a		16 28		16 31	16 42	16 43		16 51	17 02	17 05			17 13	17 18	17 30		17 36	17 44	17 49		17 53
	d		16 28		16 32		16 43		16 51	17 02	17 05			17 13		17 30		17 37	17 45			17 53
Westhoughton	d		16 36				16 50			17 10									17 52			
Hindley	d	16 28	16 40					17 03		17 17			17 24				17 52		17 56			
Ince	d		16 43					17 06					17 27				17 55		17 59			
Wigan North Western	a									17 26												
Wigan Wallgate	a	16 33	16 52				17 01	17 10					17 36				17 58		18 08			
	d	16 35					17 02	17 11					17 38				17 59					
Pemberton	d							17 15									18 03					
Orrell	d							17 19									18 07					
Upholland	d							17 22									18 11					
Rainford	d							17 26									18 14					
Kirkby	a							17 37									18 25					
Liverpool Central 10	103 a							*18 01*									*19 01*					
Gathurst	d	16 39					17 06						17 42									
Appley Bridge	d	16 43					17 10						17 46									
Parbold	d	16 47					17 14						17 50									
Hoscar	d																					
Burscough Bridge	d	16 51					17 18						17 54									
New Lane	d																					
Bescar Lane	d																					
Meols Cop	d	16 59					17 26						18 02									
Southport	a	17 10					17 37						18 11									
Lostock	d				16 36				16 56					17 18				17 42				17 58
Horwich Parkway	d				16 40				17 00					17 22				17 46				18 02
Blackrod	d								17 03					17 25				17 49				18 05
Adlington (Lancashire)	d								17 07					17 29				17 53				18 09
Chorley	d				16 47				17 12		17 17			17 34		17 42		17 57				18 14
Leyland	d			16 47	16 56				17 19			17 29		17 40				18 04			18 09	18 20
Preston 8	a			16 54	17 04				17 27		17 27	17 40		17 50		17 53		18 12			18 17	18 29
Kirkham & Wesham	97 a				17 15				17 38							18 10		18 22				18 39
Poulton-le-Fylde	97 a				17 25				17 47		*17 53*					18 20		18 32				18 48
Layton	97 a				17 28				17 51							18 24		18 36				18 52
Blackpool North	97 a				17 34				18 00		*18 03*					18 30		18 43			18 48	19 01
Preston 8	65 d			16 56							17 29					17 58						
Lancaster 6	65 a			17 16							17 44					18 13						
	d			17 17							17 45					18 14						
Oxenholme Lake District	65 a															18 28						
Windermere	83 a															*19 02*						
Carnforth	d			17 26							17 53											
Silverdale	d			17 32							18 00											
Arnside	d			17 37							18 04											
Grange-over-Sands	d			17 43							18 09											
Kents Bank	d			17 46							18 13											
Cark	d			17 51							18 17											
Ulverston	d			17 59							18 25											
Dalton	d			18 07							18 34											
Roose	d			18 13							18 39											
Barrow-in-Furness	a			18 21							18 50											

For general notes see front of timetable
For details of catering facilities see Directory of Train Operators

A From Liverpool Lime Street (Table 90) to Millom (Table 100)
B To Clitheroe (Table 94)
C 🛒 to Preston
D From Liverpool Lime Street (Table 90)
E From Stalybridge (Table 39)
G Oxenholme Lake District portion continues to Glasgow Central (Table 65)
H From Huddersfield (Table 39)
J To Blackburn (Table 94)
b Change at Manchester Piccadilly

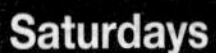

from 11 October

Manchester → Bolton → Wigan, Kirkby, Southport, Preston, Blackpool North and Barrow-in-Furness

Network Diagram - see first page of Table 82

	NT	NT	TP	NT	NT	NT	TP	NT	NT	NT	NT	NT	NT	NT	NT	TP	NT	TP		NT	NT	NT	NT	TP
			1 ◇				1 ◇									1 ◇		1 ◇						1 ◇
		A	B 🛒		C	D		E	G		D						C					D		
Manchester Airport 85 ✈ d			17 32				17 47					18 10				18 27		18 47					19 12	19 27
Heald Green 85 d							*17 22*					*17 56*				18 31							*18 56*	19 31
Buxton 86 d													17 34								18 17			
Hazel Grove 86 d													18 10								18 55			
Stockport 84 d													18 19								19 05			
Manchester Piccadilly 10 ⇌ d			17 50				18 11					18 26	18 31			18 45		19 11			19 20		19 33	19 44
Manchester Oxford Road d			17 54				18 15					18 29	18 36			18 47		19 15			19 23		19 37	19 48
Deansgate ⇌ d			17 56				18 17					18 31	18 38			18 50		19 17			19 26			19 50
Rochdale 95 d				17 33					*17 52*	18 03							*18 23*			*18 32*				
Manchester Victoria ⇌ d	17 38	17 42		17 57	18 00				18 21	18 29					18 41		18 58			19 18				
Salford Central d	17 41	17 45		18 00	18 03				18 24	18 32					18 44		19 01			19 21				
Salford Crescent a	17 45	17 48	17 59	18 03	18 07		18 19		18 28	18 35		18 38	18 41		18 47	18 59	19 04	19 21		19 24	19 31		19 42	19 54
d	17 46	17 49	18 00	18 04	18 07		18 21		18 28	18 35		18 39	18 42		18 47	19 01	19 05	19 21		19 25			19 42	19 54
Swinton d				18 10						18 42										19 31				
Moorside d				18 13						18 44										19 34				
Walkden d	17 55			18 16						18 48										19 37				
Atherton d	18 01			18 22						18 53										19 43				
Hag Fold d				18 24						18 56				←						19 45				
Daisy Hill d	18 05			18 27						18 59				18 59						19 48				
Kearsley d		17 59								→					18 55									
Farnworth d		18 01													18 57									
Moses Gate d		18 03													19 00									
Bolton a		18 07	18 10		18 19		18 32		18 44			18 49	18 52		19 04	19 11	19 17	19 31					19 52	20 04
d		18 07	18 10				18 32					18 50	18 53		19 04	19 12		19 32					19 53	20 05
Westhoughton d		18 15										18 57			19 11								20 00	
Hindley d		18 19		18 32										19 05	19 15					19 53			20 04	
Ince d				18 35										19 08						19 56				
Wigan North Western a																								
Wigan Wallgate a	18 14	18 28		18 44								19 05		19 15	19 26					20 03			20 09	
d	18 14											19 06											20 11	
Pemberton d																								
Orrell d																								
Upholland d																								
Rainford d																								
Kirkby a																								
Liverpool Central 10 103 a																								
Gathurst d	18 19											19 11											20 15	
Appley Bridge d	18 23											19 14											20 19	
Parbold d	18 27											19 18											20 23	
Hoscar d												19 21												
Burscough Bridge d	18 32											19 24											20 27	
New Lane d												19 27												
Bescar Lane d												19 30												
Meols Cop d	18 40											19 35											20 35	
Southport a	18 51											19 47											20 46	
Lostock d			18 15				18 36						18 58					19 36						
Horwich Parkway d							18 40						19 02					19 40						
Blackrod d							18 43						19 05					19 43						
Adlington (Lancashire) d													19 08					19 47						
Chorley d			18 24				18 51						19 13			19 24		19 51						20 16
Leyland d						18 44	18 58				19 07		19 19					19 58				20 07		
Preston 8 a			18 34			18 52	19 05				19 17		19 27			19 36		20 05				20 17		20 27
Kirkham & Wesham 97 a							19 16						19 38					20 15						
Poulton-le-Fylde 97 a						19 10	19 26						19 47					20 26				*20 49*		
Layton 97 a							*19 51*						19 51					20 30						
Blackpool North 97 a						19 21	19 35						19 57					20 36				*20 56*		
Preston 8 65 d			18 38													19 38								20 29
Lancaster 6 65 a			18 54			*19b14*										19 54								20 47
d			18 55					19 19								19 55								20 47
Oxenholme Lake District 65 a						*19b29*																		
Windermere 83 a						*20c19*																		
Carnforth d			19 03					19a31								20 03								20 58
Silverdale d			19 09													20 09								21 04
Arnside d			19 14													20 14								21 08
Grange-over-Sands d			19 19													20 19								21 14
Kents Bank d			19 23													20 23								21 18
Cark d			19 28													20 28								21 22
Ulverston d			19 36													20 36								21 30
Dalton d			19 44													20 44								21 39
Roose d			19 50													20 50								21 44
Barrow-in-Furness a			19 59													21 00								21 54

For general notes see front of timetable
For details of catering facilities see Directory of Train Operators

A Also stops at Clifton 1754
B 🛒 to Preston
C To Clitheroe (Table 94)
D From Liverpool Lime Street (Table 90)
E From Morecambe to Leeds (Table 36)
G To Blackburn (Table 94)
b Change at Preston
c Change at Preston and Oxenholme Lake District

Table 82

Saturdays

from 11 October

Manchester → Bolton → Wigan, Kirkby, Southport, Preston, Blackpool North and Barrow-in-Furness

Network Diagram - see first page of Table 82

		NT	TP	NT	NT	NT	NT	TP	TP	NT	NT	TP	NT	NT	NT	TP	NT	NT	NT	NT	NT	TP	NT
			1 ◇					1 ◇	1 ◇			1 ◇				1 ◇						1 ◇	
		A					A						B		C						B		
Manchester Airport	85 ✈ d		19 47		20 15	20b22			20 47		21 16	21 27				21 47		21b52		22b22		22 47	
Heald Green	85 d				19 56	20b07					20 56	21 08						21b56		22b12		22 51	
Buxton	86 d					19 50												21 33					
Hazel Grove	86 d					20 31												22 14					
Stockport	84 d					20 40												22 23		22 38			
Manchester Piccadilly 10	d		20 11		20 32	20 52			21 11		21 35	21 45				22 11		22 35		22 49		23 11	
Manchester Oxford Road	d		20 15		20 35	20 54			21 15		21 38	21 48				22 15		22 38		22 52		23 15	
Deansgate	d		20 17		20 37	20 56			21 17		21 40	21 50				22 17		22 40		22 54		23 17	
Rochdale	95 d	19 24		19 52			20 02			20 52			21 02				21 52				22 02		
Manchester Victoria	d	19 58		20 21			20 57			21 21			21 58				22 34				23 08		23 18
Salford Central	d	20 01		20 24			21 01			21 24			22 01				22 37				23 11		23 21
Salford Crescent	a	20 04	20 20	20 28	20 41	21 00	21 04		21 20	21 27	21 44	21 53	22 04			22 20	22 40	22 44		23 00	23 13	23 20	23 25
	d	20 05	20 21	20 28	20 41	21 00	21 05		21 21	21 28	21 44	21 54	22 05			22 21	22 41	22 44		23 00	23 14	23 21	23 25
Swinton	d			20 34						21 34							22 47						23 32
Moorside	d			20 37						21 37							22 50						23 34
Walkden	d			20 40						21 40							22 53						23 38
Atherton	d			20 46						21 46							22 59						23 43
Hag Fold	d			20 48						21 48							23 01		←				23 46
Daisy Hill	d			20 51						21 51							23 04		23 04				23 49
Kearsley	d																→			23 08			
Farnworth	d																			23 10			
Moses Gate	d																			23 12			
Bolton	a	20 16	20 31		20 51	21 16	21 17		21 31		21 54	22 05	22 16			22 31		22 54		23 16	23 27	23 31	
	d		20 32		20 52				21 32		21 55	22 05				22 32		22 55		23 16		23 32	
Westhoughton	d				20 59						22 02							23 02		23 24			
Hindley	d			20 56	21 03					21 56	22 06							23 06	23 13	23 28			23 53
Ince	d			20 59						21 59									23 16	23 31			23 56
Wigan North Western	a																						
Wigan Wallgate	a			21 07	21 10					22 07	22 11							23 11	23 23	23 38			00 05
	d				21 12						22 13							23 13					
Pemberton	d																						
Orrell	d																						
Upholland	d																						
Rainford	d																						
Kirkby	a																						
Liverpool Central 10	103 a																						
Gathurst	d				21 16						22 17							23 17					
Appley Bridge	d				21 20						22 21							23 21					
Parbold	d				21 24						22 25							23 25					
Hoscar	d				21 27																		
Burscough Bridge	d				21 30						22 29							23 29					
New Lane	d				21 32																		
Bescar Lane	d				21 36																		
Meols Cop	d				21 41						22 37							23 37					
Southport	a				21 51						22 49							23 48					
Lostock	d		20 36						21 36							22 36						23 36	
Horwich Parkway	d		20 40						21 40							22 40						23 40	
Blackrod	d		20 43						21 43							22 43						23 43	
Adlington (Lancashire)	d		20 47						21 47							22 47						23 47	
Chorley	d		20 51						21 51			22 17				22 51						23 51	
Leyland	d		20 58						21 58						22 54	22 58						23 58	
Preston 8	a		21 05						22 04			22 32			23 02	23 05						00 06	
Kirkham & Wesham	97 a		21 15						22 15			23 00				23 15						00 15	
Poulton-le-Fylde	97 a		21 26						22 26							23 26						00 26	
Layton	97 a		21 30						22 30							23 30						00 30	
Blackpool North	97 a		21 36						22 36						23 28	23 36						00 38	
Preston 8	65 d																						
Lancaster 6	65 a																						
	d							21 45					22 45										
Oxenholme Lake District	65 a																						
Windermere	83 a																						
Carnforth	d							21 53					22 54										
Silverdale	d							22 00					23 00										
Arnside	d							22 04					23 04										
Grange-over-Sands	d							22 09					23 10										
Kents Bank	d							22 13					23 14										
Cark	d							22 17					23 18										
Ulverston	d							22 25					23 26										
Dalton	d							22 34					23 34										
Roose	d							22 39					23 40										
Barrow-in-Furness	a							22 50					23 50										

For general notes see front of timetable
For details of catering facilities see Directory of Train Operators

A To Clitheroe (Table 94)
B To Blackburn (Table 94)
C From Liverpool Lime Street (Table 90)

b Change at Manchester Piccadilly

Table 82

Sundays

until 13 July

Manchester → Bolton → Wigan, Southport, Preston, Blackpool North and Barrow-in-Furness

Network Diagram - see first page of Table 82

	NT	TP	TP	TP	TP	NT	NT	NT	NT	NT	TP	TP	TP	NT	NT	TP	NT	TP	NT	NT	NT	NT	TP	NT
				1 ◇	1 ◇						1 ◇	1 ◇	1 ◇			1 ◇		1 ◇					1 ◇	
	A					B	A			B						C	B		A			B		
		🚌	🚌																					
Manchester Airport 85 d		00 10	05 40	06 13	07 36						08 47	08 51				09 36		09 47			10b01		10 47	11b00
Heald Green 85 d				06 16	07 16						08 16												10 17	
Buxton 86 d														08 25						09 25				10 25
Hazel Grove 86 d														08 59						09 59				10 59
Alderley Edge 84 d															09 10						10 10			
Stockport 84 d											08 39			09 10	09 29					10 10	10 29		10 36	11 10
Manchester Piccadilly 10 d		00 35	06 05	07 00	07 51						09 03	09 21		09 25	09 45	09 51		10 03		10 25	10 45		11 03	11 25
Manchester Oxford Road d				07 03	07 54						09 06	09 24		09 29	09 48	09 54		10 06		10 29	10 48		11 06	11 29
Deansgate d				07 05	07 56						09 08			09 31	09 50			10 08		10 31	10 50		11 08	11 31
Rochdale 95 d																						10 18		
Manchester Victoria d						08 00		08 28	08 49	09 00							10 00					11 00		
Salford Crescent a					08 00			08 33	08 54	09 04	09 11			09 34	09 54		10 04	10 11		10 34	10 54	11 04	11 11	11 34
d					08 00			08 33	08 54	09 05	09 12			09 35	09 54		10 05	10 12		10 35	10 54	11 05	11 12	11 35
Bolton a		01s00	06s30	07 20	08 10	08 13		08 43	09 04	09 15	09 22	09 37		09 45	10 04	10 08	10 15	10 22		10 45	11 04	11 15	11 22	11 45
d					08 10			08 44	09 05		09 22	09 38		09 45	10 05	10 09		10 22		10 45	11 05		11 22	11 45
Westhoughton d									09 12						10 12						11 12			
Hindley d									09 16						10 16						11 16			
Wigan North Western a												09 50												
Wigan Wallgate a									09 21						10 21						11 21			
d									09 23						10 23						11 23			
Gathurst d									09 27						10 27						11 27			
Appley Bridge d									09 31						10 31						11 31			
Parbold d									09 35						10 35						11 35			
Burscough Bridge d									09 39						10 39						11 39			
Southport a									09 56						10 56						11 56			
Lostock d								08 49						09 50						10 50				11 50
Horwich Parkway d								08 53						09 54						10 54				11 54
Blackrod d								08 56						09 57						10 57				11 57
Adlington (Lancashire) d								09 00						10 01						11 01				12 01
Chorley d					08 22			09 04			09 34			10 06				10 34		11 06			11 34	12 06
Leyland d	00 06		06s55		08 30		08 58	09 11						10 12					10 58	11 12				12 12
Preston 8 a	00 15	01s35	07s10		08 35		09 05	09 18			09 47	10 09		10 20		10 30		10 47	11 05	11 20			11 48	12 20
Kirkham & Wesham 97 a			07s30		08 57						09 57							10 57		11 51			11 57	
Poulton-le-Fylde 97 a			07s50		09 07		09 23	09 36			10 07			10 38				11 07	11 23	11 38			12 07	12 38
Blackpool North 97 a		02 15	08 05		09 16		09 34	09 45			10 16			10 47				11 16	11 34	11 47			12 16	12 47
Preston 8 65 d												10 13	10 25			10 35								
Lancaster 6 65 a												10 30	10 40			10 50				11c58			12c38	
d												10 31	10 41			10 51								
Oxenholme Lake District 65 a												10 46				11 06				12c13			12c51	
Windermere 83 a												11 10								12e34				
Carnforth d													10f55											
Silverdale d													11 01											
Arnside d													11 05											
Grange-over-Sands d													11 10											
Kents Bank d													11 14											
Cark d													11 18											
Ulverston d													11 26											
Dalton d													11 34											
Roose d													11 40											
Barrow-in-Furness a													11 49											

For general notes see front of timetable
For details of catering facilities see Directory of Train Operators

A From Liverpool Lime Street (Table 90)
B To Clitheroe (Table 94)
C To Glasgow Central (Table 65)
b Change at Manchester Piccadilly
c Change at Preston
e Change at Preston and Oxenholme Lake District
f Arr. 1049

Table 82

Sundays until 13 July

Manchester → Bolton → Wigan, Southport, Preston, Blackpool North and Barrow-in-Furness

Network Diagram - see first page of Table 82

Station		TP 1◇ A		NT	NT B	NT C	TP 1◇	NT D	NT	TP 1◇	NT	NT B	TP 1◇	NT	TP 1◇ A	NT C	NT	NT B	TP 1◇	NT D	NT	TP 1◇	NT	NT B	TP 1◇
Manchester Airport	85 ✈ d	11 27		11b03			11 47				12b22		12 45	12b52	13 27				13 47		13b52	14 27			14 47
Heald Green	85 d						11 17				12b16						13b15						14b19		
Buxton	86 d								11 20					12 20							13 25				
Hazel Grove	86 d								11 56					12 54							13 59				
Alderley Edge	84 d			11 10							12 10						13 10						14 10		
Stockport	84 d	11 20		11 29			11 36		12 08		12 29		12 35	13 08	13c23		13 29				14 10	14c20	14 29		
Manchester Piccadilly 10	✈ d	11 42		11 45			12 03		12 25		12 48		13 01	13 24	13 42		13 48		14 03		14 25	14 42	14 48		15 03
Manchester Oxford Road	d	11 45		11 48			12 06		12 29	12 43	12 51		13 06	13 28	13 45		13 51		14 06		14 29	14 45	14 51		15 06
Deansgate	✈ d			11 50			12 08		12 31		12 53		13 08	13 30			13 53		14 08		14 31		14 53		15 08
Rochdale	95 d				11 18							12 18						13 18						14 18	
Manchester Victoria	✈ d				12 00							13 00						14 00						15 00	
Salford Crescent	a			11 54	12 04		12 11		12 34		12 57	13 04	13 11	13 33			13 57	14 04	14 11		14 34		14 57	15 04	15 11
	d			11 54	12 05		12 12		12 35		12 57	13 05	13 12	13 34			13 57	14 05	14 12		14 35		14 57	15 05	15 12
Bolton	a	11 58		12 05	12 15		12 22		12 45	12 56	13 07	13 15	13 22	13 44	13 59		14 07	14 15	14 22		14 45	14 59	15 08	15 15	15 22
	d	11 59		12 05			12 22		12 45	13 00	13 08		13 22	13 44	14 00		14 08		14 22		14 45	15 00	15 08		15 22
Westhoughton	d			12 12							13 15						14 15						15 16		
Hindley	d			12 16							13 19						14 19						15 20		
Wigan North Western	a																								
Wigan Wallgate	a			12 23							13 24						14 24						15 25		
	d			12 23							13 26						14 26						15 27		
Gathurst	d			12 27							13 30						14 30						15 31		
Appley Bridge	d			12 31							13 34						14 34						15 35		
Parbold	d			12 35							13 38						14 38						15 39		
Burscough Bridge	d			12 39							13 42						14 42						15 43		
Southport	a			12 56							13 59						14 59						16 01		
Lostock	d								12 50					13 49							14 50				
Horwich Parkway	d								12 54					13 53							14 54				
Blackrod	d								12 57					13 56							14 57				
Adlington (Lancashire)	d								13 01					14 00							15 01				
Chorley	d						12 34		13 06				13 34	14 05					14 34		15 06				15 34
Leyland	d							12 58	13 12					14 12						14 58	15 12				
Preston 8	a	12 25					12 48	13 06	13 20	13 20			13 48	14 19	14 22				14 47	15 07	15 20	15 22			15 46
Kirkham & Wesham	97 a	12 51					12 57			13 51			13 57		14 51				14 57			15 51			15 57
Poulton-le-Fylde	97 a						13 07	13 23	13 38				14 07	14 37					15 07	15 23	15 38				16 07
Blackpool North	97 a						13 16	13 34	13 47				14 16	14 47					15 16	15 34	15 47				16 16
Preston 8	65 d	12 27								13 22					14 24							15 25			
Lancaster 6	65 a	12 43							13e47	13 37				14e47	14 39				15e32		15e55	15 40			16e19
	d	12 43				12 48				13 38					14 40	14 43						15 41			
Oxenholme Lake District	65 a	12 57								14 13				15e02	14 54										16e32
Windermere	83 a	13 18													15 36										
Carnforth	d					12a57				13 46						14a52						15 50			
Silverdale	d									13 52												15 55			
Arnside	d									13 56												16 00			
Grange-over-Sands	d									14 02												16 05			
Kents Bank	d									14 05												16 09			
Cark	d									14 10												16 13			
Ulverston	d									14 18												16 21			
Dalton	d									14 26												16 29			
Roose	d									14 31												16 35			
Barrow-in-Furness	a									14 41												16 44			

For general notes see front of timetable
For details of catering facilities see Directory of Train Operators

- **A** To Edinburgh (Table 65)
- **B** To Clitheroe (Table 94)
- **C** From Morecambe to Leeds (Table 36)
- **D** From Liverpool Lime Street (Table 90)
- **b** Change at Manchester Piccadilly
- **c** Change at Manchester Oxford Road
- **e** Change at Preston

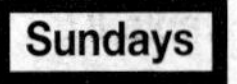

until 13 July

Manchester → Bolton → Wigan, Southport, Preston, Blackpool North and Barrow-in-Furness

Network Diagram - see first page of Table 82

		NT	TP 1 ◇ A	NT		NT B	TP 1 ◇	NT C	NT	TP 1 ◇	NT	NT B	NT D	TP 1 ◇	NT C	NT	NT	TP 1 ◇ E	NT	NT B	TP 1 ◇	NT C	NT	TP 1 ◇	NT
Manchester Airport 85	d	14b52	15 27				15 47		16b01	16 27				16 47		17b01		17 27			17 47		18b01	18 27	
Heald Green 85	d						15 17							16 17							17 17				
Buxton 86	d	14 25							15 25							16 25							17 25		
Hazel Grove 86	d	14 59							15 59							16 59							17 59		
Alderley Edge 84	d			15 10							16 10								17 10						18 10
Stockport 84	d	15 10	15c25	15 29					16 10	16c20	16 29					17 10		17c21	17 29				18 10	18c25	18 29
Manchester Piccadilly 10	d	15 25	15 42	15 45			16 03		16 25	16 42	16 45			17 03		17 25		17 42	17 45		18 03		18 25	18 42	18 45
Manchester Oxford Road	d	15 29	15 45	15 48			16 06		16 28	16 45	16 48			17 06		17 29		17 45	17 48		18 06		18 28	18 45	18 48
Deansgate	d	15 31		15 50			16 08		16 30		16 50			17 08		17 31			17 50		18 08		18 30		18 50
Rochdale 95	d					15 18						16 18								17 18					
Manchester Victoria	d					16 00						17 00								18 00					
Salford Crescent	a	15 34		15 54		16 04	16 11		16 34		16 54	17 04		17 12		17 34			17 54	18 04	18 11		18 34		18 54
	d	15 35		15 54		16 05	16 12		16 34		16 54	17 05		17 12		17 35			17 54	18 05	18 12		18 34		18 54
Bolton	a	15 45	15 59	16 05		16 15	16 22		16 45	16 59	17 05	17 15		17 22		17 45		17 59	18 05	18 15	18 22		18 45	18 59	19 04
	d	15 45	16 00	16 05			16 22		16 45	17 00	17 05			17 22		17 45		18 00	18 05		18 22		18 45	19 00	19 05
Westhoughton	d			16 12							17 12								18 12						19 12
Hindley	d			16 16							17 16								18 16						19 16
Wigan North Western	a																								
Wigan Wallgate	a			16 22							17 22								18 21						19 21
	d			16 23							17 23								18 23						19 23
Gathurst	d			16 27							17 27								18 27						19 27
Appley Bridge	d			16 31							17 31								18 31						19 31
Parbold	d			16 35							17 35								18 35						19 35
Burscough Bridge	d			16 39							17 39								18 39						19 39
Southport	a			16 56							17 56								18 56						19 57
Lostock	d	15 50							16 50							17 50							18 50		
Horwich Parkway	d	15 54							16 54							17 54							18 54		
Blackrod	d	15 57							16 57							17 57							18 57		
Adlington (Lancashire)	d	16 01							17 01							18 01							19 01		
Chorley	d	16 06					16 34		17 05					17 34		18 06					18 34		19 05		
Leyland	d	16 12						16 57	17 12						17 58	18 12						18 58	19 12		
Preston 8	a	16 20	16 22				16 46	17 04	17 20	17 23				17 46	18 05	18 20		18 23			18 48	19 05	19 19	19 21	
Kirkham & Wesham 97	a		16 51				16 57			17 51				17 57				18 51			18 57			19 51	
Poulton-le-Fylde 97	a	16 38					17 07	17 23	17 38					18 07	18 23	18 38					19 07	19 23	19 37		
Blackpool North 97	a	16 47					17 16	17 37	17 47					18 16	18 34	18 47					19 16	19 32	19 47		
Preston 8 65	d		16 25							17 25								18 25						19 25	
Lancaster 6 65	a	16e53	16 40				17e18		17e53	17 42				18e25		18e53		18 40			19e21		19e55	19 40	
	d		16 41							17 43			18 06				18 19	18 41						19 41	
Oxenholme Lake District 65	a	17e08	16 55				17f53							18e40	18e55	19e08		18 55			19e34			20 10	
Windermere 83	a		17 16				18f15											19 16			20g09				
Carnforth	d									17 51			18a15				18 29							19 49	
Silverdale	d									17 57							18 34							19 55	
Arnside	d									18 01							18 39							19 59	
Grange-over-Sands	d									18 07							18 45							20 05	
Kents Bank	d									18 10							18 48							20 08	
Cark	d									18 15							18 52							20 13	
Ulverston	d									18 23							19 01							20 21	
Dalton	d									18 31							19 09							20 29	
Roose	d									18 36							19 15							20 34	
Barrow-in-Furness	a									18 46							19 22							20 44	

For general notes see front of timetable
For details of catering facilities see Directory of Train Operators

A To Edinburgh (Table 65)

B To Clitheroe (Table 94)
C From Liverpool Lime Street (Table 90)
D From Morecambe to Leeds (Table 36)
E To Glasgow Central (Table 65)
b Change at Manchester Piccadilly

c Change at Manchester Oxford Road
e Change at Preston
f Change at Preston and Lancaster
g Change at Preston and Oxenholme Lake District

Table 82

until 13 July

Manchester → Bolton → Wigan, Southport, Preston, Blackpool North and Barrow-in-Furness

Network Diagram - see first page of Table 82

	NT	NT	TP	NT	NT	NT	TP	NT	NT	TP	NT	NT	TP	NT	NT	NT	NT	TP	NT	NT	NT	TP		
			1 ◇				1 ◇			1 ◇			1 ◇					1 ◇				1 ◇		
	A	B				A		C				A				D					C			
Manchester Airport 85 ✈ d			18 47	19b01	19b05		19 47		19b52	20 27			20 47	20b52	21b05			21 47	22b01			22 47		
Heald Green 85 d			18 17				19 17						20 17					21 17				22 17		
Buxton 86 d				18 25					19 25					20 25					21c25					
Hazel Grove 86 d				18 59					19 59					20 59					21c59					
Alderley Edge 84 d					19 10						20 10				21 10				22 10					
Stockport 84 d				19 10	19 29				20 10		20 29			21 10	21 29				22 29					
Manchester Piccadilly 10 ✈ d			19 03	19 25	19 45		20 03		20 25	20 42	20 45		21 03	21 25	21 45			22 03	22 45			23 03		
Manchester Oxford Road d			19 06	19 29	19 48		20 06		20 28	20 45	20 48		21 06	21 28	21 48			22 06	22 48			23 06		
Deansgate ✈ d			19 08	19 31	19 50		20 08		20 30		20 50		21 08	21 30	21 50			22 08	22 50			23 08		
Rochdale 95 d	18 18					19 18						20 18				21 18				21 23				
Manchester Victoria ✈ d	19 00					20 00						21 00				22 00				23 00				
Salford Crescent a	19 04		19 11	19 34	19 54	20 04	20 11		20 34		20 54	21 04	21 11	21 34	21 54	22 04		22 12	22 54	23 04		23 11		
d	19 05		19 12	19 35	19 54	20 05	20 12		20 34		20 54	21 05	21 12	21 34	21 54	22 05		22 12	22 54			23 12		
Bolton a	19 15		19 22	19 45	20 04	20 15	20 22		20 45	20 59	21 05	21 15	21 22	21 45	22 04	22 15		22 22	23 04			23 22		
d			19 22	19 45	20 05		20 22		20 45	21 00	21 05		21 22	21 45	22 05			22 22	23 05			23 22		
Westhoughton d					20 12						21 12				22 12				23 12					
Hindley d					20 16						21 16				22 16				23 16					
Wigan North Western a																								
Wigan Wallgate a					20 21						21 22				22 25				23 25					
d					20 23						21 23													
Gathurst d					20 27						21 27													
Appley Bridge d					20 31						21 31													
Parbold d					20 35						21 35													
Burscough Bridge d					20 39						21 39													
Southport a					20 56						21 56													
Lostock d				19 50					20 50					21 50										
Horwich Parkway d				19 54					20 54					21 54										
Blackrod d				19 57					20 57					21 57										
Adlington (Lancashire) d				20 01					21 01					22 01										
Chorley d			19 34	20 06			20 34		21 05				21 34	22 05				22 34				23 34		
Leyland d				20 12				20 58	21 12					22 12							23 08			
Preston 8 a			19 48	20 20			20 47	21 05	21 20	21 21			21 48	22 20				22 45			23 15	23 46		
Kirkham & Wesham 97 a			19 57	20 45			20 57						21 58					22 57				23 57		
Poulton-le-Fylde 97 a			20 07	20 38			21 07	21 23	21 37				22 07	22 37				23 07			23 33	00 07		
Blackpool North 97 a			20 16	20 47			21 16	21 34	21 47				22 16	22 47				23 16			23 43	00 16		
Preston 8 65 d										21 25														
Lancaster 6 65 a			20e23	20e54			21e24			21 40				22e52										
d		20 15								21 41							23 00							
Oxenholme Lake District 65 a			20e37	21e09			21e38							23e05										
Windermere 83 a			21f04																					
Carnforth d		20a24								21 49							23 09							
Silverdale d										21 55							23 15							
Arnside d										21 59							23 19							
Grange-over-Sands d										22 05							23 25							
Kents Bank d										22 08							23 29							
Cark d										22 13							23 33							
Ulverston d										22 21							23 41							
Dalton d										22 29							23 49							
Roose d										22 34							23 55							
Barrow-in-Furness a										22 44							00 13							

For general notes see front of timetable
For details of catering facilities see Directory of Train Operators

A To Clitheroe (Table 94)
B From Morecambe to Leeds (Table 36)
C From Liverpool Lime Street (Table 90)
D To Blackburn (Table 94)

b Change at Manchester Piccadilly
c Change at Stockport
e Change at Preston
f Change at Preston and Oxenholme Lake District

Table 82

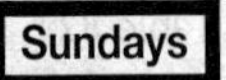

Manchester → Bolton → Wigan, Southport, Preston, Blackpool North and Barrow-in-Furness

20 July to 7 September

Network Diagram - see first page of Table 82

Station		NT	TP	TP	TP	TP	NT	NT	NT	NT	NT	TP	TP	
					1 ◇	1 ◇						1 ◇	1 ◇	
		A					B	A			B			
			🚌	🚌										
Manchester Airport	85 d		00 10	05 40	06 22	07 36						08 47		
Heald Green	85 d				06 16	07 13						08 16		
Buxton	86 d													
Hazel Grove	86 d													
Alderley Edge	84 d													
Stockport	84 d											08 39		
Manchester Piccadilly 10	d		00 35	06 05	07 00	07 51						09 03	09 21	
Manchester Oxford Road	d				07 03	07 54						09 06	09 24	
Deansgate	d				07 05	07 56						09 08		
Rochdale	95 d													
Manchester Victoria	d						08 00		08 28	08 49	09 00			
Salford Crescent	a					08 00			08 33	08 54	09 04	09 11		
	d					08 00			08 33	08 54	09 05	09 12		
Bolton	a		01s00	06s30	07 20	08 10	08 13		08 43	09 04	09 15	09 22	09 37	
	d					08 10			08 44	09 05		09 22	09 38	
Westhoughton	d									09 12				
Hindley	d									09 16				
Wigan North Western	a												09 50	
Wigan Wallgate	a									09 21				
	d									09 23				
Gathurst	d									09 27				
Appley Bridge	d									09 31				
Parbold	d									09 35				
Burscough Bridge	d									09 39				
Southport	a									09 56				
Lostock	d								08 49					
Horwich Parkway	d								08 53					
Blackrod	d								08 56					
Adlington (Lancashire)	d								09 00					
Chorley	d					08 22			09 04			09 34		
Leyland	d	00 06		06s55		08 30		08 58	09 11					
Preston 8	a	00 15	01s35	07s10		08 35		09 05	09 18			09 47	10 09	
Kirkham & Wesham	97 a			07s30		08 57						09 57		
Poulton-le-Fylde	97 a			07s50		09 07		09 23	09 36			10 07		
Blackpool North	97 a		02 15	08 05		09 16		09 34	09 45			10 16		
Preston 8	65 d												10 13	10 25
Lancaster 6	65 a												10 30	10 40
	d												10 31	10 41
Oxenholme Lake District	65 a												10 46	
Windermere	83 a												11 10	
Carnforth	d													10f55
Silverdale	d													11 01
Arnside	d													11 05
Grange-over-Sands	d													11 10
Kents Bank	d													11 14
Cark	d													11 18
Ulverston	d													11 26
Dalton	d													11 34
Roose	d													11 40
Barrow-in-Furness	a													11 49

Station		NT	NT	TP	NT	TP	NT	NT	NT	NT	TP	NT
				1 ◇		1 ◇					1 ◇	
				C	B		A			B		
Manchester Airport	85 d			09 36		09 46			09b58		10 46	10b58
Heald Green	85 d								10b02		10 17	11b02
Buxton	86 d	08 25						09 25				10 25
Hazel Grove	86 d	08 59						09 59				10 59
Alderley Edge	84 d		09 10						10 10			
Stockport	84 d	09 10	09 29					10 10	10 29			11 10
Manchester Piccadilly 10	d	09 25	09 45	09 51		10 03		10 25	10 45		11 03	11 25
Manchester Oxford Road	d	09 29	09 48	09 54		10 06		10 29	10 48		11 06	11 29
Deansgate	d	09 31	09 50			10 08		10 31	10 50		11 08	11 31
Rochdale	95 d									10c22		
Manchester Victoria	d				10 00					11 00		
Salford Crescent	a	09 34	09 54		10 04	10 11		10 34	10 54	11 04	11 11	11 34
	d	09 35	09 54		10 05	10 12		10 35	10 54	11 05	11 12	11 35
Bolton	a	09 45	10 04	10 08	10 15	10 22		10 45	11 04	11 15	11 22	11 45
	d	09 45	10 05	10 09		10 22		10 45	11 05		11 22	11 45
Westhoughton	d		10 12						11 12			
Hindley	d		10 16						11 16			
Wigan North Western	a											
Wigan Wallgate	a		10 21						11 21			
	d		10 23						11 23			
Gathurst	d		10 27						11 27			
Appley Bridge	d		10 31						11 31			
Parbold	d		10 35						11 35			
Burscough Bridge	d		10 39						11 39			
Southport	a		10 56						11 56			
Lostock	d	09 50						10 50				11 50
Horwich Parkway	d	09 54						10 54				11 54
Blackrod	d	09 57						10 57				11 57
Adlington (Lancashire)	d	10 01						11 01				12 01
Chorley	d	10 06				10 34		11 06			11 34	12 06
Leyland	d	10 12					10 58	11 12				12 12
Preston 8	a	10 20		10 30		10 47	11 06	11 20			11 48	12 20
Kirkham & Wesham	97 a					10 57		11 51			11 57	
Poulton-le-Fylde	97 a	10 38				11 07	11 23	11 38			12 07	12 38
Blackpool North	97 a	10 47				11 16	11 34	11 47			12 16	12 47
Preston 8	65 d			10 35								
Lancaster 6	65 a			10 50							12e11	12e42
	d			10 51								
Oxenholme Lake District	65 a			11 06							12e26	12e57
Windermere	83 a			12 26								
Carnforth	d											
Silverdale	d											
Arnside	d											
Grange-over-Sands	d											
Kents Bank	d											
Cark	d											
Ulverston	d											
Dalton	d											
Roose	d											
Barrow-in-Furness	a											

For general notes see front of timetable
For details of catering facilities see Directory of Train Operators

- **A** From Liverpool Lime Street (Table 90)
- **B** To Clitheroe (Table 94)
- **C** To Glasgow Central (Table 65)
- **b** Change at Manchester Piccadilly
- **c** By bus
- **e** Change at Preston
- **f** Arr. 1049

Table 82

Sundays

Manchester → Bolton → Wigan, Southport, Preston, Blackpool North and Barrow-in-Furness

20 July to 7 September

Network Diagram - see first page of Table 82

	TP		NT	NT	NT	TP	NT	NT	TP	NT	NT	TP	NT	TP	NT	NT	NT	TP	NT	NT	TP	NT	NT	TP
	1 ◇					1 ◇			1 ◇			1 ◇		1 ◇				1 ◇			1 ◇			1 ◇
	A			B	C		D				B			A	C		B		D				B	
Manchester Airport 85 d						11 46				12b13		12 46	12b49			13b22		13 46		13b49	13 58	14b22		14 46
Heald Green 85 d						*11 17*				12b16		*12 16*				13b16					*14 02*	14b19		
Buxton 86 d								11 20					12 20							13 25				
Hazel Grove 86 d								11 56					12 54							13 59				
Alderley Edge 84 d			11 10							12 10						13 10						14 10		
Stockport 84 d	*11 20*		11 28			*11 32*		12 08		12 28			13 08	*13 23*		13 29				14 10	14c20	14 29		
Manchester Piccadilly 10 d			11 45			12 03		12 25		12 45		13 01	13 25			13 48		14 03		14 25	14 42	14 48		15 03
Manchester Oxford Road d	11 45		11 48			12 06		12 29	12 43	12 48		13 06	13 29	13 45		13 51		14 06		14 29	14 45	14 51		15 06
Deansgate d			11 50			12 08		12 31		12 50		13 08	13 31			13 53		14 08		14 31		14 53		15 08
Rochdale 95 d				11e22							12e22						13e22						14e22	
Manchester Victoria d				12 00							13 00						14 00						15 00	
Salford Crescent a			11 54	12 04		12 11		12 34		12 54	13 04	13 11	13 34			13 57	14 04	14 11		14 34		14 57	15 04	15 11
d			11 54	12 05		12 12		12 35		12 54	13 05	13 12	13 35			13 57	14 05	14 12		14 35		14 57	15 05	15 12
Bolton a	11 58		12 04	12 15		12 22		12 45	12 56	13 04	13 15	13 22	13 45	13 59		14 08	14 15	14 22		14 45	14 59	15 08	15 15	15 22
d	11 59		12 05			12 22		12 45	13 00	13 05		13 22	13 45	14 00		14 08		14 22		14 45	15 00	15 08		15 22
Westhoughton d			12 12							13 12						14 15						15 16		
Hindley d			12 16							13 16						14 19						15 20		
Wigan North Western a																								
Wigan Wallgate a			12 21							13 21						14 25						15 25		
d			12 23							13 23						14 26						15 27		
Gathurst d			12 27							13 27						14 30						15 31		
Appley Bridge d			12 31							13 31						14 34						15 35		
Parbold d			12 35							13 35						14 38						15 39		
Burscough Bridge d			12 39							13 39						14 42						15 43		
Southport a			12 56							13 56						15 01						16 01		
Lostock d								12 50					13 50							14 50				
Horwich Parkway d								12 54					13 54							14 54				
Blackrod d								12 57					13 57							14 57				
Adlington (Lancashire) d								13 01					14 01							15 01				
Chorley d						12 34		13 06				13 34	14 06					14 34		15 06				15 34
Leyland d							12 58	13 12					14 12						14 57	15 12				
Preston 8 a	12 20					12 48	13 06	13 20	13 20			13 48	14 20	14 26				14 47	15 04	15 20	15 22			15 46
Kirkham & Wesham 97 a	*12 51*					12 57			*13 51*			13 57		*14 51*				14 57			*15 51*			15 57
Poulton-le-Fylde 97 a						13 07	13 23	13 38				14 07	14 37					15 07	15 23	15 38				16 07
Blackpool North 97 a						13 16	13 34	13 47				14 16	14 47					15 16	15 34	15 47				16 16
Preston 8 65 d	12 22								13 22					14 29							15 25			
Lancaster 6 65 a	12 37					*13f23*		*13f47*	13 37			*14f13*		14 44				*15f17*		*15f53*	15 40			*16f16*
d	12 38				12 48				13 38					14 45	14 54						15 41			
Oxenholme Lake District 65 a	12 52											*14f27*		14 59				*15f31*						*16f50*
Windermere 83 a	*13 18*													*15 31*				*16g19*						*17g16*
Carnforth d					12a57				13 46						15a05						15 50			
Silverdale d									13 52												15 55			
Arnside d									13 56												16 00			
Grange-over-Sands d									14 02												16 05			
Kents Bank d									14 05												16 09			
Cark d									14 10												16 13			
Ulverston d									14 18												16 21			
Dalton d									14 26												16 29			
Roose d									14 31												16 35			
Barrow-in-Furness a									14 41												16 44			

For general notes see front of timetable
For details of catering facilities see Directory of Train Operators

A To Edinburgh (Table 65)
B To Clitheroe (Table 94)
C From Morecambe to Leeds (Table 36)
D From Liverpool Lime Street (Table 90)
b Change at Manchester Piccadilly
c Change at Manchester Oxford Road
e By bus
f Change at Preston
g Change at Preston and Oxenholme Lake District

Table 82

Sundays

20 July to 7 September

Manchester → Bolton → Wigan, Southport, Preston, Blackpool North and Barrow-in-Furness

Network Diagram - see first page of Table 82

	NT	TP 1 ◇ A	NT		NT B	TP 1 ◇	NT C	NT	TP 1 ◇	NT	NT B	NT D	TP 1 ◇	NT C	NT	NT	TP 1 ◇ E	NT	NT B	TP 1 ◇	NT C	NT	TP 1 ◇	NT
Manchester Airport 85 d	14b49	14 58				15 46		15b58					16 46		16b58					17 46		17b58		
Heald Green 85 d		15 08				15 17		16b02					16 17		17b02		17 09			17 17		18b02		
Buxton 86 d	14 25							15 25							16 25							17 25		
Hazel Grove 86 d	14 59							15 59							16 59							17 59		
Alderley Edge 84 d			15 10							16 10								17 10						18 10
Stockport 84 d	15 10	15c21	15 29					16 10	16c20	16 29					17 10		17c21	17 29				18 10	18c25	18 29
Manchester Piccadilly 10 d	15 25	15 42	15 45			16 03		16 25	16 42	16 45			17 03		17 25		17 42	17 45		18 03		18 25	18 42	18 45
Manchester Oxford Road d	15 29	15 45	15 48			16 06		16 28	16 45	16 48			17 06		17 29		17 45	17 48		18 06		18 28	18 45	18 48
Deansgate d	15 31		15 50			16 08		16 30		16 50			17 08		17 31			17 50		18 08		18 30		18 50
Rochdale 95 d					15e22						16e22								17e22					
Manchester Victoria d					16 00						17 00								18 00					
Salford Crescent a	15 34		15 54		16 04	16 11		16 34		16 54	17 04		17 12		17 34			17 54	18 04	18 11		18 34		18 54
d	15 35		15 54		16 05	16 12		16 34		16 54	17 05		17 12		17 35			17 54	18 05	18 12		18 34		18 54
Bolton a	15 45	15 59	16 05		16 15	16 22		16 45	16 59	17 05	17 15		17 22		17 45		17 59	18 05	18 15	18 22		18 45	18 59	19 04
d	15 45	16 00	16 05			16 22		16 45	17 00	17 05			17 22		17 45		18 00	18 05		18 22		18 45	19 00	19 05
Westhoughton d			16 12							17 12								18 12						19 12
Hindley d			16 16							17 16								18 16						19 16
Wigan North Western a																								
Wigan Wallgate a			16 22							17 22								18 21						19 21
d			16 23							17 23								18 23						19 23
Gathurst d			16 27							17 27								18 27						19 27
Appley Bridge d			16 31							17 31								18 31						19 31
Parbold d			16 35							17 35								18 35						19 35
Burscough Bridge d			16 39							17 39								18 39						19 39
Southport a			16 56							17 56								18 56						19 57
Lostock d	15 50							16 50							17 50							18 50		
Horwich Parkway d	15 54							16 54							17 54							18 54		
Blackrod d	15 57							16 57							17 57							18 57		
Adlington (Lancashire) d	16 01							17 01							18 01							19 01		
Chorley d	16 06					16 34		17 05					17 34		18 06					18 34		19 05		
Leyland d	16 12						16 57	17 12						17 58	18 12						18 58	19 12		
Preston 8 a	16 20	16 22				16 46	17 07	17 20	17 22				17 46	18 07	18 21		18 23			18 48	19 05	19 19	19 21	
Kirkham & Wesham 97 a		*16 51*				16 57			*17 51*				17 57				*18 51*			18 57			*19 51*	
Poulton-le-Fylde 97 a	16 38					17 07	17 23	17 38					18 07	18 23	18 38					19 07	19 23	19 37		
Blackpool North 97 a	16 47					17 16	17 37	17 47					18 16	18 34	18 47					19 16	19 32	19 47		
Preston 8 65 d		16 25							17 25								18 25						19 25	
Lancaster 6 65 a		16 42				*17f11*	*17f32*		17 42					*18f33*			18 40			*19f18*		*19f45*	19 40	
d		16 43							17 43			18 06				18 19	18 41						19 41	
Oxenholme Lake District 65 a		16 55				*17f26*	*17g53*							*18f47*			18 55			*19f32*			*19 59*	
Windermere 83 a							*18g15*										*19 16*						*20h23*	
Carnforth d									17 51			18a15				18 29							19 49	
Silverdale d									17 57							18 34							19 55	
Arnside d									18 01							18 39							19 59	
Grange-over-Sands d									18 07							18 45							20 05	
Kents Bank d									18 10							18 48							20 08	
Cark d									18 15							18 52							20 13	
Ulverston d									18 23							19 01							20 21	
Dalton d									18 31							19 09							20 29	
Roose d									18 36							19 15							20 34	
Barrow-in-Furness a									18 46							19 22							20 44	

For general notes see front of timetable
For details of catering facilities see Directory of Train Operators

A To Edinburgh (Table 65)
B To Clitheroe (Table 94)
C From Liverpool Lime Street (Table 90)
D From Morecambe to Leeds (Table 36)
E To Glasgow Central (Table 65)
b Change at Manchester Piccadilly
c Change at Manchester Oxford Road
e By bus
f Change at Preston
g Change at Preston and Lancaster
h Change at Lancaster and Oxenholme Lake District

Table 82

Manchester → Bolton → Wigan, Southport, Preston, Blackpool North and Barrow-in-Furness

Sundays

20 July to 7 September

Network Diagram - see first page of Table 82

		NT	TP	NT	NT	NT	NT	TP	NT	NT	TP	NT	NT	TP	NT	NT	NT	NT	TP	NT	NT	NT	TP
			1 ◇					1 ◇			1 ◇			1 ◇					1 ◇				1 ◇
		A				A	B		C				A				D					C	
Manchester Airport	85 d		18 46	18b58				19 46		19b49	19 58			20 46	20b49	20b58			21 46	21b58			22 46
Heald Green	85 d		18 17	19b02	19b08			19 17			20 02			20 17		21b09			21 17	22b02			22 17
Buxton	86 d			18 25						19 25					20 25					21c25			
Hazel Grove	86 d			18 59						19 59					20 59					21c59			
Alderley Edge	84 d				19 10							20 10				21 10				22 10			
Stockport	84 d			19 10	19 29					20 10	20 17	20 29			21 10	21 29				22 29			
Manchester Piccadilly 10	d		19 03	19 25	19 45			20 03		20 25	20 42	20 45		21 03	21 25	21 45			22 03	22 45			23 03
Manchester Oxford Road	d		19 06	19 29	19 48			20 06		20 28	20 45	20 48		21 06	21 28	21 48			22 06	22 48			23 06
Deansgate	d		19 08	19 31	19 50			20 08		20 30		20 50		21 08	21 30	21 50			22 08	22 50			23 08
Rochdale	95 d	18e22				19e22							20e22				21e22				21e23		
Manchester Victoria	d	19 00				20 00							21 00				22 00				23 00		
Salford Crescent	a	19 04	19 11	19 34	19 54	20 04		20 11		20 34		20 54	21 04	21 11	21 34	21 54	22 04		22 12	22 54	23 04		23 11
	d	19 05	19 12	19 35	19 54	20 05		20 12		20 34		20 54	21 05	21 12	21 34	21 54	22 05		22 12	22 54			23 12
Bolton	a	19 15	19 22	19 45	20 04	20 15		20 22		20 45	20 58	21 05	21 15	21 22	21 45	22 04	22 15		22 22	23 04			23 22
	d		19 22	19 45	20 05			20 22		20 45	21 00	21 05		21 22	21 45	22 05			22 22	23 05			23 22
Westhoughton	d				20 12							21 12				22 12				23 12			
Hindley	d				20 16							21 16				22 16				23 16			
Wigan North Western	a																						
Wigan Wallgate	a				20 21							21 22				22 25				23 25			
	d				20 23							21 23											
Gathurst	d				20 27							21 27											
Appley Bridge	d				20 31							21 31											
Parbold	d				20 35							21 35											
Burscough Bridge	d				20 39							21 39											
Southport	a				20 56							21 56											
Lostock	d			19 50						20 50					21 50								
Horwich Parkway	d			19 54						20 54					21 54								
Blackrod	d			19 57						20 57					21 57								
Adlington (Lancashire)	d			20 01						21 01					22 01								
Chorley	d		19 34	20 06				20 34		21 05				21 34	22 05				22 34				23 34
Leyland	d			20 12					20 58	21 12					22 12							23 08	
Preston 8	a		19 48	20 20				20 47	21 05	21 20	21 22			21 48	22 20				22 45			23 15	23 46
Kirkham & Wesham	97 a		19 57	20 45				20 57						21 58					22 57				23 57
Poulton-le-Fylde	97 a		20 07	20 38				21 07	21 23	21 37				22 07	22 37				23 07			23 33	00 07
Blackpool North	97 a		20 16	20 47				21 16	21 34	21 47				22 16	22 47				23 16			23 43	00 16
Preston 8	65 d										21 25												
Lancaster 6	65 a		20f12					21f18			21 40												
	d						20 17				21 41						23 00						
Oxenholme Lake District	65 a		20f26					21f32															
Windermere	83 a		21g09																				
Carnforth	d						20a26				21 49						23 09						
Silverdale	d										21 55						23 15						
Arnside	d										21 59						23 19						
Grange-over-Sands	d										22 05						23 25						
Kents Bank	d										22 08						23 29						
Cark	d										22 13						23 33						
Ulverston	d										22 21						23 41						
Dalton	d										22 29						23 49						
Roose	d										22 34						23 55						
Barrow-in-Furness	a										22 44						00 13						

For general notes see front of timetable
For details of catering facilities see Directory of Train Operators

A To Clitheroe (Table 94)
B From Morecambe to Leeds (Table 36)
C From Liverpool Lime Street (Table 90)
D To Blackburn (Table 94)
b Change at Manchester Piccadilly
c Change at Stockport
e By bus
f Change at Preston
g Change at Preston and Oxenholme Lake District

Table 82

Sundays

from 14 September

Manchester → Bolton → Wigan, Southport, Preston, Blackpool North and Barrow-in-Furness

Network Diagram - see first page of Table 82

		NT	TP	TP	TP	TP	NT	NT	NT	NT	NT	TP	NT	NT	NT	TP	TP	NT	NT	NT	NT	TP	NT	TP	TP
					1 ◇	1 ◇						1 ◇				1 ◇	1 ◇					1 ◇		1 ◇	1 ◇
		A					B	A			B				B			A			B			C	D
			bus	bus																				✠	✠
Manchester Airport	85 ✈ d		00 10	05 40	06b20	07 36						08 44	08c51			09 47				10c01		10 47	11c00		11 27
Heald Green	85 d				06 16	07 13						08 16										10 17			
Buxton	86 d												08 25						09 25			09 25	10 25		
Hazel Grove	86 d												08 59						09 59			09 59	10 59		
Alderley Edge	84 d													09 10						10 10					
Stockport	84 d												09 10	09 29					10 10	10 29			11 10		
Manchester Piccadilly 10	✈ d		00 35	06 05	07 00	07 51						09 03	09 25	09 45		10 03			10 25	10 45		11 03	11 25		11 42
Manchester Oxford Road	d				07 03	07 54						09 06	09 29	09 48		10 06			10 29	10 48		11 06	11 29	11 45	11 45
Deansgate	✈ d				07 05	07 56						09 08	09 31	09 50		10 08			10 31	10 52		11 08	11 31		
Rochdale	95 d																				10 18				
Manchester Victoria	✈ d						08 00		08 28	08 49	09 00				10 00						11 00				
Salford Crescent	a					08 00			08 33	08 54	09 04	09 11	09 34	09 54	10 04	10 11			10 34	10 54	11 04	11 11	11 34		
	d					08 00			08 33	08 54	09 05	09 12	09 35	09 54	10 05	10 12			10 35	10 54	11 05	11 12	11 35		
Bolton	a		01s00	06s30	07 20	08 10	08 13		08 43	09 04	09 15	09 22	09 45	10 04	10 15	10 22			10 45	11 05	11 15	11 22	11 45	11 58	11 58
	d					08 10			08 44	09 05		09 22	09 45	10 05		10 22			10 45	11 05		11 22	11 45	11 59	11 59
Westhoughton	d									09 12				10 12						11 12					
Hindley	d									09 16				10 16						11 16					
Wigan North Western	a																								
Wigan Wallgate	a									09 21				10 21						11 23					
	d									09 23				10 23						11 23					
Gathurst	d									09 27				10 27						11 27					
Appley Bridge	d									09 31				10 31						11 31					
Parbold	d									09 35				10 35						11 35					
Burscough Bridge	d									09 39				10 39						11 39					
Southport	a									09 56				10 56						11 56					
Lostock	d								08 49				09 50						10 50				11 50		
Horwich Parkway	d								08 53				09 54						10 54				11 54		
Blackrod	d								08 56				09 57						10 57				11 57		
Adlington (Lancashire)	d								09 00				10 01						11 01				12 01		
Chorley	d					08 22			09 04			09 34	10 06			10 34			11 06			11 34	12 06		
Leyland	d	00 06		06s55		08 30		08 58	09 11				10 12					10 58	11 12				12 12		
Preston 8	a	00 15	01s35	07s10		08 35		09 06	09 18			09 47	10 20			10 47		11 06	11 20			11 47	12 20	12 22	12 22
Kirkham & Wesham	97 a			07s30		08 57						09 57				10 57			11e51			11 57			12 51
Poulton-le-Fylde	97 a			07s50		09 07		09 23	09 36			10 07	10 38			11 07		11 23	11 38			12 07	12 38		
Blackpool North	97 a		02 15	08 05		09 16		09 34	09 45			10 16	10 47			11 16		11 34	11 47			12 16	12 47		
Preston 8	65 d																11 00							12 25	12 25
Lancaster 6	65 a																11 15					12f10		12 40	12 40
	d																11 16							12 41	12 41
Oxenholme Lake District	65 a																					12f27		12 55	12 55
Windermere	83 a																					12f48		14 09	14 09
Carnforth	d																11 24								
Silverdale	d																11 30								
Arnside	d																11 34								
Grange-over-Sands	d																11 40								
Kents Bank	d																11 43								
Cark	d																11 48								
Ulverston	d																11 56								
Dalton	d																12 04								
Roose	d																12 09								
Barrow-in-Furness	a																12 18								

For general notes see front of timetable
For details of catering facilities see Directory of Train Operators

A From Liverpool Lime Street (Table 90)

B To Clitheroe (Table 94)

C From 9 November. To Edinburgh (Table 65)

D Until 2 November. To Edinburgh (Table 65)

b By bus

c Change at Manchester Piccadilly

e Until 2 November only

f Change at Preston

Table 82

from 14 September

Manchester → Bolton → Wigan, Southport, Preston, Blackpool North and Barrow-in-Furness

Network Diagram - see first page of Table 82

		NT	NT	NT	TP	TP	NT	NT	NT	NT	TP	NT	TP	TP	NT	NT	NT	TP	NT	NT	TP	NT	NT	TP	NT
					1 ◇	1 ◇					1 ◇		1 ◇	1 ◇				1 ◇			1 ◇			1 ◇	
			A	B			C			A			D	E	B		A		C				A		
Manchester Airport	85 d	11b03			11 47				12b13		12 46	12b52		13 27				13 47		13c52	14 26			14 47	14c52
Heald Green	85 d				11 17				12b16							13b16								14e18	
Buxton	86 d							11 20				12 20								13 25					14 25
Hazel Grove	86 d							11 56				12 54								13 59					14 59
Alderley Edge	84 d	11 10							12 10							13 10						14 10			
Stockport	84 d	11 29						12 08	12 29			13 08				13 33				14 10		14 29			15 10
Manchester Piccadilly 10	d	11 45			12 03			12 25	12 45		13 01	13 24		13 42		13 46		14 03		14 25	14 41	14 45		15 03	15 25
Manchester Oxford Road	d	11 48			12 06			12 29	12 48		13 06	13 28	13 45	13 45		13 51		14 06		14 29	14 44	14 48		15 06	15 29
Deansgate	d	11 50			12 08			12 31	12 50		13 08	13 30				13 53		14 08		14 31		14 50		15 08	15 31
Rochdale	95 d		11 18							12 18							13 18						14 18		
Manchester Victoria	d		12 00							13 00							14 00						15 00		
Salford Crescent	a	11 54	12 04		12 11			12 34	12 54	13 04	13 11	13 33				13 56	14 04	14 11		14 34		14 54	15 04	15 11	15 34
	d	11 54	12 05		12 12			12 35	12 54	13 05	13 12	13 34				13 57	14 05	14 12		14 35		14 54	15 05	15 12	15 35
Bolton	a	12 05	12 15		12 22			12 45	13 04	13 15	13 22	13 44	13 59	13 59		14 08	14 15	14 22		14 45	14 59	15 04	15 15	15 22	15 45
	d	12 05			12 22			12 45	13 05		13 22	13 44	14 00	14 00		14 08		14 22		14 45	15 00	15 05		15 22	15 45
Westhoughton	d	12 12							13 12							14 15						15 12			
Hindley	d	12 16							13 16							14 19						15 16			
Wigan North Western	a																								
Wigan Wallgate	a	12 23							13 21							14 25						15 21			
	d	12 23							13 23							14 26						15 23			
Gathurst	d	12 27							13 27							14 30						15 27			
Appley Bridge	d	12 31							13 31							14 34						15 31			
Parbold	d	12 35							13 35							14 38						15 35			
Burscough Bridge	d	12 39							13 39							14 42						15 39			
Southport	a	12 56							13 56							15 01						15 56			
Lostock	d							12 50				13 49								14 50					15 50
Horwich Parkway	d							12 54				13 53								14 54					15 54
Blackrod	d							12 57				13 56								14 57					15 57
Adlington (Lancashire)	d							13 01				14 00								15 01					16 01
Chorley	d				12 34			13 06			13 34	14 05						14 34		15 06				15 34	16 06
Leyland	d						12 58	13 12				14 12							14 58	15 12					16 12
Preston 8	a				12 48		13 06	13 20			13 48	14 19	14 26	14 26				14 47	15 07	15 20	15 22			15 46	16 20
Kirkham & Wesham	97 a				12 57			13f51			13 57	14g51	14 51					14 57			15f51			15 57	
Poulton-le-Fylde	97 a				13 07		13 23	13 38			14 07	14 37						15 07	15 23	15 38				16 07	16 38
Blackpool North	97 a				13 16		13 34	13 47			14 16	14 47						15 16	15 34	15 47				16 16	16 47
Preston 8	65 d					13 25							14 29	14 29							15 25				
Lancaster 6	65 a					13 40		13h54					14 44	14 44							15 40				
	d			12 48		13 41							14 45	14 45	14 54						15 41				
Oxenholme Lake District	65 a							14h09					14 59	14 59							16 07				
Windermere	83 a							14j59					16 05	16 05							16k55				
Carnforth	d			12a57		13 49									15a05						15 50				
Silverdale	d					13 55															15 55				
Arnside	d					13 59															16 00				
Grange-over-Sands	d					14 05															16 05				
Kents Bank	d					14 08															16 09				
Cark	d					14 13															16 13				
Ulverston	d					14 21															16 21				
Dalton	d					14 29															16 29				
Roose	d					14 34															16 35				
Barrow-in-Furness	a					14 44															16 44				

For general notes see front of timetable
For details of catering facilities see Directory of Train Operators

- **A** To Clitheroe (Table 94)
- **B** 14 September only. From Morecambe to Leeds (Table 36)
- **C** From Liverpool Lime Street (Table 90)
- **D** Until 2 November. To Edinburgh (Table 65)
- **E** From 9 November. To Edinburgh (Table 65)
- **b** Change at Manchester Piccadilly
- **c** Change at Manchester Piccadilly. From 9 November dep. 4 minutes later
- **e** From 9 November dep. 1 minute later
- **f** Until 2 November only
- **g** From 9 November arr. 1457
- **h** Change at Preston
- **j** Change at Preston and Oxenholme Lake District
- **k** Change at Lancaster and Oxenholme Lake District

Table 82

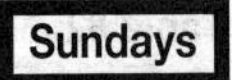

Sundays

from 14 September

Manchester → Bolton → Wigan, Southport, Preston, Blackpool North and Barrow-in-Furness

Network Diagram - see first page of Table 82

	TP	NT	NT	NT	TP	NT	NT	TP	NT	NT	NT	TP	NT	NT	NT	TP	NT	NT	TP	NT	NT	TP	NT	NT
	1 ◇				1 ◇			1 ◇				1 ◇				1 ◇			1 ◇			1 ◇		
	A	B		C		D				C	E		D		G	H		C		D				C
	⚒															⚒								
Manchester Airport 85 ✈ d	15 27				15 47		16b01	16 27				16 47		17c01		17 27			17 47		18c01	18 27		
Heald Green 85 d					15 17							16 17							17 17					
Buxton 86 d							15 25							16 25							17 25			
Hazel Grove 86 d							15 59							16 59							17 59			
Alderley Edge 84 d			15 10						16 10								17 10						18 10	
Stockport 84 d			15 29				16 10		16 29					17 10			17 29				18 10		18 29	
Manchester Piccadilly 10 ✈ d	15 42		15 45		16 03		16 25	16 42	16 45			17 03		17 25		17 42	17 45		18 03		18 25	18 42	18 45	
Manchester Oxford Road d	15 45		15 48		16 06		16 28	16 45	16 48			17 06		17 29		17 45	17 48		18 06		18 28	18 45	18 48	
Deansgate ✈ d			15 50		16 08		16 30		16 50			17 08		17 31			17 50		18 08		18 30		18 50	
Rochdale 95 d				15 18						16 18								17 18						18 18
Manchester Victoria ✈ d				16 00						17 00								18 00						19 00
Salford Crescent a			15 54	16 04	16 11		16 34		16 54	17 04		17 12		17 34			17 54	18 04	18 11		18 34		18 54	19 04
d			15 54	16 05	16 12		16 34		16 54	17 05		17 12		17 35			17 54	18 05	18 12		18 34		18 54	19 05
Bolton a	15 59		16 05	16 15	16 22		16 45	16 59	17 05	17 15		17 22		17 45		17 59	18 05	18 15	18 22		18 45	18 59	19 04	19 15
d	16 00		16 05		16 22		16 45	17 00	17 05			17 22		17 45		18 00	18 05		18 22		18 45	19 00	19 05	
Westhoughton d			16 12						17 12								18 12						19 12	
Hindley d			16 16						17 16								18 16						19 16	
Wigan North Western a																								
Wigan Wallgate a			16 22						17 22								18 21						19 21	
d			16 23						17 23								18 23						19 23	
Gathurst d			16 27						17 27								18 27						19 27	
Appley Bridge d			16 31						17 31								18 31						19 31	
Parbold d			16 35						17 35								18 35						19 35	
Burscough Bridge d			16 39						17 39								18 39						19 39	
Southport a			16 56						17 56								18 56						19 57	
Lostock d							16 50							17 50							18 50			
Horwich Parkway d							16 54							17 54							18 54			
Blackrod d							16 57							17 57							18 57			
Adlington (Lancashire) d							17 01							18 01							19 01			
Chorley d					16 34		17 05					17 34		18 06					18 34		19 05			
Leyland d						16 57	17 12						17 58	18 12						18 58	19 12			
Preston 8 a	16 22				16 46	17 04	17 20	17 22				17 46	18 05	18 20		18 23			18 48	19 05	19 19	19 21		
Kirkham & Wesham 97 a	16e51				16 57			17e51				17 57				18e51			18 57			19e51		
Poulton-le-Fylde 97 a					17 07	17 23	17 38					18 07	18 23	18 38					19 07	19 23	19 37			
Blackpool North 97 a					17 16	17 37	17 47					18 16	18 34	18 47					19 16	19 32	19 47			
Preston 8 65 d	16 25							17 25								18 25						19 25		
Lancaster 6 65 a	16 40				17f22			17 42								18 40			19f20			19 40		
d	16 41	16 46						17 43			18 04				18 19	18 41						19 41		
Oxenholme Lake District 65 a	16 55				17f36			18 15								18 55			19f34			20 15		
Windermere 83 a					18g00			18h54								19 58			19g58			21h16		
Carnforth d		16 55						17 51			18a12				18 29							19 49		
Silverdale d		17 01						17 57							18 34							19 55		
Arnside d		17 06						18 01							18 39							19 59		
Grange-over-Sands d		17 12						18 07							18 45							20 05		
Kents Bank d		17 15						18 10							18 48							20 08		
Cark d		17 20						18 15							18 52							20 13		
Ulverston d		17 28						18 23							19 01							20 21		
Dalton d		17 36						18 31							19 09							20 29		
Roose d		17 42						18 36							19 15							20 34		
Barrow-in-Furness a		17 50						18 46							19 22							20 44		

For general notes see front of timetable
For details of catering facilities see Directory of Train Operators

- **A** To Edinburgh (Table 65)
- **B** From 21 September
- **C** To Clitheroe (Table 94)
- **D** From Liverpool Lime Street (Table 90)
- **E** From Morecambe to Leeds (Table 36)
- **G** 14 September only
- **H** To Glasgow Central (Table 65)
- **b** Change at Manchester Piccadilly. From 9 November dep. 1556
- **c** Change at Manchester Piccadilly
- **e** Until 2 November only
- **f** Change at Preston
- **g** Change at Preston and Oxenholme Lake District
- **h** Change at Lancaster and Oxenholme Lake District

Manchester → Bolton → Wigan, Southport, Preston, Blackpool North and Barrow-in-Furness

Sundays from 14 September

Network Diagram - see first page of Table 82

		NT	TP	NT	NT	NT	TP	NT	NT	TP	TP	NT	NT	NT	TP	NT	NT	NT	NT	TP	NT	NT	NT	TP
			1 ◇				1 ◇			1 ◇	1 ◇				1 ◇					1 ◇				1 ◇
		A				B		C		D	E	D	E	B				G					C	
Manchester Airport 85	d		18 47	19b01	19b05		19 47		19c50	20 25	20 27	20b01	20b01		20 47	20e52	21b05			21 47	22b01			22 47
Heald Green 85	d		18 17				19 17								20 17					21 17				22 17
Buxton 86	d			18 25					19 25							20 25					21f25			
Hazel Grove 86	d			18 59					19 59							20 59					21f59			
Alderley Edge 84	d				19 10							20 10	20 10				21 10				22 10			
Stockport 84	d			19 10	19 29				20 10			20 29	20 29			21 10	21 29				22 29			
Manchester Piccadilly 10	d		19 03	19 25	19 45		20 03		20 25	20 40	20 42	20 44	20 45		21 03	21 25	21 45			22 03	22 45			23 03
Manchester Oxford Road	d		19 06	19 29	19 48		20 06		20 28	20 43	20 45	20 47	20 48		21 06	21 28	21 48			22 06	22 48			23 06
Deansgate	d		19 08	19 31	19 50		20 08		20 30			20 49	20 50		21 08	21 30	21 50			22 08	22 50			23 08
Rochdale 95	d					19 18								20 18				21 18				21 23		
Manchester Victoria	d					20 00								21 00				22 00				23 00		
Salford Crescent	a		19 11	19 34	19 54	20 04	20 11		20 34			20 53	20 54	21 04	21 11	21 34	21 54	22 04		22 12	22 54	23 04		23 11
	d		19 12	19 35	19 54	20 05	20 12		20 34			20 53	20 54	21 05	21 12	21 34	21 54	22 05		22 12	22 54			23 12
Bolton	a		19 22	19 45	20 04	20 15	20 22		20 45	20 57	20 59	21 03	21 05	21 15	21 22	21 45	22 04	22 15		22 22	23 04			23 22
	d		19 22	19 45	20 05		20 22		20 45	20 58	21 00	21 04	21 05		21 22	21 45	22 05			22 22	23 05			23 22
Westhoughton	d				20 12							21 12	21 12				22 12				23 12			
Hindley	d				20 16							21 16	21 16				22 16				23 16			
Wigan North Western	a																							
Wigan Wallgate	a				20 21							21 22	21 22				22 25				23 25			
	d				20 23							21 23	21 23											
Gathurst	d				20 27							21 27	21 27											
Appley Bridge	d				20 31							21 31	21 31											
Parbold	d				20 35							21 35	21 35											
Burscough Bridge	d				20 39							21 39	21 39											
Southport	a				20 56							21 56	21 56											
Lostock	d			19 50					20 50							21 50								
Horwich Parkway	d			19 54					20 54							21 54								
Blackrod	d			19 57					20 57							21 57								
Adlington (Lancashire)	d			20 01					21 01							22 01								
Chorley	d		19 34	20 06			20 34		21 05						21 34	22 05				22 34				23 34
Leyland	d			20 12				20 58	21 12							22 12							23 08	
Preston 8	a		19 48	20 20			20 47	21 05	21 20	21 21	21 21				21 48	22 20				22 45			23 15	23 46
Kirkham & Wesham 97	a		19 57	20g45			20 57								21 58					22 57			23 57	23 57
Poulton-le-Fylde 97	a		20 07	20 38			21 07	21 23	21 37						22 07	22 37				23 07			23 33	00 07
Blackpool North 97	a		20 16	20 47			21 16	21 34	21 47						22 16	22 47				23 16			23 43	00 16
Preston 8 65	d									21 25	21 25													
Lancaster 6 65	a									21 40	21 40													
	d	20 15								21 41	21 41								23 00					
Oxenholme Lake District 65	a																							
Windermere 83	a																							
Carnforth	d	20a24								21 49	21 49								23 09					
Silverdale	d									21 55	21 55								23 15					
Arnside	d									21 59	21 59								23 19					
Grange-over-Sands	d									22 05	22 05								23 25					
Kents Bank	d									22 08	22 08								23 29					
Cark	d									22 13	22 13								23 33					
Ulverston	d									22 21	22 21								23 41					
Dalton	d									22 29	22 29								23 49					
Roose	d									22 34	22 34								23 55					
Barrow-in-Furness	a									22 44	22 44								00 13					

For general notes see front of timetable
For details of catering facilities see Directory of Train Operators

- **A** From Morecambe to Leeds (Table 36)
- **B** To Clitheroe (Table 94)
- **C** From Liverpool Lime Street (Table 90)
- **D** From 9 November
- **E** Until 2 November
- **G** To Blackburn (Table 94)
- **b** Change at Manchester Piccadilly
- **c** Change at Manchester Piccadilly. From 9 November dep. 4 minutes later
- **e** Change at Manchester Piccadilly. From 9 November dep. 2055
- **f** Change at Stockport
- **g** Until 19 October only

Table 82

Mondays to Fridays

until 3 October

Barrow-in-Furness, Blackpool North, Preston, Southport, Kirkby and Wigan → Bolton → Manchester

Network Diagram - see first page of Table 82

Miles	Miles	Miles	Miles	Miles	Station		TP	TP	TP	TP	NT	TP	NT	TP	TP	NT	NT	NT	NT	NT	TP	NT	NT	NT	NT
										MO				MX	MO										
							[1] ◇	[1] ◇	[1] ◇	[1] ◇		[1] ◇		[1] ◇	[1] ◇						[1] ◇				
									A	B						C		D		E	✕	G			H
—	0	—	—	—	**Barrow-in-Furness**	d			04 20	04 20				05 00	05 15										
—	1¾	—	—	—	Roose	d																			
—	6	—	—	—	Dalton	d																			
—	9¼	—	—	—	Ulverston	d			04 35	04 36				05 15	05 30										
—	15¼	—	—	—	Cark	d																			
—	17¼	—	—	—	Kents Bank	d																			
—	19½	—	—	—	Grange-over-Sands	d			04 48	04 49				05 28	05 43										
—	22¾	—	—	—	Arnside	d			04 55	04 55				05 34	05 49										
—	25	—	—	—	Silverdale	d																			
—	28¾	—	—	—	Carnforth	d			05 05	05b13				05 43	05 58										
—	—	—	—	—	Windermere	83 d																			
—	—	—	—	—	Oxenholme Lake District	65 d																			
—	34¾	—	—	—	**Lancaster** [6]	65 a			05 14	05 22				05 53	06 08										
—	—	—	—	—		d				05 22				05 53	06 08						*06c33*				
—	55¾	—	—	—	**Preston** [8]	65 a				05 42				06 27	06 27										
0	—	—	—	—	**Blackpool North**	97 d	03 36	*04 45*				05 19		*05 30*	*05 30*			06 09			06 34				
1¼	—	—	—	—	Layton	97 d						*05 09*						06 13			06 37				
3¼	—	—	—	—	Poulton-le-Fylde	97 d						05 25		*05 36*	*05 36*			06 17			06 41				
9¾	—	—	—	—	Kirkham & Wesham	97 d						*05 22*						06 25			06 51				07 04
—	—	—	—	—	**Preston** [8]	d	04u01	05 17				05 58		06 28	06 28			06 39			07 03				07 20
21½	59¾	—	—	—	Leyland	d												06 44			07 08				07 25
26	64¼	—	—	—	Chorley	d		05 26						06 37	06 37			06 51			07 15				07 33
29	67½	—	—	—	Adlington (Lancashire)	d												06 56							07 38
31	69½	—	—	—	Blackrod	d												06 59			07 21				07 42
32½	70¾	—	—	—	Horwich Parkway	d								06 45	06 45			07 03			07 24				07 46
34½	72¾	—	—	—	Lostock	d		05 34						06 48	06 48			07 07			07 27				07 49
—	—	0	—	—	**Southport**	d													06 35				06 59		
—	—	1½	—	—	Meols Cop	d													06 40				07 04		
—	—	4½	—	—	Bescar Lane	d																			
—	—	6½	—	—	New Lane	d																			
—	—	7¾	—	—	Burscough Bridge	d													06 48				07 13		
—	—	9¼	—	—	Hoscar	d																			
—	—	10¾	—	—	Parbold	d													06 53				07 18		
—	—	13	—	—	Appley Bridge	d													06 57				07 22		
—	—	14¾	—	—	Gathurst	d													07 00				07 26		
—	—	—	—	—	Liverpool Central [10]	103 d																			
—	—	—	0	—	**Kirkby**	d																			
—	—	—	5¼	—	Rainford	d																			
—	—	—	7¼	—	Upholland	d																			
—	—	—	8½	—	Orrell	d																			
—	—	—	10½	—	Pemberton	d																			
—	—	17½	12¼	—	**Wigan Wallgate**	a													07 05				07 31		
—	—	—	—	—		d					06 08						06 45		07 06			07 13	07 32		
—	—	—	—	0	Wigan North Western	d						06 15												07 26	
—	—	18½	13¼	¾	Ince	d					06 11						06 48					07 16		07 29	
—	—	20	14¾	—	Hindley	d					06 14	06 20					06 51					07 19		07 33	
—	—	22½	—	—	Westhoughton	d						06 24							07 14					07 37	
37½	75¾	27	—	—	**Bolton**	a		05 40				06 31		06 52	06 52			07 12	07 22		07 33			07 45	07 54
—	—	—	—	—		d	04u29	05 40				06 31		06 54	06 54	06 58		07 12	07 23	07 30	07 33			07 46	07 55
38¼	76½	27¾	—	—	Moses Gate	d										07 01								07 49	
39¾	78	29¼	—	—	Farnworth	d										07 03								07 51	
40½	78¾	30	—	—	Kearsley	d							⟵			07 05								07 53	
—	—	—	17¼	—	Daisy Hill	d					06 18 ⟶		06 18				06 55					07 23	07 40		
—	—	—	17½	—	Hag Fold	d							06 21				06 58					07 26			
—	—	—	18¾	—	Atherton	d							06 24				07 01					07 29	07 44		
—	—	—	22¼	—	Walkden	d							06 29				07 06					07 34			
—	—	—	24	—	Moorside	d							06 33				07 10					07 38			
—	—	—	24¾	—	Swinton	d							06 35				07 12					07 40			
46½	84¾	36	28¾	—	**Salford Crescent**	a						06 43	06 46	07 06	07 06	07 17	07 19	07 25	07 35	07 42	07 45	07 47	07 59	08 03	08 07
—	—	—	—	—		d						06 43	06 46	07 06	07 06	07 17	07 19	07 25	07 36	07 43	07 46	07 47	07 59	08 03	08 07
—	—	—	29¾	—	Salford Central	d							06 49			07 20	07 22			07 46		07 50	08 02	08 06	
—	—	—	30½	—	**Manchester Victoria**	⇌ a							06 54			07 25	07 28			07 51		07 55	08 07	08 13	
—	—	—	—	—	Rochdale	95 a							*07 38*				*08 06*						08 25	*08 38*	
48	86¼	37½	—	—	Deansgate	⇌ a						06 49						07 29	07 39						08 11
48½	86½	37¾	—	—	**Manchester Oxford Road**	a						06 51		07 12	07 12			07 32	07 41		07 50				08 14
48¾	87	38¼	—	—	**Manchester Piccadilly** [10]	⇌ a		05 57				06 56		07 15	07 15			07 36	07 45		07 54				08 19
—	—	—	—	—	Stockport	84 a		*06 24*				*07 27*		*07 37*	*07 37*			07 46	*08 07*		*08 24*				08 30
—	—	—	—	—	Hazel Grove	86 a		*07 01*				*07 44*		*07 54*	*07 54*			*08 13*							*08 49*
—	—	—	—	—	Buxton	86 a		*07 45*						*08 33*	*08 33*										*09 26*
57	95¼	46½	—	—	Heald Green	85 a		*06 21*				*07 27*		07 32	07 32						08 11				*08e51*
58½	96¾	48	—	—	**Manchester Airport**	85 ✈ a	05 05	06 14				07 15		07 40	07 40				08 02		08 19				

For general notes see front of timetable
For details of catering facilities see Directory of Train Operators

- **A** Not Mondays 21 July to 8 September. To Windermere (Table 83)
- **B** 21 July to 8 September
- **C** From Blackburn (Table 94). Also stops at Clifton 0709
- **D** To Chester (Table 88)
- **E** From Colne (Table 97)
- **G** To Stalybridge (Table 39)
- **H** From St Annes-on-the-Sea (Table 97) to Greenbank (Table 88)
- **b** Arr. 0505
- **c** Change at Preston
- **e** Change at Manchester Piccadilly

Table 82

Mondays to Fridays

until 3 October

Barrow-in-Furness, Blackpool North, Preston, Southport, Kirkby and Wigan → Bolton → Manchester

Network Diagram - see first page of Table 82

		NT	NT	NT	NT	TP	TP	NT	NT	NT	NT	NT	NT	TP	NT	NT	TP	NT	NT	NT	NT	NT	NT	TP	NT
								BHX																	
						1◇	1◇							1◇			1◇							1◇	
		A		B	C	D	D					A					D	E				B	A		
						trolley	trolley							trolley			trolley							trolley	
Barrow-in-Furness	d					06 15											07 01					07 17			
Roose	d					06 19																07 21			
Dalton	d					06 25											07 10					07 27			
Ulverston	d					06 34											07 18					07 36			
Cark	d					06 42											07 26					07 44			
Kents Bank	d					06 46																07 48			
Grange-over-Sands	d					06 50											07 33					07 52			
Arnside	d					06 56											07 39					07 58			
Silverdale	d					07 01											07 43					08 03			
Carnforth	d				06 43	07 08											07 51					08 10			
Windermere 83	d										*06b20*													*07c24*	
Oxenholme Lake District 65	d			*06e22*							*06f47*													*07g53*	
Lancaster 6 65	a				06 53	07 15											07 58					08 19			
	d			*06h38*		07 16					*07 23*						07 59					08 19		*08g29*	
Preston 8 65	a					07 35											08 17					08 42			
Blackpool North 97	d			06 57			07 03	07 16						07 41						08 09				08 41	
Layton 97	d						07 06							07 44						08 12					
Poulton-le-Fylde 97	d			07 03			07 11	07 23						07 48						08 16				08 47	
Kirkham & Wesham 97	d						07 21	07 32						07 58						08 25					
Preston 8	d			07 25		07 40		07 46			07 50			08 12			08 34			08 38		08 50		09 08	
Leyland	d			07a30							07 55									08 43		08a55		09 13	
Chorley	d					07 50		07 57			08 03			08 22			08 44			08 51				09 19	
Adlington (Lancashire)	d										08 08									08 56					
Blackrod	d										08 11									09 00					
Horwich Parkway	d										08 15						08 52			09 03				09 27	
Lostock	d							08 05			08 19									09 07				09 30	
Southport	d								07 27										08 09		08 35				
Meols Cop	d								07 32										08 14		08 40				
Bescar Lane	d																		08 19						
New Lane	d																		08 23						
Burscough Bridge	d								07 41										08 25		08 48				
Hoscar	d																		08 29						
Parbold	d								07 46										08 32		08 53				
Appley Bridge	d								07 50										08 36		08 57				
Gathurst	d								07 54										08 39		09 00				
Liverpool Central 10 103	d		*06 50*							07j04						*07 50*									
Kirkby	d		07 16													08 16									
Rainford	d		07 23													08 23									
Upholland	d		07 27													08 27									
Orrell	d		07 31													08 31									
Pemberton	d		07 34													08 34									
Wigan Wallgate	a		07 39						07 59							08 40			08 44		09 05				
	d		07 43						08 00				08 13		08 32				08 45		09 07				09 16
Wigan North Western	d									07 56															
Ince	d		07 46										08 16												09 19
Hindley	d		07 49							08 01			08 19		08 37				08 50						09 22
Westhoughton	d									08 06					08 41						09 15				
Bolton	a					08 02		08 10		08 14	08 24			08 33	08 49		08 58			09 12	09 23			09 34	
	d	07 59				08 04		08 11		08 15	08 24	08 30		08 34	08 50		08 59	09 01		09 12	09 23		09 30	09 36	
Moses Gate	d									08 18								09 04							
Farnworth	d									08 20					08 53										
Kearsley	d									08 22					08 55										
Daisy Hill	d		07 53						08 08				08 23						08 54						09 26
Hag Fold	d		07 56										08 26						08 57						09 29
Atherton	d		07 59						08 13				08 29						09 00						09 32
Walkden	d		08 04										08 34						09 05						09 37
Moorside	d		08 08										08 38						09 09						09 41
Swinton	d		08 10										08 40						09 11						09 43
Salford Crescent	a	08 12	08 18						08 28	08 32	08 37	08 42	08 46		09 06		09 11	09 16	09 19	09 25	09 36		09 42	09 48	09 50
	d	08 12	08 18						08 28	08 32	08 37	08 42	08 46		09 07		09 11	09 16	09 19	09 25	09 36		09 42	09 48	09 50
Salford Central	d	08 15	08 21					08 24	08 31	08 35		08 45	08 49		09 09			09 19	09 24				09 45		09 53
Manchester Victoria	a	08 21	08 25					08 30	08 37	08 41		08 50	08 54		09 14			09 25	09 27				09 50		10 00
Rochdale 95	a		08 55							*09 08*			09 25		*09 38*				09 55						10 25
Deansgate	a										08 41						09 15			09 29	09 40				
Manchester Oxford Road	a					08 20					08 43			08 49			09 16			09 31	09 42			09 53	
Manchester Piccadilly 10	a					08 25					08 47			08 53			09 20			09 35	09 45			09 57	
Stockport 84	a					*08 53*					*09 08*			*09 13*			*09 42*			09 46	*10 12*			*10 28*	
Hazel Grove 86	a										*09 16*			*09 29*						09 55	*10 29*				
Buxton 86	a										*09 56*									10 33					
Heald Green 85	a													*09 18*			09 31							10 11	
Manchester Airport 85	a					08 42					09 06			09 13			09 40				10 01			10 19	

For general notes see front of timetable
For details of catering facilities see Directory of Train Operators

- **A** From Clitheroe (Table 94)
- **B** To Liverpool Lime Street (Table 90)
- **C** From Skipton (Table 36)
- **D** trolley from Preston
- **E** From Blackburn (Table 94)
- **b** Change at Oxenholme Lake District and Preston. By bus to Oxenholme Lake District Mondays 21 July to 8 September
- **c** Change at Oxenholme Lake District and Preston
- **e** All Tuesdays to Fridays, also Mondays until 14 July and 15, 22 and 29 September change at Preston. Mondays 21 July to 8 September dep. 0605, change at Lancaster and Preston, by bus to Lancaster
- **f** Mondays 21 July to 8 September dep. 0708
- **g** Change at Preston
- **h** Change at Preston. Mondays 21 July to 8 September dep. 0658
- **j** Liverpool Lime Street (Table 90)

Barrow-in-Furness, Blackpool North, Preston, Southport, Kirkby and Wigan → Bolton → Manchester

Network Diagram - see first page of Table 82

Station		NT	NT	TP	NT	NT	NT	NT	NT	NT	NT	TP	NT	NT	NT	TP	NT	NT	NT	NT	NT	NT	TP	NT	NT
				1 ◇								1 ◇				1 ◇							1 ◇		
		A		B	C					D	E			G		H					D	E			J
				🍴								🍴				🍴							🍴		
Barrow-in-Furness	d	07 58														09 15									09 57
Roose	d	08 02														09 19									10 01
Dalton	d	08 08														09 25									10 07
Ulverston	d	08 17														09 34									10 16
Cark	d	08 25														09 42									10 24
Kents Bank	d	08 29														09 46									10 28
Grange-over-Sands	d	08 33														09 50									10 32
Arnside	d	08 39														09 56									10 38
Silverdale	d	08 43														10 01									10 43
Carnforth	d	08 51												09 55		10 08									10 50
Windermere 83	d			*08 20*												*09b28*									
Oxenholme Lake District 65	d			08 59												*09 54*							*10c13*		
Lancaster 6 65	a	08 59		09 14										10 04		10 15									11 00
	d	09 00		09 14								*09c29*				10 16			*10c09*				*10c29*		
Preston 8 65	a	09 25		09 33												10 34									
Blackpool North 97	d							09 11		09 25		09 38							10 11		10 25		10 41		
Layton 97	d							09 14											10 14						
Poulton-le-Fylde 97	d							09 18				09 44							10 18				10 47		
Kirkham & Wesham 97	d							09 27								*10 19*			10 27						
Preston 8	d			09 38				09 41		09 50		10 08				10 38			10 41		10 50		11 08		
Leyland	d									09a55		10 13									10a55		11 13		
Chorley	d			09 47				09 51				10 19				10 47			10 51				11 19		
Adlington (Lancashire)	d							09 56											10 56						
Blackrod	d							10 00											11 00						
Horwich Parkway	d							10 03				10 27							11 03				11 27		
Lostock	d							10 07				10 30							11 07				11 30		
Southport	d					09 10			09 38								10 15			10 38					
Meols Cop	d					09 15											10 20								
Bescar Lane	d					09 20																			
New Lane	d					09 24																			
Burscough Bridge	d					09 26			09 50								10 28			10 50					
Hoscar	d					09 30																			
Parbold	d					09 33			09 55								10 33			10 55					
Appley Bridge	d					09 37			09 59								10 37			10 59					
Gathurst	d					09 40											10 40								
Liverpool Central 10 103	d												*09 20*											*10 20*	
Kirkby	d												09 51											10 51	
Rainford	d												09 58											10 58	
Upholland	d												10 02											11 02	
Orrell	d												10 06											11 06	
Pemberton	d												10 09											11 09	
Wigan Wallgate	a					09 45			10 05				10 14				10 45			11 05				11 14	
	d		09 32			09 47	09 52		10 07				10 16		10 32		10 47	10 52		11 07				11 16	
Wigan North Western	d																								
Ince	d												10 19											11 19	
Hindley	d		09 37			09 52							10 22		10 37		10 52							11 22	
Westhoughton	d		09 41						10 15						10 41					11 15					
Bolton	a		09 49	09 58			10 06	10 12	10 23			10 34			10 49	10 58		11 06	11 12	11 23			11 34		
	d		09 50	09 59	10 01		10 07	10 12	10 23		10 30	10 36			10 50	10 59		11 07	11 12	11 23		11 30	11 36		
Moses Gate	d						10 10											11 10							
Farnworth	d		09 53												10 53										
Kearsley	d		09 55												10 55										
Daisy Hill	d					09 56							10 26				10 56							11 26	
Hag Fold	d												10 29											11 29	
Atherton	d					10 00							10 32				11 00							11 32	
Walkden	d					10 05							10 37				11 05							11 37	
Moorside	d												10 41											11 41	
Swinton	d					10 10							10 43				11 10							11 43	
Salford Crescent	a		10 06	10 11	10 13	10 17	10 22	10 25	10 36		10 43	10 48	10 50		11 06	11 11	11 17	11 21	11 25	11 36		11 42	11 48	11 50	
	d		10 07	10 11	10 13	10 17	10 22	10 25	10 36		10 43	10 48	10 50		11 07	11 11	11 17	11 22	11 25	11 36		11 43	11 48	11 50	
Salford Central	d		10 09		10 16	10 20	10 24				10 45		10 53		11 09		11 20	11 24				11 45		11 53	
Manchester Victoria 🚋	a		10 14		10 21	10 24	10 32				10 50		11 00		11 14		11 24	11 29				11 50		12 00	
Rochdale 95	a		*10 38*			10 55	*11 08*						11 25		*11 38*		11 55	*12 08*						12 25	
Deansgate 🚋	a							10 29								11 15			11 29						
Manchester Oxford Road	a			10 16				10 31	10 41			10 53				11 16			11 31	11 41			11 53		
Manchester Piccadilly 10 🚋	a			10 20				10 35	10 45			10 57				11 20			11 35	11 45			11 57		
Stockport 84	a			*10 42*				10 46	*11 12*			*11 27*				*11 42*			11 46	*12 12*			*12 28*		
Hazel Grove 86	a							10 55	*11 29*										11 55	*12 29*					
Buxton 86	a							11 30											12 33						
Heald Green 85	a			10 32								11 12				11 32							12 12		
Manchester Airport 85 ✈	a			10 40					11 01			11 19				11 40				12 01			12 19		

For general notes see front of timetable
For details of catering facilities see Directory of Train Operators

A From Maryport (Table 100)
B From Glasgow Central (Table 65)
C From Blackburn (Table 94)
D To Liverpool Lime Street (Table 90)
E From Clitheroe (Table 94)
G From Leeds to Morecambe (Table 36)
H 🍴 from Preston
J From Millom (Table 100)
b Change at Oxenholme Lake District and Lancaster
c Change at Preston

Table 82

Mondays to Fridays
until 3 October

Barrow-in-Furness, Blackpool North, Preston, Southport, Kirkby and Wigan → Bolton → Manchester

Network Diagram - see first page of Table 82

Station		NT	TP 1 ◇ A 🛒		NT	NT	NT	NT	NT B	NT C	TP 1 ◇ 🛒	NT	NT D	NT	TP 1 ◇ E 🛒	NT	NT	NT	NT	NT B	NT C	TP 1 ◇ 🛒	NT	NT	TP 1 ◇ E 🛒
Barrow-in-Furness	d														11 18										
Roose	d																								
Dalton	d														11 27										
Ulverston	d														11 35										
Cark	d														11 43										
Kents Bank	d																								
Grange-over-Sands	d														11 50										
Arnside	d														11 56										
Silverdale	d														12 01										
Carnforth	d												11 52		12 08										
Windermere	83 d		*10 18*																			*11b30*			12 21
Oxenholme Lake District	65 d		10c46				*10e53*															*12e13*			12f40
Lancaster 6	65 a		11 04										12 01		12 16										12 58
	d		11c05				*11e10*				*11e29*				12 16			*12e12*				*12e29*			12f59
Preston 8	65 a		11 23												12 36										13 17
Blackpool North	97 d						11 11		11 25		11 41							12 11		12 25		12 41			
Layton	97 d						11 14											12 14							
Poulton-le-Fylde	97 d						11 18				11 47							12 18				12 47			
Kirkham & Wesham	97 d		*11 19*				11 27								*12 19*			12 27							*13 19*
Preston 8	d		11 38				11 41		11 50		12 08				12 38			12 41		12 50		13 08			13 38
Leyland	d								11a55		12 13									12a55		13 13			
Chorley	d		11 47				11 51				12 19				12 47			12 51				13 19			13 47
Adlington (Lancashire)	d						11 56											12 56							
Blackrod	d						12 00											13 00							
Horwich Parkway	d						12 03				12 27							13 03				13 27			
Lostock	d						12 07				12 30							13 07				13 30			
Southport	d				11 10			11 38								12 15			12 38						
Meols Cop	d				11 15											12 20									
Bescar Lane	d				11 20																				
New Lane	d				11 24																				
Burscough Bridge	d				11 26			11 50								12 28			12 50						
Hoscar	d				11 30																				
Parbold	d				11 33			11 55								12 33			12 55						
Appley Bridge	d				11 37			11 59								12 37			12 59						
Gathurst	d				11 40											12 40									
Liverpool Central 10	103 d											*11 20*											*12 20*		
Kirkby	d											11 51											12 51		
Rainford	d											11 58											12 58		
Upholland	d											12 02											13 02		
Orrell	d											12 06											13 06		
Pemberton	d											12 09											13 09		
Wigan Wallgate	a				11 45			12 05				12 14				12 45			13 05				13 14		
	d	11 32			11 47	11 52		12 07				12 16		12 32		12 47	12 52		13 07				13 16	13 32	
Wigan North Western	d																								
Ince	d											12 19											13 19		
Hindley	d	11 37			11 52							12 22		12 37		12 52							13 22	13 37	
Westhoughton	d	11 41						12 15						12 41					13 15					13 41	
Bolton	a	11 49	11 58			12 06	12 12	12 23			12 34			12 49	12 58		13 06	13 12	13 23			13 34		13 49	13 58
	d	11 50	11 59			12 07	12 12	12 23		12 30	12 36			12 50	12 59		13 07	13 12	13 23		13 30	13 36		13 50	13 59
Moses Gate	d					12 10											13 10								
Farnworth	d	11 53												12 53										13 53	
Kearsley	d	11 55												12 55										13 55	
Daisy Hill	d				11 56							12 26				12 56							13 26		
Hag Fold	d											12 29											13 29		
Atherton	d				12 00							12 32				13 00							13 32		
Walkden	d				12 05							12 37				13 05							13 37		
Moorside	d											12 41											13 41		
Swinton	d				12 10							12 43				13 10							13 43		
Salford Crescent	a	12 06	12 11		12 17	12 21	12 25	12 36		12 42	12 48	12 50		13 06	13 11	13 17	13 21	13 25	13 36		13 42	13 48	13 50	14 06	14 11
	d	12 07	12 11		12 17	12 22	12 25	12 36		12 43	12 48	12 50		13 07	13 11	13 17	13 22	13 25	13 36		13 43	13 48	13 50	14 07	14 11
Salford Central	d	12 09			12 20	12 24				12 45		12 53		13 09		13 20	13 24				13 45		13 53	14 09	
Manchester Victoria	🚊 a	12 14			12 24	12 29				12 50		13 00		13 14		13 24	13 30				13 50		14 00	14 14	
Rochdale	95 a	*12 38*			12 55	*13 08*						13 25		*13 38*		13 55	*14 08*						14 25	*14 38*	
Deansgate	🚊 a						12 29								13 15			13 29							14 15
Manchester Oxford Road	a		12 16				12 31	12 41			12 53				13 16			13 31	13 41			13 53			14 16
Manchester Piccadilly 10	🚊 a		12 20				12 35	12 45			12 57				13 20			13 35	13 45			13 57			14 20
Stockport	84 a		*12 42*				12 46	*13 12*			*13 28*				*13 42*			13 46	*14 12*			*14 28*			*14 42*
Hazel Grove	86 a						12 55	*13 29*										13 55	*14 29*						
Buxton	86 a						13 30											14 33							
Heald Green	85 a		12 32								13 12				13 32							14 12			14 32
Manchester Airport	85 ✈ a		12 40					13 01			13 19				13 40				14 01			14 19			14 40

For general notes see front of timetable
For details of catering facilities see Directory of Train Operators

A From Glasgow Central and from Edinburgh (Table 65)

B To Liverpool Lime Street (Table 90)
C From Clitheroe (Table 94)
D From Leeds to Morecambe (Table 36)
E 🛒 from Preston
b Change at Oxenholme Lake District and Preston

c By changing at Preston, passengers may depart Oxenholme Lake District at 1053, Lancaster at 1110
e Change at Preston
f By changing at Preston, passengers may depart Oxenholme Lake District at 1253, Lancaster at 1309

Barrow-in-Furness, Blackpool North, Preston, Southport, Kirkby and Wigan → Bolton → Manchester

Network Diagram - see first page of Table 82

	NT	NT	NT	NT	NT	NT	NT	TP	NT	NT	NT	TP	NT	NT	NT	NT	NT	NT	TP	NT	NT	TP	TP	NT
								1 ◇				1 ◇							1 ◇			1 ◇	1 ◇	
	A					B	C					D					B	C				E	E	
								🛒				🛒							🛒			🛒	🛒	
Barrow-in-Furness d	12 06									12 57													14 10	
Roose d										13 01														
Dalton d										13 07														
Ulverston d	12 22									13 15													14 26	
Cark d										13 23														
Kents Bank d										13 27														
Grange-over-Sands d	12 35									13 31													14 39	
Arnside d	12 41									13 37													14 45	
Silverdale d										13 42														
Carnforth d	12 53									13 50													14 55	
Windermere 83 d												*13 24*										14 18		
Oxenholme Lake District 65 d				*12b53*				*13b13*				13c49			*13b59*							14e37		
Lancaster 6 65 a	13 05									14 00		14 05										14 54	15 02	
d				*13b09*				*13b29*				14 06							*14b29*			15 15		
Preston 8 65 a												14 24										15 34		
Blackpool North 97 d				13 11		13 25		13 41							14 11		14 21		14 41					
Layton 97 d				13 14											14 14									
Poulton-le-Fylde 97 d				13 18				13 47							14 18				14 47					
Kirkham & Wesham 97 d				13 27								*14 19*			14 27							*15 19*		
Preston 8 d				13 41		13 50		14 08				14 38			14 41		14 46		15 08			15 38		
Leyland d						13a55		14 13									14a51		15 13					
Chorley d				13 51				14 19				14 47			14 51				15 19			15 47		
Adlington (Lancashire) d				13 56											14 56									
Blackrod d				14 00											15 00									
Horwich Parkway d				14 03				14 27							15 03				15 27					
Lostock d				14 07				14 30							15 07				15 30					
Southport d		13 10			13 38								14 15			14 38								15 10
Meols Cop d		13 15											14 20											15 15
Bescar Lane d		13 20																						15 20
New Lane d		13 24																						15 24
Burscough Bridge d		13 26			13 50								14 28			14 50								15 26
Hoscar d		13 30																						15 30
Parbold d		13 33			13 55								14 33			14 55								15 33
Appley Bridge d		13 37			13 59								14 37			14 59								15 37
Gathurst d		13 40											14 40											15 40
Liverpool Central 10 103 d									*13 20*											*14 20*				
Kirkby d									13 51											14 51				
Rainford d									13 58											14 58				
Upholland d									14 02											15 02				
Orrell d									14 06											15 06				
Pemberton d									14 09											15 09				
Wigan Wallgate a		13 45			14 05				14 14				14 45			15 05				15 14				15 45
d		13 47	13 52		14 07				14 16		14 32		14 47	14 52		15 07				15 16	15 32			15 47
Wigan North Western d																								
Ince d									14 19											15 19				
Hindley d		13 52							14 22		14 37		14 52							15 22	15 37			15 52
Westhoughton d					14 15						14 41					15 15					15 41			
Bolton a			14 06	14 12	14 23			14 34			14 49	14 58		15 06	15 12	15 23			15 34		15 49	15 58		
d			14 07	14 12	14 23		14 30	14 36			14 50	14 59		15 07	15 12	15 23		15 30	15 36		15 50	15 59		
Moses Gate d			14 10											15 10										
Farnworth d											14 53										15 53			
Kearsley d											14 55										15 55			
Daisy Hill d		13 56							14 26				14 56							15 26				15 56
Hag Fold d									14 29											15 29				
Atherton d		14 00							14 32				15 00							15 32				16 00
Walkden d		14 05							14 37				15 05							15 37				16 05
Moorside d									14 41											15 41				
Swinton d		14 10							14 43				15 10							15 43				16 10
Salford Crescent a		14 17	14 21	14 25	14 36		14 42	14 48	14 50		15 06	15 11	15 17	15 21	15 25	15 36		15 42	15 48	15 50	16 06	16 11		16 17
d		14 17	14 22	14 25	14 36		14 43	14 48	14 50		15 07	15 11	15 17	15 22	15 25	15 36		15 43	15 48	15 50	16 07	16 11		16 17
Salford Central d		14 20	14 24				14 45		14 53		15 09		15 20	15 24				15 45		15 53	16 10			16 20
Manchester Victoria 🚌 a		14 24	14 32				14 50		15 00		15 14		15 24	15 30				15 50		15 59	16 14			16 25
Rochdale 95 a		14 55	*15 08*						15 25		*15 38*		15 55	*16 08*						16 25	*16 38*			16 55
Deansgate 🚌 a				14 29											15 29							16 15		
Manchester Oxford Road a				14 31	14 41			14 53				15 16			15 31	15 41			15 53			16 16		
Manchester Piccadilly 10 🚌 a				14 35	14 45			14 57				15 20			15 35	15 45			15 57			16 20		
Stockport 84 a				14 46	*15 12*			*15 28*				*15 42*			15 46	*16 12*			*16 28*			*16 42*		
Hazel Grove 86 a				14 55	*15 28*										15 56	*16 29*								
Buxton 86 a				15 30	*16 06*										*16 41*									
Heald Green 85 a								15 12				15 32							16 11			*16 49*		
Manchester Airport 85 ✈ a					15 01			15 19				15 40				16 01			16 19			16 40		

For general notes see front of timetable
For details of catering facilities see Directory of Train Operators

A From Carlisle via Whitehaven (Table 100)
B To Liverpool Lime Street (Table 90)
C From Clitheroe (Table 94)
D From Edinburgh (Table 65)
E 🛒 from Preston
b Change at Preston
c By changing at Preston, passengers may depart at 1359
e By changing at Preston, passengers may depart at 1453

Table 82

Mondays to Fridays

until 3 October

Barrow-in-Furness, Blackpool North, Preston, Southport, Kirkby and Wigan → Bolton → Manchester

Network Diagram - see first page of Table 82

		NT	NT	NT	NT	TP	NT	NT	NT	NT	TP	NT	NT	NT	NT	NT	NT	NT	NT	TP	NT	NT	TP	NT	NT
						1 ◇					1 ◇									1 ◇			1 ◇		
				A	B				C	D	E						B	A			G		H	A	
						[trolley]					[trolley]									[trolley]			[trolley]		
Barrow-in-Furness	d																				15 28		16 21		
Roose	d																				15 32				
Dalton	d																				15 38				
Ulverston	d																				15 47		16 37		
Cark	d																				15 55				
Kents Bank	d																				15 59				
Grange-over-Sands	d																				16 03		16 50		
Arnside	d																				16 09		16 56		
Silverdale	d																				16 14				
Carnforth	d								15 26												16 22		17 07		
Windermere	83 d										15 21												16b28		
Oxenholme Lake District	65 d		14c53			15c12					15 47												16 53		
Lancaster 6	65 a								15 38		16 02										16 33		17 15		
	d		15c08			15c28					16e03		16c09							16c29			17 16		
Preston 8	65 a										16 22												17 35		
Blackpool North	97 d		15 11		15 25	15 41							16 10				16 25			16 38					
Layton	97 d		15 14										16 13							16 41					
Poulton-le-Fylde	97 d		15 18			15 47							16 17							16 45					
Kirkham & Wesham	97 d		15 27										16 26							16 56					
Preston 8	d		15 41		15 50	16 08					16 38		16 38				16 50			17 08			17 35		
Leyland	d				15a55	16 13							16 44				16a55			17 13					
Chorley	d		15 51			16 19					16 47		16 51							17 19			17 44		
Adlington (Lancashire)	d		15 56										16 56							17 23					
Blackrod	d		16 00										16 59												
Horwich Parkway	d		16 03			16 27							17 03							17 28					
Lostock	d		16 07			16 30							17 06							17 31			17 52		
Southport	d							15 51				16 16				16 43									17 14
Meols Cop	d											16 21													17 19
Bescar Lane	d																								17 24
New Lane	d																								17 28
Burscough Bridge	d							16 03				16 29				16 55									17 30
Hoscar	d																								17 34
Parbold	d							16 08				16 34				17 00									17 37
Appley Bridge	d							16 12				16 38				17 04									17 41
Gathurst	d							16 15				16 41													17 44
Liverpool Central 10	103 d						15 20								16 05										
Kirkby	d						15 51								16 38										
Rainford	d						15 58								16 45										
Upholland	d						16 02								16 49										
Orrell	d						16 06								16 52										
Pemberton	d						16 09								16 55										
Wigan Wallgate	a						16 14	16 20				16 46			17 01	17 10									17 49
	d	15 52					16 16	16 21		16 32		16 47		16 58	17 06	17 12									17 50
Wigan North Western	d																					17 31			
Ince	d						16 19							17 01	17 09							17 33			
Hindley	d						16 22			16 37		16 52		17 04	17 13							17 37			
Westhoughton	d							16 30		16 41				17 09								17 41			17 55
Bolton	a	16 07	16 12			16 34		16 40		16 49	16 58		17 11	17 17		17 27				17 36		17 50	17 59		
	d	16 10	16 12	16 20		16 36		16 43		16 50	16 59		17 12	17 17		17 27		17 30		17 36		17 50	17 59	18 03	
Moses Gate	d			16 23														17 34							
Farnworth	d									16 53												17 53			
Kearsley	d									16 55									←			17 55			
Daisy Hill	d						16 26					16 56			17 17 →				17 17						18 00
Hag Fold	d						16 29												17 20						
Atherton	d						16 32					17 00							17 22						
Walkden	d						16 37					17 06							17 28						18 04
Moorside	d						16 41												17 31						18 09
Swinton	d						16 43					17 10							17 34						18 14
Salford Crescent	a	16 22	16 25	16 34		16 48	16 50	16 55		17 06	17 11	17 18	17 24	17 30		17 40			17 45	17 48		18 07	18 11	18 14	18 21
	d	16 22	16 25	16 35		16 48	16 50	16 56		17 07	17 11	17 18	17 25	17 31		17 40			17 45	17 48		18 07	18 11	18 14	18 22
Salford Central	d	16 25		16 37			16 55			17 09		17 23		17 33				17 45	17 48			18 09		18 16	18 24
Manchester Victoria	⇌ a	16 30		16 42			16 59			17 14		17 27		17 40				17 51	17 54			18 15		18 23	18 29
Rochdale	95 a			*17 08*			17 25					17 55		*18 08*					*18 32*						*19 05*
Deansgate	⇌ a		16 29					16 59					17 28										18 15		
Manchester Oxford Road	a		16 32			16 53		17 01			17 16		17 30			17 45				17 55			18 17		
Manchester Piccadilly 10	⇌ a		16 36			16 57		17 06			17 20		17 35			17 49				17 57			18 20		
Stockport	84 a		16 45					17 19			*17 42*		17 47			*18 12*				*18 26*			*18 42*		
Hazel Grove	86 a		16 53					17 27					17 56			*18 27*									
Buxton	86 a		17 30					18 07					18 31			*19 08*									
Heald Green	85 a					17 12					*17 49*									18 12			18 35		
Manchester Airport	85 ✈ a		*17f14*			17 19					17 40					18 05				18 19			18 42		

For general notes see front of timetable
For details of catering facilities see Directory of Train Operators

A From Clitheroe (Table 94)
B To Liverpool Lime Street (Table 90)
C From Leeds to Morecambe (Table 36)
D To Huddersfield (Table 39)
E From Glasgow Central (Table 65)
G From Carlisle via Whitehaven (Table 100)
H [trolley] from Preston
b Change at Oxenholme Lake District and Lancaster
c Change at Preston
e By changing at Preston, passengers may depart at 1609
f Change at Manchester Piccadilly

Table 82

Mondays to Fridays
until 3 October

Barrow-in-Furness, Blackpool North, Preston, Southport, Kirkby and Wigan → Bolton → Manchester

Network Diagram - see first page of Table 82

	NT	NT	NT	NT	NT	TP	NT	TP	NT	TP	NT	NT	NT	NT	NT	NT	NT	NT	TP	TP	NT	NT	NT	NT
						1 ◇		1 ◇		1 ◇									1 ◇	1 ◇				
				A						B	C			A	C		D	E			G			H
Barrow-in-Furness d								17 06										17 43						
Roose d																		17 47						
Dalton d								17 15										17 53						
Ulverston d								17 24										18 01						
Cark d								17 32										18 09						
Kents Bank d																		18 13						
Grange-over-Sands d								17 39										18 17						
Arnside d								17 45										18 23						
Silverdale d																		18 28						
Carnforth d								17 55									18 31	18 34						
Windermere 83 d										17 27										18 09				
Oxenholme Lake District 65 d										17b53		18c00								18 38			18c51	
Lancaster 6 65 a								18 05		18 09							18 43	18 45		18 55				
d		17c09				17c29				18 16										18 55			19c08	
Preston 8 65 a										18 36										19 14				
Blackpool North 97 d		17 10				17 38						18 11		18 25					18 38				19 10	19 18
Layton 97 d		17 13				17 41						18 14											19 13	
Poulton-le-Fylde 97 d		17 17				17 45						18 18							18 44				19 17	
Kirkham & Wesham 97 d		17 26				17 56				18 19		18 27											19 26	19 16
Preston 8 d		17 40		17 50		18 08				18 38		18 41		18 50					19 03	19 14			19 39	19 43
Leyland d		17 45		17a55		18 13								18a55					19 08				19 44	
Chorley d		17 51				18 19				18 47		18 51							19 15				19 51	
Adlington (Lancashire) d		17 56										18 56											19 56	
Blackrod d		18 00										19 00											20 00	
Horwich Parkway d		18 03				18 27						19 03							19 22				20 03	
Lostock d		18 07				18 30						19 07							19 25				20 07	
Southport d			17 42										18 28									19 16		
Meols Cop d			17 47										18 33									19 21		
Bescar Lane d													18 38											
New Lane d													18 42											
Burscough Bridge d			17 55										18 44									19 29		
Hoscar d													18 48											
Parbold d			18 00										18 51									19 34		
Appley Bridge d			18 04										18 55									19 38		
Gathurst d													18 58									19 41		
Liverpool Central 10 103 d	17 05															18 20								
Kirkby d	17 41															18 43								
Rainford d	17 48															18 50								
Upholland d	17 52															18 54								
Orrell d	17 55															18 58								
Pemberton d	17 58															19 01								
Wigan Wallgate a	18 04		18 10										19 04			19 09						19 46		
d	18 05		18 12										19 05			19 11						19 48		
Wigan North Western d							18 18		18 31															20 01
Ince d	18 08						18 21		18 34							19 14								
Hindley d	18 12						18 25		18 38				19 10			19 17						19 53		20 06
Westhoughton d			18 21				18 29						19 15											
Bolton a		18 13	18 29			18 34	18 39			18 58		19 12	19 23						19 30	19 45			20 12	
d		18 13	18 29			18 36	18 40			18 59	19 02	19 12	19 23		19 30				19 33	19 46	20 00		20 12	
Moses Gate d							18 43																	
Farnworth d																								
Kearsley d					←																			
Daisy Hill d	18 16 →				18 16				18 42							19 21						19 57		20 10
Hag Fold d					18 19											19 24								
Atherton d					18 21				18 46							19 27						20 01		20 14
Walkden d					18 27				18 51							19 32						20 06		20 20
Moorside d					18 30											19 36								
Swinton d					18 33				18 56							19 38						20 11		
Salford Crescent a		18 26	18 41		18 43	18 48	18 54		19 05	19 11	19 13	19 25	19 36		19 42	19 44			19 48		20 13	20 18	20 25	
d		18 26	18 41		18 43	18 48	18 55		19 05	19 11	19 14	19 25	19 36		19 43	19 44			19 48		20 13	20 18	20 25	
Salford Central d					18e49		18 57		19 08		19 16				19 45	19 47					20 17	20 21		
Manchester Victoria a					18 54		19 01		19 14		19 23				19 50	19 53					20 22	20 26		20 36
Rochdale 95 a							19 38									20 38								
Deansgate a												19 29							19 52				20 29	
Manchester Oxford Road a		18 33	18 47			18 55				19 16		19 33	19 42						19 54	20 00			20 31	
Manchester Piccadilly 10 a		18 38	18 51			18 57				19 20		19 36	19 46						19 57	20 04			20 34	
Stockport 84 a		18 48	19 15			19 25				19 42		19 47	20 15							20 26			20 44	
Hazel Grove 86 a		18 56								19 55		19 55											20 52	
Buxton 86 a		19 36								20 36		20 36											21 31	
Heald Green 85 a		19f07	19 27			19 12				19 31									20 12	20 18			21f01	
Manchester Airport 85 a			19 09			19 19				19 40			20 05						20 19	20 26			21f06	

For general notes see front of timetable
For details of catering facilities see Directory of Train Operators

- **A** To Liverpool Lime Street (Table 90)
- **B** From Edinburgh (Table 65)
- **C** From Clitheroe (Table 94)
- **D** From Leeds to Morecambe (Table 36)
- **E** From Sellafield (Table 100)
- **G** From Blackburn (Table 94)
- **H** Until 12 September
- **b** By changing at Preston, passengers may depart at 1800
- **c** Change at Preston
- **e** Arr. 1846
- **f** Change at Manchester Piccadilly

Barrow-in-Furness, Blackpool North, Preston, Southport, Kirkby and Wigan → Bolton → Manchester

Network Diagram - see first page of Table 82

		NT	NT	NT	TP	NT	NT	TP	TP	NT	NT	NT	TP	NT	NT	NT	TP	NT	NT	VT	NT	NT	NT	TP
					1 ◇			1 ◇	1 ◇				1 ◇							1 ◇				1 ◇
			A	B			A	C			B				B	D			A	E	B			
								✕												⊡				
Barrow-in-Furness	d								19 10														21 45	
Roose	d								19 14														21 49	
Dalton	d								19 21														21 55	
Ulverston	d								19 29														22 04	
Cark	d								19 37														22 12	
Kents Bank	d								19 41														22 16	
Grange-over-Sands	d								19 45														22 20	
Arnside	d								19 51														22 26	
Silverdale	d								19 57														22 31	
Carnforth	d								20 07														22 38	
Windermere	83 d						19b18										20b27			21 28			22 16	
Oxenholme Lake District	65 d						19 44	19 55					20c07				20c52			22 27			22 36	
Lancaster 6	65 a							20 10	20 15											22 42			22 49	
	d						20 01	20 11	20 17				20c23				21c07			22 44			23 01	
Preston 8	65 a							20 29	20 35											23 02			23 25	
Blackpool North	97 d		19 25		19 42								20 52				21 52		22 03					23 13
Layton	97 d				19 45								20 56				21 56							23 16
Poulton-le-Fylde	97 d				19 49								21 00				22 00							23 20
Kirkham & Wesham	97 d				19 59								21 09				22 09			22 25				23 30
Preston 8	d		19 50		20 11		20 27	20 32	20 38				21 21				22 21		22 27	23 23			23 29	23 42
Leyland	d		19a55				20a32		20 43				21 26				22 26		22a32					23 47
Chorley	d				20 21			20 42	20 49				21 34				22 34							23 54
Adlington (Lancashire)	d								20 54				21 38				22 38							23 58
Blackrod	d								20 57				21 42				22 42							00 02
Horwich Parkway	d								21 01				21 45				22 45							00 05
Lostock	d								21 04				21 48				22 48							00 08
Southport	d	19 34								20 34				21 34				22 29				23 10		
Meols Cop	d	19 39								20 39				21 39				22 34				23 15		
Bescar Lane	d																	22 39						
New Lane	d																	22 43						
Burscough Bridge	d	19 47								20 47				21 47				22 45				23 23		
Hoscar	d																	22 49						
Parbold	d	19 52								20 52				21 52				22 52				23 28		
Appley Bridge	d	19 56								20 56				21 56				22 56				23 32		
Gathurst	d	19 59								20 59				21 59				22 59				23 35		
Liverpool Central 10	103 d																							
Kirkby	d																							
Rainford	d																							
Upholland	d																							
Orrell	d																							
Pemberton	d																							
Wigan Wallgate	a	20 04								21 04				22 04				23 04				23 43		
	d	20 05				20 18				21 05		21 18		22 05		22 16		23 05						
Wigan North Western	d																							
Ince	d					20 21						21 21				22 19								
Hindley	d	20 10				20 24				21 10		21 24		22 10		22 22		23 10						
Westhoughton	d	20 15								21 15				22 15				23 15						
Bolton	a	20 23			20 32			20 53	21 08	21 23			21 52	22 23			22 52	23 23					23 51	00 12
	d	20 23		20 30	20 34			20 54	21 09	21 23	21 30		21 54	22 23	22 33		22 53	23 23			23 40		23 51	00 13
Moses Gate	d																							
Farnworth	d																							
Kearsley	d																							
Daisy Hill	d					20 28						21 28				22 26								
Hag Fold	d					20 31						21 31				22 29								
Atherton	d					20 34						21 34				22 32								
Walkden	d					20 39						21 39				22 37								
Moorside	d					20 43						21 43				22 41								
Swinton	d					20 45						21 45				22 43								
Salford Crescent	a	20 36		20 42	20 46	20 52		21 06	21 21	21 36	21 42	21 52	22 07	22 36	22 46	22 51	23 05	23 36			23 52			
	d	20 36		20 43	20 47	20 52		21 06	21 22	21 36	21 43	21 52	22 07	22 36	22 46	22 52	23 05	23 36			23 53			
Salford Central	d			20 45		20 56					21 45	21 56		22e39		22e54								
Manchester Victoria	⇌ a			20 50		21 00					21 50	22 00		22 44		23 00					00 01		00 09	
Rochdale	95 a					21 38						22 38				23 38								
Deansgate	⇌ a				20 52					21 40			22 13		22 50		23 15							
Manchester Oxford Road	a	20 41			20 54			21 11	21 26	21 41			22 14		22 52		23 19	23 41						
Manchester Piccadilly 10	⇌ a	20 45			20 58			21 14	21 30	21 46			22 18		22 56		23 30	23 46		00 16				00 29
Stockport	84 a	21 14			21 26			21 34		21 59			22f37		23 06		23f50							
Hazel Grove	86 a									22 06					23 14									
Buxton	86 a									22 46					23 54									
Heald Green	85 a				21 12			21 30	21 44				22 31				23 47							00 40
Manchester Airport	85 ✈ a	21 09			21 19			21 37	21 51				22 39		23g28		23 56							00 45

For general notes see front of timetable
For details of catering facilities see Directory of Train Operators

A To Liverpool Lime Street (Table 90)
B From Clitheroe (Table 94)
C From Edinburgh (Table 65)
D To Huddersfield (Table 39)
E From Glasgow Central (Table 65)
b Change at Oxenholme Lake District and Preston
c Change at Preston
e Fridays only
f Change at Manchester Oxford Road
g Change at Manchester Piccadilly

Table 82

Mondays to Fridays
from 6 October

Barrow-in-Furness, Blackpool North, Preston, Southport, Kirkby and Wigan → Bolton → Manchester

Network Diagram - see first page of Table 82

Station			TP	TP	TP	NT	TP	NT	TP	TP	NT	NT	NT	NT	NT	TP	NT	NT	NT	NT	NT	NT	NT	NT
									MX	MO														
			1 ◇	1 ◇	1 ◇		1 ◇		1 ◇	1 ◇						1 ◇								
					A						B		C		D		E			G	H		J	K
Barrow-in-Furness		d			04 20				05 00	05 15														
Roose		d																						
Dalton		d																						
Ulverston		d			04 35				05 15	05 30														
Cark		d																						
Kents Bank		d																						
Grange-over-Sands		d			04 48				05 28	05 43														
Arnside		d			04 55				05 34	05 49														
Silverdale		d																						
Carnforth		d			05 05				05 43	05 58														06 43
Windermere	83	d																					06b22	
Oxenholme Lake District	65	d																						
Lancaster 6	65	a			05 14				05 53	06 08														06 53
		d							05 53	06 08						06b33							06b38	
Preston 8	65	a							06 27	06 27														
Blackpool North	97	d	03 36	*04 45*			05 19		*05 30*	*05 30*			06 09			06 34							06 57	
Layton	97	d					*05 09*						06 13			06 37								
Poulton-le-Fylde	97	d					*05 25*		*05 36*	*05 36*			06 17			06 41							07 03	
Kirkham & Wesham	97	d					*05 22*						06 25			06 51				07 04				
Preston 8		d	04u01	05 17			05 58		06 28	06 28			06 39			07 03				07 20			07 25	
Leyland		d											06 44			07 08				07 25			07a30	
Chorley		d		05 26					06 37	06 37			06 51			07 15				07 33				
Adlington (Lancashire)		d											06 56							07 38				
Blackrod		d											06 59			07 21				07 42				
Horwich Parkway		d							06 45	06 45			07 03			07 24				07 46				
Lostock		d		05 34					06 48	06 48			07 07			07 27				07 49				
Southport		d												06 32				06 55						
Meols Cop		d												06 37				07 00						
Bescar Lane		d																						
New Lane		d																						
Burscough Bridge		d												06 45				07 09						
Hoscar		d																						
Parbold		d												06 50				07 14						
Appley Bridge		d												06 54				07 18						
Gathurst		d												06 57				07 22						
Liverpool Central 10	103	d																				*06 50*		
Kirkby		d																				07 13		
Rainford		d																				07 20		
Upholland		d																				07 24		
Orrell		d																				07 28		
Pemberton		d																				07 31		
Wigan Wallgate		a												07 04				07 31				07 37		
		d				06 08						06 40		07 05			07 13	07 32				07 40		
Wigan North Western		d					06 15												07 26					
Ince		d				06 11						06 43					07 16		07 29			07 43		
Hindley		d				06 14	06 20					06 46					07 19		07 33			07 46		
Westhoughton		d					06 24							07 13					07 37					
Bolton		a		05 40			06 31		06 52	06 52			07 12	07 22		07 33			07 45	07 54				
		d	04u29	05 40			06 31		06 54	06 54	06 58		07 12	07 23	07 30	07 33			07 46	07 55	08 00			
Moses Gate		d									07 01								07 49					
Farnworth		d									07 03								07 51					
Kearsley		d						←			07 05								07 53					
Daisy Hill		d				06 18 →		06 18				06 50					07 23	07 40				07 50		
Hag Fold		d						06 21				06 53					07 26					07 53		
Atherton		d						06 24				06 56					07 29	07 44				07 56		
Walkden		d						06 29				07 01					07 34					08 01		
Moorside		d						06 33				07 05					07 38					08 05		
Swinton		d						06 35				07 07					07 40					08 07		
Salford Crescent		a					06 43	06 46	07 06	07 06	07 17	07 19	07 25	07 35	07 42	07 45	07 47	07 59	08 03	08 07	08 12	08 18		
		d					06 43	06 46	07 06	07 06	07 17	07 19	07 25	07 36	07 43	07 46	07 47	07 59	08 03	08 07	08 13	08 18		
Salford Central		d						06 49			07 20	07 22			07 46		07 50	08 02	08 06		08 15	08 21		
Manchester Victoria 🚊		a						06 54			07 25	07 28			07 51		07 55	08 07	08 13		08 21	08 25		
Rochdale	95	a						*07 38*				*08 06*						08 25	*08 38*			08 55		
Deansgate 🚊		a					06 49						07 29	07 39						08 11				
Manchester Oxford Road		a					06 51		07 12	07 12			07 32	07 41		07 50				08 14				
Manchester Piccadilly 10 🚊		a		05 57			06 56		07 15	07 15			07 36	07 45		07 54				08 19				
Stockport	84	a		*06 24*			*07 27*		*07 37*	*07 37*			07 46	*08 07*		*08 24*				08 30				
Hazel Grove	86	a		*07 01*			*07 44*		*07 54*	*07 54*			*08 13*							*08 49*				
Buxton	86	a		*07 47*					*08 35*	*08 35*										*09 28*				
Heald Green	85	a		*06 21*			*07 27*		07 32	07 32						08 11				*08c51*				
Manchester Airport	85 ✈	a	05 05	06 14			07 15		07 40	07 40					08 02	08 19								

For general notes see front of timetable
For details of catering facilities see Directory of Train Operators

A To Windermere (Table 83)
B From Blackburn (Table 94). Also stops at Clifton 0709
C To Chester (Table 88)
D From Colne (Table 97)
E To Stalybridge (Table 39)
G From St Annes-on-the-Sea (Table 97) to Greenbank (Table 88)
H From Clitheroe (Table 94)
J To Liverpool Lime Street (Table 90)
K From Skipton (Table 36)
b Change at Preston
c Change at Manchester Piccadilly

from 6 October

Barrow-in-Furness, Blackpool North, Preston, Southport, Kirkby and Wigan → Bolton → Manchester

Network Diagram - see first page of Table 82

	TP	TP	NT	NT	NT	NT	NT	NT	TP	NT	NT	TP	NT	NT	NT	NT	NT	NT	TP		NT	NT	NT	TP
	1 ◇ A 🍴	1 ◇ A 🍴	BHX				B		1 ◇ 🍴			1 ◇ A 🍴	C				D	B	1 ◇ 🍴			E		1 ◇ G 🍴
Barrow-in-Furness d	06 15											07 01					07 17					07 58		
Roose d	06 19																07 21					08 02		
Dalton d	06 25											07 10					07 27					08 08		
Ulverston d	06 34											07 18					07 36					08 17		
Cark d	06 42											07 26					07 44					08 25		
Kents Bank d	06 46																07 48					08 29		
Grange-over-Sands d	06 50											07 33					07 52					08 33		
Arnside d	06 56											07 39					07 58					08 39		
Silverdale d	07 01											07 43					08 03					08 43		
Carnforth d	07 08											07 51					08 10					08 51		
Windermere 83 d						06b20													07b24					08 20
Oxenholme Lake District 65 d						06 47													07c53					08 59
Lancaster 6 65 a	07 15											07 58					08 19					08 59		09 14
d	07 16					07 23						07 59					08 19		08c29			09 00		09 14
Preston 8 65 a	07 35											08 17					08 42					09 25		09 33
Blackpool North 97 d		07 03	07 16						07 41						08 09				08 41					
Layton 97 d		07 06							07 44						08 12									
Poulton-le-Fylde 97 d		07 11	07 23						07 48						08 16				08 47					
Kirkham & Wesham 97 d		07 21	07 32						07 58						08 25		08 28							
Preston 8 d	07 40		07 46			07 50			08 12			08 34			08 38		08 50		09 08					09 38
Leyland d						07 55									08 43		08a55		09 13					
Chorley d	07 50		07 57			08 03			08 22			08 44			08 51				09 19					09 47
Adlington (Lancashire) d						08 08									08 56									
Blackrod d						08 11									09 00									
Horwich Parkway d						08 15						08 52			09 03				09 27					
Lostock d			08 05			08 19									09 07				09 30					
Southport d				07 23										08 06		08 31								
Meols Cop d				07 28										08 11		08 36								
Bescar Lane d														08 16										
New Lane d														08 20										
Burscough Bridge d				07 37										08 22		08 44								
Hoscar d														08 26										
Parbold d				07 42										08 29		08 49								
Appley Bridge d				07 46										08 33		08 53								
Gathurst d				07 50										08 36		08 56								
Liverpool Central 10 103 d					07e04						07 50													
Kirkby d											08 13													
Rainford d											08 20													
Upholland d											08 24													
Orrell d											08 28													
Pemberton d											08 31													
Wigan Wallgate a				07 59							08 42			08 43		09 03								
d				08 00				08 13		08 30				08 44		09 05					09 14		09 30	
Wigan North Western d					07 56																			
Ince d								08 16													09 17			
Hindley d					08 01			08 19		08 35				08 49							09 20		09 35	
Westhoughton d					08 06					08 39						09 13							09 39	
Bolton a	08 02		08 10		08 14	08 24			08 33	08 49		08 58			09 12	09 23			09 34				09 49	09 58
d	08 04		08 11		08 15	08 24	08 30		08 34	08 50		08 59	09 01		09 12	09 23		09 30	09 36				09 50	09 59
Moses Gate d					08 18								09 04											
Farnworth d					08 20					08 53													09 53	
Kearsley d					08 22					08 55													09 55	
Daisy Hill d				08 08				08 23						08 53							09 24			
Hag Fold d								08 26						08 56							09 27			
Atherton d				08 13				08 29						08 59							09 30			
Walkden d								08 34						09 04							09 35			
Moorside d								08 38						09 08							09 39			
Swinton d								08 40						09 10							09 41			
Salford Crescent a				08 28	08 32	08 37	08 42	08 46		09 06		09 11	09 16	09 19	09 25	09 36		09 42	09 48		09 50		10 06	10 11
d				08 28	08 32	08 37	08 42	08 46		09 07		09 11	09 16	09 19	09 25	09 36		09 42	09 48		09 50		10 07	10 11
Salford Central d			08 24	08 31	08 35		08 45	08 49		09 09			09 19	09 24				09 45			09 53		10 09	
Manchester Victoria ⇌ a			08 30	08 37	08 41		08 50	08 54		09 14			09 25	09 27				09 50			10 00		10 14	
Rochdale 95 a					*09 08*			09 25		*09 38*				09 55							10 25		*10 38*	
Deansgate ⇌ a						08 41						09 15			09 29	09 40								
Manchester Oxford Road a	08 20					08 43			08 49			09 16			09 31	09 42			09 53					10 16
Manchester Piccadilly 10 ⇌ a	08 25					08 47			08 53			09 20			09 35	09 45			09 57					10 20
Stockport 84 a	*08 53*					*09 08*			*09 13*			*09 42*			09 46	*10 12*			*10 28*					*10 42*
Hazel Grove 86 a						*09 16*			*09 29*						09 55	*10 29*								
Buxton 86 a						*09 58*									10 35									
Heald Green 85 a									*09 18*			09 31							10 11					10 32
Manchester Airport 85 ✈ a	08 42					09 06			09 13			09 40				10 01			10 19					10 40

For general notes see front of timetable
For details of catering facilities see Directory of Train Operators

A 🍴 from Preston
B From Clitheroe (Table 94)
C From Blackburn (Table 94)
D To Liverpool Lime Street (Table 90)
E From Maryport (Table 100)
G From Glasgow Central (Table 65)
b Change at Oxenholme Lake District and Preston
c Change at Preston
e Liverpool Lime Street (Table 90)

Table 82

Mondays to Fridays

from 6 October

Barrow-in-Furness, Blackpool North, Preston, Southport, Kirkby and Wigan → Bolton → Manchester

Network Diagram - see first page of Table 82

		NT	NT	NT	NT	NT	NT	NT	TP	NT	NT	NT	TP	NT	NT	NT	NT	NT	NT		TP	NT	NT	NT	TP
									[1] ◇				[1] ◇								[1] ◇				[1] ◇
		A					B	C			D		E					B	C				G		H
									🛒				🛒								🛒				🛒
Barrow-in-Furness	d												09 15										09 57		
Roose	d												09 19										10 01		
Dalton	d												09 25										10 07		
Ulverston	d												09 34										10 16		
Cark	d												09 42										10 24		
Kents Bank	d												09 46										10 28		
Grange-over-Sands	d												09 50										10 32		
Arnside	d												09 56										10 38		
Silverdale	d												10 01										10 43		
Carnforth	d										09 55		10 08										10 50		
Windermere	83 d												09b28												*10 18*
Oxenholme Lake District	65 d												*09 54*								10c13				10e46
Lancaster [6]	65 a										10 04		10 15										11 00		11 04
	d								09c29				10 16			10c09					10c29				11e05
Preston [8]	65 a												10 34												11 23
Blackpool North	97 d				09 11		09 25		09 38							10 11		10 25			10 41				
Layton	97 d				09 14											10 14									
Poulton-le-Fylde	97 d				09 18				09 44							10 18					10 47				
Kirkham & Wesham	97 d				09 27								*10 19*			10 27									*11 19*
Preston [8]	d				09 41		09 50		10 08				10 38			10 41		10 50			11 08				11 38
Leyland	d						09a55		10 13									10a55			11 13				
Chorley	d				09 51				10 19				10 47			10 51					11 19				11 47
Adlington (Lancashire)	d				09 56											10 56									
Blackrod	d				10 00											11 00									
Horwich Parkway	d				10 03				10 27							11 03					11 27				
Lostock	d				10 07				10 30							11 07					11 30				
Southport	d		09 06			09 36								10 11			10 34								
Meols Cop	d		09 11											10 16											
Bescar Lane	d		09 16																						
New Lane	d		09 20																						
Burscough Bridge	d		09 22			09 48								10 24			10 46								
Hoscar	d		09 26																						
Parbold	d		09 29			09 53								10 29			10 51								
Appley Bridge	d		09 33			09 57								10 33			10 55								
Gathurst	d		09 36											10 36											
Liverpool Central [10]	103 d									*09 20*												*10 20*			
Kirkby	d									09 47												10 47			
Rainford	d									09 54												10 54			
Upholland	d									09 58												10 58			
Orrell	d									10 02												11 02			
Pemberton	d									10 05												11 05			
Wigan Wallgate	a		09 43			10 03				10 12				10 43			11 03					11 12			
	d		09 45	09 50		10 05				10 14		10 30		10 45	10 50		11 05					11 14		11 30	
Wigan North Western	d																								
Ince	d									10 17												11 17			
Hindley	d		09 50							10 20		10 35		10 50								11 20		11 35	
Westhoughton	d					10 13						10 39					11 13							11 39	
Bolton	a			10 06	10 12	10 23			10 34			10 49	10 58		11 06	11 12	11 23				11 34			11 49	11 58
	d	10 01		10 07	10 12	10 23		10 30	10 36			10 50	10 59		11 07	11 12	11 23		11 30		11 36			11 50	11 59
Moses Gate	d			10 10											11 10										
Farnworth	d											10 53												11 53	
Kearsley	d											10 55												11 55	
Daisy Hill	d		09 54							10 24				10 54								11 24			
Hag Fold	d									10 27												11 27			
Atherton	d		09 58							10 30				10 58								11 30			
Walkden	d		10 03							10 35				11 03								11 35			
Moorside	d									10 39												11 39			
Swinton	d		10 08							10 41				11 08								11 41			
Salford Crescent	a	10 13	10 17	10 22	10 25	10 36		10 42	10 48	10 50		11 06	11 11	11 17	11 21	11 25	11 36		11 42		11 48	11 50		12 06	12 11
	d	10 13	10 17	10 22	10 25	10 36		10 43	10 48	10 50		11 07	11 11	11 17	11 22	11 25	11 36		11 43		11 48	11 50		12 07	12 11
Salford Central	d	10 16	10 20	10 24				10 45		10 53		11 09		11 20	11 24				11 45			11 53		12 09	
Manchester Victoria	🚊 a	10 21	10 24	10 32				10 50		11 00		11 14		11 24	11 29				11 50			12 00		12 14	
Rochdale	95 a		10 55	*11 08*						11 25		*11 38*		11 55	*12 08*							12 25		*12 38*	
Deansgate	🚊 a				10 29								11 15			11 29									
Manchester Oxford Road	a				10 31	10 41			10 53				11 16			11 31	11 41				11 53				12 16
Manchester Piccadilly [10]	🚊 a				10 35	10 45			10 57				11 20			11 35	11 45				11 57				12 20
Stockport	84 a				10 46	*11 12*			*11 27*				*11 42*			11 46	*12 12*				*12 28*				*12 42*
Hazel Grove	86 a				10 55	*11 29*										11 55	*12 29*								
Buxton	86 a				11 32											12 35									
Heald Green	85 a								11 12				11 32								12 12				12 32
Manchester Airport	85 ✈ a					11 01			11 19				11 40				12 01				12 19				12 40

For general notes see front of timetable
For details of catering facilities see Directory of Train Operators

A From Blackburn (Table 94)

B To Liverpool Lime Street (Table 90)

C From Clitheroe (Table 94)

D From Leeds to Morecambe (Table 36)

E 🛒 from Preston

G From Millom (Table 100)

H From Glasgow Central and from Edinburgh (Table 65)

b Change at Oxenholme Lake District and Lancaster

c Change at Preston

e By changing at Preston, passengers may depart Oxenholme Lake District at 1053, Lancaster at 1110

Barrow-in-Furness, Blackpool North, Preston, Southport, Kirkby and Wigan → Bolton → Manchester

Network Diagram - see first page of Table 82

		NT	NT	NT	NT	NT	NT	TP	NT	NT	NT	TP	NT	NT	NT	NT	NT	NT		TP	NT	NT	TP	NT	NT
								1 ◇				1 ◇								1 ◇			1 ◇		
						A	B			C		D					A	B					D	E	
								✠				✠								✠			✠		
Barrow-in-Furness	d											11 18												12 06	
Roose	d																								
Dalton	d											11 27													
Ulverston	d											11 35												12 22	
Cark	d											11 43													
Kents Bank	d																								
Grange-over-Sands	d											11 50												12 35	
Arnside	d											11 56												12 41	
Silverdale	d											12 01													
Carnforth	d									11 52		12 08												12 53	
Windermere	83 d																			*11b30*			12 21		
Oxenholme Lake District	65 d			*10c53*								*10 53*								*12c13*			12e40		
Lancaster 6	65 a									12 01		12 16											12 58	13 05	
	d			*11c10*				*11c29*				12 16			*12c12*					*12c29*			12e59		
Preston 8	65 a											12 36											13 17		
Blackpool North	97 d			11 11		11 25		11 41							12 11		12 25			12 41					
Layton	97 d			11 14											12 14										
Poulton-le-Fylde	97 d			11 18				11 47							12 18					12 47					
Kirkham & Wesham	97 d			11 27								*12 19*			12 27								*13 19*		
Preston 8	d			11 41		11 50		12 08				12 38			12 41		12 50			13 08			13 38		
Leyland	d					11a55		12 13									12a55			13 13					
Chorley	d			11 51				12 19				12 47			12 51					13 19			13 47		
Adlington (Lancashire)	d			11 56											12 56										
Blackrod	d			12 00											13 00										
Horwich Parkway	d			12 03				12 27							13 03					13 27					
Lostock	d			12 07				12 30							13 07					13 30					
Southport	d	11 06			11 34								12 12			12 34									13 07
Meols Cop	d	11 11											12 17												13 12
Bescar Lane	d	11 16																							13 17
New Lane	d	11 20																							13 21
Burscough Bridge	d	11 22			11 46								12 25			12 46									13 23
Hoscar	d	11 26																							13 27
Parbold	d	11 29			11 51								12 30			12 51									13 30
Appley Bridge	d	11 33			11 55								12 34			12 55									13 34
Gathurst	d	11 36											12 37												13 37
Liverpool Central 10	103 d								*11 20*												*12 20*				
Kirkby	d								11 47												12 47				
Rainford	d								11 54												12 54				
Upholland	d								11 58												12 58				
Orrell	d								12 02												13 02				
Pemberton	d								12 05												13 05				
Wigan Wallgate	a	11 43			12 03				12 12				12 43			13 03					13 12				13 44
	d	11 45	11 50		12 05				12 14		12 30		12 45	12 50		13 05					13 14	13 26			13 45
Wigan North Western	d																								
Ince	d								12 17												13 17				
Hindley	d	11 50							12 20		12 35		12 50								13 20	13 31			13 50
Westhoughton	d				12 13						12 39					13 13						13 35			
Bolton	a		12 06	12 12	12 23			12 34			12 49	12 58		13 06	13 12	13 23				13 34		13 49	13 58		
	d		12 07	12 12	12 23		12 30	12 36			12 50	12 59		13 07	13 12	13 23		13 30		13 36		13 50	13 59		
Moses Gate	d		12 10											13 10											
Farnworth	d										12 53											13 53			
Kearsley	d										12 55											13 55			
Daisy Hill	d	11 54							12 24				12 54								13 24				13 54
Hag Fold	d								12 27												13 27				
Atherton	d	11 58							12 30				12 58								13 30				13 58
Walkden	d	12 03							12 35				13 03								13 35				14 04
Moorside	d								12 39												13 39				
Swinton	d	12 08							12 41				13 08								13 41				14 08
Salford Crescent	a	12 17	12 21	12 25	12 36		12 42	12 48	12 50		13 06	13 11	13 17	13 21	13 25	13 36		13 42		13 48	13 50	14 06	14 11		14 17
	d	12 17	12 22	12 25	12 36		12 43	12 48	12 50		13 07	13 11	13 17	13 22	13 25	13 36		13 43		13 48	13 50	14 07	14 11		14 17
Salford Central	d	12 20	12 24				12 45		12 53		13 09		13 20	13 24				13 45			13 53	14 09			14 20
Manchester Victoria	⇌ a	12 24	12 29				12 50		13 00		13 14		13 24	13 30				13 50			14 00	14 14			14 24
Rochdale	95 a	12 55	*13 08*						13 25		*13 38*		13 55	*14 08*							14 25	*14 38*			14 55
Deansgate	⇌ a			12 29								13 15			13 29								14 15		
Manchester Oxford Road	a			12 31	12 41			12 53				13 16			13 31	13 41				13 53			14 16		
Manchester Piccadilly 10	⇌ a			12 35	12 45			12 57				13 20			13 35	13 45				13 57			14 20		
Stockport	84 a			12 46	*13 12*			*13 28*				*13 42*			13 46	*14 12*				*14 28*			*14 42*		
Hazel Grove	86 a			12 55	*13 29*										13 55	*14 29*									
Buxton	86 a			13 32											14 35										
Heald Green	85 a							13 12				13 32								14 12			14 32		
Manchester Airport	85 ✈ a				13 01			13 19				13 40				14 01				14 19			14 40		

For general notes see front of timetable
For details of catering facilities see
Directory of Train Operators

A To Liverpool Lime Street (Table 90)
B From Clitheroe (Table 94)
C From Leeds to Morecambe (Table 36)
D ✠ from Preston
E From Carlisle via Whitehaven (Table 100)

b Change at Oxenholme Lake District and Preston
c Change at Preston
e By changing at Preston, passengers may depart Oxenholme Lake District at 1253, Lancaster at 1309

Barrow-in-Furness, Blackpool North, Preston, Southport, Kirkby and Wigan → Bolton → Manchester

Network Diagram - see first page of Table 82

Station		NT	NT	NT	NT	NT	TP	NT	NT	NT	TP	NT	NT	NT	NT	NT	NT		TP	NT	NT	TP	TP	NT	NT
							1 ◇				1 ◇								1 ◇			1 ◇	1 ◇		
					A	B					C					A	B					D	D		
							🍴				🍴								🍴			🍴	🍴		
Barrow-in-Furness	d								12 57														14 10		
Roose	d								13 01																
Dalton	d								13 07																
Ulverston	d								13 15														14 26		
Cark	d								13 23																
Kents Bank	d								13 27																
Grange-over-Sands	d								13 31														14 39		
Arnside	d								13 37														14 45		
Silverdale	d								13 42																
Carnforth	d								13 50														14 55		
Windermere	83 d										*13 24*											14 18			
Oxenholme Lake District	65 d		*12b53*				*13b13*				13c49			*13b59*								14e37			
Lancaster 6	65 a								14 00		14 05											14 54	15 02		
	d		*13b09*				*13b29*				14 06								*14b29*			15 15			
Preston 8	65 a										14 24											15 34			
Blackpool North	97 d		13 11		13 25		13 41							14 11		14 21			14 41						
Layton	97 d		13 14											14 14											
Poulton-le-Fylde	97 d		13 18				13 47							14 18					14 47						
Kirkham & Wesham	97 d		13 27								*14 19*			14 27								*15 19*			
Preston 8	d		13 41		13 50		14 08				14 38			14 41		14 46			15 08			15 38			
Leyland	d				13a55		14 13									14a51			15 13						
Chorley	d		13 51				14 19				14 47			14 51					15 19			15 47			
Adlington (Lancashire)	d		13 56											14 56											
Blackrod	d		14 00											15 00											
Horwich Parkway	d		14 03				14 27							15 03					15 27						
Lostock	d		14 07				14 30							15 07					15 30						
Southport	d			13 34								14 12			14 34									15 08	
Meols Cop	d											14 17												15 13	
Bescar Lane	d																							15 18	
New Lane	d																							15 22	
Burscough Bridge	d			13 46								14 25			14 46									15 24	
Hoscar	d																							15 28	
Parbold	d			13 51								14 30			14 51									15 31	
Appley Bridge	d			13 55								14 34			14 55									15 35	
Gathurst	d											14 37												15 38	
Liverpool Central 10	103 d							*13 20*												*14 20*					
Kirkby	d							13 47												14 47					
Rainford	d							13 54												14 54					
Upholland	d							13 58												14 58					
Orrell	d							14 02												15 02					
Pemberton	d							14 05												15 05					
Wigan Wallgate	a			14 03				14 12				14 43			15 03					15 12				15 43	
	d	13 50		14 05				14 14		14 30		14 45	14 50		15 05					15 14	15 30			15 45	15 50
Wigan North Western	d																								
Ince	d							14 17												15 17					
Hindley	d							14 20		14 35		14 50								15 20	15 35			15 50	
Westhoughton	d			14 13						14 39					15 13						15 39				
Bolton	a	14 06	14 12	14 23			14 34			14 49	14 58		15 06	15 12	15 23				15 34		15 49	15 58			16 07
	d	14 07	14 12	14 23		14 30	14 36			14 50	14 59		15 07	15 12	15 23		15 30		15 36		15 50	15 59			16 10
Moses Gate	d	14 10											15 10												
Farnworth	d									14 53											15 53				
Kearsley	d									14 55											15 55				
Daisy Hill	d							14 24				14 54								15 24				15 54	
Hag Fold	d							14 27												15 27					
Atherton	d							14 30				14 58								15 30				15 58	
Walkden	d							14 35				15 03								15 35				16 03	
Moorside	d							14 39												15 39					
Swinton	d							14 41				15 08								15 41				16 08	
Salford Crescent	a	14 21	14 25	14 36		14 42	14 48	14 50		15 06	15 11	15 17	15 21	15 25	15 36		15 42		15 48	15 50	16 06	16 11		16 17	16 22
	d	14 22	14 25	14 36		14 43	14 48	14 50		15 07	15 11	15 17	15 22	15 25	15 36		15 43		15 48	15 50	16 07	16 11		16 17	16 22
Salford Central	d	14 24				14 45		14 53		15 09		15 20	15 24				15 45			15 53	16 10			16 20	16 25
Manchester Victoria	⇌ a	14 32				14 50		15 00		15 14		15 24	15 30				15 50			15 59	16 14			16 25	16 30
Rochdale	95 a	*15 08*						15 25		*15 38*		15 55	*16 08*							16 25	*16 38*			16 55	
Deansgate	⇌ a		14 29											15 29								16 15			
Manchester Oxford Road	a		14 31	14 41			14 53				15 16			15 31	15 41				15 53			16 16			
Manchester Piccadilly 10	⇌ a		14 35	14 45			14 57				15 20			15 35	15 45				15 57			16 20			
Stockport	84 a		14 46	*15 12*			*15 28*				*15 42*			15 46	*16 12*				*16 28*			*16 42*			
Hazel Grove	86 a		14 55	*15 28*										15 56	*16 29*										
Buxton	86 a		15 32	*16 08*										*16 43*											
Heald Green	85 a						15 12				15 32								16 11			*16 49*			
Manchester Airport	85 ✈ a			15 01			15 19				15 40				16 01				16 19			16 40			

For general notes see front of timetable
For details of catering facilities see Directory of Train Operators

A To Liverpool Lime Street (Table 90)
B From Clitheroe (Table 94)
C From Edinburgh (Table 65)
D 🍴 from Preston

b Change at Preston
c By changing at Preston, passengers may depart at 1359
e By changing at Preston, passengers may depart at 1453

Table 82

Mondays to Fridays

from 6 October

Barrow-in-Furness, Blackpool North, Preston, Southport, Kirkby and Wigan → Bolton → Manchester

Network Diagram - see first page of Table 82

	NT	NT A	NT B	TP 1 ◇ ⊼	NT	NT	NT C	NT D	TP 1 ◇ E ⊼	NT	NT	NT	NT	NT	NT B		NT A	NT	TP 1 ◇ ⊼	NT G	NT	TP 1 ◇ H ⊼	NT A	NT
Barrow-in-Furness d																				15 28		16 21		
Roose d																				15 32				
Dalton d																				15 38				
Ulverston d																				15 47		16 37		
Cark d																				15 55				
Kents Bank d																				15 59				
Grange-over-Sands d																				16 03		16 50		
Arnside d																				16 09		16 56		
Silverdale d																				16 14				
Carnforth d							15 26													16 22		17 07		
Windermere 83 d									*15 21*													16b28		
Oxenholme Lake District 65 d	14c53			15c12					15 47													*16 53*		
Lancaster 6 65 a							15 38		16 02											16 33		17 15		
d	15c08			15c28					16e03		16c09								16c29			17 16		
Preston 8 65 a									16 22													17 35		
Blackpool North 97 d	15 11		15 25	15 41							16 10				16 25				16 38					
Layton 97 d	15 14										16 13								16 41					
Poulton-le-Fylde 97 d	15 18			15 47							16 17								16 45					
Kirkham & Wesham 97 d	15 27										16 26								16 56					
Preston 8 d	15 41		15 50	16 08					16 38		16 38				16 50				17 08			17 35		
Leyland d			15a55	16 13							16 44				16a55				17 13					
Chorley d	15 51			16 19					16 47		16 51								17 19			17 44		
Adlington (Lancashire) d	15 56										16 56								17 23					
Blackrod d	16 00										16 59													
Horwich Parkway d	16 03			16 27							17 03								17 28					
Lostock d	16 07			16 30							17 06								17 31			17 52		
Southport d						15 47				16 13				16 43										17 12
Meols Cop d										16 18														17 17
Bescar Lane d																								17 22
New Lane d																								17 26
Burscough Bridge d						15 59				16 26				16 55										17 28
Hoscar d																								17 32
Parbold d						16 04				16 31				17 00										17 35
Appley Bridge d						16 08				16 35				17 04										17 39
Gathurst d						16 11				16 38														17 42
Liverpool Central 10 103 d					*15 20*								*16 05*											
Kirkby d					15 47								16 38											
Rainford d					15 54								16 45											
Upholland d					15 58								16 49											
Orrell d					16 02								16 52											
Pemberton d					16 05								16 55											
Wigan Wallgate a					16 12	16 18				16 46			17 01	17 10										17 49
d					16 14	16 19		16 30		16 47		16 58	17 06	17 12										17 50
Wigan North Western d																					17 31			
Ince d					16 17							17 01	17 09								17 33			
Hindley d					16 20			16 35		16 52		17 04	17 13								17 37			17 55
Westhoughton d						16 28		16 39				17 09									17 41			
Bolton a	16 12			16 34		16 40		16 49	16 58		17 11	17 17		17 27					17 36		17 50	17 59		
d	16 12	16 20		16 36		16 43		16 50	16 59		17 12	17 17		17 27			17 30		17 36		17 50	17 59	18 03	
Moses Gate d		16 23															17 34							
Farnworth d								16 53													17 53			
Kearsley d								16 55										←			17 55			
Daisy Hill d					16 24					16 56			17 17					17 17						18 00
Hag Fold d					16 27								→					17 20						
Atherton d					16 30					17 00								17 22						18 04
Walkden d					16 35					17 06								17 28						18 09
Moorside d					16 39													17 31						
Swinton d					16 41					17 10								17 34						18 14
Salford Crescent a	16 25	16 34		16 48	16 50	16 55		17 06	17 11	17 18	17 24	17 30		17 40				17 45	17 48		18 07	18 11	18 14	18 21
d	16 25	16 35		16 48	16 50	16 56		17 07	17 11	17 18	17 25	17 31		17 40				17 45	17 48		18 07	18 11	18 14	18 22
Salford Central d		16 37			16 55			17 09		17 23		17 33					17 45	17 48			18 09		18 16	18 24
Manchester Victoria a		16 42			16 59			17 14		17 27		17 40					17 51	17 54			18 15		18 23	18 29
Rochdale 95 a		*17 08*			17 25					17 55		*18 08*						*18 32*						*19 05*
Deansgate a	16 29					16 59					17 28											18 15		
Manchester Oxford Road a	16 32			16 53		17 01			17 16		17 30			17 45					17 55			18 17		
Manchester Piccadilly 10 a	16 36			16 57		17 06			17 20		17 35			17 49					17 57			18 20		
Stockport 84 a	16 45					17 19			*17 42*		17 47			*18 12*					*18 26*			*18 42*		
Hazel Grove 86 a	16 53					17 27					17 56			*18 27*										
Buxton 86 a	17 32					18 09					18 33			*19 10*										
Heald Green 85 a				17 12					*17 49*										18 12			18 35		
Manchester Airport 85 a	*17f14*			17 19					17 40					18 05					18 19			18 42		

For general notes see front of timetable
For details of catering facilities see Directory of Train Operators

- **A** From Clitheroe (Table 94)
- **B** To Liverpool Lime Street (Table 90)
- **C** From Leeds to Morecambe (Table 36)
- **D** To Huddersfield (Table 39)
- **E** From Glasgow Central (Table 65)
- **G** From Carlisle via Whitehaven (Table 100)
- **H** ⊼ from Preston
- **b** Change at Oxenholme Lake District and Lancaster
- **c** Change at Preston
- **e** By changing at Preston, passengers may depart at 1609
- **f** Change at Manchester Piccadilly

Barrow-in-Furness, Blackpool North, Preston, Southport, Kirkby and Wigan → Bolton → Manchester

Network Diagram - see first page of Table 82

	NT	NT	NT	NT	NT	TP	NT	TP	NT	TP	NT	NT	NT	NT		NT	NT	NT	NT	TP	TP	NT	NT	NT
						1 ◇		1 ◇		1 ◇										1 ◇	1 ◇			
				A						B	C			A		C		D	E			G		
Barrow-in-Furness d								17 06											17 43					
Roose d																			17 47					
Dalton d								17 15											17 53					
Ulverston d								17 24											18 01					
Cark d								17 32											18 09					
Kents Bank d																			18 13					
Grange-over-Sands d								17 39											18 17					
Arnside d								17 45											18 23					
Silverdale d																			18 28					
Carnforth d								17 55										18 31	18 34					
Windermere 83 d										*17 27*											18 09			
Oxenholme Lake District 65 d						*17b13*				17c53		*18b00*								*18b00*	18 38			*18b51*
Lancaster 6 65 a								18 05		18 09								18 43	18 45		18 55			
d		*17b09*				*17b29*				18 16											18 55			*19b08*
Preston 8 65 a										18 36											19 14			
Blackpool North 97 d		17 10				17 38						18 11		18 25						18 38				19 10
Layton 97 d		17 13				17 41						18 14												19 13
Poulton-le-Fylde 97 d		17 17				17 45						18 18								18 44				19 17
Kirkham & Wesham 97 d		17 26				17 56				*18 19*		18 27												19 26
Preston 8 d		17 40		17 50		18 08				18 38		18 41		18 50						19 03	19 14			19 39
Leyland d		17 45		17a55		18 13								18a55						19 08				19 44
Chorley d		17 51				18 19				18 47		18 51								19 15				19 51
Adlington (Lancashire) d		17 56										18 56												19 56
Blackrod d		18 00										19 00												20 00
Horwich Parkway d		18 03				18 27						19 03								19 22				20 03
Lostock d		18 07				18 30						19 07								19 25				20 07
Southport d			17 40										18 24										19 13	
Meols Cop d			17 45										18 29										19 18	
Bescar Lane d													18 34											
New Lane d													18 38											
Burscough Bridge d			17 53										18 40										19 26	
Hoscar d													18 44											
Parbold d			17 58										18 47										19 31	
Appley Bridge d			18 02										18 51										19 35	
Gathurst d													18 54										19 38	
Liverpool Central 10 103 d	*17 05*																*18 20*							
Kirkby d	17 39																18 43							
Rainford d	17 46																18 50							
Upholland d	17 50																18 54							
Orrell d	17 53																18 58							
Pemberton d	17 56																19 01							
Wigan Wallgate a	18 04		18 10										19 02				19 09						19 44	
d	18 05		18 12										19 03				19 11						19 46	
Wigan North Western d							18 18		18 31															
Ince d	18 08						18 21		18 34								19 14							
Hindley d	18 12						18 25		18 38				19 08				19 17						19 51	
Westhoughton d			18 21				18 29						19 13											
Bolton a		18 13	18 29			18 34	18 39			18 58		19 12	19 23							19 30	19 45			20 12
d		18 13	18 29			18 36	18 40			18 59	19 02	19 12	19 23			19 30				19 33	19 46	20 00		20 12
Moses Gate d							18 43																	
Farnworth d																								
Kearsley d					⟵																			
Daisy Hill d	18 16 ⟶				18 16				18 42								19 21						19 55	
Hag Fold d					18 19												19 24							
Atherton d					18 21				18 46								19 27						19 59	
Walkden d					18 27				18 51								19 32						20 04	
Moorside d					18 30												19 36							
Swinton d					18 33				18 56								19 38						20 09	
Salford Crescent a		18 26	18 41		18 43	18 48	18 54		19 05	19 11	19 13	19 25	19 36			19 42	19 44			19 48		20 13	20 18	20 25
d		18 26	18 41		18 43	18 48	18 55		19 05	19 11	19 14	19 25	19 36			19 43	19 44			19 48		20 13	20 18	20 25
Salford Central d					18e49		18 57		19 08		19 16					19 45	19 47					20 17	20 21	
Manchester Victoria a					18 54		19 01		19 14		19 23					19 50	19 53					20 22	20 26	
Rochdale 95 a							*19 38*										*20 38*							
Deansgate a												19 29								19 52				20 29
Manchester Oxford Road a		18 33	18 47			18 55				19 16		19 33	19 42							19 54	20 00			20 31
Manchester Piccadilly 10 a		18 38	18 51			18 57				19 20		19 36	19 46							19 57	20 04			20 34
Stockport 84 a		18 48	*19 15*			*19 25*				*19 42*		19 47	*20 15*								*20 26*			20 44
Hazel Grove 86 a		18 56										19 55												20 52
Buxton 86 a		19 38										20 38												21 32
Heald Green 85 a		*19f07*				19 12				19 31										20 12	20 18			*21f01*
Manchester Airport 85 a			19 09			19 19				19 40			20 05							20 19	20 26			*21f06*

For general notes see front of timetable
For details of catering facilities see Directory of Train Operators

A To Liverpool Lime Street (Table 90)
B From Edinburgh (Table 65)
C From Clitheroe (Table 94)
D From Leeds to Morecambe (Table 36)
E From Sellafield (Table 100)
G From Blackburn (Table 94)
b Change at Preston
c By changing at Preston, passengers may depart at 1800
e Arr. 1846
f Change at Manchester Piccadilly

Table 82

Mondays to Fridays

from 6 October

Barrow-in-Furness, Blackpool North, Preston, Southport, Kirkby and Wigan → Bolton → Manchester

Network Diagram - see first page of Table 82

		NT	NT	NT	TP	NT	NT	TP	TP	NT	NT	NT	TP	NT	NT	NT	TP	NT	NT	VT	NT	NT	NT	TP
					1 ◇			1 ◇	1 ◇				1 ◇							1 ◇				1 ◇
			A	B			A	C			B				B	D			A	E	B			
Barrow-in-Furness	d								19 10														21 45	
Roose	d								19 14														21 49	
Dalton	d								19 21														21 55	
Ulverston	d								19 29														22 04	
Cark	d								19 37														22 12	
Kents Bank	d								19 41														22 16	
Grange-over-Sands	d								19 45														22 20	
Arnside	d								19 51														22 26	
Silverdale	d								19 57														22 31	
Carnforth	d								20 07														22 38	
Windermere	83 d						19b18										20b27			21 28			22 16	
Oxenholme Lake District	65 d						19 44	19 55					20c07				20c52			22 27			22 36	
Lancaster 6	65 a							20 10	20 15											22 42			22 49	
	d						20 01	20 11	20 17				20c23				21c07			22 44			23 01	
Preston 8	65 a							20 29	20 35											23 02			23 25	
Blackpool North	97 d		19 25		19 42								20 52				21 52		22 03					23 13
Layton	97 d				19 45								20 56				21 56							23 16
Poulton-le-Fylde	97 d				19 49								21 00				22 00							23 20
Kirkham & Wesham	97 d				19 59								21 09				22 09			22 25				23 30
Preston 8	d		19 50		20 11		20 27	20 32	20 38				21 21				22 21		22 27	23 23			23 29	23 42
Leyland	d		19a55				20a32		20 43				21 26				22 26		22a32					23 47
Chorley	d				20 21			20 42	20 49				21 34				22 34							23 54
Adlington (Lancashire)	d								20 54				21 38				22 38							23 58
Blackrod	d								20 57				21 42				22 42							00 02
Horwich Parkway	d								21 01				21 45				22 45							00 05
Lostock	d								21 04				21 48				22 48							00 08
Southport	d	19 30								20 30				21 30				22 25				23 10		
Meols Cop	d	19 35								20 35				21 35				22 30				23 15		
Bescar Lane	d																	22 35						
New Lane	d																	22 39						
Burscough Bridge	d	19 43								20 43				21 43				22 41				23 23		
Hoscar	d																	22 45						
Parbold	d	19 48								20 48				21 48				22 48				23 28		
Appley Bridge	d	19 52								20 52				21 52				22 52				23 32		
Gathurst	d	19 55								20 55				21 55				22 55				23 35		
Liverpool Central 10	103 d																							
Kirkby	d																							
Rainford	d																							
Upholland	d																							
Orrell	d																							
Pemberton	d																							
Wigan Wallgate	a	20 02								21 02				22 02				23 02				23 47		
	d	20 03				20 18				21 03		21 18		22 03		22 16		23 03						
Wigan North Western	d																							
Ince	d					20 21						21 21				22 19								
Hindley	d	20 08				20 24				21 08		21 24		22 08		22 22		23 08						
Westhoughton	d	20 13								21 13				22 13				23 13						
Bolton	a	20 23			20 32			20 53	21 08	21 23			21 52	22 23			22 52	23 23					23 51	00 12
	d	20 23		20 30	20 34			20 54	21 09	21 23	21 30		21 54	22 23	22 33		22 53	23 23			23 40		23 51	00 13
Moses Gate	d																							
Farnworth	d																							
Kearsley	d																							
Daisy Hill	d					20 28						21 28				22 26								
Hag Fold	d					20 31						21 31				22 29								
Atherton	d					20 34						21 34				22 32								
Walkden	d					20 39						21 39				22 37								
Moorside	d					20 43						21 43				22 41								
Swinton	d					20 45						21 45				22 43								
Salford Crescent	a	20 36		20 42	20 46	20 52		21 06	21 21	21 36	21 42	21 52	22 07	22 36	22 46	22 51	23 05	23 36			23 52			
	d	20 36		20 43	20 47	20 52		21 06	21 22	21 36	21 43	21 52	22 07	22 36	22 46	22 52	23 05	23 36			23 53			
Salford Central	d			20 45		20 56					21 45	21 56		22e39		22e54								
Manchester Victoria	⇌ a			20 50		21 00					21 50	22 00		22 44		23 00					00 01		00 09	
Rochdale	95 a					21 38						22 38				23 38								
Deansgate	⇌ a				20 52					21 40			22 13		22 50		23 15							
Manchester Oxford Road	a	20 41			20 54			21 11	21 26	21 41			22 14		22 52		23 19	23 41						
Manchester Piccadilly 10	⇌ a	20 45			20 58			21 14	21 30	21 46			22 18		22 56		23 30	23 46		00 16				00 29
Stockport	84 a	21 14			21 26			21 34		21 59			22f37		23 06		23f50							
Hazel Grove	86 a									22 06					23 14									
Buxton	86 a									22 48					23 56									
Heald Green	85 a				21 12			21 30	21 44				22 31				23 47							00 40
Manchester Airport	85 ✈ a	21 09			21 19			21 37	21 51				22 39		23g28		23 56							00 45

For general notes see front of timetable
For details of catering facilities see Directory of Train Operators

A To Liverpool Lime Street (Table 90)

B From Clitheroe (Table 94)
C From Edinburgh (Table 65)
D To Huddersfield (Table 39)
E From Glasgow Central (Table 65)
b Change at Oxenholme Lake District and Preston

c Change at Preston
e Fridays only
f Change at Manchester Oxford Road
g Change at Manchester Piccadilly

Saturdays

until 12 July

Barrow-in-Furness, Blackpool North, Preston, Southport, Kirkby and Wigan → Bolton → Manchester

Network Diagram - see first page of Table 82

Station		TP	TP	TP	TP	TP	NT	NT	NT	NT	NT	TP		NT	NT	NT	NT	NT	NT	TP	TP	NT	NT	NT	NT
		1 ◇	1 ◇	1 ◇	1 ◇	1 ◇						1 ◇								1 ◇	1 ◇				
				A			B		C		D					E	G	H		J	J			H	
Barrow-in-Furness	d			04 15		05 15														06 15					
Roose	d																			06 19					
Dalton	d																			06 25					
Ulverston	d			04 30		05 30														06 34					
Cark	d																			06 42					
Kents Bank	d																			06 46					
Grange-over-Sands	d			04 43		05 43														06 50					
Arnside	d			04 50		05 49														06 56					
Silverdale	d																			07 01					
Carnforth	d			05b02		05 58														07 08					
Windermere	83 d																						*06c35*		
Oxenholme Lake District	65 d																						*07 08*		
Lancaster 6	65 a			05 11		06 08														07 15					
	d				*05e33*	06 08						*06e31*								07 16			*07 24*		
Preston 8	65 a					06 27														07 35					
Blackpool North	97 d	03 36	*04 45*		05 19	*05 30*			06 08			06 34					06 57				07 03				
Layton	97 d				*05 09*				06 12			06 37					07 00				07 07				
Poulton-le-Fylde	97 d				05 25	*05 36*			06 16			06 41					07 03				07 11				
Kirkham & Wesham	97 d				*05 22*				06 24			06 51				07 04	07 13				07 20				
Preston 8	d	04u01	05 17		05 58	06 28			06 37			07 03				07 20	07 25			07 40			07 50		
Leyland	d								06 42			07 08				07 25	07a30						07 55		
Chorley	d		05 26			06 37			06 50			07 15				07 33				07 49			08 03		
Adlington (Lancashire)	d								06 55							07 38							08 08		
Blackrod	d								06 58			07 21				07 42							08 11		
Horwich Parkway	d					06 45			07 02			07 24				07 46							08 15		
Lostock	d		05 34			06 48			07 06			07 27				07 49							08 19		
Southport	d									06 35															07 41
Meols Cop	d									06 40															07 46
Bescar Lane	d																								
New Lane	d																								
Burscough Bridge	d									06 48															07 54
Hoscar	d																								
Parbold	d									06 53															07 59
Appley Bridge	d									06 57															08 03
Gathurst	d									07 00															08 06
Liverpool Central 10	103 d																		*06 50*			07f04			
Kirkby	d																		07 16						
Rainford	d																		07 23						
Upholland	d																		07 27						
Orrell	d																		07 31						
Pemberton	d																		07 34						
Wigan Wallgate	a									07 05									07 39						08 11
	d							06 45		07 06				07 13	07 27				07 43						08 13
Wigan North Western	d				06 15																	07 56			
Ince	d							06 48						07 16	07 30				07 46						08 16
Hindley	d				06 20			06 51						07 19	07 34				07 49			08 01			08 19
Westhoughton	d				06 24					07 14					07 38							08 06			
Bolton	a		05 40		06 31	06 52			07 11	07 22		07 32			07 46	07 55				08 02		08 14	08 24		
	d	04u29	05 40		06 31	06 54	06 58		07 12	07 23	07 30	07 33			07 47	07 55		08 00		08 04		08 15	08 24	08 30	
Moses Gate	d						07 01								07 50							08 18			
Farnworth	d						07 03								07 52							08 20			
Kearsley	d						07 05								07 54							08 22			
Daisy Hill	d							06 55						07 23					07 53						08 23
Hag Fold	d							06 58						07 26					07 56						08 26
Atherton	d							07 01						07 29					07 59						08 29
Walkden	d							07 06						07 34					08 04						08 34
Moorside	d							07 10						07 38					08 08						08 38
Swinton	d							07 12						07 40					08 10						08 40
Salford Crescent	a				06 43	07 06	07 17	07 18	07 25	07 35	07 42	07 45		07 47	08 04	08 07		08 13	08 18			08 32	08 37	08 42	08 50
	d				06 43	07 06	07 17	07 18	07 26	07 36	07 43	07 46		07 47	08 04	08 07		08 13	08 18			08 32	08 37	08 42	08 50
Salford Central	d						07 21	07 23			07 45			07 49	08 07			08 16	08 21			08 35		08 45	08 53
Manchester Victoria	a						07 25	07 27			07 51			07 56	08 14			08 21	08 25			08 41		08 50	09 00
Rochdale	95 a							*08 06*			*08 33*				*08 38*				08 55			*09 08*			09 25
Deansgate	a				06 49				07 29	07 39						08 12							08 41		
Manchester Oxford Road	a				06 51	07 12			07 32	07 41		07 50				08 14				08 20			08 43		
Manchester Piccadilly 10	a		05 57		06 56	07 15			07 36	07 45		07 54				08 20				08 25			08 47		
Stockport	84 a		*06 25*		*07 27*	*07 37*			07 48	*08 10*		*08 25*				08 30				*08 53*			*09 08*		
Hazel Grove	86 a		*07 07*		*07 43*	*07 54*			*08 13*			*08 51*											*09 16*		
Buxton	86 a		*07 45*			*08 33*						*09 27*											*09 56*		
Heald Green	85 a		*06 21*		*07 27*	07 32						08 11				*08g51*									
Manchester Airport	85 a	05 05	06 14		07 15	07 40				08 02		08 19								08 42			09 06		

For general notes see front of timetable
For details of catering facilities see Directory of Train Operators

- **A** To Windermere (Table 83)
- **B** From Blackburn (Table 94). Also stops at Clifton 0709
- **C** To Chester (Table 88)
- **D** From Blackburn (Table 94)
- **E** From St Annes-on-the-Sea (Table 97) to Greenbank (Table 88)
- **G** To Liverpool Lime Street (Table 90)
- **H** From Clitheroe (Table 94)
- **J** from Preston
- **b** Arr. 0459
- **c** Change at Oxenholme Lake District and Preston
- **e** Change at Preston
- **f** Liverpool Lime Street (Table 90)
- **g** Change at Manchester Piccadilly

Table 82

Saturdays until 12 July

Barrow-in-Furness, Blackpool North, Preston, Southport, Kirkby and Wigan → Bolton → Manchester

Network Diagram - see first page of Table 82

		NT A		TP 1◇ ✠	NT	NT	TP 1◇ B ✠	NT C	NT	NT	NT	NT D	NT E	TP 1◇		NT	NT G	NT	TP 1◇ H ✠	NT C	NT	NT	NT	NT	NT D
Barrow-in-Furness	d						07 05										07 58								
Roose	d																08 02								
Dalton	d						07 14										08 08								
Ulverston	d						07 22										08 17								
Cark	d						07 30										08 25								
Kents Bank	d																08 29								
Grange-over-Sands	d						07 37										08 33								
Arnside	d						07 43										08 39								
Silverdale	d						07 47										08 43								
Carnforth	d	07 42					07 55										08 51								
Windermere	83 d													*07b24*					*08 28*						
Oxenholme Lake District	65 d													*08c07*					08 59				*08c53*		
Lancaster [6]	65 a	07 53					08 02										09 02		09 14						
	d						08 03							*08c23*					09 14				*09c09*		
Preston [8]	65 a						08 21												09 35						
Blackpool North	97 d			07 41						08 09				08 41									09 11		09 25
Layton	97 d			07 44						08 12													09 14		
Poulton-le-Fylde	97 d			07 48						08 16				08 47									09 18		
Kirkham & Wesham	97 d			07 58						08 25		*08 28*											09 27		
Preston [8]	d			08 12			08 34			08 38		08 50		09 08					09 38				09 41		09 50
Leyland	d									08 43		08a55		09 13											09a55
Chorley	d			08 22			08 44			08 51				09 19					09 47				09 51		
Adlington (Lancashire)	d									08 56													09 56		
Blackrod	d									09 00													10 00		
Horwich Parkway	d						08 52			09 03				09 27									10 03		
Lostock	d									09 07				09 30									10 07		
Southport	d								08 09		08 35										09 10			09 38	
Meols Cop	d								08 14		08 40										09 15				
Bescar Lane	d								08 19												09 20				
New Lane	d								08 23												09 24				
Burscough Bridge	d								08 25		08 48										09 26			09 50	
Hoscar	d								08 29												09 30				
Parbold	d								08 32		08 53										09 33			09 55	
Appley Bridge	d								08 36		08 57										09 37			09 59	
Gathurst	d								08 39		09 00										09 40				
Liverpool Central [10]	103 d					*07 50*																			
Kirkby	d					08 16																			
Rainford	d					08 23																			
Upholland	d					08 27																			
Orrell	d					08 31																			
Pemberton	d					08 34																			
Wigan Wallgate	a					08 40			08 44		09 05										09 45			10 05	
	d				08 32				08 45		09 07					09 16		09 32			09 47	09 52		10 07	
Wigan North Western	d																								
Ince	d															09 19									
Hindley	d				08 37				08 50							09 22		09 37			09 52				
Westhoughton	d				08 41						09 15							09 41						10 15	
Bolton	a			08 33	08 49		08 58			09 12	09 23			09 34				09 49	09 58			10 06	10 12	10 23	
	d			08 34	08 50		08 59	09 01		09 12	09 23		09 30	09 36				09 50	09 59	10 01		10 07	10 12	10 23	
Moses Gate	d							09 04														10 10			
Farnworth	d				08 53													09 53							
Kearsley	d				08 55													09 55							
Daisy Hill	d								08 54							09 26					09 56				
Hag Fold	d								08 57							09 29									
Atherton	d								09 00							09 32					10 00				
Walkden	d								09 05							09 37					10 05				
Moorside	d								09 09							09 41									
Swinton	d								09 11							09 43					10 10				
Salford Crescent	a				09 06		09 11	09 16	09 20	09 25	09 36		09 42	09 48		09 50		10 06	10 11	10 13	10 17	10 22	10 25	10 36	
	d				09 07		09 11	09 16	09 20	09 25	09 36		09 42	09 48		09 50		10 07	10 11	10 13	10 17	10 22	10 25	10 36	
Salford Central	d				09 09			09 19	09 23				09 45			09 53		10 09		10 16	10 20	10 24			
Manchester Victoria	⇌ a				09 14			09 25	09 26				09 50			10 00		10 14		10 21	10 24	10 32			
Rochdale	95 a				*09 38*				09 55							10 25		*10 38*			10 55	*11 08*			
Deansgate	⇌ a						09 15			09 29													10 29		
Manchester Oxford Road	a			08 49			09 16			09 31	09 41			09 53					10 16				10 31	10 41	
Manchester Piccadilly [10]	⇌ a			08 53			09 20			09 35	09 45			09 57					10 20				10 35	10 45	
Stockport	84 a			*09 13*			*09 39*			09 49	*10 12*			*10 28*					*10 39*				10 49	*11 12*	
Hazel Grove	86 a			*09 29*						09 57	*10 29*												10 57	*11 29*	
Buxton	86 a									10 36													11 33		
Heald Green	85 a			*09 18*			09 31							10 11					10 32						
Manchester Airport	85 ✈ a			09 13			09 40				10 02			10 19					10 40					11 01	

For general notes see front of timetable
For details of catering facilities see Directory of Train Operators

A From Leeds (Table 36)
B ✠ from Preston
C From Blackburn (Table 94)
D To Liverpool Lime Street (Table 90)
E From Clitheroe (Table 94)
G From Maryport (Table 100)
H From Glasgow Central (Table 65)
b Change at Oxenholme Lake District and Preston
c Change at Preston

Table 82

Saturdays until 12 July

Barrow-in-Furness, Blackpool North, Preston, Southport, Kirkby and Wigan → Bolton → Manchester

Network Diagram - see first page of Table 82

		NT	TP	NT	NT	NT	TP	NT	NT	NT	NT	NT	NT	TP	NT	NT	NT	TP	NT	NT	NT	NT	NT
			1 ◇				1 ◇							1 ◇				1 ◇					
		A			B		C					D	A			E		G					D
			✕				✕							✕				✕					
Barrow-in-Furness	d						09 15									09 58							
Roose	d						09 19									10 02							
Dalton	d						09 25									10 08							
Ulverston	d						09 34									10 16							
Cark	d						09 42									10 24							
Kents Bank	d						09 46									10 28							
Grange-over-Sands	d						09 50									10 32							
Arnside	d						09 56									10 38							
Silverdale	d						10 01									10 43							
Carnforth	d				09 53		10 08									10 50							
Windermere	83 d						*09b26*											*10 18*					
Oxenholme Lake District	65 d						*09 51*							*10c11*				10 54					
Lancaster 6	65 a				10 04		10 15									11 01		11 11					
	d		*09c27*				10 16			*10c09*				*10c27*				11 12					
Preston 8	65 a						10 34											11 32					
Blackpool North	97 d		09 40							10 11		10 25		10 41							11 11		11 25
Layton	97 d									10 14											11 14		
Poulton-le-Fylde	97 d		09 46							10 18				10 47							11 18		
Kirkham & Wesham	97 d						*10 19*			10 27								*11 19*			11 27		
Preston 8	d		10 08				10 38			10 41		10 50		11 08				11 38			11 41		11 50
Leyland	d		10 13									10a55		11 13									11a55
Chorley	d		10 19				10 47			10 51				11 19				11 47			11 51		
Adlington (Lancashire)	d									10 56											11 56		
Blackrod	d									11 00											12 00		
Horwich Parkway	d		10 27							11 03				11 27							12 03		
Lostock	d		10 30							11 07				11 30							12 07		
Southport	d							10 15			10 38								11 10			11 38	
Meols Cop	d							10 20											11 15				
Bescar Lane	d																		11 20				
New Lane	d																		11 24				
Burscough Bridge	d							10 28			10 50								11 26			11 50	
Hoscar	d																		11 30				
Parbold	d							10 33			10 55								11 33			11 55	
Appley Bridge	d							10 37			10 59								11 37			11 59	
Gathurst	d							10 40											11 40				
Liverpool Central 10	103 d			*09 20*											*10 20*								
Kirkby	d			09 51											10 51								
Rainford	d			09 58											10 58								
Upholland	d			10 02											11 02								
Orrell	d			10 06											11 06								
Pemberton	d			10 09											11 09								
Wigan Wallgate	a			10 14				10 45			11 05				11 14				11 45			12 05	
	d			10 16		10 32		10 47	10 52		11 07				11 16		11 32		11 47	11 52		12 07	
Wigan North Western	d																						
Ince	d			10 19											11 19								
Hindley	d			10 22		10 37		10 52							11 22		11 37		11 52				
Westhoughton	d					10 41					11 15						11 41					12 15	
Bolton	a		10 34			10 49	10 58		11 06	11 12	11 23			11 34			11 49	11 58		12 06	12 12	12 23	
	d	10 30	10 36			10 50	10 59		11 07	11 12	11 23		11 30	11 36			11 50	11 59		12 07	12 12	12 23	
Moses Gate	d								11 10											12 10			
Farnworth	d					10 53											11 53						
Kearsley	d					10 55											11 55						
Daisy Hill	d			10 26				10 56							11 26				11 56				
Hag Fold	d			10 29											11 29								
Atherton	d			10 32				11 00							11 32				12 00				
Walkden	d			10 37				11 05							11 37				12 05				
Moorside	d			10 41											11 41								
Swinton	d			10 43				11 10							11 43				12 10				
Salford Crescent	a	10 43	10 48	10 50		11 06	11 11	11 17	11 21	11 25	11 36		11 43	11 48	11 50		12 06	12 11	12 17	12 21	12 25	12 36	
	d	10 43	10 48	10 50		11 07	11 11	11 17	11 22	11 25	11 36		11 43	11 48	11 50		12 07	12 11	12 17	12 22	12 25	12 36	
Salford Central	d	10 45		10 53		11 10		11 20	11 24				11 45		11 53		12 09		12 20	12 24			
Manchester Victoria	⇌ a	10 50		11 00		11 14		11 24	11 29				11 51		12 00		12 14		12 24	12 29			
Rochdale	95 a			11 25		*11 38*		11 55	*12 08*						12 25		*12 38*		12 55	*13 08*			
Deansgate	⇌ a						11 15			11 29											12 29		
Manchester Oxford Road	a		10 53				11 16			11 31	11 41			11 53				12 16			12 31	12 41	
Manchester Piccadilly 10	⇌ a		10 57				11 20			11 35	11 45			11 57				12 20			12 35	12 45	
Stockport	84 a		*11 28*				*11 39*			11 49	*12 12*			*12 28*				*12 39*			12 49	*13 12*	
Hazel Grove	86 a									11 57	*12 29*										12 57	*13 29*	
Buxton	86 a									12 36											13 33		
Heald Green	85 a		11 12				11 32							12 12				12 32					
Manchester Airport	85 ✈ a		11 19				11 40				12 01			12 19				12 40				13 01	

For general notes see front of timetable
For details of catering facilities see Directory of Train Operators

A From Clitheroe (Table 94)
B From Leeds to Morecambe (Table 36)
C ✕ from Preston
D To Liverpool Lime Street (Table 90)
E From Millom (Table 100)
G From Glasgow Central and from Edinburgh (Table 65)
b Change at Oxenholme Lake District and Lancaster
c Change at Preston

Table 82

Saturdays

until 12 July

Barrow-in-Furness, Blackpool North, Preston, Southport, Kirkby and Wigan → Bolton → Manchester

Network Diagram - see first page of Table 82

		NT	TP	NT	NT	NT		TP	NT	NT	NT	NT	NT	NT	TP	NT	NT	TP		NT	NT	NT	NT	NT	NT
			1 ◇					1 ◇							1 ◇			1 ◇							
		A			B			C					D	A				C						D	A
			🍴					🍴							🍴			🍴							
Barrow-in-Furness	d							11 18																	
Roose	d																								
Dalton	d							11 27																	
Ulverston	d							11 35																	
Cark	d							11 43																	
Kents Bank	d																								
Grange-over-Sands	d							11 50																	
Arnside	d							11 56																	
Silverdale	d							12 01																	
Carnforth	d				11 55			12 08																	
Windermere	83 d														11b27			12 23							
Oxenholme Lake District	65 d														12c11			12e42				12c53			
Lancaster 6	65 a				12 04			12 16										13 02							
	d		11c24					12 16			12c11				12c27			13e04				13c09			
Preston 8	65 a							12 36										13 22							
Blackpool North	97 d		11 41								12 11		12 25		12 41							13 11		13 25	
Layton	97 d										12 14											13 14			
Poulton-le-Fylde	97 d		11 47								12 18				12 47							13 18			
Kirkham & Wesham	97 d							12 19			12 27							13 19				13 27			
Preston 8	d		12 08					12 38			12 41		12 50		13 08			13 38				13 41		13 50	
Leyland	d		12 13										12a55		13 13									13a55	
Chorley	d		12 19					12 47			12 51				13 19			13 47				13 51			
Adlington (Lancashire)	d										12 56											13 56			
Blackrod	d										13 00											14 00			
Horwich Parkway	d		12 27								13 03				13 27							14 03			
Lostock	d		12 30								13 07				13 30							14 07			
Southport	d								12 15			12 38								13 10			13 38		
Meols Cop	d								12 20											13 15					
Bescar Lane	d																			13 20					
New Lane	d																			13 24					
Burscough Bridge	d								12 28			12 50								13 26			13 50		
Hoscar	d																			13 30					
Parbold	d								12 33			12 55								13 33			13 55		
Appley Bridge	d								12 37			12 59								13 37			13 59		
Gathurst	d								12 40											13 40					
Liverpool Central 10	103 d			11 20												12 20									
Kirkby	d			11 51												12 51									
Rainford	d			11 58												12 58									
Upholland	d			12 02												13 02									
Orrell	d			12 06												13 06									
Pemberton	d			12 09												13 09									
Wigan Wallgate	a			12 14					12 45			13 05				13 14				13 45			14 05		
	d			12 16		12 32			12 47	12 52		13 07				13 16	13 32			13 47	13 52		14 07		
Wigan North Western	d																								
Ince	d			12 19												13 19									
Hindley	d			12 22		12 37			12 52							13 22	13 37			13 52					
Westhoughton	d					12 41						13 15					13 41						14 15		
Bolton	a		12 34			12 49		12 58		13 06	13 12	13 23			13 34		13 49	13 58			14 06	14 12	14 23		
	d	12 30	12 36			12 50		12 59		13 07	13 12	13 23		13 30	13 36		13 50	13 59			14 07	14 12	14 23		14 30
Moses Gate	d									13 10											14 10				
Farnworth	d					12 53											13 53								
Kearsley	d					12 55											13 55								
Daisy Hill	d			12 26					12 56							13 26				13 56					
Hag Fold	d			12 29												13 29									
Atherton	d			12 32					13 00							13 32				14 00					
Walkden	d			12 37					13 05							13 37				14 05					
Moorside	d			12 41												13 41									
Swinton	d			12 43					13 10							13 43				14 10					
Salford Crescent	a	12 43	12 48	12 50		13 06		13 11	13 17	13 21	13 25	13 36		13 42	13 48	13 50	14 06	14 11		14 17	14 21	14 25	14 36		14 43
	d	12 43	12 48	12 50		13 07		13 11	13 17	13 22	13 25	13 36		13 43	13 48	13 50	14 07	14 11		14 17	14 22	14 25	14 36		14 43
Salford Central	d	12 45		12 53		13 09			13 20	13 24				13 45		13 53	14 09			14 20	14 25				14 45
Manchester Victoria	🚊 a	12 50		13 00		13 14			13 24	13 30				13 50		14 00	14 14			14 24	14 32				14 50
Rochdale	95 a			13 25		13 38			13 55	14 08						14 25	14 38			14 55	15 08				
Deansgate	🚊 a							13 15			13 29							14 15				14 29			
Manchester Oxford Road	a		12 53					13 16			13 31	13 41			13 53			14 16				14 31	14 41		
Manchester Piccadilly 10	🚊 a		12 57					13 20			13 35	13 45			13 57			14 20				14 35	14 45		
Stockport	84 a		13 28					13 39			13 49	14 12			14 28			14 39				14 49	15 12		
Hazel Grove	86 a										13 57	14 29										14 57	15 29		
Buxton	86 a										14 36											15 33			
Heald Green	85 a		13 12					13 32							14 12			14 32							
Manchester Airport	85 ✈ a		13 19					13 40				14 01			14 19			14 40					15 01		

For general notes see front of timetable
For details of catering facilities see Directory of Train Operators

A From Clitheroe (Table 94)
B From Leeds to Morecambe (Table 36)
C 🍴 from Preston
D To Liverpool Lime Street (Table 90)

b Change at Oxenholme Lake District and Preston
c Change at Preston
e By changing at Preston, passengers may depart Oxenholme Lake District at 1253, Lancaster at 1309

Table 82

Saturdays until 12 July

Barrow-in-Furness, Blackpool North, Preston, Southport, Kirkby and Wigan → Bolton → Manchester

Network Diagram - see first page of Table 82

		TP 1◇ 🛒	NT	NT	NT	TP 1◇ A 🛒	NT	NT	NT	NT	NT B	NT C	TP 1◇	NT	NT	TP 1◇ D 🛒	TP 1◇ D 🛒	NT	NT	NT	NT C	NT B	TP 1◇
Barrow-in-Furness	d			12 56													14 10						
Roose	d			13 00																			
Dalton	d			13 06																			
Ulverston	d			13 15													14 26						
Cark	d			13 23																			
Kents Bank	d			13 27																			
Grange-over-Sands	d			13 31													14 39						
Arnside	d			13 37													14 45						
Silverdale	d			13 42																			
Carnforth	d			13 49													14 55						
Windermere	83 d					13 25										14 18							
Oxenholme Lake District	65 d	13b11				13c50			13b58							14e37				14b53			15b11
Lancaster [6]	65 a			13 59		14 07										14 54	15 02						
	d	13b27				14 17							14b27			15 15				15b09			15b27
Preston [8]	65 a					14 36										15 34							
Blackpool North	97 d	13 41							14 11		14 25		14 41							15 11		15 25	15 41
Layton	97 d								14 14											15 14			
Poulton-le-Fylde	97 d	13 47							14 18				14 47							15 18			15 47
Kirkham & Wesham	97 d					14 19			14 27							15 19				15 27			
Preston [8]	d	14 08				14 38			14 41		14 50		15 08			15 38				15 41		15 50	16 08
Leyland	d	14 13									14a55		15 13									15a55	16 13
Chorley	d	14 19				14 47			14 51				15 19			15 47				15 51			16 19
Adlington (Lancashire)	d								14 56											15 56			
Blackrod	d								15 00											16 00			
Horwich Parkway	d	14 27							15 03				15 27							16 03			16 27
Lostock	d	14 30							15 07				15 30							16 07			16 30
Southport	d						14 15			14 38								15 10					
Meols Cop	d						14 20											15 15					
Bescar Lane	d																	15 20					
New Lane	d																	15 24					
Burscough Bridge	d						14 28			14 50								15 26					
Hoscar	d																	15 30					
Parbold	d						14 33			14 55								15 33					
Appley Bridge	d						14 37			14 59								15 37					
Gathurst	d						14 40											15 40					
Liverpool Central [10]	103 d		13 20											14 20									
Kirkby	d		13 51											14 51									
Rainford	d		13 58											14 58									
Upholland	d		14 02											15 02									
Orrell	d		14 06											15 06									
Pemberton	d		14 09											15 09									
Wigan Wallgate	a		14 14				14 45			15 05				15 14				15 45					
	d		14 16		14 32		14 47	14 52		15 07				15 16	15 32			15 47	15 52				
Wigan North Western	d																						
Ince	d		14 19											15 19									
Hindley	d		14 22		14 37		14 52							15 22	15 37			15 52					
Westhoughton	d				14 41					15 15					15 41								
Bolton	a	14 34			14 49	14 58		15 06	15 12	15 23			15 34		15 49	15 58			16 07	16 12			16 34
	d	14 36			14 50	14 59		15 07	15 12	15 23		15 30	15 36		15 50	15 59			16 10	16 12	16 20		16 36
Moses Gate	d							15 10													16 23		
Farnworth	d				14 53										15 53								
Kearsley	d				14 55										15 55								
Daisy Hill	d		14 26				14 56							15 26				15 56					
Hag Fold	d		14 29											15 29									
Atherton	d		14 32				15 00							15 32				16 00					
Walkden	d		14 37				15 05							15 37				16 05					
Moorside	d		14 41											15 41									
Swinton	d		14 43				15 10							15 43				16 10					
Salford Crescent	a	14 48	14 50		15 06	15 11	15 17	15 21	15 25	15 36		15 42	15 48	15 50	16 06	16 11		16 17	16 22	16 25	16 34		16 48
	d	14 48	14 50		15 07	15 11	15 17	15 22	15 25	15 36		15 43	15 48	15 50	16 07	16 11		16 17	16 22	16 25	16 35		16 48
Salford Central	d		14 53		15 09		15 20	15 24				15 45		15 53	16 10			16 20	16 25		16 37		
Manchester Victoria	🚢 a		15 00		15 14		15 24	15 30				15 50		15 59	16 14			16 25	16 30		16 42		
Rochdale	95 a		15 25		15 38		15 55	16 08						16 25	16 38			16 55			17 08		
Deansgate	🚢 a								15 29							16 15				16 29			
Manchester Oxford Road	a	14 53				15 16			15 31	15 41			15 53			16 16				16 32			16 53
Manchester Piccadilly [10]	🚢 a	14 57				15 20			15 35	15 45			15 57			16 20				16 36			16 57
Stockport	84 a	15 26				15 39			15 49	16 12			16 28			16 39				16 46			
Hazel Grove	86 a								15 57	16 29										16 54			
Buxton	86 a								16 36											17 30			
Heald Green	85 a	15 12				15 32							16 11			16 49							17 12
Manchester Airport	85 ✈ a	15 19				15 40				16 01			16 19			16 40				17f11			17 19

For general notes see front of timetable
For details of catering facilities see Directory of Train Operators

A From Edinburgh (Table 65)
B To Liverpool Lime Street (Table 90)
C From Clitheroe (Table 94)
D 🛒 from Preston

b Change at Preston
c By changing at Preston, passengers may depart at 1358
e By changing at Preston, passengers may depart at 1453
f Change at Manchester Piccadilly

Table 82

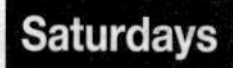
Saturdays

until 12 July

Barrow-in-Furness, Blackpool North, Preston, Southport, Kirkby and Wigan → Bolton → Manchester

Network Diagram - see first page of Table 82

		NT	NT	NT	NT	TP	NT	NT	NT	NT		NT	NT	NT	NT	TP	NT	NT	TP	NT	NT	NT		NT	NT
						1 ◇										1 ◇			1 ◇						
				A		B							C	D			E		G	D					
						𝌆													𝌆						
Barrow-in-Furness	d																15 28		16 21						
Roose	d																15 32								
Dalton	d																15 38								
Ulverston	d																15 47		16 37						
Cark	d																15 55								
Kents Bank	d																15 59								
Grange-over-Sands	d																16 03		16 50						
Arnside	d																16 09		16 56						
Silverdale	d																16 14								
Carnforth	d			15 26													16 22		17 07						
Windermere	83 d					15 22													16b22						
Oxenholme Lake District	65 d					15 47										16c05			16 48						
Lancaster 6	65 a			15 38		16 02											16 33		17 15						
	d					16e03		16c10								16c27			17 16					17c04	
Preston 8	65 a					16 22													17 34						
Blackpool North	97 d							16 10					16 25			16 38								17 10	
Layton	97 d							16 13								16 41								17 13	
Poulton-le-Fylde	97 d							16 17								16 45								17 17	
Kirkham & Wesham	97 d							16 26								16 56								17 26	
Preston 8	d					16 38		16 38					16 50			17 08			17 35					17 39	
Leyland	d							16 44					16a55			17 13								17 45	
Chorley	d					16 47		16 51								17 19			17 44					17 51	
Adlington (Lancashire)	d							16 56								17 23								17 56	
Blackrod	d							16 59																18 00	
Horwich Parkway	d							17 03								17 28								18 03	
Lostock	d							17 06								17 31			17 52					18 07	
Southport	d		15 51				16 16					16 43									17 14				17 42
Meols Cop	d						16 21														17 19				17 47
Bescar Lane	d																				17 24				
New Lane	d																				17 28				
Burscough Bridge	d		16 03				16 29					16 55									17 30				17 55
Hoscar	d																				17 34				
Parbold	d		16 08				16 34					17 00									17 37				18 00
Appley Bridge	d		16 12				16 38					17 04									17 41				18 04
Gathurst	d		16 15				16 41														17 44				
Liverpool Central 10	103 d	15 20								16 05												17 05			
Kirkby	d	15 51								16 38												17 41			
Rainford	d	15 58								16 45												17 48			
Upholland	d	16 02								16 49												17 52			
Orrell	d	16 06								16 52												17 55			
Pemberton	d	16 09								16 55												17 58			
Wigan Wallgate	a	16 14	16 20				16 46			17 01		17 10									17 49	18 04			18 10
	d	16 16	16 21		16 32		16 47		16 58	17 06		17 12						17 31			17 50	18 05			18 12
Wigan North Western	d																								
Ince	d	16 19							17 01	17 09								17 33				18 08			
Hindley	d	16 22			16 37		16 52		17 04	17 13								17 37			17 55	18 12			
Westhoughton	d		16 30		16 41				17 09									17 41							18 21
Bolton	a		16 40		16 49	16 58		17 11	17 17			17 27				17 36		17 50	17 59					18 11	18 29
	d		16 43		16 50	16 59		17 12	17 18			17 27		17 30		17 36		17 50	17 59	18 03				18 12	18 29
Moses Gate	d													17 34											
Farnworth	d				16 53													17 53							
Kearsley	d				16 55										←			17 55							
Daisy Hill	d	16 26					16 56			17 17 →					17 17						18 00	18 16 →			
Hag Fold	d	16 29													17 20										
Atherton	d	16 32					17 00								17 22						18 04				
Walkden	d	16 37					17 06								17 28						18 09				
Moorside	d	16 41													17 31										
Swinton	d	16 43					17 10								17 34						18 14				
Salford Crescent	a	16 50	16 55		17 06	17 11	17 18	17 24	17 30			17 40			17 45	17 48		18 06	18 11	18 14	18 21			18 24	18 41
	d	16 50	16 56		17 07	17 11	17 18	17 25	17 31			17 40			17 45	17 48		18 07	18 11	18 14	18 22			18 25	18 41
Salford Central	d	16 55			17 09		17 21		17 33					17 45	17 48			18 09		18 17	18 24				
Manchester Victoria	🚊 a	16 59			17 14		17 24		17 40					17 51	17 54			18 15		18 23	18 29				
Rochdale	95 a	17 25					17 55		18 08						18 32						19 05				
Deansgate	🚊 a		16 59					17 28											18 15						
Manchester Oxford Road	a		17 01			17 16		17 30				17 45				17 55			18 17					18 34	18 47
Manchester Piccadilly 10	🚊 a		17 06			17 20		17 35				17 49				17 57			18 20					18 38	18 51
Stockport	84 a		17 19			17 40		17 51				18 12				18 25			18 39					18 50	19 15
Hazel Grove	86 a		17 27					17 59				18 29												18 57	
Buxton	86 a		18 07					18 37																19 38	
Heald Green	85 a					17 49										18 12			18 35					19f07	
Manchester Airport	85 ✈ a					17 40						18 05				18 19			18 42						19 08

For general notes see front of timetable
For details of catering facilities see Directory of Train Operators

A From Leeds to Morecambe (Table 36)

B From Glasgow Central (Table 65)
C To Liverpool Lime Street (Table 90)
D From Clitheroe (Table 94)
E From Carlisle via Whitehaven (Table 100)
G 𝌆 from Preston

b Change at Oxenholme Lake District and Lancaster
c Change at Preston
e By changing at Preston, passengers may depart at 1610
f Change at Manchester Piccadilly

Saturdays

until 12 July

Barrow-in-Furness, Blackpool North, Preston, Southport, Kirkby and Wigan → Bolton → Manchester

Network Diagram - see first page of Table 82

		NT	NT	TP	NT	TP	NT	TP	NT	NT	NT	NT	NT	NT	TP	NT	TP	NT	NT	NT	NT	NT	NT	NT
				1 ◇		1 ◇		1 ◇							1 ◇		1 ◇							
		A						B	C			A	C			D		E				G		A
Barrow-in-Furness	d					17 06																18 14		
Roose	d																					18 18		
Dalton	d					17 15																18 24		
Ulverston	d					17 24																18 32		
Cark	d					17 32																18 40		
Kents Bank	d																					18 44		
Grange-over-Sands	d					17 39																18 48		
Arnside	d					17 45																18 54		
Silverdale	d																					18 59		
Carnforth	d					17 55										18 31						19 09		
Windermere	83 d							17 27									18 10							
Oxenholme Lake District	65 d			17b11				17c53		18b00					18b11		18 33			18b51		18 51		
Lancaster 6	65 a					18 05		18 09								18 43	18 49					19 17		
	d			17b27				18 16							18b27		18 51			19b07		19 18		
Preston 8	65 a							18 36									19 09					19 43		
Blackpool North	97 d			17 38						18 11		18 25			18 42					19 10			19 19	19 25
Layton	97 d			17 41						18 14										19 13				
Poulton-le-Fylde	97 d			17 45						18 18					18 48					19 17				
Kirkham & Wesham	97 d			17 56				18 19		18 27										19 26				
Preston 8	d	17 50		18 08				18 38		18 41		18 50			19 06		19 14			19 38			19 46	19 50
Leyland	d	17a55		18 13								18a55			19 11					19 44				19a55
Chorley	d			18 19				18 47		18 51					19 19		19 23			19 51				
Adlington (Lancashire)	d									18 56										19 56				
Blackrod	d									19 00										19 59				
Horwich Parkway	d			18 27						19 03					19 25					20 03				
Lostock	d			18 30						19 07					19 28					20 06				
Southport	d										18 28								19 16		19 34			
Meols Cop	d										18 33								19 21		19 39			
Bescar Lane	d										18 38													
New Lane	d										18 42													
Burscough Bridge	d										18 44								19 29		19 47			
Hoscar	d										18 48													
Parbold	d										18 51								19 34		19 52			
Appley Bridge	d										18 55								19 38		19 56			
Gathurst	d										18 58								19 41		19 59			
Liverpool Central 10	103 d													18 20										
Kirkby	d													18 43										
Rainford	d													18 50										
Upholland	d													18 54										
Orrell	d													18 58										
Pemberton	d													19 01										
Wigan Wallgate	a										19 03			19 09					19 46		20 04			
	d				18 18						19 05			19 11					19 48		20 05			
Wigan North Western	d						18 31																20 09	
Ince	d				18 21		18 34							19 14										
Hindley	d				18 25		18 38				19 10			19 17					19 53		20 10		20 15	
Westhoughton	d				18 29						19 15										20 15			
Bolton	a			18 34	18 39			18 58		19 12	19 23				19 33		19 38			20 11	20 23			
	d			18 36	18 40			18 59	19 02	19 12	19 23		19 30		19 33		19 39	20 00		20 12	20 23			
Moses Gate	d				18 43																			
Farnworth	d																							
Kearsley	d		←																					
Daisy Hill	d		18 16				18 42							19 21					19 57				20 20	
Hag Fold	d		18 19											19 24										
Atherton	d		18 21				18 46							19 27					20 01				20 24	
Walkden	d		18 27				18 51							19 32					20 06				20 29	
Moorside	d		18 30											19 36										
Swinton	d		18 33				18 56							19 38					20 11					
Salford Crescent	a		18 43	18 48	18 54		19 05	19 11	19 13	19 25	19 36		19 42	19 44	19 48		19 52	20 13	20 18	20 24	20 36			
	d		18 43	18 48	18 55		19 05	19 11	19 14	19 25	19 36		19 43	19 44	19 48		19 52	20 13	20 18	20 25	20 36			
Salford Central	d		18 46		18 57		19 08		19 16				19 45	19 47				20 16	20 21					
Manchester Victoria	a		18 54		19 01		19 14		19 23				19 50	19 53				20 22	20 26				20 44	
Rochdale	95 a						19 45							20 38										
Deansgate	a									19 29					19 52					20 28				
Manchester Oxford Road	a			18 54				19 16		19 33	19 42				19 54		19 58			20 30	20 41			
Manchester Piccadilly 10	a			18 57				19 20		19 36	19 46				19 57		20 04			20 34	20 45			
Stockport	84 a			19 26				19 42		19 47	20 14						20 28			20 44	21 10			
Hazel Grove	86 a									19 55										20 52				
Buxton	86 a									20 34										21 31				
Heald Green	85 a			19 12				19 32							20 12		20 18			21e01				
Manchester Airport	85 a			19 19				19 40			20 05				20 19		20 26			21e06	21 09			

For general notes see front of timetable
For details of catering facilities see Directory of Train Operators

A To Liverpool Lime Street (Table 90)
B From Edinburgh (Table 65)
C From Clitheroe (Table 94)
D From Leeds to Morecambe (Table 36)
E From Blackburn (Table 94)
G From Carlisle via Whitehaven (Table 100)
b Change at Preston
c By changing at Preston, passengers may depart at 1800
e Change at Manchester Piccadilly

Table 82

Saturdays until 12 July

Barrow-in-Furness, Blackpool North, Preston, Southport, Kirkby and Wigan → Bolton → Manchester

Network Diagram - see first page of Table 82

		NT	TP	NT	NT	TP	TP	NT	NT	NT	TP	NT	NT	NT	TP	NT	NT	NT	NT	NT	TP
			1 ◇			1 ◇	1 ◇				1 ◇				1 ◇						1 ◇
		A			B	C ✠			A				A	D			B		A		
Barrow-in-Furness	d						19 15											21 30			
Roose	d						19 19											21 34			
Dalton	d						19 26											21 40			
Ulverston	d						19 33											21 49			
Cark	d						19 41											21 57			
Kents Bank	d						19 46											22 01			
Grange-over-Sands	d						19 50											22 05			
Arnside	d						19 56											22 11			
Silverdale	d						20 01											22 16			
Carnforth	d						20 09											22 23			
Windermere	83 d					19 22									20b24						
Oxenholme Lake District	65 d		19c12			19 55					20c08				20b46						
Lancaster 6	65 a					20 10	20 16											22 34			
	d		19c28			20 11	20 17				20c21				21c20						
Preston 8	65 a					20 29	20 35														
Blackpool North	97 d		19 42								20 52				21 52		22 03				23 13
Layton	97 d		19 45								20 56				21 56						23 16
Poulton-le-Fylde	97 d		19 49								21 00				22 00						23 20
Kirkham & Wesham	97 d		19 59								21 09				22 09						23 30
Preston 8	d		20 11		20 27	20 32	20 37				21 21				22 21		22 28				23 42
Leyland	d				20a32		20 42				21 26				22 26		22a32				23 47
Chorley	d		20 21			20 42	20 48				21 34				22 34						23 54
Adlington (Lancashire)	d						20 53				21 38				22 38						23 58
Blackrod	d						20 56				21 42				22 42						00 02
Horwich Parkway	d						21 00				21 45				22 45						00 05
Lostock	d						21 03				21 48				22 48						00 08
Southport	d							20 34				21 34				22 29				23 10	
Meols Cop	d							20 39				21 39				22 34				23 15	
Bescar Lane	d															22 39					
New Lane	d															22 43					
Burscough Bridge	d							20 47				21 47				22 45				23 23	
Hoscar	d															22 49					
Parbold	d							20 52				21 52				22 52				23 28	
Appley Bridge	d							20 56				21 56				22 56				23 32	
Gathurst	d							20 59				21 59				22 59				23 35	
Liverpool Central 10	103 d																				
Kirkby	d																				
Rainford	d																				
Upholland	d																				
Orrell	d																				
Pemberton	d																				
Wigan Wallgate	a							21 04				22 04				23 04				23 43	
	d			20 24				21 05		21 18		22 05		22 16		23 05					
Wigan North Western	d																				
Ince	d			20 27						21 21				22 19							
Hindley	d			20 30				21 10		21 24		22 10		22 22		23 10					
Westhoughton	d							21 15				22 15				23 15					
Bolton	a		20 32			20 53	21 07	21 23			21 52	22 23			22 52	23 23					00 12
	d	20 30	20 34			20 54	21 08	21 23	21 30		21 53	22 23	22 33		22 53	23 23			23 40		00 13
Moses Gate	d																				
Farnworth	d																				
Kearsley	d																				
Daisy Hill	d			20 34						21 28				22 26							
Hag Fold	d			20 37						21 31				22 29							
Atherton	d			20 40						21 34				22 32							
Walkden	d			20 45						21 39				22 37							
Moorside	d			20 49						21 43				22 41							
Swinton	d			20 51						21 45				22 43							
Salford Crescent	a	20 42	20 46	20 58		21 06	21 20	21 36	21 42	21 52	22 05	22 36	22 46	22 51	23 05	23 36			23 53		
	d	20 43	20 47	20 58		21 06	21 21	21 36	21 43	21 52	22 05	22 36	22 46	22 52	23 05	23 36			23 53		
Salford Central	d	20 45		21 02					21 45	21 56		22 39		22 55							
Manchester Victoria ⇌	a	20 50		21 06					21 50	22 00		22 44		23 00					23 59		
Rochdale	95 a			*21 38*					*22 39*			*23 08*		*00 02*							
Deansgate ⇌	a		20 53					21 40			22 13		22 50		23 15						
Manchester Oxford Road	a		20 54			21 11	21 25	21 41			22 14		22 52		23 18	23 41					
Manchester Piccadilly 10 ⇌	a		20 58			21 14	21 29	21 46			22 18		22 56		23 30	23 46					00 29
Stockport	84 a		*21 26*			*21 34*	*21 52*	21 56			*22 42*		23 06		*23e50*						
Hazel Grove	86 a							22 05					23 14								
Buxton	86 a							22 44					23 54								
Heald Green	85 a		21 12			21 30	21 41				22 31				23 47						00 40
Manchester Airport	85 ✈ a		21 19			21 37	21 51				22 39				23 56						00 45

For general notes see front of timetable
For details of catering facilities see Directory of Train Operators

- **A** From Clitheroe (Table 94)
- **B** To Liverpool Lime Street (Table 90)
- **C** From Edinburgh (Table 65)
- **D** To Huddersfield (Table 39)
- **b** Change at Lancaster and Preston
- **c** Change at Preston
- **e** Change at Manchester Oxford Road

Table 82

Saturdays

19 July to 4 October

Barrow-in-Furness, Blackpool North, Preston, Southport, Kirkby and Wigan → Bolton → Manchester

Network Diagram - see first page of Table 82

	TP	TP	TP	TP	TP	NT	NT	NT	NT	NT	TP	NT	NT		NT	NT	NT	NT	TP	TP	NT	NT	NT	NT
	1◇	1◇	1◇	1◇	1◇						1◇								1◇	1◇				
			A			B		C		D					E	G	H		J 🍴	J 🍴			H	
Barrow-in-Furness d			04 15		05 15														06 15					
Roose d																			06 19					
Dalton d																			06 25					
Ulverston d			04 30		05 30														06 34					
Cark d																			06 42					
Kents Bank d																			06 46					
Grange-over-Sands d			04 43		05 43														06 50					
Arnside d			04 50		05 49														06 56					
Silverdale d																			07 01					
Carnforth d			05b02		05 58														07 08					
Windermere 83 d																						*06c35*		
Oxenholme Lake District 65 d																						*07 08*		
Lancaster 6 65 a			05 11		06 08														07 15					
d					06 08														07 16			*07 24*		
Preston 8 65 a					06 27														07 35					
Blackpool North 97 d	03 36	*04 45*		05 19	*05 30*			06 08			06 34					06 57				07 03				
Layton 97 d				*05 09*				06 12			06 37					07 00				07 07				
Poulton-le-Fylde 97 d				05 25	*05 36*			06 16			06 41					07 03				07 11				
Kirkham & Wesham 97 d				*05 22*				06 24			06 51				07 04	07 13				07 20				
Preston 8 d	04u01	05 17		05 58	06 28			06 37			07 03				07 20	07 25			07 40			07 50		
Leyland d								06 42			07 08				07 25	07a30						07 55		
Chorley d		05 26			06 37			06 50			07 15				07 33				07 49			08 03		
Adlington (Lancashire) d								06 55							07 38							08 08		
Blackrod d								06 58			07 21				07 42							08 11		
Horwich Parkway d					06 45			07 02			07 24				07 46							08 15		
Lostock d		05 34			06 48			07 06			07 27				07 49							08 19		
Southport d									06 35															07 41
Meols Cop d									06 40															07 46
Bescar Lane d																								
New Lane d																								
Burscough Bridge d									06 48															07 54
Hoscar d																								
Parbold d									06 53															07 59
Appley Bridge d									06 57															08 03
Gathurst d									07 00															08 06
Liverpool Central 10 103 d																		*06 50*			07e04			
Kirkby d																		07 16						
Rainford d																		07 23						
Upholland d																		07 27						
Orrell d																		07 31						
Pemberton d																		07 34						
Wigan Wallgate a									07 05									07 39						08 11
d							06 45		07 06			07 13	07 27					07 43						08 13
Wigan North Western d				06 15																	07 56			
Ince d							06 48					07 16	07 30					07 46						08 16
Hindley d				06 20			06 51					07 19	07 34					07 49			08 01			08 19
Westhoughton d				06 24					07 14				07 38								08 06			
Bolton a		05 40		06 31	06 52			07 11	07 22		07 32		07 46		07 55				08 02		08 14	08 24		
d	04u29	05 40		06 31	06 54	06 58		07 12	07 23	07 30	07 33		07 47		07 55		08 00		08 04		08 15	08 24	08 30	
Moses Gate d						07 01							07 50								08 18			
Farnworth d						07 03							07 52								08 20			
Kearsley d						07 05							07 54								08 22			
Daisy Hill d							06 55					07 23						07 53						08 23
Hag Fold d							06 58					07 26						07 56						08 26
Atherton d							07 01					07 29						07 59						08 29
Walkden d							07 06					07 34						08 04						08 34
Moorside d							07 10					07 38						08 08						08 38
Swinton d							07 12					07 40						08 10						08 40
Salford Crescent a				06 43	07 06	07 17	07 18	07 25	07 35	07 42	07 45	07 47	08 04		08 07		08 13	08 18			08 32	08 37	08 42	08 50
d				06 43	07 06	07 17	07 18	07 26	07 36	07 43	07 46	07 47	08 04		08 07		08 13	08 18			08 32	08 37	08 42	08 50
Salford Central d						07 21	07 23			07 45		07 49	08 07				08 16	08 21			08 35		08 45	08 53
Manchester Victoria ⇌ a						07 25	07 27			07 51		07 56	08 14				08 21	08 25			08 41		08 50	09 00
Rochdale 95 a							*08 06*			*08 33*			*08 38*					08 55			*09 08*			09 25
Deansgate ⇌ a				06 49				07 29	07 39						08 12							08 41		
Manchester Oxford Road a				06 51	07 12			07 32	07 41		07 50				08 14				08 20			08 43		
Manchester Piccadilly 10 ⇌ a		05 57		06 56	07 15			07 36	07 45		07 54				08 20				08 25			08 47		
Stockport 84 a								07 48							08 30									
Hazel Grove 86 a																								
Buxton 86 a																								
Heald Green 85 a		*06 21*		*07 27*	07 32						08 11				*08f51*									
Manchester Airport 85 ✈ a	05 05	06 14		07 15	07 40				08 02		08 19								08 42			09 06		

For general notes see front of timetable
For details of catering facilities see Directory of Train Operators

A To Windermere (Table 83)
B From Blackburn (Table 94). Also stops at Clifton 0709
C To Chester (Table 88)
D From Blackburn (Table 94)
E From St Annes-on-the-Sea (Table 97) to Greenbank (Table 88)
G To Liverpool Lime Street (Table 90)
H From Clitheroe (Table 94)
J 🍴 from Preston
b Arr. 0459
c Change at Oxenholme Lake District and Preston
e Liverpool Lime Street (Table 90)
f Change at Manchester Piccadilly

Table 82

Saturdays

19 July to 4 October

Barrow-in-Furness, Blackpool North, Preston, Southport, Kirkby and Wigan → Bolton → Manchester

Network Diagram - see first page of Table 82

		NT A	TP 1◇ 🛒	NT	NT	TP 1◇ B 🛒		NT C	NT	NT	NT	NT D	NT E	NT G	TP 1◇	NT	NT	TP 1◇ H 🛒	NT C	NT		NT	NT	NT	NT D
Barrow-in-Furness	d					07 05							07 58												
Roose	d												08 02												
Dalton	d					07 14							08 08												
Ulverston	d					07 22							08 17												
Cark	d					07 30							08 25												
Kents Bank	d												08 29												
Grange-over-Sands	d					07 37							08 33												
Arnside	d					07 43							08 39												
Silverdale	d					07 47							08 43												
Carnforth	d	07 42				07 55							08 51												
Windermere	83 d														*07b24*			*08 28*							
Oxenholme Lake District	65 d														*08c07*			08 59							
Lancaster 6	65 a	07 53				08 02							09 02					09 14							
	d					08 03									*08e23*			09 14							
Preston 8	65 a					08 21												09 35							
Blackpool North	97 d		07 41							08 09					08 41								09 11		09 25
Layton	97 d		07 44							08 12													09 14		
Poulton-le-Fylde	97 d		07 48							08 16					08 47								09 18		
Kirkham & Wesham	97 d		07 58							08 25		*08 28*											09 27		
Preston 8	d		08 12			08 34				08 38		08 50			09 08			09 38					09 41		09 50
Leyland	d									08 43		08a55			09 13										09a55
Chorley	d		08 22			08 44				08 51					09 19			09 47					09 51		
Adlington (Lancashire)	d									08 56													09 56		
Blackrod	d									09 00													10 00		
Horwich Parkway	d					08 52				09 03					09 27								10 03		
Lostock	d									09 07					09 30								10 07		
Southport	d								08 09		08 35									09 10				09 38	
Meols Cop	d								08 14		08 40									09 15					
Bescar Lane	d								08 19											09 20					
New Lane	d								08 23											09 24					
Burscough Bridge	d								08 25		08 48									09 26				09 50	
Hoscar	d								08 29											09 30					
Parbold	d								08 32		08 53									09 33				09 55	
Appley Bridge	d								08 36		08 57									09 37				09 59	
Gathurst	d								08 39		09 00									09 40					
Liverpool Central 10	103 d				*07 50*																				
Kirkby	d				08 16																				
Rainford	d				08 23																				
Upholland	d				08 27																				
Orrell	d				08 31																				
Pemberton	d				08 34																				
Wigan Wallgate	a				08 40				08 44		09 05									09 45				10 05	
	d			08 32					08 45		09 07					09 16	09 32			09 47		09 52		10 07	
Wigan North Western	d																								
Ince	d															09 19									
Hindley	d			08 37					08 50							09 22	09 37			09 52					
Westhoughton	d			08 41							09 15						09 41							10 15	
Bolton	a		08 33	08 49		08 58				09 12	09 23				09 34		09 49	09 58				10 06	10 12	10 23	
	d		08 34	08 50		08 59		09 01		09 12	09 23			09 30	09 36		09 50	09 59	10 01			10 07	10 12	10 23	
Moses Gate	d							09 04														10 10			
Farnworth	d			08 53													09 53								
Kearsley	d			08 55													09 55								
Daisy Hill	d								08 54							09 26				09 56					
Hag Fold	d								08 57							09 29									
Atherton	d								09 00							09 32				10 00					
Walkden	d								09 05							09 37				10 05					
Moorside	d								09 09							09 41									
Swinton	d								09 11							09 43				10 10					
Salford Crescent	a			09 06		09 11		09 16	09 20	09 25	09 36			09 42	09 48	09 50	10 06	10 11	10 13	10 17		10 22	10 25	10 36	
	d			09 07		09 11		09 16	09 20	09 25	09 36			09 42	09 48	09 50	10 07	10 11	10 13	10 17		10 22	10 25	10 36	
Salford Central	d			09 09				09 19	09 23					09 45		09 53	10 09		10 16	10 20		10 24			
Manchester Victoria	🚊 a			09 14				09 25	09 26					09 50		10 00	10 14		10 21	10 24		10 32			
Rochdale	95 a			*09 38*					09 55							10 25	*10 38*			10 55		*11 08*			
Deansgate	🚊 a					09 15				09 29													10 29		
Manchester Oxford Road	a		08 49			09 16				09 31	09 41				09 53			10 16					10 31	10 41	
Manchester Piccadilly 10	🚊 a		08 53			09 20				09 35	09 45				09 57			10 20					10 35	10 45	
Stockport	84 a									09 49													10 49		
Hazel Grove	86 a									09 57													10 57		
Buxton	86 a									10 36													11 33		
Heald Green	85 a		*09 18*			09 31									10 11			10 32							
Manchester Airport	85 ✈ a		09 13			09 40					10 02				10 19			10 40						11 01	

For general notes see front of timetable
For details of catering facilities see Directory of Train Operators

A From Leeds (Table 36)
B 🛒 from Preston
C From Blackburn (Table 94)
D To Liverpool Lime Street (Table 90)
E From Maryport (Table 100)
G From Clitheroe (Table 94)
H From Glasgow Central (Table 65)
b Change at Oxenholme Lake District and Preston
c Change at Preston
e Change at Preston. From 13 September dep. 0827

Table 82

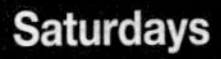

19 July to 4 October

Barrow-in-Furness, Blackpool North, Preston, Southport, Kirkby and Wigan → Bolton → Manchester

Network Diagram - see first page of Table 82

		NT	TP	NT	NT	NT	TP	NT	NT	NT	NT	NT		NT	TP	NT	NT	NT	TP	NT	NT	NT	NT	NT	NT
			1 ◇				1 ◇								1 ◇				1 ◇						
		A			B		C					D		A			E		G					D	A
			🛒				🛒								🛒				🛒						
Barrow-in-Furness	d						09 15										09 58								
Roose	d						09 19										10 02								
Dalton	d						09 25										10 08								
Ulverston	d						09 34										10 16								
Cark	d						09 42										10 24								
Kents Bank	d						09 46										10 28								
Grange-over-Sands	d						09 50										10 32								
Arnside	d						09 56										10 38								
Silverdale	d						10 01										10 43								
Carnforth	d				09 53		10 08										10 50								
Windermere	83 d						*09b26*												*10 18*						
Oxenholme Lake District	65 d						*09 51*												10 54						
Lancaster 6	65 a				10 04		10 15										11 01		11 10						
	d						10 16												11 10						
Preston 8	65 a						10 34												11 32						
Blackpool North	97 d		09 40							10 11		10 25			10 41							11 11		11 25	
Layton	97 d									10 14												11 14			
Poulton-le-Fylde	97 d		09 46							10 18					10 47							11 18			
Kirkham & Wesham	97 d						*10 19*			10 27									*11 19*			11 27			
Preston 8	d		10 08				10 38			10 41		10 50			11 08				11 38			11 41		11 50	
Leyland	d		10 13									10a55			11 13									11a55	
Chorley	d		10 19				10 47			10 51					11 19				11 47			11 51			
Adlington (Lancashire)	d									10 56												11 56			
Blackrod	d									11 00												12 00			
Horwich Parkway	d		10 27							11 03					11 27							12 03			
Lostock	d		10 30							11 07					11 30							12 07			
Southport	d							10 15			10 38									11 10			11 38		
Meols Cop	d							10 20												11 15					
Bescar Lane	d																			11 20					
New Lane	d																			11 24					
Burscough Bridge	d							10 28			10 50									11 26			11 50		
Hoscar	d																			11 30					
Parbold	d							10 33			10 55									11 33			11 55		
Appley Bridge	d							10 37			10 59									11 37			11 59		
Gathurst	d							10 40												11 40					
Liverpool Central 10	103 d			*09 20*												*10 20*									
Kirkby	d			09 51												10 51									
Rainford	d			09 58												10 58									
Upholland	d			10 02												11 02									
Orrell	d			10 06												11 06									
Pemberton	d			10 09												11 09									
Wigan Wallgate	a			10 14				10 45			11 05					11 14				11 45			12 05		
	d			10 16		10 32		10 47	10 52		11 07					11 16		11 32		11 47	11 52		12 07		
Wigan North Western	d																								
Ince	d			10 19												11 19									
Hindley	d			10 22		10 37		10 52								11 22		11 37		11 52					
Westhoughton	d					10 41					11 15							11 41					12 15		
Bolton	a		10 34			10 49	10 58		11 06	11 12	11 23				11 34			11 49	11 58		12 06	12 12	12 23		
	d	10 30	10 36			10 50	10 59		11 07	11 12	11 23			11 30	11 36			11 50	11 59		12 07	12 12	12 23		12 30
Moses Gate	d								11 10												12 10				
Farnworth	d					10 53												11 53							
Kearsley	d					10 55												11 55							
Daisy Hill	d			10 26				10 56								11 26				11 56					
Hag Fold	d			10 29												11 29									
Atherton	d			10 32				11 00								11 32				12 00					
Walkden	d			10 37				11 05								11 37				12 05					
Moorside	d			10 41												11 41									
Swinton	d			10 43				11 10								11 43				12 10					
Salford Crescent	a	10 43	10 48	10 50		11 06	11 11	11 17	11 21	11 25	11 36			11 43	11 48	11 50		12 06	12 11	12 17	12 21	12 25	12 36		12 43
	d	10 43	10 48	10 50		11 07	11 11	11 17	11 22	11 25	11 36			11 43	11 48	11 50		12 07	12 11	12 17	12 22	12 25	12 36		12 43
Salford Central	d	10 45		10 53		11 10		11 20	11 24					11 45		11 53		12 09		12 20	12 24				12 45
Manchester Victoria	🚌 a	10 50		11 00		11 14		11 24	11 29					11 51		12 00		12 14		12 24	12 29				12 50
Rochdale	95 a			11 25		*11 38*		11 55	*12 08*							12 25		*12 38*		12 55	*13 08*				
Deansgate	🚌 a						11 15			11 29												12 29			
Manchester Oxford Road	a		10 53				11 16			11 31	11 41				11 53				12 16			12 31	12 41		
Manchester Piccadilly 10	🚌 a		10 57				11 20			11 35	11 45				11 57				12 20			12 35	12 45		
Stockport	84 a									11 49												12 49			
Hazel Grove	86 a									11 57												12 57			
Buxton	86 a									12 36												13 33			
Heald Green	85 a		11 12				11 32								12 12				12 32						
Manchester Airport	85 ✈ a		11 19				11 40				12 01				12 19				12 40				13 01		

For general notes see front of timetable
For details of catering facilities see Directory of Train Operators

A From Clitheroe (Table 94)
B From Leeds to Morecambe (Table 36)
C 🛒 from Preston
D To Liverpool Lime Street (Table 90)
E From Millom (Table 100)
G From Glasgow Central and from Edinburgh (Table 65)
b Change at Oxenholme Lake District and Lancaster

Table 82

Saturdays

Barrow-in-Furness, Blackpool North, Preston, Southport, Kirkby and Wigan → Bolton → Manchester

19 July to 4 October

Network Diagram - see first page of Table 82

	TP 1 ◇ ✠	NT	NT A		NT	TP 1 ◇ B ✠	NT	NT	NT	NT	NT C	NT D	TP 1 ◇ ✠	NT	NT	TP 1 ◇ B ✠	NT		NT	NT	NT	NT C	NT D	TP 1 ◇ ✠
Barrow-in-Furness d						11 18																		
Roose d																								
Dalton d						11 27																		
Ulverston d						11 35																		
Cark d						11 43																		
Kents Bank d																								
Grange-over-Sands d						11 50																		
Arnside d						11 56																		
Silverdale d						12 01																		
Carnforth d			11 55			12 08																		
Windermere 83 d													*11b27*			12 23								
Oxenholme Lake District 65 d													*12c11*			12e42								
Lancaster 6 65 a			12 04			12 16										13 02								
d						12 16							*12c27*			13e04								
Preston 8 65 a						12 36										13 22								
Blackpool North 97 d	11 41								12 11		12 25		12 41							13 11		13 25		13 41
Layton 97 d									12 14											13 14				
Poulton-le-Fylde 97 d	11 47								12 18				12 47							13 18				13 47
Kirkham & Wesham 97 d						*12 19*			12 27							*13 19*				13 27				
Preston 8 d	12 08					12 38			12 41		12 50		13 08			13 38				13 41		13 50		14 08
Leyland d	12 13										12a55		13 13									13a55		14 13
Chorley d	12 19					12 47			12 51				13 19			13 47				13 51				14 19
Adlington (Lancashire) d									12 56											13 56				
Blackrod d									13 00											14 00				
Horwich Parkway d	12 27								13 03				13 27							14 03				14 27
Lostock d	12 30								13 07				13 30							14 07				14 30
Southport d							12 15			12 38							13 10				13 38			
Meols Cop d							12 20										13 15							
Bescar Lane d																	13 20							
New Lane d																	13 24							
Burscough Bridge d							12 28			12 50							13 26				13 50			
Hoscar d																	13 30							
Parbold d							12 33			12 55							13 33				13 55			
Appley Bridge d							12 37			12 59							13 37				13 59			
Gathurst d							12 40										13 40							
Liverpool Central 10 103 d		*11 20*												*12 20*										
Kirkby d		11 51												12 51										
Rainford d		11 58												12 58										
Upholland d		12 02												13 02										
Orrell d		12 06												13 06										
Pemberton d		12 09												13 09										
Wigan Wallgate a		12 14					12 45			13 05				13 14			13 45				14 05			
d		12 16			12 32		12 47	12 52		13 07				13 16	13 32		13 47		13 52		14 07			
Wigan North Western d																								
Ince d		12 19												13 19										
Hindley d		12 22			12 37		12 52							13 22	13 37		13 52							
Westhoughton d					12 41					13 15					13 41						14 15			
Bolton a	12 34				12 49	12 58		13 06	13 12	13 23			13 34		13 49	13 58			14 06	14 12	14 23			14 34
d	12 36				12 50	12 59		13 07	13 12	13 23		13 30	13 36		13 50	13 59			14 07	14 12	14 23		14 30	14 36
Moses Gate d								13 10											14 10					
Farnworth d					12 53										13 53									
Kearsley d					12 55										13 55									
Daisy Hill d		12 26					12 56							13 26			13 56							
Hag Fold d		12 29												13 29										
Atherton d		12 32					13 00							13 32			14 00							
Walkden d		12 37					13 05							13 37			14 05							
Moorside d		12 41												13 41										
Swinton d		12 43					13 10							13 43			14 10							
Salford Crescent a	12 48	12 50			13 06	13 11	13 17	13 21	13 25	13 36		13 42	13 48	13 50	14 06	14 11	14 17		14 21	14 25	14 36		14 43	14 48
d	12 48	12 50			13 07	13 11	13 17	13 22	13 25	13 36		13 43	13 48	13 50	14 07	14 11	14 17		14 22	14 25	14 36		14 43	14 48
Salford Central d		12 53			13 09		13 20	13 24				13 45		13 53	14 09		14 20		14 25				14 45	
Manchester Victoria a		13 00			13 14		13 24	13 30				13 50		14 00	14 14		14 24		14 32				14 50	
Rochdale 95 a		13 25			*13 38*		13 55	*14 08*						14 25	*14 38*		14 55		*15 08*					
Deansgate a						13 15			13 29							14 15				14 29				
Manchester Oxford Road a	12 53					13 16			13 31	13 41			13 53			14 16				14 31	14 41			14 53
Manchester Piccadilly 10 a	12 57					13 20			13 35	13 45			13 57			14 20				14 35	14 45			14 57
Stockport 84 a									13 49											14 49				
Hazel Grove 86 a									13 57											14 57				
Buxton 86 a									14 36											15 33				
Heald Green 85 a	13 12					13 32							14 12			14 32								15 12
Manchester Airport 85 ✈ a	13 19					13 40				14 01			14 19			14 40					15 01			15 19

For general notes see front of timetable
For details of catering facilities see Directory of Train Operators

A From Leeds to Morecambe (Table 36)

B ✠ from Preston

C To Liverpool Lime Street (Table 90)

D From Clitheroe (Table 94)

b Until 6 September only. Change at Oxenholme Lake District and Preston

c Until 6 September only. Change at Preston

e Until 6 September only, by changing at Preston, passengers may depart Oxenholme Lake District at 1253, Lancaster at 1309

Barrow-in-Furness, Blackpool North, Preston, Southport, Kirkby and Wigan → Bolton → Manchester

19 July to 4 October

Network Diagram - see first page of Table 82

		NT	NT	NT	TP	NT	NT	NT	NT	NT		NT	TP	NT	NT	TP	TP	NT	NT	NT	NT	NT	NT	TP	NT
					1 ◇								1 ◇			1 ◇	1 ◇							1 ◇	
					A					B		C				D	D				E	C	B		
					🛒											🛒	🛒								
Barrow-in-Furness	d		12 56														14 10								
Roose	d		13 00																						
Dalton	d		13 06																						
Ulverston	d		13 15														14 26								
Cark	d		13 23																						
Kents Bank	d		13 27																						
Grange-over-Sands	d		13 31														14 39								
Arnside	d		13 37														14 45								
Silverdale	d		13 42																						
Carnforth	d		13 49														14 55				15 26				
Windermere	83 d				*13 25*											14 18									
Oxenholme Lake District	65 d				13b50											14 37									
Lancaster 6	65 a		13 59		14 07											14 54	15 02				15 38				
	d				14 17											15 15									
Preston 8	65 a				14 36											15 34									
Blackpool North	97 d							14 11		14 25			14 41							15 11			15 25	15 41	
Layton	97 d							14 14												15 14					
Poulton-le-Fylde	97 d							14 18					14 47							15 18				15 47	
Kirkham & Wesham	97 d				*14 19*			14 27								*15 19*				15 27					
Preston 8	d				14 38			14 41		14 50			15 08			15 38				15 41			15 50	16 08	
Leyland	d									14a55			15 13										15a55	16 13	
Chorley	d				14 47			14 51					15 19			15 47				15 51				16 19	
Adlington (Lancashire)	d							14 56												15 56					
Blackrod	d							15 00												16 00					
Horwich Parkway	d							15 03					15 27							16 03				16 27	
Lostock	d							15 07					15 30							16 07				16 30	
Southport	d					14 15			14 38									15 10							
Meols Cop	d					14 20												15 15							
Bescar Lane	d																	15 20							
New Lane	d																	15 24							
Burscough Bridge	d					14 28			14 50									15 26							
Hoscar	d																	15 30							
Parbold	d					14 33			14 55									15 33							
Appley Bridge	d					14 37			14 59									15 37							
Gathurst	d					14 40												15 40							
Liverpool Central 10	103 d	*13 20*												*14 20*											*15 20*
Kirkby	d	13 51												14 51											15 51
Rainford	d	13 58												14 58											15 58
Upholland	d	14 02												15 02											16 02
Orrell	d	14 06												15 06											16 06
Pemberton	d	14 09												15 09											16 09
Wigan Wallgate	a	14 14				14 45			15 05					15 14				15 45							16 14
	d	14 16		14 32		14 47	14 52		15 07					15 16	15 32			15 47	15 52						16 16
Wigan North Western	d																								
Ince	d	14 19												15 19											16 19
Hindley	d	14 22		14 37		14 52								15 22	15 37			15 52							16 22
Westhoughton	d			14 41					15 15						15 41										
Bolton	a			14 49	14 58		15 06	15 12	15 23				15 34		15 49	15 58			16 07	16 12				16 34	
	d			14 50	14 59		15 07	15 12	15 23			15 30	15 36		15 50	15 59			16 10	16 12		16 20		16 36	
Moses Gate	d						15 10															16 23			
Farnworth	d			14 53											15 53										
Kearsley	d			14 55											15 55										
Daisy Hill	d	14 26				14 56								15 26				15 56							16 26
Hag Fold	d	14 29												15 29											16 29
Atherton	d	14 32				15 00								15 32				16 00							16 32
Walkden	d	14 37				15 05								15 37				16 05							16 37
Moorside	d	14 41												15 41											16 41
Swinton	d	14 43				15 10								15 43				16 10							16 43
Salford Crescent	a	14 50		15 06	15 11	15 17	15 21	15 25	15 36			15 42	15 48	15 50	16 06	16 11		16 17	16 22	16 25		16 34		16 48	16 50
	d	14 50		15 07	15 11	15 17	15 22	15 25	15 36			15 43	15 48	15 50	16 07	16 11		16 17	16 22	16 25		16 35		16 48	16 50
Salford Central	d	14 53		15 09		15 20	15 24					15 45		15 53	16 10			16 20	16 25			16 37			16 55
Manchester Victoria	🚈 a	15 00		15 14		15 24	15 30					15 50		15 59	16 14			16 25	16 30			16 42			16 59
Rochdale	95 a	15 25		*15 38*		15 55	*16 08*							16 25	*16 38*			16 55				*17 08*			17 25
Deansgate	🚈 a							15 29								16 15				16 29					
Manchester Oxford Road	a				15 16			15 31	15 41				15 53			16 16				16 32				16 53	
Manchester Piccadilly 10	🚈 a				15 20			15 35	15 45				15 57			16 20				16 36				16 57	
Stockport	84 a							15 49												16 46					
Hazel Grove	86 a							15 57												16 54					
Buxton	86 a							16 36												17 30					
Heald Green	85 a				15 32								16 11			*16 49*								17 12	
Manchester Airport	85 ✈ a				15 40				16 01				16 19			16 40				*17c11*				17 19	

For general notes see front of timetable
For details of catering facilities see Directory of Train Operators

A From Edinburgh (Table 65)
B To Liverpool Lime Street (Table 90)
C From Clitheroe (Table 94)
D 🛒 from Preston
E From Leeds to Morecambe (Table 36)
b Until 6 September only, by changing at Preston, passengers may depart at 1358
c Change at Manchester Piccadilly

Table 82

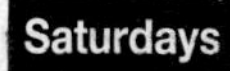

Saturdays

Barrow-in-Furness, Blackpool North, Preston, Southport, Kirkby and Wigan → Bolton → Manchester

19 July to 4 October

Network Diagram - see first page of Table 82

		NT		NT	TP	NT	NT	NT	NT	NT	NT	NT	NT	NT	NT	TP		NT	TP	NT	NT	NT	NT	NT	NT
					1 ◇											1 ◇			1 ◇						
					A			B			C	D	E	G					H	G					E
					⚒														⚒						
Barrow-in-Furness	d							15 28											16 21						
Roose	d							15 32																	
Dalton	d							15 38																	
Ulverston	d							15 47											16 37						
Cark	d							15 55																	
Kents Bank	d							15 59																	
Grange-over-Sands	d							16 03											16 50						
Arnside	d							16 09											16 56						
Silverdale	d							16 14																	
Carnforth	d							16 22											17 07						
Windermere	83 d				*15 22*														*16b22*						
Oxenholme Lake District	65 d				15 47														16c48						
Lancaster 6	65 a				16 02			16 33											17 15						
	d				16e03														17 16						
Preston 8	65 a				16 22														17 34						
Blackpool North	97 d						16 10						16 25			16 38							17 10		
Layton	97 d						16 13									16 41							17 13		
Poulton-le-Fylde	97 d						16 17									16 45							17 17		
Kirkham & Wesham	97 d						16 26									16 56							17 26		
Preston 8	d				16 38		16 38						16 50			17 08			17 35				17 39		17 50
Leyland	d						16 44						16a55			17 13							17 45		17a55
Chorley	d				16 47		16 51									17 19			17 44				17 51		
Adlington (Lancashire)	d						16 56									17 23							17 56		
Blackrod	d						16 59																18 00		
Horwich Parkway	d						17 03									17 28							18 03		
Lostock	d						17 06									17 31			17 52				18 07		
Southport	d	15 51				16 16					16 43	16 43									17 14			17 42	
Meols Cop	d					16 21															17 19			17 47	
Bescar Lane	d																				17 24				
New Lane	d																				17 28				
Burscough Bridge	d	16 03				16 29					16 55	16 55									17 30			17 55	
Hoscar	d																				17 34				
Parbold	d	16 08				16 34					17 00	17 00									17 37			18 00	
Appley Bridge	d	16 12				16 38					17 04	17 04									17 41			18 04	
Gathurst	d	16 15				16 41															17 44				
Liverpool Central 10	103 d									*16 05*												*17 05*			
Kirkby	d									16 38												17 41			
Rainford	d									16 45												17 48			
Upholland	d									16 49												17 52			
Orrell	d									16 52												17 55			
Pemberton	d									16 55												17 58			
Wigan Wallgate	a	16 20				16 46				17 01	17 10	17 10									17 49	18 04		18 10	
	d	16 21		16 32		16 47			16 58	17 06	17 12	17 12						17 31			17 50	18 05		18 12	
Wigan North Western	d																								
Ince	d								17 01	17 09								17 33				18 08			
Hindley	d			16 37		16 52			17 04	17 13								17 37			17 55	18 12			
Westhoughton	d	16 30		16 41					17 09									17 41						18 21	
Bolton	a	16 40		16 49	16 58		17 11		17 17		17 27	17 27				17 36		17 50	17 59				18 11	18 29	
	d	16 43		16 50	16 59		17 12		17 18		17 27	17 27		17 30		17 36		17 50	17 59	18 03			18 12	18 29	
Moses Gate	d													17 34											
Farnworth	d			16 53														17 53							
Kearsley	d			16 55											←			17 55							
Daisy Hill	d					16 56				17 17 →					17 17						18 00	18 16 →			
Hag Fold	d														17 20										
Atherton	d					17 00									17 22						18 04				
Walkden	d					17 06									17 28						18 09				
Moorside	d														17 31										
Swinton	d					17 10									17 34						18 14				
Salford Crescent	a	16 55		17 06	17 11	17 18	17 24		17 30			17 40			17 45	17 48		18 06	18 11	18 14	18 21		18 24	18 41	
	d	16 56		17 07	17 11	17 18	17 25		17 31			17 40			17 45	17 48		18 07	18 11	18 14	18 22		18 25	18 41	
Salford Central	d			17 09		17 21			17 33					17 45	17 48			18 09		18 17	18 24				
Manchester Victoria	🚊 a			17 14		17 24			17 40					17 51	17 54			18 15		18 23	18 29				
Rochdale	95 a					17 55			*18 08*						*18 32*						*19 05*				
Deansgate	🚊 a	16 59					17 28												18 15						
Manchester Oxford Road	a	17 01			17 16		17 30				17 43	17 45				17 55			18 17				18 34	18 47	
Manchester Piccadilly 10	🚊 a	17 06			17 20		17 35				17 47	17 49				17 57			18 20				18 38	18 51	
Stockport	84 a	17 19					17 51																18f48		
Hazel Grove	86 a	17 27					17 59																18f56		
Buxton	86 a	18 07					18 37																19f36		
Heald Green	85 a				*17 49*											18 12			18 35				*19g07*		
Manchester Airport	85 ✈ a				17 40						18 01	18 05				18 19			18 42					19 08	

For general notes see front of timetable
For details of catering facilities see Directory of Train Operators

A From Glasgow Central (Table 65)
B From Carlisle via Whitehaven (Table 100)
C From 13 September
D Until 6 September
E To Liverpool Lime Street (Table 90)
G From Clitheroe (Table 94)
H ⚒ from Preston
b Until 6 September only. Change at Oxenholme Lake District and Lancaster
c Until 6 September only
e Until 6 September only, by changing at Preston, passengers may depart at 1610
f From 13 September arr. Stockport 1850, Hazel Grove 1857, Buxton 1938
g Change at Manchester Piccadilly

Saturdays

Barrow-in-Furness, Blackpool North, Preston, Southport, Kirkby and Wigan → Bolton → Manchester

19 July to 4 October

Network Diagram - see first page of Table 82

Station		NT	TP	NT	TP	NT	TP	NT	NT	NT	NT	NT	NT	TP	NT	TP	NT	NT	NT	NT	NT	NT	NT
			1 ◇		1 ◇		1 ◇							1 ◇		1 ◇							
							A ✕	B			C	B			D		E				G	H	C
Barrow-in-Furness	d				17 06																18 14		
Roose	d																				18 18		
Dalton	d				17 15																18 24		
Ulverston	d				17 24																18 32		
Cark	d				17 32																18 40		
Kents Bank	d																				18 44		
Grange-over-Sands	d				17 39																18 48		
Arnside	d				17 45																18 54		
Silverdale	d																				18 59		
Carnforth	d				17 55										18 31						19 09		
Windermere	83 d		16b34				17 27									18 10							
Oxenholme Lake District	65 d		17c09				17e53									18 33							
Lancaster 6	65 a				18 05		18 09								18 43	18 49					19 17		
	d		17c25				18 16									18 51					19 18		
Preston 8	65 a						18 36									19 09					19 43		
Blackpool North	97 d		17 38						18 11		18 25			18 42					19 10			19 19	19 25
Layton	97 d		17 41						18 14										19 13				
Poulton-le-Fylde	97 d		17 45						18 18					18 48					19 17				
Kirkham & Wesham	97 d		17 56				*18 19*		18 27										19 26				
Preston 8	d		18 08				18 38		18 41		18 50			19 06		19 14			19 38			19 46	19 50
Leyland	d		18 13								18a55			19 11					19 44				19a55
Chorley	d		18 19				18 47		18 51					19 19		19 23			19 51				
Adlington (Lancashire)	d								18 56										19 56				
Blackrod	d								19 00										19 59				
Horwich Parkway	d		18 27						19 03					19 25					20 03				
Lostock	d		18 30						19 07					19 28					20 06				
Southport	d									18 28								19 16		19 34			
Meols Cop	d									18 33								19 21		19 39			
Bescar Lane	d									18 38													
New Lane	d									18 42													
Burscough Bridge	d									18 44								19 29		19 47			
Hoscar	d									18 48													
Parbold	d									18 51								19 34		19 52			
Appley Bridge	d									18 55								19 38		19 56			
Gathurst	d									18 58								19 41		19 59			
Liverpool Central 10	103 d												*18 20*										
Kirkby	d												18 43										
Rainford	d												18 50										
Upholland	d												18 54										
Orrell	d												18 58										
Pemberton	d												19 01										
Wigan Wallgate	a									19 03			19 09					19 46		20 04			
	d			18 18						19 05			19 11					19 48		20 05			
Wigan North Western	d					18 31																20 09	
Ince	d			18 21		18 34							19 14										
Hindley	d			18 25		18 38				19 10			19 17					19 53		20 10		20 15	
Westhoughton	d			18 29						19 15										20 15			
Bolton	a		18 34	18 39			18 58		19 12	19 23				19 33		19 38			20 11	20 23			
	d		18 36	18 40			18 59	19 02	19 12	19 23		19 30		19 33		19 39	20 00		20 12	20 23			
Moses Gate	d			18 43																			
Farnworth	d																						
Kearsley	d	⟵																					
Daisy Hill	d	18 16				18 42							19 21					19 57				20 20	
Hag Fold	d	18 19											19 24										
Atherton	d	18 21				18 46							19 27					20 01				20 24	
Walkden	d	18 27				18 51							19 32					20 06				20 29	
Moorside	d	18 30											19 36										
Swinton	d	18 33				18 56							19 38					20 11					
Salford Crescent	a	18 43	18 48	18 54		19 05	19 11	19 13	19 25	19 36		19 42	19 44	19 48		19 52	20 13	20 18	20 24	20 36			
	d	18 43	18 48	18 55		19 05	19 11	19 14	19 25	19 36		19 43	19 44	19 48		19 52	20 13	20 18	20 25	20 36			
Salford Central	d	18 46		18 57		19 08		19 16				19 45	19 47				20 16	20 21					
Manchester Victoria	⇌ a	18 54		19 01		19 14		19 23				19 50	19 53				20 22	20 26				20 44	
Rochdale	95 a					*19 45*							*20 38*										
Deansgate	⇌ a								19 29					19 52					20 28				
Manchester Oxford Road	a		18 54				19 16		19 33	19 42				19 54		19 58			20 30	20 41			
Manchester Piccadilly 10	⇌ a		18 57				19 20		19 36	19 46				19 57		20 04			20 34	20 45			
Stockport	84 a								19 47										20 44				
Hazel Grove	86 a								19 55										20 52				
Buxton	86 a								20 34										21 31				
Heald Green	85 a		19 12				19 32							20 12		20 18			*21f01*				
Manchester Airport	85 ✈ a		19 19				19 40			20 05				20 19		20 26			*21f06*	21 09			

For general notes see front of timetable
For details of catering facilities see Directory of Train Operators

A From Edinburgh (Table 65)
B From Clitheroe (Table 94)
C To Liverpool Lime Street (Table 90)
D From Leeds to Morecambe (Table 36)
E From Blackburn (Table 94)
G From Carlisle via Whitehaven (Table 100)
H Until 13 September
b From 13 September only. Change at Oxenholme Lake District and Preston
c From 13 September only. Change at Preston
e Until 6 September only, by changing at Preston, passengers may depart at 1800
f Change at Manchester Piccadilly

Saturdays

Barrow-in-Furness, Blackpool North, Preston, Southport, Kirkby and Wigan → Bolton → Manchester

19 July to 4 October

Network Diagram - see first page of Table 82

	NT	TP	NT	NT	NT	TP	TP	NT	NT	NT	TP	NT	NT		NT	TP	NT	NT	NT	NT	NT	TP	
		1 ◇				1 ◇	1 ◇				1 ◇					1 ◇						1 ◇	
	A		B	C	D	E ✠			A				A		G			D		A			
Barrow-in-Furness d							19 15												21 30				
Roose d							19 19												21 34				
Dalton d							19 26												21 40				
Ulverston d							19 33												21 49				
Cark d							19 41												21 57				
Kents Bank d							19 46												22 01				
Grange-over-Sands d							19 50												22 05				
Arnside d							19 56												22 11				
Silverdale d							20 01												22 16				
Carnforth d							20 09												22 23				
Windermere 83 d						*19 22*										*20b24*							
Oxenholme Lake District 65 d						19 55										*20b46*							
Lancaster 6 65 a						20 10	20 16												22 34				
d						20 11	20 17									*21c20*							
Preston 8 65 a						20 29	20 35																
Blackpool North 97 d		19 42									20 52					21 52		22 03				23 13	
Layton 97 d		19 45									20 56					21 56						23 16	
Poulton-le-Fylde 97 d		19 49									21 00					22 00						23 20	
Kirkham & Wesham 97 d		19 59									21 09					22 09						23 30	
Preston 8 d		20 11			20 27	20 32	20 37				21 21					22 21		22 28				23 42	
Leyland d					20a32		20 42				21 26					22 26		22a32				23 47	
Chorley d		20 21				20 42	20 48				21 34					22 34						23 54	
Adlington (Lancashire) d							20 53				21 38					22 38						23 58	
Blackrod d							20 56				21 42					22 42						00 02	
Horwich Parkway d							21 00				21 45					22 45						00 05	
Lostock d							21 03				21 48					22 48						00 08	
Southport d								20 34				21 34					22 29				23 10		
Meols Cop d								20 39				21 39					22 34				23 15		
Bescar Lane d																	22 39						
New Lane d																	22 43						
Burscough Bridge d								20 47				21 47					22 45				23 23		
Hoscar d																	22 49						
Parbold d								20 52				21 52					22 52				23 28		
Appley Bridge d								20 56				21 56					22 56				23 32		
Gathurst d								20 59				21 59					22 59				23 35		
Liverpool Central 10 103 d																							
Kirkby d																							
Rainford d																							
Upholland d																							
Orrell d																							
Pemberton d																							
Wigan Wallgate a								21 04				22 04					23 04				23 43		
d			20 18	20 24				21 05		21 18		22 05			22 16		23 05						
Wigan North Western d																							
Ince d			20 21	20 27						21 21					22 19								
Hindley d			20 24	20 30				21 10		21 24		22 10			22 22		23 10						
Westhoughton d								21 15				22 15					23 15						
Bolton a		20 32				20 53	21 07	21 23			21 52	22 23				22 52	23 23					00 12	
d	20 30	20 34				20 54	21 08	21 23	21 30		21 53	22 23	22 33			22 53	23 23			23 40		00 13	
Moses Gate d																							
Farnworth d																							
Kearsley d																							
Daisy Hill d			20 28	20 34						21 28					22 26								
Hag Fold d			20 31	20 37						21 31					22 29								
Atherton d			20 34	20 40						21 34					22 32								
Walkden d			20 39	20 45						21 39					22 37								
Moorside d			20 43	20 49						21 43					22 41								
Swinton d			20 45	20 51						21 45					22 43								
Salford Crescent a	20 42	20 46	20 52	20 58		21 06	21 20	21 36	21 42	21 52	22 05	22 36	22 46		22 51	23 05	23 36			23 53			
d	20 43	20 47	20 52	20 58		21 06	21 21	21 36	21 43	21 52	22 05	22 36	22 46		22 52	23 05	23 36			23 53			
Salford Central d	20 45		20 56	21 02					21 45	21 56		22 39			22 55								
Manchester Victoria ⇌ a	20 50		21 00	21 06					21 50	22 00		22 44			23 00					23 59			
Rochdale 95 a			*21 38*	*21 38*					*22 39*			*23 08*			*00 02*								
Deansgate ⇌ a		20 53						21 40			22 13		22 50			23 15							
Manchester Oxford Road a		20 54				21 11	21 25	21 41			22 14		22 52			23 18	23 41						
Manchester Piccadilly 10 ⇌ a		20 58				21 14	21 29	21 46			22 18		22 56			23 30	23 46					00 29	
Stockport 84 a								21 56					23 06			*23e50*							
Hazel Grove 86 a								22 05					23 14										
Buxton 86 a								22 44					23 54										
Heald Green 85 a		21 12				21 30	21 41				22 31					23 47						00 40	
Manchester Airport 85 ✈ a		21 19				21 37	21 51				22 39					23 56						00 45	

For general notes see front of timetable
For details of catering facilities see Directory of Train Operators

A From Clitheroe (Table 94)
B From 20 September
C Until 13 September
D To Liverpool Lime Street (Table 90)
E From Edinburgh (Table 65)
G To Huddersfield (from 13 September to Greenfield) (Table 39)
b Change at Lancaster and Preston
c Change at Preston
e 13 September only. Change at Manchester Oxford Road

from 11 October

Barrow-in-Furness, Blackpool North, Preston, Southport, Kirkby and Wigan → Bolton → Manchester

Network Diagram - see first page of Table 82

	TP 1◇	TP 1◇	TP 1◇	TP 1◇	TP 1◇	NT	NT	NT	NT	NT		TP 1◇	NT	NT	NT	NT	NT	NT	TP 1◇	TP 1◇	NT		NT	NT
			A			B		C		D					E	G	H		J 🚌	J 🚌				H
Barrow-in-Furness d			04 15		05 15														06 15					
Roose d																			06 19					
Dalton d																			06 25					
Ulverston d			04 30		05 30														06 34					
Cark d																			06 42					
Kents Bank d																			06 46					
Grange-over-Sands d			04 43		05 43														06 50					
Arnside d			04 50		05 49														06 56					
Silverdale d																			07 01					
Carnforth d			05b02		05 58														07 08					
Windermere 83 d																							*06c35*	
Oxenholme Lake District 65 d																							*07 08*	
Lancaster 6 65 a			05 11		06 08														07 15					
d					06 08														07 16				*07 24*	
Preston 8 65 a					06 27														07 35					
Blackpool North 97 d	03 36	*04 45*		05 19	*05 30*			06 08				06 34				06 57				07 03				
Layton 97 d				*05 09*				06 12				06 37				07 00				07 07				
Poulton-le-Fylde 97 d				05 25	*05 36*			06 16				06 41				07 03				07 11				
Kirkham & Wesham 97 d				*05 22*				06 24				06 51			07 04	07 13				07 20				
Preston 8 d	04u01	05 17		05 58	06 28			06 37				07 03			07 20	07 25			07 40				07 50	
Leyland d								06 42				07 08			07 25	07a30							07 55	
Chorley d		05 26			06 37			06 50				07 15			07 33				07 49				08 03	
Adlington (Lancashire) d								06 55							07 38								08 08	
Blackrod d								06 58				07 21			07 42								08 11	
Horwich Parkway d					06 45			07 02				07 24			07 46								08 15	
Lostock d		05 34			06 48			07 06				07 27			07 49								08 19	
Southport d									06 32															
Meols Cop d									06 37															
Bescar Lane d																								
New Lane d																								
Burscough Bridge d									06 45															
Hoscar d																								
Parbold d									06 50															
Appley Bridge d									06 54															
Gathurst d									06 57															
Liverpool Central 10 103 d																		*06 50*			07e04			
Kirkby d																		07 13						
Rainford d																		07 20						
Upholland d																		07 24						
Orrell d																		07 28						
Pemberton d																		07 31						
Wigan Wallgate a									07 04									07 37						
d							06 40		07 05				07 13	07 27				07 40						
Wigan North Western d				06 15																	07 56			
Ince d							06 43						07 16	07 30				07 43						
Hindley d				06 20			06 46						07 19	07 34				07 46			08 01			
Westhoughton d				06 24					07 13					07 38							08 06			
Bolton a		05 40		06 31	06 52			07 11	07 22			07 32		07 46	07 55				08 02		08 14		08 24	
d	04u29	05 40		06 31	06 54	06 58		07 12	07 23	07 30		07 33		07 47	07 55		08 00		08 04		08 15		08 24	08 30
Moses Gate d						07 01								07 50							08 18			
Farnworth d						07 03								07 52							08 20			
Kearsley d						07 05								07 54							08 22			
Daisy Hill d							06 50						07 23					07 50						
Hag Fold d							06 53						07 26					07 53						
Atherton d							06 56						07 29					07 56						
Walkden d							07 01						07 34					08 01						
Moorside d							07 05						07 38					08 05						
Swinton d							07 07						07 40					08 07						
Salford Crescent a				06 43	07 06	07 17	07 18	07 25	07 35	07 42		07 45	07 47	08 04	08 07		08 13	08 18			08 32		08 37	08 42
d				06 43	07 06	07 17	07 18	07 26	07 36	07 43		07 46	07 47	08 04	08 07		08 13	08 18			08 32		08 37	08 42
Salford Central d						07 21	07 23			07 45			07 49	08 07			08 16	08 21			08 35			08 45
Manchester Victoria 🚊 a						07 25	07 27			07 51			07 56	08 14			08 21	08 25			08 41			08 50
Rochdale 95 a							*08 06*							*08 38*				08 55			*09 08*			
Deansgate 🚊 a				06 49				07 29	07 39						08 12								08 41	
Manchester Oxford Road a				06 51	07 12			07 32	07 41			07 50			08 14				08 20				08 43	
Manchester Piccadilly 10 🚊 a		05 57		06 56	07 15			07 36	07 45			07 54			08 20				08 25				08 47	
Stockport 84 a								07 48							08 30									
Hazel Grove 86 a																								
Buxton 86 a																								
Heald Green 85 a		*06 21*		07 27	07 32							08 11			*08f51*									
Manchester Airport 85 ✈ a	05 05	06 14		07 15	07 40				08 02			08 19							08 42				09 06	

For general notes see front of timetable
For details of catering facilities see Directory of Train Operators

- **A** To Windermere (Table 83)
- **B** From Blackburn (Table 94). Also stops at Clifton 0709
- **C** To Chester (Table 88)
- **D** From Blackburn (Table 94)
- **E** From St Annes-on-the-Sea (Table 97) to Greenbank (Table 88)
- **G** To Liverpool Lime Street (Table 90)
- **H** From Clitheroe (Table 94)
- **J** 🚌 from Preston
- **b** Arr. 0459
- **c** Change at Oxenholme Lake District and Preston
- **e** Liverpool Lime Street (Table 90)
- **f** Change at Manchester Piccadilly

Table 82

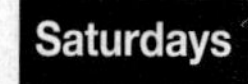

from 11 October

Barrow-in-Furness, Blackpool North, Preston, Southport, Kirkby and Wigan → Bolton → Manchester

Network Diagram - see first page of Table 82

		NT	NT	TP	NT	NT	TP	NT	NT	NT	NT	NT	NT	NT	TP	NT	NT	TP	NT	NT	NT	NT	NT
				■1 ◇			■1 ◇								■1 ◇			■1 ◇					
			A				B	C				D	E	G				H	C				
				🛒			🛒											🛒					
Barrow-in-Furness	d						07 05						07 58										
Roose	d												08 02										
Dalton	d						07 14						08 08										
Ulverston	d						07 22						08 17										
Cark	d						07 30						08 25										
Kents Bank	d												08 29										
Grange-over-Sands	d						07 37						08 33										
Arnside	d						07 43						08 39										
Silverdale	d						07 47						08 43										
Carnforth	d		07 42				07 55						08 51										
Windermere	83 d														07b24			08 28					
Oxenholme Lake District	65 d														08c07			08 59					
Lancaster [8]	65 a		07 53				08 02						09 02					09 14					
	d						08 03								08c27			09 14					
Preston [8]	65 a						08 21											09 35					
Blackpool North	97 d			07 41						08 09					08 41							09 11	
Layton	97 d			07 44						08 12												09 14	
Poulton-le-Fylde	97 d			07 48						08 16					08 47							09 18	
Kirkham & Wesham	97 d			07 58						08 25		*08 28*										09 27	
Preston [8]	d			08 12			08 34			08 38		08 50			09 08			09 38				09 41	
Leyland	d									08 43		08a55			09 13								
Chorley	d			08 22			08 44			08 51					09 19			09 47				09 51	
Adlington (Lancashire)	d									08 56												09 56	
Blackrod	d									09 00												10 00	
Horwich Parkway	d						08 52			09 03					09 27							10 03	
Lostock	d									09 07					09 30							10 07	
Southport	d	07 41							08 06		08 31									09 06			09 36
Meols Cop	d	07 46							08 11		08 36									09 11			
Bescar Lane	d								08 16											09 16			
New Lane	d								08 20											09 20			
Burscough Bridge	d	07 54							08 22		08 44									09 22			09 48
Hoscar	d								08 26											09 26			
Parbold	d	07 59							08 29		08 49									09 29			09 53
Appley Bridge	d	08 03							08 33		08 53									09 33			09 57
Gathurst	d	08 06							08 36		08 56									09 36			
Liverpool Central [10]	103 d					*07 50*																	
Kirkby	d					08 13																	
Rainford	d					08 20																	
Upholland	d					08 24																	
Orrell	d					08 28																	
Pemberton	d					08 31																	
Wigan Wallgate	a	08 11				08 42			08 43		09 03									09 43			10 03
	d	08 13			08 30				08 44		09 05					09 14	09 30			09 45	09 50		10 05
Wigan North Western	d																						
Ince	d	08 16														09 17							
Hindley	d	08 19			08 35				08 49							09 20	09 35			09 50			
Westhoughton	d				08 39						09 13						09 39						10 13
Bolton	a			08 33	08 49		08 58			09 12	09 23				09 34		09 49	09 58			10 06	10 12	10 23
	d			08 34	08 50		08 59	09 01		09 12	09 23			09 30	09 36		09 50	09 59	10 01		10 07	10 12	10 23
Moses Gate	d							09 04													10 10		
Farnworth	d				08 53												09 53						
Kearsley	d				08 55												09 55						
Daisy Hill	d	08 23							08 53							09 24				09 54			
Hag Fold	d	08 26							08 56							09 27							
Atherton	d	08 29							08 59							09 30				09 58			
Walkden	d	08 34							09 04							09 35				10 03			
Moorside	d	08 38							09 08							09 39							
Swinton	d	08 40							09 10							09 41				10 08			
Salford Crescent	a	08 50			09 06		09 11	09 16	09 20	09 25	09 36			09 42	09 48	09 50	10 06	10 11	10 13	10 17	10 22	10 25	10 36
	d	08 50			09 07		09 11	09 16	09 20	09 25	09 36			09 42	09 48	09 50	10 07	10 11	10 13	10 17	10 22	10 25	10 36
Salford Central	d	08 53			09 09			09 19	09 23					09 45		09 53	10 09		10 16	10 20	10 24		
Manchester Victoria	🚊 a	09 00			09 14			09 25	09 26					09 50		10 00	10 14		10 21	10 24	10 32		
Rochdale	95 a	09 25			*09 38*				09 55							10 25	*10 38*			10 55	*11 08*		
Deansgate	🚊 a						09 15			09 29												10 29	
Manchester Oxford Road	a			08 49			09 16			09 31	09 41				09 53			10 16				10 31	10 41
Manchester Piccadilly [10]	🚊 a			08 53			09 20			09 35	09 45				09 57			10 20				10 35	10 45
Stockport	84 a									09 49												10 49	
Hazel Grove	86 a									09 57												10 57	
Buxton	86 a									10 38												11 35	
Heald Green	85 a			*09 18*			09 31								10 11			10 32					
Manchester Airport	85 ✈ a			09 13			09 40				10 02				10 19			10 40					11 01

For general notes see front of timetable
For details of catering facilities see Directory of Train Operators

- **A** From Leeds (Table 36)
- **B** 🛒 from Preston
- **C** From Blackburn (Table 94)
- **D** To Liverpool Lime Street (Table 90)
- **E** From Maryport (Table 100)
- **G** From Clitheroe (Table 94)
- **H** From Glasgow Central (Table 65)
- **b** Change at Oxenholme Lake District and Preston
- **c** Change at Preston

Table 82

Saturdays

from 11 October

Barrow-in-Furness, Blackpool North, Preston, Southport, Kirkby and Wigan → Bolton → Manchester

Network Diagram - see first page of Table 82

		NT	NT	TP	NT	NT	NT	TP	NT	NT	NT		NT	NT	NT	TP	NT	NT	NT	TP	NT	NT		NT	NT
				1 ◇				1 ◇								1 ◇				1 ◇					
		A	B			C		D						A	B			E		G					
				🍴				🍴								🍴				🍴					
Barrow-in-Furness	d							09 15										09 58							
Roose	d							09 19										10 02							
Dalton	d							09 25										10 08							
Ulverston	d							09 34										10 16							
Cark	d							09 42										10 24							
Kents Bank	d							09 46										10 28							
Grange-over-Sands	d							09 50										10 32							
Arnside	d							09 56										10 38							
Silverdale	d							10 01										10 43							
Carnforth	d					09 53		10 08										10 50							
Windermere	83 d							*09b26*												*10 18*					
Oxenholme Lake District	65 d							*09 51*												10 54					
Lancaster 6	65 a					10 04		10 15										11 01		11 10					
	d							10 16												11 10					
Preston 8	65 a							10 34												11 32					
Blackpool North	97 d	09 25		09 40							10 11			10 25		10 41								11 11	
Layton	97 d										10 14													11 14	
Poulton-le-Fylde	97 d			09 46							10 18					10 47								11 18	
Kirkham & Wesham	97 d							*10 19*			10 27									*11 19*				11 27	
Preston 8	d	09 50		10 08				10 38			10 41			10 50		11 08				11 38				11 41	
Leyland	d	09a55		10 13										10a55		11 13									
Chorley	d			10 19				10 47			10 51					11 19				11 47				11 51	
Adlington (Lancashire)	d										10 56													11 56	
Blackrod	d										11 00													12 00	
Horwich Parkway	d			10 27							11 03					11 27								12 03	
Lostock	d			10 30							11 07					11 30								12 07	
Southport	d								10 11				10 34								11 06				11 34
Meols Cop	d								10 16												11 11				
Bescar Lane	d																				11 16				
New Lane	d																				11 20				
Burscough Bridge	d								10 24				10 46								11 22				11 46
Hoscar	d																				11 26				
Parbold	d								10 29				10 51								11 29				11 51
Appley Bridge	d								10 33				10 55								11 33				11 55
Gathurst	d								10 36												11 36				
Liverpool Central 10	103 d				*09 20*												*10 20*								
Kirkby	d				09 47												10 47								
Rainford	d				09 54												10 54								
Upholland	d				09 58												10 58								
Orrell	d				10 02												11 02								
Pemberton	d				10 05												11 05								
Wigan Wallgate	a				10 12				10 43				11 03				11 12				11 43				12 03
	d				10 14		10 30		10 45	10 50			11 05				11 14		11 30		11 45	11 50			12 05
Wigan North Western	d																								
Ince	d				10 17												11 17								
Hindley	d				10 20		10 35		10 50								11 20		11 35		11 50				
Westhoughton	d						10 39						11 13						11 39						12 13
Bolton	a			10 34			10 49	10 58		11 06	11 12		11 23			11 34			11 49	11 58		12 06		12 12	12 23
	d		10 30	10 36			10 50	10 59		11 07	11 12		11 23		11 30	11 36			11 50	11 59		12 07		12 12	12 23
Moses Gate	d									11 10												12 10			
Farnworth	d						10 53												11 53						
Kearsley	d						10 55												11 55						
Daisy Hill	d				10 24				10 54								11 24				11 54				
Hag Fold	d				10 27												11 27								
Atherton	d				10 30				10 58								11 30				11 58				
Walkden	d				10 35				11 03								11 35				12 03				
Moorside	d				10 39												11 39								
Swinton	d				10 41				11 08								11 41				12 08				
Salford Crescent	a		10 43	10 48	10 50		11 06	11 11	11 17	11 21	11 25		11 36		11 43	11 48	11 50		12 06	12 11	12 17	12 21		12 25	12 36
	d		10 43	10 48	10 50		11 07	11 11	11 17	11 22	11 25		11 36		11 43	11 48	11 50		12 07	12 11	12 17	12 22		12 25	12 36
Salford Central	d		10 45		10 53		11 10		11 20	11 24					11 45		11 53		12 09		12 20	12 24			
Manchester Victoria	🚋 a		10 50		11 00		11 14		11 24	11 29					11 52		12 00		12 14		12 24	12 29			
Rochdale	95 a				11 25		*11 38*		11 55	*12 08*							12 25		*12 38*		12 55	*13 08*			
Deansgate	🚋 a							11 15			11 29													12 29	
Manchester Oxford Road	a			10 53				11 16			11 31		11 41			11 53				12 16				12 31	12 41
Manchester Piccadilly 10	🚋 a			10 57				11 20			11 35		11 45			11 57				12 20				12 35	12 45
Stockport	84 a										11 49													12 49	
Hazel Grove	86 a										11 57													12 57	
Buxton	86 a										12 38													13 35	
Heald Green	85 a			11 12				11 32								12 12				12 32					
Manchester Airport	85 ✈ a			11 19				11 40					12 01			12 19				12 40					13 01

For general notes see front of timetable
For details of catering facilities see Directory of Train Operators

A To Liverpool Lime Street (Table 90)
B From Clitheroe (Table 94)
C From Leeds to Morecambe (Table 36)
D 🍴 from Preston
E From Millom (Table 100)
G From Glasgow Central and from Edinburgh (Table 65)
b Change at Oxenholme Lake District and Lancaster

Table 82

Saturdays

from 11 October

Barrow-in-Furness, Blackpool North, Preston, Southport, Kirkby and Wigan → Bolton → Manchester

Network Diagram - see first page of Table 82

		NT	NT	TP	NT	NT	NT	TP	NT	NT	NT	NT	NT	NT	TP	NT	NT	TP	NT	NT	NT	NT	NT
				1 ◇				1 ◇							1 ◇			1 ◇					
		A	B			C		D					A	B				D					A
				⌶				⌶							⌶			⌶					
Barrow-in-Furness	d							11 18															
Roose	d																						
Dalton	d							11 27															
Ulverston	d							11 35															
Cark	d							11 43															
Kents Bank	d																						
Grange-over-Sands	d							11 50															
Arnside	d							11 56															
Silverdale	d							12 01															
Carnforth	d					11 55		12 08															
Windermere	83 d																	12 23					
Oxenholme Lake District	65 d																	12 42					
Lancaster 6	65 a					12 04		12 16										13 02					
	d							12 16										13 04					
Preston 8	65 a							12 36										13 22					
Blackpool North	97 d	11 25		11 41							12 11		12 25		12 41						13 11		13 25
Layton	97 d										12 14										13 14		
Poulton-le-Fylde	97 d			11 47							12 18				12 47						13 18		
Kirkham & Wesham	97 d							*12 19*			12 27							*13 19*			13 27		
Preston 8	d	11 50		12 08				12 38			12 41		12 50		13 08			13 38			13 41		13 50
Leyland	d	11a55		12 13									12a55		13 13								13a55
Chorley	d			12 19				12 47			12 51				13 19			13 47			13 51		
Adlington (Lancashire)	d										12 56										13 56		
Blackrod	d										13 00										14 00		
Horwich Parkway	d			12 27							13 03				13 27						14 03		
Lostock	d			12 30							13 07				13 30						14 07		
Southport	d								12 12			12 34							13 07			13 34	
Meols Cop	d								12 17										13 12				
Bescar Lane	d																		13 17				
New Lane	d																		13 21				
Burscough Bridge	d								12 25			12 46							13 23			13 46	
Hoscar	d																		13 27				
Parbold	d								12 30			12 51							13 30			13 51	
Appley Bridge	d								12 34			12 55							13 34			13 55	
Gathurst	d								12 37										13 37				
Liverpool Central 10	103 d				*11 20*											*12 20*							
Kirkby	d				11 47											12 47							
Rainford	d				11 54											12 54							
Upholland	d				11 58											12 58							
Orrell	d				12 02											13 02							
Pemberton	d				12 05											13 05							
Wigan Wallgate	a				12 12				12 43			13 03				13 12			13 43			14 03	
	d				12 14		12 30		12 45	12 50		13 05				13 14	13 30		13 45	13 50		14 05	
Wigan North Western	d																						
Ince	d				12 17											13 17							
Hindley	d				12 20		12 35		12 50							13 20	13 35		13 50				
Westhoughton	d						12 39					13 13					13 39					14 13	
Bolton	a			12 34			12 49	12 58		13 06	13 12	13 23			13 34		13 49	13 58		14 06	14 12	14 23	
	d		12 30	12 36			12 50	12 59		13 07	13 12	13 23		13 30	13 36		13 50	13 59		14 07	14 12	14 23	
Moses Gate	d									13 10										14 10			
Farnworth	d						12 53										13 53						
Kearsley	d						12 55										13 55						
Daisy Hill	d				12 24				12 54							13 24			13 54				
Hag Fold	d				12 27											13 27							
Atherton	d				12 30				12 58							13 30			13 58				
Walkden	d				12 35				13 03							13 35			14 03				
Moorside	d				12 39											13 39							
Swinton	d				12 41				13 08							13 41			14 08				
Salford Crescent	a		12 43	12 48	12 50		13 06	13 11	13 17	13 21	13 25	13 36		13 42	13 48	13 50	14 06	14 11	14 17	14 21	14 25	14 36	
	d		12 43	12 48	12 50		13 07	13 11	13 17	13 22	13 25	13 36		13 43	13 48	13 50	14 07	14 11	14 17	14 22	14 25	14 36	
Salford Central	d		12 45		12 53		13 09		13 20	13 24				13 45		13 53	14 09		14 20	14 25			
Manchester Victoria	⇌ a		12 50		13 00		13 14		13 24	13 30				13 50		14 00	14 14		14 24	14 32			
Rochdale	95 a				13 25		*13 38*		13 55	*14 08*						14 25	*14 38*		14 55	*15 08*			
Deansgate	⇌ a							13 15			13 29							14 15			14 29		
Manchester Oxford Road	a			12 53				13 16			13 31	13 41			13 53			14 16			14 31	14 41	
Manchester Piccadilly 10	⇌ a			12 57				13 20			13 35	13 45			13 57			14 20			14 35	14 45	
Stockport	84 a										13 49										14 49		
Hazel Grove	86 a										13 57										14 57		
Buxton	86 a										14 38										15 35		
Heald Green	85 a			13 12				13 32							14 12			14 32					
Manchester Airport	85 ✈ a			13 19				13 40				14 01			14 19			14 40				15 01	

For general notes see front of timetable
For details of catering facilities see Directory of Train Operators

A To Liverpool Lime Street (Table 90)
B From Clitheroe (Table 94)
C From Leeds to Morecambe (Table 36)
D ⌶ from Preston

Table 82

Saturdays
from 11 October

Barrow-in-Furness, Blackpool North, Preston, Southport, Kirkby and Wigan → Bolton → Manchester

Network Diagram - see first page of Table 82

	NT	TP	NT	NT	NT	TP	NT	NT	NT	NT		NT	NT	TP	NT	NT	TP	TP	NT	NT	NT		NT	NT
		1 ◇				1 ◇								1 ◇			1 ◇	1 ◇						
	A					B						C	A				D	D					E	A
		✕				✕											✕	✕						
Barrow-in-Furness d				12 56														14 10						
Roose d				13 00																				
Dalton d				13 06																				
Ulverston d				13 15														14 26						
Cark d				13 23																				
Kents Bank d				13 27																				
Grange-over-Sands d				13 31														14 39						
Arnside d				13 37														14 45						
Silverdale d				13 42																				
Carnforth d				13 49														14 55					15 26	
Windermere 83 d						*13 25*											14 18							
Oxenholme Lake District 65 d						13 50											14 37							
Lancaster 6 65 a				13 59		14 07											14 54	15 02					15 38	
d						14 17											15 15							
Preston 8 65 a						14 36											15 34							
Blackpool North 97 d		13 41							14 11			14 25		14 41							15 11			
Layton 97 d									14 14												15 14			
Poulton-le-Fylde 97 d		13 47							14 18					14 47							15 18			
Kirkham & Wesham 97 d						*14 19*			14 27								*15 19*				15 27			
Preston 8 d		14 08				14 38			14 41			14 50		15 08			15 38				15 41			
Leyland d		14 13										14a55		15 13										
Chorley d		14 19				14 47			14 51					15 19			15 47				15 51			
Adlington (Lancashire) d									14 56												15 56			
Blackrod d									15 00												16 00			
Horwich Parkway d		14 27							15 03					15 27							16 03			
Lostock d		14 30							15 07					15 30							16 07			
Southport d							14 12			14 34									15 08					
Meols Cop d							14 17												15 13					
Bescar Lane d																			15 18					
New Lane d																			15 22					
Burscough Bridge d							14 25			14 46									15 24					
Hoscar d																			15 28					
Parbold d							14 30			14 51									15 31					
Appley Bridge d							14 34			14 55									15 35					
Gathurst d							14 37												15 38					
Liverpool Central 10 103 d			*13 20*												*14 20*									
Kirkby d			13 47												14 47									
Rainford d			13 54												14 54									
Upholland d			13 58												14 58									
Orrell d			14 02												15 02									
Pemberton d			14 05												15 05									
Wigan Wallgate a			14 12				14 43			15 03					15 12				15 43					
d			14 14		14 30		14 45	14 50		15 05					15 14	15 30			15 45	15 50				
Wigan North Western d																								
Ince d			14 17												15 17									
Hindley d			14 20		14 35		14 50								15 20	15 35			15 50					
Westhoughton d					14 39					15 13						15 39								
Bolton a		14 34			14 49	14 58		15 06	15 12	15 23				15 34		15 49	15 58			16 07	16 12			
d	14 30	14 36			14 50	14 59		15 07	15 12	15 23			15 30	15 36		15 50	15 59			16 10	16 13			16 20
Moses Gate d								15 10																16 23
Farnworth d					14 53											15 53								
Kearsley d					14 55											15 55								
Daisy Hill d			14 24				14 54								15 24				15 54					
Hag Fold d			14 27												15 27									
Atherton d			14 30				14 58								15 30				15 58					
Walkden d			14 35				15 03								15 35				16 03					
Moorside d			14 39												15 39									
Swinton d			14 41				15 08								15 41				16 08					
Salford Crescent a	14 43	14 48	14 50		15 06	15 11	15 17	15 21	15 25	15 36			15 42	15 48	15 50	16 06	16 11		16 17	16 22	16 25			16 34
d	14 43	14 48	14 50		15 07	15 11	15 17	15 22	15 25	15 36			15 43	15 48	15 50	16 07	16 11		16 17	16 22	16 25			16 35
Salford Central d	14 45		14 53		15 09		15 20	15 24					15 45		15 53	16 10			16 20	16 25				16 37
Manchester Victoria ⇌ a	14 50		15 00		15 14		15 24	15 30					15 50		15 59	16 14			16 25	16 30				16 42
Rochdale 95 a			15 25		*15 38*		15 55	*16 08*							16 25	*16 38*			16 55					*17 08*
Deansgate ⇌ a									15 29								16 15				16 29			
Manchester Oxford Road a		14 53				15 16			15 31	15 41				15 53			16 16				16 32			
Manchester Piccadilly 10 ⇌ a		14 57				15 20			15 35	15 45				15 57			16 20				16 36			
Stockport 84 a									15 49												16 46			
Hazel Grove 86 a									15 57												16 54			
Buxton 86 a									16 38												17 32			
Heald Green 85 a		15 12				15 32								16 11			*16 49*							
Manchester Airport 85 ✈ a		15 19				15 40				16 01				16 19			16 40				*17b11*			

For general notes see front of timetable
For details of catering facilities see Directory of Train Operators

A From Clitheroe (Table 94)
B From Edinburgh (Table 65)
C To Liverpool Lime Street (Table 90)
D ✕ from Preston
E From Leeds to Morecambe (Table 36)
b Change at Manchester Piccadilly

Saturdays

from 11 October

Barrow-in-Furness, Blackpool North, Preston, Southport, Kirkby and Wigan → Bolton → Manchester

Network Diagram - see first page of Table 82

Station		NT	TP	NT	NT	NT	TP	NT	NT	NT	NT		NT	NT	NT	NT	TP	NT	TP	NT	NT	NT		NT	NT
			1 ◇				1 ◇										1 ◇		1 ◇						
		A					B ✠			C			A			D			E ✠	D					
Barrow-in-Furness	d									15 28									16 21						
Roose	d									15 32															
Dalton	d									15 38															
Ulverston	d									15 47									16 37						
Cark	d									15 55															
Kents Bank	d									15 59															
Grange-over-Sands	d									16 03									16 50						
Arnside	d									16 09									16 56						
Silverdale	d									16 14															
Carnforth	d									16 22									17 07						
Windermere 83	d						*15 22*																		
Oxenholme Lake District 65	d						15 47																		
Lancaster 6 65	a						16 02			16 33									17 15						
	d						16 03												17 16						
Preston 8 65	a						16 22												17 34						
Blackpool North 97	d	15 25	15 41						16 10				16 25				16 38							17 10	
Layton 97	d								16 13								16 41							17 13	
Poulton-le-Fylde 97	d		15 47						16 17								16 45							17 17	
Kirkham & Wesham 97	d								16 26								16 56							17 26	
Preston 8	d	15 50	16 08				16 38		16 38				16 50				17 08		17 35					17 39	
Leyland	d	15a55	16 13						16 44				16a55				17 13							17 45	
Chorley	d		16 19				16 47		16 51								17 19		17 44					17 51	
Adlington (Lancashire)	d								16 56								17 23							17 56	
Blackrod	d								16 59															18 00	
Horwich Parkway	d		16 27						17 03								17 28							18 03	
Lostock	d		16 30						17 06								17 31		17 52					18 07	
Southport	d				15 47			16 13							16 43						17 12				17 40
Meols Cop	d							16 18													17 17				17 45
Bescar Lane	d																				17 22				
New Lane	d																				17 26				
Burscough Bridge	d				15 59			16 26							16 55						17 28				17 53
Hoscar	d																				17 32				
Parbold	d				16 04			16 31							17 00						17 35				17 58
Appley Bridge	d				16 08			16 35							17 04						17 39				18 02
Gathurst	d				16 11			16 38													17 42				
Liverpool Central 10 103	d			*15 20*										*16 05*								*17 05*			
Kirkby	d			15 47										16 38								17 39			
Rainford	d			15 54										16 45								17 46			
Upholland	d			15 58										16 49								17 50			
Orrell	d			16 02										16 52								17 53			
Pemberton	d			16 05										16 55								17 56			
Wigan Wallgate	a			16 12	16 18			16 46						17 01	17 10						17 49	18 04			18 10
	d			16 14	16 19	16 30		16 47			16 58			17 06	17 12			17 31			17 50	18 05			18 12
Wigan North Western	d																								
Ince	d			16 17							17 01			17 09				17 33				18 08			
Hindley	d			16 20		16 35		16 52			17 04			17 13				17 37			17 55	18 12			
Westhoughton	d				16 28	16 39					17 09							17 41							18 21
Bolton	a		16 34		16 40	16 49	16 58		17 11		17 17				17 27		17 36	17 50	17 59					18 11	18 29
	d		16 36		16 43	16 50	16 59		17 12		17 18				17 27	17 30	17 36	17 50	17 59	18 03				18 12	18 29
Moses Gate	d															17 34									
Farnworth	d					16 53												17 53							
Kearsley	d					16 55												17 55							
Daisy Hill	d			16 24				16 56						17 17							18 00	18 16 →			
Hag Fold	d			16 27										17 20											
Atherton	d			16 30				17 00						17 22							18 04				
Walkden	d			16 35				17 06						17 28							18 09				
Moorside	d			16 39										17 31											
Swinton	d			16 41				17 10						17 34							18 14				
Salford Crescent	a		16 48	16 50	16 55	17 06	17 11	17 18	17 24		17 30			17 45			17 48	18 06	18 11	18 14	18 21			18 24	18 41
	d		16 48	16 50	16 56	17 07	17 11	17 18	17 25		17 31			17 45			17 48	18 07	18 11	18 14	18 22			18 25	18 41
Salford Central	d			16 55		17 09		17 21			17 33			17 48		17 45		18 09		18 17	18 24				
Manchester Victoria ⇌	a			16 59		17 14		17 24			17 40			17 54		17 51		18 15		18 23	18 29				
Rochdale 95	a			17 25				17 55			*18 08*			*18 32*		*18 32*					*19 05*				
Deansgate ⇌	a				16 59				17 28										18 15						
Manchester Oxford Road	a		16 53		17 01		17 16		17 30						17 43		17 55		18 17					18 34	18 47
Manchester Piccadilly 10 ⇌	a		16 57		17 06		17 20		17 35						17 47		17 57		18 20					18 38	18 51
Stockport 84	a				17 19				17 51															18 50	
Hazel Grove 86	a				17 27				17 59															18 57	
Buxton 86	a				18 09				18 39															19 39	
Heald Green 85	a		17 12				*17 49*										18 12		18 35					*19b07*	
Manchester Airport 85 ✈	a		17 19				*17 40*								18 01		18 19		18 42						19 08

For general notes see front of timetable
For details of catering facilities see Directory of Train Operators

A To Liverpool Lime Street (Table 90)
B From Glasgow Central (Table 65)
C From Carlisle via Whitehaven (Table 100)
D From Clitheroe (Table 94)
E ✠ from Preston
b Change at Manchester Piccadilly

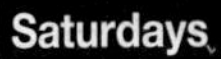

from 11 October

Barrow-in-Furness, Blackpool North, Preston, Southport, Kirkby and Wigan → Bolton → Manchester

Network Diagram - see first page of Table 82

		NT	NT	TP	NT	TP	NT	TP	NT	NT	NT		NT	NT	NT	TP	NT	TP	NT	NT	NT	NT		NT	NT
				1 ◇		1 ◇		1 ◇								1 ◇		1 ◇							
		A						B 🍴	C				A	C			D		E					G	A
Barrow-in-Furness	d					17 06																		18 14	
Roose	d																							18 18	
Dalton	d					17 15																		18 24	
Ulverston	d					17 24																		18 32	
Cark	d					17 32																		18 40	
Kents Bank	d																							18 44	
Grange-over-Sands	d					17 39																		18 48	
Arnside	d					17 45																		18 54	
Silverdale	d																							18 59	
Carnforth	d					17 55											18 31							19 09	
Windermere	83 d			*16b34*				*17 27*										*18 10*							
Oxenholme Lake District	65 d			*17c09*				*17 53*										*18 33*							
Lancaster 6	65 a					18 05		18 09									18 43	18 49						19 17	
	d			*17c25*				18 16										18 51						19 18	
Preston 8	65 a							18 36										19 09						19 43	
Blackpool North	97 d			17 38						18 11			18 25			18 42					19 10				19 25
Layton	97 d			17 41						18 14											19 13				
Poulton-le-Fylde	97 d			17 45						18 18						18 48					19 17				
Kirkham & Wesham	97 d			17 56				*18 19*		18 27											19 26				
Preston 8	d	17 50		18 08				18 38		18 41			18 50			19 06		19 14			19 38				19 50
Leyland	d	17a55		18 13									18a55			19 11					19 44				19a55
Chorley	d			18 19				18 47		18 51						19 19		19 23			19 51				
Adlington (Lancashire)	d									18 56											19 56				
Blackrod	d									19 00											19 59				
Horwich Parkway	d			18 27						19 03						19 25					20 03				
Lostock	d			18 30						19 07						19 28					20 06				
Southport	d										18 24									19 13		19 30			
Meols Cop	d										18 29									19 18		19 35			
Bescar Lane	d										18 34														
New Lane	d										18 38														
Burscough Bridge	d										18 40									19 26		19 43			
Hoscar	d										18 44														
Parbold	d										18 47									19 31		19 48			
Appley Bridge	d										18 51									19 35		19 52			
Gathurst	d										18 54									19 38		19 55			
Liverpool Central 10	103 d														*18 20*										
Kirkby	d														18 43										
Rainford	d														18 50										
Upholland	d														18 54										
Orrell	d														18 58										
Pemberton	d														19 01										
Wigan Wallgate	a										19 01				19 09					19 44		20 02			
	d				18 18						19 03				19 11					19 46		20 03			
Wigan North Western	d						18 31																		
Ince	d				18 21		18 34								19 14										
Hindley	d				18 25		18 38				19 08				19 17					19 51		20 08			
Westhoughton	d				18 29						19 13											20 13			
Bolton	a			18 34	18 39			18 58		19 12	19 23					19 33		19 38			20 11	20 23			
	d			18 36	18 40			18 59	19 02	19 12	19 23			19 30		19 33		19 39	20 00		20 12	20 23			
Moses Gate	d				18 43																				
Farnworth	d																								
Kearsley	d		←																						
Daisy Hill	d		18 16				18 42								19 21					19 55					
Hag Fold	d		18 19												19 24										
Atherton	d		18 21				18 46								19 27					19 59					
Walkden	d		18 27				18 51								19 32					20 04					
Moorside	d		18 30												19 36										
Swinton	d		18 33				18 56								19 38					20 09					
Salford Crescent	a		18 43	18 48	18 54		19 05	19 11	19 13	19 25	19 36			19 42	19 44	19 48		19 52	20 13	20 18	20 24	20 36			
	d		18 43	18 48	18 55		19 05	19 11	19 14	19 25	19 36			19 43	19 44	19 48		19 52	20 13	20 18	20 25	20 36			
Salford Central	d		18 46		18 57		19 08		19 16					19 45	19 47				20 16	20 21					
Manchester Victoria	a		18 54		19 01		19 14		19 23					19 50	19 53				20 22	20 26					
Rochdale	95 a						*19 45*								*20 38*										
Deansgate	a									19 29						19 52					20 28				
Manchester Oxford Road	a			18 54				19 16		19 33	19 42					19 54		19 58			20 30	20 41			
Manchester Piccadilly 10	a			18 57				19 20		19 36	19 46					19 57		20 04			20 34	20 45			
Stockport	84 a									19 47											20 44				
Hazel Grove	86 a									19 55											20 52				
Buxton	86 a									20 36											21 33				
Heald Green	85 a			19 12				19 32								20 12		20 18			*21e01*				
Manchester Airport	85 ✈ a			19 19				19 40			20 05					20 19		20 26			*21e06*	21 09			

For general notes see front of timetable
For details of catering facilities see Directory of Train Operators

- **A** To Liverpool Lime Street (Table 90)
- **B** From Edinburgh (Table 65)
- **C** From Clitheroe (Table 94)
- **D** From Leeds to Morecambe (Table 36)
- **E** From Blackburn (Table 94)
- **G** From Carlisle via Whitehaven (Table 100)
- **b** Change at Oxenholme Lake District and Preston
- **c** Change at Preston
- **e** Change at Manchester Piccadilly

Table 82

from 11 October

Barrow-in-Furness, Blackpool North, Preston, Southport, Kirkby and Wigan → Bolton → Manchester

Network Diagram - see first page of Table 82

Station		NT	TP	NT	NT	TP	TP	NT	NT	NT	TP	NT	NT	NT	TP	NT	NT	NT	NT	NT	TP
			1 ◇			1 ◇	1 ◇				1 ◇				1 ◇						1 ◇
		A			B	C			A				A	D			B		A		
Barrow-in-Furness	d						19 15											21 30			
Roose	d						19 19											21 34			
Dalton	d						19 26											21 40			
Ulverston	d						19 33											21 49			
Cark	d						19 41											21 57			
Kents Bank	d						19 46											22 01			
Grange-over-Sands	d						19 50											22 05			
Arnside	d						19 56											22 11			
Silverdale	d						20 01											22 16			
Carnforth	d						20 09											22 23			
Windermere	83 d					*19 22*									20b24						
Oxenholme Lake District	65 d					19 55									20b46						
Lancaster 6	65 a					20 10	20 16											22 34			
	d					20 11	20 17								21c20						
Preston 8	65 a					20 29	20 35														
Blackpool North	97 d		19 42								20 52				21 52		22 03				23 13
Layton	97 d		19 45								20 56				21 56						23 16
Poulton-le-Fylde	97 d		19 49								21 00				22 00						23 20
Kirkham & Wesham	97 d		19 59								21 09				22 09						23 30
Preston 8	d		20 11		20 27	20 32	20 37				21 21				22 21		22 28				23 42
Leyland	d				20a32		20 42				21 26				22 26		22a32				23 47
Chorley	d		20 21			20 42	20 48				21 34				22 34						23 54
Adlington (Lancashire)	d						20 53				21 38				22 38						23 58
Blackrod	d						20 56				21 42				22 42						00 02
Horwich Parkway	d						21 00				21 45				22 45						00 05
Lostock	d						21 03				21 48				22 48						00 08
Southport	d							20 30				21 34				22 25				23 10	
Meols Cop	d							20 35				21 39				22 30				23 15	
Bescar Lane	d															22 35					
New Lane	d															22 39					
Burscough Bridge	d							20 43				21 47				22 41				23 23	
Hoscar	d															22 45					
Parbold	d							20 48				21 52				22 48				23 28	
Appley Bridge	d							20 52				21 56				22 52				23 32	
Gathurst	d							20 55				21 59				22 55				23 35	
Liverpool Central 10	103 d																				
Kirkby	d																				
Rainford	d																				
Upholland	d																				
Orrell	d																				
Pemberton	d																				
Wigan Wallgate	a							21 02				22 04				23 02				23 47	
	d			20 18				21 03		21 18		22 05		22 16		23 03					
Wigan North Western	d																				
Ince	d			20 21						21 21				22 19							
Hindley	d			20 24				21 08		21 24		22 10		22 22		23 08					
Westhoughton	d							21 13				22 15				23 13					
Bolton	a		20 32			20 53	21 07	21 23			21 52	22 23			22 52	23 23					00 12
	d	20 30	20 34			20 54	21 08	21 23	21 30		21 53	22 23	22 33		22 53	23 23			23 40		00 13
Moses Gate	d																				
Farnworth	d																				
Kearsley	d																				
Daisy Hill	d			20 28						21 28				22 26							
Hag Fold	d			20 31						21 31				22 29							
Atherton	d			20 34						21 34				22 32							
Walkden	d			20 39						21 39				22 37							
Moorside	d			20 43						21 43				22 41							
Swinton	d			20 45						21 45				22 43							
Salford Crescent	a	20 42	20 46	20 52		21 06	21 20	21 36	21 42	21 52	22 05	22 36	22 46	22 51	23 05	23 36			23 53		
	d	20 43	20 47	20 52		21 06	21 21	21 36	21 43	21 52	22 05	22 36	22 46	22 52	23 05	23 36			23 53		
Salford Central	d	20 45		20 56					21 45	21 56		22 39		22 55							
Manchester Victoria	a	20 50		21 00					21 50	22 00		22 44		23 00					23 59		
Rochdale	95 a			*21 38*					*22 39*			*23 08*		*00 02*							
Deansgate	a		20 53					21 40			22 13		22 50		23 15						
Manchester Oxford Road	a		20 54			21 11	21 25	21 41			22 14		22 52		23 18	23 41					
Manchester Piccadilly 10	a		20 58			21 14	21 29	21 46			22 18		22 56		23 30	23 46					00 29
Stockport	84 a							21 56					23 06								
Hazel Grove	86 a							22 05					23 14								
Buxton	86 a							22 46					23 56								
Heald Green	85 a		21 12			21 30	21 41				22 31				23 47						00 40
Manchester Airport	85 ✈ a		21 19			21 37	21 51				22 39				23 56						00 45

For general notes see front of timetable
For details of catering facilities see Directory of Train Operators

A From Clitheroe (Table 94)
B To Liverpool Lime Street (Table 90)
C From Edinburgh (Table 65)
D To Greenfield (Table 39)

b Change at Lancaster and Preston
c Change at Preston

Table 82

Sundays

until 13 July

Barrow-in-Furness, Blackpool North, Preston, Southport and Wigan → Bolton → Manchester

Network Diagram - see first page of Table 82

	TP	TP	TP 1 ◇	TP 1 ◇	TP 1 ◇	NT	NT	NT	NT	TP 1 ◇	NT	NT	NT	TP 1 ◇	NT	NT	NT	NT	NT	TP 1 ◇	TP 1 ◇	NT	NT	NT
							A	B				C				A	D	C					C	
	🚌	🚌																						
Barrow-in-Furness d																				09 55				
Roose d																				10 00				
Dalton d																				10 06				
Ulverston d																				10 14				
Cark d																				10 22				
Kents Bank d																				10 26				
Grange-over-Sands d																				10 30				
Arnside d																				10 36				
Silverdale d																				10 41				
Carnforth d																	10 30			10 48				
Windermere 83 d																								
Oxenholme Lake District 65 d																								
Lancaster 6 65 a																	10 39			10 55				
d													*08b40*	*09b25*						10 56				
Preston 8 65 a																				11 14				
Blackpool North 97 d	03 20	05 20			08 02		08 17		08 28	09 02			09 28	10 02		10 17			10 28		11 02			11 28
Poulton-le-Fylde 97 d					08 08		08 23		08 34	09 08			09 34	10 08		10 23			10 34		11 08			11 34
Kirkham & Wesham 97 d					08 17					09 17				10 17							11 17			
Preston 8 d	04u00	06u00			08 30		08 42		08 53	09 30			09 53	10 30		10 42			10 53	11 20	11 30			11 53
Leyland d							08a47		08 59				09 59			10a47			10 59					11 59
Chorley d					08 40				09 06	09 40			10 06	10 40					11 06		11 40			12 06
Adlington (Lancashire) d									09 10				10 10						11 10					12 10
Blackrod d									09 14				10 14						11 14					12 13
Horwich Parkway d									09 17				10 17						11 17					12 17
Lostock d									09 21				10 21						11 21					12 20
Southport d											09 13				10 13							11 13		
Burscough Bridge d											09 25				10 25							11 25		
Parbold d											09 30				10 30							11 30		
Appley Bridge d											09 34				10 34							11 34		
Gathurst d											09 37				10 37							11 37		
Wigan Wallgate a											09 42				10 42							11 42		
d						08 43					09 43				10 43							11 43		
Wigan North Western d																								
Hindley d						08 48					09 48				10 48							11 48		
Westhoughton d						08 53					09 53				10 53							11 53		
Bolton a					08 51	09 01			09 26	09 51	10 01		10 26	10 51	11 01				11 26	11 39	11 51	12 01		12 25
d	04u35	06u35	06 59	07 45	08 53	09 01		09 16	09 26	09 53	10 01	10 16	10 26	10 53	11 01			11 16	11 26	11 39	11 53	12 01	12 16	12 26
Salford Crescent a					09 05	09 14		09 29	09 39	10 05	10 14	10 29	10 39	11 05	11 14			11 29	11 39		12 05	12 14	12 29	12 39
d					09 06	09 14		09 29	09 39	10 06	10 14	10 29	10 39	11 06	11 14			11 29	11 39		12 06	12 14	12 29	12 39
Manchester Victoria 🚇 a								09 35				10 35						11 35					12 35	
Rochdale a								*10 34*				*11 34*						*12 34*					*13 34*	
Deansgate 🚇 a					09 09	09 18			09 43	10 09	10 18		10 43	11 09	11 18				11 45		12 09	12 18		12 43
Manchester Oxford Road a					09 11	09 20			09 45	10 11	10 21		10 45	11 11	11 20				11 49	11 54	12 11	12 20		12 46
Manchester Piccadilly 10 🚇 a			07 14	08 00	09 15	09 24			09 49	10 15	10 25		10 49	11 15	11 24				11 52	11 58	12 17	12 24		12 49
Stockport 84 a				*08 21*		09 38			10 07		10 38		11 07		11 38				12 07	*12 18*		12 37		13 06
Alderley Edge 84 a						09 58					10 59				11 58							12 58		
Hazel Grove 86 a				*09 00*					10 15		*10c53*		11 15						12 16					13 16
Buxton 86 a				*09 53*					10 55				11 55						12 56					13 56
Heald Green 85 a			*08 04*			*10e04*					*11e05*				*12e04*							*13e03*		
Manchester Airport 85 ✈ a	05 25	07 25	07 32	08 17	09 33	*09e51*				10 33	*10e54*		*11e20*	11 33	*11e51*					12 18	12 33	*12e54*		*13e23*

For general notes see front of timetable
For details of catering facilities see Directory of Train Operators

- **A** To Liverpool Lime Street (Table 90)
- **B** From Blackburn (Table 94)
- **C** From Clitheroe (Table 94)
- **D** From Leeds to Morecambe (Table 36)
- **b** Change at Preston. By bus
- **c** Change at Stockport
- **e** Change at Manchester Piccadilly

Table 82

Sundays

until 13 July

Barrow-in-Furness, Blackpool North, Preston, Southport and Wigan → Bolton → Manchester

Network Diagram - see first page of Table 82

		TP 1 ◊	NT	NT A	NT B	NT C	NT	TP 1 ◊	TP 1 ◊	NT		NT C	NT	TP 1 ◊ D ✠	TP 1 ◊	NT	NT A	NT C	NT	TP 1 ◊	TP 1 ◊	NT	NT C	NT	TP 1 ◊ E ✠
Barrow-in-Furness	d							12 00												13 55					
Roose	d							12 05												14 00					
Dalton	d							12 11												14 06					
Ulverston	d							12 19												14 14					
Cark	d							12 27												14 22					
Kents Bank	d							12 31												14 26					
Grange-over-Sands	d							12 35												14 30					
Arnside	d							12 41												14 36					
Silverdale	d							12 46												14 41					
Carnforth	d				12 34			12 53												14 49					
Windermere	83 d							11b40					12c38	13 23										14c28	
Oxenholme Lake District	65 d	11e25						12 14					13e14	13 45										14e53	15 41
Lancaster 6	65 a				12 43			13 00						14 01						14 56					15 57
	d	11e41						13 02					13e28	14 01			14e09		14e25	14 58				15e09	15 57
Preston 8	65 a							13 20						14 20						15 16					16 16
Blackpool North	97 d	12 02		12 17			12 28		13 02				13 28		13 57		14 17		14 28		15 02			15 28	
Poulton-le-Fylde	97 d	12 08		12 23			12 34		13 08				13 34		14 03		14 23		14 34		15 08			15 34	
Kirkham & Wesham	97 d	12 17						12 51	13 17					13 51	14 12					14 51	15 17				15 51
Preston 8	d	12 30		12 42			12 53	13 22	13 30				13 53	14 22	14 30		14 42		14 53	15 22	15 30			15 53	16 22
Leyland	d			12a47			12 59						13 59				14a47		14 59					15 59	
Chorley	d	12 40					13 06		13 40				14 06		14 40				15 06		15 40			16 06	
Adlington (Lancashire)	d						13 10						14 10						15 10					16 10	
Blackrod	d						13 14						14 14						15 14					16 14	
Horwich Parkway	d						13 17						14 17						15 17					16 17	
Lostock	d						13 21						14 21						15 21					16 21	
Southport	d		12 13							13 13						14 13						15 13			
Burscough Bridge	d		12 25							13 25						14 25						15 25			
Parbold	d		12 30							13 30						14 30						15 30			
Appley Bridge	d		12 34							13 34						14 34						15 34			
Gathurst	d		12 37							13 37						14 37						15 37			
Wigan Wallgate	a		12 42							13 42						14 42						15 42			
	d		12 43							13 43						14 43						15 43			
Wigan North Western	d																								
Hindley	d		12 48							13 48						14 48						15 48			
Westhoughton	d		12 53							13 53						14 53						15 53			
Bolton	a	12 51	13 01				13 26	13 41	13 52	14 01			14 26	14 41	14 52	15 01			15 26	15 41	15 52	16 01		16 26	16 41
	d	12 53	13 01			13 16	13 26	13 42	13 52	14 01		14 16	14 26	14 42	14 53	15 01		15 16	15 26	15 42	15 53	16 01	16 16	16 26	16 42
Salford Crescent	a	13 05	13 14			13 29	13 39		14 05	14 14		14 29	14 39		15 05	15 14		15 29	15 39		16 05	16 14	16 29	16 39	
	d	13 06	13 14			13 29	13 39		14 06	14 14		14 29	14 39		15 06	15 14		15 29	15 39		16 06	16 14	16 29	16 39	
Manchester Victoria 🚊	a					13 35						14 35						15 35					16 35		
Rochdale	a					14 34						15 34						16 34					17 34		
Deansgate 🚊	a	13 09	13 18				13 43		14 09	14 18			14 43		15 09	15 18			15 43		16 09	16 18		16 43	
Manchester Oxford Road	a	13 11	13 20				13 46	13 56	14 11	14 20			14 46	14 56	15 11	15 20			15 45	15 56	16 11	16 20		16 45	16 56
Manchester Piccadilly 10 🚊	a	13 15	13 24				13 48	14 00	14 15	14 24			14 49	15 00	15 15	15 24			15 49	16 00	16 15	16 24		16 49	17 00
Stockport	84 a		13 38				14 07	14 23		14 36			15 05	15 23		15 36			16 04	16 23		16 37		17 04	17 23
Alderley Edge	84 a		13 58							14 58						15 58						16 58			
Hazel Grove	86 a						14 15						15 13						16 12					17 12	17 35
Buxton	86 a						14 55						15 53						16 52					17 52	
Heald Green	85 a		14f07							15f04						16f04						17f04			
Manchester Airport	85 ✈ a	13 33	13f55					14 18	14 33	14f51				15 18	15 33	15f51				16 18	16 33	16f51			17 18

For general notes see front of timetable
For details of catering facilities see Directory of Train Operators

- **A** To Liverpool Lime Street (Table 90)
- **B** From Leeds to Morecambe (Table 36)
- **C** From Clitheroe (Table 94)
- **D** From Edinburgh (Table 65)
- **E** From Glasgow Central (Table 65)

- **b** Change at Oxenholme Lake District and Lancaster
- **c** Change at Oxenholme Lake District and Preston
- **e** Change at Preston
- **f** Change at Manchester Piccadilly

Table 82

Sundays

until 13 July

Barrow-in-Furness, Blackpool North, Preston, Southport and Wigan → Bolton → Manchester

Network Diagram - see first page of Table 82

	TP [1] ◇	NT	NT A	NT B	NT C	NT	TP [1] ◇	TP [1] ◇	NT	NT A	NT C	NT	TP [1] ◇	TP [1] ◇	TP [1] ◇ D ⚲	TP [1] ◇	NT	NT A	NT C	NT	TP [1] ◇	TP [1] ◇	NT B	NT
Barrow-in-Furness d							16 00														18 00			
Roose d							16 05														18 05			
Dalton d							16 11														18 11			
Ulverston d							16 19														18 19			
Cark d							16 27														18 27			
Kents Bank d							16 31														18 31			
Grange-over-Sands d							16 35														18 35			
Arnside d							16 41														18 41			
Silverdale d							16 46														18 46			
Carnforth d				16 37			16 53														18 53		18 57	
Windermere 83 d										16b26			17 21											
Oxenholme Lake District 65 d										16c53		17c09	17 40		17 45			17c53		18c09				
Lancaster [6] 65 a				16 46			17 00						17 55		18 01						19 00		19 11	
d			16c08				17 02			17c09		17c25	17 55		18 01			18c10		18c25	19 02			
Preston [8] 65 a							17 20						18 15		18 20						19 20			
Blackpool North 97 d	16 02		16 17			16 28		17 02		17 17		17 28		17 58				18 17		18 28		19 02		
Poulton-le-Fylde 97 d	16 08		16 23			16 34		17 08		17 23		17 34		18 04				18 23		18 34		19 08		
Kirkham & Wesham 97 d	16 17						*16 51*	17 17						18 13	*17 51*	⟵					*18 51*	19 17		
Preston [8] d	16 30		16 42			16 53	17 22	17 30		17 42		17 53		18 30 ↦	18 22	18 30		18 42		18 53	19 22	19 30		
Leyland d			16a47			16 59				17a47		17 59						18a47		18 59				
Chorley d	16 40					17 06		17 40				18 06				18 40				19 06		19 40		
Adlington (Lancashire) d						17 10						18 10								19 10				
Blackrod d						17 14						18 14								19 14				
Horwich Parkway d						17 17						18 17								19 17				
Lostock d						17 21						18 21								19 21				
Southport d		16 13							17 13								18 13							19 13
Burscough Bridge d		16 25							17 25								18 25							19 25
Parbold d		16 30							17 30								18 30							19 30
Appley Bridge d		16 34							17 34								18 34							19 34
Gathurst d		16 37							17 37								18 37							19 37
Wigan Wallgate a		16 42							17 42								18 42							19 42
d		16 43							17 43								18 43							19 43
Wigan North Western d																								
Hindley d		16 48							17 48								18 48							19 48
Westhoughton d		16 53							17 53								18 53							19 53
Bolton a	16 52	17 01				17 26	17 41	17 52	18 01			18 26			18 41	18 52	19 01			19 26	19 41	19 51		20 01
d	16 53	17 01			17 16	17 26	17 42	17 53	18 01		18 16	18 26			18 42	18 53	19 01		19 16	19 26	19 42	19 53		20 01
Salford Crescent a	17 05	17 14			17 29	17 39		18 05	18 14		18 29	18 39				19 05	19 14		19 29	19 39		20 05		20 14
d	17 06	17 14			17 29	17 39		18 06	18 14		18 29	18 39				19 06	19 14		19 29	19 39		20 06		20 14
Manchester Victoria ⇌ a					17 35						18 35								19 35					
Rochdale a					*18 34*						*19 34*								*20 34*					
Deansgate ⇌ a	17 09	17 18				17 43		18 09	18 18			18 43				19 09	19 18			19 43		20 09		20 18
Manchester Oxford Road a	17 11	17 20				17 45	17 56	18 11	18 20			18 46			18 56	19 11	19 20			19 45	19 56	20 11		20 20
Manchester Piccadilly [10] ⇌ a	17 15	17 24				17 49	18 00	18 15	18 24			18 49			19 00	19 15	19 24			19 49	20 00	20 15		20 24
Stockport 84 a		17 37				18 04	*18 23*		18 38			19 04			*19 17*		19 38			20 04	*20 23*			20 38
Alderley Edge 84 a		17 58							18 58								19 58							20 58
Hazel Grove 86 a						18 12						19 12								20 13				
Buxton 86 a						18 52						19 52								20 53				
Heald Green 85 a		*18e04*							*19e04*								*20e04*							*21e04*
Manchester Airport 85 ✈ a	17 33	*17e51*					18 18	18 33	*18e52*						19 18	19 33	*19e51*				20 18	20 33		*20e52*

For general notes see front of timetable
For details of catering facilities see Directory of Train Operators

A To Liverpool Lime Street (Table 90)
B From Leeds to Morecambe (Table 36)
C From Clitheroe (Table 94)
D From Edinburgh (Table 65)

b Change at Oxenholme Lake District and Preston
c Change at Preston
e Change at Manchester Piccadilly

Sundays

until 13 July

Barrow-in-Furness, Blackpool North, Preston, Southport and Wigan → Bolton → Manchester

Network Diagram - see first page of Table 82

	NT	NT	TP	TP	NT	NT	NT	NT	NT	TP	NT	NT	NT	NT	TP	TP	TP	NT	NT	NT	VT	TP
	A		1 ◇ B	1 ◇		C	A			1 ◇			A		1 ◇	1 ◇	1 ◇		C	A	1 ◇ D	1 ◇
Barrow-in-Furness d												19 57			20 50							
Roose d												20 01			20 55							
Dalton d												20 07			21 01							
Ulverston d												20 15			21 09							
Cark d												20 23			21 17							
Kents Bank d												20 27			21 21							
Grange-over-Sands d												20 31			21 25							
Arnside d												20 37			21 31							
Silverdale d												20 42			21 36							
Carnforth d												20 51			21 43							
Windermere 83 d		18b30	19 20											20b23		21 20						
Oxenholme Lake District 65 d		19c10	19 45			19c52								20c58		21 40					22 09	
Lancaster 6 65 a			20 01									21 01			21 56	21 56					22 25	
d		19c26	20 01			20c08								21c14	22 02						22 26	
Preston 8 65 a			20 20												22 20						22 58	
Blackpool North 97 d		19 28		20 02		20 17		20 28		21 02				21 28			22 02		22 17			23 02
Poulton-le-Fylde 97 d		19 34		20 08		20 23		20 34		21 08				21 34			22 08		22 23			23 08
Kirkham & Wesham 97 d			19 51	20 17						21 17					21 51		22 17					23 17
Preston 8 d		19 53	20 22	20 30		20 42		20 53		21 30				21 53	22 22		22 30		22 42		23 01	23 30
Leyland d		19 59				20a47		20 59						21 59					22a47			23 35
Chorley d		20 06		20 40				21 06		21 40				22 06			22 40					23 41
Adlington (Lancashire) d		20 10						21 10						22 10								23 45
Blackrod d		20 14						21 14						22 14								23 48
Horwich Parkway d		20 17						21 17						22 17								23 51
Lostock d		20 21						21 21						22 21								23 55
Southport d					20 13						21 13							22 13				
Burscough Bridge d					20 25						21 25							22 25				
Parbold d					20 30						21 30							22 30				
Appley Bridge d					20 34						21 34							22 34				
Gathurst d					20 37						21 37							22 37				
Wigan Wallgate a					20 42						21 42							22 42				
d					20 43						21 43							22 43				
Wigan North Western d																						
Hindley d					20 48						21 48							22 48				
Westhoughton d					20 53						21 53							22 53				
Bolton a		20 26	20 41	20 51	21 01			21 26		21 50	22 01			22 26	22 41		22 51	23 01			23s37	23 59
d	20 16	20 26	20 42	20 53	21 01		21 16	21 26		21 53	22 01		22 16	22 26	22 42		22 53	23 01		23 16		00 02
Salford Crescent a	20 29	20 39		21 05	21 14		21 29	21 39		22 05	22 14		22 29	22 39			23 05	23 14		23 29		
d	20 29	20 39		21 06	21 14		21 29	21 39	21 50	22 06	22 14		22 29	22 39			23 06	23 14		23 29		
Manchester Victoria a	20 35						21 35		21 54				22 35							23 35		
Rochdale a	21 34								22 34				23 58									
Deansgate a		20 43		21 09	21 18			21 43		22 09	22 18			22 43			23 09	23 18				
Manchester Oxford Road a		20 45	20 56	21 12	21 20			21 45		22 11	22 20			22 45	22 56		23 12	23 21				
Manchester Piccadilly 10 a		20 49	21 00	21 15	21 24			21 49		22 15	22 24			22 49	23 00		23 15	23 25			23 59	00 16
Stockport 84 a		21 04	21 22		21 37			22 04			22 38			23 03	23 23			23 38				
Alderley Edge 84 a					21 58						22 59							00 01				
Hazel Grove 86 a		21 13						22 13						23 11								
Buxton 86 a		21 53						22 53						23 51								
Heald Green 85 a					22e04									23e20								
Manchester Airport 85 a			21 18	21 33	21e52					22 33	22e51				23 18		23 33	23e49				00 33

For general notes see front of timetable
For details of catering facilities see Directory of Train Operators

A From Clitheroe (Table 94)
B From Edinburgh (Table 65)
C To Liverpool Lime Street (Table 90)
D From Glasgow Central (Table 65)

b Change at Oxenholme Lake District and Preston
c Change at Preston
e Change at Manchester Piccadilly

Table 82

Sundays

20 July to 7 September

Barrow-in-Furness, Blackpool North, Preston, Southport and Wigan → Bolton → Manchester

Network Diagram - see first page of Table 82

	TP	TP	TP 1◇	TP 1◇	TP 1◇	NT	NT	NT	NT	TP 1◇	NT	NT	NT	TP 1◇	NT	NT	NT	NT		NT	TP 1◇	TP 1◇	NT	NT
	bus	bus					A	B				C				A	D	C						C
Barrow-in-Furness d																					09 55			
Roose d																					10 00			
Dalton d																					10 06			
Ulverston d																					10 14			
Cark d																					10 22			
Kents Bank d																					10 26			
Grange-over-Sands d																					10 30			
Arnside d																					10 36			
Silverdale d																					10 41			
Carnforth d																	10 30				10 48			
Windermere 83 d																								
Oxenholme Lake District 65 d																								
Lancaster 6 65 a																	10 39				10 55			
d													*08b40*	*09b25*							10 56			
Preston 8 65 a																					11 14			
Blackpool North 97 d	03 20	05 20			08 02		08 17		08 28	09 02			09 28	10 02		10 17				10 28		11 02		
Poulton-le-Fylde 97 d					08 08		08 23		08 34	09 08			09 34	10 08		10 23				10 34		11 08		
Kirkham & Wesham 97 d					08 17					09 17				10 17								11 17		
Preston 8 d	04u00	06u00			08 30		08 42		08 53	09 30			09 53	10 30		10 42				10 53	11 20	11 30		
Leyland d							08a47		08 59				09 59			10a47				10 59				
Chorley d					08 40				09 06	09 40			10 06	10 40						11 06		11 40		
Adlington (Lancashire) d									09 10				10 10							11 10				
Blackrod d									09 14				10 14							11 14				
Horwich Parkway d									09 17				10 17							11 17				
Lostock d									09 21				10 21							11 21				
Southport d											09 13				10 13								11 13	
Burscough Bridge d											09 25				10 25								11 25	
Parbold d											09 30				10 30								11 30	
Appley Bridge d											09 34				10 34								11 34	
Gathurst d											09 37				10 37								11 37	
Wigan Wallgate a											09 42				10 42								11 42	
d						08 43					09 43				10 43								11 43	
Wigan North Western d																								
Hindley d						08 48					09 48				10 48								11 48	
Westhoughton d						08 53					09 53				10 53								11 53	
Bolton a					08 51	09 01			09 26	09 51	10 01		10 26	10 51	11 01					11 26	11 39	11 51	12 01	
d	04u35	06u35	06 59	07 45	08 53	09 01		09 16	09 26	09 53	10 01	10 16	10 26	10 53	11 01			11 16		11 26	11 39	11 53	12 01	12 16
Salford Crescent a					09 05	09 14		09 29	09 39	10 05	10 14	10 29	10 39	11 05	11 14			11 29		11 39		12 05	12 14	12 29
d					09 06	09 14		09 29	09 39	10 06	10 14	10 29	10 39	11 06	11 14			11 29		11 39		12 06	12 14	12 29
Manchester Victoria ⇌ a								09 35				10 35						11 35						12 35
Rochdale a								*10c29*				*11c29*						*12c29*						*13c29*
Deansgate ⇌ a					09 09	09 18			09 43	10 09	10 18		10 43	11 09	11 18					11 45		12 09	12 18	
Manchester Oxford Road a					09 11	09 20			09 45	10 11	10 21		10 45	11 11	11 20					11 49	11 54	12 11	12 20	
Manchester Piccadilly 10 ⇌ a			07 14	08 00	09 15	09 24			09 49	10 15	10 25		10 49	11 15	11 24					11 52		12 16	12 24	
Stockport 84 a				*09 05*		09 38			10 07		10 38		11 07		11 38					12 07	*12 37*		12 37	
Alderley Edge 84 a						09 58					10 58				11 58								12 57	
Hazel Grove 86 a				*09 13*					10 15		*10e53*		11 15							12 16				
Buxton 86 a				*09 53*					10 55				11 55							12 56				
Heald Green 85 a			*08 04*			*10f04*					*11f02*		*11f18*	11 30	*12f03*								*13f04*	
Manchester Airport 85 ✈ a	05 25	07 25	07 32	08 22	09 40	*09f51*			*10f33*	10 36	*10f53*			11 36	*11f55*					*12f33*		12 36	*12f54*	

For general notes see front of timetable
For details of catering facilities see
Directory of Train Operators

- **A** To Liverpool Lime Street (Table 90)
- **B** From Blackburn (Table 94)
- **C** From Clitheroe (Table 94)
- **D** From Leeds to Morecambe (Table 36)
- **b** Change at Preston. By bus
- **c** By bus
- **e** Change at Stockport
- **f** Change at Manchester Piccadilly

Barrow-in-Furness, Blackpool North, Preston, Southport and Wigan → Bolton → Manchester

20 July to 7 September

Network Diagram - see first page of Table 82

		NT	TP	NT	NT	NT	NT	NT	TP	TP	NT	NT	NT	TP	TP	NT		NT	NT	NT	TP	TP	NT	NT	NT
			1◇						1◇	1◇				1◇	1◇						1◇	1◇			
					A	B	C					C		D (bicycle symbol)				A	C					C	
Barrow-in-Furness	d								12 00												14 00				
Roose	d								12 05												14 05				
Dalton	d								12 11												14 11				
Ulverston	d								12 19												14 19				
Cark	d								12 27												14 27				
Kents Bank	d								12 31												14 31				
Grange-over-Sands	d								12 35												14 35				
Arnside	d								12 41												14 41				
Silverdale	d								12 46												14 46				
Carnforth	d					12 34			12 53												14 54				
Windermere	83 d							11b40					12b30	13 23											14b34
Oxenholme Lake District	65 d		11c25					12c05					13c07	13 45							14 41				15c05
Lancaster 6	65 a					12 43			13 00					14 01							15 01				
	d		11c41					12c21	13 02				13c21	14 01				14c08		14c20	15 03				15c21
Preston 8	65 a								13 20					14 20							15 21				
Blackpool North	97 d	11 28	12 02		12 17			12 28		13 02			13 28		13 57			14 17		14 28		15 02			15 28
Poulton-le-Fylde	97 d	11 34	12 08		12 23			12 34		13 08			13 34		14 03			14 23		14 34		15 08			15 34
Kirkham & Wesham	97 d		12 17						12 51	13 17				13 51	14 12						14 51	15 17			
Preston 8	d	11 53	12 30		12 42			12 53	13 22	13 30			13 53	14 22	14 30			14 42		14 53	15 22	15 30			15 53
Leyland	d	11 59			12a47			12 59					13 59					14a47		14 59					15 59
Chorley	d	12 06	12 40					13 06		13 40			14 06		14 40					15 06		15 40			16 06
Adlington (Lancashire)	d	12 10						13 10					14 10							15 10					16 10
Blackrod	d	12 14						13 14					14 14							15 14					16 14
Horwich Parkway	d	12 17						13 17					14 17							15 17					16 17
Lostock	d	12 21						13 21					14 21							15 21					16 21
Southport	d			12 13							13 13					14 13							15 13		
Burscough Bridge	d			12 25							13 25					14 25							15 25		
Parbold	d			12 30							13 30					14 30							15 30		
Appley Bridge	d			12 34							13 34					14 34							15 34		
Gathurst	d			12 37							13 37					14 37							15 37		
Wigan Wallgate	a			12 42							13 42					14 42							15 42		
	d			12 43							13 43					14 43							15 43		
Wigan North Western	d																								
Hindley	d			12 48							13 48					14 48							15 48		
Westhoughton	d			12 53							13 53					14 53							15 53		
Bolton	a	12 26	12 52	13 01				13 26	13 41	13 52	14 01		14 26	14 41	14 52	15 01				15 26	15 41	15 52	16 01		16 26
	d	12 26	12 53	13 01			13 16	13 26	13 42	13 53	14 01	14 16	14 26	14 42	14 53	15 01			15 16	15 26	15 42	15 53	16 01	16 16	16 26
Salford Crescent	a	12 39	13 05	13 14			13 29	13 39		14 05	14 14	14 29	14 39		15 05	15 14			15 29	15 39		16 05	16 14	16 29	16 39
	d	12 39	13 06	13 14			13 29	13 39		14 06	14 14	14 29	14 39		15 06	15 14			15 29	15 39		16 06	16 14	16 29	16 39
Manchester Victoria	(tram symbol) a						13 35					14 35							15 35					16 35	
Rochdale	a						14e29					15e29							16e29					17e29	
Deansgate	(tram symbol) a	12 43	13 09	13 18				13 43		14 09	14 18		14 43		15 09	15 18				15 43		16 09	16 18		16 43
Manchester Oxford Road	a	12 46	13 11	13 20				13 46	13 56	14 11	14 20		14 46	14 56	15 11	15 20				15 45	15 56	16 11	16 20		16 45
Manchester Piccadilly 10	(tram symbol) a	12 49	13 18	13 24				13 49	14 00	14 15	14 24		14 49	15 00	15 15	15 24				15 49	16 00	16 15	16 24		16 49
Stockport	84 a	13 07		13 38				14 07	14 23		14 38		15 07	15 23		15 36				16 04	16 23		16 37		17 04
Alderley Edge	84 a			13 58							14 58					15 58							16 58		
Hazel Grove	86 a	13 15						14 15					15 15							16 12					17 12
Buxton	86 a	13 55						14 56					15 56							16 52					17 52
Heald Green	85 a	13f17	13 30	14f07							15f04		15f18		15 29	16f04							17f04		17f18
Manchester Airport	85 (plane symbol) a		13 36	13f53					14 33	14 36	14f53				15 36	15f53					16 33	16 36	16f53		

For general notes see front of timetable
For details of catering facilities see Directory of Train Operators

A To Liverpool Lime Street (Table 90)
B From Leeds to Morecambe (Table 36)
C From Clitheroe (Table 94)
D From Edinburgh (Table 65)

b Change at Oxenholme Lake District and Preston
c Change at Preston
e By bus
f Change at Manchester Piccadilly

Table 82

Barrow-in-Furness, Blackpool North, Preston, Southport and Wigan → Bolton → Manchester

20 July to 7 September

Network Diagram - see first page of Table 82

	TP	TP	NT	NT	NT	NT	NT	TP	TP	NT	NT	NT		NT	TP	TP	NT	NT	NT	NT	TP	TP	NT	NT
	1 ◇	1 ◇						1 ◇	1 ◇						1 ◇	1 ◇					1 ◇	1 ◇		
	A			B	C	D					B	D			E			B	D				C	
Barrow-in-Furness d								16 00													18 00			
Roose d								16 05													18 05			
Dalton d								16 11													18 11			
Ulverston d								16 19													18 19			
Cark d								16 27													18 27			
Kents Bank d								16 31													18 31			
Grange-over-Sands d								16 35													18 35			
Arnside d								16 41													18 41			
Silverdale d								16 46													18 46			
Carnforth d					16 37			16 53													18 53		18 57	
Windermere 83 d														16b26	17 21									
Oxenholme Lake District 65 d	15 41													17c10	17 45			17c51		18c09				
Lancaster 6 65 a	15 57				16 46			17 00							18 01						19 00		19 11	
d	15 57	16c04						17 02						17c26	18 01			18c10		18c25	19 02			
Preston 8 65 a	16 16							17 20							18 20						19 20			
Blackpool North 97 d		16 02		16 17			16 28		17 02		17 17			17 28		17 58		18 17		18 28		19 02		
Poulton-le-Fylde 97 d		16 08		16 23			16 34		17 08		17 23			17 34		18 04		18 23		18 34		19 08		
Kirkham & Wesham 97 d	15 51	16 17						16 51	17 17						17 51	18 13					18 51	19 17		
Preston 8 d	16 22	16 30		16 42			16 53	17 22	17 30		17 42			17 53	18 22	18 30		18 42		18 53	19 22	19 30		
Leyland d				16a47			16 59				17a47			17 59				18a47		18 59				
Chorley d		16 40					17 06		17 40					18 06		18 40				19 06		19 40		
Adlington (Lancashire) d							17 10							18 10						19 10				
Blackrod d							17 14							18 14						19 14				
Horwich Parkway d							17 17							18 17						19 17				
Lostock d							17 21							18 21						19 21				
Southport d			16 13							17 13							18 13							19 13
Burscough Bridge d			16 25							17 25							18 25							19 25
Parbold d			16 30							17 30							18 30							19 30
Appley Bridge d			16 34							17 34							18 34							19 34
Gathurst d			16 37							17 37							18 37							19 37
Wigan Wallgate a			16 42							17 42							18 42							19 42
d			16 43							17 43							18 43							19 43
Wigan North Western d																								
Hindley d			16 48							17 48							18 48							19 48
Westhoughton d			16 53							17 53							18 53							19 53
Bolton a	16 41	16 51	17 01				17 26	17 41	17 52	18 01				18 26	18 41	18 52	19 01			19 26	19 41	19 51		20 01
d	16 42	16 53	17 01			17 16	17 26	17 42	17 53	18 01		18 16		18 26	18 42	18 53	19 01		19 16	19 26	19 42	19 53		20 01
Salford Crescent a		17 05	17 14			17 29	17 39		18 05	18 14		18 29		18 39		19 05	19 14		19 29	19 39		20 05		20 14
d		17 06	17 14			17 29	17 39		18 06	18 14		18 29		18 39		19 06	19 14		19 29	19 39		20 06		20 14
Manchester Victoria ⇌ a						17 35						18 35							19 35					
Rochdale a						18e29						19e29							20e29					
Deansgate ⇌ a		17 09	17 18				17 43		18 09	18 18				18 43		19 09	19 18			19 43		20 09		20 18
Manchester Oxford Road a	16 56	17 11	17 20				17 45	17 56	18 11	18 20				18 46	18 56	19 11	19 20			19 45	19 56	20 11		20 20
Manchester Piccadilly 10 ⇌ a	17 00	17 15	17 24				17 49	18 00	18 15	18 24				18 49	19 00	19 15	19 24			19 49	20 00	20 15		20 24
Stockport 84 a	17 23		17 37				18 04	18 23		18 38				19 04	19 22		19 37			20 04	20 23			20 39
Alderley Edge 84 a			17 58							18 58							19 58							20 59
Hazel Grove 86 a	17 35						18 12							19 12						20 13				
Buxton 86 a							18 52							19 52						20 53				
Heald Green 85 a	17 28		18f04							19f04				19f18	19 28		20f04							21f04
Manchester Airport 85 ✈ a	17 32	17 36	17f53					18 33	18 36	18f53					19 32	19 36	19f53				20 32	20 36		20f54

For general notes see front of timetable
For details of catering facilities see Directory of Train Operators

- A From Glasgow Central (Table 65)
- B To Liverpool Lime Street (Table 90)
- C From Leeds to Morecambe (Table 36)
- D From Clitheroe (Table 94)
- E From Edinburgh (Table 65)
- b Change at Oxenholme Lake District and Preston
- c Change at Preston
- e By bus
- f Change at Manchester Piccadilly

Table 82

Barrow-in-Furness, Blackpool North, Preston, Southport and Wigan → Bolton → Manchester

Sundays

20 July to 7 September

Network Diagram - see first page of Table 82

	NT	NT	TP	TP	NT	NT	NT	NT	NT	NT	TP	NT	NT	NT	TP	TP	TP	NT	NT	NT	VT	TP
			1 ◇	1 ◇							1 ◇				1 ◇	1 ◇	1 ◇				1 ◇	1 ◇
	A		B			C		A					A						C	A	D	
Barrow-in-Furness d							19 57								20 50							
Roose d							20 01								20 55							
Dalton d							20 07								21 01							
Ulverston d							20 15								21 09							
Cark d							20 23								21 17							
Kents Bank d							20 27								21 21							
Grange-over-Sands d							20 31								21 25							
Arnside d							20 37								21 31							
Silverdale d							20 42								21 36							
Carnforth d							20 51								21 43							
Windermere 83 d		18b25	19 20											20b28		21 20						
Oxenholme Lake District 65 d		19c06	19 45			19c52								20c58		21 40					22 09	
Lancaster 6 65 a			20 01				21 01								21 52	21 56					22 25	
Preston 8 d		19c22	20 01			20c08								21c14	22 02						22 26	
Preston 8 65 a			20 20												22 20						22 58	
Blackpool North 97 d		19 28		20 02		20 17			20 28		21 02			21 28			22 02		22 17			23 02
Poulton-le-Fylde 97 d		19 34		20 08		20 23			20 34		21 08			21 34			22 08		22 23			23 08
Kirkham & Wesham 97 d			19 51	20 17							21 17				21 51		22 17					23 17
Preston 8 d		19 53	20 22	20 30		20 42			20 53		21 30			21 53	22 22		22 30		22 42		23 01	23 30
Leyland d		19 59				20a47			20 59					21 59					22a47			23 35
Chorley d		20 06		20 40					21 06		21 40			22 06			22 40					23 41
Adlington (Lancashire) d		20 10							21 10					22 10								23 45
Blackrod d		20 14							21 14					22 14								23 48
Horwich Parkway d		20 17							21 17					22 17								23 51
Lostock d		20 21							21 21					22 21								23 55
Southport d					20 13							21 13						22 13				
Burscough Bridge d					20 25							21 25						22 25				
Parbold d					20 30							21 30						22 30				
Appley Bridge d					20 34							21 34						22 34				
Gathurst d					20 37							21 37						22 37				
Wigan Wallgate a					20 42							21 42						22 42				
Wigan Wallgate d					20 43							21 43						22 43				
Wigan North Western d																						
Hindley d					20 48							21 48						22 48				
Westhoughton d					20 53							21 53						22 53				
Bolton a		20 26	20 41	20 51	21 01				21 26		21 50	22 01		22 26	22 41		22 51	23 01			23s37	23 59
Bolton d	20 16	20 26	20 42	20 53	21 01			21 16	21 26		21 53	22 01	22 16	22 26	22 42		22 53	23 01		23 16		00 02
Salford Crescent a	20 29	20 39		21 05	21 14			21 29	21 39		22 05	22 14	22 29	22 39			23 05	23 14		23 29		
Salford Crescent d	20 29	20 39		21 06	21 14			21 29	21 39	21 50	22 06	22 14	22 29	22 39			23 06	23 14		23 29		
Manchester Victoria a	20 35							21 35		21 54			22 35							23 35		
Rochdale a	21e29									22e50			00e40									
Deansgate a		20 43		21 09	21 18				21 43		22 09	22 18		22 43			23 09	23 18				
Manchester Oxford Road a		20 45	20 56	21 12	21 20				21 45		22 11	22 20		22 45	22 56		23 12	23 21				
Manchester Piccadilly 10 a		20 49	21 00	21 15	21 24				21 49		22 15	22 24		22 49	23 00		23 15	23 25			23 59	00 16
Stockport 84 a		21 04	21 22		21 37				22 04			22 38		23 03	23 23			23 38				
Alderley Edge 84 a					21 58							23 00						00 01				
Hazel Grove 86 a		21 13							22 13					23 11								
Buxton 86 a		21 53							22 53					23 51								
Heald Green 85 a		21f18	21 28		22f04									23f20								
Manchester Airport 85 ✈ a			21 32	21 36	21f54				22f34		22 36	22f53		23f27			23 33	23f49				00 33

For general notes see front of timetable
For details of catering facilities see Directory of Train Operators

- **A** From Clitheroe (Table 94)
- **B** From Edinburgh (Table 65)
- **C** To Liverpool Lime Street (Table 90)
- **D** From Glasgow Central (Table 65)
- **b** Change at Oxenholme Lake District and Preston
- **c** Change at Preston
- **e** By bus
- **f** Change at Manchester Piccadilly

Table 82

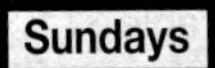
Sundays

from 14 September

Barrow-in-Furness, Blackpool North, Preston, Southport and Wigan → Bolton → Manchester

Network Diagram - see first page of Table 82

	TP	TP	TP 1 ◇	TP 1 ◇	TP 1 ◇	NT	NT	NT	NT	TP 1 ◇	NT	NT	NT	TP 1 ◇	NT	NT	NT	NT		NT	TP 1 ◇	TP 1 ◇	NT	NT
							A	B				C				A	C			D				C
	🚌	🚌																						
Barrow-in-Furness d																					09 58			
Roose d																					10 03			
Dalton d																					10 09			
Ulverston d																					10 17			
Cark d																					10 25			
Kents Bank d																					10 29			
Grange-over-Sands d																					10 33			
Arnside d																					10 39			
Silverdale d																					10 44			
Carnforth d																				10 30	10 51			
Windermere 83 d																								
Oxenholme Lake District 65 d																								
Lancaster 6 65 a																				10 39	10 58			
d																					11 00			
Preston 8 65 a																					11 18			
Blackpool North 97 d	03 20	05 20			08 02		08 14		08 28	09 02			09 28	10 02		10 17		10 28				11 02		
Poulton-le-Fylde 97 d					08 08		08 20		08 34	09 08			09 34	10 08		10 23		10 34				11 08		
Kirkham & Wesham 97 d					08 17					09 17				10 17								11 17		
Preston 8 d	04u00	06u00			08 30		08 39		08 53	09 30			09 53	10 30		10 42		10 53				11 30		
Leyland d							08a44		08 59				09 59			10a47		10 59						
Chorley d					08 40				09 06	09 40			10 06	10 40				11 06				11 40		
Adlington (Lancashire) d									09 10				10 10					11 10						
Blackrod d									09 14				10 14					11 14						
Horwich Parkway d									09 17				10 17					11 17						
Lostock d									09 21				10 21					11 21						
Southport d											09 13				10 13								11 13	
Burscough Bridge d											09 25				10 25								11 25	
Parbold d											09 30				10 30								11 30	
Appley Bridge d											09 34				10 34								11 34	
Gathurst d											09 37				10 37								11 37	
Wigan Wallgate a											09 42				10 42								11 42	
d						08 43					09 43				10 43								11 43	
Wigan North Western d																								
Hindley d						08 48					09 48				10 48								11 48	
Westhoughton d						08 53					09 53				10 53								11 53	
Bolton a					08 51	09 01			09 26	09 51	10 01		10 26	10 51	11 01			11 26				11 51	12 01	
d	04u35	06u35	06 59	07 45	08 53	09 01		09 16	09 26	09 53	10 01	10 16	10 26	10 53	11 01		11 16	11 26				11 53	12 01	12 16
Salford Crescent a					09 05	09 14		09 29	09 39	10 05	10 14	10 29	10 39	11 05	11 14		11 29	11 39				12 05	12 14	12 29
d					09 06	09 14		09 29	09 39	10 06	10 14	10 29	10 39	11 06	11 14		11 29	11 39				12 06	12 14	12 29
Manchester Victoria 🚊 a								09 35				10 35					11 35							12 35
Rochdale a								*10b34*				*11b34*					*12b34*							*13b34*
Deansgate 🚊 a					09 09	09 18			09 43	10 09	10 18		10 43	11 09	11 18			11 43				12 09	12 18	
Manchester Oxford Road a					09 11	09 20			09 45	10 11	10 21		10 45	11 11	11 20			11 46				12 11	12 20	
Manchester Piccadilly 10 🚊 a			07 14	08 00	09 15	09 24			09 49	10 15	10 25		10 49	11 15	11 24			11 51				12 15	12 24	
Stockport 84 a						09 38			10 04		10 38		11 07		11 37			12 05					12 37	
Alderley Edge 84 a						09 58					10 59				11 58								12 58	
Hazel Grove 86 a									10 12				11 15					12 13						
Buxton 86 a									10 52				11 55					12 53						
Heald Green 85 a			*08 04*			*10c04*					*11c04*				*12c04*								*13e03*	
Manchester Airport 85 ✈ a	05 25	07 25	07 32	08 17	09 33	*09c51*				10 33	*10c55*		*11c23*	11 33	*11c51*							12 33	*12e50*	

For general notes see front of timetable
For details of catering facilities see Directory of Train Operators

A To Liverpool Lime Street (Table 90)

B From Blackburn (Table 94)

C From Clitheroe (Table 94)

D 14 September only. From Leeds to Morecambe (Table 36)

b From 9 November arr. 6 minutes earlier

c Change at Manchester Piccadilly

e Change at Manchester Piccadilly. From 9 November arr. Heald Green 1305, Manchester Airport 1253

Table 82

Sundays

from 14 September

Barrow-in-Furness, Blackpool North, Preston, Southport and Wigan → Bolton → Manchester

Network Diagram - see first page of Table 82

		NT	TP 1◇	NT	NT A	NT B	NT C	NT	TP 1◇	TP 1◇	NT	NT C	NT	TP 1◇	TP 1◇ D	NT		NT A	NT E	NT C	NT	TP 1◇	TP 1◇	NT	NT C
Barrow-in-Furness	d								12 00										13 30			14 00			
Roose	d								12 05										13 34			14 05			
Dalton	d								12 11										13 40			14 11			
Ulverston	d								12 19										13 48			14 19			
Cark	d								12 27										13 57			14 27			
Kents Bank	d								12 31										14 01			14 31			
Grange-over-Sands	d								12 35										14 05			14 35			
Arnside	d								12 41										14 11			14 41			
Silverdale	d								12 46										14 16			14 46			
Carnforth	d					12 34			12 52										14 23			14 54			
Windermere	83 d														12 52							14b14			
Oxenholme Lake District	65 d														13 45							14 39			
Lancaster 6	65 a					12 43			12 59						14 01				14 34			15 01			
	d								13 01						14 01							15 03			
Preston 8	65 a								13 20						14 20							15 21			
Blackpool North	97 d	11 28	12 02		12 17			12 28		13 02			13 28	13 57				14 17			14 28		15 02		
Poulton-le-Fylde	97 d	11 34	12 08		12 23			12 34		13 08			13 34	14 03				14 23			14 34		15 08		
Kirkham & Wesham	97 d		12 17							13 17				14 12								14c51	15 17		
Preston 8	d	11 53	12 30		12 42			12 53		13 30			13 53	14 30				14 42			14 53	15 22	15 30		
Leyland	d	11 59			12a47			12 59					13 59					14a47			14 59				
Chorley	d	12 06	12 40					13 06		13 40			14 06	14 40							15 06		15 40		
Adlington (Lancashire)	d	12 10						13 10					14 10								15 10				
Blackrod	d	12 14						13 14					14 14								15 14				
Horwich Parkway	d	12 17						13 17					14 17								15 17				
Lostock	d	12 21						13 21					14 21								15 21				
Southport	d			12 13							13 13					14 13								15 13	
Burscough Bridge	d			12 25							13 25					14 25								15 25	
Parbold	d			12 30							13 30					14 30								15 30	
Appley Bridge	d			12 34							13 34					14 34								15 34	
Gathurst	d			12 37							13 37					14 37								15 37	
Wigan Wallgate	a			12 42							13 42					14 42								15 42	
	d			12 43							13 43					14 43								15 43	
Wigan North Western	d																								
Hindley	d			12 48							13 48					14 48								15 48	
Westhoughton	d			12 53							13 53					14 53								15 53	
Bolton	a	12 26	12 52	13 01				13 26		13 52	14 01		14 26	14 52		15 01					15 26	15 41	15 52	16 01	
	d	12 26	12 53	13 01			13 16	13 26		13 53	14 01	14 16	14 26	14 53		15 01				15 16	15 26	15 42	15 53	16 01	16 16
Salford Crescent	a	12 39	13 05	13 14			13 29	13 39		14 05	14 14	14 29	14 39	15 05		15 14				15 29	15 39		16 05	16 14	16 29
	d	12 39	13 06	13 14			13 29	13 39		14 06	14 14	14 29	14 39	15 06		15 14				15 29	15 39		16 06	16 14	16 29
Manchester Victoria	⇌ a						13 35					14 35								15 35					16 35
Rochdale	a						14e34					15e34								16e34					17e34
Deansgate	⇌ a	12 43	13 09	13 18				13 43		14 09	14 18		14 43	15 09		15 18					15 43		16 09	16 18	
Manchester Oxford Road	a	12 46	13 11	13 20				13 46		14 11	14 20		14 46	15 11		15 20					15 45	15 56	16 11	16 20	
Manchester Piccadilly 10	⇌ a	12 49	13 18	13 24				13 49		14 15	14 24		14 49	15 15		15 24					15 49	16 00	16 15	16 24	
Stockport	84 a	13 07		13 37				14 07			14 37		15 07			15 36					16 05			16 37	
Alderley Edge	84 a			13 58							14 58					15 58								16 58	
Hazel Grove	86 a	13 15						14 15					15 15								16 12				
Buxton	86 a	13 55						14 56					15 57								16 52				
Heald Green	85 a			14f07							15f04					16f04								17f04	
Manchester Airport	85 ✈ a	13f23	13 35	13f53				14g24		14 33	14f51		15f21	15 33		15f51						16 18	16 33	16f51	

For general notes see front of timetable
For details of catering facilities see Directory of Train Operators

A To Liverpool Lime Street (Table 90)
B 14 September only. From Leeds to Morecambe (Table 36)
C From Clitheroe (Table 94)
D From Edinburgh (Table 65)
E From 21 September
b Change at Oxenholme Lake District and Lancaster
c Until 2 November only
e From 9 November arr. 6 minutes earlier
f Change at Manchester Piccadilly
g From 9 November only. Change at Manchester Piccadilly

Table 82

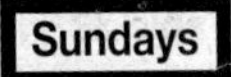

Sundays

from 14 September

Barrow-in-Furness, Blackpool North, Preston, Southport and Wigan → Bolton → Manchester

Network Diagram - see first page of Table 82

	NT	TP 1 ◇	TP 1 ◇	NT	NT	NT	NT	NT	TP 1 ◇	TP 1 ◇	NT	NT	NT	NT	TP 1 ◇	TP 1 ◇	NT	NT	NT	NT	TP 1 ◇	TP 1 ◇	NT
		A			B	C	D					B	D		E			B	D				
		✠													✠								
Barrow-in-Furness d									16 00												18 00		
Roose d									16 05												18 05		
Dalton d									16 11												18 11		
Ulverston d									16 19												18 19		
Cark d									16 27												18 27		
Kents Bank d									16 31												18 31		
Grange-over-Sands d									16 35												18 35		
Arnside d									16 41												18 41		
Silverdale d									16 46												18 46		
Carnforth d						16 37			16 53												18 53		
Windermere 83 d		*15 03*										*16b10*			*16 59*								
Oxenholme Lake District 65 d		15 41										*16c50*			17 47								
Lancaster 6 65 a		15 57				16 46			17 00						18 02						19 00		
d		15 57							17 02			*17c07*			18 03						19 02		
Preston 8 65 a		16 16							17 20						18 21						19 20		
Blackpool North 97 d	15 28		16 02		16 17			16 28		17 02		17 17		17 28		18 02		18 17		18 28		19 02	
Poulton-le-Fylde 97 d	15 34		16 08		16 23			16 34		17 08		17 23		17 34		18 08		18 23		18 34		19 08	
Kirkham & Wesham 97 d		*15e51*	16 17						*16e51*	17 17					*17e51*	18 17					*18e51*	19 17	
Preston 8 d	15 53	16 22	16 30		16 42			16 53	17 22	17 30		17 42		17 53	18 22	18 30		18 42		18 53	19 22	19 30	
Leyland d	15 59				16a47			16 59				17a47		17 59				18a47		18 59			
Chorley d	16 06		16 40					17 06		17 40				18 06		18 40				19 06		19 40	
Adlington (Lancashire) d	16 10							17 10						18 10						19 10			
Blackrod d	16 14							17 14						18 14						19 14			
Horwich Parkway d	16 17							17 17						18 17						19 17			
Lostock d	16 21							17 21						18 21						19 21			
Southport d				16 13							17 13						18 13						19 13
Burscough Bridge d				16 25							17 25						18 25						19 25
Parbold d				16 30							17 30						18 30						19 30
Appley Bridge d				16 34							17 34						18 34						19 34
Gathurst d				16 37							17 37						18 37						19 37
Wigan Wallgate a				16 42							17 42						18 42						19 42
d				16 43							17 43						18 43						19 43
Wigan North Western d																							
Hindley d				16 48							17 48						18 48						19 48
Westhoughton d				16 53							17 53						18 53						19 53
Bolton a	16 26	16 41	16 51	17 01				17 26	17 41	17 52	18 01			18 26	18 41	18 52	19 01			19 26	19 41	19 51	20 01
d	16 26	16 42	16 53	17 01			17 16	17 26	17 42	17 53	18 01		18 16	18 26	18 42	18 53	19 01		19 16	19 26	19 42	19 53	20 01
Salford Crescent a	16 39		17 05	17 14			17 29	17 39		18 05	18 14		18 29	18 39		19 05	19 14		19 29	19 39		20 05	20 14
d	16 39		17 06	17 14			17 29	17 39		18 06	18 14		18 29	18 39		19 06	19 14		19 29	19 39		20 06	20 14
Manchester Victoria ⇌ a							17 35						18 35						19 35				
Rochdale a							*18f34*						*19f34*						*20f34*				
Deansgate ⇌ a	16 43		17 09	17 18				17 43		18 09	18 18			18 43		19 09	19 18			19 43		20 09	20 18
Manchester Oxford Road a	16 45	16 56	17 11	17 20				17 46	17 56	18 11	18 20			18 45	18 56	19 11	19 20			19 45	19 56	20 11	20 20
Manchester Piccadilly 10 ⇌ a	16 49	17 00	17 15	17 24				17 51	18 00	18 15	18 24			18 47	19 00	19 15	19 24			19 49	20 00	20 15	20 24
Stockport 84 a	17 04			17 37				18 05			18 38			19 03			19 38			20 04			20 38
Alderley Edge 84 a				17 58							18 58						19 58						20 58
Hazel Grove 86 a	17 12							18 13						19 11						20 13			
Buxton 86 a	17 52							18 54						19 53						20 53			
Heald Green 85 a				*18g04*							*19g04*						*20g04*						*21g04*
Manchester Airport 85 ✈ a		17 18	17 33	*17g51*					18 18	18 33	*18g52*				19 18	19 33	*19g51*				20 18	20 33	*20g52*

For general notes see front of timetable
For details of catering facilities see Directory of Train Operators

A From Glasgow Central (Table 65)

B To Liverpool Lime Street (Table 90)
C From Leeds to Morecambe (Table 36)
D From Clitheroe (Table 94)
E From Edinburgh (Table 65)
b Change at Oxenholme Lake District and Preston

c Change at Preston
e Until 2 November only
f From 9 November arr. 6 minutes earlier
g Change at Manchester Piccadilly

Sundays from 14 September

Barrow-in-Furness, Blackpool North, Preston, Southport and Wigan → Bolton → Manchester

Network Diagram - see first page of Table 82

		NT	NT	NT	TP	TP	NT	NT	NT	NT	NT	TP	NT	NT	NT	NT	TP	TP	TP	NT	NT	NT	TP
					1 ◇	1 ◇						1 ◇					1 ◇	1 ◇	1 ◇				1 ◇
		A		B	C ✠			D	A						A						D	A	
Barrow-in-Furness	d													19 57			20 50						
Roose	d													20 01			20 55						
Dalton	d													20 07			21 01						
Ulverston	d													20 15			21 09						
Cark	d													20 23			21 17						
Kents Bank	d													20 27			21 21						
Grange-over-Sands	d													20 31			21 25						
Arnside	d													20 37			21 31						
Silverdale	d													20 42			21 36						
Carnforth	d			18 59										20 51			21 43						
Windermere	83 d		18b04		19 00											20b02		21 20					
Oxenholme Lake District	65 d		18c52		19 45											20c48		21 40					
Lancaster 6	65 a			19 13	20 01									21 01			21 52	21 56					
	d		19c08		20 01											21c07	22 02						
Preston 8	65 a				20 20												22 20						
Blackpool North	97 d		19 28			20 02		20 17		20 28		21 02				21 28			22 02		22 17		23 02
Poulton-le-Fylde	97 d		19 34			20 08		20 23		20 34		21 08				21 34			22 08		22 23		23 08
Kirkham & Wesham	97 d				19e51	20 17						21 17					21e51		22 17				23 17
Preston 8	d		19 53		20 22	20 30		20 42		20 53		21 30				21 53	22 22		22 30		22 42		23 30
Leyland	d		19 59					20a47		20 59						21 59					22a47		23 35
Chorley	d		20 06			20 40				21 06		21 40				22 06			22 40				23 41
Adlington (Lancashire)	d		20 10							21 10						22 10							23 45
Blackrod	d		20 14							21 14						22 14							23 48
Horwich Parkway	d		20 17							21 17						22 17							23 51
Lostock	d		20 21							21 21						22 21							23 55
Southport	d						20 13						21 13							22 13			
Burscough Bridge	d						20 25						21 25							22 25			
Parbold	d						20 30						21 30							22 30			
Appley Bridge	d						20 34						21 34							22 34			
Gathurst	d						20 37						21 37							22 37			
Wigan Wallgate	a						20 42						21 42							22 42			
	d						20 43						21 43							22 43			
Wigan North Western	d																						
Hindley	d						20 48						21 48							22 48			
Westhoughton	d						20 53						21 53							22 53			
Bolton	a		20 26		20 41	20 51	21 01			21 26		21 51	22 01			22 26	22 41		22 51	23 01			23 59
	d	20 16	20 26		20 42	20 53	21 01		21 16	21 26		21 53	22 01		22 16	22 26	22 42		22 53	23 01		23 16	00 02
Salford Crescent	a	20 29	20 39			21 05	21 14		21 29	21 39		22 05	22 14		22 29	22 39			23 05	23 14		23 29	
	d	20 29	20 39			21 06	21 14		21 29	21 39	21 50	22 06	22 14		22 29	22 39			23 06	23 14		23 29	
Manchester Victoria 🚋	a	20 35							21 35		21 54				22 35							23 35	
Rochdale	a	21f34									22f34				23 58								
Deansgate 🚋	a		20 43			21 09	21 18			21 43		22 09	22 18			22 43			23 09	23 18			
Manchester Oxford Road	a		20 45		20 56	21 12	21 20			21 45		22 11	22 21			22 45	22 56		23 12	23 21			
Manchester Piccadilly 10 🚋	a		20 49		21 00	21 15	21 24			21 49		22 15	22 25			22 49	23 00		23 15	23 25			00 16
Stockport	84 a		21 04				21 37			22 04			22 38			23 03				23 35			
Alderley Edge	84 a						21 58						22 59							23 56			
Hazel Grove	86 a		21 13							22 13						23 11							
Buxton	86 a		21 53							22 53						23 51							
Heald Green	85 a						22g04									23g20							
Manchester Airport	85 ✈ a				21 18	21 33	21g52					22 33	22g51				23 18		23 33	23g49			00 33

For general notes see front of timetable
For details of catering facilities see Directory of Train Operators

- **A** From Clitheroe (Table 94)
- **B** From Leeds to Morecambe (Table 36)
- **C** From Edinburgh (Table 65)
- **D** To Liverpool Lime Street (Table 90)
- **b** Change at Oxenholme Lake District and Preston
- **c** Change at Preston
- **e** Until 2 November only
- **f** From 9 November arr. 6 minutes earlier
- **g** Change at Manchester Piccadilly

Oxenholme: Lake District → Windermere

Network Diagram - see first page of Table 82

Mondays to Fridays

Miles			TP 1◇ A	TP 1	TP 1	TP 1	TP 1	TP 1◇ B	TP 1	TP 1◇ C	TP 1	TP 1◇ B	TP 1	TP 1	TP 1	TP 1◇ D	TP 1	TP 1	TP 1
0	Oxenholme Lake District	d	05ʃ53	06 51	07 56	09 05	09 53	10 43	11 55	12 57	13 54	14 51	15 51	17 04	17 48	18 52	19 59	21 05	21 53
2¼	Kendal	d	05ʃ57	06 55	08 00	09 09	09 57	10 47	11 59	13 01	13 58	14 55	15 55	17 08	17 52	18 56	20 03	21 09	21 57
4	Burneside	d	ʃ	06x58	08x03		10x00		12x02	13x04	14x01		15x58	17x11		18x59	20x06	21x12	22x00
6½	Staveley	d	ʃ	07x03	08x08		10x05		12x07	13x09	14x06		16x03	17x16		19x04	20x11	21x17	22x05
10	Windermere	a	06ʃ12	07 10	08 15	09 22	10 13	11 01	12 14	13 18	14 13	15 09	16 10	17 23	18 04	19 13	20 18	21 24	22 12

Saturdays

		TP 1◇ E	TP 1	TP 1	TP 1	TP 1	TP 1◇ B	TP 1	TP 1◇ G	TP 1◇ H	TP 1	TP 1◇ B	TP 1	TP 1	TP 1	TP 1◇ D	TP 1
Oxenholme Lake District	d	06 04	07 00	07 56	09 05	09 53	10 43	11 58	12ʃ51	12ʃ59	13 55	14 43	15 58	17 04	17 48	18 41	20 00
Kendal	d	06 08	07 04	08 00	09 09	09 57	10 47	12 02	12ʃ55	13ʃ03	13 59	14 47	16 02	17 08	17 52	18 45	20 04
Burneside	d		07x07	08x03		10x00		12x05	12x58	13x06	14x02		16x05	17x11		18x48	20x07
Staveley	d		07x12	08x08		10x05		12x10	13x03	13x11	14x07		16x10	17x16		18x53	20x12
Windermere	a	06 25	07 19	08 15	09 22	10 13	11 01	12 17	13ʃ12	13ʃ20	14 14	15 01	16 17	17 23	18 04	19 02	20 19

Sundays until 13 July

		TP 1◇ J	TP 1	TP 1	TP 1	TP 1	TP 1	TP 1	TP 1◇ D	TP 1	TP 1	TP 1
Oxenholme Lake District	d	10 47	12 18	13 02	13 50	15 17	16 03	17 00	17 54	19 00	19 50	20 45
Kendal	d	10 51	12 22	13 06	13 54	15 21	16 07	17 04	17 58	19 04	19 54	20 49
Burneside	d	10x54			13x57	15x24			18x01		19x57	20x52
Staveley	d	10x59			14x02	15x29			18x06		20x02	20x57
Windermere	a	11 10	12 34	13 18	14 09	15 36	16 19	17 16	18 15	19 16	20 09	21 04

Sundays 20 July to 7 September

		TP 1◇ J	TP 1	TP 1	TP 1	TP 1	TP 1	TP 1	TP 1◇ D	TP 1	TP 1	TP 1
Oxenholme Lake District	d	10 47	12 10	13 02	13 50	15 17	16 03	17 00	17 54	19 00	20 04	20 50
Kendal	d	10 51	12 14	13 06	13 54	15 21	16 07	17 04	17 58	19 04	20 08	20 54
Burneside	d	10x54			13x57	15x24			18x01		20x11	20x57
Staveley	d	10x59			14x02	15x29			18x06		20x16	21x02
Windermere	a	11 10	12 26	13 18	14 09	15 36	16 19	17 16	18 15	19 16	20 23	21 09

Sundays from 14 September

		TP 1◇ C	TP 1	TP 1	TP 1	TP 1	TP 1	TP 1	TP 1	TP 1 D
Oxenholme Lake District	d	12 27	13 50	14 43	15 46	16 39	17 41	18 35	19 39	20 58
Kendal	d	12 31	13 54	14 47	15 50	16 43	17 45	18 39	19 43	21 02
Burneside	d	12x35	13x57		15x53		17x48	18x42	19x46	
Staveley	d	12x40	14x02		15x58		17x53	18x47	19x51	
Windermere	a	12 48	14 09	14 59	16 05	16 55	18 00	18 54	19 58	21 16

For general notes see front of timetable
For details of catering facilities see Directory of Train Operators

- **A** Not Mondays, 21 July to 8 September. From Barrow-in-Furness (Table 82)
- **B** From Manchester Airport (Table 82)
- **C** From Preston (Table 65)
- **D** From Lancaster (Table 65)
- **E** From Barrow-in-Furness (Table 82)
- **G** From 13 September. From Preston (Table 65)
- **H** Until 6 September. From Preston (Table 65)
- **J** From Manchester Piccadilly (Table 65)

Windermere → Oxenholme: Lake District

Mondays to Fridays

Network Diagram - see first page of Table 82

Miles	Miles			TP 1 A	TP MO B 🚌	TP 1	TP 1	TP 1	TP 1◇ C	TP 1	TP 1◇ D	TP 1	TP 1◇ D	TP 1	TP 1	TP 1	TP 1◇ D	TP 1	TP 1	TP 1	TP 1◇ E
—	0	**Windermere**	d	06§20	06§20	07 24	08 20	09 28	10 18	11 30	12 21	13 24	14 18	15 21	16 28	17 27	18 09	19 18	20 27	21 28	22 16
—	3½	Staveley	d	06x25	06§30	07x29	08x25	09x33	.	11x35	.	13x29	.	15x26	16x33	.	18x15	19x23	20x32	21x33	22x21
—	6	Burneside	d	06x30	06§40	07x34	08x30	09x38	.	11x40	.	13x34	.	15x31	16x38	.	18x20	19x28	20x37	21x38	22x26
—	7¾	Kendal	d	06§34	06§50	07 38	08 34	09 42	10 29	11 44	12 32	13 38	14 29	15 35	16 42	17 38	18 23	19 32	20 41	21 42	22 30
—	10	**Oxenholme Lake District**	a	06§40	07§00	07 44	08 40	09 48	10 35	11 50	12 38	13 44	14 35	15 41	16 48	17 44	18 29	19 38	20 47	21 48	22 36

Saturdays

		TP 1	TP 1	TP 1	TP 1	TP 1◇ C	TP 1	TP 1◇ D	TP 1	TP 1◇ G	TP 1	TP 1 H	TP 1 J	TP 1	TP 1◇ D	TP 1	TP 1 G
Windermere	d	06 35	07 24	08 28	09 26	10 18	11 27	12 23	13 25	14 18	15 22	16§22	16§34	17 27	18 10	19 22	20 24
Staveley	d	06x40	07x29	08x33	09x31	.	11x32	.	13x30	.	15x27	16§27	16§39	.	18x16	19x27	20x29
Burneside	d	06x45	07x34	08x38	09x36	.	11x37	.	13x35	.	15x32	16x32	16x44	.	18x21	19x32	20x34
Kendal	d	06 49	07 38	08 42	09 40	10 29	11 41	12 34	13 39	14 29	15 36	16x36	16x48	17 38	18 24	19 36	20 38
Oxenholme Lake District	a	06 55	07 44	08 48	09 46	10 35	11 47	12 40	13 45	14 35	15 42	16§42	16§54	17 44	18 30	19 42	20 44

Sundays
until 13 July

		TP 1	TP 1	TP 1	TP 1	TP 1	TP 1	TP 1◇ D	TP 1	TP 1	TP 1	TP 1◇ D
Windermere	d	11 40	12 38	13 23	14 28	15 41	16 26	17 21	18 30	19 20	20 23	21 20
Staveley	d	11x45	.	.	14x33	.	16x31	.	18x35	19x25	.	21x25
Burneside	d	11x50	.	.	14x38	.	16x36	.	18x40	19x30	.	21x30
Kendal	d	11 54	12 49	13 34	14 42	15 52	16 40	17 32	18 44	19 34	20 34	21 34
Oxenholme Lake District	a	12 00	12 55	13 39	14 48	15 58	16 46	17 38	18 50	19 40	20 40	21 40

Sundays
20 July to 7 September

		TP 1	TP 1	TP 1	TP 1	TP 1	TP 1	TP 1◇ C	TP 1	TP 1	TP 1	TP 1◇ K
Windermere	d	11 40	12 30	13 23	14 34	15 41	16 26	17 21	18 25	19 20	20 28	21 20
Staveley	d	11x45	12x35	.	14x39	.	16x31	.	18x30	19x25	.	21x25
Burneside	d	11x50	12x40	.	14x44	.	16x36	.	18x35	19x30	.	21x30
Kendal	d	11 54	12 44	13 34	14 48	15 52	16 40	17 32	18 39	19 34	20 39	21 34
Oxenholme Lake District	a	12 00	12 50	13 39	14 54	15 58	16 46	17 38	18 45	19 40	20 45	21 40

Sundays
from 14 September

		TP 1	TP 1	TP 1	TP 1	TP 1	TP 1	TP 1	TP 1 G	TP 1◇ D
Windermere	d	12 52	14 14	15 03	16 10	16 59	18 04	19 00	20 02	21 20
Staveley	d	12x57	14x19	15x08	.	17x04	.	19x05	.	21x25
Burneside	d	13x02	14x24	15x13	.	17x09	.	19x10	.	21x30
Kendal	d	13 06	14 28	15 17	16 21	17 13	18 15	19 14	20 13	21 34
Oxenholme Lake District	a	13 12	14 34	15 23	16 27	17 19	18 21	19 20	20 19	21 40

For general notes see front of timetable
For details of catering facilities see Directory of Train Operators

A Not Mondays, 21 July to 8 September
B 21 July to 8 September
C To Preston (Table 65)
D To Manchester Airport (Table 82)
E To Barrow-in-Furness (Table 82)
G To Lancaster (Table 65)
H Until 6 September
J From 13 September
K To Manchester Piccadilly (Table 82)

Stoke-on-Trent and Crewe → Manchester Airport, Stockport and Manchester

Network Diagram - see first page of Table 78

Miles	Miles	Miles		NT MX A	NT MX	TP 1 ◇ B	NT C	NT D	NT	TP 1 ◇ E	AW	NT G	NT	NT A	NT	NT	NT H	EM ◇ J 🍴	NT G	XC 1 ◇ 🍴	NT	NT	NT K	AW ◇ L
—	—	—	London Euston 15 ⊖ 65 d																					
—	—	—	Birmingham New Street 12 68 d																	06 03				
—	—	—	Wolverhampton 7 68 d																	06 21				
—	—	—	Stafford 65, 68 d																	06 34				
0	—	—	**Stoke-on-Trent** 50, 68 d																	06 53		06 56		
3	—	—	Longport 50 d																			07 00		
6¼	—	—	Kidsgrove 50 d																			07 05		
—	0	—	**Crewe 10** 65 d		00 56				06 03		06 26					06 35					07 00			07 09
—	4¾	—	Sandbach d						06 10							06 42					07 07			
—	8½	—	Holmes Chapel d						06 14							06 46					07 11			
—	10½	—	Goostrey d						06 17							06 49					07 14			
—	14¼	—	Chelford d						06 22							06 54					07 19			
—	17¼	—	Alderley Edge d						06 26						06 49	06 58					07 23			
—	19	0	**Wilmslow** d						06 29						06 52	07 01					07 26			07 30
—	—	2	Styal d																					
—	—	4¼	**Manchester Airport** ✈ a		01 21										07 02									
—	20½	—	Handforth d						06 32							07 04					07 29			
11¾	—	—	Congleton d																	07 05		07 12		
19¾	—	—	**Macclesfield** a																	07 13		07 19		
—	—	—	d										06 45							07 14		07 20		
22½	—	—	Prestbury d										06 49									07 24		
24½	—	—	Adlington (Cheshire) d										06 52									07 27		
26½	—	—	Poynton d										06 56									07 31		
28	—	—	Bramhall d										06 58									07 34		
29½	22¾	—	Cheadle Hulme d						06 37				07 00			07 09					07 34	07 37		
31¼	25	—	**Stockport** a						06 42		06 53		07 06			07 14				07 30	07 39	07 42		07 46
—	—	—	d	00 01		05 53	06 17	06 36	06 42	06 53	06 55	07 02	07 06	07 13		07 14	07 19	07 24	07 30	07 31	07 39	07 44	07 49	07 47
31¾	26½	—	Heaton Chapel d						06 46			07 06	07 10						07 33		07 43			
34¾	28	—	Levenshulme d						06 49			07 09	07 13						07 36		07 46			
37¼	31	—	**Manchester Piccadilly 10** a	00 14	01 42	06 04	06 27	06 47	06 56	07 05	07 11	07 17	07 22	07 25	07 28	07 28	07 30	07 35	07 45	07 47	07 55	07 57	08 00	08 07
—	—	—	d				06 29										07 30	07 35					08 00	
38¼	31½	—	**Manchester Oxford Road** a				06 31										07 33	07 38					08 03	
38¾	32	—	Deansgate a				06 34										07 35						08 15	

	TP 1 ◇ N 🍴	NT G	NT	NT G	NT A	NT G	XC 1 ◇ 🍴	NT	NT	NT H	NT	EM ◇ J 🍴	NT BHX	NT	NT	VT 1 ◇ ⊠	NT G	NT	NT D	NT A	XC 1 ◇ 🍴	TP 1 ◇ N 🍴	AW ◇ L 🍴	NT
London Euston 15 ⊖ 65 d																06 20								
Birmingham New Street 12 68 d							06 30														07 18			
Wolverhampton 7 68 d							07 06														07 39			
Stafford 65, 68 d							07 18														07 54			
Stoke-on-Trent 50, 68 d			07 13				07 36				07 40					08 04					08 13			
Longport 50 d			07 20																					
Kidsgrove 50 d			07 25								07 48													
Crewe 10 65 d								07 33	07 43									08 00					08 27	
Sandbach d								07 40	07 50									08 07						
Holmes Chapel d								07 45	07 55									08 11						
Goostrey d								07 48										08 14						
Chelford d								07 52										08 19						
Alderley Edge d								07 56	08 04				08 09					08 23						
Wilmslow d								08 00	08 07				08 12					08 26					08 45	
Styal d														←										
Manchester Airport ✈ a									08 14					08 14										
Handforth d								08 03	→									08 29						
Congleton d			07 32				07 49				07 55										08 25			
Macclesfield a			07 39				07 56				08 02					08 20					08 32			
d			07 40				07 57				08 03				08 08	08 20					08 33			08 41
Prestbury d			07 44												08 13									08 45
Adlington (Cheshire) d			07 47												08 16									08 48
Poynton d			07 50												08 19									08 52
Bramhall d			07 53								08 10				08 22									08 54
Cheadle Hulme d			07 55					08 09			08 14		08 18		08 24			08 34						08 56
Stockport a			08 03				08 09	08 13			08 19		08 24		08 29	08s35		08 41			08 46		08 54	09 01
d	07 55	08 00	08 03	←	08 10	08 15	08 10	08 15		08 21	08 20	08 27	08 24		08 30		08 37	08 41	08 42	08 46	08 46	08 51	08 54	09 02
Heaton Chapel d		08 05		08 05				08 18							08 33		08 41	08 45						09 05
Levenshulme d		→		08 08				08 21							08 36		08 44	08 48						09 08
Manchester Piccadilly 10 a	08 08		08 15	08 19	08 24	08 26	08 27	08 31		08 31	08 34	08 36	08 39	08 42	08 43	08 48	08 53	08 56	08 56	08 59	09 02	09 01	09 13	09 18
d										08 31		08 37						08 56						09 19
Manchester Oxford Road a										08 35		08 40						08 58						09 21
Deansgate a										08 37								09 03						09 26

For general notes see front of timetable
For details of catering facilities see Directory of Train Operators

A From Chester (Table 88)

B From Sheffield (Table 78) to Manchester Airport (Table 85)

C To Blackpool North (Table 82)

D From Buxton (Table 86)

E From Doncaster to Manchester Airport (Table 29)

G From Hazel Grove (Table 86)

H From Buxton (Table 86) to Blackpool North (Table 82)

J From Nottingham to Liverpool Lime Street (Table 49)

K From Buxton (Table 86) to Liverpool Lime Street (Table 89)

L From Cardiff Central (Table 131)

N From Cleethorpes to Manchester Airport (Table 29)

Stoke-on-Trent and Crewe → Manchester Airport, Stockport and Manchester

Network Diagram - see first page of Table 78

Station		XC 1 ◇ A	VT 1 ◇ ⊠	NT	NT B	NT C	EM ◇ D	NT	VT 1 ◇ ⊠	NT	NT E	XC 1 ◇ G	TP 1 ◇ H	AW ◇ J	NT	XC 1 ◇ K	VT 1 ◇ ⊠	NT	NT L	NT N	EM ◇ Q	NT	VT 1 ◇ ⊠	NT	NT E
London Euston 15	⊖ 65 d		07 03						07 35								08 05						08 35		
Birmingham New Street 12	68 d	07 48										08 18				08 48									
Wolverhampton 7	68 d	08 06										08 39				09 06									
Stafford	65, 68 d	08 18										08 54				09 18									
Stoke-on-Trent	50, 68 d	08 36	08 41						09 06			09 13				09 36	09 41						10 06		
Longport	50 d																								
Kidsgrove	50 d																								
Crewe 10	65 d							08 40		09 00				09 27								09 38		10 00	
Sandbach	d							08 47		09 07												09 45		10 07	
Holmes Chapel	d							08 51		09 11												09 49		10 11	
Goostrey	d									09 14														10 14	
Chelford	d									09 19														10 19	
Alderley Edge	d			08 57				09 00		09 23								09 53				09 58		10 23	
Wilmslow	d			09 00				09 03		09 26				09 44				09 56				10 01		10 26	
Styal	d																								
Manchester Airport	✈ a							09 15														10 11			
Handforth	d			09 03						09 29								09 59						10 29	
Congleton	d																								
Macclesfield	a	08 52	08 57									09 31				09 52	09 57								
	d	08 53	08 57									09 32			09 41	09 53	09 57								
Prestbury	d														09 45										
Adlington (Cheshire)	d														09 48										
Poynton	d														09 52										
Bramhall	d														09 54										
Cheadle Hulme	d			09 09						09 34					09 56			10 04						10 34	
Stockport	a	09 05	09s12	09 14					09s34	09 39		09 46		09 54	10 01	10 05	10s12	10 09					10s34	10 39	
	d	09 06		09 14	09 19	09 20	09 24			09 39	09 49	09 46	09 53	09 56	10 02	10 06		10 11	10 18	10 21	10 25			10 39	10 49
Heaton Chapel	d				09 23					09 43					10 05			10 15						10 43	
Levenshulme	d				09 26					09 46					10 08			10 18						10 46	
Manchester Piccadilly 10	a	09 20	09 25	09 26	09 32	09 32	09 36	09 41	09 46	09 54	10 01	10 02	10 03	10 13	10 18	10 20	10 24	10 28	10 29	10 33	10 36	10 39	10 46	10 54	11 00
	d				09 33		09 37								10 19				10 30		10 37				
Manchester Oxford Road	a				09 36		09 40								10 21				10 32		10 40				
Deansgate	a				09 38										10 26				10 35						

Station		XC 1 ◇ U	TP 1 ◇ H	AW ◇ J	NT	XC 1 ◇ V	VT 1 ◇ ⊠	NT	NT B	NT C	EM ◇ X	NT	VT 1 ◇ ⊠	NT	NT E	XC 1 ◇ Y	TP 1 ◇ H	AW ◇ Z	NT	XC 1 ◇ AA	VT 1 ◇ ⊠	NT	NT B	NT C	EM ◇ Q
London Euston 15	⊖ 65 d						09 05						09 35								10 05				
Birmingham New Street 12	68 d	09 18				09 48										10 18				10 48					
Wolverhampton 7	68 d	09 39				10 06										10 39				11 06					
Stafford	65, 68 d					10 18														11 18					
Stoke-on-Trent	50, 68 d	10 13				10 36	10 41						11 06			11 13				11 36	11 41				
Longport	50 d																								
Kidsgrove	50 d																								
Crewe 10	65 d			10 27								10 38		11 00				11 27							
Sandbach	d											10 45		11 07											
Holmes Chapel	d											10 49		11 11											
Goostrey	d													11 14											
Chelford	d													11 19											
Alderley Edge	d							10 53				10 58		11 23								11 53			
Wilmslow	d			10 45				10 56				11 01		11 26				11 44				11 56			
Styal	d																								
Manchester Airport	✈ a											11 11													
Handforth	d							10 59						11 29								11 59			
Congleton	d	10 25																							
Macclesfield	a	10 32				10 52	10 57									11 31				11 52	11 57				
	d	10 33			10 41	10 53	10 57									11 32			11 41	11 53	11 57				
Prestbury	d				10 45														11 45						
Adlington (Cheshire)	d				10 48														11 48						
Poynton	d				10 52														11 52						
Bramhall	d				10 54														11 54						
Cheadle Hulme	d				10 56			11 04						11 34					11 56			12 04			
Stockport	a	10 46		10 53	11 01	11 05	11s12	11 09					11s34	11 39		11 46		11 53	12 01	12 05	12s12	12 09			
	d	10 46	10 53	10 57	11 02	11 06		11 11	11 19	11 17	11 25			11 39	11 49	11 46	11 53	11 56	12 02	12 06		12 11	12 19	12 17	12 25
Heaton Chapel	d				11 05			11 15						11 43					12 05			12 15			
Levenshulme	d				11 08			11 18						11 46					12 08			12 18			
Manchester Piccadilly 10	a	11 02	11 03	11 13	11 18	11 20	11 24	11 28	11 29	11 32	11 36	11 39	11 46	11 54	12 00	12 02	12 03	12 13	12 18	12 20	12 24	12 28	12 29	12 32	12 36
	d				11 19				11 30		11 37								12 19				12 30		12 37
Manchester Oxford Road	a				11 21				11 32		11 40								12 21				12 32		12 40
Deansgate	a				11 26				11 35										12 26				12 35		

For general notes see front of timetable
For details of catering facilities see Directory of Train Operators

- **A** From Southampton Central (Table 51)
- **B** From Buxton (Table 86) to Blackpool North (Table 82)
- **C** From Chester (Table 88)
- **D** From Nottingham to Liverpool Lime Street (Table 49)
- **E** From Hazel Grove (Table 86)
- **G** From Gatwick Airport (Table 51)
- **H** From Cleethorpes to Manchester Airport (Table 29)
- **J** From Carmarthen (Table 128)
- **K** From Derby (Table 57)
- **L** From Northwich (Table 88) to Blackpool North (Table 82)
- **N** From Buxton (Table 86)
- **Q** Until 5 September from Norwich to Liverpool Lime Street (Table 49). From 8 September from Sheffield to Liverpool Lime Street (Table 89)
- **U** From Exeter St Davids (Table 51)
- **V** From Bournemouth (Table 51)
- **X** Until 5 September from Cambridge to Liverpool Lime Street (Table 49). From 8 September from Sheffield to Liverpool Lime Street (Table 89)
- **Y** From Reading (Table 51)
- **Z** From Milford Haven (Table 128)
- **AA** From Birmingham International (Table 65)

Stoke-on-Trent and Crewe → Manchester Airport, Stockport and Manchester

Network Diagram - see first page of Table 78

	NT	VT 1 ◇ ⊠		NT	VT 1 ◇ ⊠	NT A	XC R 1 B ⊡	TP 1 ◇ C ⊥	AW ◇ D ⊥	NT	XC R 1 E ⊡	NT	VT 1 ◇ ⊡	NT G	NT	NT H	EM ◇ J ⊥	NT	VT 1 ◇ ⊡	NT	NT A	XC 1 ◇ K ⊡	TP 1 ◇ C ⊥	AW ◇ L ⊥
London Euston 15 ⊖ 65 d		10 35			09b38								11 05						11 35					
Birmingham New Street 12 68 d							11 18				11 48											12 18		
Wolverhampton 7 68 d							11 39															12 39		
Stafford 65, 68 d											12 18													
Stoke-on-Trent 50, 68 d		12 06					12 13				12 36		12 41						13 06			13 13		
Longport 50 d																								
Kidsgrove 50 d																								
Crewe 10 65 d	11 38			12 00	12 08				12 27									12 38		13 00				13 27
Sandbach d	11 45			12 07														12 45		13 07				
Holmes Chapel d	11 49			12 11														12 49		13 11				
Goostrey d				12 14																13 14				
Chelford d				12 19																13 19				
Alderley Edge d	11 58			12 23								12 53						12 58		13 23				
Wilmslow d	12 01			12 26	12 28				12 45			12 56						13 01		13 26				13 44
Styal d																								
Manchester Airport ✈ a	12 11																	13 11						
Handforth d				12 29								12 59								13 29				
Congleton d							12 25																	
Macclesfield a							12 32				12 52		12 57									13 31		
d							12 33			12 41	12 53		12 57									13 32		
Prestbury d										12 45														
Adlington (Cheshire) d										12 48														
Poynton d										12 52														
Bramhall d										12 54														
Cheadle Hulme d				12 34						12 56		13 04								13 34				
Stockport a		12s34		12 39	12s41		12 46		12 52	13 01	13 05	13 09	13s12						13s34	13 39		13 46		13 53
d				12 39		12 49	12 46	12 53	12 56	13 02	13 06	13 11		13 19	←	13 17	13 25			13 39	13 49	13 46	13 53	13 56
Heaton Chapel d				12 43						13 05		13 15			13 15					13 43				
Levenshulme d				12 46						13 08		→			13 18					13 46				
Manchester Piccadilly 10 a	12 39	12 46		12 54	12 55	13 00	13 02	13 03	13 13	13 18	13 20		13 24	13 27	13 28	13 32	13 36	13 39	13 46	13 54	14 00	14 02	14 03	14 13
d										13 19				13 30			13 37							
Manchester Oxford Road a										13 21				13 32			13 40							
Deansgate a										13 26				13 35										

	NT	XC 1 ◇ N ⊡	NT	VT 1 ◇ ⊡	NT G	NT	NT H	EM ◇ J ⊥	NT	VT 1 ◇ ⊡	NT	NT A	XC R 1 Q ⊡	TP 1 ◇ C ⊥	AW ◇ D ⊥	NT	XC R 1 E ⊡	NT	VT 1 ◇ ⊡	NT G	NT	NT H	EM ◇ J ⊥	NT
London Euston 15 ⊖ 65 d				12 05						12 35									13 05					
Birmingham New Street 12 68 d		12 48											13 18				13 48							
Wolverhampton 7 68 d		13 06											13 39				14 06							
Stafford 65, 68 d		13 18															14 18							
Stoke-on-Trent 50, 68 d		13 36		13 41						14 06			14 13				14 36		14 41					
Longport 50 d																								
Kidsgrove 50 d																								
Crewe 10 65 d									13 38		14 00				14 27									14 38
Sandbach d									13 45		14 07													14 45
Holmes Chapel d									13 49		14 11													14 49
Goostrey d											14 14													
Chelford d											14 19													
Alderley Edge d			13 53						13 58		14 23							14 53						14 58
Wilmslow d			13 56						14 01		14 26				14 45			14 56						15 01
Styal d																								
Manchester Airport ✈ a									14 11															15 11
Handforth d			13 59								14 29							14 59						
Congleton d													14 25											
Macclesfield a		13 52		13 57									14 32				14 52		14 57					
d	13 41	13 53		13 57									14 33			14 41	14 53		14 57					
Prestbury d	13 45															14 45								
Adlington (Cheshire) d	13 48															14 48								
Poynton d	13 52															14 52								
Bramhall d	13 54															14 54								
Cheadle Hulme d	13 56		14 04								14 34					14 56		15 04						
Stockport a	14 01	14 05	14 11	14s12						14s34	14 39		14 46		14 53	15 01	15 05	15 09	15s12					
d	14 02	14 06	14 11		14 19	←	14 17	14 25			14 39	14 49	14 46	14 53	14 56	15 02	15 06	15 11		15 19	←	15 17	15 25	
Heaton Chapel d	14 05		14 15			14 15					14 43					15 05		15 15			15 15			
Levenshulme d	14 08		→			14 18					14 46					15 08		→			15 18			
Manchester Piccadilly 10 a	14 18	14 20		14 24	14 27	14 28	14 32	14 36	14 39	14 46	14 54	15 00	15 02	15 03	15 13	15 18	15 20		15 24	15 27	15 28	15 32	15 36	15 39
d	14 19				14 30			14 37								15 19				15 30			15 37	
Manchester Oxford Road a	14 21				14 32			14 40								15 21				15 32			15 40	
Deansgate a	14 26				14 35											15 26				15 35				

For general notes see front of timetable
For details of catering facilities see Directory of Train Operators

- **A** From Hazel Grove (Table 86)
- **B** From Plymouth (Table 51)
- **C** From Cleethorpes to Manchester Airport (Table 29)
- **D** From Milford Haven (Table 128)
- **E** From Bournemouth (Table 51)
- **G** From Buxton (Table 86) to Blackpool North (Table 82)
- **H** From Chester (Table 88)
- **J** Until 5 September from Norwich to Liverpool Lime Street (Table 49). From 8 September from Sheffield to Liverpool Lime Street (Table 89)
- **K** From Reading (Table 51)
- **L** From Carmarthen (Table 128)
- **N** From Birmingham International (Table 65)
- **Q** From Penzance (Table 135)
- **b** By changing at Crewe, passengers may depart at 0946

Stoke-on-Trent and Crewe → Manchester Airport, Stockport and Manchester

Network Diagram - see first page of Table 78

		VT	NT	NT	XC	TP	AW	NT	XC	NT	VT	NT	NT
		1 ◇			1 ◇	1 ◇	◇		1 ◇		1 ◇		
				A	B	C	D		E			G	
		⊏P			⊏P	⌶	⌶		⊏P		⊏P		
London Euston 15	⊖ 65 d	13 35									14 05		
Birmingham New Street 12	68 d				14 18				14 48				
Wolverhampton 7	68 🚋 d				14 39				15 06				
Stafford	65, 68 d								15 18				
Stoke-on-Trent	50, 68 d	15 06			15 13				15 36		15 41		
Longport	50 d												
Kidsgrove	50 d												
Crewe 10	65 d		15 00				15 27						
Sandbach	d		15 07										
Holmes Chapel	d		15 11										
Goostrey	d		15 14										
Chelford	d		15 19										
Alderley Edge	d		15 23							15 53			
Wilmslow	d		15 26				15 45			15 56			
Styal	d												
Manchester Airport	✈ a												
Handforth	d		15 29							15 59			
Congleton	d												
Macclesfield	a				15 31				15 52		15 57		
	d				15 32			15 41	15 53		15 57		
Prestbury	d							15 45					
Adlington (Cheshire)	d							15 48					
Poynton	d							15 52					
Bramhall	d							15 54					
Cheadle Hulme	d		15 34					15 56		16 04			
Stockport	a	15s34	15 39		15 46		15 52	16 01	16 05	16 09	16s12		
	d		15 39	15 49	15 46	15 53	15 56	16 02	16 06	16 11		16 19	←
Heaton Chapel	d		15 43					16 05		16 15			16 15
Levenshulme	d		15 46					16 08		→			16 18
Manchester Piccadilly 10	🚋 a	15 46	15 54	16 00	16 02	16 03	16 13	16 18	16 20		16 24	16 27	16 28
	d							16 19				16 30	
Manchester Oxford Road	a							16 21				16 32	
Deansgate	🚋 a							16 26				16 35	

		NT	EM	NT	VT	NT	NT	NT	NT	NT	XC	TP	NT
											R		
			◇		1 ◇						1	1 ◇	
		H	J				K			A	L	C	H
			⌶		⊏P						⊏P	⌶	
London Euston 15	⊖ 65 d				14 35								
Birmingham New Street 12	68 d										15 18		
Wolverhampton 7	68 🚋 d										15 39		
Stafford	65, 68 d												
Stoke-on-Trent	50, 68 d				16 06						16 13		
Longport	50 d												
Kidsgrove	50 d												
Crewe 10	65 d			15 38					16 00				
Sandbach	d			15 45					16 07				
Holmes Chapel	d			15 49					16 11				
Goostrey	d								16 14				
Chelford	d								16 19				
Alderley Edge	d			15 58					16 23				
Wilmslow	d			16 01					16 26				
Styal	d												
Manchester Airport	✈ a			16 11									
Handforth	d								16 29				
Congleton	d										16 25		
Macclesfield	a										16 32		
	d					16 10					16 33		
Prestbury	d					16 14							
Adlington (Cheshire)	d					16 17							
Poynton	d					16 21							
Bramhall	d					16 23							
Cheadle Hulme	d					16 26							
Stockport	a				16s34	16 30			16 34		16 46		
	d	16 17	16 25			16 35	16 41	←	16 43	16 49	16 46	16 53	16 56
Heaton Chapel	d					16 38		16 38					
Levenshulme	d					→		16 41					
Manchester Piccadilly 10	🚋 a	16 32	16 35	16 41	16 46		16 50	16 54	16 54	17 00	17 02	17 03	17 09
	d		16 37				16 52	16 56					
Manchester Oxford Road	a		16 39				16 55	16 58					
Deansgate	🚋 a						16 58	17 03					

		AW	NT	XC	VT	NT	NT	NT	EM	NT	NT	VT	NT
				R									
		◇		1	1 ◇				◇			1 ◇	
		N	Q	U			H	V	J				
		⌶		⊏P	⊏P				⌶			⊠	
London Euston 15	⊖ 65 d				15 05							15 35	
Birmingham New Street 12	68 d			15 48									
Wolverhampton 7	68 🚋 d												
Stafford	65, 68 d			16 18									
Stoke-on-Trent	50, 68 d			16 36	16 41							17 06	
Longport	50 d												
Kidsgrove	50 d												
Crewe 10	65 d	16 27								16 42			17 00
Sandbach	d									16 49			17 07
Holmes Chapel	d									16 53			17 11
Goostrey	d												17 14
Chelford	d												17 19
Alderley Edge	d					16 53				17 02			17 23
Wilmslow	d	16 45				16 56				17 05			17 26
Styal	d												
Manchester Airport	✈ a									17 15			
Handforth	d					16 59							17 29
Congleton	d												
Macclesfield	a			16 52	16 57							17 21	
	d			16 53	16 57						17 10	17 22	
Prestbury	d										17 14		
Adlington (Cheshire)	d										17 17		
Poynton	d										17 21		
Bramhall	d										17 23		
Cheadle Hulme	d					17 04					17 26		17 34
Stockport	a	16 53		17 05	17s12	17 10					17 30	17s35	17 39
	d	16 55	16 59	17 06		17 11	17 16	17 18	17 26		17 32		17 39
Heaton Chapel	d		17 03			17 15	17 19						17 43
Levenshulme	d		17 06			17 18	17 22						17 46
Manchester Piccadilly 10	🚋 a	17 11	17 15	17 20	17 24	17 28	17 31	17 31	17 36	17 41	17 44	17 49	17 54
	d		17 15					17 32	17 37				
Manchester Oxford Road	a		17 17					17 34	17 39				
Deansgate	🚋 a		17 21					17 37					

		XC	NT	TP	AW	NT	XC	VT	NT	NT	NT	EM	NT
		R			R								
		1		1 ◇			1 ◇	1 ◇				◇	
		B	X	C	D		E		A	V	H	J	
		⊏P		⌶	⌶		⊏P	⊏P				⌶	
London Euston 15	⊖ 65 d							16 05					
Birmingham New Street 12	68 d	16 18					16 48						
Wolverhampton 7	68 🚋 d	16 39					17 06						
Stafford	65, 68 d						17 18						
Stoke-on-Trent	50, 68 d	17 13					17 36	17 41					
Longport	50 d												
Kidsgrove	50 d												
Crewe 10	65 d				17 27								17 38
Sandbach	d												17 45
Holmes Chapel	d												17 49
Goostrey	d												17 52
Chelford	d												17 57
Alderley Edge	d												18 01
Wilmslow	d				17 46								18 04
Styal	d												18 07
Manchester Airport	✈ a												18 15
Handforth	d												
Congleton	d	17 25											
Macclesfield	a	17 32					17 52	17 57					
	d	17 33				17 41	17 53	17 57					
Prestbury	d					17 45							
Adlington (Cheshire)	d					17 48							
Poynton	d					17 52							
Bramhall	d					17 54							
Cheadle Hulme	d					17 57							
Stockport	a	17 46			17 54	18 02	18 05	18s11					
	d	17 46	17 49	17 53	17 56	18 02	18 06		18 15	18 19	18 17	18 26	
Heaton Chapel	d					18 05							
Levenshulme	d					18 08							
Manchester Piccadilly 10	🚋 a	18 02	18 02	18 03	18 12	18 20	18 20	18 25	18 26	18 29	18 32	18 36	18 40
	d									18 31		18 37	
Manchester Oxford Road	a									18 33		18 39	
Deansgate	🚋 a									18 36			

For general notes see front of timetable
For details of catering facilities see Directory of Train Operators

- **A** From Hazel Grove (Table 86)
- **B** From Reading (Table 51)
- **C** From Cleethorpes to Manchester Airport (Table 29)
- **D** From Carmarthen (Table 128)
- **E** From Birmingham International (Table 65)
- **G** From Hazel Grove (Table 86) to Blackpool North (Table 82)
- **H** From Chester (Table 88)
- **J** Until 5 September from Norwich to Liverpool Lime Street (Table 49). From 8 September from Sheffield to Liverpool Lime Street (Table 89)
- **K** From Buxton (Table 86) to Preston (Table 82)
- **L** From Penzance (Table 135)
- **N** From Milford Haven (Table 128)
- **Q** To Blackpool North (Table 82)
- **U** From Bournemouth (Table 51)
- **V** From Buxton (Table 86) to Blackpool North (Table 82)
- **X** From Buxton (Table 86)

Table 84

Mondays to Fridays

Stoke-on-Trent and Crewe → Manchester Airport, Stockport and Manchester

Network Diagram - see first page of Table 78

	NT	NT	VT	NT	NT	XC	NT	TP	AW	NT	XC	VT	NT	VT	NT	NT	EM	NT	VT	NT	NT	XC	TP	AW
			1 ◇			R 1		1 ◇	R		R 1	1 ◇		1 ◇			◇		1 ◇			R 1	1 ◇	R
	A					B		C	D	H	G		H		J		K			L		N	C	Q
London Euston 15 ⊖ 65 d			16 35									16 49		17 05					17 35					
Birmingham New Street 12 68 d						17 18					17 48											18 18		
Wolverhampton 7 68 d						17 39					18 06											18 39		
Stafford 65, 68 d											18 18													
Stoke-on-Trent 50, 68 d			18 06			18 13					18 36			18 41					19 07			19 13		
Longport 50 d																								
Kidsgrove 50 d																								
Crewe 10 65 d					18 00		18 19		18 27			18 42									19 00			19 27
Sandbach d					18 07		18 26														19 07			
Holmes Chapel d					18 11		18 30														19 11			
Goostrey d					18 14																19 14			
Chelford d					18 19																19 19			
Alderley Edge d					18 23		18 39														19 23			
Wilmslow d					18 26		18 44		18 45			18 58									19 26			19 46
Styal d																←								
Manchester Airport a							18 54									18 54								
Handforth d					18 29		→														19 29			
Congleton d						18 25																		
Macclesfield a			18 21			18 32					18 52			18 57					19 22			19 31		
d		18 10	18 21			18 33					18 53			18 57				19 10	19 23			19 32		
Prestbury d		18 14																19 14						
Adlington (Cheshire) d		18 17																19 17						
Poynton d		18 21																19 21						
Bramhall d		18 23																19 23						
Cheadle Hulme d		18 26			18 34													19 26			19 34			
Stockport a		18 30	18s35		18 39	18 46			18 53		19 05	19s09		19s12				19 30	19s36		19 39	19 46		19 53
d	18 31	18 33		←	18 39	18 46		18 53	18 56	19 05	19 06		←		19 10		19 24	19 31		19 40	19 40	19 46	19 53	19 57
Heaton Chapel d		18 36		18 36	18 43					19 09			19 09		19 14						19 43			
Levenshulme d		→		18 39	18 46					→			19 12		19 17						19 46			
Manchester Piccadilly 10 a	18 42		18 49	18 52	18 56	19 02		19 03	19 13		19 20	19 21	19 24	19 24	19 28	19 29	19 36	19 43	19 50	19 54	19 57	20 02	20 03	20 18
d													19 26				19 37							
Manchester Oxford Road a													19 28				19 40							
Deansgate a													19 31											

	VT	NT	VT	NT	NT	NT	VT	EM	VT	NT	NT	NT	XC	TP	VT	AW	NT	NT	VT	NT	EM	XC	NT	VT
															FO									
	1 ◇		1 ◇				1 ◇	◇	1 ◇				R 1	1 ◇	1 ◇	R			1 ◇		◇	R 1		1 ◇
					J			K			U		B	C		D		J			V	G		
London Euston 15 ⊖ 65 d	17 48		18 05				17b10		18 35						18 20				19 05					19 35
Birmingham New Street 12 68 d							18 43						19 18									20 03		
Wolverhampton 7 68 d							19 06						19 39									20 21		
Stafford 65, 68 d							19 27								19 52							20 34		20 57
Stoke-on-Trent 50, 68 d		19 19	19 39				19 45		20 06				20 13						20 40					
Longport 50 d																								
Kidsgrove 50 d		19 27																						
Crewe 10 65 d	19 35									20 00					20 16	20 28						20 56	21 00	
Sandbach d										20 07													21 07	
Holmes Chapel d										20 11													21 11	
Goostrey d										20 14													21 14	
Chelford d										20 19													21 19	
Alderley Edge d										20 23													21 23	
Wilmslow d	19 51					19 51				20 26					20 33	20 45				20 50		21 16	21 26	21 31
Styal d																								
Manchester Airport a						20 02														21 02				
Handforth d										20 29													21 29	
Congleton d		19 34											20 25											
Macclesfield a		19 41	19 57				20 01		20 23				20 32						20 57					
d		19 42	19 57				20 01		20 23				20 33				20 42		20 57					
Prestbury d		19 46															20 46							
Adlington (Cheshire) d		19 49															20 49							
Poynton d		19 53															20 53							
Bramhall d		19 55															20 55							
Cheadle Hulme d		19 57								20 34							20 57						21 34	
Stockport a	20s02	20 03	20s12				20 16		20s36	20 39			20 46		20s44	20 53	21 02		21s12			21 25	21 39	21s42
d		20 03		←	20 10		20 17	20 26		20 39	20 40	←	20 46	20 53		20 57	21 03	21 10			21 17	21 26	21 39	
Heaton Chapel d		20 06		20 06						20 43		20 43					21 06						21 43	
Levenshulme d		→		20 09						→		20 46					21 09						21 46	
Manchester Piccadilly 10 a	20 14		20 20	20 23	20 28	20 31	20 35	20 36	20 51		20 52	20 54	21 02	21 03	21 04	21 13	21 18	21 24	21 24	21 28	21 30	21 39	21 54	21 54
d								20 37			20 52						21 19						21 54	
Manchester Oxford Road a								20 39			20 54						21 21						21 56	
Deansgate a											20 56						21 26						22 01	

For general notes see front of timetable
For details of catering facilities see Directory of Train Operators

- **A** From Hazel Grove (Table 86)
- **B** From Plymouth (Table 51)
- **C** From Cleethorpes to Manchester Airport (Table 29)
- **D** From Milford Haven (Table 128)
- **G** From Bournemouth (Table 51)
- **H** From Buxton (Table 86) to Salford Crescent (Table 82)
- **J** From Chester (Table 88)
- **K** Until 5 September from Norwich to Liverpool Lime Street (Table 49). From 8 September from Sheffield to Liverpool Lime Street (Table 89)
- **L** From Buxton (Table 86)
- **N** From Brighton (Table 51)
- **Q** From Carmarthen (Table 128)
- **U** From Buxton (Table 86) to Bolton (Table 82)
- **V** Until 5 September. From Norwich (Table 49)
- **b** 28 July to 22 August dep. 1702. By changing at Stafford, passengers may depart at 1745

Stoke-on-Trent and Crewe → Manchester Airport, Stockport and Manchester

Network Diagram - see first page of Table 78

Mondays to Fridays

	XC [1]◇ A	AW ◇ B	NT	VT [1]◇	NT C	NT	XC [1]◇ D	NT E	NT G	NT	XC [1]◇ H	TP [1]◇ J	NT	VT [1]◇	NT	AW ◇ K	NT L	NT N	NT FX	NT FO	XC [1]◇ Q	VT [1]◇
London Euston [15] ⊖ 65 d				20 05										21 05								22 05
Birmingham New Street [12] 68 d	20 18						20 48				21 18										22 18	
Wolverhampton [7] 68 d	20 39						21 11				21 39										22 39	
Stafford 65, 68 d							21 24				21 54										22 54	
Stoke-on-Trent 50, 68 d	21 13			21 40			21 46				22 13			22 44								
Longport 50 d																						
Kidsgrove 50 d																						
Crewe [10] 65 d		21 27								22 00						23 05			23 08	23 08		
Sandbach d										22 07									23 15	23 15		
Holmes Chapel d										22 11									23 19	23 19		
Goostrey d										22 14									23 22	23 22		
Chelford d										22 19									23 27	23 27		
Alderley Edge d										22 23									23 31	23 31		
Wilmslow d		21 46				21 55				22 26					22 53	23 23			23 34	23 34		
Styal d																						
Manchester Airport ✈ a						22 07									23 02							
Handforth d										22 29									23 36	23 36		
Congleton d											22 25											
Macclesfield a	21 31			21 57			22 02				22 32			23 00								
d	21 32		21 42	21 58			22 03				22 33		22 42	23 00								
Prestbury d			21 46										22 46									
Adlington (Cheshire) d			21 49										22 49									
Poynton d			21 53										22 53									
Bramhall d			21 55										22 55									
Cheadle Hulme d			21 57							22 34			22 57						23 42	23 42		
Stockport a	21 46	21 53	22 02	22s12			22 15			22 39	22 46		23 02	23s15		23 33			23 48	23 48		00s58
d	21 46	21 57	22 03		22 13		22 16	22 23	22 38	22 39	22 46	22 53	23 03			23 34	23 40	23 46	23 48	23 48		
Heaton Chapel d			22 06							22 43			23 06							23 52		
Levenshulme d			22 09							22 46			23 09							23 55		
Manchester Piccadilly [10] a	22 02	22 12	22 19	22 24	22 26	22 31	22 32	22 33	22 47	22 52	23 02	23 03	23 19	23 29	23 31	23 49	23 52	23 59	00 01	00 03	00 07	01 10
d			22 19					22 35	22 49	22 54												
Manchester Oxford Road a			22 21					22 37	22 51	22 56												
Deansgate a			22 26					22 40	22 54	23 00												

Saturdays

until 12 July

	NT C	NT	TP [1]◇ U	NT V	NT L	NT	TP [1]◇ X	AW	NT C	NT		NT	NT Y	EM ◇ Z	NT	NT AA	NT	NT	AW ◇ BB	XC [1]◇	TP [1]◇ J		NT AA	NT C
London Euston [15] ⊖ 65 d																								
Birmingham New Street [12] 68 d																				06 20				
Wolverhampton [7] 68 d																				06 40				
Stafford 65, 68 d																				06 54				
Stoke-on-Trent 50, 68 d															06 45					07 13				
Longport 50 d															06 49									
Kidsgrove 50 d															06 54									
Crewe [10] 65 d		00 56						06 26				06 35						07 00	07 15					
Sandbach d												06 42						07 07						
Holmes Chapel d												06 46						07 11						
Goostrey d												06 49						07 14						
Chelford d												06 54						07 19						
Alderley Edge d										06 49		06 58						07 23						
Wilmslow d										06 52		07 01						07 26	07 33					
Styal d																								
Manchester Airport ✈ a		01 21								07 02														
Handforth d												07 04						07 29						
Congleton d															07 02					07 25				
Macclesfield a															07 09					07 33				
d															07 10					07 33				
Prestbury d															07 14									
Adlington (Cheshire) d															07 17									
Poynton d															07 20									
Bramhall d															07 23									
Cheadle Hulme d												07 09			07 25			07 34						
Stockport a								06 53				07 14			07 30			07 39	07 42	07 46				
d	00 01		05 53	06 17	06 36	06 41	06 53	06 55	07 07			07 14	07 19	07 23	07 30	07 32	←	07 39	07 42	07 48	07 55		08 00	08 10
Heaton Chapel d						06 45			07 12						07 34		07 34	07 43					08 05	
Levenshulme d						06 48			07 15						→		07 37	07 46					08 08	
Manchester Piccadilly [10] a	00 14	01 40	06 04	06 27	06 47	06 55	07 05	07 11	07 25	07 28		07 28	07 30	07 35		07 42	07 45	07 55	07 59	08 02	08 08		08 14	08 24
d				06 29									07 30	07 35										
Manchester Oxford Road a				06 31									07 33	07 38										
Deansgate a				06 34									07 35											

For general notes see front of timetable
For details of catering facilities see Directory of Train Operators

- **A** From Guildford (Table 51)
- **B** From Carmarthen (Table 128)
- **C** From Chester (Table 88)
- **D** All Fridays, also Mondays to Thursdays until 4 September. From Bristol Temple Meads (Table 51)
- **E** From Buxton (Table 86) to Southport (Table 82)
- **G** To Wigan Wallgate (Table 82)
- **H** From Plymouth (Table 51)
- **J** From Cleethorpes to Manchester Airport (Table 29)
- **K** From Swansea (Fridays from Milford Haven) (Table 128)
- **L** From Buxton (Table 86)
- **N** From Sheffield (Table 78)
- **Q** From Bournemouth (Table 51)
- **U** From Sheffield to Manchester Airport (Table 78)
- **V** To Blackpool North (Table 82)
- **X** From Doncaster to Manchester Airport (Table 29)
- **Y** From Buxton (Table 86) to Blackpool North (Table 82)
- **Z** From Nottingham to Liverpool Lime Street (Table 49)
- **AA** From Hazel Grove (Table 86)
- **BB** From Cardiff Central (Table 131)

Table 84

Saturdays until 12 July

Stoke-on-Trent and Crewe → Manchester Airport, Stockport and Manchester

Network Diagram - see first page of Table 78

		NT	NT	NT	EM	NT	NT	NT	VT	NT	NT		NT
					◇				1 ◇				
			A		B			C			D		E
									🍴				
London Euston 15	⊖ 65 d								06 00				
Birmingham New Street 12	68 d												
Wolverhampton 7	68 🚊 d												
Stafford	65, 68 d												
Stoke-on-Trent	50, 68 d								08 06				
Longport	50 d												
Kidsgrove	50 d												
Crewe 10	65 d	07 33					07 43			08 00			
Sandbach	d	07 40					07 50			08 07			
Holmes Chapel	d	07 45					07 55			08 11			
Goostrey	d	07 48								08 14			
Chelford	d	07 52								08 19			
Alderley Edge	d	07 56					08 04			08 23			
Wilmslow	d	08 00					08 07			08 26			
Styal	d												
Manchester Airport	✈ a						08 14						
Handforth	d	08 03								08 29			
Congleton	d												
Macclesfield	a								08 22				
	d					08 09			08 22				
Prestbury	d					08 14							
Adlington (Cheshire)	d					08 17							
Poynton	d					08 20							
Bramhall	d					08 23							
Cheadle Hulme	d	08 09				08 24				08 34			
Stockport	a	08 13				08 30			08s36	08 41			
	d	08 14	08 20	←	08 27	08 30		08 33		08 41	08 42		08 46
Heaton Chapel	d	08 18		08 18						08 45			
Levenshulme	d	→		08 21						08 48			
Manchester Piccadilly 10	🚊 a		08 29	08 31	08 36	08 41	08 42	08 44	08 50	08 55	08 56		08 59
	d		08 31		08 37					08 56			
Manchester Oxford Road	a		08 33		08 40					08 58			
Deansgate	🚊 a		08 37							09 03			

		TP	XC	AW	NT	VT	NT	NT	XC	NT		NT	EM
		1 ◇	1 ◇	◇		1 ◇			1 ◇				◇
		G		H						E		A	B
		🛒	🍴	🛒		🍴			🍴				
London Euston 15	⊖ 65 d					06 20							
Birmingham New Street 12	68 d		07 20						07 48				
Wolverhampton 7	68 🚊 d		07 40						08 06				
Stafford	65, 68 d		07 54						08 18				
Stoke-on-Trent	50, 68 d		08 13			08 33			08 41				
Longport	50 d												
Kidsgrove	50 d												
Crewe 10	65 d			08 30									
Sandbach	d												
Holmes Chapel	d												
Goostrey	d												
Chelford	d												
Alderley Edge	d							08 53					
Wilmslow	d			08 48				08 56					
Styal	d												
Manchester Airport	✈ a												
Handforth	d							08 59					
Congleton	d		08 25										
Macclesfield	a		08 33			08 49			08 58				
	d		08 33		08 41	08 49			08 58				
Prestbury	d				08 45								
Adlington (Cheshire)	d				08 48								
Poynton	d				08 52								
Bramhall	d				08 54								
Cheadle Hulme	d				08 56			09 04					
Stockport	a		08 46	08 56	09 01	09s04		09 09	09 11				
	d	08 51	08 48	08 57	09 02		←	09 11	09 12	09 17		09 21	09 25
Heaton Chapel	d				09 05		09 05	09 15					
Levenshulme	d				→		09 08	09 18					
Manchester Piccadilly 10	🚊 a	09 01	09 02	09 12		09 17	09 18	09 26	09 27	09 30		09 32	09 36
	d						09 19					09 33	09 37
Manchester Oxford Road	a						09 21					09 36	09 40
Deansgate	🚊 a						09 26					09 38	

		NT	VT	NT	NT	XC	TP	AW	NT	VT	NT		XC
			1 ◇			1 ◇	1 ◇	◇		1 ◇			1 ◇
					C	J	G	K					
			🍴			🍴	🛒	🛒		🍴			🍴
London Euston 15	⊖ 65 d		07 04							07 36			
Birmingham New Street 12	68 d					08 20							08 48
Wolverhampton 7	68 🚊 d					08 40							09 08
Stafford	65, 68 d					08 54							09 22
Stoke-on-Trent	50, 68 d		09 07			09 13				09 34			09 42
Longport	50 d												
Kidsgrove	50 d												
Crewe 10	65 d	08 38		09 00				09 30					
Sandbach	d	08 45		09 07									
Holmes Chapel	d	08 49		09 11									
Goostrey	d			09 14									
Chelford	d			09 19									
Alderley Edge	d	08 58		09 23							09 53		
Wilmslow	d	09 01		09 26				09 48			09 56		
Styal	d												
Manchester Airport	✈ a	09 12											
Handforth	d			09 29							09 59		
Congleton	d					09 25							
Macclesfield	a					09 33				09 50			09 57
	d					09 33			09 41	09 50			09 58
Prestbury	d								09 45				
Adlington (Cheshire)	d								09 48				
Poynton	d								09 52				
Bramhall	d								09 54				
Cheadle Hulme	d			09 34					09 56		10 04		
Stockport	a		09s33	09 39		09 46		09 58	10 01	10s05	10 09		10 11
	d			09 40	09 46	09 48	09 53	09 59	10 02		10 09		10 12
Heaton Chapel	d				09 50				10 05		10 13		
Levenshulme	d				09 53				10 08		10 16		
Manchester Piccadilly 10	🚊 a	09 41	09 46	09 54	10 01	10 02	10 03	10 13	10 18	10 18	10 23		10 27
	d								10 19				
Manchester Oxford Road	a								10 21				
Deansgate	🚊 a								10 26				

		NT	NT	EM	NT	VT	NT	NT	XC	TP		AW	NT
				◇		1 ◇			1 ◇	1 ◇		◇	
		L	D	N				C	Q	G		K	
						🍴			🍴	🛒		🛒	
London Euston 15	⊖ 65 d					08 03							
Birmingham New Street 12	68 d								09 20				
Wolverhampton 7	68 🚊 d								09 40				
Stafford	65, 68 d								09 54				
Stoke-on-Trent	50, 68 d					10 03			10 13				
Longport	50 d												
Kidsgrove	50 d												
Crewe 10	65 d				09 38		10 00					10 30	
Sandbach	d				09 45		10 07						
Holmes Chapel	d				09 49		10 11						
Goostrey	d						10 14						
Chelford	d						10 19						
Alderley Edge	d				09 58		10 23						
Wilmslow	d				10 01		10 26					10 48	
Styal	d												
Manchester Airport	✈ a				10 11								
Handforth	d						10 29						
Congleton	d												
Macclesfield	a								10 32				
	d								10 33				10 41
Prestbury	d												10 45
Adlington (Cheshire)	d												10 48
Poynton	d												10 52
Bramhall	d												10 54
Cheadle Hulme	d						10 34						10 56
Stockport	a					10s33	10 39		10 46			10 58	11 01
	d	10 18	10 21	10 25			10 39	10 49	10 48	10 53		10 59	11 02
Heaton Chapel	d						10 43						11 05
Levenshulme	d						10 46						11 08
Manchester Piccadilly 10	🚊 a	10 29	10 33	10 36	10 39	10 44	10 54	11 01	11 02	11 03		11 13	11 18
	d	10 30		10 37									11 19
Manchester Oxford Road	a	10 32		10 40									11 21
Deansgate	🚊 a	10 38											11 26

For general notes see front of timetable
For details of catering facilities see Directory of Train Operators

A From Buxton (Table 86) to Blackpool North (Table 82)
B From Nottingham to Liverpool Lime Street (Table 49)
C From Hazel Grove (Table 86)
D From Buxton (Table 86)
E From Chester (Table 88)
G From Cleethorpes to Manchester Airport (Table 29)
H From Cardiff Central (Table 131)
J From Gatwick Airport (Table 51)
K From Carmarthen (Table 128)
L From Northwich (Table 88) to Blackpool North (Table 82)
N From Norwich to Liverpool Lime Street (Table 49)
Q From Bristol Temple Meads (Table 51)

Table 84

Saturdays

until 12 July

Stoke-on-Trent and Crewe → Manchester Airport, Stockport and Manchester

Network Diagram - see first page of Table 78

	NT	XC	NT	NT	EM	NT	VT	NT	NT	XC		TP	AW	NT	NT	XC	NT	NT	VT	EM	NT		VT	NT
		[1]◇			◇		[1]◇			[1]◇		[1]◇	◇			[1]◇			[1]◇	◇			[1]◇	
		A	B	C	D				E	G		H	J			K	C	B		L				
		☕					☕			☕		🍴	🍴			☕			☕				☕	
London Euston [15] ⊖ 65 d							08 28												08 37				09 31	
Birmingham New Street [12] 68 d		09 48								10 20						10 48								
Wolverhampton [7] 68 🚋 d		10 08								10 40						11 08								
Stafford 65, 68 d		10 23								10 54						11 23								
Stoke-on-Trent 50, 68 d		10 42					11 06			11 13						11 42			11 50				12 06	
Longport 50 d																								
Kidsgrove 50 d																								
Crewe [10] 65 d						10 38		11 00					11 30								11 38			12 00
Sandbach d						10 45		11 07													11 45			12 07
Holmes Chapel d						10 49		11 11													11 49			12 11
Goostrey d								11 14																12 14
Chelford d								11 19																12 19
Alderley Edge d	10 53					10 58		11 23							11 53						11 58			12 23
Wilmslow d	10 56					11 01		11 26					11 48		11 56						12 01			12 26
Styal d																								
Manchester Airport ✈ a						11 11															12 11			
Handforth d	10 59							11 29							11 59									12 29
Congleton d										11 25														
Macclesfield a		10 57					11 21			11 33						11 57							12 21	
d		10 58					11 22			11 33				11 41		11 58							12 22	
Prestbury d														11 45										
Adlington (Cheshire) d														11 48										
Poynton d														11 52										
Bramhall d														11 54										
Cheadle Hulme d	11 04							11 34						11 56	12 04									12 34
Stockport a	11 09	11 11					11s34	11 39		11 46			11 58	12 01	12 09	12 11			12s20				12s34	12 39
d	11 09	11 12	11 19	11 17	11 25			11 39	11 49	11 48		11 53	11 59	12 02	12 09	12 12	12 16	12 19		12 25				12 39
Heaton Chapel d	11 13							11 43						12 05	12 13									12 43
Levenshulme d	11 16							11 46						12 08	12 16									12 46
Manchester Piccadilly [10] 🚋 a	11 24	11 27	11 29	11 32	11 36	11 39	11 48	11 54	12 01	12 02		12 03	12 13	12 18	12 24	12 27	12 29	12 29	12 34	12 36	12 39		12 48	12 54
d			11 30		11 37									12 19				12 30		12 37				
Manchester Oxford Road a			11 32		11 40									12 21				12 33		12 40				
Deansgate 🚋 a			11 35											12 26				12 35						

	NT	XC	TP	AW	NT	NT	XC	NT	NT	VT		EM	NT	VT	NT	NT	XC	TP	AW	NT	NT		XC	NT
		[1]◇	[1]◇	◇			R [1]			[1]◇		◇		[1]◇			[1]◇	[1]◇	◇				[1]◇	
	E	N	H	J			A	B	C			L				E	G	H	Q				K	B
		☕	🍴	🍴			☕			☕				☕			☕	🍴	🍴				☕	
London Euston [15] ⊖ 65 d										09 37				10 29										
Birmingham New Street [12] 68 d		11 20					11 48										12 20						12 48	
Wolverhampton [7] 68 🚋 d		11 40					12 08										12 40						13 08	
Stafford 65, 68 d		11 54					12 23										12 54						13 23	
Stoke-on-Trent 50, 68 d		12 13					12 42			12 49				13 06			13 13						13 42	
Longport 50 d																								
Kidsgrove 50 d																								
Crewe [10] 65 d				12 30									12 38		13 00				13 30					
Sandbach d													12 45		13 07									
Holmes Chapel d													12 49		13 11									
Goostrey d															13 14									
Chelford d															13 19									
Alderley Edge d						12 53							12 58		13 23						13 53			
Wilmslow d				12 48		12 56							13 01		13 26				13 48		13 56			
Styal d																								
Manchester Airport ✈ a													13 11											
Handforth d						12 59									13 29						13 59			
Congleton d																	13 25							
Macclesfield a		12 32					12 57							13 21			13 33						13 57	
d		12 33			12 41		12 58							13 22			13 33			13 41			13 58	
Prestbury d					12 45															13 45				
Adlington (Cheshire) d					12 48															13 48				
Poynton d					12 52															13 52				
Bramhall d					12 54															13 54				
Cheadle Hulme d					12 56	13 04									13 34					13 56	14 04			
Stockport a		12 46		12 58	13 01	13 09	13 11			13s20				13s34	13 39		13 46		13 58	14 01	14 09		14 11	
d	12 49	12 48	12 53	12 59	13 02	13 09	13 12	13 19	13 16			13 25			13 39	13 49	13 48	13 53	13 59	14 02	14 09		14 12	14 19
Heaton Chapel d					13 05	13 13									13 43					14 05	14 13			
Levenshulme d					13 08	13 16									13 46					14 08	14 16			
Manchester Piccadilly [10] 🚋 a	13 01	13 02	13 03	13 13	13 18	13 24	13 27	13 28	13 29	13 34		13 36	13 39	13 48	13 54	14 01	14 02	14 03	14 13	14 18	14 24		14 27	14 28
d					13 19			13 30				13 37								14 19				14 30
Manchester Oxford Road a					13 21			13 32				13 40								14 21				14 32
Deansgate 🚋 a					13 26			13 35												14 26				14 35

For general notes see front of timetable
For details of catering facilities see Directory of Train Operators

- **A** From Bournemouth (Table 51)
- **B** From Buxton (Table 86) to Blackpool North (Table 82)
- **C** From Chester (Table 88)
- **D** From Cambridge to Liverpool Lime Street (Table 49)
- **E** From Hazel Grove (Table 86)
- **G** From Reading (Table 51)
- **H** From Cleethorpes to Manchester Airport (Table 29)
- **J** From Milford Haven (Table 128)
- **K** From Birmingham International (Table 65)
- **L** From Norwich to Liverpool Lime Street (Table 49)
- **N** From Plymouth (Table 51)
- **Q** From Carmarthen (Table 128)

Table 84

Saturdays

until 12 July

Stoke-on-Trent and Crewe → Manchester Airport, Stockport and Manchester

Network Diagram - see first page of Table 78

		NT A	VT 1◇	EM ◇ B	NT	VT 1◇	NT	NT C	XC 1◇ D	TP 1◇ E	AW ◇ G		NT	NT	XC 1◇ H	NT J	NT A	VT 1◇	EM ◇ B	NT	VT 1◇	NT		NT C	XC 1◇ K
London Euston 15	⊖ 65 d		10 38			11 29												11 38			12 29				
Birmingham New Street 12	68 d								13 20						13 48										14 20
Wolverhampton 7	68 d								13 40						14 08										14 40
Stafford	65, 68 d								13 54						14 23										14 54
Stoke-on-Trent	50, 68 d		13 49			14 06			14 13						14 42			14 49			15 06				15 13
Longport	50 d																								
Kidsgrove	50 d																								
Crewe 10	65 d				13 38		14 00				14 30									14 38		15 00			
Sandbach	d				13 45		14 07													14 45		15 07			
Holmes Chapel	d				13 49		14 11													14 49		15 11			
Goostrey	d						14 14															15 14			
Chelford	d						14 19															15 19			
Alderley Edge	d				13 58		14 23							14 53						14 58		15 23			
Wilmslow	d				14 01		14 26				14 48			14 56						15 01		15 26			
Styal	d																								
Manchester Airport	✈ a				14 11															15 11					
Handforth	d						14 29							14 59								15 29			
Congleton	d																								15 25
Macclesfield	a					14 21			14 32						14 57						15 21				15 33
	d					14 22			14 33				14 41		14 58						15 22				15 33
Prestbury	d												14 45												
Adlington (Cheshire)	d												14 48												
Poynton	d												14 52												
Bramhall	d												14 54												
Cheadle Hulme	d						14 34						14 56	15 04								15 34			
Stockport	a		14s20			14s34	14 39		14 46		14 58		15 01	15 09	15 11			15s20			15s34	15 39			15 46
	d	14 16		14 25			14 39	14 49	14 48	14 53	14 59		15 02	15 09	15 12	15 19	15 16		15 24			15 39		15 49	15 48
Heaton Chapel	d						14 43						15 05	15 13								15 43			
Levenshulme	d						14 46						15 08	15 16								15 46			
Manchester Piccadilly 10	a	14 29	14 34	14 36	14 39	14 48	14 54	15 01	15 02	15 03	15 13		15 18	15 24	15 27	15 28	15 29	15 34	15 36	15 39	15 48	15 54		16 01	16 02
	d			14 37									15 19			15 30			15 37						
Manchester Oxford Road	a			14 40									15 21			15 32			15 40						
Deansgate	a												15 26			15 35									

		TP 1◇ E	AW ◇ L	NT	NT	XC 1◇ N	NT J	NT A	VT 1◇	EM ◇ B	NT		NT	VT 1◇	NT Q	NT	NT	NT C	XC 1◇ H	TP 1◇ E	AW ◇ G	NT U		NT	XC R 1 H
London Euston 15	⊖ 65 d								12 38					13 29											
Birmingham New Street 12	68 d					14 48													15 20						15 48
Wolverhampton 7	68 d					15 08													15 40						16 08
Stafford	65, 68 d					15 23													15 54						16 23
Stoke-on-Trent	50, 68 d					15 42			15 49					16 06					16 13						16 42
Longport	50 d																								
Kidsgrove	50 d																								
Crewe 10	65 d		15 30										15 38			16 00					16 30				
Sandbach	d												15 45			16 07									
Holmes Chapel	d												15 49			16 11									
Goostrey	d															16 14									
Chelford	d															16 19									
Alderley Edge	d				15 53								15 58			16 23								16 53	
Wilmslow	d		15 48		15 56								16 01			16 26					16 48			16 56	
Styal	d																								
Manchester Airport	✈ a												16 11												
Handforth	d				15 59											16 29								16 59	
Congleton	d																								
Macclesfield	a					15 57								16 21					16 32						16 57
	d			15 41		15 58					16 10			16 22					16 33						16 58
Prestbury	d			15 45							16 14														
Adlington (Cheshire)	d			15 48							16 17														
Poynton	d			15 52							16 21														
Bramhall	d			15 54							16 23														
Cheadle Hulme	d			15 56	16 04						16 26					16 34								17 04	
Stockport	a		15 58	16 01	16 09	16 11			16s20		16 30			16s34		16 40			16 46		16 58			17 09	17 11
	d	15 53	15 59	16 02	16 09	16 12	16 19	16 16		16 25	16 35				16 40	16 43	←	16 49	16 48	16 53	16 59	17 01		17 11	17 12
Heaton Chapel	d			16 05	16 13						16 38 →						16 38					17 05		17 15	
Levenshulme	d			16 08	16 16												16 41					17 08		17 18	
Manchester Piccadilly 10	a	16 03	16 13	16 18	16 24	16 27	16 28	16 29	16 34	16 36			16 41	16 48	16 50	16 54	16 54	17 01	17 02	17 03	17 13	17 15		17 26	17 27
	d						16 30			16 37					16 52		16 56					17 15			
Manchester Oxford Road	a						16 32			16 40					16 55		16 58					17 18			
Deansgate	a						16 35								16 58		17 03					17 21			

For general notes see front of timetable
For details of catering facilities see Directory of Train Operators

- **A** From Chester (Table 88)
- **B** From Norwich to Liverpool Lime Street (Table 49)
- **C** From Hazel Grove (Table 86)
- **D** From Paignton (Table 51)
- **E** From Cleethorpes to Manchester Airport (Table 29)
- **G** From Milford Haven (Table 128)
- **H** From Bournemouth (Table 51)
- **J** From Buxton (Table 86) to Blackpool North (Table 82)
- **K** From Reading (Table 51)
- **L** From Carmarthen (Table 128)
- **N** From Birmingham International (Table 65)
- **Q** To Preston (Table 82)
- **U** To Blackpool North (Table 82)

Table 84

Saturdays

until 12 July

Stoke-on-Trent and Crewe → Manchester Airport, Stockport and Manchester

Network Diagram - see first page of Table 78

		NT	NT	VT	EM	NT	NT	VT	NT	XC	NT		TP	AW	XC	NT	NT	VT	EM	NT	NT	VT		NT	NT
														[R]											
				[1] ◇	◇			[1] ◇		[1] ◇			[1] ◇		[1] ◇			[1] ◇	◇			[1] ◇			
		A	B		C					D	E		G	H	J	B	A		C						E
				🍴				🍴		🍴			🛒	🛒	🍴			🍴				🍴			
London Euston [15]	⊖ 65 d			13 38				14 29										14 38				15 29			
Birmingham New Street [12]	68 d									16 20					16 48										
Wolverhampton [7]	68 ⛴ d									16 40					17 08										
Stafford	65, 68 d									16 54					17 23										
Stoke-on-Trent	50, 68 d			16 49				17 06		17 13					17 42			17 49				18 06			
Longport	50 d																								
Kidsgrove	50 d																								
Crewe [10]	65 d					16 42			17 00					17 30						17 38				18 00	
Sandbach	d					16 49			17 07											17 45				18 07	
Holmes Chapel	d					16 53			17 11											17 50				18 11	
Goostrey	d								17 14											17 53				18 14	
Chelford	d								17 19											17 57				18 19	
Alderley Edge	d					17 02			17 23											18 01				18 23	
Wilmslow	d					17 05			17 26					17 48						18 04				18 26	
Styal	d																			18 08					
Manchester Airport	✈ a					17 15														18 15					
Handforth	d								17 29															18 29	
Congleton	d									17 25															
Macclesfield	a							17 21		17 33					17 57							18 21			
	d						17 10	17 22		17 33					17 58						18 10	18 22			
Prestbury	d						17 14														18 14				
Adlington (Cheshire)	d						17 17														18 17				
Poynton	d						17 21														18 21				
Bramhall	d						17 23														18 23				
Cheadle Hulme	d						17 26		17 34												18 26			18 34	
Stockport	a			17s20			17 30	17s34	17 39	17 46				17 58	18 11			18s22			18 30	18s34		18 39	
	d	17 15	17 16		17 25		17 32		17 39	17 48	17 50		17 53	17 59	18 12	18 16	18 16		18 26		18 32			18 39	18 50
Heaton Chapel	d	17 19							17 43								18 20							18 43	
Levenshulme	d	17 22							17 46								18 23							18 46	
Manchester Piccadilly [10]	⛴ a	17 29	17 29	17 34	17 35	17 41	17 44	17 48	17 56	18 02	18 02		18 03	18 10	18 27	18 29	18 30	18 35	18 35	18 40	18 43	18 48		18 54	19 01
	d	17 30			17 37												18 31		18 37						
Manchester Oxford Road	a	17 32			17 39												18 34		18 39						
Deansgate	⛴ a	17 35															18 38								

		XC	TP	AW	NT	NT	XC	VT	EM	NT	NT		VT	NT	NT	NT	XC	TP	AW	NT	NT	XC		NT	EM
		[R]		[R]															[R]						
		[1]	[1] ◇				[1] ◇	[1] ◇	◇				[1] ◇				[1] ◇	[1] ◇				[1] ◇			◇
		K	G	L	N	B	Q		U						V		X	G	H		B	J			U
		🍴	🛒	🛒			🍴	🍴					🍴				🍴	🛒	🛒			🍴			
London Euston [15]	⊖ 65 d							15 38					16 29												
Birmingham New Street [12]	68 d	17 20					17 48										18 20					18 48			
Wolverhampton [7]	68 ⛴ d	17 40					18 08										18 40					19 08			
Stafford	65, 68 d	17 54					18 23										18 54					19 23			
Stoke-on-Trent	50, 68 d	18 13					18 42	18 50					19 06				19 13			19 19		19 42			
Longport	50 d																								
Kidsgrove	50 d																			19 27					
Crewe [10]	65 d			18 30						18 42				19 00					19 30						
Sandbach	d									18 49				19 07											
Holmes Chapel	d									18 53				19 11											
Goostrey	d													19 14											
Chelford	d													19 19											
Alderley Edge	d									19 02				19 23											
Wilmslow	d			18 48						19 05				19 26					19 48					19 51	
Styal	d																								
Manchester Airport	✈ a									19 16														20 02	
Handforth	d													19 29											
Congleton	d																19 25			19 34					
Macclesfield	a	18 32					18 57						19 21				19 33			19 41		19 57			
	d	18 33					18 58				19 10		19 22				19 33			19 42		19 58			
Prestbury	d										19 14									19 46					
Adlington (Cheshire)	d										19 17									19 49					
Poynton	d										19 21									19 52					
Bramhall	d										19 23									19 55					
Cheadle Hulme	d										19 26			19 34						19 57					
Stockport	a	18 46		18 59			19 11	19s19			19 30		19s34	19 39			19 46		19 59	20 02		20 11			
	d	18 48	18 53	18 59	19 05	19 10	19 12		19 24		19 31			19 39	19 40	←	19 48	19 53	19 59	20 03	20 10	20 12			20 25
Heaton Chapel	d				19 09	19 14								19 43		19 43				20 06					
Levenshulme	d				19 12	19 17								→		19 46				20 09					
Manchester Piccadilly [10]	⛴ a	19 02	19 03	19 16	19 19	19 28	19 27	19 34	19 35	19 41	19 43		19 48		19 51	19 57	20 02	20 03	20 13	20 17	20 24	20 27		20 31	20 36
	d				19 20					19 41															20 37
Manchester Oxford Road	a				19 22					19 46															20 39
Deansgate	⛴ a				19 25																				

For general notes see front of timetable
For details of catering facilities see Directory of Train Operators

- **A** From Buxton (Table 86) to Blackpool North (Table 82)
- **B** From Chester (Table 88)
- **C** From Norwich to Liverpool Lime Street (Table 49)
- **D** From Reading (Table 51)
- **E** From Hazel Grove (Table 86)
- **G** From Cleethorpes to Manchester Airport (Table 29)
- **H** From Carmarthen (Table 128)
- **J** From Birmingham International (Table 65)
- **K** From Penzance (Table 135)
- **L** From Milford Haven (Table 128)
- **N** From Buxton (Table 86) to Salford Crescent (Table 82)
- **Q** From Bournemouth (Table 51)
- **U** From Norwich (Table 49)
- **V** From Buxton (Table 86)
- **X** From Brighton (Table 51)

Table 84

Saturdays

until 12 July

Stoke-on-Trent and Crewe → Manchester Airport, Stockport and Manchester

Network Diagram - see first page of Table 78

	VT	VT	NT	NT	NT	XC	TP	AW	NT	NT		VT	EM	NT	XC	VT	NT	XC	AW	NT	NT		NT	XC
	1◇	1◇				R 1	1◇	R				1◇	◇		1◇	1◇		1◇	◇					1◇
				A		B	C	D		E			G		H			J	K				E	L
	🍽	🍽				🍽	☕	☕				🍽				🍽			☕					
London Euston 15 ⊖ 65 d	16 38	17 29										17 37				18 26								
Birmingham New Street 12 68 d						19 20						19 48			20 03			20 20						20 48
Wolverhampton 7 68 🚢 d						19 40						20 09			20 21			20 40						21 08
Stafford 65, 68 d						19 54						20 25			20 34			20 54						21 22
Stoke-on-Trent 50, 68 d	19 50	20 06				20 13						20 44				21 06		21 13						
Longport 50 d																								
Kidsgrove 50 d																								
Crewe 10 65 d			20 00					20 26							20 56		21 00		21 27					
Sandbach d			20 07														21 07							
Holmes Chapel d			20 11														21 11							
Goostrey d			20 14														21 14							
Chelford d			20 19														21 19							
Alderley Edge d			20 23														21 23							
Wilmslow d			20 26					20 45						20 50	21 13		21 26		21 46		21 55			21 59
Styal d																								
Manchester Airport ✈ a														21 02							22 05			
Handforth d			20 29														21 29				→			
Congleton d																		21 25						
Macclesfield a		20 21				20 32						20 59				21 21		21 33						
d		20 22				20 33			20 42			21 00				21 22		21 33		21 42				
Prestbury d									20 46											21 46				
Adlington (Cheshire) d									20 49											21 49				
Poynton d									20 53											21 53				
Bramhall d									20 55											21 55				
Cheadle Hulme d			20 34						20 57								21 34			21 57				
Stockport a	20s19	20s34	20 39			20 46		20 56	21 02			21s13			21 22	21s34	21 39	21 46	21 57	22 02				22 11
d			20 39	20 40	←	20 48	20 53	20 56	21 03	21 10			21 17		21 23		21 39	21 48	21 57	22 03			22 13	22 12
Heaton Chapel d			20 43		20 43				21 06								21 43			22 06				
Levenshulme d			→		20 46				21 09								21 46			22 09				
Manchester Piccadilly 10 🚢 a	20 37	20 48		20 52	20 54	21 02	21 03	21 13	21 19	21 24		21 26	21 26	21 31	21 36	21 51	21 53	22 02	22 13	22 18			22 26	22 27
d				20 52													21 54							
Manchester Oxford Road a				20 54													21 56							
Deansgate 🚢 a				20 56													22 01							

	NT	NT	VT	NT	NT	VT	XC	NT	VT	NT		NT	AW	NT	VT	NT	VT	XC	VT	NT	VT			
			1◇			1◇	R 1						◇				1◇	1◇						
		N		Q			U					V	D	X				H						
									🚌						🚌				🚌		🚌			
			🍽			🍽							☕				🍽							
London Euston 15 ⊖ 65 d			18 38			19 21											20 00							
Birmingham New Street 12 68 d							21 20											22 20						
Wolverhampton 7 68 🚢 d							21 40											22 40						
Stafford 65, 68 d			21 35			21 43	21 54								21 50		22 49	22 54			22 55			
Stoke-on-Trent 50, 68 d															22 20						23 25			
Longport 50 d																								
Kidsgrove 50 d																								
Crewe 10 65 d					22 00		22 22						23 04			23 08	23 17							
Sandbach d					22 07											23 15								
Holmes Chapel d					22 11											23 19				←				
Goostrey d					22 14											23 22				23 22				
Chelford d					22 19											→				23 38				
Alderley Edge d					22 23															23 42				
Wilmslow d			22 09		22 26	22 31	22 40		22 40	22 55			23 23				23 35	23 40	23 45	23 45				
Styal d	←																							
Manchester Airport ✈ a	22 05									23 05														
Handforth d					22 29															23 47				
Congleton d																								
Macclesfield a									23 10						23 10				00 15		00 15			
d								22 42							23 10						00 15			
Prestbury d								22 46																
Adlington (Cheshire) d								22 49																
Poynton d								22 53																
Bramhall d								22 55																
Cheadle Hulme d					22 34			22 57												23 51				
Stockport a			22s18		22 39	22s41	22 50	23 02					23 33		23 40		23s44	23s49		23 57	00 45			
d		22 23		22 38	22 39		22 51	23 03				23 22	23 33	23 40						23 57				
Heaton Chapel d					22 43			23 06												00 02				
Levenshulme d					22 46			23 09												00 05				
Manchester Piccadilly 10 🚢 a	22 31	22 33	22 36	22 47	22 52	23 01	23 07	23 19		23 31		23 37	23 50	23 52			23 57	00 06		00 10				
d		22 35		22 49	22 54																			
Manchester Oxford Road a		22 37		22 51	22 56																			
Deansgate 🚢 a		22 40		22 54	23 00																			

For general notes see front of timetable
For details of catering facilities see Directory of Train Operators

- **A** From Buxton (Table 86) to Bolton (Table 82)
- **B** From Paignton (Table 51)
- **C** From Cleethorpes to Manchester Airport (Table 29)
- **D** From Milford Haven (Table 128)
- **E** From Chester (Table 88)
- **G** From Norwich (Table 49)
- **H** From Bournemouth (Table 51)
- **J** From Guildford (Table 51)
- **K** From Carmarthen (Table 128)
- **L** From Bristol Temple Meads (Table 51)
- **N** From Buxton (Table 86) to Southport (Table 82)
- **Q** To Wigan Wallgate (Table 82)
- **U** From Newquay (Table 135)
- **V** From Sheffield (Table 78)
- **X** From Buxton (Table 86)

Saturdays

Stoke-on-Trent and Crewe → Manchester Airport, Stockport and Manchester

19 July to 6 September

Network Diagram - see first page of Table 78

		NT	NT	TP	NT	NT	NT	TP	AW	NT	NT	NT	NT	EM	NT	NT	NT	NT	AW	XC	TP	NT	NT
				1 ◇				1 ◇						◇					◇	1 ◇	1 ◇		
		A		B	C	D		E		A			G	H		J			K		L	J	A
London Euston 15	⊖ 65 d																						
Birmingham New Street 12	68 d																			06 20			
Wolverhampton 7	68 d																			06 40			
Stafford	65, 68 d																			06 54			
Stoke-on-Trent	50, 68 d														06 45					07 13			
Longport	50 d														06 49								
Kidsgrove	50 d														06 54								
Crewe 10	65 d		00 56						06 26			06 35						07 00	07 15				
Sandbach	d											06 42						07 07					
Holmes Chapel	d											06 46						07 11					
Goostrey	d											06 49						07 14					
Chelford	d											06 54						07 19					
Alderley Edge	d										06 49	06 58						07 23					
Wilmslow	d										06 52	07 01						07 26	07 33				
Styal	d																						
Manchester Airport	✈ a		01 21								07 02												
Handforth	d											07 04						07 29					
Congleton	d														07 02					07 25			
Macclesfield	a														07 09					07 33			
	d														07 10					07 33			
Prestbury	d														07 14								
Adlington (Cheshire)	d														07 17								
Poynton	d														07 20								
Bramhall	d														07 23								
Cheadle Hulme	d											07 09			07 25			07 34					
Stockport	a								06 53			07 14			07 30			07 39	07 42	07 46			
	d	00 01		05 53	06 17	06 36	06 41	06 53	06 55	07 07		07 14	07 19	07 23	07 30	07 32	←	07 39	07 42	07 48	07 55	08 00	08 10
Heaton Chapel	d						06 45			07 12					07 34 →		07 34	07 43				08 05	
Levenshulme	d						06 48			07 15							07 37	07 46				08 08	
Manchester Piccadilly 10	a	00 14	01 40	06 04	06 27	06 47	06 55	07 05	07 11	07 25	07 28	07 28	07 30	07 35		07 42	07 45	07 55	07 59	08 02	08 08	08 14	08 24
	d				06 29								07 30	07 35									
Manchester Oxford Road	a				06 31								07 33	07 38									
Deansgate	a				06 34								07 35										

		NT	NT	NT	EM	NT	NT	NT	VT	NT	NT	NT	TP	XC	AW	NT	XC	VT	NT	NT	NT	EM	NT
					◇				1 ◇				1 ◇	1 ◇	◇		1 ◇	1 ◇				◇	
			G		H			J			D	A	L		K					A	G	H	
London Euston 15	⊖ 65 d								06 00									06 57					
Birmingham New Street 12	68 d													07 20			07 48						
Wolverhampton 7	68 d													07 40			08 06						
Stafford	65, 68 d													07 54			08 18						
Stoke-on-Trent	50, 68 d								08 06					08 13			08 36	08 41					
Longport	50 d																						
Kidsgrove	50 d																						
Crewe 10	65 d	07 33					07 43			08 00					08 30								08 40
Sandbach	d	07 40					07 50			08 07													08 47
Holmes Chapel	d	07 45					07 55			08 11													08 51
Goostrey	d	07 48								08 14													
Chelford	d	07 52								08 19													
Alderley Edge	d	07 56					08 04			08 23									08 53				09 00
Wilmslow	d	08 00					08 07			08 26					08 48				08 56				09 03
Styal	d																						
Manchester Airport	✈ a						08 14																09 15
Handforth	d	08 03								08 29									08 59				
Congleton	d													08 25									
Macclesfield	a								08 22					08 33			08 52	08 56					
	d					08 09			08 22					08 33		08 41	08 53	08 57					
Prestbury	d					08 14										08 45							
Adlington (Cheshire)	d					08 17										08 48							
Poynton	d					08 20										08 52							
Bramhall	d					08 23										08 54							
Cheadle Hulme	d	08 09				08 24				08 34						08 56			09 04				
Stockport	a	08 13				08 30			08s36	08 41				08 46	08 56	09 01	09 05	09s12	09 09				
	d	08 14	08 20	←	08 27	08 30		08 33		08 41	08 42	08 46	08 51	08 48	08 57	09 02	09 06		09 11	09 17	09 21	09 25	
Heaton Chapel	d	08 18 →		08 18						08 45						09 05			09 15				
Levenshulme	d			08 21						08 48						09 08			09 18				
Manchester Piccadilly 10	a		08 29	08 31	08 36	08 41	08 42	08 44	08 50	08 55	08 56	08 59	09 01	09 02	09 12	09 18	09 20	09 24	09 26	09 30	09 32	09 36	09 41
	d		08 31		08 37					08 56						09 19					09 33	09 37	
Manchester Oxford Road	a		08 33		08 40					08 58						09 21					09 36	09 40	
Deansgate	a		08 37							09 03						09 26					09 38		

For general notes see front of timetable
For details of catering facilities see Directory of Train Operators

- **A** From Chester (Table 88)
- **B** From Sheffield to Manchester Airport (Table 78)
- **C** To Blackpool North (Table 82)
- **D** From Buxton (Table 86)
- **E** From Doncaster to Manchester Airport (Table 29)
- **G** From Buxton (Table 86) to Blackpool North (Table 82)
- **H** From Nottingham to Liverpool Lime Street (Table 49)
- **J** From Hazel Grove (Table 86)
- **K** From Cardiff Central (Table 131)
- **L** From Cleethorpes to Manchester Airport (Table 29)

Due to ongoing Engineering Operations, some services from Saturday 13 September on this Table had not been confirmed at time of going to press. These services will be issued in a special Supplement as soon as exact timings have been confirmed.

Table 84

Saturdays

19 July to 6 September

Stoke-on-Trent and Crewe → Manchester Airport, Stockport and Manchester

Network Diagram - see first page of Table 78

		VT	NT	NT	XC	TP	AW	NT	VT	NT	XC		NT	NT	EM	NT	VT	NT	NT	XC	TP	AW		NT	VT
		1 ◇			1 ◇	1 ◇	◇		1 ◇		1 ◇				◇		1 ◇			1 ◇	1 ◇	◇			1 ◇
				A	B	C	D						E	G	H				A	J	C	D			
		☕			☕	🍴	🍴		☕		☕						☕			☕	🍴	🍴			☕
London Euston 15	⊖ 65 d	07 25							07 54								08 17								08 55
Birmingham New Street 12	68 d				08 20						08 48									09 20					
Wolverhampton 7	68 ⛴ d				08 40						09 08									09 40					
Stafford	65, 68 d				08 54						09 22									09 54					
Stoke-on-Trent	50, 68 d	09 07			09 13				09 35		09 42						10 03			10 13					10 34
Longport	50 d																								
Kidsgrove	50 d																								
Crewe 10	65 d		09 00				09 30									09 38		10 00				10 30			
Sandbach	d		09 07													09 45		10 07							
Holmes Chapel	d		09 11													09 49		10 11							
Goostrey	d		09 14															10 14							
Chelford	d		09 19															10 19							
Alderley Edge	d		09 23							09 53						09 58		10 23							
Wilmslow	d		09 26				09 48			09 56						10 01		10 26				10 48			
Styal	d																								
Manchester Airport	✈ a															10 11									
Handforth	d		09 29							09 59								10 29							
Congleton	d				09 25																				
Macclesfield	a				09 33				09 51		09 57									10 32					10 50
	d				09 33			09 41	09 51		09 58									10 33				10 41	10 50
Prestbury	d							09 45																10 45	
Adlington (Cheshire)	d							09 48																10 48	
Poynton	d							09 52																10 52	
Bramhall	d							09 54																10 54	
Cheadle Hulme	d		09 34					09 56		10 04								10 34						10 56	
Stockport	a	09s33	09 39		09 46		09 58	10 01	10s05	10 09	10 11						10s33	10 39		10 46		10 58		11 01	11s05
	d		09 40	09 46	09 48	09 53	09 59	10 02		10 09	10 12		10 18	10 21	10 25			10 39	10 49	10 48	10 53	10 59		11 02	
Heaton Chapel	d			09 50				10 05		10 13								10 43						11 05	
Levenshulme	d			09 53				10 08		10 16								10 46						11 08	
Manchester Piccadilly 10	⛴ a	09 46	09 54	10 01	10 02	10 03	10 13	10 18	10 19	10 23	10 27		10 29	10 33	10 36	10 39	10 46	10 54	11 01	11 02	11 03	11 13		11 18	11 18
	d							10 19					10 30		10 37									11 19	
Manchester Oxford Road	a							10 21					10 32		10 40									11 21	
Deansgate	⛴ a							10 26					10 38											11 26	

		NT	XC	NT	NT	EM	NT	VT	NT	NT	XC		TP	AW	NT	VT	NT	XC	NT	NT	EM	NT		VT	NT
			1 ◇			◇		1 ◇			1 ◇		1 ◇	◇		1 ◇		1 ◇			◇			1 ◇	
			K	L	N	Q				A	U		C	V				X	L	N	H				
			☕					☕			☕		🍴	🍴		☕		☕						☕	
London Euston 15	⊖ 65 d							09 25								09 55								10 25	
Birmingham New Street 12	68 d		09 48								10 20							10 48							
Wolverhampton 7	68 ⛴ d		10 08								10 40							11 08							
Stafford	65, 68 d		10 23								10 54							11 23							
Stoke-on-Trent	50, 68 d		10 42					11 06			11 13					11 35		11 42						12 02	
Longport	50 d																								
Kidsgrove	50 d																								
Crewe 10	65 d						10 38		11 00					11 30								11 38			12 00
Sandbach	d						10 45		11 07													11 45			12 07
Holmes Chapel	d						10 49		11 11													11 49			12 11
Goostrey	d								11 14																12 14
Chelford	d								11 19																12 19
Alderley Edge	d	10 53					10 58		11 23								11 53					11 58			12 23
Wilmslow	d	10 56					11 01		11 26					11 48			11 56					12 01			12 26
Styal	d																								
Manchester Airport	✈ a						11 11															12 11			
Handforth	d	10 59							11 29								11 59								12 29
Congleton	d										11 25														
Macclesfield	a		10 57								11 33					11 50		11 57							
	d		10 58								11 33				11 41	11 51		11 58							
Prestbury	d														11 45										
Adlington (Cheshire)	d														11 48										
Poynton	d														11 52										
Bramhall	d														11 54										
Cheadle Hulme	d	11 04							11 34						11 56		12 04								12 34
Stockport	a	11 09	11 11					11s34	11 39		11 46			11 58	12 01	12s05	12 09	12 11						12s30	12 39
	d	11 09	11 12	11 19	11 17	11 25			11 39	11 49	11 48		11 53	11 59	12 02		12 09	12 12	12 19	12 17	12 25				12 39
Heaton Chapel	d	11 13							11 43						12 05		12 13								12 43
Levenshulme	d	11 16							11 46						12 08		12 16								12 46
Manchester Piccadilly 10	⛴ a	11 24	11 27	11 29	11 32	11 36	11 39	11 48	11 54	12 01	12 02		12 03	12 13	12 18	12 18	12 24	12 27	12 29	12 32	12 36	12 39		12 45	12 54
	d			11 30		11 37									12 19				12 30		12 37				
Manchester Oxford Road	a			11 32		11 40									12 21				12 33		12 40				
Deansgate	⛴ a			11 35											12 26				12 35						

For general notes see front of timetable
For details of catering facilities see Directory of Train Operators

- **A** From Hazel Grove (Table 86)
- **B** From Gatwick Airport (Table 51)
- **C** From Cleethorpes to Manchester Airport (Table 29)
- **D** From Carmarthen (Table 128)
- **E** From Northwich (Table 88) to Blackpool North (Table 82)
- **G** From Buxton (Table 86)
- **H** From Norwich to Liverpool Lime Street (Table 49)
- **J** From Bristol Temple Meads (Table 51)
- **K** From Bournemouth (Table 51)
- **L** From Buxton (Table 86) to Blackpool North (Table 82)
- **N** From Chester (Table 88)
- **Q** From Cambridge to Liverpool Lime Street (Table 49)
- **U** From Reading (Table 51)
- **V** From Milford Haven (Table 128)
- **X** From Birmingham International (Table 65)

Due to ongoing Engineering Operations, some services from Saturday 13 September on this Table had not been confirmed at time of going to press. These services will be issued in a special Supplement as soon as exact timings have been confirmed.

Table 84

Saturdays

Stoke-on-Trent and Crewe → Manchester Airport, Stockport and Manchester

19 July to 6 September

Network Diagram - see first page of Table 78

		NT	XC	TP	AW	NT	VT	NT	NT	XC	NT	NT	EM	NT	VT	NT	NT	XC	TP	AW	NT	VT	NT
			1 ◇	1 ◇	◇		1 ◇			R 1			◇		1 ◇			1 ◇	1 ◇	◇		1 ◇	
		A	B	C	D					E	G	H	J				A	K	C	L			
			☕	✕	✕		☕			☕					☕			☕	✕	✕		☕	
London Euston 15	⊖ 65 d						10 55								11 25							11 55	
Birmingham New Street 12	68 d		11 20							11 48								12 20					
Wolverhampton 7	68 ⛴ d		11 40							12 08								12 40					
Stafford	65, 68 d		11 54							12 23								12 54					
Stoke-on-Trent	50, 68 d		12 13				12 34			12 42					13 02			13 13				13 34	
Longport	50 d																						
Kidsgrove	50 d																						
Crewe 10	65 d				12 30									12 38		13 00				13 30			
Sandbach	d													12 45		13 07							
Holmes Chapel	d													12 49		13 11							
Goostrey	d															13 14							
Chelford	d															13 19							
Alderley Edge	d								12 53					12 58		13 23							13 53
Wilmslow	d				12 48				12 56					13 01		13 26				13 48			13 56
Styal	d																						
Manchester Airport	✈ a													13 11									
Handforth	d								12 59							13 29							13 59
Congleton	d																	13 25					
Macclesfield	a		12 32				12 49			12 57								13 33				13 50	
	d		12 33			12 41	12 50			12 58								13 33			13 41	13 50	
Prestbury	d					12 45															13 45		
Adlington (Cheshire)	d					12 48															13 48		
Poynton	d					12 52															13 52		
Bramhall	d					12 54															13 54		
Cheadle Hulme	d					12 56			13 04							13 34					13 56		14 04
Stockport	a		12 46		12 58	13 01	13s05		13 09	13 11					13s30	13 39		13 46		13 58	14 01	14s04	14 09
	d	12 49	12 48	12 53	12 59	13 02		←	13 09	13 12	13 19	13 17	13 25			13 39	13 49	13 48	13 53	13 59	14 02		14 09
Heaton Chapel	d					13 05		13 05	13 13							13 43					14 05		14 13
Levenshulme	d					→		13 08	13 16							13 46					14 08		14 16
Manchester Piccadilly 10	⛴ a	13 01	13 02	13 03	13 13		13 17	13 18	13 24	13 27	13 27	13 32	13 36	13 39	13 45	13 54	14 01	14 02	14 03	14 13	14 18	14 18	14 24
	d							13 19			13 30		13 37								14 19		
Manchester Oxford Road	a							13 21			13 32		13 40								14 21		
Deansgate	⛴ a							13 26			13 35										14 26		

		XC	NT	NT	EM	NT	VT	NT	NT	XC	TP	AW	NT	VT	NT	NT	XC	NT	EM	NT	VT	NT	NT
		1 ◇			◇		1 ◇			1 ◇	1 ◇	◇		1 ◇			1 ◇		◇		1 ◇		
		N	G	H	J				A	Q	C	D				G	E	H	J				A
		☕					☕			☕	✕	✕		☕			☕				☕		
London Euston 15	⊖ 65 d						12 25							12 55							13 25		
Birmingham New Street 12	68 d	12 48								13 20							13 48						
Wolverhampton 7	68 ⛴ d	13 08								13 40							14 08						
Stafford	65, 68 d	13 23								13 54							14 23						
Stoke-on-Trent	50, 68 d	13 42					14 02			14 13				14 34			14 42				15 02		
Longport	50 d																						
Kidsgrove	50 d																						
Crewe 10	65 d					13 38		14 00				14 30								14 38		15 00	
Sandbach	d					13 45		14 07												14 45		15 07	
Holmes Chapel	d					13 49		14 11												14 49		15 11	
Goostrey	d							14 14														15 14	
Chelford	d							14 19														15 19	
Alderley Edge	d					13 58		14 23							14 53					14 58		15 23	
Wilmslow	d					14 01		14 26				14 48			14 56					15 01		15 26	
Styal	d																						
Manchester Airport	✈ a					14 11														15 11			
Handforth	d							14 29							14 59							15 29	
Congleton	d																						
Macclesfield	a	13 57								14 32				14 50			14 57						
	d	13 58								14 33			14 41	14 50			14 58						
Prestbury	d												14 45										
Adlington (Cheshire)	d												14 48										
Poynton	d												14 52										
Bramhall	d												14 54										
Cheadle Hulme	d							14 34					14 56		15 04							15 34	
Stockport	a	14 11					14s30	14 39		14 46		14 58	15 01	15s04	15 09		15 11				15s30	15 39	
	d	14 12	14 19	14 17	14 25			14 39	14 49	14 48	14 53	14 59	15 02		15 09	15 19	15 12	15 17	15 24			15 39	15 49
Heaton Chapel	d							14 43					15 05		15 13							15 43	
Levenshulme	d							14 46					15 08		15 16							15 46	
Manchester Piccadilly 10	⛴ a	14 27	14 27	14 32	14 36	14 39	14 45	14 54	15 01	15 02	15 03	15 13	15 18	15 18	15 24	15 27	15 27	15 32	15 36	15 39	15 45	15 54	16 01
	d		14 30		14 37								15 19			15 30			15 37				
Manchester Oxford Road	a		14 32		14 40								15 21			15 32			15 40				
Deansgate	⛴ a		14 35										15 26			15 35							

For general notes see front of timetable
For details of catering facilities see Directory of Train Operators

- **A** From Hazel Grove (Table 86)
- **B** From Plymouth (Table 51)
- **C** From Cleethorpes to Manchester Airport (Table 29)
- **D** From Milford Haven (Table 128)
- **E** From Bournemouth (Table 51)
- **G** From Buxton (Table 86) to Blackpool North (Table 82)
- **H** From Chester (Table 88)
- **J** From Norwich to Liverpool Lime Street (Table 49)
- **K** From Reading (Table 51)
- **L** From Carmarthen (Table 128)
- **N** From Birmingham International (Table 65)
- **Q** From Paignton (Table 51)

Due to ongoing Engineering Operations, some services from Saturday 13 September on this Table had not been confirmed at time of going to press. These services will be issued in a special Supplement as soon as exact timings have been confirmed.

Saturdays

19 July to 6 September

Stoke-on-Trent and Crewe → Manchester Airport, Stockport and Manchester

Network Diagram - see first page of Table 78

		XC 1◇ A	TP 1◇ B	AW ◇ C	NT	VT 1◇	NT	XC 1◇ D	NT E	NT G	EM ◇ H		NT	VT 1◇	NT	NT J	NT	NT	NT K	XC 1◇ L	TP 1◇ B	AW ◇ N		NT Q	VT 1◇
London Euston 15	⊖ 65 d					13 55								14 25											14 55
Birmingham New Street 12	68 d	14 20						14 48												15 20					
Wolverhampton 7	68 d	14 40						15 08												15 40					
Stafford	65, 68 d	14 54						15 23												15 54					
Stoke-on-Trent	50, 68 d	15 13				15 35		15 42						16 02						16 13					16 34
Longport	50 d																								
Kidsgrove	50 d																								
Crewe 10	65 d			15 30									15 38					16 00				16 30			
Sandbach	d												15 45					16 07							
Holmes Chapel	d												15 49					16 11							
Goostrey	d																	16 14							
Chelford	d																	16 19							
Alderley Edge	d						15 53						15 58					16 23							
Wilmslow	d			15 48			15 56						16 01					16 26				16 48			
Styal	d																								
Manchester Airport	✈ a												16 11												
Handforth	d						15 59											16 29							
Congleton	d	15 25																							
Macclesfield	a	15 33				15 50		15 57												16 32					16 50
	d	15 33			15 41	15 51		15 58							16 10					16 33					16 50
Prestbury	d				15 45										16 14										
Adlington (Cheshire)	d				15 48										16 17										
Poynton	d				15 52										16 21										
Bramhall	d				15 54										16 23										
Cheadle Hulme	d				15 56		16 04								16 26			16 34							
Stockport	a	15 46		15 58	16 01	16s05	16 09	16 11						16s33	16 30			16 40		16 46		16 58			17s04
	d	15 48	15 53	15 59	16 02		16 09	16 12	16 19	16 17	16 25				16 35	16 40		16 43	16 49	16 48	16 53	16 59		17 01	
Heaton Chapel	d				16 05		16 13								16 38		←							17 05	
Levenshulme	d				16 08		16 16								16 41		16 41							17 08	
Manchester Piccadilly 10	a	16 02	16 03	16 13	16 18	16 18	16 24	16 27	16 27	16 32	16 36		16 41	16 45	→	16 50	16 54	16 54	17 01	17 02	17 03	17 13		17 15	17 18
	d								16 30		16 37					16 52	16 56							17 15	
Manchester Oxford Road	a								16 32		16 40					16 55	16 58							17 18	
Deansgate	a								16 35							16 58	17 03							17 21	

		NT	XC R 1 L	NT E	NT	NT G	EM ◇ H	AW G	NT	NT	VT 1◇		NT	XC 1◇ A	NT K	TP 1◇ B	AW R C	VT 1◇	XC 1◇ D	NT G	NT E	NT G		EM ◇ H	NT
London Euston 15	⊖ 65 d										15 25							15 55							
Birmingham New Street 12	68 d		15 48											16 20					16 48						
Wolverhampton 7	68 d		16 08											16 40					17 08						
Stafford	65, 68 d		16 23											16 54					17 23						
Stoke-on-Trent	50, 68 d		16 42								17 02			17 13				17 39	17 42						
Longport	50 d																								
Kidsgrove	50 d																								
Crewe 10	65 d								16 42				17 00				17 30								17 38
Sandbach	d								16 49				17 07												17 45
Holmes Chapel	d								16 53				17 11												17 50
Goostrey	d												17 14												17 53
Chelford	d												17 19												17 57
Alderley Edge	d	16 53							17 02				17 23												18 01
Wilmslow	d	16 56							17 05				17 26				17 48								18 04
Styal	d																								18 08
Manchester Airport	✈ a								17 15																18 15
Handforth	d	16 59											17 29												
Congleton	d													17 25											
Macclesfield	a		16 57								17 17			17 33				17 54	17 57						
	d		16 58							17 10	17 17			17 33				17 55	17 58						
Prestbury	d									17 14															
Adlington (Cheshire)	d									17 17															
Poynton	d									17 21															
Bramhall	d									17 23															
Cheadle Hulme	d	17 04								17 26			17 34												
Stockport	a	17 09	17 11							17 30	17s32		17 39	17 46			17 58	18s11	18 11						
	d	17 11	17 12	17 18	←	17 16	17 25	17 25		17 32			17 39	17 48	17 50	17 53	17 59		18 12	18 17	18 19	←		18 26	
Heaton Chapel	d	17 15			17 15	17 19							17 43							18 23		18 23			
Levenshulme	d	→			17 18	17 22							17 46							→		18 26			
Manchester Piccadilly 10	a		17 27	17 28	17 29	17 31	17 35	17 39	17 41	17 44	17 49		17 54	18 02	18 03	18 03	18 10	18 25	18 27		18 30	18 32		18 35	18 40
	d			17 30			17 37														18 31			18 37	
Manchester Oxford Road	a			17 32			17 39														18 34			18 39	
Deansgate	a			17 35																	18 38				

For general notes see front of timetable
For details of catering facilities see Directory of Train Operators

A From Reading (Table 51)
B From Cleethorpes to Manchester Airport (Table 29)
C From Carmarthen (Table 128)
D From Birmingham International (Table 65)
E From Buxton (Table 86) to Blackpool North (Table 82)
G From Chester (Table 88)
H From Norwich to Liverpool Lime Street (Table 49)
J To Preston (Table 82)
K From Hazel Grove (Table 86)
L From Bournemouth (Table 51)
N From Milford Haven (Table 128)
Q To Blackpool North (Table 82)

Due to ongoing Engineering Operations, some services from Saturday 13 September on this Table had not been confirmed at time of going to press. These services will be issued in a special Supplement as soon as exact timings have been confirmed.

Table 84

Saturdays

Stoke-on-Trent and Crewe → Manchester Airport, Stockport and Manchester

19 July to 6 September

Network Diagram - see first page of Table 78

Station		NT	VT	NT	NT	XC	TP	AW	NT	VT	NT
						R		R			
			1 ◇			1	1 ◇			1 ◇	
					A	B	C	D	E		G
London Euston 15	⊖ 65 d		16 25							16 55	
Birmingham New Street 12	68 d					17 20					
Wolverhampton 7	68 d					17 40					
Stafford	65, 68 d					17 54					
Stoke-on-Trent	50, 68 d		18 02			18 13				18 34	
Longport	50 d										
Kidsgrove	50 d										
Crewe 10	65 d			18 00				18 30			
Sandbach	d			18 07							
Holmes Chapel	d			18 11							
Goostrey	d			18 14							
Chelford	d			18 19							
Alderley Edge	d			18 23							
Wilmslow	d			18 26				18 48			
Styal	d										
Manchester Airport	a										
Handforth	d			18 29							
Congleton	d										
Macclesfield	a		18 17			18 32				18 50	
	d	18 10	18 17			18 33				18 50	
Prestbury	d	18 14									
Adlington (Cheshire)	d	18 17									
Poynton	d	18 21									
Bramhall	d	18 23									
Cheadle Hulme	d	18 26		18 34							
Stockport	a	18 30	18s32	18 39		18 46		18 59		19s05	
	d	18 32		18 39	18 50	18 48	18 53	18 59	19 05		19 10
Heaton Chapel	d			18 43					19 09		19 14
Levenshulme	d			18 46					19 12		19 17
Manchester Piccadilly 10	a	18 43	18 49	18 54	19 01	19 02	19 03	19 16	19 19	19 22	19 28
	d								19 20		
Manchester Oxford Road	a								19 22		
Deansgate	a								19 25		

Station		XC	EM	NT	NT	VT	NT	NT	NT	XC	TP	AW	NT
												R	
		1 ◇	◇			1 ◇				1 ◇	1 ◇		
		H	J					K		L	C	N	
London Euston 15	⊖ 65 d					17 25							
Birmingham New Street 12	68 d	17 48								18 20			
Wolverhampton 7	68 d	18 08								18 40			
Stafford	65, 68 d	18 23								18 54			
Stoke-on-Trent	50, 68 d	18 42				19 04				19 13			19 19
Longport	50 d												
Kidsgrove	50 d												19 27
Crewe 10	65 d			18 42			19 00					19 30	
Sandbach	d			18 49			19 07						
Holmes Chapel	d			18 53			19 11						
Goostrey	d						19 14						
Chelford	d						19 19						
Alderley Edge	d			19 02			19 23						
Wilmslow	d			19 05			19 26					19 48	
Styal	d												
Manchester Airport	a			19 16									
Handforth	d						19 29						
Congleton	d									19 25			19 34
Macclesfield	a	18 57				19 20				19 33			19 41
	d	18 58			19 10	19 20				19 33			19 42
Prestbury	d				19 14								19 46
Adlington (Cheshire)	d				19 17								19 49
Poynton	d				19 21								19 52
Bramhall	d				19 23								19 55
Cheadle Hulme	d				19 26		19 34						19 57
Stockport	a	19 11			19 30	19s35	19 39			19 46		19 59	20 02
	d	19 12	19 24		19 31		19 39	19 40	←	19 48	19 53	19 59	20 03
Heaton Chapel	d						19 43		19 43				20 06
Levenshulme	d						→		19 46				20 09
Manchester Piccadilly 10	a	19 27	19 35	19 41	19 43	19 48		19 51	19 57	20 02	20 03	20 13	20 17
	d			19 41									
Manchester Oxford Road	a			19 46									
Deansgate	a												

Station		VT	NT	XC	NT	EM	VT	NT	NT	XC	TP
										R	
		1 ◇		1 ◇		◇	1 ◇			1	1 ◇
			G	Q		J		U		V	C
London Euston 15	⊖ 65 d	17 55					18 25				
Birmingham New Street 12	68 d			18 48						19 20	
Wolverhampton 7	68 d			19 08						19 40	
Stafford	65, 68 d			19 23						19 54	
Stoke-on-Trent	50, 68 d	19 35		19 42			20 02			20 13	
Longport	50 d										
Kidsgrove	50 d										
Crewe 10	65 d								20 00		
Sandbach	d								20 07		
Holmes Chapel	d								20 11		
Goostrey	d								20 14		
Chelford	d								20 19		
Alderley Edge	d								20 23		
Wilmslow	d				19 51				20 26		
Styal	d										
Manchester Airport	a				20 02						
Handforth	d								20 29		
Congleton	d										
Macclesfield	a	19 50		19 57			20 17			20 32	
	d	19 51		19 58			20 18			20 33	
Prestbury	d										
Adlington (Cheshire)	d										
Poynton	d										
Bramhall	d										
Cheadle Hulme	d								20 34		
Stockport	a	20s07		20 11			20s33		20 39	20 46	
	d		20 10	20 12		20 25		20 40	20 39	20 48	20 53
Heaton Chapel	d								20 43		
Levenshulme	d								20 46		
Manchester Piccadilly 10	a	20 22	20 24	20 27	20 31	20 36	20 50	20 52	20 54	21 02	21 03
	d					20 37		20 52			
Manchester Oxford Road	a					20 39		20 54			
Deansgate	a							20 56			

Station		AW	NT	NT	VT	EM	NT	XC	NT	VT	XC	AW	NT
		R											
					1 ◇	◇		1 ◇		1 ◇	1 ◇	◇	
		D		G		J		H			X	N	
London Euston 15	⊖ 65 d				18 55					19 13			
Birmingham New Street 12	68 d							20 03			20 20		
Wolverhampton 7	68 d							20 21			20 40		
Stafford	65, 68 d							20 34			20 54		
Stoke-on-Trent	50, 68 d				20 42					21 07	21 13		
Longport	50 d												
Kidsgrove	50 d												
Crewe 10	65 d	20 26						20 56	21 00			21 27	
Sandbach	d								21 07				
Holmes Chapel	d								21 11				
Goostrey	d								21 14				
Chelford	d								21 19				
Alderley Edge	d								21 23				
Wilmslow	d	20 45					20 50	21 13	21 26			21 46	
Styal	d												
Manchester Airport	a						21 02						
Handforth	d								21 29				
Congleton	d										21 25		
Macclesfield	a				20 58					21 23	21 33		
	d		20 42		20 58					21 23	21 33		21 42
Prestbury	d		20 46										21 46
Adlington (Cheshire)	d		20 49										21 49
Poynton	d		20 53										21 53
Bramhall	d		20 55										21 55
Cheadle Hulme	d		20 57						21 34				21 57
Stockport	a	20 56	21 02		21s13			21 22	21 39	21s41	21 46	21 57	22 02
	d	20 56	21 03	21 10		21 17		21 23	21 39		21 48	21 57	22 03
Heaton Chapel	d		21 06						21 43				22 06
Levenshulme	d		21 09						21 46				22 09
Manchester Piccadilly 10	a	21 13	21 19	21 24	21 26	21 26	21 31	21 36	21 53	21 54	22 02	22 13	22 18
	d								21 54				
Manchester Oxford Road	a								21 56				
Deansgate	a								22 01				

For general notes see front of timetable
For details of catering facilities see Directory of Train Operators

- **A** From Hazel Grove (Table 86)
- **B** From Penzance (Table 135)
- **C** From Cleethorpes to Manchester Airport (Table 29)
- **D** From Milford Haven (Table 128)
- **E** From Buxton (Table 86) to Salford Crescent (Table 82)
- **G** From Chester (Table 88)
- **H** From Bournemouth (Table 51)
- **J** From Norwich (Table 49)
- **K** From Buxton (Table 86)
- **L** From Brighton (Table 51)
- **N** From Carmarthen (Table 128)
- **Q** From Birmingham International (Table 65)
- **U** From Buxton (Table 86) to Bolton (Table 82)
- **V** From Paignton (Table 51)
- **X** From Guildford (Table 51)

Due to ongoing Engineering Operations, some services from Saturday 13 September on this Table had not been confirmed at time of going to press. These services will be issued in a special Supplement as soon as exact timings have been confirmed.

Saturdays

19 July to 6 September

Stoke-on-Trent and Crewe → Manchester Airport, Stockport and Manchester

Network Diagram - see first page of Table 78

	NT	XC	NT	NT	VT	NT	VT	NT	XC	NT	NT	NT	VT	VT	AW	NT	XC	VT	VT	NT	VT
		1 ◇			1 ◇				R 1					1 ◇	◇		1 ◇		1 ◇		
	A	B		C		D			E			G			H	J	K				
							🚌						🚌					🚌			🚌
London Euston 15 ⊖ 65 d					19 27									20 23					20 36		
Birmingham New Street 12 68 d		20 48							21 20								22 20				
Wolverhampton 7 68 ⛴ d		21 08							21 40								22 40				
Stafford 65, 68 d		21 22			21 29				21 54				21 40	22 38			22 54		23 00		22 50
Stoke-on-Trent 50, 68 d		21 42											22 10								23 20
Longport 50 d																					
Kidsgrove 50 d																					
Crewe 10 65 d								22 00	22 22						23 04					23 08	
Sandbach d								22 07												23 15	
Holmes Chapel d								22 11												23 19	
Goostrey d								22 14												23 22	
Chelford d								22 19												23 27	
Alderley Edge d								22 23												23 31	
Wilmslow d			21 55		22 09		22 20	22 26	22 40		22 55			23 17	23 23			23 30		23 34	
Styal d																					
Manchester Airport ✈ a			22 05								23 05										
Handforth d								22 29												23 36	
Congleton d																					
Macclesfield a		21 57					22 50						23 00				23s29	23 59			00 10
d		21 58								22 42			23 00								00 10
Prestbury d										22 46											
Adlington (Cheshire) d										22 49											
Poynton d										22 53											
Bramhall d										22 55											
Cheadle Hulme d								22 34		22 57										23 42	
Stockport a		22 11			22s18			22 39	22 50	23 02			23 30	23s28	23 33		23s44		23s50	23 48	00 40
d	22 13	22 12		22 23		22 38		22 39	22 51	23 03		23 22			23 33	23 40				23 48	
Heaton Chapel d								22 43		23 06										23 52	
Levenshulme d								22 46		23 09										23 55	
Manchester Piccadilly 10 ⛴ a	22 26	22 27	22 31	22 33	22 36	22 47		22 52	23 07	23 19	23 31	23 37		23 41	23 50	23 52	00 04		00 04	00 05	
d				22 35		22 49		22 54													
Manchester Oxford Road a				22 37		22 51		22 56													
Deansgate ⛴ a				22 40		22 54		23 00													

Sundays

until 13 July

	NT	TP	NT	NT	TP	NT	NT	NT	XC	NT	NT	EM	NT	XC	NT	VT	TP	NT	VT	AW	EM	NT
		1 ◇			1 ◇				1 ◇			◇		1 ◇		1 ◇	1 ◇				◇	
	A	L	N	Q	U	N	G	Q			N	V	Q		G		X	N		Y	V	Q
																			🚌			
London Euston 15 ⊖ 65 d																08 35						
Birmingham New Street 12 68 d									09 03					10 03								
Wolverhampton 7 68 ⛴ d									09 32					10 32								
Stafford 65, 68 d									09 45					10 45		10 53						
Stoke-on-Trent 50, 68 d																						
Longport 50 d																						
Kidsgrove 50 d																						
Crewe 10 65 d										10 25										11 42		
Sandbach d										10 32												
Holmes Chapel d										10 36												
Goostrey d										10 39												
Chelford d										10 44												
Alderley Edge d				09 10				10 10		10 48			11 10									12 10
Wilmslow d				09 13				10 13	10 26	10 51			11 13	11 26		11 32			11 40	12 01		12 13
Styal d																						
Manchester Airport ✈ a										10 59												
Handforth d				09 17				10 17					11 17									12 17
Congleton d																						
Macclesfield a																			12 10			
d																						
Prestbury d																						
Adlington (Cheshire) d																						
Poynton d																						
Bramhall d																						
Cheadle Hulme d				09 23				10 23					11 23									12 23
Stockport a				09 28				10 28	10 35				11 28	11 35		11s41				12 11		12 28
d	00 01	08 39	09 10	09 29	09 58	10 10	10 31	10 29	10 36		11 10	11 20	11 29	11 36	11 38		11 59	12 08		12 12	12 24	12 29
Heaton Chapel d			09 14	09 33		10 14		10 33			11 14		11 33					12 11				12 33
Levenshulme d			09 17	09 36		10 17		10 36			11 17		11 36					12 14				→
Manchester Piccadilly 10 ⛴ a	00 14	08 48	09 24	09 43	10 08	10 24	10 41	10 44	10 52	11 21	11 23	11 32	11 45	11 52	11 56	11 56	12 08	12 25		12 26	12 36	
d			09 25	09 45		10 25		10 45			11 25	11 37	11 45					12 25			12 37	
Manchester Oxford Road a			09 27	09 47		10 27		10 47			11 27	11 39	11 48					12 27			12 39	
Deansgate ⛴ a			09 31	09 50		10 31		10 50			11 31		11 50					12 31				

For general notes see front of timetable
For details of catering facilities see Directory of Train Operators

- **A** From Chester (Table 88)
- **B** From Bristol Temple Meads (Table 51)
- **C** From Buxton (Table 86) to Southport (Table 82)
- **D** To Wigan Wallgate (Table 82)
- **E** From Newquay (Table 135)
- **G** From Sheffield (Table 78)
- **H** From Milford Haven (Table 128)
- **J** From Buxton (Table 86)
- **K** From Bournemouth (Table 51)
- **L** From Sheffield to Manchester Airport (Table 78)
- **N** From Buxton (Table 86) to Blackpool North (Table 82)
- **Q** To Southport (Table 82)
- **U** From Meadowhall to Manchester Airport (Table 29)
- **V** From Nottingham to Liverpool Lime Street (Table 49)
- **X** From Doncaster to Manchester Airport (Table 29)
- **Y** From Shrewsbury (Table 131)

Due to ongoing Engineering Operations, some services from Saturday 13 September on this Table had not been confirmed at time of going to press. These services will be issued in a special Supplement as soon as exact timings have been confirmed.

Sundays

until 13 July

Stoke-on-Trent and Crewe → Manchester Airport, Stockport and Manchester

Network Diagram - see first page of Table 78

		VT 1◇ ☕		NT A	VT 🚌	XC 1◇ B ☕	NT C	VT 🚌	TP 1◇ D	NT E		NT	EM ◇ G	NT A	VT 🚌	VT 1◇ ☕	NT A	VT 🚌		XC 1◇ H ☕	NT C	TP 1◇ J	AW K	NT E	VT 1◇ ☕
London Euston 15	⊖ 65 d	09 35														10 35									11 29
Birmingham New Street 12	68 d					11 03														12 03					
Wolverhampton 7	68 🚌 d					11 32														12 32					
Stafford	65, 68 d	11 39			11 05	11 45									11 50	12 39				12 45					
Stoke-on-Trent	50, 68 d				11 35										12 20										13 46
Longport	50 d																								
Kidsgrove	50 d																								
Crewe 10	65 d											12 27											13 36		
Sandbach	d											12 34													
Holmes Chapel	d											12 38													
Goostrey	d																								
Chelford	d																								
Alderley Edge	d											12 47		13 10											
Wilmslow	d	12 19				12 25		12 25				12 50		13 13		13 19		13 25		13 26			13 56		
Styal	d																								
Manchester Airport	✈ a											13 02													
Handforth	d													13 17											
Congleton	d																								
Macclesfield	a				12 25			12 55							13 10			13 55							14 01
	d				12 25										13 10										14 02
Prestbury	d																								
Adlington (Cheshire)	d																								
Poynton	d																								
Bramhall	d																								
Cheadle Hulme	d													13 23											
Stockport	a	12s30			12 55	12 34								13 28	13 40	13s30				13 35			14 06		14s15
	d			←		12 35	12 45		13 00	13 08			13 23	13 29			←			13 36	13 57	14 01	14 07	14 10	
Heaton Chapel	d			12 33						13 11				13 33			13 33							14 14	
Levenshulme	d			12 36						13 14				→			13 36							14 17	
Manchester Piccadilly 10	🚊 a	12 43		12 46		12 49	12 56		13 10	13 23		13 27	13 36			13 43	13 46			13 56	14 10	14 11	14 21	14 24	14 28
	d			12 48						13 24			13 37				13 48							14 25	
Manchester Oxford Road	a			12 50						13 26			13 39				13 50							14 27	
Deansgate	🚊 a			12 53						13 30							13 53							14 31	

		EM ◇ L	VT 1◇ ☕	NT A		XC 1◇ N ☕	NT C	AW ◇ Q 🍴	TP 1◇ D	VT 1◇ ☕	NT	NT E		EM ◇ U	VT 1◇ ☕	NT A	XC R 1 V ☕	AW ◇ X 🍴	TP 1◇ D	NT E		VT 1◇ ☕	EM ◇ G	NT A	VT 1◇ ☕
London Euston 15	⊖ 65 d		11 46							12 35					12 51							13 35			13 51
Birmingham New Street 12	68 d					13 03											14 03								
Wolverhampton 7	68 🚌 d					13 38											14 38								
Stafford	65, 68 d					13 53											14 53								
Stoke-on-Trent	50, 68 d		13 58			14 12				14 28					14 57		15 12					15 37			15 59
Longport	50 d																								
Kidsgrove	50 d																								
Crewe 10	65 d							14 19			14 27							15 24							
Sandbach	d										14 34														
Holmes Chapel	d										14 38														
Goostrey	d										14 41														
Chelford	d										14 46														
Alderley Edge	d			14 10							14 50					15 10								16 10	
Wilmslow	d			14 13				14 42			14 53					15 13		15 45						16 13	
Styal	d																								
Manchester Airport	✈ a										15 04														
Handforth	d			14 17												15 17								16 17	
Congleton	d																								
Macclesfield	a		14 13			14 27				14 43					15 12		15 27					15 54			16 14
	d		14 14			14 29				14 44					15 13		15 29					15 55			16 15
Prestbury	d																								
Adlington (Cheshire)	d																								
Poynton	d																								
Bramhall	d																								
Cheadle Hulme	d			14 21												15 23								16 23	
Stockport	a		14s30	14 28		14 42		14 53		14s58					15s30	15 28	15 41	15 55				16s12		16 28	16s30
	d	14 20		14 29		14 43	14 49	14 53	15 01			15 10		15 25		15 29	15 43	15 56	16 04	16 10			16 20	16 29	
Heaton Chapel	d			14 33								15 14				15 33				16 14				16 33	
Levenshulme	d			14 36								15 17				15 36				16 17				16 36	
Manchester Piccadilly 10	🚊 a	14 33	14 44	14 47		14 56	15 02	15 10	15 13	15 15	15 24	15 24		15 34	15 43	15 44	15 56	16 11	16 13	16 24		16 24	16 33	16 44	16 44
	d	14 37		14 48								15 25		15 37		15 45				16 25			16 37	16 45	
Manchester Oxford Road	a	14 39		14 51								15 27		15 39		15 48				16 27			16 39	16 48	
Deansgate	🚊 a			14 53								15 31				15 50				16 30				16 50	

For general notes see front of timetable
For details of catering facilities see Directory of Train Operators

- **A** To Southport (Table 82)
- **B** From Bristol Temple Meads (Table 51)
- **C** From Sheffield (Table 78)
- **D** From Cleethorpes to Manchester Airport (Table 29)
- **E** From Buxton (Table 86) to Blackpool North (Table 82)
- **G** From Nottingham to Liverpool Lime Street (Table 49)
- **H** From Southampton Central (Table 51)
- **J** From Doncaster to Manchester Airport (Table 29)
- **K** From Shrewsbury (Table 131)
- **L** From Nottingham to Liverpool Lime Street (Table 89)
- **N** From Plymouth (Table 51)
- **Q** From Cardiff Central (Table 131)
- **U** From Norwich to Liverpool Lime Street (Table 49)
- **V** From Bournemouth (Table 51)
- **X** From Milford Haven (Table 128)

Table 84

Sundays until 13 July

Stoke-on-Trent and Crewe → Manchester Airport, Stockport and Manchester

Network Diagram - see first page of Table 78

	XC R 1 A	NT B	TP 1◇ C	NT	NT		VT 1◇	NT D	EM ◇ E	NT G	VT 1◇	XC R 1 H	NT B		TP 1◇ C	VT 1◇	NT D	AW ◇ J	EM ◇ K	NT G	VT 1◇		XC R 1 L	NT B
London Euston 15 ⊖ 65 d							14 35				14 51					15 35					15 51			
Birmingham New Street 12 68 d	15 03											16 03											17 03	
Wolverhampton 7 68 d	15 38											16 38											17 38	
Stafford 65, 68 d	15 53											16 53											17 53	
Stoke-on-Trent 50, 68 d	16 12			16 19			16 37				16 59	17 12				17 36					17 59		18 12	
Longport 50 d				16 23																				
Kidsgrove 50 d				16 27																				
Crewe 10 65 d					16 27													17 39						
Sandbach d					16 34																			
Holmes Chapel d					16 38																			
Goostrey d																								
Chelford d																								
Alderley Edge d					16 47					17 10										18 10				
Wilmslow d					16 50					17 13								17 59		18 13				
Styal d																								
Manchester Airport ✈ a					16 59																			
Handforth d										17 17										18 17				
Congleton d				16 34																				
Macclesfield a	16 27			16 41			16 53				17 14	17 27				17 53					18 14		18 27	
d	16 29			16 41			16 54				17 15	17 29				17 54					18 15		18 29	
Prestbury d				16 45																				
Adlington (Cheshire) d				16 48																				
Poynton d				16 52																				
Bramhall d				16 54																				
Cheadle Hulme d				16 56						17 23										18 23				
Stockport a	16 41			17 01			17s07			17 28	17s30	17 41				18s07		18 13		18 28	18s30		18 41	
d	16 42	16 46	16 56	17 03				17 10	17 21	17 29		17 42	17 44		17 56		18 10	18 13	18 25	18 29			18 42	18 56
Heaton Chapel d								17 14		17 33							18 14			18 33				
Levenshulme d								17 17		17 36							18 17			18 36				
Manchester Piccadilly 10 a	16 56	16 56	17 11	17 15	17 23		17 24	17 24	17 36	17 44	17 44	17 56	17 57		18 12	18 23	18 24	18 28	18 35	18 43	18 45		18 56	19 10
d								17 25	17 37	17 45							18 25		18 37	18 45				
Manchester Oxford Road a								17 27	17 39	17 48							18 27		18 39	18 47				
Deansgate a								17 31		17 50							18 30			18 50				

	TP 1◇ C	NT	NT D	VT 1◇	EM ◇ E	NT G	VT 1◇		XC R 1 H	NT B	TP 1◇ C	NT	AW R N	VT 1◇	NT D		EM ◇ Q	NT G	VT 1◇	NT B	XC R 1 U	TP 1◇ C	NT	NT D
London Euston 15 ⊖ 65 d				16 35			16 51							17 35					17 51					
Birmingham New Street 12 68 d									18 03												19 03			
Wolverhampton 7 68 d									18 38												19 38			
Stafford 65, 68 d									18 53												19 53			
Stoke-on-Trent 50, 68 d				18 38			18 58		19 12			19 20		19 29					19 59		20 12			
Longport 50 d												19 24												
Kidsgrove 50 d												19 28												
Crewe 10 65 d		18 27											19 28										20 27	
Sandbach d		18 34																					20 34	
Holmes Chapel d		18 38																					20 38	
Goostrey d																								
Chelford d																								
Alderley Edge d		18 47				19 10												20 10					20 47	
Wilmslow d		18 50				19 13							19 48					20 13					20 50	
Styal d																								
Manchester Airport ✈ a		19 00																					20 59	
Handforth d						19 17												20 17						
Congleton d												19 35												
Macclesfield a				18 56			19 13		19 27			19 42		19 46					20 14		20 27			
d				18 58			19 14		19 29			19 42		19 47					20 15		20 29			
Prestbury d												19 46												
Adlington (Cheshire) d												19 49												
Poynton d												19 53												
Bramhall d												19 55												
Cheadle Hulme d						19 23						19 58						20 23						
Stockport a				19s11		19 28	19s30		19 41			20 02	19 57	20s06				20 28	20s30		20 41			
d	19 00		19 10		19 20	19 29			19 42	19 46	20 00	20 03	19 58		20 10		20 25	20 29		20 46	20 42	20 54		21 10
Heaton Chapel d			19 14			19 33									20 14			20 33						21 14
Levenshulme d			19 17			19 36									20 17			20 36						21 17
Manchester Piccadilly 10 a	19 12	19 21	19 24	19 27	19 32	19 43	19 44		19 56	19 59	20 09	20 12	20 14	20 18	20 24		20 35	20 44	20 44	20 55	20 56	21 04	21 21	21 24
d			19 25		19 37	19 45									20 25			20 45						21 25
Manchester Oxford Road a			19 27		19 39	19 47									20 27			20 48						21 27
Deansgate a			19 31			19 50									20 30			20 50						21 30

For general notes see front of timetable
For details of catering facilities see Directory of Train Operators

A From Penzance (Table 135)
B From Sheffield (Table 78)
C From Cleethorpes to Manchester Airport (Table 29)
D From Buxton (Table 86) to Blackpool North (Table 82)
E From Nottingham to Liverpool Lime Street (Table 49)
G To Southport (Table 82)
H From Bournemouth (Table 51)
J From Pembroke Dock (Table 128)
K From Norwich to Liverpool Lime Street (Table 49)
L From Newquay (Table 135)
N From Milford Haven (Table 128)
Q From Norwich (Table 49)
U From Plymouth (Table 51)

Table 84

Sundays
until 13 July

Stoke-on-Trent and Crewe → Manchester Airport, Stockport and Manchester

Network Diagram - see first page of Table 78

	VT	EM	NT	VT	XC	AW	TP	VT	NT	NT	VT	XC	NT	NT	NT	NT	VT	XC	VT
	1 ◇	◇		1 ◇	R 1	R	1 ◇	1 ◇			1 ◇	1 ◇					1 ◇	1 ◇	1 ◇
		A	B		C	D	E		G	B		H		J		G		C	
London Euston 15 ⊖ 65 d	18 35			18 51				19 35			19 51						20 35		21 50
Birmingham New Street 12 68 d					20 03							21 03						22 03	
Wolverhampton 7 68 d					20 38							21 38						22 38	
Stafford 65, 68 d					20 53							21 53					22 32	22 53	00 07
Stoke-on-Trent 50, 68 d	20 37			20 57	21 12			21 40			21 58	22 12	22 15				22 51	23 12	
Longport 50 d													22 19						
Kidsgrove 50 d													22 23						
Crewe 10 65 d						21 26									22 25				00 33
Sandbach d															22 32				
Holmes Chapel d															22 36				
Goostrey d															22 39				
Chelford d															22 44				
Alderley Edge d			21 10							22 10					22 48				
Wilmslow d			21 13			21 46				22 13					22 51				00 50
Styal d																			
Manchester Airport ✈ a															22 59				
Handforth d			21 17							22 17									
Congleton d													22 30						
Macclesfield a	20 55			21 12	21 27			21 57			22 13	22 27	22 37				23 05	23 27	
d	20 56			21 13	21 29			21 58			22 14	22 29	22 37				23 07	23 29	
Prestbury d													22 41						
Adlington (Cheshire) d													22 44						
Poynton d													22 48						
Bramhall d													22 50						
Cheadle Hulme d			21 23							22 23			22 53						
Stockport a	21s11		21 28	21s30	21 41	21 57		22s11		22 28	22s30	22 41	22 57				23s19	23 41	00s58
d		21 17	21 29		21 42	21 58	22 01		22 10	22 29		22 42	22 58	23 01		23 10		23 43	
Heaton Chapel d			21 33						22 14	22 33						23 14			
Levenshulme d			21 36						22 17	22 36						23 17			
Manchester Piccadilly 10 a	21 26	21 31	21 42	21 44	21 56	22 13	22 14	22 26	22 27	22 42	22 42	22 56	23 09	23 13	23 22	23 27	23 32	23 56	01 11
d			21 45							22 45									
Manchester Oxford Road a			21 47							22 47									
Deansgate a			21 50							22 50									

Sundays
20 July to 7 September

	NT	TP	NT	NT	TP	NT	NT	XC	NT	NT	XC	EM	NT	VT	NT	XC	TP	AW	NT	XC	EM	NT
		1 ◇			1 ◇			1 ◇			1 ◇	◇		1 ◇		1 ◇	1 ◇			1 ◇	◇	
	K	L	N	Q	U	N	Q			N		V	Q		J		X	Y	N		V	Q
London Euston 15 ⊖ 65 d														08 56								
Birmingham New Street 12 68 d								09 18			09 48					10 18				10 48		
Wolverhampton 7 68 d								09 38			10 08					10 38				11 08		
Stafford 65, 68 d								09 52			10 25					10 51				11 21		
Stoke-on-Trent 50, 68 d								10 11			10 44			11 02		11 11				11 41		
Longport 50 d																						
Kidsgrove 50 d																						
Crewe 10 65 d									10 25									11 31				
Sandbach d									10 32													
Holmes Chapel d									10 36													
Goostrey d									10 39													
Chelford d									10 44													
Alderley Edge d				09 10			10 10		10 48				11 10									12 10
Wilmslow d				09 13			10 13		10 51				11 13					11 51				12 13
Styal d																						
Manchester Airport ✈ a																						
Handforth d				09 17			10 17						11 17									12 17
Congleton d																						
Macclesfield a								10 27			11 00			11 17		11 27				11 57		
d								10 29			11 02			11 19		11 29				11 59		
Prestbury d																						
Adlington (Cheshire) d																						
Poynton d																						
Bramhall d																						
Cheadle Hulme d				09 23			10 23						11 23									12 23
Stockport a				09 28			10 28	10 41			11 14		11 28	11s32		11 41		12 01		12 11		12 28
d	00 01	08 39	09 10	09 29	09 58	10 10	10 29	10 42		11 10	11 16	11 20	11 28		11 32	11 42	11 59	12 02	12 08	12 12	12 24	12 28
Heaton Chapel d			09 14	09 33		10 14	10 33			11 14			11 32						12 11			12 32
Levenshulme d			09 17	09 36		10 17	10 36			11 17			11 35						12 14			12 35
Manchester Piccadilly 10 a	00 13	08 48	09 24	09 43	10 08	10 24	10 42	10 56	11 12	11 23	11 32	11 32	11 41	11 47	11 49	11 56	12 08	12 16	12 25	12 26	12 36	12 43
d			09 25	09 45		10 25	10 45			11 25		11 37	11 45						12 25		12 37	12 45
Manchester Oxford Road a			09 27	09 47		10 27	10 47			11 27		11 39	11 47						12 27		12 39	12 47
Deansgate a			09 31	09 50		10 31	10 50			11 31			11 50						12 31			12 50

For general notes see front of timetable
For details of catering facilities see Directory of Train Operators

- **A** From Norwich (Table 49)
- **B** To Wigan Wallgate (Table 82)
- **C** From Bournemouth (Table 51)
- **D** From Milford Haven (Table 128)
- **E** From Cleethorpes to Manchester Airport (Table 29)
- **G** From Buxton (Table 86)
- **H** From Plymouth (Table 51)
- **J** From Sheffield (Table 78)
- **K** From Chester (Table 88)
- **L** From Sheffield to Manchester Airport (Table 78)
- **N** From Buxton (Table 86) to Blackpool North (Table 82)
- **Q** To Southport (Table 82)
- **U** From Meadowhall to Manchester Airport (Table 29)
- **V** From Nottingham to Liverpool Lime Street (Table 49)
- **X** From Doncaster to Manchester Airport (Table 29)
- **Y** From Shrewsbury (Table 131)

Due to ongoing Engineering Operations, some services from Sunday 14 September on this Table had not been confirmed at time of going to press. These services will be issued in a special Supplement as soon as exact timings have been confirmed.

Table 84

Sundays

20 July to 7 September

Stoke-on-Trent and Crewe → Manchester Airport, Stockport and Manchester

Network Diagram - see first page of Table 78

	VT [1]◇ 🍴		XC [1]◇ A 🍴	TP [1]◇ B	NT C	XC [1]◇ 🍴	NT	EM ◇ D	VT [1]◇ 🍴		NT E	XC [1]◇ G 🍴	NT H	TP [1]◇ J	AW K	NT C	VT [1]◇ 🍴		XC [1]◇ 🍴	EM ◇ L	VT [1]◇ 🍴	NT E	XC [1]◇ N 🍴	AW ◇ Q 🛒
London Euston [15] ⊖ 65 d	09 31								10 30								11 29				11 46			
Birmingham New Street [12] 68 d			11 18			11 48						12 18							12 48				13 18	
Wolverhampton [7] 68 ⛴ d			11 38			12 08						12 38							13 08				13 38	
Stafford 65, 68 d			11 52			12 21						12 53							13 21				13 53	
Stoke-on-Trent 50, 68 d	11 57		12 11			12 41			12 57			13 12					13 39		13 45		14 00		14 12	
Longport 50 d																								
Kidsgrove 50 d																								
Crewe [10] 65 d							12 36								13 36									14 19
Sandbach d							12 43																	
Holmes Chapel d							12 48																	
Goostrey d																								
Chelford d																								
Alderley Edge d							12 56				13 10											14 10		
Wilmslow d							13 00				13 13				13 56							14 13		14 42
Styal d																								
Manchester Airport ✈ a																								
Handforth d											13 17											14 17		
Congleton d																								
Macclesfield a	12 11		12 27			12 57			13 11			13 30					13 53		14 01		14 16		14 28	
d	12 13		12 29			12 58			13 13			13 30					13 55		14 03		14 17		14 30	
Prestbury d																								
Adlington (Cheshire) d																								
Poynton d																								
Bramhall d																								
Cheadle Hulme d											13 23											14 21		
Stockport a	12s26		12 40			13 11			13s26		13 28	13 41			14 06		14s12		14 16		14s30	14 28	14 41	14 53
d			12 42	13 00	13 08	13 12		13 23			13 29	13 43	13 57	14 01	14 07	14 10			14 17	14 20		14 29	14 43	14 53
Heaton Chapel d					13 11						13 33					14 14						14 33		
Levenshulme d					13 14						13 36					14 17						14 36		
Manchester Piccadilly [10] ⛴ a	12 44		13 02	13 10	13 24	13 26	13 27	13 36	13 43		13 47	13 59	14 10	14 11	14 21	14 24	14 24		14 30	14 33	14 44	14 47	14 56	15 06
d					13 25			13 37			13 48					14 25				14 37		14 48		
Manchester Oxford Road a					13 27			13 39			13 51					14 27				14 39		14 51		
Deansgate ⛴ a					13 31						13 53					14 31						14 53		

	VT [1]◇ 🍴	TP [1]◇ B	NT		NT C	XC [R] [1] U 🍴	EM ◇ L	VT [1]◇ 🍴	NT E	XC [1]◇ V 🍴	AW ◇ X 🛒		TP [1]◇ B	NT C	VT [1]◇ 🍴	XC [1]◇ 🍴	EM ◇ D	NT E	VT [1]◇ 🍴		XC [R] [1] Y 🍴	TP [1]◇ B	NT	NT
London Euston [15] ⊖ 65 d	12 29							12 45							13 29				13 46					
Birmingham New Street [12] 68 d						13 48				14 18						14 48					15 18			
Wolverhampton [7] 68 ⛴ d						14 08				14 38						15 08					15 38			
Stafford 65, 68 d						14 22				14 53						15 21					15 52			
Stoke-on-Trent 50, 68 d	14 28					14 41		14 57		15 12					15 37	15 43			16 00		16 15		16 19	
Longport 50 d																							16 23	
Kidsgrove 50 d																							16 27	
Crewe [10] 65 d			14 36								15 25													16 36
Sandbach d			14 43																					16 43
Holmes Chapel d			14 47																					16 47
Goostrey d			14 50																					
Chelford d			14 55																					
Alderley Edge d			14 59						15 10									16 10						16 56
Wilmslow d			15 02						15 13		15 45							16 13						16 59
Styal d																								
Manchester Airport ✈ a																								
Handforth d									15 17									16 17						
Congleton d																							16 34	
Macclesfield a	14 43					14 57		15 12		15 30					15 54	16 00			16 16		16 34		16 41	
d	14 44					14 59		15 13		15 30					15 55	16 01			16 17		16 36		16 41	
Prestbury d																							16 45	
Adlington (Cheshire) d																							16 48	
Poynton d																							16 52	
Bramhall d																							16 54	
Cheadle Hulme d									15 23									16 23					16 56	
Stockport a	14s57					15 12		15s30	15 28	15 43	15 55				16s11	16 15		16 28	16s30		16 48		17 01	
d		15 01			15 10	15 13	15 21		15 29	15 43	15 56		16 04	16 10		16 17	16 20	16 29			16 50	16 56	17 03	
Heaton Chapel d					15 14				15 33					16 14				16 33						
Levenshulme d					15 17				15 36					16 17				16 36						
Manchester Piccadilly [10] ⛴ a	15 10	15 13	15 23		15 24	15 32	15 34	15 43	15 44	15 59	16 11		16 13	16 24	16 24	16 30	16 33	16 44	16 44		17 05	17 11	17 14	17 23
d					15 25		15 37		15 45					16 25			16 37	16 45						
Manchester Oxford Road a					15 27		15 39		15 48					16 27			16 39	16 48						
Deansgate ⛴ a					15 31				15 50					16 30				16 50						

For general notes see front of timetable
For details of catering facilities see Directory of Train Operators

- **A** From Bristol Temple Meads (Table 51)
- **B** From Cleethorpes to Manchester Airport (Table 29)
- **C** From Buxton (Table 86) to Blackpool North (Table 82)
- **D** From Nottingham to Liverpool Lime Street (Table 49)
- **E** To Southport (Table 82)
- **G** From Southampton Central (Table 51)
- **H** From Sheffield (Table 78)
- **J** From Doncaster to Manchester Airport (Table 29)
- **K** From Shrewsbury (Table 131)
- **L** From Norwich to Liverpool Lime Street (Table 49)
- **N** From Plymouth (Table 51)
- **Q** From Cardiff Central (Table 131)
- **U** From Bournemouth (Table 51)
- **V** From Reading (Table 51)
- **X** From Milford Haven (Table 128)
- **Y** From Penzance (Table 135)

Due to ongoing Engineering Operations, some services from Sunday 14 September on this Table had not been confirmed at time of going to press. These services will be issued in a special Supplement as soon as exact timings have been confirmed.

Table 84

Sundays

Stoke-on-Trent and Crewe → Manchester Airport, Stockport and Manchester

20 July to 7 September

Network Diagram - see first page of Table 78

	NT	VT	XC	EM	NT		VT	NT	XC	TP	NT	AW	VT		XC	EM	NT	VT	XC	TP	NT		NT	VT
		1 ◇	R 1	◇			1 ◇		1 ◇	1 ◇		◇	1 ◇		1 ◇	◇		1 ◇	R 1	1 ◇				1 ◇
	A		B	C	D			E	G	H	A	J				K	D		L	H			A	
		☕	☕				☕		☕			🍴	☕		☕			☕	☕					☕
London Euston 15 ⊖ 65 d		14 29					14 45						15 29					15 46						16 29
Birmingham New Street 12 68 d			15 48						16 18						16 48				17 18					
Wolverhampton 7 68 🚌 d			16 08						16 38						17 08				17 38					
Stafford 65, 68 d			16 22						16 53						17 21				17 53					
Stoke-on-Trent 50, 68 d		16 41	16 47				17 01		17 17				17 40		17 46			17 59	18 15					18 38
Longport 50 d																								
Kidsgrove 50 d																								
Crewe 10 65 d												17 39									18 36			
Sandbach d																					18 43			
Holmes Chapel d																					18 47			
Goostrey d																								
Chelford d																								
Alderley Edge d					17 10												18 10				18 56			
Wilmslow d					17 13							17 59					18 13				18 59			
Styal d																								
Manchester Airport ✈ a																								
Handforth d					17 17												18 17							
Congleton d																								
Macclesfield a		16 56	17 03				17 16		17 34				17 58		18 04			18 14	18 31					18 56
d		16 57	17 05				17 17		17 36				18 00		18 05			18 15	18 33					18 58
Prestbury d																								
Adlington (Cheshire) d																								
Poynton d																								
Bramhall d																								
Cheadle Hulme d					17 23												18 23							
Stockport a		17s12	17 17		17 28		17s30		17 48			18 11	18s15		18 19		18 28	18s30	18 50					19s11
d	17 10		17 19	17 21	17 29			17 44	17 50	17 56	18 10	18 12			18 20	18 25	18 29		18 51	19 01			19 10	
Heaton Chapel d	17 14				17 33						18 14						18 33						19 14	
Levenshulme d	17 17				17 36						18 17						18 36						19 17	
Manchester Piccadilly 10 🚌 a	17 24	17 24	17 32	17 36	17 44		17 44	17 57	18 03	18 12	18 24	18 26	18 27		18 34	18 35	18 43	18 45	19 04	19 12	19 21		19 24	19 24
d	17 25			17 37	17 45						18 25					18 37	18 45						19 25	
Manchester Oxford Road a	17 27			17 39	17 48						18 27					18 39	18 47						19 27	
Deansgate 🚌 a	17 31				17 50						18 30						18 50						19 31	

	XC	EM	NT	VT	NT	XC	TP		NT	AW	VT	NT	XC	EM	NT		VT	XC	TP	NT	NT	VT	XC	EM
	R 1	◇		1 ◇		1 ◇	1 ◇			R	1 ◇		1 ◇	◇			1 ◇	R 1	1 ◇			1 ◇	R 1	◇
	B	K	D		E	G	H			N		A		Q	D			U	H		A		B	Q
	☕			☕		☕				🍴	☕		☕				☕	☕				☕	☕	🍴
London Euston 15 ⊖ 65 d				16 45							17 29						17 45					18 29		
Birmingham New Street 12 68 d	17 48					18 18							18 48					19 18					19 48	
Wolverhampton 7 68 🚌 d	18 06					18 38							19 08					19 36					20 08	
Stafford 65, 68 d	18 20					18 53							19 22					19 50					20 22	
Stoke-on-Trent 50, 68 d	18 44			18 58		19 15			19 20		19 29		19 42				19 59	20 09				20 37	20 43	
Longport 50 d									19 24															
Kidsgrove 50 d									19 28															
Crewe 10 65 d										19 29										20 36				
Sandbach d																				20 43				
Holmes Chapel d																				20 47				
Goostrey d																								
Chelford d																								
Alderley Edge d			19 10												20 10					20 56				
Wilmslow d			19 13							19 49					20 13					20 59				
Styal d																								
Manchester Airport ✈ a																								
Handforth d			19 17												20 17									
Congleton d									19 35															
Macclesfield a	19 01			19 13		19 31			19 42		19 46		20 01				20 14	20 25				20 56	21 01	
d	19 03			19 14		19 33			19 42		19 47		20 03				20 15	20 29				20 58	21 03	
Prestbury d									19 46															
Adlington (Cheshire) d									19 49															
Poynton d									19 53															
Bramhall d									19 55															
Cheadle Hulme d			19 23						19 58						20 23									
Stockport a	19 15		19 28	19s30		19 46			20 04	19 58	20s06		20 15		20 28		20s30	20 41				21s11	21 16	
d	19 16	19 20	19 29		19 46	19 47	20 00		20 05	19 59		20 10	20 17	20 25	20 29			20 43	20 54		21 10		21 17	21 17
Heaton Chapel d			19 33									20 14			20 33						21 14			
Levenshulme d			19 36									20 17			20 36						21 17			
Manchester Piccadilly 10 🚌 a	19 30	19 32	19 43	19 44	19 59	20 01	20 09		20 15	20 17	20 23	20 24	20 32	20 35	20 44		20 44	20 56	21 04	21 21	21 24	21 26	21 31	21 31
d		19 37	19 45									20 25			20 45						21 25			
Manchester Oxford Road a		19 39	19 47									20 27			20 48						21 27			
Deansgate 🚌 a			19 50									20 30			20 50						21 30			

For general notes see front of timetable
For details of catering facilities see Directory of Train Operators

- **A** From Buxton (Table 86) to Blackpool North (Table 82)
- **B** From Bournemouth (Table 51)
- **C** From Nottingham to Liverpool Lime Street (Table 49)
- **D** To Southport (Table 82)
- **E** From Sheffield (Table 78)
- **G** From Reading (Table 51)
- **H** From Cleethorpes to Manchester Airport (Table 29)
- **J** From Pembroke Dock (Table 128)
- **K** From Norwich to Liverpool Lime Street (Table 49)
- **L** From Newquay (Table 135)
- **N** From Milford Haven (Table 128)
- **Q** From Norwich (Table 49)
- **U** From Plymouth (Table 51)

Due to ongoing Engineering Operations, some services from Sunday 14 September on this Table had not been confirmed at time of going to press. These services will be issued in a special Supplement as soon as exact timings have been confirmed.

Sundays

20 July to 7 September

Stoke-on-Trent and Crewe → Manchester Airport, Stockport and Manchester

Network Diagram - see first page of Table 78

	NT		VT	XC	TP	AW	NT	XC	VT		NT	VT	XC	NT	NT	NT	NT		VT	XC	VT			
						R																		
			1 ◇	1 ◇	1 ◇			1 ◇	1 ◇			1 ◇	1 ◇						1 ◇	1 ◇	1 ◇			
	A			B	C	D	E	G			A		H		J		E			K				
			☕			🍴			☕			☕							☕		☕			
London Euston [15] ⊖ 65 d			18 45						19 31			19 46							20 51		21 56			
Birmingham New Street [12] 68 d				20 18				20 48					21 18							22 18				
Wolverhampton [7] 68 ⛴ d				20 38				21 06					21 38							22 38				
Stafford 65, 68 d				20 53				21 20					21 52							22 52	00 05			
Stoke-on-Trent 50, 68 d			20 59	21 12				21 45	21 50			21 58	22 11	22 15					23 05					
Longport 50 d														22 19										
Kidsgrove 50 d														22 23										
Crewe [10] 65 d						21 26										22 34					00 44			
Sandbach d																22 41								
Holmes Chapel d																22 45								
Goostrey d																22 48								
Chelford d																22 53								
Alderley Edge d	21 10										22 10					22 57								
Wilmslow d	21 13					21 46					22 13					23 00					01 01			
Styal d																								
Manchester Airport ✈ a																								
Handforth d	21 17										22 17													
Congleton d														22 30										
Macclesfield a			21 17	21 30				22 04	22 09			22 14	22 27	22 37					23 20	23s27				
d			21 18	21 30				22 05	22 10			22 15	22 29	22 37					23 21					
Prestbury d														22 41										
Adlington (Cheshire) d														22 44										
Poynton d														22 48										
Bramhall d														22 50										
Cheadle Hulme d	21 23										22 23			22 53										
Stockport a	21 28		21s31	21 42		21 57		22 18	22s23		22 28	22s31	22 40	22 57					23s34	23s41	01s09			
d	21 29			21 44	22 01	21 58	22 10	22 19			22 29		22 42	22 58	23 01		23 10							
Heaton Chapel d	21 33						22 14				22 33						23 14							
Levenshulme d	21 36						22 17				22 36						23 17							
Manchester Piccadilly [10] ⛴ a	21 42		21 44	21 56	22 14	22 16	22 25	22 32	22 36		22 42	22 43	22 56	23 10	23 13	23 22	23 27		23 46	23 56	01 22			
d	21 45										22 45													
Manchester Oxford Road a	21 47										22 47													
Deansgate ⛴ a	21 50										22 50													

For general notes see front of timetable
For details of catering facilities see Directory of Train Operators

- **A** To Wigan Wallgate (Table 82)
- **B** From Reading (Table 51)
- **C** From Cleethorpes to Manchester Airport (Table 29)
- **D** From Milford Haven (Table 128)
- **E** From Buxton (Table 86)
- **G** From Bristol Temple Meads (Table 51)
- **H** From Plymouth (Table 51)
- **J** From Sheffield (Table 78)
- **K** From Bournemouth (Table 51)

Due to ongoing Engineering Operations, some services from Sunday 14 September on this Table had not been confirmed at time of going to press. These services will be issued in a special Supplement as soon as exact timings have been confirmed.

Manchester, Stockport and Manchester Airport → Crewe and Stoke-on-Trent

Network Diagram - see first page of Table 78

Miles	Miles	Miles		VT	NT	NT	TP	NT	NT	VT	NT	VT	NT	NT	VT	NT	AW	NT	NT	VT	NT	XC	NT	VT
				1 ◇			1 ◇			1 ◇		1 ◇			1 ◇		◇			1 ◇		1 ◇		1 ◇
							A	B				M				C	D	E			G	H		
				⊠						⊠		⊠			⊠		🛒			⊠		🍽		⊠
0	0	—	Deansgate d																					
½	½	—	Manchester Oxford Road d																					
1	1	—	**Manchester Piccadilly** 10 a																					
—	—	—	d	05 20	05 26	05 42	05 49	05 52		06 02	06 13	06 17	06 22	06 32	06 35	06 35	06 38	06 41		06 45	06 51	06 54	07 02	07 05
4	4	—	Levenshulme d			05 48					06 18							06 47					07 07	
5½	5½	—	Heaton Chapel d			05 51					06 21							06 50					07 10	
7	7	—	**Stockport** a			05 54	05 57	06 01			06 25	06 24	06 34			06 45	06 48	06 53			07 01		07 14	
—	—	—	d	05u31		05 55				06u11	06 25	06 25	06 34		06u44		06 48			06u53			07 14	07u14
9¼	9¼	—	Cheadle Hulme d			05 59					06 29		06 38										07 20	
9¾	—	—	Bramhall d										06 41											
12¼	—	—	Poynton d										06 44											
14¼	—	—	Adlington (Cheshire) d										06 48											
16¼	—	—	Prestbury d										06 51											
19	—	—	**Macclesfield** a							06 22		06 37	06 55							07 08				
—	—	—	d						06 04	06 24		06 38	06 57							07 09				
27	—	—	Congleton d						06 11				07 04									07 21		
—	11½	—	Handforth d			06 03					06 33								←				07 24	
—	—	0	**Manchester Airport** ✈ d		05 53									06 57 →					06 57					
—	—	2¼	Styal d																					
—	13	4	**Wilmslow** d	05 39	06 00	06 05					06 36				06 51		06 56		07 04				07 27	
—	14¾	—	Alderley Edge d		06a06	06 08					06 39								07 07				07 30	
—	17¾	—	Chelford d			06 12					06 43												07 34	
—	21½	—	Goostrey d			06 17					06 47												07 39	
—	23½	—	Holmes Chapel d			06 20					06 50								07 15				07 42	
—	27¼	—	Sandbach d			06 24					06 55								07 19				07 46	
—	32	—	**Crewe** 10 65 a	05 56		06 40					07 07				07 10		07 16		07 31				07 57	
32½	—	—	Kidsgrove 50 a						06 17				07 10											
35¾	—	—	Longport 50 a										07 14											
38¾	—	—	**Stoke-on-Trent** 50, 68 a						06 27	06 39		06 54	07 19							07 24		07 32		
—	—	—	Stafford 68 a	06 16								07 13										07 53		
—	—	—	Wolverhampton 7 68 a									07 32										08 12		
—	—	—	Birmingham New Street 12 68 a									07 55										08 30		
—	—	—	London Euston 15 ⊖ 65 a	08 04						08 27		09b44			09 01					09 07				09 11

	VT	TP	NT	XC	AW	NT	NT	NT	NT	NT	EM	VT	NT	XC	NT	NT	VT	TP	NT	XC	NT	NT	AW	NT
				R																				
	1 ◇	1 ◇		1	◇						◇	1 ◇		1 ◇			1 ◇	1 ◇		1 ◇			◇	
		A	E	J	K				G	L	N		E	Q				A	U	V	G		D	
	⊠	🛒		🍽	🛒						🛒	⊠		🍽			⊠	🛒		🍽			🛒	
Deansgate d										07 29									08 12					
Manchester Oxford Road d										07 33	07 39								08 15					
Manchester Piccadilly 10 a										07 36	07 41								08 19					
d	07 15	07 19	07 22	07 24	07 28	07 29	07 33	07 34	07 37	07 39	07 43	07 45	07 51	07 54	07 58	08 03	08 15	08 17	08 20	08 24	08 29	08 32	08 34	08 34
Levenshulme d			07 28			07 34							07 56			08 09					08 34			
Heaton Chapel d			07 31			07 37							07 59			08 12					08 37			
Stockport a		07 27	07 34	07 33	07 37	07 41	07 43		07 47	07 46	07 52		08 03	08 01	08 07	08 15		08 24	08 30	08 32	08 41	08 41	08 44	
d	07u23			07 33	07 37	07 41	07 43					07u55		08 03	08 08	08 16	08u24			08 33		08 41	08 44	
Cheadle Hulme d						07 45	07 47								08 12	08 20						08 45		
Bramhall d						07 48										08 23						08 48		
Poynton d						07 51										08 26						08 51		
Adlington (Cheshire) d						07 55										08 29						08 55		
Prestbury d						07 58										08 32						08 58		
Macclesfield a	07 36			07 46		08 03						08 07		08 15		08 37				08 46		09 03		
d	07 37			07 47								08 07		08 16						08 47				
Congleton d				07 55										08 24										
Handforth d							07 51								08 16									
Manchester Airport ✈ d								08 00																09 00
Styal d								08 04																
Wilmslow d					07 46		07 54	08 07							08 18		08 33						08 52	09 07
Alderley Edge d							08a00	08 10							08 21									09 10
Chelford d								08 14																
Goostrey d								08 19																
Holmes Chapel d								08 22							08 29									09 18
Sandbach d								08 26							08 34									09 22
Crewe 10 65 a					08 06			08 37							08 45		08 51						09 16	09 33
Kidsgrove 50 a																								
Longport 50 a																								
Stoke-on-Trent 50, 68 a	07 52			08 07								08 22		08 38						09 03				
Stafford 68 a				08 25										08 55			09 12			09 25				
Wolverhampton 7 68 a				08 41										09 12						09 41				
Birmingham New Street 12 68 a				08 58										09 30						09 58				
London Euston 15 ⊖ 65 a	09 45											10 09					10 50							

For general notes see front of timetable
For details of catering facilities see Directory of Train Operators

- **A** From Manchester Airport to Cleethorpes (Table 29)
- **B** To Sheffield (Table 78)
- **C** To Chester (Table 88)
- **D** To Milford Haven (Table 128)
- **E** To Hazel Grove (Table 86)
- **G** To Buxton (Table 86)
- **H** To Reading (Table 51)
- **J** To Bournemouth (Table 51)
- **K** To Carmarthen (Table 128)
- **L** From Blackpool North (Table 82) to Chester (Table 88)
- **M** 🍽 to Wolverhampton. ⊠ from Wolverhampton
- **N** Until 5 September from Liverpool Lime Street to Norwich (Table 49). From 8 September from Liverpool Lime Street to Sheffield (Table 89)
- **Q** To Brighton (Table 51)
- **U** From St Annes-on-the-Sea (Table 97) to Greenbank (Table 88)
- **V** To Plymouth (Table 51)
- **b** 28 July to 22 August arr. 0939. By changing at Stafford, passengers may arrive at 0858

Manchester, Stockport and Manchester Airport → Crewe and Stoke-on-Trent

Network Diagram - see first page of Table 78

Station		EM	VT		NT	XC	NT	NT	NT	VT	TP	XC	NT	NT	NT	AW	NT	EM	NT	VT	NT	XC	NT	NT	VT
												R													
		◇	1◇			1◇				1◇	1◇	1				◇		◇		1◇		1◇			1◇
		A				B	C		D		E	G	H			J	K	A				B		D	
		[trolley]	⊠			[buffet]				⊠	[trolley]	[buffet]				[trolley]		[trolley]		⊠		[buffet]			⊠
Deansgate	d													09 24			09 29								
Manchester Oxford Road	d	08 38												09 27			09 33	09 38							
Manchester Piccadilly 10	a	08 42												09 29			09 35	09 40							
	d	08 42	08 45		08 51	08 54	08 59	09 03	09 06	09 15	09 20	09 24	09 24	09 30	09 33	09 34	09 37	09 42		09 45	09 51	09 54	10 03	10 06	10 15
Levenshulme	d				08 56				09 12					09 36							09 56			10 12	
Heaton Chapel	d				08 59				09 15					09 39							09 59			10 15	
Stockport	a	08 53			09 03	09 01	09 08	09 13	09 19		09 28	09 32	09 34	09 42		09 42	09 46	09 51			10 03	10 03	10 12	10 18	
	d		08u55		09 05	09 03		09 13		09u23		09 33		09 43		09 42				09u54	10 05	10 03	10 13		10u24
Cheadle Hulme	d				09 11			09 17						09 47							10 11		10 17		
Bramhall	d													09 50											
Poynton	d													09 53											
Adlington (Cheshire)	d													09 56											
Prestbury	d													09 59											
Macclesfield	a		09 08			09 15						09 46		10 04						10 07		10 15			
	d		09 08			09 16						09 47								10 07		10 16			
Congleton	d					09 24																			
Handforth	d				09 15			09 21											←		10 15		10 21		
Manchester Airport ✈	d														10 00 →				10 00						
Styal	d																								
Wilmslow	d				09 18			09 24								09 54			10 06		10 18		10 24		
Alderley Edge	d				09a23			09 27											10 09		10a23		10 27		
Chelford	d							09 31															10 31		
Goostrey	d							09 35															10 36		
Holmes Chapel	d							09 38											10 17				10 39		
Sandbach	d							09 43											10 22				10 43		
Crewe 10	65 a							09 54								10 15			10 33				10 54		
Kidsgrove	50 a																								
Longport	50 a																								
Stoke-on-Trent	50, 68 a		09 24			09 38				09 48		10 03								10 23		10 38			10 48
Stafford	68 a											10 25													
Wolverhampton 7	68 a					10 12						10 41										11 12			
Birmingham New Street 12	68 a					10 30						10 58										11 30			
London Euston 15	⊖ 65 a		11 09							11 28										12 07					12 26

Station		TP	XC	NT	NT	NT	AW	NT	EM	NT	VT	NT	XC	NT	NT	VT	TP	XC	NT	NT	NT	AW	NT	EM	NT
																		R							
		1◇	1◇				◇		◇		1◇		1◇			1◇	1◇	1				◇		◇	
		E	L	H			N	K	A				B		D		E	G	H			J	K	A	
		[trolley]	[buffet]				[trolley]		[trolley]		⊠		[buffet]			[buffet]	[trolley]	[buffet]				[trolley]		[trolley]	
Deansgate	d				10 24			10 29												11 24			11 29		
Manchester Oxford Road	d				10 27			10 33	10 38											11 27			11 33	11 38	
Manchester Piccadilly 10	a				10 29			10 35	10 41											11 29			11 35	11 40	
	d	10 20	10 24	10 24	10 30	10 33	10 34	10 37	10 42		10 45	10 51	10 54	11 03	11 06	11 15	11 20	11 24	11 24	11 30	11 33	11 34	11 37	11 42	
Levenshulme	d				10 36							10 56			11 12					11 36					
Heaton Chapel	d				10 39							10 59			11 15					11 39					
Stockport	a	10 28	10 32	10 34	10 42		10 42	10 46	10 51			11 03	11 02	11 12	11 18		11 27	11 32	11 34	11 42		11 42	11 46	11 51	
	d		10 33		10 43		10 42				10u54	11 05	11 03	11 13		11u23		11 33		11 43		11 42			
Cheadle Hulme	d				10 47							11 11		11 17						11 47					
Bramhall	d				10 50															11 50					
Poynton	d				10 53															11 53					
Adlington (Cheshire)	d				10 56															11 56					
Prestbury	d				10 59															11 59					
Macclesfield	a		10 46		11 04						11 07		11 15					11 46		12 04					
	d		10 47								11 07		11 16					11 47							
Congleton	d												11 24												
Handforth	d									←		11 15		11 21											←
Manchester Airport ✈	d					11 00 →				11 00											12 00 →				12 00
Styal	d																								
Wilmslow	d						10 54			11 06		11 18		11 24								11 54			12 06
Alderley Edge	d									11 09		11a23		11 27											12 09
Chelford	d													11 31											
Goostrey	d													11 36											
Holmes Chapel	d									11 17				11 39											12 17
Sandbach	d									11 22				11 43											12 22
Crewe 10	65 a						11 16			11 33				11 54								12 15			12 33
Kidsgrove	50 a																								
Longport	50 a																								
Stoke-on-Trent	50, 68 a		11 03								11 23		11 38			11 48		12 03							
Stafford	68 a		11 25															12 25							
Wolverhampton 7	68 a		11 41										12 12					12 41							
Birmingham New Street 12	68 a		11 58										12 30					12 58							
London Euston 15	⊖ 65 a										13 09					13 28									

For general notes see front of timetable
For details of catering facilities see Directory of Train Operators

- **A** Until 5 September from Liverpool Lime Street to Norwich (Table 49). From 8 September from Liverpool Lime Street to Sheffield (Table 89)
- **B** To Reading (Table 51)
- **C** To Buxton (Table 86)
- **D** To Hazel Grove (Table 86)
- **E** From Manchester Airport to Cleethorpes (Table 29)
- **G** To Bournemouth (Table 51)
- **H** To Chester (Table 88)
- **J** To Carmarthen (Table 128)
- **K** From Blackpool North (Table 82) to Buxton (Table 86)
- **L** To Plymouth (Table 51)
- **N** To Milford Haven (Table 128)

Manchester, Stockport and Manchester Airport → Crewe and Stoke-on-Trent

Network Diagram - see first page of Table 78

		VT	NT		XC	NT	NT	VT	TP	XC	NT	NT	NT	AW	NT	EM	NT	VT	NT	XC	NT	NT	VT	TP	XC
		[1] ◇			[1] ◇			[1] ◇	[1] ◇	[R] [1]				[R]		◇		[1] ◇		[1] ◇			[1] ◇	[1] ◇	[1] ◇
					A		B		C	D	E			G	H	J				K		B		C	L
		⊡			⊡			⊡	⚲	⊡				⚲		⚲		⊡		⊡			⊡	⚲	⊡
Deansgate	d											12 24			12 29										
Manchester Oxford Road	d											12 27			12 33	12 38									
Manchester Piccadilly [10]	a											12 29			12 35	12 40									
	d	11 45	11 51		11 54	12 03	12 06	12 15	12 20	12 24	12 24	12 30	12 33	12 34	12 37	12 42		12 45	12 51	12 54	13 03	13 06	13 15	13 20	13 24
Levenshulme	d		11 56				12 12					12 36							12 56			13 12			
Heaton Chapel	d		11 59				12 15					12 39							12 59			13 15			
Stockport	a		12 03		12 02	12 12	12 18		12 28	12 32	12 34	12 42		12 42	12 46	12 51			13 03	13 01	13 12	13 18		13 28	13 32
	d	11u54	12 05		12 03	12 13		12u24		12 33		12 43		12 42				12u54	13 05	13 03	13 13		13u24		13 33
Cheadle Hulme	d		12 11			12 17						12 47							13 11		13 17				
Bramhall	d											12 50													
Poynton	d											12 53													
Adlington (Cheshire)	d											12 56													
Prestbury	d											12 59													
Macclesfield	a	12 07			12 15					12 46		13 04						13 07		13 15					13 46
	d	12 07			12 16					12 47								13 07		13 16					13 47
Congleton	d																			13 24					
Handforth	d		12 15			12 21											←		13 15		13 21				
Manchester Airport	d												13 00 →				13 00								
Styal	d																								
Wilmslow	d		12 18			12 24								12 54			13 06		13 18		13 24				
Alderley Edge	d		12a23			12 27											13 09		13a23		13 27				
Chelford	d					12 31															13 31				
Goostrey	d					12 36															13 36				
Holmes Chapel	d					12 39											13 17				13 39				
Sandbach	d					12 43											13 22				13 43				
Crewe [10]	65 a					12 54								13 15			13 33				13 54				
Kidsgrove	50 a																								
Longport	50 a																								
Stoke-on-Trent	50, 68 a	12 23			12 38			12 48		13 03								13 23		13 38			13 48		14 03
Stafford	68 a									13 25															14 25
Wolverhampton [7]	68 a				13 12					13 41										14 12					14 41
Birmingham New Street [12]	68 a				13 30					13 58										14 30					14 58
London Euston [15]	⊖ 65 a	14 04						14 26										15 08					15 28		

		NT	NT	NT	AW	NT	EM	NT	VT	NT	XC	NT	VT	NT	NT	VT	TP	XC	NT	NT	NT	AW	NT	EM	NT
					[R]		◇		[1] ◇		[1] ◇		[1] ◇			[1] ◇	[1] ◇	[R] [1]				[R]		◇	
		E			N	H	J				A			B			C	D	E			G	H	Q	
					⚲		⚲		⊡		⊡		⊡			⊡	⚲	⊡				⚲		⚲	
Deansgate	d		13 24			13 29														14 24			14 29		
Manchester Oxford Road	d		13 27			13 33	13 38													14 27			14 33	14 38	
Manchester Piccadilly [10]	a		13 29			13 35	13 40													14 29			14 35	14 40	
	d	13 24	13 30	13 33	13 34	13 37	13 42		13 45	13 51	13 54	14 03	14 05	14 06		14 15	14 20	14 24	14 24	14 30	14 33	14 34	14 37	14 42	
Levenshulme	d		13 36							13 56				14 12						14 36					
Heaton Chapel	d		13 39							13 59				14 15						14 39					
Stockport	a	13 34	13 42		13 42	13 46	13 51			14 03	14 02	14 12	14 15	14 18			14 28	14 32	14 34	14 42		14 42	14 46	14 51	
	d		13 43		13 42				13u54	14 05	14 03	14 13	14 15		←	14u24		14 33		14 43		14 42			
Cheadle Hulme	d		13 47							14 11		14 20 →			14 20					14 47					
Bramhall	d		13 50																	14 50					
Poynton	d		13 53																	14 53					
Adlington (Cheshire)	d		13 56																	14 56					
Prestbury	d		13 59																	14 59					
Macclesfield	a		14 04						14 07		14 15							14 46		15 04					
	d								14 07		14 16							14 47							
Congleton	d																								
Handforth	d							←		14 15					14 24										←
Manchester Airport	d			14 00 →				14 00													15 00 →				15 00
Styal	d																								
Wilmslow	d				13 54			14 06		14 18			14 25		14 26							14 54			15 06
Alderley Edge	d							14 09		14a23					14 29										15 09
Chelford	d														14 33										
Goostrey	d														14 38										
Holmes Chapel	d							14 17							14 41										15 17
Sandbach	d							14 22							14 45										15 22
Crewe [10]	65 a				14 15			14 33					14 42		14 57							15 16			15 33
Kidsgrove	50 a																								
Longport	50 a																								
Stoke-on-Trent	50, 68 a								14 23		14 38					14 48		15 03							
Stafford	68 a																	15 25							
Wolverhampton [7]	68 a										15 12							15 41							
Birmingham New Street [12]	68 a										15 30							15 58							
London Euston [15]	⊖ 65 a								16 07				17b22			16 28									

For general notes see front of timetable
For details of catering facilities see Directory of Train Operators

A To Reading (Table 51)
B To Hazel Grove (Table 86)
C From Manchester Airport to Cleethorpes (Table 29)
D To Penzance (Table 135)
E To Chester (Table 88)
G To Milford Haven (Table 128)
H From Blackpool North (Table 82) to Buxton (Table 86)
J Until 5 September from Liverpool Lime Street to Norwich (Table 49). From 8 September from Liverpool Lime Street to Sheffield (Table 89)
K To Guildford (Table 51)
L To Bournemouth (Table 51)
N To Carmarthen (Table 128)
Q Until 5 September from Liverpool Lime Street to Nottingham (Table 49) From 8 September from Liverpool Lime Street to Sheffield (Table 89)
b By changing at Crewe, passengers may arrive at 1648

Manchester, Stockport and Manchester Airport → Crewe and Stoke-on-Trent

Network Diagram - see first page of Table 78

	VT	NT		XC	NT	NT	VT	TP	XC	NT	NT	NT	AW	NT	NT	EM	NT	VT	NT	XC	NT	NT	VT	TP
	1 ◇			R 1			1 ◇	1 ◇	R 1				R			◇		1 ◇		R 1			1 ◇	1 ◇
				A		B		C	D	E			G	H	B	J				K		L		C
	☕			☕			☕	🛒	☕				🛒			🛒		☕		☕			☕	🛒
Deansgate ⇌ d											15 24			15 29										
Manchester Oxford Road d											15 27			15 33		15 38								
Manchester Piccadilly 10 ⇌ a											15 29			15 35		15 40								
d	14 45	14 51		14 54	15 03	15 06	15 15	15 20	15 24	15 24	15 30	15 33	15 34	15 37	15 40	15 42		15 45	15 51	15 54	16 03	16 06	16 15	16 20
Levenshulme d		14 56				15 11					15 36				15 46				15 56			16 12		
Heaton Chapel d		14 59				15 14					15 39				15 49				15 59			16 15		
Stockport a		15 03		15 01	15 12	15 18		15 28	15 32	15 34	15 42		15 42	15 46	15 52	15 50			16 03	16 02	16 12	16 18		16 28
d	14u54	15 05		15 03	15 13		15u24		15 33		15 43		15 42					15u54	16 05	16 03	16 13		16u24	
Cheadle Hulme d		15 11			15 17						15 47								16 11		16 17			
Bramhall d											15 50													
Poynton d											15 53													
Adlington (Cheshire) d											15 56													
Prestbury d											15 59													
Macclesfield a	15 07			15 15					15 46		16 04							16 07		16 15				
d	15 07			15 16					15 47									16 07		16 16				
Congleton d				15 24																				
Handforth d		15 15			15 21												←		16 15		16 21			
Manchester Airport ✈ d												16 00 →					16 00							
Styal d																								
Wilmslow d		15 18			15 24								15 54				16 06		16 18		16 24			
Alderley Edge d		15a23			15 27												16 09		16a23		16 27			
Chelford d					15 31												16 13				16 31			
Goostrey d					15 36												16 18				16 36			
Holmes Chapel d					15 39												16 21				16 39			
Sandbach d					15 43												16 25				16 43			
Crewe 10 65 a					15 54								16 15				16 36				16 54			
Kidsgrove 50 a																								
Longport 50 a																								
Stoke-on-Trent 50, 68 a	15 23			15 38			15 48		16 03									16 23		16 38			16 48	
Stafford 68 a									16 25															
Wolverhampton 7 68 ⇌ a				16 12					16 41											17 12				
Birmingham New Street 12 68 a				16 30					16 58											17 30				
London Euston 15 ⊖ 65 a	17 08						17 27											18 07					18 28	

	XC	NT	NT	NT	AW	NT	NT	EM	NT	NT	VT	NT	XC	NT	NT	NT	VT	NT	TP	XC	NT	NT	NT	NT
	1 ◇				R			◇			1 ◇		R 1				1 ◇		1 ◇	R 1				
	N	E			Q	U		J	L			E	V			X			C	D	E	L		
	☕				🛒			🛒			☕		☕				☕		🛒	☕				
Deansgate ⇌ d			16 24			16 29										16 59		17 10					17 24	
Manchester Oxford Road d			16 27			16 33		16 38								17 03		17 13					17 27	
Manchester Piccadilly 10 ⇌ a			16 29			16 36		16 40								17 06		17 15					17 29	
d	16 24	16 24	16 30	16 33	16 34	16 37	16 37	16 42	16 44		16 45	16 51	16 54	16 58	17 04	17 07	17 15	17 17	17 20	17 24	17 24	17 27	17 31	17 33
Levenshulme d			16 36				16 42		16 51						17 09	17 13							17 37	
Heaton Chapel d			16 39				16 45		16 54						17 12	17 16							17 40	
Stockport a	16 32	16 34	16 42		16 42	16 45	16 49	16 51	16 58			17 00	17 02	17 07	17 16	17 19		17 28	17 28	17 32	17 34	17 37	17 43	
d	16 33		16 43		16 42		16 51				16u54		17 03	17 07	17 16		17u23	17 30		17 33			17 44	
Cheadle Hulme d			16 47				16 55							17 12	17 19			17 35					17 49	
Bramhall d			16 50											17 15									17 52	
Poynton d			16 53											17 18									17 55	
Adlington (Cheshire) d			16 56											17 22										
Prestbury d			16 59											17 25									18 00	
Macclesfield a	16 46		17 04								17 08		17 15	17 30						17 46			18 05	
d	16 47										17 08		17 16							17 47				
Congleton d													17 24											
Handforth d							16 59			←					17 23									
Manchester Airport ✈ d				17 00 →						17 00														18 00 →
Styal d																								
Wilmslow d					16 54		17 02			17 06					17 26			17 41						
Alderley Edge d							17a08			17 09					17 29			17 45						
Chelford d															17 33									
Goostrey d															17 37									
Holmes Chapel d										17 17					17 40									
Sandbach d										17 23					17 45			17 56						
Crewe 10 65 a					17 16					17 33					17 56			18 07						
Kidsgrove 50 a																								
Longport 50 a																								
Stoke-on-Trent 50, 68 a	17 03										17 24		17 38				17 49			18 03				
Stafford 68 a	17 25																			18 25				
Wolverhampton 7 68 ⇌ a	17 41												18 12							18 41				
Birmingham New Street 12 68 a	17 58												18 30							18 58				
London Euston 15 ⊖ 65 a											19 11						19 28							

For general notes see front of timetable
For details of catering facilities see Directory of Train Operators

A To Brighton (Table 51)
B To Buxton (Table 86)
C From Manchester Airport to Cleethorpes (Table 29)
D To Bournemouth (Table 51)
E To Chester (Table 88)
G To Carmarthen (Table 128)
H From Blackpool North (Table 82) to Hazel Grove (Table 86)
J Until 5 September from Liverpool Lime Street to Norwich (Table 49). From 8 September from Liverpool Lime Street to Sheffield (Table 89)
K To Reading (Table 51)
L To Hazel Grove (Table 86)
N To Plymouth (Table 51)
Q To Milford Haven (Table 128)
U From Blackpool North (Table 82) to Buxton (Table 86)
V To Gatwick Airport (Table 51)
X From Southport (Table 82) to Buxton (Table 86)

Manchester, Stockport and Manchester Airport → Crewe and Stoke-on-Trent

Network Diagram - see first page of Table 78

Station		AW	NT		NT	EM	VT	NT	NT	NT	XC	NT	NT	NT	VT	TP	XC	NT	NT	AW	NT	NT	EM	VT	NT
		R				◇	1◇				1◇				1◇	1◇	1◇			◇			◇	1◇	
		A	B			C		D	E		G			H		J	K	E		L		B	N		
		⚲				⚲	☕				☕				☕	⚲	☕			⚲			⚲	☕	
Deansgate	d		17 28																						
Manchester Oxford Road	d		17 32			17 38																18 35	18 40		
Manchester Piccadilly 10	a		17 35			17 40																18 38	18 43		
	d	17 34	17 37		17 39	17 42	17 45	17 50	17 53		17 54	17 57	18 03	18 06	18 15	18 18	18 24	18 24	18 30	18 34	18 36	18 39	18 44	18 45	18 51
Levenshulme	d				17 44							18 02		18 12					18 36						18 56
Heaton Chapel	d				17 47							18 05		18 15					18 39						18 59
Stockport	a	17 42	17 47		17 51	17 50		17 59	18 04		18 02	18 09	18 12	18 18		18 26	18 32	18 34	18 43	18 42		18 48	18 54		19 03
	d	17 42			17 51		17u55				18 03	18 09	18 13		18u24		18 33		18 43	18 42				18u54	19 03
Cheadle Hulme	d				17 55							18 13	18 17						18 47						19 11
Bramhall	d											18 16							18 50						
Poynton	d											18 19							18 53						
Adlington (Cheshire)	d											18 23							18 56						
Prestbury	d											18 26							18 59						
Macclesfield	a						18 08				18 15	18 30					18 46		19 04					19 05	
	d						18 08				18 16	18 39					18 47							19 07	
Congleton	d										18 24	18 46													
Handforth	d				18 00					←			18 21												19 15
Manchester Airport ✈	d									18 00											19 01				
Styal	d									18 07															
Wilmslow	d	17 51			18 03					18 11			18 24							18 54	19 08				19 18
Alderley Edge	d				18a09					18 14			18 27								19a15				19a24
Chelford	d									18 18			18 31												
Goostrey	d									18 22			18 36												
Holmes Chapel	d									18 25			18 39												
Sandbach	d									18 30			18 43												
Crewe 10	65 a	18 15								18 41			18 54							19 15					
Kidsgrove	50 a											18 52													
Longport	50 a											18 57													
Stoke-on-Trent	50, 68 a						18 24				18 38	19 02			18 50		19 03							19 24	
Stafford	68 a																19 24								
Wolverhampton 7	68 a										19 12						19 41								
Birmingham New Street 12	68 a										19 30						19 58								
London Euston 15	⊖ 65 a						20 07								20 33									21 07	

Station		XC	NT	VT	TP	XC	NT	NT	NT	AW	NT	EM	NT	XC	NT	VT	TP	XC	NT	NT	AW	NT	EM	NT	VT
		1◇		1◇	1◇	1◇				◇		◇		1◇		1◇	1◇	1◇			◇		◇		1◇
					J	Q	E			U	B	V					J		E		U	B	V		
		☕		☕		☕						⚲				☕							⚲		☕
Deansgate	d										19 29											20 29			
Manchester Oxford Road	d										19 33	19 38										20 32	20 38		
Manchester Piccadilly 10	a										19 36	19 42										20 34	20 40		
	d	18 54	19 03	19 15	19 18	19 24	19 24	19 30	19 30	19 34	19 37	19 42		19 54	20 03	20 15	20 18	20 24	20 24	20 27	20 34	20 36	20 42	20 44	20 45
Levenshulme	d		19 08						19 36						20 08					20 32					
Heaton Chapel	d		19 11						19 39						20 11					20 35					
Stockport	a	19 02	19 15		19 25	19 32	19 34		19 42	19 42	19 47	19 53		20 01	20 15		20 26	20 32	20 34	20 39	20 46	20 44	20 51		
	d	19 03	19 15	19u24		19 33			19 43	19 43				20 03	20 15	20u24		20 33		20 40	20 46				20u54
Cheadle Hulme	d		19 19						19 47						20 19					20 44					
Bramhall	d								19 50											20 47					
Poynton	d								19 53											20 50					
Adlington (Cheshire)	d								19 56											20 53					
Prestbury	d								19 59											20 56					
Macclesfield	a	19 15		19 36		19 46			20 04					20 15		20 36		20 46		21 01					
	d	19 16		19 37		19 47								20 16		20 37		20 47							
Congleton	d	19 24												20 24											
Handforth	d		19 23										←		20 23										
Manchester Airport ✈	d							19 56 →					19 56											21 10 →	
Styal	d																								
Wilmslow	d		19 26							19 54			20a06		20 26						20 54				21 05
Alderley Edge	d		19 29												20 29										
Chelford	d		19 33												20 33										
Goostrey	d		19 38												20 37										
Holmes Chapel	d		19 41												20 40										
Sandbach	d		19 45												20 45										
Crewe 10	65 a		19 56							20 16					20 56						21 14				21 28
Kidsgrove	50 a																								
Longport	50 a																								
Stoke-on-Trent	50, 68 a	19 38		19 52		20 03								20 38		20 52		21 03							21 52
Stafford	68 a	19 57				20 25								20 56				21 25							
Wolverhampton 7	68 a	20 12				20 41								21 12				21 41							
Birmingham New Street 12	68 a	20 35				20 58								21 35				22 04							
London Euston 15	⊖ 65 a			21 36												22 52									00 09

For general notes see front of timetable
For details of catering facilities see Directory of Train Operators

- **A** To Milford Haven (Table 128)
- **B** From Blackpool North (Table 82) to Buxton (Table 86)
- **C** Until 5 September from Liverpool Lime Street to Nottingham (Table 49) From 8 September from Liverpool Lime Street to Sheffield (Table 89)
- **D** To Hazel Grove (Table 86)
- **E** To Chester (Table 88)
- **G** To Gatwick Airport (Table 51)
- **H** To Buxton (Table 86)
- **J** From Manchester Airport to Cleethorpes (Table 29)
- **K** To Plymouth (Table 51)
- **L** To Carmarthen (Table 128)
- **N** From Liverpool Lime Street to Norwich (from 8 September to Nottingham) (Table 49)
- **Q** To Southampton Central (Table 51)
- **U** To Cardiff Central (Table 131)
- **V** From Liverpool Lime Street to Nottingham (Table 49)

Manchester, Stockport and Manchester Airport → Crewe and Stoke-on-Trent

Network Diagram - see first page of Table 78

		NT	NT	TP 1◇ A	NT B	NT	AW ◇ C	NT D	NT	XC 1◇	NT	NT	TP 1◇ E	NT B	EM ◇ G	AW H	NT	NT	NT J	NT	NT B	NT	NT
Deansgate	d							21 40			21 59						22 31		22 50	23 00			23 31
Manchester Oxford Road	d							21 43			22 01				22 23		22 33		22 53	23 02		23 07	23 33
Manchester Piccadilly 10	a							21 46			22 03				22 25		22 36		22 56	23 05		23 09	23 36
	d		21 03	21 18	21 24	21 28	21 34	21 49	21 52	21 54	22 03		22 18	22 24	22 27	22 34	22 36	22 46	22 58	23 06	23 09	23 11	23 37
Levenshulme	d		21 08			21 33					22 09						22 42			23 11			23 42
Heaton Chapel	d		21 11			21 36					22 12						22 45			23 14			23 45
Stockport	a		21 14	21 26	21 34	21 40	21 46	21 59		22 01	22 16		22 26	22 33	22 37	22 42	22 49		23 06	23 18	23 19	23 21	23 50
	d		21 15			21 40	21 46			22 03	22 16					22 42	22 49			23 18		23 21	23 50
Cheadle Hulme	d		21 19			21 44					22 20						22 53			23 22		23 25	23 54
Bramhall	d					21 47											22 56					23 28	
Poynton	d					21 50											22 59					23 31	
Adlington (Cheshire)	d					21 54											23 02					23 35	
Prestbury	d					21 57											23 05					23 38	
Macclesfield	a					22 02				22 15							23 10					23 44	
	d									22 16													
Congleton	d									22 24													
Handforth	d	←	21 23								22 24	←								23 26			23 58
Manchester Airport	d	21 10							22 18 →			22 18						23 12					
Styal	d																						
Wilmslow	d	21a19	21 26				21 54				22 27	22a29				22 50		23a22		23 29			00 01
Alderley Edge	d		21 29								22 30									23a34			00 04
Chelford	d		21 33								22 34												00 08
Goostrey	d		21 37								22 38												00 12
Holmes Chapel	d		21 40								22 41												00 15
Sandbach	d		21 45								22 46												00 20
Crewe 10	65 a		21 56				22 16				22 57					23 11							00 31
Kidsgrove	50 a																						
Longport	50 a																						
Stoke-on-Trent	50, 68 a									22 38													
Stafford	68 a									22 56													
Wolverhampton 7	68 a									23 12													
Birmingham New Street 12	68 a									23 47													
London Euston 15	⊖ 65 a																						

Saturdays

until 12 July

		VT 1◇	NT	TP 1◇ A	NT K	NT	VT 1◇	NT	NT	NT B	AW ◇ L	NT	VT 1◇	NT N	XC 1◇ Q	NT U	NT	VT 1◇	TP 1◇ A	NT U	XC R 1 V	AW ◇ X	NT	NT	NT
Deansgate	d																								
Manchester Oxford Road	d																								
Manchester Piccadilly 10	a																								
	d	05 10	05 26	05 49	05 52		06 09	06 13	06 32	06 35	06 38		06 43	06 50	06 54	06 58	07 04	07 15	07 19	07 21	07 24	07 28	07 28	07 33	07 34
Levenshulme	d							06 18								07 03	07 09			07 27			07 33		
Heaton Chapel	d							06 21								07 06	07 12			07 30			07 36		
Stockport	a			05 57	06 01			06 25		06 45	06 47			07 01	07 02	07 10	07 16		07 27	07 33	07 32	07 37	07 40	07 43	
	d	05u19					06u16	06 25			06 48		06u50		07 03		07 16	07u23			07 33	07 37	07 40	07 43	
Cheadle Hulme	d							06 29									07 20						07 44	07 47	
Bramhall	d																						07 47		
Poynton	d																						07 50		
Adlington (Cheshire)	d																						07 54		
Prestbury	d																						07 57		
Macclesfield	a						06 29						07 03		07 15			07 34					08 02		
	d					06 02	06 29						07 03		07 16			07 35							
Congleton	d					06 09									07 24										
Handforth	d							06 33				←					07 24							07 51	
Manchester Airport	d		05 53						06 57 →			06 57													08 00
Styal	d																								08 04
Wilmslow	d	05 27	06 01					06 36			06 55	07 04					07 27				07 42	07 46		07 54	08 07
Alderley Edge	d		06a06					06 39				07 07					07 30							08a00	08 10
Chelford	d							06 43									07 34								
Goostrey	d							06 47									07 39								
Holmes Chapel	d							06 50				07 15					07 42								08 19
Sandbach	d							06 55				07 19					07 46								08 23
Crewe 10	65 a	05 45						07 04			07 16	07 31					07 57				08 05	08 06			08 37
Kidsgrove	50 a					06 15																			
Longport	50 a																								
Stoke-on-Trent	50, 68 a					06 25	06 45						07 20		07 38			07 50							
Stafford	68 a	06 12													07 56						08 32				
Wolverhampton 7	68 a														08 12						08 47				
Birmingham New Street 12	68 a														08 30						09 06				
London Euston 15	⊖ 65 a	08 19					08 57						09 38					10 03							

For general notes see front of timetable
For details of catering facilities see Directory of Train Operators

- **A** From Manchester Airport to Cleethorpes (Table 29)
- **B** To Chester (Table 88)
- **C** To Cardiff Central (Table 131)
- **D** From Southport (Table 82) to Buxton (Table 86)
- **E** From Manchester Airport to Sheffield (Table 78)
- **G** From Liverpool Lime Street to Nottingham (Table 49)
- **H** To Shrewsbury (Table 131)
- **J** From Clitheroe (Table 94) to Buxton (Table 86)
- **K** To Sheffield (Table 78)
- **L** To Milford Haven (Table 128)
- **N** To Buxton (Table 86)
- **Q** To Reading (Table 51)
- **U** To Hazel Grove (Table 86)
- **V** To Newquay (Table 135)
- **X** To Carmarthen (Table 128)

Table 84

Saturdays

until 12 July

Manchester, Stockport and Manchester Airport → Crewe and Stoke-on-Trent

Network Diagram - see first page of Table 78

		NT	NT	EM	VT	NT	XC	NT	NT	VT	TP	NT	XC	NT	NT	AW	NT	VT	EM	NT	XC	NT	NT	NT	VT
				◇	1 ◇		1 ◇			1 ◇	1 ◇		R 1			◇		1 ◇	◇		1 ◇				1 ◇
		A	B	C		D	E				G	H	J		A	K			C		L	A		D	
Deansgate	d		07 29									08 12													
Manchester Oxford Road	d		07 33	07 39								08 17							08 38						
Manchester Piccadilly 10	a		07 36	07 41								08 20							08 42						
	d	07 37	07 39	07 43	07 45	07 51	07 54	07 58	08 03	08 15	08 17	08 22	08 24	08 27	08 29	08 34	08 34	08 40	08 42	08 51	08 54	08 59	09 03	09 06	09 15
Levenshulme	d					07 56		08 04							08 36					08 56				09 12	
Heaton Chapel	d					07 59		08 07							08 39					08 59				09 15	
Stockport	a	07 47	07 48	07 54		08 03	08 01	08 10	08 12		08 25	08 30	08 32	08 36	08 43	08 43			08 53	09 03	09 01	09 08	09 13	09 19	
	d				07u54		08 03	08 10	08 14	08u23			08 33	08 36		08 44		08u49		09 05	09 03		09 13		09u24
Cheadle Hulme	d							08 15	08 18					08 41						09 11			09 17		
Bramhall	d								08 21					08 44											
Poynton	d								08 24					08 47											
Adlington (Cheshire)	d								08 27					08 51											
Prestbury	d								08 30					08 54											
Macclesfield	a				08 07		08 15		08 35	08 36			08 46	08 59				09 04			09 15				
	d				08 07		08 16			08 36			08 46					09 05			09 16				
Congleton	d						08 24														09 24				
Handforth	d							08 19												09 15			09 21		
Manchester Airport	d																09 00								
Styal	d																								
Wilmslow	d							08 21								08 52	09 07			09 18			09 24		
Alderley Edge	d							08 24									09 10			09a23			09 27		
Chelford	d							08 28															09 31		
Goostrey	d							08 33															09 35		
Holmes Chapel	d							08 36									09 18						09 38		
Sandbach	d							08 40									09 22						09 43		
Crewe 10	65 a							08 51								09 16	09 33						09 54		
Kidsgrove	50 a																								
Longport	50 a																								
Stoke-on-Trent	50, 68 a				08 23		08 38			08 54			09 03					09 20			09 38				09 48
Stafford	68 a						08 56						09 25								09 56				
Wolverhampton 7	68 a						09 11						09 41								10 12				
Birmingham New Street 12	68 a						09 30						09 58								10 30				10 47
London Euston 15	⊖ 65 a				10 27					11 13								12 00							12 54

		TP	XC	NT	NT	NT	AW	NT	VT	EM	NT	NT	XC	NT	NT	VT	TP	XC	NT	NT	NT	AW	NT	VT	EM
		1 ◇	1 ◇				◇		1 ◇	◇			1 ◇			1 ◇	1 ◇	R 1				◇		1 ◇	◇
		G	N	Q			U	V		C			L		D		G	J	Q			K	V		C
Deansgate	d				09 24			09 29												10 24			10 29		
Manchester Oxford Road	d				09 27			09 33		09 38										10 27			10 33		10 38
Manchester Piccadilly 10	a				09 29			09 35		09 40										10 29			10 35		10 40
	d	09 20	09 24	09 24	09 30	09 33	09 34	09 37	09 40	09 42		09 51	09 54	10 03	10 06	10 15	10 20	10 24	10 24	10 30	10 33	10 34	10 37	10 40	10 42
Levenshulme	d							09 42				09 56			10 12								10 42		
Heaton Chapel	d							09 45				09 59			10 15								10 45		
Stockport	a	09 28	09 32	09 34	09 39		09 42	09 49		09 55		10 03	10 03	10 12	10 18		10 28	10 32	10 34	10 39		10 42	10 49		10 52
	d		09 33		09 40		09 42		09u49			10 05	10 03	10 13		10u24		10 33		10 40		10 43		10u49	
Cheadle Hulme	d				09 44							10 11		10 17						10 44					
Bramhall	d				09 47															10 47					
Poynton	d				09 50															10 50					
Adlington (Cheshire)	d				09 53															10 53					
Prestbury	d				09 56															10 56					
Macclesfield	a		09 46		10 01				10 04				10 15					10 46		11 01				11 04	
	d		09 46						10 05				10 16					10 46						11 05	
Congleton	d																								
Handforth	d										←	10 15		10 21											
Manchester Airport	d					10 00 →					10 00										11 00 →				
Styal	d																								
Wilmslow	d						09 52				10 06	10 18		10 24								10 51			
Alderley Edge	d										10 09	10a24		10 27											
Chelford	d													10 31											
Goostrey	d													10 36											
Holmes Chapel	d										10 17			10 39											
Sandbach	d										10 22			10 43											
Crewe 10	65 a						10 15				10 33			10 54								11 16			
Kidsgrove	50 a																								
Longport	50 a																								
Stoke-on-Trent	50, 68 a		10 03						10 20				10 37			10 48		11 03						11 20	
Stafford	68 a		10 25										10 56					11 24							
Wolverhampton 7	68 a		10 41										11 12					11 41							
Birmingham New Street 12	68 a		10 58										11 30			11 47		11 58							
London Euston 15	⊖ 65 a								13 04							13 54								14 04	

For general notes see front of timetable
For details of catering facilities see Directory of Train Operators

- **A** To Buxton (Table 86)
- **B** From Blackpool North (Table 82) to Chester (Table 88)
- **C** From Liverpool Lime Street to Norwich (Table 49)
- **D** To Hazel Grove (Table 86)
- **E** To Brighton (Table 51)
- **G** From Manchester Airport to Cleethorpes (Table 29)
- **H** From St Annes-on-the-Sea (Table 97) to Greenbank (Table 88)
- **J** To Paignton (Table 51)
- **K** To Milford Haven (Table 128)
- **L** To Reading (Table 51)
- **N** To Bournemouth (Table 51)
- **Q** To Chester (Table 88)
- **U** To Carmarthen (Table 128)
- **V** From Blackpool North (Table 82) to Buxton (Table 86)

Manchester, Stockport and Manchester Airport → Crewe and Stoke-on-Trent

until 12 July

Network Diagram - see first page of Table 78

		NT	NT	XC	NT	NT	VT	TP	XC	NT	NT	NT	AW	NT	VT	EM	NT	NT	XC	NT	NT	VT	TP	XC	NT
				1 ◇ A ☕		B	1 ◇ ☕	1 ◇ C trolley	1 ◇ D ☕	E			◇ G trolley	H	1 ◇ ☕	◇ J			1 ◇ A ☕		B	1 ◇ ☕	1 ◇ C trolley	R 1 K ☕	E
Deansgate	d										11 24			11 29											
Manchester Oxford Road	d										11 27			11 33		11 38									
Manchester Piccadilly 10	a										11 29			11 35		11 40									
	d		10 51	10 54	11 03	11 06	11 15	11 20	11 24	11 24	11 30	11 33	11 34	11 37	11 40	11 42		11 51	11 54	12 03	12 06	12 15	12 20	12 24	12 24
Levenshulme	d		10 56			11 12								11 42				11 56			12 12				
Heaton Chapel	d		10 59			11 15								11 45				11 59			12 15				
Stockport	a		11 03	11 02	11 12	11 18		11 28	11 33	11 34	11 39		11 42	11 49		11 52		12 03	12 02	12 12	12 18		12 28	12 32	12 34
	d		11 05	11 03	11 13		11u24		11 33		11 40		11 42		11u49			12 05	12 03	12 13		12u24		12 33	
Cheadle Hulme	d		11 11		11 17						11 44							12 11		12 17					
Bramhall	d										11 47														
Poynton	d										11 50														
Adlington (Cheshire)	d										11 53														
Prestbury	d										11 56														
Macclesfield	a			11 15					11 46		12 01				12 04				12 15					12 46	
	d			11 16					11 46						12 05				12 16					12 46	
Congleton	d			11 24																					
Handforth	d	←	11 15		11 21												←	12 15		12 21					
Manchester Airport	✈ d	11 00										12 00 →					12 00								
Styal	d																								
Wilmslow	d	11 06	11 18		11 24								11 51				12 06	12 18		12 24					
Alderley Edge	d	11 09	11a24		11 27												12 09	12a24		12 27					
Chelford	d				11 31															12 31					
Goostrey	d				11 36															12 36					
Holmes Chapel	d	11 17			11 39												12 17			12 39					
Sandbach	d	11 22			11 43												12 22			12 43					
Crewe 10	65 a	11 33			11 54								12 16				12 33			12 54					
Kidsgrove	50 a																								
Longport	50 a																								
Stoke-on-Trent	50, 68 a			11 37			11 48		12 03						12 20				12 37			12 48		13 03	
Stafford	68 a			11 56	*12 43*				12 24										12 56					13 24	
Wolverhampton 7	68 a			12 12	*13 05*				12 41										13 12					13 40	
Birmingham New Street 12	68 a			12 30	*13 11*		12 47		12 58										13 30			13 47		13 58	
London Euston 15	⊖ 65 a						14 54								15 04							15 54			

		NT	NT	AW	NT	VT	EM	NT	NT	XC	NT	NT	VT	TP	XC	NT	NT	NT	AW	NT	VT	EM	NT	NT	XC
				R L trolley	H	1 ◇ ☕	◇ J			1 ◇ N ☕		B	1 ◇ ☕	1 ◇ C trolley	1 ◇ D ☕	E			R G trolley	H	1 ◇ ☕	◇ J			1 ◇ A ☕
Deansgate	d	12 24			12 29												13 24			13 29					
Manchester Oxford Road	d	12 27			12 33		12 38										13 27			13 33		13 38			
Manchester Piccadilly 10	a	12 29			12 35		12 40										13 29			13 35		13 40			
	d	12 30	12 33	12 34	12 37	12 40	12 42		12 51	12 54	13 03	13 06	13 15	13 20	13 24	13 24	13 30	13 33	13 34	13 37	13 40	13 42		13 51	13 54
Levenshulme	d				12 42				12 56			13 12								13 42				13 56	
Heaton Chapel	d				12 45				12 59			13 15								13 45				13 59	
Stockport	a	12 39		12 42	12 49		12 52		13 03	13 02	13 12	13 18		13 28	13 32	13 34	13 39		13 42	13 49		13 52		14 03	14 02
	d	12 40		12 42		12u49			13 05	13 03	13 13		13u24		13 33		13 40		13 42		13u49			14 05	14 03
Cheadle Hulme	d	12 44							13 11		13 17						13 44							14 11	
Bramhall	d	12 47															13 47								
Poynton	d	12 50															13 50								
Adlington (Cheshire)	d	12 53															13 53								
Prestbury	d	12 56															13 56								
Macclesfield	a	13 01				13 04				13 15					13 46		14 01				14 04				14 15
	d					13 05				13 16					13 46						14 05				14 16
Congleton	d									13 24															
Handforth	d							←	13 15		13 21												←	14 15	
Manchester Airport	✈ d		13 00 →					13 00										14 00 →					14 00		
Styal	d																								
Wilmslow	d			12 51				13 06	13 18		13 24								13 54				14 06	14 18	
Alderley Edge	d							13 09	13a24		13 27												14 09	14a24	
Chelford	d										13 31														
Goostrey	d										13 36														
Holmes Chapel	d							13 17			13 39												14 17		
Sandbach	d							13 22			13 43												14 22		
Crewe 10	65 a			13 15				13 33			13 54								14 15				14 33		
Kidsgrove	50 a																								
Longport	50 a																								
Stoke-on-Trent	50, 68 a					13 20				13 37			13 48		14 03						14 20				14 37
Stafford	68 a									13 56					14 24										14 56
Wolverhampton 7	68 a									14 12					14 41										15 12
Birmingham New Street 12	68 a									14 30			14 47		14 58										15 30
London Euston 15	⊖ 65 a					16 04							16 54								17 04				

For general notes see front of timetable
For details of catering facilities see Directory of Train Operators

A To Reading (Table 51)
B To Hazel Grove (Table 86)
C From Manchester Airport to Cleethorpes (Table 29)
D To Bournemouth (Table 51)
E To Chester (Table 88)
G To Carmarthen (Table 128)
H From Blackpool North (Table 82) to Buxton (Table 86)
J From Liverpool Lime Street to Norwich (Table 49)
K To Paignton (Table 51)
L To Milford Haven (Table 128)
N To Guildford (Table 51)

Table 84

Saturdays

until 12 July

Manchester, Stockport and Manchester Airport → Crewe and Stoke-on-Trent

Network Diagram - see first page of Table 78

Station		NT	NT A	VT 1◇	TP 1◇ B	XC 1◇ C	NT D	NT	NT	AW R E	NT G	VT 1◇	EM ◇ H	NT	NT	XC 1◇ J	NT	NT A	VT 1◇	TP 1◇ B	XC 1◇ K	NT D	NT	NT	AW R L
Deansgate	d							14 24			14 29												15 24		
Manchester Oxford Road	d							14 27			14 33		14 38										15 27		
Manchester Piccadilly [10]	a							14 29			14 35		14 40										15 29		
	d	14 03	14 06	14 15	14 20	14 24	14 24	14 30	14 33	14 34	14 37	14 40	14 42		14 51	14 54	15 03	15 06	15 15	15 18	15 24	15 24	15 30	15 33	15 34
Levenshulme	d		14 12								14 42				14 56			15 12							
Heaton Chapel	d		14 15								14 45				14 59			15 15							
Stockport	a	14 12	14 18		14 28	14 32	14 34	14 39		14 42	14 49		14 52		15 03	15 02	15 12	15 18		15 26	15 32	15 34	15 39		15 42
	d	14 13		14u24		14 33		14 40		14 42		14u49			15 05	15 03	15 13		15u24		15 33		15 40		15 42
Cheadle Hulme	d	14 17						14 44							15 11		15 17						15 44		
Bramhall	d							14 47															15 47		
Poynton	d							14 50															15 50		
Adlington (Cheshire)	d							14 53															15 53		
Prestbury	d							14 56															15 56		
Macclesfield	a					14 46		15 01				15 04				15 15					15 46		16 01		
	d					14 46						15 05				15 16					15 46				
Congleton	d															15 24									
Handforth	d	14 21												←	15 15		15 21								
Manchester Airport	d								15 00 →					15 00										16 00 →	
Styal	d																								
Wilmslow	d	14 24								14 51				15 06	15 18		15 24								15 51
Alderley Edge	d	14 27												15 09	15a24		15 27								
Chelford	d	14 31															15 31								
Goostrey	d	14 36															15 36								
Holmes Chapel	d	14 39												15 17			15 39								
Sandbach	d	14 43												15 22			15 43								
Crewe [10]	65 a	14 54								15 15				15 33			15 54								16 14
Kidsgrove	50 a																								
Longport	50 a																								
Stoke-on-Trent	50, 68 a			14 48		15 03						15 20				15 37			15 48		16 03				
Stafford	68 a					15 24										15 56					16 24				
Wolverhampton [7]	68 a					15 41										16 12					16 41				
Birmingham New Street [12]	68 a			15 47		15 58										16 30			16 47		16 58				
London Euston [15]	65 a			17 54								18 04							18 55						

Station		NT G	VT 1◇	EM ◇ N	NT	NT	XC 1◇ Q	NT	NT A	VT 1◇	TP 1◇ B	XC 1◇ U	NT D	NT	NT	AW R E	NT G	VT 1◇	EM ◇ N	NT	NT	XC 1◇ V	NT	NT X	NT A
Deansgate	d	15 29												16 24			16 29							16 59	
Manchester Oxford Road	d	15 33		15 38										16 27			16 33		16 38					17 03	
Manchester Piccadilly [10]	a	15 35		15 40										16 29			16 36		16 41					17 06	
	d	15 37	15 40	15 42		15 51	15 54	16 03	16 06	16 15	16 20	16 24	16 24	16 30	16 33	16 34	16 37	16 40	16 42		16 51	16 54	17 03	17 07	17 07
Levenshulme	d	15 42				15 56			16 12												16 56		17 09		17 16
Heaton Chapel	d	15 45				15 59			16 15												16 59		17 12		17 19
Stockport	a	15 49		15 53		16 03	16 02	16 12	16 18		16 28	16 32	16 34	16 39		16 42	16 46		16 52		17 03	17 02	17 15	17 19	17 22
	d		15u49			16 05	16 03	16 13		16u24		16 33		16 40		16 43		16u49			17 05	17 03	17 16		
Cheadle Hulme	d					16 11		16 17						16 44							17 11		17 19		
Bramhall	d													16 47											
Poynton	d													16 50											
Adlington (Cheshire)	d													16 53											
Prestbury	d													16 56											
Macclesfield	a		16 04				16 15					16 46		17 01				17 04				17 14			
	d		16 05				16 16					16 46						17 05				17 16			
Congleton	d																					17 24			
Handforth	d				←	16 15		16 21												←	17 15		17 23		
Manchester Airport	d				16 00										17 00 →					17 00					
Styal	d																								
Wilmslow	d				16 06	16 18		16 24								16 51				17 06	17 18		17 26		
Alderley Edge	d				16 09	16a24		16 27												17 09	17a24		17 29		
Chelford	d				16 13			16 31															17 33		
Goostrey	d				16 18			16 36															17 37		
Holmes Chapel	d				16 21			16 39												17 17			17 40		
Sandbach	d				16 25			16 43												17 22			17 45		
Crewe [10]	65 a				16 36			16 54								17 16				17 33			17 56		
Kidsgrove	50 a																								
Longport	50 a																								
Stoke-on-Trent	50, 68 a		16 20				16 37			16 48		17 03						17 20				17 37			
Stafford	68 a						16 56					17 24										17 56			
Wolverhampton [7]	68 a						17 12					17 41										18 12			
Birmingham New Street [12]	68 a						17 30			17 47		17 58										18 30			
London Euston [15]	65 a		19 05							19 48								20 01							

For general notes see front of timetable
For details of catering facilities see Directory of Train Operators

- **A** To Hazel Grove (Table 86)
- **B** From Manchester Airport to Cleethorpes (Table 29)
- **C** To Penzance (Table 135)
- **D** To Chester (Table 88)
- **E** To Milford Haven (Table 128)
- **G** From Blackpool North (Table 82) to Buxton (Table 86)
- **H** From Liverpool Lime Street to Nottingham (Table 49)
- **J** To Brighton (Table 51)
- **K** To Bournemouth (Table 51)
- **L** To Carmarthen (Table 128)
- **N** From Liverpool Lime Street to Norwich (Table 49)
- **Q** To Reading (Table 51)
- **U** To Plymouth (Table 51)
- **V** To Gatwick Airport (Table 51)
- **X** From Southport (Table 82) to Buxton (Table 86)

Table 84

Saturdays

until 12 July

Manchester, Stockport and Manchester Airport → Crewe and Stoke-on-Trent

Network Diagram - see first page of Table 78

		VT	TP	XC	NT	NT	NT	AW	NT	VT	EM	NT	NT	XC	NT	NT	NT	VT	TP	XC	NT	NT	AW	NT	NT
		1◇	1◇	1◇				R		1◇	◇			1◇				1◇	1◇	1◇			◇		
			A	B	C			D	E		G						H		A	J	C		K		E
		☕	🍴	☕				🍴		☕				☕				☕	🍴	☕			🍴		
Deansgate	d					17 24			17 28																
Manchester Oxford Road	d					17 27			17 32		17 38														18 35
Manchester Piccadilly 10	a					17 29			17 35		17 40														18 38
	d	17 15	17 20	17 24	17 24	17 31	17 33	17 34	17 37	17 40	17 42		17 49	17 54	17 54	18 03	18 06	18 15	18 17	18 24	18 24	18 30	18 34	18 36	18 39
Levenshulme	d								17 45				17 54				18 12								18 45
Heaton Chapel	d								17 48				17 57				18 15								18 48
Stockport	a		17 28	17 32	17 33	17 40		17 42	17 51		17 54		18 01	18 03	18 04	18 12	18 18		18 25	18 32	18 34	18 39	18 42		18 50
	d	17u24		17 33		17 40		17 42		17u49			18 01	18 03	18 06	18 13		18u24		18 33		18 39	18 43		
Cheadle Hulme	d					17 44							18 05		18 11	18 18						18 43			
Bramhall	d					17 47									18 14							18 46			
Poynton	d					17 50									18 17							18 49			
Adlington (Cheshire)	d					17 53									18 21							18 52			
Prestbury	d					17 56									18 24							18 55			
Macclesfield	a			17 46		18 01				18 04				18 16	18 28					18 46		19 00			
	d			17 46						18 05				18 16	18 38					18 46					
Congleton	d													18 24	18 45										
Handforth	d											⟵	18 09			18 22									
Manchester Airport ✈	d						18 00 ⟶					18 00												19 01	
Styal	d											18 07													
Wilmslow	d							17 51				18 11	18 13			18 25							18 53	19 11	
Alderley Edge	d											18 14	18a20			18 28								19a18	
Chelford	d															18 32									
Goostrey	d															18 36									
Holmes Chapel	d											18 22				18 39									
Sandbach	d											18 26				18 43									
Crewe 10	65 a							18 15				18 37				18 54							19 15		
Kidsgrove	50 a														18 51										
Longport	50 a														18 56										
Stoke-on-Trent	50, 68 a	17 48		18 03						18 20				18 37	19 01			18 48		19 04					
Stafford	68 a			18 24										18 56						19 24					
Wolverhampton 7	68 a			18 41										19 12						19 40					
Birmingham New Street 12	68 a	18 47		18 58										19 35				19 47		19 58					
London Euston 15	⊖ 65 a	21 22								21 28								22 28							

		VT	EM	NT	XC	NT	VT	TP	XC	NT	NT	NT	AW	NT	EM	NT	XC	NT	VT	TP	NT	NT	AW	NT	EM
		1◇	◇		1◇		1◇	1◇	1◇				◇		◇		1◇		1◇	1◇			◇		◇
			L					A	N	C			Q	E	G					A	C		Q	E	G
		☕			☕		☕		☕				🍴						☕						
Deansgate	d													19 29										20 28	
Manchester Oxford Road	d		18 39											19 33	19 38									20 32	20 38
Manchester Piccadilly 10	a		18 42											19 36	19 42									20 34	20 40
	d	18 40	18 44	18 50	18 54	19 03	19 15	19 18	19 24	19 24	19 30	19 30	19 34	19 37	19 42		19 54	20 03	20 15	20 20	20 24	20 27	20 34	20 36	20 42
Levenshulme	d			18 55		19 08						19 36						20 08				20 32			
Heaton Chapel	d			18 58		19 11						19 39						20 11				20 35			
Stockport	a		18 54	19 03	19 02	19 15		19 26	19 32	19 33		19 42	19 42	19 47	19 53		20 02	20 14		20 28	20 34	20 39	20 46	20 44	20 51
	d	18u49		19 03	19 03	19 15	19u24		19 33			19 43	19 42				20 03	20 15	20u24			20 40	20 46		
Cheadle Hulme	d			19 11		19 19						19 47						20 19				20 44			
Bramhall	d											19 50										20 47			
Poynton	d											19 53										20 50			
Adlington (Cheshire)	d											19 56										20 53			
Prestbury	d											19 59										20 56			
Macclesfield	a	19 04			19 15				19 46			20 04					20 14		20 37			21 01			
	d	19 05			19 16				19 46								20 16		20 38						
Congleton	d				19 24												20 24								
Handforth	d			19 15		19 23										⟵		20 23							
Manchester Airport ✈	d										19 56 ⟶					19 56									
Styal	d																								
Wilmslow	d			19 18		19 26							19 54			20a06		20 26					20 54		
Alderley Edge	d			19a24		19 29												20 29							
Chelford	d					19 33												20 33							
Goostrey	d					19 37												20 37							
Holmes Chapel	d					19 40												20 40							
Sandbach	d					19 45												20 45							
Crewe 10	65 a					19 56							20 15					20 56					21 14		
Kidsgrove	50 a																								
Longport	50 a																								
Stoke-on-Trent	50, 68 a	19 20			19 38		19 48		20 03								20 37		20 54						
Stafford	68 a				19 56				20 24								20 57		21 17						
Wolverhampton 7	68 a				20 12				20 40								21 12		21 35						
Birmingham New Street 12	68 a				20 35		20 49		20 58								21 35		21 56						
London Euston 15	⊖ 65 a	22 40					23 24												00 16						

For general notes see front of timetable
For details of catering facilities see Directory of Train Operators

A From Manchester Airport to Cleethorpes (Table 29)
B To Bournemouth (Table 51)
C To Chester (Table 88)
D To Haverfordwest (Table 128)
E From Blackpool North (Table 82) to Buxton (Table 86)
G From Liverpool Lime Street to Nottingham (Table 49)
H To Hazel Grove (Table 86)
J To Plymouth (Table 51)
K To Carmarthen (Table 128)
L From Liverpool Lime Street to Norwich (Table 49)
N To Southampton Central (Table 51)
Q To Cardiff Central (Table 131)

Table 84

Saturdays
until 12 July

Manchester, Stockport and Manchester Airport → Crewe and Stoke-on-Trent

Network Diagram - see first page of Table 78

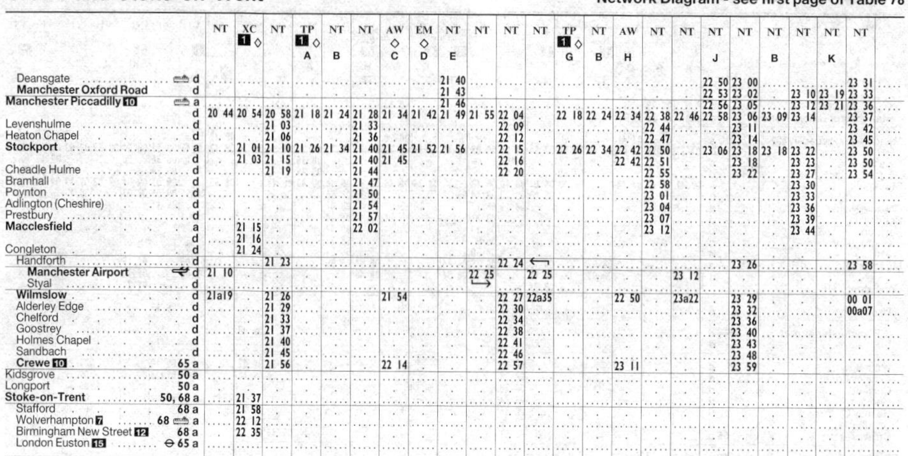

		NT	XC	NT	TP	NT	NT	AW	EM	NT	NT	NT	NT	TP	NT	AW	NT	NT	NT	NT	NT	NT	NT	NT
			1 ◇		1 ◇			◇	◇					1 ◇										
					A	B		C	D	E				G	B	H			J		B		K	
Deansgate	d									21 40									22 50	23 00				23 31
Manchester Oxford Road	d									21 43									22 53	23 02		23 10	23 19	23 33
Manchester Piccadilly 10	a									21 46									22 56	23 05		23 12	23 21	23 36
	d	20 44	20 54	20 58	21 18	21 24	21 28	21 34	21 42	21 49	21 55	22 04		22 18	22 24	22 34	22 38	22 46	22 58	23 06	23 09	23 14		23 37
Levenshulme	d			21 03			21 33					22 09					22 44			23 11				23 42
Heaton Chapel	d			21 06			21 36					22 12					22 47			23 14				23 45
Stockport	a		21 01	21 10	21 26	21 34	21 40	21 45	21 52	21 56		22 15		22 26	22 34	22 42	22 50		23 06	23 18	23 18	23 22		23 50
	d		21 03	21 15			21 40	21 45				22 16				22 42	22 51			23 18		23 23		23 50
Cheadle Hulme	d			21 19			21 44					22 20					22 55			23 22		23 27		23 54
Bramhall	d						21 47										22 58					23 30		
Poynton	d						21 50										23 01					23 33		
Adlington (Cheshire)	d						21 54										23 04					23 36		
Prestbury	d						21 57										23 07					23 39		
Macclesfield	a		21 15				22 02										23 12					23 44		
	d		21 16																					
Congleton	d		21 24																					
Handforth	d			21 23								22 24	←							23 26				23 58
Manchester Airport	d	21 10									22 25 →		22 25					23 12						
Styal	d																							
Wilmslow	d	21a19		21 26				21 54				22 27	22a35			22 50		23a22		23 29				00 01
Alderley Edge	d			21 29								22 30								23 32				00a07
Chelford	d			21 33								22 34								23 36				
Goostrey	d			21 37								22 38								23 40				
Holmes Chapel	d			21 40								22 41								23 43				
Sandbach	d			21 45								22 46								23 48				
Crewe 10	65 a			21 56				22 14				22 57				23 11				23 59				
Kidsgrove	50 a																							
Longport	50 a																							
Stoke-on-Trent	50, 68 a		21 37																					
Stafford	68 a		21 58																					
Wolverhampton 7	68 a		22 12																					
Birmingham New Street 12	68 a		22 35																					
London Euston 15	⊖ 65 a																							

Saturdays
19 July to 6 September

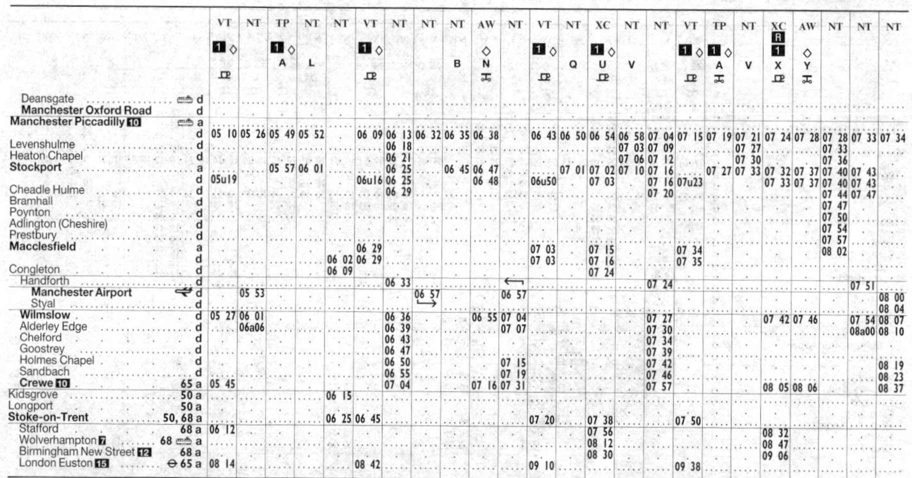

		VT	NT	TP	NT	NT	VT	NT	NT	NT	AW	NT	VT	NT	XC	NT	NT	VT	TP	NT	XC	AW	NT	NT	NT
		1 ◇		1 ◇			1 ◇				◇		1 ◇		1 ◇			1 ◇	1 ◇		R 1	◇			
				A	L					B	N			Q	U	V			A	V	X	Y			
Deansgate	d																								
Manchester Oxford Road	d																								
Manchester Piccadilly 10	a																								
	d	05 10	05 26	05 49	05 52		06 09	06 13	06 32	06 35	06 38		06 43	06 50	06 54	06 58	07 04	07 15	07 19	07 21	07 24	07 28	07 28	07 33	07 34
Levenshulme	d							06 18								07 03	07 09			07 27			07 33		
Heaton Chapel	d							06 21								07 06	07 12			07 30			07 36		
Stockport	a			05 57	06 01			06 25		06 45	06 47			07 01	07 02	07 10	07 16		07 27	07 33	07 32	07 37	07 40	07 43	
	d	05u19					06u16	06 25			06 48		06u50		07 03		07 16	07u23			07 33	07 37	07 40	07 43	
Cheadle Hulme	d							06 29									07 20						07 44	07 47	
Bramhall	d																						07 47		
Poynton	d																						07 50		
Adlington (Cheshire)	d																						07 54		
Prestbury	d																						07 57		
Macclesfield	a						06 29						07 03		07 15			07 34					08 02		
	d					06 02	06 29						07 03		07 16			07 35							
Congleton	d					06 09									07 24										
Handforth	d							06 33				←					07 24							07 51	
Manchester Airport	d		05 53						06 57 →			06 57													08 00
Styal	d																								08 04
Wilmslow	d	05 27	06 01					06 36			06 55	07 04					07 27				07 42	07 46		07 54	08 07
Alderley Edge	d		06a06					06 39				07 07					07 30							08a00	08 10
Chelford	d							06 43									07 34								
Goostrey	d							06 47									07 39								
Holmes Chapel	d							06 50				07 15					07 42								08 19
Sandbach	d							06 55				07 19					07 46								08 23
Crewe 10	65 a	05 45						07 04			07 16	07 31					07 57				08 05	08 06			08 37
Kidsgrove	50 a					06 15																			
Longport	50 a																								
Stoke-on-Trent	50, 68 a					06 25	06 45						07 20		07 38			07 50							
Stafford	68 a	06 12													07 56						08 32				
Wolverhampton 7	68 a														08 12						08 47				
Birmingham New Street 12	68 a														08 30						09 06				
London Euston 15	⊖ 65 a	08 14					08 42						09 10					09 38							

For general notes see front of timetable
For details of catering facilities see Directory of Train Operators

- **A** From Manchester Airport to Cleethorpes (Table 29)
- **B** To Chester (Table 88)
- **C** To Cardiff Central (Table 131)
- **D** To Nottingham (Table 49)
- **E** From Southport (Table 82) to Buxton (Table 86)
- **G** From Manchester Airport to Sheffield (Table 78)
- **H** To Shrewsbury (Table 131)
- **J** From Clitheroe (Table 94) to Buxton (Table 86)
- **K** To New Mills Central (Table 78)
- **L** To Sheffield (Table 78)
- **N** To Milford Haven (Table 128)
- **Q** To Buxton (Table 86)
- **U** To Reading (Table 51)
- **V** To Hazel Grove (Table 86)
- **X** To Newquay (Table 135)
- **Y** To Carmarthen (Table 128)

Due to ongoing Engineering Operations, some services from Saturday 13 September on this Table had not been confirmed at time of going to press. These services will be issued in a special Supplement as soon as exact timings have been confirmed.

19 July to 6 September

Manchester, Stockport and Manchester Airport → Crewe and Stoke-on-Trent

Network Diagram - see first page of Table 78

	NT	NT	EM	VT	NT	XC	NT	NT	VT	TP	NT	XC	NT	NT	AW	NT	EM	VT	NT	XC	NT	NT	NT	VT
			◇	1 ◇		1 ◇			1 ◇	1 ◇		R 1			◇		◇	1 ◇		1 ◇				1 ◇
	A	B	C		D					E	G	H		A	J		C			K	A		D	
				☕		☕			☕	🛒		☕			🛒			☕		☕				☕
Deansgate d		07 29									08 12													
Manchester Oxford Road d		07 33	07 39								08 17						08 38							
Manchester Piccadilly 10 a		07 36	07 41								08 20						08 42							
d	07 37	07 39	07 43	07 45	07 51	07 54	07 58	08 03	08 15	08 17	08 22	08 24	08 27	08 29	08 34	08 34	08 42	08 45	08 51	08 54	08 59	09 03	09 06	09 15
Levenshulme d					07 56		08 04							08 36					08 56				09 12	
Heaton Chapel d					07 59		08 07							08 39					08 59				09 15	
Stockport a	07 47	07 48	07 54		08 03	08 01	08 10	08 12		08 25	08 30	08 32	08 36	08 43	08 43		08 53		09 03	09 01	09 08	09 13	09 19	
d				07u54		08 03	08 10	08 14	08u23			08 33	08 36		08 44			08u55	09 05	09 03		09 13		09u22
Cheadle Hulme d							08 15	08 18					08 41						09 11			09 17		
Bramhall d								08 21					08 44											
Poynton d								08 24					08 47											
Adlington (Cheshire) d								08 27					08 51											
Prestbury d								08 30					08 54											
Macclesfield a				08 07		08 15		08 35	08 36			08 46	08 59					09 08		09 15				
d				08 07		08 16			08 36			08 46						09 08		09 16				
Congleton d						08 24														09 24				
Handforth d							08 19												09 15			09 21		
Manchester Airport ✈ d																09 00								
Styal d																								
Wilmslow d							08 21								08 52	09 07			09 18			09 24		
Alderley Edge d							08 24									09 10			09a23			09 27		
Chelford d							08 28															09 31		
Goostrey d							08 33															09 35		
Holmes Chapel d							08 36									09 18						09 38		
Sandbach d							08 40									09 22						09 43		
Crewe 10 65 a							08 51								09 16	09 33						09 54		
Kidsgrove 50 a																								
Longport 50 a																								
Stoke-on-Trent 50, 68 a				08 23		08 38			08 54			09 03						09 24		09 38				09 48
Stafford 68 a						08 56						09 25								09 56				
Wolverhampton 7 68 a						09 11						09 41								10 12				
Birmingham New Street 12 68 a						09 30						09 58								10 30				
London Euston 15 ⊖ 65 a				10 15					10 48									11 16						11 31

	TP	XC	NT	NT	NT	AW	NT	EM	NT	VT	NT	XC	NT	NT	VT	TP	XC	NT	NT	NT	AW	NT	EM	NT
	1 ◇	1 ◇				◇		◇		1 ◇		1 ◇			1 ◇	1 ◇	R 1				◇		◇	
	E	L	N			Q	U	C				K		D		E	H	N			J	U	C	
	🛒	☕				🛒				☕		☕			☕	🛒	☕				🛒			
Deansgate d				09 24			09 29												10 24			10 29		
Manchester Oxford Road d				09 27			09 33	09 38											10 27			10 33	10 38	
Manchester Piccadilly 10 a				09 29			09 35	09 40											10 29			10 35	10 40	
d	09 20	09 24	09 24	09 30	09 33	09 34	09 37	09 42		09 45	09 51	09 54	10 03	10 06	10 15	10 20	10 24	10 24	10 30	10 33	10 34	10 37	10 42	
Levenshulme d							09 42				09 56			10 12								10 42		
Heaton Chapel d							09 45				09 59			10 15								10 45		
Stockport a	09 28	09 32	09 34	09 39		09 42	09 49	09 55			10 03	10 03	10 12	10 18		10 28	10 32	10 34	10 39		10 42	10 49	10 52	
d		09 33		09 40		09 42				09u54	10 05	10 03	10 13		10u24		10 33		10 40		10 43			
Cheadle Hulme d				09 44							10 11		10 17						10 44					
Bramhall d				09 47															10 47					
Poynton d				09 50															10 50					
Adlington (Cheshire) d				09 53															10 53					
Prestbury d				09 56															10 56					
Macclesfield a		09 46		10 01						10 07		10 15					10 46		11 01					
d		09 46								10 07		10 16					10 46							
Congleton d																								
Handforth d									←		10 15		10 21											←
Manchester Airport ✈ d					10 00 →				10 00											11 00 →				11 00
Styal d																								
Wilmslow d						09 52			10 06		10 18		10 24								10 51			11 06
Alderley Edge d									10 09		10a24		10 27											11 09
Chelford d													10 31											
Goostrey d													10 36											
Holmes Chapel d									10 17				10 39											11 17
Sandbach d									10 22				10 43											11 22
Crewe 10 65 a						10 15			10 33				10 54								11 16			11 33
Kidsgrove 50 a																								
Longport 50 a																								
Stoke-on-Trent 50, 68 a		10 03								10 23		10 37			10 48		11 03							
Stafford 68 a		10 25										10 56					11 24							
Wolverhampton 7 68 a		10 41										11 12					11 41							
Birmingham New Street 12 68 a		10 58										11 30					11 58							
London Euston 15 ⊖ 65 a						12 27				12 19					12 31									

For general notes see front of timetable
For details of catering facilities see Directory of Train Operators

- **A** To Buxton (Table 86)
- **B** From Blackpool North (Table 82) to Chester (Table 88)
- **C** From Liverpool Lime Street to Norwich (Table 49)
- **D** To Hazel Grove (Table 86)
- **E** From Manchester Airport to Cleethorpes (Table 29)
- **G** From St Annes-on-the-Sea (Table 97) to Greenbank (Table 88)
- **H** To Paignton (Table 51)
- **J** To Milford Haven (Table 128)
- **K** To Reading (Table 51)
- **L** To Bournemouth (Table 51)
- **N** To Chester (Table 88)
- **Q** To Carmarthen (Table 128)
- **U** From Blackpool North (Table 82) to Buxton (Table 86)

Due to ongoing Engineering Operations, some services from Saturday 13 September on this Table had not been confirmed at time of going to press. These services will be issued in a special Supplement as soon as exact timings have been confirmed.

Table 84

Saturdays

Manchester, Stockport and Manchester Airport → Crewe and Stoke-on-Trent

19 July to 6 September

Network Diagram - see first page of Table 78

		VT	NT	XC	NT	NT	VT	TP	XC	NT	NT	NT	AW	NT	EM	NT	VT	NT	XC	NT	NT	VT	TP	XC	NT
		1 ◇		1 ◇			1 ◇	1 ◇	1 ◇				◇		◇		1 ◇		1 ◇			1 ◇	1 ◇	R 1	
				A		B		C	D	E			G	H	J				A		B		C	K	E
		🍽		🍽			🍽	🛒	🍽				🛒				🍽		🍽			🍽	🛒	🍽	
Deansgate	🚊 d										11 24			11 29											
Manchester Oxford Road	d										11 27			11 33	11 38										
Manchester Piccadilly 10	🚊 a										11 29			11 35	11 40										
	d	10 45	10 51	10 54	11 03	11 06	11 15	11 20	11 24	11 24	11 30	11 33	11 34	11 37	11 42		11 45	11 51	11 54	12 03	12 06	12 15	12 20	12 24	12 24
Levenshulme	d		10 56			11 12								11 42				11 56			12 12				
Heaton Chapel	d		10 59			11 15								11 45				11 59			12 15				
Stockport	a		11 03	11 02	11 12	11 18		11 28	11 33	11 34	11 39		11 42	11 49	11 52			12 03	12 02	12 12	12 18		12 28	12 32	12 34
	d	10u54	11 05	11 03	11 13		11u24		11 33		11 40		11 42				11u54	12 05	12 03	12 13		12u24		12 33	
Cheadle Hulme	d		11 11		11 17						11 44							12 11		12 17					
Bramhall	d										11 47														
Poynton	d										11 50														
Adlington (Cheshire)	d										11 53														
Prestbury	d										11 56														
Macclesfield	a	11 07		11 15					11 46		12 01						12 07		12 15					12 46	
	d	11 07		11 16					11 46								12 07		12 16					12 46	
Congleton	d			11 24																					
Handforth	d		11 15		11 21											←		12 15		12 21					
Manchester Airport	✈ d											12 00 →				12 00									
Styal	d																								
Wilmslow	d		11 18		11 24								11 51			12 06		12 18		12 24					
Alderley Edge	d		11a24		11 27											12 09		12a24		12 27					
Chelford	d				11 31															12 31					
Goostrey	d				11 36															12 36					
Holmes Chapel	d				11 39											12 17				12 39					
Sandbach	d				11 43											12 22				12 43					
Crewe 10	65 a				11 54								12 16			12 33				12 54					
Kidsgrove	50 a																								
Longport	50 a																								
Stoke-on-Trent	50, 68 a	11 23		11 37			11 48		12 03								12 23		12 37			12 48		13 03	
Stafford	68 a			11 56					12 24										12 56					13 24	
Wolverhampton 7	68 🚊 a			12 12					12 41										13 12					13 40	
Birmingham New Street 12	68 a			12 30					12 58										13 30					13 58	
London Euston 15	⊖ 65 a	13 20					13 31										14 19					14 31			

		NT	NT	AW	NT	EM	NT	VT	NT	XC	NT	NT	VT	TP	XC	NT	NT	NT	AW	NT	EM	NT	VT	NT	XC
				R		◇		1 ◇		1 ◇			1 ◇	1 ◇	1 ◇				R		◇		1 ◇		1 ◇
				L	H	J				N		B		C	D	E			G	H	J				A
				🛒				🍽		🍽			🍽	🛒	🍽				🛒				🍽		🍽
Deansgate	🚊 d	12 24			12 29												13 24			13 29					
Manchester Oxford Road	d	12 27			12 33	12 38											13 27			13 33	13 38				
Manchester Piccadilly 10	🚊 a	12 29			12 35	12 40											13 29			13 35	13 40				
	d	12 30	12 33	12 34	12 37	12 42		12 45	12 51	12 54	13 03	13 06	13 15	13 20	13 24	13 24	13 30	13 33	13 34	13 37	13 42		13 45	13 51	13 54
Levenshulme	d				12 42				12 56			13 12								13 42				13 56	
Heaton Chapel	d				12 45				12 59			13 15								13 45				13 59	
Stockport	a	12 39		12 42	12 49	12 52			13 03	13 02	13 12	13 18		13 28	13 32	13 34	13 39		13 42	13 49	13 52			14 03	14 02
	d	12 40		12 42				12u54	13 05	13 03	13 13		13u22		13 33		13 40		13 42				13u54	14 05	14 03
Cheadle Hulme	d	12 44							13 11		13 17						13 44							14 11	
Bramhall	d	12 47															13 47								
Poynton	d	12 50															13 50								
Adlington (Cheshire)	d	12 53															13 53								
Prestbury	d	12 56															13 56								
Macclesfield	a	13 01						13 07		13 15					13 46		14 01						14 07		14 15
	d							13 07		13 16					13 46								14 07		14 16
Congleton	d									13 24															
Handforth	d						←		13 15		13 21											←		14 15	
Manchester Airport	✈ d		13 00 →				13 00											14 00 →				14 00			
Styal	d																								
Wilmslow	d			12 51			13 06		13 18		13 24								13 54			14 06		14 18	
Alderley Edge	d						13 09		13a24		13 27											14 09		14a24	
Chelford	d										13 31														
Goostrey	d										13 36														
Holmes Chapel	d						13 17				13 39											14 17			
Sandbach	d						13 22				13 43											14 22			
Crewe 10	65 a			13 15			13 33				13 54								14 15			14 33			
Kidsgrove	50 a																								
Longport	50 a																								
Stoke-on-Trent	50, 68 a							13 23		13 37			13 48		14 03								14 23		14 37
Stafford	68 a									13 56					14 24										14 56
Wolverhampton 7	68 🚊 a									14 12					14 41										15 12
Birmingham New Street 12	68 a									14 30					14 58										15 30
London Euston 15	⊖ 65 a							15 10					15 31										16 16		

For general notes see front of timetable
For details of catering facilities see Directory of Train Operators

- **A** To Reading (Table 51)
- **B** To Hazel Grove (Table 86)
- **C** From Manchester Airport to Cleethorpes (Table 29)
- **D** To Bournemouth (Table 51)
- **E** To Chester (Table 88)
- **G** To Carmarthen (Table 128)
- **H** From Blackpool North (Table 82) to Buxton (Table 86)
- **J** From Liverpool Lime Street to Norwich (Table 49)
- **K** To Paignton (Table 51)
- **L** To Milford Haven (Table 128)
- **N** To Guildford (Table 51)

Due to ongoing Engineering Operations, some services from Saturday 13 September on this Table had not been confirmed at time of going to press. These services will be issued in a special Supplement as soon as exact timings have been confirmed.

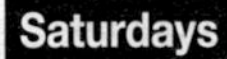

Manchester, Stockport and Manchester Airport → Crewe and Stoke-on-Trent

19 July to 6 September

Network Diagram - see first page of Table 78

	NT	NT	VT	TP	XC	NT	NT	NT	AW	NT	EM	NT	VT	NT	XC	NT	NT	VT	TP	XC	NT	NT	NT	AW
									R															R
			1 ◇	1 ◇	1 ◇						◇		1 ◇		1 ◇			1 ◇	1 ◇	1 ◇				
		A		B	C	D			E	G	H				J		A		B	K	D			L
			☕	🍴	☕				🍴				☕		☕			☕	🍴	☕				🍴
Deansgate d							14 24			14 29												15 24		
Manchester Oxford Road d							14 27			14 33	14 38											15 27		
Manchester Piccadilly 10 a							14 29			14 35	14 40											15 29		
d	14 03	14 06	14 15	14 20	14 24	14 24	14 30	14 33	14 34	14 37	14 42		14 45	14 51	14 54	15 03	15 06	15 15	15 18	15 24	15 24	15 30	15 33	15 34
Levenshulme d		14 12								14 42				14 56			15 12							
Heaton Chapel d		14 15								14 45				14 59			15 15							
Stockport a	14 12	14 18		14 28	14 32	14 34	14 39		14 42	14 49	14 52			15 03	15 02	15 12	15 18		15 26	15 32	15 34	15 39		15 42
d	14 13		14u24		14 33		14 40		14 42				14u54	15 05	15 03	15 13		15u24		15 33		15 40		15 42
Cheadle Hulme d	14 17						14 44							15 11		15 17						15 44		
Bramhall d							14 47															15 47		
Poynton d							14 50															15 50		
Adlington (Cheshire) d							14 53															15 53		
Prestbury d							14 56															15 56		
Macclesfield a					14 46		15 01						15 07		15 15					15 46		16 01		
d					14 46								15 07		15 16					15 46				
Congleton d															15 24									
Handforth d	14 21											←		15 15		15 21								
Manchester Airport ✈ d								15 00 →				15 00											16 00 →	
Styal d																								
Wilmslow d	14 24								14 51			15 06		15 18		15 24								15 51
Alderley Edge d	14 27											15 09		15a24		15 27								
Chelford d	14 31															15 31								
Goostrey d	14 36															15 36								
Holmes Chapel d	14 39											15 17				15 39								
Sandbach d	14 43											15 22				15 43								
Crewe 10 65 a	14 54								15 15			15 33				15 54								16 14
Kidsgrove 50 a																								
Longport 50 a																								
Stoke-on-Trent 50, 68 a			14 48		15 03								15 23		15 37			15 48		16 03				
Stafford 68 a					15 24										15 56					16 24				
Wolverhampton 7 68 a					15 41										16 12					16 41				
Birmingham New Street 12 68 a					15 58										16 30					16 58				
London Euston 15 ⊖ 65 a			16 36										17 10					17 31						

	NT	EM	NT	VT	NT	XC	NT	NT	VT	TP	XC	NT	NT	NT	AW	NT	EM	NT	VT	NT	XC	NT	NT	NT
															R									
		◇		1 ◇		1 ◇			1 ◇	1 ◇	1 ◇						◇		1 ◇		1 ◇			
	G	H				N		A		B	Q	D			E	G	H				U		V	A
				☕		☕			☕	🍴	☕				🍴				☕		☕			
Deansgate d	15 29												16 24			16 29							16 59	
Manchester Oxford Road d	15 33	15 38											16 27			16 33	16 38						17 03	
Manchester Piccadilly 10 a	15 35	15 40											16 29			16 36	16 41						17 06	
d	15 37	15 42		15 45	15 51	15 54	16 03	16 06	16 15	16 20	16 24	16 24	16 30	16 33	16 34	16 37	16 42		16 45	16 51	16 54	17 03	17 07	17 07
Levenshulme d	15 42				15 56			16 12												16 56		17 09		17 16
Heaton Chapel d	15 45				15 59			16 15												16 59		17 12		17 19
Stockport a	15 49	15 53			16 03	16 02	16 12	16 18		16 28	16 32	16 34	16 39		16 42	16 46	16 52			17 03	17 02	17 15	17 19	17 22
d				15u54	16 05	16 03	16 13		16u24		16 33		16 40		16 43				16u54	17 05	17 03	17 16		
Cheadle Hulme d					16 11		16 17						16 44							17 11		17 19		
Bramhall d													16 47											
Poynton d													16 50											
Adlington (Cheshire) d													16 53											
Prestbury d													16 56											
Macclesfield a				16 07		16 15					16 46		17 01						17 07		17 14			
d				16 07		16 16					16 46								17 07		17 16			
Congleton d																					17 24			
Handforth d			←		16 15		16 21											←		17 15		17 23		
Manchester Airport ✈ d			16 00											17 00 →				17 00						
Styal d																								
Wilmslow d			16 06		16 18		16 24								16 51			17 06		17 18		17 26		
Alderley Edge d			16 09		16a24		16 27											17 09		17a24		17 29		
Chelford d			16 13				16 31															17 33		
Goostrey d			16 18				16 36															17 37		
Holmes Chapel d			16 21				16 39											17 17				17 40		
Sandbach d			16 25				16 43											17 22				17 45		
Crewe 10 65 a			16 36				16 54								17 16			17 33				17 56		
Kidsgrove 50 a																								
Longport 50 a																								
Stoke-on-Trent 50, 68 a				16 23		16 37			16 48		17 03								17 23		17 37			
Stafford 68 a						16 56					17 24										17 56			
Wolverhampton 7 68 a						17 12					17 41										18 12			
Birmingham New Street 12 68 a						17 30					17 58										18 30			
London Euston 15 ⊖ 65 a				18 19					18 31										19 10					

For general notes see front of timetable
For details of catering facilities see Directory of Train Operators

- A To Hazel Grove (Table 86)
- B From Manchester Airport to Cleethorpes (Table 29)
- C To Penzance (Table 135)
- D To Chester (Table 88)
- E To Milford Haven (Table 128)
- G From Blackpool North (Table 82) to Buxton (Table 86)
- H From Liverpool Lime Street to Norwich (Table 49)
- J To Brighton (Table 51)
- K To Bournemouth (Table 51)
- L To Carmarthen (Table 128)
- N To Reading (Table 51)
- Q To Plymouth (Table 51)
- U To Gatwick Airport (Table 51)
- V From Southport (Table 82) to Buxton (Table 86)

Due to ongoing Engineering Operations, some services from Saturday 13 September on this Table had not been confirmed at time of going to press. These services will be issued in a special Supplement as soon as exact timings have been confirmed.

Table 84

Saturdays

Manchester, Stockport and Manchester Airport → Crewe and Stoke-on-Trent

19 July to 6 September

Network Diagram - see first page of Table 78

		VT	TP	XC	NT	NT	NT	AW	NT	EM	NT	VT	NT	XC	NT	NT	NT	VT	TP	XC	NT	NT	AW	NT	NT
		1 ◇	1 ◇	1 ◇				R		◇		1 ◇		1 ◇				1 ◇	1 ◇	1 ◇			◇		
			A	B	C			D	E	G							H		A	J	C		K		E
		☕	🛒	☕				🛒				☕		☕				☕	🛒	☕			🛒		
Deansgate 🚊	d					17 24			17 28																
Manchester Oxford Road	d					17 27			17 32	17 38															18 35
Manchester Piccadilly 10 🚊	a					17 29			17 35	17 40															18 38
	d	17 15	17 20	17 24	17 24	17 31	17 33	17 34	17 37	17 42		17 45	17 49	17 54	17 54	18 03	18 06	18 15	18 17	18 24	18 24	18 30	18 34	18 36	18 39
Levenshulme	d								17 45				17 54				18 12					18 35			
Heaton Chapel	d								17 48				17 57				18 15					18 38			
Stockport	a		17 28	17 32	17 33	17 40		17 42	17 51	17 54			18 01	18 03	18 04	18 12	18 18		18 25	18 32	18 34	18 42	18 42		18 48
	d	17u23		17 33		17 40		17 42				17u54	18 01	18 03	18 06	18 13		18u24		18 33		18 42	18 43		
Cheadle Hulme	d					17 44							18 05		18 11	18 17						18 46			
Bramhall	d					17 47									18 14							18 49			
Poynton	d					17 50									18 17							18 52			
Adlington (Cheshire)	d					17 53									18 21							18 55			
Prestbury	d					17 56									18 24							18 58			
Macclesfield	a			17 46		18 01						18 06		18 16	18 28					18 46		19 03			
	d			17 46								18 07		18 16	18 38					18 46					
Congleton	d													18 24	18 45										
Handforth	d										←		18 09			18 21									
Manchester Airport ✈	d						18 00 →				18 00													19 01	
Styal	d										18 07														
Wilmslow	d							17 51			18 11		18 13			18 24							18 53	19 11	
Alderley Edge	d										18 14		18a20			18 27								19a18	
Chelford	d															18 31									
Goostrey	d															18 36									
Holmes Chapel	d										18 22					18 39									
Sandbach	d										18 26					18 43									
Crewe 10	65 a							18 15			18 37					18 54							19 15		
Kidsgrove	50 a														18 51										
Longport	50 a														18 56										
Stoke-on-Trent	50, 68 a	17 49		18 03								18 22		18 37	19 01			18 50		19 04					
Stafford	68 a			18 24										18 56						19 24					
Wolverhampton 7	68 🚊 a			18 41										19 12						19 40					
Birmingham New Street 12	68 a			18 58										19 35						19 58					
London Euston 15	⊖ 65 a	19 31										20 35						21 05							

		EM	VT	NT	XC	NT	VT	TP	XC	NT	NT	NT	AW	NT	EM	NT	XC	NT	VT	TP	NT	NT	AW	NT	EM
		◇	1 ◇		1 ◇		1 ◇	1 ◇	1 ◇				◇		◇		1 ◇		1 ◇	1 ◇			◇		◇
		G						A	L	C			N	E	Q					A	C		N	E	Q
			☕		☕		☕		☕				🛒						☕						
Deansgate 🚊	d													19 29										20 28	
Manchester Oxford Road	d	18 39												19 33	19 38									20 32	20 38
Manchester Piccadilly 10 🚊	a	18 42												19 36	19 42									20 34	20 40
	d	18 44	18 45	18 50	18 54	19 03	19 15	19 18	19 24	19 24	19 30	19 30	19 34	19 37	19 42		19 54	20 03	20 15	20 20	20 24	20 27	20 34	20 36	20 42
Levenshulme	d			18 55		19 08						19 36						20 08				20 32			
Heaton Chapel	d			18 58		19 11						19 39						20 11				20 35			
Stockport	a	18 54		19 03	19 02	19 15		19 26	19 32	19 33		19 42	19 42	19 47	19 53		20 02	20 14		20 28	20 34	20 39	20 46	20 44	20 51
	d		18u56	19 03	19 03	19 15	19u24		19 33			19 43	19 42				20 03	20 15	20u24			20 40	20 46		
Cheadle Hulme	d			19 11		19 19						19 47						20 19				20 44			
Bramhall	d											19 50										20 47			
Poynton	d											19 53										20 50			
Adlington (Cheshire)	d											19 56										20 53			
Prestbury	d											19 59										20 56			
Macclesfield	a		19 07		19 15		19 36		19 46			20 04					20 14		20 36			21 01			
	d		19 09		19 16		19 37		19 46								20 16		20 37						
Congleton	d				19 24												20 24								
Handforth	d			19 15		19 23										←		20 23							
Manchester Airport ✈	d										19 56 →					19 56									
Styal	d																								
Wilmslow	d			19 18		19 26							19 54			20a06		20 26					20 54		
Alderley Edge	d			19a24		19 29												20 29							
Chelford	d					19 33												20 33							
Goostrey	d					19 37												20 37							
Holmes Chapel	d					19 40												20 40							
Sandbach	d					19 45												20 45							
Crewe 10	65 a					19 56							20 15					20 56					21 14		
Kidsgrove	50 a																								
Longport	50 a																								
Stoke-on-Trent	50, 68 a		19 23		19 38		19 52		20 03								20 37		20 52						
Stafford	68 a				19 56				20 24								20 57								
Wolverhampton 7	68 🚊 a				20 12				20 40								21 12								
Birmingham New Street 12	68 a				20 35				20 58								21 35								
London Euston 15	⊖ 65 a		21 41				22 35												23 37						

For general notes see front of timetable
For details of catering facilities see Directory of Train Operators

- A From Manchester Airport to Cleethorpes (Table 29)
- B To Bournemouth (Table 51)
- C To Chester (Table 88)
- D To Haverfordwest (Table 128)
- E From Blackpool North (Table 82) to Buxton (Table 86)
- G From Liverpool Lime Street to Norwich (Table 49)
- H To Hazel Grove (Table 86)
- J To Plymouth (Table 51)
- K To Carmarthen (Table 128)
- L To Southampton Central (Table 51)
- N To Cardiff Central (Table 131)
- Q From Liverpool Lime Street to Nottingham (Table 49)

Due to ongoing Engineering Operations, some services from Saturday 13 September on this Table had not been confirmed at time of going to press. These services will be issued in a special Supplement as soon as exact timings have been confirmed.

Table 84

Saturdays

19 July to 6 September

Manchester, Stockport and Manchester Airport → Crewe and Stoke-on-Trent

Network Diagram - see first page of Table 78

		NT	VT	XC	NT	TP	NT	NT	AW	EM	NT	NT	NT	NT	TP	NT	AW	NT	NT	NT	NT	NT	NT	NT
			1 ◇	1 ◇		1 ◇			◇	◇					1 ◇									
						A	B		C	D	E				G	B	H			J		B		
			☕																					
Deansgate 🚋	d										21 40									22 50	23 00			23 31
Manchester Oxford Road	d										21 43									22 53	23 02		23 10	23 33
Manchester Piccadilly 10 🚋	a										21 46									22 56	23 05		23 12	23 36
	d	20 44	20 45	20 54	20 58	21 18	21 24	21 28	21 34	21 42	21 49	21 55	22 04		22 18	22 24	22 34	22 38	22 46	22 58	23 06	23 09	23 14	23 37
Levenshulme	d				21 03			21 33					22 09					22 44			23 11			23 42
Heaton Chapel	d				21 06			21 36					22 12					22 47			23 14			23 45
Stockport	a			21 01	21 10	21 26	21 34	21 40	21 45	21 52	21 56		22 15		22 26	22 34	22 42	22 50		23 06	23 18	23 18	23 22	23 50
	d		20u56	21 03	21 15			21 40	21 45				22 16				22 42	22 51			23 18		23 23	23 50
Cheadle Hulme	d				21 19			21 44					22 20					22 55			23 22		23 27	23 54
Bramhall	d							21 47										22 58					23 30	
Poynton	d							21 50										23 01					23 33	
Adlington (Cheshire)	d							21 54										23 04					23 36	
Prestbury	d							21 57										23 07					23 39	
Macclesfield	a		21 07	21 15				22 02										23 12					23 44	
	d		21 09	21 16																				
Congleton	d			21 24																				
Handforth	d				21 23								22 24	←							23 26			23 58
Manchester Airport ✈	d	21 10										22 25 →		22 25					23 12					
Styal	d																							
Wilmslow	d	21a19			21 26				21 54				22 27	22a35			22 50		23a22		23 29			00 01
Alderley Edge	d				21 29								22 30								23 32			00a07
Chelford	d				21 33								22 34								23 36			
Goostrey	d				21 37								22 38								23 40			
Holmes Chapel	d				21 40								22 41								23 43			
Sandbach	d				21 45								22 46								23 48			
Crewe 10	65 a				21 56				22 14				22 57				23 11				23 59			
Kidsgrove	50 a																							
Longport	50 a																							
Stoke-on-Trent	50, 68 a		21 23	21 37																				
Stafford	68 a			21 58																				
Wolverhampton 7	68 🚋 a			22 12																				
Birmingham New Street 12	68 a			22 35																				
London Euston 15	⊖ 65 a		23 56																					

Sundays

until 13 July

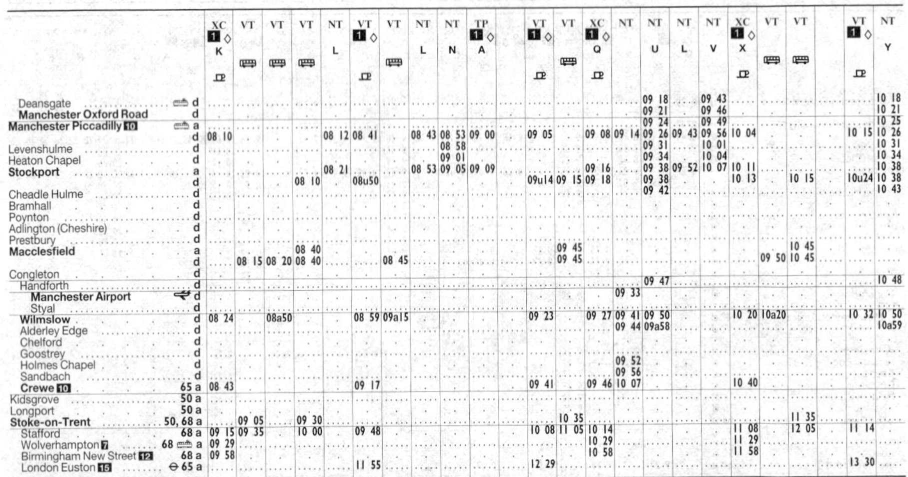

		XC	VT	VT	VT	NT	VT	VT	NT	NT	TP		VT	VT	XC	NT	NT	NT	NT	XC	VT	VT		VT	NT
		1 ◇					1 ◇				1 ◇		1 ◇		1 ◇					1 ◇				1 ◇	
		K				L			L	N	A				Q		U	L	V	X					Y
			🚌	🚌	🚌			🚌						🚌							🚌	🚌			
		☕					☕						☕		☕					☕				☕	
Deansgate 🚋	d																09 18		09 43						10 18
Manchester Oxford Road	d																09 21		09 46						10 21
Manchester Piccadilly 10 🚋	a																09 24		09 49						10 25
	d	08 10				08 12	08 41		08 43	08 53	09 00		09 05		09 08	09 14	09 26	09 43	09 56	10 04				10 15	10 26
Levenshulme	d									08 58							09 31		10 01						10 31
Heaton Chapel	d									09 01							09 34		10 04						10 34
Stockport	a					08 21			08 53	09 05	09 09				09 16		09 38	09 52	10 07	10 11					10 38
	d				08 10		08u50						09u14	09 15	09 18		09 38			10 13		10 15		10u24	10 38
Cheadle Hulme	d																09 42								10 43
Bramhall	d																								
Poynton	d																								
Adlington (Cheshire)	d																								
Prestbury	d																								
Macclesfield	a				08 40									09 45								10 45			
	d		08 15	08 20	08 40			08 45						09 45							09 50	10 45			
Congleton	d																								
Handforth	d																09 47								10 48
Manchester Airport ✈	d															09 33									
Styal	d																								
Wilmslow	d	08 24		08a50			08 59	09a15					09 23		09 27	09 41	09 50			10 20	10a20			10 32	10 50
Alderley Edge	d															09 44	09a58								10a59
Chelford	d																								
Goostrey	d																								
Holmes Chapel	d															09 52									
Sandbach	d															09 56									
Crewe 10	65 a	08 43					09 17						09 41		09 46	10 07				10 40					
Kidsgrove	50 a																								
Longport	50 a																								
Stoke-on-Trent	50, 68 a		09 05		09 30									10 35								11 35			
Stafford	68 a	09 15	09 35		10 00		09 48						10 08	11 05	10 14					11 08		12 05		11 14	
Wolverhampton 7	68 🚋 a	09 29													10 29					11 29					
Birmingham New Street 12	68 a	09 58													10 58					11 58					
London Euston 15	⊖ 65 a						11 55						12 29											13 30	

For general notes see front of timetable
For details of catering facilities see Directory of Train Operators

- **A** From Manchester Airport to Cleethorpes (Table 29)
- **B** To Chester (Table 88)
- **C** To Cardiff Central (Table 131)
- **D** To Nottingham (Table 49)
- **E** From Southport (Table 82) to Buxton (Table 86)
- **G** From Manchester Airport to Sheffield (Table 78)
- **H** To Shrewsbury (Table 131)
- **J** From Clitheroe (Table 94) to Buxton (Table 86)
- **K** To Paignton (Table 51)
- **L** To Sheffield (Table 78)
- **N** To Buxton (Table 86)
- **Q** To Bournemouth (Table 51)
- **U** From Wigan Wallgate (Table 82)
- **V** From Blackpool North (Table 82) to Buxton (Table 86)
- **X** To Plymouth (Table 51)
- **Y** From Southport (Table 82)

Due to ongoing Engineering Operations, some services from Saturday 13 September on this Table had not been confirmed at time of going to press. These services will be issued in a special Supplement as soon as exact timings have been confirmed.

Table 84

Sundays

until 13 July

Manchester, Stockport and Manchester Airport → Crewe and Stoke-on-Trent

Network Diagram - see first page of Table 78

	NT	VT	NT	NT	XC	VT	TP	VT	NT	NT		VT	NT	XC	NT	VT	NT	AW	VT	VT	EM		VT	NT
					1 ◇		1 ◇	1 ◇						R 1		1 ◇		◇			◇		1 ◇	
	A		B		C		D			E			B	G	A		E	H			J			B
		bus			catering	bus		catering				bus		catering		catering		trolley	bus	bus			catering	
Deansgate d			10 43							11 18			11 45				12 18							12 43
Manchester Oxford Road d			10 46							11 21			11 50				12 21							12 46
Manchester Piccadilly 10 a			10 49							11 24			11 52				12 24							12 49
d	10 30		10 56	11 00	11 06		11 12	11 15		11 26			11 56	12 06	12 09	12 10	12 26	12 29			12 43		12 52	12 55
Levenshulme d			11 01							11 31			12 01				12 31							13 01
Heaton Chapel d			11 04							11 34			12 04				12 34							13 04
Stockport a	10 42		11 07		11 13		11 20			11 38			12 07	12 14	12 18		12 37	12 37			12 52			13 06
d					11 15	11 15		11u24		11 38				12 15		12u22	12 38	12 40		12 15			13u00	
Cheadle Hulme d										11 42							12 42							
Bramhall d																								
Poynton d																								
Adlington (Cheshire) d																								
Prestbury d																								
Macclesfield a						11 45														12 45				
d		10 50				11 45						11 50							12 30					
Congleton d																								
Handforth d									←	11 47							12 47							
Manchester Airport ✈ d				11 32 →					11 32															
Styal d																								
Wilmslow d		11a20			11 22			11 32	11 40	11 50		12a20		12 23		12 30	12 50	12 55	13a00				13 10	
Alderley Edge d									11 43	11a58							12a58							
Chelford d																								
Goostrey d																								
Holmes Chapel d									11 51															
Sandbach d									11 55															
Crewe 10 65 a					11 41				12 06					12 41				13 17						
Kidsgrove 50 a																								
Longport 50 a																								
Stoke-on-Trent 50, 68 a						12 35																		
Stafford 68 a					12 08	13 05		12 14						13 07		13 16							13 48	
Wolverhampton 7 68 a					12 29									13 29										
Birmingham New Street 12 68 a					12 58									13 58										
London Euston 15 ⊖ 65 a								14 24								15 25							15 54	

	NT	XC	TP	VT	NT	EM	VT	NT	XC	VT		TP	NT	NT	AW	EM	VT	NT	NT	NT	NT		XC	VT
		R 1	1 ◇	1 ◇		◇	1 ◇		R 1	1 ◇		1 ◇			R	◇	1 ◇						R 1	1 ◇
		C	D		E	K		B	G			D	A	E	L	K		B			A		C	
		catering		catering			catering		catering	catering					trolley		catering						catering	catering
Deansgate d					13 18			13 43						14 18				14 43						
Manchester Oxford Road d					13 21	13 41		13 46						14 21		14 39		14 46						
Manchester Piccadilly 10 a					13 24	13 44		13 48						14 24		14 41		14 49						
d	13 04	13 06	13 12	13 15	13 27	13 46	13 49	13 56	14 08	14 10		14 15	14 19	14 26	14 34	14 43	14 45	14 53	14 56	15 05	15 05		15 06	15 08
Levenshulme d					13 31			14 01						14 31				14 58						
Heaton Chapel d					13 34			14 04						14 34				15 01						
Stockport a		13 14	13 21		13 38	13 55		14 07	14 17			14 23	14 28	14 36	14 42	14 52		15 05	15 05		15 14		15 14	
d		13 16		13u26	13 38		13u57		14 18	14u23				14 38	14 42		14u55		15 05				15 16	15u18
Cheadle Hulme d					13 42									14 42					15 09					
Bramhall d																			15 12					
Poynton d																			15 15					
Adlington (Cheshire) d																			15 19					
Prestbury d																			15 22					
Macclesfield a		13 30		13 38			14 09		14 31	14 36							15 07		15 26				15 30	15 35
d		13 31		13 39			14 10		14 32	14 36							15 08		15 39 →				15 31	15 35
Congleton d																								
Handforth d					13 47									14 47										
Manchester Airport ✈ d	13 26																			15 25				
Styal d																								
Wilmslow d	13 33				13 50									14 50	14 54					15 33				
Alderley Edge d	13 36				13a58									14a58						15 36				
Chelford d																								
Goostrey d																								
Holmes Chapel d	13 44																			15 44				
Sandbach d	13 48																			15 47				
Crewe 10 65 a	13 59														15 18					15 58				
Kidsgrove 50 a																								
Longport 50 a																								
Stoke-on-Trent 50, 68 a		13 47		13 55			14 25		14 48	14 54							15 23						15 47	15 53
Stafford 68 a		14 13							15 13														16 06	
Wolverhampton 7 68 a		14 29							15 29														16 29	
Birmingham New Street 12 68 a		14 58							15 58														16 58	
London Euston 15 ⊖ 65 a				16 03			16 25			16 56							17 27							18 03

For general notes see front of timetable
For details of catering facilities see Directory of Train Operators

A To Sheffield (Table 78)
B From Blackpool North (Table 82) to Buxton (Table 86)
C To Bournemouth (Table 51)
D From Manchester Airport to Cleethorpes (Table 29)
E From Southport (Table 82)
G To Penzance (Table 135)
H To Milford Haven (Table 128)
J To Norwich (Table 49)
K From Liverpool Lime Street to Norwich (Table 49)
L To Pembroke Dock and to Milford Haven (Table 128)

Table 84

Sundays until 13 July

Manchester, Stockport and Manchester Airport → Crewe and Stoke-on-Trent

Network Diagram - see first page of Table 78

	TP	NT	NT	AW	EM	VT	NT	XC	VT	TP	NT	NT	AW	EM	VT	NT	NT	XC	VT	TP	NT	NT
				R				R					R					R				
	1 ◇				◇	1 ◇		1	1 ◇	1 ◇				◇	1 ◇			1	1 ◇	1 ◇		
	A		B	C	D		E	G		A	H	B	J	D		E		K		A	H	B
				🛒		☕		☕	☕				🛒		☕			☕	☕			
Deansgate 🚊 d			15 18				15 43					16 18				16 43						17 18
Manchester Oxford Road d			15 21		15 39		15 46					16 21		16 39		16 46						17 21
Manchester Piccadilly 10 🚊 a			15 24		15 41		15 49					16 24		16 41		16 49						17 24
d	15 15		15 26	15 39	15 43	15 45	15 53	16 08	16 10	16 15	16 19	16 26	16 36	16 43	16 45	16 53	17 04	17 06	17 10	17 15	17 19	17 26
Levenshulme d			15 31				15 58					16 31				16 58						17 31
Heaton Chapel d			15 34				16 01					16 34				17 01						17 34
Stockport a	15 23		15 36	15 47	15 52		16 04	16 16		16 23	16 29	16 37	16 44	16 52		17 04		17 14		17 23	17 28	17 37
d			15 38	15 47		15u55		16 18	16u22			16 38	16 44		16u56			17 16	17u22			17 38
Cheadle Hulme d			15 42									16 42										17 42
Bramhall d																						
Poynton d																						
Adlington (Cheshire) d																						
Prestbury d																						
Macclesfield a		←				16 07		16 30	16 35						17 07			17 30	17 35			
d		15 39				16 08		16 31	16 36						17 09			17 31	17 35			
Congleton d		15 46																				
Handforth d			15 47									16 47										17 47
Manchester Airport ✈ d																	17 25					
Styal d																						
Wilmslow d			15 50	15 57								16 50	16 54				17 32					17 50
Alderley Edge d			15a58									16a58					17 35					17a58
Chelford d																	17 39					
Goostrey d																	17 44					
Holmes Chapel d																	17 47					
Sandbach d																	17 51					
Crewe 10 65 a				16 19									17 17				18 01					
Kidsgrove 50 a		15 52																				
Longport 50 a		15 56																				
Stoke-on-Trent 50, 68 a		16 03				16 23		16 47	16 53						17 23			17 47	17 53			
Stafford 68 a								17 07										18 14				
Wolverhampton 7 68 🚊 a								17 29										18 29				
Birmingham New Street 12 68 a								17 58										18 58				
London Euston 15 ⊖ 65 a						18 25			18 59						19 33				20 03			

	EM	VT	NT	NT	NT	XC	VT	TP	NT	NT	AW	EM	VT	NT	VT	NT	XC	TP	NT	EM	VT	NT
						R					R											
	◇	1 ◇				1	1 ◇	1 ◇				◇	1 ◇		1 ◇		1 ◇	1 ◇		◇	1 ◇	
	L		E		H	G		A		B	C	D		E			Q	A	B	L		E
		☕				☕	☕				🛒		☕		☕		☕				☕	
Deansgate 🚊 d			17 43							18 18				18 43					19 18			19 43
Manchester Oxford Road d	17 39		17 46							18 21		18 39		18 46					19 21	19 39		19 46
Manchester Piccadilly 10 🚊 a	17 41		17 49							18 24		18 41		18 49					19 24	19 41		19 49
d	17 43	17 45	17 53	17 56	18 07	18 08	18 10	18 15		18 26	18 40	18 42	18 45	18 53	19 05	19 06	19 10	19 15	19 26	19 42	19 47	19 53
Levenshulme d			17 58							18 31				18 58					19 31			19 58
Heaton Chapel d			18 01							18 34				19 01					19 34			20 01
Stockport a	17 52		18 04	18 05	18 16	18 16		18 23		18 38	18 48	18 52		19 04			19 17	19 22	19 38	19 52		20 04
d		17u55		18 05		18 18	18u22			18 38	18 48		18u55		19u13		19 18		19 38		19u55	
Cheadle Hulme d				18 09						18 42									19 42			
Bramhall d				18 12																		
Poynton d				18 15																		
Adlington (Cheshire) d				18 19																		
Prestbury d				18 22																		
Macclesfield a		18 07		18 26		18 30	18 36		←				19 09		19 25		19 33				20 07	
d		18 08		18 41 →		18 31	18 38		18 41				19 10		19 25		19 34				20 08	
Congleton d									18 48													
Handforth d										18 47									19 47			
Manchester Airport ✈ d																19 25						
Styal d																						
Wilmslow d										18 50	18 56					19 32			19 50			
Alderley Edge d										18a58						19 35			19a58			
Chelford d																						
Goostrey d																						
Holmes Chapel d																19 43						
Sandbach d																19 48						
Crewe 10 65 a											19 18					19 59						
Kidsgrove 50 a									18 54													
Longport 50 a									18 58													
Stoke-on-Trent 50, 68 a		18 23				18 47	18 53		19 04				19 25		19 46		19 52				20 22	
Stafford 68 a						19 14											20 11					
Wolverhampton 7 68 🚊 a						19 29											20 29					
Birmingham New Street 12 68 a						19 58											20 58					
London Euston 15 ⊖ 65 a		20 32					20 59						21 27		21 57						22 52	

For general notes see front of timetable
For details of catering facilities see Directory of Train Operators

A From Manchester Airport to Cleethorpes (Table 29)
B From Southport (Table 82)
C To Cardiff Central (Table 131)
D From Liverpool Lime Street to Norwich (Table 49)
E From Blackpool North (Table 82) to Buxton (Table 86)
G To Plymouth (Table 51)
H To Sheffield (Table 78)
J To Milford Haven (Table 128)
K To Bournemouth (Table 51)
L From Liverpool Lime Street to Nottingham (Table 49)
Q To Southampton Central (Table 51)

Table 84

Sundays
until 13 July

Manchester, Stockport and Manchester Airport → Crewe and Stoke-on-Trent

Network Diagram - see first page of Table 78

Station		TP 1◇ A	NT B	VT 1◇	NT C	EM ◇ D	AW ◇ E	NT G	XC 1◇	NT	NT		TP 1◇ H	NT C	NT G	XC 1◇	EM ◇ D	TP 1◇ H	NT C	AW J	NT G	TP 1◇ H	NT C		
Deansgate	d				20 18			20 43						21 18	21 43				22 18		22 43		23 18		
Manchester Oxford Road	d				20 21	20 39		20 46						21 21	21 46		22 08		22 21		22 46		23 21		
Manchester Piccadilly 10	a				20 24	20 41		20 49						21 24	21 49		22 10		22 24		22 49		23 25		
	d	20 15	20 19	20 23	20 26	20 43	20 46	20 53	20 55	20 58	21 06		21 15	21 26	21 53	21 55	22 12	22 15	22 26	22 46	22 51	23 15	23 26		
Levenshulme	d				20 31			20 58						21 31	21 58				22 31		22 56		23 31		
Heaton Chapel	d				20 34			21 01						21 34	22 01				22 34		22 59		23 34		
Stockport	a	20 23	20 28		20 38	20 52	20 54	21 04	21 03	21 07			21 22	21 37	22 04	22 03	22 21	22 22	22 38	22 54	23 03	23 23	23 38		
	d			20u32	20 38		20 54		21 04	21 08				21 38		22 04			22 38	22 54			23 38		
Cheadle Hulme	d				20 42					21 12				21 42					22 43				23 44		
Bramhall	d									21 15															
Poynton	d									21 18															
Adlington (Cheshire)	d									21 22															
Prestbury	d									21 25															
Macclesfield	a			20 43					21 16	21 28						22 16									
	d			20 45					21 16	21 29						22 16									
Congleton	d									21 36															
Handforth	d				20 47									21 47					22 47				23 49		
Manchester Airport ✈	d										21 25														
Styal	d																								
Wilmslow	d				20 50		21 02				21 32			21 50					22 51	23 02			23 52		
Alderley Edge	d				20a58						21 35			21a58					22a59				00a01		
Chelford	d																								
Goostrey	d																								
Holmes Chapel	d										21 43														
Sandbach	d										21 48														
Crewe 10	65 a						21 30				21 59									23 24					
Kidsgrove	50 a									21 42															
Longport	50 a									21 46															
Stoke-on-Trent	50, 68 a			20 59					21 35	21 51						22 35									
Stafford	68 a								21 53							22 53									
Wolverhampton 7	68 a								22 09							23 09									
Birmingham New Street 12	68 a								22 41							23 42									
London Euston 15	⊖ 65 a			23 21																					

Sundays
20 July to 7 September

Station		XC 1◇ K	VT 1◇	NT L	TP 1◇ A	NT B	VT 1◇		NT	XC 1◇ N	NT Q	XC 1◇ U	NT G	VT 1◇		XC 1◇ V	NT C	NT B	XC 1◇ U	NT G	NT		TP 1◇ A	VT 1◇	XC 1◇ N
Deansgate	d										09 18		09 43				10 18			10 43					
Manchester Oxford Road	d										09 21		09 46				10 21			10 46					
Manchester Piccadilly 10	a										09 24		09 49				10 25			10 49					
	d	08 10	08 44	08 53	09 00	09 04	09 08		09 14	09 24	09 26	09 53	09 56	10 15		10 24	10 26	10 30	10 53	10 56	11 07		11 12	11 15	11 23
Levenshulme	d			08 58							09 31		10 01				10 31			11 01					
Heaton Chapel	d			09 01							09 34		10 04				10 34			11 04					
Stockport	a			09 05	09 09	09 17				09 31	09 38	10 00	10 07			10 31	10 38	10 42	11 00	11 07			11 20		11 31
	d		08u53				09u17			09 33	09 38	10 04		10u24		10 33	10 38		11 04					11u24	11 33
Cheadle Hulme	d										09 42						10 40								
Bramhall	d																								
Poynton	d																								
Adlington (Cheshire)	d																								
Prestbury	d																								
Macclesfield	a		09 05				09 29			09 45		10 16		10 35		10 45			11 16					11 35	11 46
	d		09 06				09 30			09 46		10 16		10 37		10 46			11 16					11 37	11 47
Congleton	d																								
Handforth	d										09 47						10 46								
Manchester Airport ✈	d								09 33																
Styal	d																								
Wilmslow	d	08 24							09 41		09 50						10 51				11 28				
Alderley Edge	d								09 44		09a58						10a58				11 31				
Chelford	d																								
Goostrey	d																								
Holmes Chapel	d								09 52												11 39				
Sandbach	d								09 56												11 43				
Crewe 10	65 a	08 43							10 07												11 54				
Kidsgrove	50 a																								
Longport	50 a																								
Stoke-on-Trent	50, 68 a	09 04	09 21				09 45			10 02		10 33		10 51		11 02			11 33					11 51	12 03
Stafford	68 a	09 24								10 26		10 53				11 21			11 53						12 26
Wolverhampton 7	68 a	09 41								10 41		11 09				11 36			12 09						12 41
Birmingham New Street 12	68 a	09 58								10 58		11 28				11 58			12 31						12 58
London Euston 15	⊖ 65 a		11 36				12 06							13 05										14 05	

For general notes see front of timetable
For details of catering facilities see Directory of Train Operators

A From Manchester Airport to Cleethorpes (Table 29)
B To Sheffield (Table 78)
C From Southport (Table 82)
D From Liverpool Lime Street to Nottingham (Table 49)
E To Cardiff Central (Table 131)
G From Blackpool North (Table 82) to Buxton (Table 86)
H From Manchester Airport to Sheffield (Table 78)
J To Shrewsbury (Table 131)
K To Paignton (Table 51)
L To Buxton (Table 86)
N To Bournemouth (Table 51)
Q From Wigan Wallgate (Table 82)
U To Reading (Table 51)
V To Plymouth (Table 51)

Due to ongoing Engineering Operations, some services from Sunday 14 September on this Table had not been confirmed at time of going to press. These services will be issued in a special Supplement as soon as exact timings have been confirmed.

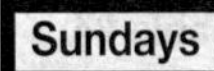

Manchester, Stockport and Manchester Airport → Crewe and Stoke-on-Trent

20 July to 7 September

Network Diagram - see first page of Table 78

		NT	XC	NT	VT	XC	NT	AW	EM	VT	XC	NT	NT	VT	TP	XC	NT	VT	EM	XC	NT	VT
			1◇		1◇	R 1		R	◇	1◇	1◇			1◇	1◇	R 1		1◇	◇	1◇		1◇
		A	B	C		D	A	E	G		B	C			H	J	A		K	B	C	
Deansgate	d	11 18		11 45			12 18					12 43					13 18				13 43	
Manchester Oxford Road	d	11 21		11 50			12 21					12 46					13 21		13 41		13 46	
Manchester Piccadilly 10	a	11 24		11 52			12 24					12 49					13 24		13 44		13 49	
	d	11 26	11 53	11 56	12 10	12 24	12 26	12 33	12 43	12 45	12 53	12 56	13 06	13 09	13 12	13 17	13 27	13 45	13 48	13 53	13 56	14 10
Levenshulme	d	11 31		12 01			12 31					13 01					13 31				14 01	
Heaton Chapel	d	11 34		12 04			12 34					13 04					13 34				14 04	
Stockport	a	11 38	12 00	12 07		12 32	12 37	12 41	12 52		13 01	13 07			13 21	13 25	13 38		13 57	14 02	14 07	
	d	11 38	12 04		12u22	12 33	12 38	12 42		12u55	13 04			13u20		13 33	13 38	13u54		14 04		14u19
Cheadle Hulme	d	11 42					12 42										13 42					
Bramhall	d																					
Poynton	d																					
Adlington (Cheshire)	d																					
Prestbury	d																					
Macclesfield	a		12 16		12 33	12 45				13 07	13 16			13 32		13 45		14 06		14 16		14 30
	d		12 16		12 35	12 47				13 09	13 16			13 33		13 47		14 07		14 16		14 31
Congleton	d																					
Handforth	d	11 47					12 46										13 47					
Manchester Airport	d																					
Styal	d																					
Wilmslow	d	11 50					12 49	12 56					13 28				13 50					
Alderley Edge	d	11a58					12a57						13 31				13a58					
Chelford	d																					
Goostrey	d																					
Holmes Chapel	d												13 39									
Sandbach	d												13 43									
Crewe 10	65 a							13 19					13 56									
Kidsgrove	50 a																					
Longport	50 a																					
Stoke-on-Trent	50, 68 a		12 33		12 49	13 03				13 24	13 33			13 50		14 03		14 25		14 33		14 50
Stafford	68 a		12 53			13 23					13 53					14 24				14 53		
Wolverhampton 7	68 a		13 09			13 41					14 09					14 40				15 09		
Birmingham New Street 12	68 a		13 31			13 58					14 31					14 58				15 31		
London Euston 15	⊖ 65 a				15 02					15 36				16 03				16 49				17 02

		TP	XC	NT	AW	EM	VT	XC	NT	NT	NT	NT	VT	TP	NT	XC	NT	AW	EM	VT	NT	XC
		1◇	R 1		R	◇	1◇	1◇					1◇	1◇		R 1		R	◇	1◇		1◇
		H	D	A	L	K		B	C			N		H		J	A	Q	K		C	U
Deansgate	d			14 18					14 43								15 18				15 43	
Manchester Oxford Road	d			14 21		14 39			14 46								15 21		15 39		15 46	
Manchester Piccadilly 10	a			14 24		14 41			14 49								15 24		15 41		15 49	
	d	14 15	14 24	14 26	14 34	14 43	14 45	14 51	14 56	15 02	15 05	15 08	15 10	15 15		15 24	15 26	15 39	15 43	15 45	15 53	15 55
Levenshulme	d			14 31					15 01								15 31				15 58	
Heaton Chapel	d			14 34					15 04								15 34				16 01	
Stockport	a	14 23	14 32	14 38	14 42	14 52		14 59	15 07	15 11		15 17		15 23		15 32	15 36	15 47	15 52		16 04	16 03
	d		14 33	14 38	14 42		14u55	15 04		15 12			15u20			15 33	15 38	15 47		15u55		16 04
Cheadle Hulme	d			14 42						15 16							15 42					
Bramhall	d									15 19												
Poynton	d									15 22												
Adlington (Cheshire)	d									15 25												
Prestbury	d									15 28												
Macclesfield	a		14 45				15 07	15 16		15 32			15 35		←	15 45				16 07		16 16
	d		14 46				15 08	15 16		15 39 →			15 36		15 39	15 46				16 08		16 16
Congleton	d														15 46							
Handforth	d			14 47													15 47					
Manchester Airport	d																					
Styal	d																					
Wilmslow	d			14 50	14 54						15 28						15 50	15 57				
Alderley Edge	d			14a58							15 31						15a58					
Chelford	d																					
Goostrey	d																					
Holmes Chapel	d										15 39											
Sandbach	d										15 42											
Crewe 10	65 a				15 19						15 53							16 19				
Kidsgrove	50 a														15 52							
Longport	50 a														15 57							
Stoke-on-Trent	50, 68 a		15 02				15 28	15 36					15 51		16 03	16 06				16 23		16 33
Stafford	68 a		15 24					15 53								16 25						16 53
Wolverhampton 7	68 a		15 41					16 09								16 41						17 09
Birmingham New Street 12	68 a		15 58					16 31								16 58						17 31
London Euston 15	⊖ 65 a						17 49						18 02							18 49		

For general notes see front of timetable
For details of catering facilities see Directory of Train Operators

- **A** From Southport (Table 82)
- **B** To Reading (Table 51)
- **C** From Blackpool North (Table 82) to Buxton (Table 86)
- **D** To Penzance (Table 135)
- **E** To Milford Haven (Table 128)
- **G** To Norwich (Table 49)
- **H** From Manchester Airport to Cleethorpes (Table 29)
- **J** To Bournemouth (Table 51)
- **K** From Liverpool Lime Street to Norwich (Table 49)
- **L** To Pembroke Dock and to Milford Haven (Table 128)
- **N** To Sheffield (Table 78)
- **Q** To Cardiff Central (Table 131)
- **U** To Brighton (Table 51)

Due to ongoing Engineering Operations, some services from Sunday 14 September on this Table had not been confirmed at time of going to press. These services will be issued in a special Supplement as soon as exact timings have been confirmed.

Table 84

Sundays

Manchester, Stockport and Manchester Airport → Crewe and Stoke-on-Trent

20 July to 7 September

Network Diagram - see first page of Table 78

		VT	TP	XC	NT	AW	EM	VT	NT	XC	NT	VT	TP	NT	XC	NT	EM	VT	NT	XC	NT	VT
		[1] ◇	[1] ◇	[R] [1]		[R]	◇	[1] ◇		[1] ◇		[1] ◇	[1] ◇		[R] [1]		◇	[1] ◇		[1] ◇		[1] ◇
			A	B	C	D	E		G	H			A	J	K	C	L		G			
		☕		☕		🍴		☕		☕		☕			☕			☕		☕		☕
Deansgate 🚊	d				16 18				16 43							17 18			17 43			
Manchester Oxford Road	d				16 21		16 39		16 46							17 21	17 39		17 46			
Manchester Piccadilly [10] 🚊	a				16 24		16 41		16 49							17 24	17 41		17 49			
	d	16 10	16 15	16 24	16 26	16 36	16 43	16 45	16 53	16 55	17 06	17 10	17 15	17 19	17 24	17 26	17 43	17 45	17 53	17 55	17 59	18 10
Levenshulme	d				16 31				16 58							17 31			17 58			
Heaton Chapel	d				16 34				17 01							17 34			18 01			
Stockport	a		16 23	16 31	16 37	16 44	16 52		17 04	17 03			17 23	17 28	17 31	17 37	17 52		18 04	18 03	18 08	
	d	16u18		16 33	16 38	16 44		16u56		17 04		17u19			17 33	17 38		17u55		18 04	18 08	18u19
Cheadle Hulme	d				16 42											17 42					18 12	
Bramhall	d																				18 15	
Poynton	d																				18 18	
Adlington (Cheshire)	d																				18 22	
Prestbury	d																				18 25	
Macclesfield	a	16 30		16 45				17 07		17 16		17 31			17 45			18 07		18 16	18 29	18 32
	d	16 31		16 46				17 09		17 16		17 31			17 46			18 08		18 16	18 36 →	18 33
Congleton	d																					
Handforth	d				16 47											17 47						
Manchester Airport ✈	d																					
Styal	d																					
Wilmslow	d				16 50	16 54					17 28					17 50						
Alderley Edge	d				16a58						17 31					17a58						
Chelford	d										17 35											
Goostrey	d										17 39											
Holmes Chapel	d										17 42											
Sandbach	d										17 47											
Crewe [10] 65	a					17 20					17 57											
Kidsgrove 50	a																					
Longport 50	a																					
Stoke-on-Trent 50, 68	a	16 49		17 02				17 23		17 33		17 47			18 02			18 23		18 35		18 53
Stafford 68	a			17 24						17 53					18 21					18 53		
Wolverhampton [7] 68 🚊	a			17 41						18 09					18 41					19 09		
Birmingham New Street [12] 68	a			17 58						18 31					18 58					19 34		
London Euston [15] ⊖ 65	a	19 05						19 35				20 08						20 38				21 06

		TP	NT	XC	NT	AW	EM	VT	NT	XC	NT	VT	TP	XC	NT	EM	VT	NT	XC	TP	VT	NT
		[1] ◇		[R] [1]		[R]	◇	[1] ◇		[1] ◇		[1] ◇	[1] ◇	[1] ◇		◇	[1] ◇		[1] ◇	[1] ◇	[1] ◇	
		A		B	C	N	E		G				A	Q	C	L		G		A		C
				☕		🍴		☕		☕		☕		☕			☕		☕		☕	
Deansgate 🚊	d				18 18				18 43						19 18			19 43				20 18
Manchester Oxford Road	d				18 21		18 39		18 46						19 21	19 39		19 46				20 21
Manchester Piccadilly [10] 🚊	a				18 24		18 41		18 49						19 24	19 41		19 49				20 24
	d	18 15		18 24	18 26	18 40	18 42	18 45	18 53	18 55	19 06	19 10	19 15	19 24	19 26	19 42	19 47	19 53	19 55	20 15	20 23	20 27
Levenshulme	d				18 31				18 58						19 31			19 58				20 32
Heaton Chapel	d				18 34				19 01						19 34			20 01				20 35
Stockport	a	18 23		18 32	18 38	18 48	18 52		19 04	19 03			19 22	19 31	19 37	19 52		20 04	20 03	20 23		20 39
	d			18 33	18 38	18 48		18u55		19 04		19u19		19 33	19 38		19u55		20 04		20u32	20 39
Cheadle Hulme	d				18 42										19 42							20 43
Bramhall	d																					
Poynton	d																					
Adlington (Cheshire)	d																					
Prestbury	d																					
Macclesfield	a		←	18 45				19 09		19 16		19 31		19 45			20 07		20 16		20 43	
	d		18 36	18 47				19 10		19 16		19 31		19 46			20 08		20 16		20 45	
Congleton	d		18 43																			
Handforth	d				18 47										19 47							20 48
Manchester Airport ✈	d																					
Styal	d																					
Wilmslow	d				18 50	18 56					19 28				19 50							20 51
Alderley Edge	d				18a58						19 31				19a58							20a59
Chelford	d																					
Goostrey	d																					
Holmes Chapel	d										19 39											
Sandbach	d										19 43											
Crewe [10] 65	a					19 19					19 54											
Kidsgrove 50	a		18 49																			
Longport 50	a		18 54																			
Stoke-on-Trent 50, 68	a		18 59	19 04				19 25		19 35		19 47		20 02			20 22		20 35		21 02	
Stafford 68	a			19 24						19 53				20 24					20 53			
Wolverhampton [7] 68 🚊	a			19 41						20 09				20 41					21 09			
Birmingham New Street [12] 68	a			19 58						20 31				20 58					21 31			
London Euston [15] ⊖ 65	a							21 36				22 06					23 02				23 33	

For general notes see front of timetable
For details of catering facilities see Directory of Train Operators

- **A** From Manchester Airport to Cleethorpes (Table 29)
- **B** To Plymouth (Table 51)
- **C** From Southport (Table 82)
- **D** To Milford Haven (Table 128)
- **E** From Liverpool Lime Street to Norwich (Table 49)
- **G** From Blackpool North (Table 82) to Buxton (Table 86)
- **H** To Gatwick Airport (Table 51)
- **J** To Sheffield (Table 78)
- **K** To Bournemouth (Table 51)
- **L** From Liverpool Lime Street to Nottingham (Table 49)
- **N** To Cardiff Central (Table 131)
- **Q** To Southampton Central (Table 51)

Due to ongoing Engineering Operations, some services from Sunday 14 September on this Table had not been confirmed at time of going to press. These services will be issued in a special Supplement as soon as exact timings have been confirmed.

Table 84

Sundays

20 July to 7 September

Manchester, Stockport and Manchester Airport → Crewe and Stoke-on-Trent

Network Diagram - see first page of Table 78

		EM		AW	NT	XC	NT	NT	TP		NT	NT	XC	EM	TP	NT		AW	NT	TP	NT				
		◇		◇		1 ◇			1 ◇				1 ◇	◇	1 ◇					1 ◇					
		A		B	C				D		E	C		A	D	E		G	C	D	E				
Deansgate	d				20 43						21 18	21 43				22 18			22 43		23 18				
Manchester Oxford Road	d	20 39			20 46						21 21	21 46		22 08		22 22			22 46		23 21				
Manchester Piccadilly 10	a	20 41			20 49						21 24	21 49		22 10		22 24			22 49		23 25				
	d	20 43		20 46	20 53	20 55	20 57	21 06	21 15		21 26	21 53	21 55	22 12	22 15	22 26		22 46	22 51	23 15	23 26				
Levenshulme	d				20 58						21 31	21 58				22 31			22 56		23 31				
Heaton Chapel	d				21 01						21 34	22 01				22 34			22 59		23 34				
Stockport	a	20 52		20 54	21 04	21 03	21 07		21 22		21 37	22 04	22 03	22 21	22 22	22 38		22 54	23 03	23 23	23 38				
	d			20 54		21 04	21 08				21 38		22 04			22 38		22 55			23 38				
Cheadle Hulme	d						21 12				21 42					22 43					23 44				
Bramhall	d						21 15																		
Poynton	d						21 18																		
Adlington (Cheshire)	d						21 22																		
Prestbury	d						21 25																		
Macclesfield	a					21 16	21 28						22 16												
	d					21 16	21 29						22 16												
Congleton	d						21 36																		
Handforth	d										21 47					22 47					23 49				
Manchester Airport ✈	d																								
Styal	d																								
Wilmslow	d			21 02				21 28			21 50					22 51		23 03			23 52				
Alderley Edge	d							21 31			21a58					23a00					00a01				
Chelford	d																								
Goostrey	d																								
Holmes Chapel	d							21 39																	
Sandbach	d							21 43																	
Crewe 10	65 a			21 30				21 54										23 24							
Kidsgrove	50 a						21 42																		
Longport	50 a						21 46																		
Stoke-on-Trent	50, 68 a					21 35	21 53						22 35												
Stafford	68 a					21 53							22 53												
Wolverhampton 7	68 a					22 16							23 09												
Birmingham New Street 12	68 a					22 41							23 30												
London Euston 15	⊖ 65 a																								

For general notes see front of timetable
For details of catering facilities see Directory of Train Operators

A From Liverpool Lime Street to Nottingham (Table 49)
B To Cardiff Central (Table 131)
C From Blackpool North (Table 82) to Buxton (Table 86)
D From Manchester Airport to Sheffield (Table 78)
E From Southport (Table 82)
G To Shrewsbury (Table 131)

Due to ongoing Engineering Operations, some services from Sunday 14 September on this Table had not been confirmed at time of going to press. These services will be issued in a special Supplement as soon as exact timings have been confirmed.

Manchester → Manchester Airport

Network Diagram - see first page of Table 78

Miles			TP MO 1◇ A	TP MX 1◇ A	TP MO 1◇ B	TP MO 1◇ C	TP MX 1◇ D	TP 1◇ E	TP 1◇ G	NT H	TP 1◇ E	TP 1◇ A	TP 1◇ G	NT J	TP 1◇ K	NT H	TP 1◇ G	TP 1◇ E	NT	TP 1◇ G	TP 1◇ A	NT H	TP 1◇ L	TP 1◇ N	TP 1◇ G
—	Deansgate	d																			06 49				
—	Manchester Oxford Road	d																			06 52	07 00		07 13	
—	Manchester Piccadilly 10	a																			06 56	07 03		07 15	
0		d	00 16	00 30	00 35	00 54	00 55	02 50	04 00	04 15	04 44	04u47	05 00	05 26	05 58	06 03	06 07	06 12	06 32	06 53	06 57	07 04	07 08	07 17	07 30
3¼	Mauldeth Road	d												05 33				06 19	06 39				07 17		
4¼	Burnage	d												05 35				06 21	06 41				07 19		
5¼	East Didsbury	d												05 37			06 15		06 43				07 22		
6¾	Gatley	d												05 39			06 18		06 45				07 24		
8¼	Heald Green	d		00 40										05 42			06 21		06 48				07 27	07 32	
9¾	Manchester Airport	a	00 33	00 45	00 54	01 11	01 11	03 06	04 15	04 30	05 01	05 05	05 19	05 47	06 14	06 19	06 29	06 34	06 53	07 12	07 15	07 20	07 35	07 40	07 48
—	Wilmslow	84 a												06 00					07 04						
—	Crewe 10	84 a																	07 31						

		NT	NT Q	TP 1◇ A	TP 1◇ G	NT H	TP 1◇ U	TP 1◇ V		TP 1◇ X	NT	NT K	TP 1◇ A	TP 1◇ Y	NT H	TP 1◇ U	TP 1◇ N	TP 1◇ Y	NT	NT Q	TP 1◇ X	TP 1◇ A	NT H	TP 1◇ U	TP 1◇ Z
Deansgate	d		07 39									08 41					09 15			09 40					
Manchester Oxford Road	d		07 43	07 52		08 03		08 20				08 45	08 50		08 59		09 17			09 43		09 55	09 59		10 18
Manchester Piccadilly 10	a		07 45	07 54		08 06		08 25				08 47	08 53		09 02		09 20			09 45		09 57	10 02		10 20
	d	07 34	07 47	07 56	08 03	08 07	08 14	08 25		08 30	08 34	08 49	08 54	08 55	09 03	09 08	09 21	09 27	09 33	09 47	09 53	09 59	10 03	10 08	10 22
Mauldeth Road	d	07 42			08 10						08 41					09 17			09 40					10 17	
Burnage	d	07 44		08 03							08 43					09 19			09 42					10 19	
East Didsbury	d	07 46		08 05				08 34			08 45		09 02		09 12				09 44				10 12		
Gatley	d	07 49		08 08							08 48				09 15				09 46				10 15		
Heald Green	d	07 52		08 11			08 25				08 51				09 18		09 32		09 49			10 12	10 18		10 32
Manchester Airport	a	07 57	08 02	08 19	08 22	08 25	08 33	08 42		08 51	08 57	09 06	09 13	09 18	09 25	09 33	09 40	09 44	09 56	10 01	10 14	10 19	10 25	10 33	10 40
Wilmslow	84 a	08 07									09 07								10 06						
Crewe 10	84 a	08 37									09 33								10 33						

		TP 1◇ D	NT	NT Q	TP 1◇ G	TP 1◇ A	NT H	TP 1◇ U	TP 1◇ N	TP 1◇ X	NT	NT Q	TP 1◇ D	TP 1◇ A	NT H		TP 1◇ U	TP 1◇ AA	TP 1◇ X	NT	NT Q	TP 1◇ D	TP 1◇ A	NT H	TP 1◇ U
Deansgate	d								11 15																
Manchester Oxford Road	d			10 43		10 55	10 59		11 18			11 43		11 55	11 59			12 18			12 43		12 55	12 59	
Manchester Piccadilly 10	a			10 45		10 57	11 02		11 20			11 45		11 57	12 02			12 20			12 45		12 57	13 02	
	d	10 27	10 33	10 47	10 53	10 59	11 03	11 08	11 22	11 27	11 33	11 47	11 53	11 59	12 03		12 08	12 22	12 27	12 33	12 47	12 53	12 59	13 03	13 08
Mauldeth Road	d		10 40					11 17			11 40						12 17			12 40					13 17
Burnage	d		10 42					11 19			11 42						12 19			12 42					13 19
East Didsbury	d		10 44				11 12				11 44				12 12					12 44				13 12	
Gatley	d		10 46				11 15				11 46				12 15					12 46				13 15	
Heald Green	d		10 49			11 12	11 18		11 32		11 49			12 12	12 18			12 32		12 49			13 12	13 18	
Manchester Airport	a	10 44	10 56	11 01	11 14	11 19	11 25	11 33	11 40	11 44	11 56	12 01	12 14	12 19	12 25		12 33	12 40	12 51	12 56	13 01	13 14	13 19	13 25	13 33
Wilmslow	84 a		11 06								12 06									13 06					
Crewe 10	84 a		11 33								12 33									13 33					

		TP 1◇ N	TP 1◇ X	NT	NT Q	TP 1◇ D	TP 1◇ A	NT H	VT 1◇ BB	TP 1◇ U	TP 1◇ CC	TP 1◇ X	NT	NT Q	TP 1◇ D	TP 1◇ A	NT H	TP 1◇ U	TP 1◇ DD	TP 1◇ X	NT	NT Q		TP 1◇ D	TP 1◇ A
Deansgate	d	13 15									14 15														
Manchester Oxford Road	d	13 18			13 43		13 55	13 59			14 18			14 43		14 55	14 59		15 18			15 43			15 55
Manchester Piccadilly 10	a	13 20			13 45		13 57	14 02			14 20			14 45		14 57	15 02		15 20			15 45			15 57
	d	13 22	13 27	13 33	13 47	13 53	13 59	14 03	14 05	14 08	14 22	14 27	14 33	14 47	14 53	14 59	15 03	15 08	15 22	15 27	15 33	15 47		15 53	15 59
Mauldeth Road	d			13 40						14 17			14 40					15 17			15 40				
Burnage	d			13 42						14 19			14 42					15 19			15 42				
East Didsbury	d			13 44				14 12					14 44				15 12				15 44				
Gatley	d			13 46				14 15					14 46				15 15				15 46				
Heald Green	d	13 32		13 49			14 12	14 18			14 32		14 49			15 12	15 18		15 32		15 49				16 12
Manchester Airport	a	13 40	13 44	13 56	14 01	14 14	14 19	14 25		14 33	14 40	14 44	14 56	15 01	15 14	15 19	15 25	15 33	15 40	15 44	15 56	16 01		16 14	16 19
Wilmslow	84 a			14 06					14 23				15 06								16 06				
Crewe 10	84 a			14 33					14 42				15 33								16 36				

		NT H	TP 1◇ U	TP 1◇ EE	TP 1◇ X	NT	TP 1◇ D	TP 1◇ A	NT H	TP 1◇ U	TP 1◇ Z	NT	NT Q	TP 1◇ D	TP 1◇ A	NT H	TP 1◇ U	TP 1◇ N	TP 1◇ X	NT J	NT Q	TP 1◇ D	TP 1◇ A	NT H	TP 1◇ U
Deansgate	d			16 15														18 15							
Manchester Oxford Road	d	15 59		16 18				16 55	16 59		17 18		17 46		17 55	17 59		18 18			18 49		18 55	19 01	
Manchester Piccadilly 10	a	16 01		16 20				16 57	17 02		17 20		17 49		17 57	18 04		18 20			18 51		18 57	19 05	
	d	16 03	16 08	16 22	16 27	16 33	16 53	16 59	17 03	17 14	17 22	17 33	17 50	17 58	17 59	18 05	18 08	18 22	18 27	18 36	18 53	18 55	18 59	19 06	19 08
Mauldeth Road	d		16 17			16 40			17 10	17 21		17 40					18 17			18 43					19 17
Burnage	d		16 19			16 42			17 13	17 24		17 42					18 19			18 45					19 19
East Didsbury	d	16 12				16 44		17 06		17 26		17 44				18 15	18 22			18 47					19 22
Gatley	d	16 15				16 46		17 09		17 29		17 46				18 18	18 24			18 49					19 24
Heald Green	d	16 18			16 38	16 49		17 12		17 32		17 49			18 12	18 21	18 27	18 35	18 40	18 52		19 07	19 12		19 27
Manchester Airport	a	16 25	16 33	16 40	16 51	16 56	17 14	17 19	17 25	17 39	17 40	17 56	18 05	18 14	18 19	18 27	18 38	18 42	18 46	18 57	19 09	19 14	19 19	19 26	19 34
Wilmslow	84 a					17 06						18 11								19 07					
Crewe 10	84 a					17 33						18 41													

For general notes see front of timetable
For details of catering facilities see Directory of Train Operators

- **A** From Blackpool North (Table 82)
- **B** Until 14 July, 15 September to 3 November. From Middlesbrough (Table 39)
- **C** 21 July to 8 September and from 10 November. From Middlesbrough (Table 39)
- **D** From Newcastle (Table 39)
- **E** From Sheffield (Table 78)
- **G** From York (Table 39)
- **H** From Liverpool Lime Street (Table 90)
- **J** To Alderley Edge (Table 84)
- **K** From Preston (Table 82)
- **L** From Doncaster (Table 29)
- **N** From Barrow-in-Furness (Table 82)
- **Q** From Southport (Table 82)
- **U** From Cleethorpes (Table 29)
- **V** From Barrow-in-Furness and from Blackpool North (Table 82)
- **X** From Middlesbrough (Table 39)
- **Y** From Scarborough (Table 39)
- **Z** From Glasgow Central (Table 65)
- **AA** From Glasgow Central and from Edinburgh (Table 65)
- **BB** To London Euston (Table 65)
- **CC** From Windermere (Table 82)
- **DD** From Edinburgh (Table 65)
- **EE** From Windermere and from Barrow-in-Furness (Table 82)

Manchester → Manchester Airport

Network Diagram - see first page of Table 78

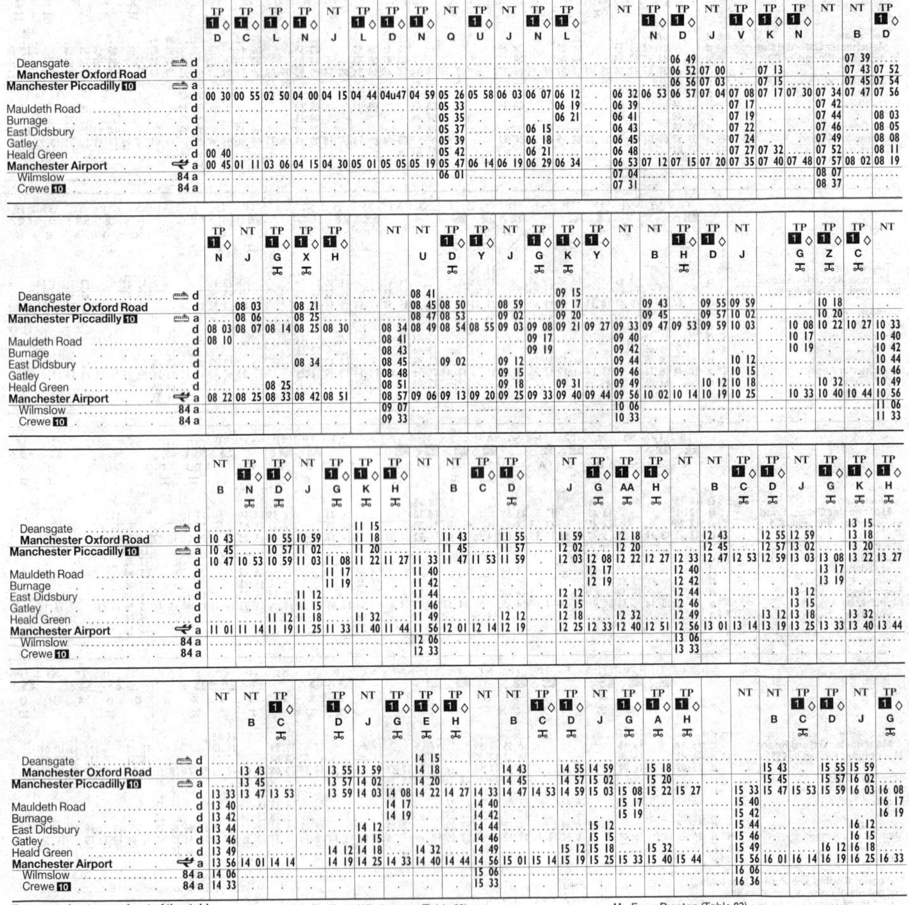

		TP 1◇ A 🚲	NT	NT B	TP 1◇ C 🚲	TP 1◇ D	TP 1◇ E	TP 1◇ G 🚲	TP 1◇ H	NT	NT B	TP 1◇ D	NT J	TP 1◇ G 🚲	TP 1◇ A 🚲	TP 1◇ K	TP 1◇ C 🚲	NT	TP 1◇ D	TP 1◇ H	NT	TP 1◇ G	TP D
Deansgate	d					19 52						20 52							22 13				23 15
Manchester Oxford Road	d	19 17		19 43		19 55	20 00				20 42	20 55	21 01		21 12	21 28			22 16				23 26
Manchester Piccadilly 10	a	19 20		19 46		19 57	20 04				20 45	20 58	21 05		21 14	21 30			22 18				23 30
	d	19 21	19 30	19 47	19 53	19 59	20 05	20 08	20 38	20 44	20 47	20 59	21 06	21 08	21 16	21 32	21 38	21 52	22 21	22 38	22 46	23 08	23 30
Mauldeth Road	d		19 37					20 17		20 51				21 17				22 00			22 53		23 37
Burnage	d		19 39					20 19		20 53				21 19				22 02			22 55		23 39
East Didsbury	d		19 41					20 22		20 55				21 22				22 04			22 57		23 42
Gatley	d		19 44					20 24		20 58				21 24				22 06			22 59		23 44
Heald Green	d	19 32	19 47			20 12	20 18	20 27		21 01		21 12		21 27	21 30	21 44		22 09	22 31		23 02		23 47
Manchester Airport ✈	a	19 40	19 52	20 05	20 12	20 19	20 26	20 34	20 58	21 06	21 09	21 19	21 28	21 34	21 37	21 51	21 58	22 15	22 39	22 58	23 09	23 28	23 56
Wilmslow	84 a		20 06							21 19								22 29			23 22		
Crewe 10	84 a																						

Saturdays

		TP 1◇ D	TP 1◇ C	TP 1◇ L	TP 1◇ N	NT J	TP 1◇ L	TP 1◇ D	TP 1◇ N	NT Q	TP 1◇ U	NT J	TP 1◇ N	TP 1◇ L		NT	TP 1◇ N	TP 1◇ D	NT J	TP 1◇ V	TP 1◇ K	TP 1◇ N	NT	NT B	TP 1◇ D
Deansgate	d																	06 49						07 39	
Manchester Oxford Road	d																	06 52	07 00		07 13			07 43	07 52
Manchester Piccadilly 10	a																	06 56	07 03		07 15			07 45	07 54
	d	00 30	00 55	02 50	04 00	04 15	04 44	04u47	04 59	05 26	05 58	06 03	06 07	06 12		06 32	06 53	06 57	07 04	07 08	07 17	07 30	07 34	07 47	07 56
Mauldeth Road	d									05 33				06 19		06 39				07 17			07 42		
Burnage	d									05 35				06 21		06 41				07 19			07 44		08 03
East Didsbury	d									05 37			06 15			06 43				07 22			07 46		08 05
Gatley	d									05 39			06 18			06 45				07 24			07 49		08 08
Heald Green	d	00 40								05 42			06 21			06 48				07 27	07 32		07 52		08 11
Manchester Airport ✈	a	00 45	01 11	03 06	04 15	04 30	05 01	05 05	05 19	05 47	06 14	06 19	06 29	06 34		06 53	07 12	07 15	07 20	07 35	07 40	07 48	07 57	08 02	08 19
Wilmslow	84 a									06 01						07 04							08 07		
Crewe 10	84 a															07 31							08 37		

		TP 1◇ N	NT J	TP 1◇ G 🚲	TP 1◇ X 🚲	TP 1◇ H		NT	NT U	TP 1◇ D 🚲	TP 1◇ Y	NT J	TP 1◇ G 🚲	TP 1◇ K 🚲	TP 1◇ Y	NT	NT B	TP 1◇ H 🚲	TP 1◇ D	NT J		TP 1◇ G 🚲	TP 1◇ Z 🚲	TP 1◇ C 🚲	NT
Deansgate	d								08 41					09 15											
Manchester Oxford Road	d		08 03		08 21				08 45	08 50		08 59		09 17			09 43		09 55	09 59			10 18		
Manchester Piccadilly 10	a		08 06		08 25				08 47	08 53		09 02		09 20			09 45		09 57	10 02			10 20		
	d	08 03	08 07	08 14	08 25	08 30		08 34	08 49	08 54	08 55	09 03	09 08	09 21	09 27	09 33	09 47	09 53	09 59	10 03		10 08	10 22	10 27	10 33
Mauldeth Road	d	08 10						08 41					09 17			09 40						10 17			10 40
Burnage	d							08 43					09 19			09 42						10 19			10 42
East Didsbury	d				08 34			08 45		09 02		09 12				09 44				10 12					10 44
Gatley	d							08 48				09 15				09 46				10 15					10 46
Heald Green	d			08 25				08 51				09 18		09 31		09 49			10 12	10 18			10 32		10 49
Manchester Airport ✈	a	08 22	08 25	08 33	08 42	08 51		08 57	09 06	09 13	09 20	09 25	09 33	09 40	09 44	09 56	10 02	10 14	10 19	10 25		10 33	10 40	10 44	10 56
Wilmslow	84 a							09 07								10 06									11 06
Crewe 10	84 a							09 33								10 33									11 33

		NT B	TP 1◇ N 🚲	TP 1◇ D 🚲	NT J	TP 1◇ G 🚲	TP 1◇ K 🚲	TP 1◇ H 🚲	NT	NT B	TP 1◇ C	TP 1◇ D 🚲		NT J	TP 1◇ G 🚲	TP 1◇ AA 🚲	TP 1◇ H 🚲	NT	NT B	TP 1◇ C 🚲	TP 1◇ D 🚲	NT J	TP 1◇ G 🚲	TP 1◇ K 🚲	TP 1◇ H 🚲
Deansgate	d						11 15																	13 15	
Manchester Oxford Road	d	10 43		10 55	10 59		11 18			11 43		11 55		11 59		12 18			12 43		12 55	12 59		13 18	
Manchester Piccadilly 10	a	10 45		10 57	11 02		11 20			11 45		11 57		12 02		12 20			12 45		12 57	13 02		13 20	
	d	10 47	10 53	10 59	11 03	11 08	11 22	11 27	11 33	11 47	11 53	11 59		12 03	12 08	12 22	12 27	12 33	12 47	12 53	12 59	13 03	13 08	13 22	13 27
Mauldeth Road	d					11 17			11 40						12 17			12 40					13 17		
Burnage	d					11 19			11 42						12 19			12 42					13 19		
East Didsbury	d				11 12				11 44					12 12				12 44				13 12			
Gatley	d				11 15				11 46					12 15				12 46				13 15			
Heald Green	d			11 12	11 18		11 32		11 49			12 12		12 18		12 32		12 49			13 12	13 18		13 32	
Manchester Airport ✈	a	11 01	11 14	11 19	11 25	11 33	11 40	11 44	11 56	12 01	12 14	12 19		12 25	12 33	12 40	12 51	12 56	13 01	13 14	13 19	13 25	13 33	13 40	13 44
Wilmslow	84 a								12 06									13 06							
Crewe 10	84 a								12 33									13 33							

		NT	NT B	TP 1◇ C 🚲		TP 1◇ D 🚲	NT J	TP 1◇ G 🚲	TP 1◇ E 🚲	TP 1◇ H 🚲	NT	NT B	TP 1◇ C 🚲	TP 1◇ D 🚲	NT J	TP 1◇ G 🚲	TP 1◇ A 🚲	TP 1◇ H 🚲		NT	NT B	TP 1◇ C 🚲	TP 1◇ D	NT J	TP 1◇ G 🚲
Deansgate	d								14 15																
Manchester Oxford Road	d		13 43			13 55	13 59		14 18			14 43		14 55	14 59		15 18				15 43		15 55	15 59	
Manchester Piccadilly 10	a		13 45			13 57	14 02		14 20			14 45		14 57	15 02		15 20				15 45		15 57	16 02	
	d	13 33	13 47	13 53		13 59	14 03	14 08	14 22	14 27	14 33	14 47	14 53	14 59	15 03	15 08	15 22	15 27		15 33	15 47	15 53	15 59	16 03	16 08
Mauldeth Road	d	13 40						14 17			14 40					15 17				15 40					16 17
Burnage	d	13 42						14 19			14 42					15 19				15 42					16 19
East Didsbury	d	13 44					14 12				14 44				15 12					15 44				16 12	
Gatley	d	13 46					14 15				14 46				15 15					15 46				16 15	
Heald Green	d	13 49				14 12	14 18		14 32		14 49			15 12	15 18		15 32			15 49			16 12	16 18	
Manchester Airport ✈	a	13 56	14 01	14 14		14 19	14 25	14 33	14 40	14 44	14 56	15 01	15 14	15 19	15 25	15 33	15 40	15 44		15 56	16 01	16 14	16 19	16 25	16 33
Wilmslow	84 a	14 06									15 06									16 06					
Crewe 10	84 a	14 33									15 33									16 36					

For general notes see front of timetable
For details of catering facilities see Directory of Train Operators

- **A** From Edinburgh (Table 65)
- **B** From Southport (Table 82)
- **C** From Newcastle (Table 39)
- **D** From Blackpool North (Table 82)
- **E** From Windermere (Table 82)
- **G** From Cleethorpes (Table 29)
- **H** From Middlesbrough (Table 39)
- **J** From Liverpool Lime Street (Table 90)
- **K** From Barrow-in-Furness (Table 82)
- **L** From Sheffield (Table 78)
- **N** From York (Table 39)
- **Q** To Alderley Edge (Table 84)
- **U** From Preston (Table 82)
- **V** From Doncaster (Table 29)
- **X** From Barrow-in-Furness and from Blackpool North (Table 82)
- **Y** From Scarborough (Table 39)
- **Z** From Glasgow Central (Table 65)
- **AA** From Glasgow Central and from Edinburgh (Table 65)

Manchester → Manchester Airport

Saturdays

Network Diagram - see first page of Table 78

		TP 1◇ A 🛒	TP 1◇ B 🛒	NT	TP 1◇ C 🛒	TP 1◇ D	NT E	TP 1◇ G 🛒	TP 1◇ H 🛒	NT		NT J	NT K	TP 1◇ C 🛒	TP 1◇ D	NT E	TP 1◇ G 🛒	TP 1◇ L 🛒	TP 1◇ B 🛒	NT N	NT Q	TP 1◇ C 🛒	TP 1◇ D	NT E	TP 1◇ G 🛒
Deansgate	d	16 15																18 15							
Manchester Oxford Road	d	16 18				16 55	16 59		17 18			17 44	17 46		17 55	17 59		18 18			18 49		18 55	19 01	
Manchester Piccadilly 10	a	16 20				16 57	17 02		17 20			17 47	17 49		17 57	18 04		18 20			18 51		18 57	19 05	
	d	16 22	16 27	16 33	16 53	16 59	17 03	17 14	17 22	17 33		17 48	17 50	17 58	17 59	18 05	18 08	18 22	18 27	18 36	18 53	18 55	18 59	19 06	19 08
Mauldeth Road	d			16 40			17 10	17 21		17 40							18 17			18 43					19 17
Burnage	d			16 42			17 13	17 24		17 42							18 19			18 45					19 19
East Didsbury	d			16 44		17 06		17 26		17 44						18 15	18 22			18 47					19 22
Gatley	d			16 46		17 09		17 29		17 46						18 18	18 24			18 49					19 24
Heald Green	d		16 38	16 49		17 12		17 32		17 49					18 12	18 21	18 27	18 35	18 40	18 52		19 07	19 12		19 27
Manchester Airport	a	16 40	16 51	16 56	17 11	17 19	17 25	17 39	17 40	17 56		18 01	18 05	18 14	18 19	18 27	18 38	18 42	18 46	18 57	19 08	19 14	19 19	19 26	19 34
Wilmslow	84 a			17 06						18 10										19 11					
Crewe 10	84 a			17 33						18 37															

		TP 1◇ U 🛒		NT	NT Q	TP 1◇ C	TP 1◇ D	TP 1◇ V	TP 1◇ G 🛒	TP 1◇ B	NT	NT Q	TP 1◇ D	NT E	TP 1◇ G 🛒	TP 1◇ U 🛒	TP 1◇ L	TP 1◇ C	NT	TP 1◇ D	TP 1◇ B	NT	TP 1◇ D		
Deansgate	d						19 52						20 53							22 13			23 15		
Manchester Oxford Road	d	19 17			19 43		19 55	19 59				20 42	20 55	21 01		21 12	21 27			22 16			23 26		
Manchester Piccadilly 10	a	19 20			19 46		19 57	20 04				20 45	20 58	21 05		21 14	21 29			22 18			23 30		
	d	19 21		19 30	19 47	19 53	19 59	20 05	20 08	20 38	20 44	20 47	20 59	21 06	21 08	21 16	21 31	21 38	21 55	22 21	22 38	22 46	23 30		
Mauldeth Road	d			19 37					20 17		20 51				21 17				22 02			22 53	23 37		
Burnage	d			19 39					20 19		20 53				21 19				22 04			22 55	23 39		
East Didsbury	d			19 41					20 22		20 55				21 22				22 06			22 57	23 42		
Gatley	d			19 44					20 24		20 58				21 24				22 08			22 59	23 44		
Heald Green	d	19 32		19 47			20 12	20 18	20 27		21 01		21 12		21 27	21 30	21 42		22 11	22 31		23 02	23 47		
Manchester Airport	a	19 40		19 52	20 05	20 12	20 19	20 26	20 34	20 58	21 06	21 09	21 19	21 28	21 34	21 37	21 51	21 58	22 16	22 39	22 58	23 08	23 56		
Wilmslow	84 a			20 06							21 19								22 35			23 22			
Crewe 10	84 a																								

Sundays

until 13 July

		TP 1◇ D	TP 1◇ B	TP 1◇ X	TP 1◇ X	NT		TP 1◇ X	NT	TP 1◇ X	TP 1◇ Y	NT		TP 1◇ Y	TP 1◇ X	TP 1◇ Z	NT	TP 1◇ D		NT E	TP 1◇ X	NT	TP 1◇ D	TP 1◇ AA	NT E
Deansgate	d																	09 09					10 09		
Manchester Oxford Road	d																	09 12		09 31			10 12		10 31
Manchester Piccadilly 10	a																	09 15		09 34			10 15		10 34
	d	00 30	00 38	04 05	05 05	05 27		06 05	06 45	07 05	07 16	07 48		08 01	08 05	08 55	09 14	09 18		09 35	09 39	09 48	10 18	10 20	10 35
Mauldeth Road	d					05 34			06 52			07 55										09 55			
Burnage	d					05 36			06 54			07 57										09 57			
East Didsbury	d					05 38			06 56			07 59										09 59			
Gatley	d					05 40			06 58			08 01										10 01			
Heald Green	d	00 40				05 43			07 01			08 04										10 04			
Manchester Airport	a	00 45	00 57	04 21	05 21	05 51		06 21	07 08	07 21	07 32	08 11		08 17	08 26	09 12	09 29	09 33		09 51	09 58	10 11	10 33	10 36	10 54
Wilmslow	84 a																09 40								
Crewe 10	84 a																10 07								

		TP 1◇ X		NT	NT	TP 1◇ D	NT E	TP 1◇ BB		NT	TP 1◇ L	TP 1◇ D	TP 1◇ CC	NT E		TP 1◇ B	NT	NT	TP 1◇ D	TP 1◇ G		NT E	TP 1◇ C	NT	TP 1◇ L
Deansgate	d					11 09						12 09							13 09						
Manchester Oxford Road	d					11 12	11 31				11 55	12 12		12 31					13 12			13 31			13 58
Manchester Piccadilly 10	a					11 15	11 35				11 58	12 17		12 35					13 15			13 35			14 00
	d	10 42		10 49	11 00	11 18	11 35	11 39		11 48	12 01	12 18	12 23	12 38		12 39	12 49	13 04	13 18	13 20		13 38	13 40	13 52	14 02
Mauldeth Road	d			10 56						11 55								13 11				13 46			
Burnage	d			10 58						11 57								13 13						14 00	
East Didsbury	d			11 00						11 59							12 57							14 02	
Gatley	d			11 02						12 01							13 00							14 04	
Heald Green	d			11 05						12 04							13 03							14 07	
Manchester Airport	a	11 04		11 12	11 20	11 33	11 51	11 58		12 11	12 18	12 33	12 37	12 54		12 58	13 10	13 23	13 33	13 39		13 55	13 58	14 14	14 18
Wilmslow	84 a				11 39													13 32							
Crewe 10	84 a				12 06													13 59							

For general notes see front of timetable
For details of catering facilities see Directory of Train Operators

- **A** From Windermere and from Barrow-in-Furness (Table 82)
- **B** From Middlesbrough (Table 39)
- **C** From Newcastle (Table 39)
- **D** From Blackpool North (Table 82)
- **E** From Liverpool Lime Street (Table 90)
- **G** From Cleethorpes (Table 29)
- **H** From Glasgow Central (Table 65)
- **J** From 13 September. From Southport (Table 82)
- **K** Until 6 September. From Southport (Table 82)
- **L** From Barrow-in-Furness (Table 82)
- **N** To Alderley Edge (Table 84)
- **Q** From Southport (Table 82)
- **U** From Edinburgh (Table 65)
- **V** From Windermere (Table 82)
- **X** From York (Table 39)
- **Y** From Bolton (Table 82)
- **Z** From Sheffield (Table 78)
- **AA** From Meadowhall (Table 29)
- **BB** From Scarborough (Table 39)
- **CC** From Doncaster (Table 29)

Table 85

Sundays
until 13 July

Manchester → Manchester Airport

Network Diagram - see first page of Table 78

		TP	TP	NT		AW	TP	NT	TP	TP		TP	NT	TP	NT	TP		TP	TP	NT	TP	NT		TP	NT
		1◇	1◇			R	1◇		1◇	1◇		1◇		1◇		1◇		1◇	1◇		1◇			1◇	
		A	B	C		D ⚲	E		G ⚲	A		H	C	J		K		A	H	C	J			L ⚲	
Deansgate	d	14 09								15 09								16 09							
Manchester Oxford Road	d	14 12		14 30					14 58	15 12			15 31			15 58		16 12		16 31				16 58	
Manchester Piccadilly 10	a	14 15		14 32					15 00	15 15			15 34			16 00		16 15		16 35				17 00	
	d	14 16	14 20	14 34		14 34	14 37	14 48	15 02	15 16		15 20	15 35	15 39	15 48	16 02		16 16	16 20	16 35	16 39	16 48		17 02	17 04
Mauldeth Road	d							14 55							15 55							16 55			
Burnage	d							14 57							15 57							16 57			
East Didsbury	d							14 59							15 59							16 59			
Gatley	d							15 01							16 01							17 01			
Heald Green	d							15 04							16 04							17 04			
Manchester Airport ✈	a	14 33	14 36	14 51			14 58	15 11	15 18	15 33		15 37	15 51	15 58	16 11	16 18		16 33	16 36	16 51	16 58	17 11		17 18	17 20
Wilmslow	84 a					14 54																			17 32
Crewe 10	84 a					15 18																			18 01

		TP	TP	NT	TP	NT		TP	TP	TP	NT	TP		NT	TP	NT	TP	TP		NT	TP	NT	TP	TP	TP
		1◇	1◇		1◇			1◇	1◇	1◇		1◇			1◇		1◇	1◇			1◇		1◇	1◇	1◇
		A	H	C	J			K	A	H	C	J			G ⚲		N	H		C	J		K	A	H
Deansgate	d	17 09							18 09								19 09							20 09	
Manchester Oxford Road	d	17 12		17 31				17 58	18 12		18 31				18 58		19 12			19 31			19 58	20 12	
Manchester Piccadilly 10	a	17 15		17 35				18 00	18 15		18 33				19 00		19 15			19 35			20 00	20 15	
	d	17 16	17 20	17 35	17 39	17 48		18 02	18 16	18 20	18 35	18 39		18 48	19 02	19 06	19 16	19 20		19 35	19 39	19 48	20 02	20 16	20 20
Mauldeth Road	d					17 55								18 55								19 55			
Burnage	d					17 57								18 57								19 57			
East Didsbury	d					17 59								18 59								19 59			
Gatley	d					18 01								19 01								20 01			
Heald Green	d					18 04								19 04								20 04			
Manchester Airport ✈	a	17 33	17 36	17 51	17 58	18 11		18 18	18 33	18 36	18 52	18 58		19 11	19 18	19 21	19 33	19 36		19 51	19 58	20 11	20 18	20 33	20 36
Wilmslow	84 a															19 32									
Crewe 10	84 a															19 59									

		NT		TP	NT	TP	NT	TP		TP	NT	NT	TP	TP		NT	TP	TP	NT	TP		NT			
				1◇		1◇		1◇		1◇			1◇	1◇			1◇	1◇		1◇					
		C		J		G ⚲		A		H	C		A	H		C	E	Q		A		C			
Deansgate	d							21 09					22 09							23 09					
Manchester Oxford Road	d	20 31				20 58		21 12			21 31		22 12			22 31		22 58		23 12		23 31			
Manchester Piccadilly 10	a	20 33				21 00		21 15			21 34		22 15			22 33		23 00		23 15		23 33			
	d	20 35		20 39	20 48	21 02	21 06	21 16		21 20	21 35	21 48	22 16	22 20		22 35	22 39	23 02	23 04	23 16		23 35			
Mauldeth Road	d				20 55							21 55							23 11						
Burnage	d				20 57							21 57							23 13						
East Didsbury	d				20 59							21 59							23 15						
Gatley	d				21 01							22 01							23 17						
Heald Green	d				21 04							22 04							23 20						
Manchester Airport ✈	a	20 52		20 58	21 11	21 18	21 21	21 33		21 36	21 52	22 11	22 33	22 36		22 51	22 58	23 18	23 27	23 33		23 49			
Wilmslow	84 a						21 32																		
Crewe 10	84 a						21 59																		

Sundays
20 July to 7 September

		TP	TP	TP	TP	TP	NT	TP	NT	TP	TP	TP	NT	TP	TP	TP	NT	TP	NT		TP	NT	TP	TP	NT
		1◇	1◇	1◇		1◇		1◇			1◇	1◇		1◇	1◇	1◇		1◇			1◇		1◇	1◇	
		A	E	U	A 🚌	U		U		A 🚌	V	U		V	U	X		A	C		U		Y	A	C
Deansgate	d																	09 09						10 09	
Manchester Oxford Road	d																	09 12	09 31					10 12	10 31
Manchester Piccadilly 10	a																	09 15	09 34					10 15	10 34
	d	00 30	00 38	04 05	05u00	05 20	05 27	06 35	06 45	07u00	07 16	07 41	07 48	08 02	08 50	08 55	09 14	09 18	09 35		09 39	09 48	10 17	10 18	10 35
Mauldeth Road	d						05 34		06 52				07 55									09 55			
Burnage	d						05 36		06 54				07 57									09 57			
East Didsbury	d						05 38		06 56				07 59									09 59			
Gatley	d						05 40		06 58				08 01									10 01			
Heald Green	d	00 40					05 43		07 01				08 04									10 04			
Manchester Airport ✈	a	00 45	00 57	04 21	05 25	05 36	05 51	06 51	07 08	07 25	07 32	07 58	08 11	08 22	09 05	09 12	09 29	09 40	09 51		10 02	10 11	10 33	10 36	10 53
Wilmslow	84 a																09 40								
Crewe 10	84 a																10 07								

For general notes see front of timetable
For details of catering facilities see Directory of Train Operators

- **A** From Blackpool North (Table 82)
- **B** From Doncaster (Table 29)
- **C** From Liverpool Lime Street (Table 90)
- **D** To Pembroke Dock (Table 128)
- **E** From Middlesbrough (Table 39)
- **G** From Edinburgh (Table 65)
- **H** From Cleethorpes (Table 29)
- **J** From Newcastle (Table 39)
- **K** From Barrow-in-Furness (Table 82)
- **L** From Glasgow Central (Table 65)
- **N** From Blackpool North and from Windermere (Table 82)
- **Q** From Windermere and from Barrow-in-Furness (Table 82)
- **U** From York (Table 39)
- **V** From Bolton (Table 82)
- **X** From Sheffield (Table 78)
- **Y** From Meadowhall (Table 29)

Manchester → Manchester Airport

Sundays

20 July to 7 September

Network Diagram - see first page of Table 78

		TP 1◇ A	NT	NT	TP 1◇ B	NT C	TP 1◇ D	NT	TP 1◇ E	TP 1◇ B	NT C	TP 1◇ G	NT	NT	TP 1◇ B	TP 1◇ H		NT C	TP 1◇ J	NT	TP 1◇ E	TP 1◇ B	NT C	TP 1◇ J	NT
Deansgate	d				11 09					12 09					13 09							14 09			
Manchester Oxford Road	d				11 12	11 31				12 12	12 31				13 15			13 31				14 12	14 30		
Manchester Piccadilly [10]	a				11 15	11 35				12 16	12 35				13 18			13 35				14 15	14 32		
	d	10 39	10 46	11 07	11 18	11 35	11 42	11 49	12 16	12 18	12 35	12 39	12 50	13 06	13 18	13 20		13 38	13 40	13 51	14 17	14 18	14 34	14 39	14 48
Mauldeth Road	d		10 53			11 44					12 43									13 57					14 55
Burnage	d		10 55			11 46					12 46									13 59					14 57
East Didsbury	d		10 57					11 57					12 58							14 01					14 59
Gatley	d		10 59					12 00					13 01							14 04					15 01
Heald Green	d		11 04	11b22	11 30			12 03					13 04	13c22	13 30					14 07					15 04
Manchester Airport ✈	a	11 02	11 11		11 36	11 55	12 02	12 10	12 33	12 36	12 54	13 02	13 11		13 36	13 39		13 53	14 02	14 14	14 33	14 36	14 53	15 02	15 11
Wilmslow	84 a			11 27										13 27											
Crewe [10]	84 a			11 54										13 56											

		NT	TP 1◇ B	TP 1◇ H	NT C	TP 1◇ G	NT	TP 1◇ H	TP 1◇ B	NT C	TP 1◇ G	NT	NT		TP 1◇ H	TP 1◇ B	NT C	TP 1◇ G	NT	TP 1◇ H	TP 1◇ B	NT C	TP 1◇ G	NT	NT
Deansgate	d		15 09						16 09							17 09					18 09				
Manchester Oxford Road	d		15 12		15 31				16 12	16 31						17 12	17 31				18 12	18 31			
Manchester Piccadilly [10]	a		15 15		15 34				16 15	16 35						17 15	17 35				18 15	18 33			
	d	15 05	15 18	15 20	15 35	15 39	15 48	16 17	16 18	16 35	16 39	16 48	17 06		17 17	17 21	17 35	17 39	17 48	18 17	18 18	18 35	18 39	18 48	19 06
Mauldeth Road	d						15 55					16 55							17 55					18 55	
Burnage	d						15 57					16 57							17 57					18 57	
East Didsbury	d						15 59					16 59							17 59					18 59	
Gatley	d						16 01					17 01							18 01					19 01	
Heald Green	d	15b22	15 29				16 04					17 04	17b22		17 28				18 04					19 04	19b22
Manchester Airport ✈	a		15 36	15 37	15 53	16 02	16 11	16 33	16 36	16 53	17 02	17 11			17 32	17 36	17 53	18 02	18 11	18 33	18 36	18 53	19 02	19 11	
Wilmslow	84 a	15 27											17 27												19 27
Crewe [10]	84 a	15 53											17 57												19 54

		TP 1◇ H	TP 1◇ B	NT C	TP 1◇ G	NT	TP 1◇ H	TP 1◇ B	NT C	TP 1◇ G	NT	NT	TP 1◇ H	TP 1◇ B	NT C	NT	TP 1◇ H	TP 1◇ B	NT C	TP 1◇ L	NT	TP 1◇ B	NT C		
Deansgate	d		19 09					20 09						21 09				22 09				23 09			
Manchester Oxford Road	d		19 12	19 31				20 12	20 31					21 12	21 31			22 12	22 31			23 12	23 31		
Manchester Piccadilly [10]	a		19 15	19 35				20 15	20 33					21 15	21 34			22 15	22 33			23 15	23 33		
	d	19 17	19 18	19 35	19 39	19 48	20 16	20 18	20 35	20 39	20 48	21 06	21 17	21 18	21 35	21 48	22 18	22 18	22 35	22 39	23 04	23 16	23 35		
Mauldeth Road	d					19 55					20 55					21 55					23 11				
Burnage	d					19 57					20 57					21 57					23 13				
East Didsbury	d					19 59					20 59					21 59					23 15				
Gatley	d					20 01					21 01					22 01					23 17				
Heald Green	d	19 28				20 04					21 04	21b22	21 28			22 04					23 20				
Manchester Airport ✈	a	19 32	19 36	19 53	20 04	20 11	20 32	20 36	20 54	21 02	21 11		21 32	21 36	21 54	22 11	22 34	22 36	22 53	23 02	23 27	23 33	23 49		
Wilmslow	84 a											21 27													
Crewe [10]	84 a											21 54													

Sundays

14 September to 2 November

		TP 1◇ B	TP 1◇ N	TP A 🚌	TP B 🚌	NT	NT	TP A 🚌	TP B 🚌	TP 1◇ Q	NT	TP 1◇ Q	TP U 🚌	TP V 🚌	NT	TP 1◇ B	NT C	NT	TP 1◇ B	TP X 🚌	NT C	TP 1◇ A	NT	NT	TP 1◇ B
Deansgate	d															09 09			10 09						11 09
Manchester Oxford Road	d															09 12	09 31		10 12		10 31				11 12
Manchester Piccadilly [10]	a															09 15	09 34		10 15		10 35				11 15
	d	00 30	00 59	04 50	05u00	05 27	06 45	06 55	07u00	07 16	07 48	08 02	08 10	09 00	09 14	09 18	09 35	09 48	10 18	10 33	10 35	10 47	10 49	11 07	11 18
Mauldeth Road	d					05 34	06 52				07 55							09 55			10 44				
Burnage	d					05 36	06 54				07 57							09 57			10 47				
East Didsbury	d					05 38	06 56				07 59							09 59					10 58		
Gatley	d					05 40	06 58				08 01							10 01					11 01		
Heald Green	d	00 40				05 43	07 01				08 04							10 04					11 04		
Manchester Airport ✈	a	00 45	01 14	05 15	05 25	05 51	07 08	07 20	07 25	07 32	08 11	08 17	08 35	09 25	09 29	09 33	09 51	10 11	10 33	10 58	10 55	11 04	11 11	11 23	11 33
Wilmslow	84 a														09 40									11 39	
Crewe [10]	84 a														10 07									12 06	

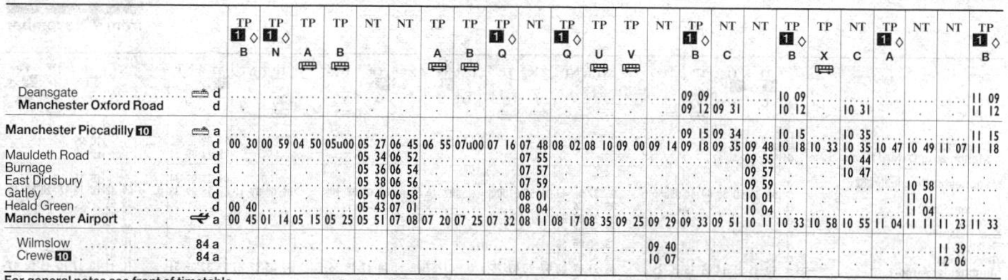

For general notes see front of timetable
For details of catering facilities see Directory of Train Operators

- **A** From York (Table 39)
- **B** From Blackpool North (Table 82)
- **C** From Liverpool Lime Street (Table 90)
- **D** From Hull (Table 39)
- **E** From Doncaster (Table 29)
- **G** From Newcastle (Table 39)
- **H** From Cleethorpes (Table 29)
- **J** From Scarborough (Table 39)
- **L** From Middlesbrough (Table 39)
- **N** From Huddersfield (Table 39)
- **Q** From Bolton (Table 82)
- **U** From Leeds (Table 39)
- **V** From Sheffield (Table 78)
- **X** From Meadowhall (Table 29)
- **b** Arr. 4 Minutes earlier
- **c** Arr. 1317

Table 85

Sundays

14 September to 2 November

Manchester → Manchester Airport

Network Diagram - see first page of Table 78

		NT A	TP 1◇ B	NT	TP 1◇ C	TP 1◇ D	NT A	TP 1◇ E	NT	NT	TP 1◇ C	TP 1◇ G	NT A	TP 1◇ H	NT	TP 1◇ C	TP 1◇ D	NT A	TP 1◇ E	NT	NT	TP 1◇ J	TP 1◇ G	NT A	TP 1◇ H
Deansgate	d				12 09						13 09					14 09						15 09			
Manchester Oxford Road	d	11 31			12 12		12 31				13 13		13 31			14 12		14 30				15 12		15 31	
Manchester Piccadilly 10	a	11 35			12 15		12 35				13 17		13 35			14 15		14 32				15 15		15 34	
	d	11 35	11 40	11 48	12 18	12 23	12 35	12 39	12 52	13 06	13 20	13 20	13 38	13 41	13 51	14 16	14 19	14 34	14 39	14 48	15 04	15 17	15 20	15 35	15 39
Mauldeth Road	d			11 55						13 13					13 57					14 55					
Burnage	d			11 57						13 15					13 59					14 57					
East Didsbury	d			11 59											14 01					14 59					
Gatley	d			12 01											14 04					15 01					
Heald Green	d			12 04					13 03						14 07					15 04					
Manchester Airport	a	11 51	11 58	12 11	12 33	12 37	12 50	12 58	13 10	13 23	13 41	13 39	13 53	13 58	14 14	14 33	14 35	14 51	14 58	15 11	15 21	15 33	15 37	15 51	15 58
Wilmslow	84 a									13 33											15 32				
Crewe 10	84 a									13 59											15 58				

		NT	TP 1◇ K	TP 1◇ C	TP 1◇ G	NT A	TP 1◇ H	NT	TP 1◇ L	NT	TP 1◇ C	TP 1◇ G	NT A	TP 1◇ H	NT	TP 1◇ K	TP 1◇ C	TP 1◇ G	NT A	TP 1◇ H	NT	TP 1◇ N	NT	TP 1◇ C	TP 1◇ G
Deansgate	d			16 09							17 09						18 09							19 09	
Manchester Oxford Road	d		15 58	16 12		16 31			16 58		17 12		17 31			17 58	18 12		18 31			18 58		19 12	
Manchester Piccadilly 10	a		16 00	16 15		16 35			17 00		17 15		17 35			18 00	18 15		18 33			19 00		19 15	
	d	15 48	16 02	16 16	16 20	16 35	16 39	16 48	17 02	17 06	17 16	17 20	17 35	17 39	17 48	18 02	18 16	18 20	18 35	18 39	18 48	19 02	19 06	19 16	19 20
Mauldeth Road	d	15 55						16 55							17 55						18 55				
Burnage	d	15 57						16 57							17 57						18 57				
East Didsbury	d	15 59						16 59							17 59						18 59				
Gatley	d	16 01						17 01							18 01						19 01				
Heald Green	d	16 04						17 04							18 04						19 04				
Manchester Airport	a	16 11	16 18	16 33	16 36	16 51	16 58	17 11	17 18	17 21	17 33	17 36	17 51	17 58	18 11	18 18	18 33	18 36	18 52	18 58	19 11	19 18	19 21	19 33	19 36
Wilmslow	84 a									17 32													19 32		
Crewe 10	84 a									18 01													19 59		

		NT A	TP 1◇ H	NT	TP 1◇ K	TP 1◇ C	TP 1◇ G	NT A	TP 1◇ H	NT	TP 1◇ N	NT	TP 1◇ C	TP 1◇ G	NT A	NT	TP 1◇ C	TP 1◇ G	NT A	TP 1◇ E	TP 1◇ Q	NT	TP 1◇ C	NT A
Deansgate	d					20 09							21 09				22 09						23 09	
Manchester Oxford Road	d	19 31			19 58	20 12		20 31			20 58		21 12		21 31		22 12		22 31		22 58		23 12	23 31
Manchester Piccadilly 10	a	19 35			20 00	20 15		20 33			21 00		21 15		21 34		22 15		22 33		23 00		23 15	23 33
	d	19 35	19 39	19 48	20 02	20 16	20 20	20 35	20 39	20 48	21 02	21 06	21 16	21 20	21 35	21 48	22 16	22 20	22 36	22 39	23 02	23 04	23 16	23 35
Mauldeth Road	d			19 55						20 55						21 55						23 11		
Burnage	d			19 57						20 57						21 57						23 13		
East Didsbury	d			19 59						20 59						21 59						23 15		
Gatley	d			20 01						21 01						22 01						23 17		
Heald Green	d			20 04						21 04						22 04						23 20		
Manchester Airport	a	19 51	19 58	20 11	20 18	20 33	20 36	20 52	20 58	21 11	21 18	21 21	21 33	21 36	21 52	22 11	22 33	22 36	22 51	22 58	23 18	23 27	23 33	23 49
Wilmslow	84 a											21 32												
Crewe 10	84 a											21 59												

Sundays

from 9 November

		TP 1◇ C	TP 1◇ U	TP V (bus)	TP C (bus)		NT	NT	TP V (bus)	TP C (bus)		TP 1◇ X	NT	TP 1◇ X	TP Y (bus)		TP Z (bus)	NT	TP 1◇ C	NT A		NT	TP 1◇ C	TP Y (bus)	TP 1◇ AA
Deansgate	d																		09 09				10 09		
Manchester Oxford Road	d																		09 12	09 31			10 12		
Manchester Piccadilly 10	a																		09 15	09 34			10 15		
	d	00 30	00 59	04 50	05u00		05 27	06 45	06 55	07u00		07 16	07 48	08 02	08 10		09 00	09 10	09 18	09 35		09 48	10 18	10 20	10 32
Mauldeth Road	d						05 34	06 52					07 55									09 55			
Burnage	d						05 36	06 54					07 57									09 57			
East Didsbury	d						05 38	06 56					07 59									09 59			
Gatley	d						05 40	06 58					08 01									10 01			
Heald Green	d	00 40					05 43	07 01					08 04									10 04			
Manchester Airport	a	00 45	01 14	05 15	05 25		05 51	07 08	07 20	07 25		07 32	08 11	08 17	08 35		09 25	09 25	09 33	09 51		10 11	10 33	10 45	10 47
Wilmslow	84 a																	09 40							
Crewe 10	84 a																	10 07							

For general notes see front of timetable
For details of catering facilities see Directory of Train Operators

- **A** From Liverpool Lime Street (Table 90)
- **B** From Scarborough (Table 39)
- **C** From Blackpool North (Table 82)
- **D** From Doncaster (Table 29)
- **E** From Middlesbrough (Table 39)
- **G** From Cleethorpes (Table 29)
- **H** From Newcastle (Table 39)
- **J** From Edinburgh (Table 65) and from Blackpool North (Table 82)
- **K** From Barrow-in-Furness (Table 82)
- **L** From Glasgow Central (Table 65)
- **N** From Edinburgh (Table 65)
- **Q** From Windermere and from Barrow-in-Furness (Table 82)
- **U** From Huddersfield (Table 39)
- **V** From York (Table 39)
- **X** From Bolton (Table 82)
- **Y** From Leeds (Table 39)
- **Z** From Sheffield (Table 78)
- **AA** From Manchester Victoria (Table 39)

Sundays

from 9 November

Manchester → Manchester Airport

Network Diagram - see first page of Table 78

	TP A	NT B		NT	NT	TP 1 ◇ C	TP 1 ◇ D		NT B	NT	TP 1 ◇ E	TP 1 ◇ C		TP 1 ◇ G	NT B	NT	NT		TP 1 ◇ H	TP 1 ◇ C	TP 1 ◇ J	NT B		NT
Deansgate d						11 09						12 09								13 09				
Manchester Oxford Road d		10 31				11 12			11 31			12 12			12 31					13 13		13 31		
Manchester Piccadilly 10 a		10 35				11 15			11 35			12 15			12 35					13 17		13 35		
d	10 33	10 35		10 49	11 07	11 18	11 32		11 35	11 48	12 08	12 18		12 23	12 35	12 52	13 06		13 08	13 18	13 20	13 38		13 51
Mauldeth Road d		10 44								11 55														13 57
Burnage d		10 47								11 57														13 59
East Didsbury d				10 58						11 59														14 01
Gatley d				11 01						12 01						13 01								14 04
Heald Green d				11 04						12 04						13 04								14 07
Manchester Airport a	10 58	10 55		11 11	11 23	11 33	11 47		11 51	12 11	12 24	12 33		12 37	12 53	13 11	13 23		13 24	13 33	13 39	13 53		14 14
Wilmslow 84 a					11 39												13 32							
Crewe 10 84 a					12 06												13 59							

	TP 1 ◇ K	TP 1 ◇ C	TP 1 ◇ G	NT B		NT	NT	TP 1 ◇ H	TP 1 ◇ N		TP 1 ◇ J	NT B	NT	TP 1 ◇ Q		TP 1 ◇ K	TP 1 ◇ C	TP 1 ◇ J	NT B		NT	TP 1 ◇ U	NT	TP 1 ◇ K
Deansgate d		14 09							15 09								16 09							
Manchester Oxford Road d		14 12		14 30					15 12			15 29		15 58			16 12		16 31			16 58		
Manchester Piccadilly 10 a		14 15		14 32					15 15			15 32		16 00			16 15		16 35			17 00		
d	14 08	14 16	14 20	14 34		14 48	15 04	15 08	15 16		15 20	15 35	15 48	16 02		16 08	16 16	16 20	16 35		16 48	17 02	17 06	17 08
Mauldeth Road d						14 55							15 55								16 55			
Burnage d						14 57							15 57								16 57			
East Didsbury d						14 59							15 59								16 59			
Gatley d						15 01							16 01								17 01			
Heald Green d						15 04							16 04								17 04			
Manchester Airport a	14 24	14 33	14 36	14 51		15 11	15 21	15 29	15 33		15 37	15 51	16 11	16 18		16 24	16 33	16 36	16 51		17 11	17 18	17 21	17 24
Wilmslow 84 a							15 32																17 32	
Crewe 10 84 a							15 58																18 01	

	TP 1 ◇ C	TP 1 ◇ J		NT B	NT	TP 1 ◇ Q	TP 1 ◇ K		TP 1 ◇ C	TP 1 ◇ J	NT B	NT		TP 1 ◇ V	NT	TP 1 ◇ K	TP 1 ◇ C		TP 1 ◇ J	NT B	NT	TP 1 ◇ Q		TP 1 ◇ K
Deansgate d	17 09								18 09								19 09							
Manchester Oxford Road d	17 12			17 31		17 58			18 12		18 31			18 58			19 12			19 31		19 58		
Manchester Piccadilly 10 a	17 15			17 35		18 00			18 15		18 33			19 00			19 15			19 35		20 00		
d	17 16	17 20		17 35	17 48	18 02	18 08		18 16	18 20	18 35	18 48		19 02	19 06	19 08	19 16		19 20	19 35	19 48	20 02		20 08
Mauldeth Road d					17 55							18 55									19 55			
Burnage d					17 57							18 57									19 57			
East Didsbury d					17 59							18 59									19 59			
Gatley d					18 01							19 01									20 01			
Heald Green d					18 04							19 04									20 04			
Manchester Airport a	17 33	17 36		17 51	18 11	18 18	18 24		18 33	18 36	18 52	19 11		19 18	19 21	19 24	19 33		19 36	19 51	20 11	20 18		20 24
Wilmslow 84 a															19 32									
Crewe 10 84 a															19 59									

	TP 1 ◇ C	TP 1 ◇ J	NT B	NT		TP 1 ◇ V	NT	TP 1 ◇ K	TP 1 ◇ C		TP 1 ◇ J	NT B	NT	TP 1 ◇ C		TP 1 ◇ J	NT B	TP 1 ◇ H	TP 1 ◇ X	NT	TP 1 ◇ C	NT B
Deansgate d	20 09								21 09					22 09							23 09	
Manchester Oxford Road d	20 12		20 31			20 58			21 12			21 31		22 12			22 31		22 58		23 12	23 31
Manchester Piccadilly 10 a	20 15		20 33			21 00			21 15			21 34		22 15			22 33		23 00		23 15	23 33
d	20 16	20 20	20 35	20 48		21 02	21 04	21 08	21 16		21 20	21 35	21 48	22 16		22 20	22 36	22 54	23 02	23 04	23 16	23 35
Mauldeth Road d				20 55									21 55							23 11		
Burnage d				20 57									21 57							23 13		
East Didsbury d				20 59									21 59							23 15		
Gatley d				21 01									22 01							23 17		
Heald Green d				21 04									22 04							23 20		
Manchester Airport a	20 33	20 36	20 52	21 11		21 16	21 19	21 24	21 33		21 36	21 52	22 11	22 33		22 36	22 51	23 09	23 18	23 27	23 33	23 49
Wilmslow 84 a							21 32															
Crewe 10 84 a							21 59															

For general notes see front of timetable
For details of catering facilities see Directory of Train Operators

- **A** From Sheffield (Table 78)
- **B** From Liverpool Lime Street (Table 90)
- **C** From Blackpool North (Table 82)
- **D** From York (Table 39)
- **E** From Scarborough (Table 39)
- **G** From Doncaster (Table 29)
- **H** From Middlesbrough (Table 39)
- **J** From Cleethorpes (Table 29)
- **K** From Newcastle (Table 39)
- **N** From Edinburgh (Table 65) and from Blackpool North (Table 82)
- **Q** From Barrow-in-Furness (Table 82)
- **U** From Glasgow Central (Table 65)
- **V** From Edinburgh (Table 65)
- **X** From Windermere and from Barrow-in-Furness (Table 82)

Manchester Airport → Manchester

Network Diagram - see first page of Table 78

Miles			NT MO	TP MO 1◇ A	TP MX 1◇ A	TP 1◇ B	NT MX	TP MO 1◇ C	TP 1◇ D	TP MO 1◇ E	TP 1◇ G	TP MO 1◇ H	TP 1◇ B	NT J	TP 1◇ K	TP 1◇ L	TP 1◇ B	TP 1◇ N	TP 1◇ Q	NT J	TP 1◇ K	TP 1◇ B	TP 1◇ U	NT V	TP 1◇ X
—	Crewe 10	84 d					00 56																		
—	Wilmslow	84 d																						06 52	
0	**Manchester Airport**	d	00 09	00 55	01 00	01 06	01 24	02 56	03 17	03 18	03 21	03 22	03 40	04 34	05 15	05 34	05 47	06 19	06 23	06 28	06 44	06 47	07 02	07 05	07 22
1½	Heald Green	d															05 51	06 23		06 32		06 51		07 09	07 26
4	Gatley	d																		06 35		06 54		07 12	
5¼	East Didsbury	d																		06 38		06 56		07 14	
6¾	Burnage	d																		06 40		06 59		07 16	07 30
7¼	Mauldeth Road	d																		06 43		07 01		07 18	07 33
9¾	**Manchester Piccadilly 10**	a	00 23	01 10	01 13	01 19	01 42	03 09	03 31	03 33	03 36	03 36	03 53	04 47	05 32	05 48	06 02	06 35	06 39	06 51	07 02	07 09	07 19	07 28	07 42
—		d															06 05	06 44		06 52		07 11			07 45
—	**Manchester Oxford Road**	a															06 07	06 46		06 54		07 15			07 47
—	Deansgate	a																							

		NT J	TP 1◇ Q	TP 1◇ B	TP 1◇ K	TP 1◇ U	NT Y	NT BHX V	NT	TP 1◇ N	NT J	TP 1◇ Q	TP 1◇ Z	TP 1◇ K	TP 1◇ U		NT Y	NT	TP 1◇ AA	NT J	TP 1◇ Q	TP 1◇ B	TP 1◇ K	TP 1◇ U	NT Y
Crewe 10	84 d							07 43	07 43									08 40							
Wilmslow	84 d							08 12	08 07									09 03							
Manchester Airport	d	07 26	07 34	07 47	07 52	08 04	08 07		08 18	08 27	08 30	08 33	08 47	08 52	09 04		09 07	09 18	09 27	09 31	09 34	09 47	09 52	10 04	10 07
Heald Green	d			07 51	07 56		08 11		08 21	08 31		08 37		08 56				09 21	09 31				09 56		
Gatley	d	07 32			07 59		08 14		08 24					08 59				09 24					09 59		
East Didsbury	d	07 35			08 01		08 17		08 27				08 53					09 27				09 53			
Burnage	d			07 55					08 29				08 56					09 29				09 56			
Mauldeth Road	d			07 58					08 31				08 58					09 31				09 58			
Manchester Piccadilly 10	a	07 47	07 48	08 10	08 11	08 19	08 26	08 39	08 42	08 44	08 49	08 49	09 10	09 11	09 19		09 22	09 41	09 42	09 48	09 48	10 10	10 11	10 19	10 21
	d	07 49		08 11			08 28			08 45	08 50		09 11				09 23		09 45	09 49		10 11			10 23
Manchester Oxford Road	a	07 51		08 14			08 30			08 47	08 52		09 14				09 25		09 47	09 51		10 14			10 25
Deansgate	a						08 33			08 50							09 28								

		NT	TP 1◇ N	NT J	TP 1◇ Q	TP 1◇ B	TP 1◇ K	TP 1◇ U	NT Y	NT	TP 1◇ X	NT J	TP 1◇ Q	TP 1◇ B	TP 1◇ K	TP 1◇ U	NT Y	NT	TP 1◇ N	NT J	TP 1◇ Q	TP 1◇ Z	TP 1◇ K	TP 1◇ U	NT Y
Crewe 10	84 d	09 38								10 38								11 38							
Wilmslow	84 d	10 01								11 01								12 01							
Manchester Airport	d	10 15	10 27	10 31	10 34	10 47	10 52	11 04	11 07	11 15	11 27	11 31	11 34	11 47	11 52	12 04	12 07	12 15	12 27	12 31	12 34	12 47	12 52	13 04	13 07
Heald Green	d	10 18	10 31				10 56			11 18	11 31				11 56			12 18	12 31				12 56		
Gatley	d	10 21					10 59			11 21					11 59			12 21					12 59		
East Didsbury	d	10 24				10 53				11 24				11 53				12 24				12 53			
Burnage	d	10 26				10 56				11 26				11 56				12 26				12 56			
Mauldeth Road	d	10 28				10 58				11 28				11 58				12 28				12 58			
Manchester Piccadilly 10	a	10 39	10 42	10 48	10 48	11 09	11 11	11 19	11 21	11 39	11 42	11 48	11 48	12 09	12 11	12 19	12 21	12 39	12 42	12 48	12 48	13 09	13 11	13 19	13 21
	d		10 45	10 49		11 11			11 23		11 45	11 49		12 11			12 23		12 45	12 49		13 11			13 23
Manchester Oxford Road	a		10 47	10 51		11 13			11 25		11 47	11 51		12 13			12 25		12 47	12 51		13 13			13 25
Deansgate	a		10 50																12 50						

		NT	TP 1◇ X	NT J	TP 1◇ Q	TP 1◇ B	TP 1◇ K		TP 1◇ A	NT Y	NT	TP 1◇ N	NT J	TP 1◇ Q	TP 1◇ B	TP 1◇ K	TP 1◇ U	NT Y	NT	TP 1◇ X	NT J	TP 1◇ L	TP 1◇ B	TP 1◇ K	TP 1◇ L
Crewe 10	84 d	12 38									13 38								14 38						
Wilmslow	84 d	13 01									14 01								15 01						
Manchester Airport	d	13 15	13 27	13 31	13 34	13 47	13 52		14 04	14 07	14 15	14 27	14 31	14 34	14 47	14 52	15 04	15 07	15 15	15 27	15 31	15 34	15 47	15 52	16 04
Heald Green	d	13 18	13 31				13 56				14 18	14 31				14 56			15 18	15 31				15 56	
Gatley	d	13 21					13 59				14 21					14 59			15 21					15 59	
East Didsbury	d	13 24				13 53					14 24				14 53				15 24				15 53		
Burnage	d	13 26				13 56					14 26				14 56				15 26				15 56		
Mauldeth Road	d	13 28				13 58					14 28				14 58				15 28				15 58		
Manchester Piccadilly 10	a	13 39	13 42	13 48	13 48	14 09	14 11		14 19	14 21	14 39	14 42	14 48	14 48	15 09	15 11	15 19	15 21	15 39	15 42	15 48	15 48	16 09	16 11	16 19
	d		13 45	13 49		14 11				14 23		14 45	14 49		15 11			15 23		15 45	15 49		16 11		
Manchester Oxford Road	a		13 47	13 51		14 13				14 25		14 47	14 51		15 13			15 25		15 47	15 51		16 13		
Deansgate	a											14 50													

For general notes see front of timetable
For details of catering facilities see Directory of Train Operators

- **A** To York (Table 39)
- **B** To Blackpool North (Table 82)
- **C** From 10 November. To Middlesbrough (Table 39)
- **D** All Tuesdays to Fridays, also Mondays 21 July to 8 September. To Middlesbrough (Table 39)
- **E** Until 14 July and from 15 September. To Doncaster (Table 29)
- **G** All Tuesdays to Fridays, also Mondays 21 July to 8 September. To Doncaster (Table 29)
- **H** Until 14 July, 15 September to 3 November. To Middlesbrough (Table 39)
- **J** To Liverpool Lime Street (Table 90)
- **K** To Cleethorpes (Table 29)
- **L** To Scarborough (Table 39)
- **N** To Barrow-in-Furness (Table 82)
- **Q** To Middlesbrough (Table 39)
- **U** To Newcastle (Table 39)
- **V** From Alderley Edge (Table 84)
- **X** To Edinburgh (Table 65)
- **Y** To Southport (Table 82)
- **Z** To Windermere and to Blackpool North (Table 82)
- **AA** To Glasgow Central (Table 65)

Manchester Airport → Manchester

Network Diagram - see first page of Table 78

Mondays to Fridays

	NT	NT	TP	NT	TP	TP	TP	TP	NT	NT	TP	TP	TP	TP	NT	NT	TP	NT	TP	TP	TP	NT	NT	TP
	A		1◇ B	C	1◇ D	1◇ E	1◇ G	1◇ H		C	1◇ J	1◇ D	1◇ K	1◇ G	A		1◇ L	C	1◇ D	1◇ K	1◇ G		A	1◇ H
Crewe 10 84 d		15 38							16 42							17 38						18 19		
Wilmslow 84 d		16 01							17 05							18 04						18 44		
Manchester Airport d	16 07	16 15	16 27	16 31	16 34	16 47	16 52	17 04	17 19	17 29	17 32	17 34	17 47	17 52	18 10	18 18	18 27	18 31	18 34	18 47	18 52	19 04	19 12	19 22
Heald Green d		16 18	16 31				16 56		17 22					17 56		18 22	18 31				18 56	19 07		
Gatley d		16 21					16 59		17 25					17 59		18 25					18 59	19 10		
East Didsbury d		16 24				16 53			17 28				17 53			18 27				18 53		19 13		
Burnage d		16 26				16 56			17 30				17 56			18 29				18 56		19 15		
Mauldeth Road d		16 28				16 58			17 32				17 58			18 31				18 58		19 17		
Manchester Piccadilly 10 a	16 21	16 41	16 42	16 47	16 48	17 10	17 11	17 19	17 41	17 44	17 47	17 49	18 09	18 11	18 24	18 40	18 43	18 48	18 49	19 09	19 11	19 29	19 31	19 38
d	16 23		16 44	16 48		17 11				17 45	17 50		18 11		18 26		18 45	18 49		19 11			19 33	
Manchester Oxford Road a	16 25		16 46	16 50		17 13				17 47	17 52		18 13		18 28		18 47	18 51		19 13			19 37	
Deansgate a	16 28												18 17		18 31		18 50			19 17				

	TP	NT	TP	TP	NT	NT	TP	TP	TP	NT	NT	TP	TP	NT	TP	TP	NT	TP	TP	NT	TP	TP
	1◇ B	C	1◇ K	1◇ G		A	1◇ N	1◇ K	1◇ G		A	1◇ H	1◇ B	C	1◇ K	1◇ Q		1◇ U	1◇ K		1◇ U	1◇ Q
Crewe 10 84 d																						
Wilmslow 84 d					19 51					20 50							21 55			22 53		
Manchester Airport d	19 27	19 30	19 47	19 52	20 04	20 15	20 22	20 47	20 52	21 04	21 16	21 22	21 27	21 30	21 47	21 52	22 08	22 22	22 47	23 04	23 22	23 52
Heald Green d	19 31			19 56	20 07				20 56	21 08						21 56	22 12		22 52	23 08		
Gatley d				19 59	20 10				20 59	21 11						21 59	22 15		22 55	23 11		
East Didsbury d			19 53		20 13			20 53		21 13					21 53		22 17		22 57	23 13		
Burnage d			19 56		20 15			20 56		21 15					21 56		22 19		23 00	23 15		
Mauldeth Road d			19 58		20 17			20 58		21 17					21 58		22 21		23 02	23 17		
Manchester Piccadilly 10 a	19 41	19 47	20 09	20 11	20 31	20 30	20 38	21 09	21 11	21 28	21 33	21 38	21 42	21 47	22 10	22 15	22 31	22 38	23 09	23 31	23 38	00 08
d	19 44	19 48	20 11			20 32		21 11			21 35		21 43	21 47	22 11				23 11			
Manchester Oxford Road a	19 46	19 50	20 13			20 34		21 13			21 37		21 45	21 49	22 14				23 15			
Deansgate a	19 49		20 17			20 37		21 17			21 40		21 48		22 17				23 17			

Saturdays

	TP	TP	NT	TP	TP	TP	NT	TP	TP	TP	TP	TP	NT		TP	TP	TP	NT	TP	NT	TP	TP	TP	TP
	1◇ U	1◇ K		1◇ D	1◇ V	1◇ K	C	1◇ G	1◇ N	1◇ K	1◇ B	1◇ D	C		1◇ G	1◇ K	1◇ H	X	1◇ Y	C	1◇ D	1◇ K	1◇ G	1◇ H
Crewe 10 84 d			00 56																					
Wilmslow 84 d																		06 52						
Manchester Airport d	01 00	01 06	01 24	03 17	03 21	03 40	04 34	05 15	05 34	05 47	06 19	06 23	06 28		06 44	06 47	07 02	07 05	07 22	07 26	07 34	07 47	07 52	08 04
Heald Green d										05 51	06 23		06 32			06 51		07 09	07 26			07 51	07 56	
Gatley d													06 35			06 54		07 12		07 32			07 59	
East Didsbury d													06 38			06 56		07 14		07 35			08 01	
Burnage d													06 40			06 59		07 16	07 30			07 55		
Mauldeth Road d													06 43			07 01		07 18	07 33			07 58		
Manchester Piccadilly 10 a	01 14	01 22	01 40	03 31	03 36	03 53	04 49	05 32	05 48	06 02	06 35	06 40	06 51		07 02	07 09	07 19	07 28	07 42	07 47	07 48	08 10	08 11	08 20
d										06 05	06 44		06 52			07 11			07 45	07 49		08 11		
Manchester Oxford Road a										06 07	06 46		06 54			07 15			07 47	07 51		08 14		
Deansgate a																								

	NT	NT	TP	NT	TP		TP	TP	TP	NT	NT	NT	TP	NT	TP	TP	TP	TP	NT		NT	TP	NT	TP
	A		1◇ B	C	1◇ D		1◇ Z	1◇ G	1◇ H	A	AA	BB	1◇ L	C	1◇ D	1◇ K	1◇ G	1◇ H	A			1◇ B	C	1◇ D
Crewe 10 84 d		07 43									08 38	08 40									09 38			
Wilmslow 84 d		08 07									09 01	09 03									10 01			
Manchester Airport d	08 07	08 18	08 27	08 30	08 33		08 47	08 52	09 04	09 07	09 16	09 18	09 27	09 31	09 34	09 47	09 52	10 04	10 07		10 15	10 27	10 31	10 34
Heald Green d	08 11	08 21	08 31		08 37			08 56			09 19	09 21	09 31				09 56				10 18	10 31		
Gatley d	08 14	08 24						08 59			09 22	09 24					09 59				10 21			
East Didsbury d		08 27					08 53				09 25	09 27				09 53					10 24			
Burnage d		08 29					08 56				09 27	09 29				09 56					10 26			
Mauldeth Road d		08 31					08 58				09 29	09 31				09 58					10 28			
Manchester Piccadilly 10 a	08 26	08 42	08 44	08 49	08 50		09 10	09 11	09 20	09 22	09 41	09 41	09 42	09 47	09 48	10 10	10 11	10 19	10 21		10 39	10 42	10 48	10 48
d	08 28		08 45	08 50			09 11			09 23			09 45	09 49		10 11			10 23			10 45	10 49	
Manchester Oxford Road a	08 30		08 47	08 52			09 14			09 25			09 47	09 51		10 14			10 25			10 47	10 51	
Deansgate a	08 33		08 50							09 28												10 50		

For general notes see front of timetable
For details of catering facilities see Directory of Train Operators

- **A** To Southport (Table 82)
- **B** To Barrow-in-Furness (Table 82)
- **C** To Liverpool Lime Street (Table 90)
- **D** To Middlesbrough (Table 39)
- **E** To Glasgow Central (Table 65) and to Blackpool North (Table 82)
- **G** To Cleethorpes (Table 29)
- **H** To Newcastle (Table 39)
- **J** To Barrow-in-Furness and to Blackpool North (Table 82)
- **K** To Blackpool North (Table 82)
- **L** To Glasgow Central (Table 65)
- **N** To Scarborough (Table 39)
- **Q** To Sheffield (Table 78)
- **U** To York (Table 39)
- **V** To Doncaster (Table 29)
- **X** From Alderley Edge (Table 84)
- **Y** To Edinburgh (Table 65)
- **Z** To Windermere and to Blackpool North (Table 82)
- **AA** Until 12 July
- **BB** From 19 July

Table 85

Saturdays

Manchester Airport → Manchester

Network Diagram - see first page of Table 78

	TP	TP	TP	NT	NT	TP	NT	TP	TP	TP	TP		NT	NT	TP	NT	TP	TP	TP	TP	NT	NT	TP	NT
	1◇	1◇	1◇			1◇		1◇	1◇	1◇	1◇				1◇		1◇	1◇	1◇	1◇			1◇	
	A	B	C	D		E	G	H	A	B	C		D		J	G	H	K	B	C	D		E	G
	⚲	⚲	⚲			⚲		⚲	⚲	⚲	⚲				⚲		⚲	⚲	⚲	⚲			⚲	
Crewe 10 84 d					10 38									11 38								12 38		
Wilmslow 84 d					11 01									12 01								13 01		
Manchester Airport ✈ d	10 47	10 52	11 04	11 07	11 15	11 27	11 31	11 34	11 47	11 52	12 04		12 07	12 15	12 27	12 31	12 34	12 47	12 52	13 04	13 07	13 15	13 27	13 31
Heald Green d		10 56			11 18	11 31				11 56				12 18	12 31				12 56			13 18	13 31	
Gatley d		10 59			11 21					11 59				12 21					12 59			13 21		
East Didsbury d	10 53				11 24				11 53					12 24				12 53				13 24		
Burnage d	10 56				11 26				11 56					12 26				12 56				13 26		
Mauldeth Road d	10 58				11 28				11 58					12 28				12 58				13 28		
Manchester Piccadilly 10 a	11 09	11 11	11 19	11 21	11 39	11 42	11 48	11 48	12 09	12 11	12 19		12 21	12 39	12 42	12 48	12 48	13 09	13 11	13 19	13 21	13 39	13 42	13 48
d	11 11			11 23		11 45	11 49		12 11				12 23		12 45	12 49		13 11			13 23		13 45	13 49
Manchester Oxford Road a	11 13			11 25		11 47	11 51		12 13				12 25		12 47	12 51		13 13			13 25		13 47	13 51
Deansgate a															12 50									

	TP	TP	TP		TP	NT	NT	TP	NT	TP	TP	TP	TP	NT	NT	TP	NT		TP	TP	TP	TP	NT	NT
	1◇	1◇	1◇		1◇			1◇		1◇	1◇	1◇	1◇			1◇			1◇	1◇	1◇	1◇		
	H	A	B		L	D		J	G	H	A	B	C	D		E	G		N	A	B	N	D	
	⚲		⚲		⚲			⚲				⚲	⚲			⚲			⚲	⚲	⚲			
Crewe 10 84 d							13 38								14 38									15 38
Wilmslow 84 d							14 01								15 01									16 01
Manchester Airport ✈ d	13 34	13 47	13 52		14 04	14 07	14 15	14 27	14 31	14 34	14 47	14 52	15 04	15 07	15 15	15 27	15 31		15 34	15 47	15 52	16 04	16 07	16 15
Heald Green d			13 56				14 18	14 31				14 56			15 18	15 31					15 56			16 18
Gatley d			13 59				14 21					14 59			15 21						15 59			16 21
East Didsbury d		13 53					14 24				14 53				15 24					15 53				16 24
Burnage d		13 56					14 26				14 56				15 26					15 56				16 26
Mauldeth Road d		13 58					14 28				14 58				15 28					15 58				16 28
Manchester Piccadilly 10 a	13 48	14 09	14 11		14 19	14 21	14 39	14 42	14 48	14 48	15 09	15 11	15 19	15 21	15 39	15 42	15 48		15 48	16 09	16 11	16 19	16 21	16 41
d		14 11				14 23		14 45	14 49		15 11			15 23		15 45	15 49			16 11			16 23	
Manchester Oxford Road a		14 13				14 25		14 47	14 51		15 13			15 25		15 47	15 51			16 13			16 25	
Deansgate a								14 50															16 28	

	TP	NT	TP	TP	TP	TP	NT	NT	TP		TP	TP	TP	NT	NT	TP	NT	TP	TP	TP	NT	TP	NT	TP
	1◇		1◇	1◇	1◇	1◇			1◇		1◇	1◇	1◇			1◇		1◇	1◇	1◇		1◇		1◇
	J	G	H	Q	B	C		G	J		H	A	B	D		J	G	H	A	B	D	C		J
	⚲			⚲	⚲				⚲				⚲											
Crewe 10 84 d							16 42								17 38								18 42	
Wilmslow 84 d							17 05								18 04								19 05	
Manchester Airport ✈ d	16 27	16 31	16 34	16 47	16 52	17 04	17 19	17 29	17 32		17 34	17 47	17 52	18 10	18 18	18 27	18 31	18 34	18 47	18 52	19 12	19 15	19 20	19 27
Heald Green d	16 31				16 56		17 22						17 56		18 22	18 31				18 56			19 23	19 31
Gatley d					16 59		17 25						17 59		18 25					18 59			19 26	
East Didsbury d				16 53			17 28					17 53			18 27				18 53				19 29	
Burnage d				16 56			17 30					17 55			18 29				18 56				19 31	
Mauldeth Road d				16 58			17 32					17 58			18 31				18 58				19 33	
Manchester Piccadilly 10 a	16 42	16 47	16 48	17 10	17 11	17 19	17 41	17 44	17 47		17 49	18 09	18 11	18 24	18 40	18 43	18 48	18 52	19 09	19 11	19 31	19 38	19 41	19 42
d	16 44	16 48		17 11				17 45	17 50			18 11		18 26		18 45	18 49		19 11		19 33		19 41	19 44
Manchester Oxford Road a	16 46	16 50		17 13				17 47	17 52			18 13		18 28		18 47	18 51		19 13		19 35		19 46	19 47
Deansgate a									17 55			18 17		18 31		18 50			19 17					19 50

	NT		TP	TP	NT	NT	TP	TP	TP	NT	NT	TP	TP	NT	TP	TP	NT	TP	TP	NT	TP	TP		
			1◇	1◇			1◇	1◇	1◇			1◇	1◇		1◇	1◇		1◇	1◇		1◇			
	G		A	B		D	N	A	B		D	L	V	G	A	X		L	A		Y	Z		
																						🚌		
Crewe 10 84 d																				22b22				
Wilmslow 84 d					19 51					20 50							21 55			22 55				
Manchester Airport ✈ d	19 30		19 47	19 52	20 04	20 15	20 22	20 47	20 52	21 04	21 16	21 22	21 27	21 30	21 47	21 52	22 08	22 22	22 47	23 07	23 22	23 25		
Heald Green d				19 56	20 07				20 56	21 08						21 56	22 12		22 51	23 10				
Gatley d				19 59	20 10				20 59	21 11						21 59	22 15		22 54	23 13				
East Didsbury d			19 53		20 13			20 53		21 13					21 53		22 17		22 56	23 16				
Burnage d			19 56		20 15			20 56		21 15					21 56		22 19		22 59	23 18				
Mauldeth Road d			19 58		20 17			20 58		21 17					21 58		22 21		23 01	23 20				
Manchester Piccadilly 10 a	19 48		20 09	20 11	20 31	20 30	20 38	21 09	21 11	21 31	21 33	21 37	21 44	21 47	22 10	22 15	22 31	22 38	23 09	23 31	23 38	23 50		
d	19 48		20 11			20 32		21 11			21 35		21 45	21 48	22 11				23 11					
Manchester Oxford Road a	19 50		20 13			20 34		21 13			21 37		21 48	21 52	22 14				23 13					
Deansgate a			20 17			20 37		21 17			21 40		21 50		22 17				23 17					

For general notes see front of timetable
For details of catering facilities see Directory of Train Operators

- **A** To Blackpool North (Table 82)
- **B** To Cleethorpes (Table 29)
- **C** To Newcastle (Table 39)
- **D** To Southport (Table 82)
- **E** To Edinburgh (Table 65)
- **G** To Liverpool Lime Street (Table 90)
- **H** To Middlesbrough (Table 39)
- **J** To Barrow-in-Furness (Table 82)
- **K** To Windermere and to Blackpool North (Table 82)
- **L** To York (Table 39)
- **N** To Scarborough (Table 39)
- **Q** To Glasgow Central (Table 65) and to Blackpool North (Table 82)
- **V** To Preston (Table 82)
- **X** To Sheffield (Table 78)
- **Y** Until 6 September to York (Table 39)
- **Z** From 13 September. To York (Table 39)
- **b** Until 6 September only

Table 85

Sundays

until 13 July

Manchester Airport → Manchester

Network Diagram - see first page of Table 78

	TP	TP	TP	TP	TP	NT	TP	NT	TP	NT	TP	TP	TP	NT	TP	TP	TP	NT	NT	TP
		1◇	1◇		1◇		1◇		1◇		1◇	1◇	1◇		1◇	1◇	1◇			1◇
	A 🚌	B	B	A 🚌	C		D		A		C	E	A	G	D	H	A	G		C
Crewe 10 84 d																				
Wilmslow 84 d																				
Manchester Airport ✈ d	00 10	01 22	04 37	05 40	06 09	06 13	07 09	07 13	07 36	08 13	08 22	08 40	08 47	08 51	09 25	09 36	09 47	10 01	10 14	10 22
Heald Green d						06 16		07 16		08 16									10 17	
Gatley d						06 19		07 19		08 19									10 20	
East Didsbury d						06 22		07 22		08 22									10 23	
Burnage d						06 24		07 24		08 24									10 25	
Mauldeth Road d						06 26		07 26		08 26									10 27	
Manchester Piccadilly 10 a	00 35	01 35	04 50	06 05	06 25	06 37	07 23	07 36	07 50	08 37	08 38	08 54	09 02	09 10	09 41	09 49	10 01	10 16	10 37	10 38
d									07 51				09 03	09 16		09 51	10 03	10 16		
Manchester Oxford Road a									07 53				09 06	09 18		09 53	10 05	10 20		
Deansgate a									07 56				09 08				10 08			

	TP	TP	NT	NT	NT	TP	TP	TP	NT	NT	TP	TP	TP	NT	NT	NT	TP	TP	TP
	1◇	1◇				1◇	1◇	1◇			1◇	1◇	1◇				1◇	1◇	1◇
	A	E	G			D	J trolley	A	G		C	A	E	G			D	J trolley	A
Crewe 10 84 d				10 25											12 27				
Wilmslow 84 d				10 51											12 50				
Manchester Airport ✈ d	10 47	10 52	11 00	11 03	11 14	11 22	11 27	11 47	12 00	12 13	12 22	12 45	12 52	13 00	13 05	13 13	13 22	13 27	13 47
Heald Green d					11 17					12 16						13 15			
Gatley d					11 20					12 19						13 18			
East Didsbury d					11 23					12 22						13 22			
Burnage d					11 25				12 07					13 07					
Mauldeth Road d					11 27				12 10					13 10					
Manchester Piccadilly 10 a	11 01	11 08	11 13	11 21	11 37	11 38	11 41	12 00	12 17	12 33	12 37	12 59	13 06	13 17	13 27	13 33	13 37	13 41	14 02
d	11 03		11 16				11 42	12 03	12 17			13 01		13 17				13 42	14 03
Manchester Oxford Road a	11 05		11 19				11 44	12 05	12 20			13 03		13 20				13 45	14 05
Deansgate a	11 08							12 08				13 08							14 08

	TP	NT	NT	TP	TP	TP	TP	NT	NT	NT	TP	TP	TP	TP	NT	NT	TP	TP	TP	TP
	1◇			1◇	1◇	1◇	1◇				1◇	1◇	1◇	1◇			1◇	1◇	1◇	1◇
	E	G		D	K	A	E	G			D	J trolley	A	E	G		C	K	A	E
Crewe 10 84 d									14 27											
Wilmslow 84 d									14 53											
Manchester Airport ✈ d	13 52	14 00	14 16	14 22	14 27	14 47	14 52	15 00	15 08	15 14	15 17	15 27	15 47	15 52	16 01	16 14	16 22	16 27	16 47	16 52
Heald Green d			14 19							15 17						16 17				
Gatley d			14 22							15 20						16 20				
East Didsbury d			14 25							15 23						16 23				
Burnage d		14 07								15 25						16 25				
Mauldeth Road d		14 10								15 27						16 27				
Manchester Piccadilly 10 a	14 07	14 17	14 36	14 37	14 41	15 01	15 09	15 16	15 24	15 37	15 39	15 41	16 01	16 09	16 15	16 37	16 38	16 41	17 00	17 08
d		14 17			14 42	15 03		15 16				15 42	16 03		16 16			16 42	17 03	
Manchester Oxford Road a		14 20			14 44	15 05		15 20				15 45	16 05		16 18			16 44	17 05	
Deansgate a						15 08							16 08						17 08	

	NT	NT	NT	TP	TP	TP	TP	NT	NT	TP	TP	TP	TP	NT	NT	NT	TP	TP	TP
				1◇	1◇	1◇	1◇			1◇	1◇	1◇	1◇				1◇	1◇	1◇
	G			D	H trolley	A	E	G		C	K	A	E	G			D	A	E
Crewe 10 84 d		16 27													18 27				
Wilmslow 84 d		16 50													18 50				
Manchester Airport ✈ d	17 01	17 05	17 14	17 22	17 27	17 47	17 52	18 01	18 14	18 22	18 27	18 47	18 52	19 01	19 05	19 14	19 22	19 47	19 52
Heald Green d			17 17						18 17							19 17			
Gatley d			17 20						18 20							19 20			
East Didsbury d			17 23						18 23							19 23			
Burnage d			17 25						18 25							19 25			
Mauldeth Road d			17 27						18 27							19 27			
Manchester Piccadilly 10 a	17 14	17 23	17 37	17 38	17 41	18 00	18 10	18 14	18 37	18 39	18 41	19 00	19 07	19 15	19 21	19 37	19 38	20 00	20 06
d	17 16				17 42	18 03		18 16			18 42	19 03		19 16				20 03	
Manchester Oxford Road a	17 18				17 45	18 05		18 18			18 44	19 05		19 19				20 05	
Deansgate a						18 08						19 08						20 08	

	NT	NT	TP	TP	TP	TP	NT	NT	NT	TP	TP	TP	NT	NT	TP	TP	NT	TP
			1◇	1◇	1◇	1◇				1◇	1◇	1◇			1◇	1◇		1◇
	G		L	K	A	N	G			B	A	N	G		A	N		B
Crewe 10 84 d								20 27									22 25	
Wilmslow 84 d								20 50									22 51	
Manchester Airport ✈ d	20 01	20 14	20 22	20 27	20 47	20 52	21 01	21 05	21 14	21 22	21 47	21 52	22 01	22 14	22 47	22 52	23 05	23 22
Heald Green d		20 17							21 17					22 17				
Gatley d		20 20							21 20					22 20				
East Didsbury d		20 23							21 23					22 23				
Burnage d		20 25							21 25					22 25				
Mauldeth Road d		20 27							21 27					22 27				
Manchester Piccadilly 10 a	20 16	20 37	20 38	20 41	21 00	21 10	21 16	21 21	21 37	21 38	22 00	22 08	22 14	22 37	23 00	23 06	23 22	23 36
d	20 16			20 42	21 03		21 16				22 03		22 16		23 03			
Manchester Oxford Road a	20 20			20 44	21 05		21 20				22 05		22 18		23 05			
Deansgate a					21 08						22 08				23 08			

For general notes see front of timetable
For details of catering facilities see Directory of Train Operators

A To Blackpool North (Table 82)
B To York (Table 39)
C To Middlesbrough (Table 39)
D To Newcastle (Table 39)
E To Cleethorpes (Table 29)
G To Liverpool Lime Street (Table 90)
H To Glasgow Central (Table 65)
J To Edinburgh (Table 65)
K To Barrow-in-Furness (Table 82)
L To Scarborough (Table 39)
N To Sheffield (Table 78)

Sundays

20 July to 7 September

Manchester Airport → Manchester

Network Diagram - see first page of Table 78

	TP A [bus]	TP 1◇ B	TP 1◇ B	TP A [bus]	NT	TP 1◇ C	NT	TP 1◇ D	TP 1◇ A	NT		TP 1◇ D	TP 1◇ E	TP 1◇ A	TP 1◇ G	TP 1◇ H	TP 1◇ A	NT J	NT	TP 1◇ K	TP 1◇ A		TP 1◇ E	NT
Crewe 10 — 84 d																								10 25
Wilmslow — 84 d																								10 51
Manchester Airport ✈ d	00 10	01 22	04 42	05 40	06 13	06 22	07 10	07 22	07 36	08 13		08 18	08 40	08 47	09 25	09 36	09 46	09 58	10 14	10 22	10 46		10 49	
Heald Green d					06 16		07 13			08 16								10 02	10 17					10 59
Gatley d					06 19		07 16			08 19									10 20					
East Didsbury d					06 22		07 19			08 22									10 23					
Burnage d					06 24		07 21			08 24									10 25					
Mauldeth Road d					06 26		07 23			08 26									10 27					
Manchester Piccadilly 10 a	00 35	01 36	04 56	06 05	06 37	06 38	07 33	07 37	07 50	08 37		08 37	08 54	09 02	09 41	09 49	10 01	10 16	10 37	10 38	11 01		11 08	11 12
d									07 51					09 03		09 51	10 03	10 16			11 03			
Manchester Oxford Road a									07 53					09 06		09 53	10 05	10 20			11 05			
Deansgate a									07 56					09 08			10 08				11 08			

	NT J	NT	TP 1◇ K	TP 1◇ A	NT J	NT	TP 1◇ B	TP 1◇ A	TP 1◇ E	NT J		NT	NT	TP 1◇ K	TP 1◇ A	TP 1◇ E	NT J	NT	TP 1◇ K	TP 1◇ A	TP 1◇ E		NT J	NT
Crewe 10 — 84 d												12 36												14 36
Wilmslow — 84 d												13 00												15 02
Manchester Airport ✈ d	10 58	11 14	11 22	11 46	11 58	12 13	12 22	12 46	12 49	12 58			13 13	13 22	13 46	13 49	13 58	14 16	14 22	14 46	14 49		14 58	
Heald Green d	11 02	11 17			12 02	12 16				13 02		13 09	13 16				14 02	14 19					15 02	15 08
Gatley d		11 20				12 19							13 19					14 22						
East Didsbury d		11 23				12 22							13 22					14 25						
Burnage d		11 25			12 07					13 07							14 07							
Mauldeth Road d		11 27			12 10					13 10							14 10							
Manchester Piccadilly 10 a	11 14	11 37	11 38	12 01	12 17	12 33	12 37	13 01	13 07	13 17		13 27	13 33	13 37	14 02	14 07	14 17	14 36	14 38	15 01	15 09		15 16	15 23
d	11 16			12 03	12 17			13 02		13 17					14 03		14 17			15 03			15 16	
Manchester Oxford Road a	11 19			12 05	12 20			13 04		13 20					14 05		14 20			15 05			15 20	
Deansgate a				12 08				13 08							14 08					15 08				

	NT	TP 1◇ K	TP 1◇ A	TP 1◇ E	NT J	NT	TP 1◇ K	TP 1◇ A	TP 1◇ E	NT J		NT	NT	TP 1◇ K	TP 1◇ A	TP 1◇ E	NT J	NT	TP 1◇ K	TP 1◇ A	TP 1◇ E		NT J	NT
Crewe 10 — 84 d												16 36												18 36
Wilmslow — 84 d												16 59												18 59
Manchester Airport ✈ d	15 14	15 20	15 46	15 49	15 58	16 14	16 22	16 46	16 49	16 58			17 14	17 22	17 46	17 49	17 58	18 14	18 22	18 46	18 49		18 58	
Heald Green d	15 17				16 02	16 17				17 02		17 09	17 17				18 02	18 17					19 02	19 08
Gatley d	15 20					16 20							17 20					18 20						
East Didsbury d	15 23					16 23							17 23					18 23						
Burnage d	15 25					16 25							17 25					18 25						
Mauldeth Road d	15 27					16 27							17 27					18 27						
Manchester Piccadilly 10 a	15 37	15 39	16 01	16 09	16 15	16 37	16 38	17 00	17 08	17 14		17 23	17 37	17 38	18 01	18 09	18 14	18 37	18 39	19 00	19 07		19 15	19 21
d			16 03		16 16			17 03		17 16					18 03		18 16			19 03			19 16	
Manchester Oxford Road a			16 05		16 18			17 05		17 18					18 05		18 18			19 05			19 19	
Deansgate a			16 08					17 08							18 08					19 08				

	NT	TP 1◇ B	TP 1◇ A	TP 1◇ E	NT J	NT	TP 1◇ B	TP 1◇ A	TP 1◇ L	NT J		NT	NT	TP 1◇ B	TP 1◇ A	TP 1◇ L	NT J	NT	TP 1◇ A	TP 1◇ L	NT	TP 1◇ B		
Crewe 10 — 84 d												20 36									22 34			
Wilmslow — 84 d												20 59									23 00			
Manchester Airport ✈ d	19 14	19 22	19 46	19 49	19 58	20 14	20 22	20 46	20 49	20 58			21 14	21 22	21 46	21 49	21 58	22 14	22 46	22 49		23 22		
Heald Green d	19 17				20 02	20 17				21 02		21 09	21 17				22 02	22 17			23 07			
Gatley d	19 20					20 20							21 20					22 20						
East Didsbury d	19 23					20 23							21 23					22 23						
Burnage d	19 25					20 25							21 25					22 25						
Mauldeth Road d	19 27					20 27							21 27					22 27						
Manchester Piccadilly 10 a	19 37	19 38	19 59	20 06	20 16	20 37	20 38	21 00	21 11	21 16		21 21	21 37	21 38	22 00	22 08	22 14	22 37	23 00	23 04	23 22	23 36		
d			20 03		20 16			21 03		21 16					22 03		22 16		23 03					
Manchester Oxford Road a			20 05		20 20			21 05		21 20					22 05		22 18		23 05					
Deansgate a			20 08					21 08							22 08				23 08					

For general notes see front of timetable
For details of catering facilities see Directory of Train Operators

A To Blackpool North (Table 82)
B To York (Table 39)
C To Middlesbrough (Table 39)
D To Newcastle (Table 39)
E To Cleethorpes (Table 29)
G To Hull (Table 39)
H To Glasgow Central (Table 65)
J To Liverpool Lime Street (Table 90)
K To Scarborough (Table 39)
L To Sheffield (Table 78)

Table 85

Sundays

14 September to 2 November

Manchester Airport → Manchester

Network Diagram - see first page of Table 78

	TP	TP	TP	TP	TP	NT	TP	NT	TP	TP	TP	NT	TP	NT	TP	TP	NT	TP	NT	TP	TP	NT	NT	NT
	bus	bus	bus	bus	bus		bus		1 ◇	1 ◇	bus		1 ◇		1 ◇	1 ◇		bus		1 ◇	1 ◇			
	A	B	C	D	A		D		A	E	G		A	H	J	A	H	G		E	A	H		
Crewe 10 84 d																							10 25	
Wilmslow 84 d																							10 51	
Manchester Airport ✈ d	00 10	01 35	01 35	05 30	05 40	06 13	06 20	07 10	07 36	07 41	08 00	08 13	08 44	08 51	09 25	09 47	10 01	10 05	10 14	10 22	10 47	11 00	11 03	11 14
Heald Green d						06 16		07 13				08 16							10 17					11 17
Gatley d						06 19		07 16				08 19							10 20					11 20
East Didsbury d						06 22		07 19				08 22							10 23					11 23
Burnage d						06 24		07 21				08 24							10 25					11 25
Mauldeth Road d						06 26		07 23				08 26							10 27					11 27
Manchester Piccadilly 10 a	00 35	02 00	02 00	05 55	06 05	06 37	06 40	07 33	07 50	07 54	08 25	08 37	09 02	09 10	09 41	10 01	10 16	10 30	10 37	10 38	11 01	11 14	11 21	11 37
d									07 51				09 03	09 16		10 03	10 16				11 03	11 16		
Manchester Oxford Road a									07 53				09 06	09 18		10 05	10 20				11 05	11 19		
Deansgate a									07 56				09 08			10 08					11 08			

	TP	TP	TP	NT	NT	TP	TP	TP	NT	NT	NT	TP	TP	TP	NT	NT	TP	TP	TP	TP	NT	NT	NT	TP
	1 ◇	1 ◇	1 ◇			1 ◇	1 ◇	1 ◇				1 ◇	1 ◇	1 ◇			1 ◇	1 ◇	1 ◇	1 ◇				1 ◇
	J	K trolley	A	H		E	A	L	H			J	A	L	H		J	N	A	L	H			J
Crewe 10 84 d										12 27												14 27		
Wilmslow 84 d										12 50												14 53		
Manchester Airport ✈ d	11 22	11 27	11 47	12 00	12 13	12 22	12 46	12 52	13 00	13 05	13 13	13 22	13 47	13 52	14 00	14 16	14 22	14 26	14 47	14 52	15 00	15 08	15 14	15 17
Heald Green d					12 16						13 16					14 18							15 17	
Gatley d					12 19						13 19					14 21							15 20	
East Didsbury d					12 22						13 22					14 25							15 23	
Burnage d				12 07					13 07						14 07								15 25	
Mauldeth Road d				12 10					13 10						14 10								15 27	
Manchester Piccadilly 10 a	11 38	11 41	12 01	12 17	12 33	12 37	13 00	13 06	13 17	13 27	13 33	13 37	14 02	14 06	14 17	14 36	14 38	14 40	15 01	15 08	15 16	15 23	15 37	15 39
d		11 42	12 03	12 17			13 02		13 17				14 03		14 17			14 41	15 03		15 16			
Manchester Oxford Road a		11 44	12 05	12 20			13 04		13 20				14 05		14 20			14 43	15 05		15 20			
Deansgate a			12 08				13 08						14 08						15 08					

	TP	TP	TP	NT	NT	TP	TP	TP	TP	NT	NT	NT	TP	TP	TP	TP	NT	NT	TP	TP	TP	TP	NT	NT
	1 ◇	1 ◇	1 ◇			1 ◇	1 ◇	1 ◇	1 ◇				1 ◇	1 ◇	1 ◇	1 ◇			1 ◇	1 ◇	1 ◇	1 ◇		
	K trolley	A	L	H		E	N	A	L	H			J	Q trolley	A	L	H		E	N	A	L	H	
Crewe 10 84 d											16 27													18 27
Wilmslow 84 d											16 50													18 50
Manchester Airport ✈ d	15 27	15 47	15 52	16 01	16 14	16 22	16 27	16 47	16 52	17 01	17 05	17 14	17 22	17 27	17 47	17 52	18 01	18 14	18 22	18 27	18 47	18 52	19 01	19 05
Heald Green d					16 17							17 17						18 17						
Gatley d					16 20							17 20						18 20						
East Didsbury d					16 23							17 23						18 23						
Burnage d					16 25							17 25						18 25						
Mauldeth Road d					16 27							17 27						18 27						
Manchester Piccadilly 10 a	15 42	16 01	16 10	16 15	16 37	16 38	16 41	17 00	17 08	17 14	17 23	17 37	17 38	17 41	18 00	18 09	18 14	18 37	18 39	18 41	19 00	19 07	19 15	19 21
d	15 42	16 03		16 16			16 42	17 03		17 16				17 42	18 03		18 16			18 42	19 03		19 16	
Manchester Oxford Road a	15 45	16 05		16 18			16 44	17 05		17 18				17 45	18 05		18 18			18 44	19 05		19 19	
Deansgate a		16 08						17 08							18 08						19 08			

	NT	TP	TP	TP	NT	NT	TP	TP	TP	TP	NT	NT	NT	TP	TP	TP	NT	NT	TP	TP	NT	TP		
		1 ◇	1 ◇	1 ◇			1 ◇	1 ◇	1 ◇	1 ◇				1 ◇	1 ◇	1 ◇			1 ◇	1 ◇		1 ◇		
		J	A	L	H		U	N	A	G	H			B	A	G	H		A	G		B		
Crewe 10 84 d												20 27									22 25			
Wilmslow 84 d												20 50									22 51			
Manchester Airport ✈ d	19 14	19 22	19 47	19 50	20 01	20 14	20 22	20 27	20 47	20 52	21 01	21 05	21 14	21 22	21 47	21 52	22 01	22 14	22 47	22 52	23 05	23 22		
Heald Green d	19 17					20 17							21 17					22 17						
Gatley d	19 20					20 20							21 20					22 20						
East Didsbury d	19 23					20 23							21 23					22 23						
Burnage d	19 25					20 25							21 25					22 25						
Mauldeth Road d	19 27					20 27							21 27					22 27						
Manchester Piccadilly 10 a	19 37	19 38	20 00	20 04	20 16	20 37	20 38	20 41	21 00	21 08	21 16	21 21	21 37	21 38	22 01	22 08	22 14	22 37	23 00	23 06	23 22	23 36		
d			20 03		20 16			20 42	21 03		21 16				22 03		22 16		23 03					
Manchester Oxford Road a			20 05		20 20			20 44	21 05		21 20				22 05		22 18		23 05					
Deansgate a			20 08						21 08						22 08				23 08					

For general notes see front of timetable
For details of catering facilities see Directory of Train Operators

A To Blackpool North (Table 82)
B To York (Table 39)
C From Leeds (Table 39)
D To Leeds (Table 39)
E To Middlesbrough (Table 39)
G To Sheffield (Table 78)
H To Liverpool Lime Street (Table 90)
J To Newcastle (Table 39)
K To Edinburgh (Table 65)
L To Cleethorpes (Table 29)
N To Barrow-in-Furness (Table 82)
Q To Glasgow Central (Table 65)
U To Scarborough (Table 39)

Sundays

from 9 November

Manchester Airport → Manchester

Network Diagram - see first page of Table 78

		TP	TP	TP	TP	TP	NT	TP	NT	TP	TP	TP	NT	TP	TP	NT	TP	TP	NT	TP	NT	TP	TP	NT	NT
										1 ◇	1 ◇			1 ◇	1 ◇		1 ◇	1 ◇				1 ◇	1 ◇		
		A	B	C	D	A		D		A	E	G		A	H	J	A	E	J	G		A	H	J	
		🚌	🚌	🚌	🚌	🚌		🚌				🚌								🚌					
Crewe 10	84 d																								10 25
Wilmslow	84 d																								10 51
Manchester Airport ✈	d	00 10	01 35	01 35	05 30	05 40	06 13	06 20	07 10	07 36	07 41	08 00	08 13	08 44	08 48	08 51	09 47	09 56	10 01	10 05	10 14	10 47	10 56	11 00	11 03
Heald Green	d						06 16		07 13				08 16								10 17				
Gatley	d						06 19		07 16				08 19								10 20				
East Didsbury	d						06 22		07 19				08 22								10 23				
Burnage	d						06 24		07 21				08 24								10 25				
Mauldeth Road	d						06 26		07 23				08 26								10 27				
Manchester Piccadilly 10	a	00 35	02 00	02 00	05 55	06 05	06 37	06 40	07 33	07 50	07 55	08 25	08 37	09 02	09 06	09 13	10 01	10 09	10 16	10 30	10 37	11 01	11 09	11 14	11 21
	d									07 51				09 03		09 16	10 03		10 16			11 03		11 16	
Manchester Oxford Road	a									07 53				09 06		09 18	10 05		10 20			11 05		11 19	
Deansgate	a									07 56				09 08			10 08					11 08			

		NT	TP	TP	NT	NT	TP	TP	TP	NT	NT	NT	TP	TP	TP	TP	NT	NT	TP	TP	TP	TP	NT	NT	NT
			1 ◇	1 ◇			1 ◇	1 ◇	1 ◇				1 ◇	1 ◇	1 ◇	1 ◇			1 ◇	1 ◇	1 ◇	1 ◇			
			A	E	J		A	H	K	J			L	A	K	H	J		N	A	K	H	J		
													trolley												
Crewe 10	84 d										12 27													14 27	
Wilmslow	84 d										12 50													14 53	
Manchester Airport ✈	d	11 14	11 47	11 56	12 00	12 13	12 46	12 49	12 52	13 00	13 05	13 13	13 27	13 47	13 52	13 56	14 00	14 16	14 26	14 47	14 52	14 56	15 00	15 08	15 14
Heald Green	d	11 17				12 16						13 16						14 19							15 17
Gatley	d	11 20				12 19						13 19						14 22							15 20
East Didsbury	d	11 23				12 22						13 22						14 25							15 23
Burnage	d	11 25			12 07					13 07							14 07								15 25
Mauldeth Road	d	11 27			12 10					13 10							14 10								15 27
Manchester Piccadilly 10	a	11 37	12 01	12 09	12 17	12 33	13 00	13 04	13 06	13 17	13 27	13 33	13 41	14 02	14 06	14 09	14 17	14 36	14 40	15 01	15 06	15 09	15 16	15 23	15 37
	d		12 03		12 17		13 02			13 17			13 42	14 03			14 17		14 41	15 03			15 16		
Manchester Oxford Road	a		12 05		12 20		13 04			13 20			13 45	14 05			14 20		14 43	15 05			15 20		
Deansgate	a		12 08				13 08							14 08						15 08					

		TP	TP	TP	TP	NT	NT	TP	TP	TP	TP	NT	NT	NT	TP	TP	TP	TP	NT	NT	TP	TP	TP	TP	NT
		1 ◇	1 ◇	1 ◇	1 ◇			1 ◇	1 ◇	1 ◇	1 ◇				1 ◇	1 ◇	1 ◇	1 ◇			1 ◇	1 ◇	1 ◇	1 ◇	
		L	A	K	E	J		N	A	K	H	J			Q	A	K	E	J		N	A	K	H	J
		trolley													trolley										
Crewe 10	84 d												16 27												
Wilmslow	84 d												16 50												
Manchester Airport ✈	d	15 27	15 47	15 52	15 56	16 01	16 14	16 27	16 47	16 52	16 56	17 01	17 05	17 14	17 27	17 47	17 52	17 56	18 01	18 14	18 27	18 47	18 52	18 56	19 01
Heald Green	d						16 17							17 17						18 17					
Gatley	d						16 20							17 20						18 20					
East Didsbury	d						16 23							17 23						18 23					
Burnage	d						16 25							17 25						18 25					
Mauldeth Road	d						16 27							17 27						18 27					
Manchester Piccadilly 10	a	15 41	16 01	16 08	16 10	16 16	16 37	16 41	17 00	17 06	17 09	17 14	17 23	17 37	17 41	18 00	18 09	18 09	18 14	18 37	18 41	19 01	19 07	19 09	19 15
	d	15 42	16 03			16 17		16 42	17 03			17 16			17 42	18 03			18 16		18 42	19 03			19 16
Manchester Oxford Road	a	15 45	16 05			16 19		16 44	17 05			17 18			17 45	18 05			18 18		18 44	19 05			19 19
Deansgate	a		16 08						17 08							18 08						19 08			

		NT	NT	TP	TP	TP	NT	NT	TP	TP	TP	TP	NT	NT	NT	TP	TP	NT	NT	TP	TP	TP	NT		
				1 ◇	1 ◇	1 ◇			1 ◇	1 ◇	1 ◇	1 ◇				1 ◇	1 ◇			1 ◇	1 ◇	1 ◇			
				A	K	U	J		N	A	G	B	J			A	G	J		A	G	B			
Crewe 10	84 d	18 27												20 27									22 25		
Wilmslow	84 d	18 50												20 50									22 51		
Manchester Airport ✈	d	19 05	19 14	19 47	19 50	19 54	20 01	20 14	20 25	20 47	20 52	20 55	21 01	21 05	21 14	21 47	21 52	22 01	22 14	22 47	22 50	22 56	23 05		
Heald Green	d		19 17					20 17							21 17				22 17						
Gatley	d		19 20					20 20							21 20				22 20						
East Didsbury	d		19 23					20 23							21 23				22 23						
Burnage	d		19 25					20 25							21 25				22 25						
Mauldeth Road	d		19 27					20 27							21 27				22 27						
Manchester Piccadilly 10	a	19 21	19 37	20 00	20 04	20 07	20 16	20 37	20 39	21 00	21 07	21 08	21 16	21 21	21 37	22 01	22 08	22 14	22 37	23 00	23 04	23 09	23 22		
	d			20 03			20 16		20 40	21 03			21 16			22 03		22 16		23 03					
Manchester Oxford Road	a			20 05			20 20		20 42	21 05			21 20			22 05		22 18		23 05					
Deansgate	a			20 08						21 08						22 08				23 08					

For general notes see front of timetable
For details of catering facilities see Directory of Train Operators

- **A** To Blackpool North (Table 82)
- **B** To York (Table 39)
- **C** From Leeds (Table 39)
- **D** To Leeds (Table 39)
- **E** To Middlesbrough (Table 39)
- **G** To Sheffield (Table 78)
- **H** To Newcastle (Table 39)
- **J** To Liverpool Lime Street (Table 90)
- **K** To Cleethorpes (Table 29)
- **L** To Edinburgh (Table 65)
- **N** To Barrow-in-Furness (Table 82)
- **Q** To Glasgow Central (Table 65)
- **U** To Scarborough (Table 39)

Table 86

Mondays to Fridays

until 3 October

Manchester → Hazel Grove and Buxton

Network Diagram - see first page of Table 78

Miles	Station		NT A	NT	NT	NT	NT	NT	NT	NT	NT	NT B	NT	NT B	NT	NT B	NT	NT B	NT	NT B
—	Deansgate	d				06 49		07 29	08 12	08 41		09 29	09 40	10 29	10b31	11 29	11b31	12 29	12b31	13 29
—	Manchester Oxford Road	d			06 24	07 07	07 13	07 39	08 15	08 45	08 50	09 33	09 43	10 33	10 43	11 33	11 43	12 33	12 43	13 33
0	**Manchester Piccadilly** 10	84 d	05 52	06 41	06 51	07 22	07 37	07 51	08 29	08 59	09 06	09 37	10 06	10 37	11 06	11 37	12 06	12 37	13 06	13 37
3	Levenshulme	84 d		06 47		07 28		07 56	08 34		09 12		10 12		11 12		12 12		13 12	
4½	Heaton Chapel	84 d		06 50		07 31		07 59	08 37		09 15		10 15		11 15		12 15		13 15	
6	**Stockport**	84 d	06 01	06 54	07 01	07 35	07 47	08 03	08 41	09 08	09 19	09 47	10 19	10 47	11 19	11 47	12 19	12 47	13 19	13 47
7	Davenport	d		06 57		07 38		08 07	08 45	09 12	09 22	09 50	10 22	10 50	11 22	11 50	12 22	12 50	13 22	13 50
7¾	Woodsmoor	d		06 59		07 40		08 09	08 47	09 14	09 24	09 52	10 24	10 52	11 24	11 52	12 24	12 52	13 24	13 52
8¾	**Hazel Grove**	a	06 08	07 01	07 07	07 44	07 54	08 13	08 49	09 16	09 29	09 55	10 29	10 55	11 29	11 55	12 29	12 55	13 29	13 55
—		d			07 08		07 54		08 49	09 18		09 55		10 55		11 55		12 55		13 55
11	Middlewood	d					07 59					09 59				11 59				13 59
12½	Disley	d			07 15		08 03		08 56	09 26		10 03		11 02		12 03		13 02		14 03
14¼	New Mills Newtown	d			07 18		08 06		08 59	09 29		10 06		11 05		12 06		13 05		14 06
15¼	Furness Vale	d			07 20		08 08		09 02	09 31		10 09		11 07		12 09		13 07		14 09
16¼	Whaley Bridge	d			07 24		08 12		09 05	09 35		10 12		11 11		12 12		13 11		14 12
20½	Chapel-en-le-Frith	d			07 31		08 19		09 13	09 42		10 20		11 18		12 20		13 18		14 20
22¾	Dove Holes	d			07 36		08 24					10 25				12 25				14 25
25¾	**Buxton**	a			07 45		08 33		09 26	09 56		10 33		11 30		12 33		13 30		14 33

Station		NT	NT B	NT	NT B	NT	NT	NT B	NT	NT C	NT	NT B	NT	NT	NT B	NT B	NT B	NT C	NT D
Deansgate	d	13b31	14 29	14b31	15 29		15b31	16 29		16 59	17 10	17 28			18 15	19 29	20 29	21 40	22 50
Manchester Oxford Road	d	13 43	14 33	14 43	15 33		15 43	16 33		17 03	17 13	17 32	17 38	17 46	18 35	19 33	20 32	21 43	22 53
Manchester Piccadilly 10	84 d	14 06	14 37	15 06	15 37	15 40	16 06	16 37	16 44	17 07	17 27	17 37	17 50	18 06	18 39	19 37	20 36	21 49	22 58
Levenshulme	84 d	14 12		15 11		15 46	16 12		16 51	17 13				18 12					
Heaton Chapel	84 d	14 15		15 14		15 49	16 15		16 54	17 16				18 15					
Stockport	84 d	14 19	14 47	15 18	15 47	15 55	16 19	16 46	16 58	17 19	17 37	17 48	17 59	18 19	18 48	19 47	20 45	21 59	23 07
Davenport	d	14 23	14 50	15 22	15 50	15 58	16 22	16 49	17 02	17 23	17 41	17 51	18 03	18 22	18 52	19 50	20 48	22 02	23 10
Woodsmoor	d	14 25	14 52	15 24	15 52	16 00	16 24	16 51	17 04	17 25	17 43	17 53	18 05	18 24	18 54	19 52	20 50	22 04	23 12
Hazel Grove	a	14 29	14 55	15 28	15 56	16 03	16 29	16 53	17 07	17 27	17 47	17 56	18 09	18 27	18 56	19 55	20 52	22 06	23 14
	d		14 55	15 28		16 03		16 54		17 27		17 56		18 27	18 56	19 55	20 52	22 07	23 15
Middlewood	d			15 32		16 07				17 32				18 32	19 01	19 59	20 56	22 11	23 19
Disley	d		15 02	15 36		16 11		17 01		17 36		18 03		18 36	19 05	20 03	21 00	22 15	23 23
New Mills Newtown	d		15 05	15 39		16 14		17 04		17 39		18 06		18 39	19 08	20 06	21 03	22 18	23 26
Furness Vale	d		15 07	15 42		16 17		17 06		17 41				18 41	19 10	20 09	21 06	22 21	23 29
Whaley Bridge	d		15 11	15 45		16 20		17 10		17 45		18 10		18 45	19 14	20 12	21 09	22 24	23 32
Chapel-en-le-Frith	d		15 18	15 53		16 28		17 17		17 52		18 18		18 52	19 21	20 20	21 17	22 32	23 40
Dove Holes	d			15 58		16 33				17 57				18 57	19 26	20 25	21 22	22 37	23 45
Buxton	a		15 30	16 06		16 41		17 30		18 07		18 31		19 08	19 36	20 36	21 31	22 46	23 54

Mondays to Fridays

from 6 October

Station		NT A	NT	NT	NT	NT	NT	NT	NT	NT	NT B	NT	NT B	NT	NT B	NT	NT B	NT	NT B	NT
Deansgate	d				06 49		07 29	08 12	08 41		09 29	09 40	10 29	10b31	11 29	11b31	12 29	12b31	13 29	13b31
Manchester Oxford Road	d			06 24	07 07	07 13	07 39	08 15	08 45	08 50	09 33	09 43	10 33	10 43	11 33	11 43	12 33	12 43	13 33	13 43
Manchester Piccadilly 10	84 d	05 52	06 41	06 51	07 22	07 37	07 51	08 29	08 59	09 06	09 37	10 06	10 37	11 06	11 37	12 06	12 37	13 06	13 37	14 06
Levenshulme	84 d		06 47		07 28		07 56	08 34		09 12		10 12		11 12		12 12		13 12		14 12
Heaton Chapel	84 d		06 50		07 31		07 59	08 37		09 15		10 15		11 15		12 15		13 15		14 15
Stockport	84 d	06 01	06 54	07 01	07 35	07 47	08 03	08 41	09 08	09 19	09 47	10 19	10 47	11 19	11 47	12 19	12 47	13 19	13 47	14 19
Davenport	d		06 57		07 38		08 07	08 45	09 12	09 22	09 50	10 22	10 50	11 22	11 50	12 22	12 50	13 22	13 50	14 23
Woodsmoor	d		06 59		07 40		08 09	08 47	09 14	09 24	09 52	10 24	10 52	11 24	11 52	12 24	12 52	13 24	13 52	14 25
Hazel Grove	a	06 08	07 01	07 07	07 44	07 54	08 13	08 49	09 16	09 29	09 55	10 29	10 55	11 29	11 55	12 29	12 55	13 29	13 55	14 29
	d			07 08		07 54		08 49	09 18		09 55		10 55		11 55		12 55		13 55	
Middlewood	d					07 59					09 59				11 59				13 59	
Disley	d			07 15		08 03		08 56	09 26		10 03		11 02		12 03		13 02		14 03	
New Mills Newtown	d			07 18		08 06		08 59	09 29		10 06		11 05		12 06		13 05		14 06	
Furness Vale	d			07 20		08 08		09 02	09 31		10 09		11 07		12 09		13 07		14 09	
Whaley Bridge	d			07 24		08 12		09 05	09 35		10 12		11 11		12 12		13 11		14 12	
Chapel-en-le-Frith	d			07 31		08 19		09 13	09 42		10 20		11 18		12 20		13 18		14 20	
Dove Holes	d			07 36		08 24					10 25				12 25				14 25	
Buxton	a			07 47		08 35		09 28	09 58		10 35		11 32		12 35		13 32		14 35	

Station		NT B	NT	NT B	NT	NT	NT B	NT	NT C	NT	NT B	NT	NT	NT B	NT B	NT B	NT C	NT D
Deansgate	d	14 29	14b31	15 29		15b31	16 29		16 59	17 10	17 28			18 15	19 29	20 29	21 40	22 50
Manchester Oxford Road	d	14 33	14 43	15 33		15 43	16 33		17 03	17 13	17 32	17 38	17 46	18 35	19 33	20 32	21 43	22 53
Manchester Piccadilly 10	84 d	14 37	15 06	15 37	15 40	16 06	16 37	16 44	17 07	17 27	17 37	17 50	18 06	18 39	19 37	20 36	21 49	22 58
Levenshulme	84 d		15 11		15 46	16 12		16 51	17 13				18 12					
Heaton Chapel	84 d		15 14		15 49	16 15		16 54	17 16				18 15					
Stockport	84 d	14 47	15 18	15 47	15 55	16 19	16 46	16 58	17 19	17 37	17 48	17 59	18 19	18 48	19 47	20 45	21 59	23 07
Davenport	d	14 50	15 22	15 50	15 58	16 22	16 49	17 02	17 23	17 41	17 51	18 03	18 22	18 52	19 50	20 48	22 02	23 10
Woodsmoor	d	14 52	15 24	15 52	16 00	16 24	16 51	17 04	17 25	17 43	17 53	18 05	18 24	18 54	19 52	20 50	22 04	23 12
Hazel Grove	a	14 55	15 28	15 56	16 03	16 29	16 53	17 07	17 27	17 47	17 56	18 09	18 27	18 56	19 55	20 52	22 06	23 14
	d	14 55	15 28		16 03		16 54		17 27		17 56		18 27	18 56	19 55	20 52	22 07	23 15
Middlewood	d		15 32		16 07				17 32				18 32	19 01	19 59	20 56	22 11	23 19
Disley	d	15 02	15 36		16 11		17 01		17 36		18 03		18 36	19 05	20 03	21 00	22 15	23 23
New Mills Newtown	d	15 05	15 39		16 14		17 04		17 39		18 06		18 39	19 08	20 06	21 03	22 18	23 26
Furness Vale	d	15 07	15 42		16 17		17 06		17 41				18 41	19 10	20 09	21 06	22 21	23 29
Whaley Bridge	d	15 11	15 45		16 20		17 10		17 45		18 10		18 45	19 14	20 12	21 09	22 24	23 32
Chapel-en-le-Frith	d	15 18	15 53		16 28		17 17		17 52		18 18		18 52	19 21	20 20	21 17	22 32	23 40
Dove Holes	d		15 58		16 33				17 57				18 57	19 26	20 25	21 22	22 37	23 45
Buxton	a	15 32	16 08		16 43		17 32		18 09		18 33		19 10	19 38	20 38	21 32	22 48	23 56

For general notes see front of timetable
For details of catering facilities see Directory of Train Operators

A To Sheffield (Table 78)
B From Blackpool North (Table 82)
C From Southport (Table 82)
D From Clitheroe (Table 94)

b Change at Manchester Oxford Road and Manchester Piccadilly

Table 86

Saturdays
until 12 July

Manchester → Hazel Grove and Buxton

Network Diagram - see first page of Table 78

		NT A	NT	NT	NT	NT	NT	NT	NT	NT	NT B	NT	NT B	NT	NT B	NT	NT B	NT
Deansgate	🚋 d				*06 49*		*07 29*	*07 39*	*08 41*		09 29	*09b31*	10 29	*10b31*	11 29	*11b31*	12 29	*12b31*
Manchester Oxford Road	d		*06 32*		*07 07*	*07 13*	*07 39*	*08 07*	*08 45*	*08 50*	09 33	*09 43*	10 33	*10 43*	11 33	*11 43*	12 33	*12 43*
Manchester Piccadilly 10	84 🚋 d	05 52	06 50	06 58	07 21	07 37	07 51	08 29	08 59	09 06	09 37	10 06	10 37	11 06	11 37	12 06	12 37	13 06
Levenshulme	84 d			07 03	07 27		07 56	08 36		09 12	09 42	10 12	10 42	11 12	11 42	12 12	12 42	13 12
Heaton Chapel	84 d			07 06	07 30		07 59	08 39		09 15	09 45	10 15	10 45	11 15	11 45	12 15	12 45	13 15
Stockport	84 d	06 01	07 01	07 10	07 34	07 47	08 03	08 43	09 08	09 19	09 49	10 19	10 49	11 19	11 49	12 19	12 49	13 19
Davenport	d			07 14	07 37		08 07	08 47	09 12	09 22	09 53	10 22	10 53	11 22	11 53	12 22	12 53	13 22
Woodsmoor	d			07 16	07 39		08 09	08 49	09 14	09 24	09 55	10 24	10 55	11 24	11 55	12 24	12 55	13 24
Hazel Grove	a	06 08	07 07	07 20	07 43	07 54	08 13	08 51	09 16	09 29	09 57	10 29	10 57	11 29	11 57	12 29	12 57	13 29
	d		07 08			07 54		08 51	09 18		09 57		10 57		11 57		12 57	
Middlewood	d					07 59					10 02				12 02			
Disley	d		07 15			08 03		08 58	09 26		10 06		11 04		12 06		13 04	
New Mills Newtown	d		07 18			08 06		09 01	09 29		10 09		11 07		12 09		13 07	
Furness Vale	d		07 20			08 08		09 04	09 31		10 11		11 10		12 11		13 10	
Whaley Bridge	d		07 24			08 12		09 07	09 35		10 15		11 13		12 15		13 13	
Chapel-en-le-Frith	d		07 31			08 19		09 15	09 42		10 22		11 21		12 22		13 21	
Dove Holes	d		07 36			08 24					10 27				12 27			
Buxton	a		07 45			08 33		09 27	09 56		10 36		11 33		12 36		13 33	

		NT B	NT	NT B	NT	NT B	NT	NT B	NT C	NT	NT B	NT	NT B	NT B	NT B	NT C	NT D
Deansgate	🚋 d	13 29	*13b31*	14 29	*14b31*	15 29	*15b31*	16 29	16 59		17 28		*18 15*	19 29	20 28	21 40	22 50
Manchester Oxford Road	d	13 33	*13 43*	14 33	*14 43*	15 33	*15 43*	16 33	17 03		17 32	*17 46*	18 35	19 33	20 32	21 43	22 53
Manchester Piccadilly 10	84 🚋 d	13 37	14 06	14 37	15 06	15 37	16 06	16 37	17 07	17 07	17 37	18 06	18 39	19 37	20 36	21 49	22 58
Levenshulme	84 d	13 42	14 12	14 42	15 12	15 42	16 12			17 16	17 45	18 12	18 45				
Heaton Chapel	84 d	13 45	14 15	14 45	15 15	15 45	16 15			17 19	17 48	18 15	18 48				
Stockport	84 d	13 49	14 19	14 49	15 19	15 49	16 19	16 46	17 19	17 23	17 51	18 19	18 50	19 48	20 45	21 57	23 07
Davenport	d	13 53	14 22	14 53	15 22	15 53	16 22	16 49	17 23	17 27	17 54	18 22	18 53	19 50	20 48	22 00	23 10
Woodsmoor	d	13 55	14 24	14 55	15 24	15 55	16 24	16 51	17 25	17 29	17 56	18 24	18 55	19 52	20 50	22 02	23 12
Hazel Grove	a	13 57	14 29	14 57	15 29	15 57	16 29	16 54	17 27	17 32	17 59	18 29	18 57	19 55	20 52	22 05	23 14
	d	13 57		14 57		15 57		16 54	17 27		17 59		18 58	19 56	20 52	22 05	23 15
Middlewood	d	14 02				16 02			17 32		18 03		19 02	19 59	20 56	22 09	23 19
Disley	d	14 06		15 04		16 06		17 01	17 36		18 07		19 06	20 03	21 00	22 13	23 23
New Mills Newtown	d	14 09		15 07		16 09		17 04	17 39		18 10		19 09	20 06	21 03	22 16	23 26
Furness Vale	d	14 11		15 10		16 11		17 06	17 41				19 12	20 10	21 06	22 19	23 29
Whaley Bridge	d	14 15		15 13		16 15		17 10	17 45		18 15		19 15	20 12	21 09	22 22	23 32
Chapel-en-le-Frith	d	14 22		15 21		16 22		17 17	17 52		18 22		19 23	20 21	21 17	22 30	23 40
Dove Holes	d	14 27				16 27			17 57		18 27		19 28	20 26	21 22	22 35	23 45
Buxton	a	14 36		15 33		16 36		17 30	18 07		18 37		19 38	20 34	21 31	22 44	23 54

Saturdays
19 July to 4 October

		NT A	NT	NT E	NT G	NT	NT	NT	NT	NT	NT E	NT G	NT B	NT	NT B	NT	NT B	NT	NT B	NT
Deansgate	🚋 d					*06 49*		*07 29*	*07 39*	*08 41*			09 29	*09b31*	10 29	*10b31*	11 29	*11b31*	12 29	*12b31*
Manchester Oxford Road	d		*06 32*			*07 07*	*07 13*	*07 39*	*08 07*	*08 45*	*08 50*	*08 50*	09 33	*09 43*	10 33	*10 43*	11 33	*11 43*	12 33	*12 43*
Manchester Piccadilly 10	84 🚋 d	05 52	06 50	06 58	07 00	07 21	07 37	07 51	08 29	08 59	09 06	09 10	09 37	10 06	10 37	11 06	11 37	12 06	12 37	13 06
Levenshulme	84 d			07 03	07 05	07 27		07 56	08 36		09 12	09 15	09 42	10 12	10 42	11 12	11 42	12 12	12 42	13 12
Heaton Chapel	84 d			07 06	07 08	07 30		07 59	08 39		09 15	09 18	09 45	10 15	10 45	11 15	11 45	12 15	12 45	13 15
Stockport	84 d	06 01	07 01	07 10	07 12	07 34	07 47	08 03	08 43	09 08	09 19	09 22	09 49	10 19	10 49	11 19	11 49	12 19	12 49	13 19
Davenport	d			07 14	07 16	07 37		08 07	08 47	09 12	09 22	09 26	09 53	10 22	10 53	11 22	11 53	12 22	12 53	13 22
Woodsmoor	d			07 16	07 18	07 39		08 09	08 49	09 14	09 24	09 28	09 55	10 24	10 55	11 24	11 55	12 24	12 55	13 24
Hazel Grove	a	06 08	07 07	07 20	07 22	07 43	07 54	08 13	08 51	09 16	09 29	09 30	09 57	10 29	10 57	11 29	11 57	12 29	12 57	13 29
	d		07 08				07 54		08 51	09 18			09 57		10 57		11 57		12 57	
Middlewood	d						07 59						10 02				12 02			
Disley	d		07 15				08 03		08 58	09 26			10 06		11 04		12 06		13 04	
New Mills Newtown	d		07 18				08 06		09 01	09 29			10 09		11 07		12 09		13 07	
Furness Vale	d		07 20				08 08		09 04	09 31			10 11		11 10		12 11		13 10	
Whaley Bridge	d		07 24				08 12		09 07	09 35			10 15		11 13		12 15		13 13	
Chapel-en-le-Frith	d		07 31				08 19		09 15	09 42			10 22		11 21		12 22		13 21	
Dove Holes	d		07 36				08 24						10 27				12 27			
Buxton	a		07 45				08 33		09 27	09 56			10 36		11 33		12 36		13 33	

		NT B	NT	NT B	NT	NT B	NT	NT B	NT C	NT	NT B	NT	NT H	NT J	NT B	NT B	NT C	NT D
Deansgate	🚋 d	13 29	*13b31*	14 29	*14b31*	15 29	*15b31*	16 29	16 59		17 28		*18 15*	*18 15*	19 29	20 28	21 40	22 50
Manchester Oxford Road	d	13 33	*13 43*	14 33	*14 43*	15 33	*15 43*	16 33	17 03		17 32	*17c46*	18 35	18 35	19 33	20 32	21 43	22 53
Manchester Piccadilly 10	84 🚋 d	13 37	14 06	14 37	15 06	15 37	16 06	16 37	17 07	17 07	17 37	18 06	18 39	18 39	19 37	20 36	21 49	22 58
Levenshulme	84 d	13 42	14 12	14 42	15 12	15 42	16 12			17 16	17 45	18 12		18 45				
Heaton Chapel	84 d	13 45	14 15	14 45	15 15	15 45	16 15			17 19	17 48	18 15		18 48				
Stockport	84 d	13 49	14 19	14 49	15 19	15 49	16 19	16 46	17 19	17 23	17 51	18 19	18 48	18 50	19 48	20 45	21 57	23 07
Davenport	d	13 53	14 22	14 53	15 22	15 53	16 22	16 49	17 23	17 27	17 54	18 22	18 52	18 53	19 50	20 48	22 00	23 10
Woodsmoor	d	13 55	14 24	14 55	15 24	15 55	16 24	16 51	17 25	17 29	17 56	18 24	18 54	18 55	19 52	20 50	22 02	23 12
Hazel Grove	a	13 57	14 29	14 57	15 29	15 57	16 29	16 54	17 27	17 32	17 59	18 29	18 56	18 57	19 55	20 52	22 05	23 14
	d	13 57		14 57		15 57		16 54	17 27		17 59		18 56	18 58	19 56	20 52	22 05	23 15
Middlewood	d	14 02				16 02			17 32		18 03		19 01	19 02	19 59	20 56	22 09	23 19
Disley	d	14 06		15 04		16 06		17 01	17 36		18 07		19 05	19 06	20 03	21 00	22 13	23 23
New Mills Newtown	d	14 09		15 07		16 09		17 04	17 39		18 10		19 08	19 09	20 06	21 03	22 16	23 26
Furness Vale	d	14 11		15 10		16 11		17 06	17 41				19 10	19 12	20 10	21 06	22 19	23 29
Whaley Bridge	d	14 15		15 13		16 15		17 10	17 45		18 15		19 14	19 15	20 12	21 09	22 22	23 32
Chapel-en-le-Frith	d	14 22		15 21		16 22		17 17	17 52		18 22		19 21	19 23	20 21	21 17	22 30	23 40
Dove Holes	d	14 27				16 27			17 57		18 27		19 26	19 28	20 26	21 22	22 35	23 45
Buxton	a	14 36		15 33		16 36		17 30	18 07		18 37		19 36	19 38	20 34	21 31	22 44	23 54

For general notes see front of timetable
For details of catering facilities see Directory of Train Operators

- **A** To Sheffield (Table 78)
- **B** From Blackpool North (Table 82)
- **C** From Southport (Table 82)
- **D** From Clitheroe (Table 94)
- **E** Until 6 September
- **G** From 13 September
- **H** Until 6 September. From Blackpool North (Table 82)
- **J** From 13 September. From Blackpool North (Table 82)
- **b** Change at Manchester Oxford Road and Manchester Piccadilly
- **c** From 13 September dep. 1744

Table 86

Saturdays
from 11 October

Manchester → Hazel Grove and Buxton

Network Diagram - see first page of Table 78

	NT A	NT	NT	NT	NT	NT	NT	NT	NT	NT B	NT	NT B	NT	NT B	NT	NT B	NT
Deansgate ⛴ d				*06 49*		*07 29*	*07 39*	*08 41*		09 29	*09b31*	10 29	*10b31*	11 29	*11b31*	12 29	*12b31*
Manchester Oxford Road d		*06 32*		*07 07*	*07 13*	*07 39*	*08 07*	*08 45*	*08 50*	09 33	*09 43*	10 33	*10 43*	11 33	*11 43*	12 33	*12 43*
Manchester Piccadilly 10 84 ⛴ d	05 52	06 50	07 00	07 21	07 37	07 51	08 29	08 59	09 10	09 37	10 06	10 37	11 06	11 37	12 06	12 37	13 06
Levenshulme 84 d			07 05	07 27		07 56	08 36		09 15	09 42	10 12	10 42	11 12	11 42	12 12	12 42	13 12
Heaton Chapel 84 d			07 08	07 30		07 59	08 39		09 18	09 45	10 15	10 45	11 15	11 45	12 15	12 45	13 15
Stockport 84 d	06 01	07 01	07 12	07 34	07 47	08 03	08 43	09 08	09 22	09 49	10 19	10 49	11 19	11 49	12 19	12 49	13 19
Davenport d			07 16	07 37		08 07	08 47	09 12	09 26	09 53	10 22	10 53	11 22	11 53	12 22	12 53	13 22
Woodsmoor d			07 18	07 39		08 09	08 49	09 14	09 28	09 55	10 24	10 55	11 24	11 55	12 24	12 55	13 24
Hazel Grove a	06 08	07 07	07 22	07 43	07 54	08 13	08 51	09 16	09 30	09 57	10 29	10 57	11 29	11 57	12 29	12 57	13 29
d		07 08			07 54		08 51	09 18		09 57		10 57		11 57		12 57	
Middlewood d					07 59					10 02				12 02			
Disley d		07 15			08 03		08 58	09 26		10 06		11 04		12 06		13 04	
New Mills Newtown d		07 18			08 06		09 01	09 29		10 09		11 07		12 09		13 07	
Furness Vale d		07 20			08 08		09 04	09 31		10 11		11 10		12 11		13 10	
Whaley Bridge d		07 24			08 12		09 07	09 35		10 15		11 13		12 15		13 13	
Chapel-en-le-Frith d		07 31			08 19		09 15	09 42		10 22		11 21		12 22		13 21	
Dove Holes d		07 36			08 24					10 27				12 27			
Buxton a		07 47			08 35		09 29	09 58		10 38		11 35		12 38		13 35	

	NT B	NT	NT B	NT	NT B	NT	NT B	NT C	NT	NT B	NT	NT B	NT B	NT B	NT C	NT D
Deansgate ⛴ d	13 29	*13b31*	14 29	*14b31*	15 29	*15b31*	16 29	16 59		17 28		*18 15*	19 29	20 28	21 40	22 50
Manchester Oxford Road d	13 33	*13 43*	14 33	*14 43*	15 33	*15 43*	16 33	17 03		17 32	*17 44*	18 35	19 33	20 32	21 43	22 53
Manchester Piccadilly 10 84 ⛴ d	13 37	14 06	14 37	15 06	15 37	16 06	16 37	17 07	17 07	17 37	18 06	18 39	19 37	20 36	21 49	22 58
Levenshulme 84 d	13 42	14 12	14 42	15 12	15 42	16 12			17 16	17 45	18 12	18 45				
Heaton Chapel 84 d	13 45	14 15	14 45	15 15	15 45	16 15			17 19	17 48	18 15	18 48				
Stockport 84 d	13 49	14 19	14 49	15 19	15 49	16 19	16 46	17 19	17 23	17 51	18 19	18 50	19 48	20 45	21 57	23 07
Davenport d	13 53	14 22	14 53	15 22	15 53	16 22	16 49	17 23	17 27	17 54	18 22	18 53	19 50	20 48	22 00	23 10
Woodsmoor d	13 55	14 24	14 55	15 24	15 55	16 24	16 51	17 25	17 29	17 56	18 24	18 55	19 52	20 50	22 02	23 12
Hazel Grove a	13 57	14 29	14 57	15 29	15 57	16 29	16 54	17 27	17 32	17 59	18 29	18 57	19 55	20 52	22 05	23 14
d	13 57		14 57		15 57		16 54	17 27		17 59		18 58	19 56	20 52	22 05	23 15
Middlewood d	14 02				16 02			17 32		18 03		19 02	19 59	20 56	22 09	23 19
Disley d	14 06		15 04		16 06		17 01	17 36		18 07		19 06	20 03	21 00	22 13	23 23
New Mills Newtown d	14 09		15 07		16 09		17 04	17 39		18 10		19 09	20 06	21 03	22 16	23 26
Furness Vale d	14 11		15 10		16 11		17 06	17 41				19 12	20 10	21 06	22 19	23 29
Whaley Bridge d	14 15		15 13		16 15		17 10	17 45		18 15		19 15	20 12	21 09	22 22	23 32
Chapel-en-le-Frith d	14 22		15 21		16 22		17 17	17 52		18 22		19 23	20 21	21 17	22 30	23 40
Dove Holes d	14 27				16 27			17 57		18 27		19 28	20 26	21 22	22 35	23 45
Buxton a	14 38		15 35		16 38		17 32	18 09		18 39		19 39	20 36	21 33	22 46	23 56

Sundays
until 13 July

	NT A	NT	NT B	NT A	NT B	NT B	NT B	NT B	NT B	NT A	NT B	NT B	NT A	NT B	NT B	NT B	NT B	NT B	NT B
Deansgate ⛴ d			09 43	*10 09*	10 43	11 45	12 43	13 43	14 43		15 43	16 43		17 43	18 43	19 43	20 43	21 43	22 43
Manchester Oxford Road d			09 46	*10 12*	10 46	11 50	12 46	13 46	14 46		15 46	16 46	*16 58*	17 46	18 46	19 46	20 46	21 46	22 46
Manchester Piccadilly 10 84 ⛴ d	08 43	08 53	09 56	10 30	10 56	11 56	12 55	13 56	14 53	15 05	15 53	16 53	17 19	17 53	18 53	19 53	20 53	21 53	22 51
Levenshulme 84 d		08 58	10 01		11 01	12 01	13 01	14 01	14 58		15 58	16 58		17 58	18 58	19 58	20 58	21 58	22 56
Heaton Chapel 84 d		09 01	10 04		11 04	12 04	13 04	14 04	15 01		16 01	17 01		18 01	19 01	20 01	21 01	22 01	22 59
Stockport 84 d	08 53	09 05	10 08	10 46	11 08	12 08	13 08	14 08	15 05	15 27	16 05	17 05	17 28	18 05	19 05	20 05	21 05	22 05	23 03
Davenport d		09 09	10 11		11 11	12 11	13 11	14 11	15 08		16 08	17 08		18 08	19 08	20 08	21 08	22 08	23 07
Woodsmoor d		09 11	10 13		11 13	12 13	13 13	14 13	15 10		16 10	17 10		18 10	19 10	20 10	21 10	22 10	23 09
Hazel Grove a	09 00	09 13	10 15	10 53	11 15	12 16	13 16	14 15	15 13	15 34	16 12	17 12	17 35	18 12	19 12	20 13	21 13	22 13	23 11
d		09 13	10 16		11 16	12 16	13 16	14 16	15 13		16 13	17 13		18 13	19 13	20 13	21 13	22 13	23 11
Middlewood d		09 18	10 20		11 20	12 21	13 20	14 20	15 17		16 17	17 17		18 17	19 17	20 17	21 17	22 17	23 16
Disley d		09 22	10 24		11 24	12 25	13 24	14 24	15 21		16 21	17 21		18 21	19 21	20 21	21 21	22 21	23 20
New Mills Newtown d		09 25	10 27		11 27	12 28	13 27	14 27	15 24		16 24	17 24		18 24	19 24	20 24	21 24	22 24	23 23
Furness Vale d		09 27	10 30		11 30	12 31	13 29	14 30	15 27		16 27	17 27		18 27	19 27	20 27	21 27	22 27	23 25
Whaley Bridge d		09 31	10 33		11 33	12 34	13 34	14 33	15 30		16 30	17 30		18 30	19 30	20 30	21 30	22 30	23 29
Chapel-en-le-Frith d		09 38	10 41		11 41	12 42	13 41	14 41	15 38		16 38	17 38		18 38	19 38	20 38	21 38	22 38	23 36
Dove Holes d		09 43	10 46		11 46	12 47	13 46	14 46	15 43		16 43	17 43		18 43	19 43	20 43	21 43	22 43	23 41
Buxton a		09 53	10 55		11 55	12 56	13 56	14 55	15 53		16 52	17 52		18 52	19 52	20 53	21 53	22 53	23 51

For general notes see front of timetable
For details of catering facilities see Directory of Train Operators

A To Sheffield (Table 78)
B From Blackpool North (Table 82)
C From Southport (Table 82)
D From Clitheroe (Table 94)

b Change at Manchester Oxford Road and Manchester Piccadilly

Table 86

Sundays

20 July to 7 September

Manchester → Hazel Grove and Buxton

Network Diagram - see first page of Table 78

		NT	NT A	NT B	NT A	NT B	NT B	NT B	NT B	NT B	NT A	NT B	NT B	NT A	NT B	NT B	NT B	NT B	NT B	NT B
Deansgate	🚋 d	.	.	09 43	*10 09*	10 43	11 45	12 43	13 43	14 43	.	15 43	16 43	.	17 43	18 43	19 43	20 43	21 43	22 43
Manchester Oxford Road	d	.	.	09 46	*10 12*	10 46	11 50	12 46	13 46	14 46	.	15 46	16 46	*16 58*	17 46	18 46	19 46	20 46	21 46	22 46
Manchester Piccadilly 10	84 🚋 d	08 53	09 04	09 56	10 30	10 56	11 56	12 56	13 56	14 56	15 08	15 53	16 53	17 19	17 53	18 53	19 53	20 53	21 53	22 51
Levenshulme	84 d	08 58	.	10 01	.	11 01	12 01	13 01	14 01	15 01	.	15 58	16 58	.	17 58	18 58	19 58	20 58	21 58	22 56
Heaton Chapel	84 d	09 01	.	10 04	.	11 04	12 04	13 04	14 04	15 04	.	16 01	17 01	.	18 01	19 01	20 01	21 01	22 01	22 59
Stockport	84 d	09 05	09 17	10 08	10 46	11 08	12 08	13 08	14 08	15 08	15 27	16 05	17 05	17 28	18 05	19 05	20 05	21 05	22 05	23 03
Davenport	d	09 09	.	10 11	.	11 11	12 11	13 11	14 11	15 11	.	16 08	17 08	.	18 08	19 08	20 08	21 08	22 08	23 07
Woodsmoor	d	09 11	.	10 13	.	11 13	12 13	13 13	14 13	15 13	.	16 10	17 10	.	18 10	19 10	20 10	21 10	22 10	23 09
Hazel Grove	a	09 13	09 24	10 15	10 53	11 15	12 16	13 16	14 15	15 15	15 34	16 12	17 12	17 35	18 12	19 12	20 13	21 13	22 13	23 11
	d	09 13	.	10 16	.	11 16	12 17	13 16	14 16	15 16	.	16 13	17 13	.	18 13	19 13	20 13	21 13	22 13	23 11
Middlewood	d	09 18	.	10 20	.	11 20	12 22	13 20	14 20	15 20	.	16 17	17 17	.	18 17	19 17	20 17	21 17	22 17	23 16
Disley	d	09 22	.	10 24	.	11 24	12 26	13 24	14 24	15 24	.	16 21	17 21	.	18 21	19 21	20 21	21 21	22 21	23 20
New Mills Newtown	d	09 25	.	10 27	.	11 27	12 29	13 27	14 27	15 27	.	16 24	17 24	.	18 24	19 24	20 24	21 24	22 24	23 23
Furness Vale	d	09 27	.	10 30	.	11 30	12 31	13 30	14 30	15 30	.	16 27	17 27	.	18 27	19 27	20 27	21 27	22 27	23 25
Whaley Bridge	d	09 31	.	10 33	.	11 33	12 35	13 33	14 33	15 33	.	16 30	17 30	.	18 30	19 30	20 30	21 30	22 30	23 29
Chapel-en-le-Frith	d	09 38	.	10 41	.	11 41	12 42	13 41	14 41	15 41	.	16 38	17 38	.	18 38	19 38	20 38	21 38	22 38	23 36
Dove Holes	d	09 43	.	10 46	.	11 46	12 47	13 46	14 46	15 46	.	16 43	17 43	.	18 43	19 43	20 43	21 43	22 43	23 41
Buxton	a	09 53	.	10 55	.	11 55	12 56	13 55	14 56	15 56	.	16 52	17 52	.	18 52	19 52	20 53	21 53	22 53	23 51

Sundays

from 14 September

		NT	NT B	NT B	NT B	NT B	NT B	NT B	NT C	NT B	NT B	NT C	NT B	NT B	NT B	NT B	NT B	NT B
Deansgate	🚋 d	.	09 43	10 43	11 43	12 43	13 43	14 43	.	15 43	16 43	.	17 43	18 43	19 43	20 43	21 43	22 43
Manchester Oxford Road	d	.	09 46	10 46	11 47	12 46	13 46	14 46	.	15 46	16 46	*16 58*	17 46	18 46	19 46	20 46	21 46	22 46
Manchester Piccadilly 10	84 🚋 d	08 53	09 53	10 56	11 53	12 56	13 53	14 56	15 08	15 53	16 53	17 19	17 53	18 51	19 53	20 53	21 53	22 51
Levenshulme	84 d	08 58	09 58	11 01	11 58	12 58	13 58	15 01		15 58	16 58		17 58	18 57	19 58	20 58	21 58	22 56
Heaton Chapel	84 d	09 01	10 01	11 04	12 01	13 01	14 01	15 04		16 01	17 01		18 01	19 00	20 01	21 01	22 01	22 59
Stockport	84 d	09 05	10 05	11 08	12 05	13 04	14 08	15 08	15 27	16 05	17 05	17 28	18 05	19 05	20 05	21 05	22 05	23 03
Davenport	d	09 09	10 08	11 11	12 09	13 08	14 11	15 11		16 08	17 08		18 09	19 08	20 08	21 08	22 08	23 07
Woodsmoor	d	09 11	10 10	11 13	12 11	13 10	14 13	15 13		16 10	17 10		18 11	19 10	20 10	21 10	22 10	23 09
Hazel Grove	a	09 13	10 12	11 15	12 13	13 15	14 15	15 15	15 34	16 12	17 12	17 35	18 13	19 11	20 13	21 13	22 13	23 11
	d	09 13	10 13	11 16	12 13	13 16	14 16	15 16	.	16 13	17 13	.	18 13	19 14	20 13	21 13	22 13	23 11
Middlewood	d	09 18	10 17	11 20	12 18	13 20	14 20	15 20	.	16 17	17 17	.	18 18	19 19	20 17	21 17	22 17	23 16
Disley	d	09 22	10 21	11 24	12 22	13 24	14 24	15 24	.	16 21	17 21	.	18 22	19 23	20 21	21 21	22 21	23 20
New Mills Newtown	d	09 25	10 24	11 27	12 25	13 27	14 27	15 27	.	16 24	17 24	.	18 25	19 26	20 24	21 24	22 24	23 23
Furness Vale	d	09 27	10 27	11 30	12 27	13 30	14 30	15 30	.	16 27	17 27	.	18 27	19 28	20 27	21 27	22 27	23 25
Whaley Bridge	d	09 31	10 30	11 33	12 31	13 33	14 33	15 33	.	16 30	17 30	.	18 31	19 32	20 30	21 30	22 30	23 29
Chapel-en-le-Frith	d	09 38	10 38	11 41	12 38	13 41	14 41	15 41	.	16 38	17 38	.	18 38	19 39	20 38	21 38	22 38	23 36
Dove Holes	d	09 43	10 43	11 46	12 43	13 46	14 46	15 46	.	16 43	17 43	.	18 43	19 44	20 43	21 43	22 43	23 41
Buxton	a	09 53	10 52	11 55	12 53	13 55	14 56	15 57	.	16 52	17 52	.	18 54	19 53	20 53	21 53	22 53	23 51

For general notes see front of timetable
For details of catering facilities see Directory of Train Operators

A To Sheffield (Table 78)
B From Blackpool North (Table 82)
C 14 September only. To Sheffield (Table 78)

Mondays to Fridays
until 3 October

Buxton and Hazel Grove → Manchester

Network Diagram - see first page of Table 78

Miles	Station		NT	NT	NT	NT	NT	NT	NT	NT	EM	NT	NT	NT	NT	NT	NT	NT	NT	NT	NT
					A		B			A	◇ C ✠			A				A		A	
0	**Buxton**	d	05 54		06 34		07 04			07 40			07 57	08 36		09 36		10 37		11 34	
3	Dove Holes	d			06 40		07 10						08 03	08 42		09 42				11 40	
5¼	Chapel-en-le-Frith	d	06 02		06 44		07 14			07 49			08 07	08 46		09 46		10 45		11 44	
9¼	Whaley Bridge	d	06 08		06 49		07 19			07 55			08 12	08 51		09 51		10 51		11 49	
10¾	Furness Vale	d	06 11		06 52		07 22						08 15	08 54		09 54		10 54		11 52	
11½	New Mills Newtown	d	06 14		06 55		07 25			08 00			08 18	08 57		09 57		10 57		11 55	
13¼	Disley	d	06 17		06 59		07 29			08 04			08 22	09 01		10 01		11 00		11 59	
14¾	Middlewood	d			07 02		07 32						08 25			10 04				12 02	
17	**Hazel Grove**	a	06 27		07 10		07 40			08 13			08 33	09 09		10 12		11 10		12 10	
—		d	06 27	06 53	07 10	07 20	07 40	07 53	08 06	08 14	08 19	08 29	08 33	09 10	09 41	10 12	10 41	11 10	11 41	12 10	12 41
18	Woodsmoor	d	06 29	06 55	07 12	07 22	07 42	07 55	08 08			08 31	08 35	09 12	09 43	10 14	10 43	11 12	11 43	12 12	12 43
18¾	Davenport	d	06 31	06 57	07 14	07 24	07 44	07 57	08 10			08 33	08 37	09 14	09 45	10 16	10 45	11 14	11 45	12 14	12 45
19¾	**Stockport**	84 a	06 36	07 02	07 19	07 29	07 49	08 00	08 14	08 21	08 26	08 37	08 41	09 19	09 49	10 21	10 49	11 18	11 49	12 18	12 49
21¼	Heaton Chapel	84 a		07 06		07 33		08 05				08 41		09 23							
22¾	Levenshulme	84 a		07 09		07 36		08 08				08 44		09 26							
25¾	**Manchester Piccadilly** 10	84 (ship) a	06 47	07 17	07 30	07 45	08 00	08 19	08 26	08 31	08 36	08 53	08 56	09 32	10 01	10 33	11 00	11 29	12 00	12 29	13 00
—	Manchester Oxford Road	a	*07 09*		07 33		08 03			08 35	08 40		*09 09*	09 36	*10 14*	10 47	*11 13*	11 32	*12 13*	12 32	*13 13*
—	Deansgate	(ship) a			07 35		08 15			08 37	*08 50*		*09 26*	09 38	*10 26*	10 50	*11 26*	11 35	*12 26*	12 35	*13 26*

Station		NT	NT	NT	NT	NT	NT	NT	NT	NT	NT	NT	NT	NT	NT	NT	NT	NT	NT	NT
		A		A		A		A	D		A			A		E		G	H	
Buxton	d	12 37		13 34		14 37			15 47		16 36	17 06		17 34		18 22	18 55	19 55	21 38	22 55
Dove Holes	d			13 40					15 53					17 40			19 01	20 01	21 44	23 01
Chapel-en-le-Frith	d	12 45		13 44		14 45			15 57		16 44	17 14		17 44		18 30	19 05	20 05	21 48	23 05
Whaley Bridge	d	12 51		13 49		14 51			16 02		16 50	17 20		17 49		18 36	19 10	20 10	21 53	23 10
Furness Vale	d	12 54		13 52		14 54			16 05		16 53	17 23		17 52		18 39	19 13	20 13	21 56	23 13
New Mills Newtown	d	12 57		13 55		14 57			16 08		16 56	17 26		17 55		18 42	19 16	20 16	21 59	23 16
Disley	d	13 00		13 59		15 00			16 12		16 59	17 29		17 59		18 45	19 20	20 20	22 03	23 20
Middlewood	d			14 02					16 15					18 02			19 23	20 23	22 06	23 23
Hazel Grove	a	13 10		14 09		15 10			16 26		17 09	17 39		18 10		18 55	19 31	20 31	22 14	23 31
	d	13 10	13 41	14 09	14 41	15 10	15 41	16 10	16 28	16 41	17 09	17 40	18 07	18 10	18 22	18 55	19 31	20 31	22 14	23 31
Woodsmoor	d	13 12	13 43	14 11	14 43	15 12	15 43	16 12	16 30	16 43	17 11	17 42	18 09	18 12	18 24	18 57	19 33	20 33	22 16	23 33
Davenport	d	13 14	13 45	14 13	14 45	15 14	15 45	16 14	16 32	16 45	17 13	17 44	18 11	18 14	18 26	18 59	19 35	20 35	22 18	23 35
Stockport	84 a	13 18	13 49	14 17	14 49	15 18	15 49	16 18	16 40	16 49	17 17	17 49	18 14	18 18	18 30	19 04	19 40	20 40	22 23	23 39
Heaton Chapel	84 a															19 09				
Levenshulme	84 a															19 12				
Manchester Piccadilly 10	84 (ship) a	13 27	14 00	14 27	15 00	15 27	16 00	16 27	16 50	17 00	17 31	18 02	18 26	18 29	18 42	19 24	19 54	20 52	22 33	23 52
Manchester Oxford Road	a	13 32	*14 13*	14 32	*15 13*	15 32	*16 13*	16 32	16 55	*17 13*	17 34	*18 18*		18 33	*19 09*	19 28	*20 09*	20 54	22 37	
Deansgate	(ship) a	13 35	*14 26*	14 35	*15 26*	15 35	*16 26*	16 35	16 58	*17 21*	17 37	*18 31*		18 36	*19 17*	19 31	*20 17*	20 56	22 40	

Mondays to Fridays
from 6 October

Station		NT	NT	NT	NT	NT	NT	NT	NT	EM	NT	NT	NT	NT	NT	NT	NT	NT	NT	NT	NT
				A		B			A	◇ C ✠			A				A		A		A
Buxton	d	05 49		06 29		06 59			07 35			07 52	08 36		09 31		10 32		11 29		12 32
Dove Holes	d			06 35		07 05						07 58	08 42		09 37				11 35		
Chapel-en-le-Frith	d	05 57		06 39		07 09			07 44			08 02	08 46		09 41		10 40		11 39		12 40
Whaley Bridge	d	06 03		06 44		07 14			07 50			08 07	08 51		09 46		10 46		11 44		12 46
Furness Vale	d	06 06		06 47		07 17						08 10	08 54		09 49		10 49		11 47		12 49
New Mills Newtown	d	06 09		06 50		07 20			07 55			08 13	08 57		09 52		10 52		11 50		12 52
Disley	d	06 12		06 54		07 24			07 59			08 17	09 01		09 56		10 55		11 54		12 55
Middlewood	d			06 57		07 27						08 20			09 59				11 57		
Hazel Grove	a	06 27		07 10		07 40			08 13			08 33	09 09		10 12		11 10		12 10		13 10
	d	06 27	06 53	07 10	07 20	07 40	07 53	08 06	08 14	08 19	08 29	08 33	09 10	09 41	10 12	10 41	11 10	11 41	12 10	12 41	13 10
Woodsmoor	d	06 29	06 55	07 12	07 22	07 42	07 55	08 08			08 31	08 35	09 12	09 43	10 14	10 43	11 12	11 43	12 12	12 43	13 12
Davenport	d	06 31	06 57	07 14	07 24	07 44	07 57	08 10			08 33	08 37	09 14	09 45	10 16	10 45	11 14	11 45	12 14	12 45	13 14
Stockport	84 a	06 36	07 02	07 19	07 29	07 49	08 00	08 14	08 21	08 26	08 37	08 41	09 19	09 49	10 21	10 49	11 18	11 49	12 18	12 49	13 18
Heaton Chapel	84 a		07 06		07 33		08 05				08 41		09 23								
Levenshulme	84 a		07 09		07 36		08 08				08 44		09 26								
Manchester Piccadilly 10	84 (ship) a	06 47	07 17	07 30	07 45	08 00	08 19	08 26	08 31	08 36	08 53	08 56	09 32	10 01	10 33	11 00	11 29	12 00	12 29	13 00	13 27
Manchester Oxford Road	a	*07 09*		07 33		08 03			08 35	08 40		*09 09*	09 36	*10 14*	10 47	*11 13*	11 32	*12 13*	12 32	*13 13*	13 32
Deansgate	(ship) a			07 35		08 15			08 37	*08 50*		*09 26*	09 38	*10 26*	10 50	*11 26*	11 35	*12 26*	12 35	*13 26*	13 35

For general notes see front of timetable
For details of catering facilities see Directory of Train Operators

- **A** To Blackpool North (Table 82)
- **B** To Liverpool Lime Street (Table 89)
- **C** From Nottingham to Liverpool Lime Street (Table 49)
- **D** To Preston (Table 82)
- **E** To Salford Crescent (Table 82)
- **G** To Bolton (Table 82)
- **H** To Southport (Table 82)

Buxton and Hazel Grove → Manchester

Network Diagram - see first page of Table 78

	NT	NT A	NT	NT A	NT	NT A	NT B	NT	NT A	NT	NT	NT A	NT	NT C	NT	NT D	NT E	NT
Buxton d		13 29		14 32			15 42		16 31	17 01		17 34		18 17	18 50	19 50	21 33	22 50
Dove Holes d		13 35					15 48					17 40			18 56	19 56	21 39	22 56
Chapel-en-le-Frith d		13 39		14 40			15 52		16 39	17 09		17 44		18 25	19 00	20 00	21 43	23 00
Whaley Bridge d		13 44		14 46			15 57		16 45	17 15		17 49		18 31	19 05	20 05	21 48	23 05
Furness Vale d		13 47		14 49			16 00		16 48	17 18		17 52		18 34	19 08	20 08	21 51	23 08
New Mills Newtown d		13 50		14 52			16 03		16 51	17 21		17 55		18 37	19 11	20 11	21 54	23 11
Disley d		13 54		14 55			16 07		16 54	17 24		17 59		18 40	19 15	20 15	21 58	23 15
Middlewood d		13 57					16 10					18 02			19 18	20 18	22 01	23 18
Hazel Grove a		14 09		15 10			16 26		17 09	17 39		18 10		18 55	19 31	20 31	22 14	23 31
d	13 41	14 09	14 41	15 10	15 41	16 10	16 28	16 41	17 09	17 40	18 07	18 10	18 22	18 55	19 31	20 31	22 14	23 31
Woodsmoor d	13 43	14 11	14 43	15 12	15 43	16 12	16 30	16 43	17 11	17 42	18 09	18 12	18 24	18 57	19 33	20 33	22 16	23 33
Davenport d	13 45	14 13	14 45	15 14	15 45	16 14	16 32	16 45	17 13	17 44	18 11	18 14	18 26	18 59	19 35	20 35	22 18	23 35
Stockport 84 a	13 49	14 17	14 49	15 18	15 49	16 18	16 40	16 49	17 17	17 49	18 14	18 18	18 30	19 04	19 40	20 40	22 23	23 39
Heaton Chapel 84 a														19 09				
Levenshulme 84 a														19 12				
Manchester Piccadilly [10] 84 a	14 00	14 27	15 00	15 27	16 00	16 27	16 50	17 00	17 31	18 02	18 26	18 29	18 42	19 24	19 54	20 52	22 33	23 52
Manchester Oxford Road a	*14 13*	14 32	*15 13*	15 32	*16 13*	16 32	16 55	*17 13*	17 34	*18 18*		18 33	*19 09*	19 28	*20 09*	20 54	22 37	
Deansgate a	*14 26*	14 35	*15 26*	15 35	*16 26*	16 35	16 58	*17 21*	17 37	*18 31*		18 36	*19 17*	19 31	*20 17*	20 56	22 40	

Saturdays

until 12 July

	NT	NT A	NT	NT	NT A	NT	NT	NT A	NT	NT	NT	NT A	NT	NT A	NT	NT A	NT
Buxton d	05 54	06 34			07 36		07 57	08 37		09 36		10 37		11 33		12 36	
Dove Holes d		06 40			07 42		08 03	08 43		09 42				11 39			
Chapel-en-le-Frith d	06 02	06 44			07 46		08 07	08 47		09 46		10 45		11 43		12 44	
Whaley Bridge d	06 08	06 49			07 51		08 12	08 52		09 51		10 51		11 48		12 50	
Furness Vale d	06 11	06 52			07 54		08 15	08 55		09 54		10 54		11 51		12 53	
New Mills Newtown d	06 14	06 55			07 57		08 18	08 58		09 57		10 57		11 54		12 56	
Disley d	06 17	06 59			08 01		08 22	09 02		10 01		11 00		11 58		12 59	
Middlewood d		07 02			08 06		08 25			10 04				12 01			
Hazel Grove a	06 27	07 10			08 13		08 33	09 11		10 12		11 10		12 09		13 09	
d	06 27	07 10	07 24	07 53	08 14	08 25	08 33	09 12	09 37	10 12	10 41	11 10	11 41	12 09	12 41	13 09	13 41
Woodsmoor d	06 29	07 12	07 26	07 55		08 27	08 35	09 14	09 39	10 14	10 43	11 12	11 43	12 11	12 43	13 11	13 43
Davenport d	06 31	07 14	07 28	07 57		08 29	08 37	09 16	09 41	10 16	10 45	11 14	11 45	12 13	12 45	13 13	13 45
Stockport 84 a	06 35	07 17	07 32	08 00	08 20	08 32	08 41	09 20		10 21	10 49	11 18	11 49	12 18	12 49	13 18	13 49
Heaton Chapel 84 a				08 05					09 50								
Levenshulme 84 a				08 08					09 53								
Manchester Piccadilly [10] 84 a	06 47	07 30	07 42	08 14	08 29	08 44	08 56	09 32	10 01	10 33	11 01	11 29	12 01	12 29	13 01	13 28	14 01
Manchester Oxford Road a	*07 09*	07 33	*08 09*	*08 31*	08 33	*08 58*	*09 09*	09 36	*10 14*	*10 47*	*11 13*	11 32	*12 13*	12 33	*13 13*	13 32	*14 13*
Deansgate a		07 35		*08 33*	08 37	*09 03*	*09 26*	09 38	*10 26*	*10 50*	*11 26*	11 35	*12 26*	12 35	*13 26*	13 35	*14 26*

	NT A	NT	NT A	NT	NT A	NT	NT A	NT	NT A	NT	NT C	NT	NT D	NT E	NT
Buxton d	13 33		14 36		15 33		16 33		17 31		18 22	18 55	19 55	21 38	22 55
Dove Holes d	13 39				15 39				17 37			19 01	20 01	21 44	23 01
Chapel-en-le-Frith d	13 43		14 44		15 43		16 41		17 41		18 30	19 05	20 05	21 48	23 05
Whaley Bridge d	13 48		14 50		15 48		16 47		17 46		18 36	19 10	20 10	21 53	23 10
Furness Vale d	13 51		14 53		15 51		16 50		17 49		18 39	19 13	20 13	21 56	23 13
New Mills Newtown d	13 54		14 56		15 54		16 53		17 52		18 42	19 16	20 16	21 59	23 16
Disley d	13 58		14 59		15 58		16 56		17 56		18 45	19 20	20 20	22 03	23 20
Middlewood d	14 01				16 01				17 59			19 23	20 23	22 06	23 23
Hazel Grove a	14 09		15 09		16 09		17 06		18 07		18 55	19 31	20 31	22 14	23 31
d	14 09	14 41	15 09	15 41	16 09	16 41	17 06	17 41	18 07	18 41	18 55	19 31	20 31	22 14	23 31
Woodsmoor d	14 11	14 43	15 11	15 43	16 11	16 43	17 08	17 43	18 09	18 43	18 57	19 33	20 33	22 16	23 33
Davenport d	14 13	14 45	15 13	15 45	16 13	16 45	17 10	17 45	18 11	18 45	18 59	19 35	20 35	22 18	23 35
Stockport 84 a	14 18	14 49	15 18	15 49	16 18	16 49	17 15	17 50	18 15	18 49	19 04	19 40	20 40	22 23	23 40
Heaton Chapel 84 a							17 19		18 20		19 09				
Levenshulme 84 a							17 22		18 23		19 12				
Manchester Piccadilly [10] 84 a	14 28	15 01	15 28	16 01	16 28	17 01	17 29	18 02	18 30	19 01	19 19	19 51	20 52	22 33	23 52
Manchester Oxford Road a	14 32	*15 13*	15 32	*16 13*	16 32	*17 13*	17 32	*18 18*	18 34	*19 13*	19 22	*20 09*	20 54	22 37	
Deansgate a	14 35	*15 26*	15 35	*16 28*	16 35	*17 21*	17 35	*18 31*	18 38	*19 17*	19 25	*20 17*	20 56	22 40	

For general notes see front of timetable
For details of catering facilities see Directory of Train Operators

A To Blackpool North (Table 82)
B To Preston (Table 82)
C To Salford Crescent (Table 82)
D To Bolton (Table 82)
E To Southport (Table 82)

19 July to 4 October

Buxton and Hazel Grove → Manchester

Network Diagram - see first page of Table 78

		NT	NT A	NT	NT	NT A	NT	NT B	NT A	NT	NT	NT B	NT A	NT	NT A	NT	NT A	NT
Buxton	d	05 54	06 34			07 36		07 57	08 37		09 36		10 37		11 34		12 37	
Dove Holes	d		06 40			07 42		08 03	08 43		09 42				11 40			
Chapel-en-le-Frith	d	06 02	06 44			07 46		08 07	08 47		09 46		10 45		11 44		12 45	
Whaley Bridge	d	06 08	06 49			07 51		08 12	08 52		09 51		10 51		11 49		12 51	
Furness Vale	d	06 11	06 52			07 54		08 15	08 55		09 54		10 54		11 52		12 54	
New Mills Newtown	d	06 14	06 55			07 57		08 18	08 58		09 57		10 57		11 55		12 57	
Disley	d	06 17	06 59			08 01		08 22	09 02		10 01		11 00		11 59		13 00	
Middlewood	d		07 02			08 06		08 25			10 04				12 02			
Hazel Grove	a	06 27	07 10			08 13		08 33	09 11		10 12		11 10		12 10		13 10	
	d	06 27	07 10	07 24	07 53	08 14	08 25	08 33	09 12	09 37	10 12	10 41	11 10	11 41	12 10	12 41	13 10	13 41
Woodsmoor	d	06 29	07 12	07 26	07 55		08 27	08 35	09 14	09 39	10 14	10 43	11 12	11 43	12 12	12 43	13 12	13 43
Davenport	d	06 31	07 14	07 28	07 57		08 29	08 37	09 16	09 41	10 16	10 45	11 14	11 45	12 14	12 45	13 14	13 45
Stockport	84 a	06 35	07 17	07 32	08 00	08 20	08 32	08 41	09 20		10 21	10 49	11 18	11 49	12 18	12 49	13 18	13 49
Heaton Chapel	84 a				08 05					09 50								
Levenshulme	84 a				08 08					09 53								
Manchester Piccadilly 10	84 a	06 47	07 30	07 42	08 14	08 29	08 44	08 56	09 32	10 01	10 33	11 01	11 29	12 01	12 29	13 01	13 27	14 01
Manchester Oxford Road	a	*07 09*	07 33	*08 09*	*08 31*	08 33	*08 58*	*09 09*	09 36	*10 14*	*10 47*	*11 13*	11 32	*12 13*	12 33	*13 13*	13 32	*14 13*
Deansgate	a	*07 35*	07 35		*08 33*	08 37	*09 03*	*09 26*	09 38	*10 26*	*10 50*	*11 26*	11 35	*12 26*	12 35	*13 26*	13 35	*14 26*

		NT A	NT	NT A	NT	NT A	NT	NT A	NT C	NT B	NT A	NT	NT D	NT	NT E	NT G	NT
Buxton	d	13 34		14 37		15 34		16 36			17 34		18 22	18 55	19 55	21 38	22 55
Dove Holes	d	13 40				15 40					17 40			19 01	20 01	21 44	23 01
Chapel-en-le-Frith	d	13 44		14 45		15 44		16 44			17 44		18 30	19 05	20 05	21 48	23 05
Whaley Bridge	d	13 49		14 51		15 49		16 50			17 49		18 36	19 10	20 10	21 53	23 10
Furness Vale	d	13 52		14 54		15 52		16 53			17 52		18 39	19 13	20 13	21 56	23 13
New Mills Newtown	d	13 55		14 57		15 55		16 56			17 55		18 42	19 16	20 16	21 59	23 16
Disley	d	13 59		15 00		15 59		16 59			17 59		18 45	19 20	20 20	22 03	23 20
Middlewood	d	14 02				16 02					18 02			19 23	20 23	22 06	23 23
Hazel Grove	a	14 10		15 10		16 10		17 09			18 10		18 55	19 31	20 31	22 14	23 31
	d	14 10	14 41	15 10	15 41	16 10	16 41	17 09	17 38	17 41	18 10	18 41	18 55	19 31	20 31	22 14	23 31
Woodsmoor	d	14 12	14 43	15 12	15 43	16 12	16 43	17 11	17 40	17 43	18 12	18 43	18 57	19 33	20 33	22 16	23 33
Davenport	d	14 14	14 45	15 14	15 45	16 14	16 45	17 13	17 42	17 45	18 14	18 45	18 59	19 35	20 35	22 18	23 35
Stockport	84 a	14 18	14 49	15 18	15 49	16 18	16 49	17 17	17 45	17 50	18 18	18 49	19 04	19 40	20 40	22 23	23 40
Heaton Chapel	84 a								17 50				19 09				
Levenshulme	84 a								17 53				19 12				
Manchester Piccadilly 10	84 a	14 27	15 01	15 27	16 01	16 27	17 01	17 28	18 02	18 03	18 30	19 01	19 19	19 51	20 52	22 33	23 52
Manchester Oxford Road	a	14 32	*15 13*	15 32	*16 13*	16 32	*17 13*	17 32	*18 18*	*18 18*	18 34	*19 13*	19 22	*20 09*	20 54	22 37	
Deansgate	a	14 35	*15 26*	15 35	*16 28*	16 35	*17 21*	17 35	*18 31*	*18 31*	18 38	*19 17*	19 25	*20 17*	20 56	22 40	

Saturdays

from 11 October

		NT	NT A	NT	NT	NT A	NT	NT	NT A	NT	NT	NT	NT A	NT	NT A	NT	NT A	NT
Buxton	d	05 49	06 29			07 31		07 52	08 37		09 31		10 32		11 29		12 32	
Dove Holes	d		06 35			07 37		07 58	08 43		09 37				11 35			
Chapel-en-le-Frith	d	05 57	06 39			07 41		08 02	08 47		09 41		10 40		11 39		12 40	
Whaley Bridge	d	06 03	06 44			07 46		08 07	08 52		09 46		10 46		11 44		12 46	
Furness Vale	d	06 06	06 47			07 49		08 10	08 55		09 49		10 49		11 47		12 49	
New Mills Newtown	d	06 09	06 50			07 52		08 13	08 58		09 52		10 52		11 50		12 52	
Disley	d	06 12	06 54			07 56		08 17	09 02		09 56		10 55		11 54		12 55	
Middlewood	d		06 57			08 01		08 20			09 59				11 57			
Hazel Grove	a	06 27	07 10			08 13		08 33	09 11		10 12		11 10		12 10		13 10	
	d	06 27	07 10	07 24	07 53	08 14	08 25	08 33	09 12	09 37	10 12	10 41	11 10	11 41	12 10	12 41	13 10	13 41
Woodsmoor	d	06 29	07 12	07 26	07 55		08 27	08 35	09 14	09 39	10 14	10 43	11 12	11 43	12 12	12 43	13 12	13 43
Davenport	d	06 31	07 14	07 28	07 57		08 29	08 37	09 16	09 41	10 16	10 45	11 14	11 45	12 14	12 45	13 14	13 45
Stockport	84 a	06 35	07 17	07 32	08 00	08 20	08 32	08 41	09 20		10 21	10 49	11 18	11 49	12 18	12 49	13 18	13 49
Heaton Chapel	84 a				08 05					09 50								
Levenshulme	84 a				08 08					09 53								
Manchester Piccadilly 10	84 a	06 46	07 30	07 42	08 14	08 29	08 44	08 56	09 32	10 01	10 33	11 01	11 29	12 01	12 29	13 01	13 27	14 01
Manchester Oxford Road	a	*07 09*	07 33	*08 09*	*08 30*	08 33	*08 58*	*09 09*	09 36	*10 14*	*10 47*	*11 13*	11 32	*12 13*	12 33	*13 13*	13 32	*14 13*
Deansgate	a	*07 35*	07 35		*08 33*	08 37	*09 03*	*09 26*	09 38	*10 26*	*10 50*	*11 26*	11 35	*12 26*	12 35	*13 26*	13 35	*14 26*

		NT A	NT	NT A	NT	NT A	NT	NT A	NT	NT A	NT	NT D	NT	NT E	NT G	NT
Buxton	d	13 29		14 32		15 29		16 31		17 34		18 17	18 50	19 50	21 33	22 50
Dove Holes	d	13 35				15 35				17 40			18 56	19 56	21 39	22 56
Chapel-en-le-Frith	d	13 39		14 40		15 39		16 39		17 44		18 25	19 00	20 00	21 43	23 00
Whaley Bridge	d	13 44		14 46		15 44		16 45		17 49		18 31	19 05	20 05	21 48	23 05
Furness Vale	d	13 47		14 49		15 47		16 48		17 52		18 34	19 08	20 08	21 51	23 08
New Mills Newtown	d	13 50		14 52		15 50		16 51		17 55		18 37	19 11	20 11	21 54	23 11
Disley	d	13 54		14 55		15 54		16 54		17 59		18 40	19 15	20 15	21 58	23 15
Middlewood	d	13 57				15 57				18 02			19 18	20 18	22 01	23 18
Hazel Grove	a	14 10		15 10		16 10		17 09		18 10		18 55	19 31	20 31	22 14	23 31
	d	14 10	14 41	15 10	15 41	16 10	16 41	17 09	17 38	18 10	18 41	18 55	19 31	20 31	22 14	23 31
Woodsmoor	d	14 12	14 43	15 12	15 43	16 12	16 43	17 11	17 40	18 12	18 43	18 57	19 33	20 33	22 16	23 33
Davenport	d	14 14	14 45	15 14	15 45	16 14	16 45	17 13	17 42	18 14	18 45	18 59	19 35	20 35	22 18	23 35
Stockport	84 a	14 18	14 49	15 18	15 49	16 18	16 49	17 17	17 45	18 18	18 50	19 04	19 40	20 40	22 23	23 40
Heaton Chapel	84 a								17 50			19 09				
Levenshulme	84 a								17 53			19 12				
Manchester Piccadilly 10	84 a	14 27	15 01	15 27	16 01	16 27	17 01	17 28	18 02	18 30	19 01	19 19	19 51	20 52	22 33	23 52
Manchester Oxford Road	a	14 32	*15 13*	15 32	*16 13*	16 32	*17 13*	17 32	*18 18*	18 34	*19 13*	19 22	*20 09*	20 54	22 37	
Deansgate	a	14 35	*15 26*	15 35	*16 28*	16 35	*17 21*	17 35	*18 31*	18 38	*19 17*	19 25	*20 17*	20 56	22 40	

For general notes see front of timetable
For details of catering facilities see Directory of Train Operators

A To Blackpool North (Table 82)
B Until 6 September
C From 13 September
D To Salford Crescent (Table 82)
E To Bolton (Table 82)
G To Southport (Table 82)

Table 86

Sundays

until 13 July

Buxton and Hazel Grove → Manchester

Network Diagram - see first page of Table 78

		NT	NT	NT	NT	NT	NT	NT	NT	NT	NT	NT	NT	NT	NT	NT	NT	NT	NT	NT	NT
		A	A	A	B	A	A	B	A	A	A	B	A	B	A	A	B	A	A		
Buxton	d	08 25	09 25	10 25		11 20	12 20		13 25	14 25	15 25		16 25		17 25	18 25		19 25	20 25	21 25	22 25
Dove Holes	d	08 31	09 31	10 31		11 26	12 26		13 31	14 31	15 31		16 31		17 31	18 31		19 31	20 31	21 31	22 31
Chapel-en-le-Frith	d	08 35	09 35	10 35		11 30	12 30		13 35	14 35	15 35		16 35		17 35	18 35		19 35	20 35	21 35	22 35
Whaley Bridge	d	08 40	09 40	10 40		11 35	12 35		13 40	14 40	15 40		16 40		17 40	18 40		19 40	20 40	21 40	22 40
Furness Vale	d	08 43	09 43	10 43		11 38	12 38		13 43	14 43	15 43		16 43		17 43	18 43		19 43	20 43	21 43	22 43
New Mills Newtown	d	08 46	09 46	10 46		11 41	12 41		13 46	14 46	15 46		16 46		17 46	18 46		19 46	20 46	21 46	22 46
Disley	d	08 50	09 50	10 50		11 45	12 45		13 50	14 50	15 50		16 50		17 50	18 50		19 50	20 50	21 50	22 50
Middlewood	d	08 53	09 53	10 53		11 48	12 48		13 53	14 53	15 53		16 53		17 53	18 53		19 53	20 53	21 53	22 53
Hazel Grove	a	08 59	09 59	10 59		11 55	12 54		13 59	14 59	15 59		16 59		17 59	18 59		19 59	20 59	21 59	22 59
	d	08 59	09 59	10 59	11 33	11 56	12 54	13 50	13 59	14 59	15 59	16 37	16 59	17 36	17 59	18 59	19 38	19 59	20 59	21 59	22 59
Woodsmoor	d	09 01	10 01	11 01		11 58	12 56		14 01	15 01	16 01		17 01		18 01	19 01		20 01	21 01	22 01	23 01
Davenport	d	09 03	10 03	11 03		12 00	12 58		14 03	15 03	16 03		17 03		18 03	19 03		20 03	21 03	22 03	23 03
Stockport	84 a	09 10	10 10	11 10	11 38	12 07	13 08	13 57	14 10	15 10	16 10	16 45	17 10	17 44	18 10	19 10	19 46	20 10	21 10	22 10	23 10
Heaton Chapel	84 a	09 14	10 14	11 14		12 11	13 11		14 14	15 14	16 14		17 14		18 14	19 14		20 14	21 14	22 14	23 14
Levenshulme	84 a	09 17	10 17	11 17		12 14	13 14		14 17	15 17	16 17		17 17		18 17	19 17		20 17	21 17	22 17	23 17
Manchester Piccadilly 10	84 ⛴ a	09 24	10 24	11 23	11 56	12 25	13 23	14 10	14 24	15 24	16 24	16 56	17 24	17 57	18 24	19 24	19 59	20 24	21 24	22 27	23 27
Manchester Oxford Road	a	09 27	10 27	11 27	*12 09*	12 27	13 26		14 27	15 27	16 27	*17 09*	17 27	*18 09*	18 27	19 27	*20 16*	20 27	21 27	*22 47*	
Deansgate	⛴ a	09 31	10 31	11 31	*12b17*	12 31	13 30		14 31	15 31	16 30	*17b17*	17 31	*18b17*	18 30	19 31		20 30	21 30	*22 50*	

Sundays

20 July to 7 September

		NT	NT	NT	NT	NT	NT	NT	NT	NT	NT	NT	NT	NT	NT	NT	NT	NT	NT	NT
		A	A	A	B	A	A	B	A	A	A	A	B	A	A	B	A	A		
Buxton	d	08 25	09 25	10 25		11 20	12 20		13 25	14 25	15 25	16 25		17 25	18 25		19 25	20 25	21 25	22 25
Dove Holes	d	08 31	09 31	10 31		11 26	12 26		13 31	14 31	15 31	16 31		17 31	18 31		19 31	20 31	21 31	22 31
Chapel-en-le-Frith	d	08 35	09 35	10 35		11 30	12 30		13 35	14 35	15 35	16 35		17 35	18 35		19 35	20 35	21 35	22 35
Whaley Bridge	d	08 40	09 40	10 40		11 35	12 35		13 40	14 40	15 40	16 40		17 40	18 40		19 40	20 40	21 40	22 40
Furness Vale	d	08 43	09 43	10 43		11 38	12 38		13 43	14 43	15 43	16 43		17 43	18 43		19 43	20 43	21 43	22 43
New Mills Newtown	d	08 46	09 46	10 46		11 41	12 41		13 46	14 46	15 46	16 46		17 46	18 46		19 46	20 46	21 46	22 46
Disley	d	08 50	09 50	10 50		11 45	12 45		13 50	14 50	15 50	16 50		17 50	18 50		19 50	20 50	21 50	22 50
Middlewood	d	08 53	09 53	10 53		11 48	12 48		13 53	14 53	15 53	16 53		17 53	18 53		19 53	20 53	21 53	22 53
Hazel Grove	a	08 59	09 59	10 59		11 55	12 54		13 59	14 59	15 59	16 59		17 59	18 59		19 59	20 59	21 59	22 59
	d	08 59	09 59	10 59	11 26	11 56	12 54	13 50	13 59	14 59	15 59	16 59	17 36	17 59	18 59	19 38	19 59	20 59	21 59	22 59
Woodsmoor	d	09 01	10 01	11 01		11 58	12 56		14 01	15 01	16 01	17 01		18 01	19 01		20 01	21 01	22 01	23 01
Davenport	d	09 03	10 03	11 03		12 00	12 58		14 03	15 03	16 03	17 03		18 03	19 03		20 03	21 03	22 03	23 03
Stockport	84 a	09 10	10 10	11 10	11 32	12 07	13 08	13 57	14 10	15 10	16 10	17 10	17 44	18 10	19 10	19 46	20 10	21 10	22 10	23 10
Heaton Chapel	84 a	09 14	10 14	11 14		12 11	13 11		14 14	15 14	16 14	17 14		18 14	19 14		20 14	21 14	22 14	23 14
Levenshulme	84 a	09 17	10 17	11 17		12 14	13 14		14 17	15 17	16 17	17 17		18 17	19 17		20 17	21 17	22 17	23 17
Manchester Piccadilly 10	84 ⛴ a	09 24	10 24	11 23	11 49	12 25	13 24	14 10	14 24	15 24	16 24	17 24	17 57	18 24	19 24	19 59	20 24	21 24	22 25	23 27
Manchester Oxford Road	a	09 27	10 27	11 27	*12 05*	12 27	13 27		14 27	15 27	16 27	17 27	*18 09*	18 27	19 27	*20 16*	20 27	21 27	*22 47*	
Deansgate	⛴ a	09 31	10 31	11 31	*12 08*	12 31	13 31		14 31	15 31	16 30	17 31	*18b17*	18 30	19 31		20 30	21 30	*22 50*	

Sundays

from 14 September

		NT	NT	NT	NT	NT	NT	NT	NT	NT	NT	NT	NT	NT	NT	NT	NT	NT
		A	A	A	A	A	C	A	A	A	A	C	A	A	C	A	A		
Buxton	d	08 25	09 25	10 25	11 20	12 20		13 25	14 25	15 25	16 25		17 25	18 25		19 25	20 25	21 25	22 25
Dove Holes	d	08 31	09 31	10 31	11 26	12 26		13 31	14 31	15 31	16 31		17 31	18 31		19 31	20 31	21 31	22 31
Chapel-en-le-Frith	d	08 35	09 35	10 35	11 30	12 30		13 35	14 35	15 35	16 35		17 35	18 35		19 35	20 35	21 35	22 35
Whaley Bridge	d	08 40	09 40	10 40	11 35	12 35		13 40	14 40	15 40	16 40		17 40	18 40		19 40	20 40	21 40	22 40
Furness Vale	d	08 43	09 43	10 43	11 38	12 38		13 43	14 43	15 43	16 43		17 43	18 43		19 43	20 43	21 43	22 43
New Mills Newtown	d	08 46	09 46	10 46	11 41	12 41		13 46	14 46	15 46	16 46		17 46	18 46		19 46	20 46	21 46	22 46
Disley	d	08 50	09 50	10 50	11 45	12 45		13 50	14 50	15 50	16 50		17 50	18 50		19 50	20 50	21 50	22 50
Middlewood	d	08 53	09 53	10 53	11 48	12 48		13 53	14 53	15 53	16 53		17 53	18 53		19 53	20 53	21 53	22 53
Hazel Grove	a	08 59	09 59	10 59	11 56	12 54		13 59	14 59	15 59	16 59		17 59	18 59		19 59	20 59	21 59	22 59
	d	08 59	09 59	10 59	11 56	12 54	13 50	13 59	14 59	15 59	16 59	17 36	17 59	18 59	19 38	19 59	20 59	21 59	22 59
Woodsmoor	d	09 01	10 01	11 01	11 58	12 56		14 01	15 01	16 01	17 01		18 01	19 01		20 01	21 01	22 01	23 01
Davenport	d	09 03	10 03	11 03	12 00	12 58		14 03	15 03	16 03	17 03		18 03	19 03		20 03	21 03	22 03	23 03
Stockport	84 a	09 10	10 10	11 10	12 07	13 08	13 57	14 10	15 10	16 10	17 10	17 44	18 10	19 10	19 46	20 10	21 10	22 10	23 10
Heaton Chapel	84 a	09 14	10 14	11 14	12 11	13 11		14 14	15 14	16 14	17 14		18 14	19 14		20 14	21 14	22 14	23 14
Levenshulme	84 a	09 17	10 17	11 17	12 14	13 14		14 17	15 17	16 17	17 17		18 17	19 17		20 17	21 17	22 17	23 17
Manchester Piccadilly 10	84 ⛴ a	09 23	10 24	11 23	12 25	13 23	14 10	14 24	15 24	16 24	17 24	17 57	18 24	19 24	19 59	20 24	21 24	22 30	23 27
Manchester Oxford Road	a	09 27	10 27	11 27	12 27	13 26		14 27	15 27	16 27	17 27	*18 09*	18 27	19 27	*20 16*	20 27	21 27	*22 47*	
Deansgate	⛴ a	09 31	10 31	11 31	12 31	13 30		14 31	15 31	16 30	17 31	*18b17*	18 30	19 31		20 30	21 30	*22 50*	

For general notes see front of timetable
For details of catering facilities see Directory of Train Operators

A To Blackpool North (Table 82)
B From Sheffield (Table 78)
C 14 September only. From Sheffield (Table 78)
b Change at Manchester Piccadilly and Manchester Oxford Road

Network Diagram for Tables 88, 89, 90, 91

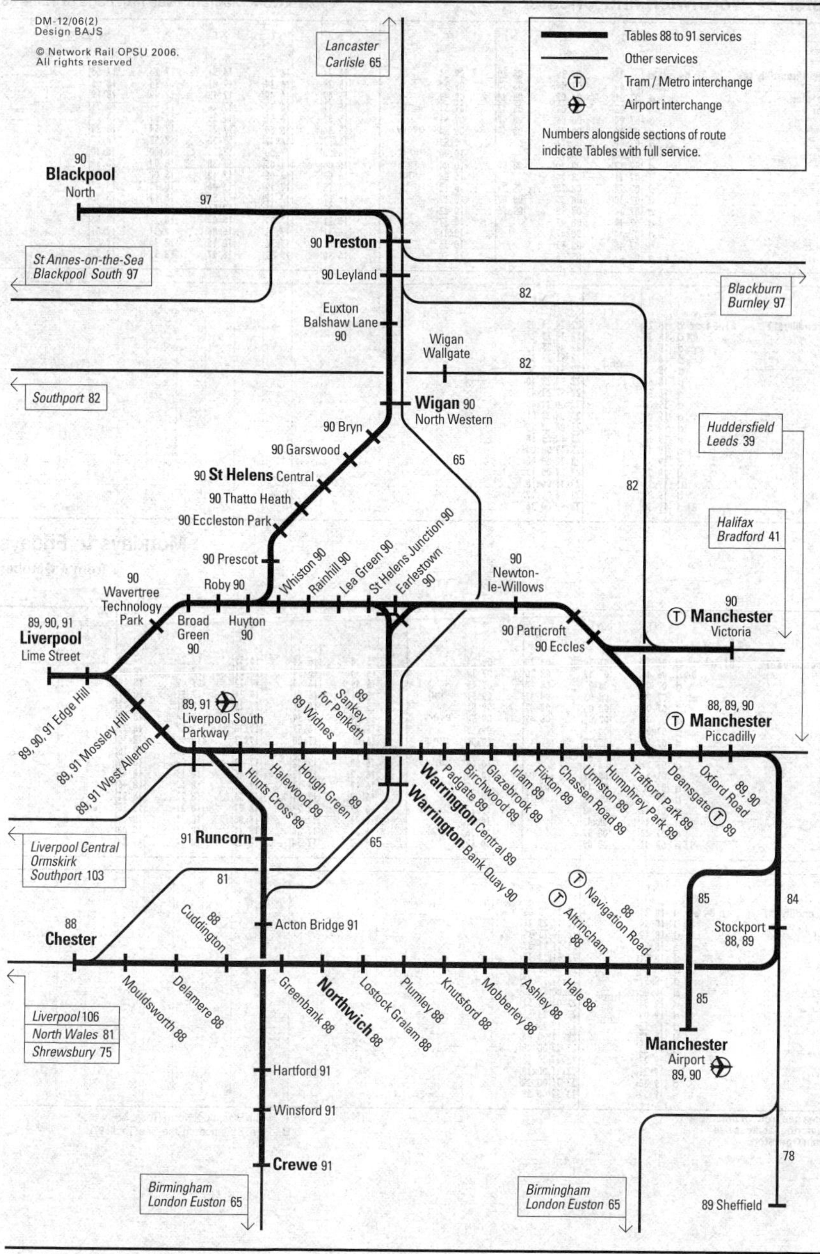

DM-12/06(2)
Design BAJS
© Network Rail OPSU 2006.
All rights reserved
Tables 88 to 91 services
Other services
Tram / Metro interchange
Airport interchange
Numbers alongside sections of route indicate Tables with full service.
Lancaster
Carlisle 65
90 Blackpool North
97
St Annes-on-the-Sea
Blackpool South 97
90 Preston
90 Leyland
Euxton Balshaw Lane 90
82
Blackburn
Burnley 97
Wigan Wallgate
Southport 82
Wigan 90 North Western
90 Bryn
90 Garswood
90 St Helens Central
90 Thatto Heath
90 Eccleston Park
90 Prescot
65
Huddersfield
Leeds 39
Halifax
Bradford 41
Roby 90
90 Wavertree Technology Park
Whiston 90
Rainhill 90
Lea Green 90
St Helens Junction 90
Earlestown 90
90 Newton-le-Willows
89, 90, 91 Liverpool Lime Street
Broad Green 90
Huyton 90
90 Patricroft
90 Eccles
90 Manchester Victoria
89, 90, 91 Edge Hill
89, 91 Mossley Hill
89, 91 West Allerton
89, 91 Liverpool South Parkway
89 Widnes
89 Sankey for Penketh
88, 89, 90 Manchester Piccadilly
Hunts Cross 89
Halewood 89
Hough Green 89
Warrington Central 89
Padgate 89
Birchwood 89
Glazebrook 89
Irlam 89
Flixton 89
Chassen Road 89
Urmston 89
Humphrey Park 89
Trafford Park 89
Deansgate 89
Oxford Road 89, 90
Warrington Bank Quay 90
Liverpool Central
Ormskirk
Southport 103
91 Runcorn
65
81
Navigation Road 88
Altrincham 88
85
84
88 Chester
Cuddington 88
Acton Bridge 91
Stockport 88, 89
Mouldsworth 88
Delamere 88
Greenbank 88
Northwich 88
Lostock Gralam 88
Plumley 88
Knutsford 88
Mobberley 88
Ashley 88
Hale 88
85
Liverpool 106
North Wales 81
Shrewsbury 75
Manchester Airport 89, 90
Hartford 91
Winsford 91
Crewe 91
78
Birmingham
London Euston 65
Birmingham
London Euston 65
89 Sheffield

Mondays to Fridays
until 3 October

Manchester → Northwich and Chester

Network Diagram - see first page of Table 88

Miles			NT	NT A	NT B	NT		NT	NT	NT	NT	NT
½	**Manchester Piccadilly** 10	81, 84 🚌 d	06 35	07 39	08 20	09 24		15 24	16 24	16 51	17 24	17 53
6½	**Stockport**	84 d	06 46	07 49	08 30	09 34		15 34	16 34	17 01	17 34	18 05
14¾	Navigation Road	🚌 d	07 01	08 03	08 44	09 49		15 49	16 49	17 22	17 49	18 19
15¼	**Altrincham**	🚌 a	07 03	08 05	08 47	09 51	and	15 51	16 51	17 24	17 51	18 21
—		d	07 04	08 05	08 47	09 51		15 51	16 51	17 25	17 51	18 22
16	Hale	d	07 06	08 08	08 49	09 54	every	15 54	16 54	17 27	17 54	18 24
17¾	Ashley	d	07x09	08x11		09x57		15x57	16x57	17x30	17x57	18x27
18½	Mobberley	d	07x12	08x15		10x00	hour	16x00	17x00	17x33	18x00	18x30
22¼	Knutsford	d	07 17	08 20	08 58	10 04		16 04	17 05	17 38	18 04	18 35
24¾	Plumley	d	07 21	08 24		10 08	until	16 08	17 08	17 42	18 08	18 39
26¾	Lostock Gralam	d	07 24	08 28	09 04	10 12		16 12	17 12	17 46	18 12	18 43
28¼	**Northwich**	d	07 30	08 33	09 07	10 17		16 17	17 17	17 51	18 17	18 46
30	Greenbank	d	07 34	08 38	09a16	10 22		16 22	17 21	17 56	18 22	18 51
32¾	Cuddington	d	07 39	08 43		10 27		16 27	17 27	18 01	18 27	18 56
35¾	Delamere	d	07x44	08x47		10x31		16x31	17x31	18x06	18x31	19x01
38¾	Mouldsworth	d	07 48	08 52		10 36		16 36	17 36	18 11	18 36	19 08
45¼	**Chester**	81 a	08 02	09 06		10 50		16 50	17 52	18 27	18 52	19 22

		NT		NT	NT
Manchester Piccadilly 10	81, 84 🚌 d	18 24		22 24	23 09
Stockport	84 d	18 34		22 34	23 21
Navigation Road	🚌 d	18 49		22 49	23 35
Altrincham	🚌 a	18 50	and	22 51	23 37
	d	18 51		22 51	23 38
Hale	d	18 54	every	22 54	23 40
Ashley	d	18x57		22x57	23x43
Mobberley	d	19x00	hour	23x00	23x46
Knutsford	d	19 04		23 04	23 51
Plumley	d	19 09	until	23 08	23 55
Lostock Gralam	d	19 12		23 12	23 58
Northwich	d	19 17		23 17	00 04
Greenbank	d	19 22		23 22	00 08
Cuddington	d	19 27		23 27	00 13
Delamere	d	19x31		23x31	00x18
Mouldsworth	d	19 36		23 36	00 22
Chester	81 a	19 50		23 50	00 36

Mondays to Fridays
from 6 October

		NT	NT A	NT B	NT		NT	NT	NT	NT	NT
Manchester Piccadilly 10	81, 84 🚌 d	06 35	07 39	08 20	09 24		15 24	16 24	16 51	17 24	17 53
Stockport	84 d	06 46	07 49	08 30	09 34		15 34	16 34	17 01	17 34	18 05
Navigation Road	🚌 d	07 01	08 03	08 44	09 49		15 49	16 49	17 22	17 49	18 19
Altrincham	🚌 a	07 03	08 05	08 47	09 51	and	15 51	16 51	17 24	17 51	18 21
	d	07 04	08 05	08 47	09 51		15 51	16 51	17 25	17 51	18 22
Hale	d	07 06	08 08	08 49	09 54	every	15 54	16 54	17 27	17 54	18 24
Ashley	d	07x09	08x11		09x57		15x57	16x57	17x30	17x57	18x27
Mobberley	d	07x12	08x15		10x00	hour	16x00	17x00	17x33	18x00	18x30
Knutsford	d	07 17	08 20	08 58	10 04		16 04	17 05	17 38	18 04	18 35
Plumley	d	07 21	08 24		10 08	until	16 08	17 08	17 42	18 09	18 39
Lostock Gralam	d	07 24	08 28	09 04	10 12		16 12	17 12	17 46	18 13	18 43
Northwich	d	07 30	08 33	09 07	10 17		16 17	17 17	17 51	18 17	18 46
Greenbank	d	07 34	08 38	09a18	10 22		16 22	17 21	17 56	18 22	18 51
Cuddington	d	07 39	08 43		10 27		16 27	17 27	18 01	18 27	18 56
Delamere	d	07x44	08x47		10x31		16x31	17x31	18x06	18x31	19x01
Mouldsworth	d	07 48	08 52		10 36		16 36	17 36	18 11	18 36	19 08
Chester	81 a	08 02	09 08		10 52		16 52	17 54	18 29	18 54	19 24

		NT		NT	NT
Manchester Piccadilly 10	81, 84 🚌 d	18 24		22 24	23 09
Stockport	84 d	18 34		22 34	23 21
Navigation Road	🚌 d	18 49		22 49	23 35
Altrincham	🚌 a	18 50	and	22 51	23 37
	d	18 51		22 51	23 38
Hale	d	18 54	every	22 54	23 40
Ashley	d	18x57		22x57	23x43
Mobberley	d	19x00	hour	23x00	23x46
Knutsford	d	19 04		23 04	23 51
Plumley	d	19 08	until	23 08	23 55
Lostock Gralam	d	19 12		23 12	23 58
Northwich	d	19 17		23 17	00 04
Greenbank	d	19 22		23 22	00 08
Cuddington	d	19 27		23 27	00 13
Delamere	d	19x31		23x31	00x18
Mouldsworth	d	19 36		23 36	00 22
Chester	81 a	19 52		23 52	00 38

For general notes see front of timetable
For details of catering facilities see Directory of Train Operators

A From Blackpool North (Table 82)
B From St Annes-on-the-Sea (Table 97)

Saturdays
until 12 July

Manchester → Northwich and Chester

Network Diagram - see first page of Table 88

			NT	NT A	NT B	NT		NT	NT	NT	NT		NT	NT
Manchester Piccadilly [10]	81, 84 🚊	d	06 35	07 39	08 22	09 24		15 24	16 24	17 24	18 24		22 24	23 09
Stockport	84	d	06 46	07 49	08 30	09 34		15 34	16 34	17 34	18 34		22 34	23 19
Navigation Road	🚊	d	07 01	08 04	08 44	09 49		15 49	16 49	17 49	18 49		22 49	23 33
Altrincham	🚊	a	07 03	08 06	08 46	09 51	and	15 51	16 51	17 51	18 50	and	22 51	23 35
		d	07 04	08 06	08 47	09 51		15 51	16 51	17 51	18 51		22 51	23 36
Hale		d	07 06	08 09	08 49	09 54	every	15 54	16 54	17 54	18 54	every	22 54	23 38
Ashley		d	07x09	08x12		09x57		15x57	16x57	17x57	18x57		22x57	23x41
Mobberley		d	07x12	08x15		10x00	hour	16x00	17x00	18x00	19x00	hour	23x00	23x44
Knutsford		d	07 17	08 20	08 58	10 04		16 04	17 05	18 04	19 04		23 04	23 49
Plumley		d	07 21	08 24		10 08	until	16 08	17 08	18 08	19 08	until	23 08	23 53
Lostock Gralam		d	07 24	08 28	09 04	10 12		16 12	17 12	18 12	19 12		23 12	23 56
Northwich		d	07 30	08 33	09 06	10 17		16 17	17 17	18 17	19 17		23 17	00 02
Greenbank		d	07 34	08 38	09a16	10 22		16 22	17 21	18 22	19 22		23 22	00 06
Cuddington		d	07 39	08 43		10 27		16 27	17 27	18 27	19 27		23 27	00 11
Delamere		d	07x44	08x47		10x31		16x31	17x31	18x31	19x31		23x31	00x16
Mouldsworth		d	07 48	08 52		10 36		16 36	17 36	18 36	19 36		23 36	00 20
Chester	81	a	08 02	09 06		10 50		16 50	17 52	18 51	19 50		23 50	00 34

Saturdays
19 July to 4 October

			NT	NT A	NT B	NT		NT	NT	NT	NT		NT	NT C
Manchester Piccadilly [10]	81, 84 🚊	d	06 35	07 39	08 22	09 24		15 24	16 24	17 24	18 24		22 24	23§09
Stockport	84	d	06 46	07 49	08 30	09 34		15 34	16 34	17 33	18 34		22 34	23§19
Navigation Road	🚊	d	07 01	08 04	08 44	09 49		15 49	16 49	17 49	18 49		22 49	23§33
Altrincham	🚊	a	07 03	08 06	08 46	09 51	and	15 51	16 51	17 51	18 50	and	22 51	23§35
		d	07 04	08 06	08 47	09 51		15 51	16 51	17 51	18 51		22 51	23§36
Hale		d	07 06	08 09	08 49	09 54	every	15 54	16 54	17 54	18 54	every	22 54	23§38
Ashley		d	07x09	08x12		09x57		15x57	16x57	17x57	18x57		22x57	23x41
Mobberley		d	07x12	08x15		10x00	hour	16x00	17x00	18x00	19x00	hour	23x00	23x44
Knutsford		d	07 17	08 20	08 58	10 04		16 04	17 05	18 05	19 04		23 04	23§49
Plumley		d	07 21	08 24		10 08	until	16 08	17 08	18 09	19 08	until	23 08	23§53
Lostock Gralam		d	07 24	08 28	09 04	10 12		16 12	17 12	18 12	19 12		23 12	23§56
Northwich		d	07 30	08 33	09 06	10 17		16 17	17 17	18 18	19 17		23 17	00§02
Greenbank		d	07 34	08 38	09a16	10 22		16 22	17 21	18 22	19 22		23 22	00§06
Cuddington		d	07 39	08 43		10 27		16 27	17 27	18 27	19 27		23 27	00§11
Delamere		d	07x44	08x47		10x31		16x31	17x31	18x32	19x31		23x31	00x16
Mouldsworth		d	07 48	08 52		10 36		16 36	17 36	18 36	19 36		23 36	00§20
Chester	81	a	08 02	09 06		10 50		16 50	17 52	18 53	19 50		23 50	00§34

			NT D
Manchester Piccadilly [10]	81, 84 🚊	d	23§16
Stockport	84	d	23§26
Navigation Road	🚊	d	23§40
Altrincham	🚊	a	23§42
		d	23§43
Hale		d	23§45
Ashley		d	23x48
Mobberley		d	23x51
Knutsford		d	23§56
Plumley		d	23§59
Lostock Gralam		d	00§03
Northwich		d	00§09
Greenbank		d	00§13
Cuddington		d	00§18
Delamere		d	00x23
Mouldsworth		d	00§27
Chester	81	a	00§41

Saturdays
from 11 October

			NT	NT A	NT B	NT		NT	NT	NT	NT		NT	NT
Manchester Piccadilly [10]	81, 84 🚊	d	06 35	07 39	08 22	09 24		15 24	16 24	17 24	18 24		22 24	23 16
Stockport	84	d	06 46	07 49	08 30	09 34		15 34	16 34	17 33	18 34		22 34	23 26
Navigation Road	🚊	d	07 01	08 04	08 44	09 49		15 49	16 49	17 49	18 49		22 49	23 40
Altrincham	🚊	a	07 03	08 06	08 46	09 51	and	15 51	16 51	17 51	18 50	and	22 51	23 42
		d	07 04	08 06	08 47	09 51		15 51	16 51	17 51	18 51		22 51	23 43
Hale		d	07 06	08 09	08 49	09 54	every	15 54	16 54	17 54	18 54	every	22 54	23 45
Ashley		d	07x09	08x12		09x57		15x57	16x57	17x57	18x57		22x57	23x48
Mobberley		d	07x12	08x15		10x00	hour	16x00	17x00	18x00	19x00	hour	23x00	23x51
Knutsford		d	07 17	08 20	08 58	10 04		16 04	17 05	18 04	19 04		23 04	23 56
Plumley		d	07 21	08 24		10 08	until	16 08	17 08	18 08	19 08	until	23 08	23 59
Lostock Gralam		d	07 24	08 28	09 04	10 12		16 12	17 12	18 12	19 12		23 12	00 03
Northwich		d	07 30	08 33	09 06	10 17		16 17	17 17	18 17	19 17		23 17	00 09
Greenbank		d	07 34	08 38	09a17	10 22		16 22	17 21	18 22	19 22		23 22	00 13
Cuddington		d	07 39	08 43		10 27		16 27	17 27	18 27	19 27		23 27	00 18
Delamere		d	07x44	08x47		10x31		16x31	17x31	18x31	19x31		23x31	00x23
Mouldsworth		d	07 48	08 52		10 36		16 36	17 36	18 36	19 36		23 36	00 27
Chester	81	a	08 02	09 08		10 52		16 52	17 54	18 55	19 52		23 52	00 43

For general notes see front of timetable
For details of catering facilities see Directory of Train Operators

A From Blackpool North (Table 82)
B From St Annes-on-the-Sea (Table 97)
C Until 6 September
D From 13 September

Table 88

Sundays

Altrincham → Northwich and Chester

		NT	NT	NT	NT	NT
Altrincham	d	10 10	13 37	16 30	18 40	21 30
Hale	d	10 12	13 39	16 32	18 42	21 32
Ashley	d	10x15	13x42	16x35	18x45	21x35
Mobberley	d	10x18	13x45	16x38	18x48	21x38
Knutsford	d	10 23	13 50	16 43	18 53	21 43
Plumley	d	10 27	13 54	16 47	18 57	21 47
Lostock Gralam	d	10 30	13 57	16 50	19 00	21 50
Northwich	d	10 36	14 03	16 56	19 06	21 56
Greenbank	d	10 40	14 07	17 00	19 10	22 00
Cuddington	d	10 45	14 12	17 05	19 15	22 05
Delamere	d	10x50	14x17	17x10	19x20	22x10
Mouldsworth	d	10 54	14 21	17 15	19 24	22 14
Chester	a	11 06	14 33	17 26	19 36	22 26

For general notes see front of timetable
For details of catering facilities see Directory of Train Operators

On Sundays only, National Rail Tickets to stations between Hale and Mouldsworth inclusive are valid for travel on Metrolink services between Manchester City Centre and Altrincham.

Table 88

Mondays to Fridays

until 3 October

Chester and Northwich → Manchester

Network Diagram - see first page of Table 88

Miles			NT	NT	NT		NT	NT	NT A		NT		NT	NT		NT	NT	NT		NT	NT	NT	NT
0	**Chester**	81 d	05 57		06 54		07 30	08 05			10 05		15 05	15 49		16 00	17 05	17 56		18 56	19 56	20 59	22 45
6½	Mouldsworth	d	06 08		07 05		07 41	08 16			10 16		15 16			16 11	17 16	18 07		19 07	20 07	21 10	22 56
9½	Delamere	d	06x13		07x10		07x46	08x21			10x21		15x21			16x16	17x21	18x12		19x12	20x12	21x15	23x01
12½	Cuddington	d	06 17		07 15		07 50	08 25			10 25	and	15 25	16 06		16 20	17 25	18 16		19 16	20 16	21 19	23 05
15¼	Greenbank	d	06 22		07 20		07 55	08 30			10 30		15 30	16 10		16 25	17 30	18 21		19 21	20 21	21 24	23 10
17	**Northwich**	d	06 27	06 50	07 25		08 00	08 35	09 33		10 35	every	15 35	16 15		16 30	17 35	18 26		19 26	20 26	21 29	23 15
18½	Lostock Gralam	d	06 30	06 53	07 28		08 03	08 38	09 36		10 38		15 38	16 18		16 33	17 38	18 29		19 29	20 29	21 32	23 18
20½	Plumley	d	06 33	06 56	07 32		08 07	08 41	09 39		10 41	hour	15 41			16 36	17 41	18 32		19 32	20 32	21 35	23 21
23	Knutsford	d	06 38	07 01	07 37		08 12	08 46	09 44		10 46		15 46	16 26		16 41	17 46	18 37		19 37	20 37	21 40	23 26
26¾	Mobberley	d	06x42	07x05	07x41		08x16	08x50	09x48		10x50	until	15x50			16x45	17x50	18x41		19x41	20x41	21x44	23x30
27½	Ashley	d	06x46	07x09	07x45		08x20	08x54	09x52		10x54		15x54			16x49	17x54	18x45		19x45	20x45	21x48	23x34
29¼	Hale	d	06 49	07 12	07 48		08 23	08 57	09 55		10 57		15 57	16 34		16 52	17 57	18 48		19 48	20 48	21 51	23 37
30	**Altrincham**	⇌ a	06 53	07 16	07 53		08 27	09 01	09 59		11 01		16 01	16 38		16 56	18 01	18 52		19 52	20 52	21 55	23 41
—		d	06 54	07 17	07 53		08 28	09 02	10 00		11 02		16 02	16 38		16 57	18 02	18 53		19 53	20 53	21 56	23 42
30½	Navigation Road	⇌ d	06 56	07 19	07 55		08 30	09 04	10 02		11 04		16 04	16 41		16 59	18 04	18 55		19 55	20 55	21 58	23 44
38¾	**Stockport**	84 a	07 09	07 35	08 10		08 45	09 20	10 16		11 17		16 17	16 56		17 14	18 17	19 09		20 09	21 09	22 12	23 59
44¾	**Manchester Piccadilly** 10	81, 84 ⇌ a	07 25	07 57	08 24		08 59	09 32	10 29		11 32		16 32	17 09		17 31	18 32	19 28		20 28	21 24	22 26	00 14

Mondays to Fridays

from 6 October

		NT	NT		NT	NT		NT	NT A		NT		NT	NT	NT	NT		NT	NT	NT	NT	NT	NT
Chester	81 d	05 53			06 53	07 22		08 05			10 01		14 01	15 03	15 45	15 58		17 01	17 56	18 56	19 56	20 59	22 45
Mouldsworth	d	06 04			07 04	07 33		08 16			10 12		14 12	15 14		16 09		17 12	18 07	19 07	20 07	21 10	22 56
Delamere	d	06x09			07x09	07x38		08x21			10x17		14x17	15x19		16x14		17x17	18x12	19x12	20x12	21x15	23x01
Cuddington	d	06 13			07 14	07 42		08 25			10 21	and	14 21	15 23	16 02	16 18		17 21	18 16	19 16	20 16	21 19	23 05
Greenbank	d	06 18			07 19	07 47		08 30			10 26		14 26	15 28	16 06	16 23		17 26	18 21	19 21	20 21	21 24	23 10
Northwich	d	06 23	06 46		07 24	07 52		08 35	09 29		10 31	every	14 31	15 33	16 11	16 28		17 31	18 26	19 26	20 26	21 29	23 15
Lostock Gralam	d	06 26	06 49		07 27	07 55		08 38	09 32		10 34		14 34	15 36	16 14	16 31		17 34	18 29	19 29	20 29	21 32	23 18
Plumley	d	06 29	06 52		07 31	07 59		08 41	09 35		10 37	hour	14 37	15 39		16 34		17 37	18 32	19 32	20 32	21 35	23 21
Knutsford	d	06 34	06 57		07 36	08 04		08 46	09 40		10 42		14 42	15 44	16 22	16 39		17 42	18 37	19 37	20 37	21 40	23 26
Mobberley	d	06x38	07x01		07x40	08x08		08x50	09x44		10x46	until	14x46	15x48		16x43		17x46	18x41	19x41	20x41	21x44	23x30
Ashley	d	06x42	07x05		07x44	08x12		08x54	09x48		10x50		14x50	15x52		16x47		17x50	18x45	19x45	20x45	21x48	23x34
Hale	d	06 45	07 08		07 47	08 15		08 57	09 51		10 53		14 53	15 55	16 30	16 50		17 53	18 48	19 48	20 48	21 51	23 37
Altrincham	⇌ a	06 49	07 12		07 52	08 19		09 01	09 55		10 57		14 57	15 59	16 34	16 54		17 57	18 52	19 52	20 52	21 55	23 41
	d	06 50	07 13		07 52	08 20		09 02	09 56		10 58		14 58	16 00	16 34	16 55		17 58	18 53	19 53	20 53	21 56	23 42
Navigation Road	⇌ d	06 52	07 15		07 54	08 22		09 04	09 58		11 00		15 00	16 02	16 37	16 57		18 00	18 55	19 55	20 55	21 58	23 44
Stockport	84 a	07 09	07 35		08 10	08 45		09 20	10 16		11 17		15 17	16 17	16 56	17 14		18 17	19 09	20 09	21 09	22 12	23 59
Manchester Piccadilly 10	81, 84 ⇌ a	07 25	07 57		08 24	08 59		09 32	10 29		11 32		15 32	16 32	17 09	17 31		18 32	19 28	20 28	21 24	22 26	00 14

Saturdays

until 12 July

		NT		NT		NT		NT		NT A		NT		NT			NT		NT	NT	NT	NT	NT
Chester	81 d	05 55		06 53		07 30		08 04				10 05		11 02			17 02		17 56	18 58	19 56	20 59	22 45
Mouldsworth	d	06 06		07 04		07 41		08 15				10 16		11 13			17 13		18 07	19 09	20 07	21 10	22 56
Delamere	d	06x11		07x09		07x46		08x20				10x21		11x18			17x18		18x12	19x14	20x12	21x15	23x01
Cuddington	d	06 15		07 14		07 50		08 24				10 25		11 22	and		17 22		18 16	19 18	20 16	21 19	23 05
Greenbank	d	06 20		07 19		07 55		08 29				10 30		11 27			17 27		18 21	19 23	20 21	21 24	23 10
Northwich	d	06 25		07 24		08 00		08 34		09 33		10 35		11 32	every		17 32		18 26	19 28	20 26	21 29	23 15
Lostock Gralam	d	06 28		07 27		08 03		08 37		09 36		10 38		11 35			17 35		18 29	19 31	20 29	21 32	23 18
Plumley	d	06 31		07 31		08 07		08 40		09 39		10 41		11 38	hour		17 38		18 32	19 34	20 32	21 35	23 21
Knutsford	d	06 36		07 36		08 12		08 45		09 44		10 46		11 43			17 43		18 37	19 39	20 37	21 40	23 26
Mobberley	d	06x40		07x40		08x16		08x49		09x48		10x50		11x47	until		17x47		18x41	19x43	20x41	21x44	23x30
Ashley	d	06x44		07x44		08x20		08x53		09x52		10x54		11x51			17x51		18x45	19x47	20x45	21x48	23x34
Hale	d	06 47		07 47		08 23		08 56		09 55		10 57		11 54			17 54		18 48	19 50	20 48	21 51	23 37
Altrincham	⇌ a	06 51		07 52		08 27		09 00		09 59		11 01		11 58			17 58		18 52	19 54	20 52	21 55	23 41
	d	06 52		07 52		08 28		09 01		10 00		11 02		11 59			17 59		18 53	19 55	20 53	21 56	23 42
Navigation Road	⇌ d	06 54		07 54		08 30		09 03		10 02		11 04		12 01			18 01		18 55	19 57	20 55	21 58	23 44
Stockport	84 a	07 07		08 09		08 46		09 16		10 16		11 17		12 16			18 16		19 10	20 10	21 09	22 12	00 01
Manchester Piccadilly 10	81, 84 ⇌ a	07 25		08 24		08 59		09 30		10 29		11 32		12 29			18 29		19 28	20 24	21 24	22 26	00 14

For general notes see front of timetable
For details of catering facilities see
Directory of Train Operators

A To Blackpool North (Table 82)

Table 88

Saturdays

19 July to 4 October

Chester and Northwich → Manchester

Network Diagram - see first page of Table 88

		NT	NT	NT	NT	NT A	NT		NT	NT	AW B	NT	NT	NT	NT	NT B	NT C	NT
Chester	81 d	05 55	06 53	07 30	08 04		10 05		15 05	16 00	16∫22	17 05	17 56	18 58	19 56	20∫59	20∫59	22 45
Mouldsworth	d	06 06	07 04	07 41	08 15		10 16		15 16	16 11		17 16	18 07	19 09	20 07	21∫10	21∫12	22 56
Delamere	d	06x11	07x09	07x46	08x20		10x21		15x21	16x16		17x21	18x12	19x14	20x12	21x15	21x16	23x01
Cuddington	d	06 15	07 14	07 50	08 24		10 25	and	15 25	16 20		17 25	18 16	19 18	20 16	21∫19	21∫21	23 05
Greenbank	d	06 20	07 19	07 55	08 29		10 30		15 30	16 25		17 30	18 21	19 23	20 21	21∫24	21∫25	23 10
Northwich	d	06 25	07 24	08 00	08 34	09 33	10 35	every	15 35	16 30		17 35	18 26	19 28	20 26	21∫29	21∫30	23 15
Lostock Gralam	d	06 28	07 27	08 03	08 37	09 36	10 38		15 38	16 33		17 38	18 29	19 31	20 29	21∫32	21∫33	23 18
Plumley	d	06 31	07 31	08 07	08 40	09 39	10 41	hour	15 41	16 36		17 41	18 32	19 34	20 32	21∫35	21∫37	23 21
Knutsford	d	06 36	07 36	08 12	08 45	09 44	10 46		15 46	16 41		17 46	18 37	19 39	20 37	21∫40	21∫42	23 26
Mobberley	d	06x40	07x40	08x16	08x49	09x48	10x50	until	15x50	16x45		17x50	18x41	19x43	20x41	21x44	21x46	23x30
Ashley	d	06x44	07x44	08x20	08x53	09x52	10x54		15x54	16x49		17x54	18x45	19x47	20x45	21x48	21x49	23x34
Hale	d	06 47	07 47	08 23	08 56	09 55	10 57		15 57	16 52		17 57	18 48	19 50	20 48	21∫51	21∫52	23 37
Altrincham	a	06 51	07 52	08 27	09 00	09 59	11 01		16 01	16 56		18 01	18 52	19 54	20 52	21∫55	21∫57	23 41
	d	06 52	07 52	08 28	09 01	10 00	11 02		16 02	16 57		18 02	18 53	19 55	20 53	21∫56	21∫57	23 42
Navigation Road	d	06 54	07 54	08 30	09 03	10 02	11 04		16 04	16 59		18 04	18 55	19 57	20 55	21∫58	21∫59	23 44
Stockport	84 a	07 07	08 09	08 46	09 16	10 16	11 17		16 17	17 14	17∫19	18 17	19 10	20 10	21 09	22∫12	22∫14	23 59
Manchester Piccadilly 10	81, 84 a	07 25	08 24	08 59	09 31	10 29	11 32		16 32	17 31	17∫39	18 32	19 28	20 24	21 24	22∫26	22∫29	00 13

Saturdays

from 11 October

		NT	NT	NT	NT	NT A	NT		NT	NT	NT	NT	NT	NT	NT	NT
Chester	81 d	05 53	06 53	07 22	08 04		10 01		15 03	15 58	17 01	17 56	18 58	19 56	20 59	22 45
Mouldsworth	d	06 04	07 04	07 33	08 15		10 12		15 14	16 09	17 12	18 07	19 09	20 07	21 12	22 56
Delamere	d	06x09	07x09	07x38	08x20		10x17		15x19	16x14	17x17	18x12	19x14	20x12	21x16	23x01
Cuddington	d	06 13	07 14	07 42	08 24		10 21	and	15 23	16 18	17 21	18 16	19 18	20 16	21 21	23 05
Greenbank	d	06 18	07 19	07 47	08 29		10 26		15 28	16 23	17 26	18 21	19 23	20 21	21 25	23 10
Northwich	d	06 23	07 24	07 52	08 34	09 29	10 31	every	15 33	16 28	17 31	18 26	19 28	20 26	21 30	23 15
Lostock Gralam	d	06 26	07 27	07 55	08 37	09 32	10 34		15 36	16 31	17 34	18 29	19 31	20 29	21 33	23 18
Plumley	d	06 29	07 31	07 59	08 40	09 35	10 37	hour	15 39	16 34	17 37	18 32	19 34	20 32	21 37	23 21
Knutsford	d	06 34	07 36	08 04	08 45	09 40	10 42		15 44	16 39	17 42	18 37	19 39	20 37	21 42	23 26
Mobberley	d	06x38	07x40	08x08	08x49	09x44	10x46	until	15x48	16x43	17x46	18x41	19x43	20x41	21x46	23x30
Ashley	d	06x42	07x44	08x12	08x53	09x48	10x50		15x52	16x47	17x50	18x45	19x47	20x45	21x49	23x34
Hale	d	06 45	07 47	08 15	08 56	09 51	10 53		15 55	16 50	17 53	18 48	19 50	20 48	21 52	23 37
Altrincham	a	06 49	07 52	08 19	09 00	09 55	10 57		15 59	16 54	17 57	18 52	19 54	20 52	21 57	23 41
	d	06 50	07 52	08 20	09 01	09 56	10 58		16 00	16 55	17 58	18 53	19 55	20 53	21 57	23 42
Navigation Road	d	06 52	07 54	08 22	09 03	09 58	11 00		16 02	16 57	18 00	18 55	19 57	20 55	21 59	23 44
Stockport	84 a	07 09	08 09	08 46	09 16	10 16	11 17		16 17	17 14	18 17	19 10	20 10	21 09	22 14	23 59
Manchester Piccadilly 10	81, 84 a	07 25	08 24	08 59	09 31	10 29	11 32		16 32	17 31	18 32	19 28	20 24	21 24	22 29	00 13

Sundays

		NT	NT	NT	NT	NT
Chester	d	08 48	12 00	15 20	17 31	20 10
Mouldsworth	d	08 59	12 13	15 31	17 42	20 21
Delamere	d	09x04	12x17	15x36	17x47	20x26
Cuddington	d	09 08	12 22	15 40	17 51	20 30
Greenbank	d	09 13	12 26	15 45	17 56	20 35
Northwich	d	09 18	12 31	15 50	18 01	20 40
Lostock Gralam	d	09 21	12 34	15 53	18 04	20 43
Plumley	d	09 24	12 38	15 56	18 07	20 46
Knutsford	d	09 29	12 43	16 01	18 12	20 51
Mobberley	d	09x33	12x47	16x05	18x16	20x55
Ashley	d	09x37	12x50	16x09	18x20	20x59
Hale	d	09 40	12 53	16 12	18 23	21 02
Altrincham	a	09 44	12 58	16 16	18 27	21 06

For general notes see front of timetable
For details of catering facilities see
Directory of Train Operators

A To Blackpool North (Table 82)
B Until 6 September
C From 13 September

On Sundays only, National Rail Tickets from stations between Mouldsworth and Hale inclusive are valid for travel on Metrolink services between Altrincham and Manchester City Centre.

Liverpool → Warrington Central → Manchester and Manchester Airport

Network Diagram - see first page of Table 88

Miles	Station		NT	NT	NT	NT	NT	TP 1 ◇ A	NT	EM ◇ B	NT	NT	NT	TP 1 ◇ C	NT	EM ◇ B	NT	NT BHX	NT	NT	TP 1 ◇ C
0	**Liverpool Lime Street** 10	90, 91 d	03 38	05 18		05 50	06 14	06 18	06 21	06 47		06 50	07 14	07 15	07 21	07 47	07 50		08 14		08 22
1¾	Edge Hill	90, 91 d				05 54						06 54					07 54				
3¾	Mossley Hill	91 d				05 59			06 29			06 59			07 29		07 59				
4½	West Allerton	91 d				06 01						07 01					08 01				
—	Liverpool Central 10	103 d										06 43			06 58	07 29	07 44				
5½	**Liverpool South Parkway** 7	91, 103 ✈ d				06 04			06 32			07 04			07 32		08 04				
7¼	Hunts Cross	103 d				06 08						07 08				08 02	08 08				
8¼	Halewood	d				06 10						07 10					08 10				
10½	Hough Green	d				06 14			06 40			07 14			07 39		08 14				
12¼	Widnes	d				06 18			06 43	07 07		07 18		07 32		08 08	08 18				
16	Sankey for Penketh	d				06 23						07 23					08 23				
18½	**Warrington Central**	a				06 30		06 41	06 50	07 15		07 30		07 39	07 48	08 16	08 27			←	08 43
—		d			06 08			06 42	06 51	07 15	07 22			07 39	07 49	08 16	08 28 →			08 28	08 44
20¼	Padgate	d			06 11				06 55		07 25				07 52					08 31	
21¾	Birchwood	d			06 14			06 47	06 58	07 20	07 28			07 44	07 55	08 21				08 34	08 49
24½	Glazebrook	d			06 19						07 33				08 00						
25¾	Irlam	d			06 22				07 04		07 36			07 49	08 03			08 32		08 40	
28	Flixton	d			06 26				07 08		07 40				08 07			08 36		08 44	
28½	Chassen Road	d			06 28				07 10		07 42				08 09			08 38			
29	Urmston	d			06 30				07 12		07 44				08 11			08 40		08 47	
30¼	Humphrey Park	d			06 32						07 46				08 14			08 42			
31	Trafford Park	d			06 35				07 15		07 49				08 17			08 45			
34	Deansgate	84, 85 🚢 a			06 43				07 25		07 56				08 25			08 52		08 58	
34½	**Manchester Oxford Road**	84, 85 a			06 47		06 58	07 02	07 30	07 37	08 01		08 01	08 04	08 29	08 38		08 57	08 58	09 04	09 06
35	**Manchester Piccadilly** 10	78, 84, 85 🚢 a	04 14	06 03	06 56		07 03	07 10		07 41			08 06	08 10		08 42			09 02		09 10
—	Stockport	84 a	05 54	06 24			07 27	07 33		07 52			08 24	08 30		08 53					09 28
—	Sheffield 7	78 🚢 a	06 48				08 09			08b34			09 09			09c35					10 08
44¾	**Manchester Airport**	85 ✈ a	04 30	06 19	07 15		07 20	07e40		08e02	08 42		08 25	08 42		09e06			09 25		09 40

Station		NT	EM ◇ B	NT	NT	NT	TP 1 ◇ C	NT	EM ◇ B	NT	NT	NT	TP 1 ◇ C	NT	EM ◇ B	NT	NT	NT	TP 1 ◇ C	NT
Liverpool Lime Street 10	90, 91 d	08 29	08 52	08 55	09 14		09 22	09 29	09 52	09 55	10 14		10 22	10 29	10 52	10 55	11 14		11 22	11 29
Edge Hill	90, 91 d			08 59						09 59						10 59				
Mossley Hill	91 d	08 37		09 04				09 37		10 04				10 37		11 04				11 37
West Allerton	91 d			09 06						10 06						11 06				
Liverpool Central 10	103 d	08 14		08 44				09 14		09 44				10 14		10 44				11 14
Liverpool South Parkway 7	91, 103 ✈ d	08 40		09 09				09 40		10 09				10 40		11 09				11 40
Hunts Cross	103 d			09 13						10 13						11 13				
Halewood	d			09 16						10 16						11 16				
Hough Green	d	08 47		09 20				09 47		10 20				10 47		11 20				11 47
Widnes	d	08 50	09 09	09 23				09 50	10 09	10 23				10 50	11 09	11 23				11 50
Sankey for Penketh	d			09 28						10 28						11 28				
Warrington Central	a	08 58	09 17	09 33		←	09 43	09 58	10 17	10 33		←	10 43	10 58	11 17	11 33		←	11 43	11 58
	d	08 59	09 17	09 34 →		09 34	09 44	09 59	10 17	10 34 →		10 34	10 44	10 59	11 17	11 34 →		11 34	11 44	11 59
Padgate	d					09 37						10 37						11 37		
Birchwood	d	09 03				09 40	09 49	10 03				10 40	10 49	11 03				11 40	11 49	12 03
Glazebrook	d							10 08												12 08
Irlam	d	09 09				09 46		10 11				10 46		11 09				11 46		12 11
Flixton	d	09 13						10 15						11 13						12 15
Chassen Road	d							10 17												12 17
Urmston	d	09 16				09 51		10 19				10 51		11 16				11 51		12 19
Humphrey Park	d	09 19												11 19						
Trafford Park	d	09 21												11 21						
Deansgate	84, 85 🚢 a	09 31				10 01		10 31				11 01		11 31				12 01		12 31
Manchester Oxford Road	84, 85 a	09 35	09 38		09 58	10 05	10 06	10 35	10 38		10 57	11 05	11 06	11 35	11 38		11 57	12 05	12 06	12 35
Manchester Piccadilly 10	78, 84, 85 🚢 a		09 40		10 02		10 10		10 41		11 02		11 10		11 40		12 02		12 10	
Stockport	84 a		09 51				10 28		10 51				11 27		11 51				12 28	
Sheffield 7	78 🚢 a		10c35				11 08		11c35				12 08		12c35				13 08	
Manchester Airport	85 ✈ a		10e01		10 25		10 40		11e01		11 25		11 40		12e01		12 25		12 40	

For general notes see front of timetable
For details of catering facilities see Directory of Train Operators

A To Scarborough and to Newcastle (Table 39)
B Until 5 September to Norwich (Table 49)
C To Scarborough (Table 39)
b From 8 September arr. 0836
c From 8 September arr. 3 minutes later
e Change at Manchester Oxford Road

Liverpool → Warrington Central → Manchester and Manchester Airport

Network Diagram - see first page of Table 88

		EM ◇ A 🍴	NT	NT	NT	TP 1 ◇ B 🍴	NT	EM ◇ A 🍴	NT	NT	NT	TP 1 ◇ B 🍴	NT	EM ◇ C 🍴	NT	NT	NT	TP 1 ◇ B 🍴	NT	EM ◇ A 🍴
Liverpool Lime Street 10	90, 91 d	11 52	11 55	12 14		12 22	12 29	12 52	12 55	13 14		13 22	13 29	13 52	13 55	14 14		14 22	14 29	14 52
Edge Hill	90, 91 d		11 59						12 59						13 59					
Mossley Hill	91 d		12 04				12 37		13 04				13 37		14 04				14 37	
West Allerton	91 d		12 06						13 06						14 06					
Liverpool Central 10	103 d		*11 44*				*12 14*		*12 44*				*13 14*		*13 44*				*14 14*	
Liverpool South Parkway 7	91, 103 ✈ d		12 09				12 40		13 09				13 40		14 09				14 40	
Hunts Cross	103 d		12 13						13 13						14 13					
Halewood	d		12 16						13 16						14 16					
Hough Green	d		12 20				12 47		13 20				13 47		14 20				14 47	
Widnes	d	12 09	12 23				12 50	13 09	13 23				13 50	14 09	14 23				14 50	15 09
Sankey for Penketh	d		12 28						13 28						14 28					
Warrington Central	a	12 17	12 33		←	12 43	12 58	13 17	13 33		←	13 43	13 58	14 17	14 33		←	14 43	14 58	15 17
	d	12 17	12 34 →		12 34	12 44	12 59	13 17	13 34 →		13 34	13 44	13 59	14 17	14 34 →		14 34	14 44	14 59	15 17
Padgate	d				12 37						13 37						14 37			
Birchwood	d				12 40	12 49	13 03				13 40	13 49	14 03				14 40	14 49	15 03	
Glazebrook	d												14 08							
Irlam	d				12 46		13 09				13 46		14 11				14 46		15 09	
Flixton	d						13 13						14 15						15 13	
Chassen Road	d												14 17							
Urmston	d				12 51		13 16				13 51		14 19				14 51		15 16	
Humphrey Park	d						13 19												15 19	
Trafford Park	d						13 21												15 21	
Deansgate	84, 85 ⛴ a				13 01		13 31				14 01		14 31				15 01		15 31	
Manchester Oxford Road	84, 85 a	12 38		12 57	13 05	13 06	13 35	13 38		13 57	14 05	14 06	14 35	14 38		14 57	15 05	15 06	15 35	15 38
Manchester Piccadilly 10	78, 84, 85 ⛴ a	12 40		13 02		13 10	*13 45*	13 40		14 02		14 10		14 40		15 02		15 10		15 40
Stockport	84 a	12 51				*13 28*		13 51				*14 28*		14 51				*15 28*		15 50
Sheffield 7	78 ⛴ a	13b35				*14 08*		14b35				*15 08*		15b35				*16 08*		16b35
Manchester Airport	85 ✈ a	*13c01*		13 25		*13 40*		*14c01*		14 25		*14 40*		*15c01*		15 25		*15 40*		*16c01*

		NT	NT	NT	TP 1 ◇ D 🍴	NT	EM ◇ A 🍴	NT	NT	NT	TP 1 ◇ B 🍴	NT	EM ◇ C 🍴	NT	NT	NT	TP 1 ◇ B 🍴	NT	EM ◇ E 🍴	NT
Liverpool Lime Street 10	90, 91 d	14 55	15 14		15 22	15 29	15 52	15 55	16 14		16 22	16 28	16 52	16 55	17 09		17 22	17 25	17 52	17 55
Edge Hill	90, 91 d	14 59						15 59						16 59				17 29		17 59
Mossley Hill	91 d	15 04				15 37		16 04				16 36		17 04				17 34		18 04
West Allerton	91 d	15 06						16 06						17 06				17 36		18 06
Liverpool Central 10	103 d	*14 44*				*15 14*		*15 44*				*16 14*		*16 44*				*17 14*		*17 44*
Liverpool South Parkway 7	91, 103 ✈ d	15 09				15 40		16 09				16 39		17 09				17 39		18 09
Hunts Cross	103 d	15 13						16 13						17 13				17 43		18 13
Halewood	d	15 16						16 16						17 15				17 45		18 15
Hough Green	d	15 20				15 47		16 20				16 46		17 19				17 49		18 19
Widnes	d	15 23				15 50	16 09	16 23				16 49	17 09	17 23				17 53	18 09	18 23
Sankey for Penketh	d	15 28						16 28						17 28				17 58		18 28
Warrington Central	a	15 33		←	15 43	15 58	16 17	16 33		←	16 43	16 57	17 17	17 33		←	17 43	18 03	18 17	18 33
	d	15 34 →		15 34	15 44	15 59	16 17	16 34 →		16 34	16 44	16 58	17 17	17 33 →		17 33	17 44	18 03	18 17	18 33 →
Padgate	d			15 37						16 37						17 36				
Birchwood	d			15 40	15 49	16 03				16 40	16 49	17 02				17 39	17 49	18 08		
Glazebrook	d					16 08						17 07								
Irlam	d			15 46		16 11				16 46		17 10				17 45		18 14		
Flixton	d					16 15				16 50		17 14				17 49				
Chassen Road	d					16 17												18 18		
Urmston	d			15 51		16 19				16 53		17 17				17 52		18 20		
Humphrey Park	d											17 20						18 23		
Trafford Park	d											17 22								
Deansgate	84, 85 ⛴ a			16 01		16 31				17 03						18 01				
Manchester Oxford Road	84, 85 a		15 57	16 05	16 06	16 35	16 37		16 57	17 06	17 06	17 35	17 37		17 58	18 05	18 06	18 34	18 38	
Manchester Piccadilly 10	78, 84, 85 ⛴ a		16 01		16 10		16 40		17 02		17 10		17 40		18 04		18 10		18 43	
Stockport	84 a				*16 28*		16 51		*17c19*		*17 28*		17 50		*18 26*		*18 32*		18 54	
Sheffield 7	78 ⛴ a				*17 08*		17 38				*18 15*		18 43		*19 08*				19e36	
Manchester Airport	85 ✈ a		16 25		*16 40*		*17f14*		17 25		*17 40*		*18f05*		18 27		*18 42*		*19f09*	

For general notes see front of timetable
For details of catering facilities see Directory of Train Operators

- **A** Until 5 September to Norwich (Table 49)
- **B** To Scarborough (Table 39)
- **C** Until 5 September to Nottingham (Table 49)
- **D** To Middlesbrough (Table 39)
- **E** To Norwich (from 8 September to Nottingham) (Table 49)
- **b** From 8 September arr. 3 minutes later
- **c** Change at Manchester Oxford Road
- **e** From 8 September arr. 1940
- **f** Change at Manchester Piccadilly

Liverpool → Warrington Central → Manchester and Manchester Airport

Network Diagram - see first page of Table 88

		NT	NT	TP [1]◇ A	NT		EM ◇ B 🛒	NT	TP [1]◇ C	NT	EM ◇ B 🛒	NT		NT	TP [1]◇ C	NT	EM ◇ B	NT	TP [1]◇ C		NT		
Liverpool Lime Street [10]	90, 91 d	18 14		18 22	18 25		18 52	18 55	19 22		19 52	19 55		20 14	20 22	20 55	21 35	21 55	22 30		23 35		
Edge Hill	90, 91 d				18 29			18 59				19 59				20 59		21 59			23 39		
Mossley Hill	91 d				18 34			19 04				20 04				21 04		22 04			23 43		
West Allerton	91 d				18 36			19 06				20 06				21 06		22 06			23 46		
Liverpool Central [10]	103 d				18 14			18 44				19 44				20 44		21 44			23 29		
Liverpool South Parkway [7]	91, 103 ✈ d				18 39			19 09				20 09				21 09		22 09			23 49		
Hunts Cross	103 d				18 43			19 13				20 13				21 13		22 13			23 52		
Halewood	d				18 45			19 15				20 15				21 15		22 15			23 55		
Hough Green	d				18 49			19 19				20 19				21 19		22 19			23 59		
Widnes	d				18 53		19 09	19 23			20 09	20 23				21 23	21 53	22 23			00 03		
Sankey for Penketh	d				18 58			19 28				20 28				21 28		22 28			00 07		
Warrington Central	a		←	18 43	19 03		19 17	19 35	19 43		20 17	20 35			20 43	21 33	22 01	22 33	22 52		00 13		
	d		18 33	18 44	19 03		19 17		19 44	19 52	20 17				20 44	21 33	22 01	22 33	22 52		00 13		
Padgate	d				19 06					19 55						21 36		22 36					
Birchwood	d		18 38	18 49	19 09				19 49	19 58					20 49	21 39		22 39	22 57				
Glazebrook	d				19 14					20 03						21 44		22 44					
Irlam	d		18 44		19 17					20 06						21 47		22 47					
Flixton	d		18 48							20 10						21 51		22 51					
Chassen Road	d									20 12						21 53		22 53					
Urmston	d		18 51		19 22					20 14						21 55		22 55					
Humphrey Park	d									20 17						21 58		22 58					
Trafford Park	d		18 54							20 19						22 00		23 00					
Deansgate	84, 85 🚊 a				19 32					20 29						22 07		23 07					
Manchester Oxford Road	84, 85 a	18 59	19 04	19 05	19 35		19 37		20 06	20 34	20 38			20 59	21 06	22 12	22 22	23 12	23 13				
Manchester Piccadilly [10]	78, 84, 85 🚊 a	19 05		19 10			19 42		20 10		20 40			21 05	21 10		22 25		23 17		00 36		
Stockport	84 a	19 25		19 32			19 53		20 32		20 51			21 26	21 34		22 37		23 50				
Sheffield [7]	78 🚊 a	20 08					20b39		21 34		21 34			22 09	23 13		23 35		01 13				
Manchester Airport	85 ✈ a	19 26		19 40			20c05		20 58		21e19			21 28	21c37		22e58		23 56		01 11		

Saturdays

until 6 September

		NT	NT	NT	NT		TP [1]◇ A 🛒	NT	EM ◇ D	NT		NT	TP [1]◇ A 🛒	NT	EM ◇ D		NT	NT	NT	TP [1]◇ A 🛒		NT	EM ◇ D
Liverpool Lime Street [10]	90, 91 d	03 38	05 18	05 50	06 10		06 18	06 21	06 47	06 50		07 14	07 18	07 21	07 47		07 50	08 14		08 21		08 29	08 52
Edge Hill	90, 91 d			05 54						06 54							07 54						
Mossley Hill	91 d			05 59				06 29		06 59				07 29			07 59					08 37	
West Allerton	91 d			06 01						07 01							08 01						
Liverpool Central [10]	103 d									06 43				06 59	07 29		07 44					08 14	
Liverpool South Parkway [7]	91, 103 ✈ d			06 04				06 32		07 04				07 32			08 04					08 40	
Hunts Cross	103 d			06 08						07 08					08 02		08 08						
Halewood	d			06 10						07 10							08 10						
Hough Green	d			06 14				06 40		07 14				07 39			08 14					08 47	
Widnes	d			06 18				06 43	07 07	07 18			07 36		08 08		08 18					08 50	09 09
Sankey for Penketh	d			06 23						07 23							08 23						
Warrington Central	a			06 30			06 41	06 51	07 15	07 30			07 43	07 48	08 16		08 28		←	08 43		08 58	09 17
	d						06 42	06 51	07 15				07 43	07 49	08 16		08 28		08 28	08 44		08 59	09 17
Padgate	d							06 55						07 52			→		08 31				
Birchwood	d						06 47	06 58	07 20				07 48	07 55	08 21				08 34	08 49		09 03	
Glazebrook	d													08 00									
Irlam	d							07 04					07 53	08 04					08 40			09 09	
Flixton	d							07 08						08 07					08 44			09 13	
Chassen Road	d							07 10						08 09									
Urmston	d							07 12						08 11					08 47			09 16	
Humphrey Park	d													08 14					08 50			09 19	
Trafford Park	d							07 15						08 17					08 52			09 21	
Deansgate	84, 85 🚊 a							07 25						08 25					09 00			09 31	
Manchester Oxford Road	84, 85 a				06 57		07 02	07 30	07 37			08 00	08 06	08 29	08 38			08 58	09 05	09 06		09 35	09 38
Manchester Piccadilly [10]	78, 84, 85 🚊 a	04 14	06 03		07 03		07 10		07 41			08 06	08 10		08 42			09 02		09 10			09 40
Stockport	84 a	05 57	06 25		07 27		07 32		07 54			08 25	08 30		08 53					09 28			09 55
Sheffield [7]	78 🚊 a	06 48	07 57		08 09		08 35		08 35			09 09			09 35					10 08			10 35
Manchester Airport	85 ✈ a	04 30	06 19		07 20		07c40		08c02			08 25	08 42		09c06			09 25		09 40			10c02

For general notes see front of timetable
For details of catering facilities see Directory of Train Operators

A To Scarborough (Table 39)
B TO Nottingham (Table 49)
C To York (Table 39)
D To Norwich (Table 49)

b From 8 September arr. 2035
c Change at Manchester Oxford Road
e Change at Manchester Piccadilly

Saturdays

until 6 September

Liverpool → Warrington Central → Manchester and Manchester Airport

Network Diagram - see first page of Table 88

Station		NT	NT	NT	TP	NT	EM	NT	NT	NT	TP	NT	EM	NT	NT	NT	TP	NT	EM
					1 ◇		◇				1 ◇		◇				1 ◇		◇
					A		B				A		B				A		B
Liverpool Lime Street 10	90, 91 d	08 55	09 14		09 22	09 29	09 52	09 55	10 14		10 22	10 29	10 52	10 55	11 14		11 22	11 29	11 52
Edge Hill	90, 91 d	08 59						09 59						10 59					
Mossley Hill	91 d	09 04				09 37		10 04				10 37		11 04				11 37	
West Allerton	91 d	09 06						10 06						11 06					
Liverpool Central 10	103 d	08 44				09 14		09 44				10 14		10 44				11 14	
Liverpool South Parkway 7	91, 103 ✈ d	09 09				09 40		10 09				10 40		11 09				11 40	
Hunts Cross	103 d	09 13						10 13						11 13					
Halewood	d	09 16						10 16						11 16					
Hough Green	d	09 20				09 47		10 20				10 47		11 20				11 47	
Widnes	d	09 23				09 50	10 09	10 23				10 50	11 09	11 23				11 50	12 09
Sankey for Penketh	d	09 28						10 28						11 28					
Warrington Central	a	09 33		←	09 43	09 58	10 17	10 33		←	10 43	10 58	11 17	11 33		←	11 43	11 58	12 17
	d	09 34 →		09 34	09 44	09 59	10 17	10 34 →		10 34	10 44	10 59	11 17	11 34 →		11 34	11 44	11 59	12 17
Padgate	d			09 37						10 37						11 37			
Birchwood	d			09 40	09 49	10 03				10 40	10 49	11 03				11 40	11 49	12 03	
Glazebrook	d					10 08												12 08	
Irlam	d			09 46		10 11				10 46		11 09				11 46		12 11	
Flixton	d					10 15						11 13						12 15	
Chassen Road	d					10 17												12 17	
Urmston	d			09 51		10 19				10 51		11 16				11 51		12 19	
Humphrey Park	d											11 19							
Trafford Park	d											11 21							
Deansgate	84, 85 🚋 a			10 01		10 31				11 01		11 31				12 01		12 31	
Manchester Oxford Road	84, 85 a		09 58	10 05	10 06	10 35	10 37		10 57	11 05	11 06	11 35	11 37		11 57	12 05	12 06	12 35	12 37
Manchester Piccadilly 10	78, 84, 85 🚋 a		10 02		10 10		10 40		11 02		11 10		11 40		12 02		12 10		12 40
Stockport	84 a				10 28		10 52				11 28		11 52				12 28		12 52
Sheffield 7	78 🚋 a				11 08		11 35				12 08		12 35				13 08		13 35
Manchester Airport	85 ✈ a		10 25		10 40		11b01		11 25		11 40		12b01		12 25		12 40		13b01

Station		NT	NT	NT	TP	NT	EM	NT	NT	NT	TP	NT	EM	NT	NT	NT	TP	NT	EM
					1 ◇		◇				1 ◇		◇				1 ◇		◇
					A		B				A		C				A		B
Liverpool Lime Street 10	90, 91 d	11 55	12 14		12 22	12 29	12 52	12 55	13 14		13 22	13 29	13 52	13 55	14 14		14 22	14 29	14 52
Edge Hill	90, 91 d	11 59						12 59						13 59					
Mossley Hill	91 d	12 04				12 37		13 04				13 37		14 04				14 37	
West Allerton	91 d	12 06						13 06						14 06					
Liverpool Central 10	103 d	11 44				12 14		12 44				13 14		13 44				14 14	
Liverpool South Parkway 7	91, 103 ✈ d	12 09				12 40		13 09				13 40		14 09				14 40	
Hunts Cross	103 d	12 13						13 13						14 13					
Halewood	d	12 16						13 16						14 16					
Hough Green	d	12 20				12 47		13 20				13 47		14 20				14 47	
Widnes	d	12 23				12 50	13 09	13 23				13 50	14 09	14 23				14 50	15 09
Sankey for Penketh	d	12 28						13 28						14 28					
Warrington Central	a	12 33		←	12 43	12 58	13 17	13 33		←	13 43	13 58	14 17	14 33		←	14 43	14 58	15 17
	d	12 34 →		12 34	12 44	12 59	13 17	13 34 →		13 34	13 44	13 59	14 17	14 34 →		14 34	14 44	14 59	15 17
Padgate	d			12 37						13 37						14 37			
Birchwood	d			12 40	12 49	13 03				13 40	13 49	14 03				14 40	14 49	15 03	
Glazebrook	d											14 08							
Irlam	d			12 46		13 09				13 46		14 11				14 46		15 09	
Flixton	d					13 13						14 15						15 13	
Chassen Road	d											14 17							
Urmston	d			12 51		13 16				13 51		14 19				14 51		15 16	
Humphrey Park	d					13 19												15 19	
Trafford Park	d					13 21												15 21	
Deansgate	84, 85 🚋 a			13 01		13 31				14 01		14 31				15 01		15 31	
Manchester Oxford Road	84, 85 a		12 57	13 05	13 06	13 35	13 37		13 57	14 05	14 06	14 35	14 37		14 57	15 05	15 06	15 35	15 37
Manchester Piccadilly 10	78, 84, 85 🚋 a		13 02		13 10		13 40		14 02		14 10		14 40		15 02		15 10		15 40
Stockport	84 a				13 28		13 52				14 28		14 52		15 26		15 32		15 53
Sheffield 7	78 🚋 a				14 08		14 35				15 08		15 35		16 08		16 35		16 35
Manchester Airport	85 ✈ a		13 25		13 40		14b01		14 25		14 40		15b01		15 25		15 40		16b01

Station		NT	NT	NT	TP	NT	EM	NT	NT	NT	TP	NT	EM	NT	NT	NT	TP	NT	EM
					1 ◇		◇				1 ◇		◇				1 ◇		◇
					D		B				A		C				A		B
Liverpool Lime Street 10	90, 91 d	14 55	15 14		15 22	15 29	15 52	15 55	16 14		16 22	16 28	16 52	16 55	17 09		17 22	17 25	17 52
Edge Hill	90, 91 d	14 59						15 59						16 59				17 29	
Mossley Hill	91 d	15 04				15 37		16 04				16 36		17 04				17 34	
West Allerton	91 d	15 06						16 06						17 06				17 36	
Liverpool Central 10	103 d	14 44				15 14		15 44				16 14		16 44				17 14	
Liverpool South Parkway 7	91, 103 ✈ d	15 09				15 40		16 09				16 39		17 09				17 39	
Hunts Cross	103 d	15 13						16 13						17 13				17 43	
Halewood	d	15 16						16 16						17 15				17 45	
Hough Green	d	15 20				15 47		16 20				16 46		17 19				17 49	
Widnes	d	15 23				15 50	16 09	16 23				16 49	17 09	17 23				17 53	18 09
Sankey for Penketh	d	15 28						16 28						17 28				17 58	
Warrington Central	a	15 33		←	15 43	15 58	16 17	16 33		←	16 43	16 57	17 17	17 33		←	17 43	18 03	18 17
	d	15 34 →		15 34	15 44	15 59	16 17	16 34 →		16 34	16 44	16 58	17 17	17 33 →		17 33	17 44	18 03	18 17
Padgate	d			15 37						16 37						17 36			
Birchwood	d			15 40	15 49	16 03				16 40	16 49	17 02				17 39	17 49	18 08	
Glazebrook	d					16 08						17 07							
Irlam	d			15 46		16 11				16 46		17 10				17 45		18 14	
Flixton	d					16 15				16 50		17 14				17 49			
Chassen Road	d					16 17												18 18	
Urmston	d			15 51		16 19				16 53		17 17				17 52		18 20	
Humphrey Park	d											17 20						18 23	
Trafford Park	d											17 22							
Deansgate	84, 85 🚋 a			16 01		16 31				17 03						18 01			
Manchester Oxford Road	84, 85 a		15 57	16 05	16 06	16 35	16 37		16 57	17 05	17 06	17 35	17 37		17 58	18 05	18 06	18 34	18 39
Manchester Piccadilly 10	78, 84, 85 🚋 a		16 02		16 10		16 41		17 02		17 10		17 40		18 04		18 10		18 42
Stockport	84 a				16 28		16 52		17b19		17 28		17 54		18 25		18 32		18 54
Sheffield 7	78 🚋 a				17 08		17 38				18 12		18 35		19 08		19 35		19 35
Manchester Airport	85 ✈ a		16 25		16 40		17c11		17 25		17 40		18c05		18 27		18 42		19c08

For general notes see front of timetable
For details of catering facilities see Directory of Train Operators

A To Scarborough (Table 39)
B To Norwich (Table 49)
C TO Nottingham (Table 49)
D To Middlesbrough (Table 39)

b Change at Manchester Oxford Road
c Change at Manchester Piccadilly

Table 89

Saturdays

until 6 September

Liverpool → Warrington Central → Manchester and Manchester Airport

Network Diagram - see first page of Table 88

		NT	NT	NT	TP 1 ◇ A		NT	EM ◇ B	NT	TP 1 ◇ C		NT	EM ◇ B	NT	NT		TP 1 ◇ C	NT	NT	TP 1 ◇ C	NT		
Liverpool Lime Street 10	90, 91 d	17 55	18 14		18 22		18 25	18 52	18 55	19 22			19 52	19 55	20 14		20 22	20 55	21 55	22 30	23 33		
Edge Hill	90, 91 d	17 59					18 29		18 59					19 59				20 59	21 59		23 37		
Mossley Hill	91 d	18 04					18 34		19 04					20 04				21 04	22 04		23 41		
West Allerton	91 d	18 06					18 36		19 06					20 06				21 06	22 06		23 44		
Liverpool Central 10	103 d	*17 44*					*18 14*		*18 44*					*19 44*				*20 44*	*21 44*		*23 14*		
Liverpool South Parkway 7	91, 103 ✈ d	18 09					18 39		19 09					20 09				21 09	22 09		23 47		
Hunts Cross	103 d	18 13					18 43		19 13					20 13				21 13	22 13		23 50		
Halewood	d	18 15					18 45		19 15					20 15				21 15	22 15		23 52		
Hough Green	d	18 19					18 49		19 19					20 19				21 19	22 19		23 56		
Widnes	d	18 23					18 53	19 09	19 23				20 09	20 23				21 23	22 23		00 01		
Sankey for Penketh	d	18 28					18 58		19 28					20 28				21 28	22 28		00 06		
Warrington Central	a	18 33		←	18 43		19 03	19 17	19 35	19 43			20 17	20 35			20 43	21 33	22 33	22 52	00 10		
	d	18 33		18 33	18 44		19 03	19 17		19 44		19 52	20 17				20 44	21 33	22 33	22 52	00 10		
Padgate	d	→					19 06					19 55						21 36	22 36				
Birchwood	d			18 38	18 49		19 09			19 49		19 58					20 49	21 39	22 39	22 57			
Glazebrook	d						19 14					20 03						21 44	22 44				
Irlam	d			18 44			19 17					20 06						21 47	22 47				
Flixton	d			18 48								20 10						21 51	22 51				
Chassen Road	d											20 12						21 53	22 53				
Urmston	d			18 51			19 22					20 14						21 55	22 55				
Humphrey Park	d											20 17						21 58	22 58				
Trafford Park	d			18 54								20 19						22 00	23 00				
Deansgate	84, 85 ⛴ a						19 32					20 30						22 07	23 07				
Manchester Oxford Road	84, 85 a		18 59	19 04	19 05		19 35	19 38		20 05		20 34	20 37		20 58		21 06	22 12	23 12	23 13			
Manchester Piccadilly 10	78, 84, 85 ⛴ a		19 05		19 10			19 42		20 10			20 40		21 05		21 10	22 56		23 17	00 33		
Stockport	84 a		*19 26*		*19 32*			19 53		*20 28*			20 51		*21 26*		*21 34*	23 06		*23 50*			
Sheffield 7	78 ⛴ a		*20 08*					20 34		*21 08*			21 34		*22 09*		*22 31*						
Manchester Airport	85 ✈ a		19 26		*19 40*			*20b05*		*20 58*			*21b09*		21 28		*21b37*			*23 56*			

Saturdays

from 13 September

		NT	NT	NT	NT		TP 1 ◇ A	NT	EM ◇	NT		NT	TP 1 ◇ A	NT	EM ◇		NT	NT	NT	TP 1 ◇ A		NT	EM ◇
Liverpool Lime Street 10	90, 91 d	03 38	05 18	05 50	06 10		06 18	06 21	06 47	06 50		07 14	07 18	07 21	07 47		07 50	08 14		08 21		08 29	08 52
Edge Hill	90, 91 d			05 54						06 54							07 54						
Mossley Hill	91 d			05 59				06 29		06 59				07 29			07 59					08 37	
West Allerton	91 d			06 01						07 01							08 01						
Liverpool Central 10	103 d									*06 43*				*06 59*	*07 29*		*07 44*					*08 14*	
Liverpool South Parkway 7	91, 103 ✈ d			06 04				06 32		07 04				07 32			08 04					08 40	
Hunts Cross	103 d			06 08						07 08					08 02		08 08						
Halewood	d			06 10						07 10							08 10						
Hough Green	d			06 14				06 40		07 14				07 39			08 14					08 47	
Widnes	d			06 18				06 43	07 07	07 18			07 36		08 08		08 18					08 50	09 09
Sankey for Penketh	d			06 23						07 23							08 23						
Warrington Central	a			06 30			06 41	06 51	07 15	07 30			07 43	07 48	08 16		08 28		←	08 43		08 58	09 17
	d						06 42	06 51	07 15				07 43	07 49	08 16		08 28		08 28	08 44		08 59	09 17
Padgate	d							06 55						07 52			→		08 31				
Birchwood	d						06 47	06 58	07 20				07 48	07 55	08 21				08 34	08 49		09 03	
Glazebrook	d													08 00									
Irlam	d							07 04					07 53	08 04					08 40			09 09	
Flixton	d							07 08						08 07					08 44			09 13	
Chassen Road	d							07 10						08 09									
Urmston	d							07 12						08 11					08 47			09 16	
Humphrey Park	d													08 14					08 50			09 19	
Trafford Park	d							07 15						08 17					08 52			09 21	
Deansgate	84, 85 ⛴ a							07 25						08 25					09 00			09 31	
Manchester Oxford Road	84, 85 a				06 57		07 02	07 30	07 37			08 00	08 06	08 29	08 38			08 58	09 05	09 06		09 35	09 38
Manchester Piccadilly 10	78, 84, 85 ⛴ a	04 14	06 03		07 03		07 10		07 41			08 06	08 10		08 42			09 02		09 10			09 40
Stockport	84 a								07 54						08 53								09 55
Sheffield 7	78 ⛴ a	*06 48*	*07 57*		*08 09*				08 35			*09 09*			09 38			*10 08*					10 38
Manchester Airport	85 ✈ a	04 30	06 19		07 20		*07b40*		*08b02*			08 25	*08 42*		*09b06*			09 25		*09 40*			*10b02*

For general notes see front of timetable
For details of catering facilities see Directory of Train Operators

A To Scarborough (Table 39)
B TO Nottingham (Table 49)
C To York (Table 39)

b Change at Manchester Oxford Road

from 13 September

Liverpool → Warrington Central → Manchester and Manchester Airport

Network Diagram - see first page of Table 88

	NT	NT	NT	TP 1 ◇ A	NT	EM ◇	NT	NT	NT	TP 1 ◇ A	NT	EM ◇	NT	NT	NT	TP 1 ◇ A	NT	EM ◇
Liverpool Lime Street 10 90, 91 d	08 55	09 14		09 22	09 29	09 52	09 55	10 14		10 22	10 29	10 52	10 55	11 14		11 22	11 29	11 52
Edge Hill 90, 91 d	08 59						09 59						10 59					
Mossley Hill 91 d	09 04				09 37		10 04				10 37		11 04				11 37	
West Allerton 91 d	09 06						10 06						11 06					
Liverpool Central 10 103 d	*08 44*				*09 14*		*09 44*				*10 14*		*10 44*				*11 14*	
Liverpool South Parkway 7 91, 103 ⇄ d	09 09				09 40		10 09				10 40		11 09				11 40	
Hunts Cross 103 d	09 13						10 13						11 13					
Halewood d	09 16						10 16						11 16					
Hough Green d	09 20				09 47		10 20				10 47		11 20				11 47	
Widnes d	09 23				09 50	10 09	10 23				10 50	11 09	11 23				11 50	12 09
Sankey for Penketh d	09 28						10 28						11 28					
Warrington Central a	09 33		←	09 43	09 58	10 17	10 33		←	10 43	10 58	11 17	11 33		←	11 43	11 58	12 17
d	09 34 →		09 34	09 44	09 59	10 17	10 34 →		10 34	10 44	10 59	11 17	11 34 →		11 34	11 44	11 59	12 17
Padgate d			09 37						10 37						11 37			
Birchwood d			09 40	09 49	10 03				10 40	10 49	11 03				11 40	11 49	12 03	
Glazebrook d					10 08												12 08	
Irlam d			09 46		10 11				10 46		11 09				11 46		12 11	
Flixton d					10 15						11 13						12 15	
Chassen Road d					10 17												12 17	
Urmston d			09 51		10 19				10 51		11 16				11 51		12 19	
Humphrey Park d											11 19							
Trafford Park d											11 21							
Deansgate 84, 85 🚋 a			10 01		10 31				11 01		11 31				12 01		12 31	
Manchester Oxford Road 84, 85 a		09 58	10 05	10 06	10 35	10 37		10 57	11 05	11 06	11 35	11 37		11 57	12 05	12 06	12 35	12 37
Manchester Piccadilly 10 78, 84, 85 🚋 a		10 02		10 10		10 40		11 02		11 10		11 40		12 02		12 10		12 40
Stockport 84 a						10 52						11 52						12 52
Sheffield 7 78 🚋 a		*11 08*				11 38		*12 08*				12 38		*13 08*				13 38
Manchester Airport 85 ⇄ a		10 25		*10 40*		*11b01*		11 25		*11 40*		*12b01*		12 25		*12 40*		*13b01*

	NT	NT	NT	TP 1 ◇ A	NT	EM ◇	NT	NT	NT	TP 1 ◇ A	NT	EM ◇	NT	NT	NT	TP 1 ◇ A	NT	EM ◇
Liverpool Lime Street 10 90, 91 d	11 55	12 14		12 22	12 29	12 52	12 55	13 14		13 22	13 29	13 52	13 55	14 14		14 22	14 29	14 52
Edge Hill 90, 91 d	11 59						12 59						13 59					
Mossley Hill 91 d	12 04				12 37		13 04				13 37		14 04				14 37	
West Allerton 91 d	12 06						13 06						14 06					
Liverpool Central 10 103 d	*11 44*				*12 14*		*12 44*				*13 14*		*13 44*				*14 14*	
Liverpool South Parkway 7 91, 103 ⇄ d	12 09				12 40		13 09				13 40		14 09				14 40	
Hunts Cross 103 d	12 13						13 13						14 13					
Halewood d	12 16						13 16						14 16					
Hough Green d	12 20				12 47		13 20				13 47		14 20				14 47	
Widnes d	12 23				12 50	13 09	13 23				13 50	14 09	14 23				14 50	15 09
Sankey for Penketh d	12 28						13 28						14 28					
Warrington Central a	12 33		←	12 43	12 58	13 17	13 33		←	13 43	13 58	14 17	14 33		←	14 43	14 58	15 17
d	12 34 →		12 34	12 44	12 59	13 17	13 34 →		13 34	13 44	13 59	14 17	14 34 →		14 34	14 44	14 59	15 17
Padgate d			12 37						13 37						14 37			
Birchwood d			12 40	12 49	13 03				13 40	13 49	14 03				14 40	14 49	15 03	
Glazebrook d											14 08							
Irlam d			12 46		13 09				13 46		14 11				14 46		15 09	
Flixton d					13 13						14 15						15 13	
Chassen Road d											14 17							
Urmston d			12 51		13 16				13 51		14 19				14 51		15 16	
Humphrey Park d					13 19												15 19	
Trafford Park d					13 21												15 21	
Deansgate 84, 85 🚋 a			13 01		13 31				14 01		14 31				15 01		15 31	
Manchester Oxford Road 84, 85 a		12 57	13 05	13 06	13 35	13 37		13 57	14 05	14 06	14 35	14 37		14 57	15 05	15 06	15 35	15 37
Manchester Piccadilly 10 78, 84, 85 🚋 a		13 02		13 10		13 40		14 02		14 10		14 40		15 02		15 10		15 40
Stockport 84 a						13 52						14 52						15 53
Sheffield 7 78 🚋 a		*14 08*				14 38		*15 08*				15 38		*16 08*				16 38
Manchester Airport 85 ⇄ a		13 25		*13 40*		*14b01*		14 25		*14 40*		*15b01*		15 25		*15 40*		*16b01*

	NT	NT	NT	TP 1 ◇ B	NT	EM ◇	NT	NT	NT	TP 1 ◇ A	NT	EM ◇	NT	NT	NT	TP 1 ◇ A	NT	EM ◇ C
Liverpool Lime Street 10 90, 91 d	14 55	15 14		15 22	15 29	15 52	15 55	16 14		16 22	16 28	16 52	16 55	17 09		17 22	17 25	17 52
Edge Hill 90, 91 d	14 59						15 59						16 59				17 29	
Mossley Hill 91 d	15 04				15 37		16 04				16 36		17 04				17 34	
West Allerton 91 d	15 06						16 06						17 06				17 36	
Liverpool Central 10 103 d	*14 44*				*15 14*		*15 44*				*16 14*		*16 44*				*17 14*	
Liverpool South Parkway 7 91, 103 ⇄ d	15 09				15 40		16 09				16 39		17 09				17 39	
Hunts Cross 103 d	15 13						16 13						17 13				17 43	
Halewood d	15 16						16 16						17 15				17 45	
Hough Green d	15 20				15 47		16 20				16 46		17 19				17 49	
Widnes d	15 23				15 50	16 09	16 23				16 49	17 09	17 23				17 53	18 09
Sankey for Penketh d	15 28						16 28						17 28				17 58	
Warrington Central a	15 33		←	15 43	15 58	16 17	16 33		←	16 43	16 57	17 17	17 33		←	17 43	18 03	18 17
d	15 34 →		15 34	15 44	15 59	16 17	16 34 →		16 34	16 44	16 58	17 17	17 33 →		17 33	17 44	18 03	18 17
Padgate d			15 37						16 37						17 36			
Birchwood d			15 40	15 49	16 03				16 40	16 49	17 02				17 39	17 49	18 08	
Glazebrook d					16 08						17 07							
Irlam d			15 46		16 11				16 46		17 10				17 45		18 14	
Flixton d					16 15				16 50		17 14				17 49			
Chassen Road d					16 17												18 18	
Urmston d			15 51		16 19				16 53		17 17				17 52		18 20	
Humphrey Park d											17 20						18 23	
Trafford Park d											17 22							
Deansgate 84, 85 🚋 a			16 01		16 31				17 03						18 01			
Manchester Oxford Road 84, 85 a		15 57	16 05	16 06	16 35	16 37		16 57	17 05	17 06	17 35	17 37		17 58	18 05	18 06	18 34	18 39
Manchester Piccadilly 10 78, 84, 85 🚋 a		16 02		16 10		16 41		17 02		17 10		17 40		18 04		18 10		18 42
Stockport 84 a						16 52						17 54						18 54
Sheffield 7 78 🚋 a		*17 08*				17 38		*18 12*				18 38		*19 08*				19 35
Manchester Airport 85 ⇄ a		16 25		*16 40*		*17c11*		17 25		*17 40*		*18b01*		18 27		*18 42*		*19c08*

For general notes see front of timetable
For details of catering facilities see Directory of Train Operators

A To Scarborough (Table 39)
B To Middlesbrough (Table 39)
C TO Nottingham (Table 49)

b Change at Manchester Oxford Road
c Change at Manchester Piccadilly

Table 89

Saturdays

from 13 September

Liverpool → Warrington Central → Manchester and Manchester Airport

Network Diagram - see first page of Table 88

		NT	NT	NT	TP 1 ◇ A	NT	EM ◇ B	NT	TP 1 ◇ C	NT	EM ◇ B	NT	NT	TP 1 ◇ C	NT	NT	TP 1 ◇ D	NT
Liverpool Lime Street 10	90, 91 d	17 55	18 14		18 22	18 25	18 52	18 55	19 22		19 52	19 55	20 14	20 22	20 55	21 55	22 30	23 33
Edge Hill	90, 91 d	17 59				18 29		18 59				19 59			20 59	21 59		23 37
Mossley Hill	91 d	18 04				18 34		19 04				20 04			21 04	22 04		23 41
West Allerton	91 d	18 06				18 36		19 06				20 06			21 06	22 06		23 44
Liverpool Central 10	103 d	17 44				18 14		18 44				19 44			20 44	21 44		23 14
Liverpool South Parkway 7	91, 103 ✈ d	18 09				18 39		19 09				20 09			21 09	22 09		23 47
Hunts Cross	103 d	18 13				18 43		19 13				20 13			21 13	22 13		23 50
Halewood	d	18 15				18 45		19 15				20 15			21 15	22 15		23 52
Hough Green	d	18 19				18 49		19 19				20 19			21 19	22 19		23 56
Widnes	d	18 23				18 53	19 09	19 23			20 09	20 23			21 23	22 23		00 01
Sankey for Penketh	d	18 28				18 58		19 28				20 28			21 28	22 28		00 06
Warrington Central	a	18 33		←	18 43	19 03	19 17	19 35	19 43		20 17	20 35		20 43	21 33	22 33	22 52	00 10
	d	18 33		18 33	18 44	19 03	19 17		19 44	19 52	20 17			20 44	21 33	22 33	22 52	00 10
Padgate	d	→				19 06				19 55					21 36	22 36		
Birchwood	d			18 38	18 49	19 09			19 49	19 58				20 49	21 39	22 39	22 57	
Glazebrook	d					19 14				20 03					21 44	22 44		
Irlam	d			18 44		19 17				20 06					21 47	22 47		
Flixton	d			18 48						20 10					21 51	22 51		
Chassen Road	d									20 12					21 53	22 53		
Urmston	d			18 51		19 22				20 14					21 55	22 55		
Humphrey Park	d									20 17					21 58	22 58		
Trafford Park	d			18 54						20 19					22 00	23 00		
Deansgate	84, 85 ⛴ a					19 32				20 30					22 07	23 07		
Manchester Oxford Road	84, 85 a		18 59	19 04	19 05	19 35	19 38		20 05	20 34	20 37		20 58	21 06	22 12	23 12	23 13	
Manchester Piccadilly 10	78, 84, 85 ⛴ a		19 05		19 10		19 42		20 10		20 40		21 05	21 10	22 56	23 21	23 17	00 33
Stockport	84 a						19 53				20 51							
Sheffield 7	78 ⛴ a		20 08				20 34				21 34		22 09	22 31				
Manchester Airport	85 ✈ a		19 26		19 40		20b05		20 58		21b09		21 28	21b37			23 56	01 14

Sundays

until 13 July

		TP 1 ◇ E	NT	NT	TP 1 ◇ A	NT	NT	NT	NT	TP 1 ◇ A	NT	NT	TP 1 ◇ G	NT	EM ◇ H	NT	TP 1 ◇ A	NT	EM ◇ H
Liverpool Lime Street 10	90, 91 d	08 22	08 30	08 57	09 22	09 30	09 57	10 30	10 57	11 22	11 30	11 57	12 22	12 30	12 52	12 57	13 22	13 30	13 52
Mossley Hill	91 d			09 05			10 05		11 05			12 05				13 05			
West Allerton	91 d			09 07			10 07		11 07			12 07				13 07			
Liverpool Central 10	103 d			08 44			09 44		10 44			11 44				12 44			
Liverpool South Parkway 7	91, 103 ✈ d			09 10			10 10		11 10			12 10				13 10			
Hunts Cross	103 d			09 14			10 14		11 14			12 14				13 14			
Halewood	d			09 16			10 16		11 16			12 16				13 16			
Hough Green	d			09 20			10 20		11 20			12 20				13 20			
Widnes	d			09 24			10 24		11 24			12 24			13 10	13 24			14 10
Warrington Central	a	08 43		09 32	09 44		10 32		11 32	11 43		12 32	12 44		13 17	13 32	13 43		14 17
	d	08 44		09 32	09 45		10 32		11 32	11 44		12 32	12 45		13 18	13 32	13 44		14 18
Birchwood	d	08 49		09 37	09 50		10 37		11 37	11 49		12 37				13 37	13 49		
Irlam	d			09 43			10 43		11 43			12 43				13 43			
Urmston	d			09 48			10 48		11 48			12 48				13 48			
Deansgate	84, 85 ⛴ a			09 58			10 58		11 58			12 58				13 58			
Manchester Oxford Road	84, 85 a	09 06	09 27	10 02	10 06	10 27	11 02	11 27	12 02	12 04	12 27	13 02	13 03	13 30	13 36	14 02	14 06	14 27	14 36
Manchester Piccadilly 10	78, 84, 85 ⛴ a	09 10	09 34		10 10	10 34	11 15	11 35		12 10	12 35		13 07	13 35	13 44		14 10	14 32	14 41
Stockport	84 a	09 38	10 07		10 38	11 07	11 38	12 07		12 37	13 06		13 38		13 55		14 36		14 52
Sheffield 7	78 ⛴ a	10 58			11 47	12 03		13 27		13 38	14 06				14 36				15 34
Manchester Airport	85 ✈ a	09b33	09 51		10b33	10 54	11 33	11 51		12b33	12 54		13 33	13 55	14c18		14b33	14 51	15c18

		NT	TP 1 ◇ G	NT	EM ◇ H	NT	TP 1 ◇ A	NT	EM ◇ H	NT	TP 1 ◇ C	NT	EM ◇ B	NT	TP 1 ◇ A	NT	EM ◇ H	NT	TP 1 ◇ A
Liverpool Lime Street 10	90, 91 d	13 57	14 22	14 30	14 52	14 57	15 22	15 30	15 52	15 57	16 22	16 30	16 52	16 57	17 22	17 30	17 52	17 57	18 22
Mossley Hill	91 d	14 05				15 05				16 05				17 05				18 05	
West Allerton	91 d	14 07				15 07				16 07				17 07				18 07	
Liverpool Central 10	103 d	13 44				14 44				15 44				16 44				17 44	
Liverpool South Parkway 7	91, 103 ✈ d	14 10				15 10				16 10				17 10				18 10	
Hunts Cross	103 d	14 14				15 14				16 14				17 14				18 14	
Halewood	d	14 16				15 16				16 16				17 16				18 16	
Hough Green	d	14 20				15 20				16 20				17 20				18 20	
Widnes	d	14 24			15 10	15 24			16 10	16 24			17 10	17 24			18 10	18 24	
Warrington Central	a	14 32	14 43		15 17	15 32	15 43		16 17	16 32	16 43		17 17	17 32	17 43		18 17	18 32	18 43
	d	14 32	14 44		15 18	15 32	15 44		16 18	16 32	16 44		17 18	17 32	17 44		18 18	18 32	18 44
Birchwood	d	14 37	14 49			15 37	15 49			16 37	16 49			17 37	17 49			18 37	18 49
Irlam	d	14 43				15 43				16 43				17 43				18 43	
Urmston	d	14 48				15 48				16 48				17 48				18 48	
Deansgate	84, 85 ⛴ a	14 58				15 58				16 58				17 58				18 58	
Manchester Oxford Road	84, 85 a	15 02	15 06	15 28	15 36	16 02	16 06	16 27	16 38	17 02	17 06	17 30	17 36	18 02	18 06	18 27	18 36	19 02	19 06
Manchester Piccadilly 10	78, 84, 85 ⛴ a		15 10	15 34	15 41		16 10	16 35	16 41		17 10	17 35	17 41		18 10	18 33	18 41		19 10
Stockport	84 a		15 36		15 52		16 37		16 52		17 37		17 52		18 38		18 52		19 38
Sheffield 7	78 ⛴ a				16 34				17 34				18 36				19 35		
Manchester Airport	85 ✈ a		15b33	15 51	16c18		16b33	16 51	17c18		17b33	17 51	18c18		18b33	18 52	19c18		19b33

For general notes see front of timetable
For details of catering facilities see Directory of Train Operators

- **A** To Scarborough (Table 39)
- **B** TO Nottingham (Table 49)
- **C** To York (Table 39)
- **D** To Huddersfield (Table 39)
- **E** To Newcastle (Table 39)
- **G** To Hull (Table 39)
- **H** To Norwich (Table 49)
- **b** Change at Manchester Oxford Road
- **c** Change at Manchester Piccadilly

Table 89

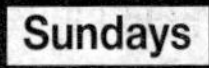

until 13 July

Liverpool → Warrington Central → Manchester and Manchester Airport

Network Diagram - see first page of Table 88

		NT	EM ◇ A	NT	TP 1 ◇ B	NT	EM ◇ A	NT	TP 1 ◇ C	NT	NT	EM ◇ A	NT	TP 1 ◇ B	NT	NT	NT	NT
Liverpool Lime Street 10	90, 91 d	18 30	18 52	18 57	19 22	19 30	19 52	19 57	20 22	20 30	20 57	21 22	21 30	21 52	21 57	22 27	22 30	
Mossley Hill	91 d			19 05				20 05			21 05				22 05	22 35		
West Allerton	91 d			19 07				20 07			21 07				22 07	22 37		
Liverpool Central 10	103 d			*18 44*				*19 44*			*20 44*				*21 44*	*22 14*		
Liverpool South Parkway 7	91, 103 ✈ d			19 10				20 10			21 10				22 10	22 40		
Hunts Cross	103 d			19 14				20 14			21 14				22 14	22 44		
Halewood	d			19 16				20 16			21 16				22 16	22 46		
Hough Green	d			19 20				20 20			21 20				22 20	22 50		
Widnes	d		19 10	19 24			20 10	20 24			21 24	21 40			22 24	22 54		←
Warrington Central	a		19 17	19 32	19 43		20 17	20 32	20 43		21 32	21 47		22 14	22 32	23 02		23 02
	d		19 18	19 32	19 44		20 18	20 32	20 44		21 32	21 47		22 15	22 32	23 02		23 02
Birchwood	d			19 37	19 49			20 37	20 49		21 37			22 20	22 37	→		23 07
Irlam	d			19 43				20 43			21 43				22 43			23 13
Urmston	d			19 48				20 48			21 48				22 48			23 18
Deansgate	84, 85 ⛴ a			19 58				20 58			21 58				22 58			23 28
Manchester Oxford Road	84, 85 a	19 28	19 36	20 02	20 06	20 28	20 39	21 02	21 06	21 28	22 02	22 06	22 27	22 36	23 02		23 27	23 32
Manchester Piccadilly 10	78, 84, 85 ⛴ a	19 35	19 41		20 10	20 33	20 41		21 10	21 34		22 10	22 33	22 40	*23 15*		23 33	*23 44*
Stockport	84 a		19 52		*20 38*		20 52		*21 37*	*22 03*		22 21	*22 54*	*23 03*	*23 38*			
Sheffield 7	78 ⛴ a		20 35				21 38			*23 06*		23 23		*00 09*				
Manchester Airport	85 ✈ a	19 51	*20b18*		*20c33*	20 52	*21b18*		*21c33*	21 52		*22c33*	22 51	*23 18*	23 33		23 49	*00e33*

Sundays

20 July to 7 September

		TP 1 ◇ D	NT	NT	TP 1 ◇ E	NT	NT	NT	NT	TP 1 ◇ E	NT	NT	TP 1 ◇ G	NT	EM ◇ H	NT	TP 1 ◇ C	NT	EM ◇ H
Liverpool Lime Street 10	90, 91 d	08 22	08 30	08 57	09 22	09 30	09 57	10 30	10 57	11 22	11 30	11 57	12 22	12 30	12 52	12 57	13 22	13 30	13 52
Edge Hill	90, 91 d																		
Mossley Hill	91 d			09 05			10 05		11 05			12 05				13 05			
West Allerton	91 d			09 07			10 07		11 07			12 07				13 07			
Liverpool Central 10	103 d			*08 44*			*09 44*		*10 44*			*11 44*				*12 44*			
Liverpool South Parkway 7	91, 103 ✈ d			09 10			10 10		11 10			12 10				13 10			
Hunts Cross	103 d			09 14			10 14		11 14			12 14				13 14			
Halewood	d			09 16			10 16		11 16			12 16				13 16			
Hough Green	d			09 20			10 20		11 20			12 20				13 20			
Widnes	d			09 24			10 24		11 24			12 24			13 10	13 24			14 10
Sankey for Penketh	d																		
Warrington Central	a	08 43		09 32	09 44		10 32		11 32	11 43		12 32	12 44		13 17	13 32	13 43		14 17
	d	08 44		09 32	09 45		10 32		11 32	11 44		12 32	12 45		13 18	13 32	13 44		14 18
Padgate	d																		
Birchwood	d	08 49		09 37	09 50		10 37		11 37	11 49		12 37	12 50			13 37	13 49		
Glazebrook	d																		
Irlam	d			09 43			10 43		11 43			12 43				13 43			
Flixton	d																		
Chassen Road	d																		
Urmston	d			09 48			10 48		11 48			12 48				13 48			
Humphrey Park	d																		
Trafford Park	d																		
Deansgate	84, 85 ⛴ a			09 58			10 58		11 58			12 58				13 58			
Manchester Oxford Road	84, 85 a	09 06	09 27	10 02	10 06	10 27	11 02	11 27	12 02	12 04	12 31	13 02	13 06	13 30	13 36	14 02	14 06	14 27	14 36
Manchester Piccadilly 10	78, 84, 85 ⛴ a	09 10	09 34		10 10	10 34	*11 15*	11 35		12 10	12 35		13 10	13 35	13 44		14 10	14 32	14 41
Stockport	84 a	*09 31*	*10 00*		*10 31*	*11 00*	*11 38*	*12 00*		*12 32*	*13 01*		*13 38*		13 57		*14 32*		14 52
Sheffield 7	78 ⛴ a	*10 56*			*11 47*	*12 03*		*13 27*		*13 38*	*14 06*				14 38				15 34
Manchester Airport	85 ✈ a	*09c40*	09 51		*10c36*	10 53	*11 36*	11 55		*12c36*	12 54		*13c36*	13 53	*14b33*		*14c36*	14 53	*15b36*

		NT	TP 1 ◇ C	NT	EM ◇ H	NT	TP 1 ◇ E	NT	EM ◇ H	NT	TP 1 ◇ C	NT	EM ◇ A	NT	TP 1 ◇ E	NT	EM ◇ H	NT	TP 1 ◇ C
Liverpool Lime Street 10	90, 91 d	13 57	14 22	14 30	14 52	14 57	15 22	15 30	15 52	15 57	16 22	16 30	16 52	16 57	17 22	17 30	17 52	17 57	18 22
Edge Hill	90, 91 d																		
Mossley Hill	91 d	14 05				15 05				16 05				17 05				18 05	
West Allerton	91 d	14 07				15 07				16 07				17 07				18 07	
Liverpool Central 10	103 d	*13 44*				*14f44*				*15 44*				*16 44*				*17 44*	
Liverpool South Parkway 7	91, 103 ✈ d	14 10				15 10				16 10				17 10				18 10	
Hunts Cross	103 d	14 14				15 14				16 14				17 14				18 14	
Halewood	d	14 16				15 16				16 16				17 16				18 16	
Hough Green	d	14 20				15 20				16 20				17 20				18 20	
Widnes	d	14 24			15 10	15 24			16 10	16 24			17 10	17 24			18 10	18 24	
Sankey for Penketh	d																		
Warrington Central	a	14 32	14 43		15 17	15 32	15 43		16 17	16 32	16 43		17 17	17 32	17 43		18 17	18 32	18 43
	d	14 32	14 44		15 18	15 32	15 44		16 18	16 32	16 44		17 18	17 32	17 44		18 18	18 32	18 44
Padgate	d																		
Birchwood	d	14 37	14 49			15 37	15 49			16 37	16 49			17 37	17 49			18 37	18 49
Glazebrook	d																		
Irlam	d	14 43				15 43				16 43				17 43				18 43	
Flixton	d																		
Chassen Road	d																		
Urmston	d	14 48				15 48				16 48				17 48				18 48	
Humphrey Park	d																		
Trafford Park	d																		
Deansgate	84, 85 ⛴ a	14 58				15 58				16 58				17 58				18 58	
Manchester Oxford Road	84, 85 a	15 02	15 06	15 28	15 36	16 02	16 06	16 27	16 38	17 02	17 06	17 30	17 36	18 02	18 06	18 27	18 36	19 02	19 06
Manchester Piccadilly 10	78, 84, 85 ⛴ a		15 10	15 34	15 41		16 10	16 35	16 41		17 10	17 35	17 41		18 10	18 33	18 41		19 10
Stockport	84 a		*15 32*		15 52		*16 31*		16 52		*17 31*		17 52		*18 32*		18 52		*19 31*
Sheffield 7	78 ⛴ a				16 34				17 34				18 36				19 35		
Manchester Airport	85 ✈ a		*15c36*	15 53	*16b33*		*16c36*	16 53	*17b32*	*17 36*	*17 36*	17 53	*18b33*		*18c36*	18 53	*19b32*		*19c36*

For general notes see front of timetable
For details of catering facilities see Directory of Train Operators

- **A** TO Nottingham (Table 49)
- **B** To York (Table 39)
- **C** To Newcastle (Table 39)
- **D** To Scarborough (Table 39)
- **E** To Middlesbrough (Table 39)
- **G** To Hull (Table 39)
- **H** To Norwich (Table 49)
- **b** Change at Manchester Piccadilly
- **c** Change at Manchester Oxford Road
- **e** Change at Manchester Oxford Road and Manchester Piccadilly
- **f** Change at Hunts Cross

Liverpool → Warrington Central → Manchester and Manchester Airport

Sundays

20 July to 7 September

Network Diagram - see first page of Table 88

	NT	EM	NT	TP	NT	EM	NT	TP	NT	NT	EM	NT	TP	NT	NT	NT	NT
		◇ A		[1] ◇ B		◇ A		[1] ◇ C			◇ A		[1] ◇ D				
Liverpool Lime Street [10] 90, 91 d	18 30	18 52	18 57	19 22	19 30	19 52	19 57	20 22	20 30	20 57	21 22	21 30	21 52	21 57	22 27	22 30	
Edge Hill 90, 91 d																	
Mossley Hill 91 d			19 05				20 05			21 05				22 05	22 35		
West Allerton 91 d			19 07				20 07			21 07				22 07	22 37		
Liverpool Central [10] 103 d			18 44				19 44			20 44				21 44	22 14		
Liverpool South Parkway [7] 91, 103 d			19 10				20 10			21 10				22 10	22 40		
Hunts Cross 103 d			19 14				20 14			21 14				22 14	22 44		
Halewood d			19 16				20 16			21 16				22 16	22 46		
Hough Green d			19 20				20 20			21 20				22 20	22 50		
Widnes d		19 10	19 24			20 10	20 24			21 24	21 40			22 24	22 54		←
Sankey for Penketh d																	
Warrington Central a		19 17	19 32	19 43		20 17	20 32	20 43		21 32	21 47		22 14	22 32	23 02		23 02
d		19 18	19 32	19 44		20 18	20 32	20 44		21 32	21 47		22 15	22 32	23 02		23 02
Padgate d																	
Birchwood d			19 37	19 49			20 37	20 49		21 37			22 20	22 37	→		23 07
Glazebrook d																	
Irlam d			19 43				20 43			21 43				22 43			23 13
Flixton d																	
Chassen Road d																	
Urmston d			19 48				20 48			21 48				22 48			23 18
Humphrey Park d																	
Trafford Park d																	
Deansgate 84, 85 a			19 58				20 58			21 58				22 58			23 28
Manchester Oxford Road 84, 85 a	19 28	19 36	20 02	20 06	20 28	20 39	21 02	21 06	21 28	22 02	22 06	22 27	22 36	23 02		23 27	23 32
Manchester Piccadilly [10] 78, 84, 85 a	19 35	19 41		20 10	20 33	20 41		21 10	21 34		22 10	22 33	22 40	23 15		23 33	23 44
Stockport 84 a		19 52		20 39		20 52		21 37	22 03		22 21	22 54	23 03	23 38			
Sheffield [7] 78 a		20 35				21 38			23 06		23 23		00 09				
Manchester Airport 85 a	19 53	20b32		20c36	20 54	21b32		21c36	21 54		22c36	22 53	23 27	23 33		23 49	00e33

Sundays

14 September to 2 November

	TP	NT	NT	TP	NT	NT	NT	NT	TP	NT	NT	TP	NT	EM	NT	TP	NT	EM
	[1] ◇ C			[1] ◇ B					[1] ◇ B			[1] ◇ E		◇ G		[1] ◇ B		◇ G
Liverpool Lime Street [10] 90, 91 d	08 22	08 30	08 57	09 22	09 30	09 57	10 30	10 57	11 22	11 30	11 57	12 22	12 30	12 52	12 57	13 22	13 30	13 52
Edge Hill 90, 91 d																		
Mossley Hill 91 d			09 05			10 05		11 05			12 05				13 05			
West Allerton 91 d			09 07			10 07		11 07			12 07				13 07			
Liverpool Central [10] 103 d			08 44			09 44		10 44			11 44				12 44			
Liverpool South Parkway [7] 91, 103 d			09 10			10 10		11 10			12 10				13 10			
Hunts Cross 103 d			09 14			10 14		11 14			12 14				13 14			
Halewood d			09 16			10 16		11 16			12 16				13 16			
Hough Green d			09 20			10 20		11 20			12 20				13 20			
Widnes d			09 24			10 24		11 24			12 24			13 10	13 24			14 10
Sankey for Penketh d																		
Warrington Central a	08 43		09 32	09 44		10 32		11 32	11 43		12 32	12 44		13 17	13 32	13 43		14 17
d	08 44		09 32	09 45		10 32		11 32	11 44		12 32	12 45		13 18	13 32	13 44		14 18
Padgate d																		
Birchwood d	08 49		09 37	09 50		10 37		11 37	11 49		12 37	12 50			13 37	13 49		
Glazebrook d																		
Irlam d			09 43			10 43		11 43			12 43				13 43			
Flixton d																		
Chassen Road d																		
Urmston d			09 48			10 48		11 48			12 48				13 48			
Humphrey Park d																		
Trafford Park d																		
Deansgate 84, 85 a			09 58			10 58		11 58			12 58				13 58			
Manchester Oxford Road 84, 85 a	09 06	09 27	10 02	10 06	10 27	11 02	11 27	12 02	12 04	12 31	13 02	13 06	13 30	13 36	14 02	14 06	14 27	14 36
Manchester Piccadilly [10] 78, 84, 85 a	09 10	09 34		10 10	10 35	11 15	11 35		12 10	12 35		13 10	13 35	13 44		14 10	14 32	14 41
Stockport 84 a														13 57				14 52
Sheffield [7] 78 a	10 58				12 03		13 27		13 37	14 06				14 38				15 34
Manchester Airport 85 a	09c33	09 51		10c33	10 55	11 33	11 51		12c33	12 50		13c33	13 53	14b33		14c33	14 51	15b21

For general notes see front of timetable
For details of catering facilities see Directory of Train Operators

A TO Nottingham (Table 49)

B To Scarborough (Table 39)
C To Newcastle (Table 39)
D To York (Table 39)
E To Hull (Table 39)
G To Norwich (Table 49)

b Change at Manchester Piccadilly
c Change at Manchester Oxford Road
e Change at Manchester Oxford Road and Manchester Piccadilly

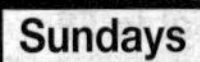

Sundays

Liverpool → Warrington Central → Manchester and Manchester Airport

14 September to 2 November

Network Diagram - see first page of Table 88

		NT	TP 1 ◇ A	NT	EM ◇ B	NT	TP 1 ◇ C	NT	EM ◇ B	NT	TP 1 ◇ D	NT	EM ◇ E	NT	TP 1 ◇ C	NT	EM ◇ B	NT	TP 1 ◇ C
Liverpool Lime Street 10	90, 91 d	13 57	14 22	14 30	14 52	14 57	15 22	15 30	15 52	15 57	16 22	16 30	16 52	16 57	17 22	17 30	17 52	17 57	18 22
Edge Hill	90, 91 d																		
Mossley Hill	91 d	14 05				15 05				16 05				17 05				18 05	
West Allerton	91 d	14 07				15 07				16 07				17 07				18 07	
Liverpool Central 10	103 d	*13 44*				*14 44*				*15 44*				*16 44*				*17 44*	
Liverpool South Parkway 7	91, 103 ✈ d	14 10				15 10				16 10				17 10				18 10	
Hunts Cross	103 d	14 14				15 14				16 14				17 14				18 14	
Halewood	d	14 16				15 16				16 16				17 16				18 16	
Hough Green	d	14 20				15 20				16 20				17 20				18 20	
Widnes	d	14 24			15 10	15 24			16 10	16 24			17 10	17 24			18 10	18 24	
Sankey for Penketh	d																		
Warrington Central	a	14 32	14 43		15 17	15 32	15 43		16 17	16 32	16 43		17 17	17 32	17 43		18 17	18 32	18 43
	d	14 32	14 44		15 18	15 32	15 44		16 18	16 32	16 44		17 18	17 32	17 44		18 18	18 32	18 44
Padgate	d																		
Birchwood	d	14 37	14 49			15 37	15 49			16 37	16 49			17 37	17 49			18 37	18 49
Glazebrook	d																		
Irlam	d	14 43				15 43				16 43				17 43				18 43	
Flixton	d																		
Chassen Road	d																		
Urmston	d	14 48				15 48				16 48				17 48				18 48	
Humphrey Park	d																		
Trafford Park	d																		
Deansgate	84, 85 ⛴ a	14 58				15 58				16 58				17 58				18 58	
Manchester Oxford Road	84, 85 a	15 02	15 06	15 28	15 36	16 02	16 06	16 27	16 38	17 02	17 06	17 30	17 36	18 02	18 06	18 27	18 36	19 02	19 06
Manchester Piccadilly 10	78, 84, 85 ⛴ a		15 10	15 34	15 41		16 10	16 35	16 41		17 10	17 35	17 41		18 10	18 33	18 41		19 10
Stockport	84 a				15 52				16 52				17 52				18 52		
Sheffield 7	78 ⛴ a				16 34				17 34				18 36				19 35		
Manchester Airport	85 ✈ a		*15*b*33*	15 51	*16*c*18*		*16*b*33*	16 51	*17*c*18*		*17*b*33*	17 51	*18*c*18*		*18*b*33*	18 52	*19*c*18*		*19*b*33*

		NT	EM ◇ E	NT	TP 1 ◇ D	NT	EM ◇ E	NT	TP 1 ◇ G	NT	NT	EM ◇ E	NT	TP 1 ◇ D	NT	NT	NT	NT
Liverpool Lime Street 10	90, 91 d	18 30	18 52	18 57	19 22	19 30	19 52	19 57	20 22	20 30	20 57	21 22	21 30	21 52	21 57	22 27	22 30	
Edge Hill	90, 91 d																	
Mossley Hill	91 d			19 05				20 05			21 05				22 05	22 35		
West Allerton	91 d			19 07				20 07			21 07				22 07	22 37		
Liverpool Central 10	103 d			*18 44*				*19 44*			*20 44*				*21 44*	*22 14*		
Liverpool South Parkway 7	91, 103 ✈ d			19 10				20 10			21 10				22 10	22 40		
Hunts Cross	103 d			19 14				20 14			21 14				22 14	22 44		
Halewood	d			19 16				20 16			21 16				22 16	22 46		
Hough Green	d			19 20				20 20			21 20				22 20	22 50		←
Widnes	d		19 10	19 24			20 10	20 24			21 24	21 40			22 24	22 54		22 54
Sankey for Penketh	d																	
Warrington Central	a		19 17	19 32	19 43		20 17	20 32	20 43		21 32	21 47		22 14	22 32	23 02		23 02
	d		19 18	19 32	19 44		20 18	20 32	20 44		21 32	21 47		22 15	22 32	23 02		23 02
Padgate	d																	
Birchwood	d			19 37	19 49			20 37	20 49		21 37			22 20	22 37	→		23 07
Glazebrook	d																	
Irlam	d			19 43				20 43			21 43				22 43			23 13
Flixton	d																	
Chassen Road	d																	
Urmston	d			19 48				20 48			21 48				22 48			23 18
Humphrey Park	d																	
Trafford Park	d																	
Deansgate	84, 85 ⛴ a			19 58				20 58			21 58				22 58			23 28
Manchester Oxford Road	84, 85 a	19 28	19 36	20 02	20 06	20 28	20 39	21 02	21 06	21 28	22 02	22 06	22 27	22 36	23 02		23 27	23 32
Manchester Piccadilly 10	78, 84, 85 ⛴ a	19 35	19 41		20 10	20 33	20 41		21 10	21 34		22 10	22 33	22 40	*23 15*		23 33	*23 41*
Stockport	84 a		19 52				20 52					22 21						
Sheffield 7	78 ⛴ a		20 35				21 38			*23 06*		23 23		*00 09*				
Manchester Airport	85 ✈ a	19 51	*20*c*18*		*20*b*33*	20 52	*21*c*18*		*21*b*33*	21 52		*22*b*33*	22 51	*23 18*	*23 33*		23 49	*00*e*33*

For general notes see front of timetable
For details of catering facilities see Directory of Train Operators

A To Hull (Table 39)
B To Norwich (Table 49)
C To Scarborough (Table 39)
D To York (Table 39)
E TO Nottingham (Table 49)
G To Newcastle (Table 39)
b Change at Manchester Oxford Road
c Change at Manchester Piccadilly
e Change at Manchester Oxford Road and Manchester Piccadilly

Table 89

Liverpool → Warrington Central → Manchester and Manchester Airport

Sundays from 9 November

Network Diagram - see first page of Table 88

		TP (bus)	TP 1 ◇ A	NT	TP (bus)	NT	TP 1 ◇ B	NT	TP (bus)	NT	NT	NT	TP 1 ◇ B	NT	TP (bus)	NT	TP 1 ◇ C	NT
Liverpool Lime Street 10	90, 91 d		08 10	08 30		08 57	09 10	09 30		09 57	10 30	10 57	11 10	11 30		11 57	12 10	12 30
Mossley Hill	91 d					09 05				10 05		11 05				12 05		
West Allerton	91 d					09 07				10 07		11 07				12 07		
Liverpool Central 10	103 d					08 44				09 44		10 44				11 44		
Liverpool South Parkway 7	91, 103 ⇄ d					09 10				10 10		11 10				12 10		
Hunts Cross	103 d					09 14				10 14		11 14				12 14		
Halewood	d					09 16				10 16		11 16				12 16		
Hough Green	d					09 20				10 20		11 20				12 20		
Widnes	d					09 24				10 24		11 24				12 24		
Warrington Central	a					09 32				10 32		11 32				12 32		
	d	07 57			08 57	09 32			09 57	10 32		11 32			11 57	12 32		
Birchwood	d					09 37				10 37		11 37				12 37		
Irlam	d					09 43				10 43		11 43				12 43		
Urmston	d					09 48				10 48		11 48				12 48		
Deansgate	84, 85 ⛴ a					09 58				10 58		11 58				12 58		
Newton-le-Willows	90 d	08a17	08 27	09 05	09a17		09 27	10 05	10a17		11 05		11 27	12 05	12a17		12 27	13 05
Manchester Victoria	90 ⛴ a		08 48				09 48						11 49				12 49	
Manchester Oxford Road	84, 85 a			09 27		10 02		10 27		11 02	11 27	12 02		12 31		13 02		13 30
Manchester Piccadilly 10	78, 84, 85 ⛴ a			09 34		10 15		10 35		11 15	11 35	12 15		12 35		13 17		13 35
Stockport	84 a																	
Sheffield 7	78 ⛴ a							12 03			13 27			14 06				
Manchester Airport	85 ⇄ a			09 51		10 33		10 55		11 33	11 51	12 33		12 53		13 33		13 53

		TP (bus)	EM ◇ D	NT	TP 1 ◇ B	NT	TP (bus)	EM ◇ D	NT	TP 1 ◇ C	NT	TP (bus)	EM ◇ D	NT	TP 1 ◇ B	NT	TP (bus)	EM ◇ D
Liverpool Lime Street 10	90, 91 d		12 52	12 57	13 10	13 30		13 52	13 57	14 10	14 30		14 52	14 57	15 10	15 30		15 52
Mossley Hill	91 d			13 05					14 05					15 05				
West Allerton	91 d			13 07					14 07					15 07				
Liverpool Central 10	103 d			12 44					13 44					14 44				
Liverpool South Parkway 7	91, 103 ⇄ d			13 10					14 10					15 10				
Hunts Cross	103 d			13 14					14 14					15 14				
Halewood	d			13 16					14 16					15 16				
Hough Green	d			13 20					14 20					15 20				
Widnes	d		13 10	13 24				14 10	14 24				15 10	15 24				16 10
Warrington Central	a		13 17	13 32				14 17	14 32				15 17	15 32				16 17
	d	12 57	13 18	13 32			13 57	14 18	14 32			14 57	15 18	15 32			15 57	16 18
Birchwood	d			13 37					14 37					15 37				
Irlam	d			13 43					14 43					15 43				
Urmston	d			13 48					14 48					15 48				
Deansgate	84, 85 ⛴ a			13 58					14 58					15 58				
Newton-le-Willows	90 d	13a17			13 27	14 05	14a17			14 27	15 05	15a17			15 27	16 05	16a17	
Manchester Victoria	90 ⛴ a				13 49					14 49					15 48			
Manchester Oxford Road	84, 85 a		13 36	14 02		14 27		14 36	15 02		15 29		15 36	16 02		16 27		16 38
Manchester Piccadilly 10	78, 84, 85 ⛴ a		13 44	14 15		14 32		14 41	15 15		15 32		15 41	16 15		16 35		16 41
Stockport	84 a		13 57					14 52					15 52					16 52
Sheffield 7	78 ⛴ a		14 38					15 34					16 34					17 34
Manchester Airport	85 ⇄ a		14b24	14 33		14 51		15b21	15 33		15 51		16b18			16 51		17b18

		NT	TP 1 ◇ E	NT	TP (bus)	EM ◇ G	NT	TP 1 ◇ B	NT	TP (bus)	EM ◇ D	NT	TP 1 ◇ B	NT	TP (bus)	EM ◇ G	NT	TP 1 ◇ E
Liverpool Lime Street 10	90, 91 d	15 57	16 10	16 30		16 52	16 57	17 10	17 30		17 52	17 57	18 09	18 30		18 52	18 57	19 10
Mossley Hill	91 d	16 05					17 05					18 05					19 05	
West Allerton	91 d	16 07					17 07					18 07					19 07	
Liverpool Central 10	103 d	15 44					16 44					17 44					18 44	
Liverpool South Parkway 7	91, 103 ⇄ d	16 10					17 10					18 10					19 10	
Hunts Cross	103 d	16 14					17 14					18 14					19 14	
Halewood	d	16 16					17 16					18 16					19 16	
Hough Green	d	16 20					17 20					18 20					19 20	
Widnes	d	16 24				17 10	17 24				18 10	18 24				19 10	19 24	
Warrington Central	a	16 32				17 17	17 32				18 17	18 32				19 17	19 32	
	d	16 32			16 57	17 18	17 32			17 57	18 18	18 32			18 57	19 18	19 32	
Birchwood	d	16 37					17 37					18 37					19 37	
Irlam	d	16 43					17 43					18 43					19 43	
Urmston	d	16 48					17 48					18 48					19 48	
Deansgate	84, 85 ⛴ a	16 58					17 58					18 58					19 58	
Newton-le-Willows	90 d		16 27	17 05	17a17			17 27	18 05	18a17			18 26	19 05	19a17			19 27
Manchester Victoria	90 ⛴ a		16 48					17 49					18 48					19 48
Manchester Oxford Road	84, 85 a	17 02		17 30		17 36	18 02		18 27		18 36	19 02		19 28		19 36	20 02	
Manchester Piccadilly 10	78, 84, 85 ⛴ a	17 15		17 35		17 41	18 15		18 33		18 41	19 15		19 35		19 41	20 15	
Stockport	84 a					17 52					18 52					19 52		
Sheffield 7	78 ⛴ a					18 36					19 35			21 06		20 35		
Manchester Airport	85 ⇄ a	17 33		17 51			18 33		18 52		19b18	19 33		19 51		20b18	20 33	

For general notes see front of timetable
For details of catering facilities see Directory of Train Operators

- **A** To Newcastle (Table 39)
- **B** To Scarborough (Table 39)
- **C** To Hull (Table 39)
- **D** To Norwich (Table 49)
- **E** To York (Table 39)
- **G** TO Nottingham (Table 49)
- **b** Change at Manchester Piccadilly

Table 89

from 9 November

Liverpool → Warrington Central → Manchester and Manchester Airport

Network Diagram - see first page of Table 88

		NT	TP	EM		NT	TP	NT		TP	NT	EM		NT	TP	NT		NT	NT	NT			
			🚌	◇ A			1 ◇ B			🚌		◇ A			1 ◇ C								
Liverpool Lime Street 10	90, 91 d	19 30		19 52		19 57	20 10	20 30			20 57	21 22		21 30	21 50	21 57		22 27	22 30				
Mossley Hill	91 d					20 05					21 05					22 05		22 35					
West Allerton	91 d					20 07					21 07					22 07		22 37					
Liverpool Central 10	103 d					*19 44*					*20 44*					*21 44*		*22 14*					
Liverpool South Parkway 7	91, 103 ✈ d					20 10					21 10					22 10		22 40					
Hunts Cross	103 d					20 14					21 14					22 14		22 44					
Halewood	d					20 16					21 16					22 16		22 46					
Hough Green	d					20 20					21 20					22 20		22 50					
Widnes	d			20 10		20 24					21 24	21 40				22 24		22 54					
Warrington Central	a			20 17		20 32					21 32	21 47				22 32		23 02		←			
	d		19 57	20 18		20 32				21 20	21 32	21 47				22 32		23 02 →		23 02			
Birchwood	d					20 37					21 37					22 37				23 07			
Irlam	d					20 43					21 43					22 43				23 13			
Urmston	d					20 48					21 48					22 48				23 18			
Deansgate	84, 85 ⛴ a					20 58					21 58					22 58				23 28			
Newton-le-Willows	90 d	20 05	20a17				20 27	21 05		21a40				22 05	22 11				23 05				
Manchester Victoria	90 ⛴ a						20 48								22 32								
Manchester Oxford Road	84, 85 a	20 28		20 39		21 02		21 28			22 02	22 06		22 27		23 02			23 27	23 32			
Manchester Piccadilly 10	78, 84, 85 ⛴ a	20 33		20 41		*21 15*		21 34				22 10		22 33		*23 15*			23 33				
Stockport	84 a			20 52								22 21											
Sheffield 7	78 ⛴ a			21 38				*23 06*				23 23		*00 09*									
Manchester Airport	85 ✈ a	20 52		*21b16*		*21 33*		21 52				*22c33*		22 51		*23 33*			23 49	*00e33*			

For general notes see front of timetable
For details of catering facilities see Directory of Train Operators

A TO Nottingham (Table 49)
B To Newcastle (Table 39)
C To York (Table 39)
b Change at Manchester Piccadilly
c Change at Manchester Oxford Road
e Change at Manchester Oxford Road and Manchester Piccadilly

Manchester Airport and Manchester → Warrington Central → Liverpool

Network Diagram - see first page of Table 88

Miles	Station		NT	NT	NT	NT	NT	NT	TP		NT	EM	NT	NT	NT	NT	TP		NT	EM	NT	NT	NT
									■1 ◇			◇ A				B	■1 ◇ C		B	◇ A			
0	**Manchester Airport**	85 ✈ d	04 34			05 47	06 19	06 28				07b02		07 26		07b34				08b07		08 30	
—	Sheffield ■7	78 d						05 11				06 20								07 37			
—	Stockport	84 d					06 17	06 17	06 42			07 24				07 49				08 27			
9¾	**Manchester Piccadilly** ■10	78, 84, 85 d	04 49			06 05	06 44	06 52	07 07			07 35		07 49		08 00	08 07		←	08 37		08 50	
10¼	**Manchester Oxford Road**	84, 85 d				06 24	06 53	06 56	07 10			07 38	07 41	07 52		08 13 →	08 10		08 13	08 41	08 43	08 55	
10¾	Deansgate	84, 85 d				06 26													08 15		08 45		
13¾	Trafford Park	d				06 31							07 47						08 20				
14½	Humphrey Park	d				06 33																	
15¾	Urmston	d				06 35	07 00						07 51						08 24		08 52		
16¼	Chassen Road	d				06 37													08 26				
16¾	Flixton	d				06 40							07 54						08 28				
19	Irlam	d				06 44	07 05						07 58						08 32		08 57		
20¼	Glazebrook	d				06 47							08 01						08 35				
23	Birchwood	d				06 51	07 11		07 24				08 05				08 24		08 40		09 02		
24½	Padgate	d				06 54							08 08						08 43				
26¼	**Warrington Central**	a				06 58	07 19		07 29			07 54	08 12		←		08 29		08 46	08 57	09 07		←
—		d		06 03	06 37	06 58			07 29		07 40	07 54	08 12 →		08 12		08 29		08 47	08 57	09 08 →		09 08
28¾	Sankey for Penketh	d		06 07	06 41	07 02					07 44				08 16								09 12
32½	Widnes	d		06 12	06 46	07 08					07 49	08 02			08 22				08 55	09 05			09 17
34¼	Hough Green	d		06 16	06 50	07 11					07 53	08 06			08 25				08 58				09 21
36½	Halewood	d		06 20	06 54	07 15					07 57				08 29								09 25
37½	Hunts Cross	89 d		06 23	06 57	07 18					08 00	08s11			08 32								09 28
39¼	**Liverpool South Parkway** ■7	91, 103 ✈ a		06 28	07 02	07 24					08 03				08 37				09 07				09 33
—	Liverpool Central ■10	103 a		06 53	07c23	07 53					08c23	08 38			09 08				09 38				09c53
40¼	West Allerton	91 a		06 31	07 05	07 27					08 06				08 40				09 10				09 36
41	Mossley Hill	91 a		06 34	07 07	07 30					08 09				08 42				09 13				09 39
43	Edge Hill	90, 91 a		06 39	07 13	07 37					08 14				08 47								09 45
44¾	**Liverpool Lime Street** ■10	90, 91 a	05 30	06 46	07 19	07 44		07 47	07 57		08 21	08 29		08 42	08 55		08 57		09 24	09 29		09 42	09 51

Station		TP	NT	EM	NT		NT	NT	TP	NT	EM	NT	NT		NT	TP	NT	EM	NT	NT	NT		TP
		■1 ◇ D		◇ A					■1 ◇ E		◇ G					■1 ◇ E		◇ H					■1 ◇ E
Manchester Airport	85 ✈ d	08 33		09b07			09 31		09 34		10b07		10 31			10 34		11b07		11 31			11 34
Sheffield ■7	78 d			08 42							09 42							10 42					
Stockport	84 d	08 42		09 24					09 39		10 25					10 39		11 25					11 39
Manchester Piccadilly ■10	78, 84, 85 d	09 07		09 37			09 49		10 07		10 37		10 49			11 07		11 37		11 49			12 07
Manchester Oxford Road	84, 85 d	09 10	09 13	09 41	09 43		09 52		10 10	10 13	10 41	10 43	10 52			11 10	11 13	11 41	11 43	11 52			12 10
Deansgate	84, 85 d		09 15		09 45					10 15		10 45					11 15		11 45				
Trafford Park	d		09 20														11 20						
Humphrey Park	d		09 22														11 22						
Urmston	d		09 24		09 52					10 21		10 52					11 24		11 52				
Chassen Road	d									10 23													
Flixton	d		09 27							10 26							11 27						
Irlam	d		09 31		09 57					10 30		10 57					11 31		11 57				
Glazebrook	d									10 33													
Birchwood	d	09 24	09 37		10 02				10 24	10 37		11 02				11 24	11 37		12 02				12 24
Padgate	d		09 40							10 40							11 40						
Warrington Central	a	09 29	09 43	09 57	10 07			←	10 28	10 44	10 57	11 07			←	11 28	11 43	11 57	12 07		←		12 28
	d	09 29	09 44	09 57	10 08 →			10 08	10 29	10 44	10 57	11 08 →			11 08	11 29	11 44	11 57	12 08 →		12 08		12 29
Sankey for Penketh	d							10 12							11 12						12 12		
Widnes	d		09 52	10 05				10 17		10 52	11 05				11 17		11 52	12 05			12 17		
Hough Green	d		09 55					10 21		10 55					11 21		11 55				12 21		
Halewood	d							10 25							11 25						12 25		
Hunts Cross	89 d							10 28							11 28						12 28		
Liverpool South Parkway ■7	91, 103 ✈ a		10 04					10 33		11 04					11 33		12 04				12 33		
Liverpool Central ■10	103 a		10 38					10c53		11 38					11c53		12 38				12c53		
West Allerton	91 a							10 36							11 36						12 36		
Mossley Hill	91 a		10 08					10 39		11 08					11 39		12 08				12 39		
Edge Hill	90, 91 a							10 45							11 45						12 45		
Liverpool Lime Street ■10	90, 91 a	09 57	10 20	10 29			10 39	10 51	10 57	11 20	11 29		11 39		11 51	11 57	12 20	12 29		12 39	12 51		12 57

Station		NT	EM	NT	NT	NT	TP	NT		EM	NT	NT	NT	TP	NT	EM		NT	NT	NT	TP	NT	EM
			◇ G				■1 ◇ E			◇ G				■1 ◇ E		◇ G					■1 ◇ E		◇ G
Manchester Airport	85 ✈ d		12b07		12 31		12 34			13b07		13 31		13 34		14b07			14 31		14 34		15b07
Sheffield ■7	78 d		11 42							12 42						13 42							14 42
Stockport	84 d		12 25				12 39			13 25				13 39		14 25					14 39		15 25
Manchester Piccadilly ■10	78, 84, 85 d		12 37		12 49		13 07			13 37		13 49		14 07		14 37			14 49		15 07		15 37
Manchester Oxford Road	84, 85 d	12 13	12 41	12 43	12 52		13 10	13 13		13 41	13 43	13 52		14 10	14 13	14 41		14 43	14 52		15 10	15 13	15 41
Deansgate	84, 85 d	12 15		12 45				13 15			13 45				14 15			14 45				15 15	
Trafford Park	d							13 20														15 20	
Humphrey Park	d							13 22														15 22	
Urmston	d	12 21		12 52				13 24			13 52				14 21			14 52				15 24	
Chassen Road	d	12 23													14 23								
Flixton	d	12 26						13 27							14 26							15 27	
Irlam	d	12 30		12 57				13 31			13 57				14 30			14 57				15 31	
Glazebrook	d	12 33													14 33								
Birchwood	d	12 37		13 02			13 24	13 37			14 02			14 24	14 37			15 02			15 24	15 37	
Padgate	d	12 40						13 40							14 40							15 40	
Warrington Central	a	12 44	12 57	13 07		←	13 28	13 43		13 57	14 07		←	14 28	14 44	14 57		15 07		←	15 28	15 44	15 57
	d	12 44	12 57	13 08 →		13 08	13 29	13 44		13 57	14 08 →		14 08	14 29	14 44	14 57		15 08 →		15 08	15 29	15 44	15 57
Sankey for Penketh	d					13 12							14 12							15 12			
Widnes	d	12 52	13 05			13 17		13 52		14 05			14 17		14 52	15 05				15 17		15 52	16 05
Hough Green	d	12 55				13 21		13 55					14 21		14 55					15 21		15 55	
Halewood	d					13 25							14 25							15 25		15 59	
Hunts Cross	89 d					13 28							14 28							15 28			
Liverpool South Parkway ■7	91, 103 ✈ a	13 04				13 33		14 04					14 33		15 04					15 33		16 06	
Liverpool Central ■10	103 a	13 38				13c53		14 38					14c53		15 38					15c53		16 38	
West Allerton	91 a					13 36							14 36							15 36			
Mossley Hill	91 a	13 08				13 39		14 08					14 39		15 08					15 39		16 10	
Edge Hill	90, 91 a					13 45							14 45							15 45			
Liverpool Lime Street ■10	90, 91 a	13 20	13 29		13 39	13 51	13 57	14 20		14 29		14 39	14 51	14 57	15 20	15 29			15 39	15 51	15 57	16 22	16 27

For general notes see front of timetable
For details of catering facilities see Directory of Train Operators

A From Nottingham (Table 49)
B From Buxton (Table 86)
C From Hull (Table 39)
D From Newcastle (Table 39)
E From Scarborough (Table 39)
G Until 5 September from Norwich (Table 49)
H Until 5 September from Cambridge (Table 49)
b Change at Manchester Piccadilly
c Change at Hunts Cross

Manchester Airport and Manchester → Warrington Central → Liverpool

Network Diagram - see first page of Table 88

		NT	NT	NT		TP	NT	EM	NT	NT	NT	TP		NT	EM	NT	NT	TP	NT	NT		EM	NT
						[1] ◇ A ✠		◇ B ✠				[1] ◇ A ✠			◇ B ✠			[1] ◇ A ✠				◇ B ✠	
Manchester Airport	85 ✈ d		15 31			*15 34*		*16b07*		16 31		*16 34*			*17b04*		17 29	*17 34*				*18b10*	
Sheffield [7]	78 d							15 42							16 42							17 42	
Stockport	84 d					*15 39*		16 25				*16 43*			17 26			*17 39*				18 26	
Manchester Piccadilly [10]	78, 84, 85 d		15 49			16 07		16 37		16 48		17 07			17 37		17 45	18 07				18 37	
Manchester Oxford Road	84, 85 d	15 43	15 52			16 10	16 13	16 41	16 43	16 52		17 10		17 13	17 41	17 43	17 49	18 10		18 13		18 41	
Deansgate	84, 85 d	15 45					16 15		16 45					17 15		17 45				18 15			
Trafford Park	d								16 50					17 20		17 50				18 20			
Humphrey Park	d													17 22		17 52				18 22			
Urmston	d	15 52					16 21		16 54					17 25		17 55				18 24			
Chassen Road	d						16 23							17 27		17 57				18 26			
Flixton	d						16 26		16 57					17 29		17 59				18 29			
Irlam	d	15 57					16 30		17 01					17 33	17 51	18 03				18 33			
Glazebrook	d						16 33							17 36		18 06							
Birchwood	d	16 02				16 24	16 37		17 06			17 24		17 41	17 57	18 11		18 24		18 38			
Padgate	d						16 40		17 09					17 44		18 14							
Warrington Central	a	16 07		←		16 28	16 44	16 57	17 13		←	17 28		17 47	18 02	18 18		18 28		18 43		18 57	
	d	16 08 →		16 08		16 29	16 44	16 57	17 13 →		17 13	17 29		17 48	18 02	18 18		18 29		18 44		18 57	
Sankey for Penketh	d			16 12							17 17			17 52						18 48			
Widnes	d			16 17			16 52	17 05			17 23			17 57	18 10					18 53		19 05	
Hough Green	d			16 21			16 55				17 26			18 01		18 28				18 57			
Halewood	d			16 25							17 30			18 05						19 01			
Hunts Cross	89 d			16 28							17 33	17 40		18 08		18 33				19 04		19 12	
Liverpool South Parkway [7]	91, 103 ✈ a			16 33			17 04				17 39			18 13		18 40				19 09			
Liverpool Central [10]	103 a			*16c53*			*17 38*					*18 08*		*18 38*		*19 08*			←			*19 38*	←
West Allerton	91 a			16 36							17 42			18 16		18 43 →			18 43	19 13 →			19 13
Mossley Hill	91 a			16 39			17 08				17 44			18 19					18 45				19 15
Edge Hill	90, 91 a			16 45							17 50			18 25					18 51				19 25
Liverpool Lime Street [10]	90, 91 a		16 39	16 51		16 57	17 24	17 27		17 38	17 58	18 00		18 32	18 32		18 40	18 57	18 59			19 29	19 32

		NT	NT	TP	NT	EM	NT	NT		TP	NT	NT	EM	NT	TP	NT	NT	NT	TP	NT	NT		
				[1] ◇ A ✠		◇ B ✠				[1] ◇ A			◇ B		[1] ◇ A				[1] ◇ A				
Manchester Airport	85 ✈ d		18 31	*18 34*		*18b52*	*19 12*	19 30					*20e15*		*20 22*		*21e16*	21 30			*22 47*		
Sheffield [7]	78 d					18 42							19 42				*20 11*	*20f31*					
Stockport	84 d			*18 39*		19 24				*19 40*			20 26		*20 40*		*21 10*	*21f17*	*21 39*		*22 39*		
Manchester Piccadilly [10]	78, 84, 85 d		18 49	19 07		19 37		19 48		20 07			20 37		21 07		21 39	21 47	22 07		*23 20*		
Manchester Oxford Road	84, 85 d	18 43	18 52	19 10		19 41	19 43	19 52		20 10			20 41	20 43	21 10		21 43	21 50	22 10		23 27		
Deansgate	84, 85 d	18 45					19 45							20 45			21 45				23 29		
Trafford Park	d	18 50					19 50							20 50			21 50				23 34		
Humphrey Park	d	18 52					19 52							20 52			21 52				23 36		
Urmston	d	18 55					19 55							20 54			21 54				23 38		
Chassen Road	d	18 57					19 57							20 56			21 56				23 40		
Flixton	d	18 59					19 59							20 59			21 59				23 43		
Irlam	d	19 03					20 03							21 03			22 03				23 47		
Glazebrook	d	19 06					20 06							21 06			22 06				23 50		
Birchwood	d	19 11		19 24			20 11			20 24				21 10	21 24		22 10		22 24		23 54		
Padgate	d	19 14					20 14							21 13			22 13				23 57		
Warrington Central	a	19 20		19 28		19 57	20 17			20 28			20 57	21 20	21 28		22 20		22 29		00 01		
	d			19 29	19 40	19 57	20 18			20 29		20 40	20 57		21 29	21 40			22 29	22 40	00 01		
Sankey for Penketh	d				19 44							20 44				21 44				22 44	00 05		
Widnes	d				19 49	20 05						20 49	21 05			21 49				22 49	00 11		
Hough Green	d				19 53		20 27					20 53				21 53				22 53	00 14		
Halewood	d				19 57							20 57				21 57				22 57			
Hunts Cross	89 d				20 00		20 32					21 00				22 00				23 00	00 19		
Liverpool South Parkway [7]	91, 103 ✈ a				20 03		20 38					21 03				22 03				23 03			
Liverpool Central [10]	103 a				*20c23*		*21 08*				←	*21c23*				*22c23*				*23c23*			
West Allerton	91 a				20 06		20 41 →				20 41	21 06				22 06				23 06			
Mossley Hill	91 a				20 09						20 43	21 09				22 09				23 09			
Edge Hill	90, 91 a				20 14							21 14				22 14				23 14			
Liverpool Lime Street [10]	90, 91 a		19 38	19 57	20 22	20 29		20 38		20 55	20 59	21 21	21 29		21 55	22 22		22 41	22 55	23 21	00 38		

For general notes see front of timetable
For details of catering facilities see Directory of Train Operators

A From Scarborough (Table 39)
B Until 5 September from Norwich (Table 49)
b Change at Manchester Piccadilly
c Change at Hunts Cross
e Change at Manchester Oxford Road
f Until 5 September only

Saturdays

until 6 September

Manchester Airport and Manchester → Warrington Central → Liverpool

Network Diagram - see first page of Table 88

		NT	NT	NT	NT	NT		TP	NT	EM	NT	NT		NT	TP	NT	EM	NT		NT	NT	TP	NT
								1 ◇		◇ A					1 ◇ B ▯		◇ A					1 ◇ C ▯	
Manchester Airport	85 ✈ d	04 34			05 47	06 28				07b02		07 26			07 34		08b07			08 30		08 33	
Sheffield 7	78 ⇌ d					05 11				06 20							07 36						
Stockport	84 d					06 17		06 41		07 23					07 39		08 27					08 42	
Manchester Piccadilly 10	78, 84, 85 ⇌ d	04 49			06 05	06 52		07 07		07 35		07 49			08 07		08 37			08 50		09 07	
Manchester Oxford Road	84, 85 d				06 29	06 56		07 10		07 38	07 41	07 52			08 10	08 13	08 41	08 43		08 55		09 10	09 13
Deansgate	84, 85 ⇌ d				06 31											08 15		08 45					09 15
Trafford Park	d				06 36						07 47					08 20							09 20
Humphrey Park	d				06 38																		09 22
Urmston	d				06 40						07 51					08 24		08 52					09 24
Chassen Road	d				06 42											08 26							
Flixton	d				06 45						07 54					08 28							09 27
Irlam	d				06 49						07 58					08 32		08 57					09 31
Glazebrook	d				06 52						08 01					08 35							
Birchwood	d				06 56			07 24			08 05				08 24	08 40		09 02				09 24	09 37
Padgate	d				06 59						08 08					08 43							09 40
Warrington Central	a				07 03			07 29		07 54	08 12			←	08 29	08 46	08 57	09 07			←	09 29	09 43
	d		06 03	06 37	07 03			07 29	07 40	07 54	08 12 →			08 12	08 29	08 47	08 57	09 08 →			09 08	09 29	09 44
Sankey for Penketh	d		06 07	06 41	07 07				07 44					08 16							09 12		
Widnes	d		06 12	06 46	07 13				07 49	08 02				08 22		08 55	09 05				09 17		09 52
Hough Green	d		06 16	06 50	07 16				07 53	08 06				08 25		08 58					09 21		09 55
Halewood	d		06 20	06 54	07 20				07 57					08 29							09 25		
Hunts Cross	89 d		06 23	06 57	07 23				08 00	08s11				08 32							09 28		
Liverpool South Parkway 7	91, 103 ✈ a		06 28	07 02	07 29				08 03					08 37		09 07					09 33		10 04
Liverpool Central 10	103 a		06 53	07 23	07 53				08c23	08 38				09 08		09 38					09c53		10 38
West Allerton	91 a		06 31	07 05	07 32				08 06					08 40		09 10					09 36		
Mossley Hill	91 a		06 34	07 07	07 35				08 09					08 42		09 13					09 39		10 08
Edge Hill	90, 91 a		06 39	07 13	07 40				08 14					08 47							09 45		
Liverpool Lime Street 10	90, 91 a	05 30	06 46	07 19	07 47	07 47		07 57	08 21	08 29		08 42		08 55	08 57	09 24	09 27			09 42	09 54	09 57	10 20

		EM	NT	NT		NT	TP	NT	EM	NT		NT	NT	TP	NT	EM		NT	NT	NT	TP	NT	EM
		◇ A					1 ◇ D ▯		◇ E					1 ◇ D ▯		◇ G					1 ◇ D ▯		◇ E
Manchester Airport	85 ✈ d	09b07		09 31			09 34		10b07			10 31		10 34		11b07			11 31		11 34		12b07
Sheffield 7	78 ⇌ d	08 42							09 42							10 42							11 42
Stockport	84 d	09 25					09 40		10 25					10 39		11 25					11 39		12 25
Manchester Piccadilly 10	78, 84, 85 ⇌ d	09 37		09 49			10 07		10 37			10 49		11 07		11 37			11 49		12 07		12 37
Manchester Oxford Road	84, 85 d	09 41	09 43	09 52			10 10	10 13	10 41	10 43		10 52		11 10	11 13	11 41		11 43	11 52		12 10	12 13	12 41
Deansgate	84, 85 ⇌ d		09 45					10 15		10 45					11 15			11 45				12 15	
Trafford Park	d														11 20								
Humphrey Park	d														11 22								
Urmston	d		09 52					10 21		10 52					11 24			11 52				12 21	
Chassen Road	d							10 23														12 23	
Flixton	d							10 26							11 27							12 26	
Irlam	d		09 57					10 30		10 57					11 31			11 57				12 30	
Glazebrook	d							10 33														12 33	
Birchwood	d		10 02				10 24	10 37		11 02				11 24	11 37			12 02			12 24	12 37	
Padgate	d							10 40							11 40							12 40	
Warrington Central	a	09 57	10 07			←	10 28	10 44	10 57	11 07			←	11 28	11 43	11 57		12 07		←	12 28	12 44	12 57
	d	09 57	10 08 →			10 08	10 29	10 44	10 57	11 08 →			11 08	11 29	11 44	11 57		12 08 →		12 08	12 29	12 44	12 57
Sankey for Penketh	d					10 12							11 12							12 12			
Widnes	d	10 05				10 17		10 52	11 05				11 17		11 52	12 05				12 17		12 52	13 05
Hough Green	d					10 21		10 55					11 21		11 55					12 21		12 55	
Halewood	d					10 25							11 25							12 25			
Hunts Cross	89 d					10 28							11 28							12 28			
Liverpool South Parkway 7	91, 103 ✈ a					10 33		11 04					11 33		12 04					12 33		13 04	
Liverpool Central 10	103 a					10c53		11 38					11c53		12 38					12c53		13 38	
West Allerton	91 a					10 36							11 36							12 36			
Mossley Hill	91 a					10 39		11 08					11 39		12 08					12 39		13 08	
Edge Hill	90, 91 a					10 45							11 45							12 45			
Liverpool Lime Street 10	90, 91 a	10 27		10 39		10 54	10 57	11 20	11 29			11 39	11 54	11 57	12 20	12 29			12 39	12 54	12 57	13 20	13 27

For general notes see front of timetable
For details of catering facilities see Directory of Train Operators

A From Nottingham (Table 49)
B From Hull (Table 39)
C From Newcastle (Table 39)
D From Scarborough (Table 39)
E From Norwich (Table 49)
G From Cambridge (Table 49)
b Change at Manchester Piccadilly
c Change at Hunts Cross

Saturdays

until 6 September

Manchester Airport and Manchester → Warrington Central → Liverpool

Network Diagram - see first page of Table 88

	NT		NT	NT	TP 1◇ A	NT	EM ◇ B		NT	NT	NT	TP 1◇ A	NT		EM ◇ B	NT	NT	NT	TP 1◇ A		NT	EM ◇ B
Manchester Airport 85 ✈ d			12 31		12 34		13b07			13 31		13 34			14b07		14 31		14 34			15b07
Sheffield 7 78 🚊 d							12 42								13 42							14 42
Stockport 84 d					12 39		13 25					13 39			14 25				14 39			15 24
Manchester Piccadilly 10 78, 84, 85 🚊 d			12 49		13 07		13 37			13 49		14 07			14 37		14 49		15 07			15 37
Manchester Oxford Road 84, 85 d	12 43		12 52		13 10	13 13	13 41		13 43	13 52		14 10	14 13		14 41	14 43	14 52		15 10		15 13	15 41
Deansgate 84, 85 🚊 d	12 45					13 15			13 45				14 15			14 45					15 15	
Trafford Park d						13 20															15 20	
Humphrey Park d						13 22															15 22	
Urmston d	12 52					13 24			13 52				14 21			14 52					15 24	
Chassen Road d													14 23									
Flixton d						13 27							14 26								15 27	
Irlam d	12 57					13 31			13 57				14 30			14 57					15 31	
Glazebrook d													14 33									
Birchwood d	13 02				13 24	13 37			14 02			14 24	14 37			15 02			15 24		15 37	
Padgate d						13 40							14 40								15 40	
Warrington Central a	13 07			←	13 28	13 43	13 57		14 07		←	14 28	14 44		14 57	15 07		←	15 28		15 44	15 57
d	13 08 →			13 08	13 29	13 44	13 57		14 08 →		14 08	14 29	14 44		14 57	15 08 →		15 08	15 29		15 44	15 57
Sankey for Penketh d				13 12							14 12							15 12				
Widnes d				13 17		13 52	14 05				14 17		14 52		15 05			15 17			15 52	16 05
Hough Green d				13 21		13 55					14 21		14 55					15 21			15 55	
Halewood d				13 25							14 25							15 25			15 59	
Hunts Cross 89 d				13 28							14 28							15 28				
Liverpool South Parkway 7 91, 103 ✈ a				13 33		14 04					14 33		15 04					15 33			16 06	
Liverpool Central 10 103 a				13c53		14 38					14c53		15 38					15c53			16 38	
West Allerton 91 a				13 36							14 36							15 36				
Mossley Hill 91 a				13 39		14 08					14 39		15 08					15 39			16 10	
Edge Hill 90, 91 a				13 45							14 45							15 45				
Liverpool Lime Street 10 90, 91 a			13 39	13 54	13 57	14 20	14 27			14 39	14 54	14 57	15 20		15 25		15 39	15 55	15 57		16 22	16 29

	NT	NT	NT	TP 1◇ A	NT		EM ◇ B	NT	NT	NT	TP 1◇ A		NT	EM ◇ B	NT	NT	NT		TP 1◇ A	NT	NT	EM ◇ B
Manchester Airport 85 ✈ d		15 31		15 34			16b07		16 31		16 34			17b04			17 29		17 34			18b10
Sheffield 7 78 🚊 d							15 42							16 42								17 42
Stockport 84 d				15 39			16 25				16 43			17 25					17 39			18 26
Manchester Piccadilly 10 78, 84, 85 🚊 d		15 49		16 07			16 37		16 48		17 07			17 37			17 45		18 07			18 37
Manchester Oxford Road 84, 85 d	15 43	15 52		16 10	16 13		16 41	16 43	16 52		17 10		17 13	17 41		17 43	17 49		18 10		18 13	18 41
Deansgate 84, 85 🚊 d	15 45				16 15			16 45					17 15			17 45					18 15	
Trafford Park d								16 50					17 20			17 50					18 20	
Humphrey Park d													17 22			17 52					18 22	
Urmston d	15 52				16 21			16 54					17 25			17 55					18 24	
Chassen Road d					16 23								17 27			17 57					18 26	
Flixton d					16 26			16 57					17 29			17 59					18 29	
Irlam d	15 57				16 30			17 01					17 33	17 51		18 03					18 33	
Glazebrook d					16 33								17 36			18 06						
Birchwood d	16 02			16 24	16 37			17 06			17 24		17 41	17 57		18 11			18 24		18 38	
Padgate d					16 40			17 09					17 44			18 14						
Warrington Central a	16 07		←	16 28	16 44		16 57	17 13		←	17 28		17 47	18 02		18 18			18 28		18 43	18 57
d	16 08 →		16 08	16 29	16 44		16 57	17 13 →		17 13	17 29		17 48	18 02		18 18			18 29		18 44	18 57
Sankey for Penketh d			16 12							17 17			17 52								18 48	
Widnes d			16 17		16 52		17 05			17 23			17 57	18 10							18 53	19 05
Hough Green d			16 21		16 55					17 26			18 01			18 28					18 57	
Halewood d			16 25							17 30			18 05								19 01	
Hunts Cross 89 d			16 28							17 33	17 40		18 08			18 33					19 04	19 12
Liverpool South Parkway 7 91, 103 ✈ a			16 33		17 04					17 39			18 13			18 38					19 09	
Liverpool Central 10 103 a			16c53		17 23						18 08		18 38		←	19 08				←		19 38
West Allerton 91 a			16 36							17 42			18 17 →		18 17	18 41 →				18 41	19 13	
Mossley Hill 91 a			16 39		17 08					17 44					18 19					18 44	19 15	
Edge Hill 90, 91 a			16 45							17 50					18 27					18 51	19 21	
Liverpool Lime Street 10 90, 91 a		16 39	16 55	16 57	17 24		17 29		17 38	17 58	18 00			18 32	18 34		18 40		18 57	18 59	19 27	19 29

	NT	NT	TP 1◇ A		NT	NT	NT	TP 1◇ A	NT		NT	NT	TP 1◇ A	NT	NT		NT	TP 1◇ A	NT	NT
Manchester Airport 85 ✈ d		18 31	18 34			19 12	19 30					20 15	20 22		21e16		21 30			22 47
Sheffield 7 78 🚊 d							18 42						19 42		20 29					
Stockport 84 d			18 39			19 05	19 24	19 40					20 40		21 17		21 23	21 39		22 39
Manchester Piccadilly 10 78, 84, 85 🚊 d		18 49	19 07			19 33	19 48	20 07				20 32	21 07		21 42		21 48	22 07		23 11
Manchester Oxford Road 84, 85 d	18 43	18 52	19 10			19 43	19 52	20 10				20 43	21 10		21 45		21 52	22 10		23 20
Deansgate 84, 85 🚊 d	18 45					19 45						20 45			21 47					23 22
Trafford Park d	18 50					19 50						20 50			21 52					23 27
Humphrey Park d	18 52					19 52						20 52			21 54					23 29
Urmston d	18 55					19 55						20 54			21 57					23 31
Chassen Road d	18 57					19 57						20 56			21 59					23 33
Flixton d	18 59					19 59						20 59			22 01					23 36
Irlam d	19 03					20 03						21 03			22 05					23 40
Glazebrook d	19 06					20 06						21 06			22 08					23 43
Birchwood d	19 11		19 24			20 11		20 24				21 10	21 24		22 13			22 24		23 47
Padgate d	19 14					20 14						21 13			22 16					23 50
Warrington Central a	19 20		19 28			20 17		20 28				21 20	21 28		22 21			22 28		23 54
d			19 29		19 40	20 18		20 29			20 40		21 29	21 40				22 29	22 40	23 54
Sankey for Penketh d					19 44						20 44			21 44					22 44	23 58
Widnes d					19 49						20 49			21 49					22 49	00 04
Hough Green d					19 53	20 27					20 53			21 53					22 53	00 07
Halewood d					19 57						20 57			21 57					22 57	
Hunts Cross 89 d					20 00	20 32					21 00			22 00					23 00	00 12
Liverpool South Parkway 7 91, 103 ✈ a					20 03	20 38					21 03			22 03					23 03	
Liverpool Central 10 103 a					20c23	21 08			←		21c23			22c23					23c23	
West Allerton 91 a					20 06	20 41 →			20 41		21 06			22 06					23 06	
Mossley Hill 91 a					20 09				20 43		21 09			22 09					23 09	
Edge Hill 90, 91 a					20 14						21 14			22 14					23 14	
Liverpool Lime Street 10 90, 91 a		19 38	19 57		20 21		20 38	20 55	20 57		21 21		21 55	22 22			22 41	22 57	23 21	00 31

For general notes see front of timetable
For details of catering facilities see Directory of Train Operators

A From Scarborough (Table 39)
B From Norwich (Table 49)
b Change at Manchester Piccadilly
c Change at Hunts Cross
e Change at Manchester Oxford Road

Table 89

Saturdays

from 13 September

Manchester Airport and Manchester → Warrington Central → Liverpool

Network Diagram - see first page of Table 88

Station		NT	NT	NT	NT	NT		TP 1◇	NT	EM ◇ A	NT	NT		NT	TP 1◇ B	NT	EM ◇ A	NT		NT	NT	TP 1◇ C	NT
Manchester Airport	85 d	04 34			05 47	06 28				07b02		07 26			07 34		08b07			08 30		08 33	
Sheffield 7	78 d					05 11				06 20							07 36						
Stockport	84 d									07 23							08 27						
Manchester Piccadilly 10	78, 84, 85 d	04 49			06 05	06 52		07 07		07 35		07 49			08 07		08 37			08 50		09 07	
Manchester Oxford Road	84, 85 d				06 29	06 56		07 10		07 38	07 41	07 52			08 10	08 13	08 41	08 43		08 55		09 10	09 13
Deansgate	84, 85 d				06 31											08 15		08 45					09 15
Trafford Park	d				06 36						07 47					08 20							09 20
Humphrey Park	d				06 38																		09 22
Urmston	d				06 40						07 51					08 24		08 52					09 24
Chassen Road	d				06 42											08 26							
Flixton	d				06 45						07 54					08 28							09 27
Irlam	d				06 49						07 58					08 32		08 57					09 31
Glazebrook	d				06 52						08 01					08 35							
Birchwood	d				06 56			07 24			08 05				08 24	08 40		09 02				09 24	09 37
Padgate	d				06 59						08 08					08 43							09 40
Warrington Central	a				07 03			07 29		07 54	08 12			←	08 29	08 46	08 57	09 07			←	09 29	09 43
	d		06 03	06 37	07 03			07 29	07 40	07 54	08 12 →			08 12	08 29	08 47	08 57	09 08 →			09 08	09 29	09 44
Sankey for Penketh	d		06 07	06 41	07 07				07 44					08 16							09 12		
Widnes	d		06 12	06 46	07 13				07 49	08 02				08 22		08 55	09 05				09 17		09 52
Hough Green	d		06 16	06 50	07 16				07 53	08 06				08 25		08 58					09 21		09 55
Halewood	d		06 20	06 54	07 20				07 57					08 29							09 25		
Hunts Cross	89 d		06 23	06 57	07 23				08 00	08s11				08 32							09 28		
Liverpool South Parkway 7	91, 103 a		06 28	07 02	07 29				08 03					08 37		09 07					09 33		10 04
Liverpool Central 10	103 a		06 53	07 23	07 53				08c23	08 38				09 08		09 38					09c53		10 38
West Allerton	91 a		06 31	07 05	07 32				08 06					08 40		09 10					09 36		
Mossley Hill	91 a		06 34	07 07	07 35				08 09					08 42		09 13					09 39		10 08
Edge Hill	90, 91 a		06 39	07 13	07 40				08 14					08 47							09 44		
Liverpool Lime Street 10	90, 91 a	05 30	06 46	07 19	07 47	07 47		07 57	08 21	08 29		08 42		08 55	08 57	09 24	09 27			09 42	09 51	09 57	10 20

Station		EM ◇ A	NT	NT		NT	TP 1◇ D	NT	EM ◇	NT		NT	NT	TP 1◇ D	NT	EM ◇		NT	NT	NT	TP 1◇ D	NT	EM ◇
Manchester Airport	85 d	09b07		09 31			09 34		10b07			10 31		10 34		11b07			11 31		11 34		12b07
Sheffield 7	78 d	08 42							09 42							10 42							11 42
Stockport	84 d	09 25							10 25							11 25							12 25
Manchester Piccadilly 10	78, 84, 85 d	09 37		09 49			10 07		10 37			10 49		11 07		11 37			11 49		12 07		12 37
Manchester Oxford Road	84, 85 d	09 41	09 43	09 52			10 10	10 13	10 41	10 43		10 52		11 10	11 13	11 41		11 43	11 52		12 10	12 13	12 41
Deansgate	84, 85 d		09 45					10 15		10 45					11 15			11 45				12 15	
Trafford Park	d														11 20								
Humphrey Park	d														11 22								
Urmston	d		09 52					10 21		10 52					11 24			11 52				12 21	
Chassen Road	d							10 23														12 23	
Flixton	d							10 26							11 27							12 26	
Irlam	d		09 57					10 30		10 57					11 31			11 57				12 30	
Glazebrook	d							10 33														12 33	
Birchwood	d		10 02				10 24	10 37		11 02				11 24	11 37			12 02			12 24	12 37	
Padgate	d							10 40							11 40							12 40	
Warrington Central	a	09 57	10 07			←	10 28	10 44	10 57	11 07			←	11 28	11 43	11 57		12 07		←	12 28	12 44	12 57
	d	09 57	10 08 →			10 08	10 29	10 44	10 57	11 08 →			11 08	11 29	11 44	11 57		12 08 →		12 08	12 29	12 44	12 57
Sankey for Penketh	d					10 12							11 12							12 12			
Widnes	d	10 05				10 17		10 52	11 05				11 17		11 52	12 05				12 17		12 52	13 05
Hough Green	d					10 21		10 55					11 21		11 55					12 21		12 55	
Halewood	d					10 25							11 25							12 25			
Hunts Cross	89 d					10 28							11 28							12 28			
Liverpool South Parkway 7	91, 103 a					10 33		11 04					11 33		12 04					12 33		13 04	
Liverpool Central 10	103 a					10c53		11 38					11c53		12 38					12c53		13 38	
West Allerton	91 a					10 36							11 36							12 36			
Mossley Hill	91 a					10 39		11 08					11 39		12 08					12 39		13 09	
Edge Hill	90, 91 a					10 44							11 44							12 44			
Liverpool Lime Street 10	90, 91 a	10 27		10 39		10 51	10 57	11 20	11 29			11 39	11 51	11 57	12 20	12 29			12 39	12 51	12 57	13 20	13 27

For general notes see front of timetable
For details of catering facilities see Directory of Train Operators

A From Nottingham (Table 49)
B From Hull (Table 39)
C From Newcastle (Table 39)
D From Scarborough (Table 39)

b Change at Manchester Piccadilly
c Change at Hunts Cross

Table 89

Saturdays
from 13 September

Manchester Airport and Manchester → Warrington Central → Liverpool

Network Diagram - see first page of Table 88

		NT		NT	NT	TP 1 ◇ A	NT	EM ◇		NT	NT	NT	TP 1 ◇ A	NT		EM ◇	NT	NT	NT	TP 1 ◇ A		NT	EM ◇
Manchester Airport	85 d			12 31		12 34		13b07			13 31		13 34			14b07		14 31		14 34			15b07
Sheffield 7	78 d							12 42								13 42							14 42
Stockport	84 d							13 25								14 25							15 24
Manchester Piccadilly 10	78, 84, 85 d			12 49		13 07		13 37			13 49		14 07			14 37		14 49		15 07			15 37
Manchester Oxford Road	84, 85 d	12 43		12 52		13 10	13 13	13 41		13 43	13 52		14 10	14 13		14 41	14 43	14 52		15 10		15 13	15 41
Deansgate	84, 85 d	12 45					13 15			13 45				14 15			14 45					15 15	
Trafford Park	d						13 20															15 20	
Humphrey Park	d						13 22															15 22	
Urmston	d	12 52					13 24			13 52				14 21			14 52					15 24	
Chassen Road	d													14 23									
Flixton	d						13 27							14 26								15 27	
Irlam	d	12 57					13 31			13 57				14 30			14 57					15 31	
Glazebrook	d													14 33									
Birchwood	d	13 02				13 24	13 37			14 02			14 24	14 37			15 02			15 24		15 37	
Padgate	d						13 40							14 40								15 40	
Warrington Central	a	13 07			←	13 28	13 43	13 57		14 07		←	14 28	14 44		14 57	15 07		←	15 28		15 44	15 57
	d	13 08 →			13 08	13 29	13 44	13 57		14 08 →		14 08	14 29	14 44		14 57	15 08 →		15 08	15 29		15 44	15 57
Sankey for Penketh	d				13 12							14 12							15 12				
Widnes	d				13 17		13 52	14 05				14 17		14 52		15 05			15 17			15 52	16 05
Hough Green	d				13 21		13 55					14 21		14 55					15 21			15 55	
Halewood	d				13 25							14 25							15 25			15 59	
Hunts Cross	89 d				13 28							14 28							15 28				
Liverpool South Parkway 7	91, 103 a				13 33		14 04					14 33		15 04					15 33			16 06	
Liverpool Central 10	103 a				13c53		14 38					14c53		15 38					15c53			16 38	
West Allerton	91 a				13 36							14 36							15 36				
Mossley Hill	91 a				13 39		14 08					14 39		15 08					15 39			16 10	
Edge Hill	90, 91 a				13 45							14 44							15 44				
Liverpool Lime Street 10	90, 91 a			13 39	13 51	13 57	14 20	14 27			14 39	14 51	14 57	15 20		15 25		15 39	15 51	15 57		16 22	16 29

		NT	NT	NT	TP 1 ◇ A	NT		EM ◇	NT	NT	NT	TP 1 ◇ A		NT	EM ◇	NT	NT	NT		TP 1 ◇ A	NT	NT	EM ◇
Manchester Airport	85 d		15 31		15 34			16b07		16 31		16 34			17b04			17 29		17 34			18b10
Sheffield 7	78 d							15 42							16 42								17 42
Stockport	84 d							16 25							17 25								18 26
Manchester Piccadilly 10	78, 84, 85 d		15 49		16 07			16 37		16 48		17 07			17 37			17 45		18 07			18 37
Manchester Oxford Road	84, 85 d	15 43	15 52		16 10	16 13		16 41	16 43	16 52		17 10		17 13	17 41		17 43	17 49		18 10		18 13	18 41
Deansgate	84, 85 d	15 45				16 15			16 45					17 15			17 45					18 15	
Trafford Park	d								16 50					17 20			17 50					18 20	
Humphrey Park	d													17 22			17 52					18 22	
Urmston	d	15 52				16 21			16 54					17 25			17 55					18 24	
Chassen Road	d					16 23								17 27			17 57					18 26	
Flixton	d					16 26			16 57					17 29			17 59					18 29	
Irlam	d	15 57				16 30			17 01					17 33	17 51		18 03					18 33	
Glazebrook	d					16 33								17 36			18 06						
Birchwood	d	16 02			16 24	16 37			17 06			17 24		17 41	17 57		18 11			18 24		18 38	
Padgate	d					16 40			17 09					17 44			18 14						
Warrington Central	a	16 07		←	16 28	16 44		16 57	17 13		←	17 28		17 47	18 02		18 18			18 28		18 43	18 57
	d	16 08 →		16 08	16 29	16 44		16 57	17 13 →		17 13	17 29		17 48	18 02		18 18			18 29		18 44	18 57
Sankey for Penketh	d			16 12							17 17			17 52								18 48	
Widnes	d			16 17		16 52		17 05			17 23			17 57	18 10							18 53	19 05
Hough Green	d			16 21		16 55					17 26			18 01			18 28					18 57	
Halewood	d			16 25							17 30			18 05								19 01	
Hunts Cross	89 d			16 28							17 33	17 40		18 08			18 33					19 04	19 12
Liverpool South Parkway 7	91, 103 a			16 33		17 04					17 39			18 13			18 38					19 09	
Liverpool Central 10	103 a			16c53		17 38						18 08		18 38		←	19 08				←		19 38
West Allerton	91 a			16 36							17 42			18 17 →		18 17	18 41 →				18 41	19 13	
Mossley Hill	91 a			16 39		17 08					17 44					18 19					18 44	19 15	
Edge Hill	90, 91 a			16 44							17 50					18 27					18 50	19 21	
Liverpool Lime Street 10	90, 91 a		16 39	16 51	16 57	17 24		17 29		17 38	17 58	18 00			18 32	18 35		18 40		18 57	18 58	19 27	19 29

		NT	NT	TP 1 ◇ A		NT	NT	NT	TP 1 ◇ A	NT		NT	NT	TP 1 ◇ A	NT	NT		NT	TP 1 ◇ A	NT	NT		
Manchester Airport	85 d		18 31	18 34			19 12	19 30					20 15	20 22		21e16		21 30			22f22		
Sheffield 7	78 d							18 42						19 42		20 11							
Stockport	84 d																						
Manchester Piccadilly 10	78, 84, 85 d		18 49	19 07			19 33	19 48	20 07				20 32	21 07		21 42		21 48	22 07		22 54		
Manchester Oxford Road	84, 85 d	18 43	18 52	19 10			19 43	19 52	20 10				20 43	21 10		21 45		21 52	22 10		23 15		
Deansgate	84, 85 d	18 45					19 45						20 45			21 47					23 17		
Trafford Park	d	18 50					19 50						20 50			21 52					23 22		
Humphrey Park	d	18 52					19 52						20 52			21 54					23 24		
Urmston	d	18 55					19 55						20 54			21 57					23 26		
Chassen Road	d	18 57					19 57						20 56			21 59					23 28		
Flixton	d	18 59					19 59						20 59			22 01					23 31		
Irlam	d	19 03					20 03						21 03			22 05					23 35		
Glazebrook	d	19 06					20 06						21 06			22 08					23 38		
Birchwood	d	19 11		19 24			20 11		20 24				21 10	21 24		22 13			22 24		23 42		
Padgate	d	19 14					20 14						21 13			22 16					23 45		
Warrington Central	a	19 20		19 28			20 17		20 28				21 20	21 28		22 21			22 28		23 49		
	d			19 29		19 40	20 18		20 29			20 40		21 29	21 40				22 29	22 40	23 49		
Sankey for Penketh	d					19 44						20 44			21 44					22 44	23 53		
Widnes	d					19 49						20 49			21 49					22 49	23 59		
Hough Green	d					19 53	20 27					20 53			21 53					22 53	00 02		
Halewood	d					19 57						20 57			21 57					22 57			
Hunts Cross	89 d					20 00	20 32					21 00			22 00					23 00	00 07		
Liverpool South Parkway 7	91, 103 a					20 03	20 38					21 03			22 03					23 03			
Liverpool Central 10	103 a					20c23	21 08			←		21c23			22c23					23c23			
West Allerton	91 a					20 06	20 41 →			20 41		21 06			22 06					23 06			
Mossley Hill	91 a					20 09				20 43		21 09			22 09					23 09			
Edge Hill	90, 91 a					20 14						21 14			22 14					23 14			
Liverpool Lime Street 10	90, 91 a		19 38	19 57		20 21		20 38	20 55	20 57		21 21		21 55	22 22			22 41	22 57	23 21	00 25		

For general notes see front of timetable
For details of catering facilities see Directory of Train Operators

A From Scarborough (Table 39)
b Change at Manchester Piccadilly
c Change at Hunts Cross
e Change at Manchester Oxford Road
f Change at Manchester Piccadilly and Manchester Oxford Road

Sundays

until 13 July

Manchester Airport and Manchester → Warrington Central → Liverpool

Network Diagram - see first page of Table 88

		NT	NT	NT	TP 1◇ A	NT	NT	TP 1◇ B	NT	NT	EM ◇ C	TP 1◇ D	NT	NT	EM ◇ C	TP 1◇ E	NT	NT
Manchester Airport	85 ✈ d	07 36	08 47	08 51	09b47		10 01	10b47		11 00	11c03	11b47		12 00		12b45		13 00
Sheffield 7	78 d			07 55				09 30			10 26	10 35			11 40	11 43		
Stockport	84 d			08 39	09 29			10 36			11 20	11 38			12 24	12 45		
Manchester Piccadilly 10	78, 84, 85 d	07 51	09 03	09 16	10 07		10 16	11 07		11 16	11 37	12 07		12 17	12 37	13 07		13 17
Manchester Oxford Road	84, 85 d	08 01	09 15	09 20	10 10	10 13	10 20	11 10	11 15	11 20	11 40	12 10	12 15	12 20	12 40	13 10	13 15	13 20
Deansgate	84, 85 d	08 03	09 17			10 15			11 17				12 17				13 17	
Urmston	d	08 09	09 23			10 21			11 23				12 23				13 23	
Irlam	d	08 14	09 28			10 26			11 28				12 28				13 28	
Birchwood	d	08 20	09 34		10 24	10 32		11 24	11 34			12 24	12 34			13 24	13 34	
Warrington Central	a	08 25	09 39		10 28	10 37		11 28	11 39		11 56	12 28	12 39		12 56	13 28	13 39	
	d	08 39	09 39		10 29	10 39		11 29	11 39		11 57	12 29	12 39		12 57	13 29	13 39	
Widnes	d	08 47	09 47			10 47			11 47		12 05		12 47		13 05		13 47	
Hough Green	d	08 51	09 51			10 51			11 51				12 51				13 51	
Halewood	d	08 55	09 55			10 55			11 55				12 55				13 55	
Hunts Cross	89 d	08 58	09 58			10 58			11 58				12 58				13 58	
Liverpool South Parkway 7	91, 103 ✈ a	09 03	10 03			11 03			12 03				13 03				14 03	
Liverpool Central 10	103 a	09e23	10e23			11e23			12e23				13e23				14e23	
West Allerton	91 a	09 06	10 06			11 06			12 06				13 06				14 06	
Mossley Hill	91 a	09 09	10 09			11 09			12 09				13 09				14 09	
Liverpool Lime Street 10	90, 91 a	09 20	10 20	10 23	10 57	11 20	11 21	11 57	12 20	12 21	12 29	12 57	13 20	13 21	13 29	13 57	14 20	14 21

		EM ◇ C	TP 1◇ G	NT	NT	EM ◇ C	TP 1◇ E	NT	NT	EM ◇ H	TP 1◇ J	NT	NT	EM ◇ C	TP 1◇ E	NT	NT	EM ◇ C
Manchester Airport	85 ✈ d	13c05	13b47		14 00		14b47		15 00	15c08	15b47		16 01		16b47		17 01	17c05
Sheffield 7	78 d	12 39				13 37			13 41	14 43				15 34	15 43			16 36
Stockport	84 d	13 23	13 36			14 20	14 43		14 49	15 25	15 43			16 20	16 46			17 21
Manchester Piccadilly 10	78, 84, 85 d	13 37	14 07		14 17	14 37	15 07		15 16	15 37	16 07		16 16	16 37	17 07		17 16	17 37
Manchester Oxford Road	84, 85 d	13 40	14 10	14 15	14 20	14 40	15 10	15 15	15 20	15 40	16 10	16 15	16 20	16 40	17 10	17 15	17 20	17 40
Deansgate	84, 85 d			14 17				15 17				16 17				17 17		
Urmston	d			14 23				15 23				16 23				17 23		
Irlam	d			14 28				15 28				16 28				17 28		
Birchwood	d		14 24	14 34			15 24	15 34			16 24	16 34			17 24	17 34		
Warrington Central	a	13 56	14 28	14 39		14 56	15 28	15 39		15 56	16 28	16 39		16 56	17 28	17 39		17 56
	d	13 57	14 29	14 39		14 57	15 29	15 39		15 57	16 29	16 39		16 57	17 29	17 39		17 57
Widnes	d	14 05		14 47		15 05		15 47		16 05		16 47		17 05		17 47		18 05
Hough Green	d			14 51				15 51				16 51				17 51		
Halewood	d			14 55				15 55				16 55				17 55		
Hunts Cross	89 d			14 58				15 58				16 58				17 58		
Liverpool South Parkway 7	91, 103 ✈ a			15 03				16 03				17 03				18 03		
Liverpool Central 10	103 a			15e23				16e23				17e23				18e23		
West Allerton	91 a			15 06				16 06				17 06				18 06		
Mossley Hill	91 a			15 09				16 09				17 09				18 09		
Liverpool Lime Street 10	90, 91 a	14 29	14 57	15 20	15 21	15 29	15 57	16 20	16 21	16 29	16 57	17 20	17 21	17 29	17 57	18 20	18 21	18 29

		TP 1◇ J	NT	NT	EM ◇ H	TP 1◇ E	NT	NT	EM ◇ C	TP 1◇ J	NT	NT	TP 1◇ E	NT	NT	TP 1◇ D	NT	NT
Manchester Airport	85 ✈ d	17b47		18 01		18b47		19 01	19c05	19b47		20 01	20b47		21 01	21b47		22 01
Sheffield 7	78 d	16 44			17 42				18 35			18 43	19 42		20 13	20 35		
Stockport	84 d	17 44			18 25	18 43			19 20	19 42		19 46	20 46		20 54	21 42		
Manchester Piccadilly 10	78, 84, 85 d	18 07		18 16	18 37	19 07		19 16	19 37	20 07		20 16	21 07		21 16	22 07		22 16
Manchester Oxford Road	84, 85 d	18 10	18 15	18 20	18 40	19 11	19 15	19 20	19 40	20 10	20 15	20 20	21 10	21 15	21 20	22 10	22 15	22 19
Deansgate	84, 85 d		18 17				19 17				20 17			21 17			22 17	
Urmston	d		18 23				19 23				20 23			21 23			22 23	
Irlam	d		18 28				19 28				20 28			21 28			22 28	
Birchwood	d	18 24	18 34			19 24	19 34			20 24	20 34		21 24	21 34		22 24	22 34	
Warrington Central	a	18 28	18 39		18 56	19 29	19 39		19 56	20 28	20 39		21 28	21 39		22 28	22 39	
	d	18 29	18 39		18 57	19 29	19 39		19 57	20 29	20 39		21 29	21 39		22 29	22 39	
Widnes	d		18 47		19 05		19 47		20 05		20 47			21 47			22 47	
Hough Green	d		18 51				19 51				20 51			21 51			22 51	
Halewood	d		18 55				19 55				20 55			21 55			22 55	
Hunts Cross	89 d		18 58				19 58				20 58			21 58			22 58	
Liverpool South Parkway 7	91, 103 ✈ a		19 03				20 03				21 03			22 03			23 03	
Liverpool Central 10	103 a		19e23				20e23				21e23			22e23			23e23	
West Allerton	91 a		19 06				20 06				21 06			22 06			23 06	
Mossley Hill	91 a		19 09				20 09				21 09			22 09			23 09	
Liverpool Lime Street 10	90, 91 a	18 57	19 20	19 21	19 29	19 57	20 20	20 21	20 29	20 57	21 20	21 21	21 57	22 20	22 21	22 57	23 20	23 20

For general notes see front of timetable
For details of catering facilities see Directory of Train Operators

A From Leeds (Table 39)
B From Hull (Table 39)
C From Nottingham (Table 49)
D From Newcastle (Table 39)
E From Scarborough (Table 39)
G From York (Table 39)
H From Norwich (Table 49)
J From Middlesbrough (Table 39)
b Change at Manchester Oxford Road
c Change at Manchester Piccadilly
e Change at Hunts Cross

Sundays

20 July to 7 September

Manchester Airport and Manchester → Warrington Central → Liverpool

Network Diagram - see first page of Table 88

		NT	NT	TP 1 ◇ A	NT	NT	TP 1 ◇ B	NT	NT	EM ◇ C	TP 1 ◇ D	NT	NT	EM ◇ C	TP 1 ◇ E	NT	NT	EM ◇ C
Manchester Airport	85 ✈ d	07 36	08 47	09b46		09 58	10b46		10 58		11b46		11 58		12b46		12 58	
Sheffield 7	78 ⛴ d			07 55			09 30			10 26	10 30			11 40				12 39
Stockport	84 d			09 29			10 42			11 20	11 42			12 24	12 28		12 42	13 23
Manchester Piccadilly 10	78, 84, 85 ⛴ d	07 51	09 03	10 07		10 16	11 07		11 16	11 37	12 07		12 17	12 37	13 07		13 17	13 37
Manchester Oxford Road	84, 85 d	08 01	09 15	10 10	10 13	10 20	11 10	11 15	11 20	11 40	12 10	12 15	12 20	12 40	13 10	13 15	13 20	13 40
Deansgate	84, 85 ⛴ d	08 03	09 17		10 15			11 17				12 17				13 17		
Urmston	d	08 09	09 23		10 21			11 23				12 23				13 23		
Irlam	d	08 14	09 28		10 26			11 28				12 28				13 28		
Birchwood	d	08 20	09 34	10 24	10 32		11 24	11 34			12 24	12 34			13 24	13 34		
Warrington Central	a	08 25	09 39	10 28	10 37		11 28	11 39		11 56	12 28	12 39		12 56	13 28	13 39		13 56
	d	08 39	09 39	10 29	10 39		11 29	11 39		11 57	12 29	12 39		12 57	13 29	13 39		13 57
Widnes	d	08 47	09 47		10 47			11 47		12 05		12 47		13 05		13 47		14 05
Hough Green	d	08 51	09 51		10 51			11 51				12 51				13 51		
Halewood	d	08 55	09 55		10 55			11 55				12 55				13 55		
Hunts Cross	89 d	08 58	09 58		10 58			11 58				12 58				13 58		
Liverpool South Parkway 7	91, 103 ✈ a	09 03	10 03		11 03			12 03				13 03				14 03		
Liverpool Central 10	103 a	09c23	10c23		11c23			12c23				13c23				14c23		
West Allerton	91 a	09 06	10 06		11 06			12 06				13 06				14 06		
Mossley Hill	91 a	09 09	10 09		11 09			12 09				13 09				14 09		
Liverpool Lime Street 10	90, 91 a	09 20	10 20	10 57	11 20	11 21	11 57	12 20	12 21	12 29	12 57	13 20	13 21	13 29	13 57	14 20	14 21	14 29

		TP 1 ◇ G	NT	NT	EM ◇ H	TP 1 ◇ J	NT	NT	EM ◇ H	TP 1 ◇ D	NT	NT	EM ◇ C	TP 1 ◇ E	NT	NT	EM ◇ C	TP 1 ◇ D
Manchester Airport	85 ✈ d	13b46		13 58		14b46		14 58		15b46		15 58		16b46		16 58		17b46
Sheffield 7	78 ⛴ d				13 37				14 37				15 34				16 36	16 44
Stockport	84 d	13 29		13 43	14 20	14 43		14 53	15 21	15 29		15 43	16 20	16 29		16 50	17 21	17 44
Manchester Piccadilly 10	78, 84, 85 ⛴ d	14 07		14 17	14 37	15 07		15 16	15 37	16 07		16 16	16 37	17 07		17 16	17 37	18 07
Manchester Oxford Road	84, 85 d	14 10	14 15	14 20	14 40	15 10	15 15	15 20	15 40	16 10	16 15	16 20	16 40	17 10	17 15	17 20	17 40	18 10
Deansgate	84, 85 ⛴ d		14 17				15 17				16 17				17 17			
Urmston	d		14 23				15 23				16 23				17 23			
Irlam	d		14 28				15 28				16 28				17 28			
Birchwood	d	14 24	14 34			15 24	15 34			16 24	16 34			17 24	17 34			18 24
Warrington Central	a	14 28	14 39		14 56	15 28	15 39		15 56	16 28	16 39		16 56	17 28	17 39		17 56	18 28
	d	14 29	14 39		14 57	15 29	15 39		15 57	16 29	16 39		16 57	17 29	17 39		17 57	18 29
Widnes	d		14 47		15 05		15 47		16 05		16 47		17 05		17 47		18 05	
Hough Green	d		14 51				15 51				16 51				17 51			
Halewood	d		14 55				15 55				16 55				17 55			
Hunts Cross	89 d		14 58				15 58				16 58				17 58			
Liverpool South Parkway 7	91, 103 ✈ a		15 03				16 03				17 03				18 03			
Liverpool Central 10	103 a		15c23				16c23				17c23				18c23			
West Allerton	91 a		15 06				16 06				17 06				18 06			
Mossley Hill	91 a		15 09				16 09				17 09				18 09			
Liverpool Lime Street 10	90, 91 a	14 57	15 20	15 21	15 29	15 57	16 20	16 21	16 29	16 57	17 20	17 21	17 29	17 57	18 20	18 21	18 29	18 57

		NT	NT	EM ◇ H	TP 1 ◇ D	NT	NT	EM ◇ H	TP 1 ◇ D	NT	NT	TP 1 ◇ D	NT	NT	TP 1 ◇ G	NT	NT
Manchester Airport	85 ✈ d		17 58		18b46		18 58		19b46		19 58	20b46		20 58	21b46		21 58
Sheffield 7	78 ⛴ d			17 42				18 35			18 43	19 35		20 13	20 35		
Stockport	84 d		17 50	18 25	18 29		18 51	19 20	19 29		19 47	20 43		20 54	21 44		
Manchester Piccadilly 10	78, 84, 85 ⛴ d		18 16	18 37	19 07		19 16	19 37	20 07		20 16	21 07		21 16	22 07		22 16
Manchester Oxford Road	84, 85 d	18 15	18 20	18 40	19 11	19 15	19 20	19 40	20 10	20 15	20 20	21 10	21 15	21 20	22 10	22 15	22 19
Deansgate	84, 85 ⛴ d	18 17				19 17				20 17			21 17			22 17	
Urmston	d	18 23				19 23				20 23			21 23			22 23	
Irlam	d	18 28				19 28				20 28			21 28			22 28	
Birchwood	d	18 34			19 24	19 34			20 24	20 34		21 24	21 34		22 24	22 34	
Warrington Central	a	18 39		18 56	19 29	19 39		19 56	20 28	20 39		21 28	21 39		22 28	22 39	
	d	18 39		18 57	19 29	19 39		19 57	20 29	20 39		21 29	21 39		22 29	22 39	
Widnes	d	18 47		19 05		19 47		20 05		20 47			21 47			22 47	
Hough Green	d	18 51				19 51				20 51			21 51			22 51	
Halewood	d	18 55				19 55				20 55			21 55			22 55	
Hunts Cross	89 d	18 58				19 58				20 58			21 58			22 58	
Liverpool South Parkway 7	91, 103 ✈ a	19 03				20 03				21 03			22 03			23 03	
Liverpool Central 10	103 a	19c23				20c23				21c23			22c23			23c23	
West Allerton	91 a	19 06				20 06				21 06			22 06			23 06	
Mossley Hill	91 a	19 09				20 09				21 09			22 09			23 09	
Liverpool Lime Street 10	90, 91 a	19 20	19 21	19 29	19 57	20 20	20 21	20 29	20 57	21 20	21 21	21 57	22 20	22 21	22 57	23 20	23 20

For general notes see front of timetable
For details of catering facilities see Directory of Train Operators

A From Leeds (Table 39)
B From York (Table 39)
C From Nottingham (Table 49)
D From Scarborough (Table 39)
E From Middlesbrough (Table 39)
G From Newcastle (Table 39)
H From Norwich (Table 49)
J From Hull (Table 39)
b Change at Manchester Oxford Road
c Change at Hunts Cross

Table 89

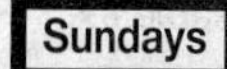

Manchester Airport and Manchester → Warrington Central → Liverpool

14 September to 2 November

Network Diagram - see first page of Table 88

		NT	NT	NT	TP 1 ◇ A	NT	NT	TP 1 ◇ B	NT	NT	EM ◇ C	TP 1 ◇ D	NT	NT	EM ◇ C	TP 1 ◇ E	NT	NT
Manchester Airport	85 ✈ d	*07 36*	*08 44*	08 51	*09b47*		10 01	*10b47*		11 00	*11c03*	*11b47*		12 00		*12b46*		13 00
Sheffield 7	78 🚌 d			*07 55*				*09 30*			10 26				11 40			
Stockport	84 d										11 20				12 24			
Manchester Piccadilly 10	78, 84, 85 🚌 d	*07 51*	*09 03*	09 16	10 07		10 16	11 07		11 16	11 37	12 07		12 17	12 37	13 07		13 17
Manchester Oxford Road	84, 85 d	08 01	09 15	09 20	10 10	10 15	10 20	11 10	11 15	11 20	11 40	12 10	12 15	12 20	12 40	13 10	13 15	13 20
Deansgate	84, 85 🚌 d	08 03	09 17			10 17			11 17				12 17				13 17	
Trafford Park	d																	
Humphrey Park	d																	
Urmston	d	08 09	09 23			10 23			11 23				12 23				13 23	
Chassen Road	d																	
Flixton	d																	
Irlam	d	08 14	09 28			10 28			11 28				12 28				13 28	
Glazebrook	d																	
Birchwood	d	08 20	09 34		10 24	10 34		11 24	11 34			12 24	12 34			13 24	13 34	
Padgate	d																	
Warrington Central	a	08 25	09 39		10 28	10 39		11 28	11 39		11 56	12 28	12 39		12 56	13 28	13 39	
	d	08 39	09 39		10 29	10 39		11 29	11 39		11 57	12 29	12 39		12 57	13 29	13 39	
Sankey for Penketh	d																	
Widnes	d	08 47	09 47			10 47			11 47		12 05		12 47		13 05		13 47	
Hough Green	d	08 51	09 51			10 51			11 51				12 51				13 51	
Halewood	d	08 55	09 55			10 55			11 55				12 55				13 55	
Hunts Cross	89 d	08 58	09 58			10 58			11 58				12 58				13 58	
Liverpool South Parkway 7	91, 103 ✈ a	09 03	10 03			11 03			12 03				13 03				14 03	
Liverpool Central 10	103 a	*09e23*	*10e23*			*11e23*			*12e23*				*13e23*				*14e23*	
West Allerton	91 a	09 06	10 06			11 06			12 06				13 06				14 06	
Mossley Hill	91 a	09 09	10 09			11 09			12 09				13 09				14 09	
Edge Hill	90, 91 a																	
Liverpool Lime Street 10	90, 91 a	09 20	10 20	10 23	10 57	11 20	11 21	11 57	12 20	12 21	12 29	12 57	13 20	13 21	13 29	13 57	14 20	14 21

		EM ◇ C	TP 1 ◇ G	NT	NT	EM ◇ C	TP 1 ◇ E	NT	NT	EM ◇ H	TP 1 ◇ J	NT	NT	EM ◇ C	TP 1 ◇ E	NT	NT	EM ◇ C
Manchester Airport	85 ✈ d	*13c05*	*13b47*		14 00		*14b47*		15 00	*15c08*	*15b47*		16 01		*16b47*		17 01	*17c05*
Sheffield 7	78 🚌 d	12 39				13 37				14 43				15 34				16 36
Stockport	84 d	13 23				14 20				15 25				16 20				17 21
Manchester Piccadilly 10	78, 84, 85 🚌 d	13 37	14 07		14 17	14 37	15 07		15 16	15 37	16 07		16 16	16 37	17 07		17 16	17 37
Manchester Oxford Road	84, 85 d	13 40	14 10	14 15	14 20	14 40	15 10	15 15	15 20	15 40	16 10	16 15	16 20	16 40	17 10	17 15	17 20	17 40
Deansgate	84, 85 🚌 d			14 17				15 17				16 17				17 17		
Trafford Park	d																	
Humphrey Park	d																	
Urmston	d			14 23				15 23				16 23				17 23		
Chassen Road	d																	
Flixton	d																	
Irlam	d			14 28				15 28				16 28				17 28		
Glazebrook	d																	
Birchwood	d		14 24	14 34			15 24	15 34			16 24	16 34			17 24	17 34		
Padgate	d																	
Warrington Central	a	13 56	14 28	14 39		14 56	15 28	15 39		15 56	16 28	16 39		16 56	17 28	17 39		17 56
	d	13 57	14 29	14 39		14 57	15 29	15 39		15 57	16 29	16 39		16 57	17 29	17 39		17 57
Sankey for Penketh	d																	
Widnes	d	14 05		14 47		15 05		15 47		16 05		16 47		17 05		17 47		18 05
Hough Green	d			14 51				15 51				16 51				17 51		
Halewood	d			14 55				15 55				16 55				17 55		
Hunts Cross	89 d			14 58				15 58				16 58				17 58		
Liverpool South Parkway 7	91, 103 ✈ a			15 03				16 03				17 03				18 03		
Liverpool Central 10	103 a			*15e23*				*16e23*				*17e23*				*18e23*		
West Allerton	91 a			15 06				16 06				17 06				18 06		
Mossley Hill	91 a			15 09				16 09				17 09				18 09		
Edge Hill	90, 91 a																	
Liverpool Lime Street 10	90, 91 a	14 29	14 57	15 20	15 21	15 29	15 57	16 20	16 21	16 29	16 57	17 20	17 21	17 29	17 57	18 20	18 21	18 29

		TP 1 ◇ J	NT	NT	EM ◇ H	TP 1 ◇ E	NT	NT	EM ◇ C	TP 1 ◇ J	NT	NT	TP 1 ◇ E	NT	NT	TP 1 ◇ D	NT	NT
Manchester Airport	85 ✈ d	*17b47*		18 01		*18b47*		19 01	*19c05*	*19b47*		20 01	*20b47*		21 01	*21b47*		22 01
Sheffield 7	78 🚌 d	*16f44*			17 42				18 35			*18f43*	*19 35*		*20 13*	*20 35*		
Stockport	84 d				18 25				19 20									
Manchester Piccadilly 10	78, 84, 85 🚌 d	18 07		18 16	18 37	19 07		19 16	19 37	20 07		20 16	21 07		21 16	22 07		22 16
Manchester Oxford Road	84, 85 d	18 10	18 15	18 20	18 40	19 11	19 15	19 20	19 40	20 10	20 15	20 20	21 10	21 15	21 20	22 10	22 15	22 19
Deansgate	84, 85 🚌 d		18 17				19 17				20 17			21 17			22 17	
Trafford Park	d																	
Humphrey Park	d																	
Urmston	d		18 23				19 23				20 23			21 23			22 23	
Chassen Road	d																	
Flixton	d																	
Irlam	d		18 28				19 28				20 28			21 28			22 28	
Glazebrook	d																	
Birchwood	d	18 24	18 34			19 24	19 34			20 24	20 34		21 24	21 34		22 24	22 34	
Padgate	d																	
Warrington Central	a	18 28	18 39		18 56	19 29	19 39		19 56	20 28	20 39		21 28	21 39		22 28	22 39	
	d	18 29	18 39		18 57	19 29	19 39		19 57	20 29	20 39		21 29	21 39		22 29	22 39	
Sankey for Penketh	d																	
Widnes	d		18 47		19 05		19 47		20 05		20 47			21 47			22 47	
Hough Green	d		18 51				19 51				20 51			21 51			22 51	
Halewood	d		18 55				19 55				20 55			21 55			22 55	
Hunts Cross	89 d		18 58				19 58				20 58			21 58			22 58	
Liverpool South Parkway 7	91, 103 ✈ a		19 03				20 03				21 03			22 03			23 03	
Liverpool Central 10	103 a		*19e23*				*20e23*				*21e23*			*22e23*			*23e23*	
West Allerton	91 a		19 06				20 06				21 06			22 06			23 06	
Mossley Hill	91 a		19 09				20 09				21 09			22 09			23 09	
Edge Hill	90, 91 a																	
Liverpool Lime Street 10	90, 91 a	18 57	19 20	19 21	19 29	19 57	20 20	20 21	20 29	20 57	21 20	21 21	21 57	22 20	22 21	22 57	23 20	23 20

For general notes see front of timetable
For details of catering facilities see Directory of Train Operators

A From Leeds (Table 39)
B From Hull (Table 39)
C From Nottingham (Table 49)
D From Newcastle (Table 39)
E From Scarborough (Table 39)
G From York (Table 39)
H From Norwich (Table 49)
J From Middlesbrough (Table 39)
b Change at Manchester Oxford Road
c Change at Manchester Piccadilly
e Change at Hunts Cross
f 14 September only

Table 89

Sundays

from 9 November

Manchester Airport and Manchester → Warrington Central → Liverpool

Network Diagram - see first page of Table 88

	NT	TP 🚌	NT	NT	TP 🚌	NT	TP [1] ◇ A	NT	NT	TP 🚌	TP [1] ◇ B	NT	TP 🚌	NT	EM ◇ C	TP [1] ◇ D	NT
Manchester Airport 85 d	07 36			08 44		08 51		09 47	10 01			10 47		11 00	11b03		11 47
Sheffield [7] 78 d						07 55								09 30	10 26		
Stockport 84 d															11 20		
Manchester Piccadilly [10] 78, 84, 85 d	07 51			09 03		09 16		10 03	10 16			11 03		11 16	11 37		12 03
Manchester Oxford Road 84, 85 d	08 01			09 15		09 20		10 15	10 20			11 15		11 20	11 40		12 15
Manchester Victoria 90 d			08 17				10 13				11 09					12 09	
Newton-le-Willows 90 d		08 35	08 40		09 35	09 40	10 35		10 40	10 45	11 28		11 35	11 40		12 28	
Deansgate d	08 03			09 17				10 17				11 17					12 17
Urmston d	08 09			09 23				10 23				11 23					12 23
Irlam d	08 14			09 28				10 28				11 28					12 28
Birchwood d	08 20			09 34				10 34				11 34					12 34
Warrington Central a	08 25	08 55		09 39	09 55			10 39		11 05		11 39	11 55		11 56		12 39
d	08 39			09 39				10 39				11 39			11 57		12 39
Widnes d	08 47			09 47				10 47				11 47			12 05		12 47
Hough Green d	08 51			09 51				10 51				11 51					12 51
Halewood d	08 55			09 55				10 55				11 55					12 55
Hunts Cross 89 d	08 58			09 58				10 58				11 58					12 58
Liverpool South Parkway [7] 91, 103 a	09 03			10 03				11 03				12 03					13 03
Liverpool Central [10] 103 a	09c23			10c23				11c23				12c23					13c23
West Allerton 91 a	09 06			10 06				11 06				12 06					13 06
Mossley Hill 91 a	09 09			10 09				11 09				12 09					13 09
Liverpool Lime Street [10] 90, 91 a	09 20		09 22	10 20		10 23	10 54	11 20	11 21		11 56	12 20		12 21	12 29	12 51	13 20

	TP 🚌	NT	EM ◇ C	TP [1] ◇ E	NT	TP 🚌	NT	EM ◇ C	TP [1] ◇ A	NT	TP 🚌	NT	EM ◇ C	TP [1] ◇ E	NT	TP 🚌	NT
Manchester Airport 85 d		12 00			12 46		13 00	13b05		13 47		14 00			14 47		15 00
Sheffield [7] 78 d			11 40					12 39					13 37				
Stockport 84 d			12 24					13 23					14 20				
Manchester Piccadilly [10] 78, 84, 85 d		12 17	12 37		13 02		13 17	13 37		14 03		14 17	14 37		15 03		15 16
Manchester Oxford Road 84, 85 d		12 20	12 40		13 15		13 20	13 40		14 15		14 20	14 40		15 15		15 20
Manchester Victoria 90 d				13 09					14 09					15 09			
Newton-le-Willows 90 d	12 35	12 40		13 28		13 35	13 40		14 28		14 35	14 40		15 28		15 35	15 40
Deansgate d					13 17					14 17					15 17		
Urmston d					13 23					14 23					15 23		
Irlam d					13 28					14 28					15 28		
Birchwood d					13 34					14 34					15 34		
Warrington Central a	12 55		12 56		13 39	13 55		13 56		14 39	14 55		14 56		15 39	15 55	
d			12 57		13 39			13 57		14 39			14 57		15 39		
Widnes d			13 05		13 47			14 05		14 47			15 05		15 47		
Hough Green d					13 51					14 51					15 51		
Halewood d					13 55					14 55					15 55		
Hunts Cross 89 d					13 58					14 58					15 58		
Liverpool South Parkway [7] 91, 103 a					14 03					15 03					16 03		
Liverpool Central [10] 103 a					14c23					15c23					16c23		
West Allerton 91 a					14 06					15 06					16 06		
Mossley Hill 91 a					14 09					15 09					16 09		
Liverpool Lime Street [10] 90, 91 a		13 21	13 29	13 55	14 20		14 21	14 29	14 51	15 20		15 21	15 29	15 51	16 20		16 21

	EM ◇ G	TP [1] ◇ H	NT	NT	EM ◇ C	TP 🚌	TP [1] ◇ E	NT	TP 🚌	NT	EM ◇ C	TP [1] ◇ H	NT	TP 🚌	NT	EM ◇ G	TP [1] ◇ E
Manchester Airport 85 d	15b08		15 47	16 01				16 47		17 01	17b05		17 47		18 01		
Sheffield [7] 78 d	14 43				15 34						16 36					17 42	
Stockport 84 d	15 25				16 20						17 21					18 25	
Manchester Piccadilly [10] 78, 84, 85 d	15 37		16 03	16 17	16 37			17 03		17 16	17 37		18 03		18 16	18 37	
Manchester Oxford Road 84, 85 d	15 40		16 15	16 20	16 40			17 15		17 20	17 40		18 15		18 20	18 40	
Manchester Victoria 90 d		16 15					17 09					18 09					19 09
Newton-le-Willows 90 d		16 33		16 40		16 45	17 28		17 35	17 40		18 28		18 35	18 40		19 28
Deansgate d			16 17					17 17					18 17				
Urmston d			16 23					17 23					18 23				
Irlam d			16 28					17 28					18 28				
Birchwood d			16 34					17 34					18 34				
Warrington Central a	15 56		16 39		16 56	17 05		17 39	17 55		17 56		18 39	18 55		18 56	
d	15 57		16 39		16 57			17 39			17 57		18 39			18 57	
Widnes d	16 05		16 47		17 05			17 47			18 05		18 47			19 05	
Hough Green d			16 51					17 51					18 51				
Halewood d			16 55					17 55					18 55				
Hunts Cross 89 d			16 58					17 58					18 58				
Liverpool South Parkway [7] 91, 103 a			17 03					18 03					19 03				
Liverpool Central [10] 103 a			17c23					18c23					19c23				
West Allerton 91 a			17 06					18 06					19 06				
Mossley Hill 91 a			17 09					18 09					19 09				
Liverpool Lime Street [10] 90, 91 a	16 29	16 55	17 20	17 21	17 29		17 51	18 20		18 21	18 29	18 51	19 20		19 21	19 29	19 51

For general notes see front of timetable
For details of catering facilities see Directory of Train Operators

A From York (Table 39)
B From Hull (Table 39)
C From Nottingham (Table 49)
D From Newcastle (Table 39)
E From Scarborough (Table 39)
G From Norwich (Table 49)
H From Middlesbrough (Table 39)
b Change at Manchester Piccadilly
c Change at Hunts Cross

Sundays

from 9 November

Manchester Airport and Manchester → Warrington Central → Liverpool

Network Diagram - see first page of Table 88

	NT	TP	NT		EM	TP	NT		TP	NT	TP		NT	NT	TP		TP	NT	NT	TP		
					◇	1 ◇					1 ◇						1 ◇					
					A	B					C						D					
		Bus							Bus						Bus					Bus		
Manchester Airport 85 ✈ d	18 47		19 01		19b05		19 47			20 01			20 47	21 01				21 47	22 01			
Sheffield 7 78 🚆 d					18 35														20 35			
Stockport 84 d					19 20																	
Manchester Piccadilly 10 78, 84, 85 🚆 d	19 03		19 16		19 37		20 03			20 16			21 03	21 16				22 03	22 16			
Manchester Oxford Road 84, 85 d	19 15		19 20		19 40		20 15			20 20			21 15	21 20				22 15	22 19			
Manchester Victoria 90 🚆 d						20 09					21 09						22 13					
Newton-le-Willows 90 d		19 35	19 40			20 28			20 35	20 40	21 27			21 40	21 42		22 31		22 39	22 45		
Deansgate 🚆 d	19 17						20 17						21 17					22 17				
Urmston d	19 23						20 23						21 23					22 23				
Irlam d	19 28						20 28						21 28					22 28				
Birchwood d	19 34						20 34						21 34					22 34				
Warrington Central a	19 39	19 55			19 56		20 39		20 55				21 39		22 02			22 39		23 05		
d	19 39				19 57		20 39						21 39					22 39				
Widnes d	19 47				20 05		20 47						21 47					22 47				
Hough Green d	19 51						20 51						21 51					22 51				
Halewood d	19 55						20 55						21 55					22 55				
Hunts Cross 89 d	19 58						20 58						21 58					22 58				
Liverpool South Parkway 7 91, 103 ✈ a	20 03						21 03						22 03					23 03				
Liverpool Central 10 103 a	20c23						21c23						22c23					23c23				
West Allerton 91 a	20 06						21 06						22 06					23 06				
Mossley Hill 91 a	20 09						21 09						22 09					23 09				
Liverpool Lime Street 10 90, 91 a	20 20		20 21		20 29	20 51	21 20			21 21	21 51		22 20	22 21			22 54	23 20	23 20			

For general notes see front of timetable
For details of catering facilities see Directory of Train Operators

A From Nottingham (Table 49)
B From Middlesbrough (Table 39)
C From Scarborough (Table 39)
D From Newcastle (Table 39)

b Change at Manchester Piccadilly
c Change at Hunts Cross

Table 90

Mondays to Fridays

Liverpool and St Helens → Newton-le-Willows, Wigan, Preston and Manchester

Network Diagram - see first page of Table 88

Miles	Miles	Miles	Miles			NT	NT	AW	NT	NT	NT	NT	NT	NT	NT	AW	NT	NT	NT	NT	AW	NT	NT	AW	NT
								A							B	A			B		A		C	◇ D	
0	0	0	—	**Liverpool Lime Street** 10	89, 91 d	03 38	05 18		05 34	05 47	06 04	06 14	06 18	06 34	06 39		07 04	07 14	07 18	07 30		07 34	07 47		08 04
1¾	1¾	1¾	—	Edge Hill	89, 91 d					05 51			06 22	06 38					07 22				07 51		
2½	2½	2½	—	Wavertree Technology Park	d				05 40	05 54	06 09	06 19	06 24	06 40	06 45		07 10	07 19	07 24			07 40	07 53		08 10
3½	3½	3½	—	Broad Green	d				05 43	05 57	06 12		06 27	06 43	06 48		07 13		07 27			07 43	07 56		08 13
5	5	5	—	Roby	d				05 46	06 01	06 16		06 31	06 46	06 51		07 16		07 31			07 46	08 00		08 16
5½	5½	5½	—	Huyton	d				05 49	06 03	06 18		06 33	06 49	06 53		07 18		07 33	07 39		07 49	08 02		08 19
—	7¾	—	—	Prescot	d				05 53		06 22			06 53			07 23					07 53			08 23
—	8¾	—	—	Eccleston Park	d				05 56		06 25			06 56			07 25					07 56			08 26
—	9¾	—	—	Thatto Heath	d				05 58		06 27			06 58			07 28					07 58			08 28
—	11¼	—	—	**St Helens Central**	a				06 02		06 31			07 02			07 31			07 47		08 02			08 32
—	—	—	—		d				06 02		06 31			07 02			07 32			07 48		08 02			08 32
—	15	—	—	Garswood	d				06 09		06 38			07 09			07 39					08 09			08 39
—	16¼	—	—	Bryn	d				06 12		06 41			07 12			07 42					08 12			08 42
7½	—	7½	—	Whiston	d					06 06			06 36		06 57				07 36				08 05		
9	—	9	—	Rainhill	d					06 09			06 39		07 00				07 39				08 08		
10¾	—	10¾	—	Lea Green	d					06 13			06 43		07 03			07 29	07 43				08 12		
12	—	12	—	**St Helens Junction**	d		05 32			06 16		06 30	06 46		07 06			07 32	07 46				08 15		
—	—	—	—	Warrington Bank Quay	d			05 53								07 16					07 54			08 21	
14¾	—	14¾	—	Earlestown 8	d			06 00		06 20			06 51		07 11	07 23			07 50		08 01		08 19	08 29	
—	—	—	—	Warrington Bank Quay	a								07 02		*07 48*								*08 48*		
16¼	—	16¼	0	**Newton-le-Willows**	d		05 38	06 03		06 23		06b38			07 14	07 26		07 38	07 53		08 04		08 22	08 32	
—	20	23¼	—	**Wigan North Western**	a				06 23		06 52			07 23			07 53			08 01		08 23			08 53
—	—	—	—		65 d												07 56			08 02					
—	28¼	31½	—	Euxton Balshaw Lane	d															08 12					
—	31	34¼	—	Leyland	82 a															08 17					
—	35	38¼	—	**Preston** 8	65, 82 a						*07 17*									08 24					*09 14*
—	52½	—	—	Blackpool North	97 a						*07c56*									08 51					*09e57*
26¾	—	—	10½	Patricroft	d					06 35									08 05				08 34		
27¾	—	—	11½	Eccles	d					06 38					07 26				08 08				08 37		
31¼	—	—	—	**Manchester Victoria**	a					06 50					07 37		08f41		08 18				08 48		
—	—	—	15¾	**Manchester Oxford Road**	a			06 22				06 58				07 45		08 01			08 31			08 52	
—	—	—	16¼	**Manchester Piccadilly** 10	a	04 14	06 03	06 32				07 03				07 54		08 06			08 40			09 02	
—	—	—	26	**Manchester Airport**	85 a	04 30	06 19					07 20						08 25							

		NT	NT	NT	NT	NT	AW	NT	NT	NT	NT	NT	NT	AW	NT	NT	NT	NT	NT	NT	NT	AW	NT	NT	NT
				E		C	◇ G						C	◇ G						C		◇ G			
Liverpool Lime Street 10	89, 91 d	08 14	08 18	08 28	08 34	08 48		08 57	09 04	09 14	09 18	09 34	09 48		09 57	10 04	10 14	10 18	10 34	10 48	10 57		11 04	11 14	11 18
Edge Hill	89, 91 d		08 22			08 52					09 22		09 52					10 22		10 52					11 22
Wavertree Technology Park	d	08 19	08 24		08 40	08 54			09 10	09 19	09 24	09 40	09 54			10 10	10 19	10 24	10 40	10 54			11 10	11 19	11 24
Broad Green	d		08 27		08 43	08 57			09 13		09 27	09 43	09 57			10 13		10 27	10 43	10 57			11 13		11 27
Roby	d		08 31		08 46	09 01			09 16		09 31	09 46	10 01			10 16		10 31	10 46	11 01			11 16		11 31
Huyton	d		08 33	08 37	08 49	09 03		09 08	09 18		09 33	09 49	10 03		10 08	10 19		10 33	10 49	11 03	11 07		11 19		11 33
Prescot	d				08 53				09 23			09 53				10 23			10 53				11 23		
Eccleston Park	d				08 56				09 25			09 56				10 26			10 56				11 26		
Thatto Heath	d				08 58				09 28			09 58				10 28			10 58				11 28		
St Helens Central	a			08 45	09 02			09 16	09 31			10 02			10 16	10 32			11 02		11 16		11 32		
	d			08 52	09 02			09 17	09 32			10 02			10 17	10 32			11 02		11 16		11 32		
Garswood	d				09 09				09 39			10 09				10 39			11 09				11 39		
Bryn	d				09 12				09 42			10 12				10 42			11 12				11 42		
Whiston	d		08 36			09 06					09 36		10 06					10 36		11 06					11 36
Rainhill	d		08 39			09 09					09 39		10 09					10 39		11 09					11 39
Lea Green	d		08 43			09 13					09 43		10 13					10 43		11 13					11 43
St Helens Junction	d	08 30	08 46			09 16				09 30	09 46		10 16				10 30	10 46		11 16				11 30	11 46
Warrington Bank Quay	d						09 20							10 20								11 20			
Earlestown 8	d		08 51			09 20	09 28				09 51		10 20	10 28				10 51		11 20		11 28			11 51
Warrington Bank Quay	a		09 02			*09 49*					10 02		*10 49*					11 02		*11 49*					12 02
Newton-le-Willows	d	08 36				09 23	09 31			09 36			10 23	10 31			10 36			11 23		11 31		11 36	
Wigan North Western	a			09 12	09 23			09 30	09 53			10 23			10 31	10 54			11 23		11 30		11 53		
	65 d			09 13				09 31							10 31						11 30				
Euxton Balshaw Lane	d			09 23				09 42							10 42						11 41				
Leyland	82 a			09 28				09 47							10 47						11 46				
Preston 8	65, 82 a			09 38				09 54	*10 14*						10 54	*11 15*					11 53		*12 15*		
Blackpool North	97 a							10 21	*10c57*						11 21	*11e54*					12 20		*12e54*		
Patricroft	d					09 35							10 35							11 35					
Eccles	d					09 38							10 38							11 38					
Manchester Victoria	a					09 48							10 48							11 48					
Manchester Oxford Road	a	08 58					09 50			09 58				10 50			10 57					11 50		11 57	
Manchester Piccadilly 10	a	09 02					09 58			10 02				10 58			11 02					11 58		12 02	
Manchester Airport	85 a	09 25								10 25							11 25							12 25	

For general notes see front of timetable
For details of catering facilities see Directory of Train Operators

A From Chester (Table 81)
B To Huddersfield (Table 39)
C To Stalybridge (Table 39)
D From Holyhead (Table 81)
E To Morecambe (Table 98)
G From Llandudno (Table 81)

b Arr. 0635
c Change at Wigan North Western and Preston
e Change at Wigan North Western and Preston. From 6 October arr. 2 minutes later.
f Via Bolton (Table 82)

Table 90

Mondays to Fridays

Liverpool and St Helens → Newton-le-Willows, Wigan, Preston and Manchester

Network Diagram - see first page of Table 88

		NT	NT	AW	NT	NT	NT	NT	NT	NT	AW	NT	NT	NT	NT	NT	NT	AW	NT	NT	NT	NT	NT	NT	AW
			A	◇ B						A	◇ B						A	◇ B				C		A	◇ B
Liverpool Lime Street [10]	89, 91 d	11 34	11 48		11 57	12 04	12 14	12 18	12 34	12 48		12 57	13 04	13 14	13 18	13 34	13 48		13 57	14 04	14 14	14 18	14 34	14 48	
Edge Hill	89, 91 d		11 52					12 22		12 52					13 22		13 52					14 22		14 52	
Wavertree Technology Park	d	11 40	11 54			12 10	12 19	12 24	12 40	12 54			13 10	13 19	13 24	13 40	13 54			14 10	14 19	14 24	14 40	14 54	
Broad Green	d	11 43	11 57			12 13		12 27	12 43	12 57			13 13		13 27	13 43	13 57			14 13		14 27	14 43	14 57	
Roby	d	11 46	12 01			12 16		12 31	12 46	13 01			13 16		13 31	13 46	14 01			14 16		14 31	14 46	15 01	
Huyton	d	11 49	12 03		12 08	12 19		12 33	12 49	13 03		13 08	13 18		13 33	13 49	14 03		14 08	14 19		14 33	14 49	15 03	
Prescot	d	11 53				12 23			12 53				13 23			13 53				14 23			14 53		
Eccleston Park	d	11 56				12 26			12 56				13 25			13 56				14 26			14 56		
Thatto Heath	d	11 58				12 28			12 58				13 28			13 58				14 28			14 58		
St Helens Central	a	12 02			12 16	12 32			13 02			13 16	13 31			14 02			14 16	14 32			15 02		
	d	12 02			12 17	12 32			13 02			13 17	13 32			14 02			14 17	14 32			15 02		
Garswood	d	12 09				12 39			13 09				13 39			14 09				14 39			15 09		
Bryn	d	12 12				12 42			13 12				13 42			14 12				14 42			15 12		
Whiston	d		12 06					12 36		13 06					13 36		14 06					14 36		15 06	
Rainhill	d		12 09					12 39		13 09					13 39		14 09					14 39		15 09	
Lea Green	d		12 13					12 43		13 13					13 43		14 13					14 43		15 13	
St Helens Junction	d		12 16				12 30	12 46		13 16				13 30	13 46		14 16				14 30	14 46		15 16	
Warrington Bank Quay	d			12 20							13 20							14 20							15 20
Earlestown [8]	d		12 20	12 28				12 51		13 20	13 28				13 51		14 20	14 27				14 51		15 20	15 28
Warrington Bank Quay	a		*12 49*					13 02		*13 49*					14 02		*14 49*					15 02		*15 50*	
Newton-le-Willows	d		12 23	12 31			12 36			13 23	13 31			13 36			14 23	14 30			14 36			15 23	15 31
Wigan North Western	a	12 23			12 31	12 53			13 23			13 31	13 53			14 23			14 31	14 53			15 23		
	65 d				12 31							13 31							14 31						
Euxton Balshaw Lane	d				12 42							13 42							14 42						
Leyland	82 a				12 47							13 47							14 47						
Preston [8]	65, 82 a				12 56	*13 15*						13 54	*14 15*						14 54	*15 15*					
Blackpool North	97 a				13 21	*13b54*						14 21	*14b54*						15 21	*15b54*					
Patricroft	d		12 35							13 35							14 35							15 35	
Eccles	d		12 38							13 38							14 38							15 38	
Manchester Victoria	a		12 48							13 48							14 48							15 48	
Manchester Oxford Road	a			12 50			12 57				13 50			13 57				14 50			14 57				15 50
Manchester Piccadilly [10]	a			12 58			13 02				13 58			14 02				14 58			15 02				15 58
Manchester Airport	85 a						13 25							14 25							15 25				

		NT	NT	NT	AW	NT	NT	NT	AW	NT	NT	NT	NT	NT	NT	NT	AW	NT	NT	NT	NT	NT	NT	NT	NT
					◇ D			E	◇ B	G			E			E	◇ B			H			J		
Liverpool Lime Street [10]	89, 91 d	14 57	15 04	15 14		15 18	15 34	15 48		15 57	16 04	16 14	16 18	16 30	16 34	16 48		17 02	17 09	17 12	17 20	17 25	17 35	17 45	17 50
Edge Hill	89, 91 d					15 22		15 52					16 22			16 52				17 16			17 39		17 54
Wavertree Technology Park	d		15 10	15 19		15 24	15 40	15 54			16 10	16 19	16 24		16 40	16 54		17 08	17 14	17 18		17 30	17 41	17 50	17 56
Broad Green	d		15 13			15 27	15 43	15 57			16 13		16 27		16 43	16 57		17 11		17 21		17 33	17 44	17 53	17 59
Roby	d		15 16			15 31	15 46	16 01			16 16		16 31		16 46	17 01		17 14		17 25		17 37	17 48		18 03
Huyton	d	15 08	15 19			15 33	15 49	16 03		16 08	16 19		16 33	16 39	16 49	17 03		17 16	17 20	17 27	17 30	17 39	17 50	17 57	18 05
Prescot	d		15 23				15 53				16 23				16 53			17 21				17 44		18 02	
Eccleston Park	d		15 26				15 56				16 26				16 56			17 23				17 46		18 04	
Thatto Heath	d		15 28				15 58				16 28				16 58			17 26				17 49		18 07	
St Helens Central	a	15 16	15 32				16 02			16 16	16 32			16 47	17 02			17 29			17 39	17 52		18 11	
	d	15 17	15 32				16 02			16 17	16 32			16 52	17 02			17 30			17 39	17 53		18 11	
Garswood	d		15 39				16 09				16 39				17 09			17 37				18 00		18 18	
Bryn	d		15 42				16 12				16 42				17 12			17 40				18 03		18 21	
Whiston	d					15 36		16 06					16 36			17 06				17 30			17 53		18 09
Rainhill	d					15 39		16 09					16 39			17 09				17 33			17 56		18 12
Lea Green	d					15 43		16 13					16 43			17 13			17 27	17 37			18 00		18 15
St Helens Junction	d			15 30		15 46		16 16				16 30	16 46			17 16			17 30	17 40			18 03		18 18
Warrington Bank Quay	d				15 33				16 20								17 20								
Earlestown [8]	d				15 44	15 51		16 20	16 27				16 50			17 20	17 28			17 44			18 07		18 23
Warrington Bank Quay	a					16 02		*16 48*								*17 55*				*18 17*					*18 48*
Newton-le-Willows	d			15 36	15 47			16 23	16 30			16 36	16 53			17 23	17 31		17 36	17 47			18 10		18 26
Wigan North Western	a	15 31	15 53				16 23			16 31	16 53			17 09	17 23			17 50			17 54	18 13		18 28	
	65 d	15 31								16 31				17 10							17 54			18 28	
Euxton Balshaw Lane	d	15 42								16 42				17 20							18 05			18 39	
Leyland	82 a	15 47								16 47				17 25							18 09			18 44	
Preston [8]	65, 82 a	15 54	*16 15*							16 54	*17 15*			17 40				*18 15*			18 17			18 54	
Blackpool North	97 a	16 21	*16b54*							*17 34*	*17c58*			*18 22*				*19b00*			18 48			19 23	
Patricroft	d							16 35					17 05			17 35				17 59			18 22		
Eccles	d							16 38					17 08			17 38				18 02			18 25		
Manchester Victoria	a							16 48					17 21			17 49				18 12			18 40		18 51
Manchester Oxford Road	a			15 57	16 13				16 50			16 57					17 51		17 58						
Manchester Piccadilly [10]	a			16 01	16 21				16 58			17 02					17 59		18 04						
Manchester Airport	85 a			16 25								17 25							18 27						

For general notes see front of timetable
For details of catering facilities see Directory of Train Operators

- **A** To Stalybridge (Table 39)
- **B** From Llandudno (Table 81)
- **C** To Ellesmere Port (Table 109)
- **D** From Holyhead (Table 81)
- **E** To Huddersfield (Table 39)
- **G** To Barrow-in-Furness (Table 82)
- **H** To Rochdale (Table 95)
- **J** To Todmorden (Table 41)
- **b** Change at Wigan North Western and Preston. From 6 October arr. 2 minutes later.
- **c** Change at Wigan North Western and Preston

Liverpool and St Helens → Newton-le-Willows, Wigan, Preston and Manchester

Network Diagram - see first page of Table 88

Mondays to Fridays

Station		AW	NT	NT	NT	NT	NT	AW	NT	NT	AW	NT	NT	NT	AW	NT	NT	AW	NT	NT	NT	NT	AW		
		◇ A 🚌						◇ A 🚌			◇ A				B			◇ A					B		
Liverpool Lime Street 10	89, 91 d		18 04	18 14	18 18	18 34	18 48		19 04	19 18		19 48	20 14	20 18		20 48	21 18		21 48	22 18	23 05	23 18			
Edge Hill	89, 91 d				18 22		18 52			19 22		19 52		20 22		20 52	21 22		21 52	22 22	23 09	23 22			
Wavertree Technology Park	d		18 10	18 19	18 24	18 40	18 54		19 10	19 24		19 54	20 19	20 24		20 54	21 24		21 54	22 24	23 11	23 24			
Broad Green	d		18 13		18 27	18 43	18 57		19 13	19 27		19 57		20 27		20 57	21 27		21 57	22 27	23 14	23 27			
Roby	d		18 16		18 31	18 46	19 01		19 16	19 31		20 01		20 31		21 01	21 31		22 01	22 31	23 17	23 31			
Huyton	d		18 19		18 33	18 49	19 03		19 19	19 33		20 03		20 33		21 03	21 33		22 03	22 33	23 20	23 33			
Prescot	d		18 23			18 53			19 23			20 08				21 08			22 08		23 24				
Eccleston Park	d		18 26			18 56			19 26			20 10				21 10			22 10		23 27				
Thatto Heath	d		18 28			18 58			19 28			20 13				21 13			22 13		23 29				
St Helens Central	a		18 32			19 02			19 32			20 16				21 16			22 16		23 33				
	d		18 32			19 02			19 32			20 17				21 17			22 17		23 34				
Garswood	d		18 39			19 09			19 39			20 24				21 24			22 24		23 41				
Bryn	d		18 42			19 12			19 42			20 27				21 27			22 27		23 44				
Whiston	d				18 36		19 06			19 36				20 36			21 36			22 36		23 36			
Rainhill	d			18 28	18 39		19 09			19 39				20 39			21 39			22 39		23 39			
Lea Green	d				18 43		19 13			19 43				20 43			21 43			22 43		23 43			
St Helens Junction	d			18 32	18 46		19 16			19 46			20 30	20 46			21 46			22 46		23 46			
Warrington Bank Quay	d	18 20						19 20			20 20				21 23			22 21					23 50		
Earlestown 8	d	18 27			18 51		19 20	19 27		19 50	20 27			20 50	21 30		21 50	22 32		22 50		23 50	23 57		
Warrington Bank Quay	a				19 02		*19 48*			*20 48*				*21 49*			*22 48*			*23 52*					
Newton-le-Willows	d	18 30		18 38			19 23	19 30		19 53	20 30		20 36	20 53	21 33		21 53	22 35		22 53		23 53	23 59		
Wigan North Western	a		18 51			19 23			19 51			20 40				21 37			22 37		23 51				
	65 d		18 51						19 51										22 38		23 51				
Euxton Balshaw Lane	d		19 02						20 02										22 49		00 01				
Leyland	82 a		19 07						20 07										22 54		00 06				
Preston 8	65, 82 a		19 17			*20 13*			20 17			*21 15*				*22 21*			23 02		00 15				
Blackpool North	97 a		*19 57*						*20 56*			*21b56*							23 28						
Patricroft	d						19 35			20 05				21 05			22 05			23 05		00 05			
Eccles	d						19 38			20 08				21 08			22 08			23 08		00 08			
Manchester Victoria	a						19 50			20 20				21 20			22 21			23 22		00 20			
Manchester Oxford Road	a	18 51		18 59				19 50			20 51		20 59		21 54			22 55							
Manchester Piccadilly 10	a	19 01		19 05				19 59			21 00		21 05		22 01			23 05					00 27		
Manchester Airport	85 a			19 26									21 28												

Saturdays

Station		NT	NT	AW	NT	NT	NT	NT	NT	NT	NT	AW	NT	NT	NT	NT	AW		NT	NT	AW	NT	NT	NT	NT
				B 🚌							C	B 🚌			C		B 🚌			D	◇ E 🚌				
Liverpool Lime Street 10	89, 91 d	03 38	05 18		05 34	05 47	06 04	06 10	06 18	06 34	06 39		07 04	07 14	07 18	07 30			07 34	07 47		08 04	08 14	08 18	08 34
Edge Hill	89, 91 d					05 51			06 22	06 38					07 22					07 51				08 22	
Wavertree Technology Park	d				05 40	05 54	06 09	06 15	06 24	06 40	06 45		07 10	07 19	07 24				07 40	07 53		08 10	08 19	08 24	08 40
Broad Green	d				05 43	05 57	06 12		06 27	06 43	06 48		07 13		07 27				07 43	07 56		08 13		08 27	08 43
Roby	d				05 46	06 01	06 16		06 31	06 46	06 51		07 16		07 31				07 46	08 00		08 16		08 31	08 46
Huyton	d				05 49	06 03	06 18		06 33	06 49	06 53		07 18		07 33	07 39			07 49	08 02		08 19		08 33	08 49
Prescot	d				05 53		06 22			06 53			07 23						07 53			08 23			08 53
Eccleston Park	d				05 56		06 25			06 56			07 25						07 56			08 26			08 56
Thatto Heath	d				05 58		06 27			06 58			07 28						07 58			08 28			08 58
St Helens Central	a				06 02		06 31			07 02			07 32			07 47			08 02			08 32			09 02
	d				06 02		06 31			07 02			07 32			07 48			08 02			08 32			09 02
Garswood	d				06 09		06 38			07 09			07 39						08 09			08 39			09 09
Bryn	d				06 12		06 41			07 12			07 42						08 12			08 42			09 12
Whiston	d					06 06			06 36		06 57				07 36					08 05				08 36	
Rainhill	d					06 09			06 39		07 00				07 39					08 08				08 39	
Lea Green	d					06 13			06 43		07 03			07 29	07 43					08 12				08 43	
St Helens Junction	d		05 32			06 16		06 28	06 46		07 06			07 32	07 46					08 15			08 30	08 46	
Warrington Bank Quay	d			06 01								07 16					07 54				08 21				
Earlestown 8	d			06 09		06 20			06 51		07 11	07 23			07 50		08 01			08 19	08 29			08 51	
Warrington Bank Quay	a								07 02		*07 48*									*08 48*				09 02	
Newton-le-Willows	d		05 38	06 12		06 23		06 32			07 14	07 26		07 38	07 53		08 04			08 22	08 32		08 36		
Wigan North Western	a				06 23		06 52			07 23			07 53			08 01			08 23			08 53			09 23
	65 d												07 56			08 02									
Euxton Balshaw Lane	d															08 12									
Leyland	82 a															08 17									
Preston 8	65, 82 a															08 24									
Blackpool North	97 a															08 51									
Patricroft	d					06 35									08 05					08 34					
Eccles	d					06 38					07 26				08 08					08 37					
Manchester Victoria	a					06 50					07 38		08c41		08 22					08 48					
Manchester Oxford Road	a			06 31				06 57				07 45		08 00			08 31				08 52		08 58		
Manchester Piccadilly 10	a	04 14	06 03	06 40				07 03				07 54		08 06			08 40				09 02		09 02		
Manchester Airport	85 a	04 30	06 19					07 20						08 25									09 25		

For general notes see front of timetable
For details of catering facilities see Directory of Train Operators

- **A** From Llandudno (Table 81)
- **B** From Chester (Table 81)
- **C** To Huddersfield (Table 39)
- **D** To Stalybridge (Table 39)
- **E** From Holyhead (Table 81)
- **b** Change at Wigan North Western and Preston
- **c** Via Bolton (Table 82)

Table 90

Saturdays

Liverpool and St Helens → Newton-le-Willows, Wigan, Preston and Manchester

Network Diagram - see first page of Table 88

		NT A	AW ◇ B	NT	NT	NT	NT	NT	NT A	AW ◇ B	NT	NT		NT	NT	NT	NT A	AW ◇ B	NT	NT	NT	NT	NT	NT A	AW ◇ B
Liverpool Lime Street 10	89, 91 d	08 48		08 57	09 04	09 14	09 18	09 34	09 48		09 57	10 04		10 14	10 18	10 34	10 48		10 57	11 04	11 14	11 18	11 34	11 48	
Edge Hill	89, 91 d	08 52					09 22		09 52						10 22		10 52					11 22		11 52	
Wavertree Technology Park	d	08 54			09 10	09 19	09 24	09 40	09 54			10 10		10 19	10 24	10 40	10 54			11 10	11 19	11 24	11 40	11 54	
Broad Green	d	08 57			09 13		09 27	09 43	09 57			10 13			10 27	10 43	10 57			11 13		11 27	11 43	11 57	
Roby	d	09 01			09 16		09 31	09 46	10 01			10 16			10 31	10 46	11 01			11 16		11 31	11 46	12 01	
Huyton	d	09 03		09 08	09 18		09 33	09 49	10 03		10 08	10 19			10 33	10 49	11 03		11 07	11 19		11 33	11 49	12 03	
Prescot	d				09 23			09 53				10 23				10 53				11 23			11 53		
Eccleston Park	d				09 25			09 56				10 26				10 56				11 26			11 56		
Thatto Heath	d				09 28			09 58				10 28				10 58				11 28			11 58		
St Helens Central	a			09 16	09 31			10 02			10 16	10 32				11 02			11 16	11 32			12 02		
	d			09 17	09 32			10 02			10 17	10 32				11 02			11 16	11 32			12 02		
Garswood	d				09 39			10 09				10 39				11 09				11 39			12 09		
Bryn	d				09 42			10 12				10 42				11 12				11 42			12 12		
Whiston	d	09 06					09 36		10 06						10 36		11 06					11 36		12 06	
Rainhill	d	09 09					09 39		10 09						10 39		11 09					11 39		12 09	
Lea Green	d	09 13					09 43		10 13						10 43		11 13					11 43		12 13	
St Helens Junction	d	09 16				09 30	09 46		10 16					10 30	10 46		11 16				11 30	11 46		12 16	
Warrington Bank Quay	d		09 20							10 20								11 20							12 20
Earlestown 8	d	09 20	09 28				09 51		10 20	10 27					10 51		11 20	11 27				11 51		12 20	12 28
Warrington Bank Quay	a	*09 49*					10 02		*10 49*						11 02		*11 48*					12 02		*12 49*	
Newton-le-Willows	d	09 23	09 31			09 36			10 23	10 30				10 36			11 23	11 30			11 36			12 23	12 31
Wigan North Western	a			09 30	09 53			10 23			10 31	10 54				11 23			11 30	11 53			12 23		
	65 d			09 31							10 31								11 30						
Euxton Balshaw Lane	d			09 42							10 42								11 41						
Leyland	82 a			09 47							10 47								11 46						
Preston 8	65, 82 a			09 54							10 55								11 53						
Blackpool North	97 a			10 21							11 22								12 20						
Patricroft	d	09 35							10 35								11 35							12 35	
Eccles	d	09 38							10 38								11 38							12 38	
Manchester Victoria	a	09 48							10 48								11 48							12 48	
Manchester Oxford Road	a		09 50			09 58				10 50				10 57				11 50			11 57				12 50
Manchester Piccadilly 10	a		09 58			10 02				10 58				11 02				11 58			12 02				12 58
Manchester Airport	85 a					10 25								11 25							12 25				

		NT	NT	NT	NT	NT	NT A		AW ◇ B	NT	NT	NT	NT	NT	NT A	AW ◇ B	NT	NT	NT	NT C	NT	NT A	AW ◇ B	NT	NT
Liverpool Lime Street 10	89, 91 d	11 57	12 04	12 14	12 18	12 34	12 48			12 57	13 04	13 14	13 18	13 34	13 48		13 57	14 04	14 14	14 18	14 34	14 48		14 57	15 04
Edge Hill	89, 91 d				12 22		12 52						13 22		13 52					14 22		14 52			
Wavertree Technology Park	d		12 10	12 19	12 24	12 40	12 54				13 10	13 19	13 24	13 40	13 54			14 10	14 19	14 24	14 40	14 54			15 10
Broad Green	d		12 13		12 27	12 43	12 57				13 13		13 27	13 43	13 57			14 13		14 27	14 43	14 57			15 13
Roby	d		12 16		12 31	12 46	13 01				13 17		13 31	13 46	14 01			14 16		14 31	14 46	15 01			15 16
Huyton	d	12 08	12 19		12 33	12 49	13 03			13 08	13 19		13 33	13 49	14 03		14 08	14 19		14 33	14 49	15 03		15 08	15 19
Prescot	d		12 23			12 53					13 23			13 53				14 23			14 53				15 23
Eccleston Park	d		12 26			12 56					13 26			13 56				14 26			14 56				15 26
Thatto Heath	d		12 28			12 58					13 28			13 58				14 28			14 58				15 28
St Helens Central	a	12 16	12 32			13 02				13 16	13 32			14 02			14 16	14 31			15 02			15 16	15 32
	d	12 17	12 32			13 02				13 17	13 32			14 02			14 17	14 32			15 02			15 17	15 32
Garswood	d		12 39			13 09					13 39			14 09				14 39			15 09				15 39
Bryn	d		12 42			13 12					13 42			14 12				14 42			15 12				15 42
Whiston	d				12 36		13 06						13 36		14 06					14 36		15 06			
Rainhill	d				12 39		13 09						13 39		14 09					14 39		15 09			
Lea Green	d				12 43		13 13						13 43		14 13					14 43		15 13			
St Helens Junction	d			12 30	12 46		13 16					13 30	13 46		14 16				14 30	14 46		15 16			
Warrington Bank Quay	d								13 20							14 20							15 20		
Earlestown 8	d				12 51		13 20		13 28				13 51		14 20	14 28				14 51		15 20	15 28		
Warrington Bank Quay	a				13 02		*13 49*						14 02		*14 49*					15 02		*15 48*			
Newton-le-Willows	d			12 36			13 23		13 31			13 36			14 23	14 31			14 36			15 23	15 31		
Wigan North Western	a	12 31	12 53			13 23				13 31	13 53			14 23			14 31	14 53			15 23			15 31	15 53
	65 d	12 31								13 31							14 31							15 31	
Euxton Balshaw Lane	d	12 42								13 42							14 42							15 42	
Leyland	82 a	12 47								13 47							14 47							15 47	
Preston 8	65, 82 a	12 56								13 54							14 54							15 54	
Blackpool North	97 a	13 21								14 21							15 21							16 21	
Patricroft	d						13 35								14 35							15 35			
Eccles	d						13 38								14 38							15 38			
Manchester Victoria	a						13 48								14 48							15 48			
Manchester Oxford Road	a			12 57					13 50			13 57				14 50			14 57				15 50		
Manchester Piccadilly 10	a			13 02					13 58			14 02				14 58			15 02				15 58		
Manchester Airport	85 a			13 25								14 25							15 25						

For general notes see front of timetable
For details of catering facilities see Directory of Train Operators

A To Stalybridge (Table 39)
B From Llandudno (Table 81)
C To Ellesmere Port (Table 109)

Liverpool and St Helens → Newton-le-Willows, Wigan, Preston and Manchester

Network Diagram - see first page of Table 88

		NT		AW A	NT	NT	NT B	AW ◇ C	NT D	NT	NT	NT E	NT	NT	NT B	AW ◇ C	NT	NT	NT G		NT	NT	NT H	NT	NT
Liverpool Lime Street 10	89, 91 d	15 14			15 18	15 34	15 48		15 57	16 04	16 14	16 18	16 30	16 34	16 48		17 02	17 09	17 12		17 20	17 25	17 35	17 45	17 48
Edge Hill	89, 91 d				15 22		15 52					16 22			16 52				17 16				17 39		17 52
Wavertree Technology Park	d	15 19			15 24	15 40	15 54			16 10	16 19	16 24		16 40	16 54		17 08	17 14	17 18			17 30	17 41	17 50	17 54
Broad Green	d				15 27	15 43	15 57			16 13		16 27		16 43	16 57		17 11		17 21			17 33	17 44	17 53	17 57
Roby	d				15 31	15 46	16 01			16 16		16 31		16 46	17 01		17 14		17 25			17 37	17 48		18 01
Huyton	d				15 33	15 49	16 03		16 08	16 19		16 33	16 39	16 49	17 03		17 16	17 20	17 27		17 30	17 39	17 50	17 57	18 03
Prescot	d					15 53				16 23				16 53			17 21					17 44		18 02	
Eccleston Park	d					15 56				16 26				16 56			17 23					17 46		18 04	
Thatto Heath	d					15 58				16 28				16 58			17 26					17 49		18 07	
St Helens Central	a					16 02			16 16	16 31			16 47	17 02			17 29				17 39	17 52		18 10	
	d					16 02			16 17	16 32			16 52	17 02			17 30				17 39	17 53		18 11	
Garswood	d					16 09				16 39				17 09			17 37					18 00		18 18	
Bryn	d					16 12				16 42				17 12			17 40					18 03		18 21	
Whiston	d				15 36		16 06					16 36			17 06				17 30				17 53		18 06
Rainhill	d				15 39		16 09					16 39			17 09				17 33				17 56		18 09
Lea Green	d				15 43		16 13					16 43			17 13			17 27	17 37				18 00		18 13
St Helens Junction	d	15 30			15 46		16 16				16 30	16 46			17 16			17 30	17 40				18 03		18 16
Warrington Bank Quay	d			15 36				16 20								17 20									
Earlestown 8	d			15 44	15 51		16 20	16 28				16 50			17 20	17 27			17 44				18 07		18 20
Warrington Bank Quay	a				16 02		*16 49*								*17 55*				*18 17*						*18 48*
Newton-le-Willows	d	15 36		15 47			16 23	16 31			16 36	16 53			17 23	17 30		17 36	17 47				18 10		18 23
Wigan North Western	a					16 23			16 31	16 53			17 11	17 23			17 50				17 54	18 13		18 28	
	65 d								16 31				17 12								17 54			18 28	
Euxton Balshaw Lane	d								16 42				17 24								18 05			18 39	
Leyland	82 a								16 47				17 29								18 09			18 44	
Preston 8	65, 82 a								16 54				17 40								18 17			18 52	
Blackpool North	97 a																				18 48			19 21	
Patricroft	d						16 35					17 05			17 35				17 59				18 22		
Eccles	d						16 38					17 08			17 38				18 02				18 25		
Manchester Victoria	a						16 48					17 21			17 49				18 12				18 40		18 46
Manchester Oxford Road	a	15 57		16 10				16 50			16 57					17 51		17 58							
Manchester Piccadilly 10	a	16 02		16 19				16 58			17 02					17 59		18 04							
Manchester Airport	85 a	16 25									17 25							18 27							

		AW ◇ C	NT	NT	NT	NT	NT	AW ◇ C	NT	NT	AW ◇ C	NT	NT	NT	AW J	NT	NT	AW ◇ K	NT	NT	NT	NT	AW J		
Liverpool Lime Street 10	89, 91 d		18 04	18 14	18 18	18 34	18 48		19 04	19 18		19 48	20 14	20 18		20 48	21 18		21 48	22 18	23 05	23 18			
Edge Hill	89, 91 d				18 22		18 52			19 22		19 52		20 22		20 52	21 22		21 52	22 22	23 09	23 22			
Wavertree Technology Park	d		18 10	18 19	18 24	18 40	18 54		19 10	19 24		19 54	20 19	20 24		20 54	21 24		21 54	22 24	23 11	23 24			
Broad Green	d		18 13		18 27	18 43	18 57		19 13	19 27		19 57		20 27		20 57	21 27		21 57	22 27	23 14	23 27			
Roby	d		18 16		18 31	18 47	19 01		19 16	19 31		20 01		20 31		21 01	21 31		22 01	22 31	23 17	23 31			
Huyton	d		18 19		18 33	18 49	19 03		19 19	19 33		20 03		20 33		21 03	21 33		22 03	22 33	23 20	23 33			
Prescot	d		18 23			18 53			19 23			20 08				21 08			22 08		23 24				
Eccleston Park	d		18 26			18 56			19 26			20 10				21 10			22 10		23 27				
Thatto Heath	d		18 28			18 58			19 28			20 13				21 13			22 13		23 29				
St Helens Central	a		18 31			19 02			19 32			20 16				21 16			22 16		23 33				
	d		18 32			19 02			19 32			20 17				21 17			22 17		23 34				
Garswood	d		18 39			19 09			19 39			20 24				21 24			22 24		23 41				
Bryn	d		18 42			19 12			19 42			20 27				21 27			22 27		23 44				
Whiston	d				18 36		19 06			19 36				20 36			21 36			22 36		23 36			
Rainhill	d			18 28	18 39		19 09			19 39				20 39			21 39			22 39		23 39			
Lea Green	d				18 43		19 13			19 43				20 43			21 43			22 43		23 43			
St Helens Junction	d			18 32	18 46		19 16			19 46			20 30	20 46			21 46			22 46		23 46			
Warrington Bank Quay	d	18 21						19 20			20 20				21 23			22 20					23 50		
Earlestown 8	d	18 27			18 51		19 20	19 28		19 50	20 27			20 50	21 30		21 50	22 27		22 50		23 50	23 57		
Warrington Bank Quay	a				19 02		*19 48*			*20 48*				*21c48*			*22c48*			*23c52*					
Newton-le-Willows	d	18 30		18 38			19 23	19 31		19 53	20 30		20 36	20 53	21 33		21 53	22 30		22 53		23 53	23 59		
Wigan North Western	a		18 51			19 23			19 51			20 40				21 37			22 37		23 51				
	65 d		18 51						19 51										22 38		23 51				
Euxton Balshaw Lane	d		19 02						20 02										22 49		00 01				
Leyland	82 a		19 07						20 07										22 54		00 06				
Preston 8	65, 82 a		19 17						20 17										23 02		00 15				
Blackpool North	97 a																		23 28						
Patricroft	d						19 35			20 05				21 05			22 05			23 05		00 05			
Eccles	d						19 38			20 08				21 08			22 08			23 08		00 08			
Manchester Victoria	a						19 50			20 20				21 20			22 21			23 22		00 20			
Manchester Oxford Road	a	18 50		18 59				19 50			20 50		20 58		21 54			22 55							
Manchester Piccadilly 10	a	18 59		19 05				19 59			20 59		21 05		22 01			23 05					00 27		
Manchester Airport	85 a			19 26									21 28												

For general notes see front of timetable
For details of catering facilities see Directory of Train Operators

- **A** Until 12 July. From Chester (Table 81)
- **B** To Stalybridge (Table 39)
- **C** From Llandudno (Table 81)
- **D** To Millom (Table 100)
- **E** To Huddersfield (Table 39)
- **G** To Rochdale (Table 95)
- **H** To Todmorden (Table 41)
- **J** Until 6 September. From Chester (Table 81)
- **K** Until 6 September. From Llandudno (Table 81)
- **c** Until 6 September only

Table 90

Sundays

until 13 July

Liverpool and St Helens → Newton-le-Willows, Wigan, Preston and Manchester

Network Diagram - see first page of Table 88

	NT	NT	NT	NT	AW	NT	NT		NT	NT	AW	NT	NT	NT	NT		AW	NT	NT	AW	NT	NT	AW	NT
					◇ A						B ⚲						B ⚲			◇ A ⚲			B	
Liverpool Lime Street 10 89, 91 d	08 00	08 30	09 00	09 30		10 00	10 30		11 00	11 30		12 00	12 30	13 00	13 30			14 00	14 30		15 00	15 30		16 00
Wavertree Technology Park d	08 06	08 36	09 06	09 36		10 06	10 36		11 06	11 36		12 06	12 36	13 06	13 36			14 06	14 36		15 06	15 36		16 06
Broad Green d	08 09	08 39	09 09	09 39		10 09	10 39		11 09	11 39		12 09	12 39	13 09	13 39			14 09	14 39		15 09	15 39		16 09
Roby d	08 12	08 42	09 12	09 42		10 12	10 42		11 12	11 42		12 12	12 42	13 12	13 42			14 12	14 42		15 12	15 42		16 12
Huyton d	08 14	08 45	09 14	09 45		10 14	10 45		11 14	11 45		12 14	12 45	13 14	13 45			14 14	14 45		15 14	15 45		16 14
Prescot d	08 19		09 19			10 19			11 19			12 19		13 19				14 19			15 19			16 19
Thatto Heath d	08 22		09 22			10 22			11 22			12 22		13 22				14 22			15 22			16 22
St Helens Central a	08 26		09 26			10 26			11 26			12 26		13 26				14 26			15 26			16 26
d	08 26		09 26			10 26			11 26			12 26		13 26				14 26			15 26			16 26
Garswood d	08 33		09 33			10 33			11 33			12 33		13 33				14 33			15 33			16 33
Whiston d		08 48		09 48			10 48			11 48			12 48		13 48				14 48			15 48		
Rainhill d		08 51		09 51			10 51			11 51			12 51		13 51				14 51			15 51		
Lea Green d		08 55		09 55			10 55			11 55			12 55		13 55				14 55			15 55		
St Helens Junction d		08 58		09 58			10 58			11 58			12 58		13 58				14 58			15 58		
Warrington Bank Quay d					10 30						12 23						13 58			15 32			16 21	
Earlestown 8 d		09 02		10 02	10 38		11 02			12 02	12 31		13 02		14 02		14 08		15 02	15 40		16 02	16 29	
Warrington Bank Quay a				*10 30*			*12 02*						*13 47*						*15 29*				*17 01*	
Newton-le-Willows d		09 05		10 05	10 41		11 05			12 05	12 33		13 05		14 05		14 11		15 05	15 43		16 05	16 32	
Wigan North Western a	08 41		09 44			10 41			11 44			12 42		13 44				14 42			15 44			16 41
65 d	08 42					10 42						12 42						14 42						16 42
Euxton Balshaw Lane d	08 53					10 53						12 53						14 53						16 52
Leyland 82 a	08 58					10 58						12 58						14 58						16 57
Preston 8 65, 82 a	09 05					11 05						13 06						15 07						17 04
Blackpool North 97 a	09 34					11 34						13 34						15 34						17 37
Eccles d		09 18		10 18			11 18			12 18			13 18		14 18				15 18			16 18		
Manchester Oxford Road a		09 27		10 27	11 00		11 27			12 27	12 52		13 30		14 27		14 31		15 28	16 03		16 27	16 51	
Manchester Piccadilly 10 a		09 34		10 34	11 04		11 35			12 35	13 02		13 35		14 32		14 41		15 34	16 12		16 35	17 00	
Manchester Airport 85 a		09 51		10 54			11 51			12 54			13 55		14 51				15 51			16 51		

	NT		AW	NT	NT	AW	NT	NT	NT		AW	NT	NT	AW	NT	NT	AW	NT	NT	NT	AW	NT		
			◇ C ⚲			◇ D					◇ D			◇ C			B				◇ A			
Liverpool Lime Street 10 89, 91 d	16 30			17 00	17 30		18 00	18 30	19 00			19 30	20 00		20 30	21 00		21 30	22 00	22 30		23 00		
Wavertree Technology Park d	16 36			17 06	17 36		18 06	18 36	19 06			19 36	20 06		20 36	21 06		21 36	22 06	22 36		23 06		
Broad Green d	16 39			17 09	17 39		18 09	18 39	19 09			19 39	20 09		20 39	21 09		21 39	22 09	22 39		23 09		
Roby d	16 42			17 12	17 42		18 12	18 42	19 12			19 42	20 12		20 42	21 12		21 42	22 12	22 42		23 12		
Huyton d	16 45			17 14	17 45		18 14	18 45	19 14			19 45	20 14		20 45	21 14		21 45	22 14	22 45		23 14		
Prescot d				17 19			18 19		19 19				20 19			21 19			22 19			23 19		
Thatto Heath d				17 22			18 22		19 22				20 22			21 22			22 22			23 22		
St Helens Central a				17 26			18 26		19 26				20 26			21 26			22 26			23 26		
d				17 26			18 26		19 26				20 26			21 26			22 26			23 26		
Garswood d				17 33			18 33		19 33				20 33			21 33			22 33			23 33		
Whiston d	16 48				17 48			18 48				19 48			20 48			21 48		22 48				
Rainhill d	16 51				17 51			18 51				19 51			20 51			21 51		22 51				
Lea Green d	16 55				17 55			18 55				19 55			20 55			21 55		22 55				
St Helens Junction d	16 58				17 58			18 58				19 58			20 58			21 58		22 58				
Warrington Bank Quay d			17 15			18 07					19 42			20 49			21 48				23 02			
Earlestown 8 d	17 02		17 23		18 02	18 15		19 02			19 52	20 02		20 56	21 02		21 56	22 02		23 02	23 10			
Warrington Bank Quay a	*18 03*				*19 04*							*20 47*			*21 47*					*23 49*				
Newton-le-Willows d	17 05		17 26		18 05	18 18		19 05			19 55	20 05		20 59	21 05		21 59	22 05		23 05	23 13			
Wigan North Western a				17 41			18 41		19 44				20 41			21 44			22 41			23 45		
65 d				17 42			18 42						20 42						22 42					
Euxton Balshaw Lane d				17 53			18 53						20 53						23 03					
Leyland 82 a				17 58			18 58						20 58						23 08					
Preston 8 65, 82 a				18 05			19 05						21 05						23 15					
Blackpool North 97 a				18 34			19 32						21 34						23 43					
Eccles d	17 18				18 18			19 18				20 18			21 18			22 18		23 18				
Manchester Oxford Road a	17 30		17 50		18 27	18 43		19 28			20 15	20 28		21 24	21 28		22 18	22 27		23 27	23 37			
Manchester Piccadilly 10 a	17 35		17 59		18 33	18 50		19 35			20 24	20 33		21 34	21 34		22 27	22 33		23 33	23 44			
Manchester Airport 85 a	17 51				18 52			19 51				20 52			21 52			22 51		23 49				

For general notes see front of timetable
For details of catering facilities see Directory of Train Operators

A From Holyhead (Table 81)
B From Chester (Table 81)
C From Bangor (Gwynedd) (Table 81)
D From Llandudno (Table 81)

Sundays

Liverpool and St Helens → Newton-le-Willows, Wigan, Preston and Manchester

20 July to 7 September

Network Diagram - see first page of Table 88

		NT	NT	NT	NT	AW ◇ A	NT	NT		NT	NT	AW B ⊥	NT	NT	NT	NT		AW B ⊥	NT	NT	AW ◇ A ⊥	NT	NT	AW B	NT
Liverpool Lime Street 10	89, 91 d	08 00	08 30	09 00	09 30		10 00	10 30		11 00	11 30		12 00	12 30	13 00	13 30			14 00	14 30		15 00	15 30		16 00
Wavertree Technology Park	d	08 06	08 36	09 06	09 36		10 06	10 36		11 06	11 36		12 06	12 36	13 06	13 36			14 06	14 36		15 06	15 36		16 06
Broad Green	d	08 09	08 39	09 09	09 39		10 09	10 39		11 09	11 39		12 09	12 39	13 09	13 39			14 09	14 39		15 09	15 39		16 09
Roby	d	08 12	08 42	09 12	09 42		10 12	10 42		11 12	11 42		12 12	12 42	13 12	13 42			14 12	14 42		15 12	15 42		16 12
Huyton	d	08 14	08 45	09 14	09 45		10 14	10 45		11 14	11 45		12 14	12 45	13 14	13 45			14 14	14 45		15 14	15 45		16 14
Prescot	d	08 19		09 19			10 19			11 19			12 19		13 19				14 19			15 19			16 19
Thatto Heath	d	08 22		09 22			10 22			11 22			12 22		13 22				14 22			15 22			16 22
St Helens Central	a	08 26		09 26			10 26			11 26			12 26		13 26				14 26			15 26			16 26
	d	08 26		09 26			10 26			11 26			12 26		13 26				14 26			15 26			16 26
Garswood	d	08 33		09 33			10 33			11 33			12 33		13 33				14 33			15 33			16 33
Whiston	d		08 48		09 48			10 48			11 48			12 48		13 48				14 48			15 48		
Rainhill	d		08 51		09 51			10 51			11 51			12 51		13 51				14 51			15 51		
Lea Green	d		08 55		09 55			10 55			11 55			12 55		13 55				14 55			15 55		
St Helens Junction	d		08 58		09 58			10 58			11 58			12 58		13 58				14 58			15 58		
Warrington Bank Quay	d					10 30						12 23						13 55			15 32			16 21	
Earlestown 8	d		09 02		10 02	10 38		11 02			12 02	12 31		13 02		14 02		14 07		15 02	15 40		16 02	16 29	
Warrington Bank Quay	a				*10 30*			*12 02*						*13 47*						*15 29*			*17 01*	*17 01*	
Newton-le-Willows	d		09 05		10 05	10 41		11 05			12 05	12 33		13 05		14 05		14 11		15 05	15 43		16 05	16 32	
Wigan North Western	a	08 41		09 44			10 41			11 44			12 42		13 44				14 41			15 44			16 42
	65 d	08 42					10 42						12 42						14 42						16 42
Euxton Balshaw Lane	d	08 53					10 53						12 53						14 52						16 52
Leyland	82 a	08 58					10 58						12 58						14 57						16 57
Preston 8	65, 82 a	09 05					11 06						13 06						15 04						17 07
Blackpool North	97 a	09 34					11 34						13 34						15 34						17 37
Eccles	d		09 18		10 18			11 18			12 18			13 18		14 18				15 18			16 18		
Manchester Oxford Road	a		09 27		10 27	11 03		11 27			12 31	12 52		13 30		14 27		14 31		15 28	16 03		16 27	16 51	
Manchester Piccadilly 10	a		09 34		10 34	11 06		11 35			12 35	13 04		13 35		14 32		14 41		15 34	16 12		16 35	17 00	
Manchester Airport	85 ✈ a		09 51		10 53			11 55			12 54			13 53		14 53				15 53			16 53		

		NT		AW ◇ C ⊥	NT	NT	AW ◇ D	NT	NT	NT		AW ◇ D	NT	NT	AW ◇ C	NT	NT	AW B	NT	NT	NT	AW ◇ A	NT		
Liverpool Lime Street 10	89, 91 d	16 30			17 00	17 30		18 00	18 30	19 00			19 30	20 00		20 30	21 00		21 30	22 00	22 30		23 00		
Wavertree Technology Park	d	16 36			17 06	17 36		18 06	18 36	19 06			19 36	20 06		20 36	21 06		21 36	22 06	22 36		23 06		
Broad Green	d	16 39			17 09	17 39		18 09	18 39	19 09			19 39	20 09		20 39	21 09		21 39	22 09	22 39		23 09		
Roby	d	16 42			17 12	17 42		18 12	18 42	19 12			19 42	20 12		20 42	21 12		21 42	22 12	22 42		23 12		
Huyton	d	16 45			17 14	17 45		18 14	18 45	19 14			19 45	20 14		20 45	21 14		21 45	22 14	22 45		23 14		
Prescot	d				17 19			18 19		19 19				20 19			21 19			22 19			23 19		
Thatto Heath	d				17 22			18 22		19 22				20 22			21 22			22 22			23 22		
St Helens Central	a				17 26			18 26		19 26				20 26			21 26			22 26			23 26		
	d				17 26			18 26		19 26				20 26			21 26			22 26			23 26		
Garswood	d				17 33			18 33		19 33				20 33			21 33			22 33			23 33		
Whiston	d	16 48				17 48			18 48				19 48			20 48			21 48		22 48				
Rainhill	d	16 51				17 51			18 51				19 51			20 51			21 51		22 51				
Lea Green	d	16 55				17 55			18 55				19 55			20 55			21 55		22 55				
St Helens Junction	d	16 58				17 58			18 58				19 58			20 58			21 58		22 58				
Warrington Bank Quay	d			17 15			18 07					19 42			20 49			21 48				23 02			
Earlestown 8	d	17 02		17 23		18 02	18 15		19 02			19 52	20 02		20 56	21 02		21 56	22 02		23 02	23 10			
Warrington Bank Quay	a	*18 03*				*19 04*							*20 47*			*21 47*					*23 49*				
Newton-le-Willows	d	17 05		17 26		18 05	18 18		19 05			19 55	20 05		20 59	21 05		21 59	22 05		23 05	23 13			
Wigan North Western	a				17 41			18 41		19 44				20 41			21 44			22 42			23 45		
	65 d				17 42			18 42						20 42						22 42					
Euxton Balshaw Lane	d				17 53			18 53						20 53						23 03					
Leyland	82 a				17 58			18 58						20 58						23 08					
Preston 8	65, 82 a				18 07			19 05						21 05						23 15					
Blackpool North	97 a				18 34			19 32						21 34						23 43					
Eccles	d	17 18				18 18			19 18				20 18			21 18			22 18		23 18				
Manchester Oxford Road	a	17 30		17 50		18 27	18 43		19 28			20 15	20 28		21 24	21 28		22 18	22 27		23 27	23 37			
Manchester Piccadilly 10	a	17 35		17 59		18 33	18 50		19 35			20 27	20 33		21 34	21 34		22 28	22 33		23 33	23 44			
Manchester Airport	85 ✈ a	17 53				18 53			19 53				20 54			21 54			22 53		23 49				

For general notes see front of timetable
For details of catering facilities see Directory of Train Operators

A From Holyhead (Table 81)
B From Chester (Table 81)
C From Bangor (Gwynedd) (Table 81)
D From Llandudno (Table 81)

Table 90

Sundays

Liverpool and St Helens → Newton-le-Willows, Wigan, Preston and Manchester

14 September to 2 November

Network Diagram - see first page of Table 88

		NT	NT	NT	NT	NT	NT	NT	NT	NT	NT	NT	NT	AW	NT	NT	AW	NT	NT	AW	NT
														A			◇ B			A	
Liverpool Lime Street 10	89, 91 d	08 00	08 30	09 00	09 30	10 00	10 30	11 00	11 30	12 00	12 30	13 00	13 30		14 00	14 30		15 00	15 30		16 00
Wavertree Technology Park	d	08 06	08 36	09 06	09 36	10 06	10 36	11 06	11 36	12 06	12 36	13 06	13 36		14 06	14 36		15 06	15 36		16 06
Broad Green	d	08 09	08 39	09 09	09 39	10 09	10 39	11 09	11 39	12 09	12 39	13 09	13 39		14 09	14 39		15 09	15 39		16 09
Roby	d	08 12	08 42	09 12	09 42	10 12	10 42	11 12	11 42	12 12	12 42	13 12	13 42		14 12	14 42		15 12	15 42		16 12
Huyton	d	08 14	08 45	09 14	09 45	10 14	10 45	11 14	11 45	12 14	12 45	13 14	13 45		14 14	14 45		15 14	15 45		16 14
Prescot	d	08 19		09 19		10 19		11 19		12 19		13 19			14 19			15 19			16 19
Thatto Heath	d	08 22		09 22		10 22		11 22		12 22		13 22			14 22			15 22			16 22
St Helens Central	a	08 26		09 26		10 26		11 26		12 26		13 26			14 26			15 26			16 26
	d	08 26		09 26		10 26		11 26		12 26		13 26			14 26			15 26			16 26
Garswood	d	08 33		09 33		10 33		11 33		12 33		13 33			14 33			15 33			16 33
Whiston	d		08 48		09 48		10 48		11 48		12 48		13 48			14 48			15 48		
Rainhill	d		08 51		09 51		10 51		11 51		12 51		13 51			14 51			15 51		
Lea Green	d		08 55		09 55		10 55		11 55		12 55		13 55			14 55			15 55		
St Helens Junction	d		08 58		09 58		10 58		11 58		12 58		13 58			14 58			15 58		
Warrington Bank Quay	d													13 58			15 32			16 21	
Earlestown 8	d		09 02		10 02		11 02		12 02		13 02		14 02	14 08		15 02	15 40		16 02	16 29	
Warrington Bank Quay	a															*15 29*			*17 01*		
Newton-le-Willows	d		09 05		10 05		11 05		12 05		13 05		14 05	14 11		15 05	15 43		16 05	16 32	
Wigan North Western	a	08 42		09 44		10 42		11 44		12 40		13 44			14 42			15 44			16 41
	65 d	08 42				10 42				12 41					14 42						16 42
Euxton Balshaw Lane	d	08 53				10 53				12 53					14 53						16 52
Leyland	82 a	08 58				10 58				12 58					14 58						16 57
Preston 8	65, 82 a	09 06				11 06				13 06					15 07						17 04
Blackpool North	97 a	09 34				11 34				13 34					15 34						17 37
Eccles	d		09 18		10 18		11 18		12 18		13 18		14 18			15 18			16 18		
Manchester Oxford Road	a		09 27		10 27		11 27		12 31		13 30		14 27	14 32		15 28	16 03		16 27	16 51	
Manchester Piccadilly 10	a		09 34		10 35		11 35		12 35		13 35		14 32	14 41		15 34	16 12		16 35	17 00	
Manchester Airport	85 a		09 51		10 55		11 51		12 50		13 53		14 51			15 51			16 51		

		NT	AW	NT	NT	AW	NT	NT	NT	NT	NT	AW	NT	NT	AW	NT	NT	NT	AW	NT
			◇ C			◇ C						A			A				◇ B	
Liverpool Lime Street 10	89, 91 d	16 30		17 00	17 30		18 00	18 30	19 00	19 30	20 00		20 30	21 00		21 30	22 00	22 30		23 00
Wavertree Technology Park	d	16 36		17 06	17 36		18 06	18 36	19 06	19 36	20 06		20 36	21 06		21 36	22 06	22 36		23 06
Broad Green	d	16 39		17 09	17 39		18 09	18 39	19 09	19 39	20 09		20 39	21 09		21 39	22 09	22 39		23 09
Roby	d	16 42		17 12	17 42		18 12	18 42	19 12	19 42	20 12		20 42	21 12		21 42	22 12	22 42		23 12
Huyton	d	16 45		17 14	17 45		18 14	18 45	19 14	19 45	20 14		20 45	21 14		21 45	22 14	22 45		23 14
Prescot	d			17 19			18 19		19 19		20 19			21 19			22 19			23 19
Thatto Heath	d			17 22			18 22		19 22		20 22			21 22			22 22			23 22
St Helens Central	a			17 26			18 26		19 26		20 26			21 26			22 26			23 26
	d			17 26			18 26		19 26		20 26			21 26			22 26			23 26
Garswood	d			17 33			18 33		19 33		20 33			21 33			22 33			23 33
Whiston	d	16 48			17 48			18 48		19 48			20 48			21 48		22 48		
Rainhill	d	16 51			17 51			18 51		19 51			20 51			21 51		22 51		
Lea Green	d	16 55			17 55			18 55		19 55			20 55			21 55		22 55		
St Helens Junction	d	16 58			17 58			18 58		19 58			20 58			21 58		22 58		
Warrington Bank Quay	d		17 12			18 19						20 49			21 46				23 02	
Earlestown 8	d	17 02	17 20		18 02	18 27		19 02		20 02		20 56	21 02		21 54	22 02		23 02	23 10	
Warrington Bank Quay	a	*18 04*			*19 04*					*20 47*			*21 47*					*23 52*		
Newton-le-Willows	d	17 05	17 23		18 05	18 30		19 05		20 05		20 59	21 05		21 57	22 05		23 05	23 13	
Wigan North Western	a			17 41			18 41		19 44		20 41			21 44			22 41			23 45
	65 d			17 42			18 42				20 42						22 42			
Euxton Balshaw Lane	d			17 53			18 53				20 53						23 03			
Leyland	82 a			17 58			18 58				20 58						23 08			
Preston 8	65, 82 a			18 05			19 05				21 05						23 15			
Blackpool North	97 a			18 34			19 32				21 34						23 43			
Eccles	d	17 18			18 18			19 18		20 18			21 18			22 18		23 18		
Manchester Oxford Road	a	17 30	17 43		18 27	18 51		19 28		20 28		21 24	21 28		22 16	22 27		23 27	23 35	
Manchester Piccadilly 10	a	17 35	17 51		18 33	18 56		19 35		20 33		21 33	21 34		22 25	22 33		23 33	23 41	
Manchester Airport	85 a	17 51			18 52			19 51		20 52			21 52			22 51		23 49		

For general notes see front of timetable
For details of catering facilities see Directory of Train Operators

A From Chester (Table 81)
B From Holyhead (Table 81)
C From Bangor (Gwynedd) (Table 81)

Sundays

from 9 November

Liverpool and St Helens → Newton-le-Willows, Wigan, Preston and Manchester

Network Diagram - see first page of Table 88

Station		NT	TP 1◇ A	NT	NT	TP 1◇ B	NT	NT	NT	NT	TP 1◇ B	NT	NT	TP 1◇ C	NT	NT	TP 1◇ B	NT	AW D	NT
Liverpool Lime Street 10 89, 91	d	07 58	08 10	08 30	08 58	09 10	09 30	09 58	10 30	10 58	11 10	11 30	11 58	12 10	12 30	12 58	13 10	13 30		13 58
Wavertree Technology Park	d	08 04		08 36	09 04		09 36	10 04	10 36	11 04		11 36	12 04		12 36	13 04		13 36		14 04
Broad Green	d	08 07		08 39	09 07		09 39	10 07	10 39	11 07		11 39	12 07		12 39	13 07		13 39		14 07
Roby	d	08 10		08 42	09 10		09 42	10 10	10 42	11 10		11 42	12 10		12 42	13 10		13 42		14 10
Huyton	d	08 12		08 45	09 12		09 45	10 12	10 45	11 12		11 45	12 12		12 45	13 12		13 45		14 12
Prescot	d	08 17			09 17			10 17		11 17			12 17			13 17				14 17
Thatto Heath	d	08 20			09 20			10 20		11 20			12 20			13 20				14 20
St Helens Central	a	08 24			09 24			10 24		11 24			12 24			13 24				14 24
	d	08 24			09 24			10 24		11 24			12 24			13 24				14 24
Garswood	d	08 31			09 31			10 31		11 31			12 31			13 31				14 31
Whiston	d			08 48			09 48		10 48			11 48			12 48			13 48		
Rainhill	d			08 51			09 51		10 51			11 51			12 51			13 51		
Lea Green	d			08 55			09 55		10 55			11 55			12 55			13 55		
St Helens Junction	d			08 58			09 58		10 58			11 58			12 58			13 58		
Warrington Bank Quay	d																		13 58	
Earlestown 8	d			09 02			10 02		11 02			12 02			13 02			14 02	14 08	
Warrington Bank Quay	a																			
Newton-le-Willows	d		08 27	09 05		09 27	10 05		11 05		11 27	12 05		12 27	13 05		13 27	14 05	14 11	
Wigan North Western	a	08 40			09 44			10 40		11 44			12 38			13 42				14 40
65	d	08 42						10 42					12 41							14 42
Euxton Balshaw Lane	d	08 53						10 53					12 53							14 53
Leyland 82	a	08 58						10 58					12 58							14 58
Preston 8 65, 82	a	09 06						11 06					13 06							15 07
Blackpool North 97	a	09 34						11 34					13 34							15 34
Eccles	d			09 18			10 18		11 18			12 18			13 18			14 18		
Manchester Victoria	a		08 48			09 48					11 49			12 49			13 49			
Manchester Oxford Road	a			09 27			10 27		11 27			12 31			13 30			14 27	14 32	
Manchester Piccadilly 10	a			09 34			10 35		11 35			12 35			13 35			14 32	14 41	
Manchester Airport 85	a			09 51			10 55		11 51			12 53			13 53			14 51		

Station		TP 1◇ C	NT	NT	TP 1◇ B	AW ◇ E	NT	NT	TP 1◇ G	AW D	NT	AW ◇ H	NT	TP 1◇ B	NT	NT	TP 1◇ B	AW ◇ H	NT
Liverpool Lime Street 10 89, 91	d	14 10	14 30	14 58	15 10		15 30	15 58	16 10		16 30		16 58	17 10	17 30	17 58	18 09		18 30
Wavertree Technology Park	d		14 36	15 04			15 36	16 04			16 36		17 04		17 36	18 04			18 36
Broad Green	d		14 39	15 07			15 39	16 07			16 39		17 07		17 39	18 07			18 39
Roby	d		14 42	15 10			15 42	16 10			16 42		17 10		17 42	18 10			18 42
Huyton	d		14 45	15 12			15 45	16 12			16 45		17 12		17 45	18 12			18 45
Prescot	d			15 17				16 17					17 17			18 17			
Thatto Heath	d			15 20				16 20					17 20			18 20			
St Helens Central	a			15 24				16 24					17 24			18 24			
	d			15 24				16 24					17 24			18 24			
Garswood	d			15 31				16 31					17 31			18 31			
Whiston	d		14 48				15 48				16 48				17 48				18 48
Rainhill	d		14 51				15 51				16 51				17 51				18 51
Lea Green	d		14 55				15 55				16 55				17 55				18 55
St Helens Junction	d		14 58				15 58				16 58				17 58				18 58
Warrington Bank Quay	d					15 32				16 21		17 12						18 19	
Earlestown 8	d		15 02			15 40	16 02			16 29	17 02	17 20			18 02			18 27	19 02
Warrington Bank Quay	a		*15 29*				*17 01*				*18 04*				*19 04*				
Newton-le-Willows	d	14 27	15 05		15 27	15 43	16 05		16 27	16 32	17 05	17 23		17 27	18 05		18 26	18 31	19 05
Wigan North Western	a			15 42				16 39					17 39			18 39			
65	d							16 42					17 42			18 42			
Euxton Balshaw Lane	d							16 52					17 53			18 53			
Leyland 82	a							16 57					17 58			18 58			
Preston 8 65, 82	a							17 04					18 05			19 05			
Blackpool North 97	a							17 37					18 34			19 32			
Eccles	d		15 18				16 18				17 18				18 18				19 18
Manchester Victoria	a	14 49			15 48				16 48					17 49			18 48		
Manchester Oxford Road	a		15 29			16 03	16 27			16 51	17 30	17 43			18 27			18 51	19 28
Manchester Piccadilly 10	a		15 32			16 12	16 35			17 00	17 35	17 51			18 33			18 56	19 35
Manchester Airport 85	a		15 51				16 51				17 51				18 52				19 51

For general notes see front of timetable
For details of catering facilities see Directory of Train Operators

- **A** To Newcastle (Table 39)
- **B** To Scarborough (Table 39)
- **C** To Hull (Table 39)
- **D** From Chester (Table 81)
- **E** From Holyhead (Table 81)
- **G** To York (Table 39)
- **H** From Bangor (Gwynedd) (Table 81)

Table 90

Sundays

from 9 November

Liverpool and St Helens → Newton-le-Willows, Wigan, Preston and Manchester

Network Diagram - see first page of Table 88

		NT	TP ◼1 ◇ A	NT	NT	TP ◼1 ◇ B	AW C	NT	NT	AW C	NT	TP ◼1 ◇ A	NT	NT	AW ◇ D	NT
Liverpool Lime Street ◼10 89, 91	d	18 58	19 10	19 30	19 58	20 10		20 30	20 58		21 30	21 50	21 58	22 30		22 58
Wavertree Technology Park	d	19 04		19 36	20 04			20 36	21 04		21 36		22 04	22 36		23 06
Broad Green	d	19 07		19 39	20 07			20 39	21 07		21 39		22 07	22 39		23 09
Roby	d	19 10		19 42	20 10			20 42	21 10		21 42		22 10	22 42		23 12
Huyton	d	19 12		19 45	20 12			20 45	21 12		21 45		22 12	22 45		23 14
Prescot	d	19 17			20 17				21 17				22 17			23 19
Thatto Heath	d	19 20			20 20				21 20				22 20			23 22
St Helens Central	a	19 24			20 24				21 24				22 24			23 26
	d	19 24			20 24				21 24				22 24			23 26
Garswood	d	19 31			20 31				21 31				22 31			23 33
Whiston	d			19 48				20 48			21 48			22 48		
Rainhill	d			19 51				20 51			21 51			22 51		
Lea Green	d			19 55				20 55			21 55			22 55		
St Helens Junction	d			19 58				20 58			21 58			22 58		
Warrington Bank Quay	d						20 49			21 46					23 02	
Earlestown ◼8	d			20 02			20 56	21 02		21 54	22 02			23 02	23 10	
Warrington Bank Quay	a			*20 47*				*21 47*						*23 52*		
Newton-le-Willows	d		19 27	20 05		20 27	20 59	21 05		21 57	22 05	22 11		23 05	23 13	
Wigan North Western	a	19 42			20 39				21 44				22 41			23 45
65	d				20 42								22 42			
Euxton Balshaw Lane	d				20 53								23 03			
Leyland 82	a				20 58								23 08			
Preston ◼8 65, 82	a				21 05								23 15			
Blackpool North 97	a				21 34								23 43			
Eccles	d			20 18				21 18			22 18			23 18		
Manchester Victoria 🚌	a		19 48			20 48						22 32				
Manchester Oxford Road	a			20 28			21 24	21 28		22 16	22 27			23 27	23 35	
Manchester Piccadilly ◼10 🚌	a			20 33			21 33	21 34		22 25	22 33			23 33	23 41	
Manchester Airport 85 ✈	a			20 52				21 52			22 51			23 49		

For general notes see front of timetable
For details of catering facilities see Directory of Train Operators

A To York (Table 39)
B To Newcastle (Table 39)
C From Chester (Table 81)
D From Holyhead (Table 81)

Manchester, Preston, Wigan and Newton-le-Willows → St Helens and Liverpool

Network Diagram - see first page of Table 88

Miles	Miles	Miles	Miles			NT	NT	NT	NT	AW ◇ A	NT	NT	NT	NT	NT	NT	NT	NT	AW ◇ A	NT B	NT	NT	NT C	NT	AW ◇ A
—	—	—	0	**Manchester Airport** 85 ✈	d	04 34								06 28							07 26				
—	—	—	9¾	**Manchester Piccadilly** 10	d	04 49				06 00				06 52					07 16		07 49				08 16
—	—	—	10¼	**Manchester Oxford Road**	d					06 03				06 56					07 19		07 52				08 19
0	—	—	—	**Manchester Victoria**	d			05 45			06 07					07 10				07 31		07b18	08 01		
4	—	—	14½	Eccles	d						06 14					07 17				07 38			08 08		
5	—	—	15½	Patricroft	d						06 17					07 20				07 41			08 11		
—	—	—	—	Blackpool North 97	d							05c30			06c09			06 57						07c03	
—	0	0	—	**Preston** 8 65, 82	d							06 15			06 51			07 25				07 29		07 43	
—	4	4	—	Leyland 82	d													07 30							
—	6¾	6¾	—	Euxton Balshaw Lane	d													07 35							
—	15	15	—	**Wigan North Western** 65	a													07 44				07 55			
—	—	—	—		d				06 08			06 39	06 45		07 09		07 29	07 45				07 59		08 29	
15½	—	22	26	**Newton-le-Willows**	d			06 04		06 21	06 29		07 01	07 14		07 32			07 37	07 53	08 10		08 23		08 37
—	—	—	—	Warrington Bank Quay	d						05 53					07 16							07 54		
17	—	23½	27½	Earlestown 8	d			06 06		06 24	06 31		07 03			07 34			07 40	07 55			08 26		08 40
—	—	—	—	Warrington Bank Quay	a					06 32									07 48						08 48
19¾	—	26¼	30¼	**St Helens Junction**	d			06 11			06 36		07 08	07 19		07 39				08 00	08 15		08 31		
21	—	27½	31½	Lea Green	d			06 14			06 39		07 11			07 42				08 03	08 18		08 34		
22¾	—	29¼	33¼	Rainhill	d			06 18			06 43		07 15	07 25		07 46				08 07	08 22		08 38		
24¼	—	30¾	34¾	Whiston	d			06 21			06 46		07 18			07 49				08 10	08 25		08 41		
—	18¾	—	—	Bryn	d				06 16			06 47			07 17		07 37					08 07		08 37	
—	20	—	—	Garswood	d				06 20			06 50			07 20		07 40	07 54				08 11		08 41	
—	23¾	—	—	**St Helens Central**	a				06 27			06 57			07 27		07 47	08 01				08 17		08 47	
—	—	—	—		d		05 57		06 27			06 57			07 27		07 47	08 01				08 18		08 48	
—	25¼	—	—	Thatto Heath	d		06 01		06 31			07 01			07 31		07 51					08 21		08 51	
—	26¼	—	—	Eccleston Park	d		06 03		06 33			07 03			07 33		07 53					08 23		08 54	
—	27¼	—	—	Prescot	d		06 05		06 35			07 05			07 35		07 55	08 07				08 26		08 56	
26¼	29½	32¾	36¾	Huyton	d		06 10	06 25	06 40		06 50	07 10	07 22	07 30	07 40	07 53	08 00	08 11		08 15		08 30	08 45	09 00	
26¾	30	33¼	37¼	Roby	d		06 12	06 27	06 42		06 52	07 12	07 24		07 42	07 55	08 02			08 17		08 32	08 47	09 02	
28¼	31½	34¾	38¾	Broad Green	d		06 15	06 30	06 45		06 55	07 15	07 27		07 45	07 58	08 05	08 15		08 20		08 35	08 50	09 05	
29¼	32½	35¾	39¾	Wavertree Technology Park	d		06 18	06 33	06 48		06 58	07 18	07 30	07 36	07 48	08 01	08 08			08 23	08 32	08 38	08 53	09 08	
30	33¼	36½	40½	Edge Hill 89, 91	d			06 36			07 01		07 33			08 04				08 26			08 56		
31¾	35	38¼	42¼	**Liverpool Lime Street** 10 89, 91	a	05 30	06 29	06 44	06 59		07 10	07 29	07 42	07 47	07 59	08 13	08 19	08 27		08 35	08 42	08 50	09 05	09 19	

		NT D	NT	NT	NT E	NT B	NT	AW ◇ A	NT	NT	NT	NT	NT D	NT	AW ◇ G	AW ◇ A	NT	NT	NT	NT	NT D	NT		AW ◇ A	NT
Manchester Airport 85 ✈	d		08 30							09 31								10 31							
Manchester Piccadilly 10	d		08 50					09 16		09 49					10 03	10 16		10 49						11 16	
Manchester Oxford Road	d		08 55					09 19		09 52					10 06	10 19		10 52						11 19	
Manchester Victoria	d	08 40				09 01							10 01								11 01				
Eccles	d					09 08							10 08								11 08				
Patricroft	d					09 11							10 11								11 11				
Blackpool North 97	d			07c41	08 09						08c41	09 25							09c38	10 25					
Preston 8 65, 82	d			08 29	08 50						09 29	09 50							10 28	10 50					
Leyland 82	d				08 55							09 55								10 55					
Euxton Balshaw Lane	d				09 00							10 00								11 00					
Wigan North Western 65	a				09 10							10 10								11 11					
	d			08 59	09 11		09 29				09 59	10 11		10 29					10 59	11 11		11 29			
Newton-le-Willows	d		09 13			09 23		09 38		10 10			10 23		10 30	10 38		11 10			11 23			11 38	
Warrington Bank Quay	d	08 21							09 48								10 48								11 48
Earlestown 8	d	08 56				09 26		09 41	09 56				10 26			10 41	10 56				11 26			11 41	11 56
Warrington Bank Quay	a							09 49							10 39	10 49								11 49	
St Helens Junction	d	09 01	09 18			09 31			10 01	10 15			10 31				11 01	11 15			11 31				12 01
Lea Green	d	09 04				09 34			10 04				10 34				11 04				11 34				12 04
Rainhill	d	09 08				09 38			10 08				10 38				11 08				11 38				12 08
Whiston	d	09 11				09 41			10 11				10 41				11 11				11 41				12 11
Bryn	d			09 07			09 37				10 07			10 37					11 07			11 37			
Garswood	d			09 11			09 41				10 11			10 41					11 11			11 41			
St Helens Central	a			09 17	09 26		09 47				10 17	10 26		10 47					11 18	11 26		11 47			
	d			09 18	09 27		09 48				10 18	10 27		10 48					11 18	11 27		11 48			
Thatto Heath	d			09 21			09 51				10 21			10 51					11 21			11 51			
Eccleston Park	d			09 24			09 54				10 24			10 54					11 24			11 54			
Prescot	d			09 26			09 56				10 26			10 56					11 26			11 56			
Huyton	d	09 15		09 30	09 37	09 45	10 00		10 15		10 30	10 37	10 45	11 00			11 15		11 30	11 37	11 45	12 00			12 15
Roby	d	09 17		09 32		09 47	10 02		10 17		10 32		10 47	11 02			11 17		11 32		11 47	12 02			12 17
Broad Green	d	09 20		09 35		09 50	10 05		10 20		10 35		10 50	11 05			11 20		11 35		11 50	12 05			12 20
Wavertree Technology Park	d	09 23	09 30	09 38		09 53	10 08		10 23	10 27	10 38		10 53	11 08			11 23	11 27	11 38		11 53	12 08			12 23
Edge Hill 89, 91	d	09 26				09 56			10 26				10 56				11 26				11 56				12 26
Liverpool Lime Street 10 89, 91	a	09 39	09 42	09 49	09 53	10 05	10 19		10 35	10 39	10 49	10 52	11 05	11 19			11 35	11 39	11 49	11 52	12 05	12 19			12 35

For general notes see front of timetable
For details of catering facilities see Directory of Train Operators

- **A** To Llandudno (Table 81)
- **B** From Huddersfield (Table 39)
- **C** From Todmorden (Table 41)
- **D** From Stalybridge (Table 39)
- **E** From Barrow-in-Furness (Table 82)
- **G** To Holyhead (Table 81)
- **b** Via Bolton (Table 82)
- **c** Change at Preston and Wigan North Western

Manchester, Preston, Wigan and Newton-le-Willows → St Helens and Liverpool

Network Diagram - see first page of Table 88

		NT	NT	NT	NT A	NT	AW ◇ B	NT	NT	NT	NT	NT A	NT	AW ◇ B	NT	NT	NT	NT	NT A	NT	AW ◇ B	NT	NT	NT	NT
Manchester Airport	85 ✈ d	11 31							12 31							13 31							14 31		
Manchester Piccadilly 10	d	11 49					12 16		12 49					13 16		13 49					14 16		14 49		
Manchester Oxford Road	d	11 52					12 19		12 52					13 19		13 52					14 19		14 52		
Manchester Victoria	d				12 01							13 01							14 01						
Eccles	d				12 08							13 08							14 08						
Patricroft	d				12 11							13 11							14 11						
Blackpool North	97 d		10b41	11 25						11b41	12 25						12b41	13 25						13b41	14 21
Preston 8	65, 82 d		11 29	11 50		11 56				12 32	12 50						13 29	13 50						14 30	14 46
Leyland	82 d			11 55							12 55							13 55							14 51
Euxton Balshaw Lane	d			12 00							13 00							14 00							14 56
Wigan North Western	65 a			12 10							13 10							14 11							15 09
	d		11 59	12 11		12 29				12 59	13 11		13 29				13 59	14 11		14 29				14 59	15 11
Newton-le-Willows	d	12 10			12 23		12 39		13 10			13 23		13 38		14 10			14 23		14 38		15 10		
Warrington Bank Quay	d							12 48							13 48							14 48			
Earlestown 8	d				12 26		12 41	12 56				13 26		13 41	13 56				14 26		14 41	14 56			
Warrington Bank Quay	a						12 49							13 49							14 49				
St Helens Junction	d	12 15			12 31			13 01	13 15			13 31			14 01	14 15			14 31			15 01	15 15		
Lea Green	d				12 34			13 04				13 34			14 04				14 34			15 04			
Rainhill	d				12 38			13 08				13 38			14 08				14 38			15 08			
Whiston	d				12 41			13 11				13 41			14 11				14 41			15 11			
Bryn	d		12 07			12 37				13 07			13 37				14 07			14 37				15 07	
Garswood	d		12 11			12 41				13 11			13 41				14 11			14 41				15 11	
St Helens Central	a		12 18	12 26		12 48				13 17	13 27		13 47				14 17	14 26		14 47				15 17	15 26
	d		12 18	12 27		12 48				13 18	13 27		13 48				14 18	14 27		14 48				15 18	15 27
Thatto Heath	d		12 21			12 51				13 21			13 51				14 21			14 51				15 21	
Eccleston Park	d		12 24			12 54				13 24			13 54				14 24			14 54				15 24	
Prescot	d		12 26			12 56				13 26			13 56				14 26			14 56				15 26	
Huyton	d		12 30	12 37	12 45	13 00		13 15		13 30	13 37	13 45	14 00		14 15		14 30	14 37	14 45	15 00		15 15		15 30	15 37
Roby	d		12 32		12 47	13 02		13 17		13 32		13 47	14 02		14 17		14 32		14 47	15 02		15 17		15 32	
Broad Green	d		12 35		12 50	13 05		13 20		13 35		13 50	14 05		14 20		14 35		14 50	15 05		15 20		15 35	
Wavertree Technology Park	d	12 27	12 38		12 53	13 08		13 23	13 27	13 38		13 53	14 08		14 23	14 27	14 38		14 53	15 08		15 23	15 27	15 38	
Edge Hill	89, 91 d				12 56			13 26				13 56			14 26				14 56			15 26			
Liverpool Lime Street 10	89, 91 a	12 39	12 49	12 52	13 05	13 19		13 35	13 39	13 49	13 52	14 05	14 19		14 35	14 39	14 49	14 52	15 05	15 19		15 35	15 39	15 49	15 52

		NT A	NT	AW ◇ B	NT C	NT	NT	NT	NT A	NT	AW ◇ B	NT D	NT	NT	NT	NT E	NT	AW ◇ B	NT	AW ◇ G	NT	NT	NT	NT	NT
Manchester Airport	85 ✈ d					15 31							16 31								17 29				
Manchester Piccadilly 10	d			15 16		15 49					16 16		16 48					17 20		17 41	17 45				
Manchester Oxford Road	d			15 19		15 52					16 19		16 52					17 23		17 47	17 49				
Manchester Victoria	d	15 01							16 01							17 01								18 01	
Eccles	d	15 08							16 08							17 08								18 08	
Patricroft	d	15 11							16 11							17 11					17 56			18 11	
Blackpool North	97 d						14b41	15 25						15b41	16 25							16b38	17 10		
Preston 8	65, 82 d		14 49				15 29	15 50						16 29	16 50							17 29	17 50		
Leyland	82 d							15 55							16 55								17 55		
Euxton Balshaw Lane	d							16 00							17 00								18 00		
Wigan North Western	65 a							16 10							17 09								18 11		
	d		15 29				15 59	16 11		16 29				16 59	17 11		17 29		17 42			17 59	18 11		18 29
Newton-le-Willows	d	15 23		15 38		16 10			16 23		16 37		17 10			17 23		17 42	17 53	18 05	18 10			18 23	
Warrington Bank Quay	d				15 48							16 48							17 20						
Earlestown 8	d	15 26		15 41	15 56				16 26		16 40	16 56				17 26		17 45	17 56	18 08				18 26	
Warrington Bank Quay	a			15 50							16 48							17 55		18 17					
St Helens Junction	d	15 31			16 01	16 15			16 31			17 01	17 15			17 31			18 01		18 15			18 31	
Lea Green	d	15 34			16 04				16 34			17 04				17 34			18 04		18 18			18 34	
Rainhill	d	15 38			16 08				16 38			17 08				17 38			18 08		18 22			18 38	
Whiston	d	15 41			16 11				16 41			17 11				17 41			18 11					18 41	
Bryn	d		15 37				16 07			16 37				17 07			17 37					18 07			18 37
Garswood	d		15 41				16 11			16 41				17 11			17 41					18 11			18 41
St Helens Central	a		15 47				16 17	16 26		16 47				17 18	17 27		17 47					18 17	18 27		18 47
	d		15 48				16 18	16 27		16 48				17 18	17 27		17 48					18 18	18 27		18 48
Thatto Heath	d		15 51				16 21			16 51				17 21			17 51					18 21			18 51
Eccleston Park	d		15 54				16 24			16 54				17 24			17 54					18 24			18 54
Prescot	d		15 56				16 26			16 56				17 26			17 56					18 26			18 56
Huyton	d	15 45	16 00		16 15		16 30	16 37	16 44	17 00		17 14		17 30	17 37	17 45	18 00		18 14			18 30	18 37	18 45	19 00
Roby	d	15 47	16 02		16 17		16 32		16 46	17 02		17 16		17 32		17 47	18 02		18 16			18 32		18 47	19 02
Broad Green	d	15 50	16 05		16 20		16 35		16 50	17 05		17 20		17 35		17 50	18 05		18 20			18 35		18 50	19 05
Wavertree Technology Park	d	15 53	16 08		16 23	16 27	16 38		16 53	17 08		17 23	17 27	17 38		17 53	18 08		18 23		18 30	18 38		18 53	19 08
Edge Hill	89, 91 d	15 56			16 26				16 56	17 11				17 41		17 56			18 26					18 56	
Liverpool Lime Street 10	89, 91 a	16 05	16 19		16 35	16 39	16 49	16 53	17 04	17 19		17 33	17 38	17 49	17 53	18 05	18 19		18 34		18 40	18 49	18 55	19 05	19 19

For general notes see front of timetable
For details of catering facilities see Directory of Train Operators

- **A** From Stalybridge (Table 39)
- **B** To Llandudno (Table 81)
- **C** From Helsby (Table 81)
- **D** From Ellesmere Port (Table 109)
- **E** From Rochdale (Table 95)
- **G** To Holyhead (Table 81)
- **b** Change at Preston and Wigan North Western

Manchester, Preston, Wigan and Newton-le-Willows → St Helens and Liverpool

Network Diagram - see first page of Table 88

Mondays to Fridays

	AW	NT	NT	NT	NT	NT	AW	NT	NT	NT	NT	AW	NT	NT	AW	NT	NT	NT	NT	AW	NT	AW		
	◇																							
	A						B					B			B					B		B		
Manchester Airport 85 ✈ d			18 31						19 30								21 30							
Manchester Piccadilly 10 d	18 16		18 49				19 16		19 48			20 16			21 16		21 47			22 16		23 20		
Manchester Oxford Road d	18 19		18 52				19 19		19 52			20 19			21 19		21 50			22 19		23 23		
Manchester Victoria d		18 31			19 01						20 01			21 01				22 01			23 11			
Eccles d		18 38			19 08						20 08			21 08				22 08			23 18			
Patricroft d		18 41			19 11						20 11			21 11				22 11			23 21			
Blackpool North 97 d				18 25		*18b38*				19 25			*19 42*			*20b52*			22 03					
Preston 8 65, 82 d				18 50		*19 10*				19 50			20 27			*21 29*			22 27					
Leyland 82 d				18 55						19 55			20 32						22 32					
Euxton Balshaw Lane d				19 00						20 00			20 37						22 37					
Wigan North Western 65 a				19 10						20 11			20 46						22 47					
d				19 11		19 29				20 11			20 47			21 47			22 47					
Newton-le-Willows d	18 37	18 53	19 10		19 23		19 37		20 10		20 23	20 37		21 23	21 37		22 10	22 23		22 37	23 33	23 41		
Warrington Bank Quay d		*18 20*						19 48				*20 20*						*21 23*			*22 21*			
Earlestown 8 d	18 40	18 56			19 26		19 40	19 56			20 26	20 40		21 26	21 40			22 26		22 40	23 35	23 44		
Warrington Bank Quay a	18 48						19 48					20 48			21 49					22 48		23 52		
St Helens Junction d		19 01	19 15		19 31			20 01	20 15		20 31			21 31			22 15	22 31			23 40			
Lea Green d		19 04			19 34			20 04			20 34			21 34				22 34			23 43			
Rainhill d		19 08			19 38			20 08			20 38			21 38				22 38			23 47			
Whiston d		19 11			19 41			20 11			20 41			21 41				22 41			23 50			
Bryn d						19 37							20 55			21 55			22 55					
Garswood d						19 41							20 58			21 58			22 58					
St Helens Central a				19 26		19 48				20 27			21 05			22 05			23 05					
d				19 27		19 48				20 27			21 05			22 05			23 05					
Thatto Heath d						19 51							21 09			22 09			23 09					
Eccleston Park d						19 54							21 11			22 11			23 11					
Prescot d						19 56							21 13			22 13			23 13					
Huyton d		19 15		19 37	19 45	20 00		20 15		20 37	20 45		21 18	21 45		22 18		22 45	23 18		23 54			
Roby d		19 17			19 47	20 02		20 17			20 47		21 20	21 47		22 20		22 47	23 20		23 56			
Broad Green d		19 20			19 50	20 05		20 20			20 50		21 23	21 50		22 23		22 50	23 23		23 59			
Wavertree Technology Park d		19 23	19 27		19 53	20 08		20 23	20 27		20 53		21 26	21 53		22 26	22 27	22 53	23 26		00 02			
Edge Hill 89, 91 d		19 26			19 56			20 26			20 56		21 29	21 56		22 29		22 56	23 29		00 05			
Liverpool Lime Street 10 89, 91 a		19 35	19 38	19 52	20 05	20 19		20 35	20 38	20 52	21 05		21 38	22 05		22 38	22 41	23 05	23 38		00 14			

Saturdays

	NT	NT	NT	NT	AW	NT	NT	NT	NT	NT	NT	NT	NT	AW	NT	NT	NT	NT	NT		AW	NT	NT	NT
					◇									◇							◇			
					A									A				C			A			
Manchester Airport 85 ✈ d	04 34								06 28							07 26							08 30	
Manchester Piccadilly 10 d	04 49				06 00				06 52					07 16		07 49					08 16		08 50	
Manchester Oxford Road d					06 03				06 56					07 19		07 52					08 19		08 55	
Manchester Victoria d			05 45			06 07					07 10				07 31		07c18	08 01				08 40		
Eccles d						06 14					07 17				07 38			08 08						
Patricroft d						06 17					07 20				07 41			08 11						
Blackpool North 97 d													06 57											
Preston 8 65, 82 d													07 25											
Leyland 82 d													07 30											
Euxton Balshaw Lane d													07 35											
Wigan North Western 65 a													07 44				07 54							
d				06 08			06 39	06 45		07 09		07 29	07 45				07 59		08 29					08 59
Newton-le-Willows d			06 04		06 21	06 29		07 01	07 14		07 32			07 37	07 53	08 10		08 23			08 37		09 13	
Warrington Bank Quay d						*06 01*					*07 16*							*07 54*				*08 21*		
Earlestown 8 d			06 06		06 24	06 31		07 03			07 34			07 40	07 55			08 26			08 40	08 56		
Warrington Bank Quay a					06 32									07 48							08 48			
St Helens Junction d			06 11			06 36		07 08	07 19		07 39				08 00	08 15		08 31				09 01	09 18	
Lea Green d			06 14			06 39		07 11			07 42				08 03	08 18		08 34				09 04		
Rainhill d			06 18			06 43		07 15	07 25		07 46				08 07	08 22		08 38				09 08		
Whiston d			06 21			06 46		07 18			07 49				08 10	08 25		08 41				09 11		
Bryn d				06 16			06 47			07 17		07 37					08 07		08 37					09 07
Garswood d				06 20			06 50			07 20		07 40	07 54				08 11		08 41					09 11
St Helens Central a				06 26			06 57			07 27		07 47	08 01				08 18		08 47					09 17
d		05 57		06 27			06 57			07 27		07 47	08 01				08 18		08 48					09 18
Thatto Heath d		06 01		06 31			07 01			07 31		07 51					08 21		08 51					09 21
Eccleston Park d		06 03		06 33			07 03			07 33		07 53					08 24		08 54					09 24
Prescot d		06 05		06 35			07 05			07 35		07 55	08 07				08 26		08 56					09 26
Huyton d		06 10	06 25	06 40		06 50	07 10	07 22	07 30	07 40	07 53	08 00	08 11		08 15		08 30	08 45	09 00			09 15		09 30
Roby d		06 12	06 27	06 42		06 52	07 12	07 24		07 42	07 55	08 02			08 17		08 32	08 47	09 02			09 17		09 32
Broad Green d		06 15	06 30	06 45		06 55	07 15	07 27		07 45	07 58	08 05	08 15		08 20		08 35	08 50	09 05			09 20		09 35
Wavertree Technology Park d		06 18	06 33	06 48		06 58	07 18	07 30	07 36	07 48	08 01	08 08			08 23	08 32	08 38	08 53	09 08			09 23	09 30	09 38
Edge Hill 89, 91 d			06 36			07 01		07 33			08 04				08 26			08 56				09 26		
Liverpool Lime Street 10 89, 91 a	05 30	06 29	06 44	06 59		07 10	07 29	07 43	07 47	07 59	08 13	08 19	08 27		08 35	08 42	08 50	09 05	09 19			09 39	09 42	09 49

For general notes see front of timetable
For details of catering facilities see Directory of Train Operators

A To Llandudno (Table 81)
B To Chester (Table 81)
C From Todmorden (Table 41)
b Change at Preston and Wigan North Western
c Via Bolton (Table 82)

Table 90

Saturdays

Manchester, Preston, Wigan and Newton-le-Willows → St Helens and Liverpool

Network Diagram - see first page of Table 88

	NT	NT	NT	AW	NT	NT	NT	NT	NT	NT	AW	AW	NT	NT	NT	NT	NT		NT	AW	NT	NT	NT	NT
		A		◇ B					C		D	◇ B					C			◇ B				
Manchester Airport 85 d						09 31								10 31								11 31		
Manchester Piccadilly 10 d				09 16		09 49					10 03	10 16		10 49						11 16		11 49		
Manchester Oxford Road d				09 19		09 52					10 06	10 18		10 52						11 19		11 52		
Manchester Victoria d		09 01							10 01								11 01							
Eccles d		09 08							10 08								11 08							
Patricroft d		09 11							10 11								11 11							
Blackpool North 97 d								09 25								10 25								11 25
Preston 8 65, 82 d	08 50							09 50								10 50								11 50
Leyland 82 d	08 55							09 55								10 55								11 55
Euxton Balshaw Lane d	09 00							10 00								11 00								12 00
Wigan North Western 65 a	09 10							10 09								11 11								12 09
d	09 11		09 29				09 59	10 11		10 29					10 59	11 11			11 29				11 59	12 11
Newton-le-Willows d		09 23		09 38		10 10			10 23		10 30	10 38		11 10			11 23			11 38		12 10		
Warrington Bank Quay d					09 48								10 48								11 48			
Earlestown 8 d		09 26		09 41	09 56				10 26			10 41	10 56				11 26			11 41	11 56			
Warrington Bank Quay a				09 49							10 39	10 49								11 49				
St Helens Junction d		09 31			10 01	10 15			10 31				11 01	11 15			11 31				12 01	12 15		
Lea Green d		09 34			10 04				10 34				11 04				11 34				12 04			
Rainhill d		09 38			10 08				10 38				11 08				11 38				12 08			
Whiston d		09 41			10 11				10 41				11 11				11 41				12 11			
Bryn d			09 37				10 07			10 37					11 07				11 37				12 07	
Garswood d			09 41				10 11			10 41					11 11				11 41				12 11	
St Helens Central a	09 26		09 47				10 17	10 26		10 48					11 17	11 26			11 47				12 17	12 26
d	09 27		09 48				10 18	10 27		10 48					11 18	11 27			11 48				12 18	12 27
Thatto Heath d			09 51				10 21			10 51					11 21				11 51				12 21	
Eccleston Park d			09 54				10 24			10 54					11 24				11 54				12 24	
Prescot d			09 56				10 26			10 56					11 26				11 56				12 26	
Huyton d	09 37	09 45	10 00		10 15		10 30	10 37	10 45	11 00			11 15		11 30	11 37	11 45		12 00		12 15		12 30	12 37
Roby d		09 47	10 02		10 17		10 32		10 47	11 02			11 17		11 32		11 47		12 02		12 17		12 32	
Broad Green d		09 50	10 05		10 20		10 35		10 50	11 05			11 20		11 35		11 50		12 05		12 20		12 35	
Wavertree Technology Park d		09 53	10 08		10 23	10 27	10 38		10 53	11 08			11 23	11 27	11 38		11 53		12 08		12 23	12 27	12 38	
Edge Hill 89, 91 d		09 56			10 26				10 56				11 26				11 56				12 26			
Liverpool Lime Street 10 89, 91 a	09 52	10 05	10 19		10 35	10 39	10 49	10 52	11 05	11 19			11 35	11 39	11 49	11 52	12 05		12 19		12 35	12 39	12 49	12 52

	NT	NT	AW	NT	NT	NT	NT	NT	NT	AW	NT	NT	NT	NT	NT		NT	AW	NT	NT	NT	NT	NT	NT
	C		◇ B					C		◇ B					C			◇ B					C	
Manchester Airport 85 d					12 31							13 31								14 31				
Manchester Piccadilly 10 d			12 16		12 49					13 16		13 49						14 16		14 49				
Manchester Oxford Road d			12 19		12 52					13 19		13 52						14 19		14 52				
Manchester Victoria d	12 01							13 01							14 01								15 01	
Eccles d	12 08							13 08							14 08								15 08	
Patricroft d	12 11							13 11							14 11								15 11	
Blackpool North 97 d							12 25							13 25								14 25		
Preston 8 65, 82 d							12 50							13 50								14 50		
Leyland 82 d							12 55							13 55								14 55		
Euxton Balshaw Lane d							13 00							14 00								15 00		
Wigan North Western 65 a							13 09							14 11								15 10		
d		12 29				12 59	13 11		13 29				13 59	14 11			14 29				14 59	15 11		15 29
Newton-le-Willows d	12 23		12 39		13 10			13 23		13 38		14 10			14 23			14 38		15 10			15 23	
Warrington Bank Quay d				12 48							13 48								14 48					
Earlestown 8 d	12 26		12 41	12 56				13 26		13 41	13 56				14 26			14 41	14 56				15 26	
Warrington Bank Quay a			12 49							13 49								14 49						
St Helens Junction d	12 31			13 01	13 15			13 31			14 01	14 15			14 31				15 01	15 15			15 31	
Lea Green d	12 34			13 04				13 34			14 04				14 34				15 04				15 34	
Rainhill d	12 38			13 08				13 38			14 08				14 38				15 08				15 38	
Whiston d	12 41			13 11				13 41			14 11				14 41				15 11				15 41	
Bryn d		12 37				13 07			13 37				14 07				14 37				15 07			15 37
Garswood d		12 41				13 11			13 41				14 11				14 41				15 11			15 41
St Helens Central a		12 47				13 17	13 26		13 47				14 17	14 26			14 47				15 17	15 26		15 47
d		12 48				13 18	13 27		13 48				14 18	14 27			14 48				15 18	15 27		15 48
Thatto Heath d		12 51				13 21			13 51				14 21				14 51				15 21			15 51
Eccleston Park d		12 54				13 24			13 54				14 24				14 54				15 24			15 54
Prescot d		12 56				13 26			13 56				14 26				14 56				15 26			15 56
Huyton d	12 45	13 00		13 15		13 30	13 37	13 45	14 00		14 15		14 30	14 37	14 45		15 00		15 15		15 30	15 37	15 45	16 00
Roby d	12 47	13 02		13 17		13 32		13 47	14 02		14 17		14 32		14 47		15 02		15 17		15 32		15 47	16 02
Broad Green d	12 50	13 05		13 20		13 35		13 50	14 05		14 20		14 35		14 50		15 05		15 20		15 35		15 50	16 05
Wavertree Technology Park d	12 53	13 08		13 23	13 27	13 38		13 53	14 08		14 23	14 27	14 38		14 53		15 08		15 23	15 27	15 38		15 53	16 08
Edge Hill 89, 91 d	12 56			13 26				13 56			14 26				14 56				15 26				15 56	
Liverpool Lime Street 10 89, 91 a	13 05	13 19		13 35	13 39	13 49	13 52	14 05	14 19		14 35	14 39	14 49	14 52	15 05		15 19		15 35	15 39	15 49	15 52	16 05	16 19

For general notes see front of timetable
For details of catering facilities see Directory of Train Operators

A From Huddersfield (Table 39)
B To Llandudno (Table 81)
C From Stalybridge (Table 39)
D To Chester (Table 81)

Table 90

Saturdays

Manchester, Preston, Wigan and Newton-le-Willows → St Helens and Liverpool

Network Diagram - see first page of Table 88

Station		AW	NT	NT	NT	NT	NT	NT	AW	NT	NT	NT	NT	NT		NT	AW	NT	AW	NT	NT	NT	NT	NT	AW
		◇ A ✕	B				C		◇ A ✕	D				E			◇ A ✕		◇ G				C		◇ A ✕
Manchester Airport 85 ✈	d			15 31							16 31									17 29					
Manchester Piccadilly 10	d	15 16		15 49					16 16		16 48						17 20		17 41	17 45					18 16
Manchester Oxford Road	d	15 19		15 52					16 19		16 52						17 26		17 47	17 49					18 19
Manchester Victoria	d						16 01							17 01									18 01		
Eccles	d						16 08							17 08						17 56			18 08		
Patricroft	d						16 11							17 11									18 11		
Blackpool North 97	d					15 25							16 25												
Preston 8 65, 82	d					15 50							16 50									17 50			
Leyland 82	d					15 55							16 55									17 55			
Euxton Balshaw Lane	d					16 00							17 00									18 00			
Wigan North Western 65	a					16 10							17 09									18 11			
	d				15 59	16 11		16 29				16 59	17 11			17 29		17 42			17 59	18 11		18 29	
Newton-le-Willows	d	15 38		16 10			16 23		16 38		17 10			17 23			17 45	17 53	18 04	18 10			18 23		18 37
Warrington Bank Quay	d		15 48							16 48								*17 20*							
Earlestown 8	d	15 41	15 56				16 26		16 41	16 56				17 26			17 47	17 56	18 07				18 26		18 40
Warrington Bank Quay	a	15 48							16 49								17 55		18 17						18 48
St Helens Junction	d		16 01	16 15			16 31			17 01	17 15			17 31				18 01		18 15			18 31		
Lea Green	d		16 04				16 34			17 04				17 34				18 04		18 18			18 34		
Rainhill	d		16 08				16 38			17 08				17 38				18 08		18 22			18 38		
Whiston	d		16 11				16 41			17 11				17 41				18 11					18 41		
Bryn	d				16 07			16 37				17 07				17 37					18 07			18 37	
Garswood	d				16 11			16 41				17 11				17 41					18 11			18 41	
St Helens Central	a				16 17	16 26		16 47				17 17	17 26			17 47					18 17	18 27		18 47	
	d				16 18	16 27		16 48				17 18	17 27			17 48					18 18	18 27		18 48	
Thatto Heath	d				16 21			16 51				17 21				17 51					18 21			18 51	
Eccleston Park	d				16 24			16 54				17 24				17 54					18 24			18 54	
Prescot	d				16 26			16 56				17 26				17 56					18 26			18 56	
Huyton	d		16 15		16 30	16 37	16 44	17 00		17 14		17 30	17 37	17 45		18 00		18 14			18 30	18 37	18 45	19 00	
Roby	d		16 17		16 32		16 46	17 02		17 16		17 32		17 47		18 02		18 16			18 32		18 47	19 02	
Broad Green	d		16 20		16 35		16 50	17 05		17 20		17 35		17 50		18 05		18 20			18 35		18 50	19 05	
Wavertree Technology Park	d		16 23	16 27	16 38		16 53	17 08		17 23	17 27	17 38		17 53		18 08		18 23		18 30	18 38		18 53	19 08	
Edge Hill 89, 91	d		16 26				16 56	17 11				17 41		17 56				18 26					18 56		
Liverpool Lime Street 10 89, 91	a		16 35	16 39	16 49	16 53	17 04	17 19		17 33	17 38	17 49	17 53	18 05		18 19		18 34		18 40	18 49	18 55	19 05	19 19	

Station		NT	NT	NT	NT	NT	AW	NT	NT	NT	NT	VT	AW	NT	NT	AW	NT	NT	NT	NT	AW	NT	AW		
					C		H					1 ◇ J ✕	H			K					K		K		
Manchester Airport 85 ✈	d		18 31						19 30									21 30							
Manchester Piccadilly 10	d		18 49				19 16		19 48				20 16			21 16		21 48			22 16		23 20		
Manchester Oxford Road	d		18 52				19 19		19 52				20 20			21 19		21 52			22 19		23 23		
Manchester Victoria	d	18 31			19 01						20 01				21 01				22 01			23 11			
Eccles	d	18 38			19 08						20 08				21 08				22 08			23 18			
Patricroft	d	18 41			19 11						20 11				21 11				22 11			23 21			
Blackpool North 97	d			18 25						19 25										22 03					
Preston 8 65, 82	d			18 50						19 50				20 27						22 28					
Leyland 82	d			18 55						19 55				20 32						22 32					
Euxton Balshaw Lane	d			19 00						20 00				20 37						22 36					
Wigan North Western 65	a			19 10						20 10				20 47						22 47					
	d			19 11		19 29				20 11				20 48			21 47			22 47					
Newton-le-Willows	d	18 53	19 10		19 23		19 37		20 10		20 23		20 37		21 23	21 37		22 10	22 23		22 37	23 33	23 41		
Warrington Bank Quay	d	*18 21*						19 48				20 44			*20 20*				*21b23*			*22b20*			
Earlestown 8	d	18 56			19 26		19 40	19 56			20 26		20 40		21 26	21 40			22 26		22 40	23 35	23 44		
Warrington Bank Quay	a						19 48						20 48			21 48					22 48		23 52		
St Helens Junction	d	19 01	19 15		19 31			20 01	20 15		20 31				21 31			22 15	22 31			23 40			
Lea Green	d	19 04			19 34			20 04			20 34				21 34				22 34			23 43			
Rainhill	d	19 08			19 38			20 08			20 38				21 38				22 38			23 47			
Whiston	d	19 11			19 41			20 11			20 41				21 41				22 41			23 50			
Bryn	d					19 37								20 55			21 55			22 55					
Garswood	d					19 41								20 59			21 58			22 58					
St Helens Central	a			19 26		19 48				20 26				21 05			22 05			23 05					
	d			19 27		19 48				20 27				21 06			22 05			23 05					
Thatto Heath	d					19 51								21 09			22 09			23 09					
Eccleston Park	d					19 54								21 11			22 11			23 11					
Prescot	d					19 56								21 13			22 13			23 13					
Huyton	d	19 15		19 37	19 45	20 00		20 15		20 37	20 45			21 18	21 45		22 18		22 45	23 18		23 54			
Roby	d	19 17			19 47	20 02		20 17			20 47			21 20	21 47		22 20		22 47	23 20		23 56			
Broad Green	d	19 20			19 50	20 05		20 20			20 50			21 23	21 50		22 23		22 50	23 23		23 59			
Wavertree Technology Park	d	19 23	19 27		19 53	20 08		20 23	20 27		20 53			21 26	21 53		22 26	22 30	22 53	23 26		00 02			
Edge Hill 89, 91	d	19 26			19 56			20 26			20 56			21 29	21 56		22 29		22 56	23 29		00 05			
Liverpool Lime Street 10 89, 91	a	19 35	19 38	19 52	20 05	20 19		20 35	20 38	20 52	21 05	21 13		21 39	22 06		22 38	22 41	23 05	23 38		00 14			

For general notes see front of timetable
For details of catering facilities see Directory of Train Operators

- **A** To Llandudno (Table 81)
- **B** Until 6 September from Helsby (Table 81)
- **C** From Stalybridge (Table 39)
- **D** From Ellesmere Port (Table 109)
- **E** From Rochdale (Table 95)
- **G** To Holyhead (Table 81)
- **H** To Chester (Table 81)
- **J** From 13 September. From London Euston (Table 65)
- **K** Until 6 September. To Chester (Table 81)
- **b** Until 6 September only

Table 90

Sundays until 13 July

Manchester, Preston, Wigan and Newton-le-Willows → St Helens and Liverpool

Network Diagram - see first page of Table 88

	NT	AW A (bus)	NT	NT	NT	NT	AW ◇ B	NT	NT	NT	AW ◇ C
Manchester Airport 85 ✈ d					08 51			10 01		11 00	
Manchester Piccadilly [10] d		07 52			09 16		09 58	10 16		11 16	
Manchester Oxford Road d		08 02	08b17		09 20		10 01	10 20		11 20	11 33
Eccles d			08 27		09 27			10 27		11 27	
Blackpool North 97 d				08 17					10 17		
Preston [8] 65, 82 d				08 42					10 42		
Leyland 82 d				08 47					10 47		
Euxton Balshaw Lane d				08 52					10 52		
Wigan North Western 65 a				09 01					10 59		
d	08 01			09 01		10 01			11 01		
Newton-le-Willows d		08 27	08 40		09 40		10 19	10 40		11 40	11 51
Warrington Bank Quay d										*10 30*	
Earlestown [8] d		08 35	08 42		09 42		10 22	10 42		11 42	11 54
Warrington Bank Quay a		08 50					10 30				12 02
St Helens Junction d			08 47		09 47			10 47		11 47	
Lea Green d			08 50		09 50			10 50		11 50	
Rainhill d			08 54		09 54			10 54		11 54	
Whiston d			08 57		09 57			10 57		11 57	
Garswood d	08 11			09 11		10 11			11 11		
St Helens Central a	08 18			09 18		10 18			11 18		
d	08 18			09 18		10 18			11 18		
Thatto Heath d	08 22			09 22		10 22			11 22		
Prescot d	08 26			09 26		10 26			11 26		
Huyton d	08 30		09 00	09 30	10 00	10 30		11 00	11 30	12 00	
Roby d	08 32		09 02	09 32	10 02	10 32		11 02	11 32	12 02	
Broad Green d	08 36		09 06	09 36	10 06	10 36		11 06	11 36	12 06	
Wavertree Technology Park d	08 39		09 09	09 39	10 09	10 39		11 09	11 39	12 09	
Liverpool Lime Street [10] 89, 91 a	08 49		09 26	09 49	10 23	10 49		11 21	11 49	12 21	

	NT	NT	NT	AW A	NT	NT	NT	NT	AW A	NT	NT
Manchester Airport 85 ✈ d		12 00			13 00		14 00			15 00	
Manchester Piccadilly [10] d		12 17		13 15	13 17		14 17		14 57	15 16	
Manchester Oxford Road d		12 20		13 18	13 20		14 20		15 00	15 20	
Eccles d		12 27			13 27		14 27			15 27	
Blackpool North 97 d			12 17					14 17			
Preston [8] 65, 82 d			12 42					14 42			
Leyland 82 d			12 47					14 47			
Euxton Balshaw Lane d			12 52					14 52			
Wigan North Western 65 a			13 02					15 00			
d	12 01		13 02			14 01		15 01			16 01
Newton-le-Willows d		12 40		13 36	13 40		14 40		15 18	15 40	
Warrington Bank Quay d		*12 23*					*13 58*				
Earlestown [8] d		12 42		13 39	13 42		14 42		15 21	15 42	
Warrington Bank Quay a				13 47					15 29		
St Helens Junction d		12 47			13 47		14 47			15 47	
Lea Green d		12 50			13 50		14 50			15 50	
Rainhill d		12 54			13 54		14 54			15 54	
Whiston d		12 57			13 57		14 57			15 57	
Garswood d	12 11		13 11			14 11		15 11			16 11
St Helens Central a	12 18		13 18			14 18		15 17			16 18
d	12 18		13 18			14 18		15 18			16 18
Thatto Heath d	12 22		13 22			14 22		15 22			16 22
Prescot d	12 26		13 26			14 26		15 26			16 26
Huyton d	12 30	13 00	13 30		14 00	14 30	15 00	15 30		16 00	16 30
Roby d	12 32	13 02	13 32		14 02	14 32	15 02	15 32		16 02	16 32
Broad Green d	12 36	13 06	13 37		14 06	14 36	15 06	15 36		16 06	16 36
Wavertree Technology Park d	12 39	13 09	13 39		14 09	14 39	15 09	15 39		16 09	16 39
Liverpool Lime Street [10] 89, 91 a	12 49	13 21	13 50		14 21	14 49	15 21	15 50		16 21	16 49

	NT	NT	AW A	NT	NT	AW ◇ C	NT	NT	AW A	NT	NT
Manchester Airport 85 ✈ d	16 01			17 01			18 01			19 01	
Manchester Piccadilly [10] d	16 16		16 29	17 16		17 32	18 16		18 32	19 16	
Manchester Oxford Road d	16 20		16 32	17 20		17 35	18 20		18 35	19 20	
Eccles d	16 27			17 27			18 27			19 27	
Blackpool North 97 d		16 17			17 17			18 17			
Preston [8] 65, 82 d		16 42			17 42			18 42			
Leyland 82 d		16 47			17 47			18 47			
Euxton Balshaw Lane d		16 52			17 52			18 52			
Wigan North Western 65 a		17 01			18 01			19 00			
d		17 01			18 01			19 01			20 01
Newton-le-Willows d	16 40		16 50	17 40		17 53	18 40		18 53	19 40	
Warrington Bank Quay d	*16 21*			*17 15*			*18 07*				
Earlestown [8] d	16 42		16 53	17 42		17 55	18 42		18 56	19 42	
Warrington Bank Quay a			17 01			18 03			19 04		
St Helens Junction d	16 47			17 47			18 47			19 47	
Lea Green d	16 50			17 50			18 50			19 50	
Rainhill d	16 54			17 54			18 54			19 54	
Whiston d	16 57			17 57			18 57			19 57	
Garswood d		17 11			18 11			19 11			20 11
St Helens Central a		17 18			18 18			19 18			20 18
d		17 18			18 18			19 18			20 18
Thatto Heath d		17 22			18 22			19 22			20 22
Prescot d		17 26			18 26			19 26			20 26
Huyton d	17 00	17 30		18 00	18 30		19 00	19 30		20 00	20 30
Roby d	17 02	17 32		18 02	18 32		19 02	19 32		20 02	20 32
Broad Green d	17 06	17 36		18 06	18 36		19 06	19 36		20 06	20 36
Wavertree Technology Park d	17 09	17 39		18 09	18 39		19 09	19 39		20 09	20 39
Liverpool Lime Street [10] 89, 91 a	17 21	17 49		18 21	18 49		19 21	19 49		20 21	20 49

	AW A	NT	NT	AW A	NT	NT	NT	NT	AW A
Manchester Airport 85 ✈ d		20 01			21 01		22 01		
Manchester Piccadilly [10] d	20 14	20 16		21 14	21 16		22 16		23 17
Manchester Oxford Road d	20 18	20 20		21 18	21 20		22 19		23 20
Eccles d		20 27			21 27		22 26		
Blackpool North 97 d			20 17					22 17	
Preston [8] 65, 82 d			20 42					22 42	
Leyland 82 d			20 47					22 47	
Euxton Balshaw Lane d			20 52					22 52	
Wigan North Western 65 a			21 01					23 10	
d			21 01			22 01		23 10	
Newton-le-Willows d	20 36	20 40		21 36	21 40		22 39		23 38
Warrington Bank Quay d		*19 42*			*20 49*		*21 48*		
Earlestown [8] d	20 39	20 42		21 39	21 42		22 42		23 41
Warrington Bank Quay a	20 47			21 47					23 49
St Helens Junction d		20 47			21 47		22 46		
Lea Green d		20 50			21 50		22 49		
Rainhill d		20 54			21 54		22 53		
Whiston d		20 57			21 57		22 56		
Garswood d			21 11			22 11		23 20	
St Helens Central a			21 18			22 18		23 27	
d			21 18			22 18		23 27	
Thatto Heath d			21 22			22 22		23 31	
Prescot d			21 26			22 26		23 35	
Huyton d		21 00	21 30		22 00	22 30	23 00	23 40	
Roby d		21 02	21 32		22 02	22 32	23 02	23 42	
Broad Green d		21 06	21 36		22 06	22 36	23 06	23 45	
Wavertree Technology Park d		21 09	21 39		22 09	22 39	23 09	23 48	
Liverpool Lime Street [10] 89, 91 a		21 21	21 49		22 21	22 49	23 20	23 59	

For general notes see front of timetable
For details of catering facilities see Directory of Train Operators

A To Chester (Table 81)
B To Holyhead (Table 81)
C To Bangor (Gwynedd) (Table 81)
b Manchester Victoria

Table 90

Sundays

Manchester, Preston, Wigan and Newton-le-Willows → St Helens and Liverpool

20 July to 7 September

Network Diagram - see first page of Table 88

	NT	AW	NT	NT	NT	NT	AW	NT	NT	NT	AW	NT	NT	NT	AW	NT	NT	NT	NT	AW	NT	NT
		A					◇ B				◇ C				A					A		
Manchester Airport 85 d								09 58		10 58			11 58			12 58		13 58			14 58	
Manchester Piccadilly 10 d		07 52					09 58	10 16		11 16			12 17		13 15	13 17		14 17		14 57	15 16	
Manchester Oxford Road d		08 02		08b17	09 20		10 01	10 20		11 20	11 33		12 20		13 18	13 20		14 20		15 00	15 20	
Eccles d			08 27		09 27			10 27		11 27			12 27			13 27		14 27			15 27	
Blackpool North 97 d				08 17					10 17					12 17					14 17			
Preston 8 65, 82 d				08 42					10 42					12 42					14 42			
Leyland 82 d				08 47					10 47					12 47					14 47			
Euxton Balshaw Lane d				08 52					10 52					12 53					14 52			
Wigan North Western 65 a				09 01					10 59					13 00					15 01			
d	08 01			09 01		10 01			11 01			12 01		13 01			14 01		15 01			16 01
Newton-le-Willows d		08 27	08 40		09 40		10 19	10 40		11 40	11 51		12 40		13 36	13 40		14 40		15 18	15 40	
Warrington Bank Quay d										*10 30*			*12 23*					*13 55*				
Earlestown 8 d		08 35	08 42		09 42		10 22	10 42		11 42	11 54		12 42		13 39	13 42		14 42		15 21	15 42	
Warrington Bank Quay a		08 50					10 30				12 02				13 47					15 29		
St Helens Junction d			08 47		09 47			10 47		11 47			12 47			13 47		14 47			15 47	
Lea Green d			08 50		09 50			10 50		11 50			12 50			13 50		14 50			15 50	
Rainhill d			08 54		09 54			10 54		11 54			12 54			13 54		14 54			15 54	
Whiston d			08 57		09 57			10 57		11 57			12 57			13 57		14 57			15 57	
Garswood d	08 11			09 11		10 11			11 11			12 11		13 11			14 11		15 11			16 11
St Helens Central a	08 18			09 18		10 18			11 18			12 18		13 18			14 18		15 17			16 18
d	08 18			09 18		10 18			11 18			12 18		13 18			14 18		15 18			16 18
Thatto Heath d	08 22			09 22		10 22			11 22			12 22		13 22			14 22		15 22			16 22
Prescot d	08 26			09 26		10 26			11 26			12 26		13 26			14 26		15 26			16 26
Huyton d	08 30		09 00	09 30	10 00	10 30		11 00	11 30	12 00		12 30	13 00	13 30		14 00	14 30	15 00	15 30		16 00	16 30
Roby d	08 32		09 02	09 32	10 02	10 32		11 02	11 32	12 02		12 32	13 02	13 32		14 02	14 32	15 02	15 32		16 02	16 32
Broad Green d	08 36		09 06	09 36	10 06	10 36		11 06	11 36	12 06		12 36	13 06	13 36		14 06	14 36	15 06	15 36		16 06	16 36
Wavertree Technology Park d	08 39		09 09	09 39	10 09	10 39		11 09	11 39	12 09		12 39	13 09	13 39		14 09	14 39	15 09	15 39		16 09	16 39
Liverpool Lime Street 10 89, 91 a	08 49		09 26	09 49	10 23	10 49		11 21	11 49	12 21		12 49	13 21	13 50		14 21	14 49	15 21	15 50		16 21	16 49

	NT	NT	AW	NT	NT	AW	NT	NT	AW	NT	NT	AW	NT	NT	AW	NT	NT	NT	NT	AW
			A			◇ C			A			A			A					A
Manchester Airport 85 d	15 58			16 58			17 58			18 58			19 58			20 58		21 58		
Manchester Piccadilly 10 d	16 16		16 29	17 16		17 32	18 16		18 32	19 16		20 14	20 16		21 14	21 16		22 16		23 17
Manchester Oxford Road d	16 20		16 32	17 20		17 35	18 20		18 35	19 20		20 18	20 20		21 18	21 20		22 19		23 20
Eccles d	16 27			17 27			18 27			19 27			20 27			21 27		22 26		
Blackpool North 97 d		16 17			17 17			18 17						20 17					22 17	
Preston 8 65, 82 d		16 42			17 42			18 42						20 42					22 42	
Leyland 82 d		16 47			17 47			18 47						20 47					22 47	
Euxton Balshaw Lane d		16 52			17 52			18 52						20 52					22 52	
Wigan North Western 65 a		17 00			18 01			19 00						21 01					23 10	
d		17 01			18 01			19 01			20 01			21 01			22 01		23 10	
Newton-le-Willows d	16 40		16 50	17 40		17 53	18 40		18 53	19 40		20 36	20 40		21 36	21 40		22 39		23 38
Warrington Bank Quay d	*16 21*			*17 15*			*18 07*						*19 42*			*20 49*		*21 48*		
Earlestown 8 d	16 42		16 53	17 42		17 55	18 42		18 56	19 42		20 39	20 42		21 39	21 42		22 42		23 41
Warrington Bank Quay a			17 01			18 03			19 04			20 47			21 47					23 49
St Helens Junction d	16 47			17 47			18 47			19 47			20 47			21 47		22 46		
Lea Green d	16 50			17 50			18 50			19 50			20 50			21 50		22 49		
Rainhill d	16 54			17 54			18 54			19 54			20 54			21 54		22 53		
Whiston d	16 57			17 57			18 57			19 57			20 57			21 57		22 56		
Garswood d		17 11			18 11			19 11			20 11			21 11			22 11		23 20	
St Helens Central a		17 17			18 18			19 18			20 18			21 18			22 18		23 27	
d		17 18			18 18			19 18			20 18			21 18			22 18		23 27	
Thatto Heath d		17 22			18 22			19 22			20 22			21 22			22 22		23 31	
Prescot d		17 26			18 26			19 26			20 26			21 26			22 26		23 35	
Huyton d	17 00	17 30		18 00	18 30		19 00	19 30		20 00	20 30		21 00	21 30		22 00	22 30	23 00	23 40	
Roby d	17 02	17 32		18 02	18 32		19 02	19 32		20 02	20 32		21 02	21 32		22 02	22 32	23 02	23 42	
Broad Green d	17 06	17 36		18 06	18 36		19 06	19 36		20 06	20 36		21 06	21 36		22 06	22 36	23 06	23 45	
Wavertree Technology Park d	17 09	17 39		18 09	18 39		19 09	19 39		20 09	20 39		21 09	21 39		22 09	22 39	23 09	23 48	
Liverpool Lime Street 10 89, 91 a	17 21	17 49		18 21	18 49		19 21	19 49		20 21	20 49		21 21	21 49		22 21	22 49	23 20	23 59	

For general notes see front of timetable
For details of catering facilities see Directory of Train Operators

A To Chester (Table 81)
B To Holyhead (Table 81)
C To Bangor (Gwynedd) (Table 81)
b Manchester Victoria

Table 90

Sundays

Manchester, Preston, Wigan and Newton-le-Willows → St Helens and Liverpool

14 September to 2 November

Network Diagram - see first page of Table 88

	NT	NT	NT	NT	NT	NT	NT	NT	NT	NT	NT	NT	NT	NT	NT	AW A	NT	NT	NT	NT
Manchester Airport 85 ✈ d				08 51		10 01		11 00		12 00		13 00		14 00			15 00		16 01	
Manchester Piccadilly 10 d				09 16		10 16		11 16		12 17		13 17		14 17		14 57	15 16		16 16	
Manchester Oxford Road d		08b17		09 20		10 20		11 20		12 20		13 20		14 20		15 00	15 20		16 20	
Eccles d		08 27		09 27		10 27		11 27		12 27		13 27		14 27			15 27		16 27	
Blackpool North 97 d			08 14				10 17				12 17				14 17					16 17
Preston 8 65, 82 d			08 39				10 42				12 42				14 42					16 42
Leyland 82 d			08 44				10 47				12 47				14 47					16 47
Euxton Balshaw Lane d			08 49				10 52				12 52				14 52					16 52
Wigan North Western 65 a			09 01				11 01				13 00				15 00					17 01
d	08 01		09 01		10 01		11 01		12 01		13 01		14 01		15 01			16 01		17 01
Newton-le-Willows d		08 40		09 40		10 40		11 40		12 40		13 40		14 40		15 18	15 40		16 40	
Warrington Bank Quay d														*13 58*					*16 21*	
Earlestown 8 d		08 42		09 42		10 42		11 42		12 42		13 42		14 42		15 21	15 42		16 42	
Warrington Bank Quay a																15 29				
St Helens Junction d		08 47		09 47		10 47		11 47		12 47		13 47		14 47			15 47		16 47	
Lea Green d		08 50		09 50		10 50		11 50		12 50		13 50		14 50			15 50		16 50	
Rainhill d		08 54		09 54		10 54		11 54		12 54		13 54		14 54			15 54		16 54	
Whiston d		08 57		09 57		10 57		11 57		12 57		13 57		14 57			15 57		16 57	
Garswood d	08 11		09 11		10 11		11 11		12 11		13 11		14 11		15 11			16 11		17 11
St Helens Central a	08 18		09 18		10 18		11 18		12 18		13 17		14 18		15 17			16 18		17 18
d	08 18		09 18		10 18		11 18		12 18		13 18		14 18		15 18			16 18		17 18
Thatto Heath d	08 22		09 22		10 22		11 22		12 22		13 22		14 22		15 22			16 22		17 22
Prescot d	08 26		09 26		10 26		11 26		12 26		13 26		14 26		15 26			16 26		17 26
Huyton d	08 30	09 00	09 30	10 00	10 30	11 00	11 30	12 00	12 30	13 00	13 30	14 00	14 30	15 00	15 30		16 00	16 30	17 00	17 30
Roby d	08 32	09 02	09 32	10 02	10 32	11 02	11 32	12 02	12 32	13 02	13 32	14 02	14 32	15 02	15 32		16 02	16 32	17 02	17 32
Broad Green d	08 36	09 06	09 36	10 06	10 36	11 06	11 36	12 06	12 36	13 06	13 36	14 06	14 36	15 06	15 36		16 06	16 36	17 06	17 36
Wavertree Technology Park d	08 39	09 09	09 39	10 09	10 39	11 09	11 39	12 09	12 39	13 09	13 39	14 09	14 39	15 09	15 39		16 09	16 39	17 09	17 39
Liverpool Lime Street 10 89, 91 a	08 49	09 26	09 49	10 23	10 49	11 21	11 49	12 21	12 49	13 21	13 50	14 21	14 49	15 21	15 50		16 21	16 49	17 21	17 49

	AW A	NT	NT	AW ◇ B	NT	NT	AW A	NT	NT	AW A	NT	VT 1 ◇ C	NT	AW A	NT	NT	NT	NT	AW A
Manchester Airport 85 ✈ d		17 01			18 01			19 01			20 01				21 01		22 01		
Manchester Piccadilly 10 d	16 29	17 16		17 32	18 16		18 32	19 16		20 14	20 16			21 14	21 16		22 16		23 21
Manchester Oxford Road d	16 32	17 20		17 35	18 20		18 35	19 20		20 18	20 20			21 18	21 20		22 19		23 24
Eccles d		17 27			18 27			19 27			20 27				21 27		22 26		
Blackpool North 97 d			17 17			18 17							20 17					22 17	
Preston 8 65, 82 d			17 42			18 42							20 42					22 42	
Leyland 82 d			17 47			18 47							20 47					22 47	
Euxton Balshaw Lane d			17 52			18 52							20 52					22 52	
Wigan North Western 65 a			18 01			19 00							21 01					23 10	
d			18 01			19 01			20 01				21 01			22 01		23 10	
Newton-le-Willows d	16 50	17 40		17 53	18 40		18 53	19 40		20 36	20 40			21 36	21 40		22 39		23 42
Warrington Bank Quay d		*17 12*			*18 19*							21 13			*20 49*		*21 46*		
Earlestown 8 d	16 53	17 42		17 56	18 42		18 56	19 42		20 39	20 42			21 39	21 42		22 42		23 44
Warrington Bank Quay a	17 01			18 04			19 04			20 47				21 47					23 52
St Helens Junction d		17 47			18 47			19 47			20 47				21 47		22 46		
Lea Green d		17 50			18 50			19 50			20 50				21 50		22 49		
Rainhill d		17 54			18 54			19 54			20 54				21 54		22 53		
Whiston d		17 57			18 57			19 57			20 57				21 57		22 56		
Garswood d			18 11			19 11			20 11				21 11			22 11		23 20	
St Helens Central a			18 18			19 18			20 18				21 18			22 18		23 27	
d			18 18			19 18			20 18				21 18			22 18		23 27	
Thatto Heath d			18 22			19 22			20 22				21 22			22 22		23 31	
Prescot d			18 26			19 26			20 26				21 26			22 26		23 35	
Huyton d		18 00	18 30		19 00	19 30		20 00	20 30		21 00		21 30		22 00	22 30	23 00	23 40	
Roby d		18 02	18 32		19 02	19 32		20 02	20 32		21 02		21 32		22 02	22 32	23 02	23 42	
Broad Green d		18 06	18 36		19 06	19 36		20 06	20 36		21 06		21 36		22 06	22 36	23 06	23 45	
Wavertree Technology Park d		18 09	18 39		19 09	19 39		20 09	20 39		21 09		21 39		22 09	22 39	23 09	23 48	
Liverpool Lime Street 10 89, 91 a		18 21	18 49		19 21	19 49		20 21	20 49		21 21	21 41	21 49		22 21	22 49	23 20	23 59	

For general notes see front of timetable
For details of catering facilities see Directory of Train Operators

A To Chester (Table 81)
B To Holyhead (Table 81)
C From London Euston (Table 65)

b Manchester Victoria

Sundays
from 9 November

Manchester, Preston, Wigan and Newton-le-Willows → St Helens and Liverpool

Network Diagram - see first page of Table 88

	NT	NT	NT		NT	NT	TP 1 ◇ A		NT	NT	TP 1 ◇ B		NT	NT	TP 1 ◇ C		NT	NT	TP 1 ◇ D		NT	NT	TP 1 ◇ A	NT
Manchester Airport 85 ✈ d					08 51				10 01				11 00				12 00				13 00			14 00
Manchester Piccadilly 10 d					09 16				10 16				11 16				12 17				13 17			14 17
Manchester Oxford Road d					09 20				10 20				11 20				12 20				13 20			14 20
Manchester Victoria d		08 17					10 13				11 09				12 09				13 09				14 09	
Eccles d		08 27			09 27				10 27				11 27				12 27				13 27			14 27
Blackpool North 97 d			08 14							10 17								12 17						
Preston 8 65, 82 d			08 39							10 42								12 42						
Leyland 82 d			08 44							10 47								12 47						
Euxton Balshaw Lane d			08 49							10 52								12 52						
Wigan North Western 65 a			09 01							11 01								13 00						
d	08 01		09 01			10 01				11 01				12 01				13 01				14 01		
Newton-le-Willows d		08 40			09 40		10 35		10 40		11 28		11 40		12 28		12 40		13 28		13 40		14 28	14 40
Warrington Bank Quay d																								*13 58*
Earlestown 8 d		08 42			09 42				10 42				11 42				12 42				13 42			14 42
Warrington Bank Quay a																								
St Helens Junction d		08 47			09 47				10 47				11 47				12 47				13 47			14 47
Lea Green d		08 50			09 50				10 50				11 50				12 50				13 50			14 50
Rainhill d		08 54			09 54				10 54				11 54				12 54				13 54			14 54
Whiston d		08 57			09 57				10 57				11 57				12 57				13 57			14 57
Garswood d	08 11		09 11			10 11				11 11				12 11				13 11				14 11		
St Helens Central a	08 18		09 18			10 18				11 18				12 18				13 17				14 18		
d	08 18		09 18			10 18				11 18				12 18				13 18				14 18		
Thatto Heath d	08 22		09 22			10 22				11 22				12 22				13 22				14 22		
Prescot d	08 26		09 26			10 26				11 26				12 26				13 26				14 26		
Huyton d	08 30	09 00	09 30		10 00	10 30			11 00	11 30			12 00	12 30			13 00	13 30			14 00	14 30		15 00
Roby d	08 32	09 02	09 32		10 02	10 32			11 02	11 32			12 02	12 32			13 02	13 32			14 02	14 32		15 02
Broad Green d	08 36	09 06	09 36		10 06	10 36			11 06	11 36			12 06	12 36			13 06	13 36			14 06	14 36		15 06
Wavertree Technology Park d	08 39	09 09	09 39		10 09	10 39			11 09	11 39			12 09	12 39			13 09	13 39			14 09	14 39		15 09
Liverpool Lime Street 10 89, 91 a	08 49	09 22	09 49		10 23	10 49	10 54		11 21	11 49	11 56		12 21	12 49	12 51		13 21	13 50	13 55		14 21	14 49	14 51	15 21

	NT		AW E	TP 1 ◇ D	NT		NT	TP 1 ◇ G	NT		NT	AW E	TP 1 ◇ D		NT	NT	AW ◇ H		TP 1 ◇ G	NT	NT		AW E	TP 1 ◇ D
Manchester Airport 85 ✈ d					15 00				16 01						17 01					18 01				
Manchester Piccadilly 10 d			14 57		15 16				16 17			16 29			17 16		17 32			18 16			18 32	
Manchester Oxford Road d			15 00		15 20				16 20			16 32			17 20		17 35			18 20			18 35	
Manchester Victoria d				15 09				16 15					17 09						18 09					19 09
Eccles d					15 27				16 27						17 27					18 27				
Blackpool North 97 d	14 17										16 17					17 17					18 17			
Preston 8 65, 82 d	14 42										16 42					17 42					18 42			
Leyland 82 d	14 47										16 47					17 47					18 47			
Euxton Balshaw Lane d	14 52										16 52					17 52					18 52			
Wigan North Western 65 a	15 00										17 01					18 01					19 00			
d	15 01						16 01				17 01					18 01					19 01			
Newton-le-Willows d			15 18	15 28	15 40			16 33	16 40			16 50	17 28		17 40		17 53		18 28	18 40			18 53	19 28
Warrington Bank Quay d									*16 21*						*17 12*					*18 19*				
Earlestown 8 d			15 21		15 42				16 42			16 53			17 42		17 56			18 42			18 56	
Warrington Bank Quay a			15 29									17 01					18 04						19 04	
St Helens Junction d					15 47				16 47						17 47					18 47				
Lea Green d					15 50				16 50						17 50					18 50				
Rainhill d					15 54				16 54						17 54					18 54				
Whiston d					15 57				16 57						17 57					18 57				
Garswood d	15 11						16 11				17 11					18 11					19 11			
St Helens Central a	15 17						16 18				17 18					18 18					19 18			
d	15 18						16 18				17 18					18 18					19 18			
Thatto Heath d	15 22						16 22				17 22					18 22					19 22			
Prescot d	15 26						16 26				17 26					18 26					19 26			
Huyton d	15 30				16 00		16 30		17 00		17 30				18 00	18 30				19 00	19 30			
Roby d	15 32				16 02		16 32		17 02		17 32				18 02	18 32				19 02	19 32			
Broad Green d	15 36				16 06		16 36		17 06		17 36				18 06	18 36				19 06	19 36			
Wavertree Technology Park d	15 39				16 09		16 39		17 09		17 39				18 09	18 39				19 09	19 39			
Liverpool Lime Street 10 89, 91 a	15 50			15 51	16 21		16 49	16 55	17 21		17 49		17 51		18 21	18 49			18 51	19 21	19 49			19 51

For general notes see front of timetable
For details of catering facilities see Directory of Train Operators

A From York (Table 39)
B From Hull (Table 39)
C From Newcastle (Table 39)
D From Scarborough (Table 39)
E To Chester (Table 81)
G From Middlesbrough (Table 39)
H To Holyhead (Table 81)

Sundays

from 9 November

Manchester, Preston, Wigan and Newton-le-Willows → St Helens and Liverpool

Network Diagram - see first page of Table 88

			NT	NT	TP 1 ◇ A	AW B	NT	VT 1 ◇ C ⊡	NT	TP 1 ◇ D	AW B	NT	NT	TP 1 ◇ E	NT	NT	AW B
Manchester Airport	85 ✈	d	19 01				20 01					21 01			22 01		
Manchester Piccadilly 10	⇌	d	19 16			20 14	20 16				21 14	21 16			22 16		23 21
Manchester Oxford Road		d	19 20			20 18	20 20				21 18	21 20			22 19		23 24
Manchester Victoria	⇌	d			20 09					21 09				22 13			
Eccles		d	19 27				20 27					21 27			22 26		
Blackpool North	97	d							20 17							22 17	
Preston 8	65, 82	d							20 42							22 42	
Leyland	82	d							20 47							22 47	
Euxton Balshaw Lane		d							20 52							22 52	
Wigan North Western	65	a							21 01							23 10	
		d		20 01					21 01				22 01			23 10	
Newton-le-Willows		d	19 40		20 28	20 36	20 40			21 27	21 36	21 40		22 31	22 39		23 42
Warrington Bank Quay		d						21 13				*20 49*			*21 46*		
Earlestown 8		d	19 42			20 39	20 42				21 39	21 42			22 42		23 44
Warrington Bank Quay		a				20 47					21 47						23 52
St Helens Junction		d	19 47				20 47					21 47			22 46		
Lea Green		d	19 50				20 50					21 50			22 49		
Rainhill		d	19 54				20 54					21 54			22 53		
Whiston		d	19 57				20 57					21 57			22 56		
Garswood		d		20 11					21 11				22 11			23 20	
St Helens Central		a		20 18					21 18				22 18			23 27	
		d		20 18					21 18				22 18			23 27	
Thatto Heath		d		20 22					21 22				22 22			23 31	
Prescot		d		20 26					21 26				22 26			23 35	
Huyton		d	20 00	20 30			21 00		21 30			22 00	22 30		23 00	23 40	
Roby		d	20 02	20 32			21 02		21 32			22 02	22 32		23 02	23 42	
Broad Green		d	20 06	20 36			21 06		21 36			22 06	22 36		23 06	23 45	
Wavertree Technology Park		d	20 09	20 39			21 09		21 39			22 09	22 39		23 09	23 48	
Liverpool Lime Street 10	89, 91	a	20 21	20 49	20 51		21 21	21 41	21 49	21 51		22 21	22 49	22 54	23 20	23 59	

For general notes see front of timetable
For details of catering facilities see Directory of Train Operators

A From Middlesbrough (Table 39)
B To Chester (Table 81)
C From London Euston (Table 65)
D From Scarborough (Table 39)
E From Newcastle (Table 39)

Liverpool → Runcorn and Crewe

Network Diagram - see first page of Table 88

Miles	Station		VT	NT	NT	VT	LM	NT	VT	LM	NT	LM	NT	VT	LM	NT	LM	NT	VT	LM
			1◇			1◇	1◇		1◇	1◇		1◇		1◇	1◇		1◇		1◇	1◇
				A	B			A			B		B			B		B		
			☒			☒	🛒		☒	🛒		🛒		☒	🛒		🛒		☒	🛒
0	**Liverpool Lime Street** 10	90 d	05 44	05 50	06 21	06 27	06 35	06 50	07 07	07 18	07 21	07 40	07 50	08 15	08 19	08 29	08 40	08 55	09 15	09 19
1¾	Edge Hill	90 d		05 54				06 54					07 54					08 59		
3¾	Mossley Hill	d		05 59	06 29			06 59			07 29		07 59			08 37		09 04		
4½	West Allerton	d		06 01				07 01					08 01					09 06		
5½	**Liverpool South Parkway** 7 ✈	a		06 04	06 32		06 45	07 04			07 32	07 49	08 04			08 40	08 49	09 09		
—		d					06 45					07 50					08 50			
13	**Runcorn**	a	05 59			06 42	06 53			07 34		07 57		08 30	08 34		08 57		09 30	09 34
—		d	06 00			06 43	06 53		07u22	07 35		07 58		08 31	08 35		08 58		09 31	09 35
21	Acton Bridge	d					07 00										09 05			
23¾	Hartford	d					07 05					08 08					09 10			
28	Winsford	d					07 09					08 12								
35½	**Crewe** 10	65 a	06 20			07 02	07 20			07 54		08 23			08 59		09 23		09 50	09 58
—	Birmingham New Street 12	65 a	07b55				08 29			08 58		09 30			09 58		10 30			10 58
—	London Euston ⊖	65 a	08 19			08 58	09b14		09 17			10c27		10 35			11c27		11 48	

Station		NT	LM	NT	VT	LM	NT	LM	NT	VT	LM	NT	LM	NT	VT	NT	LM	NT	VT
			1◇		1◇	1		1◇		1◇	1◇		1◇		1◇		1◇		1◇
		B		B			B		B			B		B		B		B	
			🛒		☒	🛒		🛒		☕	🛒		🛒		☕		🛒		☕
Liverpool Lime Street 10	90 d	09 29	09 40	09 55	10 15	10 19	10 29	10 40	10 55	11 15	11 19	11 29	11 40	11 55	12 15	12 29	12 40	12 55	13 15
Edge Hill	90 d			09 59					10 59					11 59				12 59	
Mossley Hill	d	09 37		10 04			10 37		11 04			11 37		12 04		12 37		13 04	
West Allerton	d			10 06					11 06					12 06				13 06	
Liverpool South Parkway 7 ✈	a	09 40	09 49	10 09			10 40	10 49	11 09			11 40	11 49	12 09		12 40	12 49	13 09	
	d		09 50					10 50					11 50				12 50		
Runcorn	a		09 57		10 30	10 34		10 57		11 30	11 35		11 57		12 30		12 57		13 30
	d		09 58		10 31	10 35		10 58		11 31	11 35		11 58		12 31		12 58		13 31
Acton Bridge	d																13 05		
Hartford	d		10 08			10 46		11 09					12 08				13 10		
Winsford	d		10 12					11 13					12 12						
Crewe 10	65 a		10 23		10 50	10 58		11 23		11 50	11 58		12 24		12 50		13 23		13 50
Birmingham New Street 12	65 a		11 30			11b58		12 30			12 58		13 30		13b58		14 30		
London Euston ⊖	65 a		12c26		12 48	13 18		13c27		13 47			14c40		14 49		15c26		15 48

Station		LM	NT	LM	NT	VT	NT	LM	NT	VT	LM	NT	LM	NT	VT	NT	LM	NT	VT	LM
		1◇		1◇		1◇		1◇		1◇	1◇		1◇		1◇		1◇		1◇	1◇
			B		B		B		B			B		B		B		B		
		🛒		🛒		☕		🛒		☕	🛒		🛒		☕		🛒		☕	🛒
Liverpool Lime Street 10	90 d	13 19	13 29	13 40	13 55	14 15	14 29	14 40	14 55	15 15	15 19	15 29	15 40	15 55	16 15	16 28	16 40	16 55	17 15	17 18
Edge Hill	90 d				13 59				14 59					15 59				16 59		
Mossley Hill	d		13 37		14 04		14 37		15 04			15 37		16 04		16 36		17 04		
West Allerton	d				14 06				15 06					16 06				17 06		
Liverpool South Parkway 7 ✈	a		13 40	13 49	14 09		14 40	14 49	15 09			15 40	15 49	16 09		16 39	16 49	17 09		17 27
	d			13 50				14 50					15 50				16 50			17 28
Runcorn	a	13 35		13 57		14 30		14 57		15 30	15 35		15 57		16 30		16 57		17 30	17 36
	d	13 35		13 58		14 31		14 58		15 31	15 35		15 58		16 31		16 58		17 31	17 36
Acton Bridge	d																17 04			
Hartford	d			14 08				15 08					16 08				17 09			
Winsford	d			14 12				15 12					16 12							
Crewe 10	65 a	13 58		14 23		14 50		15 23		15 50	15 58		16 23		16 50		17 23		17 51	17 58
Birmingham New Street 12	65 a	14 58		15 30		15b58		16 30			16 58		17 30		17b58		18 30			18 58
London Euston ⊖	65 a			16c27		16 48		17c40		17 47	18c21		18c27		18 50		19c25		19 50	

Station		NT	LM	NT	VT	NT	LM	NT	LM	LM	VT	NT	LM	NT	LM	NT	LM	LM	NT
			1◇		1◇		1◇		1◇	1◇	1◇		1◇		1◇		1	1	
		B		B		B		A				A		B		B			C
			🛒		☕		🛒		🛒	🛒	☕		🛒		🛒				
Liverpool Lime Street 10	90 d	17 25	17 37	17 55	18 15	18 25	18 40	18 55	19 19	19 40	19 49	19 55	20 40	20 55	21 40	21 55	22 40	23 20	23 35
Edge Hill	90 d	17 29		17 59		18 29		18 59				19 59		20 59		21 59			23 39
Mossley Hill	d	17 34		18 04		18 34		19 04				20 04		21 04	21 48	22 04			23 43
West Allerton	d	17 36		18 06		18 36		19 06				20 06		21 06		22 06			23 46
Liverpool South Parkway 7 ✈	a	17 39	17 46	18 09		18 39	18 49	19 09		19 49		20 09	20 49	21 09	21 51	22 09	22 50	23 30	23 49
	d		17 47				18 50			19 50			20 50		21 51		22 51	23 30	
Runcorn	a		17 54		18 30		18 57		19 34	19 57	20 04		20 57		21 59		22 59	23 38	
	d		17 56		18 31		18 58		19 35	19 58	20 05		20 58		21 59		22 59	23 38	
Acton Bridge	d		18 03				19 07											23 46	
Hartford	d		18 08				19 12			20 08			21 08		22 09		23 09	23 50	
Winsford	d		18 12							20 12			21 12		22 14		23 14	23 55	
Crewe 10	65 a		18 23		18 50		19 25		19 58	20 22	20 31		21 23		22 24		23 24	00 11	
Birmingham New Street 12	65 a		19 30		19b58		20 30		20 58	21 30	22b04		22 30		23 30				
London Euston ⊖	65 a		20c26		20 48		21b51			23b05	23 05		00c09						

For general notes see front of timetable
For details of catering facilities see Directory of Train Operators

- **A** To Warrington Central (Table 89)
- **B** To Manchester Oxford Road (Table 89)
- **C** To Manchester Piccadilly (Table 89)
- **b** Change at Stafford
- **c** Change at Crewe

Saturdays

until 12 July

Liverpool → Runcorn and Crewe

Network Diagram - see first page of Table 88

		NT	VT	NT	LM	NT	VT	NT	LM	NT	VT	NT	LM	NT	VT	NT	LM	NT	VT	NT	LM	NT
			1◇		1◇		1◇		1◇		1◇		1◇		1◇		1◇		1◇		1◇	
		A		B		A		B		B		B		B		B		B		B		B
			☕				☕				☕				☕				☕			
Liverpool Lime Street 10	90 d	05 50	06 15	06 21	06 33	06 50	07 15	07 21	07 39	07 50	08 15	08 29	08 38	08 55	09 15	09 29	09 37	09 55	10 15	10 29	10 37	10 55
Edge Hill	90 d	05 54				06 54				07 54				08 59				09 59				10 59
Mossley Hill	d	05 59		06 29	06 40	06 59		07 29		07 59		08 37		09 04		09 37		10 04		10 37		11 04
West Allerton	d	06 01				07 01				08 01				09 06				10 06				11 06
Liverpool South Parkway 7 ✈	a	06 04		06 32	06 44	07 04		07 32	07 48	08 04		08 40	08 47	09 09		09 40	09 47	10 09		10 40	10 47	11 09
	d				06 45				07 49				08 47				09 47				10 47	
Runcorn	a		06 30		06 52		07 30		07 56		08 29		08 55		09 30		09 55		10 30		10 55	
	d		06 31		06 53		07 30		07 57		08 30		08 55		09 31		09 55		10 31		10 55	
Acton Bridge	d				07 02								09 02									
Hartford	d				07 07				08 06				09 07				10 05				11 05	
Winsford	d				07 11				08 10								10 09				11 09	
Crewe 10	65 a		06 50		07 23		07 50		08 21		08 50		09 21		09 50		10 21		10 50		11 21	
Birmingham New Street 12	65 a		08 10		08 27		09 05		09 27		09b58		10c27		10 56		11c27		11 56		12c27	
London Euston	⊖ 65 a		09 19		09e56		10 12		10e58		11 16		12e21		13 01		13e22		13 58		14e23	

		VT	NT	LM	NT	VT	NT	LM	NT	VT	NT	LM	NT	VT	NT	LM	NT	VT	NT	LM	NT	VT
		1◇		1◇		1◇		1◇		1◇		1◇		1◇		1◇		1◇		1◇		1◇
			B		B		B		B		B		B		B		B		B		B	
		☕				☕				☕				☕				☕				☕
Liverpool Lime Street 10	90 d	11 15	11 29	11 37	11 55	12 15	12 29	12 37	12 55	13 15	13 29	13 37	13 55	14 15	14 29	14 37	14 55	15 15	15 29	15 37	15 55	16 15
Edge Hill	90 d				11 59				12 59				13 59				14 59				15 59	
Mossley Hill	d		11 37		12 04		12 37		13 04		13 37		14 04		14 37		15 04		15 37		16 04	
West Allerton	d				12 06				13 06				14 06				15 06				16 06	
Liverpool South Parkway 7 ✈	a		11 40	11 46	12 09		12 40	12 47	13 09		13 40	13 47	14 09		14 40	14 47	15 09		15 40	15 47	16 09	
	d			11 47				12 47				13 47				14 47				15 47		
Runcorn	a	11 30		11 54		12 30		12 55		13 30		13 55		14 30		14 55		15 30		15 55		16 30
	d	11 31		11 55		12 31		12 55		13 31		13 55		14 31		14 55		15 31		15 55		16 31
Acton Bridge	d							13 02														
Hartford	d			12 05				13 07				14 05				15 05				16 05		
Winsford	d			12 09								14 09				15 09				16 09		
Crewe 10	65 a	11 50		12 21		12 50		13 21		13 50		14 21		14 50		15 21		15 50		16 21		16 50
Birmingham New Street 12	65 a	12 56		13c27		13 56		14c27		14 56		15c27		15 56		16c27		16 56		17c27		17 56
London Euston	⊖ 65 a	15 01		15e24		15 59		16e25		17 01		17e23		17 58		18e23		19 02		19e21		19 55

		NT	LM	NT	VT	NT	LM	NT	VT	NT	LM	NT	LM	NT	VT	LM	NT	LM	NT	NT
			1◇		1◇		1◇		1◇		1◇		1◇		1◇	1		1◇		
		B		B		B		B		B		A		A			B		B	C
					☕				☕						☕					
Liverpool Lime Street 10	90 d	16 28	16 37	16 55	17 15	17 25	17 37	17 55	18 15	18 25	18 40	18 55	19 37	19 55	20 10	20 40	20 55	21 16	21 55	23 33
Edge Hill	90 d			16 59		17 29		17 59		18 29		18 59		19 59			20 59		21 59	23 37
Mossley Hill	d	16 36		17 04		17 34	17 45	18 04		18 34		19 04		20 04			21 04		22 04	23 41
West Allerton	d			17 06		17 36		18 06		18 36		19 06		20 06			21 06		22 06	23 44
Liverpool South Parkway 7 ✈	a	16 39	16 47	17 09		17 39	17 47	18 09		18 39	18 49	19 09	19 47	20 09		20 49	21 09	21 25	22 09	23 47
	d		16 47				17 47				18 50		19 47			20 50		21 26		
Runcorn	a		16 55		17 30		17 55		18 30		18 57		19 55		20 25	20 57		21 33		
	d		16 55		17 31		17 55		18 31		18 58		19 55		20 26	20 58		21 34		
Acton Bridge	d		17 02								19 05									
Hartford	d		17 07				18 05				19 09		20 05			21 07		21 44		
Winsford	d						18 11						20 09			21 11		21 48		
Crewe 10	65 a		17 21		17 50		18 21		18 50		19 22		20 21		20 45	21 24		21 58		
Birmingham New Street 12	65 a		18c27		18 56		19 27		19 56		20 30		21 27		22 30	23 04		23 04		
London Euston	⊖ 65 a		20e28		21 27		21e37		22 33		22b46		23e36		23 43					

Saturdays

19 July to 6 September

		NT	VT	NT	LM	NT	VT	NT	LM	NT	VT	NT	LM	NT	VT	NT	LM	NT	VT	NT	LM	NT
			1◇		1◇		1◇		1◇		1◇		1◇		1◇		1◇		1◇		1◇	
		A		B		A		B		B		B		B		B		B		B		B
			☕				☕				☕				☕				☕			
Liverpool Lime Street 10	90 d	05 50	06 15	06 21	06 33	06 50	07 15	07 21	07 39	07 50	08 15	08 29	08 38	08 55	09 15	09 29	09 37	09 55	10 15	10 29	10 37	10 55
Edge Hill	90 d	05 54				06 54				07 54				08 59				09 59				10 59
Mossley Hill	d	05 59		06 29	06 40	06 59		07 29		07 59		08 37		09 04		09 37		10 04		10 37		11 04
West Allerton	d	06 01				07 01				08 01				09 06				10 06				11 06
Liverpool South Parkway 7 ✈	a	06 04		06 32	06 44	07 04		07 32	07 48	08 04		08 40	08 47	09 09		09 40	09 47	10 09		10 40	10 47	11 09
	d				06 45				07 49				08 47				09 47				10 47	
Runcorn	a		06 30		06 52		07 30		07 56		08 29		08 55		09 30		09 55		10 30		10 55	
	d		06 31		06 53		07 30		07 57		08 30		08 55		09 31		09 55		10 31		10 55	
Acton Bridge	d				07 02								09 02									
Hartford	d				07 07				08 06				09 07				10 05				11 05	
Winsford	d				07 11				08 10								10 09				11 09	
Crewe 10	65 a		06 50		07 23		07 50		08 21		08 50		09 22		09 50		10 21		10 50		11 21	
Birmingham New Street 12	65 a		08 10		08 27		09 05		09 27		09b58		10 27		10b58		11 27		11b58		12 27	
London Euston	⊖ 65 a		09 00		09e27		09 59		10e29		11 05		11e27		12 00		12e27		12 54		13e28	

For general notes see front of timetable
For details of catering facilities see Directory of Train Operators

A To Warrington Central (Table 89)
B To Manchester Oxford Road (Table 89)
C To Manchester Piccadilly (Table 89)
b Change at Stafford
c By changing at Crewe, passengers may arrive 3 minutes earlier
e Change at Crewe

Due to ongoing Engineering Operations, some services from Saturday 13 September on this Table had not been confirmed at time of going to press. These services will be issued in a special Supplement as soon as exact timings have been confirmed.

Table 91

Saturdays

19 July to 6 September

Liverpool → Runcorn and Crewe

Network Diagram - see first page of Table 88

		VT 1◇ ☕	NT A	LM 1◇	NT A	VT 1◇ ☕		NT A	LM 1◇	NT A	VT 1◇ ☕	NT A	LM 1◇		NT A	VT 1◇ ☕	NT A	LM 1◇	NT A	VT 1◇ ☕		NT A	LM 1◇	NT A	VT 1◇ ☕
Liverpool Lime Street 10	90 d	11 15	11 29	11 37	11 55	12 15		12 29	12 37	12 55	13 15	13 29	13 37		13 55	14 15	14 29	14 37	14 55	15 15		15 29	15 37	15 55	16 15
Edge Hill	90 d				11 59					12 59					13 59				14 59					15 59	
Mossley Hill	d		11 37		12 04			12 37		13 04		13 37			14 04		14 37		15 04			15 37		16 04	
West Allerton	d				12 06					13 06					14 06				15 06					16 06	
Liverpool South Parkway 7 ✈	a		11 40	11 46	12 09			12 40	12 47	13 09		13 40	13 47		14 09		14 40	14 47	15 09			15 40	15 47	16 09	
	d			11 47					12 47				13 47					14 47					15 47		
Runcorn	a	11 29		11 54		12 30			12 55		13 30		13 55			14 30		14 55		15 30			15 55		16 30
	d	11 30		11 55		12 31			12 55		13 31		13 55			14 31		14 55		15 31			15 55		16 31
Acton Bridge	d								13 02																
Hartford	d			12 05					13 07				14 05					15 05					16 05		
Winsford	d			12 09									14 09					15 09					16 09		
Crewe 10	65 a	11 50		12 21		12 50			13 21		13 50		14 21			14 50		15 21		15 50			16 21		16 50
Birmingham New Street 12	65 a	12b58		13 27		13b58			14 27		14b58		15 27			15b58		16 27		16b58			17 27		17b58
London Euston	⊖ 65 a	14 03		14c25		15 00			15c26		16 03		16c28			17 00		17c28		18 00			18c30		19 00

		NT A	LM 1◇	NT A	VT 1◇ ☕		NT A	LM 1◇	NT A	VT 1◇ ☕	NT A	LM 1◇		NT B	VT 1◇ ☕	LM 1◇	NT B	VT 1◇ ☕	LM 1	NT A	LM 1◇	NT A	NT C		
Liverpool Lime Street 10	90 d	16 28	16 37	16 55	17 15		17 25	17 37	17 55	18 15	18 25	18 40		18 55	19 15	19 37	19 55	20 13	20 40	20 55	21 16	21 55	23 33		
Edge Hill	90 d			16 59			17 29		17 59		18 29			18 59			19 59			20 59		21 59	23 37		
Mossley Hill	d	16 36		17 04			17 34	17 45	18 04		18 34			19 04			20 04			21 04		22 04	23 41		
West Allerton	d			17 06			17 36		18 06		18 36			19 06			20 06			21 06		22 06	23 44		
Liverpool South Parkway 7 ✈	a	16 39	16 47	17 09			17 39	17 47	18 09		18 39	18 49		19 09		19 47	20 09		20 49	21 09	21 25	22 09	23 47		
	d		16 47					17 47				18 50				19 47			20 50		21 26				
Runcorn	a		16 55		17 30			17 55		18 30		18 57			19 30	19 55		20 28	20 57		21 33				
	d		16 55		17 31			17 55		18 31		18 58			19 31	19 55		20 29	20 58		21 34				
Acton Bridge	d		17 02									19 05													
Hartford	d		17 07					18 05				19 09				20 05			21 07		21 44				
Winsford	d							18 11								20 09			21 11		21 48				
Crewe 10	65 a		17 21		17 50			18 21		18 50		19 22			19 50	20 21		20 48	21 24		21 58				
Birmingham New Street 12	65 a		18 27		18b58			19 27		19b58		20 30			20b58	21 27		22b30			23 04				
London Euston	⊖ 65 a		19c24		19 57			20c58		21 34		22b45			22 45	23b45		23 45							

Sundays

until 13 July

		NT A	VT 1◇ ☕		NT A	VT 1◇ ☕		NT A	VT 1◇ ☕		LM 1◇	NT A		VT 1◇ ☕	NT A		VT 1◇ ☕	LM 1◇		NT A	VT 1◇ ☕		NT A	VT 1◇ ☕	LM 1◇
Liverpool Lime Street 10	d	08 57	09 15		09 57	10 15		10 57	11 18		11 35	11 57		12 18	12 57		13 18	13 26		13 57	14 18		14 57	15 18	15 31
Mossley Hill	d	09 05			10 05			11 05				12 05			13 05					14 05			15 05		
West Allerton	d	09 07			10 07			11 07				12 07			13 07					14 07			15 07		
Liverpool South Parkway 7 ✈	a	09 10			10 10			11 10			11 44	12 10			13 10			13 35		14 10			15 10		15 40
	d										11 45							13 36							15 41
Runcorn	a		09 31			10 31			11 34		11 52			12 33			13 33	13 44			14 33			15 33	15 48
	d		09 32			10 32			11 35		11 53			12 34			13 34	13 44			14 34			15 34	15 49
Hartford	d										12 03							13 54							
Winsford	d										12 07							13 58							
Crewe 10	65 a		09 52			10 52			11 55		12 17			12 53			13 53	14 08			14 53			15 53	16 08
Birmingham New Street 12	65 a		11b17			12 17			13 17		13 27			14 17				15 13			16 17			17 17	17 20
London Euston	⊖ 65 a		12 33			13 35			14 30		15c24			15 34			16 24	16c57			17 26			18 24	18c57

		NT A		VT 1◇ ☕	NT A		LM 1◇	VT 1◇ ☕		LM 1◇	NT A		VT 1◇ ☕	NT A		VT 1◇ ☕	LM 1◇	NT A	VT 1◇ ☕	NT A	LM 1◇	NT A	NT A		
Liverpool Lime Street 10	d	15 57		16 18	16 57		17 14	17 18			17 57		18 18	18 57		19 18	19 30	19 57	20 18	20 57	21 47	21 57	22 27		
Mossley Hill	d	16 05			17 05						18 05			19 05				20 05		21 05		22 05	22 35		
West Allerton	d	16 07			17 07						18 07			19 07				20 07		21 07		22 07	22 37		
Liverpool South Parkway 7 ✈	a	16 10			17 10		17 26			←	18 10			19 10			19 39	20 10		21 10	21 56	22 10	22 40		
	d						17 26 →			17 26							19 39				21 57				
Runcorn	a			16 33				17 33		17 37			18 33			19 33	19 47		20 33		22 04				
	d			16 34				17 34		17 38			18 34			19 34	19 47		20 34		22 05				
Hartford	d									17 47											22 15				
Winsford	d									17 52											22 19				
Crewe 10	65 a			16 53				17 53		18 02			18 53			19 53	20 07		20 53		22 33				
Birmingham New Street 12	65 a			18 17						19 11			20 17				21 10		22b17		23 53				
London Euston	⊖ 65 a			19 29				20 24		20c57			21 24			22 24	23c02		23 30						

For general notes see front of timetable
For details of catering facilities see Directory of Train Operators

A To Manchester Oxford Road (Table 89)
B To Warrington Central (Table 89)
C To Manchester Piccadilly (Table 89)

b Change at Stafford
c Change at Crewe

Due to ongoing Engineering Operations, some services from Saturday 13 September on this Table had not been confirmed at time of going to press. These services will be issued in a special Supplement as soon as exact timings have been confirmed.

Table 91

Sundays

20 July to 7 September

Liverpool → Runcorn and Crewe

Network Diagram - see first page of Table 88

		NT A	VT 1 ◇ ☕	NT A	VT 1 ◇ ☕	NT A	VT 1 ◇ ☕	LM 1 ◇	NT A	VT 1 ◇ ☕	NT A	VT 1 ◇ ☕	LM 1 ◇	NT A	VT 1 ◇ ☕	NT A	VT 1 ◇ ☕	LM 1 ◇
Liverpool Lime Street 10	d	08 57	09 15	09 57	10 15	10 57	11 15	11 35	11 57	12 15	12 57	13 15	13 26	13 57	14 15	14 57	15 15	15 31
Mossley Hill	d	09 05	.	10 05	.	11 05	.	.	12 05	.	13 05	.	.	14 05	.	15 05	.	.
West Allerton	d	09 07	.	10 07	.	11 07	.	.	12 07	.	13 07	.	.	14 07	.	15 07	.	.
Liverpool South Parkway 7 ✈	a	09 10	.	10 10	.	11 10	.	11 44	12 10	.	13 10	.	13 35	14 10	.	15 10	.	15 40
	d	.	.	.	.	.	.	11 45	.	.	.	.	13 36	.	.	.	.	15 41
Runcorn	a	.	09 31	.	10 32	.	11 31	11 52	.	12 31	.	13 30	13 44	.	14 30	.	15 30	15 48
	d	.	09 32	.	10 33	.	11 32	11 53	.	12 32	.	13 31	13 44	.	14 31	.	15 31	15 49
Hartford	d	.	.	.	.	.	.	12 03	.	.	.	.	13 54	.	.	.	.	.
Winsford	d	.	.	.	.	.	.	12 07	.	.	.	.	13 58	.	.	.	.	.
Crewe 10	65 a	.	09 51	.	10 52	.	11 52	12 17	.	12 53	.	13 51	14 09	.	14 50	.	15 52	16 08
Birmingham New Street 12	65 a	.	11b24	.	12 17	.	13b20	.	.	14 24	.	15b12	15c58	.	16 28	.	17b10	17c58
London Euston ⊖	65 a	.	12 39	.	13 36	.	14 42	15 34	.	15 53	.	16 37	17 13	.	17 39	.	18 38	19 13

		NT A	VT 1 ◇ ☕	NT A	VT 1 ◇ ☕	LM 1 ◇	NT A	VT 1 ◇ ☕	NT A	VT 1 ◇ ☕	LM 1 ◇	NT A	VT 1 ◇ ☕	NT A	LM 1 ◇	NT A	NT A
Liverpool Lime Street 10	d	15 57	16 15	16 57	17 15	17 25	17 57	18 15	18 57	19 15	19 26	19 57	20 15	20 57	21 47	21 57	22 27
Mossley Hill	d	16 05	.	17 05	.	.	18 05	.	19 05	.	.	20 05	.	21 05	.	22 05	22 35
West Allerton	d	16 07	.	17 07	.	.	18 07	.	19 07	.	.	20 07	.	21 07	.	22 07	22 37
Liverpool South Parkway 7 ✈	a	16 10	.	17 10	.	17 35	18 10	.	19 10	.	19 35	20 10	.	21 10	21 56	22 10	22 40
	d	.	.	.	.	17 35	.	.	.	.	19 35	.	.	.	21 57	.	.
Runcorn	a	.	16 30	.	17 30	17 42	.	18 30	.	19 30	19 43	.	20 30	.	22 04	.	.
	d	.	16 31	.	17 31	17 43	.	18 31	.	19 31	19 43	.	20 31	.	22 05	.	.
Hartford	d	.	.	.	.	17 52	.	.	.	.	.	.	.	.	22 15	.	.
Winsford	d	.	.	.	.	17 57	.	.	.	.	.	.	.	.	22 19	.	.
Crewe 10	65 a	.	16 51	.	17 50	18 07	.	18 51	.	19 51	20 03	.	20 50	.	22 40	.	.
Birmingham New Street 12	65 a	.	18 23	.	19b31	19c58	.	20 26	.	21 25	22 27	.	22b27	.	01e08	.	.
London Euston ⊖	65 a	.	20 04	.	20 52	21 36	.	21 52	.	22 52	23 19	.	23 52	.	.	.	.

For general notes see front of timetable
For details of catering facilities see Directory of Train Operators

A To Manchester Oxford Road (Table 89)
b Change at Stafford
c Change at Crewe and Stafford
e By bus

Due to ongoing Engineering Operations, some services from Sunday 14 September on this Table had not been confirmed at time of going to press. These services will be issued in a special Supplement as soon as exact timings have been confirmed.

Crewe and Runcorn → Liverpool

Network Diagram - see first page of Table 88

Miles			NT A	LM 1 ⊼	NT A	LM 1 ⊼	NT B	LM 1◇ ⊼	NT A	LM 1 C	NT B	LM 1◇ ⊼	NT D	LM 1◇ E ⊼	VT 1◇ ☒	NT B	LM 1 C ⊼	NT B	LM 1◇ ⊼	VT 1◇ ☒
—	London Euston	⊖ 65 d												06b46	07 13				07c46	08 17
—	Birmingham New Street 12	65 d				05 30		06 07		06e30		07 21		07 51	08 03		08 26		08 51	09 03
0	**Crewe 10**	65 d		06 12		06 47		07 23		07 47		08 24		08 52	09 08		09 24		09 47	10 08
7¼	Winsford	d		06 19				07 30		07 54		08 31					09 31			
11¾	Hartford	d		06 24				07 35		07 59		08 36					09 36			
14¾	Acton Bridge	d		06 28				07 39		08 03										
22½	**Runcorn**	a		06 35		07 03		07 47		08 10		08 45		09 08	09 25		09 45		10 03	10 25
—		d		06 36		07 03		07 47		08 11		08 45		09 08	09 25		09 45		10 03	10 25
30	**Liverpool South Parkway 7** ✈	a		06 44				07 53				08 53					09 53			
—		d	06 28	06 45	07 02		07 24	07 53	08 03		08 37	08 53	09 07			09 33	09 53	10 04		
31	West Allerton	d	06 31		07 05		07 27		08 06		08 40		09 10			09 36				
31¾	Mossley Hill	d	06 34	06 47	07 07		07 30		08 09		08 42		09 13			09 39		10 08		
33¾	Edge Hill	90 d	06 39		07 13		07 37		08 14		08 47					09 45				
35½	**Liverpool Lime Street 10**	90 a	06 46	07 01	07 19	07 27	07 44	08 11	08 21	08 35	08 55	09 09	09 24	09 31	09 47	09 51	10 09	10 20	10 26	10 47

		NT B	LM 1◇ ⊼	NT B	LM 1◇ ⊼	VT 1◇ ☒	NT B	LM 1◇ ⊼	NT B	VT 1◇ ☒	NT B	LM 1◇ ⊼	NT B	LM 1◇ ⊼	VT 1◇ ⊏	NT B	LM 1◇ ⊼	NT B	VT 1◇ ⊏
London Euston	⊖ 65 d				08c46	09 17				10 15				10c46	11 17		11c28		12 17
Birmingham New Street 12	65 d		09 21		09 51	10 03		10 21		11 03		11 21		11 51	12 03		12 21		13 03
Crewe 10	65 d		10 24		10 47	11 08		11 24		12 08		12 24		12 48	13 10		13 24		14 08
Winsford	d							11 31									13 31		
Hartford	d		10 34					11 36				12 34					13 36		
Acton Bridge	d		10 38									12 38							
Runcorn	a		10 45		11 03	11 25		11 45		12 25		12 45		13 03	13 26		13 45		14 25
	d		10 46		11 03	11 25		11 45		12 25		12 46		13 03	13 26		13 45		14 25
Liverpool South Parkway 7 ✈	a		10 53					11 53				12 53					13 53		
	d	10 33	10 53	11 04			11 33	11 53	12 04		12 33	12 53	13 04			13 33	13 53	14 04	
West Allerton	d	10 36					11 36				12 36					13 36			
Mossley Hill	d	10 39		11 08			11 39		12 08		12 39		13 08			13 39		14 08	
Edge Hill	90 d	10 45					11 45				12 45					13 45			
Liverpool Lime Street 10	90 a	10 51	11 09	11 20	11 26	11 47	11 51	12 09	12 20	12 47	12 51	13 09	13 20	13 26	13 49	13 51	14 09	14 20	14 47

		NT B	LM 1◇ ⊼	NT B	LM 1◇ ⊼	VT 1◇ ⊏	NT B	LM 1◇ ⊼	NT B	VT 1◇ ⊏	NT B	LM 1◇ ⊼	NT B	LM 1◇ ⊼	VT 1◇ ☒	NT B	LM 1◇ ⊼	NT B	VT 1◇ ⊏	NT B
London Euston	⊖ 65 d				12c46	13 17				14 17				14c46	15 17				16 17	
Birmingham New Street 12	65 d		13 21		13 51	14 03		14 21		15 03		15 21		15 51	16 03		16 21		17 03	
Crewe 10	65 d		14 24		14 47	15 08		15 24		16 08		16 24		16 47	17 08		17 24		18 08	
Winsford	d		14 31					15 31									17 31			
Hartford	d		14 36					15 36				16 34					17 36			
Acton Bridge	d											16 38								
Runcorn	a		14 45		15 03	15 25		15 45		16 25		16 45		17 03	17 25		17 45		18 25	
	d		14 45		15 03	15 25		15 45		16 25		16 46		17 03	17 25		17 45		18 25	
Liverpool South Parkway 7 ✈	a		14 53					15 53				16 53					17 53			
	d	14 33	14 53	15 04			15 33	15 53	16 06		16 33	16 53	17 04			17 39	17 53	18 13		18 40
West Allerton	d	14 36					15 36				16 36					17 42		18 16		18 43
Mossley Hill	d	14 39		15 08			15 39		16 10		16 39		17 08			17 44		18 19		18 45
Edge Hill	90 d	14 45					15 45				16 45					17 50		18 25		18 51
Liverpool Lime Street 10	90 a	14 51	15 09	15 20	15 26	15 48	15 51	16 09	16 22	16 48	16 51	17 09	17 24	17 26	17 47	17 58	18 09	18 32	18 47	18 59

		LM 1◇ ⊼	LM 1◇ ⊼	NT B	VT 1◇ ☒	LM 1◇ ⊼	NT A	LM 1◇ ⊼	VT 1◇ ☒	NT B	LM 1◇ ⊼	NT A	VT 1◇ ⊏	LM 1◇ ⊼	NT A	VT 1◇ ⊏	LM 1◇ ⊼	NT A	VT 1◇ ⊏
London Euston	⊖ 65 d		16e46		17 17	17e21		17c48	18 17		18f20		19 17			20 17			21 10
Birmingham New Street 12	65 d	17 21	17 51		18 03	18 21		18 51	19e03		19 21		20 03	20 21		21e03	21 21		
Crewe 10	65 d	18 24	18 49		19 08	19 31		19 48	20 08		20 24		21 04	21 24		22 08	22 24		23 02
Winsford	d	18 31				19 39					20 31			21 31			22 31		
Hartford	d	18 36				19 44					20 36			21 36			22 36		
Acton Bridge	d																		
Runcorn	a	18 45	19 05		19 25	19 53		20 05	20 25		20 45		21 21	21 45		22 25	22 45		23 19
	d	18 45	19 05		19 25	19 54		20 05	20 25		20 45		21 21	21 45		22 25	22 45		23 19
Liverpool South Parkway 7 ✈	a	18 53				20 01					20 53			21 53			22 54		
	d	18 53		19 09		20 02	20 03			20 38	20 53	21 03		21 53	22 03		22 54	23 03	
West Allerton	d			19 13			20 06			20 41		21 06			22 06			23 06	
Mossley Hill	d			19 15			20 09			20 43		21 09			22 09			23 09	
Edge Hill	90 d			19 25			20 14					21 14			22 14			23 14	
Liverpool Lime Street 10	90 a	19 09	19 29	19 32	19 45	20 18	20 22	20 31	20 47	20 59	21 09	21 21	21 45	22 09	22 22	22 47	23 12	23 21	23 47

For general notes see front of timetable
For details of catering facilities see Directory of Train Operators

A From Warrington Central (Table 89)
B From Manchester Oxford Road (Table 89)
C From Northampton (Table 65)
D From Buxton (Table 86)
E From Walsall (Table 70)

b Change at Crewe. 28 July to 22 August dep. 0644
c Change at Crewe
e Change at Stafford
f Fridays only. Change at Crewe

Table 91

Saturdays

until 12 July

Crewe and Runcorn → Liverpool

Network Diagram - see first page of Table 88

	NT A	LM 1	NT A	NT B	LM 1◇		NT A	NT B	LM 1◇	NT B	VT 1◇ ☕		NT B	LM 1◇	NT B	VT 1◇ ☕	NT B		LM 1◇	NT B	NT B	LM 1◇	NT B	VT 1◇ ☕
London Euston ⊖ 65 d											06 40					07 55								08 57
Birmingham New Street 12 65 d					06b07				07 21		*08 03*			08 21		*09 03*			09 21			10 21		*10 40*
Crewe 10 65 d		06 13			07 22				08 24		09 11			09 24		10 11			10 24			11 24		12 01
Winsford d		06 20			07 29				08 31					09 31								11 31		
Hartford d		06 25			07 34				08 36					09 36					10 34			11 36		
Acton Bridge d		06 29			07 38														10 38					
Runcorn a		06 36			07 46				08 46		09 27			09 45		10 28			10 45			11 45		12 17
d		06 37			07 46				08 46		09 27			09 46		10 28			10 46			11 46		12 18
Liverpool South Parkway 7 ✈ a		06 45			07 54				08 56					09 54					10 54			11 54		
d	06 28	06 45	07 02	07 29	07 54		08 03	08 37	08 56	09 07			09 33	09 54	10 04		10 33		10 54	11 04	11 33	11 54	12 04	
West Allerton d	06 31		07 05	07 32			08 06	08 40		09 10			09 36				10 36				11 36			
Mossley Hill d	06 34	06 48	07 07	07 35			08 09	08 42		09 13			09 39		10 08		10 39			11 08	11 39		12 08	
Edge Hill 90 d	06 39		07 13	07 40			08 14	08 47					09 45				10 45				11 45			
Liverpool Lime Street 10 90 a	06 46	07 02	07 19	07 47	08 10		08 21	08 55	09 10	09 24	09 50		09 54	10 09	10 20	10 50	10 54		11 09	11 20	11 54	12 09	12 20	12 40

	NT B		LM 1◇	NT B	VT 1◇ ☕	NT B	LM 1◇		NT B	VT 1◇ ☕	NT B	LM 1◇	NT B		VT 1◇ ☕	NT B	LM 1◇	NT B	VT 1◇ ☕		NT B	LM 1◇	NT B	VT 1◇ ☕
London Euston ⊖ 65 d					09 55					10 57					11 55				12 56					13 56
Birmingham New Street 12 65 d			11 21		*11 40*		12 21			*12 40*		13 21			*13 40*		14 21		*14 40*			15 21		*15 40*
Crewe 10 65 d			12 24		13 01		13 24			14 01		14 24			15 01		15 24		16 01			16 24		17 01
Winsford d							13 31					14 31					15 31							
Hartford d			12 34				13 36					14 36					15 36					16 34		
Acton Bridge d			12 38																			16 38		
Runcorn a			12 46		13 17		13 45			14 17		14 45			15 17		15 46		16 17			16 46		17 17
d			12 46		13 18		13 46			14 18		14 46			15 18		15 46		16 18			16 46		17 18
Liverpool South Parkway 7 ✈ a			12 54				13 54					14 54					15 54					16 54		
d	12 33		12 54	13 04		13 33	13 54		14 04		14 33	14 54	15 04			15 33	15 54	16 06			16 33	16 54	17 04	
West Allerton d	12 36					13 36					14 36					15 36					16 36			
Mossley Hill d	12 39			13 08		13 39			14 08		14 39		15 08			15 39		16 10			16 39		17 08	
Edge Hill 90 d	12 45					13 45					14 45					15 45					16 45			
Liverpool Lime Street 10 90 a	12 54		13 09	13 20	13 40	13 54	14 09		14 20	14 37	14 54	15 09	15 20		15 37	15 55	16 09	16 22	16 37		16 55	17 09	17 24	17 37

	NT B	LM 1◇	NT B		VT 1◇ ☕	NT B	LM 1◇	NT B	VT 1◇ ☕		LM 1◇	NT A	VT 1◇ ☕	NT B	LM 1◇		NT A	VT 1◇ ☕	NT A	VT 1◇ ☕	NT A	VT 1◇ ☕		
London Euston ⊖ 65 d					14 56				15 56				16 56					17 56		18 56		19 34		
Birmingham New Street 12 65 d		16 21			*16 40*		17 21		*17 40*		18 21		*18 40*		19 21			*19 21*		*20 21*		*21c21*		
Crewe 10 65 d		17 24			18 01		18 24		19 01		19 24		20 03		20 24			20 52		21 49		22 45		
Winsford d		17 31									19 31				20 31									
Hartford d		17 36					18 34				19 36				20 36									
Acton Bridge d																								
Runcorn a		17 45			18 17		18 43		19 17		19 45		20 18		20 45			21 08		22 05		23 00		
d		17 46			18 18		18 46		19 18		19 46		20 19		20 46			21 09		22 06		23 01		
Liverpool South Parkway 7 ✈ a		17 53					18 54				19 54				20 54									
d	17 39	17 53	18 13			18 38	18 54	19 09			19 54	20 03		20 38	20 54		21 03		22 03		23 03			
West Allerton d	17 42		18 17			18 41		19 13				20 06		20 41			21 06		22 06		23 06			
Mossley Hill d	17 44		18 19			18 44	18 57	19 15				20 09		20 43			21 09		22 09		23 09			
Edge Hill 90 d	17 50		18 27			18 51		19 21				20 14					21 14		22 14		23 14			
Liverpool Lime Street 10 90 a	17 58	18 09	18 34		18 37	18 59	19 09	19 27	19 37		20 09	20 21	20 38	20 57	21 09		21 21	21 27	22 22	22 24	23 21	23 22		

Saturdays

19 July to 6 September

	NT A	LM 1	NT A	NT B	LM 1◇		NT A	NT B	LM 1◇	NT B	VT 1◇ ☕		NT B	LM 1◇	NT B	VT 1◇ ☕	NT B		LM 1◇	NT B	VT 1◇ ☕	NT B	LM 1◇	NT B
London Euston ⊖ 65 d											07 09					08 12					09 15			
Birmingham New Street 12 65 d					06b07				07 21		*08 03*			08 21		*09 03*			09 21		*10 03*		10 21	
Crewe 10 65 d		06 13			07 22				08 24		09 11			09 24		10 11			10 24		11 11		11 24	
Winsford d		06 20			07 29				08 31					09 31									11 31	
Hartford d		06 25			07 34				08 36					09 36					10 34				11 36	
Acton Bridge d		06 29			07 38														10 38					
Runcorn a		06 36			07 46				08 46		09 27			09 45		10 28			10 45		11 28		11 45	
d		06 37			07 46				08 46		09 27			09 46		10 28			10 46		11 28		11 46	
Liverpool South Parkway 7 ✈ a		06 45			07 54				08 56					09 54					10 54				11 54	
d	06 28	06 45	07 02	07 29	07 54		08 03	08 37	08 56	09 07			09 33	09 54	10 04		10 33		10 54	11 04		11 33	11 54	12 04
West Allerton d	06 31		07 05	07 32			08 06	08 40		09 10			09 36				10 36					11 36		
Mossley Hill d	06 34	06 48	07 07	07 35			08 09	08 42		09 13			09 39		10 08		10 39			11 08		11 39		12 08
Edge Hill 90 d	06 39		07 13	07 40			08 14	08 47					09 45				10 45					11 45		
Liverpool Lime Street 10 90 a	06 46	07 02	07 19	07 47	08 10		08 21	08 55	09 10	09 24	09 50		09 54	10 09	10 20	10 50	10 54		11 09	11 20	11 50	11 54	12 09	12 20

For general notes see front of timetable
For details of catering facilities see Directory of Train Operators

A From Warrington Central (Table 89)
B From Manchester Oxford Road (Table 89)
b By changing at Stafford, passengers may depart at 0620.
c Change at Stafford

Due to ongoing Engineering Operations, some services from Saturday 13 September on this Table had not been confirmed at time of going to press. These services will be issued in a special Supplement as soon as exact timings have been confirmed.

Table 91

Saturdays

19 July to 6 September

Crewe and Runcorn → Liverpool

Network Diagram - see first page of Table 88

		VT 1◇		NT A	LM 1◇	NT A	VT 1◇	NT A		LM 1◇	NT A	VT 1◇	NT A	LM 1◇		NT A	VT 1◇	NT A	LM 1◇	NT A		VT 1◇	NT A	LM 1◇	NT A
London Euston	⊖ 65 d	10 12					11 12					12 12					13 12					14 12			
Birmingham New Street 12	65 d	*11 03*			11 21		*12 03*			12 21		*13 03*		13 21			*14 03*		14 21			*15 03*		15 21	
Crewe 10	65 d	12 11			12 24		13 11			13 24		14 11		14 24			15 11		15 24			16 11		16 24	
Winsford	d									13 31				14 31					15 31						
Hartford	d				12 34					13 36				14 36					15 36					16 34	
Acton Bridge	d				12 38																			16 38	
Runcorn	a	12 29			12 46		13 28			13 45		14 28		14 45			15 28		15 46			16 28		16 46	
	d	12 29			12 46		13 28			13 46		14 28		14 46			15 28		15 46			16 28		16 46	
Liverpool South Parkway 7	✈ a				12 54					13 54				14 54					15 54					16 54	
	d			12 33	12 54	13 04		13 33		13 54	14 04		14 33	14 54		15 04		15 33	15 54	16 06			16 33	16 54	17 04
West Allerton	d			12 36				13 36					14 36					15 36					16 36		
Mossley Hill	d			12 39		13 08		13 39			14 08		14 39			15 08		15 39		16 10			16 39		17 08
Edge Hill	90 d			12 45				13 45					14 45					15 45					16 45		
Liverpool Lime Street 10	90 a	12 50		12 54	13 09	13 20	13 50	13 54		14 09	14 20	14 50	14 54	15 09		15 20	15 50	15 55	16 09	16 22		16 50	16 55	17 09	17 24

		VT 1◇	NT A	LM 1◇		NT A	VT 1◇	NT A	LM 1◇	NT A		VT 1◇	LM 1◇	NT B	VT 1◇	NT A		LM 1◇	NT B	VT 1◇	NT B	NT B	VT 1◇		
London Euston	⊖ 65 d	15 12					16 12					17 12			18 12					19 09			20 40		
Birmingham New Street 12	65 d	*16 03*		16 21			*17 03*		17 21			*18 03*	18 21		*19b03*			19 21		*20 03*			*22b20*		
Crewe 10	65 d	17 11		17 24			18 11		18 24			19 08	19 24		20 11			20 24		21 07			23 45		
Winsford	d			17 31									19 31					20 31							
Hartford	d			17 36					18 34				19 36					20 36							
Acton Bridge	d																								
Runcorn	a	17 28		17 45			18 30		18 43			19 25	19 45		20 29			20 45		21 24			23 59		
	d	17 28		17 46			18 30		18 46			19 25	19 46		20 29			20 46		21 24			00 01		
Liverpool South Parkway 7	✈ a			17 53					18 54				19 54					20 54							
	d		17 39	17 53		18 13		18 38	18 54	19 09			19 54	20 03		20 38		20 54	21 03		22 03	23 03			
West Allerton	d		17 42			18 17		18 41		19 13				20 06		20 41			21 06		22 06	23 06			
Mossley Hill	d		17 44			18 19		18 44	18 57	19 15				20 09		20 43			21 09		22 09	23 09			
Edge Hill	90 d		17 50			18 27		18 51		19 21				20 14					21 14		22 14	23 14			
Liverpool Lime Street 10	90 a	17 50	17 58	18 09		18 34	18 52	18 59	19 09	19 27		19 45	20 09	20 21	20 52	20 57		21 09	21 21	21 48	22 22	23 21	00 22		

Sundays

until 13 July

		NT A	NT A		LM 1◇	NT A		NT A	VT 1◇		LM 1◇	NT A		VT 1◇	NT A		VT 1◇	NT A		LM 1◇	VT 1◇		NT A	LM 1◇	VT 1◇
London Euston	⊖ 65 d								09 02		*09b35*			10 50			12 05			*12c01*	13 05			*14c01*	14 05
Birmingham New Street 12	65 d				09 22				*10b03*		11 24			*12b03*			*13b06*			13 30	*14b03*			15 27	*15b03*
Crewe 10	65 d				10 29				11 49		12 29			13 31			14 32			14 37	15 30			16 28	16 33
Winsford	d				10 36															14 44					
Hartford	d				10 41															14 49					
Runcorn	a				10 50				12 04		12 46			13 46			14 48			14 58	15 46			16 44	16 49
	d				10 51				12 05		12 46			13 47			14 49			14 59	15 47			16 44	16 50
Liverpool South Parkway 7	✈ a				10 58						12 55									15 06				16 52	
	d	09 03	10 03		10 59	11 03		12 03			12 55	13 03			14 03			15 03		15 06			16 03	16 52	
West Allerton	d	09 06	10 06			11 06		12 06				13 06			14 06			15 06					16 06		
Mossley Hill	d	09 09	10 09			11 09		12 09				13 09			14 09			15 09					16 09		
Liverpool Lime Street 10	a	09 20	10 20		11 13	11 20		12 20	12 25		13 12	13 20		14 09	14 20		15 10	15 20		15 23	16 08		16 20	17 08	17 12

		NT A		VT 1◇	NT A		VT 1◇	LM 1◇		NT A	VT 1◇		NT A	VT 1◇		NT A	LM 1◇		VT 1◇	NT A	NT A	VT 1◇	VT 1◇		
London Euston	⊖ 65 d			15 05			16 05	*16c01*			17 05			18 05			*18c01*		19 05			20 05	21 00		
Birmingham New Street 12	65 d			*16b03*			*17b03*	17 26			*18b03*			*19b26*			19 26		*20b03*			*21b03*	*22b03*		
Crewe 10	65 d			17 33			18 31	18 33			19 32			20 33			20 37		21 32			22 38	23 42		
Winsford	d							18 42									20 44								
Hartford	d							18 47									20 49								
Runcorn	a			17 49			18 46	18 56			19 47			20 49			20 58		21 47			23 00	00 14		
	d			17 50			18 47	18 56			19 48			20 50			20 58		21 48			23 01	00 15		
Liverpool South Parkway 7	✈ a							19 04									21 08								
	d	17 03			18 03			19 05		19 03			20 03			21 03	21 08			22 03	23 03				
West Allerton	d	17 06			18 06					19 06			20 06			21 06				22 06	23 06				
Mossley Hill	d	17 09			18 09					19 09			20 09			21 09				22 09	23 09				
Liverpool Lime Street 10	a	17 20		18 11	18 20		19 09	19 18		19 20	20 10		20 20	21 11		21 20	21 24		22 10	22 20	23 20	23 28	00 39		

For general notes see front of timetable
For details of catering facilities see Directory of Train Operators

- **A** From Manchester Oxford Road (Table 89)
- **B** From Warrington Central (Table 89)
- **b** Change at Stafford
- **c** Change at Crewe

Due to ongoing Engineering Operations, some services from Saturday 13 September on this Table had not been confirmed at time of going to press. These services will be issued in a special Supplement as soon as exact timings have been confirmed.

Table 91

Sundays

20 July to 7 September

Crewe and Runcorn → Liverpool

Network Diagram - see first page of Table 88

		NT	NT		LM	NT		NT	VT		LM	NT		NT	VT		NT	LM		VT	NT		VT	LM	NT
					1 ◇				1 ◇		1 ◇				1 ◇			1 ◇		1 ◇			1 ◇	1 ◇	
		A	A			A		A				A		A			A				A				A
									☕						☕					☕			☕		
London Euston	⊖ 65 d								09 25						10 56			*11 13*		12 01			13 01		
Birmingham New Street 12	65 d				*09 03*				*10*b*48*		*11 03*				*12*b*18*			*13 03*		*13*b*30*			*14*b*18*	*15 03*	
Crewe 10	65 d				10 29				12 13		12 29				13 56			14 32		14 54			15 48	16 28	
Winsford	d				10 36													14 39							
Hartford	d				10 41													14 44							
Runcorn	a				10 50				12 30		12 46				14 12			14 53		15 10			16 07	16 44	
	d				10 51				12 31		12 46				14 13			14 53		15 11			16 08	16 44	
Liverpool South Parkway 7 ✈	a				10 57						12 55							15 02						16 52	
	d	09 03	10 03		10 58	11 03		12 03			12 55	13 03		14 03			15 03	15 02			16 03			16 52	17 03
West Allerton	d	09 06	10 06			11 06		12 06				13 06		14 06			15 06				16 06				17 06
Mossley Hill	d	09 09	10 09			11 09		12 09				13 09		14 09			15 09				16 09				17 09
Liverpool Lime Street 10	a	09 20	10 20		11 13	11 20		12 20	12 49		13 12	13 20		14 20	14 33		15 20	15 22		15 28	16 20		16 30	17 09	17 20

		VT		NT	VT		LM	NT		VT	NT		VT	NT		LM	VT		NT	VT	NT	VT	VT		
		1 ◇			1 ◇		1 ◇			1 ◇			1 ◇			1 ◇	1 ◇			1 ◇		1 ◇	1 ◇		
				A				A			A			A					A		A				
		☕			☕					☕			☕				☕			☕		☕	☕		
London Euston	⊖ 65 d	14 01			15 01					16 13			17 01				18 01			19 01		20 01	21 01		
Birmingham New Street 12	65 d	*15*b*30*			*16*b*18*		*17 03*			*17*b*18*			*18*b*18*			*19 03*	*19*b*21*			*20*b*18*		*21*b*21*	*22*b*18*		
Crewe 10	65 d	17 04			17 52		18 30			18 52			19 54			20 30	20 50			21 56		22 49	00 01		
Winsford	d						18 37									20 40									
Hartford	d						18 42									20 45									
Runcorn	a	17 19			18 08		18 51			19 07			20 10			20 54	21 05			22 11		23 08	00 21		
	d	17 20			18 09		18 51			19 08			20 11			20 55	21 06			22 12		23 09	00 22		
Liverpool South Parkway 7 ✈	a						18 59									21 05									
	d			18 03			19 00	19 03			20 03			21 03		21 05			22 03		23 03				
West Allerton	d			18 06				19 06			20 06			21 06					22 06		23 06				
Mossley Hill	d			18 09				19 09			20 09			21 09					22 09		23 09				
Liverpool Lime Street 10	a	17 41		18 20	18 30		19 13	19 20		19 31	20 20		20 32	21 20		21 22	21 30		22 20	22 34	23 20	23 36	00 46		

For general notes see front of timetable
For details of catering facilities see Directory of Train Operators

A From Manchester Oxford Road (Table 89)
b Change at Stafford

Due to ongoing Engineering Operations, some services from Sunday 14 September on this Table had not been confirmed at time of going to press. These services will be issued in a special Supplement as soon as exact timings have been confirmed.

Network Diagram for Tables 94, 95

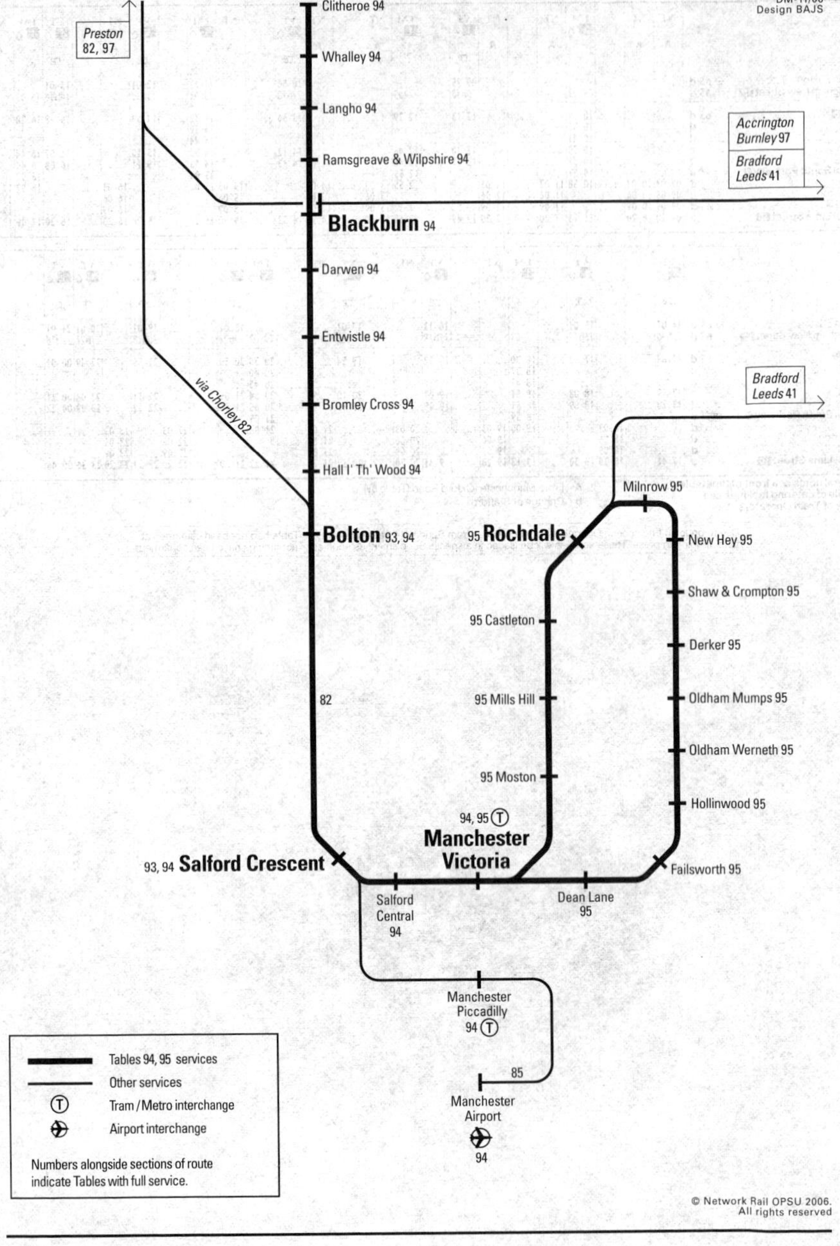
DM-11/06
Design BAJS
Preston
82, 97
Clitheroe 94
Whalley 94
Langho 94
Ramsgreave & Wilpshire 94
Accrington
Burnley 97
Bradford
Leeds 41
Blackburn 94
Darwen 94
Entwistle 94
via Chorley 82
Bromley Cross 94
Bradford
Leeds 41
Hall I' Th' Wood 94
Milnrow 95
Bolton 93, 94
95 Rochdale
New Hey 95
Shaw & Crompton 95
95 Castleton
Derker 95
82
95 Mills Hill
Oldham Mumps 95
Oldham Werneth 95
95 Moston
Hollinwood 95
94, 95 T
Manchester
Victoria
93, 94 Salford Crescent
Failsworth 95
Salford
Central
94
Dean Lane
95
Manchester
Piccadilly
94 T
85
Manchester
Airport
94
Tables 94, 95 services
Other services
Tram / Metro interchange
Airport interchange
Numbers alongside sections of route
indicate Tables with full service.

Manchester and Bolton → Blackburn → Clitheroe

Network Diagram - see first page of Table 94

Miles			NT	NT	NT	NT	NT	NT	NT	NT	NT	NT	NT	NT
0	**Manchester Victoria**	82 d		06 26	07 00	07 23	08 00	08 23	09 00	10 00	11 00	12 00	13 00	14 00
¾	Salford Central	82 d			07 03	07 26	08 03	08 26	09 03	10 03	11 03	12 03	13 03	14 03
—	Manchester Airport	82, 85 d		*05 47*	*06 19*	*06 47*	*07 22*	*07 47*	*08 27*	*09 27*	*10 27*	*11 27*	*12 27*	*13 27*
—	Manchester Piccadilly 10	82 d		*06 05*	*06 44*	*07 11*	*07 45*	*08 11*	*08 45*	*09 45*	*10 45*	*11 45*	*12 45*	*13 45*
1¾	Salford Crescent	82 d		06 31	07 06	07 31	08 07	08 29	09 07	10 07	11 07	12 07	13 07	14 07
10¾	**Bolton**	82 d		06 45	07 19	07 44	08 19	08 44	09 19	10 19	11 19	12 19	13 19	14 19
12¾	Hall I' Th' Wood	d		06 50	07 24	07 49	08 24	08 49	09 24	10 24	11 24	12 24	13 24	14 24
13¾	Bromley Cross	d		06 53	07 27	07 54	08 27	08 54	09 27	10 27	11 27	12 27	13 27	14 27
16¼	Entwistle	d				08x01	08x33		09x33			12x33		
20¼	Darwen	a		07 05	07 38	08 09	08 40	09 09	09 40	10 38	11 38	12 40	13 38	14 38
—		d		07 08	07 39	08 09	08 40	09 09	09 40	10 38	11 38	12 40	13 38	14 38
—	Blackpool North	97 d	*05 30*	*06 28*			*07 30*		*08 29*	*09 30*	*10 30*	*11 30*	*12 30*	*13 30*
—	Preston 8	97 d	*05 55*	*06 54*			*08 01*		*08 54*	*09 55*	*10 55*	*11 55*	*12 55*	*13 55*
24½	**Blackburn**	a		07 18	07 46	08 23	08 47	09 21	09 48	10 46	11 46	12 47	13 46	14 46
—		d	06 25	07 19	07 47		08 48		09 48	10 48	11 48	12 48	13 48	14 48
27¼	Ramsgreave & Wilpshire	d	06 31	07 25	07 53		08 54		09 54	10 54	11 54	12 54	13 54	14 54
29¾	Langho	d	06 35	07 29	07 57		08 58		09 58	10 58	11 58	12 58	13 58	14 58
31¾	Whalley	d	06 39	07 33	08 01		09 02		10 02	11 02	12 02	13 02	14 02	15 02
34¾	**Clitheroe**	a	06 50	07 44	08 13		09 13		10 13	11 13	12 13	13 13	14 13	15 13

		NT	NT	NT	NT	NT A	NT	NT	NT	NT	NT	NT	NT
Manchester Victoria	82 d	15 00	15 50	16 23	17 00	17 29	18 00	18 21	18 58	19 58	20 58	21 58	23 08
Salford Central	82 d	15 03	15 53	16 26	17 03	17 32	18 03	18 24	19 01	20 01	21 01	22b01	23b11
Manchester Airport	82, 85 d	*14 27*	*15 07*	*15 47*	*16c27*	*16c47*	*17 32*	*17 47*	*18 27*	*19 27*	*20e22*	*21 27*	*22e22*
Manchester Piccadilly 10	82 d	*14 45*	*15 30*	*16 11*	*16c52*	*17 15*	*17 50*	*18 11*	*18 45*	*19 44*	*20 52*	*21 43*	*22 49*
Salford Crescent	82 d	15 07	15 57	16 30	17 06	17 36	18 07	18 28	19 05	20 05	21 05	22 05	23 14
Bolton	82 d	15 19	16 09	16 42	17 18	17 51	18 19	18 44	19 18	20 18	21 18	22 18	23 28
Hall I' Th' Wood	d	15 24	16 14	16 47	17 23	17 56	18 24	18 49	19 23	20 23	21 23	22 23	23 33
Bromley Cross	d	15 27	16 17	16 50	17 26	17 59	18 27	18 53	19 26	20 26	21 26	22 26	23 36
Entwistle	d	15x33		16x57		18x06		19x00	19x32	20x32	21x32	22x32	23x42
Darwen	a	15 40	16 29	17 03	17 38	18 12	18 38	19 06	19 39	20 39	21 39	22 39	23 49
	d	15 40	16 29	17 07	17 42	18 12	18 38	19 09	19 39	20 39	21 39	22 39	23 49
Blackpool North	97 d	*14 30*	*15 30*	*15f41*	*16 30*		*17 19*		*18 30*		*20 28*		
Preston 8	97 d	*14 55*	*15 55*	*16 31*	*16 55*		*17 44*		*18 55*		*20 54*		
Blackburn	a	15 47	16 36	17 15	17 50	18 22	18 48	19 20	19 47	20 47	21 46	22 49	23 59
	d	15 48	16 38	17 15	17 50		18 48		19 48	20 48	21 48		
Ramsgreave & Wilpshire	d	15 54	16 44	17 21	17 56		18 54		19 54	20 54	21 54		
Langho	d	15 58	16 48	17 26	18 01		18 58		19 58	20 58	21 58		
Whalley	d	16 02	16 52	17 30	18 05		19 02		20 02	21 02	22 02		
Clitheroe	a	16 13	17 03	17 40	18 15		19 13		20 13	21 13	22 13		

Mondays to Fridays

from 6 October

		NT	NT	NT	NT	NT	NT	NT	NT	NT	NT	NT	NT
Manchester Victoria	82 d		06 26	07 00	07 23	08 00	08 23	09 00	10 00	11 00	12 00	13 00	14 00
Salford Central	82 d			07 03	07 26	08 03	08 26	09 03	10 03	11 03	12 03	13 03	14 03
Manchester Airport	82, 85 d		*05 47*	*06 19*	*06 47*	*07 22*	*07 47*	*08 27*	*09 27*	*10 27*	*11 27*	*12 27*	*13 27*
Manchester Piccadilly 10	82 d		*06 05*	*06 44*	*07 11*	*07 45*	*08 11*	*08 45*	*09 45*	*10 45*	*11 45*	*12 45*	*13 45*
Salford Crescent	82 d		06 31	07 06	07 31	08 07	08 29	09 07	10 07	11 07	12 07	13 07	14 07
Bolton	82 d		06 45	07 19	07 44	08 19	08 44	09 19	10 19	11 19	12 19	13 19	14 19
Hall I' Th' Wood	d		06 50	07 24	07 49	08 24	08 49	09 24	10 24	11 24	12 24	13 24	14 24
Bromley Cross	d		06 53	07 27	07 54	08 27	08 54	09 27	10 27	11 27	12 27	13 27	14 27
Entwistle	d				08x01	08x33		09x33			12x33		
Darwen	a		07 05	07 38	08 09	08 40	09 09	09 40	10 38	11 38	12 40	13 38	14 38
	d		07 08	07 39	08 09	08 40	09 09	09 40	10 38	11 38	12 40	13 38	14 38
Blackpool North	97 d	*05 30*	*06 28*			*07 30*		*08 29*	*09 30*	*10 30*	*11 30*	*12 30*	*13 30*
Preston 8	97 d	*05 55*	*06 54*			*08 01*		*08 54*	*09 55*	*10 55*	*11 55*	*12 55*	*13 55*
Blackburn	a		07 18	07 46	08 23	08 47	09 21	09 48	10 46	11 46	12 47	13 46	14 46
	d	06 25	07 19	07 47		08 48		09 48	10 48	11 48	12 48	13 48	14 48
Ramsgreave & Wilpshire	d	06 31	07 25	07 53		08 54		09 54	10 54	11 54	12 54	13 54	14 54
Langho	d	06 35	07 29	07 57		08 58		09 58	10 58	11 58	12 58	13 58	14 58
Whalley	d	06 39	07 33	08 01		09 02		10 02	11 02	12 02	13 02	14 02	15 02
Clitheroe	a	06 52	07 46	08 13		09 15		10 15	11 15	12 15	13 15	14 15	15 15

		NT	NT	NT	NT	NT A	NT	NT	NT	NT	NT	NT	NT
Manchester Victoria	82 d	15 00	15 50	16 23	17 00	17 29	18 00	18 21	18 58	19 58	20 58	21 58	23 08
Salford Central	82 d	15 03	15 53	16 26	17 03	17 32	18 03	18 24	19 01	20 01	21 01	22b01	23b11
Manchester Airport	82, 85 d	*14 27*	*15 07*	*15 47*	*16c27*	*16c47*	*17 32*	*17 47*	*18 27*	*19 27*	*20e22*	*21 27*	*22e22*
Manchester Piccadilly 10	82 d	*14 45*	*15 30*	*16 11*	*16c52*	*17 15*	*17 50*	*18 11*	*18 45*	*19 44*	*20 52*	*21 43*	*22 49*
Salford Crescent	82 d	15 07	15 57	16 29	17 06	17 36	18 07	18 28	19 05	20 05	21 05	22 05	23 14
Bolton	82 d	15 19	16 09	16 42	17 18	17 51	18 19	18 44	19 18	20 18	21 18	22 18	23 28
Hall I' Th' Wood	d	15 24	16 14	16 47	17 23	17 56	18 24	18 49	19 23	20 23	21 23	22 23	23 33
Bromley Cross	d	15 27	16 17	16 50	17 26	17 59	18 27	18 53	19 26	20 26	21 26	22 26	23 36
Entwistle	d	15x33		16x57		18x06		19x00	19x32	20x32	21x32	22x32	23x42
Darwen	a	15 40	16 29	17 03	17 38	18 12	18 38	19 06	19 39	20 39	21 39	22 39	23 49
	d	15 40	16 29	17 07	17 42	18 12	18 38	19 09	19 39	20 39	21 39	22 39	23 49
Blackpool North	97 d	*14 30*	*15 30*	*15f41*	*16 30*		*17 19*		*18 30*		*20 28*		
Preston 8	97 d	*14 55*	*15 55*	*16 31*	*16 55*		*17 44*		*18 55*		*20 54*		
Blackburn	a	15 47	16 36	17 15	17 50	18 22	18 48	19 20	19 47	20 47	21 46	22 49	23 59
	d	15 48	16 38	17 15	17 50		18 48		19 48	20 48	21 48		
Ramsgreave & Wilpshire	d	15 54	16 44	17 21	17 56		18 54		19 54	20 54	21 54		
Langho	d	15 58	16 48	17 26	18 01		18 58		19 58	20 58	21 58		
Whalley	d	16 02	16 52	17 30	18 05		19 02		20 02	21 02	22 02		
Clitheroe	a	16 15	17 05	17 42	18 17		19 15		20 15	21 15	22 15		

For general notes see front of timetable
For details of catering facilities see Directory of Train Operators

- **A** From Rochdale (Table 95) to Colne (Table 97)
- **b** Fridays only
- **c** Change at Bolton
- **e** Change at Manchester Piccadilly and Salford Crescent
- **f** Change at Preston and Blackburn

Table 94

Saturdays
until 4 October

Manchester and Bolton → Blackburn → Clitheroe

Network Diagram - see first page of Table 94

		NT	NT	NT	NT	NT	NT	NT	NT	NT	NT	NT	NT	NT	NT	NT	NT	NT A	NT	NT	NT	NT	NT	NT	NT
Manchester Victoria	82 🚇 d		06 26	07 00	07 23	08 00	08 23	09 00	10 00	11 00	12 00	13 00	14 00	15 00	15 50	16 23	17 00	17 29	18 00	18 21	18 58	19 58	20 58	21 58	23b08
Salford Central	82 d			07 03	07 26	08 03	08 26	09 03	10 03	11 03	12 03	13 03	14 03	15 03	15 53	16 26	17 03	17 32	18 03	18 24	19 01	20 01	21 01	22 01	23 11
Manchester Airport	82, 85 ✈ d		05 47	06 19	06 47	07 22	07 47	08 27	09 27	10 27	11 27	12 27	13 27	14 27	15 07	15 47	16c27	16c47	17 32	17 47	18 27	19 27	20e22	21 27	22e22
Manchester Piccadilly 10	82 🚇 d		06 05	06 44	07 11	07 45	08 11	08 45	09 45	10 45	11 45	12 45	13 45	14 45	15 30	16 11	16c52	17 15	17 50	18 11	18 45	19 44	20 52	21 45	22 49
Salford Crescent	82 d		06 31	07 06	07 31	08 07	08 29	09 07	10 07	11 07	12 07	13 07	14 07	15 07	15 57	16 29	17 07	17 36	18 07	18 28	19 05	20 05	21 05	22 05	23 14
Bolton	82 d		06 45	07 19	07 44	08 19	08 44	09 19	10 19	11 19	12 19	13 19	14 19	15 19	16 09	16 42	17 19	17 51	18 19	18 44	19 18	20 18	21 18	22 18	23 28
Hall I' Th' Wood	d		06 50	07 24	07 49	08 24	08 49	09 24	10 24	11 24	12 24	13 24	14 24	15 24	16 14	16 47	17 24	17 56	18 24	18 49	19 23	20 23	21 23	22 23	23 33
Bromley Cross	d		06 53	07 27	07 54	08 27	08 54	09 27	10 27	11 27	12 27	13 27	14 27	15 27	16 17	16 50	17 27	17 59	18 27	18 53	19 26	20 27	21 26	22 26	23 36
Entwistle	d				08x01	08x33		09x33			12x33			15x33		16x57		18x06		19x00	19x32	20x32	21x32	22x32	23x42
Darwen	a		07 05	07 38	08 09	08 40	09 09	09 40	10 38	11 38	12 40	13 38	14 38	15 40	16 29	17 03	17 38	18 12	18 38	19 06	19 39	20 40	21 39	22 39	23 49
	d		07 08	07 39	08 09	08 40	09 09	09 40	10 38	11 38	12 40	13 38	14 38	15 40	16 29	17 07	17 42	18 12	18 38	19 09	19 39	20 40	21 39	22 39	23 49
Blackpool North	97 d	05 30	06 27			07 30		08 27	09 30	10 30	11 30	12 30	13 30	14 30	15 30	15f41	16 30		17 19		18 30		20 30		
Preston 8	97 d	05 55	06 54			08 01		08 52	09 55	10 55	11 55	12 55	13 55	14 55	15 55	16 31	16 55		17 44		18 56		20 55		
Blackburn	a		07 18	07 46	08 21	08 47	09 21	09 48	10 46	11 46	12 47	13 46	14 46	15 47	16 36	17 15	17 50	18 24	18 48	19 20	19 47	20 47	21 46	22 49	23 59
	d	06 25	07 19	07 47		08 48		09 48	10 48	11 46	12 48	13 48	14 48	15 48	16 38	17 15	17 50		18 48		19 48	20 48	21 48		
Ramsgreave & Wilpshire	d	06 31	07 25	07 53		08 54		09 54	10 54	11 52	12 54	13 54	14 54	15 54	16 44	17 21	17 56		18 54		19 54	20 54	21 54		
Langho	d	06 35	07 29	07 57		08 58		09 58	10 58	11 57	12 58	13 58	14 58	15 58	16 48	17 26	18 01		18 58		19 58	20 58	21 58		
Whalley	d	06 39	07 33	08 01		09 02		10 02	11 02	12 01	13 02	14 02	15 02	16 02	16 52	17 30	18 05		19 02		20 02	21 02	22 02		
Clitheroe	a	06 50	07 44	08 13		09 13		10 13	11 13	12 11	13 13	14 13	15 13	16 13	17 03	17 40	18 15		19 13		20 13	21 13	22 13		

Saturdays
from 11 October

		NT	NT	NT	NT	NT	NT	NT	NT	NT	NT	NT	NT	NT	NT	NT	NT	NT A	NT	NT	NT	NT	NT	NT	NT
Manchester Victoria	82 🚇 d		06 26	07 00	07 23	08 00	08 23	09 00	10 00	11 00	12 00	13 00	14 00	15 00	15 50	16 23	17 00	17 29	18 00	18 21	18 58	19 58	20 57	21 58	23 08
Salford Central	82 d			07 03	07 26	08 03	08 26	09 03	10 03	11 03	12 03	13 03	14 03	15 03	15 53	16 26	17 03	17 32	18 03	18 24	19 01	20 01	21 01	22 01	23 11
Manchester Airport	82, 85 ✈ d		05 47	06 19	06 47	07 22	07 47	08 27	09 27	10 27	11 27	12 27	13 27	14 27	15 07	15 47	16c27	16c47	17 32	17 47	18 27	19 27	20e22	21 27	22e22
Manchester Piccadilly 10	82 🚇 d		06 05	06 44	07 11	07 45	08 11	08 45	09 45	10 45	11 45	12 45	13 45	14 45	15 30	16 11	16c52	17 15	17 50	18 11	18 45	19 44	20 52	21 45	22 49
Salford Crescent	82 d		06 31	07 06	07 31	08 07	08 29	09 07	10 07	11 07	12 07	13 07	14 07	15 07	15 57	16 29	17 07	17 36	18 07	18 28	19 05	20 05	21 05	22 05	23 14
Bolton	82 d		06 45	07 19	07 44	08 19	08 44	09 19	10 19	11 19	12 19	13 19	14 19	15 19	16 09	16 42	17 19	17 51	18 19	18 44	19 18	20 18	21 18	22 18	23 28
Hall I' Th' Wood	d		06 50	07 24	07 49	08 24	08 49	09 24	10 24	11 24	12 24	13 24	14 24	15 24	16 14	16 47	17 24	17 56	18 24	18 49	19 23	20 23	21 23	22 23	23 33
Bromley Cross	d		06 53	07 27	07 54	08 27	08 54	09 27	10 27	11 27	12 27	13 27	14 27	15 27	16 17	16 50	17 27	17 59	18 27	18 53	19 26	20 26	21 26	22 26	23 36
Entwistle	d				08x01	08x33		09x33			12x33			15x33		16x57		18x06		19x00	19x32	20x32	21x32	22x32	23x42
Darwen	a		07 05	07 38	08 09	08 40	09 09	09 40	10 38	11 38	12 40	13 38	14 38	15 40	16 29	17 03	17 38	18 12	18 38	19 06	19 39	20 39	21 39	22 39	23 49
	d		07 08	07 39	08 09	08 40	09 09	09 40	10 38	11 38	12 40	13 38	14 38	15 40	16 29	17 07	17 42	18 12	18 38	19 09	19 39	20 39	21 39	22 39	23 49
Blackpool North	97 d	05 30	06 27			07 30		08 27	09 30	10 30	11 30	12 30	13 30	14 30	15 30	15f41	16 30		17 19		18 30		20 30		
Preston 8	97 d	05 55	06 54			08 01		08 52	09 55	10 55	11 55	12 55	13 55	14 55	15 55	16 31	16 55		17 44		18 56		20 55		
Blackburn	a		07 18	07 46	08 21	08 47	09 21	09 48	10 46	11 46	12 47	13 46	14 46	15 47	16 36	17 15	17 50	18 24	18 48	19 20	19 47	20 47	21 46	22 49	23 59
	d	06 25	07 19	07 47		08 48		09 48	10 48	11 46	12 48	13 48	14 48	15 48	16 38	17 15	17 50		18 48		19 48	20 48	21 48		
Ramsgreave & Wilpshire	d	06 31	07 25	07 53		08 54		09 54	10 54	11 52	12 54	13 54	14 54	15 54	16 44	17 21	17 56		18 54		19 54	20 54	21 54		
Langho	d	06 35	07 29	07 57		08 58		09 58	10 58	11 57	12 58	13 58	14 58	15 58	16 48	17 26	18 01		18 58		19 58	20 58	21 58		
Whalley	d	06 39	07 33	08 01		09 02		10 02	11 02	12 01	13 02	14 02	15 02	16 02	16 52	17 30	18 05		19 02		20 02	21 02	22 02		
Clitheroe	a	06 52	07 46	08 13		09 15		10 15	11 15	12 13	13 15	14 15	15 15	16 15	17 05	17 42	18 17		19 15		20 15	21 15	22 15		

Sundays

		NT	NT B ⚮	NT	NT C ⚮	NT	NT	NT	NT	NT	NT	NT	NT	NT	NT	NT	NT	NT
Manchester Victoria	82 🚇 d	08 00		09 00		10 00	11 00	12 00	13 00	14 00	15 00	16 00	17 00	18 00	19 00	20 00	21 00	22 00
Salford Central	82 d																	
Manchester Airport	82, 85 ✈ d																	
Manchester Piccadilly 10	82 🚇 d																	
Salford Crescent	82 d			09 05		10 05	11 05	12 05	13 05	14 05	15 05	16 05	17 05	18 05	19 05	20 05	21 05	22 05
Bolton	82 d	08 13		09 18		10 18	11 18	12 18	13 18	14 18	15 18	16 18	17 18	18 18	19 18	20 18	21 18	22 18
Hall I' Th' Wood	d			09 23			11 23		13 23		15 23		17 23		19 23		21 23	
Bromley Cross	d	08 20		09 26		10 24	11 26	12 24	13 26	14 24	15 26	16 24	17 26	18 24	19 26	20 24	21 26	22 24
Entwistle	d					10x31		12x31		14x31		16x31		18x31		20x31		22x31
Darwen	a	08 31		09 37		10 37	11 37	12 37	13 37	14 37	15 37	16 37	17 37	18 37	19 37	20 37	21 37	22 37
	d	08 31		09 37		10 37	11 37	12 37	13 37	14 37	15 37	16 37	17 37	18 37	19 37	20 37	21 37	22 37
Blackpool North	97 d		08 42															
Preston 8	97 d		09 10		10 00													
Blackburn	a	08 39	09 29	09 46	10 19	10 45	11 45	12 45	13 45	14 45	15 45	16 45	17 44	18 45	19 45	20 45	21 45	22 47
	d	08 43	09 30	09 55	10 22	10 50	11 45	12 45	13 45	14 45	15 45	16 45	17 45	18 45	19 45	20 45	21 45	
Ramsgreave & Wilpshire	d	08 49	09 36	10 01	10 28	10 56	11 51	12 51	13 51	14 51	15 51	16 51	17 51	18 51	19 51	20 51	21 51	
Langho	d	08 54	09 41	10 05	10 33	11 00	11 56	12 56	13 56	14 56	15 56	16 56	17 56	18 56	19 56	20 56	21 56	
Whalley	d	08 58	09 46	10 09	10 38	11 04	12 00	13 00	14 00	15 00	16 00	17 00	18 00	19 00	20 00	21 00	22 00	
Clitheroe	a	09 08	09 52	10 20	10 44	11 15	12 10	13 10	14 10	15 10	16 10	17 10	18 10	19 10	20 10	21 10	22 10	

For general notes see front of timetable
For details of catering facilities see Directory of Train Operators

A From Rochdale (Table 95)
B Until 19 October. To Carlisle (Table 36)
C Until 14 September. To Carlisle (Table 36)
b 19 July to 6 September dep. 2307
c Change at Bolton
e Change at Manchester Piccadilly and Salford Crescent
f Change at Preston and Blackburn

Clitheroe → Blackburn → Bolton and Manchester

Mondays to Fridays
until 3 October

Network Diagram - see first page of Table 94

Miles		NT	NT A	NT	NT	NT B	NT	NT	NT	NT	NT	NT	NT
0	**Clitheroe** d			07 08	07 35	07 56		08 26		09 36	10 36	11 36	12 36
2½	Whalley d			07 14	07 41	08 02		08 32		09 42	10 42	11 42	12 42
4½	Langho d			07 18	07 45	08 06		08 36		09 46	10 46	11 46	12 46
7	Ramsgreave & Wilpshire d			07 23	07 50	08 11		08 41		09 51	10 51	11 51	12 51
9¾	**Blackburn** a			07 29	07 57	08 19		08 47		09 58	10 57	11 57	12 57
—	d	06 30	07 00	07 30	08 00	08 19	08 30	09 00	09 30	10 00	11 00	12 00	13 00
—	Preston 8 97 a			08 17	08 33	08 43		09 34		10 32	11 34	12 32	13 32
—	Blackpool North 97 a			08b51	09 04	09 32		10 02		11 02	12 01	13 00	13 59
14	Darwen a	06 37	07 07	07 37	08 07		08 37	09 07	09 37	10 07	11 07	12 07	13 07
—	d	06 37	07 07	07 40	08 10		08 41	09 10	09 41	10 07	11 07	12 07	13 07
17¾	Entwistle d	06x44		07x46						10x14		12x14	
20¾	Bromley Cross d	06 50	07 18	07 51	08 21		08 52	09 21	09 52	10 19	11 19	12 19	13 19
21¾	Hall I' Th' Wood d	06 52	07 23	07 54	08 24		08 55	09 24	09 55	10 22	11c24	12 22	13 22
23¼	**Bolton** 82 a	06 57	07 29	07 59	08 29		09 00	09 29	10 00	10 29	11 29	12 29	13 29
32½	Salford Crescent 82 a	07 17	07 42	08 12	08 42		09 16	09 42	10 13	10 43	11 42	12 42	13 42
—	Manchester Piccadilly 10 82 a	07 36	08 19	08e25	08e53		09 35	09 57	10 35	10 57	11 57	12 57	13 57
—	Manchester Airport 82, 85 a	08 02		08e42	09e13		10 01	10 19	11 01	11 19	12 19	13 19	14 19
33¼	Salford Central 82 a	07 20	07 46	08 15	08 45		09 18	09 45	10 16	10 45	11 45	12 45	13 45
34¼	**Manchester Victoria** 82 a	07 25	07 51	08 21	08 50		09 25	09 50	10 21	10 50	11 50	12 50	13 50

	NT	NT	NT	NT	NT	NT	NT	NT	NT	NT	NT C	NT
Clitheroe d	13 36	14 36	15 26	16 36	17 12	18 08	18 36		19 36	20 36	21 36	22 46
Whalley d	13 42	14 42	15 32	16 42	17 18	18 14	18 42		19 42	20 42	21 42	22 52
Langho d	13 46	14 46	15 36	16 46	17 23	18 18	18 46		19 46	20 46	21 46	22 56
Ramsgreave & Wilpshire d	13 51	14 51	15 41	16 51	17 27	18 23	18 51		19 51	20 51	21 51	23 01
Blackburn a	13 57	14 57	15 47	16 57	17 34	18 30	18 57		19 57	20 57	22 00	23 10
d	14 00	15 00	15 50	16 58	17 34	18 31	19 00	19 30	20 00	21 00	22 00	23 10
Preston 8 97 a	14 32	15 32	16 33	17 34	18 07	19 10	19 36		20 31	21 31	22 51	23 53
Blackpool North 97 a	15 00	16 00	17 00	18 03	18b48	19b57	20 03		20 56	21 56	23b28	00b38
Darwen a	14 07	15 07	15 57	17 06	17 42	18 38	19 07	19 37	20 07	21 07	22 07	23 18
d	14 07	15 07	15 57	17 06	17 42	18 41	19 07	19 40	20 07	21 07	22 07	23 18
Entwistle d		15x14		17x13	17x49		19x14		20x14	21x14	22x14	23x25
Bromley Cross d	14 19	15 19	16 08	17 18	17 54	18 52	19 19	19 51	20 19	21 19	22 19	23 30
Hall I' Th' Wood d	14 22	15 22	16c14	17c23	17 58	18 55	19 22	19 53	20 22	21 22	22 22	23 34
Bolton 82 a	14 29	15 29	16 19	17 30	18 03	19 00	19 29	19 58	20 29	21 29	22 29	23 39
Salford Crescent 82 a	14 42	15 42	16 34	17 48	18 14	19 13	19 42	20 13	20 42	21 42	22 46	23 52
Manchester Piccadilly 10 82 a	14 57	15 57	16 57	17 57	18 38	19 36	19 57	20 34	20 58	22 18	22 56	00e29
Manchester Airport 82, 85 a	15 19	16 19	17 19	18 19	19 09	20 05	20 19	21f06	21 19	22 39	23 28	00e45
Salford Central 82 a	14 45	15 45	16 37	17 45	18 16	19 16	19 45	20 16	20 45	21 45		
Manchester Victoria 82 a	14 50	15 50	16 42	17 51	18 23	19 23	19 50	20 22	20 50	21 50		00 01

Mondays to Fridays
from 6 October

	NT	NT A	NT	NT	NT B	NT	NT	NT	NT	NT	NT	NT
Clitheroe d			07 03	07 30	07 51		08 23		09 31	10 36	11 31	12 31
Whalley d			07 09	07 36	07 57		08 29		09 37	10 42	11 37	12 37
Langho d			07 13	07 40	08 01		08 33		09 41	10 46	11 41	12 41
Ramsgreave & Wilpshire d			07 18	07 45	08 06		08 38		09 46	10 51	11 46	12 46
Blackburn a			07 29	07 57	08 19		08 47		09 58	10 57	11 57	12 57
d	06 30	07 00	07 30	08 00	08 19	08 30	09 00	09 30	10 00	11 00	12 00	13 00
Preston 8 97 a			08 17	08 33	08 43		09 34		10 32	11 34	12 32	13 32
Blackpool North 97 a			08b51	09 04	09 32		10 02		11 02	12 01	13 00	13 59
Darwen a	06 37	07 07	07 37	08 07		08 37	09 07	09 37	10 07	11 07	12 07	13 07
d	06 37	07 07	07 39	08 10		08 41	09 10	09 41	10 07	11 07	12 07	13 07
Entwistle d	06x44		07x46						10x14		12x14	
Bromley Cross d	06 50	07 18	07 52	08 21		08 52	09 21	09 52	10 19	11 19	12 19	13 19
Hall I' Th' Wood d	06 52	07 23	07 54	08 24		08 55	09 24	09 55	10 22	11c24	12 22	13 22
Bolton 82 a	06 57	07 29	07 59	08 29		09 00	09 29	10 00	10 29	11 29	12 29	13 29
Salford Crescent 82 a	07 17	07 42	08 12	08 42		09 16	09 42	10 13	10 42	11 42	12 42	13 42
Manchester Piccadilly 10 82 a	07 36	08 19	08e25	08e53		09 35	09 57	10 35	10 57	11 57	12 57	13 57
Manchester Airport 82, 85 a	08 02		08e42	09e13		10 01	10 19	11 01	11 19	12 19	13 19	14 19
Salford Central 82 a	07 20	07 46	08 15	08 45		09 18	09 45	10 16	10 45	11 45	12 45	13 45
Manchester Victoria 82 a	07 25	07 51	08 21	08 50		09 25	09 50	10 21	10 50	11 50	12 50	13 50

	NT	NT	NT	NT	NT	NT	NT	NT	NT	NT	NT C	NT
Clitheroe d	13 31	14 31	15 23	16 31	17 12	18 03	18 31		19 31	20 31	21 36	22 41
Whalley d	13 37	14 37	15 29	16 37	17 18	18 09	18 37		19 37	20 37	21 42	22 47
Langho d	13 41	14 41	15 33	16 41	17 23	18 13	18 41		19 41	20 41	21 46	22 51
Ramsgreave & Wilpshire d	13 46	14 46	15 38	16 46	17 27	18 18	18 46		19 46	20 46	21 51	22 56
Blackburn a	13 57	14 57	15 47	16 57	17 34	18 29	18 57		19 57	20 57	22 00	23 10
d	14 00	15 00	15 50	16 58	17 34	18 30	19 00	19 30	20 00	21 00	22 00	23 10
Preston 8 97 a	14 32	15 32	16 33	17 34	18 07	19 10	19 36		20 31	21 31	22 51	23 53
Blackpool North 97 a	15 00	16 00	17 00	18 03	18b48	19b57	20 03		20 56	21 56	23b28	00b38
Darwen a	14 07	15 07	15 57	17 06	17 42	18 37	19 07	19 37	20 07	21 07	22 07	23 18
d	14 07	15 07	15 57	17 06	17 42	18 41	19 07	19 40	20 07	21 07	22 07	23 18
Entwistle d		15x14		17x13	17x49		19x14		20x14	21x14	22x14	23x25
Bromley Cross d	14 19	15 19	16 08	17 18	17 54	18 52	19 19	19 51	20 19	21 19	22 19	23 30
Hall I' Th' Wood d	14 22	15 22	16c14	17g23	17 58	18 55	19 22	19 53	20 22	21 22	22 22	23 34
Bolton 82 a	14 29	15 29	16 19	17 30	18 03	19 00	19 29	19 58	20 29	21 29	22 29	23 39
Salford Crescent 82 a	14 42	15 42	16 34	17 48	18 14	19 13	19 42	20 13	20 42	21 42	22 46	23 52
Manchester Piccadilly 10 82 a	14 57	15 57	16 57	17 57	18 38	19 36	19 57	20 34	20 58	22 18	22 56	00e29
Manchester Airport 82, 85 a	15 19	16 19	17 19	18 19	19 09	20 05	20 19	21f06	21 19	22 39	23 28	00e45
Salford Central 82 a	14 45	15 45	16 37	17 45	18 16	19 16	19 45	20 16	20 45	21 45		
Manchester Victoria 82 a	14 50	15 50	16 42	17 51	18 23	19 23	19 50	20 22	20 50	21 50		00 01

For general notes see front of timetable
For details of catering facilities see Directory of Train Operators

- **A** From Colne (Table 97)
- **B** To Morecambe (Table 98)
- **C** To Buxton (Table 86)
- **b** Change at Blackburn and Preston
- **c** Arr. 3 minutes earlier
- **e** Change at Bolton
- **f** Change at Salford Crescent and Manchester Piccadilly
- **g** Arr. 4 minutes earlier

Table 94

Saturdays
until 4 October

Clitheroe → Blackburn → Bolton and Manchester

Network Diagram - see first page of Table 94

		NT	NT	NT	NT	NT A	NT	NT	NT	NT	NT	NT	NT	NT	NT	NT	NT	NT	NT	NT	NT	NT	NT	NT B	NT
Clitheroe	d			07 08	07 35	07 56		08 26		09 36	10 36	11 36	12 36	13 36	14 36	15 26	16 36	17 12	18 08	18 36		19 36	20 36	21 36	22 46
Whalley	d			07 14	07 41	08 02		08 32		09 42	10 42	11 42	12 42	13 42	14 42	15 32	16 42	17 18	18 14	18 42		19 42	20 42	21 42	22 52
Langho	d			07 18	07 45	08 06		08 36		09 46	10 46	11 46	12 46	13 46	14 46	15 36	16 46	17 23	18 18	18 46		19 46	20 46	21 46	22 56
Ramsgreave & Wilpshire	d			07 23	07 50	08 11		08 41		09 51	10 51	11 51	12 51	13 51	14 51	15 41	16 51	17 27	18 23	18 51		19 51	20 51	21 51	23 01
Blackburn	a			07 29	07 57	08 19		08 47		09 57	10 57	11 57	12 57	13 57	14 57	15 47	16 57	17 34	18 29	18 57		19 57	20 57	22 00	23 10
	d	06 30	07 00	07 30	08 00	08 19	08 30	09 00	09 30	10 00	11 00	12 00	13 00	14 00	15 00	15 50	16 58	17 34	18 30	19 00	19 30	20 00	21 00	22 00	23 10
Preston 8	97 a			08 17	08 33	08 43		09 33		10 32	11 34	12 32	13 32	14 32	15 32	16 33	17 34	18 07	19 10	19 35		20 31	21 31	22 51	23 53
Blackpool North	97 a			08b51	09 03	09 32		10 02		11 03	12 01	13 01	14 00	15 01	16 01	17 01	18 03	18b48	20c01	20 07		20 56	21 56	23b28	00b38
Darwen	a	06 37	07 07	07 37	08 07		08 37	09 07	09 37	10 07	11 07	12 07	13 07	14 07	15 07	15 57	17 06	17 42	18 37	19 07	19 37	20 07	21 07	22 07	23 18
	d	06 37	07 07	07 40	08 10		08 41	09 10	09 41	10 07	11 07	12 07	13 07	14 07	15 07	15 57	17 06	17 42	18 41	19 07	19 40	20 07	21 07	22 07	23 18
Entwistle	d	06x44		07x47						10x14		12x14			15x14		17x13	17x49		19x14		20x14	21x14	22x14	23x25
Bromley Cross	d	06 50	07 18	07 52	08 21		08 52	09 21	09 52	10 19	11 19	12 19	13 19	14 19	15 19	16 08	17 18	17 54	18 52	19 19	19 51	20 19	21 19	22 19	23 30
Hall I' Th' Wood	d	06 52	07 23	07 55	08 24		08 55	09 24	09 55	10 22	11 22	12 22	13 22	14 22	15 22	16e14	17f23	17 58	18 55	19 22	19 53	20 22	21 22	22 22	23 34
Bolton	82 a	06 57	07 29	08 00	08 29		09 00	09 29	10 00	10 29	11 29	12 29	13 29	14 29	15 29	16 19	17 30	18 03	19 00	19 29	19 58	20 29	21 29	22 29	23 39
Salford Crescent	82 a	07 17	07 42	08 13	08 42		09 16	09 42	10 13	10 43	11 43	12 43	13 42	14 43	15 42	16 34	17 48	18 14	19 13	19 42	20 13	20 42	21 42	22 46	23 53
Manchester Piccadilly 10	82 a	07 36	08 20	08 47	08g53		09 35	09 57	10 35	10 57	11 57	12 57	13 57	14 57	15 57	16 57	17 57	18 38	19 36	19 57	20 34	20 58	22 18	22 56	00g29
Manchester Airport	82, 85 a	08 02	08g42	09 06	09g13		10 02	10 19	11 01	11 19	12 19	13 19	14 19	15 19	16 19	17 19	18 19	19 08	20 05	20 19	21h06	21 19	22 39	23 56	00g45
Salford Central	82 a	07 20	07 45	08 16	08 45		09 19	09 45	10 16	10 45	11 45	12 45	13 45	14 45	15 45	16 37	17 45	18 17	19 16	19 45	20 16	20 45	21 45		
Manchester Victoria	82 a	07 25	07 51	08 21	08 50		09 25	09 50	10 21	10 50	11 51	12 50	13 50	14 50	15 50	16 42	17 51	18 23	19 23	19 50	20 22	20 50	21 50		23 59

Saturdays
from 11 October

		NT	NT	NT	NT	NT A	NT	NT	NT	NT	NT	NT	NT	NT	NT	NT	NT	NT	NT	NT	NT	NT	NT	NT B	NT
Clitheroe	d			07 03	07 30	07 56		08 23		09 31	10 31	11 31	12 31	13 31	14 31	15 23	16 31	17 12	18 03	18 31		19 31	20 31	21 36	22 41
Whalley	d			07 09	07 36	08 02		08 29		09 37	10 37	11 37	12 37	13 37	14 37	15 29	16 37	17 18	18 09	18 37		19 37	20 37	21 42	22 47
Langho	d			07 13	07 40	08 06		08 33		09 41	10 41	11 41	12 41	13 41	14 41	15 33	16 41	17 23	18 13	18 41		19 41	20 41	21 46	22 51
Ramsgreave & Wilpshire	d			07 18	07 45	08 11		08 38		09 46	10 46	11 46	12 46	13 46	14 46	15 38	16 46	17 27	18 18	18 46		19 46	20 46	21 51	22 56
Blackburn	a			07 29	07 57	08 19		08 47		09 57	10 57	11 57	12 57	13 57	14 57	15 47	16 57	17 34	18 29	18 57		19 57	20 57	22 00	23 10
	d	06 30	07 00	07 30	08 00	08 19	08 30	09 00	09 30	10 00	11 00	12 00	13 00	14 00	15 00	15 50	16 58	17 34	18 30	19 00	19 30	20 00	21 00	22 00	23 10
Preston 8	97 a			08 17	08 33	08 43		09 33		10 32	11 34	12 32	13 32	14 32	15 32	16 33	17 34	18 07	19 10	19 35		20 31	21 31	22 51	23 53
Blackpool North	97 a			08b51	09 03	09 32		10 02		11 03	12 01	13 01	14 00	15 01	16 01	17 01	18 03	18b48	19b57	20 07		20 56	21 56	23b28	00b38
Darwen	a	06 37	07 07	07 37	08 07		08 37	09 07	09 37	10 07	11 07	12 07	13 07	14 07	15 07	15 57	17 06	17 42	18 37	19 07	19 37	20 07	21 07	22 07	23 18
	d	06 37	07 07	07 40	08 10		08 41	09 10	09 41	10 07	11 07	12 07	13 07	14 07	15 07	15 57	17 06	17 42	18 41	19 07	19 40	20 07	21 07	22 07	23 18
Entwistle	d	06x44		07x47						10x14		12x14			15x14		17x13	17x49		19x14		20x14	21x14	22x14	23x25
Bromley Cross	d	06 50	07 18	07 52	08 21		08 52	09 21	09 52	10 19	11 19	12 19	13 19	14 19	15 19	16 08	17 18	17 54	18 52	19 19	19 51	20 19	21 19	22 19	23 30
Hall I' Th' Wood	d	06 52	07 23	07 55	08 24		08 55	09 24	09 55	10 22	11 22	12 22	13 22	14 22	15 22	16e14	17f23	17 58	18 55	19 22	19 53	20 22	21 22	22 22	23 34
Bolton	82 a	06 57	07 29	08 00	08 29		09 00	09 29	10 00	10 29	11 29	12 29	13 29	14 29	15 29	16 19	17 30	18 03	19 00	19 29	19 58	20 29	21 29	22 29	23 39
Salford Crescent	82 a	07 17	07 42	08 13	08 42		09 16	09 42	10 13	10 43	11 43	12 43	13 42	14 43	15 42	16 34	17 48	18 14	19 13	19 42	20 13	20 42	21 42	22 46	23 53
Manchester Piccadilly 10	82 a	07 36	08 20	08 47	08g53		09 35	09 57	10 35	10 57	11 57	12 57	13 57	14 57	15 57	16 57	17 57	18 38	19 36	19 57	20 34	20 58	22 18	22 56	00g29
Manchester Airport	82, 85 a	08 02	08g42	09 06	09g13		10 02	10 19	11 01	11 19	12 19	13 19	14 19	15 19	16 19	17 19	18 19	19 08	20 05	20 19	21h06	21 19	22 39	23 56	00g45
Salford Central	82 a	07 20	07 45	08 16	08 45		09 19	09 45	10 16	10 45	11 45	12 45	13 45	14 45	15 45	16 37	17 45	18 17	19 16	19 45	20 16	20 45	21 45		
Manchester Victoria	82 a	07 25	07 51	08 21	08 50		09 25	09 50	10 21	10 50	11 52	12 50	13 50	14 50	15 50	16 42	17 51	18 23	19 23	19 50	20 22	20 50	21 50		23 59

Sundays

		NT	NT		NT	NT		NT	NT		NT	NT		NT	NT		NT C 🍴	NT	NT	NT D 🍴	NT	NT	NT		
Clitheroe	d		09 17		10 27	11 24		12 24	13 24		14 24	15 24		16 24	17 24		17 49	18 24	19 24	19 47	20 24	21 24	22 24		
Whalley	d		09 23		10 33	11 30		12 30	13 30		14 30	15 30		16 30	17 30		17 55	18 30	19 30	19 55	20 30	21 30	22 30		
Langho	d		09 27		10 37	11 34		12 34	13 34		14 34	15 34		16 34	17 34		18 00	18 34	19 34	20 00	20 34	21 34	22 34		
Ramsgreave & Wilpshire	d		09 32		10 42	11 39		12 39	13 39		14 39	15 39		16 39	17 39		18 05	18 39	19 39	20 05	20 39	21 39	22 39		
Blackburn	a		09 38		10 48	11 45		12 45	13 45		14 45	15 45		16 45	17 45		18 15	18 45	19 45	20 14	20 45	21 45	22 45		
	d	08 48	09 48		10 48	11 48		12 48	13 48		14 48	15 48		16 48	17 48		18 15	18 48	19 48	20 14	20 48	21 48	22 48		
Preston 8	97 a																18 39			20 34					
Blackpool North	97 a																			21 03					
Darwen	a	08 55	09 55		10 55	11 55		12 55	13 55		14 55	15 55		16 55	17 55			18 55	19 55		20 55	21 55	22 55		
	d	08 55	09 55		10 55	11 55		12 55	13 55		14 55	15 55		16 55	17 55			18 55	19 55		20 55	21 55	22 55		
Entwistle	d		10x02			12x02			14x02			16x02			18x02				20x02			22x02			
Bromley Cross	d	09 06	10 08		11 06	12 08		13 06	14 08		15 06	16 08		17 06	18 08			19 06	20 08		21 06	22 08	23 06		
Hall I' Th' Wood	d	09 09			11 09			13 09			15 09			17 09				19 09			21 09		23 09		
Bolton	82 a	09 14	10 14		11 16	12 14		13 14	14 14		15 14	16 14		17 14	18 14			19 14	20 14		21 14	22 14	23 15		
Salford Crescent	82 a	09 29	10 29		11 29	12 29		13 29	14 29		15 29	16 29		17 29	18 29			19 29	20 29		21 29	22 29	23 29		
Manchester Piccadilly 10	82 a																								
Manchester Airport	82, 85 a																								
Salford Central	82 a																								
Manchester Victoria	82 a	09 35	10 35		11 35	12 35		13 35	14 35		15 35	16 35		17 35	18 35			19 35	20 35		21 35	22 35	23 35		

For general notes see front of timetable
For details of catering facilities see Directory of Train Operators

- **A** To Morecambe (Table 98)
- **B** To Buxton (Table 86)
- **C** Until 14 September. From Carlisle (Table 36)
- **D** Until 19 October. From Carlisle (Table 36)
- **b** Change at Blackburn and Preston
- **c** Change at Blackburn and Preston. From 13 September arr. 1957
- **e** Arr. 3 minutes earlier
- **f** Arr. 4 minutes earlier
- **g** Change at Bolton
- **h** Change at Salford Crescent and Manchester Piccadilly

Table 95

Mondays to Saturdays
until 4 October

Manchester → Oldham and Rochdale

Network Diagram - see first page of Table 94

Miles	Miles			NT A	NT SX B	NT SO B	NT	NT B	NT	NT	NT B	NT	NT	NT B	NT	NT SX C	NT	NT	NT B	NT	NT D	NT	NT	NT B	NT
—	—	Liverpool Lime Street 10	90 d							05 47			06b39	06c39						07 18				07 47	
—	—	Bolton	82 d										06 58		07 30	07 33		07c33	07e46	07e59			08b11	08 15	08 30
—	—	Salford Crescent	82 d							06b46			07f19		07g47	07 59		07c47	08e03	08 18	08 18		08b28	08 32	08h46
—	—	Salford Central	82 d							06b49			07f22		07g50	08 02		07c49	08e06	08 21	08 21		08b31	08 35	08h49
0	0	**Manchester Victoria**	d	05 54	06 18	06 24	06 45	06 49		07 07	07 18	07 25	07 42	07 47	08 00	08 09		08 12	08 19	08 30	08 33		08 42	08 54	09 00
—	4	Moston	d		06 25			06 55			07 25			07 53					08 25		08 40				
—	5¾	Mills Hill	d		06 30			07 00			07 30			07 58					08 30		08 44				
—	8¾	Castleton	d		06 35			07 05			07 35			08 03					08 35		08 49				
2½	—	Dean Lane	d				06 51			07 13			07 48					08 18					08 48		
3½	—	Failsworth	d				06 54			07 16			07 51					08 21					08 51		
4¾	—	Hollinwood	d				06 56			07 18			07 54					08 24					08 54		
6¼	—	Oldham Werneth	d				07 01			07 23			07 58					08 28					08 58		
7½	—	**Oldham Mumps**	d				07 04			07 26		07 39	08 02		08 14			08 32		08 44			09 02		09 14
8	—	Derker	d				07 07			07 29			08 04					08 34					09 04		
10	—	Shaw & Crompton	a				07 11		←	07 35		07 44	08 11		08 19		←	08 41		08 49		←	09 11		09 19
—	—		d				07 11 →		07 11			07 44			08 19 →		08 19			08 49 →		08 49			09 19 →
11¾	—	New Hey	d						07 14			07 47					08 23					08 52			
12¾	—	Milnrow	d						07 17			07 50					08 25					08 55			
14¾	10½	**Rochdale**	a	06 08	06 38	06 38		07 08	07 25		07 38	07 57		08 06		08 25	08 33		08 38		08 55	09 03		09 08	

		NT E	NT	NT		NT B	NT	NT C	NT	NT	NT B	NT	NT G	NT	NT	NT B	NT	NT C	NT	NT	NT B	NT	NT D	NT	NT
Liverpool Lime Street 10	90 d										08 48										09 48				
Bolton	82 d					08 50	09 01					09 30				09 50	10 01			10 07		10 30			
Salford Crescent	82 d	08j46				09 07	09 16	09k19				09 42	09 50			10 07	10 17	10 17		10 22		10 43	10 50		
Salford Central	82 d	08j49				09 09	09 19	09k24				09 45	09 53			10 09	10 20	10 20		10 24		10 45	10 53		
Manchester Victoria	d	09 03		09 15		09 24	09 30	09 33		09 45	09 54	10 00	10 03		10 15	10 24	10 30	10 33		10 45	10 54	11 00	11 03		11 15
Moston	d	09 09						09 40					10 10					10 40					11 10		
Mills Hill	d	09 13						09 44					10 14					10 44					11 14		
Castleton	d	09 18						09 49					10 19					10 49					11 19		
Dean Lane	d			09 22						09 52					10 22					10 52					11 22
Failsworth	d			09 25						09 55					10 25					10 55					11 25
Hollinwood	d			09 27						09 57					10 27					10 57					11 27
Oldham Werneth	d			09 32						10 02					10 32					11 02					11 32
Oldham Mumps	d			09 35			09 44			10 05		10 14			10 35		10 44			11 05		11 14			11 35
Derker	d			09 38						10 08					10 38					11 08					11 38
Shaw & Crompton	a		←	09 44			09 49		←	10 14		10 19		←	10 44		10 49		←	11 14		11 19		←	11 44
	d		09 19				09 49 →		09 49			10 19 →		10 19			10 49 →		10 49			11 19 →		11 19	
New Hey	d		09 23						09 53					10 23					10 53					11 23	
Milnrow	d		09 25						09 55					10 25					10 55					11 25	
Rochdale	a	09 25	09 33			09 38		09 55	10 03		10 08		10 25	10 33		10 38		10 55	11 03		11 08		11 25	11 33	

		NT B	NT	NT C	NT	NT		NT B	NT	NT D	NT	NT	NT B	NT	NT C	NT	NT	NT B	NT	NT D	NT	NT	NT B	NT	NT C
Liverpool Lime Street 10	90 d							10 48										11 48							
Bolton	82 d	10 50	10m59			11 07			11 30				11 50	11m59			12 07		12 30				12 50	12m59	
Salford Crescent	82 d	11 07	11 17	11 17		11 22			11 43	11 50			12 07	12 17	12 17		12 22		12 43	12 50			13 07	13 17	13 17
Salford Central	82 d	11e09	11 20	11 20		11 24			11 45	11 53			12 09	12 20	12 20		12 24		12 45	12 53			13 09	13 20	13 20
Manchester Victoria	d	11 24	11 30	11 33		11 45		11 54	12 00	12 03		12 15	12 24	12 30	12 33		12 45	12 54	13 00	13 03		13 15	13 24	13 30	13 33
Moston	d			11 40						12 10					12 40					13 10					13 40
Mills Hill	d			11 44						12 14					12 44					13 14					13 44
Castleton	d			11 49						12 19					12 49					13 19					13 49
Dean Lane	d					11 52						12 22					12 52					13 22			
Failsworth	d					11 55						12 25					12 55					13 25			
Hollinwood	d					11 57						12 27					12 57					13 27			
Oldham Werneth	d					12 02						12 32					13 02					13 32			
Oldham Mumps	d		11 44			12 05			12 14			12 35		12 44			13 05		13 14			13 35		13 44	
Derker	d					12 08						12 38					13 08					13 38			
Shaw & Crompton	a		11 49		←	12 14			12 19		←	12 44		12 49		←	13 14		13 19		←	13 44		13 49	
	d		11 49 →		11 49				12 19 →		12 19			12 49 →		12 49			13 19 →		13 19			13 49 →	
New Hey	d				11 53						12 23					12 53					13 23				
Milnrow	d				11 55						12 25					12 55					13 25				
Rochdale	a	11 38		11 55	12 03			12 08		12 25	12 33		12 38		12 55	13 03		13 08		13 25	13 33		13 38		13 55

		NT	NT	NT B	NT	NT D	NT	NT		NT B	NT	NT C	NT	NT	NT B	NT	NT D	NT	NT	NT B	NT	NT C	NT	NT	NT B
Liverpool Lime Street 10	90 d			12 48											13 48										14 48
Bolton	82 d		13 07		13 30					13 50	13m59			14 07		14 30				14 50	14m59			15 07	
Salford Crescent	82 d		13 22		13 43	13 50				14 07	14 17	14 17		14 22		14 43	14 50			15 07	15 17	15 17		15 22	
Salford Central	82 d		13 24		13 45	13 53				14 09	14 20	14 20		14n24		14 45	14 53			15 09	15 20	15 20		15 24	
Manchester Victoria	d		13 45	13 54	14 00	14 03		14 15		14 24	14 30	14 33		14 45	14 54	15 00	15 03		15 15	15 24	15 30	15 33		15 45	15 54
Moston	d					14 10						14 40					15 10					15 40			
Mills Hill	d					14 14						14 44					15 14					15 44			
Castleton	d					14 19						14 49					15 19					15 49			
Dean Lane	d		13 52					14 22						14 52					15 22					15 52	
Failsworth	d		13 55					14 25						14 55					15 25					15 55	
Hollinwood	d		13 57					14 27						14 57					15 27					15 57	
Oldham Werneth	d		14 02					14 32						15 02					15 32					16 02	
Oldham Mumps	d		14 05		14 14			14 35			14 44			15 05		15 14			15 35		15 44			16 05	
Derker	d		14 08					14 38						15 08					15 38					16 08	
Shaw & Crompton	a	←	14 14		14 19		←	14 44			14 49		←	15 14		15 19		←	15 44		15 49		←	16 14	
	d	13 49			14 19 →		14 19				14 49 →		14 49			15 19 →		15 19			15 49 →		15 49		
New Hey	d	13 53					14 23						14 53					15 23					15 53		
Milnrow	d	13 55					14 25						14 55					15 25					15 55		
Rochdale	a	14 03		14 08		14 25	14 33			14 38		14 55	15 03		15 08		15 25	15 33		15 38		15 55	16 03		16 08

For general notes see front of timetable
For details of catering facilities see Directory of Train Operators

- **A** To Selby (Saturdays to Leeds) (Table 41)
- **B** To Leeds (Table 41)
- **C** From Southport (Table 82)
- **D** From Kirkby (Table 82)
- **E** From Wigan Wallgate (Saturdays from Southport) (Table 82)
- **G** From Wigan Wallgate (Table 82)
- **b** Mondays to Fridays only
- **c** Saturdays only
- **e** Saturdays dep. 1 minute later
- **f** Saturdays dep. Salford Crescent 0718, Salford Central 0723
- **g** Saturdays dep. Salford Central 0743, Salford Central 0745
- **h** Saturdays dep. Salford Crescent 0842, Salford Central 0845
- **j** Saturdays dep. 4 minutes later
- **k** Saturdays dep. Salford Crescent 0920, Salford Central 0923
- **m** Change at Salford Crescent and Manchester Victoria
- **n** Saturdays dep. 1425

Mondays to Saturdays
until 4 October

Manchester → Oldham and Rochdale

Network Diagram - see first page of Table 94

		NT	NT A	NT	NT	NT B	NT	NT C	NT	NT		NT B	NT	NT A	NT	NT	NT B	NT	NT C	NT	NT	NT B	NT	NT	NT
Liverpool Lime Street 10	90 d											15 48						16 18					16 48	17 12	
Bolton	82 d	15 30				15 50	15b59			16 10		16 20		16 20				16c50	16 59		17e17		17 30		
Salford Crescent	82 d	15 43	15 50			16 07	16 17	16 17		16 22		16 35		16 50				17c07	17 18		17 31		17 45		
Salford Central	82 d	15 45	15 53			16 10	16 20	16 20		16 25		16 37		16 55				17c09	17f23		17 33		17 48		
Manchester Victoria	d	16 00	16 04		16 15	16 24	16 30	16 33		16 45		16 54	17 00	17 03		17 10	17 18	17 30	17 33		17 45	17 49	18 00	18 13	
Moston	d		16 10					16 40						17 10			17 25		17 40			17 55			
Mills Hill	d		16 14					16 44						17 14			17 30		17 44			18 00		18 21	
Castleton	d		16 19					16 49						17 19			17 35		17 49			18 05		18 27	
Dean Lane	d				16 22					16 52						17 15					17 52				
Failsworth	d				16 25					16 55						17 18					17 55				
Hollinwood	d				16 27					16 57						17 21					17 57				
Oldham Werneth	d				16 32					17 02						17 25					18 02				
Oldham Mumps	d	16 14			16 35		16 44			17 05			17 14			17 29		17 44			18 05		18 14		
Derker	d				16 38					17 08						17 31					18 08				
Shaw & Crompton	a	16 19		←	16 44		16 49		←	17 14			17 19		←	17 38		17 49		←	18 14		18 19		←
	d	16 19 →		16 19			16 49 →		16 49				17 19 →		17 19			17 49 →		17 49			18 19 →		18 19
New Hey	d			16 23					16 53						17 23					17 53					18 23
Milnrow	d			16 25					16 55						17 25					17 55					18 25
Rochdale	a		16 25	16 33		16 38		16 55	17 03			17 08		17 25	17 33		17 38		17 55	18 03		18 08		18 32	18 33

		NT B	NT	NT D	NT	NT SX	NT SO	NT SX B	NT SO B	NT SX	NT SO	NT	NT B	NT	NT	NT B	NT	NT	NT SX B	NT	NT SO B	NT SX B	NT		
Liverpool Lime Street 10	90 d			17 35		17 50	17 48					18 48			19 18			20 18			21 18	21 18			
Bolton	82 d		18 03			18 40	18 40					19 30			20 30	20b34		21 30			22 23	22b33	22b33		
Salford Crescent	82 d		18 14	18 22		18 55	18 55		19 05			19 44			20 43	20g52		21 43	21 52		22 36	22 52	22 52		
Salford Central	82 d		18e16	18 24		18 57	18 57		19 08			19 47			20 45	20g56		21 45	21 56		22 39	22h54	22j55		
Manchester Victoria	d	18 19	18 30	18 47		19 07	19 07	19 18	19 26			20 07	20 19		21 00	21 19		22 00	22 19		22 49	23 19	23 21		
Moston	d	18 25		18 53				19 25	19 32				20 25			21 25			22 25		22 55	23 25			
Mills Hill	d	18 30		18 57				19 30	19 37				20 30			21 30			22 30		23 00	23 30			
Castleton	d	18 35		19 02				19 35	19 42				20 35			21 35			22 35		23 05	23 35			
Dean Lane	d		18 37			19 13	19 14					20 13			21 06			22 06					23 28		
Failsworth	d		18 40			19 16	19 17					20 16			21 09			22 09					23 31		
Hollinwood	d		18 42			19 19	19 19					20 19			21 12			22 12					23 33		
Oldham Werneth	d		18 47			19 23	19 24					20 23			21 16			22 16					23 38		
Oldham Mumps	d		18 50			19 27	19 27					20 27			21 20			22 20					23 41		
Derker	d		18 53			19 29	19 30					20 29			21 22		←	22 22					23 44		
Shaw & Crompton	a		18 56		←	19 33	19 33			←	←	20 33		←	21 26		21 26	22 26		←			23 47		
	d		18 56 →		18 56	19 36 →	19 36 →			19 36	19 36	20 33 →		20 33	21 26 →		21 26	22 26 →		22 26			23 47		
New Hey	d				19 00					19 39	19 39			20 36			21 29			22 29			23 51		
Milnrow	d				19 02					19 42	19 42			20 39			21 32			22 32			23 53		
Rochdale	a	18 38		19 05	19 13			19 38	19 45	19 49	19 56		20 38	20 46		21 38	21 39		22 38	22 39	23 08	23 38	00 02		

Mondays to Saturdays
from 6 October

		NT E	NT SX B	NT SO B	NT SX	NT SO	NT B	NT SX	NT SO	NT	NT B	NT	NT	NT B	NT SX C	NT	NT	NT B	NT A	NT	NT	NT B	NT G	NT	NT
Liverpool Lime Street 10	90 d									05 47			06k39	06j39					07m18			07 47			
Bolton	82 d												06 58		07 33		07j30	07e46	08 00		08k11	08 15	08m30		
Salford Crescent	82 d									06k46			07n19		07 59		07j47	08e03	08 18		08k28	08 32	08q46		
Salford Central	82 d									06k49			07n22		08 02		07j49	08e06	08 21		08k31	08 35	08q49		
Manchester Victoria	d	05 54	06 18	06 24	06 45	06 45	06 49			07 07	07 18		07 42	07 47	08 09		08 12	08 19	08 33		08 42	08 54	09 03		09 15
Moston	d		06 25				06 55				07 25			07 53				08 25	08 40				09 09		
Mills Hill	d		06 30				07 00				07 30			07 58				08 30	08 44				09 13		
Castleton	d		06 35				07 05				07 35			08 03				08 35	08 49				09 18		
Dean Lane	d				06 51	06 51				07 13			07 49				08 19				08 49				09 22
Failsworth	d				06 54	06 54				07 16			07 52				08 22				08 52				09 26
Hollinwood	d				06 56	06 56				07 18			07 55				08 25				08 55				09 29
Oldham Werneth	d				07 01	07 01		←	←	07 23		←	08 00			←	08 30			←	09 00			←	09 34
Oldham Mumps	d				07 05 →	07 06 →		07 05	07 06	07 26 →		07 26	08 08 →			08 08	08 38 →			08 38	09 08 →			09 08	09 40 →
Derker	d							07 08	07 09			07 34				08 11				08 41				09 11	
Shaw & Crompton	a							07 13	07 14			07 39				08 18				08 48				09 18	
	d							07 13	07 14			07 46				08 18				08 48				09 18	
New Hey	d							07 17	07 18			07 49				08 22				08 52				09 22	
Milnrow	d							07 19	07 20			07 52				08 25				08 55				09 25	
Rochdale	a	06 08	06 38	06 38			07 08	07 27	07 28		07 38	07 59		08 06	08 25	08 33		08 38	08 55	09 03		09 08	09 25	09 33	

For general notes see front of timetable
For details of catering facilities see Directory of Train Operators

- **A** From Kirkby (Table 82)
- **B** To Leeds (Table 41)
- **C** From Southport (Table 82)
- **D** To Todmorden (Table 41)
- **E** To Selby (Saturdays to Leeds) (Table 41)
- **G** From Wigan Wallgate (Saturdays from Southport) (Table 82)
- **b** Change at Salford Crescent and Manchester Victoria
- **c** Saturdays dep. Bolton 1659, Salford Crescent 1718, Salford Central 1721
- **e** Saturdays dep. 1 minute later
- **f** Saturdays dep. 1721
- **g** Saturdays until 13 September dep. Salford Crescent 2058, Salford Central 2102
- **h** Fridays only
- **j** Saturdays only
- **k** Mondays to Fridays only
- **m** Change at Manchester Victoria
- **n** Saturdays dep. Salford Crescent 0718, Salford Central 0723
- **q** Saturdays dep. 4 minutes later

Manchester → Oldham and Rochdale

Network Diagram - see first page of Table 94

		NT A	NT B	NT	NT	NT A	NT C	NT	NT	NT A	NT B	NT	NT	NT A	NT D	NT	NT	NT A	NT B	NT	NT	NT A	NT D	NT	NT
Liverpool Lime Street [10]	90 d					08 48								09 48								10 48			
Bolton	82 d	08 50	09b01				09 30			09 50	10b01		10 07		10 30			10 50	10 59		11 07		11 30		
Salford Crescent	82 d	09 07	09c19				09 50			10 07	10 17		10 22		10 50			11 07	11 17		11 22		11 50		
Salford Central	82 d	09 09	09c24				09 53			10 09	10 20		10 24		10 53			11e09	11 20		11 24		11 53		
Manchester Victoria	d	09 24	09 33		09 45	09 54	10 03		10 15	10 24	10 33		10 45	10 54	11 03		11 15	11 24	11 33		11 45	11 54	12 03		12 15
Moston	d		09 40				10 10				10 40				11 10				11 40				12 10		
Mills Hill	d		09 44				10 14				10 44				11 14				11 44				12 14		
Castleton	d		09 49				10 19				10 49				11 19				11 49				12 19		
Dean Lane	d				09 52				10 22				10 52				11 22				11 52				12 22
Failsworth	d				09 56				10 26				10 56				11 26				11 56				12 26
Hollinwood	d				09 59				10 29				10 59				11 29				11 59				12 29
Oldham Werneth	d			←	10 04			←	10 34			←	11 04			←	11 34			←	12 04			←	12 34
Oldham Mumps	d			09 40	10 10			10 10	10 40			10 40	11 10			11 10	11 40			11 40	12 10			12 10	12 40
Derker	d			09 43	→			10 13	→			10 43	→			11 13	→			11 43	→			12 13	→
Shaw & Crompton	a			09 48				10 18				10 48				11 18				11 48				12 18	
	d			09 49				10 19				10 49				11 19				11 49				12 19	
New Hey	d			09 53				10 23				10 53				11 23				11 53				12 23	
Milnrow	d			09 56				10 26				10 56				11 26				11 56				12 26	
Rochdale	a	09 38	09 55	10 03		10 08	10 25	10 33		10 38	10 55	11 03		11 08	11 25	11 33		11 38	11 55	12 03		12 08	12 25	12 33	

		NT A	NT B	NT	NT	NT A	NT D	NT	NT	NT A	NT B	NT	NT	NT A	NT D	NT	NT	NT A	NT B	NT	NT	NT A	NT D	NT	NT
Liverpool Lime Street [10]	90 d					11 48								12 48								13 48			
Bolton	82 d	11 50	11 59		12 07		12 30			12 50	12 59		13 07		13 30			13 50	13 59		14 07		14 30		
Salford Crescent	82 d	12 07	12 17		12 22		12 50			13 07	13 17		13 22		13 50			14 07	14 17		14 22		14 50		
Salford Central	82 d	12 09	12 20		12 24		12 53			13 09	13 20		13 24		13 53			14 09	14 20		14e24		14 53		
Manchester Victoria	d	12 24	12 33		12 45	12 54	13 03		13 15	13 24	13 33		13 45	13 54	14 03		14 15	14 24	14 33		14 45	14 54	15 03		15 15
Moston	d		12 40				13 10				13 40				14 10				14 40				15 10		
Mills Hill	d		12 44				13 14				13 44				14 14				14 44				15 14		
Castleton	d		12 49				13 19				13 49				14 19				14 49				15 19		
Dean Lane	d				12 52				13 22				13 52				14 22				14 52				15 22
Failsworth	d				12 56				13 26				13 56				14 26				14 56				15 26
Hollinwood	d				12 59				13 29				13 59				14 29				14 59				15 29
Oldham Werneth	d			←	13 04			←	13 34			←	14 04			←	14 34			←	15 04			←	15 34
Oldham Mumps	d			12 40	13 10			13 10	13 40			13 40	14 10			14 10	14 40			14 40	15 10			15 10	15 40
Derker	d			12 43	→			13 13	→			13 43	→			14 13	→			14 43	→			15 13	→
Shaw & Crompton	a			12 48				13 18				13 48				14 18				14 48				15 18	
	d			12 49				13 19				13 49				14 19				14 49				15 19	
New Hey	d			12 53				13 23				13 53				14 23				14 53				15 23	
Milnrow	d			12 56				13 26				13 56				14 26				14 56				15 26	
Rochdale	a	12 38	12 55	13 03		13 08	13 25	13 33		13 38	13 55	14 03		14 08	14 25	14 33		14 38	14 55	15 03		15 08	15 25	15 33	

		NT A	NT B	NT	NT	NT A	NT D	NT	NT	NT A	NT B	NT	NT	NT A	NT D	NT	NT	NT A	NT B	NT	NT	NT A	NT	NT	NT
Liverpool Lime Street [10]	90 d					14 48								15 48					16b18				16 48	17 12	
Bolton	82 d	14 50	14 59		15 07		15 30			15 50	15 59		16 10	16 20					16 59			17e17	17 30		
Salford Crescent	82 d	15 07	15 17		15 22		15 50			16 07	16 17		16 22	16 35	16 50				17 18			17 31	17 45		
Salford Central	82 d	15 09	15 20		15 24		15 53			16 10	16 20		16 25	16 37	16 55				17f23			17 33	17 48		
Manchester Victoria	d	15 24	15 33		15 45	15 54	16 04		16 15	16 24	16 33		16 45	16 54	17 03		17 10	17 18	17 33		17 36	17 49	18 00	18 13	
Moston	d		15 40				16 10				16 40				17 10			17 25	17 40			17 55			
Mills Hill	d		15 44				16 14				16 44				17 14			17 30	17 44			18 00		18 21	
Castleton	d		15 49				16 19				16 49				17 19			17 35	17 49			18 05		18 27	
Dean Lane	d				15 52				16 22				16 52				17 16				17 43				
Failsworth	d				15 56				16 26				16 56				17 19				17 46				
Hollinwood	d				15 59				16 29				16 59				17 22				17 48				
Oldham Werneth	d			←	16 04			←	16 34			←	17 04			←	17 27			←	17 53				
Oldham Mumps	d			15 40	16 10			16 10	16 40			16 40	17 10			17 10	17 36			17 36	17 56		18 14		
Derker	d			15 43	→			16 13	→			16 43	→			17 13	→			17 39	17 59				
Shaw & Crompton	a			15 48				16 18				16 48				17 18				17 46	18 07		18 19		←
	d			15 49				16 19				16 49				17 19				17 48			18 19 →		18 19
New Hey	d			15 53				16 23				16 53				17 23				17 52					18 23
Milnrow	d			15 56				16 26				16 56				17 26				17 55					18 25
Rochdale	a	15 38	15 55	16 03		16 08	16 25	16 33		16 38	16 55	17 03		17 08	17 25	17 33		17 38	17 55	18 03		18 08		18 32	18 33

		NT A	NT	NT E	NT	NT SX	NT SO	NT SX A	NT SO A	NT SX	NT SO	NT	NT A	NT	NT	NT A	NT	NT	NT SX A	NT	NT SO A	NT SX A	NT		
Liverpool Lime Street [10]	90 d			17 35		17 50	17 48					18 48			19 18			20 18			21 18	21 18			
Bolton	82 d		18 03			18 40	18 40					19 30			20 30	20g34		21 30			22 23	22g33	22g33		
Salford Crescent	82 d		18 14	18 22		18 55	18 55		19 05			19 44			20 43	20 52		21 43	21 52		22 36	22 52	22 52		
Salford Central	82 d		18e16	18 24		18 57	18 57		19 08			19 47			20 45	20 56		21 45	21 56		22 39	22h54	22j55		
Manchester Victoria	d	18 19	18 30	18 47		19 07	19 07	19 18	19 26			20 07	20 19		21 00	21 19		22 00	22 19		22 49	23 19	23 21		
Moston	d	18 25		18 53				19 25	19 32				20 25			21 25			22 25		22 55	23 25			
Mills Hill	d	18 30		18 57				19 30	19 37				20 30			21 30			22 30		23 00	23 30			
Castleton	d	18 35		19 02				19 35	19 42				20 35			21 35			22 35		23 05	23 35			
Dean Lane	d		18 37			19 13	19 14					20 13			21 06			22 06					23 28		
Failsworth	d		18 40			19 16	19 17					20 16			21 09			22 09					23 31		
Hollinwood	d		18 42			19 19	19 19					20 19			21 12			22 12					23 33		
Oldham Werneth	d		18 47		←	19 23	19 24			←	←	20 23		←	21 16		←	22 16		←			23 38		
Oldham Mumps	d		18 50		18 50	19 27	19 27			19 27	19 27	20 27		20 27	21 20		21 20	22 20		22 20			23 41		
Derker	d		→		18 53	→	→			19 29	19 30	→		20 29	→		21 22	→		22 22			23 44		
Shaw & Crompton	a				18 56					19 33	19 33			20 33			21 26			22 26			23 47		
	d				18 56					19 36	19 36			20 33			21 26			22 26			23 47		
New Hey	d				19 00					19 39	19 39			20 36			21 29			22 29			23 51		
Milnrow	d				19 02					19 42	19 42			20 39			21 32			22 32			23 53		
Rochdale	a	18 38		19 05	19 13			19 38	19 45	19 49	19 56		20 38	20 46		21 38	21 39		22 38	22 39	23 08	23 38	00 02		

For general notes see front of timetable
For details of catering facilities see Directory of Train Operators

A To Leeds (Table 41)
B From Southport (Table 82)
C From Wigan Wallgate (Table 82)
D From Kirkby (Table 82)
E To Todmorden (Table 41)
b Change at Manchester Victoria
c Saturdays dep. Salford Crescent 0920, Salford Central 0923
e Saturdays dep. 1 minute later
f Saturdays dep. 1721
g Change at Salford Crescent and Manchester Victoria
h Fridays only
j Saturdays only

Sundays

until 13 July

Manchester → Oldham and Rochdale

Network Diagram - see first page of Table 94

		NT A	NT	NT A		NT A	NT	NT A	NT	NT
Liverpool Lime Street [10]	90 d									
Bolton	82 d			*09 16*	and at	*20 16*		*21b26*		*22 16*
Salford Crescent	82 d			*09 29*	the same	*20 29*		*21 50*		*22 29*
Salford Central	82 d				minutes					
Manchester Victoria	d	09 14	09 35	10 15	past	21 15	21 35	22 15	22 35	23 20
Moston	d	09 21		10 21	each	21 21		22 21		
Mills Hill	d	09 25		10 25	hour until	21 25		22 25		
Castleton	d	09 30		10 30		21 30		22 30		
Dean Lane	d		09 41				21 41		22 41	23 26
Failsworth	d		09 44				21 44		22 44	23 29
Hollinwood	d		09 47				21 47		22 47	23 31
Oldham Werneth	d		09 51				21 51		22 51	23 36
Oldham Mumps	d		09 55				21 55		22 55	23 39
Derker	d		09 57				21 57		22 57	23 42
Shaw & Crompton	a		10 01				22 01		23 01	23 45
	d		10 01				22 01		23 01	23 45
New Hey	d		10 04				22 04		23 04	23 49
Milnrow	d		10 07				22 07		23 07	23 51
Rochdale	a	09 34	10 13	10 34		21 34	22 13	22 34	23 13	23 58

Sundays

20 July to 7 September

		NT 🚌	NT 🚌	NT 🚌	NT 🚌	NT 🚌	NT 🚌		NT 🚌	NT 🚌	NT 🚌	NT 🚌	NT 🚌	NT 🚌	NT 🚌
Liverpool Lime Street [10]	90 d														
Bolton	82 d					*09 16*		and at			*21b26*				*22 16*
Salford Crescent	82 d					*09 29*		the same			*21 50*				*22 29*
Salford Central	82 d							minutes							
Manchester Victoria	d	08 38	09 04	09 35	09 38	10 04		past		21 35	21 59	22 25		22 35	23 20
Moston	d	08 58			09 58			each			22 19				
Mills Hill	d	09 13			10 13			hour until			22 34				
Castleton	d	09 23			10 23						22 44				
Dean Lane	d			09 45						21 45				22 45	23 30
Failsworth	d			09 54						21 54				22 54	23 39
Hollinwood	d			09 59						21 59				22 59	23 44
Oldham Werneth	d			10 04			←		←	22 04			←	23 04	23 49
Oldham Mumps	d			10 12 →			10 12		21 12	22 12 →			22 12	23 12	23 57
Derker	d						10 21		21 21				22 21	23 21	00 06
Shaw & Crompton	a						10 31		21 31				22 31	23 31	00 16
	d						10 31		21 31				22 31	23 31	00 16
New Hey	d						10 40		21 40				22 40	23 40	00 25
Milnrow	d						10 45		21 45				22 45	23 45	00 30
Rochdale	a	09 29	09 29		10 29	10 29	10 55		21 55		22 50	22 50	22 55	23 55	00 40

Sundays

14 September to 2 November

		NT A	NT	NT A		NT A	NT	NT A	NT	NT
Liverpool Lime Street [10]	90 d									
Bolton	82 d			*09 16*	and at	*20 16*		*21b26*		*22 16*
Salford Crescent	82 d			*09 29*	the same	*20 29*		*21 50*		*22 29*
Salford Central	82 d				minutes					
Manchester Victoria	d	09 14	09 35	10 15	past	21 15	21 35	22 15	22 35	23 20
Moston	d	09 21		10 21	each	21 21		22 21		
Mills Hill	d	09 25		10 25	hour until	21 25		22 25		
Castleton	d	09 30		10 30		21 30		22 30		
Dean Lane	d		09 41				21 41		22 41	23 26
Failsworth	d		09 44				21 44		22 44	23 29
Hollinwood	d		09 47				21 47		22 47	23 31
Oldham Werneth	d		09 51				21 51		22 51	23 36
Oldham Mumps	d		09 55				21 55		22 55	23 39
Derker	d		09 57				21 57		22 57	23 42
Shaw & Crompton	a		10 01				22 01		23 01	23 45
	d		10 01				22 01		23 01	23 45
New Hey	d		10 04				22 04		23 04	23 49
Milnrow	d		10 07				22 07		23 07	23 51
Rochdale	a	09 34	10 13	10 34		21 34	22 13	22 34	23 13	23 58

For general notes see front of timetable
For details of catering facilities see Directory of Train Operators

A To Leeds (Table 41)
b Change at Salford Crescent and Manchester Victoria

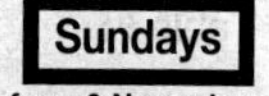

Sundays

from 9 November

Manchester → Oldham and Rochdale

Network Diagram - see first page of Table 94

	NT A	NT	NT A	NT		NT A	NT	NT A	NT		NT A		NT	NT A		NT A		NT	NT A	NT	NT		
Liverpool Lime Street 10 90 d	*08 10*		*09 10*					*11 10*			*12 10*			*13 10*		*20 10*					*21 50*		
Bolton 82 d			*09 16*			*10 16*		*11 16*			*12 16*			*13 16*		*20 16*			*21b26*		*22 16*		
Salford Crescent 82 d			*09 29*			*10 29*		*11 29*			*12 29*			*13 29*		*20 29*			*21 50*		*22 29*		
Salford Central 82 d															and at								
Manchester Victoria d	09 09	09 35	10 09	10 35		11 08	11 35	12 09	12 35		13 08		13 35	14 09	the same	21 09		21 35	22 09	22 35	23 20		
Moston d	09 16		10 15			11 15		12 15			13 15			14 15		21 15			22 15				
Mills Hill d	09 20		10 19			11 19		12 19			13 19			14 19	minutes	21 19			22 19				
Castleton d	09 25		10 24			11 24		12 24			13 24			14 24		21 24			22 24				
Dean Lane d		09 41		10 41			11 41		12 41				13 41		past			21 41		22 41	23 26		
Failsworth d		09 44		10 44			11 44		12 44				13 44		each			21 44		22 44	23 29		
Hollinwood d		09 47		10 47			11 47		12 47				13 47					21 47		22 47	23 31		
Oldham Werneth d		09 51		10 51			11 51		12 51				13 51		hour until			21 51		22 51	23 36		
Oldham Mumps d		09 55		10 55			11 55		12 55				13 55					21 55		22 55	23 39		
Derker d		09 57		10 57			11 57		12 57				13 57					21 57		22 57	23 42		
Shaw & Crompton a		10 01		11 01			12 01		13 01				14 01					22 01		23 01	23 45		
d		10 01		11 01			12 01		13 01				14 01					22 01		23 01	23 45		
New Hey d		10 04		11 04			12 04		13 04				14 04					22 04		23 04	23 49		
Milnrow d		10 07		11 07			12 07		13 07				14 07					22 07		23 07	23 51		
Rochdale a	09 29	10 13	10 28	11 13		11 28	12 13	12 28	13 13		13 28		14 13	14 28		21 28		22 13	22 28	23 13	23 58		

For general notes see front of timetable
For details of catering facilities see Directory of Train Operators

A To Leeds (Table 41)
b Change at Salford Crescent and Manchester Victoria

Rochdale and Oldham → Manchester

Network Diagram - see first page of Table 94

Miles	Miles			NT	NT SX A	NT	NT	NT A	NT	NT	NT B	NT	NT A	NT	NT	NT C	NT	NT A	NT	NT	NT D	NT	NT A	NT	NT
0	0	**Rochdale**	d	06 18	06 24		06 58	07 06		07 29	07 35		07 52		07 59	08 05		08 24		08 32	08 33		08 52		09 02
2	—	Milnrow	d	06 22			07 02			07 33					08 03					08 36					09 06
3	—	New Hey	d	06 24			07 04			07 35					08 05					08 38					09 08
4¾	—	Shaw & Crompton	a	06 28 →		←	07 08		←	07 39		←			08 13		←			08 42		←			09 12
—	—		d			06 28	07 08 →		07 08	07 39 →		07 39		07 56	08 13 →		08 13		08 26	08 42 →		08 42		08 56	09 12 →
6¾	—	Derker	d			06 32			07 12					08 00					08 30					09 00	
7¼	—	**Oldham Mumps**	d			06 35			07 15			07 44		08 02			08 18		08 32			08 47		09 02	
8½	—	Oldham Werneth	d			06 38			07 18					08 05					08 35					09 05	
10¼	—	Hollinwood	d			06 41			07 21					08 08					08 38					09 08	
11¼	—	Failsworth	d			06 43			07 23					08 11					08 41					09 11	
12¼	—	Dean Lane	d			06 46			07 26					08 13					08 43					09 13	
—	1½	Castleton	d		06 27			07 09			07 38		07 55			08 08		08 27			08 36				
—	4½	Mills Hill	d		06 32			07 14			07 42		08 00			08 12		08 32			08 40				
—	6¼	Moston	d		06 35			07 17			07 45		08 03			08 15		08 35			08 43				
14¾	10¼	**Manchester Victoria**	a		06 46	06 55		07 29	07 34		07 57	08 01	08 16	08 24		08 25	08b40	08 46	08 53		08 54	09 05	09 09	09 23	
—	—	Salford Central	82 a		06 54	07 03		07 40	07 52			08 23	08 26	08 45		08 30			09 03		09 00		09 21		
—	—	Salford Crescent	82 a		06 57	07 06		07 44	07 56			08 26	08 29	08 47		08 33			09 06		09 03		09 24		
—	—	Bolton	82 a		07 07	07 18		08 00	08 18			08 36	08 42	09 01		08 53					09c18		09 36		
—	—	Liverpool Lime Street 10	90 a			08 13					09 05					09c39					10c05				

		NT E	NT	NT G		NT	NT	NT D	NT	NT SO A	NT SX A	NT	NT	NT E	NT	NT A	NT	NT	NT D	NT	NT A	NT	NT	NT E	NT
Rochdale	d	09 03		09 23			09 32	09 33		09 50	09 53		10 02	10 03		10 23		10 32	10 33		10 50		11 02	11 03	
Milnrow	d						09 36						10 06					10 36					11 06		
New Hey	d						09 38						10 08					10 38					11 08		
Shaw & Crompton	a		←				09 42		←				10 12		←			10 42		←			11 12		←
	d		09 12			09 26	09 42 →		09 42			09 56	10 12 →		10 12		10 26	10 42 →		10 42		10 56	11 12 →		11 12
Derker	d					09 30						10 00					10 30					11 00			
Oldham Mumps	d		09 17			09 32			09 47			10 02			10 17		10 32			10 47		11 02			11 17
Oldham Werneth	d					09 35						10 05					10 35					11 05			
Hollinwood	d					09 38						10 08					10 38					11 08			
Failsworth	d					09 41						10 11					10 41					11 11			
Dean Lane	d					09 43						10 13					10 43					11 13			
Castleton	d	09 06						09 36						10 06					10 36					11 06	
Mills Hill	d	09 10						09 40						10 10					10 40					11 10	
Moston	d	09 13						09 43						10 13					10 43					11 13	
Manchester Victoria	a	09 24	09 35	09 40		09 53		09 55	10 05	10 10	10 10	10 23		10 25	10 35	10 40	10 53		10 54	11 05	11 09	11 23		11 25	11 35
Salford Central	82 a	09 32	09 44			10 03		10 00		10 21	10 21			10 32	10 44		11 03		11 00		11 21			11 32	11 44
Salford Crescent	82 a	09 35	09 47			10 06		10 03		10 24	10 24			10 35	10 47		11 06		11 03		11 24			11 35	11 47
Bolton	82 a	09 53	10 01							10 36	10 36			10e50	11 01				11c18		11 36			11 50	12 01
Liverpool Lime Street 10	90 a							11c05											12c05						

		NT SX A	NT SO A	NT	NT	NT D		NT	NT SX A	NT SO A	NT	NT	NT E	NT	NT A	NT	NT	NT D	NT	NT A	NT	NT	NT E	NT	NT A
Rochdale	d	11 23	11 24		11 32	11 33			11 50	11 50		12 02	12 03		12 23		12 32	12 33		12 52		13 02	13 03		13 23
Milnrow	d				11 36							12 06					12 36					13 06			
New Hey	d				11 38							12 08					12 38					13 08			
Shaw & Crompton	a				11 42			←				12 12		←			12 42		←			13 12		←	
	d			11 26	11 42 →			11 42			11 56	12 12 →		12 12		12 26	12 42 →		12 42		12 56	13 12 →		13 12	
Derker	d			11 30							12 00					12 30					13 00				
Oldham Mumps	d			11 32				11 47			12 02			12 17		12 32			12 47		13 02			13 17	
Oldham Werneth	d			11 35							12 05					12 35					13 05				
Hollinwood	d			11 38							12 08					12 38					13 08				
Failsworth	d			11 41							12 11					12 41					13 11				
Dean Lane	d			11 43							12 13					12 43					13 13				
Castleton	d					11 36							12 06					12 36					13 06		
Mills Hill	d					11 40							12 10					12 40					13 10		
Moston	d					11 43							12 13					12 43					13 13		
Manchester Victoria	a	11 40	11 40	11 53		11 54		12 05	12 07	12 09	12 23		12 24	12 35	12 40	12 53		12 54	13 05	13 09	13 23		13 24	13 35	13 40
Salford Central	82 a			12 03		12 00			12 21	12 21			12 32	12 44		13 03		13 00		13 21			13 32	13 44	
Salford Crescent	82 a			12 06		12 03			12 24	12 24			12 35	12 47		13 06		13 03		13 24			13 35	13 47	
Bolton	82 a					12c18			12 36	12 36			12 50	13 01				13c18		13 36			13 50	14 01	
Liverpool Lime Street 10	90 a					13c05												14c05							

		NT	NT	NT D	NT	NT A	NT	NT		NT E	NT	NT A	NT	NT	NT D	NT	NT A	NT	NT	NT E	NT	NT A	NT	NT	NT D
Rochdale	d		13 32	13 33		13 50		14 02		14 03		14 23		14 32	14 33		14 52		15 02	15 03		15 23		15 32	15 33
Milnrow	d		13 36					14 06						14 36					15 06					15 36	
New Hey	d		13 38					14 08						14 38					15 08					15 38	
Shaw & Crompton	a		13 42		←			14 12			←			14 42		←			15 12		←			15 42	
	d	13 26	13 42 →		13 42		13 56	14 12 →			14 12		14 26	14 42 →		14 42		14 56	15 12 →		15 12		15 26	15 42 →	
Derker	d	13 30					14 00						14 30					15 00					15 30		
Oldham Mumps	d	13 32			13 47		14 02				14 17		14 32			14 47		15 02			15 17		15 32		
Oldham Werneth	d	13 35					14 05						14 35					15 05					15 35		
Hollinwood	d	13 38					14 08						14 38					15 08					15 38		
Failsworth	d	13 41					14 11						14 41					15 11					15 41		
Dean Lane	d	13 43					14 13						14 43					15 13					15 43		
Castleton	d			13 36						14 06					14 36					15 06					15 36
Mills Hill	d			13 40						14 10					14 40					15 10					15 40
Moston	d			13 43						14 13					14 43					15 13					15 43
Manchester Victoria	a	13 53		13 55	14 05	14 09	14 23			14 25	14 35	14 40	14 53		14 55	15 05	15 09	15 23		15 26	15 35	15 40	15 53		15 55
Salford Central	82 a	14 03		14 00		14 21				14 32	14 44		15 03		15 00		15 21			15 32	15 44	15 53			16 00
Salford Crescent	82 a	14 06		14 03		14 24				14 35	14 47		15 06		15 03		15 24			15 35	15 47	15 56			16 03
Bolton	82 a			14c18		14 36				14 50	15 01				15c18		15 36			15 50	16 01	16 08			
Liverpool Lime Street 10	90 a			15c05											16c05										17c04

For general notes see front of timetable
For details of catering facilities see Directory of Train Operators

- **A** From Leeds (Table 41)
- **B** From Todmorden (Table 41)
- **C** From Todmorden (Table 41) to Kirkby (Table 82)
- **D** To Southport (Table 82)
- **E** To Kirkby (Table 82)
- **G** From Selby (Saturdays from Leeds) (Table 41)
- **b** Saturdays arr. 0838
- **c** Change at Manchester Victoria
- **e** Saturdays from 13 September arr. 1051

Table 95

Mondays to Saturdays

until 4 October

Rochdale and Oldham → Manchester

Network Diagram - see first page of Table 94

		NT	NT	NT	NT	NT	NT	NT	NT	NT		NT	NT	NT	NT	NT	NT	NT	NT	NT	NT	NT	NT	NT	NT
														SO	SX										SO
			A			B		A						A	A			C		A			D		A
Rochdale	d		15 54		16 02	16 03		16 23		16 32		16 33		16 52	16 52		17 02	17 03		17 23		17 32	17 33		17 52
Milnrow	d				16 06					16 36							17 06					17 36			
New Hey	d				16 08					16 38							17 08					17 38			
Shaw & Crompton	a	←			16 12		←			16 42			←				17 12		←			17 42		←	
	d	15 42		15 56	16 12		16 12		16 26	16 42			16 42			16 56	17 12		17 12		17 26	17 42		17 42	
Derker	d			16 00	→				16 30	→						17 00	→				17 30	→			
Oldham Mumps	d	15 47		16 02			16 17		16 32				16 47			17 02			17 17		17 32			17 47	
Oldham Werneth	d			16 05					16 35							17 05					17 35				
Hollinwood	d			16 08					16 38							17 08					17 38				
Failsworth	d			16 11					16 41							17 11					17 41				
Dean Lane	d			16 13					16 43							17 13					17 43				
Castleton	d					16 06						16 36						17 06					17 36		
Mills Hill	d					16 10						16 40						17 10					17 40		
Moston	d					16 13						16 43						17 13					17 43		
Manchester Victoria	a	16 04	16 10	16 23		16 27	16 35	16 40	16 53			16 57	17 05	17 08	17 10	17 23		17 26	17 35	17 40	17 53		17 53	18 05	18 08
Salford Central	82 a	16 13	16 26			16 32	16 44	16 51	17 03			17b08	17b13	17 18	17 18			17 32	17 45		18 03		18 00		18 24
Salford Crescent	82 a	16 16	16 29			16 35	16 47	16 54	17 06			17b16	17b16	17 22	17 22			17 35	17 48		18 07		18 03		18 28
Bolton	82 a	16 28	16 42			16c50	17 02	17e13	17 18			17b22	17f36	17 44	17 44			17 49	18 07				18g19		18 44
Liverpool Lime Street 10	90 a											18 05											19g05		

		NT	NT	NT	NT	NT	NT	NT	NT	NT	NT	NT	NT	NT	NT	NT	NT	NT	NT	NT	NT	NT	NT		
		SX								SX	SO	SX	SO												
		A			E		A			A	A	A	A		A		A		A		A		A		
Rochdale	d	17 52		18 02	18 03		18 23		18 32	18 52	18 54	19 23	19 24	19 24	19 52	20 02	20 52	21 02	21 52	22 02	22 52	23 02	23 52		
Milnrow	d			18 06					18 36					19 28		20 06		21 06		22 06		23 06			
New Hey	d			18 08					18 38					19 30		20 08		21 08		22 08		23 08			
Shaw & Crompton	a			18 12		←			18 42					19 34		20 12		21 12		22 12		23 12			
	d		17 56	18 12		18 12		18 26	18 42					19 34		20 12		21 12		22 12		23 12			
Derker	d		18 00	→				18 30						19 38		20 16		21 16		22 16		23 16			
Oldham Mumps	d		18 02			18 17		18 32	18 47					19 41		20 19		21 19		22 19		23 19			
Oldham Werneth	d		18 05					18 35						19 44		20 22		21 22		22 22		23 22			
Hollinwood	d		18 08					18 38						19 47		20 25		21 25		22 25		23 25			
Failsworth	d		18 11					18 41						19 49		20 27		21 27		22 27		23 27			
Dean Lane	d		18 13					18 43						19 52		20 30		21 30		22 30		23 30			
Castleton	d				18 06					18 55	18 57				19 55		20 55		21 55		22 55				
Mills Hill	d				18 10					19 00	19 02				20 00		21 00		22 00		23 00				
Moston	d				18 13					19 03	19 05				20 03		21 03		22 03		23 03				
Manchester Victoria	a	18 10	18 23		18 24	18 35	18 41	18 55	19 05	19 14	19 15	19 40	19 40	20 01	20 14	20 39	21 14	21 39	22 14	22 39	23 14	23 39	00 08		
Salford Central	82 a	18 24			18 32	18 44	19 01		19 21			20 01	20 01		20 24	21 01	21 24	22h01	22h37	23h11					
Salford Crescent	82 a	18 27			18 35	18 47	19 04		19 24			20 04	20 04		20 28	21 04	21 27	22 04	22 40	23j14					
Bolton	82 a	18 44			18k50	19c03	19 17		19e52			20 17	20 16		20e51	21 17	21e54	22 16	23e16	23j26					
Liverpool Lime Street 10	90 a				19g35			20 05				21 05	21 05			22c05		23 05		00 14					

Mondays to Saturdays

from 6 October

		NT	NT	NT	NT	NT	NT	NT	NT	NT	NT	NT	NT	NT	NT	NT	NT	NT	NT	NT	NT	NT	NT	NT	NT
			SX						SX														SX		
			A			A		G			A			H	A			J	A			B		K	
Rochdale	d	06 18	06 24		06 51	07 06		07 31		07 32	07 52		08 03	08 05	08 24		08 32	08 33	08 52		09 02	09 03		09 23	
Milnrow	d	06 22			06 55					07 36			08 07				08 36				09 06				
New Hey	d	06 24			06 57					07 38			08 10				08 38				09 08				
Shaw & Crompton	a	06 28			07 01					07 44			08 15				08 44				09 14				
	d	06 28			07 01				07 28	07 45			08 15				08 45				09 15		09 06		
Derker	d	06 32		←	07 05		←		07 32	07 49		←	08 20			←	08 49			←	09 19				←
Oldham Mumps	d	06 35		06 35	07 10		07 10		07 36	07 56		07 56	08 26			08 26	08 56			08 56	09 26		09 12		09 26
Oldham Werneth	d	→		06 38	→		07 13		07 39	→		08 00	→			08 29	→			09 00	→				09 30
Hollinwood	d			06 41			07 16		07 42			08 03				08 33				09 03					09 33
Failsworth	d			06 43			07 18		07 45			08 06				08 36				09 06					09 36
Dean Lane	d			06 46			07 21		07 47			08 09				08 39				09 09					09 39
Castleton	d		06 27			07 09		07 34			07 55			08 08	08 27			08 36				09 06			
Mills Hill	d		06 32			07 14		07 38			08 00			08 12	08 32			08 40				09 10			
Moston	d		06 35			07 17		07 41			08 03			08 15	08 35			08 43				09 13			
Manchester Victoria	a		06 46	06 55		07 29	07 34	07 53	08 01		08 16	08 24		08 25	08 46	08 53		08 55	09 09	09 23		09 24	09 32	09 40	09 53
Salford Central	82 a		06 54	07 03		07 40	07 52	08 03	08 23		08 26	08 45		08 30		09 03		09 00	09 21			09 32	09 44		10 03
Salford Crescent	82 a		06 57	07 06		07 44	07 56	08 06	08 26		08 29	08 47		08 33		09 06		09 03	09 24			09 35	09 47		10 06
Bolton	82 a		07 07	07 18		08 00		08 18	08 36		08 42	09 01		08 53				09g18	09 36			09 53	10 01		
Liverpool Lime Street 10	90 a			08 13				09 05						09g39				10g05							

For general notes see front of timetable
For details of catering facilities see Directory of Train Operators

- **A** From Leeds (Table 41)
- **B** To Kirkby (Table 82)
- **C** Mondays to Fridays to Colne (Table 97). Saturdays to Blackburn (Table 94)
- **D** To Southport (Saturdays to Wigan Wallgate)
- **E** To Wigan Wallgate (Table 82)
- **G** From Todmorden (Table 41)
- **H** From Todmorden (Table 41) to Kirkby (Table 82)
- **J** To Southport (Table 82)
- **K** From Selby (Saturdays from Leeds) (Table 41)
- **b** Mondays to Fridays only
- **c** Saturdays arr. 1 minute later
- **e** Change at Manchester Victoria and Salford Crescent
- **f** Mondays to Fridays only, change at ManchesterVict oria and Salford Crescent
- **g** Change at Manchester Victoria
- **h** Fridays and Saturdays only
- **j** Saturdays arr. Salford Crescent 2313, Bolton 2327
- **k** Saturdays until 6 September arr. 1856. Saturdays from 13 September arr. 1852

Rochdale and Oldham → Manchester

Network Diagram - see first page of Table 94

		NT	NT A	NT SO B	NT SX B	NT	NT	NT C		NT B	NT	NT	NT A	NT B	NT	NT	NT C	NT SX B	NT SO B	NT	NT	NT A	NT SX B	NT SO B	NT
Rochdale	d	09 32	09 33	09 50	09 53		10 02	10 03		10 23		10 32	10 33	10 50		11 02	11 03	11 23	11 24		11 32	11 33	11 50	11 50	
Milnrow	d	09 36					10 06					10 36				11 06					11 36				
New Hey	d	09 38					10 08					10 38				11 08					11 38				
Shaw & Crompton	a	09 44					10 14					10 44				11 14					11 44				
	d	09 45					10 15					10 45				11 15					11 45				
Derker	d	09 49				←	10 19				←	10 49			←	11 19				←	11 49				←
Oldham Mumps	d	09 56				09 56	10 26				10 26	10 56			10 56	11 26				11 26	11 56				11 56
Oldham Werneth	d	→				10 00	→				10 30	→			11 00	→				11 30	→				12 00
Hollinwood	d					10 03					10 33				11 03					11 33					12 03
Failsworth	d					10 06					10 36				11 06					11 36					12 06
Dean Lane	d					10 09					10 39				11 09					11 39					12 09
Castleton	d		09 36					10 06					10 36				11 06					11 36			
Mills Hill	d		09 40					10 10					10 40				11 10					11 40			
Moston	d		09 43					10 13					10 43				11 13					11 43			
Manchester Victoria	a		09 55	10 10	10 10	10b23		10 25		10 40	10 53		10 54	11 09	11 23		11 25	11 40	11 40	11 53		11 54	12 07	12 09	12 23
Salford Central	82 a		10 00	10 21	10 21			10 32			11 03		11 00	11 21			11 32			12 03		12 00	12 21	12 21	
Salford Crescent	82 a		10 03	10 24	10 24			10 35			11 06		11 03	11 24			11 35			12 06		12 03	12 24	12 24	
Bolton	82 a		10c18	10 36	10 36			10e50					11c18	11 36			11 50					12c18	12 36	12 36	
Liverpool Lime Street 10	90 a		11c05										12c05									13c05			

		NT	NT C	NT B	NT	NT	NT A	NT B	NT	NT	NT C	NT B	NT	NT	NT A	NT B		NT	NT	NT C	NT B	NT	NT	NT A	NT B
Rochdale	d	12 02	12 03	12 23		12 32	12 33	12 52		13 02	13 03	13 23		13 32	13 33	13 50			14 02	14 03	14 23		14 32	14 33	14 52
Milnrow	d	12 06				12 36				13 06				13 36					14 06				14 36		
New Hey	d	12 08				12 38				13 08				13 38					14 08				14 38		
Shaw & Crompton	a	12 14				12 44				13 14				13 44					14 14				14 44		
	d	12 15				12 45				13 15				13 45					14 15				14 45		
Derker	d	12 19			←	12 49			←	13 19			←	13 49				←	14 19			←	14 49		
Oldham Mumps	d	12 26			12 26	12 56			12 56	13 26			13 26	13 56				13 56	14 26			14 26	14 56		
Oldham Werneth	d	→			12 30	→			13 00	→			13 30	→				14 00	→			14 30	→		
Hollinwood	d				12 33				13 03				13 33					14 03				14 33			
Failsworth	d				12 36				13 06				13 36					14 06				14 36			
Dean Lane	d				12 39				13 09				13 39					14 09				14 39			
Castleton	d		12 06				12 36				13 06				13 36					14 06				14 36	
Mills Hill	d		12 10				12 40				13 10				13 40					14 10				14 40	
Moston	d		12 13				12 43				13 13				13 43					14 13				14 43	
Manchester Victoria	a		12 24	12 40	12 53		12 54	13 09	13 23		13 24	13 40	13 53		13 55	14 09		14 23		14 25	14 40	14 53		14 55	15 09
Salford Central	82 a		12 32		13 03		13 00	13 21			13 32		14 03		14 00	14 21				14 32		15 03		15 00	15 21
Salford Crescent	82 a		12 35		13 06		13 03	13 24			13 35		14 06		14 03	14 24				14 35		15 06		15 03	15 24
Bolton	82 a		12 50				13c18	13 36			13 50				14c18	14 36				14 50				15c18	15 36
Liverpool Lime Street 10	90 a						14c05								15c05									16c05	

		NT	NT	NT C	NT B	NT	NT	NT A	NT B	NT	NT	NT C	NT B	NT	NT	NT	NT SO B	NT SX B	NT	NT	NT D	NT B	NT	NT	NT E
Rochdale	d		15 02	15 03	15 23		15 32	15 33	15 54		16 02	16 03	16 23		16 32	16 33	16 52	16 52		17 02	17 03	17 23		17 32	17 33
Milnrow	d		15 06				15 36				16 06				16 36					17 06				17 36	
New Hey	d		15 08				15 38				16 08				16 38					17 08				17 38	
Shaw & Crompton	a		15 14				15 44				16 14				16 45					17 14				17 44	
	d		15 15				15 45				16 15				16 45					17 15				17 45	
Derker	d	←	15 19			←	15 49			←	16 19			←	16 49				←	17 19			←	17 49	
Oldham Mumps	d	14 56	15 26			15 26	15 56			15 56	16 26			16 26	16 56				16 56	17 26			17 26	17 56	
Oldham Werneth	d	15 00	→			15 30	→			16 00	→			16 30	→				17 00	→			17 30	→	
Hollinwood	d	15 03				15 33				16 03				16 33					17 03				17 33		
Failsworth	d	15 06				15 36				16 06				16 36					17 06				17 36		
Dean Lane	d	15 09				15 39				16 09				16 39					17 09				17 39		
Castleton	d			15 06				15 36				16 06				16 36					17 06				17 36
Mills Hill	d			15 10				15 40				16 10				16 40					17 10				17 40
Moston	d			15 13				15 43				16 13				16 43					17 13				17 43
Manchester Victoria	a	15 23		15 26	15 40	15 53		15 55	16 10	16 23		16 27	16 40	16 53		16 57	17 08	17 10	17 23		17 26	17 40	17 53		17 54
Salford Central	82 a			15 32	15 53	16 13		16 00	16 26			16 32	16 51	17 03		17f08	17 18	17 18			17 32		18 03		18 00
Salford Crescent	82 a			15 35	15 56	16 16		16 03	16 29			16 35	16 54	17 06		17f16	17 22	17 22			17 35		18 07		18 03
Bolton	82 a			15 50	16 08			16 28	16 42			16e50	17g13	17 18		17f22	17 44	17 44			17 49				18c19
Liverpool Lime Street 10	90 a							17c04								18 05									19c05

		NT SO B	NT SX B	NT	NT	NT G	NT B	NT	NT	NT SX B	NT SO B	NT SX B	NT SO B	NT	NT B	NT	NT B	NT	NT B	NT	NT B	NT	NT B		
Rochdale	d	17 52	17 52		18 02	18 03	18 23		18 32	18 52	18 54	19 23	19 24	19 24	19 52	20 02	20 52	21 02	21 52	22 02	22 52	23 02	23 52		
Milnrow	d				18 06				18 36					19 28		20 06		21 06		22 06		23 06			
New Hey	d				18 08				18 38					19 30		20 08		21 08		22 08		23 08			
Shaw & Crompton	a				18 14				18 42					19 34		20 12		21 12		22 12		23 12			
	d				18 15				18 42					19 34		20 12		21 12		22 12		23 12			
Derker	d			←	18 19			←						19 38		20 16		21 16		22 16		23 16			
Oldham Mumps	d			17 56	18 26			18 26	18 47					19 41		20 19		21 19		22 19		23 19			
Oldham Werneth	d			18 00	→			18 30						19 44		20 22		21 22		22 22		23 22			
Hollinwood	d			18 03				18 33						19 47		20 25		21 25		22 25		23 25			
Failsworth	d			18 06				18 36						19 49		20 27		21 27		22 27		23 27			
Dean Lane	d			18 09				18 39						19 52		20 30		21 30		22 30		23 30			
Castleton	d					18 06				18 55	18 57				19 55		20 55		21 55		22 55				
Mills Hill	d					18 10				19 00	19 02				20 00		21 00		22 00		23 00				
Moston	d					18 13				19 03	19 05				20 03		21 03		22 03		23 03				
Manchester Victoria	a	18 08	18 10	18 23		18 24	18 41	18 54	19 05	19 14	19 15	19 40	19 40	20 01	20 14	20 39	21 14	21 39	22 14	22 39	23 14	23 39	00 08		
Salford Central	82 a	18 24	18 24			18 32	19 01		19 21			20 01	20 01		20 24	21 01	21 24	22h01	22h37	23h11					
Salford Crescent	82 a	18 28	18 27			18 35	19 04		19 24			20 04	20 04		20 28	21 04	21 27	22 04	22 40	23j14					
Bolton	82 a	18 44	18 44			18k50	19 17		19g52			20 17	20 16		20g51	21 17	21g54	22 16	23g16	23j26					
Liverpool Lime Street 10	90 a					19c35		20 05				21 05	21 05			22e05		23 05		00 14					

For general notes see front of timetable
For details of catering facilities see Directory of Train Operators

- **A** To Southport (Table 82)
- **B** From Leeds (Table 41)
- **C** To Kirkby (Table 82)
- **D** Mondays to Fridays to Colne (Table 97). Saturdays to Blackburn (Table 94)
- **E** To Southport (Saturdays to Wigan Wallgate) (Table 82)
- **G** To Wigan Wallgate (Table 82)
- **b** Saturdays arr. 1020
- **c** Change at Manchester Victoria
- **e** Saturdays arr. 1 minute later
- **f** Mondays to Fridays only
- **g** Change at Manchester Victoria and Salford Crescent
- **h** Fridays and Saturdays only
- **j** Saturdays arr. Salford Crescent 2313, Bolton 2327
- **k** Saturdays arr. 1852

Table 95

until 13 July

Rochdale and Oldham → Manchester

Network Diagram - see first page of Table 94

		NT	NT A	NT A	NT		NT	NT A	NT	NT B
Rochdale	d	09 23	09 41	10 18	10 23		20 23	21 18	21 23	22 51
Milnrow	d	09 27			10 27		20 27		21 27	
New Hey	d	09 29			10 29		20 29		21 29	
Shaw & Crompton	a	09 33			10 33	and at	20 33		21 33	
	d	09 33			10 33		20 33		21 33	
Derker	d	09 37			10 37	the same	20 37		21 37	
Oldham Mumps	d	09 40			10 40		20 40		21 40	
Oldham Werneth	d	09 43			10 43	minutes	20 43		21 43	
Hollinwood	d	09 46			10 46		20 46		21 46	
Failsworth	d	09 48			10 48	past	20 48		21 48	
Dean Lane	d	09 51			10 51		20 51		21 51	
Castleton	d		09 44	10 21		each		21 21		22 54
Mills Hill	d		09 49	10 26		hour until		21 26		22 59
Moston	d		09 52	10 29				21 29		23 02
Manchester Victoria	a	09 59	10 01	10 38	10 59		20 59	21 38	21 59	23 11
Salford Central	82 a									
Salford Crescent	82 a			*11 04*				*22 04*	23 04	
Bolton	82 a			*11 15*				22 15	23b22	
Liverpool Lime Street 10	90 a									

Sundays

20 July to 7 September

		NT 🚌	NT 🚌	NT 🚌	NT 🚌	NT 🚌	NT 🚌	NT 🚌		NT 🚌	NT 🚌	NT 🚌	NT 🚌	NT 🚌	NT 🚌
Rochdale	d	09 23	09 36	09 36		10 22	10 22	10 23		20 23	21 22	21 22	21 23	22 55	22 55
Milnrow	d	09 33						10 33		20 33			21 33		
New Hey	d	09 40						10 40		20 40			21 40		
Shaw & Crompton	a	09 47						10 47	and at	20 47			21 47		
	d	09 47						10 47		20 47			21 47		
Derker	d	09 57			←			10 57	the same	20 57			21 57		
Oldham Mumps	d	10 06			10 06			11 06		21 06			22 06		
Oldham Werneth	d	→			10 14			11 14	minutes	21 14			22 14		
Hollinwood	d				10 19			11 19		21 19			22 19		
Failsworth	d				10 24			11 24	past	21 24			22 24		
Dean Lane	d				10 33			11 33		21 33			22 33		
Castleton	d			09 42			10 28		each			21 28			23 01
Mills Hill	d			09 52			10 38		hour until			21 38			23 11
Moston	d			10 07			10 53					21 53			23 26
Manchester Victoria	a		10 01	10 27	10 43	10 47	11 13	11 43		21 43	21 47	22 13	22 43	23 20	23 46
Salford Central	82 a														
Salford Crescent	82 a					*11 04*					*22 04*		*23 04*		
Bolton	82 a					*11 15*					22 15		23b22		
Liverpool Lime Street 10	90 a														

Sundays

14 September to 2 November

		NT	NT A	NT A	NT		NT	NT A	NT	NT B
Rochdale	d	09 23	09 41	10 18	10 23		20 23	21 18	21 23	22 51
Milnrow	d	09 27			10 27		20 27		21 27	
New Hey	d	09 29			10 29		20 29		21 29	
Shaw & Crompton	a	09 33			10 33	and at	20 33		21 33	
	d	09 33			10 33		20 33		21 33	
Derker	d	09 37			10 37	the same	20 37		21 37	
Oldham Mumps	d	09 40			10 40		20 40		21 40	
Oldham Werneth	d	09 43			10 43	minutes	20 43		21 43	
Hollinwood	d	09 46			10 46		20 46		21 46	
Failsworth	d	09 48			10 48	past	20 48		21 48	
Dean Lane	d	09 51			10 51		20 51		21 51	
Castleton	d		09 44	10 21		each		21 21		22 54
Mills Hill	d		09 49	10 26		hour until		21 26		22 59
Moston	d		09 52	10 29				21 29		23 02
Manchester Victoria	a	09 59	10 01	10 38	10 59		20 59	21 38	21 59	23 11
Salford Central	82 a									
Salford Crescent	82 a			*11 04*				22 04	23 04	
Bolton	82 a			*11 15*				22 15	23b22	
Liverpool Lime Street 10	90 a									

For general notes see front of timetable
For details of catering facilities see Directory of Train Operators

A From Leeds (Table 41)
B From York (Table 41)
b Change at Manchester Victoria and Salford Crescent

Table 95

from 9 November

Rochdale and Oldham → Manchester

Network Diagram - see first page of Table 94

		NT	NT A	NT A	NT	NT A	NT B		NT	NT A	NT	NT C
Rochdale	d	09 23	09 41	10 18	10 23	11 18	11 23		20 23	21 18	21 23	22 51
Milnrow	d	09 27			10 27		11 27		20 27		21 27	
New Hey	d	09 29			10 29		11 29		20 29		21 29	
Shaw & Crompton	a	09 33			10 33		11 33	and at	20 33		21 33	
	d	09 33			10 33		11 33		20 33		21 33	
Derker	d	09 37			10 37		11 37	the same	20 37		21 37	
Oldham Mumps	d	09 40			10 40		11 40		20 40		21 40	
Oldham Werneth	d	09 43			10 43		11 43	minutes	20 43		21 43	
Hollinwood	d	09 46			10 46		11 46		20 46		21 46	
Failsworth	d	09 48			10 48		11 48	past	20 48		21 48	
Dean Lane	d	09 51			10 51		11 51	each	20 51		21 51	
Castleton	d		09 44	10 21		11 21				21 21		22 54
Mills Hill	d		09 49	10 26		11 26		hour until		21 26		22 59
Moston	d		09 52	10 29		11 29				21 29		23 02
Manchester Victoria	a	09 59	10 01	10 38	10 59	11 38	11 59		20 59	21 38	21 59	23 11
Salford Central	82 a											
Salford Crescent	82 a			*11 04*		*12 04*				*22 04*	*23 04*	
Bolton	82 a			*11 15*		*12 15*				*22 15*	23b22	
Liverpool Lime Street 10	90 a		*10 54*		*11 56*		*12 51*		*21 51*		*22 54*	

For general notes see front of timetable
For details of catering facilities see Directory of Train Operators

A From Leeds (Table 41)

B 1223 from Rochdale; connection arrives Liverpool Lime Street 1355. 1523 from Rochdale; connection arrives Liverpool Lime Street 1655

C From York (Table 41)

b Change at Manchester Victoria and Salford Crescent

Network Diagram for Tables 97, 98, 99, 100

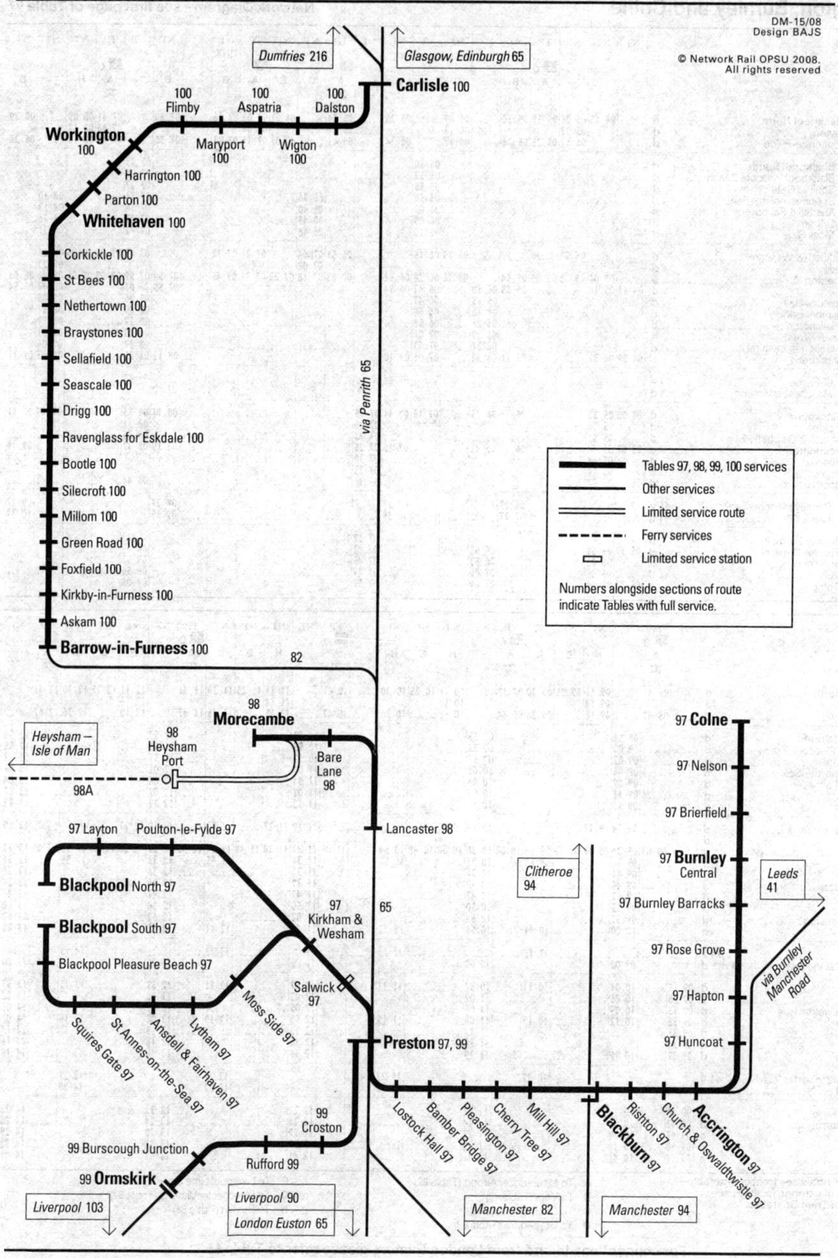

DM-15/08
Design BAJS
Dumfries 216
Glasgow, Edinburgh 65
Carlisle 100
100 Flimby
100 Aspatria
100 Dalston
Workington 100
Maryport 100
Wigton 100
Harrington 100
Parton 100
Whitehaven 100
Corkickle 100
St Bees 100
Nethertown 100
Braystones 100
Sellafield 100
Seascale 100
Drigg 100
Ravenglass for Eskdale 100
Bootle 100
Silecroft 100
Millom 100
Green Road 100
Foxfield 100
Kirkby-in-Furness 100
Askam 100
Barrow-in-Furness 100
via Penrith 65
82
98 Morecambe
Heysham – Isle of Man
98 Heysham Port
98A
Bare Lane 98
Lancaster 98
97 Layton
Poulton-le-Fylde 97
Blackpool North 97
Blackpool South 97
Blackpool Pleasure Beach 97
97 Kirkham & Wesham
65
Salwick 97
Moss Side 97
Lytham 97
Ansdell & Fairhaven 97
St Annes-on-the-Sea 97
Squires Gate 97
Preston 97, 99
99 Croston
99 Burscough Junction
Rufford 99
99 Ormskirk
Liverpool 103
Liverpool 90
London Euston 65
Lostock Hall 97
Bamber Bridge 97
Pleasington 97
Cherry Tree 97
Mill Hill 97
Manchester 82
Clitheroe 94
Blackburn 97
Rishton 97
Church & Oswaldtwistle 97
Accrington 97
Manchester 94
97 Colne
97 Nelson
97 Brierfield
97 Burnley Central
Leeds 41
97 Burnley Barracks
97 Rose Grove
97 Hapton
97 Huncoat
via Burnley Manchester Road
Tables 97, 98, 99, 100 services
Other services
Limited service route
Ferry services
Limited service station
Numbers alongside sections of route indicate Tables with full service.

Table 97

Mondays to Fridays
until 3 October

Blackpool → Preston → Blackburn, Accrington, Burnley and Colne

Network Diagram - see first page of Table 97

Miles	Miles			NT	NT	NT	TP 1◇ A	NT B	NT	NT C	NT	NT B	NT	TP 1◇ A	NT D	NT E	TP 1◇ A	NT BHX G	NT B	NT	TP 1◇ A	NT H	NT	NT B
—	0	**Blackpool North**	d		04 45	05 06	05 19	05 30		06 09		06 28		06 34		06 57	07 03	07 16	07 30		07 41	08 09		08 29
—	1¼	Layton	d			05 09				06 13				06 37			07 06				07 44	08 12		
—	3¼	Poulton-le-Fylde	d			05 13	05 25	05 36		06 17		06 34		06 41		07 03	07 11	07 23	07 36		07 48	08 16		08 35
0	—	**Blackpool South**	d								05 50									07 23				
½	—	Blackpool Pleasure Beach	d								05 52									07 25				
1¾	—	Squires Gate	d								05 55									07 27				
3¼	—	St Annes-on-the-Sea	d								05 58				06 36					07 31			08 10	
5¼	—	Ansdell & Fairhaven	d								06 02				06 40					07 34			08 13	
6½	—	Lytham	d								06 05				06 43					07 37			08 16	
9	—	Moss Side	d								06 10				06 48					07 42			08 21	
12½	9¾	Kirkham & Wesham	d			05 22				06 25	06 16			06 51	07b04		07 21	07 32		07 49	07 58	08 25	08 28	
14¾	12½	Salwick	d												07 08								08 33	
20	17½	**Preston** 8	a		05 08	05 33	05 45	05 54		06 36	06 28	06 52		07 02	07 18	07 23	07 31	07 45	07 54	07 59	08 08	08 36	08 41	08 53
—	—		d	04 43	05 16			05 55	06 10		06 42	06 54							07 55	08 01			08 42	08 54
22¾	—	Lostock Hall	d						06 15		06 47									08 06			08 48	
24	—	Bamber Bridge	d						06 18		06 50									08 09			08 51	
29	—	Pleasington	d						06 26		06 58									08 17			08 58	
30	—	Cherry Tree	d						06 29		07 01									08 20			09 01	
30¾	—	Mill Hill (Lancashire)	d						06 31		07 03									08 22			09 04	
32	—	**Blackburn**	a	04 59	05 32			06 11	06 34		07 06	07 10							08 11	08 25			09 07	09 11
—	—	Clitheroe 94	a					*06 50*				*07 44*								*09 13*				*10 13*
—	—	Manchester Victoria 94	d										←						*07 00*					*08 00*
—	—	**Blackburn**	d	05 00	05 33			06 11	06 35		07 15 →	07 11	07 15						08 11	08 26			09 15 →	09 11
35¾	—	Rishton	d		05 38								07 20							08 31				
37½	—	Church & Oswaldtwistle	d		05 41								07 23							08 34				
38¼	—	**Accrington**	d	05 07	05 44			06 19	06 42			07 18	07 26						08 19	08 37				09 19
40	—	Huncoat	d		05 48								07 30											
41½	—	Hapton	d		05 51								07 33											
43	—	Rose Grove	d		05 54								07 36							08 44				
—	—	Burnley Manchester Road 41	a					06 27				07 27							08 27					09 27
—	—	Leeds 10 41	a					07 37				08 39							09 39					10 37
44	—	Burnley Barracks	d										07 39											
44½	—	**Burnley Central**	d	05 17	05 59				06 52				07 42							08 48				
46¾	—	Brierfield	d		06 03				06 57				07 46							08 53				
48	—	Nelson	d		06 06				07 00				07 49							08 56				
50	—	**Colne**	a	05 32	06 16				07 09				07 59							09 05				

		NT	TP 1◇ A	NT	NT H	NT E	NT B	TP 1◇ A	NT	NT H	NT E	NT B	TP 1◇ A	NT	NT H	NT E	NT B	TP 1◇ A	NT	NT H	NT E	NT B	TP 1◇ A	NT
Blackpool North	d		08 41		09 11	09 25	09 30	09 38		10 11	10 25	10 30	10 41		11 11	11 25	11 30	11 41		12 11	12 25	12 30	12 41	
Layton	d				09 14					10 14					11 14					12 14				
Poulton-le-Fylde	d		08 47		09 18		09 36	09 44		10 18		10 36	10 47		11 18		11 36	11 47		12 18		12 36	12 47	
Blackpool South	d			08 58					09 53					10 53					11 53					12 53
Blackpool Pleasure Beach	d			09 00					09 55					10 55					11 55					12 55
Squires Gate	d			09 02					09 57					10 57					11 57					12 57
St Annes-on-the-Sea	d			09 06					10 01					11 01					12 01					13 01
Ansdell & Fairhaven	d			09 09					10 04					11 04					12 04					13 04
Lytham	d			09 12					10 07					11 07					12 07					13 07
Moss Side	d			09 17					10 12					11 12					12 12					13 12
Kirkham & Wesham	d			09 24	09 27				10 19	10 27				11 19	11 27				12 19	12 27				13 19
Salwick	d																							
Preston 8	a		09 05	09 34	09 39	09 48	09 54	10 02	10 30	10 38	10 48	10 54	11 05	11 29	11 38	11 48	11 54	12 05	12 29	12 38	12 48	12 53	13 05	13 29
	d			09 36			09 55		10 31			10 55		11 31			11 55		12 31			12 55		13 31
Lostock Hall	d			09 41					10 36					11 36					12 36					13 36
Bamber Bridge	d			09 44					10 39					11 39					12 39					13 39
Pleasington	d			09 52					10 47					11 47					12 47					13 47
Cherry Tree	d			09 55					10 50					11 50					12 50					13 50
Mill Hill (Lancashire)	d			09 57					10 52					11 52					12 52					13 52
Blackburn	a			10 00			10 11		10 56			11 11		11 55			12 11		12 55			13 11		13 55
Clitheroe 94	a						*11 13*					*12 13*					*13 13*					*14 13*		
Manchester Victoria 94	d	←		*09 00*					*10 00*					*11 00*					*12 00*					*13 00*
Blackburn	d	09 15		10 01			10 11		10 57			11 11		11 57			12 11		12 57			13 11		13 57
Rishton	d	09 20		10 06					11 02					12 02					13 02					14 02
Church & Oswaldtwistle	d	09 23		10 09					11 05					12 05					13 05					14 05
Accrington	d	09 26		10 12			10 19		11 08			11 19		12 08			12 19		13 08			13 19		14 08
Huncoat	d	09 31							11 13					12 13					13 13					14 13
Hapton	d	09 34							11 16					12 16					13 16					14 16
Rose Grove	d	09 37		10 19					11 19					12 19					13 19					14 19
Burnley Manchester Road 41	a						10 27					11 27					12 27					13 27		
Leeds 10 41	a						11 39					12 38					13 37					14 39		
Burnley Barracks	d	09 40		10 22					11 22					12 22					13 22					14 22
Burnley Central	d	09 42		10 24					11 24					12 24					13 24					14 24
Brierfield	d	09 47		10 29					11 29					12 29					13 29					14 29
Nelson	d	09 50		10 32					11 32					12 32					13 32					14 32
Colne	a	09 59		10 41					11 41					12 41					13 41					14 41

For general notes see front of timetable
For details of catering facilities see Directory of Train Operators

- **A** To Manchester Airport (Table 82)
- **B** To York (Table 40)
- **C** To Chester (Table 88)
- **D** To Greenbank (Table 88)
- **E** To Liverpool Lime Street (Table 90)
- **G** To Manchester Victoria (Table 82)
- **H** To Buxton (Table 86)
- **b** Arr. 0654

For connections to and from London Euston, please refer to Table 65

Table 97

Mondays to Fridays

until 3 October

Blackpool → Preston → Blackburn, Accrington, Burnley and Colne

Network Diagram - see first page of Table 97

		NT A	NT B	NT C	TP 1 ◇ D	NT		NT E	NT B	NT C	TP 1 ◇ D	NT	NT A	NT B	NT C	TP 1 ◇ D	NT	NT A	NT B	NT C	TP 1 ◇ D	NT		NT A	NT C
Blackpool North	d	13 11	13 25	13 30	13 41			14 11	14 21	14 30	14 41		15 11	15 25	15 30	15 41		16 10	16 25	16 30	16 38			17 10	17 19
Layton	d	13 14						14 14					15 14					16 13			16 41			17 13	
Poulton-le-Fylde	d	13 18		13 36	13 47			14 18		14 36	14 47		15 18		15 36	15 47		16 17		16 36	16 45			17 17	17 25
Blackpool South	d					13 53						14 53					15 53					16 53			
Blackpool Pleasure Beach	d					13 55						14 55					15 55					16 55			
Squires Gate	d					13 57						14 57					15 57					16 57			
St Annes-on-the-Sea	d					14 01						15 01					16 01					17 01			
Ansdell & Fairhaven	d					14 04						15 04					16 04					17 04			
Lytham	d					14 07						15 07					16 07					17 07			
Moss Side	d					14 12						15 12					16 12					17 12			
Kirkham & Wesham	d	13 27				14 19		14 27				15 19	15 27				16 19	16 26			16 56	17 19		17 26	
Salwick	d																16 24								
Preston 8	a	13 38	13 48	13 54	14 05	14 29		14 38	14 44	14 54	15 05	15 29	15 38	15 48	15 54	16 05	16 31	16 37	16 48	16 54	17 06	17 29		17 37	17 43
	d			13 55		14 31				14 55		15 31			15 55		16 31			16 55		17 31			17 44
Lostock Hall	d					14 36						15 36					16 36					17 36			17 50
Bamber Bridge	d					14 39						15 39					16 39					17 39			17 54
Pleasington	d					14 47						15 47					16 47					17 47			18 01
Cherry Tree	d					14 50						15 50					16 50					17 50			18 05
Mill Hill (Lancashire)	d					14 52						15 52					16 52					17 52			18 08
Blackburn	a			14 11		14 55				15 11		15 55			16 11		16 57			17 11		17 55			18 11
Clitheroe 94	a			*15 13*						*16 13*					*17 03*		*17 40*			*18 15*					*19 13*
Manchester Victoria 94	d					*14 00*						*15 00*					*15 50*					*17 00*			
Blackburn	d			14 11		14 57				15 11		15 57			16 11		16 57			17 11		17 57			18 11
Rishton	d					15 02						16 02					17 02					18 02			
Church & Oswaldtwistle	d					15 05						16 05					17 05					18 05			
Accrington	d			14 19		15 08				15 19		16 08			16 19		17 08			17 19		18 08			18 19
Huncoat	d					15 13						16 13					17 13					18 13			
Hapton	d					15 16						16 16					17 16					18 16			
Rose Grove	d					15 19						16 19					17 19					18 19			
Burnley Manchester Road 41	a			14 27						15 27					16 27					17 27					18 27
Leeds 10 41	a			15 37						16 37					17 37					18 37					19 37
Burnley Barracks	d					15 22						16 22					17 22					18 22			
Burnley Central	d					15 24						16 24					17 24					18a26			
Brierfield	d					15 29						16 29					17 29								
Nelson	d					15 32						16 32					17 32								
Colne	a					15 41						16 41					17 41								

		TP 1 ◇ D	NT G	NT	NT A	NT B	NT C	NT	TP 1 ◇ D	NT	NT A	NT H	NT B	TP 1 ◇ D	NT	NT C	TP 1 ◇ D	NT	TP D	NT B	NT	TP 1 ◇ D	NT		
Blackpool North	d	17 38			18 11	18 25	18 30		18 38		19 10	19 18	19 25	19 42		20 28	20 52		21 52	22 03		23 13			
Layton	d	17 41			18 14						19 13			19 45			20 56		21 56			23 16			
Poulton-le-Fylde	d	17 45			18 18		18 36		18 44		19 17			19 49		20 34	21 00		22 00			23 20			
Blackpool South	d			17 53						18 50					19 51			21 01			22 00		23 30		
Blackpool Pleasure Beach	d			17 55						18 52					19 53			21 03			22 02		23 32		
Squires Gate	d			17 57						18 54					19 55			21 05			22 04		23 34		
St Annes-on-the-Sea	d			18 01						18 58					19 59			21 09			22 08		23 38		
Ansdell & Fairhaven	d			18 04						19 01					20 02			21 12			22 11		23 41		
Lytham	d			18 07						19 04					20 05			21 15			22 14		23 44		
Moss Side	d			18 12						19 09					20 10			21 20			22 19		23 49		
Kirkham & Wesham	d	17 56		18 19	18 27					19 16	19 26			19 59	20 17		21 09	21 27	22 09		22 25	23 30	23 56		
Salwick	d																								
Preston 8	a	18 06		18 29	18 40	18 49	18 54		19 02	19 28	19 37	19 41	19 49	20 09	20 31	20 52	21 20	21 37	22 20	22 26	22 36	23 40	00 08		
	d			18 37			18 55								20 31	20 54		21 40			22 38				
Lostock Hall	d			18 42											20 36			21 45			22 43				
Bamber Bridge	d			18 45											20 39			21 48			22 46				
Pleasington	d			18 53											20 47			21 56			22 54				
Cherry Tree	d			18 56											20 50			21 59			22 57				
Mill Hill (Lancashire)	d			18 58											20 52			22 01			22 59				
Blackburn	a			19 01			19 11								20 56	21 10		22 04			23 02				
Clitheroe 94	a						*20 13*									*22 13*									
Manchester Victoria 94	d		*17 29*				*18 00*	←							*19 58*			*20 58*			*21 58*				
Blackburn	d		18 23	19 15			19 11	19 15							20 57	21 11		22 08			23 03				
Rishton	d		18 28	→				19 20							21 02			22 13			23 08				
Church & Oswaldtwistle	d		18 31					19 23							21 05			22 16			23 11				
Accrington	d		18 34				19 19	19 26							21 08	21 18		22 19			23 14				
Huncoat	d		18 39					19 31							21 13			22 24			23 18				
Hapton	d		18 42					19 34							21 16			22 27			23 21				
Rose Grove	d		18 45					19 37							21 19			22 30			23 24				
Burnley Manchester Road 41	a						19 27									21 27									
Leeds 10 41	a						20 37									22 38									
Burnley Barracks	d		18 48					19 40							21 22			22 33			23 27				
Burnley Central	d		18 50					19 42							21 24			22 35			23 30				
Brierfield	d		18 55					19 47							21 29			22 40			23 34				
Nelson	d		18 58					19 50							21 32			22 43			23 37				
Colne	a		19 07					19 59							21 41			22 52			23 47				

For general notes see front of timetable
For details of catering facilities see Directory of Train Operators

- **A** To Buxton (Table 86)
- **B** To Liverpool Lime Street (Table 90)
- **C** To York (Table 40)
- **D** To Manchester Airport (Table 82)
- **E** To Hazel Grove (Table 86)
- **G** From Rochdale (Table 95)
- **H** Until 12 September. To Manchester Victoria (Table 82)

For connections to and from London Euston, please refer to Table 65

Blackpool → Preston → Blackburn, Accrington, Burnley and Colne

Network Diagram - see first page of Table 97

	NT	NT	NT	TP	NT	NT	NT	NT	NT	NT		TP	NT	NT	TP	NT	NT	NT	TP	NT	NT		NT	NT
																BHX								
				1◇								1◇			1◇				1◇					
				A	B		C		B			A	D	E	A	G	B		A	H			B	
												⌶							⌶					
Blackpool North d		04 45	05 06	05 19	05 30		06 09		06 28			06 34		06 57	07 03	07 16	07 30		07 41	08 09			08 29	
Layton d			05 09				06 13					06 37			07 06				07 44	08 12				
Poulton-le-Fylde d			05 13	05 25	05 36		06 17		06 34			06 41		07 03	07 11	07 23	07 36		07 48	08 16			08 35	
Blackpool South d								05 50										07 23						
Blackpool Pleasure Beach d								05 52										07 25						
Squires Gate d								05 55										07 27						
St Annes-on-the-Sea d								05 58					06 36					07 31			08 10			
Ansdell & Fairhaven d								06 02					06 40					07 34			08 13			
Lytham d								06 05					06 43					07 37			08 16			
Moss Side d								06 10					06 48					07 42			08 21			
Kirkham & Wesham d			05 22				06 25	06 16				06 51	07b04		07 21	07 32		07 49	07 58	08 25	08 28			
Salwick d													07 08								08 33			
Preston 8 a		05 08	05 33	05 45	05 54		06 36	06 28	06 52			07 02	07 18	07 23	07 31	07 45	07 54	07 59	08 08	08 36	08 41		08 53	
d	04 43	05 16			05 55	06 10		06 42	06 54								07 55	08 01			08 42		08 54	
Lostock Hall d						06 15		06 47										08 06			08 48			
Bamber Bridge d						06 18		06 50										08 09			08 51			
Pleasington d						06 26		06 58										08 17						
Cherry Tree d						06 29		07 01										08 20			09 01			
Mill Hill (Lancashire) d						06 31		07 03										08 22			09 04			
Blackburn a	04 59	05 32			06 11	06 34		07 06	07 10								08 11	08 25			09 07		09 11	
Clitheroe 94 a					*06 52*				*07 46*									*09 15*					*10 15*	
Manchester Victoria 94 🚌 d										←							*07 00*						*08 00*	←
Blackburn d	05 00	05 33			06 11	06 35		07 15 →	07 11	07 15							08 11	08 26			09 15 →		09 11	09 15
Rishton d		05 38								07 20								08 31						09 20
Church & Oswaldtwistle d		05 41								07 23								08 34						09 23
Accrington d	05 07	05 44			06 19	06 42			07 18	07 26							08 19	08 37					09 19	09 26
Huncoat d		05 48								07 30														09 31
Hapton d		05 51								07 33														09 34
Rose Grove d		05 54								07 36								08 44						09 37
Burnley Manchester Road 41 a					06 27				07 27								08 27						09 27	
Leeds 10 41 a					07 37				08 39								09 39						10 37	
Burnley Barracks d										07 39														09 40
Burnley Central d	05 17	05 59				06 52				07 42								08 48						09 42
Brierfield d		06 03				06 57				07 46								08 53						09 47
Nelson d		06 06				07 00				07 49								08 56						09 50
Colne a	05 32	06 16				07 09				07 59								09 05						09 59

	TP	NT	NT	NT	NT	TP	NT	NT	NT	NT		TP	NT	NT	NT	NT	TP	NT	NT	NT	NT		TP	NT
	1◇					1◇						1◇					1◇						1◇	
	A		H	E	B	A		H	E	B		A		H	E	B	A		H	E	B		A	
	⌶					⌶						⌶					⌶						⌶	
Blackpool North d	08 41		09 11	09 25	09 30	09 38		10 11	10 25	10 30		10 41		11 11	11 25	11 30	11 41		12 11	12 25	12 30		12 41	
Layton d			09 14					10 14						11 14					12 14					
Poulton-le-Fylde d	08 47		09 18		09 36	09 44		10 18		10 36		10 47		11 18		11 36	11 47		12 18		12 36		12 47	
Blackpool South d		08 58					09 53						10 53					11 53						12 53
Blackpool Pleasure Beach d		09 00					09 55						10 55					11 55						12 55
Squires Gate d		09 02					09 57						10 57					11 57						12 57
St Annes-on-the-Sea d		09 06					10 01						11 01					12 01						13 01
Ansdell & Fairhaven d		09 09					10 04						11 04					12 04						13 04
Lytham d		09 12					10 07						11 07					12 07						13 07
Moss Side d		09 17					10 12						11 12					12 12						13 12
Kirkham & Wesham d		09 24	09 27				10 19	10 27					11 19	11 27				12 19	12 27					13 19
Salwick d																								
Preston 8 a	09 05	09 34	09 39	09 48	09 54	10 02	10 30	10 38	10 48	10 54		11 05	11 29	11 38	11 48	11 54	12 05	12 29	12 38	12 48	12 53		13 05	13 29
d		09 36			09 55		10 31			10 55			11 31			11 55		12 31			12 55			13 31
Lostock Hall d		09 41					10 36						11 36					12 36						13 36
Bamber Bridge d		09 44					10 39						11 39					12 39						13 39
Pleasington d		09 52											11 47											13 49
Cherry Tree d							10 50											12 50						
Mill Hill (Lancashire) d		09 57					10 52						11 52					12 52						13 52
Blackburn a		10 00			10 11		10 56			11 11			11 55			12 11		12 55			13 11			13 55
Clitheroe 94 a					*11 15*					*12 15*						*13 15*					*14 15*			
Manchester Victoria 94 🚌 d		*09 00*					*10 00*						*11 00*					*12 00*						*13 00*
Blackburn d		10 01			10 11		10 57			11 11			11 57			12 11		12 57			13 11			13 57
Rishton d		10 06					11 02						12 02					13 02						14 02
Church & Oswaldtwistle d		10 09					11 05						12 05					13 05						14 05
Accrington d		10 12			10 19		11 08			11 19			12 08			12 19		13 08			13 19			14 08
Huncoat d							11 13						12 13											14 13
Hapton d							11 16											13 16						
Rose Grove d		10 19					11 19						12 19					13 19						14 19
Burnley Manchester Road 41 a					10 27					11 27						12 27					13 27			
Leeds 10 41 a					11 39					12 38						13 37					14 39			
Burnley Barracks d		10 22					11 22						12 22					13 22						14 22
Burnley Central d		10 24					11 24						12 24					13 24						14 24
Brierfield d		10 29					11 29						12 29					13 29						14 29
Nelson d		10 32					11 32						12 32					13 32						14 32
Colne a		10 41					11 41						12 41					13 41						14 41

For general notes see front of timetable
For details of catering facilities see Directory of Train Operators

- **A** To Manchester Airport (Table 82)
- **B** To York (Table 40)
- **C** To Chester (Table 88)
- **D** To Greenbank (Table 88)
- **E** To Liverpool Lime Street (Table 90)
- **G** To Manchester Victoria (Table 82)
- **H** To Buxton (Table 86)
- **b** Arr. 0654

For connections to and from London Euston, please refer to Table 65

Table 97

Mondays to Fridays

from 6 October

Blackpool → Preston → Blackburn, Accrington, Burnley and Colne

Network Diagram - see first page of Table 97

		NT	NT	NT	TP	NT	NT	NT	NT	TP	NT	NT	NT	NT	TP	NT	NT	NT	NT	TP	NT	NT	NT
					1◇					1◇					1◇					1◇			
		A	B	C	D		E	B	C	D		A	B	C	D		A	B	C	D		A	C
Blackpool North	d	13 11	13 25	13 30	13 41		14 11	14 21	14 30	14 41		15 11	15 25	15 30	15 41		16 10	16 25	16 30	16 38		17 10	17 19
Layton	d	13 14					14 14					15 14					16 13			16 41		17 13	
Poulton-le-Fylde	d	13 18		13 36	13 47		14 18		14 36	14 47		15 18		15 36	15 47		16 17		16 36	16 45		17 17	17 25
Blackpool South	d					13 53					14 53					15 53					16 53		
Blackpool Pleasure Beach	d					13 55					14 55					15 55					16 55		
Squires Gate	d					13 57					14 57					15 57					16 57		
St Annes-on-the-Sea	d					14 01					15 01					16 01					17 01		
Ansdell & Fairhaven	d					14 04					15 04					16 04					17 04		
Lytham	d					14 07					15 07					16 07					17 07		
Moss Side	d					14 12					15 12					16 12					17 12		
Kirkham & Wesham	d	13 27				14 19	14 27				15 19	15 27				16 19	16 26			16 56	17 19	17 26	
Salwick	d															16 24							
Preston [8]	a	13 38	13 48	13 54	14 05	14 29	14 38	14 44	14 54	15 05	15 29	15 38	15 48	15 54	16 05	16 31	16 37	16 48	16 54	17 06	17 29	17 37	17 43
	d			13 55		14 31			14 55		15 31			15 55		16 31			16 55		17 31		17 44
Lostock Hall	d					14 36					15 36					16 36					17 36		17 50
Bamber Bridge	d					14 39					15 39					16 39					17 39		17 54
Pleasington	d										15 47					16 47					17 47		18 01
Cherry Tree	d					14 50					15 50					16 50					17 50		18 05
Mill Hill (Lancashire)	d					14 52					15 52					16 52					17 52		18 08
Blackburn	a			14 11		14 55			15 11		15 55			16 11		16 57			17 11		17 55		18 11
Clitheroe (94)	a			*15 15*					*16 15*					*17 05*		*17 42*			*18 17*				*19 15*
Manchester Victoria (94)	d					*14 00*					*15 00*					*15 50*					*17 00*		
Blackburn	d			14 11		14 57			15 11		15 57			16 11		16 57			17 11		17 57		18 11
Rishton	d					15 02					16 02					17 02					18 02		
Church & Oswaldtwistle	d					15 05					16 05					17 05					18 05		
Accrington	d			14 19		15 08			15 19		16 08			16 19		17 08			17 19		18 08		18 19
Huncoat	d										16 13					17 13					18 13		
Hapton	d					15 16					16 16					17 16					18 16		
Rose Grove	d					15 19					16 19					17 19					18 19		
Burnley Manchester Road (41)	a			14 27					15 27					16 27					17 27				18 27
Leeds [10] (41)	a			15 37					16 37					17 37					18 37				19 37
Burnley Barracks	d					15 22					16 22					17 22					18 22		
Burnley Central	d					15 24					16 24					17 24					18a26		
Brierfield	d					15 29					16 29					17 29							
Nelson	d					15 32					16 32					17 32							
Colne	a					15 41					16 41					17 41							

		TP	NT	NT	NT	NT	NT	NT	TP	NT	NT	NT	TP	NT	NT	TP	NT	TP	NT	NT	TP	NT
		1◇							1◇				1◇			1◇					1◇	
		D	G		A	B	C		D		A	B	D		C	D		D	B		D	
Blackpool North	d	17 38			18 11	18 25	18 30		18 38		19 10	19 25	19 42		20 28	20 52		21 52	22 03		23 13	
Layton	d	17 41			18 14						19 13		19 45			20 56		21 56			23 16	
Poulton-le-Fylde	d	17 45			18 18		18 36		18 44		19 17		19 49		20 34	21 00		22 00			23 20	
Blackpool South	d			17 53						18 50				19 51			21 01			22 00		23 30
Blackpool Pleasure Beach	d			17 55						18 52				19 53			21 03			22 02		23 32
Squires Gate	d			17 57						18 54				19 55			21 05			22 04		23 34
St Annes-on-the-Sea	d			18 01						18 58				19 59			21 09			22 08		23 38
Ansdell & Fairhaven	d			18 04						19 01				20 02			21 12			22 11		23 41
Lytham	d			18 07						19 04				20 05			21 15			22 14		23 44
Moss Side	d			18 12						19 09				20 10			21 20			22 19		23 49
Kirkham & Wesham	d	17 56		18 19	18 27					19 16	19 26		19 59	20 17		21 09	21 27	22 09		22 25	23 30	23 56
Salwick	d																					
Preston [8]	a	18 06		18 29	18 40	18 49	18 54		19 02	19 28	19 37	19 49	20 09	20 31	20 52	21 20	21 37	22 20	22 26	22 36	23 40	00 08
	d			18 37			18 55							20 31	20 54		21 40			22 38		
Lostock Hall	d			18 42										20 36			21 45			22 43		
Bamber Bridge	d			18 45										20 39			21 48			22 46		
Pleasington	d			18 53										20 47			21 56			22 54		
Cherry Tree	d			18 56										20 50			21 59			22 57		
Mill Hill (Lancashire)	d			18 58										20 52			22 01			22 59		
Blackburn	a			19 01			19 11							20 56	21 10		22 04			23 02		
Clitheroe (94)	a						*20 15*								*22 15*							
Manchester Victoria (94)	d		17 29				*18 00*	←						*19 58*			*20 58*			*21 58*		
Blackburn	d		18 23	19 15 →			19 11	19 15						20 57	21 11		22 08			23 03		
Rishton	d		18 28					19 20						21 02			22 13			23 08		
Church & Oswaldtwistle	d		18 31					19 23						21 05			22 16			23 11		
Accrington	d		18 34				19 19	19 26						21 08	21 18		22 19			23 14		
Huncoat	d		18 39					19 31						21 13			22 24			23 18		
Hapton	d		18 42					19 34						21 16			22 27			23 21		
Rose Grove	d		18 45					19 37						21 19			22 30			23 24		
Burnley Manchester Road (41)	a						19 27								21 27							
Leeds [10] (41)	a						20 37								22 38							
Burnley Barracks	d		18 48					19 40						21 22			22 33			23 27		
Burnley Central	d		18 50					19 42						21 24			22 35			23 30		
Brierfield	d		18 55					19 47						21 29			22 40			23 34		
Nelson	d		18 58					19 50						21 32			22 43			23 37		
Colne	a		19 07					19 59						21 41			22 52			23 47		

For general notes see front of timetable
For details of catering facilities see Directory of Train Operators

A To Buxton (Table 86)
B To Liverpool Lime Street (Table 90)
C To York (Table 40)
D To Manchester Airport (Table 82)
E To Hazel Grove (Table 86)
G From Rochdale (Table 95)

For connections to and from London Euston, please refer to Table 65

Table 97

Saturdays

until 4 October

Blackpool → Preston → Blackburn, Accrington, Burnley and Colne

Network Diagram - see first page of Table 97

Station		NT	NT	NT	TP 1◇	NT	NT	NT	NT	NT		NT	TP 1◇	NT	NT	TP 1◇	NT	NT	TP 1◇	NT		NT	NT	NT	TP 1◇
					A	B		C		B			A	D	E	A	B		A	G			B		A
Blackpool North	d		04 45	05 06	05 19	05 30		06 08		06 27			06 34		06 57	07 03	07 30		07 41	08 09			08 27		08 41
Layton	d			05 09				06 12					06 37		07 00	07 07			07 44	08 12					
Poulton-le-Fylde	d			05 13	05 25	05 36		06 16		06 33			06 41		07 03	07 11	07 36		07 48	08 16			08 33		08 47
Blackpool South	d								05 50									07 23							
Blackpool Pleasure Beach	d								05 52									07 25							
Squires Gate	d								05 55									07 27							
St Annes-on-the-Sea	d								05 58					06 36				07 31				08 10			
Ansdell & Fairhaven	d								06 02					06 40				07 34				08 13			
Lytham	d								06 05					06 43				07 37				08 16			
Moss Side	d								06 10					06 48				07 42				08 21			
Kirkham & Wesham	d			05 22				06 24	06 16				06 51	07b04	07 13	07 20		07 49	07 58	08 25		08 28			
Salwick	d													07 08								08 33			
Preston 8	a		05 08	05 33	05 45	05 54		06 35	06 26	06 52			07 02	07 18	07 23	07 31	07 54	07 59	08 08	08 36		08 41	08 51		09 05
	d	04 43	05 22			05 55	06 10		06 42	06 54							07 55	08 01				08 42	08 52		
Lostock Hall	d						06 15		06 47									08 06				08 48			
Bamber Bridge	d						06 18		06 50									08 09				08 51			
Pleasington	d						06 26		06 58									08 17				08 58			
Cherry Tree	d						06 29		07 01									08 20				09 01			
Mill Hill (Lancashire)	d						06 31		07 03									08 22				09 04			
Blackburn	a	04 59	05 38			06 11	06 34		07 06	07 11							08 11	08 25				09 07	09 11		
Clitheroe 94	a					*06 50*				*07 44*								*09 13*					*10 13*		
Manchester Victoria 94 🚌	d											←					*07 00*	*07 23*					*08 00*	←	
Blackburn	d	05 00	05 39			06 11	06 35		07 15 →	07 11		07 15					08 11	08 26				09 15 →	09 11	09 15	
Rishton	d		05 44									07 20						08 31						09 20	
Church & Oswaldtwistle	d		05 47									07 23						08 34						09 23	
Accrington	d	05 07	05 50			06 19	06 42			07 19		07 26					08 19	08 37					09 19	09 26	
Huncoat	d		05 54									07 30												09 31	
Hapton	d		05 57									07 33												09 34	
Rose Grove	d		06 00									07 36						08 44						09 37	
Burnley Manchester Road 41	a					06 27				07 27							08 27						09 27		
Leeds 10 41	a					07 37				08 39							09 39						10 37		
Burnley Barracks	d											07 39												09 40	
Burnley Central	d	05 17	06 05				06 52					07 42						08 48						09 42	
Brierfield	d		06 09				06 57					07 46						08 53						09 47	
Nelson	d		06 12				07 00					07 49						08 56						09 50	
Colne	a	05 32	06 22				07 09					07 59						09 05						09 59	

Station		NT	NT	NT	NT	TP 1◇	NT	NT		NT	NT	TP 1◇	NT	NT	NT	NT	TP 1◇	NT		NT	NT	NT	TP 1◇	NT	NT
			G	E	B	A		G		E	B	A		G	E	B	A			G	E	B	A		G
Blackpool North	d		09 11	09 25	09 30	09 40		10 11		10 25	10 30	10 41		11 11	11 25	11 30	11 41			12 11	12 25	12 30	12 41		13 11
Layton	d		09 14					10 14						11 14						12 14					13 14
Poulton-le-Fylde	d		09 18		09 36	09 46		10 18			10 36	10 47		11 18		11 36	11 47			12 18		12 36	12 47		13 18
Blackpool South	d	08 58					09 53						10 53					11 53						12 53	
Blackpool Pleasure Beach	d	09 00					09 55						10 55					11 55						12 55	
Squires Gate	d	09 02					09 57						10 57					11 57						12 57	
St Annes-on-the-Sea	d	09 06					10 01						11 01					12 01						13 01	
Ansdell & Fairhaven	d	09 09					10 04						11 04					12 04						13 04	
Lytham	d	09 12					10 07						11 07					12 07						13 07	
Moss Side	d	09 17					10 12						11 12					12 12						13 12	
Kirkham & Wesham	d	09 24	09 27				10 19	10 27					11 19	11 27				12 19		12 27				13 19	13 27
Salwick	d																								
Preston 8	a	09 34	09 39	09 48	09 54	10 04	10 30	10 38		10 48	10 54	11 05	11 29	11 38	11 48	11 54	12 05	12 29		12 38	12 48	12 54	13 05	13 29	13 38
	d	09 36			09 55		10 31				10 55		11 31			11 55		12 31				12 55		13 31	
Lostock Hall	d	09 41					10 36						11 36					12 36						13 36	
Bamber Bridge	d	09 44					10 39						11 39					12 39						13 39	
Pleasington	d	09 52					10 47						11 47					12 47						13 47	
Cherry Tree	d	09 55					10 50						11 50					12 50						13 50	
Mill Hill (Lancashire)	d	09 57					10 52						11 52					12 52						13 52	
Blackburn	a	10 00			10 11		10 56				11 11		11 55			12 11		12 55				13 11		13 55	
Clitheroe 94	a				*11 13*						*12 11*					*13 13*						*14 13*			
Manchester Victoria 94 🚌	d	*09 00*					*10 00*						*11 00*					*12 00*						*13 00*	
Blackburn	d	10 01			10 11		10 57				11 11		11 57			12 11		12 57				13 11		13 57	
Rishton	d	10 06					11 02						12 02					13 02						14 02	
Church & Oswaldtwistle	d	10 09					11 05						12 05					13 05						14 05	
Accrington	d	10 12			10 19		11 08				11 19		12 08			12 19		13 08				13 19		14 08	
Huncoat	d						11 13						12 13					13 13						14 13	
Hapton	d						11 16						12 16					13 16						14 16	
Rose Grove	d	10 19					11 19						12 19					13 19						14 19	
Burnley Manchester Road 41	a				10 27						11 27					12 27						13 27			
Leeds 10 41	a				11 39						12 38					13 37						14 39			
Burnley Barracks	d	10 22					11 22						12 22					13 22						14 22	
Burnley Central	d	10 24					11 24						12 24					13 24						14 24	
Brierfield	d	10 29					11 29						12 29					13 29						14 29	
Nelson	d	10 32					11 32						12 32					13 32						14 32	
Colne	a	10 41					11 41						12 41					13 41						14 41	

For general notes see front of timetable
For details of catering facilities see Directory of Train Operators

A To Manchester Airport (Table 82)
B To York (Table 40)
C To Chester (Table 88)
D To Greenbank (Table 88)
E To Liverpool Lime Street (Table 90)
G To Buxton (Table 86)
b Arr. 0654

For connections to and from London Euston, please refer to Table 65

Table 97

Saturdays

until 4 October

Blackpool → Preston → Blackburn, Accrington, Burnley and Colne

Network Diagram - see first page of Table 97

		NT	NT	TP	NT	NT	NT	NT	TP	NT	NT	NT	NT	TP	NT	NT	NT	NT	TP	NT	NT	NT	TP
				1 ◇					1 ◇					1 ◇					1 ◇				1 ◇
		A	B	C		D	A	B	C		D	A	B	C		D	A	B	C		D	B	C
Blackpool North	d	13 25	13 30	13 41		14 11	14 25	14 30	14 41		15 11	15 25	15 30	15 41		16 10	16 25	16 30	16 38		17 10	17 19	17 38
Layton	d					14 14					15 14					16 13			16 41		17 13		17 41
Poulton-le-Fylde	d		13 36	13 47		14 18		14 36	14 47		15 18		15 36	15 47		16 17		16 36	16 45		17 17	17 25	17 45
Blackpool South	d				13 53					14 53					15 53					16 53			
Blackpool Pleasure Beach	d				13 55					14 55					15 55					16 55			
Squires Gate	d				13 57					14 57					15 57					16 57			
St Annes-on-the-Sea	d				14 01					15 01					16 01					17 01			
Ansdell & Fairhaven	d				14 04					15 04					16 04					17 04			
Lytham	d				14 07					15 07					16 07					17 07			
Moss Side	d				14 12					15 12					16 12					17 12			
Kirkham & Wesham	d				14 19	14 27				15 19	15 27				16 19	16 26			16 56	17 19	17 26		17 56
Salwick	d														16 24								
Preston 8	a	13 48	13 54	14 05	14 29	14 38	14 48	14 54	15 05	15 29	15 38	15 48	15 54	16 05	16 31	16 37	16 48	16 54	17 06	17 29	17 37	17 43	18 06
	d		13 55		14 31			14 55		15 31			15 55		16 31			16 55		17 31		17 44	
Lostock Hall	d				14 36					15 36					16 36					17 36		17 50	
Bamber Bridge	d				14 39					15 39					16 39					17 39		17 54	
Pleasington	d				14 47					15 47					16 47					17 47		18 01	
Cherry Tree	d				14 50					15 50					16 50					17 50		18 05	
Mill Hill (Lancashire)	d				14 52					15 52					16 52					17 52		18 08	
Blackburn	a		14 11		14 55			15 11		15 55			16 11		16 57			17 11		17 55		18 11	
Clitheroe 94	a		*15 13*					*16 13*					*17 03*		*17 40*			*18 15*				*19 13*	
Manchester Victoria 94 🚢	d				*14 00*					*15 00*					*15 50*					*17 00*			
Blackburn	d		14 11		14 57			15 11		15 57			16 11		16 57			17 11		17 57		18 11	
Rishton	d				15 02					16 02					17 02					18 02			
Church & Oswaldtwistle	d				15 05					16 05					17 05					18 05			
Accrington	d		14 19		15 08			15 19		16 08			16 19		17 08			17 19		18 08		18 19	
Huncoat	d				15 13					16 13					17 13					18 13			
Hapton	d				15 16					16 16					17 16					18 16			
Rose Grove	d				15 19					16 19					17 19					18 19			
Burnley Manchester Road 41	a		14 27					15 27					16 27					17 27				18 27	
Leeds 10 41	a		15 37					16 37					17 37					18 37				19 37	
Burnley Barracks	d				15 22					16 22					17 22					18 22			
Burnley Central	d				15 24					16 24					17 24					18 24			
Brierfield	d				15 29					16 29					17 29					18 29			
Nelson	d				15 32					16 32					17 32					18 32			
Colne	a				15 41					16 41					17 41					18 41			

		NT	NT	NT	NT	TP	NT	NT	NT	NT	TP	NT	NT	TP	NT	TP	NT	NT	NT	TP	NT
						1 ◇					1 ◇			1 ◇		1 ◇				1 ◇	
			D	A	B	C		D	E	A	C		B	C		C	A		🚌	C	
Blackpool North	d		18 11	18 25	18 30	18 42		19 10	19 19	19 25	19 42		20 30	20 52		21 52	22 03			23 13	
Layton	d		18 14					19 13			19 45			20 56		21 56				23 16	
Poulton-le-Fylde	d		18 18		18 36	18 48		19 17			19 49		20 37	21 00		22 00				23 20	
Blackpool South	d	17 53					18 50					19 51			20 53			22 00			23 30
Blackpool Pleasure Beach	d	17 55					18 52					19 53			20 55			22 02			23 32
Squires Gate	d	17 57					18 54					19 55			20 57			22 04			23 34
St Annes-on-the-Sea	d	18 01					18 58					19 59			21 01			22 08			23 38
Ansdell & Fairhaven	d	18 04					19 01					20 02			21 04			22 11			23 41
Lytham	d	18 07					19 04					20 05			21 07			22 14			23 44
Moss Side	d	18 12					19 09					20 10			21 12			22 19			23 49
Kirkham & Wesham	d	18 19	18 27				19 16	19 26			19 59	20 17		21 09	21 19	22 09		22 25		23 30	23 56
Salwick	d																				
Preston 8	a	18 29	18 39	18 49	18 54	19 06	19 28	19 37	19 44	19 49	20 09	20 31	20 54	21 20	21 29	22 20	22 26	22 36		23 40	00 08
	d	18 31			18 56							20 31	20 55		21 31			22 38			
Lostock Hall	d	18 36										20 36			21 36			22 43			
Bamber Bridge	d	18 39										20 39			21 39			22 46			
Pleasington	d	18 47										20 47			21 47			22 54			
Cherry Tree	d	18 50										20 50			21 50			22 57			
Mill Hill (Lancashire)	d	18 52										20 52			21 52			22 59			
Blackburn	a	18 55			19 12							20 56	21 11		21 55			23 04			
Clitheroe 94	a				*20 13*								*22 13*								
Manchester Victoria 94 🚢	d	*18 00*										*19 58*			*20 58*				*21 58*		
Blackburn	d	18 57			19 13							20 57	21 11		22 00				23 10		
Rishton	d	19 02										21 02			22 05				23 20		
Church & Oswaldtwistle	d	19 05										21 05			22 08				23 32		
Accrington	d	19 08			19 20							21 08	21 19		22 11				23 36		
Huncoat	d	19 13										21 13			22 16				23 42		
Hapton	d	19 16										21 16			22 19				23 48		
Rose Grove	d	19 19										21 19			22 22				23 54		
Burnley Manchester Road 41	a				19 29								21 27								
Leeds 10 41	a				20 40								22 38								
Burnley Barracks	d	19 22										21 22			22 25				23 58		
Burnley Central	d	19 24										21 24			22 27				00 03		
Brierfield	d	19 29										21 29			22 32				00 11		
Nelson	d	19 32										21 32			22 35				00 16		
Colne	a	19 41										21 41			22 44				00 24		

For general notes see front of timetable
For details of catering facilities see Directory of Train Operators

- **A** To Liverpool Lime Street (Table 90)
- **B** To York (Table 40)
- **C** To Manchester Airport (Table 82)
- **D** To Buxton (Table 86)
- **E** Until 13 September. To Manchester Victoria (Table 82)

For connections to and from London Euston, please refer to Table 65

Table 97

Saturdays

from 11 October

Blackpool → Preston → Blackburn, Accrington, Burnley and Colne

Network Diagram - see first page of Table 97

	NT	NT	NT	TP	NT	NT	NT	NT		NT	NT	TP	NT	NT	TP	NT	NT		TP	NT	NT	NT	NT	TP
				1 ◇								**1** ◇			**1** ◇				**1** ◇					**1** ◇
				A	B		C			B		A	D	E	A	B			A 🛒	G		B		A
Blackpool North d		04 45	05 06	05 19	05 30		06 08			06 27		06 34		06 57	07 03	07 30			07 41	08 09		08 27		08 41
Layton d			05 09				06 12					06 37		07 00	07 07				07 44	08 12				
Poulton-le-Fylde d			05 13	05 25	05 36		06 16			06 33		06 41		07 03	07 11	07 36			07 48	08 16		08 33		08 47
Blackpool South d								05 50									07 23							
Blackpool Pleasure Beach d								05 52									07 25							
Squires Gate d								05 55									07 27							
St Annes-on-the-Sea d								05 58					06 36				07 31				08 10			
Ansdell & Fairhaven d								06 02					06 40				07 34				08 13			
Lytham d								06 05					06 43				07 37				08 16			
Moss Side d								06 10					06 48				07 42				08 21			
Kirkham & Wesham d			05 22				06 24	06 16				06 51	07b04	07 13	07 20		07 49		07 58	08 25	08 28			
Salwick d													07 08								08 33			
Preston 8 a		05 08	05 33	05 45	05 54		06 35	06 26		06 52		07 02	07 18	07 23	07 31	07 54	07 59		08 08	08 36	08 41	08 51		09 05
d	04 43	05 22			05 55	06 10		06 42		06 54						07 55	08 01				08 42	08 52		
Lostock Hall d						06 15		06 47									08 06				08 48			
Bamber Bridge d						06 18		06 50									08 09				08 51			
Pleasington d						06 26		06 58									08 17							
Cherry Tree d						06 29		07 01									08 20				09 01			
Mill Hill (Lancashire) d						06 31		07 03									08 22				09 04			
Blackburn a	04 59	05 38			06 11	06 34		07 06		07 11						08 11	08 25				09 07	09 11		
Clitheroe 94 a					*06 52*					*07 46*							*09 15*					*10 15*		
Manchester Victoria 94 🚌 d											←					*07 00*	*07 23*					*08 00*	←	
Blackburn d	05 00	05 39			06 11	06 35		07 15 →		07 11	07 15					08 11	08 26				09 15 →	09 11	09 15	
Rishton d		05 44									07 20						08 31						09 20	
Church & Oswaldtwistle d		05 47									07 23						08 34						09 23	
Accrington d	05 07	05 50			06 19	06 42				07 19	07 26					08 19	08 37					09 19	09 26	
Huncoat d		05 54									07 30												09 31	
Hapton d		05 57									07 33												09 34	
Rose Grove d		06 00									07 36						08 44						09 37	
Burnley Manchester Road 41 a					06 27					07 27						08 27						09 27		
Leeds 10 41 a					07 37					08 39						09 39						10 37		
Burnley Barracks d											07 39												09 40	
Burnley Central d	05 17	06 05				06 52					07 42						08 48						09 42	
Brierfield d		06 09				06 57					07 46						08 53						09 47	
Nelson d		06 12				07 00					07 49						08 56						09 50	
Colne a	05 32	06 22				07 09					07 59						09 05						09 59	

	NT	NT	NT	NT		TP	NT	NT	NT	NT	TP	NT	NT		NT	NT	TP	NT	NT	NT	NT	TP		NT
						1 ◇					**1** ◇						**1** ◇					**1** ◇		
		G	E	B		A 🛒		G	E	B	A 🛒		G		E	B	A 🛒		G	E	B	A 🛒		
Blackpool North d		09 11	09 25	09 30		09 40		10 11	10 25	10 30	10 41		11 11		11 25	11 30	11 41		12 11	12 25	12 30	12 41		
Layton d		09 14						10 14					11 14						12 14					
Poulton-le-Fylde d		09 18		09 36		09 46		10 18		10 36	10 47		11 18			11 36	11 47		12 18		12 36	12 47		
Blackpool South d	08 58						09 53					10 53						11 53						12 53
Blackpool Pleasure Beach d	09 00						09 55					10 55						11 55						12 55
Squires Gate d	09 02						09 57					10 57						11 57						12 57
St Annes-on-the-Sea d	09 06						10 01					11 01						12 01						13 01
Ansdell & Fairhaven d	09 09						10 04					11 04						12 04						13 04
Lytham d	09 12						10 07					11 07						12 07						13 07
Moss Side d	09 17						10 12					11 12						12 12						13 12
Kirkham & Wesham d	09 24	09 27					10 19	10 27				11 19	11 27					12 19	12 27					13 19
Salwick d																								
Preston 8 a	09 34	09 39	09 48	09 54		10 04	10 30	10 38	10 48	10 54	11 05	11 29	11 38		11 48	11 54	12 05	12 29	12 38	12 48	12 54	13 05		13 29
d	09 36			09 55			10 31			10 55		11 31				11 55		12 31			12 55			13 31
Lostock Hall d	09 41						10 36					11 36						12 36						13 36
Bamber Bridge d	09 44						10 39					11 39						12 39						13 39
Pleasington d	09 52											11 47												13 47
Cherry Tree d							10 50											12 50						
Mill Hill (Lancashire) d	09 57						10 52					11 52						12 52						13 52
Blackburn a	10 00			10 11			10 56			11 11		11 55				12 11		12 55			13 11			13 55
Clitheroe 94 a				*11 15*						*12 13*						*13 15*					*14 15*			
Manchester Victoria 94 🚌 d	*09 00*						*10 00*					*11 00*						*12 00*						*13 00*
Blackburn d	10 01			10 11			10 57			11 11		11 57				12 11		12 57			13 11			13 57
Rishton d	10 06						11 02					12 02						13 02						14 02
Church & Oswaldtwistle d	10 09						11 05					12 05						13 05						14 05
Accrington d	10 12			10 19			11 08			11 19		12 08				12 19		13 08			13 19			14 08
Huncoat d							11 13					12 13												14 13
Hapton d							11 16											13 16						
Rose Grove d	10 19						11 19					12 19						13 19						14 19
Burnley Manchester Road 41 a				10 27						11 27						12 27					13 27			
Leeds 10 41 a				11 39						12 38						13 37					14 39			
Burnley Barracks d	10 22						11 22					12 22						13 22						14 22
Burnley Central d	10 24						11 24					12 24						13 24						14 24
Brierfield d	10 29						11 29					12 29						13 29						14 29
Nelson d	10 32						11 32					12 32						13 32						14 32
Colne a	10 41						11 41					12 41						13 41						14 41

For general notes see front of timetable
For details of catering facilities see Directory of Train Operators

- **A** To Manchester Airport (Table 82)
- **B** To York (Table 40)
- **C** To Chester (Table 88)
- **D** To Greenbank (Table 88)
- **E** To Liverpool Lime Street (Table 90)
- **G** To Buxton (Table 86)
- **b** Arr. 0654

For connections to and from London Euston, please refer to Table 65

Table 97

Saturdays

from 11 October

Blackpool → Preston → Blackburn, Accrington, Burnley and Colne

Network Diagram - see first page of Table 97

		NT	NT	NT	TP	NT	NT	NT	NT		TP	NT	NT	NT	NT	TP	NT	NT		NT	NT	TP	NT	NT	NT
					1◇						1◇					1◇						1◇			
		A	B	C	D		A	B	C		D		A	B	C	D		A		B	C	D		A	C
					⚒																				
Blackpool North	d	13 11	13 25	13 30	13 41		14 11	14 25	14 30		14 41		15 11	15 25	15 30	15 41		16 10		16 25	16 30	16 38		17 10	17 19
Layton	d	13 14					14 14						15 14					16 13				16 41		17 13	
Poulton-le-Fylde	d	13 18		13 36	13 47		14 18		14 36		14 47		15 18		15 36	15 47		16 17			16 36	16 45		17 17	17 25
Blackpool South	d					13 53						14 53					15 53						16 53		
Blackpool Pleasure Beach	d					13 55						14 55					15 55						16 55		
Squires Gate	d					13 57						14 57					15 57						16 57		
St Annes-on-the-Sea	d					14 01						15 01					16 01						17 01		
Ansdell & Fairhaven	d					14 04						15 04					16 04						17 04		
Lytham	d					14 07						15 07					16 07						17 07		
Moss Side	d					14 12						15 12					16 12						17 12		
Kirkham & Wesham	d	13 27				14 19	14 27					15 19	15 27				16 19	16 26				16 56	17 19	17 26	
Salwick	d																16 24								
Preston 8	a	13 38	13 48	13 54	14 05	14 29	14 38	14 48	14 54		15 05	15 29	15 38	15 48	15 54	16 05	16 31	16 37		16 48	16 54	17 06	17 29	17 37	17 43
	d			13 55		14 31			14 55			15 31			15 55		16 31				16 55		17 31		17 44
Lostock Hall	d					14 36						15 36					16 36						17 36		17 50
Bamber Bridge	d					14 39						15 39					16 39						17 39		17 54
Pleasington	d											15 47					16 47						17 47		18 01
Cherry Tree	d					14 50						15 50					16 50						17 50		18 05
Mill Hill (Lancashire)	d					14 52						15 52					16 52						17 52		18 08
Blackburn	a			14 11		14 55			15 11			15 55			16 11		16 57				17 11		17 55		18 11
Clitheroe 94	a			*15 15*					*16 15*						*17 05*		*17 42*				*18 17*				*19 15*
Manchester Victoria 94 🚌	d					*14 00*						*15 00*					*15 50*						*17 00*		
Blackburn	d			14 11		14 57			15 11			15 57			16 11		16 57				17 11		17 57		18 11
Rishton	d					15 02						16 02					17 02						18 02		
Church & Oswaldtwistle	d					15 05						16 05					17 05						18 05		
Accrington	d			14 19		15 08			15 19			16 08			16 19		17 08				17 19		18 08		18 19
Huncoat	d											16 13					17 13						18 13		
Hapton	d					15 16						16 16					17 16						18 16		
Rose Grove	d					15 19						16 19					17 19						18 19		
Burnley Manchester Road 41	a			14 27					15 27						16 27						17 27				18 27
Leeds 10 41	a			15 37					16 37						17 37						18 37				19 37
Burnley Barracks	d					15 22						16 22					17 22						18 22		
Burnley Central	d					15 24						16 24					17 24						18 24		
Brierfield	d					15 29						16 29					17 29						18 29		
Nelson	d					15 32						16 32					17 32						18 32		
Colne	a					15 41						16 41					17 41						18 41		

		TP	NT	NT	NT		NT	TP	NT	NT	NT	TP	NT	NT		TP	NT	TP	NT	NT	NT	TP	NT		
		1◇						1◇				1◇				1◇		1◇				1◇			
		D		A	B		C	D		A	B	D		C		D		D	B		🚌	D			
Blackpool North	d	17 38		18 11	18 25		18 30	18 42		19 10	19 25	19 42		20 30		20 52		21 52	22 03			23 13			
Layton	d	17 41		18 14						19 13		19 45				20 56		21 56				23 16			
Poulton-le-Fylde	d	17 45		18 18			18 36	18 48		19 17		19 49		20 37		21 00		22 00				23 20			
Blackpool South	d		17 53						18 50				19 51				20 53			22 00			23 30		
Blackpool Pleasure Beach	d		17 55						18 52				19 53				20 55			22 02			23 32		
Squires Gate	d		17 57						18 54				19 55				20 57			22 04			23 34		
St Annes-on-the-Sea	d		18 01						18 58				19 59				21 01			22 08			23 38		
Ansdell & Fairhaven	d		18 04						19 01				20 02				21 04			22 11			23 41		
Lytham	d		18 07						19 04				20 05				21 07			22 14			23 44		
Moss Side	d		18 12						19 09				20 10				21 12			22 19			23 49		
Kirkham & Wesham	d	17 56	18 19	18 27					19 16	19 26		19 59	20 17			21 09	21 19	22 09		22 25		23 30	23 56		
Salwick	d																								
Preston 8	a	18 06	18 29	18 39	18 49		18 54	19 06	19 28	19 37	19 49	20 09	20 31	20 54		21 20	21 29	22 20	22 26	22 36		23 40	00 08		
	d		18 31				18 56						20 31	20 55			21 31			22 38					
Lostock Hall	d		18 36										20 36				21 36			22 43					
Bamber Bridge	d		18 39										20 39				21 39			22 46					
Pleasington	d		18 47										20 47				21 47			22 54					
Cherry Tree	d		18 50										20 50				21 50			22 57					
Mill Hill (Lancashire)	d		18 52										20 52				21 52			22 59					
Blackburn	a		18 55				19 12						20 56	21 11			21 55			23 04					
Clitheroe 94	a						*20 15*							*22 15*											
Manchester Victoria 94 🚌	d		*18 00*										*19 58*				*20 57*				*21 58*				
Blackburn	d		18 57				19 13						20 57	21 11			22 00				23 10				
Rishton	d		19 02										21 02				22 05				23 20				
Church & Oswaldtwistle	d		19 05										21 05				22 08				23 32				
Accrington	d		19 08				19 20						21 08	21 19			22 11				23 36				
Huncoat	d		19 13										21 13				22 16				23 42				
Hapton	d		19 16										21 16				22 19				23 48				
Rose Grove	d		19 19										21 19				22 22				23 54				
Burnley Manchester Road 41	a						19 29							21 27											
Leeds 10 41	a						20 40							22 38											
Burnley Barracks	d		19 22										21 22				22 25				23 58				
Burnley Central	d		19 24										21 24				22 27				00 03				
Brierfield	d		19 29										21 29				22 32				00 11				
Nelson	d		19 32										21 32				22 35				00 16				
Colne	a		19 41										21 41				22 44				00 24				

For general notes see front of timetable
For details of catering facilities see Directory of Train Operators

A To Buxton (Table 86)
B To Liverpool Lime Street (Table 90)
C To York (Table 40)
D To Manchester Airport (Table 82)

For connections to and from London Euston, please refer to Table 65

Table 97

Sundays
until 2 November

Blackpool → Preston → Blackburn, Accrington, Burnley and Colne

Network Diagram - see first page of Table 97

		NT	TP 1 ◇	NT	NT	NT	NT	TP 1 ◇	NT	NT	NT	NT	NT	TP 1 ◇	NT	NT	TP 1 ◇	NT	NT	NT	TP 1 ◇	NT	NT
			A	B	C	D	E 🍴	A	G	D	H 🍴			A	J	D	A	G	D		A	J	D
Blackpool North	d		08 02	08 14	08 17	08 28	08 42	09 02	09 10	09 28				10 02	10 17	10 28	11 02	11 12	11 28		12 02	12 17	12 28
Poulton-le-Fylde	d		08 08	08 20	08 23	08 34	08 48	09 08	09 16	09 34				10 08	10 23	10 34	11 08	11 18	11 34		12 08	12 23	12 34
Blackpool South	d												09 38							11 25			
Blackpool Pleasure Beach	d												09 40							11 27			
Squires Gate	d												09 42							11 29			
St Annes-on-the-Sea	d												09 46							11 33			
Ansdell & Fairhaven	d												09 49							11 36			
Lytham	d												09 52							11 39			
Moss Side	d												09 57							11 44			
Kirkham & Wesham	d		08 17				08 57	09 17					10 05	10 17			11 17			11 51	12 17		
Preston 8	a		08 28	08 37	08 40	08 52	09 08	09 28	09 34	09 52			10 17	10 28	10 40	10 52	11 28	11 35	11 52	12 01	12 28	12 40	12 51
	d	08 01					09 10		09 35		10 00	10 10						11 37		12 05			
Lostock Hall	d	08 06					09 15				10 05	10 15								12 11			
Bamber Bridge	d	08 09					09 18				10 08	10 18								12 14			
Pleasington	d											10 26								12 21			
Cherry Tree	d											10 29								12 24			
Mill Hill (Lancashire)	d											10 31								12 27			
Blackburn	a	08 20					09 29		09 51		10 19	10 34						11 53		12 30			
Clitheroe 94	a	*09 08*					09 52				10 44	*11 15*								*13 10*			
Manchester Victoria 94 🚌	d								*09 00*									*11 00*					
Blackburn	d	08 21							09 51			10 35						11 53		12 30			
Rishton	d											10 40								12 35			
Church & Oswaldtwistle	d											10 43								12 38			
Accrington	d	08 28							09 59			10 46						12 01		12 41			
Huncoat	d											10 50								12 46			
Hapton	d											10 53								12 49			
Rose Grove	d	08 35										10 56								12 52			
Burnley Manchester Road 41	a								10 09									12 09					
Leeds 10 41	a								11 21									13 21					
Burnley Barracks	d											10 59								12 55			
Burnley Central	d	08 40										11 02								12 57			
Brierfield	d	08 44										11 06								13 02			
Nelson	d	08 47										11 09								13 05			
Colne	a	08 57										11 19								13 14			

		NT	TP 1 ◇	NT	NT	NT	TP 1 ◇	NT	NT	NT	TP 1 ◇	NT	NT	NT	TP 1 ◇	NT	NT	NT	TP 1 ◇	NT	NT	NT	NT
			A	G	D		A	J	D		A	G	D		A	J	D		A	G	J	D	
Blackpool North	d		13 02	13 12	13 28		13 57	14 17	14 28		15 02	15 12	15 28		16 02	16 17	16 28		17 02	17 10	17 17	17 28	
Poulton-le-Fylde	d		13 08	13 18	13 34		14 03	14 23	14 34		15 08	15 18	15 34		16 08	16 23	16 34		17 08	17 16	17 23	17 34	
Blackpool South	d	12 25				13 25				14 25				15 25				16 25					17 25
Blackpool Pleasure Beach	d	12 27				13 27				14 27				15 27				16 27					17 27
Squires Gate	d	12 29				13 29				14 29				15 29				16 29					17 29
St Annes-on-the-Sea	d	12 33				13 33				14 33				15 33				16 33					17 33
Ansdell & Fairhaven	d	12 36				13 36				14 36				15 36				16 36					17 36
Lytham	d	12 39				13 39				14 39				15 39				16 39					17 39
Moss Side	d	12 44				13 44				14 44				15 44				16 44					17 44
Kirkham & Wesham	d	12 51	13 17			13 51	14 12			14 51	15 17			15 51	16 17			16 51	17 17				17 51
Preston 8	a	13 02	13 28	13 35	13 52	14 01	14 24	14 40	14 52	15 02	15 28	15 35	15 52	16 01	16 28	16 40	16 52	17 02	17 29	17 35	17 40	17 52	18 01
	d			13 37		14 05						15 37		16 05						17 37			18 05
Lostock Hall	d					14 11								16 11									18 11
Bamber Bridge	d					14 14								16 14									18 14
Pleasington	d					14 21								16 21									18 21
Cherry Tree	d					14 24								16 24									18 24
Mill Hill (Lancashire)	d					14 27								16 27									18 27
Blackburn	a			13 53		14 30						15 53		16 30						17 53			18 30
Clitheroe 94	a					*15 10*								*17 10*									*19 10*
Manchester Victoria 94 🚌	d			*13 00*								*15 00*								*17 00*			
Blackburn	d			13 53		14 30						15 53		16 30						17 53			18 30
Rishton	d					14 35								16 35									18 35
Church & Oswaldtwistle	d					14 38								16 38									18 38
Accrington	d			14 01		14 41						16 01		16 41						18 01			18 41
Huncoat	d					14 46								16 46									18 46
Hapton	d					14 49								16 49									18 49
Rose Grove	d					14 52								16 52									18 52
Burnley Manchester Road 41	a			14 09								16 09								18 09			
Leeds 10 41	a			15 21								17 21								19 21			
Burnley Barracks	d					14 55								16 55									18 55
Burnley Central	d					14 57								16 57									18 57
Brierfield	d					15 02								17 02									19 02
Nelson	d					15 05								17 05									19 05
Colne	a					15 14								17 14									19 14

For general notes see front of timetable
For details of catering facilities see Directory of Train Operators

A To Manchester Airport (Table 82)
B From 14 September. To Liverpool Lime Street (Table 90)
C Until 7 September. To Liverpool Lime Street (Table 90)
D To Buxton (Table 86)
E Until 19 October. To Carlisle (Table 36)
G Until 13 July and from 14 September to York (Table 40)
H Until 14 September. To Carlisle (Table 36)
J To Liverpool Lime Street (Table 90)

For connections to and from London Euston, please refer to Table 65

Table 97

Blackpool → Preston → Blackburn, Accrington, Burnley and Colne

Sundays until 2 November

Network Diagram - see first page of Table 97

	TP 1 ◇	TP 1 ◇	NT	NT	NT		NT	TP 1 ◇	NT	NT	NT	TP 1 ◇	NT	NT	NT	TP 1 ◇	NT	NT	NT	TP 1 ◇	NT	TP 1 ◇	
	A	B	C	D	E			G	C	E		G	D	E		G		E		G	D	G	
Blackpool North d	17 58	18 02	18 10	18 17	18 28			19 02	19 12	19 28		20 02	20 17	20 28		21 02	21 12	21 28		22 02	22 17	23 02	
Poulton-le-Fylde d	18 04	18 08	18 16	18 23	18 34			19 08	19 18	19 34		20 08	20 23	20 34		21 08	21 18	21 34		22 08	22 23	23 08	
Blackpool South d							18 25				19 25				20 25				21 25				
Blackpool Pleasure Beach d							18 27				19 27				20 27				21 27				
Squires Gate d							18 29				19 29				20 29				21 29				
St Annes-on-the-Sea d							18 33				19 33				20 33				21 33				
Ansdell & Fairhaven d							18 36				19 36				20 36				21 36				
Lytham d							18 39				19 39				20 39				21 39				
Moss Side d							18 44				19 44				20 44				21 44				
Kirkham & Wesham d	18 13	18 17					18 51	19 17			19 51	20 17			20 51	21 17			21 51	22 17		23 17	
Preston 8 a	18 24	18 28	18 35	18 40	18 52		19 02	19 28	19 35	19 52	20 01	20 28	20 40	20 52	21 01	21 28	21 35	21 52	22 01	22 28	22 40	23 28	
d			18 37						19 37		20 05				21 03		21 37		22 03				
Lostock Hall d											20 11				21 08				22 09				
Bamber Bridge d											20 14				21 11				22 12				
Pleasington d											20 21				21 19				22 19				
Cherry Tree d											20 24				21 22				22 22				
Mill Hill (Lancashire) d											20 27				21 24				22 25				
Blackburn a			18 53						19 53		20 30				21 27		21 53		22 28				
Clitheroe 94 a			*20 10*								*21 10*				*22 10*								
Manchester Victoria 94 ⛴ d			*18 00*						*19 00*						*20 00*		*21 00*						
Blackburn d			18 53						19 53		20 30				21 29		21 53		22 28				
Rishton d											20 35				21 34				22 33				
Church & Oswaldtwistle d											20 38				21 37				22 36				
Accrington d			19 01						20 01		20 41				21 40		22 01		22 39				
Huncoat d											20 46				21 44				22 44				
Hapton d											20 49				21 47				22 47				
Rose Grove d											20 52				21 50				22 50				
Burnley Manchester Road 41 a			19 09						20 09								22 09						
Leeds 10 41 a			20 22						21 21								23 21						
Burnley Barracks d											20 55				21 53				22 53				
Burnley Central d											20 57				21a58				22 55				
Brierfield d											21 02								23 00				
Nelson d											21 05								23 03				
Colne a											21 14								23 12				

Sundays from 9 November

	NT	TP 1 ◇	NT		NT	TP 1 ◇	NT		NT	NT	TP 1 ◇		NT	NT	TP 1 ◇		NT	NT	NT		TP 1 ◇	NT	NT	TP 1 ◇
		G	D		E	G	H		E		G		D	E	G		H	E			G	D	E	G
Blackpool North d		08 02	08 14		08 28	09 02	09 10		09 28		10 02		10 17	10 28	11 02		11 12	11 28			12 02	12 17	12 28	13 02
Poulton-le-Fylde d		08 08	08 20		08 34	09 08	09 16		09 34		10 08		10 23	10 34	11 08		11 18	11 34			12 08	12 23	12 34	13 08
Kirkham & Wesham d		08 17				09 17					10 17				11 17						12 17			13 17
Preston 8 a		08 28	08 37		08 52	09 28	09 34		09 52		10 28		10 40	10 52	11 28		11 35	11 52			12 28	12 40	12 51	13 28
d	08 01						09 35			10 10							11 37		12 05					
Lostock Hall d	08 06									10 15									12 11					
Bamber Bridge d	08 09									10 18									12 14					
Pleasington d										10 26									12 21					
Cherry Tree d										10 29									12 24					
Mill Hill (Lancashire) d										10 31									12 27					
Blackburn a	08 20						09 51			10 34							11 53		12 30					
Clitheroe 94 a	*09 08*									*11 15*									*13 10*					
Manchester Victoria 94 ⛴ d							*09 00*										*11 00*							
Blackburn d	08 21						09 51			10 35							11 53		12 30					
Rishton d										10 40									12 35					
Church & Oswaldtwistle d										10 43									12 38					
Accrington d	08 28						09 59			10 46							12 01		12 41					
Huncoat d										10 50									12 46					
Hapton d										10 53									12 49					
Rose Grove d	08 35									10 56									12 52					
Burnley Manchester Road 41 a							10 09										12 09							
Leeds 41 a							11 21										13 21							
Burnley Barracks d										10 59									12 55					
Burnley Central d	08 40									11 02									12 57					
Brierfield d	08 44									11 06									13 02					
Nelson d	08 47									11 09									13 05					
Colne a	08 57									11 19									13 14					

For general notes see front of timetable
For details of catering facilities see Directory of Train Operators

A Until 7 September. To Manchester Airport (Table 82)
B From 14 September. To Manchester Airport (Table 82)
C Until 13 July and from 14 September to York (Table 40)
D To Liverpool Lime Street (Table 90)
E To Buxton (Table 86)
G To Manchester Airport (Table 82)
H To York (Table 40)

For connections to and from London Euston, please refer to Table 65

Table 97

Sundays

from 9 November

Blackpool → Preston → Blackburn, Accrington, Burnley and Colne

Network Diagram - see first page of Table 97

		NT A	NT B	NT	TP ■1◇ C	NT D	NT B	TP ■1◇ C	NT A	NT B	NT	TP ■1◇ C	NT D	NT B	TP ■1◇ C	NT A	NT D	NT B	NT
Blackpool North	d	13 12	13 28		13 57	14 17	14 28	15 02	15 12	15 28		16 02	16 17	16 28	17 02	17 10	17 17	17 28	
Poulton-le-Fylde	d	13 18	13 34		14 03	14 23	14 34	15 08	15 18	15 34		16 08	16 23	16 34	17 08	17 16	17 23	17 34	
Kirkham & Wesham	d				14 12			15 17				16 17			17 17				
Preston 8	a	13 35	13 52		14 24	14 40	14 52	15 28	15 35	15 52		16 28	16 40	16 52	17 29	17 35	17 40	17 52	
	d	13 37		14 05					15 37		16 05					17 37			18 05
Lostock Hall	d			14 11							16 11								18 11
Bamber Bridge	d			14 14							16 14								18 14
Pleasington	d			14 21							16 21								18 21
Cherry Tree	d			14 24							16 24								18 24
Mill Hill (Lancashire)	d			14 27							16 27								18 27
Blackburn	a	13 53		14 30					15 53		16 30					17 53			18 30
Clitheroe 94	a			*15 10*							*17 10*								*19 10*
Manchester Victoria 94 ⛴	d	*13 00*							*15 00*							*17 00*			
Blackburn	d	13 53		14 30					15 53		16 30					17 53			18 30
Rishton	d			14 35							16 35								18 35
Church & Oswaldtwistle	d			14 38							16 38								18 38
Accrington	d	14 01		14 41					16 01		16 41					18 01			18 41
Huncoat	d			14 46							16 46								18 46
Hapton	d			14 49							16 49								18 49
Rose Grove	d			14 52							16 52								18 52
Burnley Manchester Road 41	a	14 09							16 09							18 09			
Leeds 41	a	15 21							17 21							19 21			
Burnley Barracks	d			14 55							16 55								18 55
Burnley Central	d			14 57							16 57								18 57
Brierfield	d			15 02							17 02								19 02
Nelson	d			15 05							17 05								19 05
Colne	a			15 14							17 14								19 14

		TP ■1◇ C	NT A	NT D	NT B	TP ■1◇ C	NT A	NT B	NT	TP ■1◇ C	NT D	NT B	TP ■1◇ C	NT	NT B	NT	TP ■1◇ C	NT D	TP ■1◇ C
Blackpool North	d	18 02	18 10	18 17	18 28	19 02	19 12	19 28		20 02	20 17	20 28	21 02	21 12	21 28		22 02	22 17	23 02
Poulton-le-Fylde	d	18 08	18 16	18 23	18 34	19 08	19 18	19 34		20 08	20 23	20 34	21 08	21 18	21 34		22 08	22 23	23 08
Kirkham & Wesham	d	18 17				19 17				20 17			21 17				22 17		23 17
Preston 8	a	18 28	18 35	18 40	18 52	19 28	19 35	19 52		20 28	20 40	20 52	21 28	21 35	21 52		22 28	22 40	23 28
	d		18 37				19 37		20 05					21 37		22 03			
Lostock Hall	d								20 11							22 09			
Bamber Bridge	d								20 14							22 12			
Pleasington	d								20 21							22 19			
Cherry Tree	d								20 24							22 22			
Mill Hill (Lancashire)	d								20 27							22 25			
Blackburn	a		18 53				19 53		20 30					21 53		22 28			
Clitheroe 94	a		*20 10*						*21 10*										
Manchester Victoria 94 ⛴	d		*18 00*				*19 00*							*21 00*					
Blackburn	d		18 53				19 53		20 30					21 53		22 28			
Rishton	d								20 35							22 33			
Church & Oswaldtwistle	d								20 38							22 36			
Accrington	d		19 01				20 01		20 41					22 01		22 39			
Huncoat	d								20 46							22 44			
Hapton	d								20 49							22 47			
Rose Grove	d								20 52							22 50			
Burnley Manchester Road 41	a		19 09				20 09							22 09					
Leeds 41	a		20 22				21 21							23 21					
Burnley Barracks	d								20 55							22 53			
Burnley Central	d								20 57							22 55			
Brierfield	d								21 02							23 00			
Nelson	d								21 05							23 03			
Colne	a								21 14							23 12			

For general notes see front of timetable
For details of catering facilities see Directory of Train Operators

A To York (Table 40)
B To Buxton (Table 86)
C To Manchester Airport (Table 82)
D To Liverpool Lime Street (Table 90)

For connections to and from London Euston, please refer to Table 65

Table 97

Mondays to Fridays
until 3 October

Colne, Burnley, Accrington and Blackburn → Preston → Blackpool

Network Diagram - see first page of Table 97

Miles	Miles			TP MX 1◇ A	NT	TP 1◇ A	NT B	NT	NT	NT	TP 1◇ A	NT		NT C	NT D	NT E	NT G	TP 1◇ A	NT	NT D	NT E	NT C		TP 1◇ A	NT
0	—	**Colne**	d		05 36			06 19				07 12							08 00						09 07
2	—	Nelson	d		05 41			06 24				07 17							08 05						09 12
3¼	—	Brierfield	d		05 44			06 27				07 20							08 08						09 15
5½	—	**Burnley Central**	d		05 49			06 32				07 25							08 13						09 20
6	—	Burnley Barracks	d					06 34											08 15						
—	—	Leeds 10	41 d							06 03						06 51					07 51				
—	—	Burnley Manchester Road	41 d							07 08						07 57					08 57				
7	—	Rose Grove	d		05 53			06 37				07 29							08 18						09 24
8½	—	Hapton	d					06 40				07 32							08 21						09 27
10	—	Huncoat	d					06 43				07 35							08 24						09 30
11¾	—	Accrington	d		06 00			06 47		07 17		07 40				08 06			08 29		09 06				09 35
12½	—	Church & Oswaldtwistle	d		06 03			06 50				07 42							08 31						09 37
14¼	—	Rishton	d		06 06			06 53				07 45							08 34						09 40
18	—	**Blackburn**	a		06 11			06 58		07 25		07 51				08 14			08 41		09 14				09 46
—	—	Manchester Victoria	94 a		07 25			07 51		08 21		08 50				09 25			09 50		10 21				10 50
—	—	Clitheroe	94 d									07 08				07 35	07 56				08 26				
—	—	**Blackburn**	d		06 11				07 09	07 25		07 52				08 15	08 19		08 42		09 15				09 46
19¼	—	Mill Hill (Lancashire)	d		06 14				07 12			07 55					08 22		08 45						09 49
20	—	Cherry Tree	d		06 16				07 14			07 57							08 47						09 51
21	—	Pleasington	d		06 19				07 16			07 59							08 49						09 53
26	—	Bamber Bridge	d		06 26				07 23	07 35		08 06					08 31		08 56						10 00
27¼	—	Lostock Hall	d		06 28				07 26	07 38		08 09					08 33		08 59						10 03
30	—	**Preston 8**	a		06 36				07 34	07 46		08 17				08 33	08 43		09 11		09 34				10 11
—	—		d	00 06	06 45	07 02	07 28		07 35	07 48	08 06	08 18		08 26	08 29	08 34		09 06	09 12	09 29	09 35	09 56		10 01	10 12
35¼	5¼	Salwick	d						07 42																
37¾	7¾	Kirkham & Wesham	d	00 16	06 54	07 11	07 38		07 49		08 16	08 28			08 39				09 24	09 38					10 21
41	—	Moss Side	d																09 30						10 27
43½	—	Lytham	d		07 04				07 59			08 38							09 34						10 31
44¾	—	Ansdell & Fairhaven	d		07 07				08 02			08 41							09 37						10 34
46¾	—	St Annes-on-the-Sea	d		07 11				08a07			08 45							09 41						10 38
48½	—	Squires Gate	d		07 14							08 48							09 45						10 42
49½	—	Blackpool Pleasure Beach	d		07 17							08 51							09 47						10 44
50	—	**Blackpool South**	a		07 21							08 55							09 51						10 49
—	14¼	Poulton-le-Fylde	d	00 26		07 21	07 46			08 04	08 27				08 48	08 54		09 23		09 46	09 53			10 18	
—	16¼	Layton	d	00 30		07 24	07 50				08 30				08 52					09 50					
—	17½	**Blackpool North**	a	00 38		07 31	07 56			08 12	08 36			08 51	08 59	09 04		09 32		09 57	10 02	10 21		10 28	

		NT D	NT H	NT C	TP 1◇ A	NT J	NT	NT K	NT E	NT L		NT C	TP 1◇ A	NT	NT D	NT E	NT C	TP 1◇ A	NT	NT D		NT E	NT C	TP 1◇ A	NT
Colne	d						10 00							11 00					12 00						13 00
Nelson	d						10 05							11 05					12 05						13 05
Brierfield	d						10 08							11 08					12 08						13 08
Burnley Central	d						10 13							11 13					12 13						13 13
Burnley Barracks	d						10 15							11 15					12 15						13 15
Leeds 10	41 d		08 51						09 51							10 51						11 51			
Burnley Manchester Road	41 d		09 57						10 57							11 57						12 57			
Rose Grove	d						10 18							11 18					12 18						13 18
Hapton	d						10 21							11 21											13 21
Huncoat	d						10 24							11 24					12 24						13 24
Accrington	d		10 05				10 29		11 06					11 29		12 06			12 29			13 06			13 29
Church & Oswaldtwistle	d						10 31							11 31					12 31						13 31
Rishton	d						10 34							11 34					12 34						13 34
Blackburn	a		10 13				10 40		11 14					11 39		12 14			12 39			13 14			13 39
Manchester Victoria	94 a						11 50							12 50					13 50						14 50
Clitheroe	94 d		09 36						10 36							11 36						12 36			
Blackburn	d		10 14				10 42		11 15					11 42		12 15			12 42			13 15			13 42
Mill Hill (Lancashire)	d						10 45							11 45					12 45						13 45
Cherry Tree	d						10 47							11 47											13 47
Pleasington	d						10 49							11 49					12 49						13 49
Bamber Bridge	d						10 56							11 56					12 56						13 56
Lostock Hall	d						10 59							11 59					12 59						13 59
Preston 8	a		10 32				11 10		11 34					12 12		12 32			13 12			13 32			14 12
	d	10 29	10 33	10 56	11 06	11 09	11 12	11 26	11 36	11 46		11 55	12 06	12 12	12 26	12 34	12 56	13 06	13 12	13 26		13 34	13 56	14 06	14 12
Salwick	d													12 19											
Kirkham & Wesham	d	10 38					11 21	11 35						12 23	12 35				13 21	13 35					14 21
Moss Side	d						11 27							12 29					13 27						14 27
Lytham	d						11 31							12 33					13 31						14 31
Ansdell & Fairhaven	d						11 34							12 36					13 34						14 34
St Annes-on-the-Sea	d						11 38							12 40					13 38						14 38
Squires Gate	d						11 42							12 44					13 42						14 42
Blackpool Pleasure Beach	d						11 44							12 46					13 44						14 44
Blackpool South	a						11 50							12 51					13 49						14 49
Poulton-le-Fylde	d	10 46	10 52		11 23			11 43	11 52				12 23		12 43	12 52		13 23		13 43		13 52		14 23	
Layton	d	10 50						11 47							12 47					13 47					
Blackpool North	a	10 57	11 02	11 21	11 32	11 36		11 54	12 01	12 11		12 20	12 32		12 54	13 00	13 21	13 32		13 54		13 59	14 21	14 32	

For general notes see front of timetable
For details of catering facilities see Directory of Train Operators

A From Manchester Airport (Table 82)

B From Stockport (Table 84)
C From Liverpool Lime Street (Table 90)
D From Buxton (Table 86)
E From York (Table 40)
G To Morecambe (Table 98)
H From Selby (Table 40)

J Until 12 September. From Manchester Victoria (Table 82)
K From Northwich (Table 88)
L Until 5 September. From Manchester Piccadilly (Table 82)

For connections to and from London Euston, please refer to Table 65

Colne, Burnley, Accrington and Blackburn → Preston → Blackpool

Network Diagram - see first page of Table 97

		NT	NT	NT	TP	NT	NT	NT		NT	TP	NT	NT	NT	TP	NT	NT	NT		NT BHX	TP	NT	NT	NT	NT
					1 ◇						1 ◇				1 ◇						1 ◇				
		A	B	C	D ☕		A	B		C	D ☕		A	B	D ☕		E	B		G	D ☕		H	C	A
Colne	d					14 00						15 00				16 00						17 00			
Nelson	d					14 05						15 05				16 05						17 05			
Brierfield	d					14 08						15 08				16 08						17 08			
Burnley Central	d					14 13						15 13				16 13						17 13			
Burnley Barracks	d					14 15						15 15				16 15						17 15			
Leeds 10	41 d		12 51					13 51						14 51				15 51							
Burnley Manchester Road	41 d		13 57					14 57						15 57				16 58							
Rose Grove	d					14 18						15 18				16 18						17 18			
Hapton	d					14 21						15 21				16 21						17 21			
Huncoat	d					14 24						15 24				16 24						17 24			
Accrington	d		14 06			14 29		15 06				15 29		16 06		16 29		17 06				17 29			
Church & Oswaldtwistle	d					14 31						15 31				16 31						17 31			
Rishton	d					14 34						15 34				16 34						17 34			
Blackburn	a		14 14			14 39		15 14				15 39		16 14		16 39		17 14				17 39			
Manchester Victoria	94 a					*15 50*						*16 42*				*17 51*		*18 23*							
Clitheroe	94 d		*13 36*					*14 36*						*15 26*				*16 36*				*17 12*			
Blackburn	d		14 15			14 42		15 15				15 42		16 15		16 42		17 15				17 42			
Mill Hill (Lancashire)	d					14 45						15 45				16 45						17 45			
Cherry Tree	d					14 47						15 47				16 47						17 47			
Pleasington	d					14 49						15 49				16 49						17 49			
Bamber Bridge	d					14 56						15 56				16 56						17 56			
Lostock Hall	d					14 59						15 59				16 59						17 59			
Preston 8	a		14 32			15 10		15 32				16 12		16 33		17 11		17 34				18 07			
	d	14 26	14 34	14 56	15 06	15 12	15 26	15 34		15 56	16 06	16 12	16 26	16 34	17 06	17 12	17 28	17 36		17 54	18 01	18 08	18 13	18 18	18 30
Salwick	d											16 19													
Kirkham & Wesham	d	14 35				15 21	15 35					16 23	16 35		17 15	17 21	17 38			18 04	18 10	18 19	18 22		18 40
Moss Side	d					15 27						16 29				17 27						18 25			
Lytham	d					15 31						16 33				17 31						18 29			
Ansdell & Fairhaven	d					15 34						16 36				17 34						18 32			
St Annes-on-the-Sea	d					15 38						16 40				17 38						18 36			
Squires Gate	d					15 42						16 44				17 42						18 40			
Blackpool Pleasure Beach	d					15 44						16 46				17 44						18 42			
Blackpool South	a					15 49						16 51				17 49						18 47			
Poulton-le-Fylde	d	14 43	14 52		15 23		15 43	15 52			16 23		16 43	16 52	17 25		17 47	17 53		18 13	18 20		18 32		18 49
Layton	d	14 47					15 47						16 47		17 28		17 51				18 24		18 36		18 53
Blackpool North	a	14 54	15 00	15 21	15 32		15 54	16 00		16 21	16 32		16 54	17 00	17 34		17 58	18 03		18 22	18 30		18 43	18 48	19 00

		NT	TP	NT	TP	NT		NT	NT	NT	TP	NT	NT	TP	NT	NT		NT	TP	NT	NT	TP	NT		
			1 ◇		1 ◇				1		1 ◇			1 ◇					1 ◇			1 ◇			
		B	D ☕	C	D ☕			A		B	D ☕		B	D		B			D		C	D			
Colne	d					18 00						19 12			20 05					21 44			22 56		
Nelson	d					18 05						19 17			20 10					21 49			23 01		
Brierfield	d					18 08						19 20			20 13					21 52			23 04		
Burnley Central	d					18 13			18 28			19 25			20 18					21 57			23 09		
Burnley Barracks	d					18 15						19 27			20 20					21 59			23 11		
Leeds 10	41 d	16 51								17 51			18 51			19 51									
Burnley Manchester Road	41 d	17 57								18 58			19 57			20 57									
Rose Grove	d					18 18						19 30			20 23					22 02			23 14		
Hapton	d					18 21						19 33			20 26					22 05					
Huncoat	d					18 24						19 36			20 29					22 08					
Accrington	d	18 06				18 29			18 37	19 07		19 41	20 06		20 34	21 06				22 13			23 21		
Church & Oswaldtwistle	d					18 31						19 43			20 36					22 15					
Rishton	d					18 34						19 46			20 39					22 18					
Blackburn	a	18 14				18 39			18 45	19 15		19 52	20 14		20 44	21 14				22 23			23 29		
Manchester Victoria	94 a	*19 23*							*19 50*	*20 22*		*20 50*			*21 50*					*00 01*					
Clitheroe	94 d					*18 08*				*18 36*			*19 36*			*20 36*				*21 36*			*22 46*		
Blackburn	d	18 15				18 42				19 16		19 54	20 14		20 47	21 14				22 24			23 30		
Mill Hill (Lancashire)	d					18 45						19 57			20 50					22 27			23 33		
Cherry Tree	d					18 47						19 59			20 52					22 29					
Pleasington	d					18 49						20 01			20 54					22 31					
Bamber Bridge	d					18 56						20 08			21 01					22 38			23 41		
Lostock Hall	d					18 59						20 11			21 04					22 41			23 43		
Preston 8	a	18 34				19 10				19 36		20 20	20 31		21 13	21 31				22 51			23 53		
	d	18 35	18 42	18 57	19 06	19 12		19 27		19 37	20 06	20 21	20 33	21 06	21 15	21 33		21 45	22 06	22 51	23 03	23 06			
Salwick	d																								
Kirkham & Wesham	d		18 51		19 16	19 21		19 37			20 16	20 30		21 16	21b28			21 55	22 16	23 00		23 16			
Moss Side	d					19 27						20 36			21 34					23 06					
Lytham	d					19 31						20 40			21 38					23 10					
Ansdell & Fairhaven	d					19 34						20 43			21 41					23 13					
St Annes-on-the-Sea	d					19 38						20 47			21 45					23 17					
Squires Gate	d					19 42						20 51			21 49					23 21					
Blackpool Pleasure Beach	d					19 44						20 53			21 51					23 23					
Blackpool South	a					19 49						20 58			21 56					23 28					
Poulton-le-Fylde	d	18 54	19 01	19 14	19 26			19 45		19 54	20 26		20 49	21 26		21 49		22 03	22 26			23 26			
Layton	d		19 05					19 49			20 30			21 30				22 07	22 30			23 30			
Blackpool North	a	19 03	19 11	19 23	19 35			19 57		20 03	20 36		20 56	21 36		21 56		22 12	22 36		23 28	23 36			

For general notes see front of timetable
For details of catering facilities see Directory of Train Operators

A From Buxton (Table 86)
B From York (Table 40)
C From Liverpool Lime Street (Table 90)
D From Manchester Airport (Table 82)
E From Hazel Grove (Table 86)
G From Stalybridge (Table 39)
H From Stockport (Table 84)
b Arr. 2124

For connections to and from London Euston, please refer to Table 65

Table 97

Colne, Burnley, Accrington and Blackburn → Preston → Blackpool

Mondays to Fridays

from 6 October

Network Diagram - see first page of Table 97

		TP	NT	TP	NT	NT	NT	NT	TP	NT	NT	NT	NT	NT	TP	NT	NT	NT	NT	TP	NT	NT
		MX																				
		1 ◇		1 ◇					1 ◇						1 ◇					1 ◇		
		A		A	B				A		C	D	E	G	A		D	E	C	A		D
																				🛒		
Colne	d		05 34			06 19				07 11						08 00					09 07	
Nelson	d		05 39			06 24				07 16						08 05					09 12	
Brierfield	d		05 42			06 27				07 19						08 08					09 15	
Burnley Central	d		05 47			06 32				07 24						08 13					09 20	
Burnley Barracks	d					06 34										08 15						
Leeds [10]	41 d							06 03					06 51					07 51				
Burnley Manchester Road	41 d							07 08					07 57					08 57				
Rose Grove	d		05 51			06 37				07 29						08 18					09 24	
Hapton	d					06 40				07 32						08 21					09 27	
Huncoat	d					06 43				07 35						08 24					09 30	
Accrington	d		05 58			06 47		07 17		07 40			08 06			08 29		09 06			09 35	
Church & Oswaldtwistle	d		06 01			06 50				07 42						08 31					09 37	
Rishton	d		06 04			06 53				07 45						08 34					09 40	
Blackburn	a		06 09			06 58		07 25		07 51			08 14			08 41		09 14			09 46	
Manchester Victoria	94 a		*07 25*			07 51		*08 21*		*08 50*			*09 25*			*09 50*		*10 21*			*10 50*	
Clitheroe	94 d									*07 03*			*07 30*	07 51				*08 23*				
Blackburn	d		06 09				07 06	07 25		07 52			08 15	08 19		08 42		09 15			09 46	
Mill Hill (Lancashire)	d		06 12				07 09			07 55				08 22		08 45					09 49	
Cherry Tree	d		06 14				07 11			07 57						08 47					09 51	
Pleasington	d		06 17				07 13			07 59						08 49						
Bamber Bridge	d		06 24				07 20	07 35		08 06				08 31		08 56					10 00	
Lostock Hall	d		06 26				07 23	07 38		08 09				08 33		08 59					10 03	
Preston [8]	a		06 36				07 34	07 46		08 17			08 33	08 43		09 11		09 34			10 11	
	d	00 06	06 45	07 02	07 28		07 35	07 48	08 06	08 18	08 26	08 29	08 34		09 06	09 12	09 29	09 35	09 56	10 01	10 12	10 29
Salwick	d						07 42															
Kirkham & Wesham	d	00 16	06 54	07 11	07 38		07 49		08 16	08 28		08 39				09 24	09 38				10 21	10 38
Moss Side	d															09 30					10 27	
Lytham	d		07 04				07 59			08 38						09 34					10 31	
Ansdell & Fairhaven	d		07 07				08 02			08 41						09 37					10 34	
St Annes-on-the-Sea	d		07 11				08a07			08 45						09 41					10 38	
Squires Gate	d		07 14							08 48						09 45					10 42	
Blackpool Pleasure Beach	d		07 17							08 51						09 47					10 44	
Blackpool South	a		07 21							08 55						09 51					10 49	
Poulton-le-Fylde	d	00 26		07 21	07 46			08 04	08 27			08 48	08 54		09 23		09 46	09 53		10 18		10 46
Layton	d	00 30		07 24	07 50				08 30			08 52					09 50					10 50
Blackpool North	a	00 38		07 31	07 56			08 12	08 36		08 51	09 01	09 04		09 32		09 59	10 02	10 21	10 28		10 57

		NT	NT	TP	NT	NT	NT	NT	TP	NT	NT	NT	NT	TP	NT	NT	NT	NT	TP	NT	NT	NT
				1 ◇					1 ◇					1 ◇					1 ◇			
		H	C	A		J	E	C	A		D	E	C	A		D	E	C	A		D	E
				🛒					🛒					🛒					🛒			
Colne	d				10 00					10 57					12 00					12 57		
Nelson	d				10 05					11 02					12 05					13 02		
Brierfield	d				10 08					11 05					12 08					13 05		
Burnley Central	d				10 13					11 10					12 13					13 10		
Burnley Barracks	d				10 15					11 12					12 15					13 12		
Leeds [10]	41 d	08 51					09 51					10 51					11 51					12 51
Burnley Manchester Road	41 d	09 57					10 57					11 57					12 57					13 57
Rose Grove	d				10 18					11 15					12 18					13 15		
Hapton	d									11 18										13 18		
Huncoat	d				10 24										12 24							
Accrington	d	10 05			10 29		11 06			11 26		12 06			12 29		13 06			13 26		14 06
Church & Oswaldtwistle	d				10 31					11 28					12 31					13 28		
Rishton	d				10 34					11 31					12 34					13 31		
Blackburn	a	10 13			10 40		11 14			11 36		12 14			12 39		13 14			13 36		14 14
Manchester Victoria	94 a				*11 50*					*12 50*					*13 50*					*14 50*		
Clitheroe	94 d	*09 31*					*10 36*					*11 31*					*12 31*					*13 31*
Blackburn	d	10 14			10 42		11 15			11 39		12 15			12 42		13 15			13 39		14 15
Mill Hill (Lancashire)	d				10 45					11 42					12 45					13 42		
Cherry Tree	d									11 44										13 44		
Pleasington	d				10 49										12 49							
Bamber Bridge	d				10 56					11 53					12 56					13 53		
Lostock Hall	d				10 59					11 56					12 59					13 56		
Preston [8]	a	10 32			11 10		11 34			12 12		12 32			13 12		13 32			14 12		14 32
	d	10 33	10 56	11 06	11 12	11 26	11 36	11 55	12 06	12 12	12 26	12 34	12 56	13 06	13 12	13 26	13 34	13 56	14 06	14 12	14 26	14 34
Salwick	d									12 19												
Kirkham & Wesham	d				11 21	11 35				12 23	12 35				13 21	13 35				14 21	14 35	
Moss Side	d				11 27					12 29					13 27					14 27		
Lytham	d				11 31					12 33					13 31					14 31		
Ansdell & Fairhaven	d				11 34					12 36					13 34					14 34		
St Annes-on-the-Sea	d				11 38					12 40					13 38					14 38		
Squires Gate	d				11 42					12 44					13 42					14 42		
Blackpool Pleasure Beach	d				11 44					12 46					13 44					14 44		
Blackpool South	a				11 50					12 51					13 49					14 49		
Poulton-le-Fylde	d	10 52		11 23		11 43	11 52		12 23		12 43	12 52		13 23		13 43	13 52		14 23		14 43	14 52
Layton	d					11 47					12 47					13 47					14 47	
Blackpool North	a	11 02	11 21	11 32		11 56	12 01	12 20	12 32		12 56	13 00	13 21	13 32		13 56	13 59	14 21	14 32		14 56	15 00

For general notes see front of timetable
For details of catering facilities see Directory of Train Operators

A From Manchester Airport (Table 82)
B From Stockport (Table 84)
C From Liverpool Lime Street (Table 90)
D From Buxton (Table 86)
E From York (Table 40)
G To Morecambe (Table 98)
H From Selby (Table 40)
J From Northwich (Table 88)

For connections to and from London Euston, please refer to Table 65

Table 97

Mondays to Fridays

from 6 October

Colne, Burnley, Accrington and Blackburn → Preston → Blackpool

Network Diagram - see first page of Table 97

		NT	TP	NT	NT	NT	NT	TP	NT	NT	NT	TP	NT	NT	NT	NT	TP	NT	NT	NT	NT	NT
			1 ◊					1 ◊				1 ◊				BHX	1 ◊					
		A	B		C	D	A	B		C	D	B		E	D	G	B		H	A	C	D
			(trolley)					(trolley)				(trolley)					(trolley)					
Colne	d			13 57					14 57				15 57					16 57				
Nelson	d			14 02					15 02				16 02					17 02				
Brierfield	d			14 05					15 05				16 05					17 05				
Burnley Central	d			14 10					15 10				16 10					17 10				
Burnley Barracks	d			14 12					15 12				16 12					17 12				
Leeds [10]	41 d					13 51					14 51				15 51							16 51
Burnley Manchester Road	41 d					14 57					15 57				16 58							17 57
Rose Grove	d			14 15					15 15				16 15					17 15				
Hapton	d								15 18				16 18					17 18				
Huncoat	d			14 21									16 21					17 21				
Accrington	d			14 26		15 06			15 26		16 06		16 26		17 06			17 26				18 06
Church & Oswaldtwistle	d			14 28					15 28				16 28					17 28				
Rishton	d			14 31					15 31				16 31					17 31				
Blackburn	a			14 36		15 14			15 36		16 14		16 36		17 14			17 38				18 14
Manchester Victoria	94 a			*15 50*					*16 42*				*17 51*		*18 23*							*19 23*
Clitheroe	94 d					*14 31*					*15 23*				*16 31*			*17 12*				
Blackburn	d			14 39		15 15			15 39		16 15		16 39		17 15			17 40				18 15
Mill Hill (Lancashire)	d			14 42					15 42				16 42					17 43				
Cherry Tree	d								15 44				16 44					17 45				
Pleasington	d			14 46					15 46				16 46					17 47				
Bamber Bridge	d			14 53					15 53				16 53					17 54				
Lostock Hall	d			14 56					15 56				16 56					17 57				
Preston [8]	a			15 10		15 32			16 12		16 33		17 11		17 34			18 07				18 34
	d	14 56	15 06	15 12	15 26	15 34	15 56	16 06	16 12	16 26	16 34	17 06	17 12	17 28	17 36	17 54	18 01	18 08	18 13	18 18	18 30	18 35
Salwick	d								16 19													
Kirkham & Wesham	d			15 21	15 35				16 23	16 35		17 15	17 21	17 38		18 04	18 10	18 19	18 22		18 40	
Moss Side	d			15 27					16 29				17 27					18 25				
Lytham	d			15 31					16 33				17 31					18 29				
Ansdell & Fairhaven	d			15 34					16 36				17 34					18 32				
St Annes-on-the-Sea	d			15 38					16 40				17 38					18 36				
Squires Gate	d			15 42					16 44				17 42					18 40				
Blackpool Pleasure Beach	d			15 44					16 46				17 44					18 42				
Blackpool South	a			15 49					16 51				17 49					18 47				
Poulton-le-Fylde	d		15 23		15 43	15 52		16 23		16 43	16 52	17 25		17 47	17 53	18 13	18 20		18 32		18 49	18 54
Layton	d				15 47					16 47		17 28		17 51			18 24		18 36		18 53	
Blackpool North	a	15 21	15 32		15 56	16 00	16 21	16 32		16 56	17 00	17 34		17 58	18 03	18 22	18 30		18 43	18 48	19 02	19 03

		TP	NT	TP	NT	NT	NT	NT	TP	NT	NT	TP	NT	NT	NT	TP	NT	NT	TP	NT
		1 ◊		1 ◊			1		1 ◊			1 ◊				1 ◊			1 ◊	
		B	A	B		C		D	B		D	B		D		B		A	B	
		(trolley)		(trolley)					(trolley)											
Colne	d				17 57					19 12			20 03				21 44			22 56
Nelson	d				18 02					19 17			20 08				21 49			23 01
Brierfield	d				18 05					19 20			20 11				21 52			23 04
Burnley Central	d				18 10		18 28			19 25			20 16				21 57			23 09
Burnley Barracks	d				18 12					19 27			20 18				21 59			23 11
Leeds [10]	41 d							17 51			18 51			19 51						
Burnley Manchester Road	41 d							18 58			19 57			20 57						
Rose Grove	d				18 15					19 30			20 21				22 02			23 14
Hapton	d				18 18					19 33			20 24				22 05			
Huncoat	d				18 21					19 36			20 27				22 08			
Accrington	d				18 26		18 37	19 07		19 41	20 06		20 32	21 06			22 13			23 21
Church & Oswaldtwistle	d				18 28					19 43			20 34				22 15			
Rishton	d				18 31					19 46			20 37				22 18			
Blackburn	a				18 36		18 45	19 15		19 52	20 14		20 42	21 14			22 23			23 29
Manchester Victoria	94 a						*19 50*	*20 22*		*20 50*			*21 50*				*00 01*			
Clitheroe	94 d				*18 03*			*18 31*			*19 31*			*20 31*			*21 36*			*22 41*
Blackburn	d				18 39			19 16		19 54	20 14		20 43	21 14			22 24			23 30
Mill Hill (Lancashire)	d				18 42					19 57			20 46				22 27			23 33
Cherry Tree	d				18 44					19 59			20 48				22 29			
Pleasington	d				18 46					20 01			20 50				22 31			
Bamber Bridge	d				18 53					20 08			20 57				22 38			23 41
Lostock Hall	d				18 56					20 11			21 00				22 41			23 43
Preston [8]	a				19 10			19 36		20 20	20 31		21 13	21 31			22 51			23 53
	d	18 42	18 57	19 06	19 12	19 27		19 37	20 06	20 21	20 33	21 06	21 15	21 33	21 45	22 06	22 51	23 03	23 06	
Salwick	d																			
Kirkham & Wesham	d	18 51		19 16	19 21	19 37			20 16	20 30		21 16	21b28		21 55	22 16	23 00		23 16	
Moss Side	d				19 27					20 36			21 34				23 06			
Lytham	d				19 31					20 40			21 38				23 10			
Ansdell & Fairhaven	d				19 34					20 43			21 41				23 13			
St Annes-on-the-Sea	d				19 38					20 47			21 45				23 17			
Squires Gate	d				19 42					20 51			21 49				23 21			
Blackpool Pleasure Beach	d				19 44					20 53			21 51				23 23			
Blackpool South	a				19 49					20 58			21 56				23 28			
Poulton-le-Fylde	d	19 01	19 14	19 26		19 45		19 54	20 26		20 49	21 26		21 49	22 03	22 26			23 26	
Layton	d	19 05				19 49			20 30			21 30			22 07	22 30			23 30	
Blackpool North	a	19 11	19 23	19 35		19 57		20 03	20 36		20 56	21 36		21 56	22 12	22 36		23 28	23 36	

For general notes see front of timetable
For details of catering facilities see Directory of Train Operators

A From Liverpool Lime Street (Table 90)
B From Manchester Airport (Table 82)
C From Buxton (Table 86)
D From York (Table 40)
E From Hazel Grove (Table 86)
G From Stalybridge (Table 39)
H From Stockport (Table 84)
b Arr. 2124

For connections to and from London Euston, please refer to Table 65

Colne, Burnley, Accrington and Blackburn → Preston → Blackpool

Network Diagram - see first page of Table 97

		TP	NT	TP	NT	NT	NT	TP	NT	NT	NT	NT	NT	TP	NT	NT	NT	NT	TP	NT	NT	NT
		1◇		1◇				1◇						1◇					1◇			
		A		A	B			A		C	D	E	G	A		D	E	C	A 🛒		D	E
Colne	d		05 43			06 30			07 12						08 00					09 07		
Nelson	d		05 48			06 35			07 17						08 05					09 12		
Brierfield	d		05 51			06 38			07 20						08 08					09 15		
Burnley Central	d		05 56			06 43			07 25						08 13					09 20		
Burnley Barracks	d														08 15							
Leeds 10	41 d						06 03					06 51					07 51					08 51
Burnley Manchester Road	41 d						07 09					07 57					08 57					09 58
Rose Grove	d		06 00			06 47			07 29						08 18					09 24		
Hapton	d					06 50			07 32						08 21					09 27		
Huncoat	d					06 53			07 35						08 24					09 30		
Accrington	d		06 07			06 58	07 17		07 40			08 06			08 29		09 06			09 35		10 07
Church & Oswaldtwistle	d		06 10			07 00			07 42						08 31					09 37		
Rishton	d		06 13			07 03			07 45						08 34					09 40		
Blackburn	a		06 18			07 08	07 25		07 51			08 14			08 41		09 14			09 46		10 15
Manchester Victoria	94 a		*07 25*				*08 21*		*08 50*			*09 25*			*09 50*		*10 21*			*10 50*		
Clitheroe	94 d								*07 08*			*07 35*	07 56				*08 26*					*09 36*
Blackburn	d		06 18			07 09	07 26		07 52			08 15	08 19		08 42		09 15			09 46		10 15
Mill Hill (Lancashire)	d		06 21			07 12			07 55				08 22		08 45					09 49		
Cherry Tree	d		06 23			07 14			07 57						08 47					09 51		
Pleasington	d		06 26			07 16			07 59						08 49					09 53		
Bamber Bridge	d		06 33			07 23	07 36		08 06				08 31		08 56					10 00		
Lostock Hall	d		06 35			07 26	07 39		08 09				08 33		08 59					10 03		
Preston 8	a		06 43			07 34	07 47		08 17			08 33	08 43		09 11		09 33			10 11		10 32
	d	00 06	06 45	07 02	07 28	07 38	07 48	08 06	08 18	08 26	08 29	08 34		09 06	09 12	09 29	09 34	09 56	10 03	10 12	10 29	10 33
Salwick	d					07 45																
Kirkham & Wesham	d	00 16	06 54	07 11	07 38	07 49		08 16	08 28		08 39				09 24	09 38				10 21	10 38	
Moss Side	d														09 30					10 27		
Lytham	d		07 04			07 59			08 38						09 34					10 31		
Ansdell & Fairhaven	d		07 07			08 02			08 41						09 37					10 34		
St Annes-on-the-Sea	d		07 11			08a07			08 45						09 41					10 38		
Squires Gate	d		07 14						08 48						09 45					10 42		
Blackpool Pleasure Beach	d		07 17						08 51						09 47					10 44		
Blackpool South	a		07 21						08 55						09 51					10 49		
Poulton-le-Fylde	d	00 26		07 21	07 46		08 04	08 26			08 48	08 54		09 23		09 46	09 54		10 20		10 46	10 53
Layton	d	00 30		07 24	07 50			08 30			08 52					09 50					10 50	
Blackpool North	a	00 38		07 31	07 56		08 12	08 36		08 51	09 00	09 03		09 32		09 57	10 02	10 21	10 29		10 57	11 03

		NT	TP	NT	NT	NT	NT	NT	NT	NT	TP	NT	NT	NT	NT	TP	NT	NT	NT	NT	TP
			1◇								1◇					1◇					1◇
		C	A 🛒		H	J	K	E	L	C	A 🛒		D	E	C	A 🛒		D	E	C	A 🛒
Colne	d			10 00								11 00					12 00				
Nelson	d			10 05								11 05					12 05				
Brierfield	d			10 08								11 08					12 08				
Burnley Central	d			10 13								11 13					12 13				
Burnley Barracks	d			10 15								11 15					12 15				
Leeds 10	41 d							09 51						10 51					11 51		
Burnley Manchester Road	41 d							10 57						11 57					12 57		
Rose Grove	d			10 18								11 18					12 18				
Hapton	d			10 21								11 21					12 21				
Huncoat	d			10 24								11 24					12 24				
Accrington	d			10 29				11 06				11 29		12 06			12 29		13 06		
Church & Oswaldtwistle	d			10 31								11 31					12 31				
Rishton	d			10 34								11 34					12 34				
Blackburn	a			10 40				11 14				11 39		12 14			12 39		13 14		
Manchester Victoria	94 a			*11 51*								*12 50*					*13 50*				
Clitheroe	94 d							*10 36*						*11 36*					*12 36*		
Blackburn	d			10 42				11 15				11 42		12 15			12 42		13 15		
Mill Hill (Lancashire)	d			10 45								11 45					12 45				
Cherry Tree	d			10 47								11 47					12 47				
Pleasington	d			10 49								11 49					12 49				
Bamber Bridge	d			10 56								11 56					12 56				
Lostock Hall	d			10 59								11 59					12 59				
Preston 8	a			11 08				11 34				12 12		12 32			13 12		13 32		
	d	10 56	11 06	11 10	11 15	11 18	11 27	11 36	11 48	11 55	12 06	12 12	12 26	12 34	12 56	13 06	13 12	13 26	13 34	13 56	14 06
Salwick	d											12 19									
Kirkham & Wesham	d			11 18			11 37					12 23	12 35				13 21	13 35			
Moss Side	d			11 24								12 29					13 27				
Lytham	d			11 28								12 33					13 31				
Ansdell & Fairhaven	d			11 31								12 36					13 34				
St Annes-on-the-Sea	d			11 35								12 40					13 38				
Squires Gate	d			11 39								12 44					13 42				
Blackpool Pleasure Beach	d			11 41								12 46					13 44				
Blackpool South	a			11 47								12 51					13 49				
Poulton-le-Fylde	d		11 23				11 45	11 52			12 23		12 43	12 52		13 23		13 43	13 52		14 23
Layton	d						11 49						12 47					13 47			
Blackpool North	a	11 22	11 32		11 40	11 44	11 56	12 01	12 14	12 20	12 32		12 54	13 01	13 21	13 32		13 54	14 00	14 21	14 32

For general notes see front of timetable
For details of catering facilities see Directory of Train Operators

- **A** From Manchester Airport (Table 82)
- **B** From Stockport (Table 84)
- **C** From Liverpool Lime Street (Table 90)
- **D** From Buxton (Table 86)
- **E** From York (Table 40)
- **G** To Morecambe (Table 98)
- **H** Until 6 September. From Manchester Oxford Road (Table 82)
- **J** Until 13 September. From Manchester Victoria (Table 82)
- **K** From Northwich (Table 88)
- **L** Until 6 September. From Manchester Piccadilly (Table 82)

For connections to and from London Euston, please refer to Table 65

Table 97

Saturdays

until 4 October

Colne, Burnley, Accrington and Blackburn → Preston → Blackpool

Network Diagram - see first page of Table 97

		NT	NT	NT		NT	TP	NT	NT	NT		NT	TP	NT	NT	NT		TP	NT	NT	NT	TP		NT	NT
							1 ◇						1 ◇					1 ◇				1 ◇			
			A	B		C	D		A	B		C	D		A	B		D [trolley]		A	B	D [trolley]			E
Colne	d	13 00						14 00						15 00					16 00					17 00	
Nelson	d	13 05						14 05						15 05					16 05					17 05	
Brierfield	d	13 08						14 08						15 08					16 08					17 08	
Burnley Central	d	13 13						14 13						15 13					16 13					17 13	
Burnley Barracks	d	13 15						14 15						15 15					16 15					17 15	
Leeds 10	41 d			12 51						13 51						14 51					15 51				
Burnley Manchester Road	41 d			13 57						14 57						15 57					16 58				
Rose Grove	d	13 18						14 18						15 18					16 18					17 18	
Hapton	d	13 21						14 21						15 21					16 21					17 21	
Huncoat	d	13 24						14 24						15 24					16 24					17 24	
Accrington	d	13 29		14 06				14 29		15 06				15 29		16 06			16 29		17 06			17 29	
Church & Oswaldtwistle	d	13 31						14 31						15 31					16 31					17 31	
Rishton	d	13 34						14 34						15 34					16 34					17 34	
Blackburn	a	13 39		14 14				14 39		15 14				15 42		16 14			16 39		17 14			17 39	
Manchester Victoria	94 🚌 a	*14 50*						*15 50*						*16 42*					*17 51*		*18 23*				
Clitheroe	94 d			*13 36*						*14 36*						*15 26*					*16 36*			*17 12*	
Blackburn	d	13 42		14 15				14 42		15 15				15 42		16 15			16 42		17 15			17 42	
Mill Hill (Lancashire)	d	13 45						14 45						15 45					16 45					17 45	
Cherry Tree	d	13 47						14 47						15 47					16 47					17 47	
Pleasington	d	13 49						14 49						15 49					16 49					17 49	
Bamber Bridge	d	13 56						14 56						15 56					16 56					17 56	
Lostock Hall	d	13 59						14 59						15 59					16 59					17 59	
Preston 8	a	14 12		14 32				15 10		15 32				16 12		16 33			17 11		17 34			18 07	
	d	14 12	14 26	14 34		14 56	15 06	15 12	15 26	15 34		15 56	16 06	16 12	16 26	16 34		17 06	17 12	17 28	17 36	18 01		18 08	18 14
Salwick	d													16 19											
Kirkham & Wesham	d	14 21	14 35					15 21	15 35					16 23	16 35			17 15	17 21	17 38		18 10		18 19	18 22
Moss Side	d	14 27						15 27						16 29					17 27					18 25	
Lytham	d	14 31						15 31						16 33					17 31					18 29	
Ansdell & Fairhaven	d	14 34						15 34						16 36					17 34					18 32	
St Annes-on-the-Sea	d	14 38						15 38						16 40					17 38					18 36	
Squires Gate	d	14 42						15 42						16 44					17 42					18 40	
Blackpool Pleasure Beach	d	14 44						15 44						16 46					17 44					18 42	
Blackpool South	a	14 49						15 49						16 51					17 49					18 47	
Poulton-le-Fylde	d		14 43	14 52			15 23		15 43	15 52			16 23		16 43	16 52		17 25		17 47	17 53	18 20			18 32
Layton	d		14 47						15 47						16 47			17 28		17 51		18 24			18 36
Blackpool North	a		14 54	15 01		15 21	15 32		15 54	16 01		16 21	16 32		16 54	17 01		17 34		17 58	18 03	18 30			18 43

		NT	NT	NT	NT	TP		NT	NT	NT	NT	TP		NT	NT	TP	NT	NT	TP	NT	NT	TP	NT		
						1 ◇						1 ◇				1 ◇			1 ◇			1 ◇			
		C	A	B	C	D			G	H	B	D			B	D		B	D		C	D			
Colne	d							18 00						19 00			20 00			21 44			22 56		
Nelson	d							18 05						19 05			20 05			21 49			23 01		
Brierfield	d							18 08						19 08			20 08			21 52			23 04		
Burnley Central	d							18 13						19 13			20 13			21 57			23 09		
Burnley Barracks	d							18 15						19 15			20 15			21 59			23 11		
Leeds 10	41 d			16 51							17 51				18 51			19 51							
Burnley Manchester Road	41 d			17 57							18 57				19 57			20 57							
Rose Grove	d							18 18						19 18			20 18			22 02			23 14		
Hapton	d							18 21						19 21			20 21			22 05					
Huncoat	d							18 24						19 24			20 24			22 08					
Accrington	d			18 06				18 29			19 06			19 29	20 06		20 29	21 06		22 13			23 21		
Church & Oswaldtwistle	d							18 31						19 31			20 31			22 15					
Rishton	d							18 34						19 34			20 34			22 18					
Blackburn	a			18 14				18 39			19 14			19 44	20 14		20 39	21 14		22 23			23 29		
Manchester Victoria	94 🚌 a			*19 23*				*19 50*			*20 22*			*20 50*			*21 50*			*23 59*					
Clitheroe	94 d							*18 08*			*18 36*				*19 36*			*20 36*		*21 36*			*22 46*		
Blackburn	d			18 15				18 42			19 15			19 44	20 14		20 42	21 14		22 24			23 30		
Mill Hill (Lancashire)	d							18 45						19 47			20 45			22 27			23 33		
Cherry Tree	d							18 47						19 49			20 47			22 29					
Pleasington	d							18 49						19 52			20 49			22 31					
Bamber Bridge	d							18 56						19 58			20 56			22 38			23 41		
Lostock Hall	d							18 59						19 59			20 59			22 41			23 43		
Preston 8	a			18 34				19 10			19 35			20 11	20 31		21 13	21 31		22 51			23 53		
	d	18 18	18 30	18 35	18 53	19 06		19 12	19 29	19 33	19 39	20 06		20 12	20 33	21 06	21 15	21 33	22 06	22 51	23 03	23 06			
Salwick	d																								
Kirkham & Wesham	d		18 40			19 16		19 21	19 38	19 42		20 16		20 21		21 16	21 24		22 16	23 00		23 16			
Moss Side	d							19 27						20 27			21 30			23 06					
Lytham	d							19 31						20 31			21 34			23 10					
Ansdell & Fairhaven	d							19 34						20 34			21 37			23 13					
St Annes-on-the-Sea	d							19 38						20 38			21 41			23 17					
Squires Gate	d							19 42						20 42			21 45			23 21					
Blackpool Pleasure Beach	d							19 44						20 44			21 47			23 23					
Blackpool South	a							19 49						20 49			21 52			23 28					
Poulton-le-Fylde	d		18 48	18 55	19 10	19 26			19 47	19 51	19 58	20 26			20 49	21 26		21 49	22 26			23 26			
Layton	d		18 52						19 51	19 55		20 30				21 30			22 30			23 30			
Blackpool North	a	18 48	18 59	19 04	19 21	19 35			19 57	20 01	20 07	20 36			20 56	21 36		21 56	22 36		23 28	23 36			

For general notes see front of timetable
For details of catering facilities see Directory of Train Operators

- **A** From Buxton (Table 86)
- **B** From York (Table 40)
- **C** From Liverpool Lime Street (Table 90)
- **D** From Manchester Airport (Table 82)
- **E** From Stockport (Table 84)
- **G** From 13 September. From Buxton (Table 86)
- **H** Until 6 September. From Buxton (Table 86)

For connections to and from London Euston, please refer to Table 65

Table 97

Saturdays

from 11 October

Colne, Burnley, Accrington and Blackburn → Preston → Blackpool

Network Diagram - see first page of Table 97

		TP 1◇	NT	TP 1◇	NT	NT	NT	TP 1◇	NT	NT	NT	NT	NT	TP 1◇	NT	NT	NT	NT	TP 1◇	NT	NT
		A		A	B			A		C	D	E	G	A		D	E	C	A ✠		D
Colne	d		05 41			06 30			07 11						08 00					09 07	
Nelson	d		05 46			06 35			07 16						08 05					09 12	
Brierfield	d		05 49			06 38			07 19						08 08					09 15	
Burnley Central	d		05 54			06 43			07 24						08 13					09 20	
Burnley Barracks	d														08 15						
Leeds 10	41 d						06 03					06 51					07 51				
Burnley Manchester Road	41 d						07 09					07 57					08 57				
Rose Grove	d		05 58			06 47			07 29						08 18					09 24	
Hapton	d					06 50			07 32						08 21					09 27	
Huncoat	d					06 53			07 35						08 24					09 30	
Accrington	d		06 05			06 58	07 17		07 40			08 06			08 29		09 06			09 35	
Church & Oswaldtwistle	d		06 08			07 00			07 42						08 31					09 37	
Rishton	d		06 11			07 03			07 45						08 34					09 40	
Blackburn	a		06 16			07 08	07 25		07 51			08 14			08 41		09 14			09 46	
Manchester Victoria	94 ⛴ a		*07 25*				*08 21*		*08 50*			*09 25*			*09 50*		*10 21*			*10 50*	
Clitheroe	94 d								*07 03*			*07 30*	07 56				*08 23*				
Blackburn	d		06 16			07 09	07 26		07 52			08 15	08 19		08 42		09 15			09 46	
Mill Hill (Lancashire)	d		06 19			07 12			07 55				08 22		08 45					09 49	
Cherry Tree	d		06 21			07 14			07 57						08 47					09 51	
Pleasington	d		06 24			07 16			07 59						08 49						
Bamber Bridge	d		06 31			07 23	07 36		08 06				08 31		08 56					10 00	
Lostock Hall	d		06 33			07 26	07 39		08 09				08 33		08 59					10 03	
Preston 8	a		06 43			07 34	07 47		08 17			08 33	08 43		09 11		09 33			10 11	
	d	00 06	06 45	07 02	07 28	07 38	07 48	08 06	08 18	08 26	08 29	08 34		09 06	09 12	09 29	09 34	09 56	10 03	10 12	10 29
Salwick	d					07 45															
Kirkham & Wesham	d	00 16	06 54	07 11	07 38	07 49		08 16	08 28		08 39				09 24	09 38				10 21	10 38
Moss Side	d														09 30					10 27	
Lytham	d		07 04			07 59			08 38						09 34					10 31	
Ansdell & Fairhaven	d		07 07			08 02			08 41						09 37					10 34	
St Annes-on-the-Sea	d		07 11			08a07			08 45						09 41					10 38	
Squires Gate	d		07 14						08 48						09 45					10 42	
Blackpool Pleasure Beach	d		07 17						08 51						09 47					10 44	
Blackpool South	a		07 21						08 55						09 51					10 49	
Poulton-le-Fylde	d	00 26		07 21	07 46		08 04	08 26			08 48	08 54		09 23		09 46	09 54		10 20		10 46
Layton	d	00 30		07 24	07 50			08 30			08 52					09 50					10 50
Blackpool North	a	00 38		07 31	07 56		08 12	08 36		08 51	09 02	09 03		09 32		09 59	10 02	10 21	10 29		10 57

		NT	NT	TP 1◇	NT	NT	NT	NT	TP 1◇	NT	NT	NT	NT	TP 1◇	NT	NT	NT	NT	TP 1◇	NT
		E	C	A ✠		H	E	C	A ✠		D	E	C	A ✠		D	E	C	A ✠	
Colne	d				10 00					10 57					11 57					12 57
Nelson	d				10 05					11 02					12 02					13 02
Brierfield	d				10 08					11 05					12 05					13 05
Burnley Central	d				10 13					11 10					12 10					13 10
Burnley Barracks	d				10 15					11 12					12 12					13 12
Leeds 10	41 d	08 51					09 51					10 51					11 51			
Burnley Manchester Road	41 d	09 58					10 57					11 57					12 57			
Rose Grove	d				10 18					11 15					12 15					13 15
Hapton	d									11 18										13 18
Huncoat	d				10 24										12 21					13 23
Accrington	d	10 07			10 29		11 06			11 26		12 06			12 26		13 06			13 28
Church & Oswaldtwistle	d				10 31					11 28					12 28					13 30
Rishton	d				10 34					11 31					12 31					13 33
Blackburn	a	10 15			10 40		11 14			11 36		12 14			12 36		13 14			13 38
Manchester Victoria	94 ⛴ a				*11 52*					*12 50*					*13 50*					*14 50*
Clitheroe	94 d	*09 31*					*10 31*					*11 31*					*12 31*			
Blackburn	d	10 15			10 42		11 15			11 39		12 15			12 39		13 15			13 41
Mill Hill (Lancashire)	d				10 45					11 42					12 42					13 44
Cherry Tree	d									11 44										13 46
Pleasington	d				10 49										12 46					
Bamber Bridge	d				10 56					11 53					12 53					13 53
Lostock Hall	d				10 59					11 56					12 56					13 56
Preston 8	a	10 32			11 08		11 34			12 12		12 32			13 12		13 32			14 12
	d	10 33	10 56	11 06	11 10	11 27	11 36	11 55	12 06	12 12	12 26	12 34	12 56	13 06	13 12	13 26	13 34	13 56	14 06	14 12
Salwick	d									12 19										
Kirkham & Wesham	d				11 18	11 37				12 23	12 35				13 21	13 35				14 21
Moss Side	d				11 24					12 29					13 27					14 27
Lytham	d				11 28					12 33					13 31					14 31
Ansdell & Fairhaven	d				11 31					12 36					13 34					14 34
St Annes-on-the-Sea	d				11 35					12 40					13 38					14 38
Squires Gate	d				11 39					12 44					13 42					14 42
Blackpool Pleasure Beach	d				11 41					12 46					13 44					14 44
Blackpool South	a				11 47					12 51					13 49					14 49
Poulton-le-Fylde	d	10 53		11 23		11 45	11 52		12 23		12 43	12 52		13 23		13 43	13 52		14 23	
Layton	d					11 49					12 47					13 47				
Blackpool North	a	11 03	11 22	11 32		11 58	12 01	12 20	12 32		12 56	13 01	13 21	13 32		13 56	14 00	14 21	14 32	

For general notes see front of timetable
For details of catering facilities see Directory of Train Operators

- **A** From Manchester Airport (Table 82)
- **B** From Stockport (Table 84)
- **C** From Liverpool Lime Street (Table 90)
- **D** From Buxton (Table 86)
- **E** From York (Table 40)
- **G** To Morecambe (Table 98)
- **H** From Northwich (Table 88)

For connections to and from London Euston, please refer to Table 65

Table 97

Saturdays

from 11 October

Colne, Burnley, Accrington and Blackburn → Preston → Blackpool

Network Diagram - see first page of Table 97

	NT	NT	NT	TP	NT	NT	NT	NT	TP	NT	NT	NT	TP	NT	NT	NT	TP	NT	NT	NT
				1 ◇					1 ◇				1 ◇				1 ◇			
	A	B	C	D		A	B	C	D		A	B	D 🚲		A	B	D 🚲		E	C
Colne d					13 57					14 57				15 57				16 57		
Nelson d					14 02					15 02				16 02				17 02		
Brierfield d					14 05					15 05				16 05				17 05		
Burnley Central d					14 10					15 10				16 10				17 10		
Burnley Barracks d					14 12					15 12				16 12				17 12		
Leeds 10 41 d		12 51					13 51					14 51				15 51				
Burnley Manchester Road 41 d		13 57					14 57					15 57				16 58				
Rose Grove d					14 15					15 15				16 15				17 15		
Hapton d										15 18				16 18				17 18		
Huncoat d					14 21									16 21				17 21		
Accrington d		14 06			14 26		15 06			15 26		16 06		16 26		17 06		17 26		
Church & Oswaldtwistle d					14 28					15 28				16 28				17 28		
Rishton d					14 31					15 31				16 31				17 31		
Blackburn a		14 14			14 36		15 14			15 39		16 14		16 36		17 14		17 38		
Manchester Victoria 94 🚌 a					15 50					16 42				17 51		18 23				
Clitheroe 94 d		13 31					14 31					15 23				16 31		17 12		
Blackburn d		14 15			14 39		15 15			15 39		16 15		16 39		17 15		17 40		
Mill Hill (Lancashire) d					14 42					15 42				16 42				17 43		
Cherry Tree d										15 44				16 44				17 45		
Pleasington d					14 46					15 46				16 46				17 47		
Bamber Bridge d					14 53					15 53				16 53				17 54		
Lostock Hall d					14 56					15 56				16 56				17 57		
Preston 8 a		14 32			15 10		15 32			16 12		16 33		17 11		17 34		18 07		
d	14 26	14 34	14 56	15 06	15 12	15 26	15 34	15 56	16 06	16 12	16 26	16 34	17 06	17 12	17 28	17 36	18 01	18 08	18 14	18 18
Salwick d										16 19										
Kirkham & Wesham d	14 35				15 21	15 35				16 23	16 35		17 15	17 21	17 38		18 10	18 19	18 22	
Moss Side d					15 27					16 29				17 27				18 25		
Lytham d					15 31					16 33				17 31				18 29		
Ansdell & Fairhaven d					15 34					16 36				17 34				18 32		
St Annes-on-the-Sea d					15 38					16 40				17 38				18 36		
Squires Gate d					15 42					16 44				17 42				18 40		
Blackpool Pleasure Beach d					15 44					16 46				17 44				18 42		
Blackpool South a					15 49					16 51				17 49				18 47		
Poulton-le-Fylde d	14 43	14 52		15 23		15 43	15 52		16 23		16 43	16 52	17 25		17 47	17 53	18 20		18 32	
Layton d	14 47					15 47					16 47		17 28		17 51		18 24		18 36	
Blackpool North a	14 56	15 01	15 21	15 32		15 56	16 01	16 21	16 32		16 56	17 01	17 34		18 00	18 03	18 30		18 43	18 48

	NT	NT	NT	TP	NT	NT	NT	TP	NT	NT	TP	NT	NT	TP	NT	NT	TP	NT
				1 ◇				1 ◇			1 ◇			1 ◇			1 ◇	
	A	B	C	D		A	B	D		B	D		B	D		C	D	
Colne d					17 57				18 57			19 57			21 44			22 56
Nelson d					18 02				19 02			20 02			21 49			23 01
Brierfield d					18 05				19 05			20 05			21 52			23 04
Burnley Central d					18 10				19 10			20 10			21 57			23 09
Burnley Barracks d					18 12				19 12			20 12			21 59			23 11
Leeds 10 41 d		16 51					17 51			18 51			19 51					
Burnley Manchester Road 41 d		17 57					18 57			19 57			20 57					
Rose Grove d					18 15				19 15			20 15			22 02			23 14
Hapton d					18 18				19 18			20 18			22 05			
Huncoat d					18 21				19 21			20 21			22 08			
Accrington d		18 06			18 26		19 06		19 26	20 06		20 26	21 06		22 13			23 21
Church & Oswaldtwistle d					18 28				19 28			20 28			22 15			
Rishton d					18 31				19 31			20 31			22 18			
Blackburn a		18 14			18 36		19 14		19 39	20 14		20 36	21 14		22 23			23 29
Manchester Victoria 94 🚌 a		19 23			19 50		20 22		20 50			21 50			23 59			
Clitheroe 94 d					18 03		18 31			19 31			20 31		21 36			22 41
Blackburn d		18 15			18 39		19 15		19 39	20 14		20 39	21 14		22 24			23 30
Mill Hill (Lancashire) d					18 42				19 42			20 42			22 27			23 33
Cherry Tree d					18 44				19 44			20 44			22 29			
Pleasington d					18 46				19 47			20 46			22 31			
Bamber Bridge d					18 53				19 53			20 53			22 38			23 41
Lostock Hall d					18 56				19 54			20 56			22 41			23 43
Preston 8 a		18 34			19 10		19 35		20 11	20 31		21 13	21 31		22 51			23 53
d	18 30	18 35	18 53	19 06	19 12	19 29	19 39	20 06	20 12	20 33	21 06	21 15	21 33	22 06	22 51	23 03	23 06	
Salwick d																		
Kirkham & Wesham d	18 40			19 16	19 21	19 38		20 16	20 21		21 16	21 24		22 16	23 00		23 16	
Moss Side d					19 27				20 27			21 30			23 06			
Lytham d					19 31				20 31			21 34			23 10			
Ansdell & Fairhaven d					19 34				20 34			21 37			23 13			
St Annes-on-the-Sea d					19 38				20 38			21 41			23 17			
Squires Gate d					19 42				20 42			21 45			23 21			
Blackpool Pleasure Beach d					19 44				20 44			21 47			23 23			
Blackpool South a					19 49				20 49			21 52			23 28			
Poulton-le-Fylde d	18 48	18 55	19 10	19 26		19 47	19 58	20 26		20 49	21 26		21 49	22 26			23 26	
Layton d	18 52					19 51		20 30			21 30			22 30			23 30	
Blackpool North a	19 01	19 04	19 21	19 35		19 57	20 07	20 36		20 56	21 36		21 56	22 36		23 28	23 36	

For general notes see front of timetable
For details of catering facilities see Directory of Train Operators

A From Buxton (Table 86)
B From York (Table 40)
C From Liverpool Lime Street (Table 90)
D From Manchester Airport (Table 82)
E From Stockport (Table 84)

For connections to and from London Euston, please refer to Table 65

Table 97

Sundays

until 2 November

Colne, Burnley, Accrington and Blackburn → Preston → Blackpool

Network Diagram - see first page of Table 97

		TP 1◇ A	TP 1◇ A	NT	NT B	NT C	TP 1◇ A	NT	NT D	NT	TP 1◇ A	NT B	NT E	NT D	NT	TP 1◇ A	NT D	NT	TP 1◇ A	NT B	NT E	NT D	NT
Colne	d							09 01										11 35					
Nelson	d							09 06										11 40					
Brierfield	d							09 09										11 43					
Burnley Central	d							09 14										11 48					
Burnley Barracks	d							09 16										11 50					
Leeds 10	41 d									08 45			09 35								11 35		
Burnley Manchester Road	41 d									09 49			10 41								12 39		
Rose Grove	d							09 19										11 53					
Hapton	d							09 22										11 56					
Huncoat	d							09 25										11 59					
Accrington	d							09 30		09 57			10 50					12 04			12 47		
Church & Oswaldtwistle	d							09 32										12 06					
Rishton	d							09 35										12 09					
Blackburn	a							09 42		10 05			10 58					12 14			12 55		
Manchester Victoria	94 🚌 a							*10 35*		*11 35*			*12 35*					*13 35*			*14 35*		
Clitheroe	94 d							*09 17*					*10 27*					*11 24*			*12 24*		
Blackburn	d							09 43		10 06			10 58					12 15			12 56		
Mill Hill (Lancashire)	d							09 46										12 18					
Cherry Tree	d							09 48										12 20					
Pleasington	d							09 50										12 22					
Bamber Bridge	d							09 57										12 29					
Lostock Hall	d							10 00										12 32					
Preston 8	a							10 08		10 29			11 15					12 40			13 13		
	d	00 06	08 48	08 56	09 07	09 20	09 48	10 10	10 21	10 31	10 48	11 07	11 17	11 21	11 42	11 48	12 21	12 42	12 48	13 07	13 14	13 21	13 42
Kirkham & Wesham	d	00 16	08 58	09 05			09 58	10 19			10 58				11 51	11 58		12 51	12 58				13 51
Moss Side	d			09 11				10 25							11 57			12 57					13 57
Lytham	d			09 15				10 29							12 01			13 01					14 01
Ansdell & Fairhaven	d			09 18				10 32							12 04			13 04					14 04
St Annes-on-the-Sea	d			09 22				10 36							12 08			13 08					14 08
Squires Gate	d			09 26				10 40							12 12			13 12					14 12
Blackpool Pleasure Beach	d			09 28				10 42							12 14			13 14					14 14
Blackpool South	a			09 33				10 47							12 19			13 19					14 19
Poulton-le-Fylde	d	00 26	09 07		09 23	09 36	10 07		10 38	10 47	11 07	11 23	11 33	11 38		12 07	12 38		13 07	13 23	13 31	13 38	
Blackpool North	a	00 38	09 16		09 34	09 45	10 16		10 47	10 54	11 16	11 34	11 40	11 47		12 16	12 47		13 16	13 34	13 39	13 47	

		TP 1◇ A	NT D	NT	TP 1◇ A	NT B	NT E	NT D	NT	TP 1◇ A	NT D	NT	TP 1◇ A	NT B	NT E	NT D	NT	TP 1◇ A	NT B	NT E	NT D	NT
Colne	d			13 35								15 35										17 28
Nelson	d			13 40								15 40										17 33
Brierfield	d			13 43								15 43										17 36
Burnley Central	d			13 48								15 48										17 41
Burnley Barracks	d			13 50								15 50										17 43
Leeds 10	41 d						13 35								15 35					16 35		
Burnley Manchester Road	41 d						14 39								16 39					17 39		
Rose Grove	d			13 53								15 53										17 46
Hapton	d			13 56								15 56										17 49
Huncoat	d			13 59								15 59										17 52
Accrington	d			14 04			14 47					16 04			16 47					17 47		17 57
Church & Oswaldtwistle	d			14 06								16 06										17 59
Rishton	d			14 09								16 09										18 02
Blackburn	a			14 14			14 55					16 14			16 55					17 55		18 07
Manchester Victoria	94 🚌 a			*15 35*			*16 35*					*17 35*			*18 35*							*19 35*
Clitheroe	94 d			*13 24*			*14 24*					*15 24*			*16 24*					*17 24*		
Blackburn	d			14 15			14 56					16 15			16 56					17 56		18 08
Mill Hill (Lancashire)	d			14 18								16 18										18 11
Cherry Tree	d			14 20								16 20										18 13
Pleasington	d			14 22								16 22										18 15
Bamber Bridge	d			14 29								16 29										18 22
Lostock Hall	d			14 32								16 32										18 25
Preston 8	a			14 40			15 13					16 40			17 13					18 13		18 33
	d	13 48	14 21	14 42	14 48	15 07	15 14	15 21	15 42	15 48	16 21	16 42	16 48	17 07	17 14	17 21	17 42	17 48	18 07	18 14	18 21	18 42
Kirkham & Wesham	d	13 58		14 51	14 58				15 51	15 58		16 51	16 58				17 51	17 58				18 51
Moss Side	d			14 57					15 57			16 57					17 57					18 57
Lytham	d			15 01					16 01			17 01					18 01					19 01
Ansdell & Fairhaven	d			15 04					16 04			17 04					18 04					19 04
St Annes-on-the-Sea	d			15 08					16 08			17 08					18 08					19 08
Squires Gate	d			15 12					16 12			17 12					18 12					19 12
Blackpool Pleasure Beach	d			15 14					16 14			17 14					18 14					19 14
Blackpool South	a			15 19					16 19			17 19					18 19					19 19
Poulton-le-Fylde	d	14 07	14 37		15 07	15 23	15 32	15 38		16 07	16 38		17 07	17 23	17 31	17 38		18 07	18 23	18 31	18 38	
Blackpool North	a	14 16	14 47		15 16	15 34	15 40	15 47		16 16	16 47		17 16	17 37	17 40	17 47		18 16	18 34	18 38	18 47	

For general notes see front of timetable
For details of catering facilities see Directory of Train Operators

A From Manchester Airport (Table 82)
B From Liverpool Lime Street (Table 90)
C From Manchester Victoria (Table 82)
D From Buxton (Table 86)
E Until 13 July and from 14 September from York (Table 40)

For connections to and from London Euston, please refer to Table 65

Sundays
until 2 November

Colne, Burnley, Accrington and Blackburn → Preston → Blackpool

Network Diagram - see first page of Table 97

	NT A	TP 1 ◇ B	NT C	NT D	NT E	NT	TP 1 ◇ B	NT E	NT	NT G	NT	TP 1 ◇ B	NT C	NT D	NT E	TP 1 ◇ B	NT E	NT	TP 1 ◇ B	NT C	TP 1 ◇ B
Colne d									19 21									21 29			
Nelson d									19 26									21 34			
Brierfield d									19 29									21 37			
Burnley Central d									19 34									21 42			
Burnley Barracks d									19 36									21 44			
Leeds 10 41 d				17 35										19 35							
Burnley Manchester Road 41 d				18 39										20 39							
Rose Grove d									19 39									21 47			
Hapton d									19 42									21 50			
Huncoat d									19 45									21 53			
Accrington d				18 47					19 50					20 47				21 57			
Church & Oswaldtwistle d									19 52									22 00			
Rishton d									19 55									22 03			
Blackburn a				18 55					20 00					20 55				22 08			
Manchester Victoria 94 a				*20 35*					*21 35*					*22 35*				*23 35*			
Clitheroe 94 d	17 49			*18 24*					*19 24*	19 47				*20 24*				*21 24*			
Blackburn d	18 15			18 56					20 01	20 14				20 56				22 09			
Mill Hill (Lancashire) d									20 04									22 12			
Cherry Tree d									20 06									22 14			
Pleasington d									20 08									22 16			
Bamber Bridge d	18 25								20 15	20 24								22 23			
Lostock Hall d	18 29								20 18	20 26								22 26			
Preston 8 a	18 39			19 13					20 26	20 34	←			21 13				22 36			
d		18 48	19 07	19 14	19 21	19 42	19 48	20 21	20 42	20 36	20 42	20 48	21 07	21 14	21 21	21 48	22 21		22 48	23 17	23 48
Kirkham & Wesham d		18 57				19 51	19 58		→	20 46	20 51	20 58				21 58			22 58		23 58
Moss Side d						19 57					20 57										
Lytham d						20 01					21 01										
Ansdell & Fairhaven d						20 04					21 04										
St Annes-on-the-Sea d						20 08					21 08										
Squires Gate d						20 12					21 12										
Blackpool Pleasure Beach d						20 14					21 14										
Blackpool South a						20 19					21 19										
Poulton-le-Fylde d		19 07	19 23	19 31	19 37		20 07	20 38		20 54		21 07	21 23	21 31	21 37	22 07	22 37		23 07	23 33	00 07
Blackpool North a		19 16	19 32	19 38	19 47		20 16	20 47		21 03		21 16	21 34	21 38	21 47	22 16	22 47		23 16	23 43	00 16

Sundays
from 9 November

	TP 1 ◇ B	TP 1 ◇ B	NT C	NT H	TP 1 ◇ B	NT	NT E	NT	TP 1 ◇ B	NT C	NT J	NT E	TP 1 ◇ B	NT E	NT	TP 1 ◇ B	NT C	NT J	NT E
Colne d						09 01									11 35				
Nelson d						09 06									11 40				
Brierfield d						09 09									11 43				
Burnley Central d						09 14									11 48				
Burnley Barracks d						09 16									11 50				
Leeds 41 d								08 45			09 35							11 35	
Burnley Manchester Road 41 d								09 49			10 41							12 39	
Rose Grove d						09 19									11 53				
Hapton d						09 22									11 56				
Huncoat d						09 25									11 59				
Accrington d						09 30		09 57			10 50				12 04			12 47	
Church & Oswaldtwistle d						09 32									12 06				
Rishton d						09 35									12 09				
Blackburn a						09 42		10 05			10 58				12 14			12 55	
Manchester Victoria 94 a						*10 35*		*11 35*			*12 35*				*13 35*			*14 35*	
Clitheroe 94 d						*09 17*					*10 27*				*11 24*			*12 24*	
Blackburn d						09 43		10 06			10 58				12 15			12 56	
Mill Hill (Lancashire) d						09 46									12 18				
Cherry Tree d						09 48									12 20				
Pleasington d						09 50									12 22				
Bamber Bridge d						09 57									12 29				
Lostock Hall d						10 00									12 32				
Preston 8 a						10 10		10 29			11 15				12 42			13 13	
d	00 06	08 48	09 07	09 20	09 48		10 21	10 31	10 48	11 07	11 17	11 21	11 48	12 21		12 48	13 07	13 14	13 21
Kirkham & Wesham d	00 16	08 58			09 58				10 58				11 58			12 58			
Poulton-le-Fylde d	00 26	09 07	09 23	09 36	10 07		10 38	10 47	11 07	11 23	11 33	11 38	12 07	12 38		13 07	13 23	13 31	13 38
Blackpool North a	00 38	09 16	09 34	09 45	10 16		10 47	10 54	11 16	11 34	11 40	11 47	12 16	12 47		13 16	13 34	13 39	13 47

For general notes see front of timetable
For details of catering facilities see Directory of Train Operators

A Until 14 September. From Carlisle (Table 36)
B From Manchester Airport (Table 82)
C From Liverpool Lime Street (Table 90)
D Until 13 July and from 14 September from York (Table 40)
E From Buxton (Table 86)
G Until 19 October. From Carlisle (Table 36)
H From Manchester Victoria (Table 82)
J From York (Table 40)

For connections to and from London Euston, please refer to Table 65

Table 97

Sundays

from 9 November

Colne, Burnley, Accrington and Blackburn → Preston → Blackpool

Network Diagram - see first page of Table 97

		TP 1 ◇ A	NT B	NT	TP 1 ◇ A	NT C	NT D	NT B	TP 1 ◇ A	NT B	NT	TP 1 ◇ A	NT C	NT D	NT B	TP 1 ◇ A	NT C	NT D	NT B
Colne	d			13 35							15 35								
Nelson	d			13 40							15 40								
Brierfield	d			13 43							15 43								
Burnley Central	d			13 48							15 48								
Burnley Barracks	d			13 50							15 50								
Leeds 41	d						13 35							15 35				16 35	
Burnley Manchester Road 41	d						14 39							16 39				17 39	
Rose Grove	d			13 53							15 53								
Hapton	d			13 56							15 56								
Huncoat	d			13 59							15 59								
Accrington	d			14 04			14 47				16 04			16 47				17 47	
Church & Oswaldtwistle	d			14 06							16 06								
Rishton	d			14 09							16 09								
Blackburn	a			14 14			14 55				16 14			16 55				17 55	
Manchester Victoria 94 ⛴	a			*15 35*			*16 35*				*17 35*			*18 35*					
Clitheroe 94	d			*13 24*			*14 24*				*15 24*			*16 24*				*17 24*	
Blackburn	d			14 15			14 56				16 15			16 56				17 56	
Mill Hill (Lancashire)	d			14 18							16 18								
Cherry Tree	d			14 20							16 20								
Pleasington	d			14 22							16 22								
Bamber Bridge	d			14 29							16 29								
Lostock Hall	d			14 32							16 32								
Preston 8	a			14 42			15 13				16 42			17 13				18 13	
	d	13 48	14 21		14 48	15 07	15 14	15 21	15 48	16 21		16 48	17 07	17 14	17 21	17 48	18 07	18 14	18 21
Kirkham & Wesham	d	13 58			14 58				15 58			16 58				17 58			
Poulton-le-Fylde	d	14 07	14 37		15 07	15 23	15 32	15 38	16 07	16 38		17 07	17 23	17 31	17 38	18 07	18 23	18 31	18 38
Blackpool North	a	14 16	14 47		15 16	15 34	15 40	15 47	16 16	16 47		17 16	17 37	17 40	17 47	18 16	18 34	18 38	18 47

		NT	TP 1 ◇ A	NT C	NT D	NT B	TP 1 ◇ A	NT B	NT	TP 1 ◇ A	NT C	NT D	NT B	TP 1 ◇ A	NT B	NT	TP 1 ◇ A	NT C	TP 1 ◇ A
Colne	d	17 28							19 21							21 29			
Nelson	d	17 33							19 26							21 34			
Brierfield	d	17 36							19 29							21 37			
Burnley Central	d	17 41							19 34							21 42			
Burnley Barracks	d	17 43							19 36							21 44			
Leeds 41	d				17 35							19 35							
Burnley Manchester Road 41	d				18 39							20 39							
Rose Grove	d	17 46							19 39							21 47			
Hapton	d	17 49							19 42							21 50			
Huncoat	d	17 52							19 45							21 53			
Accrington	d	17 57			18 47				19 50			20 47				21 57			
Church & Oswaldtwistle	d	17 59							19 52							22 00			
Rishton	d	18 02							19 55							22 03			
Blackburn	a	18 07			18 55				20 00			20 55				22 08			
Manchester Victoria 94 ⛴	a	*19 35*			*20 35*				*21 35*			*22 35*				*23 35*			
Clitheroe 94	d				*18 24*				*19 24*			*20 24*				*21 24*			
Blackburn	d	18 08			18 56				20 01			20 56				22 09			
Mill Hill (Lancashire)	d	18 11							20 04							22 12			
Cherry Tree	d	18 13							20 06							22 14			
Pleasington	d	18 15							20 08							22 16			
Bamber Bridge	d	18 22							20 15							22 23			
Lostock Hall	d	18 25							20 18							22 26			
Preston 8	a	18 35			19 13				20 28			21 13				22 36			
	d		18 48	19 07	19 14	19 21	19 48	20 21		20 48	21 07	21 14	21 21	21 48	22 21		22 48	23 17	23 48
Kirkham & Wesham	d		18 57				19 58			20 58				21 58			22 58		23 58
Poulton-le-Fylde	d		19 07	19 23	19 31	19 37	20 07	20 38		21 07	21 23	21 31	21 37	22 07	22 37		23 07	23 33	00 07
Blackpool North	a		19 16	19 32	19 38	19 47	20 16	20 47		21 16	21 34	21 38	21 47	22 16	22 47		23 16	23 43	00 16

For general notes see front of timetable
For details of catering facilities see Directory of Train Operators

A From Manchester Airport (Table 82)
B From Buxton (Table 86)
C From Liverpool Lime Street (Table 90)
D From York (Table 40)

For connections to and from London Euston, please refer to Table 65

Table 98

Mondays to Fridays

Lancaster → Morecambe and Heysham

Network Diagram - see first page of Table 97

Miles			NT	NT	NT	NT	NT	NT	NT	NT	NT	NT	NT	NT	NT	NT	NT	NT	NT	NT	NT	NT	NT	NT	NT	TP
																										1 ◊
							A	B	C			C				C					C					D
0	Lancaster 6	82 d	06 28	07 10	07 49	08 19	09 07	10 03	10 10	11 14	12 03	12 10	13 22	14 40	15 24	16 02	16 50	17 23	18 04	18 37	18 45	19 15	20 14	21 07	21 45	22 57
2½	Bare Lane	d	06 34	07 16	07 55	08 25	09 13	10 10	10 16	11 20	12 09	12 16	13 28	14 46	15 30	16 08	16 56	17 28	18 10	18 43	18 51	19 21	20 20	21 13	21 51	23 02
4¼	Morecambe	a	06 38	07 20	08 00	08 29	09 21	10 17	10 22	11 25	12 13	12 21	13 32	14 50	15 36	16 13	17 00	17 34	18 15	18 48	18 57	19 26	20 24	21 17	21 55	23 06
—		d									12 17		13 36													
8½	Heysham Port	a									12 31		13 50													

Saturdays

		NT	NT	NT	NT	NT	NT	NT	NT	NT	NT	NT	NT	NT	NT	NT	NT	NT	NT	NT	NT	NT	NT	NT	NT
					A			C			C				C					C					E
																								🚌	🚌
Lancaster 6	82 d	07 10	07 49	08 19	09 07	09 16	10 00	10 10	11 06	12 00	12 14	13 20	14 35	15 24	16 02	16 49	17 23	17 58	18 33	18 45	19 10	20 14	20 56	21 25	22 45
Bare Lane	d	07 16	07 55	08 25	09 13	09 22	10 06	10 16	11 12	12 06	12 20	13 26	14 41	15 30	16 08	16 55	17 29	18 04	18 39	18 51	19 16	20 20	21 02	21 35	22 55
Morecambe	a	07 20	07 59	08 29	09 21	09 27	10 12	10 22	11 16	12 10	12 25	13 30	14 47	15 36	16 13	16 59	17 34	18 10	18 44	18 57	19 22	20 24	21 06	21 45	23 05
	d									12 14		13 34													
Heysham Port	a									12 28		13 48													

Sundays

until 13 July

		NT	NT	NT	NT	NT	NT	NT	NT	NT	NT	NT	NT	NT
		C				C						C	C	
Lancaster 6	82 d	10 45	11 10	11 54	12 05	12 52	13 23	14 06	15 03	15 45	16 23	16 50	19 14	21 46
Bare Lane	d	10 51	11 16	12 00	12 11	12 58	13 29	14 12	15 09	15 51	16 29	16 56	19 20	21 51
Morecambe	a	10 55	11 20	12 05	12 15	13 02	13 34	14 16	15 13	15 55	16 33	17 01	19 24	21 55
	d			12 08			13 37							
Heysham Port	a			12 23			13 52							

Sundays

20 July to 14 September

		NT	NT	NT	NT	NT	NT	NT	NT	NT	NT	NT	NT	NT	NT
		C				C						C	G	H	
Lancaster 6	82 d	10 45	11 10	11 54	12 05	12 52	13 19	14 06	15 00	15 45	16 23	16 50	19 16	19 23	21 46
Bare Lane	d	10 51	11 16	12 00	12 11	12 58	13 25	14 12	15 06	15 51	16 29	16 56	19 22	19 29	21 51
Morecambe	a	10 55	11 20	12 05	12 15	13 02	13 30	14 16	15 10	15 55	16 33	17 01	19 26	19 33	21 55
	d			12 08			13 33								
Heysham Port	a			12 23			13 48								

Sundays

from 21 September

		NT	NT	NT	NT
			C	C	
Lancaster 6	82 d	15 00	16 50	19 16	21 46
Bare Lane	d	15 06	16 56	19 22	21 51
Morecambe	a	15 10	17 01	19 26	21 55
	d				
Heysham Port	a				

For general notes see front of timetable
For details of catering facilities see Directory of Train Operators

A From Clitheroe (Table 94)
B From Liverpool Lime Street (Table 90)
C From Leeds (Table 36)
D From Windermere (Table 83) to Barrow-in-Furness (Table 82)
E Until 6 September
G 14 September only. From Leeds (Table 36)
H Until 7 September. From Leeds (Table 36)

Table 98

Mondays to Fridays

Heysham and Morecambe → Lancaster

Network Diagram - see first page of Table 97

Miles			NT	NT	NT	NT	NT	NT	NT	NT	NT	NT	NT	NT	NT	NT	NT	NT	NT	NT	NT	NT	NT	NT	NT	NT	TP
								A		B		B					C					B					1 ◇ D
0	**Heysham Port**	d											12 48	13 53													
4¼	**Morecambe**	a											12 58	14 03													
—		d	06 13	06 55	07 34	08 05	08 33	09 25	10 22	10 45	11 33	12 44	13 02	14 07	15 08	15 40	16 38	17 09	17 48	18 20	18 52	19 05	19 39	20 29	21 28	22 25	23 10
6	Bare Lane	d	06 17	06 59	07 38	08 09	08 37	09 29	10 26	10 49	11 37	12 48	13 09	14 14	15 12	15 44	16 42	17 13	17 52	18 24	18 56	19 09	19 43	20 33	21 32	22 29	23a14
8½	**Lancaster** 3	82 a	06 23	07 06	07 44	08 15	08 43	09 34	10 35	10 56	11 43	12 53	13 16	14 20	15 18	15 52	16 48	17 20	17 59	18 30	19 04	19 18	19 49	20 40	21 39	22 36	

Saturdays

		NT	NT	NT	NT	NT	NT	NT	NT	NT	NT	NT	NT	NT	NT	NT	NT	NT	NT	NT	NT	NT	NT	NT	NT	NT
									B	E	G	B					C					B			A	🚌
Heysham Port	d												12 44	14 01												
Morecambe	a												12 54	14 11												
	d	06 55	07 34	08 05	08 33	09 25	09 48	10 25	10 34	11⟆23	11⟆26	12 47	12 58	14 15	15 08	15 40	16 38	17 09	17 40	18 20	18 52	19 00	19 39	20 29	21 10	22 05
Bare Lane	d	06 59	07 38	08 09	08 37	09 29	09 52	10 29	10 38	11⟆27	11⟆30	12 51	13 05	14 22	15 12	15 44	16 42	17 13	17 44	18 24	18 56	19 05	19 43	20 33	21 14	22 15
Lancaster 6	82 a	07 06	07 44	08 15	08 43	09 38	09 59	10 36	10 45	11⟆33	11⟆37	12 59	13 14	14 28	15 18	15 52	16 49	17 20	17 51	18 30	19 04	19 13	19 49	20 40	21 20	22 25

Sundays

until 13 July

		NT	NT	NT	NT	NT	NT	NT	NT	NT	NT	NT	NT	NT
				B				B				B	B	
Heysham Port	d				12 42		14 00							
Morecambe	a				12 52		14 10							
	d	11 15	11 40	12 23	12 56	13 11	14 14	14 28	15 21	16 03	16 44	17 54	20 00	22 19
Bare Lane	d	11 19	11 44	12 27	13 03	13 15	14 21	14 32	15 25	16 07	16 48	17 58	20 04	22 23
Lancaster 6	82 a	11 25	11 50	12 33	13 12	13 21	14 30	14 38	15 34	16 15	16 54	18 06	20 11	22 29

Sundays

20 July to 14 September

		NT	NT	NT	NT	NT	NT	NT	NT	NT	NT	NT	NT	NT	NT
				B				B				H	J	B	
Heysham Port	d				12 42		14 00								
Morecambe	a				12 52		14 10								
	d	11 15	11 40	12 23	12 56	13 07	14 14	14 28	15 21	16 03	16 44	17⟆42	17⟆54	20 00	22 19
Bare Lane	d	11 19	11 44	12 27	13 03	13 11	14 21	14 32	15 25	16 07	16 48	17⟆46	17⟆58	20 04	22 23
Lancaster 6	82 a	11 25	11 50	12 33	13 12	13 17	14 30	14 38	15 31	16 15	16 54	17⟆53	18⟆06	20 11	22 29

Sundays

from 21 September

		NT	NT	NT	NT
			B	B	
Heysham Port	d				
Morecambe	a				
	d	15 21	17 42	20 00	22 19
Bare Lane	d	15 25	17 46	20 04	22 23
Lancaster 6	82 a	15 31	17 53	20 11	22 29

For general notes see front of timetable
For details of catering facilities see Directory of Train Operators

- **A** To Preston (Table 65)
- **B** To Leeds (Table 36)
- **C** To Skipton (Table 36)
- **D** From Windermere (Table 83) to Barrow-in-Furness (Table 82)
- **E** Until 6 September
- **G** From 13 September
- **H** 14 September only. To Leeds (Table 36)
- **J** Until 7 September. To Leeds (Table 36)

To and from The Isle of Man via Heysham and Liverpool

One Class only on ship

		VT A	VT MTX B	VT FX C	VT MX D	VT MFX E	NT	NT	VT	VT MTO G	VT ThX H	VT J	VT MTX K
		R	R	R	R	R			R	R	R	R	R
London Euston [15]	65 d												
Birmingham New Street [12]	65 d												
Crewe [10]	65 d												
Manchester Piccadilly [10]	82, 89 ⛴ d												
Preston [10]	82 d												
Lancaster [8]	98 d						12 03	13 22					
Morecambe	98 d						12 17	13 36					
Heysham Port	a						12 31	13 50					
Liverpool Lime Street	a	11 15	11 15	11 15	11 15	11 15							
Liverpool Landing Stage	⛴ d									19 00	19 00	19 00	21 30
Heysham Port	⛴ d								14 15				
Douglas (Isle of Man)	⛴ a	13 45	13 45	13 45	13 45	13 45			17 45	21 30	21 30	21 30	23 59

Saturdays

until 12 July

One Class only on ship

		NT	NT	VT	VT L	VT N
				R	R	R
London Euston [15]	65 d					
Birmingham New Street [12]	65 d					
Crewe [10]	65 d					
Manchester Piccadilly [10]	82, 89 ⛴ d					
Preston [10]	82 d					
Lancaster [8]	98 d	12 00	13 20			
Morecambe	98 d	12 14	13 34			
Heysham Port	a	12 28	13 48			
Liverpool Lime Street	a					
Liverpool Landing Stage	⛴ d				19 00	21 30
Heysham Port	⛴ d			14 15		
Douglas (Isle of Man)	⛴ a			17 45	21 30	23 59

Saturdays

19 July to 6 September

One Class only on ship

		NT	NT	VT	VT
				R	R
London Euston [15]	65 d				
Birmingham New Street [12]	65 d				
Crewe [10]	65 d				
Manchester Piccadilly [10]	82, 89 ⛴ d				
Preston [10]	82 d				
Lancaster [8]	98 d	12 00	13 20		
Morecambe	98 d	12 14	13 34		
Heysham Port	a	12 28	13 48		
Liverpool Lime Street	a				
Liverpool Landing Stage	⛴ d				19 00
Heysham Port	⛴ d			14 15	
Douglas (Isle of Man)	⛴ a			17 45	21 30

For general notes see front of timetable
For details of catering facilities see Directory of Train Operators

- **A** 19 to 23 May, 16 June to 15 August and 25 August to 3 October
- **B** 11 to 13 June
- **C** 18 to 21 August
- **D** 7 to 17 October
- **E** 21 to 30 October
- **G** 9 and 10 June
- **H** 16 June to 15 August and 1 to 26 September
- **J** 18 to 29 August
- **K** 21 to 23 May
- **L** From 21 June
- **N** 24 May

Reservations: Customers, including all children, must obtain an advance reservation for the ship. This can be obtained free of charge from stations, appointed Agents or direct from The Isle of Man Steam Packet Company Offices in Douglas, Isle of Man. Customers without a reservation may not be able to travel if the ship is fully reserved.

Customers travelling via Liverpool should allow a minimum of 45 minutes for the transfer to and from the ship. Bus transfers between Liverpool Lime Street and the Landing Stage are available free of charge for customers with through rail tickets.

To and from The Isle of Man via Heysham and Liverpool

Sundays
until 13 July

One Class only on ship

		NT			NT			VT R			VT R A			VT R B			VT R C
London Euston 15	65 d																
Birmingham New Street 12	65 d																
Crewe 10	65 d																
Manchester Piccadilly 10	82, 89 ⛴ d																
Preston 10	82 d																
Lancaster 8	98 d	11 54			13 23												
Morecambe	98 d	12 08			13 37												
Heysham Port	a	12 23			13 52												
Liverpool Lime Street	a																
Liverpool Landing Stage	⛴ d										17 00			19 00			20 00
Heysham Port	⛴ d							14 15									
Douglas (Isle of Man)	⛴ a							17 45			19 30			21 30			22 30

Sundays
20 July to 7 September

One Class only on ship

		NT					NT					VT R					VT R
London Euston 15	65 d																
Birmingham New Street 12	65 d																
Crewe 10	65 d																
Manchester Piccadilly 10	82, 89 ⛴ d																
Preston 10	82 d																
Lancaster 8	98 d	11 54					13 19										
Morecambe	98 d	12 08					13 33										
Heysham Port	a	12 23					13 48										
Liverpool Lime Street	a																
Liverpool Landing Stage	⛴ d																19 00
Heysham Port	⛴ d											14 15					
Douglas (Isle of Man)	⛴ a											17 45					21 30

For general notes see front of timetable
For details of catering facilities see Directory of Train Operators

A 1 June
B 18 May and from 15 June
C 25 May

Reservations: Customers, including all children, must obtain an advance reservation for the ship. This can be obtained free of charge from stations, appointed Agents or direct from The Isle of Man Steam Packet Company Offices in Douglas, Isle of Man.Customers without a reservation may not be able to travel if the ship is fully reserved.

Customers travelling via Liverpool should allow a minimum of 45 minutes for the transfer to and from the ship. Bus transfers between Liverpool Lime Street and the Landing Stage are available free of charge for customers with through rail tickets.

To and from The Isle of Man via Heysham and Liverpool

One Class only on ship

Mondays to Fridays

		VT MTO R A	VT MTX R B	VT R C	VT FX R D	VT MX R E	VT MFX R G	VT ThFO R H	VT MX R J	VT ThFX R K	VT MO R L	VT MWO R N	VT R Q	NT	VT TO R U	NT	VT MTO R V	VT ThX R X	VT ThFX R Y	VT R Z	VT FX R D	VT MTX R AA
Douglas (Isle of Man)	⛴ d	07 30	07 30	07 30	07 30	07 30	07 30	08 00	08 00	08 45	08 45	08 45	08 45		09 15		15 00	15 00	15 00	15 00	15 00	17 15
Heysham Port	⛴ a							11 30	11 30	12 15	12 15	12 15	12 15		12 45							
Liverpool Landing Stage	⛴ a	10 00	10 00	10 00	10 00	10 00	10 00										17 30	17 30	17 30	17 30	17 30	19 45
Liverpool Lime Street	d																					
Heysham Port	d													12 48		13 53						
Morecambe	98 a													12 58		14 03						
Lancaster 8	98 a													13 16		14 20						
Preston 10	82 a																					
Manchester Piccadilly 10	82, 89 ⛴ a																					
Crewe 10	65 a																					
Birmingham New Street 12	65 a																					
London Euston 15	65 a																					

Saturdays

until 12 July

One Class only on ship

		VT R BB	NT	VT R CC	NT	VT R DD	VT R EE
Douglas (Isle of Man)	⛴ d	08 00		08 45		15 00	17 15
Heysham Port	⛴ a	11 30		12 45			
Liverpool Landing Stage	⛴ a					17 30	19 45
Liverpool Lime Street	d						
Heysham Port	d		12 44		14 01		
Morecambe	98 a		12 54		14 11		
Lancaster 8	98 a		13 14		14 28		
Preston 10	82 a						
Manchester Piccadilly 10	82, 89 ⛴ a						
Crewe 10	65 a						
Birmingham New Street 12	65 a						
London Euston 15	65 a						

Saturdays

19 July to 6 September

One Class only on ship

		VT R	NT	NT	VT R FF
Douglas (Isle of Man)	⛴ d	08 45			15 00
Heysham Port	⛴ a	12 15			
Liverpool Landing Stage	⛴ a				17 30
Liverpool Lime Street	d				
Heysham Port	d		12 44	14 01	
Morecambe	98 a		12 54	14 11	
Lancaster 8	98 a		13 14	14 28	
Preston 10	82 a				
Manchester Piccadilly 10	82, 89 ⛴ a				
Crewe 10	65 a				
Birmingham New Street 12	65 a				
London Euston 15	65 a				

For general notes see front of timetable
For details of catering facilities see Directory of Train Operators

- **A** 19 and 20 May
- **B** 11 to 13 June
- **C** 16 June to 15 August and 25 August to 3 October
- **D** 18 to 21 August
- **E** 7 to 17 October
- **G** 21 to 30 October
- **H** 22 and 23 May
- **J** 27 to 30 May
- **K** 19 to 21 May
- **L** 26 May
- **N** 2 and 4 June
- **Q** From 9 June
- **U** 3 June
- **V** 9 and 10 June
- **X** 16 June to 4 July, 14 to 25 July and 4 to 15 August
- **Y** 7 to 9 July and 1 to 3 September
- **Z** 28 July to 1 August and 25 to 29 August
- **AA** 21 to 23 May
- **BB** 24 and 31 May
- **CC** From 7 June
- **DD** From 15 June
- **EE** 24 May
- **FF** Until 16 August and from 30 August

Reservations: Customers, including all children, must obtain an advance reservation for the ship. This can be obtained free of charge from stations, appointed Agents or direct from The Isle of Man Steam Packet Company Offices in Douglas, Isle of Man.Customers without a reservation may not be able to travel if the ship is fully reserved.

Customers travelling via Liverpool should allow a minimum of 45 minutes for the transfer to and from the ship. Bus transfers between Liverpool Lime Street and the Landing Stage are available free of charge for customers with through rail tickets.

To and from The Isle of Man via Heysham and Liverpool

Sundays
until 13 July

One Class only on ship

		VT R	NT	NT	VT R A	VT R B	VT R C	VT R D
Douglas (Isle of Man)	d	08 45			11 45	12 45	15 00	15 30
Heysham Port	a	12 15						
Liverpool Landing Stage	a				14 15	15 15	17 30	18 00
Liverpool Lime Street	d							
Heysham Port	d		12 42	14 00				
Morecambe	98 a		12 52	14 10				
Lancaster 8	98 a		13 12	14 30				
Preston 10	82 a							
Manchester Piccadilly 10	82, 89 a							
Crewe 10	65 a							
Birmingham New Street 12	65 a							
London Euston 15	65 a							

Sundays
20 July to 7 September

One Class only on ship

		VT R	NT	NT	VT R
Douglas (Isle of Man)	d	08 45			15 00
Heysham Port	a	12 15			
Liverpool Landing Stage	a				17 30
Liverpool Lime Street	d				
Heysham Port	d		12 42	14 00	
Morecambe	98 a		12 52	14 10	
Lancaster 8	98 a		13 12	14 30	
Preston 10	82 a				
Manchester Piccadilly 10	82, 89 a				
Crewe 10	65 a				
Birmingham New Street 12	65 a				
London Euston 15	65 a				

For general notes see front of timetable
For details of catering facilities see Directory of Train Operators

A 1 June
B 8 June
C 18 May and from 15 June
D 25 May

Reservations: Customers, including all children, must obtain an advance reservation for the ship. This can be obtained free of charge from stations, appointed Agents or direct from The Isle of Man Steam Packet Company Offices in Douglas, Isle of Man.Customers without a reservation may not be able to travel if the ship is fully reserved.

Customers travelling via Liverpool should allow a minimum of 45 minutes for the transfer to and from the ship. Bus transfers between Liverpool Lime Street and the Landing Stage are available free of charge for customers with through rail tickets.

Table 99

Mondays to Saturdays

Ormskirk — Preston

Network Diagram - see first page of Table 97

Miles			NT	NT	NT	NT	NT	NT	NT	NT	NT	NT	NT	NT
—	Liverpool Central 10	103 d	*06 10*	*07 40*	*08 55*	*10 10*	*11 40*	*12 55*	*14 25*	*15 55*	*17 10*	*18 25*	*19 40*	*21 40*
0	**Ormskirk**	d	07 15	08 22	09 35	10 50	12 23	13 38	15 04	16 32	17 51	19 02	20 19	22 17
2½	Burscough Junction	d	07 19	08 26	09 39	10 54	12 27	13 42	15 08	16 36	17 55	19 06	20 23	22 21
5½	Rufford	d	07 23	08 30	09 43	10 58	12 31	13 46	15 12	16 40	17 59	19 10	20 27	22 25
8	Croston	d	07 28	08 35	09 48	11 03	12 36	13 51	15 17	16 45	18 04	19 15	20 32	22 30
15	**Preston 3**	a	07 44	08 51	10 05	11 19	12 52	14 07	15 39	17 01	18 21	19 34	20 49	22 46

Mondays to Saturdays

Miles			NT	NT	NT	NT	NT	NT	NT	NT	NT	NT	NT	NT
0	**Preston 3**	d	06 28	07 48	09 02	10 12	11 26	13 02	14 26	15 45	17 06	18 25	19 39	21 36
7	Croston	d	06 39	07 59	09 14	10 23	11 37	13 13	14 37	15 57	17 17	18 36	19 50	21 48
9½	Rufford	d	06 44	08 03	09 18	10 28	11 42	13 18	14 42	16 01	17 22	18 41	19 55	21 52
12½	Burscough Junction	d	06 49	08 08	09 23	10 33	11 47	13 23	14 47	16 06	17 27	18 46	20 00	21 57
15	**Ormskirk**	a	06 58	08 15	09 30	10 42	11 56	13 30	14 56	16 15	17 36	18 54	20 09	22 06
—	Liverpool Central 10	103 a	*07 35*	*08 50*	*10 05*	*11 20*	*12 35*	*14 05*	*15 35*	*16 50*	*18 20*	*19 35*	*20 50*	*22 50*

For general notes see front of timetable
For details of catering facilities see
Directory of Train Operators

No Sunday Service

Barrow-in-Furness → Whitehaven and Carlisle

Network Diagram - see first page of Table 97

Mondays to Fridays

Miles			NT	NT	NT	NT	NT	NT	NT	NT A	NT	NT	NT	NT	NT	NT	NT	NT	NT	NT	NT	NT	NT
—	Lancaster 3	82 d							08 54	10 30	*11 45*		13 12	*13 45*	14 17		*15 52*	16 39		*17 45*			*19 39*
0	**Barrow-in-Furness**	d		05 56	06 47		08 46		09 58	11 35	13 00		14 09	14 51	15 30		17 12	17 58		19 10			21 19
6	Askam	d		06 06	06 57		08 56		10 08	11 45	13 10		14 19	15 01	15 40		17 22	18 08		19 20			21 29
9¼	Kirkby-in-Furness	d		06x10	07x01		09x00		10x12	11x49	13x14			15x05	15x44		17x26	18x12		19x24			21x33
11¼	Foxfield	d		06x14	07x05		09x03		10x16	11x52	13x17			15x08	15x47		17x29	18x16		19x27			21x36
13½	Green Road	d		06x17	07x08				10x19	11x56	13x21			15x12	15x51		17x33	18x19		19x31			21x40
16	Millom	a		06 24	07 15		09 15		10 26	12 02	13 30		14 33	15 18	15 57		17 39	18 29		19 40			21 49
—		d		06 25	07 16				10 26	12 02			14 33	15 18	15 58		17 39						
19	Silecroft	d		06x30	07x21				10x31	12x07				15x23	16x02		17x44						
24½	Bootle	d		06x37	07x28				10x37	12x13				15x29	16x09		17x50						
29¼	Ravenglass for Eskdale	d		06 43	07 34				10 43	12 19			14 48	15 35	16 15		17 56						
31	Drigg	d		06x47	07x37				10x46	12x22				15x38	16x18		17x59						
33¼	Seascale	d		06x50	07x41				10x49	12x25				15x41	16x21		18x02						
35	Sellafield	d		06 58	07 48				10 55	12 31			14 56	15 47	16a31		18 08						
37	Braystones	d		07x02	07x51									15x51			18x12						
38½	Nethertown	d		07x04	07x54									15x53			18x14						
41¼	St Bees	d		07 09	07 58				11 05	12 40			15 06	15 58			18 19						
44¾	Corkickle	d		07x14	08x03				11x10	12x45			15x11	16x04			18x24						
45¾	**Whitehaven**	a		07 17	08 07				11 13	12 48			15 13	16 06			18 27						
—		d	06 34	07 22	08 08	08 59		09 49	11 14	12 49		14 03	15 15	16 08		16 54	18 29		19 19		19 50	21 22	
47	Parton	d	06x38	07x25	08x12	09x02		09x52	11x18	12x53		14x06	15x20	16x11		16x57	18x32		19x22		19x53	21x25	
50½	Harrington	d	06x46	07x33	08x20	09x10		10x00	11x26	13x01		14x14	15x28	16x19		17x05	18x40		19x30		20x01	21x33	
52¼	**Workington**	d	06 51	07 40	08 26	09 16		10 06	11 32	13 07		14 21	15 34	16 26		17 12	18 47		19 37		20 08	21a38	
56	Flimby	d	06x56	07x44	08x31			10x11	11x37	13x12		14x25	15x39	16x30		17x16	18x51		19x41		20x12		
58	Maryport	d	06 59	07 48	08 34	09 24		10 14	11 40	13 15		14 29	15 42	16 34		17 20	18 55		19 45		20 16		
65½	Aspatria	d	07x09	07x57	08x44	09x33		10x24	11x50	13x25		14x38	15x52	16x43		17x29	19x04		19x54		20x25		
71¾	Wigton	d	07 19	08 07	08 54	09 43		10 34	12 00	13 35		14 48	16 02	16 53		17 39	19 14		20 04		20 35		
81¼	Dalston	d	07x27	08x16	09x02	09x52		10x42	12x08	13x43		14x57	16x10	17x02		17x48	19x23		20x13		20x44		
85¼	**Carlisle** 3	a	07 43	08 31	09 17	10 07		10 58	12 22	13 58		15 12	16 24	17 17		18 03	19 38		20 28		20 59		

Saturdays

		NT	NT	NT	NT	NT	NT	NT	NT	NT	NT	NT	NT	NT	NT	NT	NT B	NT	NT	NT	NT
Lancaster 6	82 d								08 50	*09 48*	11 01	*11 45*			14 18	16 14	17 17		*17 45*		*19 55*
Barrow-in-Furness	d			05 57	07 34		08 47		09 58	11 09	11 58	12 58	13 55		15 25	17 19	18 24		19 10		21 19
Askam	d			06 07	07 44		08 57		10 08	11 19	12 08	13 08	14 05		15 35	17 29	18 34		19 20		21 29
Kirkby-in-Furness	d			06x11	07x48		09x01		10x12		12x12	13x12	14x09		15x39	17x33	18x38		19x24		21x33
Foxfield	d			06x14	07x51		09x04		10x15		12x15	13x15	14x12		15x42	17x36	18x41		19x27		21x36
Green Road	d			06x18	07x55				10x19		12x19	13x19	14x16		15x46	17x40	18x45		19x31		21x40
Millom	a			06 24	08 01		09 16		10 25	11 36	12 25	13 25	14 22		15 52	17 46	18 54		19 40		21 49
	d			06 25	08 01				10 26		12 25	13 25	14 22		15 53	17 47					
Silecroft	d			06x30	08x06				10x30		12x30		14x27		15x57	17x51					
Bootle	d			06x37	08x12				10x37		12x36	13x35	14x33		16x04	17x58					
Ravenglass for Eskdale	d			06 43	08 18				10 43		12 42	13 41	14 39		16 10	18 04					
Drigg	d			06x47	08x21				10x46		12x45		14x42		16x13	18x07					
Seascale	d			06x50	08x24				10x49		12x48	13x47	14x45		16x16	18x10					
Sellafield	d			06 56	08 30				10 55		12 54	13 51	14 51		16 22	18 16					
Braystones	d			07x00	08x34										16x25	18x19					
Nethertown	d			07x02	08x36										16x28	18x22					
St Bees	d			07 07	08 41				11 04		13 03	14 02	15 00		16 32	18 26					
Corkickle	d			07x12	08x46				11x09		13x08	14x07	15x05		16x37	18x31					
Whitehaven	a			07 15	08 52				11 12		13 11	14 10	15 08		16 41	18 35					
	d	05 54	06 37	07 17		08 57		09 47	11 13		13 12	14 11	15 09	16 04	16 42	18 36		19 15		19 50	
Parton	d	05x57	06x41	07x20		09x00		09x50	11x17		13x16	14x15	15x13	16x07	16x46	18x40		19x18		19x53	
Harrington	d	06x05	06x49	07x28		09x08		09x58	11x25		13x24	14x23	15x21	16x15	16x54	18x48		19x26		20x01	
Workington	d	06 12	06 55	07 35		09 15		10 05	11 31		13 30	14 29	15 27	16 22	17 00	18 54		19 33		20 08	
Flimby	d	06x16	07x00	07x39		09x19		10x09	11x36		13x35	14x34	15x32	16x26	17x05	18x59		19x37		20x12	
Maryport	d	06 20	07 03	07 43		09 23		10 13	11 39		13 38	14 37	15 35	16 30	17 08	19 02		19 41		20 16	
Aspatria	d	06x29	07x13	07x52		09x32		10x22	11x49		13x48	14x47	15x45	16x39	17x18	19x12		19x50		20x25	
Wigton	d	06 39	07 23	08 02		09 42		10 32	11 59		13 58	14 57	15 55	16 49	17 28	19 22		20 00		20 35	
Dalston	d	06x48	07x31	08x11		09x51		10x41	12x07		14x06	15x05	16x03	16x58	17x36	19x30		20x09		20x44	
Carlisle 8	a	07 03	07 46	08 26		10 05		10 56	12 22		14 21	15 20	16 18	17 12	17 51	19 46		20 24		20 59	

Sundays

		NT	NT	NT
Whitehaven	d	12 50	16 10	20 15
Parton	d	12x53	16x13	20x18
Harrington	d	13x01	16x21	20x26
Workington	d	13 07	16 27	20 32
Flimby	d	13x11	16x31	20x36
Maryport	d	13 15	16 35	20 40
Aspatria	d	13x24	16x44	20x49
Wigton	d	13 34	16 54	20 59
Dalston	d	13x43	17x03	21x08
Carlisle 8	a	13 57	17 17	21 22

For general notes see front of timetable
For details of catering facilities see Directory of Train Operators

A From Preston (Table 65)
B From Liverpool Lime Street (Table 90)

No Sunday Service Whitehaven to Barrow-in-Furness

Carlisle and Whitehaven → Barrow-in-Furness

Network Diagram - see first page of Table 97

Mondays to Fridays

Miles	Station		NT	NT	NT	NT	NT	NT	NT	NT	NT	NT	NT	NT	NT	NT	NT	NT	NT	NT	NT	NT	NT	NT	NT	NT
				A														FO	FX	B					FO	
0	**Carlisle 8**	d				07 46		08 35	09 27	10 14	11 44		12 41	14 18		15 40	16 33	17 27	17 27	18 04	18 36		20 09		20 50	21 53
4	Dalston	d				07x54		08x43	09x35	10x22	11x52		12x49	14x26		15x48	16x41	17x35	17x35	18x12	18x44		20x17		20x58	22x01
11½	Wigton	d				08 03		08 52	09 44	10 31	12 01		12 58	14 35		15 57	16 50	17 44	17 44	18 21	18 53		20 26		21 07	22 10
19¾	Aspatria	d				08x13		09x02	09x54	10x41	12x11		13x08	14x45		16x07	17x00	17x54	17x54	18x31	19x03		20x36		21x17	22x20
27¼	Maryport	d		06 04		08 23		09 12	10 04	10 51	12 21		13 18	14 55		16 17	17 10	18 04	18 04	18 41	19 13		20 46		21 27	22 30
29¼	Flimby	d		06x07		08x26		09x15	10x07	10x54	12x24		13x21	14x58		16x20	17x13	18x07	18x07	18x44	19x16		20x49		21x30	22x33
33	**Workington**	d		06 15		08 35		09 24	10b17	11 03	12 33		13 30	15 07		16 29	17 22	18 16	18 16	18 53	19 25		20 58		21 39	22 42
34¾	Harrington	d		06x18		08x38		09x27	10x20	11x06	12x36		13x33	15x10		16x32	17x25	18x19	18x19	18x56	19x28		21x01		21x42	22x45
38¼	Parton	d		06x27		08x47		09x36	10x29	11x15	12x46		13x42	15x19		16x41	17x34	18x28	18x28	19x05	19x37		21x10		21x51	22x54
39½	**Whitehaven**	a		06 33		08 56		09 45	10 35	11 21	12 54		13 48	15 25		16 50	17 40	18 35	18 36	19 14	19 46		21 19		22 00	23 02
—		d		06 35	07 23				10 36	11 24			13 49	15 26			17 41	18 36	18 36							
40½	Corkickle	d		06x37	07x25				10x38	11x26			13x51	15x28			17x43	18x38	18x38							
44	St Bees	d		06 42	07 30				10 44	11 32			13 58	15 34			17 49	18 43	18 43							
47	Nethertown	d		06x46						11x36			14x02				17x53									
48¾	Braystones	d		06x49						11x38			14x05				17x55									
50¼	Sellafield	d		06 55	07 41				10 54	11 45			14 11	15c54	16 40		18 03	18 54	18 54							
52	Seascale	d		06x58	07x44				10x57	11x48			14x14	15x57	16x43		18x06	18x57	18x57							
54¼	Drigg	d		07x01	07x47				11x00	11x51			14x17	16x00	16x46		18x09	19x00	19x00							
56	Ravenglass for Eskdale	d		07 04	07 50				11 04	11 54			14 20	16 04	16 49		18 12	19 03	19 03							
60¾	Bootle	d		07x10	07x56				11x10	12x00			14x26	16x09	16x55		18x18	19x09	19x09							
66¼	Silecroft	d		07x16	08x02				11x16	12x06			14x32	16x16	17x01		18x24	19x15	19x15							
69¼	Millom	a		07 23	08 09				11 23	12 13			14 39	16 23	17 08		18 31	19 22	19 22							
—		d	06 08	07 23	08 10		09 24		11 24	12 14		13 56	14 40	16 24	17 09		18 32	19 22	19 22			19 55		21 55		
71¾	Green Road	d	06x12	07x27	08x14		09x28			12x18		14x00	14x44	16x28	17x13		18x36	19x26	19x26			19x59		21x59		
73¾	Foxfield	d	06x15	07x31	08x17		09x31		11x31	12x21		14x03	14x47	16x31	17x16		18x39	19x30	19x30			20x02		22x02		
76	Kirkby-in-Furness	d	06x19	07x35	08x21		09x35		11x35	12x25		14x07	14x51	16x36	17x20		18x43	19x34	19x34			20x06		22x06		
79¼	Askam	d	06 24	07 40	08 26		09 40		11 40	12 30		14 12	14 56	16 41	17 25		18 48	19 39	19 39			20 11		22 11		
85¼	**Barrow-in-Furness**	a	06 40	07 56	08 42		09 55		11 56	12 46		14 28	15 16	16 57	17 41		19 04	19 55	19 55			20 27		22 27		
—	Lancaster 6	82 a	*07 58*	08 59	*10 15*		11 00		13 05	*14 00*			16 33	*18 05*	18 45		*20 15*					22 49				

Saturdays

Station		NT	NT	NT	NT	NT	NT	NT		NT	NT	NT	NT	NT	NT	NT	NT	NT	NT	NT	NT	NT	NT	NT		
																A			B							
Carlisle 8	d				07 28		08 15	08 39			10 14	11 11	12 41	13 46	14 28	15 45	16 33	17 34	17 57	18 36		20 09		21 45		
Dalston	d				07x36		08x23	08x47			10x22	11x19	12x49	13x54	14x36	15x53	16x41	17x42	18x05	18x44		20x17		21x53		
Wigton	d				07 45		08 32	08 56			10 31	11 28	12 58	14 03	14 45	16 02	16 50	17 51	18 14	18 53		20 26		22 02		
Aspatria	d				07x55		08x42	09x06			10x41	11x38	13x08	14x13	14x55	16x12	17x00	18x01	18x25	19x03		20x36		22x12		
Maryport	d		06 04		08 05		08 52	09 16			10 51	11 48	13 18	14 23	15 05	16 22	17 10	18 11	18 35	19 13		20 46		22 22		
Flimby	d		06x07		08x08		08x55				10x54	11x51	13x21	14x26	15x08	16x25	17x13	18x14	18x39	19x16		20x49		22x25		
Workington	d		06 15		08 17		09 04	09 28			11 03	12 00	13 30	14 35	15 17	16 34	17 22	18 23	18 47	19 25		20 58		22 34		
Harrington	d		06x19		08x20		09x07	09x31			11x06	12x03	13x33	14x38	15x20	16x37	17x25	18x26	18x51	19x28		21x01		22x37		
Parton	d		06x27		08x29		09x16	09x40			11x15	12x12	13x42	14x47	15x29	16x46	17x34	18x35	19x00	19x37		21x10		22x46		
Whitehaven	a		06 33		08 38		09 25	09 46			11 21	12 18	13 48	14 56	15 35	16 52	17 40	18 41	19 09	19 46		21 19		22 55		
	d		06 35					09 47			11 24	12 19	13 49		15 36	16 53	17 41	18 43								
Corkickle	d		06x37					09x49			11x26	12x21	13x51		15x38	16x55	17x43	18x45								
St Bees	d		06 42					09x55			11 32	12 27	14e02		15 44	17x01	17 49	18 50								
Nethertown	d		06x46								11x36		14x06		15x48		17x53									
Braystones	d		06x49								11x38		14x09		15x50		17x55									
Sellafield	d		06 55					10 05			11 45	12 38	14 15		15 56	17 11	18 03	19 01								
Seascale	d		06x58					10x08			11x48	12x41	14x18		15x59	17x14	18x06	19x04								
Drigg	d		07x01					10x11			11x51	12x44	14x21		16x02	17x17	18x09	19x07								
Ravenglass for Eskdale	d		07 04					10 15			11 54	12 47	14 24		16 06	17 21	18 12	19 10								
Bootle	d		07x10					10x20			12x00	12x53	14x30		16x11	17x26	18x18	19x16								
Silecroft	d		07x16					10x27			12x06	12x59	14x36		16x18	17x33	18x24	19x22								
Millom	a		07 23					10 34			12 13	13 06	14 43		16 25	17 40	18 31	19 29								
	d	06 15	07 23	08 10		09 25		10 34		11 47	12 14	13 07	14 44		16 25	17 40	18 32	19 29			19 55		21 55			
Green Road	d	06x19	07x27	08x14		09x29				11x51	12x18	13 11	14x48		16x29	17x44	18x36	19x33			19x59		21x59			
Foxfield	d	06x22	07x31	08x17		09x32		10x41		11x54	12x21	13x14	14x51		16x32	17x47	18x39	19x37			20x02		22x02			
Kirkby-in-Furness	d	06x26	07x35	08x21		09x36				11x58	12x25	13x18	14x55		16x36	17x51	18x43	19x41			20x06		22x06			
Askam	d	06 31	07 40	08 26		09 41		10 49		12 03	12 30	13 23	15 00		16 41	17 56	18 48	19 46			20 11		22 11			
Barrow-in-Furness	a	06 47	07 56	08 42		09 56		11 06		12 19	12 46	13 39	15 16		16 57	18 14	19 04	20 02			20 27		22 27			
Lancaster 6	82 a	*08 02*	09 02	*10 15*		11 01		*12 16*			*13 59*	*15 02*	16 33		*18 05*	19 17	*20 16*				22 34					

Sundays

Station		NT	NT	NT
Carlisle 8	d	14 47	18 56	21 42
Dalston	d	14x55	19x04	21x50
Wigton	d	15 04	19 13	21 59
Aspatria	d	15x14	19x23	22x09
Maryport	d	15 24	19 33	22 19
Flimby	d	15x27	19x36	22x22
Workington	d	15 36	19 45	22 31
Harrington	d	15x39	19x48	22x34
Parton	d	15x48	19x57	22x43
Whitehaven	a	15 57	20 06	22 52

For general notes see front of timetable
For details of catering facilities see Directory of Train Operators

A To Preston (Table 65)
B From Newcastle (Table 48)
b Arr. 1014
c Arr. 1544
e Arr. 1357

No Sunday Service Whitehaven to Barrow-in-Furness

Network Diagram for Tables 101, 103, 106, 109

DM-14/06(2)
Design BAJS

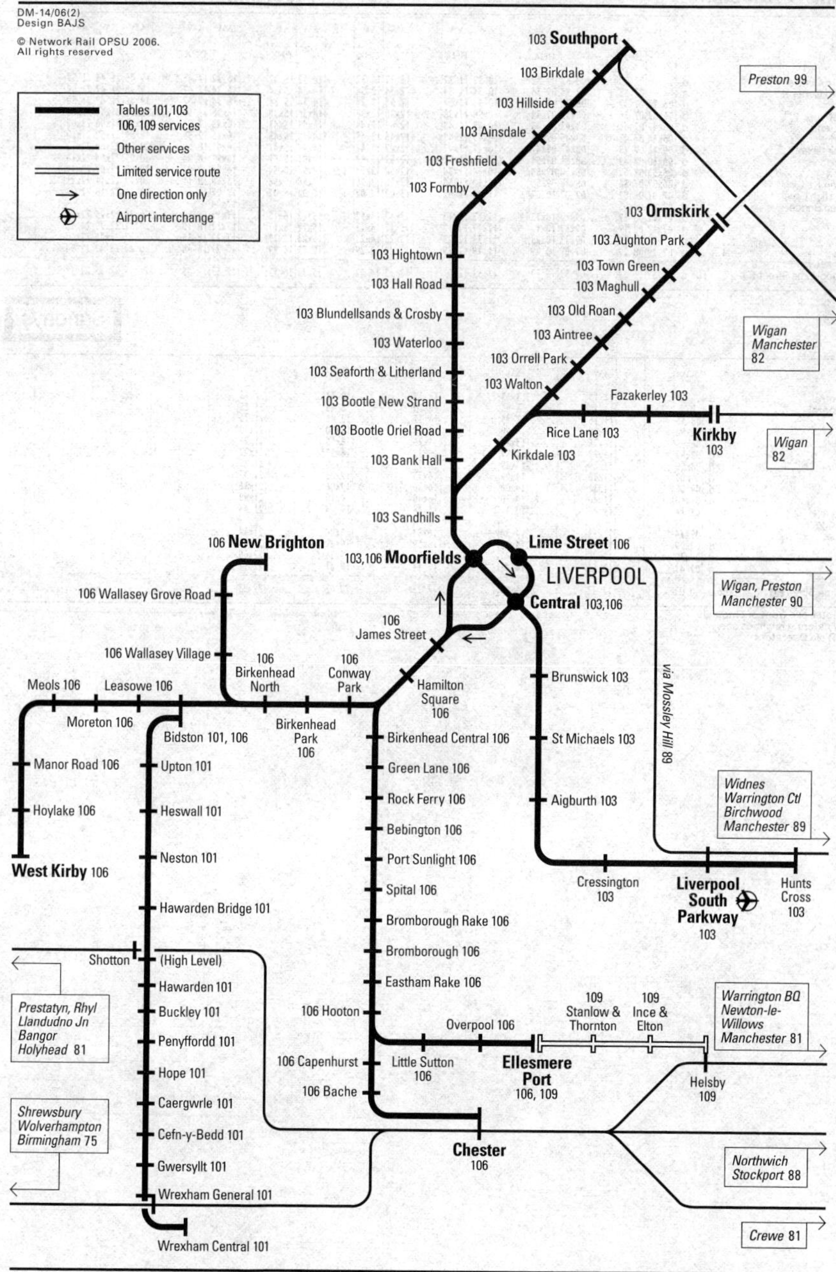
Tables 101,103 106, 109 services
Other services
Limited service route
One direction only
Airport interchange
103 Southport
103 Birkdale
103 Hillside
103 Ainsdale
103 Freshfield
103 Formby
103 Hightown
103 Hall Road
103 Blundellsands & Crosby
103 Waterloo
103 Seaforth & Litherland
103 Bootle New Strand
103 Bootle Oriel Road
103 Bank Hall
103 Sandhills
Preston 99
103 Ormskirk
103 Aughton Park
103 Town Green
103 Maghull
103 Old Roan
103 Aintree
103 Orrell Park
103 Walton
Wigan Manchester 82
Fazakerley 103
Rice Lane 103
Kirkby 103
Kirkdale 103
Wigan 82
106 New Brighton
103,106 Moorfields
Lime Street 106
LIVERPOOL
Central 103,106
Wigan, Preston Manchester 90
106 Wallasey Grove Road
106 Wallasey Village
106 James Street
106 Birkenhead North
106 Conway Park
Hamilton Square 106
Meols 106
Leasowe 106
Moreton 106
Bidston 101, 106
Birkenhead Park 106
Birkenhead Central 106
Brunswick 103
St Michaels 103
via Mossley Hill 89
Manor Road 106
Upton 101
Green Lane 106
Rock Ferry 106
Aigburth 103
Widnes Warrington Ctl Birchwood Manchester 89
Hoylake 106
Heswall 101
Bebington 106
West Kirby 106
Neston 101
Port Sunlight 106
Spital 106
Cressington 103
Liverpool South Parkway 103
Hunts Cross 103
Hawarden Bridge 101
Bromborough Rake 106
Bromborough 106
Shotton (High Level)
Eastham Rake 106
Hawarden 101
109 Stanlow & Thornton
109 Ince & Elton
Warrington BQ Newton-le-Willows Manchester 81
Prestatyn, Rhyl Llandudno Jn Bangor Holyhead 81
Buckley 101
106 Hooton
Overpool 106
Penyffordd 101
106 Capenhurst
Little Sutton 106
Ellesmere Port 106, 109
Hope 101
106 Bache
Helsby 109
Caergwrle 101
Shrewsbury Wolverhampton Birmingham 75
Cefn-y-Bedd 101
Chester 106
Gwersyllt 101
Northwich Stockport 88
Wrexham General 101
Wrexham Central 101
Crewe 81

Wrexham → Bidston

Network Diagram - see first page of Table 101

Miles			AW	AW	AW	AW	AW	AW	AW	AW	AW	AW	AW	AW	AW	AW	AW
																SO	SX
				BHX		BHX		BHX		BHX		BHX		BHX			
0	**Wrexham Central**	d		07 30	08 32	09 32	10 32	11 32	12 32	13 32	14 32	15 32	16 32	17 45	19 46	21 45	21 57
½	**Wrexham General**	a		07 32	08 34	09 34	10 34	11 34	12 34	13 34	14 34	15 34	16 34	17 47	19 48	21 47	21 59
—		d	06 33	07 32	08 34	09 34	10 34	11 34	12 34	13 34	14 34	15 34	16 34	17 47	19 48	21 47	21 59
2¼	Gwersyllt	d	06x37	07 36	08x38	09x38	10x38	11x38	12x38	13x38	14x38	15x38	16x38	17 51	19x52	21x51	22x03
4	Cefn-y-Bedd	d	06x42	07 41	08x43	09x43	10x43	11x43	12x43	13x43	14x43	15x43	16x43	17 56	19x57	21x56	22x08
4¾	Caergwrle	d	06x44	07 43	08x45	09x45	10x45	11x45	12x45	13x45	14x45	15x45	16x45	17 58	19x59	21x58	22x10
5¼	Hope (Flintshire)	d	06x46	07 45	08x47	09x47	10x47	11x47	12x47	13x47	14x47	15x47	16x47	18 00	20x01	22x00	22x12
7¼	Penyffordd	d	06x50	07 49	08x51	09x51	10x51	11x51	12x51	13x51	14x51	15x51	16x51	18 04	20x05	22x04	22x16
8½	Buckley	d	06x53	07 52	08x54	09x54	10x54	11x54	12x54	13x54	14x54	15x54	16x54	18 07	20x08	22x07	22x19
10½	Hawarden	d	06x57	07 56	08x58	09x58	10x58	11x58	12x58	13x58	14x58	15x58	16x58	18 11	20x12	22x11	22x23
12¾	Shotton High Level	d	07 01	08 01	09 02	10 02	11 02	12 02	13 02	14 02	15 02	16 02	17 02	18 15	20 16	22 15	22 27
13¼	Hawarden Bridge	d	07x03	08x03									17x04				
18¾	Neston	d	07x12	08 12	09x12	10x12	11x12	12x12	13x12	14x12	15x12	16x12	17x12	18 25	20x26	22x25	22x37
21¼	Heswall	d	07x17	08 17	09x17	10x17	11x17	12x17	13x17	14x17	15x17	16x17	17x17	18 30	20x31	22x30	22x42
25½	Upton	d	07x23	08 23	09x23	10x23	11x23	12x23	13x23	14x23	15x23	16x23	17x23	18 36	20x37	22x36	22x48
27½	**Bidston**	a	07 29	08 29	09 29	10 29	11 29	12 29	13 29	14 29	15 29	16 29	17 29	18 44	20 43	22 42	22 54
—	Liverpool Lime Street 10	106 a	*07 53*	*08 53*	*09 53*	*10 53*	*11 53*	*12 53*	*13 53*	*14 53*	*15 53*	*16 53*	*17 53*	*19 08*	*21 33*	*23 33*	*23 33*

Sundays

		AW	AW	AW	AW	AW	AW
Wrexham Central	d		11 13	13 43	16 13	18 43	21 13
Wrexham General	a		11 15	13 45	16 15	18 45	21 15
	d	08 46	11 16	13 46	16 17	18 46	21 16
Gwersyllt	d	08x50	11x20	13x50	16x20	18x50	21x20
Cefn-y-Bedd	d	08x55	11x25	13x55	16x25	18x55	21x25
Caergwrle	d	08x57	11x27	13x57	16x27	18x57	21x27
Hope (Flintshire)	d	08x59	11x29	13x59	16x29	18x59	21x29
Penyffordd	d	09x03	11x33	14x03	16x33	19x03	21x33
Buckley	d	09x06	11x36	14x06	16x36	19x06	21x36
Hawarden	d	09x10	11x40	14x10	16x40	19x10	21x40
Shotton High Level	d	09 14	11 44	14 14	16 44	19 14	21 44
Hawarden Bridge	d						
Neston	d	09x24	11x54	14x24	16x54	19x24	21x54
Heswall	d	09x29	11x59	14x29	16x59	19x29	21x59
Upton	d	09x35	12x05	14x35	17x05	19x35	22x05
Bidston	a	09 41	12 11	14 41	17 11	19 41	22 11
Liverpool Lime Street 10	106 a	*10 03*	*12 33*	*15 03*	*17 33*	*20 03*	*22 33*

For general notes see front of timetable
For details of catering facilities see Directory of Train Operators

Bidston → Wrexham

Network Diagram - see first page of Table 101

Miles			AW BHX	AW	AW BHX		AW	AW BHX	AW		AW BHX	AW	AW BHX		AW	AW BHX	AW		AW BHX	AW SO	AW SX	AW SO	AW SX		
—	Liverpool Lime Street 10	106 d		06 53	08 08		09 08	10 08	11 08		12 08	13 08	14 08		15 08	16 08	17 23		18 23	20 03	20 33	22 03	22 33		
0	**Bidston**	d		07 31	08 31		09 32	10 32	11 32		12 32	13 32	14 32		15 32	16 31	17 45		18 46	20 45	20 56	22 45	22 56		
2	Upton	d		07 35	08x35		09x36	10x36	11x36		12x36	13x36	14x36		15x36	16x35	17 49		18x50	20x49	21x00	22x49	23x00		
6¼	Heswall	d		07 42	08x42		09x43	10x43	11x43		12x43	13x43	14x43		15x43	16x42	17 56		18x57	20x56	21x07	22x56	23x07		
8¾	Neston	d		07 47	08x47		09x48	10x48	11x48		12x48	13x48	14x48		15x48	16x47	18 01		19x02	21x01	21x12	23x01	23x12		
14¼	Hawarden Bridge	d		07x55	08x55											16x55	18x09								
14¾	Shotton High Level	d		07 57	08 57		09 57	10 57	11 57		12 57	13 57	14 57		15 57	16 57	18 11		19 11	21 10	21 21	23 11	23 22		
17½	Hawarden	d		08 02	09x02		10x02	11x02	12x02		13x02	14x02	15x02		16x02	17x02	18 16		19x16	21x15	21x26	23x16	23x27		
19	Buckley	d		08 07	09x07		10x07	11x07	12x07		13x07	14x07	15x07		16x07	17x07	18 21		19x21	21x20	21x31	23x21	23x32		
20¼	Penyffordd	d		08 10	09x10		10x10	11x10	12x10		13x10	14x10	15x10		16x10	17x10	18 24		19x24	21x23	21x34	23x24	23x35		
22¼	Hope (Flintshire)	d		08 14	09x14		10x14	11x14	12x14		13x14	14x14	15x14		16x14	17x14	18 28		19x28	21x27	21x38	23x28	23x39		
22¾	Caergwrle	d		08 16	09x16		10x16	11x16	12x16		13x16	14x16	15x16		16x16	17x16	18 30		19x30	21x29	21x40	23x30	23x41		
23½	Cefn-y-Bedd	d		08 18	09x18		10x18	11x18	12x18		13x18	14x18	15x18		16x18	17x18	18 32		19x32	21x31	21x42	23x32	23x43		
25¼	Gwersyllt	d		08 22	09x22		10x22	11x22	12x22		13x22	14x22	15x22		16x22	17x22	18 36		19x36	21x35	21x46	23 36	23 47		
27	**Wrexham General**	a		08 27	09 27		10 27	11 27	12 27		13 27	14 27	15 27		16 27	17 27	18 41		19 41	21 40	21 51	23 41	23 52		
—		d	07 10	08 27	09 27		10 27	11 27	12 27		13 27	14 27	15 27		16 27	17 27	18 41		19 41	21 40	21 51				
27½	**Wrexham Central**	a	07 13	08 32	09 30		10 30	11 30	12 30		13 30	14 30	15 30		16 30	17 30	18 44		19 44	21 43	21 54				

Sundays

		AW			AW			AW			AW			AW			AW
Liverpool Lime Street 10	106 d	09 33			12 03			14 33			17 03			19 33			22 03
Bidston	d	09 57			12 27			14 57			17 27			19 57			22 27
Upton	d	10x01			12x31			15x01			17x31			20x01			22x31
Heswall	d	10x08			12x38			15x08			17x38			20x08			22x38
Neston	d	10x13			12x43			15x13			17x43			20x13			22x43
Hawarden Bridge	d																
Shotton High Level	d	10 22			12 52			15 22			17 52			20 22			22 52
Hawarden	d	10x27			12x57			15x27			17x57			20x27			22x57
Buckley	d	10x32			13x02			15x32			18x02			20x32			23x02
Penyffordd	d	10x35			13x05			15x35			18x05			20x35			23x05
Hope (Flintshire)	d	10x39			13x09			15x39			18x09			20x39			23x09
Caergwrle	d	10x41			13x11			15x41			18x11			20x41			23x11
Cefn-y-Bedd	d	10x43			13x13			15x43			18x13			20x43			23x13
Gwersyllt	d	10x47			13x17			15x47			18x17			20x47			23x17
Wrexham General	a	10 52			13 22			15 52			18 22			20 52			23 22
	d	10 53			13 23			15 53			18 23			20 53			
Wrexham Central	a	10 56			13 26			15 56			18 26			20 56			

For general notes see front of timetable
For details of catering facilities see Directory of Train Operators

Llandudno → Blaenau Ffestiniog

Network Diagram - see first page of Table 81

Miles	Station		AW ◇	AW ◇	AW ◇	AW ◇	AW ◇	AW ◇
0	**Llandudno**	81 d		07 03	10 14	13 14	16 14	18 53
1¾	Deganwy	81 d		07 07	10x18	13x18	16x18	18x57
—	Crewe 10	81 d		06b18	09 03	12c03	15 03	17e35
—	Chester	81 d		06b45	09 35	12 35	15 35	18e00
—	Rhyl	81 d		07b17	10 08	13 08	16 08	18e33
—	Bangor (Gwynedd)	81 d	05 00	07 12	10 07	13 04	15 04	18e06
3	**Llandudno Junction**	81 d	05 35	07 39	10 33	13 33	16 33	19 03
5	Glan Conwy	d		07x42	10x36	13x36	16x36	19x06
8½	Tal-y-Cafn	d		07 48	10 42	13 42	16 42	19 12
11½	Dolgarrog	d		07x53	10x47	13x47	16x47	19x17
14½	North Llanrwst	d		08x00	10x53	13x53	16x53	19x23
15	Llanrwst	d	05 53	08 02	10 55	13 55	16 55	19 25
18½	Betws-y-Coed	d	05 59	08 08	11 01	14 01	17 01	19 31
22¾	Pont-y-Pant	d		08x16	11x09	14x09	17x09	19x39
24¼	Dolwyddelan	d		08x19	11x12	14x12	17x12	19x42
26	Roman Bridge	d		08x23	11x16	14x16	17x16	19x46
31	**Blaenau Ffestiniog**	a	06 27	08 40	11 33	14 33	17 33	20 01

Sundays

until 7 September

Station		AW ◇	AW ◇	AW ◇
Llandudno	81 d	10 22	13 30	15 50
Deganwy	81 d	10x26	13x34	15 54
Crewe 10	81 d	09 00	12c06	14 55
Chester	81 d	09 20	12 35	15 15
Rhyl	81 d	09 54	13 09	15 49
Bangor (Gwynedd)	81 d	08 51	12 10	15 45
Llandudno Junction	81 d	10 32	13 40	16 15
Glan Conwy	d	10x35	13x43	16x18
Tal-y-Cafn	d	10 41	13 49	16 24
Dolgarrog	d	10x46	13x54	16x29
North Llanrwst	d	10x52	14x00	16x35
Llanrwst	d	10 54	14 02	16 37
Betws-y-Coed	d	11 00	14 08	16 43
Pont-y-Pant	d	11x08	14x16	16x51
Dolwyddelan	d	11x11	14x19	16x54
Roman Bridge	d	11x15	14x23	16x58
Blaenau Ffestiniog	a	11 30	14 38	17 13

Sundays

from 14 September

Station		AW 🚌	AW 🚌	AW 🚌
Llandudno	81 d	10 15	13 15	16 00
Deganwy	81 d	10 30	13 30	16 15
Crewe 10	81 d		11 15	14c25
Chester	81 d		11 38	15 02
Rhyl	81 d		12 12	15 37
Bangor (Gwynedd)	81 d		13 00	15 42
Llandudno Junction	81 d	10 35	13 35	16 20
Glan Conwy	d	10 40	13 40	16 25
Tal-y-Cafn	d	10 48	13 48	16 33
Dolgarrog	d	10 53	13 53	16 38
North Llanrwst	d	10 58	13 58	16 43
Llanrwst	d	11 00	14 00	16 45
Betws-y-Coed	d	11 10	14 10	16 55
Pont-y-Pant	d	11 20	14 20	17 05
Dolwyddelan	d	11 25	14 25	17 10
Roman Bridge	d	11 32	14 32	17 17
Blaenau Ffestiniog	a	11 45	14 45	17 30

For general notes see front of timetable
For details of catering facilities see Directory of Train Operators

b Applies all Mondays to Fridays, also Saturdays until 6 September
c Change at Chester and Llandudno Junction
e Saturdays dep. Crewe 1703, Chester 1735, Rhyl 1809, Bangor (Gwynedd) 1814

Blaenau Ffestiniog → Llandudno

Network Diagram - see first page of Table 81

Miles			AW ◇	AW ◇	AW ◇	AW ◇	AW ◇	AW ◇
—	**Blaenau Ffestiniog**	d	06 30	08 52	11 52	14 52	17 37	20 04
—	Roman Bridge	d	06x40	09x02	12x02	15x02	17x47	20x14
6¾	Dolwyddelan	d	06x43	09x06	12x06	15x06	17x51	20x17
8¼	Pont-y-Pant	d	06x46	09x09	12x09	15x09	17x54	20x20
12½	Betws-y-Coed	d	06 56	09 19	12 19	15 19	18 04	20 30
16	Llanrwst	d	07 02	09 25	12 25	15 25	18 10	20 36
16½	North Llanrwst	d	07x03	09x26	12x26	15x26	18x11	20x37
19½	Dolgarrog	d	07x09	09x33	12x33	15x33	18x18	20x43
22½	Tal-y-Cafn	d	07x14	09x39	12x39	15x39	18x24	20x49
26	Glan Conwy	d	07x20	09x45	12x45	15x45	18x30	20x55
28	**Llandudno Junction**	81 a	07 26	09 50	12 50	15 50	18 35	21 00
—	Bangor (Gwynedd)	81 a	*07b49*	*10 46*	*13 48*	*16 46*	*19c05*	*21e51*
—	Rhyl	81 a	*07f47*	*10 15*	*13 15*	*16 15*	*19 15*	*21 46*
—	Chester	81 a	*08f21*	*10 51*	*13 51*	*16 51*	*19 51*	*22 23*
—	Crewe 10	81 a	*08g45*	*11h24*	*14j24*	*17k24*	*20h29*	*23m07*
29¼	Deganwy	81 a	*07 36*	09x55	12x55	15x55	18x40	21x05
31	**Llandudno**	81 a	*07 43*	10 01	13 01	16 01	18 46	21 12

Sundays

until 7 September

		AW ◇	AW ◇	AW ◇
Blaenau Ffestiniog	d	11 45	15 03	17 30
Roman Bridge	d	11x55	15x13	17x40
Dolwyddelan	d	11x58	15x16	17x44
Pont-y-Pant	d	12x01	15x19	17x48
Betws-y-Coed	d	12 11	15 29	17 57
Llanrwst	d	12 17	15 35	18 03
North Llanrwst	d	12x18	15x36	18x05
Dolgarrog	d	12x24	15x42	18x11
Tal-y-Cafn	d	12x29	15x47	18x17
Glan Conwy	d	12x35	15x53	18x23
Llandudno Junction	81 a	12 40	15 59	18 29
Bangor (Gwynedd)	81 a	*13 59*	*17 25*	*19 05*
Rhyl	81 a	*13 38*	*16n59*	*19 22*
Chester	81 a	*14 14*	*17n31*	*19 59*
Crewe 10	81 a	*14 37*	*17n57*	*20h50*
Deganwy	81 a	12x45	*16 14*	18x34
Llandudno	81 a	12 51	*16 14*	18 40

Sundays

from 14 September

		AW 🚌	AW 🚌	AW 🚌
Blaenau Ffestiniog	d	11 50	15 00	17 50
Roman Bridge	d	12 00	15 10	18 00
Dolwyddelan	d	12 05	15 15	18 05
Pont-y-Pant	d	12 09	15 19	18 09
Betws-y-Coed	d	12 20	15 30	18 20
Llanrwst	d	12 30	15 40	18 30
North Llanrwst	d	12 33	15 43	18 33
Dolgarrog	d	12 38	15 48	18 38
Tal-y-Cafn	d	12 43	15 53	18 43
Glan Conwy	d	12 51	16 01	18 51
Llandudno Junction	81 a	13 00	16 10	19 00
Bangor (Gwynedd)	81 a	*14 04*	*17 29*	*19 52*
Rhyl	81 a	*13 41*	*17 18*	*19 43*
Chester	81 a	*14 18*	*17 51*	*20 17*
Crewe 10	81 a	*14 45*	*18 27*	*20h49*
Deganwy	81 a	13 05	16 15	19 05
Llandudno	81 a	13 20	16 30	19 20

For general notes see front of timetable
For details of catering facilities see Directory of Train Operators

- b Saturdays from 13 September arr. 0806
- c Saturdays arr. 1949
- e Saturdays from 13 September arr. 2128
- f Saturdays until 12 July and from 13 September arr. Ryhl 0815, Chester 0851
- g Saturdays until 12 July and from 13 September arr. 0924, change at Llandudno Junction and Chester
- h Change at Llandudno Junction and Chester
- j Change at Llandudno Junction and Chester. Saturdays until 6 September arr. 1427
- k Change at Llandudno Junction and Chester. Saturdays arr. 1726
- m Change at Llandudno Junction and Chester. Saturdays arr. 2256
- n From 20 July arr. Rhyl 1658, Chester 1727, Crewe 1756

Merseyrail

These notes apply to Tables 103 and 106

Spring Holiday

Monday 26 May — A normal Saturday service will operate

Late Summer Holiday

Monday 25 August — A normal Saturday service will operate

Hunts Cross and Liverpool → Kirkby, Ormskirk and Southport

Network Diagram - see first page of Table 101

Miles	Miles	Miles			ME	ME	ME	ME		ME	ME	ME	ME		ME	ME	ME	ME			ME	ME	ME	ME
0	—	—	**Hunts Cross** 89	d						06 06		06 21				06 36		06 51					07 06	
1½	—	—	**Liverpool South Parkway 7** 89 ⇌	d						06 09		06 24				06 39		06 54					07 09	
2½	—	—	Cressington	d						06 12		06 27				06 42		06 57					07 12	
3¼	—	—	Aigburth	d						06 14		06 29				06 44		06 59					07 14	
4½	—	—	St Michaels	d						06 16		06 31				06 46		07 01					07 16	
5¾	—	—	Brunswick	d						06 19		06 34				06 49		07 04					07 19	
7¼	—	—	**Liverpool Central 10**	a						06 23		06 38				06 53		07 08					07 23	
—	0	0		d		05 55	06 08	06 10		06 23	06 25	06 38	06 40		06 50	06 53	06 55	07 08			07 10	07 20	07 23	07 25
7¾	½	½	**Moorfields 10**	d		05 57	06 10	06 12		06 25	06 27	06 40	06 42		06 52	06 55	06 57	07 10			07 12	07 22	07 25	07 27
9¼	2	2	Sandhills	d	05 59	06 01	06 14	06 16		06 29	06 31	06 44	06 46		06 56	06 59	07 01	07 14			07 16	07 26	07 29	07 31
—	3	3	Kirkdale	d		06 04		06 19			06 34		06 49		06 59		07 04				07 19	07 29		07 34
—	—	4¼	Rice Lane	d		06 07					06 37				07 02							07 32		
—	—	5¾	Fazakerley	d		06 10					06 40				07 03							07 34		
—	—	7½	**Kirkby**	a		06 13					06 43				07 08							07 38		
—	4¼	—	Walton (Merseyside)	d				06 22					06 52				07 07				07 22			07 37
—	4½	—	Orrell Park	d				06 23					06 53				07 08				07 23			07 38
—	5½	—	Aintree	d				06 26					06 56				07 11				07 26			07 41
—	6¼	—	Old Roan	d				06 28					06 58				07 13				07 28			07 43
—	8	—	Maghull	d				06 31					07 01				07 16				07 31			07 46
—	10½	—	Town Green	d				06 35					07 05				07 20				07 35			07 50
—	11½	—	Aughton Park	d				06 37					07 07				07 22				07 37			07 52
—	12¾	—	**Ormskirk**	a				06 42					07 12				07 27				07 42			07 57
10	—	—	Bank Hall	d	06 01		06 16			06 31		06 46				07 01		07 16					07 31	
10¾	—	—	Bootle Oriel Road	d	06 03		06 18			06 33		06 48				07 03		07 18					07 33	
11	—	—	Bootle New Strand	d	06 05		06 20			06 35		06 50				07 05		07 20					07 35	
12	—	—	Seaforth & Litherland	d	06 07		06 22			06 37		06 52				07 07		07 22					07 37	
13¼	—	—	Waterloo (Merseyside)	d	06 09		06 24			06 39		06 54				07 09		07 24					07 39	
14¼	—	—	Blundellsands & Crosby	d	06 12		06 27			06 42		06 57				07 12		07 27					07 42	
15	—	—	Hall Road	d	06 14		06 29			06 44		06 59				07 14		07 29					07 44	
17	—	—	Hightown	d	06 17		06 32			06 47		07 02				07 17		07 32					07 47	
19	—	—	Formby	d	06 21		06 36			06 51		07 06				07 21		07 36					07 51	
20	—	—	Freshfield	d	06 23		06 38			06 53		07 08				07 23		07 38					07 53	
22¾	—	—	Ainsdale	d	06 27		06 42			06 57		07 12				07 27		07 42					07 57	
24½	—	—	Hillside	d	06 30		06 45			07 00		07 15				07 30		07 45					08 00	
25¼	—	—	Birkdale	d	06 32		06 47			07 02		07 17				07 32		07 47					08 02	
26¼	—	—	**Southport**	a	06 37		06 52			07 07		07 22				07 37		07 52					08 07	

		ME	ME	ME	ME	ME	ME	ME	ME			ME	ME	ME SX	ME		ME	ME	ME	ME		ME	ME
Hunts Cross 89	d		07 21			07 36			07 51	and at the same minutes past each hour until		16 51					17 06			17 21			
Liverpool South Parkway 7 89 ⇌	d		07 24			07 39			07 54			16 54					17 09			17 24			
Cressington	d		07 27			07 42			07 57			16 57					17 12			17 27			
Aigburth	d		07 29			07 44			07 59			16 59					17 14			17 29			
St Michaels	d		07 31			07 46			08 01			17 01					17 16			17 31			
Brunswick	d		07 34			07 49			08 04			17 04					17 19			17 34			
Liverpool Central 10	a		07 38			07 53			08 08			17 08					17 23			17 38			
	d	07 35	07 38	07 40	07 50	07 53	07 55	08 05	08 08			17 08	17 10	17 13	17 20		17 23	17 25	17 35	17 38		17 40	17 50
Moorfields 10	d	07 37	07 40	07 42	07 52	07 55	07 57	08 07	08 10			17 10	17 12	17 15	17 22		17 25	17 27	17 37	17 40		17 42	17 52
Sandhills	d	07 41	07 44	07 46	07 56	07 59	08 01	08 11	08 14			17 14	17 16	17 19	17 26		17 29	17 31	17 41	17 44		17 46	17 56
Kirkdale	d	07 44		07 49	07 59		08 04	08 14					17 19		17 29			17 34	17 44			17 49	17 59
Rice Lane	d	07 47			08 02			08 17							17 32				17 47				18 02
Fazakerley	d	07 49			08 04			08 19							17 34				17 49				18 04
Kirkby	a	07 53			08 08			08 23							17 38				17 53				18 08
Walton (Merseyside)	d			07 52			08 07						17 22					17 37				17 52	
Orrell Park	d			07 53			08 08						17 23					17 38				17 53	
Aintree	d			07 56			08 11						17 26					17 41				17 56	
Old Roan	d			07 58			08 13						17 28					17 43				17 58	
Maghull	d			08 01			08 16						17 31					17 46				18 01	
Town Green	d			08 05			08 20						17 35					17 50				18 05	
Aughton Park	d			08 07			08 22						17 37					17 52				18 07	
Ormskirk	a			08 12			08 27						17 42					17 57				18 12	
Bank Hall	d		07 46			08 01			08 16			17 16		17 21			17 31			17 46			
Bootle Oriel Road	d		07 48			08 03			08 18			17 18		17 23			17 33			17 48			
Bootle New Strand	d		07 50			08 05			08 20			17 20		17 25			17 35			17 50			
Seaforth & Litherland	d		07 52			08 07			08 22			17 22		17 27			17 37			17 52			
Waterloo (Merseyside)	d		07 54			08 09			08 24			17 24		17 29			17 39			17 54			
Blundellsands & Crosby	d		07 57			08 12			08 27			17 27		17 32			17 42			17 57			
Hall Road	d		07 59			08 14			08 29			17 29		17 34			17 44			17 59			
Hightown	d		08 02			08 17			08 32			17 32		17 37			17 47			18 02			
Formby	d		08 06			08 21			08 36			17 36		17 41			17 51			18 06			
Freshfield	d		08 08			08 23			08 38			17 38		17 43			17 53			18 08			
Ainsdale	d		08 12			08 27			08 42			17 42		17 47			17 57			18 12			
Hillside	d		08 15			08 30			08 45			17 45		17 50			18 00			18 15			
Birkdale	d		08 17			08 32			08 47			17 47		17 52			18 02			18 17			
Southport	a		08 22			08 37			08 52			17 52		17 57			18 07			18 22			

For general notes see front of timetable
For details of catering facilities see Directory of Train Operators

Hunts Cross and Liverpool → Kirkby, Ormskirk and Southport

Network Diagram - see first page of Table 101

Station		ME	ME	ME	ME	ME	ME	ME	ME	ME	ME	ME	ME	ME	ME	ME	ME	ME	ME	ME
Hunts Cross	89 d	17 36			17 51			18 06			18 21			18 36			18 51		19 06	
Liverpool South Parkway 7	89 ✈ d	17 39			17 54			18 09			18 24			18 39			18 54		19 09	
Cressington	d	17 42			17 57			18 12			18 27			18 42			18 57		19 12	
Aigburth	d	17 44			17 59			18 14			18 29			18 44			18 59		19 14	
St Michaels	d	17 46			18 01			18 16			18 31			18 46			19 01		19 16	
Brunswick	d	17 49			18 04			18 19			18 34			18 49			19 04		19 19	
Liverpool Central 10	a	17 53			18 08			18 23			18 38			18 53			19 08		19 23	
	d	17 53	17 55	18 05	18 08	18 10	18 20	18 23	18 25	18 35	18 38	18 40	18 50	18 53	18 55	19 05	19 08	19 10	19 23	19 25
Moorfields 10	d	17 55	17 57	18 07	18 10	18 12	18 22	18 25	18 27	18 37	18 40	18 42	18 52	18 55	18 57	19 07	19 10	19 12	19 25	19 27
Sandhills	d	17 59	18 01	18 11	18 14	18 16	18 26	18 29	18 31	18 41	18 44	18 46	18 56	18 59	19 01	19 11	19 14	19 16	19 29	19 31
Kirkdale	d		18 04	18 14		18 19	18 29		18 34	18 44		18 49	18 59		19 04	19 14		19 19		19 34
Rice Lane	d			18 17			18 32			18 47			19 02			19 17				19 37
Fazakerley	d			18 19			18 34			18 49			19 04			19 19				19 40
Kirkby	a			18 23			18 38			18 53			19 08			19 23				19 43
Walton (Merseyside)	d		18 07			18 22			18 37			18 52			19 07			19 22		
Orrell Park	d		18 08			18 23			18 38			18 53			19 08			19 23		
Aintree	d		18 11			18 26			18 41			18 56			19 11			19 26		
Old Roan	d		18 13			18 28			18 43			18 58			19 13			19 28		
Maghull	d		18 16			18 31			18 46			19 01			19 16			19 31		
Town Green	d		18 20			18 35			18 50			19 05			19 20			19 35		
Aughton Park	d		18 22			18 37			18 52			19 07			19 22			19 37		
Ormskirk	a		18 27			18 42			18 57			19 12			19 27			19 42		
Bank Hall	d	18 01			18 16			18 31			18 46			19 01			19 16		19 31	
Bootle Oriel Road	d	18 03			18 18			18 33			18 48			19 03			19 18		19 33	
Bootle New Strand	d	18 05			18 20			18 35			18 50			19 05			19 20		19 35	
Seaforth & Litherland	d	18 07			18 22			18 37			18 52			19 07			19 22		19 37	
Waterloo (Merseyside)	d	18 09			18 24			18 39			18 54			19 09			19 24		19 39	
Blundellsands & Crosby	d	18 12			18 27			18 42			18 57			19 12			19 27		19 42	
Hall Road	d	18 14			18 29			18 44			18 59			19 14			19 29		19 44	
Hightown	d	18 17			18 32			18 47			19 02			19 17			19 32		19 47	
Formby	d	18 21			18 36			18 51			19 06			19 21			19 36		19 51	
Freshfield	d	18 23			18 38			18 53			19 08			19 23			19 38		19 53	
Ainsdale	d	18 27			18 42			18 57			19 12			19 27			19 42		19 57	
Hillside	d	18 30			18 45			19 00			19 15			19 30			19 45		20 00	
Birkdale	d	18 32			18 47			19 02			19 17			19 32			19 47		20 02	
Southport	a	18 37			18 52			19 07			19 22			19 37			19 52		20 07	

Station		ME	ME	ME	ME		ME	ME	ME	ME	ME	ME	ME	ME
Hunts Cross	89 d	19 21		19 36				22 51		23 06		23 21		
Liverpool South Parkway 7	89 ✈ d	19 24		19 39				22 54		23 09		23 24		
Cressington	d	19 27		19 42				22 57		23 12		23 27		
Aigburth	d	19 29		19 44				22 59		23 14		23 29		
St Michaels	d	19 31		19 46				23 01		23 16		23 31		
Brunswick	d	19 34		19 49				23 04		23 19		23 34		
Liverpool Central 10	a	19 38		19 53				23 08		23 23		23 38		
	d	19 38	19 40	19 53	19 55		22 55	23 08	23 10	23 23	23 25	23 38	23 40	23 55
Moorfields 10	d	19 40	19 42	19 55	19 57		22 57	23 10	23 12	23 25	23 27	23 40	23 42	23 57
Sandhills	d	19 44	19 46	19 59	20 01		23 01	23 14	23 16	23 29	23 31	23 44	23 46	00 01
Kirkdale	d		19 49		20 04		23 04		23 19		23 34		23 49	00 04
Rice Lane	d				20 07	and at	23 07				23 37			00 07
Fazakerley	d				20 10	the same	23 10				23 40			00 10
Kirkby	a				20 13	minutes	23 13				23 43			00 13
Walton (Merseyside)	d		19 52			past			23 22				23 52	
Orrell Park	d		19 53			each			23 23				23 53	
Aintree	d		19 56			hour until			23 26				23 56	
Old Roan	d		19 58						23 28				23 58	
Maghull	d		20 01						23 31				00 01	
Town Green	d		20 05						23 35				00 05	
Aughton Park	d		20 07						23 37				00 07	
Ormskirk	a		20 12						23 42				00 12	
Bank Hall	d	19 46		20 01				23 16		23 31		23 46		
Bootle Oriel Road	d	19 48		20 03				23 18		23 33		23 48		
Bootle New Strand	d	19 50		20 05				23 20		23 35		23 50		
Seaforth & Litherland	d	19 52		20 07				23 22		23 37		23 52		
Waterloo (Merseyside)	d	19 54		20 09				23 24		23 39		23 54		
Blundellsands & Crosby	d	19 57		20 12				23 27		23 42		23 57		
Hall Road	d	19 59		20 14				23 29		23 44		23 59		
Hightown	d	20 02		20 17				23 32		23 47		00 02		
Formby	d	20 06		20 21				23 36		23 51		00 06		
Freshfield	d	20 08		20 23				23 38		23 53		00 08		
Ainsdale	d	20 12		20 27				23 42		23 57		00 12		
Hillside	d	20 15		20 30				23 45		23 59		00 15		
Birkdale	d	20 17		20 32				23 47		00 02		00 17		
Southport	a	20 22		20 37				23 52		00 07		00 22		

For general notes see front of timetable
For details of catering facilities see
Directory of Train Operators

Table 103

Sundays

Hunts Cross and Liverpool → Kirkby, Ormskirk and Southport

Network Diagram - see first page of Table 101

		ME	ME	ME	ME	ME	ME	ME	ME	ME	ME	ME	ME	ME	ME A	ME	ME	ME	ME A
Hunts Cross	89 d			08b06			08 36			09 06			09 36				10 06		
Liverpool South Parkway 7	89 ⇌ d			08 09			08 39			09 09			09 39				10 09		
Cressington	d			08 12			08 42			09 12			09 42				10 12		
Aigburth	d			08 14			08 44			09 14			09 44				10 14		
St Michaels	d			08 16			08 46			09 16			09 46				10 16		
Brunswick	d			08 19			08 49			09 19			09 49				10 19		
Liverpool Central 10	a			08 23			08 53			09 23			09 53				10 23		
	d	08 08	08 10	08 23	08 25	08 40	08 53	08 55	09 10	09 23	09 25	09 40	09 53	09 55	10 08	10 10	10 23	10 25	10 38
Moorfields 10	d	08 10	08 12	08 25	08 27	08 42	08 55	08 57	09 12	09 25	09 27	09 42	09 55	09 57	10 10	10 12	10 25	10 27	10 40
Sandhills	d	08 14	08 16	08 29	08 31	08 46	08 59	09 01	09 16	09 29	09 31	09 46	09 59	10 01	10 14	10 16	10 29	10 31	10 44
Kirkdale	d		08 19		08 34	08 49		09 04	09 19		09 34	09 49		10 04		10 19		10 34	
Rice Lane	d				08 37			09 07			09 37			10 07				10 37	
Fazakerley	d				08 40			09 10			09 40			10 10				10 40	
Kirkby	a				08 43			09 13			09 43			10 13				10 43	
Walton (Merseyside)	d		08 22			08 52			09 22			09 52				10 22			
Orrell Park	d		08 23			08 53			09 23			09 53				10 23			
Aintree	d		08 26			08 56			09 26			09 56				10 26			
Old Roan	d		08 28			08 58			09 28			09 58				10 28			
Maghull	d		08 31			09 01			09 31			10 01				10 31			
Town Green	d		08 35			09 05			09 35			10 05				10 35			
Aughton Park	d		08 37			09 07			09 37			10 07				10 37			
Ormskirk	a		08 42			09 12			09 42			10 12				10 42			
Bank Hall	d	08 16		08 31			09 01			09 31			10 01		10 16		10 31		10 46
Bootle Oriel Road	d	08 18		08 33			09 03			09 33			10 03		10 18		10 33		10 48
Bootle New Strand	d	08 20		08 35			09 05			09 35			10 05		10 20		10 35		10 50
Seaforth & Litherland	d	08 22		08 37			09 07			09 37			10 07		10 22		10 37		10 52
Waterloo (Merseyside)	d	08 24		08 39			09 09			09 39			10 09		10 24		10 39		10 54
Blundellsands & Crosby	d	08 27		08 42			09 12			09 42			10 12		10 27		10 42		10 57
Hall Road	d	08 29		08 44			09 14			09 44			10 14		10 29		10 44		10 59
Hightown	d	08 32		08 47			09 17			09 47			10 17		10 32		10 47		11 02
Formby	d	08 36		08 51			09 21			09 51			10 21		10 36		10 51		11 06
Freshfield	d	08 38		08 53			09 23			09 53			10 23		10 38		10 53		11 08
Ainsdale	d	08 42		08 57			09 27			09 57			10 27		10 42		10 57		11 12
Hillside	d	08 45		09 00			09 30			10 00			10 30		10 45		11 00		11 15
Birkdale	d	08 47		09 02			09 32			10 02			10 32		10 47		11 02		11 17
Southport	a	08 52		09 07			09 37			10 07			10 37		10 52		11 07		11 22

		ME	ME		ME	ME	ME A	ME	ME A	ME B	ME	ME	ME	ME
Hunts Cross	89 d		10 36		22 36				23 06	23 06				
Liverpool South Parkway 7	89 ⇌ d		10 39		22 39				23 09	23 09				
Cressington	d		10 42		22 42				23 12	23 12				
Aigburth	d		10 44		22 44				23 14	23 14				
St Michaels	d		10 46		22 46				23 16	23 16				
Brunswick	d		10 49		22 49				23 19	23 19				
Liverpool Central 10	a		10 53		22 53				23 23	23 23				
	d	10 40	10 53		22 53	22 55	23 08	23 10	23 23	23 23	23 25	23 38	23 40	23 55
Moorfields 10	d	10 42	10 55		22 55	22 57	23 10	23 12	23 25	23 25	23 27	23 40	23 42	23 57
Sandhills	d	10 46	10 59		22 59	23 01	23 14	23 16	23a29	23 29	23 31	23 44	23 46	00 01
Kirkdale	d	10 49		and at the same minutes past each hour until		23 04		23 19			23 34		23 49	00 04
Rice Lane	d					23 07					23 37			00 07
Fazakerley	d					23 10					23 40			00 10
Kirkby	a					23 13					23 43			00 13
Walton (Merseyside)	d	10 52						23 22					23 52	
Orrell Park	d	10 53						23 23					23 53	
Aintree	d	10 56						23 26					23 56	
Old Roan	d	10 58						23 28					23 58	
Maghull	d	11 01						23 31					00 01	
Town Green	d	11 05						23 35					00 05	
Aughton Park	d	11 07						23 37					00 07	
Ormskirk	a	11 12						23 42					00 12	
Bank Hall	d		11 01		23 01		23 16			23 31		23 46		
Bootle Oriel Road	d		11 03		23 03		23 18			23 33		23 48		
Bootle New Strand	d		11 05		23 05		23 20			23 35		23 50		
Seaforth & Litherland	d		11 07		23 07		23 22			23 37		23 52		
Waterloo (Merseyside)	d		11 09		23 09		23 24			23 39		23 54		
Blundellsands & Crosby	d		11 12		23 12		23 27			23 42		23 57		
Hall Road	d		11 14		23 14		23 29			23 44		23 59		
Hightown	d		11 17		23 17		23 32			23 47		00 02		
Formby	d		11 21		23 21		23 36			23 51		00 06		
Freshfield	d		11 23		23 23		23 38			23 53		00 08		
Ainsdale	d		11 27		23 27		23 42			23 57		00 12		
Hillside	d		11 30		23 30		23 45			00 01		00 15		
Birkdale	d		11 32		23 32		23 47			00 02		00 17		
Southport	a		11 37		23 37		23 52			00 07		00 22		

For general notes see front of timetable
For details of catering facilities see Directory of Train Operators

A Until 21 September
B From 28 September
b From 14 September only

Southport, Ormskirk and Kirkby → Liverpool and Hunts Cross

Network Diagram - see first page of Table 101

Miles	Miles	Miles			ME	ME	ME	ME	ME	ME	ME	ME	ME		ME	ME	ME	ME	ME	ME	ME	ME	ME	ME
0	—	—	**Southport**	d				05 43		05 58		06 13			06 28		06 43			06 58			07 13	
1	—	—	Birkdale	d				05 47		06 02		06 17			06 32		06 47			07 02			07 17	
2	—	—	Hillside	d				05 49		06 04		06 19			06 34		06 49			07 04			07 19	
3½	—	—	Ainsdale	d				05 52		06 07		06 22			06 37		06 52			07 07			07 22	
6¼	—	—	Freshfield	d				05 56		06 11		06 26			06 41		06 56			07 11			07 26	
7¼	—	—	Formby	d				05 58		06 13		06 28			06 43		06 58			07 13			07 28	
9¼	—	—	Hightown	d				06 02		06 17		06 32			06 47		07 02			07 17			07 32	
11¼	—	—	Hall Road	d				06 05		06 20		06 35			06 50		07 05			07 20			07 35	
12	—	—	Blundellsands & Crosby	d				06 07		06 22		06 37			06 52		07 07			07 22			07 37	
13	—	—	Waterloo (Merseyside)	d				06 10		06 25		06 40			06 55		07 10			07 25			07 40	
14¼	—	—	Seaforth & Litherland	d				06 12		06 27		06 42			06 57		07 12			07 27			07 42	
15¼	—	—	Bootle New Strand	d				06 15		06 30		06 45			07 00		07 15			07 30			07 45	
15½	—	—	Bootle Oriel Road	d				06 16		06 31		06 46			07 01		07 16			07 31			07 46	
16¼	—	—	Bank Hall	d				06 18		06 33		06 48			07 03		07 18			07 33			07 48	
—	0	—	**Ormskirk**	d			05 50				06 20					06 50			07 05			07 20		
—	1¼	—	Aughton Park	d			05 53				06 23					06 53			07 08			07 23		
—	2¾	—	Town Green	d			05 55				06 25					06 55			07 10			07 25		
—	4¾	—	Maghull	d			06 00				06 30					07 00			07 15			07 30		
—	6½	—	Old Roan	d			06 03				06 33					07 03			07 18			07 33		
—	7¼	—	Aintree	d			06 05				06 35					07 05			07 20			07 35		
—	8¼	—	Orrell Park	d			06 07				06 37					07 07			07 22			07 37		
—	8½	—	Walton (Merseyside)	d			06 09				06 39					07 09			07 24			07 39		
—	—	0	**Kirkby**	d	05 48				06 18				06 48					07 13			07 28			07 43
—	—	1¾	Fazakerley	d	05 51				06 21				06 51					07 16			07 31			07 46
—	—	3¼	Rice Lane	d	05 54				06 24				06 54					07 19			07 34			07 49
—	9¾	4½	Kirkdale	d	05 57		06 12		06 27		06 42		06 57			07 12		07 22	07 27		07 37	07 42		07 52
17	10¾	5½	Sandhills	d	06 00	06 06	06 14	06 21	06 30	06 36	06 44	06 51	07 00		07 06	07 14	07 21	07 25	07 29	07 36	07 40	07 44	07 51	07 55
18½	12¼	7	**Moorfields 10**	d	06 03	06 10	06 18	06 25	06 33	06 40	06 48	06 55	07 03		07 10	07 18	07 25	07 28	07 33	07 40	07 43	07 48	07 55	07 58
19	12¾	7½	**Liverpool Central 10**	a	06 06	06 13	06 20	06 28	06 36	06 43	06 50	06 58	07 06		07 13	07 20	07 28	07 31	07 35	07 43	07 46	07 50	07 58	08 01
—	—	—		d		06 14		06 29		06 43		06 59			07 14		07 29			07 44			07 59	
20½	—	—	Brunswick	d		06 17		06 32		06 47		07 02			07 17		07 32			07 47			08 02	
21¾	—	—	St Michaels	d		06 20		06 35		06 49		07 05			07 20		07 35			07 50			08 05	
23	—	—	Aigburth	d		06 22		06 37		06 52		07 07			07 22		07 37			07 52			08 07	
23¾	—	—	Cressington	d		06 24		06 39		06 54		07 09			07 24		07 39			07 54			08 09	
24¾	—	—	**Liverpool South Parkway 7** 89 ✈	d		06 27		06 42		06 56		07 12			07 27		07 42			07 57			08 12	
26¼	—	—	**Hunts Cross** 89	a		06 31		06 46		07 01		07 16			07 31		07 46			08 01			08 16	

		ME		ME	ME	ME	ME	ME	ME SX	ME	ME	ME		ME SX	ME	ME		ME	ME	ME	ME	ME	ME	ME
Southport	d			07 28			07 43		07 48		07 58			08 03		08 13				08 28			08 43	
Birkdale	d			07 32			07 47		07 52		08 02			08 07		08 17				08 32			08 47	
Hillside	d			07 34			07 49		07 54		08 04			08 09		08 19				08 34			08 49	
Ainsdale	d			07 37			07 52		07 57		08 07			08 12		08 22				08 37			08 52	
Freshfield	d			07 41			07 56		08 01		08 11			08 16		08 26				08 41			08 56	
Formby	d			07 43			07 58		08 03		08 13			08 18		08 28				08 43			08 58	
Hightown	d			07 47			08 02		08 07		08 17			08 22		08 32				08 47			09 02	
Hall Road	d			07 50			08 05		08 10		08 20			08 25		08 35				08 50			09 05	
Blundellsands & Crosby	d			07 52			08 07		08 12		08 22			08 27		08 37				08 52			09 07	
Waterloo (Merseyside)	d			07 55			08 10		08 15		08 25			08 30		08 40				08 55			09 10	
Seaforth & Litherland	d			07 57			08 12		08 17		08 27			08 32		08 42				08 57			09 12	
Bootle New Strand	d			08 00			08 15		08 20		08 30			08 35		08 45				09 00			09 15	
Bootle Oriel Road	d			08 01			08 16		08 21		08 31			08 36		08 46				09 01			09 16	
Bank Hall	d			08 03			08 18		08 23		08 33			08 38		08 48				09 03			09 18	
Ormskirk	d	07 35				07 50				08 05					08 20				08 35			08 50		
Aughton Park	d	07 38				07 53				08 08					08 23				08 38			08 53		
Town Green	d	07 40				07 55				08 10					08 25				08 40			08 55		
Maghull	d	07 45				08 00				08 15					08 30				08 45			09 00		
Old Roan	d	07 48				08 03				08 18					08 33				08 48			09 03		
Aintree	d	07 50				08 05				08 20					08 35				08 50			09 05		
Orrell Park	d	07 52				08 07				08 22					08 37				08 52			09 07		
Walton (Merseyside)	d	07 54				08 09				08 24					08 39				08 54			09 09		
Kirkby	d				07 58			08 13				08 28						08 43			08 58			09 13
Fazakerley	d				08 01			08 16				08 31						08 46			09 01			09 16
Rice Lane	d				08 04			08 19				08 34						08 49			09 04			09 19
Kirkdale	d	07 57			08 07	08 12		08 22		08 27		08 37			08 42			08 52	08 57		09 07	09 12		09 22
Sandhills	d	07 59		08 06	08 10	08 14	08 21	08 25	08 27	08 29	08 36	08 40		08 42	08 44	08 51		08 55	08 59	09 06	09 10	09 14	09 21	09 25
Moorfields 10	d	08 03		08 10	08 13	08 18	08 25	08 28	08 31	08 33	08 40	08 43		08 46	08 48	08 55		08 58	09 03	09 10	09 13	09 18	09 25	09 28
Liverpool Central 10	a	08 05		08 13	08 16	08 20	08 28	08 31	08 33	08 35	08 43	08 46		08 48	08 50	08 58		09 01	09 05	09 13	09 16	09 20	09 28	09 31
	d			08 14			08 29				08 44					08 59				09 14			09 29	
Brunswick	d			08 17			08 32				08 47					09 02				09 17			09 32	
St Michaels	d			08 20			08 35				08 50					09 05				09 20			09 35	
Aigburth	d			08 22			08 37				08 52					09 07				09 22			09 37	
Cressington	d			08 24			08 39				08 54					09 09				09 24			09 39	
Liverpool South Parkway 7 89 ✈	d			08 27			08 42				08 57					09 12				09 27			09 42	
Hunts Cross 89	a			08 31			08 46				09 01					09 16				09 31			09 46	

For general notes see front of timetable
For details of catering facilities see Directory of Train Operators

Table 103

Mondays to Saturdays

Southport, Ormskirk and Kirkby → Liverpool and Hunts Cross

Network Diagram - see first page of Table 101

		ME	ME	ME	ME	ME			ME	ME	ME	ME	ME	ME	ME	ME	ME		ME	ME		ME	ME
Southport	d		08 58			09 13	and at the same minutes past each hour until		18 13			18 28			18 43				18 58				19 13
Birkdale	d		09 02			09 17			18 17			18 32			18 47				19 02				19 17
Hillside	d		09 04			09 19			18 19			18 34			18 49				19 04				19 19
Ainsdale	d		09 07			09 22			18 22			18 37			18 52				19 07				19 22
Freshfield	d		09 11			09 26			18 26			18 41			18 56				19 11				19 26
Formby	d		09 13			09 28			18 28			18 43			18 58				19 13				19 28
Hightown	d		09 17			09 32			18 32			18 47			19 02				19 17				19 32
Hall Road	d		09 20			09 35			18 35			18 50			19 05				19 20				19 35
Blundellsands & Crosby	d		09 22			09 37			18 37			18 52			19 07				19 22				19 37
Waterloo (Merseyside)	d		09 25			09 40			18 40			18 55			19 10				19 25				19 40
Seaforth & Litherland	d		09 27			09 42			18 42			18 57			19 12				19 27				19 42
Bootle New Strand	d		09 30			09 45			18 45			19 00			19 15				19 30				19 45
Bootle Oriel Road	d		09 31			09 46			18 46			19 01			19 16				19 31				19 46
Bank Hall	d		09 33			09 48			18 48			19 03			19 18				19 33				19 48
Ormskirk	d	09 05			09 20						18 35			18 50			19 05					19 20	
Aughton Park	d	09 08			09 23						18 38			18 53			19 08					19 23	
Town Green	d	09 10			09 25						18 40			18 55			19 10					19 25	
Maghull	d	09 15			09 30						18 45			19 00			19 15					19 30	
Old Roan	d	09 18			09 33						18 48			19 03			19 18					19 33	
Aintree	d	09 20			09 35						18 50			19 05			19 20					19 35	
Orrell Park	d	09 22			09 37						18 52			19 07			19 22					19 37	
Walton (Merseyside)	d	09 24			09 39						18 54			19 09			19 24					19 39	
Kirkby	d			09 28						18 43			18 58			19 13				19 28			
Fazakerley	d			09 31						18 46			19 01			19 16				19 31			
Rice Lane	d			09 34						18 49			19 04			19 19				19 34			
Kirkdale	d	09 27		09 37	09 42					18 52	18 57		19 07	19 12		19 22	19 27			19 37		19 42	
Sandhills	d	09 29	09 36	09 40	09 44	09 51			18 51	18 55	18 59	19 06	19 10	19 14	19 21	19 25	19 29		19 36	19 40		19 44	19 51
Moorfields [10]	d	09 33	09 40	09 43	09 48	09 55			18 55	18 58	19 03	19 10	19 13	19 18	19 25	19 28	19 33		19 40	19 43		19 48	19 55
Liverpool Central [10]	a	09 35	09 43	09 46	09 50	09 58			18 58	19 01	19 05	19 13	19 16	19 20	19 28	19 31	19 35		19 43	19 46		19 50	19 58
	d		09 44			09 59			18 59			19 14			19 29				19 44				19 59
Brunswick	d		09 47			10 02			19 02			19 17			19 32				19 47				20 02
St Michaels	d		09 50			10 05			19 05			19 20			19 35				19 50				20 05
Aigburth	d		09 52			10 07			19 07			19 22			19 37				19 52				20 07
Cressington	d		09 54			10 09			19 09			19 24			19 39				19 54				20 09
Liverpool South Parkway [7] 89 ⇌	d		09 57			10 12			19 12			19 27			19 42				19 57				20 12
Hunts Cross 89	a		10 01			10 16			19 16			19 31			19 46				20 01				20 16

		ME	ME	ME	ME	ME	ME		ME		ME	ME	ME	ME	ME	ME	ME	ME	ME		ME		
Southport	d		19 28		19 43		19 58	and at the same minutes past each hour until	21 58			22 13		22 28		22 43		22 58			23 16		
Birkdale	d		19 32		19 47		20 02		22 02			22 17		22 32		22 47		23 02			23 20		
Hillside	d		19 34		19 49		20 04		22 04			22 19		22 34		22 49		23 04			23 22		
Ainsdale	d		19 37		19 52		20 07		22 07			22 22		22 37		22 52		23 07			23 25		
Freshfield	d		19 41		19 56		20 11		22 11			22 26		22 41		22 56		23 11			23 29		
Formby	d		19 43		19 58		20 13		22 13			22 28		22 43		22 58		23 13			23 31		
Hightown	d		19 47		20 02		20 17		22 17			22 32		22 47		23 02		23 17			23 35		
Hall Road	d		19 50		20 05		20 20		22 20			22 35		22 50		23 05		23 20			23 38		
Blundellsands & Crosby	d		19 52		20 07		20 22		22 22			22 37		22 52		23 07		23 22			23 40		
Waterloo (Merseyside)	d		19 55		20 10		20 25		22 25			22 40		22 55		23 10		23 25			23 43		
Seaforth & Litherland	d		19 57		20 12		20 27		22 27			22 42		22 57		23 12		23 27			23 45		
Bootle New Strand	d		20 00		20 15		20 30		22 30			22 45		23 00		23 15		23 30			23 48		
Bootle Oriel Road	d		20 01		20 16		20 31		22 31			22 46		23 01		23 16		23 31			23 49		
Bank Hall	d		20 03		20 18		20 33		22 33			22 48		23 03		23 18		23 33			23 51		
Ormskirk	d			19 50							22 20				22 50				23 20				
Aughton Park	d			19 53							22 23				22 53				23 23				
Town Green	d			19 55							22 25				22 55				23 25				
Maghull	d			20 00							22 30				23 00				23 30				
Old Roan	d			20 03							22 33				23 03				23 33				
Aintree	d			20 05							22 35				23 05				23 35				
Orrell Park	d			20 07							22 37				23 07				23 37				
Walton (Merseyside)	d			20 09							22 39				23 09				23 39				
Kirkby	d	19 48				20 18							22 48				23 18						
Fazakerley	d	19 51				20 21							22 51				23 21						
Rice Lane	d	19 54				20 24							22 54				23 24						
Kirkdale	d	19 57		20 12		20 27					22 42		22 57		23 12		23 27		23 42				
Sandhills	d	20 00	20 06	20 14	20 21	20 30	20 36		22 36		22 44	22 51	23 00	23 06	23 14	23 21	23 30	23 36	23 44		23 55		
Moorfields [10]	d	20 03	20 10	20 18	20 25	20 33	20 40		22 40		22 48	22 55	23 03	23 10	23 18	23 25	23 33	23 40	23 48		23 58		
Liverpool Central [10]	a	20 06	20 13	20 20	20 28	20 36	20 43		22 43		22 50	22 58	23 06	23 13	23 20	23 28	23 36	23 43	23 50		00 01		
	d		20 14		20 29		20 44		22 44			22 59		23 14		23 29		23 44					
Brunswick	d		20 17		20 32		20 47		22 47			23 02		23 17		23 32		23 47					
St Michaels	d		20 20		20 35		20 50		22 50			23 05		23 20		23 35		23 50					
Aigburth	d		20 22		20 37		20 52		22 52			23 07		23 22		23 37		23 52					
Cressington	d		20 24		20 39		20 54		22 54			23 09		23 24		23 39		23 54					
Liverpool South Parkway [7] 89 ⇌	d		20 27		20 42		20 57		22 57			23 12		23 27		23 42		23 57					
Hunts Cross 89	a		20 31		20 46		21 01		23 01			23 18		23 32		23 46		00 01					

For general notes see front of timetable
For details of catering facilities see Directory of Train Operators

Table 103

Sundays

Southport, Ormskirk and Kirkby → Liverpool and Hunts Cross

Network Diagram - see first page of Table 101

Station		ME	ME	ME	ME	ME	ME	ME	ME	ME	ME	ME	ME	ME	ME	ME	ME	ME A	ME	ME
Southport	d			07 58			08 28			08 58			09 28			09 58		10 13		10 28
Birkdale	d			08 02			08 32			09 02			09 32			10 02		10 17		10 32
Hillside	d			08 04			08 34			09 04			09 34			10 04		10 19		10 34
Ainsdale	d			08 07			08 37			09 07			09 37			10 07		10 22		10 37
Freshfield	d			08 11			08 41			09 11			09 41			10 11		10 26		10 41
Formby	d			08 13			08 43			09 13			09 43			10 13		10 28		10 43
Hightown	d			08 17			08 47			09 17			09 47			10 17		10 32		10 47
Hall Road	d			08 20			08 50			09 20			09 50			10 20		10 35		10 50
Blundellsands & Crosby	d			08 22			08 52			09 22			09 52			10 22		10 37		10 52
Waterloo (Merseyside)	d			08 25			08 55			09 25			09 55			10 25		10 40		10 55
Seaforth & Litherland	d			08 27			08 57			09 27			09 57			10 27		10 42		10 57
Bootle New Strand	d			08 30			09 00			09 30			10 00			10 30		10 45		11 00
Bootle Oriel Road	d			08 31			09 01			09 31			10 01			10 31		10 46		11 01
Bank Hall	d			08 33			09 03			09 33			10 03			10 33		10 48		11 03
Ormskirk	d				08 20			08 50			09 20			09 50			10 20			
Aughton Park	d				08 23			08 53			09 23			09 53			10 23			
Town Green	d				08 25			08 55			09 25			09 55			10 25			
Maghull	d				08 30			09 00			09 30			10 00			10 30			
Old Roan	d				08 33			09 03			09 33			10 03			10 33			
Aintree	d				08 35			09 05			09 35			10 05			10 35			
Orrell Park	d				08 37			09 07			09 37			10 07			10 37			
Walton (Merseyside)	d				08 39			09 09			09 39			10 09			10 39			
Kirkby	d		08 18			08 48			09 18			09 48			10 18				10 48	
Fazakerley	d		08 21			08 51			09 21			09 51			10 21				10 51	
Rice Lane	d		08 24			08 54			09 24			09 54			10 24				10 54	
Kirkdale	d		08 27		08 42	08 57		09 12	09 27		09 42	09 57		10 12	10 27		10 42		10 57	
Sandhills	d		08 30	08 36	08 44	09 00	09 06	09 14	09 30	09 36	09 44	10 00	10 06	10 14	10 30	10 36	10 44	10 51	11 00	11 06
Moorfields 10	d		08 33	08 40	08 48	09 03	09 10	09 18	09 33	09 40	09 48	10 03	10 10	10 18	10 33	10 40	10 48	10 55	11 03	11 10
Liverpool Central 10	a		08 36	08 43	08 50	09 06	09 13	09 20	09 36	09 43	09 50	10 06	10 13	10 20	10 36	10 43	10 50	10 58	11 06	11 13
	d	08 14		08 44			09 14			09 44			10 14			10 44				11 14
Brunswick	d	08 17		08 47			09 17			09 47			10 17			10 47				11 17
St Michaels	d	08 20		08 50			09 20			09 50			10 20			10 50				11 20
Aigburth	d	08 22		08 52			09 22			09 52			10 22			10 52				11 22
Cressington	d	08 24		08 54			09 24			09 54			10 24			10 54				11 24
Liverpool South Parkway 7	89 ⇌ d	08 27		08 57			09 27			09 57			10 27			10 57				11 27
Hunts Cross	89 a	08 31		09 01			09 31			10 01			10 31			11 01				11 31

Station		ME	ME A		ME A	ME	ME	ME	ME A	ME	ME	ME	ME A	ME	ME	ME	ME
Southport	d		10 43		21 43		21 58		22 13		22 28		22 43		22 58		23 16
Birkdale	d		10 47		21 47		22 02		22 17		22 32		22 47		23 02		23 20
Hillside	d		10 49		21 49		22 04		22 19		22 34		22 49		23 04		23 22
Ainsdale	d		10 52		21 52		22 07		22 22		22 37		22 52		23 07		23 25
Freshfield	d		10 56		21 56		22 11		22 26		22 41		22 56		23 11		23 29
Formby	d		10 58		21 58		22 13		22 28		22 43		22 58		23 13		23 31
Hightown	d		11 02		22 02		22 17		22 32		22 47		23 02		23 17		23 35
Hall Road	d		11 05		22 05		22 20		22 35		22 50		23 05		23 20		23 38
Blundellsands & Crosby	d		11 07		22 07		22 22		22 37		22 52		23 07		23 22		23 40
Waterloo (Merseyside)	d		11 10		22 10		22 25		22 40		22 55		23 10		23 25		23 43
Seaforth & Litherland	d		11 12		22 12		22 27		22 42		22 57		23 12		23 27		23 45
Bootle New Strand	d		11 15		22 15		22 30		22 45		23 00		23 15		23 30		23 48
Bootle Oriel Road	d		11 16		22 16		22 31		22 46		23 01		23 16		23 31		23 49
Bank Hall	d		11 18	and at	22 18		22 33		22 48		23 03		23 18		23 33		23 51
Ormskirk	d	10 50		the same				22 20				22 50				23 20	
Aughton Park	d	10 53						22 23				22 53				23 23	
Town Green	d	10 55		minutes				22 25				22 55				23 25	
Maghull	d	11 00						22 30				23 00				23 30	
Old Roan	d	11 03		past				22 33				23 03				23 33	
Aintree	d	11 05						22 35				23 05				23 35	
Orrell Park	d	11 07		each				22 37				23 07				23 37	
Walton (Merseyside)	d	11 09						22 39				23 09				23 39	
Kirkby	d			hour until		22 18				22 48				23 18			
Fazakerley	d					22 21				22 51				23 21			
Rice Lane	d					22 24				22 54				23 24			
Kirkdale	d	11 12				22 27		22 42		22 57		23 12		23 27		23 42	
Sandhills	d	11 14	11 21		22 21	22 30	22 36	22 44	22 51	23 00	23 06	23 14	23 21	23 30	23 36	23 44	23 55
Moorfields 10	d	11 18	11 25		22 25	22 33	22 40	22 48	22 55	23 03	23 10	23 18	23 25	23 33	23 40	23 48	23 58
Liverpool Central 10	a	11 20	11 28		22 28	22 36	22 43	22 50	22 58	23 06	23 13	23 20	23 28	23 36	23 43	23 50	00 01
	d						22 44				23 14				23 44		
Brunswick	d						22 47				23 17				23 47		
St Michaels	d						22 50				23 20				23 50		
Aigburth	d						22 52				23 22				23 52		
Cressington	d						22 54				23 24				23 54		
Liverpool South Parkway 7	89 ⇌ d						22 57				23 27				23 57		
Hunts Cross	89 a						23 01				23 31				00 01		

For general notes see front of timetable
For details of catering facilities see
Directory of Train Operators

A Until 21 September

Table 106

Mondays to Saturdays

Liverpool and Birkenhead → New Brighton, West Kirby, Ellesmere Port and Chester

Network Diagram - see first page of Table 101

Miles	Miles	Miles	Miles			ME	ME	ME	ME	ME	ME	ME	ME	ME	ME	ME	ME		ME	ME	ME	ME	ME	ME	ME	ME
0	—	0	0	**Moorfields 10**	d	05 41	05 56	06 11	06 16	06 21	06 26	06 41	06 46	06 51	06 56	07 11	07 16		07 21	07 26	07 31	07 36	07 41	07 46	07 51	07 56
½	—	½	½	**Liverpool Lime Street 10**	d	05 43	05 58	06 13	06 18	06 23	06 28	06 43	06 48	06 53	06 58	07 13	07 18		07 23	07 28	07 33	07 38	07 43	07 48	07 53	07 58
1	—	1	1	**Liverpool Central 10**	d	05 45	06 00	06 15	06 20	06 25	06 30	06 45	06 50	06 55	07 00	07 15	07 20		07 25	07 30	07 35	07 40	07 45	07 50	07 55	08 00
1½	—	1½	1½	James Street	d	05 47	06 02	06 17	06 22	06 27	06 32	06 47	06 52	06 57	07 02	07 17	07 22		07 27	07 32	07 37	07 42	07 47	07 52	07 57	08 02
2¾	—	2¾	2¾	Hamilton Square	d	05 50	06 05	06 20	06 25	06 30	06 35	06 50	06 55	07 00	07 05	07 20	07 25		07 30	07 35	07 40	07 45	07 50	07 55	08 00	08 05
—	—	3¼	3¼	Conway Park	d				06 27	06 32			06 57	07 02			07 27		07 32		07 42	07 47		07 57	08 02	
—	—	4	4	Birkenhead Park	d				06 29	06 34			06 59	07 04			07 29		07 34		07 44	07 49		07 59	08 04	
—	—	4¾	4¾	Birkenhead North	d				06 32	06 37			07 02	07 07			07 32		07 37		07 47	07 52		08 02	08 07	
—	—	—	6¼	Wallasey Village	d				06 37				07 07				07 37				07 52			08 07		
—	—	—	6½	Wallasey Grove Road	d				06 38				07 08				07 38				07 53			08 08		
—	—	—	7¾	**New Brighton**	a				06 43				07 13				07 43				07 58			08 13		
—	—	5¼	—	Bidston	d					06 40				07 10					07 40			07 55			08 10	
—	—	6½	—	Leasowe	d					06 42				07 12					07 42			07 57			08 12	
—	—	7	—	Moreton (Merseyside)	d					06 44				07 14					07 44			07 59			08 14	
—	—	8¼	—	Meols	d					06 48				07 18					07 48			08 03			08 18	
—	—	9½	—	Manor Road	d					06 50				07 20					07 50			08 05			08 20	
—	—	10	—	Hoylake	d					06 52				07 22					07 52			08 07			08 22	
—	—	11¼	—	**West Kirby**	a					06 57				07 27					07 57			08 12			08 27	
3	—	—	—	Birkenhead Central	d	05 52	06 07	06 22			06 37	06 52			07 07	07 22				07 37			07 52			08 07
3¾	—	—	—	Green Lane	d	05 54	06 09	06 24			06 39	06 54			07 09	07 24				07 39			07 54			08 09
4½	—	—	—	Rock Ferry	d	05 57	06 12	06 27			06 42	06 57			07 12	07 27				07 42			07 57			08 12
5½	—	—	—	Bebington	d	05 59	06 14	06 29			06 44	06 59			07 14	07 29				07 44			07 59			08 14
6½	—	—	—	Port Sunlight	d	06 01	06 16	06 31			06 46	07 01			07 16	07 31				07 46			08 01			08 16
7	—	—	—	Spital	d	06 03	06 18	06 33			06 48	07 03			07 18	07 33				07 48			08 03			08 18
7¾	—	—	—	Bromborough Rake	d	06 05	06 20	06 35			06 50	07 05			07 20	07 35				07 50			08 05			08 20
8½	—	—	—	Bromborough	d	06 07	06 22	06 37			06 52	07 07			07 22	07 37				07 52			08 07			08 22
9	—	—	—	Eastham Rake	d	06 10	06 25	06 40			06 55	07 10			07 25	07 40				07 55			08 10			08 25
10	0	—	—	Hooton	d	06 12	06 27	06 42			06 57	07 12			07 27	07 42				07 57			08 12			08 27
—	1½	—	—	Little Sutton	d		06 31				07 01				07 31					08 01						08 31
—	2½	—	—	Overpool	d		06 33				07 03				07 33					08 03						08 33
—	4	—	—	**Ellesmere Port**	a		06 37				07 07				07 37					08 07						08 37
13	—	—	—	Capenhurst	d	06 17		06 47				07 17				07 47							08 17			
16¾	—	—	—	Bache	d	06 22		06 52				07 22				07 52							08 22			
18¼	—	—	—	**Chester**	a	06 26		06 56				07 26				07 56							08 26			

		ME	ME SX	ME	ME	ME	ME SX		ME	ME	ME	ME SX	ME	ME	ME	ME SX	ME	ME	ME	ME SX		ME	ME	ME	ME SX	
Moorfields 10	d	08 01	08 03	08 06	08 11	08 16	08 18		08 21	08 26	08 31	08 33	08 36	08 41	08 46	08 48	08 51	08 56	09 01	09 03		09 06	09 11	09 16	09 18	
Liverpool Lime Street 10	d	08 03	08 05	08 08	08 13	08 18	08 20		08 23	08 28	08 33	08 35	08 38	08 43	08 48	08 50	08 53	08 58	09 03	09 05		09 08	09 13	09 18	09 20	
Liverpool Central 10	d	08 05	08a07	08 10	08 15	08 20	08a22		08 25	08 30	08 35	08a37	08 40	08 45	08 50	08a52	08 55	09 00	09 05	09a07		09 10	09 15	09 20	09a22	
James Street	d	08 07		08 12	08 17	08 22			08 27	08 32	08 37		08 42	08 47	08 52		08 57	09 02	09 07			09 12	09 17	09 22		
Hamilton Square	d	08 10		08 15	08 20	08 25			08 30	08 35	08 40		08 45	08 50	08 55		09 00	09 05	09 10			09 15	09 20	09 25		
Conway Park	d	08 12		08 17		08 27			08 32		08 42		08 47		08 57		09 02		09 12			09 17		09 27		
Birkenhead Park	d	08 14		08 19		08 29			08 34		08 44		08 49		08 59		09 04		09 14			09 19		09 29		
Birkenhead North	d	08 17		08 22		08 32			08 37		08 47		08 52		09 02		09 07		09 17			09 22		09 32		
Wallasey Village	d	08 22				08 37					08 52				09 07				09 22					09 37		
Wallasey Grove Road	d	08 23				08 38					08 53				09 08				09 23					09 38		
New Brighton	a	08 28				08 43					08 58				09 13				09 28					09 43		
Bidston	d			08 25					08 40				08 55				09 10					09 25				
Leasowe	d			08 27					08 42				08 57				09 12					09 27				
Moreton (Merseyside)	d			08 29					08 44				08 59				09 14					09 29				
Meols	d			08 33					08 48				09 03				09 18					09 33				
Manor Road	d			08 35					08 50				09 05				09 20					09 35				
Hoylake	d			08 37					08 52				09 07				09 22					09 37				
West Kirby	a			08 42					08 57				09 12				09 27					09 42				
Birkenhead Central	d				08 22					08 37				08 52				09 07					09 22			
Green Lane	d				08 24					08 39				08 54				09 09					09 24			
Rock Ferry	d				08 27					08 42				08 57				09 12					09 27			
Bebington	d				08 29					08 44				08 59				09 14					09 29			
Port Sunlight	d				08 31					08 46				09 01				09 16					09 31			
Spital	d				08 33					08 48				09 03				09 18					09 33			
Bromborough Rake	d				08 35					08 50				09 05				09 20					09 35			
Bromborough	d				08 37					08 52				09 07				09 22					09 37			
Eastham Rake	d				08 40					08 55				09 10				09 25					09 40			
Hooton	d				08 42					08 57				09 12				09 27					09 42			
Little Sutton	d									09 01								09 31								
Overpool	d									09 03								09 33								
Ellesmere Port	a									09 07								09 37								
Capenhurst	d				08 47									09 17									09 47			
Bache	d				08 52									09 22									09 52			
Chester	a				08 56									09 26									09 56			

For general notes see front of timetable
For details of catering facilities see Directory of Train Operators

Liverpool and Birkenhead → New Brighton, West Kirby, Ellesmere Port and Chester

Network Diagram - see first page of Table 101

		ME	ME	ME	ME	ME	ME	ME	ME	ME	ME	ME	ME		ME	ME	ME	ME	ME	ME	ME	ME	ME
Moorfields 10	d	09 21	09 26	09 31	09 36	09 41	09 46	09 51	09 56	10 01	10 06	10 11	10 16		15 16	15 21	15 26	15 31	15 36	15 41	15 46	15 51	15 56
Liverpool Lime Street 10	d	09 23	09 28	09 33	09 38	09 43	09 48	09 53	09 58	10 03	10 08	10 13	10 18		15 18	15 23	15 28	15 33	15 38	15 43	15 48	15 53	15 58
Liverpool Central 10	d	09 25	09 30	09 35	09 40	09 45	09 50	09 55	10 00	10 05	10 10	10 15	10 20		15 20	15 25	15 30	15 35	15 40	15 45	15 50	15 55	16 00
James Street	d	09 27	09 32	09 37	09 42	09 47	09 52	09 57	10 02	10 07	10 12	10 17	10 22		15 22	15 27	15 32	15 37	15 42	15 47	15 52	15 57	16 02
Hamilton Square	d	09 30	09 35	09 40	09 45	09 50	09 55	10 00	10 05	10 10	10 15	10 20	10 25		15 25	15 30	15 35	15 40	15 45	15 50	15 55	16 00	16 05
Conway Park	d	09 32		09 42	09 47		09 57	10 02		10 12	10 17		10 27		15 27	15 32		15 42	15 47		15 57	16 02	
Birkenhead Park	d	09 34		09 44	09 49		09 59	10 04		10 14	10 19		10 29		15 29	15 34		15 44	15 49		15 59	16 04	
Birkenhead North	d	09 37		09 47	09 52		10 02	10 07		10 17	10 22		10 32		15 32	15 37		15 47	15 52		16 02	16 07	
Wallasey Village	d			09 52			10 07			10 22			10 37		15 37			15 52			16 07		
Wallasey Grove Road	d			09 53			10 08			10 23			10 38		15 38			15 53			16 08		
New Brighton	a			09 58			10 13			10 28			10 43		15 43			15 58			16 13		
Bidston	d	09 40			09 55			10 10			10 25			and at		15 40			15 55			16 10	
Leasowe	d	09 42			09 57			10 12			10 27			the same		15 42			15 57			16 12	
Moreton (Merseyside)	d	09 44			09 59			10 14			10 29					15 44			15 59			16 14	
Meols	d	09 48			10 03			10 18			10 33			minutes		15 48			16 03			16 18	
Manor Road	d	09 50			10 05			10 20			10 35					15 50			16 05			16 20	
Hoylake	d	09 52			10 07			10 22			10 37			past		15 52			16 07			16 22	
West Kirby	a	09 57			10 12			10 27			10 42			each		15 57			16 12			16 27	
Birkenhead Central	d		09 37			09 52			10 07			10 22		hour until			15 37			15 52			16 07
Green Lane	d		09 39			09 54			10 09			10 24					15 39			15 54			16 09
Rock Ferry	d		09 42			09 57			10 12			10 27					15 42			15 57			16 12
Bebington	d		09 44			09 59			10 14			10 29					15 44			15 59			16 14
Port Sunlight	d		09 46			10 01			10 16			10 31					15 46			16 01			16 16
Spital	d		09 48			10 03			10 18			10 33					15 48			16 03			16 18
Bromborough Rake	d		09 50			10 05			10 20			10 35					15 50			16 05			16 20
Bromborough	d		09 52			10 07			10 22			10 37					15 52			16 07			16 22
Eastham Rake	d		09 55			10 10			10 25			10 40					15 55			16 10			16 25
Hooton	d		09 57			10 12			10 27			10 42					15 57			16 12			16 27
Little Sutton	d		10 01						10 31								16 01						16 31
Overpool	d		10 03						10 33								16 03						16 33
Ellesmere Port	a		10 07						10 37								16 07						16 37
Capenhurst	d					10 17						10 47								16 17			
Bache	d					10 22						10 52								16 22			
Chester	a					10 26						10 56								16 26			

		ME	ME SX	ME	ME	ME	ME SX	ME	ME	ME	ME SX	ME	ME SX	ME SO	ME	ME SX	ME	ME	ME	ME SX	ME	ME SX	ME SO	ME
Moorfields 10	d	16 01	16 03	16 06	16 11	16 16	16 18	16 21	16 26	16 31	16 33	16 36	16 41	16 41	16 46	16 48	16 51	16 56	17 01	17 03	17 06	17 11	17 11	17 16
Liverpool Lime Street 10	d	16 03	16 05	16 08	16 13	16 18	16 20	16 23	16 28	16 33	16 35	16 38	16 43	16 43	16 48	16 50	16 53	16 58	17 03	17 05	17 08	17 13	17 13	17 18
Liverpool Central 10	d	16 05	16 07	16 10	16 15	16 20	16 22	16 25	16 30	16 35	16 37	16 40	16 45	16 45	16 50	16 52	16 55	17 00	17 05	17 07	17 10	17 15	17 15	17 20
James Street	d	16 07	16 09	16 12	16 17	16 22	16 24	16 27	16 32	16 37	16 39	16 42	16 47	16 47	16 52	16 54	16 57	17 02	17 07	17 09	17 12	17 17	17 17	17 22
Hamilton Square	d	16 10	16 12	16 15	16 20	16 25	16 27	16 30	16 35	16 40	16 42	16 45	16 50	16 50	16 55	16 57	17 00	17 05	17 10	17 12	17 15	17 20	17 20	17 25
Conway Park	d	16 12		16 17		16 27		16 32		16 42		16 47			16 57		17 02		17 12		17 17			17 27
Birkenhead Park	d	16 14		16 19		16 29		16 34		16 44		16 49			16 59		17 04		17 14		17 19			17 29
Birkenhead North	d	16 17		16 22		16 32		16 37		16 47		16 52			17 02		17 07		17 17		17 22			17 32
Wallasey Village	d	16 22				16 37				16 52					17 07				17 22					17 37
Wallasey Grove Road	d	16 23				16 38				16 53					17 08				17 23					17 38
New Brighton	a	16 28				16 43				16 58					17 13				17 28					17 43
Bidston	d			16 25				16 40				16 55					17 10				17 25			
Leasowe	d			16 27				16 42				16 57					17 12				17 27			
Moreton (Merseyside)	d			16 29				16 44				16 59					17 14				17 29			
Meols	d			16 33				16 48				17 03					17 18				17 33			
Manor Road	d			16 35				16 50				17 05					17 20				17 35			
Hoylake	d			16 37				16 52				17 07					17 22				17 37			
West Kirby	a			16 42				16 57				17 12					17 27				17 42			
Birkenhead Central	d				16 22				16 37		16 45		16 52	16 52		17 00		17 07		17 15		17 22	17 22	
Green Lane	d				16 24				16 39		16 47		16 54	16 54		17 02		17 09		17 17		17 24	17 24	
Rock Ferry	d				16 27				16 42		16 49		16 57	16 57		17 04		17 12		17 19		17 27	17 27	
Bebington	d				16 29				16 44		16 52		16 59	16 59		17 07		17 14		17 22		17 29	17 29	
Port Sunlight	d				16 31				16 46		16 54		17 01	17 01		17 09		17 16		17 24		17 31	17 31	
Spital	d				16 33				16 48		16 56		17 03	17 03		17 11		17 18		17 26		17 33	17 33	
Bromborough Rake	d				16 35				16 50		16 58		17 05	17 05		17 13		17 20		17 28		17 35	17 35	
Bromborough	d				16 37				16 52		17 00		17 07	17 07		17 15		17 22		17 30		17 37	17 37	
Eastham Rake	d				16 40				16 55		17 02		17 10	17 10		17 17		17 25		17 32		17 40	17 40	
Hooton	d				16 42				16 57		17 04		17 12	17 12		17 19		17 27		17 34		17 42	17 42	
Little Sutton	d								17 01				17 16					17 31				17 46		
Overpool	d								17 03				17 18					17 33				17 48		
Ellesmere Port	a								17 07				17 23					17 37				17 53		
Capenhurst	d				16 47						17 09			17 17		17 24				17 39			17 47	
Bache	d				16 52						17 15			17 22		17 30				17 45			17 52	
Chester	a				16 56						17 18			17 26		17 33				17 48			17 56	

For general notes see front of timetable
For details of catering facilities see
Directory of Train Operators

Liverpool and Birkenhead → New Brighton, West Kirby, Ellesmere Port and Chester

Network Diagram - see first page of Table 101

		ME SX	ME	ME	ME	ME SX	ME	ME SX	ME SO	ME	ME SX	ME	ME	ME	ME	ME	ME	ME	ME	ME	ME	ME	ME	ME
Moorfields 10	d	17 18	17 21	17 26	17 31	17 33	17 36	17 41	17 41	17 46	17 48	17 51	17 56	18 01	18 06	18 11	18 16	18 21	18 26	18 31	18 36	18 41	18 46	18 51
Liverpool Lime Street 10	d	17 20	17 23	17 28	17 33	17 35	17 38	17 43	17 43	17 48	17 50	17 53	17 58	18 03	18 08	18 13	18 18	18 23	18 28	18 33	18 38	18 43	18 48	18 53
Liverpool Central 10	d	17 22	17 25	17 30	17 35	17 37	17 40	17 45	17 45	17 50	17 52	17 55	18 00	18 05	18 10	18 15	18 20	18 25	18 30	18 35	18 40	18 45	18 50	18 55
James Street	d	17 24	17 27	17 32	17 37	17 39	17 42	17 47	17 47	17 52	17 54	17 57	18 02	18 07	18 12	18 17	18 22	18 27	18 32	18 37	18 42	18 47	18 52	18 57
Hamilton Square	d	17 27	17 30	17 35	17 40	17 42	17 45	17 50	17 50	17 55	17 57	18 00	18 05	18 10	18 15	18 20	18 25	18 30	18 35	18 40	18 45	18 50	18 55	19 00
Conway Park	d		17 32		17 42		17 47			17 57		18 02		18 12	18 17		18 27	18 32		18 42	18 47		18 57	19 02
Birkenhead Park	d		17 34		17 44		17 49			17 59		18 04		18 14	18 19		18 29	18 34		18 44	18 49		18 59	19 04
Birkenhead North	d		17 37		17 47		17 52			18 02		18 07		18 17	18 22		18 32	18 37		18 47	18 52		19 02	19 07
Wallasey Village	d				17 52					18 07				18 22			18 37			18 52			19 07	
Wallasey Grove Road	d				17 53					18 08				18 23			18 38			18 53			19 08	
New Brighton	a				17 58					18 13				18 28			18 43			18 58			19 13	
Bidston	d		17 40				17 55					18 10			18 25			18 40			18 55			19 10
Leasowe	d		17 42				17 57					18 12			18 27			18 42			18 57			19 12
Moreton (Merseyside)	d		17 44				17 59					18 14			18 29			18 44			18 59			19 14
Meols	d		17 48				18 03					18 18			18 33			18 48			19 03			19 18
Manor Road	d		17 50				18 05					18 20			18 35			18 50			19 05			19 20
Hoylake	d		17 52				18 07					18 22			18 37			18 52			19 07			19 22
West Kirby	a		17 57				18 12					18 27			18 42			18 57			19 12			19 27
Birkenhead Central	d	17 30		17 37		17 45		17 52	17 52		18 00		18 07			18 22			18 37			18 52		
Green Lane	d	17 32		17 39		17 47		17 54	17 54		18 02		18 09			18 24			18 39			18 54		
Rock Ferry	d	17 34		17 42		17 49		17 57	17 57		18 04		18 12			18 27			18 42			18 57		
Bebington	d	17 37		17 44		17 52		17 59	17 59		18 07		18 14			18 29			18 44			18 59		
Port Sunlight	d	17 39		17 46		17 54		18 01	18 01		18 09		18 16			18 31			18 46			19 01		
Spital	d	17 41		17 48		17 56		18 03	18 03		18 11		18 18			18 33			18 48			19 03		
Bromborough Rake	d	17 43		17 50		17 58		18 05	18 05		18 13		18 20			18 35			18 50			19 05		
Bromborough	d	17 45		17 52		18 00		18 07	18 07		18 15		18 22			18 37			18 52			19 07		
Eastham Rake	d	17 47		17 55		18 02		18 10	18 10		18 17		18 25			18 40			18 55			19 10		
Hooton	d	17 49		17 57		18 04		18 12	18 12		18 19		18 27			18 42			18 57			19 12		
Little Sutton	d			18 01				18 16					18 31						19 01					
Overpool	d			18 03				18 18					18 33						19 03					
Ellesmere Port	a			18 07				18 23					18 37						19 07					
Capenhurst	d	17 54				18 09			18 17		18 24					18 47						19 17		
Bache	d	18 00				18 15			18 22		18 30					18 52						19 22		
Chester	a	18 03				18 18			18 26		18 33					18 56						19 26		

		ME	ME	ME	ME	ME	ME	ME	ME	ME	ME	ME		ME	ME	ME	ME	ME	ME	ME	ME
Moorfields 10	d	18 56	19 01	19 06	19 11	19 16	19 26	19 31	19 41	19 46	19 56	20 01		23 01	23 11	23 16	23 26	23 31	23 41	23 46	23 56
Liverpool Lime Street 10	d	18 58	19 03	19 08	19 13	19 18	19 28	19 33	19 43	19 48	19 58	20 03		23 03	23 13	23 18	23 28	23 33	23 43	23 48	23 58
Liverpool Central 10	d	19 00	19 05	19 10	19 15	19 20	19 30	19 35	19 45	19 50	20 00	20 05		23 05	23 15	23 20	23 30	23 35	23 45	23 50	23 59
James Street	d	19 02	19 07	19 12	19 17	19 22	19 32	19 37	19 47	19 52	20 02	20 07		23 07	23 17	23 22	23 32	23 37	23 47	23 52	00 02
Hamilton Square	d	19 05	19 10	19 15	19 20	19 25	19 35	19 40	19 50	19 55	20 05	20 10		23 10	23 20	23 25	23 35	23 40	23 50	23 55	00a05
Conway Park	d		19 12	19 17		19 27		19 42		19 57		20 12		23 12		23 27		23 42		23 57	
Birkenhead Park	d		19 14	19 19		19 29		19 44		19 59		20 14		23 14		23 29		23 44		23 59	
Birkenhead North	d		19 17	19 22		19 32		19 47		20 02		20 17		23 17		23 32		23 47		00 02	
Wallasey Village	d		19 22			19 37				20 07						23 37				00 07	
Wallasey Grove Road	d		19 23			19 38				20 08						23 38				00 08	
New Brighton	a		19 28			19 43				20 13						23 43				00 13	
Bidston	d			19 25				19 50				20 20	and at	23 20				23 50			
Leasowe	d			19 27				19 52				20 22	the same	23 22				23 52			
Moreton (Merseyside)	d			19 29				19 54				20 24	minutes	23 24				23 54			
Meols	d			19 33				19 58				20 28	past	23 28				23 58			
Manor Road	d			19 35				20 00				20 30	each	23 30				23 59			
Hoylake	d			19 37				20 02				20 32	hour until	23 32				00 02			
West Kirby	a			19 42				20 07				20 37		23 37				00 07			
Birkenhead Central	d	19 07			19 22		19 37		19 52		20 07				23 22		23 37		23 52		
Green Lane	d	19 09			19 24		19 39		19 54		20 09				23 24		23 39		23 54		
Rock Ferry	d	19 12			19 27		19 42		19 57		20 12				23 27		23 42		23 57		
Bebington	d	19 14			19 29		19 44		19 59		20 14				23 29		23 44		23 59		
Port Sunlight	d	19 16			19 31		19 46		20 01		20 16				23 31		23 46		00 01		
Spital	d	19 18			19 33		19 48		20 03		20 18				23 33		23 48		00 03		
Bromborough Rake	d	19 20			19 35		19 50		20 05		20 20				23 35		23 50		00 05		
Bromborough	d	19 22			19 37		19 52		20 07		20 22				23 37		23 52		00 07		
Eastham Rake	d	19 25			19 40		19 55		20 10		20 25				23 40		23 55		00 10		
Hooton	d	19 27			19 42		19 57		20 12		20 27				23 42		23 57		00 12		
Little Sutton	d	19 31					20 01				20 31						00 01				
Overpool	d	19 33					20 03				20 33						00 03				
Ellesmere Port	a	19 37					20 07				20 37						00 07				
Capenhurst	d				19 47				20 17						23 47				00 17		
Bache	d				19 52				20 22						23 52				00 22		
Chester	a				19 56				20 26						23 56				00 26		

For general notes see front of timetable
For details of catering facilities see Directory of Train Operators

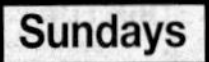

Liverpool and Birkenhead → New Brighton, West Kirby, Ellesmere Port and Chester

Network Diagram - see first page of Table 101

Station		ME	ME		ME	ME	ME	ME	ME	ME	ME	ME			ME	ME	ME	ME	ME		ME	ME	ME		
Moorfields 10	d	07 56	08 01		08 11	08 16	08 26	08 31	08 41	08 46	08 56	09 01	and at the same minutes past each hour until		23 01	23 11	23 16	23 26	23 31		23 41	23 46	23 56		
Liverpool Lime Street 10	d	07 58	08 03		08 13	08 18	08 28	08 33	08 43	08 48	08 58	09 03			23 03	23 13	23 18	23 28	23 33		23 43	23 48	23 58		
Liverpool Central 10	d	08 00	08 05		08 15	08 20	08 30	08 35	08 45	08 50	09 00	09 05			23 05	23 15	23 20	23 30	23 35		23 45	23 50	23 59		
James Street	d	08 02	08 07		08 17	08 22	08 32	08 37	08 47	08 52	09 02	09 07			23 07	23 17	23 22	23 32	23 37		23 47	23 52	00 02		
Hamilton Square	d	08 05	08 10		08 20	08 25	08 35	08 40	08 50	08 55	09 05	09 10			23 10	23 20	23 25	23 35	23 40		23 50	23 55	00a05		
Conway Park	d		08 12			08 27		08 42		08 57		09 12			23 12		23 27		23 42			23 57			
Birkenhead Park	d		08 14			08 29		08 44		08 59		09 14			23 14		23 29		23 44			23 59			
Birkenhead North	d		08 17			08 32		08 47		09 02		09 17			23 17		23 32		23 47			00 02			
Wallasey Village	d					08 37				09 07							23 37					00 07			
Wallasey Grove Road	d					08 38				09 08							23 38					00 08			
New Brighton	a					08 43				09 13							23 43					00 13			
Bidston	d		08 20					08 50				09 20			23 20				23 50						
Leasowe	d		08 22					08 52				09 22			23 22				23 52						
Moreton (Merseyside)	d		08 24					08 54				09 24			23 24				23 54						
Meols	d		08 28					08 58				09 28			23 28				23 58						
Manor Road	d		08 30					09 00				09 30			23 30				23 59						
Hoylake	d		08 32					09 02				09 32			23 32				00 02						
West Kirby	a		08 37					09 07				09 37			23 37				00 07						
Birkenhead Central	d	08 07			08 22		08 37		08 52		09 07					23 22		23 37			23 52				
Green Lane	d	08 09			08 24		08 39		08 54		09 09					23 24		23 39			23 54				
Rock Ferry	d	08 12			08 27		08 42		08 57		09 12					23 27		23 42			23 57				
Bebington	d	08 14			08 29		08 44		08 59		09 14					23 29		23 44			23 59				
Port Sunlight	d	08 16			08 31		08 46		09 01		09 16					23 31		23 46			00 01				
Spital	d	08 18			08 33		08 48		09 03		09 18					23 33		23 48			00 03				
Bromborough Rake	d	08 20			08 35		08 50		09 05		09 20					23 35		23 50			00 05				
Bromborough	d	08 22			08 37		08 52		09 07		09 22					23 37		23 52			00 07				
Eastham Rake	d	08 25			08 40		08 55		09 10		09 25					23 40		23 55			00 10				
Hooton	d	08 27			08 42		08 57		09 12		09 27					23 42		23 57			00 12				
Little Sutton	d	08 31					09 01				09 31							00 01							
Overpool	d	08 33					09 03				09 33							00 03							
Ellesmere Port	a	08 37					09 07				09 37							00 07							
Capenhurst	d				08 47				09 17							23 47					00 17				
Bache	d				08 52				09 22							23 52					00 22				
Chester	a				08 56				09 26							23 56					00 26				

For general notes see front of timetable
For details of catering facilities see Directory of Train Operators

Table 106

Mondays to Saturdays

Chester, Ellesmere Port, West Kirby and New Brighton → Birkenhead and Liverpool

Network Diagram - see first page of Table 101

Miles	Miles	Miles	Miles			ME	ME	ME	ME	ME	ME	ME	ME	ME	ME		ME	ME	ME	ME	ME	ME	ME	ME	ME	ME
0	—	—	—	**Chester**	d						06 00				06 30							07 00				
1½	—	—	—	Bache	d						06 03				06 33							07 03				
5¼	—	—	—	Capenhurst	d						06 09				06 39							07 09				
—	0	—	—	**Ellesmere Port**	d									06 19					06 49						07 19	
—	1½	—	—	Overpool	d									06 22					06 52						07 22	
—	2½	—	—	Little Sutton	d									06 24					06 54						07 24	
8¼	4	—	—	Hooton	d		05 44			05 59	06 14			06 29	06 44				06 59			07 14			07 29	
9¼	—	—	—	Eastham Rake	d		05 46			06 01	06 16			06 31	06 46				07 01			07 16			07 31	
9¾	—	—	—	Bromborough	d		05 48			06 03	06 18			06 33	06 48				07 03			07 18			07 33	
10½	—	—	—	Bromborough Rake	d		05 50			06 05	06 20			06 35	06 50				07 05			07 20			07 35	
11¼	—	—	—	Spital	d		05 52			06 07	06 22			06 37	06 52				07 07			07 22			07 37	
11¾	—	—	—	Port Sunlight	d		05 54			06 09	06 24			06 39	06 54				07 09			07 24			07 39	
12¾	—	—	—	Bebington	d		05 56			06 11	06 26			06 41	06 56				07 11			07 26			07 41	
13¾	—	—	—	Rock Ferry	d	05 44	05 59			06 14	06 29			06 44	06 59				07 14			07 29			07 44	
14½	—	—	—	Green Lane	d	05 47	06 02			06 17	06 32			06 47	07 02				07 17			07 32			07 47	
15	—	—	—	Birkenhead Central	d	05 49	06 04			06 19	06 34			06 49	07 04				07 19			07 34			07 49	
—	—	0	—	**West Kirby**	d				05 51				06 21					06 51			07 06			07 21		
—	—	1	—	Hoylake	d				05 54				06 24					06 54			07 09			07 24		
—	—	1¾	—	Manor Road	d				05 56				06 26					06 56			07 11			07 26		
—	—	3	—	Meols	d				05 58				06 28					06 58			07 13			07 28		
—	—	4¼	—	Moreton (Merseyside)	d				06 01				06 31					07 01			07 16			07 31		
—	—	4¾	—	Leasowe	d				06 03				06 33					07 03			07 18			07 33		
—	—	5¾	—	Bidston	d				06 06				06 36					07 06			07 21			07 36		
—	—	—	0	**New Brighton**	d			05 53				06 23					06 53			07 08			07 23			07 38
—	—	—	1¼	Wallasey Grove Road	d			05 57				06 27					06 57			07 12			07 27			07 42
—	—	—	1½	Wallasey Village	d			05 59				06 29					06 59			07 14			07 29			07 44
—	—	6½	3	Birkenhead North	d			06 04	06 09			06 34	06 39				07 04	07 09		07 19	07 24		07 34	07 39		07 49
—	—	7¼	3¾	Birkenhead Park	d			06 06	06 11			06 36	06 41				07 06	07 11		07 21	07 26		07 36	07 41		07 51
—	—	8¼	4½	Conway Park	d			06 09	06 14			06 39	06 44				07 09	07 14		07 24	07 29		07 39	07 44		07 54
15½	—	8¾	5	Hamilton Square	d	05 51	06 06	06 11	06 16	06 21	06 36	06 41	06 46	06 51	07 06		07 11	07 16	07 21	07 26	07 31	07 36	07 41	07 46	07 51	07 56
16¾	—	9¾	6¼	James Street	d	05 54	06 09	06 14	06 19	06 24	06 39	06 44	06 49	06 54	07 09		07 14	07 19	07 24	07 29	07 34	07 39	07 44	07 49	07 54	07 59
17¼	—	10¼	7¾	**Moorfields** 10	a	05 56	06 11	06 16	06 21	06 26	06 41	06 46	06 51	06 56	07 11		07 16	07 21	07 26	07 31	07 36	07 41	07 46	07 51	07 56	08 01
17¾	—	10¾	8¼	**Liverpool Lime Street** 10	a	05 58	06 13	06 18	06 23	06 28	06 43	06 48	06 53	06 58	07 13		07 18	07 23	07 28	07 33	07 38	07 43	07 48	07 53	07 58	08 03
18½	—	11¼	8¾	**Liverpool Central** 10	a	06 00	06 15	06 20	06 25	06 30	06 45	06 50	06 55	07 00	07 15		07 20	07 25	07 30	07 35	07 40	07 45	07 50	07 55	08 00	08 05

		ME SX	ME		ME SX	ME SO	ME	ME SX	ME	ME	ME	ME SX	ME	ME SX		ME SO	ME	ME SX	ME	ME	ME	ME SX	ME	ME	ME	ME SX
Chester	d	07 22				07 30		07 37				07 52				08 00		08 07						08 30		
Bache	d	07 26				07 33		07 41				07 56				08 03		08 11						08 33		
Capenhurst	d	07 32				07 39		07 47				08 02				08 09		08 17						08 39		
Ellesmere Port	d				07 31					07 49				08 01						08 19						
Overpool	d				07 34					07 52				08 04						08 22						
Little Sutton	d				07 36					07 54				08 06						08 24						
Hooton	d	07 36			07b44	07 44		07 51		07 59		08 06		08b14		08 14		08 21		08 29		08 36		08 44		08 51
Eastham Rake	d	07 38			07 46	07 46		07 53		08 01		08 08		08 16		08 16		08 23		08 31		08 38		08 46		08 53
Bromborough	d	07 41			07 48	07 48		07 56		08 03		08 11		08 18		08 18		08 26		08 33		08 41		08 48		08 56
Bromborough Rake	d	07 43			07 50	07 50		07 58		08 05		08 13		08 20		08 20		08 28		08 35		08 43		08 50		08 58
Spital	d	07 45			07 52	07 52		08 00		08 07		08 15		08 22		08 22		08 30		08 37		08 45		08 52		09 00
Port Sunlight	d	07 47			07 54	07 54		08 02		08 09		08 17		08 24		08 24		08 32		08 39		08 47		08 54		09 02
Bebington	d	07 49			07 56	07 56		08 04		08 11		08 19		08 26		08 26		08 34		08 41		08 49		08 56		09 04
Rock Ferry	d	07 52			07 59	07 59		08 07		08 14		08 22		08 29		08 29		08 37		08 44		08 52		08 59		09 07
Green Lane	d	07 54			08 02	08 02		08 09		08 17		08 24		08 32		08 32		08 39		08 47		08 54		09 02		09 09
Birkenhead Central	d	07 57			08 04	08 04		08 12		08 19		08 27		08 34		08 34		08 42		08 49		08 57		09 04		09 12
West Kirby	d		07 36						07 51				08 06						08 21				08 36			
Hoylake	d		07 39						07 54				08 09						08 24				08 39			
Manor Road	d		07 41						07 56				08 11						08 26				08 41			
Meols	d		07 43						07 58				08 13						08 28				08 43			
Moreton (Merseyside)	d		07 46						08 01				08 16						08 31				08 46			
Leasowe	d		07 48						08 03				08 18						08 33				08 48			
Bidston	d		07 51						08 06				08 21						08 36				08 51			
New Brighton	d						07 53				08 08						08 23				08 38				08 53	
Wallasey Grove Road	d						07 57				08 12						08 27				08 42				08 57	
Wallasey Village	d						07 59				08 14						08 29				08 44				08 59	
Birkenhead North	d		07 54				08 04		08 09		08 19		08 24				08 34		08 39		08 49		08 54		09 04	
Birkenhead Park	d		07 56				08 06		08 11		08 21		08 26				08 36		08 41		08 51		08 56		09 06	
Conway Park	d		07 59				08 09		08 14		08 24		08 29				08 39		08 44		08 54		08 59		09 09	
Hamilton Square	d	07 59	08 01		08 06	08 06	08 11	08 14	08 16	08 21	08 26	08 29	08 31	08 36		08 36	08 41	08 44	08 46	08 51	08 56	08 59	09 01	09 06	09 11	09 14
James Street	d	08 02	08 04		08 09	08 09	08 14	08 17	08 19	08 24	08 29	08 32	08 34	08 39		08 39	08 44	08 47	08 49	08 54	08 59	09 02	09 04	09 09	09 14	09 17
Moorfields 10	a	08 03	08 06		08 11	08 11	08 16	08 18	08 21	08 26	08 31	08 33	08 36	08 41		08 41	08 46	08 48	08 51	08 56	09 01	09 03	09 06	09 11	09 16	09 18
Liverpool Lime Street 10	a	08 05	08 08		08 13	08 13	08 18	08 20	08 23	08 28	08 33	08 35	08 38	08 43		08 43	08 48	08 50	08 53	08 58	09 03	09 05	09 08	09 13	09 18	09 20
Liverpool Central 10	a	08 07	08 10		08 15	08 15	08 20	08 22	08 25	08 30	08 35	08 37	08 40	08 45		08 45	08 50	08 52	08 55	09 00	09 05	09 07	09 10	09 15	09 20	09 22

For general notes see front of timetable
For details of catering facilities see Directory of Train Operators

b Arr. 4 minutes earlier

Chester, Ellesmere Port, West Kirby and New Brighton → Birkenhead and Liverpool

Network Diagram - see first page of Table 101

		ME	ME	ME	ME	ME	ME	ME	ME	ME	ME	ME	ME		ME	ME	ME	ME	ME	ME	ME	ME	ME
Chester	d					09 00						09 30								18 00			
Bache	d					09 03						09 33								18 03			
Capenhurst	d					09 09						09 39								18 09			
Ellesmere Port	d		08 49						09 19								17 49						18 19
Overpool	d		08 52						09 22								17 52						18 22
Little Sutton	d		08 54						09 24								17 54						18 24
Hooton	d		08 59			09 14			09 29			09 44					17 59			18 14			18 29
Eastham Rake	d		09 01			09 16			09 31			09 46					18 01			18 16			18 31
Bromborough	d		09 03			09 18			09 33			09 48					18 03			18 18			18 33
Bromborough Rake	d		09 05			09 20			09 35			09 50					18 05			18 20			18 35
Spital	d		09 07			09 22			09 37			09 52					18 07			18 22			18 37
Port Sunlight	d		09 09			09 24			09 39			09 54		and at			18 09			18 24			18 39
Bebington	d		09 11			09 26			09 41			09 56					18 11			18 26			18 41
Rock Ferry	d		09 14			09 29			09 44			09 59		the same			18 14			18 29			18 44
Green Lane	d		09 17			09 32			09 47			10 02					18 17			18 32			18 47
Birkenhead Central	d		09 19			09 34			09 49			10 04		minutes			18 19			18 34			18 49
West Kirby	d	08 51			09 06			09 21			09 36			past		17 51			18 06			18 21	
Hoylake	d	08 54			09 09			09 24			09 39					17 54			18 09			18 24	
Manor Road	d	08 56			09 11			09 26			09 41			each		17 56			18 11			18 26	
Meols	d	08 58			09 13			09 28			09 43					17 58			18 13			18 28	
Moreton (Merseyside)	d	09 01			09 16			09 31			09 46			hour until		18 01			18 16			18 31	
Leasowe	d	09 03			09 18			09 33			09 48					18 03			18 18			18 33	
Bidston	d	09 06			09 21			09 36			09 51					18 06			18 21			18 36	
New Brighton	d			09 08			09 23			09 38			09 53		17 53			18 08			18 23		
Wallasey Grove Road	d			09 12			09 27			09 42			09 57		17 57			18 12			18 27		
Wallasey Village	d			09 14			09 29			09 44			09 59		17 59			18 14			18 29		
Birkenhead North	d	09 09		09 19	09 24		09 34	09 39		09 49	09 54		10 04		18 04	18 09		18 19	18 24		18 34	18 39	
Birkenhead Park	d	09 11		09 21	09 26		09 36	09 41		09 51	09 56		10 06		18 06	18 11		18 21	18 26		18 36	18 41	
Conway Park	d	09 14		09 24	09 29		09 39	09 44		09 54	09 59		10 09		18 09	18 14		18 24	18 29		18 39	18 44	
Hamilton Square	d	09 16	09 21	09 26	09 31	09 36	09 41	09 46	09 51	09 56	10 01	10 06	10 11		18 11	18 16	18 21	18 26	18 31	18 36	18 41	18 46	18 51
James Street	d	09 19	09 24	09 29	09 34	09 39	09 44	09 49	09 54	09 59	10 04	10 09	10 14		18 14	18 19	18 24	18 29	18 34	18 39	18 44	18 49	18 54
Moorfields 10	a	09 21	09 26	09 31	09 36	09 41	09 46	09 51	09 56	10 01	10 06	10 11	10 16		18 16	18 21	18 26	18 31	18 36	18 41	18 46	18 51	18 56
Liverpool Lime Street 10	a	09 23	09 28	09 33	09 38	09 43	09 48	09 53	09 58	10 03	10 08	10 13	10 18		18 18	18 23	18 28	18 33	18 38	18 43	18 48	18 53	18 58
Liverpool Central 10	a	09 25	09 30	09 35	09 40	09 45	09 50	09 55	10 00	10 05	10 10	10 15	10 20		18 20	18 25	18 30	18 35	18 40	18 45	18 50	18 55	19 00

		ME	ME	ME	ME	ME	ME	ME	ME	ME	ME	ME	ME	ME	ME	ME	ME	ME	ME	VT SO 1 ◊ A	ME	ME	ME	ME
Chester	d			18 30				19 00				19 30				20 00				20 20	20 30			
Bache	d			18 33				19 03				19 33				20 03					20 33			
Capenhurst	d			18 39				19 09				19 39				20 09					20 39			
Ellesmere Port	d					18 49				19 19				19 49				20 19					20 49	
Overpool	d					18 52				19 22				19 52				20 22					20 52	
Little Sutton	d					18 54				19 24				19 54				20 24					20 54	
Hooton	d			18 44		18 59		19 14		19 29		19 44		19 59		20 14		20 29			20 44		20 59	
Eastham Rake	d			18 46		19 01		19 16		19 31		19 46		20 01		20 16		20 31			20 46		21 01	
Bromborough	d			18 48		19 03		19 18		19 33		19 48		20 03		20 18		20 33			20 48		21 03	
Bromborough Rake	d			18 50		19 05		19 20		19 35		19 50		20 05		20 20		20 35			20 50		21 05	
Spital	d			18 52		19 07		19 22		19 37		19 52		20 07		20 22		20 37			20 52		21 07	
Port Sunlight	d			18 54		19 09		19 24		19 39		19 54		20 09		20 24		20 39			20 54		21 09	
Bebington	d			18 56		19 11		19 26		19 41		19 56		20 11		20 26		20 41			20 56		21 11	
Rock Ferry	d			18 59		19 14		19 29		19 44		19 59		20 14		20 29		20 44			20 59		21 14	
Green Lane	d			19 02		19 17		19 32		19 47		20 02		20 17		20 32		20 47			21 02		21 17	
Birkenhead Central	d			19 04		19 19		19 34		19 49		20 04		20 19		20 34		20 49			21 04		21 19	
West Kirby	d		18 36				19 01				19 31				20 01				20 31					21 01
Hoylake	d		18 39				19 04				19 34				20 04				20 34					21 04
Manor Road	d		18 41				19 06				19 36				20 06				20 36					21 06
Meols	d		18 43				19 08				19 38				20 08				20 38					21 08
Moreton (Merseyside)	d		18 46				19 11				19 41				20 11				20 41					21 11
Leasowe	d		18 48				19 13				19 43				20 13				20 43					21 13
Bidston	d		18 51				19 16				19 46				20 16				20 46					21 16
New Brighton	d	18 38			18 53				19 23				19 53				20 23					20 53		
Wallasey Grove Road	d	18 42			18 57				19 27				19 57				20 27					20 57		
Wallasey Village	d	18 44			18 59				19 29				19 59				20 29					20 59		
Birkenhead North	d	18 49	18 54		19 04		19 19		19 34		19 49		20 04		20 19		20 34		20 49			21 04		21 19
Birkenhead Park	d	18 51	18 56		19 06		19 21		19 36		19 51		20 06		20 21		20 36		20 51			21 06		21 21
Conway Park	d	18 54	18 59		19 09		19 24		19 39		19 54		20 09		20 24		20 39		20 54			21 09		21 24
Hamilton Square	d	18 56	19 01	19 06	19 11	19 21	19 26	19 36	19 41	19 51	19 56	20 06	20 11	20 21	20 26	20 36	20 41	20 51	20 56		21 06	21 11	21 21	21 26
James Street	d	18 59	19 04	19 09	19 14	19 24	19 29	19 39	19 44	19 54	19 59	20 09	20 14	20 24	20 29	20 39	20 44	20 54	20 59		21 09	21 14	21 24	21 29
Moorfields 10	a	19 01	19 06	19 11	19 16	19 26	19 31	19 41	19 46	19 56	20 01	20 11	20 16	20 26	20 31	20 41	20 46	20 56	21 01		21 11	21 16	21 26	21 31
Liverpool Lime Street 10	a	19 03	19 08	19 13	19 18	19 28	19 33	19 43	19 48	19 58	20 03	20 13	20 18	20 28	20 33	20 43	20 48	20 58	21 03	21b13	21 13	21 18	21 28	21 33
Liverpool Central 10	a	19 05	19 10	19 15	19 20	19 30	19 35	19 45	19 50	20 00	20 05	20 15	20 20	20 30	20 35	20 45	20 50	21 00	21 05		21 15	21 20	21 30	21 35

For general notes see front of timetable
For details of catering facilities see Directory of Train Operators

A From 13 September. From London Euston (Table 65)
b Liverpool Lime Street (Mainline)

Chester, Ellesmere Port, West Kirby and New Brighton → Birkenhead and Liverpool

Network Diagram - see first page of Table 101

Mondays to Saturdays

		ME	ME	ME	ME	ME	ME	ME	ME	ME	ME	ME	ME
Chester	d	21 00				21 30				22 00			
Bache	d	21 03				21 33				22 03			
Capenhurst	d	21 09				21 39				22 09			
Ellesmere Port	d			21 19				21 49				22 19	
Overpool	d			21 22				21 52				22 22	
Little Sutton	d			21 24				21 54				22 24	
Hooton	d	21 14		21 29		21 44		21 59		22 14		22 29	
Eastham Rake	d	21 16		21 31		21 46		22 01		22 16		22 31	
Bromborough	d	21 18		21 33		21 48		22 03		22 18		22 33	
Bromborough Rake	d	21 20		21 35		21 50		22 05		22 20		22 35	
Spital	d	21 22		21 37		21 52		22 07		22 22		22 37	
Port Sunlight	d	21 24		21 39		21 54		22 09		22 24		22 39	
Bebington	d	21 26		21 41		21 56		22 11		22 26		22 41	
Rock Ferry	d	21 29		21 44		21 59		22 14		22 29		22 44	
Green Lane	d	21 32		21 47		22 02		22 17		22 32		22 47	
Birkenhead Central	d	21 34		21 49		22 04		22 19		22 34		22 49	
West Kirby	d				21 31				22 01				22 31
Hoylake	d				21 34				22 04				22 34
Manor Road	d				21 36				22 06				22 36
Meols	d				21 38				22 08				22 38
Moreton (Merseyside)	d				21 41				22 11				22 41
Leasowe	d				21 43				22 13				22 43
Bidston	d				21 46				22 16				22 46
New Brighton	d		21 23				21 53				22 23		
Wallasey Grove Road	d		21 27				21 57				22 27		
Wallasey Village	d		21 29				21 59				22 29		
Birkenhead North	d		21 34		21 49		22 04		22 19		22 34		22 49
Birkenhead Park	d		21 36		21 51		22 06		22 21		22 36		22 51
Conway Park	d		21 39		21 54		22 09		22 24		22 39		22 54
Hamilton Square	d	21 36	21 41	21 51	21 56	22 06	22 11	22 21	22 26	22 36	22 41	22 51	22 56
James Street	d	21 39	21 44	21 54	21 59	22 09	22 14	22 24	22 29	22 39	22 44	22 54	22 59
Moorfields 10	a	21 41	21 46	21 56	22 01	22 11	22 16	22 26	22 31	22 41	22 46	22 56	23 01
Liverpool Lime Street 10	a	21 43	21 48	21 58	22 03	22 13	22 18	22 28	22 33	22 43	22 48	22 58	23 03
Liverpool Central 10	a	21 45	21 50	22 00	22 05	22 15	22 20	22 30	22 35	22 45	22 50	23 00	23 05

		ME	ME	ME	ME	ME	ME	ME	ME
Chester	d	22 30				23 00			23 30
Bache	d	22 33				23 03			23 33
Capenhurst	d	22 39				23 09			23 39
Ellesmere Port	d			22 49				23 19	
Overpool	d			22 52				23 22	
Little Sutton	d			22 54				23 24	
Hooton	d	22 44		22 59		23 14		23 29	23a45
Eastham Rake	d	22 46		23 01		23 16		23 31	
Bromborough	d	22 48		23 03		23 18		23 33	
Bromborough Rake	d	22 50		23 05		23 20		23 35	
Spital	d	22 52		23 07		23 22		23 37	
Port Sunlight	d	22 54		23 09		23 24		23 39	
Bebington	d	22 56		23 11		23 26		23 41	
Rock Ferry	d	22 59		23 14		23 29		23 44	
Green Lane	d	23 02		23 17		23 32		23 47	
Birkenhead Central	d	23 04		23 19		23 34		23 49	
West Kirby	d				23 01				
Hoylake	d				23 04				
Manor Road	d				23 06				
Meols	d				23 08				
Moreton (Merseyside)	d				23 11				
Leasowe	d				23 13				
Bidston	d				23 16				
New Brighton	d		22 53				23 23		
Wallasey Grove Road	d		22 57				23 27		
Wallasey Village	d		22 59				23 29		
Birkenhead North	d		23 04		23 19		23 34		
Birkenhead Park	d		23 06		23 21		23 36		
Conway Park	d		23 09		23 24		23 39		
Hamilton Square	d	23 06	23 11	23 21	23 26	23 36	23 41	23 51	
James Street	d	23 09	23 14	23 24	23 29	23 39	23 44	23 54	
Moorfields 10	a	23 11	23 16	23 26	23 31	23 41	23 46	23 56	
Liverpool Lime Street 10	a	23 13	23 18	23 28	23 33	23 43	23 48	23 58	
Liverpool Central 10	a	23 15	23 20	23 30	23 35	23 45	23 50	23 59	

Sundays

		ME	ME	ME	ME	ME	ME	ME	ME	ME	ME	ME
Chester	d							08 00				08 30
Bache	d							08 03				08 33
Capenhurst	d							08 09				08 39
Ellesmere Port	d					07 49				08 19		
Overpool	d					07 52				08 22		
Little Sutton	d					07 54				08 24		
Hooton	d			07 44		07 59		08 14		08 29		08 44
Eastham Rake	d			07 46		08 01		08 16		08 31		08 46
Bromborough	d			07 48		08 03		08 18		08 33		08 48
Bromborough Rake	d			07 50		08 05		08 20		08 35		08 50
Spital	d			07 52		08 07		08 22		08 37		08 52
Port Sunlight	d			07 54		08 09		08 24		08 39		08 54
Bebington	d			07 56		08 11		08 26		08 41		08 56
Rock Ferry	d	07 44	07 49	07 59		08 14		08 29		08 44		08 59
Green Lane	d	07 47	07 52	08 02		08 17		08 32		08 47		09 02
Birkenhead Central	d	07 49	07 54	08 04		08 19		08 34		08 49		09 04
West Kirby	d						08 01				08 31	
Hoylake	d						08 04				08 34	
Manor Road	d						08 06				08 36	
Meols	d						08 08				08 38	
Moreton (Merseyside)	d						08 11				08 41	
Leasowe	d						08 13				08 43	
Bidston	d						08 16				08 46	
New Brighton	d				07 53				08 23			
Wallasey Grove Road	d				07 57				08 27			
Wallasey Village	d				07 59				08 29			
Birkenhead North	d				08 04		08 19		08 34		08 49	
Birkenhead Park	d				08 06		08 21		08 36		08 51	
Conway Park	d				08 09		08 24		08 39		08 54	
Hamilton Square	d	07 51	07 56	08 06	08 11	08 21	08 26	08 36	08 41	08 51	08 56	09 06
James Street	d	07 54	07 59	08 09	08 14	08 24	08 29	08 39	08 44	08 54	08 59	09 09
Moorfields 10	a	07 56	08 01	08 11	08 16	08 26	08 31	08 41	08 46	08 56	09 01	09 11
Liverpool Lime Street 10	a	07 58	08 03	08 13	08 18	08 28	08 33	08 43	08 48	08 58	09 03	09 13
Liverpool Central 10	a	08 00	08 05	08 15	08 20	08 30	08 35	08 45	08 50	09 00	09 05	09 15

and at the same minutes past each hour until

		ME	ME	ME	ME	VT 1 ◇ A	ME	ME	ME	ME
Chester	d	20 30				20 50	21 00			
Bache	d	20 33					21 03			
Capenhurst	d	20 39					21 09			
Ellesmere Port	d			20 49					21 19	
Overpool	d			20 52					21 22	
Little Sutton	d			20 54					21 24	
Hooton	d	20 44		20 59			21 14		21 29	
Eastham Rake	d	20 46		21 01			21 16		21 31	
Bromborough	d	20 48		21 03			21 18		21 33	
Bromborough Rake	d	20 50		21 05			21 20		21 35	
Spital	d	20 52		21 07			21 22		21 37	
Port Sunlight	d	20 54		21 09			21 24		21 39	
Bebington	d	20 56		21 11			21 26		21 41	
Rock Ferry	d	20 59		21 14			21 29		21 44	
Green Lane	d	21 02		21 17			21 32		21 47	
Birkenhead Central	d	21 04		21 19			21 34		21 49	
West Kirby	d				21 01					21 31
Hoylake	d				21 04					21 34
Manor Road	d				21 06					21 36
Meols	d				21 08					21 38
Moreton (Merseyside)	d				21 11					21 41
Leasowe	d				21 13					21 43
Bidston	d				21 16					21 46
New Brighton	d		20 53					21 23		
Wallasey Grove Road	d		20 57					21 27		
Wallasey Village	d		20 59					21 29		
Birkenhead North	d		21 04		21 19			21 34		21 49
Birkenhead Park	d		21 06		21 21			21 36		21 51
Conway Park	d		21 09		21 24			21 39		21 54
Hamilton Square	d	21 06	21 11	21 21	21 26		21 36	21 41	21 51	21 56
James Street	d	21 09	21 14	21 24	21 29		21 39	21 44	21 54	21 59
Moorfields 10	a	21 11	21 16	21 26	21 31		21 41	21 46	21 56	22 01
Liverpool Lime Street 10	a	21 13	21 18	21 28	21 33	21b41	21 43	21 48	21 58	22 03
Liverpool Central 10	a	21 15	21 20	21 30	21 35		21 45	21 50	22 00	22 05

For general notes see front of timetable
For details of catering facilities see Directory of Train Operators

A From 14 September. From London Euston (Table 65)
b Liverpool Lime Street (Mainline)

Table 106

Sundays

Chester, Ellesmere Port, West Kirby and New Brighton → Birkenhead and Liverpool

Network Diagram - see first page of Table 101

		ME		ME	ME	ME	ME		ME	ME	ME	ME		ME	ME	ME	ME		ME	ME	ME					
Chester	d	21 30					22 00					22 30					23 00				23 30					
Bache	d	21 33					22 03					22 33					23 03				23 33					
Capenhurst	d	21 39					22 09					22 39					23 09				23 39					
Ellesmere Port	d				21 49					22 19					22 49					23 19						
Overpool	d				21 52					22 22					22 52					23 22						
Little Sutton	d				21 54					22 24					22 54					23 24						
Hooton	d	21 44			21 59		22 14			22 29		22 44			22 59		23 14			23 29	23a45					
Eastham Rake	d	21 46			22 01		22 16			22 31		22 46			23 01		23 16			23 31						
Bromborough	d	21 48			22 03		22 18			22 33		22 48			23 03		23 18			23 33						
Bromborough Rake	d	21 50			22 05		22 20			22 35		22 50			23 05		23 20			23 35						
Spital	d	21 52			22 07		22 22			22 37		22 52			23 07		23 22			23 37						
Port Sunlight	d	21 54			22 09		22 24			22 39		22 54			23 09		23 24			23 39						
Bebington	d	21 56			22 11		22 26			22 41		22 56			23 11		23 26			23 41						
Rock Ferry	d	21 59			22 14		22 29			22 44		22 59			23 14		23 29			23 44						
Green Lane	d	22 02			22 17		22 32			22 47		23 02			23 17		23 32			23 47						
Birkenhead Central	d	22 04			22 19		22 34			22 49		23 04			23 19		23 34			23 49						
West Kirby	d					22 01					22 31					23 01										
Hoylake	d					22 04					22 34					23 04										
Manor Road	d					22 06					22 36					23 06										
Meols	d					22 08					22 38					23 08										
Moreton (Merseyside)	d					22 11					22 41					23 11										
Leasowe	d					22 13					22 43					23 13										
Bidston	d					22 16					22 46					23 16										
New Brighton	d			21 53					22 23					22 53					23 23							
Wallasey Grove Road	d			21 57					22 27					22 57					23 27							
Wallasey Village	d			21 59					22 29					22 59					23 29							
Birkenhead North	d			22 04		22 19			22 34		22 49			23 04		23 19			23 34							
Birkenhead Park	d			22 06		22 21			22 36		22 51			23 06		23 21			23 36							
Conway Park	d			22 09		22 24			22 39		22 54			23 09		23 24			23 39							
Hamilton Square	d	22 06		22 11	22 21	22 26	22 36		22 41	22 51	22 56	23 06		23 11	23 21	23 26	23 36		23 41	23 51						
James Street	d	22 09		22 14	22 24	22 29	22 39		22 44	22 54	22 59	23 09		23 14	23 24	23 29	23 39		23 44	23 54						
Moorfields 10	a	22 11		22 16	22 26	22 31	22 41		22 46	22 56	23 01	23 11		23 16	23 26	23 31	23 41		23 46	23 56						
Liverpool Lime Street 10	a	22 13		22 18	22 28	22 33	22 43		22 48	22 58	23 03	23 13		23 18	23 28	23 33	23 43		23 48	23 58						
Liverpool Central 10	a	22 15		22 20	22 30	22 35	22 45		22 50	23 00	23 05	23 15		23 20	23 30	23 35	23 45		23 50	23 59						

For general notes see front of timetable
For details of catering facilities see
Directory of Train Operators

Mondays to Saturdays

Helsby — Ellesmere Port

Network Diagram - see first page of Table 101

Miles			NT	NT	NT A	NT
—	Warrington Bank Quay	81 d	06 00		15 02	
0	**Helsby**	d	06 14	06 46	15 30	16 03
2	Ince & Elton	d	06 17	06 49	15 33	16 06
2¾	Stanlow & Thornton	d	06 19	06 51	15 35	16 08
5¼	**Ellesmere Port**	a	06 27	06 57	15 41	16 14
—	Hooton	106 a	06 59	07 29	15 59	16 29
—	Liverpool Lime Street	106 a	07 28	07 58	16 28	16 58

Mondays to Saturdays

Miles			NT	NT SX	NT SO	NT	NT B
—	Liverpool Lime Street	106 d		05 58	05 58	14 58	15 28
—	Hooton	106 d		06 27	06 27	15 27	15 57
0	**Ellesmere Port**	d	06 32	07 02	07 02	15 47	16 17
2½	Stanlow & Thornton	d	06 36	07 06	07 06	15 51	16 21
3¼	Ince & Elton	d	06 39	07 09	07 09	15 54	16 24
5¼	**Helsby**	a	06 42	07 12	07 12	15 57	16 27
—	Warrington Bank Quay	81 a	07 15	07 27	07 52	16 19	16 45

For general notes see front of timetable
For details of catering facilities see Directory of Train Operators

A From Liverpool Lime Street (Table 90)
B To Liverpool Lime Street (Table 90)

No Sunday Service

Network Diagram for Tables 114, 115

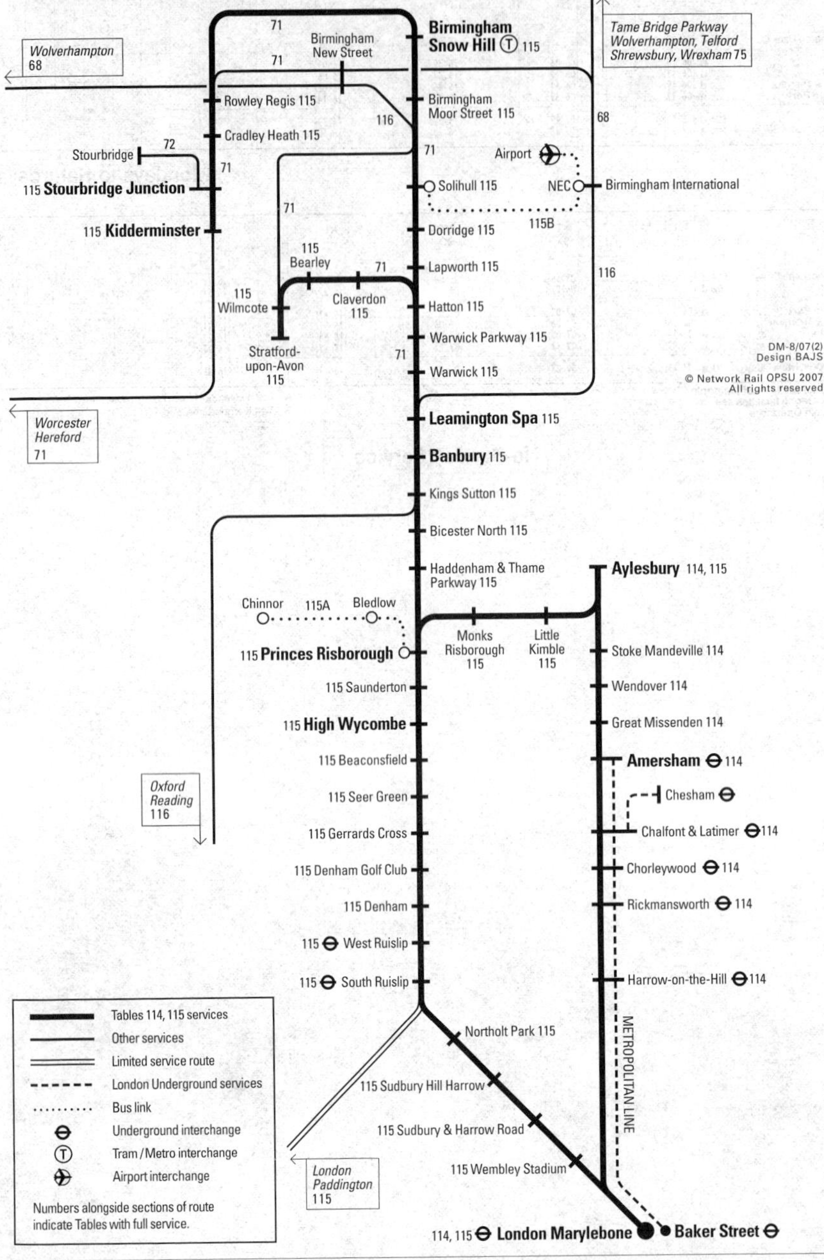

Birmingham Snow Hill 115
Birmingham New Street
Wolverhampton 68
Tame Bridge Parkway Wolverhampton, Telford Shrewsbury, Wrexham 75
71
Rowley Regis 115
Birmingham Moor Street 115
116
68
Cradley Heath 115
Stourbridge
72
115 Stourbridge Junction
Airport
Solihull 115
NEC
Birmingham International
115 Kidderminster
Dorridge 115
115B
115 Bearley
Lapworth 115
116
Claverdon 115
115 Wilmcote
Hatton 115
Warwick Parkway 115
Stratford-upon-Avon 115
Warwick 115
DM-8/07(2)
Design BAJS
© Network Rail OPSU 2007
All rights reserved
Worcester Hereford 71
Leamington Spa 115
Banbury 115
Kings Sutton 115
Bicester North 115
Haddenham & Thame Parkway 115
Aylesbury 114, 115
Chinnor
115A
Bledlow
115 Princes Risborough
Monks Risborough 115
Little Kimble 115
Stoke Mandeville 114
115 Saunderton
Wendover 114
115 High Wycombe
Great Missenden 114
115 Beaconsfield
Amersham 114
Oxford Reading 116
115 Seer Green
Chesham
115 Gerrards Cross
Chalfont & Latimer 114
115 Denham Golf Club
Chorleywood 114
115 Denham
Rickmansworth 114
115 West Ruislip
115 South Ruislip
Harrow-on-the-Hill 114
Northolt Park 115
115 Sudbury Hill Harrow
METROPOLITAN LINE
115 Sudbury & Harrow Road
115 Wembley Stadium
London Paddington 115
114, 115 London Marylebone
Baker Street
Tables 114, 115 services
Other services
Limited service route
London Underground services
Bus link
Underground interchange
Tram/Metro interchange
Airport interchange
Numbers alongside sections of route indicate Tables with full service.

London → Amersham and Aylesbury

Network Diagram - See first page of Table 114

Mondays to Fridays

Miles			CH	CH MX	CH	CH	CH	CH	CH		CH	CH	CH	CH	CH	CH	CH		CH	CH	CH	CH	CH	CH	CH	CH
0	**London Marylebone 10**	⊖ d	23p27	23p57	06 35	07 07	07 29	07 56	08 27		09 00	09 27	09 57	10 27	10 57	11 27	11 57		12 27	12 57	13 27	13 57	14 27	14 57	15 27	15 57
9	Harrow-on-the-Hill 3 §	⊖ d	23p39	00 09	06 47	07 19	07 41	08 08	08 39		09 12	09 39	10 09	10 39	11 09	11 39	12 09		12 39	13 09	13 39	14 09	14 39	15 09	15 39	16 09
17	Rickmansworth §	⊖ d	23p49	00 19	06 58	07 29	07 51	08 18	08 49		09 22	09 49	10 19	10 49	11 19	11 49	12 20		12 49	13 19	13 49	14 19	14 49	15 19	15 49	16 19
19¾	Chorleywood §	⊖ d	23p54	00 24	07 02	07 34	07 56	08 23	08 54		09 27	09 54	10 24	10 54	11 24	11 54	12 24		12 54	13 24	13 54	14 24	14 54	15 24	15 54	16 24
21½	Chalfont & Latimer §	⊖ d	23p58	00 28	07 06	07 38	08 00	08 27	08 58		09 31	09 58	10 28	10 58	11 28	11 58	12 28		12 58	13 28	13 58	14 28	14 58	15 28	15 58	16 28
23½	**Amersham §**	⊖ d	00 02	00 32	07 10	07 42	08 04	08 31	09 02		09 35	10 02	10 32	11 02	11 32	12 02	12 32		13 02	13 32	14 02	14 32	15 02	15 32	16 02	16 32
28¾	Great Missenden	d	00 08	00 38	07 17	07 48	08 10	08 37	09 08		09 41	10 08	10 38	11 08	11 38	12 08	12 39		13 08	13 38	14 08	14 38	15 08	15 38	16 08	16 38
33¾	Wendover	d	00 14	00 44	07 23	07 54	08 16	08 43	09 14		09 47	10 14	10 44	11 14	11 44	12 14	12 45		13 14	13 44	14 14	14 44	15 14	15 44	16 14	16 44
35¾	Stoke Mandeville	d	00 18	00 48	07 27	07 58	08 20	08 47	09 18		09 51	10 18	10 48	11 18	11 48	12 18	12 49		13 18	13 48	14 18	14 48	15 18	15 48	16 18	16 48
37¾	**Aylesbury**	a	00 26	00 56	07 34	08 06	08 28	08 55	09 26		09 59	10 26	10 56	11 26	11 56	12 26	12 56		13 26	13 56	14 26	14 56	15 26	15 56	16 26	16 56

		CH		CH	CH	CH	CH	CH	CH	CH		CH	CH	CH	CH	CH	CH	CH	CH	CH	CH	CH	CH	CH		
London Marylebone 10	⊖ d	16 25		16 42	16 56	17 16	17 27	17 50	18 06	18 23		18 40	18 57	19 15	19 27	19 57	20 27	20 57	21 27	21 57	22 27	22 57	23 27	23 57		
Harrow-on-the-Hill 3 §	⊖ d	16 37			17 08		17 39		18 18			18 52	19 09		19 39	20 09	20 39	21 09	21 39	22 09	22 39	23 09	23 39	00 09		
Rickmansworth §	⊖ d				17 18		17 50								19 50	20 19	20 49	21 19	21 49	22 19	22 49	23 19	23 49	00 19		
Chorleywood §	⊖ d	16 51			17 23		17 54		18 32			19 06	19 23		19 54	20 24	20 54	21 24	21 54	22 24	22 54	23 24	23 54	00 24		
Chalfont & Latimer §	⊖ d	16 55			17 27		18 00		18 36			19 10	19 27		19 58	20 28	20 58	21 28	21 58	22 28	22 58	23 28	23 58	00 28		
Amersham §	⊖ d	16 59		17 12	17 31		18 04	18 20	18 41			19 15	19 31		20 02	20 32	21 02	21 32	22 02	22 32	23 02	23 32	00 02	00 32		
Great Missenden	d	17 05		17 19	17 37	17 51	18 10	18 26	18 47	18 59		19 21	19 37	19 51	20 09	20 38	21 08	21 38	22 08	22 38	23 08	23 38	00 08	00 38		
Wendover	d	17 11		17 25	17 43	17 57	18 16	18 32	18 53	19 05		19 27	19 43	19 57	20 15	20 44	21 14	21 44	22 14	22 44	23 14	23 44	00 14	00 44		
Stoke Mandeville	d	17 15		17 29	17 47	18 01	18 20	18 36	18 57	19 09		19 31	19 47	20 01	20 19	20 48	21 18	21 48	22 18	22 48	23 18	23 48	00 18	00 48		
Aylesbury	a	17 23		17 39	17 55	18 12	18 26	18 47	19 05	19 19		19 39	19 55	20 13	20 26	20 56	21 26	21 56	22 26	22 56	23 26	23 56	00 26	00 56		

Saturdays

		CH	CH		CH	CH		CH	CH		CH	CH		CH	CH		CH	CH		CH	CH		CH	CH		CH
London Marylebone 10	⊖ d	23p27	23p57			07 27		07 57	08 27		08 57	09 27		09 57	10 27		10 57	11 27		11 57	12 27		12 57	13 27		13 57
Harrow-on-the-Hill 3 §	⊖ d	23p39	00 09			07 39		08 09	08 39		09 09	09 39		10 09	10 39		11 09	11 39		12 09	12 39		13 09	13 39		14 09
Rickmansworth §	⊖ d	23p49	00 19			07 49		08 19	08 49		09 19	09 49		10 19	10 49		11 19	11 49		12 19	12 49		13 19	13 49		14 19
Chorleywood §	⊖ d	23p54	00 24			07 54		08 24	08 54		09 24	09 54		10 24	10 54		11 24	11 54		12 24	12 54		13 24	13 54		14 24
Chalfont & Latimer §	⊖ d	23p58	00 28			07 58		08 28	08 58		09 28	09 58		10 28	10 58		11 28	11 58		12 28	12 58		13 28	13 58		14 28
Amersham §	⊖ d	00 02	00 32		07 05	08 02		08 32	09 02		09 32	10 02		10 32	11 02		11 32	12 02		12 32	13 02		13 32	14 02		14 32
Great Missenden	d	00 08	00 38		07 11	08 08		08 38	09 08		09 38	10 08		10 38	11 08		11 38	12 08		12 38	13 08		13 38	14 08		14 38
Wendover	d	00 14	00 44		07 17	08 14		08 44	09 14		09 44	10 14		10 44	11 14		11 44	12 14		12 44	13 14		13 44	14 14		14 44
Stoke Mandeville	d	00 18	00 48		07 21	08 18		08 48	09 18		09 48	10 18		10 48	11 18		11 48	12 18		12 48	13 18		13 48	14 18		14 48
Aylesbury	a	00 26	00 56		07 29	08 26		08 56	09 26		09 56	10 26		10 56	11 26		11 56	12 26		12 56	13 26		13 56	14 26		14 56

		CH	CH		CH	CH		CH	CH		CH	CH		CH	CH		CH	CH		CH	CH		CH	CH		
London Marylebone 10	⊖ d	14 27	14 57		15 27	15 57		16 27	16 57		17 27	17 57		18 27	18 57		19 27	19 57		20 57	21 57		22 57	23 57		
Harrow-on-the-Hill 3 §	⊖ d	14 39	15 09		15 39	16 09		16 39	17 09		17 39	18 09		18 39	19 09		19 39	20 09		21 09	22 09		23 09	00 09		
Rickmansworth §	⊖ d	14 49	15 19		15 49	16 19		16 49	17 19		17 49	18 19		18 49	19 19		19 49	20 19		21 19	22 19		23 19	00 19		
Chorleywood §	⊖ d	14 54	15 24		15 54	16 24		16 54	17 24		17 54	18 24		18 54	19 24		19 54	20 24		21 24	22 24		23 24	00 24		
Chalfont & Latimer §	⊖ d	14 58	15 28		15 58	16 28		16 58	17 28		17 58	18 28		18 58	19 28		19 58	20 28		21 28	22 28		23 28	00 28		
Amersham §	⊖ d	15 02	15 32		16 02	16 32		17 02	17 32		18 02	18 32		19 02	19 32		20 02	20 32		21 32	22 32		23 32	00 32		
Great Missenden	d	15 08	15 38		16 08	16 38		17 08	17 38		18 08	18 38		19 08	19 38		20 08	20 38		21 38	22 38		23 38	00 38		
Wendover	d	15 14	15 44		16 14	16 44		17 14	17 44		18 14	18 44		19 14	19 44		20 14	20 44		21 44	22 44		23 44	00 44		
Stoke Mandeville	d	15 18	15 48		16 18	16 48		17 18	17 48		18 18	18 48		19 18	19 48		20 18	20 48		21 48	22 48		23 48	00 48		
Aylesbury	a	15 26	15 56		16 26	16 56		17 26	17 56		18 26	18 56		19 26	19 56		20 26	20 56		21 56	22 56		23 56	00 56		

Sundays

		CH		CH		CH		CH		CH		CH		CH		CH		CH		CH		CH		CH		CH
London Marylebone 10	⊖ d			23p57				08 27		09 27		10 27		11 27		12 27		13 27		14 27				15 27		
Harrow-on-the-Hill 3 §	⊖ d			00 09				08 39		09 39		10 39		11 39		12 39		13 39		14 39				15 39		
Rickmansworth §	⊖ d			00 19				08 50		09 50		10 49		11 49		12 49		13 49		14 49				15 49		
Chorleywood §	⊖ d			00 24				08 54		09 54		10 54		11 54		12 54		13 54		14 54				15 54		
Chalfont & Latimer §	⊖ d			00 28				08 58		09 58		10 58		11 58		12 58		13 58		14 58				15 58		
Amersham §	⊖ d	00 02		00 32		08 32		09 02		10 02		11 02		12 02		13 02		14 02		15 02		15 32		16 02		16 32
Great Missenden	d	00 08		00 38		08 38		09 09		10 09		11 08		12 08		13 08		14 08		15 08		15 38		16 08		16 38
Wendover	d	00 14		00 44		08 44		09 15		10 15		11 14		12 14		13 14		14 14		15 14		15 44		16 14		16 44
Stoke Mandeville	d	00 18		00 48		08 48		09 19		10 19		11 18		12 18		13 18		14 18		15 18		15 48		16 18		16 48
Aylesbury	a	00 26		00 56		08 56		09 26		10 26		11 26		12 26		13 26		14 26		15 26		15 56		16 26		16 56

		CH		CH		CH		CH		CH		CH		CH		CH		CH		CH		CH	CH	CH		
London Marylebone 10	⊖ d	16 27				17 27				18 27				19 27				20 27				21 27	22 27	23 27		
Harrow-on-the-Hill 3 §	⊖ d	16 39				17 39				18 39				19 39				20 39				21 39	22 39	23 39		
Rickmansworth §	⊖ d	16 49				17 49				18 49				19 49				20 49				21 49	22 49	23 49		
Chorleywood §	⊖ d	16 54				17 54				18 54				19 54				20 54				21 54	22 54	23 54		
Chalfont & Latimer §	⊖ d	16 58				17 58				18 58				19 58				20 58				21 58	22 58	23 58		
Amersham §	⊖ d	17 02		17 32		18 02		18 32		19 02		19 32		20 02		20 32		21 02		21 32		22 02	23 02	00 02		
Great Missenden	d	17 08		17 38		18 08		18 38		19 08		19 38		20 08		20 38		21 08		21 38		22 08	23 08	00 08		
Wendover	d	17 14		17 44		18 14		18 44		19 14		19 44		20 14		20 44		21 14		21 44		22 14	23 14	00 14		
Stoke Mandeville	d	17 18		17 48		18 18		18 48		19 18		19 48		20 18		20 48		21 18		21 48		22 18	23 18	00 18		
Aylesbury	a	17 26		17 56		18 26		18 56		19 26		19 56		20 26		20 56		21 26		21 56		22 26	23 26	00 26		

For general notes see front of timetable
For details of catering facilities see Directory of Train Operators

§ London Underground Limited (Metropolitan Line) services operate between Harrow-on-the-Hill, Rickmansworth, Chorleywood, Chalfont & Latimer and Amersham

Mondays to Fridays
until 3 October

Aylesbury and Amersham → London

Network Diagram - See first page of Table 114

Miles			CH	CH	CH	CH	CH	CH	CH	CH	CH	CH	CH	CH	CH	CH	CH	CH	CH	CH	CH	CH
0	**Aylesbury**	d	05 31	06 06	06 26	06 43	06 57	07 16	07 30	07 50	08 06	08 25	08 39	09 06	09 37	10 05	10 35	11 05	11 35	12 05	12 35	13 05
2¼	Stoke Mandeville	d	05 35	06 10	06 30	06 47	07 01	07 20	07 34	07 54	08 10	08 29	08 43	09 10	09 41	10 09	10 39	11 09	11 39	12 09	12 39	13 09
4¼	Wendover	d	05 39	06 14	06 34	06 51	07 05	07 24	07 38	07 58	08 14	08 33	08 47	09 14	09 45	10 13	10 43	11 13	11 43	12 13	12 43	13 13
9	Great Missenden	d	05 45	06 20	06 40	06 57	07 11	07 30	07 44	08 04	08 20	08 39	08 53	09 20	09 51	10 19	10 49	11 19	11 49	12 19	12 49	13 19
14¼	**Amersham §**	⊖ d	05 52	06 27	06 47		07 18	07 38	07 51	08 12	08 27		09 00	09 27	09 58	10 26	10 56	11 26	11 56	12 26	12 56	13 26
16¼	Chalfont & Latimer §	⊖ d		06 32	06 51		07 22		07 55		08 31		09 04	09 31	10 02	10 30	11 00	11 30	12 00	12 30	13 00	13 30
18¼	Chorleywood §	⊖ d		06 36	06 54		07 25		07 58		08 34		09 07	09 34	10 05	10 33	11 03	11 33	12 03	12 33	13 03	13 33
20¾	Rickmansworth §	⊖ d			06 59				08 03				09 12	09 39	10 10	10 38	11 08	11 38	12 08	12 38	13 08	13 38
28¾	Harrow-on-the-Hill 3 §	⊖ d	06 10	06 50	07 10		07 39		08 14		08 48		09 23	09 50	10 21	10 49	11 19	11 49	12 19	12 49	13 19	13 49
37¾	**London Marylebone 10**	⊖ a	06 26	07 04	07 25	07 37	07 55	08 14	08 29	08 44	09 05	09 20	09 38	10 05	10 37	11 05	11 35	12 05	12 34	13 05	13 35	14 04

		CH	CH	CH	CH	CH	CH	CH	CH	CH	CH	CH	CH	CH	CH	CH	CH	CH	CH	CH	CH	CH
Aylesbury	d	13 35	14 05	14 35	15 05	15 35	16 05	16 35	17 05	17 35	17 55	18 26	18 45	19 15	19 35	20 05	20 35	21 05	21 35	22 35
Stoke Mandeville	d	13 39	14 09	14 39	15 09	15 39	16 09	16 39	17 09	17 39	17 59	18 30	18 49	19 19	19 39	20 09	20 39	21 09	21 39	22 39
Wendover	d	13 43	14 13	14 43	15 13	15 43	16 13	16 43	17 13	17 43	18 03	18 34	18 53	19 23	19 43	20 13	20 43	21 13	21 43	22 43
Great Missenden	d	13 49	14 19	14 49	15 19	15 49	16 19	16 49	17 19	17 49	18 09	18 40	18 59	19 29	19 49	20 19	20 49	21 19	21 49	22 49
Amersham §	⊖ d	13 56	14 26	14 56	15 26	15 56	16 26	16 56	17 26	17 56	18 16	18 47	19 06	19 36	19 56	20 26	20 56	21 26	21 56	22 56
Chalfont & Latimer §	⊖ d	14 00	14 30	15 00	15 30	16 00	16 30	17 00	17 30	18 00	18 20	18 51	19 10	19 40	20 00	20 30	21 00	21 30	22 00	23 00
Chorleywood §	⊖ d	14 03	14 33	15 03	15 33	16 03	16 33	17 03	17 33	18 03	18 23	18 54	19 13	19 43	20 03	20 33	21 03	21 33	22 03	23 03
Rickmansworth §	⊖ d	14 08	14 38	15 08	15 38	16 08	16 38	17 08	17 38	18 08	18 28	18 59	19 18	19 48	20 08	20 38	21 08	21 38	22 08	23 08
Harrow-on-the-Hill 3 §	⊖ d	14 19	14 49	15 19	15 49	16 19	16 49	17 19	17 49	18 19	18 39	19 10	19 29	19 59	20 19	20 49	21 19	21 49	22 19	23 19
London Marylebone 10	⊖ a	14 34	15 05	15 34	16 05	16 35	17 05	17 35	18 05	18 35	18 55	19 26	19 45	20 15	20 35	21 05	21 34	22 05	22 35	23 35

Mondays to Fridays
from 6 October

		CH	CH	CH	CH	CH	CH	CH	CH	CH	CH	CH	CH	CH	CH	CH	CH	CH	CH	CH	CH	CH
Aylesbury	d	05 28	06 03	06 23	06 40	06 54	07 13	07 27	07 47	08 03	08 22	08 36	09 03	09 34	10 02	10 32	11 02	11 32	12 02	12 32	13 02	13 32
Stoke Mandeville	d	05 32	06 07	06 27	06 44	06 58	07 17	07 31	07 51	08 07	08 26	08 40	09 07	09 38	10 06	10 36	11 06	11 36	12 06	12 36	13 06	13 36
Wendover	d	05 36	06 11	06 31	06 48	07 02	07 21	07 35	07 55	08 11	08 30	08 44	09 11	09 42	10 10	10 40	11 10	11 40	12 10	12 40	13 10	13 40
Great Missenden	d	05 42	06 17	06 37	06 54	07 08	07 27	07 41	08 01	08 17	08 36	08 50	09 17	09 48	10 16	10 46	11 16	11 46	12 16	12 46	13 16	13 46
Amersham §	⊖ d	05 49	06 24	06 44		07 15	07 35	07 48	08 09	08 24		09 57	09 24	09 55	10 23	10 53	11 23	11 53	12 23	12 53	13 23	13 53
Chalfont & Latimer §	⊖ d		06 30	06 48		07 19		07 52		08 28		09 01	09 28	09 59	10 27	10 57	11 27	11 57	12 27	12 57	13 27	13 57
Chorleywood §	⊖ d		06 34	06 53		07 24		07 57		08 33		09 06	09 33	10 04	10 32	11 02	11 32	12 02	12 32	13 02	13 32	14 02
Rickmansworth §	⊖ d			06 59				08 03				09 12	09 39	10 10	10 38	11 08	11 38	12 08	12 38	13 08	13 38	14 08
Harrow-on-the-Hill 3 §	⊖ d	06 10	06 50	07 10		07 39		08 14		08 48		09 23	09 50	10 21	10 49	11 19	11 49	12 19	12 49	13 19	13 49	14 19
London Marylebone 10	⊖ a	06 26	07 04	07 25	07 37	07 55	08 14	08 29	08 44	09 05	09 20	09 38	10 05	10 37	11 05	11 35	12 05	12 34	13 05	13 35	14 04	14 34

		CH	CH	CH	CH	CH	CH	CH	CH	CH	CH	CH	CH	CH	CH	CH	CH	CH	CH
Aylesbury	d	14 02	14 32	15 02	15 32	16 02	16 32	17 02	17 32	17 52	18 23	18 42	19 12	19 32	20 02	20 32	21 02	21 32	22 32
Stoke Mandeville	d	14 06	14 36	15 06	15 36	16 06	16 36	17 06	17 36	17 56	18 27	18 46	19 16	19 36	20 06	20 36	21 06	21 36	22 36
Wendover	d	14 10	14 40	15 10	15 40	16 10	16 40	17 10	17 40	18 00	18 31	18 50	19 20	19 40	20 10	20 40	21 10	21 40	22 40
Great Missenden	d	14 16	14 46	15 16	15 46	16 16	16 46	17 16	17 46	18 06	18 37	18 56	19 26	19 46	20 16	20 46	21 16	21 46	22 46
Amersham §	⊖ d	14 23	14 53	15 23	15 53	16 23	16 53	17 23	17 53	18 13	18 44	19 03	19 33	19 53	20 23	20 53	21 23	21 53	22 53
Chalfont & Latimer §	⊖ d	14 27	14 57	15 27	15 57	16 27	16 57	17 27	17 57	18 17	18 48	19 07	19 37	19 57	20 27	20 57	21 27	21 57	22 57
Chorleywood §	⊖ d	14 32	15 02	15 32	16 02	16 32	17 02	17 32	18 02	18 22	18 43	19 12	19 42	20 02	20 32	21 02	21 32	22 02	23 02
Rickmansworth §	⊖ d	14 38	15 08	15 38	16 08	16 38	17 08	17 38	18 08	18 28	18 59	19 18	19 48	20 08	20 38	21 08	21 38	22 08	23 08
Harrow-on-the-Hill 3 §	⊖ d	14 49	15 19	15 49	16 19	16 49	17 19	17 49	18 19	18 39	19 10	19 29	19 59	20 19	20 49	21 19	21 49	22 19	23 19
London Marylebone 10	⊖ a	15 05	15 34	16 05	16 35	17 05	17 35	18 05	18 35	18 55	19 26	19 45	20 15	20 35	21 05	21 34	22 05	22 35	23 35

Saturdays
until 4 October

		CH	CH	CH	CH	CH	CH	CH	CH	CH	CH	CH	CH	CH	CH	CH	CH	CH
Aylesbury	d	06 05	06 35	07 05	07 35	08 05	08 35	09 05	09 35	10 05	10 35	11 05	11 35	12 05	12 35	13 05	13 35	14 05
Stoke Mandeville	d	06 09	06 39	07 09	07 39	08 09	08 39	09 09	09 39	10 09	10 39	11 09	11 39	12 09	12 39	13 09	13 39	14 09
Wendover	d	06 13	06 43	07 13	07 43	08 13	08 43	09 13	09 43	10 13	10 43	11 13	11 43	12 13	12 43	13 13	13 43	14 13
Great Missenden	d	06 19	06 49	07 19	07 49	08 19	08 49	09 19	09 49	10 19	10 49	11 19	11 49	12 19	12 49	13 19	13 49	14 19
Amersham §	⊖ d	06 26	06a58	07 26	07 56	08 26	08 56	09 26	09 56	10 26	10 56	11 26	11 56	12 26	12 56	13 26	13 56	14 26
Chalfont & Latimer §	⊖ d	06 30		07 30	08 00	08 30	09 00	09 30	10 00	10 30	11 00	11 30	12 00	12 30	13 00	13 30	14 00	14 30
Chorleywood §	⊖ d	06 33		07 33	08 03	08 33	09 03	09 33	10 03	10 33	11 03	11 33	12 03	12 33	13 03	13 33	14 03	14 33
Rickmansworth §	⊖ d	06 38		07 38	08 08	08 38	09 08	09 38	10 08	10 38	11 08	11 38	12 08	12 38	13 08	13 38	14 08	14 38
Harrow-on-the-Hill 3 §	⊖ d	06 49		07 49	08 19	08 49	09 19	09 49	10 19	10 49	11 19	11 49	12 19	12 49	13 19	13 49	14 19	14 49
London Marylebone 10	⊖ a	07 04		08 04	08 34	09 04	09 34	10 05	10 35	11 04	11 35	12 04	12 35	13 05	13 35	14 05	14 35	15 05

		CH	CH	CH	CH	CH	CH	CH	CH	CH	CH	CH	CH	CH	CH
Aylesbury	d	14 35	15 05	15 35	16 05	16 35	17 05	17 35	18 05	18 35	19 05	20 05	21 05	22 05	23 20
Stoke Mandeville	d	14 39	15 09	15 39	16 09	16 39	17 09	17 39	18 09	18 39	19 09	20 09	21 09	22 09	23 24
Wendover	d	14 43	15 13	15 43	16 13	16 43	17 13	17 43	18 13	18 43	19 13	20 13	21 13	22 13	23 28
Great Missenden	d	14 49	15 19	15 49	16 19	16 49	17 19	17 49	18 19	18 49	19 19	20 19	21 19	22 19	23 34
Amersham §	⊖ d	14 56	15 26	15 56	16 26	16 56	17 26	17 56	18 26	18 56	19 26	20 26	21 26	22 26	23a43
Chalfont & Latimer §	⊖ d	15 00	15 30	16 00	16 30	17 00	17 30	18 00	18 30	19 00	19 30	20 30	21 30	22 30	
Chorleywood §	⊖ d	15 03	15 33	16 03	16 33	17 03	17 33	18 03	18 33	19 03	19 33	20 33	21 33	22 33	
Rickmansworth §	⊖ d	15 08	15 38	16 08	16 38	17 08	17 38	18 08	18 38	19 08	19 38	20 38	21 38	22 38	
Harrow-on-the-Hill 3 §	⊖ d	15 19	15 49	16 19	16 49	17 19	17 49	18 19	18 49	19 19	19 49	20 49	21 49	22 49	
London Marylebone 10	⊖ a	15 34	16 05	16 35	17 04	17 35	18 05	18 35	19 05	19 35	20 04	21 04	22 04	23 04	

For general notes see front of timetable
For details of catering facilities see Directory of Train Operators

§ London Underground Limited (Metropolitan Line) services operate between Harrow-on-the-Hill, Rickmansworth, Chorleywood, Chalfont & Latimer and Amersham

from 11 October

Aylesbury and Amersham → London

Network Diagram - See first page of Table 114

		CH	CH	CH	CH	CH	CH	CH	CH	CH	CH	CH	CH	CH	CH	CH	CH	CH
Aylesbury	d	06 02	06 32	07 02	07 32	08 02	08 32	09 02	09 32	10 02	10 32	11 02	11 32	12 02	12 32	13 02	13 32	14 02
Stoke Mandeville	d	06 06	06 36	07 06	07 36	08 06	08 36	09 06	09 36	10 06	10 36	11 06	11 36	12 06	12 36	13 06	13 36	14 06
Wendover	d	06 10	06 40	07 10	07 40	08 10	08 40	09 10	09 40	10 10	10 40	11 10	11 40	12 10	12 40	13 10	13 40	14 10
Great Missenden	d	06 16	06 46	07 16	07 46	08 16	08 46	09 16	09 46	10 16	10 46	11 16	11 46	12 16	12 46	13 16	13 46	14 16
Amersham §	⊖ d	06 23	06a55	07 23	07 53	08 23	08 53	09 23	09 53	10 23	10 53	11 23	11 53	12 23	12 53	13 23	13 53	14 23
Chalfont & Latimer §	⊖ d	06 27	.	07 27	07 57	08 27	08 57	09 27	09 57	10 27	10 57	11 27	11 57	12 27	12 57	13 27	13 57	14 27
Chorleywood §	⊖ d	06 32	.	07 32	08 02	08 32	09 02	09 32	10 02	10 32	11 02	11 32	12 02	12 32	13 02	13 32	14 02	14 32
Rickmansworth §	⊖ d	06 38	.	07 38	08 08	08 38	09 08	09 38	10 08	10 38	11 08	11 38	12 08	12 38	13 08	13 38	14 08	14 38
Harrow-on-the-Hill 3 §	⊖ d	06 49	.	07 49	08 19	08 49	09 19	09 49	10 19	10 49	11 19	11 49	12 19	12 49	13 19	13 49	14 19	14 49
London Marylebone 10	⊖ a	07 04	.	08 04	08 34	09 04	09 34	10 05	10 35	11 04	11 35	12 04	12 35	13 05	13 35	14 05	14 35	15 05

		CH	CH	CH	CH	CH	CH	CH	CH	CH	CH	CH	CH	CH	CH
Aylesbury	d	14 32	15 02	15 32	16 02	16 32	17 02	17 32	18 02	18 32	19 02	20 02	21 02	22 02	23 17
Stoke Mandeville	d	14 36	15 06	15 36	16 06	16 36	17 06	17 36	18 06	18 36	19 06	20 06	21 06	22 06	23 21
Wendover	d	14 40	15 10	15 40	16 10	16 40	17 10	17 40	18 10	18 40	19 10	20 10	21 10	22 10	23 25
Great Missenden	d	14 46	15 16	15 46	16 16	16 46	17 16	17 46	18 16	18 46	19 16	20 16	21 16	22 16	23 31
Amersham §	⊖ d	14 53	15 23	15 53	16 23	16 53	17 23	17 53	18 23	18 53	19 23	20 23	21 23	22 23	23a40
Chalfont & Latimer §	⊖ d	14 57	15 27	15 57	16 27	16 57	17 27	17 57	18 27	18 57	19 27	20 27	21 27	22 27	.
Chorleywood §	⊖ d	15 02	15 32	16 02	16 32	17 02	17 32	18 02	18 32	19 02	19 32	20 32	21 32	22 32	.
Rickmansworth §	⊖ d	15 08	15 38	16 08	16 38	17 08	17 38	18 08	18 38	19 08	19 38	20 38	21 38	22 38	.
Harrow-on-the-Hill 3 §	⊖ d	15 19	15 49	16 19	16 49	17 19	17 49	18 19	18 49	19 19	19 49	20 49	21 49	22 49	.
London Marylebone 10	⊖ a	15 34	16 05	16 35	17 04	17 35	18 05	18 35	19 05	19 35	20 04	21 04	22 04	23 04	.

Sundays

until 28 September

		CH	CH	CH	CH	CH	CH	CH	CH	CH	CH	CH	CH	CH	CH	CH	CH	CH	CH	CH	CH	CH	CH	CH	CH
Aylesbury	d	07 35	08 35	09 05	10 05	11 05	12 05	13 05	14 05	15 05	15 35	16 05	16 35	17 05	17 35	18 05	18 35	19 05	19 35	20 05	20 35	21 05	21 35	22 05	22 35
Stoke Mandeville	d	07 39	08 39	09 09	10 09	11 09	12 09	13 09	14 09	15 09	15 39	16 09	16 39	17 09	17 39	18 09	18 39	19 09	19 39	20 09	20 39	21 09	21 39	22 09	22 39
Wendover	d	07 43	08 43	09 13	10 13	11 13	12 13	13 13	14 13	15 13	15 43	16 13	16 43	17 13	17 43	18 13	18 43	19 13	19 43	20 13	20 43	21 13	21 43	22 13	22 43
Great Missenden	d	07 49	08 49	09 19	10 19	11 19	12 19	13 19	14 19	15 19	15 49	16 19	16 49	17 19	17 49	18 19	18 49	19 19	19 49	20 19	20 49	21 19	21 49	22 19	22 49
Amersham §	⊖ d	07 56	08 56	09 26	10 26	11 26	12 26	13 26	14 26	15 26	15a58	16 26	16a58	17 26	17a58	18 26	18a58	19 26	19a58	20 26	20a58	21 26	21a58	22a28	22 56
Chalfont & Latimer §	⊖ d	08 00	09 00	09 30	10 30	11 30	12 30	13 30	14 30	15 30	.	16 30	.	17 30	.	18 30	.	19 30	.	20 30	.	21 30	.	.	23 00
Chorleywood §	⊖ d	08 03	09 03	09 33	10 33	11 33	12 33	13 33	14 33	15 33	.	16 33	.	17 33	.	18 33	.	19 33	.	20 33	.	21 33	.	.	23 03
Rickmansworth §	⊖ d	08 08	09 08	09 38	10 38	11 38	12 38	13 38	14 38	15 38	.	16 38	.	17 38	.	18 38	.	19 38	.	20 38	.	21 38	.	.	23 08
Harrow-on-the-Hill 3 §	⊖ d	08 19	09 19	09 49	10 49	11 49	12 49	13 49	14 49	15 49	.	16 49	.	17 49	.	18 49	.	19 49	.	20 49	.	21 49	.	.	23 19
London Marylebone 10	⊖ a	08 34	09 34	10 04	11 04	12 05	13 04	14 05	15 04	16 05	.	17 04	.	18 05	.	19 05	.	20 04	.	21 04	.	22 04	.	.	23 34

Sundays

from 5 October

		CH	CH	CH	CH	CH	CH	CH	CH	CH	CH	CH	CH	CH	CH	CH	CH	CH	CH	CH	CH	CH	CH	CH	CH
Aylesbury	d	07 32	08 32	09 02	10 02	11 02	12 02	13 02	14 02	15 02	15 32	16 02	16 32	17 02	17 32	18 02	18 32	19 02	19 32	20 02	20 32	21 02	21 32	22 02	22 32
Stoke Mandeville	d	07 36	08 36	09 06	10 06	11 06	12 06	13 06	14 06	15 06	15 36	16 06	16 36	17 06	17 36	18 06	18 36	19 06	19 36	20 06	20 36	21 06	21 36	22 06	22 36
Wendover	d	07 40	08 40	09 10	10 10	11 10	12 10	13 10	14 10	15 10	15 40	16 10	16 40	17 10	17 40	18 10	18 40	19 10	19 40	20 10	20 40	21 10	21 40	22 10	22 40
Great Missenden	d	07 46	08 46	09 16	10 16	11 16	12 16	13 16	14 16	15 16	15 46	16 16	16 46	17 16	17 46	18 16	18 46	19 16	19 46	20 16	20 46	21 16	21 46	22 16	22 46
Amersham §	⊖ d	07 53	08 53	09 23	10 23	11 23	12 23	13 23	14 23	15 23	15a55	16 23	16a55	17 23	17a55	18 23	18a55	19 23	19a55	20 23	20a55	21 23	21a55	22a25	22 53
Chalfont & Latimer §	⊖ d	07 57	08 57	09 27	10 27	11 27	12 27	13 27	14 37	15 27	.	16 27	.	17 27	.	18 27	.	19 27	.	20 27	.	21 27	.	.	22 57
Chorleywood §	⊖ d	08 02	09 02	09 32	10 32	11 32	12 32	13 32	14 32	15 32	.	16 32	.	17 32	.	18 32	.	19 32	.	20 32	.	21 32	.	.	23 02
Rickmansworth §	⊖ d	08 08	09 08	09 38	10 38	11 38	12 38	13 38	14 38	15 38	.	16 38	.	17 38	.	18 38	.	19 38	.	20 38	.	21 38	.	.	23 08
Harrow-on-the-Hill 3 §	⊖ d	08 19	09 19	09 49	10 49	11 49	12 49	13 49	14 49	15 49	.	16 49	.	17 49	.	18 49	.	19 49	.	20 49	.	21 49	.	.	23 19
London Marylebone 10	⊖ a	08 34	09 34	10 04	11 04	12 05	13 04	14 05	15 04	16 05	.	17 04	.	18 05	.	19 05	.	20 04	.	21 04	.	22 04	.	.	23 34

For general notes see front of timetable
For details of catering facilities see Directory of Train Operators

§ London Underground Limited (Metropolitan Line) services operate between Harrow-on-the-Hill, Rickmansworth, Chorleywood, Chalfont & Latimer and Amersham

London → High Wycombe, Aylesbury, Banbury, Stratford-upon-Avon, Birmingham Snow Hill and Kidderminster

Network Diagram - See first page of Table 114

Miles	Miles	Miles		CH MX	CH MO	CH MX	CH MX	CH MX	CH MO	CH MO	CH MX	LM A	CH	CH B	CH C	CH	CH	CH	CH	CH	CH	CH	CH	CH
0	—	—	**London Marylebone** ⊖ d	22p10	22p45	23p10	23p30	23p54	23p45		00 10					06 00		06 27	06 50	06 54	07 20	07 23	07 26	
—	—	0	**London Paddington** ⊖ d																					
6½	—	—	Wembley Stadium d		22p54	23p19	23p39		23p54		00 19					06 09		06 36		07 03		07 32	07 35	
8	—	—	Sudbury & Harrow Road d																					
8¾	—	—	Sudbury Hill Harrow d																				07 39	
9¾	—	—	Northolt Park d		22p59		23p44		00 01		00 24					06 14		06 41					07 42	
11¼	—	—	South Ruislip § ⊖ d		23p03		23p48		00 03		00 28					06 18		06 45					07 45	
13¼	—	12	West Ruislip § ⊖ d		23p06		23p51		00 06		00 31							06 48		07 12			07 49	
16	—	—	Denham d		23p11		23p56		00 11		00 36					06 24		06 53		07 17			07 53	
17	—	—	Denham Golf Club d		23p13		23p58		00 13		00 38							06 55					07 56	
18¾	—	—	Gerrards Cross d	22p31	23p16	23p33	00 01	00 15	00 16		00 41					06 28		06 58		07 21		07 46	07 59	
21¼	—	—	Seer Green d		23p21		00 06		00 21		00 46					06 33				07 26		07 50		
23	—	—	Beaconsfield d	22p37	23p24	23p39	00 09	00 21	00 24		00 49					06 36		07 04		07 29		07 54	08 05	
27¾	—	—	**High Wycombe** d	22p43	23p30	23p45	00 15	00 28	00 30		00 55			06 07	06 10	06 42		07a14	07 20	07a38	07 50	08 00	08a15	
32¼	—	—	Saunderton d		23p37		00 22	00 34	00 37		01 02			06 13	06 16	06 49						08 07		
36	0	—	**Princes Risborough** d	22p54	23p43	23p56	00 27	00 41	00 43	00 48	01 07			06 18	06 21	06 55	07 08		07 31		08 00	08 12		08 18
—	1½	—	Monks Risborough d				00 31			00 51	01 11						07 11							08 21
—	3	—	Little Kimble d				00 34			00 55	01 14						07 15							08 25
—	7¼	—	**Aylesbury** a				00 48			01 05	01 28						07 25							08 36
41¾	—	—	Haddenham & Thame Parkway d	23p01	23p50	00 03		00 47	00 50					06 25	06 28	07 02			07 37		08 06			
54¼	—	—	**Bicester North** a	23p12	00 02	00 16		00 59	01 03					06 40	06 42	07 15			07 48		08 18	08 28		
—	—	—	d	23p12	00 04	00 16		01 00	01 03					06 41	06 43	07 15			07 49		08 19	08 28		
65½	—	—	Kings Sutton d		00 16	00 30								06 54	06 56	07 29						08 39		
68¾	—	—	**Banbury** d	23p29	00a25	00a42		01a21	01a23					07 02	07 02	07a37			08 05		08 35	08a50		
88¾	—	0	**Leamington Spa** d	23p48									06 55	07 22	07 22				08 24		08 53			
90¾	—	2	Warwick d	23p53									06 58	07 26	07 26				08 28		08 57			
92	—	3¼	Warwick Parkway d	23p56									07 01	07 30	07 30				08 32		09 01			
94¼	—	6	Hatton d										07 07	07 34	07 34						09 07			
—	—	7¾	Claverdon d									06x36	07 12											
—	—	10	Bearley d									06x40	07 17											
—	—	11½	Wilmcote d									06 44	07 20											
—	—	15¼	**Stratford-upon-Avon** a									06 48	07 30											
99	—	—	Lapworth a																		09 12			
101½	—	—	Dorridge a	00 07										07 43	07 42				08 42		09 16			
104¾	—	—	Solihull a	00 12										07 50	07 50				08 48		09 20			
111¼	—	—	**Birmingham Moor Street** a	00 23										08 03	08 03				08 59		09 32			
112	—	—	**Birmingham Snow Hill** a	00 31										08 14	08 11				09 07		09 41			
—	—	—	Rowley Regis a																					
—	—	—	Cradley Heath a																					
—	—	—	**Stourbridge Junction** a																					
—	—	—	**Kidderminster** a																					

	CH	CH	CH	CH	CH	CH	CH	CH	CH	CH	CH	CH	CH	CH	CH	CH		CH	CH	CH	CH	CH	CH	CH
London Marylebone ⊖ d		07 50	07 53	08 00	08 20	08 24	08 31		08 50	08 54	09 04	09 20		09 24	09 30	09 50		09 54	10 00	10 20		10 24	10 30	10 50
London Paddington ⊖ d																								
Wembley Stadium d				08 09			08 40				09 13				09 39				10 09				10 39	
Sudbury & Harrow Road d																								
Sudbury Hill Harrow d				08 13			08 44								09 43								10 43	
Northolt Park d						08 37									09 46				10 14				10 46	
South Ruislip § ⊖ d				08 18							09 21								10 18					
West Ruislip § ⊖ d				08 21			08 51								09 51								10 51	
Denham d				08 26			08 55				09 26				09 56				10 24				10 56	
Denham Golf Club d							08 58								09 58								10 58	
Gerrards Cross d			08 14	08 30		08 47	09 01				09 31			09 45	10 01			10 15	10 28			10 45	11 01	
Seer Green d			08 19	08 35		08 51					09 35				10 06				10 33				11 06	
Beaconsfield d			08 22	08 38		08 54	09 07				09 39			09 51	10 09			10 21	10 36			10 51	11 09	
High Wycombe d		08 20	08 29	08a47	08 50	09 01	09a16		09 20	09 25	09a48	09 50		09 58	10a19	10 20		10 28	10a45	10 50		10 58	11a18	
Saunderton d			08 35			09 07								10 04								11 04		
Princes Risborough d			08 41		09 01	09 13		09 17		09 35		10 01	10 06	10a13				10 37		11 01	11 06	11 10		
Monks Risborough d								09 20					10 09								11 09			
Little Kimble d								09 24					10 13								11 13			
Aylesbury a								09 35					10 24								11 24			
Haddenham & Thame Parkway d			08 48		09 07	09 19				09 42		10 07						10 44		11 07		11 16		
Bicester North a			09 06		09 18	09 36				09 55		10 18						11 01		11 18		11 34		11 38
d					09 19					09 55		10 19								11 19				11 39
Kings Sutton d										10 08														
Banbury d		08 56			09 35				09 56	10 14		10 35				10 56				11 35				11 56
Leamington Spa d	09 04	09 14			09 54				10 14	10 34		10 54				11 14				11 54				12 15
Warwick d	09 07	09 19			09 58				10 19	10 38		10 59				11 19				11 59				12 19
Warwick Parkway d	09 10	09 22			10 02				10 22			11 02				11 22				12 02				12 23
Hatton d	09 16				10 07					10 45										12 07				
Claverdon d	09 21																							
Bearley d										10 53														
Wilmcote d										10 57														
Stratford-upon-Avon a	09 37									11 08														
Lapworth a					10 12															12 13				
Dorridge a		09 33			10 16				10 33			11 13				11 33				12 17				12 33
Solihull a		09 38			10 22				10 38			11 18				11 38				12 22				12 39
Birmingham Moor Street a		09 50			10 33				10 51			11 30				11 50				12 34				12 51
Birmingham Snow Hill a		10 01			10 41				11 01			11 41				12 01				12 42				13 02
Rowley Regis a																								
Cradley Heath a																								
Stourbridge Junction a																								
Kidderminster a																								

For general notes see front of timetable
For details of catering facilities see Directory of Train Operators

§ London Underground Limited (Central Line) also operate services between South Ruislip and West Ruislip at frequent intervals

A From Birmingham Snow Hill (Table 71)
B From 6 October
C Until 3 October

Wrexham & Shropshire services are expected to start operating during the currency of this timetable. Please visit the Wrexham & Shropshire website www.wrexhamandshropshire.co.uk for updated information

London → High Wycombe, Aylesbury, Banbury, Stratford-upon-Avon, Birmingham Snow Hill and Kidderminster

Network Diagram - See first page of Table 114

Station		CH	CH	CH	CH	CH	CH	CH	CH	CH	CH	CH	CH	CH	CH	CH	CH	CH	CH	CH	CH	CH	CH	CH	CH
London Marylebone 10 ⊖	d	10 54	11 00	11 20			11 30	11 50	11 54	12 00	12 20		12 24	12 30	12 50	12 54	13 00	13 20		13 24	13 30	13 50	13 54	14 00	14 20
London Paddington 15 ⊖	d					11 12																			
Wembley Stadium	d		11 09				11 39			12 09				12 39			13 09				13 39			14 09	
Sudbury & Harrow Road	d																								
Sudbury Hill Harrow	d						11 43							12 43							13 43				
Northolt Park	d		11 14				11 46			12 14				12 46			13 14				13 46			14 14	
South Ruislip § ⊖	d		11 18							12 18							13 18							14 18	
West Ruislip 3 § ⊖	d						11 51							12 51							13 51				
Denham	d		11 24				11 56			12 24				12 56			13 24				13 56			14 24	
Denham Golf Club	d						11 58							12 58							13 58				
Gerrards Cross 1	d	11 15	11 28			11 45	12 01		12 15	12 28			12 45	13 01		13 15	13 28			13 45	14 01		14 15	14 28	
Seer Green	d		11 33				12 06			12 33				13 06			13 33				14 06			14 33	
Beaconsfield	d	11 21	11 36			11 51	12 09		12 21	12 36			12 51	13 09		13 21	13 36			13 51	14 09		14 21	14 36	
High Wycombe 1	d	11 28	11a45	11 50		11 58	12a18		12 28	12a45	12 50		12 58	13a18		13 28	13a45	13 50		13 58	14a18		14 28	14a45	14 50
Saunderton	d					12 04							13 04							14 04					
Princes Risborough 2	d	11 38		12 01	12 06	12a13			12 37		13 00	13 06	13 10			13 38		14 01	14 08	14a13			14 38		15 01
Monks Risborough	d				12 09							13 09							14 11						
Little Kimble	d				12 13							13 13							14 15						
Aylesbury	a				12 24							13 24							14 26						
Haddenham & Thame Parkway	d	11 45		12 07					12 44		13 06		13 16			13 45		14 07					14 45		15 07
Bicester North 3	a	11 58		12 18				12 39	13 01		13 18		13 34		13 39	13 58		14 18				14 39	15 01		15 18
	d	11 59		12 19				12 39			13 19				13 39	13 59		14 19				14 39			15 19
Kings Sutton	d	12 12														14 12									
Banbury	d	12 17		12 35				12 56			13 35				13 56	14 17		14 35				14 56			15 35
Leamington Spa 8	d	12 38		12 54				13 14			13 54				14 15	14 38		14 54				15 15			15 54
Warwick	d	12 42		12 59				13 19			13 59				14 19	14 42		14 59				15 19			15 59
Warwick Parkway	d			13 02				13 22			14 02				14 23			15 02				15 23			16 02
Hatton	d	12 50									14 07					14 49									16 07
Claverdon	d	12 54																							
Bearley	d	12 59														14 57									
Wilmcote	d																								
Stratford-upon-Avon	a	13 11														15 09									
Lapworth	a										14 13														16 13
Dorridge	a			13 13				13 33			14 17				14 33			15 13				15 33			16 17
Solihull	a			13 20				13 38			14 22				14 39			15 20				15 39			16 22
Birmingham Moor Street	a			13 31				13 50			14 34				14 51			15 33				15 50			16 34
Birmingham Snow Hill	a			13 41				14 01			14 42				15 02			15 41				16 01			16 42
Rowley Regis	a																								
Cradley Heath	a																								
Stourbridge Junction 2	a																								
Kidderminster	a																								

Station		CH	CH	CH	CH	CH	CH	CH	CH		CH	CH	CH	CH	CH	CH	CH	CH	CH	CH	CH	CH	CH	CH	CH
																								A	
														🛒					🛒					🛒	
London Marylebone 10 ⊖	d		14 24	14 30	14 50	14 54	15 00	15 20			15 24	15 30	15 42	16 00	16 03	16 06	16 13	16 17	16 30		16 34	16 38	16 48	17 00	17 03
London Paddington 15 ⊖	d																								
Wembley Stadium	d			14 39			15 09					15 39						16 26				16 47			
Sudbury & Harrow Road	d																	16 29							
Sudbury Hill Harrow	d			14 43								15 43						16 32							
Northolt Park	d			14 46			15 14					15 46						16 35				16 52			
South Ruislip § ⊖	d						15 18									16 21						16 56			
West Ruislip 3 § ⊖	d			14 51								15 51					16 30						17 05		
Denham	d			14 56			15 24					15 56					16 34					17 02			
Denham Golf Club	d			14 58													16 36								
Gerrards Cross 1	d		14 45	15 01		15 15	15 28				15 48	16 00	16 03			16 29	16 40	16a48				17 06	17 11		
Seer Green	d			15 06			15 33				15 53						16 44					17 11			
Beaconsfield	d		14 51	15 09		15 21	15 36				15 56	16 06	16 09			16 35	16 48					17 14	17 18		
High Wycombe 1	d		14 58	15a18		15 28	15a45	15 50			16 02	16a15	16 17		16 32	16 41	16a57				17 04	17 20	17a27		17 33
Saunderton	d		15 04								16 09					16 48									
Princes Risborough 2	d	15 06	15 10			15 38		16 00	16 05		16a21		16 26		16 43	16a57				17 00	17 14	17a33			17 44
Monks Risborough	d	15 09							16 08											17 03					
Little Kimble	d	15 13							16 12											17 07					
Aylesbury	a	15 24							16 23											17 18					
Haddenham & Thame Parkway	d		15 16			15 45		16 07					16 33		16 49						17 21				17 50
Bicester North 3	a		15 34		15 38	15 58		16 18					16 50		17 00						17 32				18 01
	d				15 39	15 59		16 19							17 01						17 32				18 01
Kings Sutton	d					16 12									17 12										18 14
Banbury	d				15 56	16 17		16 35						17 03	17a25				17 34		17 49			18 03	18a24
Leamington Spa 8	d				16 14	16 38		16 54						17 22					17 52		18 07			18 23	
Warwick	d				16 19	16 42		16 58											17 57						
Warwick Parkway	d				16 22			17 02						17 28					18 00		18 13			18 29	
Hatton	d					16 49															18 19				
Claverdon	d					16 54																			
Bearley	d					16 59																			
Wilmcote	d					17 02															18 30				
Stratford-upon-Avon	a					17 12															18 40				
Lapworth	a																		18 09						
Dorridge	a				16 33			17 12						17 38					18 13					18 39	
Solihull	a				16 38			17 20						17 44					18 18					18 45	
Birmingham Moor Street	a				16 50			17 32						17 58					18 29					18 56	
Birmingham Snow Hill	a				17 01			17 41						18 12					18 40					19 01	
Rowley Regis	a																							19 24	
Cradley Heath	a																							19 29	
Stourbridge Junction 2	a																							19 35	
Kidderminster	a																							19 48	

For general notes see front of timetable
For details of catering facilities see Directory of Train Operators

A 🛒 to Birmingham Snow Hill

§ London Underground Limited (Central Line) also operate services between South Ruislip and West Ruislip at frequent intervals

Wrexham & Shropshire services are expected to start operating during the currency of this timetable. Please visit the Wrexham & Shropshire website www.wrexhamandshropshire.co.uk for updated information

London → High Wycombe, Aylesbury, Banbury, Stratford-upon-Avon, Birmingham Snow Hill and Kidderminster

Network Diagram - See first page of Table 114

		CH	CH	CH	CH	CH	CH	CH	CH	CH	CH	CH	CH	CH	CH	CH	CH	CH	CH	CH	CH	CH	CH	CH	CH
												A ⊼											A ⊼		
London Marylebone 10	⊖ d		17 06	17 09	17 20	17 30	17 33	17 36	17 41	17 45	17 53	18 00	18 03	18 09		18 12	18 15	18 19	18 30	18 33	18 36	18 47	19 00	19 03	19 07
London Paddington 15	⊖ d																								
Wembley Stadium	d		17 15	17 18					17 50	17 54							18 24	18 28			18 45				
Sudbury & Harrow Road	d			17 21														18 31							
Sudbury Hill Harrow	d							17 48									18 28								
Northolt Park	d		17 20				17 46				18 06							18 35				19 00			
South Ruislip §	⊖ d			17 27					17 58								18 33				18 53				19 22
West Ruislip 3 §	⊖ d		17 26					17 54								18 29					18 56				
Denham	d		17 30				17 53										18 39				19 00				
Denham Golf Club	d			17 34												18 34									
Gerrards Cross 1	d		17 34		17 41			18a04		18 08				18 30			18 43	18a49			19 05	19 10			19 30
Seer Green	d			17 40			18 00			18 12						18 40					19 09				19 34
Beaconsfield	d		17 40		17 47		18 04			18 16	18 21					18 43	18 49			18 58	19 12	19 16			19 38
High Wycombe 1	d		17 47	17a52	17 53		18a13		18 15	18 22	18a29			18 41		18 50	18a59			19 05	19 18	19 22		19 33	19 44
Saunderton	d		17 53							18 29						18 56						19 29			19 51
Princes Risborough 2	d	17 48	17 59		18a07				18 25	18 34			18 42	18 50	18 54	19a05				19 14	19 28	19 34		19 43	19a59
Monks Risborough	d	17 51								18 38												19 39			
Little Kimble	d	17 55								18 41												19 44			
Aylesbury	a	18 06								18 56					19 10						19 49	19 59			
Haddenham & Thame Parkway	d		18 05			18 12			18 31				18 48	18 59						19 21				19 50	
Bicester North 3	a		18 22			18 24			18 42				19 03	19 15					19 20	19 39				20 03	
	d					18 24			18 42										19 21					20 03	
Kings Sutton	d																							20 15	
Banbury	d					18 39			18 58			19 03							19 36				20 03	20a26	
Leamington Spa 8	d					18 58			19 16			19 22							19 54				20 23		
Warwick	d					19 03			19 20										19 59						
Warwick Parkway	d					19 06						19 28							20 02				20 29		
Hatton	d					19 11			19 27										20 07						
Claverdon	d								19 33																
Bearley	d																								
Wilmcote	d																								
Stratford-upon-Avon	a								19 51																
Lapworth	a					19 17													20 13						
Dorridge	a					19 21						19 38							20 17				20 39		
Solihull	a					19 27						19 44							20 23				20 45		
Birmingham Moor Street	a					19 38						19 56							20 33				20 57		
Birmingham Snow Hill	a					19 47						20 01							20 44				21 03		
Rowley Regis	a											20 24											21 19		
Cradley Heath	a											20 29											21 25		
Stourbridge Junction 2	a											20 35											21 32		
Kidderminster	a											20 50											21 49		

		CH	CH	CH	CH	CH	CH	CH	CH	CH	CH	CH	CH	CH	CH	CH	CH	CH	CH	CH	CH	CH	CH
																						FX	FO
London Marylebone 10	⊖ d	19 11	19 30	19 33	19 36	19 40	20 00	20 06	20 10	20 30	20 33	21 00	21 06	21 10	21 30	21 40	22 10	22 20	22 40	23 10	23 30	23 54	23 54
London Paddington 15	⊖ d																						
Wembley Stadium	d	19 20				19 49			20 19		20 42			21 19		21 49		22 29	22 49	23 19	23 39		
Sudbury & Harrow Road	d	19 23									20 45												
Sudbury Hill Harrow	d	19 26									20 48												
Northolt Park	d	19 29				19 54			20 24					21 24				22 34			23 44		
South Ruislip §	⊖ d					19 58					20 53					21 57			22 57		23 48		
West Ruislip 3 §	⊖ d	19 34				20 01			20 30					21 30				22 40			23 51		
Denham	d	19 38				20 06			20 34		20 58			21 34		22 02		22 44	23 02		23 56		
Denham Golf Club	d	19 40							20 36					21 36				22 46			23 58		
Gerrards Cross 1	d	19 44			19 57	20 10		20 27	20 40		21 03		21 27	21 40		22 07	22 31	22 50	23 07	23 33	00 01	00 15	00 15
Seer Green	d					20 14			20 44		21 07			21 44		22 11		22 54	23 11		00 06		
Beaconsfield	d			19 57	20 03	20 18		20 33	20 47		21 11		21 33	21 47		22 15	22 37	22 57	23 15	23 39	00 09	00 21	00 21
High Wycombe 1	d	19a58		20 04	20 10	20a27		20 40	20 54	21 00	21 17		21 40	21 54	22 00	22 21	22 43	23 04	23 21	23 45	00 15	00 28	00 28
Saunderton	d								21 00				21 46			22 27		23 10			00 22	00 34	00 34
Princes Risborough 2	d			20 15	20 20			20 49	21 06	21 11	21a30		21 57	22a07	22 11	22 36	22 54	23 19	23 31	23 56	00 27	00 41	00 41
Monks Risborough	d								21 09				22 01					23 22			00 31		
Little Kimble	d								21 13				22 05					23 26			00 34		
Aylesbury	a								21 27				22 19			22 54		23 38			00 48		
Haddenham & Thame Parkway	d		20 11	20 21	20 27			20 56		21 17		21 41			22 17		23 01		23 38	00 03		00 47	00 47
Bicester North 3	a		20 22	20 32	20 43		20 50	21 13		21 28		21 52			22 28		23 12		23 51	00 16		00 59	01 00
	d		20 22	20 32			20 50			21 28		21 52			22 28		23 12		23 52	00 16		01 00	01 00
Kings Sutton	d									21 41					22 41					00 30			
Banbury	d		20 38	20 49			21 06			21 47		22 08			22 47		23 29		00a12	00a42		01a21	01 17
Leamington Spa 8	d		20 56	21 07			21 25			22 05		22 27			23 06		23 48						01a39
Warwick	d		21 00	21 12						22 10					23 10		23 53						
Warwick Parkway	d		21 04				21 31			22 14		22 32			23 14		23 56						
Hatton	d		21 09	21 19						22 19													
Claverdon	d			21 24																			
Bearley	d			21 29																			
Wilmcote	d			21 33																			
Stratford-upon-Avon	a			21 43																			
Lapworth	a		21 14							22 24													
Dorridge	a		21 18				21 41			22 28		22 43			23 24		00 07						
Solihull	a		21 24				21 47			22 35		22 49			23 30		00 12						
Birmingham Moor Street	a		21 36				21 58			22 50		23 00			23 41		00 23						
Birmingham Snow Hill	a		21 47				22 04			22 58		23 05			23 51		00 31						
Rowley Regis	a						22 24					23 31											
Cradley Heath	a						22 29					23 37											
Stourbridge Junction 2	a						22 35					23 50											
Kidderminster	a						22 50																

For general notes see front of timetable
For details of catering facilities see Directory of Train Operators

A ⊼ to Birmingham Snow Hill

§ London Underground Limited (Central Line) also operate services between South Ruislip and West Ruislip at frequent intervals

Wrexham & Shropshire services are expected to start operating during the currency of this timetable. Please visit the Wrexham & Shropshire website www.wrexhamandshropshire.co.uk for updated information

Table 115

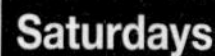

London → High Wycombe, Aylesbury, Banbury, Stratford-upon-Avon, Birmingham Snow Hill and Kidderminster

Network Diagram - See first page of Table 114

		CH	CH	CH	CH	CH	CH	CH	CH	CH		CH	CH	CH	CH	CH	CH	CH	CH	CH		CH	CH	CH	CH
London Marylebone 10	⊖ d	22p10	23p10	23p30	23p54	00 10		06 27				07 23		08 20	08 23		08 54	09 18		09 24		09 45	10 00	10 18	10 24
London Paddington 15	⊖ d																								
Wembley Stadium	d		23p19	23p39		00 19		06 36				07 32			08 32					09 33			10 09		10 33
Sudbury & Harrow Road	d																								
Sudbury Hill Harrow	d																								
Northolt Park	d			23p44		00 24		06 41				07 37			08 37					09 38			10 14		10 38
South Ruislip §	⊖ d			23p48		00 28		06 45				07 41			08 41					09 42			10 18		
West Ruislip 3 §	⊖ d			23p51		00 31		06 48				07 44			08 44					09 45					10 44
Denham	d			23p56		00 36		06 53				07 49			08 49					09 50			10 24		10 48
Denham Golf Club	d			23p58		00 38		06 55				07 51			08 51					09 52					10 50
Gerrards Cross 1	d	22p31	23p33	00 01	00 15	00 41		06 59				07 54		08 41	08 54		09 15	09 39		09 55			10 28		10 54
Seer Green	d			00 06		00 46		07 03				07 59			08 59					10 00			10 33		10 58
Beaconsfield	d	22p37	23p39	00 09	00 21	00 49		07 07				08 02		08 47	09 02		09 21	09 45		10 03			10 36		11 01
High Wycombe 1	d	22p43	23p45	00 15	00 28	00 55	06 12	07 13				08 08		08 53	09 08		09 28	09 51		10a12		10 15	10a45	10 48	11a11
Saunderton	d			00 22	00 34	01 02	06 18	07 21				08 15			09 15			09 58						10 54	
Princes Risborough 2	d	22p54	23p56	00 27	00 41	01 07	06 24	07 26	07 30			08 22	08 30	09 04	09 21	09 26	09 38	10 04	10 11					11 01	
Monks Risborough	d			00 31		01 11			07 33				08 33			09 29			10 14						
Little Kimble	d			00 34		01 14			07 37				08 37			09 33			10 18						
Aylesbury	a			00 48		01 28			07 47				08 47			09 43			10 28						
Haddenham & Thame Parkway	d	23p01	00 03		00 47		06 31	07 33				08 28		09 11	09 28		09 45	10 11				10 30		11 07	
Bicester North 3	a	23p12	00 16		01 00		06 42	07 44				08 39		09 22	09 40		09 58	10 22				10 41		11 18	
	d	23p12	00 16		01 00		06 42	07 44				08 40		09 22	09 40		09 59	10 22				10 41		11 19	
Kings Sutton	d		00 30				06 53					08 50					10 10								
Banbury	d	23p29	00a42		01 17		07 00	08 01		08 40		08 55		09 39	09 56		10 17	10 39				10 58		11 35	
Leamington Spa 8	d	23p48			01a39		07 19	08 20		09 00		09 14		09 58	10 14		10 38	10 58				11 16		11 54	
Warwick	d	23p53					07 24	08 24		09 04		09 20		10 02	10 18		10 42	11 02				11 20		11 59	
Warwick Parkway	d	23p56					07 27	08 28		09 08		09 23		10 06	10 22			11 06				11 24		12 02	
Hatton	d							08 33		09 12					10 27		10 49							12 07	
Claverdon	d																10 54								
Bearley	d																10 59								
Wilmcote	d																11 02								
Stratford-upon-Avon	a									09 35							11 12								
Lapworth	a							08 38							10 32									12 13	
Dorridge	a	00 07					07 38	08 42				09 34		10 16	10 36			11 16				11 34		12 17	
Solihull	a	00 12					07 43	08 50				09 43		10 22	10 44			11 22				11 40		12 22	
Birmingham Moor Street	a	00 23					07 58	09 00				09 54		10 33	10 54			11 33				11 51		12 34	
Birmingham Snow Hill	a	00 31					08 07	09 11				10 04		10 41	11 03			11 41				12 01		12 42	
Rowley Regis	a																								
Cradley Heath	a																								
Stourbridge Junction 2	a																								
Kidderminster	a																								

For general notes see front of timetable
For details of catering facilities see Directory of Train Operators

§ London Underground Limited (Central Line) also operate services between South Ruislip and West Ruislip at frequent intervals

Wrexham & Shropshire services are expected to start operating during the currency of this timetable. Please visit the Wrexham & Shropshire website www.wrexhamandshropshire.co.uk for updated information

Table 115

Saturdays

London → High Wycombe, Aylesbury, Banbury, Stratford-upon-Avon, Birmingham Snow Hill and Kidderminster

Network Diagram - See first page of Table 114

		CH	CH	CH	CH	CH	CH	CH		CH	CH	CH	CH	CH	CH	CH	CH	CH		CH	CH	CH	CH	CH	CH
London Marylebone 10 ⊖	d	10 50		10 53	11 00	11 20	11 24	11 50			11 53	12 20	12 23	12 50		12 53	13 20	13 23		13 50		13 53	14 20	14 23	14 50
London Paddington 15 ⊖	d																								
Wembley Stadium	d				11 09		11 33				12 02		12 32					13 32				14 02		14 32	
Sudbury & Harrow Road	d																								
Sudbury Hill Harrow	d																								
Northolt Park	d				11 14		11 38						12 37					13 37						14 37	
South Ruislip § ⊖	d				11 18		11 42						12 41					13 41						14 41	
West Ruislip 3 § ⊖	d						11 45						12 44					13 44						14 44	
Denham	d				11 24		11 50						12 49					13 49						14 49	
Denham Golf Club	d						11 52						12 51					13 51						14 51	
Gerrards Cross 1	d			11 14	11 28		11 55				12 16		12 54			13 14		13 54				14 16		14 54	
Seer Green	d				11 33		12 00						12 59					13 59						14 59	
Beaconsfield	d			11 20	11 36		12 03				12 22		13 02			13 20		14 02				14 22		15 02	
High Wycombe 1	d			11 27	11a45	11 50	12a12				12 28	12 50	13a11			13 27	13 50	14a11				14 28	14 50	15a11	
Saunderton	d			11 33							12 35					13 33						14 35			
Princes Risborough 2	d		11 08	11 40		12 01				12 11	12 41	13 01			13 05	13 40	14 01				14 05	14 41	15 01		
Monks Risborough	d		11 11							12 14					13 08						14 08				
Little Kimble	d		11 15							12 18					13 12						14 12				
Aylesbury	a		11 25							12 28					13 22						14 22				
Haddenham & Thame Parkway	d			11 46		12 07					12 48	13 07				13 46	14 07					14 48	15 07		
Bicester North 3	a	11 41		11 59		12 18		12 41			13 04	13 18		13 41		13 59	14 18			14 41		15 04	15 18		15 41
	d	11 42		12 00		12 19		12 42				13 19		13 42		14 00	14 19			14 42			15 19		15 42
Kings Sutton	d			12 11												14 11									
Banbury	d	11 58		12 19		12 35		12 58				13 35		13 58		14 19	14 35			14 58			15 35		15 58
Leamington Spa 8	d	12 17		12 39		12 54		13 17				13 54		14 17		14 39	14 54			15 17			15 54		16 17
Warwick	d	12 22		12 43		12 59		13 22				13 59		14 22		14 43	14 59			15 22			15 59		16 21
Warwick Parkway	d	12 25				13 02		13 25				14 02		14 25			15 02			15 25			16 02		16 25
Hatton	d			12 49								14 07				14 49							16 07		
Claverdon	d																								
Bearley	d			12 58																					
Wilmcote	d			13 01												15 00									
Stratford-upon-Avon	a			13 11												15 10									
Lapworth	a											14 13											16 13		
Dorridge	a	12 36				13 13		13 36				14 17		14 36			15 13			15 36			16 17		16 35
Solihull	a	12 41				13 19		13 41				14 22		14 41			15 19			15 41			16 22		16 41
Birmingham Moor Street	a	12 52				13 32		13 52				14 34		14 53			15 32			15 53			16 33		16 53
Birmingham Snow Hill	a	13 01				13 41		14 01				14 42		15 01			15 41			16 01			16 41		17 02
Rowley Regis	a																								
Cradley Heath	a																								
Stourbridge Junction 2	a																								
Kidderminster	a																								

		CH	CH	CH	CH	CH		CH	CH	CH	CH	CH	CH	CH	CH	CH		CH	CH	CH	CH	CH	CH	CH	CH
London Marylebone 10 ⊖	d		14 53	15 00	15 20	15 24		15 50		15 53	16 00	16 20	16 24	16 50		16 53		17 00	17 20	17 24	17 50		17 53	18 00	18 15
London Paddington 15 ⊖	d																								
Wembley Stadium	d			15 09		15 33					16 09		16 33					17 09		17 33				18 09	
Sudbury & Harrow Road	d																								
Sudbury Hill Harrow	d																								
Northolt Park	d			15 14		15 38					16 14		16 38					17 14		17 38				18 14	
South Ruislip § ⊖	d			15 18							16 18		16 42					17 18						18 18	
West Ruislip 3 § ⊖	d					15 44							16 45							17 44					
Denham	d			15 24		15 48					16 24		16 50					17 24		17 48				18 24	
Denham Golf Club	d					15 50							16 52							17 50					
Gerrards Cross 1	d		15 14	15 28		15 54				16 14	16 28		16 55			17 14		17 28		17 54			18 14	18 28	
Seer Green	d			15 33		15 58					16 33		17 00					17 33		17 58				18 33	
Beaconsfield	d		15 20	15 36		16 01				16 20	16 36		17 03			17 20		17 36		18 01			18 20	18 36	
High Wycombe 1	d		15 27	15a45	15 50	16a11				16 27	16a45	16 50	17a12			17 27		17a45	17 50	18a11			18 27	18a45	18 47
Saunderton	d		15 33							16 33						17 33							18 33		
Princes Risborough 2	d	15 05	15 40		16 01				16 05	16 40		17 01			17 05	17 40			18 01			18 05	18 40		18 56
Monks Risborough	d	15 08							16 08						17 08							18 08			
Little Kimble	d	15 12							16 12						17 12							18 12			
Aylesbury	a	15 22							16 22						17 22							18 22			19 14
Haddenham & Thame Parkway	d		15 46		16 07					16 46		17 07				17 46			18 07				18 46		
Bicester North 3	a		15 59		16 18			16 41		17 02		17 18		17 42		17 59			18 18		18 46		19 02		
	d		16 00		16 19			16 42				17 19		17 42		18 00			18 19		18 46				
Kings Sutton	d		16 11													18 11									
Banbury	d		16 19		16 35			16 57				17 35		17 59		18 19			18 35		19 03				
Leamington Spa 8	d		16 39		16 53			17 16				17 54		18 18		18 39			18 54		19 23				
Warwick	d		16 43		16 58			17 21				17 59		18 23		18 43			18 59		19 27				
Warwick Parkway	d				17 01			17 24				18 02		18 26					19 02		19 31				
Hatton	d		16 49		17 06							18 07				18 50			19 07						
Claverdon	d		16 54													18 54									
Bearley	d		16 59													18 59									
Wilmcote	d															19 03									
Stratford-upon-Avon	a		17 11													19 13									
Lapworth	a				17 12							18 13							19 14						
Dorridge	a				17 16			17 35				18 17		18 37					19 18		19 42				
Solihull	a				17 22			17 40				18 22		18 42					19 23		19 48				
Birmingham Moor Street	a				17 33			17 52				18 33		18 54					19 33		19 58				
Birmingham Snow Hill	a				17 41			18 01				18 41		19 03					19 41		20 06				
Rowley Regis	a																								
Cradley Heath	a																								
Stourbridge Junction 2	a																								
Kidderminster	a																								

For general notes see front of timetable
For details of catering facilities see Directory of Train Operators

§ London Underground Limited (Central Line) also operate services between South Ruislip and West Ruislip at frequent intervals

Wrexham & Shropshire services are expected to start operating during the currency of this timetable. Please visit the Wrexham & Shropshire website www.wrexhamandshropshire.co.uk for updated information

Table 115

Saturdays

London → High Wycombe, Aylesbury, Banbury, Stratford-upon-Avon, Birmingham Snow Hill and Kidderminster

Network Diagram - See first page of Table 114

		CH	CH	CH		CH	CH	CH	CH	CH	CH	CH	CH	CH		CH	CH	CH	CH	CH	CH	CH	CH		
London Marylebone 10	⊖ d	18 20	18 24	18 50			18 53	19 00	19 20		19 30	20 00	20 05	20 40		20 50	21 15	21 40	22 10	22 45	23 10	23 14	23 45		
London Paddington 15	⊖ d																								
Wembley Stadium	d		18 33					19 09			19 39		20 14				21 24		22 19	22 54	23 19	23 23	23 54		
Sudbury & Harrow Road	d																								
Sudbury Hill Harrow	d																								
Northolt Park	d		18 38					19 14			19 44		20 19				21 29		22 24			23 28			
South Ruislip §	⊖ d							19 18					20 23				21 33		22 28			23 32			
West Ruislip 3 §	⊖ d		18 44								19 50		20 26				21 36		22 31			23 35			
Denham	d		18 48					19 24			19 54		20 31				21 41		22 36			23 40			
Denham Golf Club	d		18 50								19 56		20 33				21 43		22 38			23 42			
Gerrards Cross 1	d		18 54				19 14	19 28			20 00		20 36	21 02			21 46	22 02	22 41	23 08	23 33	23 45	00 08		
Seer Green	d		18 58					19 33			20 04		20 41				21 51		22 46			23 50			
Beaconsfield	d		19 01				19 20	19 36			20 07		20 44	21 08			21 54	22 08	22 49	23 14	23 39	23 53	00 14		
High Wycombe 1	d	18 50	19a11				19 27	19 42	19 50		20 14	20 30	20 50	21 14		21 22	22 00	22 14	22 55	23 20	23 45	00 01	00 20		
Saunderton	d						19 33				20 20			21 21			22 07		23 02			00 06			
Princes Risborough 2	d	19 01				19 05	19 40	19 54	20 01	20 05	20 27	20 41	21 00	21 27		21 31	22 14	22 25	23 07	23 32	23 56	00 12	00 32		
Monks Risborough	d					19 08				20 08	20 30			21 30			22 17		23 11			00 16			
Little Kimble	d					19 12				20 12	20 34			21 34			22 21		23 14			00 19			
Aylesbury	a					19 22		20 12		20 22	20 46		21 19	21 47			22 33		23 28			00 32			
Haddenham & Thame Parkway	d	19 07					19 46		20 07			20 48				21 38		22 32		23 38	00 03		00 38		
Bicester North 3	a	19 18		19 46			19 59		20 18			21 01				21 51		22 45		23 51	00 16		00 51		
	d	19 19		19 46			20 00		20 19			21 01				21 51		22 46		23 52	00 16		00 52		
Kings Sutton	d						20 11		20 30											00 03			01 03		
Banbury	d	19 35		20 03			20 19		20 37			21 19				22 07		23 03		00a14	00a38		01a14		
Leamington Spa 8	d	19 54		20 23			20 39		20 55			21 39				22 28		23 24							
Warwick	d	19 59		20 27			20 43		21 00			21 43				22 32		23 28							
Warwick Parkway	d	20 02		20 31					21 03			21 47				22 35		23 31							
Hatton	d	20 07					20 49		21 08																
Claverdon	d						20 54																		
Bearley	d																								
Wilmcote	d																								
Stratford-upon-Avon	a						21 10																		
Lapworth	a	20 13							21 14																
Dorridge	a	20 17		20 42					21 18			21 58				22 46		23 42							
Solihull	a	20 22		20 47					21 24			22 03				22 52		23 49							
Birmingham Moor Street	a	20 34		20 58					21 35			22 16				23 02		00 01							
Birmingham Snow Hill	⛴ a	20 42		21 06					21 43			22 26				23 10		00 09							
Rowley Regis	a																								
Cradley Heath	a																								
Stourbridge Junction 2	a																								
Kidderminster	a																								

For general notes see front of timetable
For details of catering facilities see Directory of Train Operators

§ London Underground Limited (Central Line) also operate services between South Ruislip and West Ruislip at frequent intervals

Wrexham & Shropshire services are expected to start operating during the currency of this timetable. Please visit the Wrexham & Shropshire website www.wrexhamandshropshire.co.uk for updated information

Table 115

Sundays

until 13 July

London → High Wycombe, Aylesbury, Banbury, Stratford-upon-Avon, Birmingham Snow Hill and Kidderminster

Network Diagram - See first page of Table 114

Station		CH	CH	CH	CH	CH		CH	CH	CH	CH	CH		CH	CH	CH	CH	CH		CH	CH	CH	CH	CH	CH
London Marylebone 10 ⊖	d	21p40	22p45	23p10	23p14	23p45		00 10	07 35		08 00	08 54		09 15	09 33	09 54	10 15	10 50		10 54	11 20	11 33	11 50	11 54	12 20
London Paddington 15 ⊖	d																								
Wembley Stadium	d		22p54	23p19	23p23	23p54		00 19	07 44		08 09	09 03			09 42	10 03				11 03		11 42		12 03	
Sudbury & Harrow Road	d																								
Sudbury Hill Harrow	d																								
Northolt Park	d				23p28			00 24	07 49		08 14	09 08				10 08				11 08				12 08	
South Ruislip § ⊖	d				23p32			00 28	07 53		08 18	09 12				10 12				11 12				12 12	
West Ruislip 3 § ⊖	d				23p35			00 31	07 56		08 21	09 15				10 15				11 15				12 15	
Denham	d				23p40			00 36	08 01		08 26	09 20				10 20				11 20				12 20	
Denham Golf Club	d				23p42			00 38	08 03			09 22								11 22					
Gerrards Cross 1	d	22p02	23p08	23p33	23p45	00 08		00 41	08 06		08 30	09 25		09 36	09 56	10 24	10 36			11 25	11 41	11 56		12 24	12 41
Seer Green	d				23p50			00 46	08 11		08 34	09 30				10 28				11 30				12 28	
Beaconsfield	d	22p08	23p14	23p39	23p53	00 14		00 49	08 14		08 38	09 33		09 42	10 02	10 32	10 42			11 33	11 47	12 02		12 32	12 47
High Wycombe 1	d	22p14	23p20	23p45	00 01	00 20		00 55	08 20		08 44	09 39		09 49	10 08	10 38	10 49			11 39	11 54	12 08		12 38	12 54
Saunderton	d				00 06			01 02	08 27		08 51	09 46				10 45				11 46				12 45	
Princes Risborough 2	d	22p25	23p32	23p56	00 12	00 32		01 07	08 33	08 38	08 57	09 51		09 59	10 19	10 50	10 59			11 51	12 04	12 19		12 50	13 04
Monks Risborough	d				00 16			01 11		08 41		09 55				10 54				11 55				12 54	
Little Kimble	d				00 19			01 14		08 45		09 58				10 57				11 58				12 57	
Aylesbury	a				00 32			01 28		08 56		10 12				11 11				12 12				13 11	
Haddenham & Thame Parkway	d	22p32	23p38	00 03		00 38			08 40		09 04			10 06	10 26		11 06				12 11	12 26			13 11
Bicester North 3	a	22p45	23p51	00 16		00 51			08 53		09 17			10 19	10 39		11 19	11 45			12 24	12 39	12 45		13 24
	d	22p46	23p52	00 16		00 52			08 54		09 17			10 20	10 39		11 20	11 45			12 25	12 39	12 45		13 25
Kings Sutton	d		00 03			01 03			09 07						10 55		11 33					12 55			13 38
Banbury	d	23p03	00a14	00a38		01a14			09a15		09 34			10 36	11 01		11 38	12 02			12 41	13 01	13 05		13 43
Leamington Spa 8	d	23p24									09 54			10 57	11 21		11 59	12 22			13 02	13 21	13 26		14 03
Warwick	d	23p28									09 59			11 01	11 25		12 03				13 06	13 25			14 07
Warwick Parkway	d	23p31									10 02			11 04			12 06	12 28			13 09		13 31		14 10
Hatton	d										10 07				11 33		12 11					13 33			
Claverdon	d																								
Bearley	d																								
Wilmcote	d														11 48							13 43			
Stratford-upon-Avon	a														11 59							13 54			
Lapworth	a										10 11			11 13							13 18				
Dorridge	a	23p42									10 16			11 18			12 19	12 39			13 22		13 42		14 21
Solihull	a	23p49									10 21			11 23			12 24	12 44			13 27		13 48		14 28
Birmingham Moor Street	a	00 01									10 32			11 33			12 35	12 55			13 35		14 00		14 39
Birmingham Snow Hill	a	00 09									10 40			11 41			12 43	13 03			13 46		14 08		14 47
Rowley Regis	a																								
Cradley Heath	a																								
Stourbridge Junction 2	a																								
Kidderminster	a																								

For general notes see front of timetable
For details of catering facilities see Directory of Train Operators

§ London Underground Limited (Central Line) also operate services between South Ruislip and West Ruislip at frequent intervals

Wrexham & Shropshire services are expected to start operating during the currency of this timetable. Please visit the Wrexham & Shropshire website www.wrexhamandshropshire.co.uk for updated information

Table 115

Sundays

until 13 July

London → High Wycombe, Aylesbury, Banbury, Stratford-upon-Avon, Birmingham Snow Hill and Kidderminster

Network Diagram - See first page of Table 114

		CH ⊼		CH	CH	CH	CH	CH		CH	CH	CH ⊼	CH	CH		CH	CH	CH	CH	CH		CH ⊼	CH	CH	CH
London Marylebone 10 ⊖	d	12 33		12 50	12 54	13 20	13 33	13 50		13 54	14 20	14 33	14 50	14 54		15 20	15 33	15 50	15 54	16 20		16 35	16 57	17 00	17 20
London Paddington 15 ⊖	d																								
Wembley Stadium	d	12 42			13 03		13 42			14 03		14 42		15 03			15 42		16 03			16 44		17 09	
Sudbury & Harrow Road	d																								
Sudbury Hill Harrow	d																								
Northolt Park	d				13 08					14 08				15 08					16 08					17 14	
South Ruislip § ⊖	d				13 12					14 12				15 12					16 12					17 18	
West Ruislip 3 § ⊖	d				13 15					14 15				15 15					16 15					17 21	
Denham	d				13 20					14 20				15 20					16 20					17 26	
Denham Golf Club	d				13 22									15 22										17 28	
Gerrards Cross 1	d	12 56			13 25	13 41	13 56			14 24	14 41	14 56		15 25		15 41	15 56		16 24	16 41		16 58		17 31	17 41
Seer Green	d				13 30					14 28				15 30					16 28					17 36	
Beaconsfield	d	13 02			13 33	13 47	14 02			14 32	14 47	15 02		15 33		15 47	16 02		16 32	16 47		17 04		17 39	17 47
High Wycombe 1	d	13 08			13 39	13 54	14 08			14 38	14 54	15 08		15 39		15 54	16 08		16 38	16 54		17 10		17 45	17 54
Saunderton	d				13 46					14 45				15 46					16 45					17 52	
Princes Risborough 2	d	13 18			13 51	14 04	14 19			14 50	15 04	15 18		15 51		16 04	16 19		16 50	17 04		17 20		17 57	18 04
Monks Risborough	d				13 55					14 54				15 55					16 54					18 01	
Little Kimble	d				13 58					14 57				15 58					16 57					18 04	
Aylesbury	a				14 12					15 11				16 12					17 11					18 18	
Haddenham & Thame Parkway	d	13 25				14 11	14 26				15 11	15 25				16 11	16 26			17 11		17 27			18 11
Bicester North 3	a	13 41		13 45		14 24	14 39	14 45			15 24	15 41	15 45			16 24	16 39	16 45		17 24		17 43	17 52		18 24
	d			13 45		14 25	14 39	14 45			15 25		15 45			16 25	16 39	16 45		17 25			17 52		18 25
Kings Sutton	d						14 55										16 55								
Banbury	d			14 02		14 41	15 01	15 05			15 41		16 02			16 40	17 01	17 05		17 41			18 09		18 41
Leamington Spa 8	d			14 22		15 02	15 21	15 26			16 02		16 22			17 01	17 21	17 26		18 02			18 29		19 02
Warwick	d					15 06	15 25				16 06					17 06	17 26			18 06					19 06
Warwick Parkway	d			14 28		15 09		15 31			16 09		16 28			17 09		17 31		18 09			18 35		19 09
Hatton	d						15 33				16 14						17 33			18 14					
Claverdon	d																								
Bearley	d																								
Wilmcote	d						15 43										17 43								
Stratford-upon-Avon	a						15 49										17 49								
Lapworth	a					15 18										17 18									19 18
Dorridge	a			14 39		15 22		15 42			16 22		16 39			17 22		17 42		18 22			18 46		19 22
Solihull	a			14 44		15 27		15 48			16 27		16 44			17 27		17 48		18 29			18 51		19 29
Birmingham Moor Street	a			14 55		15 38		15 58			16 38		16 55			17 38		17 59		18 40			19 01		19 40
Birmingham Snow Hill	a			15 03		15 46		16 06			16 46		17 03			17 46		18 07		18 49			19 10		19 48
Rowley Regis	a																								
Cradley Heath	a																								
Stourbridge Junction 2	a																								
Kidderminster	a																								

		CH	CH	CH		CH	CH	CH	CH	CH		CH	CH	CH	CH	CH		CH	CH	CH	CH	CH	CH		
London Marylebone 10 ⊖	d	17 35	17 57	18 00		18 20	18 35	18 57	19 00	19 22		19 35	19 57	20 00	20 20	20 50		21 10	21 40	22 10	22 45		23 45		
London Paddington 15 ⊖	d																								
Wembley Stadium	d	17 44		18 09			18 44		19 09			19 44		20 09				21 19		22 19	22 54		23 54		
Sudbury & Harrow Road	d																								
Sudbury Hill Harrow	d																								
Northolt Park	d			18 14					19 14					20 14				21 24		22 24	22 59		00 01		
South Ruislip § ⊖	d			18 18					19 18					20 18				21 28		22 28	23 03		00 03		
West Ruislip 3 § ⊖	d			18 21					19 21					20 21				21 31		22 31	23 06		00 06		
Denham	d			18 26					19 26					20 26				21 36		22 36	23 11		00 11		
Denham Golf Club	d								19 28									21 38			23 13		00 13		
Gerrards Cross 1	d	17 58		18 30		18 41	18 58		19 31	19 43		19 58		20 30	20 41	21 11		21 41	22 01	22 40	23 16		00 16		
Seer Green	d			18 34					19 36					20 34				21 46		22 44	23 21		00 21		
Beaconsfield	d	18 04		18 38		18 47	19 04		19 39	19 49		20 04		20 38	20 47	21 17		21 49	22 07	22 48	23 24		00 24		
High Wycombe 1	d	18 10		18 44		18 54	19 10		19 45	19 56		20 10		20 44	20 54	21 24		21 55	22 14	22 54	23 30		00 30		
Saunderton	d			18 51					19 52					20 51				22 01		23 00	23 37		00 37		
Princes Risborough 2	d	18 21		18 56		19 04	19 20		19 57	20 07		20 21		20 56	21 04	21 34		22 07	22 24	23 05	23 43	23 49	00 43		
Monks Risborough	d			19 00					20 01					21 00				22 10		23 09		23 52			
Little Kimble	d			19 03					20 04					21 03				22 14		23 12		23 56			
Aylesbury	a			19 17					20 18					21 17				22 28		23 26		00 07			
Haddenham & Thame Parkway	d	18 28				19 11	19 27			20 14		20 28			21 11	21 41			22 31		23 50		00 50		
Bicester North 3	a	18 41	18 52			19 24	19 40	19 52		20 27		20 41	20 52		21 24	21 54			22 44		00 02		01 03		
	d	18 41	18 52			19 25	19 40	19 52		20 27		20 41	20 52		21 25	21 55			22 45		00 04		01 03		
Kings Sutton	d	18 55										20 55									00 16				
Banbury	d	19 01	19 09			19 41	20a02	20 09		20 44		21a04	21 09		21 41	22 10			23 01		00a25		01a23		
Leamington Spa 8	d	19 21	19 29			20 02		20 29		21 04			21 29		22 02	22 31			23 22						
Warwick	d	19 25				20 06				21 09					22 06	22 35			23 26						
Warwick Parkway	d		19 35			20 09		20 35		21 12			21 35		22 09	22 38			23 29						
Hatton	d	19 32														22 43									
Claverdon	d																								
Bearley	d																								
Wilmcote	d	19 43																							
Stratford-upon-Avon	a	19 48																							
Lapworth	a															22 48									
Dorridge	a		19 46			20 20		20 46		21 23			21 46		22 20	22 52			23 40						
Solihull	a		19 51			20 28		20 51		21 30			21 51		22 26	22 59			23 46						
Birmingham Moor Street	a		20 01			20 38		21 01		21 40			22 01		22 37	23 10			23 56						
Birmingham Snow Hill	a		20 10			20 46		21 10		21 48			22 10		22 45	23 18			00 04						
Rowley Regis	a																								
Cradley Heath	a																								
Stourbridge Junction 2	a																								
Kidderminster	a																								

For general notes see front of timetable
For details of catering facilities see Directory of Train Operators

§ London Underground Limited (Central Line) also operate services between South Ruislip and West Ruislip at frequent intervals

Wrexham & Shropshire services are expected to start operating during the currency of this timetable. Please visit the Wrexham & Shropshire website www.wrexhamandshropshire.co.uk for updated information

Table 115

Sundays

20 July to 7 September

London → High Wycombe, Aylesbury, Banbury, Stratford-upon-Avon, Birmingham Snow Hill and Kidderminster

Network Diagram - See first page of Table 114

Station		CH	CH	CH	CH	CH	CH	CH	CH	CH	CH	CH	CH	CH	CH	CH	CH	CH	CH	CH	CH	CH
London Marylebone 10 ⊖	d	21p40	22p45	23p10	23p14	23p45	00 10	07 35		08 00	08 54	09 15	09 33	09 54	10 15	10 50	10 54	11 15	11 33	11 50	11 54	12 20
London Paddington 15 ⊖	d																					
Wembley Stadium	d		22p54	23p19	23p23	23p54	00 19	07 44		08 09	09 03		09 42	10 03			11 03		11 42		12 03	
Sudbury & Harrow Road	d																					
Sudbury Hill Harrow	d																					
Northolt Park	d				23p28		00 24	07 49		08 14	09 08			10 08			11 08				12 08	
South Ruislip § ⊖	d				23p32		00 28	07 53		08 18	09 12			10 12			11 12				12 12	
West Ruislip 3 § ⊖	d				23p35		00 31	07 56		08 21	09 15			10 15			11 15				12 15	
Denham	d				23p40		00 36	08 01		08 26	09 20			10 20			11 20				12 20	
Denham Golf Club	d				23p42		00 38	08 03			09 22						11 22					
Gerrards Cross 1	d	22p02	23p08	23p33	23p45	00 08	00 41	08 06		08 30	09 25	09 36	09 56	10 24	10 36		11 25	11 36	11 56		12 24	12 41
Seer Green	d				23p50		00 46	08 11		08 34	09 30			10 28			11 30				12 28	
Beaconsfield	d	22p08	23p14	23p39	23p53	00 14	00 49	08 14		08 38	09 33	09 42	10 02	10 32	10 42		11 33	11 42	12 02		12 32	12 47
High Wycombe 1	d	22p14	23p20	23p45	00 01	00 20	00 55	08 20		08 44	09 39	09 49	10 08	10 38	10 49		11 39	11 49	12 08		12 38	12 54
Saunderton	d				00 06		01 02	08 27		08 51	09 46			10 45			11 46				12 45	
Princes Risborough 2	d	22p25	23p32	23p56	00 12	00 32	01 07	08 33	08 38	08 57	09 51	09 59	10 19	10 50	10 59		11 51	11 59	12 19		12 50	13 04
Monks Risborough	d				00 16		01 11		08 41		09 55			10 54			11 55				12 54	
Little Kimble	d				00 19		01 14		08 45		09 58			10 57			11 58				12 57	
Aylesbury	a				00 32		01 28		08 56		10 12			11 11			12 12				13 11	
Haddenham & Thame Parkway	d	22p32	23p38	00 03		00 38		08 40		09 04		10 06	10 26		11 06			12 06	12 26			13 11
Bicester North 3	a	22p45	23p51	00 16		00 51		08 53		09 17		10 19	10 39		11 19	11 45		12 19	12 39	12 45		13 24
	d	22p46	23p52	00 16		00 52		08 54		09 17		10 20	10 39		11 20	11 45		12 20	12 39	12 45		13 25
Kings Sutton	d		00 03			01 03		09 07					10 55		11 33				12 55			13 38
Banbury	d	23p03	00a14	00a38		01a14		09a15		09 34		10 36	11 01		11 38	12 02		12 36	13 01	13 05		13 43
Leamington Spa 8	d	23p24								09 54		10 57	11 21		11 59	12 22		12 57	13 21	13 26		14 03
Warwick	d	23p28								09 59		11 01	11 25		12 03			13 01	13 25			14 07
Warwick Parkway	d	23p31								10 02		11 04			12 06	12 28		13 04		13 31		14 10
Hatton	d									10 07			11 33		12 11				13 33			
Claverdon	d																					
Bearley	d																					
Wilmcote	d												11 48						13 43			
Stratford-upon-Avon	a												11 59						13 54			
Lapworth	a									10 11		11 13						13 13				
Dorridge	a	23p42								10 16		11 18			12 19	12 39		13 17		13 42		14 21
Solihull	a	23p49								10 21		11 23			12 24	12 44		13 22		13 48		14 28
Birmingham Moor Street	a	00 01								10 32		11 33			12 35	12 55		13 30		14 00		14 39
Birmingham Snow Hill ⛴	a	00 09								10 40		11 41			12 43	13 03		13 41		14 08		14 47
Rowley Regis	a																					
Cradley Heath	a																					
Stourbridge Junction 2	a																					
Kidderminster	a																					

For general notes see front of timetable
For details of catering facilities see Directory of Train Operators

§ London Underground Limited (Central Line) also operate services between South Ruislip and West Ruislip at frequent intervals

Wrexham & Shropshire services are expected to start operating during the currency of this timetable. Please visit the Wrexham & Shropshire website www.wrexhamandshropshire.co.uk for updated information

Table 115

Sundays

London → High Wycombe, Aylesbury, Banbury, Stratford-upon-Avon, Birmingham Snow Hill and Kidderminster

20 July to 7 September

Network Diagram - See first page of Table 114

		CH 🚌		CH	CH	CH	CH	CH		CH	CH	CH 🚌	CH	CH		CH	CH	CH	CH	CH		CH 🚌	CH	CH	CH
London Marylebone 10	⊖ d	12 33		12 50	12 54	13 15	13 33	13 50		13 54	14 20	14 33	14 50	14 54		15 15	15 33	15 50	15 54	16 20		16 35	16 57	17 00	17 20
London Paddington 15	⊖ d																								
Wembley Stadium	d	12 42			13 03		13 42			14 03		14 42		15 03			15 42		16 03			16 44		17 09	
Sudbury & Harrow Road	d																								
Sudbury Hill Harrow	d																								
Northolt Park	d				13 08					14 08				15 08					16 08					17 14	
South Ruislip §	⊖ d				13 12					14 12				15 12					16 12					17 18	
West Ruislip 3 §	⊖ d				13 15					14 15				15 15					16 15					17 21	
Denham	d				13 20					14 20				15 20					16 20					17 26	
Denham Golf Club	d				13 22									15 22										17 28	
Gerrards Cross 1	d	12 56			13 25	13 36	13 56			14 24	14 41	14 56		15 25		15 36	15 56		16 24	16 41		16 58		17 31	17 41
Seer Green	d				13 30					14 28				15 30					16 28					17 36	
Beaconsfield	d	13 02			13 33	13 42	14 02			14 32	14 47	15 02		15 33		15 42	16 02		16 32	16 47		17 04		17 39	17 47
High Wycombe 1	d	13 08			13 39	13 49	14 08			14 38	14 54	15 08		15 39		15 49	16 08		16 38	16 54		17 10		17 45	17 54
Saunderton	d				13 46					14 45				15 46					16 45					17 52	
Princes Risborough 2	d	13 18			13 51	13 59	14 19			14 50	15 04	15 18		15 51		15 59	16 19		16 50	17 04		17 20		17 57	18 04
Monks Risborough	d				13 55					14 54				15 55					16 54					18 01	
Little Kimble	d				13 58					14 57				15 58					16 57					18 04	
Aylesbury	a				14 12					15 11				16 12					17 11					18 18	
Haddenham & Thame Parkway	d	13 25				14 06	14 26				15 11	15 25				16 06	16 26			17 11		17 27			18 11
Bicester North 3	a	13 41		13 45		14 19	14 39	14 45			15 24	15 41	15 45			16 19	16 39	16 45		17 24		17 43	17 52		18 24
	d			13 45		14 20	14 39	14 45			15 25		15 45			16 20	16 39	16 45		17 25			17 52		18 25
Kings Sutton	d						14 55										16 55								
Banbury	d			14 02		14 36	15 01	15 05			15 41		16 02			16 35	17 01	17 05		17 41			18 09		18 41
Leamington Spa 8	d			14 22		14 57	15 21	15 26			16 02		16 22			16 56	17 21	17 26		18 02			18 29		19 02
Warwick	d					15 01	15 25				16 06					17 01	17 26			18 06					19 06
Warwick Parkway	d			14 28		15 04		15 31			16 09		16 28			17 04		17 31		18 09			18 35		19 09
Hatton	d						15 33				16 14						17 33			18 14					
Claverdon	d																								
Bearley	d																								
Wilmcote	d						15 43										17 43								
Stratford-upon-Avon	a						15 49										17 49								
Lapworth	a					15 13										17 13									19 18
Dorridge	a			14 39		15 17		15 42			16 22		16 39			17 17		17 42		18 22			18 46		19 22
Solihull	a			14 44		15 22		15 48			16 27		16 44			17 22		17 48		18 29			18 51		19 29
Birmingham Moor Street	a			14 55		15 30		15 58			16 38		16 55			17 33		17 59		18 40			19 01		19 40
Birmingham Snow Hill ⛴	a			15 03		15 41		16 06			16 46		17 03			17 41		18 07		18 49			19 10		19 48
Rowley Regis	a																								
Cradley Heath	a																								
Stourbridge Junction 2	a																								
Kidderminster	a																								

		CH	CH	CH		CH	CH	CH	CH	CH		CH	CH	CH	CH	CH		CH	CH	CH	CH	CH	CH		
London Marylebone 10	⊖ d	17 35	17 57	18 00		18 20	18 35	18 57	19 00	19 22		19 35	19 57	20 00	20 20	20 50		21 10	21 40	22 10	22 45		23 45		
London Paddington 15	⊖ d																								
Wembley Stadium	d	17 44		18 09			18 44		19 09			19 44		20 09				21 19		22 19	22 54		23 54		
Sudbury & Harrow Road	d																								
Sudbury Hill Harrow	d																								
Northolt Park	d			18 14					19 14					20 14				21 24		22 24	22 59		00 01		
South Ruislip §	⊖ d			18 18					19 18					20 18				21 28		22 28	23 03		00 03		
West Ruislip 3 §	⊖ d			18 21					19 21					20 21				21 31		22 31	23 06		00 06		
Denham	d			18 26					19 26					20 26				21 36		22 36	23 11		00 11		
Denham Golf Club	d								19 28									21 38			23 13		00 13		
Gerrards Cross 1	d	17 58		18 30		18 41	18 58		19 31	19 43		19 58		20 30	20 41	21 11		21 41	22 01	22 40	23 16		00 16		
Seer Green	d			18 34					19 36					20 34				21 46		22 44	23 21		00 21		
Beaconsfield	d	18 04		18 38		18 47	19 04		19 39	19 49		20 04		20 38	20 47	21 17		21 49	22 07	22 48	23 24		00 24		
High Wycombe 1	d	18 10		18 44		18 54	19 10		19 45	19 56		20 10		20 44	20 54	21 24		21 55	22 14	22 54	23 30		00 30		
Saunderton	d			18 51					19 52					20 51				22 01		23 00	23 37		00 37		
Princes Risborough 2	d	18 21		18 56		19 04	19 20		19 57	20 07		20 21		20 56	21 04	21 34		22 07	22 24	23 05	23 43	23 49	00 43		
Monks Risborough	d			19 00					20 01					21 00				22 10		23 09		23 52			
Little Kimble	d			19 03					20 04					21 03				22 14		23 12		23 56			
Aylesbury	a			19 17					20 18					21 17				22 28		23 26		00 07			
Haddenham & Thame Parkway	d	18 28				19 11	19 27			20 14		20 28			21 11	21 41			22 31		23 50		00 50		
Bicester North 3	a	18 41	18 52			19 24	19 40	19 52		20 27		20 41	20 52		21 24	21 54			22 44		00 02		01 03		
	d	18 41	18 52			19 25	19 40	19 52		20 27		20 41	20 52		21 25	21 55			22 45		00 04		01 03		
Kings Sutton	d	18 55										20 55									00 16				
Banbury	d	19 01	19 09			19 41	20a02	20 09		20 44		21a04	21 09		21 41	22 10			23 01		00a25		01a23		
Leamington Spa 8	d	19 21	19 29			20 02		20 29		21 04			21 29		22 02	22 31			23 22						
Warwick	d	19 25				20 06				21 09					22 06	22 35			23 26						
Warwick Parkway	d		19 35			20 09		20 35		21 12			21 35		22 09	22 38			23 29						
Hatton	d	19 32														22 43									
Claverdon	d																								
Bearley	d																								
Wilmcote	d	19 43																							
Stratford-upon-Avon	a	19 48																							
Lapworth	a															22 48									
Dorridge	a		19 46			20 20		20 46		21 23			21 46		22 20	22 52			23 40						
Solihull	a		19 51			20 28		20 51		21 30			21 51		22 26	22 59			23 46						
Birmingham Moor Street	a		20 01			20 38		21 01		21 40			22 01		22 37	23 10			23 56						
Birmingham Snow Hill ⛴	a		20 10			20 46		21 10		21 48			22 10		22 45	23 18			00 04						
Rowley Regis	a																								
Cradley Heath	a																								
Stourbridge Junction 2	a																								
Kidderminster	a																								

For general notes see front of timetable
For details of catering facilities see Directory of Train Operators

§ London Underground Limited (Central Line) also operate services between South Ruislip and West Ruislip at frequent intervals

Wrexham & Shropshire services are expected to start operating during the currency of this timetable. Please visit the Wrexham & Shropshire website www.wrexhamandshropshire.co.uk for updated information

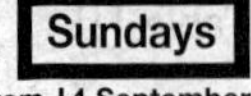

from 14 September

London → High Wycombe, Aylesbury, Banbury, Stratford-upon-Avon, Birmingham Snow Hill and Kidderminster

Network Diagram - See first page of Table 114

Station		CH	CH	CH	CH	CH	CH	CH	CH	CH	CH	CH	CH	CH	CH	CH	CH	CH	CH	CH	CH	CH
London Marylebone 10	⊖ d	21p40	22p45	23p10	23p14	23p45	00 10	07 35		08 00	08 54	09 15	09 33	09 54	10 15	10 50	10 54	11 20	11 33	11 50	11 54	12 20
London Paddington 15	⊖ d																					
Wembley Stadium	d		22p54	23p19	23p23	23p54	00 19	07 44		08 09	09 03		09 42	10 03			11 03		11 42		12 03	
Sudbury & Harrow Road	d																					
Sudbury Hill Harrow	d																					
Northolt Park	d				23p28		00 24	07 49		08 14	09 08			10 08			11 08				12 08	
South Ruislip §	⊖ d				23p32		00 28	07 53		08 18	09 12			10 12			11 12				12 12	
West Ruislip 3 §	⊖ d				23p35		00 31	07 56		08 21	09 15			10 15			11 15				12 15	
Denham	d				23p40		00 36	08 01		08 26	09 20			10 20			11 20				12 20	
Denham Golf Club	d				23p42		00 38	08 03			09 22						11 22					
Gerrards Cross 1	d	22p02	23p08	23p33	23p45	00 08	00 41	08 06		08 30	09 25	09 36	09 56	10 24	10 36		11 25	11 41	11 56		12 24	12 41
Seer Green	d				23p50		00 46	08 11		08 34	09 30			10 28			11 30				12 28	
Beaconsfield	d	22p08	23p14	23p39	23p53	00 14	00 49	08 14		08 38	09 33	09 42	10 02	10 32	10 42		11 33	11 47	12 02		12 32	12 47
High Wycombe 1	d	22p14	23p20	23p45	00 01	00 20	00 55	08 20		08 44	09 39	09 49	10 08	10 38	10 49		11 39	11 54	12 08		12 38	12 54
Saunderton	d				00 06		01 02	08 27		08 51	09 46			10 45			11 46				12 45	
Princes Risborough 2	d	22p25	23p32	23p56	00 12	00 32	01 07	08 33	08 38	08 57	09 51	09 59	10 19	10 50	10 59		11 51	12 04	12 19		12 50	13 04
Monks Risborough	d				00 16		01 11		08 41		09 55			10 54			11 55				12 54	
Little Kimble	d				00 19		01 14		08 45		09 58			10 57			11 58				12 57	
Aylesbury	a				00 32		01 28		08 56		10 12			11 11			12 12				13 11	
Haddenham & Thame Parkway	d	22p32	23p38	00 03		00 38		08 40		09 04		10 06	10 26		11 06			12 11	12 26			13 11
Bicester North 3	a	22p45	23p51	00 16		00 51		08 53		09 17		10 19	10 39		11 19	11 45		12 24	12 39	12 45		13 24
	d	22p46	23p52	00 16		00 52		08 54		09 17		10 20	10 39		11 20	11 45		12 25	12 39	12 45		13 25
Kings Sutton	d		00 03			01 03		09 07					10 55		11 33				12 55			13 38
Banbury	d	23p03	00a14	00a38		01a14		09a15		09 34		10 36	11 01		11 38	12 02		12 41	13 01	13 05		13 43
Leamington Spa 8	d	23p24								09 54		10 57	11 21		11 59	12 22		13 02	13 21	13 26		14 03
Warwick	d	23p28								09 59		11 01	11 25		12 03			13 06	13 25			14 07
Warwick Parkway	d	23p31								10 02		11 04			12 06	12 28		13 09		13 31		14 10
Hatton	d									10 07			11 33		12 11				13 33			
Claverdon	d																					
Bearley	d																					
Wilmcote	d												11 48						13 43			
Stratford-upon-Avon	a												11 59						13 54			
Lapworth	a									10 11		11 13						13 18				
Dorridge	a	23p42								10 16		11 18			12 19	12 39		13 22		13 42		14 21
Solihull	a	23p49								10 21		11 23			12 24	12 44		13 27		13 48		14 28
Birmingham Moor Street	a	00 01								10 32		11 33			12 35	12 55		13 35		14 00		14 39
Birmingham Snow Hill	a	00 09								10 40		11 41			12 43	13 03		13 46		14 08		14 47
Rowley Regis	a																					
Cradley Heath	a																					
Stourbridge Junction 2	a																					
Kidderminster	a																					

For general notes see front of timetable
For details of catering facilities see Directory of Train Operators

§ London Underground Limited (Central Line) also operate services between South Ruislip and West Ruislip at frequent intervals

Wrexham & Shropshire services are expected to start operating during the currency of this timetable. Please visit the Wrexham & Shropshire website www.wrexhamandshropshire.co.uk for updated information

Sundays from 14 September

London → High Wycombe, Aylesbury, Banbury, Stratford-upon-Avon, Birmingham Snow Hill and Kidderminster

Network Diagram - See first page of Table 114

		CH 🛒		CH	CH	CH	CH	CH		CH	CH	CH 🛒	CH	CH		CH	CH	CH	CH	CH		CH 🛒	CH	CH	CH
London Marylebone [10]	⊖ d	12 33		12 50	12 54	13 20	13 33	13 50		13 54	14 20	14 33	14 50	14 54		15 20	15 33	15 50	15 54	16 20		16 35	16 57	17 00	17 20
London Paddington [15]	⊖ d																								
Wembley Stadium	d	12 42			13 03		13 42			14 03		14 42		15 03			15 42		16 03			16 44		17 09	
Sudbury & Harrow Road	d																								
Sudbury Hill Harrow	d																								
Northolt Park	d				13 08					14 08				15 08					16 08					17 14	
South Ruislip §	⊖ d				13 12					14 12				15 12					16 12					17 18	
West Ruislip [3] §	⊖ d				13 15					14 15				15 15					16 15					17 21	
Denham	d				13 20					14 20				15 20					16 20					17 26	
Denham Golf Club	d				13 22									15 22										17 28	
Gerrards Cross [1]	d	12 56			13 25	13 41	13 56			14 24	14 41	14 56		15 25		15 41	15 56		16 24	16 41		16 58		17 31	17 41
Seer Green	d				13 30					14 28				15 30					16 28					17 36	
Beaconsfield	d	13 02			13 33	13 47	14 02			14 32	14 47	15 02		15 33		15 47	16 02		16 32	16 47		17 04		17 39	17 47
High Wycombe [1]	d	13 08			13 39	13 54	14 08			14 38	14 54	15 08		15 39		15 54	16 08		16 38	16 54		17 10		17 45	17 54
Saunderton	d				13 46					14 45				15 46					16 45					17 52	
Princes Risborough [2]	d	13 18			13 51	14 04	14 19			14 50	15 04	15 18		15 51		16 04	16 19		16 50	17 04		17 20		17 57	18 04
Monks Risborough	d				13 55					14 54				15 55					16 54					18 01	
Little Kimble	d				13 58					14 57				15 58					16 57					18 04	
Aylesbury	a				14 12					15 11				16 12					17 11					18 18	
Haddenham & Thame Parkway	d	13 25				14 11	14 26				15 11	15 25				16 11	16 26			17 11		17 27			18 11
Bicester North [3]	a	13 41		13 45		14 24	14 39	14 45			15 24	15 41	15 45			16 24	16 39	16 45		17 24		17 43	17 52		18 24
	d			13 45		14 25	14 39	14 45			15 25		15 45			16 25	16 39	16 45		17 25			17 52		18 25
Kings Sutton	d						14 55										16 55								
Banbury	d			14 02		14 41	15 01	15 05			15 41		16 02			16 40	17 01	17 05		17 41			18 09		18 41
Leamington Spa [8]	d			14 22		15 02	15 21	15 26			16 02		16 22			17 01	17 21	17 26		18 02			18 29		19 02
Warwick	d					15 06	15 25				16 06					17 06	17 26			18 06					19 06
Warwick Parkway	d			14 28		15 09		15 31			16 09		16 28			17 09		17 31		18 09			18 35		19 09
Hatton	d						15 33				16 14						17 33			18 14					
Claverdon	d																								
Bearley	d																								
Wilmcote	d						15 43										17 43								
Stratford-upon-Avon	a						15 49										17 49								
Lapworth	a					15 18										17 18									19 18
Dorridge	a			14 39		15 22		15 42			16 22		16 39			17 22		17 42		18 22			18 46		19 22
Solihull	a			14 44		15 27		15 48			16 27		16 44			17 27		17 48		18 29			18 51		19 29
Birmingham Moor Street	a			14 55		15 38		15 58			16 38		16 55			17 38		17 59		18 40			19 01		19 40
Birmingham Snow Hill	a			15 03		15 46		16 06			16 46		17 03			17 46		18 07		18 49			19 10		19 48
Rowley Regis	a																								
Cradley Heath	a																								
Stourbridge Junction [2]	a																								
Kidderminster	a																								

		CH	CH	CH		CH	CH	CH	CH	CH		CH	CH	CH	CH	CH		CH	CH	CH	CH	CH	CH		
London Marylebone [10]	⊖ d	17 35	17 57	18 00		18 20	18 35	18 57	19 00	19 22		19 35	19 57	20 00	20 20	20 50		21 10	21 40	22 10	22 45		23 45		
London Paddington [15]	⊖ d																								
Wembley Stadium	d	17 44		18 09			18 44		19 09			19 44		20 09				21 19		22 19	22 54		23 54		
Sudbury & Harrow Road	d																								
Sudbury Hill Harrow	d																								
Northolt Park	d			18 14					19 14					20 14				21 24		22 24	22 59		00 01		
South Ruislip §	⊖ d			18 18					19 18					20 18				21 28		22 28	23 03		00 03		
West Ruislip [3] §	⊖ d			18 21					19 21					20 21				21 31		22 31	23 06		00 06		
Denham	d			18 26					19 26					20 26				21 36		22 36	23 11		00 11		
Denham Golf Club	d								19 28									21 38			23 13		00 13		
Gerrards Cross [1]	d	17 58		18 30		18 41	18 58		19 31	19 43		19 58		20 30	20 41	21 11		21 41	22 01	22 40	23 16		00 16		
Seer Green	d			18 34					19 36					20 34				21 46		22 44	23 21		00 21		
Beaconsfield	d	18 04		18 38		18 47	19 04		19 39	19 49		20 04		20 38	20 47	21 17		21 49	22 07	22 48	23 24		00 24		
High Wycombe [1]	d	18 10		18 44		18 54	19 10		19 45	19 56		20 10		20 44	20 54	21 24		21 55	22 14	22 54	23 30		00 30		
Saunderton	d			18 51					19 52					20 51				22 01		23 00	23 37		00 37		
Princes Risborough [2]	d	18 21		18 56		19 04	19 20		19 57	20 07		20 21		20 56	21 04	21 34		22 07	22 24	23 05	23 43	23 49	00 43		
Monks Risborough	d			19 00					20 01					21 00				22 10		23 09		23 52			
Little Kimble	d			19 03					20 04					21 03				22 14		23 12		23 56			
Aylesbury	a			19 17					20 18					21 17				22 28		23 26		00 07			
Haddenham & Thame Parkway	d	18 28				19 11	19 27			20 14		20 28			21 11	21 41			22 31		23 50		00 50		
Bicester North [3]	a	18 41	18 52			19 24	19 40	19 52		20 27		20 41	20 52		21 24	21 54			22 44		00 02		01 03		
	d	18 41	18 52			19 25	19 40	19 52		20 27		20 41	20 52		21 25	21 55			22 45		00 04		01 03		
Kings Sutton	d	18 55										20 55									00 16				
Banbury	d	19 01	19 09			19 41	20a02	20 09		20 44		21a04	21 09		21 41	22 10			23 01		00a25		01a23		
Leamington Spa [8]	d	19 21	19 29			20 02		20 29		21 04			21 29		22 02	22 31			23 22						
Warwick	d	19 25				20 06				21 09					22 06	22 35			23 26						
Warwick Parkway	d		19 35			20 09		20 35		21 12			21 35		22 09	22 38			23 29						
Hatton	d	19 32														22 43									
Claverdon	d																								
Bearley	d																								
Wilmcote	d	19 43																							
Stratford-upon-Avon	a	19 48																							
Lapworth	a															22 48									
Dorridge	a		19 46			20 20		20 46		21 23			21 46		22 20	22 52			23 40						
Solihull	a		19 51			20 28		20 51		21 30			21 51		22 26	22 59			23 46						
Birmingham Moor Street	a		20 01			20 38		21 01		21 40			22 01		22 37	23 10			23 56						
Birmingham Snow Hill	a		20 10			20 46		21 10		21 48			22 10		22 45	23 18			00 04						
Rowley Regis	a																								
Cradley Heath	a																								
Stourbridge Junction [2]	a																								
Kidderminster	a																								

For general notes see front of timetable
For details of catering facilities see Directory of Train Operators

§ London Underground Limited (Central Line) also operate services between South Ruislip and West Ruislip at frequent intervals

Wrexham & Shropshire services are expected to start operating during the currency of this timetable. Please visit the Wrexham & Shropshire website www.wrexhamandshropshire.co.uk for updated information

Kidderminster, Birmingham Snow Hill, Stratford-upon-Avon, Banbury, Aylesbury and High Wycombe → London

Network Diagram - See first page of Table 114

Miles	Miles	Miles	Station		CH A	CH B	CH	CH	CH A	CH B	CH	CH 🛒	CH	CH	CH		CH 🛒	CH	CH	CH	CH	CH	CH	CH 🛒	CH
—	—	—	**Kidderminster**	d																					
—	—	—	**Stourbridge Junction 2**	d																					
—	—	—	Cradley Heath	d																					
—	—	—	Rowley Regis	d																					
0	—	—	**Birmingham Snow Hill**	d													05 43							06 14	
$\frac{3}{4}$	—	—	**Birmingham Moor Street**	d													05 46							06 17	
$7\frac{1}{4}$	—	—	Solihull	d													05 56							06 27	
$10\frac{1}{2}$	—	—	Dorridge	d													06 01							06 32	
13	—	—	Lapworth	d																					
—	—	0	**Stratford-upon-Avon**	d														06 10							
—	—	$2\frac{3}{4}$	Wilmcote	d														06 14							
—	—	$4\frac{1}{4}$	Bearley	d														06 20							
—	—	$7\frac{1}{2}$	Claverdon	d														06 25							
$17\frac{1}{4}$	—	$9\frac{1}{4}$	Hatton	d														06 31							
20	—	12	Warwick Parkway	d								05 40					06 12							06 44	
$21\frac{1}{4}$	—	$13\frac{1}{4}$	Warwick	d													06 15	06 38							
$23\frac{1}{4}$	—	$15\frac{1}{4}$	**Leamington Spa 8**	d								05 45					06 20	06a45						06 49	
$43\frac{1}{4}$	—	—	**Banbury**	d				05 24				06 03					06 38			06 25			06 53	07 07	
$46\frac{3}{4}$	—	—	Kings Sutton	d				05 28												06 29					
$57\frac{1}{4}$	—	—	**Bicester North 3**	a				05 40				06 18					06 53			06 41			07 07		
—	—	—		d				05 40				06 18					06 54			06 42		06 59	07 12		
$70\frac{1}{4}$	—	—	Haddenham & Thame Parkway	d				05 53				06 29								06 55		07 12	07 24		
—	0	—	**Aylesbury**	d	05 02	05 05	05 35				05 59		06 25		06 35										
—	$4\frac{1}{2}$	—	Little Kimble	d	05 10	05 13					06 07				06 43										
—	6	—	Monks Risborough	d	05 14	05 17					06 11				06 47										
76	$7\frac{1}{2}$	—	**Princes Risborough 2**	d	05 18	05 20	05 48	06 02			06 14	06 36	06 39		06 50					07 02		07 19			
$79\frac{1}{4}$	—	—	Saunderton	d	05 23	05 25					06 19				06 55							07 24			
$84\frac{1}{4}$	—	—	**High Wycombe 1**	d	05 30	05 32	05 58	06 12	06 18	06 19	06 26		06 50	06 55	07 02				07 08	07 13	07 21	07 30			07 45
89	—	—	Beaconsfield	d	05 37	05 38	06 04	06 18	06 24	06 25	06 32		06 56	07 01	07 08				07 14	07 19	07 27	07 37			
$90\frac{3}{4}$	—	—	Seer Green	d	05 40	05 41	06 07				06 35				07 12						07 30				
$93\frac{1}{4}$	—	—	Gerrards Cross 1	d	05 45	05 45	06 12	06 24	06 29	06 30	06 40		07 01	07 07	07 16				07 20		07 34	07 42			07 54
95	—	—	Denham Golf Club	d	05 48	05 48			06 32	06 33				07 10											
96	—	—	Denham	d	05 51	05 51	06 16				06 44			07 12							07 38				
$98\frac{3}{4}$	—	0	West Ruislip 3 §	⊖ d	05 55	05 55			06 38	06 38	06 48			07 17					07b35						
$100\frac{1}{2}$	—	—	South Ruislip §	⊖ d	05 59	05 59			06 42	06 42			07 09								07 44				
$102\frac{1}{4}$	—	—	Northolt Park	d	06 02	06 02			06 46	06 46	06 54			07 22					07 41						08 04
$103\frac{1}{4}$	—	—	Sudbury Hill Harrow	d					06 48	06 48									07 43						
104	—	—	Sudbury & Harrow Road	d					06 51	06 51									07 46						
$105\frac{1}{2}$	—	—	Wembley Stadium	d	06 07	06 07		06 37	06 53	06 53	06 59			07 27							07 51				08 09
—	—	12	**London Paddington 15**	⊖ a																					
112	—	—	**London Marylebone 10**	⊖ a	06 24	06 21	06 39	06 50	07 10	07 07	07 12	07 18	07 29	07 40	07 44		07 52		08 01	07 48	08 04	08 07	08 10	08 16	08 25

Station		CH	CH	CH	CH		CH	CH C 🛒	CH	CH	CH	CH	CH C 🛒	CH	CH	CH	CH		CH C 🛒	CH	CH	CH	CH	CH	CH
Kidderminster	d							06 09					06 30						06 56				07 30		
Stourbridge Junction 2	d							06 17					06 39						07 07				07 40		
Cradley Heath	d							06 24					06 44						07 14				07 45		
Rowley Regis	d							06 30					06 50						07 22				07 53		
Birmingham Snow Hill	d							06 50					07 13						07 45				08 12		
Birmingham Moor Street	d							06 53					07 16						07 48				08 15		
Solihull	d							07 04					07 26						07 58				08 25		
Dorridge	d							07 09					07 31						08 03				08 30		
Lapworth	d																		08 07						
Stratford-upon-Avon	d						06 46										07 36								
Wilmcote	d																07 40								
Bearley	d																07 46								
Claverdon	d																07 51								
Hatton	d						07 03										07 56		08 13						
Warwick Parkway	d						07 09	07 21					07 43						08 19				08 41		
Warwick	d						07 13						07 46				08 05		08 23				08 44		
Leamington Spa 8	d						07 18	07 26					07 50				08 09		08 27				08 49		
Banbury	d			07 18			07 36	07 44				07 50	08 08				08 28		08 45				09 09	09 15	
Kings Sutton	d																08 33								
Bicester North 3	a			07 33			07 51					08 04	08 24				08 46		08 59					09 30	
	d			07 35			07 51					08 04	08 24				08 47		08 59			09 11		09 30	
Haddenham & Thame Parkway	d			07 47			08 03					08 16	08 36				08 58		09 11			09 24		09 42	
Aylesbury	d		07 29		07 44				07 55						08 35	08 45									09 41
Little Kimble	d		07 37						08 03							08 53									09 49
Monks Risborough	d		07 41						08 07							08 57									09 53
Princes Risborough 2	d		07 44	07 53	07 58				08a13			08 22			08 49	09a03	09 06					09 31		09 49	09a59
Saunderton	d				08 03							08 29										09 36			
High Wycombe 1	d	07 50	07 55		08 10						08 25	08 36		08 54	09 00		09 16				09 35	09 42	09 46	09 59	
Beaconsfield	d	07 56	08 01		08 16						08 31	08 42		09 00	09 06		09 22				09 41	09 49			
Seer Green	d		08 05								08 34				09 09						09 44				
Gerrards Cross 1	d	08 02			08 21					08 16	08 38	08 47		09 05	09 13		09 27			09 40	09 48	09 54			
Denham Golf Club	d									08 19				09 08											
Denham	d	08 06								08 21	08 42			09 11						09 44					
West Ruislip 3 §	⊖ d		08 14							08c33				09e21						09 48					
South Ruislip §	⊖ d	08 12									08 48			09 24						09 51					
Northolt Park	d									08 38					09 23					09 55					
Sudbury Hill Harrow	d									08 41				09 29											
Sudbury & Harrow Road	d									08 43				09 31											
Wembley Stadium	d	08 19		08 24							08 55	09 00		09 34							10 03				
London Paddington 15	⊖ a																								
London Marylebone 10	⊖ a	08 32	08 35	08 38	08 47		08 50	08 53		09 02	09 09	09 16	09 23	09 49	09 41		09 53		09 59	10 13	10 17	10 21	10 25	10 36	

For general notes see front of timetable
For details of catering facilities see Directory of Train Operators

§ London Underground Limited (Central Line) also operate services between South Ruislip and West Ruislip at frequent intervals

A From 6 October
B Until 3 October
C 🛒 from Birmingham Snow Hill
b Arr. 0727
c Arr. 0825
e Arr. 0914

Wrexham & Shropshire services are expected to start operating during the currency of this timetable. Please visit the Wrexham & Shropshire website www.wrexhamandshropshire.co.uk for updated information

Kidderminster, Birmingham Snow Hill, Stratford-upon-Avon, Banbury, Aylesbury and High Wycombe → London

Network Diagram - See first page of Table 114

Station		CH	CH	CH	CH	CH	CH		CH	CH	CH	CH	CH	CH	CH	CH	CH	CH	CH		CH	CH	CH	CH	CH
Kidderminster	d				08 10																				
Stourbridge Junction 2	d				08 23																				
Cradley Heath	d				08 28																				
Rowley Regis	d				08 34																				
Birmingham Snow Hill	d				08 52				09 12				09 52			10 12					10 52			11 12	
Birmingham Moor Street	d				08 55				09 15				09 55			10 15					10 55			11 15	
Solihull	d				09 05				09 25				10 05			10 25					11 05			11 25	
Dorridge	d				09 10				09 30				10 11			10 30					11 10			11 31	
Lapworth	d								09 34							10 34									
Stratford-upon-Avon	d											09 41													
Wilmcote	d											09 45													
Bearley	d											09 51													
Claverdon	d																								
Hatton	d								09 40			10 00				10 40									
Warwick Parkway	d				09 21				09 45				10 22			10 45					11 21			11 41	
Warwick	d				09 24				09 49			10 06	10 25			10 49					11 24			11 45	
Leamington Spa 8	d				09 29				09 54			10 11	10 29			10 54					11 29			11 52	
Banbury	d				09 47				10 12			10 29	10 47			11 13					11 47			12 09	
Kings Sutton	d											10 34													
Bicester North 3	a				10 03				10 28			10 46	11 03			11 28					12 03			12 24	
	d			09 47	10 04				10 28			10 46	11 04		11 12	11 28			11 44		12 04			12 24	
Haddenham & Thame Parkway	d			10 00					10 40			10 59			11 25	11 40			11 57					12 36	
Aylesbury	d									10 38							11 38								12 38
Little Kimble	d									10 46							11 46								12 46
Monks Risborough	d									10 50							11 50								12 50
Princes Risborough 2	d			10 06			10 33		10 47	10a56		11 06			11 32	11 47	11a56		12 05				12 33	12 43	12a56
Saunderton	d						10 38								11 37								12 38		
High Wycombe 1	d		10 04	10 18		10 32	10 44		10 57		11 02	11 16		11 32	11 43	11 57		12 02	12 15			12 32	12 44	12 53	
Beaconsfield	d		10 10	10 24		10 38	10 51				11 08	11 22		11 38	11 50			12 08	12 21			12 38	12 50		
Seer Green	d		10 13			10 41					11 11			11 41				12 11				12 41			
Gerrards Cross 1	d	10 03	10 17	10 29		10 45	10 56				11 15	11 27		11 45	11 55			12 15	12 26			12 45	12 56		
Denham Golf Club	d	10 06				10 48								11 48								12 48			
Denham	d	10 08	10 21			10 50					11 19			11 50				12 19				12 50			
West Ruislip 3 §	⊖ d	10 12				10 55								11 55								12 55			
South Ruislip §	⊖ d		10 27								11 25							12 25							
Northolt Park	d		10 30			11 00					11 28			12 00				12 28				13 00			
Sudbury Hill Harrow	d		10 33								11 31							12 31							
Sudbury & Harrow Road	d																								
Wembley Stadium	d		10 37			11 05					11 35			12 05				12 35				13 05			
London Paddington 15	⊖ a	10 43																							
London Marylebone 10	⊖ a		10 50	10 55	10 59	11 19	11 22		11 30		11 48	11 56	12 00	12 18	12 21	12 30		12 48	12 51		12 59	13 18	13 21	13 29	

Station		CH	CH	CH	CH	CH	CH	CH	CH		CH	CH	CH	CH	CH	CH	CH	CH	CH	CH	CH		CH	CH	CH
Kidderminster	d																								
Stourbridge Junction 2	d																								
Cradley Heath	d																								
Rowley Regis	d																								
Birmingham Snow Hill	d			11 52			12 12					12 52			13 12				13 52				14 12		
Birmingham Moor Street	d			11 55			12 15					12 55			13 15				13 55				14 15		
Solihull	d			12 05			12 25					13 05			13 25				14 05				14 25		
Dorridge	d			12 10			12 31					13 10			13 31				14 10				14 31		
Lapworth	d						12 35																14 35		
Stratford-upon-Avon	d		11 40															13 39							
Wilmcote	d																								
Bearley	d		11 48																						
Claverdon	d																	13 50							
Hatton	d		11 59				12 41											13 57					14 41		
Warwick Parkway	d			12 21			12 46					13 21			13 41				14 21				14 46		
Warwick	d		12 05	12 24			12 49					13 24			13 45			14 03	14 24				14 49		
Leamington Spa 8	d		12 08	12 29			12 54					13 29			13 50			14 08	14 29				14 54		
Banbury	d		12 28	12 47			13 12					13 47			14 08			14 27	14 47				15 12		
Kings Sutton	d		12 33															14 32							
Bicester North 3	a		12 45	13 03			13 28					14 03			14 23			14 44	15 03				15 28		
	d		12 45	13 04		13 13	13 28				13 44	14 04			14 24			14 44	15 04		15 13		15 28		
Haddenham & Thame Parkway	d		12 58			13 26	13 40				13 57				14 35			14 57			15 26		15 40		
Aylesbury	d							13 42								14 38								15 38	
Little Kimble	d							13 50								14 46								15 46	
Monks Risborough	d							13 54								14 50								15 50	
Princes Risborough 2	d		13 06			13 33	13 47	14a00			14 05			14 33	14 43	14a56		15 06			15 33		15 47	15a56	
Saunderton	d					13 38								14 38							15 38				
High Wycombe 1	d	13 02	13 17		13 32	13 44	13 57		14 02		14 15		14 32	14 44	14 53		15 02	15 16		15 32	15 44		15 57		16 02
Beaconsfield	d	13 08	13 23		13 38	13 51			14 08		14 21		14 38	14 51			15 08	15 22		15 38	15 51				16 08
Seer Green	d	13 11			13 41				14 11				14 41				15 11			15 41					16 11
Gerrards Cross 1	d	13 15	13 28		13 45	13 56			14 15		14 26		14 45	14 56			15 15	15 27		15 45	15 56				16 15
Denham Golf Club	d				13 48								14 48							15 48					
Denham	d	13 20			13 50				14 19				14 50				15 19			15 50					16 20
West Ruislip 3 §	⊖ d				13 55								14 55							15 55					
South Ruislip §	⊖ d	13 26							14 25								15 25								16 26
Northolt Park	d	13 29			14 00				14 28				15 00				15 28			16 00					16 29
Sudbury Hill Harrow	d	13 32							14 31								15 31								16 32
Sudbury & Harrow Road	d																								
Wembley Stadium	d	13 36			14 05				14 35				15 05				15 35			16 05					16 36
London Paddington 15	⊖ a																								
London Marylebone 10	⊖ a	13 49	13 55	13 59	14 18	14 21	14 30		14 48		14 51	14 59	15 18	15 21	15 28		15 48	15 53	16 00	16 18	16 22		16 31		16 49

For general notes see front of timetable
For details of catering facilities see Directory of Train Operators

§ London Underground Limited (Central Line) also operate services between South Ruislip and West Ruislip at frequent intervals

Wrexham & Shropshire services are expected to start operating during the currency of this timetable. Please visit the Wrexham & Shropshire website www.wrexhamandshropshire.co.uk for updated information

Kidderminster, Birmingham Snow Hill, Stratford-upon-Avon, Banbury, Aylesbury and High Wycombe → London

Network Diagram - See first page of Table 114

		CH	CH	CH	CH	CH	CH	CH	CH	CH	CH		CH	CH	CH	CH	CH	CH	CH	CH	CH	CH	CH		CH
Kidderminster	d																								
Stourbridge Junction [2]	d																								
Cradley Heath	d																								
Rowley Regis	d																								
Birmingham Snow Hill	d		14 52			15 12					15 52					16 12					16 52				17 10
Birmingham Moor Street	d		14 55			15 15					15 55					16 15					16 55				17 13
Solihull	d		15 05			15 25					16 05					16 25					17 05				17 23
Dorridge	d		15 10			15 30					16 10					16 30					17 10				17 30
Lapworth	d															16 34									17 34
Stratford-upon-Avon	d									15 41															
Wilmcote	d																								
Bearley	d									15 49															
Claverdon	d																								
Hatton	d									15 58						16 40									17 40
Warwick Parkway	d		15 21			15 41					16 21					16 45					17 20				17 45
Warwick	d		15 24			15 44				16 04	16 24					16 49					17 23				17 48
Leamington Spa [8]	d		15 29			15 49				16 08	16 29					16 54					17 28				17 53
Banbury	d		15 47			16 07				16 27	16 47					17 12					17 46		17 51		18 11
Kings Sutton	d									16 32													17 56		
Bicester North [3]	a		16 03			16 23				16 44	17 03					17 28					18 02		18 08		18 27
	d	15 44	16 04			16 23				16 45	17 04			17 17		17 28					18 03		18 08		18 27
Haddenham & Thame Parkway	d	15 57				16 35				16 59				17 30		17 40					18 14		18 21		18 39
Aylesbury	d						16 39								17 21					18 09					
Little Kimble	d						16 47								17 29					18 17					
Monks Risborough	d						16 51								17 33					18 21					
Princes Risborough [2]	d	16 05			16 36	16 44	16a57			17 06				17 37	17a42	17 47		17 55	18 15	18a28			18 30		18 46
Saunderton	d				16 40					17 12				17 42									18 35		
High Wycombe [1]	d	16 15		16 33	16 47	16 54			17 04	17 19	17 26		17 36	17 48		17 57	18 01	18 06	18 25		18 30	18 35	18 41		18 56
Beaconsfield	d	16 21		16 39	16 53				17 10	17 25			17 42	17 55			18 07	18 12	18 31			18 41	18 47		
Seer Green	d			16 42					17 13				17 45				18 10						18 51		
Gerrards Cross [1]	d	16 26		16 46	16 59			17 10	17 17	17 30			17 49	18 00			18 14	18 17	18 36			18 46	18 55		
Denham Golf Club	d			16 49				17 13										18 20							
Denham	d			16 51				17 15	17 21				17 53					18 23				18 50			
West Ruislip [3] §	⊖ d			16 56					17 25				17 57				18 21					18 55			
South Ruislip §	⊖ d							17 21										18 28							
Northolt Park	d			17 01					17 31				18 03					18 32				19 00			
Sudbury Hill Harrow	d								17 33								18 27								
Sudbury & Harrow Road	d																								
Wembley Stadium	d			17 06				17 28	17 37				18 08				18 31					19 05			
London Paddington [15]	⊖ a																								
London Marylebone [10]	⊖ a	16 53	17 01	17 21	17 25	17 31		17 42	17 51	17 55	18 04		18 24	18 27		18 33	18 45	18 49	19 01		19 08	19 18	19 21		19 33

		CH	CH	CH	CH	CH	CH	CH	CH	CH	CH	CH		CH	CH	CH	CH	CH	CH	CH	CH	CH	CH		
Kidderminster	d																								
Stourbridge Junction [2]	d																								
Cradley Heath	d																								
Rowley Regis	d																								
Birmingham Snow Hill	d			17 52				18 12						19 12				20 12			21 15				
Birmingham Moor Street	d			17 55				18 15						19 15				20 15			21 18				
Solihull	d			18 05				18 25						19 25				20 25			21 27				
Dorridge	d			18 12				18 30						19 32				20 32			21 33				
Lapworth	d							18 34						19 36				20 36			21 37				
Stratford-upon-Avon	d		17 42													19 43	20 00						23 00		
Wilmcote	d		17 46														20 04								
Bearley	d		17 52																						
Claverdon	d		17 57													19 54									
Hatton	d		18 02					18 40						19 42		19 59	20 17	20 42			21 42				
Warwick Parkway	d			18 23				18 45						19 47		20 06		20 47			21 47				
Warwick	d		18 08	18 26				18 49						19 50		20 09	20 23	20 50			21 50		23 21		
Leamington Spa [8]	d		18 12	18 30				18 54						19 54		20 15	20a33	20 54			21 55		23 25		
Banbury	d		18 32	18 48				19 12						20 11		20 33		21 12			22 14		23a43		
Kings Sutton	d							19 17								20 38					22 19				
Bicester North [3]	a		18 47	19 04				19 30						20 26		20 51		21 27			22 32				
	d		18 48	19 04			19 20	19 30		19 50	20 03			20 26		20 51		21 27			22 32				
Haddenham & Thame Parkway	d		19 02				19 33	19 42		20 03				20 37		21 03		21 39			22 45				
Aylesbury	d					19 13						20 16							21 37			23 00			
Little Kimble	d											20 24							21 45			23 08			
Monks Risborough	d					19 24						20 28							21 49			23 12			
Princes Risborough [2]	d		19 09		19 25	19a32	19 40	19 49		20 11		20a34		20 44		21 09		21 46	21 52		22 53	23 15			
Saunderton	d						19 45							20 50					21 57		22 58				
High Wycombe [1]	d	19 07	19 19	19 28	19 36		19 51	19 59	20 06	20 21	20 27			20 58	21 05	21 19		21 56	22 06		23 05	23 25			
Beaconsfield	d	19 13	19 25		19 42		19 58		20 12	20 27				21 04	21 11	21 25			22 12		23 11	23 31			
Seer Green	d	19 16			19 45				20 15						21 14				22 15		23 14				
Gerrards Cross [1]	d	19 20	19 31		19 49		20 03		20 19	20 32				21 10	21 18	21 31			22 19		23 18	23 37			
Denham Golf Club	d	19 23							20 22						21 21				22 22		23 21				
Denham	d	19 25			19 53				20 24						21 23				22 25		23 24				
West Ruislip [3] §	⊖ d				19 57				20 29						21 28				22 29		23 28				
South Ruislip §	⊖ d	19 31							20 32						21 31				22 33		23 32				
Northolt Park	d	19 35			20 03				20 36						21 35				22 36		23 35				
Sudbury Hill Harrow	d	19 37																							
Sudbury & Harrow Road	d																								
Wembley Stadium	d	19 41			20 08				20 41		20 49			21 23	21 40			22 18	22 41	23 00	23 40	23 50			
London Paddington [15]	⊖ a																								
London Marylebone [10]	⊖ a	19 54	19 57	20 06	20 21		20 28	20 35	20 54	20 58	21 02			21 38	21 53	21 57		22 32	22 55	23 15	23 53	00 04			

For general notes see front of timetable
For details of catering facilities see Directory of Train Operators

§ London Underground Limited (Central Line) also operate services between South Ruislip and West Ruislip at frequent intervals

Wrexham & Shropshire services are expected to start operating during the currency of this timetable. Please visit the Wrexham & Shropshire website www.wrexhamandshropshire.co.uk for updated information

Table 115

Kidderminster, Birmingham Snow Hill, Stratford-upon-Avon, Banbury, Aylesbury and High Wycombe → London

Network Diagram - See first page of Table 114

		CH	CH	CH	CH	CH		CH	CH	CH	CH	CH		CH	CH	CH	CH	CH		CH	CH	CH	CH	CH	CH
Kidderminster	d										06 37				07 11							08 13			
Stourbridge Junction 2	d										06 45				07 20							08 26			
Cradley Heath	d										06 50				07 27							08 31			
Rowley Regis	d										06 56				07 33							08 37			
Birmingham Snow Hill	d							06 12	06 37		07 12				07 52		08 12					08 52		09 12	
Birmingham Moor Street	d							06 15	06 40		07 15				07 55		08 15					08 55		09 15	
Solihull	d							06 25	06 50		07 25				08 04		08 25					09 06		09 25	
Dorridge	d							06 30	06 55		07 30				08 10		08 31					09 13		09 31	
Lapworth	d										07 34						08 35							09 35	
Stratford-upon-Avon	d													07 35											
Wilmcote	d																								
Bearley	d																								
Claverdon	d													07 47											
Hatton	d										07 40			07 56			08 40								
Warwick Parkway	d							06 41	07 06		07 45				08 20		08 45					09 23		09 43	
Warwick	d							06 44	07 09		07 50			08 03	08 23		08 48					09 27		09 46	
Leamington Spa 8	d							06 49	07 14		07 54			08 08	08 29		08 52					09 32		09 50	
Banbury	d			06 05	06 34			07 08	07 33		08 12			08 27	08 47		09 12				09 28	09 50		10 10	
Kings Sutton	d			06 09										08 32							09 32				
Bicester North 3	a			06 21	06 49			07 23	07 48		08 28			08 45			09 27				09 44			10 26	
	d			06 22	06 49			07 24	07 49		08 28			08 45			09 28				09 46			10 26	
Haddenham & Thame Parkway	d			06 35	07 01			07 35	08 00		08 40			08 58			09 41				09 59			10 39	
Aylesbury	d	05 15	05 56			06 56				07 56						09 06				09 46					10 38
Little Kimble	d	05 23	06 04			07 04				08 04						09 14				09 54					10 46
Monks Risborough	d	05 27	06 08			07 08				08 08						09 18				09 58					10 50
Princes Risborough 2	d	05 30	06 11	06 43		07 11		07 43		08 11	08 47			09 06		09 21	09 49			10a04	10 08			10 47	10a59
Saunderton	d	05 35	06 16			07 16				08 16						09 26					10 13				
High Wycombe 1	d	05 42	06 23	06 53		07 23		07 53		08 23	08 57	09 04		09 17		09 39	09 59	10 04			10 20		10 34	10 57	
Beaconsfield	d	05 48	06 29	06 59		07 29		07 59		08 29		09 10		09 23		09 45		10 10			10 26		10 40		
Seer Green	d	05 51	06 32			07 32				08 32		09 13				09 48		10 13					10 43		
Gerrards Cross 1	d	05 55	06 36	07 05		07 36		08 04		08 36		09 17		09 28		09 52		10 17			10 31		10 47		
Denham Golf Club	d	05 58	06 39			07 39				08 39						09 55							10 50		
Denham	d	06 01	06 42			07 42				08 42		09 21				09 58		10 21					10 52		
West Ruislip 3 §	⊖ d	06 05	06 46			07 46				08 46						10 02							10 57		
South Ruislip §	⊖ d	06 09	06 50			07 50				08 50		09 27						10 27							
Northolt Park	d	06 12	06 53			07 53				08 53		09 30				10 07		10 30					11 02		
Sudbury Hill Harrow	d																								
Sudbury & Harrow Road	d																								
Wembley Stadium	d	06 17	06 58	07 18		07 58				08 58		09 35				10 12		10 35					11 07		
London Paddington 15	⊖ a																								
London Marylebone 10	⊖ a	06 31	07 11	07 31	07 47	08 11		08 29	08 47	09 12	09 30	09 50		09 55	10 01	10 26	10 32	10 49			10 56	11 01	11 20	11 31	

For general notes see front of timetable
For details of catering facilities see Directory of Train Operators

§ London Underground Limited (Central Line) also operate services between South Ruislip and West Ruislip at frequent intervals

Wrexham & Shropshire services are expected to start operating during the currency of this timetable. Please visit the Wrexham & Shropshire website www.wrexhamandshropshire.co.uk for updated information

Table 115

Saturdays

Kidderminster, Birmingham Snow Hill, Stratford-upon-Avon, Banbury, Aylesbury and High Wycombe → London

Network Diagram - See first page of Table 114

Station		CH		CH	CH	CH	CH	CH		CH	CH	CH	CH	CH		CH	CH	CH	CH	CH		CH	CH	CH	CH
Kidderminster	d				09 03																				
Stourbridge Junction	d				09 15																				
Cradley Heath	d				09 21																				
Rowley Regis	d				09 26																				
Birmingham Snow Hill	d				09 52		10 12					10 52		11 12				11 52		12 12				12 52	
Birmingham Moor Street	d				09 55		10 15					10 55		11 15				11 55		12 15				12 55	
Solihull	d				10 05		10 25					11 05		11 25				12 05		12 25				13 05	
Dorridge	d				10 12		10 31					11 12		11 31				12 12		12 31				13 10	
Lapworth	d						10 35													12 35					
Stratford-upon-Avon	d			09 36													11 38								
Wilmcote	d			09 40													11 42								
Bearley	d			09 46													11 48								
Claverdon	d			09 51																					
Hatton	d			09 56			10 41										11 57			12 40					
Warwick Parkway	d				10 22		10 46					11 22		11 41				12 22		12 45				13 21	
Warwick	d			10 04	10 26		10 49					11 26		11 45			12 03	12 26		12 48				13 24	
Leamington Spa	d			10 08	10 30		10 54					11 31		11 49			12 07	12 30		12 52				13 29	
Banbury	d			10 28	10 48		11 12				11 29	11 49		12 07			12 27	12 49		13 11				13 47	
Kings Sutton	d										11 33						12 32								
Bicester North	a			10 44	11 04		11 28				11 46	12 05		12 23			12 45	13 04		13 27				14 03	
	d			10 44	11 04		11 28				11 46	12 05		12 24			12 45	13 04		13 28			13 47	14 04	
Haddenham & Thame Parkway	d			10 57			11 40				11 59			12 35			12 58			13 41			14 00		
Aylesbury	d							11 38								12 38						13 38			
Little Kimble	d							11 46								12 46						13 46			
Monks Risborough	d							11 50								12 50						13 50			
Princes Risborough	d			11 05			11 47	11a56			12 06			12 43		12a56	13 06			13 49		13a56	14 06		
Saunderton	d			11 10							12 11						13 11						14 12		
High Wycombe	d	11 04		11 17		11 34	11 57			12 04	12 19		12 34	12 53			13 18		13 38	13 59			14 18		14 38
Beaconsfield	d	11 10		11 23		11 40				12 10	12 25		12 40				13 24		13 44				14 25		14 44
Seer Green	d	11 13				11 43				12 13			12 43						13 47						14 47
Gerrards Cross	d	11 17		11 28		11 47				12 17	12 31		12 47				13 30		13 51				14 30		14 51
Denham Golf Club	d					11 50							12 50						13 55						14 55
Denham	d	11 21				11 52				12 21			12 52						13 57						14 57
West Ruislip §	d					11 57							13 03						14 01						15 01
South Ruislip §	d	11 27								12 27			13 06						14 05						15 05
Northolt Park	d	11 30				12 02				12 30			13 10						14 08						15 08
Sudbury Hill Harrow	d																								
Sudbury & Harrow Road	d																								
Wembley Stadium	d	11 35				12 07				12 35			13 15				13 43		14 13				14 43		15 13
London Paddington	a																								
London Marylebone	a	11 48		11 56	11 59	12 22	12 30			12 48	12 58	13 01	13 28	13 31			13 58	14 01	14 28	14 33			14 58	15 01	15 27

Station		CH	CH	CH		CH	CH	CH	CH	CH		CH	CH	CH	CH	CH		CH	CH	CH	CH	CH		CH	CH
Kidderminster	d																								
Stourbridge Junction	d																								
Cradley Heath	d																								
Rowley Regis	d																								
Birmingham Snow Hill	d	13 12				13 52		14 12					14 52		15 12					15 52		16 12			
Birmingham Moor Street	d	13 15				13 55		14 15					14 55		15 15					15 55		16 15			
Solihull	d	13 25				14 05		14 25					15 05		15 25					16 05		16 25			
Dorridge	d	13 31				14 10		14 31					15 10		15 31					16 10		16 30			
Lapworth	d							14 35														16 34			
Stratford-upon-Avon	d			13 40															15 39						
Wilmcote	d																		15 43						
Bearley	d																								
Claverdon	d																		15 52						
Hatton	d			13 59				14 40											15 58			16 40			
Warwick Parkway	d	13 41				14 21		14 45					15 21		15 41					16 21		16 45			
Warwick	d	13 45		14 06		14 24		14 48					15 24		15 45				16 04	16 24		16 49			
Leamington Spa	d	13 49		14 11		14 29		14 52					15 29		15 49				16 09	16 29		16 54			
Banbury	d	14 07		14 30		14 47		15 11					15 47		16 07				16 28	16 47		17 12			
Kings Sutton	d			14 35															16 33						
Bicester North	a	14 23		14 47		15 03		15 27					16 03		16 23				16 46	17 03		17 28			
	d	14 24		14 47		15 04		15 28				15 47	16 04		16 24				16 46	17 04		17 28			
Haddenham & Thame Parkway	d	14 35		15 00				15 41				16 00			16 35				16 59			17 40			
Aylesbury	d		14 38						15 38							16 38								17 38	
Little Kimble	d		14 46						15 46							16 46								17 46	
Monks Risborough	d		14 50						15 50							16 50								17 50	
Princes Risborough	d	14 43	14a56	15 06				15 49	15a56			16 06			16 43	16a56			17 06			17 46		17a56	
Saunderton	d			15 14								16 12							17 13						
High Wycombe	d	14 53		15 20			15 38	15 59		16 04		16 18		16 34	16 53			17 04	17 19		17 34	17 56			18 04
Beaconsfield	d			15 26			15 44			16 10		16 25		16 40				17 10	17 25		17 40				18 10
Seer Green	d						15 47			16 13				16 43				17 13			17 43				18 13
Gerrards Cross	d			15 32			15 51			16 17		16 30		16 47				17 17	17 31		17 47				18 17
Denham Golf Club	d						15 55							16 50							17 50				
Denham	d						15 57			16 21				16 52				17 21			17 52				18 21
West Ruislip §	d						16 01							16 57							17 57				
South Ruislip §	d						16 05			16 27								17 27							18 27
Northolt Park	d						16 08			16 30				17 02				17 30			18 02				18 30
Sudbury Hill Harrow	d																								
Sudbury & Harrow Road	d																								
Wembley Stadium	d			15 45			16 13			16 35				17 07				17 35			18 07				18 35
London Paddington	a																								
London Marylebone	a	15 30		15 58		16 01	16 27	16 33		16 48		16 55	16 59	17 20	17 29			17 48	17 57	18 00	18 20	18 32			18 48

For general notes see front of timetable
For details of catering facilities see Directory of Train Operators

§ London Underground Limited (Central Line) also operate services between South Ruislip and West Ruislip at frequent intervals

Wrexham & Shropshire services are expected to start operating during the currency of this timetable. Please visit the Wrexham & Shropshire website www.wrexhamandshropshire.co.uk for updated information

Table 115

Kidderminster, Birmingham Snow Hill, Stratford-upon-Avon, Banbury, Aylesbury and High Wycombe → London

Network Diagram - See first page of Table 114

		CH	CH	CH	CH	CH		CH	CH	CH	CH	CH		CH	CH	CH	CH	CH		CH	CH	CH
Kidderminster	d																					
Stourbridge Junction 2	d																					
Cradley Heath	d																					
Rowley Regis	d																					
Birmingham Snow Hill	d		16 52		17 12					17 52				18 12		19 10		20 10				21 11
Birmingham Moor Street	d		16 55		17 15					17 55				18 15		19 13		20 13				21 14
Solihull	d		17 06		17 25					18 06				18 25		19 23		20 23				21 23
Dorridge	d		17 12		17 31					18 11				18 32		19 30		20 30				21 30
Lapworth	d				17 35									18 36		19 34		20 34				21 34
Stratford-upon-Avon	d								17 36								19 53			21 15		
Wilmcote	d								17 40													
Bearley	d								17 46								20 01					
Claverdon	d								17 51													
Hatton	d				17 41				17 56					18 42		19 40	20 10	20 40		21a33		21 40
Warwick Parkway	d		17 22		17 46					18 22				18 46		19 44	20 16	20 45				21 44
Warwick	d		17 26		17 49				18 04	18 25				18 48		19 47	20 19	20 48				21 47
Leamington Spa 8	d		17 30		17 54				18 08	18 29				18 52		19 51	20 23	20 53				21 52
Banbury	d		17 49		18 12				18 28	18 47				19 12		20 10	20 42	21 15				22 15
Kings Sutton	d								18 32							20 15						22 20
Bicester North 3	a		18 04		18 28				18 45	19 03				19 28		20 28	20 59	21 29				22 32
	d	17 47	18 04		18 28				18 46	19 04				19 28	19 59	20 29	21 00	21 30				22 32
Haddenham & Thame Parkway	d	18 00			18 40				18 59					19 41	20 12	20 42	21 13	21 43				22 45
Aylesbury	d					18 38						19 27									21 55	
Little Kimble	d					18 46						19 35									22 03	
Monks Risborough	d					18 50						19 39									22 07	
Princes Risborough 2	d	18 06			18 47	18a56			19 06			19a45		19 50	20 19	20 49	21 21	21 52			22 10	22 54
Saunderton	d	18 11							19 12						20 25		21 26				22 15	
High Wycombe 1	d	18 17	18 28	18 34	18 57			19 04	19 19	19 28	19 34			20 00	20 31	20 59	21 32	22 02			22b30	23 04
Beaconsfield	d	18 24		18 40				19 10	19 25		19 40			20 06	20 38	21 06	21 39	22 08			22 36	23 10
Seer Green	d			18 43				19 13			19 43				20 41		21 42				22 39	
Gerrards Cross 1	d	18 29		18 47				19 17	19 30		19 47			20 12	20 45	21 11	21 46	22 13			22 43	23 16
Denham Golf Club	d			18 50							19 50				20 48		21 49				22 46	
Denham	d			18 52				19 21			19 52				20 50		21 51				22 49	23 20
West Ruislip 3 §	⊖ d			18 57							19 57				20 55		21 56				22 53	
South Ruislip §	⊖ d							19 27			20 00				20 58		21 59				22 57	23 25
Northolt Park	d			19 02				19 30			20 04				21 02		22 03				23 00	
Sudbury Hill Harrow	d																					
Sudbury & Harrow Road	d																					
Wembley Stadium	d			19 07				19 35			20 09				21 07		22 08	22 27			23 05	23 32
London Paddington 15	⊖ a																					
London Marylebone 10	⊖ a	18 57	19 02	19 20	19 30			19 48	19 56	20 01	20 22			20 37	21 20	21 36	22 21	22 40			23 19	23 46

For general notes see front of timetable
For details of catering facilities see Directory of Train Operators

b Arr. 2221

§ London Underground Limited (Central Line) also operate services between South Ruislip and West Ruislip at frequent intervals

Wrexham & Shropshire services are expected to start operating during the currency of this timetable. Please visit the Wrexham & Shropshire website www.wrexhamandshropshire.co.uk for updated information

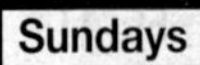
Sundays

until 13 July

Kidderminster, Birmingham Snow Hill, Stratford-upon-Avon, Banbury, Aylesbury and High Wycombe → London

Network Diagram - See first page of Table 114

Station	CH	CH	CH	CH	CH	CH	CH	CH	CH	CH	CH	CH	CH	CH	CH	CH	CH
Kidderminster d																	
Stourbridge Junction 2 d																	
Cradley Heath d																	
Rowley Regis d																	
Birmingham Snow Hill d							09 10		09 40		10 10		10 40		11 10		11 40
Birmingham Moor Street d							09 13		09 43		10 13		10 43		11 13		11 43
Solihull d							09 22		09 52		10 22		10 52		11 22		11 52
Dorridge d							09 28		09 58		10 28		10 58		11 28		11 58
Lapworth d									10 02								12 02
Stratford-upon-Avon d										10 00							
Wilmcote d										10 04							
Bearley d																	
Claverdon d																	
Hatton d										10 17			11 05				
Warwick Parkway d							09 39		10 10		10 38		11 10		11 38		12 10
Warwick d							09 42			10 24	10 41				11 41		
Leamington Spa 8 d							09 47		10 16	10 29	10 47		11 16		11 47		12 16
Banbury d				09 00		09 47	10 06		10 36	10 48	11 06		11 36		12 06		12 36
Kings Sutton d				09 04						10 53							
Bicester North 3 a				09 17		10 01	10 22		10 51	11 06	11 22		11 51		12 22		12 51
d			08 24	09 17		10 02	10 22		10 52	11 06	11 22		11 52	12 11	12 22		12 52
Haddenham & Thame Parkway d			08 37	09 30		10 15			11 05	11 19			12 05	12 24			13 05
Aylesbury d	07 27	08 18			09 30			10 28				11 30				12 28	
Little Kimble d	07 35	08 26			09 38			10 36				11 38				12 36	
Monks Risborough d	07 39	08 30			09 42			10 40				11 42				12 40	
Princes Risborough 2 d	07 42	08 33	08 44	09 37	09 45	10 23		10 43	11 13	11 28		11 45	12 13	12 31		12 43	13 13
Saunderton d	07 47		08 49		09 50			10 48				11 50				12 48	
High Wycombe 1 d	07 54	08 43	08 55	09 47	09 57	10 33		10 55	11 23	11 38		11 57	12 23	12 41		12 55	13 23
Beaconsfield d	08 00	08 49	09 02	09 53	10 03	10 39		11 01	11 29	11 44		12 03	12 29	12 47		13 01	13 29
Seer Green d	08 03		09 05		10 06			11 04				12 06				13 04	
Gerrards Cross 1 d	08 07	08 55	09 09	09 59	10 10	10 45		11 08	11 35	11 49		12 10	12 35	12 52		13 08	13 35
Denham Golf Club d	08 10				10 13							12 13					
Denham d	08 13		09 13		10 16			11 12				12 16				13 12	
West Ruislip 3 § ⊖ d	08 17		09 17		10 20			11 16				12 20				13 16	
South Ruislip § ⊖ d	08 21		09 21		10 24			11 20				12 24				13 20	
Northolt Park d	08 24		09 24		10 27			11 24				12 27				13 24	
Sudbury Hill Harrow d																	
Sudbury & Harrow Road d																	
Wembley Stadium d	08 29		09 29		10 32			11 29		12 02		12 32		13 06		13 29	
London Paddington 15 ⊖ a																	
London Marylebone 10 ⊖ a	08 42	09 20	09 43	10 27	10 47	11 10	11 23	11 42	12 00	12 16	12 22	12 47	13 00	13 19	13 22	13 42	14 00

For general notes see front of timetable
For details of catering facilities see Directory of Train Operators

§ London Underground Limited (Central Line) also operate services between South Ruislip and West Ruislip at frequent intervals

Wrexham & Shropshire services are expected to start operating during the currency of this timetable. Please visit the Wrexham & Shropshire website www.wrexhamandshropshire.co.uk for updated information

Table 115

Sundays

until 13 July

Kidderminster, Birmingham Snow Hill, Stratford-upon-Avon, Banbury, Aylesbury and High Wycombe → London

Network Diagram - See first page of Table 114

Station		CH	CH	CH	CH	CH 🚌	CH	CH	CH	CH	CH	CH	CH	CH 🚌	CH	CH	CH
Kidderminster	d																
Stourbridge Junction 2	d																
Cradley Heath	d																
Rowley Regis	d																
Birmingham Snow Hill	d		12 10		12 40		13 10		13 40		14 10		14 40		15 10		15 40
Birmingham Moor Street	d		12 13		12 43		13 13		13 43		14 13		14 43		15 13		15 43
Solihull	d		12 22		12 52		13 23		13 52		14 22		14 52		15 22		15 52
Dorridge	d		12 28		12 58		13 29		13 58		14 28		14 58		15 28		15 58
Lapworth	d								14 02								16 02
Stratford-upon-Avon	d	12 00								14 00							
Wilmcote	d	12 04								14 04							
Bearley	d																
Claverdon	d																
Hatton	d	12 19			13 05					14 19			15 05				
Warwick Parkway	d		12 38		13 10		13 39		14 10		14 38		15 10		15 38		16 10
Warwick	d	12 24	12 41				13 42			14 24	14 41				15 41		
Leamington Spa 8	d	12 29	12 46		13 16		13 47		14 16	14 29	14 47		15 16		15 47		16 16
Banbury	d	12 48	13 06		13 36		14 06		14 36	14 48	15 06		15 36		16 06		16 36
Kings Sutton	d	12 53								14 53							
Bicester North 3	a	13 06	13 22		13 51		14 22		14 51	15 06	15 22		15 51		16 22		16 51
	d	13 06	13 22		13 52	14 11	14 22		14 52	15 06	15 22		15 52	16 11	16 22		16 52
Haddenham & Thame Parkway	d	13 19			14 05	14 24			15 05	15 19			16 05	16 24			17 05
Aylesbury	d			13 30				14 28				15 30				16 28	
Little Kimble	d			13 38				14 36				15 38				16 36	
Monks Risborough	d			13 42				14 40				15 42				16 40	
Princes Risborough 2	d	13 28		13 45	14 13	14 31		14 43	15 13	15 28		15 45	16 13	16 31		16 43	17 13
Saunderton	d			13 50				14 48				15 50				16 48	
High Wycombe 1	d	13 38		13 57	14 23	14 41		14 55	15 23	15 38		15 57	16 23	16 41		16 55	17 23
Beaconsfield	d	13 44		14 03	14 29	14 47		15 01	15 29	15 44		16 03	16 29	16 47		17 01	17 29
Seer Green	d			14 06				15 04				16 06				17 04	
Gerrards Cross 1	d	13 49		14 10	14 35	14 52		15 08	15 35	15 49		16 10	16 35	16 52		17 08	17 35
Denham Golf Club	d			14 13								16 13					
Denham	d			14 16				15 12				16 16				17 12	
West Ruislip 3 §	⊖ d			14 20				15 16				16 20				17 16	
South Ruislip §	⊖ d			14 24				15 20				16 24				17 20	
Northolt Park	d			14 27				15 24				16 27				17 24	
Sudbury Hill Harrow	d																
Sudbury & Harrow Road	d																
Wembley Stadium	d	14 02		14 32		15 06		15 29		16 02		16 32		17 06		17 29	
London Paddington 15	⊖ a																
London Marylebone 10	⊖ a	14 16	14 22	14 47	15 00	15 19	15 22	15 42	16 00	16 16	16 22	16 47	17 00	17 19	17 22	17 42	18 00

Station		CH	CH	CH	CH	CH 🚌	CH	CH	CH	CH	CH	CH	CH	CH	CH	CH	CH	CH
Kidderminster	d																	
Stourbridge Junction 2	d																	
Cradley Heath	d																	
Rowley Regis	d																	
Birmingham Snow Hill	d		16 10		16 40		17 10		17 40		18 10		18 40	19 15		20 15		21 15
Birmingham Moor Street	d		16 13		16 43		17 13		17 43		18 13		18 43	19 18		20 18		21 18
Solihull	d		16 22		16 52		17 22		17 52		18 22		18 52	19 27		20 27		21 27
Dorridge	d		16 28		16 58		17 28		17 58		18 28		18 58	19 34		20 34		21 34
Lapworth	d								18 02									
Stratford-upon-Avon	d	16 00								18 00					20 00			
Wilmcote	d	16 04								18 04					20 04			
Bearley	d																	
Claverdon	d																	
Hatton	d	16 17			17 05					18 17			19 05		20 17			
Warwick Parkway	d		16 38		17 10		17 38		18 10		18 38		19 10	19 45		20 45		21 45
Warwick	d	16 24	16 41				17 41			18 24	18 41			19 48	20 24	20 48		21 48
Leamington Spa 8	d	16 29	16 47		17 16		17 47		18 16	18 29	18 47		19 16	19 53	20 29	20 53		21 53
Banbury	d	16 48	17 06		17 36		18 06		18 36	18 48	19 06		19 35	20 13	20 48	21 13		22 15
Kings Sutton	d	16 53								18 53					20 53			22 20
Bicester North 3	a	17 06	17 22		17 51		18 22		18 51	19 06	19 22		19 51	20 29	21 06	21 29		22 33
	d	17 06	17 22		17 52	18 11	18 22		18 52	19 06	19 22		19 52	20 29	21 06	21 29		22 33
Haddenham & Thame Parkway	d	17 19			18 05	18 24			19 05	19 19			20 05	20 42	21 19	21 42		22 46
Aylesbury	d			17 30				18 28				19 30					22 32	
Little Kimble	d			17 38				18 36				19 38					22 40	
Monks Risborough	d			17 42				18 40				19 42					22 44	
Princes Risborough 2	d	17 28		17 45	18 13	18 31		18 43	19 13	19 28		19 45	20 13	20 50	21 28	21 50	22a50	22 54
Saunderton	d			17 50				18 48				19 50		20 55		21 55		22 59
High Wycombe 1	d	17 38		17 57	18 23	18 41		18 55	19 23	19 38		19 57	20 23	21 02	21 38	22 02		23 06
Beaconsfield	d	17 44		18 03	18 29	18 47		19 01	19 29	19 44		20 03	20 29	21 08	21 44	22 08		23 12
Seer Green	d			18 06				19 04				20 06		21 11				23 15
Gerrards Cross 1	d	17 49		18 10	18 35	18 52		19 08	19 34	19 49		20 10	20 35	21 15	21 49	22 14		23 19
Denham Golf Club	d			18 13								20 13				22 17		
Denham	d			18 16				19 12				20 16		21 19		22 19		23 23
West Ruislip 3 §	⊖ d			18 20				19 16				20 20		21 24		22 23		23 28
South Ruislip §	⊖ d			18 24				19 20				20 24		21 27		22 27		23 31
Northolt Park	d			18 27				19 24				20 27		21 31		22 31		23 35
Sudbury Hill Harrow	d																	
Sudbury & Harrow Road	d																	
Wembley Stadium	d	18 04		18 32		19 06		19 29		20 02		20 32		21 36	22 02	22 36		23 40
London Paddington 15	⊖ a																	
London Marylebone 10	⊖ a	18 17	18 21	18 47	19 00	19 19	19 22	19 42	20 00	20 16	20 21	20 48	21 00	21 50	22 16	22 50		23 53

For general notes see front of timetable
For details of catering facilities see Directory of Train Operators

§ London Underground Limited (Central Line) also operate services between South Ruislip and West Ruislip at frequent intervals

Wrexham & Shropshire services are expected to start operating during the currency of this timetable. Please visit the Wrexham & Shropshire website www.wrexhamandshropshire.co.uk for updated information

Table 115

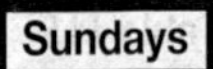

20 July to 7 September

Kidderminster, Birmingham Snow Hill, Stratford-upon-Avon, Banbury, Aylesbury and High Wycombe → London

Network Diagram - See first page of Table 114

		CH	CH	CH	CH	CH	CH	CH	CH	CH	CH	CH	CH	CH	CH	CH	CH	CH
Kidderminster	d																	
Stourbridge Junction 2	d																	
Cradley Heath	d																	
Rowley Regis	d																	
Birmingham Snow Hill	d							09 10		09 40		10 10		10 40		11 10		11 40
Birmingham Moor Street	d							09 13		09 43		10 13		10 43		11 13		11 43
Solihull	d							09 22		09 52		10 22		10 52		11 22		11 52
Dorridge	d							09 28		09 58		10 28		10 58		11 28		11 58
Lapworth	d									10 02								12 02
Stratford-upon-Avon	d										10 00							
Wilmcote	d										10 04							
Bearley	d																	
Claverdon	d																	
Hatton	d										10 17			11 05				
Warwick Parkway	d							09 39		10 10		10 38		11 10		11 38		12 10
Warwick	d							09 42			10 24	10 41				11 41		
Leamington Spa 8	d							09 47		10 16	10 29	10 47		11 16		11 47		12 16
Banbury	d				09 00		09 47	10 06		10 36	10 48	11 06		11 36		12 06		12 36
Kings Sutton	d				09 04						10 53							
Bicester North 3	a				09 17		10 01	10 22		10 51	11 06	11 22		11 51		12 22		12 51
	d			08 24	09 17		10 02	10 22		10 52	11 06	11 22		11 52	12 11	12 22		12 52
Haddenham & Thame Parkway	d			08 37	09 30		10 15			11 05	11 19			12 05	12 24			13 05
Aylesbury	d	07 27	08 18			09 30			10 28				11 30				12 28	
Little Kimble	d	07 35	08 26			09 38			10 36				11 38				12 36	
Monks Risborough	d	07 39	08 30			09 42			10 40				11 42				12 40	
Princes Risborough 2	d	07 42	08 33	08 44	09 37	09 45	10 23		10 43	11 13	11 28		11 45	12 13	12 31		12 43	13 13
Saunderton	d	07 47		08 49		09 50			10 48				11 50				12 48	
High Wycombe 1	d	07 54	08 43	08 55	09 47	09 57	10 33		10 55	11 23	11 38		11 57	12 23	12 41		12 55	13 23
Beaconsfield	d	08 00	08 49	09 02	09 53	10 03	10 39		11 01	11 29	11 44		12 03	12 29	12 47		13 01	13 29
Seer Green	d	08 03		09 05		10 06			11 04				12 06				13 04	
Gerrards Cross 1	d	08 07	08 55	09 09	09 59	10 10	10 45		11 08	11 35	11 49		12 10	12 35	12 52		13 08	13 35
Denham Golf Club	d	08 10				10 13							12 13					
Denham	d	08 13		09 13		10 16			11 12				12 16				13 12	
West Ruislip 3 §	⊖ d	08 17		09 17		10 20			11 16				12 20				13 16	
South Ruislip §	⊖ d	08 21		09 21		10 24			11 20				12 24				13 20	
Northolt Park	d	08 24		09 24		10 27			11 24				12 27				13 24	
Sudbury Hill Harrow	d																	
Sudbury & Harrow Road	d																	
Wembley Stadium	d	08 29		09 29		10 32			11 29		12 02		12 32		13 06		13 29	
London Paddington 15	⊖ a																	
London Marylebone 10	⊖ a	08 42	09 20	09 43	10 27	10 47	11 10	11 23	11 42	12 00	12 16	12 22	12 47	13 00	13 19	13 22	13 42	14 00

For general notes see front of timetable
For details of catering facilities see Directory of Train Operators

§ London Underground Limited (Central Line) also operate services between South Ruislip and West Ruislip at frequent intervals

Wrexham & Shropshire services are expected to start operating during the currency of this timetable. Please visit the Wrexham & Shropshire website www.wrexhamandshropshire.co.uk for updated information

Table 115

Sundays

Kidderminster, Birmingham Snow Hill, Stratford-upon-Avon, Banbury, Aylesbury and High Wycombe → London

20 July to 7 September

Network Diagram - See first page of Table 114

		CH	CH	CH	CH	CH (trolley)	CH	CH	CH	CH	CH	CH	CH	CH (trolley)	CH	CH	CH
Kidderminster	d																
Stourbridge Junction 2	d																
Cradley Heath	d																
Rowley Regis	d																
Birmingham Snow Hill	d		12 10		12 40		13 10		13 40		14 10		14 40		15 10		15 40
Birmingham Moor Street	d		12 13		12 43		13 13		13 43		14 13		14 43		15 13		15 43
Solihull	d		12 22		12 52		13 23		13 52		14 22		14 52		15 22		15 52
Dorridge	d		12 28		12 58		13 29		13 58		14 28		14 58		15 28		15 58
Lapworth	d								14 02								16 02
Stratford-upon-Avon	d	12 00								14 00							
Wilmcote	d	12 04								14 04							
Bearley	d																
Claverdon	d																
Hatton	d	12 19			13 05					14 19			15 05				
Warwick Parkway	d		12 38		13 10		13 39		14 10		14 38		15 10		15 38		16 10
Warwick	d	12 24	12 41				13 42			14 24	14 41				15 41		
Leamington Spa 8	d	12 29	12 46		13 16		13 47		14 16	14 29	14 47		15 16		15 47		16 16
Banbury	d	12 48	13 06		13 36		14 06		14 36	14 48	15 06		15 36		16 06		16 36
Kings Sutton	d	12 53								14 53							
Bicester North 3	a	13 06	13 22		13 51		14 22		14 51	15 06	15 22		15 51		16 22		16 51
	d	13 06	13 22		13 52	14 11	14 22		14 52	15 06	15 22		15 52	16 11	16 22		16 52
Haddenham & Thame Parkway	d	13 19			14 05	14 24			15 05	15 19			16 05	16 24			17 05
Aylesbury	d			13 30				14 28				15 30				16 28	
Little Kimble	d			13 38				14 36				15 38				16 36	
Monks Risborough	d			13 42				14 40				15 42				16 40	
Princes Risborough 2	d	13 28		13 45	14 13	14 31		14 43	15 13	15 28		15 45	16 13	16 31		16 43	17 13
Saunderton	d			13 50				14 48				15 50				16 48	
High Wycombe 1	d	13 38		13 57	14 23	14 41		14 55	15 23	15 38		15 57	16 23	16 41		16 55	17 23
Beaconsfield	d	13 44		14 03	14 29	14 47		15 01	15 29	15 44		16 03	16 29	16 47		17 01	17 29
Seer Green	d			14 06				15 04				16 06				17 04	
Gerrards Cross 1	d	13 49		14 10	14 35	14 52		15 08	15 35	15 49		16 10	16 35	16 52		17 08	17 35
Denham Golf Club	d			14 13								16 13					
Denham	d			14 16				15 12				16 16				17 12	
West Ruislip 3 §	⊖ d			14 20				15 16				16 20				17 16	
South Ruislip §	⊖ d			14 24				15 20				16 24				17 20	
Northolt Park	d			14 27				15 24				16 27				17 24	
Sudbury Hill Harrow	d																
Sudbury & Harrow Road	d																
Wembley Stadium	d	14 02		14 32		15 06		15 29		16 02		16 32		17 06		17 29	
London Paddington 15	⊖ a																
London Marylebone 10	⊖ a	14 16	14 22	14 47	15 00	15 19	15 22	15 42	16 00	16 16	16 22	16 47	17 00	17 19	17 22	17 42	18 00

		CH	CH	CH	CH	CH (trolley)	CH	CH	CH	CH	CH	CH	CH	CH	CH	CH	CH	CH
Kidderminster	d																	
Stourbridge Junction 2	d																	
Cradley Heath	d																	
Rowley Regis	d																	
Birmingham Snow Hill	d		16 10		16 40		17 10		17 40		18 10		18 40	19 15		20 15		21 15
Birmingham Moor Street	d		16 13		16 43		17 13		17 43		18 13		18 43	19 18		20 18		21 18
Solihull	d		16 22		16 52		17 22		17 52		18 22		18 52	19 27		20 27		21 27
Dorridge	d		16 28		16 58		17 28		17 58		18 28		18 58	19 34		20 34		21 34
Lapworth	d								18 02									
Stratford-upon-Avon	d	16 00								18 00					20 00			
Wilmcote	d	16 04								18 04					20 04			
Bearley	d																	
Claverdon	d																	
Hatton	d	16 17			17 05					18 17			19 05		20 17			
Warwick Parkway	d		16 38		17 10		17 38		18 10		18 38		19 10	19 45		20 45		21 45
Warwick	d	16 24	16 41				17 41			18 24	18 41			19 48	20 24	20 48		21 48
Leamington Spa 8	d	16 29	16 47		17 16		17 47		18 16	18 29	18 47		19 16	19 53	20 29	20 53		21 53
Banbury	d	16 48	17 06		17 36		18 06		18 36	18 48	19 06		19 35	20 13	20 48	21 13		22 15
Kings Sutton	d	16 53								18 53					20 53			22 20
Bicester North 3	a	17 06	17 22		17 51		18 22		18 51	19 06	19 22		19 51	20 29	21 06	21 29		22 33
	d	17 06	17 22		17 52	18 11	18 22		18 52	19 06	19 22		19 52	20 29	21 06	21 29		22 33
Haddenham & Thame Parkway	d	17 19			18 05	18 24			19 05	19 19			20 05	20 42	21 19	21 42		22 46
Aylesbury	d			17 30				18 28				19 30					22 32	
Little Kimble	d			17 38				18 36				19 38					22 40	
Monks Risborough	d			17 42				18 40				19 42					22 44	
Princes Risborough 2	d	17 28		17 45	18 13	18 31		18 43	19 13	19 28		19 45	20 13	20 50	21 28	21 50	22a50	22 54
Saunderton	d			17 50				18 48				19 50		20 55		21 55		22 59
High Wycombe 1	d	17 38		17 57	18 23	18 41		18 55	19 23	19 38		19 57	20 23	21 02	21 38	22 02		23 06
Beaconsfield	d	17 44		18 03	18 29	18 47		19 01	19 29	19 44		20 03	20 29	21 08	21 44	22 08		23 12
Seer Green	d			18 06				19 04				20 06		21 11				23 15
Gerrards Cross 1	d	17 49		18 10	18 35	18 52		19 08	19 34	19 49		20 10	20 35	21 15	21 49	22 14		23 19
Denham Golf Club	d			18 13								20 13				22 17		
Denham	d			18 16				19 12				20 16		21 19		22 19		23 23
West Ruislip 3 §	⊖ d			18 20				19 16				20 20		21 24		22 23		23 28
South Ruislip §	⊖ d			18 24				19 20				20 24		21 27		22 27		23 31
Northolt Park	d			18 27				19 24				20 27		21 31		22 31		23 35
Sudbury Hill Harrow	d																	
Sudbury & Harrow Road	d																	
Wembley Stadium	d	18 04		18 32		19 06		19 29		20 02		20 32		21 36	22 02	22 36		23 40
London Paddington 15	⊖ a																	
London Marylebone 10	⊖ a	18 17	18 21	18 47	19 00	19 19	19 22	19 42	20 00	20 16	20 21	20 48	21 00	21 50	22 16	22 50		23 53

For general notes see front of timetable
For details of catering facilities see Directory of Train Operators

§ London Underground Limited (Central Line) also operate services between South Ruislip and West Ruislip at frequent intervals

Wrexham & Shropshire services are expected to start operating during the currency of this timetable. Please visit the Wrexham & Shropshire website www.wrexhamandshropshire.co.uk for updated information

Table 115

Sundays

from 14 September

Kidderminster, Birmingham Snow Hill, Stratford-upon-Avon, Banbury, Aylesbury and High Wycombe → London

Network Diagram - See first page of Table 114

		CH	CH	CH 🚌	CH 🚌	CH	CH	CH	CH	CH	CH	CH	CH	CH	CH 🚌	CH	CH	CH
Kidderminster	d																	
Stourbridge Junction 2	d																	
Cradley Heath	d																	
Rowley Regis	d																	
Birmingham Snow Hill	d							09 10		09 40		10 10		10 40		11 10		11 40
Birmingham Moor Street	d							09 13		09 43		10 13		10 43		11 13		11 43
Solihull	d							09 22		09 52		10 22		10 52		11 22		11 52
Dorridge	d							09 28		09 58		10 28		10 58		11 28		11 58
Lapworth	d									10 02								12 02
Stratford-upon-Avon	d										10 00							
Wilmcote	d										10 04							
Bearley	d																	
Claverdon	d																	
Hatton	d										10 17			11 05				
Warwick Parkway	d							09 39		10 10		10 38		11 10		11 38		12 10
Warwick	d							09 42			10 24	10 41				11 41		
Leamington Spa 8	d							09 47		10 16	10 29	10 47		11 16		11 47		12 16
Banbury	d				09 00		09 47	10 06		10 36	10 48	11 06		11 36		12 06		12 36
Kings Sutton	d				09 04						10 53							
Bicester North 3	a				09 17		10 01	10 22		10 51	11 06	11 22		11 51		12 22		12 51
	d			08 24	09 17		10 02	10 22		10 52	11 06	11 22		11 52	12 11	12 22		12 52
Haddenham & Thame Parkway	d			08 37	09 30		10 15			11 05	11 19			12 05	12 24			13 05
Aylesbury	d	07 27	08 18			09 30			10 28				11 30				12 28	
Little Kimble	d	07 35	08 26			09 38			10 36				11 38				12 36	
Monks Risborough	d	07 39	08 30			09 42			10 40				11 42				12 40	
Princes Risborough 2	d	07 42	08 33	08 44	09 37	09 45	10 23		10 43	11 13	11 28		11 45	12 13	12 31		12 43	13 13
Saunderton	d	07 47		08 49		09 50			10 48				11 50				12 48	
High Wycombe 1	d	07 54	08 43	08 55	09 47	09 57	10 33		10 55	11 23	11 38		11 57	12 23	12 41		12 55	13 23
Beaconsfield	d	08 00	08 49	09 02	09 53	10 03	10 39		11 01	11 29	11 44		12 03	12 29	12 47		13 01	13 29
Seer Green	d	08 03		09 05		10 06			11 04				12 06				13 04	
Gerrards Cross 1	d	08 07	08 55	09 09	09 59	10 10	10 45		11 08	11 35	11 49		12 10	12 35	12 52		13 08	13 35
Denham Golf Club	d	08 10				10 13							12 13					
Denham	d	08 13		09 13		10 16			11 12				12 16				13 12	
West Ruislip 3 §	⊖ d	08 17		09 17		10 20			11 16				12 20				13 16	
South Ruislip §	⊖ d	08 21		09 21		10 24			11 20				12 24				13 20	
Northolt Park	d	08 24		09 24		10 27			11 24				12 27				13 24	
Sudbury Hill Harrow	d																	
Sudbury & Harrow Road	d																	
Wembley Stadium	d	08 29		09 29		10 32			11 29		12 02		12 32		13 06		13 29	
London Paddington 15	⊖ a																	
London Marylebone 10	⊖ a	08 42	09 20	09 43	10 27	10 47	11 10	11 23	11 42	12 00	12 16	12 22	12 47	13 00	13 19	13 22	13 42	14 00

For general notes see front of timetable
For details of catering facilities see Directory of Train Operators

§ London Underground Limited (Central Line) also operate services between South Ruislip and West Ruislip at frequent intervals

Wrexham & Shropshire services are expected to start operating during the currency of this timetable. Please visit the Wrexham & Shropshire website www.wrexhamandshropshire.co.uk for updated information

Sundays

from 14 September

Kidderminster, Birmingham Snow Hill, Stratford-upon-Avon, Banbury, Aylesbury and High Wycombe → London

Network Diagram - See first page of Table 114

		CH	CH	CH	CH	CH 🚌	CH	CH	CH	CH	CH	CH	CH	CH 🚌	CH	CH	CH
Kidderminster	d																
Stourbridge Junction [2]	d																
Cradley Heath	d																
Rowley Regis	d																
Birmingham Snow Hill 🚊	d		12 10		12 40		13 10		13 40		14 10		14 40		15 10		15 40
Birmingham Moor Street	d		12 13		12 43		13 13		13 43		14 13		14 43		15 13		15 43
Solihull	d		12 22		12 52		13 23		13 52		14 22		14 52		15 22		15 52
Dorridge	d		12 28		12 58		13 29		13 58		14 28		14 58		15 28		15 58
Lapworth	d								14 02								16 02
Stratford-upon-Avon	d	12 00								14 00							
Wilmcote	d	12 04								14 04							
Bearley	d																
Claverdon	d																
Hatton	d	12 19			13 05					14 19			15 05				
Warwick Parkway	d		12 38		13 10		13 39		14 10		14 38		15 10		15 38		16 10
Warwick	d	12 24	12 41				13 42			14 24	14 41				15 41		
Leamington Spa [8]	d	12 29	12 46		13 16		13 47		14 16	14 29	14 47		15 16		15 47		16 16
Banbury	d	12 48	13 06		13 36		14 06		14 36	14 48	15 06		15 36		16 06		16 36
Kings Sutton	d	12 53								14 53							
Bicester North [3]	a	13 06	13 22		13 51		14 22		14 51	15 06	15 22		15 51		16 22		16 51
	d	13 06	13 22		13 52	14 11	14 22		14 52	15 06	15 22		15 52	16 11	16 22		16 52
Haddenham & Thame Parkway	d	13 19			14 05	14 24			15 05	15 19			16 05	16 24			17 05
Aylesbury	d			13 30				14 28				15 30				16 28	
Little Kimble	d			13 38				14 36				15 38				16 36	
Monks Risborough	d			13 42				14 40				15 42				16 40	
Princes Risborough [2]	d	13 28		13 45	14 13	14 31		14 43	15 13	15 28		15 45	16 13	16 31		16 43	17 13
Saunderton	d			13 50				14 48				15 50				16 48	
High Wycombe [1]	d	13 38		13 57	14 23	14 41		14 55	15 23	15 38		15 57	16 23	16 41		16 55	17 23
Beaconsfield	d	13 44		14 03	14 29	14 47		15 01	15 29	15 44		16 03	16 29	16 47		17 01	17 29
Seer Green	d			14 06				15 04				16 06				17 04	
Gerrards Cross [1]	d	13 49		14 10	14 35	14 52		15 08	15 35	15 49		16 10	16 35	16 52		17 08	17 35
Denham Golf Club	d			14 13								16 13					
Denham	d			14 16				15 12				16 16				17 12	
West Ruislip [3] §	⊖ d			14 20				15 16				16 20				17 16	
South Ruislip §	⊖ d			14 24				15 20				16 24				17 20	
Northolt Park	d			14 27				15 24				16 27				17 24	
Sudbury Hill Harrow	d																
Sudbury & Harrow Road	d																
Wembley Stadium	d	14 02		14 32		15 06		15 29		16 02		16 32		17 06		17 29	
London Paddington [15]	⊖ a																
London Marylebone [10]	⊖ a	14 16	14 22	14 47	15 00	15 19	15 22	15 42	16 00	16 16	16 22	16 47	17 00	17 19	17 22	17 42	18 00

		CH	CH	CH	CH	CH 🚌	CH	CH	CH	CH	CH	CH	CH	CH	CH	CH	CH	CH
Kidderminster	d																	
Stourbridge Junction [2]	d																	
Cradley Heath	d																	
Rowley Regis	d																	
Birmingham Snow Hill 🚊	d		16 10		16 40		17 10		17 40		18 10		18 40	19 15		20 15		21 15
Birmingham Moor Street	d		16 13		16 43		17 13		17 43		18 13		18 43	19 18		20 18		21 18
Solihull	d		16 22		16 52		17 22		17 52		18 22		18 52	19 27		20 27		21 27
Dorridge	d		16 28		16 58		17 28		17 58		18 28		18 58	19 34		20 34		21 34
Lapworth	d								18 02									
Stratford-upon-Avon	d	16 00								18 00					20 00			
Wilmcote	d	16 04								18 04					20 04			
Bearley	d																	
Claverdon	d																	
Hatton	d	16 17			17 05					18 17			19 05		20 17			
Warwick Parkway	d		16 38		17 10		17 38		18 10		18 38		19 10	19 45		20 45		21 45
Warwick	d	16 24	16 41				17 41			18 24	18 41			19 48	20 24	20 48		21 48
Leamington Spa [8]	d	16 29	16 47		17 16		17 47		18 16	18 29	18 47		19 16	19 53	20 29	20 53		21 53
Banbury	d	16 48	17 06		17 36		18 06		18 36	18 48	19 06		19 35	20 13	20 48	21 13		22 15
Kings Sutton	d	16 53								18 53					20 53			22 20
Bicester North [3]	a	17 06	17 22		17 51		18 22		18 51	19 06	19 22		19 51	20 29	21 06	21 29		22 33
	d	17 06	17 22		17 52	18 11	18 22		18 52	19 06	19 22		19 52	20 29	21 06	21 29		22 33
Haddenham & Thame Parkway	d	17 19			18 05	18 24			19 05	19 19			20 05	20 42	21 19	21 42		22 46
Aylesbury	d			17 30				18 28				19 30					22 32	
Little Kimble	d			17 38				18 36				19 38					22 40	
Monks Risborough	d			17 42				18 40				19 42					22 44	
Princes Risborough [2]	d	17 28		17 45	18 13	18 31		18 43	19 13	19 28		19 45	20 13	20 50	21 28	21 50	22a50	22 54
Saunderton	d			17 50				18 48				19 50		20 55		21 55		22 59
High Wycombe [1]	d	17 38		17 57	18 23	18 41		18 55	19 23	19 38		19 57	20 23	21 02	21 38	22 02		23 06
Beaconsfield	d	17 44		18 03	18 29	18 47		19 01	19 29	19 44		20 03	20 29	21 08	21 44	22 08		23 12
Seer Green	d			18 06				19 04				20 06		21 11				23 15
Gerrards Cross [1]	d	17 49		18 10	18 35	18 52		19 08	19 34	19 49		20 10	20 35	21 15	21 49	22 14		23 19
Denham Golf Club	d			18 13								20 13				22 17		
Denham	d			18 16				19 12				20 16		21 19		22 19		23 23
West Ruislip [3] §	⊖ d			18 20				19 16				20 20		21 24		22 23		23 28
South Ruislip §	⊖ d			18 24				19 20				20 24		21 27		22 27		23 31
Northolt Park	d			18 27				19 24				20 27		21 31		22 31		23 35
Sudbury Hill Harrow	d																	
Sudbury & Harrow Road	d																	
Wembley Stadium	d	18 04		18 32		19 06		19 29		20 02		20 32		21 36	22 02	22 36		23 40
London Paddington [15]	⊖ a																	
London Marylebone [10]	⊖ a	18 17	18 21	18 47	19 00	19 19	19 22	19 42	20 00	20 16	20 21	20 48	21 00	21 50	22 16	22 50		23 53

For general notes see front of timetable
For details of catering facilities see Directory of Train Operators

§ London Underground Limited (Central Line) also operate services between South Ruislip and West Ruislip at frequent intervals

Wrexham & Shropshire services are expected to start operating during the currency of this timetable. Please visit the Wrexham & Shropshire website www.wrexhamandshropshire.co.uk for updated information

Chinnor — Princes Risborough

Bus Service

		CH	CH	CH	CH	CH	CH
Chinnor, Lower Road	d	06 12	06 40	07 34	08 00	09 07	09 36
Chinnor, Estover Way	d	06 14	06 42	07 36	08 02	09 09	09 38
Chinnor, The Wheatsheaf	d	06 15	06 43	07 37	08 03	09 10	09 39
Chinnor, The Red Lion	d	06 18	06 46	07 40	08 06	09 13	09 42
Bledlow, Village Hall	d	06 21	06 49	07 43	08 09	09 16	09 45
Princes Risborough	a	06 28	06 56	07 50	08 16	09 23	09 52

Mondays to Fridays

		CH	CH	CH	CH	CH	CH	CH
Princes Risborough	d	16 50	17 19	18 12	18 47	19 17	20 19	20 54
Bledlow, Village Hall	d	16 57	17 26	18 19	18 54	19 24	20 26	21 01
Chinnor, Lower Road	d	17 00	17 29	18 22	18 57	19 27	20 29	21 04
Chinnor, Estover Way	d	17 02	17 31	18 24	18 59	19 29	20 31	21 06
Chinnor, The Wheatsheaf	d	17 03	17 32	18 25	19 00	19 30	20 32	21 07
Chinnor, The Red Lion	a	17 06	17 35	18 28	19 03	19 33	20 35	21 10

For general notes see front of timetable
For details of catering facilities see Directory of Train Operators

NO SATURDAY OR SUNDAY SERVICE

Solihull → Birmingham International Airport

Bus Service

		CH	CH	CH		CH	CH	CH		CH	CH	CH		CH	CH	CH		CH	CH	CH		CH	CH	CH		CH
Solihull	d	05 50	06 20	06 50	.....	07 20	07 50	08 20	.....	08 50	09 20	09 50	.....	10 20	10 50	11 20	.....	11 50	12 20	12 50	.....	13 20	13 50	14 20	.....	14 50
Birmingham Nec (Bus)	d	06 07	06 37	07 07	.	07 44	08 14	08 44	.	09 14	09 44	10 14	.	10 44	11 14	11 44	.	12 14	12 44	13 14	.	13 44	14 14	14 44	.	15 14
Birmingham Airport (Bus)	a	06 09	06 39	07 09	.....	07 46	08 16	08 46	.....	09 16	09 46	10 16	.....	10 46	11 16	11 46	.....	12 16	12 46	13 16	.....	13 46	14 16	14 46	.....	15 16

		CH	CH	CH		CH	CH	CH		CH	CH	CH		CH	CH	CH		CH	CH	CH		CH	CH			
Solihull	d	15 20	15 50	16 20	.....	16 50	17 15	17 45	.....	18 15	18 48	19 18	.....	19 48	20 18	20 48	.....	21 18	21 48	22 18	.....	22 48	23 18	.....	.....	.....
Birmingham Nec (Bus)	d	15 44	16 14	16 44	.	17 14	17 39	18 05	.	18 35	19 05	19 35	.	20 05	20 35	21 05	.	21 35	22 05	22 35	.	23 05	23 35	.	.	.
Birmingham Airport (Bus)	a	15 46	16 16	16 46	.....	17 16	17 41	18 07	.....	18 37	19 07	19 37	.....	20 07	20 37	21 07	.....	21 37	22 07	22 37	.....	23 07	23 37	.....	.....	.....

Saturdays

		CH	CH	CH		CH	CH	CH		CH	CH	CH		CH	CH	CH		CH	CH	CH		CH	CH	CH		CH
Solihull	d	05 50	06 20	06 50	.....	07 20	07 50	08 20	.....	08 50	09 20	09 50	.....	10 20	10 50	11 20	.....	11 50	12 20	12 50	.....	13 20	13 50	14 20	.....	14 50
Birmingham Nec (Bus)	d	06 07	06 37	07 07	.	07 44	08 14	08 44	.	09 14	09 44	10 14	.	10 44	11 14	11 44	.	12 14	12 44	13 14	.	13 44	14 14	14 44	.	15 14
Birmingham Airport (Bus)	a	06 09	06 39	07 09	.....	07 46	08 16	08 46	.....	09 16	09 46	10 16	.....	10 46	11 16	11 46	.....	12 16	12 46	13 16	.....	13 46	14 16	14 46	.....	15 16

		CH	CH	CH		CH	CH	CH		CH	CH	CH		CH	CH	CH		CH	CH	CH		CH	CH			
Solihull	d	15 20	15 50	16 20	.....	16 50	17 15	17 45	.....	18 15	18 48	19 18	.....	19 48	20 18	20 48	.....	21 18	21 48	22 18	.....	22 48	23 18	.....	.....	.....
Birmingham Nec (Bus)	d	15 44	16 14	16 44	.	17 14	17 39	18 09	.	18 39	19 05	19 35	.	20 05	20 35	21 05	.	21 35	22 05	22 35	.	23 05	23 35	.	.	.
Birmingham Airport (Bus)	a	15 46	16 16	16 46	.....	17 16	17 41	18 11	.....	18 41	19 07	19 37	.....	20 07	20 37	21 07	.....	21 37	22 07	22 37	.....	23 07	23 37	.....	.....	.....

Sundays

		CH		CH		CH		CH		CH		CH		CH		CH		CH		CH		CH		CH		CH
Solihull	d	09 48	.....	10 18	.....	10 48	.....	11 18	.....	11 48	.....	12 18	.....	12 48	.....	13 18	.....	13 48	.....	14 18	.....	14 48	.....	15 18	.....	15 48
Birmingham Nec (Bus)	d	10 05	.	10 35	.	11 05	.	11 35	.	12 05	.	12 35	.	13 05	.	13 35	.	14 05	.	14 35	.	15 05	.	15 35	.	16 05
Birmingham Airport (Bus)	a	10 07	.....	10 37	.....	11 07	.....	11 37	.....	12 07	.....	12 37	.....	13 07	.....	13 37	.....	14 07	.....	14 37	.....	15 07	.....	15 37	.....	16 07

		CH		CH		CH		CH		CH		CH		CH		CH		CH	CH	CH	CH	CH	CH	CH		
Solihull	d	16 18	.....	16 48	.....	17 18	.....	17 48	.....	18 18	.....	18 48	.....	19 18	.....	19 48	.....	20 18	20 48	21 18	21 48	22 18	22 48	23 18	.....	.....
Birmingham Nec (Bus)	d	16 35	.	17 05	.	17 35	.	18 05	.	18 35	.	19 05	.	19 35	.	20 05	.	20 35	21 05	21 35	22 05	22 35	23 05	23 35	.	.
Birmingham Airport (Bus)	a	16 37	.....	17 07	.....	17 37	.....	18 07	.....	18 37	.....	19 07	.....	19 37	.....	20 07	.....	20 37	21 07	21 37	22 07	22 37	23 07	23 37	.....	.....

For general notes see front of timetable
For details of catering facilities see
Directory of Train Operators

Birmingham International Airport → Solihull

Bus Service

Mondays to Fridays

		CH	CH		CH	CH		CH	CH		CH	CH		CH	CH		CH	CH		CH	CH		CH	CH		CH
Birmingham Airport (Bus)	d	06 12	06 42		07 06	07 39		08 12	08 42		09 12	09 42		10 12	10 42		11 12	11 42		12 12	12 42		13 12	13 42		14 12
Birmingham Nec (Bus)	d	06 14	06 44		07 10	07 43		08 16	08 46		09 16	09 46		10 16	10 46		11 16	11 46		12 16	12 46		13 16	13 46		14 16
Solihull	a	06 31	07 01		07 30	08 03		08 37	09 07		09 37	10 07		10 37	11 07		11 37	12 07		12 37	13 07		13 37	14 07		14 37

		CH	CH		CH	CH		CH	CH		CH	CH		CH	CH		CH	CH		CH	CH	CH	CH	CH		
Birmingham Airport (Bus)	d	14 42	15 12		15 42	16 12		16 42	17 12		17 42	18 12		18 42	19 19		19 49	20 19		20 49	21 19	21 49	22 19	22 49		
Birmingham Nec (Bus)	d	14 46	15 16		15 46	16 16		16 46	17 16		17 46	18 16		18 46	19 21		19 51	20 21		20 51	21 21	21 51	22 21	22 51		
Solihull	a	15 07	15 37		16 07	16 37		17 07	17 37		18 07	18 37		19 07	19 40		20 10	20 40		21 10	21 40	22 10	22 40	23 10		

Saturdays

		CH	CH		CH	CH		CH	CH		CH	CH		CH	CH		CH	CH		CH	CH		CH	CH		CH
Birmingham Airport (Bus)	d	05 41	06 12		06 42	07 06		07 39	08 12		08 42	09 12		09 42	10 12		10 42	11 12		11 42	12 12		12 42	13 12		13 42
Birmingham Nec (Bus)	d	05 43	06 14		06 44	07 10		07 43	08 16		08 46	09 16		09 46	10 16		10 46	11 16		11 46	12 16		12 46	13 16		13 46
Solihull	a	06 00	06 31		07 01	07 30		08 03	08 37		09 07	09 37		10 07	10 37		11 07	11 37		12 07	12 37		13 07	13 37		14 07

		CH	CH		CH	CH		CH	CH		CH	CH		CH	CH		CH	CH	CH	CH	CH	CH	CH	CH		
Birmingham Airport (Bus)	d	14 12	14 42		15 12	15 42		16 12	16 42		17 12	17 42		18 12	18 42		19 19	19 49	20 19	21 19	21 49	22 19	22 49	22 49		
Birmingham Nec (Bus)	d	14 16	14 46		15 16	15 46		16 16	16 46		17 16	17 46		18 16	18 46		19 21	19 51	20 21	21 21	21 51	22 21	22 51	22 51		
Solihull	a	14 37	15 07		15 37	16 07		16 37	17 07		17 37	18 07		18 37	19 07		19 40	20 10	20 40	21 40	22 10	22 40	23 10	23 10		

Sundays

		CH		CH		CH		CH		CH		CH		CH		CH		CH		CH		CH		CH		CH
Birmingham Airport (Bus)	d	10 19		10 49		11 19		11 49		12 19		12 49		13 19		13 49		14 19		14 49		15 19		15 49		16 19
Birmingham Nec (Bus)	d	10 21		10 51		11 21		11 51		12 21		12 51		13 21		13 51		14 21		14 51		15 21		15 51		16 21
Solihull	a	10 40		11 10		11 40		12 10		12 40		13 10		13 40		14 10		14 40		15 10		15 40		16 10		16 40

		CH		CH		CH		CH		CH		CH		CH		CH		CH		CH		CH	CH	CH		
Birmingham Airport (Bus)	d	16 49		17 19		17 49		18 19		18 49		19 19		19 49		20 19		20 49		21 19		21 49	22 19	22 49		
Birmingham Nec (Bus)	d	16 51		17 21		17 51		18 21		18 51		19 21		19 51		20 21		20 51		21 21		21 51	22 21	22 51		
Solihull	a	17 10		17 40		18 10		18 40		19 10		19 40		20 10		20 40		21 10		21 40		22 10	22 40	23 10		

For general notes see front of timetable
For details of catering facilities see
Directory of Train Operators

Network Diagram for Tables 116, 117, 118, 119, 120, 121, 122, 126

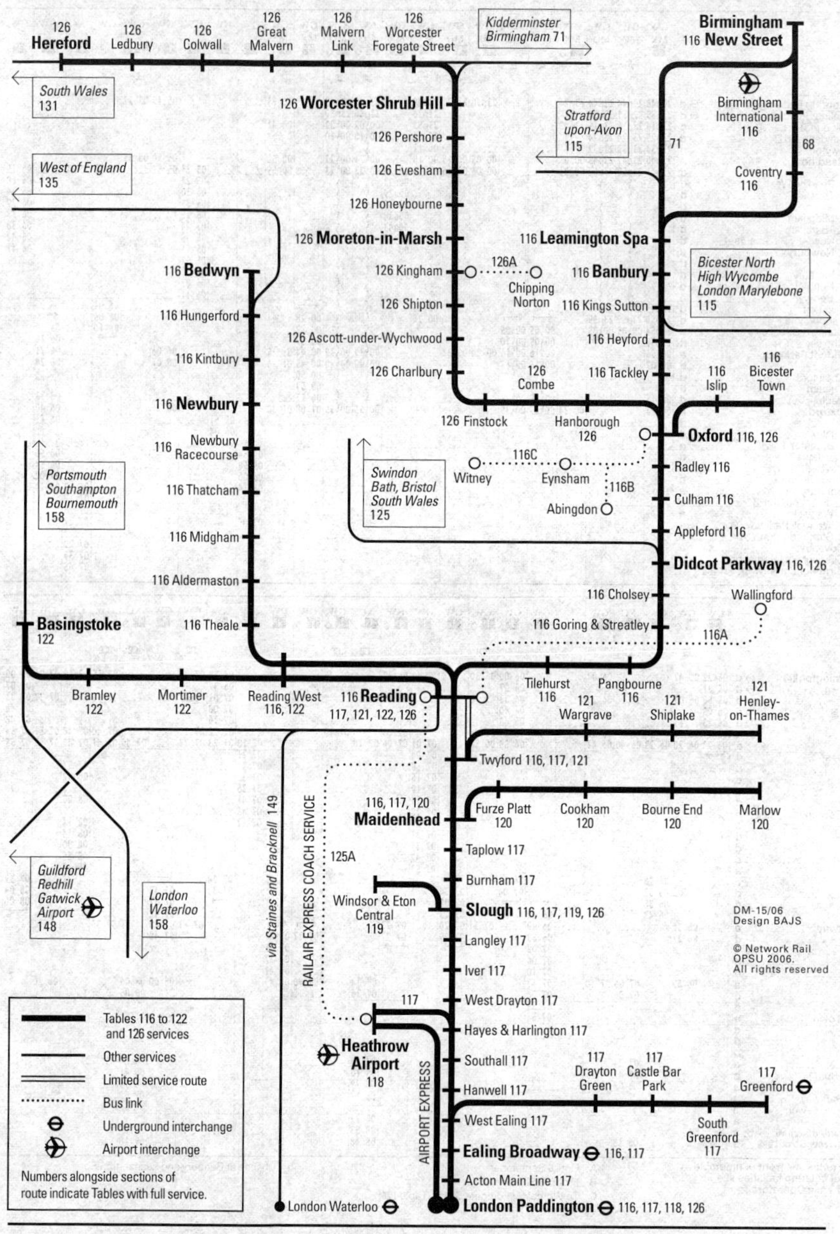

London and Reading → Bedwyn, Oxford, Bicester, Banbury and Birmingham

Network Diagram - see first page of Table 116

Miles	Miles			GW MX 1	GW MO A	GW MO B	GW MX 1◇	GW MO A	GW MO B	GW MX 1◇ 🛏	GW MO 1◇ ☕	GW MX 1	GW MX 1	GW MO 1◇ A 🛏	GW MO 1◇ B 🛏	GW MX 1	GW MX 1◇	GW 1	GW 1	GW 1	GW 1◇	GW 1◇ ☕	GW 1	XC 1◇ ☕	GW 1	GW 1
0	—	**London Paddington** [15] ⊖	d	22p46	22p44	22p44	23p21			23p30	23p37	23p29		23p42	23p42		00 21				05 19	05 27				
5¾	—	Ealing Broadway ⊖	d	22p55	22p51	22p51						23p36		23p50	23p50											
18½	—	Slough [3]	d	23p14	23p16	23p15	23p43					23p55		00 02	00 03		00 41									
24¼	—	Maidenhead [3]	d	23p25	23p24	23p24						00 03		00 10	00 10											
31	—	Twyford [3]	d	23p33	23p32	23p32						00 11														
36	—	**Reading** [7]	a	23p40	23p42	23p43	00 01			00 05	00 15	00 18		00 23	00 23		00 58				05 50	05 55				
—	0		d	23p41	23p50	23p50	00 01			00 06	00 15	00 19	00 20	00 23	00 23		00 59			05 21	05 51		05 57	06 10		06 15
—	1	Reading West	d										00s23							05 24						06 18
—	5¼	Theale	d										00s29							05 30						06 24
—	8¾	Aldermaston	d										00s35							05 35						06 29
—	10¾	Midgham	d										00s38							05 39						06 33
—	13¾	Thatcham	d										00s43							05 44						06 38
—	16½	Newbury Racecourse	d										00s48							05 48						06 42
—	17	**Newbury**	a										00 51							05 51						06 47
—	—		d																	05 51						
—	22½	Kintbury	d																	05 57						
—	25¾	Hungerford	d																	06 02						
—	30½	**Bedwyn**	a																	06 11						
38¾	—	Tilehurst	d	23p45	23p55	23p55						00 23				←							06 01			
41½	—	Pangbourne	d	23p50	23p59	23p59		←	←			00 28				00 28							06 06		←	
44¾	—	Goring & Streatley	d	23p54	00 05	00 05		00 05	00 05			→				00 32							06 10		06 10	
48¼	—	Cholsey	d	23p59	→	→		00 09	00 10							00 37							→		06 15	
53¼	—	**Didcot Parkway**	a	00 06				00 16	00 16	00 24	00s33			00 39	00 39	00 44	01 15				06 06				06 21	
—	—		d	00 07				00 16	00 17					00 40	00 40	00 45	01 16				06 07				06 24	
55½	—	Appleford	d													00 50										
56¾	—	Culham	d													00 53										
58¼	—	Radley	d	00 15				00 25	00 25							00 57									06 33	
63½	—	**Oxford**	a	00 23			00 34	00 35	00 35					00 55	00 55	01 08	01 30				06 21			06 34	06 40	
—	0		d															05 45	05 51					06 36	06 41	
—	5¾	Islip	d																06 04							
—	11¼	**Bicester Town**	a																06 17							
72½	—	Tackley	d															05 54							06 50	
75¾	—	Heyford	d															05 58							06 54	
82¾	—	Kings Sutton	d															06 06							07 02	
86¼	—	**Banbury**	a															06 14						06 52	07 10	
106¼	—	Leamington Spa [8]	a																					07 10		
—	—	Warwick	a																					*07 26*		
—	—	Warwick Parkway	a															*07b09*						*07 29*		
—	—	Stratford-upon-Avon	a																							
115¾	—	Coventry	a																					07 22		
126½	—	Birmingham International	a																					07 33		
135	—	**Birmingham New Street** [12]	a																					07 45		

		GW 1	GW 1◇ ☕	GW 1	XC 1◇ ☕	GW 1◇		GW 1	GW 1	GW 1◇ ☕	GW 1	GW 1	GW 1◇	XC 1◇ ☕	GW 1◇ ☕	GW 1◇	GW 1	GW 1	GW 1 C	GW 1◇ ☕	GW 1 C	XC 1◇ ☕	GW 1◇ ☕	GW 1	GW 1◇	GW 1
London Paddington [15] ⊖	d	05 22	05 42			06 07			06 00	06 30			06 33		06 45				06 30	07 00			07 15	07 18	07 21	07 00
Ealing Broadway ⊖	d	05 31							06 07										06 37							07 07
Slough [3]	d	05 58	06 03			06 23			06 33				06 49						07 01						07 37	07 33
Maidenhead [3]	d	06 05							06 40										07 08							07 40
Twyford [3]	d	06 13							06 48										07 16							07 48
Reading [7]	a	06 19	06 20	←		06 39			06 54	06 55			07 03		07 10				07 22	07 25			07 40	07 48	07 51	07 54
	d	06 23	06 20	06 23	06 40	06 41			06 55	06 57		07 01	07 06	07 10				07 18	07 23	07 27		07 40	07 41	07 48	07 53	07 55
Reading West	d	→										07 04						07 21								
Theale	d											07 10						07 27						07 57		
Aldermaston	d											07 15						07 32						08 02		
Midgham	d											07 19						07 36								
Thatcham	d											07 24						07 41						08 08		
Newbury Racecourse	d											07 28						07 45								
Newbury	a											07 31						07 52						08 14		
	d											07 31												08 14		
Kintbury	d											07 37												08 20		
Hungerford	d											07 42												08 25		
Bedwyn	a											07 51												08 35		
Tilehurst	d			06 28					06 59		←								07 28		←					07 59
Pangbourne	d			06 33					07 04		07 04								07 32		07 32					08 04
Goring & Streatley	d			06 38				←	→		07 08								→		07 37					08 08
Cholsey	d			06 43				06 43			07 13										07 42					→
Didcot Parkway	a		06 36	→				06 49		07 11	07 20		07 23			←	←			07 41	07 48		07 56			
	d		06 37					06 58			07 29		07 27			07 27	07 29				07 48					
Appleford	d							07 03			→		→				07 35									
Culham	d							07 06									07 37									
Radley	d							07 10									07 41									
Oxford	a		06 52		07 06	07 10		07 17						07 34		07 40	07 49				08 00	08 06			08 20	
	d				07 06			07 26						07 36								08 06				
Islip	d							07 39																		
Bicester Town	a							07 51																		
Tackley	d																									
Heyford	d																									
Kings Sutton	d																									
Banbury	a				07 24									07 52								08 24				
Leamington Spa [8]	a				07 41									08 10								08 41				
Warwick	a				*08 07*									*08 28*								*08 56*				
Warwick Parkway	a				*07 42*									*08 19*								*09 01*				
Stratford-upon-Avon	a																					*09 37*				
Coventry	a													08 22												
Birmingham International	a													08 33												
Birmingham New Street [12]	a				08 18									08 48								09 18				

For general notes see front of timetable
For details of catering facilities see Directory of Train Operators

A Until 8 September
B From 15 September
C To Worcester Foregate Street (Table 126)
b Change at Banbury and Leamington Spa

London and Reading → Bedwyn, Oxford, Bicester, Banbury and Birmingham

Network Diagram - see first page of Table 116

Station		GW	GW	XC	GW	GW	GW	GW	GW	GW		GW	GW	GW	XC	GW	GW	GW	GW	GW	GW	GW	XC	GW	GW	GW
		1◇	1	1◇	1◇	1	1	1	1◇	1		1◇	1◇	1	1◇	1	1◇	1◇	1◇	1	1	1◇	1◇	1	1◇	1
					A																					
		⊠		☕	⊠				☕			☕	☕		☕		☕	☕				☕	☕		☕	
London Paddington 15 ⊖	d	07 30			07 45				07 48	07 30		07 51	08 00				08 15	08 18	08 21		08 00	08 30			08 45	
Ealing Broadway ⊖	d									07 37											08 07					
Slough 3	d									08 03		08 07							08 37		08 33					
Maidenhead 3	d									08 10											08 40					
Twyford 3	d									08 18											08 48					
Reading 7	a	07 57			08 10				08 15	08 24		08 21	08 26				08 40	08 45	08 51		08 54	08 57			09 10	
	d			08 10				08 11	08 16	08 25		08 23	08 27		08 40		08 41	08 47	08 53	08 54	08 55	08 57	09 10			09 11
Reading West	d							08 14																		09 14
Theale	d							08 20										08 55		09 03						09 20
Aldermaston	d							08 25												09 08						09 25
Midgham	d							08 29																		09 29
Thatcham	d							08 34										09 04		09 14						09 34
Newbury Racecourse	d							08 38																		09 38
Newbury	a							08 41										09 10		09 22						09 43
	d							08 41										09 10								
Kintbury	d							08 48																		
Hungerford	d							08 53										09 20								
Bedwyn	a							09 01										09 28								
Tilehurst	d									08 29						←					08 59			←		
Pangbourne	d						←			08 34						08 34					09 04			09 04		
Goring & Streatley	d						08 08			→						08 38					→			09 08		
Cholsey	d						08 13									08 43								09 13		
Didcot Parkway	a						08 19		08 33				08 42			08 49	08 56					09 12		09 19		
	d		08 08				08 25									08 55								09 25		
Appleford	d		08 13													09 00										
Culham	d		08 16													09 03										
Radley	d		08 20				08 33									09 07										
Oxford	a		08 28	08 34			08 42					08 47			09 06	09 15			09 24				09 34	09 40		
	d			08 36		08 39								08 54	09 06								09 36			
Islip	d					08 52																				
Bicester Town	a					09 05																				
Tackley	d													09 03												
Heyford	d													09 07												
Kings Sutton	d													09 16												
Banbury	a			08 52										09 23	09 24								09 52			
Leamington Spa 8	a			09 10										*09 53*	09 41								10 10			
Warwick	a													*09 58*	*09 58*								*10 38*			
Warwick Parkway	a			*09 20*										*10 01*	*09 45*								*10 21*			
Stratford-upon-Avon	a																						*11 08*			
Coventry	a			09 22																			10 22			
Birmingham International	a			09 33																			10 33			
Birmingham New Street 12	a			09 45											10 18								10 45			

Station		GW	GW	GW	GW	XC	GW	GW	GW	GW	GW	GW	GW	XC		GW	GW	GW	GW	GW	GW	GW	XC	GW	GW	GW
														R												
		1◇	1	1◇	1◇	1◇	1	1◇	1	1◇	1	1◇	1	1		1◇	1	1◇	1◇	1	1◇	1◇	1◇	1	1◇	1
																					B	C				
		☕		☕	☕	☕		☕				☕		☕		⊠		☕	☕		☕	☕	☕		☕	
London Paddington 15 ⊖	d	08 51	08 30	09 00	09 06			09 15	09 18	09 21	09 00	09 30				09 45		09 48	09 51	09 30	10 00	10 06			10 15	10 18
Ealing Broadway ⊖	d		08 37								09 07									09 37						
Slough 3	d	09 07	09 03							09 37	09 31								10 07	10 01						
Maidenhead 3	d		09 10								09 38									10 08						
Twyford 3	d		09 18								09 46									10 16						
Reading 7	a	09 21	09 24	09 26	09 31			09 40	09 48	09 51	09 52	09 57				10 10		10 15	10 21	10 22	10 26	10 31			10 40	10 48
	d	09 23	09 25			09 40		09 41	09 48	09 53	09 53	09 57		10 10			10 11	10 16	10 23	10 23			10 40		10 41	10 48
Reading West	d																10 14									
Theale	d								09 56								10 20									10 56
Aldermaston	d																10 25									
Midgham	d																10 29									
Thatcham	d								10 04								10 34									11 04
Newbury Racecourse	d																10 38									
Newbury	a								10 10								10 43									11 10
	d								10 11																	11 11
Kintbury	d								10 17																	11 17
Hungerford	d								10 22																	11 22
Bedwyn	a								10 32																	11 32
Tilehurst	d		09 29								09 57		←							10 27						
Pangbourne	d		09 34								10 02		10 02							10 32						
Goring & Streatley	d		09 38				←				→		10 06							10 36				←		
Cholsey	d		09 43				09 43						10 11							10 41				10 41		
Didcot Parkway	a	09 37	→				09 49	09 56				10 12	10 17					10 33		→				10 47	10 56	
	d	09 38					09 55						10 18											10 55		
Appleford	d																							11 00		
Culham	d						10 00																			
Radley	d						10 04																	11 04		
Oxford	a	09 51				10 06	10 13			10 18			10 31	10 34					10 47				11 06	11 14		
	d					10 06								10 36									11 06			
Islip	d																									
Bicester Town	a																									
Tackley	d																									
Heyford	d																									
Kings Sutton	d																									
Banbury	a					10 24								10 52									11 24			
Leamington Spa 8	a					10 41								11 10									11 41			
Warwick	a					*10 58*																	*11 58*			
Warwick Parkway	a					*10 45*								*11 20*									*11 41*			
Stratford-upon-Avon	a																						*13 11*			
Coventry	a													11 22												
Birmingham International	a													11 33												
Birmingham New Street 12	a					11 18								11 45									12 18			

For general notes see front of timetable
For details of catering facilities see Directory of Train Operators

A The St David
B Torbay Express
C Cornish Riviera

London and Reading → Bedwyn, Oxford, Bicester, Banbury and Birmingham

Network Diagram - see first page of Table 116

		GW	GW	GW	GW	GW	XC	GW	GW	GW	GW	GW	GW	XC	GW	GW	GW	GW		GW	GW	GW	XC	GW	GW	GW
		1◇	1	1◇	1	1	R 1	1◇	1	1◇	1	1◇	1◇	1◇	1	1◇	1	1◇		1	1◇	1	R 1	1◇	1	1◇
													A													B
				☕			☕	⊠				☕	⊠	☕		☕					☕		☕	⊠		☕
London Paddington 15 ⊖	d	10 21	10 00	10 30				10 45		10 51	10 30	11 00	11 06			11 15	11 18	11 21		11 00	11 30			11 45		11 48
Ealing Broadway ⊖	d		10 07								10 37									11 07						
Slough 3	d	10 37	10 31							11 07	11 01							11 37		11 31						
Maidenhead 3	d		10 38								11 08									11 38						
Twyford 3	d		10 46								11 16									11 46						
Reading 7	a	10 51	10 52	10 57				11 10		11 21	11 22	11 26	11 31			11 40	11 48	11 51		11 52	11 56			12 10		12 15
	d	10 53	10 53	10 57			11 10		11 11	11 23	11 23			11 40		11 41	11 48	11 53		11 53	11 57		12 10		12 11	12 16
Reading West	d								11 14																12 14	
Theale	d								11 20								11 56								12 20	
Aldermaston	d								11 25																12 25	
Midgham	d								11 29																12 29	
Thatcham	d								11 34								12 04								12 34	
Newbury Racecourse	d								11 38																12 38	
Newbury	a								11 43								12 10								12 43	
	d																12 11									
Kintbury	d																12 17									
Hungerford	d																12 22									
Bedwyn	a																12 32									
Tilehurst	d		10 57			←					11 27									11 57		←				
Pangbourne	d		11 02 →			11 02					11 32									12 02 →		12 02				
Goring & Streatley	d					11 06					11 36				←							12 06				
Cholsey	d					11 11					11 41 →				11 41							12 11				
Didcot Parkway	a			11 12		11 17				11 37					11 47	11 56					12 12	12 17				12 33
	d					11 18				11 38					11 55							12 18				
Appleford	d																									
Culham	d														12 00											
Radley	d														12 04											
Oxford	a	11 18				11 31	11 34			11 51				12 06	12 13			12 18				12 31	12 34			
	d				11 23		11 36							12 06									12 36			
Islip	d																									
Bicester Town	a																									
Tackley	d				11 32																					
Heyford	d				11 36																					
Kings Sutton	d				11 44																					
Banbury	a				11 51		11 52							12 24									12 52			
Leamington Spa 8	a				*12 14*		12 10							12 41									13 10			
Warwick	a				*12 19*		*12 41*							*12 58*												
Warwick Parkway	a				*12b20*		*12 20*							*12 45*									*13 20*			
Stratford-upon-Avon	a				*13 11*		*13 11*																			
Coventry	a						12 22																13 21			
Birmingham International	a						12 33																13 33			
Birmingham New Street 12	a						12 45							13 18									13 45			

		GW	GW	GW	GW	XC	GW	GW	GW	GW	GW	GW	GW	GW	XC	GW	GW	GW	GW	GW	GW	XC		GW	GW	GW
		1◇	1	1◇	1◇	1◇	1	1◇	1◇	1◇	1	1◇	1	1	R 1	1◇	1	1◇	1	1◇	1◇	1◇		1	1◇	1
					C																					
		☕		☕	✕	☕		☕	☕			☕			☕	⊠				☕	⊠	☕			☕	
London Paddington 15 ⊖	d	11 51	11 30	12 00	12 06			12 15	12 18	12 21	12 00	12 30				12 45		12 51	12 30	13 00	13 06				13 15	13 18
Ealing Broadway ⊖	d		11 37								12 07								12 37							
Slough 3	d	12 07	12 01							12 37	12 31							13 07	13 01							
Maidenhead 3	d		12 08								12 38								13 08							
Twyford 3	d		12 16								12 46								13 16							
Reading 7	a	12 21	12 22	12 26	12 31			12 40	12 45	12 51	12 52	12 57				13 10		13 21	13 22	13 26	13 31				13 40	13 48
	d	12 23	12 23			12 40		12 41	12 47	12 53	12 53	12 57			13 10		13 11	13 23	13 23			13 40			13 41	13 48
Reading West	d																13 14									
Theale	d								12 55								13 20									13 56
Aldermaston	d																13 25									
Midgham	d																13 29									
Thatcham	d								13 04								13 34									14 04
Newbury Racecourse	d																13 38									
Newbury	a								13 10								13 43									14 10
	d								13 10																	14 11
Kintbury	d																									14 17
Hungerford	d								13 20																	14 22
Bedwyn	a								13 29																	14 32
Tilehurst	d		12 27								12 57			←					13 27							
Pangbourne	d		12 32								13 02 →			13 02					13 32							
Goring & Streatley	d		12 36				←							13 06					13 36					←		
Cholsey	d		12 41 →				12 41							13 11					13 41 →					13 41		
Didcot Parkway	a						12 47	12 56				13 12		13 17				13 37						13 47	13 56	
	d						12 55							13 18				13 38						13 55		
Appleford	d						13 00																			
Culham	d																							14 00		
Radley	d						13 04																	14 04		
Oxford	a	12 47				13 06	13 14			13 18				13 31	13 34			13 51				14 06		14 13		
	d					13 06							13 23		13 36							14 06				
Islip	d												13 36													
Bicester Town	a												13 50													
Tackley	d																									
Heyford	d																									
Kings Sutton	d																									
Banbury	a					13 24									13 52							14 24				
Leamington Spa 8	a					13 41									14 10							14 41				
Warwick	a					*13 58*									*14 41*							*14 58*				
Warwick Parkway	a					*13 41*									*14 20*							*14 45*				
Stratford-upon-Avon	a														*15 09*											
Coventry	a														14 22											
Birmingham International	a														14 33											
Birmingham New Street 12	a					14 18									14 45							15 18				

For general notes see front of timetable
For details of catering facilities see Directory of Train Operators

A The Mayflower
B Cheltenham Spa Express
C The Royal Duchy

b Change at Banbury and Leamington Spa

London and Reading → Bedwyn, Oxford, Bicester, Banbury and Birmingham

Network Diagram - see first page of Table 116

		GW	GW	GW	GW	GW	XC	GW	GW	GW	GW	GW	GW	GW	XC	GW	GW	GW	GW	GW	GW	GW	XC	GW	GW	GW
		1◇	1	1◇	1	1	R 1	1◇	1	1◇	1◇	1	1◇	1◇	R 1	1	1◇	1	1◇	1	1◇	1	R 1	1◇	1	1◇
																					A					
				☕			☕	☕		☕	☕		☕	⊠	☕		☕				☕		☕	☕		
London Paddington 15	⊖ d	13 21	13 00	13 30				13 45		13 48	13 51	13 30	14 00	14 06			14 15	14 18	14 21	14 00	14 30			14 45		14 51
Ealing Broadway	⊖ d		13 07									13 37								14 07						
Slough 3	d	13 37	13 31								14 07	14 01								14 31						15 07
Maidenhead 3	d		13 38									14 08								14 38						
Twyford 3	d		13 46									14 16								14 46						
Reading 7	a	13 51	13 52	13 57				14 10		14 15	14 21	14 22	14 26	14 31			14 40	14 48	14 51	14 52	14 57			15 10		15 21
	d	13 53	13 53	13 57			14 10		14 11	14 16	14 23	14 23			14 40		14 41	14 48	14 53	14 53	14 57		15 10		15 11	15 23
Reading West	d								14 14																15 14	
Theale	d								14 20									14 56							15 20	
Aldermaston	d								14 25																15 25	
Midgham	d								14 29																15 29	
Thatcham	d								14 34									15 04							15 34	
Newbury Racecourse	d								14 38																15 38	
Newbury	a								14 43									15 10							15 43	
	d																	15 11								
Kintbury	d																	15 17								
Hungerford	d																	15 22								
Bedwyn	a																	15 32								
Tilehurst	d		13 57			←						14 27								14 57		←				
Pangbourne	d		14 02			14 02						14 32								15 02		15 02				
Goring & Streatley	d		→			14 06						14 36				←				→		15 06				
Cholsey	d					14 11						14 41				14 41						15 11				
Didcot Parkway	a			14 12		14 17				14 33		→				14 47	14 56				15 12	15 17				15 37
	d					14 18										14 55						15 18				15 38
Appleford	d															15 00										
Culham	d																									
Radley	d															15 04										
Oxford	a	14 18				14 31	14 34				14 47				15 06	15 13			15 21			15 31	15 34			15 51
	d				14 23		14 36								15 06								15 36			
Islip	d																									
Bicester Town	a																									
Tackley	d				14 32																					
Heyford	d				14 36																					
Kings Sutton	d				14 44																					
Banbury	a				14 51		14 52								15 24								15 52			
Leamington Spa 8	a				*15 14*		15 10								15 41								16 10			
Warwick	a				*15 19*										*15 58*								*16 41*			
Warwick Parkway	a				*15b20*		*15 20*								*16 02*								*16 20*			
Stratford-upon-Avon	a																						*17 12*			
Coventry	a						15 22																16 22			
Birmingham International	a						15 33																16 33			
Birmingham New Street 12	a						15 45								16 18								16 45			

		GW	GW		GW	XC	GW	GW	GW	GW	GW	GW	GW	GW	GW	GW	XC	GW	GW	GW	GW	GW	GW	GW	XC	GW
		1	1◇		1◇	R 1	1	1◇	1	1◇	1◇	1	1◇	1	1	1	R 1	1◇	1	1◇	1◇	1	1◇	1◇	R 1	1
						B				C	D		A													
			☕		☕	☕		☕					☕				☕	☕		☕	☕		☕	☕	☕	
London Paddington 15	⊖ d	14 30	15 00		15 06			15 15	15 18	15 21	15 21	15 00	15 30					15 45		15 48	15 51	15 30	16 00	16 06		
Ealing Broadway	⊖ d	14 37										15 07										15 37				
Slough 3	d	15 01								15 37		15 31									16 07	15 58				
Maidenhead 3	d	15 08										15 38										16 06				
Twyford 3	d	15 16										15 46										16 14				
Reading 7	a	15 22	15 26		15 31			15 40	15 48	15 51	15 51	15 52	15 57					16 10		16 15	16 21	16 23	16 26	16 31		
	d	15 23				15 40		15 41	15 48	15 53	15 53	15 53	15 57				16 10		16 11	16 16	16 23	16 25			16 40	
Reading West	d																		16 14							
Theale	d								15 56										16 20							
Aldermaston	d																		16 25							
Midgham	d																		16 29							
Thatcham	d								16 04										16 34							
Newbury Racecourse	d																		16 38							
Newbury	a								16 10										16 43							
	d								16 11																	
Kintbury	d								16 17																	
Hungerford	d								16 22																	
Bedwyn	a								16 32																	
Tilehurst	d	15 27										15 57				←						16 29				
Pangbourne	d	15 32										16 02				16 02						16 34				
Goring & Streatley	d	15 36					←					→				16 06						16 38				←
Cholsey	d	15 41					15 41									16 11						16 43				16 43
Didcot Parkway	a	→					15 47	15 56					16 12			16 17				16 33		→				16 49
	d						15 55									16 18										16 54
Appleford	d																									17 00
Culham	d						16 00																			17 03
Radley	d						16 04																			17 07
Oxford	a					16 06	16 13			16 18	16 18					16 31	16 34				16 47				17 06	17 15
	d					16 06								16 23	16 28		16 36								17 06	
Islip	d														16 41											
Bicester Town	a														16 54											
Tackley	d													16 32												
Heyford	d													16 36												
Kings Sutton	d													16 44												
Banbury	a					16 24								16 51			16 52								17 24	
Leamington Spa 8	a					16 41								*17 22*			17 10								17 41	
Warwick	a					*16 58*																			*17 56*	
Warwick Parkway	a					*16 45*								*17 27*			*17 19*								*17 44*	
Stratford-upon-Avon	a																								*18 40*	
Coventry	a																17 22									
Birmingham International	a																17 33									
Birmingham New Street 12	a					17 18											17 45								18 18	

For general notes see front of timetable
For details of catering facilities see Directory of Train Operators

A To Weston-super-Mare (Table 134)
B To Derby (Table 57)
C Until 27 June and from 8 September
D 30 June to 5 September
b Change at Banbury and Leamington Spa

London and Reading → Bedwyn, Oxford, Bicester, Banbury and Birmingham

Network Diagram - see first page of Table 116

		GW	GW	GW	GW	GW	GW	GW	XC	GW	GW	GW	GW	GW	GW	GW	GW	GW	GW	GW	XC	GW	GW	GW	GW
		1◇	1	1	1◇	1	1◇	1◇	R 1	1	1◇	1	1	1◇	1	1◇	1◇	1	1	1◇	R 1	1◇	1◇	1	1◇
							A													B					A
		☕					☕	☕	☕		☕					☕	☕			☕	☕	☕	☕		☕
London Paddington 15 ⊖	d	16 15		16 18	16 21	16 00	16 30	16 33			16 45			16 51	16 30	17 00	17 03			17 06		17 15	17 21	17 18	17 30
Ealing Broadway ⊖	d					16 07									16 37										
Slough 3	d				16 37	16 30		16 48							16 57										
Maidenhead 3	d					16 38									17 04									17 40	
Twyford 3	d					16 46									17 12					17 28				17 48	
Reading 7	a	16 40		16 48	16 51	16 52	16 56	17 03			17 10			17 16	17 19	17 25	17 30			17 35		17 40	17 49	17 54	17 55
	d	16 41		16 48	16 53	16 54	16 57	17 04	17 10		17 11		17 11	17 18	17 20	17 27	17 32			17 37	17 40	17 41	17 50	17 56	17 57
Reading West	d												17 14												
Theale	d			16 56									17 20							17 45					
Aldermaston	d			17 02									17 25												
Midgham	d												17 29												
Thatcham	d			17 08									17 34							17 54					
Newbury Racecourse	d												17 39												
Newbury	a			17 15				17 19				←	17 43				17 46			17 59					
	d		17 05	17 25 →				17 20				17 25								18 01					
Kintbury	d		17 12									17 31								18 08					
Hungerford	d		17 17					17a29				17 36								18 14					
Bedwyn	a		17 25									17 46								18 21					
Tilehurst	d					16 58				←					17 25				←					18 01	
Pangbourne	d					17 03 →				17 03					17 29 →				17 29					18 05 →	
Goring & Streatley	d									17 07									17 34						
Cholsey	d									17 12									17 39						
Didcot Parkway	a	16 56			17 08		17 12			17 18	17 26			17 32		17 41			17 45			17 56			18 11
	d				17 09					17 24				17 34					17 45						
Appleford	d									17 29															
Culham	d									17 32									17 51						
Radley	d									17 36									17 55						
Oxford	a				17 23				17 34	17 43				17 48					18 03		18 06		18 15		
	d								17 36	17 44								17 54			18 06				
Islip	d																	18 07							
Bicester Town	a																	18 20							
Tackley	d									17 53															
Heyford	d									17 58															
Kings Sutton	d									18 08															
Banbury	a								17 52	18 13											18 24				
Leamington Spa 8	a								18 10												18 41				
Warwick	a																				*19 03*				
Warwick Parkway	a								*18 22*												*18 45*				
Stratford-upon-Avon	a																								
Coventry	a								18 22																
Birmingham International	a								18 33																
Birmingham New Street 12	a								18 45												19 18				

		GW	XC	GW	GW	GW	GW	GW	GW	GW	GW	GW	GW	GW	GW	XC	GW	GW	GW	GW	GW	GW	GW	GW	XC
		1◇	R 1	1	1◇	1	1	1◇	1	1◇	1◇	1	1	1◇	1◇	1◇	1	1	1◇	1◇	1	1◇	1◇	1◇	1◇
											C			D	E				G	H		J	K	L	
		☕	☕		☕			☕		☕	☕			✕	☕	☕			☕	☕		☕	☕	☕	☕
London Paddington 15 ⊖	d	17 33			17 45			17 48	17 36	17 51	18 00		17 25	18 03	18 06				18 15	18 21	18 18	18 30	18 33	18 36	
Ealing Broadway ⊖	d												17 33												
Slough 3	d												18 01												
Maidenhead 3	d								17 59				18 10								18 40				
Twyford 3	d								18 08				18 18		18 27						18 48				
Reading 7	a	18 00			18 10			18 15	18 15	18 20	18 25		18 25	18 30	18 35				18 40	18 50	18 54	18 55	19 00	19 02	
	d	18 02	18 10				18 11	18 16	18 17	18 21	18 27		18 28		18 36	18 40			18 41	18 51	18 56	18 57	19 03	19 03	19 10
Reading West	d						18 14																		
Theale	d						18 20								18 45										
Aldermaston	d						18 25																		
Midgham	d						18 29																		
Thatcham	d						18 34								18 54										
Newbury Racecourse	d						18 38																		
Newbury	a	18 16					18 43								19 00								19 18	19 18	
	d					18 22									19 01								19 19	19 19	
Kintbury	d					18 29									19 09										
Hungerford	d					18 34									19 15								19a28	19a28	
Bedwyn	a					18 42									19 23										
Tilehurst	d			←					18 24				18 33								19 00				
Pangbourne	d			18 05					18 28			←	18 38								19 05 →				
Goring & Streatley	d			18 10					18 33 →			18 33	18 42					←							
Cholsey	d			18 15								18 38	18 47 →					18 47							
Didcot Parkway	a			18 21				18 33			18 41	18 44						18 53	18 56			19 11			
	d			18 25								18 45						18 54							
Appleford	d																	19 00							
Culham	d																								
Radley	d											18 53						19 05							
Oxford	a		18 34	18 40						18 47		19 01				19 06		19 12		19 18					19 34
	d		18 36													19 06	19 10	19 14							19 36
Islip	d																19 23								
Bicester Town	a																19 36								
Tackley	d																	19 23							
Heyford	d																	19 28							
Kings Sutton	d																	19 39							
Banbury	a		18 52													19 24		19 45							19 52
Leamington Spa 8	a		19 10													19 41									20 10
Warwick	a		*19b20*													*19 58*									
Warwick Parkway	a		*19 27*													*19 46*									*20 28*
Stratford-upon-Avon	a		*19b51*																						
Coventry	a		19 22																						20 22
Birmingham International	a		19 33																						20 33
Birmingham New Street 12	a		19 45													20 18									20 48

For general notes see front of timetable
For details of catering facilities see Directory of Train Operators

A To Taunton (Table 134)
B To Westbury (Table 135)
C **The Bristolian**
D **The Golden Hind**
E To Frome (Table 123)
G **The Red Dragon**
H **Cathedrals Express**
J To Weston-super-Mare (Table 134)
K 30 June to 5 September
L Until 27 June and from 8 September
b Change at Banbury

London and Reading → Bedwyn, Oxford, Bicester, Banbury and Birmingham

Network Diagram - see first page of Table 116

		GW	GW	GW	GW	GW	GW	GW	GW	GW	GW	GW	GW	GW	GW		XC	GW	GW	GW	GW	GW	GW	GW	GW	GW
		1	1	1 ◇	1	1	1	1 ◇	1	1	1 ◇	1	1 ◇	1	1		1 ◇	1	1	1	1 ◇	1	1 ◇	1	1 ◇	1
			A				B		A	B								A	B							
				☕				☕					☕		✕		☕				☕		☕		☕	
London Paddington 15 ⊖	d		18 33	18 45			18 36	18 48			18 51	18 25	19 00		19 03						19 15		19 21	19 15	19 30	
Ealing Broadway ⊖	d											18 33														
Slough 3	d										19 07	19 01											19 37			
Maidenhead 3	d		18 53				18 58					19 10												19 40		
Twyford 3	d		19 03				19 06					19 18												19 48		
Reading 7	a		19 10	19 10			19 13	19 15	←	←	19 21	19 25	19 26	←	19 31						19 40		19 51	19 55	19 57	
	d		19 17 →			19 11	19 17 →	19 16	19 17	19 17	19 23	19 28 →	19 27	19 28	19 32		19 40				19 41	19 42	19 53	19 57	19 57	
Reading West	d					19 14																19 45				
Theale	d					19 20																19 51				
Aldermaston	d					19 25																19 56				
Midgham	d					19 29																20 00				
Thatcham	d					19 34																20 05				
Newbury Racecourse	d					19 38																20 09				
Newbury	a					19 43									19 48							20 16				
	d				19 24																	20 32				
Kintbury	d				19 30																	20 38				
Hungerford	d				19 35																	20 43				
Bedwyn	a				19 44																	20 52				
Tilehurst	d	←							19 24	19 24				19 32										20 01		
Pangbourne	d	19 05							19 30	19 30				19 37				←	←	←				20 06		
Goring & Streatley	d	19 09							19 35 →	19 35 →				19 41 →				19 35	19 35	19 41				20 10		
Cholsey	d	19 14																19 41	19 41	19 46				20 15 →		
Didcot Parkway	a	19 20						19 33					19 42					19 48	19 48	19 52	19 56				20 12	
	d	19 24																19 55	19 55	20 08						
Appleford	d	19 31																								
Culham	d	19 33																								←
Radley	d	19 37																20 03	20 03	20 16 →						20 16
Oxford	a	19 46									19 50						20 06	20 12	20 12				20 19			20 24
	d																20 06									
Islip	d																									
Bicester Town	a																									
Tackley	d																									
Heyford	d																									
Kings Sutton	d																									
Banbury	a																20 24									
Leamington Spa 8	a																20 41									
Warwick	a																*21 00*									
Warwick Parkway	a																*20 46*									
Stratford-upon-Avon	a																*21 43*									
Coventry	a																									
Birmingham International	a																									
Birmingham New Street 12	a																21 18									

		XC	GW	GW	GW	GW	GW	GW	GW	GW	GW	GW	GW	GW	GW	XC	GW	GW	GW		GW	GW	GW	GW	GW	GW
		1 ◇	1	1 ◇	1 ◇	1 ◇	1	1 ◇	1	1	1 ◇	1	1 ◇	1	1 ◇	1 ◇	1 ◇	1	1 ◇		1	1 ◇	1 ◇	1	1	1
				☕	☕			☕			☕		☕		☕		☕					☕				
London Paddington 15 ⊖	d			19 45	19 48	19 51	19 30	20 00			20 15		20 20	20 00	20 35		20 45		20 51		20 30	21 15	21 21	21 00		21 30
Ealing Broadway ⊖	d						19 37							20 07							20 37			21 07		21 37
Slough 3	d					20 07	20 03						20 36	20 31					21 07		21 01		21 37	21 31		21 58
Maidenhead 3	d						20 12							20 38							21 08			21 38		22 05
Twyford 3	d						20 19							20 46							21 16			21 46		22 13
Reading 7	a			20 10	20 15	20 21	20 26	20 26			20 40		20 50	20 52	21 00		21 10		21 23		21 24	21 40	21 51	21 52		22 20
	d	20 10		20 11	20 16	20 23	20 26	20 27			20 41	20 44	20 52	20 53	21 02	21 10	21 11		21 23		21 28	21 41	21 53	21 58	22 00	22 26 →
Reading West	d											20 47													22 03	
Theale	d											20 53													22 09	
Aldermaston	d											20 58													22 14	
Midgham	d											21 02													22 18	
Thatcham	d											21 07													22 23	
Newbury Racecourse	d											21 11													22 27	
Newbury	a			20 26								21 14			21 17										22 30	
	d											21 23													22 30	
Kintbury	d											21 29													22 37	
Hungerford	d											21 34													22 42	
Bedwyn	a											21 43													22 51	
Tilehurst	d						20 31			←				20 57							21 32			22 02		
Pangbourne	d						20 35 →			20 35				21 02							21 37			22 07		
Goring & Streatley	d		←							20 40				21 06							21 41			22 11		
Cholsey	d		20 15							20 45				21 11							21 46			22 16		
Didcot Parkway	a		20 21		20 33			20 42		20 51	20 56			21 17			21 26				21 53	22 00		22 23		
	d		20 25							20 51				21 18							21 54			22 24		
Appleford	d		20 30																		21 59					
Culham	d		20 33																		22 02					
Radley	d		20 37							20 59											22 06					
Oxford	a	20 34	20 45			20 49				21 09			21 16	21 31		21 34			21 51		22 14		22 22	22 37		
	d	20 36							20 54							21 36		21 39								
Islip	d																									
Bicester Town	a																									
Tackley	d								21 02									21 48								
Heyford	d								21 08									21 52								
Kings Sutton	d								21 19									22 01								
Banbury	a	20 52							21 25							21 52		22 08								
Leamington Spa 8	a	21 10							*22 04*							22 10		*23 05*								
Warwick	a								*22 10*									*23 10*								
Warwick Parkway	a								*22 13*							*22 32*		*23 13*								
Stratford-upon-Avon	a																									
Coventry	a	21 22														22 22										
Birmingham International	a	21 33														22 33										
Birmingham New Street 12	a	21 45														22 52										

For general notes see front of timetable
For details of catering facilities see Directory of Train Operators

A Until 27 June and from 8 September
B 30 June to 5 September

London and Reading → Bedwyn, Oxford, Bicester, Banbury and Birmingham

Network Diagram - see first page of Table 116

		GW	GW	GW	GW	GW	GW	GW	GW	GW	GW	GW	GW	GW	GW	GW	GW	GW	GW	GW	GW	GW	GW	GW
						FO	FO	FX	FO	FX	FO		FX	FX	FO	FX	FX	FO		FO	FX	FO	FX	
		1 ◇	1 ◇	1	1	1 ◇	1	1 ◇	1	1	1 ◇	1	1 ◇	1	1 ◇	1 ◇	1 ◇	1 ◇	1	1 ◇	1 ◇	1 ◇	1 ◇	1
						☕		☕							☕	☕						trolley	trolley	
London Paddington 15 ⊖	d	21 45	21 48			22 15	21 59	22 15		21 57	22 21		22 21		22 45	22 45	22 48	22 51	22 46	23 21	23 21	23 30	23 30	23 29
Ealing Broadway ⊖	d						22 06			22 04									22 55					23 36
Slough 3	d		22 05				22 23			22 33	22 39		22 46				23 07	23 09	23 14	23 39	23 43			23 55
Maidenhead 3	d						22 33			22 41									23 25					00 03
Twyford 3	d						22 40			22 48									23 33					00 11
Reading 7	a	22 10	22 21		←	22 40	22 47	22 48		22 56	22 55		23 06		23 10	23 18	23 34	23 25	23 40	23 55	00 01	00 01	00 05	00 18
	d	22 11	22 21		22 26	22 41	22 48	22 49		22 56	22 56	23 00	23 07		23 11	23 18	23 35	23 25	23 41	23 55	00 01	00 02	00 06	00 19
Reading West	d											23 03												
Theale	d											23 09												
Aldermaston	d											23 14												
Midgham	d											23 18												
Thatcham	d											23 23												
Newbury Racecourse	d											23 27												
Newbury	a											23 30												
	d											23 30												
Kintbury	d											23 37												
Hungerford	d											23 42												
Bedwyn	a											23 51												
Tilehurst	d				22 32		22 52		←	23 01									23 45					00 23
Pangbourne	d				22 36		22 57		22 57	23 05				←					23 50					00 28
Goring & Streatley	d				22 41		→		23 01	23 10				23 10					23 54					00 32
Cholsey	d				22 46				23 06	→				23 15					23 59					00 37
Didcot Parkway	a	22 31			22 53	23 00		23 07	23 12					23 20	23 30	23 37			00 06			00 20	00 24	00 44
	d				22 53				23 17					23 25					00 07					00 45
Appleford	d				22 59																			00 50
Culham	d				23 01																			00 53
Radley	d				23 05														00 15					00 57
Oxford	a		22 50		23 13				23 33		23 26		23 37	23 43			00 09	23 52	00 23	00 28	00 34			01 08
	d			22 56																				
Islip	d																							
Bicester Town	a																							
Tackley	d			23 05																				
Heyford	d			23 10																				
Kings Sutton	d			23 18																				
Banbury	a			23 25																				
Leamington Spa 8	a																							
Warwick	a																							
Warwick Parkway	a																							
Stratford-upon-Avon	a																							
Coventry	a																							
Birmingham International	a																							
Birmingham New Street 12	a																							

For general notes see front of timetable
For details of catering facilities see Directory of Train Operators

Table 116

Saturdays

until 6 September

London and Reading → Bedwyn, Oxford, Bicester, Banbury and Birmingham

Network Diagram - see first page of Table 116

		GW	GW	GW	GW	GW	GW	GW	GW	GW	GW	GW	GW	GW	GW	XC	GW		GW	GW	GW	GW	XC	GW	GW	GW
		1	1 ◇	1	1	1 ◇	1	1	1	1 ◇	1	1	1	1 ◇	1	1 ◇	1		1	1 ◇	1 ◇	1	1 ◇	1	1	1 ◇
			🚌											☕		☕					☕		☕			☕
London Paddington [15] ⊖	d	22p46	23p30	23p29		00 21				05 12				05 42	05 25		05 45			06 21	06 30				06 15	06 51
Ealing Broadway ⊖	d	22p55		23p36											05 32		05 52								06 22	
Slough [3]	d	23p14		23p55		00 41				05 29				05 57	05 51		06 18			06 38					06 48	07 07
Maidenhead [3]	d	23p25		00 03											06 03		06 29								06 59	
Twyford [3]	d	23p33		00 11											06 10		06 37								07 07	
Reading [7]	a	23p40	00 01	00 18		00 58				05 46				06 13	06 17		06 43			06 52	06 55				07 13	07 21
	d	23p41	00 02	00 19	00 20	00 59	05 11		05 41	05 48	05 48	06 11		06 14	06 19	06 40	06 48		06 48	06 53	06 55		07 10	07 11	07 16	07 23
Reading West	d				00s23		05 14		05 44			06 14												07 14		
Theale	d				00s29		05 20		05 50			06 20							06 56					07 20		
Aldermaston	d				00s35		05 25		05 55			06 25												07 25		
Midgham	d				00s38		05 29		05 59			06 29												07 29		
Thatcham	d				00s43		05 34		06 04			06 34							07 04					07 34		
Newbury Racecourse	d				00s48		05 38		06 08			06 38												07 38		
Newbury	a				00 51		05 41		06 11			06 42							07 10					07 42		
	d						05 41		06 11										07 10							
Kintbury	d						05 47		06 17										07 16							
Hungerford	d						05 52		06 22										07 21							
Bedwyn	a						06 01		06 31										07 30							
Tilehurst	d	23p45		00 23							05 52				06 24		06 53								07 20	
Pangbourne	d	23p50		00 28							05 57				06 28		06 57					←			07 25	
Goring & Streatley	d	23p54		00 32							06 01				06 33		07 02					07 02			07 29	
Cholsey	d	23p59		00 37							06 06				06 38		→					07 07			07 34	
Didcot Parkway	a	00 06	00 20	00 44		01 14				06 01	06 12			06 28	06 44						07 12	07 15			→	
	d	00 07		00 45		01 15				06 02	06 13			06 29	06 44							07 16				
Appleford	d			00 50							06 18				06 50											
Culham	d			00 53							06 21															
Radley	d	00 15		00 57							06 25				06 55											
Oxford	a	00 23		01 08		01 30				06 17	06 32			06 45	07 02	07 06				07 19		07 28	07 34			07 48
	d							06 16					06 44			07 07							07 36			
Islip	d												06 57													
Bicester Town	a												07 10													
Tackley	d							06 25																		
Heyford	d							06 29																		
Kings Sutton	d							06 37																		
Banbury	a							06 44								07 24							07 52			
Leamington Spa [8]	a							*07 19*								07 42							08 10			
Warwick	a							*07 23*								*08 00*							*08 24*			
Warwick Parkway	a							*07 27*								*07 45*							*08 20*			
Stratford-upon-Avon	a																									
Coventry	a																						08 22			
Birmingham International	a																						08 33			
Birmingham New Street [12]	a															08 18							08 45			

For general notes see front of timetable
For details of catering facilities see Directory of Train Operators

Due to Engineering Operations, services from Saturday 13 September on this Table had not been confirmed at time of going to press. These services will be issued in a special Supplement as soon as exact timings have been confirmed

Table 116

Saturdays

until 6 September

London and Reading → Bedwyn, Oxford, Bicester, Banbury and Birmingham

Network Diagram - see first page of Table 116

		GW	GW	GW	XC	GW	GW	GW	GW	GW	XC		GW	GW	GW	GW	GW	GW	GW	XC	GW	GW	GW	GW	GW	GW
		1 ◇ ☕	1	1	1 ◇ ☕	1	1	1 ◇	1 ◇ ☕	1	1 ◇ ☕		1 ◇ ☕	1	1	1	1 ◇ ☕	1 ◇ ☕	1 ☕	1 ◇ ☕	1	1 ◇ ☕	1	1	1	1 ◇
London Paddington 15 ⊖	d	07 00					07 00	07 21	07 30				07 45			07 30	07 51	08 00	08 06			08 15		08 18	08 00	08 21
Ealing Broadway ⊖	d						07 07									07 37									08 07	
Slough 3	d						07 31	07 38								08 01	08 07								08 31	08 38
Maidenhead 3	d						07 38									08 08									08 38	
Twyford 3	d						07 46									08 16									08 46	
Reading 7	a	07 26					07 52	07 52	07 56				08 10			08 21	08 21	08 26	08 31			08 40		08 48	08 52	08 52
	d				07 40	07 48	07 53	07 54			08 10				08 11	08 23	08 23			08 40		08 41		08 48	08 53	08 54
Reading West	d														08 14											
Theale	d					07 56									08 20									08 56		
Aldermaston	d														08 25											
Midgham	d														08 29											
Thatcham	d					08 04									08 34									09 04		
Newbury Racecourse	d														08 38											
Newbury	a					08 10									08 42									09 10		
	d					08 10																	08 58			
Kintbury	d					08 16																	09 04			
Hungerford	d					08 21																	09 09			
Bedwyn	a					08 30																	09 18			
Tilehurst	d						07 57									08 27									08 57	
Pangbourne	d						08 02							←		08 32									09 02	
Goring & Streatley	d			←			08 06 →							08 06		08 36					←				09 06 →	
Cholsey	d			07 34										08 11		08 41 →					08 41					
Didcot Parkway	a			07 40										08 17							08 47	08 56				
	d			07 41										08 25							08 55					
Appleford	d																				09 03					
Culham	d			07 46																						
Radley	d			07 50																	09 07					
Oxford	a			08 00	08 05			08 21			08 34			08 39			08 47			09 05	09 15					09 22
	d		07 53		08 07					08 24	08 36									09 07						
Islip	d									08 37																
Bicester Town	a									08 50																
Tackley	d		08 02																							
Heyford	d		08 06																							
Kings Sutton	d		08 14																							
Banbury	a		08 21		08 24						08 52									09 24						
Leamington Spa 8	a		08 59		08 42						09 10									09 42						
Warwick	a		09 04		09 04															10 02						
Warwick Parkway	a		09 07		08 44						09 23									09 43						
Stratford-upon-Avon	a		09 35		09 35															11 12						
Coventry	a										09 22															
Birmingham International	a										09 33															
Birmingham New Street 12	a				09 18						09 45									10 18						

		GW	GW	GW	XC		GW	GW	GW	GW	GW	GW	GW	XC	GW	GW	GW	GW	GW	GW	GW	GW		XC	GW	GW
		1 ◇ ☕	1 ☕	1	R 1 ☕		1 ◇ A ☕	1	1	1	1 ◇ ☕	1 ◇ ☕	1 ☕	1 ◇ ☕	1	1	1	1	1 ◇	1 ◇ ☕	1	1		R 1 ☕	1 ◇ ☕	1
London Paddington 15 ⊖	d	08 30	08 35				08 45			08 30	08 51	09 00	09 06			09 18	09 00		09 21	09 30					09 45	
Ealing Broadway ⊖	d									08 37							09 07									
Slough 3	d									09 01	09 07						09 31		09 38							
Maidenhead 3	d									09 08							09 38									
Twyford 3	d									09 16							09 46									
Reading 7	a	08 57	09 02				09 10			09 21	09 21	09 26	09 32			09 48	09 52		09 52	09 57					10 10	
	d	08 58	09 03		09 10				09 11	09 23	09 23			09 40		09 48	09 53		09 54	09 57				10 10		10 11
Reading West	d								09 14																	10 14
Theale	d								09 20							09 56										10 20
Aldermaston	d								09 25																	10 25
Midgham	d								09 29																	10 29
Thatcham	d								09 34							10 04										10 34
Newbury Racecourse	d								09 38																	10 38
Newbury	a		09 18						09 43							10 10										10 43
	d							09 27								10 11										
Kintbury	d							09 33								10 17										
Hungerford	d							09 38								10 22										
Bedwyn	a							09 46								10 31										
Tilehurst	d									09 27							09 57									
Pangbourne	d			←						09 32							10 02					←				
Goring & Streatley	d			09 06						09 36					←		10 06 →					10 06				
Cholsey	d			09 11						09 41 →					09 41							10 11				
Didcot Parkway	a	09 13		09 17											09 47					10 12		10 17				
	d			09 18											09 55							10 18				
Appleford	d																									
Culham	d														10 00											
Radley	d														10 02											
Oxford	a			09 31	09 34						09 47			10 05	10 12				10 21			10 30		10 34		
	d				09 36									10 07				10 16			10 22			10 36		
Islip	d																				10 35					
Bicester Town	a																				10 48					
Tackley	d																	10 25								
Heyford	d																	10 29								
Kings Sutton	d																	10 39								
Banbury	a				09 52									10 24				10 46						10 52		
Leamington Spa 8	a				10 10									10 42										11 10		
Warwick	a				10 41									11 02										11b20		
Warwick Parkway	a				10 22									10 45										11 22		
Stratford-upon-Avon	a				11 12																					
Coventry	a				10 22																			11 22		
Birmingham International	a				10 33																			11 33		
Birmingham New Street 12	a				10 45									11 18										11 45		

For general notes see front of timetable
For details of catering facilities see
Directory of Train Operators

A **Pembroke Coast Express**
b Change at Banbury

Due to Engineering Operations, services from Saturday 13 September on this Table had not been confirmed at time of going to press. These services will be issued in a special Supplement as soon as exact timings have been confirmed

London and Reading → Bedwyn, Oxford, Bicester, Banbury and Birmingham

Network Diagram - see first page of Table 116

	GW	GW	GW	GW	XC	GW	GW	GW	GW	GW	GW	GW	GW	GW	GW		GW	GW	GW	GW	XC	GW	GW	GW	GW
	1	1◊	1◊	1	1◊	1	1◊	1	1	1◊	1◊	1	1◊	1	1		1	1◊	1◊	1	1◊	1	1	1	1
				A								B													
		☕	☕	☕	☕		☕				☕	☕	☕					☕	☕	☕	☕				
London Paddington 15 ⊖ d	09 30	09 51	10 00	10 06			10 15	10 18	10 00	10 21	10 30	10 35	10 45				10 30	10 51	11 00	11 06			11 18	11 00	
Ealing Broadway ⊖ d	09 37								10 07								10 37							11 07	
Slough 3 d	10 01	10 07							10 31	10 38							11 01	11 07						11 31	
Maidenhead 3 d	10 08								10 38								11 08							11 38	
Twyford 3 d	10 16								10 46								11 16							11 46	
Reading 7 a	10 21	10 21	10 26	10 32			10 40	10 47	10 52	10 52	10 57	11 02	11 10				11 21	11 21	11 26	11 31			11 47	11 52	
d	10 23	10 23			10 40		10 41	10 48	10 53	10 54	10 57				11 11		11 23	11 23			11 40		11 48	11 53	
Reading West d															11 14										
Theale d								10 56							11 20								11 56		
Aldermaston d															11 25										
Midgham d															11 29										
Thatcham d								11 04							11 34								12 04		
Newbury Racecourse d															11 38										
Newbury a								11 11							11 43								12 11		
d								11 22															12 21		
Kintbury d								11 28															12 27		
Hungerford d								11 33															12 32		
Bedwyn a								11 42															12 42		
Tilehurst d	10 27								10 57								11 27							11 57	
Pangbourne d	10 32								11 02					←			11 32							12 02	
Goring & Streatley d	10 36					←			11 06					11 06			11 36					←		12 06	
Cholsey d	10 41					10 41			→					11 11			11 41					11 41		→	
Didcot Parkway a	→					10 47	10 56				11 13			11 17			→					11 48			
d						10 55								11 18								11 55			
Appleford d						11 00																			
Culham d																						12 00			
Radley d						11 04																12 02			
Oxford a		10 47			11 05	11 13				11 19				11 30				11 47			12 05	12 12			
d					11 07																12 07				12 16
Islip d																									
Bicester Town a																									
Tackley d																									12 25
Heyford d																									12 29
Kings Sutton d																									12 37
Banbury a					11 24																12 24				12 44
Leamington Spa 8 a					11 42																12 42				*13 17*
Warwick a					*11 58*																*12 58*				*13 21*
Warwick Parkway a					*12 02*																*12 44*				*13b20*
Stratford-upon-Avon a					*13 11*																				
Coventry a																									
Birmingham International a																									
Birmingham New Street 12 a					12 18																13 18				

	GW	GW	GW	GW	GW	GW	GW	GW	GW		GW	XC	GW	GW	GW	GW	GW	GW	GW	GW	GW	XC	GW	GW	GW
	1◊	1◊	1◊	1◊	1	1	1	1◊	1◊		1	1◊	1	1◊	1	1	1◊	1◊	1	1	1	1◊	1◊	1	1
											C														
		☕	☕	☕				☕	☕		☕	☕		☕				☕	☕			☕	☕		
London Paddington 15 ⊖ d	11 21	11 30	11 35	11 45			11 30	11 51	12 00		12 06			12 15	12 18	12 00	12 21	12 30	12 35				12 45		
Ealing Broadway ⊖ d							11 37									12 07									
Slough 3 d	11 38						12 01	12 07								12 31	12 38								
Maidenhead 3 d							12 08									12 38									
Twyford 3 d							12 16									12 46									
Reading 7 a	11 52	11 58	12 01	12 10			12 21	12 21	12 26		12 31			12 40	12 48	12 52	12 52	12 57	13 03				13 10		
d	11 54	11 58				12 11	12 23	12 23				12 40		12 41	12 48	12 53	12 54	12 57	13 05			13 10			13 13
Reading West d						12 14																			13 16
Theale d						12 20									12 56										13 22
Aldermaston d						12 25																			13 27
Midgham d						12 29																			13 31
Thatcham d						12 34									13 04										13 36
Newbury Racecourse d						12 38																			13 40
Newbury a						12 43									13 10				13 20						13 45
d																								13 25	
Kintbury d																								13 31	
Hungerford d																								13 36	
Bedwyn a																								13 44	
Tilehurst d							12 27									12 57									
Pangbourne d					←		12 32									13 02					←				
Goring & Streatley d					12 06		12 36						←			13 06					13 06				
Cholsey d					12 11		12 41						12 41			→					13 11				
Didcot Parkway a		12 13			12 17		→						12 47	12 56				13 13			13 17				
d					12 18								12 55								13 18				
Appleford d													13 00												
Culham d																									
Radley d													13 04												
Oxford a	12 21				12 30			12 47				13 05	13 13				13 21				13 30	13 34			
d												13 07								13 23		13 36			
Islip d																				13 36					
Bicester Town a																				13 49					
Tackley d																									
Heyford d																									
Kings Sutton d																									
Banbury a												13 24										13 52			
Leamington Spa 8 a												13 42										14 10			
Warwick a												*13 58*										*14c21*			
Warwick Parkway a												*14 02*										*14 20*			
Stratford-upon-Avon a																						*15 10*			
Coventry a																						14 22			
Birmingham International a																						14 33			
Birmingham New Street 12 a												14 18										14 45			

For general notes see front of timetable
For details of catering facilities see Directory of Train Operators

A **Cornish Riviera**
B **Torbay Express**
C **The Royal Duchy**

b Change at Banbury and Leamington Spa
c Change at Banbury

Due to Engineering Operations, services from Saturday 13 September on this Table had not been confirmed at time of going to press. These services will be issued in a special Supplement as soon as exact timings have been confirmed

Saturdays

until 6 September

London and Reading → Bedwyn, Oxford, Bicester, Banbury and Birmingham

Network Diagram - see first page of Table 116

		GW	GW	GW		GW	XC	GW	GW	GW	GW	GW	GW	GW	XC	GW	GW	GW	GW	GW	GW		XC	GW	GW	GW
		1 ◇	1	1 ◇ ☕		1 ☕	1 ◇ ☕	1	1	1	1	1 ◇	1 ◇ ☕	1	R 1 ☕	1 ◇ ☕	1	1	1 ◇ ☕	1 ◇ ☕	1 ◇ ☕		1 ◇ ☕	1	1 ◇ ☕	1
London Paddington 15 ⊖	d	12 51	12 30	13 00		13 06			13 18	13 00		13 21	13 30			13 45		13 30	13 51	14 00	14 06				14 15	14 18
Ealing Broadway ⊖	d		12 37							13 07								13 37								
Slough 3	d		13 01							13 31		13 38						14 01	14 07							
Maidenhead 3	d		13 08							13 38								14 08								
Twyford 3	d		13 16							13 46								14 16								
Reading 7	a	13 21	13 21	13 26		13 31			13 47	13 52		13 52	13 56			14 10		14 21	14 21	14 26	14 31				14 40	14 47
	d	13 22	13 23				13 40		13 48	13 53		13 54	13 57		14 10		14 11	14 23	14 23				14 40		14 41	14 48
Reading West	d																14 14									
Theale	d								13 56								14 20									14 56
Aldermaston	d																14 25									
Midgham	d																14 29									
Thatcham	d								14 04								14 34									15 04
Newbury Racecourse	d																14 38									
Newbury	a								14 11								14 43									15 11
	d								14 11																	15 11
Kintbury	d								14 18																	15 17
Hungerford	d								14 23																	15 22
Bedwyn	a								14 32																	15 31
Tilehurst	d		13 27							13 57								14 27								
Pangbourne	d		13 32							14 02				←				14 32								
Goring & Streatley	d		13 36					←		14 06				14 06				14 36						←		
Cholsey	d		13 41					13 41		→				14 11				14 41						14 41		
Didcot Parkway	a		→					13 47					14 12	14 17				→						14 47	14 56	
	d							13 55						14 18										14 55		
Appleford	d																							15 00		
Culham	d							14 00																		
Radley	d							14 02																15 04		
Oxford	a	13 46					14 05	14 12				14 21		14 30	14 34				14 47				15 05	15 13		
	d						14 07				14 16				14 36								15 07			
Islip	d																									
Bicester Town	a																									
Tackley	d										14 25															
Heyford	d										14 29															
Kings Sutton	d										14 37															
Banbury	a						14 24				14 44				14 52								15 24			
Leamington Spa 8	a						14 42								15 10								15 42			
Warwick	a						*14 58*								*15b21*								*15 58*			
Warwick Parkway	a						*14 44*								*15 20*								*16 02*			
Stratford-upon-Avon	a																									
Coventry	a														15 22											
Birmingham International	a														15 33											
Birmingham New Street 12	a						15 18								15 45								16 18			

		GW	GW	GW	GW	GW	XC	GW	GW	GW	GW	GW	GW	XC	GW		GW	GW	GW	GW	GW	GW	XC	GW	GW	GW
		1	1 ◇	1 ◇ ☕	1	1	1 ◇ ☕	1 ◇ ☕	1	1	1 ◇ ☕	1 ◇ ☕	1 ◇ ☕	1 ◇ ☕	1		1	1	1	1 ◇	1 ◇ ☕	1	1 ◇ ☕	1 ◇ ☕	1	1
London Paddington 15 ⊖	d	14 00	14 21	14 30				14 45		14 30	14 51	15 00	15 06				15 18	15 00		15 21	15 30			15 45		15 30
Ealing Broadway ⊖	d	14 07								14 37								15 07								15 37
Slough 3	d	14 31	14 38							15 01	15 07							15 31		15 38						16 01
Maidenhead 3	d	14 38								15 08								15 38								16 08
Twyford 3	d	14 46								15 16								15 46								16 16
Reading 7	a	14 52	14 52	14 58				15 10		15 21	15 21	15 26	15 31				15 47	15 52		15 52	15 57			16 10		16 21
	d	14 53	14 54	14 59			15 10		15 11	15 23	15 23			15 40			15 48	15 53		15 54	15 58		16 10		16 15	16 23
Reading West	d								15 14																16 18	
Theale	d								15 20								15 56								16 24	
Aldermaston	d								15 25																16 29	
Midgham	d								15 29																16 33	
Thatcham	d								15 34								16 04								16 38	
Newbury Racecourse	d								15 38																16 42	
Newbury	a								15 43								16 11								16 47	
	d																16 11									
Kintbury	d																16 17									
Hungerford	d																16 22									
Bedwyn	a																16 31									
Tilehurst	d	14 57								15 27								15 57								16 27
Pangbourne	d	15 02				←				15 32								16 02				←				16 32
Goring & Streatley	d	15 06				15 06				15 36					←			16 06				16 06				16 36
Cholsey	d	→				15 11				15 41					15 41			→				16 11				16 41
Didcot Parkway	a			15 13		15 17				→					15 47						16 13	16 17				→
	d					15 18									15 55							16 18				
Appleford	d																									
Culham	d														16 00											
Radley	d														16 02											
Oxford	a		15 21			15 30	15 34				15 47			16 05	16 12					16 21		16 30	16 34			
	d				15 24		15 36							16 07					16 16				16 36			
Islip	d				15 37																					
Bicester Town	a				15 50																					
Tackley	d																		16 25							
Heyford	d																		16 29							
Kings Sutton	d																		16 37							
Banbury	a						15 52							16 24					16 44				16 52			
Leamington Spa 8	a						16 10							16 42									17 10			
Warwick	a						*16b21*							*16 57*									*17b20*			
Warwick Parkway	a						*16 20*							*16 45*									*17 22*			
Stratford-upon-Avon	a						*17 11*																			
Coventry	a						16 22																17 22			
Birmingham International	a						16 33																17 33			
Birmingham New Street 12	a						16 45							17 18									17 45			

For general notes see front of timetable
For details of catering facilities see Directory of Train Operators

b Change at Banbury

Due to Engineering Operations, services from Saturday 13 September on this Table had not been confirmed at time of going to press. These services will be issued in a special Supplement as soon as exact timings have been confirmed

Saturdays

until 6 September

London and Reading → Bedwyn, Oxford, Bicester, Banbury and Birmingham

Network Diagram - see first page of Table 116

		GW	GW	GW	XC	GW	GW	GW	GW	GW	GW	GW	GW	XC	GW	GW	GW	GW	GW	GW	XC	GW	GW	GW	GW
		1◇	1◇	1◇	1◇	1	1◇	1	1	1◇	1◇	1	1	1◇	1◇	1	1	1◇	1◇	1◇	1◇	1	1	1	1
		☕	☕	☕	☕		☕				☕			☕	☕			☕	☕	☕	☕				
London Paddington 15	⊖ d	15 51	16 00	16 06			16 15	16 18	16 00	16 21	16 30				16 45		16 30	16 51	17 00	17 06			17 18	17 00	
Ealing Broadway	⊖ d								16 07								16 37							17 07	
Slough 3	d	16 07							16 31	16 38							17 01	17 07						17 31	
Maidenhead 3	d								16 38								17 08							17 38	
Twyford 3	d								16 46								17 16							17 46	
Reading 7	a	16 21	16 26	16 31			16 40	16 47	16 52	16 52	16 57				17 10		17 21	17 21	17 26	17 31			17 47	17 52	
	d	16 23			16 40		16 41	16 48	16 53	16 54	16 58			17 10		17 11	17 23	17 23			17 40		17 48	17 53	
Reading West	d															17 14									
Theale	d							16 56								17 20							17 56		
Aldermaston	d															17 25									
Midgham	d															17 29									
Thatcham	d							17 04								17 34							18 04		
Newbury Racecourse	d															17 38									
Newbury	a							17 11								17 43							18 11		
	d							17 11															18 11		
Kintbury	d							17 17															18 17		
Hungerford	d							17 22															18 22		
Bedwyn	a							17 31															18 31		
Tilehurst	d								16 57								17 27							17 57	
Pangbourne	d								17 02				←				17 32							18 02	
Goring & Streatley	d					←			17 06				17 06				17 36					←		18 06	
Cholsey	d					16 41			→				17 11				17 41					17 41		→	
Didcot Parkway	a					16 47	16 56				17 13		17 17				→					17 47			
	d					16 55							17 18									17 55			
Appleford	d					17 00																			
Culham	d																					18 00			
Radley	d					17 04																18 02			
Oxford	a	16 47			17 05	17 13				17 21			17 30	17 34				17 47			18 05	18 12			
	d				17 07							17 24		17 36							18 07				18 16
Islip	d											17 37													
Bicester Town	a											17 50													
Tackley	d																								18 25
Heyford	d																								18 29
Kings Sutton	d																								18 37
Banbury	a				17 24									17 52							18 24				18 44
Leamington Spa 8	a				17 42									18 10							18 42				
Warwick	a				*17 58*									*18 22*							*18 58*				
Warwick Parkway	a				*17 45*									*18 21*							*18 46*				
Stratford-upon-Avon	a													*19 13*											
Coventry	a													18 22											
Birmingham International	a													18 33											
Birmingham New Street 12	a				18 18									18 45							19 18				

		GW	GW	GW	XC	GW	GW	GW	GW	GW	GW	XC	GW	GW	GW	GW	GW	GW	GW	GW	XC	GW	GW	GW
		1◇	1◇	1	1◇	1	1◇	1	1◇	1◇	1◇	1◇	1	1◇	1	1	1◇	1	1◇	1	1◇	1◇	1	1◇
			A								B													
			☕		☕		☕			☕	☕	☕		☕			☕		☕		☕	☕		
London Paddington 15	⊖ d	17 21	17 30				17 45	17 30	17 51	18 00	18 06			18 15	18 18		18 21	18 00	18 30			18 45	18 30	18 51
Ealing Broadway	⊖ d							17 37										18 07					18 37	
Slough 3	d	17 38						18 01									18 38	18 31					19 01	19 07
Maidenhead 3	d							18 08										18 38					19 08	
Twyford 3	d							18 16										18 46					19 16	
Reading 7	a	17 52	17 57				18 11	18 21	18 21	18 27	18 31			18 40	18 47		18 51	18 52	18 56			19 11	19 21	19 21
	d	17 54	17 57		18 10	18 11		18 23	18 23			18 40		18 41	18 48		18 53	18 53	18 57		19 10		19 23	19 23
Reading West	d					18 14																		
Theale	d					18 20									18 56									
Aldermaston	d					18 25																		
Midgham	d					18 29																		
Thatcham	d					18 34									19 04									
Newbury Racecourse	d					18 38																		
Newbury	a					18 43									19 11									
	d														19 11									
Kintbury	d														19 17									
Hungerford	d														19 22									
Bedwyn	a														19 31									
Tilehurst	d							18 27										18 57		←			19 27	
Pangbourne	d			←				18 32										19 02		19 02			19 32	
Goring & Streatley	d			18 06				18 36					←					→		19 06			19 36	
Cholsey	d			18 11				18 41					18 41							19 11			19 41	
Didcot Parkway	a		18 13	18 17				→					18 47	18 56					19 12	19 17			→	
	d			18 18									18 55							19 18				
Appleford	d												19 00											
Culham	d																							
Radley	d												19 04											
Oxford	a	18 21		18 30	18 34				18 47			19 05	19 13				19 18			19 30	19 34			19 48
	d				18 36							19 07				19 16					19 36			
Islip	d																							
Bicester Town	a																							
Tackley	d															19 25								
Heyford	d															19 29								
Kings Sutton	d															19 37								
Banbury	a				18 52							19 24				19 44					19 52			
Leamington Spa 8	a				19 10							19 42									20 10			
Warwick	a				*19 27*							*19 58*									*20 27*			
Warwick Parkway	a				*19 30*							*19 44*									*20 15*			
Stratford-upon-Avon	a																				*21 10*			
Coventry	a				19 22																20 21			
Birmingham International	a				19 33																20 33			
Birmingham New Street 12	a				19 45							20 18									20 45			

For general notes see front of timetable
For details of catering facilities see Directory of Train Operators

A To Weston-super-Mare (Table 134)
B **The Golden Hind**

Due to Engineering Operations, services from Saturday 13 September on this Table had not been confirmed at time of going to press. These services will be issued in a special Supplement as soon as exact timings have been confirmed

Table 116

Saturdays

until 6 September

London and Reading → Bedwyn, Oxford, Bicester, Banbury and Birmingham

Network Diagram - see first page of Table 116

		GW 1◇ ☕	GW 1◇ ☕	GW 1	XC 1◇ ☕	GW 1	GW 1	GW 1	GW 1◇	GW 1◇ ☕	GW 1	XC 1◇ ☕	GW 1◇ ☕	GW 1		GW 1◇	GW 1◇ ☕	GW 1◇ ☕	GW 1	GW 1	GW 1◇ ☕	GW 1	GW 1	GW 1	GW 1◇	GW 1◇ ☕
London Paddington 15 ⊖	d	19 00	19 06					19 00	19 21	19 30			19 45	19 30		19 51	20 00	20 06			20 15		20 00		20 21	20 30
Ealing Broadway ⊖	d							19 07						19 37									20 07			
Slough 3	d							19 31	19 38					20 01		20 07							20 31		20 38	
Maidenhead 3	d							19 38						20 08									20 38			
Twyford 3	d							19 46						20 16									20 46			
Reading 7	a	19 26	19 32					19 52	19 52	19 57			20 10	20 21		20 21	20 26	20 31			20 40		20 52		20 52	20 57
	d		19 32		19 40		19 49	19 53	19 54	19 59		20 10		20 23		20 23	20 26	20 31			20 41	20 49	20 53		20 54	20 58
Reading West	d						19 52															20 52				
Theale	d						19 58															20 58				
Aldermaston	d						20 03															21 03				
Midgham	d						20 07															21 07				
Thatcham	d						20 12															21 12				
Newbury Racecourse	d						20 16															21 16				
Newbury	a		19 48				20 19											20 46				21 19				
	d						20 19															21 33				
Kintbury	d						20 25															21 39				
Hungerford	d						20 30															21 44				
Bedwyn	a						20 39															21 53				
Tilehurst	d							19 57						20 27						←			20 57			
Pangbourne	d							20 02			←			20 32 →						20 32			21 02			
Goring & Streatley	d					←		20 06 →			20 06									20 36			21 06 →			
Cholsey	d					19 41					20 11									20 41						
Didcot Parkway	a					19 47				20 13	20 17						20 41			20 47	20 56					21 12
	d					19 58					20 18									20 55						
Appleford	d																			21 00						
Culham	d					20 03																				
Radley	d					20 06														21 04						
Oxford	a				20 05	20 15			20 21		20 30	20 34				20 47				21 13					21 21	
	d			19 56	20 07							20 36							20 52					21 20		
Islip	d																		21 05							
Bicester Town	a																		21 18							
Tackley	d			20 05																				21 29		
Heyford	d			20 09																				21 33		
Kings Sutton	d			20 17																				21 41		
Banbury	a			20 24	20 24							20 52												21 48		
Leamington Spa 8	a			*20 55*	20 42							21 10														
Warwick	a			*20 59*	*20 59*							*21 43*														
Warwick Parkway	a			*21 03*	20 44							*21 44*														
Stratford-upon-Avon	a																									
Coventry	a											21 22														
Birmingham International	a											21 33														
Birmingham New Street 12	a				21 22							21 45														

		GW 1	XC 1◇	GW 1◇ ☕	GW 1	GW 1◇	GW 1	GW 1		GW 1	GW 1◇	GW 1◇ ☕	GW 1	GW 1◇	GW 1◇	GW 1	GW 1◇ ☕	GW 1◇	GW 🚌	GW 1◇	GW 1	GW 1◇ ☕	GW 1◇	GW 1
London Paddington 15 ⊖	d			20 45	20 30	20 51				21 00	21 21	21 30		21 51	22 00	22 00	22 30	22 32		23 00	22 45	23 30	23 33	23 20
Ealing Broadway ⊖	d				20 37					21 07						22 07					22 54			23 27
Slough 3	d				21 01	21 08				21 31	21 38			22 08		22 31		22 50		23 17	23 20		23 50	23 53
Maidenhead 3	d				21 08					21 38						22 38					23 29			00 05
Twyford 3	d				21 16					21 46						22 46					23 36			00 12
Reading 7	a			21 10	21 21	21 22				21 52	21 55	22 00		22 23	22 27	22 52	22 55	23 06		23 33	23 44	23 59	00 07	00 19
	d		21 10		21 23	21 23		21 42		21 53	21 55	22 00		22 23	22 27	22 53	23 00	23 07		23 34	23 49	23 59	00 08	00 19
Reading West	d							21 45																
Theale	d							21 51																
Aldermaston	d							21 57																
Midgham	d							22 00																
Thatcham	d							22 05																
Newbury Racecourse	d							22 10																
Newbury	a							22 12																
	d							22 12																
Kintbury	d							22 19																
Hungerford	d							22 24																
Bedwyn	a							22 32																
Tilehurst	d				21 27		←			21 57			←			22 57					23 53			00 24
Pangbourne	d	←			21 32 →		21 32			22 02 →			22 02			23 02					23 58			
Goring & Streatley	d	21 06					21 36						22 06			23 06					00 02			00 31
Cholsey	d	21 11					21 41						22 11			23 11					00 07			00 36
Didcot Parkway	a	21 17				21 38	21 48				22 11	22 15	22 17		22 42	23 17	23 22	23 25		23 51	00 13	00 16	00 24	00 43
	d	21 18				21 39	21 52				22 11		22 18			23 18		23 26		23 52	00 14		00 25	00 44
Appleford	d																							00s49
Culham	d						21 57																	00s52
Radley	d						22 00														00s22			00s56
Oxford	a	21 30	21 34			21 51	22 09				22 23		22 30	22 46		23 30		23 40		00 06	00 32		00 39	01 07
	d		21 36																23 37					
Islip	d																							
Bicester Town	a																							
Tackley	d																		23s57					
Heyford	d																		00s12					
Kings Sutton	d																		00b27					
Banbury	a		21 52																00 37					
Leamington Spa 8	a		22 10																					
Warwick	a		*22 31*																					
Warwick Parkway	a		*22 35*																					
Stratford-upon-Avon	a																							
Coventry	a		22 22																					
Birmingham International	a		22 33																					
Birmingham New Street 12	a		22 50																					

For general notes see front of timetable
For details of catering facilities see Directory of Train Operators

b Kings Sutton V. Square. Stops to set down only

Due to Engineering Operations, services from Saturday 13 September on this Table had not been confirmed at time of going to press. These services will be issued in a special Supplement as soon as exact timings have been confirmed

London and Reading → Bedwyn, Oxford, Bicester, Banbury and Birmingham

Sundays until 13 July

Network Diagram - see first page of Table 116

		GW 1	GW 1◇	GW 1	GW	GW	GW 1◇ ☕	GW	GW 1◇ ☕	GW 🚌	GW 1◇ A	GW	GW 1◇ 🍴	GW 1◇ ☕	GW		GW 1◇ ☕	GW 1	GW 1	GW	GW 🚌	GW 1◇ ☕	XC 1◇ ☕	GW 1◇ ☕	GW 1◇ B ☕	GW
London Paddington 15 ⊖	d	22p45	23p33	23p20		07 43	07 57		08 00		08 03		08 42	08 57	08 44		09 07					09 27		09 35	09 57	09 44
Ealing Broadway ⊖	d	22p54		23p27		07 50									08 51											09 51
Slough 3	d	23p20	23p50	23p53		08 14					08 25		09 01		09 15									09 53		10 15
Maidenhead 3	d	23p29		00 05		08 23					08 35				09 24											10 24
Twyford 3	d	23p36		00 12		08 31									09 32											10 32
Reading 7	a	23p44	00 07	00 19		08 37	08 40		08 45		08 50	←	09 21	09 32	09 39		09 41			←		10 03		10 13	10 30	10 38
	d	23p49	00 08	00 19	08 14	08 54	08 42	08 44			08 50	08 54	09 21		09 46		09 41		09 44	09 46			10 10	10 13		10 43
Reading West	d				08 17	↪									↪				09 47							
Theale	d				08 23			08 52											09 53							
Aldermaston	d				08 28														09 58							
Midgham	d				08 32														10 02							
Thatcham	d				08 37			09 00											10 07							
Newbury Racecourse	d																									
Newbury	a				08 43			09 07											10 13							
	d									09 15											10 18					
Kintbury	d									09 35											10 38					
Hungerford	d									09 45											10 48					
Bedwyn	a									10 00											11 03					
Tilehurst	d	23p53		00 24								08 59								09 50						10 47
Pangbourne	d	23p58										09 03								09 54						10 51
Goring & Streatley	d	00 02		00 31								09 08								10 00						→
Cholsey	d	00 07		00 36								09 14								10 05						
Didcot Parkway	a	00 13	00 24	00 43			08 57				09 04	09 18	09 36				09 57			10 11				10 29		
	d	00 14	00 25	00 44							09 04	09 18	09 36							10 11				10 29		
Appleford	d			00s49																10 17						
Culham	d			00s52																						
Radley	d	00s22		00s56								09 28								10 22						
Oxford	a	00 32	00 39	01 07							09 17	09 35	09 51							10 29			10 34	10 42		
	d																	10 00					10 36			
Islip	d																									
Bicester Town	a																									
Tackley	d																	10 09								
Heyford	d																	10 14								
Kings Sutton	d																	10 23								
Banbury	a																	10 29					10 52			
Leamington Spa 8	a																	*10 56*					11 10			
Warwick	a																	*11 00*					*11 25*			
Warwick Parkway	a																	*11 04*					*11 38*			
Stratford-upon-Avon	a																						*11 59*			
Coventry	a																									
Birmingham International	a																									
Birmingham New Street 12	a																						11 51			

For general notes see front of timetable
For details of catering facilities see Directory of Train Operators

A To Great Malvern (Table 126)
B **Atlantic Coast Express**

until 13 July

London and Reading → Bedwyn, Oxford, Bicester, Banbury and Birmingham

Network Diagram - see first page of Table 116

		GW	GW	GW	GW	XC	GW		GW	XC	GW	GW	GW	GW	GW	XC	GW	GW	GW	GW	GW	GW		GW	GW	XC
		1◇ A ☕		1	1◇ ☕	R 1◇ ☕	1◇ ☕		1◇ ☕	1◇ ☕		1◇ ☕		1	1◇ ☕	R 1 ☕	🚌	1◇	1◇ ☕		1◇ ☕			1	1◇ ☕	R 1 ☕
London Paddington 15 ⊖	d	10 07			10 27		10 42		10 57		10 44	11 07			11 27			11 42	11 57	11 44	12 07				12 27	
Ealing Broadway ⊖	d										10 51									11 51						
Slough 3	d						10 58				11 15							12 00		12 15						
Maidenhead 3	d										11 24									12 24						
Twyford 3	d										11 32									12 32						
Reading 7	a	10 43			11 01		11 19		11 31		11 37	11 43			12 01			12 17	12 31	12 38	12 41	←			13 01	
	d	10 44		10 44		11 10	11 20			11 40	11 43	11 44		11 44		12 10		12 23		12 43 →	12 42	12 43		12 44		13 10
Reading West	d			10 47																				12 47		
Theale	d			10 53										11 52										12 53		
Aldermaston	d			10 58																				12 58		
Midgham	d			11 02																				13 02		
Thatcham	d			11 07										12 00										13 07		
Newbury Racecourse	d			11 11																				13 11		
Newbury	a			11 15										12 07										13 15		
	d																12 15									
Kintbury	d																12 35									
Hungerford	d																12 45									
Bedwyn	a																13 00									
Tilehurst	d		←								11 47		←									12 47				
Pangbourne	d		10 51								11 51 →		11 51									12 51				
Goring & Streatley	d		10 57										11 57									12 57				
Cholsey	d		11 02										12 02									13 02				
Didcot Parkway	a	10 59	11 08				11 35					11 59	12 08					12 38			12 57	13 08				
	d		11 08				11 36						12 08					12 39				13 08				
Appleford	d																					13 15				
Culham	d																									
Radley	d		11 17										12 17									13 20				
Oxford	a		11 25			11 34	11 49			12 04			12 27			12 34		12 51				13 27				13 34
	d					11 36				12 07						12 36										13 36
Islip	d																									
Bicester Town	a																									
Tackley	d																									
Heyford	d																									
Kings Sutton	d																									
Banbury	a					11 52				12 24						12 52										13 52
Leamington Spa 8	a					12 10				12 41						13 10										14 10
Warwick	a									*13 05*						*13 25*										*15 05*
Warwick Parkway	a									*13 09*						*13 31*										*14 27*
Stratford-upon-Avon	a															*13 54*										
Coventry	a																									
Birmingham International	a																									
Birmingham New Street 12	a					12 46				13 15						13 57										14 57

		GW	GW	GW	GW	GW	GW	GW	GW	XC	GW	GW	GW	GW		GW	GW	GW	GW	XC	GW	GW	GW	GW	GW	GW
		1◇ ☕	1◇ ☕		1◇ ☕	1		1	1◇ ☕	R 1 ☕	🚌	1◇ ☕	1◇ ☕			1◇ ☕		1	1◇ ☕	R 1 ☕	1◇ ☕	1◇ ☕		1◇ B ☕		1
London Paddington 15 ⊖	d	12 42	12 57	12 44	13 07				13 27			13 42	13 57	13 44		14 07			14 27		14 42	14 57	14 44	15 07		
Ealing Broadway ⊖	d			12 51										13 51									14 51			
Slough 3	d	12 58		13 15								13 58		14 15							14 58		15 15			
Maidenhead 3	d			13 24										14 24									15 24			
Twyford 3	d			13 32										14 32									15 32			
Reading 7	a	13 20	13 31	13 38	13 41		←		14 01			14 19	14 30	14 38		14 41	←		15 01		15 19	15 31	15 38	15 41	←	
	d	13 20		13 43 →	13 42		13 43	13 44		14 10		14 20		14 43 →		14 42	14 43	14 44		15 10	15 20		15 43 →	15 42	15 43	15 44
Reading West	d																	14 47								
Theale	d							13 52										14 53								15 52
Aldermaston	d																	14 58								
Midgham	d																	15 02								
Thatcham	d							14 00										15 07								16 00
Newbury Racecourse	d																	15 11								
Newbury	a							14 07										15 15								16 07
	d										14 15															
Kintbury	d										14 35															
Hungerford	d										14 45															
Bedwyn	a										15 00															
Tilehurst	d						13 47										14 47								15 47	
Pangbourne	d						13 51										14 51								15 51	
Goring & Streatley	d						13 57										14 57								15 57	
Cholsey	d						14 02										15 02								16 02	
Didcot Parkway	a	13 36			13 57		14 08					14 35				14 57	15 08				15 35			15 57	16 08	
	d	13 37					14 08					14 36					15 08				15 36				16 08	
Appleford	d																15 15									
Culham	d																									
Radley	d						14 17										15 20								16 17	
Oxford	a	13 49					14 25			14 34		14 49					15 27			15 34	15 48				16 25	
	d					14 20				14 36										15 36						
Islip	d																									
Bicester Town	a																									
Tackley	d					14 29																				
Heyford	d					14 33																				
Kings Sutton	d					14 42																				
Banbury	a					14 48				14 52										15 52						
Leamington Spa 8	a									15 10										16 10						
Warwick	a									*15 25*										*17 05*						
Warwick Parkway	a									*15 31*										*16 27*						
Stratford-upon-Avon	a									*15 49*																
Coventry	a																									
Birmingham International	a																									
Birmingham New Street 12	a									15 57										16 57						

For general notes see front of timetable
For details of catering facilities see Directory of Train Operators

A To Weston-super-Mare (Table 134)
B To Taunton (Table 134)

Table 116

Sundays

until 13 July

London and Reading → Bedwyn, Oxford, Bicester, Banbury and Birmingham

Network Diagram - see first page of Table 116

		GW	XC	GW	GW	GW	GW	GW	GW	GW	GW	GW
		1 ◇	R 1		1 ◇	1 ◇		1 ◇	1		1	1 ◇
				🚌								
		☕	☕		☕	☕		☕				☕
London Paddington 15 ⊖	d	15 27			15 42	15 57	15 44	16 07				16 27
Ealing Broadway ⊖	d						15 51					
Slough 3	d				15 58		16 15					
Maidenhead 3	d						16 24					
Twyford 3	d						16 32					
Reading 7	a	16 01			16 19	16 30	16 38	16 41		←		17 01
	d		16 10		16 20		16 43 →	16 42		16 43	16 44	
Reading West	d										16 47	
Theale	d										16 53	
Aldermaston	d										16 58	
Midgham	d										17 02	
Thatcham	d										17 07	
Newbury Racecourse	d										17 11	
Newbury	a										17 15	
	d			16 15								
Kintbury	d			16 35								
Hungerford	d			16 45								
Bedwyn	a			17 00								
Tilehurst	d									16 47		
Pangbourne	d									16 51		
Goring & Streatley	d									16 57		
Cholsey	d									17 02		
Didcot Parkway	a				16 35			16 57		17 08		
	d				16 36					17 08		
Appleford	d											
Culham	d											
Radley	d									17 17		
Oxford	a		16 34		16 49					17 25		
	d		16 36						17 20			
Islip	d											
Bicester Town	a											
Tackley	d								17 29			
Heyford	d								17 33			
Kings Sutton	d								17 42			
Banbury	a		16 52						17 48			
Leamington Spa 8	a		17 10									
Warwick	a		*17 24*									
Warwick Parkway	a		*17 31*									
Stratford-upon-Avon	a		*17 49*									
Coventry	a											
Birmingham International	a											
Birmingham New Street 12	a		17 57									

		XC	GW	GW	GW	GW	GW	GW	GW	XC	GW	GW	GW
		R 1	1 ◇	1 ◇		1 ◇		1	1 ◇	R 1	1 ◇		1 ◇
						A						🚌	
		☕	☕	☕		☕			☕	☕	☕		☕
London Paddington 15 ⊖	d		16 42	16 57	16 44	17 07			17 27		17 37		17 42
Ealing Broadway ⊖	d				16 51								
Slough 3	d		16 58		17 15								17 58
Maidenhead 3	d				17 24								
Twyford 3	d				17 32								
Reading 7	a		17 19	17 31	17 38	17 41	←		18 01		18 12		18 19
	d	17 10	17 20		17 43 →	17 42	17 43	17 44		18 10	18 13		18 20
Reading West	d												
Theale	d							17 52					
Aldermaston	d												
Midgham	d												
Thatcham	d							18 00					
Newbury Racecourse	d												
Newbury	a							18 07					
	d											18 15	
Kintbury	d											18 35	
Hungerford	d											18 45	
Bedwyn	a											19 00	
Tilehurst	d						17 47						
Pangbourne	d						17 51						
Goring & Streatley	d						17 57						
Cholsey	d						18 02						
Didcot Parkway	a		17 35			17 57	18 08				18 28		18 35
	d		17 36				18 08						18 36
Appleford	d						18 15						
Culham	d												
Radley	d						18 20						
Oxford	a	17 35	17 49				18 27			18 34			18 49
	d	17 36								18 36			
Islip	d												
Bicester Town	a												
Tackley	d												
Heyford	d												
Kings Sutton	d												
Banbury	a	17 52								18 52			
Leamington Spa 8	a	18 10								19 10			
Warwick	a	*19 05*								*19 25*			
Warwick Parkway	a	*18 34*								*19 34*			
Stratford-upon-Avon	a									*19 48*			
Coventry	a												
Birmingham International	a												
Birmingham New Street 12	a	18 51								19 51			

		GW	GW	GW	GW	GW	GW	XC	GW	GW	GW	GW	GW
		1 ◇		1 ◇		1	1 ◇	1 ◇	1 ◇	1 ◇		1 ◇	
		☕		☕			☕	☕	☕	☕		☕	
London Paddington 15 ⊖	d	17 57	17 44	18 07			18 27		18 42	18 57	18 44	19 07	
Ealing Broadway ⊖	d		17 51								18 51		
Slough 3	d		18 15						18 58		19 15		
Maidenhead 3	d		18 24								19 24		
Twyford 3	d		18 32								19 32		
Reading 7	a	18 31	18 38	18 41	←		19 02		19 20	19 30	19 38	19 41	←
	d		18 43 →	18 42	18 43	18 44		19 10	19 20		19 43 →	19 42	19 43
Reading West	d					18 47							
Theale	d					18 53							
Aldermaston	d					18 58							
Midgham	d					19 02							
Thatcham	d					19 07							
Newbury Racecourse	d					19 11							
Newbury	a					19 15							
	d												
Kintbury	d												
Hungerford	d												
Bedwyn	a												
Tilehurst	d				18 47								19 47
Pangbourne	d				18 51								19 51
Goring & Streatley	d				18 57								19 57
Cholsey	d				19 02								20 02
Didcot Parkway	a			18 57	19 08				19 36			19 57	20 08
	d				19 08				19 36				20 08
Appleford	d												
Culham	d												
Radley	d				19 17								20 17
Oxford	a				19 25			19 35	19 50				20 25
	d							19 36					
Islip	d												
Bicester Town	a												
Tackley	d												
Heyford	d												
Kings Sutton	d												
Banbury	a							19 52					
Leamington Spa 8	a							20 10					
Warwick	a							*21 08*					
Warwick Parkway	a							*20 34*					
Stratford-upon-Avon	a												
Coventry	a												
Birmingham International	a												
Birmingham New Street 12	a							20 51					

		GW	GW	XC	GW	GW	GW	GW	GW	GW	GW	GW	XC
		1	1 ◇	1 ◇		1 ◇	1 ◇		1 ◇		1	1 ◇	1 ◇
					🚌								
			☕	☕			☕		☕			☕	
London Paddington 15 ⊖	d		19 27			19 42	19 57	19 44	20 07			20 27	
Ealing Broadway ⊖	d							19 51					
Slough 3	d					19 57		20 15					
Maidenhead 3	d							20 24					
Twyford 3	d							20 32					
Reading 7	a		20 01			20 17	20 31	20 38	20 41	←		21 01	
	d	19 44		20 10		20 20		20 43 →	20 42	20 43	20 44		21 10
Reading West	d										20 47		
Theale	d	19 52									20 56		
Aldermaston	d										21 01		
Midgham	d										21 05		
Thatcham	d	20 00									21 10		
Newbury Racecourse	d										21 14		
Newbury	a	20 07									21 18		
	d				20 15								
Kintbury	d				20 35								
Hungerford	d				20 45								
Bedwyn	a				21 00								
Tilehurst	d									20 47			
Pangbourne	d									20 51			
Goring & Streatley	d									20 57			
Cholsey	d									21 02			
Didcot Parkway	a					20 35			20 57	21 08			
	d					20 36				21 08			
Appleford	d												
Culham	d												
Radley	d									21 17			
Oxford	a			20 34		20 48				21 25			21 34
	d			20 36									21 36
Islip	d												
Bicester Town	a												
Tackley	d												
Heyford	d												
Kings Sutton	d												
Banbury	a			20 52									21 52
Leamington Spa 8	a			21 10									22 10
Warwick	a			*22 05*									*22 34*
Warwick Parkway	a			*21 34*									*22 38*
Stratford-upon-Avon	a												
Coventry	a												
Birmingham International	a												
Birmingham New Street 12	a			21 51									22 51

For general notes see front of timetable
For details of catering facilities see Directory of Train Operators

A To Weston-super-Mare (Table 134)

Table 116

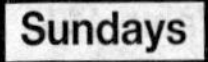

Sundays

until 13 July

London and Reading → Bedwyn, Oxford, Bicester, Banbury and Birmingham

Network Diagram - see first page of Table 116

		GW	GW	GW	GW	GW	GW	GW	XC	GW	GW	GW	GW	GW	GW	GW	GW	GW	GW	GW	GW	GW	GW
		1 ◇	1 ◇		1 ◇	1		1 ◇	1 ◇		1 ◇			1 ◇			1 ◇	1 ◇		1 ◇		1 ◇	1 ◇
					A						B												
		[trolley]	[buffet]					[buffet]		[bus]				[buffet]			[buffet]			[buffet]		[buffet]	
London Paddington 15 ⊖	d	20 42	20 57	20 44	21 07			21 27			21 42	21 44		22 07		22 15	22 37	22 42	22 44	23 07		23 37	23 42
Ealing Broadway ⊖	d			20 51								21 51				22 24			22 51				23 50
Slough 3	d	20 58		21 15							21 59	22 16				22 47		23 00	23 16				00 02
Maidenhead 3	d			21 24							22 08	22 29				22 55			23 24				00 10
Twyford 3	d			21 32								22 36				23 04			23 32				
Reading 7	a	21 20	21 31	21 38	21 41		⟵	22 01			22 20	22 43		22 46	⟵	23 10	23 14	23 18	23 42	23 46	⟵	00 15	00 23
	d	21 22		21 46	21 42	21 44	21 46		22 10		22 20	22 50	22 44	22 46	22 50	23 12	23 14	23 19	23 50	23 46	23 50	00 15	00 23
Reading West	d			↪								↪	22 47			23 15			↪				
Theale	d					21 53							22 53			23 22							
Aldermaston	d												22 58										
Midgham	d												23 02										
Thatcham	d					22 01							23 07			23 30							
Newbury Racecourse	d												23 11										
Newbury	a					22 08							23 15			23 37							
	d									22 15													
Kintbury	d									22 35													
Hungerford	d									22 45													
Bedwyn	a									23 00													
Tilehurst	d						21 50								22 54						23 55		
Pangbourne	d						21 55								22 59						23 59		
Goring & Streatley	d						22 00								23 03						00 05		
Cholsey	d						22 05								23 08						00 09		
Didcot Parkway	a	21 37			21 59		22 11				22 37			23 02	23 14		23s30	23 34		00s02	00 16	00s33	00 39
	d	21 38					22 12				22 39				23 15			23 35			00 16		00 40
Appleford	d																						
Culham	d																						
Radley	d						22 19								23 22						00 25		
Oxford	a	21 50					22 29		22 34		22 50				23 30			23 48			00 35		00 55
	d								22 36														
Islip	d																						
Bicester Town	a																						
Tackley	d																						
Heyford	d																						
Kings Sutton	d																						
Banbury	a								22 52														
Leamington Spa 8	a								23 10														
Warwick	a								23 25														
Warwick Parkway	a								23 29														
Stratford-upon-Avon	a																						
Coventry	a																						
Birmingham International	a																						
Birmingham New Street 12	a								23 43														

For general notes see front of timetable
For details of catering facilities see Directory of Train Operators

A To Weston-super-Mare (Table 134)
B To Worcester Shrub Hill (Table 126)

Table 116

Sundays

London and Reading → Bedwyn, Oxford, Bicester, Banbury and Birmingham

20 July to 7 September

Network Diagram - see first page of Table 116

Station		GW	GW	GW	GW	GW	GW	GW	GW	GW	GW	GW	GW	GW	GW	GW	GW	GW	GW	GW	GW	GW	XC	GW	GW	GW
		(bus)	1	1 ◇	1			1 ◇ (buffet)		1 ◇ (buffet)	(bus)	1 ◇ A		1 ◇ (trolley)	1 ◇ (buffet)		1 ◇ (buffet)	1	1		(bus)	1 ◇ (buffet)	1 ◇ (buffet)	1 ◇ (buffet)	1 ◇ B (buffet)	
London Paddington 15 ⊖	d		22p45	23p33	23p20		07 43	07 57		08 00		08 03		08 42	08 57	08 44	09 07					09 27		09 35	09 57	09 44
Ealing Broadway ⊖	d		22p54		23p27		07 50									08 51										09 51
Slough 3	d		23p20	23p50	23p53		08 14					08 25		09 01		09 15								09 53		10 15
Maidenhead 3	d		23p29		00 05		08 23					08 35				09 24										10 24
Twyford 3	d		23p36		00 12		08 31									09 32										10 32
Reading 7	a		23p44	00 07	00 19		08 37	08 40		08 45		08 50	←	09 21	09 32	09 39	09 41			←		10 03		10 13	10 30	10 38
	d		23p49	00 08	00 19	08 14	08 54	08 42	08 44			08 50	08 54	09 21		09 46	09 41		09 44	09 46			10 10	10 13		10 43
Reading West	d					08 17	→									→			09 47							
Theale	d					08 23			08 52										09 53							
Aldermaston	d					08 28													09 58							
Midgham	d					08 32													10 02							
Thatcham	d					08 37			09 00										10 07							
Newbury Racecourse	d																									
Newbury	a					08 43			09 07										10 13							
	d										09 15										10 18					
Kintbury	d										09 35										10 38					
Hungerford	d										09 45										10 48					
Bedwyn	a										10 00										11 03					
Tilehurst	d		23p53		00 24								08 59							09 50						10 47
Pangbourne	d		23p58										09 03							09 54						10 51
Goring & Streatley	d		00 02		00 31								09 08							10 00						→
Cholsey	d		00 07		00 36								09 14							10 05						
Didcot Parkway	a		00 13	00 24	00 43			08 57				09 04	09 18	09 36			09 57			10 11				10 29		
	d		00 14	00 25	00 44							09 04	09 18	09 36						10 11				10 29		
Appleford	d				00s49															10 17						
Culham	d				00s52																					
Radley	d		00s22		00s56								09 28							10 22						
Oxford	a		00 32	00 39	01 07							09 17	09 35	09 51						10 29			10 34	10 42		
	d	23p42																10 00					10 36			
Islip	d																									
Bicester Town	a																									
Tackley	d	00s02																10 09								
Heyford	d	00s17																10 14								
Kings Sutton	d	00b32																10 23								
Banbury	a	00 42																10 29					10 52			
Leamington Spa 8	a																	*10 56*					11 10			
Warwick	a																	*11 00*					*11 25*			
Warwick Parkway	a																	*11 04*					*11 38*			
Stratford-upon-Avon	a																						*11 59*			
Coventry	a																									
Birmingham International	a																									
Birmingham New Street 12	a																						11 51			

For general notes see front of timetable
For details of catering facilities see
Directory of Train Operators

A To Great Malvern (Table 126)
B **Atlantic Coast Express**

b Kings Sutton V. Square. Stops to set down only

Due to Engineering Operations, services from Sunday 14 September on this Table had not been confirmed at time of going to press. These services will be issued in a special Supplement as soon as exact timings have been confirmed

Table 116

Sundays

London and Reading → Bedwyn, Oxford, Bicester, Banbury and Birmingham

20 July to 7 September

Network Diagram - see first page of Table 116

		GW	GW	GW	GW	XC	GW	GW	XC	GW	GW	GW	GW	GW	XC	GW	GW	GW	GW	XC	GW	GW	GW	GW	XC	GW
		1 ◇		1	1 ◇	1 ◇	1 ◇	1 ◇	1 ◇		1 ◇		1	1 ◇	R 1		1 ◇	1 ◇		1 ◇	1 ◇		1	1 ◇	R 1	1 ◇
		A														bus										
		☕			☕	☕	☕	☕	☕		☕			☕	☕			☕		☕	☕			☕	☕	☕
London Paddington 15 ⊖	d	10 07			10 27		10 42	10 57		10 44	11 07			11 27			11 42	11 57	11 44		12 07			12 27		12 42
Ealing Broadway ⊖	d									10 51									11 51							
Slough 3	d						10 58			11 15							12 00		12 15							12 58
Maidenhead 3	d									11 24									12 24							
Twyford 3	d									11 32									12 32							
Reading 7	a	10 43			11 01		11 19	11 31		11 37	11 43			12 01			12 17	12 31	12 38		12 41	←		13 01		13 20
	d	10 44		10 44		11 10	11 20		11 40	11 43	11 44		11 44		12 10		12 23		12 43 →	12 40	12 42	12 43	12 44		13 10	13 20
Reading West	d			10 47																			12 47			
Theale	d			10 53									11 52										12 53			
Aldermaston	d			10 58																			12 58			
Midgham	d			11 02																			13 02			
Thatcham	d			11 07									12 00										13 07			
Newbury Racecourse	d			11 11																			13 11			
Newbury	a			11 15									12 07										13 15			
	d															12 15										
Kintbury	d															12 35										
Hungerford	d															12 45										
Bedwyn	a															13 00										
Tilehurst	d		←							11 47		←										12 47				
Pangbourne	d		10 51							11 51 →		11 51										12 51				
Goring & Streatley	d		10 57									11 57										12 57				
Cholsey	d		11 02									12 02										13 02				
Didcot Parkway	a	10 59	11 08				11 35				11 59	12 08					12 38				12 57	13 08				13 36
	d		11 08				11 36					12 08					12 39					13 08				13 37
Appleford	d																					13 15				
Culham	d																									
Radley	d		11 17									12 17										13 20				
Oxford	a		11 25			11 34	11 49		12 04			12 27			12 34		12 51			13 04		13 27			13 34	13 49
	d					11 36			12 07						12 36					13 07					13 36	
Islip	d																									
Bicester Town	a																									
Tackley	d																									
Heyford	d																									
Kings Sutton	d																									
Banbury	a					11 52			12 24						12 52					13 24					13 52	
Leamington Spa 8	a					12 10			12 41						13 10					13 41					14 10	
Warwick	a								*13 00*						*13 25*					*14 06*						
Warwick Parkway	a					*12 27*			*13 04*						*13 31*					*14 10*						
Stratford-upon-Avon	a								*13 54*						*13 54*											
Coventry	a																									
Birmingham International	a																									
Birmingham New Street 12	a					12 46			13 15						13 45					14 15					14 54	

		GW	GW	XC		GW	GW	GW	GW	GW	XC	GW	GW	GW	GW	XC	GW	GW	GW	GW	XC	GW	GW	GW	XC	GW
		1 ◇		1 ◇		1 ◇	1		1	1 ◇	R 1		1 ◇	1 ◇		1 ◇	1 ◇		1	1 ◇	R 1	1 ◇	1 ◇		1 ◇	1 ◇
												bus														B
		☕		☕		☕				☕	☕		☕	☕		☕	☕			☕	☕	☕	☕		☕	☕
London Paddington 15 ⊖	d	12 57	12 44			13 07				13 27			13 42	13 57	13 44		14 07			14 27		14 42	14 57	14 44		15 07
Ealing Broadway ⊖	d		12 51												13 51									14 51		
Slough 3	d		13 15										13 58		14 15							14 58		15 15		
Maidenhead 3	d		13 24												14 24									15 24		
Twyford 3	d		13 32												14 32									15 32		
Reading 7	a	13 31	13 38			13 41		←		14 01			14 19	14 30	14 38		14 41	←		15 01		15 19	15 31	15 38		15 41
	d		13 43 →	13 40		13 42		13 43	13 44		14 10		14 20		14 43 →	14 40	14 42	14 43	14 44		15 10	15 20		15 43 →	15 40	15 42
Reading West	d																		14 47							
Theale	d								13 52										14 53							
Aldermaston	d																		14 58							
Midgham	d																		15 02							
Thatcham	d								14 00										15 07							
Newbury Racecourse	d																		15 11							
Newbury	a								14 07										15 15							
	d											14 15														
Kintbury	d											14 35														
Hungerford	d											14 45														
Bedwyn	a											15 00														
Tilehurst	d							13 47										14 47								
Pangbourne	d							13 51										14 51								
Goring & Streatley	d							13 57										14 57								
Cholsey	d							14 02										15 02								
Didcot Parkway	a					13 57		14 08					14 35				14 57	15 08				15 35				15 57
	d							14 08					14 36					15 08				15 36				
Appleford	d																	15 15								
Culham	d																									
Radley	d							14 17										15 20								
Oxford	a			14 05				14 25			14 34		14 49			15 05		15 27			15 34	15 48			16 04	
	d			14 07			14 20				14 36					15 07					15 36				16 07	
Islip	d																									
Bicester Town	a																									
Tackley	d						14 29																			
Heyford	d						14 33																			
Kings Sutton	d						14 42																			
Banbury	a			14 24			14 48				14 52					15 24					15 52				16 24	
Leamington Spa 8	a			14 41							15 10					15 41					16 10				16 41	
Warwick	a			*15 00*							*15 25*					*16 05*									*17 00*	
Warwick Parkway	a			*15 04*							*15 31*					*16 09*					*16 27*				*17 04*	
Stratford-upon-Avon	a			*15 49*							*15 49*														*17 49*	
Coventry	a																									
Birmingham International	a																									
Birmingham New Street 12	a			15 15							15 46					16 15					16 57				17 15	

For general notes see front of timetable
For details of catering facilities see Directory of Train Operators

A To Weston-super-Mare (Table 134)
B To Taunton (Table 134)

Due to Engineering Operations, services from Sunday 14 September on this Table had not been confirmed at time of going to press. These services will be issued in a special Supplement as soon as exact timings have been confirmed

Table 116

Sundays

London and Reading → Bedwyn, Oxford, Bicester, Banbury and Birmingham

20 July to 7 September

Network Diagram - see first page of Table 116

		GW	GW	GW	XC	GW	GW	GW	GW	XC	GW	GW	GW	GW	XC	GW	GW	GW	XC	GW	GW	GW	GW	XC	GW	GW
			1	1 ◇	R 1		1 ◇	1 ◇		1 ◇	1 ◇		1	1 ◇	R 1	1 ◇	1 ◇		1 ◇	1 ◇ A		1	1 ◇	R 1	1 ◇	
				☕	☕	🚌	☕	☕		☕	☕			☕	☕	☕	☕		☕	☕			☕	☕	☕	🚌
London Paddington 15 ⊖	d			15 27			15 42	15 57	15 44		16 07			16 27		16 42	16 57	16 44		17 07			17 27		17 37	
Ealing Broadway ⊖	d								15 51									16 51								
Slough 3	d						15 58		16 15							16 58		17 15								
Maidenhead 3	d								16 24									17 24								
Twyford 3	d								16 32									17 32								
Reading 7	a	←		16 01			16 19	16 30	16 38		16 41	←		17 01		17 19	17 31	17 38		17 41	←		18 01		18 12	
	d	15 43	15 44		16 10		16 20		16 43 →	16 40	16 42	16 43	16 44		17 10	17 20		17 43 →	17 40	17 42	17 43	17 44		18 10	18 13	
Reading West	d												16 47													
Theale	d		15 52										16 53									17 52				
Aldermaston	d												16 58													
Midgham	d												17 02													
Thatcham	d		16 00										17 07									18 00				
Newbury Racecourse	d												17 11													
Newbury	a		16 07										17 15									18 07				
	d					16 15																				18 15
Kintbury	d					16 35																				18 35
Hungerford	d					16 45																				18 45
Bedwyn	a					17 00																				19 00
Tilehurst	d	15 47										16 47									17 47					
Pangbourne	d	15 51										16 51									17 51					
Goring & Streatley	d	15 57										16 57									17 57					
Cholsey	d	16 02										17 02									18 02					
Didcot Parkway	a	16 08					16 35				16 57	17 08				17 35				17 57	18 08				18 28	
	d	16 08					16 36					17 08				17 36					18 08					
Appleford	d																				18 15					
Culham	d																									
Radley	d	16 17										17 17									18 20					
Oxford	a	16 25			16 34		16 49			17 04		17 25			17 35	17 49			18 04		18 27			18 34		
	d				16 36					17 07					17 36				18 07					18 36		
Islip	d																									
Bicester Town	a																									
Tackley	d																									
Heyford	d																									
Kings Sutton	d																									
Banbury	a				16 52					17 24					17 52				18 24					18 52		
Leamington Spa 8	a				17 10					17 41					18 10				18 41					19 10		
Warwick	a				*17 24*					*18 05*									*19 05*					*19 25*		
Warwick Parkway	a				*17 31*					*18 09*					*18 34*				*19 09*					*19 34*		
Stratford-upon-Avon	a				*17 49*														*19 48*					*19 48*		
Coventry	a																									
Birmingham International	a																									
Birmingham New Street 12	a				17 46					18 15					18 51				19 15					19 46		

		GW	GW	GW	XC	GW	GW	GW	GW	XC	GW	GW	GW	GW	GW	GW	GW	XC	GW	GW	GW	GW	GW	GW	GW	GW
		1 ◇	1 ◇		1 ◇	1 ◇		1	1 ◇	1 ◇	1 ◇	1 ◇		1 ◇		1	1 ◇	1 ◇		1 ◇	1 ◇		1 ◇		1	1 ◇
		☕	☕		☕	☕			☕	☕	☕	☕		☕			☕	☕	🚌		☕		☕			☕
London Paddington 15 ⊖	d	17 42	17 57	17 44		18 07			18 27		18 42	18 57	18 44	19 07			19 27			19 42	19 57	19 44	20 07			20 27
Ealing Broadway ⊖	d			17 51									18 51									19 51				
Slough 3	d	17 58		18 15							18 58		19 15							19 57		20 15				
Maidenhead 3	d			18 24									19 24									20 24				
Twyford 3	d			18 32									19 32									20 32				
Reading 7	a	18 19	18 31	18 38		18 41	←		19 02		19 20	19 30	19 38	19 41	←		20 01			20 17	20 31	20 38	20 41	←		21 01
	d	18 20		18 43 →	18 40	18 42	18 43	18 44		19 10	19 20		19 43 →	19 42	19 43	19 44		20 10		20 20		20 43 →	20 42	20 43	20 44	
Reading West	d							18 47																	20 47	
Theale	d							18 53								19 52									20 56	
Aldermaston	d							18 58																	21 01	
Midgham	d							19 02																	21 05	
Thatcham	d							19 07								20 00									21 10	
Newbury Racecourse	d							19 11																	21 14	
Newbury	a							19 15								20 07									21 18	
	d																		20 15							
Kintbury	d																		20 35							
Hungerford	d																		20 45							
Bedwyn	a																		21 00							
Tilehurst	d						18 47								19 47									20 47		
Pangbourne	d						18 51								19 51									20 51		
Goring & Streatley	d						18 57								19 57									20 57		
Cholsey	d						19 02								20 02									21 02		
Didcot Parkway	a	18 35				18 57	19 08				19 36			19 57	20 08					20 35			20 57	21 08		
	d	18 36					19 08				19 36				20 08					20 36				21 08		
Appleford	d																									
Culham	d																									
Radley	d						19 17								20 17									21 17		
Oxford	a	18 49			19 04		19 25			19 35	19 50				20 25			20 34		20 48				21 25		
	d				19 07					19 36								20 36								
Islip	d																									
Bicester Town	a																									
Tackley	d																									
Heyford	d																									
Kings Sutton	d																									
Banbury	a				19 24					19 52								20 52								
Leamington Spa 8	a				19 41					20 10								21 10								
Warwick	a				*20 05*					*21 08*								*22 05*								
Warwick Parkway	a				*19 45*					*20 34*								*21 34*								
Stratford-upon-Avon	a																									
Coventry	a																									
Birmingham International	a																									
Birmingham New Street 12	a				20 15					20 51								21 51								

For general notes see front of timetable
For details of catering facilities see Directory of Train Operators

A To Weston-super-Mare (Table 134)

Due to Engineering Operations, services from Sunday 14 September on this Table had not been confirmed at time of going to press. These services will be issued in a special Supplement as soon as exact timings have been confirmed

Table 116

Sundays

20 July to 7 September

London and Reading → Bedwyn, Oxford, Bicester, Banbury and Birmingham

Network Diagram - see first page of Table 116

		XC	GW	GW	GW	GW	GW	GW	GW	XC	GW	GW	GW	GW	GW	GW	GW	GW	GW	GW	GW	GW	GW	GW
		1 ◇	1 ◇	1 ◇		1 ◇	1		1 ◇	1 ◇		1 ◇			1 ◇			1 ◇	1 ◇		1 ◇		1 ◇	1 ◇
						A					🚌	B												
			🛒	☕					☕						☕			☕			☕		☕	
London Paddington 15 ⊖	d		20 42	20 57	20 44	21 07			21 27			21 42	21 44		22 07		22 15	22 37	22 42	22 44	23 07		23 37	23 42
Ealing Broadway ⊖	d				20 51								21 51				22 24			22 51				23 50
Slough 3	d		20 58		21 15							21 59	22 16				22 47		23 00	23 16				00 02
Maidenhead 3	d				21 24							22 08	22 29				22 55			23 24				00 10
Twyford 3	d				21 32								22 36				23 04			23 32				
Reading 7	a		21 20	21 31	21 38	21 41		⟵	22 01			22 20	22 43		22 46	⟵	23 10	23 14	23 18	23 42	23 46	⟵	00 15	00 23
	d	21 10	21 22		21 46	21 42	21 44	21 46		22 10		22 20	22 50	22 44	22 46	22 50	23 12	23 14	23 19	23 50	23 46	23 50	00 15	00 23
Reading West	d				⟶								⟶	22 47			23 15			⟶				
Theale	d						21 53							22 53			23 22							
Aldermaston	d													22 58										
Midgham	d													23 02										
Thatcham	d						22 01							23 07			23 30							
Newbury Racecourse	d													23 11										
Newbury	a						22 08							23 15			23 37							
	d										22 15													
Kintbury	d										22 35													
Hungerford	d										22 45													
Bedwyn	a										23 00													
Tilehurst	d							21 50								22 54						23 55		
Pangbourne	d							21 55								22 59						23 59		
Goring & Streatley	d							22 00								23 03						00 05		
Cholsey	d							22 05								23 08						00 09		
Didcot Parkway	a		21 37			21 59		22 11				22 37			23 02	23 14		23s30	23 34		00s02	00 16	00s33	00 39
	d		21 38					22 12				22 39				23 15			23 35			00 16		00 40
Appleford	d																							
Culham	d																							
Radley	d							22 19								23 22						00 25		
Oxford	a	21 34	21 50					22 29		22 34		22 50				23 30			23 48			00 35		00 55
	d	21 36								22 36														
Islip	d																							
Bicester Town	a																							
Tackley	d																							
Heyford	d																							
Kings Sutton	d																							
Banbury	a	21 52								22 52														
Leamington Spa 8	a	22 10								23 10														
Warwick	a	22 34								23 25														
Warwick Parkway	a	22 38								23 29														
Stratford-upon-Avon	a																							
Coventry	a																							
Birmingham International	a																							
Birmingham New Street 12	a	22 51								23 43														

For general notes see front of timetable
For details of catering facilities see Directory of Train Operators

A To Weston-super-Mare (Table 134)
B To Worcester Shrub Hill (Table 126)

Due to Engineering Operations, services from Sunday 14 September on this Table had not been confirmed at time of going to press. These services will be issued in a special Supplement as soon as exact timings have been confirmed

Birmingham, Banbury, Bicester, Oxford and Bedwyn → Reading and London

Network Diagram - see first page of Table 116

Miles	Miles			GW	GW	GW	GW	GW	GW	GW	GW	GW	GW	GW	GW	GW	GW	GW	GW	GW	GW	GW		GW	GW
				MO	MO	MO	MX	MX																	
						[1]◇	[1]◇	[1]	[1]	[1]	[1]◇	[1]	[1]	[1]	[1]	[1]◇	[1]	[1]	[1]	[1]	[1]◇	[1]		[1]◇	[1]
				A	B																				
						🚲					☕					☕					☕			🚲	
0	—	**Birmingham New Street** [12]	d																						
8½	—	Birmingham International	d																						
19¼	—	Coventry	d																						
—	—	Stratford-upon-Avon	d																						
—	—	Warwick Parkway	d																						
—	—	Warwick	d																						
28¾	—	Leamington Spa [3]	d																						
48¾	—	**Banbury**	d					23p50																	
52½	—	Kings Sutton	d					23p55																	
59¾	—	Heyford	d					00 04																	
62½	—	Tackley	d					00 08																	
—	0	**Bicester Town**	d																						
—	6	Islip	d																						
71½	11¾	**Oxford**	a					00 18																	
—	—		d			00 01	00 05	00 20	04 00	05 06			05 50		06 02				06 07		06 30				
76¼	—	Radley	d					00 26		05 12			05 56						06 13						
78¾	—	Culham	d					00 30											06 17						
79¾	—	Appleford	d					00 33											06 20						
81¾	—	**Didcot Parkway**	a			00 12	00 19	00 38	04 12	05 19			06 03		06 14				06 25		06 42				
—	—		d			00 13	00 20	00 39	04 12	05 20	05 41		06 04	06 12	06 16	06 29			06 34	06 39	06 43			06 46	
86½	—	Cholsey	d					00 47	04 18	05 26				06 19			←		06 40	06 45		←			←
90¼	—	Goring & Streatley	d					00 52	04 23	05 31				06 25			06 25		06 45	06 50		06 45			06 50
93½	—	Pangbourne	d					00 56	04 28	05 35				→			06 30		→	→		06 49			06 55
96¼	—	Tilehurst	d					01 01	04 32	05 40							06 36					06 54			06 59
—	0	**Bedwyn**	d															06 03							
—	5	Hungerford	d															06 09							
—	8	Kintbury	d															06 13							
—	13½	**Newbury**	a															06 20							
—	—		d	23p45	23p47							05 40						06 25							
—	14	Newbury Racecourse	d	23p47	23p49							05 42													
—	17	Thatcham	d	23p51	23p53							05 46						06 30							
—	19¾	Midgham	d	23p56	23p58							05 51													
—	21¾	Aldermaston	d	23p59	00ʃ02							05 55													
—	25¾	Theale	d	00ʃ05	00ʃ07							06 00						06 38							
—	29¾	Reading West	d	00s12	00s14							06 07						06 46							
99	30½	**Reading** [7]	a	00ʃ17	00ʃ17	00 30	00 38	01 09	04 38	05 44	05 57	06 11	06 20		06 30	06 43	06 42	06 49			06 57	06 59		07 02	07 05
—	—		d			00 31	00 39	01 09	04 40	05 45	05 57		06 21		06 32	06 45	06 46	06 50			06 59	07 10 →		07 03	07 07
104	—	Twyford [3]	a			00 37		01 15	04 46	05 51			06 28				06 54								
110¾	—	Maidenhead [3]	a			00 44		01 23	04 54	05 58					06 42		07 03	07 01							07 18
116½	—	Slough [3]	a			00 52	00 56	01 31	05 02	06 10	06 11		06 39		06 50	06 58									
129½	—	Ealing Broadway	⊖ a			01 12		01 48	05 30	06 33															
135	—	**London Paddington** [15]	⊖ a			01 22	01 17	01 57	05 42	06 46	06 30		07 00		07 08	07 16	07 27	07 25			07 29			07 32	07 41

		GW	GW	GW	GW	GW	GW	GW	GW	GW	GW	GW	GW	GW	XC	GW	GW	GW	GW	GW		GW	GW	GW	GW
		[1]	[1]	[1]◇	[1]◇	[1]	[1]	[1]◇	[1]	[1]	[1]◇	[1]◇	[1]	[1]	[1]◇	[1]◇	[1]◇	[1]	[1]	[1]◇		[1]	[1]◇	[1]◇	[1]◇
																C									
				☕	☕			☕			⊠	☕			☕	☕	☕			⊠				☕	☕
Birmingham New Street [12]	d														06 03										
Birmingham International	d														06 15										
Coventry	d														06 25										
Stratford-upon-Avon	d																								
Warwick Parkway	d					*05 40*									*06 12*										
Warwick	d														*06 15*										
Leamington Spa [3]	d					*05 45*									06 38										
Banbury	d					06 08							06 31		06 55										
Kings Sutton	d					06 13							06 36												
Heyford	d					06 21							06 45												
Tackley	d					06 26							06 49												
Bicester Town	d						06 24																		
Islip	d						06 36																		
Oxford	a					06 36	06 50						07 00		07 14										
	d					06 37		06 58					07 02	07 10	07 15							07 22	07 30		
Radley	d					06 43							07 08									07 28			
Culham	d					06 47							07 12									07 32			
Appleford	d					06 50							07 15									07 35			
Didcot Parkway	a					06 55		07 10					07 22					←				07 40			
	d			07 00		07 02		07 11				07 20	07 30 →				07 30	07 30		07 44		07 48 →			07 54
Cholsey	d					07 08				←				07 26				07 36							
Goring & Streatley	d					07 13 →				07 13				07 32				07 41							
Pangbourne	d									07 17				07 38				07 45							
Tilehurst	d									07 22				07 43				07 50							
Bedwyn	d		06 23													06 50			07 08						
Hungerford	d		06 29		06 40											06 57			07 14					07 37	
Kintbury	d		06 33													07 04			07 18						
Newbury	a		06 40		06 48											07 10			07 25					07 45	
	d		06 40		06 48				06 56							07 10			07 25					07 45	
Newbury Racecourse	d		06 42						06 58										07 27						
Thatcham	d		06 47		06 57				07 03							07 19			07 32						
Midgham	d		06 51						07 07										07 36						
Aldermaston	d		06 55						07 11										07 40						
Theale	d		07 00		07 07				07 16							07 29			07 45						
Reading West	d		07 07						07 23							07 38			07 52						
Reading [7]	a	←	07 12	07 16	07 17			07 25	07 28	07 29		07 35			07 39	07 41	07 44	07 54	07 56	07 58			07 59	08 07	08 12
	d	07 10		07 18	07 21			07 27		07 30	07 31	07 37				07 42	07 46	07 56		08 00			08 03	08 08	08 14
Twyford [3]	a	07 16								07 36								08 02							
Maidenhead [3]	a	07 24								07 45				07 59				08 10							
Slough [3]	a	07 37								07 55								08 20							
Ealing Broadway	⊖ a	08 01								08 19															
London Paddington [15]	⊖ a	08 12		07 44	07 52			07 58		08 31	08 01	08 06		08 22		08 09	08 14	08 43		08 30			08 32	08 38	08 41

For general notes see front of timetable
For details of catering facilities see Directory of Train Operators

A From 15 September
B Until 8 September
C From Frome (Table 123)

Birmingham, Banbury, Bicester, Oxford and Bedwyn → Reading and London

Network Diagram - see first page of Table 116

		XC	GW	GW	GW	GW	GW	GW	GW	GW	GW	XC	GW	GW	GW	GW	GW	GW	GW	GW	GW	XC	GW	GW
		1◇	1◇	1	1◇	1	1	1	1◇	1◇	1◇	1◇	1◇	1	1◇	1	1	1◇	1	1◇	1	1◇	1◇	1◇
			A										A B					C					D	
		☕	☕		⊠				☕	☕		☕	⊠		☕			✕		☕		☕	⊠	⊠
Birmingham New Street 12	d	06 33										07 03										07 33		
Birmingham International	d											07 15												
Coventry	d											07 25												
Stratford-upon-Avon	d	*06 10*										*06 46*												
Warwick Parkway	d	*06 44*										*07 21*										*07 43*		
Warwick	d	*06 38*										*07 13*										*07 46*		
Leamington Spa 8	d	07 00										07 38										08 00		
Banbury	d	07 19						07 28				07 55										08 19		
Kings Sutton	d							07 33																
Heyford	d							07 42																
Tackley	d							07 46																
Bicester Town	d																07 57							
Islip	d																08 09							
Oxford	a	07 41						07 56				08 14					08 23					08 41		
	d	07 42			07 52			07 57			08 07	08 15				08 21						08 42	08 49	
Radley	d							08 04								08 27								
Culham	d							08 08																
Appleford	d							08 10																
Didcot Parkway	a			←				08 15			08 19			←		08 37								
	d		08 00	07 48				08 17		08 17	08 20		08 30	08 17		08 37		08 47		08 53				09 02
Cholsey	d			07 54				→						08 23		08 43			←					
Goring & Streatley	d			07 59										08 29		08 48 →			08 48					
Pangbourne	d			08 03										08 34					08 53					
Tilehurst	d			08 08										08 39					08 57					
Bedwyn	d						07 57																	
Hungerford	d						08 03																	
Kintbury	d						08 07																	
Newbury	a						08 15																	
	d					07 57									08 30						08 37			
Newbury Racecourse	d					07 59															08 39			
Thatcham	d					08 03															08 43			
Midgham	d					08 08															08 48			
Aldermaston	d					08 12															08 52			
Theale	d					08 17															08 57			
Reading West	d					08 23															09 04			
Reading 7	a	08 13	08 15	08 17	08 22	08 27				08 33	08 36	08 39	08 44	08 44	08 51			09 01	09 03	09 06	09 08	09 13	09 14	09 16
	d		08 17	08 19	08 24				08 34	08 35	08 38		08 45	08 48	08 52			09 02	09 04	09 09			09 15	09 18
Twyford 3	a			08 25										08 54					09 10					
Maidenhead 3	a			08 33										09 02					09 18					
Slough 3	a																		09 25					
Ealing Broadway	⊖ a																		09 49					
London Paddington 15	⊖ a		08 44	08 59	08 51				09 00	09 06	09 09		09 14	09 28	09 22			09 29	10 02	09 36			09 41	09 44

		GW	GW	GW	GW	GW	XC	GW	GW	GW	GW	GW	GW	GW	GW	XC	GW	GW	GW	GW	GW	GW	XC	GW
		1	1◇	1	1◇	1◇	1◇	1◇	1	1◇	1	1	1◇	1◇	1◇	1◇	1	1	1◇	1	1◇	1	R 1	1◇
					E																			
			☕		✕		☕	☕		☕				☕	☕	☕			☕		⊠		☕	☕
Birmingham New Street 12	d						08 03									08 33							09 03	
Birmingham International	d						08 15																09 15	
Coventry	d						08 25																09 25	
Stratford-upon-Avon	d						*07 36*																	
Warwick Parkway	d						*08 19*									*08 41*							*09 21*	
Warwick	d						*08 23*									*08 44*							*09 24*	
Leamington Spa 8	d						08 38									09 00							09 38	
Banbury	d						08 55									09 19				09 38			09 55	
Kings Sutton	d																			09 43				
Heyford	d																			09 52				
Tackley	d																			09 56				
Bicester Town	d											09 07												
Islip	d											09 19												
Oxford	a						09 14					09 33				09 41				10 07			10 14	
	d			08 55		09 06	09 15				09 20		09 38			09 42		09 55	10 01				10 15	
Radley	d										09 26													
Culham	d										09 30													
Appleford	d			09 03																				
Didcot Parkway	a			09 07		09 18					09 35							10 07						
	d			09 07		09 19		09 29			09 37			09 53				10 07			10 17			10 29
Cholsey	d			09 13							09 43							10 13				←		
Goring & Streatley	d			09 18							09 48							10 18 →				10 18		
Pangbourne	d			09 22							09 52											10 22		
Tilehurst	d			09 27							09 57											10 27		
Bedwyn	d	08 40															09 37							
Hungerford	d	08 46															09 43							
Kintbury	d	08 50															09 47							
Newbury	a	08 57															09 54							
	d	08 57							09 23								09 54							
Newbury Racecourse	d								09 26															
Thatcham	d	09 02							09 30								09 59							
Midgham	d								09 35															
Aldermaston	d								09 39															
Theale	d	09 10							09 44								10 07							
Reading West	d								09 51															
Reading 7	a	09 20		09 33		09 35	09 39	09 44	09 55		10 02		10 03	10 09		10 13	10 16		10 24		10 32	10 32	10 39	10 44
	d	09 22	09 28	09 34	09 35	09 38		09 45		09 58	10 04		10 04	10 10	10 11		10 18		10 25		10 33	10 34		10 45
Twyford 3	a			09 40							10 10											10 40		
Maidenhead 3	a			09 48							10 18											10 48		
Slough 3	a			09 55		09 51					10 25		10 17						10 38			10 55		
Ealing Broadway	⊖ a			10 19							10 49											11 19		
London Paddington 15	⊖ a	09 57	09 59	10 32	10 03	10 10		10 14		10 27	11 02		10 36	10 39	10 44		10 54		10 59		11 02	11 32		11 15

For general notes see front of timetable
For details of catering facilities see Directory of Train Operators

A From Weston-super-Mare (Table 134)
B **The Bristolian**
C **The Red Dragon**
D **Cathedrals Express**
E **The Golden Hind**

Birmingham, Banbury, Bicester, Oxford and Bedwyn → Reading and London

Network Diagram - see first page of Table 116

		GW	GW	GW	GW	GW	GW	XC	GW	GW	GW	GW	GW	GW		XC	GW	GW	GW	GW	GW	GW	GW	GW	GW
																R									
		1	1	1◊	1◊	1◊	1	1◊	1◊	1	1	1◊	1◊	1		1	1◊	1	1	1◊	1◊	1◊	1	1◊	1◊
				⊠		⊠		☕	☕				☕			☕	☕			⊠		☕		☕	☕
Birmingham New Street 12	d							09 33								10 03									
Birmingham International	d															10 15									
Coventry	d															10 25									
Stratford-upon-Avon	d															*09 41*									
Warwick Parkway	d							09b45								*10 22*									
Warwick	d							09b49								*10 25*									
Leamington Spa 8	d							10 00								10 38									
Banbury	d							10 19								10 55									
Kings Sutton	d																								
Heyford	d																								
Tackley	d																								
Bicester Town	d																								
Islip	d																								
Oxford	a							10 41								11 14									
	d		10 21		10 31			10 42			10 55	11 01				11 15			11 21		11 31				
Radley	d		10 27																11 27						
Culham	d																		11 31						
Appleford	d		10 32																						
Didcot Parkway	a		10 36								11 06								11 36						
	d		10 37			10 47	←				11 07		11 17				11 29		11 37			11 47	←	11 53	
Cholsey	d		10 43 →				10 43				11 13			←					11 43 →				11 43		
Goring & Streatley	d						10 48				11 18 →			11 18									11 48		
Pangbourne	d						10 52							11 22									11 52		
Tilehurst	d						10 57							11 27									11 57		
Bedwyn	d									10 37															
Hungerford	d									10 43															
Kintbury	d									10 47															
Newbury	a									10 54															
	d	10 13								10 54								11 13							
Newbury Racecourse	d	10 15																11 15							
Thatcham	d	10 19								10 59								11 19							
Midgham	d	10 24																11 24							
Aldermaston	d	10 28																11 28							
Theale	d	10 33								11 07								11 33							
Reading West	d	10 40																11 40							
Reading 7	a	10 45			10 55	11 01	11 02	11 09		11 17		11 25	11 32	11 32		11 39	11 44	11 45			11 55	12 01	12 02	12 07	
	d			10 52	10 56	11 03	11 04		11 11	11 18		11 26	11 33	11 34			11 45			11 52	11 56	12 03	12 04	12 09	12 11
Twyford 3	a						11 10							11 40									12 10		
Maidenhead 3	a						11 18							11 48									12 18		
Slough 3	a				11 09		11 25							11 55							12 09		12 25		
Ealing Broadway	⊖ a						11 49							12 19									12 49		
London Paddington 15	⊖ a			11 23	11 27	11 30	12 02		11 42	11 54		11 58	12 01	12 32			12 16			12 23	12 29	12 32	13 02	12 39	12 42

		XC	GW	GW	GW	GW	GW	XC	GW	GW	GW	GW		GW	GW	GW	XC	GW	GW	GW	GW	GW	GW	XC	GW
								R																R	
		1◊	1	1	1◊	1◊	1	1	1◊	1	1	1◊		1◊	1	1◊	1◊	1	1	1◊	1	1◊	1	1	1◊
																		A							
		☕				☕		☕	☕					☕		☕	☕	☕		☕		☕		☕	🛒
Birmingham New Street 12	d	10 33						11 03									11 33							12 03	
Birmingham International	d							11 15																12 15	
Coventry	d							11 25																12 25	
Stratford-upon-Avon	d																				*11 40*				
Warwick Parkway	d	10b45						*11 21*									*11 41*				*11 41*			*12 21*	
Warwick	d	10b49						*11 24*									*11 45*				*12 05*			*12 24*	
Leamington Spa 8	d	11 00						11 38									12 00				*12 08*			12 38	
Banbury	d	11 19						11 55									12 19				12 38			12 55	
Kings Sutton	d																				12 43				
Heyford	d																				12 52				
Tackley	d																				12 56				
Bicester Town	d																								
Islip	d																								
Oxford	a	11 41						12 14									12 41				13 07			13 14	
	d	11 42		11 55	12 01			12 15			12 21	12 31					12 42		12 55	13 01				13 15	
Radley	d										12 27														
Culham	d																								
Appleford	d										12 32														
Didcot Parkway	a			12 06							12 36								13 06						
	d			12 07		12 17			12 29		12 37			12 47	←				13 07			13 17			13 29
Cholsey	d			12 13			←				12 43 →				12 43				13 13				←		
Goring & Streatley	d			12 18 →			12 18								12 48				13 18 →				13 18		
Pangbourne	d						12 22								12 52								13 22		
Tilehurst	d						12 27								12 57								13 27		
Bedwyn	d		11 37																						
Hungerford	d		11 43																						
Kintbury	d		11 47																						
Newbury	a		11 54																						
	d		11 54							12 13															
Newbury Racecourse	d									12 15															
Thatcham	d		11 59							12 19															
Midgham	d									12 24															
Aldermaston	d									12 28															
Theale	d		12 07							12 33															
Reading West	d									12 40															
Reading 7	a	12 13	12 16		12 25	12 32	12 32	12 39	12 44	12 45		12 55		13 01	13 02		13 13			13 25		13 32	13 32	13 39	13 44
	d		12 18		12 27	12 33	12 34		12 45			12 56		13 03	13 04	13 11		13 18		13 27		13 33	13 34		13 45
Twyford 3	a						12 40								13 10								13 40		
Maidenhead 3	a						12 48								13 18								13 48		
Slough 3	a				12 40		12 55					13 09			13 25					13 40			13 55		
Ealing Broadway	⊖ a						13 19								13 49								14 19		
London Paddington 15	⊖ a		12 54		12 59	13 02	13 32		13 15			13 27		13 30	14 02	13 42		13 44		13 59		14 02	14 32		14 15

For general notes see front of timetable
For details of catering facilities see
Directory of Train Operators

A Cornish Riviera
b Change at Banbury

Birmingham, Banbury, Bicester, Oxford and Bedwyn → Reading and London

Network Diagram - see first page of Table 116

		GW	GW	GW	GW	GW	GW	GW	GW	XC		GW	GW	GW	GW	GW	XC	GW	GW	GW	GW	GW	GW	GW	GW
																	R								
		1	1	1	1◇	1◇	1	1◇	1◇	1◇		1◇	1	1◇	1◇	1	1	1◇	1	1	1	1◇	1	1◇	1
						A																			
						⊠		☕	🛒	☕		☕		☕	☕		☕	🛒			✕			☕	
Birmingham New Street 12	d									12 33							13 03								
Birmingham International	d																13 15								
Coventry	d																13 25								
Stratford-upon-Avon	d																								
Warwick Parkway	d									12b46							13 21								
Warwick	d									12b49							13 24								
Leamington Spa 8	d									13 00							13 38								
Banbury	d									13 19							13 55								
Kings Sutton	d																								
Heyford	d																								
Tackley	d																								
Bicester Town	d																						14 00		
Islip	d																						14 12		
Oxford	a									13 41							14 14						14 32		
	d			13 21	13 31					13 42			13 55	14 01			14 15			14 21		14 31			
Radley	d			13 27																14 27					
Culham	d			13 31																					
Appleford	d																			14 32					
Didcot Parkway	a			13 36									14 06							14 36					
	d			13 37		13 47	←	13 53					14 07		14 17			14 29		14 37				14 47	←
Cholsey	d			13 43			13 43						14 13			←				14 43					14 43
Goring & Streatley	d			→			13 48						14 18			14 18				→					14 48
Pangbourne	d						13 52						→			14 22									14 52
Tilehurst	d						13 57									14 27									14 57
Bedwyn	d		13 12									13 32													
Hungerford	d		13 18									13 39													
Kintbury	d		13 22																						
Newbury	a		13 29									13 47													
	d	13 13	13 29									13 47							14 13						
Newbury Racecourse	d	13 15																	14 15						
Thatcham	d	13 19	13 34									13 56							14 19						
Midgham	d	13 24																	14 24						
Aldermaston	d	13 28																	14 28						
Theale	d	13 33	13 42									14 05							14 33						
Reading West	d	13 40																	14 40						
Reading 7	a	13 45	13 51		13 55	14 01	14 02	14 07		14 13		14 17		14 25	14 32	14 32	14 39	14 44	14 45			14 55		15 01	15 03
	d		13 52		13 55	14 03	14 04	14 09	14 11			14 18		14 27	14 33	14 34		14 45			14 52	14 56		15 03	15 04
Twyford 3	a						14 10									14 40									15 10
Maidenhead 3	a						14 18									14 48									15 18
Slough 3	a				14 09		14 25							14 40		14 55						15 09			15 25
Ealing Broadway	⊖ a						14 49									15 19									15 49
London Paddington 15	⊖ a		14 25		14 29	14 32	15 02	14 39	14 42			14 44		14 59	15 02	15 32		15 15			15 21	15 27		15 30	16 02

		GW	XC	GW	GW	GW	GW	GW		XC	GW	GW	GW	GW	GW	GW	GW	GW	GW	XC	GW	GW	GW	GW	GW
										R															
		1◇	1◇	1	1	1◇	1◇	1		1	1◇	1	1	1◇	1◇	1	1◇	1	1◇	1◇	1◇	1	1	1◇	1◇
																			B						
		🛒	☕				☕			☕	☕			⊠			☕		☕	☕	☕			☕	☕
Birmingham New Street 12	d		13 33							14 03										14 33					
Birmingham International	d									14 15															
Coventry	d									14 25															
Stratford-upon-Avon	d									13 39						13 39									
Warwick Parkway	d		13 41							14 21						14 21				14b46					
Warwick	d		13 45							14 24						14 24				14b49					
Leamington Spa 8	d		14 00							14 38						14 38				15 00					
Banbury	d		14 19							14 55						15 05				15 19					
Kings Sutton	d															15 10									
Heyford	d															15 18									
Tackley	d															15 23									
Bicester Town	d																								
Islip	d																								
Oxford	a		14 41							15 14						15 34				15 41					
	d		14 42		14 55	15 01				15 15			15 21		15 31					15 42			15 55	16 01	
Radley	d												15 27												
Culham	d												15 31												
Appleford	d																								
Didcot Parkway	a				15 06								15 36										16 06		
	d				15 07		15 17				15 29		15 37				15 47	←	15 53				16 07		16 17
Cholsey	d				15 13			←					15 43					15 43					16 13		
Goring & Streatley	d				15 18			15 18					→					15 48					16 18		
Pangbourne	d				→			15 22										15 52					→		
Tilehurst	d							15 27										15 57							
Bedwyn	d			14 37																		15 37			
Hungerford	d			14 43																		15 43			
Kintbury	d			14 47																		15 47			
Newbury	a			14 54																		15 54			
	d			14 54								15 13										15 54			
Newbury Racecourse	d											15 15													
Thatcham	d			14 59								15 19										15 59			
Midgham	d											15 24													
Aldermaston	d											15 28													
Theale	d			15 07								15 33										16 07			
Reading West	d											15 40													
Reading 7	a		15 13	15 16		15 25	15 32	15 32		15 39	15 44	15 45			15 55		16 01	16 02	16 07	16 11		16 17		16 25	16 32
	d	15 11		15 18		15 27	15 33	15 34			15 45			15 52	15 56		16 03	16 04	16 09		16 14	16 18		16 27	16 33
Twyford 3	a							15 40										16 10							
Maidenhead 3	a							15 48										16 18							
Slough 3	a					15 40		15 55							16 09			16 25						16 40	
Ealing Broadway	⊖ a							16 19										16 49							
London Paddington 15	⊖ a	15 42		15 54		15 59	16 02	16 32			16 16			16 22	16 27		16 30	17 02	16 39		16 44	16 54		16 59	17 02

For general notes see front of timetable
For details of catering facilities see Directory of Train Operators

A **The St David**
B **Cheltenham Spa Express**
b Change at Banbury

Table 116

Mondays to Fridays

Birmingham, Banbury, Bicester, Oxford and Bedwyn → Reading and London

Network Diagram - see first page of Table 116

		GW	XC	GW	GW	GW		GW	GW	GW	GW	GW	XC	GW	GW	GW	GW	GW	GW	GW	XC	GW	GW	GW	GW
																					R				
		1	1◇	1◇	1	1		1◇	1◇	1◇	1	1◇	1◇	1◇	1	1	1◇	1◇	1◇	1	1	1◇	1	1◇	1◇
																	A	B						C	
			☕	☕				☕		☕		☕	☕	🛒					☕		☕	☕		✕	☕
Birmingham New Street 12	d		15 03										15 33								16 03				
Birmingham International	d		15 15																		16 15				
Coventry	d		15 25																		16 25				
Stratford-upon-Avon	d																				15 41				
Warwick Parkway	d		15 21										15 41								16 21				
Warwick	d		15 24										15 44								16 24				
Leamington Spa 8	d		15 38										16 00								16 38				
Banbury	d		15 55										16 19								16 55				
Kings Sutton	d																								
Heyford	d																								
Tackley	d																								
Bicester Town	d																								
Islip	d																								
Oxford	a		16 14										16 41								17 14				
	d		16 15			16 21			16 31				16 42			16 53	17 01	17 01			17 15				
Radley	d					16 27										16 59									
Culham	d																								
Appleford	d					16 32																			
Didcot Parkway	a					16 36										17 06									
	d			16 29		16 37				16 47	←					17 07			17 17	←		17 29			
Cholsey	d	←				16 43 →					16 43					17 13 →				17 13					
Goring & Streatley	d	16 18									16 48									17 18					
Pangbourne	d	16 22									16 52									17 22					
Tilehurst	d	16 27									16 57									17 27					
Bedwyn	d														16 44										
Hungerford	d													16 41	16 50										
Kintbury	d														16 54										
Newbury	a													16 50	17 02										
	d				16 13									16 51									17 16		
Newbury Racecourse	d				16 15																		17 18		
Thatcham	d				16 19									16 57									17 22		
Midgham	d				16 24																		17 27		
Aldermaston	d				16 28																		17 31		
Theale	d				16 33									17 06									17 36		
Reading West	d				16 40																		17 42		
Reading 7	a	16 32	16 39	16 44	16 45				16 55	17 01	17 02		17 13	17 17			17 25	17 25	17 32	17 32	17 39	17 44	17 45		
	d	16 34		16 45				16 52	16 56	17 03	17 04	17 11		17 18			17 27	17 27	17 33	17 34		17 45		17 52	17 58
Twyford 3	a	16 40									17 10									17 40					
Maidenhead 3	a	16 48									17 18									17 48					
Slough 3	a	16 55							17 09		17 25			17 31			17 40			17 55					
Ealing Broadway	⊖ a	17 19									17 49									18 19					
London Paddington 15	⊖ a	17 32		17 15				17 24	17 27	17 30	18 02	17 41		17 53			17 58	17 58	18 02	18 32		18 15		18 21	18 27

		GW	GW	GW		GW	XC	GW	GW	GW	GW	GW	GW	GW	XC	GW	GW	GW	GW	GW	GW	GW	GW	XC	GW
							R								R									R	
		1	1	1◇		1◇	1	1	1	1◇	1	1◇	1◇	1	1	1◇	1	1	1◇	1◇	1◇	1	1◇	1	1
				☕		☕	☕			☕			☕		☕	☕			☕		☕		☕	☕	
Birmingham New Street 12	d						16 33								17 03									17 33	
Birmingham International	d														17 15										
Coventry	d														17 25										
Stratford-upon-Avon	d																								
Warwick Parkway	d						16b45		16 45						17 20									17b45	
Warwick	d						16b49		16 49						17 23									17b48	
Leamington Spa 8	d						17 00		16 54						17 38									18 00	
Banbury	d						17 19		17 22						17 55									18 19	
Kings Sutton	d								17 27																
Heyford	d								17 36																
Tackley	d								17 40																
Bicester Town	d		16 56																						18 26
Islip	d		17 08																						18 38
Oxford	a		17 22				17 41		17 51						18 14									18 41	18 52
	d	17 21		17 38			17 42	17 49				18 01			18 15			18 21		18 31				18 42	
Radley	d	17 27						17 55										18 27							
Culham	d	17 31																18 31							
Appleford	d							18 00																	
Didcot Parkway	a	17 36						18 04										18 36							
	d	17 37				17 53		18 07					18 17	←		18 29		18 37			18 47	←			
Cholsey	d	17 43						18 13 →						18 13				18 43 →				18 43			
Goring & Streatley	d	17 48												18 18								18 48			
Pangbourne	d	17 52												18 22								18 52			
Tilehurst	d	17 57												18 27								18 57			
Bedwyn	d										17 37						17 56								
Hungerford	d										17 43						18 02								
Kintbury	d										17 47						18 06								
Newbury	a										17 54						18 13								
	d										17 54						18 13								
Newbury Racecourse	d																18 15								
Thatcham	d										17 59						18 19								
Midgham	d																18 24								
Aldermaston	d										18 04						18 28								
Theale	d										18 09						18 33								
Reading West	d																18 40								
Reading 7	a	18 02		18 03		18 07	18 11				18 22	18 25	18 32	18 32	18 39	18 44	18 45			18 55	19 01	19 02		19 13	
	d	18 04		18 04		18 09				18 15	18 22	18 27	18 33	18 34		18 46			18 52	18 56	19 03	19 04	19 11		
Twyford 3	a	18 10												18 40								19 10			
Maidenhead 3	a	18 18												18 48								19 18			
Slough 3	a	18 25										18 40		18 55						19 09		19 25			
Ealing Broadway	⊖ a	18 49												19 19								19 49			
London Paddington 15	⊖ a	19 02		18 30		18 39				18 44	18 54	18 59	19 02	19 32		19 15			19 24	19 29	19 32	20 02	19 42		

For general notes see front of timetable
For details of catering facilities see Directory of Train Operators

A Until 27 June and from 8 September
B 30 June to 5 September
C **The Mayflower**
b Change at Banbury

Birmingham, Banbury, Bicester, Oxford and Bedwyn → Reading and London

Network Diagram - see first page of Table 116

		GW		GW	GW	GW	GW	GW	XC	GW	GW	GW	GW	GW	GW	XC	GW	GW	GW	GW	GW	GW		XC	GW
									R							R								R	
		1		1	1 ◇	1	1 ◇	1	1	1 ◇	1	1 ◇	1 ◇	1	1 ◇	1	1 ◇	1	1	1 ◇	1	1 ◇		1	1
																						A			
					🍴		🍴		🍴	🍴			🍴		🍴		🍴					🍴		🍴	
Birmingham New Street 12	d								18 03							18 33								19 03	
Birmingham International	d								18 15															19 15	
Coventry	d								18 25															19 25	
Stratford-upon-Avon	d								*17 42*																
Warwick Parkway	d								*18 23*							*18b45*								*18 45*	
Warwick	d								*18 26*							*18b49*								*18 49*	
Leamington Spa 8	d								18 38							19 00								19 38	
Banbury	d								18 55			19 01				19 19								19 55	
Kings Sutton	d											19 06													
Heyford	d											19 15													
Tackley	d											19 19													
Bicester Town	d																								
Islip	d																								
Oxford	a								19 14			19 28				19 41								20 14	
	d			18 55	19 01				19 15		19 21	19 30				19 42			19 55	20 01				20 15	
Radley	d										19 27														
Culham	d																								
Appleford	d										19 32														
Didcot Parkway	a			19 06							19 36								20 06						
	d			19 07			19 17			19 29	19 37		19 47	←			19 53		20 07						
Cholsey	d			19 13				←			19 43			19 43					20 13		←				
Goring & Streatley	d			19 18				19 18			→			19 48					20 18		20 18				
Pangbourne	d			→				19 22						19 52					→		20 22				
Tilehurst	d							19 27						19 57							20 27				
Bedwyn	d					19 03																19 45			19 56
Hungerford	d					19 09																19 52			20 02
Kintbury	d					19 13																19 58			20 06
Newbury	a					19 21																20 04			20 13
	d	18 54													19 45			19 51				20 04			20 13
Newbury Racecourse	d																	19 53							20 15
Thatcham	d	18 59																19 57				20 12			20 19
Midgham	d																	20 02							20 24
Aldermaston	d																	20 06							20 28
Theale	d	19 07																20 11				20 21			20 33
Reading West	d																	20 18							20 40
Reading 7	a	19 16			19 26		19 32	19 32	19 39	19 45		19 54	20 01	20 02	20 07	20 09	20 12	20 22		20 25	20 32	20 33		20 39	20 44
	d	19 18			19 27		19 33	19 34		19 46		19 54	20 03	20 04	20 10		20 14			20 26	20 34	20 35			
Twyford 3	a							19 40						20 10							20 40				
Maidenhead 3	a							19 48						20 18							20 48				
Slough 3	a				19 40			19 55				20 09		20 25							20 55				
Ealing Broadway	⊖ a							20 19						20 49							21 19				
London Paddington 15	⊖ a	19 52			19 59		20 02	20 32		20 15		20 29	20 31	21 02	20 39		20 44			20 57	21 32	21 02			

		GW	GW	GW	GW	GW	GW	GW	XC	GW	GW	GW	GW	GW	XC	GW	GW	GW	GW	GW		GW	GW	GW	GW
																				FO		FX	FO	FX	
															R										
		1	1 ◇	1	1 ◇	1 ◇	1	1 ◇	1 ◇	1	1	1 ◇	1 ◇	1	1	1 ◇	1	1 ◇	1	1 ◇		1 ◇	1 ◇	1 ◇	1
												B	C												
			🍴		⊠	🍴		🍴	🍴							🍴		🍴					🍴	🍴	
Birmingham New Street 12	d								19 33						20 03										
Birmingham International	d														20 15										
Coventry	d														20 25										
Stratford-upon-Avon	d														*19 43*										
Warwick Parkway	d														*20 06*										
Warwick	d														*20 09*										
Leamington Spa 8	d								20 00						20 38										
Banbury	d						20 05		20 19						20 55										
Kings Sutton	d						20 10																		
Heyford	d						20 19																		
Tackley	d						20 23																		
Bicester Town	d	19 51																							
Islip	d	20 03																							
Oxford	a	20 17					20 34		20 41						21 14										
	d			20 21		20 31			20 42		20 53	21 01	21 01		21 15				21 20	21 38		21 38			21 53
Radley	d			20 27															21 26						21 59
Culham	d			20 31															21 30						
Appleford	d										21 01														
Didcot Parkway	a			20 37							21 06								21 36						22 06
	d		20 29	20 37				20 47		←	21 07			←		21 29			21 37				21 51	21 51	22 07
Cholsey	d			20 43						20 43	21 13			21 13					21 43						22 13
Goring & Streatley	d			→						20 48	→			21 18					21 48						22 18
Pangbourne	d									20 52				21 23					21 53						22 23
Tilehurst	d									20 57				21 27					21 57						22 27
Bedwyn	d																21 06								
Hungerford	d																21 12								
Kintbury	d																21 16								
Newbury	a																21 23								
	d																21 23	21 41							
Newbury Racecourse	d																21 25								
Thatcham	d																21 29								
Midgham	d																21 34								
Aldermaston	d																21 38								
Theale	d																21 43								
Reading West	d																21 50								
Reading 7	a		20 44			20 55		21 02	21 06	21 05		21 25	21 25	21 32	21 39	21 44	21 54	22 00	22 03	22 10		22 10	22 15	22 15	22 34
	d		20 45		20 52	20 56		21 04				21 27	21 27	21 34		21 46		22 00		22 11		22 11	22 17	22 17	22 50 →
Twyford 3	a													21 40											
Maidenhead 3	a													21 47											
Slough 3	a					21 09						21 40	21 41	21 59						22 26		22 26			
Ealing Broadway	⊖ a													22 20											
London Paddington 15	⊖ a		21 15		21 21	21 29		21 32				21 59	22 01	22 32		22 15		22 30		22 45		22 52	22 53	22 56	

For general notes see front of timetable
For details of catering facilities see Directory of Train Operators

A From Westbury (Table 135)
B Until 27 June and from 8 September
C 30 June to 5 September
b Change at Banbury

Table 116

Birmingham, Banbury, Bicester, Oxford and Bedwyn → Reading and London

Network Diagram - see first page of Table 116

		GW	XC	GW	GW FO	GW FX	GW	GW FO	GW FX	GW FO	GW FX	GW FO	GW FX	GW	GW	GW	GW	GW		GW FO	GW FX	CH	GW	
		1	1 ◇	1	1 ◇	1 ◇	1	1 ◇	1 ◇	1 ◇	1 ◇	1 ◇	1 ◇	1	1	1 ◇	1	1		1 ◇	1 ◇		1	
																				A	A			
					✕	ꝑ		ꝑ	ꝑ			ꝑ	ꝑ							✕	✕			
Birmingham New Street 12	d		21 03																					
Birmingham International	d		21 15																					
Coventry	d		21 25																					
Stratford-upon-Avon	d	*20b00*																				23 00		
Warwick Parkway	d	*20 47*												*21 47*								22c53		
Warwick	d	*20 50*												*21 50*								23 21		
Leamington Spa 3	d	*20 54*	21 38											*21 55*								23 25		
Banbury	d	21 40	21 55											22 19								23 44	23 50	
Kings Sutton	d	21 45												22 24									23 55	
Heyford	d	21 54												22 33									00 04	
Tackley	d	21 58												22 37									00 08	
Bicester Town	d																							
Islip	d																							
Oxford	a	22 09	22 14											22 48								00 18	00 18	
	d		22 15		22 21	22 21				22 34	22 34				22 55	23 05							00 20	
Radley	d														23 01								00 26	
Culham	d														23 05								00 30	
Appleford	d														23 08								00 33	
Didcot Parkway	a									22 46	22 46				23 13	23 17	←						00 38	
	d									22 47	22 47	22 47	22 47		23 21 →	23 18	23 21			23 32	23 32		00 39	
Cholsey	d																23 27						00 47	
Goring & Streatley	d																23 32						00 52	
Pangbourne	d																23 36						00 56	
Tilehurst	d																23 41						01 01	
Bedwyn	d			21 54														23 00						
Hungerford	d			22 00														23 06						
Kintbury	d			22 04														23 10						
Newbury	a			22 11														23 17						
	d			22 11														23 17						
Newbury Racecourse	d			22 13														23 19						
Thatcham	d			22 18														23 23						
Midgham	d			22 22														23 28						
Aldermaston	d			22 26														23 32						
Theale	d			22 31														23 37						
Reading West	d			22 38														23 44						
Reading 7	a		22 39	22 42	22 46	22 46	←			23 02	23 02	23 06	23 06			23 33	23 48	23 49		23 55	23 55		01 09	
	d				22 48	22 48	22 50	22 55	22 55	23 04	23 04	23 07	23 07			23 35				23 56	23 56		01 09	
Twyford 3	a						22 56																01 15	
Maidenhead 3	a						23 04																01 23	
Slough 3	a				23 01	23 02	23 17			23 17	23 21					23 52							01 31	
Ealing Broadway	⊖ a						23 50																01 48	
London Paddington 15	⊖ a				23 22	23 25	23 59	23 29	23 36	23 36	23 41	23 42	23 50			00 22				00 25	00 32		01 57	

For general notes see front of timetable
For details of catering facilities see Directory of Train Operators

A From Taunton (Table 134)
b Change at Warwick and Banbury
c Change at Leamington Spa

Table 116

Saturdays

until 6 September

Birmingham, Banbury, Bicester, Oxford and Bedwyn → Reading and London

Network Diagram - see first page of Table 116

		GW	GW	GW	GW	GW	GW	GW	GW	GW	GW	GW	GW	GW	GW	GW	GW	XC	GW	GW	GW	GW	GW	GW	GW
		1◇ 🛏	1	1	1	1	1◇ ☕	1	1	1◇	1	1◇ ☕	1	1	1◇	1◇ ☕	1	1◇ ☕	1	1◇ ☕	1	1	1◇ ☕	1	1◇
Birmingham New Street 12	d																	06 03							
Birmingham International	d																	06 15							
Coventry	d																	06 25							
Stratford-upon-Avon	d																								
Warwick Parkway	d																								
Warwick	d																								
Leamington Spa 8	d																	06 38							
Banbury	d		23p50															06 55				07 02			
Kings Sutton	d		23p55																			07 07			
Heyford	d		00 04																			07 16			
Tackley	d		00 08																			07 20			
Bicester Town	d																								
Islip	d																								
Oxford	a		00 18															07 14				07 30			
	d	00 05	00 20	04 00	05 21	05 55			06 20	06 30				06 55	07 00			07 15			07 21				07 37
Radley	d		00 26		05 27				06 26												07 27				
Culham	d		00 30		05 31																07 31				
Appleford	d		00 33						06 31																
Didcot Parkway	a	00 19	00 38	04 11	05 37	06 06			06 35					07 06							07 37				
	d	00 20	00 39	04 12	05 38	06 08	06 29		06 36		←	06 59		07 08		07 17				07 30	07 38		07 47	←	
Cholsey	d		00 47		05 44	06 14			06 42		06 42			07 14			←				07 44				
Goring & Streatley	d		00 52		05 49	06 19			→		06 47			07 19			07 19				07 49			07 49	
Pangbourne	d		00 56		05 53	06 24					06 52			→			07 23				→			07 53	
Tilehurst	d		01 01		05 58	06 28					06 56						07 28							07 58	
Bedwyn	d							06 07					06 37												
Hungerford	d							06 13					06 43												
Kintbury	d							06 17					06 47												
Newbury	a							06 24					06 54												
	d							06 24					06 54						07 13						
Newbury Racecourse	d							06 26											07 15						
Thatcham	d							06 30					06 59						07 19						
Midgham	d							06 35											07 24						
Aldermaston	d							06 39											07 28						
Theale	d							06 44					07 07						07 33						
Reading West	d																		07 40						
Reading 7	a	00 38	01 09	04 29	06 03	06 34	06 43	06 52		06 57	07 02	07 14	07 20		07 25	07 32	07 34	07 44	07 44	07 44			08 02	08 03	08 08
	d	00 39	01 09	04 40	06 04	06 34	06 45	06 52		06 58	07 03	07 15	07 21		07 27	07 33	07 34			07 46			08 03	08 04	08 09
Twyford 3	a		01 15	04 46	06 10	06 40					07 09						07 40							08 10	
Maidenhead 3	a		01 23	04 54	06 18	06 48					07 17						07 48							08 18	
Slough 3	a	00 52	01 31	05 01	06 25	06 56				07 11	07 24				07 40		07 56							08 25	
Ealing Broadway	⊖ a		01 48	05 19	06 49	07 19					07 48						08 19							08 49	
London Paddington 15	⊖ a	01 10	01 57	05 30	06 58	07 29	07 14	07 25		07 29	07 58	07 45	07 53		07 58	08 00	08 28			08 14			08 30	08 59	08 40

For general notes see front of timetable
For details of catering facilities see Directory of Train Operators

Due to Engineering Operations, services from Saturday 13 September on this Table had not been confirmed at time of going to press. These services will be issued in a special Supplement as soon as exact timings have been confirmed

Table 116

Saturdays

until 6 September

Birmingham, Banbury, Bicester, Oxford and Bedwyn → Reading and London

Network Diagram - see first page of Table 116

		GW		GW	GW	GW	GW	GW	GW	XC	GW	GW	GW	GW	GW	GW	GW	GW	XC	GW	GW	GW	GW	GW	GW
		1◇		1	1	1◇	1	1◇	1	1◇	1	1◇	1◇	1	1◇	1◇	1	1◇	1◇	1◇	1	1	1◇	1◇	1
																				A					
		☕						☕		☕		☕	☕			☕		☕	☕	☕			☕	☕	
Birmingham New Street 12	d									07 03									07 33						
Birmingham International	d									07 15															
Coventry	d									07 25															
Stratford-upon-Avon	d																								
Warwick Parkway	d									*07 06*									07b45						
Warwick	d									*07 09*									07b50						
Leamington Spa 8	d									07 38									08 00						
Banbury	d									07 55									08 19						
Kings Sutton	d																								
Heyford	d																								
Tackley	d																								
Bicester Town	d						07 41																		
Islip	d						07 53																		
Oxford	a						08 08			08 14									08 41						
	d				07 55	08 00				08 15				08 21	08 30				08 43			08 55	08 59		
Radley	d													08 27								09 01			
Culham	d																								
Appleford	d													08 32											
Didcot Parkway	a				08 06									08 36								09 09			
	d	08 00			08 08			08 17				08 30		08 37		08 47	←	08 52		09 00		09 09		09 17	←
Cholsey	d				08 14				←					08 43 →			08 43					09 15 →			09 15
Goring & Streatley	d				08 19 →				08 19								08 48								09 20
Pangbourne	d								08 24								08 53								09 25
Tilehurst	d								08 28								08 57								09 29
Bedwyn	d			07 37																	08 37				
Hungerford	d			07 43																	08 43				
Kintbury	d			07 47																	08 47				
Newbury	a			07 54																	08 54				
	d			07 54							08 13		08 34								08 54				
Newbury Racecourse	d										08 15														
Thatcham	d			07 59							08 19										08 59				
Midgham	d										08 24														
Aldermaston	d										08 28														
Theale	d			08 07							08 33										09 07				
Reading West	d										08 40														
Reading 7	a	08 14		08 16		08 25		08 32	08 34	08 39	08 44	08 44	08 52		08 55	09 02	09 03	09 07	09 13	09 14	09 20		09 25	09 32	09 35
	d	08 16		08 18		08 27		08 33	08 34			08 46	08 52		08 57	09 04	09 04	09 09		09 16	09 21		09 27	09 33	09 35
Twyford 3	a								08 40								09 10								09 41
Maidenhead 3	a								08 48								09 18								09 49
Slough 3	a					08 40			08 56						09 10		09 25						09 40		09 57
Ealing Broadway	⊖ a								09 19								09 49								10 20
London Paddington 15	⊖ a	08 45		08 52		08 58		09 05	09 28			09 15	09 21		09 28	09 30	09 59	09 36		09 44	09 52		09 58	10 01	10 30

		GW	XC	GW		GW	GW	GW	GW	GW	GW	GW	XC	GW	GW		GW	GW	GW	XC	GW	GW	GW	GW	GW
		1◇	1◇	1◇		1	1	1◇	1	1◇	1	1◇	1◇	1	1		1◇	1	1◇	R 1	1	1◇	1	1◇	1◇
		☕	☕	☕						☕		☕	☕				☕		☕	☕		☕		☕	
Birmingham New Street 12	d		08 03										08 33							09 03					
Birmingham International	d		08 15																	09 15					
Coventry	d		08 25																	09 25					
Stratford-upon-Avon	d		*07 35*																						
Warwick Parkway	d		*08 20*										*08 45*							09b23					
Warwick	d		*08 23*										*08 48*							09b27					
Leamington Spa 8	d		08 38										09 00							09 38					
Banbury	d		08 55						09 02				09 19							09 55					
Kings Sutton	d								09 07																
Heyford	d								09 16																
Tackley	d								09 20																
Bicester Town	d														09 19										
Islip	d														09 31										
Oxford	a		09 14						09 30				09 41		09 46					10 14					
	d		09 15				09 20	09 30					09 43				09 49	09 55		10 15			10 21		10 30
Radley	d						09 26																10 27		
Culham	d						09 30																		
Appleford	d																						10 32		
Didcot Parkway	a						09 35											10 06					10 36		
	d			09 29			09 37			09 47	←							10 08	10 22			10 29	10 37		
Cholsey	d						09 43 →				09 43							10 14					10 43 →		
Goring & Streatley	d										09 48							10 19							
Pangbourne	d										09 52							10 24							
Tilehurst	d										09 57							10 28							
Bedwyn	d													09 37											
Hungerford	d													09 43											
Kintbury	d													09 47											
Newbury	a													09 54											
	d					09 23								09 54							10 13				
Newbury Racecourse	d					09 26															10 15				
Thatcham	d					09 30								09 59							10 19				
Midgham	d					09 35															10 24				
Aldermaston	d					09 39															10 28				
Theale	d					09 44								10 07							10 33				
Reading West	d					09 51															10 40				
Reading 7	a		09 39	09 44		09 55		09 55		10 01	10 02		10 13	10 15			10 20	10 34	10 37	10 39	10 45	10 45			10 58
	d	09 38		09 45				09 56		10 03	10 04	10 10		10 16			10 22	10 34	10 38			10 45		10 56	11 00
Twyford 3	a										10 10							10 40							
Maidenhead 3	a										10 18							10 48							
Slough 3	a							10 09			10 25						10 35	10 56							
Ealing Broadway	⊖ a										10 49							11 19							
London Paddington 15	⊖ a	10 06		10 14				10 27		10 31	10 59	10 43		10 52			10 54	11 29	11 09			11 15		11 23	11 26

For general notes see front of timetable
For details of catering facilities see
Directory of Train Operators

A From Taunton (Table 134)
b Change at Banbury

Due to Engineering Operations, services from Saturday 13 September on this Table had not been confirmed at time of going to press. These services will be issued in a special Supplement as soon as exact timings have been confirmed

Saturdays

until 6 September

Birmingham, Banbury, Bicester, Oxford and Bedwyn → Reading and London

Network Diagram - see first page of Table 116

		GW	GW	GW	XC	GW	GW	GW	GW	XC	GW	GW	GW	GW	GW	GW	GW	GW	GW	XC	GW	GW	GW	GW
										R														
		1◇	1	1◇	1◇	1	1	1◇	1	1	1◇	1	1	1	1	1◇	1◇	1	1◇	1◇	1	1	1	1◇
		☕		☕	☕			☕		☕	☕				☕		☕		☕	☕				☕
Birmingham New Street 12	d				09 33					10 03										10 33				
Birmingham International	d									10 15														
Coventry	d									10 25														
Stratford-upon-Avon	d									*09 36*														
Warwick Parkway	d				*09 43*					*10 22*										*10b46*				
Warwick	d				*09 46*					*10 26*										*10b49*				
Leamington Spa 8	d				10 00					10 38										11 00				
Banbury	d				10 19					10 55				11 02						11 19				
Kings Sutton	d													11 07										
Heyford	d													11 16										
Tackley	d													11 20										
Bicester Town	d																				11 19			
Islip	d																				11 31			
Oxford	a				10 41					11 14				11 30						11 41	11 46			
	d				10 43		10 55	11 00		11 15			11 21			11 30				11 43			11 55	12 00
Radley	d												11 27											
Culham	d												11 31											
Appleford	d																							
Didcot Parkway	a						11 06						11 37										12 06	
	d	10 47	←				11 08				11 29		11 37				11 47	←					12 08	
Cholsey	d		10 43				11 14		←				11 43 →					11 43					12 14	
Goring & Streatley	d		10 48				11 19 →		11 19									11 48					12 19 →	
Pangbourne	d		10 53						11 24									11 53						
Tilehurst	d		10 57						11 28									11 57						
Bedwyn	d					10 40																11 48		
Hungerford	d					10 46																11 54		
Kintbury	d					10 50																11 58		
Newbury	a					10 57																12 05		
	d					10 57						11 13										12 05		
Newbury Racecourse	d											11 15												
Thatcham	d					11 02						11 19										12 10		
Midgham	d											11 24												
Aldermaston	d											11 28												
Theale	d					11 10						11 33										12 18		
Reading West	d											11 40												
Reading 7	a	10 59	11 03		11 13	11 21		11 25	11 34	11 39	11 44	11 45				11 56	12 03	12 03		12 13		12 25		12 27
	d	11 02	11 04	11 11		11 22		11 27	11 34		11 45				11 52	11 58	12 04	12 04	12 11			12 27		12 29
Twyford 3	a		11 10						11 40									12 10						
Maidenhead 3	a		11 18						11 48									12 18						
Slough 3	a		11 25					11 40	11 56									12 25						12 44
Ealing Broadway	⊖ a		11 49						12 19									12 49						
London Paddington 15	⊖ a	11 30	11 59	11 41		11 53		11 59	12 29		12 15				12 21	12 24	12 30	12 59	12 42			12 59		13 08

		GW	GW	XC	GW	GW	GW	GW	GW	GW	GW	GW	GW	XC	GW	GW	GW	GW	XC	GW	GW	GW	GW	GW
		1	1	1◇	1◇	1◇	1	1◇	1	1	1◇	1	1	1◇	1	1	1◇	1	1◇	1◇	1	1	1	1◇
																A								
			☕	☕	☕	☕					☕		☕	☕		☕	☕		☕	☕				
Birmingham New Street 12	d			11 03										11 33					12 03					
Birmingham International	d			11 15															12 15					
Coventry	d			11 25															12 25					
Stratford-upon-Avon	d																		*11 38*					
Warwick Parkway	d			*11 22*										*11 41*					*12 22*					
Warwick	d			*11 26*										*11 45*					*12 26*					
Leamington Spa 8	d			11 38										12 00					12 38					
Banbury	d			11 55										12 19					12 55					
Kings Sutton	d																							
Heyford	d																							
Tackley	d																							
Bicester Town	d																							
Islip	d																							
Oxford	a			12 14										12 41					13 14					
	d			12 15			12 21	12 30						12 43	12 55		13 00		13 15				13 21	13 30
Radley	d						12 27																13 27	
Culham	d																						13 31	
Appleford	d						12 32																	
Didcot Parkway	a						12 36								13 06								13 37	
	d				12 22	12 27	12 37				12 47	←			13 08					13 29			13 38	
Cholsey	d	←					12 43 →					12 43			13 14			←					13 44 →	
Goring & Streatley	d	12 19										12 48			13 19 →			13 19						
Pangbourne	d	12 24										12 53						13 24						
Tilehurst	d	12 28										12 57						13 28						
Bedwyn	d									12 32														
Hungerford	d									12 38														
Kintbury	d									12 42														
Newbury	a									12 49														
	d								12 24												13 13	13 29		
Newbury Racecourse	d								12 26												13 15			
Thatcham	d								12 30												13 19	13 34		
Midgham	d								12 35												13 24			
Aldermaston	d								12 39												13 28			
Theale	d								12 44												13 33	13 42		
Reading West	d								12 51												13 40			
Reading 7	a	12 34		12 39	12 41	12 46		12 54	12 56		13 01	13 03		13 13			13 24	13 34	13 39	13 44	13 45	13 50		13 57
	d	12 34	12 35		12 42	12 47		12 56			13 02	13 04	13 11			13 20	13 26	13 34		13 45		13 51		13 58
Twyford 3	a	12 40										13 10						13 40						
Maidenhead 3	a	12 48										13 18						13 48						
Slough 3	a	12 56						13 09				13 25					13 39	13 56						
Ealing Broadway	⊖ a	13 19										13 49						14 19						
London Paddington 15	⊖ a	13 29	13 13		13 13	13 17		13 27			13 30	13 59	13 41			13 54	13 58	14 28		14 14		14 25		14 27

For general notes see front of timetable
For details of catering facilities see Directory of Train Operators

A Cornish Riviera
b Change at Banbury

Due to Engineering Operations, services from Saturday 13 September on this Table had not been confirmed at time of going to press. These services will be issued in a special Supplement as soon as exact timings have been confirmed

Table 116

Saturdays
until 6 September

Birmingham, Banbury, Bicester, Oxford and Bedwyn → Reading and London

Network Diagram - see first page of Table 116

		GW	GW	GW	GW	XC	GW	GW	GW	GW		GW	XC	GW	GW	GW	GW	GW	GW	GW	GW	XC	GW	GW	GW
		1	1◇	1	1◇	1◇	1	1	1◇	1		1◇	1◇	1◇	1	1	1	1◇	1	1	1◇	1◇	1	1	1
			☕		☕	☕			☕			☕	☕	☕			☕		A ✕		☕	☕			
Birmingham New Street 12	d					12 33							13 03									13 33			
Birmingham International	d												13 15												
Coventry	d												13 25												
Stratford-upon-Avon	d																								
Warwick Parkway	d					12 45							13 21									13 41			
Warwick	d					12 48							13 24									13 45			
Leamington Spa 8	d					13 00							13 38									14 00			
Banbury	d	13 02				13 19							13 55									14 19			
Kings Sutton	d	13 07																							
Heyford	d	13 16																							
Tackley	d	13 20																							
Bicester Town	d																							14 19	
Islip	d																							14 31	
Oxford	a	13 30				13 41							14 14									14 41		14 46	
	d					13 43		13 55	14 00				14 15			14 21		14 30				14 43			14 55
Radley	d															14 27									
Culham	d																								
Appleford	d															14 32									
Didcot Parkway	a							14 06								14 36									15 06
	d		13 47	←				14 08				14 22		14 29		14 37				←					15 08
Cholsey	d			13 44				14 14		←						14 43				14 43					15 14
Goring & Streatley	d			13 49				14 19		14 19						→				14 48					15 19
Pangbourne	d			13 53				→		14 24										14 53					→
Tilehurst	d			13 58						14 28										14 57					
Bedwyn	d						13 40																14 37		
Hungerford	d						13 46																14 43		
Kintbury	d						13 50																14 47		
Newbury	a						13 57																14 54		
	d						13 57								14 13								14 54		
Newbury Racecourse	d														14 15										
Thatcham	d						14 02								14 19								14 59		
Midgham	d														14 24										
Aldermaston	d														14 28										
Theale	d						14 10								14 33								15 07		
Reading West	d														14 40										
Reading 7	a		14 01	14 03		14 13	14 17		14 25	14 34		14 36	14 39	14 43	14 45			14 59		15 03		15 13	15 16		
	d		14 03	14 04	14 11		14 19		14 27	14 34		14 38		14 45			14 52	15 00	15 04	15 04	15 11		15 18		
Twyford 3	a			14 10						14 40										15 10					
Maidenhead 3	a			14 18						14 48										15 18					
Slough 3	a			14 25					14 40	14 56										15 25					
Ealing Broadway	⊖ a			14 49						15 19										15 49					
London Paddington 15	⊖ a		14 30	14 59	14 42		14 51		14 58	15 28		15 09		15 14			15 24	15 26	15 30	15 59	15 42		15 52		

		GW	GW	XC	GW	GW	GW	GW	GW	GW	GW	GW		GW	GW	XC	GW	GW	GW	GW	GW	GW	XC	GW	GW
		1◇	1	R 1	1	1◇	1	1	1◇	1	1◇	1		1◇	1	1◇	1	1	1	1◇	1	1◇	1◇	1◇	1
		☕		☕	☕	☕		☕			☕			☕		☕			B ☕	☕		☕	☕	☕	
Birmingham New Street 12	d			14 03												14 33							15 03		
Birmingham International	d																						15 15		
Coventry	d																						15 25		
Stratford-upon-Avon	d									13 40						13 40									
Warwick Parkway	d									14 21						14 45							15 21		
Warwick	d									14 24						14 48							15 24		
Leamington Spa 8	d									14 29						15 00							15 38		
Banbury	d									15 02						15 19							15 55		
Kings Sutton	d									15 07															
Heyford	d									15 16															
Tackley	d									15 20															
Bicester Town	d																								
Islip	d																								
Oxford	a			15 14						15 31						15 41							16 14		
	d	15 00		15 15			15 21		15 30							15 43		15 55		16 00			16 15		
Radley	d						15 27																		
Culham	d						15 31																		
Appleford	d																								
Didcot Parkway	a						15 37											16 06							
	d					15 29	15 38				15 47	←						16 08				16 22		16 29	
Cholsey	d		←				15 44					15 44						16 14			←				
Goring & Streatley	d		15 19				→					15 49						16 19			16 19				
Pangbourne	d		15 24									15 53						→			16 24				
Tilehurst	d		15 28									15 58									16 28				
Bedwyn	d																15 37								
Hungerford	d																15 43								
Kintbury	d																15 47								
Newbury	a																15 54								
	d				15 22										15 31		15 54								16 14
Newbury Racecourse	d														15 33										16 16
Thatcham	d														15 37		15 59								16 20
Midgham	d														15 42										16 25
Aldermaston	d														15 46										16 29
Theale	d														15 51		16 07								16 34
Reading West	d														16 04										16 41
Reading 7	a	15 25	15 34	15 39	15 42	15 45			15 55		16 01	16 03			16 12	16 13	16 16			16 28	16 34	16 36	16 39	16 44	16 46
	d	15 27	15 34		15 43	15 47		15 50	15 57		16 03	16 04		16 11			16 18		16 28	16 30	16 34	16 38		16 45	
Twyford 3	a		15 40									16 10									16 40				
Maidenhead 3	a		15 48									16 18									16 48				
Slough 3	a	15 40	15 56						16 10			16 25								16 46	16 56				
Ealing Broadway	⊖ a		16 19									16 49									17 19				
London Paddington 15	⊖ a	15 58	16 29		16 13	16 15		16 24	16 28		16 30	16 59		16 42			16 52		16 58	17 06	17 28	17 09		17 16	

For general notes see front of timetable
For details of catering facilities see
Directory of Train Operators

A Pembroke Coast Express
B Atlantic Coast Express

Due to Engineering Operations, services from Saturday 13 September on this Table had not been confirmed at time of going to press. These services will be issued in a special Supplement as soon as exact timings have been confirmed

Table 116

Saturdays

until 6 September

Birmingham, Banbury, Bicester, Oxford and Bedwyn → Reading and London

Network Diagram - see first page of Table 116

		GW 1	GW 1 ☕	GW 1◇	GW 1◇ ☕	GW 1	GW 1◇ ☕	XC 1◇ ☕	GW 1	GW 1	GW 1	GW 1◇	GW 1	GW 1 ☕		XC 1◇ ☕	GW 1◇ ☕	GW 1	GW 1	GW 1 ☕	GW 1◇	GW 1	GW 1◇ ☕	GW 1	GW 1◇ ☕
Birmingham New Street 12	d							15 33								16 03									
Birmingham International	d															16 15									
Coventry	d															16 25									
Stratford-upon-Avon	d															*15 39*									
Warwick Parkway	d							*15 41*								*16 21*									
Warwick	d							*15 45*								*16 24*									
Leamington Spa 8	d							16 00								16 38									
Banbury	d							16 19								16 55						17 02			
Kings Sutton	d																					17 07			
Heyford	d																					17 16			
Tackley	d																					17 20			
Bicester Town	d									16 19															
Islip	d									16 31															
Oxford	a							16 41		16 46						17 14						17 30			
	d	16 21		16 30				16 43			16 55	17 00				17 15			17 21		17 30				
Radley	d	16 27																	17 27						
Culham	d																		17 31						
Appleford	d	16 32																							
Didcot Parkway	a	16 36									17 06								17 37						
	d	16 37			16 47	←					17 08						17 29		17 37				17 47	←	
Cholsey	d	16 43				16 43					17 14		←						17 43					17 43	
Goring & Streatley	d	→				16 48					17 19		17 19						→					17 48	
Pangbourne	d					16 53					→		17 24											17 53	
Tilehurst	d					16 57							17 28											17 57	
Bedwyn	d								16 40																
Hungerford	d								16 46																
Kintbury	d								16 50																
Newbury	a								16 57																
	d								16 57									17 14							
Newbury Racecourse	d																	17 16							
Thatcham	d								17 02									17 20							
Midgham	d																	17 25							
Aldermaston	d																	17 29							
Theale	d								17 10									17 34							
Reading West	d																	17 41							
Reading 7	a			16 55	17 01	17 03		17 13	17 17			17 25	17 34			17 39	17 44	17 46			17 54		18 01	18 03	
	d		16 51	16 56	17 03	17 04	17 11		17 19			17 27	17 34	17 35			17 45			17 52	17 56		18 03	18 04	18 11
Twyford 3	a					17 10							17 40											18 10	
Maidenhead 3	a					17 18							17 48											18 18	
Slough 3	a					17 25						17 40	17 56								18 09			18 25	
Ealing Broadway	⊖ a					17 49							18 19											18 49	
London Paddington 15	⊖ a		17 23	17 27	17 31	17 59	17 40		17 51			17 58	18 29	18 05			18 15			18 24	18 27		18 29	18 59	18 40

		XC 1◇ ☕	GW 1	GW 1	GW 1◇ ☕	GW 1	GW 1◇ ☕	XC 1◇ ☕	GW 1◇ ☕	GW 1	GW 1	GW 1◇ A ☕	GW 1◇	GW 1◇ ☕	GW 1	GW 1◇ ☕		XC 1◇ ☕	GW 1	GW 1	GW 1	GW 1◇ ☕	GW 1	XC 1◇ ☕	GW 1◇ ☕
Birmingham New Street 12	d	16 33						17 03										17 33						18 03	
Birmingham International	d							17 15																18 15	
Coventry	d							17 25																18 25	
Stratford-upon-Avon	d																							*17 36*	
Warwick Parkway	d	*16b45*						*17 22*										*17b46*						*18 22*	
Warwick	d	*16b49*						*17 26*										*17b49*						*18 25*	
Leamington Spa 8	d	17 00						17 38										18 00						18 38	
Banbury	d	17 19						17 55										18 19						18 55	
Kings Sutton	d																								
Heyford	d																								
Tackley	d																								
Bicester Town	d																			18 19					
Islip	d																			18 31					
Oxford	a	17 41						18 14										18 41		18 46				19 14	
	d	17 43		17 55	18 00			18 15			18 21		18 30					18 43			18 55	19 00		19 15	
Radley	d										18 27														
Culham	d																								
Appleford	d										18 32														
Didcot Parkway	a			18 06							18 36										19 06				
	d			18 08			18 22		18 29		18 37			18 47	←						19 08				19 29
Cholsey	d			18 14		←					18 43				18 43						19 14		←		
Goring & Streatley	d			18 19		18 19					→				18 48						19 19		19 19		
Pangbourne	d			→		18 24									18 52						→		19 24		
Tilehurst	d					18 28									18 57								19 28		
Bedwyn	d		17 37																18 37						
Hungerford	d		17 43																18 43						
Kintbury	d		17 47																18 47						
Newbury	a		17 54																18 54						
	d		17 54							18 13									18 54						
Newbury Racecourse	d									18 15															
Thatcham	d		17 59							18 19									18 59						
Midgham	d									18 24															
Aldermaston	d									18 28															
Theale	d		18 07							18 33									19 07						
Reading West	d									18 40															
Reading 7	a	18 13	18 16		18 25	18 34	18 36	18 39	18 43	18 45			18 56	19 02	19 02			19 13	19 16			19 25	19 34	19 39	19 43
	d		18 18		18 27	18 34	18 38		18 45			18 50	18 58	19 04	19 04	19 11			19 18			19 27	19 34		19 45
Twyford 3	a					18 40									19 10								19 40		
Maidenhead 3	a					18 48									19 18								19 48		
Slough 3	a				18 40	18 56									19 25							19 40	19 55		
Ealing Broadway	⊖ a					19 19									19 49								20 19		
London Paddington 15	⊖ a		18 52		18 58	19 29	19 06		19 14			19 23	19 24	19 30	19 59	19 42			19 52			19 58	20 28		20 14

For general notes see front of timetable
For details of catering facilities see Directory of Train Operators

A **The Royal Duchy**
b Change at Banbury

Due to Engineering Operations, services from Saturday 13 September on this Table had not been confirmed at time of going to press. These services will be issued in a special Supplement as soon as exact timings have been confirmed

Table 116

Saturdays

until 6 September

Birmingham, Banbury, Bicester, Oxford and Bedwyn → Reading and London

Network Diagram - see first page of Table 116

	GW 1	GW 1	GW 1 ◇	GW 1	GW 1 ◇ ☕	GW 1 ◇ ☕	GW 1	GW 1 ◇ ☕	XC 1 ◇ ☕	GW 1	GW 1	GW 1 ◇ ☕
Birmingham New Street 12 d									18 33			
Birmingham International d												
Coventry d												
Stratford-upon-Avon d												
Warwick Parkway d									*18 46*			
Warwick d									*18 48*			
Leamington Spa 8 d									19 00			
Banbury d				19 01					19 19			
Kings Sutton d				19 06								
Heyford d				19 15								
Tackley d				19 19								
Bicester Town d												
Islip d												
Oxford a				19 32					19 41			
d		19 21	19 30						19 43		19 55	20 06
Radley d		19 27										
Culham d		19 31										
Appleford d												
Didcot Parkway a		19 37									20 06	
d		19 38					←				20 08	
Cholsey d		19 44 →					19 44				20 14	
Goring & Streatley d							19 49				20 19 →	
Pangbourne d							19 53					
Tilehurst d							19 58					
Bedwyn d										19 37		
Hungerford d										19 43		
Kintbury d										19 47		
Newbury a										19 54		
d	19 13				19 36					19 54		
Newbury Racecourse d	19 15									19 56		
Thatcham d	19 19									20 00		
Midgham d	19 24									20 05		
Aldermaston d	19 28									20 09		
Theale d	19 33									20 14		
Reading West d	19 40									20 21		
Reading 7 a	19 45		19 55		19 56		20 03	←	20 13	20 24		20 30
d			19 56		20 05 →	20 02	20 04	20 05				20 32
Twyford 3 a							20 10					
Maidenhead 3 a							20 18					
Slough 3 a							20 25					20 45
Ealing Broadway ⊖ a							20 49					
London Paddington 15 ⊖ a			20 27			20 31	20 59	20 36				21 05

	GW 1	GW 1 ◇ ☕	XC 1 ◇ ☕	GW 1 ◇ ☕	GW 1		GW 1 ◇	GW 1	GW 1 ◇ ☕	GW 1	GW 1 ◇ ☕	GW 1
Birmingham New Street 12 d			19 03									
Birmingham International d			19 15									
Coventry d			19 25									
Stratford-upon-Avon d												
Warwick Parkway d								*18 46*				
Warwick d								*18 48*				
Leamington Spa 8 d			19 38									
Banbury d			19 55					20 02				
Kings Sutton d								20 07				
Heyford d								20 16				
Tackley d								20 20				
Bicester Town d												
Islip d												
Oxford a			20 14					20 30				
d			20 15		20 20		20 30					20 55
Radley d					20 26							21 01
Culham d												
Appleford d					20 32							
Didcot Parkway a					20 36							21 08
d		20 22		20 29	20 38					←	20 47	21 09
Cholsey d	←				20 44 →					20 44		21 15 →
Goring & Streatley d	20 19									20 49		
Pangbourne d	20 24									20 53		
Tilehurst d	20 28									20 58		
Bedwyn d												
Hungerford d												
Kintbury d												
Newbury a												
d												
Newbury Racecourse d												
Thatcham d												
Midgham d												
Aldermaston d												
Theale d												
Reading West d												
Reading 7 a	20 34	20 38	20 39	20 44			20 54			21 03	21 07	
d	20 34	20 39		20 45			20 55		20 59	21 09	21 09	
Twyford 3 a	20 40									21 15		
Maidenhead 3 a	20 48									21 23		
Slough 3 a	20 55									21 35		
Ealing Broadway ⊖ a	21 19									21 58		
London Paddington 15 ⊖ a	21 28	21 09		21 15			21 26		21 29	22 08	21 36	

	GW 1 ◇ ☕	GW 1	GW 1	GW 1	XC 1 ◇ ☕	GW 1 ◇ ☕	GW 1 ◇	GW 1 ◇ ☕	GW 1	GW 1 ☕	GW 1
Birmingham New Street 12 d					20 03						
Birmingham International d					20 15						
Coventry d					20 25						
Stratford-upon-Avon d					*19 53*						
Warwick Parkway d		*19 44*			*20 16*						
Warwick d		*19 47*			*20 19*						
Leamington Spa 8 d		*19 51*			20 38						
Banbury d		20 38			20 55						
Kings Sutton d		20 43									
Heyford d		20 52									
Tackley d		20 56									
Bicester Town d									21 21		
Islip d									21 33		
Oxford a		21 06			21 14				21 47		
d	21 00				21 15		21 37				21 55
Radley d											22 01
Culham d											
Appleford d											
Didcot Parkway a							21 48				22 08
d			←			21 34	21 52	21 47			22 11
Cholsey d			21 15								22 17 →
Goring & Streatley d			21 20								
Pangbourne d			21 24								
Tilehurst d			21 29								
Bedwyn d				20 48							
Hungerford d				20 54							
Kintbury d				20 58							
Newbury a				21 05							
d				21 05							
Newbury Racecourse d				21 07							
Thatcham d				21 11							
Midgham d				21 16							
Aldermaston d				21 20							
Theale d				21 25							
Reading West d				21 32							
Reading 7 a	21 25		21 34	21 36	21 39	21 48	22 05	21 58			
d	21 27		21 35			21 50	22 07	22 00		22 06	
Twyford 3 a			21 41								
Maidenhead 3 a			21 49								
Slough 3 a	21 40		21 56				22 24				
Ealing Broadway ⊖ a			22 19								
London Paddington 15 ⊖ a	21 58		22 28			22 16	22 42	22 31		22 37	

	GW 1 ◇	GW 1	XC 1 ◇	GW 1	GW 1 ◇	GW 1	GW 1 ◇ ☕	GW 1 ◇ ☕	GW 1	GW 1 ◇ A	GW 1
Birmingham New Street 12 d			21 03								
Birmingham International d			21 15								
Coventry d			21 25								
Stratford-upon-Avon d											
Warwick Parkway d			*20 45*								
Warwick d			*20 48*								
Leamington Spa 8 d			21 38								
Banbury d			21 55			22 02					
Kings Sutton d						22 07					
Heyford d						22 16					
Tackley d						22 20					
Bicester Town d											
Islip d											
Oxford a			22 14			22 30					
d	22 08		22 15		22 30			23 00			23 09
Radley d											23 15
Culham d											23 20
Appleford d											23 23
Didcot Parkway a	22 19				22 41			23 12			23 27
d	22 20	←			22 42		22 52	23 13		23 32	23 36
Cholsey d		22 17									23 42
Goring & Streatley d		22 22									23 47
Pangbourne d		22 26									23 51
Tilehurst d		22 31									23 56
Bedwyn d				22 00					22 40		
Hungerford d				22 06					22 46		
Kintbury d				22 10					22 50		
Newbury a				22 17					22 57		
d				22 17					22 57		
Newbury Racecourse d				22 19					22 59		
Thatcham d				22 23					23 03		
Midgham d				22 28					23 08		
Aldermaston d				22 32					23 12		
Theale d				22 37					23 17		
Reading West d				22 44					23 24		
Reading 7 a	22 35	22 36	22 39	22 49	22 54		23 07	23 28	23 29	23 52	00 01
d	22 36	22 37			22 56		23 08	23 29		23 53	00 05
Twyford 3 a		22 43									00 11
Maidenhead 3 a		22 51									00 18
Slough 3 a	22 51	22 59			23 12			23 48			00 30
Ealing Broadway ⊖ a		23 21									00 53
London Paddington 15 ⊖ a	23 11	23 30			23 29		23 38	00 09		00 32	01 02

For general notes see front of timetable
For details of catering facilities see Directory of Train Operators

A From Taunton (Table 134)

Due to Engineering Operations, services from Saturday 13 September on this Table had not been confirmed at time of going to press. These services will be issued in a special Supplement as soon as exact timings have been confirmed

Table 116

Sundays

until 13 July

Birmingham, Banbury, Bicester, Oxford and Bedwyn → Reading and London

Network Diagram - see first page of Table 116

		GW 1	GW 1	GW 1	GW 1 ◇ ☕	GW 1 ◇	GW 1	GW 🚌	GW 1 ◇ ☕	GW 1	GW 1 ◇	GW 1 ◇ ☕	GW 1		GW 🚌	GW 1 ◇ ☕	GW 1	XC 1 ◇ ☕	GW 1 ◇ ☕	GW 1	GW 1 ◇ trolley	GW 1 ◇ ☕	GW 1	GW 🚌	GW 1
Birmingham New Street 12	d																	09 03							
Birmingham International	d																								
Coventry	d																								
Stratford-upon-Avon	d																								
Warwick Parkway	d																								
Warwick	d																								
Leamington Spa 8	d																	09 38							
Banbury	d																	09 55							
Kings Sutton	d																								
Heyford	d																								
Tackley	d																								
Bicester Town	d																								
Islip	d																								
Oxford	a																	10 14							
	d	23p09		08 05		08 38				09 05	09 38						10 05	10 16			10 38				11 05
Radley	d	23p15		08 11						09 11							10 11								11 11
Culham	d	23p20																							
Appleford	d	23p23		08 16													10 16								
Didcot Parkway	a	23p27		08 20		08 49				09 20	09 49						10 20				10 49				11 20
	d	23p36	07 45	08 21	08 39	08 50			09 10	09 21	09 50	09 59				10 12	10 21			←	10 50	10 58			11 21
Cholsey	d	23p42		08 27						09 27							10 27 →			10 27					11 27 →
Goring & Streatley	d	23p47	07 52	08 32						09 32										10 32					
Pangbourne	d	23p51		08 37						09 37										10 37					
Tilehurst	d	23p56		08 42						09 42										10 42					
Bedwyn	d							09 04							10 10									11 04	
Hungerford	d							09 19							10 25									11 19	
Kintbury	d							09 29							10 35									11 29	
Newbury	a							09 48							10 54									11 48	
	d						08 53						09 53										11 00		
Newbury Racecourse	d						08 55						09 55												
Thatcham	d						08 59						09 59										11 05		
Midgham	d						09 04						10 04												
Aldermaston	d						09 08						10 08												
Theale	d						09 13						10 13										11 13		
Reading West	d						09 20						10 20												
Reading 7	a	00 01	08 02	08 46	08 55	09 05	09 23		09 26	09 46	10 05	10 13	10 23			10 26		10 44		10 46	11 06	11 13	11 21		
	d	00 05	08 03	08 48	08 55	09 05			09 26	09 48	10 05	10 15				10 28			10 45	10 46	11 07	11 15			
Twyford 3	a	00 11		08 54						09 54										10 55					
Maidenhead 3	a	00 18		09 01						10 01										11 02					
Slough 3	a	00 30	08 21	09 09		09 24				10 09	10 26									11 10	11 26				
Ealing Broadway	⊖ a	00 53		09 32						10 32										11 32					
London Paddington 15	⊖ a	01 02	08 44	09 40	09 35	09 43			10 03	10 40	10 45	10 54				11 10			11 26	11 40	11 46	11 55			

For general notes see front of timetable
For details of catering facilities see Directory of Train Operators

Table 116

Sundays

until 13 July

Birmingham, Banbury, Bicester, Oxford and Bedwyn → Reading and London

Network Diagram - see first page of Table 116

		GW	GW	XC		GW	GW	GW	GW	GW	GW	GW	GW	XC	GW	GW	GW		GW	GW	GW	GW	XC	GW	GW
		1	1◇	1◇		1◇	1	1◇	1◇	1◇	1	1	1◇	1◇	1	1◇	1◇		1	1◇	🚌	1	1◇	1◇	1◇
			☕	☕		☕		☕	trolley	☕			☕	☕		☕				☕			☕	☕	
Birmingham New Street 12	d			10 03										11 03									12 03		
Birmingham International	d																								
Coventry	d																								
Stratford-upon-Avon	d			*10 00*																					
Warwick Parkway	d	*10 10*												*11 10*											
Warwick	d	*09 42*		*10 24*										*10 41*											
Leamington Spa 8	d	*10 16*		10 38										11 38									12 38		
Banbury	d	10 40		10 55										11 55									12 55		
Kings Sutton	d	10 45																							
Heyford	d	10 54																							
Tackley	d	10 58																							
Bicester Town	d																								
Islip	d																								
Oxford	a	11 08		11 14										12 14									13 14		
	d			11 16					11 38			12 05		12 16			12 50					13 05	13 16		13 38
Radley	d											12 11										13 11			
Culham	d																								
Appleford	d											12 16													
Didcot Parkway	a								11 50			12 20					13 01					13 20			13 49
	d						←		11 51	11 58		12 21			←	12 58	13 03					13 21			13 50
Cholsey	d						11 27					12 27			12 27							13 27			
Goring & Streatley	d						11 32					→			12 32							13 32			
Pangbourne	d						11 37								12 37							13 37			
Tilehurst	d						11 42								12 42							13 42			
Bedwyn	d																				13 04				
Hungerford	d																				13 19				
Kintbury	d																				13 29				
Newbury	a																				13 48				
	d										11 53								13 00						
Newbury Racecourse	d										11 55														
Thatcham	d										11 59								13 05						
Midgham	d										12 04														
Aldermaston	d										12 08														
Theale	d										12 13								13 13						
Reading West	d										12 20														
Reading 7	a			11 44			11 46		12 06	12 13	12 23			12 44	12 46	13 13	13 20		13 21			13 46	13 44		14 04
	d		11 41			11 50	11 52	11 56	12 07	12 15			12 44		12 46	13 15	13 22			13 46		13 46		13 52	14 06
Twyford 3	a						11 59								12 55							13 55			
Maidenhead 3	a						12 06								13 02							14 02			
Slough 3	a						12 14		12 28						13 10		13 47					14 10			14 25
Ealing Broadway	⊖ a						12 35								13 32							14 32			
London Paddington 15	⊖ a		12 15			12 29	12 44	12 41	12 46	12 55			13 26		13 40	13 55	14 08			14 24		14 40		14 30	14 44

		GW	GW	GW	XC	GW	GW	GW		GW	GW	GW	GW	GW	XC	GW	GW	GW	GW	GW	GW		GW	GW	GW
		1◇	1	1	1◇	1◇	1	1◇		1◇	1◇	1	🚌	1	R 1	1◇	1	1	1◇	1◇	1◇		1	1	1◇
		☕			☕	☕		☕			☕				☕	☕			☕	☕	☕				☕
Birmingham New Street 12	d				13 03										14 03										
Birmingham International	d																								
Coventry	d																								
Stratford-upon-Avon	d				*12 00*										*14 00*										
Warwick Parkway	d				*13 10*										*14 10*										
Warwick	d				*12 41*										*14 24*										
Leamington Spa 8	d				13 38										14 38										
Banbury	d				13 55										14 55			15 10							
Kings Sutton	d																	15 15							
Heyford	d																	15 24							
Tackley	d																	15 28							
Bicester Town	d																								
Islip	d																								
Oxford	a				14 14										15 14			15 38							
	d			14 05	14 16					14 38				15 05	15 16						15 50			16 05	
Radley	d			14 11										15 11										16 11	
Culham	d																								
Appleford	d			14 16																				16 16	
Didcot Parkway	a			14 20						14 49				15 20							16 01			16 20	
	d	13 58		14 21			←			14 50	14 58			15 21			←			15 58	16 01			16 21	
Cholsey	d			14 27			14 27							15 27			15 27							16 27	
Goring & Streatley	d			→			14 32							→			15 32							→	
Pangbourne	d						14 37										15 37								
Tilehurst	d						14 42										15 42								
Bedwyn	d												15 04												
Hungerford	d												15 19												
Kintbury	d												15 29												
Newbury	a												15 48												
	d		13 53									15 00											15 53		
Newbury Racecourse	d		13 55																				15 55		
Thatcham	d		13 59									15 05											15 59		
Midgham	d		14 04																				16 04		
Aldermaston	d		14 08																				16 08		
Theale	d		14 13									15 13											16 13		
Reading West	d		14 20																				16 20		
Reading 7	a	14 14	14 23		14 44		14 46			15 04	15 15	15 21			15 44		15 46			16 14	16 18		16 23		
	d	14 15				14 45	14 46	14 51		15 05	15 16					15 45	15 46		15 52	16 15	16 21				16 31
Twyford 3	a						14 55										15 55								
Maidenhead 3	a						15 02										16 02								
Slough 3	a						15 10			15 23							16 12				16 47				
Ealing Broadway	⊖ a						15 32										16 33								
London Paddington 15	⊖ a	14 54				15 21	15 40	15 31		15 43	15 55					16 22	16 42		16 31	16 54	17 07				17 10

For general notes see front of timetable
For details of catering facilities see Directory of Train Operators

Table 116

Sundays

until 13 July

Birmingham, Banbury, Bicester, Oxford and Bedwyn → Reading and London

Network Diagram - see first page of Table 116

Station		XC	GW	GW	GW	GW	GW	GW	GW	GW	GW	GW	XC	GW	GW	GW	GW	GW	GW	GW	XC	GW	GW	GW
		[R] [1]	[1]	[1] ◇	[1] ◇	[1] ◇	[1] ◇	[1]	[1]	[1] ◇	[1] ◇	🚌	[R] [1]	[1]	[1] ◇	[1] ◇	[1] ◇	[1]	[1]	[1] ◇	[R] [1]	[1]	[1]	[1] ◇
		☕		☕	☕	☕	☕			☕	☕		☕		☕	☕	☕			☕	☕			☕
Birmingham New Street [12]	d	15 03											16 03								17 03			
Birmingham International	d																							
Coventry	d																							
Stratford-upon-Avon	d												*16 00*											
Warwick Parkway	d	*15 10*											*16 10*								*17 10*			
Warwick	d	*14 41*											*16 24*								*16 41*			
Leamington Spa [8]	d	15 38											16 38								17 38			
Banbury	d	15 55											16 55								17 55		18 00	
Kings Sutton	d																						18 05	
Heyford	d																						18 14	
Tackley	d																						18 18	
Bicester Town	d																							
Islip	d																							
Oxford	a	16 14											17 14								18 14		18 28	
	d	16 16					16 50		17 05				17 16				17 50		18 05		18 16			
Radley	d								17 11										18 11					
Culham	d																							
Appleford	d																		18 16					
Didcot Parkway	a						17 01		17 20								18 01		18 20					
	d		←			16 58	17 03		17 21					←		17 58	18 03		18 21			←		
Cholsey	d		16 27						17 27 →					17 27					18 27 →			18 27		
Goring & Streatley	d		16 32											17 32								18 32		
Pangbourne	d		16 37											17 37								18 37		
Tilehurst	d		16 42											17 42								18 42		
Bedwyn	d											17 04												
Hungerford	d											17 19												
Kintbury	d											17 29												
Newbury	a											17 48												
	d							17 00										17 53						
Newbury Racecourse	d																	17 55						
Thatcham	d							17 05										17 59						
Midgham	d																	18 04						
Aldermaston	d																	18 08						
Theale	d							17 13										18 13						
Reading West	d																	18 20						
Reading [7]	a	16 44	16 46			17 14	17 18	17 21					17 44	17 46		18 15	18 18	18 23			18 44	18 46		
	d		16 46	16 56	17 06	17 15	17 21			17 31	17 43			17 46	17 56	18 15	18 21			18 44		18 46		18 52
Twyford [3]	a		16 55											17 55								18 55		
Maidenhead [3]	a		17 02											18 02								19 02		
Slough [3]	a		17 12				17 48							18 12			18 45					19 12		
Ealing Broadway	⊖ a		17 33											18 33								19 33		
London Paddington [15]	⊖ a		17 42	17 34	17 40	17 54	18 08			18 15	18 24			18 42	18 36	18 54	19 08			19 24		19 42		19 30

Station		GW	GW	GW	XC	GW	GW	GW	GW	GW	GW	XC	GW	GW	GW	GW	GW	GW	XC	GW	GW	GW	GW
		[1] ◇	[1] ◇	[1] ◇	[1] ◇	[1] ◇	[1]	[1] ◇	🚌	[1] ◇	[1]	[R] [1]	[1] ◇	[1] ◇	[1] ◇	[1]	[1]	[1] ◇	[R] [1]	[1]	[1] ◇	[1] ◇	[1] ◇
		☕	☕	☕	☕	☕		☕		☕		☕	☕	☕	☕			☕	☕		☕	☕	☕
Birmingham New Street [12]	d				17 33							18 03							19 03				
Birmingham International	d																						
Coventry	d																						
Stratford-upon-Avon	d											*18 00*											
Warwick Parkway	d				*17 38*							*18 10*							*19 10*				
Warwick	d				*17 41*							*18 24*							*18 41*				
Leamington Spa [8]	d				18 00							18 38							19 38				
Banbury	d				18 19							18 55							19 55				
Kings Sutton	d																						
Heyford	d																						
Tackley	d																						
Bicester Town	d																						
Islip	d																						
Oxford	a				18 41							19 14							20 14				
	d			18 41	18 43						19 05	19 16			19 50		20 05		20 16				
Radley	d										19 11						20 11						
Culham	d																						
Appleford	d																						
Didcot Parkway	a			18 52							19 20				20 03		20 20						
	d			18 52		18 58					19 21			19 58	20 05		20 21			←			20 58
Cholsey	d										19 27						20 27 →			20 27			
Goring & Streatley	d										19 32									20 32			
Pangbourne	d										19 37									20 37			
Tilehurst	d										19 42									20 42			
Bedwyn	d								19 04														
Hungerford	d								19 19														
Kintbury	d								19 29														
Newbury	a								19 48														
	d						19 00									19 53							
Newbury Racecourse	d															19 55							
Thatcham	d						19 05									19 59							
Midgham	d															20 04							
Aldermaston	d															20 08							
Theale	d						19 13									20 13							
Reading West	d															20 20							
Reading [7]	a			19 07	19 13	19 14	19 21				19 46	19 44		20 14	20 20	20 23			20 44	20 46			21 13
	d	18 57	19 02	19 07		19 15		19 32		19 44	19 46		19 58	20 15	20 24			20 43		20 46	20 51	20 57	21 14
Twyford [3]	a										19 55									20 55			
Maidenhead [3]	a										20 02									21 02			
Slough [3]	a			19 32							20 12				20 47					21 12			
Ealing Broadway	⊖ a										20 33									21 33			
London Paddington [15]	⊖ a	19 39	19 40	19 52		19 58		20 06		20 21	20 42		20 38	20 55	21 08			21 22		21 42	21 30	21 37	21 53

For general notes see front of timetable
For details of catering facilities see
Directory of Train Operators

Table 116

Sundays

until 13 July

Birmingham, Banbury, Bicester, Oxford and Bedwyn → Reading and London

Network Diagram - see first page of Table 116

		GW	GW	XC	GW	GW	GW		GW	GW	GW	GW	GW	XC	GW	GW	GW	GW	GW	GW	GW	GW	GW
		1 ◇		R 1	1 ◇	1 ◇			1	1 ◇	1 ◇		1 ◇	1 ◇	1	1 ◇		1 ◇	1 ◇	1			
					A		🚌															🚌	
		☕		☕	☕	☕					☕		☕	☕		🛒		☕	☕				
Birmingham New Street 12	d			20 03										21 03									
Birmingham International	d																						
Coventry	d																						
Stratford-upon-Avon	d			*20 00*																			
Warwick Parkway	d			*19 45*										*20 45*									
Warwick	d			*20 24*										*20 48*									
Leamington Spa 8	d			20 38										21 38									
Banbury	d			20 55										21 55									
Kings Sutton	d																						
Heyford	d																						
Tackley	d																						
Bicester Town	d																						
Islip	d																						
Oxford	a			21 14										22 14									
	d	20 50		21 16					21 21		21 50			22 16	22 21	22 50				22 58			
Radley	d								21 27						22 27					23 04			
Culham	d																						
Appleford	d																						
Didcot Parkway	a	21 02							21 34		22 01				22 34	22 59				23 13			
	d	21 03							21 35	22 01	22 03				22 35	23 00				23 15			
Cholsey	d								21 41						22 41					23 21			
Goring & Streatley	d								21 46						22 46					23 26			
Pangbourne	d								21 50						22 50					23 30			
Tilehurst	d								21 55						22 55					23 35			
Bedwyn	d						21 04															22 58	
Hungerford	d						21 19															23 13	
Kintbury	d						21 29															23 23	
Newbury	a						21 48															23 42	
	d		21 00									21 53					22 53				23 23		23 47
Newbury Racecourse	d											21 55					22 55				23 25		23 49
Thatcham	d		21 05									21 59					22 59				23 29		23 53
Midgham	d											22 04					23 04				23 34		23 58
Aldermaston	d											22 08					23 08				23 38		00 02
Theale	d		21 13									22 13					23 13				23 43		00 07
Reading West	d											22 20					23 20				23s50		00s14
Reading 7	a	21 19	21 21	21 44					21 59	22 16	22 19	22 23		22 44	22 59	23 15	23 23			23 40	23 53		00 17
	d	21 19			21 28	21 47			21 59	22 17	22 19		22 42		22 59	23 15		23 24	23 30	23 41			
Twyford 3	a								22 06						23 06					23 48			
Maidenhead 3	a								22 13						23 14					23 56			
Slough 3	a	21 41							22 23		22 40				23 23	23 36				00 05			
Ealing Broadway	⊖ a								22 44						23 45					00 27			
London Paddington 15	⊖ a	22 03			22 25	22 28			22 53	22 59	23 04		23 23		23 53	00 01		00 05	00 17	00 40			

For general notes see front of timetable
For details of catering facilities see Directory of Train Operators

A Atlantic Coast Express

Table 116

Sundays

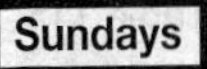

20 July to 7 September

Birmingham, Banbury, Bicester, Oxford and Bedwyn → Reading and London

Network Diagram - see first page of Table 116

		GW	GW	GW	GW	GW	GW	GW	GW	GW	GW	GW	GW	GW	GW	GW	XC	GW	GW	GW	GW	GW	GW	GW	GW
		1	1	1	1 ◇	1 ◇	1	bus	1 ◇	1	1 ◇	1 ◇	1	bus	1 ◇	1	1 ◇	1 ◇	1	1 ◇	1 ◇	1	bus	1	1
					☕				☕		trolley	☕			☕		☕	☕		trolley	☕				
Birmingham New Street 12	d																09 03								
Birmingham International	d																								
Coventry	d																								
Stratford-upon-Avon	d																								*10 10*
Warwick Parkway	d																								*09 42*
Warwick	d																								
Leamington Spa 8	d																09 38								*10 16*
Banbury	d																09 55								10 40
Kings Sutton	d																								10 45
Heyford	d																								10 54
Tackley	d																								10 58
Bicester Town	d																								
Islip	d																								
Oxford	a																10 14								11 08
	d	23p09		08 05		08 38				09 05	09 38					10 05	10 16			10 38				11 05	
Radley	d	23p15		08 11						09 11						10 11								11 11	
Culham	d	23p20																							
Appleford	d	23p23		08 16												10 16									
Didcot Parkway	a	23p27		08 20		08 49				09 20	09 49					10 20				10 49				11 20	
	d	23p36	07 45	08 21	08 39	08 50			09 10	09 21	09 50	09 59			10 12	10 21			←	10 50	10 58			11 21	
Cholsey	d	23p42		08 27						09 27						10 27 →			10 27					11 27 →	
Goring & Streatley	d	23p47	07 52	08 32						09 32									10 32						
Pangbourne	d	23p51		08 37						09 37									10 37						
Tilehurst	d	23p56		08 42						09 42									10 42						
Bedwyn	d							09 04						10 10									11 04		
Hungerford	d							09 19						10 25									11 19		
Kintbury	d							09 29						10 35									11 29		
Newbury	a							09 48						10 54									11 48		
	d						08 53						09 53									11 00			
Newbury Racecourse	d						08 55						09 55												
Thatcham	d						08 59						09 59									11 05			
Midgham	d						09 04						10 04												
Aldermaston	d						09 08						10 08												
Theale	d						09 13						10 13									11 13			
Reading West	d						09 20						10 20												
Reading 7	a	00 01	08 02	08 46	08 55	09 05	09 23		09 26	09 46	10 05	10 13	10 23		10 26		10 44		10 46	11 06	11 13	11 21			
	d	00 05	08 03	08 48	08 55	09 05			09 26	09 48	10 05	10 15			10 28			10 45	10 46	11 07	11 15				
Twyford 3	a	00 11		08 54						09 54									10 55						
Maidenhead 3	a	00 18		09 01						10 01									11 02						
Slough 3	a	00 30	08 21	09 09		09 24				10 09	10 26								11 10	11 26					
Ealing Broadway	⊖ a	00 53		09 32						10 32									11 32						
London Paddington 15	⊖ a	01 02	08 44	09 40	09 35	09 43			10 03	10 40	10 45	10 54			11 10			11 26	11 40	11 46	11 55				

For general notes see front of timetable
For details of catering facilities see Directory of Train Operators

Due to Engineering Operations, services from Sunday 14 September on this Table had not been confirmed at time of going to press. These services will be issued in a special Supplement as soon as exact timings have been confirmed

Table 116

Sundays

Birmingham, Banbury, Bicester, Oxford and Bedwyn → Reading and London

20 July to 7 September

Network Diagram - see first page of Table 116

		GW	XC	GW	GW	GW	GW	GW	XC	GW	GW	GW	XC	GW	XC	GW	GW	GW	GW	GW	XC	GW	GW	GW	GW
		1 ◇	1 ◇	1 ◇	1	1 ◇	1 ◇	1 ◇	1 ◇	1	1	1 ◇	1 ◇	1	1 ◇	1 ◇	1 ◇	1	🚌	1	1 ◇	1 ◇	1	1 ◇	1 ◇
		☕	☕	☕		☕	trolley	☕	☕			☕	☕		☕	☕					☕	☕		☕	
Birmingham New Street 12	d		10 03						10 33				11 03		11 33						12 03				
Birmingham International	d																								
Coventry	d																								
Stratford-upon-Avon	d		*10 00*																		*12 00*				
Warwick Parkway	d								*10 38*				*11 10*		*11 38*						*12 10*				
Warwick	d		*10 24*						*10 41*						*11 41*						*12 24*				
Leamington Spa 8	d		10 38						11 00				11 38		12 00						12 38				
Banbury	d		10 55						11 19				11 55		12 19						12 55				
Kings Sutton	d																								
Heyford	d																								
Tackley	d																								
Bicester Town	d																								
Islip	d																								
Oxford	a		11 14						11 41				12 14		12 41						13 14				
	d		11 16				11 38		11 43		12 05		12 16		12 43		12 50			13 05	13 16				13 38
Radley	d										12 11									13 11					
Culham	d																								
Appleford	d										12 16														
Didcot Parkway	a						11 50				12 20						13 01			13 20					13 49
	d				←		11 51	11 58			12 21			←		12 58	13 03			13 21			←		13 50
Cholsey	d				11 27						12 27			12 27						13 27			13 27		
Goring & Streatley	d				11 32						→			12 32						→			13 32		
Pangbourne	d				11 37									12 37									13 37		
Tilehurst	d				11 42									12 42									13 42		
Bedwyn	d																		13 04						
Hungerford	d																		13 19						
Kintbury	d																		13 29						
Newbury	a																		13 48						
	d									11 53								13 00							
Newbury Racecourse	d									11 55															
Thatcham	d									11 59								13 05							
Midgham	d									12 04															
Aldermaston	d									12 08															
Theale	d									12 13								13 13							
Reading West	d									12 20															
Reading 7	a		11 44		11 46		12 06	12 13	12 13	12 23			12 44	12 46	13 13	13 13	13 20	13 21			13 44		13 46		14 04
	d	11 41		11 50	11 52	11 56	12 07	12 15				12 44		12 46		13 15	13 22					13 46	13 46	13 52	14 06
Twyford 3	a				11 59									12 55									13 55		
Maidenhead 3	a				12 06									13 02									14 02		
Slough 3	a				12 14		12 28							13 10			13 47						14 10		14 25
Ealing Broadway	⊖ a				12 35									13 32									14 32		
London Paddington 15	⊖ a	12 15		12 29	12 44	12 41	12 46	12 55				13 26		13 40		13 55	14 08					14 24	14 40	14 30	14 44

		XC	GW	GW	GW	XC	GW	GW	GW	GW	XC	GW	GW	GW	GW	XC	GW	GW	GW	GW	XC	GW	GW	GW	GW
																R									
		1 ◇	1 ◇	1	1	1 ◇	1 ◇	1	1 ◇	1 ◇	1 ◇	1 ◇	1	🚌	1	1	1 ◇	1	1 ◇	1	1 ◇	1 ◇	1 ◇	1	1
		☕	☕			☕	☕		☕		☕	☕				☕	☕		☕		☕	☕	☕		
Birmingham New Street 12	d	12 33				13 03					13 33					14 03					14 33				
Birmingham International	d																								
Coventry	d																								
Stratford-upon-Avon	d															*14 00*									
Warwick Parkway	d	*12 38*				*13 10*					*13 39*					*14 10*					*14 38*				
Warwick	d	*12 41*									*13 42*					*14 24*					*14 41*				
Leamington Spa 8	d	13 00				13 38					14 00					14 38					15 00				
Banbury	d	13 19				13 55					14 19					14 55				15 10	15 19				
Kings Sutton	d																			15 15					
Heyford	d																			15 24					
Tackley	d																			15 28					
Bicester Town	d																								
Islip	d																								
Oxford	a	13 41				14 14					14 41					15 14				15 38	15 41				
	d	13 43			14 05	14 16				14 38	14 43				15 05	15 16					15 43		15 50		16 05
Radley	d				14 11										15 11										16 11
Culham	d																								
Appleford	d				14 16																				16 16
Didcot Parkway	a				14 20					14 49					15 20								16 01		16 20
	d		13 58		14 21			←		14 50		14 58			15 21			←				15 58	16 01		16 21
Cholsey	d				14 27			14 27							15 27			15 27							16 27
Goring & Streatley	d				→			14 32							→			15 32							→
Pangbourne	d							14 37										15 37							
Tilehurst	d							14 42										15 42							
Bedwyn	d													15 04											
Hungerford	d													15 19											
Kintbury	d													15 29											
Newbury	a													15 48											
	d			13 53									15 00											15 53	
Newbury Racecourse	d			13 55																				15 55	
Thatcham	d			13 59									15 05											15 59	
Midgham	d			14 04																				16 04	
Aldermaston	d			14 08																				16 08	
Theale	d			14 13									15 13											16 13	
Reading West	d			14 20																				16 20	
Reading 7	a	14 13	14 14	14 23		14 44		14 46		15 04	15 13	15 15	15 21			15 44		15 46			16 13	16 14	16 18	16 23	
	d		14 15				14 45	14 46	14 51	15 05		15 16					15 45	15 46	15 52			16 15	16 21		
Twyford 3	a							14 55										15 55							
Maidenhead 3	a							15 02										16 02							
Slough 3	a							15 10		15 23								16 12					16 47		
Ealing Broadway	⊖ a							15 32										16 33							
London Paddington 15	⊖ a		14 54				15 21	15 40	15 31	15 43		15 55					16 22	16 42	16 31			16 54	17 07		

For general notes see front of timetable
For details of catering facilities see Directory of Train Operators

Due to Engineering Operations, services from Sunday 14 September on this Table had not been confirmed at time of going to press. These services will be issued in a special Supplement as soon as exact timings have been confirmed

Sundays

20 July to 7 September

Birmingham, Banbury, Bicester, Oxford and Bedwyn → Reading and London

Network Diagram - see first page of Table 116

		GW	XC	GW	GW	GW	XC	GW	GW	GW	GW	GW	GW	GW	XC	GW	GW	XC	GW	GW	GW	GW	GW	XC	GW
		1 ◇	R 1	1	1 ◇	1 ◇	1 ◇	1 ◇	1 ◇	1	1	1 ◇	1 ◇	🚌	R 1	1	1 ◇	1 ◇	1 ◇	1 ◇	1	1	1 ◇	R 1	1
		☕	☕		☕	☕	☕	☕	☕			☕	☕		☕		☕	☕	☕	☕			☕	☕	
Birmingham New Street 12	d		15 03				15 33								16 03			16 33						17 03	
Birmingham International	d																								
Coventry	d																								
Stratford-upon-Avon	d														*16 00*										
Warwick Parkway	d		*15 10*				*15 38*								*16 10*			*16 38*						*17 10*	
Warwick	d						*15 41*								*16 24*			*16 41*							
Leamington Spa 8	d		15 38				16 00								16 38			17 00						17 38	
Banbury	d		15 55				16 19								16 55			17 19						17 55	
Kings Sutton	d																								
Heyford	d																								
Tackley	d																								
Bicester Town	d																								
Islip	d																								
Oxford	a		16 14				16 41								17 14			17 41						18 14	
	d		16 16				16 43		16 50		17 05				17 16			17 43		17 50		18 05		18 16	
Radley	d										17 11											18 11			
Culham	d																								
Appleford	d																					18 16			
Didcot Parkway	a								17 01		17 20									18 01		18 20			
	d			←				16 58	17 03		17 21					←			17 58	18 03		18 21			←
Cholsey	d			16 27							17 27 →					17 27						18 27 →			18 27
Goring & Streatley	d			16 32												17 32									18 32
Pangbourne	d			16 37												17 37									18 37
Tilehurst	d			16 42												17 42									18 42
Bedwyn	d													17 04											
Hungerford	d													17 19											
Kintbury	d													17 29											
Newbury	a													17 48											
	d									17 00											17 53				
Newbury Racecourse	d																				17 55				
Thatcham	d									17 05											17 59				
Midgham	d																				18 04				
Aldermaston	d																				18 08				
Theale	d									17 13											18 13				
Reading West	d																				18 20				
Reading 7	a		16 44	16 46			17 13	17 14	17 18	17 21					17 44	17 46		18 13	18 15	18 18	18 23			18 44	18 46
	d	16 31		16 46	16 56	17 06		17 15	17 21			17 31	17 43			17 46	17 56		18 15	18 21			18 44		18 46
Twyford 3	a			16 55												17 55									18 55
Maidenhead 3	a			17 02												18 02									19 02
Slough 3	a			17 12					17 48							18 12				18 45					19 12
Ealing Broadway	⊖ a			17 33												18 33									19 33
London Paddington 15	⊖ a	17 10		17 42	17 34	17 40		17 54	18 08			18 15	18 24			18 42	18 36		18 54	19 08			19 24		19 42

		GW	GW	GW	GW	GW	XC	GW	GW	GW	GW	GW	GW	XC	GW	GW	XC	GW	GW	GW	GW	GW	XC	GW	GW
		1 ◇	1	1 ◇	1 ◇	1 ◇	1 ◇	1 ◇	1	1	1 ◇	1 ◇	🚌	R 1	1	1 ◇	1 ◇	1 ◇	1 ◇	1	1	1 ◇	R 1	1	1 ◇
		☕		☕	☕	☕	☕	☕			☕	☕		☕		☕	☕	☕	☕			☕	☕		☕
Birmingham New Street 12	d						17 33							18 03			18 33						19 03		
Birmingham International	d																								
Coventry	d																								
Stratford-upon-Avon	d													*18 00*			*18 00*								
Warwick Parkway	d						*17 38*							*18 10*			*18 38*						*19 10*		
Warwick	d						*17 41*							*18 24*			*18 41*								
Leamington Spa 8	d						18 00							18 38			19 00						19 38		
Banbury	d		18 00				18 19							18 55			19 19						19 55		
Kings Sutton	d		18 05																						
Heyford	d		18 14																						
Tackley	d		18 18																						
Bicester Town	d																								
Islip	d																								
Oxford	a		18 28				18 41							19 14			19 41						20 14		
	d					18 41	18 43			19 05				19 16			19 43		19 50		20 05		20 16		
Radley	d									19 11											20 11				
Culham	d																								
Appleford	d																								
Didcot Parkway	a					18 52				19 20									20 03		20 20				
	d					18 52		18 58		19 21					←			19 58	20 05		20 21			←	
Cholsey	d									19 27 →					19 27						20 27 →			20 27	
Goring & Streatley	d														19 32									20 32	
Pangbourne	d														19 37									20 37	
Tilehurst	d														19 42									20 42	
Bedwyn	d												19 04												
Hungerford	d												19 19												
Kintbury	d												19 29												
Newbury	a												19 48												
	d								19 00											19 53					
Newbury Racecourse	d																			19 55					
Thatcham	d								19 05											19 59					
Midgham	d																			20 04					
Aldermaston	d																			20 08					
Theale	d								19 13											20 13					
Reading West	d																			20 20					
Reading 7	a					19 07	19 13	19 14	19 21					19 44	19 46		20 13	20 14	20 20	20 23			20 44	20 46	
	d	18 52		18 57	19 02	19 07		19 15			19 32	19 44			19 46	19 58		20 15	20 24			20 43		20 46	20 51
Twyford 3	a														19 55									20 55	
Maidenhead 3	a														20 02									21 02	
Slough 3	a					19 32									20 12				20 47					21 12	
Ealing Broadway	⊖ a														20 33									21 33	
London Paddington 15	⊖ a	19 30		19 39	19 40	19 52		19 58			20 06	20 21			20 42	20 38		20 55	21 08			21 22		21 42	21 30

For general notes see front of timetable
For details of catering facilities see
Directory of Train Operators

Due to Engineering Operations, services from Sunday 14 September on this Table had not been confirmed at time of going to press. These services will be issued in a special Supplement as soon as exact timings have been confirmed

Table 116

Sundays

Birmingham, Banbury, Bicester, Oxford and Bedwyn → Reading and London

20 July to 7 September

Network Diagram - see first page of Table 116

		GW	GW	GW	GW	GW	XC	GW	GW	GW	GW	GW	GW	GW	XC	GW	GW	GW	GW	GW	GW	GW	GW	GW
		1 ◇	1 ◇	1 ◇		1 ◇	R 1	1 ◇		1	1 ◇	1 ◇		1 ◇	1 ◇	1	1 ◇		1 ◇	1 ◇	1			
						A			🚌														🚌	
		☕	☕	☕		☕	☕	☕				☕		☕	☕		trolley		☕	☕				
Birmingham New Street 12	d						20 03								21 03									
Birmingham International	d																							
Coventry	d																							
Stratford-upon-Avon	d						20 00																	
Warwick Parkway	d						19 45								20 45									
Warwick	d						20 24								20 48									
Leamington Spa 8	d						20 38								21 38									
Banbury	d						20 55								21 55									
Kings Sutton	d																							
Heyford	d																							
Tackley	d																							
Bicester Town	d																							
Islip	d																							
Oxford	a						21 14								22 14									
	d			20 50			21 16			21 21		21 50			22 16	22 21	22 50				22 58			
Radley	d									21 27						22 27					23 04			
Culham	d																							
Appleford	d																							
Didcot Parkway	a			21 02						21 34		22 01				22 34	22 59				23 13			
	d		20 58	21 03						21 35	22 01	22 03				22 35	23 00				23 15			
Cholsey	d									21 41						22 41					23 21			
Goring & Streatley	d									21 46						22 46					23 26			
Pangbourne	d									21 50						22 50					23 30			
Tilehurst	d									21 55						22 55					23 35			
Bedwyn	d								21 04														22 58	
Hungerford	d								21 19														23 13	
Kintbury	d								21 29														23 23	
Newbury	a								21 48														23 42	
	d				21 00								21 53					22 53				23 23		23 47
Newbury Racecourse	d												21 55					22 55				23 25		23 49
Thatcham	d				21 05								21 59					22 59				23 29		23 53
Midgham	d												22 04					23 04				23 34		23 58
Aldermaston	d												22 08					23 08				23 38		00 02
Theale	d				21 13								22 13					23 13				23 43		00 07
Reading West	d												22 20					23 20				23s50		00s14
Reading 7	a		21 13	21 19	21 21		21 44			21 59	22 16	22 19	22 23		22 44	22 59	23 15	23 23			23 40	23 53		00 17
	d	20 57	21 14	21 19		21 28		21 47		21 59	22 17	22 19		22 42		22 59	23 15		23 24	23 30	23 41			
Twyford 3	a									22 06						23 06					23 48			
Maidenhead 3	a									22 13						23 14					23 56			
Slough 3	a			21 41						22 23		22 40				23 23	23 36				00 05			
Ealing Broadway	⊖ a									22 44						23 45					00 27			
London Paddington 15	⊖ a	21 37	21 53	22 03		22 25		22 28		22 53	22 59	23 04		23 23		23 54	00 01		00 05	00 17	00 40			

For general notes see front of timetable
For details of catering facilities see Directory of Train Operators

A Atlantic Coast Express

Due to Engineering Operations, services from Sunday 14 September on this Table had not been confirmed at time of going to press. These services will be issued in a special Supplement as soon as exact timings have been confirmed

Table 116A

Mondays to Fridays

Reading — Wallingford
Bus Service

		GW MX	GW	GW	GW	GW	GW	GW	GW	GW	GW	GW	GW	GW	GW	GW	GW	GW	GW FO
Reading	d	00 35	07 27	08 27	09 25	10 25	11 25	12 25	13 25	14 25	15 25	16 35	17 35	18 35	19 35	20 35	21 35	22 35	23 35
Wallingford Market Place	a	01 10	07 59	08 59	09 58	10 58	11 58	12 58	13 58	14 58	15 58	17 10	18 10	19 10	20 10	21 10	22 10	23 10	00 10

Saturdays

		GW	GW	GW	GW	GW	GW	GW	GW	GW	GW	GW	GW	GW	GW	GW	GW	GW
Reading	d	00 35	08 27	09 25	10 25	11 25	12 25	13 25	14 25	15 25	16 35	17 35	18 35	19 35	20 35	21 35	22 35	23 35
Wallingford Market Place	a	01 10	08 59	09 58	10 58	11 58	12 58	13 58	14 58	15 58	17 10	18 10	19 10	20 10	21 10	22 10	23 10	00 10

Sundays

		GW	GW	GW	GW	GW	GW	GW	GW	GW
Reading	d	00 35	11 25	13 25	15 25	17 25	19 25	21 25	23 25	23 35
Wallingford Market Place	a	01 10	11 58	13 58	15 58	17 58	19 58	21 58	23 58	00 10

Mondays to Fridays

		GW	GW	GW	GW	GW	GW	GW	GW	GW	GW	GW	GW	GW	GW	GW	GW	GW	GW	GW FO
Wallingford Market Place	d	06 07	06 47	07 40	08 40	09 40	10 40	11 40	12 40	13 40	14 40	15 50	16 50	17 50	18 50	19 50	20 50	21 50	22 50	23 50
Reading	a	06 40	07 25	08 20	09 18	10 18	11 18	12 18	13 18	14 18	15 18	16 28	17 28	18 28	19 28	20 28	21 28	22 28	23 28	00 28

Saturdays

		GW	GW	GW	GW	GW	GW	GW	GW	GW	GW	GW	GW	GW	GW	GW	GW	GW
Wallingford Market Place	d	07 40	08 40	09 40	10 40	11 40	12 40	13 40	14 40	15 50	16 50	17 50	18 50	19 50	20 50	21 50	22 50	23 50
Reading	a	08 20	09 18	10 18	11 18	12 18	13 18	14 18	15 18	16 28	17 28	18 28	19 28	20 28	21 28	22 28	23 28	00 28

Sundays

		GW	GW	GW	GW	GW	GW	GW	GW
Wallingford Market Place	d	10 40	12 40	14 40	16 40	18 40	20 40	22 40	23 50
Reading	a	11 18	13 18	15 18	17 18	19 18	21 18	23 18	00 28

For general notes see front of timetable
For details of catering facilities see
Directory of Train Operators

Oxford → Abingdon

Bus Service

		GW 🚌	GW 🚌	GW 🚌	GW 🚌	GW 🚌	GW 🚌	GW 🚌	GW 🚌	GW 🚌	GW 🚌	GW 🚌
Oxford	d	06 30	06 50	07 10	07 30	07 47	07 55	08 10	08 25	08 40	08 55	09 13
Abingdon High Street	a	07 00	07 20	07 40	08 00	08 17	08 25	08 40	08 55	09 10	09 25	09 43

		GW 🚌	GW 🚌	GW 🚌	GW 🚌	GW 🚌	GW 🚌	GW 🚌	GW 🚌	GW 🚌	GW 🚌
Oxford	d	09 23	09 43	10 03	10 23	10 43	11 03	11 23	11 43	12 03	12 23
Abingdon High Street	a	09 53	10 13	10 33	10 53	11 13	11 33	11 53	12 13	12 33	12 53

		GW 🚌	GW 🚌	GW 🚌	GW 🚌	GW 🚌	GW 🚌	GW 🚌	GW 🚌	GW 🚌	GW 🚌	GW 🚌
Oxford	d	12 43	13 03	13 23	13 43	14 03	14 23	14 43	15 03	15 23	15 43	16 03
Abingdon High Street	a	13 13	13 33	13 53	14 13	14 33	14 53	15 13	15 33	15 53	16 13	16 33

		GW 🚌	GW 🚌	GW 🚌	GW 🚌	GW 🚌	GW 🚌	GW 🚌	GW 🚌	GW 🚌	GW FO 🚌
Oxford	d	16 23	16 38	16 53	17 08	17 23	17 38	17 53	18 13	18 30	18 40
Abingdon High Street	a	16 53	17 08	17 23	17 38	17 53	18 08	18 23	18 43	19 00	19 10

		GW FX 🚌	GW FO 🚌	GW 🚌	GW FO 🚌	GW FX 🚌	GW FO 🚌	GW FX 🚌	GW FO 🚌	GW 🚌	GW FO 🚌	GW FX 🚌	GW FX 🚌	GW 🚌
Oxford	d	18 50	18 55	19 10	19 25	19 30	19 40	19 50	19 55	20 10	20 25	20 30	20 50	21 10
Abingdon High Street	a	19 20	19 25	19 40	19 55	20 00	20 10	20 20	20 25	20 40	20 55	21 00	21 20	21 40

		GW 🚌	GW 🚌	GW 🚌	GW 🚌	GW 🚌	GW 🚌	GW 🚌	GW 🚌	GW 🚌
Oxford	d	21 30	21 50	22 10	22 30	22 50	23 10	23 30	23 50	
Abingdon High Street	a	22 00	22 20	22 40	23 00	23 20	23 40	23 59	00 20	

Saturdays

		GW 🚌	GW 🚌	GW 🚌	GW 🚌	GW 🚌	GW 🚌	GW 🚌	GW 🚌	GW 🚌	GW 🚌
Oxford	d	06 50	07 10	07 30	07 50	08 10	08 30	08 50	09 03	09 23	09 43
Abingdon High Street	a	07 20	07 40	08 00	08 20	08 40	09 00	09 20	09 33	09 53	10 13

		GW 🚌	GW 🚌	GW 🚌	GW 🚌	GW 🚌	GW 🚌	GW 🚌	GW 🚌	GW 🚌
Oxford	d	10 03	10 23	10 43	11 03	11 23	11 43	12 03	12 23	12 43
Abingdon High Street	a	10 33	10 53	11 13	11 33	11 53	12 13	12 33	12 53	13 13

		GW 🚌	GW 🚌	GW 🚌	GW 🚌	GW 🚌	GW 🚌	GW 🚌	GW 🚌	GW 🚌	GW 🚌
Oxford	d	13 03	13 23	13 43	14 03	14 23	14 43	15 03	15 23	15 43	16 03
Abingdon High Street	a	13 33	13 53	14 13	14 33	14 53	15 13	15 33	15 53	16 13	16 33

		GW 🚌	GW 🚌	GW 🚌	GW 🚌	GW 🚌	GW 🚌	GW 🚌	GW 🚌	GW 🚌
Oxford	d	16 23	16 43	17 03	17 23	17 43	18 03	18 26	18 40	18 55
Abingdon High Street	a	16 53	17 13	17 33	17 53	18 13	18 33	18 56	19 10	19 25

		GW 🚌	GW 🚌	GW 🚌	GW 🚌	GW 🚌	GW 🚌	GW 🚌	GW 🚌	GW 🚌
Oxford	d	19 10	19 25	19 40	19 55	20 10	20 25	20 40	20 55	21 10
Abingdon High Street	a	19 40	19 55	20 10	20 25	20 40	20 55	21 10	21 25	21 40

		GW 🚌	GW 🚌	GW 🚌	GW 🚌	GW 🚌	GW 🚌	GW 🚌	GW 🚌
Oxford	d	21 30	21 50	22 10	22 30	22 50	23 10	23 30	23 50
Abingdon High Street	a	22 00	22 20	22 40	23 00	23 20	23 40	23 59	00 20

Sundays

		GW 🚌	GW 🚌	GW 🚌	GW 🚌	GW 🚌	GW 🚌	GW 🚌	GW 🚌	GW 🚌
Oxford	d	08 00	08 20	08 40	09 00	09 20	09 40	10 10	10 40	11 10
Abingdon High Street	a	08 30	08 50	09 10	09 30	09 50	10 10	10 40	11 10	11 40

		GW 🚌	GW 🚌	GW 🚌	GW 🚌	GW 🚌	GW 🚌	GW 🚌	GW 🚌
Oxford	d	11 40	12 10	12 40	13 10	13 40	14 10	14 40	15 10
Abingdon High Street	a	12 10	12 40	13 10	13 40	14 10	14 40	15 10	15 40

		GW 🚌	GW 🚌	GW 🚌	GW 🚌	GW 🚌	GW 🚌	GW 🚌	GW 🚌	GW 🚌
Oxford	d	15 40	16 10	16 40	17 10	17 40	18 10	18 40	19 10	19 40
Abingdon High Street	a	16 10	16 40	17 10	17 40	18 10	18 40	19 10	19 40	20 10

		GW 🚌	GW 🚌	GW 🚌	GW 🚌	GW 🚌	GW 🚌	GW 🚌	GW 🚌
Oxford	d	20 10	20 40	21 10	21 40	22 10	22 40	23 10	23 50
Abingdon High Street	a	20 40	21 10	21 40	22 10	22 40	23 10	23 40	00 20

For general notes see front of timetable
For details of catering facilities see
Directory of Train Operators

Abingdon → Oxford
Bus Service

		GW 🚌	GW 🚌	GW 🚌	GW 🚌	GW 🚌	GW 🚌	GW 🚌		GW 🚌	GW 🚌	GW 🚌	GW 🚌	GW 🚌	GW 🚌	GW 🚌		GW 🚌	GW 🚌	GW 🚌	GW 🚌	GW 🚌	GW 🚌	GW 🚌		GW 🚌
Abingdon High Street	d	05 50	06 10	06 30	06 50	07 10	07 30	07 45	.....	08 00	08 15	08 30	08 45	09 00	09 15	09 30	.....	09 50	10 10	10 30	10 50	11 10	11 30	11 50	.....	12 10
Oxford	a	06 20	06 40	07 00	07 20	07 40	08 00	08 15	.	08 30	08 45	09 00	09 15	09 30	09 45	10 00	.	10 20	10 40	11 00	11 20	11 40	12 00	12 20	.	12 40

		GW 🚌	GW 🚌	GW 🚌	GW 🚌	GW 🚌	GW 🚌	GW 🚌		GW 🚌	GW 🚌	GW 🚌	GW 🚌	GW 🚌	GW 🚌	GW 🚌		GW 🚌	GW 🚌	GW 🚌	GW 🚌	GW 🚌	GW 🚌	GW 🚌		GW FO 🚌
Abingdon High Street	d	12 30	12 50	13 10	13 30	13 50	14 10	14 30	.....	14 50	15 10	15 30	15 50	16 10	16 30	16 50	.....	17 05	17 20	17 35	17 50	18 05	18 25	18 40	.....	18 55
Oxford	a	13 00	13 20	13 40	14 00	14 20	14 40	15 00	.	15 20	15 40	16 00	16 20	16 40	17 00	17 20	.	17 35	17 50	18 05	18 20	18 35	18 55	19 10	.	19 25

		GW FX 🚌	GW FO 🚌	GW FX 🚌	GW FO 🚌	GW 🚌	GW FO 🚌	GW FX 🚌		GW FO 🚌	GW FX 🚌	GW FO 🚌	GW 🚌	GW FO 🚌	GW FX 🚌	GW FO 🚌	GW FX 🚌	GW FO 🚌	GW 🚌	GW 🚌	GW 🚌	GW 🚌	GW 🚌	GW 🚌		
Abingdon High Street	d	19 00	19 10	19 20	19 25	19 40	19 55	20 00	.....	20 10	20 20	20 25	20 40	20 55	21 00	21 10	21 20	21 25	21 40	22 00	22 20	22 40	23 00	23 20	.....	.....
Oxford	a	19 30	19 40	19 50	19 55	20 10	20 25	20 30	.	20 40	20 50	20 55	21 10	21 25	21 30	21 40	21 50	21 55	22 10	22 30	22 50	23 10	23 30	23 50	.	.

Saturdays

		GW 🚌	GW 🚌	GW 🚌		GW 🚌	GW 🚌	GW 🚌		GW 🚌	GW 🚌	GW 🚌		GW 🚌	GW 🚌	GW 🚌		GW 🚌	GW 🚌	GW 🚌		GW 🚌	GW 🚌	GW 🚌		GW 🚌
Abingdon High Street	d	06 20	06 40	07 00	.....	07 20	07 40	08 00	.....	08 20	08 30	08 50	.....	09 10	09 30	09 50	.....	10 10	10 30	10 50	.....	11 10	11 30	11 50	.....	12 10
Oxford	a	06 50	07 10	07 30	.	07 50	08 10	08 30	.	08 50	09 00	09 20	.	09 40	10 00	10 20	.	10 40	11 00	11 20	.	11 40	12 00	12 20	.	12 40

		GW 🚌	GW 🚌	GW 🚌		GW 🚌	GW 🚌	GW 🚌		GW 🚌	GW 🚌	GW 🚌		GW 🚌	GW 🚌	GW 🚌		GW 🚌	GW 🚌	GW 🚌		GW 🚌	GW 🚌	GW 🚌		GW 🚌
Abingdon High Street	d	12 30	12 50	13 10	.....	13 30	13 50	14 10	.....	14 30	14 50	15 10	.....	15 30	15 50	16 10	.....	16 30	16 50	17 10	.....	17 30	17 50	18 10	.....	18 25
Oxford	a	13 00	13 20	13 40	.	14 00	14 20	14 40	.	15 00	15 20	15 40	.	16 00	16 20	16 40	.	17 00	17 20	17 40	.	18 00	18 20	18 40	.	18 53

		GW 🚌	GW 🚌	GW 🚌		GW 🚌	GW 🚌	GW 🚌		GW 🚌	GW 🚌	GW 🚌		GW 🚌	GW 🚌	GW 🚌		GW 🚌	GW 🚌	GW 🚌		GW 🚌	GW 🚌	GW 🚌		
Abingdon High Street	d	18 40	18 55	19 10	.....	19 25	19 40	19 55	.....	20 10	20 25	20 40	.....	20 55	21 10	21 25	.....	21 40	22 00	22 20	.....	22 40	23 00	23 20	.....	.....
Oxford	a	19 08	19 23	19 38	.	19 53	20 08	20 23	.	20 38	20 53	21 08	.	21 23	21 38	21 53	.	22 10	22 30	22 50	.	23 10	23 30	23 50	.	.

Sundays

		GW 🚌	GW 🚌		GW 🚌	GW 🚌		GW 🚌	GW 🚌		GW 🚌	GW 🚌		GW 🚌	GW 🚌		GW 🚌	GW 🚌		GW 🚌	GW 🚌		GW 🚌	GW 🚌		GW 🚌
Abingdon High Street	d	07 30	07 50	.....	08 10	08 30	.....	08 50	09 10	.....	09 40	10 10	.....	10 40	11 10	.....	11 40	12 10	.....	12 40	13 10	.....	13 40	14 10	.....	14 40
Oxford	a	08 00	08 20	.	08 40	09 00	.	09 20	09 40	.	10 10	10 40	.	11 10	11 40	.	12 10	12 40	.	13 10	13 40	.	14 10	14 40	.	15 10

		GW 🚌	GW 🚌		GW 🚌	GW 🚌		GW 🚌	GW 🚌		GW 🚌	GW 🚌		GW 🚌	GW 🚌		GW 🚌	GW 🚌		GW 🚌	GW 🚌		GW 🚌	GW 🚌		
Abingdon High Street	d	15 10	15 40	.....	16 10	16 40	.....	17 10	17 40	.....	18 10	18 40	.....	19 10	19 40	.....	20 10	20 40	.....	21 10	21 40	.....	22 10	22 40	.....	.....
Oxford	a	15 40	16 10	.	16 40	17 10	.	17 40	18 10	.	18 40	19 10	.	19 40	20 10	.	20 40	21 10	.	21 40	22 10	.	22 40	23 10	.	.

For general notes see front of timetable
For details of catering facilities see
Directory of Train Operators

Table 116C

Mondays to Fridays

Oxford → Eynsham → Witney
Bus Service

		GW MX	GW MO	GW MFO	GW		GW	GW	GW	GW		GW	GW	GW	GW		GW	GW	GW	GW		GW	GW	GW	GW		GW
Oxford	d	23p47	23p52	00 47	05 59		06 54	07 14	07 19	07 39		07 59	08 19	08 39	08 59		09 14	09 29	09 44	09 59		10 14	10 29	10 44	10 59		11 14
Eynsham Church	a	00 01	00 08	01 00	06 14		07 09	07 29	07 36	07 57		08 17	08 37	08 57	09 17		09 32	09 47	10 02	10 17		10 32	10 47	11 02	11 17		11 32
Witney Market Place	a	00 12	00 24	01 12	06 27		07 21	07 41	07 51	08 14		08 34	08 54	09 14	09 34		09 49	10 04	10 19	10 34		10 49	11 04	11 19	11 34		11 49

		GW	GW	GW	GW		GW	GW	GW	GW		GW	GW	GW	GW		GW	GW	GW	GW		GW	GW	GW	GW		GW
Oxford	d	11 29	11 44	11 59	12 14		12 29	12 44	12 59	13 14		13 29	13 44	13 59	14 14		14 29	14 44	14 59	15 14		15 29	15 44	15 59	16 14		16 29
Eynsham Church	a	11 47	12 02	12 17	12 32		12 47	13 02	13 17	13 32		13 47	14 02	14 17	14 32		14 47	15 02	15 17	15 32		15 47	16 02	16 17	16 32		16 47
Witney Market Place	a	12 04	12 19	12 34	12 49		13 04	13 19	13 34	13 49		14 04	14 19	14 34	14 49		15 04	15 19	15 34	15 49		16 04	16 19	16 34	16 49		17 04

		GW	GW	GW	GW		GW	GW	GW	GW		GW	GW	GW	GW		GW	GW	GW	GW	GW	GW	GW	GW	GW		
Oxford	d	16 39	16 49	16 59	17 09		17 19	17 29	17 39	17 49		17 59	18 12	18 27	18 47		19 22	19 57	20 37	20 52	21 17	21 57	22 27	23 07	23 47		
Eynsham Church	a	17 03	17 14	17 24	17 34		17 44	17 54	18 04	18 14		18 24	18 35	18 45	19 05		19 37	20 10	20 50	21 05	21 30	22 10	22 40	23 20	00 01		
Witney Market Place	a	17 22	17 35	17 43	17 53		18 03	18 13	18 23	18 33		18 43	18 52	19 02	19 22		19 52	20 22	21 02	21 17	21 42	22 22	22 52	23 32	00 12		

Saturdays

		GW	GW	GW		GW	GW	GW		GW	GW	GW		GW	GW	GW		GW	GW	GW		GW	GW	GW		GW	GW
Oxford	d	23p47	00 17	00 47		01 47	06 35	07 22		07 52	08 17	08 38		08 59	09 14	09 29		09 44	09 59	10 14		10 29	10 44	10 59		11 14	11 29
Eynsham Church	a	00 01	00 30	01 00		02 00	06 50	07 37		08 07	08 33	08 55		09 16	09 32	09 47		10 02	10 17	10 32		10 47	11 02	11 17		11 32	11 47
Witney Market Place	a	00 12	00 42	01 12		02 12	07 02	07 49		08 19	08 48	09 10		09 31	09 49	10 04		10 19	10 32	10 49		11 04	11 19	11 32		11 49	12 04

		GW	GW	GW		GW	GW	GW		GW	GW	GW		GW	GW	GW		GW	GW	GW		GW	GW	GW		GW	GW
Oxford	d	11 44	11 59	12 14		12 29	12 44	12 59		13 14	13 29	13 44		13 59	14 14	14 29		14 44	14 59	15 14		15 29	15 44	15 59		16 14	16 29
Eynsham Church	a	12 02	12 17	12 32		12 47	13 02	13 17		13 32	13 47	14 02		14 17	14 32	14 47		15 02	15 17	15 32		15 47	16 02	16 17		16 32	16 47
Witney Market Place	a	12 19	12 32	12 49		13 04	13 19	13 32		13 49	14 04	14 19		14 32	14 49	15 04		15 19	15 32	15 49		16 04	16 19	16 32		16 49	17 04

		GW	GW	GW		GW	GW	GW		GW	GW	GW		GW	GW	GW		GW	GW	GW		GW	GW	GW			
Oxford	d	16 44	16 59	17 14		17 29	17 44	17 54		18 09	18 29	18 47		19 22	19 57	20 37		20 52	21 17	21 57		22 27	23 07	23 47			
Eynsham Church	a	17 02	17 17	17 32		17 47	17 52	18 02		18 17	18 39	18 55		19 37	20 10	20 50		21 05	21 30	22 10		22 40	23 20	23 59			
Witney Market Place	a	17 19	17 32	17 49		18 04	18 19	18 29		18 44	19 04	19 22		19 52	20 22	21 02		21 17	21 42	22 22		22 52	23 32	00 12			

Sundays

		GW		GW		GW		GW		GW		GW		GW		GW		GW		GW		GW		GW		GW	GW
Oxford	d	00 17		00 47		01 17		01 47		08 22		09 22		10 22		11 22		11 52		12 22		12 52		13 22		13 52	14 22
Eynsham Church	a	00 30		01 00		01 30		02 00		08 38		09 38		10 38		11 38		12 08		12 38		13 08		13 38		14 08	14 38
Witney Market Place	a	00 42		01 12		01 42		02 12		08 54		09 54		10 54		11 54		12 24		12 54		13 24		13 54		14 24	14 54

		GW		GW		GW		GW		GW		GW		GW		GW		GW	GW	GW	GW	GW	GW	GW	GW		
Oxford	d	14 52		15 22		15 52		16 22		16 52		17 22		17 52		18 22		18 52	19 22	20 22	21 22	22 22	23 12	23 47	23 52		
Eynsham Church	a	15 08		15 38		16 08		16 38		17 08		17 38		18 08		18 38		19 08	19 38	20 38	21 38	22 38	23 28	23 59	00 08		
Witney Market Place	a	15 24		15 54		16 24		16 54		17 24		17 54		18 24		18 54		19 24	19 54	20 54	21 54	22 54	23 44	00 12	00 24		

For general notes see front of timetable
For details of catering facilities see
Directory of Train Operators

Table 116C

Mondays to Fridays

Witney → Eynsham → Oxford

Bus Service

		GW	GW	GW	GW		GW	GW	GW	GW		GW	GW	GW	GW		GW	GW	GW	GW		GW	GW	GW	GW		GW
Witney Market Place	d	05 20	06 12	06 28	06 44	.....	06 59	07 14	07 24	07 34	.....	07 44	07 54	08 05	08 25	.....	08 40	08 55	09 10	09 25	.....	09 40	09 55	10 10	10 25	.....	10 40
Eynsham Witney Road	d	05 29	06 26	06 42	06 58	.	07 13	07 28	07 38	07 48	.	07 58	08 08	08 19	08 39	.	08 54	09 09	09 24	09 39	.	09 54	10 09	10 24	10 39	.	10 54
Oxford	a	05 50	06 50	07 10	07 30	.....	07 45	08 10	08 20	08 30	.....	08 40	08 50	09 11	09 21	.....	09 32	09 37	09 52	10 07	.....	10 22	10 37	10 52	11 07	.....	11 22

		GW	GW	GW	GW		GW	GW	GW	GW		GW	GW	GW	GW		GW	GW	GW	GW		GW	GW	GW	GW		GW
Witney Market Place	d	10 55	11 10	11 25	11 40	.....	11 55	12 10	12 25	12 40	.....	12 55	13 10	13 25	13 40	.....	13 55	14 10	14 25	14 40	.....	14 55	15 10	15 25	15 40	.....	16 00
Eynsham Witney Road	d	11 09	11 24	11 39	11 54	.	12 09	12 24	12 39	12 54	.	13 09	13 24	13 39	13 54	.	14 09	14 24	14 39	14 54	.	15 09	15 24	15 39	15 54	.	16 14
Oxford	a	11 37	11 52	12 07	12 22	.....	12 37	12 52	13 07	13 22	.....	13 37	13 52	14 07	14 22	.....	14 37	14 52	15 07	15 22	.....	15 37	15 52	16 07	16 22	.....	16 42

		GW	GW	GW	GW		GW	GW	GW	GW		GW	GW	GW	GW		GW	GW	GW	GW		GW	GW	GW	GW		
															FX		FO										
Witney Market Place	d	16 10	16 30	16 50	17 10	.....	17 21	17 34	17 56	18 22	.....	18 52	19 00	19 35	20 04	.....	20 12	20 34	20 40	21 04	.....	21 44	22 24	23 04	23 34	.....	.....
Eynsham Witney Road	d	16 24	16 44	17 04	17 24	.	17 35	17 48	18 10	18 38	.	19 08	19 16	19 50	20 19	.	20 28	20 49	20 55	21 18	.	21 58	22 38	23 18	23 48	.	.
Oxford	a	16 52	17 12	17 32	17 52	.....	18 03	18 16	18 38	19 03	.....	19 33	19 41	20 11	20 40	.....	20 53	21 10	21 19	21 40	.....	22 20	23 00	23 40	00 10	.....	.....

Saturdays

		GW	GW		GW	GW		GW	GW		GW	GW		GW	GW		GW	GW		GW	GW		GW	GW		GW	GW
Witney Market Place	d	05 52	06 42	.....	07 12	07 32	.....	07 53	08 10	.....	08 25	08 40	.....	08 55	09 10	.....	09 25	09 40	.....	09 55	10 10	.....	10 25	10 40	.....	10 55	11 10
Eynsham Witney Road	d	06 01	06 51	.	07 21	07 45	.	08 07	08 24	.	08 39	08 54	.	09 09	09 24	.	09 39	09 54	.	10 09	10 24	.	10 39	10 54	.	11 09	11 24
Oxford	a	06 25	07 15	.....	07 45	08 09	.....	08 31	08 52	.....	09 07	09 22	.....	09 37	09 52	.....	10 07	10 22	.....	10 37	10 52	.....	11 07	11 22	.....	11 37	11 52

		GW	GW		GW	GW		GW	GW		GW	GW		GW	GW		GW	GW		GW	GW		GW	GW		GW	GW
Witney Market Place	d	11 25	11 40	.....	11 55	12 10	.....	12 25	12 40	.....	12 55	13 10	.....	13 25	13 40	.....	13 55	14 10	.....	14 25	14 40	.....	14 55	15 10	.....	15 25	15 40
Eynsham Witney Road	d	11 39	11 54	.	12 09	12 24	.	12 39	12 54	.	13 09	13 24	.	13 39	13 54	.	14 09	14 24	.	14 39	14 54	.	15 09	15 24	.	15 39	15 54
Oxford	a	12 07	12 22	.....	12 37	12 52	.....	13 07	13 22	.....	13 37	13 52	.....	14 07	14 22	.....	14 37	14 52	.....	15 07	15 22	.....	15 37	15 52	.....	16 07	16 22

		GW	GW		GW	GW		GW	GW		GW	GW		GW	GW		GW	GW	GW	GW	GW	GW	GW	GW	GW		
Witney Market Place	d	15 55	16 10	.....	16 25	16 40	.....	16 55	17 15	.....	17 35	17 58	.....	18 25	18 52	.....	19 00	19 38	20 12	20 40	21 04	21 44	22 24	23 04	23 34	.....	.....
Eynsham Witney Road	d	16 09	16 24	.	16 39	16 54	.	17 09	17 29	.	17 49	18 12	.	18 41	19 08	.	19 16	19 54	20 29	20 55	21 18	21 58	22 38	23 18	23 48	.	.
Oxford	a	16 37	16 52	.....	17 07	17 22	.....	17 37	17 57	.....	18 17	18 40	.....	19 06	19 33	.....	19 41	20 19	20 53	21 19	21 40	22 20	23 00	23 40	00 10	.....	.....

Sundays

		GW	GW	GW	GW	GW	GW	GW	GW	GW	GW	GW	GW	GW	GW	GW	GW	GW	GW	GW	GW	GW	GW	GW	GW	GW	
Witney Market Place	d	07 35	08 35	09 35	10 35	11 05	11 35	12 05	12 35	13 05	13 35	14 05	14 35	15 05	15 35	16 05	16 35	17 05	17 35	18 05	18 35	19 35	20 35	21 35	22 35	23 34	.....
Eynsham Witney Road	d	07 51	08 51	09 51	10 51	11 21	11 51	12 21	12 51	13 21	13 51	14 21	14 51	15 21	15 51	16 21	16 51	17 21	17 51	18 21	18 51	19 51	20 51	21 51	22 51	23 48	.
Oxford	a	08 08	09 08	10 08	11 08	11 38	12 08	12 38	13 08	13 38	14 08	14 38	15 08	15 38	16 08	16 38	17 08	17 38	18 08	18 38	19 08	20 08	21 08	22 08	23 08	00 10	.....

For general notes see front of timetable
For details of catering facilities see
Directory of Train Operators

London → Greenford and Reading

(Local services only)

Network Diagram - see first page of Table 116

Miles	Miles	Miles			GW MX 1◇	GW MO 1 A	GW MO 1 B	GW MX 1	GW MX 1	GW MO 1◇ A	GW MO 1◇ B	GW MO 1 A	GW MO 1 B	GW MX 1	GW MX 1◇	GW MO 1	GW MX 1	GW 1	GW 1	HC	HC	GW 1 C	GW 1◇ ☕	GW 1 C	HC
0	0	0	**London Paddington 15** ⊖	d	23p21	23p15	23p15		23p29	23p42	23p42	23p53	23p53	23p48	00 21	00 34	00 34	01 34	03 34	04 42	05 13	05 22	05 30		05 33
4¼	4¼	4¼	Acton Main Line	d										23p54											
5¾	5¾	5¾	**Ealing Broadway** ⊖	d		23p22	23p24		23p36	23p50	23p50	00 01	00 01	23p58		00 41	00 41	01 41	03 41	04 50	05 21	05 31			05 41
6½	6½	6½	West Ealing	d										23p59											05 43
—	7¼	—	Drayton Green	d																					
—	7¾	—	Castle Bar Park	d																					
—	8¼	—	South Greenford	d																					
—	9¼	—	**Greenford** ⊖	a																					
7¼	—	7¼	Hanwell	d										00 03											05 46
9	—	9	Southall	d		23p29	23p29					00 06	00 06	00 07		00 46	00 46	01 46	03 47	04 54	05 25	05 37			05 49
10¾	—	10¾	Hayes & Harlington	d		23p33	23p33		23p44			00 10	00 10	00 12		00 50	00 50	01 50	03 51	04 58	05 29	05 42			05 53
—	—	14¾	**Heathrow Terminals 1-2-3** ✈	a																05 04	05 35				05 59
—	—	16½	**Heathrow Terminal 4** ✈	a																05 10	05 41				06 10
—	—	—	**Heathrow Terminal 5** ✈	a																*05b32*	*05b46*			←	*06b16*
13¼	—	—	West Drayton	d		23p36	23p37					00 14	00 14	00 16		00 55	00 55	01 55	03 55			05 46 →		05 46	
14¾	—	—	Iver	d										00 19										05 49	
16¼	—	—	Langley	d		23p42	23p42					00 19	00 19	00 22		00 59	00 59							05 52	
18½	—	—	**Slough 3**	a	23p42	23p47	23p47		23p55	23p59	00 02	00 24	00 24	00 28	00 40	01 05	01 04	02 04	04 04				05 47	05 57	
—	—	—		d	23p43	23p47	23p47		23p55	00 02	00 03	00 24	00 24	00 29	00 41	01 05	01 05	02 04	04 05				05 49	05 58	
21	—	—	Burnham	d		23p51	23p51					00 28	00 28	00 33		01 09	01 09								
22½	—	—	Taplow	d									00 32	00 36			01 12								
24¼	—	—	**Maidenhead 3**	d		23p55	23p56		00 03	00 10	00 10	00 33	00 36	00 40		01 13	01 16	02 12	04 12					06 05	
31	—	—	**Twyford 3**	d		00 04	00 04	00 07	00 11			00 41	00 44	00 48		01 22	01 24	02 19	04 20					06 13	
36	—	—	**Reading 7**	a	00 01	00 10	00 10	00 17	00 18	00 23	00 23	00 48	00 50	00 55	00 58	01 32	01 33	02 29	04 29				06 04	06 19	
—	—	—	Oxford	a	00 34				01 08	00 55	00 55				01 30				*06 21*					07 22	

		GW 1◇ ☕	GW 1	GW 1	GW 1	HC	GW 1◇	GW 1	GW 1	GW 1	GW 1	GW 1	GW 1◇	GW 1	GW 1	HC	GW 1	GW 1	GW 1	HC	GW 1	GW 1◇	GW 1	GW 1	GW 1
London Paddington 15 ⊖	d	05 42	05 44	05 55	06 00	06 03	06 07			06 15	06 25	06 30	06 33			06 33	06 45	06 55	07 00	07 03	07 15	07 21			07 25
Acton Main Line	d			06 01							06 31							07 01							07 31
Ealing Broadway ⊖	d		05 51	06 04	06 07	06 11				06 22	06 34	06 37				06 41	06 52	07 04	07 07	07 11	07 22				07 34
West Ealing	d			06 06		06 13					06 36					06 43		07 06		07 13					07 36
Drayton Green	d			06 09							06 39							07 09							07 39
Castle Bar Park	d			06 10							06 40							07 10							07 40
South Greenford	d			06 13							06 43							07 13							07 43
Greenford ⊖	a			06 19							06 49							07 19							07 49
Hanwell	d					06 16										06 46				07 16				←	
Southall	d		05 56		06 13	06 19				06 27						06 49	06 57		07 13	07 19	07 27 →			07 27	
Hayes & Harlington	d		06 00		06 17	06 23				06 31		06 45				06 53	07 01		07 17	07 23				07 31	
Heathrow Terminals 1-2-3 ✈	a					06 29										06 59				07 29					
Heathrow Terminal 4 ✈	a					06 40										07 10				07 40					
Heathrow Terminal 5 ✈	a					*06b46*			←						←	*07b16*				*07b46*					
West Drayton	d		06 05		06 21 →				06 21	06 36		06 49 →			06 49		07 06		07 21					07 36	
Iver	d								06 24						06 52				07 24						
Langley	d								06 27						06 55				07 27						
Slough 3	a	06 03	06 13				06 22		06 32	06 44			06 48		07 00		07 14		07 32			07 37		07 44	
	d	06 03	06 13				06 23		06 33	06 44			06 49		07 01		07 14		07 33			07 37		07 44	
Burnham	d		06 17					←		06 48				←			07 18							07 48	
Taplow	d		06 21 →					06 21		06 52 →				06 52			07 22						←	07 52	
Maidenhead 3	d							06 25	06 40					06 56	07 08		07 26		07 40 →				07 40	07 56	
Twyford 3	d							06 32	06 48					07 03	07 16		07 33						07 48	08 03	
Reading 7	a	06 20					06 39	06 41	06 54				07 05	07 12	07 22		07 42					07 51	07 54	08 12	
Oxford	a	06 52					07 10	*07 35*	07 49				07 40		08 05							08 20	08 42	*09 06*	

		GW 1	HC	GW 1	GW 1◇ ☕	GW 1	GW 1	GW 1	GW 1	HC	GW 1	GW 1◇	GW 1	GW 1	GW 1	GW 1	HC	GW 1	GW 1	GW 1◇ ☕	GW 1	GW 1	GW 1	GW 1	GW 1
London Paddington 15 ⊖	d	07 30	07 33	07 45	07 51			07 55	08 00	08 03	08 15	08 21			08 25	08 30	08 33	08 40	08 45	08 51				08 55	09 00
Acton Main Line	d							08 01							08 31									09 01	
Ealing Broadway ⊖	d	07 37	07 41	07 52				08 04	08 07	08 11	08 22				08 34	08 37	08 41	08 47	08 52					09 04	09 07
West Ealing	d		07 43					08 06		08 13					08 36		08 43		08 55					09 06	
Drayton Green	d							08 09							08 39									09 09	
Castle Bar Park	d							08 10							08 40									09 10	
South Greenford	d							08 13							08 43									09 13	
Greenford ⊖	a							08 19							08 49									09 19	
Hanwell	d		07 46							08 16				←			08 46		08 57				←		
Southall	d	07 43	07 49	07 57					08 13	08 19	08 27 →			08 27		08 43	08 49	08 52	09 01 →				09 01		
Hayes & Harlington	d	07 47	07 53	08 01					08 17	08 23				08 31		08 47	08 53	08 56					09 05		09 15
Heathrow Terminals 1-2-3 ✈	a		07 59							08 29							08 59								
Heathrow Terminal 4 ✈	a		08 10							08 40							09 10								
Heathrow Terminal 5 ✈	a		*08b16*				←			*08b46*							*09b16*								
West Drayton	d	07 51		08 06 →			08 06		08 21					08 36		08 51							09 09		09 19
Iver	d	07 54							08 24							08 54							09 12		09 22
Langley	d	07 57							08 27							08 57							09 15		09 25
Slough 3	a	08 02			08 06		08 14		08 32			08 37		08 44		09 02		09 06		09 06			09 20		09 30
	d	08 03			08 07		08 14		08 33			08 37		08 44		09 03		09 06		09 07			09 21		09 31
Burnham	d						08 18							08 48				09 10				←			
Taplow	d					←	08 22						←	08 52				09 14 →			←	09 14			
Maidenhead 3	d	08 10 →				08 10	08 26		08 40 →				08 40	08 56		09 10 →					09 10	09 18	09 28		09 38 →
Twyford 3	d					08 18	08 33						08 48	09 03							09 18	09 25	09a35		
Reading 7	a				08 21	08 24	08 43					08 51	08 54	09 12						09 21	09 24	09 33			
Oxford	a				08 47	09 15						09 24	09 40							09 51	10 13	*10 06*			

For general notes see front of timetable
For details of catering facilities see Directory of Train Operators

For fast services between London Paddington and Reading see Table 116

A Until 8 September
B From 15 September
C To Bicester Town (Table 116)

b Change at Heathrow Terminals 1-2-3

London → Greenford and Reading
(Local services only)

Network Diagram - see first page of Table 116

Station		HC	GW 1	GW 1 ◊	GW 1	GW 1	GW 1	GW 1	HC	GW 1	GW 1 ◊ ☕	GW 1	GW 1	GW 1	GW 1	HC	GW 1	GW 1 ◊	GW 1	GW 1	GW 1	GW 1	HC	GW 1	GW 1 ◊
London Paddington 15 ⊖	d	09 03	09 15	09 21			09 25	09 30	09 33	09 45	09 51			09 55	10 00	10 03	10 15	10 21			10 25	10 30	10 33	10 45	10 51
Acton Main Line	d						09 31							10 01							10 31				
Ealing Broadway ⊖	d	09 11	09 22				09 34	09 37	09 41	09 52				10 04	10 07	10 11	10 22				10 34	10 37	10 41	10 52	
West Ealing	d	09 13					09 36		09 43					10 06		10 13					10 36		10 43		
Drayton Green	d						09 39							10 09							10 39				
Castle Bar Park	d						09 40							10 10							10 40				
South Greenford	d						09 43							10 13							10 43				
Greenford ⊖	a						09 49							10 19							10 49				
Hanwell	d	09 16				←			09 46				←			10 16				←			10 46		
Southall	d	09 19	09 27			09 27			09 49	09 57			09 57			10 19	10 27			10 27			10 49	10 57	
Hayes & Harlington	d	09 23	→			09 31		09 45	09 53	→			10 01		10 15	10 23	→			10 31		10 45	10 53	→	
Heathrow Terminals 1-2-3 ✈	a	09 29							09 59							10 29							10 59		
Heathrow Terminal 4 ✈	a	09 40							10 10							10 40							11 10		
Heathrow Terminal 5 ✈	a	09b46							10b16							10b46							11b16		
West Drayton	d					09 36		09 49					10 06		10 19					10 36		10 49			
Iver	d							09 52							10 22							10 52			
Langley	d							09 55							10 25							10 55			
Slough 3	a			09 37		09 44		10 00			10 06		10 14		10 30			10 37		10 44		11 00			11 06
	d			09 37		09 44		10 01			10 07		10 14		10 31			10 37		10 44		11 01			11 07
Burnham	d					09 48							10 18							10 48					
Taplow	d				←	09 52						←	10 22						←	10 52					
Maidenhead 3	d				09 38	09 56		10 08				10 08	10 26		10 38				10 38	10 56		11 08			
Twyford 3	d				09 46	10 03		→				10 16	10 33		→				10 46	11 03		→			
Reading 7	a			09 51	09 52	10 15					10 21	10 22	10 43					10 51	10 52	11 13					11 21
Oxford	a			10 18	10 31						10 47	11 14						11 18	11 31						11 51

Station		GW 1	GW 1	GW 1	GW 1	HC	GW 1	GW 1 ◊	GW 1	GW 1	GW 1		GW 1	HC	GW 1	GW 1 ◊ ☕	GW 1	GW 1	GW 1	GW 1	HC	GW 1	GW 1 ◊	GW 1	GW 1
London Paddington 15 ⊖	d			10 55	11 00	11 03	11 15	11 21			11 25		11 30	11 33	11 45	11 51			11 55	12 00	12 03	12 15	12 21		
Acton Main Line	d			11 01							11 31								12 01						
Ealing Broadway ⊖	d			11 04	11 07	11 11	11 22				11 34		11 37	11 41	11 52				12 04	12 07	12 11	12 22			
West Ealing	d			11 06		11 13					11 36			11 43					12 06		12 13				
Drayton Green	d			11 09							11 39								12 09						
Castle Bar Park	d			11 10							11 40								12 10						
South Greenford	d			11 13							11 43								12 13						
Greenford ⊖	a			11 19							11 49								12 19						
Hanwell	d		←			11 16				←				11 46				←			12 16				←
Southall	d		10 57			11 19	11 27			11 27				11 49	11 57			11 57			12 19	12 27			12 27
Hayes & Harlington	d		11 01		11 15	11 23	→			11 31			11 45	11 53	→			12 01		12 15	12 23	→			12 31
Heathrow Terminals 1-2-3 ✈	a					11 29								11 59							12 29				
Heathrow Terminal 4 ✈	a					11 40								12 10							12 40				
Heathrow Terminal 5 ✈	a					11b46								12b16							12b46				
West Drayton	d		11 06		11 19					11 36			11 49					12 06		12 19					12 36
Iver	d				11 22								11 52							12 22					
Langley	d				11 25								11 55							12 25					
Slough 3	a		11 14		11 30			11 37		11 44			12 00			12 06		12 14		12 30			12 37		12 44
	d		11 14		11 31			11 37		11 44			12 01			12 07		12 14		12 31			12 37		12 44
Burnham	d		11 18							11 48								12 18							12 48
Taplow	d	←	11 22						←	11 52							←	12 22						←	12 52
Maidenhead 3	d	11 08	11 26		11 38				11 38	11 56			12 08				12 08	12 26		12 38				12 38	12 56
Twyford 3	d	11 16	11 33		→				11 46	12 03			→				12 16	12 33		→				12 46	13 03
Reading 7	a	11 22	11 43					11 51	11 52	12 13						12 21	12 22	12 43					12 51	12 52	13 13
Oxford	a	12 13						12 18	12 31							12 47	13 14						13 18	13 31	

Station		GW 1	GW 1	HC	GW 1	GW 1 ◊	GW 1	GW 1	GW 1	GW 1	HC	GW 1	GW 1 ◊	GW 1	GW 1	GW 1	GW 1	HC	GW 1	GW 1 ◊ ☕	GW 1	GW 1	GW 1	GW 1	HC
London Paddington 15 ⊖	d	12 25	12 30	12 33	12 45	12 51			12 55	13 00	13 03	13 15	13 21			13 25	13 30	13 33	13 45	13 51			13 55	14 00	14 03
Acton Main Line	d	12 31							13 01							13 31							14 01		
Ealing Broadway ⊖	d	12 34	12 37	12 41	12 52				13 04	13 07	13 11	13 22				13 34	13 37	13 41	13 52				14 04	14 07	14 11
West Ealing	d	12 36		12 43					13 06		13 13					13 36		13 43					14 06		14 13
Drayton Green	d	12 39							13 09							13 39							14 09		
Castle Bar Park	d	12 40							13 10							13 40							14 10		
South Greenford	d	12 43							13 13							13 43							14 13		
Greenford ⊖	a	12 49							13 19							13 49							14 19		
Hanwell	d			12 46				←			13 16				←			13 46				←			14 16
Southall	d			12 49	12 57			12 57			13 19	13 27			13 27			13 49	13 57			13 57			14 19
Hayes & Harlington	d		12 45	12 53	→			13 01		13 15	13 23	→			13 31		13 45	13 53	→			14 01		14 15	14 23
Heathrow Terminals 1-2-3 ✈	a			12 59							13 29							13 59							14 29
Heathrow Terminal 4 ✈	a			13 10							13 40							14 10							14 40
Heathrow Terminal 5 ✈	a			13b16							13b46							14b16							14b46
West Drayton	d		12 49					13 06		13 19					13 36		13 49					14 06		14 19	
Iver	d		12 52							13 22							13 52							14 22	
Langley	d		12 55							13 25							13 55							14 25	
Slough 3	a		13 00			13 06		13 14		13 30			13 37		13 44		14 00			14 06		14 14		14 30	
	d		13 01			13 07		13 14		13 31			13 37		13 44		14 01			14 07		14 14		14 31	
Burnham	d							13 18							13 48							14 18			
Taplow	d						←	13 22						←	13 52						←	14 22			
Maidenhead 3	d		13 08				13 08	13 26		13 38				13 38	13 56		14 08				14 08	14 26		14 38	
Twyford 3	d		→				13 16	13 33		→				13 46	14 03		→				14 16	14 33		14 46	
Reading 7	a					13 21	13 22	13 43					13 51	13 52	14 13					14 21	14 22	14 43		14 52	
Oxford	a					13 51	14 13						14 18	14 31						14 47	15 13	*15 21*		15 31	

For general notes see front of timetable
For details of catering facilities see Directory of Train Operators

For fast services between London Paddington and Reading see Table 116

b Change at Heathrow Terminals 1-2-3

London → Greenford and Reading

(Local services only)

Network Diagram - see first page of Table 116

Station		GW 1	GW 1	GW 1	HC	GW 1	GW 1 ◇	GW 1	GW 1	GW 1	GW 1	HC	GW 1	GW 1 ◇ A	GW 1	GW 1	GW 1	GW 1	HC	GW 1	GW 1 ◇ ☕	GW 1	GW 1	GW 1	GW 1 B
London Paddington 15 ⊖	d	14 15	14 25	14 30	14 33	14 45	14 51			14 55	15 00	15 03	15 15	15 21			15 25	15 30	15 33	15 45	15 51			15 55	16 00
Acton Main Line	d		14 31							15 01							15 31							16 01	
Ealing Broadway ⊖	d	14 22	14 34	14 37	14 41	14 52				15 04	15 07	15 11	15 22				15 34	15 37	15 41	15 52				16 04	16 07
West Ealing	d		14 36		14 43					15 06		15 13					15 36		15 43					16 06	
Drayton Green	d		14 39							15 09							15 39							16 09	
Castle Bar Park	d		14 40							15 10							15 40							16 10	
South Greenford	d		14 43							15 13							15 43							16 13	
Greenford ⊖	a		14 49							15 19							15 49							16 19	
Hanwell	d				14 46				←			15 16							15 46						
Southall	d	14 27			14 49	14 57			14 57			15 19	15 27			←			15 49	15 57			←		16 13
Hayes & Harlington	d	14 31		14 45	14 53	→			15 01		15 15	15 23	15 31			15 31		15 45	15 53	16 01			16 01		16 17
Heathrow Terminals 1-2-3 ✈	a				14 59							15 29	→						15 59	→					
Heathrow Terminal 4 ✈	a				15 10							15 40							16 10						
Heathrow Terminal 5 ✈	a				15b16							15b46							16b16						
West Drayton	d	14 36		14 49					15 06		15 19					15 36		15 51					16 06		16 22
Iver	d			14 52							15 22					15 39							16 10		
Langley	d			14 55							15 25					15 42							16 13		
Slough 3	a	14 44		15 00			15 06		15 14		15 30			15 37		15 47		15 58			16 06		16 18		16 30
	d	14 44		15 01			15 07		15 14		15 31			15 37		15 47		15 58			16 07		16 19		16 30
Burnham	d	14 48							15 18							15 51							16 23		
Taplow	d	14 52						←	15 22						←	15 55						←	16 26		
Maidenhead 3	d	14 56		15 08				15 08	15 26		15 38				15 38	15 59		16 06				16 06	16 30		16 38
Twyford 3	d	15 03		→				15 16	15 33		→				15 46	16 07		→				16 14	16 38		→
Reading 7	a	15 13					15 21	15 22	15 43					15 51	15 52	16 15					16 21	16 23	16 45		
Oxford	a						15 51	16 13	*16 18*					16 18	16 31						16 47	17 15			

Station		HC	GW 1	GW 1 ◇	GW 1 B	GW 1	GW 1	GW 1 ◇ ☕	GW 1	GW 1	HC	GW 1	GW 1	GW 1	HC	GW 1 ◇ C ☕	GW 1	GW 1	GW 1 D	GW 1	GW 1	GW 1	GW 1 B	GW 1 D	GW 1
London Paddington 15 ⊖	d	16 03	16 14	16 21		16 25	16 30	16 33			16 33	16 44	16 55	17 00	17 03	17 06			17 14	17 17	17 18		17 25		17 27
Acton Main Line	d					16 31							17 01												17 34
Ealing Broadway ⊖	d	16 11	16 22			16 34	16 37				16 41	16 52	17 04	17 07	17 11					17 25			17 33		17 37
West Ealing	d	16 13				16 36					16 43		17 06		17 13										17 39
Drayton Green	d					16 39							17 09												17 42
Castle Bar Park	d					16 40							17 10												17 43
South Greenford	d					16 43							17 13												17 46
Greenford ⊖	a					16 49							17 19												17 51
Hanwell	d	16 16								←	16 46				17 16										
Southall	d	16 19	16 27				16 43		←	16 43	16 49	16 57		17 13	17 19					17 30			17 38		
Hayes & Harlington	d	16 23	16 31				→		16 31	16 47	16 53	17 01		17 17	17 23					17 34			17 42		
Heathrow Terminals 1-2-3 ✈	a	16 29	→								16 59				17 29										
Heathrow Terminal 4 ✈	a	16 40									17 10				17 40										
Heathrow Terminal 5 ✈	a	16b46									17b16				17b46			←							
West Drayton	d								16 36			17 06		17 21			←	17 21		17 39			17 47		
Iver	d								16 40			17 09		→			17 09	17 24		17 43			→		
Langley	d								16 43			→					17 12	17 27		→					
Slough 3	a			16 37				16 48	16 48	16 56							17 17	17 32	17 36					←	
	d			16 37				16 48	16 49	16 57							17 17	17 33	17 37					17 37	
Burnham	d								16 53								17 21	17 37	→			←			
Taplow	d				←				16 56								17 25	17 40				17 40			
Maidenhead 3	d				16 38				17 00	17 04							17 29	→			17 40	17 44		17 48	
Twyford 3	d				16 46				17 08	17 12						17 28	17 37				17 48	17 52		17a58	
Reading 7	a			16 51	16 52			17 03	17 15	17 19						17 35	17 43				17 54	17 59			
Oxford	a			17 23	17 43			*17 34*		18 03							*18 15*				18 40	*18 34*			

Station		HC	GW 1	GW 1	GW 1 B	GW 1 E	GW 1	GW 1	GW 1	HC	GW 1 ◇ G ☕	GW 1	GW 1	GW 1 D	GW 1	GW 1	GW 1	GW 1	GW 1 D	GW 1	GW 1 A	HC	GW 1 H	GW 1	GW 1
London Paddington 15 ⊖	d	17 33	17 36			17 44	17 47	17 55	18 00	18 03	18 06			18 14	18 17	18 18		18 25		18 27	18 33	18 33	18 36		
Acton Main Line	d							18 01												18 34					
Ealing Broadway ⊖	d	17 41					17 55	18 04	18 07	18 11					18 25			18 33		18 37		18 41			
West Ealing	d	17 43						18 06		18 13										18 39		18 43			
Drayton Green	d							18 09												18 42					
Castle Bar Park	d							18 10												18 43					
South Greenford	d							18 13												18 46					
Greenford ⊖	a							18 19												18 51					
Hanwell	d	17 46								18 16												18 46			
Southall	d	17 49					18 00		18 13	18 19					18 30			18 38				18 49			
Hayes & Harlington	d	17 53					18 04		18 17	18 23					18 34			18 42				18 53			
Heathrow Terminals 1-2-3 ✈	a	17 59								18 29												18 59			
Heathrow Terminal 4 ✈	a	18 10								18 40												19 10			
Heathrow Terminal 5 ✈	a	18b16			←					18b46												19b16			←
West Drayton	d			←	17 47		18 09		18 21				←		18 39			18 47							18 47
Iver	d			17 43	17 51				18 24			←	18 24					→						←	18 51
Langley	d			17 46	17 54		18 14		→			18 14	18 27		18 44									18 44	18 54
Slough 3	a			17 51	17 59	18 06	→					18 19	18 32	18 36	→				←					18 49	18 59
	d			17 52	18 01	18 07						18 20	18 33	18 37					18 37					18 50	19 01
Burnham	d			17 56	18 05							18 24	18 37	→			←							18 54	19 05
Taplow	d			17 59								18 27	18 40				18 40							18 57	
Maidenhead 3	d		17 59	18 03	18 10	18a14						18 31	→			18 40	18 44		18 48		18 53		18 58	19 01	19 10
Twyford 3	d		18 08	18 12	18 18						18 27	18 39				18 48	18 52		18a58		19 03		19 06	19 09	19 18
Reading 7	a		18 15	18 18	18 25						18 35	18 46				18 54	19 01				19 10		19 13	19 16	→
Oxford	a		19 02	*19 06*	19 12						*19 17*					19 46	*19 34*				20 12		20 12		

For general notes see front of timetable
For details of catering facilities see Directory of Train Operators

For fast services between London Paddington and Reading see Table 116

- **A** Until 27 June and from 8 September
- **B** To Banbury (Table 116)
- **C** To Westbury (Table 135)
- **D** To Henley-on-Thames (Table 121)
- **E** To Bourne End (Table 120)
- **G** To Frome (Table 123)
- **H** 30 June to 5 September
- **b** Change at Heathrow Terminals 1-2-3

London → Greenford and Reading

(Local services only)

Network Diagram - see first page of Table 116

Station		GW 1 A	GW 1	GW 1 ◇	GW 1	GW 1	GW 1	HC	GW 1 B	GW 1	GW 1	GW 1	GW 1	GW 1 ◇ ☐P	GW 1	GW 1	GW 1	GW 1	GW 1	HC	GW 1	GW 1 ◇	GW 1	GW 1	GW 1
London Paddington 15 ⊖	d	18 44	18 47	18 51		18 55	19 00	19 03	19 06		19 15		19 18	19 21		19 25			19 30	19 33	19 45	19 51			19 55
Acton Main Line	d					19 01										19 31									20 01
Ealing Broadway ⊖	d		18 55			19 04	19 07	19 11					19 25			19 34			19 37	19 41	19 52				20 04
West Ealing	d					19 06		19 13								19 36				19 43					20 06
Drayton Green	d					19 09										19 39									20 09
Castle Bar Park	d					19 10										19 40									20 10
South Greenford	d					19 13										19 43									20 13
Greenford ⊖	a					19 19										19 49									20 19
Hanwell	d							19 16										←		19 46					
Southall	d		19 00				19 13	19 19					19 31 →					19 31	19 43	19 49	19 57			←	
Hayes & Harlington	d		19 04				19 17	19 23										19 35	19 47	19 53	20 01 →			20 01	
Heathrow Terminals 1-2-3 ✈	a							19 29												19 59					
Heathrow Terminal 4 ✈	a							19 40												20 10					
Heathrow Terminal 5 ✈	a							19b46				←								20b16					
West Drayton	d		19 09				19 22 →					19 22							19 51					20 06	
Iver	d									←		19 25							19 54					20 09	
Langley	d		19 14 →							19 14		19 28							19 57					20 12	
Slough 3	a	19 06		19 06						19 19		19 33		19 37				19 44	20 02			20 06		20 17	
	d	19 07		19 07						19 20		19 34		19 37			←	19 45	20 03			20 07		20 17	
Burnham	d									19 24		19 38 →					19 38	19 49	20 07					20 21	
Taplow	d									19 27					←			19 52					←	20 25	
Maidenhead 3	d	19a14			←				19 27	19 31	19 40 →				19 40		19 44	19 56	20 12 →				20 12	20 29	
Twyford 3	d				19 18				19a35	19 40					19 48		19 51	20 04					20 19	20 36	
Reading 7	a			19 21	19 25					19 46				19 51	19 55		19 58	20 13				20 21	20 26	20 43	
Oxford	a			19 50	20 24									20 19	20 46		20 34					20 49	21 09		

Station		GW 1	HC	GW 1	GW 1 ◇ ☐P	GW 1	GW 1	GW 1	GW 1	HC	GW 1	GW 1 ◇	GW 1	GW 1	GW 1	HC	GW 1	GW 1 ◇	GW 1	GW 1	GW 1	GW 1	HC	GW 1	GW 1 ◇
London Paddington 15 ⊖	d	20 00	20 03	20 15	20 20			20 25	20 30	20 33	20 45	20 51		20 55	21 00	21 03	21 15	21 21			21 25	21 30	21 33	21 45	21 48
Acton Main Line	d							20 31						21 01							21 31				
Ealing Broadway ⊖	d	20 07	20 11	20 22				20 34	20 37	20 41	20 52			21 04	21 07	21 11	21 22				21 34	21 37	21 41	21 52	
West Ealing	d		20 13					20 36		20 43				21 06		21 13					21 36		21 43		
Drayton Green	d							20 39						21 09							21 39				
Castle Bar Park	d							20 40						21 10							21 40				
South Greenford	d							20 43						21 13							21 43				
Greenford ⊖	a							20 49						21 19							21 49				
Hanwell	d		20 16				←			20 46			←			21 16				←			21 46		
Southall	d		20 19	20 27 →			20 27			20 49	20 57 →		20 57			21 19	21 27 →			21 27			21 49	21 57	
Hayes & Harlington	d	20 15	20 23				20 31		20 45	20 53			21 01		21 15	21 23				21 31		21 45	21 53	22 01 →	
Heathrow Terminals 1-2-3 ✈	a		20 29							20 59						21 29							21 59		
Heathrow Terminal 4 ✈	a		20 40							21 10						21 40							22 10		
Heathrow Terminal 5 ✈	a		20b46							21b16						21b46							22b16		
West Drayton	d	20 19					20 36		20 49				21 06		21 19					21 36		21 49			
Iver	d	20 22							20 52						21 22										
Langley	d	20 25							20 55						21 25										
Slough 3	a	20 30			20 35		20 44		21 00			21 07	21 14		21 30			21 37		21 44		21 57			22 04
	d	20 31			20 36		20 44		21 01			21 07	21 14		21 31			21 37		21 44		21 58			22 05
Burnham	d						20 48						21 18							21 48					
Taplow	d					←	20 52						21 22						←	21 52					
Maidenhead 3	d	20 38 →				20 38	20 56		21 08				21 26		21 38 →				21 38	21 56		22 05			
Twyford 3	d					20 46	21 03		21 16				21 33						21 46	22 03		22 13			
Reading 7	a				20 50	20 52	21 12		21 24			21 23	21 42					21 51	21 52	22 13		22 20			22 21
Oxford	a				21 16	21 31			22 14			21 51						22 22	22 37			23 14			22 50

Station		GW 1	GW FO 1	GW FX 1	HC	GW FX 1	GW FO 1	GW FO 1 ◇	GW FX 1 ◇	GW FO 1	GW FX 1	HC	GW 1	GW FX 1 ◇	GW FO 1 ◇	GW 1	GW 1	HC	GW FO 1 ◇	GW 1	GW FX 1 ◇	GW 1	GW 1
London Paddington 15 ⊖	d		21 59	21 57	22 03	22 14	22 14	22 21	22 21			22 33	22 46	22 48	22 51		22 59	23 03	23 21		23 21	23 29	23 48
Acton Main Line	d												22 52			←							23 54
Ealing Broadway ⊖	d		22 06	22 04	22 11	22 21	22 21					22 41	22 55 →			22 55	23 06	23 11				23 36	23 58
West Ealing	d				22 13							22 43						23 13					23 59
Drayton Green	d																						
Castle Bar Park	d																						
South Greenford	d																						
Greenford ⊖	a																						
Hanwell	d				22 16							22 46						23 16					00 03
Southall	d	←		22 09	22 19	22 26	22 26					22 49					23 13	23 19					00 07
Hayes & Harlington	d	22 01	22 13	22 13	22 23	22 30	22 30					22 53				23 03	23 17	23 23				23 44	00 12
Heathrow Terminals 1-2-3 ✈	a				22 29							22 59						23 29					
Heathrow Terminal 4 ✈	a				22 40							23 10						23 40					
Heathrow Terminal 5 ✈	a				22b46							23b16						23b46					
West Drayton	d	22 06		22 19		22 35	22 35										23 24						00 16
Iver	d	22 09		22 22			22 38			←							23 27						00 19
Langley	d	22 12		22 25			22 41			22 41							23 30						00 22
Slough 3	a	22 17	22 23	22 30		22 43	→	22 38	22 46	22 46	←			23 06	23 08	23 13	23 34		23 38		23 42	23 55	00 28
	d	22 17	22 23	22 33		22 48 →		22 39	22 46	22 48	22 48			23 07	23 09	23 14	23 34		23 39		23 43	23 55	00 29
Burnham	d	22 21								22 52	22 52					23 18							00 33
Taplow	d	22 25								22 56	22 56					23 21				←			00 36
Maidenhead 3	d	22 29	22 33	22 41						23 00	23 00					23 25	23 42 →			23 42		00 03	00 40
Twyford 3	d	22 36	22 40	22 48						23 07	23 07					23 33				23 49		00 11	00 48
Reading 7	a	22 45	22 47	22 56				22 55	23 06	23 15	23 15			23 34	23 25	23 40			23 55	23 57	00 01	00 18	00 55
Oxford	a		23 33	23 43				23 26	23 37					00 09	23 52	00 23			00 28		00 34	01 08	

For general notes see front of timetable
For details of catering facilities see Directory of Train Operators

For fast services between London Paddington and Reading see Table 116

A To Bourne End (Table 120)
B To Henley-on-Thames (Table 121)
b Change at Heathrow Terminals 1-2-3

Saturdays

until 6 September

London → Greenford and Reading

(Local services only)

Network Diagram - see first page of Table 116

		GW 1	GW 1	GW 1	GW 1 ◇	GW 1	GW 1	GW 1	HC	GW 1 ◇		HC	GW 1
London Paddington 15 ⊖	d		23p29	23p48	00 21	00 34	01 44	03 34	04 42	05 12		05 16	05 25
Acton Main Line	d			23p54									
Ealing Broadway ⊖	d		23p36	23p58		00 41	01 51	03 41	04 50			05 24	05 32
West Ealing	d			23p59									
Drayton Green	d												
Castle Bar Park	d												
South Greenford	d												
Greenford ⊖	a												
Hanwell	d			00 03									
Southall	d			00 07		00 46	01 56	03 46	04 54				05 37
Hayes & Harlington	d		23p44	00 12		00 50	02 00	03 50	04 58			05 30	05 41
Heathrow Terminals 1-2-3 ✈	a								05 04			05 36	
Heathrow Terminal 4 ✈	a								05 10			05 42	
Heathrow Terminal 5 ✈	a								05b32			05b46	
West Drayton	d			00 16		00 55	02 05	03 55					
Iver	d			00 19									
Langley	d			00 22		00 59							
Slough 3	a		23p55	00 28	00 40	01 04	02 13	04 03		05 29			05 51
	d		23p55	00 29	00 41	01 05	02 13	04 03		05 29			05 51
Burnham	d			00 33		01 09							05 55
Taplow	d			00 36		01 12							05 59 →
Maidenhead 3	d		00 03	00 40		01 16	02 21	04 11					
Twyford 3	d	00 07	00 11	00 48		01 24	02 29	04 19					
Reading 7	a	00 17	00 18	00 55	00 58	01 33	02 37	04 28		05 46			
Oxford	a		01 08		01 30					06 17			

		HC	GW 1 ◇ ☕	GW 1	GW 1	GW 1	HC	GW 1		GW 1 ◇	GW 1	GW 1	GW 1
London Paddington 15 ⊖	d	05 33	05 42		05 45	05 55	06 03	06 15		06 21		06 25	06 30
Acton Main Line	d					06 01						06 31	
Ealing Broadway ⊖	d	05 41			05 52	06 04	06 11	06 22				06 34	06 37
West Ealing	d	05 43				06 06	06 13					06 36	
Drayton Green	d					06 09						06 39	
Castle Bar Park	d					06 10						06 40	
South Greenford	d					06 13						06 43	
Greenford ⊖	a					06 19						06 49	
Hanwell	d	05 46					06 16						
Southall	d	05 49			05 57		06 19	06 27			←		06 42
Hayes & Harlington	d	05 53			06 02		06 23	06 32 →			06 32		06 47
Heathrow Terminals 1-2-3 ✈	a	05 59					06 29						
Heathrow Terminal 4 ✈	a	06 10					06 40						
Heathrow Terminal 5 ✈	a	06b16					06b46						
West Drayton	d				06 06						06 36		06 51
Iver	d				06 09						06 39		
Langley	d				06 12						06 42		
Slough 3	a		05 57		06 17					06 37	06 47		06 58
	d		05 57		06 18					06 38	06 48		06 59
Burnham	d			←	06 22						06 52		07 03
Taplow	d			05 59	06 25						06 55		07 06 →
Maidenhead 3	d			06 03	06 29						06 59		
Twyford 3	d			06 10	06 37						07 07		
Reading 7	a		06 13	06 17	06 43					06 52	07 13		
Oxford	a		06 45	07 02	07 28					07 19	08 00		

		HC	GW 1	GW 1 ◇ ☕	GW 1	GW 1	GW 1	GW 1		HC	GW 1	GW 1 ◇	GW 1
London Paddington 15 ⊖	d	06 33	06 45	06 51			06 55	07 00		07 03	07 15	07 21	
Acton Main Line	d						07 01						
Ealing Broadway ⊖	d	06 41	06 52				07 04	07 07		07 11	07 22		
West Ealing	d	06 43					07 06			07 13			
Drayton Green	d						07 09						
Castle Bar Park	d						07 10						
South Greenford	d						07 13						
Greenford ⊖	a						07 19						
Hanwell	d	06 46				←				07 16			←
Southall	d	06 49	06 57			06 57				07 19	07 27		07 27
Hayes & Harlington	d	06 53	→			07 01		07 15		07 23	→		07 31
Heathrow Terminals 1-2-3 ✈	a	06 59								07 29			
Heathrow Terminal 4 ✈	a	07 10								07 40			
Heathrow Terminal 5 ✈	a	07b16								07b46			
West Drayton	d					07 06		07 19					07 36
Iver	d							07 22					
Langley	d							07 25					
Slough 3	a			07 06		07 14		07 30				07 37	07 44
	d			07 07		07 14		07 31				07 38	07 44
Burnham	d				←	07 18							07 48
Taplow	d				07 06	07 22							07 52
Maidenhead 3	d				07 10	07 26		07 38					07 56
Twyford 3	d				07 18	07 33		07 46					08 03
Reading 7	a			07 21	07 26	07 42		07 52				07 52	08 12
Oxford	a			07 48	*08 05*			08 39				08 21	

		GW 1	GW 1	HC	GW 1	GW 1 ◇ ☕		GW 1	GW 1	GW 1	HC	GW 1	GW 1 ◇
London Paddington 15 ⊖	d	07 25	07 30	07 33	07 45	07 51			07 55	08 00	08 03	08 15	08 21
Acton Main Line	d	07 31							08 01				
Ealing Broadway ⊖	d	07 34	07 37	07 41	07 52				08 04	08 07	08 11	08 22	
West Ealing	d	07 36		07 43					08 06		08 13		
Drayton Green	d	07 39							08 09				
Castle Bar Park	d	07 40							08 10				
South Greenford	d	07 43							08 13				
Greenford ⊖	a	07 49							08 19				
Hanwell	d			07 46				←			08 16		
Southall	d			07 49	07 57			07 57			08 19	08 27	
Hayes & Harlington	d		07 45	07 53	→			08 01		08 14	08 23	→	
Heathrow Terminals 1-2-3 ✈	a			07 59							08 29		
Heathrow Terminal 4 ✈	a			08 10							08 40		
Heathrow Terminal 5 ✈	a			08b16							08b46		
West Drayton	d		07 49					08 06		08 19			
Iver	d		07 52							08 22			
Langley	d		07 55							08 25			
Slough 3	a		08 00			08 06		08 14		08 30			08 37
	d		08 01			08 07		08 14		08 31			08 38
Burnham	d							08 18					
Taplow	d							08 22					
Maidenhead 3	d		08 08					08 26		08 38			
Twyford 3	d		08 16					08 33		08 46			
Reading 7	a		08 21			08 21		08 42		08 52			08 52
Oxford	a		09 15			08 47				09 31			09 22

		GW 1	GW 1	GW 1	HC	GW 1		GW 1 ◇ ☕	GW 1	GW 1	GW 1	HC	GW 1
London Paddington 15 ⊖	d		08 25	08 30	08 33	08 45		08 51		08 55	09 00	09 03	09 15
Acton Main Line	d		08 31							09 01			
Ealing Broadway ⊖	d		08 34	08 37	08 41	08 52				09 04	09 07	09 11	09 22
West Ealing	d		08 36		08 43					09 06		09 13	
Drayton Green	d		08 39							09 09			
Castle Bar Park	d		08 40							09 10			
South Greenford	d		08 43							09 13			
Greenford ⊖	a		08 49							09 19			
Hanwell	d	←			08 46				←			09 16	
Southall	d	08 27			08 49	08 57			08 57			09 19	09 27
Hayes & Harlington	d	08 31		08 45	08 53	→			09 01		09 15	09 23	→
Heathrow Terminals 1-2-3 ✈	a				08 59							09 29	
Heathrow Terminal 4 ✈	a				09 10							09 40	
Heathrow Terminal 5 ✈	a				09b16							09b46	
West Drayton	d	08 36		08 49					09 06		09 19		
Iver	d			08 52							09 22		
Langley	d			08 55							09 25		
Slough 3	a	08 44		09 00				09 06	09 14		09 30		
	d	08 44		09 01				09 07	09 14		09 31		
Burnham	d	08 48							09 18				
Taplow	d	08 52							09 22				
Maidenhead 3	d	08 56		09 08					09 26		09 38		
Twyford 3	d	09 03		09 16					09 33		09 46		
Reading 7	a	09 12		09 21				09 21	09 42		09 52		
Oxford	a			10 12				09 47			10 30		

		GW 1 ◇	GW 1	GW 1		GW 1	HC	GW 1	GW 1 ◇ ☕	GW 1	GW 1	GW 1	HC
London Paddington 15 ⊖	d	09 21		09 25		09 30	09 33	09 45	09 51		09 55	10 00	10 03
Acton Main Line	d			09 31							10 01		
Ealing Broadway ⊖	d			09 34		09 37	09 41	09 52			10 04	10 07	10 11
West Ealing	d			09 36			09 43				10 06		10 13
Drayton Green	d			09 39							10 09		
Castle Bar Park	d			09 40							10 10		
South Greenford	d			09 43							10 13		
Greenford ⊖	a			09 49							10 19		
Hanwell	d		←				09 46			←			10 16
Southall	d		09 27				09 49	09 57		09 57			10 19
Hayes & Harlington	d		09 31			09 45	09 53	→		10 01		10 15	10 23
Heathrow Terminals 1-2-3 ✈	a						09 59						10 29
Heathrow Terminal 4 ✈	a						10 10						10 40
Heathrow Terminal 5 ✈	a						10b16						10b46
West Drayton	d		09 36			09 49				10 06		10 19	
Iver	d					09 52						10 22	
Langley	d					09 55						10 25	
Slough 3	a	09 37	09 44			10 00			10 06	10 14		10 30	
	d	09 38	09 44			10 01			10 07	10 14		10 31	
Burnham	d		09 48							10 18			
Taplow	d		09 52							10 22			
Maidenhead 3	d		09 56			10 08				10 26		10 38	
Twyford 3	d		10 03			10 16				10 33		10 46	
Reading 7	a	09 52	10 12			10 21			10 21	10 42		10 52	
Oxford	a	10 21				11 13			10 47			11 30	

For general notes see front of timetable
For details of catering facilities see Directory of Train Operators

For fast services between London Paddington and Reading see Table 116

b Change at Heathrow Terminals 1-2-3

London → Greenford and Reading

(Local services only)

Saturdays

until 6 September

Network Diagram - see first page of Table 116

		GW 1	GW 1 ◇	GW 1		GW 1	GW 1	HC	GW 1	GW 1 ◇ 🍴	GW 1	GW 1	GW 1	HC		GW 1	GW 1 ◇	GW 1	GW 1	GW 1	HC	GW 1	GW 1 ◇ 🍴	GW 1	GW 1
London Paddington 15 ⊖	d	10 15	10 21			10 25	10 30	10 33	10 45	10 51		10 55	11 00	11 03		11 15	11 21		11 25	11 30	11 33	11 45	11 51		11 55
Acton Main Line	d					10 31						11 01							11 31						12 01
Ealing Broadway ⊖	d	10 22				10 34	10 37	10 41	10 52			11 04	11 07	11 11		11 22			11 34	11 37	11 41	11 52			12 04
West Ealing	d					10 36		10 43				11 06		11 13					11 36		11 43				12 06
Drayton Green	d					10 39						11 09							11 39						12 09
Castle Bar Park	d					10 40						11 10							11 40						12 10
South Greenford	d					10 43						11 13							11 43						12 13
Greenford ⊖	a					10 49						11 19							11 49						12 19
Hanwell	d			←				10 46			←			11 16				←			11 46			←	
Southall	d	10 27		10 27				10 49	10 57		10 57			11 19		11 27		11 27			11 49	11 57		11 57	
Hayes & Harlington	d	→		10 31			10 45	10 53	→		11 01		11 15	11 23		→		11 31		11 45	11 53	→		12 01	
Heathrow Terminals 1-2-3 ✈	a							10 59						11 29							11 59				
Heathrow Terminal 4 ✈	a							11 10						11 40							12 10				
Heathrow Terminal 5 ✈	a							11b16						11b46							12b16				
West Drayton	d			10 36			10 49				11 06		11 19					11 36		11 49				12 06	
Iver	d						10 52						11 22							11 52					
Langley	d						10 55						11 25							11 55					
Slough 3	a		10 37	10 44			11 00			11 06	11 14		11 30				11 37	11 44		12 00			12 06	12 14	
	d		10 38	10 44			11 01			11 07	11 14		11 31				11 38	11 44		12 01			12 07	12 14	
Burnham	d			10 48							11 18							11 48						12 18	
Taplow	d			10 52							11 22							11 52						12 22	
Maidenhead 3	d			10 56			11 08				11 26		11 38					11 56		12 08				12 26	
Twyford 3	d			11 03			11 16				11 33		11 46					12 03		12 16				12 33	
Reading 7	a		10 52	11 12			11 21			11 21	11 42		11 52				11 52	12 12		12 21			12 21	12 42	
Oxford	a		11 19				12 12			11 47			12 30				12 21			13 13			12 47		

		GW 1		HC	GW 1	GW 1 ◇	GW 1	GW 1	GW 1	HC	GW 1	GW 1		GW 1	HC	GW 1	GW 1 ◇	GW 1	GW 1	GW 1	HC	GW 1		GW 1 ◇ 🍴	GW 1
London Paddington 15 ⊖	d	12 00		12 03	12 15	12 21		12 25	12 30	12 33	12 45	12 55		13 00	13 03	13 15	13 21		13 25	13 30	13 33	13 45		13 51	
Acton Main Line	d							12 31				13 01							13 31						
Ealing Broadway ⊖	d	12 07		12 11	12 22			12 34	12 37	12 41	12 52	13 04		13 07	13 11	13 22			13 34	13 37	13 41	13 52			
West Ealing	d			12 13				12 36		12 43		13 06			13 13				13 36		13 43				
Drayton Green	d							12 39				13 09							13 39						
Castle Bar Park	d							12 40				13 10							13 40						
South Greenford	d							12 43				13 13							13 43						
Greenford ⊖	a							12 49				13 19							13 49						
Hanwell	d			12 16			←			12 46					13 16			←			13 46				←
Southall	d			12 19	12 27		12 27			12 49	12 57				13 19	13 27		13 27			13 49	13 57			13 57
Hayes & Harlington	d	12 15		12 23	→		12 31		12 45	12 53	13 01			13 15	13 23	→		13 31		13 45	13 53	→			14 01
Heathrow Terminals 1-2-3 ✈	a			12 29						12 59					13 29						13 59				
Heathrow Terminal 4 ✈	a			12 40						13 10					13 40						14 10				
Heathrow Terminal 5 ✈	a			12b46						13b16					13b46						14b16				
West Drayton	d	12 19					12 36		12 49		13 06			13 19				13 36		13 49					14 06
Iver	d	12 22							12 52					13 22						13 52					
Langley	d	12 25							12 55					13 25						13 55					
Slough 3	a	12 30				12 37	12 44		13 00		13 14			13 30			13 37	13 44		14 00				14 06	14 14
	d	12 31				12 38	12 44		13 01		13 14			13 31			13 38	13 44		14 01				14 07	14 14
Burnham	d						12 48				13 18							13 48							14 18
Taplow	d						12 52				13 22							13 52							14 22
Maidenhead 3	d	12 38					12 56		13 08		13 26			13 38				13 56		14 08					14 26
Twyford 3	d	12 46					13 03		13 16		13 33			13 46				14 03		14 16					14 33
Reading 7	a	12 52				12 52	13 12		13 21		13 42			13 52			13 52	14 12		14 21				14 21	14 42
Oxford	a	13 30				13 21	*13 46*		14 12					14 30			14 21			15 13				14 47	

		GW 1	GW 1	HC	GW 1	GW 1 ◇	GW 1	GW 1	GW 1	HC		GW 1	GW 1 ◇ 🍴	GW 1	GW 1	GW 1	HC	GW 1	GW 1 ◇	GW 1		GW 1	GW 1	HC	GW 1
London Paddington 15 ⊖	d	13 55	14 00	14 03	14 15	14 21		14 25	14 30	14 33		14 45	14 51		14 55	15 00	15 03	15 15	15 21			15 25	15 30	15 33	15 45
Acton Main Line	d	14 01						14 31							15 01							15 31			
Ealing Broadway ⊖	d	14 04	14 07	14 11	14 22			14 34	14 37	14 41		14 52			15 04	15 07	15 11	15 22				15 34	15 37	15 41	15 52
West Ealing	d	14 06		14 13				14 36		14 43					15 06		15 13					15 36		15 43	
Drayton Green	d	14 09						14 39							15 09							15 39			
Castle Bar Park	d	14 10						14 40							15 10							15 40			
South Greenford	d	14 13						14 43							15 13							15 43			
Greenford ⊖	a	14 19						14 49							15 19							15 49			
Hanwell	d			14 16			←			14 46				←			15 16			←				15 46	
Southall	d			14 19	14 27		14 27			14 49		14 57		14 57			15 19	15 27		15 27				15 49	15 57
Hayes & Harlington	d		14 15	14 23	→		14 31		14 45	14 53		→		15 01		15 15	15 23	→		15 31			15 45	15 53	→
Heathrow Terminals 1-2-3 ✈	a			14 29						14 59							15 29							15 59	
Heathrow Terminal 4 ✈	a			14 40						15 10							15 40							16 10	
Heathrow Terminal 5 ✈	a			14b46						15b16							15b46							16b16	
West Drayton	d		14 19				14 36		14 49					15 06		15 19				15 36			15 49		
Iver	d		14 22						14 52							15 22							15 52		
Langley	d		14 25						14 55							15 25							15 55		
Slough 3	a		14 30			14 37	14 44		15 00				15 06	15 14		15 30			15 37	15 44			16 00		
	d		14 31			14 38	14 44		15 01				15 07	15 14		15 31			15 38	15 44			16 01		
Burnham	d						14 48							15 18						15 48					
Taplow	d						14 52							15 22						15 52					
Maidenhead 3	d		14 38				14 56		15 08					15 26		15 38				15 56			16 08		
Twyford 3	d		14 46				15 03		15 16					15 33		15 46				16 03			16 16		
Reading 7	a		14 52			14 52	15 12		15 21				15 21	15 42		15 52			15 52	16 12			16 21		
Oxford	a		15 30			15 21			16 12				15 47			16 30			16 21				17 13		

For general notes see front of timetable
For details of catering facilities see
Directory of Train Operators

For fast services between London Paddington and
Reading see Table 116

b Change at Heathrow Terminals 1-2-3

London → Greenford and Reading
(Local services only)

Saturdays
until 6 September

Network Diagram - see first page of Table 116

		GW 1◇	GW 1	GW 1	GW 1	HC	GW 1	GW 1◇		GW 1	GW 1	GW 1	HC	GW 1	GW 1◇	GW 1	GW 1	GW 1		HC	GW 1	GW 1◇	GW 1	GW 1	GW 1
London Paddington 15 ⊖	d	15 51		15 55	16 00	16 03	16 15	16 21			16 25	16 30	16 33	16 45	16 51		16 55	17 00		17 03	17 15	17 21		17 25	17 30
Acton Main Line	d			16 01							16 31						17 01							17 31	
Ealing Broadway ⊖	d			16 04	16 07	16 11	16 22				16 34	16 37	16 41	16 52			17 04	17 07		17 11	17 22			17 34	17 37
West Ealing	d			16 06		16 13					16 36		16 43				17 06			17 13				17 36	
Drayton Green	d			16 09							16 39						17 09							17 39	
Castle Bar Park	d			16 10							16 40						17 10							17 40	
South Greenford	d			16 13							16 43						17 13							17 43	
Greenford ⊖	a			16 19							16 49						17 19							17 49	
Hanwell	d		←			16 16				←			16 46			←				17 16			←		
Southall	d		15 57			16 19	16 27 →			16 27			16 49	16 57 →		16 57				17 19	17 27 →		17 27		
Hayes & Harlington	d		16 01		16 15	16 23				16 31		16 45	16 53			17 01		17 15		17 23			17 31		17 45
Heathrow Terminals 1-2-3 ✈	a					16 29							16 59							17 29					
Heathrow Terminal 4 ✈	a					16 40							17 10							17 40					
Heathrow Terminal 5 ✈	a					16b46							17b16							17b46					
West Drayton	d		16 06		16 19					16 36		16 49				17 06		17 19					17 36		17 49
Iver	d				16 22							16 52						17 22							17 52
Langley	d				16 25							16 55						17 25							17 55
Slough 3	a	16 06	16 14		16 30			16 37		16 44		17 00			17 06	17 14		17 30				17 37	17 44		18 00
	d	16 07	16 14		16 31			16 38		16 44		17 01			17 07	17 14		17 31				17 38	17 44		18 01
Burnham	d		16 18							16 48						17 18							17 48		
Taplow	d		16 22							16 52						17 22							17 52		
Maidenhead 3	d		16 26		16 38					16 56		17 08				17 26		17 38					17 56		18 08
Twyford 3	d		16 33		16 46					17 03		17 16				17 33		17 46					18 03		18 16
Reading 7	a	16 21	16 42		16 52			16 52		17 12		17 21			17 21	17 42		17 52				17 52	18 12		18 21
Oxford	a	16 47			17 30			17 21				18 12			17 47			18 30				18 21	*18 47*		19 13

		HC	GW 1	GW 1	GW 1	HC		GW 1	GW 1◇	GW 1	GW 1	GW 1	GW 1	HC	GW 1	GW 1◇		GW 1	GW 1	GW 1	HC	GW 1	GW 1◇	GW 1	GW 1
London Paddington 15 ⊖	d	17 33	17 45	17 55	18 00	18 03		18 15	18 21			18 25	18 30	18 33	18 45	18 51			18 55	19 00	19 03	19 15	19 21		19 25
Acton Main Line	d			18 01								18 31							19 01						19 31
Ealing Broadway ⊖	d	17 41	17 52	18 04	18 07	18 11		18 22				18 34	18 37	18 41	18 52				19 04	19 07	19 11	19 22			19 34
West Ealing	d	17 43		18 06		18 13						18 36		18 43					19 06		19 13				19 36
Drayton Green	d			18 09								18 39							19 09						19 39
Castle Bar Park	d			18 10								18 40							19 10						19 40
South Greenford	d			18 13								18 43							19 13						19 43
Greenford ⊖	a			18 19								18 49							19 19						19 49
Hanwell	d	17 46				18 16					←			18 46				←			19 16			←	
Southall	d	17 49	17 57			18 19		18 27 →			18 27			18 49	18 57 →			18 57			19 19	19 27 →		19 27	
Hayes & Harlington	d	17 53	18 01		18 15	18 23					18 31		18 45	18 53				19 01		19 15	19 23			19 31	
Heathrow Terminals 1-2-3 ✈	a	17 59				18 29								18 59							19 29				
Heathrow Terminal 4 ✈	a	18 10				18 40								19 10							19 40				
Heathrow Terminal 5 ✈	a	18b16				18b46								19b16							19b46				
West Drayton	d		18 06		18 19						18 36		18 49					19 06		19 19				19 36	
Iver	d				18 22								18 52							19 22					
Langley	d				18 25								18 55							19 25					
Slough 3	a		18 14		18 30				18 37		18 44		19 00			19 07		19 14		19 30			19 37	19 44	
	d		18 14		18 31				18 38		18 44		19 01			19 08		19 14		19 31			19 38	19 44	
Burnham	d		18 18								18 48							19 18						19 48	
Taplow	d		18 22							←	18 52							19 22						19 52	
Maidenhead 3	d		18 26		18 38 →					18 38	18 56		19 08					19 26		19 38				19 56	
Twyford 3	d		18 33							18 46	19 03		19 16					19 33		19 46				20 03	
Reading 7	a		18 42						18 51	18 52	19 12		19 21			19 22		19 42		19 52			19 52	20 12	
Oxford	a								19 18	19 30			20 15			19 48				20 30			20 21		

		GW 1	HC	GW 1		GW 1◇	GW 1	GW 1	GW 1	HC	GW 1	GW 1◇	GW 1	GW 1		GW 1	HC	GW 1	GW 1◇	GW 1	GW 1	GW 1	HC	GW 1	GW 1◇
London Paddington 15 ⊖	d	19 30	19 33	19 45		19 51		19 55	20 00	20 03	20 15	20 21		20 25		20 30	20 33	20 47	20 51		20 55	21 00	21 03	21 15	21 21
Acton Main Line	d							20 01						20 31							21 01				
Ealing Broadway ⊖	d	19 37	19 41	19 52				20 04	20 07	20 11	20 22			20 34		20 37	20 41	20 54			21 04	21 07	21 11	21 22	
West Ealing	d		19 43					20 06		20 13				20 36			20 43				21 06		21 13		
Drayton Green	d							20 09						20 39							21 09				
Castle Bar Park	d							20 10						20 40							21 10				
South Greenford	d							20 13						20 43							21 13				
Greenford ⊖	a							20 19						20 49							21 19				
Hanwell	d		19 46				←			20 16			←				20 46			←			21 16		
Southall	d		19 49	19 57 →			19 57			20 19	20 27 →		20 27				20 49	20 59 →		20 59			21 19	21 27 →	
Hayes & Harlington	d	19 45	19 53				20 01		20 15	20 23			20 31			20 45	20 53			21 04		21 15	21 23		
Heathrow Terminals 1-2-3 ✈	a		19 59							20 29							20 59						21 29		
Heathrow Terminal 4 ✈	a		20 10							20 40							21 10						21 40		
Heathrow Terminal 5 ✈	a		20b16							20b46							21b16						21b46		
West Drayton	d	19 49					20 06		20 19				20 36			20 49				21 08		21 19			
Iver	d	19 52							20 22							20 52						21 22			
Langley	d	19 55							20 25							20 55						21 25			
Slough 3	a	20 00				20 07	20 14		20 30			20 37	20 44			21 00			21 07	21 15		21 30			21 38
	d	20 01				20 07	20 14		20 31			20 38	20 44			21 01			21 08	21 16		21 31			21 39
Burnham	d						20 18						20 48							21 20					
Taplow	d						20 22						20 52							21 23					
Maidenhead 3	d	20 08					20 26		20 38				20 56			21 08				21 27		21 38			
Twyford 3	d	20 16					20 33		20 46				21 03			21 16				21 35		21 46			
Reading 7	a	20 21				20 21	20 42		20 52			20 52	21 12			21 21			21 22	21 43		21 52			21 55
Oxford	a	21 13				20 47			21 30			21 21				22 09			21 51			22 30			22 23

For general notes see front of timetable
For details of catering facilities see Directory of Train Operators

For fast services between London Paddington and Reading see Table 116

b Change at Heathrow Terminals 1-2-3

London → Greenford and Reading
(Local services only)

Saturdays
until 6 September

Network Diagram - see first page of Table 116

	GW 1		GW 1	HC	GW 1	GW 1 ◇	GW 1	GW 1	HC	GW 1	GW 1 ◇		GW 1	HC	GW 1	GW 1 ◇	GW 1	HC	GW 1	GW 1 ◇	GW 1	GW 1		
London Paddington 15 ⊖ d			21 25	21 33	21 45	21 51		22 00	22 03	22 20	22 32			22 33	22 45	23 00		23 03	23 20	23 33		23 45		
Acton Main Line d			21 31												22 51							23 51		
Ealing Broadway ⊖ d			21 34	21 41	21 52			22 07	22 11	22 27				22 41	22 54			23 11	23 27			23 54		
West Ealing d			21 36	21 43					22 13					22 43				23 13				23 56		
Drayton Green d			21 39																					
Castle Bar Park d			21 40																					
South Greenford d			21 43																					
Greenford ⊖ a			21 49																					
Hanwell d	←			21 46					22 16					22 46				23 16				23 59		
Southall d	21 27			21 49	21 57		←		22 19	22 32			←	22 49	22 59		←	23 19	23 32		←	00 02		
Hayes & Harlington d	21 31			21 53	22 01		22 01	22 15	22 23	22 36			22 36	22 53	23 03		23 03	23 23	23 36		23 36	00 06		
Heathrow Terminals 1-2-3 ✈ a				21 59	→				22 29	→				22 59	→			23 29	→					
Heathrow Terminal 4 ✈ a				22 10					22 40					23 10				23 40						
Heathrow Terminal 5 ✈ a				22b16					22b46					23b16				23b46						
West Drayton d	21 36						22 06	22 19					22 41				23 07				23 41	00 11		
Iver d							22 09	22 22					22 44				23 10				23 44	00 14		
Langley d							22 12	22 25					22 47				23 13				23 47	00 17		
Slough 3 a	21 44					22 07	22 17	22 30			22 49		22 52			23 16	23 18			23 49	23 52	00 22		
d	21 44					22 08	22 17	22 31			22 50		22 52			23 17	23 20			23 50	23 53	00 22		
Burnham d	21 48						22 21						22 56				23 24				23 57	00 26		
Taplow d	21 52						22 25						23 00								00 01			
Maidenhead 3 d	21 56						22 29	22 38					23 04				23 29				00 05	00 31		
Twyford 3 d	22 03						22 36	22 46					23 11				23 36				00 12	00 39		
Reading 7 a	22 12					22 23	22 43	22 52			23 06		23 19			23 33	23 44			00 07	00 19	00 46		
Oxford a						22 46		23 31			23 40					00 06	00 32			00 39	01 07			

Saturdays
from 13 September

	GW 1	GW 1	GW 1	GW 1 ◇	GW 1	GW 1	GW 1	HC	GW 1 ◇	HC	GW 1		HC	GW 1 ◇ ☕	GW 1	GW 1	GW 1	HC	GW 1	GW 1 ◇	GW 1	GW 1	GW 1	HC
London Paddington 15 ⊖ d		23p29	23p48	00 21	00 34	01 44	03 34	04 42	05 12	05 16	05 25		05 33	05 42		05 45	05 55	06 03	06 15	06 21		06 25	06 30	06 33
Acton Main Line d			23p54														06 01					06 31		
Ealing Broadway ⊖ d		23p36	23p58		00 41	01 51	03 41	04 50		05 24	05 32		05 41			05 52	06 04	06 11	06 22			06 34	06 37	06 41
West Ealing d			23p59										05 43				06 06	06 13				06 36		06 43
Drayton Green d																	06 09					06 39		
Castle Bar Park d																	06 10					06 40		
South Greenford d																	06 13					06 43		
Greenford ⊖ a																	06 19					06 49		
Hanwell d			00 03										05 46					06 16						06 46
Southall d			00 07		00 46	01 56	03 46	04 54			05 37		05 49			05 57		06 19	06 27		←		06 42	06 49
Hayes & Harlington d		23p44	00 12		00 50	02 00	03 50	04 58		05 30	05 41		05 53			06 02		06 23	06 32		06 32		06 47	06 53
Heathrow Terminals 1-2-3 ✈ a								05 04		05 36			05 59					06 29	→					06 59
Heathrow Terminal 4 ✈ a								05 10		05 42			06 10					06 40						07 10
Heathrow Terminal 5 ✈ a								05b32		05b46			06b16					06b46						07b16
West Drayton d			00 16		00 55	02 05	03 55									06 06					06 36		06 51	
Iver d			00 19													06 09					06 39			
Langley d			00 22		00 59											06 12					06 42			
Slough 3 a		23p55	00 28	00 40	01 04	02 13	04 03		05 29		05 51			05 57		06 17				06 37	06 47		06 58	
d		23p55	00 29	00 41	01 05	02 13	04 03		05 29		05 51			05 57		06 18				06 38	06 48		06 59	
Burnham d			00 33		01 09						05 55				←	06 22					06 52		07 03	
Taplow d			00 36		01 12						05 59				05 59	06 25					06 55		07 06	
Maidenhead 3 d		00 03	00 40		01 16	02 21	04 11				→				06 03	06 29					06 59		→	
Twyford 3 d	00 07	00 11	00 48		01 24	02 29	04 19								06 10	06 37					07 07			
Reading 7 a	00 17	00 18	00 55	00 58	01 33	02 37	04 28		05 46					06 13	06 17	06 43				06 52	07 13			
Oxford a		01 08		01 30					06 17					06 45	07 02	07 28				07 19	08 00			

	GW 1		GW 1 ◇ ☕	GW 1	GW 1	GW 1	GW 1	HC	GW 1	GW 1 ◇	GW 1	GW 1	GW 1		HC	GW 1	GW 1 ◇ ☕	GW 1	GW 1	GW 1	HC	GW 1	GW 1 ◇	GW 1
London Paddington 15 ⊖ d	06 45		06 51			06 55	07 00	07 03	07 15	07 21		07 25	07 30		07 33	07 45	07 51		07 55	08 00	08 03	08 15	08 21	
Acton Main Line d						07 01						07 31							08 01					
Ealing Broadway ⊖ d	06 52					07 04	07 07	07 11	07 22			07 34	07 37		07 41	07 52			08 04	08 07	08 11	08 22		
West Ealing d						07 06		07 13				07 36			07 43				08 06		08 13			
Drayton Green d						07 09						07 39							08 09					
Castle Bar Park d						07 10						07 40							08 10					
South Greenford d						07 13						07 43							08 13					
Greenford ⊖ a						07 19						07 49							08 19					
Hanwell d					←			07 16			←				07 46			←			08 16			
Southall d	06 57				06 57			07 19	07 27		07 27				07 49	07 57		07 57			08 19	08 27		
Hayes & Harlington d	→				07 01		07 15	07 23	→		07 31		07 45		07 53	→		08 01		08 14	08 23	→		
Heathrow Terminals 1-2-3 ✈ a								07 29							07 59						08 29			
Heathrow Terminal 4 ✈ a								07 40							08 10						08 40			
Heathrow Terminal 5 ✈ a								07b46							08b16						08b46			
West Drayton d					07 06		07 19				07 36		07 49					08 06		08 19				
Iver d							07 22						07 52							08 22				
Langley d							07 25						07 55							08 25				
Slough 3 a			07 06		07 14		07 30			07 37	07 44		08 00				08 06	08 14		08 30			08 36	
d			07 07		07 14		07 31			07 38	07 44		08 01				08 07	08 14		08 31			08 37	
Burnham d				←	07 18						07 48							08 18						
Taplow d				07 06	07 22						07 52							08 22						←
Maidenhead 3 d				07 10	07 26		07 38				07 56		08 08					08 26		08 38				08 38
Twyford 3 d				07 18	07 33		07 46				08 03		08 16					08 33		→				08 46
Reading 7 a			07 21	07 26	07 42		07 52			07 52	08 12		08 21				08 21	08 42					08 50	08 52
Oxford a			07 48				08 39			08 21			09 15				08 47						09 21	09 31

For general notes see front of timetable
For details of catering facilities see
Directory of Train Operators

For fast services between London Paddington and
Reading see Table 116

b Change at Heathrow Terminals 1-2-3

Saturdays

from 13 September

London → Greenford and Reading

(Local services only)

Network Diagram - see first page of Table 116

		GW 1	GW 1	GW 1		HC	GW 1	GW 1 ◇ ☕	GW 1	GW 1	GW 1	HC	GW 1	GW 1 ◇	GW 1	GW		GW 1	HC	GW 1	GW 1 ◇ ☕	GW 1	GW 1	GW 1	HC
London Paddington 15	Θ d		08 25	08 30		08 33	08 45	08 51		08 55	09 00	09 03	09 15	09 21		09 25		09 30	09 33	09 45	09 51		09 55	10 00	10 03
Acton Main Line	d		08 31							09 01						09 31							10 01		
Ealing Broadway	Θ d		08 34	08 37		08 41	08 52			09 04	09 07	09 11	09 22			09 34		09 37	09 41	09 52			10 04	10 07	10 11
West Ealing	d		08 36			08 43				09 06		09 13				09 36			09 43				10 06		10 13
Drayton Green	d		08 39							09 09						09 39							10 09		
Castle Bar Park	d		08 40							09 10						09 40							10 10		
South Greenford	d		08 43							09 13						09 43							10 13		
Greenford	Θ a		08 49							09 19						09 49							10 19		
Hanwell	d	←				08 46			←			09 16			←				09 46			←			10 16
Southall	d	08 27				08 49	08 57		08 57			09 19	09 27		09 27				09 49	09 57		09 57			10 19
Hayes & Harlington	d	08 31		08 45		08 53	→		09 01		09 15	09 23	→		09 31			09 45	09 53	→		10 01		10 15	10 23
Heathrow Terminals 1-2-3	✈ a					08 59						09 29							09 59						10 29
Heathrow Terminal 4	✈ a					09 10						09 40							10 10						10 40
Heathrow Terminal 5	✈ a					09b16						09b46							10b16						10b46
West Drayton	d	08 36		08 49					09 06		09 19				09 36			09 49				10 06		10 19	
Iver	d			08 52							09 22							09 52						10 22	
Langley	d			08 55							09 25							09 55						10 25	
Slough 3	a	08 44		09 00				09 06	09 14		09 30			09 37	09 44			10 00			10 06	10 14		10 30	
	d	08 44		09 01				09 07	09 14		09 31			09 38	09 44			10 01			10 07	10 14		10 31	
Burnham	d	08 48							09 18						09 48							10 18			
Taplow	d	08 52							09 22						09 52							10 22			
Maidenhead 3	d	08 56		09 08					09 26		09 38				09 56			10 08				10 26		10 38	
Twyford 3	d	09 03		09 16					09 33		09 46				10 03			10 16				10 33		10 46	
Reading 7	a	09 12		09 21				09 21	09 42		09 52			09 52	10 12			10 21			10 21	10 42		10 52	
Oxford	a			10 12				09 47			10 30			10 21				11 13			10 47			11 30	

		GW 1	GW 1 ◇	GW 1	GW 1	GW 1		HC	GW 1	GW 1 ◇ ☕	GW 1	GW 1	GW 1	HC	GW 1	GW 1 ◇	GW 1	GW 1		GW 1	HC	GW 1	GW 1 ◇ ☕	GW 1	GW 1
London Paddington 15	Θ d	10 15	10 21		10 25	10 30		10 33	10 45	10 51		10 55	11 00	11 03	11 15	11 21		11 25		11 30	11 33	11 45	11 51		11 55
Acton Main Line	d				10 31							11 01						11 31							12 01
Ealing Broadway	Θ d	10 22			10 34	10 37		10 41	10 52			11 04	11 07	11 11	11 22			11 34		11 37	11 41	11 52			12 04
West Ealing	d				10 36			10 43				11 06		11 13				11 36			11 43				12 06
Drayton Green	d				10 39							11 09						11 39							12 09
Castle Bar Park	d				10 40							11 10						11 40							12 10
South Greenford	d				10 43							11 13						11 43							12 13
Greenford	Θ a				10 49							11 19						11 49							12 19
Hanwell	d			←				10 46			←			11 16			←				11 46			←	
Southall	d	10 27		10 27				10 49	10 57		10 57			11 19	11 27		11 27				11 49	11 57		11 57	
Hayes & Harlington	d	→		10 31		10 45		10 53	→		11 01		11 15	11 23	→		11 31			11 45	11 53	→		12 01	
Heathrow Terminals 1-2-3	✈ a							10 59						11 29							11 59				
Heathrow Terminal 4	✈ a							11 10						11 40							12 10				
Heathrow Terminal 5	✈ a							11b16						11b46							12b16				
West Drayton	d			10 36		10 49					11 06		11 19				11 36			11 49				12 06	
Iver	d					10 52							11 22							11 52					
Langley	d					10 55							11 25							11 55					
Slough 3	a		10 37	10 44		11 00				11 06	11 14		11 30			11 37	11 44			12 00			12 06	12 14	
	d		10 38	10 44		11 01				11 07	11 14		11 31			11 38	11 44			12 01			12 07	12 14	
Burnham	d			10 48							11 18						11 48							12 18	
Taplow	d			10 52							11 22						11 52							12 22	
Maidenhead 3	d			10 56		11 08					11 26		11 38				11 56			12 08				12 26	
Twyford 3	d			11 03		11 16					11 33		11 46				12 03			12 16				12 33	
Reading 7	a		10 52	11 12		11 21				11 21	11 42		11 52			11 52	12 12			12 21			12 21	12 42	
Oxford	a		11 18			12 12				11 47			12 30			12 21				13 13			12 47		

		GW 1	HC	GW 1	GW 1 ◇ ☕	GW 1 ◇	GW 1	GW 1		GW 1	GW 1	HC	GW 1	GW 1	GW 1	HC	GW 1	GW 1 ◇	GW 1	GW 1		GW 1	HC	GW 1	GW 1 ◇ ☕
London Paddington 15	Θ d	12 00	12 03	12 15	12 18	12 21				12 25	12 30	12 33	12 45	12 55	13 00	13 03	13 15	13 21		13 25		13 30	13 33	13 45	13 51
Acton Main Line	d									12 31				13 01						13 31					
Ealing Broadway	Θ d	12 07	12 11	12 22						12 34	12 37	12 41	12 52	13 04	13 07	13 11	13 22			13 34		13 37	13 41	13 52	
West Ealing	d		12 13							12 36		12 43		13 06		13 13				13 36			13 43		
Drayton Green	d									12 39				13 09						13 39					
Castle Bar Park	d									12 40				13 10						13 40					
South Greenford	d									12 43				13 13						13 43					
Greenford	Θ a									12 49				13 19						13 49					
Hanwell	d		12 16					←				12 46				13 16			←				13 46		
Southall	d		12 19	12 27				12 27				12 49	12 57			13 19	13 27		13 27				13 49	13 57	
Hayes & Harlington	d	12 15	12 23	→				12 31			12 45	12 53	13 01		13 15	13 23	→		13 31			13 45	13 53	→	
Heathrow Terminals 1-2-3	✈ a		12 29									12 59				13 29							13 59		
Heathrow Terminal 4	✈ a		12 40									13 10				13 40							14 10		
Heathrow Terminal 5	✈ a		12b46									13b16				13b46							14b16		
West Drayton	d	12 19						12 36			12 49		13 06		13 19				13 36			13 49			
Iver	d	12 22									12 52				13 22							13 52			
Langley	d	12 25									12 55				13 25							13 55			
Slough 3	a	12 30			12 33	12 37		12 44			13 00		13 14		13 30			13 37	13 44			14 00			14 06
	d	12 31			12 34	12 38		12 44			13 01		13 14		13 31			13 38	13 44			14 01			14 07
Burnham	d							12 48					13 18						13 48						
Taplow	d						←	12 52					13 22						13 52						
Maidenhead 3	d	12 38					12 38	12 56			13 08		13 26		13 38				13 56			14 08			
Twyford 3	d	→					12 46	13 03			13 16		13 33		13 46				14 03			14 16			
Reading 7	a				12 48	12 52	12 52	13 12			13 21		13 42		13 52			13 52	14 12			14 21			14 21
Oxford	a					13 21	13 30				14 12				14 30			14 21				15 13			14 47

For general notes see front of timetable
For details of catering facilities see Directory of Train Operators

For fast services between London Paddington and Reading see Table 116

b Change at Heathrow Terminals 1-2-3

Table 117

London → Greenford and Reading

(Local services only)

Saturdays

from 13 September

Network Diagram - see first page of Table 116

		GW 1	GW 1	GW 1	HC	GW 1	GW 1 ◇	GW 1	GW 1	GW 1		HC	GW 1	GW 1 ◇	GW 1	GW 1	GW 1	HC	GW 1	GW 1 ◇	GW 1	GW 1		GW 1	HC
London Paddington 15 ⊖	d		13 55	14 00	14 03	14 15	14 21		14 25	14 30		14 33	14 45	14 51		14 55	15 00	15 03	15 15	15 21		15 25		15 30	15 33
Acton Main Line	d		14 01						14 31							15 01						15 31			
Ealing Broadway ⊖	d		14 04	14 07	14 11	14 22			14 34	14 37		14 41	14 52			15 04	15 07	15 11	15 22			15 34		15 37	15 41
West Ealing	d		14 06		14 13				14 36			14 43				15 06		15 13				15 36			15 43
Drayton Green	d		14 09						14 39							15 09						15 39			
Castle Bar Park	d		14 10						14 40							15 10						15 40			
South Greenford	d		14 13						14 43							15 13						15 43			
Greenford ⊖	a		14 19						14 49							15 19						15 49			
Hanwell	d	←			14 16			←				14 46			←			15 16			←				15 46
Southall	d	13 57			14 19	14 27 →		14 27				14 49	14 57 →		14 57			15 19	15 27 →		15 27				15 49
Hayes & Harlington	d	14 01		14 15	14 23			14 31		14 45		14 53			15 01		15 15	15 23			15 31			15 45	15 53
Heathrow Terminals 1-2-3 ✈	a				14 29							14 59						15 29							15 59
Heathrow Terminal 4 ✈	a				14 40							15 10						15 40							16 10
Heathrow Terminal 5 ✈	a				14b46							15b16						15b46							16b16
West Drayton	d	14 06		14 19				14 36		14 49					15 06		15 19				15 36			15 49	
Iver	d			14 22						14 52							15 22							15 52	
Langley	d			14 25						14 55							15 25							15 55	
Slough 3	a	14 14		14 30			14 37	14 44		15 00				15 06	15 14		15 30			15 37	15 44			16 00	
	d	14 14		14 31			14 38	14 44		15 01				15 07	15 14		15 31			15 38	15 44			16 01	
Burnham	d	14 18						14 48							15 18						15 48				
Taplow	d	14 22						14 52							15 22						15 52				
Maidenhead 3	d	14 26		14 38				14 56		15 08					15 26		15 38				15 56			16 08	
Twyford 3	d	14 33		14 46				15 03		15 16					15 33		15 46				16 03			16 16	
Reading 7	a	14 42		14 52			14 52	15 12		15 21				15 21	15 42		15 52			15 52	16 12			16 21	
Oxford	a			15 30			15 21			16 12				15 47			16 30			16 21				17 13	

		GW 1	GW 1 ◇	GW 1	GW 1	GW 1	HC	GW 1	GW 1 ◇	GW 1	GW 1	GW 1		HC	GW 1	GW 1 ◇	GW 1	GW 1	GW 1	HC	GW 1	GW 1 ◇	GW 1	GW 1	GW 1
London Paddington 15 ⊖	d	15 45	15 51		15 55	16 00	16 03	16 15	16 21		16 25	16 30		16 33	16 45	16 51		16 55	17 00	17 03	17 15	17 21		17 25	17 30
Acton Main Line	d				16 01						16 31							17 01						17 31	
Ealing Broadway ⊖	d	15 52			16 04	16 07	16 11	16 22			16 34	16 37		16 41	16 52			17 04	17 07	17 11	17 22			17 34	17 37
West Ealing	d				16 06		16 13				16 36			16 43				17 06		17 13				17 36	
Drayton Green	d				16 09						16 39							17 09						17 39	
Castle Bar Park	d				16 10						16 40							17 10						17 40	
South Greenford	d				16 13						16 43							17 13						17 43	
Greenford ⊖	a				16 19						16 49							17 19						17 49	
Hanwell	d			←			16 16			←				16 46			←			17 16			←		
Southall	d	15 57 →		15 57			16 19	16 27 →		16 27				16 49	16 57 →		16 57			17 19	17 27 →		17 27		
Hayes & Harlington	d			16 01		16 15	16 23			16 31		16 45		16 53			17 01		17 15	17 23			17 31		17 45
Heathrow Terminals 1-2-3 ✈	a						16 29							16 59						17 29					
Heathrow Terminal 4 ✈	a						16 40							17 10						17 40					
Heathrow Terminal 5 ✈	a						16b46							17b16						17b46					
West Drayton	d			16 06		16 19				16 36		16 49					17 06		17 19				17 36		17 49
Iver	d					16 22						16 52							17 22						17 52
Langley	d					16 25						16 55							17 25						17 55
Slough 3	a		16 06	16 14		16 30			16 37	16 44		17 00				17 06	17 14		17 30			17 37	17 44		18 00
	d		16 07	16 14		16 31			16 38	16 44		17 01				17 07	17 14		17 31			17 38	17 44		18 01
Burnham	d			16 18						16 48							17 18						17 48		
Taplow	d			16 22						16 52							17 22						17 52		
Maidenhead 3	d			16 26		16 38				16 56		17 08					17 26		17 38				17 56		18 08
Twyford 3	d			16 33		16 46				17 03		17 16					17 33		17 46				18 03		18 16
Reading 7	a		16 21	16 42		16 52			16 52	17 12		17 21				17 21	17 42		17 52			17 52	18 12		18 21
Oxford	a		16 47			17 30			17 21			18 12				17 47			18 30			18 21			19 13

		HC		GW 1	GW 1	GW 1	HC	GW 1	GW 1 ◇	GW 1	GW 1	GW 1	GW 1	HC		GW 1	GW 1 ◇	GW 1	GW 1	GW 1	HC	GW 1	GW 1 ◇	GW 1	GW 1
London Paddington 15 ⊖	d	17 33		17 45	17 55	18 00	18 03	18 15	18 21			18 25	18 30	18 33		18 45	18 51		18 55	19 00	19 03	19 15	19 21		19 25
Acton Main Line	d				18 01							18 31							19 01						19 31
Ealing Broadway ⊖	d	17 41		17 52	18 04	18 07	18 11	18 22				18 34	18 37	18 41		18 52			19 04	19 07	19 11	19 22			19 34
West Ealing	d	17 43			18 06		18 13					18 36		18 43					19 06		19 13				19 36
Drayton Green	d				18 09							18 39							19 09						19 39
Castle Bar Park	d				18 10							18 40							19 10						19 40
South Greenford	d				18 13							18 43							19 13						19 43
Greenford ⊖	a				18 19							18 49							19 19						19 49
Hanwell	d	17 46					18 16				←			18 46				←			19 16			←	
Southall	d	17 49		17 57			18 19	18 27 →			18 27			18 49		18 57 →		18 57			19 19	19 27 →		19 27	
Hayes & Harlington	d	17 53		18 01		18 15	18 23				18 31		18 45	18 53				19 01		19 15	19 23			19 31	
Heathrow Terminals 1-2-3 ✈	a	17 59					18 29							18 59							19 29				
Heathrow Terminal 4 ✈	a	18 10					18 40							19 10							19 40				
Heathrow Terminal 5 ✈	a	18b16					18b46							19b16							19b46				
West Drayton	d			18 06		18 19					18 36		18 49					19 06		19 19				19 36	
Iver	d					18 22							18 52							19 22					
Langley	d					18 25							18 55							19 25					
Slough 3	a			18 14		18 30			18 37		18 44		19 00				19 07	19 14		19 30			19 37	19 44	
	d			18 14		18 31			18 38		18 44		19 01				19 08	19 14		19 31			19 38	19 44	
Burnham	d			18 18							18 48							19 18						19 48	
Taplow	d			18 22						←	18 52							19 22						19 52	
Maidenhead 3	d			18 26		18 38 →				18 38	18 56		19 08					19 26		19 38				19 56	
Twyford 3	d			18 33						18 46	19 03		19 16					19 33		19 46				20 03	
Reading 7	a			18 42					18 51	18 52	19 12		19 21				19 22	19 42		19 52			19 52	20 12	
Oxford	a								19 18	19 30			20 15				19 48			20 30			20 21		

For general notes see front of timetable
For details of catering facilities see Directory of Train Operators

For fast services between London Paddington and Reading see Table 116

b Change at Heathrow Terminals 1-2-3

Saturdays

from 13 September

London → Greenford and Reading
(Local services only)

Network Diagram - see first page of Table 116

		GW 1	HC	GW 1		GW 1 ◇	GW 1	GW 1	GW 1	HC	GW 1	GW 1 ◇	GW 1	GW 1	GW 1	HC		GW 1	GW 1 ◇	GW 1	GW 1	GW 1	HC	GW 1	GW 1 ◇
London Paddington 15 ⊖	d	19 30	19 33	19 45		19 51		19 55	20 00	20 03	20 15	20 21		20 25	20 30	20 33		20 47	20 51		20 55	21 00	21 03	21 15	21 21
Acton Main Line	d							20 01						20 31							21 01				
Ealing Broadway ⊖	d	19 37	19 41	19 52				20 04	20 07	20 11	20 22			20 34	20 37	20 41		20 54			21 04	21 07	21 11	21 22	
West Ealing	d		19 43					20 06		20 13				20 36		20 43					21 06		21 13		
Drayton Green	d							20 09						20 39							21 09				
Castle Bar Park	d							20 10						20 40							21 10				
South Greenford	d							20 13						20 43							21 13				
Greenford ⊖	a							20 19						20 49							21 19				
Hanwell	d		19 46				←			20 16			←			20 46				←			21 16		
Southall	d		19 49	19 57			19 57			20 19	20 27		20 27			20 49		20 59		20 59			21 19	21 27	
Hayes & Harlington	d	19 45	19 53	→			20 01		20 15	20 23	→		20 31		20 45	20 53		→		21 04		21 15	21 23	→	
Heathrow Terminals 1-2-3	a		19 59							20 29						20 59							21 29		
Heathrow Terminal 4	a		20 10							20 40						21 10							21 40		
Heathrow Terminal 5	a		*20b16*							*20b46*						*21b16*							*21b46*		
West Drayton	d	19 49					20 06		20 19				20 36		20 49					21 08		21 19			
Iver	d	19 52							20 22						20 52							21 22			
Langley	d	19 55							20 25						20 55							21 25			
Slough 3	a	20 00				20 07	20 14		20 30			20 37	20 44		21 00				21 07	21 15		21 30			21 38
	d	20 01				20 07	20 14		20 31			20 38	20 44		21 01				21 08	21 16		21 31			21 39
Burnham	d						20 18						20 48							21 20					
Taplow	d						20 22						20 52							21 23					
Maidenhead 3	d	20 08					20 26		20 38				20 56		21 08					21 27		21 38			
Twyford 3	d	20 16					20 33		20 46				21 03		21 16					21 35		21 46			
Reading 7	a	20 21				20 21	20 42		20 52			20 52	21 12		21 21				21 22	21 43		21 52			21 55
Oxford	a	21 13				20 47			21 30			21 21			22 09				21 51			22 30			22 23

		GW 1	GW 1	HC	GW 1	GW 1 ◇		GW 1	GW 1	HC	GW 1	GW 1 ◇	GW 1	HC	GW 1 A	GW 1 ◇	GW 1 A	HC		GW 1 A	GW 1 ◇	GW 1 A	GW 1		
London Paddington 15 ⊖	d		21 25	21 33	21 45	21 51			22 00	22 03	22 20	22 32		22 33	22 45	23 00		23 03		23 20	23 33		23 45		
Acton Main Line	d		21 31												22 51								23 51		
Ealing Broadway ⊖	d		21 34	21 41	21 52				22 07	22 11	22 27			22 41	22 54			23 11		23 27			23 54		
West Ealing	d		21 36	21 43						22 13				22 43				23 13					23 56		
Drayton Green	d		21 39																						
Castle Bar Park	d		21 40																						
South Greenford	d		21 43																						
Greenford ⊖	a		21 49																						
Hanwell	d	←		21 46						22 16				22 46				23 16					23 59		
Southall	d	21 27		21 49	21 57			←		22 19	22 32		←	22 49	22 59		←	23 19		23 32		←	00 02		
Hayes & Harlington	d	21 31		21 53	22 01			22 01	22 15	22 23	22 36		22 36	22 53	23 03		23 03	23 23		23 36		23 36	00 06		
Heathrow Terminals 1-2-3	a			21 59	→					22 29	→			22 59	→			23 29		→					
Heathrow Terminal 4	a			22 10						22 40				23 10				23 40							
Heathrow Terminal 5	a			*22b16*						*22b46*				*23b16*				*23b46*							
West Drayton	d	21 36						22 06	22 19				22 41				23 07					23 41	00 11		
Iver	d							22 09	22 22				22 44				23 10					23 44	00 14		
Langley	d							22 12	22 25				22 47				23 13					23 47	00 17		
Slough 3	a	21 44				22 07		22 17	22 30			22 49	22 52			23 16	23 18				23 49	23 52	00 22		
	d	21 44				22 08		22 17	22 31			22 50	22 52			23 17	23 20				23 50	23 53	00 22		
Burnham	d	21 48						22 21					22 56				23 24					23 57	00 26		
Taplow	d	21 52						22 25					23 00									00 01			
Maidenhead 3	d	21 56						22 29	22 38				23 04				23 29					00 05	00 31		
Twyford 3	d	22 03						22 36	22 46				23 11				23 36					00 12	00 39		
Reading 7	a	22 12				22 23		22 43	22 52			23 06	23 19			23 33	23 43				00 07	00 19	00 46		
Oxford	a					22 46			23 31							*00 32*	*00 39*				*01 07*				

Sundays

until 7 September

		GW 1	GW 1	GW 1	GW 1	GW 1	HC	HC	GW 1	HC	GW		GW 1 ◇ B	HC	GW 1	GW 1 ◇	GW	HC	GW 1	GW 1 ◇	HC	GW		HC	GW 1
London Paddington 15 ⊖	d	23p20	23p45	00 05	00 30	01 00		06 12	06 43	07 12	07 43		08 03	08 12	08 15	08 42	08 44	09 07	09 15	09 35	09 37	09 44		10 07	10 15
Acton Main Line	d		23p51																						
Ealing Broadway ⊖	d	23p27	23p54	00 12	00 37	01 07	05 20	06 20	06 50	07 20	07 50			08 20	08 22		08 51	09 15	09 22		09 45	09 51		10 15	10 22
West Ealing	d		23p56																						
Drayton Green	d																								
Castle Bar Park	d																								
South Greenford	d																								
Greenford ⊖	a																								
Hanwell	d		23p59																						
Southall	d	23p32	00 02	00 17	00 42	01 12	05 24	06 24	06 55	07 24	07 55			08 24	08 27		08 56	09 19	09 27		09 49	09 56		10 19	10 27
Hayes & Harlington	d	23p36	00 06	00 21	00 46	01 16	05 28	06 28	06 59	07 28	07 59			08 28	08 31		08 59	09 23	09 31		09 53	09 59		10 23	10 31
Heathrow Terminals 1-2-3	a						05 34	06 34		07 34				08 34				09 29			09 59			10 29	
Heathrow Terminal 4	a						05 40	06 40		07 40				08 40				09 40			10 10			10 40	
Heathrow Terminal 5	a						*05b47*	*06b50*		*07b50*				*08b50*				*09b46*			*10b16*			*10b46*	
West Drayton	d	23p41	00 11	00 26	00 51				07 04		08 04				08 36		09 06		09 36			10 06			10 36
Iver	d	23p44	00 14	00 29																					
Langley	d	23p47	00 17	00 32	00 55				07 08		08 08				08 40		09 10		09 40			10 10			10 40
Slough 3	a	23p52	00 22	00 37	01 00	01 26			07 12		08 14		08 24		08 47	09 01	09 15		09 45	09 52		10 15			10 45
	d	23p53	00 22	00 37	01 01	01 26			07 14		08 14		08 25		08 47	09 01	09 15		09 46	09 53		10 15			10 46
Burnham	d	23p57	00 26	00 41					07 18		08 18						09 19					10 19			
Taplow	d	00 01		00 45																					
Maidenhead 3	d	00 05	00 31	00 49	01 08	01 34			07 25		08 23		08 35		08 54		09 24		09 53			10 24			10 53
Twyford 3	d	00 12	00 39	00 56	01 16	01 41			07 33		08 31				09 01		09 32		10 01			10 32			11 01
Reading 7	a	00 19	00 46	01 04	01 23	01 49			07 40		08 37		08 50		09 08	09 21	09 39		10 11	10 13		10 38			11 07
Oxford	a	01 07									09 35		09 17			09 51	10 29		*11 25*	10 42		11 25			

For general notes see front of timetable
For details of catering facilities see Directory of Train Operators

For fast services between London Paddington and Reading see Table 116

A To Didcot Parkway (Table 116)
B To Great Malvern (Table 126)
b Change at Heathrow Terminals 1-2-3

Table 117

Sundays
until 7 September

London → Greenford and Reading
(Local services only)

Network Diagram - see first page of Table 116

		HC	GW 1 ◇ ☕	GW	HC	GW 1	HC	GW 1 ◇	GW	HC	GW 1	HC	GW 1 ◇ ☕	GW	HC	GW 1	HC	GW 1 ◇ ☕	GW	HC	GW 1	HC	GW 1 ◇ ☕
London Paddington 15 ⊖	d	10 37	10 42	10 44	11 07	11 15	11 37	11 42	11 44	12 07	12 15	12 37	12 42	12 44	13 07	13 15	13 37	13 42	13 44	14 07	14 15	14 37	14 42
Acton Main Line	d																						
Ealing Broadway ⊖	d	10 45		10 51	11 15	11 22	11 45		11 51	12 15	12 22	12 45		12 51	13 15	13 22	13 45		13 51	14 15	14 22	14 45	
West Ealing	d																						
Drayton Green	d																						
Castle Bar Park	d																						
South Greenford	d																						
Greenford ⊖	a																						
Hanwell	d																						
Southall	d	10 49		10 56	11 19	11 27	11 49		11 56	12 19	12 27	12 49		12 56	13 19	13 27	13 49		13 56	14 19	14 27	14 49	
Hayes & Harlington	d	10 53		10 59	11 23	11 31	11 53		11 59	12 23	12 31	12 53		12 59	13 23	13 31	13 53		13 59	14 23	14 31	14 53	
Heathrow Terminals 1-2-3 ✈	a	10 59			11 29		11 59			12 29		12 59			13 29		13 59			14 29		14 59	
Heathrow Terminal 4 ✈	a	11 10			11 40		12 10			12 40		13 10			13 40		14 10			14 40		15 10	
Heathrow Terminal 5 ✈	a	11b16			11b46		12b16			12b46		13b16			13b46		14b16			14b46		15b16	
West Drayton	d			11 06		11 36			12 06		12 36			13 06		13 36			14 06		14 36		
Iver	d																						
Langley	d			11 10		11 40			12 10		12 40			13 10		13 40			14 10		14 40		
Slough 3	a		10 57	11 15		11 45		11 59	12 15		12 45		12 57	13 15		13 45		13 57	14 15		14 45		14 57
	d		10 58	11 15		11 46		12 00	12 15		12 46		12 58	13 15		13 46		13 58	14 15		14 46		14 58
Burnham	d			11 19					12 19					13 19					14 19				
Taplow	d																						
Maidenhead 3	d			11 24		11 53			12 24		12 53			13 24		13 53			14 24		14 53		
Twyford 3	d			11 32		12 01			12 32		13 01			13 32		14 01			14 32		15 01		
Reading 7	a		11 19	11 37		12 07		12 17	12 38		13 07		13 20	13 38		14 07		14 19	14 38		15 08		15 19
Oxford	a		11 49	12 27				12 51	13 27				13 49	14 25				14 49	15 27				15 48

		GW	HC	GW 1	HC	GW 1 ◇ ☕	GW	HC	GW 1	HC	GW 1 ◇ ☕	GW	HC	GW 1	HC	GW 1 ◇ ☕	GW	HC	GW 1	HC	GW 1 ◇ ☕	GW	HC
London Paddington 15 ⊖	d	14 44	15 07	15 15	15 37	15 42	15 44	16 07	16 15	16 37	16 42	16 44	17 07	17 15	17 37	17 42	17 44	18 07	18 15	18 37	18 42	18 44	19 07
Acton Main Line	d																						
Ealing Broadway ⊖	d	14 51	15 15	15 22	15 45		15 51	16 15	16 22	16 45		16 51	17 15	17 22	17 45		17 51	18 15	18 22	18 45		18 51	19 15
West Ealing	d																						
Drayton Green	d																						
Castle Bar Park	d																						
South Greenford	d																						
Greenford ⊖	a																						
Hanwell	d																						
Southall	d	14 56	15 19	15 27	15 49		15 56	16 19	16 27	16 49		16 56	17 19	17 27	17 49		17 56	18 19	18 27	18 49		18 56	19 19
Hayes & Harlington	d	14 59	15 23	15 31	15 53		15 59	16 23	16 31	16 53		16 59	17 23	17 31	17 53		17 59	18 23	18 31	18 53		18 59	19 23
Heathrow Terminals 1-2-3 ✈	a		15 29		15 59			16 29		16 59			17 29		17 59			18 29		18 59			19 29
Heathrow Terminal 4 ✈	a		15 40		16 10			16 40		17 10			17 40		18 10			18 40		19 10			19 40
Heathrow Terminal 5 ✈	a		15b46		16b16			16b46		17b16			17b46		18b16			18b46		19b16			19b46
West Drayton	d	15 06		15 36			16 06		16 36			17 06		17 36			18 06		18 36			19 06	
Iver	d																						
Langley	d	15 10		15 40			16 10		16 40			17 10		17 40			18 10		18 40			19 10	
Slough 3	a	15 15		15 45		15 57	16 15		16 45		16 57	17 15		17 45		17 57	18 15		18 45		18 57	19 15	
	d	15 15		15 46		15 58	16 15		16 46		16 58	17 15		17 46		17 58	18 15		18 46		18 58	19 15	
Burnham	d	15 19		15 50			16 19		16 50			17 19		17 50			18 19		18 50			19 19	
Taplow	d																						
Maidenhead 3	d	15 24		15 55			16 24		16 55			17 24		17 55			18 24		18 55			19 24	
Twyford 3	d	15 32		16 03			16 32		17 03			17 32		18 03			18 32		19 03			19 32	
Reading 7	a	15 38		16 09		16 19	16 38		17 10		17 19	17 38		18 09		18 19	18 38		19 09		19 20	19 38	
Oxford	a	16 25				16 49	17 25				17 49	18 27				18 49	19 25				19 50	20 25	

		GW 1	HC	GW 1 ◇	GW	HC	GW 1	HC	GW 1 ◇ 🛒	GW	HC	GW 1	GW 1 ◇ A	GW	HC	GW B	GW 1 ◇	GW	HC	GW 1	GW 1 ◇	GW 1
London Paddington 15 ⊖	d	19 15	19 37	19 42	19 44	20 07	20 15	20 37	20 42	20 44	21 07	21 15	21 42	21 44	22 12	22 15	22 42	22 44	23 12	23 15	23 42	23 53
Acton Main Line	d																					
Ealing Broadway ⊖	d	19 22	19 45		19 51	20 15	20 22	20 45		20 51	21 15	21 22		21 51	22 20	22 24		22 51	23 20	23 22	23 50	00 01
West Ealing	d																					
Drayton Green	d																					
Castle Bar Park	d																					
South Greenford	d																					
Greenford ⊖	a																					
Hanwell	d																					
Southall	d	19 27	19 49		19 56	20 19	20 27	20 49		20 56	21 19	21 27		21 56	22 24	22 28		22 56	23 24	23 29		00 06
Hayes & Harlington	d	19 31	19 53		19 59	20 23	20 31	20 53		20 59	21 23	21 31		21 59	22 28	22 32		22 59	23 28	23 33		00 10
Heathrow Terminals 1-2-3 ✈	a		19 59			20 29		20 59			21 29				22 34				23 34			
Heathrow Terminal 4 ✈	a		20 10			20 40		21 10			21 40				22 40				23 40			
Heathrow Terminal 5 ✈	a		20b16			20b46		21b16			21b46				22b50				23b50			
West Drayton	d	19 36			20 06		20 36			21 06		21 36		22 06		22 36		23 06		23 36		00 14
Iver	d																					
Langley	d	19 40			20 10		20 40			21 10		21 40		22 10		22 40		23 10		23 42		00 19
Slough 3	a	19 45		19 57	20 15		20 45		20 57	21 15		21 45	21 59	22 16		22 47	22 59	23 16		23 47	23 59	00 24
	d	19 46		19 57	20 15		20 46		20 58	21 15		21 46	21 59	22 16		22 47	23 00	23 16		23 47	00 02	00 24
Burnham	d	19 50			20 19		20 50			21 19		21 50		22 19		22 51		23 19		23 51		00 28
Taplow	d																					
Maidenhead 3	d	19 55			20 24		20 55			21 24		21 55	22 08	22c29		22 55		23 24		23 55	00 10	00 33
Twyford 3	d	20 02			20 32		21 02			21 32		22 02		22 36		23 04		23 32		00 04		00 41
Reading 7	a	20 10		20 17	20 38		21 09		21 20	21 38		22 09	22 20	22 43		23 10	23 18	23 42		00 10	00 23	00 48
Oxford	a			20 48	21 25				21 50	22 29			22 50	23 30			23 48	00 35			00 55	

For general notes see front of timetable
For details of catering facilities see Directory of Train Operators

For fast services between London Paddington and Reading see Table 116

A To Worcester Shrub Hill (Table 126)
B To Newbury (Table 116)
b Change at Heathrow Terminals 1-2-3
c Arr. 2224

Table 117

Sundays

London → Greenford and Reading

(Local services only)

from 14 September

Network Diagram - see first page of Table 116

Station		GW 1 A	GW 1	GW 1	GW 1	GW 1	HC	HC	GW 1	HC	GW	GW 1 ◇ B	HC	GW 1	GW 1 ◇ 🛒	GW	HC	GW 1	GW 1 ◇ ☕	GW	HC
London Paddington 15 ⊖	d	23p20	23p45	00 05	00 30	01 00		06 12	06 44	07 12	07 44	08 03	08 12	08 16	08 42	08 44	09 12	09 15	09 35	09 44	10 12
Acton Main Line	d		23p51																		
Ealing Broadway ⊖	d	23p27	23p54	00 12	00 37	01 07	05 20	06 20	06 51	07 20	07 51		08 20	08 24		08 51	09 20	09 24		09 51	10 20
West Ealing	d		23p56																		
Drayton Green	d																				
Castle Bar Park	d																				
South Greenford	d																				
Greenford ⊖	a																				
Hanwell	d		23p59																		
Southall	d	23p32	00 02	00 17	00 42	01 12	05 24	06 24	06 56	07 24	07 56		08 24	08 29		08 56	09 24	09 29		09 56	10 24
Hayes & Harlington	d	23p36	00 06	00 21	00 46	01 16	05 28	06 28	07 00	07 28	08 00		08 28	08 33		09 00	09 28	09 33		10 00	10 28
Heathrow Terminals 1-2-3 ✈	a						05 34	06 34		07 34			08 34				09 34				10 34
Heathrow Terminal 4 ✈	a						05 40	06 40		07 40			08 40				09 40				10 40
Heathrow Terminal 5 ✈	a						05b47	06b50		07b50			08b50				09b50				10b50
West Drayton	d	23p41	00 11	00 26	00 51				07 05		08 05			08 37		09 05		09 37		10 05	
Iver	d	23p44	00 14	00 29																	
Langley	d	23p47	00 17	00 32	00 55				07 10		08 10			08 42		09 10		09 42		10 10	
Slough 3	a	23p52	00 22	00 37	01 00	01 26			07 14		08 14	08 24		08 47	09 00	09 14		09 47	09 54	10 14	
	d	23p53	00 22	00 37	01 01	01 26			07 14		08 14	08 25		08 47	09 01	09 14		09 47	09 55	10 14	
Burnham	d	23p57	00 26	00 41					07 19		08 19					09 19				10 19	
Taplow	d	00 01		00 45																	
Maidenhead 3	d	00 05	00 31	00 49	01 08	01 34			07 23		08 24	08 32		08 55		09 24		09 55		10 24	
Twyford 3	d	00 12	00 39	00 56	01 16	01 41			07 32		08 32			09 03		09 32		10 03		10 32	
Reading 7	a	00 19	00 46	01 04	01 23	01 49			07 39		08 39	08 43		09 09	09 20	09 39		10 11	10 12	10 39	
Oxford	a										09 32	09 15			09 51	10 27			10 42	11 25	

Station		GW 1	GW 1 ◇ ☕	GW	HC	GW 1	GW 1 ◇	GW	HC	GW 1	GW 1 ◇ ☕	GW	HC	GW 1	GW 1 ◇ ☕	GW	HC	GW 1	GW 1 ◇ ☕	GW
London Paddington 15 ⊖	d	10 15	10 42	10 44	11 12	11 15	11 42	11 44	12 12	12 15	12 42	12 44	13 12	13 15	13 42	13 44	14 12	14 15	14 42	14 44
Acton Main Line	d																			
Ealing Broadway ⊖	d	10 24		10 51	11 20	11 24		11 51	12 20	12 24		12 51	13 20	13 24		13 51	14 20	14 24		14 51
West Ealing	d																			
Drayton Green	d																			
Castle Bar Park	d																			
South Greenford	d																			
Greenford ⊖	a																			
Hanwell	d																			
Southall	d	10 29		10 56	11 24	11 29		11 56	12 24	12 29		12 56	13 24	13 29		13 56	14 24	14 29		14 56
Hayes & Harlington	d	10 33		11 00	11 28	11 33		12 00	12 28	12 33		13 00	13 28	13 33		14 00	14 28	14 33		15 00
Heathrow Terminals 1-2-3 ✈	a				11 34				12 34				13 34				14 34			
Heathrow Terminal 4 ✈	a				11 40				12 40				13 40				14 40			
Heathrow Terminal 5 ✈	a				11b50				12b50				13b50				14b50			
West Drayton	d	10 37		11 05		11 37		12 05		12 37		13 05		13 37		14 05		14 37		15 05
Iver	d																			
Langley	d	10 42		11 10		11 42		12 10		12 42		13 10		13 42		14 10		14 42		15 10
Slough 3	a	10 47	11 02	11 14		11 47	12 00	12 14		12 47	13 00	13 14		13 47	14 04	14 14		14 47	15 04	15 14
	d	10 47	11 03	11 14		11 47	12 00	12 14		12 47	13 01	13 14		13 47	14 05	14 14		14 47	15 05	15 14
Burnham	d			11 19				12 19				13 19				14 19				15 19
Taplow	d																			
Maidenhead 3	d	10 55		11 24		11 55		12 24		12 55		13 24		13 55		14 24		14 55		15 24
Twyford 3	d	11 03		11 32		12 03		12 32		13 03		13 32		14 03		14 32		15 03		15 32
Reading 7	a	11 11	11 19	11 39		12 09	12 19	12 39		13 09	13 19	13 39		14 10	14 19	14 39		15 09	15 19	15 39
Oxford	a		11 49	12 25			12 50	13 27			13 49	14 25			14 49	15 27			15 48	16 25

Station		HC	GW 1	GW 1 ◇ ☕	GW	HC	GW 1	GW 1 ◇ ☕	GW	HC	GW 1	GW 1 ◇ ☕	GW	HC	GW 1	GW 1 ◇ ☕	GW	HC	GW 1	GW 1 ◇	GW
London Paddington 15 ⊖	d	15 12	15 15	15 42	15 44	16 12	16 15	16 42	16 44	17 12	17 15	17 42	17 44	18 12	18 15	18 42	18 44	19 12	19 15	19 42	19 44
Acton Main Line	d																				
Ealing Broadway ⊖	d	15 20	15 24		15 51	16 20	16 24		16 51	17 20	17 24		17 51	18 20	18 24		18 51	19 20	19 24		19 51
West Ealing	d																				
Drayton Green	d																				
Castle Bar Park	d																				
South Greenford	d																				
Greenford ⊖	a																				
Hanwell	d																				
Southall	d	15 24	15 29		15 56	16 24	16 29		16 56	17 24	17 29		17 56	18 24	18 29		18 56	19 24	19 29		19 56
Hayes & Harlington	d	15 28	15 33		16 00	16 28	16 33		17 00	17 28	17 33		18 00	18 28	18 33		19 00	19 28	19 33		20 00
Heathrow Terminals 1-2-3 ✈	a	15 34				16 34				17 34				18 34				19 34			
Heathrow Terminal 4 ✈	a	15 40				16 40				17 40				18 40				19 40			
Heathrow Terminal 5 ✈	a	15b50				16b50				17b50				18b50				19b50			
West Drayton	d		15 37		16 05		16 37		17 05		17 37		18 05		18 37		19 05		19 37		20 05
Iver	d																				
Langley	d		15 42		16 10		16 42		17 10		17 42		18 10		18 42		19 10		19 42		20 10
Slough 3	a		15 47	16 04	16 14		16 47	17 04	17 14		17 47	18 04	18 14		18 47	19 04	19 14		19 47	20 04	20 14
	d		15 47	16 05	16 14		16 47	17 05	17 14		17 47	18 05	18 14		18 47	19 05	19 14		19 47	20 04	20 14
Burnham	d		15 51		16 19		16 51		17 19		17 51		18 19		18 51		19 19		19 51		20 19
Taplow	d																				
Maidenhead 3	d		15 56		16 24		16 56		17 24		17 56		18 24		18 56		19 24		19 56		20 24
Twyford 3	d		16 04		16 32		17 04		17 32		18 04		18 32		19 04		19 32		20 04		20 32
Reading 7	a		16 10	16 19	16 39		17 10	17 19	17 39		18 10	18 19	18 39		19 10	19 19	19 39		20 10	20 17	20 39
Oxford	a			16 49	17 25			17 49	18 27			18 49	19 25			19 50	20 25			20 48	21 25

For general notes see front of timetable
For details of catering facilities see Directory of Train Operators

For fast services between London Paddington and Reading see Table 116

A To Didcot Parkway (Table 116)
B To Great Malvern (Table 126)
b Change at Heathrow Terminals 1-2-3

Table 117

Sundays

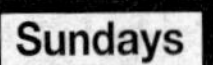

from 14 September

London → Greenford and Reading

(Local services only)

Network Diagram - see first page of Table 116

		HC	GW		GW	GW	HC	GW		GW	GW	HC	GW		GW	GW	HC	GW		GW	GW
			1		1 ◇			1		1 ◇					1 ◇			1		1 ◇	1
													A								
					🚌																
London Paddington 15 ⊖	d	20 12	20 15		20 42	20 44	21 12	21 15		21 27	21 44	22 12	22 15		22 42	22 44	23 12	23 15		23 42	23 53
Acton Main Line	d																				
Ealing Broadway ⊖	d	20 20	20 24			20 51	21 20	21 24			21 51	22 20	22 24			22 51	23 20	23 24		23 50	00 01
West Ealing	d																				
Drayton Green	d																				
Castle Bar Park	d																				
South Greenford	d																				
Greenford ⊖	a																				
Hanwell	d																				
Southall	d	20 24	20 29			20 56	21 24	21 29			21 56	22 24	22 29			22 56	23 24	23 29			00 06
Hayes & Harlington	d	20 28	20 33			21 00	21 28	21 33			22 00	22 28	22 33			23 00	23 28	23 33			00 10
Heathrow Terminals 1-2-3 ✈	a	20 34					21 34					22 34					23 34				
Heathrow Terminal 4 ✈	a	20 40					21 40					22 40					23 40				
Heathrow Terminal 5 ✈	a	*20b50*					*21b50*					*22b50*					*23b50*				
West Drayton	d		20 37			21 05		21 37			22 05		22 37			23 05		23 37			00 14
Iver	d																				
Langley	d		20 42			21 10		21 42			22 10		22 42			23 10		23 42			00 19
Slough 3	a		20 47		21 00	21 14		21 47		21 51	22 14		22 47		22 59	23 15		23 47		00 02	00 24
	d		20 47		21 01	21 14		21 47		21 51	22 14		22 47		23 01	23 15		23 47		00 03	00 24
Burnham	d		20 51			21 19		21 51			22 19		22 51			23 19		23 51			00 28
Taplow	d																				00 32
Maidenhead 3	d		20 56			21 24		21 56			22 29		22 56			23 24		23 56		00 10	00 36
Twyford 3	d		21 04			21 32		22 04			22 35		23 04			23 32		00 04			00 44
Reading 7	a		21 10		21 17	21 39		22 10		22 07	22 43		23 10		23 18	23 43		00 10		00 23	00 50
Oxford	a				21 51	22 27				22 41	23 30				23 48	00 35		*00 55*		00 55	

For general notes see front of timetable
For details of catering facilities see Directory of Train Operators

For fast services between London Paddington and Reading see Table 116

A To Newbury (Table 116)
b Change at Heathrow Terminals 1-2-3

Reading and Greenford → London

(Local services only)

Network Diagram - see first page of Table 116

Miles	Miles	Miles			GW MX 1	HC	GW MO 1 A	GW MO 1 B	GW MX 1	GW MO 1	GW MO 1 ◇	GW MX 1 ◇	GW MX 1 C	GW MX 1	GW 1	GW 1	HC 1	GW 1	HC 1	GW 1	GW 1	GW 1 ◇	GW 1	GW 1	HC 1
—	—	—	Oxford	d			22p58	22p58			00 01	00 05	00 20			04 00					05 06				
0	—	—	**Reading 7**	d	23p15		23p40	23p41	00 15	00 24	00 31	00 39	01 09	02 24	03 54	04 40		05 16		05 39	05 45	05 57			
5	—	—	**Twyford 3**	d	23p21		23p48	23p48	00 21	00 30	00 37		01 15	02 30	04 00	04 46		05 23		05 45	05 51				
11¾	—	—	**Maidenhead 3**	d	23p29		23p56	23p56	00 29	00 38	00 45		01 23	02 38	04 08	04 54		05 31		05 53	05 59				
13½	—	—	Taplow	d	23p32				00 33									05 34			06 02				
15	—	—	Burnham	d	23p36		00 01	00 01	00 36									05 38			06 06				
17½	—	—	**Slough 3**	a	23p41		00 05	00 05	00 42	00 46	00 52	00 56	01 31	02 46	04 16	05 02		05 42		06 00	06 10	06 11			
—	—	—		d	23p42		00 06	00 06	00 42	00 47	00 52	00 57	01 32	02 47	04 17	05 04		05 43		06 01	06 11	06 12			
19¾	—	—	Langley	d	23p46		00 10	00 10	00 46	00 51						05 09		05 47			06 15				
21¼	—	—	Iver	d	23p49											05 13		05 50			06 18				
22¾	—	—	West Drayton	d	23p52		00 14	00 14	00 51	00 55				02 53	04 23	05 16		05 53			06 21				
—	—	—	**Heathrow Terminal 5** ✈	d													05b07		05b42						06b12
—	—	0	**Heathrow Terminal 4** ✈	d		00 01											05 23		05 51						06 21
—	—	1¾	**Heathrow Terminals 1-2-3** ✈	d		00 06											05 29		05 56				←		06 26
25¼	—	5¾	Hayes & Harlington	d	23p56	00 12	00 19	00 19	00 55	01 00	01 03		01 41	02 58	04 28	05 21	05 34	05 57	06 03	06 10	06 25		06 25		06 33
27	—	7½	Southall	d	00 01	00 15	00 22	00 22	01 00	01 04				03 02	04 32	05 25	05 38	06 01	06 06	06 13	→		06 29		06 36
28¾	—	9¼	Hanwell	d													05 41		06 09						06 39
—	0	—	**Greenford** ⊖	d																				06 25	
—	1	—	South Greenford	d																				06 28	
—	1¾	—	Castle Bar Park	d																				06 31	
—	2	—	Drayton Green	d																				06 33	
29½	2¾	10	West Ealing	d													05 43		06 12					06 36	06 42
30¼	3½	11	**Ealing Broadway** ⊖	d	00 06	00 20	00 27	00 27	01 05	01 09	01 13		01 48	03 07	04 37	05 30	05 46	06 07	06 14	06 19			06 34	06 39	06 44
31¾	5	12¼	Acton Main Line	d												05 34		06 10					06 37	06 42	
36	9¼	16½	**London Paddington 15** ⊖	a	00 15	00 29	00 35	00 40	01 15	01 19	01 22	01 17	01 57	03 18	04 47	05 43	05 57	06 19	06 24	06 31		06 30	06 46	06 51	06 54

		GW 1	GW 1	GW 1	GW 1	GW 1	GW 1	GW 1	GW 1	GW 1	GW 1 ◇	GW 1	HC 1	GW 1	GW 1	GW 1	GW 1	GW 1	GW 1	GW 1	GW 1	GW 1	GW 1	HC 1	GW 1
Oxford	d		05 34	05 50			06 02														*06 30*				06 07
Reading 7	d	06 05	06 15	06 21			06 32		06 32	06 37	06 45			06 46	06 50	←			06 57	07 02	07 07				07 10
Twyford 3	d	06 11	06 21	06 28					06 38	06 43				06 55		06 55		←	07 03	07 08					07 16
Maidenhead 3	d	06 19	06 29			←	06 43		06 46	06 53				→	07 02	07 04		06 53	07 11	07 16	07 19				07 24
Taplow	d	06 23	06 33			06 33				→								06 58							07 28
Burnham	d	06 26	→			06 36			06 50									07 02		07 21					→
Slough 3	a	06 31		06 39		06 41	06 50		06 55		06 58							07 07	07 18	→		←			
	d	06 31		06 40		06 41	06 51		06 55		06 59							07 08	07 19			07 19			
Langley	d	06 35				06 45			06 59									07 12	→						
Iver	d					06 48		←	07 03								←	07 15							
West Drayton	d	06 40				06 51		06 51	07 06								07 06	07 19							
Heathrow Terminal 5 ✈	d					→			→				06b42											07b12	
Heathrow Terminal 4 ✈	d												06 51											07 21	
Heathrow Terminals 1-2-3 ✈	d				←								06 56											07 26	
Hayes & Harlington	d	06 44			06 44			06 56					07 03				07 10	07 23						07 33	
Southall	d	→			06 48			07 00					07 06				07 15	07 27						07 36	
Hanwell	d												07 09											07 39	
Greenford ⊖	d											06 55											07 25		
South Greenford	d											06 58											07 28		
Castle Bar Park	d											07 01											07 31		
Drayton Green	d											07 03											07 33		
West Ealing	d											07 06	07 12										07 36	07 42	
Ealing Broadway ⊖	d				06 53			07 05				07 09	07 14				07 20	07 32					07 39	07 44	
Acton Main Line	d											07 12											07 42		
London Paddington 15 ⊖	a			07 00	07 03		07 08	07 15			07 16	07 21	07 24		07 26	07 29	07 31	07 40			07 43	07 45	07 51	07 54	

		GW 1 D	GW 1	GW 1	GW 1 E	GW 1	GW 1 C	GW 1	GW 1	HC 1	GW 1 D	GW 1 C		GW 1	GW 1 C	GW 1	GW 1	HC 1	GW 1	GW 1	GW 1	GW 1	GW 1 E	GW 1	HC 1
Oxford	d						06 37	*06 57*	07 10						07 02	*07 30*				07 22					
Reading 7	d						07 30	07 41							07 56	08 06			08 12	08 19					
Twyford 3	d	07 23					07 37	07 47			07 56				08 02	08a12			08 18	08 26					
Maidenhead 3	d	07 31		←	07 42		07 46	07 55	08 00		08 04				08 11				08 26	08 34			08 42		
Taplow	d		←	07 28				07 59											08 30			←			
Burnham	d		07 21	07 32			07 51	08 02							08 15				08 33			08 33			
Slough 3	a		07 26	07 37	07 49		07 55	08 07							08 20				→			08 38	08 49		
	d		07 26	07 37	07 50		07 56	08 07							08 20						08 25	08 38	08 49		
Langley	d		07 30	07 42			08 00	08 12						←							08 29	08 43			
Iver	d			07 45				08 15				←		08 15								08 46			
West Drayton	d		07 36	07 48			08 05	→				08 05		08 18							08 34	08 49			
Heathrow Terminal 5 ✈	d						→			07b42								08b12							08b42
Heathrow Terminal 4 ✈	d									07 51								08 21							08 51
Heathrow Terminals 1-2-3 ✈	d									07 56								08 26							08 56
Hayes & Harlington	d		07 40	07 53						08 03		08 10		08 23				08 33			08 39	08 54			09 03
Southall	d		07 44	07 57						08 06		08 14		08 27				08 36			08 43	08 58			09 06
Hanwell	d									08 09								08 39							09 09
Greenford ⊖	d					07 55											08 25							08 55	
South Greenford	d					07 58											08 28							08 58	
Castle Bar Park	d					08 01											08 31							09 01	
Drayton Green	d					08 03											08 33							09 03	
West Ealing	d					08 06				08 12							08 36	08 42						09 06	09 12
Ealing Broadway ⊖	d		07 49	08 02		08 09				08 14		08 19		08 32			08 39	08 44			08 49	09 03		09 09	09 14
Acton Main Line	d					08 12											08 42							09 12	
London Paddington 15 ⊖	a	07 57	08 01	08 12	08 15	08 21			08 22	08 24	08 29	08 31		08 42	08 45		08 51	08 54		08 59	09 01	09 13	09 16	09 21	09 24

For general notes see front of timetable
For details of catering facilities see Directory of Train Operators

For fast services between Reading and London Paddington see Table 116

A From 15 September
B Until 8 September
C From Banbury (Table 116)
D From Henley-on-Thames (Table 121)
E From Bourne End (Table 120)
b Change at Heathrow Terminals 1-2-3

Reading and Greenford → London

(Local services only)

Network Diagram - see first page of Table 116

	GW 1	GW 1	GW 1	GW 1	HC 1	GW 1	GW 1	GW 1	GW 1 ◇	GW 1	GW 1	HC 1
Oxford d	*07 52*	07 57				08 21		08 55	09 06			
Reading 7 d	08 31	08 48				09 04	09 18	09 34	09 38			
Twyford 3 d	08 37	08 55				09 10	09 25	09 40 →				
Maidenhead 3 d	08 45	09 04				09 18	09 33					
Taplow d	08 49						09 37					
Burnham d	08 52						09 40					
Slough 3 a	08 57					09 25	09 45		09 51			
d	08 57					09 26	09 45		09 52			
Langley d	09 01		←			09 30						
Iver d	09 04		09 04			09 33						
West Drayton d	→		09 07			09 36	09 52					
Heathrow Terminal 5 ✈ d					*09*b*12*							*09*b*42*
Heathrow Terminal 4 ✈ d					09 21							09 51
Heathrow Terminals 1-2-3 ✈ d					09 26					←		09 56
Hayes & Harlington d			09 12		09 33	09 40	09 56 →			09 56		10 03
Southall d			09 15		09 36	09 44						10 06
Hanwell d					09 39							10 09
Greenford ⊖ d				09 25							09 53	
South Greenford d				09 28							09 56	
Castle Bar Park d				09 31							09 59	
Drayton Green d				09 33							10 01	
West Ealing d				09 36	09 42						10 04	10 12
Ealing Broadway ⊖ d			09 20	09 39	09 44	09 49				10 03	10 07	10 14
Acton Main Line d				09 42							10 10	
London Paddington 15 ⊖ a		09 28	09 31	09 51	09 54	10 02			10 10	10 13	10 21	10 24

	GW 1	GW 1	GW 1 ◇	GW 1	GW 1	HC 1	GW 1	GW 1	GW 1 ◇ (catering)	GW 1	GW 1	GW 1
Oxford d		*09 15*	09 38				09 21		10 01			
Reading 7 d	←	09 49	10 04				10 04	10 19	10 25			
Twyford 3 d	09 40	09 55					10 10	10 25			←	
Maidenhead 3 d	09 48	10 03					10 18	10 33 →			10 33	
Taplow d		10 07									10 37	
Burnham d		10 10									10 40	
Slough 3 a	09 55	10 15	10 17				10 25		10 38		10 45	
d	09 56	10 15	10 18				10 26		10 39		10 45	
Langley d	10 00						10 30					
Iver d	10 03						10 33			←		
West Drayton d	10 06	10 22					10 36			10 36	10 52	
Heathrow Terminal 5 ✈ d						*10*b*12*	→					
Heathrow Terminal 4 ✈ d						10 21						
Heathrow Terminals 1-2-3 ✈ d				←		10 26						
Hayes & Harlington d	10 10	10 26 →		10 26		10 33				10 40	10 56	
Southall d	10 14					10 36				10 44		
Hanwell d						10 39						
Greenford ⊖ d					10 25							10 53
South Greenford d					10 28							10 56
Castle Bar Park d					10 31							10 59
Drayton Green d					10 33							11 01
West Ealing d					10 36	10 42						11 04
Ealing Broadway ⊖ d	10 19			10 33	10 39	10 44				10 49	11 03	11 07
Acton Main Line d					10 42							11 10
London Paddington 15 ⊖ a	10 32		10 36	10 43	10 51	10 54			10 59	11 02	11 13	11 19

	HC 1	GW 1	GW 1	GW 1 ◇	GW 1	GW 1	GW 1	HC 1	GW 1	GW 1	GW 1	HC 1
Oxford d		09 55	*10 15*	10 31					10 21	*10 43*		
Reading 7 d		10 34	10 49	10 56					11 04	11 19		
Twyford 3 d		10 40	10 55			←			11 10	11 25		
Maidenhead 3 d		10 48	11 03			11 03			11 18	11 33		
Taplow d			→			11 07				11 37		
Burnham d						11 10				11 40		
Slough 3 a		10 55		11 09		11 15			11 25	11 45		
d		10 56		11 10		11 15			11 26	11 45		
Langley d		11 00							11 30			
Iver d		11 03			←				11 33			
West Drayton d		11 06			11 06	11 22			11 36	11 52		
Heathrow Terminal 5 ✈ d	*10*b*42*	→						*11*b*12*				*11*b*42*
Heathrow Terminal 4 ✈ d	10 51							11 21				11 51
Heathrow Terminals 1-2-3 ✈ d	10 56							11 26				11 56
Hayes & Harlington d	11 03				11 10	11 26		11 33	11 40	11 56		12 03
Southall d	11 06				11 14			11 36	11 44			12 06
Hanwell d	11 09							11 39				12 09
Greenford ⊖ d							11 23				11 53	
South Greenford d							11 26				11 56	
Castle Bar Park d							11 29				11 59	
Drayton Green d							11 31				12 01	
West Ealing d	11 12						11 34	11 42			12 04	12 12
Ealing Broadway ⊖ d	11 14				11 19	11 33	11 37	11 44	11 49	12 03	12 07	12 14
Acton Main Line d							11 40				12 10	
London Paddington 15 ⊖ a	11 24			11 27	11 32	11 43	11 49	11 54	12 02	12 13	12 19	12 24

	GW 1	GW 1	GW 1 ◇	GW 1	GW 1	GW 1	HC 1	GW 1		GW 1	GW 1 ◇	GW 1
Oxford d	10 55	*11 15*	11 31					11 21			12 01	
Reading 7 d	11 34	11 49	11 56					12 04		12 19	12 27	
Twyford 3 d	11 40	11 55			←			12 10		12 25		
Maidenhead 3 d	11 48	12 03			12 03			12 18		12 33		
Taplow d		→			12 07					→		
Burnham d					12 10							
Slough 3 a	11 55		12 09		12 15			12 25			12 40	
d	11 56		12 10		12 15			12 26			12 41	
Langley d	12 00							12 30				
Iver d	12 03			←				12 33				←
West Drayton d	12 06			12 06	12 22			12 36				12 36
Heathrow Terminal 5 ✈ d	→						*12*b*12*	→				
Heathrow Terminal 4 ✈ d							12 21					
Heathrow Terminals 1-2-3 ✈ d							12 26					
Hayes & Harlington d				12 10	12 26		12 33					12 40
Southall d				12 14			12 36					12 44
Hanwell d							12 39					
Greenford ⊖ d						12 23						
South Greenford d						12 26						
Castle Bar Park d						12 29						
Drayton Green d						12 31						
West Ealing d						12 34	12 42					
Ealing Broadway ⊖ d				12 19	12 33	12 37	12 44					12 49
Acton Main Line d						12 40						
London Paddington 15 ⊖ a			12 29	12 32	12 43	12 49	12 54				12 59	13 02

	GW 1	GW 1	HC 1	GW 1	GW 1	GW 1 ◇	GW 1	GW 1	GW 1	HC 1	GW 1	GW 1
Oxford d				11 55	*12 15*	12 31					12 21	
Reading 7 d				12 34	12 49	12 56					13 04	13 19
Twyford 3 d	←			12 40	12 55			←			13 10	13 25
Maidenhead 3 d	12 33			12 48	13 03			13 03			13 18	13 33
Taplow d	12 37				→			13 07				→
Burnham d	12 40							13 10				
Slough 3 a	12 45			12 55		13 09		13 15			13 25	
d	12 45			12 56		13 10		13 15			13 26	
Langley d				13 00							13 30	
Iver d				13 03			←				13 33	
West Drayton d	12 52			13 06			13 06	13 22			13 36	
Heathrow Terminal 5 ✈ d			*12*b*42*	→						*13*b*12*	→	
Heathrow Terminal 4 ✈ d			12 51							13 21		
Heathrow Terminals 1-2-3 ✈ d			12 56							13 26		
Hayes & Harlington d	12 56		13 03				13 10	13 26		13 33		
Southall d			13 06				13 14			13 36		
Hanwell d			13 09							13 39		
Greenford ⊖ d		12 53							13 23			
South Greenford d		12 56							13 26			
Castle Bar Park d		12 59							13 29			
Drayton Green d		13 01							13 31			
West Ealing d		13 04	13 12						13 34	13 42		
Ealing Broadway ⊖ d	13 03	13 07	13 14				13 19	13 33	13 37	13 44		
Acton Main Line d		13 10							13 40			
London Paddington 15 ⊖ a	13 13	13 19	13 24			13 27	13 32	13 43	13 49	13 54		

	GW 1 ◇ (catering)	GW 1	GW 1	GW 1	HC 1	GW 1	GW 1	GW 1 ◇	GW 1	GW 1	GW 1	HC 1
Oxford d	13 01					12 55	*13 15*	13 31				
Reading 7 d	13 27					13 34	13 49	13 55				
Twyford 3 d			←			13 40	13 55			←		
Maidenhead 3 d			13 33			13 48	14 03			14 03		
Taplow d			13 37				→			14 07		
Burnham d			13 40							14 10		
Slough 3 a	13 40		13 45			13 55		14 09		14 15		
d	13 41		13 45			13 56		14 10		14 15		
Langley d						14 00						
Iver d		←				14 03			←			
West Drayton d		13 36	13 52			14 06			14 06	14 22		
Heathrow Terminal 5 ✈ d					*13*b*42*	→						*14*b*12*
Heathrow Terminal 4 ✈ d					13 51							14 21
Heathrow Terminals 1-2-3 ✈ d					13 56							14 26
Hayes & Harlington d		13 40	13 56		14 03				14 10	14 26		14 33
Southall d		13 44			14 06				14 14			14 36
Hanwell d					14 09							14 39
Greenford ⊖ d				13 53							14 23	
South Greenford d				13 56							14 26	
Castle Bar Park d				13 59							14 29	
Drayton Green d				14 01							14 31	
West Ealing d				14 04	14 12						14 34	14 42
Ealing Broadway ⊖ d		13 49	14 03	14 07	14 14				14 19	14 33	14 37	14 44
Acton Main Line d				14 10							14 40	
London Paddington 15 ⊖ a	13 59	14 02	14 13	14 19	14 24			14 29	14 32	14 43	14 49	14 54

For general notes see front of timetable
For details of catering facilities see Directory of Train Operators

For fast services between Reading and London Paddington see Table 116

b Change at Heathrow Terminals 1-2-3

Reading and Greenford → London
(Local services only)

Network Diagram - see first page of Table 116

	GW 1	GW 1	GW 1 ◇	GW 1	GW 1	GW 1	HC 1	GW 1	GW 1	GW 1 ◇	GW 1	GW 1	GW 1	HC 1	GW 1	GW 1	GW 1 ◇	GW 1	GW 1	GW 1	HC 1	GW 1	GW 1	GW 1 ◇
Oxford d	13 21		14 01					13 55	*14 15*	14 31					14 21		15 01					14 55	*15 15*	15 31
Reading 7 d	14 04	14 19	14 27					14 34	14 49	14 56					15 04	15 19	15 27					15 34	15 49	15 56
Twyford 3 d	14 10	14 25			←			14 40	14 55			←			15 10	15 25			←			15 40	15 55	
Maidenhead 3 d	14 18	14 33			14 33			14 48	15 03			15 03			15 18	15 33			15 33			15 48	16 03	
Taplow d		→			14 37				→			15 07				→			15 37				→	
Burnham d					14 40							15 10							15 40					
Slough 3 a	14 25		14 40		14 45			14 55		15 09		15 15			15 25		15 40		15 45			15 55		16 09
d	14 26		14 41		14 45			14 56		15 10		15 15			15 26		15 41		15 45			15 56		16 10
Langley d	14 30							15 00							15 30							16 00		
Iver d	14 33			←				15 03			←				15 33			←				16 03		
West Drayton d	14 36			14 36	14 52			15 06			15 06	15 22			15 36			15 36	15 52			16 06		
Heathrow Terminal 5 ✈ d	→						*14b42*	→						*15b12*	→						*15b42*	→		
Heathrow Terminal 4 ✈ d							14 51							15 21							15 51			
Heathrow Terminals 1-2-3 ✈ d							14 56							15 26							15 56			
Hayes & Harlington d				14 40	14 56		15 03				15 10	15 26		15 33				15 40	15 56		16 03			
Southall d				14 44			15 06				15 14			15 36				15 44			16 06			
Hanwell d							15 09							15 39							16 09			
Greenford ⊖ d						14 53							15 23							15 53				
South Greenford d						14 56							15 26							15 56				
Castle Bar Park d						14 59							15 29							15 59				
Drayton Green d						15 01							15 31							16 01				
West Ealing d						15 04	15 12						15 34	15 42						16 04	16 12			
Ealing Broadway ⊖ d				14 49	15 03	15 07	15 14				15 19	15 33	15 37	15 44				15 49	16 03	16 07	16 14			
Acton Main Line d						15 10							15 40							16 10				
London Paddington 15 ⊖ a			14 59	15 02	15 13	15 19	15 24			15 27	15 32	15 43	15 49	15 54			15 59	16 02	16 13	16 19	16 24			16 27

	GW 1	GW 1	GW 1	HC 1	GW 1	GW 1	GW 1 ◇		GW 1	GW 1	GW 1	HC 1	GW 1	GW 1	GW 1 ◇	GW 1	GW 1	GW 1	GW 1	GW 1 ◇	HC 1	GW 1	GW 1 ◇ A	GW 1
Oxford d					15 21	*15 43*	16 01						15 55	*16 15*	16 31				16 21				17 01	
Reading 7 d					16 04	16 19	16 27						16 34	16 49	16 56				17 04	17 18		17 18	17 27	
Twyford 3 d		←			16 10	16 25				←			16 40	16 55			←		17 10			17 25		
Maidenhead 3 d		16 03			16 18	16 33				16 33			16 48	17 03			17 03		17 18			17 33		
Taplow d		16 07				→				16 37				→			17 07					→		
Burnham d		16 10								16 40							17 10							
Slough 3 a		16 15			16 25		16 40			16 45			16 55		17 09		17 15		17 25	17 31			17 40	
d		16 15			16 26		16 41			16 45			16 56		17 10		17 15		17 26	17 32			17 41	
Langley d					16 30								17 00						17 30					
Iver d	←				16 33				←				17 03			←			17 33					←
West Drayton d	16 06	16 22			16 36				16 36	16 52			17 06			17 06	17 22		17 36					17 36
Heathrow Terminal 5 ✈ d				*16b12*	→							*16b42*	→						→		*17b12*			
Heathrow Terminal 4 ✈ d				16 21								16 51									17 21			
Heathrow Terminals 1-2-3 ✈ d				16 26								16 56									17 26			
Hayes & Harlington d	16 10	16 26		16 33					16 40	16 56		17 03				17 10	17 26				17 33			17 40
Southall d	16 14			16 36					16 44			17 06				17 14					17 36			17 44
Hanwell d				16 39								17 09									17 39			
Greenford ⊖ d			16 23								16 53							17 23						
South Greenford d			16 26								16 56							17 26						
Castle Bar Park d			16 29								16 59							17 29						
Drayton Green d			16 31								17 01							17 31						
West Ealing d			16 34	16 42							17 04	17 12						17 34			17 42			
Ealing Broadway ⊖ d	16 19	16 33	16 37	16 44					16 49	17 03	17 07	17 14				17 19	17 33	17 37			17 44			17 49
Acton Main Line d			16 40								17 10							17 40						
London Paddington 15 ⊖ a	16 32	16 43	16 49	16 54			16 59		17 02	17 13	17 19	17 24			17 27	17 33	17 43	17 49		17 53	17 54		17 58	18 02

	GW 1	GW 1	HC 1	GW 1	GW 1	GW 1	GW 1	HC 1	GW 1	GW 1	GW 1 ◇	GW 1	GW 1	GW 1	HC 1	GW 1	GW 1	GW 1 ◇	GW 1	GW 1	GW 1	HC 1	GW 1	GW 1
Oxford d				16 53	*17 01*	*17 15*			17 21	*17 43*	18 01					17 49	*18 15*	18 31					18 21	
Reading 7 d				17 34	17 44	17 49			18 04	18 18	18 27					18 34	18 49	18 56					19 04	19 19
Twyford 3 d	←			17 40	17 50	17 55			18 10	18 25			←			18 40	18 55			←			19 10	19 25
Maidenhead 3 d	17 33			17 48	17 58	18 03			18 18	18 33			18 33			18 48	19 03			19 03			19 18	19 33
Taplow d	17 37					18 07				→			18 37				→			19 07				→
Burnham d	17 40					18 10							18 40							19 10				
Slough 3 a	17 45			17 55	18 05	18 15			18 25		18 40		18 45			18 55		19 09		19 15			19 25	
d	17 45			17 56	18 06	18 15			18 26		18 41		18 45			18 56		19 10		19 15			19 26	
Langley d				18 00					18 30							19 00							19 30	
Iver d				18 03					18 33			←				19 03			←				19 33	
West Drayton d	17 52			18 06		18 22			18 36			18 36	18 52			19 06			19 06	19 22			19 36	
Heathrow Terminal 5 ✈ d			*17b42*					*18b12*	→						*18b42*	→						*19b12*	→	
Heathrow Terminal 4 ✈ d			17 51					18 21							18 51							19 21		
Heathrow Terminals 1-2-3 ✈ d			17 56					18 26							18 56							19 26		
Hayes & Harlington d	17 56		18 03	18 10	18 15	18 26		18 33				18 40	18 56		19 03				19 10	19 26		19 33		
Southall d			18 06	18 14				18 36				18 44			19 06				19 14			19 36		
Hanwell d			18 09					18 39							19 09							19 39		
Greenford ⊖ d		17 53					18 23							18 53							19 23			
South Greenford d		17 56					18 26							18 56							19 26			
Castle Bar Park d		17 59					18 29							18 59							19 29			
Drayton Green d		18 01					18 31							19 01							19 31			
West Ealing d		18 04	18 12				18 34	18 42						19 04	19 12						19 34	19 42		
Ealing Broadway ⊖ d	18 03	18 07	18 14	18 19	18 24	18 33	18 37	18 44				18 49	19 03	19 07	19 14				19 19	19 33	19 37	19 44		
Acton Main Line d		18 10					18 40							19 10							19 40			
London Paddington 15 ⊖ a	18 14	18 19	18 24	18 33	18 34	18 43	18 51	18 54			18 59	19 02	19 13	19 19	19 24			19 29	19 32	19 43	19 49	19 54		

For general notes see front of timetable
For details of catering facilities see Directory of Train Operators

For fast services between Reading and London Paddington see Table 116

A Until 27 June and from 8 September
b Change at Heathrow Terminals 1-2-3

Reading and Greenford → London

(Local services only)

Network Diagram - see first page of Table 116

Station		GW 1◇	GW 1	GW 1	GW 1	HC 1	GW 1	GW 1	GW 1◇	GW 1	GW 1	GW 1	HC 1	GW 1	GW 1	GW 1	HC 1	GW 1	GW 1	GW 1◇	GW 1	GW 1	GW 1	HC 1	GW 1
Oxford	d	19 01					18 55	*19 15*	19 30					19 21	*19 43*			19 55	*20 15*	20 31					
Reading 7	d	19 27					19 34	19 49	19 54					20 04	20 18			20 34	20 46	20 56					21 20
Twyford 3	d			←			19 40	19 55			←			20 10	20 25			20 40	20 52			←			21 26
Maidenhead 3	d			19 33			19 48	20 03			20 03			20 18	20 33			20 48	21 00			21 00			→
Taplow	d			19 37				→			20 06				20 37				→			21 03			
Burnham	d			19 40							20 10				20 40							21 07			
Slough 3	a	19 40		19 45			19 55		20 09		20 14			20 25	20 45			20 55		21 09		21 11			
	d	19 41		19 45			19 56		20 10		20 15			20 26	20 45			20 56		21 10		21 12			
Langley	d						20 00							20 30				21 00				21 16			
Iver	d		←				20 03			←				20 33				21 03			←	21 19			
West Drayton	d		19 36	19 52			20 06			20 06	20 21			20 36	20 52			21 06			21 06	21 22			
Heathrow Terminal 5	d					19b42	→						20b12				20b42	→						21b12	
Heathrow Terminal 4	d					19 51							20 21				20 51							21 21	
Heathrow Terminals 1-2-3	d					19 56							20 26				20 56							21 26	
Hayes & Harlington	d		19 40	19 56		20 03				20 10	20 26		20 33	20 40	20 56		21 03				21 10	21 26		21 33	
Southall	d		19 44			20 06				20 14			20 36	20 44			21 06				21 14			21 36	
Hanwell	d					20 09							20 39				21 09							21 39	
Greenford	⊖ d				19 53							20 23				20 53							21 23		
South Greenford	d				19 56							20 26				20 56							21 26		
Castle Bar Park	d				19 59							20 29				20 59							21 29		
Drayton Green	d				20 01							20 31				21 01							21 31		
West Ealing	d				20 04	20 12						20 34	20 42			21 04	21 12						21 34	21 42	
Ealing Broadway	⊖ d		19 49	20 03	20 07	20 14				20 19	20 32	20 37	20 44	20 49	21 03	21 07	21 14				21 19	21 33	21 37	21 44	
Acton Main Line	d				20 10							20 40				21 10							21 40		
London Paddington 15	⊖ a	19 59	20 02	20 13	20 19	20 24			20 29	20 32	20 42	20 49	20 54	21 02	21 13	21 19	21 24			21 29	21 32	21 43	21 49	21 54	

Station		GW 1◇ A	GW 1◇ B	GW 1	GW 1	HC 1	GW 1	GW FX 1	GW FO 1◇	GW FX 1◇	HC 1	GW FX 1	GW FO 1	GW FO 1◇	HC 1	GW FX 1◇	GW 1	GW FO 1◇	GW FX 1◇	HC 1	GW 1	GW 1	GW 1◇
Oxford	d	21 01	21 01				20 53	*21 15*	21 38	21 38			*21 20*	22 21		22 21	21 53	22 34	22 34				23 05
Reading 7	d	21 27	21 27	←			21 34	22 00	22 11	22 11			22 16	22 48		22 48	22 50	23 04	23 04			23 15	23 35
Twyford 3	d			21 26			21 40	22 06				←	22 22				22 56					23 21	
Maidenhead 3	d			21 34			21 48	22 14				22 14	22 30				23 04					23 29	
Taplow	d						21 51	→				22 17	22 33				23 08					23 32	
Burnham	d						21 55					22 21	22 37				23 11					23 36	
Slough 3	a	21 40	21 41	21 41			21 59		22 26	22 26		22 26	22 42	23 01		23 02	23 17	23 17	23 21		←	23 41	23 52
	d	21 41	21 41	21 42			22 00		22 26	22 26		22 36	22 42	23 02		23 02	23 27	23 18	23 22		23 27	23 42	23 53
Langley	d			21 46			22 04					22 40	22 46				→				23 31	23 46	
Iver	d			21 49			22 07					22 43	22 49								23 34	23 49	
West Drayton	d			21 52			22 10					22 46	22 52								23 37	23 52	
Heathrow Terminal 5	d					21b42					22b12				22b42					23b12			
Heathrow Terminal 4	d					21 51					22 21				22 51					23 21			
Heathrow Terminals 1-2-3	d					21 56					22 26				22 56					23 26			
Hayes & Harlington	d			21 56		22 03	22 14				22 33	22 50	22 57		23 03					23 33	23 41	23 56	
Southall	d			22 00		22 06					22 36	22 55	23 00		23 06					23 36	23 46	00 01	
Hanwell	d					22 09					22 39				23 09					23 39			
Greenford	⊖ d				21 53																		
South Greenford	d				21 56																		
Castle Bar Park	d				21 59																		
Drayton Green	d				22 01																		
West Ealing	d				22 04	22 12					22 42				23 12					23 42			
Ealing Broadway	⊖ d			22 05	22 07	22 14	22 21				22 44	23 00	23 05		23 14					23 44	23 51	00 06	
Acton Main Line	d				22 10																		
London Paddington 15	⊖ a	21 59	22 01	22 14	22 19	22 24	22 32		22 45	22 52	22 54	23 08	23 15	23 22	23 24	23 25		23 36	23 41	23 54	23 59	00 15	00 22

Saturdays

until 6 September

Station		GW 1	HC	GW 1	GW 1◇	GW 1	GW 1 C	GW 1	GW 1	HC 1	GW 1	HC 1	GW 1	GW 1	GW 1	HC 1	GW 1	GW 1	GW 1	HC 1	GW 1	GW 1	GW 1◇	GW 1	GW 1
Oxford	d				00 05		00 20		04 00								05 21				05 55		06 30		
Reading 7	d	23p15		00 15	00 39		01 09	04 10	04 40		05 10		05 34	05 48			06 04	06 18			06 34	06 48	06 58		
Twyford 3	d	23p21		00 21			01 15	04 16	04 46		05 16		05 40	05 55			06 10	06 25			06 41	06 56		←	
Maidenhead 3	d	23p29		00 29			01 23	04 24	04 54		05 24		05 48	06 03			06 18	06 33			06 49	07 04		07 04	
Taplow	d	23p32		00 33							05 28			06 07				06 37				→		07 07	
Burnham	d	23p36		00 36							05 31			06 10				06 40						07 11	
Slough 3	a	23p41		00 42	00 52		01 31	04 31	05 01		05 36		05 55	06 15			06 25	06 45			06 56		07 11	07 15	
	d	23p42		00 42	00 53		01 32	04 32	05 02		05 36		05 56	06 15			06 26	06 45			06 56		07 12	07 16	
Langley	d	23p46		00 46							05 40		06 00				06 30				07 00				
Iver	d	23p49									05 43		06 03				06 33				07 03				
West Drayton	d	23p52		00 51				04 38			05 45		06 06	06 22			06 36	06 52			07 06			07 22	
Heathrow Terminal 5	d									05b07		05b42				06b12				06b42					
Heathrow Terminal 4	d		00 01							05 23		05 51				06 21				06 51					
Heathrow Terminals 1-2-3	d		00 06			←				05 29		05 56				06 26				06 56					
Hayes & Harlington	d	23p56	00 12	00 55		00 55	01 41	04 43	05 11	05 34	05 51	06 03	06 10	06 26		06 33	06 40	06 56		07 03	07 11			07 27	
Southall	d	00 01	00 15	→		01 00		04 46	05 14	05 38	05 54	06 06	06 14			06 36	06 44			07 06	07 14				
Hanwell	d									05 41		06 09				06 39				07 09					
Greenford	⊖ d														06 23				06 53						07 23
South Greenford	d														06 26				06 56						07 26
Castle Bar Park	d														06 29				06 59						07 29
Drayton Green	d														06 31				07 01						07 31
West Ealing	d									05 43		06 12			06 34	06 42			07 04	07 12					07 34
Ealing Broadway	⊖ d	00 06	00 20			01 05	01 48	04 51	05 19	05 46	05 59	06 14	06 19	06 33	06 37	06 44	06 49	07 03	07 07	07 14	07 19			07 33	07 37
Acton Main Line	d								05 23		06 03			06 36	06 40				07 10						07 40
London Paddington 15	⊖ a	00 15	00 29		01 10	01 13	01 57	05 00	05 30	05 57	06 10	06 24	06 28	06 44	06 48	06 54	06 58	07 12	07 18	07 24	07 29		07 29	07 42	07 49

For general notes see front of timetable
For details of catering facilities see Directory of Train Operators

For fast services between Reading and London Paddington see Table 116

A Until 27 June and from 8 September
B 30 June to 5 September
C From Banbury (Table 116)

b Change at Heathrow Terminals 1-2-3

Saturdays

Reading and Greenford → London

(Local services only)

until 6 September

Network Diagram - see first page of Table 116

Station		HC 1	GW 1	GW 1	GW 1 ◇		GW 1	GW 1	GW 1	HC 1	GW 1	GW 1	GW 1	HC 1	GW 1	GW 1	GW 1 ◇	GW 1	GW 1	GW 1	HC 1	GW 1	GW 1	GW 1 ◇	GW 1
Oxford	d		06 20		07 00						06 55				07 21	*07 37*	08 00					07 55	*08 15*	08 30	
Reading 7	d		07 06	07 18	07 27						07 34	07 48			08 04	08 18	08 27					08 34	08 48	08 57	
Twyford 3	d		07 12	07 25				←			07 41	07 55			08 10	08 25			←			08 40	08 55		←
Maidenhead 3	d		07 20	07 33				07 33			07 49	08 03			08 18	08 33			08 33			08 48	09 03		09 03
Taplow	d			→				07 37				08 07				→			08 37				→		09 07
Burnham	d							07 40				08 10							08 40						09 10
Slough 3	a		07 27		07 40			07 45			07 56	08 15			08 25		08 40		08 45			08 56		09 10	09 15
	d		07 28		07 41			07 45			07 56	08 15			08 26		08 41		08 45			08 56		09 11	09 15
Langley	d		07 32								08 00				08 30							09 00			
Iver	d		07 35				←				08 03				08 33			←				09 03			
West Drayton	d		07 38				07 38	07 52			08 06	08 22			08 36			08 36	08 52			09 06			09 22
Heathrow Terminal 5 ✈	d	*07b12*	→							*07b42*				*08b12*	→						*08b42*				
Heathrow Terminal 4 ✈	d	07 21								07 51				08 21							08 51				
Heathrow Terminals 1-2-3 ✈	d	07 26								07 56				08 26							08 56				
Hayes & Harlington	d	07 33					07 42	07 56		08 03	08 11	08 26		08 33				08 40	08 56		09 03	09 11			09 26
Southall	d	07 36					07 46			08 06	08 14			08 36				08 44			09 06	09 14			
Hanwell	d	07 39								08 09				08 39							09 09				
Greenford ⊖	d								07 53				08 23							08 53					
South Greenford	d								07 56				08 26							08 56					
Castle Bar Park	d								07 59				08 29							08 59					
Drayton Green	d								08 01				08 31							09 01					
West Ealing	d	07 42							08 04	08 12			08 34	08 42						09 04	09 12				
Ealing Broadway ⊖	d	07 44					07 51	08 03	08 07	08 14	08 19	08 33	08 37	08 44				08 49	09 03	09 07	09 14	09 19			09 33
Acton Main Line	d								08 10				08 40							09 10					
London Paddington 15 ⊖	a	07 54			07 58		07 59	08 12	08 18	08 24	08 28	08 42	08 48	08 54			08 58	08 59	09 12	09 18	09 24	09 28		09 28	09 42

Station		GW 1	HC 1	GW 1	GW 1	GW 1 ◇ ☕	GW 1	GW 1	GW 1	HC 1		GW 1	GW 1	GW 1 ◇	GW 1	GW 1	GW 1	HC 1	GW 1	GW 1	GW 1 ◇ ☕	GW 1	GW 1	GW 1	HC 1
Oxford	d			08 21		08 59						08 55	*09 15*	09 30					09 20		09 50				
Reading 7	d			09 04	09 18	09 27						09 35	09 48	09 56					10 04	10 18	10 22				
Twyford 3	d			09 10	09 25			←				09 42	09 55			←			10 10	10 25			←		
Maidenhead 3	d			09 18	09 33			09 33				09 50	10 03			10 03			10 18	10 33			10 33		
Taplow	d				→			09 37					→			10 07				→			10 37		
Burnham	d							09 40								10 10							10 40		
Slough 3	a			09 25		09 40		09 45				09 57		10 09		10 15			10 25		10 35		10 45		
	d			09 26		09 41		09 45				09 57		10 10		10 15			10 26		10 36		10 45		
Langley	d			09 30								10 01							10 30						
Iver	d			09 33			←					10 04			←				10 33			←			
West Drayton	d			09 36			09 36	09 52				10 07			10 07	10 22			10 36			10 36	10 52		
Heathrow Terminal 5 ✈	d		*09b12*	→						*09b42*		→						*10b12*	→						*10b42*
Heathrow Terminal 4 ✈	d		09 21							09 51								10 21							10 51
Heathrow Terminals 1-2-3 ✈	d		09 26							09 56								10 26							10 56
Hayes & Harlington	d		09 33				09 40	09 56		10 03					10 12	10 26		10 33				10 40	10 56		11 03
Southall	d		09 36				09 44			10 06					10 15			10 36				10 44			11 06
Hanwell	d		09 39							10 09								10 39							11 09
Greenford ⊖	d	09 23							09 53								10 23							10 53	
South Greenford	d	09 26							09 56								10 26							10 56	
Castle Bar Park	d	09 29							09 59								10 29							10 59	
Drayton Green	d	09 31							10 01								10 31							11 01	
West Ealing	d	09 34	09 42						10 04	10 12							10 34	10 42						11 04	11 12
Ealing Broadway ⊖	d	09 37	09 44				09 49	10 03	10 07	10 14					10 20	10 33	10 37	10 44				10 49	11 03	11 07	11 14
Acton Main Line	d	09 40							10 10								10 40							11 10	
London Paddington 15 ⊖	a	09 48	09 54			09 58	09 59	10 12	10 18	10 24				10 27	10 30	10 42	10 48	10 54			10 54	10 59	11 12	11 18	11 24

Station		GW 1	GW 1	GW 1	HC 1	GW 1	GW 1	GW 1 ◇ ☕	GW 1	GW 1	HC 1	GW 1	GW 1	GW 1	HC 1		GW 1	GW 1	GW 1 ◇ ☕	GW 1	GW 1	HC 1	GW 1	GW 1	GW 1 ◇
Oxford	d	09 55				10 21		11 00				10 55	*11 15*				11 21		12 00				11 55	*12 15*	12 30
Reading 7	d	10 34	10 48			11 04	11 18	11 27				11 34	11 48				12 04	12 18	12 29				12 34	12 48	12 56
Twyford 3	d	10 40	10 55			11 10	11 25		←			11 41	11 55				12 10	12 25					12 41	12 55	
Maidenhead 3	d	10 48	11 03			11 18	11 33		11 33			11 49	12 03				12 18	12 33					12 49	13 03	
Taplow	d		11 07				→		11 37				12 07					12 37						→	
Burnham	d		11 10						11 40				12 10					12 40							
Slough 3	a	10 56	11 15			11 25		11 40	11 45			11 56	12 15				12 25	12 45	12 45				12 56		13 09
	d	10 56	11 15			11 26		11 41	11 45			11 56	12 15				12 26	12 45	12 46				12 56		13 10
Langley	d	11 00				11 30						12 00					12 30						13 00		
Iver	d	11 03				11 33						12 03					12 33			←			13 03		
West Drayton	d	11 06	11 22			11 36			11 52			12 06	12 22				12 36	12 52		12 52			13 06		
Heathrow Terminal 5 ✈	d				*11b12*						*11b42*				*12b12*			→				*12b42*	→		
Heathrow Terminal 4 ✈	d				11 21						11 51				12 21							12 51			
Heathrow Terminals 1-2-3 ✈	d				11 26						11 56				12 26							12 56			
Hayes & Harlington	d	11 10	11 26		11 33	11 40			11 56		12 03	12 11	12 26		12 33		12 40			12 56		13 03			
Southall	d	11 14			11 36	11 44					12 06	12 14			12 36		12 44					13 06			
Hanwell	d				11 39						12 09				12 39							13 09			
Greenford ⊖	d			11 23						11 53				12 23							12 53				
South Greenford	d			11 26						11 56				12 26							12 56				
Castle Bar Park	d			11 29						11 59				12 29							12 59				
Drayton Green	d			11 31						12 01				12 31							13 01				
West Ealing	d			11 34	11 42					12 04	12 12			12 34	12 42						13 04	13 12			
Ealing Broadway ⊖	d	11 19	11 33	11 37	11 44	11 49			12 03	12 07	12 14	12 19	12 33	12 37	12 44		12 49			13 03	13 07	13 14			
Acton Main Line	d			11 40						12 10				12 40							13 10				
London Paddington 15 ⊖	a	11 28	11 42	11 48	11 54	11 59		11 58	12 12	12 18	12 24	12 29	12 42	12 48	12 54		12 59		13 08	13 12	13 18	13 24			13 27

For general notes see front of timetable
For details of catering facilities see Directory of Train Operators

For fast services between Reading and London Paddington see Table 116

b Change at Heathrow Terminals 1-2-3

Saturdays

until 6 September

Reading and Greenford → London

(Local services only)

Network Diagram - see first page of Table 116

Station		GW 1	GW 1	GW 1	HC 1	GW 1	GW 1	GW 1◇	GW 1	GW 1	HC 1	GW 1	GW 1	GW 1	HC 1	GW 1	GW 1	GW 1◇	GW 1	GW 1		HC 1	GW 1	GW 1	GW 1
Oxford	d					12 21		13 00				12 55	*13 15*			13 21	*13 30*	14 00					13 55	*14 15*	
Reading 7	d					13 04	13 18	13 26				13 34	13 48			14 04	14 18	14 27					14 34	14 48	
Twyford 3	d		←			13 10	13 25		←			13 40	13 55			14 10	14 25		←				14 41	14 55	
Maidenhead 3	d		13 03			13 18	13 33		13 33			13 48	14 03			14 18	14 33		14 33				14 49	15 03	
Taplow	d		13 07				→		13 37				14 07				→		14 37					15 07	
Burnham	d		13 10						13 40				14 10						14 40					15 10	
Slough 3	a		13 15			13 25		13 39	13 45			13 56	14 15			14 25		14 40	14 45				14 56	15 15	
	d		13 15			13 26		13 40	13 45			13 56	14 15			14 26		14 41	14 45				14 56	15 15	
Langley	d					13 30						14 00				14 30							15 00		
Iver	d	←				13 33						14 03				14 33							15 03		
West Drayton	d	13 06	13 22			13 36			13 52			14 06	14 22			14 36			14 52				15 06	15 22	
Heathrow Terminal 5 ✈	d				*13b12*						*13b42*				*14b12*							*14b42*			
Heathrow Terminal 4 ✈	d				13 21						13 51				14 21							14 51			
Heathrow Terminals 1-2-3 ✈	d				13 26						13 56				14 26							14 56			
Hayes & Harlington	d	13 11	13 26		13 33	13 40			13 56		14 03	14 10	14 26		14 33	14 40			14 56			15 03	15 11	15 26	
Southall	d	13 14			13 36	13 44					14 06	14 14			14 36	14 44						15 06	15 14		
Hanwell	d				13 39						14 09				14 39							15 09			
Greenford ⊖	d			13 23						13 53				14 23						14 53					15 23
South Greenford	d			13 26						13 56				14 26						14 56					15 26
Castle Bar Park	d			13 29						13 59				14 29						14 59					15 29
Drayton Green	d			13 31						14 01				14 31						15 01					15 31
West Ealing	d			13 34	13 42					14 04	14 12			14 34	14 42					15 04		15 12			15 34
Ealing Broadway ⊖	d	13 20	13 33	13 37	13 44	13 49			14 03	14 07	14 14	14 19	14 33	14 37	14 44	14 49			15 03	15 07		15 14	15 19	15 33	15 37
Acton Main Line	d			13 40						14 10				14 40						15 10					15 40
London Paddington 15 ⊖	a	13 29	13 42	13 48	13 54	13 59		13 58	14 12	14 18	14 24	14 28	14 42	14 48	14 54	14 59		14 58	15 12	15 18		15 24	15 29	15 42	15 48

Station		HC 1	GW 1	GW 1	GW 1◇	GW 1	GW 1	HC 1	GW 1	GW 1	GW 1◇	GW 1	GW 1	HC 1	GW 1	GW 1	GW 1◇	GW 1	GW 1	HC 1	GW 1	GW 1	GW 1	HC 1	GW 1
Oxford	d		14 21		15 00				14 55	*15 15*	15 30				15 21		16 00				15 55	*16 15*			16 21
Reading 7	d		15 04	15 18	15 27				15 34	15 48	15 57				16 04	16 18	16 30				16 34	16 48			17 04
Twyford 3	d		15 10	15 25		←			15 41	15 55		←			16 10	16 25					16 41	16 55			17 10
Maidenhead 3	d		15 18	15 33		15 33			15 49	16 03		16 03			16 18	16 33					16 49	17 03			17 18
Taplow	d			→		15 37				→		16 07				16 37						17 07			
Burnham	d					15 40						16 10				16 40						17 10			
Slough 3	a		15 25		15 40	15 45			15 56		16 10	16 15			16 25	16 45	16 46				16 56	17 15			17 25
	d		15 26		15 41	15 45			15 56		16 11	16 15			16 26	16 45	16 47				16 56	17 15			17 26
Langley	d		15 30						16 00						16 30						17 00				17 30
Iver	d		15 33						16 03						16 33						17 03				17 33
West Drayton	d		15 36			15 52			16 06			16 22			16 36	16 52					17 06	17 22			17 36
Heathrow Terminal 5 ✈	d	*15b12*						*15b42*						*16b12*						*16b42*				*17b12*	
Heathrow Terminal 4 ✈	d	15 21						15 51						16 21						16 51				17 21	
Heathrow Terminals 1-2-3 ✈	d	15 26						15 56						16 26				←		16 56				17 26	
Hayes & Harlington	d	15 33	15 40			15 56		16 03	16 10			16 26		16 33	16 40	16 56		16 56		17 03	17 11	17 26		17 33	17 40
Southall	d	15 36	15 44					16 06	16 14					16 36	16 44	→				17 06	17 14			17 36	17 44
Hanwell	d	15 39						16 09						16 39						17 09				17 39	
Greenford ⊖	d						15 53						16 23						16 53				17 23		
South Greenford	d						15 56						16 26						16 56				17 26		
Castle Bar Park	d						15 59						16 29						16 59				17 29		
Drayton Green	d						16 01						16 31						17 01				17 31		
West Ealing	d	15 42					16 04	16 12					16 34	16 42					17 04	17 12			17 34	17 42	
Ealing Broadway ⊖	d	15 44	15 49			16 03	16 07	16 14	16 19			16 33	16 37	16 44	16 49			17 03	17 07	17 14	17 19	17 33	17 37	17 44	17 49
Acton Main Line	d						16 10						16 40						17 10				17 40		
London Paddington 15 ⊖	a	15 54	15 59		15 58	16 12	16 18	16 24	16 28		16 28	16 42	16 48	16 54	16 59		17 06	17 12	17 18	17 24	17 28	17 42	17 48	17 54	17 59

Station		GW 1	GW 1◇		GW 1	GW 1	HC 1	GW 1	GW 1	GW 1◇	GW 1	GW 1	HC 1	GW 1	GW 1	GW 1◇	GW 1	GW 1	HC 1	GW 1	GW 1	GW 1	HC 1	GW 1	GW 1
Oxford	d	*16 30*	17 00					16 55		17 30				17 21		18 00				17 55	*18 15*			18 21	*18 30*
Reading 7	d	17 18	17 27					17 34	17 48	17 56				18 04	18 18	18 27				18 34	18 48			19 04	19 18
Twyford 3	d	17 25			←			17 41	17 55					18 10	18 25		←			18 41	18 55			19 10	19 25
Maidenhead 3	d	17 33			17 33			17 49	18 03					18 18	18 33		18 33			18 49	19 03			19 18	19 33
Taplow	d	→			17 37				18 07						→		18 37				19 07				→
Burnham	d				17 40				18 10								18 40				19 10				
Slough 3	a		17 40		17 45			17 56	18 15	18 09				18 25		18 40	18 45			18 56	19 15			19 25	
	d		17 41		17 45			17 56	18 15	18 10				18 26		18 41	18 45			18 56	19 15			19 26	
Langley	d							18 00						18 30						19 00				19 30	
Iver	d							18 03						18 33						19 03				19 33	
West Drayton	d				17 52			18 06	18 22					18 36			18 52			19 06	19 22			19 36	
Heathrow Terminal 5 ✈	d						*17b42*						*18b12*						*18b42*				*19b12*	→	
Heathrow Terminal 4 ✈	d						17 51						18 21						18 51				19 21		
Heathrow Terminals 1-2-3 ✈	d						17 56				←		18 26						18 56				19 26		
Hayes & Harlington	d				17 56		18 03	18 11	18 26		18 26		18 33	18 40			18 56		19 03	19 11	19 26		19 33		
Southall	d						18 06	18 14					18 36	18 44					19 06	19 14			19 36		
Hanwell	d						18 09						18 39						19 09				19 39		
Greenford ⊖	d					17 53						18 23						18 53				19 23			
South Greenford	d					17 56						18 26						18 56				19 26			
Castle Bar Park	d					17 59						18 29						18 59				19 29			
Drayton Green	d					18 01						18 31						19 01				19 31			
West Ealing	d					18 04	18 12					18 34	18 42					19 04	19 12			19 34	19 42		
Ealing Broadway ⊖	d				18 03	18 07	18 14	18 19	18 33		18 33	18 37	18 44	18 49			19 03	19 07	19 14	19 19	19 33	19 37	19 44		
Acton Main Line	d					18 10						18 40						19 10				19 40			
London Paddington 15 ⊖	a		17 58		18 12	18 18	18 24	18 28	18 42	18 27	18 42	18 48	18 54	18 59		18 58	19 12	19 18	19 24	19 29	19 42	19 48	19 54		

For general notes see front of timetable
For details of catering facilities see Directory of Train Operators

For fast services between Reading and London Paddington see Table 116

b Change at Heathrow Terminals 1-2-3

Table 117

Saturdays

until 6 September

Reading and Greenford → London

(Local services only)

Network Diagram - see first page of Table 116

		GW	GW	GW	GW	HC	GW	GW		GW	GW	GW	HC	GW	GW	GW	GW	GW	HC	GW	GW	GW	GW	GW	HC
		1 ◇ ☕	1	1	1	1	1	1		1 ◇	1	1	1	1	1	1 ◇ ☕	1	1	1	1	1	1 ◇	1	1	1
Oxford	d	19 00					18 55			19 30				19 21		20 06				19 55	*20 15*	20 30			
Reading 7	d	19 27					19 34	19 48		19 56				20 04	20 18	20 32				20 34	20 48	20 54			
Twyford 3	d			←			19 40	19 55			←			20 10	20 25					20 40	20 55		←		
Maidenhead 3	d			19 33			19 48	20 03			20 03			20 18	20 33					20 48	21 03		21 03		
Taplow	d			19 37				→			20 07				20 37						→		21 07		
Burnham	d			19 40							20 10				20 40								21 10		
Slough 3	a	19 40		19 45			19 55			20 09	20 15			20 25	20 45	20 45				20 55		21 08	21 15		
	d	19 41		19 45			19 56			20 10	20 15			20 26	20 45	20 46				20 56		21 09	21 15		
Langley	d						20 00							20 30						21 00					
Iver	d		←				20 03							20 33						21 03					
West Drayton	d		19 36	19 52			20 06				20 22			20 36	20 52					21 06			21 22		
Heathrow Terminal 5 ✈	d					19b42							20b12						20b42						21b12
Heathrow Terminal 4 ✈	d					19 51							20 21						20 51						21 21
Heathrow Terminals 1-2-3 ✈	d					19 56							20 26				←		20 56						21 26
Hayes & Harlington	d		19 40	19 56		20 03	20 10				20 26		20 33	20 40	20 56		20 56		21 03	21 10			21 26		21 33
Southall	d		19 44			20 06	20 14						20 36	20 44	→				21 06	21 14					21 36
Hanwell	d					20 09							20 39						21 09						21 39
Greenford ⊖	d				19 53							20 23						20 53						21 23	
South Greenford	d				19 56							20 26						20 56						21 26	
Castle Bar Park	d				19 59							20 29						20 59						21 29	
Drayton Green	d				20 01							20 31						21 01						21 31	
West Ealing	d				20 04	20 12						20 34	20 42					21 04	21 12					21 34	21 42
Ealing Broadway ⊖	d		19 49	20 03	20 07	20 14	20 19				20 33	20 37	20 44	20 49			21 03	21 07	21 14	21 19			21 33	21 37	21 44
Acton Main Line	d				20 10							20 40						21 10						21 40	
London Paddington 15 ⊖	a	19 58	19 59	20 12	20 18	20 24	20 28			20 27	20 42	20 48	20 54	20 59		21 06	21 12	21 18	21 24	21 28		21 26	21 42	21 48	21 54

		GW	GW	GW	GW	HC	GW	GW	GW	HC	GW	GW	GW	HC	GW	GW	GW	GW	HC	GW	GW	GW	GW		
		1	1 ◇ ☕	1	1	1	1	1	1 ◇	1	1	1 ◇	1	1	1	1	1 ◇	1	1	1	1 ◇ ☕	1	1		
Oxford	d	20 20	21 00				20 55		21 37			22 08			21 55		22 30			*22 30*	23 00		23 09		
Reading 7	d	21 09	21 27				21 35	21 44	22 07		22 16	22 36			22 35	22 45	22 56			23 16	23 29		00 05		
Twyford 3	d	21 15					21 41	21 50			22 22				22 40	22 52				23 23			00 11		
Maidenhead 3	d	21 23					21 49	21 58			22 30				22 48	23 00				23 32			00 19		
Taplow	d	21 27						22 02			22 34					23 04				23 35			00 22		
Burnham	d	21 30						22 05			22 37					23 07				23 38			00 26		
Slough 3	a	21 35	21 40				21 56	22 10	22 24		22 42	22 51			22 57	23 12	23 12			23 42	23 48		00 30		
	d	21 35	21 41				21 57	22 10	22 24		22 42	22 52			22 57	23 12	23 13			23 42	23 49		00 31		
Langley	d	21 39						22 14			22 46					23 16				23 46			00 35		
Iver	d	21 42		←				22 17			22 49		←			23 19				23 49		←	00 38		
West Drayton	d	21 45		21 45				22 20			22 52		22 52			23 22				23 52		23 52	00 41		
Heathrow Terminal 5 ✈	d	→				21b42				22b12	→			22b42					23b12	→					
Heathrow Terminal 4 ✈	d					21 51				22 21				22 51					23 21						
Heathrow Terminals 1-2-3 ✈	d					21 56				22 26				22 56					23 26						
Hayes & Harlington	d			21 50		22 03	22 06	22 25		22 33			22 57	23 03	23 06	23 27		←	23 33			23 57	00 45		
Southall	d			21 53		22 06	22 10	22 28		22 36			23 00	23 06	23 10	23 30		23 30	23 36			23 59	00 49		
Hanwell	d					22 09				22 39				23 09		→			23 39						
Greenford ⊖	d				21 53																				
South Greenford	d				21 56																				
Castle Bar Park	d				21 59																				
Drayton Green	d				22 01																				
West Ealing	d				22 04	22 12				22 42				23 12					23 42						
Ealing Broadway ⊖	d			21 58	22 07	22 14	22 19	22 33		22 44			23 05	23 14	23 19			23 35	23 44			00 07	00 54		
Acton Main Line	d				22 10																				
London Paddington 15 ⊖	a		21 58	22 08	22 18	22 24	22 28	22 42	22 42	22 54		23 11	23 14	23 24	23 28		23 30	23 44	23 54		00 09	00 16	01 02		

For general notes see front of timetable
For details of catering facilities see Directory of Train Operators

For fast services between Reading and London Paddington see Table 116

b Change at Heathrow Terminals 1-2-3

Table 117

Saturdays

from 13 September

Reading and Greenford → London
(Local services only)

Network Diagram - see first page of Table 116

		GW 1	HC	GW 1	GW 1 ◇	GW 1	GW 1	GW 1	GW 1	HC 1	GW 1	HC 1	GW 1	GW 1	GW 1	HC 1	GW 1	GW 1	GW 1	HC 1	GW 1	GW 1	GW 1 ◇	GW 1	GW 1
					⊼		A																		
Oxford	d				00 05		00 20		04 00								05 21				05 55		06 30		
Reading 7	d	23p15		00 15	00 39		01 09	04 10	04 40		05 10		05 34	05 48			06 04	06 18			06 34	06 48	06 58		
Twyford 3	d	23p21		00 21			01 15	04 16	04 46		05 16		05 40	05 55			06 10	06 25			06 41	06 56		←	
Maidenhead 3	d	23p29		00 29			01 23	04 24	04 54		05 24		05 48	06 03			06 18	06 33			06 49	07 04 →		07 04	
Taplow	d	23p32		00 33							05 28			06 07				06 37						07 07	
Burnham	d	23p36		00 36							05 31			06 10				06 40						07 11	
Slough 3	a	23p41		00 42	00 52		01 31	04 31	05 01		05 36		05 55	06 15			06 25	06 45			06 56		07 11	07 15	
	d	23p42		00 42	00 53		01 32	04 32	05 02		05 36		05 56	06 15			06 26	06 45			06 56		07 12	07 16	
Langley	d	23p46		00 46							05 40		06 00				06 30				07 00				
Iver	d	23p49									05 43		06 03				06 33				07 03				
West Drayton	d	23p52		00 51				04 38			05 45		06 06	06 22			06 36	06 52			07 06			07 22	
Heathrow Terminal 5 ✈	d									05b07		05b42				06b12				06b42					
Heathrow Terminal 4 ✈	d		00 01							05 23		05 51				06 21				06 51					
Heathrow Terminals 1-2-3 ✈	d		00 06			←				05 29		05 56				06 26				06 56					
Hayes & Harlington	d	23p56	00 12	00 55 →		00 55	01 41	04 43	05 11	05 34	05 51	06 03	06 10	06 26		06 33	06 40	06 56		07 03	07 11			07 27	
Southall	d	00 01	00 15			01 00		04 46	05 14	05 38	05 54	06 06	06 14			06 36	06 44			07 06	07 14				
Hanwell	d									05 41		06 09				06 39				07 09					
Greenford ⊖	d														06 23				06 53						07 23
South Greenford	d														06 26				06 56						07 26
Castle Bar Park	d														06 29				06 59						07 29
Drayton Green	d														06 31				07 01						07 31
West Ealing	d									05 43		06 12			06 34	06 42			07 04	07 12					07 34
Ealing Broadway ⊖	d	00 06	00 20			01 05	01 48	04 51	05 19	05 46	05 59	06 14	06 19	06 33	06 37	06 44	06 49	07 03	07 07	07 14	07 19			07 33	07 37
Acton Main Line	d								05 23		06 03			06 36	06 40				07 10						07 40
London Paddington 15 ⊖	a	00 15	00 29		01 10	01 13	01 57	05 00	05 30	05 57	06 10	06 24	06 28	06 44	06 48	06 54	06 58	07 12	07 18	07 24	07 29		07 29	07 42	07 49

		HC 1	GW 1	GW 1	GW 1 ◇	GW 1	GW 1	GW 1	HC 1	GW 1	GW 1	GW 1	HC 1	GW 1	GW 1	GW 1 ◇	GW 1	GW 1	GW 1	HC 1	GW 1		GW 1	GW 1 ◇	GW 1
Oxford	d		06 20		07 00					06 55				07 21		08 00					07 55			08 30	
Reading 7	d		07 06	07 18	07 27					07 34	07 48			08 04	08 18	08 27					08 34		08 48	08 57	
Twyford 3	d		07 12	07 25			←			07 41	07 55			08 10	08 25			←			08 41		08 55		←
Maidenhead 3	d		07 20	07 33 →			07 33			07 49	08 03			08 18	08 33 →			08 33			08 49		09 03 →		09 03
Taplow	d						07 37				08 07							08 37							09 07
Burnham	d						07 40				08 10							08 40							09 10
Slough 3	a		07 27		07 40		07 45			07 56	08 15			08 25		08 40		08 45			08 56			09 10	09 15
	d		07 28		07 41		07 45			07 56	08 15			08 26		08 41		08 45			08 56			09 11	09 15
Langley	d		07 32							08 00				08 30							09 00				
Iver	d		07 35			←				08 03				08 33			←				09 03				
West Drayton	d		07 38			07 38	07 52			08 06	08 22			08 36			08 36	08 52			09 06				09 22
Heathrow Terminal 5 ✈	d	07b12	→						07b42				08b12	→						08b42					
Heathrow Terminal 4 ✈	d	07 21							07 51				08 21							08 51					
Heathrow Terminals 1-2-3 ✈	d	07 26							07 56				08 26							08 56					
Hayes & Harlington	d	07 33				07 42	07 56		08 03	08 11	08 26		08 33				08 40	08 56		09 03	09 11				09 26
Southall	d	07 36				07 46			08 06	08 14			08 36				08 44			09 06	09 14				
Hanwell	d	07 39							08 09				08 39							09 09					
Greenford ⊖	d							07 53				08 23							08 53						
South Greenford	d							07 56				08 26							08 56						
Castle Bar Park	d							07 59				08 29							08 59						
Drayton Green	d							08 01				08 31							09 01						
West Ealing	d	07 42						08 04	08 12			08 34	08 42						09 04	09 12					
Ealing Broadway ⊖	d	07 44				07 51	08 03	08 07	08 14	08 19	08 33	08 37	08 44				08 49	09 03	09 07	09 14	09 19				09 33
Acton Main Line	d							08 10				08 40							09 10						
London Paddington 15 ⊖	a	07 54			07 58	07 59	08 12	08 18	08 24	08 28	08 42	08 48	08 54			08 58	08 59	09 12	09 18	09 24	09 28			09 28	09 42

		GW 1	HC 1	GW 1	GW 1	GW 1 ◇	GW 1	GW 1	GW 1	HC 1	GW 1	GW 1	GW 1 ◇	GW 1	GW 1	GW 1	HC 1	GW 1	GW 1	GW 1 ◇	GW 1	GW 1	GW 1	HC 1	GW 1
						ꟼ														ꟼ					
Oxford	d			08 21		08 59					08 55		09 30					09 20		09 50					09 55
Reading 7	d			09 04	09 18	09 27					09 34	09 48	09 56					10 04	10 18	10 22					10 34
Twyford 3	d			09 10	09 25			←			09 40	09 55			←			10 10	10 25			←			10 41
Maidenhead 3	d			09 18	09 33 →			09 33			09 48	10 03 →			10 03			10 18	10 33 →			10 33			10 49
Taplow	d							09 37							10 07							10 37			
Burnham	d							09 40							10 10							10 40			
Slough 3	a			09 25		09 40		09 45			09 56		10 09		10 15			10 25		10 35		10 45			10 56
	d			09 26		09 41		09 45			09 56		10 10		10 15			10 26		10 36		10 45			10 56
Langley	d			09 30							10 00							10 30							11 00
Iver	d			09 33			←				10 00			←				10 33			←				11 03
West Drayton	d			09 36			09 36	09 52			10 06			10 06	10 22			10 36			10 36	10 52			11 06
Heathrow Terminal 5 ✈	d		09b12	→						09b42	→						10b12	→						10b42	
Heathrow Terminal 4 ✈	d		09 21							09 51							10 21							10 51	
Heathrow Terminals 1-2-3 ✈	d		09 26							09 56							10 26							10 56	
Hayes & Harlington	d		09 33				09 40	09 56		10 03				10 10	10 26		10 33				10 40	10 56		11 03	11 11
Southall	d		09 36				09 44			10 06				10 14			10 36				10 44			11 06	11 14
Hanwell	d		09 39							10 09							10 39							11 09	
Greenford ⊖	d	09 23							09 53							10 23							10 53		
South Greenford	d	09 26							09 56							10 26							10 56		
Castle Bar Park	d	09 29							09 59							10 29							10 59		
Drayton Green	d	09 31							10 01							10 31							11 01		
West Ealing	d	09 34	09 42						10 04	10 12						10 34	10 42						11 04	11 12	
Ealing Broadway ⊖	d	09 37	09 44				09 49	10 03	10 07	10 14				10 20	10 33	10 37	10 44				10 49	11 03	11 07	11 14	
Acton Main Line	d	09 40							10 10							10 40							11 10		
London Paddington 15 ⊖	a	09 48	09 54			09 58	09 59	10 12	10 18	10 24			10 27	10 30	10 42	10 48	10 54			10 54	10 59	11 12	11 18	11 24	11 28

For general notes see front of timetable
For details of catering facilities see Directory of Train Operators

For fast services between Reading and London Paddington see Table 116

A From Banbury (Table 116)
b Change at Heathrow Terminals 1-2-3

Table 117

Saturdays

from 13 September

Reading and Greenford → London

(Local services only)

Network Diagram - see first page of Table 116

		GW 1	GW 1	HC 1	GW 1	GW 1	GW 1 ◇	GW 1	GW 1	HC 1	GW 1	GW 1	GW 1	HC 1	GW 1	GW 1	GW 1 ◇	GW 1	GW 1	HC 1	GW 1	GW 1	GW 1
Oxford	d				10 21		11 00				10 55				11 21		12 00				11 55		
Reading 7	d	10 48			11 04	11 18	11 27				11 34	11 48			12 04	12 18	12 27				12 34		12 48
Twyford 3	d	10 55			11 10	11 25		←			11 41	11 55			12 10	12 25		←			12 41		12 55
Maidenhead 3	d	11 03			11 18	11 33		11 33			11 49	12 03			12 18	12 33		12 33			12 49		13 03
Taplow	d	11 07				→		11 37				12 07				→		12 37					13 07
Burnham	d	11 10						11 40				12 10						12 40					13 10
Slough 3	a	11 15			11 25		11 40	11 45			11 56	12 15			12 25		12 40	12 45			12 56		13 15
	d	11 15			11 26		11 41	11 45			11 56	12 15			12 26		12 41	12 45			12 56		13 15
Langley	d				11 30						12 00				12 30						13 00		
Iver	d				11 33						12 03				12 33						13 03	←	
West Drayton	d	11 22			11 36			11 52			12 06	12 22			12 36			12 52			13 06 →	13 06	13 22
Heathrow Terminal 5	d			11b12						11b42				12b12						12b42			
Heathrow Terminal 4	d			11 21						11 51				12 21						12 51			
Heathrow Terminals 1-2-3	d			11 26						11 56				12 26						12 56			
Hayes & Harlington	d	11 26		11 33	11 40			11 56		12 03	12 11	12 26		12 33	12 40			12 56		13 03		13 11	13 26
Southall	d			11 36	11 44					12 06	12 14			12 36	12 44					13 06		13 14	
Hanwell	d			11 39						12 09				12 39						13 09			
Greenford	⊖ d		11 23						11 53				12 23						12 53				
South Greenford	d		11 26						11 56				12 26						12 56				
Castle Bar Park	d		11 29						11 59				12 29						12 59				
Drayton Green	d		11 31						12 01				12 31						13 01				
West Ealing	d		11 34	11 42					12 04	12 12			12 34	12 42					13 04	13 12			
Ealing Broadway	⊖ d	11 33	11 37	11 44	11 49			12 03	12 07	12 14	12 19	12 33	12 37	12 44	12 49			13 03	13 07	13 14		13 20	13 33
Acton Main Line	d		11 40						12 10				12 40						13 10				
London Paddington 15	⊖ a	11 42	11 48	11 54	11 59		11 58	12 12	12 18	12 24	12 29	12 42	12 48	12 54	12 59		12 59	13 12	13 18	13 24		13 29	13 42

		GW 1	HC 1	GW 1	GW 1	GW 1 ◇	GW 1	GW 1	HC 1	GW 1	GW 1	GW 1	HC 1	GW 1	GW 1	GW 1 ◇	GW 1	GW 1	HC 1	GW 1	GW 1	GW 1	HC 1	GW 1	GW 1
Oxford	d			12 21		13 00				12 55				13 21		14 00				13 55				14 21	
Reading 7	d			13 04	13 18	13 26				13 34	13 48			14 04	14 18	14 27				14 34	14 48			15 04	15 18
Twyford 3	d			13 10	13 25		←			13 41	13 55			14 10	14 25		←			14 41	14 55			15 10	15 25
Maidenhead 3	d			13 18	13 33		13 33			13 49	14 03			14 18	14 33		14 33			14 49	15 03			15 18	15 33
Taplow	d				→		13 37				14 07				→		14 37				15 07				→
Burnham	d						13 40				14 10						14 40				15 10				
Slough 3	a			13 25		13 39	13 45			13 56	14 15			14 25		14 40	14 45			14 56	15 15			15 25	
	d			13 26		13 40	13 45			13 56	14 15			14 26		14 41	14 45			14 56	15 15			15 26	
Langley	d			13 30						14 00				14 30						15 00				15 30	
Iver	d			13 33						14 03				14 33						15 03				15 33	
West Drayton	d			13 36			13 52			14 06	14 22			14 36			14 52			15 06	15 22			15 36	
Heathrow Terminal 5	d		13b12						13b42				14b12						14b42				15b12		
Heathrow Terminal 4	d		13 21						13 51				14 21						14 51				15 21		
Heathrow Terminals 1-2-3	d		13 26						13 56				14 26						14 56				15 26		
Hayes & Harlington	d		13 33	13 40			13 56		14 03	14 11	14 26		14 33	14 40			14 56		15 03	15 11	15 26		15 33	15 40	
Southall	d		13 36	13 44					14 06	14 14			14 36	14 44					15 06	15 14			15 36	15 44	
Hanwell	d		13 39						14 09				14 39						15 09				15 39		
Greenford	⊖ d	13 23						13 53				14 23						14 53				15 23			
South Greenford	d	13 26						13 56				14 26						14 56				15 26			
Castle Bar Park	d	13 29						13 59				14 29						14 59				15 29			
Drayton Green	d	13 31						14 01				14 31						15 01				15 31			
West Ealing	d	13 34	13 42					14 04	14 12			14 34	14 42					15 04	15 12			15 34	15 42		
Ealing Broadway	⊖ d	13 37	13 44	13 49			14 03	14 07	14 14	14 19	14 33	14 37	14 44	14 49			15 03	15 07	15 14	15 19	15 33	15 37	15 44	15 49	
Acton Main Line	d	13 40						14 10				14 40						15 10				15 40			
London Paddington 15	⊖ a	13 48	13 54	13 59		13 58	14 12	14 18	14 24	14 28	14 42	14 48	14 54	14 59		14 58	15 12	15 18	15 24	15 28	15 42	15 48	15 54	15 59	

		GW 1 ◇	GW 1	GW 1	HC 1	GW 1	GW 1	GW 1 ◇	GW 1	GW 1	HC 1	GW 1	GW 1	GW 1 ◇	GW 1	GW 1	HC 1	GW 1	GW 1	GW 1	HC 1	GW 1	GW 1	GW 1 ◇
Oxford	d	15 00				14 55		15 30				15 21		16 00				15 55				16 21		17 00
Reading 7	d	15 27				15 34	15 48	15 57				16 04	16 18	16 27				16 34	16 48			17 04	17 18	17 27
Twyford 3	d		←			15 41	15 55		←			16 10	16 25		←			16 41	16 55			17 10	17 25	
Maidenhead 3	d		15 33			15 49	16 03		16 03			16 18	16 33		16 33			16 49	17 03			17 18	17 33	
Taplow	d		15 37				→		16 07				→		16 37				17 07				→	
Burnham	d		15 40						16 10						16 40				17 10					
Slough 3	a	15 40	15 45			15 56		16 10	16 15			16 25		16 40	16 45			16 56	17 15			17 25		17 40
	d	15 41	15 45			15 56		16 11	16 15			16 26		16 41	16 45			16 56	17 15			17 26		17 41
Langley	d					16 00						16 30						17 00				17 30		
Iver	d					16 03						16 33						17 03				17 33		
West Drayton	d		15 52			16 06			16 22			16 36			16 52			17 06	17 22			17 36		
Heathrow Terminal 5	d				15b42						16b12						16b42				17b12			
Heathrow Terminal 4	d				15 51						16 21						16 51				17 21			
Heathrow Terminals 1-2-3	d				15 56						16 26						16 56				17 26			
Hayes & Harlington	d		15 56		16 03	16 10			16 26		16 33	16 40			16 56		17 03	17 11	17 26		17 33	17 40		
Southall	d				16 06	16 14					16 36	16 44					17 06	17 14			17 36	17 44		
Hanwell	d				16 09						16 39						17 09				17 39			
Greenford	⊖ d			15 53						16 23						16 53				17 23				
South Greenford	d			15 56						16 26						16 56				17 26				
Castle Bar Park	d			15 59						16 29						16 59				17 29				
Drayton Green	d			16 01						16 31						17 01				17 31				
West Ealing	d			16 04	16 12					16 34	16 42					17 04	17 12			17 34	17 42			
Ealing Broadway	⊖ d		16 03	16 07	16 14	16 19			16 33	16 37	16 44	16 49			17 03	17 07	17 14	17 19	17 33	17 37	17 44	17 49		
Acton Main Line	d			16 10						16 40						17 10				17 40				
London Paddington 15	⊖ a	15 58	16 12	16 18	16 24	16 28		16 28	16 42	16 48	16 54	16 59		16 58	17 12	17 18	17 24	17 28	17 42	17 48	17 54	17 59		17 58

For general notes see front of timetable
For details of catering facilities see Directory of Train Operators

For fast services between Reading and London Paddington see Table 116

b Change at Heathrow Terminals 1-2-3

Reading and Greenford → London

(Local services only)

from 13 September

Network Diagram - see first page of Table 116

Station		GW 1	GW 1	GW 1◇ ⊡	GW 1	GW 1	HC 1	GW 1	GW 1	GW 1◇	GW 1	GW 1	HC 1	GW 1	GW 1	GW 1◇ ⊡	GW 1	GW 1	HC 1	GW 1	GW 1	GW 1	HC 1	GW 1	GW 1
Oxford	d	16 55								17 30				17 21		18 00				17 55				18 21	
Reading 7	d	17 34		17 40				←	17 48	17 57	←			18 04	18 18	18 27				18 34	18 48			19 04	19 18
Twyford 3	d	17 40 →	←					17 40	17 55		17 55			18 10	18 25		←			18 41	18 55			19 10	19 25
Maidenhead 3	d		17 33					17 48	→		18 03			18 18	18 33 →		18 33			18 49	19 03			19 18	19 33 →
Taplow	d		17 37								18 07						18 37				19 07				
Burnham	d		17 40								18 10						18 40				19 10				
Slough 3	a		17 45	17 53				17 56		18 10	18 15			18 25		18 40	18 45			18 56	19 15			19 25	
	d		17 45	17 54				17 56		18 11	18 15			18 26		18 41	18 45			18 56	19 15			19 26	
Langley	d							18 00						18 30						19 00				19 30	
Iver	d							18 03						18 33						19 03				19 33	
West Drayton	d		17 52					18 06			18 22			18 36			18 52			19 06	19 22			19 36 →	
Heathrow Terminal 5 ✈	d						17b42						18b12						18b42				19b12		
Heathrow Terminal 4 ✈	d						17 51						18 21						18 51				19 21		
Heathrow Terminals 1-2-3 ✈	d				←		17 56						18 26						18 56				19 26		
Hayes & Harlington	d		17 56 →		17 56		18 03	18 10			18 26		18 33	18 40			18 56		19 03	19 11	19 26		19 33		
Southall	d						18 06	18 14					18 36	18 44					19 06	19 14			19 36		
Hanwell	d						18 09						18 39						19 09				19 39		
Greenford ⊖	d					17 53						18 23						18 53				19 23			
South Greenford	d					17 56						18 26						18 56				19 26			
Castle Bar Park	d					17 59						18 29						18 59				19 29			
Drayton Green	d					18 01						18 31						19 01				19 31			
West Ealing	d					18 04	18 12					18 34	18 42					19 04	19 12			19 34	19 42		
Ealing Broadway ⊖	d				18 03	18 07	18 14	18 19			18 33	18 37	18 44	18 49			19 03	19 07	19 14	19 19	19 33	19 37	19 44		
Acton Main Line	d					18 10						18 40						19 10				19 40			
London Paddington 15 ⊖	a			18 11	18 12	18 18	18 24	18 28		18 28	18 42	18 48	18 54	18 59		18 58	19 12	19 18	19 24	19 28	19 42	19 48	19 54		

Station		GW 1◇ ⊡	GW 1	GW 1	GW 1	HC 1	GW 1	GW 1	GW 1◇	GW 1	GW 1	HC 1	GW 1	GW 1	GW 1◇ ⊡	GW 1	GW 1	HC 1	GW 1	GW 1	GW 1◇	GW 1	GW 1	HC 1	GW 1
Oxford	d	19 00					18 55		19 30				19 21		20 06				19 55		20 30				20 20
Reading 7	d	19 27					19 34	19 48	19 56				20 04	20 18	20 32				20 34	20 48	20 54				21 09
Twyford 3	d			←			19 40	19 55		←			20 10	20 25					20 40	20 55		←			21 15
Maidenhead 3	d			19 33			19 48	20 03 →		20 03			20 18	20 33					20 48	21 03 →		21 03			21 23
Taplow	d			19 37						20 07				20 37								21 07			21 27
Burnham	d			19 40						20 10				20 40								21 10			21 30
Slough 3	a	19 40		19 45			19 55		20 09	20 15			20 25	20 45	20 45				20 55		21 08	21 15			21 35
	d	19 41		19 45			19 56		20 10	20 15			20 26	20 45	20 46				20 56		21 09	21 15			21 35
Langley	d						20 00						20 30						21 00						21 39
Iver	d		←				20 03						20 33						21 03						21 42
West Drayton	d		19 36	19 52			20 06			20 22			20 36	20 52					21 06			21 22			21 45 →
Heathrow Terminal 5 ✈	d					19b42						20b12						20b42						21b12	
Heathrow Terminal 4 ✈	d					19 51						20 21						20 51						21 21	
Heathrow Terminals 1-2-3 ✈	d					19 56						20 26				←		20 56						21 26	
Hayes & Harlington	d		19 40	19 56		20 03	20 10			20 26		20 33	20 40	20 56 →		20 56		21 03	21 10			21 26		21 33	
Southall	d		19 44			20 06	20 14					20 36	20 44					21 06	21 14					21 36	
Hanwell	d					20 09						20 39						21 09						21 39	
Greenford ⊖	d				19 53						20 23						20 53						21 23		
South Greenford	d				19 56						20 26						20 56						21 26		
Castle Bar Park	d				19 59						20 29						20 59						21 29		
Drayton Green	d				20 01						20 31						21 01						21 31		
West Ealing	d				20 04	20 12					20 34	20 42					21 04	21 12					21 34	21 42	
Ealing Broadway ⊖	d		19 49	20 03	20 07	20 14	20 19			20 33	20 37	20 44	20 49			21 03	21 07	21 14	21 19			21 33	21 37	21 44	
Acton Main Line	d				20 10						20 40						21 10						21 40		
London Paddington 15 ⊖	a	19 58	19 59	20 12	20 18	20 24	20 28		20 27	20 42	20 48	20 54	20 59		21 06	21 12	21 18	21 24	21 28		21 26	21 42	21 48	21 54	

Station		GW 1◇ ⊡	GW 1	GW 1	HC 1	GW 1	GW 1	GW 1◇	GW 1	HC 1	GW 1	GW 1◇	GW 1	HC 1	GW 1	GW 1	GW 1◇	GW 1	HC 1	GW 1	GW 1◇ ⊡	GW 1	GW 1
Oxford	d	21 00				20 55		21 37				22 08			21 55		22 30				23 00		23 09
Reading 7	d	21 27				21 35	21 44	22 07			22 16	22 36			22 35	22 45	22 56			23 16	23 29		00 04
Twyford 3	d					21 41	21 50				22 22				22 40	22 52				23 23			00 10
Maidenhead 3	d					21 49	21 58				22 30				22 48	23 00				23 32			00 18
Taplow	d						22 02				22 34					23 04				23 35			00 22
Burnham	d						22 05				22 37					23 07				23 38			00 26
Slough 3	a	21 40				21 56	22 10	22 22			22 42	22 51			22 57	23 12	23 12			23 42	23 48		00 30
	d	21 41				21 57	22 10	22 22			22 42	22 52			22 57	23 12	23 13			23 42	23 49		00 31
Langley	d						22 14				22 46					23 16				23 46			00 35
Iver	d		←				22 17		←		22 49		←			23 19				23 49		←	00 38
West Drayton	d		21 45				22 20 →		22 20		22 52 →		22 52			23 22				23 52 →		23 52	00 41
Heathrow Terminal 5 ✈	d				21b42					22b12				22b42					23b12				
Heathrow Terminal 4 ✈	d				21 51					22 21				22 51					23 21				
Heathrow Terminals 1-2-3 ✈	d				21 56					22 26				22 56					23 26				
Hayes & Harlington	d		21 50		22 03	22 06			22 25	22 33			22 57	23 03	23 06	23 27		←	23 33			23 57	00 45
Southall	d		21 53		22 06	22 10			22 28	22 36			23 00	23 06	23 10	23 30 →		23 30	23 36			23 59	00 49
Hanwell	d				22 09					22 39				23 09					23 39				
Greenford ⊖	d			21 53																			
South Greenford	d			21 56																			
Castle Bar Park	d			21 59																			
Drayton Green	d			22 01																			
West Ealing	d			22 04	22 12					22 42				23 12					23 42				
Ealing Broadway ⊖	d		21 58	22 07	22 14	22 19			22 33	22 44			23 05	23 14	23 19			23 35	23 44			00 07	00 54
Acton Main Line	d			22 10																			
London Paddington 15 ⊖	a	21 58	22 08	22 18	22 24	22 28		22 40	22 42	22 54		23 11	23 14	23 24	23 28		23 30	23 44	23 54		00 09	00 16	01 02

For general notes see front of timetable
For details of catering facilities see
Directory of Train Operators

For fast services between Reading and London
Paddington see Table 116

b Change at Heathrow Terminals 1-2-3

Table 117

Sundays

until 7 September

Reading and Greenford → London

(Local services only)

Network Diagram - see first page of Table 116

		GW 1	HC	GW 1	HC	GW 1	HC	GW 1	HC	GW 1	GW 1	GW 1	GW 1 ◇	HC	GW 1	HC	GW 1	GW 1 ◇	HC	GW 1	HC	GW 1	GW 1 ◇
Oxford	d			23p09								08 05	08 38				09 05	09 38				10 05	10 38
Reading 7	d	23p16		00 04		06 22		07 22		08 03	08 22	08 48	09 05		09 18		09 48	10 05		10 18		10 46	11 07
Twyford 3	d	23p23		00 10		06 28		07 28			08 28	08 54			09 24		09 54			10 24		10 55	
Maidenhead 3	d	23p32		00 18		06 36		07 36			08 36	09 02			09 32		10 02			10 32		11 03	
Taplow	d	23p35		00 22																			
Burnham	d	23p38		00 26		06 40		07 40			08 40				09 36					10 36			
Slough 3	a	23p42		00 30		06 45		07 45		08 21	08 45	09 09	09 24		09 40		10 09	10 26		10 41		11 10	11 26
	d	23p42		00 31		06 45		07 45		08 21	08 45	09 11	09 25		09 41		10 11	10 27		10 41		11 11	11 27
Langley	d	23p46		00 35		06 49		07 49			08 49	09 15			09 45		10 15			10 45		11 15	
Iver	d	23p49		00 38																			
West Drayton	d	23p52		00 41		06 54		07 54			08 54	09 19			09 49		10 19			10 49		11 19	
Heathrow Terminal 5 ✈	d				06b03		07b03		08b03					09b13		09b42			10b12		10b42		
Heathrow Terminal 4 ✈	d		00 01		06 07		07 07		08 07					09 21		09 51			10 21		10 51		
Heathrow Terminals 1-2-3 ✈	d		00 06		06 13		07 13		08 13					09 26		09 56			10 26		10 56		
Hayes & Harlington	d	23p57	00 12	00 45	06 18	07 01	07 18	08 01	08 18		09 01	09 24		09 32	09 55	10 02	10 24		10 32	10 55	11 02	11 24	
Southall	d	23p59	00 15	00 49	06 22	07 05	07 22	08 05	08 22		09 05	09 27		09 35	09 58	10 05	10 27		10 35	10 58	11 05	11 27	
Hanwell	d																						
Greenford ⊖	d																						
South Greenford	d																						
Castle Bar Park	d																						
Drayton Green	d																						
West Ealing	d																						
Ealing Broadway ⊖	d	00 07	00 20	00 54	06 27	07 10	07 27	08 10	08 27		09 10	09 32		09 40	10 03	10 10	10 32		10 40	11 03	11 10	11 32	
Acton Main Line	d																						
London Paddington 15 ⊖	a	00 16	00 29	01 02	06 35	07 19	07 35	08 19	08 35	08 44	09 19	09 41	09 43	09 49	10 12	10 19	10 40	10 45	10 49	11 12	11 19	11 40	11 46

		HC	GW 1	HC	GW 1	GW 1 ◇	HC	GW 1	HC	GW 1	HC	GW 1	GW 1 ◇	GW 1	HC	GW 1	GW 1 ◇	HC	GW 1	HC	GW 1	GW 1 ◇	HC
Oxford	d				11 05	11 38				12 05		*12 16*	12 50			13 05	13 38				14 05	14 38	
Reading 7	d		11 18		11 52	12 07		12 18		12 46		13 18	13 22			13 46	14 06		14 18		14 46	15 05	
Twyford 3	d		11 24		11 59			12 24		12 55		13 24				13 55			14 24		14 55		
Maidenhead 3	d		11 32		12 07			12 32		13 03		13 32				14 03			14 32		15 03		
Taplow	d																						
Burnham	d		11 36					12 36				13 36							14 36				
Slough 3	a		11 41		12 14	12 28		12 41		13 10		13 41	13 47			14 10	14 25		14 41		15 10	15 23	
	d		11 41		12 14	12 29		12 41		13 11		13 41	13 47			14 11	14 26		14 41		15 11	15 23	
Langley	d		11 45		12 18			12 45		13 15		13 45				14 15			14 45		15 15		
Iver	d																						
West Drayton	d		11 49		12 23			12 49		13 19		13 49				14 19			14 49		15 19		
Heathrow Terminal 5 ✈	d	11b12		11b42			12b12		12b42		13b12				13b42			14b12		14b42			15b12
Heathrow Terminal 4 ✈	d	11 21		11 51			12 21		12 51		13 21				13 51			14 21		14 51			15 21
Heathrow Terminals 1-2-3 ✈	d	11 26		11 56			12 26		12 56		13 26			←	13 56			14 26		14 56			15 26
Hayes & Harlington	d	11 32	11 55	12 02	12 27		12 32	12 55	13 02	13 24	13 32	13 55 →		13 55	14 02	14 24		14 32	14 55	15 02	15 24		15 32
Southall	d	11 35	11 58	12 05	12 31		12 35	12 58	13 05	13 27	13 35			13 58	14 05	14 27		14 35	14 58	15 05	15 27		15 35
Hanwell	d																						
Greenford ⊖	d																						
South Greenford	d																						
Castle Bar Park	d																						
Drayton Green	d																						
West Ealing	d																						
Ealing Broadway ⊖	d	11 40	12 03	12 10	12 36		12 40	13 03	13 10	13 32	13 40			14 03	14 10	14 32		14 40	15 03	15 10	15 32		15 40
Acton Main Line	d																						
London Paddington 15 ⊖	a	11 49	12 12	12 19	12 44	12 46	12 49	13 12	13 19	13 40	13 49		14 08	14 12	14 19	14 40	14 44	14 49	15 12	15 19	15 40	15 43	15 49

		GW 1	HC	GW 1	HC	GW 1	GW 1 ◇	GW 1	HC	GW 1	HC	GW 1	GW 1 ◇	GW 1	HC	GW 1	HC	GW 1	GW 1 ◇	GW 1	HC	GW 1	HC
Oxford	d			15 05		*15 16*	15 50			16 05		*16 16*	16 50			17 05		*17 16*	17 50			18 05	
Reading 7	d	15 18		15 46		16 18	16 21			16 46		17 18	17 21			17 46		18 18	18 21			18 46	
Twyford 3	d	15 24		15 55		16 24				16 55		17 24				17 55		18 24				18 55	
Maidenhead 3	d	15 32		16 03		16 32				17 03		17 32				18 03		18 32				19 03	
Taplow	d																						
Burnham	d	15 36		16 07		16 36				17 07		17 36				18 07		18 36				19 07	
Slough 3	a	15 41		16 12		16 41	16 47			17 12		17 41	17 48			18 12		18 41	18 45			19 12	
	d	15 41		16 12		16 41	16 47			17 12		17 41	17 48			18 12		18 41	18 45			19 12	
Langley	d	15 45		16 16		16 45				17 16		17 45				18 16		18 45				19 16	
Iver	d																						
West Drayton	d	15 51		16 21		16 49				17 21		17 49				18 21		18 49				19 21	
Heathrow Terminal 5 ✈	d		15b42		16b12				16b42		17b12				17b42		18b12				18b42		19b12
Heathrow Terminal 4 ✈	d		15 51		16 21				16 51		17 21				17 51		18 21				18 51		19 21
Heathrow Terminals 1-2-3 ✈	d		15 56		16 26			←	16 56		17 26			←	17 56		18 26			←	18 56		19 26
Hayes & Harlington	d	15 54	16 02	16 25	16 32	16 55 →		16 55	17 02	17 25	17 32	17 55 →		17 55	18 02	18 25	18 32	18 55 →		18 55	19 02	19 25	19 32
Southall	d	15 59	16 05	16 29	16 35			16 58	17 05	17 29	17 35			17 58	18 05	18 29	18 35			18 58	19 05	19 29	19 35
Hanwell	d																						
Greenford ⊖	d																						
South Greenford	d																						
Castle Bar Park	d																						
Drayton Green	d																						
West Ealing	d																						
Ealing Broadway ⊖	d	16 04	16 10	16 34	16 40			17 03	17 10	17 34	17 40			18 03	18 10	18 34	18 40			19 03	19 10	19 34	19 40
Acton Main Line	d																						
London Paddington 15 ⊖	a	16 12	16 19	16 42	16 49		17 07	17 12	17 19	17 42	17 49		18 08	18 12	18 19	18 42	18 49		19 08	19 12	19 19	19 42	19 49

For general notes see front of timetable
For details of catering facilities see Directory of Train Operators

For fast services between Reading and London Paddington see Table 116

b Change at Heathrow Terminals 1-2-3

Reading and Greenford → London
(Local services only)

Sundays
until 7 September

Network Diagram - see first page of Table 116

		GW 1 ◇	GW 1	HC	GW 1	HC	GW 1	GW 1 ◇	GW 1	HC	GW 1	HC	GW 1 ◇	GW 1	HC	GW 1	GW 1 ◇	GW 1	HC	GW 1	GW 1 ◇	GW 1
Oxford	d	18 41			19 05		*19 16*	19 50			20 05		20 50	*20 16*		21 09	21 50			22 21	22 50	22 58
Reading 7	d	19 07	19 18		19 46		20 18	20 24			20 46		21 19	21 24		21 56	22 19	22 24		22 59	23 15	23 41
Twyford 3	d		19 24		19 55		20 24				20 55			21 30		22 03		22 30		23 06		23 48
Maidenhead 3	d		19 32		20 03		20 32				21 03			21 38		22 11		22 38		23 14		23 56
Taplow	d																					
Burnham	d		19 36		20 07		20 36				21 07			21 42		22 15		22 42		23 18		00 01
Slough 3	a	19 32	19 41		20 12		20 41	20 47			21 12		21 41	21 47		22 20	22 40	22 47		23 23	23 36	00 05
	d	19 32	19 41		20 12		20 41	20 47			21 12		21 41	21 47		22 20	22 41	22 47		23 23	23 36	00 06
Langley	d		19 45		20 16		20 45				21 16			21 51		22 24		22 51		23 27		00 10
Iver	d																					
West Drayton	d		19 49		20 21		20 49				21 21			21 56		22 29		22 56		23 32		00 14
Heathrow Terminal 5 ✈	d			*19c42*		*20c12*				*20c42*		*21c12*			*22c03*				*23c03*			
Heathrow Terminal 4 ✈	d			19 51		20 21				20 51		21 21			22 07				23 07			
Heathrow Terminals 1-2-3 ✈	d			19 56		20 26				20 56		21 26			22 13				23 13			
Hayes & Harlington	d		19 55	20 02	20 25	20 32	20 55 →		← 20 55	21 02	21 25	21 32		22 01	22 18	22 33		23 01	23 18	23 36		00 19
Southall	d		19 58	20 05	20 29	20 35			20 58	21 05	21 29	21 35		22 05	22 22	22 37		23 05	23 22	23 40		00 22
Hanwell	d																					
Greenford ⊖	d																					
South Greenford	d																					
Castle Bar Park	d																					
Drayton Green	d																					
West Ealing	d																					
Ealing Broadway ⊖	d		20 03	20 10	20 34	20 40			21 03	21 10	21 34	21 40		22 10	22 27	22 42		23 10	23 27	23 45		00 27
Acton Main Line	d																					
London Paddington 15 ⊖	a	19 52	20 12	20 19	20 42	20 49		21 08	21 12	21 19	21 42	21 49	22 03	22 18	22 35	22 51	23 04	23 18	23 35	23 53	00 01	00 40

Sundays
from 14 September

		GW 1	HC	GW 1	HC	GW 1	HC	GW 1	HC	GW 1	GW 1	HC	GW 1 A	GW 1 ◇	GW 1	HC	GW 1	GW 1 ◇	GW 1	HC
Oxford	d			23p09													09 05	09 38		
Reading 7	d	23p16		00 04		06 22		07 22		08 04	08 22		08 52	09 06	09 18		09 52	10 06	10 18	
Twyford 3	d	23p23		00 10		06 28		07 28			08 28		08 58		09 24		09 58		10 24	
Maidenhead 3	d	23p32		00 18		06 36		07 36			08 36		09 06		09e36		10 06		10f36	
Taplow	d	23p35		00 22																
Burnham	d	23p38		00 26		06 40		07 40			08 40				09 40				10 40	
Slough 3	a	23p42		00 30		06 45		07 45		08 23	08 45		09 18	09 29	09 46		10 18	10 23	10 48	
	d	23p42		00 31		06 45		07 45		08 23	08 45		09 18	09 30	09 46		10 18	10 23	10 48	
Langley	d	23p46		00 35		06 49		07 49			08 49		09 22		09 50		10 22		10 52	
Iver	d	23p49		00 38																
West Drayton	d	23p52		00 41		06 54		07 54			08 54		09 27		09 55		10 27		10 57	
Heathrow Terminal 5 ✈	d				*06c03*		*07c03*		*08c03*			*09c03*				*10c03*				*11c03*
Heathrow Terminal 4 ✈	d		00 01		06 07		07 07		08 07			09 07				10 07				11 07
Heathrow Terminals 1-2-3 ✈	d		00 06		06 13		07 13		08 13			09 13				10 13				11 13
Hayes & Harlington	d	23p57	00 12	00 45	06 18	07 01	07 18	08 01	08 18		09 01	09 18	09 31		10 00	10 18	10 31		11 01	11 18
Southall	d	23p59	00 15	00 49	06 22	07 05	07 22	08 05	08 22		09 05	09 22	09 35		10 04	10 22	10 35		11 05	11 22
Hanwell	d																			
Greenford ⊖	d																			
South Greenford	d																			
Castle Bar Park	d																			
Drayton Green	d																			
West Ealing	d																			
Ealing Broadway ⊖	d	00 07	00 20	00 54	06 27	07 10	07 27	08 10	08 27		09 10	09 27	09 40		10 09	10 27	10 40		11 10	11 27
Acton Main Line	d																			
London Paddington 15 ⊖	a	00 16	00 29	01 02	06 35	07 18	07 35	08 20	08 35	08 43	09 20	09 35	09 49	09 52	10 20	10 35	10 49	10 51	11 20	11 35

		GW 1	GW 1 ◇	GW 1	HC	GW 1	GW 1 ◇	GW 1	HC	GW 1	GW 1	GW 1 ◇	GW 1	HC	GW 1	GW 1 ◇	GW 1	HC	GW 1
Oxford	d	10 05	10 38			11 05	11 38			12 05		12 50			13 05	13 38			14 05
Reading 7	d	10 52	11 06	11 18		11 52	12 10	12 18		12 52	13 18	13 19			13 52	14 06	14 18		14 52
Twyford 3	d	10 58		11 24		11 58		12 24		12 58	13 24		←		13 58		14 24		14 58
Maidenhead 3	d	11 06		11g36		12 06		12h36		13 06	13j36 →		13 36		14 06		14k36		15 06
Taplow	d																		
Burnham	d			11 40				12 40					13 40				14 40		
Slough 3	a	11 18	11 24	11 48		12 18	12 28	12 48		13 18		13 37	13 48		14 18	14 23	14 48		15 18
	d	11 18	11 25	11 48		12 18	12 29	12 48		13 18		13 37	13 48		14 18	14 24	14 48		15 18
Langley	d	11 22		11 52		12 22		12 52		13 22			13 52		14 22		14 52		15 22
Iver	d																		
West Drayton	d	11 27		11 57		12 27		12 57		13 27			13 57		14 27		14 57		15 27
Heathrow Terminal 5 ✈	d				*12c03*				*13c03*					*14c03*				*15c03*	
Heathrow Terminal 4 ✈	d				12 07				13 07					14 07				15 07	
Heathrow Terminals 1-2-3 ✈	d				12 13				13 13					14 13				15 13	
Hayes & Harlington	d	11 31		12 01	12 18	12 31		13 01	13 18	13 31			14 01	14 18	14 31		15 01	15 18	15 31
Southall	d	11 35		12 05	12 22	12 35		13 05	13 22	13 35			14 05	14 22	14 35		15 05	15 22	15 35
Hanwell	d																		
Greenford ⊖	d																		
South Greenford	d																		
Castle Bar Park	d																		
Drayton Green	d																		
West Ealing	d																		
Ealing Broadway ⊖	d	11 40		12 10	12 27	12 40		13 10	13 27	13 40			14 10	14 27	14 40		15 10	15 27	15 40
Acton Main Line	d																		
London Paddington 15 ⊖	a	11 49	11 53	12 20	12 35	12 49	12 51	13 20	13 35	13 49		14 00	14 20	14 35	14 49	14 52	15 20	15 35	15 49

For general notes see front of timetable
For details of catering facilities see Directory of Train Operators
For fast services between Reading and London Paddington see Table 116

A From Didcot Parkway (Table 116)
c Change at Heathrow Terminals 1-2-3
e Arr. 0930
f Arr. 1030
g Arr. 1131
h Arr. 1230
j Arr. 1330
k Arr. 1430

Reading and Greenford → London

(Local services only)

from 14 September

Network Diagram - see first page of Table 116

	GW 1 ◇	GW 1	HC		GW 1	GW 1	GW 1 ◇ ☕		GW 1	HC	GW 1		GW 1	GW 1 ◇ ☕	GW 1		HC	GW 1	GW 1		GW 1 ◇ ☕	GW 1	HC	GW 1
Oxford d	14 38				15 05		15 50				16 05			16 50				17 05			17 50			18 05
Reading 7 d	15 10	15 18			15 52	16 18	16 20				16 52		17 18	17 22				17 52	18 18		18 21			18 52
Twyford 3 d		15 24			15 58	16 24			←		16 58		17 24		←			17 58	18 24			←		18 58
Maidenhead 3 d		15b36			16 06	16c36 →			16 36		17 06		17e36 →		17 36			18 06	18f36 →			18 36		19 06
Taplow d																								
Burnham d		15 40			16 11				16 40		17 11				17 40			18 11				18 40		19 11
Slough 3 a	15 34	15 48			16 18		16 36		16 48		17 18			17 40	17 48			18 18			18 36	18 48		19 18
d	15 34	15 48			16 18		16 36		16 48		17 18			17 40	17 48			18 18			18 36	18 48		19 18
Langley d		15 52			16 22				16 52		17 22				17 52			18 22				18 52		19 22
Iver d																								
West Drayton d		15 57			16 27				16 57		17 27				17 57			18 27				18 57		19 27
Heathrow Terminal 5 ✈ d			16g03							17g03							18g03						19g03	
Heathrow Terminal 4 ✈ d			16 07							17 07							18 07						19 07	
Heathrow Terminals 1-2-3 ✈ d			16 13							17 13							18 13						19 13	
Hayes & Harlington d		16 01	16 18		16 31				17 01	17 18	17 31				18 01		18 18	18 31				19 01	19 18	19 31
Southall d		16 05	16 22		16 35				17 05	17 22	17 35				18 05		18 22	18 35				19 05	19 22	19 35
Hanwell d																								
Greenford ⊖ d																								
South Greenford d																								
Castle Bar Park d																								
Drayton Green d																								
West Ealing d																								
Ealing Broadway ⊖ d		16 10	16 27		16 40				17 10	17 27	17 40				18 10		18 27	18 40				19 10	19 27	19 40
Acton Main Line d																								
London Paddington 15 ⊖ a	15 58	16 20	16 35		16 49		17 00		17 20	17 35	17 49			18 06	18 20		18 35	18 49			19 02	19 20	19 35	19 49

	GW 1 ◇ ☕		GW 1	HC	GW 1		GW 1	GW 1 ◇ ☕	GW 1		HC	GW 1	GW 1 ◇ ☕		HC	GW 1	GW 1 ◇ ☕		HC	GW 1	GW 1 ◇ 🛒	GW 1		
Oxford d	18 41				19 05			19 50				20 05	20 50			21 05	21 50			22 05	22 50	22 58		
Reading 7 d	19 08		19 18		19 52		20 18	20 20				20 52	21 19			21 55	22 19			22 55	23 15	23 40		
Twyford 3 d			19 24		19 58		20 24		←			20 58				22 01				23 01		23 48		
Maidenhead 3 d			19h36		20 06		20j36 →		20 36			21 06				22 09				23 09		23 56		
Taplow d																								
Burnham d			19 41		20 11				20 40			21 10				22 13				23 13		00 01		
Slough 3 a	19 28		19 48		20 18			20 35	20 48			21 18	21 35			22 18	22 42			23 18	23 36	00 05		
d	19 28		19 48		20 18			20 36	20 48			21 18	21 35			22 18	22 43			23 18	23 36	00 06		
Langley d			19 52		20 22				20 52			21 22				22 22				23 22		00 10		
Iver d																								
West Drayton d			19 57		20 27				20 57			21 27				22 27				23 27		00 14		
Heathrow Terminal 5 ✈ d				20g03							21g03				22g03				23g03					
Heathrow Terminal 4 ✈ d				20 07							21 07				22 07				23 07					
Heathrow Terminals 1-2-3 ✈ d				20 13							21 13				22 13				23 13					
Hayes & Harlington d			20 01	20 18	20 31				21 01		21 18	21 31			22 18	22 31			23 18	23 31		00 19		
Southall d			20 05	20 22	20 35				21 05		21 22	21 35			22 22	22 35			23 22	23 35		00 22		
Hanwell d																								
Greenford ⊖ d																								
South Greenford d																								
Castle Bar Park d																								
Drayton Green d																								
West Ealing d																								
Ealing Broadway ⊖ d			20 10	20 27	20 40				21 10		21 27	21 40			22 27	22 40			23 27	23 40		00 27		
Acton Main Line d																								
London Paddington 15 ⊖ a	19 53		20 20	20 35	20 49			21 00	21 20		21 35	21 49	22 03		22 35	22 48	23 05		23 35	23 48	23 59	00 35		

For general notes see front of timetable
For details of catering facilities see Directory of Train Operators

For fast services between Reading and London Paddington see Table 116

b Arr. 1530
c Arr. 1630
e Arr. 1730
f Arr. 1830
g Change at Heathrow Terminals 1-2-3
h Arr. 1930
j Arr. 2030

Table 118

Mondays to Fridays

London → Heathrow Airport

Network Diagram - see first page of Table 116

Miles			HX 1	HX 1	HX 1	HX 1		HX 1	HX 1	HX 1	HX 1		HX 1	HX 1	HX 1	HX 1		HX 1	HX 1	HX 1	HX 1		HX 1	HX 1	HX 1
0	London Paddington 15	d	05 10	05 25	05 40	05 55		06 10	06 25	06 40	06 55		07 10	07 25	07 40	07 55		08 10	08 25	08 40	08 55		09 10	09 25	09 40
14¾	Heathrow Terminals 1-2-3	a	05 26	05 40	05 55	06 10		06 25	06 40	06 55	07 10		07 25	07 40	07 55	08 10		08 25	08 40	08 55	09 10		09 25	09 40	09 55
16½	Heathrow Terminal 4	a	*05 41*	*06 10*		*06 40*			*07 10*		*07 40*			*08 10*		*08 40*			*09 10*		*09 40*			*10 10*	
—	Heathrow Terminal 5	a	05 32	05 46	06 01	06 16		06 31	06 46	07 01	07 16		07 31	07 46	08 01	08 16		08 31	08 46	09 01	09 16		09 31	09 46	10 01

		HX 1	HX 1	HX 1		HX 1	HX 1	HX 1	HX 1		HX 1	HX 1	HX 1	HX 1		HX 1	HX 1	HX 1	HX 1		HX 1	HX 1	HX 1	HX 1	HX 1
London Paddington 15	d	09 55	10 10	10 25		10 40	10 55	11 10	11 25		11 40	11 55	12 10	12 25		12 40	12 55	13 10	13 25		13 40	13 55	14 10	14 25	14 40
Heathrow Terminals 1-2-3	a	10 10	10 25	10 40		10 55	11 10	11 25	11 40		11 55	12 10	12 25	12 40		12 55	13 10	13 25	13 40		13 55	14 10	14 25	14 40	14 55
Heathrow Terminal 4	a	*10 40*		*11 10*			*11 40*		*12 10*			*12 40*		*13 10*			*13 40*		*14 10*			*14 40*		*15 10*	
Heathrow Terminal 5	a	10 16	10 31	10 46		11 01	11 16	11 31	11 46		12 01	12 16	12 31	12 46		13 01	13 16	13 31	13 46		14 01	14 16	14 31	14 46	15 01

		HX 1		HX 1	HX 1	HX 1	HX 1		HX 1	HX 1	HX 1	HX 1		HX 1	HX 1	HX 1	HX 1		HX 1	HX 1	HX 1	HX 1		HX 1	HX 1
London Paddington 15	d	14 55		15 10	15 25	15 40	15 55		16 10	16 25	16 40	16 55		17 10	17 25	17 40	17 55		18 10	18 25	18 40	18 55		19 10	19 25
Heathrow Terminals 1-2-3	a	15 10		15 25	15 40	15 55	16 10		16 25	16 40	16 55	17 10		17 25	17 40	17 55	18 10		18 25	18 40	18 55	19 10		19 25	19 40
Heathrow Terminal 4	a	*15 40*			*16 10*		*16 40*			*17 10*		*17 40*			*18 10*		*18 40*			*19 10*		*19 40*			*20 10*
Heathrow Terminal 5	a	15 16		15 31	15 46	16 01	16 16		16 31	16 46	17 01	17 16		17 31	17 46	18 01	18 16		18 31	18 46	19 01	19 16		19 31	19 46

		HX 1	HX 1	HX 1	HX 1		HX 1	HX 1	HX 1	HX 1		HX 1	HX 1	HX 1	HX 1		HX 1	HX 1	HX 1	HX 1					
London Paddington 15	d	19 40	19 55	20 10	20 25		20 40	20 55	21 10	21 25		21 40	21 55	22 10	22 25		22 40	22 55	23 10	23 25					
Heathrow Terminals 1-2-3	a	19 55	20 10	20 25	20 40		20 55	21 10	21 25	21 40		21 55	22 10	22 25	22 40		22 55	23 10	23 25	23 40					
Heathrow Terminal 4	a		*20 40*		*21 10*			*21 40*		*22 10*			*22 40*		*23 10*			*23 40*							
Heathrow Terminal 5	a	20 01	20 16	20 31	20 46		21 01	21 16	21 31	21 46		22 01	22 16	22 31	22 46		23 01	23 16	23 31	23 46					

Saturdays

		HX 1	HX 1	HX 1		HX 1	HX 1	HX 1		HX 1	HX 1	HX 1		HX 1	HX 1	HX 1		HX 1	HX 1	HX 1		HX 1	HX 1	HX 1	HX 1
London Paddington 15	d	05 10	05 25	05 40		05 55	06 10	06 25		06 40	06 55	07 10		07 25	07 40	07 55		08 10	08 25	08 40		08 55	09 10	09 25	09 40
Heathrow Terminals 1-2-3	a	05 26	05 40	05 55		06 10	06 25	06 40		06 55	07 10	07 25		07 40	07 55	08 10		08 25	08 40	08 55		09 10	09 25	09 40	09 55
Heathrow Terminal 4	a	*05 42*	*06 10*			*06 40*		*07 10*			*07 40*			*08 10*		*08 40*			*09 10*			*09 40*		*10 10*	
Heathrow Terminal 5	a	05 32	05 46	06 01		06 16	06 31	06 46		07 01	07 16	07 31		07 46	08 01	08 16		08 31	08 46	09 01		09 16	09 31	09 46	10 01

		HX 1		HX 1	HX 1	HX 1		HX 1	HX 1	HX 1		HX 1	HX 1	HX 1		HX 1	HX 1	HX 1		HX 1	HX 1	HX 1		HX 1	HX 1
London Paddington 15	d	09 55		10 10	10 25	10 40		10 55	11 10	11 25		11 40	11 55	12 10		12 25	12 40	12 55		13 10	13 25	13 40		13 55	14 10
Heathrow Terminals 1-2-3	a	10 10		10 25	10 40	10 55		11 10	11 25	11 40		11 55	12 10	12 25		12 40	12 55	13 10		13 25	13 40	13 55		14 10	14 25
Heathrow Terminal 4	a	*10 40*			*11 10*			*11 40*		*12 10*			*12 40*			*13 10*		*13 40*			*14 10*			*14 40*	
Heathrow Terminal 5	a	10 16		10 31	10 46	11 01		11 16	11 31	11 46		12 01	12 16	12 31		12 46	13 01	13 16		13 31	13 46	14 01		14 16	14 31

		HX 1	HX 1	HX 1		HX 1	HX 1	HX 1		HX 1	HX 1	HX 1		HX 1	HX 1	HX 1		HX 1	HX 1	HX 1		HX 1	HX 1	HX 1	HX 1
London Paddington 15	d	14 25	14 40	14 55		15 10	15 25	15 40		15 55	16 10	16 25		16 40	16 55	17 10		17 25	17 40	17 55		18 10	18 25	18 40	18 55
Heathrow Terminals 1-2-3	a	14 40	14 55	15 10		15 25	15 40	15 55		16 10	16 25	16 40		16 55	17 10	17 25		17 40	17 55	18 10		18 25	18 40	18 55	19 10
Heathrow Terminal 4	a	*15 10*		*15 40*			*16 10*			*16 40*		*17 10*			*17 40*			*18 10*		*18 40*			*19 10*		*19 40*
Heathrow Terminal 5	a	14 46	15 01	15 16		15 31	15 46	16 01		16 16	16 31	16 46		17 01	17 16	17 31		17 46	18 01	18 16		18 31	18 46	19 01	19 16

		HX 1		HX 1	HX 1	HX 1		HX 1	HX 1	HX 1		HX 1	HX 1	HX 1		HX 1	HX 1	HX 1	HX 1	HX 1	HX 1	HX 1	HX 1		
London Paddington 15	d	19 10		19 25	19 40	19 55		20 10	20 25	20 40		20 55	21 10	21 25		21 40	21 55	22 10	22 25	22 40	22 55	23 10	23 25		
Heathrow Terminals 1-2-3	a	19 25		19 40	19 55	20 10		20 25	20 40	20 55		21 10	21 25	21 40		21 55	22 10	22 25	22 40	22 55	23 10	23 25	23 40		
Heathrow Terminal 4	a			*20 10*		*20 40*			*21 10*			*21 40*		*22 10*			*22 40*		*23 10*		*23 40*				
Heathrow Terminal 5	a	19 31		19 46	20 01	20 16		20 31	20 46	21 01		21 16	21 31	21 46		22 01	22 16	22 31	22 46	23 01	23 16	23 31	23 46		

Sundays

until 7 September

		HX 1	HX 1	HX 1		HX 1	HX 1	HX 1		HX 1	HX 1	HX 1		HX 1	HX 1	HX 1		HX 1	HX 1	HX 1		HX 1	HX 1	HX 1	HX 1
London Paddington 15	d	05 10	05 25	05 40		05 55	06 10	06 25		06 40	06 55	07 10		07 25	07 40	07 55		08 10	08 25	08 40		08 55	09 10	09 25	09 40
Heathrow Terminals 1-2-3	a	05 26	05 41	05 56		06 11	06 26	06 41		06 56	07 11	07 26		07 41	07 56	08 11		08 27	08 41	08 56		09 11	09 25	09 40	09 55
Heathrow Terminal 4	a	*05 40*		*06 06*			*06 35*	*06 53*		*07 06*		*07 35*		*07 53*	*08 06*	*08 35*		*08 40*	*08 53*	*09 06*		*09 40*	*09 48*	*10 10*	*10 18*
Heathrow Terminal 5	a	05 32	05 47	06 03		06 17	06 32	06 50		07 03	07 17	07 32		07 50	08 03	08 17		08 33	08 50	09 03		09 17	09 31	09 46	10 01

		HX 1		HX 1	HX 1	HX 1		HX 1	HX 1	HX 1		HX 1	HX 1	HX 1		HX 1	HX 1	HX 1		HX 1	HX 1	HX 1		HX 1	HX 1
London Paddington 15	d	09 55		10 10	10 25	10 40		10 55	11 10	11 25		11 40	11 55	12 10		12 25	12 40	12 55		13 10	13 25	13 40		13 55	14 10
Heathrow Terminals 1-2-3	a	10 10		10 25	10 40	10 55		11 10	11 25	11 40		11 55	12 10	12 25		12 40	12 55	13 10		13 25	13 40	13 55		14 10	14 25
Heathrow Terminal 4	a	*10 40*		*10 48*	*11 10*	*11 18*		*11 40*	*11 48*	*12 10*		*12 18*	*12 40*	*12 48*		*13 10*	*13 18*	*13 40*		*13 48*	*14 10*	*14 18*		*14 40*	*14 48*
Heathrow Terminal 5	a	10 16		10 31	10 46	11 01		11 16	11 31	11 46		12 01	12 16	12 31		12 46	13 01	13 16		13 31	13 46	14 01		14 16	14 31

For general notes see front of timetable
For details of catering facilities see
Directory of Train Operators

Table 118

London → Heathrow Airport

Sundays
until 7 September

Network Diagram - see first page of Table 116

		HX 1	HX 1	HX 1		HX 1	HX 1	HX 1		HX 1	HX 1	HX 1		HX 1	HX 1	HX 1		HX 1	HX 1	HX 1		HX 1	HX 1	HX 1	HX 1
London Paddington 15	⊖ d	14 25	14 40	14 55	.....	15 10	15 25	15 40	.....	15 55	16 10	16 25	.....	16 40	16 55	17 10	.....	17 25	17 40	17 55	.....	18 10	18 25	18 40	18 55
Heathrow Terminals 1-2-3	a	14 40	14 55	15 10	.	15 25	15 40	15 55	.	16 10	16 25	16 40	.	16 55	17 10	17 25	.	17 40	17 55	18 10	.	18 25	18 40	18 55	19 10
Heathrow Terminal 4	a	*15 10*	*15 18*	*15 40*	.....	*15 48*	*16 10*	*16 18*	.....	*16 40*	*16 48*	*17 10*	.....	*17 18*	*17 40*	*17 48*	.....	*18 10*	*18 18*	*18 40*	.....	*18 48*	*19 10*	*19 18*	*19 40*
Heathrow Terminal 5	a	14 46	15 01	15 16	.	15 31	15 46	16 01	.	16 16	16 31	16 46	.	17 01	17 16	17 31	.	17 46	18 01	18 16	.	18 31	18 46	19 01	19 16

		HX 1		HX 1	HX 1	HX 1		HX 1	HX 1	HX 1		HX 1	HX 1	HX 1		HX 1	HX 1	HX 1	HX 1	HX 1	HX 1	HX 1	HX 1		
London Paddington 15	⊖ d	19 10	.....	19 25	19 40	19 55	.....	20 10	20 25	20 40	.....	20 55	21 10	21 25	.....	21 40	21 55	22 10	22 25	22 40	22 55	23 10	23 25	.....	.....
Heathrow Terminals 1-2-3	a	19 25	.	19 40	19 55	20 10	.	20 25	20 40	20 55	.	21 10	21 25	21 40	.	21 56	22 11	22 26	22 41	22 56	23 11	23 26	23 41	.	.
Heathrow Terminal 4	a	*19 48*	.....	*20 10*	*20 18*	*20 40*	.....	*20 48*	*21 10*	*21 18*	.....	*21 40*	.....	*21 53*	.....	*22 06*	.....	*22 35*	*22 53*	*23 06*	.....	*23 35*	*23 53*	.....	.....
Heathrow Terminal 5	a	19 31	.	19 46	20 01	20 16	.	20 31	20 46	21 01	.	21 16	21 31	21 46	.	22 03	22 17	22 32	22 50	23 03	23 17	23 32	23 50	.	.

Sundays
from 14 September

		HX 1	HX 1	HX 1		HX 1	HX 1	HX 1		HX 1	HX 1	HX 1		HX 1	HX 1	HX 1		HX 1	HX 1	HX 1		HX 1	HX 1	HX 1	HX 1
London Paddington 15	⊖ d	05 10	05 25	05 40	.....	05 55	06 10	06 25	.....	06 40	06 55	07 10	.....	07 25	07 40	07 55	.....	08 10	08 25	08 40	.....	08 55	09 10	09 25	09 40
Heathrow Terminals 1-2-3	a	05 26	05 41	05 56	.	06 11	06 26	06 41	.	06 56	07 11	07 26	.	07 41	07 56	08 11	.	08 27	08 41	08 56	.	09 11	09 26	09 41	09 55
Heathrow Terminal 4	a	*05 40*	*05 51*	*06 06*	.....	.....	*06 35*	*06 53*	.....	*07 06*	.....	*07 35*	.....	*07 53*	.....	*08 35*	.....	*08 40*	*08 53*	*09 06*	.....	.....	*09 35*	.....	*10 06*
Heathrow Terminal 5	a	05 32	05 47	06 03	.	06 17	06 32	06 50	.	07 03	07 17	07 32	.	07 50	08 03	08 17	.	08 33	08 50	09 03	.	09 17	09 32	09 50	10 03

		HX 1		HX 1	HX 1	HX 1		HX 1	HX 1	HX 1		HX 1	HX 1	HX 1		HX 1	HX 1	HX 1		HX 1	HX 1	HX 1		HX 1	HX 1
London Paddington 15	⊖ d	09 55	.....	10 10	10 25	10 40	.....	10 55	11 10	11 25	.....	11 40	11 55	12 10	.....	12 25	12 40	12 55	.....	13 10	13 25	13 40	.....	13 55	14 10
Heathrow Terminals 1-2-3	a	10 11	.	10 26	10 41	10 56	.	11 11	11 26	11 41	.	11 56	12 11	12 26	.	12 41	12 56	13 11	.	13 26	13 41	13 56	.	14 11	14 26
Heathrow Terminal 4	a	.....	.....	*10 35*	.....	*11 06*	.....	.....	*11 35*	.....	.....	*12 06*	.....	*12 35*	.....	.....	*13 06*	.....	.....	*13 35*	.....	*14 06*	.....	.....	*14 35*
Heathrow Terminal 5	a	10 17	.	10 32	10 50	11 03	.	11 17	11 32	11 50	.	12 03	12 17	12 32	.	12 50	13 03	13 17	.	13 32	13 50	14 03	.	14 17	14 32

		HX 1	HX 1	HX 1		HX 1	HX 1	HX 1		HX 1	HX 1	HX 1		HX 1	HX 1	HX 1		HX 1	HX 1	HX 1		HX 1	HX 1	HX 1	HX 1
London Paddington 15	⊖ d	14 25	14 40	14 55	.....	15 10	15 25	15 40	.....	15 55	16 10	16 25	.....	16 40	16 55	17 10	.....	17 25	17 40	17 55	.....	18 10	18 25	18 40	18 55
Heathrow Terminals 1-2-3	a	14 41	14 56	15 11	.	15 26	15 41	15 56	.	16 11	16 26	16 41	.	16 56	17 11	17 26	.	17 41	17 56	18 11	.	18 26	18 41	18 56	19 11
Heathrow Terminal 4	a	.....	*15 06*	.....	.....	*15 35*	.....	*16 06*	.....	.....	*16 35*	.....	.....	*17 06*	.....	*17 35*	.....	.....	*17 48*	.....	.....	*18 35*	.....	*19 06*	.....
Heathrow Terminal 5	a	14 50	15 03	15 17	.	15 32	15 50	16 03	.	16 17	16 32	16 50	.	17 03	17 17	17 32	.	17 50	18 03	18 17	.	18 32	18 50	19 03	19 17

		HX 1		HX 1	HX 1	HX 1		HX 1	HX 1	HX 1		HX 1	HX 1	HX 1		HX 1	HX 1	HX 1	HX 1	HX 1	HX 1	HX 1	HX 1		
London Paddington 15	⊖ d	19 10	.....	19 25	19 40	19 55	.....	20 10	20 25	20 40	.....	20 55	21 10	21 25	.....	21 40	21 55	22 10	22 25	22 40	22 55	23 10	23 25	.....	.....
Heathrow Terminals 1-2-3	a	19 26	.	19 41	19 56	20 11	.	20 26	20 41	20 56	.	21 11	21 26	21 41	.	21 56	22 11	22 26	22 41	22 56	23 11	23 26	23 41	.	.
Heathrow Terminal 4	a	*19 35*	.....	.....	*19 48*	.....	.....	*20 35*	.....	*21 06*	.....	.....	*21 35*	*21 53*	.....	*22 06*	.....	*22 35*	*22 53*	*23 06*	.....	*23 35*	*23 53*	.	.
Heathrow Terminal 5	a	19 32	.	19 50	20 03	20 17	.	20 32	20 50	21 03	.	21 17	21 32	21 50	.	22 03	22 17	22 32	22 50	23 03	23 17	23 32	23 50	.	.

For general notes see front of timetable
For details of catering facilities see
Directory of Train Operators

Heathrow Airport → London

Network Diagram - see first page of Table 116

Mondays to Fridays

Miles	Station		HX 1	HX 1	HX 1	HX 1		HX 1	HX 1	HX 1	HX 1		HX 1	HX 1	HX 1	HX 1		HX 1	HX 1	HX 1	HX 1		HX 1	HX 1	HX 1
—	Heathrow Terminal 5	d	05 07	05 27	05 42	05 57	.....	06 12	06 27	06 42	06 57	.....	07 12	07 27	07 42	07 57	.....	08 12	08 27	08 42	08 57	.....	09 12	09 27	09 42
0	Heathrow Terminal 4	d	.	*05 23*	.	*05 51*	.	.	*06 21*	.	*06 51*	.	.	*07 21*	.	*07 51*	.	.	*08 21*	.	*08 51*	.	.	*09 21*	.
1¾	Heathrow Terminals 1-2-3	d	05 12	05 33	05 48	06 03	.....	06 18	06 33	06 48	07 03	.....	07 18	07 33	07 48	08 03	.....	08 18	08 33	08 48	09 03	.....	09 18	09 33	09 48
16½	London Paddington 15	⊖ a	05 28	05 49	06 04	06 19	.	06 34	06 49	07 04	07 19	.	07 34	07 49	08 04	08 19	.	08 34	08 49	09 04	09 19	.	09 34	09 49	10 04

Station		HX 1	HX 1	HX 1		HX 1	HX 1	HX 1	HX 1		HX 1	HX 1	HX 1	HX 1		HX 1	HX 1	HX 1	HX 1		HX 1	HX 1	HX 1	HX 1	HX 1
Heathrow Terminal 5	d	09 57	10 12	10 27	.....	10 42	10 57	11 12	11 27	.....	11 42	11 57	12 12	12 27	.....	12 42	12 57	13 12	13 27	.....	13 42	13 57	14 12	14 27	14 42
Heathrow Terminal 4	d	*09 51*	.	*10 21*	.	.	*10 51*	.	*11 21*	.	.	*11 51*	.	*12 21*	.	.	*12 51*	.	*13 21*	.	.	*13 51*	.	*14 21*	.
Heathrow Terminals 1-2-3	d	10 03	10 18	10 33	.....	10 48	11 03	11 18	11 33	.....	11 48	12 03	12 18	12 33	.....	12 48	13 03	13 18	13 33	.....	13 48	14 03	14 18	14 33	14 48
London Paddington 15	⊖ a	10 19	10 34	10 49	.	11 04	11 19	11 34	11 49	.	12 04	12 19	12 34	12 49	.	13 04	13 19	13 34	13 49	.	14 04	14 19	14 34	14 49	15 04

Station		HX 1		HX 1	HX 1	HX 1	HX 1		HX 1	HX 1	HX 1	HX 1		HX 1	HX 1	HX 1	HX 1		HX 1	HX 1	HX 1	HX 1		HX 1	HX 1
Heathrow Terminal 5	d	14 57	.....	15 12	15 27	15 42	15 57	.....	16 12	16 27	16 42	16 57	.....	17 12	17 27	17 42	17 57	.....	18 12	18 27	18 42	18 57	.....	19 12	19 27
Heathrow Terminal 4	d	*14 51*	.	.	*15 21*	.	*15 51*	.	.	*16 21*	.	*16 51*	.	.	*17 21*	.	*17 51*	.	.	*18 21*	.	*18 51*	.	.	*19 21*
Heathrow Terminals 1-2-3	d	15 03	.....	15 18	15 33	15 48	16 03	.....	16 18	16 33	16 48	17 03	.....	17 18	17 33	17 48	18 03	.....	18 18	18 33	18 48	19 03	.....	19 18	19 33
London Paddington 15	⊖ a	15 19	.	15 34	15 49	16 04	16 19	.	16 34	16 49	17 04	17 19	.	17 34	17 49	18 04	18 18	.	18 34	18 49	19 04	19 19	.	19 34	19 49

Station		HX 1	HX 1	HX 1	HX 1		HX 1	HX 1	HX 1	HX 1		HX 1	HX 1	HX 1	HX 1		HX 1	HX 1	HX 1	HX 1		HX 1	HX 1		
Heathrow Terminal 5	d	19 42	19 57	20 12	20 27	.....	20 42	20 57	21 12	21 27	.....	21 42	21 57	22 12	22 27	.....	22 42	22 57	23 12	23 27	.....	23 42	23 53	.....	.....
Heathrow Terminal 4	d	.	*19 51*	.	*20 21*	.	.	*20 51*	.	*21 21*	.	.	*21 51*	.	*22 21*	.	.	*22 51*	.	*23 21*	.	.	.	.	.
Heathrow Terminals 1-2-3	d	19 48	20 03	20 18	20 33	.....	20 48	21 03	21 18	21 33	.....	21 48	22 03	22 18	22 33	.....	22 48	23 03	23 18	23 33	.....	23 48	23 57	.....	.....
London Paddington 15	⊖ a	20 04	20 19	20 34	20 49	.	21 04	21 19	21 34	21 49	.	22 04	22 19	22 34	22 49	.	23 04	23 19	23 34	23 49	.	00 04	00 18	.	.

Saturdays

Station		HX 1	HX 1	HX 1	HX 1		HX 1	HX 1	HX 1	HX 1		HX 1	HX 1	HX 1	HX 1		HX 1	HX 1	HX 1	HX 1		HX 1	HX 1	HX 1	HX 1
Heathrow Terminal 5	d	05 07	05 27	05 42	05 57	.....	06 12	06 27	06 42	06 57	.....	07 12	07 27	07 42	07 57	.....	08 12	08 27	08 42	08 57	.....	09 12	09 27	09 42	09 57
Heathrow Terminal 4	d	.	*05 23*	.	*05 51*	.	.	*06 21*	.	*06 51*	.	.	*07 21*	.	*07 51*	.	.	*08 21*	.	*08 51*	.	.	*09 21*	.	*09 51*
Heathrow Terminals 1-2-3	d	05 12	05 33	05 48	06 03	.....	06 18	06 33	06 48	07 03	.....	07 18	07 33	07 48	08 03	.....	08 18	08 33	08 48	09 03	.....	09 18	09 33	09 48	10 03
London Paddington 15	⊖ a	05 28	05 49	06 04	06 19	.	06 34	06 49	07 04	07 19	.	07 34	07 49	08 04	08 19	.	08 34	08 49	09 04	09 19	.	09 34	09 49	10 04	10 19

Station		HX 1	HX 1		HX 1	HX 1	HX 1	HX 1		HX 1	HX 1	HX 1	HX 1		HX 1	HX 1	HX 1	HX 1		HX 1	HX 1	HX 1	HX 1		HX 1
Heathrow Terminal 5	d	10 12	10 27	.....	10 42	10 57	11 12	11 27	.....	11 42	11 57	12 12	12 27	.....	12 42	12 57	13 12	13 27	.....	13 42	13 57	14 12	14 27	.....	14 42
Heathrow Terminal 4	d	.	*10 21*	.	.	*10 51*	.	*11 21*	.	.	*11 51*	.	*12 21*	.	.	*12 51*	.	*13 21*	.	.	*13 51*	.	*14 21*	.	.
Heathrow Terminals 1-2-3	d	10 18	10 33	.....	10 48	11 03	11 18	11 33	.....	11 48	12 03	12 18	12 33	.....	12 48	13 03	13 18	13 33	.....	13 48	14 03	14 18	14 33	.....	14 48
London Paddington 15	⊖ a	10 34	10 49	.	11 04	11 19	11 34	11 49	.	12 04	12 19	12 34	12 49	.	13 04	13 19	13 34	13 49	.	14 04	14 19	14 34	14 49	.	15 04

Station		HX 1	HX 1	HX 1	HX 1		HX 1	HX 1	HX 1	HX 1		HX 1	HX 1	HX 1	HX 1		HX 1	HX 1	HX 1	HX 1		HX 1	HX 1	HX 1	HX 1
Heathrow Terminal 5	d	14 57	15 12	15 27	15 42	.....	15 57	16 12	16 27	16 42	.....	16 57	17 12	17 27	17 42	.....	17 57	18 12	18 27	18 42	.....	18 57	19 12	19 27	19 42
Heathrow Terminal 4	d	*14 51*	.	*15 21*	.	.	*15 51*	.	*16 21*	.	.	*16 51*	.	*17 21*	.	.	*17 51*	.	*18 21*	.	.	*18 51*	.	*19 21*	.
Heathrow Terminals 1-2-3	d	15 03	15 18	15 33	15 48	.....	16 03	16 18	16 33	16 48	.....	17 03	17 18	17 33	17 48	.....	18 03	18 18	18 33	18 48	.....	19 03	19 18	19 33	19 48
London Paddington 15	⊖ a	15 19	15 34	15 49	16 04	.	16 19	16 34	16 49	17 04	.	17 19	17 34	17 49	18 04	.	18 19	18 34	18 49	19 04	.	19 19	19 34	19 49	20 04

Station		HX 1	HX 1		HX 1	HX 1	HX 1	HX 1		HX 1	HX 1	HX 1	HX 1		HX 1	HX 1	HX 1	HX 1		HX 1	HX 1	HX 1			
Heathrow Terminal 5	d	19 57	20 12	.....	20 27	20 42	20 57	21 12	.....	21 27	21 42	21 57	22 12	.....	22 27	22 42	22 57	23 12	.....	23 27	.....	23 42	.....	.....	.....
Heathrow Terminal 4	d	*19 51*	.	.	*20 21*	.	*20 51*	.	.	*21 21*	.	*21 51*	.	.	*22 21*	.	*22 51*	.	.	*23 21*	23 40	.	.	.	.
Heathrow Terminals 1-2-3	d	20 03	20 18	.....	20 33	20 48	21 03	21 18	.....	21 33	21 48	22 03	22 18	.....	22 33	22 48	23 03	23 18	.....	23 33	23 48	23 48	.....	.....	.....
London Paddington 15	⊖ a	20 19	20 34	.	20 49	21 04	21 19	21 34	.	21 49	22 04	22 19	22 34	.	22 49	23 04	23 19	23 34	.	23 49	00 04	00 04	.	.	.

Sundays

until 7 September

Station		HX 1	HX 1	HX 1	HX 1		HX 1	HX 1	HX 1	HX 1		HX 1	HX 1	HX 1	HX 1		HX 1	HX 1	HX 1	HX 1		HX 1	HX 1	HX 1	HX 1
Heathrow Terminal 5	d	05 03	05 18	05 33	05 48	.....	06 03	06 18	06 33	06 48	.....	07 03	07 18	07 33	07 48	.....	08 03	08 18	08 33	08 48	.....	09 00	09 13	09 27	09 42
Heathrow Terminal 4	d	.	.	.	.	.	.	*06 07*	.	.	.	.	*07 07*	.	.	.	.	*08 07*	.	.	.	.	.	*09 21*	.
Heathrow Terminals 1-2-3	d	05 08	05 23	05 38	05 53	.....	06 08	06 23	06 38	06 53	.....	07 08	07 23	07 38	07 53	.....	08 08	08 23	08 38	08 53	.....	09 06	09 19	09 33	09 48
London Paddington 15	⊖ a	05 24	05 39	05 54	06 09	.	06 24	06 39	06 54	07 09	.	07 24	07 39	07 54	08 09	.	08 24	08 39	08 54	09 09	.	09 22	09 35	09 49	10 04

Station		HX 1	HX 1		HX 1	HX 1	HX 1	HX 1		HX 1	HX 1	HX 1	HX 1		HX 1	HX 1	HX 1	HX 1		HX 1	HX 1	HX 1	HX 1		HX 1
Heathrow Terminal 5	d	09 57	10 12	.....	10 27	10 42	10 57	11 12	.....	11 27	11 42	11 57	12 12	.....	12 27	12 42	12 57	13 12	.....	13 27	13 42	13 57	14 12	.....	14 27
Heathrow Terminal 4	d	*09 51*	.	.	*10 21*	.	*10 51*	.	.	*11 21*	.	*11 51*	.	.	*12 21*	.	*12 51*	.	.	*13 21*	.	*13 51*	.	.	*14 21*
Heathrow Terminals 1-2-3	d	10 03	10 18	.....	10 33	10 48	11 03	11 18	.....	11 33	11 48	12 03	12 18	.....	12 33	12 48	13 03	13 18	.....	13 33	13 48	14 03	14 18	.....	14 33
London Paddington 15	⊖ a	10 19	10 34	.	10 49	11 04	11 19	11 34	.	11 49	12 04	12 19	12 34	.	12 49	13 04	13 19	13 34	.	13 49	14 04	14 19	14 34	.	14 49

For general notes see front of timetable
For details of catering facilities see Directory of Train Operators

Table 118

Sundays

until 7 September

Heathrow Airport → London

Network Diagram - see first page of Table 116

		HX 1	HX 1	HX 1	HX 1		HX 1	HX 1	HX 1	HX 1		HX 1	HX 1	HX 1	HX 1		HX 1	HX 1	HX 1	HX 1		HX 1	HX 1	HX 1	HX 1
Heathrow Terminal 5	✈ d	14 42	14 57	15 12	15 27		15 42	15 57	16 12	16 27		16 42	16 57	17 12	17 27		17 42	17 57	18 12	18 27		18 42	18 57	19 12	19 27
Heathrow Terminal 4	✈ d	.	*14 51*	.	*15 21*		.	*15 51*	.	*16 21*		.	*16 51*	.	*17 21*		.	*17 51*	.	*18 21*		.	*18 51*	.	*19 21*
Heathrow Terminals 1-2-3	✈ d	14 48	15 03	15 18	15 33		15 48	16 03	16 18	16 33		16 48	17 03	17 18	17 33		17 48	18 03	18 18	18 33		18 48	19 03	19 18	19 33
London Paddington 15	⊖ a	15 04	15 19	15 34	15 49		16 04	16 19	16 34	16 49		17 04	17 19	17 34	17 49		18 04	18 19	18 34	18 49		19 04	19 19	19 34	19 48

		HX 1	HX 1		HX 1	HX 1	HX 1	HX 1		HX 1	HX 1	HX 1	HX 1		HX 1	HX 1	HX 1	HX 1		HX 1	HX 1	HX 1			
Heathrow Terminal 5	✈ d	19 42	19 57		20 12	20 27	20 42	20 57		21 12	21 27	21 48	22 03		22 18	22 33	22 48	23 03		23 18	23 33	23 48			
Heathrow Terminal 4	✈ d	.	*19 51*		.	*20 21*	.	*20 51*		.	*21 21*	.	.		*22 07*	.	.	.		*23 07*	.	.			
Heathrow Terminals 1-2-3	✈ d	19 48	20 03		20 18	20 33	20 48	21 03		21 18	21 33	21 53	22 08		22 23	22 38	22 53	23 08		23 23	23 38	23 53			
London Paddington 15	⊖ a	20 04	20 19		20 34	20 49	21 04	21 19		21 34	21 49	22 09	22 24		22 40	22 56	23 09	23 24		23 39	23 57	00 09			

Sundays

from 14 September

		HX 1	HX 1	HX 1	HX 1		HX 1	HX 1	HX 1	HX 1		HX 1	HX 1	HX 1	HX 1		HX 1	HX 1	HX 1	HX 1		HX 1	HX 1	HX 1	HX 1
Heathrow Terminal 5	✈ d	05 03	05 18	05 33	05 48		06 03	06 18	06 33	06 48		07 03	07 18	07 33	07 48		08 03	08 18	08 33	08 48		09 03	09 18	09 33	09 48
Heathrow Terminal 4	✈ d	.	.	.	.		.	*06 07*	.	.		.	*07 07*	.	.		.	*08 07*	.	.		.	*09 07*	.	.
Heathrow Terminals 1-2-3	✈ d	05 08	05 23	05 38	05 53		06 08	06 23	06 38	06 53		07 08	07 23	07 38	07 53		08 08	08 23	08 38	08 53		09 08	09 23	09 38	09 53
London Paddington 15	⊖ a	05 24	05 39	05 54	06 09		06 24	06 39	06 54	07 09		07 24	07 39	07 54	08 09		08 24	08 39	08 54	09 09		09 24	09 41	09 54	10 09

		HX 1	HX 1		HX 1	HX 1	HX 1	HX 1		HX 1	HX 1	HX 1	HX 1		HX 1	HX 1	HX 1	HX 1		HX 1	HX 1	HX 1	HX 1		HX 1
Heathrow Terminal 5	✈ d	10 03	10 18		10 33	10 48	11 03	11 18		11 33	11 48	12 03	12 18		12 33	12 48	13 03	13 18		13 33	13 48	14 03	14 18		14 33
Heathrow Terminal 4	✈ d	.	*10 07*		.	.	.	*11 07*		.	.	.	*12 07*		.	.	.	*13 07*		.	.	.	*14 07*		.
Heathrow Terminals 1-2-3	✈ d	10 08	10 23		10 38	10 53	11 08	11 23		11 38	11 53	12 08	12 23		12 38	12 53	13 08	13 23		13 38	13 53	14 08	14 23		14 38
London Paddington 15	⊖ a	10 24	10 39		10 54	11 09	11 25	11 39		11 54	12 09	12 24	12 39		12 54	13 09	13 24	13 39		13 54	14 09	14 24	14 39		14 54

		HX 1	HX 1	HX 1	HX 1		HX 1	HX 1	HX 1	HX 1		HX 1	HX 1	HX 1	HX 1		HX 1	HX 1	HX 1	HX 1		HX 1	HX 1	HX 1	HX 1
Heathrow Terminal 5	✈ d	14 48	15 03	15 18	15 33		15 48	16 03	16 18	16 33		16 48	17 03	17 18	17 33		17 48	18 03	18 18	18 33		18 48	19 03	19 18	19 33
Heathrow Terminal 4	✈ d	.	.	*15 07*	.		.	.	*16 07*	.		.	.	*17 07*	.		.	.	*18 07*	.		.	.	*19 07*	.
Heathrow Terminals 1-2-3	✈ d	14 53	15 08	15 23	15 38		15 53	16 08	16 23	16 38		16 53	17 08	17 23	17 38		17 53	18 08	18 23	18 38		18 53	19 08	19 23	19 38
London Paddington 15	⊖ a	15 09	15 24	15 39	15 54		16 09	16 24	16 39	16 54		17 09	17 24	17 39	17 54		18 09	18 24	18 40	18 54		19 09	19 24	19 41	19 54

		HX 1	HX 1		HX 1	HX 1	HX 1	HX 1		HX 1	HX 1	HX 1	HX 1		HX 1	HX 1	HX 1	HX 1		HX 1	HX 1	HX 1			
Heathrow Terminal 5	✈ d	19 48	20 03		20 18	20 33	20 48	21 03		21 18	21 33	21 48	22 03		22 18	22 33	22 48	23 03		23 18	23 33	23 48			
Heathrow Terminal 4	✈ d	.	.		*20 07*	.	.	.		*21 07*	.	.	.		*22 07*	.	.	.		*23 07*	.	.			
Heathrow Terminals 1-2-3	✈ d	19 53	20 08		20 23	20 38	20 53	21 08		21 23	21 38	21 53	22 08		22 23	22 38	22 53	23 08		23 23	23 38	23 53			
London Paddington 15	⊖ a	20 09	20 24		20 41	20 54	21 09	21 24		21 41	21 54	22 09	22 24		22 39	22 54	23 09	23 24		23 39	23 54	00 09			

For general notes see front of timetable
For details of catering facilities see
Directory of Train Operators

Table 119

Mondays to Fridays

Slough → Windsor & Eton

Network Diagram - see first page of Table 116

Miles			GW 1	GW 1	GW 1	GW 1	GW 1	GW 1	GW 1	GW 1	GW 1	GW 1	GW 1	GW 1	GW 1	GW 1	GW 1	GW 1		GW 1	GW 1	GW 1	GW 1	GW 1	GW 1	GW 1
—	London Paddington 15	⊖ d	03 34	.....	05 44	06 07	06 33	.....	06 45	07 21	07 30	07 45	08 21	08 51	09 00	09 21	09 51	10 21	.....	10 51	11 21	11 51	12 21	12 51	13 21	13 51
—	Reading 7	d	04 40	05 16	05 57	06 05	06 32	06 45	07 02	07 10	07 41	07 56	08 12	08 31	09 04	09 19	10 04	10 25	.	10 56	11 19	11 56	12 27	12 56	13 27	13 55
0	**Slough 3**	d	**05 38**	**05 58**	**06 18**	**06 37**	**06 55**	**07 13**	**07 31**	**07 55**	**08 13**	**08 31**	**08 55**	**09 13**	**09 34**	**09 53**	**10 20**	**10 50**	.....	**11 20**	**11 50**	**12 20**	**12 50**	**13 20**	**13 50**	**14 20**
2¾	**Windsor & Eton Central**	a	**05 44**	**06 04**	**06 24**	**06 43**	**07 01**	**07 19**	**07 37**	**08 01**	**08 19**	**08 37**	**09 01**	**09 19**	**09 40**	**09 59**	**10 26**	**10 56**	.	**11 26**	**11 56**	**12 26**	**12 56**	**13 26**	**13 56**	**14 26**

		GW 1	GW 1	GW 1	GW 1	GW 1	GW 1	GW 1	GW 1	GW 1	GW 1	GW 1	GW 1	GW 1	GW 1	GW 1	GW 1	GW 1	GW 1	GW 1	GW 1	GW 1	GW 1	GW 1		
London Paddington 15	⊖ d	14 15	14 51	.....	15 51	16 21	16 30	16 44	17 14	17 17	17 44	18 14	18 17	18 51	19 21	19 51	20 00	20 20	20 51	21 00	21 21	21 48	.....	.....	.....	.....
Reading 7	d	14 27	14 56	15 27	15 56	16 04	16 34	16 56	17 18	17 34	17 44	18 14	18 34	18 56	19 04	19 34	20 04	20 19	20 34	20 56	21 27	21 34	.	22 50	.	.
Slough 3	d	**14 50**	**15 20**	**15 50**	**16 21**	**16 42**	**17 00**	**17 21**	**17 40**	**17 58**	**18 16**	**18 40**	**18 58**	**19 16**	**19 42**	**20 10**	**20 33**	**20 51**	**21 10**	**21 33**	**21 57**	**22 20**	**22 50**	**23 21**	.....	.....
Windsor & Eton Central	a	**14 56**	**15 26**	**15 56**	**16 27**	**16 48**	**17 06**	**17 27**	**17 46**	**18 04**	**18 22**	**18 46**	**19 04**	**19 22**	**19 48**	**20 16**	**20 39**	**20 57**	**21 16**	**21 39**	**22 03**	**22 26**	**22 56**	**23 27**	.	.

Saturdays

		GW 1	GW 1	GW 1		GW 1	GW 1	GW 1		GW 1	GW 1	GW 1		GW 1	GW 1	GW 1		GW 1	GW 1	GW 1		GW 1	GW 1	GW 1		GW 1
London Paddington 15	⊖ d	05 45	06 21	06 51	.....	07 21	07 51	08 21	.....	08 51	09 21	09 51	.....	10 21	10 51	11 21	.....	11 51	12 21	12 45	.....	13 21	13 51	14 21	.....	14 51
Reading 7	d	05 49	06 19	06 58	.	07 26	07 49	08 27	.	08 57	09 27	09 56	.	10 23	10 55	11 26	.	11 56	12 29	12 56	.	13 28	13 49	14 27	.	14 58
Slough 3	d	**06 20**	**06 50**	**07 20**	.....	**07 50**	**08 20**	**08 50**	.....	**09 20**	**09 50**	**10 20**	.....	**10 50**	**11 20**	**11 50**	.....	**12 20**	**12 50**	**13 20**	.....	**13 50**	**14 20**	**14 50**	.....	**15 20**
Windsor & Eton Central	a	**06 26**	**06 56**	**07 26**	.	**07 56**	**08 26**	**08 56**	.	**09 26**	**09 56**	**10 26**	.	**10 56**	**11 26**	**11 56**	.	**12 26**	**12 56**	**13 26**	.	**13 56**	**14 26**	**14 56**	.	**15 26**

		GW 1	GW 1	GW 1		GW 1	GW 1	GW 1		GW 1	GW 1	GW 1		GW 1	GW 1	GW 1		GW 1	GW 1	GW 1		GW 1	GW 1			
London Paddington 15	⊖ d	15 21	15 51	16 21	.....	16 51	17 21	17 45	.....	18 21	18 51	19 21	.....	19 51	20 21	20 51	.....	21 21	21 51	22 32	.....	23 00	23 33	.....	.....	.....
Reading 7	d	15 27	15 56	16 29	.	16 49	17 25	17 49	.	18 27	18 49	19 27	.	19 49	20 34	20 49	.	21 25	21 55	22 33	.	22 45	23 29	.	.	.
Slough 3	d	**15 50**	**16 20**	**16 50**	.....	**17 20**	**17 50**	**18 20**	.....	**18 50**	**19 20**	**19 50**	.....	**20 20**	**20 50**	**21 20**	.....	**21 50**	**22 20**	**22 55**	.....	**23 21**	**23 55**	.....	.....	.....
Windsor & Eton Central	a	**15 56**	**16 26**	**16 56**	.	**17 26**	**17 56**	**18 26**	.	**18 56**	**19 26**	**19 56**	.	**20 26**	**20 56**	**21 26**	.	**21 56**	**22 26**	**23 01**	.	**23 27**	**00 01**	.	.	.

Sundays

		GW 1	GW 1		GW 1	GW 1		GW 1	GW 1		GW 1	GW 1		GW 1	GW 1		GW 1	GW 1		GW 1	GW 1		GW 1	GW 1		GW 1
London Paddington 15	⊖ d	07 43	08 15	.....	08 44	09 15	.....	09 44	10 15	.....	10 44	11 15	.....	11 44	12 15	.....	12 44	13 15	.....	13 44	14 15	.....	14 44	15 15	.....	15 44
Reading 7	d	07 22	08 22	.	08 48	09 18	.	09 48	10 18	.	10 46	11 18	.	11 52	12 18	.	12 46	.	.	13 46	14 18	.	14 46	15 18	.	15 46
Slough 3	d	**08 22**	**08 52**	.....	**09 22**	**09 52**	.....	**10 22**	**10 52**	.....	**11 22**	**11 52**	.....	**12 22**	**12 52**	.....	**13 22**	**13 52**	.....	**14 22**	**14 52**	.....	**15 22**	**15 52**	.....	**16 22**
Windsor & Eton Central	a	**08 28**	**08 58**	.	**09 28**	**09 58**	.	**10 28**	**10 58**	.	**11 28**	**11 58**	.	**12 28**	**12 58**	.	**13 28**	**13 58**	.	**14 28**	**14 58**	.	**15 28**	**15 58**	.	**16 28**

		GW 1	GW 1		GW 1	GW 1		GW 1	GW 1		GW 1	GW 1		GW 1	GW 1		GW 1	GW 1		GW 1	GW 1				
London Paddington 15	⊖ d	16 15	16 44	.....	17 15	17 44	.....	18 15	18 44	.....	19 15	19 44	.....	20 15	20 44	.....	21 15	21 44	.....	.....	22 44	.....	.....	.....	.....	.....
Reading 7	d	.	16 46	.	17 21	17 46	.	18 21	18 46	.	19 18	19 46	.	.	20 46	.	.	.	.	22 24	.	.	.	.	.	.
Slough 3	d	**16 52**	**17 22**	.....	**17 52**	**18 22**	.....	**18 52**	**19 22**	.....	**19 52**	**20 22**	.....	**20 52**	**21 22**	.....	**21 52**	**22 22**	.....	**22 52**	**23 22**	.....	.....	.....	.....	.....
Windsor & Eton Central	a	**16 58**	**17 28**	.	**17 58**	**18 28**	.	**18 58**	**19 28**	.	**19 58**	**20 28**	.	**20 58**	**21 28**	.	**21 58**	**22 28**	.	**22 58**	**23 28**	.	.	.	.	.

For general notes see front of timetable
For details of catering facilities see Directory of Train Operators

Windsor & Eton → Slough

Network Diagram - see first page of Table 116

Mondays to Fridays

Miles		GW 1	GW 1	GW 1	GW 1	GW 1	GW 1	GW 1	GW 1	GW 1	GW 1	GW 1	GW 1	GW 1	GW 1	GW 1	GW 1		GW 1	GW 1	GW 1	GW 1	GW 1	GW 1	GW 1
0	Windsor & Eton Central d	05 48	06 08	06 28	06 46	07 04	07 22	07 40	08 04	08 22	08 40	09 04	09 22	09 44	10 02	10 30	11 00	.....	11 30	12 00	12 30	13 00	13 30	14 00	14 30
2¾	Slough 3 a	05 54	06 14	06 34	06 52	07 10	07 28	07 46	08 10	08 28	08 46	09 10	09 28	09 50	10 08	10 36	11 06	.	11 36	12 06	12 36	13 06	13 36	14 06	14 36
—	Reading 7 a	06 19	06 39	07 05	07 22	07 42	07 51	08 24	08 42	08 51	09 21	.....	09 51	10 21	10 42	11 12	11 42	.....	12 12	12 42	13 12	13 42	14 12	14 42	15 12
—	London Paddington 15 a	06 30	.	07 01	07 16	07 44	08 12	08 14	08 43	09 11	09 15	10 02	10 10	10 32	10 36	10 59	11 27	.	12 12	12 29	12 59	13 27	13 59	14 29	14 59

	GW 1	GW 1	GW 1	GW 1	GW 1	GW 1	GW 1	GW 1	GW 1	GW 1	GW 1	GW 1	GW 1	GW 1	GW 1	GW 1	GW 1	GW 1	GW 1	GW 1	GW 1	GW 1	GW 1		
Windsor & Eton Central d	15 00	15 30	16 00	16 30	16 51	17 10	17 30	17 49	18 07	18 28	18 49	19 07	19 26	19 53	20 20	20 42	21 00	21 20	21 44	22 08	22 30	23 00	23 32	.....	.....
Slough 3 a	15 06	15 36	16 06	16 36	16 57	17 16	17 36	17 55	18 13	18 34	18 55	19 13	19 32	19 59	20 26	20 48	21 06	21 26	21 50	22 14	22 36	23 06	23 38	.	.
Reading 7 a	15 42	16 15	16 45	17 03	17 43	17 59	18 18	18 25	18 46	19 16	19 21	19 46	19 51	20 21	20 50	21 23	21 42	21 51	.....	22 45	.....	23 40	.....	.....	.....
London Paddington 15 a	15 27	15 59	16 27	16 59	17 27	17 53	.	18 34	.	18 59	19 29	.	19 59	20 29	21 12	.	21 29	21 59	22 32	.	.	23 41	00 15	.	.

Saturdays

	GW 1	GW 1		GW 1	GW 1		GW 1	GW 1		GW 1	GW 1		GW 1	GW 1		GW 1	GW 1		GW 1	GW 1		GW 1	GW 1		GW 1
Windsor & Eton Central d	06 30	07 00	.....	07 30	08 00	.....	08 30	09 00	.....	09 30	10 00	.....	10 30	11 00	.....	11 30	12 00	.....	12 30	13 00	.....	13 30	14 00	.....	14 30
Slough 3 a	06 36	07 06	.	07 36	08 06	.	08 36	09 06	.	09 36	10 06	.	10 36	11 06	.	11 36	12 06	.	12 36	13 06	.	13 36	14 06	.	14 36
Reading 7 a	07 13	07 42	.....	08 12	08 42	.....	09 12	09 42	.....	10 12	10 42	.....	11 12	11 42	.....	12 12	12 42	.....	13 12	13 42	.....	14 12	14 42	.....	15 12
London Paddington 15 a	07 12	07 29	.	07 57	08 42	.	08 58	09 28	.	09 58	10 27	.	11 12	11 26	.	11 59	12 29	.	13 08	13 27	.	14 00	14 42	.	14 59

	GW 1	GW 1		GW 1	GW 1		GW 1	GW 1		GW 1	GW 1		GW 1	GW 1		GW 1	GW 1	GW 1	GW 1	GW 1	GW 1	GW 1	GW 1		
Windsor & Eton Central d	15 00	15 30	.....	16 00	16 30	.....	17 00	17 30	.....	18 00	18 30	.....	19 00	19 30	.....	20 00	20 30	21 00	21 30	22 00	22 30	23 04	23 32	.....	.....
Slough 3 a	15 06	15 36	.	16 06	16 36	.	17 06	17 36	.	18 06	18 36	.	19 06	19 36	.	20 06	20 36	21 06	21 36	22 06	22 36	23 10	23 38	.	.
Reading 7 a	15 42	16 12	.....	16 42	17 12	.....	17 42	18 12	.....	18 42	19 12	.....	19 42	20 12	.....	20 42	21 12	21 43	22 12	22 43	23 06	23 33	00 07	.....	.....
London Paddington 15 a	15 29	15 59	.	16 27	17 06	.	17 42	17 59	.	18 42	18 59	.	19 42	19 58	.	20 42	21 06	21 42	21 58	22 29	23 07	.	00 09	.	.

Sundays

	GW 1	GW 1		GW 1	GW 1		GW 1	GW 1		GW 1	GW 1		GW 1	GW 1		GW 1	GW 1		GW 1	GW 1		GW 1	GW 1		GW 1
Windsor & Eton Central d	08 32	09 02	.....	09 32	10 02	.....	10 32	11 02	.....	11 32	12 02	.....	12 32	13 02	.....	13 32	14 02	.....	14 32	15 02	.....	15 32	16 02	.....	16 32
Slough 3 a	08 38	09 08	.	09 38	10 08	.	10 38	11 08	.	11 38	12 08	.	12 38	13 08	.	13 38	14 08	.	14 38	15 08	.	15 38	16 08	.	16 38
Reading 7 a	.....	09 39	.....	10 11	.....	.....	.....	.....	.....	.....	.....	.....	.....	.....	.....	.....	.....	.....	.....	.....	.....	.....	.....	.....	17 10
London Paddington 15 a	.	.	.	.	.	.	.	.	.	.	.	.	.	.	.	.	.	.	.	.	.	.	.	.	.

	GW 1	GW 1		GW 1	GW 1		GW 1	GW 1		GW 1	GW 1		GW 1	GW 1		GW 1	GW 1		GW 1	GW 1					
Windsor & Eton Central d	17 02	17 32	.....	18 02	18 32	.....	19 02	19 32	.....	20 02	20 32	.....	21 02	21 32	.....	22 02	22 32	.....	23 02	23 32	.....	.....	.....	.....	.....
Slough 3 a	17 08	17 38	.	18 08	18 38	.	19 08	19 38	.	20 08	20 38	.	21 08	21 38	.	22 08	22 38	.	23 08	23 38	.	.	.	.	.
Reading 7 a	.....	.....	.....	.....	.....	.....	.....	20 10	.....	.....	.....	.....	22 43	.....	.....	.....	23 10	.....	.....	.....	.....	.....	.....	.....	.....
London Paddington 15 a	.	.	.	.	.	.	.	.	.	.	.	.	.	.	.	.	.	.	.	.	.	.	.	.	.

For general notes see front of timetable
For details of catering facilities see
Directory of Train Operators

Maidenhead → Marlow

Network Diagram - see first page of Table 116

Miles			GW MX 1	GW 1	GW 1	GW 1	GW 1	GW 1	GW 1	GW 1	GW 1	GW 1	GW 1	GW 1	GW 1	GW 1	GW 1	GW 1	GW 1
—	London Paddington 15	⊖ d		03 34			05 44		06b33		06 45		07 30		08b21	08b51	09b51	10b51	11b51
—	Reading 7	d		04 40	05 16		06 15		06 50		07 10		07 56		08 48	09 19	10 04	11 04	12 04
0	**Maidenhead 3**	d	23p45	05 25	05 49		06 32		07 11		07 41		08 13		09 06	09 37	10 35	11 35	12 35
1¼	Furze Platt	d	23p49	05 29	05 53		06 36		07 15		07 45		08 17		09 10	09 41	10 39	11 39	12 39
3	Cookham	d	23p53	05 33							07 49		08 21		09 14	09 45	10 43	11 43	12 43
4½	Bourne End 3	a	23p57	05 37	06 01		06 44		07 23		07 53		08 25		09 18	09 49	10 47	11 47	12 47
—		d	00 01	05 41		06 18		06 49		07 27		07 58		08 28		09 53	10 51	11 51	12 51
7¼	**Marlow**	a	00 08	05 48		06 25		06 56		07 34		08 05		08 35		10 01	10 58	11 58	12 58

		GW 1	GW 1	GW 1	GW 1	GW 1	GW 1	GW 1	GW 1	GW 1	GW 1	GW 1	GW 1	GW 1	GW 1	GW 1	GW 1	GW 1
London Paddington 15	⊖ d	12b51	13b51	14b51	16 00	17 18	17 44		18 18		18 44		19 15		20 00	21 00	21c57	22 59
Reading 7	d	13 04	14 04	15 04	16 19	17 34	17 49		18 19		18 49		19 19		20 19	21 20	22e00	23 15
Maidenhead 3	d	13 35	14 35	15 35	16 41	17 52	18 15		18 47		19 15		19 47		20 42	21 41	22 45	23 45
Furze Platt	d	13 39	14 39	15 39	16 45	17 56	18 20		18 51		19 20		19 51		20 46	21 45	22 49	23 49
Cookham	d	13 43	14 43	15 43	16 49	18 00	18 23		18 55		19 23		19 55		20 50	21 49	22 53	23 53
Bourne End 3	a	13 47	14 47	15 47	16 53	18 04	18 28		18 59		19 28		19 59		20 54	21 53	22 57	23 57
	d	13 51	14 51	15 51	16 57	18 08		18 33		19 02		19 33		20 02	20 58	21 57	23 01	00 01
Marlow	a	13 58	14 58	15 58	17 04	18 15		18 40		19 09		19 40		20 09	21 05	22 04	23 08	00 08

Saturdays

		GW 1	GW 1	GW 1	GW 1	GW 1	GW 1	GW 1	GW 1	GW 1	GW 1	GW 1	GW 1	GW 1	GW 1	GW 1	GW 1	GW 1	GW 1	GW 1
London Paddington 15	⊖ d		05 45	06b51	07b51	08b51	09b51	10b51	11b51	12 45	13b51	14b51	15b51	16b51	17 45	18b51	19b51	20b51	21b51	23b00
Reading 7	d		06 04	07 03	08 04	09 04	10 04	11 04	12 04	13 04	14 04	15 04	16 04	17 04	18 04	19 04	20 04	21 09	22 16	23 16
Maidenhead 3	d	23p45	06 33	07 33	08 33	09 33	10 33	11 33	12 33	13 33	14 33	15 33	16 33	17 33	18 33	19 33	20 33	21 33	22 33	23 37
Furze Platt	d	23p49	06 37	07 37	08 37	09 37	10 37	11 37	12 37	13 37	14 37	15 37	16 37	17 37	18 37	19 37	20 37	21 37	22 37	23 41
Cookham	d	23p53	06 40	07 40	08 40	09 40	10 40	11 40	12 40	13 40	14 40	15 40	16 40	17 40	18 40	19 40	20 40	21 40	22 40	23 44
Bourne End 3	a	23p57	06 44	07 44	08 44	09 44	10 44	11 44	12 44	13 44	14 44	15 44	16 44	17 44	18 44	19 44	20 44	21 44	22 44	23 48
	d	00 01	06 48	07 48	08 48	09 48	10 48	11 48	12 48	13 48	14 48	15 48	16 48	17 48	18 48	19 48	20 48	21 48	22 48	23 52
Marlow	a	00 08	06 57	07 57	08 57	09 57	10 57	11 57	12 57	13 57	14 57	15 57	16 57	17 57	18 57	19 57	20 57	21 57	22 57	00 01

Sundays

		GW 1	GW 1	GW 1	GW 1	GW 1	GW 1	GW 1	GW 1	GW 1	GW 1	GW 1	GW 1
London Paddington 15	⊖ d	09 44	10 44	11 44	12 44	13 44	14 44	15 44	16 44	17 44	18 44	19 44	20 44
Reading 7	d	10 18	11 18	12 18	13 18	14 18	15 18	16 18	17 18	18 18	19 18	20 18	
Maidenhead 3	d	10 34	11 34	12 34	13 34	14 34	15 34	16 34	17 34	18 34	19 34	20 34	21 40
Furze Platt	d	10 38	11 38	12 38	13 38	14 38	15 38	16 38	17 38	18 38	19 38	20 38	21 44
Cookham	d	10 41	11 41	12 41	13 41	14 41	15 41	16 41	17 41	18 41	19 41	20 42	21 48
Bourne End 3	a	10 45	11 45	12 45	13 45	14 45	15 45	16 45	17 45	18 45	19 45	20 45	21 51
	d	10 49	11 49	12 49	13 49	14 49	15 49	16 49	17 49	18 49	19 49	20 49	21 55
Marlow	a	10 56	11 56	12 56	13 56	14 56	15 56	16 56	17 56	18 56	19 56	20 56	22 02

For general notes see front of timetable
For details of catering facilities see Directory of Train Operators

b Change at Slough and Maidenhead
c Fridays dep. 2159
e Fridays dep. 2216

Marlow → Maidenhead

Network Diagram - see first page of Table 116

Miles			GW MX 1	GW 1	GW 1	GW 1	GW 1	GW 1	GW 1	GW 1	GW 1	GW 1	GW 1	GW 1	GW 1	GW 1	GW 1	GW 1	GW 1
0	**Marlow**	d	00 11	06 05		06 39		07 17		07 46		08 16		08 38		10 05	11 05	12 05	13 05
2¾	Bourne End 3	a	00 18	06 12		06 46		07 24		07 53		08 23		08 45		10 12	11 12	12 12	13 12
—		d	00 22		06 15		06 49		07 27		07 56		08 28	08 49	09 21	10 16	11 16	12 16	13 16
4¼	Cookham	d	00 26		06 19		06 53		07 31		08 00		08 32	08 53	09 25	10 20	11 20	12 20	13 20
6	Furze Platt	d	00 30		06 22		06 56		07 34		08 03		08 35	08 57	09 28	10 24	11 24	12 24	13 24
7¼	**Maidenhead 3**	a	00 34		06 27		07 01		07 39		08 08		08 40	09 01	09 33	10 28	11 28	12 28	13 28
—	Reading 7	a	*00 55*		*06 54*		*07 22*		*08 12*		*08 42*		*09 12*	*09 24*	*09 52*	*10 52*	*11 52*	*12 52*	*13 52*
—	London Paddington 15 ⊖	a	*01 57*		*07 08*		*07 27*		*08 15*		*08 43*		*09 16*	*09 28*	*10 32*	*11 12*	*12 12*	*13 12*	*14 12*

		GW 1	GW 1	GW 1	GW 1	GW 1	GW 1	GW 1	GW 1	GW 1	GW 1	GW 1	GW 1	GW 1	GW 1	GW 1	GW 1
Marlow	d	14 05	15 05	16 05	17 07	18 20		18 52		19 20		19 52		20 14	21 08	22 07	23 15
Bourne End 3	a	14 12	15 12	16 12	17 14	18 27		18 59		19 27		19 59		20 21	21 15	22 14	23 22
	d	14 16	15 16	16 16	17 18		18 30		19 02		19 30		20 11	20 25	21 19	22 18	23 26
Cookham	d	14 20	15 20	16 20	17 22		18 34		19 06		19 34		20 15	20 29	21 23	22 22	23 30
Furze Platt	d	14 24	15 24	16 24	17 26		18 37		19 09		19 37		20 18	20 33	21 27	22 26	23 34
Maidenhead 3	a	14 28	15 28	16 28	17 30		18 42		19 13		19 42		20 23	20 37	21 31	22 30	23 38
Reading 7	a	*14 52*	*15 52*	*16 52*	*17 54*				*19 46*		*20 12*		*20 43*	*21 12*	*21 52*		*23 57*
London Paddington 15 ⊖	a	*15 12*	*16 12*	*17 12*	*18 12*		*19e29*		*19e59*		*20e29*		*21 12*	*21e29*	*22 14*	*23 59*	

Saturdays

		GW 1	GW 1	GW 1	GW 1	GW 1	GW 1	GW 1	GW 1	GW 1	GW 1	GW 1	GW 1	GW 1	GW 1	GW 1	GW 1	GW 1	GW 1
Marlow	d	00 11	07 07	08 07	09 07	10 07	11 07	12 07	13 07	14 07	15 07	16 07	17 07	18 07	19 07	20 07	21 07	22 07	23 07
Bourne End 3	a	00 18	07 14	08 14	09 14	10 14	11 14	12 14	13 14	14 14	15 14	16 14	17 14	18 14	19 14	20 14	21 14	22 14	23 14
	d	00 22	07 18	08 18	09 18	10 18	11 18	12 18	13 18	14 18	15 18	16 18	17 18	18 18	19 18	20 18	21 18	22 18	23 18
Cookham	d	00 26	07 22	08 22	09 22	10 22	11 22	12 22	13 22	14 22	15 22	16 22	17 22	18 22	19 22	20 22	21 22	22 22	23 22
Furze Platt	d	00 30	07 25	08 25	09 25	10 25	11 25	12 25	13 25	14 25	15 25	16 25	17 25	18 25	19 25	20 25	21 25	22 25	23 25
Maidenhead 3	a	00 34	07 29	08 29	09 29	10 29	11 29	12 29	13 29	14 29	15 29	16 29	17 29	18 29	19 29	20 29	21 29	22 29	23 29
Reading 7	a	*00 55*	*07 52*	*08 52*	*09 52*	*10 52*	*11 52*	*12 52*	*13 52*	*14 52*	*15 52*	*16 52*	*17 52*	*18 52*	*19 52*	*20 52*	*21 52*	*22 52*	*00 19*
London Paddington 15 ⊖	a	*01 57*	*08 12*	*09 12*	*10 12*	*11 12*	*12 12*	*13 12*	*14 12*	*15 12*	*16 12*	*17 12*		*19 12*	*20 12*	*21e06*	*22 21*	*23 28*	*00e09*

Sundays

		GW 1	GW 1	GW 1	GW 1	GW 1	GW 1	GW 1	GW 1	GW 1	GW 1	GW 1	GW 1	GW 1	GW 1
Marlow	d	00 07	09 59	10 59	11 59	12 59	13 59	14 59	15 59	16 59	17 59	18 59	19 59	20 59	22 05
Bourne End 3	a	00 14	10 06	11 06	12 06	13 06	14 06	15 06	16 06	17 06	18 06	19 06	20 06	21 06	22 12
	d	00 18	10 10	11 10	12 10	13 10	14 10	15 10	16 10	17 10	18 10	19 10	20 10	21 10	22 16
Cookham	d	00 22	10 14	11 14	12 14	13 14	14 14	15 14	16 14	17 14	18 14	19 14	20 14	21 14	22 20
Furze Platt	d	00 25	10 17	11 17	12 17	13 17	14 17	15 17	16 17	17 17	18 17	19 17	20 17	21 17	22 23
Maidenhead 3	a	00 30	10 20	11 20	12 20	13 20	14 20	15 20	16 20	17 20	18 20	19 20	20 20	21 20	22 26
Reading 7	a	*01 03*													*22 43*
London Paddington 15 ⊖	a														

For general notes see front of timetable
For details of catering facilities see Directory of Train Operators

e Change at Maidenhead and Slough

Twyford → Henley-on-Thames

Network Diagram - see first page of Table 116

Mondays to Fridays

Miles			GW 1	GW 1	GW 1	GW 1	GW 1	GW 1	GW 1	GW 1	GW 1	GW 1	GW 1	GW 1	GW 1
—	London Paddington 15 ⊖	d	03b34	05 22	06c07	06c33	07c21	07 45	08 30	09 00	10 00	11 00	12 00	13 00	14 00
—	Reading 7	d	05 33	06 05	06 36	07 10	08 06	08 31	09 04	09 34	10 34	11 34	12 34	13 34	14 34
0	**Twyford 3**	d	05 42	06 22	06 51	07 27	08 14	08 44	09 22	09 52	10 50	11 50	12 50	13 50	14 50
1¾	Wargrave	d	05 46	06 26	06 55	07 31	08 19	08 48	09 26	09 56	10 54	11 54	12 54	13 54	14 54
2¾	Shiplake	d	05 49	06 29	06 58	07 34	08 22	08 51	09 29	09 59	10 57	11 57	12 57	13 57	14 57
4½	**Henley-on-Thames**	a	05 54	06 34	07 03	07 39	08 26	08 56	09 34	10 04	11 02	12 02	13 02	14 02	15 02

		GW 1	GW 1	GW 1	GW 1	GW 1	GW 1	GW 1	GW 1	GW 1	GW 1	GW 1	GW 1
London Paddington 15 ⊖	d	15 00	16 00	17 06	17 14	18 06	18 14	19 06	19c21	20 00	21 00	.	....
Reading 7	d	15 34	16 34	17 19	17 49	18 19	18 49	19 19	19 49	20 34	21 34	.	23 15
Twyford 3	d	15 50	16 50	17 30	17 59	18 30	18 59	19 36	20 08	20 50	21 50	22 52	23 37
Wargrave	d	15 54	16 54	17 34	18 04	18 34	19 04	19 41	20 12	20 54	21 54	22 56	23 41
Shiplake	d	15 57	16 57	17 37	18 07	18 37	19 07	19 44	20 15	20 57	21 57	22 59	23 44
Henley-on-Thames	a	16 02	17 02	17 42	18 12	18 42	19 12	19 49	20 20	21 02	22 02	23 04	23 49

Saturdays

		GW 1	GW 1	GW 1	GW 1	GW 1	GW 1	GW 1	GW 1	GW 1	GW 1	GW 1	GW 1	GW 1	GW 1	GW 1	GW 1	GW 1	GW 1
London Paddington 15 ⊖	d	05 45	07 00	08 00	09 00	10 00	11 00	12 00	13 00	14 00	15 00	16 00	17 00	18 00	19 00	20 00	21 00	22 00	23c00
Reading 7	d	06 34	07 34	08 34	09 35	10 34	11 34	12 34	13 34	14 34	15 34	16 34	17 34	18 34	19 34	20 34	21 33	22 35	23 16
Twyford 3	d	06 50	07 50	08 50	09 50	10 50	11 50	12 50	13 50	14 50	15 50	16 50	17 50	18 50	19 50	20 50	21 50	22 50	23 50
Wargrave	d	06 54	07 54	08 54	09 54	10 54	11 54	12 54	13 54	14 54	15 54	16 54	17 54	18 54	19 54	20 54	21 54	22 54	23 54
Shiplake	d	06 57	07 57	08 57	09 57	10 57	11 57	12 57	13 57	14 57	15 57	16 57	17 57	18 57	19 57	20 57	21 57	22 57	23 57
Henley-on-Thames	a	07 02	08 02	09 02	10 02	11 02	12 02	13 02	14 02	15 02	16 02	17 02	18 02	19 02	20 02	21 02	22 02	23 02	00 02

Sundays

		GW 1	GW 1	GW 1	GW 1	GW 1	GW 1	GW 1	GW 1	GW 1	GW 1	GW 1	GW 1
London Paddington 15 ⊖	d	....	09 44	10 44	11 44	12 44	14 44	15 44	16 44	17 44	18 44	19 44	20 44
Reading 7	d	.	10 18	11 18	12 18	13 18	15 18	16 18	17 18	18 18	19 18	20 18	.
Twyford 3	d	09 38	10 38	11 38	12 38	13 38	15 38	16 38	17 38	18 38	19 38	20 38	21 38
Wargrave	d	09 42	10 42	11 42	12 42	13 42	15 42	16 42	17 42	18 42	19 42	20 42	21 42
Shiplake	d	09 45	10 45	11 45	12 45	13 45	15 45	16 45	17 45	18 45	19 45	20 45	21 45
Henley-on-Thames	a	09 51	10 50	11 50	12 50	13 50	15 50	16 50	17 50	18 50	19 50	20 50	21 50

For general notes see front of timetable
For details of catering facilities see Directory of Train Operators

b Change at Twyford
c Change at Slough and Twyford

Table 121

Mondays to Fridays

Henley-on-Thames → Twyford

Network Diagram - see first page of Table 116

Mondays to Fridays

Miles			GW 1	GW 1	GW 1	GW 1	GW 1	GW 1	GW 1	GW 1	GW 1	GW 1	GW 1	GW 1	GW 1
0	**Henley-on-Thames**	d	06 06	06 37	07 09	07 43	08 29	09 02	09 37	10 08	11 08	12 08	13 08	14 08	15 08
1¾	Shiplake	d	06 10	06 41	07 14	07 48	08 33	09 06	09 41	10 12	11 12	12 12	13 12	14 12	15 12
2¾	Wargrave	d	06 13	06 44	07 17	07 51	08 36	09 09	09 44	10 15	11 15	12 15	13 15	14 15	15 15
4½	**Twyford 3**	a	06 18	06 49	07 22	07 56	08 41	09 14	09 49	10 20	11 20	12 20	13 20	14 20	15 20
—	Reading 7	a	06 40	07 12	07 42	08 12	08 54	09 24	10 15	10 42	11 42	12 42	13 42	14 42	15 42
—	London Paddington 15	⊖ a	07 01	07 27	07 57	08 29	09 28	10b10	10b36	11 12	12 12	13 12	14 12	15 12	16 12

		GW 1	GW 1	GW 1	GW 1	GW 1	GW 1	GW 1	GW 1	GW 1	GW 1	GW 1	GW 1
Henley-on-Thames	d	16 20	17 09	17 45	18 14	18 45	19 16	19 52	20 25	21 07	22 07	23 07	23 52
Shiplake	d	16 24	17 13	17 49	18 18	18 49	19 20	19 56	20 29	21 11	22 11	23 11	23 56
Wargrave	d	16 27	17 16	17 52	18 21	18 52	19 23	19 59	20 32	21 14	22 14	23 14	23 59
Twyford 3	a	16 32	17 21	17 57	18 28	18 57	19 28	20 04	20 37	21 19	22 19	23 19	00 04
Reading 7	a	16 45	17 35	18 15	18 46	.	19 46	20 26	20 52	21 42	22 45	23 40	00 17
London Paddington 15	⊖ a	17b27	18 12	18b59	19b29	19b59	20b29	21 02	21b29	22 14	23b15	01 13	01f13

Saturdays

		GW 1	GW 1	GW 1	GW 1	GW 1	GW 1	GW 1	GW 1	GW 1	GW 1	GW 1	GW 1	GW 1	GW 1	GW 1	GW 1	GW 1	GW 1
Henley-on-Thames	d	23p52	07 08	08 08	09 08	10 08	11 08	12 08	13 08	14 08	15 08	16 08	17 08	18 08	19 08	20 08	21 08	22 08	23 08
Shiplake	d	23p56	07 12	08 12	09 12	10 12	11 12	12 12	13 12	14 12	15 12	16 12	17 12	18 12	19 12	20 12	21 12	22 12	23 12
Wargrave	d	23p59	07 15	08 15	09 15	10 15	11 15	12 15	13 15	14 15	15 15	16 15	17 15	18 15	19 15	20 15	21 15	22 15	23 15
Twyford 3	a	00 04	07 20	08 20	09 20	10 20	11 20	12 20	13 20	14 20	15 20	16 20	17 20	18 20	19 20	20 20	21 20	22 20	23 20
Reading 7	a	00 17	07 42	08 42	09 42	10 42	11 42	12 42	13 42	14 42	15 42	16 42	17 42	18 42	19 42	20 42	21 43	22 43	23b44
London Paddington 15	⊖ a	01b10	08 12	09 12	10 12	11 12	12 12	13 12	14 12	15 12	16 12	17 12	18b12	19 12	20 12	21b06	22 21	23 28	00b09

Sundays

		GW 1	GW 1	GW 1	GW 1	GW 1	GW 1	GW 1	GW 1	GW 1	GW 1	GW 1	GW 1	GW 1	GW 1
Henley-on-Thames	d	00 08	10 03	11 03	12 03	13 03	14 03	15 03	16 03	17 03	18 03	19 03	20 03	21 03	22 03
Shiplake	d	00 12	10 07	11 07	12 07	13 07	14 07	15 07	16 07	17 07	18 07	19 07	20 07	21 07	22 07
Wargrave	d	00 15	10 10	11 10	12 10	13 10	14 10	15 10	16 10	17 10	18 10	19 10	20 10	21 10	22 10
Twyford 3	a	00 20	10 15	11 15	12 15	13 15	14 15	15 15	16 15	17 15	18 15	19 15	20 15	21 15	22 15
Reading 7	a	00 45	10 38	11 37	12 38	13 38	14 38	15 38	16 38	17 38	18 38	19 38	20 38	21 38	22 43
London Paddington 15	⊖ a	.	.	.	.	.	.	.	.	.	.	.	.	.	.

For general notes see front of timetable
For details of catering facilities see
Directory of Train Operators

b Change at Twyford and Slough
f Change at Twyford

Reading → Basingstoke

Network Diagram - see first page of Table 116

Mondays to Fridays

Miles			GW 1	GW 1	GW 1	GW 1	GW 1	XC 1◇ ☕	GW 1	GW 1	XC 1◇ ☕	GW 1	GW 1	XC 1◇ ☕	GW 1	GW 1	XC R 1 ☕	GW 1	GW 1
—	London Paddington 15 ⊖	d	03 34	05 27	05 42	06 30	07 00		07 30	08 00		08 30	09 06		09 30	10 06		10 30	11 06
0	**Reading 7**	d	05 37	06 06	06 39	07 07	07 39	07 45	08 07	08 39	08 45	09 07	09 39	09 45	10 07	10 39	10 45	11 07	11 39
1	Reading West	d	05 40	06 09	06 42	07 10	07 42	.	08 10	08 42	.	09 10	09 42	.	10 10	10 42	.	11 10	11 42
7¼	Mortimer	d	05 48	06 17	06 50	07 18	07 50	.	08 18	08 50	.	09 18	09 50	.	10 18	10 50	.	11 18	11 50
10½	Bramley (Hants)	d	05 53	06 22	06 55	07 23	07 55	.	08 23	08 55	.	09 23	09 55	.	10 23	10 55	.	11 23	11 55
15½	**Basingstoke**	a	06 01	06 30	07 03	07 31	08 03	08 08	08 31	09 03	09 08	09 32	10 03	10 08	10 32	11 03	11 08	11 31	12 03

		XC R 1 ☕	GW 1	GW 1	XC R 1 ☕	GW 1	GW 1	XC R 1 ☕	GW 1	GW 1	XC R 1 ☕	GW 1	GW 1	XC R 1 ☕	GW 1	GW 1	XC 1◇ ☕	GW 1
London Paddington 15 ⊖	d		11 30	12 06		12 30	13 06		13 30	14 06		14 30	15 06		15 30	16 06		16 30
Reading 7	d	11 45	12 07	12 39	12 45	13 07	13 39	13 45	14 07	14 39	14 45	15 07	15 39	15 45	16 07	16 39	16 45	17 07
Reading West	d	.	12 10	12 42	.	13 10	13 42	.	14 10	14 42	.	15 10	15 42	.	16 10	16 42	.	17 10
Mortimer	d	.	12 18	12 50	.	13 18	13 50	.	14 18	14 50	.	15 18	15 50	.	16 18	16 50	.	17 18
Bramley (Hants)	d	.	12 23	12 55	.	13 23	13 55	.	14 23	14 55	.	15 23	15 55	.	16 23	16 55	.	17 23
Basingstoke	a	12 08	12 31	13 03	13 08	13 31	14 03	14 08	14 31	15 03	15 08	15 31	16 03	16 08	16 32	17 03	17 08	17 32

		GW 1	XC R 1 ☕	GW 1	GW 1	XC R 1 ☕	GW 1	GW 1	XC R 1 ☕	GW 1	GW 1	XC R 1	GW 1	GW 1	XC R 1	GW 1	XC 1◇	GW 1	GW 1		
London Paddington 15 ⊖	d	17 03	17 06	17 33	18 03	18 06	18b30	19 00	19 03	19 30	20 00		20 35	20 51		21 21	21 48	21c48	22 45		
Reading 7	d	17 39	17 45	18 07	18 39	18 45	19 07	19 37	19 45	20 07	20 39	20 45	21 07	21 41	21 45	22 10	22 45	22 51	23 34		
Reading West	d	17 42	.	18 10	18 42	.	19 10	19 40	.	20 10	20 42	.	21 10	21 44	.	22 13	.	22 54	23 37		
Mortimer	d	17 50	.	18 18	18 50	.	19 18	19 48	.	20 18	20 50	.	21 18	21 52	.	22 21	.	23 02	23 45		
Bramley (Hants)	d	17 55	.	18 23	18 55	.	19 23	19 53	.	20 23	20 55	.	21 23	21 57	.	22 26	.	23 07	23 50		
Basingstoke	a	18 03	18 08	18 32	19 04	19 08	19 31	20 02	20 08	20 31	21 03	21 08	21 31	22 05	22 08	22 34	23 08	23 15	23 58		

Saturdays

until 6 September

		GW 1	GW 1	GW 1	GW 1	GW 1	GW 1	XC 1◇ ☕	GW 1	GW 1	XC 1◇ ☕	GW 1	GW 1	XC R 1 ☕	GW 1	GW 1	XC R 1 ☕	GW 1
London Paddington 15 ⊖	d	05 12	05 42	06 30	07 00	07 30	08 06		08 30	09 06		09 30	10 06		10 30	11 06		11 30
Reading 7	d	06 07	06 39	07 07	07 39	08 07	08 39	08 45	09 07	09 39	09 45	10 07	10 39	10 45	11 07	11 39	11 45	12 07
Reading West	d	06 10	06 42	07 10	07 42	08 10	08 42	.	09 10	09 42	.	10 10	10 42	.	11 10	11 42	.	12 10
Mortimer	d	06 18	06 50	07 18	07 50	08 18	08 50	.	09 18	09 50	.	10 18	10 50	.	11 18	11 50	.	12 18
Bramley (Hants)	d	06 23	06 55	07 23	07 55	08 23	08 55	.	09 23	09 55	.	10 23	10 55	.	11 23	11 55	.	12 23
Basingstoke	a	06 32	07 03	07 32	08 03	08 31	09 03	09 08	09 31	10 03	10 08	10 31	11 03	11 08	11 31	12 03	12 08	12 31

		GW 1	XC 1◇ ☕	GW 1	GW 1	XC 1◇ ☕	GW 1	GW 1	XC 1◇ ☕	GW 1	GW 1	XC R 1 ☕	GW 1	GW 1	XC 1◇ ☕	GW 1	GW 1	XC 1◇ ☕
London Paddington 15 ⊖	d	12 06		12 35	13 06		13 30	14 06		14 30	15 06		15 30	16 06		16 30	17 06	
Reading 7	d	12 39	12 45	13 10	13 39	13 45	14 07	14 39	14 45	15 07	15 39	15 45	16 07	16 39	16 45	17 07	17 39	17 45
Reading West	d	12 42	.	13 13	13 42	.	14 10	14 42	.	15 10	15 42	.	16 10	16 42	.	17 10	17 42	.
Mortimer	d	12 50	.	13 21	13 50	.	14 18	14 50	.	15 18	15 50	.	16 18	16 50	.	17 18	17 50	.
Bramley (Hants)	d	12 55	.	13 26	13 55	.	14 23	14 55	.	15 23	15 55	.	16 23	16 55	.	17 23	17 55	.
Basingstoke	a	13 03	13 08	13 34	14 03	14 08	14 31	15 03	15 08	15 31	16 03	16 08	16 31	17 03	17 08	17 31	18 03	18 08

		GW 1	GW 1	XC 1◇ ☕	GW 1	GW 1	XC 1◇ ☕	GW 1	GW 1	XC 1◇ ☕	GW 1	GW 1	XC 1◇ ☕	GW 1	GW 1	XC 1◇	GW 1	
London Paddington 15 ⊖	d	17 30	18 06		18 30	19 06		19 30	20 06		20 30	20 51		21 30	22 00		22 30	
Reading 7	d	18 08	18 39	18 45	19 07	19 39	19 45	20 07	20 39	20 45	21 07	21 39	21 45	22 07	22 39	22 45	23 07	
Reading West	d	18 11	18 42	.	19 10	19 42	.	20 10	20 42	.	21 10	21 42	.	22 10	22 42	.	23 10	
Mortimer	d	18 19	18 50	.	19 18	19 50	.	20 18	20 50	.	21 18	21 50	.	22 18	22 50	.	23 18	
Bramley (Hants)	d	18 24	18 55	.	19 23	19 55	.	20 23	20 55	.	21 23	21 55	.	22 23	22 55	.	23 23	
Basingstoke	a	18 32	19 03	19 08	19 31	20 03	20 08	20 31	21 03	21 08	21 31	22 03	22 08	22 31	23 03	23 08	23 31	

For general notes see front of timetable
For details of catering facilities see Directory of Train Operators

b 30 June to 5 September dep. 1833
c Fridays dep. 2215

Due to Engineering Operations, services from Saturday 13 September on this Table had not been confirmed at time of going to press. These services will be issued in a special Supplement as soon as exact timings have been confirmed

Sundays
until 7 September

Reading → Basingstoke

Network Diagram - see first page of Table 116

		GW 1	GW 1		GW 1	GW 1		XC 1◇ ☕	GW 1		XC 1◇ ☕	GW 1		XC 1◇ ☕	GW 1		XC 1◇ ☕	GW 1		XC 1◇ ☕	GW 1		XC R 1 ☕	GW 1		XC R 1 ☕
London Paddington 15 ⊖	d		06 43		08 42	09 57		10 07	10 42		11 07	11 42		12 07	12 42		13 07	13 57		14 07	14 42		15 07	15 57		16 07
Reading 7	d	07 37	08 37		09 37	10 37		10 50	11 37		11 50	12 37		12 50	13 37		13 50	14 37		14 50	15 37		15 50	16 37		16 50
Reading West	d	07 40	08 40		09 40	10 40			11 40			12 40			13 40			14 40			15 40			16 40		
Mortimer	d	07 48	08 48		09 48	10 48			11 48			12 48			13 48			14 48			15 48			16 48		
Bramley (Hants)	d	07 53	08 53		09 53	10 53			11 53			12 53			13 53			14 53			15 53			16 53		
Basingstoke	a	08 01	09 01		10 01	11 01		11 08	12 01		12 08	13 01		13 08	14 01		14 08	15 01		15 08	16 01		16 08	17 01		17 08

		GW 1	XC R 1 ☕		GW 1	XC R 1 ☕		GW 1	XC R 1 ☕		GW 1	XC R 1 ☕		GW 1	XC R 1 ☕		GW 1	XC 1◇ ☕		GW 1						
London Paddington 15 ⊖	d	16 42	17 07		17 42	18 07		18 57	19 07		19 42	20 07		20 42	21 07		21 42	21 44		22 42						
Reading 7	d	17 37	17 50		18 37	18 50		19 37	19 50		20 37	20 50		21 37	21 50		22 37	22 50		23 37						
Reading West	d	17 40			18 40			19 40			20 40			21 40			22 41			23 40						
Mortimer	d	17 48			18 48			19 48			20 48			21 48			22 49			23 48						
Bramley (Hants)	d	17 53			18 53			19 53			20 53			21 53			22 54			23 53						
Basingstoke	a	18 01	18 08		19 01	19 08		20 01	20 08		21 01	21 08		22 01	22 08		23 02	23 08		00 01						

For general notes see front of timetable
For details of catering facilities see Directory of Train Operators

Due to Engineering Operations, services from Sunday 14 September on this Table had not been confirmed at time of going to press. These services will be issued in a special Supplement as soon as exact timings have been confirmed

Basingstoke → Reading

Network Diagram - see first page of Table 116

Miles			GW MX	GW MO	XC	GW	GW	XC	GW	GW	XC	GW	GW	XC	GW	GW	XC	GW	GW	XC	GW
			1	1	1 ◇ ☕	1	1	1 ◇ ☕	1	1	1 ◇ ☕	1	1	1 ◇ ☕	1	1	R 1 ☕	1	1	R 1 ☕	1
0	**Basingstoke**	d	00 02	00 07	05 47	06 07	06 37	06 47	07 07	07 37	07 47	08 07	08 37	08 47	09 07	09 37	09 47	10 07	10 37	10 47	11 07
5	Bramley (Hants)	d	00 09	00 14	.	06 14	06 44	.	07 14	07 44	.	08 14	08 44	.	09 14	09 44	.	10 14	10 44	.	11 14
8¼	Mortimer	d	00 14	00 19	.	06 19	06 49	.	07 19	07 49	.	08 19	08 49	.	09 19	09 49	.	10 19	10 49	.	11 19
14½	Reading West	d	00 22	00 27	.	06 27	06 57	.	07 27	07 57	.	08 27	08 57	.	09 27	09 57	.	10 27	10 57	.	11 27
15½	**Reading 7**	a	00 26	00 30	06 04	06 30	07 00	07 04	07 30	08 00	08 04	08 30	09 00	09 04	09 30	10 00	10 04	10 30	11 00	11 04	11 30
—	London Paddington 15 ⊖	a	*01 17*	.	*07 01*	*07 16*	*07 41*	*07 44*	*08 06*	*08 38*	*08 41*	*09 06*	*09 36*	*09 41*	*10 10*	*10 39*	*10 44*	*11 15*	*11 42*	*11 42*	*12 16*

		GW	XC	GW	GW	XC	GW	GW	XC	GW	GW	XC	GW	GW	XC	GW	GW	XC	GW	GW
		1	R 1 ☕	1	1	R 1 ☕	1	1	R 1 ☕	1	1	R 1 ☕	1	1	R 1 ☕	1	1	R 1 ☕	1	1
Basingstoke	d	11 37	11 47	12 07	12 37	12 47	13 07	13 37	13 47	14 07	14 37	14 47	15 07	15 37	15 47	16 07	16 37	16 47	17 07	17 37
Bramley (Hants)	d	11 44	.	12 14	12 44	.	13 14	13 44	.	14 14	14 44	.	15 14	15 44	.	16 14	16 44	.	17 14	17 44
Mortimer	d	11 49	.	12 19	12 49	.	13 19	13 49	.	14 19	14 49	.	15 19	15 49	.	16 19	16 49	.	17 19	17 49
Reading West	d	11 57	.	12 27	12 57	.	13 27	13 57	.	14 27	14 57	.	15 27	15 57	.	16 27	16 57	.	17 27	17 57
Reading 7	a	12 00	12 04	12 31	13 00	13 04	13 30	14 00	14 04	14 30	15 00	15 04	15 31	16 00	16 04	16 30	17 00	17 04	17 30	18 00
London Paddington 15 ⊖	a	*12 39*	*12 42*	*13 15*	*13 42*	*13 42*	*14 15*	*14 39*	*14 42*	*15 15*	*15 42*	*15 42*	*16 16*	*16 39*	*16 44*	*17 15*	*17 41*	*17 41*	*18 15*	*18 39*

		XC	GW	GW	XC	GW	GW	XC	GW	GW	XC	GW	GW	GW	GW	GW
		R 1 ☕	1	1	1 ◇ ☕	1	1	1 ◇ ☕	1	1	1 ◇ ☕	1	1	1	1	1
Basingstoke	d	17 47	18 07	18 37	18 47	19 07	19 37	19 47	20 07	20 37	20 47	21 10	21 40	22 22	22 55	23 30
Bramley (Hants)	d	.	18 14	18 44	.	19 14	19 44	.	20 14	20 44	.	21 17	21 47	22 29	23 02	23 37
Mortimer	d	.	18 19	18 49	.	19 19	19 49	.	20 19	20 49	.	21 22	21 52	22 34	23 07	23 42
Reading West	d	.	18 27	18 57	.	19 27	19 57	.	20 27	20 57	.	21 30	22 01	22 41	23 15	23 50
Reading 7	a	18 04	18 31	19 00	19 04	19 31	20 00	20 04	20 30	21 01	21 04	21 33	22 04	22 45	23 18	23 53
London Paddington 15 ⊖	a	*18 44*	*19 15*	.	*19 42*	*20 15*	*20 39*	*20 44*	*21 15*	.	*21b59*	*22 15*	*22c52*	*23e36*	*00 22*	*01f13*

Saturdays
until 6 September

		GW	GW	XC	GW	GW	XC	GW	GW	XC	GW	GW	XC	GW	GW	GW	GW	GW	GW	XC	GW	GW	XC	GW	GW	XC
		1	1	1 ◇ ☕	1	1	1 ◇ ☕	1	1	R 1 ☕	1	1	R 1 ☕	1	1	1	1	1	1	1 ◇ ☕	1	1	R 1 ☕	1	1	1 ◇ ☕
Basingstoke	d	00 02	06 37	06 47	07 07	07 37	07 47	08 07	08 37	08 47	09 07	09 37	09 47	10 07	10 37	11 07	11 37	12 07	12 37	12 47	13 07	13 37	13 47	14 07	14 37	14 47
Bramley (Hants)	d	00 09	06 44	.	07 14	07 44	.	08 14	08 44	.	09 14	09 44	.	10 14	10 44	11 14	11 44	12 14	12 44	.	13 14	13 44	.	14 14	14 44	.
Mortimer	d	00 14	06 49	.	07 19	07 49	.	08 19	08 49	.	09 19	09 49	.	10 19	10 49	11 19	11 49	12 19	12 49	.	13 19	13 49	.	14 19	14 49	.
Reading West	d	00 22	06 57	.	07 27	07 57	.	08 27	08 57	.	09 27	09 57	.	10 27	10 57	11 27	11 57	12 27	12 57	.	13 27	13 57	.	14 27	14 57	.
Reading 7	a	00 26	07 00	07 05	07 31	08 00	08 05	08 31	09 00	09 05	09 31	10 00	10 05	10 31	11 00	11 31	12 00	12 31	13 00	13 05	13 31	14 00	14 05	14 31	15 00	15 05
London Paddington 15 ⊖	a	*01 10*	.	*07 45*	*08 14*	*08 40*	*08 45*	*09 15*	*09 36*	*09 44*	*10 06*	*10 43*	*10 53*	*11 09*	*11 41*	*12 15*	*12 42*	*13 13*	*13 41*	*13 54*	*14 14*	*14 42*	*14 51*	*15 09*	*15 42*	*15 52*

		GW	GW	XC	GW	GW	XC	GW	GW	XC	GW	GW	XC	GW	GW	XC	GW	GW	XC	GW	GW	GW	GW	GW	GW
		1	1	1 ◇ ☕	1	1	1 ◇ ☕	1	1	1 ◇ ☕	1	1	1 ◇ ☕	1	1	1 ◇ ☕	1	1	1 ◇	1	1	1	1	1	1
Basingstoke	d	15 07	15 37	15 47	16 07	16 37	16 47	17 07	17 37	17 47	18 07	18 37	18 47	19 07	19 37	19 47	20 07	20 37	20 47	21 07	21 37	22 07	22 37	23 07	23 37
Bramley (Hants)	d	15 14	15 44	.	16 14	16 44	.	17 14	17 44	.	18 14	18 44	.	19 14	19 44	.	20 14	20 44	.	21 14	21 44	22 14	22 44	23 14	23 44
Mortimer	d	15 19	15 49	.	16 19	16 49	.	17 19	17 49	.	18 19	18 49	.	19 19	19 49	.	20 19	20 49	.	21 19	21 49	22 19	22 49	23 19	23 49
Reading West	d	15 27	15 57	.	16 27	16 57	.	17 27	17 57	.	18 27	18 57	.	19 27	19 57	.	20 27	20 57	.	21 27	21 57	22 27	22 57	23 27	23 57
Reading 7	a	15 31	16 00	16 05	16 31	17 00	17 05	17 31	18 00	18 05	18 31	19 00	19 05	19 31	20 00	20 05	20 31	21 00	21 05	21 31	22 00	22 31	23 00	23 31	00 01
London Paddington 15 ⊖	a	*16 13*	*16 42*	*16 52*	*17 09*	*17 40*	*17 51*	*18 15*	*18 42*	*18 52*	*19 06*	*19 42*	*19 52*	*20 14*	.	*21 06*	*21 09*	*21 36*	*21 58*	*22 16*	*23 07*	*23 29*	*23 38*	*00 32*	.

Sundays
until 7 September

		GW	GW	XC	GW	XC	GW	XC	GW	XC	GW	XC	GW	XC
		1	1	1 ◇ ☕	1	1 ◇ ☕	1	R 1 ☕	1	R 1 ☕	1	R 1 ☕	1	R 1 ☕
Basingstoke	d	08 07	09 07	09 47	10 07	10 47	11 07	11 47	12 07	12 47	13 07	13 47	14 07	14 47
Bramley (Hants)	d	08 14	09 14	.	10 14	.	11 14	.	12 14	.	13 14	.	14 14	.
Mortimer	d	08 19	09 19	.	10 19	.	11 19	.	12 19	.	13 19	.	14 19	.
Reading West	d	08 27	09 27	.	10 27	.	11 27	.	12 27	.	13 27	.	14 27	.
Reading 7	a	08 30	09 30	10 05	10 30	11 05	11 30	12 05	12 30	13 05	13 30	14 05	14 30	15 05
London Paddington 15 ⊖	a	*09 35*	*10 40*	*10 54*	*11 26*	*11 55*	*12 15*	*12 55*	*13 26*	*13 55*	*14 24*	*14 54*	*15 21*	*15 55*

For general notes see front of timetable
For details of catering facilities see Directory of Train Operators

b 30 June to 5 September arr. 2201
c Fridays arr. 2253
e Fridays arr. 2329
f Fridays arr. 0110

Due to Engineering Operations, services from Saturday 13 September on this Table had not been confirmed at time of going to press. These services will be issued in a special Supplement as soon as exact timings have been confirmed

Due to Engineering Operations, services from Sunday 14 September on this Table had not been confirmed at time of going to press. These services will be issued in a special Supplement as soon as exact timings have been confirmed

Table 122

Sundays

until 7 September

Basingstoke → Reading

Network Diagram - see first page of Table 116

	GW	XC	GW	XC	GW	XC	GW	XC	GW	XC	GW	XC	GW	XC	GW	GW
	1	R 1 ☕	1	R 1 ☕	1	R 1 ☕	1	1 ◊ ☕	1	1 ◊ ☕	1	1 ◊	1	1 ◊	1	1
Basingstoke d	15 07	15 47	16 07	16 47	17 07	17 47	18 07	18 47	19 07	19 47	20 07	20 47	21 07	21 47	22 07	23 07
Bramley (Hants) d	15 14	.	16 14	.	17 14	.	18 14	.	19 14	.	20 14	.	21 14	.	22 15	23 14
Mortimer d	15 19		16 19		17 19		18 19		19 19		20 19		21 19		22 20	23 19
Reading West d	15 27	.	16 27	.	17 27	.	18 27	.	19 27	.	20 27	.	21 27	.	22 30	23 27
Reading 7 a	15 30	16 05	16 30	17 05	17 30	18 05	18 30	19 05	19 30	20 05	20 30	21 05	21 30	22 05	22 33	23 30
London Paddington 15 ⊖ a	*16 22*	*16 54*	*17 34*	*17 54*	*18 24*	*18 54*	*19 24*	*19 58*	*20 21*	*20 55*	*21 22*	*21 53*	*22 28*	*22 59*	*23 23*	*00 40*

For general notes see front of timetable
For details of catering facilities see
Directory of Train Operators

Due to Engineering Operations, services from Sunday 14 September on this Table had not been confirmed at time of going to press. These services will be issued in a special Supplement as soon as exact timings have been confirmed

Network Diagram for Table 123

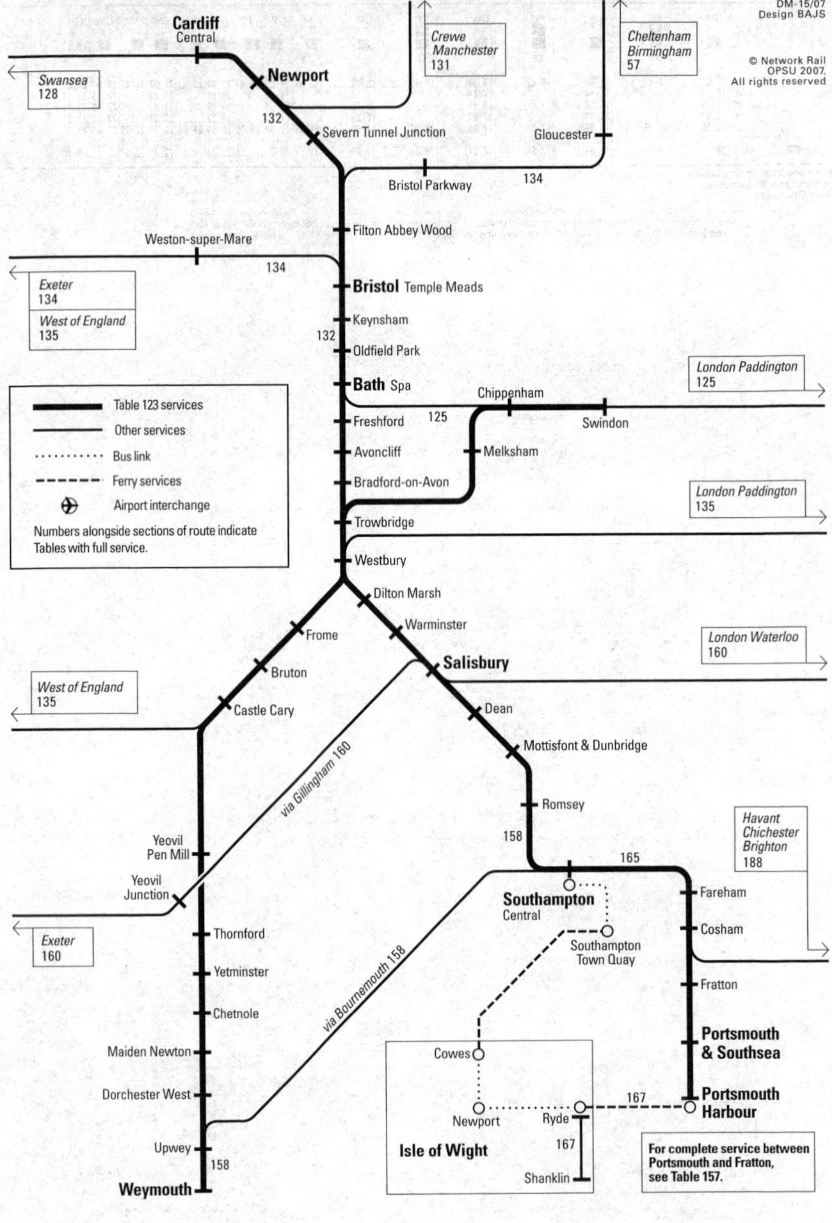

DM-15/07
Design BAJS
© Network Rail OPSU 2007. All rights reserved
Cardiff Central
Newport
Swansea 128
Crewe Manchester 131
Cheltenham Birmingham 57
132
Severn Tunnel Junction
Gloucester
Bristol Parkway
134
Filton Abbey Wood
Weston-super-Mare
134
Exeter 134
West of England 135
Bristol Temple Meads
Keynsham
132
Oldfield Park
Bath Spa
London Paddington 125
Chippenham
Swindon
125
Freshford
Avoncliff
Melksham
Bradford-on-Avon
London Paddington 135
Trowbridge
Westbury
Table 123 services
Other services
Bus link
Ferry services
Airport interchange
Numbers alongside sections of route indicate Tables with full service.
Dilton Marsh
Frome
Warminster
London Waterloo 160
Salisbury
Bruton
West of England 135
Castle Cary
Dean
Mottisfont & Dunbridge
via Gillingham 160
Romsey
Havant Chichester Brighton 188
158
165
Yeovil Pen Mill
Yeovil Junction
Southampton Central
Fareham
Exeter 160
Thornford
Southampton Town Quay
Cosham
Yetminster
via Bournemouth 158
Fratton
Chetnole
Portsmouth & Southsea
Maiden Newton
Cowes
Dorchester West
Newport
Ryde
167
Portsmouth Harbour
Upwey
Isle of Wight
167
158
Shanklin
Weymouth
For complete service between Portsmouth and Fratton, see Table 157.

South Wales and Bristol → Weymouth and Portsmouth

Network Diagram - see first page of Table 123

Miles	Miles	Miles	Station		GW MX	GW	GW	GW	GW ◇	GW ◇	GW A		GW	GW ◇	GW B	GW ◇	GW ◇ C	SW [1] ◇ D	GW		GW ◇	GW [1] ◇	GW	GW ◇ E	GW ◇	GW
—	—	—	Swansea [7]	d										05 24		06 29			06b59		07 29				08 29	
0	0	—	**Cardiff Central [7]**	d										06 25		07 30			08 00		08 30				09 30	
11¾	11¾	—	Newport (South Wales)	d										06 39		07 44			08 15		08 44				09 44	
21¾	21¾	—	Severn Tunnel Jn	d										06 50		07 55			08 25						09c25	
33¾	33¾	—	Filton Abbey Wood	d										07 09	07 28	08 09	08 27		08 42		09 09			09 22	10 09	
38¼	38¼	—	**Bristol Temple Meads [10]**	d	23p16				05 44				06 44	07 22	07 49	08 22	08 40	08 50	09 05		09 22			09 49	10 22	
42¾	42¾	—	Keynsham	d	23p23				05 51				06 51		07 56		08 47	08 57						09 56		
48¾	48¾	—	Oldfield Park	d	23p29				05 58				06 58		08 03		08 54		09 16					10 03		
—	—	—	London Paddington [15] ⊖	d									05 27		06 30	07 00		07 30			08 00	08 18		08 30	09 00	
—	—	0	Swindon	d							06 15		06 26		07 31	08 01		08 26			09 01			09 31	09 56	
—	—	16¾	Chippenham	d							06 31		06 40		07 45	08 15		08 40			09 15			09 45	10 10	
—	—	23	Melksham	d							06 40															
49¾	49¾	—	**Bath Spa [7]**	d	23p35				06 01				07 02	07 36	08 07	08 37	08 57	09 05	09 20		09 35			10 07	10 36	
56¾	56¾	—	Freshford	d	23p45				06 11				07 11		08 18		09 08							10 17		
57¾	57¾	—	Avoncliff	d	23e47				06x13				07x14		08x19		09x09							10x18		
59	59	—	Bradford-on-Avon	d	23p51				06 17				07 17	07 47	08 23	08 47	09 13	09 20	09 32					10 23	10 47	
62¼	62¼	28½	Trowbridge	d	23p57				06 24		06 50		07 23	07 53	08 29	08 53	09 19	09 27	09 38		09 50			10 29	10 53	
—	—	—	Plymouth	d										05 35			07f47				06g40		07 47			08 55
—	—	—	Exeter St Davids [6]	d						05f46	05h10			06 38		06h41	08f49				08h25		08 49			09 57
66¼	66¼	32½	**Westbury**	a	00 04				06 31		06 57		07 32	08 01	08 36	09 01	09 26	09 33	09 46		09 57	09 57		10 36	11 00	
—	—	—		d	00 04	05 26	05 49	06 25	06 35	06 44	06 58			08 01		09 01	09 30	09 39			09 58	10 00	10 08	10 36	11 01	11 07
—	72	—	Frome	d	00a15			06a35		06 54							09 39							10 46		
—	82½	—	Bruton	d						07 05							09 51							10 57		
—	86	—	Castle Cary	a						07 10							09 55					10 16		11 02		
—	—	—		d						07 10							09 56							11 03		
—	97¾	—	Yeovil Pen Mill	d						07j34							10 09							11 16		
—	101	—	Thornford	d						07x38							10x13							11x21		
—	102	—	Yetminster	d						07x41							10x16							11x24		
—	104	—	Chetnole	d						07x45							10x20							11x28		
—	110½	—	Maiden Newton	d						07 57							10 31							11 40		
—	118¼	—	Dorchester West	d						08 08							10 42							11 50		
—	122¾	—	Upwey	a						08 14							10 48							12 01		
—	125¼	—	**Weymouth**	a						08 20							10 55							12 08		
67¾	—	—	Dilton Marsh	d							07x01												10 11			11x09
71	—	—	Warminster	d		05 34	05 56		06 43		07 10			08 08		09 08		09 46			10 07		10a18		11 08	11 16
90¾	—	—	**Salisbury**	a		05 58	06 19		07 10		07 36			08 32		09 32		10 09			10 29				11 32	11 38
—	—	—		d			06 20		07 11		07 36			08 32		09 32					10 30				11 32	11 39
99¾	—	—	Dean	d																						
103½	—	—	Mottisfont & Dunbridge	d																						
107¼	—	—	Romsey	d			06 38		07 30		07 56			08 50		09 50					10 50				11 50	12 02
115½	—	—	**Southampton Central**	a			06 49		07 41		08 09			09 03		10 02					11 02				12 02	12 19
—	—	—	Bournemouth	a			07 45		08 43		09 10			10 00		11 00					12 00					13 00
130	—	—	Fareham	a			07 14		08 05		08 59			09 26		10 26					11 26				12 26	12 59
—	—	—		d			07 15		08 06					09 26		10 26					11 26				12 26	
135¾	—	—	Cosham	a			07 23		08 14		09 08			09 34		10 34					11 34				12 34	13 08
139½	—	—	Fratton	a			07 34		08 21		09 35			09 41		10 41					11 41				12 41	13 36
140½	—	—	Portsmouth & Southsea	a			07 38		08 24		09 40			09 45		10 45					11 45				12 45	13 40
141¼	—	—	**Portsmouth Harbour**	a			07 45		08 30					09 54		10 54					11 54				12 54	
—	—	—	Havant	a			07k46		08m40					09k51		10k51					11k51				12k50	
—	—	—	Chichester [4]	a			08k08		08m55					10k09		11k08					12k08				13k08	
—	—	—	Barnham	a			08k16		09m03					10k18		11k18					12k18				13k18	
—	—	—	Worthing [4]	a			08k56		09m25					10k54		11k54					12k54				13k54	
—	—	—	Shoreham-by-Sea	a			09k05		09m34					11k04		12k04					13k04				14k04	
—	—	—	Hove [2]	a			09k14		09m43					11k13		12k13					13k13				14k13	
—	—	—	Brighton [10]	a			09k19		09m48					11k18		12k18					13k18				14k18	

For general notes see front of timetable
For details of catering facilities see Directory of Train Operators

- **A** From Gloucester (Table 125)
- **B** From Bristol Parkway (Table 132)
- **C** From Worcester Shrub Hill (Table 57)
- **D** To London Waterloo (Table 160)
- **E** From Gloucester (Table 134)
- **b** Change at Cardiff Central and Bristol Temple Meads
- **c** Change at Bristol Temple Meads
- **e** Previous night.
  Stops on request, passengers wishing to alight must inform the guard and those wishing to join must give a hand signal to the driver
- **f** Change at Castle Cary
- **g** Change at Exeter St Davids and Salisbury
- **h** Change at Salisbury
- **j** Arr. 0722
- **k** Change at Fareham
- **m** Change at Fratton

South Wales and Bristol → Weymouth and Portsmouth

Network Diagram - see first page of Table 123

Station		GW A	GW ◇ ⊼	GW 1◇ B ⊠	GW ◇ C	GW ◇ ⊼	GW ◇ A	SW 1◇	GW 1◇ D ⊔	GW ◇ ⊼	GW C	GW ◇ ⊼	GW	GW ◇ A	GW ◇ ⊼	GW 1◇ ⊔	GW C	SW 1◇	GW ◇ ⊼	GW	GW ◇ A	GW E	GW ◇ ⊼
Swansea 7	d		09 29			10 29		10b55		11 29		12 29			13 29				14 29			14b55	15 29
Cardiff Central 7	d		10 30			11 30		12 00		12 30		13 30			14 30				15 30			16c00	16 30
Newport (South Wales)	d		10 44			11 44		12 15		12 44		13 44			14 44				15 44			16c15	16 44
Severn Tunnel Jn	d		10c25			11c25		12 25				13c25			14c25				15c25			16c25	16 55
Filton Abbey Wood	d	10 22	11 09		11 22	12 09	12 22	12 42		13 09	13 22	14 09		14 22	15 09		15 22		16 09		16 22	16 49	17 09
Bristol Temple Meads 10	d	10 49	11 22		11 49	12 22	12 39	13 10		13 22	13 49	14 22		14 49	15 22		15 43	15 52	16 22		16 49	17 07	17 22
Keynsham	d	10 56			11 56		12 46				13 56			14 56			15 50				16 56	17 14	
Oldfield Park	d	11 03			12 03		12 53				14 03			15 03			15 57				17 03	17 21	17 32
London Paddington 15 ⊖	d	09 30	10 00	11 06	10 30	11 00		11 30	12 18	12 00	12 30	13 00		13 30	14 00	15 06			15 00		15 30		16 00
Swindon	d	10 31	10 56		11 31	11 56		12 31		12 56	13 31	13 56		14 31	14 56				15 56		16 31		16 56
Chippenham	d	10 45	11 10		11 45	12 10		12 45		13 10	13 45	14 10		14 45	15 10				16 10		16 45		17 10
Melksham	d																						
Bath Spa 7	d	11 07	11 36		12 07	12 36	12 57	13 22		13 36	14 07	14 36		15 07	15 36		16 01	16 06	16 36		17 07	17 25	17 36
Freshford	d	11 17			12 17		13 06				14 17			15 17			16 09				17 17	17 34	
Avoncliff	d	11x18			12x18		13x07				14x18			15x18			16x11				17x18	17x36	
Bradford-on-Avon	d	11 23	11 47		12 23	12 47	13 12	13 35		13 47	14 23	14 47		15 23	15 47		16 15	16 22	16 47		17 23	17 40	
Trowbridge	d	11 29	11 53		12 29	12 53	13 18	13 42		13 53	14 29	14 53		15 29	15 53		16 21	16 28	16 53		17 29	17 46	17 53
Plymouth	d				10e45		10f45					12g25	12 55										15g00
Exeter St Davids 6	d		10h10		11j54		11 54			12h10		13h35	13 57		14h10								16h10
Westbury	a	11 36	12 01	12 21	12 36	13 01	13 25	13 48	13 56	14 01	14 36	15 01		15 36	16 01	16 21	16 29	16 36	17 01		17 36	17 56	18 00
	d		12 01	12 22	12 37	13 01	13 27	13 53	13 58	14 01		15 01	15 08	15 36	16 01	16 22		16 39	17 01	17 08	17 38		18 01
Frome	d				12 47				14 08					15 46							17 47		
Bruton	d				12 57									15 57							17 59		
Castle Cary	a			12 39	13 03				14 21					16 01		16 39					18 04		
	d				13 04									16 10							18 10		
Yeovil Pen Mill	d				13 17									16 23							18 24		
Thornford	d				13x22									16x27							18x28		
Yetminster	d				13x25									16x30							18x31		
Chetnole	d				13x29									16x34							18x35		
Maiden Newton	d				13 41									16 45							18 47		
Dorchester West	d				13 54									16 55							18 58		
Upwey	a				14 01									17 01							19 06		
Weymouth	a				14 09									17 08							19 13		
Dilton Marsh	d						13x29						15x11							17 11			
Warminster	d		12 08			13 08	13 36	14 00		14 08		15 08	15a17		16 08			16 47	17 08	17a18			18 08
Salisbury	a		12 32			13 32	13 58	14 24		14 32		15 32			16 32			17 09	17 32				18 31
	d		12 32			13 32	13 59			14 32		15 32			16 32				17 32				18 32
Dean	d																						
Mottisfont & Dunbridge	d																						
Romsey	d		12 50			13 50	14 19			14 50		15 50			16 50				17 50				18 50
Southampton Central	a		13 02			14 02	14 33			15 02		16 02			17 02				18 02				19 01
Bournemouth	a		14 00			15 00	15 15			16 00		17 04			18 04				18 49				20 02
Fareham	a		13 26			14 26	14 55			15 26		16 26			17 26				18 26				19 26
	d		13 26			14 26	14 56			15 26		16 26			17 26				18 26				19 26
Cosham	a		13 34			14 34	15 04			15 34		16 34			17 34				18 34				19 34
Fratton	a		13 41			14 41	15 36			15 41		16 47			17 41				18 47				19 41
Portsmouth & Southsea	a		13 45			14 45	15 40			15 45		16 51			17 45				18 51				19 45
Portsmouth Harbour	a		13 54			14 54				15 54		16 59			17 54				18 59				19 54
Havant	a		13k51			14k51	15 10			15k50		16k51			17k50				18k50				19k51
Chichester 4	a		14k08			15k08	15 21			16k08		17k09			18k08				19k05				20k06
Barnham	a		14k18			15k18	15 29			16k20		17k18			18k20				19k14				20k14
Worthing 4	a		14k54				15 45			16k54		17m43			18k52				19k50				20k52
Shoreham-by-Sea	a		15k04				15 56			17k04		17m53			19k02				20k02				21k02
Hove 2	a		15k13				16 07			17k13		18m04			19k14				20k13				21k14
Brighton 10	a		15k18				16 14			17k18		18m09			19k18				20k18				21k18

For general notes see front of timetable
For details of catering facilities see Directory of Train Operators

- **A** From Great Malvern (Table 71)
- **B** **The Mayflower**
- **C** From Gloucester (Table 134)
- **D** To Taunton (Table 135)
- **E** From Bristol Parkway (Table 132)
- **b** Change at Cardiff Central and Bristol Temple Meads
- **c** Change at Bristol Temple Meads
- **e** Change at Exeter St Davids and Castle Cary
- **f** Change at Exeter St Davids and Westbury
- **g** Change at Exeter St Davids and Salisbury
- **h** Change at Salisbury
- **j** Change at Castle Cary
- **k** Change at Fareham
- **m** Change at Fareham and Barnham

South Wales and Bristol → Weymouth and Portsmouth

Network Diagram - see first page of Table 123

		GW	GW	GW	GW	GW	GW	GW	GW	GW	GW	GW	GW	GW	GW	GW	GW	GW	GW	GW	SW	GW
		1 ◇	◇	1 ◇		1 ◇	◇			1 ◇	◇	1 ◇	1 ◇		◇	1 ◇	◇	1 ◇	◇		1	
			A		B			C	D			E	G	A			H					
		🍴		🍴		🍴	🛒			🍴	🛒	🍴	🍴		🛒	🍴		🍴	🛒			
Swansea 7	d				15b55		16 29				17 29				18 29				19 29	19 55		20b55
Cardiff Central 7	d				17c00		17 30				18 30				19 30				20 30	21 00		22 00
Newport (South Wales)	d				17c15		17 44				18 44				19 44				20 44	21 14		22 17
Severn Tunnel Jn	d				17c25		17 55				18 54				19c25				20c21	21 24		22 32
Filton Abbey Wood	d		17 22		17 49		18 09		18 22		19 09			19 22	20 09		20 22		21 09	21 41		22 51
Bristol Temple Meads 10	d		17 49		18 07		18 22		18 49		19 22			19 49	20 22		20 49		21 22	22 00	22 25	23 16
Keynsham	d		17 56		18 14				18 56					19 56			20 56			22 08		23 23
Oldfield Park	d		18 03		18 21				19 03					20 03			21 03			22 15		23 29
London Paddington 15 ⊖	d	16 33	16 30	17 06		17 33	17 00	17 45	17 30	18 06	18 00	18 33	18 36	18 30	19 00	19 45	19 30	20 35	20 00	20 45		
Swindon	d		17 31				18 01	18 45	18 31		19 01			19 31	20 01		20 26		21 01	21 45		
Chippenham	d		17 45				18 15	19 01	18 45		19 15			19 45	20 15		20 40		21 15	22 00		
Melksham	d							19 11														
Bath Spa 7	d		18 07		18 25		18 36		19 07		19 37			20 07	20 37		21 07		21 37	22 19	22 38	23 35
Freshford	d		18 17		18 34				19 17					20 17			21 17			22 27		23 45
Avoncliff	d		18x18		18x36				19x18					20x18			21x18			22x30		23x47
Bradford-on-Avon	d		18 23		18 40		18 47		19 22		19 47			20 23	20 47		21 23		21 47	22 33	22 51	23 51
Trowbridge	d		18 29		18 46		18 53	19 20	19 28		19 53			20 29	20 53		21 29		21 53	22 39	22 57	23 57
Plymouth	d		17e00					17 00							18f00		18g43		18h43			
Exeter St Davids 6	d		18e00					18 00			18j10				19j10		19e53		19 53			
Westbury	a	18 04	18 36	18 51	18 56	18 57	19 00	19 27	19 35	19 52	20 01	20 04	20 04	20 36	21 01	21 05	21 36	21 56	22 01	22 46	23 04	00 04
	d	18 04	18 36			18 58	19 01	19 40		19 53	20 01	20 05	20 05	20 36	21 01	21 06	21 36	21 57	22 01		23 04	00 04
Frome	d		18 46							20a03				20a47			21 46					00a15
Bruton	d		18 57														21 57					
Castle Cary	a	18 22	19 02			19 15						20 22	20 22			21 24	22 03	22 14				
	d		19 03														22 03					
Yeovil Pen Mill	d		19 16														22 17					
Thornford	d		19x21														22x21					
Yetminster	d		19x24														22x24					
Chetnole	d		19x28														22x28					
Maiden Newton	d		19 40														22 40					
Dorchester West	d		19 52														22 50					
Upwey	a		19 58														22 57					
Weymouth	a		20 06														23 05					
Dilton Marsh	d							19x42											22x04			
Warminster	d						19 08	19 49			20 08				21 08				22 08		23 11	
Salisbury	a						19 32	20 12			20 32				21 32				22 32		23 34	
	d						19 32	20 13			20 32				21 32				22 32			
Dean	d																					
Mottisfont & Dunbridge	d																					
Romsey	d						19 50	20 35			20 49				21 50				22 50			
Southampton Central	a						20 02	20 46			21 02				22 02				23 03			
Bournemouth	a						21 00	21 22			22 09				23 16				00 16			
Fareham	a						20 26				21 26				22 39				23 26			
	d						20 26				21 26				22 39				23 26			
Cosham	a						20 44				21 48				22k45				23 59			
Fratton	a						20 47				21 40				22 55				23 41			
Portsmouth & Southsea	a						20 51				21 45				22 59				23 45			
Portsmouth Harbour	a						20 59				21 52				23 04				23 54			
Havant	a						20m50				21m54				23m14							
Chichester 4	a						21m05				22m05				23m25							
Barnham	a						21m14				22m13				23m33							
Worthing 4	a						21m55				22n52											
Shoreham-by-Sea	a						22m05				23n02											
Hove 2	a						22m17				23n13											
Brighton 10	a						22m22				23n18											

For general notes see front of timetable
For details of catering facilities see Directory of Train Operators

A From Gloucester (Table 134)
B From Bristol Parkway (Table 132)
C From Worcester Foregate Street (Table 71)
D From Cheltenham Spa (Table 57)
E 30 June to 5 September
G Until 27 June and from 8 September
H From Great Malvern (Table 71)
b Change at Cardiff Central and Bristol Temple Meads
c Change at Bristol Temple Meads
e Change at Castle Cary
f Change at Exeter St Davids and Salisbury
g Change at Exeter St Davids and Castle Cary
h Change at Exeter St Davida and Westbury
j Change at Salisbury
k Change at Southampton Central
m Change at Fareham
n Change at Fratton

Saturdays

until 6 September

South Wales and Bristol → Weymouth and Portsmouth

Network Diagram - see first page of Table 123

		GW	GW ◇	GW ◇		GW	GW	GW ◇		GW	GW ◇	GW A		SW 1 ◇ B	GW C	GW 1		GW C	GW ◇	GW		GW ◇ D	GW ◇	GW		GW E
Swansea 7	d						03 59	05 29			06 29				06b59				07 29				08 29			
Cardiff Central 7	d						04 54	06 30			07 30				08 00				08 30				09 30			
Newport (South Wales)	d						05 08	06 44			07 44				08 15				08 44				09 44			
Severn Tunnel Jn	d							06 55			07 55				08 25				08c25							
Filton Abbey Wood	d							07 09			08 09	08 23			08 43				09 09			09 23	10 09			10 25
Bristol Temple Meads 10	d	23p16	05 45	05 50			06 43	07 22		07 49	08 22	08 40		08 50	09 09				09 22			09 49	10 22			10 49
Keynsham	d	23p23	05 52	05 57			06 50			07 56		08 47		08 57	09 16							09 56				10 56
Oldfield Park	d	23p29	05 59	06 04			06 56			08 02		08 54			09 23							10 03				11 03
London Paddington 15 ⊖	d										07 00			07 30		08 35			08 00				09 00			09 30
Swindon	d										07 56			08 27					08 56				09 56			10 31
Chippenham	d										08 10			08 41					09 10				10 10			10 45
Melksham	d																									
Bath Spa 7	d	23p35	06 02	06 08			07 00	07 36		08 06	08 36	08 57		09 05	09 26				09 36			10 07	10 36			11 07
Freshford	d	23p45	06 12	06 17			07 09			08 15		09 08										10 16				11 16
Avoncliff	d	23e47	06x14	06x20			07x11			08x17		09x09										10x19				11x19
Bradford-on-Avon	d	23p51	06 18	06 23			07 15	07 47		08 21	08 47	09 14		09 20	09 40				09 47			10 22	10 47			11 22
Trowbridge	d	23p57	06 24	06 33			07 21	07 53		08 27	08 53	09 20		09 27	09 47				09 53			10 28	10 53			11 28
Plymouth	d							05 40				07f54							06g55				07 54	08 52		
Exeter St Davids 6	d		05h10					06 41				08f56							08h25				08 56	09 54		
Westbury	a	00 04	06 31	06 43			07 28	08 00		08 34	09 00	09 27		09 33	09 54	09 55		←	10 00			10 34	11 00			11 35
	d	00 04	06 39	06 45		07 03		08 01			09 01	09 28		09 39	10 00	09 56		10 00	10 01	10 08		10 35	11 01	11 07		
Frome	d	00a15		06 54								09 38			→			10 10				10 45				
Bruton	d			07 06								09 49				10 13		10 21				10 57				
Castle Cary	a			07 12								09 53						10 26				11 02				
	d			07 15								09 54						10 30				11 02				
Yeovil Pen Mill	d			07j39								10 08						10 48				11 16				
Thornford	d			07x44								10x13										11x20				
Yetminster	d			07x47								10x16										11x23				
Chetnole	d			07x51								10x19										11x27				
Maiden Newton	d			08 03								10 31						11 13				11 41				
Dorchester West	d			08 14								10 38						11 29				11k56				
Upwey	a			08 20								10 48										12 02				
Weymouth	a			08 26								10 54						11 42				12 08				
Dilton Marsh	d					07x06														10x10				11x10		
Warminster	d		06 46			07 13		08 08			09 08			09 46					10 08	10a16			11 08	11 16		
Salisbury	a		07 15			07 35		08 32			09 32			10 09					10 31				11 32	11 38		
	d		07 24			07 37		08 32			09 32								10 32				11 32	11 39		
Dean	d																									
Mottisfont & Dunbridge	d																									
Romsey	d		07 44			07 56		08 50			09 50								10 50				11 50	12 02		
Southampton Central	a		08 02			08 07		09 02			10 02								11 02				12 02	12 18		
Bournemouth	a					09 10		10 00			11 00								12 00					13 00		
Fareham	a		08 26			08 59		09 26			10 26								11 26				12 26	12 59		
	d		08 26					09 26			10 26								11 26				12 26			
Cosham	a		08 34			09 08		09 34			10 34								11 34				12 34	13 08		
Fratton	a		08 41			09 36		09 41			10 41								11 41				12 41	13 36		
Portsmouth & Southsea	a		08 45			09 40		09 45			10 45								11 45				12 45	13 40		
Portsmouth Harbour	a		08 49					09 51			10 51								11 51				12 51			
Havant	a		08m50					09m50			10m50								11m50				12m50			
Chichester 4	a		09m08					10m08			11m08								12m08				13m08			
Barnham	a		09m18					10m18			11m18								12m18				13m18			
Worthing 4	a		09m54					10m54			11m54								12m54				13m54			
Shoreham-by-Sea	a		10m04					11m04			12m04								13m04				14m04			
Hove 2	a		10m13					11m13			12m13								13m13				14m13			
Brighton 10	a		10m18					11m18			12m18								13m18				14m18			

For general notes see front of timetable
For details of catering facilities see Directory of Train Operators

- **A** From Worcester Shrub Hill (Table 57)
- **B** To London Waterloo (Table 160)
- **C** From 5 July
- **D** From Gloucester (Table 134)
- **E** From Great Malvern (Table 71)
- **b** Change at Cardiff Central and Bristol Temple Meads
- **c** Change at Bristol Temple Meads
- **e** Previous night.
  Stops on request, passengers wishing to alight must inform the guard and those wishing to join must give a hand signal to the driver
- **f** Change at Castle Cary
- **g** Change at Exeter St Davids and Salisbury
- **h** Change at Salisbury
- **j** Arr. 0727
- **k** Arr. 1151
- **m** Change at Fareham

South Wales and Bristol → Weymouth and Portsmouth

Network Diagram - see first page of Table 123

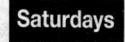

		GW	GW	GW	GW	GW	SW	GW	GW	GW	GW	GW	GW	GW	GW	GW	GW	GW	SW	GW
		1	◇	◇	◇	◇	1 ◇	1	◇		◇		◇	◇			1 ◇		1 ◇	◇
		A		B		C				B			C					B		
		🍴	⊼		⊼			🍴	⊼		⊼		⊼	⊼			🍴			⊼
Swansea 7	d		09 29		10 29		10b55		11 29		12 29			13 29						14 29
Cardiff Central 7	d		10 30		11 30		12 00		12 30		13 30			14 30						15 30
Newport (South Wales)	d		10 44		11 44		12 15		12 44		13 44			14 44						15 44
Severn Tunnel Jn	d		10c25		11c25		12 25				13c26			14c25						15c25
Filton Abbey Wood	d		11 09	11 23	12 09	12 25	12 42		13 09	13 23	14 09		14 23	15 09				15 23		16 09
Bristol Temple Meads 10	d		11 22	11 49	12 22	12 40	13 10		13 22	13 49	14 22		14 49	15 22				15 43	15 52	16 22
Keynsham	d			11 56		12 47				13 56			14 56					15 50		
Oldfield Park	d			12 03		12 54				14 03			15 03					15 57		
London Paddington 15 ⊖	d	10 35	10 00	10 30	11 00		11 30	12 35	12 00		13 00			14 00			15 06			15 00
Swindon	d		10 56	11 31	11 56		12 32		12 56		13 56			14 56	15 19					15 56
Chippenham	d		11 10	11 45	12 10		12 46		13 10		14 10			15 10	15 35					16 10
Melksham	d														15 45					
Bath Spa 7	d		11 36	12 07	12 36	12 57	13 22		13 36	14 07	14 36		15 07	15 36				16 01	16 06	16 36
Freshford	d			12 16						14 16			15 17					16 10		
Avoncliff	d			12x19						14x19			15x19					16x13		
Bradford-on-Avon	d		11 47	12 22	12 47	13 10	13 35		13 47	14 22	14 47		15 22	15 47				16 16	16 22	16 47
Trowbridge	d		11 53	12 28	12 53	13 17	13 42		13 53	14 28	14 53		15 28	15 53	15 59			16 22	16 28	16 53
Plymouth	d		09 28		09e57				10e43		11f59			12e56					14f25	
Exeter St Davids 6	d		10 35		11g08				12g10		13 36			14g10					15 30	
Westbury	a	11 52	12 00	12 35	13 00	13 24	13 48	13 59	14 00	14 35	15 00		15 35	16 00	16 06		16 22	16 29	16 36	17 00
	d	11 54	12 01	12 36	13 01	13 27	13 53	14 00	14 01		15 01	15 08	15 36	16 01		16 08	16 22		16 39	17 01
Frome	d			12 48									15 46							
Bruton	d			12 59									15 57							
Castle Cary	a	12 10		13 04				14 17					16 02				16 40			
	d			13 05									16 02							
Yeovil Pen Mill	d			13 18									16 13							
Thornford	d			13x23									16x18							
Yetminster	d			13x26									16x21							
Chetnole	d			13x30									16x24							
Maiden Newton	d			13 42									16 37							
Dorchester West	d			13 55									16h54							
Upwey	a			14 02									17 02							
Weymouth	a			14 08									17 08							
Dilton Marsh	d					13x30						15x11				16 11				
Warminster	d		12 08		13 08	13 36	14 00		14 08		15 08	15a17		16 08		16a17			16 47	17 08
Salisbury	a		12 32		13 32	13 58	14 24		14 32		15 32			16 32					17 09	17 32
	d		12 32		13 32	13 59			14 32		15 32			16 32						17 32
Dean	d																			
Mottisfont & Dunbridge	d																			
Romsey	d		12 50		13 50	14 19			14 50		15 50			16 50						17 50
Southampton Central	a		13 02		14 02	14 33			15 02		16 02			17 02						18 02
Bournemouth	a		14 00		15 00	15 15			16 00		17 00			18 00						19 00
Fareham	a		13 26		14 26	14 55			15 26		16 26			17 26						18 26
	d		13 26		14 26	14 56			15 26		16 26			17 26						18 26
Cosham	a		13 34		14 34	15 04			15 34		16 34			17 34						18 34
Fratton	a		13 41		14 41	15 36			15 41		16 41			17 41						18 41
Portsmouth & Southsea	a		13 45		14 45	15 40			15 45		16 45			17 45						18 45
Portsmouth Harbour	a		13 51		14 51				15 51		16 51			17 51						18 51
Havant	a		13j50		14j50	15 11			15j50		16j50			17j50						18j50
Chichester 4	a		14j08		15j08	15 22			16j08		17j08			18j08						19j05
Barnham	a		14j18		15j18	15 30			16j18		17j18			18j18						19j14
Worthing 4	a		14j54			15 45			16j54		17j54			18j54						19j54
Shoreham-by-Sea	a		15j04			15 56			17j04		18j04			19j04						20j04
Hove 2	a		15j13			16 07			17j13		18j13			19j13						20j15
Brighton 10	a		15j18			16 14			17j18		18j18			19j18						20j20

For general notes see front of timetable
For details of catering facilities see Directory of Train Operators

A **Torbay Express**

- **B** From Gloucester (Table 134)
- **C** From Great Malvern (Table 71)
- **b** Change at Cardiff Central and Bristol Temple Meads
- **c** Change at Bristol Temple Meads
- **e** Change at Exeter St Davids and Salisbury
- **f** Change at Exeter St Davids and Westbury
- **g** Change at Salisbury
- **h** Arr. 1646
- **j** Change at Fareham

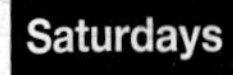

Saturdays

until 6 September

South Wales and Bristol → Weymouth and Portsmouth

Network Diagram - see first page of Table 123

		GW ◇ A	GW ◇	GW **1** ◇	GW ◇ B	GW ◇	GW	GW C	GW ◇	GW **1** ◇	GW B	GW ◇	GW **1** ◇	GW ◇ D	GW E	GW ◇	GW	SW **1**	GW
Swansea 7	d		15 29			16 29			17 29			18 29				19 29		19b55	20b55
Cardiff Central 7	d		16 30			17 30			18 30			19 30				20 30		21 00	22 00
Newport (South Wales)	d		16 44			17 44			18 44			19 44				20 44		21 15	22 16
Severn Tunnel Jn	d		16 55			17 55			18c25			19c25				20c15		21 25	22 33
Filton Abbey Wood	d	16 23	17 09		17 23	18 09		18 27	19 09		19 22	20 09		20 27		21 09		21 42	22 52
Bristol Temple Meads 10	d	16 49	17 22		17 49	18 22		18 49	19 22		19 49	20 22		20 49		21 22	21 51	22 23	23 10
Keynsham	d	16 56			17 56			18 56			19 56			20 56			21 58		23 17
Oldfield Park	d	17 02			18 03			19 03			20 03			21 03			22 04		23 23
London Paddington 15 ⊖	d		16 00	17 06		17 00			18 00	19 06	18 30	19 00	20 06		20 00	19 30	20 30		21 30
Swindon	d		16 56			17 56			18 56		19 31	19 56			21 08	20 33	21 31		22 33
Chippenham	d		17 10			18 10			19 11		19 45	20 11			21 24	20 46	21 45		22 48
Melksham	d														21 34				
Bath Spa 7	d	17 07	17 36		18 07	18 36		19 07	19 36		20 07	20 36		21 07		21 36	22 07	22 36	23 27
Freshford	d	17 15			18 16			19 17			20 16			21 17			22 17		23 36
Avoncliff	d	17x18			18x19			19x18			20x18			21x19			22x18		23x38
Bradford-on-Avon	d	17 21	17 47		18 22	18 47		19 23	19 47		20 22	20 47		21 23		21 47	22 23	22 47	23 42
Trowbridge	d	17 27	17 53		18 28	18 53		19 29	19 53		20 28	20 53		21 29	21 43	21 53	22 29	22 53	23 48
Plymouth	d		14e50		16f00		16g00					17 54				19h04			
Exeter St Davids 6	d		16e10		17j56		17 56		18e10			18 56				20e15			
Westbury	a	17 34	18 00	18 22	18 35	19 00		19 36	20 00	20 27	20 35	21 00	21 24	21 36	21 51	22 00	22 36	23 02	23 55
	d	17 35	18 01	18 22	18 36	19 01	19 09		20 01	20 28	20 37	21 01	21 24	21 36		22 01		23 04	23 55
Frome	d	17 44			18 46						20a46			21 46					00a05
Bruton	d	17 55			18 57									21 57					
Castle Cary	a	18 00		18 40	19 02					20 45			21 43	22 02					
	d	18 14			19 03									22 03					
Yeovil Pen Mill	d	18 29			19 17									22 13					
Thornford	d	18x34			19x22									22x18					
Yetminster	d	18x38			19x26									22x21					
Chetnole	d	18x41			19x30									22x24					
Maiden Newton	d	18 55			19 43									22k37					
Dorchester West	d	19m12			19 54									22 47					
Upwey	a	19 20			20 02									22 53					
Weymouth	a	19 26			20 08									22 59					
Dilton Marsh	d						19x12									22x04			
Warminster	d		18 08			19 08	19 18		20 08			21 08				22 09		23 11	
Salisbury	a		18 32			19 32	19 41		20 32			21 32				22 31		23 34	
	d		18 32			19 32	19 41		20 32			21 32				22 32			
Dean	d																		
Mottisfont & Dunbridge	d																		
Romsey	d		18 50			19 50	20 02		20 50			21 50				22 51			
Southampton Central	a		19 02			20 02	20 18		21 02			22 02				23 02			
Bournemouth	a		20 00				21 00		22 09			23 16				00 16			
Fareham	a		19 26			20 26	20 59		21 26			22 25				23 25			
	d		19 26			20 26			21 26			22 26				23 26			
Cosham	a		19 34			20 44	21 08		21 48			22 48				23 58			
Fratton	a		19 41			20 40	21 36		21 41			22 39				23 40			
Portsmouth & Southsea	a		19 45			20 44	21 40		21 45			22 43				23 44			
Portsmouth Harbour	a		19 51			20 51			21 51			22 51				23 51			
Havant	a		19n51			20n50			21n54			22n54							
Chichester 4	a		20n06			21n05			22n05			23n09							
Barnham	a		20n14			21n14			22n13			23q24							
Worthing 4	a		20n52			21n55			22q52			23q58							
Shoreham-by-Sea	a		21n02			22n05			23q02			00q08							
Hove 2	a		21n14			22n17			23q13			00q20							
Brighton 10	a		21n18			22n22			23q18			00q25							

For general notes see front of timetable
For details of catering facilities see Directory of Train Operators

A From Worcester Foregate Street (Table 71)
B From Gloucester (Table 134)
C From Great Malvern (Table 71)
D From Worcester Shrub Hill (Table 57)
E From Cheltenham Spa (Table 125)
b Change at Cardiff Central and Bristol Temple Meads
c Change at Bristol Temple Meads
e Change at Salisbury
f Change at Exeter St Davids and Castle Cary
g Change at Exeter St Davids and Westbury
h Change at Exeter St Davids and Salisbury
j Change at Castle Cary
k Arr. 2234
m Arr. 1903
n Change at Fareham
q Change at Fratton

Table 123

Saturdays

from 13 September

South Wales and Bristol → Weymouth and Portsmouth

Network Diagram - see first page of Table 123

		GW	GW ◇	GW ◇	GW	GW	GW ◇	GW	GW ◇ 🍴	GW A	SW 1 ◇ B	GW 1 ◇ 🍽	GW ◇ 🍴	GW	GW ◇ C	GW ◇ 🍴	GW	GW D	GW ◇ 🍴	GW 1 ◇ 🍽
Swansea 7	d						05 29		06 29				07 29			08 29			09 29	
Cardiff Central 7	d						06 30		07 30				08 30			09 30			10 30	
Newport (South Wales)	d						06 44		07 44				08 44			09 44			10 44	
Severn Tunnel Jn	d						06 55		07 55											
Filton Abbey Wood	d						07 09		08 09	08 23			09 09		09 23	10 09		10 25	11 09	
Bristol Temple Meads 10	d	23p16	05 45	05 50		06 43	07 22	07 49	08 22	08 40	08 50		09 22		09 49	10 22		10 49	11 22	
Keynsham	d	23p23	05 52	05 57		06 50		07 56		08 47	08 57				09 56			10 56		
Oldfield Park	d	23p29	05 59	06 04		06 56		08 02		08 54					10 03			11 03		
London Paddington 15 ⊖	d								07 00			08 18	08 00			09 00		09 30	10 00	11 06
Swindon	d								07 56				08 56			09 56		10 31	10 56	
Chippenham	d								08 10				09 10			10 10		10 45	11 10	
Melksham	d																			
Bath Spa 7	d	23p35	06 02	06 08		07 00	07 36	08 06	08 36	08 57	09 05		09 36		10 07	10 36		11 07	11 36	
Freshford	d	23p45	06 12	06 17		07 09		08 15		09 06					10 16			11 16		
Avoncliff	d	23b47	06x14	06x20		07x11		08x17		09x08					10x19			11x19		
Bradford-on-Avon	d	23p51	06 18	06 23		07 15	07 47	08 21	08 47	09 12	09 20		09 47		10 22	10 47		11 22	11 47	
Trowbridge	d	23p57	06 24	06 33		07 21	07 53	08 27	08 53	09 18	09 27		09 53		10 28	10 53		11 28	11 53	
Plymouth	d						05 40			07c54			06e55			07 54	08 52			
Exeter St Davids 6	d		05f10				06 41			08c56			08f25			08 56	09 54		10f10	
Westbury	a	00 04	06 31	06 43		07 28	08 00	08 34	09 00	09 25	09 33	09 57	10 00		10 34	11 00		11 35	12 00	12 22
	d	00 04	06 39	06 45	07 03		08 01		09 01	09 28	09 39	09 59	10 01	10 08	10 35	11 01	11 07		12 01	12 22
Frome	d	00a15		06 54						09 38					10 45					
Bruton	d			07 06						09 49					10 57					
Castle Cary	a			07 12						09 53		10 15			11 02					12 40
	d			07 15						09 54					11 02					
Yeovil Pen Mill	d			07g39						10 08					11 16					
Thornford	d			07x44						10x13					11x20					
Yetminster	d			07x47						10x16					11x23					
Chetnole	d			07x51						10x19					11x27					
Maiden Newton	d			08 03						10 31					11 41					
Dorchester West	d			08 14						10 38					11h56					
Upwey	a			08 20						10 48					12 02					
Weymouth	a			08 26						10 54					12 08					
Dilton Marsh	d				07x06									10x10			11x10			
Warminster	d		06 46		07 13		08 08		09 08		09 46		10 08	10a16		11 08	11 16		12 08	
Salisbury	a		07 15		07 35		08 32		09 32		10 09		10 31			11 32	11 38		12 32	
	d		07 24		07 37		08 32		09 32				10 32			11 32	11 39		12 32	
Dean	d																			
Mottisfont & Dunbridge	d																			
Romsey	d		07 44		07 56		08 50		09 50				10 50			11 50	12 02		12 50	
Southampton Central	a		08 02		08 07		09 02		10 02				11 02			12 02	12 18		13 02	
Bournemouth	a				09 10		10 00		11 00				12 00				13 00		14 00	
Fareham	a		08 26		08 59		09 26		10 26				11 26			12 26	12 59		13 26	
	d		08 26				09 26		10 26				11 26			12 26			13 26	
Cosham	a		08 34		09 08		09 34		10 34				11 34			12 34	13 08		13 34	
Fratton	a		08 41		09 36		09 41		10 41				11 41			12 41	13 36		13 41	
Portsmouth & Southsea	a		08 45		09 40		09 45		10 45				11 45			12 45	13 40		13 45	
Portsmouth Harbour	a		08 49				09 51		10 51				11 51			12 51			13 51	
Havant	a		08j50				09j50		10j50				11j50			12j50			13j50	
Chichester 4	a		09j08				10j08		11j08				12j08			13j08			14j08	
Barnham	a		09j18				10j18		11j18				12j18			13j18			14j18	
Worthing 4	a		09j54				10j54		11j54				12j54			13j54			14j54	
Shoreham-by-Sea	a		10j04				11j04		12j04				13j04			14j04			15j04	
Hove 2	a		10j13				11j13		12j13				13j13			14j13			15j13	
Brighton 10	a		10j18				11j18		12j18				13j18			14j18			15j18	

For general notes see front of timetable
For details of catering facilities see Directory of Train Operators

- **A** From Worcester Shrub Hill (Table 57)
- **B** To London Waterloo (Table 160)
- **C** From Gloucester (Table 134)
- **D** From Great Malvern (Table 71)
- **b** Previous night.
- Stops on request, passengers wishing to alight must inform the guard and those wishing to join must give a hand signal to the driver
- **c** Change at Castle Cary
- **e** Change at Exeter St Davids and Salisbury
- **f** Change at Salisbury
- **g** Arr. 0727
- **h** Arr. 1151
- **j** Change at Fareham

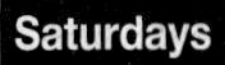

from 13 September

South Wales and Bristol → Weymouth and Portsmouth

Network Diagram - see first page of Table 123

		GW	GW	GW		SW	GW	GW		GW	GW	GW		GW	GW	GW		GW	GW	SW		GW	GW	GW		GW
		◇	◇	◇		1 ◇	1 ◇	◇			◇			◇	◇			1 ◇		1 ◇		◇		◇		◇
		A		B			C			A				B					A					D		
			🛒				🍴	🛒			🛒			🛒	🛒			🍴				🛒				🛒
Swansea [7]	d		10 29					11 29			12 29				13 29							14 29				15 29
Cardiff Central [7]	d		11 30					12 30			13 30				14 30							15 30				16 30
Newport (South Wales)	d		11 44					12 44			13 44				14 44							15 44				16 44
Severn Tunnel Jn	d																									16 55
Filton Abbey Wood	d	11 23	12 09	12 22		12 42		13 09		13 23	14 09			14 23	15 09				15 23			16 09		16 23		17 09
Bristol Temple Meads [10]	d	11 49	12 22	12 39		13 10		13 22		13 49	14 22			14 49	15 22				15 43	15 52		16 22		16 49		17 22
Keynsham	d	11 56		12 46						13 56				14 56					15 50					16 56		
Oldfield Park	d	12 03		12 53						14 03				15 03					15 57					17 02		
London Paddington [15] ⊖	d	10 30	11 00			11 30	12 18	12 00			13 00				14 00			15 06				15 00				16 00
Swindon	d	11 31	11 56			12 32		12 56			13 56				14 56	15 19						15 56				16 56
Chippenham	d	11 45	12 10			12 46		13 10			14 10				15 10	15 35						16 10				17 10
Melksham	d															15 45										
Bath Spa [7]	d	12 07	12 36	12 56		13 22		13 36		14 07	14 36			15 07	15 36				16 01	16 06		16 36		17 07		17 36
Freshford	d	12 16								14 16				15 15					16 10					17 15		
Avoncliff	d	12x19								14x19				15x18					16x13					17x18		
Bradford-on-Avon	d	12 22	12 47	13 08		13 35		13 47		14 22	14 47			15 21	15 47				16 16	16 22		16 47		17 21		17 47
Trowbridge	d	12 28	12 53	13 15		13 42		13 53		14 28	14 53			15 27	15 53	15 59			16 22	16 28		16 53		17 27		17 53
Plymouth	d	10b46	09c25	10e46							12c00	12 54														15c04
Exeter St Davids [6]	d	11f54	11g08	11 54				12g10			13g35	13 56			14g10											16g10
Westbury	a	12 35	13 00	13 22		13 48	13 59	14 00		14 35	15 00			15 34	16 00	16 06		16 22	16 29	16 36		17 00		17 34		18 00
	d	12 36	13 01	13 27		13 53	13 59	14 01			15 01	15 08		15 35	16 01			16 22		16 39		17 01	17 08	17 35		18 01
Frome	d	12 48					14 10							15 44										17 44		
Bruton	d	12 59												15 55										17 55		
Castle Cary	a	13 04					14 22							16 00				16 40						18 00		
	d	13 05												16 10										18 14		
Yeovil Pen Mill	d	13 18																						18 29		
Thornford	d	13x23												16x27										18x34		
Yetminster	d	13x25												16x30										18x38		
Chetnole	d	13x30												16x34										18x41		
Maiden Newton	d	13 42																						18 55		
Dorchester West	d	13 55												16 55										19h12		
Upwey	a	14 02												17 02										19 20		
Weymouth	a	14 08												17 08										19 26		
Dilton Marsh	d			13x30								15 11											17 11			
Warminster	d		13 08	13 36		14 00		14 08			15 08	15a17			16 08					16 47		17 08	17a17			18 08
Salisbury	a		13 32	13 58		14 24		14 32			15 32				16 32					17 09		17 32				18 32
	d		13 32	13 59				14 32			15 32				16 32							17 32				18 32
Dean	d																									
Mottisfont & Dunbridge	d																									
Romsey	d		13 50	14 19				14 50			15 50				16 50							17 50				18 50
Southampton Central	a		14 02	14 33				15 02			16 02				17 02							18 02				19 02
Bournemouth	a		15 00	15 15				16 00			17 00				18 00							19 00				20 00
Fareham	a		14 26	14 55				15 26			16 26				17 26							18 26				19 26
	d		14 26	14 56				15 26			16 26				17 26							18 26				19 26
Cosham	a		14 34	15 04				15 34			16 34				17 34							18 34				19 34
Fratton	a		14 41	15 36				15 41			16 41				17 41							18 41				19 41
Portsmouth & Southsea	a		14 45	15 40				15 45			16 45				17 45							18 45				19 45
Portsmouth Harbour	a		14 51	15 51				15 51			16 51				17 51							18 51				19 51
Havant	a		14j50	15 11				15j50			16j50				17j50							18j50				19j51
Chichester [4]	a		15j08	15 22				16j08			17j08				18j08							19j05				20j06
Barnham	a		15j18	15 30				16j18			17j18				18j18							19j14				20j14
Worthing [4]	a			15 45				16j54			17j54				18j54							19j54				20j52
Shoreham-by-Sea	a			15 56				17j04			18j04				19j04							20j04				21j02
Hove [2]	a			16 07				17j13			18j13				19j13							20j15				21j14
Brighton [10]	a			16 14				17j18			18j18				19j18							20j20				21j18

For general notes see front of timetable
For details of catering facilities see Directory of Train Operators

A From Gloucester (Table 134)
B From Great Malvern (Table 71)
C To Taunton (Table 135)
D From Worcester Foregate Street (Table 71)
b Change at Exeter St Davids and Castle Cary
c Change at Exeter St Davids and Salisbury
e Change at Exeter St Davids and Westbury
f Change at Castle Cary
g Change at Salisbury
h Arr. 1903
j Change at Fareham

Table 123

from 13 September

South Wales and Bristol → Weymouth and Portsmouth

Network Diagram - see first page of Table 123

		GW	GW	GW		GW	GW	GW		GW	GW	GW		GW	GW	GW		GW	GW	SW		GW
		1 ◇	◇ A	◇			B	◇		1 ◇	A	◇		1 ◇	◇ C	D		◇		1		
		🍴		🛒				🛒		🍴		🛒		🍴				🛒				
Swansea 7	d			16 29				17 29				18 29						19 29				
Cardiff Central 7	d			17 30				18 30				19 30						20 30				
Newport (South Wales)	d			17 44				18 44				19 44						20 44				
Severn Tunnel Jn	d			17 55																		
Filton Abbey Wood	d		17 23	18 09			18 27	19 09			19 22	20 09			20 27			21 09		21 42		22 52
Bristol Temple Meads 10	d		17 49	18 22			18 49	19 22			19 49	20 22			20 49			21 22	21 51	22 23		23 10
Keynsham	d		17 56				18 56				19 56				20 56				21 58			23 17
Oldfield Park	d		18 03				19 03				20 03				21 03				22 04			23 23
London Paddington 15 ⊖	d	17 06		17 00				18 00		19 06	18 30	19 00		20 06		20 00		19 30	20 30			21 30
Swindon	d			17 56				18 56			19 31	19 56				21 08		20 33	21 31			22 33
Chippenham	d			18 10				19 11			19 45	20 11				21 24		20 46	21 45			22 48
Melksham	d															21 34						
Bath Spa 7	d		18 07	18 36			19 07	19 36			20 07	20 36			21 07			21 36	22 07	22 36		23 27
Freshford	d		18 16				19 17				20 16				21 17				22 17			23 36
Avoncliff	d		18x19				19x18				20x18				21x19				22x18			23x38
Bradford-on-Avon	d		18 22	18 47			19 23	19 47			20 22	20 47			21 23			21 47	22 23	22 47		23 42
Trowbridge	d		18 28	18 53			19 29	19 53			20 28	20 53			21 29	21 43		21 53	22 29	22 53		23 48
Plymouth	d		16b54			16 54						17 54						18c45				
Exeter St Davids 6	d		17b53			17 53		18e10				18 56						20e15				
Westbury	a	18 22	18 35	19 00			19 36	20 00		20 27	20 35	21 00		21 24	21 36	21 51		22 00	22 36	23 02		23 55
	d	18 22	18 36	19 01		19 06		20 01		20 28	20 37	21 01		21 24	21 36			22 01		23 04		23 55
Frome	d		18 46								20a46				21 46							00a05
Bruton	d		18 57												21 57							
Castle Cary	a	18 40	19 02							20 45				21 43	22 02							
	d		19 03												22 03							
Yeovil Pen Mill	d		19 17												22 13							
Thornford	d		19x22												22x18							
Yetminster	d		19x26												22x21							
Chetnole	d		19x30												22x24							
Maiden Newton	d		19 43												22 37							
Dorchester West	d		19 54												22 47							
Upwey	a		20 02												22 53							
Weymouth	a		20 08												22 59							
Dilton Marsh	d					19x09												22x04				
Warminster	d			19 08		19 15		20 08				21 08						22 09		23 11		
Salisbury	a			19 32		19 38		20 32				21 32						22 31		23 34		
	d			19 32		19 39		20 32				21 32						22 32				
Dean	d																					
Mottisfont & Dunbridge	d																					
Romsey	d			19 50		20 02		20 50				21 50						22 51				
Southampton Central	a			20 02		20 18		21 02				22 02						23 02				
Bournemouth	a					21 00		22 09				23 16						00 16				
Fareham	a			20 26		20 59		21 26				22 25						23 25				
	d			20 26				21 26				22 26						23 26				
Cosham	a			20 44		21 08		21 48				22 48						23 58				
Fratton	a			20 40		21 36		21 41				22 39						23 40				
Portsmouth & Southsea	a			20 44		21 40		21 45				22 43						23 44				
Portsmouth Harbour	a			20 51				21 51				22 50						23 49				
Havant	a			20f50				21f54				22f54										
Chichester 4	a			21f05				22f05				23f09										
Barnham	a			21f14				22f13				23g24										
Worthing 4	a			21f55				22g52				23g58										
Shoreham-by-Sea	a			22f05				23g02				00g08										
Hove 2	a			22f17				23g13				00g20										
Brighton 10	a			22f22				23g18				00g25										

For general notes see front of timetable
For details of catering facilities see Directory of Train Operators

- **A** From Gloucester (Table 134)
- **B** From Great Malvern (Table 71)
- **C** From Worcester Shrub Hill (Table 57)
- **D** From Cheltenham Spa (Table 125)
- **b** Change at Castle Cary
- **c** Change at Exeter St Davids and Salisbury
- **e** Change at Salisbury
- **f** Change at Fareham
- **g** Change at Fratton

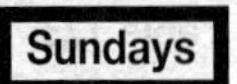

Sundays

until 7 September

South Wales and Bristol → Weymouth and Portsmouth

Network Diagram - see first page of Table 123

		GW	GW	GW	GW	GW	GW	GW	GW	GW	GW	GW	GW	GW	SW	GW	GW	GW
		◇	◇	◇	■1 ◇	■1 ◇	◇	◇	◇	◇	◇	◇	■1 ◇	◇	■1 ◇	■1 ◇	◇	◇
			A			B	A	A	A	A		A		A	C		A	D
Swansea 7	d																	
Cardiff Central 7	d		07b28				08b28	09b28	10b28	11b28		12b28		13b28			15b28	
Newport (South Wales)	d		07b58				08b58	09b58	10b58	11b58		12b58		13b58			15b58	
Severn Tunnel Jn	d		08b18				09b18	10b18	11b18	12b18		13b18		14b18			16b18	
Filton Abbey Wood	d		08 55				09 55	10 53	11 54	12 53		13 54		14 54			16 53	
Bristol Temple Meads 10	d		09 10	09 15			10 10	11 10	12 10	13 10		14 10		15 10	16 04		17 10	17 42
Keynsham	d		09 17	09 22				11 17		13 17				15 17	16 11		17 17	17 49
Oldfield Park	d		09 24	09 30				11 24		13 24				15 24			17 24	17 56
London Paddington 15 ⊖	d				08 57	09 57	07 57	09 07	10 07	11 07		12 07	13 57	13 07	14 07	15 57	15 07	16 07
Swindon	d					11 03	09 17	10 15	11 18	12 19		13 17		14 17	15 17		16 17	17 17
Chippenham	d						09 33	10 30	11 33	12 32		13 31		14 31	15 31		16 31	17 31
Melksham	d																	
Bath Spa 7	d		09 27	09 33			10 22	11 27	12 23	13 27		14 23		15 27	16 20		17 27	17 59
Freshford	d			09 43			10 32		12 32			14 33						18 09
Avoncliff	d			09x45			10x34		12x34			14x36						18x12
Bradford-on-Avon	d		09 39	09 49			10 38	11 39	12 38	13 39		14 39		15 39	16 31		17 39	18 15
Trowbridge	d		09 45	09 55			10 44	11 46	12 44	13 46		14 45		15 45	16 37		17 45	18 21
Plymouth	d						08 40		10 35			11c45		13 44	13 44		15 43	
Exeter St Davids 6	d	08e30	08 30				09 50		11 38			13f18		14 45	14 45		16 45	
Westbury	a		09 52	10 02	10 35		10 51	11 53	12 51	13 53		14 52	15 34	15 54	16 44	17 35	17 52	18 28
	d	09 00	09 53	10 04			11 00	12 03	12 55	14 03	14 15	15 00	15 36	15 58	16 46	17 36	18 00	18 30
Frome	d	09 09		10 13							14 26							18 39
Bruton	d	09 21		10 25							14 39							18 51
Castle Cary	a	09 26		10 30		11 51					14 44		15 53			17 53		18 56
	d	09 26		10 30							14 46							19 00
Yeovil Pen Mill	d	09 40		10 44							15 00							19 14
Thornford	d	09x44		10x48							15x04							19x18
Yetminster	d	09x47		10x51							15x07							19x21
Chetnole	d	09x51		10x55							15x11							19x25
Maiden Newton	d	10 03		11 07							15 23							19 37
Dorchester West	d	10 13		11 17							15 33							19 48
Upwey	a	10 20		11 24							15 40							19 55
Weymouth	a	10 25		11 29							15 45							20 01
Dilton Marsh	d		09x56					12x06		14x06				16x01				
Warminster	d		10 02				11 07	12 12	13 02	14 12		15 07		16 07	16 53		18 07	
Salisbury	a		10 26				11 29	12 34	13 25	14 39		15 32		16 30	17 16		18 30	
	d		10 31				11 31	12 36	13 29	14 48		15 33		16 31			18 31	
Dean	d																	
Mottisfont & Dunbridge	d																	
Romsey	d		10 50				11 49	12 56	13 47	15 10		15 51		16 49			18 49	
Southampton Central	a		11 00				12 04	13 06	13 58	15 20		16 02		17 04			19 04	
Bournemouth	a		12 23				13 23	14 23	14 35	16 23		17 23		18 23			20 23	
Fareham	a		11 25				12 28	13 33	14 22	15 50		16 26		17 28			19 28	
	d		11 26				12 29	13 34	14 23	15 51		16 27		17 29			19 29	
Cosham	a		11 33				12 37	13 41	14 31	16 00		16 35		17 37			19 37	
Fratton	a		11 40				12 44	14 04	14 38	16 30		16 42		17 44			19 44	
Portsmouth & Southsea	a		11 44				12 47	14 08	14 41	16 33		16 45		17 47			19 47	
Portsmouth Harbour	a		11 51				12 51	14 13	14 46			16 51		17 51			19 51	
Havant	a		11g59				12g59	14 03	14g59	16 11		16g59		17g59			19g59	
Chichester 4	a		12g14				13g14	14 19	15g14	16 22		17g14		18g14			20g14	
Barnham	a		12g22				13g22	14 27	15g22	16 30		17g22		18g22			20g22	
Worthing 4	a		12g37				13g37	14 44	15g37	16 45		17g37		18g37			20g37	
Shoreham-by-Sea	a		12g47				13g47	14 51	15g47	16 51		17g47		18g47			20g47	
Hove 2	a		12g53				13g53	14 59	15g53	16 58		17g53		18g53			20g53	
Brighton 10	a		13h00				14h00	15 06	16h00	17 05		18h00		19h00			21h00	

For general notes see front of timetable
For details of catering facilities see Directory of Train Operators

A From Bristol Parkway (Table 132)
B **Atlantic Coast Express**
C To London Waterloo (Table 160)
D From Weston-super-Mare (Table 134)
b Change at Bristol Parkway. By bus
c Change at Exeter St Davids and Salisbury
e Change at Castle Cary
f Change at Salisbury
g Change at Fratton
h Change at Fratton and Hove

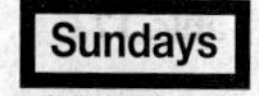

until 7 September

South Wales and Bristol → Weymouth and Portsmouth

Network Diagram - see first page of Table 123

		GW ◇ A	GW	GW ◇ A	GW 1 ◇	GW ◇ A	GW ◇ A	GW ◇ A	GW ◇	GW 1 ◇	GW ◇ A	GW ◇	SW 1	GW ◇ A
Swansea 7	d													
Cardiff Central 7	d	16b28		17b00		17b28	17b58	18b30			19b28			21b28
Newport (South Wales)	d	16b58		17b30		17b58	18b28	19b00			19b58			21b58
Severn Tunnel Jn	d	17b18				18b18	18b48				20b18			22b18
Filton Abbey Wood	d	17 54		18 23		18 53	19 23	19 53	19 58		20 53			22 56
Bristol Temple Meads 10	d	18 10		18 50		19 10	19 50	20 10	20 50		21 10		21 35	23 10
Keynsham	d	18 17				19 17			20 57					
Oldfield Park	d	18 24				19 24			21 04					
London Paddington 15 ⊖	d		17 07	17 07	17 57	17 37	18 07		19 07	19 57				21 07
Swindon	d		18 25	18 17	19 03	18 49	19 17		20 17	21 03				22 20
Chippenham	d		18 41	18 31		19 01	19 31		20 31					22 33
Melksham	d		18 51											
Bath Spa 7	d	18 27		19 02		19 27	20 02	20 22	21 07		21 22		21 49	23 22
Freshford	d	18 37						20 32	21 18					
Avoncliff	d	18x39						20x34	21x21					
Bradford-on-Avon	d	18 43		19 14		19 39		20 38	21 24		21 34		22 00	23 34
Trowbridge	d	18 50	19 00	19 20		19 45	20 18	20 44	21 30		21 40		22 06	23 40
Plymouth	d	16c02						18 10	19 15					
Exeter St Davids 6	d	17c18						19 14	20 20					
Westbury	a	18 57	19 07	19 27	19 38	19 52	20 25	20 51	21 37	21 42	21 50		22 13	23 47
	d	19 01		19 29	19 39	19 53	20 27	20 55	21 38	21 43	21 55	←	22 15	23 50
Frome	d								21e53 →			21 53		
Bruton	d											22 04		
Castle Cary	a				19 56					22 00		22 09		
	d											22 10		
Yeovil Pen Mill	d											22 23		
Thornford	d											22x28		
Yetminster	d											22x31		
Chetnole	d											22x35		
Maiden Newton	d											22 47		
Dorchester West	d											22 57		
Upwey	a											23 03		
Weymouth	a											23 08		
Dilton Marsh	d	19x04				19x56								23x53
Warminster	d	19 10		19 37		20 02	20 34	21 02			22 02		22 22	23a58
Salisbury	a	19 33		19 59		20 25	20 58	21 25			22 25		22 46	
	d	19 36		20 00		20 30	20 59	21 29			22 29			
Dean	d													
Mottisfont & Dunbridge	d													
Romsey	d	19 55		20 19		20 48	21 17	21 47			22 48			
Southampton Central	a	20 06		20 31		20 59	21 28	21 58			22 59			
Bournemouth	a	21 23		21 32			22 23	22 35			00 21			
Fareham	a	20 28		20 54		21 22	21 50	22 22			23 21			
	d	20 29		20 55		21 23	21 51	22 23			23 22			
Cosham	a	20 44		21 19		21 54	22 19	22 54			23 54			
Fratton	a	21 04		21 09		21 36	22 08	22 36			23 37			
Portsmouth & Southsea	a	21 08		21 15		21 39	22 13	22 39			23 40			
Portsmouth Harbour	a	21 13		21 23		21 46	22 20	22 46			23 44			
Havant	a	20 52		21f32		21f49	22f32	22f49						
Chichester 4	a	21 03		21f53		22f14	22f53	23f14						
Barnham	a	21 11		22f01		22f22	23f01	23f22						
Worthing 4	a	21 34		22f29		23f00								
Shoreham-by-Sea	a	21 44		22f39		23f09								
Hove 2	a	21 55		22f51		23f21								
Brighton 10	a	22 01		22f56		23f25								

For general notes see front of timetable
For details of catering facilities see Directory of Train Operators

- **A** From Bristol Parkway (Table 132)
- **b** Change at Bristol Parkway. By bus
- **c** Change at Salisbury
- **e** Arr. 2147
- **f** Change at Fratton

Table 123

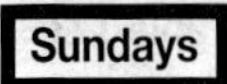

from 14 September

South Wales and Bristol → Weymouth and Portsmouth

Network Diagram - see first page of Table 123

Station		GW ◇	GW 1 ◇	GW 1 ◇	GW ◇	GW ◇	GW ◇	GW 1 ◇	GW ◇	GW 1 ◇	GW ◇	GW ◇	GW 1 ◇	GW ◇	SW 1 ◇ A	GW ◇	GW 1 ◇	GW ◇
Swansea 7	d				07 59	08 59	09 59		10 59			11 59		12 59		13 59		14 59
Cardiff Central 7	d	08 05			09 15	10 15	11 15		12 15			13 15		14 15		15 15		16 15
Newport (South Wales)	d	08 23			09 29	10 29	11 29		12 29			13 29		14 29		15 29		16 29
Severn Tunnel Jn	d	08 39			09 39	10 39	11 39		12 39			13 39		14 39		15 39		16 39
Filton Abbey Wood	d	08 54			09 56	10 54	11 54		12 57		13 01	13 54		14 54		15 58		16 57
Bristol Temple Meads 10	d	09 10			10 10	11 10	12 10		13 10		13 40	14 10		15 10	16 04	16 10		17 10
Keynsham	d	09 17				11 17			13 17		13 47			15 17	16 11			17 17
Oldfield Park	d	09 24				11 24			13 24		13 54			15 24				17 24
London Paddington 15 ⊖	d		08 57	09 57	08 00	09 03	10 03	11 27	11 03	12 57	12 03		13 57	13 03	14 03		15 57	15 03
Swindon	d				09 12	10 10	11 11		12 17		13 12			14 12	15 12			16 12
Chippenham	d				09 28	10 26	11 26		12 31		13 26			14 26	15 26			16 26
Melksham	d																	
Bath Spa 7	d	09 27			10 22	11 27	12 22		13 27		13 57	14 23		15 27	16 20	16 25		17 27
Freshford	d				10 32		12 32				14 08	14 33				16 35		
Avoncliff	d				10x34		12x34				14x11	14x36				16x37		
Bradford-on-Avon	d	09 39			10 38	11 39	12 38		13 39		14 14	14 39		15 39	16 31	16 41		17 39
Trowbridge	d	09 45			10 44	11 46	12 44		13 46		14 20	14 45		15 45	16 37	16 47		17 45
Plymouth	d				08 40		10 35					11b45		13 44		14c06		15b25
Exeter St Davids 6	d	08 30			09 49		11 38					13c18		14 46		15c20		16c33
Westbury	a	09 52	10 22		10 51	11 53	12 52	12 59	13 53	14 17	14 27	14 52		15 54	16 44	16 54	17 22	17 52
	d	09 53			11 00	12 03	12 55	12 59	14 03		14 30	15 00		15 58	16 46	16 58	17 24	18 00
Frome	d										14e49							
Bruton	d										15 00							
Castle Cary	a			11 33				13 17			15 05		15 34				17 40	
	d										15 06							
Yeovil Pen Mill	d										15 19							
Thornford	d										15x24							
Yetminster	d										15x27							
Chetnole	d										15x31							
Maiden Newton	d										15 43							
Dorchester West	d										15 53							
Upwey	a										15 59							
Weymouth	a										16 05							
Dilton Marsh	d	09x56				12x06			14x06					16x01		17x01		
Warminster	d	10 02			11 07	12 12	13 02		14 12			15 06		16 07	16 53	17 07		18 07
Salisbury	a	10 26			11 29	12 34	13 25		14 39			15 32		16 30	17 16	17 30		18 30
	d	10 31			11 31	12 36	13 29		14 48			15 33		16 31		17 31		18 31
Dean	d																	
Mottisfont & Dunbridge	d																	
Romsey	d	10 50			11 49	12 56	13 47		15 10			15 51		16 49		17 49		18 49
Southampton Central	a	11 00			12 04	13 06	13 58		15 20			16 02		17 04		18 04		19 04
Bournemouth	a	12 23			13 23	14 23	14 35		16 23			17 23		18 23		19 23		20 23
Fareham	a	11 25			12 28	13 33	14 22		15 50			16 26		17 28		18 28		19 28
	d	11 26			12 29	13 34	14 23		15 51			16 26		17 29		18 29		19 29
Cosham	a	11 33			12 37	13 41	14 31		16 00			16 34		17 37		18 37		19 37
Fratton	a	11 40			12 44	14 04	14 38		16 30			16 41		17 44		18 44		19 44
Portsmouth & Southsea	a	11 44			12 47	14 08	14 41		16 33			16 45		17 47		18 47		19 47
Portsmouth Harbour	a	11 51			12 51	14 13	14 46					16 51		17 51		18 51		19 51
Havant	a	11f59			12f59	14 03	14f59		16 11			16f59		17f59		18f59		19f59
Chichester 4	a	12f14			13f14	14 19	15f14		16 22			17f14		18f14		19f14		20f14
Barnham	a	12f22			13f22	14 27	15f22		16 30			17f22		18f22		19f22		20f22
Worthing 4	a	12f37			13f37	14 44	15f37		16 45			17f37		18f37		19f37		20f37
Shoreham-by-Sea	a	12f47			13f47	14 51	15f47		16 51			17f47		18f47		19f47		20f47
Hove 2	a	12f53			13f53	14 59	15f53		16 58			17f53		18f53		19f53		20f53
Brighton 10	a	13g00			14g00	15 06	16g00		17 05			18g00		19g00		20g00		21g00

For general notes see front of timetable
For details of catering facilities see Directory of Train Operators

- A To London Waterloo (Table 160)
- b Change at Exeter St Davids and Salisbury
- c Change at Salisbury
- e Arr. 1439
- f Change at Fratton
- g Change at Fratton and Hove

from 14 September

South Wales and Bristol → Weymouth and Portsmouth

Network Diagram - see first page of Table 123

		GW ◇ A	GW ◇	GW	GW [1] ◇	GW ◇	GW ◇	GW ◇	GW [1] ◇	GW ◇	GW [1] ◇	GW ◇	GW ◇	SW [1]	GW ◇
Swansea [7]	d		15 59			16 29		17 35					18 29		20 35
Cardiff Central [7]	d		17 15			17 45	18 15	18 45		19 15			20 15		22 05
Newport (South Wales)	d		17 29			18 00	18 29	18 59		19 29			20 29		22 23
Severn Tunnel Jn	d		17 40				18 39	19 09					20 39		22 40
Filton Abbey Wood	d		17 55			18 23	18 56	19 25		19 52		19 58	20 54		22 57
Bristol Temple Meads [10]	d	17 42	18 10			18 50	19 10	19 50		20 10		20 50	21 10	21 35	23 10
Keynsham	d	17 49	18 17				19 17					20 57			
Oldfield Park	d	17 56	18 24				19 24					21 04			
London Paddington [15] ⊖	d	16 03		17 03	17 57			18 03	18 57		19 57	19 03		20 03	21 03
Swindon	d	17 12		18 31		18 12		19 12				20 12		21 12	22 15
Chippenham	d	17 26		18 47		18 26		19 26				20 26		21 26	22 28
Melksham	d			18 57											
Bath Spa [7]	d	17 59	18 27			19 02	19 27	20 02		20 22		21 07	21 22	21 49	23 22
Freshford	d	18 09	18 37							20 32		21 18			
Avoncliff	d	18x12	18x39							20x34		21x21			
Bradford-on-Avon	d	18 15	18 43			19 14	19 39			20 38		21 24	21 36	22 00	23 34
Trowbridge	d	18 21	18 50	19 06		19 20	19 45	20 18		20 44		21 30	21 42	22 06	23 40
Plymouth	d	15b43	16c02							18 10		19b15	19 15		
Exeter St Davids [6]	d	16b45	17c18							19c20		20b19	20 19		
Westbury	a	18 28	18 57	19 13	19 26	19 29	19 52	20 25		20 51	21 27	21 37	21 49	22 13	23 47
	d	18 30	19 01			19 30	19 53	20 28		20 55	21 28	21 38	21 55	22 15	23 50
Frome	d	18 39										21 48			
Bruton	d	18 51										21 59			
Castle Cary	a	18 56							20 29		21 45	22 04			
	d	19 00										22 05			
Yeovil Pen Mill	d	19 14										22 18			
Thornford	d	19x18										22x23			
Yetminster	d	19x21										22x26			
Chetnole	d	19x25										22x30			
Maiden Newton	d	19 37										22 42			
Dorchester West	d	19 48										22 52			
Upwey	a	19 55										22 58			
Weymouth	a	20 01										23 03			
Dilton Marsh	d		19x04				19x56								23x53
Warminster	d		19 10			19 38	20 02	20 35		21 02			22 02	22 22	23a58
Salisbury	a		19 33			19 59	20 25	20 58		21 25			22 25	22 46	
	d		19 36			20 00	20 30	20 59		21 29			22 29		
Dean	d														
Mottisfont & Dunbridge	d														
Romsey	d		19 55			20 19	20 48	21 17		21 47			22 48		
Southampton Central	a		20 06			20 31	20 59	21 28		21 58			22 59		
Bournemouth	a		21 23			21 32		22 23		22 35			00 21		
Fareham	a		20 28			20 54	21 22	21 50		22 22			23 21		
	d		20 29			20 55	21 23	21 51		22 23			23 22		
Cosham	a		20 44			21 19	21 54	22 19		22 54			23 54		
Fratton	a		21 04			21 09	21 36	22 08		22 36			23 37		
Portsmouth & Southsea	a		21 08			21 15	21 39	22 13		22 39			23 40		
Portsmouth Harbour	a		21 13			21 23	21 46	22 20		22 46			23 44		
Havant	a		20 52			21e32	21e49	22e32		22e49					
Chichester [4]	a		21 03			21e53	22e14	22e53		23e14					
Barnham	a		21 11			22e01	22e22	23e01		23e22					
Worthing [4]	a		21 34			22e29	23e00								
Shoreham-by-Sea	a		21 44			22e39	23e09								
Hove [2]	a		21 55			22e51	23e21								
Brighton [10]	a		22 01			22e56	23e25								

For general notes see front of timetable
For details of catering facilities see Directory of Train Operators

A From Weston-super-Mare (Table 134)
b Change at Castle Cary
c Change at Salisbury
e Change at Fratton

Portsmouth and Weymouth → Bristol and South Wales

Network Diagram - see first page of Table 123

Miles	Miles	Miles			GW	GW	GW	GW	GW		GW	GW	SW	GW	GW		GW	GW	GW	GW	GW		GW	GW	GW	GW
						1 ◇	1 ◇					1 ◇		◇			1 ◇	◇	◇		◇			◇	1 ◇	◇
								A			B			C	D				C	A				D		
						⎍	⎍					⎍					⎍	⊼			⊼				⊠	⊼
—	—	—	Brighton [10]	d																						
—	—	—	Hove [2]	d																						
—	—	—	Shoreham-by-Sea	d																						
—	—	—	Worthing [4]	d																						
—	—	—	Barnham	d																						
—	—	—	Chichester [4]	d																						
—	—	—	Havant	d																						
0	—	—	**Portsmouth Harbour**	d														06 00			06 51					08 22
¾	—	—	Portsmouth & Southsea	d														06 04			06 55					08 27
1¾	—	—	Fratton	d														06 08			06 59					08 31
5½	—	—	Cosham	d														06 15			07 07		*07 38*			08 39
11¼	—	—	Fareham	a														06 23			07 17					08 46
—	—	—		d														06 24			07 18		*07 47*			08 47
—	—	—	Bournemouth	d														*05b57*			*06 56*		*07 30*			*08 10*
25¾	—	—	**Southampton Central**	d														06 46			07 47		08 23			09 10
34	—	—	Romsey	d														07 00			08 00		08 35			09 21
37¾	—	—	Mottisfont & Dunbridge	d																						
41½	—	—	Dean	d																						
50½	—	—	**Salisbury**	a														07 18			08 20		09 00			09 40
—	—	—		d				06 12					06 40					07 20			08 21		09 03			09 41
70¼	—	—	Warminster	d				06 32					07 00		07 23			07 41			08 43		09 23			10 01
73½	—	—	Dilton Marsh	d				06x36							07x27			07x45					09x27			
—	0	—	**Weymouth**	d										05 40					06 40							
—	2½	—	Upwey	d										05 45					06 45							
—	7	—	Dorchester West	d										05 54					06 53							
—	14¾	—	Maiden Newton	d										06 05					07 05							
—	21¼	—	Chetnole	d										06x13					07x12							
—	23¼	—	Yetminster	d										06x16					07x15							
—	24¼	—	Thornford	d										06x18					07x18							
—	27½	—	Yeovil Pen Mill	d										06 26					07c31							
—	39¼	—	Castle Cary	a										06 38					07 43							
—	—	—		d								06 43		06 46			07 30		07 43						09 40	
—	42¾	—	Bruton	d										06 52					07 49							
—	53¼	—	Frome	d			06 10		06 47					07 04					08 02							
75	59	0	**Westbury**	a			06 20	06 40	06 56			07 02	07 06	07 13	07 32		07 48	07 50	08 12		08 49		09 33		09 58	10 07
—	—	—		d	05 58	06 08	06 21	06 42	06 57		07 02	07 05	07 07	07 18	07 38		07 51	07 52	08 17	08 45	08 54			09 38	09 59	10 08
—	—	—	Exeter St Davids [6]	a																	*10e33*		*11 12*			*11e42*
—	—	—	Plymouth	a																	*11f48*		*12g23*			*13f10*
79	63	4	Trowbridge	d	06 04			06 48	07 03		07 08		07 13	07 24	07 44			07 58	08 23	08 51	09 00			09 44		10 14
82¼	66¼	—	Bradford-on-Avon	d	06 10			06 54	07 09				07 20	07 30	07 50			08 04	08 29	08 57	09 08			09 50		10 20
83½	67½	—	Avoncliff	d	06x12			06x56	07x11					07x32	07x52			08x06	08x31	08x59	09x11			09x52		
84½	68½	—	Freshford	d	06 15			06 59	07 15					07 36	07 55			08 09	08 34	09 02	09 12			09 55		
91½	75½	—	Bath Spa [7]	a	06 26			07 10	07 26				07 32	07 47	08 06			08 20	08 45	09 13	09 22			10 06		10 33
—	—	9½	Melksham	d							07 17															
—	—	15¾	Chippenham	a	*06 54*						07 30		*07 54*		*08 24*			*08 44*	*09 24*		*09 54*			*10 24*		*10 54*
—	—	32½	Swindon	a	*07 09*						07 48		*08 09*		*08 39*			*09 03*	*09 39*		*10 09*			*10 39*		*11 09*
—	—	—	London Paddington [15] ⊖	a	*08 14*	07 52	08 09				*09 06*	08 38	*09 14*		*09 44*		09 22	*10 14*	*10 44*		*11 15*			*11 42*	11 23	*12 16*
92½	76½	—	Oldfield Park	a	06 30			07 14	07 30				07 36	07 51	08 10			08 24	08 49	09 17				10 10		
98½	82½	—	Keynsham	a	06 38			07 21	07 37				07 43	07 57	08 17			08 31	08 56	09 24	09 32			10 17		
103	87	—	**Bristol Temple Meads [10]**	a	06 46			07 29	07 45				07 52	08 06	08 29			08 39	09 04	09 32	09 39			10 29		10 47
107½	91½	—	Filton Abbey Wood	a	07 01			07 48	08 00					08 21	08 48			09 01	09 20	09 47	10 01			10 47		11 01
119½	119½	—	Severn Tunnel Jn	a	07 14									*08h46*					*09h45*		*10h46*					*11h45*
129½	113½	—	Newport (South Wales)	a	07 26				08 24					*08h59*				09 23	*09h58*		10 23					11 24
141¼	125¼	—	**Cardiff Central [7]**	a	07 44				08 42					*09j22*				09 41	*10h17*		10 41					11 43
—	—	—	Swansea [7]	a	*08 49*				*09k44*									*10 45*			*11 43*					*12k45*

For general notes see front of timetable
For details of catering facilities see Directory of Train Operators

A To Gloucester (Table 134)
B To Cheltenham Spa (Table 125)
C To Bristol Parkway (Table 132)
D To Great Malvern (Table 71)
b From 29 September dep. 0554
c Arr. 0726
e Change at Salisbury
f Change at Salisbury and Exeter St Davids
g Change at Westbury and Exeter St Davids
h Change at Bristol Temple Meads
j Change at Bristol Parkway
k Change at Newport (South Wales)

Portsmouth and Weymouth → Bristol and South Wales

Network Diagram - see first page of Table 123

Station		GW	GW	GW		GW	SW	GW	GW	GW		GW	GW	GW	GW	GW		SW	GW	GW	GW	GW		GW	GW	GW
				1◇		◇	1◇	◇	◇	◇		1◇	◇			◇		1◇	◇	1◇	◇			1◇	◇	◇
		A					B	C		A				D	E			B	A			C				A
				⊠		🍴			🍴			🍽	🍴			🍴				⊠	🍴			🍴	🍴	
Brighton 10	d							09 00																		
Hove 2	d							09 04																		
Shoreham-by-Sea	d							09 13																		
Worthing 4	d							09 22																		
Barnham	d							09 38																		
Chichester 4	d							09 47																		
Havant	d							09 59																		
Portsmouth Harbour	d					09 22		09 32	10 22				11 22			12 22					13 22				14 22	
Portsmouth & Southsea	d					09 27		09 36	10 27				11 27			12 27					13 27				14 27	
Fratton	d					09 31		09 40	10 31				11 31			12 31					13 31				14 31	
Cosham	d					09 39		10 05	10 39				11 39		11 45	12 39					13 39				14 39	
Fareham	a					09 46		10 13	10 46				11 46			12 46					13 46				14 46	
	d					09 47		10 14	10 47				11 47		11 53	12 47					13 47				14 47	
Bournemouth	d					09 18		09 55	10 21				11 21		11 45	12 21					13 21				14 21	
Southampton Central	d					10 10		10 40	11 10				12 10		12 26	13 10					14 10				15 10	
Romsey	d					10 21		10 51	11 21				12 21		12 39	13 21					14 21				15 21	
Mottisfont & Dunbridge	d																									
Dean	d																									
Salisbury	a					10 40		11 10	11 40				12 40		13 02	13 40					14 40				15 40	
	d					10 41	10 52	11 11	11 41				12 41		13 06	13 41		13 52			14 41				15 41	
Warminster	d		10 25			11 01	11 12	11 31	12 01				13 01		13 31	14 01		14 12			15 01	15 28			16 01	
Dilton Marsh	d		10x29												13x35							15x32				
Weymouth	d	08 50								11 10									13 10							15 10
Upwey	d	08 55								11 16									13 16							15 16
Dorchester West	d	09 04								11 24									13 25							15 25
Maiden Newton	d	09 15								11b42									13c43							15 36
Chetnole	d	09x23								11x49									13x50							15x45
Yetminster	d	09x26								11x52									13x53							15x48
Thornford	d	09x28								11x55									13x56							15x50
Yeovil Pen Mill	d	09 36								12 03									14 04							15 57
Castle Cary	a	09 48								12 14									14 16							16 09
	d	09 51								12 22		12 45							14 16	14 44				15 40		16 10
Bruton	d	09 57								12 27									14 22							16 16
Frome	d	10e15								12 39									14 35					15 55		16 29
Westbury	a	10 25	10 33			11 07	11 18	11 38	12 07	12 48		13 03	13 07		13 39	14 07		14 18	14 44	15 02	15 07	15 36		16 05	16 07	16 38
	d	10 38		11 03		11 08	11 19	11 38	12 08	12 49		13 04	13 08	13 38	13 42	14 08		14 19	14 45	15 03	15 08	15 38		16 07	16 08	16 38
Exeter St Davids 6	a	11f12				12g27			13 32	13f32						15g42									17 33	17f33
Plymouth	a	12h23				13j48			14 36	14f36						16g58									18 39	18f39
Trowbridge	d	10 44				11 14	11 25	11 44	12 14	12 55			13 14	13 44	13 51	14 14		14 25	14 51		15 14	15 44			16 14	16 44
Bradford-on-Avon	d	10 50				11 20	11 31	11 50	12 20	13 01			13 20	13 50	13 57	14 20		14 31	14 57		15 20	15 50			16 20	16 50
Avoncliff	d	10x52						11x52		13x03				13x52	13x59				14x59			15x52				16x52
Freshford	d	10 55						11 55		13 05				13 55	14 02				15 02			15 55				16 55
Bath Spa 7	a	11 06				11 33	11 45	12 06	12 33	13 17			13 33	14 06	14 13	14 33		14 45	15 13		15 33	16 05			16 33	17 06
Melksham	d																									
Chippenham	a	11 24				11 54		12 24	12 54				13 54	14 24		14 54		15 24			15 54	16 24			16 54	17 24
Swindon	a	11 39				12 09		12 39	13 09				14 09	14 39		15 09		15 39			16 09	16 39			17 09	17 39
London Paddington 15 ⊖	a	12 42		12 23		13 15		13 42	14 15			14 44	15 15	15 42		16 16		16 44		16 22	17 15	17 41		17 53	18 15	18 44
Oldfield Park	a	11 10						12 10		13 20					14 17				15 17			16 09				17 10
Keynsham	a	11 17						12 17		13 27					14 25				15 24			16 16				17 17
Bristol Temple Meads 10	a	11 29				11 47	12 05	12 29	12 47	13 36			13 47		14 35	14 47		15 05	15 32		15 47	16 29			16 47	17 29
Filton Abbey Wood	a	11 47				12 01	12 29	12 47	13 01	13 47			14 01	14 26	14 47	15 01		15 29	15 47		16 01	16 47			17 01	17 47
Severn Tunnel Jn	a						12 45		13m45				14m45					15 45			16m48				17 14	
Newport (South Wales)	a					12 24	13 04		13 24				14 24			15 24		15 58			16 24				17 26	
Cardiff Central 7	a					12 43	13 27		13 45				14 43			15 43		16 17			16 43				17 47	
Swansea 7	a					13n45			14n45				15n43			16n43					17n43				18n46	

For general notes see front of timetable
For details of catering facilities see Directory of Train Operators

- **A** To Gloucester (Table 134)
- **B** From London Waterloo (Table 160)
- **C** To Great Malvern (Table 71)
- **D** To Bristol Parkway (Table 134)
- **E** To Worcester Foregate Street (Table 71)
- **b** Arr. 1133
- **c** Arr. 1334
- **e** Arr. 1009
- **f** Change at Castle Cary
- **g** Change at Salisbury
- **h** Change at Castle Cary and Exeter St Davids
- **j** Change at Salisbury and Exeter St Davids
- **m** Change at Bristol Temple Meads
- **n** Change at Newport (South Wales)

Portsmouth and Weymouth → Bristol and South Wales

Network Diagram - see first page of Table 123

	GW	GW	GW	GW		GW	GW	GW	GW	GW		GW	GW	GW	GW	GW		GW	SW	GW	GW	GW	GW		
																FX					FX				
	◇		◇	◇		1 ◇	◇	1 ◇		◇		◇	1		1 ◇	◇			1 ◇	◇	◇				
		A							B	C															
	⊤		⊤	⊤		⊡		⊡				⊤			⊡	⊤					⊤				
Brighton [10] d										17 00															
Hove [2] d										17 04															
Shoreham-by-Sea d										17 13															
Worthing [4] d										17 22															
Barnham d										17 39															
Chichester [4] d										17 47															
Havant d										17 58															
Portsmouth Harbour d	15 22		16 22	17 22						17b28		18 22				19 22					20 22		21 22		
Portsmouth & Southsea d	15 27		16 27	17 27						17 36		18 27				19 27					20 27		21 27		
Fratton d	15 31		16 31	17 31						17 40		18 31				19 31					20 31		21 31		
Cosham d	15 39		16 39	17 39						18 05		18 39				19 39					20 33		21c44		
Fareham a	15 46		16 46	17 46						18 12		18 46				19 46					20 46		21 46		
Fareham d	15 47		16 47	17 47						18 13		18 47				19 47					20 47		21 47		
Bournemouth d	15 21		16 21	17 21						17 59		18 21				19 21					20 21		21 12		
Southampton Central d	16 10		17 10	18 10						18 40		19 10				20 10					21 10	21 20	22 22		
Romsey d	16 21		17 21	18 21						18 51		19 21				20 21					21 21	21 31	22 33		
Mottisfont & Dunbridge d																									
Dean d																									
Salisbury a	16 40		17 40	18 40						19 10		19 40				20 40					21 40	21 56	22 58		
Salisbury d	16 41		17 41	18 41						19 11		19 41				20 41			20 57		21 41	21 58	23 00		
Warminster d	17 01	17 28	18 01	19 01						19 30		20 01				21 01			21 17		22 01	22 18	23 20		
Dilton Marsh d		17x32								19x35												22x22	23x24		
Weymouth d							17 30													20 01					
Upwey d							17 35													20 06					
Dorchester West d							17 45													20 16					
Maiden Newton d							17 56													20 28					
Chetnole d							18x03													20x35					
Yetminster d							18x06													20x38					
Thornford d							18x09													20x41					
Yeovil Pen Mill d							18e23													20 49					
Castle Cary a							18 34													21 01					
Castle Cary d						18 53	18 35								20 44					21 02					
Bruton d							18 41													21 08					
Frome d							19f05						20 17					20 57		21 21					
Westbury a	17 07	17 36	18 07	19 08		19 11	19 17			19 38		20 07	20 28		21 02	21 07		21 10	21 23	21 31	22 07	22 26	23 30		
Westbury d	17 08	17 38	18 08	19 08		19 11	19 17	19 17	19 32	19 38		20 08		20 38	21 04	21 08			21 24	21 38	22 08	22 40			
Exeter St Davids [6] a		19 17	20g07	20g36			20h08			21 16		21g55	22 16						23 48	22h16	00g01	00g01			
Plymouth a		20j48	21j17	21k48			21m17			22j24			23 22						00 52	23h22					
Trowbridge d	17 14	17 44	18 14	19 14			19 23		19 38	19 44		20 14		20 44		21 14			21 30	21 44	22 14	22 46			
Bradford-on-Avon d	17 20	17 50	18 20	19 20			19 29			19 50		20 20		20 50		21 20			21 36	21 50	22 20	22 52			
Avoncliff d		17x52					19x31			19x52				20x52						21x52		22x54			
Freshford d		17 55					19 35			19 55				20 55						21 55		22 57			
Bath Spa [7] a	17 33	18 06	18 35	19 35			19 46			20 08		20 35		21 06		21 35			21 50	22 06	22 33	23 08			
Melksham d									19 47																
Chippenham a	17 54	18 24	18 54	19 54					20 01			20 54				22 07					22 57				
Swindon a	18 09	18 39	19 09	20 09					20 19			21 09				22 23					23 13				
London Paddington [15] ⊖ a	19 15	19 42	20 15	21 15		20 39		21 02	21 32			22 15			22 30	23 36					00 32				
Oldfield Park a		18 10					19 50			20 10				21 10						22 10		23 12			
Keynsham a		18 17					19 57			20 17				21 17					21 58	22 17		23 20			
Bristol Temple Meads [10] a	17 47	18 28	18 50	19 49			20 05			20 29		20 50		21 29		21 50			22 06	22 27	22 47	23 29			
Filton Abbey Wood a	18 01	18 47	19 01	20 00			20 30			20 47		21 01				22 00					23 00				
Severn Tunnel Jn a	18 14		19 15				20 46					21n45				22 16					23 16				
Newport (South Wales) a	18 26		19 27	20 23			21 00					21 28				22 35					23 35				
Cardiff Central [7] a	18 45		19 45	20 43			21q22					21 47				22 54					23 55				
Swansea [7] a	19 48		20r46	21r42								23 00				00 28					02 10				

For general notes see front of timetable
For details of catering facilities see Directory of Train Operators

- **A** To Great Malvern (Table 71)
- **B** To Cheltenham Spa (Table 125)
- **C** To Worcester Shrub Hill (Table 57)
- **b** Change at Fratton and Cosham
- **c** Change at Southampton Central
- **e** Arr. 1815
- **f** Arr. 1856
- **g** Change at Salisbury
- **h** Change at Castle Cary
- **j** Change at Westbury and Exeter St Davids
- **k** Change at Salisbury and Exeter St Davids
- **m** Change at Castle Cary and Exeter St Davids
- **n** Change at Bristol Temple Meads
- **q** Change at Bristol Temple Meads and Newport (South Wales)
- **r** Change at Newport (South Wales)

Table 123

Saturdays
until 6 September

Portsmouth and Weymouth → Bristol and South Wales

Network Diagram - see first page of Table 123

		GW	GW	SW	GW	GW	GW	GW	GW	GW	GW	GW	GW	GW	GW	GW	GW	GW
				1		1 ◇	◇	◇		◇		◇	1 ◇	◇			1	◇
		A			B			A				B			A			
						☕							☕				☕	
Brighton 10	d																	
Hove 2	d																	
Shoreham-by-Sea	d																	
Worthing 4	d																	
Barnham	d																	
Chichester 4	d																	
Havant	d																	
Portsmouth Harbour	d						06 00			07 04				08 22				09 22
Portsmouth & Southsea	d						06 04			07 08				08 27				09 27
Fratton	d						06 08			07 13				08 31				09 31
Cosham	d						06 16			07 20	*07 44*			08 39				09 39
Fareham	a						06 26			07 28				08 46				09 46
	d						06 27			07 29	*07 53*			08 47				09 47
Bournemouth	d						*05 42*			*06 42*	*07 45*			*08 21*				*09 21*
Southampton Central	d						06 52			07 52	08 27			09 10				10 10
Romsey	d						07 11			08 09	08 38			09 21				10 21
Mottisfont & Dunbridge	d																	
Dean	d																	
Salisbury	a						07 29			08 29	09 03			09 40				10 40
	d	06 03		06 40			07 30			08 32	09 04			09 41				10 41
Warminster	d	06 23		07 00	07 23		07 50			08 53	09 25			10 01		10 28		11 01
Dilton Marsh	d	06x27			07x28						09x29					10x33		
Weymouth	d							06 40							08 53			
Upwey	d							06 45							08 58			
Dorchester West	d							06 53							09 05			
Maiden Newton	d							07 05							09 17			
Chetnole	d							07x12							09x24			
Yetminster	d							07x15							09x27			
Thornford	d							07x18							09x30			
Yeovil Pen Mill	d							07b30							09 38			
Castle Cary	a							07 42							09 49			
	d					07 33		07 43					09 45		09 56			
Bruton	d							07 49							10 01			
Frome	d		06 37					08 02							10 17			
Westbury	a	06 31	06 46	07 06	07 31	07 51	07 56	08 12		08 59	09 33		10 03	10 07	10 27	10 36		11 07
	d	06 38	06 47	07 07	07 38	07 56	07 59	08 17	09 03	09 08		09 38	10 13	10 08	10 38		11 00	11 08
Exeter St Davids 6	a									*10c32*	*11 01*			*11c56*	*11e01*			*12c30*
Plymouth	a									*11f48*	*12g26*			*13f11*	*11h26*			*13c59*
Trowbridge	d	06 44	06 53	07 13	07 44		08 05	08 23	09 09	09 14		09 44		10 14	10 44			11 14
Bradford-on-Avon	d	06 49	06 59	07 19	07 50		08 11	08 29		09 20		09 50		10 20	10 50			11 20
Avoncliff	d	06x51	07x01		07x53			08x32				09x52			10x53			
Freshford	d	06 55	07 05		07 55			08 34				09 55			10 55			
Bath Spa 7	a	07 06	07 16	07 32	08 07		08 31	08 45		09 33		10 06		10 34	11 06			11 33
Melksham	d								09 18									
Chippenham	a	*07 24*		*07 54*			*08 54*	*09 24*	09 31	*09 54*		*10 24*		*10 54*	*11 24*			*11 54*
Swindon	a	*07 40*		*08 09*			*09 09*	*09 39*	09 49	*10 09*		*10 39*		*11 09*	*11 39*			*12 09*
London Paddington 15 ⊖	a	*08 45*		*09 15*		09 21	*10 14*	*10 43*	11 09	*11 15*		*11 41*	11 23	*12 15*	*12 42*		12 21	*13 17*
Oldfield Park	a	07 10	07 20	07 36	08 11			08 49				10 10			11 10			
Keynsham	a	07 17	07 27	07 43	08 18			08 56				10 17			11 17			
Bristol Temple Meads 10	a	07 29	07 35	07 52	08 29		08 45	09 04		09 47		10 28		10 48	11 29			11 47
Filton Abbey Wood	a	07 47	08 00	*08 29*	08 47		09 00	09 16		10 00		10 47		11 00	11 47			12 00
Severn Tunnel Jn	a			*08 45*				*09j45*		*10j45*				*11j45*				
Newport (South Wales)	a		08 24	*09 00*			09 23	*09j58*		10 23				11 22				12 22
Cardiff Central 7	a		08 41	*09 21*			09 41	*10j16*		10 41				11 41				12 41
Swansea 7	a		*09 56*				*10 43*			*11 42*				*12 43*				*13 42*

For general notes see front of timetable
For details of catering facilities see
Directory of Train Operators

- **A** To Gloucester (Table 134)
- **B** To Great Malvern (Table 71)
- **b** Arr. 0724
- **c** Change at Salisbury
- **e** Change at Castle Cary
- **f** Change at Salisbury and Exeter St Davids
- **g** Change at Westbury and Exeter St Davids
- **h** Change at Castle Cary and Exeter St Davids
- **j** Change at Bristol Temple Meads

Table 123

until 6 September

Portsmouth and Weymouth → Bristol and South Wales

Network Diagram - see first page of Table 123

		SW 1 ◇ A	GW ◇ B	GW 1 ☕	GW ◇	GW ◇ C	GW ◇	GW ◇ C	GW D	GW 1 ☕	GW ◇	SW 1 ◇ A	GW 1 ☕	GW ◇ C	GW	GW ◇	GW D	GW ◇
Brighton 10	d		09 00															
Hove 2	d		09 04															
Shoreham-by-Sea	d		09 13															
Worthing 4	d		09 22															
Barnham	d		09 41															
Chichester 4	d		09 49															
Havant	d		10 00															
Portsmouth Harbour	d		09b28		10 22		11 22				12 22					13 22		14 22
Portsmouth & Southsea	d		09 36		10 27		11 27				12 27					13 27		14 27
Fratton	d		09 40		10 31		11 31				12 31					13 31		14 31
Cosham	d		10 06		10 39		11 39		11 45		12 39					13 39		14 39
Fareham	a		10 14		10 46		11 46				12 46					13 46		14 46
	d		10 15		10 47		11 47		11 53		12 47					13 47		14 47
Bournemouth	d		09 59		10 21		11 21		11 45		12 21					13 21		14 21
Southampton Central	d		10 40		11 10		12 10		12 27		13 10					14 10		15 10
Romsey	d		10 51		11 21		12 21		12 38		13 21					14 21		15 21
Mottisfont & Dunbridge	d																	
Dean	d																	
Salisbury	a		11 10		11 40		12 40		13 03		13 40					14 40		15 40
	d	10 52	11 11		11 41		12 41		13 04		13 41	13 52				14 41		15 41
Warminster	d	11 12	11 32		12 01		13 01		13 25		14 01	14 12				15 01	15 28	16 01
Dilton Marsh	d								13x29								15x33	
Weymouth	d					11 10		13 10										
Upwey	d					11 15		13 15										
Dorchester West	d					11 26		13 24										
Maiden Newton	d					11c42		13e44										
Chetnole	d					11x49		13x51										
Yetminster	d					11x53		13x54										
Thornford	d					11x55		13x57										
Yeovil Pen Mill	d					12 03		14 05										
Castle Cary	a					12 15		14 16										
	d			11 21		12 26		14 17		14 18			14 24	←				
Bruton	d					12 31		14 22 →						14 22				
Frome	d					12 43								14 34				
Westbury	a	11 18	11 38	11 39	12 07	12 52	13 07		13 33		14 07	14 18	14 43	14 47		15 07	15 36	16 07
	d	11 19	11 38	11 40	12 08	12 52	13 08		13 38	14 00	14 08	14 19	14 44	14 48	15 04	15 08	15 38	16 08
Exeter St Davids 6	a		13 03		13f42		14f23		15 06	15 06	15f42							17 32
Plymouth	a		14g23		15h11				16g26	16 26	16f57							18 39
Trowbridge	d	11 25	11 44		12 14	12 58	13 14		13 44		14 14	14 25		14 54	15 10	15 14	15 44	16 14
Bradford-on-Avon	d	11 31	11 50		12 20	13 04	13 20		13 50		14 20	14 31		15 00		15 20	15 50	16 20
Avoncliff	d		11x52						13x52					15x02			15x53	
Freshford	d		11 55						13 55					15 06			15 55	
Bath Spa 7	a	11 45	12 06		12 33	13 17	13 33		14 09		14 33	14 45		15 17		15 33	16 06	16 33
Melksham	d														15 19			
Chippenham	a	12 24	12 24		12 54		13 54				14 54	15 24			15 28	15 54	16 24	16 54
Swindon	a	12 40	12 40		13 10		14 09				15 09	15 39			15 48	16 10	16 39	17 09
London Paddington 15 ⊖	a	13 41	13 41	13 13	14 14		15 14				16 15	16 42	16 13		17 09	17 16	17 40	18 15
Oldfield Park	a		12 10			13 21			14 13					15 21			16 10	
Keynsham	a		12 17			13 27			14 19					15 27			16 17	
Bristol Temple Meads 10	a	12 00	12 29		12 47	13 36	13 47		14 29		14 47	15 05		15 35		15 47	16 29	16 47
Filton Abbey Wood	a	12 29	12 47		13 00	13 47	14 00		14 47		15 00	15 29		15 47		16 00	16 47	17 00
Severn Tunnel Jn	a	12 45			13j45		14j45					15 47				16j45		17 13
Newport (South Wales)	a	12 58			13 22		14 22				15 22	15 59				16 24		17 25
Cardiff Central 7	a	13 18			13 41		14 41				15 41	16 15				16 41		17 45
Swansea 7	a				14 42		15 43				16 43					17 43		18k46

For general notes see front of timetable
For details of catering facilities see Directory of Train Operators

A From London Waterloo (Table 160)
B To Worcester Foregate Street (Table 71)
C To Gloucester (Table 134)
D To Great Malvern (Table 71)
b Change at Fratton and Cosham
c Arr. 1136
e Arr. 1333
f Change at Salisbury
g Change at Westbury and Exeter St Davids
h Change at Salisbury and Exeter St Davids
j Change at Bristol Temple Meads
k Change at Newport (South Wales)

Table 123

Saturdays
until 6 September

Portsmouth and Weymouth → Bristol and South Wales

Network Diagram - see first page of Table 123

		GW 1	GW ◇	GW ◇	GW	GW ◇	GW ◇	GW 1 ◇	GW ◇	GW ◇	GW	GW 1 ◇	GW ◇	GW	GW 1	GW ◇	SW 1 ◇	GW ◇	GW ◇	GW
			A		B		C				D						E			
		☕						☕				☕								
Brighton 10	d										17 00									
Hove 2	d										17 04									
Shoreham-by-Sea	d										17 13									
Worthing 4	d										17 22									
Barnham	d										17 41									
Chichester 4	d										17 49									
Havant	d										18 00									
Portsmouth Harbour	d			15 22		16 22			17 22		17 32		18 22			19 22			20 22	
Portsmouth & Southsea	d			15 27		16 27			17 27		17 36		18 27			19 27			20 27	
Fratton	d			15 31		16 31			17 31		17 40		18 31			19 31			20 31	
Cosham	d			15 39		16 39			17 39		18 06		18 39			19 39			20 32	20 45
Fareham	a			15 46		16 46			17 46		18 14		18 46			19 46			20 45	
	d			15 47		16 47			17 47		18 15		18 47			19 47			20 48	20 53
Bournemouth	d			15 21		16 21			17 21		17 59		18 21			19 21			20 21	
Southampton Central	d			16 10		17 10			18 10		18 40		19 10			20 10			21 12	21 27
Romsey	d			16 21		17 21			18 21		18 51		19 21			20 21			21 23	21 38
Mottisfont & Dunbridge	d																			
Dean	d																			
Salisbury	a			16 40		17 40			18 40		19 10		19 40			20 40			21 43	22 03
	d			16 41		17 41			18 41		19 11		19 41			20 41	20 57		21 44	22 04
Warminster	d		16 28	17 01		18 01			19 01		19 31		20 01			21 01	21 17		22 03	22 25
Dilton Marsh	d		16x33								19x36									22x29
Weymouth	d				16 10		16 55			17 30								19 58		
Upwey	d				16 15					17 35								20 03		
Dorchester West	d				16 23		17b12			17 44								20 11		
Maiden Newton	d						17c29			17 55								20 23		
Chetnole	d				16x45					18x02								20x30		
Yetminster	d				16x48					18x05								20x33		
Thornford	d				16x51					18x08								20x36		
Yeovil Pen Mill	d						17e54			18f26								20 44		
Castle Cary	a				17 10		18 09			18 37								20 56		
	d	16 16			17 11		18 09	18 43		18 47		19 47						20 56		
Bruton	d				17 16		18 15			18 52								21 02		
Frome	d				17 28		18 26			19 05					20 53			21 15		
Westbury	a	16 34	16 36	17 07	17 37	18 07	18 37	19 01	19 07	19 14	19 39	20 05	20 07		21 02	21 07	21 23	21 26	22 10	22 33
	d	16 36	16 38	17 08	17 38	18 08	18 38	19 02	19 08	19 17	19 39	20 06	20 08	20 38		21 08	21 24	21 38	22 11	22 38
Exeter St Davids 6	a					19 32	19g32						21 38			22 35		22g35		
Plymouth	a					20 36	20g36						22 43			23 47		23g47		
Trowbridge	d		16 44	17 14	17 44	18 14	18 45		19 14	19 23	19 45		20 14	20 44		21 14	21 30	21 44	22 17	22 44
Bradford-on-Avon	d		16 50	17 20	17 50	18 20	18 51		19 20	19 29	19 51		20 20	20 50		21 20	21 36	21 50	22 23	22 50
Avoncliff	d		16x52		17x52					19x31	19x53			20x52				21x52		22x52
Freshford	d		16 55		17 55					19 35	19 55			20 55				21 55		22 55
Bath Spa 7	a		17 06	17 33	18 06	18 33	19 08		19 33	19 46	20 08		20 33	21 06		21 37	21 50	22 06	22 36	23 09
Melksham	d																			
Chippenham	a		17 24	17 54		18 54			19 54				20 57				22 11		22 57	
Swindon	a		17 39	18 09		19 09			20 09				21 13				22 27		23 13	
London Paddington 15	⊖ a	18 05	18 42	19 14		20 14		20 36	21 15			21 30	22 16				23 38		00 32	
Oldfield Park	a		17 10		18 10		19 12			19 50	20 11			21 10				22 10		23 13
Keynsham	a		17 17		18 17		19 18			19 56	20 18			21 17			21 58	22 17		23 19
Bristol Temple Meads 10	a		17 29	17 47	18 29	18 47	19 26		19 47	20 04	20 27		20 47	21 29		21 51	22 06	22 31	22 50	23 27
Filton Abbey Wood	a		17 47	18 00	18 47	19 00	19 47		20 00	20 29	20 47		21 00			22 00			23 00	
Severn Tunnel Jn	a			18 13		19h47				20 45			21h45			22 18			23 16	
Newport (South Wales)	a			18 25		19 24			20 22	20 58			21 23			22 35			23 33	
Cardiff Central 7	a			18 41		19 41			20 41	21 24			21 41			22 56			23 54	
Swansea 7	a			19 42		20 48			21 47				22 46			00 01				

For general notes see front of timetable
For details of catering facilities see Directory of Train Operators

A To Gloucester (Table 134)
B To Great Malvern (Table 71)
C From 5 July
D To Cheltenham Spa (Table 57)
E From London Waterloo (Table 160)
b Arr. 1706
c Arr. 1724
e Arr. 1747
f Arr. 1814
g Change at Castle Cary
h Change at Bristol Temple Meads

Table 123

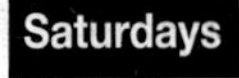

Saturdays

from 13 September

Portsmouth and Weymouth → Bristol and South Wales

Network Diagram - see first page of Table 123

		GW	GW	SW	GW	GW	GW	GW	GW	GW	GW	GW	GW	GW	GW	GW	GW	GW
				1		1 ◇	◇	◇		◇		◇	1 ◇	◇			1	◇
		A			B			A				B			A			
						⊏							⊏				⊏	
Brighton 10	d																	
Hove 2	d																	
Shoreham-by-Sea	d																	
Worthing 4	d																	
Barnham	d																	
Chichester 4	d																	
Havant	d																	
Portsmouth Harbour	d						06 00			07 04	*07 04*			08 22				09 22
Portsmouth & Southsea	d						06 04			07 08	*07 08*			08 27				09 27
Fratton	d						06 08			07 13	*07 13*			08 31				09 31
Cosham	d						06 16			07 20	*07 44*			08 39				09 39
Fareham	a						06 26			07 28				08 46				09 46
	d						06 27			07 29	*07 53*			08 47				09 47
Bournemouth	d						*05 42*			*06 42*	*07 45*			*08 21*				*09 21*
Southampton Central	d						06 52			07 52	08 27			09 10				10 10
Romsey	d						07 11			08 09	08 38			09 21				10 21
Mottisfont & Dunbridge	d																	
Dean	d																	
Salisbury	a						07 29			08 29	09 03			09 40				10 40
	d	06 03		06 40			07 30			08 32	09 04			09 41				10 41
Warminster	d	06 23		07 00	07 23		07 50			08 53	09 25			10 01		10 28		11 01
Dilton Marsh	d	06x27			07x28						09x29					10x33		
Weymouth	d							06 40							08 53			
Upwey	d							06 45							08 58			
Dorchester West	d							06 53							09 05			
Maiden Newton	d							07 05							09 17			
Chetnole	d							07x12							09x24			
Yetminster	d							07x15							09x27			
Thornford	d							07x18							09x30			
Yeovil Pen Mill	d							07b30							09 38			
Castle Cary	a							07 42							09 49			
	d					07 33		07 43					09 45		09 56			
Bruton	d							07 49							10 01			
Frome	d		06 37					08 02							10 17			
Westbury	a	06 31	06 46	07 06	07 31	07 51	07 56	08 12		08 59	09 33		10 03	10 07	10 27	10 36		11 07
	d	06 38	06 47	07 07	07 38	07 56	07 59	08 17	09 03	09 08		09 38	10 05	10 08	10 38		11 00	11 08
Exeter St Davids 6	a									*10c32*	*11 07*			*11c56*	*11e07*			*12c30*
Plymouth	a									*11f48*	*12g24*			*13f10*	*12h24*			*13f48*
Trowbridge	d	06 44	06 53	07 13	07 44		08 05	08 23	09 09	09 14		09 44		10 14	10 44			11 14
Bradford-on-Avon	d	06 49	06 59	07 19	07 50		08 11	08 29		09 20		09 50		10 20	10 50			11 20
Avoncliff	d	06x51	07x01		07x53			08x32				09x52			10x53			
Freshford	d	06 55	07 05		07 55			08 34				09 55			10 55			
Bath Spa 7	a	07 06	07 16	07 32	08 07		08 31	08 45		09 33		10 06		10 34	11 06			11 33
Melksham	d								09 18									
Chippenham	a	*07 24*		*07 54*			*08 54*	*09 24*	09 31	*09 54*		*10 24*		*10 54*	*11 24*			*11 54*
Swindon	a	*07 40*		*08 09*			*09 09*	*09 39*	09 48	*10 09*		*10 39*		*11 09*	*11 39*			*12 09*
London Paddington 15 ⊖	a	*08 45*		*09 15*		09 21	*10 14*	*10 43*	*10 59*	*11 15*		*11 41*	11 23	*12 15*	*12 42*		12 21	*13 15*
Oldfield Park	a	07 10	07 20	07 36	08 11			08 49				10 10			11 10			
Keynsham	a	07 17	07 27	07 43	08 18			08 56				10 17			11 17			
Bristol Temple Meads 10	a	07 29	07 35	07 52	08 29		08 45	09 04		09 47		10 28		10 48	11 29			11 47
Filton Abbey Wood	a	07 47	08 00	*08 29*	08 47		09 00	09 16		10 00		10 47		11 00	11 47			12 00
Severn Tunnel Jn	a																	
Newport (South Wales)	a		08 24				09 23			10 23				11 22				12 22
Cardiff Central 7	a		08 41				09 41			10 41				11 41				12 41
Swansea 7	a		*09 56*				*10 43*			*11 43*				*12 43*				*13 42*

For general notes see front of timetable
For details of catering facilities see Directory of Train Operators

- **A** To Gloucester (Table 134)
- **B** To Great Malvern (Table 71)
- **b** Arr. 0724
- **c** Change at Salisbury
- **e** Change at Castle Cary
- **f** Change at Salisbury and Exeter St Davids
- **g** Change at Westbury and Exeter St Davids
- **h** Change at Castle Cary and Exeter St Davids

Table 123

Saturdays

from 13 September

Portsmouth and Weymouth → Bristol and South Wales

Network Diagram - see first page of Table 123

		SW 1 ◇ A	GW ◇ B	GW ◇	GW ◇ C	GW 1 ◇ ⊡	GW ◇	GW D	GW ◇	SW 1 ◇ A	GW ◇ C	GW 1 ◇ ⊡	GW	GW ◇	GW E	GW ◇	GW 1 ◇ G ⊡	GW C
Brighton 10	d		09 00															
Hove 2	d		09 04															
Shoreham-by-Sea	d		09 13															
Worthing 4	d		09 22															
Barnham	d		09 41															
Chichester 4	d		09 49															
Havant	d		10 00															
Portsmouth Harbour	d		09b28	10 22			11 22		12 22					13 22		14 22		
Portsmouth & Southsea	d		09 36	10 27			11 27		12 27					13 27		14 27		
Fratton	d		09 40	10 31			11 31		12 31					13 31		14 31		
Cosham	d		10 06	10 39			11 39	11 45	12 39					13 39		14 39		
Fareham	a		10 14	10 46			11 46		12 46					13 46		14 46		
	d		10 15	10 47			11 47	11 53	12 47					13 47		14 47		
Bournemouth	d		09 59	10 21			11 21		12 21					13 21		14 21		
Southampton Central	d		10 40	11 10			12 10	12 27	13 10					14 10		15 10		
Romsey	d		10 51	11 21			12 21	12 38	13 21					14 21		15 21		
Mottisfont & Dunbridge	d																	
Dean	d																	
Salisbury	a		11 10	11 40			12 40	13 03	13 40					14 40		15 40		
	d	10 52	11 11	11 41			12 41	13 04	13 41	13 52				14 41		15 41		
Warminster	d	11 12	11 32	12 01			13 01	13 25	14 01	14 12				15 01	15 28	16 01		
Dilton Marsh	d							13x29							15x33			
Weymouth	d				11 10						13 10							15 10
Upwey	d				11 15						13 15							15 15
Dorchester West	d				11 26						13 24							15 23
Maiden Newton	d				11c42						13e44							15 34
Chetnole	d				11x49						13x51							15x41
Yetminster	d				11x53						13x54							15x45
Thornford	d				11x55						13x57							15x47
Yeovil Pen Mill	d				12 03						14 05							15 55
Castle Cary	a				12 15						14 16							16 07
	d				12 26	12 45					14 17	14 44					16 00	16 07
Bruton	d				12 31						14 22							16 13
Frome	d				12 43						14 34						16 14	16 25
Westbury	a	11 18	11 38	12 07	12 52	13 03	13 07	13 33	14 07	14 18	14 47	15 02		15 07	15 36	16 07	16 23	16 34
	d	11 19	11 38	12 08	12 52	13 05	13 08	13 38	14 08	14 19	14 48	15 03	15 04	15 08	15 38	16 08	16 25	16 38
Exeter St Davids 6	a			13 32	13f32		14g23		15g42							17 32		17f32
Plymouth	a			14 37	14f37		15h48		16g57							18 39		18f39
Trowbridge	d	11 25	11 44	12 14	12 58		13 14	13 44	14 14	14 25	14 54		15 10	15 14	15 44	16 14		16 44
Bradford-on-Avon	d	11 31	11 50	12 20	13 04		13 20	13 50	14 20	14 31	15 00			15 20	15 50	16 20		16 50
Avoncliff	d		11x52					13x52			15x02				15x53			16x52
Freshford	d		11 55					13 55			15 06				15 55			16 55
Bath Spa 7	a	11 45	12 06	12 33	13 17		13 33	14 08	14 33	14 45	15 17			15 33	16 06	16 33		17 07
Melksham	d												15 19					
Chippenham	a		12 24	12 54			13 54		14 54	15 24			15 28	15 54	16 24	16 54		17 24
Swindon	a		12 40	13 09			14 09		15 09	15 39			15 48	16 09	16 39	17 09		17 39
London Paddington 15 ⊖	a		13 41	14 15		14 46	15 15		16 15	16 42		16 22	17 06	17 15	17 40	18 14	18 11	18 42
Oldfield Park	a		12 10		13 21			14 12			15 21				16 10			17 11
Keynsham	a		12 17		13 27			14 18			15 27				16 17			17 18
Bristol Temple Meads 10	a	12 00	12 29	12 47	13 36		13 47	14 26	14 47	15 05	15 35			15 47	16 29	16 47		17 29
Filton Abbey Wood	a	12 29	12 47	13 00	13 47		14 00	14 47	15 00	15 29	15 47			16 00	16 47	17 00		17 47
Severn Tunnel Jn	a															17 13		
Newport (South Wales)	a			13 22			14 22		15 22					16 24		17 25		
Cardiff Central 7	a			13 41			14 41		15 41					16 41		17 45		
Swansea 7	a			14 42			15 43		16 43					17 43		18 56		

For general notes see front of timetable
For details of catering facilities see Directory of Train Operators

A From London Waterloo (Table 160)

B To Worcester Foregate Street (Table 71)
C To Gloucester (Table 134)
D To Great Malvern
E To Great Malvern (Table 71)
G From Taunton (Table 135)
b Change at Fratton and Cosham

c Arr. 1136
e Arr. 1333
f Change at Castle Cary
g Change at Salisbury
h Change at Salisbury and Exeter St Davids

Table 123

Saturdays

from 13 September

Portsmouth and Weymouth → Bristol and South Wales

Network Diagram - see first page of Table 123

		GW ◇	GW	GW ◇	GW 1 ◇	GW ◇	GW ◇	GW	GW 1 ◇	GW ◇	GW	GW	GW ◇	SW 1 ◇	GW ◇	GW ◇	GW
			A					B						C			
					⊡				⊡								
Brighton 10	d							17 00									
Hove 2	d							17 04									
Shoreham-by-Sea	d							17 13									
Worthing 4	d							17 22									
Barnham	d							17 41									
Chichester 4	d							17 49									
Havant	d							18 00									
Portsmouth Harbour	d	15 22		16 22		17 22		17 32		18 22			19 22			20 22	
Portsmouth & Southsea	d	15 27		16 27		17 27		17 36		18 27			19 27			20 27	
Fratton	d	15 31		16 31		17 31		17 40		18 31			19 31			20 31	
Cosham	d	15 39		16 39		17 39		18 06		18 39			19 39			20 32	20 45
Fareham	a	15 46		16 46		17 46		18 14		18 46			19 46			20 45	
	d	15 47		16 47		17 47		18 15		18 47			19 47			20 48	20 53
Bournemouth	d	15 21		16 21		17 21		17 59		18 21			19 21			20 21	
Southampton Central	d	16 10		17 10		18 10		18 40		19 10			20 10			21 12	21 27
Romsey	d	16 21		17 21		18 21		18 51		19 21			20 21			21 23	21 38
Mottisfont & Dunbridge	d																
Dean	d																
Salisbury	a	16 40		17 40		18 40		19 10		19 40			20 40			21 43	22 03
	d	16 41		17 41		18 41		19 11		19 41			20 41	20 57		21 44	22 04
Warminster	d	17 01	17 25	18 01		19 01		19 31		20 01			21 01	21 17		22 03	22 25
Dilton Marsh	d		17 30					19x36									22x29
Weymouth	d						17 30								19 58		
Upwey	d						17 35								20 03		
Dorchester West	d						17 44								20 11		
Maiden Newton	d						17 55								20 23		
Chetnole	d						18x02								20x30		
Yetminster	d						18x05								20x33		
Thornford	d						18x08								20x36		
Yeovil Pen Mill	d						18b26								20 44		
Castle Cary	a						18 37								20 56		
	d				18 39		18 47		19 47						20 56		
Bruton	d						18 52								21 02		
Frome	d						19 05					20 53			21 15		
Westbury	a	17 07	17 33	18 07	18 57	19 07	19 14	19 39	20 05	20 07		21 02	21 07	21 23	21 26	22 10	22 33
	d	17 08	17 35	18 08	18 59	19 08	19 17	19 39	20 06	20 08	20 38		21 08	21 24	21 38	22 11	22 38
Exeter St Davids 6	a			19 32						21 38			22 35		22c35		
Plymouth	a			20 36						22 43			23 47		23c47		
Trowbridge	d	17 14	17 41	18 14		19 14	19 23	19 45		20 14	20 44		21 14	21 30	21 44	22 17	22 44
Bradford-on-Avon	d	17 20	17 47	18 20		19 20	19 29	19 51		20 20	20 50		21 20	21 36	21 50	22 23	22 50
Avoncliff	d		17x49				19x31	19x53			20x52				21x52		22x52
Freshford	d		17 52				19 35	19 55			20 55				21 55		22 55
Bath Spa 7	a	17 33	18 03	18 33		19 33	19 46	20 08		20 33	21 06		21 37	21 50	22 06	22 36	23 09
Melksham	d																
Chippenham	a	17 54	18 24	18 54		19 54				20 57				22 11		22 57	
Swindon	a	18 09	18 39	19 09		20 09				21 13				22 27		23 13	
London Paddington 15	⊖ a	19 15	19 42	20 15	20 21	21 15			21 30	22 16				23 38		00 32	
Oldfield Park	a		18 07				19 50	20 11			21 10				22 10		23 13
Keynsham	a		18 14				19 56	20 18			21 17			21 58	22 17		23 19
Bristol Temple Meads 10	a	17 47	18 27	18 47		19 47	20 04	20 27		20 47	21 29		21 51	22 06	22 31	22 50	23 27
Filton Abbey Wood	a	18 00	18 45	19 00		20 00	20 29	20 47		21 00			22 00			23 00	
Severn Tunnel Jn	a	18 13											22 18			23 16	
Newport (South Wales)	a	18 25		19 24		20 22				21 23			22 35			23 33	
Cardiff Central 7	a	18 41		19 41		20 41				21 41			22 56			23 54	
Swansea 7	a	19 42		20 41		21 47				22 46			00 01				

For general notes see front of timetable
For details of catering facilities see Directory of Train Operators

A To Great Malvern (Table 71)
B To Cheltenham Spa (Table 57)
C From London Waterloo (Table 160)

b Arr. 1814
c Change at Castle Cary

Table 123

until 7 September

Portsmouth and Weymouth → Bristol and South Wales

Network Diagram - see first page of Table 123

		GW	GW	GW	GW	GW	GW	GW	GW	SW	GW	GW	GW	GW	GW	GW	GW	GW
		1 ◇		1 ◇	◇		1 ◇	◇	◇	1 ◇	◇		1 ◇	◇	◇			1 ◇
					A			A	A	B	A			A	A			
		🛏		🛏	✕	✕	🛏	✕			✕		🛏	✕	✕			🛏
Brighton 10	d								11 10									
Hove 2	d								11 14									
Shoreham-by-Sea	d								11 20									
Worthing 4	d								11 29									
Barnham	d								11 46									
Chichester 4	d								11 58									
Havant	d								12 10									
Portsmouth Harbour	d				09 08			11 08	*11b32*		13 08			14 08	15 08			
Portsmouth & Southsea	d				09 12			11 12	*11 42*		13 12			14 12	15 12			
Fratton	d				09 16			11 16	*11 46*		13 16			14 16	15 16			
Cosham	d				09 23			11 23	12 23		13 23			14 23	15 23			
Fareham	a				09 31			11 31	12 31		13 31			14 31	15 31			
	d				09 32			11 32	12 32		13 32			14 32	15 32			
Bournemouth	d				*08 50*			*10 50*	*11 50*		*12 50*			*13 50*	*14 50*			
Southampton Central	d				09 54			11 54	12 54		13 54			14 54	15 54			
Romsey	d				10 05			12 06	13 06		14 06			15 06	16 06			
Mottisfont & Dunbridge	d																	
Dean	d																	
Salisbury	a				10 24			12 24	13 24		14 24			15 24	16 24			
	d				10 30			12 28	13 28	13 58	14 28			15 28	16 28			
Warminster	d				10 50			12 48	13 47	14 18	14 48			15 48	16 48			
Dilton Marsh	d				10x55						14x53			15x53	16x53			
Weymouth	d					11 11						14 08					16 13	
Upwey	d					11 16						14 13					16 18	
Dorchester West	d					11 24						14 21					16 26	
Maiden Newton	d					11 36						14 35					16 38	
Chetnole	d					11x44						14x43					16x46	
Yetminster	d					11x47						14x46					16x49	
Thornford	d					11x50						14x49					16x52	
Yeovil Pen Mill	d					11 57						14c59					16 59	
Castle Cary	a					12 09						15 11					17 11	
	d	09 21				12 11	12 30					15 12	15 33				17 11	17 37
Bruton	d					12 16						15 18					17 17	
Frome	d		09 35			12 29						15 31					17 30	
Westbury	a	09 38	09 46		10 57	12 39	12 48	12 53	13 54	14 24	14 55	15 40	15 50	15 55	16 55		17 39	17 54
	d	09 40	09 56	10 54	10 58		12 48	12 55	13 55	14 25	15 01	15 41	15 51	15 58	17 00	17 20	17 40	17 57
Exeter St Davids 6	a				*12e49*			*14e46*			*16 49*	*16f49*			*18e51*		*18f51*	
Plymouth	a				*14g29*			*16g03*			*17 58*	*17f58*			*19 54*		*19f54*	
Trowbridge	d		10 02		11 04			13 01	14 01	14 32	15 07	15 47		16 04	17 06	17 26	17 46	
Bradford-on-Avon	d		10 07		11 10			13 07	14 07	14 38	15 13	15 52		16 10	17 12		17 52	
Avoncliff	d		10x10					13x10	14x10			15x55		16x13			17x55	
Freshford	d		10 12					13 13	14 12			15 57		16 16			17 57	
Bath Spa 7	a		10 23		11 25			13 26	14 23	14 52	15 27	16 08		16 28	17 26		18 08	
Melksham	d															17 36		
Chippenham	a		*10 54*		*12 24*			*14 24*		*15 24*	*16 24*			*16 54*		17 46		
Swindon	a	10 13	*11 09*		*12 40*		13 22	*14 40*		*15 40*	*16 40*		16 25	*17 10*		18 03		
London Paddington 15	⊖ a	11 26	*12 15*	12 41	*13 55*		14 30	*15 55*		*16 54*	*17 54*		17 34	*18 24*		*19 24*		19 39
Oldfield Park	a		10 27		11 28			13 29	14 27			16 12			17 29		18 12	
Keynsham	a		10 34		11 35			13 36	14 34			16 19			17 36		18 20	
Bristol Temple Meads 10	a		10 43		11 43			13 44	14 42	15 06	15 40	16 28		16 41	17 44		18 28	
Filton Abbey Wood	a				11 54			13 55	14 55		15 54	*16 50*		16 55	17 55		*18 50*	
Severn Tunnel Jn	a				*12h32*			*14h32*	*15h32*		*16h32*			*17h32*	*18h32*			
Newport (South Wales)	a				*12h52*			*14h52*	*15h52*		*16h52*			*17h52*	*18h52*			
Cardiff Central 7	a				*13h22*			*15h22*	*16h22*		*17h22*			*18h22*	*19h22*			
Swansea 7	a																	

For general notes see front of timetable
For details of catering facilities see Directory of Train Operators

- **A** To Bristol Parkway (Table 132)
- **B** From London Waterloo (Table 160)
- **b** Change at Fratton and Cosham
- **c** Arr. 1454
- **e** Change at Salisbury
- **f** Change at Castle Cary
- **g** Change at Salisbury and Exeter St Davids
- **h** Change at Bristol Parkway. By bus

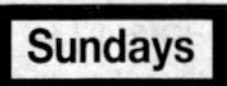

until 7 September

Portsmouth and Weymouth → Bristol and South Wales

Network Diagram - see first page of Table 123

		GW	GW	GW	GW	GW	GW	GW	SW	GW	GW	GW	GW	GW	GW
		◇	◇	◇	◇		◇	1 ◇	1 ◇	◇	◇	1 ◇	◇	◇	◇
		A		A			A	B	C		A			A	
		🛒		🛒			🛒	⊡			🛒	⊡		🛒	🛒
Brighton 10	d		15 47							17 47					
Hove 2	d		15 51							17 51					
Shoreham-by-Sea	d		15 57							17 57					
Worthing 4	d		16 08							18 08					
Barnham	d		16 25							18 25					
Chichester 4	d		16 34							18 34					
Havant	d		16 48							18 48					
Portsmouth Harbour	d	16 08	16 17	17 08			18 08			18 17	19 08			20 08	22 07
Portsmouth & Southsea	d	16 12	16 22	17 12			18 12			18 22	19 12			20 12	22 12
Fratton	d	16 16	16 26	17 16			18 16			18 26	19 16			20 16	22 16
Cosham	d	16 23	16 55	17 23			18 23			18 35	19 23			20 23	22 23
Fareham	a	16 31	17 02	17 31			18 31			19 00	19 31			20 31	22 31
	d	16 32	17 03	17 32			18 32			19 01	19 32			20 32	22 32
Bournemouth	d	15 50	16 40	16 50			17 50			18 50				19 50	21 06
Southampton Central	d	16 54	17 26	17 54			18 54			19 30	19 54			20 54	22 54
Romsey	d	17 06	17 39	18 06			19 06			19 42	20 06			21 06	23 05
Mottisfont & Dunbridge	d														
Dean	d														
Salisbury	a	17 24	18 01	18 24			19 24			20 00	20 24			21 24	23 29
	d	17 28	18 02	18 28			19 28		19 58	20 03	20 28			21 28	23 30
Warminster	d	17 48	18 22	18 48			19 48		20 18	20 28	20 48			21 48	23 50
Dilton Marsh	d		18x27							20x33				21x53	23x55
Weymouth	d				18 00								20 09		
Upwey	d				18 05								20 14		
Dorchester West	d				18 13								20 22		
Maiden Newton	d				18 25								20 34		
Chetnole	d				18x32								20x41		
Yetminster	d				18x35								20x44		
Thornford	d				18x38								20x47		
Yeovil Pen Mill	d				18 46								20 55		
Castle Cary	a				18 57								21 06		
	d				18 59			20 06				21 12	21 15		
Bruton	d				19 05								21 21		
Frome	d				19 18										
Westbury	a	17 57	18 30	18 53	19 27		19 53	20 24	20 24	20 36	20 53	21 30		21 55	23 57
	d	18 01	18 34	19 01	19 30	19 35	20 01	20 25	20 32	20 39	21 01	21 30		22 01	
Exeter St Davids 6	a			20b49	20 50						22 52		22c52	00b30	
Plymouth	a				21 54						00 06		00c06		
Trowbridge	d	18 08	18 40	19 07	19 36	19 42	20 07		20 38	20 45	21 07		21 52	22 07	
Bradford-on-Avon	d		18 46	19 13	19 42		20 13		20 44	20 51	21 13		21 58	22 13	
Avoncliff	d		18x49		19x45					20x54			22x01		
Freshford	d		18 52		19 48					20 56			22 04		
Bath Spa 7	a	18 27	19 03	19 26	20 01		20 27		20 59	21 09	21 27		22 15	22 29	
Melksham	d					19 52									
Chippenham	a	18 55	19 24	19 54	20 24	20 02			21 25		22 30				
Swindon	a	19 11	19 40	20 10	20 40	20 20			21 41		22 46	22 06			
London Paddington 15	⊖ a	20 21	20 55	21 22	21 53	21 53		22 25	22 59		00 17	23 23			
Oldfield Park	a		19 06		20 04					21 13			22 18		
Keynsham	a		19 14		20 12				21 08	21 20			22 26		
Bristol Temple Meads 10	a	18 40	19 22	19 40	20 20		20 40		21 16	21 28	21 44		22 34	22 42	
Filton Abbey Wood	a	18 55		19 55	20 49		20 55				21 55			22 55	
Severn Tunnel Jn	a			20f32			21f32				22f32			23f32	
Newport (South Wales)	a			20f52			21f52				22f52			23f52	
Cardiff Central 7	a			21f22			22f22				23f22			00f22	
Swansea 7	a														

For general notes see front of timetable
For details of catering facilities see Directory of Train Operators

A To Bristol Parkway (Table 132)
B **Atlantic Coast Express**
C From London Waterloo (Table 160)
b Change at Salisbury
c Change at Castle Cary
f Change at Bristol Parkway. By bus

Table 123

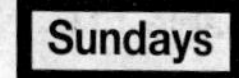

Sundays

from 14 September

Portsmouth and Weymouth → Bristol and South Wales

Network Diagram - see first page of Table 123

		GW 1 ◇	GW	GW 1 ◇	GW ◇	GW 1 ◇	GW ◇	GW ◇	SW 1 ◇	GW ◇	GW ◇	GW 1 ◇	GW ◇	GW ◇
									A					
		🍴		🍴	🛒	🍴	🛒			🛒		🍴	🛒	🛒
Brighton 10	d							11 10						
Hove 2	d							11 14						
Shoreham-by-Sea	d							11 20						
Worthing 4	d							11 29						
Barnham	d							11 46						
Chichester 4	d							11 58						
Havant	d							12 10						
Portsmouth Harbour	d				09 08		11 08	*11b32*		13 08			14 08	15 08
Portsmouth & Southsea	d				09 12		11 12	*11 42*		13 12			14 12	15 12
Fratton	d				09 16		11 16	*11 46*		13 16			14 16	15 16
Cosham	d				09 23		11 23	12 23		13 23			14 23	15 23
Fareham	a				09 31		11 31	12 31		13 31			14 31	15 31
	d				09 32		11 32	12 32		13 32			14 32	15 32
Bournemouth	d				*08 50*		*10 50*	*11 50*		*12 50*			*13 50*	*14 50*
Southampton Central	d				09 54		11 54	12 54		13 54			14 54	15 54
Romsey	d				10 05		12 06	13 06		14 06			15 06	16 06
Mottisfont & Dunbridge	d													
Dean	d													
Salisbury	a				10 24		12 24	13 24		14 24			15 24	16 24
	d				10 30		12 28	13 28	13 58	14 28			15 28	16 28
Warminster	d				10 50		12 48	13 47	14 18	14 48			15 48	16 48
Dilton Marsh	d				10x55					14x53			15x53	16x53
Weymouth	d										14 00			
Upwey	d										14 05			
Dorchester West	d										14 13			
Maiden Newton	d										14 25			
Chetnole	d										14x32			
Yetminster	d										14x35			
Thornford	d										14x38			
Yeovil Pen Mill	d										14 46			
Castle Cary	a										14 57			
	d	09 21				12 30					14 59	15 33		
Bruton	d										15 05			
Frome	d		09 35								15 18			
Westbury	a	09 38	09 46		10 57	12 48	12 53	13 54	14 24	14 55	15 27	15 50	15 55	16 55
	d	09 40	09 56	10 53	10 58	12 48	12 55	13 55	14 25	15 01	15 27	15 52	15 58	16 59
Exeter St Davids 6	a		*11 29*		*12c49*		*14 09*	*15 25*		*16c50*	*16e28*			*18 35*
Plymouth	a		*12 32*		*14f11*		*15g27*	*16 28*		*18f22*	*17e38*			*19 38*
Trowbridge	d		10 02		11 04		13 01	14 01	14 32	15 07	15 33		16 04	17 05
Bradford-on-Avon	d		10 07		11 10		13 07	14 07	14 38	15 13	15 39		16 10	17 11
Avoncliff	d		10x10				13x10	14x10			15x42		16x13	
Freshford	d		10 12				13 13	14 12			15 45		16 16	
Bath Spa 7	a		10 23		11 25		13 25	14 23	14 52	15 27	15 56		16 28	17 25
Melksham	d													
Chippenham	a		*10 54*		*12 24*		*14 24*		*15 24*		*16 24*		*16 54*	*17 54*
Swindon	a		*11 09*		*12 40*		*14 40*		*15 40*		*16 40*		*17 10*	*18 10*
London Paddington 15 ⊖	a	11 28	*12 22*	12 32	*13 55*	14 21	*15 56*		*16 55*		*17 55*	17 33	*18 30*	*19 23*
Oldfield Park	a		10 27		11 28		13 28	14 27			16 00			17 28
Keynsham	a		10 34		11 35		13 35	14 34			16 08			17 35
Bristol Temple Meads 10	a		10 43		11 43		13 43	14 42	15 06	15 40	16 16		16 41	17 43
Filton Abbey Wood	a				11 54		13 54	14 54		15 54	*16 49*		16 54	17 54
Severn Tunnel Jn	a				12 10		14 07	15 07		16 07			17 10	18 07
Newport (South Wales)	a				12 24		14 20	15 20		16 21			17 23	18 21
Cardiff Central 7	a				12 39		14 35	15 37		16 36			17 38	18 36
Swansea 7	a				*13 41*		*15 41*	*16 42*		*17 41*			*18 45*	*19 44*

For general notes see front of timetable
For details of catering facilities see Directory of Train Operators

- **A** From London Waterloo (Table 160)
- **b** Change at Fratton and Cosham
- **c** Change at Salisbury
- **e** Change at Castle Cary
- **f** Change at Salisbury and Exeter St Davids
- **g** Change at Westbury and Exeter St Davids

Sundays

from 14 September

Portsmouth and Weymouth → Bristol and South Wales

Network Diagram - see first page of Table 123

		GW	GW	GW	GW	GW	GW	GW	GW	GW	SW	GW	GW	GW	GW	GW	GW
			1 ◇	◇	◇	◇	◇		◇	1 ◇	1 ◇	◇	◇	1 ◇	◇	◇	◇
								A			B						
			⊓	⊼		⊼			⊼	⊓			⊼	⊓		⊼	⊼
Brighton 10	d				15 47							17 47					
Hove 2	d				15 51							17 51					
Shoreham-by-Sea	d				15 57							17 57					
Worthing 4	d				16 08							18 08					
Barnham	d				16 25							18 25					
Chichester 4	d				16 34							18 34					
Havant	d				16 48							18 48					
Portsmouth Harbour	d			16 08	16 17	17 08			18 08			18 17	19 08			20 08	22 07
Portsmouth & Southsea	d			16 12	16 22	17 12			18 12			18 22	19 12			20 12	22 12
Fratton	d			16 16	16 26	17 16			18 16			18 26	19 16			20 16	22 16
Cosham	d			16 23	16 55	17 23			18 23			18 35	19 23			20 23	22 23
Fareham	a			16 31	17 02	17 31			18 31			19 00	19 31			20 31	22 31
	d			16 32	17 03	17 32			18 32			19 01	19 32			20 32	22 32
Bournemouth	d			15 50	16 40	16 50			17 50			18 50				19 50	21 06
Southampton Central	d			16 54	17 26	17 54			18 54			19 30	19 54			20 54	22 54
Romsey	d			17 06	17 39	18 06			19 06			19 42	20 06			21 06	23 05
Mottisfont & Dunbridge	d																
Dean	d																
Salisbury	a			17 24	18 01	18 24			19 24			20 00	20 24			21 24	23 29
	d			17 28	18 02	18 28			19 28		19 58	20 03	20 28			21 28	23 30
Warminster	d			17 48	18 22	18 48			19 48		20 18	20 28	20 48			21 48	23 50
Dilton Marsh	d				18x27							20x33				21x53	23x55
Weymouth	d						18 00								20 09		
Upwey	d						18 05								20 14		
Dorchester West	d						18 13								20 22		
Maiden Newton	d						18 25								20 34		
Chetnole	d						18x32								20x41		
Yetminster	d						18x35								20x44		
Thornford	d						18x38								20x47		
Yeovil Pen Mill	d						18 46								20 55		
Castle Cary	a						18 57								21 06		
	d		17 37				18 59			20 08				21 12	21 15		
Bruton	d						19 05								21 21		
Frome	d						19 18								21 34		
Westbury	a		17 54	17 53	18 30	18 53	19 27		19 53	20 26	20 24	20 36	20 53	21 30	21 43	21 55	23 57
	d	17 05	17 57	18 01	18 34	19 01	19 30	19 35	20 01	20 27	20 32	20 39	21 01	21 30	21 46	22 01	
Exeter St Davids 6	a					20 33	21b21						22 37		22b37	00c30	
Plymouth	a					21 37	22b31						23 44		23b44		
Trowbridge	d	17 11		18 07	18 40	19 07	19 36	19 42	20 07		20 38	20 45	21 07		21 52	22 07	
Bradford-on-Avon	d				18 46	19 13	19 42		20 13		20 44	20 51	21 13		21 58	22 13	
Avoncliff	d				18x49		19x45					20x54			22x01		
Freshford	d				18 52		19 48					20 56			22 04		
Bath Spa 7	a			18 25	19 03	19 27	20 01		20 27		20 59	21 09	21 27		22 15	22 28	
Melksham	d	17 21						19 52									
Chippenham	a	17 31		18 55	19 24	19 54	20 24	20 02			21 25		22 30				
Swindon	a	17 48		19 11	19 40	20 10	20 40	20 20			21 41		22 46				
London Paddington 15 ⊖	a	19 05	19 35	20 27	20 56	21 28	22 02	21 42		21 53	22 59		00 05	23 08			
Oldfield Park	a				19 06		20 04					21 13			22 18		
Keynsham	a				19 14		20 12				21 08	21 20			22 26		
Bristol Temple Meads 10	a			18 38	19 22	19 40	20 20		20 40		21 16	21 28	21 40		22 34	22 41	
Filton Abbey Wood	a			18 55		19 54	20 49		20 54		21 56		21 56			22 54	
Severn Tunnel Jn	a			19 08		20 10			21 07				22 13			23 09	
Newport (South Wales)	a			19 21		20 23			21 20				22 34			23 32	
Cardiff Central 7	a			19 36		20 38			21 37				22 53			23 51	
Swansea 7	a			20 44		21 43			22 44				23 58			00 57	

For general notes see front of timetable
For details of catering facilities see Directory of Train Operators

A To Cheltenham Spa (Table 125)
B From London Waterloo (Table 160)
b Change at Castle Cary
c Change at Salisbury

Route Diagram for Table 125

DM-12/06
Design BAJS

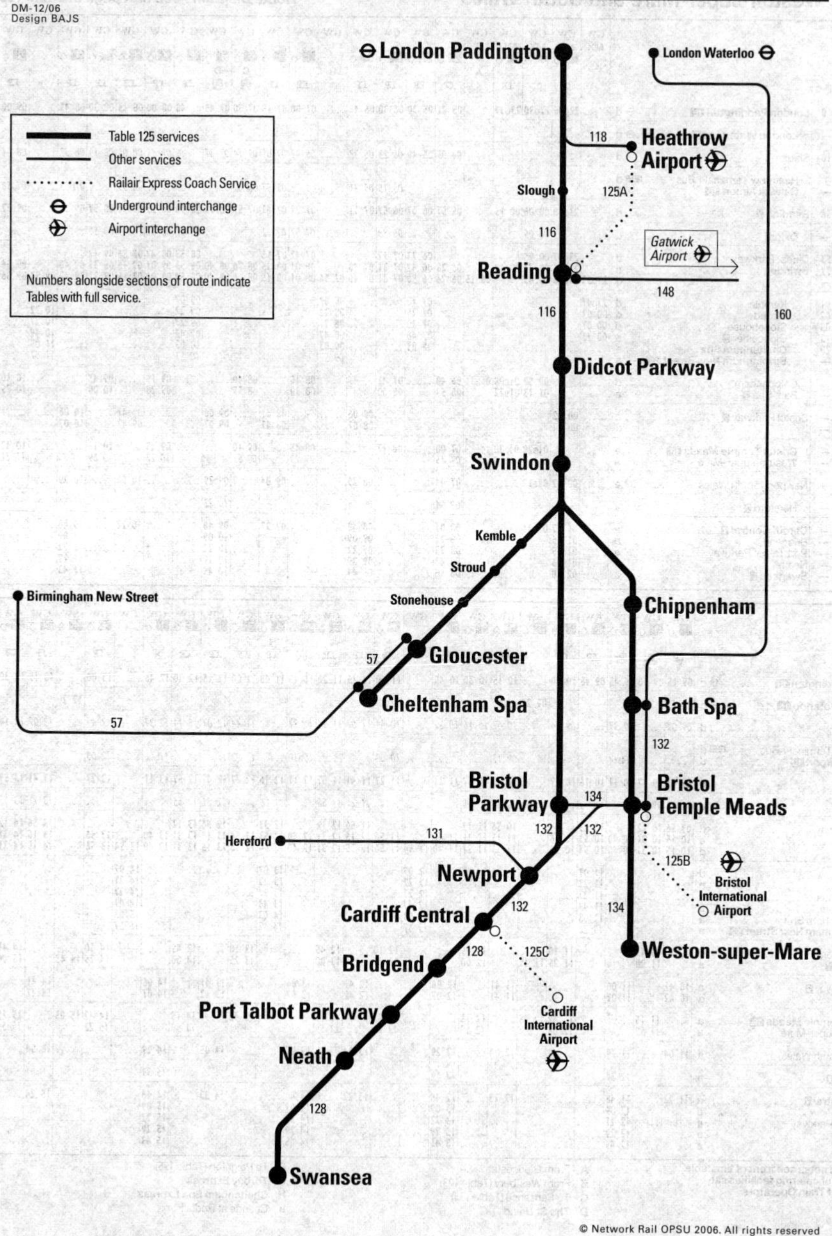

London Paddington
London Waterloo
Table 125 services
Other services
Railair Express Coach Service
Underground interchange
Airport interchange
Numbers alongside sections of route indicate Tables with full service.
118
Heathrow Airport
Slough
125A
116
Gatwick Airport
Reading
148
116
160
Didcot Parkway
Swindon
Kemble
Stroud
Stonehouse
Birmingham New Street
Chippenham
Gloucester
57
Cheltenham Spa
57
Bath Spa
132
Bristol Parkway
134
Bristol Temple Meads
132
132
Hereford
131
125B
Bristol International Airport
Newport
132
134
Cardiff Central
128
125C
Weston-super-Mare
Bridgend
Cardiff International Airport
Port Talbot Parkway
Neath
128
Swansea

London and Oxford → Swindon, Cheltenham Spa, Bristol, Weston-super-Mare and South Wales

Route Diagram - see first page of Table 125

Miles	Miles	Miles			GW MX	GW MX 1◇ ☕	GW MX 1◇ 🛏	GW MO 1◇ ☕	GW A	GW 1◇ ☕	GW 1◇ ☕	GW 1◇ ☕	GW 1◇ ☕	GW B	GW 1◇ ☕	GW 1◇ ☕	GW 1◇ C ☒	GW 1◇ D ☒	GW 1◇ ☕	GW 1◇ ☕	GW 1◇ ☕	GW 1◇ ☕	GW 1◇ ☕	GW	GW 1◇ ☕
0	0	0	**London Paddington 15** ⊖	d		22p45	23p30	23p37		05 27	05 30	06 30	06 45		07 00	07 15	07 30	07 45	07 48	08 00	08 15	08 30	08 45		09 00
—	—	—	**London Waterloo 15** ⊖	d																					
18½	18½	18½	Slough 3	d						*04 05*	05 49	*06 23*	*06 33*		*06 49*	*07 01*	*07 14*	*07 37*		*07 44*	*08 03*	*08 14*	*08 37*		*08 44*
—	—	—	Heathrow Terminal 1 Bus 🚌	d																					
—	—	—	Gatwick Airport 10	d								*05 15*	*05 31*			*05 57*	*06b02*				*06 59*		*07b03*		*07 58*
36	36	36	**Reading 7**	d		23p18	00 06	00 15		05 57	06 07	06 57	07 11		07 27	07 41	07 57	08 11	08 16	08 27	08 41	08 57	09 11		09 27
—	—	—	Oxford	d			*00 05*					*06 38*			*07 02*	*07 22*			*08 07*	*08 21*		*08 55*			
53¼	53¼	53¼	Didcot Parkway	d		23p37	00 25				06 23	07 12			07 42	07 56			08 33	08 42	08 56	09 12			
77¼	77¼	77¼	**Swindon**	a		23p56	00 43	00s53		06 25	06 42	07 31	07 40		08 01	08 15	08 26	08 40	08 53	09 01	09 15	09 31	09 40		09 56
—	—	—		d	23p33	23p56	00 43		06 15	06 26	06 50	07 31	07 40	07 54	08 01	08 15	08 26	08 40	08 54	09 01	09 15	09 31	09 40	09 54	09 56
—	—	91	Kemble	d	23p47						07 10			08 07					09 07					10 07	
—	—	102¼	Stroud	d	00 02						07 25			08 22					09 22					10 22	
—	—	105	Stonehouse	d	00 07						07 30			08 27					09 27					10 27	
—	—	113¾	Gloucester 7	a	00 23						07 48			08 47					09 43					10 49	
—	—	120¼	**Cheltenham Spa**	a							08 03			09 03					10 03					11 05	
—	—	—	**Birmingham New Street 12**	a										*09 57*					*10 57*					*11 57*	
—	94	—	Chippenham	d			00 58	01s08	06a31	06 40		07 45			08 15		08 40			09 15		09 45			10 10
—	107	—	Bath Spa 7	a			01 13	01s22		06 53		08 00			08 30		08 55			09 28		10 00			10 25
111¾	—	—	Bristol Parkway 7	a		00 22							08 06			08 41		09 06			09 41		10 06		
—	—	—		d		00 22							08 07			08 42		09 07			09 42		10 07		
117¾	118½	—	**Bristol Temple Meads 10**	a			01s29	01 38		07 08		08 17			08 45		09 10			09 45		10 15			10 42
—	137½	—	Weston-super-Mare	a						*07 46*					*09 23*		*09 59*			*10 22*		*10 59*			*11 21*
133½	—	—	Newport (South Wales)	a		00 52	02s10			07 44			08 29			09 04		09 29			10 04		10 29		
—	—	—	Hereford 7	a						*08 54*			*09 54*					*10 22*					*11 54*		
145¼	—	—	**Cardiff Central 7**	a		01 12	02 31			08 01			08 48			09 22		09 48			10 22		10 48		
165½	—	—	Bridgend	a		01 36				08 22			09 09					10 09					11 09		
177¾	—	—	Port Talbot Parkway	a		01 49				08 35			09 22					10 22					11 22		
183¼	—	—	Neath	a		01 56				08 43			09 29					10 29					11 29		
192¾	—	—	**Swansea 7**	a		02 10				08 56			09 44					10 45					11 43		

		GW 1◇ ☕	GW 1◇ ☕	GW 1◇ ☒	GW 1◇ ☕	GW 1◇ E G ☕	SW 1◇	GW 1◇ ☕	GW 1◇ ☕	GW 1◇ ☒	GW	GW 1◇ ☕	GW 1◇ ☕	GW 1◇ ☕	GW 1◇ ☒	GW 1◇ H ☕	GW 1◇ ☕	GW 1◇ ☕	GW 1◇ ☕	GW 1◇ ☒	GW	GW 1◇ ☕	SW 1◇	GW 1◇ ☕	GW 1◇ ☕
London Paddington 15 ⊖	d	09 15	09 30	09 45	09 48	10 00		10 15	10 30	10 45		11 00	11 15	11 30	11 45	11 48	12 00	12 15	12 30	12 45		13 00		13 15	13 30
London Waterloo 15 ⊖	d						09 20																12 20		
Slough 3	d	*09 07*		*09 37*		*09 44*		*10 07*	*10 14*	*10 37*		*10 44*	*11 07*	*11 14*	*11 37*		*11 44*	*12 07*	*12 14*	*12 37*		*12 44*		*13 07*	*13 14*
Heathrow Terminal 1 Bus 🚌	d																								
Gatwick Airport 10	d			*08b14*				*09 17*				*10 03*			*10b10*		*11 03*			*11b08*		*12 03*			
Reading 7	d	09 41	09 57	10 11	10 16	10 27		10 41	10 57	11 11		11 27	11 41	11 57	12 11	12 16	12 27	12 41	12 57	13 11		13 27		13 41	13 57
Oxford	d	*09 20*	*09 55*					*10 21*	*10 55*				*11 21*	*11 55*				*12 21*	*12 55*					*13 21*	*13 55*
Didcot Parkway	d	09 56	10 12		10 33			10 56	11 12				11 56	12 12		12 33		12 56	13 12					13 56	14 12
Swindon	a	10 15	10 31	10 40	10 53	10 56		11 15	11 31	11 40		11 56	12 15	12 31	12 40	12 53	12 56	13 15	13 31	13 40		13 56		14 15	14 31
	d	10 15	10 31	10 40	10 54	10 56		11 15	11 31	11 40	11 54	11 56	12 15	12 31	12 40	12 54	12 56	13 15	13 31	13 40	13 54	13 56		14 15	14 31
Kemble	d				11 07						12 07					13 07					14 07				
Stroud	d				11 22						12 22					13 22					14 22				
Stonehouse	d				11 27						12 27					13 27					14 27				
Gloucester 7	a				11 43						12 47					13 43					14 47				
Cheltenham Spa	a				12 03						13 03					14 03					15 03				
Birmingham New Street 12	a				*13 26*						*13 57*					*14 57*					*15 57*				
Chippenham	d		10 45			11 10			11 45			12 10		12 45			13 10		13 45			14 10			14 45
Bath Spa 7	a		11 00			11 25	11 45		12 00			12 25		13 00			13 25		14 00			14 25	14 45		15 00
Bristol Parkway 7	a	10 41		11 06				11 41		12 06			12 41		13 06			13 41		14 06				14 41	
	d	10 42		11 07				11 42		12 07			12 42		13 07			13 42		14 07				14 42	
Bristol Temple Meads 10	a		11 15			11 42	12 05		12 15			12 42		13 15			13 42		14 15			14 42	15 05		15 15
Weston-super-Mare	a		*11 59*			12 06			*12 59*			*13 21*		*13 59*			*14 21*		*14 59*			*15 22*			*15 59*
Newport (South Wales)	a	11 04		11 29				12 04		12 29			13 04		13 29			14 05		14 29				15 04	
Hereford 7	a			*12 24*						*13 54*					*14 25*					*15 53*					
Cardiff Central 7	a	11 23		11 48				12 22		12 48			13 22		13 48			14 23		14 48				15 24	
Bridgend	a			12 09						13 09					14 09					15 09					
Port Talbot Parkway	a			12 21						13 22					14 22					15 22					
Neath	a			12 29						13 29					14 29					15 29					
Swansea 7	a			12 45						13 45					14 45					15 43					

For general notes see front of timetable
For details of catering facilities see Directory of Train Operators

- **A** From Gloucester
- **B** From Westbury (Table 123)
- **C** To Penzance (Table 135)
- **D** **The St David**
- **E** To Paignton (Table 135)
- **G** **Torbay Express**
- **H** **Cheltenham Spa Express**
- **b** Change at Redhill

London and Oxford → Swindon, Cheltenham Spa, Bristol, Weston-super-Mare and South Wales

Route Diagram - see first page of Table 125

		GW	GW	GW	GW	GW	GW	GW	GW	GW	GW	GW	GW	GW	GW	GW	GW	GW	GW	GW	GW	GW	GW	GW	GW
		1◇	1◇	1◇	1◇	1◇	1◇		1◇	1◇	1◇	1◇	1◇	1◇	1◇	1◇	1◇		1◇	1◇	1◇	1◇		1◇	1◇
																A					A	B	C		D
		⊡	⊡	⊡	⊡	⊡	⊡		⊡	⊡	⊡	⊡	⊡	⊡	⊡	⊡	⊡		⊡	⊡	⊡	⊡		⊡	⊡
London Paddington [15] ⊖	d	13 45	13 48	14 00	14 15	14 30	14 45		15 00	15 15	15 30	15 45	15 48	16 00	16 15	16 30	16 45		17 00	17 15	17 30	17 45		17 48	18 00
London Waterloo [15] ⊖	d																								
Slough [3]	d	13 37		13 44	14 07	14 14	14 31		14 44	15 07	15 14	15b37		15 47	16 07	16 19	16 48		16 57		17 17	17 33			17 52
Heathrow Terminal 1 Bus	d																								
Gatwick Airport [10]	d	12c08		13 03			13c08		14 03			14c08			15 03		15c08		16 03			16c08			
Reading [7]	d	14 11	14 16	14 27	14 41	14 57	15 11		15 27	15 41	15 57	16 11	16 16	16 27	16 41	16 57	17 11		17 27	17 41	17 57	18 11		18 16	18 27
Oxford	d				14 21	14 55				15 21	15 55				16 21	16 53			17 21		17 51				18 21
Didcot Parkway	d		14 33		14 56	15 12				15 56	16 12		16 33		16 56	17 12	17 26		17 42	17 56	18 12			18 33	18 42
Swindon	a	14 40	14 53	14 56	15 15	15 31	15 40		15 56	16 15	16 31	16 40	16 54	16 56	17 15	17 31	17 45		18 01	18 15	18 31	18 40		18 53	19 01
	d	14 40	14 54	14 56	15 15	15 31	15 40	15 54	15 56	16 15	16 31	16 40	16 54	16 56	17 15	17 31	17 45	17 54	18 01	18 15	18 31	18 40	18 45	18 54	19 01
Kemble	d		15 07					16 07					17 07					18 07						19 07	
Stroud	d		15 22					16 22					17 22					18 22						19 22	
Stonehouse	d		15 27					16 27					17 27					18 27						19 27	
Gloucester [7]	a		15 43					16 47					17 47					18 47						19 47	
Cheltenham Spa	a		16 03					17 03					18 03					19 03						20 03	
Birmingham New Street [12]	a		16 57					17 57					18 57					19 57						20 57	
Chippenham	d			15 10		15 45			16 10		16 45			17 10		17 45			18 15		18 45		19a01		19 15
Bath Spa [7]	a			15 25		16 00			16 25		17 00			17 25		18 00			18 28		19 00				19 28
Bristol Parkway [7]	a	15 06			15 41		16 06			16 41		17 06			17 41		18 12			18 41		19 11			
	d	15 07			15 42		16 07			16 42		17 07			17 42		18 13			18 42		19 11			
Bristol Temple Meads [10]	a			15 42		16 15			16 42		17 15			17 42		18 15			18 45		19 15				19 45
Weston-super-Mare	a			16 25		16 48			17 25		17 51			18 24		18 52			19 29		19 47				20 29
Newport (South Wales)	a	15 29			16 04		16 29			17 04		17 29			18 04		18 36			19 08		19 34			
Hereford [7]	a	16 24					17 54					18 24					19 54					20 39			
Cardiff Central [7]	a	15 48			16 22		16 48			17 22		17 48			18 22		18 53			19 23		19 50			
Bridgend	a	16 09					17 09					18 09			18 53		19 15			19 49		20 12			
Port Talbot Parkway	a	16 22					17 22					18 22			19 06		19 28			20 02		20 25			
Neath	a	16 29					17 29					18 29			19 13		19 35			20 09		20 32			
Swansea [7]	a	16 43					17 43					18 46			19 34		19 48			20 27		20 46			

		GW	GW	GW	GW	GW	GW	GW	GW	GW	GW	GW	GW	GW	GW	GW	GW	GW	GW	GW	GW	GW	GW		
																	FO	FX		FO	FX	FO	FX		
		1◇	1◇	1◇	1◇	1◇	1◇		1◇	1◇	1◇	1◇	1◇		1◇	1◇	1◇	1◇		1◇	1◇	1◇	1◇		
		E						G								H				J					
		⊡	⊡	⊡	⊡	⊡	⊡		⊡	⊡	⊡	⊡	⊡		⊡	⊡	⊡	⊡		⊡	⊡	⊼	⊼		
London Paddington [15] ⊖	d	18 15	18 30	18 45	18 48	19 00	19 15		19 30	19 48	20 00	20 15	20 45		21 15	21 45	22 15	22 15		22 45	22 45	23 30	23 30		
London Waterloo [15] ⊖	d																								
Slough [3]	d	18 01	18 20	18 33		18 50	19 07		19 20	19 37	19 45	20 07	20 36		21 07		22 05	22 05		22 23	22 46	23 39			
Heathrow Terminal 1 Bus	d																								
Gatwick Airport [10]	d	17 03				17c23	18 03				18c23		19 16		20 03		21 03	21 03		21e11					
Reading [7]	d	18 41	18 57	19 11	19 16	19 27	19 41		19 57	20 16	20 27	20 41	21 11		21 41	22 11	22 41	22 49		23 11	23 18	00 02	00 06		
Oxford	d		18 55			19 21				19 55	20 21		20 53		21 20		22 34	22 34		23 05	23 05				
Didcot Parkway	d	18 56	19 12		19 33	19 42	19 56			20 33	20 42	20 56	21 27		22 00	22 32	23 00	23 07		23 30	23 37	00 25	00 25		
Swindon	a	19 15	19 31	19 40	19 53	20 01	20 15		20 12	20 53	21 01	21 15	21 45		22 20	22 50	23 19	23 26		23 50	23 56	00 43	00 43		
	d	19 15	19 31	19 40	19 54	20 01	20 15	20 23	20 31	20 54	21 01	21 15	21 45	21 54	22 20	22 52	23 19	23 26	23 33	23 50	23 56	00 43	00 43		
Kemble	d				20 07			20 37		21 11				22 07					23 47						
Stroud	d				20 22			20 52		21 26				22 22					00 02						
Stonehouse	d				20 27			20 57		21 31				22 27					00 07						
Gloucester [7]	a				20 43			21 13		21 47				22 47					00 23						
Cheltenham Spa	a				21 03			21 27		22 05				23 03					00 52						
Birmingham New Street [12]	a				21g52			22 48		23 43															
Chippenham	d		19 45			20 15			20 45		21 15		22 00			23 06	23 33	23 40				00 58	00 58		
Bath Spa [7]	a		20 00			20 28			21 00		21 28		22 12			23 19	23 48	23 55				01 13	01 13		
Bristol Parkway [7]	a	19 41		20 06			20 41					21 41			22 46					00 16	00 22				
	d	19 42		20 07			20 42					21 42			22 46					00 17	00 22				
Bristol Temple Meads [10]	a		20 15			20 45			21 15		21 45		22 30			23 33	00 05	00 11				01s29	01s29		
Weston-super-Mare	a		20 53			21 28			21 48		22 28		23 40			00s04									
Newport (South Wales)	a	20 04		20 29			21 04					22 04			23 15					00 48	00 52	02s06	02s10		
Hereford [7]	a	21 14					22 00					23 05			01 46					01 46	01 53				
Cardiff Central [7]	a	20 21		20 48			21 24					22 25			23 37					01 04	01 12	02 23	02 31		
Bridgend	a	20 42		21 09			21 45					22 55			23 59					01 28	01 36				
Port Talbot Parkway	a	20 57		21 22			21 58					23 08			00 11					01 41	01 49				
Neath	a	21 04		21 29			22 05					23 15			00 18					01 48	01 56				
Swansea [7]	a	21 21		21 42			22 20					23 31			00 33					02 10	02 10				

For general notes see front of timetable
For details of catering facilities see Directory of Train Operators

- **A** To Taunton (Table 134)
- **B** To Carmarthen (Table 128)
- **C** From Worcester Foregate Street (Table 71) to Southampton Central (Table 123)
- **D** **The Bristolian**
- **E** **The Red Dragon**
- **G** From Westbury (Table 123)
- **H** To Exeter St Davids (Table 135)
- **J** ⊡ to Reading
- **b** 30 June to 5 September dep. 1531
- **c** Change at Redhill
- **e** Change at Redhill and Reading
- **g** Change at Gloucester

Table 125

until 6 September

London and Oxford → Swindon, Cheltenham Spa, Bristol, Weston-super-Mare and South Wales

Route Diagram - see first page of Table 125

	GW	GW	GW	GW	GW	GW	GW	GW	GW	GW	GW	GW	GW	GW	GW	GW	GW	SW	GW	GW	GW	GW	GW	GW
		1◇	1◇		1◇	1◇	1◇	1◇	1◇	1◇	1◇	1◇	1◇		1◇	1◇	1◇	1◇	1◇	1◇	1◇	1◇		1◇
							A					B C												
			🛒		☕	☕	☕	☕	☕	☕	☕	☕	☕		☕	☕	☕		☕	☕	☕	☕		☕
London Paddington 15 ⊖ d		22p45	23p30		06 30	07 00	07 30	07 45	08 00	08 15	08 30	08 45	09 00		09 30	09 45	10 00		10 15	10 30	10 45	11 00		11 30
London Waterloo 15 ⊖ d																		09 20						
Slough 3 d					*06 18*	*06 48*	*07 14*	*07 38*	*07 44*	*08 07*	*08 14*	*08 38*	*08 44*		*09 14*	*09 38*	*09 44*		*10 07*	*10 14*	*10 38*	*10 44*		*11 14*
Heathrow Terminal 1 Bus d																								
Gatwick Airport 10 d					*05 15*	*06 03*			*07 03*			*07b08*	*08 03*			*08b08*	*09 03*				*09b08*	*10 03*		
Reading 7 d		23p11	00 02		06 55	07 27	07 56	08 11	08 27	08 41	08 58	09 11	09 27		09 57	10 11	10 27		10 41	10 57	11 11	11 27		11 58
Oxford d			*00 05*		*06 55*					*08 21*					*09 52*				*10 21*	*10 55*				*11 55*
Didcot Parkway d		23p30	00 25		07 13					08 56	09 13				10 12				10 56	11 13				12 13
Swindon a		23p50	00 43		07 31	07 56	08 26	08 40	08 56	09 15	09 32	09 40	09 56		10 31	10 40	10 56		11 15	11 31	11 40	11 56		12 32
Swindon d	23p33	23p50	00 43	07 16	07 31	07 56	08 26	08 40	08 56	09 15	09 32	09 40	09 56	10 14	10 31	10 40	10 56		11 15	11 31	11 40	11 56	12 14	12 32
Kemble d	23p47			07 30						09 30				10 28					11 30				12 28	
Stroud d	00 02			07 45						09 45				10 43					11 45				12 43	
Stonehouse d	00 07			07 50						09 50				10 48					11 50				12 48	
Gloucester 7 a	00 23			08 06						10 06				11 04					12 06				13 04	
Cheltenham Spa a	*00 52*			08 23						10 23				11 20					12 23				13 20	
Birmingham New Street 12 a				*09 26*						*11 26*				*12 26*					*13 26*				*14 26*	
Chippenham d			00 58		07 46	08 10	08 40		09 10		09 46		10 10		10 45		11 10		11 45			12 10		12 46
Bath Spa 7 a			01 13		08 01	08 24	08 55		09 24		10 01		10 25		11 00		11 25	11 45	12 00			12 25		13 01
Bristol Parkway 7 a		00 16						09 06				10 06				11 06					12 06			
Bristol Parkway 7 d		00 17						09 07				10 07				11 07					12 07			
Bristol Temple Meads 10 a			01s29		08 15	08 40	09 10		09 40		10 15		10 39		11 15		11 42	12 00	12 15			12 42		13 15
Weston-super-Mare a						*09 21*	*09 59*		*10 24*				11 05		*11 59*		*12 21*		12 35			*13 21*		*14 01*
Newport (South Wales) a		00 48	02s06					09 30				10 31				11 29					12 31			
Hereford 7 a		*01 53*						*10 54*				*11 54*				*12 25*					*13 54*			
Cardiff Central 7 a		01 04	02 23					09 48				10 47				11 48					12 47			
Bridgend a		01 28						10 09				11 09				12 09					13 09			
Port Talbot Parkway a		01 41						10 22				11 22				12 22					13 22			
Neath a		01 48						10 29				11 29				12 30					13 29			
Swansea 7 a		02 10						10 43				11 42				12 43					13 42			

	GW	GW	GW	GW	GW	GW	SW	GW	GW	GW	GW	GW	GW	GW	GW	GW	GW	GW	GW	GW	GW	GW	GW	GW
	1◇	1◇	1◇	1◇	1◇	1◇	1◇		1◇	1◇	1◇	1◇		1◇	1◇	1◇		1◇	1◇	1◇	1◇	1◇	1◇	1◇
																						D		
	☕	☕	☕	☕	☕	☕			☕	☕	☕	☕		☕	☕	☕		☕	☕	☕	☕	☕	☕	☕
London Paddington 15 ⊖ d	11 45	12 00	12 15	12 30	12 45	13 00			13 30	13 45	14 00	14 15		14 30	14 45	15 00		15 30	15 45	16 00	16 15	16 30	16 45	17 00
London Waterloo 15 ⊖ d							12 20																	
Slough 3 d	*11 38*	*11 44*	*12 07*	*12 14*	*12 38*	*12 44*			*13 14*	*13 38*	*13 44*	*14 07*		*14 38*		*14 44*		*15 14*	*15 38*	*15 44*	*16 07*	*16 14*	*16 38*	*16 44*
Heathrow Terminal 1 Bus d																								
Gatwick Airport 10 d	*10b08*	*11 03*			*11b08*	*12 03*				*12b08*	*13 03*			*13b08*		*14 03*			*14b08*	*15 03*			*15b08*	*16 03*
Reading 7 d	12 11	12 27	12 41	12 57	13 11	13 27			13 57	14 11	14 27	14 41		14 59	15 11	15 27		15 58	16 11	16 27	16 41	16 58	17 11	17 27
Oxford d			*12 21*	*12 55*					*13 55*			*14 21*		*14 55*				*15 55*			*16 21*	*16 55*		
Didcot Parkway d			12 56	13 14					14 13			14 56		15 13				16 13			16 56	17 13		
Swindon a	12 40	12 56	13 15	13 32	13 40	13 56			14 32	14 40	14 56	15 15		15 32	15 40	15 56		16 32	16 40	16 56	17 15	17 32	17 40	17 56
Swindon d	12 40	12 56	13 15	13 34	13 40	13 56		14 14	14 33	14 40	14 56	15 15	15 19	15 32	15 40	15 56	16 14	16 32	16 40	16 56	17 15	17 32	17 40	17 56
Kemble d			13 30					14 28				15 30					16 28				17 30			
Stroud d			13 45					14 43				15 45					16 43				17 45			
Stonehouse d			13 50					14 48				15 50					16 48				17 50			
Gloucester 7 a			14 06					15 04				16 06					17 04				18 06			
Cheltenham Spa a			14 23					15 20				16 23					17 20				18 23			
Birmingham New Street 12 a			*15 26*					*16 26*				*17 26*					*18 26*				*19 26*			
Chippenham d		13 10		13 48		14 10			14 46		15 10		15a35	15 46		16 10		16 46		17 10		17 46		18 10
Bath Spa 7 a		13 25		14 01		14 25	14 45		15 01		15 25			16 01		16 25		17 01		17 25		18 01		18 25
Bristol Parkway 7 a	13 06				14 06					15 06					16 06				17 06				18 06	
Bristol Parkway 7 d	13 07				14 07					15 07					16 07				17 07				18 07	
Bristol Temple Meads 10 a		13 42		14 15		14 42	15 05		15 15		15 42			16 15		16 42		17 15		17 42		18 15		18 42
Weston-super-Mare a		*14 21*		14 36		*15 21*	*15 59*				*16 21*			16 35		*17 21*		17 35		*18 21*		18 36		*19 23*
Newport (South Wales) a	13 29				14 32					15 29					16 32				17 29				18 31	
Hereford 7 a	*14 25*				*15 52*					*16 25*					*17 54*				*18 25*				*19 54*	
Cardiff Central 7 a	13 47				14 48					15 48					16 48				17 47				18 47	
Bridgend a	14 08				15 10					16 09					17 10				18 09				19 09	
Port Talbot Parkway a	14 21				15 23					16 22					17 23				18 24				19 22	
Neath a	14 29				15 30					16 30					17 30				18 32				19 29	
Swansea 7 a	14 42				15 43					16 43					17 43				18 46				19 42	

For general notes see front of timetable
For details of catering facilities see Directory of Train Operators

- **A** To Penzance (Table 135)
- **B** To Pembroke Dock (Table 128)
- **C** **Pembroke Coast Express**
- **D** To Paignton (Table 135)
- **b** Change at Redhill

London and Oxford → Swindon, Cheltenham Spa, Bristol, Weston-super-Mare and South Wales

until 6 September

Route Diagram - see first page of Table 125

		GW	GW	GW	GW	GW	GW	GW	GW	GW	GW	GW	GW	SW	GW	GW	GW	GW	GW	GW	GW	GW	GW		
			1◇	1◇	1◇	1◇	1◇	1◇	1◇		1◇	1◇	1◇	1◇		1◇	1◇	1◇	1◇		1◇	1◇	1◇		
				A			B		C						D		C								
			☕	☕	☕	☕	☕	☕	☕		☕	☕	☕			☕	☕	☕	☕			☕	☕		
London Paddington 15 ⊖	d		17 30	17 45	18 00	18 15	18 30	18 45	19 00		19 30	19 45	20 00			20 15	20 30	20 45	21 30		22 00	22 30	23 30		
London Waterloo 15 ⊖	d													19 20											
Slough 3	d		*17 14*	*17 38*	*17 44*	*18 01*	*18 14*	*18 38*	*18 44*		*19 38*		*19 44*			*20 07*	*20 14*	*20 38*	*21 31*		*21 44*	*22 31*	*23 20*		
Heathrow Terminal 1 Bus	d																								
Gatwick Airport 10	d			*16b08*	*17 03*			*17b08*	*18 03*		*18b08*		*19 03*					*19b08*	*20b11*		*21 03*		*21b11*		
Reading 7	d		17 57	18 11	18 27	18 41	18 57	19 11	19 27		19 59	20 11	20 26			20 41	20 58	21 11	22 00		22 27	23 00	23 59		
Oxford	d		*17 55*			*18 21*	*18 55*				*19 55*		*20 20*				*20 53*		*21 53*			*23 00*	*23 09*		
Didcot Parkway	d		18 13			18 56	19 12				20 14		20 42			20 56	21 12		22 15		22 42	23 22	00 16		
Swindon	a		18 32	18 40	18 56	19 15	19 31	19 40	19 56		20 32	20 40	21 01			21 15	21 31	21 47	22 34		23 01	23 42	00 36		
	d	18 14	18 32	18 40	18 56	19 15	19 31	19 40	19 56	20 00	20 33	20 40	21 01		21 08	21 15	21 31	21 48	22 34	22 35	23 01	23 42	00 36		
Kemble	d	18 28				19 30				20 15						21 30				22 49					
Stroud	d	18 43				19 45				20 30						21 45				23 04					
Stonehouse	d	18 48				19 50				20 35						21 50				23 09					
Gloucester 7	a	19 04				20 07				20 51						22 05				23 25					
Cheltenham Spa	a	19 20				20 23				21 16						22 23									
Birmingham New Street 12	a	*20 26*				*21 52*				*22 25*															
Chippenham	d		18 46		19 11		19 45		20 10		20 46		21 15		21a24		21 45		22 49			23 56	00 50		
Bath Spa 7	a		19 01		19 25		20 00		20 25		21 01		21 30	21 50			21 59		23 03			00 10	01 05		
Bristol Parkway 7	a			19 12				20 07				21 06						22 13			23 27				
	d			19 12				20 07				21 06						22 14			23 29				
Bristol Temple Meads 10	a		19 16		19 42		20 15		20 42		21 16		21 47	22 06			22 16		23 18			00 26	01 21		
Weston-super-Mare	a		19 52		*20 23*		20 37		21 24		*22 25*						22s45								
Newport (South Wales)	a			19 35				20 31				21 31						22 45			00 01				
Hereford 7	a			*20 39*				*21 57*				*22 59*													
Cardiff Central 7	a			19 52				20 48				21 47						23 06			00 23				
Bridgend	a			20 13				21 09				22 09						23 27							
Port Talbot Parkway	a			20 26				21 22				22 22						23 40							
Neath	a			20 34				21 30				22 29						23 48							
Swansea 7	a			20 48				21 47				22 46						00 01							

Saturdays

from 13 September

		GW	GW	GW	GW	GW	GW	GW	GW	GW	GW	GW	GW	GW	GW	GW	GW	GW	SW	GW	GW	GW	GW	GW	GW
			1◇	1◇		1◇	1◇	1◇	1◇	1◇	1◇	1◇	1◇	1◇		1◇	1◇	1◇	1◇	1◇	1◇	1◇	1◇		1◇
								E																	
				🛒		☕	☕	☕	☕	☕	☕	☕	☕	☕		☕	☕	☕		☕	☕	☕	☕		☕
London Paddington 15 ⊖	d		22p45	23p30		06 30	07 00	07 30	07 45	08 00	08 15	08 30	08 45	09 00		09 30	09 45	10 00		10 15	10 30	10 45	11 00		11 30
London Waterloo 15 ⊖	d																		09 20						
Slough 3	d					*06 18*	*06 48*	*07 14*	*07 38*	*07 44*	*08 07*	*08 37*		*08 44*		*09 14*	*09 38*	*09 44*		*10 07*	*10 14*	*10 38*	*10 44*		*11 14*
Heathrow Terminal 1 Bus	d																								
Gatwick Airport 10	d					*05 15*	*06 03*			*07 03*			*07b08*	*08 03*			*08b08*	*09 03*				*09b08*	*10 03*		
Reading 7	d		23p11	00 02		06 55	07 27	07 57	08 11	08 27	08 41	08 58	09 11	09 27		09 57	10 11	10 27		10 41	10 57	11 11	11 27		11 58
Oxford	d																								
Didcot Parkway	d		23p30	00 25		07 13		08 12			08 56	09 13				10 12				10 56	11 12				12 13
Swindon	a		23p50	00 43		07 31	07 56	08 30	08 40	08 56	09 15	09 32	09 40	09 56		10 31	10 40	10 56		11 15	11 31	11 40	11 56		12 32
	d	23p33	23p50	00 43	07 16	07 31	07 56	08 30	08 40	08 56	09 15	09 32	09 40	09 56	10 14	10 31	10 40	10 56		11 15	11 31	11 40	11 56	12 14	12 32
Kemble	d	23p47			07 30						09 30				10 28					11 30				12 28	
Stroud	d	00 02			07 45						09 45				10 43					11 45				12 43	
Stonehouse	d	00 07			07 50						09 50				10 48					11 50				12 48	
Gloucester 7	a	00 23			08 06						10 06				11 04					12 06				13 04	
Cheltenham Spa	a	*00 52*			08 23						10 23				11 20					12 23				13 20	
Birmingham New Street 12	a																								
Chippenham	d			00 58		07 46	08 10	08 45		09 10		09 46		10 10		10 45		11 10			11 45		12 10		12 46
Bath Spa 7	a			01 13		08 01	08 24	09 00		09 24		10 01		10 25		11 00		11 25	11 45		12 00		12 25		13 01
Bristol Parkway 7	a		00 16						09 06				10 06				11 06					12 06			
	d		00 17						09 07				10 07				11 07					12 07			
Bristol Temple Meads 10	a			01s29		08 15	08 40	09 15		09 40		10 15		10 39		11 15		11 42	12 00		12 15		12 42		13 15
Weston-super-Mare	a						*09 21*	*09 59*		*10 24*						*11 59*		*12 21*			*12 59*		*13 21*		
Newport (South Wales)	a		00 48	02s06					09 30				10 31				11 29					12 31			
Hereford 7	a		*01 53*						*10 54*				*11 54*				*12 25*					*13 54*			
Cardiff Central 7	a		01 04	02 23					09 48				10 48				11 48					12 47			
Bridgend	a		01 28						10 09				11 09				12 09					13 09			
Port Talbot Parkway	a		01 41						10 22				11 22				12 22					13 22			
Neath	a		01 48						10 29				11 29				12 30					13 29			
Swansea 7	a		02 10						10 43				11 43				12 43					13 42			

For general notes see front of timetable
For details of catering facilities see Directory of Train Operators

- **A** To Carmarthen (Table 128)
- **B** To Taunton (Table 134)
- **C** To Exeter St Davids (Table 135)
- **D** From Cheltenham Spa
- **E** To Penzance (Table 135)
- **b** Change at Redhill

Table 125

Saturdays

from 13 September

London and Oxford → Swindon, Cheltenham Spa, Bristol, Weston-super-Mare and South Wales

Route Diagram - see first page of Table 125

		GW	GW	GW	GW	GW	GW	SW	GW	GW	GW	GW	GW	GW	GW	GW	GW	GW	GW	GW	GW	GW	GW	GW	GW
		1 ◇	1 ◇	1 ◇	1 ◇	1 ◇	1 ◇	1 ◇		1 ◇	1 ◇	1 ◇	1 ◇		1 ◇	1 ◇	1 ◇		1 ◇	1 ◇	1 ◇	1 ◇	1 ◇	1 ◇	1 ◇
																							A		
		☕	☕	☕	☕	☕	☕			☕	☕	☕	☕		☕	☕	☕		☕	☕	☕	☕	☕	☕	☕
London Paddington 15 ⊖	d	11 45	12 00	12 15	12 30	12 45	13 00			13 30	13 45	14 00	14 15		14 30	14 45	15 00		15 30	15 45	16 00	16 15	16 30	16 45	17 00
London Waterloo 15 ⊖	d							12 20																	
Slough 3	d	*11 38*	*11 44*	*12 07*	*12 34*	*12 38*	*12 44*			*13 14*	*13 38*	*13 44*	*14 07*		*14 14*	*14 38*	*14 44*		*15 14*	*15 38*	*15 44*	*16 07*	*16 14*	*16 38*	*16 44*
Heathrow Terminal 1 Bus	d																								
Gatwick Airport 10	d	*10b08*	*11 03*			*11b08*	*12 03*				*12b08*	*13 03*				*13b08*	*14 03*			*14b08*	*15 03*			*15b08*	*16 03*
Reading 7	d	12 11	12 27	12 41	12 58	13 11	13 27			13 57	14 11	14 27	14 41		14 58	15 11	15 27		15 58	16 11	16 27	16 41	16 58	17 11	17 27
Oxford	d																								
Didcot Parkway	d			12 56	13 15					14 13			14 56		15 13				16 13			16 56	17 13		
Swindon	a	12 40	12 56	13 15	13 33	13 40	13 56			14 32	14 40	14 56	15 15		15 32	15 40	15 56		16 32	16 40	16 56	17 15	17 32	17 40	17 56
	d	12 40	12 56	13 15	13 35	13 40	13 56		14 14	14 33	14 40	14 56	15 15	15 19	15 32	15 40	15 56	16 14	16 32	16 40	16 56	17 15	17 32	17 40	17 56
Kemble	d			13 30					14 28				15 30					16 28				17 30			
Stroud	d			13 45					14 43				15 45					16 43				17 45			
Stonehouse	d			13 50					14 48				15 50					16 48				17 50			
Gloucester 7	a			14 06					15 04				16 06					17 04				18 06			
Cheltenham Spa	a			14 23					15 20				16 23					17 20				18 23			
Birmingham New Street 12	a																								
Chippenham	d		13 10		13 49		14 10			14 46		15 10		15a35	15 46		16 10		16 46		17 10		17 46		18 10
Bath Spa 7	a		13 25		14 02		14 25	14 45		15 01		15 25			16 01		16 25		17 01		17 25		18 01		18 25
Bristol Parkway 7	a	13 06				14 06					15 06					16 06				17 06				18 06	
	d	13 07				14 07					15 07					16 07				17 07				18 07	
Bristol Temple Meads 10	a		13 42		14 16		14 42	15 05		15 15		15 42			16 15		16 42		17 15		17 42		18 15		18 42
Weston-super-Mare	a		*14 21*				*15 21*	*15 59*				*16 21*					*17 21*				*18 21*		18 36		*19 23*
Newport (South Wales)	a	13 29				14 32					15 29					16 32				17 29				18 31	
Hereford 7	a	*14 25*				*15 52*					*16 25*					*17 54*				*18 25*				*19 54*	
Cardiff Central 7	a	13 47				14 48					15 48					16 48				17 47				18 47	
Bridgend	a	14 08				15 10					16 09					17 10				18 09				19 09	
Port Talbot Parkway	a	14 21				15 23					16 22					17 23				18 24				19 22	
Neath	a	14 29				15 30					16 30					17 30				18 32				19 29	
Swansea 7	a	14 42				15 43					16 43					17 43				18 46				19 42	

		GW	GW	GW	GW	GW	GW	GW	GW	GW	GW	GW	GW	GW	SW	GW	GW	GW	GW	GW	GW	GW	GW	GW
			1 ◇	1 ◇	1 ◇	1 ◇	1 ◇	1 ◇	1 ◇		1 ◇	1 ◇	1 ◇	1 ◇	1 ◇		1 ◇	1 ◇	1 ◇	1 ◇		1 ◇	1 ◇	1 ◇
				B			C		D							E		C						
			☕	☕	☕	☕	☕	☕	☕		☕	☕	☕	☕			☕	☕	☕	☕			☕	☕
London Paddington 15 ⊖	d		17 30	17 45	18 00	18 15	18 30	18 45	19 00		19 15	19 30	19 45	20 00			20 15	20 30	20 45	21 30		22 00	22 30	23 30
London Waterloo 15 ⊖	d														19 20									
Slough 3	d		*17 14*	*17 38*	*17 44*	*18 01*	*18 14*	*18 38*	*18 44*		*19 08*	*19 38*		*19 44*			*20 07*	*20 14*	*20 38*	*21 31*		*21 44*	*22 31*	*23 20*
Heathrow Terminal 1 Bus	d																							
Gatwick Airport 10	d			*16b08*	*17 03*			*17b08*	*18 03*			*18b08*		*19 03*					*19b08*	*20b11*		*21 03*		*21b11*
Reading 7	d		17 57	18 11	18 27	18 41	18 57	19 11	19 27		19 41	19 59	20 11	20 26			20 41	20 58	21 11	22 00		22 27	23 00	23 59
Oxford	d																							*23 09*
Didcot Parkway	d		18 13			18 56	19 12				19 56	20 14		20 42			20 56	21 12		22 15		22 42	23 22	00 16
Swindon	a		18 32	18 40	18 56	19 15	19 31	19 40	19 56		20 15	20 32	20 40	21 01			21 15	21 31	21 47	22 34		23 01	23 42	00 36
	d	18 14	18 32	18 40	18 56	19 15	19 31	19 40	19 56	20 00	20 15	20 33	20 40	21 01		21 08	21 15	21 31	21 48	22 34	22 35	23 01	23 42	00 36
Kemble	d	18 28				19 30				20 15							21 30				22 49			
Stroud	d	18 43				19 45				20 30							21 45				23 04			
Stonehouse	d	18 48				19 50				20 35							21 50				23 09			
Gloucester 7	a	19 04				20 07				20 51							22 05				23 25			
Cheltenham Spa	a	19 20				20 23				21 16							22 23							
Birmingham New Street 12	a																							
Chippenham	d		18 46		19 11		19 45		20 10			20 46		21 15		21a24		21 45		22 49			23 56	00 50
Bath Spa 7	a		19 01		19 25		20 00		20 25			21 01		21 30	21 50			21 59		23 03			00 10	01 05
Bristol Parkway 7	a			19 12				20 07			20 41		21 06						22 13			23 27		
	d			19 12				20 07			20 42		21 06						22 14			23 29		
Bristol Temple Meads 10	a		19 16		19 42		20 15		20 42			21 16		21 47	22 06			22 16		23 18			00 26	01 21
Weston-super-Mare	a		19 52		*20 23*		20 37		21 24			*22 25*						22s45						
Newport (South Wales)	a			19 35				20 31			21 04		21 31						22 45			00 01		
Hereford 7	a			*20 39*							*21 57*		*22 59*											
Cardiff Central 7	a			19 52				20 48			21 22		21 47						23 06			00 23		
Bridgend	a			20 13				21 09			21 42		22 09						23 27					
Port Talbot Parkway	a			20 26				21 22			21 55		22 22						23 40					
Neath	a			20 34				21 30			22 03		22 29						23 48					
Swansea 7	a			20 48				21 47			22 18		22 46						00 01					

For general notes see front of timetable
For details of catering facilities see Directory of Train Operators

A To Paignton (Table 135)
B To Carmarthen (Table 128)
C To Exeter St Davids (Table 135)
D To Taunton (Table 134)
E From Cheltenham Spa
b Change at Redhill

Table 125

Sundays

London and Oxford → Swindon, Cheltenham Spa, Bristol, Weston-super-Mare and South Wales

until 7 September

Route Diagram - see first page of Table 125

		GW 1◇	GW 1◇ A	GW 1◇	GW 🚌	GW 1◇	GW 1◇ B	GW 🚌	GW 1◇ C	GW 1◇	GW 1◇	GW 🚌	GW 1◇ D	GW 1◇ B	GW 🚌	GW 1◇ E	GW 1◇	GW 🚌	GW 1◇	SW 1◇
London Paddington [15] ⊖	d	23p30	07 57	08 00		09 07	09 27		09 57	10 07	10 27		11 07	11 27		12 07	12 27		13 07	
London Waterloo [15] ⊖	d																			12 15
Slough [3]	d		*07 14*	*08 14*		*09 01*	*09 15*		*09 53*		*10 15*		*11 15*			*12 00*	*12 15*		*12 58*	
Heathrow Terminal 1 Bus 🚌	d																			
Gatwick Airport [10]	d		*07 07*			*08 07*				*09 07*			*10 12*			*11 07*			*12 07*	
Reading [7]	d	23p59	08 42	08 46		09 41	10 05		10 30	10 44	11 02		11 44	12 02		12 42	13 02		13 42	
Oxford	d		*08 38*			*09 38*				*10 38*			*11 38*			*12 05*			*13 38*	
Didcot Parkway	d	00 16	08 57			09 58				11 00			12 00			12 58			13 58	
Swindon	a	00 36	09 17	09 22		10 14	10 35		11 01	11 18	11 31		12 18	12 31		13 17	13 31		14 16	
	d	00 36	09 17	09 23	09 27	10 15	10 36	10 40		11 18	11 33	11 40	12 19	12 33	12 40	13 17	13 33	13 40	14 17	
Kemble	d			09 37			10 50				11 46			12 46			13 46			
Stroud	d			09 52			11 05				12 01			13 01			14 01			
Stonehouse	d			09 57			11 10				12 07			13 07			14 07			
Gloucester [7]	a			10 12			11 25				12 22			13 27			14 25			
Cheltenham Spa	a			*10 46*			*11 57*				*12 50*			*13 49*			*14 49*			
Birmingham New Street [12]	a			*11b51*			*12b51*				*13 45*			*14b57*			*15 44*			
Chippenham	d	00 50	09 33			10 30				11 33			12 32			13 31			14 31	
Bath Spa [7]	a	01 05	09 46			10 45				11 48			12 47			13 45			14 45	14 52
Bristol Parkway [7]	a				10 22			11 35				12 35			13 35			14 35		
	d																			
Bristol Temple Meads [10]	a	01 21	10 00			11 00				12 04			13 01			14 01			15 00	15 06
Weston-super-Mare	a		*10 40*			*12 01*				12 34			13 31							*15 49*
Newport (South Wales)	a			10 57			12 09				13 05			14 10			15 09			
Hereford [7]	a			*12 41*			*13 41*							*15 41*			*16 37*			
Cardiff Central [7]	a			11 14			12 25				13 22			14 27			15 25			
Bridgend	a			11 35			12 47				13 43			14 48			15 47			
Port Talbot Parkway	a			11 48			13 00				13 56			15 01			16 00			
Neath	a			11 56			13 07				14 04			15 09			16 07			
Swansea [7]	a			12 10			13 20				14 17			15 27			16 20			

		GW 1◇ B	GW 🚌	GW 1◇	GW 1◇	GW 🚌	GW 1◇ G	GW 1◇	GW 🚌	GW 1◇	GW 1◇	GW 🚌	GW 1◇	GW	GW 1◇	GW 🚌	GW 1◇	GW 1◇	GW 1◇
London Paddington [15] ⊖	d	13 27		14 07	14 27		15 07	15 27		16 07	16 27		17 07		17 27		17 37	17 57	18 07
London Waterloo [15] ⊖	d																		
Slough [3]	d	*13 15*		*13 58*	*14 15*		*14 58*	*15 15*		*15 58*	*16 15*		*16 58*		*17 15*			*17 58*	
Heathrow Terminal 1 Bus 🚌	d																		
Gatwick Airport [10]	d			*13 07*			*14 07*			*15 07*			*16 07*						*17 07*
Reading [7]	d	14 02		14 42	15 02		15 42	16 02		16 42	17 02		17 42		18 05		18 13	18 31	18 42
Oxford	d			*14 38*			*15 05*			*16 05*			*17 05*				*18 05*		*18 41*
Didcot Parkway	d			14 58			15 58			16 58			17 58				18 29		18 58
Swindon	a	14 31		15 17	15 31		16 17	16 31		17 17	17 31		18 15		18 34		18 47	19 01	19 17
	d	14 33	14 40	15 17	15 33	15 40	16 17	16 33	16 40	17 17	17 33	17 40	18 17	18 25	18 36	18 40	18 49		19 17
Kemble	d	14 46			15 46			16 47			17 46				18 49				
Stroud	d	15 01			16 01			17 02			18 01				19 04				
Stonehouse	d	15 07			16 07			17 08			18 07				19 10				
Gloucester [7]	a	15 29			16 29			17 31			18 26				19 28				
Cheltenham Spa	a	*15 51*			*16 49*			*17 51*			*18 55*				*19 47*				
Birmingham New Street [12]	a	*16 45*			*17 45*			*18 45*			*19 45*				*20 45*				
Chippenham	d			15 31			16 31			17 31			18 31	18a41			19 01		19 31
Bath Spa [7]	a			15 45			16 45			17 45			18 45				19 16		19 45
Bristol Parkway [7]	a		15 35			16 35			17 35			18 35				19 35			
	d																		
Bristol Temple Meads [10]	a			16 00			17 00			18 00			19 00				19 38		20 00
Weston-super-Mare	a			*16 48*			17 38			*18 42*			19 32						*20 53*
Newport (South Wales)	a	16 13			17 12			18 15			19 09				20 11				
Hereford [7]	a	*17 41*			*18 12*			*19 39*							*21 40*				
Cardiff Central [7]	a	16 29			17 29			18 31			19 27				20 28				
Bridgend	a	16 56			17 50			18 53			19 48				20 49				
Port Talbot Parkway	a	17 09			18 03			19 06			20 01				21 02				
Neath	a	17 17			18 11			19 13			20 08				21 10				
Swansea [7]	a	17 34			18 24			19 30			20 21				21 24				

For general notes see front of timetable
For details of catering facilities see Directory of Train Operators

- **A** To Penzance (Table 135)
- **B** To Carmarthen (Table 128)
- **C** **Atlantic Coast Express**
- **D** To Paignton (Table 135)
- **E** To Plymouth (Table 135)
- **G** To Taunton (Table 134)
- **b** Change at Gloucester and Cheltenham Spa

Table 125

Sundays
until 7 September

London and Oxford → Swindon, Cheltenham Spa, Bristol, Weston-super-Mare and South Wales

Route Diagram - see first page of Table 125

		GW 1◇ ☕	GW 🚌	GW 1◇ A ☕	SW 1◇	GW 1◇ ☕	GW 🚌	GW 1◇ ☕	GW 1◇ ☕	GW 1◇ ☕
London Paddington 15 ⊖	d	18 27		19 07		19 27		19 57	20 07	20 27
London Waterloo 15 ⊖	d				18 15					
Slough 3	d	18 15		18 58		19 15		19 57		20 15
Heathrow Terminal 1 Bus 🚌	d									
Gatwick Airport 10	d			18 07					19 07	
Reading 7	d	19 05		19 42		20 05		20 33	20 42	21 04
Oxford	d			19 05					20 05	
Didcot Parkway	d			19 58					20 58	
Swindon	a	19 34		20 17		20 34		21 01	21 16	21 34
	d	19 36	19 40	20 17		20 36	20 40		21 17	21 36
Kemble	d	19 49				20 49				21 49
Stroud	d	20 04				21 04				22 04
Stonehouse	d	20 10				21 10				22 10
Gloucester 7	a	20 25				21 30				22 25
Cheltenham Spa	a	20 47				21 49				23 11
Birmingham New Street 12	a	21 45				22 45				
Chippenham	d			20 31					21 31	
Bath Spa 7	a			20 45	20 59				21 45	
Bristol Parkway 7	a		20 35				21 35			
	d									
Bristol Temple Meads 10	a			21 00	21 16				22 02	
Weston-super-Mare	a			21 31					23 03	
Newport (South Wales)	a	21 08				22 21				23 16
Hereford 7	a					00 03				
Cardiff Central 7	a	21 25				22 41				23 36
Bridgend	a	21 46				23 03				23 58
Port Talbot Parkway	a	21 59				23 16				00 14
Neath	a	22 07				23 23				00 21
Swansea 7	a	22 20				23 36				00 34

		GW 🚌	GW 1◇	GW 1◇ ☕	GW 🚌	GW 1◇ ☕	GW 1◇ ☕	GW 1◇ ☕	GW 1◇ ☕
London Paddington 15 ⊖	d		21 07	21 27		22 07	22 37	23 07	23 37
London Waterloo 15 ⊖	d								
Slough 3	d		20 58	21 15		21 59	22 16	23 00	23 16
Heathrow Terminal 1 Bus 🚌	d								
Gatwick Airport 10	d		20 07			21 07		22 07	22 07
Reading 7	d		21 42	22 02		22 46	23 14	23 46	00 15
Oxford	d		21 21			22 21			
Didcot Parkway	d		22 00			23 02			
Swindon	a		22 20	22 35		23 22	23s50	00s22	00s53
	d	21 40	22 20	22 37	22 40	23 23			
Kemble	d			22 51					
Stroud	d			23 06					
Stonehouse	d			23 12					
Gloucester 7	a			23 27					
Cheltenham Spa	a								
Birmingham New Street 12	a								
Chippenham	d		22 33			23 37		00s37	01s08
Bath Spa 7	a		22 47			23 51		00s52	01s22
Bristol Parkway 7	a	22 35			23 35		00s16		
	d								
Bristol Temple Meads 10	a		23 03			00 06	00 30	01 06	01 38
Weston-super-Mare	a		23 33						
Newport (South Wales)	a			00 18					
Hereford 7	a								
Cardiff Central 7	a			00 40					
Bridgend	a			01 00					
Port Talbot Parkway	a			01 14					
Neath	a			01 21					
Swansea 7	a			01 34					

Sundays
from 14 September

		GW 1◇ ☕	GW 1◇ B ☕	GW 1◇ ☕	GW 1◇ ☕	GW 1◇ ☕	GW 1◇ ☕	GW	GW 1◇ ☕	GW 1◇ ☕
London Paddington 15 ⊖	d	23p30	08 00	08 30		09 03	09 30		10 03	
London Waterloo 15 ⊖	d									
Slough 3	d		07 14	08 25		09 01	09 14		09 55	
Heathrow Terminal 1 Bus 🚌	d									
Gatwick Airport 10	d		06 09	07 07			08 07			
Reading 7	d	23p59	08 37	09 06		09 36	10 07		10 37	
Oxford	d									
Didcot Parkway	d	00 16	08 52	09 24		09 53			10 53	
Swindon	a	00 36	09 12	09 43		10 09	10 36		11 11	
	d	00 36	09 12	09 45	09 55	10 10	10 38	10 45	11 11	11 29
Kemble	d				10 08			10 59		11 44
Stroud	d				10 23			11 14		11 59
Stonehouse	d				10 28			11 19		12 04
Gloucester 7	a				10 44			11 35		12 20
Cheltenham Spa	a				11 00			11 48		12 36
Birmingham New Street 12	a									
Chippenham	d	00 50	09 28			10 26			11 26	
Bath Spa 7	a	01 05	09 41			10 41			11 41	
Bristol Parkway 7	a			10 09			11 02			
	d			10 11			11 04			
Bristol Temple Meads 10	a	01 21	09 55			10 56			11 57	
Weston-super-Mare	a		10 40			11 36			12 29	
Newport (South Wales)	a			10 32			11 30			
Hereford 7	a						12 41			
Cardiff Central 7	a			10 49			11 47			
Bridgend	a			11 10			12 08			
Port Talbot Parkway	a			11 25			12 21			
Neath	a			11 33			12 29			
Swansea 7	a			11 47			12 43			

		GW 1◇ C ☕	GW 1◇ ☕	GW 1◇ ☕	GW 1◇ D ☕	GW 1◇ ☕	GW 1◇ C ☕	GW 1◇ ☕	SW 1◇
London Paddington 15 ⊖	d	10 37	11 03	11 37	12 03		12 37	13 03	
London Waterloo 15 ⊖	d								12 15
Slough 3	d	10 14	11 03	11 14	12 00		12 14	13 01	
Heathrow Terminal 1 Bus 🚌	d								
Gatwick Airport 10	d	09 07	10 11				11 07		
Reading 7	d	11 11	11 43	12 11	12 37		13 11	13 37	
Oxford	d								
Didcot Parkway	d		11 58		12 53			13 53	
Swindon	a	11 40	12 16	12 39	13 12		13 40	14 11	
	d	11 42	12 17	12 42	13 12	13 29	13 42	14 12	
Kemble	d					13 46			
Stroud	d					14 02			
Stonehouse	d					14 07			
Gloucester 7	a					14 24			
Cheltenham Spa	a					14 41			
Birmingham New Street 12	a								
Chippenham	d		12 31		13 26			14 26	
Bath Spa 7	a		12 46		13 40			14 40	14 52
Bristol Parkway 7	a	12 07		13 05			14 07		
	d	12 08		13 06			14 08		
Bristol Temple Meads 10	a		13 00		13 56			14 55	15 06
Weston-super-Mare	a		13 29		14 37				15 49
Newport (South Wales)	a	12 30		13 33			14 30		
Hereford 7	a	13 41					15 41		
Cardiff Central 7	a	12 46		13 49			14 46		
Bridgend	a	13 08		14 11			15 08		
Port Talbot Parkway	a	13 21		14 24			15 21		
Neath	a	13 28		14 31			15 28		
Swansea 7	a	13 41		14 49			15 41		

For general notes see front of timetable
For details of catering facilities see Directory of Train Operators

A To Exeter St Davids (Table 135)
B To Penzance (Table 135)
C To Carmarthen (Table 128)
D To Plymouth (Table 135)

Sundays

from 14 September

London and Oxford → Swindon, Cheltenham Spa, Bristol, Weston-super-Mare and South Wales

Route Diagram - see first page of Table 125

		GW	GW 1◇	GW 1◇	GW 1◇	GW 1◇ A	GW 1◇ B	GW 1◇	GW 1◇	GW 1◇	GW 1◇	GW 1◇	GW	GW	GW 1◇	GW 1◇	GW 1◇
London Paddington 15	⊖ d		13 37	14 03		14 37	15 03	15 37	16 03	16 27	16 37	17 03			17 30	17 37	18 03
London Waterloo 15	⊖ d																
Slough 3	d		*13 14*	*14 05*		*14 14*	*15 05*	*15 14*	*16 05*	*16 14*		*17 05*				*17 14*	*18 05*
Heathrow Terminal 1 Bus	d																
Gatwick Airport 10	d		*12 07*			*13 07*		*14 07*		*15 07*						*16 07*	
Reading 7	d		14 11	14 37		15 11	15 37	16 11	16 37	17 05	17 11	17 37			18 04	18 11	18 37
Oxford	d																
Didcot Parkway	d			14 53			15 53		16 53	17 20		17 53			18 20		18 53
Swindon	a		14 39	15 12		15 40	16 12	16 40	17 12	17 39	17 43	18 10			18 39	18 44	19 12
	d	14 21	14 42	15 12	15 29	15 42	16 12	16 42	17 12	17 40	17 45	18 12	18 22	18 31	18 39	18 46	19 12
Kemble	d	14 36			15 44					17 54			18 36				
Stroud	d	14 51			16 00					18 10			18 50				
Stonehouse	d	14 56			16 05					18 15			18 55				
Gloucester 7	a	15 17			16 24					18 31			19 18				
Cheltenham Spa	a	15 31			16 41					18 48							
Birmingham New Street 12	a																
Chippenham	d			15 26			16 26		17 26			18 26		18a47	18 54		19 26
Bath Spa 7	a			15 40			16 40		17 40			18 40			19 09		19 40
Bristol Parkway 7	a		15 08			16 07		17 06			18 09					19 10	
	d		15 09			16 08		17 08			18 11					19 12	
Bristol Temple Meads 10	a			15 55			16 55		17 55			18 56			19 28		19 55
Weston-super-Mare	a			*16 48*			17 26		*18 37*			19 30					*20 53*
Newport (South Wales)	a		15 31			16 30		17 32			18 32					19 35	
Hereford 7	a		*16 37*			*17 41*					*19 39*						
Cardiff Central 7	a		15 47			16 46		17 49			18 49					19 52	
Bridgend	a		16 09			17 08		18 10			19 10					20 13	
Port Talbot Parkway	a		16 22			17 21		18 23			19 23					20 26	
Neath	a		16 29			17 28		18 31			19 31					20 34	
Swansea 7	a		16 42			17 41		18 45			19 44					20 50	

		GW 1◇	GW 1◇	GW 1◇ C	SW 1◇	GW D	GW 1◇	GW 1◇	GW 1◇	GW 1◇	GW 1◇	GW 1◇	GW	GW 1◇	GW 1◇	GW 1◇	GW 1◇
London Paddington 15	⊖ d	18 27	18 37	19 03			19 37	20 03	20 27	20 37	21 03	21 37		22 03	22 37	23 03	23 37
London Waterloo 15	⊖ d				18 15												
Slough 3	d	*18 14*		*19 05*			*19 14*	*20 04*	*20 14*		*21 01*	*21 14*		*21 59*	*22 14*	*23 01*	*23 15*
Heathrow Terminal 1 Bus	d																
Gatwick Airport 10	d	*17 07*					*18 07*		*19 07*			*20 07*		*21 07*		*22 07*	*22 07*
Reading 7	d	19 05	19 09	19 37			20 11	20 37	21 05	21 11	21 37	22 11		22 46	23 14	23 46	00 15
Oxford	d																
Didcot Parkway	d	19 19		19 53				20 53	21 19		21 55			23 02			
Swindon	a	19 38	19 41	20 12			20 40	21 11	21 38	21 43	22 15	22 47		23 22	23s50	00s22	00s53
	d	19 39	19 44	20 12		20 28	20 42	21 12	21 40	21 44	22 15	22 49	22 57	23 23			
Kemble	d	19 53				20 42			21 53				23 11				
Stroud	d	20 08				20 57			22 08				23 26				
Stonehouse	d	20 14				21 02			22 13				23 31				
Gloucester 7	a	20 29				21 17			22 29				23 50				
Cheltenham Spa	a	20 44				21 30			22 44				00 04				
Birmingham New Street 12	a																
Chippenham	d			20 26				21 26			22 28			23 37		00s37	01s08
Bath Spa 7	a			20 40	20 59			21 40			22 42			23 51		00s52	01s22
Bristol Parkway 7	a		20 08				21 06			22 08		23 13			00s16		
	d		20 10				21 08			22 10		23 15					
Bristol Temple Meads 10	a			20 55	21 16			21 55			22 58			00 06	00 30	01 06	01 38
Weston-super-Mare	a			21 29				*23 03*			23 30						
Newport (South Wales)	a		20 31				21 30			22 41		23 44					
Hereford 7	a		*21 40*							*00 03*							
Cardiff Central 7	a		20 48				21 47			23 03		00 04					
Bridgend	a		21 09				22 08			23 25		00 26					
Port Talbot Parkway	a		21 22				22 23			23 38		00 39					
Neath	a		21 30				22 31			23 45		00 46					
Swansea 7	a		21 43				22 44			23 58		00 59					

For general notes see front of timetable
For details of catering facilities see Directory of Train Operators

A To Carmarthen (Table 128)
B To Taunton (Table 134)
C To Exeter St Davids (Table 135)
D From Westbury (Table 123)

South Wales, Weston-super-Mare, Bristol, Cheltenham Spa and Swindon → Oxford and London

Route Diagram - see first page of Table 125

Miles	Miles	Miles			GW	GW	GW	GW	GW	GW	GW	GW	GW	GW	GW	GW	GW	GW	GW	GW	GW	GW	GW	GW	GW
					1◇		1◇	1◇	1◇	1◇	1◇	1◇	1◇	1◇	1◇	1◇		1◇	1◇	1◇	1◇	1◇	1◇		1◇
						A							B				C		D	E		G			H
					☕		☕	🛒	☕	⊠	☕	☕	☕ 🛒	⊠	☕	☕		☕	⊠	✕	☕	⊠	☕		☕
0	—	—	**Swansea 7**	d				03 59		04 58				05 24				05 59		06 29			06 59		
9½	—	—	Neath	d				04 11		05 09				05 36				06 10		06 40			07 10		
15	—	—	Port Talbot Parkway	d				04 18		05 17				05 43				06 18		06 48			07 18		
27¼	—	—	Bridgend	d				04 30		05 28				05 55				06 29		06 59			07 29		
47½	—	—	**Cardiff Central 7**	d				05 15		05 54				06 20				06 55		07 25			07 55		
—	—	—	Hereford 7	d										*05 23*						*06 42*			*07 16*		
59¼	—	—	Newport (South Wales)	d				05 33		06 08				06 34				07 09		07 39			08 09		
—	0	—	Weston-super-Mare	d												06 23			06 48			07 25			07 50
—	19	—	**Bristol Temple Meads 10**	d	04 47		05 30		06 00			06 30	06 40			07 00			07 30			08 00		08 13	08 30
81	—	—	Bristol Parkway 7	a				06 00		06 29				06 55				07 30		08 00			08 30		
—	—	—		d	04u57			06 01		06 31				06 57				07 32		08 02			08 32		
—	30½	—	Bath Spa 7	d			05 43		06 13			06 43	06 52			07 13			07 43			08 13		08 31	08 43
—	43½	—	Chippenham	d			05 55		06 25			06 55	07 05			07 25	07 30		07 55			08 25		08 45	08 55
—	—	—	Birmingham New Street 12	d																	*06 10*				
—	—	0	**Cheltenham Spa**	d							05 56				06 31						07 27				
—	—	6½	Gloucester 7	d		05 19					06 12				06 47						07 43				
—	—	15½	Stonehouse	d		05 32					06 25				07 00						07 55				
—	—	18	Stroud	d		05 37					06 31				07 06						08 01				
—	—	29¼	Kemble	d		05 51					06 46				07 21						08 15				
115½	60¼	43	**Swindon**	a	05 23	06 06	06 09	06 27	06 39	06 56	07 00	07 09	07 19	07 24	07 35	07 39	07 48	07 57	08 09	08 27	08 31	08 39	08 57	09 03	09 10
—	—	—		d	05 23		06 11	06 28	06 41	06 58	07 02	07 11	07 21	07 25	07 36	07 41		07 59	08 11	08 29	08 33	08 41	08 59		09 11
139½	84¼	67	Didcot Parkway	a	05 41		06 28	06 45	06 58		07 19	07 28		07 42	07 54	08 00		08 16	08 28	08 46	08 52	09 00			09 28
—	—	—	Oxford	a	*06 21*		*06 52*	*07 17*			*07 40*			*08 00*		*08 28*		*08 42*		*09 15*		*09 40*			*09 51*
156¾	101½	84½	**Reading 7**	a	05 57		06 43	07 02	07 16	07 29	07 35	07 44		07 58	08 12	08 15		08 33	08 44	09 01	09 06	09 16	09 27		09 44
—	—	—	Gatwick Airport 10	a	*07 54*				*09 02*							*09 59*							*10 50*		
—	—	—	Heathrow Terminal 1 Bus	🚌 a	*07 17*		*07 57*	*08 17*	*08 37*			*08 57*		*09 17*		*09 37*			*09 45*		*10 05*		*10 25*		*10 45*
174¼	119	101¾	Slough 3	a	06 11		06 58	*07 37*	*07 55*	*08 07*		*08 20*		*08 38*		*08 57*			*09 25*		*09 45*		*09 51*		
—	—	—	**London Waterloo 15**	⊖ a																					
192¾	137½	120¼	**London Paddington 15**	⊖ a	06 30		07 16	07 32	07 44	08 01	08 06	08 14	08 18	08 30	08 41	08 44		09 06	09 14	09 29	09 36	09 44	09 59		10 14

		GW	GW	SW	GW	GW	GW	GW	GW	GW	GW	GW	GW	GW	GW	GW	GW	GW	GW	GW	GW	GW	GW	GW	GW
		1◇	1◇	1◇	1◇	1◇	1◇	1◇		1◇	1◇	1◇	1◇	1◇	1◇	1◇	1◇	1◇		1◇	1◇	1◇	1◇	1◇	1◇
								J		K										L			N		
		☕	☕		☕	⊠	☕	⊠		☕	☕	☕	☕	☕	☕	☕	☕	☕		☕	☕	🛒	⊠	☕	🛒
Swansea 7	d	07 29				07 59		08 29					09 29					10 29					11 29		
Neath	d	07 40				08 10		08 40					09 40					10 40					11 40		
Port Talbot Parkway	d	07 48				08 18		08 48					09 48					10 48					11 48		
Bridgend	d	07 59				08 29		08 59					09 59					10 59					11 59		
Cardiff Central 7	d	08 25				08 55		09 25			09 55		10 25			10 55		11 25			11 55		12 25		
Hereford 7	d	*07 48*				*08 09*		*08 48*					*09 47*			*10 09*		*10 48*					*11 48*		
Newport (South Wales)	d	08 39				09 09		09 39			10 09		10 39			11 09		11 39			12 09		12 39		
Weston-super-Mare	d				*08 30*		*08 40*			09 28		*09 40*			*10 10*		*10 40*			*11 10*		*11 40*			*12 10*
Bristol Temple Meads 10	d			08 50	09 00		09 30			10 00		10 30			11 00		11 30			12 00		12 30			13 00
Bristol Parkway 7	a	09 00				09 30		10 00			10 30		11 00			11 30		12 00			12 30		13 00		
	d	09 02				09 32		10 02			10 32		11 02			11 32		12 02			12 32		13 02		
Bath Spa 7	d			09 05	09 13		09 43			10 13		10 43			11 13		11 43			12 13		12 43			13 13
Chippenham	d				09 25		09 55			10 25		10 55			11 25		11 55			12 25		12 55			13 25
Birmingham New Street 12	d		*07 40*						*08 40*					*09 40*					*10 40*					*11 40*	
Cheltenham Spa	d		08 31						09 38					10 31					11 38					12 31	
Gloucester 7	d		08 46						09 51					10 46					11 51					12 46	
Stonehouse	d		08 59						10 03					10 59					12 03					12 59	
Stroud	d		09 04						10 08					11 04					12 08					13 04	
Kemble	d		09 19						10 22					11 19					12 22					13 19	
Swindon	a	09 27	09 34		09 39	09 57	10 09	10 27	10 38	10 39	10 57	11 09	11 27	11 34	11 39	11 57	12 09	12 27	12 38	12 40	12 57	13 09	13 27	13 34	13 39
	d	09 29	09 35		09 41	09 59	10 11	10 29		10 41	10 59	11 11	11 29	11 35	11 41	11 59	12 11	12 29		12 41	12 59	13 11	13 29	13 35	13 41
Didcot Parkway	a		09 52			10 16	10 28	10 46			11 16	11 28	11 46	11 52		12 16	12 28	12 46			13 16	13 28	13 46	13 52	
Oxford	a		*10 31*					*11 14*				*11 51*	*12 13*	*12 31*				*13 14*				*13 51*	*14 13*	*14 31*	
Reading 7	a	09 57	10 09		10 09	10 32	10 44	11 01		11 09	11 32	11 44	12 01	12 07	12 09	12 32	12 44	13 01		13 11	13 32	13 44	14 01	14 07	14 09
Gatwick Airport 10	a							*12 33*		*12 50*					*13 50*					*14 50*					*15 50*
Heathrow Terminal 1 Bus	🚌 a				*11 05*		*11 45*			*12 05*		*12 45*			*13 05*		*13 45*			*14 05*		*14 45*			*15 05*
Slough 3	a	*10 17*			*10 38*		*11 09*			*11 45*		*12 09*			*12 40*		*13 09*			*13 40*		*14 09*			*14 40*
London Waterloo 15	⊖ a			11 49																					
London Paddington 15	⊖ a	10 27	10 39		10 44	11 02	11 15	11 30		11 42	12 01	12 16	12 32	12 39	12 42	13 02	13 15	13 30		13 42	14 02	14 15	14 32	14 39	14 42

For general notes see front of timetable
For details of catering facilities see Directory of Train Operators

A To Southampton Central (Table 123)
B Until 27 June and from 8 September. ☕ until 27 June. 🛒 from 8 September
C to Cheltenham Spa
D **The Bristolian**
E **The Red Dragon**
G From Plymouth (Table 135)
H From Exeter St Davids (Table 135)
J From Carmarthen (Table 128)
K From Paignton (Table 135)
L From Penzance (Table 135)
N **The St David**

South Wales, Weston-super-Mare, Bristol, Cheltenham Spa and Swindon → Oxford and London

Route Diagram - see first page of Table 125

	SW	GW	GW	GW	GW	GW	GW	GW	GW	GW	GW	GW	GW	GW	GW	SW	GW	GW	GW	GW	GW	GW	GW	GW
	1◇	1◇	1◇	1◇		1◇	1◇	1◇	1◇	1◇	1◇	1◇	1◇	1◇		1◇	1◇	1◇	1◇	1◇	1◇	1◇	1◇	1◇
										A														
		🍴	⊼	🍴		⊼	🍴	🍴	🍴	🍴	🍴	🍴	🍴	🍴			🍴	🍴	🍴	🍴	🍴	🍴	🍴	🍴
Swansea 7 d				12 29					13 29					14 29						15 29				
Neath d				12 40					13 40					14 40						15 40				
Port Talbot Parkway d				12 48					13 48					14 48						15 48				
Bridgend d				12 59					13 59					14 59						15 59				
Cardiff Central 7 d		12 55		13 25			13 55		14 25			14 55		15 25				15 55		16 25			16 55	
Hereford 7 d		*12 09*		*12 48*					*13 48*			*14 09*		*14 48*						*15 48*			*16 09*	
Newport (South Wales) d		13 09		13 39			14 09		14 39			15 09		15 39				16 09		16 39			17 09	
Weston-super-Mare d			*12 40*			*13 10*		*13 40*			*14 10*		*14 40*				*15 10*		*15 36*			*16 10*		*17 08*
Bristol Temple Meads 10 d	13 10		13 30			14 00		14 30			15 00		15 30			15 52	16 00		16 30			17 00		17 30
Bristol Parkway 7 a		13 30		14 00			14 30		15 00			15 30		16 00				16 30		17 00			17 30	
Bristol Parkway 7 d		13 32		14 02			14 32		15 02			15 32		16 02				16 32		17 02			17 32	
Bath Spa 7 d	13 22		13 43			14 13		14 43			15 13		15 43			16 06	16 13		16 43			17 13		17 43
Chippenham d			13 55			14 25		14 55			15 25		15 55				16 25		16 55			17 25		17 55
Birmingham New Street 12 d					*12 40*					*13 40*					*14 40*						*15 40*			
Cheltenham Spa d					13 38					14 31					15 38						16 31			
Gloucester 7 d					13 51					14 46					15 51						16 46			
Stonehouse d					14 03					14 59					16 03						16 59			
Stroud d					14 08					15 04					16 08						17 04			
Kemble d					14 22					15 19					16 22						17 19			
Swindon a		13 57	14 09	14 27	14 38	14 39	14 57	15 09	15 27	15 34	15 39	15 57	16 09	16 27	16 38		16 39	16 57	17 09	17 27	17 34	17 39	17 57	18 09
Swindon d		13 59	14 11	14 29		14 41	14 59	15 11	15 29	15 35	15 41	15 59	16 11	16 29			16 41	16 59	17 11	17 29	17 35	17 41	17 59	18 11
Didcot Parkway a		14 16	14 28	14 46			15 16	15 28	15 46	15 52		16 16	16 28	16 46				17 16	17 28		17 52		18 16	18 28
Oxford a				*15 13*				*15 51*	*16 13*	*16 31*				*17 15*				*17 43*	*17 48*				*18 40*	*19 01*
Reading 7 a		14 32	14 44	15 01		15 09	15 32	15 44	16 01	16 07	16 12	16 32	16 44	17 01			17 09	17 32	17 44	17 57	18 07	18 13	18 32	18 44
Gatwick Airport 10 a						*17 00*					*17 50*									*19 52*		*19 50*		
Heathrow Terminal 1 Bus 🚌 a			*15 45*			*16 05*		*16 45*		*17 05*	*17 25*		*17 45*				*18 05*		*18 45*			*19 15*		*19 45*
Slough 3 a			*15 09*			*15 40*		*16 09*			*16 40*		*17 09*				*17 31*	*18 05*		*18 25*	*18 35*	*18 40*		*19 09*
London Waterloo 15 ⊖ a	16 19															18 45								
London Paddington 15 ⊖ a		15 02	15 15	15 30		15 42	16 02	16 16	16 30	16 39	16 44	17 02	17 15	17 30			17 41	18 02	18 15	18 27	18 39	18 44	19 02	19 15

	GW	GW	GW	GW	GW	GW	GW	GW	GW	GW	GW	GW	GW	GW	GW	GW	GW	GW	GW	GW	GW	GW		
													FO	FX		FO	FX	FO	FX		FO	FX		
	1◇		1◇	1◇	1◇	1◇	1◇	1◇		1◇		1◇	1◇	1◇	1	1◇	1◇	1◇	1◇		1◇	1◇		
		B							C							D	D				E	G		
	🍴		🍴	🍴	🍴	🍴	🍴	🍴		🍴		🍴	🍴	🍴	🍴	🍴	🍴	🍴	🍴		⊼	⊼		
Swansea 7 d	16 29					17 29				18 29			19 29	19 29				20 29	20 29					
Neath d	16 40					17 40				18 40			19 40	19 40				20 40	20 40					
Port Talbot Parkway d	16 48					17 48				18 48			19 48	19 48				20 48	20 48					
Bridgend d	16 59					17 59				18 59			19 59	19 59				20 59	20 59					
Cardiff Central 7 d	17 25			17 55		18 25				19 25			20 25	20 25				21 25	21 25					
Hereford 7 d	*16 48*									*18 48*								*20 48*	*20 48*					
Newport (South Wales) d	17 39			18 09		18 39				19 39			20 39	20 39				21 39	21 39					
Weston-super-Mare d			*17 14*		*18 09*			*18 40*				*19 48*									22 00	22 00		
Bristol Temple Meads 10 d			18 00		18 30			19 30				20 30				21 40	21 40				22 33	22 33		
Bristol Parkway 7 a	18 00			18 30		19 00				20 00			21 00	21 00				22 00	22 00					
Bristol Parkway 7 d	18 02			18 32		19 02				20 02			21 02	21 02				22 02	22 02					
Bath Spa 7 d			18 13		18 43			19 43				20 43				21 56	21 56				22 46	22 46		
Chippenham d			18 25		18 55			19 55	20 02			20 55				22 09	22 09				22 58	22 58		
Birmingham New Street 12 d		*16 40*					*17 40*				*19 10*				*19 40*					*21 10*				
Cheltenham Spa d		17 33					18 31				20 00				20 48					22 00				
Gloucester 7 d		17 51					18 46				20 13				21 05					22 13				
Stonehouse d		18 03					18 59				20 25				21 18					22 25				
Stroud d		18 08					19 04				20 30				21 23					22 30				
Kemble d		18 22					19 19				20 44				21 37					22 45				
Swindon a	18 27	18 38	18 39	18 57	19 09	19 27	19 34	20 09	20 19	20 27	21 00	21 09	21 27	21 27	21 53	22 23	22 23	22 27	22 27	23 00	23 13	23 13		
Swindon d	18 29		18 41	18 59	19 11	19 29	19 35	20 11		20 29		21 11	21 29	21 29		22 25	22 25	22 30	22 30		23 14	23 14		
Didcot Parkway a	18 46			19 16	19 28	19 46	19 52	20 28		20 46		21 28	21 49	21 49				22 47	22 47		23 31	23 31		
Oxford a	*19 12*			*19 46*		*20 12*	*20 24*			*21 08*			*22 14*	*22 14*				*23 13*	*23 13*		*00 23*	*00 23*		
Reading 7 a	19 01		19 09	19 32	19 45	20 01	20 12	20 44		21 02		21 44	22 15	22 15		22 55	22 55	23 06	23 06		23 55	23 55		
Gatwick Airport 10 a						*21 47*	*22 04*			*23 04*			*00 11*	*00 11*				*01 01*	*01 01*					
Heathrow Terminal 1 Bus 🚌 a			*20 15*		*20 45*		*21 15*	*21 45*				*22 45*	*23 45*	*23 45*										
Slough 3 a			*19 40*		*20 09*		*20 45*	*21 09*		*21b40*		*22c26*	*23 01*	*23 02*		*23 17*	*23 21*	*23 41*	*23 41*		*00 42*	*00 42*		
London Waterloo 15 ⊖ a																								
London Paddington 15 ⊖ a	19 32		19 42	20 02	20 15	20 31	20 44	21 15		21 32		22 15	22 53	22 56		23 29	23 36	23 42	23 50		00 25	00 32		

For general notes see front of timetable
For details of catering facilities see Directory of Train Operators

A **Cheltenham Spa Express**

B From Worcester Foregate Street (Table 71) to Southampton Central (Table 123)

C to Cheltenham Spa

D From Penzance (Table 135)

E From Taunton (Table 134)

G From Taunton (Table 134). ⊼ to Reading

b 30 June to 5 September arr. 2141

c Fridays arr. 2242

Table 125

Saturdays

until 6 September

South Wales, Weston-super-Mare, Bristol, Cheltenham Spa and Swindon → Oxford and London

Route Diagram - see first page of Table 125

		GW	GW	GW	GW	GW	GW	GW	GW	GW	GW	GW	GW	GW	GW	GW	SW	GW	GW	GW	GW	GW	GW	GW	GW
		1 ◇		1 ◇	1 ◇	1 ◇	1 ◇	1 ◇	1 ◇	1 ◇	1 ◇	1 ◇	1 ◇	1 ◇	1 ◇	1 ◇	1 ◇	1 ◇	1 ◇		1 ◇	1 ◇	1 ◇		1 ◇
													A					B							
		☕		☕	☕	☕	☕	☕	☕	☕	☕	☕	☕	☕	☕	☕		☕	☕		☕	☕	☕		☕
Swansea [7]	d			03 59	04 59		05 29		05 59		06 29			06 59		07 29							08 29		
Neath	d			04 10	05 10		05 40		06 10		06 40			07 10		07 40							08 40		
Port Talbot Parkway	d			04 18	05 18		05 48		06 18		06 48			07 18		07 48							08 48		
Bridgend	d			04 29	05 29		05 59		06 29		06 59			07 29		07 59							08 59		
Cardiff Central [7]	d			04 54	05 55		06 25		06 55		07 25			07 55		08 25							09 25		
Hereford [7]	d						*05 42*							*07 16*		*07 48*							*08 48*		
Newport (South Wales)	d			05 08	06 09		06 39		07 09		07 39			08 09		08 39							09 39		
Weston-super-Mare	d							06 24					07 28		*07 34*			08 30	*09 09*			*08 40*			*09 40*
Bristol Temple Meads [10]	d	05 30		06 00		06 30		07 00		07 30			08 00		08 30		08 50	09 00	10 00			09 30			10 30
Bristol Parkway [7]	a			05 36	06 30		07 00		07 30		08 00			08 30		09 00							10 00		
	d			05 41	06 32		07 02		07 32		08 02			08 32		09 02							10 02		
Bath Spa [7]	d	05 43		06 13		06 43		07 13		07 43			08 13		08 43		09 05	09 13	10 13			09 43			10 43
Chippenham	d	05 55		06 26		06 55		07 25		07 55			08 25		08 55			09 25	10 25	09 31		09 55			10 55
Birmingham New Street [12]	d											*05 30*									*08 10*			*09 10*	
Cheltenham Spa	d		05 30									07 27									09 00			10 01	
Gloucester [7]	d		05 44									07 43									09 16			10 15	
Stonehouse	d		05 56									07 55									09 29			10 27	
Stroud	d		06 01									08 01									09 34			10 32	
Kemble	d		06 16									08 15									09 48			10 47	
Swindon	a	06 09	06 32	06 39	06 57	07 09	07 27	07 40	07 57	08 09	08 27	08 31	08 39	08 57	09 09	09 27		09 39	10 39	09 49	10 02	10 09	10 27	11 03	11 09
	d	06 11		06 41	06 59	07 11	07 29	07 42	07 59	08 11	08 29	08 33	08 41	08 59	09 11	09 29		09 41	10 41		10 04	10 11	10 29		11 11
Didcot Parkway	a	06 28		06 58	07 16	07 28	07 46	07 59	08 16	08 28	08 46	08 51	08 58	09 16	09 28	09 46					10 21	10 28	10 46		11 28
Oxford	a	*07 02*		*07 28*		*08 00*			*08 39*		*09 15*		*09 31*			*10 12*							*11 13*		
Reading [7]	a	06 43		07 14	07 32	07 44	08 02	08 14	08 32	08 44	09 02	09 07	09 14	09 32	09 44	10 01		10 09	11 09		10 37	10 45	10 59		11 44
Gatwick Airport [10]	a			*08 50*				*09 50*					*10 50*					*11 50*	*12 50*						
Heathrow Terminal 1 Bus	a	*07 55*		*08 25*		*08 55*		*09 25*		*09 55*			*10 25*		*10 55*			*11 25*	*12 25*				*11 55*		*12 55*
Slough [3]	a	*07 11*		*07 39*	*08 15*	*08 25*		*08 40*		*09 10*			*09 40*		*10 09*			*10 36*	*11 40*			*11 08*			*12 09*
London Waterloo [15]	⊖ a																11 49								
London Paddington [15]	⊖ a	07 14		07 45	08 00	08 14	08 30	08 45	09 05	09 15	09 30	09 36	09 44	10 00	10 14	10 31		10 43	11 41		11 09	11 15	11 30		12 15

		GW	GW	GW	GW	GW	GW	GW	GW	GW	GW	GW	SW	GW		GW	GW	GW	GW	GW	GW	GW	GW	GW	GW
		1 ◇	1 ◇	1 ◇	1 ◇	1 ◇	1		1 ◇	1 ◇	1 ◇	1 ◇	1 ◇	1 ◇		1	1 ◇		1 ◇	1 ◇	1 ◇		1 ◇	1 ◇	1 ◇
					C	D										E G									
		☕	☕	☕	☕	☕	☕		☕	☕	☕	☕		☕		✕	☕		☕	☕	☕		☕	☕	☕
Swansea [7]	d	09 29				10 29				11 29						12 29				13 29					14 29
Neath	d	09 40				10 40				11 40						12 40				13 40					14 40
Port Talbot Parkway	d	09 48				10 48				11 48						12 48				13 48					14 48
Bridgend	d	09 59				10 59				11 59						12 59				13 59					14 59
Cardiff Central [7]	d	10 25				11 25				12 25						13 25				14 25					15 25
Hereford [7]	d	*09 47*				*10 48*				*11 48*						*12 48*				*13 48*					*14 48*
Newport (South Wales)	d	10 39				11 39				12 39						13 39				14 39					15 39
Weston-super-Mare	d		*10 08*		*10 43*		11 30		*11 41*		*12 08*			13 01			*13 08*		*13 39*		*14 08*			15 01	
Bristol Temple Meads [10]	d		11 00		11 30		12 00		12 30		13 00		13 10	13 30			14 00		14 30		15 00			15 30	
Bristol Parkway [7]	a	11 00				12 00				13 00						14 00				15 00					16 00
	d	11 02				12 02				13 02						14 02				15 02					16 02
Bath Spa [7]	d		11 13		11 43		12 13		12 43		13 13		13 22	13 43			14 13		14 43		15 13			15 43	
Chippenham	d		11 25		11 55		12 25		12 55		13 25			13 55			14 25		14 55		15 25	15 28		15 55	
Birmingham New Street [12]	d			*10 10*				*11 10*				*12 10*						*12 40*					*14 10*		
Cheltenham Spa	d			11 00				12 01				13 00						14 01					15 00		
Gloucester [7]	d			11 16				12 15				13 16						14 15					15 16		
Stonehouse	d			11 29				12 27				13 29						14 27					15 29		
Stroud	d			11 34				12 32				13 34						14 32					15 34		
Kemble	d			11 48				12 47				13 48						14 47					15 48		
Swindon	a	11 27	11 39	12 02	12 09	12 27	12 40	13 02	13 10	13 27	13 39	14 02		14 09		14 27	14 39	15 02	15 09	15 27	15 39	15 48	16 02	16 10	16 27
	d	11 29	11 41	12 04	12 11	12 29	12 41		13 11	13 29	13 41	14 04		14 11		14 29	14 41		15 11	15 29	15 41		16 04	16 11	16 29
Didcot Parkway	a	11 46		12 21	12 26	12 46			13 28	13 46		14 21		14 28					15 28	15 46			16 21	16 28	16 46
Oxford	a	*12 12*				*13 13*				*14 12*				*15 13*						*16 12*					*17 13*
Reading [7]	a	12 03	12 09	12 41	12 46	13 01	13 09		13 44	14 01	14 09	14 36		14 43		15 01	15 09		15 45	16 01	16 09		16 36	16 44	17 01
Gatwick Airport [10]	a		*13 50*			*14 50*	*14 50*				*15 50*						*16 50*				*17 50*				
Heathrow Terminal 1 Bus	a		*13 25*		*13 55*	*14 25*	*14 25*		*14 55*		*15 25*			*15 55*			*16 25*		*16 55*		*17 25*			*17 55*	
Slough [3]	a		*12 44*		*13 09*	*13 41*	*13 41*		*14 25*		*14 40*			*15 11*			*15 40*		*16 09*		*16 45*		*17 15*	*17 25*	
London Waterloo [15]	⊖ a												16 19												
London Paddington [15]	⊖ a	12 30	12 42	13 13	13 17	13 36	13 41		14 14	14 30	14 42	15 09		15 14		15 30	15 42		16 15	16 30	16 42		17 09	17 16	17 31

For general notes see front of timetable
For details of catering facilities see Directory of Train Operators

A From Taunton (Table 134)
B From Exeter St Davids (Table 135)
C From Paignton (Table 135)
D From Carmarthen (Table 128)
E From Pembroke Dock (Table 128)
G **Pembroke Coast Express**

Saturdays until 6 September

South Wales, Weston-super-Mare, Bristol, Cheltenham Spa and Swindon → Oxford and London

Route Diagram - see first page of Table 125

		SW 1◇	GW 1◇ ☕	GW	GW 1◇ ☕	GW 1◇ ☕	GW 1◇ ☕	GW 1◇ ☕	GW 1◇ ☕	GW 1◇ ☕	GW 1◇ ☕	GW	GW 1◇ ☕	GW 1◇ A ☕	GW 1◇ ☕	GW 1◇ ☕	GW 1◇ ☕	GW B	GW 1◇ ☕	GW 1◇ ☕	GW 1◇ C ☕	GW	GW 1◇ D
Swansea 7	d					15 29				16 29				17 29			18 29			19 29			
Neath	d					15 40				16 40				17 40			18 40			19 40			
Port Talbot Parkway	d					15 48				16 48				17 48			18 48			19 48			
Bridgend	d					15 59				16 59				17 59			18 59			19 59			
Cardiff Central 7	d					16 25				17 25				18 25			19 25			20 25			
Hereford 7	d					15 48				16 48							18 11			18 48			
Newport (South Wales)	d					16 39				17 39				18 39			19 39			20 39			
Weston-super-Mare	d	15 08			15 42		16 08		17 01		17 08		18 01			18 41			20 10		20 40		22 01
Bristol Temple Meads 10	d	15 52	16 00		16 30		17 00		17 30		18 00		18 30			19 30			20 33		21 44		22 33
Bristol Parkway 7	a					17 00				18 00				19 00			20 00			21 00			
	d					17 02				18 02				19 02			20 02			21 02			
Bath Spa 7	d	16 06	16 13		16 43		17 13		17 43		18 13		18 43			19 43			20 46		22 00		22 46
Chippenham	d		16 25		16 55		17 25		17 55		18 25		18 55			19 55			20 58		22 12		22 58
Birmingham New Street 12	d			15 10				16 10				17 10			18 10			19 10				20 10	
Cheltenham Spa	d			16 01				17 00				18 01			19 00			20 01				21 30	
Gloucester 7	d			16 15				17 16				18 15			19 15			20 15				21 44	
Stonehouse	d			16 27				17 29				18 27			19 29			20 27				21 56	
Stroud	d			16 32				17 34				18 32			19 33			20 32				22 01	
Kemble	d			16 47				17 48				18 47			19 47			20 47				22 16	
Swindon	a		16 39	17 02	17 09	17 27	17 39	18 02	18 09	18 27	18 39	19 02	19 09	19 27	20 02	20 09	20 27	21 03	21 13	21 27	22 27	22 31	23 13
	d		16 41		17 11	17 29	17 41	18 04	18 11	18 29	18 41		19 11	19 29	20 04	20 11	20 29		21 14	21 29	22 34		23 14
Didcot Parkway	a				17 28	17 46		18 21	18 28	18 46			19 28		20 21	20 28	20 46		21 31	21 46	22 51		23 31
Oxford	a					18 12				19 13			20 15				21 13		21 51	22 09	23 31		00 06
Reading 7	a		17 09		17 44	18 01	18 09	18 36	18 43	19 01	19 09		19 43	20 00	20 38	20 44	21 07		21 48	21 58	23 07		23 52
Gatwick Airport 10	a					19 52	19 50							21 47			23 03		00 10		01 02		
Heathrow Terminal 1 Bus	a		18 25		18 55		19 25		19 55		20 25			21 05	21 35				22 45	23 45			
Slough 3	a		17 40		18 25		18 40	19 15	19 25		19 40		20 25	20 45	21 15	21 35	21 38		22 09	22 42	23 42		00 30
London Waterloo 15 ⊖	a	18 49																					
London Paddington 15 ⊖	a		17 40		18 15	18 31	18 40	19 06	19 14	19 30	19 42		20 14	20 31	21 09	21 15	21 36		22 16	22 31	23 38		00 32

Saturdays from 13 September

		GW 1◇ ☕	GW	GW 1◇ ☕	GW 1◇ ☕	GW 1◇ ☕	GW 1◇ ☕	GW 1◇ ☕	GW 1◇ ☕	GW 1◇ ☕	GW 1◇ ☕	GW 1◇ ☕	GW 1◇ D ☕	GW 1◇ ☕	GW 1◇ ☕	GW 1◇ ☕	SW 1◇	GW 1◇ E ☕	GW	GW 1◇ ☕	GW 1◇ ☕	GW 1◇ G ☕	GW 1◇ ☕	GW 1◇ ☕	GW
Swansea 7	d			03 59	04 59		05 29		05 59		06 29			06 59		07 29				07 59			08 29		
Neath	d			04 10	05 10		05 40		06 10		06 40			07 10		07 40				08 10			08 40		
Port Talbot Parkway	d			04 18	05 18		05 48		06 18		06 48			07 18		07 48				08 18			08 48		
Bridgend	d			04 29	05 29		05 59		06 29		06 59			07 29		07 59				08 29			08 59		
Cardiff Central 7	d			04 54	05 55		06 25		06 55		07 25			07 55		08 25				08 55			09 25		
Hereford 7	d						05 42							07 16		07 48				08 10			08 48		
Newport (South Wales)	d			05 08	06 09		06 39		07 09		07 39			08 09		08 39				09 08			09 39		
Weston-super-Mare	d							06 24					07 28		07 34			08 30				09 01			
Bristol Temple Meads 10	d	05 30		06 00		06 30		07 00		07 30			08 00		08 30		08 50	09 00				09 30		10 00	
Bristol Parkway 7	a			05 36	06 30		07 00		07 30		08 00			08 30		09 00				09 30			10 00		
	d			05 41	06 32		07 02		07 32		08 02			08 32		09 02				09 32			10 02		
Bath Spa 7	d	05 43		06 13		06 43		07 13		07 43			08 13		08 43		09 05	09 13				09 43		10 13	
Chippenham	d	05 55		06 26		06 55		07 25		07 55			08 25		08 55			09 25	09 31			09 55		10 25	
Birmingham New Street 12	d																								
Cheltenham Spa	d		05 30									07 27									09 00				10 01
Gloucester 7	d		05 44									07 43									09 16				10 15
Stonehouse	d		05 56									07 55									09 29				10 27
Stroud	d		06 01									08 01									09 34				10 32
Kemble	d		06 16									08 15									09 48				10 47
Swindon	a	06 09	06 32	06 39	06 57	07 09	07 27	07 40	07 57	08 09	08 27	08 31	08 39	08 57	09 09	09 27		09 39	09 48	09 57	10 02	10 09	10 27	10 39	11 03
	d	06 11		06 41	06 59	07 11	07 29	07 42	07 59	08 11	08 29	08 33	08 41	08 59	09 11	09 29		09 41		09 59	10 04	10 11	10 29	10 41	
Didcot Parkway	a	06 28		06 58	07 16	07 28	07 46	07 59	08 16	08 28	08 46	08 51	08 58	09 16	09 28	09 46				10 16	10 21	10 28	10 46		
Oxford	a																								
Reading 7	a	06 43		07 14	07 32	07 44	08 02	08 14	08 32	08 44	09 02	09 07	09 14	09 33	09 44	10 01		10 09		10 32	10 37	10 45	10 59	11 09	
Gatwick Airport 10	a			08 50				09 50					10 50	11 50									12 53	12 50	
Heathrow Terminal 1 Bus	a	07 55		08 25		08 55		09 25		09 55			10 25		10 55			11 25					11 55	12 25	
Slough 3	a	07 11		07 39	08 15	08 25		08 40		09 10			09 40		10 09			10 36				11 08		11 40	
London Waterloo 15 ⊖	a																11 49								
London Paddington 15 ⊖	a	07 14		07 45	08 00	08 14	08 30	08 45	09 05	09 15	09 30	09 36	09 44	10 00	10 14	10 31		10 43		10 59	11 09	11 15	11 30	11 41	

For general notes see front of timetable
For details of catering facilities see Directory of Train Operators

- **A** From Pembroke Dock (Table 128)
- **B** To Westbury (Table 123)
- **C** From Penzance (Table 135)
- **D** From Taunton (Table 134)
- **E** From Exeter St Davids (Table 135)
- **G** From Paignton (Table 135)

Table 125

Saturdays

from 13 September

South Wales, Weston-super-Mare, Bristol, Cheltenham Spa and Swindon → Oxford and London

Route Diagram - see first page of Table 125

		GW 1◇ ☕	GW 1◇ ☕	GW 1◇ ☕	GW 1◇ ☕	GW 1◇ ☕	GW 1◇ A ☕	GW 1◇ ☕	GW	GW 1◇ ☕	GW 1◇ ☕	GW 1◇ ☕	GW 1◇ ☕	SW 1◇	GW 1◇ ☕	GW 1◇ ☕	GW 1◇ ☕	GW	GW 1◇ ☕	GW 1◇ ☕	GW 1◇ ☕	GW	GW 1◇ ☕	GW 1◇ ☕	GW 1◇ ☕
Swansea 7	d		09 29				10 29				11 29					12 29				13 29					14 29
Neath	d		09 40				10 40				11 40					12 40				13 40					14 40
Port Talbot Parkway	d		09 48				10 48				11 48					12 48				13 48					14 48
Bridgend	d		09 59				10 59				11 59					12 59				13 59					14 59
Cardiff Central 7	d		10 25				11 25				12 25					13 25				14 25					15 25
Hereford 7	d		*09 47*				*10 48*				*11 48*					*12 48*				*13 48*					*14 48*
Newport (South Wales)	d		10 39				11 39				12 39					13 39				14 39					15 39
Weston-super-Mare	d	*09 40*		*10 08*		*10 43*				*11 41*		*12 08*			*12 41*		*13 08*		*13 39*		*14 08*			*14 39*	
Bristol Temple Meads 10	d	10 30		11 00		11 30		12 00		12 30		13 00		13 10	13 30		14 00		14 30		15 00			15 30	
Bristol Parkway 7	a		11 00				12 00				13 00					14 00				15 00					16 00
	d		11 02				12 02				13 02					14 02				15 02					16 02
Bath Spa 7	d	10 43		11 13		11 43		12 13		12 43		13 13		13 22	13 43		14 13		14 43		15 13			15 43	
Chippenham	d	10 55		11 25		11 55		12 25		12 55		13 25			13 55		14 25		14 55		15 25	15 28		15 55	
Birmingham New Street 12	d																								
Cheltenham Spa	d				11 00				12 01				13 00					14 01					15 00		
Gloucester 7	d				11 16				12 15				13 16					14 15					15 16		
Stonehouse	d				11 29				12 27				13 29					14 27					15 29		
Stroud	d				11 34				12 32				13 34					14 32					15 34		
Kemble	d				11 48				12 47				13 48					14 47					15 48		
Swindon	a	11 09	11 27	11 39	12 02	12 09	12 27	12 40	13 02	13 09	13 27	13 39	14 02		14 09	14 27	14 39	15 02	15 09	15 27	15 39	15 48	16 02	16 09	16 27
	d	11 11	11 29	11 41	12 04	12 11	12 29	12 41		13 11	13 29	13 41	14 04		14 11	14 29	14 41		15 11	15 29	15 41		16 04	16 11	16 29
Didcot Parkway	a	11 28	11 46		12 21	12 28	12 46			13 28	13 46		14 21		14 28	14 46			15 28	15 46			16 21	16 28	16 46
Oxford	a																								
Reading 7	a	11 44	12 03	12 09	12 36	12 44	13 01	13 09		13 44	14 01	14 09	14 36		14 44	15 01	15 09		15 44	16 01	16 09		16 36	16 44	17 01
Gatwick Airport 10	a			*13 50*				*14 50*				*15 50*					*16 50*				*17 50*				
Heathrow Terminal 1 Bus	a	*12 55*		*13 25*		*13 55*		*14 25*		*14 55*		*15 25*			*15 55*		*16 25*		*16 55*		*17 25*			*17 55*	
Slough 3	a	*12 09*		*12 40*		*13 09*		*13 41*		*14 25*		*14 40*			*15 11*		*15 40*		*16 09*		*16 40*		*17 15*	*17 25*	
London Waterloo 15	⊖ a													16 19											
London Paddington 15	⊖ a	12 15	12 30	12 42	13 07	13 15	13 30	13 41		14 15	14 30	14 42	15 09		15 15	15 30	15 42		16 15	16 30	16 42		17 06	17 15	17 31

		SW 1◇	GW 1◇ ☕	GW	GW 1◇ ☕	GW 1◇ ☕	GW 1◇ ☕	GW 1◇ ☕	GW 1◇ ☕	GW 1◇ ☕	GW 1◇ ☕	GW	GW 1◇ ☕	GW 1◇ ☕	GW 1◇ ☕	GW 1◇ ☕	GW 1◇ ☕	GW B	GW 1◇ ☕	GW 1◇ ☕	GW 1◇ C ☕	GW	GW 1◇ D		
Swansea 7	d					15 29				16 29				17 29			18 29			19 29					
Neath	d					15 40				16 40				17 40			18 40			19 40					
Port Talbot Parkway	d					15 48				16 48				17 48			18 48			19 48					
Bridgend	d					15 59				16 59				17 59			18 59			19 59					
Cardiff Central 7	d					16 25				17 25				18 25			19 25			20 25					
Hereford 7	d					*15 48*				*16 48*							*18 11*			*18 48*					
Newport (South Wales)	d					16 39				17 39				18 39			19 39			20 39					
Weston-super-Mare	d	*15 08*			*15 42*		*16 08*		*16 42*		*17 08*		*17 39*			*18 41*			20 10		*20 40*		22 01		
Bristol Temple Meads 10	d	15 52	16 00		16 30		17 00		17 30		18 00		18 30			19 30			20 33		21 44		22 33		
Bristol Parkway 7	a					17 00				18 00				19 00			20 00			21 00					
	d					17 02				18 02				19 02			20 02			21 02					
Bath Spa 7	d	16 06	16 13		16 43		17 13		17 43		18 13		18 43			19 43			20 46		22 00		22 46		
Chippenham	d		16 25		16 55		17 25		17 55		18 25		18 55			19 55			20 58		22 12		22 58		
Birmingham New Street 12	d																								
Cheltenham Spa	d			16 01				17 00				18 01			19 00			20 01				21 30			
Gloucester 7	d			16 15				17 16				18 15			19 15			20 15				21 44			
Stonehouse	d			16 27				17 29				18 27			19 29			20 27				21 56			
Stroud	d			16 32				17 34				18 32			19 33			20 32				22 01			
Kemble	d			16 47				17 48				18 47			19 47			20 47				22 16			
Swindon	a		16 39	17 02	17 09	17 27	17 39	18 02	18 09	18 27	18 39	19 02	19 09	19 27	20 02	20 09	20 27	21 03	21 13	21 27	22 27	22 31	23 13		
	d		16 41		17 11	17 29	17 41	18 04	18 11	18 29	18 41		19 11	19 29	20 04	20 11	20 29		21 14	21 29	22 34		23 14		
Didcot Parkway	a				17 28	17 46		18 21	18 28	18 46			19 28	19 46	20 21	20 28	20 46		21 31	21 46	22 51		23 31		
Oxford	a																						*00 32*		
Reading 7	a		17 09		17 44	18 01	18 09	18 36	18 44	19 02	19 09		19 44	20 01	20 38	20 44	21 05		21 48	21 58	23 07		23 52		
Gatwick Airport 10	a					*19 52*	*19 50*							*21 47*			*23 03*		*00 10*		*01 02*				
Heathrow Terminal 1 Bus	a		*18 25*		*18 55*		*19 25*		*19 55*		*20 25*			*21 05*	*21 35*				*22 45*	*23 45*					
Slough 3	a		*17 40*		*18 25*		*18 40*	*19 15*	*19 25*		*19 40*		*20 25*	*20 45*	*21 15*	*21 35*	*21 38*		*22 09*	*22 42*	*23 42*		*00 30*		
London Waterloo 15	⊖ a	18 49																							
London Paddington 15	⊖ a		17 40		18 14	18 29	18 42	19 06	19 15	19 30	19 42		20 15	20 31	21 09	21 15	21 36		22 16	22 31	23 38		00 32		

For general notes see front of timetable
For details of catering facilities see Directory of Train Operators

A From Carmarthen (Table 128)
B To Westbury (Table 123)
C From Penzance (Table 135)
D From Taunton (Table 134)

Sundays

until 7 September

South Wales, Weston-super-Mare, Bristol, Cheltenham Spa and Swindon → Oxford and London

Route Diagram - see first page of Table 125

		GW	GW	GW	GW		GW	GW	GW	GW		GW	GW	GW	GW		GW	GW	GW	GW		GW	GW	GW	GW
		1 ◇	1 ◇	1 ◇			1 ◇	1 ◇	1 ◇			1 ◇	1 ◇	1 ◇			1 ◇	1 ◇		1 ◇		1 ◇	1 ◇		1 ◇
																		A					A		
		☕	☕	☕	🚌		☕	☕	☕	🚌		☕	☕	☕	🚌		☕	☕	🚌	☕		☕	☕	🚌	☕
Swansea 7	d												08 29				09 29			10 29					11 29
Neath	d												08 41				09 41			10 41					11 41
Port Talbot Parkway	d												08 48				09 48			10 48					11 48
Bridgend	d												09 00				10 00			11 00					12 00
Cardiff Central 7	d						07 55						09 25				10 25			11 25					12 25
Hereford 7	d																			10 00					
Newport (South Wales)	d						08 13						09 39				10 39			11 39					12 39
Weston-super-Mare	d			08 28					09 14					10 28				10 50					12 09		
Bristol Temple Meads 10	d	07 40	08 10	09 00					10 00			10 30		11 00				12 00					13 00		
Bristol Parkway 7	a																								
	d				08 50					10 09					11 09				12 09					13 09	
Bath Spa 7	d	07 53	08 23	09 13					10 13			10 43		11 13				12 13					13 13		
Chippenham	d	08 05	08 35	09 25					10 25			10 55		11 25				12 25					13 25		
Birmingham New Street 12	d																			11b10					11 46
Cheltenham Spa	d												09 58				10 06			12 00					12 45
Gloucester 7	d						09 05						10 22				11 22			12 22					13 22
Stonehouse	d						09 19						10 36				11 36			12 36					13 36
Stroud	d						09 24						10 42				11 42			12 42					13 42
Kemble	d						09 38						10 57				11 57			12 57					13 57
Swindon	a	08 20	08 50	09 39	09 45		09 52		10 40	11 04		11 09	11 10	11 40	12 04		12 09	12 40	13 04	13 10			13 40	14 04	14 10
	d	08 20	08 50	09 41			09 54	10 15	10 41			11 11	11 14	11 41			12 11	12 41		13 12		13 24	13 41		14 11
Didcot Parkway	a	08 39	09 09	09 58			10 11		10 58					11 58				12 58					13 58		
Oxford	a	09 17	09 35	10 29			10 42		11 25					12 27				13 27					14 25		
Reading 7	a	08 55	09 26	10 13			10 26	10 43	11 13			11 38	11 48	12 13			12 43	13 13		13 44		13 52	14 14		14 43
Gatwick Airport 10	a	10 30	11 31					12 30					13 31				14 30					15 31			16 30
Heathrow Terminal 1 Bus 🚌	a	09 55	10 25				11 25	11 55	12 25				12 55	13 25			13 55	14 25				14 55	15 25		15 55
Slough 3	a	09 24	10 09				11 10	11 26				12 14	12 28	13 10			13 41	13 47				14 25	15 10		15 23
London Waterloo 15	⊖ a																								
London Paddington 15	⊖ a	09 35	10 03	10 54			11 10	11 26	11 55			12 15	12 29	12 55			13 26	13 55		14 24		14 30	14 54		15 21

		GW	GW		GW	GW	GW	GW		GW	GW	GW	GW		SW	GW	GW	GW		GW	GW	GW	GW		GW
		1 ◇			1 ◇	1 ◇	1 ◇			1 ◇	1 ◇	1 ◇	1 ◇		1 ◇		1 ◇	1 ◇				1 ◇	1 ◇		1 ◇
																						A			
		☕	🚌		☕	☕	☕	🚌		☕	☕	☕	☕			🚌	☕	☕			🚌	☕	☕		☕
Swansea 7	d				12 29		13 29						14 29										15 29		
Neath	d				12 41		13 41						14 41										15 41		
Port Talbot Parkway	d				12 48		13 48						14 48										15 48		
Bridgend	d				13 00		14 00						15 00										16 00		
Cardiff Central 7	d				13 25		14 25						15 25										16 25		
Hereford 7	d						12 44						14 15										15 11		
Newport (South Wales)	d				13 39		14 39						15 39										16 39		
Weston-super-Mare	d	13 30				14 26											14c26	16 14				16 59			
Bristol Temple Meads 10	d	14 00				15 00						16 00			16 04		16 30	17 00				17 30			
Bristol Parkway 7	a																								
	d		14 09					15 09								16 09					17 09				
Bath Spa 7	d	14 13				15 13						16 13			16 20		16 43	17 13				17 43			
Chippenham	d	14 25				15 25						16 25					16 55	17 25		17 46		17 55			
Birmingham New Street 12	d				13b10		14b10				14e30		15b10										16b10		16f30
Cheltenham Spa	d				14 02		15 01				15 31		16 02										17 06		17 31
Gloucester 7	d				14 22		15 22				15 48		16 22										17 22		17 48
Stonehouse	d				14 36						16 01												17 36		18 00
Stroud	d				14 42						16 06												17 42		18 06
Kemble	d				14 57						16 20												17 57		18 20
Swindon	a	14 40	15 04		15 10	15 40	16 00	16 04			16 34	16 40	17 00			17 04	17 10	17 40		18 03	18 04	18 10	18 10		18 34
	d	14 41			15 11	15 41	16 01			16 26	16 36	16 41	17 01				17 11	17 41				18 11	18 15		18 35
Didcot Parkway	a	14 58				15 58						16 58						17 58							
Oxford	a	15 27				16 25						17 25						18 27							
Reading 7	a	15 15			15 43	16 14	16 29			16 54	17 04	17 14	17 29				17 42	18 15				18 44	18 49		19 02
Gatwick Airport 10	a				17 33					18 29							19 33						20 30		20 44
Heathrow Terminal 1 Bus 🚌	a	16 25			16 55		17 25			17 55			18 25				18 55	19 25					19 55		
Slough 3	a	16 12			16 41	16 47	17 12				17 41	17 48	18 12				18 41	19 12					19 32		19 41
London Waterloo 15	⊖ a														18 58										
London Paddington 15	⊖ a	15 55			16 22	16 54	17 10			17 34	17 40	17 54	18 15				18 24	18 54				19 24	19 30		19 40

For general notes see front of timetable
For details of catering facilities see Directory of Train Operators

A From Plymouth (Table 135)
b Change at Cheltenham Spa and Gloucester
c From 20 July dep. 1530
e From 20 July dep. 1440
f From 20 July dep. 1640

Table 125

Sundays

until 7 September

South Wales, Weston-super-Mare, Bristol, Cheltenham Spa and Swindon → Oxford and London

Route Diagram - see first page of Table 125

		GW 1◇ A ☕	GW 1◇ B ☕	GW 🚌	GW 1◇ C ☕		GW 1◇ ☕	GW 🚌	GW 1◇ ☕	GW 1◇ D ☕		GW 1◇ ☕	GW	GW 1◇ ☕	GW 🚌		GW 1◇ B ☕	GW 1◇	GW 1◇ ☕	GW 🚌		GW 1◇ B ☕	GW 1◇ C ☕		
Swansea 7	d		16 29						17 29								18 29					19 59			
Neath	d		16 41						17 41								18 41					20 11			
Port Talbot Parkway	d		16 48						17 48								18 48					20 18			
Bridgend	d		17 00						18 00								19 00					20 30			
Cardiff Central 7	d		17 25						18 25								19 25					20 55			
Hereford 7	d								*17 09*								*17 51*					*19 10*			
Newport (South Wales)	d		17 39						18 39								19 39					21 09			
Weston-super-Mare	d	17 25			*17 50*					18 54								20 38					*21 17*		
Bristol Temple Meads 10	d	18 00			18 30		19 00			19 30				20 00				21 00					22 05		
Bristol Parkway 7	a																								
	d			18 09				19 09							20 09					21 39					
Bath Spa 7	d	18 13			18 43		19 13			19 43				20 13				21 13					22 19		
Chippenham	d	18 25			18 55		19 25			19 56			20 04	20 25				21 27					22 31		
Birmingham New Street 12	d		*17b10*						*18b10*								*19b10*					*20 30*			
Cheltenham Spa	d		*18 02*						*19 03*								*20 02*					*21 35*			
Gloucester 7	d		18 22						19 22								20 22					21 52			
Stonehouse	d								19 36								20 36					22 06			
Stroud	d								19 42								20 42					22 12			
Kemble	d								19 57								20 57					22 26			
Swindon	a	18 40	19 01	19 04	19 11		19 40	20 04	20 09	20 10		←	20 20	20 40	21 04		21 10	21 41		22 34		22 40	22 46		
	d	18 41	19 03		19 11		19 41		20 15 →	20 12		20 15		20 41			21 11	21 42	22 08			22 45	22 53		
Didcot Parkway	a	18 58					19 58							20 58				22 00							
Oxford	a	*19 25*					*20 25*							*21 25*				*22 29*							
Reading 7	a	19 14	19 31		19 43		20 14			20 43		20 50		21 13			21 45	22 16	22 41			23 23	23 29		
Gatwick Airport 10	a				*21 31*							*22 30*					*23 31*		*00 41*						
Heathrow Terminal 1 Bus 🚌	a	*20 25*			*21 05*		*21 35*					*21 55*					*22 45*		*23 45*						
Slough 3	a		*20 12*		*20 41*		*20 47*					*21 41*		*21 47*			*22 23*	*22 47*	*23 23*				*00 05*		
London Waterloo 15	⊖ a																								
London Paddington 15	⊖ a	19 58	20 06		20 21		20 55			21 22		21 30		21 53			22 28	22 59	23 23			00 05	00 17		

Sundays

from 14 September

		GW 1◇ ☕	GW 1◇ ☕		GW 1◇ ☕	GW 1◇ ☕		GW 1◇ ☕	GW		GW 1◇ ☕	GW 1◇ ☕		GW 1◇ ☕	GW 1◇ ☕		GW 1◇ ☕	GW 1◇ C ☕		GW 1◇ ☕	GW 1◇ ☕		GW 1◇ C ☕	GW	GW 1◇ ☕
Swansea 7	d							07 59				08 59					09 59				10 59				11 59
Neath	d							08 11				09 11					10 11				11 11				12 11
Port Talbot Parkway	d							08 18				09 18					10 18				11 18				12 18
Bridgend	d							08 30				09 30					10 30				11 30				12 30
Cardiff Central 7	d				07 45			08 55				09 55					10 55				11 55				12 55
Hereford 7	d																*10 11*								
Newport (South Wales)	d				08 03			09 13				10 09					11 09				12 09				13 09
Weston-super-Mare	d					08 28					*09 14*				10 28			*10 50*					*12 09*		
Bristol Temple Meads 10	d	07 40	08 10			09 00					10 00			10 30	11 00			12 00					13 00		
Bristol Parkway 7	a				08 34			09 34				10 30					11 30				12 30				13 30
	d				08 34			09 36				10 31					11 32				12 32				13 32
Bath Spa 7	d	07 53	08 23			09 13					10 13			10 43	11 13			12 13					13 13		
Chippenham	d	08 05	08 35			09 25					10 25			10 55	11 25			12 25					13 25		
Birmingham New Street 12	d																								
Cheltenham Spa	d								09 35											11 46				12 35	
Gloucester 7	d								09 49											12 04				12 49	
Stonehouse	d								10 01											12 17				13 01	
Stroud	d								10 06											12 22				13 06	
Kemble	d								10 20											12 36				13 20	
Swindon	a	08 20	08 50		09 00	09 39		10 01	10 35		10 40	10 56		11 09	11 40		11 57	12 40		12 50	12 57		13 40	13 36	13 57
	d	08 20	08 50		09 00	09 41		10 02			10 41	10 59		11 11	11 41		11 59	12 41			12 59		13 41		13 59
Didcot Parkway	a	08 39	09 09			09 58					10 58				11 58			12 58					13 58		
Oxford	a																								
Reading 7	a	08 55	09 26		09 32	10 13		10 31			11 13	11 27		11 38	12 13		12 27	13 13			13 27		14 13		14 27
Gatwick Airport 10	a	*10 30*			*11 31*			*12 30*						*13 31*			*14 30*				*15 31*				*16 30*
Heathrow Terminal 1 Bus 🚌	a	*09 55*	*10 25*		*10 55*	*11 25*		*11 55*				*12 25*		*12 55*			*13 25*				*14 25*				*15 25*
Slough 3	a	*09 29*			*10 18*			*11 18*						*12 18*			*13 18*				*14 18*				*15 18*
London Waterloo 15	⊖ a																								
London Paddington 15	⊖ a	09 43	10 05		10 22	11 00		11 09			12 01	12 05		12 22	13 00		13 05	13 55			14 05		15 03		15 05

For general notes see front of timetable
For details of catering facilities see Directory of Train Operators

A From Paignton (Table 135)
B From Carmarthen (Table 128)
C From Plymouth (Table 135)
D From Taunton (Table 134)
b Change at Cheltenham Spa and Gloucester

Table 125

Sundays

from 14 September

South Wales, Weston-super-Mare, Bristol, Cheltenham Spa and Swindon → Oxford and London

Route Diagram - see first page of Table 125

		GW 1◇ ☕	GW 1◇ ☕	GW 1◇ ☕	GW 1◇ ☕	GW 1◇ ☕	GW 1◇ ☕	GW 1◇ ☕	SW 1◇	GW 1◇ ☕	GW 1◇ ☕	GW	GW 1◇ ☕	GW	GW 1◇ ☕	GW 1◇ A ☕	GW 1◇ B ☕
Swansea [7]	d			12 59		13 59				14 59					15 59		16 29
Neath	d			13 11		14 11				15 11					16 11		16 41
Port Talbot Parkway	d			13 18		14 18				15 18					16 18		16 48
Bridgend	d			13 30		14 30				15 30					16 30		17 00
Cardiff Central [7]	d			13 55		14 55				15 55					16 55		17 25
Hereford [7]	d			12 44						15 11							
Newport (South Wales)	d			14 09		15 09				16 09					17 09		17 39
Weston-super-Mare	d	13 30			14 26								16 14			16 59	
Bristol Temple Meads [10]	d	14 00			15 00		16 00		16 04		16 30		17 00			17 30	
Bristol Parkway [7]	a			14 30		15 30				16 30					17 30		18 00
	d			14 32		15 32				16 32					17 32		18 02
Bath Spa [7]	d	14 13			15 13		16 13		16 20		16 43		17 13			17 43	
Chippenham	d	14 25			15 25		16 25				16 55		17 25	17 31		17 55	
Birmingham New Street [12]	d																
Cheltenham Spa	d		13 46					15 46				16 35					
Gloucester [7]	d		14 03					16 04				16 49					
Stonehouse	d		14 17					16 16				17 01					
Stroud	d		14 22					16 22				17 06					
Kemble	d		14 36					16 36				17 21					
Swindon	a	14 40	14 50	14 57	15 40	15 57	16 40	16 50		16 57	17 10	17 36	17 40	17 48	17 57	18 10	18 27
	d	14 41		14 59	15 41	15 59	16 41	16 51		16 59	17 11		17 41		17 59	18 11	18 29
Didcot Parkway	a	14 58			15 58		16 58						17 58				
Oxford	a																
Reading [7]	a	15 14		15 27	16 14	16 27	17 14	17 19		17 27	17 43		18 15		18 27	18 39	18 59
Gatwick Airport [10]	a			17 33		18 29					19 33				20 30		
Heathrow Terminal 1 Bus	a			16 25		17 25				18 25	18 55				19 25		19 55
Slough [3]	a			16 18		17 18	17 40				18 18					19 18	19 28
London Waterloo [15]	⊖ a								18 58								
London Paddington [15]	⊖ a	15 56		16 05	16 55	17 05	17 55	17 57		18 08	18 30		18 55		19 05	19 23	19 39

		GW 1◇ C ☕	GW 1◇ ☕	GW 1◇ A ☕	GW 1◇ ☕	GW 1◇ ☕	GW 1◇ D ☕	GW E	GW	GW 1◇ B ☕	GW 1◇ ☕	GW 1◇ ☕	GW 1◇	GW 1◇ B ☕	GW 1◇ A ☕	GW
Swansea [7]	d				17 29					18 29				19 59		
Neath	d				17 41					18 41				20 11		
Port Talbot Parkway	d				17 48					18 48				20 18		
Bridgend	d				18 00					19 00				20 30		
Cardiff Central [7]	d				18 25					19 25				20 55		
Hereford [7]	d				17 09					18 35				19 10		
Newport (South Wales)	d				18 39					19 39				21 09		
Weston-super-Mare	d	17 26		17 50			18 54						20 38		21 17	
Bristol Temple Meads [10]	d	18 00		18 30		19 00	19 30				20 00		21 00		22 05	
Bristol Parkway [7]	a				19 00					20 00				21 30		
	d				19 02					20 02				21 32		
Bath Spa [7]	d	18 13		18 43		19 13	19 43				20 13		21 13		22 19	
Chippenham	d	18 25		18 55		19 25	19 55	20 04			20 25		21 25		22 31	
Birmingham New Street [12]	d															
Cheltenham Spa	d		17 46									19 46				21 42
Gloucester [7]	d		18 04						19 28			20 03				22 00
Stonehouse	d		18 17						19 47			20 15				22 12
Stroud	d		18 22						19 52			20 21				22 17
Kemble	d		18 36						20 07			20b43				22 32
Swindon	a	18 41	18 50	19 11	19 27	19 40	20 10	20 20	20 22	20 27	20 40	20 57	21 41	21 57	22 46	22 47
	d	18 41	18 52	19 11	19 29	19 41	20 11			20 29	20 41	21 02	21 42	21 59	22 52	
Didcot Parkway	a	19 01				19 58					20 58		22 00			
Oxford	a															
Reading [7]	a	19 18	19 20	19 45	19 58	20 14	20 45			20 57	21 16	21 31	22 16	22 35	23 26	
Gatwick Airport [10]	a				21c46		22 30					23 31		00 41		
Heathrow Terminal 1 Bus	a		20 25		21 05	21 35				21 55		22 45		23 45		
Slough [3]	a			20 18	20 35		21 18			21 35		22 18		23 18	00 05	
London Waterloo [15]	⊖ a															
London Paddington [15]	⊖ a	20 01	20 02	20 27	20 42	20 56	21 28			21 42	22 02	22 16	22 59	23 15	00 05	

For general notes see front of timetable
For details of catering facilities see Directory of Train Operators

- **A** From Plymouth (Table 135)
- **B** From Carmarthen (Table 128)
- **C** From Paignton (Table 135)
- **D** From Taunton (Table 134)
- **E** To Cheltenham Spa
- **b** Arr. 2035
- **c** Change at Reading and Redhill

Reading → Heathrow Railair Link
Express Coach Service

Sunday service operates on Bank Holiday Mondays.

Mondays to Fridays

		GW	GW	GW	GW	GW	GW	GW	GW	GW	GW	GW	GW	GW	GW	GW	GW	GW	GW	GW	GW	GW	GW	GW	GW	GW
Reading	d	04 00	05 00	05 30	06 00	06 20	06 40	07 00	07 20	07 40	08 00	08 20	08 40	09 05	09 25	09 45	10 05	10 25	10 45	11 05	11 25	11 45	12 05	12 25	12 45	13 05
Heathrow Terminal 1 Bus	a	04 40	05 40	06 10	06 40	07 17	07 37	07 57	08 17	08 37	08 57	09 17	09 37	09 45	10 05	10 25	10 45	11 05	11 25	11 45	12 05	12 25	12 45	13 05	13 25	13 45
Heathrow Terminal 2 Bus	a	04 42	05 42	06 12	06 42	07 19	07 39	07 59	08 19	08 39	08 59	09 19	09 39	09 47	10 07	10 27	10 47	11 07	11 27	11 47	12 07	12 27	12 47	13 07	13 27	13 47
Heathrow Terminal 3 Bus	a	04 45	05 45	06 15	06 45	07 22	07 42	08 02	08 22	08 42	09 02	09 22	09 42	09 50	10 10	10 30	10 50	11 10	11 30	11 50	12 10	12 30	12 50	13 10	13 30	13 50

		GW	GW	GW	GW	GW	GW	GW	GW	GW	GW	GW	GW	GW	GW	GW	GW	GW	GW	GW	GW	GW	GW	GW		
Reading	d	13 25	13 45	14 05	14 25	14 45	15 05	15 25	15 45	16 05	16 25	16 45	17 05	17 25	17 45	18 05	18 35	19 05	19 35	20 05	20 35	21 05	22 05	23 05		
Heathrow Terminal 1 Bus	a	14 05	14 25	14 45	15 05	15 25	15 45	16 05	16 25	16 45	17 05	17 25	17 45	18 05	18 25	18 45	19 15	19 45	20 15	20 45	21 15	21 45	22 45	23 45		
Heathrow Terminal 2 Bus	a	14 07	14 27	14 47	15 07	15 27	15 47	16 07	16 27	16 47	17 07	17 27	17 47	18 07	18 27	18 47	19 17	19 47	20 17	20 47	21 17	21 47	22 47	23 47		
Heathrow Terminal 3 Bus	a	14 10	14 30	14 50	15 10	15 30	15 50	16 10	16 30	16 50	17 10	17 30	17 50	18 10	18 30	18 50	19 20	19 50	20 20	20 50	21 20	21 50	22 50	23 50		

Saturdays

		GW	GW		GW	GW		GW	GW		GW	GW		GW	GW		GW	GW		GW	GW		GW	GW		GW
Reading	d	04 00	05 15		05 45	06 15		06 45	07 15		07 45	08 15		08 45	09 15		09 45	10 15		10 45	11 15		11 45	12 15		12 45
Heathrow Terminal 1 Bus	a	04 40	05 55		06 25	06 55		07 25	07 55		08 25	08 55		09 25	09 55		10 25	10 55		11 25	11 55		12 25	12 55		13 25
Heathrow Terminal 2 Bus	a	04 42	05 57		06 27	06 57		07 27	07 57		08 27	08 57		09 27	09 57		10 27	10 57		11 27	11 57		12 27	12 57		13 27
Heathrow Terminal 3 Bus	a	04 45	06 00		06 30	07 00		07 30	08 00		08 30	09 00		09 30	10 00		10 30	11 00		11 30	12 00		12 30	13 00		13 30

		GW	GW		GW	GW		GW	GW		GW	GW		GW	GW		GW	GW	GW	GW	GW	GW	GW	GW		
Reading	d	13 15	13 45		14 15	14 45		15 15	15 45		16 15	16 45		17 15	17 45		18 15	18 45	19 15	19 45	20 25	20 55	22 05	23 05		
Heathrow Terminal 1 Bus	a	13 55	14 25		14 55	15 25		15 55	16 25		16 55	17 25		17 55	18 25		18 55	19 25	19 55	20 25	21 05	21 35	22 45	23 45		
Heathrow Terminal 2 Bus	a	13 57	14 27		14 57	15 27		15 57	16 27		16 57	17 27		17 57	18 27		18 57	19 27	19 57	20 27	21 07	21 37	22 47	23 47		
Heathrow Terminal 3 Bus	a	14 00	14 30		15 00	15 30		16 00	16 30		17 00	17 30		18 00	18 30		19 00	19 30	20 00	20 30	21 10	21 40	22 50	23 50		

Sundays

Also Bank Holiday Mondays.

		GW	GW	GW		GW	GW	GW		GW	GW	GW		GW	GW	GW		GW	GW	GW		GW	GW	GW		GW
Reading	d	04 00	05 15	05 45		06 15	06 45	07 15		07 45	08 15	08 45		09 15	09 45	10 15		10 45	11 15	11 45		12 15	12 45	13 15		13 45
Heathrow Terminal 1 Bus	a	04 40	05 55	06 25		06 55	07 25	07 55		08 25	08 55	09 25		09 55	10 25	10 55		11 25	11 55	12 25		12 55	13 25	13 55		14 25
Heathrow Terminal 2 Bus	a	04 42	05 57	06 27		06 57	07 27	07 57		08 27	08 57	09 27		09 57	10 27	10 57		11 27	11 57	12 27		12 57	13 27	13 57		14 27
Heathrow Terminal 3 Bus	a	04 45	06 00	06 30		07 00	07 30	08 00		08 30	09 00	09 30		10 00	10 30	11 00		11 30	12 00	12 30		13 00	13 30	14 00		14 30

		GW	GW	GW		GW	GW	GW		GW	GW	GW		GW	GW	GW		GW	GW	GW		GW	GW			
Reading	d	14 15	14 45	15 15		15 45	16 15	16 45		17 15	17 45	18 15		18 45	19 15	19 45		20 25	20 55	21 15		22 05	23 05			
Heathrow Terminal 1 Bus	a	14 55	15 25	15 55		16 25	16 55	17 25		17 55	18 25	18 55		19 25	19 55	20 25		21 05	21 35	21 55		22 45	23 45			
Heathrow Terminal 2 Bus	a	14 57	15 27	15 57		16 27	16 57	17 27		17 57	18 27	18 57		19 27	19 57	20 27		21 07	21 37	21 57		22 47	23 47			
Heathrow Terminal 3 Bus	a	15 00	15 30	16 00		16 30	17 00	17 30		18 00	18 30	19 00		19 30	20 00	20 30		21 10	21 40	22 00		22 50	23 50			

For general notes see front of timetable
For details of catering facilities see
Directory of Train Operators

Table 125A **Mondays to Fridays**

Heathrow → Reading Railair Link
Express Coach Service

Sunday service operates on Bank Holiday Mondays.

		GW	GW	GW	GW	GW	GW	GW	GW	GW	GW	GW	GW	GW	GW	GW	GW	GW	GW	GW	GW	GW	GW	GW	GW	GW
Heathrow Central Bus Stn	d	05 05	06 05	06 35	07 05	07 32	07 52	08 12	08 32	08 52	09 12	09 32	09 52	10 05	10 25	10 45	11 05	11 25	11 45	12 05	12 25	12 45	13 05	13 25	13 45	14 05
Reading	a	05 48	06 48	07 18	07 48	08 28	08 48	09 08	09 21	09 41	09 55	10 15	10 35	10 48	11 08	11 28	11 48	12 08	12 28	12 48	13 08	13 28	13 48	14 08	14 28	14 48

		GW	GW	GW	GW	GW	GW	GW	GW	GW	GW	GW	GW	GW	GW	GW	GW	GW	GW	GW	GW	GW	GW	GW		
Heathrow Central Bus Stn	d	14 25	14 45	15 05	15 25	15 45	16 05	16 25	16 45	17 05	17 25	17 45	18 05	18 25	18 45	19 05	19 35	20 05	20 35	21 05	21 35	22 05	23 05	23 59	.....	.....
Reading	a	15 08	15 28	15 48	16 08	16 28	16 48	17 08	17 28	17 48	18 08	18 28	18 48	19 08	19 28	19 48	20 18	20 48	21 18	21 48	22 18	22 48	23 48	00 43	.	.

Saturdays

		GW	GW		GW	GW		GW	GW		GW	GW		GW	GW		GW	GW		GW	GW		GW	GW		GW
Heathrow Central Bus Stn	d	05 05	06 10	.....	06 40	07 10	.....	07 40	08 10	.....	08 40	09 10	.....	09 40	10 10	.....	10 40	11 10	.....	11 40	12 10	.....	12 40	13 10	.....	13 40
Reading	a	05 48	06 53	.	07 23	07 53	.	08 23	08 53	.	09 23	09 53	.	10 23	10 53	.	11 23	11 53	.	12 23	12 53	.	13 23	13 53	.	14 23

		GW	GW		GW	GW		GW	GW		GW	GW		GW	GW		GW	GW	GW	GW	GW	GW	GW	GW		
Heathrow Central Bus Stn	d	14 10	14 40	.....	15 10	15 40	.....	16 10	16 40	.....	17 10	17 40	.....	18 10	18 40	.....	19 10	19 40	20 10	20 40	21 20	22 00	23 05	23 59	.....	.....
Reading	a	14 53	15 23	.	15 53	16 23	.	16 53	17 23	.	17 53	18 23	.	18 53	19 23	.	19 53	20 23	20 53	21 23	22 03	22 43	23 48	00 43	.	.

Sundays

Also Bank Holiday Mondays.

		GW	GW	GW		GW	GW	GW		GW	GW	GW		GW	GW	GW		GW	GW	GW		GW	GW	GW		GW
Heathrow Central Bus Stn	d	05 05	06 10	06 40	.....	07 10	07 40	08 10	.....	08 40	09 10	09 40	.....	10 10	10 40	11 10	.....	11 40	12 10	12 40	.....	13 10	13 40	14 10	.....	14 40
Reading	a	05 48	06 53	07 23	.	07 53	08 23	08 53	.	09 23	09 53	10 23	.	10 53	11 23	11 53	.	12 23	12 53	13 23	.	13 53	14 23	14 53	.	15 23

		GW	GW	GW		GW	GW	GW		GW	GW	GW		GW	GW	GW		GW	GW	GW		GW	GW			
Heathrow Central Bus Stn	d	15 10	15 40	16 10	.....	16 40	17 10	17 40	.....	18 10	18 40	19 10	.....	19 40	20 10	20 40	.....	21 20	22 00	23 05	.....	23 59	23 59	.....	.....	.....
Reading	a	15 53	16 23	16 53	.	17 23	17 53	18 23	.	18 53	19 23	19 53	.	20 23	20 53	21 23	.	22 03	22 43	23 48	.	00 43	00 43	.	.	.

For general notes see front of timetable
For details of catering facilities see Directory of Train Operators

Table 125B

Mondays to Saturdays

Bristol — Bristol International Airport
Bus service

		GW 🚌	GW 🚌	GW 🚌	GW 🚌		GW 🚌	GW 🚌	GW 🚌	GW 🚌		GW 🚌	GW 🚌	GW 🚌	GW 🚌		GW 🚌	GW 🚌	GW 🚌	GW 🚌		GW 🚌	GW 🚌	GW 🚌	GW 🚌		GW 🚌
Bristol Temple Meads	d	05 25	06 10	06 25	06 40	.....	06 55	07 10	07 25	07 40	.....	07 55	08 10	08 25	08 40	.....	08 55	09 10	09 25	09 40	.....	09 55	10 10	10 25	10 40	.....	10 55
Bristol Internatl Airport	a	05 50	06 35	06 50	07 05	.	07 20	07 35	07 50	08 05	.	08 20	08 35	08 50	09 05	.	09 20	09 35	09 50	10 05	.	10 20	10 35	10 50	11 05	.	11 20

		GW 🚌	GW 🚌	GW 🚌	GW 🚌		GW 🚌	GW 🚌	GW 🚌	GW 🚌		GW 🚌	GW 🚌	GW 🚌	GW 🚌		GW 🚌	GW 🚌	GW 🚌	GW 🚌		GW 🚌	GW 🚌	GW 🚌	GW 🚌		GW SX 🚌
Bristol Temple Meads	d	11 10	11 25	11 40	11 55	.....	12 10	12 25	12 40	12 55	.....	13 10	13 25	13 40	13 55	.....	14 10	14 25	14 40	14 55	.....	15 10	15 25	15 40	15 55	.....	16 10
Bristol Internatl Airport	a	11 35	11 50	12 05	12 20	.	12 35	12 50	13 05	13 20	.	13 35	13 50	14 05	14 20	.	14 35	14 50	15 05	15 20	.	15 35	15 50	16 05	16 20	.	16 35

		GW 🚌	GW SX 🚌	GW 🚌	GW SX 🚌		GW 🚌	GW SX 🚌	GW 🚌	GW SX 🚌		GW 🚌	GW SX 🚌	GW 🚌	GW SX 🚌		GW 🚌	GW 🚌	GW 🚌	GW 🚌		GW 🚌	GW 🚌	GW 🚌	GW 🚌		
Bristol Temple Meads	d	16 25	16 40	16 55	17 10	.....	17 25	17 40	17 55	18 10	.....	18 25	18 40	18 55	19 10	.....	19 25	19 55	20 25	20 55	.....	21 25	21 55	22 25	22 55	.....	.....
Bristol Internatl Airport	a	16 50	17 05	17 20	17 35	.	17 50	18 05	18 20	18 35	.	18 50	19 05	19 20	19 35	.	19 50	20 20	20 50	21 20	.	21 50	22 20	22 50	23 20	.	.

Sundays

		GW 🚌	GW 🚌	GW 🚌	GW 🚌	GW 🚌	GW 🚌	GW 🚌	GW 🚌	GW 🚌	GW 🚌	GW 🚌	GW 🚌	GW 🚌	GW 🚌	GW 🚌	GW 🚌	GW 🚌	GW 🚌	GW 🚌	GW 🚌	GW 🚌	GW 🚌	GW 🚌	GW 🚌	GW 🚌	GW 🚌
Bristol Temple Meads	d	05 25	05 55	06 25	06 55	07 25	07 55	08 25	08 55	09 25	09 55	10 25	10 55	11 25	11 55	12 25	12 55	13 25	13 55	14 25	14 40	14 55	15 10	15 25	15 40	15 55	16 10
Bristol Internatl Airport	a	05 45	06 20	06 50	07 20	07 50	08 20	08 50	09 20	09 50	10 20	10 50	11 20	11 50	12 20	12 50	13 20	13 50	14 20	14 50	15 05	15 20	15 35	15 50	16 05	16 20	16 35

		GW 🚌	GW 🚌	GW 🚌	GW 🚌	GW 🚌	GW 🚌	GW 🚌	GW 🚌	GW 🚌	GW 🚌	GW 🚌	GW 🚌	GW 🚌	GW 🚌	GW 🚌	GW 🚌	GW 🚌	GW 🚌	GW 🚌	GW 🚌	GW 🚌	GW 🚌	GW 🚌	GW 🚌		
Bristol Temple Meads	d	16 25	16 40	16 55	17 10	17 25	17 40	17 55	18 10	18 25	18 40	18 55	19 10	19 25	19 55	20 10	20 25	20 40	20 55	21 10	21 40	21 55	22 10	22 25	22 55	.....	.....
Bristol Internatl Airport	a	16 50	17 05	17 20	17 35	17 50	18 05	18 20	18 35	18 50	19 05	19 20	19 35	19 50	20 20	20 35	20 50	21 05	21 20	21 35	22 05	22 20	22 35	22 50	23 20	.	.

Mondays to Saturdays

		GW 🚌	GW 🚌	GW 🚌	GW 🚌		GW 🚌	GW 🚌	GW 🚌	GW 🚌		GW 🚌	GW 🚌	GW 🚌	GW 🚌		GW 🚌	GW 🚌	GW 🚌	GW 🚌		GW 🚌	GW 🚌	GW 🚌	GW 🚌		GW 🚌
Bristol Internatl Airport	d	06 15	06 45	07 00	07 15	.....	07 30	07 45	08 00	08 15	.....	08 30	08 45	09 00	09 15	.....	09 30	09 45	10 00	10 15	.....	10 30	10 45	11 00	11 15	.....	11 30
Bristol Temple Meads	a	06 40	07 10	07 25	07 40	.	07 55	08 10	08 25	08 40	.	08 55	09 10	09 25	09 40	.	09 55	10 10	10 25	10 40	.	10 55	11 10	11 25	11 40	.	11 55

		GW 🚌	GW 🚌	GW 🚌	GW 🚌		GW 🚌	GW 🚌	GW 🚌	GW 🚌		GW 🚌	GW 🚌	GW 🚌	GW 🚌		GW 🚌	GW 🚌	GW 🚌	GW 🚌		GW 🚌	GW 🚌	GW SX 🚌	GW 🚌		GW SX 🚌
Bristol Internatl Airport	d	11 45	12 00	12 15	12 30	.....	12 45	13 00	13 15	13 30	.....	13 45	14 00	14 15	14 30	.....	14 45	15 00	15 15	15 30	.....	15 45	16 00	16 15	16 30	.....	16 45
Bristol Temple Meads	a	12 10	12 25	12 40	12 55	.	13 10	13 25	13 40	13 55	.	14 10	14 25	14 40	14 55	.	15 10	15 25	15 40	15 55	.	16 10	16 25	16 40	16 55	.	17 10

		GW 🚌	GW SX 🚌	GW 🚌	GW SX 🚌		GW 🚌	GW SX 🚌	GW 🚌	GW SX 🚌		GW 🚌	GW SX 🚌	GW 🚌	GW 🚌		GW 🚌	GW 🚌	GW 🚌	GW 🚌		GW 🚌	GW 🚌	GW 🚌	GW 🚌		
Bristol Internatl Airport	d	17 00	17 15	17 30	17 45	.....	18 00	18 15	18 30	18 45	.....	19 00	19 15	19 30	20 00	.....	20 30	21 00	21 30	22 00	.....	22 15	22 45	23 15	23 45	.....	.....
Bristol Temple Meads	a	17 25	17 40	17 55	18 10	.	18 25	18 40	18 55	19 10	.	19 25	19 40	19 55	20 25	.	20 55	21 25	21 55	22 25	.	22 40	23 10	23 40	00 10	.	.

Sundays

		GW 🚌	GW 🚌	GW 🚌	GW 🚌	GW 🚌	GW 🚌	GW 🚌	GW 🚌	GW 🚌	GW 🚌	GW 🚌	GW 🚌	GW 🚌	GW 🚌	GW 🚌	GW 🚌	GW 🚌	GW 🚌	GW 🚌	GW 🚌	GW 🚌	GW 🚌	GW 🚌	GW 🚌	GW 🚌	GW 🚌
Bristol Internatl Airport	d	06 00	07 00	07 30	08 00	08 30	09 00	09 30	10 00	10 30	11 00	12 00	12 30	13 00	13 30	14 00	14 30	14 45	15 00	15 15	15 30	15 45	16 00	16 15	16 30	16 45	17 00
Bristol Temple Meads	a	06 25	07 25	07 55	08 25	08 55	09 25	09 55	10 25	10 55	11 25	12 25	12 55	13 25	13 55	14 25	14 55	15 10	15 25	15 40	15 55	16 10	16 25	16 40	16 55	17 10	17 25

		GW 🚌	GW 🚌	GW 🚌	GW 🚌	GW 🚌	GW 🚌	GW 🚌	GW 🚌	GW 🚌	GW 🚌	GW 🚌	GW 🚌	GW 🚌	GW 🚌	GW 🚌	GW 🚌	GW 🚌	GW 🚌	GW 🚌	GW 🚌	GW 🚌	GW 🚌	GW 🚌	GW 🚌	GW 🚌	
Bristol Internatl Airport	d	17 15	17 30	17 45	18 00	18 15	18 30	18 45	19 00	19 15	19 30	19 45	20 00	20 15	20 30	20 45	21 15	21 30	21 45	22 00	22 15	22 30	22 45	23 00	23 15	23 30	.....
Bristol Temple Meads	a	17 40	17 55	18 10	18 25	18 40	18 55	19 10	19 25	19 40	19 55	20 10	20 25	20 40	20 55	21 10	21 40	21 55	22 10	22 25	22 40	22 55	23 10	23 25	23 40	23 55	.

For general notes see front of timetable
For details of catering facilities see Directory of Train Operators

Table 125C

Mondays to Fridays

Cardiff — Cardiff International Airport
Bus Service

		GW	GW	GW	GW	GW	GW	GW	GW	GW	GW	GW	GW	GW
Cardiff Central Bus Stn	d	05 10	08 00	08 57	10 02	11 02	12 02	13 02	14 02	15 02	16 02	17 12	17 40	18 20
Cardiff International Apt	a	05 39	08 35	09 26	10 31	11 31	12 31	13 31	14 31	15 31	16 33	17 50	18 12	18 50

Saturdays

		GW	GW	GW	GW	GW	GW	GW	GW	GW	GW	GW	GW	GW
Cardiff Central Bus Stn	d	05 10	08 02	09 02	10 02	11 02	12 02	13 02	14 02	15 02	16 02	17 12	17 40	18 20
Cardiff International Apt	a	05 39	08 31	09 31	10 31	11 31	12 31	13 31	14 31	15 31	16 31	17 41	18 12	18 49

Sundays

		GW	GW	GW	GW	GW	GW	GW
Cardiff Central Bus Stn	d	08 30	10 02	12 02	14 02	16 02	18 02	19 15
Cardiff International Apt	a	08 59	10 31	12 31	14 31	16 31	18 31	19 44

Mondays to Fridays

		GW	GW	GW	GW	GW	GW	GW	GW	GW	GW	GW	GW	GW	GW	GW
Cardiff International Apt	d	07 16	07 51	09 35	10 35	11 05	11 35	12 35	13 35	14 35	15 05	15 35	16 40	17 41	18 51	20 25
Cardiff Central Bus Stn	a	07 50	08 32	10 06	11 06	11 36	12 06	13 06	14 06	15 06	15 36	16 06	17 16	18 12	19 21	20 55

Saturdays

		GW	GW	GW	GW	GW	GW	GW	GW	GW	GW	GW	GW	GW
Cardiff International Apt	d	07 25	08 00	09 35	10 35	11 35	12 35	13 35	14 35	15 35	16 40	17 40	18 51	20 25
Cardiff Central Bus Stn	a	07 56	08 31	10 06	11 06	12 06	13 06	14 06	15 06	16 06	17 11	18 11	19 23	20 55

Sundays

		GW	GW	GW	GW	GW	GW	GW
Cardiff International Apt	d	09 05	10 40	12 40	14 40	16 40	18 40	20 25
Cardiff Central Bus Stn	a	09 35	11 10	13 10	15 10	17 10	19 10	21 01

For general notes see front of timetable
For details of catering facilities see
Directory of Train Operators

London and Oxford → Worcester and Hereford

Network Diagram - see first page of Table 116

Mondays to Fridays

Miles			GW 1 ◇ ☕		GW 1	GW 1 ◇ ☕		GW 1 ◇ ☕	GW 1 ◇ ☕		GW 1 ◇ ☕	GW 1 ◇ ☕		GW 1 ◇ ☕	GW 1		GW 1 ◇ ☕	GW 1 ◇ ☕	GW 1 ◇ A ☕	GW 1 ◇ ☕	GW 1 ◇ ☕	GW 1 ◇			
0	**London Paddington** 15 ⊖	d		05 42		06 30	07 51		08 51	09 51		11 51	13 51		15 51			17 21	17 51	18 21	19 21	20 20	21 48		
18½	Slough 3	d		06 03		07 01	08 07		09 07	10 07		12 07	14 07		16 07						19 37	20 36	22 05		
36	Reading 7	d		06 20		07 23	08 23		09 23	10 23		12 23	14 23		16 23			17 50	18 21	18 50	19 53	20 52	22 21		
53¼	Didcot Parkway	d		06 37		07 48			09 38																
63½	**Oxford**	d		06 54		08 02	08 49		09 55	10 49		12 48	14 49		16 48	17 31		18 16	18 55	19 21	20 21	21 17	22 52		
70½	Hanborough	d		07 04		08 13	08 59		10 06	10 59		12 59	14 59		16 58	17 40		18 27	19 05		20 31	21 28	23 01		
71½	Combe	d														17x41									
75	Finstock	d														17x47									
76¾	Charlbury	d		07 12		08 21	09 07		10 14	11 07		13 07	15 07		17 06	17 51		18 35	19 13	19 35	20 39	21 36	23 09		
80½	Ascott-under-Wychwood	d														17x55									
81¾	Shipton	d														17x58			19x21				23x14		
84¾	Kingham	d		07 22		08 30	09 17		10 23	11 17		13 16	15 17		17 16	18 03		18 45	19 27	19 46	20 49	21 45	23 19		
91¾	Moreton-in-Marsh	a		07 30		08 37	09 25		10 31	11 25		13 25	15 25		17 24	18 14		18 53	19 37	19 54	20 57	21 53	23 28		
—		d		07 30		08 38	09 25		10 32	11 25		13 25	15 25		17 25	18 15		18 54	19 37	19 58	20 57	21 54	23 28		
101¾	Honeybourne	d		07 42		08 49	09 37		10 43	11 37		13 36	15 37		17 36	18 26		19 05		20 09	21 09	22 05	23 39		
106¾	Evesham	a		07 50		08 56	09 45		10 51	11 45		13 45	15 45		17 45	18 33		19 14	19 54	20 18	21 17	22 13	23 47		
—		d	06 11	07 56		09 02	10 00		10 52	11 56		13 45	15 46		17 46	18 42		19 20	19 56	20 19	21 23	22 14	23 47		
112¾	Pershore	d	06 18	08 04		09 09	10 08		10 59	12 04		13 53	15 54		17 54	18 49		19 28	20 04	20 27	21 31	22 22	23 55		
120½	**Worcester Shrub Hill** 7	a	06 29	08 15		09 21	10 22		11 12	12 21		14 05	16 14		18 09	19 10		19 44	20 22	20 41	21 41	22 33	00 08		
121¼	**Worcester Foregate Street** 7	a	06 36	08 20		09 26	10 26		11 16	12 26		14 12	16 18			19 15		19 48		20 44	21 57	22 37			
128	Malvern Link	a					10 36		11 26				16 27					19 57		20 54	22 09	22 47			
128¾	Great Malvern	a					10 43		11 30			14 22	16 34					20 01		20 58	22 13	22 53			
131¾	Colwall	a							11 35			14 28						20 07		21 04					
136	Ledbury	a							11 43			14 36						20 15		21 12					
149¾	**Hereford** 7	a							12 03			14 58						20 36		21 33					

Saturdays

		GW 1 ◇ ☕		GW 1 ◇ ☕		GW 1 ◇ ☕		GW 1 ◇ ☕		GW 1 ◇ ☕		GW 1 ◇ ☕		GW 1 ◇ ☕		GW 1 ◇ ☕		GW 1 ◇ ☕	GW 1 ◇ ☕	GW 1 ◇ ☕	GW 1 ◇ ☕	GW 1 ◇	GW 1 ◇		
London Paddington 15 ⊖	d	05 42		06 51		07 51		08 51		09 51		10 51		11 51		13 51		14 51	15 51	16 51	18 21	19 51	21 51		
Slough 3	d	05 57		07 07		08 07		09 07		10 07		11 07		12 07		14 07		15 07	16 07	17 07	18 38	20 07	22 08		
Reading 7	d	06 14		07 23		08 23		09 23		10 23		11 23		12 23		14 23		15 23	16 23	17 23	18 53	20 23	22 23		
Didcot Parkway	d	06 29																							
Oxford	d	06 48		07 48		08 48		09 48		10 48		11 48		12 48		14 48		15 48	16 48	17 48	19 19	20 49	22 48		
Hanborough	d	06 58		07 59		08 59		09 59		10 59		11 59		12 59		14 59		15 59	16 59	17 59	19 30	20 58	22 57		
Combe	d																								
Finstock	d																								
Charlbury	d	07 07		08 07		09 07		10 07		11 07		12 07		13 07		15 07		16 07	17 07	18 07	19 38	21 06	23 05		
Ascott-under-Wychwood	d																								
Shipton	d															15x15				18x15		21x12	23x11		
Kingham	d	07 17		08 17		09 17		10 17		11 17		12 17		13 17		15 21		16 17	17 17	18 21	19 48	21 17	23 16		
Moreton-in-Marsh	a	07 25		08 25		09 25		10 25		11 25		12 25		13 25		15 29		16 25	17 25	18 29	19 56	21 25	23 24		
	d	07 26		08 27		09 27		10 27		11 27		12 27		13 27		15 30		16 27	17 27	18 30	19 58	21 25	23 24		
Honeybourne	d	07 38		08 38		09 38		10 38		11 38		12 38		13 38		15 42		16 38	17 38	18 42	20 09	21 36	23 35		
Evesham	a	07 45		08 46		09 46		10 46		11 46		12 46		13 46		15 49		16 46	17 46	18 49	20 17	21 44	23 42		
	d	07 59		08 48		10 00		10 48		11 48		12 48		13 48		16 00		16 48	17 48	18 52	20 19	21 46	23 44		
Pershore	d	08 07		08 56		10 08		10 56		11 56		12 56		13 56		16 08		16 56	17 56	19 00	20 27	21 54	23 52		
Worcester Shrub Hill 7	a	08 22		09 08		10 22		11 08		12 07		13 08		14 07		16 22		17 08	18 08	19 14	20 39	22 05	00 03		
Worcester Foregate Street 7	a	08 26		09 12		10 26		11 12		12 11		13 12		14 11		16 26		17 12	18 12	19 18	20 46	22 08			
Malvern Link	a	08 36		09 21		10 36		11 21								16 35		17 21	18 21	19 28	20 55	22 17			
Great Malvern	a	08 41		09 26		10 41		11 26		12 22				14 22		16 39		17 26	18 26	19 32	20 59	22 21			
Colwall	a									12 28				14 28						19 38	21 05				
Ledbury	a									12 35				14 35						19 45	21 13				
Hereford 7	a									12 54				14 54						20 02	21 33				

For general notes see front of timetable
For details of catering facilities see Directory of Train Operators

A Cathedrals Express

Table 126

London and Oxford → Worcester and Hereford

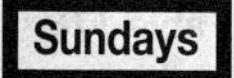

Sundays

until 7 September

Network Diagram - see first page of Table 116

		GW 1 ◇	GW 1 ◇ ☕	GW 1 ◇ ☕	GW 1 ◇ ☕	GW 1 ◇ ☕	GW 1 ◇ ☕	GW 1 ◇ ☕	GW 1 ◇ ☕	GW 1 ◇ ☕	GW 1 ◇ ☕	GW 1 ◇	GW 1 ◇
London Paddington [15] ⊖	d	08 03	09 35	10 42	12 42	13 42	14 42	15 42	16 42	17 42	18 42	19 42	21 42
Slough [3]	d	08 25	09 53	10 58	12 58	13 58	14 58	15 58	16 58	17 58	18 58	19 57	21 59
Reading [7]	d	08 50	10 13	11 20	13 20	14 20	15 20	16 20	17 20	18 20	19 20	20 20	22 20
Didcot Parkway	d	09 04	10 29	11 36	13 37	14 36	15 36	16 36	17 36	18 36	19 36	20 36	22 39
Oxford	d	09 18	10 45	11 50	13 50	14 50	15 50	16 50	17 50	18 50	19 50	20 49	22 50
Hanborough	d	09 29	10 55	12 00	14 01		16 00		18 00	19 00	20 01	20 58	23 02
Combe	d												
Finstock	d												
Charlbury	d	09 36	11 03	12 09	14 09	15 04	16 08	17 04	18 09	19 09	20 10	21 07	23 10
Ascott-under-Wychwood	d												
Shipton	d												
Kingham	d	09 45	11 13	12 19	14 19	15 15	16 18	17 14	18 19	19 19	20 20	21 16	23 19
Moreton-in-Marsh	a	09 53	11 21	12 27	14 27	15 23	16 26	17 22	18 27	19 27	20 28	21 24	23 26
	d	09 57	11 23	12 28	14 29	15 24	16 28	17 24	18 28	19 28	20 29	21 24	23 27
Honeybourne	d	10 08	11 34	12 39		15 35	16 39	17 35	18 39	19 39	20 40	21 35	23 38
Evesham	a	10 14	11 41	12 47	14 45	15 44	16 46	17 44	18 47	19 47	20 48	21 41	23 44
	d	10 16	11 44	12 48	14 47	15 48	16 49	17 49	18 49	19 49	20 50	21 49	23 46
Pershore	d	10 23	11 51	12 56	14 55	15 55	16 56	17 56	18 57	19 57	20 58	21 58	23 53
Worcester Shrub Hill [7]	a	10 34	12 03	13 07	15 06	16 07	17 08	18 08	19 08	20 06	21 09	22 07	00 04
Worcester Foregate Street [7]	a	10 37	12 07	13 11	15 10		17 12		19 12	20 12	21 13	22 24	
Malvern Link	a	10 47	12 17	13 21			17 21		19 22	20 22	21 23	22 33	
Great Malvern	a	10 50	12 20	13 25	15 21		17 25		19 26	20 26	21 27	22 40	
Colwall	a		12 27	13 31			17 32				21 33		
Ledbury	a		12 34	13 39	15 32		17 39				21 40		
Hereford [7]	a		12 54	14 04	15 51		17 58				22 02		

Sundays

from 14 September

		GW 1 ◇	GW 1 ◇ ☕	GW 1 ◇ ☕	GW 1 ◇ ☕	GW 1 ◇ ☕	GW 1 ◇ ☕	GW 1 ◇ ☕	GW 1 ◇ ☕	GW 1 ◇ ☕	GW 1 ◇ ☕	GW 1 ◇	GW 1 ◇	GW 1 ◇
London Paddington [15] ⊖	d	08 03	09 35	10 42	12 42	13 42	14 42	15 42	16 42	17 42	18 42	19 42	21 27	21 51
Slough [3]	d	08 25	09 55	11 03	13 01	14 05	15 05	16 05	17 05	18 05	19 05	20 04	21 57	22 08
Reading [7]	d	08 43	10 12	11 20	13 20	14 20	15 20	16 20	17 20	18 20	19 20	20 20	22 08	22 23
Didcot Parkway	d	09 03	10 29	11 36	13 37	14 36	15 36	16 36	17 36	18 36	19 36	20 36	22 28	
Oxford	d	09 15	10 45	11 50	13 50	14 50	15 50	16 50	17 50	18 50	19 50	20 49	22 42	22 48
Hanborough	d	09 26	10 55	12 00	14 01		16 00		18 00	19 00	20 01	20 58	22 52	22 57
Combe	d													
Finstock	d													
Charlbury	d	09 33	11 03	12 09	14 09	15 04	16 08	17 04	18 09	19 09	20 10	21 07	23 00	23 05
Ascott-under-Wychwood	d													
Shipton	d													23 11
Kingham	d	09 42	11 13	12 19	14 19	15 15	16 18	17 14	18 19	19 19	20 20	21 16	23 09	23 16
Moreton-in-Marsh	a	09 50	11 21	12 27	14 27	15 23	16 26	17 22	18 27	19 27	20 28	21 24	23 16	23 24
	d	09 57	11 23	12 28	14 29	15 24	16 28	17 24	18 28	19 28	20 29	21 24	23 17	23 24
Honeybourne	d	10 08	11 34	12 39		15 35	16 39	17 35	18 39	19 39	20 40	21 35	23 28	23 35
Evesham	a	10 14	11 41	12 47	14 45	15 44	16 46	17 44	18 47	19 47	20 48	21 41	23 34	23 35
	d	10 16	11 44	12 48	14 47	15 48	16 49	17 49	18 49	19 49	20 50	21 49	23 36	23 42
Pershore	d	10 23	11 51	12 56	14 55	15 55	16 56	17 56	18 57	19 57	20 58	21 58	23 43	23 44
Worcester Shrub Hill [7]	a	10 34	12 03	13 07	15 06	16 07	17 08	18 08	19 08	20 06	21 09	22 07	23 54	23 52
Worcester Foregate Street [7]	a	10 37	12 07	13 11	15 10		17 12		19 12	20 12	21 13	22 24		00 03
Malvern Link	a	10 47	12 17	13 21			17 21		19 22	20 22	21 23	22 33		
Great Malvern	a	10 50	12 20	13 25	15 21		17 25		19 26	20 26	21 27	22 40		
Colwall	a		12 27	13 31			17 32				21 33			
Ledbury	a		12 34	13 39	15 32		17 39				21 40			
Hereford [7]	a		12 54	14 04	15 51		17 58				22 02			

For general notes see front of timetable
For details of catering facilities see
Directory of Train Operators

Hereford and Worcester → Oxford and London

Network Diagram - see first page of Table 116

Mondays to Fridays

Miles	Station		GW	GW	GW	GW	GW	GW	GW
			MX						
			1 ◇	1	1 ◇	1 ◇	1 ◇	1	1 ◇
							A		A B
					☕	☕	⊠		⊠
0	**Hereford 7**	d					05 41		06 43
13¾	Ledbury	d					05 59		07 00
18	Colwall	d					06 07		07 08
20¾	Great Malvern	d	22p33			05 30	06 12		07 15
21¾	Malvern Link	d				05 34	06 16		07 19
28½	**Worcester Foregate Street 7**	d	22p44				06 27	06 52	07 29
29¼	**Worcester Shrub Hill 7**	d	22p49			05 45	06 32	06 55	07 34
37	Pershore	d	22p58	05 24			06 41	07 03	07 43
43	Evesham	a	23p06	05 32		05 59	06 49	07 11	07 52
—		d	23p07			06 00	06 49	07 12	07 54
48	Honeybourne	d	23p13			06 06	06 56		08 01
58	Moreton-in-Marsh	a	23p26			06 19	07 09	07 27	08 13
—		d	23p26		05 49	06 19	07 09	07 27	08 14
65	Kingham	d	23p35		05 57	06 28	07 18	07 35	08 23
68	Shipton	d			06 02			07 40	
69¼	Ascott-under-Wychwood	d						07 44	
73	Charlbury	d	23p46		06 09	06 38	07 29	07 50	08 33
74¾	Finstock	d						07 53	
78¼	Combe	d						07 58	
79¼	Hanborough	d			06 17	06 45	07 37	08 01	
86¼	**Oxford**	a	23p59		06 28	06 56	07 48	08 12	08 48
96½	Didcot Parkway	a	00 19		06 42	07 10			
113¾	Reading 7	a	00 38		06 57	07 25	08 22		09 14
131¼	Slough 3	a	00 56						
149¾	**London Paddington 15**	⊖ a	01 17		07 29	07 58	08 51		09 41

Miles	Station		GW	GW	GW	GW	GW	GW	GW	GW	GW	GW	GW	GW	GW
												FO	FX	FO	FX
			1 ◇	1 ◇	1 ◇	1 ◇	1 ◇	1 ◇	1 ◇	1 ◇	1	1 ◇	1 ◇	1 ◇	1 ◇
			☕		☕	☕	☕	☕	☕	☕		🛒	☕	🛒	☕
0	**Hereford 7**	d					13 20	15 19							
13¾	Ledbury	d					13 48	15 36							
18	Colwall	d					13 45	15 44							
20¾	Great Malvern	d			11 06		13 51	15 51	17 06					22 33	22 33
21¾	Malvern Link	d			11 10		13 55	15 55	17 10						
28½	**Worcester Foregate Street 7**	d	08 37	09 37	11 26	12 40	14 06	16 06	17 21	18 49	19 27	20 58	20 58	22 44	22 44
29¼	**Worcester Shrub Hill 7**	d	08 41	09 40	11 31	12 44	14 12	16 10	17 25	18 53	19 30	21 02	21 02	22 49	22 49
37	Pershore	d	08 50	09 48	11 40	12 53	14 27	16 26	17 35	19 09	19 45	21 11	21 11	22 58	22 58
43	Evesham	a	08 58	09 56	11 48	13 01	14 37	16 34	17 43	19 17	19 53	21 19	21 19	23 06	23 06
—		d	09 00	09 58	11 49	13 02	14 44	16 35	17 48	19 18	20 21	21 21	21 21	23 07	23 07
48	Honeybourne	d	09 06	10 04	11 56	13 08	14 52	16 42	17 55		20 29	21 27	21 27	23 13	23 13
58	Moreton-in-Marsh	a	09 19	10 17	12 08	13 21	15 03	16 55	18 08	19 34	20 41	21 40	21 40	23 26	23 26
—		d	09 19	10 18	12 13	13 21	15 16	16 56	18 11	19 35	20 41	21 40	21 40	23 26	23 26
65	Kingham	d	09 28	10 25	12 21	13 30	15 25	17 05	18 25	19 43	20 50	21 49	21 49	23 35	23 35
68	Shipton	d							18 30						
69¼	Ascott-under-Wychwood	d													
73	Charlbury	d	09 38	10 34	12 31	13 40	15 35	17 17	18 46	19 53	20 59	21 59	21 59	23 45	23 46
74¾	Finstock	d													
78¼	Combe	d													
79¼	Hanborough	d	09 45	10 41	12 39	13 47	15 43	17 25		20 01	21 06	22 06	22 06		
86¼	**Oxford**	a	09 58	10 58	12 58	13 58	15 58	17 36	18 59	20 24	21 22	22 19	22 19	23 59	23 59
96½	Didcot Parkway	a												00 19	00 19
113¾	Reading 7	a	10 24	11 25	13 25	14 25	16 25	18 03	19 26	20 55		22 46	22 46	00 38	00 38
131¼	Slough 3	a	10 38		13 40	14 40	16 40		19 40	21 09		23 01	23 02	00 52	00 56
149¾	**London Paddington 15**	⊖ a	10 59	11 58	13 59	14 59	16 59	18 30	19 59	21 29		23 22	23 25	01 10	01 17

Saturdays

Station		GW	GW	GW	GW	GW	GW	GW	GW	GW	GW
		1 ◇	1 ◇	1 ◇	1 ◇	1 ◇	1 ◇	1 ◇	1 ◇	1 ◇	1 ◇
							C	D			
		🛒		☕	☕	☕	☕	☕	☕	☕	☕
Hereford 7	d				07 22						
Ledbury	d				07 40						
Colwall	d				07 47						
Great Malvern	d	22p33	06 07	07 07	07 53	09 07	09 55	09 55	11 07	11 45	
Malvern Link	d		06 10	07 11	07 57	09 11	09 59	09 59	11 11	11 49	
Worcester Foregate Street 7	d	22p44	06 19	07 22	08 08	09 20	10 10	10 10	11 22	12 00	13 22
Worcester Shrub Hill 7	d	22p49	06 23	07 26	08 17	09 26	10 26	10 26	11 26	12 26	13 26
Pershore	d	22p58	06 32	07 35	08 31	09 35	10 35	10 35	11 35	12 35	13 35
Evesham	a	23p06	06 39	07 43	08 39	09 43	10 43	10 43	11 43	12 43	13 43
	d	23p07	06 41	07 53	08 50	09 56	10 56	10 56	11 56	12 56	13 56
Honeybourne	d	23p13	06 48	08 00	08 57	10 03	11 03	11 03	12 03	13 03	14 03
Moreton-in-Marsh	a	23p26	07 00	08 11	09 09	10 14	11 14	11 14	12 14	13 14	14 14
	d	23p26	07 00	08 13	09 10	10 16	11 16	11 16	12 16	13 16	14 16
Kingham	d	23p35	07 08	08 22	09 19	10 25	11 25	11 25	12 25	13 24	14 25
Shipton	d		07x13	08x27							
Ascott-under-Wychwood	d										
Charlbury	d	23p45	07 19	08 35	09 30	10 35	11 35	11 35	12 35	13 36	14 35
Finstock	d										
Combe	d										
Hanborough	d		07 26	08 43	09 38	10 43	11 43	11 43	12 43	13 44	14 43
Oxford	a	23p59	07 36	08 57	09 48	10 58	11 58	11 58	12 58	13 58	14 58
Didcot Parkway	a	00 19									
Reading 7	a	00 38	08 08	09 25	10 20	11 25	12 25	12 27	13 24	14 25	15 25
Slough 3	a	00 52		09 40	10 35	11 40	12 40	12 45	13 39	14 40	15 40
London Paddington 15	⊖ a	01 10	08 40	09 58	10 54	11 58	12 59	13 08	13 58	14 58	15 59

Station		GW	GW	GW	GW	GW	GW	GW	GW	GW	GW
		1 ◇	1 ◇	1 ◇	1 ◇	1 ◇	1 ◇	1 ◇	1 ◇	1 ◇	1
		C	D					C	D		
		☕	☕	☕	☕	☕	☕			☕	
Hereford 7	d	13 20	13 20	15 23						20 22	
Ledbury	d	13 39	13 39	15 40						20 45	
Colwall	d	13 47	13 47	15 48						20 52	
Great Malvern	d	14 07	14 07	15 53	17 07	18 07	18 45	19 20	19 20	20 58	22 40
Malvern Link	d	14 11	14 11	15 57	17 11	18 11	18 49	19 23	19 23	21 02	22 43
Worcester Foregate Street 7	d	14 22	14 22	16 06	17 22	18 22	19 01	19 35	19 35	21 19	22 51
Worcester Shrub Hill 7	d	14 26	14 26	16 26	17 26	18 26	19 15	19 55	19 55	21 24	22 55
Pershore	d	14 35	14 35	16 35	17 35	18 35	19 24	20 04	20 04	21 33	23 04
Evesham	a	14 43	14 43	16 43	17 43	18 43	19 32	20 12	20 12	21 41	23 12
	d	14 53	14 53	16 56	17 56	18 56	19 34	20 35	20 35	21 53	
Honeybourne	d	15 00	15 00	17 03	18 03	19 03	19 41	20 41	20 41	22 00	
Moreton-in-Marsh	a	15 12	15 12	17 14	18 14	19 14	19 52	20 54	20 54	22 11	
	d	15 13	15 13	17 16	18 16	19 26	20 16	20 54	20 54	22 13	
Kingham	d	15 22	15 22	17 25	18 25	19 35	20 25	21 03	21 03	22 22	
Shipton	d	15x28	15x28							22x27	
Ascott-under-Wychwood	d										
Charlbury	d	15 35	15 35	17 35	18 35	19 50	20 35	21 17	21 17	22 35	
Finstock	d										
Combe	d										
Hanborough	d	15 43	15 43	17 43	18 43		20 43	21 24	21 24	22 43	
Oxford	a	15 58	15 58	17 58	18 58	20 05	20 58	21 35	21 35	22 58	
Didcot Parkway	a							21 48	21 48	23 12	
Reading 7	a	16 25	16 28	18 25	19 25	20 30	21 24	22 05	22 05	23 28	
Slough 3	a	16 40	16 46	18 40	19 40	20 45	21 38	22 22	22 24	23 48	
London Paddington 15	⊖ a	16 58	17 06	18 58	19 58	21 05	21 58	22 40	22 42	00 09	

For general notes see front of timetable
For details of catering facilities see
Directory of Train Operators

A From Abergavenny (Table 131)
B **Cathedrals Express**
C From 13 September
D Until 6 September

Sundays

until 7 September

Hereford and Worcester → Oxford and London

Network Diagram - see first page of Table 116

		GW	GW	GW	GW	GW	GW	GW	GW	GW	GW	GW
		1 ◇	1 ◇	1 ◇	1 ◇	1 ◇	1 ◇	1 ◇	1 ◇	1 ◇	1 ◇	1 ◇
		🛒			☕	☕	☕	☕	☕	☕	☕	🛒
Hereford 7	d				13 30	14 30		16 30		18 30		
Ledbury	d				13 48	14 57		16 47		18 48		
Colwall	d				13 55	15 04		16 55		18 55		
Great Malvern	d	09 01	11 08	13 06	14 01	15 09		17 00		19 08	20 08	21 05
Malvern Link	d	09 04	11 11	13 09	14 05	15 13		17 04		19 12	20 12	21 09
Worcester Foregate Street 7	d	09 13	11 19	13 20	14 16	15 24		17 21		19 23	20 23	21 23
Worcester Shrub Hill 7	d	09 17	11 23	13 24	14 20	15 28	16 25	17 26	18 25	19 27	20 27	21 27
Pershore	d	09 26	11 32	13 34	14 29	15 37	16 34	17 34	18 34	19 36	20 36	21 36
Evesham	a	09 33	11 39	13 41	14 37	15 45	16 42	17 42	18 44	19 44	20 44	21 44
	d	09 35	11 46	13 42	14 51	15 50	16 51	17 47	18 53	19 51	20 51	21 47
Honeybourne	d	09 40	11 52	13 48	14 58	15 55	16 57	17 53	19 00	19 58	20 58	21 53
Moreton-in-Marsh	a	09 53	12 04	14 01	15 09	16 08	17 09	18 05	19 11	20 09	21 09	22 05
	d	09 53	12 05	14 01	15 11	16 09	17 09	18 06	19 13	20 11	21 11	22 06
Kingham	d	10 00	12 12	14 09	15 19	16 18	17 19	18 15	19 22	20 20	21 20	22 15
Shipton	d											
Ascott-under-Wychwood	d											
Charlbury	d	10 10	12 21	14 20	15 30	16 28	17 30	18 26	19 32	20 30	21 30	22 25
Finstock	d											
Combe	d											
Hanborough	d	10 17	12 28	14 27	15 38	16 36	17 37		19 40	20 38	21 38	
Oxford	a	10 27	12 41	14 37	15 48	16 46	17 47	18 40	19 50	20 48	21 48	22 38
Didcot Parkway	a	10 49	13 01	14 49	16 01	17 01	18 01	18 52	20 03	21 02	22 01	22 59
Reading 7	a	11 06	13 20	15 04	16 18	17 18	18 18	19 07	20 20	21 19	22 19	23 15
Slough 3	a	11 26	13 47	15 23	16 47	17 48	18 45	19 32	20 47	21 41	22 40	23 36
London Paddington 15	⊖ a	11 46	14 08	15 43	17 07	18 08	19 08	19 52	21 08	22 03	23 04	00 01

Sundays

from 14 September

		GW	GW	GW	GW	GW	GW	GW	GW	GW	GW	GW
		1 ◇	1 ◇	1 ◇	1 ◇	1 ◇	1 ◇	1 ◇	1 ◇	1 ◇	1 ◇	1 ◇
		🛒			☕	☕	☕	☕	☕	☕	☕	🛒
Hereford 7	d				13 30	14 30		16 30		18 30		
Ledbury	d				13 48	14 57		16 47		18 48		
Colwall	d				13 55	15 04		16 55		18 55		
Great Malvern	d	09 01	11 08	13 06	14 01	15 09		17 00		19 08	20 08	21 05
Malvern Link	d	09 04	11 11	13 09	14 05	15 13		17 04		19 12	20 12	21 09
Worcester Foregate Street 7	d	09 13	11 19	13 20	14 16	15 24		17 21		19 23	20 23	21 23
Worcester Shrub Hill 7	d	09 17	11 23	13 24	14 20	15 28	16 25	17 26	18 25	19 27	20 27	21 27
Pershore	d	09 26	11 32	13 34	14 29	15 37	16 34	17 34	18 34	19 36	20 36	21 36
Evesham	a	09 33	11 39	13 41	14 37	15 45	16 42	17 42	18 44	19 44	20 44	21 44
	d	09 35	11 46	13 42	14 51	15 50	16 51	17 47	18 53	19 51	20 51	21 47
Honeybourne	d	09 40	11 52	13 48	14 58	15 55	16 57	17 53	19 00	19 58	20 58	21 53
Moreton-in-Marsh	a	09 53	12 04	14 01	15 09	16 08	17 09	18 05	19 12	20 09	21 09	22 05
	d	09 53	12 05	14 01	15 11	16 09	17 09	18 06	19 13	20 11	21 11	22 06
Kingham	d	10 00	12 12	14 09	15 19	16 18	17 19	18 15	19 22	20 20	21 20	22 15
Shipton	d											
Ascott-under-Wychwood	d											
Charlbury	d	10 10	12 21	14 20	15 30	16 28	17 30	18 26	19 31	20 30	21 30	22 25
Finstock	d											
Combe	d											
Hanborough	d	10 17	12 28	14 27	15 38	16 36	17 37		19 40	20 38	21 38	
Oxford	a	10 27	12 41	14 37	15 48	16 46	17 47	18 40	19 50	20 48	21 48	22 38
Didcot Parkway	a	10 49	13 01	14 49	16 01	17 01	18 01	18 52	20 03	21 02	22 01	22 59
Reading 7	a	11 06	13 19	15 04	16 18	17 18	18 18	19 07	20 18	21 19	22 19	23 15
Slough 3	a	11 24	13 37	15 34	16 36	17 40	18 36	19 28	20 35	21 35	22 42	23 36
London Paddington 15	⊖ a	11 53	14 00	15 58	17 00	18 06	19 02	19 53	21 00	22 03	23 05	23 59

For general notes see front of timetable
For details of catering facilities see
Directory of Train Operators

Table 126A

Mondays to Fridays

Kingham — Chipping Norton

Bus Service

		GW	GW	GW	GW	GW	GW	GW	GW	GW	GW	GW	GW	GW
Kingham	d	07 07	07 43	08 35	09 32	11 30	13 15	14 05	16 20	17 15	18 08	18 50	19 20	19 50
Chipping Norton West St	a	07 18	07 56	08 48	09 50	11 48	13 28	14 18	16 33	17 28	18 21	19 03	19 33	20 03

Saturdays

		GW	GW	GW	GW	GW	GW	GW	GW	GW	GW	GW
Kingham	d	08 10	09 15	10 10	11 15	12 10	13 10	15 15	16 15	17 15	18 18	19 45
Chipping Norton West St	a	08 23	09 28	10 29	11 34	12 29	13 23	15 28	16 28	17 28	18 31	19 58

Mondays to Fridays

		GW	GW	GW	GW	GW	GW	GW	GW	GW	GW	GW	GW	GW
Chipping Norton West St	d	06 52	07 20	08 00	09 00	10 48	12 35	13 35	15 55	16 40	17 35	18 25	19 05	19 35
Kingham	a	07 05	07 33	08 13	09 13	11 03	12 50	13 48	16 08	16 55	17 48	18 38	19 16	19 47

Saturdays

		GW	GW	GW	GW	GW	GW	GW	GW	GW	GW	GW
Chipping Norton West St	d	07 40	08 35	09 30	10 40	11 40	12 40	13 35	15 40	16 45	17 40	19 25
Kingham	a	07 53	08 48	09 43	10 58	11 58	12 53	13 48	15 53	16 58	17 53	19 38

For general notes see front of timetable
For details of catering facilities see
Directory of Train Operators

No Sunday Service

Route Diagram for Tables 127, 128

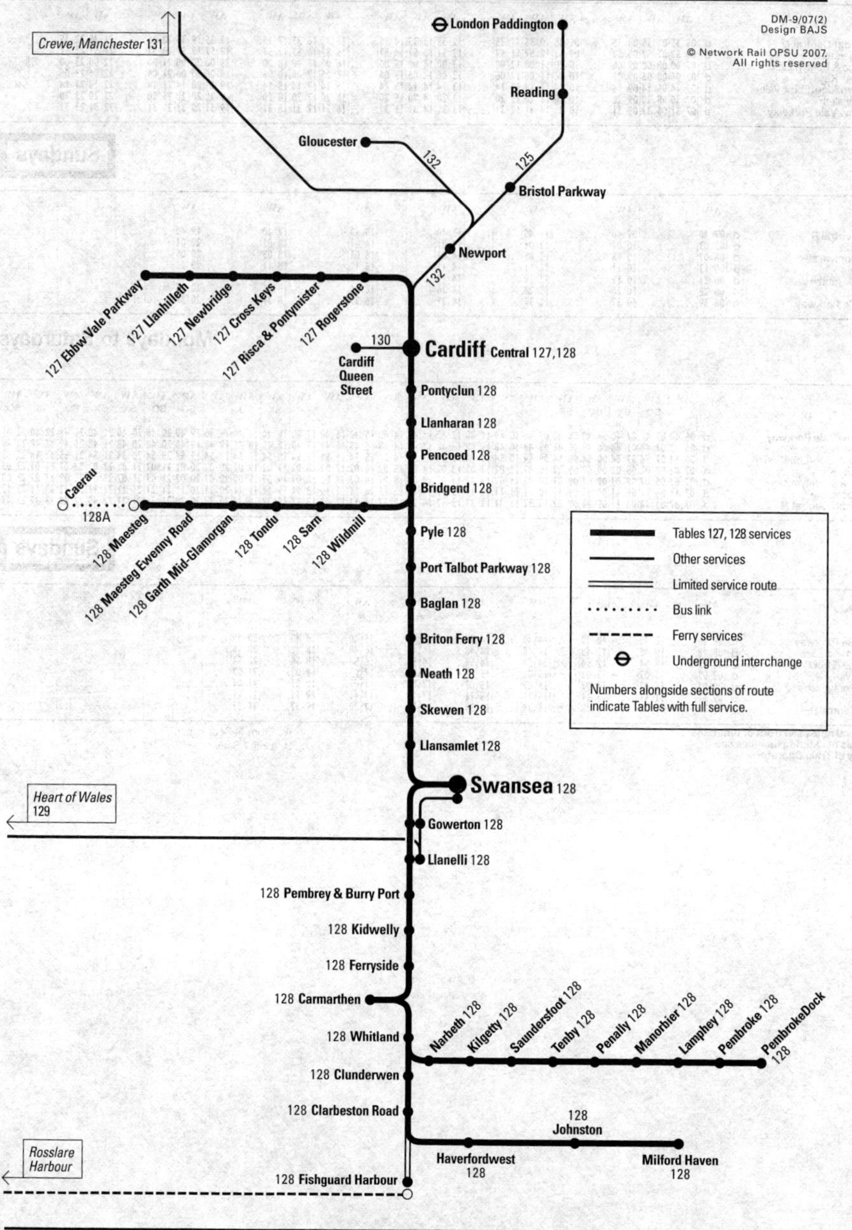

DM-9/07(2)
Design BAJS
© Network Rail OPSU 2007.
All rights reserved
Crewe, Manchester 131
London Paddington
Reading
Gloucester
132
125
Bristol Parkway
Newport
132
127 Ebbw Vale Parkway
127 Llanhilleth
127 Newbridge
127 Cross Keys
127 Risca & Pontymister
127 Rogerstone
130
Cardiff Central 127,128
Cardiff Queen Street
Pontyclun 128
Llanharan 128
Pencoed 128
Bridgend 128
Caerau
128A
128 Maesteg
128 Maesteg Ewenny Road
128 Garth Mid-Glamorgan
128 Tondu
128 Sarn
128 Wildmill
Pyle 128
Port Talbot Parkway 128
Baglan 128
Briton Ferry 128
Neath 128
Skewen 128
Llansamlet 128
Tables 127, 128 services
Other services
Limited service route
Bus link
Ferry services
Underground interchange
Numbers alongside sections of route indicate Tables with full service.
Swansea 128
Heart of Wales 129
Gowerton 128
Llanelli 128
128 Pembrey & Burry Port
128 Kidwelly
128 Ferryside
128 Carmarthen
128 Whitland
128 Clunderwen
128 Clarbeston Road
Narbeth 128
Kilgetty 128
Saundersfoot 128
Tenby 128
Penally 128
Manorbier 128
Lamphey 128
Pembroke 128
PembrokeDock 128
128 Johnston
Haverfordwest 128
Milford Haven 128
Rosslare Harbour
128 Fishguard Harbour

Cardiff Central — Ebbw Vale Parkway

Route Diagram - see first page of Table 127

Miles			AW	AW	AW	AW	AW	AW	AW	AW	AW	AW	AW	AW	AW	AW	AW	AW	AW
0	**Cardiff Central 7**	d	06 35	07 35	08 35	09 35	10 35	11 35	12 35	13 35	14 35	15 35	16 35	17 35	18 35	19 35	20 35	21 35	22 35
14	Rogerstone	d	06 57	07 57	08 57	09 57	10 57	11 57	12 57	13 57	14 57	15 57	16 57	17 57	18 57	19 57	20 57	21 57	22 57
15¼	Risca & Pontymister	d	07 00	08 00	09 00	10 00	11 00	12 00	13 00	14 00	15 00	16 00	17 00	18 00	19 00	20 00	21 00	22 00	23 00
17¼	Cross Keys	d	07 06	08 06	09 06	10 06	11 06	12 06	13 06	14 06	15 06	16 06	17 06	18 06	19 06	20 06	21 06	22 06	23 06
20¾	Newbridge (Ebbw Vale)	d	07 14	08 14	09 14	10 14	11 14	12 14	13 14	14 14	15 14	16 14	17 14	18 14	19 14	20 14	21 14	22 14	23 14
23½	Llanhilleth	d	07 20	08 20	09 20	10 20	11 20	12 20	13 20	14 20	15 20	16 20	17 20	18 20	19 20	20 20	21 20	22 20	23 20
28¾	**Ebbw Vale Parkway**	a	07 31	08 31	09 31	10 31	11 31	12 31	13 31	14 31	15 31	16 31	17 31	18 31	19 31	20 31	21 31	22 31	23 31

Sundays

		AW	AW	AW	AW	AW	AW	AW
Cardiff Central 7	d	07 40	09 40	11 40	13 40	15 40	17 40	19 40
Rogerstone	d	08 03	10 01	12 01	14 01	16 01	18 01	20 01
Risca & Pontymister	d	08 07	10 05	12 05	14 05	16 05	18 05	20 05
Cross Keys	d	08 13	10 11	12 11	14 11	16 11	18 11	20 11
Newbridge (Ebbw Vale)	d	08 21	10 19	12 19	14 19	16 19	18 19	20 19
Llanhilleth	d	08 28	10 26	12 26	14 26	16 26	18 26	20 26
Ebbw Vale Parkway	a	08 39	10 37	12 37	14 37	16 37	18 37	20 37

Mondays to Saturdays

Miles			AW	AW SO	AW SX	AW SO	AW SX	AW	AW	AW	AW	AW	AW	AW	AW	AW	AW SX	AW SO	AW SX	AW SO	AW SO	AW SX	AW SX	AW SO	AW SX	AW SO
0	**Ebbw Vale Parkway**	d	06 40	07 40	07 40	08 40	08 40	09 40	10 40	11 40	12 40	13 40	14 40	15 40	16 40	17 40	18 40	18 40	19 40	19 40	20 40	20 40	21 40	21 41	22 40	22 41
5¼	Llanhilleth	d	06 48	07 48	07 48	08 48	08 48	09 48	10 48	11 48	12 48	13 48	14 48	15 48	16 48	17 48	18 48	18 48	19 48	19 48	20 48	20 48	21 48	21 49	22 48	22 49
8	Newbridge (Ebbw Vale)	d	06 54	07 54	07 54	08 54	08 54	09 54	10 54	11 54	12 54	13 54	14 54	15 54	16 54	17 54	18 54	18 54	19 54	19 54	20 54	20 54	21 54	21 55	22 54	22 55
11½	Cross Keys	d	07 02	08 02	08 02	09 02	09 02	10 02	11 02	12 02	13 02	14 02	15 02	16 02	17 02	18 02	19 02	19 02	20 02	20 02	21 02	21 02	22 02	22 03	23 02	23 03
13½	Risca & Pontymister	d	07 07	08 07	08 07	09 07	09 07	10 07	11 07	12 07	13 07	14 07	15 07	16 07	17 07	18 07	19 07	19 07	20 07	20 07	21 07	21 07	22 07	22 08	23 07	23 08
14¾	Rogerstone	d	07 11	08 11	08 11	09 11	09 11	10 11	11 11	12 11	13 11	14 11	15 11	16 11	17 11	18 11	19 11	19 11	20 11	20 11	21 11	21 11	22 11	22 12	23 11	23 12
28¾	**Cardiff Central 7**	a	07 37	08 34	08 37	09 36	09 37	10 37	11 37	12 37	13 37	14 37	15 37	16 37	17 43	18 37	19 37	19 38	20 37	20 38	21 36	21 37	22 40	22 40	23 37	23 43

Sundays

		AW	AW	AW	AW A	AW B	AW A	AW B	AW	AW
Ebbw Vale Parkway	d	08 40	10 40	12 40	14 40	14 40	16 40	16 40	18 40	20 40
Llanhilleth	d	08 48	10 48	12 48	14 48	14 48	16 48	16 48	18 48	20 48
Newbridge (Ebbw Vale)	d	08 54	10 54	12 54	14 54	14 54	16 54	16 54	18 54	20 54
Cross Keys	d	09 02	11 02	13 02	15 02	15 02	17 02	17 02	19 02	21 02
Risca & Pontymister	d	09 07	11 07	13 07	15 07	15 07	17 07	17 07	19 07	21 07
Rogerstone	d	09 11	11 11	13 11	15 11	15 11	17 11	17 11	19 11	21 11
Cardiff Central 7	a	09 37	11 37	13 38	15 38	15 39	17 37	17 38	19 37	21 37

For general notes see front of timetable
For details of catering facilities see
Directory of Train Operators

A From 14 September
B Until 7 September

Cardiff → Maesteg, Swansea and West Wales

Route Diagram - see first page of Table 127

Miles	Miles			AW	AW	AW	AW	AW	GW	GW	GW	GW	GW	AW	AW	AW	AW	AW	AW	AW	AW
				MX	MO	MX	MO	MX	MX	MO	MO	MO	MX								
					◇	◇	◇	◇	[1] ◇	[1] ◇	[1] ◇	[1] ◇	[1] ◇		◇					◇	
					A		B			B	A	B		C							
									🍴	🍴		🍴	🍴						🛒	🛒	
—	—	London Paddington [15] ⊖	d						21p15	20p27	21p37	21p27	22p45								
—	—	Reading [7]	d						21p41	21p04	22p14	22p02	23p18								
—	—	Manchester Piccadilly [10] 🚊	d																		
—	—	Gloucester [7]	d							22p31		23p28									
—	—	Bristol Parkway [7]	d						22p46		23p15		00 22								
—	—	Newport (South Wales)	d						23p16	23p22	23p45	00 20	00 52								
—	—	Cardiff Queen Street [3]	d																		
0	—	**Cardiff Central** [7]	d	21p09	22p35		22p35	23p15	23p40	23p43	00 07	00 41	01 12							05 40	05 51
11	—	Pontyclun	d					23p29												05 52	06 03
14	—	Llanharan	d					23p34												05 57	06 08
16¼	—	Pencoed	d					23p39												06 02	06 12
20¼	0	Bridgend	d	21p28	22p54		22p54	23p45	23p59	00 03	00 27	01 01	01 36							06 08	06 20
—	1	Wildmill	d																		06 22
—	2¼	Sarn	d																		06 25
—	3	Tondu	d																		06 29
—	7	Garth (Mid Glamorgan)	d																		06 38
—	7¾	Maesteg (Ewenny Road)	d																		06 41
—	8¼	Maesteg	a																		06 46
26¼	—	Pyle	d	21p35				23p53												06 16	
32½	—	Port Talbot Parkway	d	21p43	23p07		23p07	00 01	00 11	00 17	00 40	01 15	01 49							06 24	
34½	—	Baglan	d					00 05												06 28	
36¼	—	Briton Ferry	d					00 08												06 31	
38	—	Neath	d	21p50	23p14		23p14	00 12	00 18	00 24	00 47	01 22	01 56							06 35	
41¾	—	Skewen	d					00 16												06 39	
43½	—	Llansamlet	d					00 20												06 43	
47½	—	**Swansea** [7]	a	22p03	23p26		23p26	00 28	00 33	00 36	00 59	01 34	02 10							06 52	
—	—		d	22p27	23p30	23p45	23p45	00 45							04 36				05 50	06 54	
53	—	Gowerton	d	22b37	23b40		23b55	00c56											06x01		
58¾	—	Llanelli	a	22p44	23p47	00 01	00 02	01s02							04 52				06 08	07 10	
—	—		d	22p44	23p47	00 01	00 02												06 08	07 11	
62¾	—	Pembrey & Burry Port	d	22p50	23p53	00 07	00 08	01s08											06 14	07 17	
68	—	Kidwelly	d	22b56	23b59		00x13	01c14											06x21	07x23	
72¼	—	Ferryside	d	23b01	00x05		00x20	01c20											06x27	07x29	
79¼	—	**Carmarthen**	a	23p13	00 17	00 27	00 32	01 37											06 40	07 42	
—	—		d	23p17	00 19	00 30	00 40									04 55	05 45	06 05	06 43	07 44	
93¼	0	Whitland	a	23p31	00 34	00 45	00 55									05 11	06 01	06 19	07 00	07 59	
—	—		d	23p32	00 34	00 45	00 55									05 11	06 01	06 20	07 00	08 00	
—	5¼	Narberth	d														06x10		07x09		
—	10¾	Kilgetty	d														06x19		07x19		
—	11½	Saundersfoot	d														06x20		07x21		
—	15¾	**Tenby**	a														06 27		07 28		
—	—		d														06 30		07 42		
—	17	Penally	d														06x33		07x45		
—	20¼	Manorbier	d														06 39		07 52		
—	23¾	Lamphey	d														06x46		07x59		
—	25¼	Pembroke	d														06 49		08 02		
—	27¼	**Pembroke Dock**	a														07 04		08 17		
98¾	—	Clunderwen	d	23b38												05x18		06x26		08x06	
105¼	0	Clarbeston Road	d	23b45	00x46	00x59	01x07									05x26		06x33		08x13	
—	5¼	Haverfordwest	d	23p54												05e40		06 41		08 22	
—	10	Johnston	d	00x01												05x47		06x49		08x29	
—	14	**Milford Haven**	a	00 11												05 57		07 04		08 44	
121	—	**Fishguard Harbour**	a		01 15	01 26	01 35														
—	—	⛴	d											02 45							
—	—	Rosslare Harbour ⛴	a											06 15							

For general notes see front of timetable
For details of catering facilities see Directory of Train Operators

A From 15 September
B Until 8 September
C Ship service

b Previous night.
Stops on request, passengers wishing to alight must inform the guard and those wishing to join must give a hand signal to the driver
c Stops, on request, to set down only
e Arr. 0534

Table 128

Cardiff → Maesteg, Swansea and West Wales

Route Diagram - see first page of Table 127

		AW	AW	AW	AW	GW	AW	AW	GW	AW	AW	AW	AW	GW	AW	AW	GW	AW	AW	AW	AW
			◇		◇	**1** ◇	◇		**1** ◇		◇			**1** ◇	◇		**1** ◇	◇		◇	
				A	B		C				B		A	D		A					
		🛒			🛒	🍴			🍴	🛒	🛒			⊠	🛒		🍴	🛒	🛒	🛒	
London Paddington 15	⊖ d					05 27			06 45					07 45			08 45				
Reading 7	d					05 57			07 11					08 11			09 11				
Manchester Piccadilly 10	🚌 d														06 38					07 28	
Gloucester 7	d			05 50									07 58			08 58					
Bristol Parkway 7	d								08 07					09 07			10 07				
Newport (South Wales)	d			06 44	07 35	07 45			08 31		08 37		08 51	09 31	09 37	09 52	10 32			10 38	
Cardiff Queen Street 3	d																				
Cardiff Central 7	d		06 52	07 04	07 58	08 01	08 09	08 21	08 48		09 04	09 14	09 21	09 49	10 04	10 21	10 48	10 55		11 04	11 14
Pontyclun	d			07 16				08 33					09 33			10 33					
Llanharan	d			07 21				08 38					09 38			10 38					
Pencoed	d			07 25				08 42					09 42			10 42					
Bridgend	d		07 12	07 32	08 17	08 22	08 29	08 49	09 09		09 23	09 34	09 49	10 09	10 23	10 49	11 09			11 23	11 34
Wildmill	d			07 35				08 52					09 52			10 52					
Sarn	d			07 38				08 55					09 55			10 55					
Tondu	d			07 41				08 58					09 58			10 58					
Garth (Mid Glamorgan)	d			07 51				09 08					10 08			11 08					
Maesteg (Ewenny Road)	d			07 53				09 10					10 10			11 10					
Maesteg	a			07 59				09 15					10 15			11 15					
Pyle	d		07 19				08 37					09 42									11 42
Port Talbot Parkway	d		07 28		08 30	08 35	08 45		09 22		09 36	09 50		10 22	10 36		11 22			11 36	11 50
Baglan	d		07 31				08 49					09 54									11 54
Briton Ferry	d		07 35				08 52					09 57									11 57
Neath	d		07 39		08 37	08 43	08 56		09 29		09 43	10 01		10 29	10 43		11 29			11 43	12 01
Skewen	d		07 42				09 00					10 05									12 05
Llansamlet	d		07 46				09 04					10 09									12 09
Swansea 7	a		07 54		08 49	08 56	09 13		09 44		09 56	10 20		10 45	10 58		11 43			11 56	12 20
	d	07 50	08 05		09 00		09 15			09 50	10 05				11 05				11 50	12 05	
Gowerton	d	08x01			09x15					10x01									12x01		
Llanelli	a	08 08	08 23		09 19		09 31			10 08	10 23				11 20			11 58	12 08	12 20	
	d	08 08	08 23		09 19					10 08	10 24				11 21			11 58	12 08	12 21	
Pembrey & Burry Port	d	08 14	08 29		09 24					10 14	10 29				11 26				12 14	12 26	
Kidwelly	d	08x21								10x21									12x21		
Ferryside	d	08x27								10x27									12x27		
Carmarthen	a	08 40	08 51		09 47					10 40	10 51				11 46				12 40	12 51	
	d	08 56			09 52					10 56					11 52				12 56		
Whitland	a	09 12			10 13					11 12					12 13			12 33	13 12		
	d	09 12			10 14					11 12					12 14			12 34	13 12		
Narberth	d	09x21								11x21									13x21		
Kilgetty	d	09x30								11x30									13x30		
Saundersfoot	d	09x31								11x31									13x31		
Tenby	a	09 38								11 38									13 38		
	d	09 43								11 43									13 43		
Penally	d	09x46								11x46									13x46		
Manorbier	d	09 52								11 52									13 52		
Lamphey	d	09x59								11x59									13x59		
Pembroke	d	10 02								12 02									14 02		
Pembroke Dock	a	10 17								12 17									14 17		
Clunderwen	d				10x20										12x20						
Clarbeston Road	d				10x27										12x27						
Haverfordwest	d				10 35										12 35						
Johnston	d				10x43										12x43						
Milford Haven	a				10 58										12 58						
Fishguard Harbour	a																	13 15			
	⛴ d																				
Rosslare Harbour	⛴ a																				

For general notes see front of timetable
For details of catering facilities see Directory of Train Operators

A From Cheltenham Spa (Table 57)
B From Crewe (Table 131)
C To Shrewsbury (Table 129)
D **The St David**

Cardiff → Maesteg, Swansea and West Wales

Route Diagram - see first page of Table 127

		AW	GW 1 ◇ ⊠	AW ◇ ⌶	AW	AW ◇	GW 1 ◇ ⊠	AW ◇ ⌶	AW ⌶	AW	AW	AW	GW 1 ◇ ⊠	AW ◇ ⌶	AW	GW 1 ◇ ⊠	AW ⌶	AW ◇ ⌶	AW	AW
					A						A	B								A
London Paddington 15 ⊖	d		09 45				10 45						11 45			12 45				
Reading 7	d		10 11				11 11						12 11			13 11				
Manchester Piccadilly 10	d			08 34				09 34						10 34				11 34		
Gloucester 7	d				10 58						11 58									13 58
Bristol Parkway 7	d		11 07				12 07						13 07			14 07				
Newport (South Wales)	d		11 31	11 38	11 52		12 31	12 38			12 52		13 31	13 38		14 31		14 38		14 52
Cardiff Queen Street 3	d																			
Cardiff Central 7	d	11 21	11 48	12 04	12 21		12 48	13 04		13 14	13 21		13 48	14 04	14 21	14 48		15 04	15 14	15 21
Pontyclun	d	11 33			12 33						13 33				14 33					15 33
Llanharan	d	11 38			12 38						13 38				14 38					15 38
Pencoed	d	11 42			12 42						13 42				14 42					15 42
Bridgend	d	11 49	12 09	12 23	12 49		13 09	13 23		13 34	13 49		14 09	14 23	14 49	15 09		15 23	15 34	15 49
Wildmill	d	11 52			12 52						13 52				14 52					15 52
Sarn	d	11 55			12 55						13 55				14 55					15 55
Tondu	d	11 58			12 58						13 58				14 58					15 58
Garth (Mid Glamorgan)	d	12 08			13 08						14 08				15 08					16 08
Maesteg (Ewenny Road)	d	12 10			13 10						14 10				15 10					16 10
Maesteg	a	12 15			13 15						14 15				15 15					16 15
Pyle	d									13 42									15 42	
Port Talbot Parkway	d		12 22	12 36			13 22	13 36		13 50			14 22	14 36		15 22		15 36	15 50	
Baglan	d									13 54									15 54	
Briton Ferry	d									13 57									15 57	
Neath	d		12 29	12 43			13 29	13 43		14 01			14 29	14 43		15 29		15 43	16 01	
Skewen	d									14 05									16 05	
Llansamlet	d									14 09									16 09	
Swansea 7	a		12 45	12 56			13 45	13 56		14 20			14 45	14 56		15 43		15 56	16 20	
	d			13 05		13 16		14 00	14 05					15 05			15 50	16 05		
Gowerton	d								14x17								16x01			
Llanelli	a			13 20		13 32		14 15	14 24					15 23			16 08	16 20		
	d			13 21				14 16	14 24					15 24			16 08	16 21		
Pembrey & Burry Port	d			13 26				14 21	14 30					15 29			16 14	16 26		
Kidwelly	d								14x37								16x21			
Ferryside	d								14x43								16x27			
Carmarthen	a			13 46				14 47	14 56					15 49			16 40	16 51		
	d			13 52					14 59					15 52			16 56			
Whitland	a			14 06					15 15					16 15			17 12			
	d			14 07					15 15					16 16			17 12			
Narberth	d								15x24								17x21			
Kilgetty	d								15x33								17x30			
Saundersfoot	d								15x34								17x31			
Tenby	a								15 41								17 38			
	d								15 43								17 43			
Penally	d								15x46								17x46			
Manorbier	d								15 52								17 52			
Lamphey	d								15x59								17x59			
Pembroke	d								16 02								18 02			
Pembroke Dock	a								16 17								18 17			
Clunderwen	d			14x13										16x22						
Clarbeston Road	d			14x20										16x29						
Haverfordwest	d			14 28										16 37						
Johnston	d			14x36										16x45						
Milford Haven	a			14 51										17 00						
Fishguard Harbour	a																			
	⛴ d											14 30								
Rosslare Harbour	⛴ a											18 00								

For general notes see front of timetable
For details of catering facilities see Directory of Train Operators

A From Cheltenham Spa (Table 57)
B Ship service

Cardiff → Maesteg, Swansea and West Wales

Route Diagram - see first page of Table 127

		GW	AW	AW	GW	AW	AW	AW	AW	AW	GW	AW	AW	GW	GW	AW	AW	AW	GW	AW	GW
		1 ◇	R	A	1 ◇		R		◇		1 ◇	R	A	1 ◇	1 ◇	R		A	1 ◇		1 ◇
		🍴	🛒		🍴	🛒	🛒				🍴	🛒		🍴	🍴	🛒			🍴		🍴
London Paddington [15] ⊖	d	13 45			14 45						15 45			16 15	16 45				17 15		17 45
Reading [7]	d	14 11			15 11						16 11			16 41	17 11				17 41		18 11
Manchester Piccadilly [10]	d		12 34				13 34					14 34				15 34					
Gloucester [7]	d			14 58									16 58					17 58			
Bristol Parkway [7]	d	15 07			16 07						17 07			17 42	18 13				18 42		19 11
Newport (South Wales)	d	15 31	15 38	15 52	16 31		16 38				17 31	17 38	17 52	18 05	18 38	18 47		18 52	19 10		19 34
Cardiff Queen Street [3]	d																				
Cardiff Central [7]	d	15 48	16 04	16 21	16 48		17 04	17 21		17 38	17 48	18 04	18 21	18 28	18 53	19 04		19 12	19 24	19 37	19 50
Pontyclun	d			16 33				17 32					18 33					19 26			
Llanharan	d			16 38				17 38					18 38					19 31			
Pencoed	d			16 42				17 41					18 42					19 35			
Bridgend	d	16 09	16 23	16 49	17 09		17 25	17 48		17 58	18 09	18 26	18 49	18 53	19 15	19 23		19 45	19 49	19 56	20 12
Wildmill	d			16 52				17 51					18 52					19 48			
Sarn	d			16 55				17 54					18 55					19 51			
Tondu	d			16 58				17 57					18 58					19 54			
Garth (Mid Glamorgan)	d			17 08				18 07					19 08					20 04			
Maesteg (Ewenny Road)	d			17 10				18 09					19 10					20 06			
Maesteg	a			17 15				18 14					19 15					20 11			
Pyle	d						17 31			18 06										20 04	
Port Talbot Parkway	d	16 22	16 36		17 22		17 39			18 14	18 22	18 42		19 06	19 28	19 35			20 02	20 12	20 25
Baglan	d						17 41			18 18										20 16	
Briton Ferry	d						17 46			18 21										20 19	
Neath	d	16 29	16 43		17 29		17 50			18 25	18 29	18 49		19 13	19 35	19 42			20 09	20 23	20 32 →
Skewen	d						17 53			18 29										20 27	
Llansamlet	d						17 57			18 33										20 31	
Swansea [7]	a	16 43	16 56		17 43		18 05			18 44	18 46	19 01		19 34	19 48	19 56			20 27	20 42	
	d		17 05			17 50	18 09		18 21			19 05				20 00	20 05				
Gowerton	d		17x16			18x01	18x19										20x17				
Llanelli	a		17 23			18 08	18 26		18 37			19 20				20 15	20 24				
	d		17 23			18 08	18 26					19 21				20 16	20 24				
Pembrey & Burry Port	d		17 29			18 14	18 32					19 26				20 21	20 30				
Kidwelly	d		17x35			18x21	18x38										20x37				
Ferryside	d		17x40			18x27	18x43										20x43				
Carmarthen	a		17 52			18 40	19 00					19 46				20 46	20 56				
	d		17 55			19 05						19 52					20 59				
Whitland	a		18 13			19 21						20 06					21 15				
	d		18 14			19 21						20 07					21 15				
Narberth	d					19x30											21x24				
Kilgetty	d					19x39											21x34				
Saundersfoot	d					19x40											21x36				
Tenby	a					19 47											21 43				
	d					19 52											21 44				
Penally	d					19x55											21x47				
Manorbier	d					20 02											21 54				
Lamphey	d					20x09											22x01				
Pembroke	d					20 12											22 04				
Pembroke Dock	a					20 22											22 17				
Clunderwen	d		18x20									20x13									
Clarbeston Road	d		18x27									20x20									
Haverfordwest	d		18 35									20 28									
Johnston	d		18x43									20x36									
Milford Haven	a		18 58									20 51									
Fishguard Harbour	a																				
⛴	d																				
Rosslare Harbour ⛴	a																				

For general notes see front of timetable
For details of catering facilities see Directory of Train Operators

A From Cheltenham Spa (Table 57)

Cardiff → Maesteg, Swansea and West Wales

Route Diagram - see first page of Table 127

		AW	AW	GW	GW	AW	GW	AW	AW	GW	AW	AW	AW	GW	AW	AW	AW	GW	GW	GW
																			FO	FX
		R		1 ◇	1 ◇		1 ◇			1 ◇		◇		1 ◇		◇	◇	1 ◇	1 ◇	1 ◇
			A		B	A			A		A								C	
		ㅈ		ᗡP	ᗡP		ᗡP			ᗡP		ㅈ		ᗡP				ᗡP	ᗡP	ᗡP
London Paddington 15 ⊖	d				18 15		18 45			19 15				20 15				21 15	22 45	22 45
Reading 7	d				18 41		19 11			19 41				20 41				21 41	23 11	23 18
Manchester Piccadilly 10	d	16 34										18 34								
Gloucester 7	d		18 58						19 58											
Bristol Parkway 7	d				19 42		20 07			20 42				21 42				22 46	00 17	00 22
Newport (South Wales)	d	19 40	19 51		20 05		20 31		20 52	21 05		21 38		22 05				23 16	00 48	00 52
Cardiff Queen Street 3	d																			
Cardiff Central 7	d	20 00	20 15		20 22		20 48	21 09	21 21	21 25		22 09	22 25	22 35			23 15	23 40	01 05	01 12
Pontyclun	d		20 39			←			21 42		←		22 37		←		23 29			
Llanharan	d		20 44 →			20 44			21 47 →		21 47		22 42 →		22 42		23 34			
Pencoed	d					20 48					21 51				22 46		23 39			
Bridgend	d	20 19			20 42	20 55	21 09	21 28		21 45	21 58	22 28		22 55	23 02		23 45	23 59	01 28	01 36
Wildmill	d					20 58					22 01				23 05					
Sarn	d					21 01					22 04				23 08					
Tondu	d					21 04					22 07				23 11					
Garth (Mid Glamorgan)	d					21 14					22 17				23 21					
Maesteg (Ewenny Road)	d					21 16					22 19				23 23					
Maesteg	a					21 20					22 23				23 29					
Pyle	d							21 35									23 53			
Port Talbot Parkway	d	20 35			20 57		21 22	21 43		21 58		22 41		23 08			00 01	00 11	01 41	01 49
Baglan	d																00 05			
Briton Ferry	d			←													00 08			
Neath	d			20 32	21 04		21 29	21 50		22 05		22 48		23 15			00 12	00 18	01 48	01 56
Skewen	d																00 16			
Llansamlet	d																00 20			
Swansea 7	a			20 46	21 21		21 42	22 03		22 20		23 00		23 31			00 28	00 33	02 10	02 10
	d			21 00				22 27				23 06				23 45	00 45			
Gowerton	d							22x37				23x21					00b56			
Llanelli	a	21 05		21 16				22 44				23 27				00 01	01s02			
	d	21 05		21 16				22 44				23 28				00 01				
Pembrey & Burry Port	d	21 11		21 23				22 50				23 33				00 07	01s08			
Kidwelly	d							22x56				23x39					01b14			
Ferryside	d							23x01				23x45					01b20			
Carmarthen	a	21 30		21 49				23 13				00 03				00 27	01 37			
	d	22 04						23 17								00 30				
Whitland	a	22 20						23 31								00 45				
	d	22 21						23 32								00 45				
Narberth	d																			
Kilgetty	d																			
Saundersfoot	d																			
Tenby	a																			
	d																			
Penally	d																			
Manorbier	d																			
Lamphey	d																			
Pembroke	d																			
Pembroke Dock	a																			
Clunderwen	d	22x27						23x38												
Clarbeston Road	d	22x34						23x45								00x59				
Haverfordwest	d	22 42						23 54												
Johnston	d	22x50						00x01												
Milford Haven	a	23 05						00 11												
Fishguard Harbour	a															01 26				
	⛴ d																			
Rosslare Harbour	⛴ a																			

For general notes see front of timetable
For details of catering facilities see Directory of Train Operators

A From Cheltenham Spa (Table 57)
B **The Red Dragon**
C ᗡP to Reading

b Stops, on request, to set down only

Saturdays

until 6 September

Cardiff → Maesteg, Swansea and West Wales

Route Diagram - see first page of Table 127

		AW	AW ◇	AW	AW ◇	GW 1 ◇ ⊡	GW 1 ◇	AW A	AW ◇	AW	AW	AW	AW ⊤	AW ◇ ⊤	AW	GW 1 ◇ ⊡	AW ⊤	AW ◇	AW	GW 1 ⊡	GW 1 ◇ B ⊡	AW	AW ◇ C ⊤
London Paddington 15 ⊖	d					21p15	22p45																
Reading 7	d					21p41	23p11																
Manchester Piccadilly 10 🚌	d																						
Gloucester 7	d																		05 50				
Bristol Parkway 7	d					22p46	00 17														07 13		
Newport (South Wales)	d					23p16	00 48												06 44		07 36		07 40
Cardiff Queen Street 3	d																						
Cardiff Central 7	d	21p09			23p15	23p40	01 05							05 40	05 51			06 52	07 04		07 53		08 04
Pontyclun	d				23p29									05 52	06 03				07 16				
Llanharan	d				23p34									05 57	06 08				07 21				
Pencoed	d				23p39									06 02	06 12				07 25				
Bridgend	d	21p28			23p45	23p59	01 28							06 08	06 20			07 12	07 32		08 13		08 23
Wildmill	d														06 22				07 35				
Sarn	d														06 25				07 38				
Tondu	d														06 29				07 41				
Garth (Mid Glamorgan)	d														06 38				07 51				
Maesteg (Ewenny Road)	d														06 41				07 53				
Maesteg	a														06 46				07 59				
Pyle	d	21p35			23p53									06 16				07 20					
Port Talbot Parkway	d	21p43			00 01	00 11	01 41							06 24				07 28			08 26		08 36
Baglan	d				00 05									06 28				07 32					
Briton Ferry	d				00 08									06 31				07 35					
Neath	d	21p50			00 12	00 18	01 48							06 35				07 39			08 34		08 43
Skewen	d				00 16									06 39				07 43					
Llansamlet	d				00 20									06 43				07 47					
Swansea 7	a	22p03			00 28	00 33	02 10							06 51				07 55			08 48		08 55
	d	22p27	23p45	00 05	00 45				04 36				05 50	06 54		07 25	07 50	08 05		08 13			09 00
Gowerton	d	22b37		00x16	00c56								06x01				08x01						09x15
Llanelli	a	22p44	00 01	00 23	01s02				04 52				06 08	07 10		07 44	08 08	08 23		08 29			09 19
	d	22p44	00 01	00 23									06 08	07 11		07 45	08 08	08 23		08 34			09 19
Pembrey & Burry Port	d	22p50	00 07	00 29	01s08								06 14	07 17		07 52	08 14	08 29		08 41			09 24
Kidwelly	d	22b56		00x36	01c14								06x21	07x23			08x21						
Ferryside	d	23b01		00x41	01c20								06x27	07x29			08x27						
Carmarthen	a	23p13	00 27	00 59	01 37								06 40	07 42		08 13	08 45	08 51		09 08			09 47
	d	23p17	00 30							04 55	05 45	06 05	06 43	07 44		08 20						09 40	09 52
Whitland	a	23p31	00 45							05 11	06 01	06 19	07 00	07 59		08 37						09 56	10 13
	d	23p32	00 45							05 11	06 01	06 20	07 00	08 00		08 39						09 56	10 14
Narberth	d										06x10		07x09			08x48						10x05	
Kilgetty	d										06x19		07x19			08x57						10x14	
Saundersfoot	d										06x20		07x21			09x00						10x15	
Tenby	a										06 27		07 28			09 08						10 27	
	d										06 30		07 42			09 12							
Penally	d										06x33		07x45			09x16							
Manorbier	d										06 39		07 52			09 24							
Lamphey	d										06x46		07x59			09x33							
Pembroke	d										06 49		08 02			09 38							
Pembroke Dock	a										07 04		08 17			09 49							
Clunderwen	d	23b38								05x18		06x26		08x06									10x20
Clarbeston Road	d	23b45	00x59							05x26		06x33		08x13									10x27
Haverfordwest	d	23p54								05e40		06 41		08 22									10 35
Johnston	d	00x01								05x47		06x49		08x29									10x43
Milford Haven	a	00 11								05 57		07 04		08 44									10 58
Fishguard Harbour	a		01 26																				
⛴	d							02 45															
Rosslare Harbour ⛴	a							06 15															

For general notes see front of timetable
For details of catering facilities see Directory of Train Operators

A Ship service
B From Bristol Temple Meads (Table 132)
C From Crewe (Table 131)

b Previous night.
Stops on request, passengers wishing to alight must inform the guard and those wishing to join must give a hand signal to the driver
c Stops, on request, to set down only
e Arr. 0534

Table 128

Saturdays

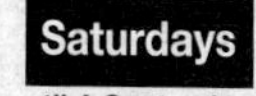

until 6 September

Cardiff → Maesteg, Swansea and West Wales

Route Diagram - see first page of Table 127

		AW	AW	AW	AW		AW	AW	GW	AW	AW	GW	AW	GW		AW	AW	AW	AW	GW	AW	AW	AW		AW
		◇			◇				1 ◇	◇		1 ◇	◇	1 ◇		◇				1 ◇	◇		◇		
		A			B			C			C	D		D								C			
				🛒	🛒				🍴	🛒		🍴	🛒	🍴		🛒			🛒	🍴	🛒				🛒
London Paddington 15 ⊖	d								07 45			08 45								09 45					
Reading 7	d								08 11			09 11								10 11					
Manchester Piccadilly 10 ⛴	d									06 38						07 28					08 34				
Gloucester 7	d							07 58			08 58											10 58			
Bristol Parkway 7	d								09 07			10 07								11 07					
Newport (South Wales)	d				08 37			08 52	09 32	09 36	09 52	10 31				10 36				11 32	11 38	11 52			
Cardiff Queen Street 3	d																								
Cardiff Central 7	d	08 09	08 21		09 04		09 14	09 21	09 49	10 04	10 21	10 49	10 55			11 04	11 14	11 21		11 48	12 04	12 21			
Pontyclun	d		08 33					09 33			10 33							11 33				12 33			
Llanharan	d		08 38					09 38			10 38							11 38				12 38			
Pencoed	d		08 42					09 42			10 42							11 42				12 42			
Bridgend	d	08 29	08 49		09 23		09 34	09 49	10 09	10 23	10 49	11 09				11 23	11 34	11 49		12 09	12 23	12 49			
Wildmill	d		08 52					09 52			10 52							11 52				12 52			
Sarn	d		08 55					09 55			10 55							11 55				12 55			
Tondu	d		08 58					09 58			10 58							11 58				12 58			
Garth (Mid Glamorgan)	d		09 08					10 08			11 08							12 08				13 08			
Maesteg (Ewenny Road)	d		09 10					10 10			11 10							12 10				13 10			
Maesteg	a		09 15					10 15			11 15							12 15				13 15			
Pyle	d	08 37					09 42							←			11 42								
Port Talbot Parkway	d	08 45			09 36		09 50		10 22	10 36		11 22 →		11 22		11 36	11 50			12 22	12 36				
Baglan	d	08 49					09 54										11 54								
Briton Ferry	d	08 52					09 57										11 57								
Neath	d	08 56			09 43		10 01		10 30	10 43				11 29		11 43	12 01			12 30	12 43				
Skewen	d	09 00					10 05										12 05								
Llansamlet	d	09 04					10 09										12 09								
Swansea 7	a	09 13			09 56		10 20		10 43	11 01				11 42		11 56	12 20			12 43	12 56				
	d	09 15		09 50	10 05					11 05				11 51		12 05			12 35		13 05		13 16		13 35
Gowerton	d			10x01															12x52						13x46
Llanelli	a	09 31		10 08	10 23					11 21			11 58	12 07		12 20			12 59		13 20		13 32		13 53
	d			10 08	10 24					11 21			11 58	12 09		12 21			12 59		13 21				13 53
Pembrey & Burry Port	d			10 14	10 29					11 27				12 15		12 26			13 05		13 26				13 59
Kidwelly	d			10x21															13x12						14x06
Ferryside	d			10x27															13x18						14x12
Carmarthen	a			10 40	10 51					11 47				12 39		12 51			13 31		13 46				14 27
	d			10 56						11 52				12 45							13 52				14 47
Whitland	a			11 14						12 13			12 33	13 03							14 06				15 03
	d			11 14						12 14			12 34	13 04							14 07				15 03
Narberth	d			11x23																					15x12
Kilgetty	d			11x32																					15x21
Saundersfoot	d			11x33										13 24											15x22
Tenby	a			11 40										13 34											15 31
	d			11 43										13 40											15 33
Penally	d			11x46																					15x36
Manorbier	d			11 52										13 50											15 42
Lamphey	d			11x59																					15x49
Pembroke	d			12 02										14 02											15 52
Pembroke Dock	a			12 17										14 13											16 07
Clunderwen	d									12x20											14x13				
Clarbeston Road	d									12x27											14x20				
Haverfordwest	d									12 36											14 28				
Johnston	d									12x43											14x36				
Milford Haven	a									12 58											14 51				
Fishguard Harbour	a												13 15												
⛴	d																								
Rosslare Harbour ⛴	a																								

For general notes see front of timetable
For details of catering facilities see Directory of Train Operators

A To Shrewsbury (Table 129)
B From Crewe (Table 131)
C From Cheltenham Spa (Table 57)
D **Pembroke Coast Express**

Saturdays
until 6 September

Cardiff → Maesteg, Swansea and West Wales

Route Diagram - see first page of Table 127

		GW	AW	AW	AW	AW	GW	AW	AW		GW	AW	AW	AW	AW	GW	AW	AW		GW	AW	AW	AW	AW	AW
																	R					R			
		1 ◇	◇				1 ◇	◇			1 ◇	◇				1 ◇				1 ◇				◇	
					A	B									A			A							
		🍴	🛒				🍴	🛒			🍴	🛒	🛒			🍴	🛒			🍴		🛒			
London Paddington 15 ⊖	d	10 45					11 45				12 45					13 45				14 45					
Reading 7	d	11 11					12 11				13 11					14 11				15 11					
Manchester Piccadilly 10	d		09 34					10 34				11 34					12 34					13 34			
Gloucester 7	d				11 58										13 58			14 58							
Bristol Parkway 7	d	12 07					13 07				14 07					15 07				16 07					
Newport (South Wales)	d	12 31	12 38		12 52		13 31	13 38			14 32	14 38			14 52	15 32	15 38	15 52		16 32		16 38			
Cardiff Queen Street 3	d																								
Cardiff Central 7	d	12 48	13 04	13 14	13 21		13 47	14 04	14 21		14 49	15 04		15 14	15 21	15 48	16 04	16 21		16 49		17 04	17 21		17 38
Pontyclun	d				13 33				14 33						15 33			16 33					17 33		
Llanharan	d				13 38				14 38						15 38			16 38					17 38		
Pencoed	d				13 42				14 42						15 42			16 42					17 42		
Bridgend	d	13 09	13 23	13 34	13 49		14 08	14 23	14 49		15 10	15 23		15 34	15 49	16 09	16 23	16 49		17 10		17 25	17 49		17 58
Wildmill	d				13 52				14 52						15 52			16 52					17 52		
Sarn	d				13 55				14 55						15 55			16 55					17 55		
Tondu	d				13 58				14 58						15 58			16 58					17 58		
Garth (Mid Glamorgan)	d				14 08				15 08						16 08			17 08					18 08		
Maesteg (Ewenny Road)	d				14 10				15 10						16 10			17 10					18 10		
Maesteg	a				14 15				15 15						16 15			17 15					18 15		
Pyle	d			13 42										15 42								17 32			18 06
Port Talbot Parkway	d	13 22	13 36	13 50			14 21	14 36			15 23	15 36		15 50		16 22	16 36			17 23		17 40			18 14
Baglan	d			13 54										15 54								17 43			18 18
Briton Ferry	d			13 57										15 57								17 47			18 21
Neath	d	13 29	13 43	14 01			14 29	14 43			15 30	15 43		16 01		16 30	16 43			17 30		17 51			18 25
Skewen	d			14 05										16 05								17 55			18 29
Llansamlet	d			14 09										16 09								17 59			18 33
Swansea 7	a	13 42	13 56	14 20			14 42	14 56			15 43	15 56		16 20		16 43	16 56			17 43		18 06			18 44
	d		14 00					15 05				16 00	16 05				17 05				17 50	18 09		18 21	
Gowerton	d												16x17				17x20				18x01	18x19			
Llanelli	a		14 15					15 23				16 15	16 24				17 27				18 08	18 26		18 37	
	d		14 16					15 24				16 16	16 24				17 27				18 08	18 26			
Pembrey & Burry Port	d		14 21					15 29				16 21	16 30				17 33				18 14	18 32			
Kidwelly	d												16x37				17x39				18x21	18x38			
Ferryside	d												16x45				17x44				18x27	18x43			
Carmarthen	a		14 47					15 49				16 42	16 58				17 56				18 40	19 00			
	d							15 52					17 05				17 59				19 05				
Whitland	a							16 15					17 21				18 13				19 21				
	d							16 16					17 34				18 14				19 21				
Narberth	d												17x42								19x30				
Kilgetty	d												17x51								19x39				
Saundersfoot	d												17x53								19x40				
Tenby	a												18 00								19 47				
	d												18 01								19 52				
Penally	d												18x04								19x55				
Manorbier	d												18 10								20 02				
Lamphey	d												18x17								20x09				
Pembroke	d												18 20								20 12				
Pembroke Dock	a												18 35								20 22				
Clunderwen	d							16x22									18x20								
Clarbeston Road	d							16x29									18x27								
Haverfordwest	d							16 37									18 35								
Johnston	d							16x45									18x43								
Milford Haven	a							17 00									18 58								
Fishguard Harbour	a																								
	⛴ d					14 30																			
Rosslare Harbour	⛴ a					18 00																			

For general notes see front of timetable
For details of catering facilities see Directory of Train Operators

A From Cheltenham Spa (Table 57)
B Ship service

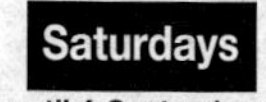

Saturdays

until 6 September

Cardiff → Maesteg, Swansea and West Wales

Route Diagram - see first page of Table 127

Station		GW 1 ◇	AW R	AW A	GW 1 ◇		AW R	AW	AW A	AW	GW 1 ◇	AW R	GW 1 ◇	AW A		GW 1 ◇	AW R	AW A	GW 1 ◇	AW ◇	AW ◇	AW ◇	GW 1 ◇		
London Paddington 15 ⊖	d	15 45			16 45						17 45					18 45			19 45				20 45		
Reading 7	d	16 11			17 11						18 11					19 11			20 11				21 11		
Manchester Piccadilly 10	d		14 34				15 34					16 34					17 34			18 34					
Gloucester 7	d			16 58					17 58					18 58				19 58							
Bristol Parkway 7	d	17 07			18 07						19 12					20 07			21 06				22 14		
Newport (South Wales)	d	17 31	17 38	17 52	18 31		18 40		18 52		19 35	19 43		19 52		20 32	20 47	20 52	21 31	21 37			22 46		
Cardiff Queen Street 3	d																								
Cardiff Central 7	d	17 47	18 02	18 21	18 48		19 04		19 21	19 38	19 53	20 00		20 21		20 48	21 07	21 21	21 48	22 09		22 41	23 06		
Pontyclun	d			18 33					19 33					20 33				21 40				22 55			
Llanharan	d			18 38					19 38					20 38				21 45				23 00			
Pencoed	d			18 42					19 42					20 42				21 49				23 05			
Bridgend	d	18 09	18 21	18 49	19 09		19 23		19 49	19 58	20 13	20 19		20 49		21 09	21 28	21 56	22 09	22 28		23 11	23 27		
Wildmill	d			18 52					19 52					20 52				21 59							
Sarn	d			18 55					19 55					20 55				22 02							
Tondu	d			18 58					19 58					20 58				22 05							
Garth (Mid Glamorgan)	d			19 08					20 08					21 08				22 15							
Maesteg (Ewenny Road)	d			19 10					20 10					21 10				22 17							
Maesteg	a			19 15					20 15					21 15				22 21							
Pyle	d									20 06							21 35					23 19			
Port Talbot Parkway	d	18 24	18 34		19 22		19 36			20 14	20 26	20 32				21 22	21 43		22 22	22 41		23 26	23 40		
Baglan	d									20 18												23 30			
Briton Ferry	d									20 21			←									23 33			
Neath	d	18 32	18 41		19 29		19 43			20 25	20 34		20 34			21 30	21 50		22 29	22 48		23 37	23 48		
Skewen	d									20 29	→											23 41			
Llansamlet	d									20 33												23 45			
Swansea 7	a	18 46	18 56		19 42		19 56			20 44			20 48			21 47	22 03		22 46	23 00		23 54	00 01		
	d		19 05				20 00	20 05					21 00				22 25			23 06	23 45	00 08			
Gowerton	d							20x17									22x35			23x21		00b19			
Llanelli	a		19 20				20 15	20 24				21 04	21 25				22 42			23 27	00 01	00s25			
	d		19 21				20 16	20 24				21 04	21 25				22 42			23 28	00 01				
Pembrey & Burry Port	d		19 26				20 21	20 30				21 10	21 32				22 48			23 33	00 07	00s31			
Kidwelly	d							20x37									22x54			23x39		00b38			
Ferryside	d							20x43									22x59			23x45		00b44			
Carmarthen	a		19 46				20 46	20 56				21 29	21 55				23 11			00 03	00 27	01 01			
	d		19 52					20 59				22 04					23 17				00 30				
Whitland	a		20 06					21 15				22 21					23 31				00 45				
	d		20 07					21 15				22 21					23 32				00 45				
Narberth	d							21x24																	
Kilgetty	d							21x34																	
Saundersfoot	d							21x36																	
Tenby	a							21 43																	
	d							21 44																	
Penally	d							21x47																	
Manorbier	d							21 54																	
Lamphey	d							22x01																	
Pembroke	d							22 04																	
Pembroke Dock	a							22 19																	
Clunderwen	d		20x13									22x27					23x38								
Clarbeston Road	d		20x20									22x34					23x45				00x59				
Haverfordwest	d		20 28									22 43					23a58								
Johnston	d		20x36									22x50													
Milford Haven	a		20 51									23 05													
Fishguard Harbour	a																				01 26				
	⛴ d																								
Rosslare Harbour	⛴ a																								

For general notes see front of timetable
For details of catering facilities see Directory of Train Operators

A From Cheltenham Spa (Table 57)
b Stops, on request, to set down only

Table 128

Saturdays

from 13 September

Cardiff → Maesteg, Swansea and West Wales

Route Diagram - see first page of Table 127

		AW	AW	AW	AW	GW	GW	AW		AW	AW	AW	AW	AW	AW	AW		AW	AW	AW	GW	GW	AW	AW	AW
			◇		◇	1 ◇	1 ◇			◇					◇				◇		1	1 ◇	◇	◇	
								A														B	C	D	
						🍴								🛒	🛒			🛒			🍴	🍴	🛒		
London Paddington 15	⊖ d					21p15	22p45																		
Reading 7	d					21p41	23p11																		
Manchester Piccadilly 10	🚌 d																								
Gloucester 7	d																			05 50					
Bristol Parkway 7	d					22p46	00 17															07 13			
Newport (South Wales)	d					23p16	00 48													06 44		07 36	07 40		
Cardiff Queen Street 3	d																								
Cardiff Central 7	d	21p09			23p15	23p40	01 05								05 40	05 51			06 52	07 04		07 53	08 04	08 09	08 21
Pontyclun	d				23p29										05 52	06 03				07 16					08 33
Llanharan	d				23p34										05 57	06 08				07 21					08 38
Pencoed	d				23p39										06 02	06 12				07 25					08 42
Bridgend	d	21p28			23p45	23p59	01 28								06 08	06 20			07 12	07 32		08 13	08 23	08 29	08 49
Wildmill	d															06 22				07 35					08 52
Sarn	d															06 25				07 38					08 55
Tondu	d															06 29				07 41					08 58
Garth (Mid Glamorgan)	d															06 38				07 51					09 08
Maesteg (Ewenny Road)	d															06 41				07 53					09 10
Maesteg	a															06 46				07 59					09 15
Pyle	d	21p35			23p53										06 16				07 20					08 37	
Port Talbot Parkway	d	21p43			00 01	00 11	01 41								06 24				07 28			08 26	08 36	08 45	
Baglan	d				00 05										06 28				07 32					08 49	
Briton Ferry	d				00 08										06 31				07 35					08 52	
Neath	d	21p50			00 12	00 18	01 48								06 35				07 39			08 34	08 43	08 56	
Skewen	d				00 16										06 39				07 43					09 00	
Llansamlet	d				00 20										06 43				07 47					09 04	
Swansea 7	a	22p03			00 28	00 33	02 10								06 51				07 55			08 48	08 55	09 13	
	d	22p27	23p45	00 05	00 45					04 36				05 50	06 54			07 50	08 05		08 13		09 00	09 15	
Gowerton	d	22b37		00x16	00c56									06x01				08x01					09x15		
Llanelli	a	22p44	00 01	00 23	01s02					04 52				06 08	07 10			08 08	08 23		08 29		09 19	09 31	
	d	22p44	00 01	00 23										06 08	07 11			08 08	08 23		08 34		09 19		
Pembrey & Burry Port	d	22p50	00 07	00 29	01s08									06 14	07 17			08 14	08 29		08 41		09 24		
Kidwelly	d	22b56		00x36	01c14									06x21	07x23			08x21							
Ferryside	d	23b01		00x41	01c20									06x27	07x29			08x27							
Carmarthen	a	23p13	00 27	00 59	01 37									06 40	07 42			08 40	08 51		09 08		09 47		
	d	23p17	00 30								04 55	05 45	06 05	06 43	07 44			08 56					09 52		
Whitland	a	23p31	00 45								05 11	06 01	06 19	07 00	07 59			09 12					10 13		
	d	23p32	00 45								05 11	06 01	06 20	07 00	08 00			09 12					10 14		
Narberth	d											06x10		07x09				09x21							
Kilgetty	d											06x19		07x19				09x30							
Saundersfoot	d											06x20		07x21				09x31							
Tenby	a											06 27		07 28				09 38							
	d											06 30		07 42				09 43							
Penally	d											06x33		07x45				09x46							
Manorbier	d											06 39		07 52				09 52							
Lamphey	d											06x46		07x59				09x59							
Pembroke	d											06 49		08 02				10 02							
Pembroke Dock	a											07 04		08 17				10 17							
Clunderwen	d	23b38									05x18		06x26		08x06								10x20		
Clarbeston Road	d	23b45	00x59								05x26		06x33		08x13								10x27		
Haverfordwest	d	23p54									05e40		06 41		08 22								10 35		
Johnston	d	00x01									05x47		06x49		08x29								10x43		
Milford Haven	a	00 11									05 57		07 04		08 44								10 58		
Fishguard Harbour	a		01 26																						
	⛴ d							02 45																	
Rosslare Harbour	⛴ a							06 15																	

For general notes see front of timetable
For details of catering facilities see Directory of Train Operators

A Ship service

B From Bristol Temple Meads (Table 132)

C From Crewe (Table 131)

D To Shrewsbury (Table 129)

b Previous night. Stops on request, passengers wishing to alight must inform the guard and those wishing to join must give a hand signal to the driver

c Stops, on request, to set down only

e Arr. 0534

Saturdays

from 13 September

Cardiff → Maesteg, Swansea and West Wales

Route Diagram - see first page of Table 127

		AW		AW	AW	AW	GW	AW	AW	GW		AW	AW	AW	AW	AW	GW	AW		AW	AW	GW	AW	AW	AW
				◇			1 ◇	◇		1 ◇		◇		◇			1 ◇	◇			◇	1 ◇	◇		
				A		B			B											B					
		🛒		🛒			🍴	🛒		🍴		🛒	🛒	🛒			🍴	🛒				🍴	🛒	🛒	
London Paddington 15 ⊖	d						07 45			08 45							09 45					10 45			
Reading 7	d						08 11			09 11							10 11					11 11			
Manchester Piccadilly 10 ⛴	d							06 38						07 28				08 34					09 34		
Gloucester 7	d					07 58			08 58											10 58					
Bristol Parkway 7	d						09 07			10 07							11 07					12 07			
Newport (South Wales)	d			08 37		08 52	09 32	09 36	09 52	10 32				10 36			11 32	11 38		11 52		12 31	12 38		
Cardiff Queen Street 3	d																								
Cardiff Central 7	d			09 04	09 14	09 21	09 49	10 04	10 21	10 49		10 55		11 04	11 14	11 21	11 48	12 04		12 21		12 48	13 04		13 14
Pontyclun	d					09 33			10 33							11 33				12 33					
Llanharan	d					09 38			10 38							11 38				12 38					
Pencoed	d					09 42			10 42							11 42				12 42					
Bridgend	d			09 23	09 34	09 49	10 09	10 23	10 49	11 09				11 23	11 34	11 49	12 09	12 23		12 49		13 09	13 23		13 34
Wildmill	d					09 52			10 52							11 52				12 52					
Sarn	d					09 55			10 55							11 55				12 55					
Tondu	d					09 58			10 58							11 58				12 58					
Garth (Mid Glamorgan)	d					10 08			11 08							12 08				13 08					
Maesteg (Ewenny Road)	d					10 10			11 10							12 10				13 10					
Maesteg	a					10 15			11 15							12 15				13 15					
Pyle	d				09 42										11 42										13 42
Port Talbot Parkway	d			09 36	09 50		10 22	10 36		11 22				11 36	11 50		12 22	12 36				13 22	13 36		13 50
Baglan	d				09 54										11 54										13 54
Briton Ferry	d				09 57										11 57										13 57
Neath	d			09 43	10 01		10 30	10 43		11 30				11 43	12 01		12 30	12 43				13 29	13 43		14 01
Skewen	d				10 05										12 05										14 05
Llansamlet	d				10 09										12 09										14 09
Swansea 7	a			09 56	10 20		10 43	11 01		11 43				11 56	12 20		12 43	12 56				13 42	13 56		14 20
	d	09 50		10 05				11 05					11 50	12 05				13 05			13 16		14 00	14 05	
Gowerton	d	10x01											12x01											14x17	
Llanelli	a	10 08		10 23				11 21				11 58	12 08	12 20				13 20			13 32		14 15	14 24	
	d	10 08		10 24				11 21				11 58	12 08	12 21				13 21					14 16	14 24	
Pembrey & Burry Port	d	10 14		10 29				11 27					12 14	12 26				13 26					14 21	14 30	
Kidwelly	d	10x21											12x21											14x37	
Ferryside	d	10x27											12x27											14x43	
Carmarthen	a	10 40		10 51				11 47					12 40	12 51				13 46					14 47	14 56	
	d	10 56						11 52					12 56					13 52						14 59	
Whitland	a	11 12						12 13				12 33	13 12					14 06						15 15	
	d	11 12						12 14				12 34	13 12					14 07						15 15	
Narberth	d	11x21											13x21											15x24	
Kilgetty	d	11x30											13x30											15x33	
Saundersfoot	d	11x31											13x31											15x34	
Tenby	a	11 38											13 38											15 41	
	d	11 43											13 43											15 43	
Penally	d	11x46											13x46											15x46	
Manorbier	d	11 52											13 52											15 52	
Lamphey	d	11x59											13x59											15x59	
Pembroke	d	12 02											14 02											16 02	
Pembroke Dock	a	12 17											14 17											16 17	
Clunderwen	d							12x20										14x13							
Clarbeston Road	d							12x27										14x20							
Haverfordwest	d							12 36										14 28							
Johnston	d							12x43										14x36							
Milford Haven	a							12 58										14 51							
Fishguard Harbour	a											13 15													
⛴	d																								
Rosslare Harbour ⛴	a																								

For general notes see front of timetable
For details of catering facilities see
Directory of Train Operators

A From Crewe (Table 131)
B From Cheltenham Spa (Table 57)

Table 128

Saturdays

from 13 September

Cardiff → Maesteg, Swansea and West Wales

Route Diagram - see first page of Table 127

		AW	AW	GW		AW	AW	GW	AW	AW	AW	AW		GW	AW	AW	GW	AW	AW	AW		AW	AW	GW	AW
															R				R						R
				1 ◇		◇		1 ◇		◇				1 ◇			1 ◇					◇		1 ◇	
		A	B									A				A									
				🍽		🛒		🍽	🛒	🛒				🍽	🛒		🍽		🛒					🍽	🛒
London Paddington 15 ⊖	d			11 45				12 45						13 45			14 45							15 45	
Reading 7	d			12 11				13 11						14 11			15 11							16 11	
Manchester Piccadilly 10 🚌	d					10 34				11 34					12 34				13 34						14 34
Gloucester 7	d	11 58										13 58				14 58									
Bristol Parkway 7	d			13 07				14 07						15 07			16 07							17 07	
Newport (South Wales)	d	12 52		13 31		13 38		14 32		14 38		14 52		15 32	15 38	15 52	16 32		16 38					17 31	17 38
Cardiff Queen Street 3	d																								
Cardiff Central 7	d	13 21		13 47		14 04	14 21	14 49		15 04	15 14	15 21		15 48	16 04	16 21	16 49		17 04	17 21			17 38	17 47	18 02
Pontyclun	d	13 33					14 33					15 33				16 33				17 33					
Llanharan	d	13 38					14 38					15 38				16 38				17 38					
Pencoed	d	13 42					14 42					15 42				16 42				17 42					
Bridgend	d	13 49		14 08		14 23	14 49	15 10		15 23	15 34	15 49		16 09	16 23	16 49	17 10		17 25	17 49			17 58	18 09	18 21
Wildmill	d	13 52					14 52					15 52				16 52				17 52					
Sarn	d	13 55					14 55					15 55				16 55				17 55					
Tondu	d	13 58					14 58					15 58				16 58				17 58					
Garth (Mid Glamorgan)	d	14 08					15 08					16 08				17 08				18 08					
Maesteg (Ewenny Road)	d	14 10					15 10					16 10				17 10				18 10					
Maesteg	a	14 15					15 15					16 15				17 15				18 15					
Pyle	d										15 42								17 32				18 06		
Port Talbot Parkway	d			14 21		14 36		15 23		15 36	15 50			16 22	16 36		17 23		17 40				18 14	18 24	18 34
Baglan	d										15 54								17 43				18 18		
Briton Ferry	d										15 57								17 47				18 21		
Neath	d			14 29		14 43		15 30		15 43	16 01			16 30	16 43		17 30		17 51				18 25	18 32	18 41
Skewen	d										16 05								17 55				18 29		
Llansamlet	d										16 09								17 59				18 33		
Swansea 7	a			14 42		14 56		15 43		15 56	16 20			16 43	16 56		17 43		18 06				18 44	18 46	18 56
	d					15 05			15 50	16 05					17 05			17 50	18 09			18 21			19 05
Gowerton	d								16x01						17x20			18x01	18x19						
Llanelli	a					15 23			16 08	16 20					17 27			18 08	18 26			18 37			19 20
	d					15 24			16 08	16 21					17 27			18 08	18 26						19 21
Pembrey & Burry Port	d					15 29			16 14	16 26					17 33			18 14	18 32						19 26
Kidwelly	d								16x21						17x39			18x21	18x38						
Ferryside	d								16x27						17x44			18x27	18x43						
Carmarthen	a					15 49			16 40	16 51					17 56			18 40	19 00						19 46
	d					15 52			16 56						17 59			19 05							19 52
Whitland	a					16 15			17 12						18 13			19 21							20 06
	d					16 16			17 12						18 14			19 21							20 07
Narberth	d								17x21									19x30							
Kilgetty	d								17x30									19x39							
Saundersfoot	d								17x31									19x40							
Tenby	a								17 38									19 47							
	d								17 43									19 52							
Penally	d								17x46									19x55							
Manorbier	d								17 52									20 02							
Lamphey	d								17x59									20x09							
Pembroke	d								18 02									20 12							
Pembroke Dock	a								18 17									20 22							
Clunderwen	d					16x22									18x20										20x13
Clarbeston Road	d					16x29									18x27										20x20
Haverfordwest	d					16 37									18 35										20 28
Johnston	d					16x45									18x43										20x36
Milford Haven	a					17 00									18 58										20 51
Fishguard Harbour	a																								
⛴	d		14 30																						
Rosslare Harbour ⛴	a		18 00																						

For general notes see front of timetable
For details of catering facilities see Directory of Train Operators

A From Cheltenham Spa (Table 57)
B Ship service

Table 128

Saturdays

from 13 September

Cardiff → Maesteg, Swansea and West Wales

Route Diagram - see first page of Table 127

		AW	GW	AW	AW	AW	AW	GW	AW	GW	AW	GW	AW	AW	GW	AW	GW	AW	AW	AW	GW
				R					R				R								
			1 ◇					1 ◇		1 ◇		1 ◇			1 ◇		1 ◇	◇	◇	◇	1 ◇
		A				A					A			A		A					
			buffet	restaurant				buffet	restaurant	buffet		buffet	restaurant		buffet		buffet	restaurant			buffet
London Paddington 15 ⊖	d		16 45					17 45				18 45			19 15		19 45				20 45
Reading 7	d		17 11					18 11				19 11			19 41		20 11				21 11
Manchester Piccadilly 10	d			15 34					16 34				17 34					18 34			
Gloucester 7	d	16 58				17 58					18 58			19 58							
Bristol Parkway 7	d		18 07					19 12				20 07			20 42		21 06				22 14
Newport (South Wales)	d	17 52	18 31	18 40		18 52		19 35	19 43		19 52	20 32	20 47	20 52	21 05		21 31	21 37			22 46
Cardiff Queen Street 3	d																				
Cardiff Central 7	d	18 21	18 48	19 04		19 21	19 38	19 53	20 00		20 21	20 48	21 07	21 21	21 22		21 48	22 09		22 41	23 06
Pontyclun	d	18 33				19 33					20 33			21 40		←				22 55	
Llanharan	d	18 38				19 38					20 38			21 45		21 45				23 00	
Pencoed	d	18 42				19 42					20 42			→		21 49				23 05	
Bridgend	d	18 49	19 09	19 23		19 49	19 58	20 13	20 19		20 49	21 09	21 28		21 42	21 56	22 09	22 28		23 11	23 27
Wildmill	d	18 52				19 52					20 52					21 59					
Sarn	d	18 55				19 55					20 55					22 02					
Tondu	d	18 58				19 58					20 58					22 05					
Garth (Mid Glamorgan)	d	19 08				20 08					21 08					22 15					
Maesteg (Ewenny Road)	d	19 10				20 10					21 10					22 17					
Maesteg	a	19 15				20 15					21 15					22 21					
Pyle	d						20 06						21 35							23 19	
Port Talbot Parkway	d		19 22	19 36			20 14	20 26	20 32			21 22	21 43		21 55		22 22	22 41		23 26	23 40
Baglan	d						20 18													23 30	
Briton Ferry	d						20 21			←										23 33	
Neath	d		19 29	19 43			20 25	20 34		20 34		21 30	21 50		22 03		22 29	22 48		23 37	23 48
Skewen	d						20 29	→												23 41	
Llansamlet	d						20 33													23 45	
Swansea 7	a		19 42	19 56			20 44			20 48		21 47	22 03		22 18		22 46	23 00		23 54	00 01
	d			20 00	20 05					21 00			22 25					23 06	23 45	00 08	
Gowerton	d				20x17								22x35					23x21		00b19	
Llanelli	a			20 15	20 24				21 04	21 25			22 42					23 27	00 01	00s25	
	d			20 16	20 24				21 04	21 25			22 42					23 28	00 01		
Pembrey & Burry Port	d			20 21	20 30				21 10	21 32			22 48					23 33	00 07	00s31	
Kidwelly	d				20x37								22x54					23x39		00b38	
Ferryside	d				20x43								22x59					23x45		00b44	
Carmarthen	a			20 46	20 56				21 29	21 55			23 11					00 03	00 27	01 01	
	d				20 59				22 04				23 17						00 30		
Whitland	a				21 15				22 21				23 31						00 45		
	d				21 15				22 21				23 32						00 45		
Narberth	d				21x24																
Kilgetty	d				21x34																
Saundersfoot	d				21x36																
Tenby	a				21 43																
	d				21 44																
Penally	d				21x47																
Manorbier	d				21 54																
Lamphey	d				22x01																
Pembroke	d				22 04																
Pembroke Dock	a				22 19																
Clunderwen	d								22x27				23x38								
Clarbeston Road	d								22x34				23x45						00x59		
Haverfordwest	d								22 43				23a58								
Johnston	d								22x50												
Milford Haven	a								23 05												
Fishguard Harbour	a																		01 26		
⛴	d																				
Rosslare Harbour ⛴	a																				

For general notes see front of timetable
For details of catering facilities see Directory of Train Operators

A From Cheltenham Spa (Table 57)
b Stops, on request, to set down only

Table 128

Sundays

until 7 September

Cardiff → Maesteg, Swansea and West Wales

Route Diagram - see first page of Table 127

		AW	AW	AW	AW	AW	AW	AW	AW	AW	GW	AW	AW	AW	GW	GW	AW	AW	AW	AW	GW
		◇	◇	R			◇			◇	1 ◇	◇			1 ◇	1 ◇	R	◇	◇		1 ◇
				A													A	B	C		
											🍴		🛒		🍴	🍴		🛒		🛒	🍴
London Paddington 15 ⊖	d										08 00				09 27	10 27					11 27
Reading 7	d										08 46				10 05	11 02					12 02
Manchester Piccadilly 10 🚆	d																				
Gloucester 7	d										10 14				11 27	12 23					13 28
Bristol Parkway 7	d																				
Newport (South Wales)	d						08 07				10 59				12 10	13 06		13 38			14 12
Cardiff Queen Street 3	d																				
Cardiff Central 7	d		22p41				08 30		09 55		11 16	11 21			12 27	13 24		14 03			14 29
Pontyclun	d		22p55				08 42														
Llanharan	d		23p00				08 47														
Pencoed	d		23p05				08 51														
Bridgend	d		23p11				08 58		10 15		11 36	11 42			12 48	13 44		14 24			14 49
Wildmill	d																				
Sarn	d																				
Tondu	d																				
Garth (Mid Glamorgan)	d																				
Maesteg (Ewenny Road)	d																				
Maesteg	a																				
Pyle	d		23p19				09 06														
Port Talbot Parkway	d		23p26				09 14		10 29		11 49	11 55			13 00	13 57		14 38			15 02
Baglan	d		23p30				09 17														
Briton Ferry	d		23p33				09 21														
Neath	d		23p37				09 25		10 37		11 57	12 03			13 08	14 05		14 46			15 10
Skewen	d		23p41				09 29														
Llansamlet	d		23p45				09 33														
Swansea 7	a		23p54				09 40		10 49		12 10	12 15			13 20	14 17		14 58			15 27
	d	23p45	00 08				09 45		10 54	11 03		12 18			13 40			15 06	15 10		15 35
Gowerton	d		00b19				09x56		11x05	11x14		12x28							15x23		
Llanelli	a	00 01	00s25				10 02		11 11	11 21		12 35			13 56			15 22	15 30		15 51
	d	00 01					10 06		11 12			12 35			13 57			15 22			15 52
Pembrey & Burry Port	d	00 07	00s31				10 12		11 18			12 41			14 04			15 28			15 59
Kidwelly	d		00b38				10x18		11x24			12x47									
Ferryside	d		00b44				10x24		11x30			12x52									
Carmarthen	a	00 27	01 01				10 37		11 43			13 04			14 25			15 53			16 20
	d	00 30			08 20	09 35	10 39	10 46	11 50			13 07	14 09	14 20						16 05	
Whitland	a	00 45			08 34	09 49	10 54	11 02	12 07			13 21	14 25	14 36						16 21	
	d	00 45			08 35	09 50	10 55	11 02	12 07			13 22	14 25	14 36						16 21	
Narberth	d					09x57		11x11	12x15					14x45							
Kilgetty	d					10x06		11x20	12x24					14x55							
Saundersfoot	d					10x07		11x21	12x25					14x57							
Tenby	a					10 14		11 28	12 39					15 04							
	d					10 16		11 32						15 21							
Penally	d					10x18		11x34						15x24							
Manorbier	d					10 24		11 41						15 31							
Lamphey	d					10x31		11x48						15x38							
Pembroke	d					10 34		11 51						15 42							
Pembroke Dock	a					10 49		12 02						15 53							
Clunderwen	d				08x41		11x01						14x32							16x28	
Clarbeston Road	d	00x59			08x45		11x09						14x40							16x36	
Haverfordwest	d				08 56		11 18						14 48							16 44	
Johnston	d				09x04		11x26						14x56							16x52	
Milford Haven	a				09 15		11 37						15 09							17 05	
Fishguard Harbour	a	01 26										14 00									
⛴	d			02 45													14 30				
Rosslare Harbour ⛴	a			06 15													18 00				

For general notes see front of timetable
For details of catering facilities see Directory of Train Operators

A Ship service
B From Crewe (Table 131). 🛒 to Swansea
C To Crewe (Table 131)
b Stops, on request, to set down only

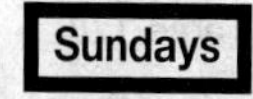

until 7 September

Cardiff → Maesteg, Swansea and West Wales

Route Diagram - see first page of Table 127

		GW	AW	AW	AW	GW	GW	AW		GW	GW	AW	GW	GW	AW	AW	GW	GW	GW
					R			R				R							
		1 ◇		◇		1 ◇	1 ◇			1 ◇	1 ◇		1 ◇	1 ◇	◇	◇	1 ◇	1 ◇	1 ◇
				A	B														
		🍽		⊥	⊥	🍽	🍽	⊥		🍽	🍽	⊥	🍽	🍽			🍽	🍽	🍽
London Paddington 15 ⊖	d	12 27				13 27	14 27			15 27	16 27		17 27	18 27			19 27	20 27	21 27
Reading 7	d	13 02				14 02	15 02			16 02	17 02		18 05	19 05			20 05	21 04	22 02
Manchester Piccadilly 10 ⛴	d			12 29	12 33			14 34				16 36							
Gloucester 7	d	14 26				15 30	16 30			17 33	18 27		19 29	20 26			21 31	22 26	23 28
Bristol Parkway 7	d																		
Newport (South Wales)	d	15 09		16 01	16 01	16 14	17 13	18 01		18 15	19 09	20 01	20 12	21 10			22 22	23 17	00 20
Cardiff Queen Street 3	d																		
Cardiff Central 7	d	15 28		16 18	16 18	16 37	17 31	18 22		18 33	19 27	20 22	20 29	21 25	21 32	22 35	22 43	23 38	00 41
Pontyclun	d			16 32	16 32										21 44				
Llanharan	d			16 37	16 37										21 48				
Pencoed	d			16 41	16 41										21 52				
Bridgend	d	15 48		16 45	16 45	16 57	17 51	18 42		18 54	19 48	20 42	20 50	21 47	21 59	22 54	23 04	23 58	01 01
Wildmill	d																		
Sarn	d																		
Tondu	d																		
Garth (Mid Glamorgan)	d																		
Maesteg (Ewenny Road)	d																		
Maesteg	a																		
Pyle	d														22 06				
Port Talbot Parkway	d	16 01		16 59	16 59	17 10	18 04	18 57		19 07	20 01	20 56	21 03	21 59	22 14	23 07	23 16	00 15	01 15
Baglan	d														22 18				
Briton Ferry	d														22 21				
Neath	d	16 08		17 07	17 07	17 18	18 12	19 05		19 14	20 09	21 04	21 11	22 08	22 25	23 14	23 24	00 22	01 22
Skewen	d														22 30				
Llansamlet	d														22 34				
Swansea 7	a	16 20		17 20	17 20	17 34	18 24	19 17		19 30	20 21	21 16	21 24	22 20	22 41	23 26	23 36	00 34	01 34
	d			17 24	17 24	17 41		19 20				21 19			22 51	23 45			
Gowerton	d			17x35	17x35			19x30				21x30				23x55			
Llanelli	a			17 42	17 42	17 57		19 38				21 36			23 06	00 02			
	d			17 42	17 42	17 58		19 38				21 37			23 07	00 02			
Pembrey & Burry Port	d			17 48	17 48	18 05		19 45				21 43			23 13	00 08			
Kidwelly	d			17x55	17x55							21x49				00x13			
Ferryside	d			18x01	18x01							21x55				00x20			
Carmarthen	a			18 13	18 13	18 29		20 05				22 08			23 35	00 32			
	d		17 05	18 16	18 16			20 12				22 10				00 40			
Whitland	a		17 21	18 31	18 31			20 27				22 25				00 55			
	d		17 21	18 32	18 32			20 30	20 37			22 27				00 55			
Narberth	d		17x30						20x46										
Kilgetty	d		17x40						20x55										
Saundersfoot	d		17x42						20x57										
Tenby	a		17 49						21 04										
	d		17 50						21 08										
Penally	d		17x53						21x11										
Manorbier	d		18 00						21 17										
Lamphey	d		18x07						21x25										
Pembroke	d		18 11						21 28										
Pembroke Dock	a		18 25						21 43										
Clunderwen	d			18x39	18x39			20x37				22x33							
Clarbeston Road	d			18x46	18x46			20x44				22x40				01x07			
Haverfordwest	d			18 54	18 54			20 54				22 49							
Johnston	d			19x02	19x02			21x02				22x56							
Milford Haven	a			19 17	19 17			21 15				23 11							
Fishguard Harbour	a															01 35			
⛴	d																		
Rosslare Harbour ⛴	a																		

For general notes see front of timetable
For details of catering facilities see
Directory of Train Operators

A Until 13 July
B From 20 July

Table 128

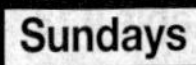

Sundays

from 14 September

Cardiff → Maesteg, Swansea and West Wales

Route Diagram - see first page of Table 127

		AW	AW	AW	AW	AW	GW	AW	AW	GW	AW	AW	AW	GW	GW	AW	AW	AW
		◇	◇	R	◇	◇	1 ◇		◇	1 ◇	R			1 ◇	1 ◇	◇	◇	
				A					B		A					C	D	
							🍽			🍽		🛒		🍽	🍽	🛒		🛒
London Paddington 15 ⊖	d						08 30			09 30				10 37	11 37			
Reading 7	d						09 06			10 07				11 11	12 11			
Manchester Piccadilly 10 ⛴	d																	
Gloucester 7	d																	
Bristol Parkway 7	d						10 11			11 04				12 08	13 06			
Newport (South Wales)	d				09 10		10 34		11 02	11 32				12 30	13 34	13 38		
Cardiff Queen Street 3	d																	
Cardiff Central 7	d		22p41		09 30		10 51		11 20	11 49				12 49	13 52	14 03		
Pontyclun	d		22p55		09 42													
Llanharan	d		23p00		09 48													
Pencoed	d		23p05		09 52													
Bridgend	d		23p11		09 58		11 11		11 40	12 09				13 08	14 12	14 24		
Wildmill	d																	
Sarn	d																	
Tondu	d																	
Garth (Mid Glamorgan)	d																	
Maesteg (Ewenny Road)	d																	
Maesteg	a																	
Pyle	d		23p19		10 06													
Port Talbot Parkway	d		23p26		10 14		11 26		11 54	12 22				13 22	14 25	14 38		
Baglan	d		23p30		10 17													
Briton Ferry	d		23p33		10 21													
Neath	d		23p37		10 25		11 34		12 02	12 30				13 28	14 32	14 46		
Skewen	d		23p41		10 29													
Llansamlet	d		23p45		10 33													
Swansea 7	a		23p54		10 40		11 47		12 14	12 43				13 41	14 49	14 58		
	d	23p45	00 08		10 43	11 09			12 17					13 47		15 06	15 16	
Gowerton	d		00b19		10x54	11x20			12x28								15x27	
Llanelli	a	00 01	00s25		11 00	11 27			12 34					14 04		15 25	15 34	
	d	00 01			11 06				12 35					14 04		15 25		
Pembrey & Burry Port	d	00 07	00s31		11 12				12 40					14 10		15 31		
Kidwelly	d		00b38		11x18				12x47									
Ferryside	d		00b44		11x24				12x53									
Carmarthen	a	00 27	01 01		11 37				13 05					14 37		15 56		
	d	00 30			12 05				13 08			14 05	14 20					16 05
Whitland	a	00 45			12 20				13 23			14 21	14 36					16 21
	d	00 45			12 24			12 30	13 24			14 21	14 36					16 21
Narberth	d							12x39					14x45					
Kilgetty	d							12x48					14x55					
Saundersfoot	d							12x50					14x57					
Tenby	a							13 00					15 04					
	d												15 21					
Penally	d												15x24					
Manorbier	d												15 31					
Lamphey	d												15x38					
Pembroke	d												15 42					
Pembroke Dock	a												15 53					
Clunderwen	d				12x31							14x28						16x28
Clarbeston Road	d	00x59			12x38							14x36						16x36
Haverfordwest	d				12 47							14 44						16 44
Johnston	d				12x55							14x52						16x52
Milford Haven	a				13 06							15 05						17 05
Fishguard Harbour	a	01 26							14 00									
⛴	d			02 45							14 30							
Rosslare Harbour ⛴	a			06 15							18 00							

For general notes see front of timetable
For details of catering facilities see Directory of Train Operators

A Ship service
B From Hereford (Table 131)
C From Crewe (Table 131). 🛒 to Swansea
D To Crewe (Table 131)
b Stops, on request, to set down only

Sundays

from 14 September

Cardiff → Maesteg, Swansea and West Wales

Route Diagram - see first page of Table 127

		GW		GW	AW		AW	GW		GW	AW			GW	GW		AW	GW	AW	GW	AW	GW	GW		
		1 ◇		1 ◇			R	1 ◇		1 ◇	R			1 ◇	1 ◇		R	1 ◇	◇	1 ◇	◇	1 ◇	1 ◇		
London Paddington 15 ⊖	d	12 37		13 37				14 37		15 37				16 37	17 37			18 37		19 37		20 37	21 37		
Reading 7	d	13 11		14 11				15 11		16 11				17 11	18 11			19 09		20 11		21 11	22 14		
Manchester Piccadilly 10	d						12 33				14 34						16 36								
Gloucester 7	d																								
Bristol Parkway 7	d	14 08		15 09				16 08		17 08				18 11	19 12			20 10		21 08		22 10	23 15		
Newport (South Wales)	d	14 30		15 32			16 01	16 30		17 34	18 01			18 32	19 40		20 01	20 33		21 32		22 41	23 45		
Cardiff Queen Street 3	d																								
Cardiff Central 7	d	14 49		15 49			16 18	16 49		17 51	18 18			18 49	19 57		20 22	20 48	21 32	21 48	22 35	23 05	00 07		
Pontyclun	d						16 32												21 44						
Llanharan	d						16 37												21 48						
Pencoed	d						16 41												21 52						
Bridgend	d	15 08		16 10			16 45	17 09		18 11	18 38			19 10	20 18		20 42	21 10	21 59	22 09	22 54	23 25	00 27		
Wildmill	d																								
Sarn	d																								
Tondu	d																								
Garth (Mid Glamorgan)	d																								
Maesteg (Ewenny Road)	d																								
Maesteg	a																								
Pyle	d																		22 06						
Port Talbot Parkway	d	15 22		16 22			16 59	17 22		18 24	18 52			19 23	20 31		20 56	21 22	22 14	22 23	23 07	23 39	00 40		
Baglan	d																		22 18						
Briton Ferry	d																		22 21						
Neath	d	15 28		16 30			17 07	17 29		18 32	19 00			19 32	20 39		21 04	21 31	22 25	22 32	23 14	23 46	00 47		
Skewen	d																		22 30						
Llansamlet	d																		22 34						
Swansea 7	a	15 41		16 42			17 20	17 41		18 45	19 12			19 44	20 54		21 16	21 43	22 41	22 44	23 26	23 58	00 59		
	d	15 51					17 24	17 47			19 17						21 19		22 51		23 30				
Gowerton	d						17x35				19x27						21x30				23x40				
Llanelli	a	16 09					17 42	18 04			19 35						21 36		23 06		23 47				
	d	16 09					17 42	18 05			19 35						21 37		23 07		23 47				
Pembrey & Burry Port	d	16 16					17 48	18 12			19 42						21 43		23 13		23 53				
Kidwelly	d						17x55										21x49				23x59				
Ferryside	d						18x01										21x55				00x05				
Carmarthen	a	16 42					18 13	18 37			20 02						22 08		23 35		00 17				
	d				17 05		18 16				20 09						22 10				00 19				
Whitland	a				17 21		18 31				20 24						22 25				00 34				
	d				17 21		18 32				20 30	20 34					22 27				00 34				
Narberth	d				17x30							20x43													
Kilgetty	d				17x40							20x52													
Saundersfoot	d				17x42							20x54													
Tenby	a				17 49							21 01													
	d				17 50							21 05													
Penally	d				17x53							21x08													
Manorbier	d				18 00							21 14													
Lamphey	d				18x07							21x22													
Pembroke	d				18 11							21 25													
Pembroke Dock	a				18 25							21 40													
Clunderwen	d						18x39				20x37						22x33								
Clarbeston Road	d						18x46				20x44						22x40				00x46				
Haverfordwest	d						18 54				20 54						22 49								
Johnston	d						19x02				21x02						22x56								
Milford Haven	a						19 17				21 15						23 11								
Fishguard Harbour	a																				01 15				
	⛴ d																								
Rosslare Harbour	⛴ a																								

For general notes see front of timetable
For details of catering facilities see Directory of Train Operators

West Wales, Swansea and Maesteg → Cardiff

Route Diagram - see first page of Table 127

Miles	Miles																							
				AW	AW	AW	GW	GW	GW	GW	AW	GW	GW	AW	AW	GW	AW	GW	AW	AW	GW	GW	AW	AW
				MO	MX		MO	MX																
				◇		◇	■1 ◇	■1 ◇	■1 ◇	■1 ◇	◇	■1 ◇	■1 ◇		◇	■1 ◇		■1 ◇	◇		■1 ◇	■1 ◇	◇	
													A											B
							🛒	🛒	⊠	⊠	🛒	☕	✕		🛒	☕		☕	🛒		⊠	⊠	🛒	
—	—	Rosslare Harbour ⛴	d																					
—	—	**Fishguard Harbour** ⛴	a																					
0	—		d			01 50																		
—	0	**Milford Haven**	d	21p35	00 15														06 05				07 05	
—	4	Johnston	d	21b42	00x22														06x12				07x12	
—	8¾	Haverfordwest	d	21p50	00 30														06 20				07 20	
15¾	14	Clarbeston Road	d	21b58	00x37	02x10													06x27				07x27	
22¼	—	Clunderwen	d	22b06	00x44														06x33				07x33	
—	0	**Pembroke Dock**	d																					
—	2	Pembroke	d																					
—	3½	Lamphey	d																					
—	7	Manorbier	d																					
—	10¼	Penally	d																					
—	11½	**Tenby**	a																					
—	—		d																					
—	15¾	Saundersfoot	d																					
—	16½	Kilgetty	d																					
—	22	Narberth	d																					
27¾	27¼	Whitland	a	22p12	00 50	02 22													06 39				07 39	
—	—		d	22p13	00 50	02 22													06 40				07 40	
41¾	—	**Carmarthen**	a	22p30	01 12	02 39													06 56				07 56	
—	—		d	22p35		02 44					05 04				05 50		06 18		07 00			07 30	07 59	
48¾	—	Ferryside	d	22b45											06x00		06x28					07 42	08x09	
53	—	Kidwelly	d	22b51											06x05		06x33					07 49	08x14	
58¼	—	Pembrey & Burry Port	d	22p59							05 22				06 12		06 40		07 18			07 56	08 21	
62¼	—	Llanelli	a	23p05		03 06					05 27				06 17		06 45		07 23			08 02	08 26	
—	—		d	23p05		03 07					05 28				06 18		06 46		07 24			08 04	08 27	
68	—	Gowerton	d	23b12											06x24		06x52		07x30				08x33	
73½	—	**Swansea** 7	a	23p26		03 25									06 37		07 06		07 43			08 22	08 46	
—	—		d	23p35			03 59	03 59	04 58	05 24		05 59	06 29		06 40	06 59	07 09	07 29	07 45		07 59	08 29	08 55	
77½	—	Llansamlet	d														07 16							
79¼	—	Skewen	d														07 20							
83	—	Neath	d	23p46			04 11	04 11	05 09	05 36		06 10	06 40		06 51	07 10	07 24	07 40	07 56		08 10	08 40	09 06	
84¾	—	Briton Ferry	d														07 27							
86½	—	Baglan	d														07 31							
88½	—	Port Talbot Parkway	d	23p54			04 18	04 18	05 17	05 43	06 01	06 18	06 48		06 58	07 18	07 35	07 48	08 03		08 18	08 48	09 13	
94¾	—	Pyle	d												07 04		07 42		08 10					
—	0	Maesteg	d											06 49						08 00				09 17
—	½	Maesteg (Ewenny Road)	d											06 51						08 02				09 19
—	1¼	Garth (Mid Glamorgan)	d											06 54						08 05				09 22
—	5¼	Tondu	d											07 03						08 14				09 31
—	6	Sarn	d											07 06						08 17				09 34
—	7¼	Wildmill	d											07 08						08 19				09 36
100¾	8¼	Bridgend	d	00 07			04 30	04 30	05 28	05 55	06 13	06 29	06 59	07 12	07 17	07 29	07 50	07 59	08 18	08 23	08 29	08 59	09 25	09 40
104¼	—	Pencoed	d								06 19			07 18			07 56		08 24					09 46
107	—	Llanharan	d											07 22			08 00			08 31				09 50
110	—	Pontyclun	d								06 26			07 26			08 04		08 31					09 54
121	—	**Cardiff Central** 7	a	00 50			04 52	04 55	05 51	06 17	06 40	06 52	07 22	07 43	07 45	07 52	08 18	08 22	08 44	08 48	08 52	09 22	09 47	10 09
—	—	Cardiff Queen Street 3	a																					
—	—	Newport (South Wales)	a				05 32	05 32	06 07	06 33	07 02	07 08	07 38		08 03	08 08		08 38	09 03		09 08	09 38	10 03	10 25
—	—	Bristol Parkway 7	a				06 00	06 00	06 29	06 55		07 30	08 00			08 30		09 00			09 30	10 00		
—	—	Gloucester 7	a																					11 20
—	—	Manchester Piccadilly 10 🚌	a								10 13				11 13				12 13				13 13	
—	—	Reading 7	a				07 02	07 02	07 29	07 58		08 33	09 01			09 27		09 57			10 32	11 01		
—	—	London Paddington 15 ⊖	a				07 32	07 32	08 01	08 30		09 06	09 29			09 59		10 27			11 02	11 30		

For general notes see front of timetable
For details of catering facilities see Directory of Train Operators

A **The Red Dragon**
B To Cheltenham Spa (Table 57)

b Previous night.
Stops on request, passengers wishing to alight must inform the guard and those wishing to join must give a hand signal to the driver

West Wales, Swansea and Maesteg → Cardiff

Route Diagram - see first page of Table 127

		AW	AW	GW	AW	AW	GW	AW	AW	AW	AW	GW	AW	AW	GW	AW	AW	AW	AW	AW	AW	GW	AW	AW
		◇		1 ◇	◇		1 ◇	◇				1 ◇	◇		1 ◇	◇		◇				1 ◇	R	
		A							B			C		B			D							B
			🛒	🍽	🛒		🍽	🛒			🛒	⊠	🛒		🍽	🛒					🛒	🍽	🛒	
Rosslare Harbour	⛴ d																09 00							
Fishguard Harbour	⛴ a																12 30							
	d																							
Milford Haven	d							09 10								11 10								
Johnston	d							09x17								11x17								
Haverfordwest	d							09 25								11 25								
Clarbeston Road	d							09x32								11x32								
Clunderwen	d							09x38								11x38								
Pembroke Dock	d		07 05								09 05										11 05			
Pembroke	d		07 13								09 13										11 13			
Lamphey	d		07x16								09x16										11x16			
Manorbier	d		07 25								09 24										11 24			
Penally	d		07x30								09x29										11x29			
Tenby	a		07 33								09 32										11 32			
	d		07 40								09 42										11 42			
Saundersfoot	d		07x48								09x49										11x49			
Kilgetty	d		07x50								09x51										11x51			
Narberth	d		08x00								10x00										12x00			
Whitland	a		08 08					09 44			10 08					11 44					12 08			
	d		08 08					09 45			10 09					11 45					12 09			
Carmarthen	a		08 27					10 01			10 26					12 01					12 26			
	d		08 30		09 00			10 05			10 30		11 05			12 05					12 30		13 05	
Ferryside	d		08x40								10x40										12x40			
Kidwelly	d		08x46								10x46										12x46			
Pembrey & Burry Port	d		08 53		09 18			10 22			10 53		11 23			12 23					12 53		13 23	
Llanelli	a		08 59		09 23			10 28			10 59		11 28			12 28					12 59		13 28	
	d	08 45	09 00		09 26			10 28			11 00		11 29			12 29		12 33			13 00		13 29	
Gowerton	d	08x53	09x07								11x07										13x07			
Swansea 7	a	09 07	09 22		09 46			10 45			11 22		11 46			12 46		13 01			13 22		13 48	
	d	09 10		09 29	09 55		10 29	10 55		11 10		11 29	11 55		12 29	12 50				13 10		13 29	13 55	
Llansamlet	d	09 17								11 17										13 17				
Skewen	d	09 21								11 21										13 21				
Neath	d	09 25		09 40	10 06		10 40	11 06		11 25		11 40	12 06		12 40	13 06				13 25		13 40	14 06	
Briton Ferry	d	09 29								11 28										13 28				
Baglan	d	09 32								11 32										13 32				
Port Talbot Parkway	d	09 36		09 48	10 13		10 48	11 13		11 36		11 48	12 13		12 48	13 13				13 36		13 48	14 13	
Pyle	d	09 43								11 43										13 43				
Maesteg	d					10 17			11 17					12 17					13 17					14 17
Maesteg (Ewenny Road)	d					10 19			11 19					12 19					13 19					14 19
Garth (Mid Glamorgan)	d					10 22			11 22					12 22					13 22					14 22
Tondu	d					10 31			11 31					12 31					13 31					14 31
Sarn	d					10 34			11 34					12 34					13 34					14 34
Wildmill	d					10 36			11 36					12 36					13 36					14 36
Bridgend	d	09 55		09 59	10 25	10 40	10 59	11 25	11 40	11 55		11 59	12 25	12 40	12 59	13 25			13 40	13 55		13 59	14 25	14 40
Pencoed	d					10 46			11 46					12 46					13 46					14 46
Llanharan	d					10 50			11 50					12 50					13 50					14 50
Pontyclun	d					10 54			11 54					12 54					13 54					14 54
Cardiff Central 7	a	10 17		10 22	10 47	11 13	11 22	11 47	12 09	12 17		12 22	12 47	13 09	13 22	13 47			14 13	14 17		14 22	14 47	15 09
Cardiff Queen Street 3	a																							
Newport (South Wales)	a			10 38	11 03		11 38	12 03	12 25			12 38	13 03	13 25	13 38	14 03						14 38	15 03	15 25
Bristol Parkway 7	a			11 00			12 00					13 00			14 00							15 00		
Gloucester 7	a								13 20					14 20										16 21
Manchester Piccadilly 10	⛴ a				14 13			15 13					16 13			17 11							18 12	
Reading 7	a			12 01			13 01					14 01			15 01							16 01		
London Paddington 15	⊖ a			12 32			13 30					14 32			15 30							16 30		

For general notes see front of timetable
For details of catering facilities see Directory of Train Operators

A From Shrewsbury (Table 129)
B To Cheltenham Spa (Table 57)
C **The St David**
D Ship service

Table 128 — Mondays to Fridays

West Wales, Swansea and Maesteg → Cardiff

Route Diagram - see first page of Table 127

		GW	AW	AW	AW	AW	AW	GW	AW	AW	GW	AW	AW	AW	AW	GW	AW	AW	AW	GW	AW FX	AW FO	AW	AW FX
		1 ◇ 🍴	R 🛒	◇ 🛒	A		🛒	1 ◇ 🍴	R 🛒	A	1 ◇ 🍴	R 🛒	A		🛒	1 ◇ 🍴	◇ 🛒	◇		1 ◇ 🍴	◇	◇	A	◇
Rosslare Harbour ⛴	d																							
Fishguard Harbour ⛴	a																							
	d			13 27																				
Milford Haven	d		13 10									15 10										17 10		17 10
Johnston	d		13x17									15x17										17x17		17x17
Haverfordwest	d		13 25									15 25										17 25		17 25
Clarbeston Road	d		13x32									15x32										17x32		17x32
Clunderwen	d		13x38									15x38										17x38		17x39
Pembroke Dock	d						13 05								15 05									
Pembroke	d						13 13								15 13									
Lamphey	d						13x16								15x16									
Manorbier	d						13 24								15 24									
Penally	d						13x29								15x29									
Tenby	a						13 32								15 32									
	d						13 42								15 44									
Saundersfoot	d						13x49								15x51									
Kilgetty	d						13x51								15x53									
Narberth	d						14x00								16x02									
Whitland	a		13 44	13 59			14 13					15 44			16 10							17 44		17 45
	d		13 45	13 59			14 13					15 45			16 11							17 45		17 45
Carmarthen	a		14 01	14 16			14 31					16 01			16 28							18 01		18 02
	d		14 05	14 19			14 34		15 05			16 05			16 31		17 01					18 05		18 06
Ferryside	d						14x44								16x41		17x11					18x15		18x16
Kidwelly	d						14x50								16x47		17x16					18x20		18x21
Pembrey & Burry Port	d		14 23				14 57		15 23			16 23			16 54		17 23					18 27		18 28
Llanelli	a		14 28	14 43			15 03		15 28			16 28			17 00		17 28					18 32		18 34
	d		14 29	14 43			15 04		15 29			16 29			17 01		17 29	17 36				18 33		18 34
Gowerton	d		14x35									16x35			17x08			17x44						
Swansea 7	a		14 48				15 22		15 46			16 48			17 22		17 46	18 06				18 51		18 51
	d	14 29	14 55			15 10		15 29	15 55		16 29	16 55		17 10		17 29	17 55			18 29	18 58	18 58		19 10
Llansamlet	d					15 17								17 17										19 17
Skewen	d					15 21								17 21										19 21
Neath	d	14 40	15 06			15 25		15 40	16 06		16 40	17 06		17 25		17 40	18 06			18 40	19 09	19 09		19 25
Briton Ferry	d					15 28								17 28										19 28
Baglan	d					15 32								17 32										19 32
Port Talbot Parkway	d	14 48	15 13			15 36		15 48	16 13		16 48	17 13		17 36		17 48	18 13			18 48	19 16	19 16		19 36
Pyle	d					15 43								17 43										19 43
Maesteg	d				15 17					16 17			17 17						18 20				19 20	
Maesteg (Ewenny Road)	d				15 19					16 19			17 19						18 22				19 22	
Garth (Mid Glamorgan)	d				15 22					16 22			17 22						18 25				19 25	
Tondu	d				15 31					16 31			17 31						18 34				19 34	
Sarn	d				15 34					16 34			17 34						18 37				19 37	
Wildmill	d				15 36					16 36			17 36						18 39				19 39	
Bridgend	d	14 59	15 25		15 40	15 55		15 59	16 25	16 40	16 59	17 25	17 40	17 55		17 59	18 25		18 43	18 59	19 28	19 28	19 43	19 54
Pencoed	d				15 46					16 46			17 46						18 49				19 49	
Llanharan	d				15 50					16 50			17 50						18 53				19 53	
Pontyclun	d				15 54					16 54			17 54	18 05					18 57				19 57	
Cardiff Central 7	a	15 22	15 47	16 04	16 10	16 18		16 22	16 47	17 10	17 22	17 47	18 09	18 18		18 22	18 48		19 13	19 22	19 50	19 50	20 12	20 18
Cardiff Queen Street 3	a																							
Newport (South Wales)	a	15 38	16 03		16 25			16 38	17 03	17 27	17 38	18 03	18 25			18 38	19 05			19 38	20 22	20 22	20 28	
Bristol Parkway 7	a	16 00						17 00			18 00					19 00				20 00				
Gloucester 7	a				17 21					18 20			19 20										21 21	
Manchester Piccadilly 10 ⛴	a		19 13						20 18			21 13					22 12				23 49	23 49		
Reading 7	a	17 01						17 57			19 01					20 01				21 02				
London Paddington 15 ⊖	a	17 30						18 27			19 32					20 31				21 32				

For general notes see front of timetable
For details of catering facilities see Directory of Train Operators

A To Cheltenham Spa (Table 57)

West Wales, Swansea and Maesteg → Cardiff

Route Diagram - see first page of Table 127

		AW	AW	GW	GW	AW	AW	GW	GW	AW	AW	AW	AW	AW	AW	AW	AW	AW	AW	AW	AW	AW	AW
		FO		FO	FX			FO	FX				FX	FO	FX								
				1 ◇	1 ◇	◇		1 ◇	1 ◇	◇				◇	◇	◇							
						A	B			C								B					D
			🚌	☕	☕			☕	☕			🚌											
Rosslare Harbour ⛴	d																						21 15
Fishguard Harbour ⛴	a																						00 45
	d																						
Milford Haven	d									19 10							21 20					23 15	
Johnston	d									19x17							21x27					23x22	
Haverfordwest	d									19 25							21 35					23 30	
Clarbeston Road	d									19x32							21x42					23x39	
Clunderwen	d									19x38							21x48					23x47	
Pembroke Dock	d		17 05									19 16								21 11	22 24		
Pembroke	d		17 13									19 24								21 19	22 32		
Lamphey	d		17x16									19x27								21x22	22x35		
Manorbier	d		17 24									19 36								21 31	22 43		
Penally	d		17x29									19x41								21x36	22x48		
Tenby	a		17 32									19 44								21 39	22 51		
	d		17 42									19 49								21 45	22 53		
Saundersfoot	d		17x49									19x56								21x53	23x00		
Kilgetty	d		17x51									19x58								21x55	23x02		
Narberth	d		18x00									20x07								22x05	23x11		
Whitland	a		18 08							19 44		20 15					21 54			22 13	23 19	23 56	
	d		18 09							19 45		20 16					21 55			22 14	23 20	23 57	
Carmarthen	a		18 26							20 01		20 33					22 16			22 32	23 40	00 18	
	d		18 30			19 10				20 05		20 36	21 05	21 05						22 35			
Ferryside	d		18x40									20x46	21x15	21x15						22x45			
Kidwelly	d		18x46									20x52	21x20	21x20						22x51			
Pembrey & Burry Port	d		18 53			19 28				20 23		20 59	21 27	21 27						22 58			
Llanelli	a		18 59			19 33				20 28		21 05	21 32	21 32						23 04			
	d		19 00			19 34				20 29		21 10	21 33	21 33		21 44				23 05			
Gowerton	d		19x07													21x52				23x12			
Swansea 7	a		19 22			19 51				20 50		21 33	21 52	21 52		22 13				23 27			
	d	19 10		19 29	19 29	19 55		20 29	20 29	20 55		21 35		22 00	22 00				22 32				
Llansamlet	d	19 17										21 42							22 39				
Skewen	d	19 21										21 46							22 43				
Neath	d	19 25		19 40	19 40	20 06		20 40	20 40	21 06		21 50		22 11	22 11				22 47				
Briton Ferry	d	19 28										21 53							22 50				
Baglan	d	19 32										21 57							22 54				
Port Talbot Parkway	d	19 36		19 48	19 48	20 13		20 48	20 48	21 13		22 01		22 18	22 18				22 58				
Pyle	d	19 43										22 08							23 05				
Maesteg	d						20 20				21 22							22 25					
Maesteg (Ewenny Road)	d						20 22				21 24							22 27					
Garth (Mid Glamorgan)	d						20 25				21 27							22 30					
Tondu	d						20 34				21 36							22 39					
Sarn	d						20 37				21 39							22 42					
Wildmill	d						20 39				21 41							22 44					
Bridgend	d	19 54		19 59	19 59	20 25	20 43	20 59	20 59	21 25	21 45	22 16		22 30	22 32			22 49	23 13				
Pencoed	d						20 49				21 51							22 55					
Llanharan	d						20 53				21 55			22 38	22 40			22 59					
Pontyclun	d						20 57				21 59							23 03					
Cardiff Central 7	a	20 18		20 22	20 22	20 47	21 11	21 22	21 22	21 47	22 17	22 39		22 55	22 58			23 18	23 38				
Cardiff Queen Street 3	a																						
Newport (South Wales)	a			20 38	20 38	21 08	21 27	21 38	21 38	22 13								23 37					
Bristol Parkway 7	a			21 00	21 00			22 00	22 00														
Gloucester 7	a						22 22											00 38					
Manchester Piccadilly 10 🚆	a																						
Reading 7	a			22 15	22 15			23 06	23 06														
London Paddington 15 ⊖	a			22 53	22 56			23 42	23 50														

For general notes see front of timetable
For details of catering facilities see Directory of Train Operators

A To Chester (Table 131)
B To Cheltenham Spa (Table 57)
C To Crewe (Table 131)
D Ship service

Saturdays

until 6 September

West Wales, Swansea and Maesteg → Cardiff

Route Diagram - see first page of Table 127

Station		AW	AW	GW	GW	GW	AW	GW		GW	AW	AW	GW	AW	GW	AW		AW	GW	AW	AW	AW	AW	GW
			◇	1 ◇	1 ◇	1 ◇	◇	1 ◇		1 ◇		◇	1 ◇		1 ◇	◇			1 ◇	◇		◇		1 ◇
																					A	B		
				⊡	⊡	⊡	⚲	⊡		⊡		⚲	⊡		⊡	⚲			⊡	⚲			⚲	⊡
Rosslare Harbour ⛴	d																							
Fishguard Harbour ⛴	a																							
	d		01 50																					
Milford Haven	d	00 15														06 05				07 05				
Johnston	d	00x22														06x12				07x12				
Haverfordwest	d	00 30														06 20				07 20				
Clarbeston Road	d	00x37	02x10													06x27				07x27				
Clunderwen	d	00x44														06x33				07x33				
Pembroke Dock	d																						07 05	
Pembroke	d																						07 13	
Lamphey	d																						07x16	
Manorbier	d																						07 25	
Penally	d																						07x30	
Tenby	a																						07 33	
	d																						07 40	
Saundersfoot	d																						07x48	
Kilgetty	d																						07x50	
Narberth	d																						08x00	
Whitland	a	00 50	02 22													06 39				07 39			08 08	
	d	00 50	02 22													06 40				07 40			08 08	
Carmarthen	a	01 12	02 39													06 56				07 56			08 27	
	d		02 44				05 04					05 50		06 18		07 00				07 59			08 30	
Ferryside	d											06x00		06x28						08x09			08x40	
Kidwelly	d											06x05		06x33						08x14			08x46	
Pembrey & Burry Port	d						05 22					06 12		06 40		07 18				08 21			08 53	
Llanelli	a		03 06				05 27					06 17		06 45		07 23				08 26			08 59	
	d		03 06				05 28					06 18		06 46		07 24				08 27		08 45	09 00	
Gowerton	d											06x24		06x52		07x30				08x33		08x53	09x07	
Swansea 7	a		03 25									06 37		07 06		07 43				08 48		09 07	09 22	
	d			03 59	04 59	05 29		05 59		06 29		06 40	06 59	07 09	07 29	07 45			08 29	08 55		09 10		09 29
Llansamlet	d													07 16								09 17		
Skewen	d													07 20								09 21		
Neath	d			04 10	05 10	05 40		06 10		06 40		06 51	07 10	07 24	07 40	07 56			08 40	09 06		09 25		09 40
Briton Ferry	d													07 27								09 29		
Baglan	d													07 31								09 32		
Port Talbot Parkway	d			04 18	05 18	05 48	06 01	06 18		06 48		06 58	07 18	07 35	07 48	08 03			08 48	09 13		09 36		09 48
Pyle	d											07 04		07 42		08 10						09 43		
Maesteg	d										06 49							08 00			09 17			
Maesteg (Ewenny Road)	d										06 51							08 02			09 19			
Garth (Mid Glamorgan)	d										06 54							08 05			09 22			
Tondu	d										07 03							08 14			09 31			
Sarn	d										07 06							08 17			09 34			
Wildmill	d										07 08							08 19			09 36			
Bridgend	d			04 29	05 29	05 59	06 13	06 29		06 59	07 12	07 17	07 29	07 50	07 59	08 18		08 23	08 59	09 25	09 40	09 55		09 59
Pencoed	d						06 19				07 18			07 56		08 24					09 46			
Llanharan	d										07 22			08 00				08 31			09 50			
Pontyclun	d						06 26				07 26			08 04		08 31					09 54			
Cardiff Central 7	a			04 52	05 52	06 22	06 40	06 52		07 22	07 43	07 45	07 52	08 18	08 22	08 44		08 48	09 22	09 47	10 09	10 17		10 22
Cardiff Queen Street 3	a																							
Newport (South Wales)	a			05 08	06 08	06 38	07 02	07 08		07 38		08 02	08 08		08 38	09 02			09 38	10 03	10 25			10 38
Bristol Parkway 7	a			05 36	06 30	07 00		07 30		08 00			08 30		09 00				10 00					11 00
Gloucester 7	a																				11 21			
Manchester Piccadilly 10 ⛴	a						10 13					11 13				12 13				13 13				
Reading 7	a			07 14	07 32	08 02		08 32		09 02			09 32		10 01				10 59					12 03
London Paddington 15 ⊖	a			07 45	08 00	08 30		09 05		09 30			10 01		10 31				11 30					12 30

For general notes see front of timetable
For details of catering facilities see Directory of Train Operators

A To Cheltenham Spa (Table 57)
B From Shrewsbury (Table 129)

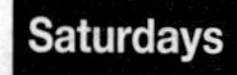

until 6 September

West Wales, Swansea and Maesteg → Cardiff

Route Diagram - see first page of Table 127

		AW	AW	AW	GW	AW	AW	AW	AW	GW	AW	AW	GW	AW	AW	AW	AW	AW	AW	GW	AW
		◇			1 ◇	◇	A			1 ◇	◇	A	1 B	◇	C	◇				1 ◇	R
		⊼	⊼		☕	⊼				☕	⊼		✕	⊼					⊼	☕	⊼
Rosslare Harbour ⛴	d														09 00						
Fishguard Harbour ⛴	a														12 30						
	d																				
Milford Haven	d					09 10								11 10							
Johnston	d					09x17								11x17							
Haverfordwest	d					09 25								11 25							
Clarbeston Road	d					09x32								11x32							
Clunderwen	d					09x38								11x38							
Pembroke Dock	d		08 35										10 02								
Pembroke	d		08 43										10 12								
Lamphey	d		08x46																		
Manorbier	d		08 54										10 25								
Penally	d		08x59																		
Tenby	a		09 02										10 34								
	d		09 10										10 38						11 42		
Saundersfoot	d		09x17										10 48						11x49		
Kilgetty	d		09x19																11x51		
Narberth	d		09x28																12x00		
Whitland	a		09 36			09 44							11 08	11 44					12 08		
	d					09 45			10 08				11 09	11 45					12 09		
Carmarthen	a					10 01			10 26				11 27	12 01					12 26		
	d	09 00			09 35	10 05			10 30		11 05		11 36	12 05					12 30		13 05
Ferryside	d								10x40										12x40		
Kidwelly	d								10x45										12x46		
Pembrey & Burry Port	d	09 18			09 56	10 22			10 52		11 23		11 57	12 23					12 53		13 23
Llanelli	a	09 23			10 01	10 28			10 58		11 28		12 02	12 28					12 59		13 28
	d	09 26			10 03	10 28			10 59		11 29		12 03	12 29		12 33			13 00		13 29
Gowerton	d								11x06										13x07		
Swansea 7	a	09 46			10 21	10 45			11 22		11 46		12 20	12 46		13 01			13 22		13 46
	d	09 55			10 29	10 55		11 10		11 29	11 55		12 29	12 50				13 10		13 29	13 55
Llansamlet	d							11 17										13 17			
Skewen	d							11 21										13 21			
Neath	d	10 06			10 40	11 06		11 25		11 40	12 06		12 40	13 06				13 25		13 40	14 06
Briton Ferry	d							11 28										13 28			
Baglan	d							11 32										13 32			
Port Talbot Parkway	d	10 13			10 48	11 13		11 36		11 48	12 13		12 48	13 13				13 36		13 48	14 13
Pyle	d							11 43										13 43			
Maesteg	d			10 17			11 17					12 17					13 17				
Maesteg (Ewenny Road)	d			10 19			11 19					12 19					13 19				
Garth (Mid Glamorgan)	d			10 22			11 22					12 22					13 22				
Tondu	d			10 31			11 31					12 31					13 31				
Sarn	d			10 34			11 34					12 34					13 34				
Wildmill	d			10 36			11 36					12 36					13 36				
Bridgend	d	10 25		10 40	10 59	11 25	11 40	11 55		11 59	12 25	12 40	12 59	13 25			13 40	13 55		13 59	14 25
Pencoed	d			10 46			11 46					12 46					13 46				
Llanharan	d			10 50			11 50					12 50					13 50				
Pontyclun	d			10 54			11 54					12 54					13 54				
Cardiff Central 7	a	10 47		11 13	11 22	11 47	12 09	12 17		12 22	12 47	13 09	13 22	13 47			14 13	14 16		14 22	14 47
Cardiff Queen Street 3	a																				
Newport (South Wales)	a	11 03			11 38	12 03	12 25			12 38	13 03	13 25	13 38	14 03						14 38	15 03
Bristol Parkway 7	a				12 00					13 00			14 00							15 00	
Gloucester 7	a						13 20					14 20									
Manchester Piccadilly 10	a	14 13				15 13					16 13			17 13							18 10
Reading 7	a				13 01					14 01			15 01							16 01	
London Paddington 15 ⊖	a				13 30					14 30			15 30							16 30	

For general notes see front of timetable
For details of catering facilities see Directory of Train Operators

A To Cheltenham Spa (Table 57)
B **Pembroke Coast Express**
C Ship service

Table 128

Saturdays

until 6 September

West Wales, Swansea and Maesteg → Cardiff

Route Diagram - see first page of Table 127

		AW	GW	AW	AW	AW	AW	AW	GW	AW	AW	GW	AW	AW	AW	GW	AW	AW	AW	AW	GW
			1 ◇	R	◇				1 ◇	R		1 ◇	R			1 ◇	◇	◇			1 ◇
		A				A					A			A							
			[buffet]	[trolley]	[trolley]			[trolley]	[buffet]	[trolley]		[buffet]	[trolley]			[buffet]	[trolley]		[trolley]		[buffet]
Rosslare Harbour	⛴ d																				
Fishguard Harbour	⛴ a																				
	d				13 27																
Milford Haven	d			13 10									15 10								
Johnston	d			13x17									15x17								
Haverfordwest	d			13 25									15 25								
Clarbeston Road	d			13x32									15x32								
Clunderwen	d			13x38									15x38								
Pembroke Dock	d							13 05								14 55			16 35		
Pembroke	d							13 13								15 05			16 43		
Lamphey	d							13x16								15x08			16x46		
Manorbier	d							13 24								15 20			16 54		
Penally	d							13x29								15x26			16x59		
Tenby	a							13 32								15 29			17 02		
	d							13 42								15 35			17 04		
Saundersfoot	d							13x49								15 45			17x11		
Kilgetty	d							13x51								15x48			17x13		
Narberth	d							14x00								15x58			17x22		
Whitland	a			13 44	13 59			14 13					15 44			16 07			17 30		
	d			13 45	13 59			14 13					15 45			16 09			17 31		
Carmarthen	a			14 01	14 16			14 31					16 01			16 26			17 48		
	d			14 05	14 19			14 34		15 05			16 05			16 33	17 01		18 30 →		
Ferryside	d							14x44								16x44	17x11				
Kidwelly	d							14x50								16x50	17x16				
Pembrey & Burry Port	d			14 23				14 57		15 23			16 23			16 57	17 23				
Llanelli	a			14 28	14 43			15 03		15 28			16 28			17 03	17 28				
	d			14 29	14 43			15 04		15 29			16 29			17 04	17 29	17 36			
Gowerton	d			14x35									16x35					17x44			
Swansea 7	a			14 48				15 22		15 46			16 48			17 21	17 46	18 06			
	d		14 29	14 55			15 10		15 29	15 55		16 29	16 55		17 10	17 29	17 55				18 29
Llansamlet	d						15 17								17 17						
Skewen	d						15 21								17 21						
Neath	d		14 40	15 06			15 25		15 40	16 06		16 40	17 06		17 25	17 40	18 06				18 40
Briton Ferry	d						15 28								17 28						
Baglan	d						15 32								17 32						
Port Talbot Parkway	d		14 48	15 13			15 36		15 48	16 13		16 48	17 13		17 36	17 48	18 13				18 48
Pyle	d						15 43								17 43						
Maesteg	d	14 17				15 17					16 17			17 17						18 20	
Maesteg (Ewenny Road)	d	14 19				15 19					16 19			17 19						18 22	
Garth (Mid Glamorgan)	d	14 22				15 22					16 22			17 22						18 25	
Tondu	d	14 31				15 31					16 31			17 31						18 34	
Sarn	d	14 34				15 34					16 34			17 34						18 37	
Wildmill	d	14 36				15 36					16 36			17 36						18 39	
Bridgend	d	14 40	14 59	15 25		15 40	15 55		15 59	16 26	16 40	16 59	17 25	17 40	17 55	17 59	18 25			18 43	18 59
Pencoed	d	14 46				15 46					16 46			17 46						18 49	
Llanharan	d	14 50				15 50					16 50			17 50						18 53	
Pontyclun	d	14 54				15 54					16 54			17 54	18 05					18 57	
Cardiff Central 7	a	15 09	15 22	15 46	16 02	16 09	16 17		16 22	16 47	17 09	17 22	17 47	18 09	18 18	18 22	18 47			19 16	19 22
Cardiff Queen Street 3	a																				
Newport (South Wales)	a	15 25	15 38	16 03		16 23			16 38	17 03	17 27	17 38	18 03	18 25		18 38	19 05				19 38
Bristol Parkway 7	a		16 00						17 00			18 00				19 00					20 00
Gloucester 7	a	16 20				17 20					18 20			19 20							
Manchester Piccadilly 10	🚢 a			19 16						20 13			21 13				22 13				
Reading 7	a		17 01						18 01			19 02				20 00					21 07
London Paddington 15	⊖ a		17 31						18 31			19 30				20 31					21 36

For general notes see front of timetable
For details of catering facilities see
Directory of Train Operators

A To Cheltenham Spa (Table 57)

Saturdays

until 6 September

West Wales, Swansea and Maesteg → Cardiff

Route Diagram - see first page of Table 127

		AW	AW	AW	AW	GW	AW	AW		AW	AW	AW	AW	AW	AW	AW	AW	AW	AW	AW	AW	AW		
		◇				1 ◇	◇			◇				◇	◇									
			A				B			C												D		
Rosslare Harbour	d																					21 15		
Fishguard Harbour	a																					00 45		
	d																							
Milford Haven	d	17 10								19 10						21 20					23 15			
Johnston	d	17x17								19x17						21x27					23x22			
Haverfordwest	d	17 25								19 25						21 35					23 30			
Clarbeston Road	d	17x32								19x32						21x42					23x39			
Clunderwen	d	17x38								19x38						21x48					23x47			
Pembroke Dock	d											19 16							21 11	22 22				
Pembroke	d											19 24							21 19	22 30				
Lamphey	d											19x27							21x22	22x33				
Manorbier	d											19 36							21 31	22 41				
Penally	d											19x41							21x36	22x46				
Tenby	a											19 44							21 39	22 49				
	d											19 47							21 45	22 51				
Saundersfoot	d											19x54							21x53	22x58				
Kilgetty	d											19x56							21x55	23x00				
Narberth	d											20x05							22x05	23x09				
Whitland	a	17 44								19 44		20 13				21 54			22 13	23 17	23 56			
	d	17 45								19 45		20 14				21 55			22 14	23 18	23 57			
Carmarthen	a	18 05			←					20 01		20 33				22 16			22 32	23 40	00 18			
	d	18 07			18 30		19 10			20 05		20 35		21 05					22 35					
Ferryside	d	18x17			18x40							20x46		21x15					22x45					
Kidwelly	d	18x23			18x46							20x52		21x20					22x51					
Pembrey & Burry Port	d	18 29			18 53		19 28			20 23		20 59		21 27					22 58					
Llanelli	a	18 35			18 59		19 33			20 28		21 05		21 32					23 04					
	d	18 35			19 00		19 34			20 29		21 06		21 33	21 44				23 05					
Gowerton	d				19x07										21x52				23x12					
Swansea 7	a	18 52			19 22		19 51			20 50		21 24		21 50	22 13				23 29					
	d	18 55		19 10		19 29	19 55			20 55			21 35	21 55				22 20						
Llansamlet	d			19 17									21 42					22 27						
Skewen	d			19 21									21 46					22 31						
Neath	d	19 06		19 25		19 40	20 06			21 06			21 50	22 06				22 35						
Briton Ferry	d			19 28									21 53					22 38						
Baglan	d			19 32									21 57					22 42						
Port Talbot Parkway	d	19 13		19 36		19 48	20 13			21 13			22 01	22 13				22 46						
Pyle	d			19 43									22 08					22 53						
Maesteg	d		19 20					20 20			21 22						22 23							
Maesteg (Ewenny Road)	d		19 22					20 22			21 24						22 25							
Garth (Mid Glamorgan)	d		19 25					20 25			21 27						22 28							
Tondu	d		19 34					20 34			21 36						22 37							
Sarn	d		19 37					20 37			21 39						22 40							
Wildmill	d		19 39					20 39			21 41						22 42							
Bridgend	d	19 25	19 43	19 53		19 59	20 25	20 43		21 25	21 45		22 16	22 25			22 47	23 01						
Pencoed	d		19 49					20 49			21 51						22 53							
Llanharan	d		19 53					20 53			21 55			22 33			22 57							
Pontyclun	d		19 57					20 57			21 59						23 01							
Cardiff Central 7	a	19 47	20 12	20 17		20 22	20 47	21 12		21 47	22 17		22 39	22 50			23 16	23 26						
Cardiff Queen Street 3	a																							
Newport (South Wales)	a	20 23	20 28			20 38	21 07	21 28		22 06							23 37							
Bristol Parkway 7	a					21 00																		
Gloucester 7	a		21 22					22 22									00 42							
Manchester Piccadilly 10	a	23 50																						
Reading 7	a					21 58																		
London Paddington 15 ⊖	a					22 31																		

For general notes see front of timetable
For details of catering facilities see Directory of Train Operators

A To Cheltenham Spa (Table 57)
B To Chester (Table 131)
C To Crewe (Table 131)
D Ship service

West Wales, Swansea and Maesteg → Cardiff

Route Diagram - see first page of Table 127

		AW	AW	GW	GW	GW	AW	GW		GW	AW	AW	GW	AW	GW	AW		AW	GW	GW	AW	AW	AW	AW
			◇	1 ◇	1 ◇	1 ◇	◇	1 ◇		1 ◇		◇	1 ◇		1 ◇	◇			1 ◇	1 ◇	◇		◇	
							A															B	C	
				⊡	⊡	⊡	⏚	⊡		⊡		⏚	⊡		⊡	⏚			⊡	⊡	⏚			⏚
Rosslare Harbour ⛴	d																							
Fishguard Harbour ⛴	a																							
	d		01 50																					
Milford Haven	d	00 15														06 05					07 05			
Johnston	d	00x22														06x12					07x12			
Haverfordwest	d	00 30														06 20					07 20			
Clarbeston Road	d	00x37	02x10													06x27					07x27			
Clunderwen	d	00x44														06x33					07x33			
Pembroke Dock	d																							07 05
Pembroke	d																							07 13
Lamphey	d																							07x16
Manorbier	d																							07 25
Penally	d																							07x30
Tenby	a																							07 33
	d																							07 40
Saundersfoot	d																							07x48
Kilgetty	d																							07x50
Narberth	d																							08x00
Whitland	a	00 50	02 22													06 39					07 39			08 08
	d	00 50	02 22													06 40					07 40			08 08
Carmarthen	a	01 12	02 39													06 56					07 56			08 27
	d		02 44				05 04					05 50		06 18		07 00					07 59			08 30
Ferryside	d											06x00		06x28							08x09			08x40
Kidwelly	d											06x05		06x33							08x14			08x46
Pembrey & Burry Port	d						05 22					06 12		06 40		07 18					08 21			08 53
Llanelli	a		03 06				05 27					06 17		06 45		07 23					08 26			08 59
	d		03 06				05 28					06 18		06 46		07 24					08 27		08 45	09 00
Gowerton	d											06x24		06x52		07x30					08x33		08x53	09x07
Swansea 7	a		03 25									06 37		07 06		07 43					08 48		09 07	09 22
	d			03 59	04 59	05 29		05 59		06 29		06 40	06 59	07 09	07 29	07 45			07 59	08 29	08 55		09 10	
Llansamlet	d													07 16									09 17	
Skewen	d													07 20									09 21	
Neath	d			04 10	05 10	05 40		06 10		06 40		06 51	07 10	07 24	07 40	07 56			08 10	08 40	09 06		09 25	
Briton Ferry	d													07 27									09 29	
Baglan	d													07 31									09 32	
Port Talbot Parkway	d			04 18	05 18	05 48	06 01	06 18		06 48		06 58	07 18	07 35	07 48	08 03			08 18	08 48	09 13		09 36	
Pyle	d											07 04		07 42		08 10							09 43	
Maesteg	d										06 49							08 00				09 17		
Maesteg (Ewenny Road)	d										06 51							08 02				09 19		
Garth (Mid Glamorgan)	d										06 54							08 05				09 22		
Tondu	d										07 03							08 14				09 31		
Sarn	d										07 06							08 17				09 34		
Wildmill	d										07 08							08 19				09 36		
Bridgend	d			04 29	05 29	05 59	06 13	06 29		06 59	07 12	07 17	07 29	07 50	07 59	08 18		08 23	08 29	08 59	09 25	09 40	09 55	
Pencoed	d						06 19				07 18			07 56		08 24						09 46		
Llanharan	d										07 22			08 00				08 31				09 50		
Pontyclun	d						06 26				07 26			08 04		08 31						09 54		
Cardiff Central 7	a			04 52	05 52	06 22	06 40	06 52		07 22	07 43	07 45	07 52	08 18	08 22	08 44		08 48	08 52	09 22	09 47	10 09	10 17	
Cardiff Queen Street 3	a																							
Newport (South Wales)	a			05 08	06 08	06 38	07 02	07 08		07 38		08 02	08 08		08 38	09 02			09 08	09 38	10 03	10 25		
Bristol Parkway 7	a			05 36	06 30	07 00		07 30		08 00			08 30		09 00				09 30	10 00				
Gloucester 7	a																					11 21		
Manchester Piccadilly 10 ⛴	a						10 13					11 13				12 13					13 13			
Reading 7	a			07 14	07 32	08 02		08 32		09 02			09 32		10 01				10 32	10 59				
London Paddington 15 ⊖	a			07 45	08 00	08 30		09 05		09 30			10 01		10 31				10 59	11 30				

For general notes see front of timetable
For details of catering facilities see Directory of Train Operators

A ⏚ from Cardiff Central
B To Cheltenham Spa (Table 57)
C From Shrewsbury (Table 129)

Table 128

Saturdays

from 13 September

West Wales, Swansea and Maesteg → Cardiff

Route Diagram - see first page of Table 127

		GW	AW		AW	GW	AW	AW	AW	AW	GW		AW	AW	GW	AW	AW	AW	AW		AW	AW	GW	AW
		1 ◇	◇			1 ◇	◇				1 ◇		◇		1 ◇	◇		◇					1 ◇	R
								A						A			B							
		🍽	🛒			🍽	🛒			🛒	🍽		🛒		🍽	🛒						🛒	🍽	🛒
Rosslare Harbour ⛴	d																09 00							
Fishguard Harbour ⛴	a																12 30							
	d																							
Milford Haven	d						09 10									11 10								
Johnston	d						09x17									11x17								
Haverfordwest	d						09 25									11 25								
Clarbeston Road	d						09x32									11x32								
Clunderwen	d						09x38									11x38								
Pembroke Dock	d									09 05												11 05		
Pembroke	d									09 13												11 13		
Lamphey	d									09x16												11x16		
Manorbier	d									09 24												11 24		
Penally	d									09x29												11x29		
Tenby	a									09 32												11 32		
	d									09 42												11 42		
Saundersfoot	d									09x49												11x49		
Kilgetty	d									09x51												11x51		
Narberth	d									10x00												12x00		
Whitland	a						09 44			10 08						11 44						12 08		
	d						09 45			10 09						11 45						12 09		
Carmarthen	a						10 01			10 26						12 01						12 26		
	d		09 00			09 35	10 05			10 30			11 05			12 05						12 30		13 05
Ferryside	d									10x40												12x40		
Kidwelly	d									10x46												12x46		
Pembrey & Burry Port	d		09 18			09 56	10 22			10 53			11 23			12 23						12 53		13 23
Llanelli	a		09 23			10 01	10 28			10 59			11 28			12 28						12 59		13 28
	d		09 26			10 03	10 28			11 00			11 29			12 29		12 33				13 00		13 29
Gowerton	d									11x07												13x07		
Swansea 7	a		09 46			10 21	10 45			11 22			11 46			12 46		13 01				13 22		13 48
	d	09 29	09 55			10 29	10 55		11 10		11 29		11 55		12 29	12 50					13 10		13 29	13 55
Llansamlet	d								11 17												13 17			
Skewen	d								11 21												13 21			
Neath	d	09 40	10 06			10 40	11 06		11 25		11 40		12 06		12 40	13 06					13 25		13 40	14 06
Briton Ferry	d								11 28												13 28			
Baglan	d								11 32												13 32			
Port Talbot Parkway	d	09 48	10 13			10 48	11 13		11 36		11 48		12 13		12 48	13 13					13 36		13 48	14 13
Pyle	d								11 43												13 43			
Maesteg	d				10 17			11 17						12 17					13 17					
Maesteg (Ewenny Road)	d				10 19			11 19						12 19					13 19					
Garth (Mid Glamorgan)	d				10 22			11 22						12 22					13 22					
Tondu	d				10 31			11 31						12 31					13 31					
Sarn	d				10 34			11 34						12 34					13 34					
Wildmill	d				10 36			11 36						12 36					13 36					
Bridgend	d	09 59	10 25		10 40	10 59	11 25	11 40	11 55		11 59		12 25	12 40	12 59	13 25			13 40		13 55		13 59	14 25
Pencoed	d				10 46			11 46						12 46					13 46					
Llanharan	d				10 50			11 50						12 50					13 50					
Pontyclun	d				10 54			11 54						12 54					13 54					
Cardiff Central 7	a	10 22	10 47		11 13	11 22	11 47	12 09	12 17		12 22		12 47	13 09	13 22	13 47			14 13		14 16		14 22	14 47
Cardiff Queen Street 3	a																							
Newport (South Wales)	a	10 38	11 03			11 38	12 03	12 25			12 38		13 03	13 25	13 38	14 03							14 38	15 03
Bristol Parkway 7	a	11 00				12 00					13 00				14 00								15 00	
Gloucester 7	a							13 20						14 20										
Manchester Piccadilly 10 ⛴	a		14 13				15 13						16 13			17 13								18 10
Reading 7	a	12 03				13 01					14 01				15 01								16 01	
London Paddington 15	⊖ a	12 30				13 30					14 30				15 30								16 30	

For general notes see front of timetable
For details of catering facilities see
Directory of Train Operators

A To Cheltenham Spa (Table 57)
B Ship service

Table 128

Saturdays

from 13 September

West Wales, Swansea and Maesteg → Cardiff

Route Diagram - see first page of Table 127

		AW	GW	AW	AW	AW		AW	AW	GW	AW	AW	GW	AW		AW	AW	AW	GW	AW	AW	AW		GW
				R							R			R										
			1 ◇		◇					1 ◇			1 ◇						1 ◇	◇	◇			1 ◇
		A				A						A		B		A								
			☕	🍴	🍴				🍴	☕	🍴		☕	🍴					☕	🍴				☕
Rosslare Harbour ⛴	d																							
Fishguard Harbour ⛴	a																							
	d				13 27																			
Milford Haven	d			13 10										15 10										
Johnston	d			13x17										15x17										
Haverfordwest	d			13 25										15 25										
Clarbeston Road	d			13x32										15x32										
Clunderwen	d			13x38										15x38										
Pembroke Dock	d								13 05									15 05						
Pembroke	d								13 13									15 13						
Lamphey	d								13x16									15x16						
Manorbier	d								13 24									15 24						
Penally	d								13x29									15x29						
Tenby	a								13 32									15 32						
	d								13 42									15 44						
Saundersfoot	d								13x49									15x51						
Kilgetty	d								13x51									15x53						
Narberth	d								14x00									16x02						
Whitland	a			13 44	13 59				14 13					15 44				16 10						
	d			13 45	13 59				14 13					15 45				16 11						
Carmarthen	a			14 01	14 16				14 31					16 01				16 28						
	d			14 05	14 19				14 34		15 05			16 05				16 31		17 01				
Ferryside	d								14x44									16x41		17x11				
Kidwelly	d								14x50									16x47		17x16				
Pembrey & Burry Port	d			14 23					14 57		15 23			16 23				16 54		17 23				
Llanelli	a			14 28	14 43				15 03		15 28			16 28				17 00		17 28				
	d			14 29	14 43				15 04		15 29			16 29				17 01		17 29	17 36			
Gowerton	d			14x35										16x35				17x08			17x44			
Swansea 7	a			14 48					15 22		15 46			16 48				17 22		17 46	18 06			
	d		14 29	14 55				15 10		15 29	15 55		16 29	16 55			17 10		17 29	17 55				18 29
Llansamlet	d							15 17									17 17							
Skewen	d							15 21									17 21							
Neath	d		14 40	15 06				15 25		15 40	16 06		16 40	17 06			17 25		17 40	18 06				18 40
Briton Ferry	d							15 28									17 28							
Baglan	d							15 32									17 32							
Port Talbot Parkway	d		14 48	15 13				15 36		15 48	16 13		16 48	17 13			17 36		17 48	18 13				18 48
Pyle	d							15 43									17 43							
Maesteg	d	14 17				15 17						16 17				17 17						18 20		
Maesteg (Ewenny Road)	d	14 19				15 19						16 19				17 19						18 22		
Garth (Mid Glamorgan)	d	14 22				15 22						16 22				17 22						18 25		
Tondu	d	14 31				15 31						16 31				17 31						18 34		
Sarn	d	14 34				15 34						16 34				17 34						18 37		
Wildmill	d	14 36				15 36						16 36				17 36						18 39		
Bridgend	d	14 40	14 59	15 25		15 40		15 55		15 59	16 26	16 40	16 59	17 25		17 40	17 55		17 59	18 25		18 43		18 59
Pencoed	d	14 46				15 46						16 46				17 46						18 49		
Llanharan	d	14 50				15 50						16 50				17 50						18 53		
Pontyclun	d	14 54				15 54						16 54				17 54	18 05					18 57		
Cardiff Central 7	a	15 09	15 22	15 46	16 02	16 09		16 17		16 22	16 47	17 09	17 22	17 47		18 09	18 18		18 22	18 47		19 16		19 22
Cardiff Queen Street 3	a																							
Newport (South Wales)	a	15 25	15 38	16 03		16 23				16 38	17 03	17 27	17 38	18 03		18 25			18 38	19 05				19 38
Bristol Parkway 7	a		16 00							17 00			18 00						19 00					20 00
Gloucester 7	a	16 20				17 20						18 20				19 20								
Manchester Piccadilly 10 🚢	a			19 16							20 13			21 13						22 13				
Reading 7	a		17 01							18 01			19 02						20 01					21 05
London Paddington 15 ⊖	a		17 31							18 31			19 30						20 31					21 36

For general notes see front of timetable
For details of catering facilities see
Directory of Train Operators

A To Cheltenham Spa (Table 57)
B 🍴 from Swansea

Saturdays

from 13 September

West Wales, Swansea and Maesteg → Cardiff

Route Diagram - see first page of Table 127

		AW ◇ 🛒	AW A	AW	AW 🛒	GW 1 ◇ 🍽	AW ◇ B 🛒	AW		AW ◇ C	AW	AW	AW	AW ◇	AW ◇	AW	AW	AW	AW	AW	AW	AW D		
Rosslare Harbour ⛴	d																					21 15		
Fishguard Harbour ⛴	a																					00 45		
	d																							
Milford Haven	d	17 10								19 10						21 20					23 15			
Johnston	d	17x17								19x17						21x27					23x22			
Haverfordwest	d	17 25								19 25						21 35					23 30			
Clarbeston Road	d	17x32								19x32						21x42					23x39			
Clunderwen	d	17x38								19x38						21x48					23x47			
Pembroke Dock	d				17 05							19 16							21 11	22 22				
Pembroke	d				17 13							19 24							21 19	22 30				
Lamphey	d				17x16							19x27							21x22	22x33				
Manorbier	d				17 24							19 36							21 31	22 41				
Penally	d				17x29							19x41							21x36	22x46				
Tenby	a				17 32							19 44							21 39	22 49				
	d				17 42							19 47							21 45	22 51				
Saundersfoot	d				17x49							19x54							21x53	22x58				
Kilgetty	d				17x51							19x56							21x55	23x00				
Narberth	d				18x00							20x05							22x05	23x09				
Whitland	a	17 44			18 08					19 44		20 13				21 54			22 13	23 17	23 56			
	d	17 45			18 09					19 45		20 14				21 55			22 14	23 18	23 57			
Carmarthen	a	18 05			18 26					20 01		20 33				22 16			22 32	23 40	00 18			
	d	18 07			18 30		19 10			20 05		20 35		21 05					22 35					
Ferryside	d	18x17			18x40							20x46		21x15					22x45					
Kidwelly	d	18x23			18x46							20x52		21x20					22x51					
Pembrey & Burry Port	d	18 29			18 53		19 28			20 23		20 59		21 27					22 58					
Llanelli	a	18 35			18 59		19 33			20 28		21 05		21 32					23 04					
	d	18 35			19 00		19 34			20 29		21 06		21 33	21 44				23 05					
Gowerton	d				19x07										21x52				23x12					
Swansea 7	a	18 52			19 22		19 51			20 50		21 24		21 50	22 13				23 29					
	d	18 55		19 10		19 29	19 55			20 55			21 35	21 55				22 20						
Llansamlet	d			19 17									21 42					22 27						
Skewen	d			19 21									21 46					22 31						
Neath	d	19 06		19 25		19 40	20 06			21 06			21 50	22 06				22 35						
Briton Ferry	d			19 28									21 53					22 38						
Baglan	d			19 32									21 57					22 42						
Port Talbot Parkway	d	19 13		19 36		19 48	20 13			21 13			22 01	22 13				22 46						
Pyle	d			19 43									22 08					22 53						
Maesteg	d		19 20					20 20			21 22						22 23							
Maesteg (Ewenny Road)	d		19 22					20 22			21 24						22 25							
Garth (Mid Glamorgan)	d		19 25					20 25			21 27						22 28							
Tondu	d		19 34					20 34			21 36						22 37							
Sarn	d		19 37					20 37			21 39						22 40							
Wildmill	d		19 39					20 39			21 41						22 42							
Bridgend	d	19 25	19 43	19 53		19 59	20 25	20 43		21 25	21 45		22 16	22 25			22 47	23 01						
Pencoed	d		19 49					20 49			21 51						22 53							
Llanharan	d		19 53					20 53			21 55			22 33			22 57							
Pontyclun	d		19 57					20 57			21 59						23 01							
Cardiff Central 7	a	19 47	20 12	20 17		20 22	20 47	21 12		21 47	22 17		22 39	22 50			23 16	23 26						
Cardiff Queen Street 3	a																							
Newport (South Wales)	a	20 23	20 28			20 38	21 07	21 28		22 06							23 37							
Bristol Parkway 7	a					21 00																		
Gloucester 7	a		21 22					22 22									00 42							
Manchester Piccadilly 10 ⛴	a	23 50																						
Reading 7	a					21 58																		
London Paddington 15 ⊖	a					22 31																		

For general notes see front of timetable
For details of catering facilities see Directory of Train Operators

A To Cheltenham Spa (Table 57)
B To Chester (Table 131)
C To Crewe (Table 131)
D Ship service

Table 128

Sundays

until 7 September

West Wales, Swansea and Maesteg → Cardiff

Route Diagram - see first page of Table 127

		AW	GW	GW	GW	AW	GW	AW	GW	AW	AW	GW	AW	AW	AW	AW	GW	AW	AW	AW	AW
		◇	[1] ◇	[1] ◇	[1] ◇	◇	[1] ◇	◇	[1] ◇	◇	◇	[1] ◇	◇	◇		[R]	[1] ◇	[R]	[R]		
						A		A		B	C		B	C		D		C	B		
			⊡	⊡	⊡	⌶	⊡	⌶	⊡	⌶	⌶	⊡	⌶	⌶			⊡	⌶	⌶		
Rosslare Harbour ⛴	d															09 00					
Fishguard Harbour ⛴	a															12 30					
	d	01 50																			14 30
Milford Haven	d					09 25												13 35	13 35		
Johnston	d					09x32												13x42	13x42		
Haverfordwest	d					09 40												13 50	13 50		
Clarbeston Road	d					09x47												13x57	13x57		
Clunderwen	d					09x54												14x04	14x04		
Pembroke Dock	d									11 00	11 00				12 12						
Pembroke	d									11 08	11 08				12 20						
Lamphey	d									11x11	11x11				12x23						
Manorbier	d									11 19	11 19				12 31						
Penally	d									11x24	11x24				12x36						
Tenby	a									11 27	11 27				12 39						
	d									11 36	11 36				12 41					14 00	
Saundersfoot	d									11x43	11x43				12x49					14x08	
Kilgetty	d									11x44	11x44				12x51					14x10	
Narberth	d									11x53	11x53				13x01					14x20	
Whitland	a	02 21				10 00				12 01	12 01				13 09			14 10	14 10	14 30	15 01
	d	02 22				10 00				12 02	12 02				13 10			14 11	14 11	14 31	15 02
Carmarthen	a	02 38				10 17				12 18	12 18				13 27			14 30	14 30	14 50	15 20
	d	02 41				10 20				12 35	12 35				13 30			14 35	14 35		
Ferryside	d					10x30				12x45	12x45				13x40						
Kidwelly	d					10x35				12x51	12x51				13x46						
Pembrey & Burry Port	d					10 42				12 58	12 58				13 53			14 53	14 53		
Llanelli	a	03 03				10 48				13 04	13 04				13 59			14 59	14 59		
	d	03 04				10 48				13 04	13 04				14 00			14 59	14 59		
Gowerton	d					10x55									14x07						
Swansea 7	a	03 21				11 09				13 21	13 21		←	←	14 21			15 18	15 18		
	d	03 35	08 29	09 29	10 29	11 12	11 29		12 29	13 35 →	13 35 →	13 29	13 35	13 35			14 29	15 19	15 19		
Llansamlet	d					11 19															
Skewen	d					11 23															
Neath	d	03 46	08 41	09 41	10 41	11 27	11 41		12 41			13 41	13 47	13 47			14 41	15 30	15 30		
Briton Ferry	d					11 30															
Baglan	d					11 34															
Port Talbot Parkway	d	03 53	08 48	09 48	10 48	11 38	11 48	←	12 48			13 48	13 55	13 55			14 48	15 38	15 38		
Pyle	d					11 45		11 45													
Maesteg	d					→															
Maesteg (Ewenny Road)	d																				
Garth (Mid Glamorgan)	d																				
Tondu	d																				
Sarn	d																				
Wildmill	d																				
Bridgend	d	04 05	09 00	10 00	11 00		12 00	12 10	13 00			14 00	14 08	14 08			15 00	15 51	15 51		
Pencoed	d							12 16										15 57	15 57		
Llanharan	d																	16 01	16 01		
Pontyclun	d							12 23										16 05	16 05		
Cardiff Central 7	a	04 30	09 22	10 22	11 22		12 22	12 36	13 22			14 22	14 30	14 30			15 22	16 18	16 18		
Cardiff Queen Street 3	a																				
Newport (South Wales)	a		09 38	10 38	11 38		12 38	12 48	13 38			14 38	14 48	14 48			15 38	16 48	16 48		
Bristol Parkway 7	a																				
Gloucester 7	a		10 21	11 21	12 21		13 21		14 21			15 21					16 21				
Manchester Piccadilly 10 ⛴	a							16 11					18 26	18 28				20 14	20 17		
Reading 7	a		11 48	12 43	13 44		14 43		15 43			16 29					17 29				
London Paddington 15 ⊖	a		12 29	13 26	14 24		15 21		16 22			17 10					18 15				

For general notes see front of timetable
For details of catering facilities see Directory of Train Operators

A ⌶ to Cardiff Central
B From 20 July
C Until 13 July
D Ship service

Table 128

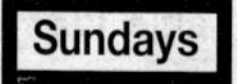

until 7 September

West Wales, Swansea and Maesteg → Cardiff

Route Diagram - see first page of Table 127

	GW	AW	GW	AW	AW	GW	AW	AW	AW	GW	AW	GW	AW	AW	AW	AW	AW	AW	AW
	1 ◇	◇	1 ◇	R	R	1 ◇	R	R		1 ◇	R	1 ◇	◇	◇		◇			R
				A	B		A	B			C		D	E					G
Rosslare Harbour d																			21 15
Fishguard Harbour a																			00 45
d																			
Milford Haven d				15 35	15 35						17 35				19 35	21 35		23 15	
Johnston d				15x42	15x42						17x42				19x42	21x42		23x22	
Haverfordwest d				15 50	15 50						17 50				19 50	21 50		23 30	
Clarbeston Road d				15x57	15x57						17x57				19x58	21x58		23x37	
Clunderwen d				16x04	16x04						18x05				20x05	22x06		23x44	
Pembroke Dock d									16 05					19 05			22 05		
Pembroke d									16 13					19 13			22 13		
Lamphey d									16x16					19x16			22x16		
Manorbier d									16 25					19 24			22 25		
Penally d									16x30					19x29			22x30		
Tenby a									16 33					19 32			22 33		
d									16 35					19 35			22 35		
Saundersfoot d									16x43					19x42			22x43		
Kilgetty d									16x45					19x44			22x45		
Narberth d									16x55					19x53			22x55		
Whitland a				16 10	16 10				17 03		18 11			20 01	20 11	22 12	23 03	23 50	
d				16 10	16 10				17 04		18 11			20 04	20 12	22 13	23 04	23 51	
Carmarthen a				16 28	16 28				17 25		18 30			20 21	20 30	22 30	23 25	00 07	
d			15 39	16 32	16 32					17 39	18 35	19 09		20 35		22 35			
Ferryside d				16x42	16x42						18x45			20x45		22x45			
Kidwelly d				16x47	16x47						18x50			20x51		22x51			
Pembrey & Burry Port d			15 59	16 54	16 54					17 59	18 57	19 29		20 59		22 59			
Llanelli a			16 04	17 00	17 00					18 04	19 03	19 34		21 05		23 05			
d		15 45	16 06	17 00	17 00					18 06	19 03	19 36	19 52	21 05		23 05			
Gowerton d		15x52		17x07	17x07						19x10		19x59	21x12		23x12			
Swansea 7 a		16 13	16 22	17 20	17 20					18 22	19 26	19 52	20 13	21 26		23 26			
d	15 29		16 29	17 35	17 35	17 29	17 35	17 35		18 29	19 35	19 59	20 35	21 35		23 35			
Llansamlet d														21 42					
Skewen d														21 46					
Neath d	15 41		16 41			17 41	17 48	17 48		18 41	19 46	20 11	20 46	21 50		23 46			
Briton Ferry d														21 53					
Baglan d														21 57					
Port Talbot Parkway d	15 48		16 48			17 48	17 56	17 56		18 48	19 54	20 18	20 54	22 01		23 54			
Pyle d														22 08					
Maesteg d																			
Maesteg (Ewenny Road) d																			
Garth (Mid Glamorgan) d																			
Tondu d																			
Sarn d																			
Wildmill d																			
Bridgend d	16 00		17 00			18 00	18 09	18 09		19 00	20 07	20 30	21 07	22 16		00 07			
Pencoed d														22 22					
Llanharan d														22 26					
Pontyclun d														22 30					
Cardiff Central 7 a	16 23		17 22			18 22	18 28	18 28		19 22	20 29	20 52	21 30	22 44		00 50			
Cardiff Queen Street 3 a																			
Newport (South Wales) a	16 38		17 38			18 38	18 48	18 48		19 38	20 48	21 08		23 07					
Bristol Parkway 7 a																			
Gloucester 7 a	17 21		18 21			19 21				20 21		21 51							
Manchester Piccadilly 10 a							22 13	22 16											
Reading 7 a	18 49		19 31			20 50				21 45		23 23							
London Paddington 15 ⊖ a	19 30		20 06			21 30				22 28		00 05							

For general notes see front of timetable
For details of catering facilities see Directory of Train Operators

A Until 13 July. Conveys portion to Holyhead (Table 81). to Cardiff Central

B From 20 July. Conveys portion to Holyhead (Table 81). to Cardiff Central

C To Crewe (Table 131)

D From Shrewsbury (Table 129)

E To Hereford (Table 131)

G Ship service

Table 128

Sundays

from 14 September

West Wales, Swansea and Maesteg → Cardiff

Route Diagram - see first page of Table 127

		AW	GW	GW	GW	GW	AW	GW	AW	GW	AW	AW	GW	GW	AW	AW	GW
		◇	1 ◇	1 ◇	1 ◇	1 ◇	◇	1 ◇	R	1 ◇	◇		1 ◇	1 ◇	R		1 ◇
									A								
			FP	FP	FP	FP		FP		FP	trolley		FP	FP	trolley		FP
Rosslare Harbour (ship)	d								09 00								
Fishguard Harbour (ship)	a								12 30								
	d	01 50														14 10	
Milford Haven	d														13 35		
Johnston	d														13x42		
Haverfordwest	d														13 50		
Clarbeston Road	d														13x57		
Clunderwen	d														14x04		
Pembroke Dock	d																
Pembroke	d																
Lamphey	d																
Manorbier	d																
Penally	d																
Tenby	a																
	d											13 10					
Saundersfoot	d											13x18					
Kilgetty	d											13x20					
Narberth	d											13x30					
Whitland	a	02 21										13 38			14 10	14 41	
	d	02 22													14 11	14 42	
Carmarthen	a	02 38													14 28	15 00	
	d	02 41					10 30				12 35				14 42		
Ferryside	d						10x40				12x45						
Kidwelly	d						10x45				12x51						
Pembrey & Burry Port	d						10 52				12 58				15 00		
Llanelli	a	03 03					10 58				13 04				15 06		
	d	03 04					10 58				13 04				15 06		
Gowerton	d						11x05										
Swansea 7	a	03 21					11 18				13 21				15 25		
	d	03 35	07 59	08 59	09 59	10 59	11 22	11 59		12 59	13 35		13 59	14 59	15 30		15 59
Llansamlet	d						11 29										
Skewen	d						11 33										
Neath	d	03 46	08 11	09 11	10 11	11 11	11 37	12 11		13 11	13 47		14 11	15 11	15 41		16 11
Briton Ferry	d						11 40										
Baglan	d						11 44										
Port Talbot Parkway	d	03 53	08 18	09 18	10 18	11 18	11 48	12 18		13 18	13 55		14 18	15 18	15 49		16 18
Pyle	d						11 55										
Maesteg	d																
Maesteg (Ewenny Road)	d																
Garth (Mid Glamorgan)	d																
Tondu	d																
Sarn	d																
Wildmill	d																
Bridgend	d	04 05	08 30	09 30	10 30	11 30	12 03	12 30		13 30	14 08		14 30	15 30	16 02		16 30
Pencoed	d						12 09										
Llanharan	d						12 13										
Pontyclun	d						12 17										
Cardiff Central 7	a	04 30	08 52	09 52	10 52	11 52	12 31	12 52		13 52	14 30		14 52	15 52	16 23		16 52
Cardiff Queen Street 3	a																
Newport (South Wales)	a		09 12	10 08	11 08	12 08	12 48	13 08		14 08	14 48		15 08	16 08	16 48		17 08
Bristol Parkway 7	a		09 34	10 30	11 30	12 30		13 30		14 30			15 30	16 30			17 30
Gloucester 7	a																
Manchester Piccadilly 10 (ship)	a						16 10				18 19				20 15		
Reading 7	a		10 31	11 27	12 27	13 27		14 27		15 27			16 27	17 27			18 27
London Paddington 15 ⊖	a		11 09	12 05	13 05	14 05		15 05		16 05			17 05	18 08			19 05

For general notes see front of timetable
For details of catering facilities see Directory of Train Operators

A Ship service

Table 128

Sundays

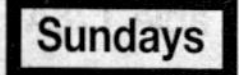

from 14 September

West Wales, Swansea and Maesteg → Cardiff

Route Diagram - see first page of Table 127

		AW	GW		AW	GW		AW	AW		GW	AW		GW	AW		AW	AW	AW	AW	AW	AW		
		◇	1 ◇		R	1 ◇		R			1 ◇	R		1 ◇	◇		◇		◇			R		
					A			A				C			D		E					G		
Rosslare Harbour	d																					21 15		
Fishguard Harbour	a																					00 45		
	d																							
Milford Haven	d				15 35							17 35						19 35	21 35		23 15			
Johnston	d				15x42							17x42						19x42	21x42		23x22			
Haverfordwest	d				15 50							17 50						19 50	21 50		23 30			
Clarbeston Road	d				15x57							17x57						19x58	21x58		23x37			
Clunderwen	d				16x04							18x05						20x05	22x06		23x44			
Pembroke Dock	d								16 05								19 05			22 05				
Pembroke	d								16 13								19 13			22 13				
Lamphey	d								16x16								19x16			22x16				
Manorbier	d								16 25								19 24			22 25				
Penally	d								16x30								19x29			22x30				
Tenby	a								16 33								19 32			22 33				
	d								16 35								19 35			22 35				
Saundersfoot	d								16x43								19x42			22x43				
Kilgetty	d								16x45								19x44			22x45				
Narberth	d								16x55								19x53			22x55				
Whitland	a				16 10				17 03			18 11					20 01	20 11	22 12	23 03	23 50			
	d				16 10				17 04			18 11					20 04	20 12	22 13	23 04	23 51			
Carmarthen	a				16 27				17 25			18 28					20 21	20 30	22 30	23 25	00 07			
	d		15 39		16 31						17 39	18 37		19 09			20 35		22 35					
Ferryside	d				16x41							18x47					20x45		22x45					
Kidwelly	d				16x46							18x52					20x51		22x51					
Pembrey & Burry Port	d		15 59		16 53						17 59	18 59		19 29			20 59		22 59					
Llanelli	a		16 04		16 59						18 04	19 05		19 34			21 05		23 05					
	d	15 45	16 06		16 59						18 06	19 05		19 36	19 52		21 05		23 05					
Gowerton	d	15x52			17x06							19x12			19x59		21x12		23x12					
Swansea 7	a	16 13	16 22		17 19			←			18 22	19 27		19 52	20 13		21 26		23 26					
	d		16 29		17 35 →	17 29		17 35			18 29	19 35		19 59	20 35		21 35		23 35					
Llansamlet	d																21 42							
Skewen	d																21 46							
Neath	d		16 41			17 41		17 47			18 41	19 46		20 11	20 46		21 50		23 46					
Briton Ferry	d																21 53							
Baglan	d																21 57							
Port Talbot Parkway	d		16 48			17 48		17 55			18 48	19 54		20 18	20 54		22 01		23 54					
Pyle	d																22 08							
Maesteg	d																							
Maesteg (Ewenny Road)	d																							
Garth (Mid Glamorgan)	d																							
Tondu	d																							
Sarn	d																							
Wildmill	d																							
Bridgend	d		17 00			18 00		18 08			19 00	20 07		20 30	21 07		22 16		00 07					
Pencoed	d																22 22							
Llanharan	d																22 26							
Pontyclun	d																22 30							
Cardiff Central 7	a		17 22			18 22		18 27			19 22	20 29		20 52	21 30		22 44		00 50					
Cardiff Queen Street 3	a																							
Newport (South Wales)	a		17 38			18 38		18 48			19 38	20 48		21 08			23 08							
Bristol Parkway 7	a		18 00			19 00					20 00			21 30										
Gloucester 7	a																							
Manchester Piccadilly 10	a							22 13																
Reading 7	a		18 59			19 58					20 57			22 35										
London Paddington 15 ⊖	a		19 39			20 42					21 42			23 15										

For general notes see front of timetable
For details of catering facilities see
Directory of Train Operators

A Conveys portion to Holyhead (Table 81)
C To Crewe (Table 131)
D From Shrewsbury (Table 129)
E To Hereford (Table 131)
G Ship service

Table 128A

Mondays to Fridays

Maesteg — Caerau
Bus Service

		AW	AW	AW	AW	AW	AW	AW	AW	AW	AW	AW	AW	AW	AW	AW	AW	AW
Cardiff Central	128 d	05 51	07 04	08 21	09 21	10 21	11 21	12 21	13 21	14 21	15 21	16 21	17 21	18 21	19 12	20b22	21b22	22b35
Bridgend	128 d	06 20	07 32	08 49	09 49	10 49	11 49	12 49	13 49	14 49	15 49	16 49	17 48	18 49	19 45	20 55	21 56	23 02
Maesteg	d	06 51	08 05	09 20	10 20	11 20	12 20	13 20	14 20	15 20	16 20	17 20	18 22	19 21	20 26	21 25	22 28	23 34
Caerau (Square)	a	07 00	08 14	09 29	10 29	11 29	12 29	13 29	14 29	15 29	16 29	17 29	18 31	19 30	20 35	21 34	22 37	23 43
Caerau Park	a	07 10	08 24	09 39	10 39	11 39	12 39	13 39	14 39	15 39	16 39	17 39	18 41	19 40	20 45	21 44	22 47	23 53

Saturdays

		AW	AW	AW	AW	AW	AW	AW	AW	AW	AW	AW	AW	AW	AW	AW	AW
Cardiff Central	128 d	05 51	07 04	08 21	09 21	10 21	11 21	12 21	13 21	14 21	15 21	16 21	17 21	18 21	19 21	20 21	21 21
Bridgend	128 d	06 20	07 32	08 49	09 49	10 49	11 49	12 49	13 49	14 49	15 49	16 49	17 49	18 49	19 49	20 49	21 56
Maesteg	d	06 51	08 05	09 20	10 20	11 20	12 20	13 20	14 20	15 20	16 20	17 20	18 22	19 21	20 26	21 25	22 26
Caerau (Square)	a	07 00	08 14	09 29	10 29	11 29	12 29	13 29	14 29	15 29	16 29	17 29	18 31	19 30	20 35	21 34	22 35
Caerau Park	a	07 10	08 24	09 39	10 39	11 39	12 39	13 39	14 39	15 39	16 39	17 39	18 41	19 40	20 45	21 44	22 45

Mondays to Fridays

		AW	AW	AW	AW	AW	AW	AW	AW	AW	AW	AW	AW	AW	AW	AW	AW
Caerau Park	d	06 24	07 35	08 50	09 50	10 50	11 50	12 50	13 50	14 50	15 50	16 50	17 50	18 50	19 50	20 50	21 50
Caerau (Square)	d	06 34	07 45	09 00	10 00	11 00	12 00	13 00	14 00	15 00	16 00	17 00	18 00	19 00	20 00	21 00	22 00
Maesteg	a	06 44	07 55	09 10	10 10	11 10	12 10	13 10	14 10	15 10	16 10	17 10	18 10	19 10	20 10	21 10	22 12
Bridgend	128 a	07 11	08 22	09 39	10 39	11 39	12 39	13 39	14 39	15 39	16 39	17 39	18 42	19 42	20 42	21 44	22 45
Cardiff Central	128 a	07 43	08 48	10 09	11 15	12 09	13 09	14 13	15 09	16 10	17 10	18 09	19 13	20 12	21 11	22 17	23 16

Saturdays

		AW	AW	AW	AW	AW	AW	AW	AW	AW	AW	AW	AW	AW	AW	AW	AW
Caerau Park	d	06 24	07 35	08 50	09 50	10 50	11 50	12 50	13 50	14 50	15 50	16 50	17 50	18 50	19 50	20 50	21 50
Caerau (Square)	d	06 34	07 45	09 00	10 00	11 00	12 00	13 00	14 00	15 00	16 00	17 00	18 00	19 00	20 00	21 00	22 00
Maesteg	a	06 44	07 55	09 10	10 10	11 10	12 10	13 10	14 10	15 10	16 10	17 10	18 10	19 10	20 10	21 10	22 10
Bridgend	128 a	07 11	08 22	09 39	10 39	11 39	12 39	13 39	14 39	15 39	16 39	17 39	18 42	19 42	20 42	21 44	22 45
Cardiff Central	128 a	07 43	08 48	10 09	11 15	12 09	13 09	14 13	15 09	16 09	17 09	18 09	19 16	20 12	21 12	22 17	23 16

For general notes see front of timetable
For details of catering facilities see
Directory of Train Operators

b Change at Bridgend and Maesteg

No Sunday Service

Network Diagram for Tables 129, 131

DM-16/08
Design BAJS

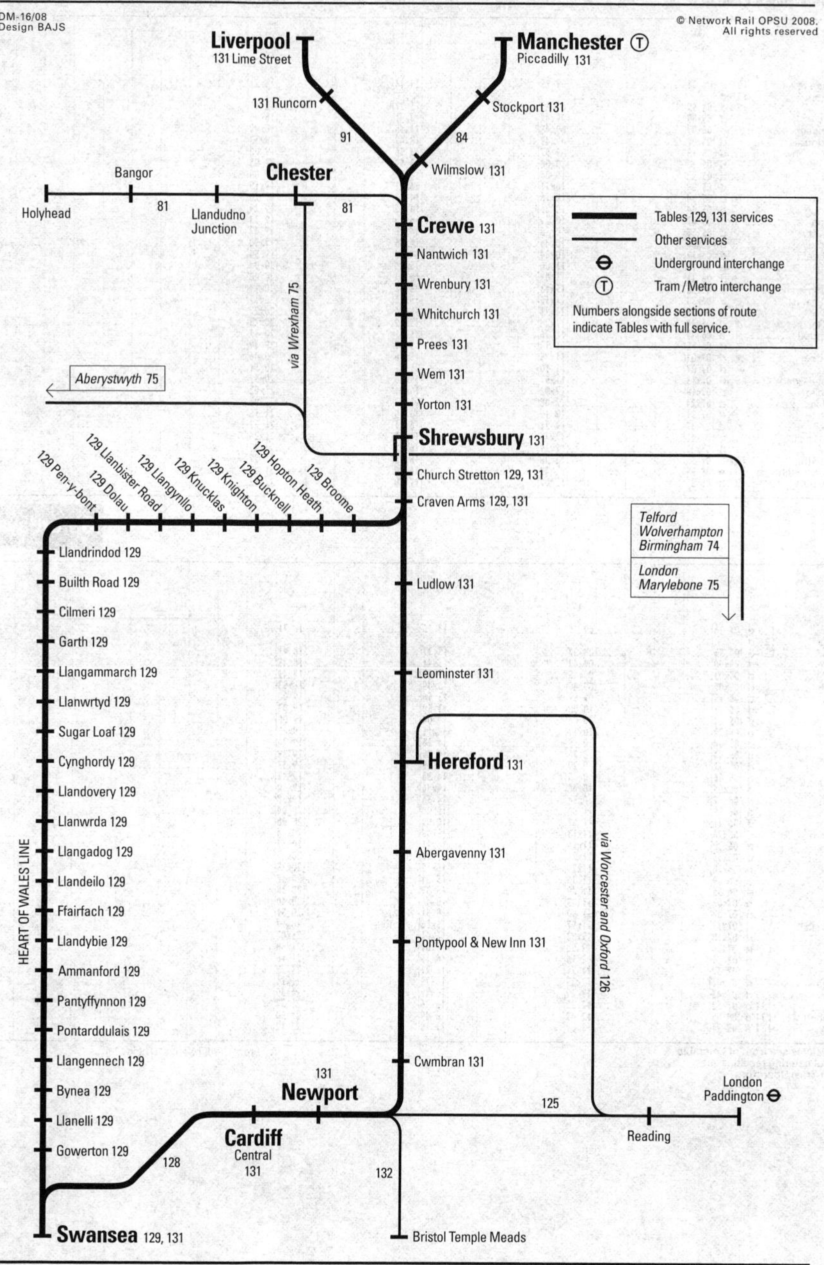
Liverpool
131 Lime Street
Manchester
Piccadilly 131
131 Runcorn
Stockport 131
91
84
Wilmslow 131
Bangor
Chester
Holyhead
81
Llandudno Junction
81
Crewe 131
Nantwich 131
Wrenbury 131
Whitchurch 131
Prees 131
Wem 131
Yorton 131
via Wrexham 75
Aberystwyth 75
Shrewsbury 131
Tables 129, 131 services
Other services
Underground interchange
Tram / Metro interchange
Numbers alongside sections of route indicate Tables with full service.
129 Pen-y-bont
129 Llanbister Road
129 Dolau
129 Llangynllo
129 Knucklas
129 Knighton
129 Bucknell
129 Hopton Heath
129 Broome
Church Stretton 129, 131
Craven Arms 129, 131
Telford
Wolverhampton
Birmingham 74
London
Marylebone 75
Llandrindod 129
Builth Road 129
Cilmeri 129
Garth 129
Llangammarch 129
Llanwrtyd 129
Sugar Loaf 129
Cynghordy 129
Llandovery 129
Llanwrda 129
Llangadog 129
Llandeilo 129
Ffairfach 129
Llandybie 129
Ammanford 129
Pantyffynnon 129
Pontarddulais 129
Llangennech 129
Bynea 129
Llanelli 129
Gowerton 129
HEART OF WALES LINE
Ludlow 131
Leominster 131
Hereford 131
Abergavenny 131
Pontypool & New Inn 131
Cwmbran 131
via Worcester and Oxford 126
131
Newport
Cardiff
Central
131
128
132
125
London
Paddington
Reading
Swansea 129, 131
Bristol Temple Meads

Swansea → Shrewsbury
HEART OF WALES LINE

Route Diagram - see first page of Table 129

Miles			AW ◇	AW ◇ A	AW ◇	AW ◇
0	**Swansea 7**	128 d	04 36	09 15	13 16	18 21
5½	Gowerton	128 d	.	.	.	.
11¼	Llanelli	128 d	04 55	09 37	13 37	18 41
14	Bynea	d	05x00	09x42	13x41	18x45
16	Llangennech	d	05x03	09x45	13x45	18x49
18¼	Pontarddulais	d	05x07	09x49	13x49	18x53
23	Pantyffynnon	d	05 15	09 57	13 56	19 00
24¼	Ammanford	d	05 18	10 00	13 59	19 03
26	Llandybie	d	05 22	10 04	14 04	19 08
30	Ffairfach	d	05x29	10x11	14x11	19x15
30¾	Llandeilo	d	05 34	10 16	14 16	19 20
36½	Llangadog	d	05 44	10 26	14 25	19 29
38¼	Llanwrda	d	05 47	10 29	14 29	19 33
42	Llandovery	d	05 56	10 38	14 38	19 42
46¾	Cynghordy	d	06x04	10x46	14x46	19x50
49½	Sugar Loaf	d	06x12	10x54	14x54	19x58
53½	Llanwrtyd	a	06 18	11 00	15 00	20 04
—		d	06 21	11 07	15 02	20 08
56¾	Llangammarch	d	06x26	11x13	15x08	20x14
58½	Garth (Powys)	d	06x30	11x16	15x11	20x17
62	Cilmeri	d	06x35	11x21	15x16	20x22
64	Builth Road	d	06x38	11x24	15x19	20x25
69¾	Llandrindod	a	06 49	11 36	15 31	20 37
—		d	06 55	11 38	15 39	20 39
73¼	Pen-y-bont	d	07x02	11x45	15x46	20x46
76¼	Dolau	d	07 07	11 50	15 51	20 51
79¾	Llanbister Road	d	07x13	11x57	15x56	20x57
82¾	Llangynllo	d	07x18	12x02	16x01	21x02
86¾	Knucklas	d	07x24	12x08	16x07	21x08
89¼	Knighton	d	07 31	12 15	16 15	21 16
93½	Bucknell	d	07 37	12 21	16 21	21 22
96½	Hopton Heath	d	07x41	12x25	16x25	21x26
99	Broome	d	07x45	12x29	16x29	21x30
101½	Craven Arms	131 a	07 52	12 36	16 36	21 37
108¾	Church Stretton	131 a	08 05	12 49	16 49	21 50
121½	**Shrewsbury**	131 a	08 21	13 07	17 10	22 12

Saturdays

		AW ◇	AW ◇ A	AW ◇	AW ◇
Swansea 7	128 d	04 36	09 15	13 16	18 21
Gowerton	128 d	.	.	.	.
Llanelli	128 d	04 55	09 37	13 37	18 41
Bynea	d	05x00	09x42	13x41	18x45
Llangennech	d	05x03	09x45	13x45	18x49
Pontarddulais	d	05x07	09x49	13x49	18x53
Pantyffynnon	d	05 15	09 57	13 56	19 00
Ammanford	d	05 18	10 00	13 59	19 03
Llandybie	d	05 22	10 04	14 04	19 08
Ffairfach	d	05x29	10x11	14x11	19x15
Llandeilo	d	05 34	10 16	14 16	19 20
Llangadog	d	05 44	10 26	14 25	19 29
Llanwrda	d	05 47	10 29	14 29	19 33
Llandovery	d	05 56	10 38	14 38	19 42
Cynghordy	d	06x04	10x46	14x46	19x50
Sugar Loaf	d	06x12	10x54	14x54	19x58
Llanwrtyd	a	06 18	11 00	15 00	20 04
	d	06 21	11 07	15 02	20 08
Llangammarch	d	06x26	11x13	15x08	20x14
Garth (Powys)	d	06x30	11x16	15x11	20x17
Cilmeri	d	06x35	11x21	15x16	20x22
Builth Road	d	06x38	11x24	15x19	20x25
Llandrindod	a	06 49	11 36	15 31	20 37
	d	06 55	11 38	15 39	20 39
Pen-y-bont	d	07x02	11x45	15x46	20x46
Dolau	d	07 07	11 50	15 51	20 51
Llanbister Road	d	07x13	11x57	15x56	20x57
Llangynllo	d	07x18	12x02	16x01	21x02
Knucklas	d	07x24	12x08	16x07	21x08
Knighton	d	07 31	12 15	16 15	21 16
Bucknell	d	07 37	12 21	16 21	21 22
Hopton Heath	d	07x41	12x25	16x25	21x26
Broome	d	07x45	12x29	16x29	21x30
Craven Arms	131 a	07 52	12 36	16 36	21 37
Church Stretton	131 a	08 05	12 49	16 49	21 50
Shrewsbury	131 a	08 21	13 07	17 10	22 12

For general notes see front of timetable
For details of catering facilities see Directory of Train Operators

A From Cardiff Central (Table 128)

Table 129

Sundays

Swansea → Shrewsbury
HEART OF WALES LINE

Route Diagram - see first page of Table 129

		AW ◇ A	AW ◇ B	AW ◇ D	AW ◇ C
Swansea 7	128 d	11 03	11 09	15 10	15 16
Gowerton	128 d	11x14	11x20	15 23	15x27
Llanelli	128 d	11 29	11 29	15 38	15 38
Bynea	d	11x34	11x34	15x43	15x43
Llangennech	d	11x38	11x38	15x46	15x46
Pontarddulais	d	11x42	11x42	15x50	15x50
Pantyffynnon	d	11 49	11 49	15 58	15 58
Ammanford	d	11 52	11 52	16 01	16 01
Llandybie	d	11 57	11 57	16 05	16 05
Ffairfach	d	12x04	12x04	16 12	16x12
Llandeilo	d	12 09	12 09	16 17	16 17
Llangadog	d	12 18	12 18	16 27	16 27
Llanwrda	d	12 22	12 22	16 30	16 30
Llandovery	d	12 31	12 31	16 39	16 39
Cynghordy	d	12x39	12x39	16 47	16x47
Sugar Loaf	d	12x47	12x47	16 55	16x55
Llanwrtyd	a	12 53	12 53	17 01	17 01
	d	12 55	12 55	17 04	17 04
Llangammarch	d	13x01	13x01	17 09	17x09
Garth (Powys)	d	13x04	13x04	17 13	17x13
Cilmeri	d	13x09	13x09	17 18	17x18
Builth Road	d	13x12	13x12	17 21	17x21
Llandrindod	a	13 24	13 24	17 32	17 32
	d	14 05	14 05	17 58	17 58
Pen-y-bont	d	14x12	14x12	18 05	18x05
Dolau	d	14 17	14 17	18 10	18 10
Llanbister Road	d	14x22	14x22	18 15	18x15
Llangynllo	d	14x27	14x27	18 20	18x20
Knucklas	d	14x33	14x33	18 26	18x26
Knighton	d	14 41	14 41	18 34	18 34
Bucknell	d	14 47	14 47	18 40	18 40
Hopton Heath	d	14x51	14x51	18 44	18x44
Broome	d	14x55	14x55	18 48	18x48
Craven Arms	131 a	15 02	15 02	18 55	18x55
Church Stretton	131 a	15 15	15 15	19 08	19 08
Shrewsbury	131 a	15 33	15 33	19 23	19 23

For general notes see front of timetable
For details of catering facilities see Directory of Train Operators

A Until 7 September
B From 14 September
C From 14 September to Crewe (Table 131)
D Until 7 September to Crewe (Table 131)

Shrewsbury → Swansea
HEART OF WALES LINE

Route Diagram - see first page of Table 129

Miles			AW ◇ A	AW ◇	AW ◇	AW ◇
0	**Shrewsbury**	131 d	05 19	09 05	14 05	18 05
12¾	Church Stretton	131 d	05 36	09 22	14 23	18 23
20	Craven Arms	131 d	05 50	09 35	14 36	18 35
22½	Broome	d	05x55	09x40	14x41	18x40
25	Hopton Heath	d	05x59	09x44	14x45	18x44
28	Bucknell	d	06x03	09x48	14x49	18x48
32½	Knighton	d	06 12	09 57	14 58	18 57
34¾	Knucklas	d	06x17	10x02	15x03	19x02
38¾	Llangynllo	d	06x25	10x10	15x11	19x10
41¾	Llanbister Road	d	06x29	10x14	15x15	19x14
45¼	Dolau	d	06x35	10x20	15x21	19x20
48¼	Pen-y-bont	d	06x39	10x24	15x25	19x24
51¾	Llandrindod	a	06 48	10 33	15 34	19 33
—		d	06 55	10 35	15 38	19 35
57½	Builth Road	d	07x04	10x44	15x47	19x44
59½	Cilmeri	d	07x07	10x47	15x50	19x47
63	Garth (Powys)	d	07x12	10x52	15x55	19x52
64¾	Llangammarch	d	07x15	10x56	15x59	19x56
68	Llanwrtyd	a	07 21	11 02	16 05	20 02
—		d	07 24	11 09	16 07	20 13
70¾	Sugar Loaf	d	07x30	11x15	16x13	20x19
74¾	Cynghordy	d	07x36	11x21	16x20	20x25
79½	Llandovery	d	07 48	11 33	16 32	20 37
83¼	Llanwrda	d	07x54	11x39	16x37	20x43
85	Llangadog	d	07x57	11x42	16x41	20x46
90¾	Llandeilo	d	08 09	11 54	16 52	20 58
91½	Ffairfach	d	08 11	11 56	16 55	21 00
95½	Llandybie	d	08x18	12x03	17x02	21x07
97¼	Ammanford	d	08x22	12x07	17x06	21x11
98½	Pantyffynnon	d	08 25	12 10	17 09	21 14
103¼	Pontarddulais	d	08x32	12x17	17x15	21x21
105½	Llangennech	d	08x36	12x21	17x19	21x25
107½	Bynea	d	08x39	12x24	17x22	21x28
110¼	Llanelli	128 a	08 43	12 30	17 28	21 42
116	Gowerton	128 a	08x53		17x44	21x52
121½	**Swansea** 7	128 a	09 07	13 01	18 06	22 13

Saturdays

		AW ◇ A	AW ◇	AW ◇	AW ◇
Shrewsbury	131 d	05 19	09 05	14 05	18 05
Church Stretton	131 d	05 36	09 22	14 23	18 23
Craven Arms	131 d	05 50	09 35	14 36	18 35
Broome	d	05x55	09x40	14x41	18x40
Hopton Heath	d	05x59	09x44	14x45	18x44
Bucknell	d	06x03	09x48	14x49	18x48
Knighton	d	06 12	09 57	14 58	18 57
Knucklas	d	06x17	10x02	15x03	19x02
Llangynllo	d	06x25	10x10	15x11	19x10
Llanbister Road	d	06x29	10x14	15x15	19x14
Dolau	d	06x35	10x20	15x21	19x20
Pen-y-bont	d	06x39	10x24	15x25	19x24
Llandrindod	a	06 48	10 33	15 34	19 33
	d	06 55	10 35	15 38	19 35
Builth Road	d	07x04	10x44	15x47	19x44
Cilmeri	d	07x07	10x47	15x50	19x47
Garth (Powys)	d	07x12	10x52	15x55	19x52
Llangammarch	d	07x15	10x56	15x59	19x56
Llanwrtyd	a	07 21	11 02	16 05	20 02
	d	07 24	11 09	16 07	20 13
Sugar Loaf	d	07x30	11x15	16x13	20x19
Cynghordy	d	07x36	11x21	16x20	20x25
Llandovery	d	07 48	11 33	16 32	20 37
Llanwrda	d	07x54	11x39	16x37	20x43
Llangadog	d	07x57	11x42	16x41	20x46
Llandeilo	d	08 09	11 54	16 52	20 58
Ffairfach	d	08 11	11 56	16 55	21 00
Llandybie	d	08x18	12x03	17x02	21x07
Ammanford	d	08x22	12x07	17x06	21x11
Pantyffynnon	d	08 25	12 10	17 09	21 14
Pontarddulais	d	08x32	12x17	17x15	21x21
Llangennech	d	08x36	12x21	17x19	21x25
Bynea	d	08x39	12x24	17x22	21x28
Llanelli	128 a	08 43	12 30	17 34	21 42
Gowerton	128 a	08x53		17x44	21x52
Swansea 7	128 a	09 07	13 01	18 06	22 13

For general notes see front of timetable
For details of catering facilities see Directory of Train Operators

A To Cardiff Central (Table 128)

Table 129

Sundays

Shrewsbury → Swansea
HEART OF WALES LINE

Route Diagram - see first page of Table 129

			AW ◇	AW ◇ A
Shrewsbury	131	d	12 07	16 24
Church Stretton	131	d	12 24	16 42
Craven Arms	131	d	12 36	16 53
Broome		d	12x42	16x59
Hopton Heath		d	12x46	17x03
Bucknell		d	12x50	17x07
Knighton		d	12 59	17 16
Knucklas		d	13x04	17x21
Llangynllo		d	13x12	17x29
Llanbister Road		d	13x16	17x33
Dolau		d	13x22	17x39
Pen-y-bont		d	13x26	17x43
Llandrindod		a	13 34	17 52
		d	13 38	17 57
Builth Road		d	13x47	18x06
Cilmeri		d	13x50	18x09
Garth (Powys)		d	13x55	18x14
Llangammarch		d	13x59	18x18
Llanwrtyd		a	14 05	18 24
		d	14 10	18 26
Sugar Loaf		d	14x16	18x32
Cynghordy		d	14x22	18x39
Llandovery		d	14 34	18 51
Llanwrda		d	14x40	18x56
Llangadog		d	14x43	19x00
Llandeilo		d	15b07	19 11
Ffairfach		d	15 09	19 14
Llandybie		d	15x16	19x21
Ammanford		d	15x20	19x25
Pantyffynnon		d	15 23	19 28
Pontarddulais		d	15x30	19x34
Llangennech		d	15x34	19x38
Bynea		d	15x37	19x41
Llanelli	128	a	15 42	19 49
Gowerton	128	a	15x52	19x59
Swansea 7	128	a	16 13	20 13

For general notes see front of timetable
For details of catering facilities see Directory of Train Operators

A To Cardiff Central (Table 128)
b Arr. 1452

Network Diagram for Table 130

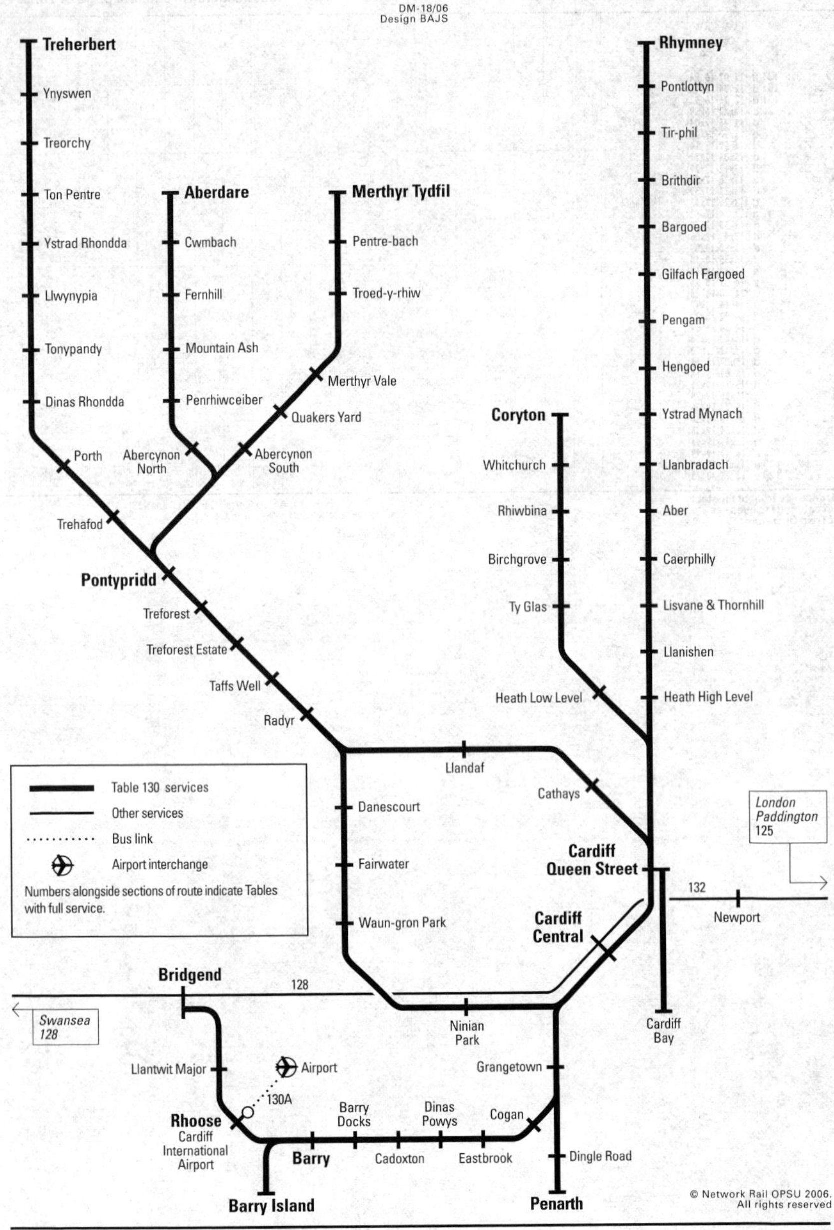

DM-18/06
Design BAJS
Treherbert
Ynyswen
Treorchy
Ton Pentre
Ystrad Rhondda
Llwynypia
Tonypandy
Dinas Rhondda
Porth
Trehafod
Aberdare
Cwmbach
Fernhill
Mountain Ash
Penrhiwceiber
Abercynon North
Merthyr Tydfil
Pentre-bach
Troed-y-rhiw
Merthyr Vale
Quakers Yard
Abercynon South
Pontypridd
Treforest
Treforest Estate
Taffs Well
Radyr
Rhymney
Pontlottyn
Tir-phil
Brithdir
Bargoed
Gilfach Fargoed
Pengam
Hengoed
Ystrad Mynach
Llanbradach
Aber
Caerphilly
Lisvane & Thornhill
Llanishen
Heath High Level
Coryton
Whitchurch
Rhiwbina
Birchgrove
Ty Glas
Heath Low Level
Llandaf
Cathays
Danescourt
Fairwater
Waun-gron Park
Cardiff Queen Street
Cardiff Central
London Paddington 125
132
Newport
Cardiff Bay
Table 130 services
Other services
Bus link
Airport interchange
Numbers alongside sections of route indicate Tables with full service.
Bridgend
128
Swansea 128
Ninian Park
Llantwit Major
Airport
130A
Rhoose Cardiff International Airport
Barry Docks
Dinas Powys
Cogan
Grangetown
Barry
Cadoxton
Eastbrook
Dingle Road
Barry Island
Penarth

Table 130

Mondays to Fridays
until 5 September

Treherbert, Aberdare, Merthyr, Pontypridd, Rhymney and Coryton → Cardiff, Penarth, Barry, Barry Island and Bridgend

Network Diagram - see first page of Table 130

Miles	Miles	Miles	Miles	Miles	Station		AW	AW	AW	AW	AW	AW	AW	AW	AW	AW	AW	AW	AW A	AW	AW	AW B	AW	AW B	AW	AW
0	—	—	—	—	**Treherbert**	d									05 47											
½	—	—	—	—	Ynyswen	d									05 49											
1¼	—	—	—	—	Treorchy	d									05 51											
2¾	—	—	—	—	Ton Pentre	d									05 53											
3¼	—	—	—	—	Ystrad Rhondda	a									05 56											
—	—	—	—	—		d									05 58											
4½	—	—	—	—	Llwynypia	d									06 00											
5½	—	—	—	—	Tonypandy	d									06 03											
6	—	—	—	—	Dinas Rhondda	d									06 05											
7½	—	—	—	—	Porth	d									06 09											
8¾	—	—	—	—	Trehafod	d									06 12											
—	—	0	—	—	**Merthyr Tydfil**	d																				
—	—	1½	—	—	Pentre-bach	d																				
—	—	2¾	—	—	Troed Y Rhiw	d																				
—	—	4½	—	—	Merthyr Vale	d																				
—	—	6¾	—	—	Quakers Yard	d																				
—	—	—	—	0	**Aberdare [3]**	d																			06 22	
—	—	—	—	1½	Cwmbach	d																			06 25	
—	—	—	—	2¾	Fernhill	d																			06 28	
—	—	—	—	3¾	Mountain Ash	a																			06 31	
—	—	—	—	—		d																			06 34	
—	—	—	—	5	Penrhiwceiber	d																			06 37	
—	—	8¼	—	7¾	Abercynon	d																			06 43	
10¾	—	11½	—	11	**Pontypridd [3]**	a									06 17										06 53	
—	—	—	—	—		d			05 24						06 18										06 54	
11½	—	—	—	—	Trefforest	d			05 27						06 21										06 57	
14	—	—	—	—	Trefforest Estate	d			05 31						06 25										07 01	
16¼	—	—	—	—	Taffs Well [3]	d			05 34						06 28							06 53			07 04	
18¼	—	—	0	—	Radyr [3]	a			05 37						06 31							06 56		←	07 07	
—	—	—	—	—		d			05 37						06 31							07 04		07 04	07 07	
—	—	—	1½	—	Danescourt	d																→		07 08		
—	—	—	2	—	Fairwater	d																		07 10		
—	—	—	2¼	—	Waun-gron Park	d																		07 12		
—	—	—	3¾	—	Ninian Park	d																		07 15		
19¼	—	—	—	—	Llandaf	d			05 40						06 34										07 10	
21¾	—	—	—	—	Cathays	d			05 45						06 39										07 15	
—	0	—	—	—	**Rhymney [3]**	d															06 14					
—	1	—	—	—	Pontlottyn	d															06 17					
—	3½	—	—	—	Tir-phil	d															06 21					
—	4½	—	—	—	Brithdir	d															06 24					
—	6	—	—	—	Bargoed	d																				
—	6½	—	—	—	Gilfach Fargoed	d															06 34					
—	7½	—	—	—	Pengam	d															06 37					
—	9¼	—	—	—	Hengoed	d															06 40					
—	10½	—	—	—	Ystrad Mynach [3]	d															06 43					
—	13	—	—	—	Llanbradach	d															06 48					
—	15	—	—	—	Aber	d															06 52					
—	15¾	—	—	—	Caerphilly [3]	d							06 10								06 55					
—	18¼	—	—	—	Lisvane & Thornhill	d							06 14								06 59					
—	19¼	—	—	—	Llanishen	d							06 16								07 01					
—	20¼	—	—	—	Heath High Level	d							06 19								07 04					
—	—	0	—	—	**Coryton**	d													06 45							
—	—	½	—	—	Whitchurch (Cardiff)	d													06 46							
—	—	¾	—	—	Rhiwbina	d													06 48							
—	—	1¼	—	—	Birchgrove	d													06 50							
—	—	1½	—	—	Ty Glas	d													06 51							
—	—	2¼	—	—	Heath Low Level	d													06 54							
22½	22¾	4¾	—	—	**Cardiff Queen Street [3]**	a			05 48				06 25		06 44				06 59		07 09				07 19	
—	—	—	—	—		d			05 51				06 26	06 42	06 45			06 57	07 00		07 11		07 12		07 21	07 27
—	—	5¾	—	—	**Cardiff Bay**	a								06 46				07 01					07 16			07 31
23	23¼	—	4¾	—	**Cardiff Central [7]**	a			05 54				06 29		06 48				07 03		07 14			07 20	07 24	
—	—	—	—	—		d	05 25	05 41	05 55	06 16	06 25	06 36	06 41			06 55	07 01			07 10	07 16				07 25	
24	24¼	—	—	—	Grangetown	d	05 29	05 45	05 59	06 20	06 29	06 40	06 45			06 59	07 05			07 14	07 20				07 29	
—	26¾	—	—	—	Dingle Road	d				06 26		06 44					07 11				07 26					
—	27	—	—	—	**Penarth**	a				06 31		06 49					07 16				07 31					
25¾	—	—	—	—	Cogan	d	05 33	05 48	06 03		06 33		06 48			07 03				07 18					07 33	
26½	—	—	—	—	Eastbrook	d	05 35	05 51	06 05		06 35		06 51			07 05				07 20					07 35	
27½	—	—	—	—	Dinas Powys	d	05 37	05 53	06 07		06 37		06 53			07 07				07 22					07 37	
29½	—	—	—	—	Cadoxton	d	05 42	05 57	06 12		06 42		06 57			07 12				07 27					07 42	
30¼	—	—	—	—	Barry Docks	d	05 45	06 00	06 15		06 45		07 00			07 15				07 30					07 45	
31½	—	0	—	—	**Barry [3]**	d	05 49	06 05	06 19		06 49		07 05			07 19				07 34					07 49	
32¼	—	—	—	—	**Barry Island**	a	05 55		06 25		06 55					07 25				07 40					07 55	
—	—	3¼	—	—	Rhoose Cardiff Int Airport ✈	d		06 12					07 12													
—	—	9¾	—	—	Llantwit Major	d		06 22					07 22													
—	—	19	—	—	**Bridgend**	a		06 39					07 39													

For general notes see front of timetable
For details of catering facilities see Directory of Train Operators

A To Radyr
B To Coryton

Treherbert, Aberdare, Merthyr, Pontypridd, Rhymney and Coryton → Cardiff, Penarth, Barry, Barry Island and Bridgend

Network Diagram - see first page of Table 130

		AW	AW	AW	AW		AW	AW	AW	AW	AW	AW	AW	AW	AW	AW	AW	AW	AW	AW	AW	AW	AW	AW	AW	AW
			A						B						A					B					A		
Treherbert	d							06 47									07 17									
Ynyswen	d							06 49									07 19									
Treorchy	d							06 51									07 21									
Ton Pentre	d							06 53									07 23									
Ystrad Rhondda	a							06 56									07 26									
	d							06 58									07 28									
Llwynypia	d							07 00									07 30									
Tonypandy	d							07 03									07 33									
Dinas Rhondda	d							07 05									07 35									
Porth	d							07 09									07 39									
Trehafod	d							07 12									07 42									
Merthyr Tydfil	d			06 38																					07 38	
Pentre-bach	d			06 42																					07 42	
Troed Y Rhiw	d			06 45																					07 45	
Merthyr Vale	d			06 50																					07 50	
Quakers Yard	d			06 55																					07 55	
Aberdare 3	d										06 52										07 22					
Cwmbach	d										06 55										07 25					
Fernhill	d										06 58										07 28					
Mountain Ash	a										07 01										07 31					
	d										07 04										07 34					
Penrhiwceiber	d										07 07										07 37					
Abercynon	d			06 59							07 13										07 43				07 59	
Pontypridd 3	a			07 07				07 17			07 23						07 47				07 53				08 07	
	d			07 09				07 18			07 24				07 39		07 48				07 54				08 09	
Trefforest	d			07 12				07 21			07 27				07 42		07 51				07 57				08 12	
Trefforest Estate	d			07 16											07 46										08 16	
Taffs Well 3	d			07 20				07 28			07 34				07 50		07 58				08 04				08 20	
Radyr 3	a			07 23				07 31			07 37				07 53		08 01				08 07				08 23	
	d			07 23				07 31	07 34		07 37				07 53		08 01		08 04		08 07				08 23	
Danescourt	d								07 38										08 08							
Fairwater	d								07 40										08 10							
Waun-gron Park	d								07 42										08 12							
Ninian Park	d								07 45										08 15							
Llandaf	d			07 26				07 34		←	07 40				07 56		08 04			←	08 10				08 26	
Cathays	d			07 31				07 39		07 39	07 45				08 01		08 09			08 09	08 15				08 31	
Rhymney 3	d	06 37						→				07 02					→					07 24				07 44
Pontlottyn	d	06 40										07 05										07 27				07 47
Tir-phil	d	06 44										07 09										07 31				07 51
Brithdir	d	06 47										07 12										07 34				07 54
Bargoed	d	06 51			07 02							07 17				07 32						07b45				08 02
Gilfach Fargoed	d				07 04							07 19										07 47				
Pengam	d	06 55			07 07							07 22				07 37						07 50				08 07
Hengoed	d	06 59			07 10							07 25				07 40						07 54				08 10
Ystrad Mynach 3	d	07 01			07 13							07 28				07 43						07 57				08 13
Llanbradach	d	07 06			07 18							07 33				07 48						08 02				08 18
Aber	d	07 10			07 22							07 37				07 52						08 07				08 22
Caerphilly 3	d	07 13			07 25							07 40				07 55						08 10				08 25
Lisvane & Thornhill	d	07 17			07 29							07 44				07 59						08 14				08 29
Llanishen	d	07 19			07 31							07 46				08 01						08 16				08 31
Heath High Level	d	07 22			07 34							07 49				08 04						08 19				08 34
Coryton	d		07 15											07 45										08 15		
Whitchurch (Cardiff)	d		07 16											07 46										08 16		
Rhiwbina	d		07 18											07 48										08 18		
Birchgrove	d		07 20											07 50										08 20		
Ty Glas	d		07 21											07 51										08 21		
Heath Low Level	d		07 24											07 54										08 24		
Cardiff Queen Street 3	a	07 27	07 29	07 34	07 38					07 44	07 49	07 54		07 59	08 04	08 09				08 14	08 19	08 24		08 29	08 34	08 39
	d	07 28	07 31	07 36	07 41		07 42			07 46	07 51	07 56	07 57	08 01	08 06	08 11		08 12		08 16	08 21	08 26	08 27	08 31	08 36	08 41
Cardiff Bay	a						07 46						08 01					08 16					08 31			
Cardiff Central 7	a	07 31	07 34	07 39	07 44				07 50	07 52	07 54	07 59		08 04	08 09	08 14			08 20	08 22	08 24	08 29		08 34	08 39	08 47
	d	07 32		07 41	07 46						07 55	08 01			08 10	08 16					08 25	08 31			08 41	
Grangetown	d	07 36		07 45	07 50						07 59	08 05			08 14	08 20					08 29	08 35			08 45	
Dingle Road	d	07 41			07 56							08 11				08 26						08 41				
Penarth	a	07 46			08 01							08 16				08 31						08 46				
Cogan	d			07 48							08 03				08 18						08 33				08 48	
Eastbrook	d			07 51							08 05				08 20						08 35				08 51	
Dinas Powys	d			07 53							08 07				08 22						08 37				08 53	
Cadoxton	d			07 57							08 12				08 27						08 42				08 57	
Barry Docks	d			08 00							08 15				08 30						08 45				09 00	
Barry 3	d			08 05							08 19				08 34						08 49				09 05	
Barry Island	a										08 25				08 40						08 55					
Rhoose Cardiff Int Airport ✈	d			08 12																					09 12	
Llantwit Major	d			08 22																					09 22	
Bridgend	a			08 39																					09 39	

For general notes see front of timetable
For details of catering facilities see Directory of Train Operators

A To Radyr
B To Coryton
b Arr. 0737

Table 130

Mondays to Fridays

until 5 September

Treherbert, Aberdare, Merthyr, Pontypridd, Rhymney and Coryton → Cardiff, Penarth, Barry, Barry Island and Bridgend

Network Diagram - see first page of Table 130

		AW	AW	AW A	AW		AW	AW	AW	AW B	AW	AW	AW	AW	AW A	AW	AW	AW	AW	AW B	AW	AW	AW	AW	AW A	AW
Treherbert	d		07 47										08 17											08 47		
Ynyswen	d		07 49										08 19											08 49		
Treorchy	d		07 51										08 21											08 51		
Ton Pentre	d		07 53										08 23											08 53		
Ystrad Rhondda	a		07 56										08 26											08 56		
	d		07 58										08 28											08 58		
Llwynypia	d		08 00										08 30											09 00		
Tonypandy	d		08 03										08 33											09 03		
Dinas Rhondda	d		08 05										08 35											09 05		
Porth	d		08 09										08 39											09 09		
Trehafod	d		08 12										08 42											09 12		
Merthyr Tydfil	d																				08 38					
Pentre-bach	d																				08 42					
Troed Y Rhiw	d																				08 45					
Merthyr Vale	d																				08 50					
Quakers Yard	d																				08 55					
Aberdare 3	d						07 52										08 22									
Cwmbach	d						07 55										08 25									
Fernhill	d						07 58										08 28									
Mountain Ash	a						08 01										08 31									
	d						08 04										08 34									
Penrhiwceiber	d						08 07										08 37									
Abercynon	d						08 13										08 43				08 59					
Pontypridd 3	a		08 17				08 23						08 47				08 53				09 07			09 17		
	d		08 18				08 24				08 39		08 48				08 54				09 09			09 18		
Trefforest	d		08 21				08 27				08 42		08 51				08 57				09 12			09 21		
Trefforest Estate	d										08 46										09 16					
Taffs Well 3	d		08 28				08 34				08 50		08 58				09 04				09 20			09 28		
Radyr 3	a		08 31				08 37				08 53		09 01				09 07				09 23			09 31		
	d		08 31	08 34			08 37				08 53		09 01		09 04		09 07				09 23			09 31	09 34	
Danescourt	d			08 38											09 08										09 38	
Fairwater	d			08 40											09 10										09 40	
Waun-gron Park	d			08 42											09 12										09 42	
Ninian Park	d			08 45											09 15										09 45	
Llandaf	d		08 34		←		08 40				08 56		09 04			←	09 10				09 26			09 34		←
Cathays	d		08 39		08 39		08 45				09 01		09 09			09 09	09 15				09 31			09 39		09 39
Rhymney 3	d		→										→					08 30						→		
Pontlottyn	d																	08 33								
Tir-phil	d																	08 37								
Brithdir	d																	08 40								
Bargoed	d							08 17				08 32						08 47				09 02				
Gilfach Fargoed	d							08 19																		
Pengam	d							08 22				08 37						08 52				09 07				
Hengoed	d							08 25				08 40						08 55				09 10				
Ystrad Mynach 3	d							08 28				08 43						08 58				09 13				
Llanbradach	d							08 33				08 48						09 03				09 18				
Aber	d							08 37				08 52						09 07				09 22				
Caerphilly 3	d							08 40				08 55						09 10				09 25				
Lisvane & Thornhill	d							08 44				08 59						09 14				09 29				
Llanishen	d							08 46				09 01						09 16				09 31				
Heath High Level	d							08 49				09 04						09 19				09 34				
Coryton	d									08 45										09 15						
Whitchurch (Cardiff)	d									08 46										09 16						
Rhiwbina	d									08 48										09 18						
Birchgrove	d									08 50										09 20						
Ty Glas	d									08 51										09 21						
Heath Low Level	d									08 54										09 24						
Cardiff Queen Street 3	a				08 44		08 49	08 54		08 59	09 04	09 09				09 14	09 19	09 24		09 29	09 34	09 39				09 44
	d	08 42			08 46		08 51	08 56	08 57	09 01	09 06	09 11		09 12		09 16	09 21	09 26	09 27	09 31	09 36	09 41	09 42			09 46
Cardiff Bay	a	08 46							09 01					09 16					09 31				09 46			
Cardiff Central 7	a			08 50	08 52		08 54	08 59		09 04	09 09	09 14			09 20	09 22	09 24	09 29		09 34	09 39	09 46			09 50	09 52
	d						08 55	09 01			09 10	09 16					09 25	09 31			09 41	09 46				
Grangetown	d						08 59	09 05			09 14	09 20					09 29	09 35			09 45	09 50				
Dingle Road	d							09 11				09 26						09 41				09 56				
Penarth	a							09 16				09 31						09 46				10 01				
Cogan	d						09 03				09 18						09 33				09 48					
Eastbrook	d						09 05				09 20						09 35				09 51					
Dinas Powys	d						09 07				09 22						09 37				09 53					
Cadoxton	d						09 12				09 27						09 42				09 57					
Barry Docks	d						09 15				09 30						09 45				10 00					
Barry 3	d						09 19				09 34						09 49				10 05					
Barry Island	a						09 25				09 40						09 55									
Rhoose Cardiff Int Airport ✈	d																				10 12					
Llantwit Major	d																				10 22					
Bridgend	a																				10 39					

For general notes see front of timetable
For details of catering facilities see Directory of Train Operators

A To Coryton
B To Radyr

Table 130

Mondays to Fridays
until 5 September

Treherbert, Aberdare, Merthyr, Pontypridd, Rhymney and Coryton → Cardiff, Penarth, Barry, Barry Island and Bridgend

Network Diagram - see first page of Table 130

Station		AW	AW	AW	AW A		AW	AW	AW	AW	AW B	AW	AW	AW	AW	AW A	AW	AW	AW	AW	AW B	AW	AW	AW	AW	AW A
Treherbert	d								09 17											09 47						
Ynyswen	d								09 19											09 49						
Treorchy	d								09 21											09 51						
Ton Pentre	d								09 23											09 53						
Ystrad Rhondda	a								09 26											09 56						
	d								09 28											09 58						
Llwynypia	d								09 30											10 00						
Tonypandy	d								09 33											10 03						
Dinas Rhondda	d								09 35											10 05						
Porth	d								09 39											10 09						
Trehafod	d								09 42											10 12						
Merthyr Tydfil	d																09 38									
Pentre-bach	d																09 42									
Troed Y Rhiw	d																09 45									
Merthyr Vale	d																09 50									
Quakers Yard	d																09 55									
Aberdare [3]	d	08 52											09 22										09 52			
Cwmbach	d	08 55											09 25										09 55			
Fernhill	d	08 58											09 28										09 58			
Mountain Ash	a	09 01											09 31										10 01			
	d	09 04											09 34										10 04			
Penrhiwceiber	d	09 07											09 37										10 07			
Abercynon	d	09 13											09 43				09 59						10 13			
Pontypridd [3]	a	09 23							09 47				09 53				10 07			10 17			10 23			
	d	09 24					09 39		09 48				09 54				10 09			10 18			10 24			
Trefforest	d	09 27					09 42		09 51				09 57				10 12			10 21			10 27			
Trefforest Estate	d						09 46										10 16									
Taffs Well [3]	d	09 34					09 50		09 58				10 04				10 20			10 28			10 34			
Radyr [3]	a	09 37					09 53		10 01				10 07				10 23			10 31			10 37			
	d	09 37					09 53		10 01		10 04		10 07				10 23			10 31	10 34		10 37			
Danescourt	d										10 08										10 38					
Fairwater	d										10 10										10 40					
Waun-gron Park	d										10 12										10 42					
Ninian Park	d										10 15										10 45					
Llandaf	d	09 40					09 56		10 04			←	10 10				10 26			10 34		←	10 40			
Cathays	d	09 45					10 01		10 09			10 09	10 15				10 31			10 39		10 39	10 45			
Rhymney [3]	d								→					09 29						→						
Pontlottyn	d													09 32												
Tir-phil	d													09 36												
Brithdir	d													09 39												
Bargoed	d		09 17					09 32						09 47				10 02						10 17		
Gilfach Fargoed	d		09 19																					10 19		
Pengam	d		09 22					09 37						09 52				10 07						10 22		
Hengoed	d		09 25					09 40						09 55				10 10						10 25		
Ystrad Mynach [3]	d		09 28					09 43						09 58				10 13						10 28		
Llanbradach	d		09 33					09 48						10 03				10 18						10 33		
Aber	d		09 37					09 52						10 07				10 22						10 37		
Caerphilly [3]	d		09 40					09 55						10 10				10 25						10 40		
Lisvane & Thornhill	d		09 44					09 59						10 14				10 29						10 44		
Llanishen	d		09 46					10 01						10 16				10 31						10 46		
Heath High Level	d		09 49					10 04						10 19				10 34						10 49		
Coryton	d				09 45											10 15										10 45
Whitchurch (Cardiff)	d				09 46											10 16										10 46
Rhiwbina	d				09 48											10 18										10 48
Birchgrove	d				09 50											10 20										10 50
Ty Glas	d				09 51											10 21										10 51
Heath Low Level	d				09 54											10 24										10 54
Cardiff Queen Street [3]	a	09 49	09 54		09 59		10 04	10 09				10 14	10 19	10 24		10 29	10 34	10 39				10 44	10 49	10 54		10 59
	d	09 51	09 56	09 57	10 01		10 06	10 11		10 12		10 16	10 21	10 26	10 27	10 31	10 36	10 41	10 42			10 46	10 51	10 56	10 57	11 01
Cardiff Bay	a			10 01						10 16					10 31				10 46						11 01	
Cardiff Central [7]	a	09 54	09 59		10 04		10 09	10 14			10 20	10 22	10 24	10 29		10 34	10 39	10 44			10 50	10 52	10 54	10 59		11 04
	d	09 55	10 01				10 10	10 16					10 25	10 31			10 41	10 46					10 55	11 01		
Grangetown	d	09 59	10 05				10 14	10 20					10 29	10 35			10 45	10 50					10 59	11 05		
Dingle Road	d		10 11					10 26						10 41				10 56						11 11		
Penarth	a		10 17					10 31						10 46				11 01						11 16		
Cogan	d	10 03					10 18						10 33				10 49						11 03			
Eastbrook	d	10 05					10 20						10 35				10 51						11 05			
Dinas Powys	d	10 07					10 22						10 37				10 53						11 07			
Cadoxton	d	10 12					10 27						10 42				10 58						11 12			
Barry Docks	d	10 15					10 30						10 45				11 01						11 15			
Barry [3]	d	10 19					10 34						10 49				11 05						11 19			
Barry Island	a	10 25					10 40						10 55										11 25			
Rhoose Cardiff Int Airport ✈	d																11 12									
Llantwit Major	d																11 22									
Bridgend	a																11 39									

For general notes see front of timetable
For details of catering facilities see Directory of Train Operators

A To Radyr
B To Coryton

Table 130

Mondays to Fridays
until 5 September

Treherbert, Aberdare, Merthyr, Pontypridd, Rhymney and Coryton → Cardiff, Penarth, Barry, Barry Island and Bridgend

Network Diagram - see first page of Table 130

		AW	AW	AW	AW A		AW	AW	AW B	AW	AW	AW C	AW	AW	AW	AW	AW A	AW	AW	AW	AW	AW C	AW	AW	AW	AW
Treherbert	d									10 17						10 47									11 17	
Ynyswen	d									10 19						10 49									11 19	
Treorchy	d									10 21						10 51									11 21	
Ton Pentre	d									10 23						10 53									11 23	
Ystrad Rhondda	a									10 26						10 56									11 26	
	d									10 28						10 58									11 28	
Llwynypia	d									10 30						11 00									11 30	
Tonypandy	d									10 33						11 03									11 33	
Dinas Rhondda	d									10 35						11 05									11 35	
Porth	d									10b52						11 09									11 39	
Trehafod	d									10 55						11 12									11 42	
Merthyr Tydfil	d												10 38													
Pentre-bach	d												10 42													
Troed Y Rhiw	d												10 45													
Merthyr Vale	d												10 50													
Quakers Yard	d												10 55													
Aberdare 3	d						10 22												10 52							
Cwmbach	d						10 25		10a39										10 55							
Fernhill	d						10 28												10 58							
Mountain Ash	a						10 31												11 01							
	d						10 34												11 04							
Penrhiwceiber	d						10 37		10a27										11 07							
Abercynon	d						10 43						10 59						11 13							
Pontypridd 3	a						10 53			11 00			11 07			11 17			11 23						11 47	
	d	10 39					10 54			11 04			11 09			11 18			11 24				11 39		11 48	
Trefforest	d	10 42					10 57			11 07			11 12			11 21			11 27				11 42		11 51	
Trefforest Estate	d	10 46											11 16										11 46			
Taffs Well 3	d	10 50					11 04			11 13			11 20			11 28			11 34				11 50		11 58	
Radyr 3	a	10 53					11 07			11 17			11 23			11 31			11 37				11 53		12 01	
	d	10 53			11 04		11 07			11 17			11 23			11 31	11 34		11 37				11 53		12 01	
Danescourt	d				11 08												11 38									
Fairwater	d				11 10												11 40									
Waun-gron Park	d				11 12												11 42									
Ninian Park	d				11 15												11 45									
Llandaf	d	10 56					11 10						11 26			11 34		←	11 40				11 56		12 04	
Cathays	d	11 01					11 15						11 31			11 39		11 39	11 45				12 01		12 09	
Rhymney 3	d							10 29								→									→	
Pontlottyn	d							10 32																		
Tir-phil	d							10 36																		
Brithdir	d							10 39																		
Bargoed	d		10 32					10 47						11 02						11 17				11 32		
Gilfach Fargoed	d																			11 19						
Pengam	d		10 37					10 52						11 07						11 22				11 37		
Hengoed	d		10 40					10 55						11 10						11 25				11 40		
Ystrad Mynach 3	d		10 43					10 58						11 13						11 28				11 43		
Llanbradach	d		10 48					11 03						11 18						11 33				11 48		
Aber	d		10 52					11 07						11 22						11 37				11 52		
Caerphilly 3	d		10 55					11 10						11 25						11 40				11 55		
Lisvane & Thornhill	d		10 59					11 14						11 29						11 44				11 59		
Llanishen	d		11 01					11 16						11 31						11 46				12 01		
Heath High Level	d		11 04					11 19						11 34						11 49				12 04		
Coryton	d											11 15										11 45				
Whitchurch (Cardiff)	d											11 16										11 46				
Rhiwbina	d											11 18										11 48				
Birchgrove	d											11 20										11 50				
Ty Glas	d											11 21										11 51				
Heath Low Level	d											11 24										11 54				
Cardiff Queen Street 3	a	11 04	11 09				11 19	11 24				11 29	11 34	11 39				11 44	11 49	11 54		11 59	12 04	12 09		
	d	11 06	11 11	11 12			11 21	11 26			11 27	11 31	11 36	11 41	11 42			11 46	11 51	11 56	11 57	12 01	12 06	12 11		12 12
Cardiff Bay	a			11 16							11 31				11 46						12 01					12 16
Cardiff Central 7	a	11 09	11 14		11 20		11 24	11 29		11 34		11 34	11 39	11 44			11 50	11 52	11 54	11 59		12 04	12 09	12 14		
	d	11 10	11 16				11 25	11 31					11 41	11 46					11 55	12 01			12 10	12 16		
Grangetown	d	11 14	11 20				11 29	11 35					11 45	11 50					11 59	12 05			12 14	12 20		
Dingle Road	d		11 26					11 41						11 56						12 11				12 26		
Penarth	a		11 31					11 46						12 01						12 16				12 31		
Cogan	d	11 18					11 33						11 48						12 03				12 18			
Eastbrook	d	11 20					11 35						11 51						12 05				12 20			
Dinas Powys	d	11 22					11 37						11 53						12 07				12 22			
Cadoxton	d	11 27					11 42						11 57						12 12				12 27			
Barry Docks	d	11 30					11 45						12 00						12 15				12 30			
Barry 3	d	11 34					11 49						12 05						12 19				12 34			
Barry Island	a	11 40					11 55												12 25				12 40			
Rhoose Cardiff Int Airport ✈	d												12 12													
Llantwit Major	d												12 22													
Bridgend	a												12 39													

For general notes see front of timetable
For details of catering facilities see Directory of Train Operators

A To Coryton
B To Aberdare
C To Radyr

b Arr. 1038

Table 130

Treherbert, Aberdare, Merthyr, Pontypridd, Rhymney and Coryton → Cardiff, Penarth, Barry, Barry Island and Bridgend

Mondays to Fridays
until 5 September

Network Diagram - see first page of Table 130

	AW A	AW	AW	AW		AW	AW B	AW	AW	AW	AW	AW A	AW	AW	AW	AW B	AW	AW	AW	AW	AW A	AW	AW	AW	AW
Treherbert d											11 47									12 17					
Ynyswen d											11 49									12 19					
Treorchy d											11 51									12 21					
Ton Pentre d											11 53									12 23					
Ystrad Rhondda a											11 56									12 26					
d											11 58									12 28					
Llwynypia d											12 00									12 30					
Tonypandy d											12 03									12 33					
Dinas Rhondda d											12 05									12 35					
Porth d											12 09									12 39					
Trehafod d											12 12									12 42					
Merthyr Tydfil d								11 38																	
Pentre-bach d								11 42																	
Troed Y Rhiw d								11 45																	
Merthyr Vale d								11 50																	
Quakers Yard d								11 55																	
Aberdare 3 d			11 22																				12 22		
Cwmbach d			11 25																				12 25		
Fernhill d			11 28																				12 28		
Mountain Ash a			11 31																				12 31		
d			11 34																				12 34		
Penrhiwceiber d			11 37																				12 37		
Abercynon d			11 43					11 59															12 43		
Pontypridd 3 a			11 53					12 07			12 17									12 48			12 53		
d			11 54					12 09			12 18						12 39			12 48			12 54		
Trefforest d			11 57					12 12			12 21						12 42			12 51			12 57		
Trefforest Estate d								12 16									12 46								
Taffs Well 3 d			12 04					12 20			12 28						12 50			12 58			13 04		
Radyr 3 a			12 07					12 23			12 31						12 53			13 01			13 07		
d	12 04		12 07					12 23			12 31	12 34					12 53			13 01	13 04		13 07		
Danescourt d	12 08											12 38									13 08				
Fairwater d	12 10											12 40									13 10				
Waun-gron Park d	12 12											12 42									13 12				
Ninian Park d	12 15											12 45									13 15				
Llandaf d		←	12 10					12 26			12 34		←				12 56			13 04		←	13 10		
Cathays d		12 09	12 15					12 31			12 39		12 39				13 01			13 09		13 09	13 15		
Rhymney 3 d				11 29							→									→				12 29	
Pontlottyn d				11 32																				12 32	
Tir-phil d				11 36																				12 36	
Brithdir d				11 39																				12 39	
Bargoed d				11 47					12 02					12 17				12 32						12 47	
Gilfach Fargoed d														12 19											
Pengam d				11 52					12 07					12 22				12 37						12 52	
Hengoed d				11 55					12 10					12 25				12 40						12 55	
Ystrad Mynach 3 d				11 58					12 13					12 28				12 43						12 58	
Llanbradach d				12 03					12 18					12 33				12 48						13 03	
Aber d				12 07					12 22					12 37				12 52						13 07	
Caerphilly 3 d				12 10					12 25					12 40				12 55						13 10	
Lisvane & Thornhill d				12 14					12 29					12 44				12 59						13 14	
Llanishen d				12 16					12 31					12 46				13 01						13 16	
Heath High Level d				12 19					12 34					12 49				13 04						13 19	
Coryton d							12 15									12 45									
Whitchurch (Cardiff) d							12 16									12 46									
Rhiwbina d							12 18									12 48									
Birchgrove d							12 20									12 50									
Ty Glas d							12 21									12 51									
Heath Low Level d							12 24									12 54									
Cardiff Queen Street 3 a		12 14	12 19	12 24			12 29	12 34	12 39				12 44	12 54		12 59	13 04	13 09				13 14	13 19	13 24	
d		12 16	12 21	12 26		12 27	12 31	12 36	12 41	12 42			12 46	12 56	12 57	13 01	13 06	13 11	13 12			13 16	13 21	13 26	13 27
Cardiff Bay a						12 31				12 46					13 01				13 16						13 31
Cardiff Central 7 a	12 20	12 22	12 24	12 29			12 34	12 39	12 44			12 50	12 52	12 59		13 04	13 09	13 14			13 20	13 22	13 24	13 29	
d			12 25	12 31				12 41	12 46				12 55	13 01			13 10	13 16					13 25	13 31	
Grangetown d			12 29	12 35				12 45	12 50				12 59	13 05			13 14	13 20					13 29	13 35	
Dingle Road d				12 41					12 56					13 11				13 26						13 41	
Penarth a				12 46					13 01					13 16				13 31						13 46	
Cogan d			12 33					12 48					13 03				13 18						13 33		
Eastbrook d			12 35					12 51					13 05				13 20						13 35		
Dinas Powys d			12 37					12 53					13 07				13 22						13 37		
Cadoxton d			12 42					12 57					13 12				13 27						13 42		
Barry Docks d			12 45					13 00					13 15				13 30						13 45		
Barry 3 d			12 49					13 05					13 19				13 34						13 49		
Barry Island a			12 55										13 25				13 40						13 55		
Rhoose Cardiff Int Airport ✈ d								13 12																	
Llantwit Major d								13 22																	
Bridgend a								13 39																	

For general notes see front of timetable
For details of catering facilities see Directory of Train Operators

A To Coryton
B To Radyr

Table 130

Treherbert, Aberdare, Merthyr, Pontypridd, Rhymney and Coryton → Cardiff, Penarth, Barry, Barry Island and Bridgend

Mondays to Fridays
until 5 September

Network Diagram - see first page of Table 130

		AW A	AW	AW	AW		AW	AW B	AW	AW	AW	AW	AW A	AW	AW	AW	AW	AW B	AW	AW	AW	AW	AW A	AW	AW	AW
Treherbert	d						12 47									13 17										
Ynyswen	d						12 49									13 19										
Treorchy	d						12 51									13 21										
Ton Pentre	d						12 53									13 23										
Ystrad Rhondda	a						12 56									13 26										
	d						12 58									13 28										
Llwynypia	d						13 00									13 30										
Tonypandy	d						13 03									13 33										
Dinas Rhondda	d						13 05									13 35										
Porth	d						13 09									13 39										
Trehafod	d						13 12									13 42										
Merthyr Tydfil	d		12 38																					13 38		
Pentre-bach	d		12 42																					13 42		
Troed Y Rhiw	d		12 45																					13 45		
Merthyr Vale	d		12 50																					13 50		
Quakers Yard	d		12 55																					13 55		
Aberdare 3	d									12 52																
Cwmbach	d									12 55																
Fernhill	d									12 58																
Mountain Ash	a									13 01																
	d									13 04																
Penrhiwceiber	d									13 07																
Abercynon	d		12 59							13 13										13 45				13 59		
Pontypridd 3	a		13 07				13 17			13 23						13 47				13 53				14 07		
	d		13 09				13 18			13 24				13 39		13 48				13 54				14 09		
Trefforest	d		13 12				13 21			13 27				13 42		13 51				13 57				14 12		
Trefforest Estate	d		13 16											13 46										14 16		
Taffs Well 3	d		13 20				13 28			13 34				13 50		13 58				14 04				14 20		
Radyr 3	a		13 23				13 31			13 37				13 53		14 01				14 07				14 23		
	d		13 23				13 31	13 34		13 37				13 53		14 01		14 04		14 07				14 23		
Danescourt	d							13 38										14 08								
Fairwater	d							13 40										14 10								
Waun-gron Park	d							13 42										14 12								
Ninian Park	d							13 45										14 15								
Llandaf	d		13 26				13 34		←	13 40				13 56		14 04			←	14 10				14 26		
Cathays	d		13 31				13 39		13 39	13 45				14 01		14 09			14 09	14 15				14 31		
Rhymney 3	d						→									→					13 29					
Pontlottyn	d																				13 32					
Tir-phil	d																				13 36					
Brithdir	d																				13 39					
Bargoed	d			13 02							13 17				13 32						13 47				14 02	
Gilfach Fargoed	d										13 19															
Pengam	d			13 07							13 22				13 37						13 52				14 07	
Hengoed	d			13 10							13 25				13 40						13 55				14 10	
Ystrad Mynach 3	d			13 13							13 28				13 43						13 58				14 13	
Llanbradach	d			13 18							13 33				13 48						14 03				14 18	
Aber	d			13 22							13 37				13 52						14 07				14 22	
Caerphilly 3	d			13 25							13 40				13 55						14 10				14 25	
Lisvane & Thornhill	d			13 29							13 44				13 59						14 14				14 29	
Llanishen	d			13 31							13 46				14 01						14 16				14 31	
Heath High Level	d			13 34							13 49				14 04						14 19				14 34	
Coryton	d	13 15											13 45										14 15			
Whitchurch (Cardiff)	d	13 16											13 46										14 16			
Rhiwbina	d	13 18											13 48										14 18			
Birchgrove	d	13 20											13 50										14 20			
Ty Glas	d	13 21											13 51										14 21			
Heath Low Level	d	13 24											13 54										14 24			
Cardiff Queen Street 3	a	13 29	13 34	13 39					13 44	13 49	13 54		13 59	14 04	14 09				14 14	14 19	14 24		14 29	14 34	14 39	
	d	13 31	13 36	13 41	13 42				13 46	13 51	13 56	13 57	14 01	14 06	14 11		14 12		14 16	14 21	14 26	14 27	14 31	14 36	14 41	14 42
Cardiff Bay	a				13 46							14 01					14 16					14 31				14 46
Cardiff Central 7	a	13 34	13 40	13 44				13 50	13 52	13 54	13 59		14 04	14 09	14 14			14 20	14 22	14 24	14 29		14 34	14 39	14 44	
	d		13 41	13 46						13 55	14 01			14 10	14 16					14 25	14 31			14 41	14 46	
Grangetown	d		13 45	13 50						13 59	14 05			14 14	14 20					14 29	14 35			14 45	14 50	
Dingle Road	d			13 56							14 11				14 26						14 41				14 56	
Penarth	a			14 01							14 16				14 31						14 46				15 01	
Cogan	d		13 48							14 03				14 18						14 33				14 48		
Eastbrook	d		13 51							14 05				14 20						14 35				14 51		
Dinas Powys	d		13 53							14 07				14 22						14 37				14 53		
Cadoxton	d		13 57							14 12				14 27						14 41				14 57		
Barry Docks	d		14 00							14 15				14 30						14 44				15 00		
Barry 3	d		14 05							14 19				14 34						14 48				15 05		
Barry Island	a									14 25				14 40						14 55						
Rhoose Cardiff Int Airport ✈	d		14 12																					15 12		
Llantwit Major	d		14 22																					15 22		
Bridgend	a		14 39																					15 39		

For general notes see front of timetable
For details of catering facilities see Directory of Train Operators

A To Radyr
B To Coryton

Table 130

Mondays to Fridays

until 5 September

Treherbert, Aberdare, Merthyr, Pontypridd, Rhymney and Coryton → Cardiff, Penarth, Barry, Barry Island and Bridgend

Network Diagram - see first page of Table 130

		AW	AW A	AW	AW		AW	AW	AW B	AW	AW	AW	AW A	AW	AW	AW	AW	AW B	AW	AW	AW	AW	AW A	AW	AW	AW
Treherbert	d	13 47														14 17						14 47				
Ynyswen	d	13 49														14 19						14 49				
Treorchy	d	13 51														14 21						14 51				
Ton Pentre	d	13 53														14 23						14 53				
Ystrad Rhondda	a	13 56														14 26						14 56				
	d	13 58														14 28						14 58				
Llwynypia	d	14 00														14 30						15 00				
Tonypandy	d	14 03														14 33						15 03				
Dinas Rhondda	d	14 05														14 35						15 05				
Porth	d	14 09														14b52						15 09				
Trehafod	d	14 12														14 55						15 12				
Merthyr Tydfil	d																		14 38							
Pentre-bach	d																		14 42							
Troed Y Rhiw	d																		14 45							
Merthyr Vale	d																		14 50							
Quakers Yard	d																		14 55							
Aberdare 3	d				13 52									14 22											14 52	
Cwmbach	d				13 55									14 25											14 55	
Fernhill	d				13 58									14 28											14 58	
Mountain Ash	a				14 01									14 31											15 01	
	d				14 04									14 34											15 04	
Penrhiwceiber	d				14 07									14 37											15 07	
Abercynon	d				14 13									14 43					14 59						15 13	
Pontypridd 3	a	14 17			14 23									14 53		15 00			15 07			15 17			15 23	
	d	14 18			14 24					14 39				14 54		15 04			15 09			15 18			15 24	
Trefforest	d	14 21			14 27					14 42				14 57		15 07			15 12			15 21			15 27	
Trefforest Estate	d									14 46									15 16							
Taffs Well 3	d	14 28			14 34					14 50				15 04		15 13			15 20			15 28			15 34	
Radyr 3	a	14 31			14 37					14 53				15 07		15 17			15 23			15 31			15 37	
	d	14 31	14 34		14 37					14 53			15 04	15 07		15 17			15 23			15 31	15 34		15 37	
Danescourt	d		14 38										15 08										15 38			
Fairwater	d		14 40										15 10										15 40			
Waun-gron Park	d		14 42										15 12										15 42			
Ninian Park	d		14 45										15 15										15 45			
Llandaf	d	14 34		←	14 40					14 56				15 10					15 26			15 34		←	15 40	
Cathays	d	14 39		14 39	14 45					15 01				15 15					15 31			15 39		15 39	15 45	
Rhymney 3	d	↦													14 29							↦				
Pontlottyn	d														14 32											
Tir-phil	d														14 36											
Brithdir	d														14 39											
Bargoed	d						14 17				14 32				14 47					15 02						15 17
Gilfach Fargoed	d						14 19																			15 19
Pengam	d						14 22				14 37				14 52					15 07						15 22
Hengoed	d						14 25				14 40				14 55					15 10						15 25
Ystrad Mynach 3	d						14 28				14 43				14 58					15 13						15 28
Llanbradach	d						14 33				14 48				15 03					15 18						15 33
Aber	d						14 37				14 52				15 07					15 22						15 37
Caerphilly 3	d						14 40				14 55				15 10					15 25						15 40
Lisvane & Thornhill	d						14 44				14 59				15 14					15 29						15 44
Llanishen	d						14 46				15 01				15 16					15 31						15 46
Heath High Level	d						14 49				15 04				15 19					15 34						15 49
Coryton	d								14 45									15 15								
Whitchurch (Cardiff)	d								14 46									15 16								
Rhiwbina	d								14 48									15 18								
Birchgrove	d								14 50									15 20								
Ty Glas	d								14 51									15 21								
Heath Low Level	d								14 54									15 24								
Cardiff Queen Street 3	a			14 44	14 49		14 54		14 59	15 04	15 09			15 19	15 24			15 29	15 34	15 39				15 44	15 49	15 54
	d			14 46	14 51		14 56	14 57	15 01	15 06	15 11	15 12		15 21	15 26		15 27	15 31	15 36	15 41	15 42			15 46	15 51	15 56
Cardiff Bay	a							15 01				15 16					15 31				15 46					
Cardiff Central 7	a		14 50	14 52	14 54		14 59		15 04	15 09	15 14		15 20	15 24	15 29	15 34		15 34	15 39	15 44			15 50	15 52	15 54	15 59
	d				14 55		15 01			15 10	15 16			15 25	15 31				15 41	15 46					15 55	16 01
Grangetown	d				14 59		15 05			15 14	15 20			15 29	15 35				15 45	15 50					15 59	16 05
Dingle Road	d						15 11				15 26				15 41					15 56						16 11
Penarth	a						15 16				15 31				15 46					16 01						16 16
Cogan	d				15 03					15 18				15 33					15 48						16 03	
Eastbrook	d				15 05					15 20				15 35					15 51						16 05	
Dinas Powys	d				15 07					15 22				15 37					15 53						16 07	
Cadoxton	d				15 12					15 27				15 42					15 57						16 12	
Barry Docks	d				15 15					15 30				15 45					16 00						16 15	
Barry 3	d				15 19					15 34				15 49					16 05						16 19	
Barry Island	a				15 25					15 40				15 55											16 25	
Rhoose Cardiff Int Airport ✈	d																		16 12							
Llantwit Major	d																		16 22							
Bridgend	a																		16 39							

For general notes see front of timetable
For details of catering facilities see Directory of Train Operators

A To Coryton
B To Radyr
b Arr. 1438

Treherbert, Aberdare, Merthyr, Pontypridd, Rhymney and Coryton → Cardiff, Penarth, Barry, Barry Island and Bridgend

Network Diagram - see first page of Table 130

		AW	AW	AW	AW		AW	AW	AW	AW	AW	AW	AW	AW	AW	AW	AW	AW	AW	AW	AW	AW	AW	AW	AW	AW
			A						B					A					B					A		
Treherbert	d						15 17											15 47								
Ynyswen	d						15 19											15 49								
Treorchy	d						15 21											15 51								
Ton Pentre	d						15 23											15 53								
Ystrad Rhondda	a						15 26											15 56								
	d						15 28											15 58								
Llwynypia	d						15 30											16 00								
Tonypandy	d						15 33											16 03								
Dinas Rhondda	d						15 35											16 05								
Porth	d						15 39											16 09								
Trehafod	d						15 42											16 12								
Merthyr Tydfil	d														15 38											
Pentre-bach	d														15 42											
Troed Y Rhiw	d														15 45											
Merthyr Vale	d														15 50											
Quakers Yard	d														15 55											
Aberdare 3	d										15 22										15 52					
Cwmbach	d										15 25										15 55					
Fernhill	d										15 28										15 58					
Mountain Ash	a										15 31										16 01					
	d										15 34										16 04					
Penrhiwceiber	d										15 37										16 07					
Abercynon	d										15 43										16 13					
Pontypridd 3	a						15 47				15 53				16 07			16 17			16 23					
	d			15 39			15 48				15 54				16 09			16 18			16 24				16 39	
Trefforest	d			15 42			15 51				15 57				16 12			16 21			16 27				16 42	
Trefforest Estate	d			15 46											16 16										16 46	
Taffs Well 3	d			15 50			15 58				16 04				16 20			16 28			16 34				16 50	
Radyr 3	a			15 53			16 01				16 07				16 23			16 31			16 37				16 53	
	d			15 53			16 01		16 04		16 07				16 23			16 31	16 34		16 37				16 53	
Danescourt	d								16 08										16 38							
Fairwater	d								16 10										16 40							
Waun-gron Park	d								16 12										16 42							
Ninian Park	d								16 15										16 45							
Llandaf	d			15 56			16 04			←	16 10				16 26			16 34		←	16 40				16 56	
Cathays	d			16 01			16 09			16 09	16 15				16 31			16 39		16 39	16 45				17 01	
Rhymney 3	d						→					15 29						→								
Pontlottyn	d											15 32														
Tir-phil	d											15 36														
Brithdir	d											15 39														
Bargoed	d				15 32							15 47				16 02						16 17				16 32
Gilfach Fargoed	d																					16 19				
Pengam	d				15 37							15 52				16 07						16 22				16 37
Hengoed	d				15 40							15 55				16 10						16 25				16 40
Ystrad Mynach 3	d				15 43							15 58				16 13						16 28				16 43
Llanbradach	d				15 48							16 03				16 18						16 33				16 48
Aber	d				15 52							16 07				16 22						16 37				16 52
Caerphilly 3	d				15 55							16 10				16 25						16 40				16 55
Lisvane & Thornhill	d				15 59							16 14				16 29						16 44				16 59
Llanishen	d				16 01							16 16				16 31						16 46				17 01
Heath High Level	d				16 04							16 19				16 34						16 49				17 04
Coryton	d		15 45											16 15										16 45		
Whitchurch (Cardiff)	d		15 46											16 16										16 46		
Rhiwbina	d		15 48											16 18										16 48		
Birchgrove	d		15 50											16 20										16 50		
Ty Glas	d		15 51											16 21										16 51		
Heath Low Level	d		15 54											16 24										16 54		
Cardiff Queen Street 3	a		15 59	16 04	16 09					16 14	16 19	16 24		16 29	16 34	16 39				16 44	16 49	16 54		16 59	17 04	17 09
	d	15 57	16 01	16 06	16 11			16 12		16 16	16 21	16 26	16 27	16 31	16 36	16 41	16 42			16 46	16 51	16 56	16 57	17 01	17 06	17 11
Cardiff Bay	a	16 01						16 16					16 31				16 46						17 01			
Cardiff Central 7	a		16 04	16 09	16 14				16 20	16 22	16 24	16 32		16 34	16 39	16 44			16 50	16 52	16 54	16 59		17 04	17 09	17 14
	d			16 10	16 16						16 25				16 41	16 46					16 55	17 01			17 10	17 16
Grangetown	d			16 14	16 20						16 29				16 45	16 50					16 59	17 05			17 14	17 20
Dingle Road	d				16 26											16 56						17 11				17 26
Penarth	a				16 31											17 01						17 16				17 31
Cogan	d			16 18							16 33				16 48						17 03				17 18	
Eastbrook	d			16 20							16 35				16 51						17 05				17 20	
Dinas Powys	d			16 22							16 37				16 53						17 07				17 22	
Cadoxton	d			16 27							16 42				16 57						17 12				17 27	
Barry Docks	d			16 30							16 45				17 00						17 15				17 30	
Barry 3	d			16 34							16 49				17 05						17 19				17 34	
Barry Island	a			16 40							16 55										17 25				17 40	
Rhoose Cardiff Int Airport ✈	d														17 12											
Llantwit Major	d														17 22											
Bridgend	a														17 39											

For general notes see front of timetable
For details of catering facilities see Directory of Train Operators

A To Radyr
B To Coryton

Treherbert, Aberdare, Merthyr, Pontypridd, Rhymney and Coryton → Cardiff, Penarth, Barry, Barry Island and Bridgend

Network Diagram - see first page of Table 130

		AW	AW	AW A	AW	AW	AW	AW	AW B	AW	AW	AW	AW	AW A	AW	AW	AW	AW	AW B	AW	AW	AW	AW	AW A	AW
Treherbert	d	16 17											16 47									17 17			
Ynyswen	d	16 19											16 49									17 19			
Treorchy	d	16 21											16 51									17 21			
Ton Pentre	d	16 23											16 53									17 23			
Ystrad Rhondda	a	16 26											16 56									17 26			
	d	16 28											16 58									17 28			
Llwynypia	d	16 30											17 00									17 30			
Tonypandy	d	16 33											17 03									17 33			
Dinas Rhondda	d	16 35											17 05									17 35			
Porth	d	16 39											17 09									17 39			
Trehafod	d	16 42											17 12									17 42			
Merthyr Tydfil	d									16 38															
Pentre-bach	d									16 42															
Troed Y Rhiw	d									16 45															
Merthyr Vale	d									16 50															
Quakers Yard	d									16 55															
Aberdare 3	d					16 22										16 52									
Cwmbach	d					16 25										16 55									
Fernhill	d					16 28										16 58									
Mountain Ash	a					16 31										17 01									
	d					16 34										17 04									
Penrhiwceiber	d					16 37										17 07									
Abercynon	d					16 43				16 59						17 13									
Pontypridd 3	a	16 47				16 53				17 07			17 17			17 23						17 47			
	d	16 48				16 54				17 09			17 18			17 24				17 39		17 48			
Trefforest	d	16 51				16 57				17 12			17 21			17 27				17 42		17 51			
Trefforest Estate	d									17 16										17 46					
Taffs Well 3	d	16 58				17 04				17 20			17 28			17 34				17 50		17 58			
Radyr 3	a	17 01				17 07				17 23			17 31			17 37				17 53		18 01			
	d	17 01		17 04		17 07				17 23			17 31	17 34		17 37				17 53		18 01		18 04	
Danescourt	d			17 08										17 38										18 08	
Fairwater	d			17 10										17 40										18 10	
Waun-gron Park	d			17 12										17 42										18 12	
Ninian Park	d			17 15										17 45										18 15	
Llandaf	d	17 04			←	17 10				17 26			17 34		←	17 40				17 56		18 04			←
Cathays	d	17 09			17 09	17 15				17 31			17 39		17 39	17 45				18 01		18 09			18 09
Rhymney 3	d	→					16 29						→									→			
Pontlottyn	d						16 32																		
Tir-phil	d						16 36																		
Brithdir	d						16 39																		
Bargoed	d						16 47				17 02						17 17				17 32				
Gilfach Fargoed	d																17 19								
Pengam	d						16 52				17 07						17 22				17 37				
Hengoed	d						16 55				17 10						17 25				17 40				
Ystrad Mynach 3	d						16 58				17 13						17 28				17 43				
Llanbradach	d						17 03				17 18						17 33				17 48				
Aber	d						17 07				17 22						17 37				17 52				
Caerphilly 3	d						17 10				17 25						17 40				17 55				
Lisvane & Thornhill	d						17 14				17 29						17 44				17 59				
Llanishen	d						17 16				17 31						17 46				18 01				
Heath High Level	d						17 19				17 34						17 49				18 04				
Coryton	d								17 15										17 45						
Whitchurch (Cardiff)	d								17 16										17 46						
Rhiwbina	d								17 18										17 48						
Birchgrove	d								17 20										17 50						
Ty Glas	d								17 21										17 51						
Heath Low Level	d								17 24										17 54						
Cardiff Queen Street 3	a				17 14	17 19	17 24		17 29	17 34	17 39				17 44	17 49	17 54		17 59	18 04	18 09				18 14
	d		17 12		17 16	17 21	17 26	17 27	17 31	17 36	17 41	17 42			17 46	17 51	17 56	17 57	18 01	18 06	18 11		18 12		18 16
Cardiff Bay	a		17 16					17 31				17 46						18 01					18 16		
Cardiff Central 7	a			17 20	17 22	17 24	17 29		17 34	17 39	17 44			17 50	17 52	17 54	17 59		18 04	18 09	18 14			18 20	18 22
	d					17 25	17 31			17 41	17 46					17 55	18 01			18 10	18 16				
Grangetown	d					17 29	17 35			17 45	17 50					17 59	18 05			18 14	18 20				
Dingle Road	d						17 41				17 56						18 11				18 26				
Penarth	a						17 46				18 01						18 16				18 31				
Cogan	d					17 33				17 48						18 03				18 18					
Eastbrook	d					17 35				17 51						18 05				18 20					
Dinas Powys	d					17 37				17 53						18 07				18 22					
Cadoxton	d					17 42				17 57						18 12				18 27					
Barry Docks	d					17 45				18 00						18 15				18 30					
Barry 3	d					17 49				18 05						18 19				18 34					
Barry Island	a					17 55										18 25				18 40					
Rhoose Cardiff Int Airport ✈	d									18 12															
Llantwit Major	d									18 22															
Bridgend	a									18 39															

For general notes see front of timetable
For details of catering facilities see Directory of Train Operators

A To Coryton
B To Radyr

Table 130

Mondays to Fridays

until 5 September

Treherbert, Aberdare, Merthyr, Pontypridd, Rhymney and Coryton → Cardiff, Penarth, Barry, Barry Island and Bridgend

Network Diagram - see first page of Table 130

		AW	AW	AW	AW A	AW	AW	AW	AW B	AW	AW	AW	AW	AW	AW	AW	AW	AW	AW	AW	AW	AW A	AW	AW	AW
Treherbert	d						17 47										18 17								18 47
Ynyswen	d						17 49										18 19								18 49
Treorchy	d						17 51										18 21								18 51
Ton Pentre	d						17 53										18 23								18 53
Ystrad Rhondda	a						17 56										18 26								18 56
	d						17 58										18 28								18 58
Llwynypia	d						18 00										18 30								19 00
Tonypandy	d						18 03										18 33								19 03
Dinas Rhondda	d						18 05										18 35								19 05
Porth	d						18 09										18 39								19 09
Trehafod	d						18 12										18 42								19 12
Merthyr Tydfil	d					17 38																	18 38		
Pentre-bach	d					17 42																	18 42		
Troed Y Rhiw	d					17 45																	18 45		
Merthyr Vale	d					17 50																	18 50		
Quakers Yard	d					17 55																	18 55		
Aberdare 3	d	17 22									17 52								18 22						
Cwmbach	d	17 25									17 55								18 25						
Fernhill	d	17 28									17 58								18 28						
Mountain Ash	a	17 31									18 01								18 31						
	d	17 34									18 04								18 34						
Penrhiwceiber	d	17 37									18 07								18 37						
Abercynon	d	17 43				17 59					18 13								18 43				18 59		
Pontypridd 3	a	17 53				18 07	18 17				18 23						18 47		18 53				19 07		19 17
	d	17 54				18 09	18 18				18 24				18 39		18 48		18 54				19 09		19 18
Trefforest	d	17 57				18 12	18 21				18 27				18 42		18 51		18 57				19 12		19 21
Trefforest Estate	d					18 16									18 46								19 16		
Taffs Well 3	d	18 04				18 20	18 28				18 34				18 50		18 58		19 04				19 20		19 28
Radyr 3	a	18 07				18 23	18 31				18 37				18 53		19 01		19 07				19 23		19 31
	d	18 07				18 23	18 31		18 34		18 37				18 53		19 01	19 04	19 07				19 23		19 31
Danescourt	d								18 38									19 08							
Fairwater	d								18 40									19 10							
Waun-gron Park	d								18 42									19 12							
Ninian Park	d								18 45									19 15							
Llandaf	d	18 10				18 26	18 34			←	18 40				18 56		19 04		19 10				19 26		19 34
Cathays	d	18 15				18 31	18 39			18 39	18 45				19 01		19 09		19 15				19 31		19 39
Rhymney 3	d		17 29				→																		
Pontlottyn	d		17 32																						
Tir-phil	d		17 36																						
Brithdir	d		17 39																						
Bargoed	d		17 47									18 17								18 48					
Gilfach Fargoed	d											18 19								18 50					
Pengam	d		17 52									18 22								18 53					
Hengoed	d		17 55									18 25								18 56					
Ystrad Mynach 3	d		17 58									18 28								18 59					
Llanbradach	d		18 03									18 33								19 04					
Aber	d		18 07									18 37								19 08					
Caerphilly 3	d		18 10									18 40								19 11					
Lisvane & Thornhill	d		18 14									18 44								19 15					
Llanishen	d		18 16									18 46								19 17					
Heath High Level	d		18 19									18 49								19 20					
Coryton	d				18 15									18 45								19 15			
Whitchurch (Cardiff)	d				18 16									18 46								19 16			
Rhiwbina	d				18 18									18 48								19 18			
Birchgrove	d				18 20									18 50								19 20			
Ty Glas	d				18 21									18 51								19 21			
Heath Low Level	d				18 24									18 54								19 24			
Cardiff Queen Street 3	a	18 19	18 24		18 29	18 34				18 44	18 49	18 54		18 59	19 04		19 14		19 19	19 24		19 29	19 34		19 44
	d	18 21	18 26	18 27	18 31	18 36		18 42		18 46	18 51	18 56	18 57	19 01	19 06	19 12	19 16		19 21	19 26	19 27	19 31	19 36	19 42	19 46
Cardiff Bay	a			18 31				18 46					19 01			19 16					19 31			19 46	
Cardiff Central 7	a	18 24	18 29		18 34	18 39			18 50	18 52	18 54	18 59		19 06	19 10		19 22	19 22	19 24	19 29		19 34	19 39		19 52
	d	18 25	18 31			18 41					18 55	19 01							19 25	19 31			19 41		
Grangetown	d	18 29	18 35			18 45					18 59	19 05							19 29	19 35			19 45		
Dingle Road	d		18 41									19 11								19 41					
Penarth	a		18 46									19 16								19 46					
Cogan	d	18 33				18 48					19 03								19 33				19 48		
Eastbrook	d	18 35				18 51					19 05								19 35				19 51		
Dinas Powys	d	18 37				18 53					19 07								19 37				19 53		
Cadoxton	d	18 42				18 57					19 12								19 42				19 57		
Barry Docks	d	18 45				19 00					19 15								19 45				20 00		
Barry 3	d	18 49				19 05					19 19								19 49				20 05		
Barry Island	a	18 55									19 25								19 55						
Rhoose Cardiff Int Airport ✈	d					19 12																	20 12		
Llantwit Major	d					19 22																	20 22		
Bridgend	a					19 39																	20 39		

For general notes see front of timetable
For details of catering facilities see Directory of Train Operators

A To Radyr
B To Coryton

Treherbert, Aberdare, Merthyr, Pontypridd, Rhymney and Coryton → Cardiff, Penarth, Barry, Barry Island and Bridgend

Mondays to Fridays
until 5 September

Network Diagram - see first page of Table 130

Station		AW	AW	AW	AW	AW	AW	AW	AW	AW A	AW	AW	AW	AW	AW	AW	AW	AW	AW	AW	AW	AW	AW	AW	AW A
Treherbert	d					19 17								19 47					20 17						
Ynyswen	d					19 19								19 49					20 19						
Treorchy	d					19 21								19 51					20 21						
Ton Pentre	d					19 23								19 53					20 23						
Ystrad Rhondda	a					19 26								19 56					20 26						
	d					19 28								19 58					20 28						
Llwynypia	d					19 30								20 00					20 30						
Tonypandy	d					19 33								20 03					20 33						
Dinas Rhondda	d					19 35								20 05					20 35						
Porth	d					19 39								20 09					20 39						
Trehafod	d					19 42								20 12					20 42						
Merthyr Tydfil	d										19 38														
Pentre-bach	d										19 42														
Troed Y Rhiw	d										19 45														
Merthyr Vale	d										19 50														
Quakers Yard	d										19 55														
Aberdare 3	d	18 52													19 52						20 22				
Cwmbach	d	18 55													19 55						20 25				
Fernhill	d	18 58													19 58						20 28				
Mountain Ash	a	19 01													20 01						20 31				
	d	19 04													20 04						20 34				
Penrhiwceiber	d	19 07													20 07						20 37				
Abercynon	d	19 13									19 59				20 13						20 43				
Pontypridd 3	a	19 23				19 47		19 53			20 07			20 17	20 23				20 47		20 53				
	d	19 24				19 48		19 54			20 09			20 18	20 24				20 48		20 54				
Trefforest	d	19 27				19 51		19 57			20 12			20 21	20 27				20 51		20 57				
Trefforest Estate	d										20 16														
Taffs Well 3	d	19 34				19 58		20 04			20 20			20 28	20 34				20 58		21 04				
Radyr 3	a	19 37				20 01		20 07			20 23			20 31	20 37				21 01		21 07				
	d	19 37				20 01	20 04	20 07			20 23			20 31	20 37				21 01	21 04	21 07				
Danescourt	d						20 08													21 08		←			
Fairwater	d						20 10													21 10 →		21 10			
Waun-gron Park	d						20 12															21 12			
Ninian Park	d						20 15															21 15			
Llandaf	d	19 40				20 04		20 10			20 26			20 34	20 40				21 04		21 10				
Cathays	d	19 45				20 09		20 15			20 31			20 39	20 45				21 09		21 15				
Rhymney 3	d											19 45													
Pontlottyn	d											19 48													
Tir-phil	d											19 52													
Brithdir	d											19 55													
Bargoed	d											19 59													
Gilfach Fargoed	d											20 01													
Pengam	d											20 04													
Hengoed	d											20 07													
Ystrad Mynach 3	d											20 10													
Llanbradach	d											20 15													
Aber	d											20 19													
Caerphilly 3	d		19 40									20 22				20 40									
Lisvane & Thornhill	d		19 44									20 26				20 44									
Llanishen	d		19 46									20 28				20 46									
Heath High Level	d		19 49									20 31				20 49									
Coryton	d									20 15															21 15
Whitchurch (Cardiff)	d									20 16															21 16
Rhiwbina	d									20 18															21 18
Birchgrove	d									20 20															21 20
Ty Glas	d									20 21															21 21
Heath Low Level	d									20 24															21 24
Cardiff Queen Street 3	a	19 49	19 54			20 14		20 19		20 29	20 34	20 39		20 44	20 50	20 54			21 14		21 19				21 29
	d	19 51	19 56	19 57	20 12	20 16		20 21	20 27	20 31	20 36	20 41	20 42	20 46	20 51	20 56	20 57	21 12	21 16		21 21			21 27	21 31
Cardiff Bay	a			20 01	20 16				20 31				20 46				21 01	21 16						21 31	
Cardiff Central 7	a	19 57	19 59			20 19	20 22	20 24		20 34	20 39	20 47		20 52	20 58	20 59			21 21		21 24	21 25			21 34
	d		20 01			20 20		20 31			20 41					21 01					21 25		21 31		
Grangetown	d		20 05			20 24		20 35			20 45					21 05					21 29		21 35		
Dingle Road	d		20 11					20 41								21 11							21 41		
Penarth	a		20 16					20 46								21 16							21 46		
Cogan	d					20 28					20 48										21 33				
Eastbrook	d					20 30					20 51										21 35				
Dinas Powys	d					20 32					20 53										21 37				
Cadoxton	d					20 37					20 57										21 42				
Barry Docks	d					20 40					21 00										21 45				
Barry 3	d					20 44					21 05										21 49				
Barry Island	a					20 50															21 55				
Rhoose Cardiff Int Airport ✈	d										21 12														
Llantwit Major	d										21 22														
Bridgend	a										21 39														

For general notes see front of timetable
For details of catering facilities see Directory of Train Operators

A To Radyr

Table 130

Mondays to Fridays

until 5 September

Treherbert, Aberdare, Merthyr, Pontypridd, Rhymney and Coryton → Cardiff, Penarth, Barry, Barry Island and Bridgend

Network Diagram - see first page of Table 130

		AW	AW	AW	AW		AW	AW	AW	AW	AW	AW	AW	AW	AW	AW	AW	AW	AW	AW	AW	AW	AW	AW		
Treherbert	d									21 17																
Ynyswen	d									21 19																
Treorchy	d									21 21																
Ton Pentre	d									21 23																
Ystrad Rhondda	a									21 26																
	d									21 28																
Llwynypia	d									21 30																
Tonypandy	d									21 33																
Dinas Rhondda	d									21 35																
Porth	d									21 39																
Trehafod	d									21 42																
Merthyr Tydfil	d	20 38													21 38							22 38				
Pentre-bach	d	20 42													21 42							22 42				
Troed Y Rhiw	d	20 45													21 45							22 45				
Merthyr Vale	d	20 50													21 50							22 50				
Quakers Yard	d	20 55													21 55							22 55				
Aberdare 3	d				20 52												21 52							22 52		
Cwmbach	d				20 55												21 55							22 55		
Fernhill	d				20 58												21 58							22 58		
Mountain Ash	a				21 01												22 01							23 01		
	d				21 04												22 04							23 04		
Penrhiwceiber	d				21 07												22 07							23 07		
Abercynon	d	20 59			21 13												22 14					22 59		23 13		
Pontypridd 3	a	21 07			21 23					21 47					22 07		22 24					23 07		23 23		
	d	21 09			21 24					21 48					22 09		22 29					23 09		23 29		
Trefforest	d	21 12			21 27					21 51					22 12		22 32					23 12		23 32		
Trefforest Estate	d	21 16													22 16											
Taffs Well 3	d	21 20			21 34					21 58					22 20		22 39					23 20		23 38		
Radyr 3	a	21 23			21 37					22 01					22 23		22 42					23 23		23 42		
	d	21 23			21 37					22 01	22 04				22 23		22 42					23 23		23 42		
Danescourt	d										22 08															
Fairwater	d										22 10															
Waun-gron Park	d										22 12															
Ninian Park	d										22 15															
Llandaf	d	21 26			21 40					22 04					22 26		22 45					23 26		23 45		
Cathays	d	21 31			21 45					22 09					22 31		22 50					23 31		23 49		
Rhymney 3	d			20 48									21 33													
Pontlottyn	d			20 51									21 36													
Tir-phil	d			20 55									21 40													
Brithdir	d			20 58									21 43													
Bargoed	d			21 02									21 47													
Gilfach Fargoed	d			21 04									21 49													
Pengam	d			21 07									21 52													
Hengoed	d			21 10									21 55													
Ystrad Mynach 3	d			21 13									21 58													
Llanbradach	d			21 18									22 03													
Aber	d			21 22									22 07													
Caerphilly 3	d			21 25			21 40						22 10													
Lisvane & Thornhill	d			21 29			21 45						22 14													
Llanishen	d			21 31			21 47						22 16													
Heath High Level	d			21 34			21 49						22 19													
Coryton	d																									
Whitchurch (Cardiff)	d																									
Rhiwbina	d																									
Birchgrove	d																									
Ty Glas	d																									
Heath Low Level	d																									
Cardiff Queen Street 3	a	21 34		21 42	21 50		21 54			22 14			22 24		22 34		22 54					23 34		23 53		
	d	21 36	21 42	21 44	21 51		21 56	21 57	22 12	22 16			22 26	22 27	22 36	22 42	22 55	22 57	23 12		23 27	23 36	23 42	23 56		
Cardiff Bay	a		21 46					22 01	22 16					22 31		22 46		23 01	23 16		23 31		23 46			
Cardiff Central 7	a	21 39		21 47	21 57		21 59			22 22	22 22		22 29		22 39		23 01					23 42		00 02		
	d	21 41					22 01					22 25	22 35		22 41		23 12			23 30						
Grangetown	d	21 45					22 05					22 29	22 39		22 45		23 16			23 34						
Dingle Road	d						22 11						22 43				23 20									
Penarth	a						22 16						22 46				23 25									
Cogan	d	21 48										22 33			22 48					23 37						
Eastbrook	d	21 51										22 35			22 51					23 40						
Dinas Powys	d	21 53										22 37			22 53					23 42						
Cadoxton	d	21 57										22 42			22 57					23 46						
Barry Docks	d	22 00										22 45			23 00					23 49						
Barry 3	d	22 05										22 49			23 05					23 54						
Barry Island	a											22 55								23 59						
Rhoose Cardiff Int Airport ✈	d	22 12													23 12											
Llantwit Major	d	22 22													23 22											
Bridgend	a	22 39													23 39											

For general notes see front of timetable
For details of catering facilities see
Directory of Train Operators

Table 130

Mondays to Fridays

from 8 September

Treherbert, Aberdare, Merthyr, Pontypridd, Rhymney and Coryton → Cardiff, Penarth, Barry, Barry Island and Bridgend

Network Diagram - see first page of Table 130

		AW	AW	AW	AW	AW	AW	AW	AW	AW	AW	AW	AW	AW	AW	AW	AW	AW		AW	AW	AW	AW	AW	AW	AW
														A	B						B				A	
Treherbert	d									05 47										06 17						
Ynyswen	d									05 49										06 19						
Treorchy	d									05 51										06 21						
Ton Pentre	d									05 53										06 23						
Ystrad Rhondda	a									05 56										06 26						
	d									05 58										06 28						
Llwynypia	d									06 00										06 30						
Tonypandy	d									06 03										06 33						
Dinas Rhondda	d									06 05										06 35						
Porth	d									06 09										06 39						
Trehafod	d									06 12										06 42						
Merthyr Tydfil	d																									06 38
Pentre-bach	d																									06 42
Troed Y Rhiw	d																									06 45
Merthyr Vale	d																									06 50
Quakers Yard	d																									06 55
Aberdare 3	d																					06 21				
Cwmbach	d																					06 24				
Fernhill	d																					06 28				
Mountain Ash	a																					06 31				
	d																					06 34				
Penrhiwceiber	d																					06 38				
Abercynon	d																					06 44				06 59
Pontypridd 3	a									06 17										06 47		06 53				07 07
	d			05 24						06 18										06 48		06 54				07 09
Trefforest	d			05 27						06 21										06 51		06 57				07 12
Trefforest Estate	d			05 31						06 25												07 01				07 16
Taffs Well 3	d			05 34						06 28					06 53					06 58		07 04				07 20
Radyr 3	a			05 37						06 31					06 56					07 01	←	07 07				07 23
	d			05 37						06 31					07 04					07 01	07 04	07 07				07 23
Danescourt	d														→						07 08					
Fairwater	d																				07 10					
Waun-gron Park	d																				07 12					
Ninian Park	d																				07 15					
Llandaf	d			05 40						06 34										07 04		07 10				07 26
Cathays	d			05 45						06 39										07 09		07 15				07 31
Rhymney 3	d																06 14							06 37		
Pontlottyn	d																06 17							06 40		
Tir-phil	d																06 21							06 44		
Brithdir	d																06 24							06 47		
Bargoed	d																06 32							06 51		
Gilfach Fargoed	d																06 34									
Pengam	d																06 37							06 55		
Hengoed	d																06 40							06 59		
Ystrad Mynach 3	d																06 43							07 01		
Llanbradach	d																06 48							07 06		
Aber	d																06 52							07 10		
Caerphilly 3	d							06 10									06 55							07 13		
Lisvane & Thornhill	d							06 14									06 59							07 17		
Llanishen	d							06 16									07 01							07 19		
Heath High Level	d							06 19									07 04							07 22		
Coryton	d													06 45											07 15	
Whitchurch (Cardiff)	d													06 46											07 16	
Rhiwbina	d													06 48											07 18	
Birchgrove	d													06 50											07 20	
Ty Glas	d													06 51											07 21	
Heath Low Level	d													06 54											07 24	
Cardiff Queen Street 3	a			05 48				06 25		06 44				06 59			07 09			07 14		07 19		07 27	07 29	07 34
	d			05 51				06 26	06 42	06 45			06 57	07 00			07 11	07 12		07 16		07 21	07 27	07 28	07 31	07 36
Cardiff Bay	a								06 46				07 01					07 16					07 31			
Cardiff Central 7	a			05 54				06 29		06 48				07 03			07 14			07 18	07 20	07 24		07 31	07 34	07 39
	d	05 25	05 41	05 55	06 16	06 25	06 36	06 41			06 55	07 01				07 10	07 16					07 25		07 32		07 41
Grangetown	d	05 29	05 45	05 59	06 20	06 29	06 40	06 45			06 59	07 05				07 14	07 20					07 29		07 36		07 45
Dingle Road	d				06 26		06 44					07 11					07 26							07 41		
Penarth	a				06 32		06 49					07 17					07 32							07 47		
Cogan	d	05 33	05 48	06 03		06 33		06 48			07 03					07 18						07 33				07 48
Eastbrook	d	05 35	05 51	06 05		06 35		06 51			07 05					07 20						07 35				07 51
Dinas Powys	d	05 37	05 53	06 07		06 37		06 53			07 07					07 22						07 37				07 53
Cadoxton	d	05 42	05 57	06 12		06 42		06 57			07 12					07 27						07 42				07 57
Barry Docks	d	05 45	06 00	06 15		06 45		07 00			07 15					07 30						07 45				08 00
Barry 3	d	05 49	06 05	06 19		06 49		07 05			07 19					07 34						07 49				08 05
Barry Island	a	05 56		06 26		06 56					07 26					07 40						07 56				
Rhoose Cardiff Int Airport ✈	d		06 12					07 12																		08 12
Llantwit Major	d		06 22					07 22																		08 22
Bridgend	a		06 40					07 40																		08 40

For general notes see front of timetable
For details of catering facilities see
Directory of Train Operators

A To Radyr
B To Coryton

Table 130

Mondays to Fridays
from 8 September

Treherbert, Aberdare, Merthyr, Pontypridd, Rhymney and Coryton → Cardiff, Penarth, Barry, Barry Island and Bridgend

Network Diagram - see first page of Table 130

		AW	AW	AW	AW A	AW	AW	AW	AW	AW B	AW	AW	AW		AW	AW A	AW	AW	AW	AW	AW B	AW	AW	AW	AW	AW A
Treherbert	d			06 47									07 17												07 47	
Ynyswen	d			06 49									07 19												07 49	
Treorchy	d			06 51									07 21												07 51	
Ton Pentre	d			06 53									07 23												07 53	
Ystrad Rhondda	a			06 56									07 26												07 56	
	d			06 58									07 28												07 58	
Llwynypia	d			07 00									07 30												08 00	
Tonypandy	d			07 03									07 33												08 03	
Dinas Rhondda	d			07 05									07 35												08 05	
Porth	d			07 09									07 39												08 09	
Trehafod	d			07 12									07 42												08 12	
Merthyr Tydfil	d																					07 38				
Pentre-bach	d																					07 42				
Troed Y Rhiw	d																					07 45				
Merthyr Vale	d																					07 50				
Quakers Yard	d																					07 55				
Aberdare 3	d						06 51											07 21								
Cwmbach	d						06 54											07 24								
Fernhill	d						06 58											07 28								
Mountain Ash	a						07 01											07 31								
	d						07 04											07 34								
Penrhiwceiber	d						07 08											07 38								
Abercynon	d						07 14											07 44				07 59				
Pontypridd 3	a			07 17			07 23						07 47					07 53				08 07			08 17	
	d			07 18			07 24				07 39		07 48					07 54				08 09			08 18	
Trefforest	d			07 21			07 27				07 42		07 51					07 57				08 12			08 21	
Trefforest Estate	d										07 46											08 16				
Taffs Well 3	d			07 28			07 34				07 50		07 58					08 04				08 20			08 28	
Radyr 3	a			07 31			07 37				07 53		08 01					08 07				08 23			08 31	
	d			07 31	07 34		07 37				07 53		08 01			08 04		08 07				08 23			08 31	08 34
Danescourt	d				07 38											08 08										08 38
Fairwater	d				07 40											08 10										08 40
Waun-gron Park	d				07 42											08 12										08 42
Ninian Park	d				07 45											08 15										08 45
Llandaf	d			07 34		←	07 40				07 56		08 04				←	08 10				08 26			08 34	
Cathays	d			07 39		07 39	07 45				08 01		08 09				08 09	08 15				08 31			08 39	
Rhymney 3	d			→				07 02					→						07 24				07 44		→	
Pontlottyn	d							07 05											07 27				07 47			
Tir-phil	d							07 09											07 31				07 51			
Brithdir	d							07 12											07 34				07 54			
Bargoed	d	07 02						07 17				07 32							07b45				08 02			
Gilfach Fargoed	d	07 04						07 19											07 47							
Pengam	d	07 07						07 22				07 37							07 50				08 07			
Hengoed	d	07 10						07 25				07 40							07 54				08 10			
Ystrad Mynach 3	d	07 13						07 28				07 43							07 57				08 13			
Llanbradach	d	07 18						07 33				07 48							08 02				08 18			
Aber	d	07 22						07 37				07 52							08 07				08 22			
Caerphilly 3	d	07 25						07 40				07 55							08 10				08 25			
Lisvane & Thornhill	d	07 29						07 44				07 59							08 14				08 29			
Llanishen	d	07 31						07 46				08 01							08 16				08 31			
Heath High Level	d	07 34						07 49				08 04							08 19				08 34			
Coryton	d									07 45											08 15					
Whitchurch (Cardiff)	d									07 46											08 16					
Rhiwbina	d									07 48											08 18					
Birchgrove	d									07 50											08 20					
Ty Glas	d									07 51											08 21					
Heath Low Level	d									07 54											08 24					
Cardiff Queen Street 3	a	07 38				07 44	07 49	07 54		07 59	08 04	08 09					08 14	08 19	08 24		08 29	08 34	08 39			
	d	07 41	07 42			07 46	07 51	07 56	07 57	08 01	08 06	08 11			08 12		08 16	08 21	08 26	08 27	08 31	08 36	08 41	08 42		
Cardiff Bay	a		07 46						08 01						08 16					08 31				08 46		
Cardiff Central 7	a	07 44			07 50	07 53	07 54	07 59		08 04	08 09	08 14				08 20	08 23	08 24	08 29		08 34	08 39	08 48			08 50
	d	07 46					07 55	08 01			08 10	08 16						08 25	08 31			08 41				
Grangetown	d	07 50					07 59	08 05			08 14	08 20						08 29	08 35			08 45				
Dingle Road	d	07 56						08 11				08 26							08 41							
Penarth	a	08 02						08 17				08 32							08 47							
Cogan	d						08 03				08 18							08 33				08 48				
Eastbrook	d						08 05				08 20							08 35				08 51				
Dinas Powys	d						08 07				08 22							08 37				08 53				
Cadoxton	d						08 12				08 27							08 42				08 57				
Barry Docks	d						08 15				08 30							08 45				09 00				
Barry 3	d						08 19				08 34							08 49				09 05				
Barry Island	a						08 26				08 41							08 56								
Rhoose Cardiff Int Airport ✈	d																					09 12				
Llantwit Major	d																					09 22				
Bridgend	a																					09 40				

For general notes see front of timetable
For details of catering facilities see Directory of Train Operators

A To Coryton
B To Radyr
b Arr. 0737

Table 130

Mondays to Fridays

from 8 September

Treherbert, Aberdare, Merthyr, Pontypridd, Rhymney and Coryton → Cardiff, Penarth, Barry, Barry Island and Bridgend

Network Diagram - see first page of Table 130

		AW	AW	AW	AW	AW A	AW	AW	AW	AW	AW B	AW	AW	AW	AW	AW A	AW	AW	AW	AW	AW B	AW	AW	AW	AW
Treherbert	d								08 17											08 47					
Ynyswen	d								08 19											08 49					
Treorchy	d								08 21											08 51					
Ton Pentre	d								08 23											08 53					
Ystrad Rhondda	a								08 26											08 56					
	d								08 28											08 58					
Llwynypia	d								08 30											09 00					
Tonypandy	d								08 33											09 03					
Dinas Rhondda	d								08 35											09 05					
Porth	d								08 39											09 09					
Trehafod	d								08 42											09 12					
Merthyr Tydfil	d																08 38								
Pentre-bach	d																08 42								
Troed Y Rhiw	d																08 45								
Merthyr Vale	d																08 50								
Quakers Yard	d																08 55								
Aberdare 3	d		07 51										08 21										08 51		
Cwmbach	d		07 54										08 24										08 54		
Fernhill	d		07 58										08 28										08 58		
Mountain Ash	a		08 01										08 31										09 01		
	d		08 04										08 34										09 04		
Penrhiwceiber	d		08 08										08 38										09 08		
Abercynon	d		08 14										08 44				08 59						09 14		
Pontypridd 3	a		08 23						08 47				08 53				09 07			09 17			09 23		
	d		08 24				08 39		08 48				08 54				09 09			09 18			09 24		
Trefforest	d		08 27				08 42		08 51				08 57				09 12			09 21			09 27		
Trefforest Estate	d						08 46										09 16								
Taffs Well 3	d		08 34				08 50		08 58				09 04				09 20			09 28			09 34		
Radyr 3	a		08 37				08 53		09 01				09 07				09 23			09 31			09 37		
	d		08 37				08 53		09 01		09 04		09 07				09 23			09 31	09 34		09 37		
Danescourt	d										09 08										09 38				
Fairwater	d										09 10										09 40				
Waun-gron Park	d										09 12										09 42				
Ninian Park	d										09 15										09 45				
Llandaf	d	←	08 40				08 56		09 04			←	09 10				09 26			09 34		←	09 40		
Cathays	d	08 39	08 45				09 01		09 09			09 09	09 15				09 31			09 39		09 39	09 45		
Rhymney 3	d								→					08 30						→					
Pontlottyn	d													08 33											
Tir-phil	d													08 37											
Brithdir	d													08 40											
Bargoed	d			08 17				08 32						08 47				09 02							
Gilfach Fargoed	d			08 19																					
Pengam	d			08 22				08 37						08 52				09 07							
Hengoed	d			08 25				08 40						08 55				09 10							
Ystrad Mynach 3	d			08 28				08 43						08 58				09 13						09 28	
Llanbradach	d			08 33				08 48						09 03				09 18						09 33	
Aber	d			08 37				08 52						09 07				09 22						09 37	
Caerphilly 3	d			08 40				08 55						09 10				09 25						09 40	
Lisvane & Thornhill	d			08 44				08 59						09 14				09 29						09 44	
Llanishen	d			08 46				09 01						09 16				09 31						09 46	
Heath High Level	d			08 49				09 04						09 19				09 34						09 49	
Coryton	d					08 45										09 15									
Whitchurch (Cardiff)	d					08 46										09 16									
Rhiwbina	d					08 48										09 18									
Birchgrove	d					08 50										09 20									
Ty Glas	d					08 51										09 21									
Heath Low Level	d					08 54										09 24									
Cardiff Queen Street 3	a	08 44	08 49	08 54		08 59	09 04	09 09				09 14	09 19	09 24		09 29	09 34	09 39				09 44	09 49	09 54	
	d	08 46	08 51	08 56	08 57	09 01	09 06	09 11		09 12		09 16	09 21	09 26	09 27	09 31	09 36	09 41	09 42			09 46	09 51	09 56	09 57
Cardiff Bay	a				09 01					09 16					09 31				09 46						10 01
Cardiff Central 7	a	08 53	08 54	08 59		09 04	09 09	09 14			09 20	09 23	09 24	09 29		09 34	09 39	09 46			09 50	09 53	09 54	09 59	
	d		08 55	09 01			09 10	09 16					09 25	09 31			09 41	09 46					09 55	10 01	
Grangetown	d		08 59	09 05			09 14	09 20					09 29	09 35			09 45	09 50					09 59	10 05	
Dingle Road	d			09 11				09 26						09 41				09 56						10 11	
Penarth	a			09 17				09 32						09 47				10 02						10 17	
Cogan	d		09 03				09 18						09 33				09 48						10 03		
Eastbrook	d		09 05				09 20						09 35				09 51						10 05		
Dinas Powys	d		09 07				09 22						09 37				09 53						10 07		
Cadoxton	d		09 12				09 27						09 42				09 57						10 12		
Barry Docks	d		09 15				09 30						09 45				10 00						10 15		
Barry 3	d		09 19				09 34						09 49				10 05						10 19		
Barry Island	a		09 26				09 41						09 56										10 25		
Rhoose Cardiff Int Airport ✈	d																10 12								
Llantwit Major	d																10 22								
Bridgend	a																10 40								

For general notes see front of timetable
For details of catering facilities see Directory of Train Operators

A To Radyr
B To Coryton

Table 130

Mondays to Fridays

from 8 September

Treherbert, Aberdare, Merthyr, Pontypridd, Rhymney and Coryton → Cardiff, Penarth, Barry, Barry Island and Bridgend

Network Diagram - see first page of Table 130

		AW A	AW		AW	AW	AW	AW B	AW	AW	AW	AW	AW A	AW	AW	AW	AW	AW B	AW	AW	AW		AW	AW A	AW	AW
Treherbert	d					09 17											09 47									
Ynyswen	d					09 19											09 49									
Treorchy	d					09 21											09 51									
Ton Pentre	d					09 23											09 53									
Ystrad Rhondda	a					09 26											09 56									
	d					09 28											09 58									
Llwynypia	d					09 30											10 00									
Tonypandy	d					09 33											10 03									
Dinas Rhondda	d					09 35											10 05									
Porth	d					09 39											10 09									
Trehafod	d					09 42											10 12									
Merthyr Tydfil	d													09 38												
Pentre-bach	d													09 42												
Troed Y Rhiw	d													09 45												
Merthyr Vale	d													09 50												
Quakers Yard	d													09 55												
Aberdare 3	d									09 21										09 51						
Cwmbach	d									09 24										09 54						
Fernhill	d									09 28										09 58						
Mountain Ash	a									09 31										10 01						
	d									09 34										10 04						
Penrhiwceiber	d									09 38										10 08						
Abercynon	d									09 44				09 59						10 14						
Pontypridd 3	a					09 47				09 53				10 07			10 17			10 23						
	d		09 39			09 48				09 54				10 09			10 18			10 24					10 39	
Trefforest	d		09 42			09 51				09 57				10 12			10 21			10 27					10 42	
Trefforest Estate	d		09 46											10 16											10 46	
Taffs Well 3	d		09 50			09 58				10 04				10 20			10 28			10 34					10 50	
Radyr 3	a		09 53			10 01				10 07				10 23			10 31			10 37					10 53	
	d		09 53			10 01		10 04		10 07				10 23			10 31	10 34		10 37					10 53	
Danescourt	d							10 08										10 38								
Fairwater	d							10 10										10 40								
Waun-gron Park	d							10 12										10 42								
Ninian Park	d							10 15										10 45								
Llandaf	d		09 56			10 04			←	10 10				10 26			10 34		←	10 40					10 56	
Cathays	d		10 01			10 09			10 09	10 15				10 31			10 39		10 39	10 45					11 01	
Rhymney 3	d					→					09 29						→									
Pontlottyn	d										09 32															
Tir-phil	d										09 36															
Brithdir	d										09 39															
Bargoed	d				09 25						09 47				10 02											10 25
Gilfach Fargoed	d				09 27																					10 27
Pengam	d				09 30						09 52				10 07											10 30
Hengoed	d				09 33						09 55				10 10											10 33
Ystrad Mynach 3	d				09b43						09 58				10 13						10 28					10c43
Llanbradach	d				09 48						10 03				10 18						10 33					10 48
Aber	d				09 52						10 07				10 22						10 37					10 52
Caerphilly 3	d				09 55						10 10				10 25						10 40					10 55
Lisvane & Thornhill	d				09 59						10 14				10 29						10 44					10 59
Llanishen	d				10 01						10 16				10 31						10 46					11 01
Heath High Level	d				10 04						10 19				10 34						10 49					11 04
Coryton	d	09 45											10 15											10 45		
Whitchurch (Cardiff)	d	09 46											10 16											10 46		
Rhiwbina	d	09 48											10 18											10 48		
Birchgrove	d	09 50											10 20											10 50		
Ty Glas	d	09 51											10 21											10 51		
Heath Low Level	d	09 54											10 24											10 54		
Cardiff Queen Street 3	a	09 59	10 04		10 09				10 14	10 19	10 24		10 29	10 34	10 39				10 44	10 49	10 54			10 59	11 04	11 09
	d	10 01	10 06		10 11		10 12		10 16	10 21	10 26	10 27	10 31	10 36	10 41	10 42			10 46	10 51	10 56		10 57	11 01	11 06	11 11
Cardiff Bay	a						10 16					10 31				10 46							11 01			
Cardiff Central 7	a	10 04	10 09		10 14			10 20	10 23	10 24	10 29		10 34	10 39	10 44			10 50	10 53	10 54	10 59			11 04	11 09	11 14
	d		10 10		10 16					10 25	10 31			10 41	10 46					10 55	11 01				11 10	11 16
Grangetown	d		10 14		10 20					10 29	10 35			10 45	10 50					10 59	11 05				11 14	11 20
Dingle Road	d				10 26						10 41				10 56						11 11					11 26
Penarth	a				10 32						10 47				11 02						11 17					11 32
Cogan	d		10 18							10 33				10 49						11 03					11 18	
Eastbrook	d		10 20							10 35				10 51						11 05					11 20	
Dinas Powys	d		10 22							10 37				10 53						11 07					11 22	
Cadoxton	d		10 27							10 42				10 58						11 12					11 27	
Barry Docks	d		10 30							10 45				11 01						11 15					11 30	
Barry 3	d		10 34							10 49				11 05						11 19					11 34	
Barry Island	a		10 41							10 56										11 26					11 41	
Rhoose Cardiff Int Airport ✈	d													11 12												
Llantwit Major	d													11 22												
Bridgend	a													11 40												

For general notes see front of timetable
For details of catering facilities see Directory of Train Operators

A To Radyr
B To Coryton
b Arr. 0936
c Arr. 1036

Table 130

Mondays to Fridays

from 8 September

Treherbert, Aberdare, Merthyr, Pontypridd, Rhymney and Coryton → Cardiff, Penarth, Barry, Barry Island and Bridgend

Network Diagram - see first page of Table 130

		AW	AW A	AW	AW	AW	AW	AW B	AW	AW	AW	AW	AW A	AW	AW	AW		AW	AW B	AW	AW	AW	AW	AW A	AW	AW
Treherbert	d					10 17						10 47										11 17				
Ynyswen	d					10 19						10 49										11 19				
Treorchy	d					10 21						10 51										11 21				
Ton Pentre	d					10 23						10 53										11 23				
Ystrad Rhondda	a					10 26						10 56										11 26				
	d					10 28						10 58										11 28				
Llwynypia	d					10 30						11 00										11 30				
Tonypandy	d					10 33						11 03										11 33				
Dinas Rhondda	d					10 35						11 05										11 35				
Porth	d					10b52						11 09										11 39				
Trehafod	d					10 55						11 12										11 42				
Merthyr Tydfil	d								10 38																	
Pentre-bach	d								10 42																	
Troed Y Rhiw	d								10 45																	
Merthyr Vale	d								10 50																	
Quakers Yard	d								10 55																	
Aberdare 3	d			10 21											10 51											11 21
Cwmbach	d			10 24											10 54											11 24
Fernhill	d			10 28											10 58											11 28
Mountain Ash	a			10 31											11 01											11 31
	d			10 34											11 04											11 34
Penrhiwceiber	d			10 38											11 08											11 38
Abercynon	d			10 44					10 59						11 14											11 44
Pontypridd 3	a			10 53		11 00			11 07			11 17			11 23							11 47				11 53
	d			10 54		11 04			11 09			11 18			11 24					11 39		11 48				11 54
Trefforest	d			10 57		11 07			11 12			11 21			11 27					11 42		11 51				11 57
Trefforest Estate	d								11 16											11 46						
Taffs Well 3	d			11 04		11 13			11 20			11 28			11 34					11 50		11 58				12 04
Radyr 3	a			11 07		11 17			11 23			11 31			11 37					11 53		12 01				12 07
	d		11 04	11 07		11 17			11 23			11 31	11 34		11 37					11 53		12 01		12 04		12 07
Danescourt	d		11 08										11 38											12 08		
Fairwater	d		11 10										11 40											12 10		
Waun-gron Park	d		11 12										11 42											12 12		
Ninian Park	d		11 15										11 45											12 15		
Llandaf	d			11 10					11 26			11 34		←	11 40					11 56		12 04			←	12 10
Cathays	d			11 15					11 31			11 39		11 39	11 45					12 01		12 09			12 09	12 15
Rhymney 3	d				10 29							→										→				
Pontlottyn	d				10 32																					
Tir-phil	d				10 36																					
Brithdir	d				10 39																					
Bargoed	d				10 47					11 02											11 25					
Gilfach Fargoed	d																				11 27					
Pengam	d				10 52					11 07											11 30					
Hengoed	d				10 55					11 10											11 33					
Ystrad Mynach 3	d				10 58					11 13						11 28					11c43					
Llanbradach	d				11 03					11 18						11 33					11 48					
Aber	d				11 07					11 22						11 37					11 52					
Caerphilly 3	d				11 10					11 25						11 40					11 55					
Lisvane & Thornhill	d				11 14					11 29						11 44					11 59					
Llanishen	d				11 16					11 31						11 46					12 01					
Heath High Level	d				11 19					11 34						11 49					12 04					
Coryton	d							11 15											11 45							
Whitchurch (Cardiff)	d							11 16											11 46							
Rhiwbina	d							11 18											11 48							
Birchgrove	d							11 20											11 50							
Ty Glas	d							11 21											11 51							
Heath Low Level	d							11 24											11 54							
Cardiff Queen Street 3	a			11 19	11 24			11 29	11 34	11 39				11 44	11 49	11 54			11 59	12 04	12 09				12 14	12 19
	d	11 12		11 21	11 26		11 27	11 31	11 36	11 41	11 42			11 46	11 51	11 56		11 57	12 01	12 06	12 11		12 12		12 16	12 21
Cardiff Bay	a	11 16					11 31				11 46							12 01					12 16			
Cardiff Central 7	a		11 20	11 24	11 29	11 34		11 34	11 39	11 44			11 50	11 53	11 54	11 59			12 04	12 09	12 14			12 20	12 23	12 24
	d			11 25	11 31				11 41	11 46					11 55	12 01				12 10	12 16					12 25
Grangetown	d			11 29	11 35				11 45	11 50					11 59	12 05				12 14	12 20					12 29
Dingle Road	d				11 41					11 56						12 11					12 26					
Penarth	a				11 47					12 02						12 17					12 32					
Cogan	d			11 33					11 48						12 03					12 18						12 33
Eastbrook	d			11 35					11 51						12 05					12 20						12 35
Dinas Powys	d			11 37					11 53						12 07					12 22						12 37
Cadoxton	d			11 42					11 57						12 12					12 27						12 42
Barry Docks	d			11 45					12 00						12 15					12 30						12 45
Barry 3	d			11 49					12 05						12 19					12 34						12 49
Barry Island	a			11 56											12 26					12 41						12 56
Rhoose Cardiff Int Airport ✈	d								12 12																	
Llantwit Major	d								12 22																	
Bridgend	a								12 40																	

For general notes see front of timetable
For details of catering facilities see Directory of Train Operators

A To Coryton
B To Radyr
b Arr. 1038
c Arr. 1136

Table 130

Mondays to Fridays

from 8 September

Treherbert, Aberdare, Merthyr, Pontypridd, Rhymney and Coryton → Cardiff, Penarth, Barry, Barry Island and Bridgend

Network Diagram - see first page of Table 130

		AW	AW	AW A	AW	AW	AW	AW	AW B	AW	AW		AW	AW A	AW	AW	AW	AW	AW B	AW	AW	AW	AW	AW A	AW	AW
Treherbert	d							11 47										12 17								
Ynyswen	d							11 49										12 19								
Treorchy	d							11 51										12 21								
Ton Pentre	d							11 53										12 23								
Ystrad Rhondda	a							11 56										12 26								
	d							11 58										12 28								
Llwynypia	d							12 00										12 30								
Tonypandy	d							12 03										12 33								
Dinas Rhondda	d							12 05										12 35								
Porth	d							12 09										12 39								
Trehafod	d							12 12										12 42								
Merthyr Tydfil	d				11 38																				12 38	
Pentre-bach	d				11 42																				12 42	
Troed Y Rhiw	d				11 45																				12 45	
Merthyr Vale	d				11 50																				12 50	
Quakers Yard	d				11 55																				12 55	
Aberdare 3	d																				12 21					
Cwmbach	d																				12 24					
Fernhill	d																				12 28					
Mountain Ash	a																				12 31					
	d																				12 34					
Penrhiwceiber	d																				12 38					
Abercynon	d				11 59																12 44				12 59	
Pontypridd 3	a				12 07			12 17										12 48			12 53				13 07	
	d				12 09			12 18							12 39			12 48			12 54				13 09	
Trefforest	d				12 12			12 21							12 42			12 51			12 57				13 12	
Trefforest Estate	d				12 16										12 46										13 16	
Taffs Well 3	d				12 20			12 28							12 50			12 58			13 04				13 20	
Radyr 3	a				12 23			12 31							12 53			13 01			13 07				13 23	
	d				12 23			12 31	12 34						12 53			13 01	13 04		13 07				13 23	
Danescourt	d								12 38										13 08							
Fairwater	d								12 40										13 10							
Waun-gron Park	d								12 42										13 12							
Ninian Park	d								12 45										13 15							
Llandaf	d				12 26			12 34		←					12 56			13 04		←	13 10				13 26	
Cathays	d				12 31			12 39		12 39					13 01			13 09		13 09	13 15				13 31	
Rhymney 3	d	11 29						→										→				12 29				
Pontlottyn	d	11 32																				12 32				
Tir-phil	d	11 36																				12 36				
Brithdir	d	11 39																				12 39				
Bargoed	d	11 47				12 02										12 25						12 47				13 02
Gilfach Fargoed	d															12 27										
Pengam	d	11 52				12 07										12 30						12 52				13 07
Hengoed	d	11 55				12 10										12 33						12 55				13 10
Ystrad Mynach 3	d	11 58				12 13					12 28					12b43						12 58				13 13
Llanbradach	d	12 03				12 18					12 33					12 48						13 03				13 18
Aber	d	12 07				12 22					12 37					12 52						13 07				13 22
Caerphilly 3	d	12 10				12 25					12 40					12 55						13 10				13 25
Lisvane & Thornhill	d	12 14				12 29					12 44					12 59						13 14				13 29
Llanishen	d	12 16				12 31					12 46					13 01						13 16				13 31
Heath High Level	d	12 19				12 34					12 49					13 04						13 19				13 34
Coryton	d			12 15										12 45										13 15		
Whitchurch (Cardiff)	d			12 16										12 46										13 16		
Rhiwbina	d			12 18										12 48										13 18		
Birchgrove	d			12 20										12 50										13 20		
Ty Glas	d			12 21										12 51										13 21		
Heath Low Level	d			12 24										12 54										13 24		
Cardiff Queen Street 3	a	12 24		12 29	12 34	12 39				12 44	12 54			12 59	13 04	13 09				13 14	13 19	13 24		13 29	13 34	13 39
	d	12 26	12 27	12 31	12 36	12 41	12 42			12 46	12 56		12 57	13 01	13 06	13 11	13 12			13 16	13 21	13 26	13 27	13 31	13 36	13 41
Cardiff Bay	a		12 31				12 46						13 01				13 16						13 31			
Cardiff Central 7	a	12 29		12 34	12 39	12 44			12 50	12 52	12 59			13 04	13 09	13 14			13 20	13 23	13 24	13 29		13 34	13 40	13 44
	d	12 31			12 41	12 46				12 55	13 01				13 10	13 16					13 25	13 31			13 41	13 46
Grangetown	d	12 35			12 45	12 50				12 59	13 05				13 14	13 20					13 29	13 35			13 45	13 50
Dingle Road	d	12 41				12 56					13 11					13 26						13 41				13 56
Penarth	a	12 47				13 02					13 17					13 32						13 47				14 02
Cogan	d				12 48					13 03					13 18						13 33				13 48	
Eastbrook	d				12 51					13 05					13 20						13 35				13 51	
Dinas Powys	d				12 53					13 07					13 22						13 37				13 53	
Cadoxton	d				12 57					13 12					13 27						13 42				13 57	
Barry Docks	d				13 00					13 15					13 30						13 45				14 00	
Barry 3	d				13 05					13 19					13 34						13 49				14 05	
Barry Island	a									13 26					13 41						13 56					
Rhoose Cardiff Int Airport ✈	d				13 12																				14 12	
Llantwit Major	d				13 22																				14 22	
Bridgend	a				13 40																				14 40	

For general notes see front of timetable
For details of catering facilities see Directory of Train Operators

A To Radyr
B To Coryton
b Arr. 1236

Table 130

Mondays to Fridays
from 8 September

Treherbert, Aberdare, Merthyr, Pontypridd, Rhymney and Coryton → Cardiff, Penarth, Barry, Barry Island and Bridgend

Network Diagram - see first page of Table 130

		AW	AW	AW A	AW	AW	AW	AW	AW B	AW	AW	AW	AW	AW A	AW	AW	AW	AW	AW B	AW	AW	AW	AW	AW A
Treherbert	d		12 47									13 17											13 47	
Ynyswen	d		12 49									13 19											13 49	
Treorchy	d		12 51									13 21											13 51	
Ton Pentre	d		12 53									13 23											13 53	
Ystrad Rhondda	a		12 56									13 26											13 56	
	d		12 58									13 28											13 58	
Llwynypia	d		13 00									13 30											14 00	
Tonypandy	d		13 03									13 33											14 03	
Dinas Rhondda	d		13 05									13 35											14 05	
Porth	d		13 09									13 39											14 09	
Trehafod	d		13 12									13 42											14 12	
Merthyr Tydfil	d																			13 38				
Pentre-bach	d																			13 42				
Troed Y Rhiw	d																			13 45				
Merthyr Vale	d																			13 50				
Quakers Yard	d																			13 55				
Aberdare 3	d					12 51																		
Cwmbach	d					12 54																		
Fernhill	d					12 58																		
Mountain Ash	a					13 01																		
	d					13 04																		
Penrhiwceiber	d					13 08																		
Abercynon	d					13 14										13 45				13 59				
Pontypridd 3	a		13 17			13 23						13 47				13 53				14 07			14 17	
	d		13 18			13 24				13 39		13 48				13 54				14 09			14 18	
Trefforest	d		13 21			13 27				13 42		13 51				13 57				14 12			14 21	
Trefforest Estate	d									13 46										14 16				
Taffs Well 3	d		13 28			13 34				13 50		13 58				14 04				14 20			14 28	
Radyr 3	a		13 31			13 37				13 53		14 01				14 07				14 23			14 31	
	d		13 31	13 34		13 37				13 53		14 01		14 04		14 07				14 23			14 31	14 34
Danescourt	d			13 38										14 08										14 38
Fairwater	d			13 40										14 10										14 40
Waun-gron Park	d			13 42										14 12										14 42
Ninian Park	d			13 45										14 15										14 45
Llandaf	d		13 34		←	13 40				13 56		14 04			←	14 10				14 26			14 34	
Cathays	d		13 39		13 39	13 45				14 01		14 09			14 09	14 15				14 31			14 39	
Rhymney 3	d		→									→					13 29						→	
Pontlottyn	d																13 32							
Tir-phil	d																13 36							
Brithdir	d																13 39							
Bargoed	d										13 25						13 47				14 02			
Gilfach Fargoed	d										13 27													
Pengam	d										13 30						13 52				14 07			
Hengoed	d										13 33						13 55				14 10			
Ystrad Mynach 3	d						13 28				13b43						13 58				14 13			
Llanbradach	d						13 33				13 48						14 03				14 18			
Aber	d						13 37				13 52						14 07				14 22			
Caerphilly 3	d						13 40				13 55						14 10				14 25			
Lisvane & Thornhill	d						13 44				13 59						14 14				14 29			
Llanishen	d						13 46				14 01						14 16				14 31			
Heath High Level	d						13 49				14 04						14 19				14 34			
Coryton	d								13 45										14 15					
Whitchurch (Cardiff)	d								13 46										14 16					
Rhiwbina	d								13 48										14 18					
Birchgrove	d								13 50										14 20					
Ty Glas	d								13 51										14 21					
Heath Low Level	d								13 54										14 24					
Cardiff Queen Street 3	a				13 44	13 49	13 54		13 59	14 04	14 09				14 14	14 19	14 24		14 29	14 34	14 39			
	d	13 42			13 46	13 51	13 56	13 57	14 01	14 06	14 11		14 12		14 16	14 21	14 26	14 27	14 31	14 36	14 41	14 42		
Cardiff Bay	a	13 46						14 01					14 16					14 31				14 46		
Cardiff Central 7	a			13 50	13 53	13 54	13 59		14 04	14 09	14 14			14 20	14 23	14 24	14 29		14 34	14 39	14 44			14 50
	d					13 55	14 01			14 10	14 16					14 25	14 31			14 41	14 46			
Grangetown	d					13 59	14 05			14 14	14 20					14 29	14 35			14 45	14 50			
Dingle Road	d						14 11				14 26						14 41				14 56			
Penarth	a						14 17				14 32						14 47				15 02			
Cogan	d					14 03				14 18						14 33				14 48				
Eastbrook	d					14 05				14 20						14 35				14 51				
Dinas Powys	d					14 07				14 22						14 37				14 53				
Cadoxton	d					14 12				14 27						14 41				14 57				
Barry Docks	d					14 15				14 30						14 44				15 00				
Barry 3	d					14 19				14 34						14 48				15 05				
Barry Island	a					14 26				14 41						14 56								
Rhoose Cardiff Int Airport ✈	d																			15 12				
Llantwit Major	d																			15 22				
Bridgend	a																			15 40				

For general notes see front of timetable
For details of catering facilities see
Directory of Train Operators

A To Coryton
B To Radyr
b Arr. 1336

Treherbert, Aberdare, Merthyr, Pontypridd, Rhymney and Coryton → Cardiff, Penarth, Barry, Barry Island and Bridgend

Network Diagram - see first page of Table 130

Station		AW	AW	AW	AW	AW	AW	AW	AW	AW	AW	AW	AW	AW	AW	AW	AW	AW		AW	AW	AW	AW	AW	AW	AW
						A				B					A					B					A	
Treherbert	d												14 17					14 47								
Ynyswen	d												14 19					14 49								
Treorchy	d												14 21					14 51								
Ton Pentre	d												14 23					14 53								
Ystrad Rhondda	a												14 26					14 56								
	d												14 28					14 58								
Llwynypia	d												14 30					15 00								
Tonypandy	d												14 33					15 03								
Dinas Rhondda	d												14 35					15 05								
Porth	d												14b52					15 09								
Trehafod	d												14 55					15 12								
Merthyr Tydfil	d															14 38										
Pentre-bach	d															14 42										
Troed Y Rhiw	d															14 45										
Merthyr Vale	d															14 50										
Quakers Yard	d															14 55										
Aberdare 3	d		13 51								14 21											14 51				
Cwmbach	d		13 54								14 24											14 54				
Fernhill	d		13 58								14 28											14 58				
Mountain Ash	a		14 01								14 31											15 01				
	d		14 04								14 34											15 04				
Penrhiwceiber	d		14 08								14 38											15 08				
Abercynon	d		14 14								14 44					14 59						15 14				
Pontypridd 3	a		14 23								14 53		15 00			15 07		15 17				15 23				
	d		14 24				14 39				14 54		15 04			15 09		15 18				15 24				15 39
Trefforest	d		14 27				14 42				14 57		15 07			15 12		15 21				15 27				15 42
Trefforest Estate	d						14 46									15 16										15 46
Taffs Well 3	d		14 34				14 50				15 04		15 13			15 20		15 28				15 34				15 50
Radyr 3	a		14 37				14 53				15 07		15 17			15 23		15 31				15 37				15 53
	d		14 37				14 53			15 04	15 07		15 17			15 23		15 31		15 34		15 37				15 53
Danescourt	d									15 08										15 38						
Fairwater	d									15 10										15 40						
Waun-gron Park	d									15 12										15 42						
Ninian Park	d									15 15										15 45						
Llandaf	d	←	14 40				14 56				15 10					15 26		15 34			←	15 40				15 56
Cathays	d	14 39	14 45				15 01				15 15					15 31		15 39			15 39	15 45				16 01
Rhymney 3	d											14 29						→								
Pontlottyn	d											14 32														
Tir-phil	d											14 36														
Brithdir	d											14 39														
Bargoed	d							14 25				14 47														
Gilfach Fargoed	d							14 27																		
Pengam	d							14 30				14 52														
Hengoed	d							14 33				14 55														
Ystrad Mynach 3	d			14 28				14c43				14 58											15 28			
Llanbradach	d			14 33				14 48				15 03											15 33			
Aber	d			14 37				14 52				15 07											15 37			
Caerphilly 3	d			14 40				14 55				15 10											15 40			
Lisvane & Thornhill	d			14 44				14 59				15 14											15 44			
Llanishen	d			14 46				15 01				15 16											15 46			
Heath High Level	d			14 49				15 04				15 19											15 49			
Coryton	d					14 45									15 15										15 45	
Whitchurch (Cardiff)	d					14 46									15 16										15 46	
Rhiwbina	d					14 48									15 18										15 48	
Birchgrove	d					14 50									15 20										15 50	
Ty Glas	d					14 51									15 21										15 51	
Heath Low Level	d					14 54									15 24										15 54	
Cardiff Queen Street 3	a	14 44	14 49	14 54		14 59	15 04	15 09			15 19	15 24			15 29	15 34					15 44	15 49	15 54		15 59	16 04
	d	14 46	14 51	14 56	14 57	15 01	15 06	15 11	15 12		15 21	15 26		15 27	15 31	15 36	15 42				15 46	15 51	15 56	15 57	16 01	16 06
Cardiff Bay	a				15 01				15 16					15 31			15 46							16 01		
Cardiff Central 7	a	14 53	14 54	14 59		15 04	15 09	15 14		15 20	15 24	15 29	15 34		15 34	15 39				15 50	15 53	15 54	15 59		16 04	16 09
	d		14 55	15 01			15 10	15 16			15 25	15 31				15 41						15 55	16 01			16 10
Grangetown	d		14 59	15 05			15 14	15 20			15 29	15 35				15 45						15 59	16 05			16 14
Dingle Road	d			15 11				15 26				15 41											16 11			
Penarth	a			15 17				15 32				15 47											16 17			
Cogan	d		15 03				15 18				15 33					15 48						16 03				16 18
Eastbrook	d		15 05				15 20				15 35					15 51						16 05				16 20
Dinas Powys	d		15 07				15 22				15 37					15 53						16 07				16 22
Cadoxton	d		15 12				15 27				15 42					15 57						16 12				16 27
Barry Docks	d		15 15				15 30				15 45					16 00						16 15				16 30
Barry 3	d		15 19				15 34				15 49					16 05						16 19				16 34
Barry Island	a		15 26				15 41				15 56											16 26				16 41
Rhoose Cardiff Int Airport ✈	d															16 12										
Llantwit Major	d															16 22										
Bridgend	a															16 40										

For general notes see front of timetable
For details of catering facilities see Directory of Train Operators

A To Radyr
B To Coryton
b Arr. 1438
c Arr. 1436

Treherbert, Aberdare, Merthyr, Pontypridd, Rhymney and Coryton → Cardiff, Penarth, Barry, Barry Island and Bridgend

Network Diagram - see first page of Table 130

		AW	AW	AW	AW A	AW	AW	AW	AW	AW B	AW	AW	AW	AW	AW A	AW	AW	AW	AW	AW B	AW	AW	AW	AW	AW A
Treherbert	d		15 17											15 47									16 17		
Ynyswen	d		15 19											15 49									16 19		
Treorchy	d		15 21											15 51									16 21		
Ton Pentre	d		15 23											15 53									16 23		
Ystrad Rhondda	a		15 26											15 56									16 26		
	d		15 28											15 58									16 28		
Llwynypia	d		15 30											16 00									16 30		
Tonypandy	d		15 33											16 03									16 33		
Dinas Rhondda	d		15 35											16 05									16 35		
Porth	d		15 39											16 09									16 39		
Trehafod	d		15 42											16 12									16 42		
Merthyr Tydfil	d										15 38														
Pentre-bach	d										15 42														
Troed Y Rhiw	d										15 45														
Merthyr Vale	d										15 50														
Quakers Yard	d										15 55														
Aberdare 3	d						15 21										15 51								
Cwmbach	d						15 24										15 54								
Fernhill	d						15 28										15 58								
Mountain Ash	a						15 31										16 01								
	d						15 34										16 04								
Penrhiwceiber	d						15 38										16 08								
Abercynon	d						15 44				15 59						16 14								
Pontypridd 3	a		15 47				15 53				16 07			16 17			16 23						16 47		
	d		15 48				15 54				16 09			16 18			16 24				16 39		16 48		
Trefforest	d		15 51				15 57				16 12			16 21			16 27				16 42		16 51		
Trefforest Estate	d										16 16										16 46				
Taffs Well 3	d		15 58				16 04				16 20			16 28			16 34				16 50		16 58		
Radyr 3	a		16 01				16 07				16 23			16 31			16 37				16 53		17 01		
	d		16 01		16 04		16 07				16 23			16 31	16 34		16 37				16 53		17 01		17 04
Danescourt	d				16 08										16 38										17 08
Fairwater	d				16 10										16 40										17 10
Waun-gron Park	d				16 12										16 42										17 12
Ninian Park	d				16 15										16 45										17 15
Llandaf	d		16 04			←	16 10				16 26			16 34		←	16 40				16 56		17 04		
Cathays	d		16 09			16 09	16 15				16 31			16 39		16 39	16 45				17 01		17 09		
Rhymney 3	d		↳					15 29						↳									↳		
Pontlottyn	d							15 32																	
Tir-phil	d							15 36																	
Brithdir	d							15 39																	
Bargoed	d	15 25						15 47				16 02						16 17				16 32			
Gilfach Fargoed	d	15 27																16 19							
Pengam	d	15 30						15 52				16 07						16 22				16 37			
Hengoed	d	15 33						15 55				16 10						16 25				16 40			
Ystrad Mynach 3	d	15b43						15 58				16 13						16 28				16 43			
Llanbradach	d	15 48						16 03				16 18						16 33				16 48			
Aber	d	15 52						16 07				16 22						16 37				16 52			
Caerphilly 3	d	15 55						16 10				16 25						16 40				16 55			
Lisvane & Thornhill	d	15 59						16 14				16 29						16 44				16 59			
Llanishen	d	16 01						16 16				16 31						16 46				17 01			
Heath High Level	d	16 04						16 19				16 34						16 49				17 04			
Coryton	d									16 15										16 45					
Whitchurch (Cardiff)	d									16 16										16 46					
Rhiwbina	d									16 18										16 48					
Birchgrove	d									16 20										16 50					
Ty Glas	d									16 21										16 51					
Heath Low Level	d									16 24										16 54					
Cardiff Queen Street 3	a	16 09				16 14	16 19	16 24		16 29	16 34	16 39				16 44	16 49	16 54		16 59	17 04	17 09			
	d	16 11		16 12		16 16	16 21	16 26	16 27	16 31	16 36	16 41	16 42			16 46	16 51	16 56	16 57	17 01	17 06	17 11		17 12	
Cardiff Bay	a			16 16					16 31				16 46						17 01					17 16	
Cardiff Central 7	a	16 14			16 20	16 23	16 24	16 33		16 34	16 39	16 44			16 50	16 53	16 54	16 59		17 04	17 09	17 14			17 20
	d	16 16					16 25				16 41	16 46					16 55	17 01			17 10	17 16			
Grangetown	d	16 20					16 29				16 45	16 50					16 59	17 05			17 14	17 20			
Dingle Road	d	16 26										16 56						17 11				17 26			
Penarth	a	16 32										17 02						17 17				17 32			
Cogan	d						16 33				16 48						17 03				17 18				
Eastbrook	d						16 35				16 51						17 05				17 20				
Dinas Powys	d						16 37				16 53						17 07				17 22				
Cadoxton	d						16 42				16 57						17 12				17 27				
Barry Docks	d						16 45				17 00						17 15				17 30				
Barry 3	d						16 49				17 05						17 19				17 34				
Barry Island	a						16 56										17 26				17 41				
Rhoose Cardiff Int Airport ✈	d										17 12														
Llantwit Major	d										17 22														
Bridgend	a										17 40														

For general notes see front of timetable
For details of catering facilities see Directory of Train Operators

A To Coryton
B To Radyr
b Arr. 1536

Treherbert, Aberdare, Merthyr, Pontypridd, Rhymney and Coryton → Cardiff, Penarth, Barry, Barry Island and Bridgend

Network Diagram - see first page of Table 130

		AW	AW	AW	AW	AW	AW	AW		AW	AW	AW	AW	AW	AW	AW	AW	AW	AW	AW	AW	AW	AW	AW	AW	AW
						A						B					A					B				
Treherbert	d										16 47									17 17						
Ynyswen	d										16 49									17 19						
Treorchy	d										16 51									17 21						
Ton Pentre	d										16 53									17 23						
Ystrad Rhondda	a										16 56									17 26						
	d										16 58									17 28						
Llwynypia	d										17 00									17 30						
Tonypandy	d										17 03									17 33						
Dinas Rhondda	d										17 05									17 35						
Porth	d										17 09									17 39						
Trehafod	d										17 12									17 42						
Merthyr Tydfil	d						16 38																			
Pentre-bach	d						16 42																			
Troed Y Rhiw	d						16 45																			
Merthyr Vale	d						16 50																			
Quakers Yard	d						16 55																			
Aberdare 3	d		16 21											16 51										17 21		
Cwmbach	d		16 24											16 54										17 24		
Fernhill	d		16 28											16 58										17 28		
Mountain Ash	a		16 31											17 01										17 31		
	d		16 34											17 04										17 34		
Penrhiwceiber	d		16 38											17 08										17 38		
Abercynon	d		16 44				16 59							17 14										17 44		
Pontypridd 3	a		16 53				17 07				17 17			17 23						17 47				17 53		
	d		16 54				17 09				17 18			17 24				17 39		17 48				17 54		
Trefforest	d		16 57				17 12				17 21			17 27				17 42		17 51				17 57		
Trefforest Estate	d						17 16											17 46								
Taffs Well 3	d		17 04				17 20				17 28			17 34				17 50		17 58				18 04		
Radyr 3	a		17 07				17 23				17 31			17 37				17 53		18 01				18 07		
	d		17 07				17 23				17 31	17 34		17 37				17 53		18 01		18 04		18 07		
Danescourt	d											17 38										18 08				
Fairwater	d											17 40										18 10				
Waun-gron Park	d											17 42										18 12				
Ninian Park	d											17 45										18 15				
Llandaf	d	←	17 10				17 26				17 34		←	17 40				17 56		18 04			←	18 10		
Cathays	d	17 09	17 15				17 31				17 39		17 39	17 45				18 01		18 09			18 09	18 15		
Rhymney 3	d			16 29							→									→					17 29	
Pontlottyn	d			16 32																					17 32	
Tir-phil	d			16 36																					17 36	
Brithdir	d			16 39																					17 39	
Bargoed	d			16 47				17 02							17 17				17 32						17 47	
Gilfach Fargoed	d														17 19											
Pengam	d			16 52				17 07							17 22				17 37						17 52	
Hengoed	d			16 55				17 10							17 25				17 40						17 55	
Ystrad Mynach 3	d			16 58				17 13							17 28				17 43						17 58	
Llanbradach	d			17 03				17 18							17 33				17 48						18 03	
Aber	d			17 07				17 22							17 37				17 52						18 07	
Caerphilly 3	d			17 10				17 25							17 40				17 55						18 10	
Lisvane & Thornhill	d			17 14				17 29							17 44				17 59						18 14	
Llanishen	d			17 16				17 31							17 46				18 01						18 16	
Heath High Level	d			17 19				17 34							17 49				18 04						18 19	
Coryton	d					17 15											17 45									
Whitchurch (Cardiff)	d					17 16											17 46					18a38				
Rhiwbina	d					17 18											17 48									
Birchgrove	d					17 20											17 50									
Ty Glas	d					17 21											17 51									
Heath Low Level	d					17 24											17 54									
Cardiff Queen Street 3	a	17 14	17 19	17 24		17 29	17 34	17 39					17 44	17 49	17 54		17 59	18 04	18 09				18 14	18 19	18 24	
	d	17 16	17 21	17 26	17 27	17 31	17 36	17 41		17 42			17 46	17 51	17 56	17 57	18 01	18 06	18 11		18 12		18 16	18 21	18 26	18 27
Cardiff Bay	a				17 31					17 46						18 01					18 16					18 31
Cardiff Central 7	a	17 23	17 24	17 29		17 34	17 39	17 44				17 50	17 53	17 54	17 59		18 04	18 09	18 14			18 20	18 23	18 24	18 29	
	d		17 25	17 31			17 41	17 46						17 55	18 01			18 10	18 16					18 25	18 31	
Grangetown	d		17 29	17 35			17 45	17 50						17 59	18 05			18 14	18 20					18 29	18 35	
Dingle Road	d			17 41				17 56							18 11				18 26						18 41	
Penarth	a			17 47				18 02							18 17				18 32						18 47	
Cogan	d		17 33				17 48							18 03				18 18						18 33		
Eastbrook	d		17 35				17 51							18 05				18 20						18 35		
Dinas Powys	d		17 37				17 53							18 07				18 22						18 37		
Cadoxton	d		17 42				17 57							18 12				18 27						18 42		
Barry Docks	d		17 45				18 00							18 15				18 30						18 45		
Barry 3	d		17 49				18 05							18 19				18 34						18 49		
Barry Island	a		17 56											18 26				18 41						18 56		
Rhoose Cardiff Int Airport ✈	d						18 12																			
Llantwit Major	d						18 22																			
Bridgend	a						18 40																			

For general notes see front of timetable
For details of catering facilities see Directory of Train Operators

A To Radyr
B To Coryton

Table 130

Mondays to Fridays

from 8 September

Treherbert, Aberdare, Merthyr, Pontypridd, Rhymney and Coryton → Cardiff, Penarth, Barry, Barry Island and Bridgend

Network Diagram - see first page of Table 130

		AW A	AW		AW	AW	AW B	AW	AW	AW	AW	AW	AW	AW	AW	AW	AW	AW	AW	AW	AW A		AW	AW	AW	AW
Treherbert	d				17 47									18 17											18 47	
Ynyswen	d				17 49									18 19											18 49	
Treorchy	d				17 51									18 21											18 51	
Ton Pentre	d				17 53									18 23											18 53	
Ystrad Rhondda	a				17 56									18 26											18 56	
	d				17 58									18 28											18 58	
Llwynypia	d				18 00									18 30											19 00	
Tonypandy	d				18 03									18 33											19 03	
Dinas Rhondda	d				18 05									18 35											19 05	
Porth	d				18 09									18 39											19 09	
Trehafod	d				18 12									18 42											19 12	
Merthyr Tydfil	d		17 38																				18 38			
Pentre-bach	d		17 42																				18 42			
Troed Y Rhiw	d		17 45																				18 45			
Merthyr Vale	d		17 50																				18 50			
Quakers Yard	d		17 55																				18 55			
Aberdare 3	d								17 51									18 21								18 51
Cwmbach	d								17 54									18 24								18 54
Fernhill	d								17 58									18 28								18 58
Mountain Ash	a								18 01									18 31								19 01
	d								18 04									18 34								19 04
Penrhiwceiber	d								18 08									18 38								19 08
Abercynon	d		17 59						18 14									18 44					18 59			19 14
Pontypridd 3	a		18 07		18 17				18 23					18 47				18 53					19 07		19 17	19 23
	d		18 09		18 18				18 24				18 39	18 48				18 54					19 09		19 18	19 24
Trefforest	d		18 12		18 21				18 27				18 42	18 51				18 57					19 12		19 21	19 27
Trefforest Estate	d		18 16										18 46										19 16			
Taffs Well 3	d		18 20		18 28				18 34				18 50	18 58				19 04					19 20		19 28	19 34
Radyr 3	a		18 23		18 31				18 37				18 53	19 01				19 07					19 23		19 31	19 37
	d		18 23		18 31		18 34		18 37				18 53	19 01		19 04		19 07					19 23		19 31	19 37
Danescourt	d						18 38									19 08										
Fairwater	d						18 40									19 10										
Waun-gron Park	d						18 42									19 12										
Ninian Park	d						18 45									19 15										
Llandaf	d		18 26		18 34			←	18 40				18 56	19 04			←	19 10					19 26		19 34	19 40
Cathays	d		18 31		18 39			18 39	18 45				19 01	19 09			19 09	19 15					19 31		19 39	19 45
Rhymney 3	d				↪									↪												
Pontlottyn	d																									
Tir-phil	d																									
Brithdir	d																									
Bargoed	d									18 17									18 48							
Gilfach Fargoed	d									18 19									18 50							
Pengam	d									18 22									18 53							
Hengoed	d									18 25									18 56							
Ystrad Mynach 3	d									18 28									18 59							
Llanbradach	d									18 33									19 04							
Aber	d									18 37									19 08							
Caerphilly 3	d									18 40									19 11							
Lisvane & Thornhill	d									18 44									19 15							
Llanishen	d									18 46									19 17							
Heath High Level	d									18 49									19 20							
Coryton	d	18 15										18 45									19 15					
Whitchurch (Cardiff)	d	18 16										18 46									19 16					
Rhiwbina	d	18 18										18 48									19 18					
Birchgrove	d	18 20										18 50									19 20					
Ty Glas	d	18 21										18 51									19 21					
Heath Low Level	d	18 24										18 54									19 24					
Cardiff Queen Street 3	a	18 29	18 34					18 44	18 49	18 54		18 59	19 04				19 14	19 19	19 24		19 29		19 34		19 44	19 49
	d	18 31	18 36			18 42		18 46	18 51	18 56	18 57	19 01	19 06		19 12		19 16	19 21	19 26	19 27	19 31		19 36	19 42	19 46	19 51
Cardiff Bay	a					18 46					19 01				19 16					19 31				19 46		
Cardiff Central 7	a	18 34	18 39				18 50	18 53	18 54	18 59		19 07	19 10			19 22	19 23	19 24	19 29		19 34		19 39		19 53	19 57
	d		18 41						18 55	19 01								19 25	19 31				19 41			
Grangetown	d		18 45						18 59	19 05								19 29	19 35				19 45			
Dingle Road	d									19 11									19 41							
Penarth	a									19 17									19 47							
Cogan	d		18 48						19 03									19 33					19 48			
Eastbrook	d		18 51						19 05									19 35					19 51			
Dinas Powys	d		18 53						19 07									19 37					19 53			
Cadoxton	d		18 57						19 12									19 42					19 57			
Barry Docks	d		19 00						19 15									19 45					20 00			
Barry 3	d		19 05						19 19									19 49					20 05			
Barry Island	a								19 26									19 56								
Rhoose Cardiff Int Airport ✈	d		19 12																				20 12			
Llantwit Major	d		19 22																				20 22			
Bridgend	a		19 40																				20 40			

For general notes see front of timetable
For details of catering facilities see Directory of Train Operators

A To Radyr
B To Coryton

from 8 September

Treherbert, Aberdare, Merthyr, Pontypridd, Rhymney and Coryton → Cardiff, Penarth, Barry, Barry Island and Bridgend

Network Diagram - see first page of Table 130

		AW	AW	AW	AW	AW	AW	AW	AW	AW	AW	AW	AW	AW	AW	AW		AW	AW	AW	AW	AW	AW	AW	AW	AW
									A																A	
Treherbert	d				19 17								19 47						20 17							
Ynyswen	d				19 19								19 49						20 19							
Treorchy	d				19 21								19 51						20 21							
Ton Pentre	d				19 23								19 53						20 23							
Ystrad Rhondda	a				19 26								19 56						20 26							
	d				19 28								19 58						20 28							
Llwynypia	d				19 30								20 00						20 30							
Tonypandy	d				19 33								20 03						20 33							
Dinas Rhondda	d				19 35								20 05						20 35							
Porth	d				19 39								20 09						20 39							
Trehafod	d				19 42								20 12						20 42							
Merthyr Tydfil	d									19 38																20 38
Pentre-bach	d									19 42																20 42
Troed Y Rhiw	d									19 45																20 45
Merthyr Vale	d									19 50																20 50
Quakers Yard	d									19 55																20 55
Aberdare 3	d													19 51							20 21					
Cwmbach	d													19 54							20 24					
Fernhill	d													19 58							20 28					
Mountain Ash	a													20 01							20 31					
	d													20 04							20 34					
Penrhiwceiber	d													20 08							20 38					
Abercynon	d						19 43			19 59				20 14							20 44					20 59
Pontypridd 3	a				19 47		19 53			20 07			20 17	20 23					20 47		20 53					21 07
	d				19 48		19 54			20 09			20 18	20 24					20 48		20 54					21 09
Trefforest	d				19 51		19 57			20 12			20 21	20 27					20 51		20 57					21 12
Trefforest Estate	d									20 16																21 16
Taffs Well 3	d				19 58		20 04			20 20			20 28	20 34					20 58		21 04					21 20
Radyr 3	a				20 01		20 07			20 23			20 31	20 37					21 01		21 07					21 23
	d				20 01	20 04	20 07			20 23			20 31	20 37					21 01	21 04	21 07					21 23
Danescourt	d					20 08														21 08		←				
Fairwater	d					20 10														21 10		21 10				
Waun-gron Park	d					20 12														→		21 12				
Ninian Park	d					20 15																21 15				
Llandaf	d				20 04		20 10			20 26			20 34	20 40					21 04		21 10					21 26
Cathays	d				20 09		20 15			20 31			20 39	20 45					21 09		21 15					21 31
Rhymney 3	d										19 45															
Pontlottyn	d										19 48															
Tir-phil	d										19 52															
Brithdir	d										19 55															
Bargoed	d										19 59															
Gilfach Fargoed	d										20 01															
Pengam	d										20 04															
Hengoed	d										20 07															
Ystrad Mynach 3	d										20 10															
Llanbradach	d										20 15															
Aber	d										20 19															
Caerphilly 3	d	19 40									20 22				20 40											
Lisvane & Thornhill	d	19 44									20 26				20 44											
Llanishen	d	19 46									20 28				20 46											
Heath High Level	d	19 49									20 31				20 49											
Coryton	d								20 15																21 15	
Whitchurch (Cardiff)	d								20 16																21 16	
Rhiwbina	d								20 18																21 18	
Birchgrove	d								20 20																21 20	
Ty Glas	d								20 21																21 21	
Heath Low Level	d								20 24																21 24	
Cardiff Queen Street 3	a	19 54			20 14		20 19		20 29	20 34	20 39		20 44	20 50	20 54				21 14		21 19				21 29	21 34
	d	19 56	19 57	20 12	20 16		20 21	20 27	20 31	20 36	20 41	20 42	20 46	20 51	20 56	20 57		21 12	21 16		21 21			21 27	21 31	21 36
Cardiff Bay	a		20 01	20 16				20 31				20 46				21 01		21 16						21 31		
Cardiff Central 7	a	19 59			20 19	20 22	20 24		20 34	20 39	20 48		20 53	20 58	20 59				21 22		21 24	21 25			21 34	21 39
	d	20 01			20 20		20 31			20 41					21 01						21 25		21 31			21 41
Grangetown	d	20 05			20 24		20 35			20 45					21 05						21 29		21 35			21 45
Dingle Road	d	20 11					20 41								21 11								21 41			
Penarth	a	20 17					20 47								21 17								21 47			
Cogan	d				20 28					20 48											21 33					21 48
Eastbrook	d				20 30					20 51											21 35					21 51
Dinas Powys	d				20 32					20 53											21 37					21 53
Cadoxton	d				20 37					20 57											21 42					21 57
Barry Docks	d				20 40					21 00											21 45					22 00
Barry 3	d				20 44					21 05											21 49					22 05
Barry Island	a				20 51																21 56					
Rhoose Cardiff Int Airport ✈	d									21 12																22 12
Llantwit Major	d									21 22																22 22
Bridgend	a									21 40																22 40

For general notes see front of timetable
For details of catering facilities see Directory of Train Operators

A To Radyr

Table 130

Mondays to Fridays
from 8 September

Treherbert, Aberdare, Merthyr, Pontypridd, Rhymney and Coryton → Cardiff, Penarth, Barry, Barry Island and Bridgend

Network Diagram - see first page of Table 130

Station		AW	AW	AW	AW	AW	AW	AW	AW	AW	AW		AW	AW	AW	AW	AW	AW	AW	AW	AW	AW	AW	AW
Treherbert	d						21 17																	
Ynyswen	d						21 19																	
Treorchy	d						21 21																	
Ton Pentre	d						21 23																	
Ystrad Rhondda	a						21 26																	
	d						21 28																	
Llwynypia	d						21 30																	
Tonypandy	d						21 33																	
Dinas Rhondda	d						21 35																	
Porth	d						21 39																	
Trehafod	d						21 42																	
Merthyr Tydfil	d														21 38							22 38		
Pentre-bach	d														21 42							22 42		
Troed Y Rhiw	d														21 45							22 45		
Merthyr Vale	d														21 50							22 50		
Quakers Yard	d														21 55							22 55		
Aberdare 3	d			20 51													21 51							22 51
Cwmbach	d			20 54													21 54							22 54
Fernhill	d			20 58													21 58							22 58
Mountain Ash	a			21 01													22 01							23 01
	d			21 04													22 04							23 04
Penrhiwceiber	d			21 08													22 08							23 08
Abercynon	d			21 14											21 59		22 14					22 59		23 14
Pontypridd 3	a			21 23			21 47								22 07		22 22					23 07		23 22
	d			21 24			21 48								22 09		22 29					23 09		23 29
Trefforest	d			21 27			21 51								22 12		22 32					23 12		23 32
Trefforest Estate	d														22 16									
Taffs Well 3	d			21 34			21 58								22 20		22 39					23 20		23 38
Radyr 3	a			21 37			22 01								22 23		22 42					23 23		23 42
	d			21 37			22 01		22 04						22 23		22 42					23 23		23 42
Danescourt	d								22 08															
Fairwater	d								22 10															
Waun-gron Park	d								22 12															
Ninian Park	d								22 15															
Llandaf	d			21 40			22 04			←					22 26		22 45					23 26		23 45
Cathays	d			21 45			22 09			22 09					22 31		22 50					23 31		23 49
Rhymney 3	d		20 48				→						21 33											
Pontlottyn	d		20 51										21 36											
Tir-phil	d		20 55										21 40											
Brithdir	d		20 58										21 43											
Bargoed	d		21 02										21 47											
Gilfach Fargoed	d		21 04										21 49											
Pengam	d		21 07										21 52											
Hengoed	d		21 10										21 55											
Ystrad Mynach 3	d		21 13										21 58											
Llanbradach	d		21 18										22 03											
Aber	d		21 22										22 07											
Caerphilly 3	d		21 25		21 40								22 10											
Lisvane & Thornhill	d		21 29		21 45								22 14											
Llanishen	d		21 31		21 47								22 16											
Heath High Level	d		21 34		21 49								22 19											
Coryton	d																							
Whitchurch (Cardiff)	d																							
Rhiwbina	d																							
Birchgrove	d																							
Ty Glas	d																							
Heath Low Level	d																							
Cardiff Queen Street 3	a		21 42	21 50	21 54					22 14			22 24		22 34		22 54					23 34		23 53
	d	21 42	21 44	21 51	21 56	21 57		22 12		22 16			22 26	22 27	22 36	22 42	22 55	22 57	23 12		23 27	23 36	23 42	23 56
Cardiff Bay	a	21 46				22 01		22 16						22 31		22 46		23 01	23 16		23 31		23 46	
Cardiff Central 7	a		21 51	21 58	21 59				22 22	22 23			22 29		22 39		23 01					23 43		00 03
	d				22 01						22 25		22 35		22 41		23 12			23 30				
Grangetown	d				22 05						22 29		22 39		22 45		23 16			23 34				
Dingle Road	d				22 11								22 43				23 20							
Penarth	a				22 17								22 47				23 26							
Cogan	d										22 33				22 48					23 37				
Eastbrook	d										22 35				22 51					23 40				
Dinas Powys	d										22 37				22 53					23 42				
Cadoxton	d										22 42				22 57					23 46				
Barry Docks	d										22 45				23 00					23 49				
Barry 3	d										22 49				23 05					23 54				
Barry Island	a										22 56									00 01				
Rhoose Cardiff Int Airport ✈	d														23 12									
Llantwit Major	d														23 22									
Bridgend	a														23 40									

For general notes see front of timetable
For details of catering facilities see Directory of Train Operators

Table 130

until 6 September

Treherbert, Aberdare, Merthyr, Pontypridd, Rhymney and Coryton → Cardiff, Penarth, Barry, Barry Island and Bridgend

Network Diagram - see first page of Table 130

		AW	AW	AW	AW	AW	AW	AW	AW	AW	AW A	AW	AW	AW B	AW	AW	AW C	AW		AW	AW C	AW	AW	AW	AW B	AW
Treherbert	d									05 47										06 17						
Ynyswen	d									05 49										06 19						
Treorchy	d									05 51										06 21						
Ton Pentre	d									05 53										06 23						
Ystrad Rhondda	a									05 56										06 26						
	d									05 58										06 28						
Llwynypia	d									06 00										06 30						
Tonypandy	d									06 03										06 33						
Dinas Rhondda	d									06 05										06 35						
Porth	d									06 09										06 39						
Trehafod	d									06 12										06 42						
Merthyr Tydfil	d																									06 38
Pentre-bach	d																									06 42
Troed Y Rhiw	d																									06 45
Merthyr Vale	d																									06 50
Quakers Yard	d																									06 55
Aberdare 3	d																					06 22				
Cwmbach	d																					06 25				
Fernhill	d																					06 28				
Mountain Ash	a																					06 31				
	d																					06 34				
Penrhiwceiber	d																					06 37				
Abercynon	d																					06 43				06 59
Pontypridd 3	a									06 17										06 47		06 53				07 07
	d			05 24						06 18										06 48		06 54				07 09
Trefforest	d			05 27						06 21										06 51		06 57				07 12
Trefforest Estate	d			05 31						06 25												07 01				07 16
Taffs Well 3	d			05 34						06 28							06 53			06 58		07 04				07 20
Radyr 3	a			05 37						06 31							06 56			07 01	←	07 07				07 23
	d			05 37						06 31							07 04			07 01	07 04	07 07				07 23
Danescourt	d																→				07 08					
Fairwater	d																				07 10					
Waun-gron Park	d																				07 12					
Ninian Park	d																				07 15					
Llandaf	d			05 40						06 34										07 04		07 10				07 26
Cathays	d			05 45						06 39										07 09		07 15				07 31
Rhymney 3	d															06 14								06 37		
Pontlottyn	d															06 17								06 40		
Tir-phil	d															06 21								06 44		
Brithdir	d															06 24								06 47		
Bargoed	d															06 32								06 51		
Gilfach Fargoed	d															06 34										
Pengam	d															06 37								06 55		
Hengoed	d															06 40								06 59		
Ystrad Mynach 3	d															06 43								07 01		
Llanbradach	d															06 48								07 06		
Aber	d															06 52								07 10		
Caerphilly 3	d							06 10								06 55								07 13		
Lisvane & Thornhill	d							06 14								06 59								07 17		
Llanishen	d							06 16								07 01								07 19		
Heath High Level	d							06 19								07 04								07 22		
Coryton	d													06 45											07 15	
Whitchurch (Cardiff)	d													06 46											07 16	
Rhiwbina	d													06 48											07 18	
Birchgrove	d													06 50											07 20	
Ty Glas	d													06 51											07 21	
Heath Low Level	d													06 54											07 24	
Cardiff Queen Street 3	a			05 49				06 25		06 44				06 59		07 09				07 14		07 19		07 27	07 29	07 34
	d			05 51				06 26	06 42	06 45			06 57	07 00		07 11		07 12		07 16		07 21	07 27	07 28	07 31	07 36
Cardiff Bay	a								06 46				07 01					07 16					07 31			
Cardiff Central 7	a			05 53				06 29		06 48				07 04		07 14				07 18	07 20	07 24		07 31	07 34	07 39
	d	05 25	05 41	05 55	06 16	06 25	06 36	06 41			06 55	06 59			07 10	07 16						07 25		07 32		07 41
Grangetown	d	05 29	05 45	05 59	06 20	06 29	06 40	06 45			06 59	07 03			07 14	07 20						07 29		07 36		07 45
Dingle Road	d				06 26		06 44					07 09				07 26								07 41		
Penarth	a				06 31		06 49					07 14				07 31								07 46		
Cogan	d	05 33	05 48	06 03		06 33		06 48			07 03				07 18							07 33				07 48
Eastbrook	d	05 35	05 51	06 05		06 35		06 51			07 05				07 20							07 35				07 51
Dinas Powys	d	05 37	05 53	06 07		06 37		06 53			07 07				07 22							07 37				07 53
Cadoxton	d	05 42	05 57	06 12		06 42		06 57			07 12				07 27							07 42				07 57
Barry Docks	d	05 45	06 00	06 15		06 45		07 00			07 15				07 30							07 45				08 00
Barry 3	d	05 49	06 05	06 19		06 49		07 05			07 19				07 34							07 49				08 05
Barry Island	a	05 55		06 25		06 55					07 25				07 40							07 55				
Rhoose Cardiff Int Airport ✈	d		06 12					07 12																		08 12
Llantwit Major	d		06 22					07 22																		08 22
Bridgend	a		06 39					07 39																		08 39

For general notes see front of timetable
For details of catering facilities see Directory of Train Operators

A From Hereford (Table 131)
B To Radyr
C To Coryton

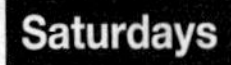

until 6 September

Treherbert, Aberdare, Merthyr, Pontypridd, Rhymney and Coryton → Cardiff, Penarth, Barry, Barry Island and Bridgend

Network Diagram - see first page of Table 130

		AW	AW	AW	AW	AW	AW	AW	AW	AW	AW	AW	AW	AW	AW	AW	AW	AW	AW	AW	AW	AW	AW	AW	AW
					A					B					A					B					A
Treherbert	d			06 47									07 17											07 47	
Ynyswen	d			06 49									07 19											07 49	
Treorchy	d			06 51									07 21											07 51	
Ton Pentre	d			06 53									07 23											07 53	
Ystrad Rhondda	a			06 56									07 26											07 56	
	d			06 58									07 28											07 58	
Llwynypia	d			07 00									07 30											08 00	
Tonypandy	d			07 03									07 33											08 03	
Dinas Rhondda	d			07 05									07 35											08 05	
Porth	d			07 09									07 39											08 09	
Trehafod	d			07 12									07 42											08 12	
Merthyr Tydfil	d																				07 38				
Pentre-bach	d																				07 42				
Troed Y Rhiw	d																				07 45				
Merthyr Vale	d																				07 50				
Quakers Yard	d																				07 55				
Aberdare 3	d						06 52										07 22								
Cwmbach	d						06 55										07 25								
Fernhill	d						06 58										07 28								
Mountain Ash	a						07 01										07 31								
	d						07 04										07 34								
Penrhiwceiber	d						07 07										07 37								
Abercynon	d						07 13										07 43				07 59				
Pontypridd 3	a			07 17			07 23						07 47				07 53				08 07			08 17	
	d			07 18			07 24				07 39		07 48				07 54				08 09			08 18	
Trefforest	d			07 21			07 27				07 42		07 51				07 57				08 12			08 21	
Trefforest Estate	d										07 46										08 16				
Taffs Well 3	d			07 28			07 34				07 50		07 58				08 04				08 20			08 28	
Radyr 3	a			07 31			07 37				07 53		08 01				08 07				08 23			08 31	
	d			07 31	07 34		07 37				07 53		08 01		08 04		08 07				08 23			08 31	08 34
Danescourt	d				07 38										08 08										08 38
Fairwater	d				07 40										08 10										08 40
Waun-gron Park	d				07 42										08 12										08 42
Ninian Park	d				07 45										08 15										08 45
Llandaf	d			07 34		←	07 40				07 56		08 04			←	08 10				08 26			08 34	
Cathays	d			07 39		07 39	07 45				08 01		08 09			08 09	08 15				08 31			08 39	
Rhymney 3	d			↪				07 02					↪					07 24				07 44		↪	
Pontlottyn	d							07 05										07 27				07 47			
Tir-phil	d							07 09										07 31				07 51			
Brithdir	d							07 12										07 34				07 54			
Bargoed	d	07 02						07 17				07 32						07b45				08 02			
Gilfach Fargoed	d	07 04						07 19										07 47							
Pengam	d	07 07						07 22				07 37						07 50				08 07			
Hengoed	d	07 10						07 25				07 40						07 54				08 10			
Ystrad Mynach 3	d	07 13						07 28				07 43						07 57				08 13			
Llanbradach	d	07 18						07 33				07 48						08 02				08 18			
Aber	d	07 22						07 37				07 52						08 07				08 22			
Caerphilly 3	d	07 25						07 40				07 55						08 10				08 25			
Lisvane & Thornhill	d	07 29						07 44				07 59						08 14				08 29			
Llanishen	d	07 31						07 46				08 01						08 16				08 31			
Heath High Level	d	07 34						07 49				08 04						08 19				08 34			
Coryton	d									07 45										08 15					
Whitchurch (Cardiff)	d									07 46										08 16					
Rhiwbina	d									07 48										08 18					
Birchgrove	d									07 50										08 20					
Ty Glas	d									07 51										08 21					
Heath Low Level	d									07 54										08 24					
Cardiff Queen Street 3	a	07 39				07 44	07 49	07 54		07 59	08 04	08 09				08 14	08 19	08 24		08 29	08 34	08 39			
	d	07 41	07 42			07 46	07 51	07 56	07 57	08 01	08 06	08 11		08 12		08 16	08 21	08 26	08 27	08 31	08 36	08 41	08 42		
Cardiff Bay	a		07 46						08 01					08 16					08 31				08 46		
Cardiff Central 7	a	07 44			07 50	07 52	07 54	07 59		08 04	08 09	08 14			08 20	08 22	08 24	08 29		08 34	08 39	08 47			08 50
	d	07 46					07 55	08 01			08 10	08 16					08 25	08 31			08 41				
Grangetown	d	07 50					07 59	08 05			08 14	08 20					08 29	08 35			08 45				
Dingle Road	d	07 56						08 11				08 26						08 41							
Penarth	a	08 01						08 16				08 31						08 46							
Cogan	d						08 03				08 18						08 33				08 48				
Eastbrook	d						08 05				08 20						08 35				08 51				
Dinas Powys	d						08 07				08 22						08 37				08 53				
Cadoxton	d						08 12				08 27						08 42				08 57				
Barry Docks	d						08 15				08 30						08 45				09 00				
Barry 3	d						08 19				08 34						08 49				09 05				
Barry Island	a						08 25				08 40						08 55								
Rhoose Cardiff Int Airport ✈	d																				09 12				
Llantwit Major	d																				09 22				
Bridgend	a																				09 39				

For general notes see front of timetable
For details of catering facilities see Directory of Train Operators

A To Coryton
B To Radyr
b Arr. 0737

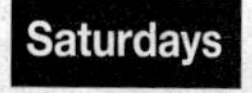

Saturdays

until 6 September

Treherbert, Aberdare, Merthyr, Pontypridd, Rhymney and Coryton → Cardiff, Penarth, Barry, Barry Island and Bridgend

Network Diagram - see first page of Table 130

		AW	AW	AW	AW	AW	AW	AW	AW	AW	AW	AW	AW	AW	AW	AW	AW	AW	AW	AW	AW	AW	AW	AW	AW
						A					B					A					B			C	
Treherbert	d								08 17											08 47					
Ynyswen	d								08 19											08 49					
Treorchy	d								08 21											08 51					
Ton Pentre	d								08 23											08 53					
Ystrad Rhondda	a								08 26											08 56					
	d								08 28											08 58					
Llwynypia	d								08 30											09 00					
Tonypandy	d								08 33											09 03					
Dinas Rhondda	d								08 35											09 05					
Porth	d								08 39											09 09					
Trehafod	d								08 42											09 12					
Merthyr Tydfil	d																08 38								
Pentre-bach	d																08 42								
Troed Y Rhiw	d																08 45								
Merthyr Vale	d																08 50								
Quakers Yard	d																08 55								
Aberdare [3]	d		07 52										08 22										08 52		
Cwmbach	d		07 55										08 25										08 55	09a09	
Fernhill	d		07 58										08 28										08 58		
Mountain Ash	a		08 01										08 31										09 01		
	d		08 04										08 34										09 04		
Penrhiwceiber	d		08 07										08 37										09 07	08a57	
Abercynon	d		08 13										08 43				08 59						09 13		
Pontypridd [3]	a		08 23						08 47				08 53				09 07			09 17			09 23		
	d		08 24				08 39		08 48				08 54				09 09			09 18			09 24		
Trefforest	d		08 27				08 42		08 51				08 57				09 12			09 21			09 27		
Trefforest Estate	d						08 46										09 16								
Taffs Well [3]	d		08 34				08 50		08 58				09 04				09 20			09 28			09 34		
Radyr [3]	a		08 37				08 53		09 01				09 07				09 23			09 31			09 37		
	d		08 37				08 53		09 01		09 04		09 07				09 23			09 31	09 34		09 37		
Danescourt	d										09 08										09 38				
Fairwater	d										09 10										09 40				
Waun-gron Park	d										09 12										09 42				
Ninian Park	d										09 15										09 45				
Llandaf	d	⟵	08 40				08 56		09 04			⟵	09 10				09 26			09 34		⟵	09 40		
Cathays	d	08 39	08 45				09 01		09 09			09 09	09 15				09 31			09 39		09 39	09 45		
Rhymney [3]	d								⟶					08 30						⟶					
Pontlottyn	d													08 33											
Tir-phil	d													08 37											
Brithdir	d													08 40											
Bargoed	d			08 17				08 32						08 47				09 02							09 17
Gilfach Fargoed	d			08 19																					09 19
Pengam	d			08 22				08 37						08 52				09 07							09 22
Hengoed	d			08 25				08 40						08 55				09 10							09 25
Ystrad Mynach [3]	d			08 28				08 43						08 58				09 13							09 28
Llanbradach	d			08 33				08 48						09 03				09 18							09 33
Aber	d			08 37				08 52						09 07				09 22							09 37
Caerphilly [3]	d			08 40				08 55						09 10				09 25							09 40
Lisvane & Thornhill	d			08 44				08 59						09 14				09 29							09 44
Llanishen	d			08 46				09 01						09 16				09 31							09 46
Heath High Level	d			08 49				09 04						09 19				09 34							09 49
Coryton	d					08 45										09 15									
Whitchurch (Cardiff)	d					08 46										09 16									
Rhiwbina	d					08 48										09 18									
Birchgrove	d					08 50										09 20									
Ty Glas	d					08 51										09 21									
Heath Low Level	d					08 54										09 24									
Cardiff Queen Street [3]	a	08 44	08 49	08 54		08 59	09 04	09 09				09 14	09 19	09 24		09 29	09 34	09 39				09 44	09 49		09 54
	d	08 46	08 51	08 56	08 57	09 01	09 06	09 11		09 12		09 16	09 21	09 26	09 27	09 31	09 36	09 41	09 42			09 46	09 51		09 56
Cardiff Bay	a				09 01					09 16					09 31				09 46						
Cardiff Central [7]	a	08 52	08 54	08 59		09 04	09 09	09 14			09 20	09 22	09 24	09 29		09 34	09 39	09 44			09 50	09 52	09 54		09 59
	d		08 55	09 01			09 10	09 16					09 25	09 31			09 41	09 46					09 55		10 01
Grangetown	d		08 59	09 05			09 14	09 20					09 29	09 35			09 45	09 50					09 59		10 05
Dingle Road	d			09 11				09 26						09 41				09 56							10 11
Penarth	a			09 16				09 31						09 46				10 01							10 16
Cogan	d		09 03				09 18						09 33				09 48						10 03		
Eastbrook	d		09 05				09 20						09 35				09 51						10 05		
Dinas Powys	d		09 07				09 22						09 37				09 53						10 07		
Cadoxton	d		09 12				09 27						09 42				09 57						10 12		
Barry Docks	d		09 15				09 30						09 45				10 00						10 15		
Barry [3]	d		09 19				09 34						09 49				10 05						10 19		
Barry Island	a		09 25				09 40						09 55										10 25		
Rhoose Cardiff Int Airport ✈	d																10 12								
Llantwit Major	d																10 22								
Bridgend	a																10 39								

For general notes see front of timetable
For details of catering facilities see Directory of Train Operators

A To Radyr
B To Coryton
C To Aberdare

Table 130

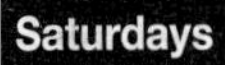

until 6 September

Treherbert, Aberdare, Merthyr, Pontypridd, Rhymney and Coryton → Cardiff, Penarth, Barry, Barry Island and Bridgend

Network Diagram - see first page of Table 130

		AW	AW		AW	AW	AW	AW	AW	AW	AW	AW	AW	AW	AW	AW	AW	AW	AW	AW	AW		AW	AW	AW	AW
								A					B					A						B		
Treherbert	d					09 17											09 47									
Ynyswen	d					09 19											09 49									
Treorchy	d					09 21											09 51									
Ton Pentre	d					09 23											09 53									
Ystrad Rhondda	a					09 26											09 56									
	d					09 28											09 58									
Llwynypia	d					09 30											10 00									
Tonypandy	d					09 33											10 03									
Dinas Rhondda	d					09 35											10 05									
Porth	d					09 39											10 09									
Trehafod	d					09 42											10 12									
Merthyr Tydfil	d													09 38												
Pentre-bach	d													09 42												
Troed Y Rhiw	d													09 45												
Merthyr Vale	d													09 50												
Quakers Yard	d													09 55												
Aberdare 3	d									09 22										09 52						
Cwmbach	d									09 25										09 55						
Fernhill	d									09 28										09 58						
Mountain Ash	a									09 31										10 01						
	d									09 34										10 04						
Penrhiwceiber	d									09 37										10 07						
Abercynon	d									09 43				09 59						10 13						
Pontypridd 3	a					09 47				09 53				10 07			10 17			10 23						
	d		09 39			09 48				09 54				10 09			10 18			10 24					10 39	
Trefforest	d		09 42			09 51				09 57				10 12			10 21			10 27					10 42	
Trefforest Estate	d		09 46											10 16											10 46	
Taffs Well 3	d		09 50			09 58				10 04				10 20			10 28			10 34					10 50	
Radyr 3	a		09 53			10 01				10 07				10 23			10 31			10 37					10 53	
	d		09 53			10 01		10 04		10 07				10 23			10 31	10 34		10 37					10 53	
Danescourt	d							10 08										10 38								
Fairwater	d							10 10										10 40								
Waun-gron Park	d							10 12										10 42								
Ninian Park	d							10 15										10 45								
Llandaf	d		09 56			10 04			←	10 10				10 26			10 34		←	10 40					10 56	
Cathays	d		10 01			10 09			10 09	10 15				10 31			10 39		10 39	10 45					11 01	
Rhymney 3	d					→					09 29						→									
Pontlottyn	d										09 32															
Tir-phil	d										09 36															
Brithdir	d										09 39															
Bargoed	d				09 32						09 47				10 02						10 17					10 32
Gilfach Fargoed	d																				10 19					
Pengam	d				09 37						09 52				10 07						10 22					10 37
Hengoed	d				09 40						09 55				10 10						10 25					10 40
Ystrad Mynach 3	d				09 43						09 58				10 13						10 28					10 43
Llanbradach	d				09 48						10 03				10 18						10 33					10 48
Aber	d				09 52						10 07				10 22						10 37					10 52
Caerphilly 3	d				09 55						10 10				10 25						10 40					10 55
Lisvane & Thornhill	d				09 59						10 14				10 29						10 44					10 59
Llanishen	d				10 01						10 16				10 31						10 46					11 01
Heath High Level	d				10 04						10 19				10 34						10 49					11 04
Coryton	d												10 15											10 45		
Whitchurch (Cardiff)	d												10 16											10 46		
Rhiwbina	d												10 18											10 48		
Birchgrove	d												10 20											10 50		
Ty Glas	d												10 21											10 51		
Heath Low Level	d												10 24											10 54		
Cardiff Queen Street 3	a		10 04		10 09				10 14	10 19	10 24		10 29	10 34	10 39				10 44	10 49	10 54			10 59	11 04	11 09
	d	09 57	10 06		10 11		10 12		10 16	10 21	10 26	10 27	10 31	10 36	10 41	10 42			10 46	10 51	10 56		10 57	11 01	11 06	11 11
Cardiff Bay	a	10 01					10 16					10 31				10 46							11 01			
Cardiff Central 7	a		10 09		10 14			10 20	10 22	10 24	10 29		10 34	10 39	10 44			10 50	10 52	10 54	10 59			11 04	11 09	11 14
	d		10 10		10 16					10 25	10 31			10 41	10 46					10 55	11 01				11 10	11 16
Grangetown	d		10 14		10 20					10 29	10 35			10 45	10 50					10 59	11 05				11 14	11 20
Dingle Road	d				10 26						10 41				10 56						11 11					11 26
Penarth	a				10 31						10 46				11 01						11 16					11 31
Cogan	d		10 18							10 33				10 48						11 03					11 18	
Eastbrook	d		10 20							10 35				10 51						11 05					11 20	
Dinas Powys	d		10 22							10 37				10 53						11 07					11 22	
Cadoxton	d		10 27							10 42				10 57						11 12					11 27	
Barry Docks	d		10 30							10 45				11 00						11 15					11 30	
Barry 3	d		10 34							10 49				11 05						11 19					11 34	
Barry Island	a		10 40							10 55										11 25					11 40	
Rhoose Cardiff Int Airport ✈	d													11 12												
Llantwit Major	d													11 22												
Bridgend	a													11 39												

For general notes see front of timetable
For details of catering facilities see Directory of Train Operators

A To Coryton
B To Radyr

Table 130

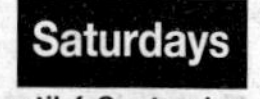

Saturdays

until 6 September

Treherbert, Aberdare, Merthyr, Pontypridd, Rhymney and Coryton → Cardiff, Penarth, Barry, Barry Island and Bridgend

Network Diagram - see first page of Table 130

		AW	AW A	AW	AW	AW	AW	AW B	AW	AW	AW	AW	AW A	AW	AW	AW		AW	AW B	AW	AW	AW	AW	AW A	AW	AW
Treherbert	d					10 17						10 47										11 17				
Ynyswen	d					10 19						10 49										11 19				
Treorchy	d					10 21						10 51										11 21				
Ton Pentre	d					10 23						10 53										11 23				
Ystrad Rhondda	a					10 26						10 56										11 26				
	d					10 28						10 58										11 28				
Llwynypia	d					10 30						11 00										11 30				
Tonypandy	d					10 33						11 03										11 33				
Dinas Rhondda	d					10 35						11 05										11 35				
Porth	d					10b52						11 09										11 39				
Trehafod	d					10 55						11 12										11 42				
Merthyr Tydfil	d								10 38																	
Pentre-bach	d								10 42																	
Troed Y Rhiw	d								10 45																	
Merthyr Vale	d								10 50																	
Quakers Yard	d								10 55																	
Aberdare 3	d			10 22											10 52											11 22
Cwmbach	d			10 25											10 55											11 25
Fernhill	d			10 28											10 58											11 28
Mountain Ash	a			10 31											11 01											11 31
	d			10 34											11 04											11 34
Penrhiwceiber	d			10 37											11 07											11 37
Abercynon	d			10 43					10 59						11 13											11 43
Pontypridd 3	a			10 53		11 00			11 07			11 17			11 23							11 47				11 53
	d			10 54		11 04			11 09			11 18			11 24					11 39		11 48				11 54
Trefforest	d			10 57		11 07			11 12			11 21			11 27					11 42		11 51				11 57
Trefforest Estate	d								11 16											11 46						
Taffs Well 3	d			11 04		11 13			11 20			11 28			11 34					11 50		11 58				12 04
Radyr 3	a			11 07		11 17			11 23			11 31			11 37					11 53		12 01				12 07
	d		11 04	11 07		11 17			11 23			11 31	11 34		11 37					11 53		12 01		12 04		12 07
Danescourt	d		11 08										11 38											12 08		
Fairwater	d		11 10										11 40											12 10		
Waun-gron Park	d		11 12										11 42											12 12		
Ninian Park	d		11 15										11 45											12 15		
Llandaf	d			11 10					11 26			11 34		←	11 40					11 56		12 04			←	12 10
Cathays	d			11 15					11 31			11 39		11 39	11 45					12 01		12 09			12 09	12 15
Rhymney 3	d				10 29							→										→				
Pontlottyn	d				10 32																					
Tir-phil	d				10 36																					
Brithdir	d				10 39																					
Bargoed	d				10 47					11 02						11 17					11 32					
Gilfach Fargoed	d															11 19										
Pengam	d				10 52					11 07						11 22					11 37					
Hengoed	d				10 55					11 10						11 25					11 40					
Ystrad Mynach 3	d				10 58					11 13						11 28					11 43					
Llanbradach	d				11 03					11 18						11 33					11 48					
Aber	d				11 07					11 22						11 37					11 52					
Caerphilly 3	d				11 10					11 25						11 40					11 55					
Lisvane & Thornhill	d				11 14					11 29						11 44					11 59					
Llanishen	d				11 16					11 31						11 46					12 01					
Heath High Level	d				11 19					11 34						11 49					12 04					
Coryton	d							11 15											11 45							
Whitchurch (Cardiff)	d							11 16											11 46							
Rhiwbina	d							11 18											11 48							
Birchgrove	d							11 20											11 50							
Ty Glas	d							11 21											11 51							
Heath Low Level	d							11 24											11 54							
Cardiff Queen Street 3	a			11 20	11 24			11 29	11 34	11 39				11 44	11 49	11 54			11 59	12 04	12 09				12 14	12 19
	d	11 12		11 21	11 26		11 27	11 31	11 36	11 41	11 42			11 46	11 51	11 56		11 57	12 01	12 06	12 11		12 12		12 16	12 21
Cardiff Bay	a	11 16					11 31				11 46							12 01					12 16			
Cardiff Central 7	a		11 20	11 24	11 29	11 34		11 34	11 39	11 44			11 50	11 52	11 54	11 59			12 04	12 09	12 14			12 20	12 22	12 24
	d			11 25	11 31				11 41	11 46					11 55	12 01				12 10	12 16					12 25
Grangetown	d			11 29	11 35				11 45	11 50					11 59	12 05				12 14	12 20					12 29
Dingle Road	d				11 41					11 56						12 11					12 26					
Penarth	a				11 46					12 01						12 16					12 31					
Cogan	d			11 33					11 48						12 03					12 18						12 33
Eastbrook	d			11 35					11 51						12 05					12 20						12 35
Dinas Powys	d			11 37					11 53						12 07					12 22						12 37
Cadoxton	d			11 42					11 57						12 12					12 27						12 42
Barry Docks	d			11 45					12 00						12 15					12 30						12 45
Barry 3	d			11 49					12 05						12 19					12 34						12 49
Barry Island	a			11 55											12 25					12 40						12 55
Rhoose Cardiff Int Airport ✈	d								12 12																	
Llantwit Major	d								12 22																	
Bridgend	a								12 39																	

For general notes see front of timetable
For details of catering facilities see Directory of Train Operators

A To Coryton
B To Radyr
b Arr. 1038

Table 130

Saturdays

until 6 September

Treherbert, Aberdare, Merthyr, Pontypridd, Rhymney and Coryton → Cardiff, Penarth, Barry, Barry Island and Bridgend

Network Diagram - see first page of Table 130

Station		AW	AW	AW A	AW	AW	AW	AW	AW B	AW	AW	AW	AW A	AW	AW	AW	AW	AW B	AW	AW	AW	AW	AW A	AW	AW
Treherbert	d							11 47									12 17								
Ynyswen	d							11 49									12 19								
Treorchy	d							11 51									12 21								
Ton Pentre	d							11 53									12 23								
Ystrad Rhondda	a							11 56									12 26								
	d							11 58									12 28								
Llwynypia	d							12 00									12 30								
Tonypandy	d							12 03									12 33								
Dinas Rhondda	d							12 05									12 35								
Porth	d							12 09									12 39								
Trehafod	d							12 12									12 42								
Merthyr Tydfil	d				11 38																			12 38	
Pentre-bach	d				11 42																			12 42	
Troed Y Rhiw	d				11 45																			12 45	
Merthyr Vale	d				11 50																			12 50	
Quakers Yard	d				11 55																			12 55	
Aberdare 3	d																			12 22					
Cwmbach	d																			12 25					
Fernhill	d																			12 28					
Mountain Ash	a																			12 31					
	d																			12 34					
Penrhiwceiber	d																			12 37					
Abercynon	d				11 59															12 43				12 59	
Pontypridd 3	a				12 07			12 17									12 48			12 53				13 07	
	d				12 09			12 18						12 39			12 48			12 54				13 09	
Trefforest	d				12 12			12 21						12 42			12 51			12 57				13 12	
Trefforest Estate	d				12 16									12 46										13 16	
Taffs Well 3	d				12 20			12 28						12 50			12 58			13 04				13 20	
Radyr 3	a				12 23			12 31						12 53			13 01			13 07				13 23	
	d				12 23			12 31	12 34					12 53			13 01	13 04		13 07				13 23	
Danescourt	d								12 38									13 08							
Fairwater	d								12 40									13 10							
Waun-gron Park	d								12 42									13 12							
Ninian Park	d								12 45									13 15							
Llandaf	d				12 26			12 34		⟵				12 56			13 04		⟵	13 10				13 26	
Cathays	d				12 31			12 39		12 39				13 01			13 09		13 09	13 15				13 31	
								⟶									⟶								
Rhymney 3	d	11 29																			12 29				
Pontlottyn	d	11 32																			12 32				
Tir-phil	d	11 36																			12 36				
Brithdir	d	11 39																			12 39				
Bargoed	d	11 47				12 02					12 17				12 32						12 47				13 02
Gilfach Fargoed	d										12 19														
Pengam	d	11 52				12 07					12 22				12 37						12 52				13 07
Hengoed	d	11 55				12 10					12 25				12 40						12 55				13 10
Ystrad Mynach 3	d	11 58				12 13					12 28				12 43						12 58				13 13
Llanbradach	d	12 03				12 18					12 33				12 48						13 03				13 18
Aber	d	12 07				12 22					12 37				12 52						13 07				13 22
Caerphilly 3	d	12 10				12 25					12 40				12 55						13 10				13 25
Lisvane & Thornhill	d	12 14				12 29					12 44				12 59						13 14				13 29
Llanishen	d	12 16				12 31					12 46				13 01						13 16				13 31
Heath High Level	d	12 19				12 34					12 49				13 04						13 19				13 34
Coryton	d			12 15									12 45										13 15		
Whitchurch (Cardiff)	d			12 16									12 46										13 16		
Rhiwbina	d			12 18									12 48										13 18		
Birchgrove	d			12 20									12 50										13 20		
Ty Glas	d			12 21									12 51										13 21		
Heath Low Level	d			12 24									12 54										13 24		
Cardiff Queen Street 3	a	12 24		12 29	12 34	12 39				12 44	12 54		12 59	13 04	13 09				13 14	13 19	13 24		13 29	13 34	13 39
	d	12 26	12 27	12 31	12 36	12 41	12 42			12 46	12 56	12 57	13 01	13 06	13 11	13 12			13 16	13 21	13 26	13 27	13 31	13 36	13 41
Cardiff Bay	a		12 31				12 46					13 01				13 16						13 31			
Cardiff Central 7	a	12 29		12 34	12 39	12 44			12 50	12 52	12 59		13 04	13 09	13 14			13 20	13 22	13 24	13 29		13 34	13 40	13 44
	d	12 31			12 41	12 46				12 55	13 01			13 10	13 16					13 25	13 31			13 41	13 46
Grangetown	d	12 35			12 45	12 50				12 59	13 05			13 14	13 20					13 29	13 35			13 45	13 50
Dingle Road	d	12 41				12 56					13 11				13 26						13 41				13 56
Penarth	a	12 46				13 01					13 16				13 31						13 46				14 01
Cogan	d				12 48					13 03				13 18						13 33				13 48	
Eastbrook	d				12 51					13 05				13 20						13 35				13 51	
Dinas Powys	d				12 53					13 07				13 22						13 37				13 53	
Cadoxton	d				12 57					13 12				13 27						13 42				13 57	
Barry Docks	d				13 00					13 15				13 30						13 45				14 00	
Barry 3	d				13 05					13 19				13 34						13 49				14 05	
Barry Island	a									13 25				13 40						13 55					
Rhoose Cardiff Int Airport ✈	d				13 12																			14 12	
Llantwit Major	d				13 22																			14 22	
Bridgend	a				13 39																			14 39	

For general notes see front of timetable
For details of catering facilities see Directory of Train Operators

A To Radyr
B To Coryton

Table 130

until 6 September

Treherbert, Aberdare, Merthyr, Pontypridd, Rhymney and Coryton → Cardiff, Penarth, Barry, Barry Island and Bridgend

Network Diagram - see first page of Table 130

		AW	AW	AW A	AW	AW		AW	AW	AW B	AW	AW	AW	AW	AW	AW	AW	AW	AW	AW B	AW	AW	AW	AW		AW A
Treherbert	d		12 47										13 17											13 47		
Ynyswen	d		12 49										13 19											13 49		
Treorchy	d		12 51										13 21											13 51		
Ton Pentre	d		12 53										13 23											13 53		
Ystrad Rhondda	a		12 56										13 26											13 56		
	d		12 58										13 28											13 58		
Llwynypia	d		13 00										13 30											14 00		
Tonypandy	d		13 03										13 33											14 03		
Dinas Rhondda	d		13 05										13 35											14 05		
Porth	d		13 09										13 39											14 09		
Trehafod	d		13 12										13 42											14 12		
Merthyr Tydfil	d																				13 38					
Pentre-bach	d																				13 42					
Troed Y Rhiw	d																				13 45					
Merthyr Vale	d																				13 50					
Quakers Yard	d																				13 55					
Aberdare 3	d					12 52																				
Cwmbach	d					12 55																				
Fernhill	d					12 58																				
Mountain Ash	a					13 01																				
	d					13 04																				
Penrhiwceiber	d					13 07																				
Abercynon	d					13 13											13 45				13 59					
Pontypridd 3	a		13 17			13 23							13 47				13 53				14 07			14 17		
	d		13 18			13 24					13 39		13 48				13 54				14 09			14 18		
Trefforest	d		13 21			13 27					13 42		13 51				13 57				14 12			14 21		
Trefforest Estate	d										13 46										14 16					
Taffs Well 3	d		13 28			13 34					13 50		13 58				14 04				14 20			14 28		
Radyr 3	a		13 31			13 37					13 53		14 01				14 07				14 23			14 31		
	d		13 31	13 34		13 37					13 53		14 01		14 04		14 07				14 23			14 31		14 34
Danescourt	d			13 38											14 08											14 38
Fairwater	d			13 40											14 10											14 40
Waun-gron Park	d			13 42											14 15											14 42
Ninian Park	d			13 45																						14 45
Llandaf	d		13 34		←	13 40					13 56		14 04			←	14 10				14 26			14 34		
Cathays	d		13 39		13 39	13 45					14 01		14 09			14 09	14 15				14 31			14 39		
Rhymney 3	d		→										→					13 29						→		
Pontlottyn	d																	13 32								
Tir-phil	d																	13 36								
Brithdir	d																	13 39								
Bargoed	d							13 17				13 32						13 47				14 02				
Gilfach Fargoed	d							13 19																		
Pengam	d							13 22				13 37						13 52				14 07				
Hengoed	d							13 25				13 40						13 55				14 10				
Ystrad Mynach 3	d							13 28				13 43						13 58				14 13				
Llanbradach	d							13 33				13 48						14 03				14 18				
Aber	d							13 37				13 52						14 07				14 22				
Caerphilly 3	d							13 40				13 55						14 10				14 25				
Lisvane & Thornhill	d							13 44				13 59						14 14				14 29				
Llanishen	d							13 46				14 01						14 16				14 31				
Heath High Level	d							13 49				14 04						14 19				14 34				
Coryton	d									13 45										14 15						
Whitchurch (Cardiff)	d									13 46										14 16						
Rhiwbina	d									13 48										14 18						
Birchgrove	d									13 50										14 20						
Ty Glas	d									13 51										14 21						
Heath Low Level	d									13 54										14 24						
Cardiff Queen Street 3	a				13 44	13 49		13 54		13 59	14 04	14 09				14 14	14 19	14 24		14 29	14 34	14 39				
	d	13 42			13 46	13 51		13 56	13 57	14 01	14 06	14 11		14 12		14 16	14 21	14 26	14 27	14 31	14 36	14 41	14 42			
Cardiff Bay	a	13 46							14 01					14 16					14 31				14 46			
Cardiff Central 7	a			13 50	13 52	13 54		13 59		14 04	14 09	14 14			14 20	14 22	14 24	14 29		14 34	14 39	14 44				14 50
	d					13 55		14 01			14 10	14 16					14 25	14 31			14 41	14 46				
Grangetown	d					13 59		14 05			14 14	14 20					14 29	14 35			14 45	14 50				
Dingle Road	d							14 11				14 26						14 41				14 56				
Penarth	a							14 16				14 31						14 46				15 01				
Cogan	d					14 03					14 18						14 33				14 48					
Eastbrook	d					14 05					14 20						14 35				14 51					
Dinas Powys	d					14 07					14 22						14 37				14 53					
Cadoxton	d					14 12					14 27						14 42				14 57					
Barry Docks	d					14 15					14 30						14 45				15 00					
Barry 3	d					14 19					14 34						14 49				15 05					
Barry Island	a					14 25					14 40						14 55									
Rhoose Cardiff Int Airport ✈	d																				15 12					
Llantwit Major	d																				15 22					
Bridgend	a																				15 39					

For general notes see front of timetable
For details of catering facilities see Directory of Train Operators

A To Coryton
B To Radyr

Table 130

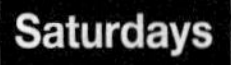

until 6 September

Treherbert, Aberdare, Merthyr, Pontypridd, Rhymney and Coryton → Cardiff, Penarth, Barry, Barry Island and Bridgend

Network Diagram - see first page of Table 130

		AW	AW	AW	AW	AW	AW	AW	AW	AW	AW	AW	AW	AW	AW	AW	AW	AW		AW	AW	AW	AW	AW	AW	AW
						A				B					A						B					A
Treherbert	d												14 17							14 47						
Ynyswen	d												14 19							14 49						
Treorchy	d												14 21							14 51						
Ton Pentre	d												14 23							14 53						
Ystrad Rhondda	a												14 26							14 56						
	d												14 28							14 58						
Llwynypia	d												14 30							15 00						
Tonypandy	d												14 33							15 03						
Dinas Rhondda	d												14 35							15 05						
Porth	d												14b52							15 09						
Trehafod	d												14 55							15 12						
Merthyr Tydfil	d															14 38										
Pentre-bach	d															14 42										
Troed Y Rhiw	d															14 45										
Merthyr Vale	d															14 50										
Quakers Yard	d															14 55										
Aberdare 3	d		13 52								14 22												14 52			
Cwmbach	d		13 55								14 25												14 55			
Fernhill	d		13 58								14 28												14 58			
Mountain Ash	a		14 01								14 31												15 01			
	d		14 04								14 34												15 04			
Penrhiwceiber	d		14 07								14 37												15 07			
Abercynon	d		14 13								14 43					14 59							15 13			
Pontypridd 3	a		14 23								14 53		15 00			15 07				15 17			15 23			
	d		14 24				14 39				14 54		15 04			15 09				15 18			15 24			
Trefforest	d		14 27				14 42				14 57		15 07			15 12				15 21			15 27			
Trefforest Estate	d						14 46									15 16										
Taffs Well 3	d		14 34				14 50				15 04		15 13			15 20				15 28			15 34			
Radyr 3	a		14 37				14 53				15 07		15 17			15 23				15 31			15 37			
	d		14 37				14 53			15 04	15 07		15 17			15 23				15 31	15 34		15 37			
Danescourt	d									15 08											15 38					
Fairwater	d									15 10											15 40					
Waun-gron Park	d									15 12											15 42					
Ninian Park	d									15 15											15 45					
Llandaf	d	←	14 40				14 56				15 10					15 26				15 34		←	15 40			
Cathays	d	14 39	14 45				15 01				15 15					15 31				15 39		15 39	15 45			
Rhymney 3	d											14 29								→						
Pontlottyn	d											14 32														
Tir-phil	d											14 36														
Brithdir	d											14 39														
Bargoed	d			14 17				14 32				14 47					15 02							15 17		
Gilfach Fargoed	d			14 19																				15 19		
Pengam	d			14 22				14 37				14 52					15 07							15 22		
Hengoed	d			14 25				14 40				14 55					15 10							15 25		
Ystrad Mynach 3	d			14 28				14 43				14 58					15 13							15 28		
Llanbradach	d			14 33				14 48				15 03					15 18							15 33		
Aber	d			14 37				14 52				15 07					15 22							15 37		
Caerphilly 3	d			14 40				14 55				15 10					15 25							15 40		
Lisvane & Thornhill	d			14 44				14 59				15 14					15 29							15 44		
Llanishen	d			14 46				15 01				15 16					15 31							15 46		
Heath High Level	d			14 49				15 04				15 19					15 34							15 49		
Coryton	d					14 45									15 15											15 45
Whitchurch (Cardiff)	d					14 46									15 16											15 46
Rhiwbina	d					14 48									15 18											15 48
Birchgrove	d					14 50									15 20											15 50
Ty Glas	d					14 51									15 21											15 51
Heath Low Level	d					14 54									15 24											15 54
Cardiff Queen Street 3	a	14 44	14 49	14 54		14 59	15 04	15 09			15 19	15 24			15 29	15 34	15 39					15 44	15 49	15 54		15 59
	d	14 46	14 51	14 56	14 57	15 01	15 06	15 11	15 12		15 21	15 26		15 27	15 31	15 36	15 41	15 42				15 46	15 51	15 56	15 57	16 01
Cardiff Bay	a				15 01				15 16					15 31				15 46							16 01	
Cardiff Central 7	a	14 52	14 54	14 59		15 04	15 09	15 14		15 20	15 24	15 29	15 34		15 34	15 39	15 44				15 50	15 52	15 54	15 59		16 04
	d		14 55	15 01			15 10	15 16			15 25	15 31				15 41	15 46						15 55	16 01		
Grangetown	d		14 59	15 05			15 14	15 20			15 29	15 35				15 45	15 50						15 59	16 05		
Dingle Road	d			15 11				15 26				15 41					15 56							16 11		
Penarth	a			15 16				15 31				15 46					16 01							16 16		
Cogan	d		15 03				15 18				15 33					15 48							16 03			
Eastbrook	d		15 05				15 20				15 35					15 51							16 05			
Dinas Powys	d		15 07				15 22				15 37					15 53							16 07			
Cadoxton	d		15 12				15 27				15 42					15 57							16 12			
Barry Docks	d		15 15				15 30				15 45					16 00							16 15			
Barry 3	d		15 19				15 34				15 49					16 05							16 19			
Barry Island	a		15 25				15 40				15 55												16 25			
Rhoose Cardiff Int Airport ✈	d															16 12										
Llantwit Major	d															16 22										
Bridgend	a															16 39										

For general notes see front of timetable
For details of catering facilities see Directory of Train Operators

A To Radyr
B To Coryton
b Arr. 1438

Table 130

Saturdays

until 6 September

Treherbert, Aberdare, Merthyr, Pontypridd, Rhymney and Coryton → Cardiff, Penarth, Barry, Barry Island and Bridgend

Network Diagram - see first page of Table 130

		AW	AW	AW	AW	AW	AW	AW	AW	AW	AW	AW	AW	AW	AW	AW	AW	AW	AW	AW	AW	AW	AW	AW	AW
						A					B					A					B				
Treherbert	d			15 17											15 47									16 17	
Ynyswen	d			15 19											15 49									16 19	
Treorchy	d			15 21											15 51									16 21	
Ton Pentre	d			15 23											15 53									16 23	
Ystrad Rhondda	a			15 26											15 56									16 26	
	d			15 28											15 58									16 28	
Llwynypia	d			15 30											16 00									16 30	
Tonypandy	d			15 33											16 03									16 33	
Dinas Rhondda	d			15 35											16 05									16 35	
Porth	d			15 39											16 09									16 39	
Trehafod	d			15 42											16 12									16 42	
Merthyr Tydfil	d											15 38													
Pentre-bach	d											15 42													
Troed Y Rhiw	d											15 45													
Merthyr Vale	d											15 50													
Quakers Yard	d											15 55													
Aberdare 3	d							15 22										15 52							
Cwmbach	d							15 25										15 55							
Fernhill	d							15 28										15 58							
Mountain Ash	a							15 31										16 01							
	d							15 34										16 04							
Penrhiwceiber	d							15 37										16 07							
Abercynon	d							15 43				15 59						16 13							
Pontypridd 3	a			15 47				15 53				16 07			16 17			16 23						16 47	
	d	15 39		15 48				15 54				16 09			16 18			16 24				16 39		16 48	
Trefforest	d	15 42		15 51				15 57				16 12			16 21			16 27				16 42		16 51	
Trefforest Estate	d	15 46										16 16										16 46			
Taffs Well 3	d	15 50		15 58				16 04				16 20			16 28			16 34				16 50		16 58	
Radyr 3	a	15 53		16 01				16 07				16 23			16 31			16 37				16 53		17 01	
	d	15 53		16 01		16 04		16 07				16 23			16 31	16 34		16 37				16 53		17 01	
Danescourt	d					16 08										16 38									
Fairwater	d					16 10										16 40									
Waun-gron Park	d					16 12										16 42									
Ninian Park	d					16 15										16 45									
Llandaf	d	15 56		16 04			←	16 10				16 26			16 34		←	16 40				16 56		17 04	
Cathays	d	16 01		16 09			16 09	16 15				16 31			16 39		16 39	16 45				17 01		17 09	
Rhymney 3	d			→					15 29						→									→	
Pontlottyn	d								15 32																
Tir-phil	d								15 36																
Brithdir	d								15 39																
Bargoed	d		15 32						15 47				16 02						16 17				16 32		
Gilfach Fargoed	d																		16 19						
Pengam	d		15 37						15 52				16 07						16 22				16 37		
Hengoed	d		15 40						15 55				16 10						16 25				16 40		
Ystrad Mynach 3	d		15 43						15 58				16 13						16 28				16 43		
Llanbradach	d		15 48						16 03				16 18						16 33				16 48		
Aber	d		15 52						16 07				16 22						16 37				16 52		
Caerphilly 3	d		15 55						16 10				16 25						16 40				16 55		
Lisvane & Thornhill	d		15 59						16 14				16 29						16 44				16 59		
Llanishen	d		16 01						16 16				16 31						16 46				17 01		
Heath High Level	d		16 04						16 19				16 34						16 49				17 04		
Coryton	d										16 15										16 45				
Whitchurch (Cardiff)	d										16 16										16 46				
Rhiwbina	d										16 18										16 48				
Birchgrove	d										16 20										16 50				
Ty Glas	d										16 21										16 51				
Heath Low Level	d										16 24										16 54				
Cardiff Queen Street 3	a	16 04	16 09				16 14	16 19	16 24		16 29	16 34	16 39				16 44	16 49	16 54		16 59	17 04	17 09		
	d	16 06	16 11		16 12		16 16	16 21	16 26	16 27	16 31	16 36	16 41	16 42			16 46	16 51	16 56	16 57	17 01	17 06	17 11		17 12
Cardiff Bay	a				16 16					16 31				16 46						17 01					17 16
Cardiff Central 7	a	16 09	16 14			16 20	16 22	16 24	16 32		16 34	16 39	16 44			16 50	16 52	16 54	16 59		17 04	17 09	17 14		
	d	16 10	16 16					16 25				16 41	16 46					16 55	17 01			17 10	17 16		
Grangetown	d	16 14	16 20					16 29				16 45	16 50					16 59	17 05			17 14	17 20		
Dingle Road	d		16 26										16 56						17 11				17 26		
Penarth	a		16 31										17 01						17 16				17 31		
Cogan	d	16 18						16 33				16 48						17 03				17 18			
Eastbrook	d	16 20						16 35				16 51						17 05				17 20			
Dinas Powys	d	16 22						16 37				16 53						17 07				17 22			
Cadoxton	d	16 27						16 42				16 57						17 12				17 27			
Barry Docks	d	16 30						16 45				17 00						17 15				17 30			
Barry 3	d	16 34						16 49				17 05						17 19				17 34			
Barry Island	a	16 40						16 55										17 25				17 40			
Rhoose Cardiff Int Airport ✈	d											17 12													
Llantwit Major	d											17 22													
Bridgend	a											17 39													

For general notes see front of timetable
For details of catering facilities see Directory of Train Operators

A To Coryton
B To Radyr

Table 130

until 6 September

Treherbert, Aberdare, Merthyr, Pontypridd, Rhymney and Coryton → Cardiff, Penarth, Barry, Barry Island and Bridgend

Network Diagram - see first page of Table 130

		AW	AW	AW	AW	AW	AW	AW		AW	AW	AW	AW	AW	AW	AW	AW	AW	AW	AW	AW	AW	AW	AW	AW	AW
		A					B						A					B					A			
Treherbert	d											16 47									17 17					
Ynyswen	d											16 49									17 19					
Treorchy	d											16 51									17 21					
Ton Pentre	d											16 53									17 23					
Ystrad Rhondda	a											16 56									17 26					
	d											16 58									17 28					
Llwynypia	d											17 00									17 30					
Tonypandy	d											17 03									17 33					
Dinas Rhondda	d											17 05									17 35					
Porth	d											17 09									17 39					
Trehafod	d											17 12									17 42					
Merthyr Tydfil	d							16 38																		
Pentre-bach	d							16 42																		
Troed Y Rhiw	d							16 45																		
Merthyr Vale	d							16 50																		
Quakers Yard	d							16 55																		
Aberdare 3	d			16 22											16 52										17 22	
Cwmbach	d			16 25											16 55										17 25	
Fernhill	d			16 28											16 58										17 28	
Mountain Ash	a			16 31											17 01										17 31	
	d			16 34											17 04										17 34	
Penrhiwceiber	d			16 37											17 07										17 37	
Abercynon	d			16 43				16 59							17 13										17 43	
Pontypridd 3	a			16 53				17 07				17 17			17 23						17 47				17 53	
	d			16 54				17 09				17 18			17 24				17 39		17 48				17 54	
Trefforest	d			16 57				17 12				17 21			17 27				17 42		17 51				17 57	
Trefforest Estate	d							17 16											17 46							
Taffs Well 3	d			17 04				17 20				17 28			17 34				17 50		17 58				18 04	
Radyr 3	a			17 07				17 23				17 31			17 37				17 53		18 01				18 07	
	d	17 04		17 07				17 23				17 31	17 34		17 37				17 53		18 01		18 04		18 07	
Danescourt	d	17 08											17 38										18 08			
Fairwater	d	17 10											17 40										18 10			
Waun-gron Park	d	17 12											17 42										18 12			
Ninian Park	d	17 15											17 45										18 15			
Llandaf	d		←	17 10				17 26				17 34		←	17 40				17 56		18 04			←	18 10	
Cathays	d		17 09	17 15				17 31				17 39		17 39	17 45				18 01		18 09			18 09	18 15	
Rhymney 3	d				16 29							→									→					17 29
Pontlottyn	d				16 32																					17 32
Tir-phil	d				16 36																					17 36
Brithdir	d				16 39																					17 39
Bargoed	d				16 47					17 02						17 17				17 32						17 47
Gilfach Fargoed	d															17 19										
Pengam	d				16 52					17 07						17 22				17 37						17 52
Hengoed	d				16 55					17 10						17 25				17 40						17 55
Ystrad Mynach 3	d				16 58					17 13						17 28				17 43						17 58
Llanbradach	d				17 03					17 18						17 33				17 48						18 03
Aber	d				17 07					17 22						17 37				17 52						18 07
Caerphilly 3	d				17 10					17 25						17 40				17 55						18 10
Lisvane & Thornhill	d				17 14					17 29						17 44				17 59						18 14
Llanishen	d				17 16					17 31						17 46				18 01						18 16
Heath High Level	d				17 19					17 34						17 49				18 04						18 19
Coryton	d						17 15											17 45								
Whitchurch (Cardiff)	d						17 16											17 46								
Rhiwbina	d						17 18											17 48								
Birchgrove	d						17 20											17 50								
Ty Glas	d						17 21											17 51								
Heath Low Level	d						17 24											17 54								
Cardiff Queen Street 3	a		17 14	17 19	17 24		17 29	17 34		17 39				17 44	17 49	17 54		17 59	18 04	18 09				18 14	18 19	18 24
	d		17 16	17 21	17 26	17 27	17 31	17 36		17 41	17 42			17 46	17 51	17 56	17 57	18 01	18 06	18 11		18 12		18 16	18 21	18 26
Cardiff Bay	a					17 31					17 46						18 01					18 16				
Cardiff Central 7	a	17 20	17 22	17 24	17 29		17 34	17 39		17 44			17 50	17 52	17 54	17 59		18 04	18 09	18 14			18 20	18 22	18 24	18 29
	d			17 25	17 31			17 41		17 46					17 55	18 01			18 10	18 16					18 25	18 31
Grangetown	d			17 29	17 35			17 45		17 50					17 59	18 05			18 14	18 20					18 29	18 35
Dingle Road	d				17 41					17 56						18 11				18 26						18 41
Penarth	a				17 46					18 01						18 16				18 31						18 46
Cogan	d			17 33				17 48							18 03				18 18						18 33	
Eastbrook	d			17 35				17 51							18 05				18 20						18 35	
Dinas Powys	d			17 37				17 53							18 07				18 22						18 37	
Cadoxton	d			17 42				17 57							18 12				18 27						18 42	
Barry Docks	d			17 45				18 00							18 15				18 30						18 45	
Barry 3	d			17 49				18 05							18 19				18 34						18 49	
Barry Island	a			17 55											18 25				18 40						18 55	
Rhoose Cardiff Int Airport ✈	d							18 12																		
Llantwit Major	d							18 22																		
Bridgend	a							18 39																		

For general notes see front of timetable
For details of catering facilities see Directory of Train Operators

A To Coryton
B To Radyr

Table 130

Saturdays

until 6 September

Treherbert, Aberdare, Merthyr, Pontypridd, Rhymney and Coryton → Cardiff, Penarth, Barry, Barry Island and Bridgend

Network Diagram - see first page of Table 130

		AW	AW A	AW	AW	AW	AW B	AW	AW	AW	AW	AW	AW	AW	AW	AW	AW	AW	AW	AW A	AW	AW	AW	AW
Treherbert	d				17 47										18 17								18 47	
Ynyswen	d				17 49										18 19								18 49	
Treorchy	d				17 51										18 21								18 51	
Ton Pentre	d				17 53										18 23								18 53	
Ystrad Rhondda	a				17 56										18 26								18 56	
	d				17 58										18 28								18 58	
Llwynypia	d				18 00										18 30								19 00	
Tonypandy	d				18 03										18 33								19 03	
Dinas Rhondda	d				18 05										18 35								19 05	
Porth	d				18 09										18 39								19 09	
Trehafod	d				18 12										18 42								19 12	
Merthyr Tydfil	d			17 38																	18 38			
Pentre-bach	d			17 42																	18 42			
Troed Y Rhiw	d			17 45																	18 45			
Merthyr Vale	d			17 50																	18 50			
Quakers Yard	d			17 55																	18 55			
Aberdare 3	d								17 52								18 22							18 52
Cwmbach	d								17 55								18 25							18 55
Fernhill	d								17 58								18 28							18 58
Mountain Ash	a								18 01								18 31							19 01
	d								18 04								18 34							19 04
Penrhiwceiber	d								18 07								18 37							19 07
Abercynon	d			17 59					18 13								18 43				18 59			19 13
Pontypridd 3	a			18 07	18 17				18 23						18 47		18 53				19 07		19 17	19 23
	d			18 09	18 18				18 24				18 39		18 48		18 54				19 09		19 18	19 24
Trefforest	d			18 12	18 21				18 27				18 42		18 51		18 57				19 12		19 21	19 27
Trefforest Estate	d			18 16									18 46								19 16			
Taffs Well 3	d			18 20	18 28				18 34				18 50		18 58		19 04				19 20		19 28	19 34
Radyr 3	a			18 23	18 31				18 37				18 53		19 01		19 07				19 23		19 31	19 37
	d			18 23	18 31		18 34		18 37				18 53		19 01	19 04	19 07				19 23		19 31	19 37
Danescourt	d						18 38									19 08								
Fairwater	d						18 40									19 10								
Waun-gron Park	d						18 42									19 12								
Ninian Park	d						18 45									19 15								
Llandaf	d			18 26	18 34			⟵	18 40				18 56		19 04		19 10				19 26		19 34	19 40
Cathays	d			18 31	18 39			18 39	18 45				19 01		19 09		19 15				19 31		19 39	19 45
Rhymney 3	d				⟶																			
Pontlottyn	d																							
Tir-phil	d																							
Brithdir	d																							
Bargoed	d									18 17								18 48						
Gilfach Fargoed	d									18 19								18 50						
Pengam	d									18 22								18 53						
Hengoed	d									18 25								18 56						
Ystrad Mynach 3	d									18 28								18 59						
Llanbradach	d									18 33								19 04						
Aber	d									18 37								19 08						
Caerphilly 3	d									18 40								19 11						
Lisvane & Thornhill	d									18 44								19 15						
Llanishen	d									18 46								19 17						
Heath High Level	d									18 49								19 20						
Coryton	d		18 15									18 45								19 15				
Whitchurch (Cardiff)	d		18 16									18 46								19 16				
Rhiwbina	d		18 18									18 48								19 18				
Birchgrove	d		18 20									18 50								19 20				
Ty Glas	d		18 21									18 51								19 21				
Heath Low Level	d		18 24									18 54								19 24				
Cardiff Queen Street 3	a		18 29	18 34				18 44	18 49	18 54		18 59	19 04		19 14		19 19	19 24		19 29	19 34		19 44	19 49
	d	18 27	18 31	18 36		18 42		18 46	18 51	18 56	18 57	19 01	19 06	19 12	19 16		19 21	19 26	19 27	19 31	19 36	19 42	19 46	19 51
Cardiff Bay	a	18 31				18 46					19 01			19 16					19 31			19 46		
Cardiff Central 7	a		18 34	18 39			18 50	18 52	18 54	18 59		19 06	19 10		19 22	19 22	19 24	19 29		19 34	19 39		19 52	19 57
	d			18 41					18 55	19 01							19 25	19 31			19 41			
Grangetown	d			18 45					18 59	19 05							19 29	19 35			19 45			
Dingle Road	d									19 11								19 41						
Penarth	a									19 16								19 46						
Cogan	d			18 48					19 03								19 33				19 48			
Eastbrook	d			18 51					19 05								19 35				19 51			
Dinas Powys	d			18 53					19 07								19 37				19 53			
Cadoxton	d			18 57					19 12								19 42				19 57			
Barry Docks	d			19 00					19 15								19 45				20 00			
Barry 3	d			19 05					19 19								19 49				20 05			
Barry Island	a								19 25								19 55							
Rhoose Cardiff Int Airport ✈	d			19 12																	20 12			
Llantwit Major	d			19 22																	20 22			
Bridgend	a			19 39																	20 39			

For general notes see front of timetable
For details of catering facilities see Directory of Train Operators

A To Radyr
B To Coryton

Table 130

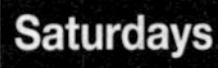

Saturdays

until 6 September

Treherbert, Aberdare, Merthyr, Pontypridd, Rhymney and Coryton → Cardiff, Penarth, Barry, Barry Island and Bridgend

Network Diagram - see first page of Table 130

		AW	AW	AW	AW	AW	AW	AW	AW	AW A	AW	AW	AW	AW	AW	AW		AW	AW	AW	AW	AW	AW	AW	AW	AW A
Treherbert	d				19 17									19 47						20 17						
Ynyswen	d				19 19									19 49						20 19						
Treorchy	d				19 21									19 51						20 21						
Ton Pentre	d				19 23									19 53						20 23						
Ystrad Rhondda	a				19 26									19 56						20 26						
	d				19 28									19 58						20 28						
Llwynypia	d				19 30									20 00						20 30						
Tonypandy	d				19 33									20 03						20 33						
Dinas Rhondda	d				19 35									20 05						20 35						
Porth	d				19 39									20 09						20 39						
Trehafod	d				19 42									20 12						20 42						
Merthyr Tydfil	d										19 38															
Pentre-bach	d										19 42															
Troed Y Rhiw	d										19 45															
Merthyr Vale	d										19 50															
Quakers Yard	d										19 55															
Aberdare 3	d														19 52							20 22				
Cwmbach	d														19 55							20 25				
Fernhill	d														19 58							20 28				
Mountain Ash	a														20 01							20 31				
	d														20 04							20 34				
Penrhiwceiber	d														20 07							20 37				
Abercynon	d						19 43				19 59				20 13							20 43				
Pontypridd 3	a				19 47		19 53				20 07			20 17	20 23					20 47		20 53				
	d				19 48		19 54				20 09			20 18	20 24					20 48		20 54				
Trefforest	d				19 51		19 57				20 12			20 21	20 27					20 51		20 57				
Trefforest Estate	d										20 16															
Taffs Well 3	d				19 58		20 04				20 20			20 28	20 34					20 58		21 04				
Radyr 3	a				20 01		20 07				20 23			20 31	20 37					21 01		21 07				
	d				20 01	20 04	20 07				20 23			20 31	20 37					21 01	21 04	21 07				
Danescourt	d					20 08															21 08					
Fairwater	d					20 10 →		← 20 10													21 10 →		← 21 10			
Waun-gron Park	d							20 12															21 12			
Ninian Park	d							20 15															21 15			
Llandaf	d				20 04		20 10				20 26			20 34	20 40					21 04		21 10				
Cathays	d				20 09		20 15				20 31			20 39	20 45					21 09		21 15				
Rhymney 3	d											19 45														
Pontlottyn	d											19 48														
Tir-phil	d											19 52														
Brithdir	d											19 55														
Bargoed	d											19 59														
Gilfach Fargoed	d											20 01														
Pengam	d											20 04														
Hengoed	d											20 07														
Ystrad Mynach 3	d											20 10														
Llanbradach	d											20 15														
Aber	d											20 19														
Caerphilly 3	d	19 40										20 22				20 40										
Lisvane & Thornhill	d	19 44										20 26				20 44										
Llanishen	d	19 46										20 28				20 46										
Heath High Level	d	19 49										20 31				20 49										
Coryton	d									20 15																21 15
Whitchurch (Cardiff)	d									20 16																21 16
Rhiwbina	d									20 18																21 18
Birchgrove	d									20 20																21 20
Ty Glas	d									20 21																21 21
Heath Low Level	d									20 24																21 24
Cardiff Queen Street 3	a	19 54			20 14		20 19			20 29	20 34	20 39		20 44	20 50	20 54				21 14		21 19				21 29
	d	19 56	19 57	20 12	20 16		20 21		20 27	20 31	20 36	20 41	20 42	20 46	20 51	20 56		20 57	21 12	21 16		21 21			21 27	21 31
Cardiff Bay	a		20 01	20 16					20 31				20 46					21 01	21 16						21 31	
Cardiff Central 7	a	19 59			20 19		20 24	20 26		20 34	20 39	20 47		20 52	20 57	20 59				21 21		21 24	21 25			21 34
	d	20 01			20 20		20 31				20 41					21 01						21 25		21 31		
Grangetown	d	20 05			20 24		20 35				20 45					21 05						21 29		21 35		
Dingle Road	d	20 11					20 41									21 11								21 41		
Penarth	a	20 16					20 46									21 16								21 46		
Cogan	d				20 28						20 48											21 33				
Eastbrook	d				20 30						20 51											21 35				
Dinas Powys	d				20 32						20 53											21 37				
Cadoxton	d				20 37						20 57											21 42				
Barry Docks	d				20 40						21 00											21 45				
Barry 3	d				20 44						21 05											21 49				
Barry Island	a				20 50																	21 55				
Rhoose Cardiff Int Airport ✈	d										21 12															
Llantwit Major	d										21 22															
Bridgend	a										21 39															

For general notes see front of timetable
For details of catering facilities see Directory of Train Operators

A To Radyr

until 6 September

Treherbert, Aberdare, Merthyr, Pontypridd, Rhymney and Coryton → Cardiff, Penarth, Barry, Barry Island and Bridgend

Network Diagram - see first page of Table 130

Station		AW	AW	AW	AW	AW	AW	AW	AW	AW	AW	AW	AW	AW	AW	AW	AW	AW	AW	AW	AW	AW	AW
Treherbert	d								21 17														
Ynyswen	d								21 19														
Treorchy	d								21 21														
Ton Pentre	d								21 23														
Ystrad Rhondda	a								21 26														
	d								21 28														
Llwynypia	d								21 30														
Tonypandy	d								21 33														
Dinas Rhondda	d								21 35														
Porth	d								21 39														
Trehafod	d								21 42														
Merthyr Tydfil	d	20 38												21 38							22 38		
Pentre-bach	d	20 42												21 42							22 42		
Troed Y Rhiw	d	20 45												21 45							22 45		
Merthyr Vale	d	20 50												21 50							22 50		
Quakers Yard	d	20 55												21 55							22 55		
Aberdare 3	d				20 52											21 52							22 52
Cwmbach	d				20 55											21 55							22 55
Fernhill	d				20 58											21 58							22 58
Mountain Ash	a				21 01											22 01							23 01
	d				21 04											22 04							23 04
Penrhiwceiber	d				21 07											22 07							23 07
Abercynon	d	20 59			21 13									21 59		22 14					22 59		23 13
Pontypridd 3	a	21 07			21 23				21 47					22 07		22 24					23 07		23 23
	d	21 09			21 24				21 48					22 09		22 29					23 09		23 29
Trefforest	d	21 12			21 27				21 51					22 12		22 32					23 12		23 32
Trefforest Estate	d	21 16												22 16									
Taffs Well 3	d	21 20			21 34				21 58					22 20		22 39					23 20		23 38
Radyr 3	a	21 23			21 37				22 01					22 23		22 42					23 23		23 42
	d	21 23			21 37				22 01	22 04				22 23		22 42					23 23		23 42
Danescourt	d									22 08													
Fairwater	d									22 10													
Waun-gron Park	d									22 12													
Ninian Park	d									22 15													
Llandaf	d	21 26			21 40				22 04					22 26		22 45					23 26		23 45
Cathays	d	21 31			21 45				22 09					22 31		22 50					23 31		23 49
Rhymney 3	d			20 48								21 33											
Pontlottyn	d			20 51								21 36											
Tir-phil	d			20 55								21 40											
Brithdir	d			20 58								21 43											
Bargoed	d			21 02								21 47											
Gilfach Fargoed	d			21 04								21 49											
Pengam	d			21 07								21 52											
Hengoed	d			21 10								21 55											
Ystrad Mynach 3	d			21 13								21 58											
Llanbradach	d			21 18								22 03											
Aber	d			21 22								22 07											
Caerphilly 3	d			21 25		21 40						22 10											
Lisvane & Thornhill	d			21 29		21 45						22 14											
Llanishen	d			21 31		21 47						22 16											
Heath High Level	d			21 34		21 49						22 19											
Coryton	d																						
Whitchurch (Cardiff)	d																						
Rhiwbina	d																						
Birchgrove	d																						
Ty Glas	d																						
Heath Low Level	d																						
Cardiff Queen Street 3	a	21 34		21 42	21 50	21 54			22 14			22 24		22 34		22 54					23 34		23 53
	d	21 36	21 42	21 44	21 51	21 56	21 57	22 12	22 16			22 26	22 27	22 36	22 42	22 55	22 57	23 12		23 27	23 36	23 42	23 56
Cardiff Bay	a		21 46				22 01	22 16					22 31		22 46		23 01	23 16		23 31		23 46	
Cardiff Central 7	a	21 39		21 47	21 57	21 59			22 22	22 22		22 29		22 42		23 01					23 42		00 02
	d	21 41				22 01					22 25	22 31				23 12			23 30				
Grangetown	d	21 45				22 05					22 29	22 35				23 16			23 34				
Dingle Road	d					22 11						22 41				23 20							
Penarth	a					22 16						22 46				23 25							
Cogan	d	21 48									22 33								23 37				
Eastbrook	d	21 51									22 35								23 40				
Dinas Powys	d	21 53									22 37								23 42				
Cadoxton	d	21 57									22 42								23 46				
Barry Docks	d	22 00									22 45								23 49				
Barry 3	d	22 05									22 49								23 54				
Barry Island	a										22 55								23 59				
Rhoose Cardiff Int Airport ✈	d	22 12																					
Llantwit Major	d	22 22																					
Bridgend	a	22 39																					

For general notes see front of timetable
For details of catering facilities see Directory of Train Operators

Table 130

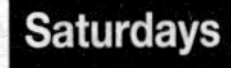

Saturdays

from 13 September

Treherbert, Aberdare, Merthyr, Pontypridd, Rhymney and Coryton → Cardiff, Penarth, Barry, Barry Island and Bridgend

Network Diagram - see first page of Table 130

		AW	AW	AW	AW	AW	AW	AW	AW	AW	AW	AW	AW	AW	AW	AW	AW	AW	AW	AW	AW	AW	AW	AW	AW
											A			B			C			C				B	
Treherbert	d									05 47									06 17						
Ynyswen	d									05 49									06 19						
Treorchy	d									05 51									06 21						
Ton Pentre	d									05 53									06 23						
Ystrad Rhondda	a									05 56									06 26						
	d									05 58									06 28						
Llwynypia	d									06 00									06 30						
Tonypandy	d									06 03									06 33						
Dinas Rhondda	d									06 05									06 35						
Porth	d									06 09									06 39						
Trehafod	d									06 12									06 42						
Merthyr Tydfil	d																								06 38
Pentre-bach	d																								06 42
Troed Y Rhiw	d																								06 45
Merthyr Vale	d																								06 50
Quakers Yard	d																								06 55
Aberdare 3	d																				06 21				
Cwmbach	d																				06 24				
Fernhill	d																				06 28				
Mountain Ash	a																				06 31				
	d																				06 34				
Penrhiwceiber	d																				06 38				
Abercynon	d																				06 44				06 59
Pontypridd 3	a									06 17									06 47		06 53				07 07
	d			05 24						06 18									06 48		06 54				07 09
Trefforest	d			05 27						06 21									06 51		06 57				07 12
Trefforest Estate	d			05 31						06 25											07 01				07 16
Taffs Well 3	d			05 34						06 28							06 53		06 58	⟵	07 04				07 20
Radyr 3	a			05 37						06 31							06 56		07 01		07 07				07 23
	d			05 37						06 31							07 04		07 01	07 04	07 07				07 23
Danescourt	d																⟶			07 08					
Fairwater	d																			07 10					
Waun-gron Park	d																			07 12					
Ninian Park	d																			07 15					
Llandaf	d			05 40						06 34									07 04		07 10				07 26
Cathays	d			05 45						06 39									07 09		07 15				07 31
Rhymney 3	d															06 14							06 37		
Pontlottyn	d															06 17							06 40		
Tir-phil	d															06 21							06 44		
Brithdir	d															06 24							06 47		
Bargoed	d															06 32							06 51		
Gilfach Fargoed	d															06 34									
Pengam	d															06 37							06 55		
Hengoed	d															06 40							06 59		
Ystrad Mynach 3	d															06 43							07 01		
Llanbradach	d															06 48							07 06		
Aber	d															06 52							07 10		
Caerphilly 3	d							06 10								06 55							07 13		
Lisvane & Thornhill	d							06 14								06 59							07 17		
Llanishen	d							06 16								07 01							07 19		
Heath High Level	d							06 19								07 04							07 22		
Coryton	d													06 45										07 15	
Whitchurch (Cardiff)	d													06 46										07 16	
Rhiwbina	d													06 48										07 18	
Birchgrove	d													06 50										07 20	
Ty Glas	d													06 51										07 21	
Heath Low Level	d													06 54										07 24	
Cardiff Queen Street 3	a			05 49				06 25		06 44				06 59		07 09			07 14		07 19		07 27	07 29	07 34
	d			05 51				06 26	06 42	06 45			06 57	07 00		07 11		07 12	07 16		07 21	07 27	07 28	07 31	07 36
Cardiff Bay	a								06 46				07 01					07 16				07 31			
Cardiff Central 7	a			05 53				06 29		06 48				07 04		07 14			07 18	07 20	07 24		07 31	07 34	07 39
	d	05 25	05 41	05 55	06 16	06 25	06 36	06 41			06 55	06 59			07 10	07 16					07 25		07 32		07 41
Grangetown	d	05 29	05 45	05 59	06 20	06 29	06 40	06 45			06 59	07 03			07 14	07 20					07 29		07 36		07 45
Dingle Road	d				06 26		06 44					07 09				07 26							07 41		
Penarth	a				06 32		06 49					07 15				07 32							07 47		
Cogan	d	05 33	05 48	06 03		06 33		06 48			07 03				07 18						07 33				07 48
Eastbrook	d	05 35	05 51	06 05		06 35		06 51			07 05				07 20						07 35				07 51
Dinas Powys	d	05 37	05 53	06 07		06 37		06 53			07 07				07 22						07 37				07 53
Cadoxton	d	05 42	05 57	06 12		06 42		06 57			07 12				07 27						07 42				07 57
Barry Docks	d	05 45	06 00	06 15		06 45		07 00			07 15				07 30						07 45				08 00
Barry 3	d	05 49	06 05	06 19		06 49		07 05			07 19				07 34						07 49				08 05
Barry Island	a	05 56		06 26		06 56					07 25				07 40						07 56				
Rhoose Cardiff Int Airport ✈	d		06 12					07 12																	08 12
Llantwit Major	d		06 22					07 22																	08 22
Bridgend	a		06 40					07 40																	08 40

For general notes see front of timetable
For details of catering facilities see Directory of Train Operators

A From Hereford (Table 131)
B To Radyr
C To Coryton

Saturdays

from 13 September

Treherbert, Aberdare, Merthyr, Pontypridd, Rhymney and Coryton → Cardiff, Penarth, Barry, Barry Island and Bridgend

Network Diagram - see first page of Table 130

		AW	AW	AW	AW A	AW	AW	AW	AW	AW B	AW	AW	AW	AW	AW A	AW	AW	AW	AW	AW B	AW	AW	AW	AW	AW A
Treherbert	d			06 47									07 17											07 47	
Ynyswen	d			06 49									07 19											07 49	
Treorchy	d			06 51									07 21											07 51	
Ton Pentre	d			06 53									07 23											07 53	
Ystrad Rhondda	a			06 56									07 26											07 56	
	d			06 58									07 28											07 58	
Llwynypia	d			07 00									07 30											08 00	
Tonypandy	d			07 03									07 33											08 03	
Dinas Rhondda	d			07 05									07 35											08 05	
Porth	d			07 09									07 39											08 09	
Trehafod	d			07 12									07 42											08 12	
Merthyr Tydfil	d																				07 38				
Pentre-bach	d																				07 42				
Troed Y Rhiw	d																				07 45				
Merthyr Vale	d																				07 50				
Quakers Yard	d																				07 55				
Aberdare 3	d						06 51										07 21								
Cwmbach	d						06 54										07 24								
Fernhill	d						06 58										07 28								
Mountain Ash	a						07 01										07 31								
	d						07 04										07 34								
Penrhiwceiber	d						07 08										07 38								
Abercynon	d						07 14										07 44				07 59				
Pontypridd 3	a			07 17			07 23						07 47				07 53				08 07			08 17	
	d			07 18			07 24				07 39		07 48				07 54				08 09			08 18	
Trefforest	d			07 21			07 27				07 42		07 51				07 57				08 12			08 21	
Trefforest Estate	d										07 46										08 16				
Taffs Well 3	d			07 28			07 34				07 50		07 58				08 04				08 20			08 28	
Radyr 3	a			07 31			07 37				07 53		08 01				08 07				08 23			08 31	
	d			07 31	07 34		07 37				07 53		08 01		08 04		08 07				08 23			08 31	08 34
Danescourt	d				07 38										08 08										08 38
Fairwater	d				07 40										08 10										08 40
Waun-gron Park	d				07 42										08 12										08 42
Ninian Park	d				07 45										08 15										08 45
Llandaf	d			07 34		←	07 40				07 56		08 04			←	08 10				08 26			08 34	
Cathays	d			07 39		07 39	07 45				08 01		08 09			08 09	08 15				08 31			08 39	
Rhymney 3	d			→				07 02					→					07 24				07 44		→	
Pontlottyn	d							07 05										07 27				07 47			
Tir-phil	d							07 09										07 31				07 51			
Brithdir	d							07 12										07 34				07 54			
Bargoed	d	07 02						07 17				07 32						07b45				08 02			
Gilfach Fargoed	d	07 04						07 19										07 47							
Pengam	d	07 07						07 22				07 37						07 50				08 07			
Hengoed	d	07 10						07 25				07 40						07 54				08 10			
Ystrad Mynach 3	d	07 13						07 28				07 43						07 57				08 13			
Llanbradach	d	07 18						07 33				07 48						08 02				08 18			
Aber	d	07 22						07 37				07 52						08 07				08 22			
Caerphilly 3	d	07 25						07 40				07 55						08 10				08 25			
Lisvane & Thornhill	d	07 29						07 44				07 59						08 14				08 29			
Llanishen	d	07 31						07 46				08 01						08 16				08 31			
Heath High Level	d	07 34						07 49				08 04						08 19				08 34			
Coryton	d									07 45										08 15					
Whitchurch (Cardiff)	d									07 46										08 16					
Rhiwbina	d									07 48										08 18					
Birchgrove	d									07 50										08 20					
Ty Glas	d									07 51										08 21					
Heath Low Level	d									07 54										08 24					
Cardiff Queen Street 3	a	07 39				07 44	07 49	07 54		07 59	08 04	08 09				08 14	08 19	08 24		08 29	08 34	08 39			
	d	07 41	07 42			07 46	07 51	07 56	07 57	08 01	08 06	08 11		08 12		08 16	08 21	08 26	08 27	08 31	08 36	08 41	08 42		
Cardiff Bay	a		07 46						08 01					08 16					08 31				08 46		
Cardiff Central 7	a	07 44			07 50	07 53	07 54	07 59		08 04	08 09	08 14			08 20	08 23	08 24	08 29		08 34	08 39	08 48			08 50
	d	07 46					07 55	08 01			08 10	08 16					08 25	08 31			08 41				
Grangetown	d	07 50					07 59	08 05			08 14	08 20					08 29	08 35			08 45				
Dingle Road	d	07 56						08 11				08 26						08 41							
Penarth	a	08 02						08 17				08 32						08 47							
Cogan	d						08 03				08 18						08 33				08 48				
Eastbrook	d						08 05				08 20						08 35				08 51				
Dinas Powys	d						08 07				08 22						08 37				08 53				
Cadoxton	d						08 12				08 27						08 42				08 57				
Barry Docks	d						08 15				08 30						08 45				09 00				
Barry 3	d						08 19				08 34						08 49				09 05				
Barry Island	a						08 26				08 41						08 56								
Rhoose Cardiff Int Airport ✈	d																				09 12				
Llantwit Major	d																				09 22				
Bridgend	a																				09 40				

For general notes see front of timetable
For details of catering facilities see Directory of Train Operators

A To Coryton
B To Radyr
b Arr. 0737

Table 130

from 13 September

Treherbert, Aberdare, Merthyr, Pontypridd, Rhymney and Coryton → Cardiff, Penarth, Barry, Barry Island and Bridgend

Network Diagram - see first page of Table 130

		AW	AW	AW	AW	AW A	AW	AW	AW	AW	AW B	AW	AW	AW		AW	AW A	AW	AW	AW	AW	AW B	AW	AW	AW	AW
Treherbert	d								08 17												08 47					
Ynyswen	d								08 19												08 49					
Treorchy	d								08 21												08 51					
Ton Pentre	d								08 23												08 53					
Ystrad Rhondda	a								08 26												08 56					
	d								08 28												08 58					
Llwynypia	d								08 30												09 00					
Tonypandy	d								08 33												09 03					
Dinas Rhondda	d								08 35												09 05					
Porth	d								08 39												09 09					
Trehafod	d								08 42												09 12					
Merthyr Tydfil	d																	08 38								
Pentre-bach	d																	08 42								
Troed Y Rhiw	d																	08 45								
Merthyr Vale	d																	08 50								
Quakers Yard	d																	08 55								
Aberdare 3	d		07 51										08 21											08 51		
Cwmbach	d		07 54										08 24											08 54		
Fernhill	d		07 58										08 28											08 58		
Mountain Ash	a		08 01										08 31											09 01		
	d		08 04										08 34											09 04		
Penrhiwceiber	d		08 08										08 38											09 08		
Abercynon	d		08 14										08 44					08 59						09 14		
Pontypridd 3	a		08 23						08 47				08 53					09 07			09 17			09 23		
	d		08 24				08 39		08 48				08 54					09 09			09 18			09 24		
Trefforest	d		08 27				08 42		08 51				08 57					09 12			09 21			09 27		
Trefforest Estate	d						08 46											09 16								
Taffs Well 3	d		08 34				08 50		08 58				09 04					09 20			09 28			09 34		
Radyr 3	a		08 37				08 53		09 01				09 07					09 23			09 31			09 37		
	d		08 37				08 53		09 01		09 04		09 07					09 23			09 31	09 34		09 37		
Danescourt	d										09 08											09 38				
Fairwater	d										09 10											09 40				
Waun-gron Park	d										09 12											09 42				
Ninian Park	d										09 15											09 45				
Llandaf	d	←	08 40				08 56		09 04			←	09 10					09 26			09 34		←	09 40		
Cathays	d	08 39	08 45				09 01		09 09			09 09	09 15					09 31			09 39		09 39	09 45		
Rhymney 3	d								→					08 30							→					
Pontlottyn	d													08 33												
Tir-phil	d													08 37												
Brithdir	d													08 40												
Bargoed	d			08 17				08 32						08 47					09 02							
Gilfach Fargoed	d			08 19																						
Pengam	d			08 22				08 37						08 52					09 07							
Hengoed	d			08 25				08 40						08 55					09 10							
Ystrad Mynach 3	d			08 28				08 43						08 58					09 13						09 28	
Llanbradach	d			08 33				08 48						09 03					09 18						09 33	
Aber	d			08 37				08 52						09 07					09 22						09 37	
Caerphilly 3	d			08 40				08 55						09 10					09 25						09 40	
Lisvane & Thornhill	d			08 44				08 59						09 14					09 29						09 44	
Llanishen	d			08 46				09 01						09 16					09 31						09 46	
Heath High Level	d			08 49				09 04						09 19					09 34						09 49	
Coryton	d					08 45											09 15									
Whitchurch (Cardiff)	d					08 46											09 16									
Rhiwbina	d					08 48											09 18									
Birchgrove	d					08 50											09 20									
Ty Glas	d					08 51											09 21									
Heath Low Level	d					08 54											09 24									
Cardiff Queen Street 3	a	08 44	08 49	08 54		08 59	09 04	09 09				09 14	09 19	09 24			09 29	09 34	09 39				09 44	09 49	09 54	
	d	08 46	08 51	08 56	08 57	09 01	09 06	09 11		09 12		09 16	09 21	09 26		09 27	09 31	09 36	09 41	09 42			09 46	09 51	09 56	09 57
Cardiff Bay	a				09 01					09 16						09 31				09 46						10 01
Cardiff Central 7	a	08 53	08 54	08 59		09 04	09 09	09 14			09 20	09 23	09 24	09 29			09 34	09 39	09 44			09 50	09 53	09 54	09 59	
	d		08 55	09 01			09 10	09 16					09 25	09 31				09 41	09 46					09 55	10 01	
Grangetown	d		08 59	09 05			09 14	09 20					09 29	09 35				09 45	09 50					09 59	10 05	
Dingle Road	d			09 11				09 26						09 41					09 56						10 11	
Penarth	a			09 17				09 32						09 47					10 02						10 17	
Cogan	d		09 03				09 18						09 33					09 48						10 03		
Eastbrook	d		09 05				09 20						09 35					09 51						10 05		
Dinas Powys	d		09 07				09 22						09 37					09 53						10 07		
Cadoxton	d		09 12				09 27						09 42					09 57						10 12		
Barry Docks	d		09 15				09 30						09 45					10 00						10 15		
Barry 3	d		09 19				09 34						09 49					10 05						10 19		
Barry Island	a		09 26				09 41						09 56											10 26		
Rhoose Cardiff Int Airport ✈	d																	10 12								
Llantwit Major	d																	10 22								
Bridgend	a																	10 40								

For general notes see front of timetable
For details of catering facilities see Directory of Train Operators

A To Radyr
B To Coryton

Table 130

from 13 September

Treherbert, Aberdare, Merthyr, Pontypridd, Rhymney and Coryton → Cardiff, Penarth, Barry, Barry Island and Bridgend

Network Diagram - see first page of Table 130

		AW A	AW	AW	AW	AW	AW B	AW	AW	AW	AW	AW A	AW	AW	AW	AW	AW B	AW	AW	AW	AW	AW A	AW	AW	AW
Treherbert	d				09 17											09 47									
Ynyswen	d				09 19											09 49									
Treorchy	d				09 21											09 51									
Ton Pentre	d				09 23											09 53									
Ystrad Rhondda	a				09 26											09 56									
	d				09 28											09 58									
Llwynypia	d				09 30											10 00									
Tonypandy	d				09 33											10 03									
Dinas Rhondda	d				09 35											10 05									
Porth	d				09 39											10 09									
Trehafod	d				09 42											10 12									
Merthyr Tydfil	d												09 38												
Pentre-bach	d												09 42												
Troed Y Rhiw	d												09 45												
Merthyr Vale	d												09 50												
Quakers Yard	d												09 55												
Aberdare [3]	d								09 21										09 51						
Cwmbach	d								09 24										09 54						
Fernhill	d								09 28										09 58						
Mountain Ash	a								09 31										10 01						
	d								09 34										10 04						
Penrhiwceiber	d								09 38										10 08						
Abercynon	d								09 44				09 59						10 14						
Pontypridd [3]	a				09 47				09 53				10 07			10 17			10 23						
	d		09 39		09 48				09 54				10 09			10 18			10 24				10 39		
Trefforest	d		09 42		09 51				09 57				10 12			10 21			10 27				10 42		
Trefforest Estate	d		09 46										10 16										10 46		
Taffs Well [3]	d		09 50		09 58				10 04				10 20			10 28			10 34				10 50		
Radyr [3]	a		09 53		10 01				10 07				10 23			10 31			10 37				10 53		
	d		09 53		10 01		10 04		10 07				10 23			10 31	10 34		10 37				10 53		
Danescourt	d						10 08										10 38								
Fairwater	d						10 10										10 40								
Waun-gron Park	d						10 12										10 42								
Ninian Park	d						10 15										10 45								
Llandaf	d		09 56		10 04			←	10 10				10 26			10 34		←	10 40				10 56		
Cathays	d		10 01		10 09			10 09	10 15				10 31			10 39		10 39	10 45				11 01		
Rhymney [3]	d				→					09 29						→									
Pontlottyn	d									09 32															
Tir-phil	d									09 36															
Brithdir	d									09 39															
Bargoed	d			09 25						09 47				10 02										10 25	
Gilfach Fargoed	d			09 27																				10 27	
Pengam	d			09 30						09 52				10 07										10 30	
Hengoed	d			09 33						09 55				10 10										10 33	
Ystrad Mynach [3]	d			09b43						09 58				10 13						10 28				10c43	
Llanbradach	d			09 48						10 03				10 18						10 33				10 48	
Aber	d			09 52						10 07				10 22						10 37				10 52	
Caerphilly [3]	d			09 55						10 10				10 25						10 40				10 55	
Lisvane & Thornhill	d			09 59						10 14				10 29						10 44				10 59	
Llanishen	d			10 01						10 16				10 31						10 46				11 01	
Heath High Level	d			10 04						10 19				10 34						10 49				11 04	
Coryton	d	09 45										10 15										10 45			
Whitchurch (Cardiff)	d	09 46										10 16										10 46			
Rhiwbina	d	09 48										10 18										10 48			
Birchgrove	d	09 50										10 20										10 50			
Ty Glas	d	09 51										10 21										10 51			
Heath Low Level	d	09 54										10 24										10 54			
Cardiff Queen Street [3]	a	09 59	10 04	10 09				10 14	10 19	10 24		10 29	10 34	10 39				10 44	10 49	10 54		10 59	11 04	11 09	
	d	10 01	10 06	10 11		10 12		10 16	10 21	10 26	10 27	10 31	10 36	10 41	10 42			10 46	10 51	10 56	10 57	11 01	11 06	11 11	11 12
Cardiff Bay	a					10 16					10 31				10 46						11 01				11 16
Cardiff Central [7]	a	10 04	10 09	10 14			10 20	10 23	10 24	10 29		10 34	10 39	10 44			10 50	10 53	10 54	10 59		11 04	11 09	11 14	
	d		10 10	10 16					10 25	10 31			10 41	10 46					10 55	11 01			11 10	11 16	
Grangetown	d		10 14	10 20					10 29	10 35			10 45	10 50					10 59	11 05			11 14	11 20	
Dingle Road	d			10 26						10 41				10 56						11 11				11 26	
Penarth	a			10 32						10 47				11 02						11 17				11 32	
Cogan	d		10 18						10 33				10 48						11 03				11 18		
Eastbrook	d		10 20						10 35				10 51						11 05				11 20		
Dinas Powys	d		10 22						10 37				10 53						11 07				11 22		
Cadoxton	d		10 27						10 42				10 57						11 12				11 27		
Barry Docks	d		10 30						10 45				11 00						11 15				11 30		
Barry [3]	d		10 34						10 49				11 05						11 19				11 34		
Barry Island	a		10 41						10 56										11 26				11 41		
Rhoose Cardiff Int Airport ✈	d												11 12												
Llantwit Major	d												11 22												
Bridgend	a												11 40												

For general notes see front of timetable
For details of catering facilities see Directory of Train Operators

A To Radyr
B To Coryton
b Arr. 0936
c Arr. 1036

Table 130

from 13 September

Treherbert, Aberdare, Merthyr, Pontypridd, Rhymney and Coryton → Cardiff, Penarth, Barry, Barry Island and Bridgend

Network Diagram - see first page of Table 130

		AW A	AW	AW	AW	AW	AW B	AW		AW	AW	AW	AW A	AW	AW	AW	AW	AW B	AW	AW	AW	AW	AW A	AW	AW	AW
Treherbert	d				10 17							10 47									11 17					
Ynyswen	d				10 19							10 49									11 19					
Treorchy	d				10 21							10 51									11 21					
Ton Pentre	d				10 23							10 53									11 23					
Ystrad Rhondda	a				10 26							10 56									11 26					
	d				10 28							10 58									11 28					
Llwynypia	d				10 30							11 00									11 30					
Tonypandy	d				10 33							11 03									11 33					
Dinas Rhondda	d				10 35							11 05									11 35					
Porth	d				10b52							11 09									11 39					
Trehafod	d				10 55							11 12									11 42					
Merthyr Tydfil	d							10 38																		
Pentre-bach	d							10 42																		
Troed Y Rhiw	d							10 45																		
Merthyr Vale	d							10 50																		
Quakers Yard	d							10 55																		
Aberdare [3]	d		10 21												10 51										11 21	
Cwmbach	d		10 24												10 54										11 24	
Fernhill	d		10 28												10 58										11 28	
Mountain Ash	a		10 31												11 01										11 31	
	d		10 34												11 04										11 34	
Penrhiwceiber	d		10 38												11 08										11 38	
Abercynon	d		10 44					10 59							11 14										11 44	
Pontypridd [3]	a		10 53		11 00			11 07				11 17			11 23						11 47				11 53	
	d		10 54		11 04			11 09				11 18			11 24				11 39		11 48				11 54	
Trefforest	d		10 57		11 07			11 12				11 21			11 27				11 42		11 51				11 57	
Trefforest Estate	d							11 16											11 46							
Taffs Well [3]	d		11 04		11 13			11 20				11 28			11 34				11 50		11 58				12 04	
Radyr [3]	a		11 07		11 17			11 23				11 31			11 37				11 53		12 01				12 07	
	d	11 04	11 07		11 17			11 23				11 31	11 34		11 37				11 53		12 01		12 04		12 07	
Danescourt	d	11 08											11 38										12 08			
Fairwater	d	11 10											11 40										12 10			
Waun-gron Park	d	11 12											11 42										12 12			
Ninian Park	d	11 15											11 45										12 15			
Llandaf	d		11 10					11 26				11 34		←	11 40				11 56		12 04			←	12 10	
Cathays	d		11 15					11 31				11 39		11 39	11 45				12 01		12 09			12 09	12 15	
Rhymney [3]	d			10 29								→									→					11 29
Pontlottyn	d			10 32																						11 32
Tir-phil	d			10 36																						11 36
Brithdir	d			10 39																						11 39
Bargoed	d			10 47						11 02										11 25						11 47
Gilfach Fargoed	d																			11 27						
Pengam	d			10 52						11 07										11 30						11 52
Hengoed	d			10 55						11 10										11 33						11 55
Ystrad Mynach [3]	d			10 58						11 13						11 28				11c43						11 58
Llanbradach	d			11 03						11 18						11 33				11 48						12 03
Aber	d			11 07						11 22						11 37				11 52						12 07
Caerphilly [3]	d			11 10						11 25						11 40				11 55						12 10
Lisvane & Thornhill	d			11 14						11 29						11 44				11 59						12 14
Llanishen	d			11 16						11 31						11 46				12 01						12 16
Heath High Level	d			11 19						11 34						11 49				12 04						12 19
Coryton	d						11 15											11 45								
Whitchurch (Cardiff)	d						11 16											11 46								
Rhiwbina	d						11 18											11 48								
Birchgrove	d						11 20											11 50								
Ty Glas	d						11 21											11 51								
Heath Low Level	d						11 24											11 54								
Cardiff Queen Street [3]	a		11 20	11 24			11 29	11 34		11 39				11 44	11 49	11 54		11 59	12 04	12 09				12 14	12 19	12 24
	d		11 21	11 26		11 27	11 31	11 36		11 41	11 42			11 46	11 51	11 56	11 57	12 01	12 06	12 11		12 12		12 16	12 21	12 26
Cardiff Bay	a					11 31					11 46						12 01					12 16				
Cardiff Central [7]	a	11 20	11 24	11 29	11 34		11 34	11 39		11 44			11 50	11 53	11 54	11 59		12 04	12 09	12 14			12 20	12 23	12 24	12 29
	d		11 25	11 31				11 41		11 46					11 55	12 01			12 10	12 16					12 25	12 31
Grangetown	d		11 29	11 35				11 45		11 50					11 59	12 05			12 14	12 20					12 29	12 35
Dingle Road	d			11 41						11 56						12 11				12 26						12 41
Penarth	a			11 47						12 02						12 17				12 32						12 47
Cogan	d		11 33					11 48							12 03				12 18						12 33	
Eastbrook	d		11 35					11 51							12 05				12 20						12 35	
Dinas Powys	d		11 37					11 53							12 07				12 22						12 37	
Cadoxton	d		11 42					11 57							12 12				12 27						12 42	
Barry Docks	d		11 45					12 00							12 15				12 30						12 45	
Barry [3]	d		11 49					12 05							12 19				12 34						12 49	
Barry Island	a		11 56												12 26				12 41						12 56	
Rhoose Cardiff Int Airport ✈	d							12 12																		
Llantwit Major	d							12 22																		
Bridgend	a							12 40																		

For general notes see front of timetable
For details of catering facilities see Directory of Train Operators

A To Coryton
B To Radyr
b Arr. 1038
c Arr. 1136

Table 130

Saturdays

from 13 September

Treherbert, Aberdare, Merthyr, Pontypridd, Rhymney and Coryton → Cardiff, Penarth, Barry, Barry Island and Bridgend

Network Diagram - see first page of Table 130

		AW	AW A	AW	AW		AW	AW	AW	AW B	AW	AW	AW	AW C	AW	AW	AW	AW	AW B	AW	AW	AW	AW	AW C	AW	AW
Treherbert	d								11 47									12 17								
Ynyswen	d								11 49									12 19								
Treorchy	d								11 51									12 21								
Ton Pentre	d								11 53									12 23								
Ystrad Rhondda	a								11 56									12 26								
	d								11 58									12 28								
Llwynypia	d								12 00									12 30								
Tonypandy	d								12 03									12 33								
Dinas Rhondda	d								12 05									12 35								
Porth	d								12 09									12 39								
Trehafod	d								12 12									12 42								
Merthyr Tydfil	d				11 38																				12 38	
Pentre-bach	d				11 42																				12 42	
Troed Y Rhiw	d				11 45																				12 45	
Merthyr Vale	d				11 50																				12 50	
Quakers Yard	d				11 55																				12 55	
Aberdare 3	d																				12 21					
Cwmbach	d																				12 24					
Fernhill	d																				12 28					
Mountain Ash	a																				12 31					
	d																				12 34					
Penrhiwceiber	d																				12 38					
Abercynon	d				11 59																12 44				12 59	
Pontypridd 3	a				12 07				12 17									12 48			12 53				13 07	
	d				12 09				12 18						12 39			12 48			12 54				13 09	
Trefforest	d				12 12				12 21						12 42			12 51			12 57				13 12	
Trefforest Estate	d				12 16										12 46										13 16	
Taffs Well 3	d				12 20				12 28						12 50			12 58			13 04				13 20	
Radyr 3	a				12 23				12 31						12 53			13 01			13 07				13 23	
	d				12 23				12 31	12 34					12 53			13 01	13 04		13 07				13 23	
Danescourt	d									12 38									13 08							
Fairwater	d									12 40									13 10							
Waun-gron Park	d									12 42									13 12							
Ninian Park	d									12 45									13 15							
Llandaf	d				12 26				12 34		←				12 56			13 04		←	13 10				13 26	
Cathays	d				12 31				12 39		12 39				13 01			13 09		13 09	13 15				13 31	
Rhymney 3	d								→									→				12 29				
Pontlottyn	d																					12 32				
Tir-phil	d																					12 36				
Brithdir	d																					12 39				
Bargoed	d						12 02									12 25						12b47				13 02
Gilfach Fargoed	d															12 27										
Pengam	d						12 07									12 30						12 52				13 07
Hengoed	d						12 10									12 33						12 55				13 10
Ystrad Mynach 3	d						12 13					12 28				12c43						12 58				13 13
Llanbradach	d						12 18					12 33				12 48						13 03				13 18
Aber	d						12 22					12 37				12 52						13 07				13 22
Caerphilly 3	d						12 25					12 40				12 55						13 10				13 25
Lisvane & Thornhill	d						12 29					12 44				12 59						13 14				13 29
Llanishen	d						12 31					12 46				13 01						13 16				13 31
Heath High Level	d						12 34					12 49				13 04						13 19				13 34
Coryton	d		12 15											12 45										13 15		
Whitchurch (Cardiff)	d		12 16											12 46										13 16		
Rhiwbina	d		12 18											12 48										13 18		
Birchgrove	d		12 20											12 50										13 20		
Ty Glas	d		12 21											12 51										13 21		
Heath Low Level	d		12 24											12 54										13 24		
Cardiff Queen Street 3	a		12 29		12 34		12 39				12 44	12 54		12 59	13 04	13 09				13 14	13 19	13 24		13 29	13 34	13 39
	d	12 27	12 31		12 36		12 41	12 42			12 46	12 56	12 57	13 01	13 06	13 11	13 12			13 16	13 21	13 26	13 27	13 31	13 36	13 41
Cardiff Bay	a	12 31						12 46					13 01				13 16						13 31			
Cardiff Central 7	a		12 34		12 39		12 44			12 50	12 52	12 59		13 04	13 09	13 14			13 20	13 23	13 24	13 29		13 34	13 40	13 44
	d				12 41		12 46				12 55	13 01			13 10	13 16					13 25	13 31			13 41	13 46
Grangetown	d				12 45		12 50				12 59	13 05			13 14	13 20					13 29	13 35			13 45	13 50
Dingle Road	d						12 56					13 11				13 26						13 41				13 56
Penarth	a						13 02					13 17				13 32						13 47				14 02
Cogan	d				12 48						13 03				13 18						13 33				13 48	
Eastbrook	d				12 51						13 05				13 20						13 35				13 51	
Dinas Powys	d				12 53						13 07				13 22						13 37				13 53	
Cadoxton	d				12 57						13 12				13 27						13 42				13 57	
Barry Docks	d				13 00						13 15				13 30						13 45				14 00	
Barry 3	d				13 05						13 19				13 34						13 49				14 05	
Barry Island	a										13 26				13 41						13 56					
Rhoose Cardiff Int Airport ✈	d				13 12																				14 12	
Llantwit Major	d				13 22																				14 22	
Bridgend	a				13 40																				14 40	

For general notes see front of timetable
For details of catering facilities see Directory of Train Operators

A To Radyr
B To Coryton
C To Radyr

b Arr. 1242
c Arr. 1236

Table 130

from 13 September

Treherbert, Aberdare, Merthyr, Pontypridd, Rhymney and Coryton → Cardiff, Penarth, Barry, Barry Island and Bridgend

Network Diagram - see first page of Table 130

		AW		AW	AW A	AW	AW	AW	AW	AW B	AW	AW	AW	AW	AW A	AW	AW	AW	AW	AW B	AW	AW		AW	AW	AW A
Treherbert	d			12 47									13 17												13 47	
Ynyswen	d			12 49									13 19												13 49	
Treorchy	d			12 51									13 21												13 51	
Ton Pentre	d			12 53									13 23												13 53	
Ystrad Rhondda	a			12 56									13 26												13 56	
	d			12 58									13 28												13 58	
Llwynypia	d			13 00									13 30												14 00	
Tonypandy	d			13 03									13 33												14 03	
Dinas Rhondda	d			13 05									13 35												14 05	
Porth	d			13 09									13 39												14 09	
Trehafod	d			13 12									13 42												14 12	
Merthyr Tydfil	d																				13 38					
Pentre-bach	d																				13 42					
Troed Y Rhiw	d																				13 45					
Merthyr Vale	d																				13 50					
Quakers Yard	d																				13 55					
Aberdare 3	d						12 51																			
Cwmbach	d						12 54																			
Fernhill	d						12 58																			
Mountain Ash	a						13 01																			
	d						13 04																			
Penrhiwceiber	d						13 08																			
Abercynon	d						13 14										13 45				13 59					
Pontypridd 3	a			13 17			13 23						13 47				13 53				14 07				14 17	
	d			13 18			13 24				13 39		13 48				13 54				14 09				14 18	
Trefforest	d			13 21			13 27				13 42		13 51				13 57				14 12				14 21	
Trefforest Estate	d										13 46										14 16					
Taffs Well 3	d			13 28			13 34				13 50		13 58				14 04				14 20				14 28	
Radyr 3	a			13 31			13 37				13 53		14 01				14 07				14 23				14 31	
	d			13 31	13 34		13 37				13 53		14 01		14 04		14 07				14 23				14 31	14 34
Danescourt	d				13 38										14 08											14 38
Fairwater	d				13 40										14 10											14 40
Waun-gron Park	d				13 42										14 12											14 42
Ninian Park	d				13 45										14 15											14 45
Llandaf	d			13 34		←	13 40				13 56		14 04			←	14 10				14 26				14 34	
Cathays	d			13 39		13 39	13 45				14 01		14 09			14 09	14 15				14 31				14 39	
Rhymney 3	d			↪									↪					13 29							↪	
Pontlottyn	d																	13 32								
Tir-phil	d																	13 36								
Brithdir	d																	13 39								
Bargoed	d											13 25						13 47				14 02				
Gilfach Fargoed	d											13 27														
Pengam	d											13 30						13 52				14 07				
Hengoed	d											13 33						13 55				14 10				
Ystrad Mynach 3	d							13 28				13b43						13 58				14 13				
Llanbradach	d							13 33				13 48						14 03				14 18				
Aber	d							13 37				13 52						14 07				14 22				
Caerphilly 3	d							13 40				13 55						14 10				14 25				
Lisvane & Thornhill	d							13 44				13 59						14 14				14 29				
Llanishen	d							13 46				14 01						14 16				14 31				
Heath High Level	d							13 49				14 04						14 19				14 34				
Coryton	d									13 45										14 15						
Whitchurch (Cardiff)	d									13 46										14 16						
Rhiwbina	d									13 48										14 18						
Birchgrove	d									13 50										14 20						
Ty Glas	d									13 51										14 21						
Heath Low Level	d									13 54										14 24						
Cardiff Queen Street 3	a					13 44	13 49	13 54		13 59	14 04	14 09				14 14	14 19	14 24		14 29	14 34	14 39				
	d	13 42				13 46	13 51	13 56	13 57	14 01	14 06	14 11		14 12		14 16	14 21	14 26	14 27	14 31	14 36	14 41		14 42		
Cardiff Bay	a	13 46							14 01					14 16					14 31					14 46		
Cardiff Central 7	a				13 50	13 53	13 54	13 59		14 04	14 09	14 14			14 20	14 23	14 24	14 29		14 34	14 39	14 44				14 50
	d						13 55	14 01			14 10	14 16					14 25	14 31			14 41	14 46				
Grangetown	d						13 59	14 05			14 14	14 20					14 29	14 35			14 45	14 50				
Dingle Road	d							14 11				14 26						14 41				14 56				
Penarth	a							14 17				14 32						14 47				15 02				
Cogan	d						14 03				14 18						14 33				14 48					
Eastbrook	d						14 05				14 20						14 35				14 51					
Dinas Powys	d						14 07				14 22						14 37				14 53					
Cadoxton	d						14 12				14 27						14 42				14 57					
Barry Docks	d						14 15				14 30						14 45				15 00					
Barry 3	d						14 19				14 34						14 49				15 05					
Barry Island	a						14 26				14 41						14 55									
Rhoose Cardiff Int Airport ✈	d																				15 12					
Llantwit Major	d																				15 22					
Bridgend	a																				15 40					

For general notes see front of timetable
For details of catering facilities see Directory of Train Operators

A To Coryton
B To Radyr
b Arr. 1336

Table 130

Saturdays
from 13 September

Treherbert, Aberdare, Merthyr, Pontypridd, Rhymney and Coryton → Cardiff, Penarth, Barry, Barry Island and Bridgend

Network Diagram - see first page of Table 130

		AW	AW	AW	AW	AW	AW	AW	AW	AW	AW	AW	AW	AW	AW	AW	AW	AW	AW	AW	AW	AW	AW	AW	AW
						A				B					A				B					A	
Treherbert	d												14 17					14 47							
Ynyswen	d												14 19					14 49							
Treorchy	d												14 21					14 51							
Ton Pentre	d												14 23					14 53							
Ystrad Rhondda	a												14 26					14 56							
	d												14 28					14 58							
Llwynypia	d												14 30					15 00							
Tonypandy	d												14 33					15 03							
Dinas Rhondda	d												14 35					15 05							
Porth	d												14b52					15 09							
Trehafod	d												14 55					15 12							
Merthyr Tydfil	d															14 38									
Pentre-bach	d															14 42									
Troed Y Rhiw	d															14 45									
Merthyr Vale	d															14 50									
Quakers Yard	d															14 55									
Aberdare 3	d		13 51								14 21										14 51				
Cwmbach	d		13 54								14 24										14 54				
Fernhill	d		13 58								14 28										14 58				
Mountain Ash	a		14 01								14 31										15 01				
	d		14 04								14 34										15 04				
Penrhiwceiber	d		14 08								14 38										15 08				
Abercynon	d		14 14								14 44					14 59					15 14				
Pontypridd 3	a		14 23								14 53		15 00			15 07		15 17			15 23				
	d		14 24				14 39				14 54		15 04			15 09		15 18			15 24				15 39
Trefforest	d		14 27				14 42				14 57		15 07			15 12		15 21			15 27				15 42
Trefforest Estate	d						14 46									15 16									15 46
Taffs Well 3	d		14 34				14 50				15 04		15 13			15 20		15 28			15 34				15 50
Radyr 3	a		14 37				14 53				15 07		15 17			15 23		15 31			15 37				15 53
	d		14 37				14 53			15 04	15 07		15 17			15 23		15 31	15 34		15 37				15 53
Danescourt	d									15 08									15 38						
Fairwater	d									15 10									15 40						
Waun-gron Park	d									15 12									15 42						
Ninian Park	d									15 15									15 45						
Llandaf	d	←	14 40				14 56				15 10					15 26		15 34		←	15 40				15 56
Cathays	d	14 39	14 45				15 01				15 15					15 31		15 39		15 39	15 45				16 01
Rhymney 3	d											14 29						→							
Pontlottyn	d											14 32													
Tir-phil	d											14 36													
Brithdir	d											14 39													
Bargoed	d							14 25				14 47													
Gilfach Fargoed	d							14 27																	
Pengam	d							14 30				14 52													
Hengoed	d							14 33				14 55													
Ystrad Mynach 3	d			14 28				14c43				14 58										15 28			
Llanbradach	d			14 33				14 48				15 03										15 33			
Aber	d			14 37				14 52				15 07										15 37			
Caerphilly 3	d			14 40				14 55				15 10										15 40			
Lisvane & Thornhill	d			14 44				14 59				15 14										15 44			
Llanishen	d			14 46				15 01				15 16										15 46			
Heath High Level	d			14 49				15 04				15 19										15 49			
Coryton	d					14 45									15 15									15 45	
Whitchurch (Cardiff)	d					14 46									15 16									15 46	
Rhiwbina	d					14 48									15 18									15 48	
Birchgrove	d					14 50									15 20									15 50	
Ty Glas	d					14 51									15 21									15 51	
Heath Low Level	d					14 54									15 24									15 54	
Cardiff Queen Street 3	a	14 44	14 49	14 54		14 59	15 04	15 09			15 19	15 24			15 29	15 34				15 44	15 49	15 54		15 59	16 04
	d	14 46	14 51	14 56	14 57	15 01	15 06	15 11	15 12		15 21	15 26		15 27	15 31	15 36	15 42			15 46	15 51	15 56	15 57	16 01	16 06
Cardiff Bay	a				15 01				15 16					15 31			15 46						16 01		
Cardiff Central 7	a	14 53	14 54	14 59		15 04	15 09	15 14		15 20	15 24	15 29	15 34		15 34	15 39			15 50	15 53	15 54	15 59		16 04	16 09
	d		14 55	15 01			15 10	15 16			15 25	15 31				15 41					15 55	16 01			16 10
Grangetown	d		14 59	15 05			15 14	15 20			15 29	15 35				15 45					15 59	16 05			16 14
Dingle Road	d			15 11				15 26				15 41										16 11			
Penarth	a			15 17				15 32				15 47										16 17			
Cogan	d		15 03				15 18				15 33					15 48					16 03				16 18
Eastbrook	d		15 05				15 20				15 35					15 51					16 05				16 20
Dinas Powys	d		15 07				15 22				15 37					15 53					16 07				16 22
Cadoxton	d		15 12				15 27				15 42					15 57					16 12				16 27
Barry Docks	d		15 15				15 30				15 45					16 00					16 15				16 30
Barry 3	d		15 19				15 34				15 49					16 05					16 19				16 34
Barry Island	a		15 26				15 41				15 56										16 25				16 41
Rhoose Cardiff Int Airport	d															16 12									
Llantwit Major	d															16 22									
Bridgend	a															16 40									

For general notes see front of timetable
For details of catering facilities see Directory of Train Operators

A To Radyr
B To Coryton
b Arr. 1438
c Arr. 1436

Treherbert, Aberdare, Merthyr, Pontypridd, Rhymney and Coryton → Cardiff, Penarth, Barry, Barry Island and Bridgend

Network Diagram - see first page of Table 130

		AW	AW	AW	AW	AW	AW	AW	AW	AW	AW	AW	AW	AW	AW	AW		AW	AW	AW	AW	AW	AW	AW	AW	AW
					A					B					A						B					A
Treherbert	d		15 17											15 47										16 17		
Ynyswen	d		15 19											15 49										16 19		
Treorchy	d		15 21											15 51										16 21		
Ton Pentre	d		15 23											15 53										16 23		
Ystrad Rhondda	a		15 26											15 56										16 26		
	d		15 28											15 58										16 28		
Llwynypia	d		15 30											16 00										16 30		
Tonypandy	d		15 33											16 03										16 33		
Dinas Rhondda	d		15 35											16 05										16 35		
Porth	d		15 39											16 09										16 39		
Trehafod	d		15 42											16 12										16 42		
Merthyr Tydfil	d										15 38															
Pentre-bach	d										15 42															
Troed Y Rhiw	d										15 45															
Merthyr Vale	d										15 50															
Quakers Yard	d										15 55															
Aberdare 3	d						15 21											15 51								
Cwmbach	d						15 24											15 54								
Fernhill	d						15 28											15 58								
Mountain Ash	a						15 31											16 01								
	d						15 34											16 04								
Penrhiwceiber	d						15 38											16 08								
Abercynon	d						15 44				15 59							16 14								
Pontypridd 3	a		15 47				15 53				16 07			16 17				16 23						16 47		
	d		15 48				15 54				16 09			16 18				16 24				16 39		16 48		
Trefforest	d		15 51				15 57				16 12			16 21				16 27				16 42		16 51		
Trefforest Estate	d										16 16											16 46				
Taffs Well 3	d		15 58				16 04				16 20			16 28				16 34				16 50		16 58		
Radyr 3	a		16 01				16 07				16 23			16 31				16 37				16 53		17 01		
	d		16 01		16 04		16 07				16 23			16 31	16 34			16 37				16 53		17 01		17 04
Danescourt	d				16 08										16 38											17 08
Fairwater	d				16 10										16 40											17 10
Waun-gron Park	d				16 12										16 42											17 12
Ninian Park	d				16 15										16 45											17 15
Llandaf	d		16 04			←	16 10				16 26			16 34		←		16 40				16 56		17 04		
Cathays	d		16 09			16 09	16 15				16 31			16 39		16 39		16 45				17 01		17 09		
Rhymney 3	d		→					15 29						→										→		
Pontlottyn	d							15 32																		
Tir-phil	d							15 36																		
Brithdir	d							15 39																		
Bargoed	d	15 25						15 47				16 02							16 17				16 32			
Gilfach Fargoed	d	15 27																	16 19							
Pengam	d	15 30						15 52				16 07							16 22				16 37			
Hengoed	d	15 33						15 55				16 10							16 25				16 40			
Ystrad Mynach 3	d	15b43						15 58				16 13							16 28				16 43			
Llanbradach	d	15 48						16 03				16 18							16 33				16 48			
Aber	d	15 52						16 07				16 22							16 37				16 52			
Caerphilly 3	d	15 55						16 10				16 25							16 40				16 55			
Lisvane & Thornhill	d	15 59						16 14				16 29							16 44				16 59			
Llanishen	d	16 01						16 16				16 31							16 46				17 01			
Heath High Level	d	16 04						16 19				16 34							16 49				17 04			
Coryton	d									16 15											16 45					
Whitchurch (Cardiff)	d									16 16											16 46					
Rhiwbina	d									16 18											16 48					
Birchgrove	d									16 20											16 50					
Ty Glas	d									16 21											16 51					
Heath Low Level	d									16 24											16 54					
Cardiff Queen Street 3	a	16 09				16 14	16 19	16 24		16 29	16 34	16 39				16 44		16 49	16 54		16 59	17 04	17 09			
	d	16 11		16 12		16 16	16 21	16 26	16 27	16 31	16 36	16 41	16 42			16 46		16 51	16 56	16 57	17 01	17 06	17 11		17 12	
Cardiff Bay	a			16 16					16 31				16 46							17 01					17 16	
Cardiff Central 7	a	16 14			16 20	16 23	16 24	16 33		16 34	16 39	16 44			16 50	16 53		16 54	16 59		17 04	17 09	17 14			17 20
	d	16 16					16 25				16 41	16 46						16 55	17 01			17 10	17 16			
Grangetown	d	16 20					16 29				16 45	16 50						16 59	17 05			17 14	17 20			
Dingle Road	d	16 26										16 56							17 11				17 26			
Penarth	a	16 32										17 02							17 17				17 32			
Cogan	d						16 33				16 48							17 03				17 18				
Eastbrook	d						16 35				16 51							17 05				17 20				
Dinas Powys	d						16 37				16 53							17 07				17 22				
Cadoxton	d						16 42				16 57							17 12				17 27				
Barry Docks	d						16 45				17 00							17 15				17 30				
Barry 3	d						16 49				17 05							17 19				17 34				
Barry Island	a						16 56											17 26				17 41				
Rhoose Cardiff Int Airport ✈	d										17 12															
Llantwit Major	d										17 22															
Bridgend	a										17 40															

For general notes see front of timetable
For details of catering facilities see Directory of Train Operators

A To Coryton
B To Radyr
b Arr. 1536

Table 130

from 13 September

Treherbert, Aberdare, Merthyr, Pontypridd, Rhymney and Coryton → Cardiff, Penarth, Barry, Barry Island and Bridgend

Network Diagram - see first page of Table 130

		AW	AW	AW	AW	AW	AW	AW	AW	AW	AW	AW	AW		AW	AW	AW	AW	AW	AW	AW	AW	AW	AW	AW	AW
						A					B				C							B				
Treherbert	d									16 47										17 17						
Ynyswen	d									16 49										17 19						
Treorchy	d									16 51										17 21						
Ton Pentre	d									16 53										17 23						
Ystrad Rhondda	a									16 56										17 26						
	d									16 58										17 28						
Llwynypia	d									17 00										17 30						
Tonypandy	d									17 03										17 33						
Dinas Rhondda	d									17 05										17 35						
Porth	d									17 09										17 39						
Trehafod	d									17 12										17 42						
Merthyr Tydfil	d						16 38																			
Pentre-bach	d						16 42																			
Troed Y Rhiw	d						16 45																			
Merthyr Vale	d						16 50																			
Quakers Yard	d						16 55																			
Aberdare 3	d		16 21										16 51											17 21		
Cwmbach	d		16 24										16 54		17a10									17 24		
Fernhill	d		16 28										16 58											17 28		
Mountain Ash	a		16 31										17 01											17 31		
	d		16 34										17 04											17 34		
Penrhiwceiber	d		16 38										17 08		16a57									17 38		
Abercynon	d		16 44				16 59						17 14											17 44		
Pontypridd 3	a		16 53				17 07			17 17			17 23							17 47				17 53		
	d		16 54				17 09			17 18			17 24					17 39		17 48				17 54		
Trefforest	d		16 57				17 12			17 21			17 27					17 42		17 51				17 57		
Trefforest Estate	d						17 16											17 46								
Taffs Well 3	d		17 04				17 20			17 28			17 34					17 50		17 58				18 04		
Radyr 3	a		17 07				17 23			17 31			17 37					17 53		18 01				18 07		
	d		17 07				17 23			17 31	17 34		17 37					17 53		18 01		18 04		18 07		
Danescourt	d										17 38											18 08				
Fairwater	d										17 40											18 10				
Waun-gron Park	d										17 42											18 12				
Ninian Park	d										17 45											18 15				
Llandaf	d	←	17 10				17 26			17 34		←	17 40					17 56		18 04			←	18 10		
Cathays	d	17 09	17 15				17 31			17 39		17 39	17 45					18 01		18 09			18 09	18 15		
Rhymney 3	d			16 29						→										→					17 29	
Pontlottyn	d			16 32																					17 32	
Tir-phil	d			16 36																					17 36	
Brithdir	d			16 39																					17 39	
Bargoed	d			16 47				17 02								17 17			17 32						17 47	
Gilfach Fargoed	d															17 19										
Pengam	d			16 52				17 07								17 22			17 37						17 52	
Hengoed	d			16 55				17 10								17 25			17 40						17 55	
Ystrad Mynach 3	d			16 58				17 13								17 28			17 43						17 58	
Llanbradach	d			17 03				17 18								17 33			17 48						18 03	
Aber	d			17 07				17 22								17 37			17 52						18 07	
Caerphilly 3	d			17 10				17 25								17 40			17 55						18 10	
Lisvane & Thornhill	d			17 14				17 29								17 44			17 59						18 14	
Llanishen	d			17 16				17 31								17 46			18 01						18 16	
Heath High Level	d			17 19				17 34								17 49			18 04						18 19	
Coryton	d					17 15																				
Whitchurch (Cardiff)	d					17 16																				
Rhiwbina	d					17 18																				
Birchgrove	d					17 20																				
Ty Glas	d					17 21																				
Heath Low Level	d					17 24																				
Cardiff Queen Street 3	a	17 14	17 19	17 24		17 29	17 34	17 39				17 44	17 49			17 54		18 04	18 09				18 14	18 19	18 24	
	d	17 16	17 21	17 26	17 27	17 31	17 36	17 41	17 42			17 46	17 51			17 56	17 57	18 06	18 11		18 12		18 16	18 21	18 26	18 27
Cardiff Bay	a				17 31				17 46								18 01				18 16					18 31
Cardiff Central 7	a	17 23	17 24	17 29		17 34	17 39	17 44			17 50	17 53	17 54			17 59		18 09	18 14			18 20	18 23	18 24	18 29	
	d		17 25	17 31			17 41	17 46					17 55			18 01		18 10	18 16					18 25	18 31	
Grangetown	d		17 29	17 35			17 45	17 50					17 59			18 05		18 14	18 20					18 29	18 35	
Dingle Road	d			17 41				17 56								18 11			18 26						18 41	
Penarth	a			17 47				18 02								18 17			18 32						18 47	
Cogan	d		17 33				17 48						18 03					18 18						18 33		
Eastbrook	d		17 35				17 51						18 05					18 20						18 35		
Dinas Powys	d		17 37				17 53						18 07					18 22						18 37		
Cadoxton	d		17 42				17 57						18 12					18 27						18 42		
Barry Docks	d		17 45				18 00						18 15					18 30						18 45		
Barry 3	d		17 49				18 05						18 19					18 34						18 49		
Barry Island	a		17 56										18 26					18 41						18 56		
Rhoose Cardiff Int Airport ✈	d						18 12																			
Llantwit Major	d						18 22																			
Bridgend	a						18 40																			

For general notes see front of timetable
For details of catering facilities see Directory of Train Operators

A To Radyr
B To Coryton
C To Aberdare

Table 130

from 13 September

Treherbert, Aberdare, Merthyr, Pontypridd, Rhymney and Coryton → Cardiff, Penarth, Barry, Barry Island and Bridgend

Network Diagram - see first page of Table 130

		AW A	AW	AW	AW	AW B	AW	AW	AW	AW		AW	AW	AW	AW	AW	AW	AW	AW	AW	AW A	AW	AW	AW	AW	AW
Treherbert	d			17 47										18 17										18 47		
Ynyswen	d			17 49										18 19										18 49		
Treorchy	d			17 51										18 21										18 51		
Ton Pentre	d			17 53										18 23										18 53		
Ystrad Rhondda	a			17 56										18 26										18 56		
	d			17 58										18 28										18 58		
Llwynypia	d			18 00										18 30										19 00		
Tonypandy	d			18 03										18 33										19 03		
Dinas Rhondda	d			18 05										18 35										19 05		
Porth	d			18 09										18 39										19 09		
Trehafod	d			18 12										18 42										19 12		
Merthyr Tydfil	d		17 38																			18 38				
Pentre-bach	d		17 42																			18 42				
Troed Y Rhiw	d		17 45																			18 45				
Merthyr Vale	d		17 50																			18 50				
Quakers Yard	d		17 55																			18 55				
Aberdare 3	d							17 51										18 21							18 51	
Cwmbach	d							17 54										18 24							18 54	
Fernhill	d							17 58										18 28							18 58	
Mountain Ash	a							18 01										18 31							19 01	
	d							18 04										18 34							19 04	
Penrhiwceiber	d							18 08										18 38							19 08	
Abercynon	d		17 59					18 14										18 44				18 59			19 14	
Pontypridd 3	a		18 07	18 17				18 23						18 47				18 53				19 07		19 17	19 23	
	d		18 09	18 18				18 24					18 39	18 48				18 54				19 09		19 18	19 24	
Trefforest	d		18 12	18 21				18 27					18 42	18 51				18 57				19 12		19 21	19 27	
Trefforest Estate	d		18 16										18 46									19 16				
Taffs Well 3	d		18 20	18 28				18 34					18 50	18 58				19 04				19 20		19 28	19 34	
Radyr 3	a		18 23	18 31				18 37					18 53	19 01				19 07				19 23		19 31	19 37	
	d		18 23	18 31		18 34		18 37					18 53	19 01		19 04		19 07				19 23		19 31	19 37	
Danescourt	d					18 38										19 08										
Fairwater	d					18 40										19 10										
Waun-gron Park	d					18 42										19 12										
Ninian Park	d					18 45										19 15										
Llandaf	d		18 26	18 34			←	18 40					18 56	19 04			←	19 10				19 26		19 34	19 40	
Cathays	d		18 31	18 39			18 39	18 45					19 01	19 09			19 09	19 15				19 31		19 39	19 45	
Rhymney 3	d			→										→												
Pontlottyn	d																									
Tir-phil	d																									
Brithdir	d																									
Bargoed	d								18 17										18 48							
Gilfach Fargoed	d								18 19										18 50							
Pengam	d								18 22										18 53							
Hengoed	d								18 25										18 56							
Ystrad Mynach 3	d								18 28										18 59							
Llanbradach	d								18 33										19 04							
Aber	d								18 37										19 08							19 40
Caerphilly 3	d								18 40										19 11							19 44
Lisvane & Thornhill	d								18 44										19 15							19 46
Llanishen	d								18 46										19 17							19 49
Heath High Level	d								18 49										19 20							
Coryton	d	18 15										18 45									19 15					
Whitchurch (Cardiff)	d	18 16										18 46									19 16					
Rhiwbina	d	18 18										18 48									19 18					
Birchgrove	d	18 20										18 50									19 20					
Ty Glas	d	18 21										18 51									19 21					
Heath Low Level	d	18 24										18 54									19 24					
Cardiff Queen Street 3	a	18 29	18 34				18 44	18 49	18 54			18 59	19 04				19 14	19 19	19 24		19 29	19 34		19 44	19 49	19 54
	d	18 31	18 36		18 42		18 46	18 51	18 56	18 57		19 01	19 06		19 12		19 16	19 21	19 26	19 27	19 31	19 36	19 42	19 46	19 51	19 56
Cardiff Bay	a				18 46					19 01					19 16					19 31			19 46			
Cardiff Central 7	a	18 34	18 39			18 50	18 53	18 54	18 59			19 07	19 10			19 22	19 23	19 24	19 29		19 34	19 39		19 53	19 57	19 59
	d		18 41					18 55	19 01									19 25	19 31			19 41				20 01
Grangetown	d		18 45					18 59	19 05									19 29	19 35			19 45				20 05
Dingle Road	d								19 11										19 41							20 11
Penarth	a								19 17										19 47							20 17
Cogan	d		18 48					19 03										19 33				19 48				
Eastbrook	d		18 51					19 05										19 35				19 51				
Dinas Powys	d		18 53					19 07										19 37				19 53				
Cadoxton	d		18 57					19 12										19 42				19 57				
Barry Docks	d		19 00					19 15										19 45				20 00				
Barry 3	d		19 05					19 19										19 49				20 05				
Barry Island	a							19 26										19 56								
Rhoose Cardiff Int Airport ✈	d		19 12																			20 12				
Llantwit Major	d		19 22																			20 22				
Bridgend	a		19 40																			20 40				

For general notes see front of timetable
For details of catering facilities see Directory of Train Operators

A To Radyr
B To Coryton

Table 130

Saturdays

from 13 September

Treherbert, Aberdare, Merthyr, Pontypridd, Rhymney and Coryton → Cardiff, Penarth, Barry, Barry Island and Bridgend

Network Diagram - see first page of Table 130

		AW	AW	AW	AW	AW	AW		AW	AW A	AW	AW	AW	AW	AW	AW	AW	AW	AW	AW	AW	AW	AW	AW	AW A	AW
Treherbert	d			19 17										19 47					20 17							
Ynyswen	d			19 19										19 49					20 19							
Treorchy	d			19 21										19 51					20 21							
Ton Pentre	d			19 23										19 53					20 23							
Ystrad Rhondda	a			19 26										19 56					20 26							
	d			19 28										19 58					20 28							
Llwynypia	d			19 30										20 00					20 30							
Tonypandy	d			19 33										20 03					20 33							
Dinas Rhondda	d			19 35										20 05					20 35							
Porth	d			19 39										20 09					20 39							
Trehafod	d			19 42										20 12					20 42							
Merthyr Tydfil	d										19 38															20 38
Pentre-bach	d										19 42															20 42
Troed Y Rhiw	d										19 45															20 45
Merthyr Vale	d										19 50															20 50
Quakers Yard	d										19 55															20 55
Aberdare [3]	d														19 51						20 21					
Cwmbach	d														19 54						20 24					
Fernhill	d														19 58						20 28					
Mountain Ash	a														20 01						20 31					
	d														20 04						20 34					
Penrhiwceiber	d														20 08						20 38					
Abercynon	d					19 43					19 59				20 14						20 44					20 59
Pontypridd [3]	a			19 47		19 53					20 07			20 17	20 23				20 47		20 53					21 07
	d			19 48		19 54					20 09			20 18	20 24				20 48		20 54					21 09
Trefforest	d			19 51		19 57					20 12			20 21	20 27				20 51		20 57					21 12
Trefforest Estate	d										20 16															21 16
Taffs Well [3]	d			19 58		20 04					20 20			20 28	20 34				20 58		21 04					21 20
Radyr [3]	a			20 01		20 07					20 23			20 31	20 37				21 01		21 07					21 23
	d			20 01	20 04	20 07					20 23			20 31	20 37				21 01	21 04	21 07					21 23
Danescourt	d				20 08		←													21 08		←				
Fairwater	d				20 10 →		20 10													21 10 →		21 10				
Waun-gron Park	d						20 12															21 12				
Ninian Park	d						20 15															21 15				
Llandaf	d			20 04		20 10					20 26			20 34	20 40				21 04		21 10					21 26
Cathays	d			20 09		20 15					20 31			20 39	20 45				21 09		21 15					21 31
Rhymney [3]	d											19 45														
Pontlottyn	d											19 48														
Tir-phil	d											19 52														
Brithdir	d											19 55														
Bargoed	d											19 59														
Gilfach Fargoed	d											20 01														
Pengam	d											20 04														
Hengoed	d											20 07														
Ystrad Mynach [3]	d											20 10														
Llanbradach	d											20 15														
Aber	d											20 19														
Caerphilly [3]	d											20 22				20 40										
Lisvane & Thornhill	d											20 26				20 44										
Llanishen	d											20 28				20 46										
Heath High Level	d											20 31				20 49										
Coryton	d									20 15															21 15	
Whitchurch (Cardiff)	d									20 16															21 16	
Rhiwbina	d									20 18															21 18	
Birchgrove	d									20 20															21 20	
Ty Glas	d									20 21															21 21	
Heath Low Level	d									20 24															21 24	
Cardiff Queen Street [3]	a			20 14		20 19				20 29	20 34	20 39		20 44	20 50	20 54			21 14		21 19				21 29	21 34
	d	19 57	20 12	20 16		20 21			20 27	20 31	20 36	20 41	20 42	20 46	20 51	20 56	20 57	21 12	21 16		21 21			21 27	21 31	21 36
Cardiff Bay	a	20 01	20 16						20 31				20 46				21 01	21 16						21 31		
Cardiff Central [7]	a			20 19		20 24	20 26			20 34	20 39	20 48		20 53	20 58	20 59			21 22		21 24	21 25			21 34	21 39
	d			20 20		20 31					20 41					21 01					21 25		21 31			21 41
Grangetown	d			20 24		20 35					20 45					21 05					21 29		21 35			21 45
Dingle Road	d					20 41										21 11							21 41			
Penarth	a					20 47										21 17							21 47			
Cogan	d			20 28							20 48										21 33					21 48
Eastbrook	d			20 30							20 51										21 35					21 51
Dinas Powys	d			20 32							20 53										21 37					21 53
Cadoxton	d			20 37							20 57										21 42					21 57
Barry Docks	d			20 40							21 00										21 45					22 00
Barry [3]	d			20 44							21 05										21 49					22 05
Barry Island	a			20 51																	21 56					
Rhoose Cardiff Int Airport ✈	d										21 12															22 12
Llantwit Major	d										21 22															22 22
Bridgend	a										21 40															22 40

For general notes see front of timetable
For details of catering facilities see Directory of Train Operators

A To Radyr

from 13 September

Treherbert, Aberdare, Merthyr, Pontypridd, Rhymney and Coryton → Cardiff, Penarth, Barry, Barry Island and Bridgend

Network Diagram - see first page of Table 130

		AW	AW	AW		AW	AW	AW	AW	AW	AW	AW	AW	AW	AW	AW	AW	AW	AW	AW	AW	AW	AW	AW		
Treherbert	d							21 17																		
Ynyswen	d							21 19																		
Treorchy	d							21 21																		
Ton Pentre	d							21 23																		
Ystrad Rhondda	a							21 26																		
	d							21 28																		
Llwynypia	d							21 30																		
Tonypandy	d							21 33																		
Dinas Rhondda	d							21 35																		
Porth	d							21 39																		
Trehafod	d							21 42																		
Merthyr Tydfil	d														21 38							22 38				
Pentre-bach	d														21 42							22 42				
Troed Y Rhiw	d														21 45							22 45				
Merthyr Vale	d														21 50							22 50				
Quakers Yard	d														21 55							22 55				
Aberdare 3	d			20 51													21 51							22 51		
Cwmbach	d			20 54													21 54							22 54		
Fernhill	d			20 58													21 58							22 58		
Mountain Ash	a			21 01													22 01							23 01		
	d			21 04													22 04							23 04		
Penrhiwceiber	d			21 08													22 08							23 08		
Abercynon	d			21 14											21 59		22 14							23 14		
Pontypridd 3	a			21 23				21 47							22 07		22 22					23 07		23 22		
	d			21 24				21 48							22 09		22 29					23 09		23 29		
Trefforest	d			21 27				21 51							22 12		22 32					23 12		23 32		
Trefforest Estate	d														22 16											
Taffs Well 3	d			21 34				21 58							22 20		22 39					23 20		23 38		
Radyr 3	a			21 37				22 01							22 23		22 42					23 23		23 42		
	d			21 37				22 01		22 04					22 23		22 42					23 23		23 42		
Danescourt	d									22 08																
Fairwater	d									22 10																
Waun-gron Park	d									22 12																
Ninian Park	d									22 15																
Llandaf	d			21 40				22 04			←				22 26		22 45					23 26		23 45		
Cathays	d			21 45				22 09			22 09				22 31		22 50					23 31		23 49		
Rhymney 3	d		20 48					↳					21 33													
Pontlottyn	d		20 51										21 36													
Tir-phil	d		20 55										21 40													
Brithdir	d		20 58										21 43													
Bargoed	d		21 02										21 47													
Gilfach Fargoed	d		21 04										21 49													
Pengam	d		21 07										21 52													
Hengoed	d		21 10										21 55													
Ystrad Mynach 3	d		21 13										21 58													
Llanbradach	d		21 18										22 03													
Aber	d		21 22										22 07													
Caerphilly 3	d		21 25			21 40							22 10													
Lisvane & Thornhill	d		21 29			21 45							22 14													
Llanishen	d		21 31			21 47							22 16													
Heath High Level	d		21 34			21 49							22 19													
Coryton	d																									
Whitchurch (Cardiff)	d																									
Rhiwbina	d																									
Birchgrove	d																									
Ty Glas	d																									
Heath Low Level	d																									
Cardiff Queen Street 3	a		21 42	21 50		21 54					22 14		22 24		22 34		22 54					23 34		23 53		
	d	21 42	21 44	21 51		21 56	21 57		22 12		22 16		22 26	22 27	22 36	22 42	22 55	22 57	23 12		23 27	23 36	23 42	23 56		
Cardiff Bay	a	21 46					22 01		22 16					22 31		22 46		23 01	23 16		23 31		23 46			
Cardiff Central 7	a		21 51	21 58		21 59				22 22	22 23		22 29		22 42		23 01					23 43		00 03		
	d					22 01						22 25	22 31				23 12			23 30						
Grangetown	d					22 05						22 29	22 35				23 16			23 34						
Dingle Road	d					22 11							22 41				23 20									
Penarth	a					22 17							22 47				23 26									
Cogan	d											22 33								23 37						
Eastbrook	d											22 35								23 40						
Dinas Powys	d											22 37								23 42						
Cadoxton	d											22 42								23 46						
Barry Docks	d											22 45								23 49						
Barry 3	d											22 49								23 54						
Barry Island	a											22 56								00 01						
Rhoose Cardiff Int Airport ✈	d																									
Llantwit Major	d																									
Bridgend	a																									

For general notes see front of timetable
For details of catering facilities see Directory of Train Operators

Table 130

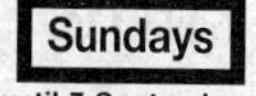

until 7 September

Treherbert, Aberdare, Merthyr, Pontypridd, Rhymney and Coryton → Cardiff, Penarth, Barry, Barry Island and Bridgend

Network Diagram - see first page of Table 130

Station		AW	AW	AW	AW	AW	AW	AW	AW		AW A	AW	AW B	AW	AW	AW	AW	AW		AW	AW	AW	AW	AW	AW	AW
Treherbert	d			08 17										10 17												
Ynyswen	d			08 19										10 19												
Treorchy	d			08 21										10 21												
Ton Pentre	d			08 23										10 23												
Ystrad Rhondda	a			08 26										10 26												
	d			08 28										10 28												
Llwynypia	d			08 30										10 30												
Tonypandy	d			08 33										10 33												
Dinas Rhondda	d			08 35										10 35												
Porth	d			08 39										10 39												
Trehafod	d			08 42										10 42												
Merthyr Tydfil	d							09 38																11 38		
Pentre-bach	d							09 42																11 42		
Troed Y Rhiw	d							09 45																11 45		
Merthyr Vale	d							09 50																11 50		
Quakers Yard	d							09 55																11 55		
Aberdare 3	d								09 52								10 52									
Cwmbach	d								09 55								10 55									
Fernhill	d								09 58								10 58									
Mountain Ash	a								10 01								11 01									
	d								10 04								11 04									
Penrhiwceiber	d								10 07								11 07									
Abercynon	d							09 59	10 13								11 13							11 59		
Pontypridd 3	a			08 47				10 07	10 23					10 47			11 23							12 07		
	d			08 48				10 09	10 24					10 48			11 24							12 09		
Trefforest	d			08 51				10 12	10 27					10 51			11 27							12 12		
Trefforest Estate	d																									
Taffs Well 3	d			08 58				10 20	10 34					10 58			11 34							12 20		
Radyr 3	a			09 01				10 23	10 37					11 01			11 37							12 23		
	d			09 01				10 23	10 37					11 01			11 37							12 23		
Danescourt	d																									
Fairwater	d																									
Waun-gron Park	d																									
Ninian Park	d																									
Llandaf	d			09 04				10 26	10 40					11 04			11 40							12 26		
Cathays	d			09 09				10 31	10 45					11 09			11 45							12 31		
Rhymney 3	d						09 29															11 29				
Pontlottyn	d						09 32															11 32				
Tir-phil	d						09 36															11 36				
Brithdir	d						09 39															11 39				
Bargoed	d						09 47															11 47				
Gilfach Fargoed	d						09 49															11 49				
Pengam	d						09 52															11 52				
Hengoed	d						09 55															11 55				
Ystrad Mynach 3	d						09 58															11 58				
Llanbradach	d						10 03															12 03				
Aber	d						10 07															12 07				
Caerphilly 3	d						10 10															12 10				
Lisvane & Thornhill	d						10 14															12 14				
Llanishen	d						10 16															12 16				
Heath High Level	d						10 19															12 19				
Coryton	d																									
Whitchurch (Cardiff)	d																									
Rhiwbina	d																									
Birchgrove	d																									
Ty Glas	d																									
Heath Low Level	d																									
Cardiff Queen Street 3	a			09 14			10 24	10 34	10 49					11 14			11 49					12 24		12 34		
	d			09 16			10 26	10 36	10 51		10 57	11 12		11 16	11 27	11 42	11 51	11 57		12 12		12 26	12 27	12 36	12 42	
Cardiff Bay	a										11 01	11 16			11 31	11 46		12 01		12 16			12 31		12 46	
Cardiff Central 7	a			09 19			10 29	10 39	10 54					11 19			11 54					12 29		12 39		
	d	08 25	08 41	09 25	09 55	10 25	10 31	10 41	10 55				11 17	11 25			11 55				12 25	12 31		12 41		12 55
Grangetown	d	08 29	08 45	09 29	09 59	10 29	10 35	10 45	10 59					11 29			11 59				12 29	12 35		12 45		12 59
Dingle Road	d						10 41															12 41				
Penarth	a						10 46															12 46				
Cogan	d	08 33	08 49	09 33	10 03	10 33		10 48	11 03					11 33			12 03				12 33			12 48		13 03
Eastbrook	d	08 35	08 51	09 35	10 05	10 35		10 51	11 05					11 35			12 05				12 35			12 51		13 05
Dinas Powys	d	08 37	08 53	09 37	10 07	10 37		10 53	11 07					11 37			12 07				12 37			12 53		13 07
Cadoxton	d	08 42	08 58	09 42	10 12	10 42		10 57	11 12					11 42			12 12				12 42			12 57		13 12
Barry Docks	d	08 45	09 01	09 45	10 15	10 45		11 00	11 15					11 45			12 15				12 45			13 00		13 15
Barry 3	d	08 49	09 05	09 49	10 19	10 49		11 05	11 19				11 34	11 49			12 19				12 49			13 05		13 19
Barry Island	a	08 55		09 55	10 25	10 55			11 25				11 41	11 55			12 25				12 55					13 25
Rhoose Cardiff Int Airport ✈	d		09 12					11 12																13 12		
Llantwit Major	d		09 22					11 22																13 22		
Bridgend	a		09 39					11 39																13 39		

For general notes see front of timetable
For details of catering facilities see Directory of Train Operators

A From Cardiff Central
B From Hereford (Table 131)

Table 130

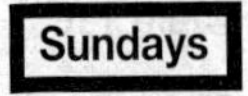

until 7 September

Treherbert, Aberdare, Merthyr, Pontypridd, Rhymney and Coryton → Cardiff, Penarth, Barry, Barry Island and Bridgend

Network Diagram - see first page of Table 130

		AW	AW	AW		AW	AW	AW	AW	AW	AW	AW	AW		AW	AW	AW	AW	AW	AW	AW	AW		AW	AW	AW
Treherbert	d			12 17																14 17						
Ynyswen	d			12 19																14 19						
Treorchy	d			12 21																14 21						
Ton Pentre	d			12 23																14 23						
Ystrad Rhondda	a			12 26																14 26						
	d			12 28																14 28						
Llwynypia	d			12 30																14 30						
Tonypandy	d			12 33																14 33						
Dinas Rhondda	d			12 35																14 35						
Porth	d			12 39																14 39						
Trehafod	d			12 42																14 42						
Merthyr Tydfil	d														13 38											
Pentre-bach	d														13 42											
Troed Y Rhiw	d														13 45											
Merthyr Vale	d														13 50											
Quakers Yard	d														13 55											
Aberdare 3	d							12 52																14 52		
Cwmbach	d							12 55																14 55		
Fernhill	d							12 58																14 58		
Mountain Ash	a							13 01																15 01		
	d							13 04																15 04		
Penrhiwceiber	d							13 07																15 07		
Abercynon	d							13 13							13 59									15 13		
Pontypridd 3	a			12 47				13 23							14 07					14 47				15 23		
	d			12 48				13 24							14 09					14 48				15 24		
Trefforest	d			12 51				13 27							14 12					14 51				15 27		
Trefforest Estate	d																									
Taffs Well 3	d			12 58				13 34							14 20					14 58				15 34		
Radyr 3	a			13 01				13 37							14 23					15 01				15 37		
	d			13 01				13 37							14 23					15 01				15 37		
Danescourt	d																									
Fairwater	d																									
Waun-gron Park	d																									
Ninian Park	d																									
Llandaf	d			13 04				13 40							14 26					15 04				15 40		
Cathays	d			13 09				13 45							14 31					15 09				15 45		
Rhymney 3	d											13 29														
Pontlottyn	d											13 32														
Tir-phil	d											13 36														
Brithdir	d											13 39														
Bargoed	d											13 47														
Gilfach Fargoed	d											13 49														
Pengam	d											13 52														
Hengoed	d											13 55														
Ystrad Mynach 3	d											13 58														
Llanbradach	d											14 03														
Aber	d											14 07														
Caerphilly 3	d											14 10														
Lisvane & Thornhill	d											14 14														
Llanishen	d											14 16														
Heath High Level	d											14 19														
Coryton	d																									
Whitchurch (Cardiff)	d																									
Rhiwbina	d																									
Birchgrove	d																									
Ty Glas	d																									
Heath Low Level	d																									
Cardiff Queen Street 3	a			13 14				13 49				14 24			14 34					15 14				15 49		
	d	12 57	13 12	13 16		13 27	13 42	13 51	13 57	14 12		14 26	14 27		14 36	14 42		14 57	15 12	15 16	15 27	15 42		15 51	15 57	16 12
Cardiff Bay	a	13 01	13 16			13 31	13 46		14 01	14 16			14 31			14 46		15 01	15 16		15 31	15 46			16 01	16 16
Cardiff Central 7	a			13 19				13 54				14 29			14 39					15 19				15 54		
	d			13 25				13 55			14 25	14 31			14 41		14 55			15 25				15 55		
Grangetown	d			13 29				13 59			14 29	14 35			14 45		14 59			15 29				15 59		
Dingle Road	d											14 41														
Penarth	a											14 46														
Cogan	d			13 33				14 03			14 33				14 48		15 03			15 33				16 03		
Eastbrook	d			13 35				14 05			14 35				14 51		15 05			15 35				16 05		
Dinas Powys	d			13 37				14 07			14 37				14 53		15 07			15 37				16 07		
Cadoxton	d			13 42				14 12			14 42				14 57		15 12			15 42				16 12		
Barry Docks	d			13 45				14 15			14 45				15 00		15 15			15 45				16 15		
Barry 3	d			13 49				14 19			14 49				15 05		15 19			15 49				16 19		
Barry Island	a			13 55				14 25			14 55						15 25			15 55				16 25		
Rhoose Cardiff Int Airport ✈	d														15 12											
Llantwit Major	d														15 22											
Bridgend	a														15 39											

For general notes see front of timetable
For details of catering facilities see Directory of Train Operators

Table 130

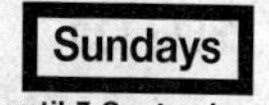
Sundays

until 7 September

Treherbert, Aberdare, Merthyr, Pontypridd, Rhymney and Coryton → Cardiff, Penarth, Barry, Barry Island and Bridgend

Network Diagram - see first page of Table 130

		AW	AW	AW	AW	AW A	AW	AW		AW	AW	AW	AW	AW	AW	AW	AW	AW	AW	AW	AW	AW	AW	AW		
Treherbert	d							16 17							18 17						20 17					
Ynyswen	d							16 19							18 19						20 19					
Treorchy	d							16 21							18 21						20 21					
Ton Pentre	d							16 23							18 23						20 23					
Ystrad Rhondda	a							16 26							18 26						20 26					
	d							16 28							18 28						20 28					
Llwynypia	d							16 30							18 30						20 30					
Tonypandy	d							16 33							18 33						20 33					
Dinas Rhondda	d							16 35							18 35						20 35					
Porth	d							16 39							18 39						20 39					
Trehafod	d							16 42							18 42						20 42					
Merthyr Tydfil	d				15 38								17 38						19 38					21 38		
Pentre-bach	d				15 42								17 42						19 42					21 42		
Troed Y Rhiw	d				15 45								17 45						19 45					21 45		
Merthyr Vale	d				15 50								17 50						19 50					21 50		
Quakers Yard	d				15 55								17 55						19 55					21 55		
Aberdare 3	d									16 52						18 52						20 52				
Cwmbach	d									16 55						18 55						20 55				
Fernhill	d									16 58						18 58						20 58				
Mountain Ash	a									17 01						19 01						21 01				
	d									17 04						19 04						21 04				
Penrhiwceiber	d									17 07						19 07						21 07				
Abercynon	d				15 59					17 13			17 59			19 13			19 59			21 13		21 59		
Pontypridd 3	a				16 07			16 47		17 23			18 07		18 47	19 23			20 07		20 47	21 23		22 07		
	d				16 09			16 48		17 24			18 09		18 48	19 24			20 09		20 48	21 24		22 09		
Trefforest	d				16 12			16 51		17 27			18 12		18 51	19 27			20 12		20 51	21 27		22 12		
Trefforest Estate	d																									
Taffs Well 3	d				16 20			16 58		17 34			18 20		18 58	19 34			20 20		20 58	21 34		22 20		
Radyr 3	a				16 23			17 01		17 37			18 23		19 01	19 37			20 23		21 01	21 37		22 23		
	d				16 23			17 01		17 37			18 23		19 01	19 37			20 23		21 01	21 37		22 23		
Danescourt	d																									
Fairwater	d																									
Waun-gron Park	d																									
Ninian Park	d																									
Llandaf	d				16 26			17 04		17 40			18 26		19 04	19 40			20 26		21 04	21 40		22 26		
Cathays	d				16 31			17 09		17 45			18 31		19 09	19 45			20 31		21 09	21 45		22 31		
Rhymney 3	d		15 29									17 29						19 29								
Pontlottyn	d		15 32									17 32						19 32								
Tir-phil	d		15 36									17 36						19 36								
Brithdir	d		15 39									17 39						19 39								
Bargoed	d		15 47									17 47						19 47								
Gilfach Fargoed	d		15 49									17 49						19 49								
Pengam	d		15 52									17 52						19 52								
Hengoed	d		15 55									17 55						19 55								
Ystrad Mynach 3	d		15 58									17 58						19 58								
Llanbradach	d		16 03									18 03						20 03								
Aber	d		16 07									18 07						20 07								
Caerphilly 3	d		16 10									18 10						20 10								
Lisvane & Thornhill	d		16 14									18 14						20 14								
Llanishen	d		16 16									18 16						20 16								
Heath High Level	d		16 19									18 19						20 19								
Coryton	d																									
Whitchurch (Cardiff)	d																									
Rhiwbina	d																									
Birchgrove	d																									
Ty Glas	d																									
Heath Low Level	d																									
Cardiff Queen Street 3	a		16 24		16 34			17 14		17 49		18 24	18 34		19 14	19 49		20 24	20 34		21 14	21 49		22 34		
	d		16 26	16 27	16 36	16 40		17 16		17 51		18 26	18 36		19 16	19 51		20 26	20 36		21 16	21 51		22 36		
Cardiff Bay	a			16 31																						
Cardiff Central 7	a		16 29		16 39	16 44		17 19		17 54		18 29	18 39		19 19	19 54		20 30	20 39		21 19	21 57		22 42		
	d	16 25	16 31		16 41		16 55	17 25		17 55	18 25	18 31	18 41	18 55	19 25	19 55	20 25	20 31	20 41	20 55	21 25		22 25			
Grangetown	d	16 29	16 35		16 45		16 59	17 29		17 59	18 29	18 35	18 45	18 59	19 29	19 59	20 29	20 35	20 45	20 59	21 29		22 29			
Dingle Road	d		16 41									18 41						20 41								
Penarth	a		16 46									18 46						20 46								
Cogan	d	16 33			16 48		17 03	17 33		18 03	18 33		18 48	19 03	19 33	20 03	20 33		20 48	21 03	21 33		22 33			
Eastbrook	d	16 35			16 51		17 05	17 35		18 05	18 35		18 51	19 05	19 35	20 05	20 35		20 51	21 05	21 35		22 35			
Dinas Powys	d	16 37			16 53		17 07	17 37		18 07	18 37		18 53	19 07	19 37	20 07	20 37		20 53	21 07	21 37		22 37			
Cadoxton	d	16 42			16 57		17 12	17 42		18 12	18 42		18 57	19 12	19 42	20 12	20 42		20 57	21 12	21 42		22 42			
Barry Docks	d	16 45			17 00		17 15	17 45		18 15	18 45		19 00	19 15	19 45	20 15	20 45		21 00	21 15	21 45		22 45			
Barry 3	d	16 49			17 05		17 19	17 49		18 19	18 49		19 05	19 19	19 49	20 19	20 49		21 05	21 19	21 49		22 49			
Barry Island	a	16 55					17 25	17 55		18 25	18 55			19 25	19 55	20 25	20 55			21 25	21 55		22 55			
Rhoose Cardiff Int Airport ✈	d				17 12								19 12						21 12							
Llantwit Major	d				17 22								19 22						21 22							
Bridgend	a				17 39								19 39						21 39							

For general notes see front of timetable
For details of catering facilities see Directory of Train Operators

A From Cardiff Bay

Table 130

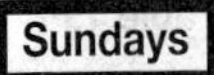

Sundays

from 14 September

Treherbert, Aberdare, Merthyr, Pontypridd, Rhymney and Coryton → Cardiff, Penarth, Barry, Barry Island and Bridgend

Network Diagram - see first page of Table 130

		AW	AW	AW	AW	AW	AW	AW	AW	AW	AW	AW	AW	AW	AW	AW	AW	AW	AW	AW	AW	AW	AW
										A													
Treherbert	d			08 17								10 17											
Ynyswen	d			08 19								10 19											
Treorchy	d			08 21								10 21											
Ton Pentre	d			08 23								10 23											
Ystrad Rhondda	a			08 26								10 26											
	d			08 28								10 28											
Llwynypia	d			08 30								10 30											
Tonypandy	d			08 33								10 33											
Dinas Rhondda	d			08 35								10 35											
Porth	d			08 39								10 39											
Trehafod	d			08 42								10 42											
Merthyr Tydfil	d							09 38													11 38		
Pentre-bach	d							09 42													11 42		
Troed Y Rhiw	d							09 45													11 45		
Merthyr Vale	d							09 50													11 50		
Quakers Yard	d							09 55													11 55		
Aberdare 3	d								09 51						10 51								
Cwmbach	d								09 54						10 54								
Fernhill	d								09 58						10 58								
Mountain Ash	a								10 01						11 01								
	d								10 04						11 04								
Penrhiwceiber	d								10 08						11 08								
Abercynon	d							09 59	10 14						11 14						11 59		
Pontypridd 3	a			08 47				10 07	10 23			10 47			11 23						12 07		
	d			08 48				10 09	10 24			10 48			11 24						12 09		
Trefforest	d			08 51				10 12	10 27			10 51			11 27						12 12		
Trefforest Estate	d																						
Taffs Well 3	d			08 58				10 20	10 34			10 58			11 34						12 20		
Radyr 3	a			09 01				10 23	10 37			11 01			11 37						12 23		
	d			09 01				10 23	10 37			11 01			11 37						12 23		
Danescourt	d																						
Fairwater	d																						
Waun-gron Park	d																						
Ninian Park	d																						
Llandaf	d			09 04				10 26	10 40			11 04			11 40						12 26		
Cathays	d			09 09				10 31	10 45			11 09			11 45						12 31		
Rhymney 3	d						09 29												11 29				
Pontlottyn	d						09 32												11 32				
Tir-phil	d						09 36												11 36				
Brithdir	d						09 39												11 39				
Bargoed	d						09 47												11 47				
Gilfach Fargoed	d						09 49												11 49				
Pengam	d						09 52												11 52				
Hengoed	d						09 55												11 55				
Ystrad Mynach 3	d						09 58												11 58				
Llanbradach	d						10 03												12 03				
Aber	d						10 07												12 07				
Caerphilly 3	d						10 10												12 10				
Lisvane & Thornhill	d						10 14												12 14				
Llanishen	d						10 16												12 16				
Heath High Level	d						10 19												12 19				
Coryton	d																						
Whitchurch (Cardiff)	d																						
Rhiwbina	d																						
Birchgrove	d																						
Ty Glas	d																						
Heath Low Level	d																						
Cardiff Queen Street 3	a			09 14			10 24	10 34	10 49			11 14			11 49				12 24		12 34		
	d			09 16			10 26	10 36	10 51	10 57	11 12	11 16	11 27	11 42	11 51	11 57	12 12		12 26	12 27	12 36	12 42	
Cardiff Bay	a									11 01	11 16		11 31	11 46		12 01	12 16			12 31		12 46	
Cardiff Central 7	a			09 19			10 29	10 39	10 54			11 19			11 54				12 29		12 39		
	d	08 25	08 41	09 25	09 55	10 25	10 31	10 41	10 55			11 25			11 55			12 25	12 31		12 41		12 55
Grangetown	d	08 29	08 45	09 29	09 59	10 29	10 35	10 45	10 59			11 29			11 59			12 29	12 35		12 45		12 59
Dingle Road	d						10 41												12 41				
Penarth	a						10 47												12 47				
Cogan	d	08 33	08 49	09 33	10 03	10 33		10 48	11 03			11 33			12 03			12 33			12 48		13 03
Eastbrook	d	08 35	08 51	09 35	10 05	10 35		10 51	11 05			11 35			12 05			12 35			12 51		13 05
Dinas Powys	d	08 37	08 53	09 37	10 07	10 37		10 53	11 07			11 37			12 07			12 37			12 53		13 07
Cadoxton	d	08 42	08 58	09 42	10 12	10 42		10 57	11 12			11 42			12 12			12 42			12 57		13 12
Barry Docks	d	08 45	09 01	09 45	10 15	10 45		11 00	11 15			11 45			12 15			12 45			13 00		13 15
Barry 3	d	08 49	09 05	09 49	10 19	10 49		11 05	11 19			11 49			12 19			12 49			13 05		13 19
Barry Island	a	08 56		09 56	10 26	10 56			11 26			11 56			12 26			12 56					13 26
Rhoose Cardiff Int Airport ✈	d		09 12					11 12													13 12		
Llantwit Major	d		09 22					11 22													13 22		
Bridgend	a		09 40					11 40													13 40		

For general notes see front of timetable
For details of catering facilities see Directory of Train Operators

A From Cardiff Central

Table 130

from 14 September

Treherbert, Aberdare, Merthyr, Pontypridd, Rhymney and Coryton → Cardiff, Penarth, Barry, Barry Island and Bridgend

Network Diagram - see first page of Table 130

Station		AW	AW	AW	AW	AW	AW	AW		AW	AW	AW	AW	AW	AW	AW		AW	AW	AW	AW	AW	AW	AW		AW
Treherbert	d			12 17																14 17						
Ynyswen	d			12 19																14 19						
Treorchy	d			12 21																14 21						
Ton Pentre	d			12 23																14 23						
Ystrad Rhondda	a			12 26																14 26						
	d			12 28																14 28						
Llwynypia	d			12 30																14 30						
Tonypandy	d			12 33																14 33						
Dinas Rhondda	d			12 35																14 35						
Porth	d			12 39																14 39						
Trehafod	d			12 42																14 42						
Merthyr Tydfil	d													13 38												
Pentre-bach	d													13 42												
Troed Y Rhiw	d													13 45												
Merthyr Vale	d													13 50												
Quakers Yard	d													13 55												
Aberdare [3]	d						12 51																14 51			
Cwmbach	d						12 54																14 54			
Fernhill	d						12 58																14 58			
Mountain Ash	a						13 01																15 01			
	d						13 04																15 04			
Penrhiwceiber	d						13 08																15 08			
Abercynon	d						13 14							13 59									15 14			
Pontypridd [3]	a			12 47			13 23							14 07						14 47			15 23			
	d			12 48			13 24							14 09						14 48			15 24			
Trefforest	d			12 51			13 27							14 12						14 51			15 27			
Trefforest Estate	d																									
Taffs Well [3]	d			12 58			13 34							14 20						14 58			15 34			
Radyr [3]	a			13 01			13 37							14 23						15 01			15 37			
	d			13 01			13 37							14 23						15 01			15 37			
Danescourt	d																									
Fairwater	d																									
Waun-gron Park	d																									
Ninian Park	d																									
Llandaf	d			13 04			13 40							14 26						15 04			15 40			
Cathays	d			13 09			13 45							14 31						15 09			15 45			
Rhymney [3]	d											13 29														
Pontlottyn	d											13 32														
Tir-phil	d											13 36														
Brithdir	d											13 39														
Bargoed	d											13 47														
Gilfach Fargoed	d											13 49														
Pengam	d											13 52														
Hengoed	d											13 55														
Ystrad Mynach [3]	d											13 58														
Llanbradach	d											14 03														
Aber	d											14 07														
Caerphilly [3]	d											14 10														
Lisvane & Thornhill	d											14 14														
Llanishen	d											14 16														
Heath High Level	d											14 19														
Coryton	d																									
Whitchurch (Cardiff)	d																									
Rhiwbina	d																									
Birchgrove	d																									
Ty Glas	d																									
Heath Low Level	d																									
Cardiff Queen Street [3]	a			13 14			13 49					14 24		14 34						15 14			15 49			
	d	12 57	13 12	13 16	13 27	13 42	13 51	13 57		14 12		14 26	14 27	14 36	14 42			14 57	15 12	15 16	15 27	15 42	15 51	15 57		16 12
Cardiff Bay	a	13 01	13 16		13 31	13 46		14 01		14 16			14 31		14 46			15 01	15 16		15 31	15 46		16 01		16 16
Cardiff Central [7]	a			13 19			13 54					14 29		14 39						15 19			15 54			
	d			13 25			13 55				14 25	14 31		14 41		14 55				15 25			15 55			
Grangetown	d			13 29			13 59				14 29	14 35		14 45		14 59				15 29			15 59			
Dingle Road	d											14 41														
Penarth	a											14 47														
Cogan	d			13 33			14 03				14 33			14 48		15 03				15 33			16 03			
Eastbrook	d			13 35			14 05				14 35			14 51		15 05				15 35			16 05			
Dinas Powys	d			13 37			14 07				14 37			14 53		15 07				15 37			16 07			
Cadoxton	d			13 42			14 12				14 42			14 57		15 12				15 42			16 12			
Barry Docks	d			13 45			14 15				14 45			15 00		15 15				15 45			16 15			
Barry [3]	d			13 49			14 19				14 49			15 05		15 19				15 49			16 19			
Barry Island	a			13 56			14 26				14 56					15 26				15 56			16 26			
Rhoose Cardiff Int Airport ✈	d													15 12												
Llantwit Major	d													15 22												
Bridgend	a													15 40												

For general notes see front of timetable
For details of catering facilities see Directory of Train Operators

Table 130

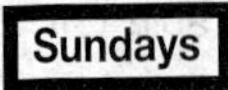

Sundays

from 14 September

Treherbert, Aberdare, Merthyr, Pontypridd, Rhymney and Coryton → Cardiff, Penarth, Barry, Barry Island and Bridgend

Network Diagram - see first page of Table 130

		AW	AW	AW	AW	AW A	AW	AW	AW	AW	AW	AW	AW	AW	AW	AW	AW	AW	AW	AW	AW	AW	AW
Treherbert	d							16 17						18 17						20 17			
Ynyswen	d							16 19						18 19						20 19			
Treorchy	d							16 21						18 21						20 21			
Ton Pentre	d							16 23						18 23						20 23			
Ystrad Rhondda	a							16 26						18 26						20 26			
	d							16 28						18 28						20 28			
Llwynypia	d							16 30						18 30						20 30			
Tonypandy	d							16 33						18 33						20 33			
Dinas Rhondda	d							16 35						18 35						20 35			
Porth	d							16 39						18 39						20 39			
Trehafod	d							16 42						18 42						20 42			
Merthyr Tydfil	d				15 38							17 38						19 38					21 38
Pentre-bach	d				15 42							17 42						19 42					21 42
Troed Y Rhiw	d				15 45							17 45						19 45					21 45
Merthyr Vale	d				15 50							17 50						19 50					21 50
Quakers Yard	d				15 55							17 55						19 55					21 55
Aberdare [3]	d								16 51						18 51						20 51		
Cwmbach	d								16 54						18 54						20 54		
Fernhill	d								16 58						18 58						20 58		
Mountain Ash	a								17 01						19 01						21 01		
	d								17 04						19 04						21 04		
Penrhiwceiber	d								17 08						19 08						21 08		
Abercynon	d				15 59				17 14			17 59			19 14			19 59			21 14		21 59
Pontypridd [3]	a				16 07			16 47	17 23			18 07		18 47	19 23			20 07		20 47	21 23		22 07
	d				16 09			16 48	17 24			18 09		18 48	19 24			20 09		20 48	21 24		22 09
Trefforest	d				16 12			16 51	17 27			18 12		18 51	19 27			20 12		20 51	21 27		22 12
Trefforest Estate	d																						
Taffs Well [3]	d				16 20			16 58	17 34			18 20		18 58	19 34			20 20		20 58	21 34		22 20
Radyr [3]	a				16 23			17 01	17 37			18 23		19 01	19 37			20 23		21 01	21 37		22 23
	d				16 23			17 01	17 37			18 23		19 01	19 37			20 23		21 01	21 37		22 23
Danescourt	d																						
Fairwater	d																						
Waun-gron Park	d																						
Ninian Park	d																						
Llandaf	d				16 26			17 04	17 40			18 26		19 04	19 40			20 26		21 04	21 40		22 26
Cathays	d				16 31			17 09	17 45			18 31		19 09	19 45			20 31		21 09	21 45		22 31
Rhymney [3]	d		15 29								17 29						19 29						
Pontlottyn	d		15 32								17 32						19 32						
Tir-phil	d		15 36								17 36						19 36						
Brithdir	d		15 39								17 39						19 39						
Bargoed	d		15 47								17 47						19 47						
Gilfach Fargoed	d		15 49								17 49						19 49						
Pengam	d		15 52								17 52						19 52						
Hengoed	d		15 55								17 55						19 55						
Ystrad Mynach [3]	d		15 58								17 58						19 58						
Llanbradach	d		16 03								18 03						20 03						
Aber	d		16 07								18 07						20 07						
Caerphilly [3]	d		16 10								18 10						20 10						
Lisvane & Thornhill	d		16 14								18 14						20 14						
Llanishen	d		16 16								18 16						20 16						
Heath High Level	d		16 19								18 19						20 19						
Coryton	d																						
Whitchurch (Cardiff)	d																						
Rhiwbina	d																						
Birchgrove	d																						
Ty Glas	d																						
Heath Low Level	d																						
Cardiff Queen Street [3]	a		16 24		16 34			17 14	17 49		18 24	18 34		19 14	19 49		20 24	20 34		21 14	21 49		22 34
	d		16 26	16 27	16 36	16 40		17 16	17 51		18 26	18 36		19 16	19 51		20 26	20 36		21 16	21 51		22 36
Cardiff Bay	a			16 31																			
Cardiff Central [7]	a		16 29		16 39	16 44		17 19	17 54		18 29	18 39		19 19	19 54		20 30	20 39		21 19	21 57		22 43
	d	16 25	16 31		16 41		16 55	17 25	17 55	18 25	18 31	18 41	18 55	19 25	19 55	20 25	20 31	20 41	20 55	21 25		22 25	
Grangetown	d	16 29	16 35		16 45		16 59	17 29	17 59	18 29	18 35	18 45	18 59	19 29	19 59	20 29	20 35	20 45	20 59	21 29		22 29	
Dingle Road	d		16 41								18 41						20 41						
Penarth	a		16 47								18 47						20 47						
Cogan	d	16 33			16 48		17 03	17 33	18 03	18 33		18 48	19 03	19 33	20 03	20 33		20 48	21 03	21 33		22 33	
Eastbrook	d	16 35			16 51		17 05	17 35	18 05	18 35		18 51	19 05	19 35	20 05	20 35		20 51	21 05	21 35		22 35	
Dinas Powys	d	16 37			16 53		17 07	17 37	18 07	18 37		18 53	19 07	19 37	20 07	20 37		20 53	21 07	21 37		22 37	
Cadoxton	d	16 42			16 57		17 12	17 42	18 12	18 42		18 57	19 12	19 42	20 12	20 42		20 57	21 12	21 42		22 42	
Barry Docks	d	16 45			17 00		17 15	17 45	18 15	18 45		19 00	19 15	19 45	20 15	20 45		21 00	21 15	21 45		22 45	
Barry [3]	d	16 49			17 05		17 19	17 49	18 19	18 49		19 05	19 19	19 49	20 19	20 49		21 05	21 19	21 49		22 49	
Barry Island	a	16 56					17 26	17 56	18 26	18 56			19 26	19 56	20 26	20 56			21 26	21 56		22 56	
Rhoose Cardiff Int Airport ✈	d				17 12							19 12						21 12					
Llantwit Major	d				17 22							19 22						21 22					
Bridgend	a				17 40							19 40						21 40					

A From Cardiff Bay

For general notes see front of timetable
For details of catering facilities see Directory of Train Operators

Table 130

Mondays to Fridays

until 5 September

Bridgend, Barry Island, Barry, Penarth and Cardiff → Coryton. Rhymney, Pontypridd, Merthyr, Aberdare and Treherbert

Network Diagram - see first page of Table 130

Miles	Miles	Miles	Miles	Miles			AW		AW	AW	AW	AW	AW	AW	AW	AW	AW	AW	AW	AW	AW	AW A	AW	AW	AW	AW B
—	—	0	—	—	**Bridgend**	d									05 42											
—	—	9½	—	—	Llantwit Major	d									05 56											
—	—	15¾	—	—	Rhoose Cardiff Int Airport ✈	d									06 06											
0	—	—	—	—	**Barry Island**	d							05 56						06 26							
¾	—	19	—	—	**Barry** 3	d							06 00		06 15				06 30							
2	—	—	—	—	Barry Docks	d							06 04		06 19				06 34							
2¾	—	—	—	—	Cadoxton	d							06 07		06 22				06 37							
4¼	—	—	—	—	Dinas Powys	d							06 11		06 26				06 41							
5¼	—	—	—	—	Eastbrook	d							06 13		06 28				06 43							
6½	—	—	—	—	Cogan	d							06 15		06 30				06 45							
—	0	—	—	—	**Penarth**	d										06 32								07 02		
—	¼	—	—	—	Dingle Road	d										06 34								07 04		
8¼	2¾	—	—	—	Grangetown	d							06 19		06 34	06 38			06 49					07 08		
9¼	3½	—	—	—	**Cardiff Central** 7	a							06 24		06 39	06 44			06 54					07 14		
—	—	—	0	—		d	05 26		05 46	06 11	06 16	06 21	06 26	06 36	06 41	06 46		06 51	06 56		07 06	07 06	07 11	07 16		07 21
—	—	0	—	—	**Cardiff Bay**	d											06 49			07 04					07 19	
9¾	4¼	1	—	—	**Cardiff Queen Street** 3	a	05 29		05 49	06 14	06 19	06 24	06 29	06 39	06 44	06 49	06 53	06 54	06 59	07 08	07 09		07 14	07 19	07 23	07 24
—	—	—	—	—		d	05 30		05 50	06 15	06 20	06 25	06 30	06 40	06 45	06 50		06 55	07 00		07 10		07 15	07 20		07 25
—	—	3½	—	—	Heath Low Level	d						06 30						07 00								07 30
—	—	4¼	—	—	Ty Glas	d						06 33						07 03								07 33
—	—	4¾	—	—	Birchgrove	d						06 34						07 04								07 34
—	—	5¼	—	—	Rhiwbina	d						06 36						07 06								07 36
—	—	5½	—	—	Whitchurch (Cardiff)	d						06 38						07 08								07 38
—	—	6	—	—	**Coryton**	a						06 43						07 13								07 43
—	6¾	—	—	—	Heath High Level	d			05 54		06 25					06 55								07 25		
—	7¾	—	—	—	Llanishen	d			05 57		06 28					06 58								07 28		
—	8¾	—	—	—	Lisvane & Thornhill	d			06 00		06 30					07 00								07 30		
—	11¼	—	—	—	Caerphilly 3	d			06a09		06 36					07 06								07 36		
—	12	—	—	—	Aber	d					06 38					07 08								07 38		
—	14	—	—	—	Llanbradach	d					06 42					07 12								07 42		
—	16¾	—	—	—	Ystrad Mynach 3	d					06 47					07 17								07 47		
—	17¾	—	—	—	Hengoed	d					06 50					07 20								07 50		
—	19½	—	—	—	Pengam	d					06 53					07 23								07 53		
—	20½	—	—	—	Gilfach Fargoed	d																				
—	21	—	—	—	Bargoed	d					07a01					07a31								08a01		
—	22½	—	—	—	Brithdir	d																				
—	23½	—	—	—	Tir-phil	d																				
—	26	—	—	—	Pontlottyn	d																				
—	27	—	—	—	**Rhymney** 3	a																				
10½	—	—	—	—	Cathays	d	05 33			06 18			06 33	06 43	06 48				07 03		07 13		07 18			
13	—	—	—	—	Llandaf	d	05 37			06 22			06 37	06 47	06 52				07 07		07 17		07 22			
—	—	—	1	—	Ninian Park	d																07 10				
—	—	—	2½	—	Waun-gron Park	d																07 13				
—	—	—	3	—	Fairwater	d																07 15				
—	—	—	3½	—	Danescourt	d																07 17				
14	—	—	4¾	—	Radyr 3	a	05 39			06 24			06 40	06 50	06 54				07 10		07 20	07 24	07 25			
—	—	—	—	—		d	05 40			06 24			06 40	06 50	06 55				07 10		07 20		07 25			
16	—	—	—	—	Taffs Well 3	d	05 43			06 28			06 44	06 54	06 59				07 14		07 24		07 29			
18¼	—	—	—	—	Trefforest Estate	d	05 47						06 48						07 18							
20¾	—	—	—	—	Trefforest	d	05 52			06 35			06 52	07 01	07 06				07 22		07 31		07 36			
21¾	—	0	—	0	**Pontypridd** 3	a	05 55			06 38			06 55	07 04	07 09				07 32		07 34		07 39			
—	—	—	—	—		d	05 56	06 11		06 41			06 56	07 06	07 11						07 36		07 40			
—	—	3¼	—	3¼	Abercynon	d	06 06	06 21		06 51			07 06		07 21								07 51			
—	—	—	—	6	Penrhiwceiber	d		06 27		06 57					07 27								07 57			
—	—	—	—	7¼	Mountain Ash	a		06 30		07 00					07 30								08 00			
—	—	—	—	—		d		06 33		07 03					07 33								08 03			
—	—	—	—	8¼	Fernhill	d		06 35		07 05					07 35								08 05			
—	—	—	—	9½	Cwmbach	d		06 39		07 09					07 39								08 09			
—	—	—	—	11	**Aberdare** 3	a		06 46		07 16					07 46								08 16			
—	—	4¾	—	—	Quakers Yard	d	06 10						07 10													
—	—	7	—	—	Merthyr Vale	d	06 18						07 18													
—	—	8¾	—	—	Troed Y Rhiw	d	06 21						07 21													
—	—	10	—	—	Pentre-bach	d	06 24						07 24													
—	—	11½	—	—	**Merthyr Tydfil**	a	06 32						07 32													
23½	—	—	—	—	Trehafod	d								07 11							07 41					
24¾	—	—	—	—	Porth	d								07 15							07 45					
26¼	—	—	—	—	Dinas Rhondda	d								07 19							07 49					
26¾	—	—	—	—	Tonypandy	d								07 21							07 51					
27¾	—	—	—	—	Llwynypia	d								07 23							07 53					
29	—	—	—	—	Ystrad Rhondda	a								07 26							07 56					
—	—	—	—	—		d								07 29							07 59					
29½	—	—	—	—	Ton Pentre	d								07 31							08 01					
30¾	—	—	—	—	Treorchy	d								07 34							08 04					
31¾	—	—	—	—	Ynyswen	d								07 37							08 07					
32¼	—	—	—	—	**Treherbert**	a								07 43							08 13					

For general notes see front of timetable
For details of catering facilities see Directory of Train Operators

A From Coryton
B From Taffs Well

Table 130

Mondays to Fridays
until 5 September

Bridgend, Barry Island, Barry, Penarth and Cardiff → Coryton. Rhymney, Pontypridd, Merthyr, Aberdare and Treherbert

Network Diagram - see first page of Table 130

		AW	AW	AW	AW	AW A	AW	AW	AW	AW B	AW	AW	AW	AW	AW A	AW	AW	AW	AW B	AW	AW	AW	AW	AW A	AW
Bridgend	d						06 42																		07 42
Llantwit Major	d						06 56																		07 56
Rhoose Cardiff Int Airport ✈	d						07 06																		08 06
Barry Island	d	06 56									07 26					07 41				07 56					
Barry 3	d	07 00					07 15				07 30					07 45				08 00					08 15
Barry Docks	d	07 04					07 19				07 34					07 49				08 04					08 19
Cadoxton	d	07 07					07 22				07 37					07 52				08 07					08 22
Dinas Powys	d	07 11					07 26				07 41					07 56				08 11					08 26
Eastbrook	d	07 13					07 28				07 43					07 58				08 13					08 28
Cogan	d	07 15					07 30				07 45					08 00				08 15					08 30
Penarth	d		07 17					07 32				07 47					08 02				08 17				
Dingle Road	d		07 19					07 34				07 49					08 04				08 19				
Grangetown	d	07 19	07 23				07 34	07 38			07 49	07 53				08 04	08 08			08 19	08 23				08 34
Cardiff Central 7	a	07 24	07 29				07 39	07 44			07 55	07 59				08 09	08 14			08 24	08 29				08 39
	d	07 26	07 31		07 36	07 36	07 41	07 46		07 51	07 56	08 01		08 06	08 06	08 11	08 16		08 21	08 26	08 31		08 36	08 36	08 41
Cardiff Bay	d			07 34					07 49				08 04					08 19				08 34			
Cardiff Queen Street 3	a	07 29	07 34	07 38	07 39		07 44	07 49	07 53	07 54	08 00	08 04	08 08	08 09		08 14	08 19	08 23	08 24	08 29	08 34	08 38	08 39		08 44
	d	07 30	07 35		07 40		07 45	07 50		07 55	08 00	08 05		08 10		08 15	08 20		08 25	08 30	08 35		08 40		08 45
Heath Low Level	d									08 00									08 30						
Ty Glas	d									08 03									08 33						
Birchgrove	d									08 04									08 34						
Rhiwbina	d									08 06									08 36						
Whitchurch (Cardiff)	d									08 08									08 38						
Coryton	a									08 13									08 43						
Heath High Level	d		07 40					07 55				08 10					08 25				08 40				
Llanishen	d		07 43					07 58				08 13					08 28				08 43				
Lisvane & Thornhill	d		07 45					08 00				08 15					08 30				08 45				
Caerphilly 3	d		07 51					08 06				08 21					08 36				08 51				
Aber	d		07 53					08 08				08 23					08 38				08 53				
Llanbradach	d		07 57					08 12				08 27					08 42				08 57				
Ystrad Mynach 3	d		08 02					08 17				08 32					08 47				09 02				
Hengoed	d		08 05					08 20				08 35					08 50				09 05				
Pengam	d		08 08					08 23				08 38					08 53				09 08				
Gilfach Fargoed	d											08 41													
Bargoed	d		08 14					08a31				08a48					08 59				09a16				
Brithdir	d		08 18														09 03								
Tir-phil	d		08 21														09 06								
Pontlottyn	d		08 25														09 10								
Rhymney 3	a		08 31														09 16								
Cathays	d	07 33			07 43		07 48				08 03			08 13		08 18				08 33			08 43		08 48
Llandaf	d	07 37			07 47		07 52				08 07			08 17		08 22				08 37			08 47		08 52
Ninian Park	d					07 40									08 10									08 40	
Waun-gron Park	d					07 43									08 13									08 43	
Fairwater	d					07 45									08 15									08 45	
Danescourt	d					07 47									08 17									08 47	
Radyr 3	a	07 40			07 50	07 54	07 55				08 10			08 20	08 24	08 25				08 40			08 50	08 54	08 55
	d	07 40			07 50		07 55				08 10			08 20		08 25				08 40			08 50		08 55
Taffs Well 3	d	07 44			07 54		07 59				08 14			08 24		08 29				08 44			08 54		08 59
Trefforest Estate	d	07 48									08 18									08 48					
Trefforest	d	07 52			08 01		08 06				08 22			08 31		08 36				08 52			09 01		09 06
Pontypridd 3	a	07 55			08 04		08 09				08 32			08 34		08 39				08 55			09 04		09 09
	d	07 56			08 06		08 11							08 36		08 41				08 56			09 06		09 11
Abercynon	d	08 06					08 21									08 51				09 06					09 21
Penrhiwceiber	d						08 27									08 57									09 27
Mountain Ash	a						08 30									09 00									09 30
	d						08 33									09 03									09 33
Fernhill	d						08 35									09 05									09 35
Cwmbach	d						08 39									09 09									09 39
Aberdare 3	a						08 46									09 16									09 46
Quakers Yard	d	08 10																		09 10					
Merthyr Vale	d	08 18																		09 18					
Troed Y Rhiw	d	08 21																		09 21					
Pentre-bach	d	08 24																		09 24					
Merthyr Tydfil	a	08 32																		09 32					
Trehafod	d				08 11									08 41									09 11		
Porth	d				08 15									08 45									09 15		
Dinas Rhondda	d				08 19									08 49									09 19		
Tonypandy	d				08 21									08 51									09 21		
Llwynypia	d				08 23									08 53									09 23		
Ystrad Rhondda	a				08 26									08 56									09 26		
	d				08 29									08 59									09 29		
Ton Pentre	d				08 31									09 01									09 31		
Treorchy	d				08 34									09 04									09 34		
Ynyswen	d				08 37									09 07									09 37		
Treherbert	a				08 43									09 13									09 43		

For general notes see front of timetable
For details of catering facilities see Directory of Train Operators

A From Coryton
B From Radyr

Table 130

Mondays to Fridays

until 5 September

Bridgend, Barry Island, Barry, Penarth and Cardiff → Coryton. Rhymney, Pontypridd, Merthyr, Aberdare and Treherbert

Network Diagram - see first page of Table 130

Station		AW	AW	AW A	AW	AW	AW	AW	AW B
Bridgend	d								
Llantwit Major	d								
Rhoose Cardiff Int Airport ✈	d								
Barry Island	d				08 26				
Barry 3	d				08 30				
Barry Docks	d				08 34				
Cadoxton	d				08 37				
Dinas Powys	d				08 41				
Eastbrook	d				08 43				
Cogan	d				08 45				
Penarth	d	08 32				08 47			
Dingle Road	d	08 34				08 49			
Grangetown	d	08 38			08 49	08 53			
Cardiff Central 7	a	08 44			08 54	08 59			
	d	08 46		08 51	08 56	09 01		09 06	09 06
Cardiff Bay	d		08 49				09 04		
Cardiff Queen Street 3	a	08 49	08 53	08 54	08 59	09 04	09 08	09 09	
	d	08 50		08 55	09 00	09 05		09 10	
Heath Low Level	d			09 00					
Ty Glas	d			09 03					
Birchgrove	d			09 04					
Rhiwbina	d			09 06					
Whitchurch (Cardiff)	d			09 08					
Coryton	a			09 13					
Heath High Level	d	08 55				09 10			
Llanishen	d	08 58				09 13			
Lisvane & Thornhill	d	09 00				09 15			
Caerphilly 3	d	09 06				09 21			
Aber	d	09 08				09 23			
Llanbradach	d	09 12				09 27			
Ystrad Mynach 3	d	09 17				09 32			
Hengoed	d	09 20				09 35			
Pengam	d	09 23				09 38			
Gilfach Fargoed	d					09 41			
Bargoed	d	09a31				09a48			
Brithdir	d								
Tir-phil	d								
Pontlottyn	d								
Rhymney 3	a								
Cathays	d				09 03			09 13	
Llandaf	d				09 07			09 17	
Ninian Park	d								09 10
Waun-gron Park	d								09 13
Fairwater	d								09 15
Danescourt	d								09 17
Radyr 3	a				09 10			09 20	09 24
	d				09 10			09 20	
Taffs Well 3	d				09 14			09 24	
Trefforest Estate	d				09 18				
Trefforest	d				09 22			09 31	
Pontypridd 3	a				09 32			09 34	
	d							09 36	
Abercynon	d								
Penrhiwceiber	d								
Mountain Ash	a								
	d								
Fernhill	d								
Cwmbach	d								
Aberdare 3	a								
Quakers Yard	d								
Merthyr Vale	d								
Troed Y Rhiw	d								
Pentre-bach	d								
Merthyr Tydfil	a								
Trehafod	d							09 41	
Porth	d							09 45	
Dinas Rhondda	d							09 49	
Tonypandy	d							09 51	
Llwynypia	d							09 53	
Ystrad Rhondda	a							09 56	
	d							09 59	
Ton Pentre	d							10 01	
Treorchy	d							10 04	
Ynyswen	d							10 07	
Treherbert	a							10 13	

Station		AW	AW	AW	AW A	AW	AW	AW	AW	AW B	AW	AW	AW	AW A	AW	AW	AW
Bridgend	d										08 42						
Llantwit Major	d										08 56						
Rhoose Cardiff Int Airport ✈	d										09 06						
Barry Island	d	08 41				08 56									09 26		
Barry 3	d	08 45				09 00					09 15				09 30		
Barry Docks	d	08 49				09 04					09 19				09 34		
Cadoxton	d	08 52				09 07					09 22				09 37		
Dinas Powys	d	08 56				09 11					09 26				09 41		
Eastbrook	d	08 58				09 13					09 28				09 43		
Cogan	d	09 00				09 15					09 30				09 45		
Penarth	d						09 17					09 32				09 47	
Dingle Road	d						09 19					09 34				09 49	
Grangetown	d	09 04				09 19	09 23				09 34	09 38			09 49	09 53	
Cardiff Central 7	a	09 09				09 24	09 29				09 39	09 44			09 54	09 59	
	d	09 11	09 16		09 21	09 26	09 31		09 36	09 36	09 41	09 46		09 51	09 56	10 01	
Cardiff Bay	d			09 19				09 34					09 49				10 04
Cardiff Queen Street 3	a	09 14	09 19	09 23	09 24	09 29	09 34	09 38	09 39		09 44	09 49	09 53	09 54	09 59	10 04	10 08
	d	09 15	09 20		09 25	09 30	09 35		09 40		09 45	09 50		09 55	10 00	10 05	
Heath Low Level	d				09 30									10 00			
Ty Glas	d				09 33									10 03			
Birchgrove	d				09 34									10 04			
Rhiwbina	d				09 36									10 06			
Whitchurch (Cardiff)	d				09 38									10 08			
Coryton	a				09 43									10 13			
Heath High Level	d		09 25				09 40					09 55				10 10	
Llanishen	d		09 28				09 43					09 58				10 13	
Lisvane & Thornhill	d		09 30				09 45					10 00				10 15	
Caerphilly 3	d		09 36				09 51					10 06				10 21	
Aber	d		09 38				09 53					10 08				10 23	
Llanbradach	d		09 42				09 57					10 12				10 27	
Ystrad Mynach 3	d		09 47				10 02					10 17				10 32	
Hengoed	d		09 50				10 05					10 20				10 35	
Pengam	d		09 53				10 08					10 23				10 38	
Gilfach Fargoed	d															10 41	
Bargoed	d		09 59				10a16					10a31				10a48	
Brithdir	d		10 03														
Tir-phil	d		10 06														
Pontlottyn	d		10 10														
Rhymney 3	a		10 16														
Cathays	d	09 18				09 33			09 43		09 48				10 03		
Llandaf	d	09 22				09 37			09 47		09 52				10 07		
Ninian Park	d									09 40							
Waun-gron Park	d									09 43							
Fairwater	d									09 45							
Danescourt	d									09 47							
Radyr 3	a	09 25				09 40			09 50	09 54	09 55				10 10		
	d	09 25				09 40			09 50		09 55				10 10		
Taffs Well 3	d	09 29				09 44			09 54		09 59				10 14		
Trefforest Estate	d					09 48									10 18		
Trefforest	d	09 36				09 52			10 01		10 06				10 22		
Pontypridd 3	a	09 39				09 55			10 04		10 09				10 32		
	d	09 41				09 56			10 06		10 11						
Abercynon	d	09 51				10 06					10 21						
Penrhiwceiber	d	09 57									10 27						
Mountain Ash	a	10 00									10 30						
	d	10 03									10 33						
Fernhill	d	10 05									10 35						
Cwmbach	d	10 09									10 39						
Aberdare 3	a	10 16									10 46						
Quakers Yard	d					10 10											
Merthyr Vale	d					10 18											
Troed Y Rhiw	d					10 21											
Pentre-bach	d					10 24											
Merthyr Tydfil	a					10 32											
Trehafod	d								10 11								
Porth	d								10 15								
Dinas Rhondda	d								10 19								
Tonypandy	d								10 21								
Llwynypia	d								10 23								
Ystrad Rhondda	a								10 26								
	d								10 29								
Ton Pentre	d								10 31								
Treorchy	d								10 34								
Ynyswen	d								10 37								
Treherbert	a								10 43								

For general notes see front of timetable
For details of catering facilities see Directory of Train Operators

A From Radyr
B From Coryton

Table 130

Mondays to Fridays

until 5 September

Bridgend, Barry Island, Barry, Penarth and Cardiff → Coryton. Rhymney, Pontypridd, Merthyr, Aberdare and Treherbert

Network Diagram - see first page of Table 130

		AW	AW	AW	AW	AW	AW	AW	AW	AW	AW	AW	AW	AW	AW	AW	AW	AW	AW	AW	AW	AW	AW	AW	AW
			A				B					A					B				A				B
Bridgend	d												09 42												
Llantwit Major	d												09 56												
Rhoose Cardiff Int Airport ✈	d												10 06												
Barry Island	d			09 41				09 56										10 26				10 41			
Barry 3	d			09 45				10 00					10 15					10 30				10 45			
Barry Docks	d			09 49				10 04					10 19					10 34				10 49			
Cadoxton	d			09 52				10 07					10 22					10 37				10 52			
Dinas Powys	d			09 56				10 11					10 26					10 41				10 56			
Eastbrook	d			09 58				10 13					10 28					10 43				10 58			
Cogan	d			10 00				10 15					10 30					10 45				11 00			
Penarth	d				10 02				10 17					10 32					10 47				11 02		
Dingle Road	d				10 04				10 19					10 34					10 49				11 04		
Grangetown	d			10 04	10 08			10 19	10 23				10 34	10 38				10 49	10 53			11 04	11 08		
Cardiff Central 7	a			10 09	10 14			10 24	10 29				10 43	10 44				10 54	10 59			11 09	11 14		
	d	10 06	10 06	10 11	10 16		10 21	10 26	10 31		10 36	10 36		10 46	10 51		10 51	10 56	11 01		11 06	11 11	11 16		11 21
Cardiff Bay	d					10 19				10 34						10 49				11 04				11 19	
Cardiff Queen Street 3	a	10 09		10 14	10 19	10 23	10 24	10 29	10 34	10 38	10 39			10 49		10 53	10 54	10 59	11 04	11 08		11 14	11 19	11 23	11 24
	d	10 10		10 15	10 20		10 25	10 30	10 35		10 40			10 50			10 55	11 00	11 05			11 15	11 20		11 25
Heath Low Level	d						10 30										11 00								11 30
Ty Glas	d						10 33										11 03								11 33
Birchgrove	d						10 34										11 04								11 34
Rhiwbina	d						10 36										11 06								11 36
Whitchurch (Cardiff)	d		09 46				10 38										11 08								11 38
Coryton	a						10 43										11 13								11 43
Heath High Level	d				10 25				10 40					10 55					11 10				11 25		
Llanishen	d				10 28				10 43					10 58					11 13				11 28		
Lisvane & Thornhill	d				10 30				10 45					11 00					11 15				11 30		
Caerphilly 3	d				10 36				10 51					11 06					11 21				11 36		
Aber	d				10 38				10 53					11 08					11 23				11 38		
Llanbradach	d				10 42				10 57					11 12					11 27				11 42		
Ystrad Mynach 3	d				10 47				11 02					11 17					11 32				11 47		
Hengoed	d				10 50				11 05					11 20					11 35				11 50		
Pengam	d				10 53				11 08					11 23					11 38				11 53		
Gilfach Fargoed	d																		11 41						
Bargoed	d				10 59				11a16					11a31					11a48				11 59		
Brithdir	d				11 03																		12 03		
Tir-phil	d				11 06																		12 06		
Pontlottyn	d				11 10																		12 10		
Rhymney 3	a				11 16																		12 16		
Cathays	d	10 13		10 18				10 33			10 43							11 03				11 18			
Llandaf	d	10 17		10 22				10 37			10 47							11 07				11 22			
Ninian Park	d		10 10									10 40									11 10				
Waun-gron Park	d		10 13									10 43									11 13				
Fairwater	d		10 15									10 45									11 15				
Danescourt	d		10 17									10 47									11 17				
Radyr 3	a	10 20	10 24	10 25				10 40			10 50	10 54			11 02			11 10			11 24	11 25			
	d	10 20		10 25				10 40			10 50				11 05			11 10				11 25			
Taffs Well 3	d	10 24		10 29				10 44			10 54				11 09			11 14				11 29			
Trefforest Estate	d							10 48										11 18							
Trefforest	d	10 31		10 36				10 52			11 01				11 16			11 22				11 36			
Pontypridd 3	a	10 34		10 39				10 55			11 04				11 19			11 32				11 39			
	d	10 36		10 41				10 56			11 06				11 22							11 41			
Abercynon	d			10 51				11 06														11 51			
Penrhiwceiber	d			10 57																		11 57			
Mountain Ash	a			11 00																		12 00			
	d			11 03																		12 03			
Fernhill	d			11 05																		12 05			
Cwmbach	d			11 09																		12 09			
Aberdare 3	a			11 16																		12 16			
Quakers Yard	d							11 10																	
Merthyr Vale	d							11 18																	
Troed Y Rhiw	d							11 21																	
Pentre-bach	d							11 24																	
Merthyr Tydfil	a							11 32																	
Trehafod	d	10 41									11 11				11 27										
Porth	d	10 45									11 15				11b45										
Dinas Rhondda	d	10 49									11 19				11 49										
Tonypandy	d	10 51									11 21				11 51										
Llwynypia	d	10 53									11 23				11 53										
Ystrad Rhondda	a	10 56									11 26				11 56										
	d	10 59									11 29				11 59										
Ton Pentre	d	11 01									11 31				12 01										
Treorchy	d	11 04									11 34				12 04										
Ynyswen	d	11 07									11 37				12 07										
Treherbert	a	11 13									11 43				12 13										

For general notes see front of timetable
For details of catering facilities see Directory of Train Operators

A From Coryton
B From Radyr
b Arr. 1130

Table 130

Mondays to Fridays

until 5 September

Bridgend, Barry Island, Barry, Penarth and Cardiff → Coryton. Rhymney, Pontypridd, Merthyr, Aberdare and Treherbert

Network Diagram - see first page of Table 130

		AW	AW	AW	AW	AW	AW	AW	AW	AW	AW	AW	AW	AW	AW	AW	AW	AW	AW	AW	AW	AW	AW	AW	AW
						A					B					A				B					A
Bridgend	d							10 42																	
Llantwit Major	d							10 56																	
Rhoose Cardiff Int Airport ✈	d							11 06																	
Barry Island	d	10 56										11 26					11 41				11 56				
Barry 3	d	11 00						11 15				11 30					11 45				12 00				
Barry Docks	d	11 04						11 19				11 34					11 49				12 04				
Cadoxton	d	11 07						11 22				11 37					11 52				12 07				
Dinas Powys	d	11 11						11 26				11 41					11 56				12 11				
Eastbrook	d	11 13						11 28				11 43					11 58				12 13				
Cogan	d	11 15						11 30				11 45					12 00				12 15				
Penarth	d		11 17						11 32				11 47					12 02				12 17			
Dingle Road	d		11 19						11 34				11 49					12 04				12 19			
Grangetown	d	11 19	11 23					11 34	11 38			11 49	11 53				12 04	12 08			12 19	12 23			
Cardiff Central 7	a	11 24	11 29					11 44	11 44			11 54	11 59				12 09	12 14			12 24	12 29			
	d	11 26	11 31		11 36	11 36	11 41		11 46		11 51	11 56	12 01		12 06	12 06	12 11	12 16		12 21	12 26	12 31		12 36	12 36
Cardiff Bay	d			11 34						11 49				12 04					12 19				12 34		
Cardiff Queen Street 3	a	11 29	11 34	11 38	11 39		11 44		11 49	11 53	11 54	11 59	12 04	12 08	12 09		12 14	12 19	12 23	12 24	12 29	12 34	12 38	12 39	
	d	11 30	11 35		11 40		11 45		11 50		11 55	12 00	12 05		12 10		12 15	12 20		12 25	12 30	12 35		12 40	
Heath Low Level	d										12 00									12 30					
Ty Glas	d										12 03									12 33					
Birchgrove	d										12 04									12 34					
Rhiwbina	d										12 06									12 36					
Whitchurch (Cardiff)	d										12 08									12 38					
Coryton	a										12 13									12 43					
Heath High Level	d		11 40						11 55				12 10					12 25				12 40			
Llanishen	d		11 43						11 58				12 13					12 28				12 43			
Lisvane & Thornhill	d		11 45						12 00				12 15					12 30				12 45			
Caerphilly 3	d		11 51						12 06				12 21					12 36				12 51			
Aber	d		11 53						12 08				12 23					12 38				12 53			
Llanbradach	d		11 57						12 12				12 27					12 42				12 57			
Ystrad Mynach 3	d		12 02						12 17				12 32					12 47				13 02			
Hengoed	d		12 05						12 20				12 35					12 50				13 05			
Pengam	d		12 08						12 23				12 38					12 53				13 08			
Gilfach Fargoed	d												12 41												
Bargoed	d		12a16						12a31				12a48					12 59				13a16			
Brithdir	d																	13 03							
Tir-phil	d																	13 06							
Pontlottyn	d																	13 10							
Rhymney 3	a																	13 16							
Cathays	d	11 33			11 43		11 48					12 03			12 13		12 18				12 33			12 43	
Llandaf	d	11 37			11 47		11 52					12 07			12 17		12 22				12 37			12 47	
Ninian Park	d					11 40										12 10									
Waun-gron Park	d					11 43										12 13									12 40
Fairwater	d					11 45										12 15									12 43
Danescourt	d					11 47										12 17									12 45
																									12 47
Radyr 3	a	11 40			11 50	11 54	11 55					12 10			12 20	12 24	12 25				12 40			12 50	12 54
	d	11 40			11 50		11 55					12 10			12 20		12 25				12 40			12 50	
Taffs Well 3	d	11 44			11 54		11 59					12 14			12 24		12 29				12 44			12 54	
Trefforest Estate	d	11 48										12 18									12 48				
Trefforest	d	11 52			12 01		12 06					12 22			12 31		12 36				12 52			13 01	
Pontypridd 3	a	11 55			12 04		12 09					12 32			12 34		12 42				12 55			13 04	
	d	11 56			12 06		12 11								12 36						12 56			13 06	
Abercynon	d	12 06					12 22														13 06				
Penrhiwceiber	d						12 28																		
Mountain Ash	a						12 31																		
	d						12 33																		
Fernhill	d						12 35																		
Cwmbach	d						12 39																		
Aberdare 3	a						12 46																		
Quakers Yard	d	12 10																			13 10				
Merthyr Vale	d	12 18																			13 18				
Troed Y Rhiw	d	12 21																			13 21				
Pentre-bach	d	12 24																			13 24				
Merthyr Tydfil	a	12 32																			13 32				
Trehafod	d				12 11										12 41									13 11	
Porth	d				12 15										12 45									13 15	
Dinas Rhondda	d				12 19										12 49									13 19	
Tonypandy	d				12 21										12 51									13 21	
Llwynypia	d				12 23										12 53									13 23	
Ystrad Rhondda	a				12 26										12 56									13 26	
	d				12 29										12 59									13 29	
Ton Pentre	d				12 31										13 01									13 31	
Treorchy	d				12 34										13 04									13 34	
Ynyswen	d				12 37										13 07									13 37	
Treherbert	a				12 43										13 13									13 43	

For general notes see front of timetable
For details of catering facilities see
Directory of Train Operators

A From Coryton
B From Radyr

Table 130

Mondays to Fridays

until 5 September

Bridgend, Barry Island, Barry, Penarth and Cardiff → Coryton. Rhymney, Pontypridd, Merthyr, Aberdare and Treherbert

Network Diagram - see first page of Table 130

Station		AW	AW	AW	AW A	AW	AW	AW	AW	AW B	AW	AW	AW	AW A	AW	AW	AW	AW	AW B	AW	AW	AW	AW A	AW	AW
Bridgend	d	11 42																		12 42					
Llantwit Major	d	11 56																		12 56					
Rhoose Cardiff Int Airport ✈	d	12 06																		13 06					
Barry Island	d					12 26					12 41				12 56									13 26	
Barry 3	d	12 15				12 30					12 45				13 00					13 15				13 30	
Barry Docks	d	12 19				12 34					12 49				13 04					13 19				13 34	
Cadoxton	d	12 22				12 37					12 52				13 07					13 22				13 37	
Dinas Powys	d	12 26				12 41					12 56				13 11					13 26				13 41	
Eastbrook	d	12 28				12 43					12 58				13 13					13 28				13 43	
Cogan	d	12 30				12 45					13 00				13 15					13 30				13 45	
Penarth	d		12 32				12 47					13 02				13 17					13 32				13 47
Dingle Road	d		12 34				12 49					13 04				13 19					13 34				13 49
Grangetown	d	12 34	12 38			12 49	12 53				13 04	13 08			13 19	13 23				13 34	13 38			13 49	13 53
Cardiff Central 7	a	12 39	12 44			12 54	12 59				13 09	13 14			13 24	13 29				13 39	13 44			13 54	13 59
	d	12 41	12 46		12 51	12 56	13 01		13 06	13 06	13 11	13 16		13 21	13 26	13 31		13 36	13 36	13 41	13 46		13 51	13 56	14 01
Cardiff Bay	d			12 49				13 04					13 19				13 34					13 49			
Cardiff Queen Street 3	a	12 44	12 49	12 53	12 54	12 59	13 04	13 08	13 09		13 14	13 19	13 23	13 24	13 29	13 34	13 38	13 39		13 44	13 49	13 53	13 54	13 59	14 04
	d	12 45	12 50		12 55	13 00	13 05		13 10		13 15	13 20		13 25	13 30	13 35		13 40		13 45	13 50		13 55	14 00	14 05
Heath Low Level	d				13 00									13 30									14 00		
Ty Glas	d				13 03									13 33									14 03		
Birchgrove	d				13 04									13 34									14 04		
Rhiwbina	d				13 06									13 36									14 06		
Whitchurch (Cardiff)	d				13 08									13 38									14 08		
Coryton	a				13 13									13 43									14 13		
Heath High Level	d		12 55				13 10					13 25				13 40					13 55				14 10
Llanishen	d		12 58				13 13					13 28				13 43					13 58				14 13
Lisvane & Thornhill	d		13 00				13 15					13 30				13 45					14 00				14 15
Caerphilly 3	d		13 06				13 21					13 36				13 51					14 06				14 21
Aber	d		13 08				13 23					13 38				13 53					14 08				14 23
Llanbradach	d		13 12				13 27					13 42				13 57					14 12				14 27
Ystrad Mynach 3	d		13 17				13 32					13 47				14 02					14 17				14 32
Hengoed	d		13 20				13 35					13 50				14 05					14 20				14 35
Pengam	d		13 23				13 38					13 53				14 08					14 23				14 38
Gilfach Fargoed	d						13 41																		14 41
Bargoed	d		13a31				13a48					13 59				14a16					14a31				14a48
Brithdir	d											14 03													
Tir-phil	d											14 06													
Pontlottyn	d											14 10													
Rhymney 3	a											14 16													
Cathays	d	12 48				13 03			13 13		13 18				13 33			13 43		13 48				14 03	
Llandaf	d	12 52				13 07			13 17		13 22				13 37			13 47		13 52				14 07	
Ninian Park	d									13 10									13 40						
Waun-gron Park	d									13 13									13 43						
Fairwater	d									13 15									13 45						
Danescourt	d									13 17									13 47						
Radyr 3	a	12 55				13 10			13 20	13 24	13 25				13 40			13 50	13 54	13 55				14 10	
	d	12 55				13 10			13 20		13 25				13 40			13 50		13 55				14 10	
Taffs Well 3	d	12 59				13 14			13 24		13 29				13 44			13 54		13 59				14 14	
Trefforest Estate	d					13 18									13 48									14 18	
Trefforest	d	13 06				13 22			13 31		13 36				13 52			14 01		14 06				14 22	
Pontypridd 3	a	13 09				13 32			13 34		13 39				13 55			14 04		14 09				14 32	
	d	13 11							13 36		13 41				13 56			14 06		14 11					
Abercynon	d	13 21									13 51				14 06					14 21					
Penrhiwceiber	d	13 27									13 57									14 27					
Mountain Ash	a	13 30									14 00									14 30					
	d	13 33									14 03									14 33					
Fernhill	d	13 35									14 05									14 35					
Cwmbach	d	13 39									14 09									14 39					
Aberdare 3	a	13 46									14 16									14 46					
Quakers Yard	d														14 10										
Merthyr Vale	d														14 18										
Troed Y Rhiw	d														14 21										
Pentre-bach	d														14 24										
Merthyr Tydfil	a														14 32										
Trehafod	d								13 41									14 11							
Porth	d								13 45									14 15							
Dinas Rhondda	d								13 49									14 19							
Tonypandy	d								13 51									14 21							
Llwynypia	d								13 53									14 23							
Ystrad Rhondda	a								13 56									14 26							
	d								13 59									14 29							
Ton Pentre	d								14 01									14 31							
Treorchy	d								14 04									14 34							
Ynyswen	d								14 07									14 37							
Treherbert	a								14 13									14 43							

For general notes see front of timetable
For details of catering facilities see Directory of Train Operators

A From Radyr
B From Coryton

Table 130

Mondays to Fridays

until 5 September

Bridgend, Barry Island, Barry, Penarth and Cardiff → Coryton. Rhymney, Pontypridd, Merthyr, Aberdare and Treherbert

Network Diagram - see first page of Table 130

		AW	AW	AW	AW	AW	AW	AW	AW	AW	AW	AW	AW	AW	AW	AW	AW		AW	AW	AW	AW	AW	AW	AW	AW
				A				B					A				B						A			
Bridgend	d													13 42												
Llantwit Major	d													13 56												
Rhoose Cardiff Int Airport ✈	d													14 06												
Barry Island	d				13 41				13 56											14 26				14 41		
Barry 3	d				13 45				14 00					14 15						14 30				14 45		
Barry Docks	d				13 49				14 04					14 19						14 34				14 49		
Cadoxton	d				13 52				14 07					14 22						14 37				14 52		
Dinas Powys	d				13 56				14 11					14 26						14 41				14 56		
Eastbrook	d				13 58				14 13					14 28						14 43				14 58		
Cogan	d				14 00				14 15					14 30						14 45				15 00		
Penarth	d					14 02				14 17					14 32						14 47				15 02	
Dingle Road	d					14 04				14 19					14 34						14 49				15 04	
Grangetown	d				14 04	14 08			14 19	14 23				14 34	14 38					14 49	14 53			15 04	15 08	
Cardiff Central 7	a				14 09	14 14			14 24	14 29				14 39	14 44					14 54	14 59			15 09	15 14	
	d		14 06	14 06	14 11	14 16		14 21	14 26	14 31		14 36	14 36	14 41	14 46		14 51		14 51	14 56	15 01		15 06	15 11	15 16	
Cardiff Bay	d	14 04					14 19				14 34					14 49						15 04				15 19
Cardiff Queen Street 3	a	14 08	14 09		14 14	14 19	14 23	14 24	14 29	14 34	14 38	14 39		14 44	14 49	14 53	14 54			14 59	15 04	15 08		15 14	15 19	15 23
	d		14 10		14 15	14 20		14 25	14 30	14 35		14 40		14 45	14 50		14 55			15 00	15 05			15 15	15 20	
Heath Low Level	d							14 30									15 00									
Ty Glas	d							14 33									15 03									
Birchgrove	d							14 34									15 04									
Rhiwbina	d							14 36									15 06									
Whitchurch (Cardiff)	d							14 38									15 08									
Coryton	a							14 43									15 13									
Heath High Level	d					14 25				14 40					14 55						15 10				15 25	
Llanishen	d					14 28				14 43					14 58						15 13				15 28	
Lisvane & Thornhill	d					14 30				14 45					15 00						15 15				15 30	
Caerphilly 3	d					14 36				14 51					15 06						15 21				15 36	
Aber	d					14 38				14 53					15 08						15 23				15 38	
Llanbradach	d					14 42				14 57					15 12						15 27				15 42	
Ystrad Mynach 3	d					14 47				15 02					15 17						15 32				15 47	
Hengoed	d					14 50				15 05					15 20						15 35				15 50	
Pengam	d					14 53				15 08					15 23						15 38				15 53	
Gilfach Fargoed	d																				15 41					
Bargoed	d					14 59				15a16					15a31						15a48				15 59	
Brithdir	d					15 03																			16 03	
Tir-phil	d					15 06																			16 06	
Pontlottyn	d					15 10																			16 10	
Rhymney 3	a					15 16																			16 16	
Cathays	d		14 13		14 18				14 33			14 43		14 48						15 03				15 18		
Llandaf	d		14 17		14 22				14 37			14 47		14 52						15 07				15 22		
Ninian Park	d			14 10									14 40										15 10			
Waun-gron Park	d			14 13									14 43										15 13			
Fairwater	d			14 15									14 45										15 15			
Danescourt	d			14 17									14 47										15 17			
Radyr 3	a		14 20	14 24	14 25				14 40			14 50	14 54	14 55					15 02	15 10			15 24	15 25		
	d		14 20		14 25				14 40			14 50		14 55					15 02	15 10				15 25		
Taffs Well 3	d		14 24		14 29				14 44			14 54		14 59					15 06	15 14				15 29		
Trefforest Estate	d								14 48											15 18						
Trefforest	d		14 31		14 36				14 52			15 01		15 06					15 13	15 22				15 36		
Pontypridd 3	a		14 34		14 39				14 55			15 04		15 09					15 16	15 32				15 39		
	d		14 36		14 41				14 56			15 06		15 11					15 22					15 41		
Abercynon	d				14 51				15 06					15 21										15 51		
Penrhiwceiber	d				14 57									15 27										15 57		
Mountain Ash	a				15 00									15 30										16 00		
	d				15 03									15 33										16 03		
Fernhill	d				15 05									15 35										16 05		
Cwmbach	d				15 09									15 39										16 09		
Aberdare 3	a				15 16									15 46										16 16		
Quakers Yard	d								15 10																	
Merthyr Vale	d								15 18																	
Troed Y Rhiw	d								15 21																	
Pentre-bach	d								15 24																	
Merthyr Tydfil	a								15 32																	
Trehafod	d		14 41									15 11							15 27							
Porth	d		14 45									15 15							15b45							
Dinas Rhondda	d		14 49									15 19							15 49							
Tonypandy	d		14 51									15 21							15 51							
Llwynypia	d		14 53									15 23							15 53							
Ystrad Rhondda	a		14 56									15 26							15 56							
	d		14 59									15 29							15 59							
Ton Pentre	d		15 01									15 31							16 01							
Treorchy	d		15 04									15 34							16 04							
Ynyswen	d		15 07									15 37							16 07							
Treherbert	a		15 13									15 43							16 13							

For general notes see front of timetable
For details of catering facilities see Directory of Train Operators

A From Coryton
B From Radyr
b Arr. 1530

Table 130

Mondays to Fridays
until 5 September

Bridgend, Barry Island, Barry, Penarth and Cardiff → Coryton. Rhymney, Pontypridd, Merthyr, Aberdare and Treherbert

Network Diagram - see first page of Table 130

Station		AW A	AW	AW	AW	AW	AW B	AW	AW	AW	AW A	AW	AW	AW	AW	AW B	AW	AW	AW		AW A	AW	AW	AW	AW	AW B
Bridgend	d							14 42																		
Llantwit Major	d							14 56																		
Rhoose Cardiff Int Airport ✈	d							15 06																		
Barry Island	d		14 56									15 26					15 41					15 56				
Barry 3	d		15 00					15 15				15 30					15 45					16 00				
Barry Docks	d		15 04					15 19				15 34					15 49					16 04				
Cadoxton	d		15 07					15 22				15 37					15 52					16 07				
Dinas Powys	d		15 11					15 26				15 41					15 56					16 11				
Eastbrook	d		15 13					15 28				15 43					15 58					16 13				
Cogan	d		15 15					15 30				15 45					16 00					16 15				
Penarth	d			15 17					15 32				15 47					16 02					16 17			
Dingle Road	d			15 19					15 34				15 49					16 04					16 19			
Grangetown	d		15 19	15 23				15 34	15 38			15 49	15 53				16 04	16 08				16 19	16 23			
Cardiff Central 7	a		15 24	15 29				15 39	15 44			15 54	15 59				16 09	16 14				16 24	16 29			
	d	15 21	15 26	15 31		15 36	15 36	15 41	15 46		15 51	15 56	16 01		16 06	16 06	16 11	16 16			16 21	16 26	16 31		16 36	16 36
Cardiff Bay	d				15 34					15 49				16 04					16 19					16 34		
Cardiff Queen Street 3	a	15 24	15 29	15 34	15 38	15 39		15 44	15 49	15 53	15 54	15 59	16 04	16 08	16 09		16 14	16 19	16 23		16 24	16 29	16 34	16 38	16 39	
	d	15 25	15 30	15 35		15 40		15 45	15 50		15 55	16 00	16 05		16 10		16 15	16 20			16 25	16 30	16 35		16 40	
Heath Low Level	d	15 30									16 00										16 30					
Ty Glas	d	15 33									16 03										16 33					
Birchgrove	d	15 34									16 04										16 34					
Rhiwbina	d	15 36									16 06										16 36					
Whitchurch (Cardiff)	d	15 38									16 08										16 38					
Coryton	a	15 43									16 13										16 43					
Heath High Level	d			15 40					15 55				16 10					16 25					16 40			
Llanishen	d			15 43					15 58				16 13					16 28					16 43			
Lisvane & Thornhill	d			15 45					16 00				16 15					16 30					16 45			
Caerphilly 3	d			15 51					16 06				16 21					16 36					16 51			
Aber	d			15 53					16 08				16 23					16 38					16 53			
Llanbradach	d			15 57					16 12				16 27					16 42					16 57			
Ystrad Mynach 3	d			16 02					16 17				16 32					16 47					17 02			
Hengoed	d			16 05					16 20				16 35					16 50					17 05			
Pengam	d			16 08					16 23				16 38					16 53					17 08			
Gilfach Fargoed	d												16 41													
Bargoed	d			16a16					16a31				16a48					16 59					17a16			
Brithdir	d																	17 03								
Tir-phil	d																	17 06								
Pontlottyn	d																	17 10								
Rhymney 3	a																	17 16								
Cathays	d		15 33			15 43		15 48				16 03			16 13		16 18					16 33			16 43	
Llandaf	d		15 37			15 47		15 52				16 07			16 17		16 22					16 37			16 47	
Ninian Park	d						15 40									16 10										16 40
Waun-gron Park	d						15 43									16 13										16 43
Fairwater	d						15 45									16 15										16 45
Danescourt	d						15 47									16 17										16 47
Radyr 3	a		15 40			15 50	15 54	15 55				16 10			16 20	16 24	16 25					16 40			16 50	16 54
	d		15 40			15 50		15 55				16 10			16 20		16 25					16 40			16 50	
Taffs Well 3	d		15 44			15 54		15 59				16 14			16 24		16 29					16 44			16 54	
Trefforest Estate	d		15 48									16 18										16 48				
Trefforest	d		15 52			16 01		16 06				16 22			16 31		16 36					16 52			17 01	
Pontypridd 3	a		15 55			16 04		16 09				16 32			16 34		16 39					16 55			17 04	
	d		15 56			16 06		16 11							16 36		16 41					16 56			17 06	
Abercynon	d		16 06					16 21									16 51					17 06				
Penrhiwceiber	d							16 27									16 57									
Mountain Ash	a							16 30									17 00									
	d							16 33									17 03									
Fernhill	d							16 35									17 05									
Cwmbach	d							16 39									17 09									
Aberdare 3	a							16 46									17 16									
Quakers Yard	d		16 10																			17 10				
Merthyr Vale	d		16 18																			17 18				
Troed Y Rhiw	d		16 21																			17 21				
Pentre-bach	d		16 24																			17 24				
Merthyr Tydfil	a		16 32																			17 32				
Trehafod	d					16 11									16 41										17 11	
Porth	d					16 15									16 45										17 15	
Dinas Rhondda	d					16 19									16 49										17 19	
Tonypandy	d					16 21									16 51										17 21	
Llwynypia	d					16 23									16 53										17 23	
Ystrad Rhondda	a					16 26									16 56										17 26	
	d					16 29									16 59										17 29	
Ton Pentre	d					16 31									17 01										17 31	
Treorchy	d					16 34									17 04										17 34	
Ynyswen	d					16 37									17 07										17 37	
Treherbert	a					16 43									17 13										17 43	

For general notes see front of timetable
For details of catering facilities see Directory of Train Operators

A From Radyr
B From Coryton

Mondays to Fridays

until 5 September

Bridgend, Barry Island, Barry, Penarth and Cardiff → Coryton. Rhymney, Pontypridd, Merthyr, Aberdare and Treherbert

Network Diagram - see first page of Table 130

		AW	AW	AW	AW	AW	AW	AW	AW	AW	AW	AW	AW	AW	AW	AW	AW	AW	AW	AW	AW	AW	AW	AW	AW
					A					B				A					B				A		
Bridgend	d	15 42																		16 42					
Llantwit Major	d	15 56																		16 56					
Rhoose Cardiff Int Airport ✈	d	16 06																		17 06					
Barry Island	d					16 26					16 41				16 56									17 26	
Barry 3	d	16 15				16 30					16 45				17 00					17 15				17 30	
Barry Docks	d	16 19				16 34					16 49				17 04					17 19				17 34	
Cadoxton	d	16 22				16 37					16 52				17 07					17 22				17 37	
Dinas Powys	d	16 26				16 41					16 56				17 11					17 26				17 41	
Eastbrook	d	16 28				16 43					16 58				17 13					17 28				17 43	
Cogan	d	16 30				16 45					17 00				17 15					17 30				17 45	
Penarth	d		16 32									17 02				17 17					17 32				17 47
Dingle Road	d		16 34									17 04				17 19					17 34				17 49
Grangetown	d	16 34	16 38			16 49					17 04	17 08			17 19	17 23				17 34	17 38			17 49	17 53
Cardiff Central 7	a	16 39	16 44			16 54					17 09	17 14			17 24	17 29				17 39	17 44			17 54	17 59
	d	16 41	16 46		16 51	16 56	17 01		17 06	17 06	17 11	17 16		17 21	17 26	17 31		17 36	17 36	17 41	17 46		17 51	17 56	18 01
Cardiff Bay	d			16 49				17 04					17 19				17 34					17 49			
Cardiff Queen Street 3	a	16 44	16 49	16 53	16 54	16 59	17 04	17 08	17 09		17 14	17 19	17 23	17 24	17 29	17 34	17 38	17 39		17 44	17 49	17 53	17 54	17 59	18 04
	d	16 45	16 50		16 55	17 00	17 05		17 10		17 15	17 20		17 25	17 30	17 35		17 40		17 45	17 50		17 55	18 00	18 05
Heath Low Level	d				17 00									17 30									18 00		
Ty Glas	d				17 03									17 33									18 03		
Birchgrove	d				17 04									17 34									18 04		
Rhiwbina	d				17 06									17 36									18 06		
Whitchurch (Cardiff)	d				17 08									17 38									18 08		
Coryton	a				17 13									17 43									18 13		
Heath High Level	d		16 55				17 10					17 25				17 40					17 55				18 10
Llanishen	d		16 58				17 13					17 28				17 43					17 59				18 13
Lisvane & Thornhill	d		17 00				17 15					17 30				17 45					18 02				18 15
Caerphilly 3	d		17 06				17 21					17 36				17 51					18 07				18 21
Aber	d		17 08				17 23					17 38				17 53					18 10				18 23
Llanbradach	d		17 12				17 27					17 42				17 57					18 14				18 27
Ystrad Mynach 3	d		17 17				17 33					17 47				18 02					18 20				18 32
Hengoed	d		17 20				17 35					17 50				18 05					18 23				18 35
Pengam	d		17 23				17 39					17 53				18 08					18 27				18 38
Gilfach Fargoed	d						17 42									18 11					18 30				18 41
Bargoed	d		17a31				17 47					18a01				18 16					18b44				18a48
Brithdir	d						17 50									18 20					18 48				
Tir-phil	d						17 53									18 23					18 51				
Pontlottyn	d						17 58									18 27					18 55				
Rhymney 3	a						18 04									18 33					19 01				
Cathays	d	16 48				17 03			17 13		17 18				17 33			17 43		17 48				18 03	
Llandaf	d	16 52				17 07			17 17		17 22				17 37			17 47		17 52				18 07	
Ninian Park	d									17 10									17 40						
Waun-gron Park	d									17 13									17 43						
Fairwater	d									17 15									17 45						
Danescourt	d									17 17									17 47						
Radyr 3	a	16 55				17 10			17 20	17 24	17 25				17 40			17 50	17 54	17 55				18 10	
	d	16 55				17 10			17 20		17 25				17 40			17 50		17 55				18 10	
Taffs Well 3	d	16 59				17 14			17 24		17 29				17 44			17 54		17 59				18 14	
Trefforest Estate	d					17 18									17 48									18 18	
Trefforest	d	17 06				17 22			17 31		17 36				17 52			18 01		18 06				18 22	
Pontypridd 3	a	17 09				17 32			17 34		17 39				17 55			18 04		18 09				18 32	
	d	17 11							17 36		17 41				17 56			18 06		18 11					
Abercynon	d	17 21									17 51				18 06					18 21					
Penrhiwceiber	d	17 27									17 57									18 27					
Mountain Ash	a	17 30									18 00									18 30					
	d	17 33									18 03									18 33					
Fernhill	d	17 35									18 05									18 35					
Cwmbach	d	17 39									18 09									18 39					
Aberdare 3	a	17 46									18 16									18 46					
Quakers Yard	d														18 10										
Merthyr Vale	d														18 18										
Troed Y Rhiw	d														18 21										
Pentre-bach	d														18 24										
Merthyr Tydfil	a														18 32										
Trehafod	d								17 41									18 11							
Porth	d								17 45									18 15							
Dinas Rhondda	d								17 49									18 19							
Tonypandy	d								17 51									18 21							
Llwynypia	d								17 53									18 23							
Ystrad Rhondda	a								17 56									18 26							
	d								17 59									18 29							
Ton Pentre	d								18 01									18 31							
Treorchy	d								18 04									18 34							
Ynyswen	d								18 07									18 37							
Treherbert	a								18 13									18 43							

For general notes see front of timetable
For details of catering facilities see Directory of Train Operators

A From Radyr
B From Coryton
b Arr. 1834

Table 130

Mondays to Fridays

until 5 September

Bridgend, Barry Island, Barry, Penarth and Cardiff → Coryton. Rhymney, Pontypridd, Merthyr, Aberdare and Treherbert

Network Diagram - see first page of Table 130

		AW	AW	AW	AW	AW	AW	AW	AW	AW		AW	AW	AW	AW	AW	AW	AW	AW	AW	AW	AW	AW		AW	AW
				A				B					A				B									
Bridgend	d													17 42												
Llantwit Major	d													17 56												
Rhoose Cardiff Int Airport ✈	d													18 06												
Barry Island	d				17 41				17 56									18 26				18 41			18 56	
Barry [3]	d				17 45				18 00					18 15				18 30				18 45			19 00	
Barry Docks	d				17 49				18 04					18 19				18 34				18 49			19 04	
Cadoxton	d				17 52				18 07					18 22				18 37				18 52			19 07	
Dinas Powys	d				17 56				18 11					18 26				18 41				18 56			19 11	
Eastbrook	d				17 58				18 13					18 28				18 43				18 58			19 13	
Cogan	d				18 00				18 15					18 30				18 45				19 00			19 15	
Penarth	d					18 02				18 17					18 32				18 47							19 17
Dingle Road	d					18 04				18 19					18 34				18 49							19 19
Grangetown	d				18 04	18 08			18 19	18 23				18 34	18 38			18 49	18 53			19 04			19 19	19 23
Cardiff Central [7]	a				18 09	18 14			18 24	18 29				18 39	18 44			18 54	18 59			19 09			19 24	19 29
	d		18 06	18 06	18 11	18 16		18 21	18 26	18 31	18 36		18 36	18 41			18 51		19 01		19 06	19 11			19 26	19 31
Cardiff Bay	d	18 04					18 19					18 34				18 49				19 04			19 19			
Cardiff Queen Street [3]	a	18 08	18 09		18 14	18 19	18 23	18 24	18 29	18 34	18 38	18 38		18 44		18 53	18 54		19 04	19 08	19 09	19 14	19 23		19 29	19 34
	d		18 10		18 15	18 20		18 25	18 30	18 35	18 40			18 50			18 55		19 05		19 10	19 15			19 30	19 35
Heath Low Level	d							18 30									19 00									
Ty Glas	d							18 33									19 03									
Birchgrove	d							18 34									19 04									
Rhiwbina	d							18 36									19 06									
Whitchurch (Cardiff)	d							18 38									19 08									
Coryton	a							18 43									19 13									
Heath High Level	d					18 25				18 40									19 10							19 40
Llanishen	d					18 28				18 43									19 13							19 43
Lisvane & Thornhill	d					18 30				18 45									19 15							19 45
Caerphilly [3]	d					18 36				18 51									19a24							19 51
Aber	d					18 38				18 53																19 53
Llanbradach	d					18 42				18 57																19 57
Ystrad Mynach [3]	d					18a51				19 02																20 02
Hengoed	d									19 05																20 05
Pengam	d									19 08																20 08
Gilfach Fargoed	d									19 11																20 11
Bargoed	d									19 16																20 16
Brithdir	d									19 20																20 20
Tir-phil	d									19 23																20 23
Pontlottyn	d									19 27																20 27
Rhymney [3]	a									19 33																20 33
Cathays	d		18 13		18 18				18 33		18 43			18 52							19 13	19 18			19 33	
Llandaf	d		18 17		18 22				18 37		18 47			18 56							19 17	19 22			19 37	
Ninian Park	d			18 10									18 40													
Waun-gron Park	d			18 13									18 43													
Fairwater	d			18 15									18 45													
Danescourt	d			18 17									18 47													
Radyr [3]	a		18 20	18 24	18 25				18 40		18 50		18 54	18 58							19 20	19 25			19 40	
	d		18 20		18 25				18 40		18 50			18 58							19 20	19 25			19 40	
Taffs Well [3]	d		18 24		18 29				18 44		18 54			19 03							19 24	19 29			19 44	
Trefforest Estate	d								18 48																19 48	
Trefforest	d		18 31		18 36				18 52		19 01			19 10							19 31	19 36			19 52	
Pontypridd [3]	a		18 34		18 42				18 55		19 04			19 13							19 34	19 39			19 55	
	d		18 36						18 56		19 06			19 14							19 36	19 41			19 56	
Abercynon	d								19 06					19 21								19 53			20 06	
Penrhiwceiber	d													19 26								19 57				
Mountain Ash	a													19 30								20 00				
	d													19 33								20 03				
Fernhill	d													19 35								20 05				
Cwmbach	d													19 39								20 09				
Aberdare [3]	a													19 46								20 16				
Quakers Yard	d								19 10																20 10	
Merthyr Vale	d								19 18																20 18	
Troed Y Rhiw	d								19 21																20 21	
Pentre-bach	d								19 24																20 24	
Merthyr Tydfil	a								19 32																20 32	
Trehafod	d		18 41								19 11										19 41					
Porth	d		18 45								19 15										19 45					
Dinas Rhondda	d		18 49								19 19										19 49					
Tonypandy	d		18 51								19 21										19 51					
Llwynypia	d		18 53								19 23										19 53					
Ystrad Rhondda	a		18 56								19 26										19 56					
	d		18 59								19 29										19 59					
Ton Pentre	d		19 01								19 31										20 01					
Treorchy	d		19 04								19 34										20 04					
Ynyswen	d		19 07								19 37										20 07					
Treherbert	a		19 13								19 43										20 13					

For general notes see front of timetable
For details of catering facilities see
Directory of Train Operators

A From Coryton
B From Radyr

Table 130

Mondays to Fridays

until 5 September

Bridgend, Barry Island, Barry, Penarth and Cardiff → Coryton. Rhymney, Pontypridd, Merthyr, Aberdare and Treherbert

Network Diagram - see first page of Table 130

Station		AW	AW	AW	AW	AW	AW	AW	AW	AW	AW	AW	AW	AW	AW	AW	AW	AW	AW	AW	AW	AW	AW	AW	AW	AW
			A												A											
Bridgend	d			18 42												19 42										
Llantwit Major	d			18 56												19 56										
Rhoose Cardiff Int Airport ✈	d			19 06												20 06										
Barry Island	d						19 26					19 56											20 56			
Barry 3	d			19 15			19 30					20 00				20 15							21 00			
Barry Docks	d			19 19			19 34					20 04				20 19							21 04			
Cadoxton	d			19 22			19 37					20 07				20 22							21 07			
Dinas Powys	d			19 26			19 41					20 11				20 26							21 11			
Eastbrook	d			19 28			19 43					20 13				20 28							21 13			
Cogan	d			19 30			19 45					20 15				20 30							21 15			
Penarth	d							19 47					20 17						20 47						21 17	
Dingle Road	d							19 49					20 19						20 49						21 19	
Grangetown	d			19 34			19 49	19 53				20 19	20 24			20 34			20 53				21 19		21 23	
Cardiff Central 7	a			19 39			19 56	19 59				20 24	20 30			20 39			20 59				21 25		21 33	
	d		19 36	19 41		19 51		20 01		20 06		20 26	20 31		20 36	20 41		20 51	21 01		21 06		21 26	21 31		
Cardiff Bay	d	19 34			19 49				20 04		20 19			20 34			20 49			21 04		21 19				21 34
Cardiff Queen Street 3	a	19 38		19 44	19 53	19 54		20 04	20 08	20 09	20 23	20 29	20 34	20 38		20 44	20 53	20 54	21 04	21 08	21 09	21 23	21 29	21 34		21 38
	d			19 45		19 55		20 05		20 10		20 30	20 35			20 45		20 55	21 05		21 10		21 30	21 35		
Heath Low Level	d					20 00												21 00								
Ty Glas	d					20 03												21 03								
Birchgrove	d					20 04												21 04								
Rhiwbina	d					20 06												21 06								
Whitchurch (Cardiff)	d					20 08												21 08								
Coryton	a					20 13												21 13								
Heath High Level	d							20 10					20 40						21 10					21 40		
Llanishen	d							20 13					20 43						21 13					21 43		
Lisvane & Thornhill	d							20 15					20 45						21 15					21 45		
Caerphilly 3	d							20a28					20 51						21a28					21 51		
Aber	d												20 53											21 53		
Llanbradach	d												20 57											21 57		
Ystrad Mynach 3	d												21 02											22 02		
Hengoed	d												21 05											22 05		
Pengam	d												21 08											22 08		
Gilfach Fargoed	d												21 11											22 11		
Bargoed	d												21 16											22 16		
Brithdir	d												21 20											22 20		
Tir-phil	d												21 23											22 23		
Pontlottyn	d												21 27											22 27		
Rhymney 3	a												21 33											22 33		
Cathays	d			19 48						20 13		20 33				20 48					21 13		21 33			
Llandaf	d			19 52						20 17		20 37				20 52					21 17		21 37			
Ninian Park	d		19 40												20 40											
Waun-gron Park	d		19 43												20 43											
Fairwater	d		19 45												20 45											
Danescourt	d		19 47												20 47											
Radyr 3	a		19 54	19 55						20 20		20 40			20 54	20 55					21 20		21 40			
	d			19 55						20 20		20 40				20 55					21 20		21 40			
Taffs Well 3	d			19 59						20 24		20 44				20 59					21 24		21 44			
Trefforest Estate	d											20 48											21 48			
Trefforest	d			20 06						20 31		20 52				21 06					21 31		21 52			
Pontypridd 3	a			20 09						20 34		20 55				21 09					21 34		21 55			
	d			20 11						20 36		20 56				21 11					21 36		21 56			
Abercynon	d			20 21								21 06				21 21							22 06			
Penrhiwceiber	d			20 27												21 27										
Mountain Ash	a			20 30												21 30										
	d			20 33												21 33										
Fernhill	d			20 35												21 35										
Cwmbach	d			20 39												21 39										
Aberdare 3	a			20 46												21 46										
Quakers Yard	d											21 10											22 10			
Merthyr Vale	d											21 18											22 18			
Troed Y Rhiw	d											21 21											22 21			
Pentre-bach	d											21 24											22 24			
Merthyr Tydfil	a											21 32											22 32			
Trehafod	d									20 41											21 41					
Porth	d									20 45											21 45					
Dinas Rhondda	d									20 49											21 49					
Tonypandy	d									20 51											21 51					
Llwynypia	d									20 53											21 53					
Ystrad Rhondda	a									20 56											21 56					
	d									20 59											21 59					
Ton Pentre	d									21 01											22 01					
Treorchy	d									21 04											22 04					
Ynyswen	d									21 07											22 07					
Treherbert	a									21 13											22 13					

For general notes see front of timetable
For details of catering facilities see Directory of Train Operators

A From Coryton

Table 130

Mondays to Fridays
until 5 September

Bridgend, Barry Island, Barry, Penarth and Cardiff → Coryton. Rhymney, Pontypridd, Merthyr, Aberdare and Treherbert

Network Diagram - see first page of Table 130

		AW A		AW	AW	AW	AW	AW	AW	AW	AW	AW	AW	AW	AW	AW	AW	AW	AW	AW	AW	AW	AW	AW		
Bridgend	d			20 42										21 42									22 42			
Llantwit Major	d			20 56										21 56									22 56			
Rhoose Cardiff Int Airport ✈	d			21 06										22 06									23 06			
Barry Island	d										21 56									22 56						
Barry 3	d			21 15							22 00			22 15						23 00			23 15			
Barry Docks	d			21 19							22 04			22 19						23 04			23 19			
Cadoxton	d			21 22							22 07			22 22						23 07			23 22			
Dinas Powys	d			21 26							22 11			22 26						23 11			23 26			
Eastbrook	d			21 28							22 13			22 28						23 13			23 28			
Cogan	d			21 30							22 15			22 30						23 15			23 30			
Penarth	d					21 47						22 17						22 47				23 26				
Dingle Road	d					21 49						22 19						22 49				23 28				
Grangetown	d			21 34		21 53					22 19	22 23		22 34				22 53		23 19		23 32	23 34			
Cardiff Central 7	a			21 39		21 59					22 25	22 31		22 39				23 00		23 24		23 38	23 41			
	d	21 36		21 41		22 00		22 06	22 11		22 26	22 35		22 41	22 46			23 15		23 26						
Cardiff Bay	d				21 49		22 04			22 19			22 34			22 49	23 04		23 19		23 34			23 49		
Cardiff Queen Street 3	a			21 44	21 53	22 04	22 08	22 09	22 14	22 23	22 29	22 38	22 38	22 44	22 49	22 53	23 08	23 18	23 23	23 29	23 38			23 53		
	d			21 45		22 05		22 10	22 15		22 30	22 39		22 45	22 50			23 19		23 30						
Heath Low Level	d																									
Ty Glas	d																									
Birchgrove	d																									
Rhiwbina	d																									
Whitchurch (Cardiff)	d																									
Coryton	a																									
Heath High Level	d					22 10						22 44						23 24								
Llanishen	d					22 13						22 47						23 27								
Lisvane & Thornhill	d					22 15						22 49						23 29								
Caerphilly 3	d					22a24						22 55						23 35								
Aber	d											22 57						23 37								
Llanbradach	d											23 01						23 41								
Ystrad Mynach 3	d											23 06						23a50								
Hengoed	d											23 09														
Pengam	d											23 12														
Gilfach Fargoed	d											23 15														
Bargoed	d											23 20														
Brithdir	d											23 24														
Tir-phil	d											23 27														
Pontlottyn	d											23 31														
Rhymney 3	a											23 37														
Cathays	d			21 48				22 13	22 18		22 33			22 48	22 53					23 33						
Llandaf	d			21 52				22 17	22 22		22 37			22 52	22 57					23 37						
Ninian Park	d	21 40																								
Waun-gron Park	d	21 43																								
Fairwater	d	21 45																								
Danescourt	d	21 47																								
Radyr 3	a	21 54		21 55				22 20	22 25		22 40			22 55	22 59					23 40						
	d			21 55				22 20	22 25		22 40			22 55	22 59					23 40						
Taffs Well 3	d			21 59				22 24	22 29		22 44			22 59	23 03					23 44						
Trefforest Estate	d										22 48									23 48						
Trefforest	d			22 06				22 31	22 36		22 52			23 06	23 10					23 52						
Pontypridd 3	a			22 09				22 34	22 43		22 55			23 09	23 14					23 58						
	d			22 11				22 36			22 56			23 11	23 15											
Abercynon	d			22 21							23 06			23 21												
Penrhiwceiber	d			22 27										23 27												
Mountain Ash	a			22 30										23 30												
	d			22 33										23 33												
Fernhill	d			22 35										23 35												
Cwmbach	d			22 39										23 39												
Aberdare 3	a			22 46										23 46												
Quakers Yard	d										23 10															
Merthyr Vale	d										23 18															
Troed Y Rhiw	d										23 21															
Pentre-bach	d										23 24															
Merthyr Tydfil	a										23 32															
Trehafod	d							22 41							23 20											
Porth	d							22 45							23 24											
Dinas Rhondda	d							22 49							23 28											
Tonypandy	d							22 51							23 30											
Llwynypia	d							22 53							23 32											
Ystrad Rhondda	a							22 56							23 35											
	d							22 59							23 38											
Ton Pentre	d							23 01							23 40											
Treorchy	d							23 04							23 43											
Ynyswen	d							23 07							23 46											
Treherbert	a							23 13							23 52											

For general notes see front of timetable
For details of catering facilities see Directory of Train Operators

A From Coryton

Table 130

Mondays to Fridays
from 8 September

Bridgend, Barry Island, Barry, Penarth and Cardiff → Coryton, Rhymney, Pontypridd, Merthyr, Aberdare and Treherbert

Network Diagram - see first page of Table 130

		AW		AW	AW	AW	AW	AW	AW	AW	AW	AW	AW	AW	AW	AW A	AW	AW	AW A		AW	AW	AW B	AW	AW	AW
Bridgend	d									05 42																
Llantwit Major	d									05 56																
Rhoose Cardiff Int Airport ✈	d									06 06																
Barry Island	d							05 56						06 26											06 56		
Barry 3	d							06 00		06 15				06 30											07 00		
Barry Docks	d							06 04		06 19				06 34											07 04		
Cadoxton	d							06 07		06 22				06 37											07 07		
Dinas Powys	d							06 11		06 26				06 41											07 11		
Eastbrook	d							06 13		06 28				06 43											07 13		
Cogan	d							06 15		06 30				06 45											07 15		
Penarth	d										06 32										07 02				07 17	
Dingle Road	d										06 34										07 04				07 19	
Grangetown	d							06 19		06 34	06 38			06 49							07 08			07 19	07 23	
Cardiff Central 7	a							06 24		06 39	06 44			06 54							07 14			07 24	07 29	
	d	05 26		05 46	06 11	06 16	06 21	06 26	06 36	06 41	06 46		06 51	06 56		07 06	07 06	07 11			07 16		07 21	07 26	07 31	
Cardiff Bay	d											06 49			07 04							07 19				07 34
Cardiff Queen Street 3	a	05 29		05 49	06 14	06 19	06 24	06 29	06 39	06 44	06 49	06 53	06 54	06 59	07 08		07 09	07 14			07 19	07 23	07 24	07 29	07 34	07 38
	d	05 30		05 50	06 15	06 20	06 25	06 30	06 40	06 45	06 50		06 55	07 00			07 10	07 15			07 20		07 25	07 30	07 35	
Heath Low Level	d						06 30						07 00										07 30			
Ty Glas	d						06 33						07 03										07 33			
Birchgrove	d						06 34						07 04										07 34			
Rhiwbina	d						06 36						07 06										07 36			
Whitchurch (Cardiff)	d						06 38						07 08										07 38			
Coryton	a						06 44						07 14										07 44			
Heath High Level	d			05 54		06 25					06 55										07 25				07 40	
Llanishen	d			05 57		06 28					06 58										07 28				07 43	
Lisvane & Thornhill	d			06 00		06 30					07 00										07 30				07 45	
Caerphilly 3	d			06a09		06 36					07 06										07 36				07 51	
Aber	d					06 38					07 08										07 38				07 53	
Llanbradach	d					06 42					07 12										07 42				07 57	
Ystrad Mynach 3	d					06 47					07 17										07 47				08 02	
Hengoed	d					06 50					07 20										07 50				08 05	
Pengam	d					06 53					07 23										07 53				08 08	
Gilfach Fargoed	d																									
Bargoed	d					07a02					07a32										08a02				08 14	
Brithdir	d																								08 18	
Tir-phil	d																								08 21	
Pontlottyn	d																								08 25	
Rhymney 3	a																								08 32	
Cathays	d	05 33			06 18			06 33	06 43	06 48				07 03			07 13	07 18						07 33		
Llandaf	d	05 37			06 22			06 37	06 47	06 52				07 07			07 17	07 22						07 37		
Ninian Park	d															07 10			←							
Waun-gron Park	d															07 14 →			07 14							
Fairwater	d																		07 16							
Danescourt	d																		07 19							
Radyr 3	a	05 39			06 24			06 40	06 50	06 54				07 10			07 20	07 25	07 27					07 40		
	d	05 40			06 24			06 40	06 50	06 55				07 10			07 20	07 25						07 40		
Taffs Well 3	d	05 43			06 28			06 44	06 54	06 59				07 14			07 24	07 29						07 44		
Trefforest Estate	d	05 47						06 48						07 18										07 48		
Trefforest	d	05 52			06 35			06 52	07 01	07 06				07 22			07 31	07 36						07 52		
Pontypridd 3	a	05 55			06 39			06 55	07 04	07 09				07 32			07 34	07 39						07 55		
	d	05 56	06 11		06 41			06 56	07 06	07 11							07 36	07 41						07 56		
Abercynon	d	06 06	06 21		06 51			07 06		07 21								07 51						08 06		
Penrhiwceiber	d		06 27		06 57					07 27								07 57								
Mountain Ash	a		06 31		07 01					07 31								08 01								
	d		06 34		07 04					07 34								08 04								
Fernhill	d		06 37		07 07					07 37								08 07								
Cwmbach	d		06 41		07 11					07 41								08 11								
Aberdare 3	a		06 49		07 19					07 49								08 19								
Quakers Yard	d	06 11						07 11																08 11		
Merthyr Vale	d	06 18						07 18																08 18		
Troed Y Rhiw	d	06 22						07 22																08 22		
Pentre-bach	d	06 25						07 25																08 25		
Merthyr Tydfil	a	06 34						07 34																08 34		
Trehafod	d								07 11								07 41									
Porth	d								07 15								07 45									
Dinas Rhondda	d								07 19								07 49									
Tonypandy	d								07 21								07 51									
Llwynypia	d								07 23								07 53									
Ystrad Rhondda	a								07 26								07 56									
	d								07 29								07 59									
Ton Pentre	d								07 31								08 01									
Treorchy	d								07 34								08 04									
Ynyswen	d								07 37								08 07									
Treherbert	a								07 44								08 14									

For general notes see front of timetable
For details of catering facilities see Directory of Train Operators

A From Coryton
B From Taffs Well

Table 130

Mondays to Fridays
from 8 September

Bridgend, Barry Island, Barry, Penarth and Cardiff → Coryton, Rhymney, Pontypridd, Merthyr, Aberdare and Treherbert

Network Diagram - see first page of Table 130

		AW	AW A	AW	AW A	AW	AW	AW B	AW	AW	AW	AW	AW A	AW	AW A		AW	AW	AW B	AW	AW	AW	AW	AW A	AW	AW A
Bridgend	d			06 42																					07 42	
Llantwit Major	d			06 56																					07 56	
Rhoose Cardiff Int Airport ✈	d			07 06																					08 06	
Barry Island	d								07 26					07 41						07 56						
Barry [3]	d			07 15					07 30					07 45						08 00					08 15	
Barry Docks	d			07 19					07 34					07 49						08 04					08 19	
Cadoxton	d			07 22					07 37					07 52						08 07					08 22	
Dinas Powys	d			07 26					07 41					07 56						08 11					08 26	
Eastbrook	d			07 28					07 43					07 58						08 13					08 28	
Cogan	d			07 30					07 45					08 00						08 15					08 30	
Penarth	d					07 32				07 47							08 02				08 17					
Dingle Road	d					07 34				07 49							08 04				08 19					
Grangetown	d			07 34		07 38			07 49	07 53				08 04			08 08			08 19	08 23				08 34	
Cardiff Central [7]	a			07 39		07 44			07 55	07 59				08 09			08 14			08 24	08 29				08 39	
	d	07 36	07 36	07 41		07 46		07 51	07 56	08 01		08 06	08 06	08 11			08 16		08 21	08 26	08 31		08 36	08 36	08 41	
Cardiff Bay	d						07 49				08 04							08 19				08 34				
Cardiff Queen Street [3]	a	07 39		07 44		07 49	07 53	07 54	08 00	08 04	08 08	08 09		08 14			08 19	08 23	08 24	08 29	08 34	08 38	08 39		08 44	
	d	07 40		07 45		07 50		07 55	08 00	08 05		08 10		08 15			08 20		08 25	08 30	08 35		08 40		08 45	
Heath Low Level	d							08 00											08 30							
Ty Glas	d							08 03											08 33							
Birchgrove	d							08 04											08 34							
Rhiwbina	d							08 06											08 36							
Whitchurch (Cardiff)	d							08 08											08 38					08 16		
Coryton	a							08 14											08 44							
Heath High Level	d					07 55				08 10							08 25				08 40					
Llanishen	d					07 58				08 13							08 28				08 43					
Lisvane & Thornhill	d					08 00				08 15							08 30				08 45					
Caerphilly [3]	d					08 06				08 21							08 36				08 51					
Aber	d					08 08				08 23							08 38				08 53					
Llanbradach	d					08 12				08 27							08 42				08 57					
Ystrad Mynach [3]	d					08 17				08 32							08 47				09 07					
Hengoed	d					08 20				08 35							08 50				09 10					
Pengam	d					08 23				08 38							08 53				09 13					
Gilfach Fargoed	d									08 41																
Bargoed	d					08a32				08a49							08 59				09a25					
Brithdir	d																09 03									
Tir-phil	d																09 06									
Pontlottyn	d																09 10									
Rhymney [3]	a																09 17									
Cathays	d	07 43		07 48					08 03			08 13		08 18						08 33			08 43		08 48	
Llandaf	d	07 47		07 52					08 07			08 17		08 22						08 37			08 47		08 52	
Ninian Park	d		07 40		←								08 10		←									08 40		←
Waun-gron Park	d		07 44 →		07 44								08 14 →		08 14									08 44 →		08 44
Fairwater	d				07 46										08 16											08 46
Danescourt	d				07 49										08 19											08 49
Radyr [3]	a	07 50		07 55	07 57				08 10			08 20		08 25	08 27					08 40			08 50		08 55	08 57
	d	07 50		07 55					08 10			08 20		08 25						08 40			08 50		08 55	
Taffs Well [3]	d	07 54		07 59					08 14			08 24		08 29						08 44			08 54		08 59	
Trefforest Estate	d								08 18											08 48						
Trefforest	d	08 01		08 06					08 22			08 31		08 36						08 52			09 01		09 06	
Pontypridd [3]	a	08 04		08 09					08 32			08 34		08 39						08 55			09 04		09 09	
	d	08 06		08 11								08 36		08 41						08 56			09 06		09 11	
Abercynon	d			08 21										08 51						09 06					09 21	
Penrhiwceiber	d			08 27										08 57											09 27	
Mountain Ash	a			08 31										09 01											09 31	
	d			08 34										09 04											09 34	
Fernhill	d			08 37										09 07											09 37	
Cwmbach	d			08 41										09 11											09 41	
Aberdare [3]	a			08 49										09 19											09 49	
Quakers Yard	d																			09 11						
Merthyr Vale	d																			09 18						
Troed Y Rhiw	d																			09 22						
Pentre-bach	d																			09 25						
Merthyr Tydfil	a																			09 34						
Trehafod	d	08 11										08 41											09 11			
Porth	d	08 15										08 45											09 15			
Dinas Rhondda	d	08 19										08 49											09 19			
Tonypandy	d	08 21										08 51											09 21			
Llwynypia	d	08 23										08 53											09 23			
Ystrad Rhondda	a	08 26										08 56											09 26			
	d	08 29										08 59											09 29			
Ton Pentre	d	08 31										09 01											09 31			
Treorchy	d	08 34										09 04											09 34			
Ynyswen	d	08 37										09 07											09 37			
Treherbert	a	08 44										09 14											09 44			

For general notes see front of timetable
For details of catering facilities see Directory of Train Operators

A From Coryton
B From Radyr

Table 130

Mondays to Fridays

from 8 September

Bridgend, Barry Island, Barry, Penarth and Cardiff → Coryton, Rhymney, Pontypridd, Merthyr, Aberdare and Treherbert

Network Diagram - see first page of Table 130

		AW	AW	AW	AW	AW	AW	AW	AW	AW	AW	AW	AW	AW	AW	AW	AW	AW	AW	AW	AW	AW	AW	AW	AW
				A					B		B			A					B		B			A	
Bridgend	d																			08 42					
Llantwit Major	d																			08 56					
Rhoose Cardiff Int Airport ✈	d																			09 06					
Barry Island	d				08 26					08 41					08 56										09 26
Barry 3	d				08 30					08 45					09 00					09 15					09 30
Barry Docks	d				08 34					08 49					09 04					09 19					09 34
Cadoxton	d				08 37					08 52					09 07					09 22					09 37
Dinas Powys	d				08 41					08 56					09 11					09 26					09 41
Eastbrook	d				08 43					08 58					09 13					09 28					09 43
Cogan	d				08 45					09 00					09 15					09 30					09 45
Penarth	d	08 32				08 47										09 17						09 32			
Dingle Road	d	08 34				08 49										09 19						09 34			
Grangetown	d	08 38			08 49	08 53				09 04					09 19	09 23				09 34		09 38			09 49
Cardiff Central 7	a	08 44			08 54	08 59				09 09					09 24	09 29				09 39		09 44			09 54
	d	08 46		08 51	08 56	09 01		09 06	09 06	09 11		09 16		09 21	09 26	09 31		09 36	09 36	09 41		09 46		09 51	09 56
Cardiff Bay	d		08 49				09 04						09 19				09 34						09 49		
Cardiff Queen Street 3	a	08 49	08 53	08 54	08 59	09 04	09 08	09 09		09 14		09 19	09 23	09 24	09 29	09 34	09 38	09 39		09 44		09 49	09 53	09 54	09 59
	d	08 50		08 55	09 00	09 05		09 10		09 15		09 20		09 25	09 30	09 35		09 40		09 45		09 50		09 55	10 00
Heath Low Level	d			09 00										09 30										10 00	
Ty Glas	d			09 03										09 33										10 03	
Birchgrove	d			09 04										09 34										10 04	
Rhiwbina	d			09 06										09 36										10 06	
Whitchurch (Cardiff)	d			09 08					08 46					09 38					09 16					10 08	
Coryton	a			09 14										09 44										10 14	
Heath High Level	d	08 55				09 10						09 25				09 40						09 55			
Llanishen	d	08 58				09 13						09 28				09 43						09 58			
Lisvane & Thornhill	d	09 00				09 15						09 30				09 45						10 00			
Caerphilly 3	d	09 06				09 21						09 36				09 51						10 06			
Aber	d	09 08				09 23						09 38				09 53						10 08			
Llanbradach	d	09 12				09 27						09 42				09 57						10 12			
Ystrad Mynach 3	d	09a22				09 32						09 47				10 07						10a22			
Hengoed	d					09 35						09 50				10 10									
Pengam	d					09 38						09 53				10 13									
Gilfach Fargoed	d					09 41																			
Bargoed	d					09a49						09 59				10a25									
Brithdir	d											10 03													
Tir-phil	d											10 06													
Pontlottyn	d											10 10													
Rhymney 3	a											10 17													
Cathays	d				09 03			09 13		09 18					09 33			09 43		09 48					10 03
Llandaf	d				09 07			09 17		09 22					09 37			09 47		09 52					10 07
Ninian Park	d								09 10		←								09 40		←				
Waun-gron Park	d								09 14		09 14								09 44		09 44				
Fairwater	d								→		09 16								→		09 46				
Danescourt	d										09 19										09 49				
Radyr 3	a				09 10			09 20		09 25	09 27				09 40			09 50		09 55	09 57				10 10
	d				09 10			09 20		09 25					09 40			09 50		09 55					10 10
Taffs Well 3	d				09 14			09 24		09 29					09 44			09 54		09 59					10 14
Trefforest Estate	d				09 18										09 48										10 18
Trefforest	d				09 22			09 31		09 36					09 52			10 01		10 06					10 22
Pontypridd 3	a				09 32			09 34		09 39					09 55			10 04		10 09					10 32
	d							09 36		09 41					09 56			10 06		10 11					
Abercynon	d									09 51					10 06					10 21					
Penrhiwceiber	d									09 57										10 27					
Mountain Ash	a									10 01										10 31					
	d									10 04										10 34					
Fernhill	d									10 07										10 37					
Cwmbach	d									10 11										10 41					
Aberdare 3	a									10 19										10 49					
Quakers Yard	d														10 11										
Merthyr Vale	d														10 18										
Troed Y Rhiw	d														10 22										
Pentre-bach	d														10 25										
Merthyr Tydfil	a														10 34										
Trehafod	d							09 41										10 11							
Porth	d							09 45										10 15							
Dinas Rhondda	d							09 49										10 19							
Tonypandy	d							09 51										10 21							
Llwynypia	d							09 53										10 23							
Ystrad Rhondda	a							09 56										10 26							
	d							09 59										10 29							
Ton Pentre	d							10 01										10 31							
Treorchy	d							10 04										10 34							
Ynyswen	d							10 07										10 37							
Treherbert	a							10 14										10 44							

For general notes see front of timetable
For details of catering facilities see Directory of Train Operators

A From Radyr
B From Coryton

Table 130

Mondays to Fridays

from 8 September

Bridgend, Barry Island, Barry, Penarth and Cardiff → Coryton, Rhymney, Pontypridd, Merthyr, Aberdare and Treherbert

Network Diagram - see first page of Table 130

		AW	AW	AW	AW	AW	AW		AW	AW	AW	AW	AW	AW	AW	AW	AW	AW	AW	AW	AW	AW	AW	AW	AW	AW
					A		A				B					A					B				A	
Bridgend	d																09 42									
Llantwit Major	d																09 56									
Rhoose Cardiff Int Airport ✈	d																10 06									
Barry Island	d					09 41						09 56										10 26				10 41
Barry 3	d					09 45						10 00					10 15					10 30				10 45
Barry Docks	d					09 49						10 04					10 19					10 34				10 49
Cadoxton	d					09 52						10 07					10 22					10 37				10 52
Dinas Powys	d					09 56						10 11					10 26					10 41				10 56
Eastbrook	d					09 58						10 13					10 28					10 43				10 58
Cogan	d					10 00						10 15					10 30					10 45				11 00
Penarth	d	09 47							10 02				10 17					10 32					10 47			
Dingle Road	d	09 49							10 04				10 19					10 34					10 49			
Grangetown	d	09 53				10 04			10 08			10 19	10 23				10 34	10 38				10 49	10 53			11 04
Cardiff Central 7	a	09 59				10 09			10 14			10 24	10 29				10 43	10 44				10 54	10 59			11 09
	d	10 01		10 06	10 06	10 11			10 16		10 21	10 26	10 31		10 36	10 36		10 46	10 48		10 51	10 56	11 01		11 06	11 11
Cardiff Bay	d		10 04							10 19				10 34						10 49				11 04		
Cardiff Queen Street 3	a	10 04	10 08	10 09		10 14			10 19	10 23	10 24	10 29	10 34	10 38	10 39			10 49		10 53	10 54	10 59	11 04	11 08		11 14
	d	10 05		10 10		10 15			10 20		10 25	10 30	10 35		10 40			10 50			10 55	11 00	11 05			11 15
Heath Low Level	d										10 30										11 00					
Ty Glas	d										10 33										11 03					
Birchgrove	d										10 34										11 04					
Rhiwbina	d										10 36										11 06					
Whitchurch (Cardiff)	d										10 38										11 08					
Coryton	a										10 44										11 14					
Heath High Level	d	10 10							10 25				10 40					10 55					11 10			
Llanishen	d	10 13							10 28				10 43					10 58					11 13			
Lisvane & Thornhill	d	10 15							10 30				10 45					11 00					11 15			
Caerphilly 3	d	10 21							10 36				10 51					11 06					11 21			
Aber	d	10 23							10 38				10 53					11 08					11 23			
Llanbradach	d	10 27							10 42				10 57					11 12					11 27			
Ystrad Mynach 3	d	10 32							10 47				11 07					11a22					11 32			
Hengoed	d	10 35							10 50				11 10										11 35			
Pengam	d	10 38							10 53				11 13										11 38			
Gilfach Fargoed	d	10 41																					11 41			
Bargoed	d	10a49							10 59				11a25										11a49			
Brithdir	d								11 03																	
Tir-phil	d								11 06																	
Pontlottyn	d								11 10																	
Rhymney 3	a								11 17																	
Cathays	d			10 13		10 18						10 33			10 43							11 03				11 18
Llandaf	d			10 17		10 22						10 37			10 47							11 07				11 22
Ninian Park	d				10 10		←									10 40									11 10	
Waun-gron Park	d				10 14 →		10 14									10 44									11 14 →	
Fairwater	d						10 16									10 46										
Danescourt	d						10 19									10 49										
Radyr 3	a			10 20		10 25	10 27					10 40			10 50	10 57			11 02			11 10				11 25
	d			10 20		10 25						10 40			10 50				11 05			11 10				11 25
Taffs Well 3	d			10 24		10 29						10 44			10 54				11 09			11 14				11 29
Trefforest Estate	d											10 48										11 18				
Trefforest	d			10 31		10 36						10 52			11 01				11 16			11 22				11 36
Pontypridd 3	a			10 34		10 39						10 55			11 04				11 19			11 32				11 39
	d			10 36		10 41						10 56			11 06				11 22							11 41
Abercynon	d					10 51						11 06														11 51
Penrhiwceiber	d					10 57																				11 57
Mountain Ash	a					11 01																				12 01
	d					11 04																				12 04
Fernhill	d					11 07																				12 07
Cwmbach	d					11 11																				12 11
Aberdare 3	a					11 19																				12 19
Quakers Yard	d											11 11														
Merthyr Vale	d											11 18														
Troed Y Rhiw	d											11 22														
Pentre-bach	d											11 25														
Merthyr Tydfil	a											11 34														
Trehafod	d			10 41											11 11				11 27							
Porth	d			10 45											11 15				11b45							
Dinas Rhondda	d			10 49											11 19				11 49							
Tonypandy	d			10 51											11 21				11 51							
Llwynypia	d			10 53											11 23				11 53							
Ystrad Rhondda	a			10 56											11 26				11 56							
	d			10 59											11 29				11 59							
Ton Pentre	d			11 01											11 31				12 01							
Treorchy	d			11 04											11 34				12 04							
Ynyswen	d			11 07											11 37				12 07							
Treherbert	a			11 14											11 44				12 14							

For general notes see front of timetable
For details of catering facilities see
Directory of Train Operators

A From Coryton
B From Radyr
b Arr. 1130

Table 130

Mondays to Fridays

from 8 September

Bridgend, Barry Island, Barry, Penarth and Cardiff → Coryton, Rhymney, Pontypridd, Merthyr, Aberdare and Treherbert

Network Diagram - see first page of Table 130

		AW A	AW		AW	AW B	AW	AW	AW	AW A	AW	AW	AW A	AW	AW	AW	AW B	AW	AW	AW	AW	AW A		AW	AW A	AW
Bridgend	d														10 42											
Llantwit Major	d														10 56											
Rhoose Cardiff Int Airport ✈	d														11 06											
Barry Island	d						10 56											11 26						11 41		
Barry 3	d						11 00								11 15			11 30						11 45		
Barry Docks	d						11 04								11 19			11 34						11 49		
Cadoxton	d						11 07								11 22			11 37						11 52		
Dinas Powys	d						11 11								11 26			11 41						11 56		
Eastbrook	d						11 13								11 28			11 43						11 58		
Cogan	d						11 15								11 30			11 45						12 00		
Penarth	d		11 02					11 17						11 32					11 47							12 02
Dingle Road	d		11 04					11 19						11 34					11 49							12 04
Grangetown	d		11 08				11 19	11 23						11 38	11 34			11 49	11 53					12 04		12 08
Cardiff Central 7	a		11 14				11 24	11 29						11 44	11 45			11 54	11 59					12 09		12 14
	d		11 16			11 21	11 26	11 31		11 36	11 36	11 41		11 46			11 51	11 56	12 01		12 06	12 06		12 11		12 16
Cardiff Bay	d				11 19				11 34							11 49				12 04						
Cardiff Queen Street 3	a		11 19		11 23	11 24	11 29	11 34	11 38		11 39	11 44		11 49		11 53	11 54	11 59	12 04	12 08	12 09			12 14		12 19
	d		11 20			11 25	11 30	11 35			11 40	11 45		11 50			11 55	12 00	12 05		12 10			12 15		12 20
Heath Low Level	d					11 30											12 00									
Ty Glas	d					11 33											12 03									
Birchgrove	d					11 34											12 04									
Rhiwbina	d					11 36											12 06									
Whitchurch (Cardiff)	d					11 38											12 08									
Coryton	a					11 44											12 14									
Heath High Level	d		11 25					11 40						11 55					12 10							12 25
Llanishen	d		11 28					11 43						11 58					12 13							12 28
Lisvane & Thornhill	d		11 30					11 45						12 00					12 15							12 30
Caerphilly 3	d		11 36					11 51						12 06					12 21							12 36
Aber	d		11 38					11 53						12 08					12 23							12 38
Llanbradach	d		11 42					11 57						12 12					12 27							12 42
Ystrad Mynach 3	d		11 47					12b07						12a22					12 32							12 47
Hengoed	d		11 50					12 10											12 35							12 50
Pengam	d		11 53					12 13											12 38							12 53
Gilfach Fargoed	d																		12 41							
Bargoed	d		11 59					12a25											12a49							12 59
Brithdir	d		12 03																							13 03
Tir-phil	d		12 06																							13 06
Pontlottyn	d		12 10																							13 10
Rhymney 3	a		12 17																							13 17
Cathays	d						11 33				11 43	11 48						12 03			12 13			12 18		
Llandaf	d						11 37				11 47	11 52						12 07			12 17			12 22		
Ninian Park	d	←								11 40			←									12 10			←	
Waun-gron Park	d	11 14								11 44 →			11 44									12 14 →			12 14	
Fairwater	d	11 16											11 46												12 16	
Danescourt	d	11 19											11 49												12 19	
Radyr 3	a	11 27					11 40				11 50	11 55	11 57					12 10			12 20			12 25	12 27	
	d						11 40				11 50	11 55						12 10			12 20			12 25		
Taffs Well 3	d						11 44				11 54	11 59						12 14			12 24			12 29		
Trefforest Estate	d						11 48											12 18								
Trefforest	d						11 52				12 01	12 06						12 22			12 31			12 36		
Pontypridd 3	a						11 55				12 04	12 09						12 32			12 34			12 43		
	d						11 56				12 06	12 11									12 36					
Abercynon	d						12 06					12 21														
Penrhiwceiber	d											12 27														
Mountain Ash	a											12 31														
	d											12 34														
Fernhill	d											12 37														
Cwmbach	d											12 41														
Aberdare 3	a											12 49														
Quakers Yard	d						12 11																			
Merthyr Vale	d						12 18																			
Troed Y Rhiw	d						12 22																			
Pentre-bach	d						12 25																			
Merthyr Tydfil	a						12 34																			
Trehafod	d										12 11										12 41					
Porth	d										12 15										12 45					
Dinas Rhondda	d										12 19										12 49					
Tonypandy	d										12 21										12 51					
Llwynypia	d										12 23										12 53					
Ystrad Rhondda	a										12 26										12 56					
	d										12 29										12 59					
Ton Pentre	d										12 31										13 01					
Treorchy	d										12 34										13 04					
Ynyswen	d										12 37										13 07					
Treherbert	a										12 44										13 14					

For general notes see front of timetable
For details of catering facilities see
Directory of Train Operators

A From Coryton
B From Radyr
b Arr. 1202

Bridgend, Barry Island, Barry, Penarth and Cardiff → Coryton, Rhymney, Pontypridd, Merthyr, Aberdare and Treherbert

Network Diagram - see first page of Table 130

Station		AW	AW A	AW	AW	AW	AW	AW B	AW	AW B	AW	AW	AW A	AW	AW	AW	AW	AW B		AW	AW B	AW	AW	AW A	AW	AW
Bridgend	d								11 42																	
Llantwit Major	d								11 56																	
Rhoose Cardiff Int Airport ✈	d								12 06																	
Barry Island	d			11 56										12 26						12 41					12 56	
Barry 3	d			12 00					12 15					12 30						12 45					13 00	
Barry Docks	d			12 04					12 19					12 34						12 49					13 04	
Cadoxton	d			12 07					12 22					12 37						12 52					13 07	
Dinas Powys	d			12 11					12 26					12 41						12 56					13 11	
Eastbrook	d			12 13					12 28					12 43						12 58					13 13	
Cogan	d			12 15					12 30					12 45						13 00					13 15	
Penarth	d				12 17						12 32				12 47							13 02				13 17
Dingle Road	d				12 19						12 34				12 49							13 04				13 19
Grangetown	d			12 19	12 23				12 34		12 38			12 49	12 53					13 04		13 08			13 19	13 23
Cardiff Central 7	a			12 24	12 29				12 39		12 44			12 54	12 59					13 09		13 14			13 24	13 29
	d		12 21	12 26	12 31		12 36	12 36	12 41		12 46		12 51	12 56	13 01		13 06	13 06		13 11		13 16		13 21	13 26	13 31
Cardiff Bay	d	12 19				12 34						12 49				13 04							13 19			
Cardiff Queen Street 3	a	12 23	12 24	12 29	12 34	12 38	12 39		12 44		12 49	12 53	12 54	12 59	13 04	13 08	13 09			13 14		13 19	13 23	13 24	13 29	13 34
	d		12 25	12 30	12 35		12 40		12 45		12 50		12 55	13 00	13 05		13 10			13 15		13 20		13 25	13 30	13 35
Heath Low Level	d		12 30										13 00											13 30		
Ty Glas	d		12 33										13 03											13 33		
Birchgrove	d		12 34										13 04											13 34		
Rhiwbina	d		12 36										13 06											13 36		
Whitchurch (Cardiff)	d		12 38										13 08											13 38		
Coryton	a		12 44										13 14											13 44		
Heath High Level	d				12 40						12 55				13 10							13 25				13 40
Llanishen	d				12 43						12 58				13 13							13 28				13 43
Lisvane & Thornhill	d				12 45						13 00				13 15							13 30				13 45
Caerphilly 3	d				12 51						13 06				13 21							13 36				13 51
Aber	d				12 53						13 08				13 23							13 38				13 53
Llanbradach	d				12 57						13 12				13 27							13 42				13 57
Ystrad Mynach 3	d				13 07						13a22				13 32							13 47				14 07
Hengoed	d				13 10										13 35							13 50				14 10
Pengam	d				13 13										13 38							13 53				14 13
Gilfach Fargoed	d														13 41											
Bargoed	d				13a25										13a49							13 59				14a25
Brithdir	d																					14 03				
Tir-phil	d																					14 06				
Pontlottyn	d																					14 10				
Rhymney 3	a																					14 17				
Cathays	d			12 33			12 43		12 48					13 03			13 13			13 18					13 33	
Llandaf	d			12 37			12 47		12 52					13 07			13 17			13 22					13 37	
Ninian Park	d							12 40		←								13 10			←					
Waun-gron Park	d							12 44 →		12 44								13 14 →			13 14					
Fairwater	d									12 46											13 16					
Danescourt	d									12 49											13 19					
Radyr 3	a			12 40			12 50		12 55	12 57				13 10			13 20			13 25	13 27				13 40	
	d			12 40			12 50		12 55					13 10			13 20			13 25					13 40	
Taffs Well 3	d			12 44			12 54		12 59					13 14			13 24			13 29					13 44	
Trefforest Estate	d			12 48										13 18											13 48	
Trefforest	d			12 52			13 01		13 06					13 22			13 31			13 36					13 52	
Pontypridd 3	a			12 55			13 04		13 09					13 32			13 34			13 39					13 55	
	d			12 56			13 06		13 11								13 36			13 41					13 56	
Abercynon	d			13 06					13 21											13 51					14 06	
Penrhiwceiber	d								13 27											13 57						
Mountain Ash	a								13 31											14 01						
	d								13 34											14 04						
Fernhill	d								13 37											14 07						
Cwmbach	d								13 41											14 11						
Aberdare 3	a								13 49											14 19						
Quakers Yard	d			13 11																					14 11	
Merthyr Vale	d			13 18																					14 18	
Troed Y Rhiw	d			13 22																					14 22	
Pentre-bach	d			13 25																					14 25	
Merthyr Tydfil	a			13 34																					14 34	
Trehafod	d						13 11										13 41									
Porth	d						13 15										13 45									
Dinas Rhondda	d						13 19										13 49									
Tonypandy	d						13 21										13 51									
Llwynypia	d						13 23										13 53									
Ystrad Rhondda	a						13 26										13 56									
	d						13 29										13 59									
Ton Pentre	d						13 31										14 01									
Treorchy	d						13 34										14 04									
Ynyswen	d						13 37										14 07									
Treherbert	a						13 44										14 14									

For general notes see front of timetable
For details of catering facilities see Directory of Train Operators

A From Radyr
B From Coryton

Table 130

Bridgend, Barry Island, Barry, Penarth and Cardiff → Coryton, Rhymney, Pontypridd, Merthyr, Aberdare and Treherbert

Mondays to Fridays

from 8 September

Network Diagram - see first page of Table 130

		AW	AW	AW A	AW	AW A	AW	AW	AW B	AW	AW	AW	AW	AW A	AW	AW A	AW	AW	AW B	AW	AW	AW	AW	AW A	AW
Bridgend	d				12 42																				13 42
Llantwit Major	d				12 56																				13 56
Rhoose Cardiff Int Airport ✈	d				13 06																				14 06
Barry Island	d									13 26					13 41					13 56					
Barry 3	d				13 15					13 30					13 45					14 00					14 15
Barry Docks	d				13 19					13 34					13 49					14 04					14 19
Cadoxton	d				13 22					13 37					13 52					14 07					14 22
Dinas Powys	d				13 26					13 41					13 56					14 11					14 26
Eastbrook	d				13 28					13 43					13 58					14 13					14 28
Cogan	d				13 30					13 45					14 00					14 15					14 30
Penarth	d						13 32				13 47						14 02				14 17				
Dingle Road	d						13 34				13 49						14 04				14 19				
Grangetown	d				13 34		13 38			13 49	13 53				14 04		14 08			14 19	14 23				14 34
Cardiff Central 7	a				13 39		13 44			13 54	14 02				14 09		14 14			14 24	14 29				14 39
	d		13 36	13 36	13 41		13 46		13 51	13 56			14 06	14 06	14 11		14 16		14 21	14 26	14 31		14 36	14 36	14 41
Cardiff Bay	d	13 34						13 49				14 04						14 19				14 34			
Cardiff Queen Street 3	a	13 38	13 39		13 44		13 49	13 53	13 54	13 59		14 08	14 09		14 14		14 19	14 23	14 24	14 29	14 34	14 38	14 39		14 44
	d		13 40		13 45		13 50		13 55	14 00			14 10		14 15		14 20		14 25	14 30	14 35		14 40		14 45
Heath Low Level	d								14 00										14 30						
Ty Glas	d								14 03										14 33						
Birchgrove	d								14 04										14 34						
Rhiwbina	d								14 06										14 36						
Whitchurch (Cardiff)	d								14 08										14 38						
Coryton	a								14 14										14 44						
Heath High Level	d						13 55										14 25				14 40				
Llanishen	d						13 58										14 28				14 43				
Lisvane & Thornhill	d						14 00										14 30				14 45				
Caerphilly 3	d						14 06										14 36				14 51				
Aber	d						14 08										14 38				14 53				
Llanbradach	d						14 12										14 42				14 57				
Ystrad Mynach 3	d						14a22										14 47				15 07				
Hengoed	d																14 50				15 10				
Pengam	d																14 53				15 13				
Gilfach Fargoed	d																								
Bargoed	d																14 59				15a25				
Brithdir	d																15 03								
Tir-phil	d																15 06								
Pontlottyn	d																15 10								
Rhymney 3	a																15 17								
Cathays	d		13 43		13 48					14 03			14 13		14 18					14 33			14 43		14 48
Llandaf	d		13 47		13 52					14 07			14 17		14 22					14 37			14 47		14 52
Ninian Park	d			13 40		←								14 10		←								14 40	
Waun-gron Park	d			13 44		13 44								14 14		14 14								14 44	
Fairwater	d			→		13 46								→		14 16								→	
Danescourt	d					13 49										14 19									
Radyr 3	a		13 50		13 55	13 57				14 10			14 20		14 25	14 27				14 40			14 50		14 55
	d		13 50		13 55					14 10			14 20		14 25					14 40			14 50		14 55
Taffs Well 3	d		13 54		13 59					14 14			14 24		14 29					14 44			14 54		14 59
Trefforest Estate	d									14 18										14 48					
Trefforest	d		14 01		14 06					14 22			14 31		14 36					14 52			15 01		15 06
Pontypridd 3	a		14 04		14 09					14 32			14 34		14 39					14 55			15 04		15 09
	d		14 06		14 11								14 36		14 41					14 56			15 06		15 11
Abercynon	d				14 21										14 51					15 06					15 21
Penrhiwceiber	d				14 27										14 57										15 27
Mountain Ash	a				14 31										15 01										15 31
	d				14 34										15 04										15 34
Fernhill	d				14 37										15 07										15 37
Cwmbach	d				14 41										15 11										15 41
Aberdare 3	a				14 49										15 19										15 49
Quakers Yard	d																			15 11					
Merthyr Vale	d																			15 18					
Troed Y Rhiw	d																			15 22					
Pentre-bach	d																			15 25					
Merthyr Tydfil	a																			15 34					
Trehafod	d		14 11										14 41										15 11		
Porth	d		14 15										14 45										15 15		
Dinas Rhondda	d		14 19										14 49										15 19		
Tonypandy	d		14 21										14 51										15 21		
Llwynypia	d		14 23										14 53										15 23		
Ystrad Rhondda	a		14 26										14 56										15 26		
	d		14 29										14 59										15 29		
Ton Pentre	d		14 31										15 01										15 31		
Treorchy	d		14 34										15 04										15 34		
Ynyswen	d		14 37										15 07										15 37		
Treherbert	a		14 44										15 14										15 44		

For general notes see front of timetable
For details of catering facilities see Directory of Train Operators

A From Coryton
B From Radyr

Table 130

Mondays to Fridays
from 8 September

Bridgend, Barry Island, Barry, Penarth and Cardiff → Coryton, Rhymney, Pontypridd, Merthyr, Aberdare and Treherbert

Network Diagram - see first page of Table 130

		AW A	AW	AW	AW B	AW	AW	AW	AW	AW A		AW	AW A	AW	AW	AW B	AW	AW	AW	AW	AW A	AW	AW A	AW	AW	AW B
Bridgend	d																					14 42				
Llantwit Major	d																					14 56				
Rhoose Cardiff Int Airport ✈	d																					15 06				
Barry Island	d						14 26					14 41					14 56									
Barry [3]	d						14 30					14 45					15 00					15 15				
Barry Docks	d						14 34					14 49					15 04					15 19				
Cadoxton	d						14 37					14 52					15 07					15 22				
Dinas Powys	d						14 41					14 56					15 11					15 26				
Eastbrook	d						14 43					14 58					15 13					15 28				
Cogan	d						14 45					15 00					15 15					15 30				
Penarth	d		14 32					14 47						15 02				15 17						15 32		
Dingle Road	d		14 34					14 49						15 04				15 19						15 34		
Grangetown	d		14 38				14 49	14 53				15 04		15 08			15 19	15 23				15 34		15 38		
Cardiff Central [7]	a		14 44				14 54	14 59				15 09		15 14			15 24	15 29				15 39		15 44		
	d		14 46		14 51	14 51	14 56	15 01		15 06		15 11		15 16		15 21	15 26	15 31		15 36	15 36	15 41		15 46		15 51
Cardiff Bay	d			14 49					15 04						15 19				15 34						15 49	
Cardiff Queen Street [3]	a		14 49	14 53	14 54		14 59	15 04	15 08			15 14		15 19	15 23	15 24	15 29	15 34	15 38	15 39		15 44		15 49	15 53	15 54
	d		14 50		14 55		15 00	15 05				15 15		15 20		15 25	15 30	15 35		15 40		15 45		15 50		15 55
Heath Low Level	d				15 00											15 30										16 00
Ty Glas	d				15 03											15 33										16 03
Birchgrove	d				15 04											15 34										16 04
Rhiwbina	d				15 06											15 36										16 06
Whitchurch (Cardiff)	d				15 08											15 38										16 08
Coryton	a				15 14											15 44										16 14
Heath High Level	d		14 55					15 10						15 25				15 40						15 55		
Llanishen	d		14 58					15 13						15 28				15 43						15 58		
Lisvane & Thornhill	d		15 00					15 15						15 30				15 45						16 00		
Caerphilly [3]	d		15 06					15 21						15 36				15 51						16 06		
Aber	d		15 08					15 23						15 38				15 53						16 08		
Llanbradach	d		15 12					15 27						15 42				15 57						16 12		
Ystrad Mynach [3]	d		15a22					15 32						15 47				16 02						16 17		
Hengoed	d							15 35						15 50				16 05						16 20		
Pengam	d							15 38						15 53				16 08						16 23		
Gilfach Fargoed	d							15 41																		
Bargoed	d							15a49						15 59				16a17						16a32		
Brithdir	d													16 03												
Tir-phil	d													16 06												
Pontlottyn	d													16 10												
Rhymney [3]	a													16 17												
Cathays	d						15 03					15 18					15 33			15 43		15 48				
Llandaf	d						15 07					15 22					15 37			15 47		15 52				
Ninian Park	d	←								15 10			←								15 40		←			
Waun-gron Park	d	14 44								15 14 →			15 14								15 44 →		15 44			
Fairwater	d	14 46											15 16										15 46			
Danescourt	d	14 49											15 19										15 49			
Radyr [3]	a	14 57				15 02	15 10					15 25	15 27				15 40			15 50		15 55	15 57			
	d					15 02	15 10					15 25					15 40			15 50		15 55				
Taffs Well [3]	d					15 06	15 14					15 29					15 44			15 54		15 59				
Trefforest Estate	d						15 18										15 48									
Trefforest	d					15 13	15 22					15 36					15 52			16 01		16 06				
Pontypridd [3]	a					15 16	15 32					15 39					15 55			16 04		16 09				
	d					15 22						15 41					15 56			16 06		16 11				
Abercynon	d											15 51					16 06					16 21				
Penrhiwceiber	d											15 57										16 27				
Mountain Ash	a											16 01										16 31				
	d											16 04										16 34				
Fernhill	d											16 07										16 37				
Cwmbach	d											16 11										16 41				
Aberdare [3]	a											16 19										16 49				
Quakers Yard	d																16 11									
Merthyr Vale	d																16 18									
Troed Y Rhiw	d																16 22									
Pentre-bach	d																16 25									
Merthyr Tydfil	a																16 34									
Trehafod	d					15 27														16 11						
Porth	d					15b45														16 15						
Dinas Rhondda	d					15 49														16 19						
Tonypandy	d					15 51														16 21						
Llwynypia	d					15 53														16 23						
Ystrad Rhondda	a					15 56														16 26						
	d					15 59														16 29						
Ton Pentre	d					16 01														16 31						
Treorchy	d					16 04														16 34						
Ynyswen	d					16 07														16 37						
Treherbert	a					16 14														16 44						

For general notes see front of timetable
For details of catering facilities see Directory of Train Operators

A From Coryton
B From Radyr
b Arr. 1530

Table 130

Mondays to Fridays

from 8 September

Bridgend, Barry Island, Barry, Penarth and Cardiff → Coryton, Rhymney, Pontypridd, Merthyr, Aberdare and Treherbert

Network Diagram - see first page of Table 130

Station		AW	AW	AW	AW	AW		AW	AW	AW	AW	AW	AW	AW	AW	AW	AW	AW	AW	AW	AW	AW	AW	AW	AW	AW
						A			A			B					A		A			B				
Bridgend	d																	15 42								
Llantwit Major	d																	15 56								
Rhoose Cardiff Int Airport ✈	d																	16 06								
Barry Island	d	15 26						15 41					15 56										16 26			
Barry 3	d	15 30						15 45					16 00					16 15					16 30			
Barry Docks	d	15 34						15 49					16 04					16 19					16 34			
Cadoxton	d	15 37						15 52					16 07					16 22					16 37			
Dinas Powys	d	15 41						15 56					16 11					16 26					16 41			
Eastbrook	d	15 43						15 58					16 13					16 28					16 43			
Cogan	d	15 45						16 00					16 15					16 30					16 45			
Penarth	d		15 47											16 17						16 32						
Dingle Road	d		15 49											16 19						16 34						
Grangetown	d	15 49	15 53					16 04					16 19	16 23				16 34		16 38			16 49			
Cardiff Central 7	a	15 54	15 59					16 09					16 24	16 29				16 39		16 44			16 54			
	d	15 56	16 01		16 06	16 06		16 11		16 16		16 21	16 26	16 31		16 36	16 36	16 41		16 46		16 51	16 56	17 01		17 06
Cardiff Bay	d			16 04							16 19				16 34						16 49				17 04	
Cardiff Queen Street 3	a	15 59	16 04	16 08	16 09			16 14		16 19	16 23	16 24	16 29	16 34	16 38	16 39		16 44		16 49	16 53	16 54	16 59	17 04	17 08	17 09
	d	16 00	16 05		16 10			16 15		16 20		16 25	16 30	16 35		16 40		16 45		16 50		16 55	17 00	17 05		17 10
Heath Low Level	d											16 30										17 00				
Ty Glas	d											16 33										17 03				
Birchgrove	d											16 34										17 04				
Rhiwbina	d											16 36										17 06				
Whitchurch (Cardiff)	d											16 38					16 16					17 08				
Coryton	a											16 44										17 14				
Heath High Level	d		16 10							16 25				16 40						16 55				17 10		
Llanishen	d		16 13							16 28				16 43						16 58				17 13		
Lisvane & Thornhill	d		16 15							16 30				16 45						17 00				17 15		
Caerphilly 3	d		16 21							16 36				16 51						17 06				17 21		
Aber	d		16 23							16 38				16 53						17 08				17 23		
Llanbradach	d		16 27							16 42				16 57						17 12				17 27		
Ystrad Mynach 3	d		16 32							16 47				17 02						17 17				17 33		
Hengoed	d		16 35							16 50				17 05						17 20				17 35		
Pengam	d		16 38							16 53				17 08						17 23				17 39		
Gilfach Fargoed	d		16 41																					17 42		
Bargoed	d		16a49							16 59				17a17						17a32				17 47		
Brithdir	d									17 03														17 50		
Tir-phil	d									17 06														17 53		
Pontlottyn	d									17 10														17 58		
Rhymney 3	a									17 17														18 05		
Cathays	d	16 03			16 13			16 18					16 33			16 43		16 48					17 03			17 13
Llandaf	d	16 07			16 17			16 22					16 37			16 47		16 52					17 07			17 17
Ninian Park	d					16 10			←								16 40		←							
Waun-gron Park	d					16 14 →			16 14								16 44 →		16 44							
Fairwater	d								16 16										16 46							
Danescourt	d								16 19										16 49							
Radyr 3	a	16 10			16 20			16 25	16 27				16 40			16 50		16 55	16 57				17 10			17 20
	d	16 10			16 20			16 25					16 40			16 50		16 55					17 10			17 20
Taffs Well 3	d	16 14			16 24			16 29					16 44			16 54		16 59					17 14			17 24
Trefforest Estate	d	16 18											16 48										17 18			
Trefforest	d	16 22			16 31			16 36					16 52			17 01		17 06					17 22			17 31
Pontypridd 3	a	16 32			16 34			16 39					16 55			17 04		17 09					17 29			17 34
	d				16 36			16 41					16 56			17 06		17 11								17 36
Abercynon	d							16 51					17 06					17 21								
Penrhiwceiber	d							16 57										17 27								
Mountain Ash	a							17 01										17 31								
	d							17 04										17 34								
Fernhill	d							17 07										17 37								
Cwmbach	d							17 11										17 41								
Aberdare 3	a							17 19										17 49								
Quakers Yard	d												17 11													
Merthyr Vale	d												17 18													
Troed Y Rhiw	d												17 22													
Pentre-bach	d												17 25													
Merthyr Tydfil	a												17 34													
Trehafod	d				16 41											17 11										17 41
Porth	d				16 45											17 15										17 45
Dinas Rhondda	d				16 49											17 19										17 49
Tonypandy	d				16 51											17 21										17 51
Llwynypia	d				16 53											17 23										17 53
Ystrad Rhondda	a				16 56											17 26										17 56
	d				16 59											17 29										17 59
Ton Pentre	d				17 01											17 31										18 01
Treorchy	d				17 04											17 34										18 04
Ynyswen	d				17 07											17 37										18 07
Treherbert	a				17 14											17 44										18 14

For general notes see front of timetable
For details of catering facilities see
Directory of Train Operators

A From Coryton
B From Radyr

Table 130

Mondays to Fridays
from 8 September

Bridgend, Barry Island, Barry, Penarth and Cardiff → Coryton, Rhymney, Pontypridd, Merthyr, Aberdare and Treherbert

Network Diagram - see first page of Table 130

Station		AW A	AW	AW A	AW	AW	AW B	AW	AW	AW	AW	AW A	AW	AW A	AW	AW	AW B	AW	AW	AW	AW	AW A	AW	AW A
Bridgend	d												16 42											
Llantwit Major	d												16 56											
Rhoose Cardiff Int Airport ✈	d												17 06											
Barry Island	d		16 41					16 56										17 26					17 41	
Barry 3	d		16 45					17 00					17 15					17 30					17 45	
Barry Docks	d		16 49					17 04					17 19					17 34					17 49	
Cadoxton	d		16 52					17 07					17 22					17 37					17 52	
Dinas Powys	d		16 56					17 11					17 26					17 41					17 56	
Eastbrook	d		16 58					17 13					17 28					17 43					17 58	
Cogan	d		17 00					17 15					17 30					17 45					18 00	
Penarth	d				17 02				17 17						17 32				17 47					
Dingle Road	d				17 04				17 19						17 34				17 49					
Grangetown	d		17 04		17 08			17 19	17 23				17 34		17 38			17 49	17 53				18 04	
Cardiff Central 7	a		17 09		17 14			17 24	17 29				17 39		17 44			17 54	17 59				18 09	
	d	17 06	17 11		17 16		17 21	17 26	17 31		17 36	17 36	17 41		17 46		17 51	17 56	18 01		18 06	18 06	18 11	
Cardiff Bay	d					17 19				17 34						17 49				18 04				
Cardiff Queen Street 3	a		17 14		17 19	17 23	17 24	17 29	17 34	17 38	17 39		17 44		17 49	17 53	17 54	17 59	18 04	18 08	18 09		18 14	
	d		17 15		17 20		17 25	17 30	17 35		17 40		17 45		17 50		17 55	18 00	18 05		18 10		18 15	
Heath Low Level	d						17 30										18 00							
Ty Glas	d						17 33										18 03							
Birchgrove	d						17 34										18 04							
Rhiwbina	d						17 36										18 06							
Whitchurch (Cardiff)	d						17 38										18 08							
Coryton	a						17 44										18 14							
Heath High Level	d				17 25				17 40						17 55				18 10					
Llanishen	d				17 28				17 43						17 59				18 13					
Lisvane & Thornhill	d				17 30				17 45						18 02				18 15					
Caerphilly 3	d				17 36				17 51						18 07				18 21					
Aber	d				17 38				17 53						18 10				18 23					
Llanbradach	d				17 42				17 57						18 14				18 27					
Ystrad Mynach 3	d				17 47				18 02						18 20				18 32					
Hengoed	d				17 50				18 05						18 23				18 35					
Pengam	d				17 53				18 08						18 27				18 38					
Gilfach Fargoed	d								18 11						18 30				18 41					
Bargoed	d				18a02				18 16						18b44				18a49					
Brithdir	d								18 20						18 48									
Tir-phil	d								18 23						18 51									
Pontlottyn	d								18 27						18 55									
Rhymney 3	a								18 34						19 02									
Cathays	d		17 18					17 33			17 43		17 48					18 03			18 13		18 18	
Llandaf	d		17 22					17 37			17 47		17 52					18 07			18 17		18 22	
Ninian Park	d	17 10		←								17 40		←								18 10		←
Waun-gron Park	d	17 14 →		17 14								17 44 →		17 44								18 14 →		18 14
Fairwater	d			17 16										17 46										18 16
Danescourt	d			17 19										17 49										18 19
Radyr 3	a		17 25	17 27				17 40			17 50		17 55	17 57				18 10			18 20		18 25	18 27
	d		17 25					17 40			17 50		17 55					18 10			18 20		18 25	
Taffs Well 3	d		17 29					17 44			17 54		17 59					18 14			18 24		18 29	
Trefforest Estate	d							17 48										18 18						
Trefforest	d		17 36					17 52			18 01		18 06					18 22			18 31		18 36	
Pontypridd 3	a		17 39					17 55			18 04		18 09					18 32			18 34		18 42	
	d		17 41					17 56			18 06		18 11								18 36			
Abercynon	d		17 51					18 06					18 21											
Penrhiwceiber	d		17 57										18 27											
Mountain Ash	a		18 01										18 31											
	d		18 04										18 34											
Fernhill	d		18 07										18 37											
Cwmbach	d		18 11										18 41											
Aberdare 3	a		18 19										18 49											
Quakers Yard	d							18 11																
Merthyr Vale	d							18 18																
Troed Y Rhiw	d							18 22																
Pentre-bach	d							18 25																
Merthyr Tydfil	a							18 34																
Trehafod	d										18 11										18 41			
Porth	d										18 15										18 45			
Dinas Rhondda	d										18 19										18 49			
Tonypandy	d										18 21										18 51			
Llwynypia	d										18 23										18 53			
Ystrad Rhondda	a										18 26										18 56			
	d										18 29										18 59			
Ton Pentre	d										18 31										19 01			
Treorchy	d										18 34										19 04			
Ynyswen	d										18 37										19 07			
Treherbert	a										18 44										19 14			

For general notes see front of timetable
For details of catering facilities see Directory of Train Operators

A From Coryton
B From Radyr
b Arr. 1834

Mondays to Fridays
from 8 September

Bridgend, Barry Island, Barry, Penarth and Cardiff → Coryton, Rhymney, Pontypridd, Merthyr, Aberdare and Treherbert

Network Diagram - see first page of Table 130

		AW	AW	AW A	AW	AW		AW	AW B	AW	AW	AW	AW A	AW	AW	AW	AW		AW	AW	AW	AW	AW	AW B	AW	AW B
Bridgend	d									17 42															18 42	
Llantwit Major	d									17 56															18 56	
Rhoose Cardiff Int Airport ✈	d									18 06															19 06	
Barry Island	d				17 56									18 26					18 41		18 56					
Barry 3	d				18 00					18 15				18 30					18 45		19 00				19 15	
Barry Docks	d				18 04					18 19				18 34					18 49		19 04				19 19	
Cadoxton	d				18 07					18 22				18 37					18 52		19 07				19 22	
Dinas Powys	d				18 11					18 26				18 41					18 56		19 11				19 26	
Eastbrook	d				18 13					18 28				18 43					18 58		19 13				19 28	
Cogan	d				18 15					18 30				18 45					19 00		19 15				19 30	
Penarth	d	18 02				18 17					18 32				18 47							19 17				
Dingle Road	d	18 04				18 19					18 34				18 49							19 19				
Grangetown	d	18 08			18 19	18 23				18 34	18 38			18 49	18 53				19 04		19 19	19 23			19 34	
Cardiff Central 7	a	18 14			18 24	18 29				18 39	18 47			18 54	18 59				19 09		19 24	19 29			19 39	
	d	18 16		18 21	18 26	18 31	18 36		18 36	18 41			18 51		19 01		19 06		19 11		19 26	19 31		19 36	19 41	
Cardiff Bay	d		18 19					18 34				18 49				19 04				19 19			19 34			
Cardiff Queen Street 3	a	18 19	18 23	18 24	18 29	18 34	18 38	18 38		18 44		18 53	18 54		19 04	19 08	19 09		19 14	19 23	19 29	19 34	19 38		19 44	
	d	18 20		18 25	18 30	18 35	18 40			18 50			18 55		19 05		19 10		19 15		19 30	19 35			19 45	
Heath Low Level	d			18 30									19 00													
Ty Glas	d			18 33									19 03													
Birchgrove	d			18 34									19 04													
Rhiwbina	d			18 36									19 06													
Whitchurch (Cardiff)	d			18 38					18 16				19 08													
Coryton	a			18 44									19 14													
Heath High Level	d	18 25				18 40									19 10							19 40				
Llanishen	d	18 28				18 43									19 13							19 43				
Lisvane & Thornhill	d	18 30				18 45									19 15							19 45				
Caerphilly 3	d	18 36				18 51									19a24							19 51				
Aber	d	18 38				18 53																19 53				
Llanbradach	d	18 42				18 57																19 57				
Ystrad Mynach 3	d	18a52				19 02																20 02				
Hengoed	d					19 05																20 05				
Pengam	d					19 08																20 08				
Gilfach Fargoed	d					19 11																20 11				
Bargoed	d					19 16																20 16				
Brithdir	d					19 20																20 20				
Tir-phil	d					19 23																20 23				
Pontlottyn	d					19 27																20 27				
Rhymney 3	a					19 34																20 34				
Cathays	d				18 33		18 43			18 52							19 13		19 18		19 33				19 48	
Llandaf	d				18 37		18 47			18 56							19 17		19 22		19 37				19 52	
Ninian Park	d								18 40															19 40		←
Waun-gron Park	d								18 44															19 44		19 44
Fairwater	d								18 46															→		19 46
Danescourt	d								18 49																	19 49
Radyr 3	a				18 40		18 50		18 57	18 58							19 20		19 25		19 40				19 55	19 57
	d				18 40		18 50			18 58							19 20		19 25		19 40				19 55	
Taffs Well 3	d				18 44		18 54			19 03							19 24		19 29		19 44				19 59	
Trefforest Estate	d				18 48																19 48					
Trefforest	d				18 52		19 01			19 10							19 31		19 36		19 52				20 06	
Pontypridd 3	a				18 55		19 04			19 13							19 34		19 39		19 55				20 09	
	d				18 56		19 06			19 14							19 36		19 41		19 56				20 11	
Abercynon	d				19 06					19 21									19 51		20 06				20 21	
Penrhiwceiber	d									19 27									19 57						20 27	
Mountain Ash	a									19 30									20 01						20 31	
	d									19 34									20 04						20 34	
Fernhill	d									19 37									20 07						20 37	
Cwmbach	d									19 41									20 11						20 41	
Aberdare 3	a									19 49									20 19						20 49	
Quakers Yard	d				19 11																20 11					
Merthyr Vale	d				19 18																20 18					
Troed Y Rhiw	d				19 22																20 22					
Pentre-bach	d				19 25																20 25					
Merthyr Tydfil	a				19 34																20 34					
Trehafod	d						19 11										19 41									
Porth	d						19 15										19 45									
Dinas Rhondda	d						19 19										19 49									
Tonypandy	d						19 21										19 51									
Llwynypia	d						19 23										19 53									
Ystrad Rhondda	a						19 26										19 56									
	d						19 29										19 59									
Ton Pentre	d						19 31										20 01									
Treorchy	d						19 34										20 04									
Ynyswen	d						19 37										20 07									
Treherbert	a						19 44										20 14									

For general notes see front of timetable
For details of catering facilities see Directory of Train Operators

A From Radyr
B From Coryton

Bridgend, Barry Island, Barry, Penarth and Cardiff → Coryton, Rhymney, Pontypridd, Merthyr, Aberdare and Treherbert

Network Diagram - see first page of Table 130

		AW	AW	AW	AW	AW	AW	AW	AW	AW	AW	AW A	AW	AW A	AW	AW	AW	AW	AW	AW	AW	AW	AW	AW	AW A
Bridgend	d												19 42												
Llantwit Major	d												19 56												
Rhoose Cardiff Int Airport ✈	d												20 06												
Barry Island	d			19 26					19 56												20 56				
Barry 3	d			19 30					20 00				20 15								21 00				
Barry Docks	d			19 34					20 04				20 19								21 04				
Cadoxton	d			19 37					20 07				20 22								21 07				
Dinas Powys	d			19 41					20 11				20 26								21 11				
Eastbrook	d			19 43					20 13				20 28								21 13				
Cogan	d			19 45					20 15				20 30								21 15				
Penarth	d				19 47					20 17							20 47						21 17		
Dingle Road	d				19 49					20 19							20 49						21 19		
Grangetown	d			19 49	19 53				20 19	20 24			20 34				20 53				21 19		21 23		
Cardiff Central 7	a			19 56	19 59				20 24	20 30			20 39				20 59				21 25		21 33		
	d		19 51		20 01		20 06		20 26	20 31		20 36	20 41			20 51	21 01		21 06		21 26	21 31			21 36
Cardiff Bay	d	19 49				20 04		20 19			20 34				20 49			21 04		21 19				21 34	
Cardiff Queen Street 3	a	19 53	19 54		20 04	20 08	20 09	20 23	20 29	20 34	20 38		20 44		20 53	20 54	21 04	21 08	21 09	21 23	21 29	21 34		21 38	
	d		19 55		20 05		20 10		20 30	20 35			20 45			20 55	21 05		21 10		21 30	21 35			
Heath Low Level	d		20 00													21 00									
Ty Glas	d		20 03													21 03									
Birchgrove	d		20 04													21 04									
Rhiwbina	d		20 06													21 06									
Whitchurch (Cardiff)	d		20 08													21 08									
Coryton	a		20 14													21 14									
Heath High Level	d				20 10					20 40							21 10					21 40			
Llanishen	d				20 13					20 43							21 13					21 43			
Lisvane & Thornhill	d				20 15					20 45							21 15					21 45			
Caerphilly 3	d				20a28					20 51							21a28					21 51			
Aber	d									20 53												21 53			
Llanbradach	d									20 57												21 57			
Ystrad Mynach 3	d									21 02												22 02			
Hengoed	d									21 05												22 05			
Pengam	d									21 08												22 08			
Gilfach Fargoed	d									21 11												22 11			
Bargoed	d									21 16												22 16			
Brithdir	d									21 20												22 20			
Tir-phil	d									21 23												22 23			
Pontlottyn	d									21 27												22 27			
Rhymney 3	a									21 34												22 34			
Cathays	d						20 13		20 33				20 48						21 13		21 33				
Llandaf	d						20 17		20 37				20 52						21 17		21 37				
Ninian Park	d											20 40		←											21 40
Waun-gron Park	d											20 44 →		20 44											21 44 →
Fairwater	d													20 46											
Danescourt	d													20 49											
Radyr 3	a						20 20		20 40				20 55	20 57					21 20		21 40				
	d						20 20		20 40				20 55						21 20		21 40				
Taffs Well 3	d						20 24		20 44				20 59						21 24		21 44				
Trefforest Estate	d								20 48												21 48				
Trefforest	d						20 31		20 52				21 06						21 31		21 52				
Pontypridd 3	a						20 34		20 55				21 09						21 34		21 55				
	d						20 36		20 56				21 11						21 36		21 56				
Abercynon	d								21 06				21 21								22 06				
Penrhiwceiber	d												21 27												
Mountain Ash	a												21 31												
	d												21 34												
Fernhill	d												21 37												
Cwmbach	d												21 41												
Aberdare 3	a												21 49												
Quakers Yard	d								21 11												22 11				
Merthyr Vale	d								21 18												22 18				
Troed Y Rhiw	d								21 22												22 22				
Pentre-bach	d								21 25												22 25				
Merthyr Tydfil	a								21 34												22 34				
Trehafod	d						20 41												21 41						
Porth	d						20 45												21 45						
Dinas Rhondda	d						20 59												21 49						
Tonypandy	d						20 51												21 51						
Llwynypia	d						20 53												21 53						
Ystrad Rhondda	a						20 56												21 56						
	d						20 59												21 59						
Ton Pentre	d						21 01												22 01						
Treorchy	d						21 04												22 04						
Ynyswen	d						21 07												22 07						
Treherbert	a						21 14												22 14						

For general notes see front of timetable
For details of catering facilities see
Directory of Train Operators

A From Coryton

from 8 September

Bridgend, Barry Island, Barry, Penarth and Cardiff → Coryton, Rhymney, Pontypridd, Merthyr, Aberdare and Treherbert

Network Diagram - see first page of Table 130

Station		AW	AW A	AW	AW	AW	AW	AW	AW	AW	AW	AW	AW	AW	AW	AW	AW	AW	AW	AW	AW	AW	AW
Bridgend	d	20 42											21 42									22 42	
Llantwit Major	d	20 56											21 56									22 56	
Rhoose Cardiff Int Airport ✈	d	21 06											22 06									23 06	
Barry Island	d									21 56									22 56				
Barry 3	d	21 15								22 00			22 15						23 00			23 15	
Barry Docks	d	21 19								22 04			22 19						23 04			23 19	
Cadoxton	d	21 22								22 07			22 22						23 07			23 22	
Dinas Powys	d	21 26								22 11			22 26						23 11			23 26	
Eastbrook	d	21 28								22 13			22 28						23 13			23 28	
Cogan	d	21 30								22 15			22 30						23 15			23 30	
Penarth	d				21 47						22 17						22 47				23 26		
Dingle Road	d				21 49						22 19						22 49				23 28		
Grangetown	d	21 34			21 53					22 19	22 23		22 34				22 53		23 19		23 32	23 34	
Cardiff Central 7	a	21 39			21 59					22 25	22 31		22 39				23 00		23 24		23 40	23 42	
	d	21 41			22 00		22 06	22 11		22 26	22 35		22 41	22 46			23 15		23 26				
Cardiff Bay	d			21 49		22 04			22 19			22 34			22 49	23 04		23 19		23 34			23 49
Cardiff Queen Street 3	a	21 44		21 53	22 04	22 08	22 09	22 14	22 23	22 29	22 38	22 38	22 44	22 49	22 53	23 08	23 18	23 23	23 29	23 38			23 53
	d	21 45			22 05		22 10	22 15		22 30	22 39		22 45	22 50			23 19		23 30				
Heath Low Level	d																						
Ty Glas	d																						
Birchgrove	d																						
Rhiwbina	d																						
Whitchurch (Cardiff)	d																						
Coryton	a																						
Heath High Level	d				22 10						22 44						23 24						
Llanishen	d				22 13						22 47						23 27						
Lisvane & Thornhill	d				22 15						22 49						23 29						
Caerphilly 3	d				22a24						22 55						23 35						
Aber	d										22 57						23 37						
Llanbradach	d										23 01						23 41						
Ystrad Mynach 3	d										23 06						23a51						
Hengoed	d										23 09												
Pengam	d										23 12												
Gilfach Fargoed	d										23 15												
Bargoed	d										23 20												
Brithdir	d										23 24												
Tir-phil	d										23 27												
Pontlottyn	d										23 31												
Rhymney 3	a										23 38												
Cathays	d	21 48					22 13	22 18		22 33			22 48	22 53					23 33				
Llandaf	d	21 52					22 17	22 22		22 37			22 52	22 57					23 37				
Ninian Park	d		←																				
Waun-gron Park	d		21 44																				
Fairwater	d		21 46																				
Danescourt	d		21 49																				
Radyr 3	a	21 55	21 57				22 20	22 25		22 40			22 55	22 59					23 40				
	d	21 55					22 20	22 25		22 40			22 55	22 59					23 40				
Taffs Well 3	d	21 59					22 24	22 29		22 44			22 59	23 03					23 44				
Trefforest Estate	d									22 48									23 48				
Trefforest	d	22 06					22 31	22 36		22 52			23 06	23 10					23 52				
Pontypridd 3	a	22 09					22 34	22 43		22 55			23 09	23 14					00 01				
	d	22 11					22 36			22 56			23 11	23 15									
Abercynon	d	22 21								23 06			23 21										
Penrhiwceiber	d	22 27											23 27										
Mountain Ash	a	22 31											23 31										
	d	22 34											23 34										
Fernhill	d	22 37											23 37										
Cwmbach	d	22 41											23 41										
Aberdare 3	a	22 49											23 49										
Quakers Yard	d									23 11													
Merthyr Vale	d									23 18													
Troed Y Rhiw	d									23 22													
Pentre-bach	d									23 25													
Merthyr Tydfil	a									23 34													
Trehafod	d						22 41							23 20									
Porth	d						22 45							23 24									
Dinas Rhondda	d						22 49							23 28									
Tonypandy	d						22 51							23 30									
Llwynypia	d						22 53							23 32									
Ystrad Rhondda	a						22 56							23 35									
	d						22 59							23 38									
Ton Pentre	d						23 01							23 40									
Treorchy	d						23 04							23 43									
Ynyswen	d						23 07							23 46									
Treherbert	a						23 14							23 53									

For general notes see front of timetable
For details of catering facilities see Directory of Train Operators

A From Coryton

Table 130

until 6 September

Bridgend, Barry Island, Barry, Penarth and Cardiff → Coryton, Rhymney, Pontypridd, Merthyr, Aberdare and Treherbert

Network Diagram - see first page of Table 130

		AW		AW	AW	AW	AW	AW	AW	AW	AW	AW	AW	AW	AW	AW	AW	AW		AW	AW	AW	AW	AW	AW	AW
																	A					B				
Bridgend	d									05 42																
Llantwit Major	d									05 56																
Rhoose Cardiff Int Airport ✈	d									06 06																
Barry Island	d							05 56						06 26									06 56			
Barry 3	d							06 00		06 15				06 30									07 00			
Barry Docks	d							06 04		06 19				06 34									07 04			
Cadoxton	d							06 07		06 22				06 37									07 07			
Dinas Powys	d							06 11		06 26				06 41									07 11			
Eastbrook	d							06 13		06 28				06 43									07 13			
Cogan	d							06 15		06 30				06 45									07 15			
Penarth	d										06 32									07 02				07 17		
Dingle Road	d										06 34									07 04				07 19		
Grangetown	d							06 19		06 34	06 38			06 49						07 08			07 19	07 23		
Cardiff Central 7	a							06 24		06 39	06 44			06 54						07 14			07 24	07 29		
	d	05 26		05 46	06 11	06 16	06 21	06 26	06 36	06 41	06 46		06 51	06 56		07 06	07 06	07 11		07 16		07 21	07 26	07 31		07 36
Cardiff Bay	d											06 49			07 04						07 19				07 34	
Cardiff Queen Street 3	a	05 29		05 49	06 14	06 19	06 24	06 29	06 39	06 44	06 49	06 53	06 54	06 59	07 08	07 09		07 14		07 19	07 23	07 24	07 29	07 34	07 38	07 39
	d	05 30		05 50	06 15	06 20	06 25	06 30	06 40	06 45	06 50		06 55	07 00		07 10		07 15		07 20		07 25	07 30	07 35		07 40
Heath Low Level	d						06 30						07 00									07 30				
Ty Glas	d						06 33						07 03									07 33				
Birchgrove	d						06 34						07 04									07 34				
Rhiwbina	d						06 36						07 06									07 36				
Whitchurch (Cardiff)	d						06 38						07 08									07 38				
Coryton	a						06 43						07 13									07 43				
Heath High Level	d			05 54		06 25					06 55									07 25				07 40		
Llanishen	d			05 57		06 28					06 58									07 28				07 43		
Lisvane & Thornhill	d			06 00		06 30					07 00									07 30				07 45		
Caerphilly 3	d			06a09		06 36					07 06									07 36				07 51		
Aber	d					06 38					07 08									07 38				07 53		
Llanbradach	d					06 42					07 12									07 42				07 57		
Ystrad Mynach 3	d					06 47					07 17									07 47				08 02		
Hengoed	d					06 50					07 20									07 50				08 05		
Pengam	d					06 53					07 23									07 53				08 08		
Gilfach Fargoed	d																									
Bargoed	d					07a01					07a31									08a01				08 14		
Brithdir	d																							08 18		
Tir-phil	d																							08 21		
Pontlottyn	d																							08 25		
Rhymney 3	a																							08 31		
Cathays	d	05 33			06 18			06 33	06 43	06 48				07 03		07 13		07 18					07 33			07 43
Llandaf	d	05 37			06 22			06 37	06 47	06 52				07 07		07 17		07 22					07 37			07 47
Ninian Park	d																07 10									
Waun-gron Park	d																07 13									
Fairwater	d																07 15									
Danescourt	d																07 17									
Radyr 3	a	05 39			06 24			06 40	06 50	06 54				07 10		07 20	07 24	07 25					07 40			07 50
	d	05 40			06 24			06 40	06 50	06 55				07 10		07 20		07 25					07 40			07 50
Taffs Well 3	d	05 43			06 28			06 44	06 54	06 59				07 14		07 24		07 29					07 44			07 54
Trefforest Estate	d	05 47						06 48						07 18									07 48			
Trefforest	d	05 52			06 35			06 52	07 01	07 06				07 22		07 31		07 36					07 52			08 01
Pontypridd 3	a	05 55			06 38			06 55	07 04	07 09				07 32		07 34		07 39					07 55			08 04
	d	05 56	06 11		06 41			06 56	07 06	07 11						07 36		07 41					07 56			08 06
Abercynon	d	06 06	06 21		06 51			07 06		07 21								07 51					08 06			
Penrhiwceiber	d		06 27		06 57					07 27								07 57								
Mountain Ash	a		06 30		07 00					07 30								08 00								
	d		06 33		07 03					07 33								08 03								
Fernhill	d		06 35		07 05					07 35								08 05								
Cwmbach	d		06 39		07 09					07 39								08 09								
Aberdare 3	a		06 46		07 16					07 46								08 16								
Quakers Yard	d	06 10						07 10															08 10			
Merthyr Vale	d	06 18						07 18															08 18			
Troed Y Rhiw	d	06 21						07 21															08 21			
Pentre-bach	d	06 24						07 24															08 24			
Merthyr Tydfil	a	06 32						07 32															08 32			
Trehafod	d								07 11							07 41										08 11
Porth	d								07 15							07 45										08 15
Dinas Rhondda	d								07 19							07 49										08 19
Tonypandy	d								07 21							07 51										08 21
Llwynypia	d								07 23							07 53										08 23
Ystrad Rhondda	a								07 26							07 56										08 26
	d								07 29							07 59										08 29
Ton Pentre	d								07 31							08 01										08 31
Treorchy	d								07 34							08 04										08 34
Ynyswen	d								07 37							08 07										08 37
Treherbert	a								07 43							08 13										08 43

For general notes see front of timetable
For details of catering facilities see Directory of Train Operators

A From Coryton
B From Taffs Well

Table 130

Saturdays until 6 September

Bridgend, Barry Island, Barry, Penarth and Cardiff → Coryton, Rhymney, Pontypridd, Merthyr, Aberdare and Treherbert

Network Diagram - see first page of Table 130

		AW A	AW	AW	AW	AW B	AW	AW	AW	AW	AW A	AW	AW	AW	AW B	AW	AW	AW	AW	AW A	AW	AW	AW	AW B	AW
Bridgend	d		06 42																		07 42				
Llantwit Major	d		06 56																		07 56				
Rhoose Cardiff Int Airport ✈	d		07 06																		08 06				
Barry Island	d						07 26					07 41				07 56									08 26
Barry 3	d		07 15				07 30					07 45				08 00					08 15				08 30
Barry Docks	d		07 19				07 34					07 49				08 04					08 19				08 34
Cadoxton	d		07 22				07 37					07 52				08 07					08 22				08 37
Dinas Powys	d		07 26				07 41					07 56				08 11					08 26				08 41
Eastbrook	d		07 28				07 43					07 58				08 13					08 28				08 43
Cogan	d		07 30				07 45					08 00				08 15					08 30				08 45
Penarth	d			07 32				07 47					08 02				08 17					08 32			
Dingle Road	d			07 34				07 49					08 04				08 19					08 34			
Grangetown	d		07 34	07 38			07 49	07 53				08 04	08 08			08 19	08 23				08 34	08 38			08 49
Cardiff Central 7	a		07 39	07 44			07 55	07 59				08 09	08 14			08 24	08 29				08 39	08 44			08 54
	d	07 36	07 41	07 46		07 51	07 56	08 01		08 06	08 06	08 11	08 16		08 21	08 26	08 31		08 36	08 36	08 41	08 46		08 51	08 56
Cardiff Bay	d				07 49				08 04					08 19				08 34					08 49		
Cardiff Queen Street 3	a		07 44	07 49	07 53	07 54	07 59	08 04	08 08	08 09		08 14	08 19	08 23	08 24	08 29	08 34	08 38	08 39		08 44	08 49	08 53	08 54	08 59
	d		07 45	07 50		07 55	08 00	08 05		08 10		08 15	08 20		08 25	08 30	08 35		08 40		08 45	08 50		08 55	09 00
Heath Low Level	d					08 00									08 30									09 00	
Ty Glas	d					08 03									08 33									09 03	
Birchgrove	d					08 04									08 34									09 04	
Rhiwbina	d					08 06									08 36									09 06	
Whitchurch (Cardiff)	d	07 16				08 08					07 46				08 38									09 08	
Coryton	a					08 13									08 43									09 13	
Heath High Level	d			07 55				08 10					08 25				08 40					08 55			
Llanishen	d			07 58				08 13					08 28				08 43					08 58			
Lisvane & Thornhill	d			08 00				08 15					08 30				08 45					09 00			
Caerphilly 3	d			08 06				08 21					08 36				08 51					09 06			
Aber	d			08 08				08 23					08 38				08 53					09 08			
Llanbradach	d			08 12				08 27					08 42				08 57					09 12			
Ystrad Mynach 3	d			08 17				08 32					08 47				09 02					09 17			
Hengoed	d			08 20				08 35					08 50				09 05					09 20			
Pengam	d			08 23				08 38					08 53				09 08					09 23			
Gilfach Fargoed	d							08 41																	
Bargoed	d			08a31				08a48					08 59				09a16					09a31			
Brithdir	d												09 03												
Tir-phil	d												09 06												
Pontlottyn	d												09 10												
Rhymney 3	a												09 16												
Cathays	d		07 48				08 03			08 13		08 18				08 33			08 43		08 48				09 03
Llandaf	d		07 52				08 07			08 17		08 22				08 37			08 47		08 52				09 07
Ninian Park	d	07 40									08 10									08 40					
Waun-gron Park	d	07 43									08 13									08 43					
Fairwater	d	07 45									08 15									08 45					
Danescourt	d	07 47									08 17									08 47					
Radyr 3	a	07 54	07 55				08 10			08 20	08 24	08 25				08 40			08 50	08 54	08 55				09 10
	d		07 55				08 10			08 20		08 25				08 40			08 50		08 55				09 10
Taffs Well 3	d		07 59				08 14			08 24		08 29				08 44			08 54		08 59				09 14
Trefforest Estate	d						08 18									08 48									09 18
Trefforest	d		08 06				08 22			08 31		08 36				08 52			09 01		09 06				09 22
Pontypridd 3	a		08 09				08 32			08 34		08 39				08 55			09 04		09 09				09 32
	d		08 11							08 36		08 41				08 56			09 06		09 11				
Abercynon	d		08 21									08 51				09 06					09 21				
Penrhiwceiber	d		08 27									08 57									09 27				
Mountain Ash	a		08 30									09 00									09 30				
	d		08 33									09 03									09 33				
Fernhill	d		08 35									09 05									09 35				
Cwmbach	d		08 39									09 09									09 39				
Aberdare 3	a		08 46									09 16									09 46				
Quakers Yard	d															09 10									
Merthyr Vale	d															09 18									
Troed Y Rhiw	d															09 21									
Pentre-bach	d															09 24									
Merthyr Tydfil	a															09 32									
Trehafod	d									08 41									09 11						
Porth	d									08 45									09 15						
Dinas Rhondda	d									08 49									09 19						
Tonypandy	d									08 51									09 21						
Llwynypia	d									08 53									09 23						
Ystrad Rhondda	a									08 56									09 26						
	d									08 59									09 29						
Ton Pentre	d									09 01									09 31						
Treorchy	d									09 04									09 34						
Ynyswen	d									09 07									09 37						
Treherbert	a									09 13									09 43						

For general notes see front of timetable
For details of catering facilities see Directory of Train Operators

A From Coryton
B From Radyr

until 6 September

Bridgend, Barry Island, Barry, Penarth and Cardiff → Coryton, Rhymney, Pontypridd, Merthyr, Aberdare and Treherbert

Network Diagram - see first page of Table 130

		AW	AW	AW	AW	AW	AW	AW		AW	AW	AW	AW	AW	AW	AW	AW	AW	AW	AW	AW	AW	AW	AW	AW	AW
					A					B					A				B					A		
Bridgend	d															08 42										
Llantwit Major	d															08 56										
Rhoose Cardiff Int Airport ✈	d															09 06										
Barry Island	d					08 41					08 56									09 26					09 41	
Barry 3	d					08 45					09 00					09 15				09 30					09 45	
Barry Docks	d					08 49					09 04					09 19				09 34					09 49	
Cadoxton	d					08 52					09 07					09 22				09 37					09 52	
Dinas Powys	d					08 56					09 11					09 26				09 41					09 56	
Eastbrook	d					08 58					09 13					09 28				09 43					09 58	
Cogan	d					09 00					09 15					09 30				09 45					10 00	
Penarth	d	08 47										09 17					09 32				09 47					10 02
Dingle Road	d	08 49										09 19					09 34				09 49					10 04
Grangetown	d	08 53				09 04					09 19	09 23				09 34	09 38			09 49	09 53				10 04	10 08
Cardiff Central 7	a	08 59				09 09					09 24	09 29				09 39	09 44			09 54	09 59				10 09	10 14
	d	09 01		09 06	09 06	09 11	09 16			09 21	09 26	09 31		09 36	09 36	09 41	09 46		09 51	09 56	10 01		10 06	10 06	10 11	10 16
Cardiff Bay	d		09 04					09 19					09 34					09 49				10 04				
Cardiff Queen Street 3	a	09 04	09 08	09 09		09 14	09 19	09 23		09 24	09 29	09 34	09 38	09 39		09 44	09 49	09 53	09 54	09 59	10 04	10 08	10 09		10 14	10 19
	d	09 05		09 10		09 15	09 20			09 25	09 30	09 35		09 40		09 45	09 50		09 55	10 00	10 05		10 10		10 15	10 20
Heath Low Level	d									09 30									10 00							
Ty Glas	d									09 33									10 03							
Birchgrove	d									09 34									10 04							
Rhiwbina	d									09 36									10 06							
Whitchurch (Cardiff)	d									09 38									10 08							
Coryton	a									09 43									10 13							
Heath High Level	d	09 10					09 25					09 40					09 55				10 10					10 25
Llanishen	d	09 13					09 28					09 43					09 58				10 13					10 28
Lisvane & Thornhill	d	09 15					09 30					09 45					10 00				10 15					10 30
Caerphilly 3	d	09 21					09 36					09 51					10 06				10 21					10 36
Aber	d	09 23					09 38					09 53					10 08				10 23					10 38
Llanbradach	d	09 27					09 42					09 57					10 12				10 27					10 42
Ystrad Mynach 3	d	09 32					09 47					10 02					10 17				10 32					10 47
Hengoed	d	09 35					09 50					10 05					10 20				10 35					10 50
Pengam	d	09 38					09 53					10 08					10 23				10 38					10 53
Gilfach Fargoed	d	09 41																			10 41					
Bargoed	d	09a48					09 59					10a16					10a31				10a48					10 59
Brithdir	d						10 03																			11 03
Tir-phil	d						10 06																			11 06
Pontlottyn	d						10 10																			11 10
Rhymney 3	a						10 16																			11 16
Cathays	d			09 13		09 18					09 33			09 43		09 48				10 03			10 13		10 18	
Llandaf	d			09 17		09 22					09 37			09 47		09 52				10 07			10 17		10 22	
Ninian Park	d				09 10										09 40									10 10		
Waun-gron Park	d				09 13										09 43									10 13		
Fairwater	d				09 15										09 45									10 15		
Danescourt	d				09 17										09 47									10 17		
Radyr 3	a			09 20	09 24	09 25					09 40			09 50	09 54	09 55				10 10			10 20	10 24	10 25	
	d			09 20		09 25					09 40			09 50		09 55				10 10			10 20		10 25	
Taffs Well 3	d			09 24		09 29					09 44			09 54		09 59				10 14			10 24		10 29	
Trefforest Estate	d										09 48									10 18						
Trefforest	d			09 31		09 36					09 52			10 01		10 06				10 22			10 31		10 36	
Pontypridd 3	a			09 34		09 39					09 55			10 04		10 09				10 32			10 34		10 39	
	d			09 36		09 41					09 56			10 06		10 11							10 36		10 41	
Abercynon	d					09 51					10 06					10 21									10 51	
Penrhiwceiber	d					09 57										10 27									10 57	
Mountain Ash	a					10 00										10 30									11 00	
	d					10 03										10 33									11 03	
Fernhill	d					10 05										10 35									11 05	
Cwmbach	d					10 09										10 39									11 09	
Aberdare 3	a					10 16										10 46									11 16	
Quakers Yard	d										10 10															
Merthyr Vale	d										10 18															
Troed Y Rhiw	d										10 21															
Pentre-bach	d										10 24															
Merthyr Tydfil	a										10 32															
Trehafod	d			09 41										10 11									10 41			
Porth	d			09 45										10 15									10 45			
Dinas Rhondda	d			09 49										10 19									10 49			
Tonypandy	d			09 51										10 21									10 51			
Llwynypia	d			09 53										10 23									10 53			
Ystrad Rhondda	a			09 56										10 26									10 56			
	d			09 59										10 29									10 59			
Ton Pentre	d			10 01										10 31									11 01			
Treorchy	d			10 04										10 34									11 04			
Ynyswen	d			10 07										10 37									11 07			
Treherbert	a			10 13										10 43									11 13			

For general notes see front of timetable
For details of catering facilities see Directory of Train Operators

A From Coryton
B From Radyr

Table 130

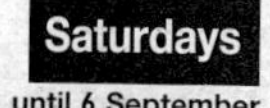

until 6 September

Bridgend, Barry Island, Barry, Penarth and Cardiff → Coryton, Rhymney, Pontypridd, Merthyr, Aberdare and Treherbert

Network Diagram - see first page of Table 130

		AW	AW A		AW	AW	AW	AW	AW B	AW	AW	AW	AW A	AW	AW	AW	AW	AW B	AW	AW	AW		AW A	AW	AW	AW
Bridgend	d									09 42																
Llantwit Major	d									09 56																
Rhoose Cardiff Int Airport ✈	d									10 06																
Barry Island	d				09 56										10 26				10 41					10 56		
Barry 3	d				10 00					10 15					10 30				10 45					11 00		
Barry Docks	d				10 04					10 19					10 34				10 49					11 04		
Cadoxton	d				10 07					10 22					10 37				10 52					11 07		
Dinas Powys	d				10 11					10 26					10 41				10 56					11 11		
Eastbrook	d				10 13					10 28					10 43				10 58					11 13		
Cogan	d				10 15					10 30					10 45				11 00					11 15		
Penarth	d					10 17					10 32					10 47				11 02					11 17	
Dingle Road	d					10 19					10 34					10 49				11 04					11 19	
Grangetown	d				10 19	10 23				10 34	10 38				10 49	10 53			11 04	11 08				11 19	11 23	
Cardiff Central 7	a				10 24	10 29				10 42	10 44				10 54	10 59			11 09	11 14				11 24	11 29	
	d		10 21		10 26	10 31		10 36	10 36		10 46		10 51	10 51	10 56	11 01		11 06	11 11	11 16			11 21	11 26	11 31	
Cardiff Bay	d	10 19					10 34					10 49					11 04				11 19					11 34
Cardiff Queen Street 3	a	10 23	10 24		10 29	10 34	10 38	10 39			10 49	10 53	10 54		10 59	11 04	11 08		11 14	11 19	11 23		11 24	11 29	11 34	11 38
	d		10 25		10 30	10 35		10 40			10 50		10 55		11 00	11 05			11 15	11 20			11 25	11 30	11 35	
Heath Low Level	d		10 30										11 00										11 30			
Ty Glas	d		10 33										11 03										11 33			
Birchgrove	d		10 34										11 04										11 34			
Rhiwbina	d		10 36										11 06										11 36			
Whitchurch (Cardiff)	d		10 38										11 08										11 38			
Coryton	a		10 43										11 13										11 43			
Heath High Level	d					10 40					10 55					11 10				11 25					11 40	
Llanishen	d					10 43					10 58					11 13				11 28					11 43	
Lisvane & Thornhill	d					10 45					11 00					11 15				11 30					11 45	
Caerphilly 3	d					10 51					11 06					11 21				11 36					11 51	
Aber	d					10 53					11 08					11 23				11 38					11 53	
Llanbradach	d					10 57					11 12					11 27				11 42					11 57	
Ystrad Mynach 3	d					11 02					11 17					11 32				11 47					12 02	
Hengoed	d					11 05					11 20					11 35				11 50					12 05	
Pengam	d					11 08					11 23					11 38				11 53					12 08	
Gilfach Fargoed	d															11 41										
Bargoed	d					11a16					11a31					11a48				11 59					12a16	
Brithdir	d																			12 03						
Tir-phil	d																			12 06						
Pontlottyn	d																			12 10						
Rhymney 3	a																			12 16						
Cathays	d				10 33			10 43							11 03				11 18					11 33		
Llandaf	d				10 37			10 47							11 07				11 22					11 37		
Ninian Park	d								10 40									11 10								
Waun-gron Park	d								10 43									11 13								
Fairwater	d								10 45									11 15								
Danescourt	d								10 47									11 17								
Radyr 3	a				10 40			10 50	10 54					11 02	11 10			11 24	11 25					11 40		
	d				10 40			10 50						11 05	11 10				11 25					11 40		
Taffs Well 3	d				10 44			10 54						11 09	11 14				11 29					11 44		
Trefforest Estate	d				10 48										11 18									11 48		
Trefforest	d				10 52			11 01						11 16	11 22				11 36					11 52		
Pontypridd 3	a				10 55			11 04						11 19	11 32				11 39					11 55		
	d				10 56			11 06						11 22					11 41					11 56		
Abercynon	d				11 06														11 51					12 06		
Penrhiwceiber	d																		11 57							
Mountain Ash	a																		12 00							
	d																		12 03							
Fernhill	d																		12 05							
Cwmbach	d																		12 09							
Aberdare 3	a																		12 16							
Quakers Yard	d				11 10																			12 10		
Merthyr Vale	d				11 18																			12 18		
Troed Y Rhiw	d				11 21																			12 21		
Pentre-bach	d				11 24																			12 24		
Merthyr Tydfil	a				11 32																			12 32		
Trehafod	d							11 11						11 27												
Porth	d							11 15						11b45												
Dinas Rhondda	d							11 19						11 49												
Tonypandy	d							11 21						11 51												
Llwynypia	d							11 23						11 53												
Ystrad Rhondda	a							11 26						11 56												
	d							11 29						11 59												
Ton Pentre	d							11 31						12 01												
Treorchy	d							11 34						12 04												
Ynyswen	d							11 37						12 07												
Treherbert	a							11 43						12 13												

For general notes see front of timetable
For details of catering facilities see Directory of Train Operators

A From Radyr
B From Coryton
b Arr. 1130

Table 130

until 6 September

Bridgend, Barry Island, Barry, Penarth and Cardiff → Coryton, Rhymney, Pontypridd, Merthyr, Aberdare and Treherbert

Network Diagram - see first page of Table 130

		AW	AW A	AW	AW	AW	AW	AW B	AW	AW	AW	AW	AW A	AW	AW	AW	AW B	AW	AW	AW	AW	AW A	AW	AW	AW
Bridgend	d				10 42																		11 42		
Llantwit Major	d				10 56																		11 56		
Rhoose Cardiff Int Airport ✈	d				11 06																		12 06		
Barry Island	d								11 26					11 41				11 56							
Barry [3]	d				11 15				11 30					11 45				12 00					12 15		
Barry Docks	d				11 19				11 34					11 49				12 04					12 19		
Cadoxton	d				11 22				11 37					11 52				12 07					12 22		
Dinas Powys	d				11 26				11 41					11 56				12 11					12 26		
Eastbrook	d				11 28				11 43					11 58				12 13					12 28		
Cogan	d				11 30				11 45					12 00				12 15					12 30		
Penarth	d					11 32				11 47					12 02				12 17					12 32	
Dingle Road	d					11 34				11 49					12 04				12 19					12 34	
Grangetown	d				11 34	11 38			11 49	11 53				12 04	12 08			12 19	12 23				12 34	12 38	
Cardiff Central [7]	a				11 44	11 44			11 54	11 59				12 09	12 14			12 24	12 29				12 39	12 44	
	d	11 36	11 36	11 41		11 46		11 51	11 56	12 01		12 06	12 06	12 11	12 16		12 21	12 26	12 31		12 36	12 36	12 41	12 46	
Cardiff Bay	d						11 49				12 04					12 19				12 34					12 49
Cardiff Queen Street [3]	a	11 39		11 44		11 49	11 53	11 54	11 59	12 04	12 08	12 09		12 14	12 19	12 23	12 24	12 29	12 34	12 38	12 39		12 44	12 49	12 53
	d	11 40		11 45		11 50		11 55	12 00	12 05		12 10		12 15	12 20		12 25	12 30	12 35		12 40		12 45	12 50	
Heath Low Level	d							12 00									12 30								
Ty Glas	d							12 03									12 33								
Birchgrove	d							12 04									12 34								
Rhiwbina	d							12 06									12 36								
Whitchurch (Cardiff)	d							12 08									12 38								
Coryton	a							12 13									12 43								
Heath High Level	d					11 55				12 10					12 25				12 40					12 55	
Llanishen	d					11 58				12 13					12 28				12 43					12 58	
Lisvane & Thornhill	d					12 00				12 15					12 30				12 45					13 00	
Caerphilly [3]	d					12 06				12 21					12 36				12 51					13 06	
Aber	d					12 08				12 23					12 38				12 53					13 08	
Llanbradach	d					12 12				12 27					12 42				12 57					13 12	
Ystrad Mynach [3]	d					12 17				12 32					12 47				13 02					13 17	
Hengoed	d					12 20				12 35					12 50				13 05					13 20	
Pengam	d					12 23				12 38					12 53				13 08					13 23	
Gilfach Fargoed	d									12 41															
Bargoed	d					12a31				12a48					12 59				13a16					13a31	
Brithdir	d														13 03										
Tir-phil	d														13 06										
Pontlottyn	d														13 10										
Rhymney [3]	a														13 16										
Cathays	d	11 43		11 48					12 03			12 13		12 18				12 33			12 43		12 48		
Llandaf	d	11 47		11 52					12 07			12 17		12 22				12 37			12 47		12 52		
Ninian Park	d		11 40										12 10									12 40			
Waun-gron Park	d		11 43										12 13									12 43			
Fairwater	d		11 45										12 15									12 45			
Danescourt	d		11 47										12 17									12 47			
Radyr [3]	a	11 50	11 54	11 54					12 10			12 20	12 24	12 25				12 40			12 50	12 54	12 55		
	d	11 50		11 55					12 10			12 20		12 25				12 40			12 50		12 55		
Taffs Well [3]	d	11 54		11 59					12 14			12 24		12 29				12 44			12 54		12 59		
Trefforest Estate	d								12 18									12 48							
Trefforest	d	12 01		12 06					12 22			12 31		12 36				12 52			13 01		13 06		
Pontypridd [3]	a	12 04		12 09					12 32			12 34		12 42				12 55			13 04		13 09		
	d	12 06		12 11								12 36						12 56			13 06		13 11		
Abercynon	d			12 22														13 06					13 21		
Penrhiwceiber	d			12 28																			13 27		
Mountain Ash	a			12 31																			13 30		
	d			12 33																			13 33		
Fernhill	d			12 35																			13 35		
Cwmbach	d			12 39																			13 39		
Aberdare [3]	a			12 46																			13 46		
Quakers Yard	d																	13 10							
Merthyr Vale	d																	13 18							
Troed Y Rhiw	d																	13 21							
Pentre-bach	d																	13 24							
Merthyr Tydfil	a																	13 32							
Trehafod	d	12 11										12 41									13 11				
Porth	d	12 15										12 45									13 15				
Dinas Rhondda	d	12 19										12 49									13 19				
Tonypandy	d	12 21										12 51									13 21				
Llwynypia	d	12 23										12 53									13 23				
Ystrad Rhondda	a	12 26										12 56									13 26				
	d	12 29										12 59									13 29				
Ton Pentre	d	12 31										13 01									13 31				
Treorchy	d	12 34										13 04									13 34				
Ynyswen	d	12 37										13 07									13 37				
Treherbert	a	12 43										13 13									13 43				

For general notes see front of timetable
For details of catering facilities see Directory of Train Operators

A From Coryton
B From Radyr

Table 130

until 6 September

Bridgend, Barry Island, Barry, Penarth and Cardiff → Coryton, Rhymney, Pontypridd, Merthyr, Aberdare and Treherbert

Network Diagram - see first page of Table 130

Station		AW A	AW	AW	AW	AW	AW B	AW	AW	AW	AW A	AW	AW	AW	AW	AW B	AW	AW	AW	AW A	AW	AW	AW	AW	AW B
Bridgend	d																12 42								
Llantwit Major	d																12 56								
Rhoose Cardiff Int Airport ✈	d																13 06								
Barry Island	d		12 26					12 41				12 56									13 26				
Barry 3	d		12 30					12 45				13 00					13 15				13 30				
Barry Docks	d		12 34					12 49				13 04					13 19				13 34				
Cadoxton	d		12 37					12 52				13 07					13 22				13 37				
Dinas Powys	d		12 41					12 56				13 11					13 26				13 41				
Eastbrook	d		12 43					12 58				13 13					13 28				13 43				
Cogan	d		12 45					13 00				13 15					13 30				13 45				
Penarth	d			12 47					13 02				13 17					13 32				13 47			
Dingle Road	d			12 49					13 04				13 19					13 34				13 49			
Grangetown	d		12 49	12 53				13 04	13 08			13 19	13 23				13 34	13 38			13 49	13 53			
Cardiff Central 7	a		12 54	12 59				13 09	13 14			13 24	13 29				13 39	13 44			13 54	13 59			
	d	12 51	12 56	13 01		13 06	13 06	13 11	13 16		13 21	13 26	13 31		13 36	13 36	13 41	13 46		13 51	13 56	14 01		14 06	14 06
Cardiff Bay	d				13 04					13 19				13 34					13 49				14 04		
Cardiff Queen Street 3	a	12 54	12 59	13 04	13 08	13 09		13 14	13 19	13 23	13 24	13 29	13 34	13 38	13 39		13 44	13 49	13 53	13 54	13 59	14 04	14 08	14 09	
	d	12 55	13 00	13 05		13 10		13 15	13 20		13 25	13 30	13 35		13 40		13 45	13 50		13 55	14 00	14 05		14 10	
Heath Low Level	d	13 00									13 30									14 00					
Ty Glas	d	13 03									13 33									14 03					
Birchgrove	d	13 04									13 34									14 04					
Rhiwbina	d	13 06									13 36									14 06					
Whitchurch (Cardiff)	d	13 08					12 46				13 38									14 08					
Coryton	a	13 13									13 43									14 13					
Heath High Level	d			13 10					13 25				13 40					13 55				14 10			
Llanishen	d			13 13					13 28				13 43					13 58				14 13			
Lisvane & Thornhill	d			13 15					13 30				13 45					14 00				14 15			
Caerphilly 3	d			13 21					13 36				13 51					14 06				14 21			
Aber	d			13 23					13 38				13 53					14 08				14 23			
Llanbradach	d			13 27					13 42				13 57					14 12				14 27			
Ystrad Mynach 3	d			13 32					13 47				14 02					14 17				14 32			
Hengoed	d			13 35					13 50				14 05					14 20				14 35			
Pengam	d			13 38					13 53				14 08					14 23				14 38			
Gilfach Fargoed	d			13 41																		14 41			
Bargoed	d			13a48					13 59				14a16					14a31				14a48			
Brithdir	d								14 03																
Tir-phil	d								14 06																
Pontlottyn	d								14 10																
Rhymney 3	a								14 16																
Cathays	d		13 03			13 13		13 18				13 33			13 43		13 48				14 03			14 13	
Llandaf	d		13 07			13 17		13 22				13 37			13 47		13 52				14 07			14 17	
Ninian Park	d						13 10									13 40									14 10
Waun-gron Park	d						13 13									13 43									14 13
Fairwater	d						13 15									13 45									14 15
Danescourt	d						13 17									13 47									14 17
Radyr 3	a		13 10			13 20	13 24	13 25				13 40			13 50	13 54	13 55				14 10			14 20	14 24
	d		13 10			13 20		13 25				13 40			13 50		13 55				14 10			14 20	
Taffs Well 3	d		13 14			13 24		13 29				13 44			13 54		13 59				14 14			14 24	
Trefforest Estate	d		13 18									13 48									14 18				
Trefforest	d		13 22			13 31		13 36				13 52			14 01		14 06				14 22			14 31	
Pontypridd 3	a		13 32			13 34		13 39				13 55			14 04		14 09				14 32			14 34	
	d					13 36		13 41				13 56			14 06		14 11							14 36	
Abercynon	d							13 51				14 06					14 21								
Penrhiwceiber	d							13 57									14 27								
Mountain Ash	a							14 00									14 30								
	d							14 03									14 33								
Fernhill	d							14 05									14 35								
Cwmbach	d							14 09									14 39								
Aberdare 3	a							14 16									14 46								
Quakers Yard	d											14 10													
Merthyr Vale	d											14 18													
Troed Y Rhiw	d											14 21													
Pentre-bach	d											14 24													
Merthyr Tydfil	a											14 32													
Trehafod	d					13 41									14 11									14 41	
Porth	d					13 45									14 15									14 45	
Dinas Rhondda	d					13 49									14 19									14 49	
Tonypandy	d					13 51									14 21									14 51	
Llwynypia	d					13 53									14 23									14 53	
Ystrad Rhondda	a					13 56									14 26									14 56	
	d					13 59									14 29									14 59	
Ton Pentre	d					14 01									14 31									15 01	
Treorchy	d					14 04									14 34									15 04	
Ynyswen	d					14 07									14 37									15 07	
Treherbert	a					14 13									14 43									15 13	

For general notes see front of timetable
For details of catering facilities see Directory of Train Operators

A From Radyr
B From Coryton

until 6 September

Bridgend, Barry Island, Barry, Penarth and Cardiff → Coryton, Rhymney, Pontypridd, Merthyr, Aberdare and Treherbert

Network Diagram - see first page of Table 130

Station		AW	AW	AW	AW	AW	AW	AW	AW	AW	AW	AW	AW	AW	AW	AW	AW	AW	AW	AW	AW	AW	AW	AW
					A					B				A					B				A	
Bridgend	d										13 42													
Llantwit Major	d										13 56													
Rhoose Cardiff Int Airport ✈	d										14 06													
Barry Island	d	13 41				13 56										14 26				14 41				14 56
Barry 3	d	13 45				14 00					14 15					14 30				14 45				15 00
Barry Docks	d	13 49				14 04					14 19					14 34				14 49				15 04
Cadoxton	d	13 52				14 07					14 22					14 37				14 52				15 07
Dinas Powys	d	13 56				14 11					14 26					14 41				14 56				15 11
Eastbrook	d	13 58				14 13					14 28					14 43				14 58				15 13
Cogan	d	14 00				14 15					14 30					14 45				15 00				15 15
Penarth	d		14 02				14 17					14 32					14 47				15 02			
Dingle Road	d		14 04				14 19					14 34					14 49				15 04			
Grangetown	d	14 04	14 08			14 19	14 23				14 34	14 38				14 49	14 53			15 04	15 08			15 19
Cardiff Central 7	a	14 09	14 14			14 24	14 29				14 39	14 44				14 54	14 59			15 09	15 14			15 24
	d	14 11	14 16		14 21	14 26	14 31		14 36	14 36	14 41	14 46		14 51	14 51	14 56	15 01		15 06	15 11	15 16		15 21	15 26
Cardiff Bay	d			14 19				14 34					14 49					15 04				15 19		
Cardiff Queen Street 3	a	14 14	14 19	14 23	14 24	14 29	14 34	14 38	14 39		14 44	14 49	14 53	14 54		14 59	15 04	15 08		15 14	15 19	15 23	15 24	15 29
	d	14 15	14 20		14 25	14 30	14 35		14 40		14 45	14 50		14 55		15 00	15 05			15 15	15 20		15 25	15 30
Heath Low Level	d				14 30									15 00									15 30	
Ty Glas	d				14 33									15 03									15 33	
Birchgrove	d				14 34									15 04									15 34	
Rhiwbina	d				14 36									15 06									15 36	
Whitchurch (Cardiff)	d				14 38					14 16				15 08									15 38	
Coryton	a				14 43									15 13									15 43	
Heath High Level	d		14 25				14 40					14 55					15 10				15 25			
Llanishen	d		14 28				14 43					14 58					15 13				15 28			
Lisvane & Thornhill	d		14 30				14 45					15 00					15 15				15 30			
Caerphilly 3	d		14 36				14 51					15 06					15 21				15 36			
Aber	d		14 38				14 53					15 08					15 23				15 38			
Llanbradach	d		14 42				14 57					15 12					15 27				15 42			
Ystrad Mynach 3	d		14 47				15 02					15 17					15 32				15 47			
Hengoed	d		14 50				15 05					15 20					15 35				15 50			
Pengam	d		14 53				15 08					15 23					15 38				15 53			
Gilfach Fargoed	d																15 41							
Bargoed	d		14 59				15a16					15a31					15a48				15 59			
Brithdir	d		15 03																		16 03			
Tir-phil	d		15 06																		16 06			
Pontlottyn	d		15 10																		16 10			
Rhymney 3	a		15 16																		16 16			
Cathays	d	14 18				14 33			14 43		14 48					15 03				15 18				15 33
Llandaf	d	14 22				14 37			14 47		14 52					15 07				15 22				15 37
Ninian Park	d									14 40									15 10					
Waun-gron Park	d									14 43									15 13					
Fairwater	d									14 45									15 15					
Danescourt	d									14 47									15 17					
Radyr 3	a	14 25				14 40			14 50	14 54	14 55				15 02	15 10			15 24	15 25				15 40
	d	14 25				14 40			14 50		14 55				15 02	15 10				15 25				15 40
Taffs Well 3	d	14 29				14 44			14 54		14 59				15 06	15 14				15 29				15 44
Trefforest Estate	d					14 48										15 18								15 48
Trefforest	d	14 36				14 52			15 01		15 06				15 13	15 22				15 36				15 52
Pontypridd 3	a	14 39				14 55			15 04		15 09				15 16	15 32				15 39				15 55
	d	14 41				14 56			15 06		15 11				15 22					15 41				15 56
Abercynon	d	14 51				15 06					15 21									15 51				16 06
Penrhiwceiber	d	14 57									15 27									15 57				
Mountain Ash	a	15 00									15 30									16 00				
	d	15 03									15 33									16 03				
Fernhill	d	15 05									15 35									16 05				
Cwmbach	d	15 09									15 39									16 09				
Aberdare 3	a	15 16									15 46									16 16				
Quakers Yard	d					15 10																		16 10
Merthyr Vale	d					15 18																		16 18
Troed Y Rhiw	d					15 21																		16 21
Pentre-bach	d					15 24																		16 24
Merthyr Tydfil	a					15 32																		16 32
Trehafod	d								15 11						15 27									
Porth	d								15 15						15b45									
Dinas Rhondda	d								15 19						15 49									
Tonypandy	d								15 21						15 51									
Llwynypia	d								15 23						15 53									
Ystrad Rhondda	a								15 26						15 56									
	d								15 29						15 59									
Ton Pentre	d								15 31						16 01									
Treorchy	d								15 34						16 04									
Ynyswen	d								15 37						16 07									
Treherbert	a								15 43						16 13									

For general notes see front of timetable
For details of catering facilities see Directory of Train Operators

A From Radyr
B From Coryton
b Arr. 1530

Table 130

until 6 September

Bridgend, Barry Island, Barry, Penarth and Cardiff → Coryton, Rhymney, Pontypridd, Merthyr, Aberdare and Treherbert

Network Diagram - see first page of Table 130

		AW	AW	AW	AW A	AW	AW	AW	AW B	AW	AW	AW	AW
Bridgend	d					14 42							
Llantwit Major	d					14 56							
Rhoose Cardiff Int Airport ✈	d					15 06							
Barry Island	d									15 26			
Barry 3	d					15 15				15 30			
Barry Docks	d					15 19				15 34			
Cadoxton	d					15 22				15 37			
Dinas Powys	d					15 26				15 41			
Eastbrook	d					15 28				15 43			
Cogan	d					15 30				15 45			
Penarth	d	15 17					15 32				15 47		
Dingle Road	d	15 19					15 34				15 49		
Grangetown	d	15 23				15 34	15 38			15 49	15 53		
Cardiff Central 7	a	15 29				15 39	15 44			15 54	15 59		
	d	15 31		15 36	15 36	15 41	15 46		15 51	15 56	16 01		16 06
Cardiff Bay	d		15 34					15 49				16 04	
Cardiff Queen Street 3	a	15 34	15 38	15 39		15 44	15 49	15 53	15 54	15 59	16 04	16 08	16 09
	d	15 35		15 40		15 45	15 50		15 55	16 00	16 05		16 10
Heath Low Level	d								16 00				
Ty Glas	d								16 03				
Birchgrove	d								16 04				
Rhiwbina	d								16 06				
Whitchurch (Cardiff)	d								16 08				
Coryton	a								16 13				
Heath High Level	d	15 40					15 55				16 10		
Llanishen	d	15 43					15 58				16 13		
Lisvane & Thornhill	d	15 45					16 00				16 15		
Caerphilly 3	d	15 51					16 06				16 21		
Aber	d	15 53					16 08				16 23		
Llanbradach	d	15 57					16 12				16 27		
Ystrad Mynach 3	d	16 02					16 17				16 32		
Hengoed	d	16 05					16 20				16 35		
Pengam	d	16 08					16 23				16 38		
Gilfach Fargoed	d										16 41		
Bargoed	d	16a16					16a31				16a48		
Brithdir	d												
Tir-phil	d												
Pontlottyn	d												
Rhymney 3	a												
Cathays	d			15 43		15 48				16 03			16 13
Llandaf	d			15 47		15 52				16 07			16 17
Ninian Park	d				15 40								
Waun-gron Park	d				15 43								
Fairwater	d				15 45								
Danescourt	d				15 47								
Radyr 3	a			15 50	15 54	15 55				16 10			16 20
	d			15 50		15 55				16 10			16 20
Taffs Well 3	d			15 54		15 59				16 14			16 24
Trefforest Estate	d									16 18			
Trefforest	d			16 01		16 06				16 22			16 31
Pontypridd 3	a			16 04		16 09				16 32			16 34
	d			16 06		16 11							16 36
Abercynon	d					16 21							
Penrhiwceiber	d					16 27							
Mountain Ash	a					16 30							
	d					16 33							
Fernhill	d					16 35							
Cwmbach	d					16 39							
Aberdare 3	a					16 46							
Quakers Yard	d												
Merthyr Vale	d												
Troed Y Rhiw	d												
Pentre-bach	d												
Merthyr Tydfil	a												
Trehafod	d			16 11									16 41
Porth	d			16 15									16 45
Dinas Rhondda	d			16 19									16 49
Tonypandy	d			16 21									16 51
Llwynypia	d			16 23									16 53
Ystrad Rhondda	a			16 26									16 56
	d			16 29									16 59
Ton Pentre	d			16 31									17 01
Treorchy	d			16 34									17 04
Ynyswen	d			16 37									17 07
Treherbert	a			16 43									17 13

		AW A	AW	AW	AW	AW B		AW	AW	AW	AW	AW A	AW	AW
Bridgend	d												15 42	
Llantwit Major	d												15 56	
Rhoose Cardiff Int Airport ✈	d												16 06	
Barry Island	d		15 41					15 56						
Barry 3	d		15 45					16 00					16 15	
Barry Docks	d		15 49					16 04					16 19	
Cadoxton	d		15 52					16 07					16 22	
Dinas Powys	d		15 56					16 11					16 26	
Eastbrook	d		15 58					16 13					16 28	
Cogan	d		16 00					16 15					16 30	
Penarth	d			16 02					16 17					16 32
Dingle Road	d			16 04					16 19					16 34
Grangetown	d		16 04	16 08				16 19	16 23				16 34	16 38
Cardiff Central 7	a		16 09	16 14				16 24	16 29				16 39	16 44
	d	16 06	16 11	16 16		16 21		16 26	16 31		16 36	16 36	16 41	16 46
Cardiff Bay	d				16 19					16 34				
Cardiff Queen Street 3	a		16 14	16 19	16 23	16 24		16 29	16 34	16 38	16 39		16 44	16 49
	d		16 15	16 20		16 25		16 30	16 35		16 40		16 45	16 50
Heath Low Level	d					16 30								
Ty Glas	d					16 33								
Birchgrove	d					16 34								
Rhiwbina	d					16 36								
Whitchurch (Cardiff)	d	15 46				16 38								
Coryton	a					16 43								
Heath High Level	d			16 25					16 40					16 55
Llanishen	d			16 28					16 43					16 58
Lisvane & Thornhill	d			16 30					16 45					17 00
Caerphilly 3	d			16 36					16 51					17 06
Aber	d			16 38					16 53					17 08
Llanbradach	d			16 42					16 57					17 12
Ystrad Mynach 3	d			16 47					17 02					17 17
Hengoed	d			16 50					17 05					17 20
Pengam	d			16 53					17 08					17 23
Gilfach Fargoed	d													
Bargoed	d			16 59					17a16					17a31
Brithdir	d			17 03										
Tir-phil	d			17 06										
Pontlottyn	d			17 10										
Rhymney 3	a			17 16										
Cathays	d		16 18					16 33			16 43		16 48	
Llandaf	d		16 22					16 37			16 47		16 52	
Ninian Park	d	16 10										16 40		
Waun-gron Park	d	16 13										16 43		
Fairwater	d	16 15										16 45		
Danescourt	d	16 17										16 47		
Radyr 3	a	16 24	16 25					16 40			16 50	16 54	16 55	
	d		16 25					16 40			16 50		16 55	
Taffs Well 3	d		16 29					16 44			16 54		16 59	
Trefforest Estate	d							16 48						
Trefforest	d		16 36					16 52			17 01		17 06	
Pontypridd 3	a		16 39					16 55			17 04		17 09	
	d		16 41					16 56			17 06		17 11	
Abercynon	d		16 51					17 06					17 21	
Penrhiwceiber	d		16 57										17 27	
Mountain Ash	a		17 00										17 30	
	d		17 03										17 33	
Fernhill	d		17 05										17 35	
Cwmbach	d		17 09										17 39	
Aberdare 3	a		17 16										17 46	
Quakers Yard	d							17 10						
Merthyr Vale	d							17 18						
Troed Y Rhiw	d							17 21						
Pentre-bach	d							17 24						
Merthyr Tydfil	a							17 32						
Trehafod	d										17 11			
Porth	d										17 15			
Dinas Rhondda	d										17 19			
Tonypandy	d										17 21			
Llwynypia	d										17 23			
Ystrad Rhondda	a										17 26			
	d										17 29			
Ton Pentre	d										17 31			
Treorchy	d										17 34			
Ynyswen	d										17 37			
Treherbert	a										17 43			

For general notes see front of timetable
For details of catering facilities see Directory of Train Operators

A From Coryton
B From Radyr

Table 130

until 6 September

Bridgend, Barry Island, Barry, Penarth and Cardiff → Coryton, Rhymney, Pontypridd, Merthyr, Aberdare and Treherbert

Network Diagram - see first page of Table 130

		AW	AW	AW	AW	AW	AW	AW	AW	AW	AW	AW	AW		AW	AW	AW	AW	AW	AW	AW	AW	AW	AW	AW	AW
			A					B				A						B				A				
Bridgend	d																		16 42							
Llantwit Major	d																		16 56							
Rhoose Cardiff Int Airport ✈	d																		17 06							
Barry Island	d			16 26					16 41				16 56										17 26			
Barry 3	d			16 30					16 45				17 00						17 15				17 30			
Barry Docks	d			16 34					16 49				17 04						17 19				17 34			
Cadoxton	d			16 37					16 52				17 07						17 22				17 37			
Dinas Powys	d			16 41					16 56				17 11						17 26				17 41			
Eastbrook	d			16 43					16 58				17 13						17 28				17 43			
Cogan	d			16 45					17 00				17 15						17 30				17 45			
Penarth	d									17 02					17 17					17 32				17 47		
Dingle Road	d									17 04					17 19					17 34				17 49		
Grangetown	d			16 49					17 04	17 08			17 19		17 23				17 34	17 38			17 49	17 53		
Cardiff Central 7	a			16 54					17 09	17 14			17 24		17 29				17 39	17 44			17 54	17 59		
	d		16 51	16 56	17 01		17 06	17 06	17 11	17 16		17 21	17 26		17 31		17 36	17 36	17 41	17 46		17 51	17 56	18 01		18 06
Cardiff Bay	d	16 49				17 04					17 19					17 34					17 49				18 04	
Cardiff Queen Street 3	a	16 53	16 54	16 59	17 04	17 08	17 09		17 14	17 19	17 23	17 24	17 29		17 34	17 38	17 39		17 44	17 49	17 53	17 54	17 59	18 04	18 08	18 09
	d		16 55	17 00	17 05		17 10		17 15	17 20		17 25	17 30		17 35		17 40		17 45	17 50		17 55	18 00	18 05		18 10
Heath Low Level	d		17 00									17 30										18 00				
Ty Glas	d		17 03									17 33										18 03				
Birchgrove	d		17 04									17 34										18 04				
Rhiwbina	d		17 06									17 36										18 06				
Whitchurch (Cardiff)	d		17 08									17 38										18 08				
Coryton	a		17 13									17 43										18 13				
Heath High Level	d				17 10					17 25					17 40					17 55				18 10		
Llanishen	d				17 13					17 28					17 43					17 59				18 13		
Lisvane & Thornhill	d				17 15					17 30					17 45					18 02				18 15		
Caerphilly 3	d				17 21					17 36					17 51					18 07				18 21		
Aber	d				17 23					17 38					17 53					18 10				18 23		
Llanbradach	d				17 27					17 42					17 57					18 14				18 27		
Ystrad Mynach 3	d				17 33					17 47					18 02					18 20				18 32		
Hengoed	d				17 35					17 50					18 05					18 23				18 35		
Pengam	d				17 39					17 53					18 08					18 27				18 38		
Gilfach Fargoed	d				17 42										18 11					18 30				18 41		
Bargoed	d				17 47					18a01					18 16					18b44				18a48		
Brithdir	d				17 50										18 20					18 48						
Tir-phil	d				17 53										18 23					18 51						
Pontlottyn	d				17 58										18 27					18 55						
Rhymney 3	a				18 04										18 33					19 01						
Cathays	d			17 03			17 13		17 18				17 33				17 43		17 48				18 03			18 13
Llandaf	d			17 07			17 17		17 22				17 37				17 47		17 52				18 07			18 17
Ninian Park	d							17 10										17 40								
Waun-gron Park	d							17 13										17 43								
Fairwater	d							17 15										17 45								
Danescourt	d							17 17										17 47								
Radyr 3	a			17 10			17 20	17 24	17 25				17 40				17 50	17 54	17 55				18 10			18 20
	d			17 10			17 20		17 25				17 40				17 50		17 55				18 10			18 20
Taffs Well 3	d			17 14			17 24		17 29				17 44				17 54		17 59				18 14			18 24
Trefforest Estate	d			17 18									17 48										18 18			
Trefforest	d			17 22			17 31		17 36				17 52				18 01		18 06				18 22			18 31
Pontypridd 3	a			17 32			17 34		17 39				17 55				18 04		18 09				18 32			18 34
	d						17 36		17 41				17 56				18 06		18 11							18 36
Abercynon	d								17 51				18 06						18 21							
Penrhiwceiber	d								17 57										18 27							
Mountain Ash	a								18 00										18 30							
	d								18 03										18 33							
Fernhill	d								18 05										18 35							
Cwmbach	d								18 09										18 39							
Aberdare 3	a								18 16										18 46							
Quakers Yard	d												18 10													
Merthyr Vale	d												18 18													
Troed Y Rhiw	d												18 21													
Pentre-bach	d												18 24													
Merthyr Tydfil	a												18 32													
Trehafod	d						17 41										18 11									18 41
Porth	d						17 45										18 15									18 45
Dinas Rhondda	d						17 49										18 19									18 49
Tonypandy	d						17 51										18 21									18 51
Llwynypia	d						17 53										18 23									18 53
Ystrad Rhondda	a						17 56										18 26									18 56
	d						17 59										18 29									18 59
Ton Pentre	d						18 01										18 31									19 01
Treorchy	d						18 04										18 34									19 04
Ynyswen	d						18 07										18 37									19 07
Treherbert	a						18 13										18 43									19 13

For general notes see front of timetable
For details of catering facilities see Directory of Train Operators

A From Radyr
B From Coryton
b Arr. 1834

Table 130

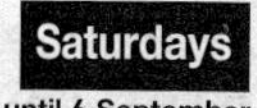

until 6 September

Bridgend, Barry Island, Barry, Penarth and Cardiff → Coryton, Rhymney, Pontypridd, Merthyr, Aberdare and Treherbert

Network Diagram - see first page of Table 130

		AW A	AW	AW	AW	AW B	AW	AW			AW	AW A	AW	AW	AW	AW B	AW	AW	AW	AW	AW	AW	AW	AW	AW	AW A
Bridgend	d												17 42													
Llantwit Major	d												17 56													
Rhoose Cardiff Int Airport ✈	d												18 06													
Barry Island	d		17 41				17 56										18 26				18 41		18 56			
Barry [3]	d		17 45				18 00						18 15				18 30				18 45		19 00			
Barry Docks	d		17 49				18 04						18 19				18 34				18 49		19 04			
Cadoxton	d		17 52				18 07						18 22				18 37				18 52		19 07			
Dinas Powys	d		17 56				18 11						18 26				18 41				18 56		19 11			
Eastbrook	d		17 58				18 13						18 28				18 43				18 58		19 13			
Cogan	d		18 00				18 15						18 30				18 45				19 00		19 15			
Penarth	d			18 02				18 17						18 32				18 47						19 17		
Dingle Road	d			18 04				18 19						18 34				18 49						19 19		
Grangetown	d		18 04	18 08			18 19	18 23					18 34	18 38			18 49	18 53			19 04		19 19	19 23		
Cardiff Central [7]	a		18 09	18 14			18 24	18 29					18 39	18 45			18 54	18 59			19 09		19 24	19 29		
	d	18 06	18 11	18 16		18 21	18 26	18 31	18 36			18 36	18 41			18 51		19 01		19 06	19 11		19 26	19 31		19 36
Cardiff Bay	d				18 19						18 34				18 49				19 04			19 19			19 34	
Cardiff Queen Street [3]	a		18 14	18 19	18 23	18 24	18 29	18 34	18 38		18 38		18 44		18 53	18 54		19 04	19 08	19 09	19 14	19 23	19 29	19 34	19 38	
	d		18 15	18 20		18 25	18 30	18 35	18 40				18 50			18 55		19 05		19 10	19 15		19 30	19 35		
Heath Low Level	d					18 30										19 00										
Ty Glas	d					18 33										19 03										
Birchgrove	d					18 34										19 04										
Rhiwbina	d					18 36										19 06										
Whitchurch (Cardiff)	d					18 38										19 08										
Coryton	a					18 43										19 13										
Heath High Level	d			18 25				18 40										19 10						19 40		
Llanishen	d			18 28				18 43										19 13						19 43		
Lisvane & Thornhill	d			18 30				18 45										19 15						19 45		
Caerphilly [3]	d			18 36				18 51										19a24						19 51		
Aber	d			18 38				18 53																19 53		
Llanbradach	d			18 42				18 57																19 57		
Ystrad Mynach [3]	d			18a51				19 02																20 02		
Hengoed	d							19 05																20 05		
Pengam	d							19 08																20 08		
Gilfach Fargoed	d							19x11																20 11		
Bargoed	d							19 16																20 16		
Brithdir	d							19 20																20 20		
Tir-phil	d							19 23																20 23		
Pontlottyn	d							19 27																20 27		
Rhymney [3]	a							19 33																20 33		
Cathays	d		18 18				18 33		18 43				18 52							19 13	19 18		19 33			
Llandaf	d		18 22				18 37		18 47				18 56							19 17	19 22		19 37			
Ninian Park	d	18 10										18 40														19 40
Waun-gron Park	d	18 13										18 43														19 43
Fairwater	d	18 15										18 45														19 45
Danescourt	d	18 17										18 47														19 47
Radyr [3]	a	18 24	18 25				18 40		18 50			18 54	18 58							19 20	19 25		19 40			19 54
	d		18 25				18 40		18 50				18 58							19 20	19 25		19 40			
Taffs Well [3]	d		18 29				18 44		18 54				19 03							19 24	19 29		19 44			
Trefforest Estate	d						18 48																19 48			
Trefforest	d		18 36				18 52		19 01				19 10							19 31	19 36		19 52			
Pontypridd [3]	a		18 42				18 55		19 04				19 13							19 34	19 39		19 55			
	d						18 56		19 06				19 14							19 36	19 41		19 56			
Abercynon	d						19 06						19 21								19 51					
Penrhiwceiber	d												19 26								19 57					
Mountain Ash	a												19 30								20 00					
	d												19 33								20 03					
Fernhill	d												19 35								20 05					
Cwmbach	d												19 39								20 09					
Aberdare [3]	a												19 46								20 16					
Quakers Yard	d						19 10																20 10			
Merthyr Vale	d						19 18																20 18			
Troed Y Rhiw	d						19 21																20 21			
Pentre-bach	d						19 24																20 24			
Merthyr Tydfil	a						19 32																20 32			
Trehafod	d								19 11											19 41						
Porth	d								19 15											19 45						
Dinas Rhondda	d								19 19											19 49						
Tonypandy	d								19 21											19 51						
Llwynypia	d								19 23											19 53						
Ystrad Rhondda	a								19 26											19 56						
	d								19 29											19 59						
Ton Pentre	d								19 31											20 01						
Treorchy	d								19 34											20 04						
Ynyswen	d								19 37											20 07						
Treherbert	a								19 43											20 13						

For general notes see front of timetable
For details of catering facilities see
Directory of Train Operators

A From Coryton
B From Radyr

Saturdays

until 6 September

Bridgend, Barry Island, Barry, Penarth and Cardiff → Coryton, Rhymney, Pontypridd, Merthyr, Aberdare and Treherbert

Network Diagram - see first page of Table 130

		AW	AW	AW		AW	AW	AW	AW	AW	AW	AW	AW	AW A	AW	AW	AW	AW	AW	AW	AW	AW		AW	AW	AW
Bridgend	d	18 42													19 42											
Llantwit Major	d	18 56													19 56											
Rhoose Cardiff Int Airport ✈	d	19 06													20 06											
Barry Island	d					19 26					19 56											20 56				
Barry 3	d	19 15				19 30					20 00				20 15							21 00				
Barry Docks	d	19 19				19 34					20 04				20 19							21 04				
Cadoxton	d	19 22				19 37					20 07				20 22							21 07				
Dinas Powys	d	19 26				19 41					20 11				20 26							21 11				
Eastbrook	d	19 28				19 43					20 13				20 28							21 13				
Cogan	d	19 30				19 45					20 15				20 30							21 15				
Penarth	d						19 47					20 17						20 47							21 17	
Dingle Road	d						19 49					20 19						20 49							21 19	
Grangetown	d	19 34				19 49	19 53				20 19	20 23			20 34			20 53				21 19			21 23	
Cardiff Central 7	a	19 39				19 56	19 59				20 24	20 29			20 39			20 59				21 24			21 33	
	d	19 41		19 51			20 01		20 06		20 26	20 31		20 36	20 41		20 51	21 01		21 06		21 26		21 31		
Cardiff Bay	d		19 49					20 04		20 19			20 34			20 49			21 04		21 19					21 34
Cardiff Queen Street 3	a	19 44	19 53	19 54			20 04	20 08	20 09	20 23	20 29	20 34	20 38		20 44	20 53	20 54	21 04	21 08	21 09	21 23	21 29		21 34		21 38
	d	19 45		19 55			20 05		20 15		20 30	20 35			20 45		20 55	21 05		21 10		21 30		21 35		
Heath Low Level	d			20 00													21 00									
Ty Glas	d			20 03													21 03									
Birchgrove	d			20 04													21 04									
Rhiwbina	d			20 06													21 06									
Whitchurch (Cardiff)	d			20 08													21 08									
Coryton	a			20 13													21 13									
Heath High Level	d						20 10					20 40						21 10						21 40		
Llanishen	d						20 13					20 43						21 13						21 43		
Lisvane & Thornhill	d						20 15					20 45						21 15						21 45		
Caerphilly 3	d						20a28					20 51						21a28						21 51		
Aber	d											20 53												21 53		
Llanbradach	d											20 57												21 57		
Ystrad Mynach 3	d											21 02												22 02		
Hengoed	d											21 05												22 05		
Pengam	d											21 08												22 08		
Gilfach Fargoed	d											21 11												22 11		
Bargoed	d											21 16												22 16		
Brithdir	d											21 20												22 20		
Tir-phil	d											21 23												22 23		
Pontlottyn	d											21 27												22 27		
Rhymney 3	a											21 33												22 33		
Cathays	d	19 48							20 13		20 33				20 48					21 13		21 33				
Llandaf	d	19 52							20 17		20 37				20 52					21 17		21 37				
Ninian Park	d													20 40												
Waun-gron Park	d													20 43												
Fairwater	d													20 45												
Danescourt	d													20 47												
Radyr 3	a	19 55							20 20		20 40			20 54	20 55					21 20		21 40				
	d	19 55							20 20		20 40				20 55					21 20		21 40				
Taffs Well 3	d	19 59							20 24		20 44				20 59					21 24		21 44				
Trefforest Estate	d										20 48											21 48				
Trefforest	d	20 06							20 31		20 52				21 06					21 31		21 52				
Pontypridd 3	a	20 09							20 34		20 55				21 09					21 34		21 55				
	d	20 11							20 36		20 56				21 11					21 36		21 56				
Abercynon	d	20 21									21 06				21 21							22 06				
Penrhiwceiber	d	20 27													21 27											
Mountain Ash	a	20 30													21 30											
	d	20 33													21 33											
Fernhill	d	20 35													21 35											
Cwmbach	d	20 39													21 39											
Aberdare 3	a	20 46													21 46											
Quakers Yard	d										21 10											22 10				
Merthyr Vale	d										21 18											22 18				
Troed Y Rhiw	d										21 21											22 21				
Pentre-bach	d										21 24											22 24				
Merthyr Tydfil	a										21 32											22 32				
Trehafod	d								20 41											21 41						
Porth	d								20 45											21 45						
Dinas Rhondda	d								20 49											21 49						
Tonypandy	d								20 51											21 51						
Llwynypia	d								20 53											21 53						
Ystrad Rhondda	a								20 56											21 56						
	d								20 59											21 59						
Ton Pentre	d								21 01											22 01						
Treorchy	d								21 04											22 04						
Ynyswen	d								21 07											22 07						
Treherbert	a								21 13											22 13						

For general notes see front of timetable
For details of catering facilities see Directory of Train Operators

A From Coryton

until 6 September

Bridgend, Barry Island, Barry, Penarth and Cardiff → Coryton, Rhymney, Pontypridd, Merthyr, Aberdare and Treherbert

Network Diagram - see first page of Table 130

		AW A	AW	AW	AW	AW	AW	AW	AW	AW	AW	AW	AW	AW	AW	AW	AW	AW	AW	AW	AW	AW	AW
Bridgend	d		20 42										21 42									22 42	
Llantwit Major	d		20 56										21 56									22 56	
Rhoose Cardiff Int Airport ✈	d		21 06										22 06									23 06	
Barry Island	d									21 56									22 56				
Barry 3	d		21 15							22 00			22 15						23 00			23 15	
Barry Docks	d		21 19							22 04			22 19						23 04			23 19	
Cadoxton	d		21 22							22 07			22 22						23 07			23 22	
Dinas Powys	d		21 26							22 11			22 26						23 11			23 26	
Eastbrook	d		21 28							22 13			22 28						23 13			23 28	
Cogan	d		21 30							22 15			22 30						23 15			23 30	
Penarth	d				21 47						22 17						22 47				23 26		
Dingle Road	d				21 49						22 19						22 49				23 28		
Grangetown	d		21 34		21 53					22 19	22 23		22 34				22 53		23 19		23 32	23 34	
Cardiff Central 7	a		21 39		21 59					22 25	22 31		22 39				23 00		23 24		23 39	23 42	
	d	21 36	21 41		22 01		22 06	22 11		22 26	22 35		22 41	22 46			23 15		23 26				
Cardiff Bay	d			21 49		22 04			22 19			22 34			22 49	23 04		23 19		23 34			23 49
Cardiff Queen Street 3	a		21 44	21 53	22 04	22 08	22 09	22 14	22 23	22 29	22 38	22 38	22 44	22 49	22 53	23 08	23 18	23 23	23 29	23 38			23 53
	d		21 45		22 05		22 10	22 15		22 30	22 39		22 45	22 50			23 19		23 30				
Heath Low Level	d																						
Ty Glas	d																						
Birchgrove	d																						
Rhiwbina	d																						
Whitchurch (Cardiff)	d																						
Coryton	a																						
Heath High Level	d				22 10						22 44						23 24						
Llanishen	d				22 13						22 47						23 27						
Lisvane & Thornhill	d				22 15						22 49						23 29						
Caerphilly 3	d				22a24						22 55						23 35						
Aber	d										22 57						23 37						
Llanbradach	d										23 01						23 41						
Ystrad Mynach 3	d										23 06						23a50						
Hengoed	d										23 09												
Pengam	d										23 12												
Gilfach Fargoed	d										23 15												
Bargoed	d										23 20												
Brithdir	d										23 24												
Tir-phil	d										23 27												
Pontlottyn	d										23 31												
Rhymney 3	a										23 37												
Cathays	d		21 48				22 13	22 18		22 33			22 48	22 53					23 33				
Llandaf	d		21 52				22 17	22 22		22 37			22 52	22 57					23 37				
Ninian Park	d	21 40																					
Waun-gron Park	d	21 43																					
Fairwater	d	21 45																					
Danescourt	d	21 47																					
Radyr 3	a	21 54	21 55				22 20	22 25		22 40			22 55	22 59					23 40				
	d		21 55				22 20	22 25		22 40			22 55	22 59					23 40				
Taffs Well 3	d		21 59				22 24	22 29		22 44			22 59	23 03					23 44				
Trefforest Estate	d									22 48									23 48				
Trefforest	d		22 06				22 31	22 36		22 52			23 06	23 10					23 52				
Pontypridd 3	a		22 09				22 34	22 43		22 55			23 09	23 14					23 58				
	d		22 11				22 36			22 56			23 11	23 15									
Abercynon	d		22 21							23 06			23 21										
Penrhiwceiber	d		22 27										23 27										
Mountain Ash	a		22 30										23 30										
	d		22 33										23 33										
Fernhill	d		22 35										23 35										
Cwmbach	d		22 39										23 39										
Aberdare 3	a		22 46										23 46										
Quakers Yard	d									23 10													
Merthyr Vale	d									23 18													
Troed Y Rhiw	d									23 21													
Pentre-bach	d									23 24													
Merthyr Tydfil	a									23 32													
Trehafod	d						22 41							23 20									
Porth	d						22 45							23 24									
Dinas Rhondda	d						22 49							23 28									
Tonypandy	d						22 51							23 30									
Llwynypia	d						22 53							23 32									
Ystrad Rhondda	a						22 56							23 35									
	d						22 59							23 38									
Ton Pentre	d						23 01							23 40									
Treorchy	d						23 04							23 43									
Ynyswen	d						23 07							23 46									
Treherbert	a						23 13							23 52									

For general notes see front of timetable
For details of catering facilities see Directory of Train Operators

A From Coryton

Table 130

from 13 September

Bridgend, Barry Island, Barry, Penarth and Cardiff → Coryton, Rhymney, Pontypridd, Merthyr, Aberdare and Treherbert

Network Diagram - see first page of Table 130

		AW		AW	AW	AW	AW	AW	AW	AW	AW	AW	AW	AW	AW	AW A	AW	AW	AW A		AW	AW	AW B	AW	AW	AW
Bridgend	d									05 42																
Llantwit Major	d									05 56																
Rhoose Cardiff Int Airport ✈	d									06 06																
Barry Island	d							05 56						06 26										06 56		
Barry 3	d							06 00		06 15				06 30										07 00		
Barry Docks	d							06 04		06 19				06 34										07 04		
Cadoxton	d							06 07		06 22				06 37										07 07		
Dinas Powys	d							06 11		06 26				06 41										07 11		
Eastbrook	d							06 13		06 28				06 43										07 13		
Cogan	d							06 15		06 30				06 45										07 15		
Penarth	d										06 32										07 02				07 17	
Dingle Road	d										06 34										07 04				07 19	
Grangetown	d							06 19		06 34	06 38			06 49							07 08			07 19	07 23	
Cardiff Central 7	a							06 24		06 39	06 44			06 54							07 14			07 24	07 29	
	d	05 26		05 46	06 11	06 16	06 21	06 26	06 36	06 41	06 46		06 51	06 56		07 06	07 06	07 11			07 16		07 21	07 26	07 31	
Cardiff Bay	d											06 49			07 04							07 19				07 34
Cardiff Queen Street 3	a	05 29		05 49	06 14	06 19	06 24	06 29	06 39	06 44	06 49	06 53	06 54	06 59	07 08		07 09	07 14			07 19	07 23	07 24	07 29	07 34	07 38
	d	05 30		05 50	06 15	06 20	06 25	06 30	06 40	06 45	06 50		06 55	07 00			07 10	07 15			07 20		07 25	07 30	07 35	
Heath Low Level	d						06 30						07 00										07 30			
Ty Glas	d						06 33						07 03										07 33			
Birchgrove	d						06 34						07 04										07 34			
Rhiwbina	d						06 36						07 06										07 36			
Whitchurch (Cardiff)	d						06 38						07 08										07 38			
Coryton	a						06 44						07 14										07 44			
Heath High Level	d			05 54		06 25					06 55										07 25				07 40	
Llanishen	d			05 57		06 28					06 58										07 28				07 43	
Lisvane & Thornhill	d			06 00		06 30					07 00										07 30				07 45	
Caerphilly 3	d			06a09		06 36					07 06										07 36				07 51	
Aber	d					06 38					07 08										07 38				07 53	
Llanbradach	d					06 42					07 12										07 42				07 57	
Ystrad Mynach 3	d					06 47					07 17										07 47				08 02	
Hengoed	d					06 50					07 20										07 50				08 05	
Pengam	d					06 53					07 23										07 53				08 08	
Gilfach Fargoed	d																									
Bargoed	d					07a02					07a32										08a02				08 14	
Brithdir	d																								08 18	
Tir-phil	d																								08 21	
Pontlottyn	d																								08 25	
Rhymney 3	a																								08 32	
Cathays	d	05 33			06 18			06 33	06 43	06 48				07 03			07 13	07 18						07 33		
Llandaf	d	05 37			06 22			06 37	06 47	06 52				07 07			07 17	07 22						07 37		
Ninian Park	d															07 10			←							
Waun-gron Park	d															07 14			07 14							
Fairwater	d															→			07 16							
Danescourt	d																		07 19							
Radyr 3	a	05 39			06 24			06 40	06 50	06 54				07 10			07 20	07 25	07 27					07 40		
	d	05 40			06 24			06 40	06 50	06 55				07 10			07 20	07 25						07 40		
Taffs Well 3	d	05 43			06 28			06 44	06 54	06 59				07 14			07 24	07 29						07 44		
Trefforest Estate	d	05 47						06 48						07 18										07 48		
Trefforest	d	05 52			06 35			06 52	07 01	07 06				07 22			07 31	07 36						07 52		
Pontypridd 3	a	05 55			06 39			06 55	07 04	07 09				07 32			07 34	07 39						07 55		
	d	05 56	06 11		06 41			06 56	07 06	07 11							07 36	07 11						07 56		
Abercynon	d	06 06	06 21		06 51			07 06		07 21								07 51						08 06		
Penrhiwceiber	d		06 27		06 57					07 27								07 57								
Mountain Ash	a		06 31		07 01					07 31								08 01								
	d		06 34		07 04					07 34								08 04								
Fernhill	d		06 37		07 07					07 37								08 07								
Cwmbach	d		06 41		07 11					07 41								08 11								
Aberdare 3	a		06 49		07 19					07 49								08 19								
Quakers Yard	d	06 11						07 11																08 11		
Merthyr Vale	d	06 18						07 18																08 18		
Troed Y Rhiw	d	06 22						07 22																08 22		
Pentre-bach	d	06 25						07 25																08 25		
Merthyr Tydfil	a	06 34						07 34																08 34		
Trehafod	d								07 11								07 41									
Porth	d								07 15								07 45									
Dinas Rhondda	d								07 19								07 49									
Tonypandy	d								07 21								07 51									
Llwynypia	d								07 23								07 53									
Ystrad Rhondda	a								07 26								07 56									
	d								07 29								07 59									
Ton Pentre	d								07 31								08 01									
Treorchy	d								07 34								08 04									
Ynyswen	d								07 37								08 07									
Treherbert	a								07 44								08 14									

For general notes see front of timetable
For details of catering facilities see Directory of Train Operators

A From Coryton
B From Taffs Well

Table 130

from 13 September

Bridgend, Barry Island, Barry, Penarth and Cardiff → Coryton, Rhymney, Pontypridd, Merthyr, Aberdare and Treherbert

Network Diagram - see first page of Table 130

Station		AW	AW	AW	AW	AW	AW	AW	AW	AW	AW	AW	AW	AW	AW	AW	AW	AW	AW	AW	AW	AW	AW	AW	AW
			A		A			B					A		A			B					A		A
Bridgend	d			06 42																				07 42	
Llantwit Major	d			06 56																				07 56	
Rhoose Cardiff Int Airport ✈	d			07 06																				08 06	
Barry Island	d								07 26					07 41					07 56						
Barry 3	d			07 15					07 30					07 45					08 00					08 15	
Barry Docks	d			07 19					07 34					07 49					08 04					08 19	
Cadoxton	d			07 22					07 37					07 52					08 07					08 22	
Dinas Powys	d			07 26					07 41					07 56					08 11					08 26	
Eastbrook	d			07 28					07 43					07 58					08 13					08 28	
Cogan	d			07 30					07 45					08 00					08 15					08 30	
Penarth	d					07 32				07 47						08 02				08 17					
Dingle Road	d					07 34				07 49						08 04				08 19					
Grangetown	d			07 34		07 38			07 49	07 53				08 04		08 08			08 19	08 23				08 34	
Cardiff Central 7	a			07 39		07 44			07 55	07 59				08 09		08 14			08 24	08 29				08 39	
	d	07 36	07 36	07 41		07 46		07 51	07 56	08 01		08 06	08 06	08 11		08 16		08 21	08 26	08 31		08 36	08 36	08 41	
Cardiff Bay	d						07 49				08 04						08 19				08 34				
Cardiff Queen Street 3	a	07 39		07 44		07 49	07 53	07 54	07 59	08 04	08 08	08 09		08 14		08 19	08 23	08 24	08 29	08 34	08 38	08 39		08 44	
	d	07 40		07 45		07 50		07 55	08 00	08 05		08 10		08 15		08 20		08 25	08 30	08 35		08 40		08 45	
Heath Low Level	d							08 00										08 30							
Ty Glas	d							08 03										08 33							
Birchgrove	d							08 04										08 34							
Rhiwbina	d							08 06										08 36							
Whitchurch (Cardiff)	d							08 08										08 38							
Coryton	a							08 14										08 44							
Heath High Level	d					07 55				08 10						08 25				08 40					
Llanishen	d					07 58				08 13						08 28				08 43					
Lisvane & Thornhill	d					08 00				08 15						08 30				08 45					
Caerphilly 3	d					08 06				08 21						08 36				08 51					
Aber	d					08 08				08 23						08 38				08 53					
Llanbradach	d					08 12				08 27						08 42				08 57					
Ystrad Mynach 3	d					08 17				08 32						08 47				09 07					
Hengoed	d					08 20				08 35						08 50				09 10					
Pengam	d					08 23				08 38						08 53				09 13					
Gilfach Fargoed	d									08 41															
Bargoed	d					08a32				08a49						08 59				09a25					
Brithdir	d															09 03									
Tir-phil	d															09 06									
Pontlottyn	d															09 10									
Rhymney 3	a															09 17									
Cathays	d	07 43		07 48					08 03			08 13		08 18					08 33			08 43		08 48	
Llandaf	d	07 47		07 52					08 07			08 17		08 22					08 37			08 47		08 52	
Ninian Park	d		07 40		←								08 10		←								08 40		←
Waun-gron Park	d		07 44 →		07 44								08 14 →		08 14								08 44 →		08 44
Fairwater	d				07 46										08 16										08 46
Danescourt	d				07 49										08 19										08 49
Radyr 3	a	07 50		07 55	07 57				08 10			08 20		08 25	08 27				08 40			08 50		08 55	08 57
	d	07 50		07 55					08 10			08 20		08 25					08 40			08 50		08 55	
Taffs Well 3	d	07 54		07 59					08 14			08 24		08 29					08 44			08 54		08 59	
Trefforest Estate	d								08 18										08 48						
Trefforest	d	08 01		08 06					08 22			08 31		08 36					08 52			09 01		09 06	
Pontypridd 3	a	08 04		08 09					08 32			08 34		08 39					08 55			09 04		09 09	
	d	08 06		08 11								08 36		08 41					08 56			09 06		09 11	
Abercynon	d			08 21										08 51					09 06					09 21	
Penrhiwceiber	d			08 27										08 57										09 27	
Mountain Ash	a			08 31										09 01										09 31	
	d			08 34										09 04										09 34	
Fernhill	d			08 37										09 07										09 37	
Cwmbach	d			08 41										09 11										09 41	
Aberdare 3	a			08 49										09 19										09 49	
Quakers Yard	d																		09 11						
Merthyr Vale	d																		09 18						
Troed Y Rhiw	d																		09 22						
Pentre-bach	d																		09 25						
Merthyr Tydfil	a																		09 34						
Trehafod	d	08 11										08 41										09 11			
Porth	d	08 15										08 45										09 15			
Dinas Rhondda	d	08 19										08 49										09 19			
Tonypandy	d	08 21										08 51										09 21			
Llwynypia	d	08 23										08 53										09 23			
Ystrad Rhondda	a	08 26										08 56										09 26			
	d	08 29										08 59										09 29			
Ton Pentre	d	08 31										09 01										09 31			
Treorchy	d	08 34										09 04										09 34			
Ynyswen	d	08 37										09 07										09 37			
Treherbert	a	08 44										09 14										09 44			

For general notes see front of timetable
For details of catering facilities see Directory of Train Operators

A From Coryton
B From Radyr

from 13 September

Bridgend, Barry Island, Barry, Penarth and Cardiff → Coryton, Rhymney, Pontypridd, Merthyr, Aberdare and Treherbert

Network Diagram - see first page of Table 130

		AW	AW	AW A	AW	AW	AW	AW	AW B	AW	AW B	AW	AW	AW A	AW	AW	AW	AW	AW B	AW	AW B	AW	AW	AW A	AW
Bridgend	d																			08 42					
Llantwit Major	d																			08 56					
Rhoose Cardiff Int Airport ✈	d																			09 06					
Barry Island	d				08 26					08 41					08 56										09 26
Barry 3	d				08 30					08 45					09 00					09 15					09 30
Barry Docks	d				08 34					08 49					09 04					09 19					09 34
Cadoxton	d				08 37					08 52					09 07					09 22					09 37
Dinas Powys	d				08 41					08 56					09 11					09 26					09 41
Eastbrook	d				08 43					08 58					09 13					09 28					09 43
Cogan	d				08 45					09 00					09 15					09 30					09 45
Penarth	d	08 32				08 47										09 17						09 32			
Dingle Road	d	08 34				08 49										09 19						09 34			
Grangetown	d	08 38			08 49	08 53				09 04					09 19	09 23				09 34		09 38			09 49
Cardiff Central 7	a	08 44			08 54	08 59				09 09					09 24	09 29				09 39		09 44			09 54
	d	08 46		08 51	08 56	09 01		09 06	09 06	09 11		09 16		09 21	09 26	09 31		09 36	09 36	09 41		09 46		09 51	09 56
Cardiff Bay	d		08 49				09 04						09 19				09 34						09 49		
Cardiff Queen Street 3	a	08 49	08 53	08 54	08 59	09 04	09 08	09 09		09 14		09 19	09 23	09 24	09 29	09 34	09 38	09 39		09 44		09 49	09 53	09 54	09 59
	d	08 50		08 55	09 00	09 05		09 10		09 15		09 20		09 25	09 30	09 35		09 40		09 45		09 50		09 55	10 00
Heath Low Level	d			09 00										09 30										10 00	
Ty Glas	d			09 03										09 33										10 03	
Birchgrove	d			09 04										09 34										10 04	
Rhiwbina	d			09 06										09 36										10 06	
Whitchurch (Cardiff)	d			09 08										09 38										10 08	
Coryton	a			09 14										09 44										10 14	
Heath High Level	d	08 55				09 10						09 25				09 40						09 55			
Llanishen	d	08 58				09 13						09 28				09 43						09 58			
Lisvane & Thornhill	d	09 00				09 15						09 30				09 45						10 00			
Caerphilly 3	d	09 06				09 21						09 36				09 51						10 06			
Aber	d	09 08				09 23						09 38				09 53						10 08			
Llanbradach	d	09 12				09 27						09 42				09 57						10 12			
Ystrad Mynach 3	d	09a22				09 32						09 47				10 07						10a22			
Hengoed	d					09 35						09 50				10 10									
Pengam	d					09 38						09 53				10 13									
Gilfach Fargoed	d					09 41																			
Bargoed	d					09a49						09 59				10a25									
Brithdir	d											10 03													
Tir-phil	d											10 06													
Pontlottyn	d											10 10													
Rhymney 3	a											10 17													
Cathays	d				09 03			09 13		09 18					09 33			09 43		09 48					10 03
Llandaf	d				09 07			09 17		09 22					09 37			09 47		09 52					10 07
Ninian Park	d								09 10		←								09 40		←				
Waun-gron Park	d								09 14 →		09 14								09 44 →		09 44				
Fairwater	d										09 16										09 46				
Danescourt	d										09 19										09 49				
Radyr 3	a				09 10			09 20		09 25	09 27				09 40			09 50		09 55	09 57				10 10
	d				09 10			09 20		09 25					09 40			09 50		09 55					10 10
Taffs Well 3	d				09 14			09 24		09 29					09 44			09 54		09 59					10 14
Trefforest Estate	d				09 18										09 48										10 18
Trefforest	d				09 22			09 31		09 36					09 52			10 01		10 06					10 22
Pontypridd 3	a				09 32			09 34		09 39					09 55			10 04		10 09					10 32
	d							09 36		09 41					09 56			10 06		10 11					
Abercynon	d									09 51					10 06					10 21					
Penrhiwceiber	d									09 57										10 27					
Mountain Ash	a									10 01										10 31					
	d									10 04										10 34					
Fernhill	d									10 07										10 37					
Cwmbach	d									10 11										10 41					
Aberdare 3	a									10 19										10 49					
Quakers Yard	d														10 11										
Merthyr Vale	d														10 18										
Troed Y Rhiw	d														10 22										
Pentre-bach	d														10 25										
Merthyr Tydfil	a														10 34										
Trehafod	d							09 41										10 11							
Porth	d							09 45										10 15							
Dinas Rhondda	d							09 49										10 19							
Tonypandy	d							09 51										10 21							
Llwynypia	d							09 53										10 23							
Ystrad Rhondda	a							09 56										10 26							
	d							09 59										10 29							
Ton Pentre	d							10 01										10 31							
Treorchy	d							10 04										10 34							
Ynyswen	d							10 07										10 37							
Treherbert	a							10 14										10 44							

For general notes see front of timetable
For details of catering facilities see Directory of Train Operators

A From Radyr
B From Coryton

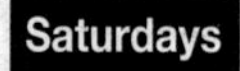

from 13 September

Bridgend, Barry Island, Barry, Penarth and Cardiff → Coryton, Rhymney, Pontypridd, Merthyr, Aberdare and Treherbert

Network Diagram - see first page of Table 130

		AW	AW	AW	AW A	AW	AW A	AW	AW	AW B	AW	AW	AW	AW	AW A	AW	AW	AW	AW B	AW	AW	AW	AW	AW A	AW
Bridgend	d															09 42									
Llantwit Major	d															09 56									
Rhoose Cardiff Int Airport ✈	d															10 06									
Barry Island	d					09 41					09 56										10 26				10 41
Barry 3	d					09 45					10 00					10 15					10 30				10 45
Barry Docks	d					09 49					10 04					10 19					10 34				10 49
Cadoxton	d					09 52					10 07					10 22					10 37				10 52
Dinas Powys	d					09 56					10 11					10 26					10 41				10 56
Eastbrook	d					09 58					10 13					10 28					10 43				10 58
Cogan	d					10 00					10 15					10 30					10 45				11 00
Penarth	d	09 47						10 02				10 17					10 32					10 47			
Dingle Road	d	09 49						10 04				10 19					10 34					10 49			
Grangetown	d	09 53				10 04		10 08			10 19	10 23				10 34	10 38				10 49	10 53			11 04
Cardiff Central 7	a	09 59				10 09		10 14			10 24	10 29				10 42	10 44				10 54	10 59			11 09
	d	10 01		10 06	10 06	10 11		10 16		10 21	10 26	10 31		10 36	10 36		10 46		10 51	10 51	10 56	11 01		11 06	11 11
Cardiff Bay	d		10 04						10 19				10 34					10 49					11 04		
Cardiff Queen Street 3	a	10 04	10 08	10 09		10 14		10 19	10 23	10 24	10 29	10 34	10 38	10 39			10 49	10 53	10 54		10 59	11 04	11 08		11 14
	d	10 05		10 10		10 15		10 20		10 25	10 30	10 35		10 40			10 50		10 55		11 00	11 05			11 15
Heath Low Level	d									10 30									11 00						
Ty Glas	d									10 33									11 03						
Birchgrove	d									10 34									11 04						
Rhiwbina	d									10 36									11 06						
Whitchurch (Cardiff)	d									10 38					10 16				11 08						
Coryton	a									10 44									11 14						
Heath High Level	d	10 10						10 25				10 40					10 55					11 10			
Llanishen	d	10 13						10 28				10 43					10 58					11 13			
Lisvane & Thornhill	d	10 15						10 30				10 45					11 00					11 15			
Caerphilly 3	d	10 21						10 36				10 51					11 06					11 21			
Aber	d	10 23						10 38				10 53					11 08					11 23			
Llanbradach	d	10 27						10 42				10 57					11 12					11 27			
Ystrad Mynach 3	d	10 32						10 47				11 07					11a22					11 32			
Hengoed	d	10 35						10 50				11 10										11 35			
Pengam	d	10 38						10 53				11 13										11 38			
Gilfach Fargoed	d	10 41																				11 41			
Bargoed	d	10a49						10 59				11a25										11a49			
Brithdir	d							11 03																	
Tir-phil	d							11 06																	
Pontlottyn	d							11 10																	
Rhymney 3	a							11 17																	
Cathays	d			10 13		10 18					10 33			10 43							11 03				11 18
Llandaf	d			10 17		10 22					10 37			10 47							11 07				11 22
Ninian Park	d				10 10		←								10 40									11 10	
Waun-gron Park	d				10 14 →		10 14								10 44									11 14 →	
Fairwater	d						10 16								10 46										
Danescourt	d						10 19								10 49										
Radyr 3	a			10 20		10 25	10 27				10 40			10 50	10 57					11 02	11 10				11 25
	d			10 20		10 25					10 40			10 50						11 05	11 10				11 25
Taffs Well 3	d			10 24		10 29					10 44			10 54						11 09	11 14				11 29
Trefforest Estate	d										10 48										11 18				
Trefforest	d			10 31		10 36					10 52			11 01						11 16	11 22				11 36
Pontypridd 3	a			10 34		10 39					10 55			11 04						11 19	11 32				11 39
	d			10 36		10 41					10 56			11 06						11 22					11 41
Abercynon	d					10 51					11 06														11 51
Penrhiwceiber	d					10 57																			11 57
Mountain Ash	a					11 01																			12 01
	d					11 04																			12 04
Fernhill	d					11 07																			12 07
Cwmbach	d					11 11																			12 11
Aberdare 3	a					11 19																			12 19
Quakers Yard	d										11 11														
Merthyr Vale	d										11 18														
Troed Y Rhiw	d										11 22														
Pentre-bach	d										11 25														
Merthyr Tydfil	a										11 34														
Trehafod	d			10 41										11 11						11 27					
Porth	d			10 45										11 15						11b45					
Dinas Rhondda	d			10 49										11 19						11 49					
Tonypandy	d			10 51										11 21						11 51					
Llwynypia	d			10 53										11 23						11 53					
Ystrad Rhondda	a			10 56										11 26						11 56					
	d			10 59										11 29						11 59					
Ton Pentre	d			11 01										11 31						12 01					
Treorchy	d			11 04										11 34						12 04					
Ynyswen	d			11 07										11 37						12 07					
Treherbert	a			11 14										11 44						12 14					

For general notes see front of timetable
For details of catering facilities see Directory of Train Operators

A From Coryton
B From Radyr
b Arr. 1130

Table 130

from 13 September

Bridgend, Barry Island, Barry, Penarth and Cardiff → Coryton, Rhymney, Pontypridd, Merthyr, Aberdare and Treherbert

Network Diagram - see first page of Table 130

		AW A	AW		AW	AW B	AW	AW	AW	AW A	AW	AW	AW A	AW	AW	AW	AW B	AW	AW	AW	AW	AW A		AW	AW A	AW
Bridgend	d														10 42											
Llantwit Major	d														10 56											
Rhoose Cardiff Int Airport ✈	d														11 06											
Barry Island	d						10 56											11 26						11 41		
Barry 3	d						11 00								11 15			11 30						11 45		
Barry Docks	d						11 04								11 19			11 34						11 49		
Cadoxton	d						11 07								11 22			11 37						11 52		
Dinas Powys	d						11 11								11 26			11 41						11 56		
Eastbrook	d						11 13								11 28			11 43						11 58		
Cogan	d						11 15								11 30			11 45						12 00		
Penarth	d		11 02					11 17						11 32					11 47							12 02
Dingle Road	d		11 04					11 19						11 34					11 49							12 04
Grangetown	d		11 08				11 19	11 23						11 38	11 34			11 49	11 53					12 04		12 08
Cardiff Central 7	a		11 14				11 24	11 29						11 44	11 45			11 54	11 59					12 09		12 14
	d		11 16			11 21	11 26	11 31		11 36	11 36	11 41		11 46			11 51	11 56	12 01		12 06	12 06		12 11		12 16
Cardiff Bay	d				11 19				11 34							11 49				12 04						
Cardiff Queen Street 3	a		11 19		11 23	11 24	11 29	11 34	11 38		11 39	11 44		11 49		11 53	11 54	11 59	12 04	12 08	12 09			12 14		12 19
	d		11 20			11 25	11 30	11 35			11 40	11 45		11 50			11 55	12 00	12 05		12 10			12 15		12 20
Heath Low Level	d					11 30											12 00									
Ty Glas	d					11 33											12 03									
Birchgrove	d					11 34											12 04									
Rhiwbina	d					11 36											12 06									
Whitchurch (Cardiff)	d					11 38											12 08									
Coryton	a					11 44											12 14									
Heath High Level	d		11 25					11 40						11 55					12 10							12 25
Llanishen	d		11 28					11 43						11 58					12 13							12 28
Lisvane & Thornhill	d		11 30					11 45						12 00					12 15							12 30
Caerphilly 3	d		11 36					11 51						12 06					12 21							12 36
Aber	d		11 38					11 53						12 08					12 23							12 38
Llanbradach	d		11 42					11 57						12 12					12 27							12 42
Ystrad Mynach 3	d		11 47					12 07						12a22					12 32							12 47
Hengoed	d		11 50					12 10											12 35							12 50
Pengam	d		11 53					12 13											12 38							12 53
Gilfach Fargoed	d																		12 41							
Bargoed	d		11 59					12a25											12a49							12 59
Brithdir	d		12 03																							13 03
Tir-phil	d		12 06																							13 06
Pontlottyn	d		12 10																							13 10
Rhymney 3	a		12 17																							13 17
Cathays	d						11 33				11 43	11 48						12 03			12 13			12 18		
Llandaf	d						11 37				11 47	11 52						12 07			12 17			12 22		
Ninian Park	d	←								11 40			←									12 10			←	
Waun-gron Park	d	11 14								11 44			11 44									12 14			12 14	
Fairwater	d	11 16								→			11 46									→			12 16	
Danescourt	d	11 19											11 49												12 19	
Radyr 3	a	11 27					11 40				11 50	11 54	11 57					12 10			12 20			12 25	12 27	
	d						11 40				11 50	11 55						12 10			12 20			12 25		
Taffs Well 3	d						11 44				11 54	11 59						12 14			12 24			12 29		
Trefforest Estate	d						11 48											12 18								
Trefforest	d						11 52				12 01	12 06						12 22			12 31			12 36		
Pontypridd 3	a						11 55				12 04	12 09						12 32			12 34			12 43		
	d						11 56				12 06	12 11									12 36					
Abercynon	d						12 06					12 21														
Penrhiwceiber	d											12 27														
Mountain Ash	a											12 31														
	d											12 34														
Fernhill	d											12 37														
Cwmbach	d											12 41														
Aberdare 3	a											12 49														
Quakers Yard	d						12 11																			
Merthyr Vale	d						12 18																			
Troed Y Rhiw	d						12 22																			
Pentre-bach	d						12 25																			
Merthyr Tydfil	a						12 34																			
Trehafod	d										12 11										12 41					
Porth	d										12 15										12 45					
Dinas Rhondda	d										12 19										12 49					
Tonypandy	d										12 21										12 51					
Llwynypia	d										12 23										12 53					
Ystrad Rhondda	a										12 26										12 56					
	d										12 29										12 59					
Ton Pentre	d										12 31										13 01					
Treorchy	d										12 34										13 04					
Ynyswen	d										12 37										13 07					
Treherbert	a										12 44										13 14					

For general notes see front of timetable
For details of catering facilities see Directory of Train Operators

A From Coryton
B From Radyr

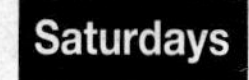

Bridgend, Barry Island, Barry, Penarth and Cardiff → Coryton, Rhymney, Pontypridd, Merthyr, Aberdare and Treherbert

Saturdays from 13 September

Network Diagram - see first page of Table 130

		AW	AW A	AW	AW	AW	AW	AW B	AW	AW B	AW	AW	AW A	AW	AW	AW	AW	AW B		AW	AW B	AW	AW	AW A	AW	AW
Bridgend	d								11 42																	
Llantwit Major	d								11 56																	
Rhoose Cardiff Int Airport ✈	d								12 06																	
Barry Island	d			11 56										12 26						12 41					12 56	
Barry 3	d			12 00					12 15					12 30						12 45					13 00	
Barry Docks	d			12 04					12 19					12 34						12 49					13 04	
Cadoxton	d			12 07					12 22					12 37						12 52					13 07	
Dinas Powys	d			12 11					12 26					12 41						12 56					13 11	
Eastbrook	d			12 13					12 28					12 43						12 58					13 13	
Cogan	d			12 15					12 30					12 45						13 00					13 15	
Penarth	d				12 17						12 32				12 47							13 02				13 17
Dingle Road	d				12 19						12 34				12 49							13 04				13 19
Grangetown	d			12 19	12 23				12 34		12 38			12 49	12 53					13 04		13 08			13 19	13 23
Cardiff Central 7	a			12 24	12 29				12 39		12 44			12 54	12 59					13 09		13 14			13 24	13 29
	d		12 21	12 26	12 31		12 36	12 36	12 41		12 46		12 51	12 56	13 01		13 06	13 06		13 11		13 16		13 21	13 26	13 31
Cardiff Bay	d	12 19				12 34						12 49				13 04							13 19			
Cardiff Queen Street 3	a	12 23	12 24	12 29	12 34	12 38	12 39		12 44		12 49	12 53	12 54	12 59	13 04	13 08	13 09			13 14		13 19	13 23	13 24	13 29	13 34
	d		12 25	12 30	12 35		12 40		12 45		12 50		12 55	13 00	13 05		13 10			13 15		13 20		13 25	13 30	13 35
Heath Low Level	d		12 30										13 00											13 30		
Ty Glas	d		12 33										13 03											13 33		
Birchgrove	d		12 34										13 04											13 34		
Rhiwbina	d		12 36										13 06											13 36		
Whitchurch (Cardiff)	d		12 38										13 08					12 46						13 38		
Coryton	a		12 44										13 14											13 44		
Heath High Level	d				12 40						12 55				13 10							13 25				13 40
Llanishen	d				12 43						12 58				13 13							13 28				13 43
Lisvane & Thornhill	d				12 45						13 00				13 15							13 30				13 45
Caerphilly 3	d				12 51						13 06				13 21							13 36				13 51
Aber	d				12 53						13 08				13 23							13 38				13 53
Llanbradach	d				12 57						13 12				13 27							13 42				13 57
Ystrad Mynach 3	d				13 07						13a22				13 32							13 47				14 07
Hengoed	d				13 10										13 35							13 50				14 10
Pengam	d				13 13										13 38							13 53				14 13
Gilfach Fargoed	d														13 41											
Bargoed	d				13a25										13a49							13 59				14a25
Brithdir	d																					14 03				
Tir-phil	d																					14 06				
Pontlottyn	d																					14 10				
Rhymney 3	a																					14 17				
Cathays	d			12 33			12 43		12 48					13 03			13 13			13 18					13 33	
Llandaf	d			12 37			12 47		12 52					13 07			13 17			13 22					13 37	
Ninian Park	d							12 40		←								13 10			←					
Waun-gron Park	d							12 44 →		12 44								13 14 →			13 14					
Fairwater	d									12 46											13 16					
Danescourt	d									12 49											13 19					
Radyr 3	a			12 40			12 50		12 55	12 57				13 10			13 20			13 25	13 27				13 40	
	d			12 40			12 50		12 55					13 10			13 20			13 25					13 40	
Taffs Well 3	d			12 44			12 54		12 59					13 14			13 24			13 29					13 44	
Trefforest Estate	d			12 48										13 18											13 48	
Trefforest	d			12 52			13 01		13 06					13 22			13 31			13 36					13 52	
Pontypridd 3	a			12 55			13 04		13 09					13 32			13 34			13 39					13 55	
	d			12 56			13 06		13 11								13 36			13 41					13 56	
Abercynon	d			13 06					13 21											13 51					14 06	
Penrhiwceiber	d								13 27											13 57						
Mountain Ash	a								13 31											14 01						
	d								13 34											14 04						
Fernhill	d								13 37											14 07						
Cwmbach	d								13 41											14 11						
Aberdare 3	a								13 49											14 19						
Quakers Yard	d			13 11																					14 11	
Merthyr Vale	d			13 18																					14 18	
Troed Y Rhiw	d			13 22																					14 22	
Pentre-bach	d			13 25																					14 25	
Merthyr Tydfil	a			13 34																					14 34	
Trehafod	d						13 11										13 41									
Porth	d						13 15										13 45									
Dinas Rhondda	d						13 19										13 49									
Tonypandy	d						13 21										13 51									
Llwynypia	d						13 23										13 53									
Ystrad Rhondda	a						13 26										13 56									
	d						13 29										13 59									
Ton Pentre	d						13 31										14 01									
Treorchy	d						13 34										14 04									
Ynyswen	d						13 37										14 07									
Treherbert	a						13 44										14 14									

For general notes see front of timetable
For details of catering facilities see Directory of Train Operators

A From Radyr
B From Coryton

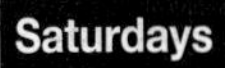

from 13 September

Bridgend, Barry Island, Barry, Penarth and Cardiff → Coryton, Rhymney, Pontypridd, Merthyr, Aberdare and Treherbert

Network Diagram - see first page of Table 130

Station		AW	AW	AW A	AW	AW A	AW	AW	AW B	AW	AW	AW	AW	AW A		AW	AW A	AW	AW	AW B	AW	AW	AW	AW	AW A	AW
Bridgend	d				12 42																					13 42
Llantwit Major	d				12 56																					13 56
Rhoose Cardiff Int Airport ✈	d				13 06																					14 06
Barry Island	d									13 26						13 41					13 56					
Barry 3	d				13 15					13 30						13 45					14 00					14 15
Barry Docks	d				13 19					13 34						13 49					14 04					14 19
Cadoxton	d				13 22					13 37						13 52					14 07					14 22
Dinas Powys	d				13 26					13 41						13 56					14 11					14 26
Eastbrook	d				13 28					13 43						13 58					14 13					14 28
Cogan	d				13 30					13 45						14 00					14 15					14 30
Penarth	d						13 32				13 47							14 02				14 17				
Dingle Road	d						13 34				13 49							14 04				14 19				
Grangetown	d				13 34		13 38			13 49	13 53					14 04		14 08			14 19	14 23				14 34
Cardiff Central 7	a				13 39		13 44			13 54	14 02					14 09		14 14			14 24	14 29				14 39
	d		13 36	13 36	13 41		13 46		13 51	13 56			14 06	14 06		14 11		14 16		14 21	14 26	14 31		14 36	14 36	14 41
Cardiff Bay	d	13 34						13 49				14 04							14 19				14 34			
Cardiff Queen Street 3	a	13 38	13 39		13 44		13 49	13 53	13 54	13 59		14 08	14 09			14 14		14 19	14 23	14 24	14 29	14 34	14 38	14 39		14 44
	d		13 40		13 45		13 50		13 55	14 00			14 10			14 15		14 20		14 25	14 30	14 35		14 40		14 45
Heath Low Level	d								14 00											14 30						
Ty Glas	d								14 03											14 33						
Birchgrove	d								14 04											14 34						
Rhiwbina	d								14 06											14 36						
Whitchurch (Cardiff)	d								14 08											14 38						
Coryton	a								14 14											14 44						
Heath High Level	d						13 55											14 25				14 40				
Llanishen	d						13 58											14 28				14 43				
Lisvane & Thornhill	d						14 00											14 30				14 45				
Caerphilly 3	d						14 06											14 36				14 51				
Aber	d						14 08											14 38				14 53				
Llanbradach	d						14 12											14 42				14 57				
Ystrad Mynach 3	d						14a22											14 47				15 07				
Hengoed	d																	14 50				15 10				
Pengam	d																	14 53				15 13				
Gilfach Fargoed	d																									
Bargoed	d																	14 59				15a25				
Brithdir	d																	15 03								
Tir-phil	d																	15 06								
Pontlottyn	d																	15 10								
Rhymney 3	a																	15 17								
Cathays	d		13 43		13 48					14 03			14 13			14 18					14 33			14 43		14 48
Llandaf	d		13 47		13 52					14 07			14 17			14 22					14 37			14 47		14 52
Ninian Park	d			13 40		←								14 10			←								14 40	
Waun-gron Park	d			13 44		13 44								14 14			14 14								14 44	
Fairwater	d			→		13 46								→			14 16								→	
Danescourt	d					13 49											14 19									
Radyr 3	a		13 50		13 55	13 57				14 10			14 20			14 25	14 27				14 40			14 50		14 55
	d		13 50		13 55					14 10			14 20			14 25					14 40			14 50		14 55
Taffs Well 3	d		13 54		13 59					14 14			14 24			14 29					14 44			14 54		14 59
Trefforest Estate	d									14 18											14 48					
Trefforest	d		14 01		14 06					14 22			14 31			14 36					14 52			15 01		15 06
Pontypridd 3	a		14 04		14 09					14 32			14 34			14 39					14 55			15 04		15 09
	d		14 06		14 11								14 36			14 41					14 56			15 06		15 11
Abercynon	d				14 21											14 51					15 06					15 21
Penrhiwceiber	d				14 27											14 57										15 27
Mountain Ash	a				14 31											15 01										15 31
	d				14 34											15 04										15 34
Fernhill	d				14 37											15 07										15 37
Cwmbach	d				14 41											15 11										15 41
Aberdare 3	a				14 49											15 19										15 49
Quakers Yard	d																				15 11					
Merthyr Vale	d																				15 18					
Troed Y Rhiw	d																				15 22					
Pentre-bach	d																				15 25					
Merthyr Tydfil	a																				15 34					
Trehafod	d		14 11										14 41											15 11		
Porth	d		14 15										14 45											15 15		
Dinas Rhondda	d		14 19										14 49											15 19		
Tonypandy	d		14 21										14 51											15 21		
Llwynypia	d		14 23										14 53											15 23		
Ystrad Rhondda	a		14 26										14 56											15 26		
	d		14 29										14 59											15 29		
Ton Pentre	d		14 31										15 01											15 31		
Treorchy	d		14 34										15 04											15 34		
Ynyswen	d		14 37										15 07											15 37		
Treherbert	a		14 44										15 14											15 44		

For general notes see front of timetable
For details of catering facilities see Directory of Train Operators

A From Coryton
B From Radyr

Table 130

Saturdays

from 13 September

Bridgend, Barry Island, Barry, Penarth and Cardiff → Coryton, Rhymney, Pontypridd, Merthyr, Aberdare and Treherbert

Network Diagram - see first page of Table 130

		AW A	AW	AW	AW B	AW	AW	AW	AW	AW A	AW	AW A	AW	AW	AW B	AW	AW	AW	AW	AW A	AW	AW A	AW	AW	AW B
Bridgend	d																				14 42				
Llantwit Major	d																				14 56				
Rhoose Cardiff Int Airport ✈	d																				15 06				
Barry Island	d						14 26				14 41					14 56									
Barry 3	d						14 30				14 45					15 00					15 15				
Barry Docks	d						14 34				14 49					15 04					15 19				
Cadoxton	d						14 37				14 52					15 07					15 22				
Dinas Powys	d						14 41				14 56					15 11					15 26				
Eastbrook	d						14 43				14 58					15 13					15 28				
Cogan	d						14 45				15 00					15 15					15 30				
Penarth	d		14 32					14 47					15 02				15 17						15 32		
Dingle Road	d		14 34					14 49					15 04				15 19						15 34		
Grangetown	d		14 38				14 49	14 53			15 04		15 08			15 19	15 23				15 34		15 38		
Cardiff Central 7	a		14 44				14 54	14 59			15 09		15 14			15 24	15 29				15 39		15 44		
	d		14 46		14 51	14 51	14 56	15 01		15 06	15 11		15 16		15 21	15 26	15 31		15 36	15 36	15 41		15 46		15 51
Cardiff Bay	d			14 49					15 04					15 19				15 34						15 49	
Cardiff Queen Street 3	a		14 49	14 53	14 54		14 59	15 04	15 08		15 14		15 19	15 23	15 24	15 29	15 34	15 38	15 39		15 44		15 49	15 53	15 54
	d		14 50		14 55		15 00	15 05			15 15		15 20		15 25	15 30	15 35		15 40		15 45		15 50		15 55
Heath Low Level	d				15 00										15 30										16 00
Ty Glas	d				15 03										15 33										16 03
Birchgrove	d				15 04										15 34										16 04
Rhiwbina	d				15 06										15 36										16 06
Whitchurch (Cardiff)	d				15 08										15 38										16 08
Coryton	a				15 14										15 44										16 14
Heath High Level	d		14 55					15 10					15 25				15 40						15 55		
Llanishen	d		14 58					15 13					15 28				15 43						15 58		
Lisvane & Thornhill	d		15 00					15 15					15 30				15 45						16 00		
Caerphilly 3	d		15 06					15 21					15 36				15 51						16 06		
Aber	d		15 08					15 23					15 38				15 53						16 08		
Llanbradach	d		15 12					15 27					15 42				15 57						16 12		
Ystrad Mynach 3	d		15a22					15 32					15 47				16 02						16 17		
Hengoed	d							15 35					15 50				16 05						16 20		
Pengam	d							15 38					15 53				16 08						16 23		
Gilfach Fargoed	d							15 41																	
Bargoed	d							15a49					15 59				16a17						16a32		
Brithdir	d												16 03												
Tir-phil	d												16 06												
Pontlottyn	d												16 10												
Rhymney 3	a												16 17												
Cathays	d						15 03				15 18					15 33			15 43		15 48				
Llandaf	d						15 07				15 22					15 37			15 47		15 52				
Ninian Park	d	←								15 10		←								15 40		←			
Waun-gron Park	d	14 44								15 14 →		15 14								15 44 →		15 44			
Fairwater	d	14 46										15 16										15 46			
Danescourt	d	14 49										15 19										15 49			
Radyr 3	a	14 57				15 02	15 10				15 25	15 27				15 40			15 50		15 55	15 57			
	d					15 02	15 10				15 25					15 40			15 50		15 55				
Taffs Well 3	d					15 06	15 14				15 29					15 44			15 54		15 59				
Trefforest Estate	d						15 18									15 48									
Trefforest	d					15 13	15 22				15 36					15 52			16 01		16 06				
Pontypridd 3	a					15 16	15 32				15 39					15 55			16 04		16 09				
	d					15 22					15 41					15 56			16 06		16 11				
Abercynon	d										15 51					16 06					16 21				
Penrhiwceiber	d										15 57										16 27				
Mountain Ash	a										16 01										16 31				
	d										16 04										16 34				
Fernhill	d										16 07										16 37				
Cwmbach	d										16 11										16 41				
Aberdare 3	a										16 19										16 49				
Quakers Yard	d															16 11									
Merthyr Vale	d															16 18									
Troed Y Rhiw	d															16 22									
Pentre-bach	d															16 25									
Merthyr Tydfil	a															16 34									
Trehafod	d					15 27													16 11						
Porth	d					15b45													16 15						
Dinas Rhondda	d					15 49													16 19						
Tonypandy	d					15 51													16 21						
Llwynypia	d					15 53													16 23						
Ystrad Rhondda	a					15 56													16 26						
	d					15 59													16 29						
Ton Pentre	d					16 01													16 31						
Treorchy	d					16 04													16 34						
Ynyswen	d					16 07													16 37						
Treherbert	a					16 14													16 44						

For general notes see front of timetable
For details of catering facilities see Directory of Train Operators

A From Coryton
B From Radyr
b Arr. 1530

Table 130

from 13 September

Bridgend, Barry Island, Barry, Penarth and Cardiff → Coryton, Rhymney, Pontypridd, Merthyr, Aberdare and Treherbert

Network Diagram - see first page of Table 130

		AW	AW	AW	AW	AW A		AW	AW A	AW	AW	AW B	AW	AW	AW	AW	AW A	AW	AW A	AW	AW	AW B	AW	AW	AW	AW
Bridgend	d																	15 42								
Llantwit Major	d																	15 56								
Rhoose Cardiff Int Airport ✈	d																	16 06								
Barry Island	d	15 26						15 41					15 56										16 26			
Barry 3	d	15 30						15 45					16 00					16 15					16 30			
Barry Docks	d	15 34						15 49					16 04					16 19					16 34			
Cadoxton	d	15 37						15 52					16 07					16 22					16 37			
Dinas Powys	d	15 41						15 56					16 11					16 26					16 41			
Eastbrook	d	15 43						15 58					16 13					16 28					16 43			
Cogan	d	15 45						16 00					16 15					16 30					16 45			
Penarth	d		15 47											16 17						16 32						
Dingle Road	d		15 49											16 19						16 34						
Grangetown	d	15 49	15 53					16 04					16 19	16 23				16 34		16 38			16 49			
Cardiff Central 7	a	15 54	15 59					16 09					16 24	16 29				16 39		16 44			16 54			
	d	15 56	16 01		16 06	16 06		16 11		16 16		16 21	16 26	16 31		16 36	16 36	16 41		16 46		16 51	16 56	17 01		17 06
Cardiff Bay	d			16 04							16 19				16 34						16 49				17 04	
Cardiff Queen Street 3	a	15 59	16 04	16 08	16 09			16 14		16 19	16 23	16 24	16 29	16 34	16 38	16 39		16 44		16 49	16 53	16 54	16 59	17 04	17 08	17 09
	d	16 00	16 05		16 10			16 15		16 20		16 25	16 30	16 35		16 40		16 45		16 50		16 55	17 00	17 05		17 10
Heath Low Level	d											16 30										17 00				
Ty Glas	d											16 33										17 03				
Birchgrove	d											16 34										17 04				
Rhiwbina	d											16 36										17 06				
Whitchurch (Cardiff)	d					15 46						16 38					16 16					17 08				
Coryton	a											16 44										17 14				
Heath High Level	d		16 10							16 25				16 40						16 55				17 10		
Llanishen	d		16 13							16 28				16 43						16 58				17 13		
Lisvane & Thornhill	d		16 15							16 30				16 45						17 00				17 15		
Caerphilly 3	d		16 21							16 36				16 51						17 06				17 21		
Aber	d		16 23							16 38				16 53						17 08				17 23		
Llanbradach	d		16 27							16 42				16 57						17 12				17 27		
Ystrad Mynach 3	d		16 32							16 47				17 02						17 17				17 33		
Hengoed	d		16 35							16 50				17 05						17 20				17 35		
Pengam	d		16 38							16 53				17 08						17 23				17 39		
Gilfach Fargoed	d		16 41																					17 42		
Bargoed	d		16a49							16 59				17a17						17a32				17 47		
Brithdir	d									17 03														17 50		
Tir-phil	d									17 06														17 53		
Pontlottyn	d									17 10														17 58		
Rhymney 3	a									17 17														18 05		
Cathays	d	16 03			16 13			16 18					16 33			16 43		16 48					17 03			17 13
Llandaf	d	16 07			16 17			16 22					16 37			16 47		16 52					17 07			17 17
Ninian Park	d					16 10			←								16 40		←							
Waun-gron Park	d					16 14 →			16 14								16 44 →		16 44							
Fairwater	d								16 16										16 46							
Danescourt	d								16 19										16 49							
Radyr 3	a	16 10			16 20			16 25	16 27				16 40			16 50		16 55	16 57				17 10			17 20
	d	16 10			16 20			16 25					16 40			16 50		16 55					17 10			17 20
Taffs Well 3	d	16 14			16 24			16 29					16 44			16 54		16 59					17 14			17 24
Trefforest Estate	d	16 18											16 48										17 18			
Trefforest	d	16 22			16 31			16 36					16 52			17 01		17 06					17 22			17 31
Pontypridd 3	a	16 32			16 34			16 39					16 55			17 04		17 09					17 32			17 34
	d				16 36			16 41					16 56			17 06		17 11								17 36
Abercynon	d							16 51					17 06					17 21								
Penrhiwceiber	d							16 57										17 27								
Mountain Ash	a							17 01										17 31								
	d							17 04										17 34								
Fernhill	d							17 07										17 37								
Cwmbach	d							17 11										17 41								
Aberdare 3	a							17 19										17 49								
Quakers Yard	d												17 11													
Merthyr Vale	d												17 18													
Troed Y Rhiw	d												17 22													
Pentre-bach	d												17 25													
Merthyr Tydfil	a												17 34													
Trehafod	d				16 41											17 11										17 41
Porth	d				16 45											17 15										17 45
Dinas Rhondda	d				16 49											17 19										17 49
Tonypandy	d				16 51											17 21										17 51
Llwynypia	d				16 53											17 23										17 53
Ystrad Rhondda	a				16 56											17 26										17 56
	d				16 59											17 29										17 59
Ton Pentre	d				17 01											17 31										18 01
Treorchy	d				17 04											17 34										18 04
Ynyswen	d				17 07											17 37										18 07
Treherbert	a				17 14											17 44										18 14

For general notes see front of timetable
For details of catering facilities see Directory of Train Operators

A From Coryton
B From Radyr

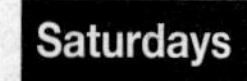

from 13 September

Bridgend, Barry Island, Barry, Penarth and Cardiff → Coryton, Rhymney, Pontypridd, Merthyr, Aberdare and Treherbert

Network Diagram - see first page of Table 130

		AW	AW	AW	AW	AW	AW	AW	AW	AW	AW	AW	AW	AW	AW	AW	AW	AW	AW	AW	AW	AW	AW	AW
		A		A			B					A		A			B					A		A
Bridgend	d												16 42											
Llantwit Major	d												16 56											
Rhoose Cardiff Int Airport ✈	d												17 06											
Barry Island	d		16 41					16 56										17 26					17 41	
Barry 3	d		16 45					17 00					17 15					17 30					17 45	
Barry Docks	d		16 49					17 04					17 19					17 34					17 49	
Cadoxton	d		16 52					17 07					17 22					17 37					17 52	
Dinas Powys	d		16 56					17 11					17 26					17 41					17 56	
Eastbrook	d		16 58					17 13					17 28					17 43					17 58	
Cogan	d		17 00					17 15					17 30					17 45					18 00	
Penarth	d				17 02				17 17						17 32				17 47					
Dingle Road	d				17 04				17 19						17 34				17 49					
Grangetown	d		17 04		17 08			17 19	17 23				17 34		17 38			17 49	17 53				18 04	
Cardiff Central 7	a		17 09		17 14			17 24	17 29				17 39		17 44			17 54	17 59				18 09	
	d	17 06	17 11		17 16		17 21	17 26	17 31		17 36	17 36	17 41		17 46		17 51	17 56	18 01		18 06	18 06	18 11	
Cardiff Bay	d					17 19				17 34						17 49				18 04				
Cardiff Queen Street 3	a		17 14		17 19	17 23	17 24	17 29	17 34	17 38	17 39		17 44		17 49	17 53	17 54	17 59	18 04	18 08	18 09		18 14	
	d		17 15		17 20		17 25	17 30	17 35		17 40		17 45		17 50		17 55	18 00	18 05		18 10		18 15	
Heath Low Level	d						17 30										18 00							
Ty Glas	d						17 33										18 03							
Birchgrove	d						17 34										18 04							
Rhiwbina	d						17 36										18 06							
Whitchurch (Cardiff)	d	16 46					17 38										18 08					17 46		
Coryton	a						17 44										18 14							
Heath High Level	d				17 25				17 40						17 55				18 10					
Llanishen	d				17 28				17 43						17 59				18 13					
Lisvane & Thornhill	d				17 30				17 45						18 02				18 15					
Caerphilly 3	d				17 36				17 51						18 07				18 21					
Aber	d				17 38				17 53						18 10				18 23					
Llanbradach	d				17 42				17 57						18 14				18 27					
Ystrad Mynach 3	d				17 47				18 02						18 20				18 32					
Hengoed	d				17 50				18 05						18 23				18 35					
Pengam	d				17 53				18 08						18 27				18 38					
Gilfach Fargoed	d								18 11						18 30				18 41					
Bargoed	d				18a02				18 16						18b44				18a49					
Brithdir	d								18 20						18 48									
Tir-phil	d								18 23						18 51									
Pontlottyn	d								18 27						18 55									
Rhymney 3	a								18 34						19 02									
Cathays	d		17 18					17 33			17 43		17 48					18 03			18 13		18 18	
Llandaf	d		17 22					17 37			17 47		17 52					18 07			18 17		18 22	
Ninian Park	d	17 10		←								17 40		←								18 10		←
Waun-gron Park	d	17 14		17 14								17 44		17 44								18 14		18 14
Fairwater	d	→		17 16								→		17 46								→		18 16
Danescourt	d			17 19										17 49										18 19
Radyr 3	a		17 25	17 27				17 40			17 50		17 55	17 57				18 10			18 20		18 25	18 27
	d		17 25					17 40			17 50		17 55					18 10			18 20		18 25	
Taffs Well 3	d		17 29					17 44			17 54		17 59					18 14			18 24		18 29	
Trefforest Estate	d							17 48										18 18						
Trefforest	d		17 36					17 52			18 01		18 06					18 22			18 31		18 36	
Pontypridd 3	a		17 39					17 55			18 04		18 09					18 32			18 34		18 42	
	d		17 41					17 56			18 06		18 11								18 36			
Abercynon	d							18 06					18 21											
Penrhiwceiber	d		17 57										18 27											
Mountain Ash	a		18 01										18 31											
	d		18 04										18 34											
Fernhill	d		18 07										18 37											
Cwmbach	d		18 11										18 41											
Aberdare 3	a		18 19										18 49											
Quakers Yard	d							18 11																
Merthyr Vale	d							18 18																
Troed Y Rhiw	d							18 22																
Pentre-bach	d							18 25																
Merthyr Tydfil	a							18 34																
Trehafod	d										18 11										18 41			
Porth	d										18 15										18 45			
Dinas Rhondda	d										18 19										18 49			
Tonypandy	d										18 21										18 51			
Llwynypia	d										18 23										18 53			
Ystrad Rhondda	a										18 26										18 56			
	d										18 29										18 59			
Ton Pentre	d										18 31										19 01			
Treorchy	d										18 34										19 04			
Ynyswen	d										18 37										19 07			
Treherbert	a										18 44										19 14			

For general notes see front of timetable
For details of catering facilities see Directory of Train Operators

A From Coryton
B From Radyr
b Arr. 1834

Table 130

Saturdays

from 13 September

Bridgend, Barry Island, Barry, Penarth and Cardiff → Coryton, Rhymney, Pontypridd, Merthyr, Aberdare and Treherbert

Network Diagram - see first page of Table 130

		AW	AW	AW A	AW	AW		AW	AW B	AW	AW	AW	AW A	AW	AW	AW	AW		AW	AW	AW	AW	AW	AW B	AW	AW B
Bridgend	d									17 42															18 42	
Llantwit Major	d									17 56															18 56	
Rhoose Cardiff Int Airport ✈	d									18 06															19 06	
Barry Island	d				17 56									18 26					18 41		18 56					
Barry 3	d				18 00					18 15				18 30					18 45		19 00				19 15	
Barry Docks	d				18 04					18 19				18 34					18 49		19 04				19 19	
Cadoxton	d				18 07					18 22				18 37					18 52		19 07				19 22	
Dinas Powys	d				18 11					18 26				18 41					18 56		19 11				19 26	
Eastbrook	d				18 13					18 28				18 43					18 58		19 13				19 28	
Cogan	d				18 15					18 30				18 45					19 00		19 15				19 30	
Penarth	d	18 02				18 17					18 32				18 47							19 17				
Dingle Road	d	18 04				18 19					18 34				18 49							19 19				
Grangetown	d	18 08			18 19	18 23				18 34	18 38			18 49	18 53				19 04		19 19	19 23			19 34	
Cardiff Central 7	a	18 14			18 24	18 29				18 39	18 47			18 54	18 59				19 09		19 24	19 29			19 39	
	d	18 16		18 21	18 26	18 31	18 36		18 36	18 41			18 51		19 01		19 06		19 11		19 26	19 31		19 36	19 41	
Cardiff Bay	d		18 19					18 34				18 49				19 04				19 19			19 34			
Cardiff Queen Street 3	a	18 19	18 23	18 24	18 29	18 34	18 38	18 38		18 44		18 53	18 54		19 04	19 08	19 09		19 14	19 23	19 29	19 34	19 38		19 44	
	d	18 20		18 25	18 30	18 35	18 40			18 50			18 55		19 05		19 10		19 15		19 30	19 35			19 45	
Heath Low Level	d			18 30									19 00													
Ty Glas	d			18 33									19 03													
Birchgrove	d			18 34									19 04													
Rhiwbina	d			18 36									19 06													
Whitchurch (Cardiff)	d			18 38					18 16				19 08													
Coryton	a			18 44									19 14													
Heath High Level	d	18 25				18 40									19 10							19 40				
Llanishen	d	18 28				18 43									19 13							19 43				
Lisvane & Thornhill	d	18 30				18 45									19 15							19 45				
Caerphilly 3	d	18 36				18 51									19a24							19 51				
Aber	d	18 38				18 53																19 53				
Llanbradach	d	18 42				18 57																19 57				
Ystrad Mynach 3	d	18a52				19 02																20 02				
Hengoed	d					19 05																20 05				
Pengam	d					19 08																20 08				
Gilfach Fargoed	d					19x11																20 11				
Bargoed	d					19 16																20 16				
Brithdir	d					19 20																20 20				
Tir-phil	d					19 23																20 23				
Pontlottyn	d					19 27																20 27				
Rhymney 3	a					19 34																20 34				
Cathays	d				18 33		18 43			18 52							19 13		19 18		19 33				19 48	
Llandaf	d				18 37		18 47			18 56							19 17		19 22		19 37				19 52	
Ninian Park	d								18 40															19 40		←
Waun-gron Park	d								18 44															19 44 →		19 44
Fairwater	d								18 46																	19 46
Danescourt	d								18 49																	19 49
Radyr 3	a				18 40		18 50		18 57	18 58							19 20		19 25		19 40				19 55	19 57
	d				18 40		18 50			18 58							19 20		19 25		19 40				19 55	
Taffs Well 3	d				18 44		18 54			19 03							19 24		19 29		19 44				19 59	
Trefforest Estate	d				18 48																19 48					
Trefforest	d				18 52		19 01			19 10							19 31		19 36		19 52				20 06	
Pontypridd 3	a				18 55		19 04			19 13							19 34		19 39		19 55				20 09	
	d				18 56		19 06			19 14							19 36		19 41		19 56				20 11	
Abercynon	d				19 06					19 21									19 51		20 06				20 21	
Penrhiwceiber	d									19 27									19 57						20 27	
Mountain Ash	a									19 30									20 01						20 31	
	d									19 34									20 04						20 34	
Fernhill	d									19 37									20 07						20 37	
Cwmbach	d									19 41									20 11						20 41	
Aberdare 3	a									19 49									20 19						20 49	
Quakers Yard	d				19 11																20 11					
Merthyr Vale	d				19 18																20 18					
Troed Y Rhiw	d				19 22																20 22					
Pentre-bach	d				19 25																20 25					
Merthyr Tydfil	a				19 34																20 34					
Trehafod	d						19 11										19 41									
Porth	d						19 15										19 45									
Dinas Rhondda	d						19 19										19 49									
Tonypandy	d						19 21										19 51									
Llwynypia	d						19 23										19 53									
Ystrad Rhondda	a						19 26										19 56									
	d						19 29										19 59									
Ton Pentre	d						19 31										20 01									
Treorchy	d						19 34										20 04									
Ynyswen	d						19 37										20 07									
Treherbert	a						19 44										20 14									

For general notes see front of timetable
For details of catering facilities see Directory of Train Operators

A From Radyr
B From Coryton

Saturdays

from 13 September

Bridgend, Barry Island, Barry, Penarth and Cardiff → Coryton, Rhymney, Pontypridd, Merthyr, Aberdare and Treherbert

Network Diagram - see first page of Table 130

		AW	AW	AW	AW	AW	AW	AW	AW	AW	AW	AW	AW	AW	AW	AW	AW	AW	AW	AW	AW	AW	AW	AW	AW
												A		A											A
Bridgend	d												19 42												
Llantwit Major	d												19 56												
Rhoose Cardiff Int Airport ✈	d												20 06												
Barry Island	d			19 26					19 56												20 56				
Barry 3	d			19 30					20 00				20 15								21 00				
Barry Docks	d			19 34					20 04				20 19								21 04				
Cadoxton	d			19 37					20 07				20 22								21 07				
Dinas Powys	d			19 41					20 11				20 26								21 11				
Eastbrook	d			19 43					20 13				20 28								21 13				
Cogan	d			19 45					20 15				20 30								21 15				
Penarth	d				19 47					20 17							20 47						21 17		
Dingle Road	d				19 49					20 19							20 49						21 19		
Grangetown	d			19 49	19 53				20 19	20 23			20 34				20 53				21 19		21 23		
Cardiff Central 7	a			19 56	19 59				20 24	20 29			20 39				20 59				21 24		21 33		
	d		19 51		20 01		20 06		20 26	20 31		20 36	20 41			20 51	21 01		21 06		21 26	21 31			21 36
Cardiff Bay	d	19 49				20 04		20 19			20 34				20 49			21 04		21 19				21 34	
Cardiff Queen Street 3	a	19 53	19 54		20 04	20 08	20 09	20 23	20 29	20 34	20 38		20 44		20 53	20 54	21 04	21 08	21 09	21 23	21 29	21 34		21 38	
	d		19 55		20 05		20 10		20 30	20 35			20 45			20 55	21 05		21 10		21 30	21 35			
Heath Low Level	d		20 00													21 00									
Ty Glas	d		20 03													21 03									
Birchgrove	d		20 04													21 04									
Rhiwbina	d		20 06													21 06									
Whitchurch (Cardiff)	d		20 08													21 08									
Coryton	a		20 14													21 13									
Heath High Level	d				20 10					20 40							21 10					21 40			
Llanishen	d				20 13					20 43							21 13					21 43			
Lisvane & Thornhill	d				20 15					20 45							21 15					21 45			
Caerphilly 3	d				20a28					20 51							21a28					21 51			
Aber	d									20 53												21 53			
Llanbradach	d									20 57												21 57			
Ystrad Mynach 3	d									21 02												22 02			
Hengoed	d									21 05												22 05			
Pengam	d									21 08												22 08			
Gilfach Fargoed	d									21 11												22 11			
Bargoed	d									21 16												22 16			
Brithdir	d									21 20												22 20			
Tir-phil	d									21 23												22 23			
Pontlottyn	d									21 27												22 27			
Rhymney 3	a									21 34												22 34			
Cathays	d						20 13		20 33				20 48						21 13		21 33				
Llandaf	d						20 17		20 37				20 52						21 17		21 37				
Ninian Park	d											20 40		←											21 40
Waun-gron Park	d											20 44 →		20 44											21 44 →
Fairwater	d													20 46											
Danescourt	d													20 49											
Radyr 3	a						20 20		20 40				20 55	20 57					21 20		21 40				
	d						20 20		20 40				20 55						21 20		21 40				
Taffs Well 3	d						20 24		20 44				20 59						21 24		21 44				
Trefforest Estate	d								20 48												21 48				
Trefforest	d						20 31		20 52				21 06						21 31		21 52				
Pontypridd 3	a						20 34		20 55				21 09						21 34		21 55				
	d						20 36		20 56				21 11						21 36		21 56				
Abercynon	d								21 06				21 21								22 06				
Penrhiwceiber	d												21 27												
Mountain Ash	a												21 31												
	d												21 34												
Fernhill	d												21 37												
Cwmbach	d												21 41												
Aberdare 3	a												21 49												
Quakers Yard	d								21 11												22 11				
Merthyr Vale	d								21 18												22 18				
Troed Y Rhiw	d								21 22												22 22				
Pentre-bach	d								21 25												22 25				
Merthyr Tydfil	a								21 34												22 34				
Trehafod	d						20 41												21 41						
Porth	d						20 45												21 45						
Dinas Rhondda	d						20 49												21 49						
Tonypandy	d						20 51												21 51						
Llwynypia	d						20 53												21 53						
Ystrad Rhondda	a						20 56												21 56						
	d						20 59												21 59						
Ton Pentre	d						21 01												22 01						
Treorchy	d						21 04												22 04						
Ynyswen	d						21 09												22 07						
Treherbert	a						21 17												22 14						

For general notes see front of timetable
For details of catering facilities see Directory of Train Operators

A From Coryton

Table 130

Saturdays

from 13 September

Bridgend, Barry Island, Barry, Penarth and Cardiff → Coryton, Rhymney, Pontypridd, Merthyr, Aberdare and Treherbert

Network Diagram - see first page of Table 130

		AW	AW	AW	AW	AW	AW	AW	AW	AW	AW	AW	AW	AW	AW	AW	AW	AW	AW	AW	AW	AW	AW
			A																				
Bridgend	d	20 42											21 42									22 42	
Llantwit Major	d	20 56											21 56									22 56	
Rhoose Cardiff Int Airport ✈	d	21 06											22 06									23 06	
Barry Island	d									21 56									22 56				
Barry 3	d	21 15								22 00			22 15						23 00			23 15	
Barry Docks	d	21 19								22 04			22 19						23 04			23 19	
Cadoxton	d	21 22								22 07			22 22						23 07			23 22	
Dinas Powys	d	21 26								22 11			22 26						23 11			23 26	
Eastbrook	d	21 28								22 13			22 28						23 13			23 28	
Cogan	d	21 30								22 15			22 30						23 15			23 30	
Penarth	d				21 47						22 17						22 47				23 26		
Dingle Road	d				21 49						22 19						22 49				23 28		
Grangetown	d	21 34			21 53					22 19	22 23		22 34				22 53		23 19		23 32	23 34	
Cardiff Central 7	a	21 39			21 59					22 25	22 31		22 39				23 00		23 24		23 40	23 42	
	d	21 41			22 01		22 06	22 11		22 26	22 35		22 41	22 46			23 15		23 26				
Cardiff Bay	d			21 49		22 04			22 19			22 34			22 49	23 04		23 19		23 34			23 49
Cardiff Queen Street 3	a	21 44		21 53	22 04	22 08	22 09	22 14	22 23	22 29	22 38	22 38	22 44	22 49	22 53	23 08	23 18	23 23	23 29	23 38			23 53
	d	21 45			22 05		22 10	22 15		22 30	22 39		22 45	22 50			23 19		23 30				
Heath Low Level	d																						
Ty Glas	d																						
Birchgrove	d																						
Rhiwbina	d																						
Whitchurch (Cardiff)	d																						
Coryton	a																						
Heath High Level	d				22 10						22 44						23 24						
Llanishen	d				22 13						22 47						23 27						
Lisvane & Thornhill	d				22 15						22 49						23 29						
Caerphilly 3	d				22a24						22 55						23 35						
Aber	d										22 57						23 37						
Llanbradach	d										23 01						23 41						
Ystrad Mynach 3	d										23 06						23a51						
Hengoed	d										23 09												
Pengam	d										23 12												
Gilfach Fargoed	d										23 15												
Bargoed	d										23 20												
Brithdir	d										23 24												
Tir-phil	d										23 27												
Pontlottyn	d										23 31												
Rhymney 3	a										23 38												
Cathays	d	21 48					22 13	22 18		22 33			22 48	22 53					23 33				
Llandaf	d	21 52					22 17	22 22		22 37			22 52	22 57					23 37				
Ninian Park	d		←																				
Waun-gron Park	d		21 44																				
Fairwater	d		21 46																				
Danescourt	d		21 49																				
Radyr 3	a	21 55	21 57				22 20	22 25		22 40			22 55	22 59					23 40				
	d	21 55					22 20	22 25		22 40			22 55	22 59					23 40				
Taffs Well 3	d	21 59					22 24	22 29		22 44			22 59	23 03					23 44				
Trefforest Estate	d									22 48									23 48				
Trefforest	d	22 06					22 31	22 36		22 52			23 06	23 10					23 52				
Pontypridd 3	a	22 09					22 34	22 43		22 55			23 09	23 14					00 01				
	d	22 11					22 36			22 56			23 11	23 15									
Abercynon	d	22 21								23 06			23 21										
Penrhiwceiber	d	22 27											23 27										
Mountain Ash	a	22 31											23 31										
	d	22 34											23 34										
Fernhill	d	22 37											23 37										
Cwmbach	d	22 41											23 41										
Aberdare 3	a	22 49											23 49										
Quakers Yard	d									23 11													
Merthyr Vale	d									23 18													
Troed Y Rhiw	d									23 22													
Pentre-bach	d									23 25													
Merthyr Tydfil	a									23 34													
Trehafod	d						22 41							23 20									
Porth	d						22 45							23 24									
Dinas Rhondda	d						22 49							23 28									
Tonypandy	d						22 51							23 30									
Llwynypia	d						22 53							23 32									
Ystrad Rhondda	a						22 56							23 35									
	d						22 59							23 38									
Ton Pentre	d						23 01							23 40									
Treorchy	d						23 04							23 43									
Ynyswen	d						23 07							23 46									
Treherbert	a						23 14							23 53									

For general notes see front of timetable
For details of catering facilities see Directory of Train Operators

A From Coryton

Table 130

Sundays until 7 September

Bridgend, Barry Island, Barry, Penarth and Cardiff → Coryton, Rhymney, Pontypridd, Merthyr, Aberdare and Treherbert

Network Diagram - see first page of Table 130

		AW	AW	AW	AW	AW	AW	AW	AW	AW	AW	AW	AW		AW	AW	AW	AW	AW	AW	AW	AW	AW	AW	AW	AW
									A																	
Bridgend	d							09 42															11 42			
Llantwit Major	d							09 56															11 56			
Rhoose Cardiff Int Airport ✈	d							10 06															12 06			
Barry Island	d				08 56		09 56				10 26					10 56			11 26		11 56					12 26
Barry 3	d				09 00		10 00	10 15			10 30					11 00			11 30		12 00		12 15			12 30
Barry Docks	d				09 04		10 04	10 19			10 34					11 04			11 34		12 04		12 19			12 34
Cadoxton	d				09 07		10 07	10 22			10 37					11 07			11 37		12 07		12 22			12 37
Dinas Powys	d				09 11		10 11	10 26			10 41					11 11			11 41		12 11		12 26			12 41
Eastbrook	d				09 13		10 13	10 28			10 43					11 13			11 43		12 13		12 28			12 43
Cogan	d				09 15		10 15	10 30			10 45					11 15			11 45		12 15		12 30			12 45
Penarth	d											10 47														
Dingle Road	d											10 49														
Grangetown	d				09 19		10 19	10 34			10 49	10 53				11 19			11 49		12 19		12 34			12 49
Cardiff Central 7	a				09 24		10 24	10 42			10 54	10 59				11 24			11 57		12 24		12 42			12 54
	d	08 26	08 41	09 06	09 41	10 16	10 26		10 51		11 06					11 41			12 16		12 26					13 06
Cardiff Bay	d									11 04			11 19		11 34		11 49	12 04		12 19		12 34		12 49	13 04	
Cardiff Queen Street 3	a	08 29	08 44	09 09	09 44	10 19	10 29		10 54	11 08	11 09		11 23		11 38	11 44	11 53	12 08	12 19	12 23	12 29	12 38		12 53	13 08	13 09
	d	08 30	08 45	09 10	09 45	10 20	10 30				11 10					11 45			12 20		12 30					13 10
Heath Low Level	d																									
Ty Glas	d																									
Birchgrove	d																									
Rhiwbina	d																									
Whitchurch (Cardiff)	d																									
Coryton	a																									
Heath High Level	d					10 25													12 25							
Llanishen	d					10 28													12 28							
Lisvane & Thornhill	d					10 30													12 30							
Caerphilly 3	d					10 36													12 36							
Aber	d					10 38													12 38							
Llanbradach	d					10 42													12 42							
Ystrad Mynach 3	d					10 47													12 47							
Hengoed	d					10 50													12 50							
Pengam	d					10 53													12 53							
Gilfach Fargoed	d					10 56													12 56							
Bargoed	d					10 59													12 59							
Brithdir	d					11 03													13 03							
Tir-phil	d					11 06													13 06							
Pontlottyn	d					11 10													13 10							
Rhymney 3	a					11 16													13 16							
Cathays	d	08 33	08 48	09 13	09 48		10 33				11 13					11 48					12 33					13 13
Llandaf	d	08 37	08 52	09 17	09 52		10 37				11 17					11 52					12 37					13 17
Ninian Park	d																									
Waun-gron Park	d																									
Fairwater	d																									
Danescourt	d																									
Radyr 3	a	08 40	08 55	09 20	09 55		10 40				11 20					11 55					12 40					13 20
	d	08 40	08 55	09 20	09 55		10 40				11 20					11 55					12 40					13 20
Taffs Well 3	d	08 44	08 59	09 24	09 59		10 44				11 24					11 59					12 44					13 24
Trefforest Estate	d																									
Trefforest	d	08 52	09 06	09 31	10 06		10 52				11 31					12 06					12 52					13 31
Pontypridd 3	a	08 55	09 09	09 34	10 09		10 55				11 34					12 09					12 55					13 34
	d	08 57	09 11	09 36	10 11		10 57				11 36					12 11					12 57					13 36
Abercynon	d	09 06	09 21		10 21		11 06									12 21					13 06					
Penrhiwceiber	d		09 27		10 27											12 27										
Mountain Ash	a		09 30		10 30											12 30										
	d		09 33		10 33											12 33										
Fernhill	d		09 35		10 35											12 35										
Cwmbach	d		09 39		10 39											12 39										
Aberdare 3	a		09 46		10 46											12 46										
Quakers Yard	d	09 10					11 10														13 10					
Merthyr Vale	d	09 18					11 18														13 18					
Troed Y Rhiw	d	09 21					11 21														13 21					
Pentre-bach	d	09 24					11 24														13 24					
Merthyr Tydfil	a	09 32					11 32														13 32					
Trehafod	d			09 41							11 41															13 41
Porth	d			09 45							11 45															13 45
Dinas Rhondda	d			09 49							11 49															13 49
Tonypandy	d			09 51							11 51															13 51
Llwynypia	d			09 53							11 53															13 53
Ystrad Rhondda	a			09 56							11 56															13 56
	d			09 59							11 59															13 59
Ton Pentre	d			10 01							12 01															14 01
Treorchy	d			10 04							12 04															14 04
Ynyswen	d			10 07							12 07															14 07
Treherbert	a			10 13							12 13															14 13

For general notes see front of timetable
For details of catering facilities see Directory of Train Operators

A To Cardiff Bay

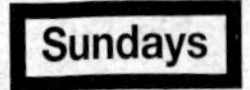

until 7 September

Bridgend, Barry Island, Barry, Penarth and Cardiff → Coryton, Rhymney, Pontypridd, Merthyr, Aberdare and Treherbert

Network Diagram - see first page of Table 130

		AW	AW		AW	AW	AW	AW	AW	AW	AW	AW	AW	AW	AW	AW		AW	AW	AW	AW	AW	AW	AW	AW	AW
Bridgend	d												13 42													
Llantwit Major	d												13 56													
Rhoose Cardiff Int Airport ✈	d												14 06													
Barry Island	d					12 56			13 26		13 56					14 26					14 56			15 26		15 56
Barry 3	d					13 00			13 30		14 00		14 15			14 30					15 00			15 30		16 00
Barry Docks	d					13 04			13 34		14 04		14 19			14 34					15 04			15 34		16 04
Cadoxton	d					13 07			13 37		14 07		14 22			14 37					15 07			15 37		16 07
Dinas Powys	d					13 11			13 41		14 11		14 26			14 41					15 11			15 41		16 11
Eastbrook	d					13 13			13 43		14 13		14 28			14 43					15 13			15 43		16 13
Cogan	d					13 15			13 45		14 15		14 30			14 45					15 15			15 45		16 15
Penarth	d	12 47																14 47								
Dingle Road	d	12 49																14 49								
Grangetown	d	12 53				13 19			13 49		14 19		14 34			14 49		14 53			15 19			15 49		16 19
Cardiff Central 7	a	12 59				13 24			13 57		14 24		14 42			14 54		14 59			15 24			15 57		16 24
	d					13 41			14 16		14 26					15 06					15 41			16 16		16 26
Cardiff Bay	d		13 19		13 34		13 49	14 04		14 19		14 34		14 49	15 04				15 19	15 34		15 49	16 04		16 19	
Cardiff Queen Street 3	a		13 23		13 38	13 44	13 53	14 08	14 19	14 23	14 29	14 38		14 53	15 08	15 09			15 23	15 38	15 44	15 53	16 08	16 19	16 23	16 29
	d					13 45			14 20		14 30					15 10					15 45			16 20		16 30
Heath Low Level	d																									
Ty Glas	d																									
Birchgrove	d																									
Rhiwbina	d																									
Whitchurch (Cardiff)	d																									
Coryton	a																									
Heath High Level	d								14 25															16 25		
Llanishen	d								14 28															16 28		
Lisvane & Thornhill	d								14 30															16 30		
Caerphilly 3	d								14 36															16 36		
Aber	d								14 38															16 38		
Llanbradach	d								14 42															16 42		
Ystrad Mynach 3	d								14 47															16 47		
Hengoed	d								14 50															16 50		
Pengam	d								14 53															16 53		
Gilfach Fargoed	d								14 56															16 56		
Bargoed	d								14 59															16 59		
Brithdir	d								15 03															17 03		
Tir-phil	d								15 06															17 06		
Pontlottyn	d								15 10															17 10		
Rhymney 3	a								15 16															17 16		
Cathays	d					13 48					14 33					15 13					15 48					16 33
Llandaf	d					13 52					14 37					15 17					15 52					16 37
Ninian Park	d																									
Waun-gron Park	d																									
Fairwater	d																									
Danescourt	d																									
Radyr 3	a					13 55					14 40					15 20					15 55					16 40
	d					13 55					14 40					15 20					15 55					16 40
Taffs Well 3	d					13 59					14 44					15 24					15 59					16 44
Trefforest Estate	d																									
Trefforest	d					14 06					14 52					15 31					16 06					16 52
Pontypridd 3	a					14 09					14 55					15 34					16 09					16 55
	d					14 11					14 57					15 36					16 11					16 57
Abercynon	d					14 21					15 06										16 21					17 06
Penrhiwceiber	d					14 27															16 27					
Mountain Ash	a					14 30															16 30					
	d					14 33															16 33					
Fernhill	d					14 35															16 35					
Cwmbach	d					14 39															16 39					
Aberdare 3	a					14 46															16 46					
Quakers Yard	d										15 10															17 10
Merthyr Vale	d										15 18															17 18
Troed Y Rhiw	d										15 21															17 21
Pentre-bach	d										15 24															17 24
Merthyr Tydfil	a										15 32															17 32
Trehafod	d															15 41										
Porth	d															15 45										
Dinas Rhondda	d															15 49										
Tonypandy	d															15 51										
Llwynypia	d															15 53										
Ystrad Rhondda	a															15 56										
	d															15 59										
Ton Pentre	d															16 01										
Treorchy	d															16 04										
Ynyswen	d															16 07										
Treherbert	a															16 13										

For general notes see front of timetable
For details of catering facilities see Directory of Train Operators

Table 130

until 7 September

Bridgend, Barry Island, Barry, Penarth and Cardiff → Coryton, Rhymney, Pontypridd, Merthyr, Aberdare and Treherbert

Network Diagram - see first page of Table 130

		AW A	AW	AW	AW	AW B	AW	AW	AW	AW	AW	AW	AW	AW	AW	AW	AW	AW	AW	AW	AW	AW	AW
Bridgend	d		15 42							17 42						19 42						21 42	
Llantwit Major	d		15 56							17 56						19 56						21 56	
Rhoose Cardiff Int Airport ✈	d		16 06							18 06						20 06						22 06	
Barry Island	d			16 26		16 41	16 56	17 26	17 56		18 26		18 56	19 26	19 56		20 26		20 56	21 26	21 56		22 56
Barry 3	d		16 15	16 30		16 45	17 00	17 30	18 00	18 15	18 30		19 00	19 30	20 00	20 15	20 30		21 00	21 30	22 00	22 15	23 00
Barry Docks	d		16 19	16 34			17 04	17 34	18 04	18 19	18 34		19 04	19 34	20 04	20 19	20 34		21 04	21 34	22 04	22 19	23 04
Cadoxton	d		16 22	16 37			17 07	17 37	18 07	18 22	18 37		19 07	19 37	20 07	20 22	20 37		21 07	21 37	22 07	22 22	23 07
Dinas Powys	d		16 26	16 41			17 11	17 41	18 11	18 26	18 41		19 11	19 41	20 11	20 26	20 41		21 11	21 41	22 11	22 26	23 11
Eastbrook	d		16 28	16 43			17 13	17 43	18 13	18 28	18 43		19 13	19 43	20 13	20 28	20 43		21 13	21 43	22 13	22 28	23 13
Cogan	d		16 30	16 45			17 15	17 45	18 15	18 30	18 45		19 15	19 45	20 15	20 30	20 45		21 15	21 45	22 15	22 30	23 15
Penarth	d				16 47							18 47						20 47					
Dingle Road	d				16 49							18 49						20 49					
Grangetown	d		16 34	16 49	16 53		17 19	17 49	18 19	18 34	18 49	18 53	19 19	19 49	20 19	20 34	20 49	20 53	21 19	21 49	22 19	22 34	23 19
Cardiff Central 7	a		16 42	16 54	16 59	17 02	17 24	17 57	18 24	18 42	18 54	18 59	19 24	19 57	20 24	20 42	20 54	20 59	21 27	21 54	22 27	22 42	23 27
	d			17 06			17 41	18 16	18 26		19 06		19 41	20 16	20 26		21 06	21 16		22 06			
Cardiff Bay	d	16 34																					
Cardiff Queen Street 3	a	16 37		17 09			17 44	18 19	18 29		19 09		19 44	20 19	20 29		21 09	21 19		22 09			
	d			17 10			17 45	18 20	18 30		19 10		19 45	20 20	20 30		21 10	21 20		22 10			
Heath Low Level	d																						
Ty Glas	d																						
Birchgrove	d																						
Rhiwbina	d																						
Whitchurch (Cardiff)	d																						
Coryton	a																						
Heath High Level	d							18 25						20 25				21 25					
Llanishen	d							18 28						20 28				21 28					
Lisvane & Thornhill	d							18 30						20 30				21 30					
Caerphilly 3	d							18 36						20 36				21 36					
Aber	d							18 38						20 38				21 38					
Llanbradach	d							18 42						20 42				21 42					
Ystrad Mynach 3	d							18 47						20 47				21 47					
Hengoed	d							18 50						20 50				21 50					
Pengam	d							18 53						20 53				21 53					
Gilfach Fargoed	d							18 56						20 56				21 56					
Bargoed	d							18 59						20 59				21 59					
Brithdir	d							19 03						21 03				22 03					
Tir-phil	d							19 06						21 06				22 06					
Pontlottyn	d							19 10						21 10				22 10					
Rhymney 3	a							19 17						21 17				22 17					
Cathays	d			17 13			17 48		18 33		19 13		19 48		20 33		21 13			22 13			
Llandaf	d			17 17			17 52		18 37		19 17		19 52		20 37		21 17			22 17			
Ninian Park	d																						
Waun-gron Park	d																						
Fairwater	d																						
Danescourt	d																						
Radyr 3	a			17 20			17 55		18 40		19 20		19 55		20 40		21 20			22 20			
	d			17 20			17 55		18 40		19 20		19 55		20 40		21 20			22 20			
Taffs Well 3	d			17 24			17 59		18 44		19 24		19 59		20 44		21 24			22 24			
Trefforest Estate	d																						
Trefforest	d			17 31			18 06		18 52		19 31		20 06		20 52		21 31			22 31			
Pontypridd 3	a			17 34			18 09		18 55		19 34		20 09		20 55		21 34			22 34			
	d			17 36			18 11		18 57		19 36		20 11		20 57		21 36			22 36			
Abercynon	d						18 21		19 06				20 21		21 06								
Penrhiwceiber	d						18 27						20 27										
Mountain Ash	a						18 30						20 30										
	d						18 33						20 33										
Fernhill	d						18 35						20 35										
Cwmbach	d						18 39						20 39										
Aberdare 3	a						18 46						20 46										
Quakers Yard	d								19 10						21 10								
Merthyr Vale	d								19 18						21 18								
Troed Y Rhiw	d								19 21						21 21								
Pentre-bach	d								19 24						21 24								
Merthyr Tydfil	a								19 32						21 32								
Trehafod	d			17 41							19 41						21 41			22 41			
Porth	d			17 45							19 45						21 45			22 45			
Dinas Rhondda	d			17 49							19 49						21 49			22 49			
Tonypandy	d			17 51							19 51						21 51			22 51			
Llwynypia	d			17 53							19 53						21 53			22 53			
Ystrad Rhondda	a			17 56							19 56						21 56			22 56			
	d			17 59							19 59						21 59			22 59			
Ton Pentre	d			18 01							20 01						22 01			23 01			
Treorchy	d			18 04							20 04						22 04			23 04			
Ynyswen	d			18 07							20 07						22 07			23 07			
Treherbert	a			18 13							20 13						22 13			23 13			

For general notes see front of timetable
For details of catering facilities see Directory of Train Operators

A To Cardiff Central
B To Hereford (Table 131)

Table 130

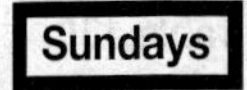

from 14 September

Bridgend, Barry Island, Barry, Penarth and Cardiff → Coryton, Rhymney, Pontypridd, Merthyr, Aberdare and Treherbert

Network Diagram - see first page of Table 130

		AW	AW	AW	AW	AW	AW	AW	AW A	AW	AW	AW	AW	AW	AW	AW	AW	AW	AW	AW	AW	AW	AW	AW
Bridgend	d							09 42														11 42		
Llantwit Major	d							09 56														11 56		
Rhoose Cardiff Int Airport ✈	d							10 06														12 06		
Barry Island	d				08 56		09 56				10 26				10 56			11 26		11 56				
Barry 3	d				09 00		10 00	10 15			10 30				11 00			11 30		12 00		12 15		
Barry Docks	d				09 04		10 04	10 19			10 34				11 04			11 34		12 04		12 19		
Cadoxton	d				09 07		10 07	10 22			10 37				11 07			11 37		12 07		12 22		
Dinas Powys	d				09 11		10 11	10 26			10 41				11 11			11 41		12 11		12 26		
Eastbrook	d				09 13		10 13	10 28			10 43				11 13			11 43		12 13		12 28		
Cogan	d				09 15		10 15	10 30			10 45				11 15			11 45		12 15		12 30		
Penarth	d											10 47												
Dingle Road	d											10 49												
Grangetown	d				09 19		10 19	10 34			10 49	10 53			11 19			11 49		12 19		12 34		
Cardiff Central 7	a				09 24		10 24	10 42			10 54	10 59			11 24			11 57		12 24		12 43		
	d	08 26	08 41	09 06	09 41	10 16	10 26		10 51		11 06				11 41			12 16		12 26				
Cardiff Bay	d									11 04			11 19	11 34		11 49	12 04		12 19		12 34		12 49	13 04
Cardiff Queen Street 3	a	08 29	08 44	09 09	09 44	10 19	10 29		10 54	11 08	11 09		11 23	11 38	11 44	11 53	12 08	12 19	12 23	12 29	12 38		12 53	13 08
	d	08 30	08 45	09 10	09 45	10 20	10 30				11 10				11 45			12 20		12 30				
Heath Low Level	d																							
Ty Glas	d																							
Birchgrove	d																							
Rhiwbina	d																							
Whitchurch (Cardiff)	d																							
Coryton	a																							
Heath High Level	d					10 25												12 25						
Llanishen	d					10 28												12 28						
Lisvane & Thornhill	d					10 30												12 30						
Caerphilly 3	d					10 36												12 36						
Aber	d					10 38												12 38						
Llanbradach	d					10 42												12 42						
Ystrad Mynach 3	d					10 47												12 47						
Hengoed	d					10 50												12 50						
Pengam	d					10 53												12 53						
Gilfach Fargoed	d					10 56												12 56						
Bargoed	d					10 59												12 59						
Brithdir	d					11 03												13 03						
Tir-phil	d					11 06												13 06						
Pontlottyn	d					11 10												13 10						
Rhymney 3	a					11 17												13 17						
Cathays	d	08 33	08 48	09 13	09 48		10 33				11 13				11 48					12 33				
Llandaf	d	08 37	08 52	09 17	09 52		10 37				11 17				11 52					12 37				
Ninian Park	d																							
Waun-gron Park	d																							
Fairwater	d																							
Danescourt	d																							
Radyr 3	a	08 40	08 55	09 20	09 55		10 40				11 20				11 55					12 40				
	d	08 40	08 55	09 20	09 55		10 40				11 20				11 55					12 40				
Taffs Well 3	d	08 44	08 59	09 24	09 59		10 44				11 24				11 59					12 44				
Trefforest Estate	d						10 48													12 48				
Trefforest	d	08 52	09 06	09 31	10 06		10 52				11 31				12 06					12 52				
Pontypridd 3	a	08 55	09 09	09 34	10 09		10 55				11 34				12 09					12 55				
	d	08 57	09 11	09 36	10 11		10 57				11 36				12 11					12 57				
Abercynon	d	09 06	09 21		10 21		11 06								12 21					13 06				
Penrhiwceiber	d		09 27		10 27										12 27									
Mountain Ash	a		09 31		10 31										12 31									
	d		09 34		10 34										12 34									
Fernhill	d		09 37		10 37										12 37									
Cwmbach	d		09 41		10 41										12 41									
Aberdare 3	a		09 49		10 49										12 49									
Quakers Yard	d	09 11					11 11													13 11				
Merthyr Vale	d	09 18					11 18													13 18				
Troed Y Rhiw	d	09 22					11 22													13 22				
Pentre-bach	d	09 25					11 25													13 25				
Merthyr Tydfil	a	09 34					11 34													13 34				
Trehafod	d			09 41							11 41													
Porth	d			09 45							11 45													
Dinas Rhondda	d			09 49							11 49													
Tonypandy	d			09 51							11 51													
Llwynypia	d			09 53							11 53													
Ystrad Rhondda	a			09 56							11 56													
	d			09 59							11 59													
Ton Pentre	d			10 01							12 01													
Treorchy	d			10 04							12 04													
Ynyswen	d			10 07							12 07													
Treherbert	a			10 14							12 14													

For general notes see front of timetable
For details of catering facilities see
Directory of Train Operators

A To Cardiff Bay

Table 130

from 14 September

Bridgend, Barry Island, Barry, Penarth and Cardiff → Coryton, Rhymney, Pontypridd, Merthyr, Aberdare and Treherbert

Network Diagram - see first page of Table 130

		AW	AW	AW	AW	AW	AW	AW	AW	AW	AW	AW	AW	AW	AW	AW	AW	AW	AW	AW	AW	AW	AW	AW
Bridgend	d												13 42											
Llantwit Major	d												13 56											
Rhoose Cardiff Int Airport ✈	d												14 06											
Barry Island	d	12 26				12 56			13 26		13 56					14 26				14 56			15 26	
Barry 3	d	12 30				13 00			13 30		14 00		14 15			14 30				15 00			15 30	
Barry Docks	d	12 34				13 04			13 34		14 04		14 19			14 34				15 04			15 34	
Cadoxton	d	12 37				13 07			13 37		14 07		14 22			14 37				15 07			15 37	
Dinas Powys	d	12 41				13 11			13 41		14 11		14 26			14 41				15 11			15 41	
Eastbrook	d	12 43				13 13			13 43		14 13		14 28			14 43				15 13			15 43	
Cogan	d	12 45				13 15			13 45		14 15		14 30			14 45				15 15			15 45	
Penarth	d		12 47														14 47							
Dingle Road	d		12 49														14 49							
Grangetown	d	12 49	12 53			13 19			13 49		14 19		14 34			14 49	14 53			15 19			15 49	
Cardiff Central 7	a	12 54	12 59			13 24			13 57		14 24		14 43			14 54	14 59			15 24			15 57	
	d	13 06				13 41			14 16		14 26					15 06				15 41			16 16	
Cardiff Bay	d			13 19	13 34		13 49	14 04		14 19		14 34		14 49	15 04			15 19	15 34		15 49	16 04		16 19
Cardiff Queen Street 3	a	13 09		13 23	13 38	13 44	13 53	14 08	14 19	14 23	14 29	14 38		14 53	15 08	15 09		15 23	15 38	15 44	15 53	16 08	16 19	16 23
	d	13 10				13 45			14 20		14 30					15 10				15 45			16 20	
Heath Low Level	d																							
Ty Glas	d																							
Birchgrove	d																							
Rhiwbina	d																							
Whitchurch (Cardiff)	d																							
Coryton	a																							
Heath High Level	d								14 25														16 25	
Llanishen	d								14 28														16 28	
Lisvane & Thornhill	d								14 30														16 30	
Caerphilly 3	d								14 36														16 36	
Aber	d								14 38														16 38	
Llanbradach	d								14 42														16 42	
Ystrad Mynach 3	d								14 47														16 47	
Hengoed	d								14 50														16 50	
Pengam	d								14 53														16 53	
Gilfach Fargoed	d								14 56														16 56	
Bargoed	d								14 59														16 59	
Brithdir	d								15 03														17 03	
Tir-phil	d								15 06														17 06	
Pontlottyn	d								15 10														17 10	
Rhymney 3	a								15 17														17 17	
Cathays	d	13 13				13 48					14 33					15 13				15 48				
Llandaf	d	13 17				13 52					14 37					15 17				15 52				
Ninian Park	d																							
Waun-gron Park	d																							
Fairwater	d																							
Danescourt	d																							
Radyr 3	a	13 20				13 55					14 40					15 20				15 55				
	d	13 20				13 55					14 40					15 20				15 55				
Taffs Well 3	d	13 24				13 59					14 44					15 24				15 59				
Trefforest Estate	d										14 48													
Trefforest	d	13 31				14 06					14 52					15 31				16 06				
Pontypridd 3	a	13 34				14 09					14 55					15 34				16 09				
	d	13 36				14 11					14 57					15 36				16 11				
Abercynon	d					14 21					15 06									16 21				
Penrhiwceiber	d					14 27														16 27				
Mountain Ash	a					14 31														16 31				
	d					14 34														16 34				
Fernhill	d					14 37														16 37				
Cwmbach	d					14 41														16 41				
Aberdare 3	a					14 49														16 49				
Quakers Yard	d										15 11													
Merthyr Vale	d										15 18													
Troed Y Rhiw	d										15 22													
Pentre-bach	d										15 25													
Merthyr Tydfil	a										15 34													
Trehafod	d	13 41														15 41								
Porth	d	13 45														15 45								
Dinas Rhondda	d	13 49														15 49								
Tonypandy	d	13 51														15 51								
Llwynypia	d	13 53														15 53								
Ystrad Rhondda	a	13 56														15 56								
	d	13 59														15 59								
Ton Pentre	d	14 01														16 01								
Treorchy	d	14 04														16 04								
Ynyswen	d	14 07														16 07								
Treherbert	a	14 14														16 14								

For general notes see front of timetable
For details of catering facilities see Directory of Train Operators

Table 130

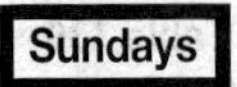

from 14 September

Bridgend, Barry Island, Barry, Penarth and Cardiff → Coryton, Rhymney, Pontypridd, Merthyr, Aberdare and Treherbert

Network Diagram - see first page of Table 130

		AW	AW	AW	AW	AW	AW	AW	AW	AW	AW	AW	AW	AW	AW	AW	AW	AW	AW	AW	AW	AW	AW
			A																				
Bridgend	d			15 42						17 42						19 42						21 42	
Llantwit Major	d			15 56						17 56						19 56						21 56	
Rhoose Cardiff Int Airport ✈	d			16 06						18 06						20 06						22 06	
Barry Island	d	15 56			16 26		16 56	17 26	17 56		18 26		18 56	19 26	19 56		20 26		20 56	21 26	21 56		22 56
Barry 3	d	16 00		16 15	16 30		17 00	17 30	18 00	18 15	18 30		19 00	19 30	20 00	20 15	20 30		21 00	21 30	22 00	22 15	23 00
Barry Docks	d	16 04		16 19	16 34		17 04	17 34	18 04	18 19	18 34		19 04	19 34	20 04	20 19	20 34		21 04	21 34	22 04	22 19	23 04
Cadoxton	d	16 07		16 22	16 37		17 07	17 37	18 07	18 22	18 37		19 07	19 37	20 07	20 22	20 37		21 07	21 37	22 07	22 22	23 07
Dinas Powys	d	16 11		16 26	16 41		17 11	17 41	18 11	18 26	18 41		19 11	19 41	20 11	20 26	20 41		21 11	21 41	22 11	22 26	23 11
Eastbrook	d	16 13		16 28	16 43		17 13	17 43	18 13	18 28	18 43		19 13	19 43	20 13	20 28	20 43		21 13	21 43	22 13	22 28	23 13
Cogan	d	16 15		16 30	16 45		17 15	17 45	18 15	18 30	18 45		19 15	19 45	20 15	20 30	20 45		21 15	21 45	22 15	22 30	23 15
Penarth	d					16 47						18 47						20 47					
Dingle Road	d					16 49						18 49						20 49					
Grangetown	d	16 19		16 34	16 49	16 53	17 19	17 49	18 19	18 34	18 49	18 53	19 19	19 49	20 19	20 34	20 49	20 53	21 19	21 49	22 19	22 34	23 19
Cardiff Central 7	a	16 24		16 43	16 54	16 59	17 24	17 57	18 24	18 43	18 54	19 01	19 24	19 57	20 24	20 43	20 57	20 59	21 28	21 54	22 28	22 43	23 28
	d	16 26			17 06		17 41	18 16	18 26		19 06		19 41	20 16	20 26		21 06	21 16		22 06			
Cardiff Bay	d		16 34																				
Cardiff Queen Street 3	a	16 29	16 37		17 09		17 44	18 19	18 29		19 09		19 44	20 19	20 29		21 09	21 19		22 09			
	d	16 30			17 10		17 45	18 20	18 30		19 10		19 45	20 20	20 30		21 10	21 20		22 10			
Heath Low Level	d																						
Ty Glas	d																						
Birchgrove	d																						
Rhiwbina	d																						
Whitchurch (Cardiff)	d																						
Coryton	a																						
Heath High Level	d							18 25						20 25				21 25					
Llanishen	d							18 28						20 28				21 28					
Lisvane & Thornhill	d							18 30						20 30				21 30					
Caerphilly 3	d							18 36						20 36				21 36					
Aber	d							18 38						20 38				21 38					
Llanbradach	d							18 42						20 42				21 42					
Ystrad Mynach 3	d							18 47						20 47				21 47					
Hengoed	d							18 50						20 50				21 50					
Pengam	d							18 53						20 53				21 53					
Gilfach Fargoed	d							18 56						20 56				21 56					
Bargoed	d							18 59						20 59				21 59					
Brithdir	d							19 03						21 03				22 03					
Tir-phil	d							19 06						21 06				22 06					
Pontlottyn	d							19 10						21 10				22 10					
Rhymney 3	a							19 18						21 18				22 18					
Cathays	d	16 33			17 13		17 48		18 33		19 13		19 48		20 33		21 13			22 13			
Llandaf	d	16 37			17 17		17 52		18 37		19 17		19 52		20 37		21 17			22 17			
Ninian Park	d																						
Waun-gron Park	d																						
Fairwater	d																						
Danescourt	d																						
Radyr 3	a	16 40			17 20		17 55		18 40		19 20		19 55		20 40		21 20			22 20			
	d	16 40			17 20		17 55		18 40		19 20		19 55		20 40		21 20			22 20			
Taffs Well 3	d	16 44			17 24		17 59		18 44		19 24		19 59		20 44		21 24			22 24			
Trefforest Estate	d	16 48							18 48						20 48								
Trefforest	d	16 52			17 31		18 06		18 52		19 31		20 06		20 52		21 31			22 31			
Pontypridd 3	a	16 55			17 34		18 09		18 55		19 34		20 09		20 55		21 34			22 34			
	d	16 57			17 36		18 11		18 57		19 36		20 11		20 57		21 36			22 36			
Abercynon	d	17 06					18 21		19 06				20 21		21 06								
Penrhiwceiber	d						18 27						20 27										
Mountain Ash	a						18 31						20 31										
	d						18 34						20 34										
Fernhill	d						18 37						20 37										
Cwmbach	d						18 41						20 41										
Aberdare 3	a						18 49						20 49										
Quakers Yard	d	17 11							19 11						21 11								
Merthyr Vale	d	17 18							19 18						21 18								
Troed Y Rhiw	d	17 22							19 22						21 22								
Pentre-bach	d	17 25							19 25						21 25								
Merthyr Tydfil	a	17 34							19 34						21 34								
Trehafod	d				17 41						19 41						21 41			22 41			
Porth	d				17 45						19 45						21 45			22 45			
Dinas Rhondda	d				17 49						19 49						21 49			22 49			
Tonypandy	d				17 51						19 51						21 51			22 51			
Llwynypia	d				17 53						19 53						21 53			22 53			
Ystrad Rhondda	a				17 56						19 56						21 56			22 56			
	d				17 59						19 59						21 59			22 59			
Ton Pentre	d				18 01						20 01						22 01			23 01			
Treorchy	d				18 04						20 04						22 04			23 04			
Ynyswen	d				18 07						20 07						22 07			23 07			
Treherbert	a				18 14						20 14						22 14			23 14			

For general notes see front of timetable
For details of catering facilities see Directory of Train Operators

A To Cardiff Central

Table 130A

Mondays to Saturdays

Rhoose (Cardiff Intl Airport) — Cardiff International Airport
Bus Service

		AW	AW	AW		AW	AW	AW		AW	AW	AW		AW	AW	AW		AW	AW	AW		AW	AW	AW		
Rhoose Cardiff Int Airport	d	06 16	07 16	08 16	.....	09 16	10 16	11 16	.....	12 16	13 16	14 16	.....	15 16	16 16	17 16	.....	18 16	19 16	20 16	.....	21 16	22 16	23 16	.....	.....
Cardiff International Apt	a	06 23	07 23	08 23	.	09 23	10 23	11 23	.	12 23	13 23	14 23	.	15 23	16 23	17 23	.	18 23	19 23	20 23	.	21 23	22 23	23 23	.	.

Sundays

		AW		AW		AW		AW		AW		AW		AW		AW		AW		AW	AW	AW	AW	AW		
Rhoose Cardiff Int Airport	d	09 16	.....	10 16	.....	11 16	.....	12 16	.....	13 16	.....	14 16	.....	15 16	.....	16 16	.....	17 16	.....	18 16	19 16	20 16	21 16	22 16	.....	.....
Cardiff International Apt	a	09 23	.	10 23	.	11 23	.	12 23	.	13 23	.	14 23	.	15 23	.	16 23	.	17 23	.	18 23	19 23	20 23	21 23	22 23	.	.

Mondays to Saturdays

		AW	AW	AW		AW	AW	AW		AW	AW	AW		AW	AW	AW		AW	AW	AW		AW	AW	AW		
Cardiff International Apt	d	05 51	06 51	07 51	.....	08 51	09 51	10 51	.....	11 51	12 51	13 51	.....	14 51	15 51	16 51	.....	17 51	18 51	19 51	.....	20 51	21 51	22 51	.....	.....
Rhoose Cardiff Int Airport	a	05 58	06 58	07 58	.	08 58	09 58	10 58	.	11 58	12 58	13 58	.	14 58	15 58	16 58	.	17 58	18 58	19 58	.	20 58	21 58	22 58	.	.

Sundays

		AW	AW		AW	AW		AW	AW		AW	AW		AW	AW		AW	AW		AW	AW		AW		
Cardiff International Apt	d	08 51	09 51	.....	10 51	11 51	.....	12 51	13 51	.....	14 51	15 51	.....	16 51	17 51	.....	18 51	19 51	.....	20 51	21 51	.....	22 51	.....	.....
Rhoose Cardiff Int Airport	a	08 58	09 58	.	10 58	11 58	.	12 58	13 58	.	14 58	15 58	.	16 58	17 58	.	18 58	19 58	.	20 58	21 58	.	22 58	.	.

For general notes see front of timetable
For details of catering facilities see
Directory of Train Operators

Cardiff → Crewe, Liverpool and Manchester

Route Diagram - see first page of Table 129

Miles	Miles	Station		AW	AW	AW	AW	AW	GW	AW	GW	AW	AW	AW	AW	AW	AW	AW
				MO ◇ A	MX ◇ B	MX		◇	1 ◇ C ⊠	◇ buffet	1 ◇ D E ⊠	◇ buffet	◇		◇ G buffet	◇	◇ G buffet	
—	—	Swansea 7	d		20p55					03 59			04 36		05 24	05 59	06 40	
0	0	**Cardiff Central 7**	d		21p56	00 30		04 00		05 10		05 35			06 50	07 20	07 50	
—	—	London Paddington 15 ⊖	d														05 27	
—	—	Reading 7	d														05 57	
—	—	Bristol Temple Meads 10	d												05 54	06 50	07 15	
11¾	11¾	**Newport (South Wales)**	d		22p15	00 57		04 18		05 28		05 53			07 04	07 34	08 04	
18¾	18¾	Cwmbran	d		22p25	01 08		04 28		05 38		06 03			07 15	07 44	08 16	
21¾	21¾	Pontypool and New Inn	d		22p31	01 14		04 34		05 44		06 09				07 49		
31¼	31¼	Abergavenny	d		22p40	01 25		04 45	05 10	05 54	06 09	06 22			07 28	08 00	08 29	
55¼	55¼	**Hereford 7**	a		23p05	01 53		05 12	05 33	06 18	06 32	06 47			07 54	08 25	08 54	
—	—		d		23p06			05 23		06 25		06 48			07 56	08 28	08 56	
67¾	67¾	Leominster	d		23p20			05 36		06 38		07 02			08 09		09 09	
78¾	78¾	Ludlow	d		23p31			05 47		06 49		07 13			08 20	08 49	09 20	
86	86	Craven Arms	d		23p39			05 56		06 58		07 21	07 53		08 29		09 29	
93¼	93¼	Church Stretton	d		23p48			06 08		07 07		07 30	08 06		08 38		09 38	
106	106	**Shrewsbury**	a		00 02			06 22		07 22		07 44	08 21		08 52	09 15	09 52	
—	—		d	00 03	00 12		06 03	06 26		07 30		07 46		08 26	08 54	09 30	09 54	10 26
113¼	113¼	Yorton	d		00x20		06x13							08x36				10x36
116¾	116¾	Wem	d		00 25		06 19	06 38				07 58		08 42				10 42
120	120	Prees	d		00x30		06x23							08x46				10x46
125	125	Whitchurch (Shrops)	d		00 37		06 31	06 47				08 07		08 54				10 54
129¾	129¾	Wrenbury	d		00x42		06x37							09x00				11x00
134¼	134¼	Nantwich	d		00 48		06 44	06 56				08 16		09 07				11 07
138¾	138¾	**Crewe 10**	a	00 33	00 58		06 54	07 05				08 25		09 17	09 25		10 25	11 17
—	—	Chester	a	00 53				07 59		08 28		09 26		09 57		10 28	11 16	11 59
—	—	Llandudno Junction	a	01 40				09b19		09 26		10 24		11b17		11 24	12 06	13b17
—	—	Bangor (Gwynedd)	a	01 57						09 43		10 46				11 41	12 26	
—	—	Holyhead	a							10 20		11 30				12 20	13 03	
—	161¼	Runcorn	a					07 47				09 08			10 03		11 03	
—	174½	**Liverpool Lime Street 10**	a					08 11				09 31			10 26		11 26	
157¾	—	Wilmslow	a					07 29				08 44			09 44		10 44	
163¾	—	Stockport	a					07 46				08 54			09 54		10 53	
169¾	—	**Manchester Piccadilly 10**	a					08 07				09 13			10 13		11 13	

Station		AW	AW	AW	AW	AW	GW	AW	AW	AW	AW	AW	AW	AW	GW	AW	AW	AW
		◇ B buffet	◇ buffet	◇ B buffet		◇ G buffet	1 ◇ trolley	◇	◇ buffet	◇ B buffet		◇ G buffet	◇ buffet	◇ B buffet	1 ◇ trolley		R G buffet	◇
Swansea 7	d	07 45	07 59	08 55		09 55		09 15		10 55		11 55		12 50			13 55	13 16
Cardiff Central 7	d	08 50	09 20	09 50		10 50		08 09	11 20	11 50		12 50	13 20	13 50			14 50	
London Paddington 15 ⊖	d	06 45	07 45			08 45	08 51		09 45			10 45	11 45		11 51		12 45	
Reading 7	d	07 11	08 11			09 11	09 23		10 11			11 11	12 11		12 23		13 11	
Bristol Temple Meads 10	d	08 22	08 54	09 19		09 54			10 54	11 19		11 54	12 54	13 19			14 19	
Newport (South Wales)	d	09 04	09 34	10 04		11 04			11 34	12 04		13 04	13 34	14 04			15 04	
Cwmbran	d	09 15	09 44	10 15		11 15			11 44	12 15		13 15	13 43	14 15			15 15	
Pontypool and New Inn	d	09 20							11 49				13 48					
Abergavenny	d	09 28	09 57	10 28		11 28			12 00	12 28		13 28	14 00	14 28			15 28	
Hereford 7	a	09 54	10 22	10 54		11 54	12 01		12 24	12 54		13 54	14 25	14 54	14 59		15 53	
	d	09 56	10 23	10 56		11 56			12 28	12 56		13 56	14 28	14 56			15 55	
Leominster	d	10 09		11 09		12 09				13 09		14 09		15 09			16 08	
Ludlow	d	10 20	10 45	11 20		12 20			12 49	13 20		14 20	14 49	15 20			16 19	
Craven Arms	d	10 29		11 29		12 29		12 36		13 29		14 29		15 29			16 28	16 37
Church Stretton	d	10 38		11 38		12 38		12 50		13 38		14 38		15 38				16 50
Shrewsbury	a	10 52	11 11	11 51		12 52		13 07	13 15	13 52		14 52	15 17	15 52			16 48	17 10
	d	10 54	11 30	11 54	12 26	12 54			13 30	13 54	14 26	14 54	15 30	15 54		16 26	16 50	
Yorton	d				12x36						14x36					16x36		
Wem	d				12 42						14 42					16 42	17 01	
Prees	d				12x46						14x46					16x46		
Whitchurch (Shrops)	d				12 54						14 54					16 54	17 10	
Wrenbury	d				13x00						15x00					17x00		
Nantwich	d				13 07						15 07					17 07		
Crewe 10	a	11 25		12 25	13 17	13 24				14 24	15 18	15 24		16 25		17 17	17 26	
Chester	a		12 28	13 32	13 57				14 28	15 26	15 57		16 28	17 26		17 53	18 28	
Llandudno Junction	a		13 24	14 22	15b18				15 25	16 24	17 17		17 24	18 25		18 49	19b25	
Bangor (Gwynedd)	a		13 48	14 55					15 47	16 46			17 47	18 47		19 05	19b48	
Holyhead	a		14 30	15 30					16 30	17 20			18 30	19 20		19 41	20b29	
Runcorn	a	12 25		13 03		14 25				15 03		16 25		17 03			18 25	
Liverpool Lime Street 10	a	12 47		13 26		14 47				15 26		16 48		17 26			18 47	
Wilmslow	a	11 44		12 44		13 44				14 44		15 44		16 44			17 44	
Stockport	a	11 53		12 52		13 53				14 53		15 52		16 53			17 54	
Manchester Piccadilly 10	a	12 13		13 13		14 13				15 13		16 13		17 11			18 12	

For general notes see front of timetable
For details of catering facilities see Directory of Train Operators

- **A** Until 14 July. From Birmingham New Street(Table 74)
- **B** From Milford Haven (Table 128)
- **C** All Tuesdays to Fridays, also Mondays from 15 September. To London Paddington (Table 126)
- **D** To London Paddington (Table 126)
- **E** **Cathedrals Express**
- **G** From Carmarthen (Table 128)
- **b** Change at Crewe and Chester

Cardiff → Crewe, Liverpool and Manchester

Route Diagram - see first page of Table 129

Mondays to Fridays

		AW ◇ ✠		AW R A ✠	AW		AW	AW R B ✠		AW R ✠	AW R A ✠		AW	AW ◇ B ✠		GW 1 ◇ ⊡	AW ◇ ✠	AW ◇	AW ◇ C	GW 1 ◇ D ⊡	AW ◇ B	AW ◇ E	AW ◇ A		
Swansea 7	d			14 55				15 55			16 55			17 55			18 29	18 21	18 58		19 55		20 55		
Cardiff Central 7	d	15 20		15 50	16 06			16 50		17 20	17 50			18 50			19 34		20 10		20 53		21 56		
London Paddington 15 ⊖	d	13 45			14 15			14 45		15 45				16 45		17 21	17 45		18 15	18 21	19 15		20 15		
Reading 7	d	14 11			14 41			15 11		16 11				17 11		17 50	18 11		18 41	18 51	19 41		20 41		
Bristol Temple Meads 10	d	14 54		15 19				15 54		16 54	17 19			17 54			18 54		19 25		20 19		21 19		
Newport (South Wales)	d	15 34		16 04	16 23			17 04		17 34	18 04			19 06			19 49		20 25		21 10		22 15		
Cwmbran	d	15 44		16 15	16 34			17 15		17 44	18 15			19 15			19 58		20 35		21 21		22 25		
Pontypool and New Inn	d	15 50			16 40					17 49	18 20						20 03		20 41				22 31		
Abergavenny	d	16 00		16 28	16a55			17 28		18 00	18 28			19 28			20 13		20 48		21 34		22 40		
Hereford 7	a	16 24		16 54				17 54		18 24	18 54			19 54		20 36	20 39		21 14	21 33	22 00		23 05		
	d	16 28		16 56				17 56		18 26	18 56			19 56			20 40		21 16		22 01		23 06		
Leominster	d			17 09				18 09		18 39	19 09			20 09			20 54		21 29		22 15		23 20		
Ludlow	d	16 49		17 20				18 20		18 49	19 20			20 20			21 01		21 40		22 26		23 31		
Craven Arms	d			17 29				18 29			19 29			20 29			21 13	21 37	21 49		22 34		23 39		
Church Stretton	d			17 38				18 38			19 38			20 38			21 22	21 50	22 02		22 43		23 48		
Shrewsbury	a	17 15		17 52				18 52		19 16	19 54			20 52			21 36	22 12	22 16		22 57		00 02		
	d	17 30		17 54			18 26	18 54		19 30	19 56		20 26	20 54			21 38		22 17		22 59	23 32	00 12		
Yorton	d						18x36						20x36						22x26		23x08		00x20		
Wem	d						18 42						20 42						22 31		23 13		00 25		
Prees	d						18x46						20x46						22x35		23x17		00x30		
Whitchurch (Shrops)	d						18 54						20 54						22 42		23 24		00 37		
Wrenbury	d						19x00						21x00						22x48		23x30		00x42		
Nantwich	d						19 07						21 07						22 54		23 36		00 48		
Crewe 10	a			18 24			19 17	19 25			20 26		21 17	21 24					23 03		23 46	00 01	00 58		
Chester	a	18 25		19 25				20 02		20 31	21 27		21 49	22 11			22 32				00 16	00 26			
Llandudno Junction	a	19 25		20 44						21 28			22 39				23 38					01 25			
Bangor (Gwynedd)	a	19 48		21 03						21 51			22 55				00 01					01 42			
Holyhead	a	20 29		21 40						22 35			23 30				00 47					02 15			
Runcorn	a			19 05			19 53	20 25			21 21			22 25											
Liverpool Lime Street 10	a			19 29			20 18	20 47			21 45			22 47											
Wilmslow	a			18 44				19 44			20 45			21 44					23 23						
Stockport	a			18 53				19 53			20 53			21 53					23 33						
Manchester Piccadilly 10 ⇌	a			19 13				20 18			21 13			22 12					23 49			01b42			

Saturdays

		AW ◇ A	AW		AW	AW ◇ G		AW ◇ H	AW ◇ ✠		AW ◇ ✠	AW ◇		AW	AW ◇ B ✠		AW ◇ ✠	AW ◇ B ✠		AW	AW ◇ A ✠		AW ◇ ✠	AW ◇ A ✠	AW
Swansea 7	d	20p55							03 59			04 36			05 29		05 59	06 40			07 45			08 55	
Cardiff Central 7	d	21p56	00 30			04 00		04 00	05 10		05 35				06 50		07 20	07 50			08 50		09 20	09 50	
London Paddington 15 ⊖	d																							07 45	
Reading 7	d																							08 11	
Bristol Temple Meads 10	d																								
Newport (South Wales)	d	22p15	00 53			04 18		04 18	05 25		05 53				07 04		07 34	08 04			09 04		09 34	10 04	
Cwmbran	d	22p25	01 04			04 28		04 28	05 39		06 03				07 15		07 44	08 15			09 15		09 44	10 15	
Pontypool and New Inn	d	22p31	01 10			04 34		04 34	05 45		06 09						07 49				09 20				
Abergavenny	d	22p40	01 20			04 45		04 45	05 55		06 18				07 28		08 00	08 28			09 28		09 57	10 28	
Hereford 7	a	23p05	01 46			05 12		05 12	06 19		06 47				07 54		08 25	08 54			09 54		10 22	10 54	
	d	23p06	01 48			05 23		05 23	06 25		06 48				07 56		08 28	08 56			09 56		10 24	10 56	
Leominster	d	23p20	02 01			05 36		05 36	06 38		07 02				08 09			09 09			10 09			11 09	
Ludlow	d	23p31	02 12			05 47		05 47	06 49		07 13				08 20		08 49	09 20			10 20		10 46	11 20	
Craven Arms	d	23p39	02 22			05 56		05 56	06 58		07 21	07 53			08 29			09 29			10 29			11 29	
Church Stretton	d	23p48	02 31			06 05		06 05	07 07		07 30	08 06			08 38			09 38			10 38			11 38	
Shrewsbury	a	00 02	02 49			06 22		06 22	07 22		07 44	08 21			08 52		09 15	09 52			10 52		11 12	11 52	
	d	00 12			06 03	06 26		06 26	07 30		07 46			08 26	08 54		09 30	09 54		10 26	10 54		11 30	11 54	12 26
Yorton	d	00x20			06x13									08x36						10x36					12x36
Wem	d	00 25			06 19	06 38		06 38			07 58			08 42						10 42					12 42
Prees	d	00x30			06x23									08x46						10x46					12x46
Whitchurch (Shrops)	d	00 37			06 31	06 47		06 47			08 07			08 54						10 54					12 54
Wrenbury	d	00x42			06x37									09x00						11x00					13x00
Nantwich	d	00 48			06 44	06 56		06 56			08 16			09 07						11 07					13 07
Crewe 10	a	00 58			06 57	07 05		07 05			08 28			09 16	09 28			10 28		11 20	11 28			12 28	13 20
Chester	a					07 57		07 57	08 28		09 26			09 57			10 28			11 59			12 25		
Llandudno Junction	a					09c19		09c19	09 26		10 24			11c17			11 26			13c17			13 24		
Bangor (Gwynedd)	a								09 43		10 46						11 43						13 48		
Holyhead	a								10 20		11 30						12 20						14 30		
Runcorn	a																								
Liverpool Lime Street 10	a																								
Wilmslow	a					07 33		07 33			08 48				09 48			10 48			11 48			12 48	
Stockport	a					07 42		07 42			08 56				09 58			10 58			11 58			12 58	
Manchester Piccadilly 10 ⇌	a					07 59		08 00			09 12				10 13			11 13			12 13			13 13	

For general notes see front of timetable
For details of catering facilities see Directory of Train Operators

- **A** From Milford Haven (Table 128)
- **B** From Carmarthen (Table 128)
- **C** Fridays from Milford Haven (Table 128)
- **D** **Cathedrals Express**
- **E** From Birmingham New Street (Table 74)
- **G** Until 6 September
- **H** From 13 September
- **b** Change at Crewe. Saturday mornings arr. 0140
- **c** Change at Crewe and Chester

Cardiff → Crewe, Liverpool and Manchester

Route Diagram - see first page of Table 129

Station		AW	AW	AW	GW	AW	AW	AW	AW	GW	AW	AW	AW	AW	AW	AW	AW
		◇ A ⚯	◇	◇ ⚯	[1] ◇ ⊏	◇ B ⚯		◇ A ⚯	◇ ⚯	[1] ◇ ⊏	◇ B ⚯		[R] A ⚯	◇	◇ ⚯	[R] B ⚯	
Swansea [7]	d	09 55	09 15			10 55		11 55			12 50		13 55	13 16		14 55	
Cardiff Central [7]	d	10 50	08 09	11 20		11 50		12 50	13 20		13 50		14 50		15 20	15 50	16 06
London Paddington [15] ⊖	d	08 45		09 45	09 51			10 45	11 45	11 51			12 45		13 45		
Reading [7]	d	09 11		10 11	10 23			11 11	12 11	12 23			13 11		14 11		
Bristol Temple Meads [10]	d																
Newport (South Wales)	d	11 04		11 34		12 04		13 04	13 34		14 04		15 04		15 34	16 04	16 22
Cwmbran	d	11 15		11 44		12 15		13 15	13 44		14 15		15 15		15 44	16 15	16 32
Pontypool and New Inn	d			11 49					13 49						15 49		16 38
Abergavenny	d	11 28		12 00		12 28		13 28	14 00		14 28		15 28		16 00	16 28	16a53
Hereford [7]	a	11 54		12 25	12 54	12 54		13 54	14 25	14 54	14 54		15 52		16 25	16 54	
	d	11 56		12 28		12 56		13 56	14 28		14 56		15 54		16 28	16 56	
Leominster	d	12 09				13 09		14 09			15 09		16 07			17 09	
Ludlow	d	12 20		12 49		13 20		14 20	14 49		15 20		16 18		16 49	17 20	
Craven Arms	d	12 29	12 36			13 29		14 29			15 29		16 27	16 37		17 29	
Church Stretton	d	12 38	12 50			13 38		14 38			15 38			16 50		17 38	
Shrewsbury	a	12 52	13 07	13 15		13 52		14 52	15 17		15 52		16 47	17 10	17 15	17 52	
	d	12 54		13 30		13 54	14 26	14 54	15 30		15 54	16 26	16 49		17 30	17 54	
Yorton	d						14x36					16x36					
Wem	d						14 42					16 42	17 01				
Prees	d						14x46					16x46					
Whitchurch (Shrops)	d						14 54					16 54	17 10				
Wrenbury	d						15x00					17x00					
Nantwich	d						15 07					17 07					
Crewe [10]	a	13 28				14 28	15 20	15 28			16 28	17 20	17 28			18 28	
Chester	a			14 28			15 57		16 28		17 26	17 54	18 29		18 25	19 04	
Llandudno Junction	a			15 25			17b17		17 24		18 25	19b17	19b26		19 26	19 54	
Bangor (Gwynedd)	a			15 47					17 47		18 47		19b49		19 49	20 11	
Holyhead	a			16 30					18 30		19 20		20b30		20 30	20 55	
Runcorn	a																
Liverpool Lime Street [10]	a																
Wilmslow	a	13 48				14 48		15 48			16 48		17 48			18 48	
Stockport	a	13 58				14 58		15 58			16 58		17 58			18 59	
Manchester Piccadilly [10] ⛴	a	14 13				15 13		16 13			17 13		18 10			19 16	

Station		AW	AW	AW	AW	AW	AW	GW	AW	AW	AW	AW	GW	AW	AW	AW
			[R] A ⚯	◇ ⚯	[R] B ⚯		◇ A ⚯	[1] ◇ ⊏	◇ C ⚯	◇ D ⚯	◇	◇ B ⚯	[1] ◇ ⊏	◇ A ⚯	◇ E	◇ B
Swansea [7]	d		15 55		16 55		17 55		18 29	18 29	18 21	18 55		19 55		20 55
Cardiff Central [7]	d		16 50	17 20	17 50		18 50		19 34	19 34		20 10		20 53		21 50
London Paddington [15] ⊖	d		14 45	15 45			16 45	16 51	17 45	17 45			18 21			19 45
Reading [7]	d		15 11	16 11			17 11	17 23	18 11	18 11			18 53			20 11
Bristol Temple Meads [10]	d								18 53							
Newport (South Wales)	d		17 04	17 34	18 04		19 05		19 49	19 49		20 25		21 09		22 08
Cwmbran	d		17 15	17 44	18 15		19 16		20 00	20 00		20 35		21 20		22 19
Pontypool and New Inn	d			17 49	18 21				20 04	20 04		20 41				22 25
Abergavenny	d		17 28	18 00	18 28		19 29		20 15	20 15		20 48		21 33		22 34
Hereford [7]	a		17 54	18 25	18 54		19 54	20 02	20 39	20 39		21 14	21 33	21 57		22 59
	d		17 56	18 26	18 56		19 56		20 41	20 41		21 16		21 59		23 00
Leominster	d		18 09	18 39	19 09		20 09		20 54	20 54		21 29		22 12		23 13
Ludlow	d		18 20	18 49	19 20		20 20		21 01	21 01		21 40		22 23		23 24
Craven Arms	d		18 29		19 29		20 29		21 13	21 13	21 37	21 49		22 32		23 33
Church Stretton	d		18 38		19 38		20 38		21 22	21 22	21 50	22 02		22 41		23 42
Shrewsbury	a		18 52	19 16	19 52		20 52		21 36	21 36	22 12	22 16		22 55		23 56
	d	18 26	18 54	19 30	19 54	20 26	20 54		21 38	21 38		22 17		22 56	23 29	23 57
Yorton	d	18x36				20x36						22x26		23x05		00x06
Wem	d	18 42				20 42						22 31		23 10		00 10
Prees	d	18x46				20x46						22x35		23x15		00x15
Whitchurch (Shrops)	d	18 54				20 54						22 42		23 22		00 21
Wrenbury	d	19x00				21x00						22x48		23x28		00x27
Nantwich	d	19 07				21 07						22 54		23 34		00 32
Crewe [10]	a	19 23	19 28		20 26	21 20	21 27					23 03		23 44	00 01	00 44
Chester	a			20 26	21 27		22 09		22 32	22 32				00 10	00 24	
Llandudno Junction	a			21 28	22 25				23 30	23 33						
Bangor (Gwynedd)	a			21 51	22 42				23 52	00c25						
Holyhead	a			22 35	23 30				00 31	01c45						
Runcorn	a						22 05									
Liverpool Lime Street [10]	a						22 24					00 22				
Wilmslow	a		19 48		20 45		21 46					23 22				
Stockport	a		19 59		20 56		21 57					23 33				
Manchester Piccadilly [10] ⛴	a		20 13		21 13		22 13					23 50				

For general notes see front of timetable
For details of catering facilities see Directory of Train Operators

- **A** From Carmarthen (Table 128)
- **B** From Milford Haven (Table 128)
- **C** Until 6 September
- **D** From 13 September
- **E** From Birmingham New Street (Table 74)
- **b** Change at Crewe and Chester
- **c** By bus

Table 131

Sundays

until 13 July

Cardiff → Crewe, Liverpool and Manchester

Route Diagram - see first page of Table 129

		AW	AW	AW	AW	AW	AW		GW	AW	GW	AW	AW	GW	AW	AW	GW	AW	AW	AW		AW	GW	AW
																R				R		R		
		◇ A			🚌		◇		1 ◇	◇ A	1 ◇	◇	◇ B	1 ◇	◇	A	1 ◇	◇	C	A		A	1 ◇	◇ B
Swansea 7	d	20p55					10 29			11b12		11 03	13 35		14 29	15 19		15 10	15 29	17 35		19 35		21 35
Cardiff Central 7	d	21p50	08 34				11 35			12 39			14 35		15 35	16 35			17 05	18 35		20 35		22 46
London Paddington 15 ⊖	d						08 00		09 35	09 27	10 42		11 27	12 42	12 27	13 27	14 42		14 27	15 27		17 27	18 42	19 27
Reading 7	d						08 46		10 13	10 05	11 20		12 02	13 20	13 02	14 02	15 20		15 02	16 02		18 05	19 20	20 05
Bristol Temple Meads 10	d																							
Newport (South Wales)	d	22p08	08 50				11 50			12 50			14 50		15 49	16 50			17 19	18 50		20 50		23 08
Cwmbran	d	22p19	09 01				12 00			13 01			15 01		15 59	17 01			17 29	19 00		21 01		23 19
Pontypool and New Inn	d	22p25	09 07							13 07			15 07			17 07			17 35			21 06		23 24
Abergavenny	d	22p34	09 16				12 14			13 16			15 16		16 12	17 16			17 44	19 14		21 16		23 34
Hereford 7	a	22p59	09 46				12 41		12 54	13 41	14 04		15 41	15 51	16 37	17 41	17 58		18 12	19 39		21 40	22 02	00 03
	d	23p00			10 00		12 42			13 42			15 42		16 38	17 42				19 40		21 42		
Leominster	d	23p13			10 25		12 55			13 56			15 56		16 52	17 56				19 53		21 56		
Ludlow	d	23p24			10 50		13 07			14 07			16 07		17 03	18 07				20 05		22 07		
Craven Arms	d	23p33			11 10		13 15			14 15		15 02	16 15			18 15		18 55		20 13		22 15		
Church Stretton	d	23p42			11 30		13 24			14 25		15 15	16 24			18 24		19 08		20 22		22 24		
Shrewsbury	a	23p56			12 00		13 38			14 38		15 33	16 40		17 29	18 38		19 23		20 36		22 38		
	d	23p57		11 05		12 40	13 40	13 50		14 40			16 42		17 30	18 40		19 25		20 41	20 48	22 40		
Yorton	d	00x06				12x49							16x50					19x34				22x48		
Wem	d	00 10				12 54							16 55					19 39				22 53		
Prees	d	00x15				12x59							17x00					19x44				22x58		
Whitchurch (Shrops)	d	00 21				13 06							17 07					19 51				23 05		
Wrenbury	d	00x27				13x12							17x12					19x57				23x10		
Nantwich	d	00 32				13 18							17 18					20 03				23 16		
Crewe 10	a	00 44		11 41		13 35	14 19			15 23			17 37		18 12	19 27		20 15		21 25		23 35		
Chester	a			12 30		14 13		14 39		16 18			18 25		19 08	20 33		21 00			21 36			
Llandudno Junction	a			13c28		15 08		15 40		17 08			19c34		20 15	21 28		22 28			22 49			
Bangor (Gwynedd)	a			13c59		15 29		16 03		17 25			20c05		20 34	21 51		22 44			23 12			
Holyhead	a							16 38		17 55					21 06	22 21		23 14			23 57			
Runcorn	a			12 46			14 48			16 44					18 46			20 49		23 00		00 21		
Liverpool Lime Street 10	a			13 12			15 10			17 08					19 09			21 11		23 28		00 46		
Wilmslow	a			12 00		13 55	14 42			15 44			17 58		18 50	19 48		20 50		21 46		00 49		
Stockport	a			12 11		14 06	14 53			15 55			18 13		19f28	19 57		21f28		21 57		00 58		
Manchester Piccadilly 10 ✈	a	01 42		12 26		14 21	15 10			16 11			18 28		19 21	20 14		21 21		22 13		01 11		

Sundays

20 July to 7 September

		AW	AW	AW	AW	AW	AW		GW	AW	GW	AW	AW	GW	AW	AW	GW	AW	AW	AW		AW	GW	AW	AW
																R				R		R			
		◇ A			🚌		◇		1 ◇	◇ A	1 ◇	◇	◇ B	1 ◇	◇	A	1 ◇	◇	C	A		A	1 ◇	◇ D	◇ B
Swansea 7	d	20p55					10 29			11b12		11 03	13 35		14 29	15 19		15 10	15 29	17 35		19 35			21 35
Cardiff Central 7	d	21p50	08 34				11 35			12 39			14 35		15 35	16 35			17 05	18 35		20 35			22 47
London Paddington 15 ⊖	d						08 00		09 35	09 27	10 42		11 27	12 42	12 27	13 27	14 42		14 27	15 27		17 27	18 42		19 27
Reading 7	d						08 46		10 13	10 05	11 20		12 02	13 20	13 02	14 02	15 20		15 02	16 02		18 05	19 20		20 05
Bristol Temple Meads 10	d																								
Newport (South Wales)	d	22p08	08 50				11 50			12 50			14 50		15 49	16 50			17 19	18 50		20 50			23 09
Cwmbran	d	22p19	09 01				12 00			13 01			15 01		15 59	17 01			17 29	19 00		21 01			23 20
Pontypool and New Inn	d	22p25	09 07							13 07			15 07			17 07			17 35			21 06			23 25
Abergavenny	d	22p34	09 16				12 14			13 16			15 16		16 12	17 16			17 44	19 14		21 16			23 35
Hereford 7	a	22p59	09 46				12 41		12 54	13 41	14 04		15 41	15 51	16 37	17 41	17 58		18 12	19 39		21 40	22 02		00 04
	d	23p00			10 00		12 42			13 42			15 42		16 38	17 42				19 40		21 42			
Leominster	d	23p13			10 25		12 55			13 56			15 56		16 52	17 56				19 53		21 56			
Ludlow	d	23p24			10 50		13 07			14 07			16 07		17 03	18 07				20 05		22 07			
Craven Arms	d	23p33			11 10		13 15			14 15		15 02	16 15			18 15		18 55		20 13		22 15			
Church Stretton	d	23p42			11 30		13 24			14 25		15 15	16 24			18 24		19 08		20 22		22 24			
Shrewsbury	a	23p56			12 00		13 38			14 38		15 33	16 40		17 29	18 38		19 23		20 36		22 38			
	d	23p57		10 54		12 40	13 40	13 50		14 40			16 42		17 30	18 40		19 25		20 41	20 48	22 40		23 50	
Yorton	d	00x06				12x49							16x50					19x34				22x48			
Wem	d	00 10				12 54							16 55					19 39				22 53			
Prees	d	00x15				12x59							17x00					19x44				22x58			
Whitchurch (Shrops)	d	00 21				13 06							17 07					19 51				23 05			
Wrenbury	d	00x27				13x12							17x12					19x57				23x10			
Nantwich	d	00 32				13 18							17 18					20 03				23 16			
Crewe 10	a	00 44		11 30		13 35	14 19			15 23			17 37		18 12	19 28		20 15		21 24		23 35			
Chester	a			12 30		14 13		14 39		16 18			18 25		19 08	20 33		21 00			21 36			00 41	
Llandudno Junction	a			13c28		15 08		15 40		17 08			19c34		20 15	21 28		22 28			22 49			01 28	
Bangor (Gwynedd)	a			13c59		15 29		16 03		17 25			20c05		20 34	21 51		22 44			23 12			01 45	
Holyhead	a							16 38		17 55					21 06	22 21		23 14			23 57			02 16	
Runcorn	a			12 30		14 12	14 53			16 07			18 08		18 51	20 10		20 54		22 11		00 21			
Liverpool Lime Street 10	a			12 49		14 33	15 22			16 30			18 30		19 13	20 32		21 22		22 34		00 46			
Wilmslow	a			11 50		13 55	14 42			15 44			17 58		18 59	19 49		20 59		21 46		01 00			
Stockport	a			12 01		14 06	14 53			15 55			18 11		19f28	19 58		21f28		21 57		01 09			
Manchester Piccadilly 10 ✈	a	01 42		12 16		14 21	15 06			16 11			18 26		19 21	20 17		21 21		22 16		01 22			

For general notes see front of timetable
For details of catering facilities see Directory of Train Operators

- **A** From Milford Haven (Table 128)
- **B** From Pembroke Dock (Table 128)
- **C** From Barry Island (Table 130)
- **D** From Birmingham New Street (Table 74)
- **b** By changing at Cardiff Central, passengers may depart at 1129
- **c** Change at Crewe and Chester
- **e** Change at Crewe and Bangor (Gwynedd)

Table 131

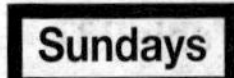

from 14 September

Cardiff → Crewe, Liverpool and Manchester

Route Diagram - see first page of Table 129

		AW	AW	AW	AW	AW	AW		GW	AW	AW	GW	AW	AW
		◇ A			bus		◇ ✠		1 ◇ ⊡		◇ B	1 ◇ ⊡	◇	◇ B ✠
Swansea 7	d	20p55					09 59				11 22		11 09	13 35
Cardiff Central 7	d	21p50	08 34				11 35				12 35			14 35
London Paddington 15	⊖ d						09 30		09 35		10 37	10 42		12 37
Reading 7	d						10 07		10 12		11 11	11 20		13 11
Bristol Temple Meads 10	d													
Newport (South Wales)	d	22p08	08 50				11 50				12 50			14 50
Cwmbran	d	22p19	09 01				12 00				13 00			15 01
Pontypool and New Inn	d	22p25	09 07								13 06			15 07
Abergavenny	d	22p34	09 16				12 14				13 16			15 16
Hereford 7	a	22p59	09 46				12 41		12 54		13 41	14 04		15 41
	d	23p00			10 00		12 42				13 42			15 42
Leominster	d	23p13			10 25		12 55				13 55			15 56
Ludlow	d	23p24			10 50		13 07				14 07			16 07
Craven Arms	d	23p33			11 10		13 15				14 15		15 02	16 15
Church Stretton	d	23p42			11 30		13 24				14 25		15 15	16 24
Shrewsbury	a	23p56			12 00		13 38				14 38		15 33	16 40
	d	23p57		11 05		12 40	13 40	13 50		14 24	14 40			16 42
Yorton	d	00x06				12x49								16x50
Wem	d	00 10				12 54								16 55
Prees	d	00x15				12x59								17x00
Whitchurch (Shrops)	d	00 21				13 06								17 07
Wrenbury	d	00x27				13x12								17x12
Nantwich	d	00 32				13 18								17 18
Crewe 10	a	00 44		11 41		13 35	14 19			14 54	15 23			17 32
Chester	a			12 20		14 15	15 20	14 58			16 06			18 09
Llandudno Junction	a			13b34		15 09		15 56			17 12			19b29
Bangor (Gwynedd)	a			14b04		15 33		16 18			17 29			19b52
Holyhead	a							16 55			18 05			20b30
Runcorn	a													
Liverpool Lime Street 10	a													
Wilmslow	a			12 00		13 55	14 42				15 44			17 53
Stockport	a			12 11		14 06	14 53				15 55			18 04
Manchester Piccadilly 10	⇌ a	01 42		12 26		14 21	15 06				16 10			18 19

		GW	AW	AW	AW	GW	AW	AW	AW	AW		AW	GW	AW	AW
		1 ◇ ⊡		◇ ✠	R A ✠	1 ◇ ⊡		◇		R A ✠		R A ✠	1 ◇ ⊡	◇ C	◇ D
Swansea 7	d			13 59	15 30			15 16	15 59	17 35		19 35			21 35
Cardiff Central 7	d			15 35	16 35				17 05	18 35		20 35			22 46
London Paddington 15	⊖ d	12 42		13 37	14 37	14 42				16 37		18 37	18 42		20 37
Reading 7	d	13 20		14 11	15 11	15 20				17 11		19 09	19 20		21 11
Bristol Temple Meads 10	d														
Newport (South Wales)	d			15 49	16 50				17 19	18 50		20 50			23 08
Cwmbran	d			15 59	17 01				17 29	19 00		21 01			23 19
Pontypool and New Inn	d				17 07				17 35			21 06			23 24
Abergavenny	d			16 12	17 16				17 44	19 14		21 16			23 34
Hereford 7	a	15 51		16 37	17 41	17 58			18 10	19 39		21 40	22 02		00 03
	d			16 38	17 42					19 40		21 42			
Leominster	d			16 52	17 56					19 53		21 56			
Ludlow	d			17 03	18 07					20 05		22 07			
Craven Arms	d				18 15			18 55		20 13		22 15			
Church Stretton	d				18 24			19 08		20 22		22 24			
Shrewsbury	a			17 29	18 38			19 23		20 36		22 38			
	d		17 28	17 37	18 40		19 15	19 25		20 41	20 48	22 40		23 50	
Yorton	d							19x34				22x48			
Wem	d							19 39				22 53			
Prees	d							19x44				22x58			
Whitchurch (Shrops)	d							19 51				23 05			
Wrenbury	d							19x57				23x10			
Nantwich	d							20 03				23 16			
Crewe 10	a		17 58	18 12	19 27		19 45	20 15		21 24		23 36		00 20	
Chester	a			18 50	20 20			20 56			21 36			00 41	
Llandudno Junction	a			20 51				21 51			22 46			01 28	
Bangor (Gwynedd)	a			21 10				22 14			23 09			01 45	
Holyhead	a			21 42				22 50			23 54			02 16	
Runcorn	a														
Liverpool Lime Street 10	a														
Wilmslow	a				19 48					21 45					
Stockport	a				19 58					21 56					
Manchester Piccadilly 10	⇌ a				20 15					22 13					

For general notes see front of timetable
For details of catering facilities see Directory of Train Operators

A From Milford Haven (Table 128)
B From Carmarthen (Table 128)
C From Birmingham New Street (Table 74)
D From Pembroke Dock (Table 128)
b Change at Crewe and Chester

Manchester, Liverpool and Crewe → Cardiff

Route Diagram - see first page of Table 129

Miles	Miles	Station		AW MX ◇	AW MO A	AW MO B	AW	GW **1** ◇ C ☒	GW MO **1** ◇ D ☒	AW ◇	AW ◇ E ⚲	GW **1** ◇ G ☒	AW ◇	AW ◇ H ⚲	AW ◇ ⚲	AW ◇ E ⚲	AW	AW ◇ H ⚲
0	—	**Manchester Piccadilly 10**	d	21p34	22p46	22p46										06 38		07 28
6	—	Stockport	d	21p46	22p54	22p55										06 48		07 37
12	—	Wilmslow	d	21p54	23p02	23p03										06 56		07 46
—	0	**Liverpool Lime Street 10**	d													06 27		07 18
—	13	Runcorn	d													06 43		07 35
—	—	Holyhead	d								02 15				04 27			05 32
—	—	Bangor (Gwynedd)	d								02 42				05 00			06 01
—	—	Llandudno Junction	d								03 00				05 18			06 21
—	—	Chester	d								03 40		05 07	04 55	06 12	06 30		07 30
31	35½	**Crewe 10**	d	22p18	23p26	23p26					04 54			05 55		07 18	07 27	08 08
35½	40	Nantwich	d	22p25	23p33	23p33					05 01			06 02			07 34	08 15
40	44½	Wrenbury	d	22b31	23b39	23b39								06x08			07x41	
44¾	49¼	Whitchurch (Shrops)	d	22p38	23p46	23p46					05 12			06 14			07 49	08 26
49¾	54¼	Prees	d	22b44	23b51	23b51								06x20			07x55	
53	57½	Wem	d	22p48	23p56	23p56					05 20			06 24			08 01	08 35
56½	61	Yorton	d	22b54	00x01	00x01								06x29			08x06	
63¾	68¼	**Shrewsbury**	a	23p04	00 13	00 13					05 32		06 07	06 40	07 07	07 47	08 17	08 44
—	—		d	23p06						05 19	05 40		06 20	06 45	07 16	07 49		08 49
76½	81	Church Stretton	d	23p22						05 36	05 55			07 00		08 04		09 04
83¾	88¼	Craven Arms	d	23p30						05 50	06 03			07 08		08 12		09 12
91	95½	Ludlow	d	23p38							06 11		06 47	07 16	07 43	08 20		09 20
102	106½	Leominster	d	23p48							06 22		06 58	07 27	07 53	08 31		09 31
114½	119	**Hereford 7**	a	00 03							06 36		07 12	07 45	08 08	08 45		09 45
—	—		d	00 04			05 23	05 35	05 41		06 42	06 43	07 16	07 48	08 09	08 48		09 47
138½	143	Abergavenny	d	00 27			05 48				07 05		07 39	08 11	08 32	09 11		10 10
148	152½	Pontypool and New Inn	d	00 37			05 59				07 15		07 49		08 42			10 20
151	155½	Cwmbran	d	00 42			06 04				07 20		07 54	08 23	08 47	09 23		10 24
158	162½	**Newport (South Wales)**	a	00 56			06 16				07 33		08 04	08 34	08 58	09 34		10 34
—	—	Bristol Temple Meads 10	a				07 18				08 18		08 52	09 18	09 52	10 18		11 18
—	—	Reading 7	a				07 58	08 22	08 22		09 01	09 14	09 27	09 57	10 32	11 01		12 01
—	—	London Paddington 15	⊖ a				08 30	08 51	08 51		09 29	09 41	09 59	10 27	11 02	11 30		12 32
169¾	174¼	**Cardiff Central 7**	a	01 22			06 59			10 17	07 50		08 29	08 53	09 18	09 53		10 54
—	—	Swansea 7	a							09 07	08 49		09 44	09 56	10 45	10 58		11 56

Station		AW ◇	AW ◇ ⚲	AW ◇ E ⚲	AW	AW ◇ H ⚲	AW ◇ ⚲	AW ◇ E ⚲	AW	GW **1** ◇	AW ◇ H ⚲	AW ◇ ⚲	AW **R** E ⚲	AW ◇	AW	GW **1** ◇	AW **R** H ⚲	AW ◇ ⚲
Manchester Piccadilly 10	d			08 34		09 34		10 34			11 34		12 34				13 34	
Stockport	d			08 44		09 42		10 42			11 42		12 42				13 42	
Wilmslow	d			08 52		09 54		10 54			11 54		12 54				13 54	
Liverpool Lime Street 10	d			08 19		09 19		10 19			11 19		12 15				13 19	
Runcorn	d			08 35		09 35		10 35			11 35		12 31				13 35	
Holyhead	d		06 15	06 45		07 15	08 10				09 50	10 30					11 40	12 35
Bangor (Gwynedd)	d		06 59	07 12		08 01	09 04				10 18	11 03					12 19	13 04
Llandudno Junction	d		07 17	07 31		08 27	09 27				10 36	11 26					12 42	13 27
Chester	d		08 20	08 30		09 19	10 20	10 29			11 28	12 20	12 29				13 33	14 20
Crewe 10	d			09 17	09 27	10 17		11 18	11 26		12 18		13 18		13 26		14 18	
Nantwich	d				09 34				11 34						13 34			
Wrenbury	d				09x41				11x41						13x41			
Whitchurch (Shrops)	d				09 49				11 49						13 49			
Prees	d				09x55				11x55						13x55			
Wem	d				10 01				12 01						14 01			
Yorton	d				10x06				12x06						14x06			
Shrewsbury	a		09 15	09 46	10 17	10 46	11 15	11 46	12 17		12 46	13 15	13 46		14 17		14 46	15 15
	d	09 05	09 18	09 49		10 49	11 18	11 48			12 49	13 18	13 49	14 05			14 49	15 18
Church Stretton	d	09 22		10 04		11 04		12 03			13 04		14 04	14 23			15 04	
Craven Arms	d	09 35		10 12		11 12		12 11			13 12		14 12	14 36			15 12	
Ludlow	d		09 45	10 20		11 20	11 45	12 19			13 20	13 45	14 20				15 20	15 45
Leominster	d			10 31		11 31		12 30			13 31		14 31				15 31	
Hereford 7	a		10 08	10 45		11 45	12 08	12 44			13 45	14 08	14 45				15 44	16 08
	d		10 09	10 48		11 48	12 09	12 48		13 21	13 48	14 09	14 48			15 19	15 48	16 09
Abergavenny	d		10 32	11 11		12 11	12 32	13 11			14 11	14 32	15 11				16 11	16 32
Pontypool and New Inn	d						12 42					14 42						16 42
Cwmbran	d		10 47	11 23		12 23	12 47	13 23			14 23	14 47	15 23				16 23	16 47
Newport (South Wales)	a		10 58	11 34		12 34	12 58	13 34			14 34	14 58	15 34				16 34	16 57
Bristol Temple Meads 10	a		11 52	12 18		13 17	13 52	14 19			15 18	15 51	16 18				17 18	17 52
Reading 7	a		12 32	13 01		14 01	14 32	15 01		16 25	16 01	16 32	17 01			18 03	17 57	18 32
London Paddington 15	⊖ a		13 02	13 30		14 32	15 02	15 30		16 59	16 30	17 02	17 30			18 30	18 27	19 02
Cardiff Central 7	a		11 20	11 54		12 54	13 20	13 54			14 54	15 20	15 54				16 54	17 15
Swansea 7	a	13 01	12 45	12 56		13 56	14 45	14 56			15 56	16 43	16 56	18 06			18 05	18 44

For general notes see front of timetable
For details of catering facilities see Directory of Train Operators

A Until 14 July and from 15 September
B 21 July to 8 September
C All Tuesdays to Fridays, also Mondays From 15 September
D Until 8 September
E To Milford Haven (Table 128)
G **Cathedrals Express**
H To Carmarthen (Table 128)
b Previous night.
Stops on request, passengers wishing to alight must inform the guard and those wishing to join must give a hand signal to the driver

Manchester, Liverpool and Crewe → Cardiff

Route Diagram - see first page of Table 129

Mondays to Fridays

		AW	AW	AW	AW	AW	AW	AW	AW	AW	AW	AW	AW	AW	AW	AW	AW
															FO	FX	
		R		R		R			R								
					◇		◇			◇	◇		◇	◇	◇	◇	
		A		B		A					B						
		🛒		🛒	🛒	🛒			🛒	🛒	🛒						
Manchester Piccadilly [10] ✈	d	14 34		15 34		16 34			17 34		18 34		19 34	20 34	21 34	21 34	22 34
Stockport	d	14 42		15 42		16 42			17 42		18 42		19 43	20 46	21 46	21 46	22 42
Wilmslow	d	14 54		15 54		16 54			17 51		18 54		19 54	20 54	21 54	21 54	22 50
Liverpool Lime Street [10]	d	*14 15*		*15 19*		*16 15*			*17 18*		*18 15*		*19 19*	*19 49*	*20 40*	*20 40*	*21 40*
Runcorn	d	*14 31*		*15 35*		*16 31*			*17 36*		*18 31*		*19 35*	*20 05*	*20 58*	*20 58*	*21 59*
Holyhead	d			*13 35*	14 35				*15 39*	16 35			*17 27*	*18b35*	*19 35*	*19 35*	
Bangor (Gwynedd)	d			*14 14*	15 04				*16 17*	17 04			*18 06*	*19b14*	*20 14*	*20 14*	
Llandudno Junction	d			*14 37*	15 27				*16 40*	17 27			*18 29*	*19b32*	*20 37*	*20 37*	*20b56*
Chester	d	*14 30*		*15 30*	16 20	*16 31*			*17 31*	18 20	*18 30*		*19 22*	*20 30*	*21 33*	*21 33*	*22 14*
Crewe [10]	d	15 18	15 26	16 18		17 18		17 27	18 18		19 18	19 26	20 18	21 18	22 18	22 18	23 16
Nantwich	d		15 34	16 25				17 34	18 25			19 34		21 25	22 25	22 25	23 23
Wrenbury	d		15x41					17x41				19x41		21x32	22x31	22x31	23x30
Whitchurch (Shrops)	d		15 49	16 36				17 49	18 36			19 49		21 39	22 38	22 38	23 38
Prees	d		15x55					17x55				19x55		21x45	22x44	22x44	23x44
Wem	d		16 01	16 45				18 01	18 45			20 01		21 50	22 48	22 48	23 50
Yorton	d		16x06					18x06				20x06		21x56	22x54	22x54	23x55
Shrewsbury	a	15 46	16 17	16 57	17 15	17 46		18 17	18 57	19 15	19 46	20 17	20 46	22 04	23 04	23 04	00 07
	d	15 48		16 59	17 18	17 49	18 05		18 59	19 17	19 49		20 49	22 07	23 06	23 06	
Church Stretton	d	16 03		17 14		18 04	18 23		19 14		20 04		21 04	22 22	23 22	23 22	
Craven Arms	d	16 11		17 22		18 12	18 35		19 22		20 12		21 12	22 30	23 30	23 30	
Ludlow	d	16 19		17 30	17 45	18 20			19 30	19 45	20 20		21 20	22 38	23 38	23 38	
Leominster	d	16 30		17 41		18 31			19 41		20 31		21 31	22 49	23 48	23 48	
Hereford [7]	a	16 44		17 52	18 08	18 45			19 55	20 08	20 45		21 45	23 03	00 03	00 03	
	d	16 48		17 56	18 09	18 48			19 57	20 09	20 48		21 49	23 05	00 04	00 04	
Abergavenny	d	17 11		18 19	18 33	19 11			20 20	20 33	21 11		22 12	23 28	00 27	00 27	
Pontypool and New Inn	d				18 42					20 42			22 22		00 37	00 37	
Cwmbran	d	17 23		18 31	18 47	19 23			20 32	20 47	21 23		22 24	23 40	00 42	00 42	
Newport (South Wales)	a	17 34		18 45	18 57	19 34			20 45	20 58	21 34		22 38	23 51	00 53	00 56	
Bristol Temple Meads [10]	a	*18 18*			*19 52*	*20 18*				*21 53*	*23 00*		*00 04*				
Reading [7]	a	*19 01*				*21 01*					*23 06*						
London Paddington [15] ⊖	a	*19 32*				*21 32*					*23c50*						
Cardiff Central [7]	a	17 54		19 01	19 20	19 54			21 01	21 19	21 57		23 04	00 17	01 14	01 22	
Swansea [7]	a	19 01		19 56	*20 42*	*21 21*	22 13				23 00		*00 28*	*02 10*			

Saturdays

		AW	AW	AW	AW	AW	GW	AW	AW	AW	AW	AW	AW	AW	AW	AW	AW	AW
		◇		◇	◇	◇	[1] ◇	◇	◇	◇		◇	◇	◇	◇		◇	◇
			C		A			B		A		B			A		B	
					🛒		🍽	🛒	🛒	🛒		🛒		🛒	🛒		🛒	🛒
Manchester Piccadilly [10] ✈	d	21p34								06 38		07 28			08 34		09 34	
Stockport	d	21p46								06 48		07 37			08 44		09 42	
Wilmslow	d	21p54								06 55		07 46			08 52		09 52	
Liverpool Lime Street [10]	d																	
Runcorn	d																	
Holyhead	d								04 27			*05 30*		06 15	*06 45*		*07 15*	08 25
Bangor (Gwynedd)	d								05 00			*05 59*		06 59	*07 12*		*08 01*	09 04
Llandudno Junction	d								05 18			*06 19*		07 17			*08 27*	09 27
Chester	d							*04 55*	06 12	*06 30*		*07 30*		08 20	*08 30*		*09 19*	10 20
Crewe [10]	d	22p18			04 54			05 55		07 18	07 27	08 08			09 17	09 27	10 17	
Nantwich	d	22p25			05 01			06 02			07 34	08 15				09 34		
Wrenbury	d	22e31						06x08			07x41					09x41		
Whitchurch (Shrops)	d	22p38			05 12			06 14			07 49	08 26				09 49		
Prees	d	22e44						06x20			07x55					09x55		
Wem	d	22p48			05 20			06 24			08 01	08 35				10 01		
Yorton	d	22e54						06x29			08x06					10x06		
Shrewsbury	a	23p04			05 32			06 40	07 07	07 46	08 18	08 44		09 16	09 46	10 19	10 46	11 15
	d	23p06		05 19	05 40	06 23		06 45	07 16	07 49		08 49	09 05	09 18	09 49		10 49	11 18
Church Stretton	d	23p22		05 36	05 55			07 00		08 04		09 04	09 22		10 04		11 04	
Craven Arms	d	23p30		05 50	06 03			07 08		08 12		09 12	09 35		10 12		11 12	
Ludlow	d	23p38			06 11	06 49		07 16	07 43	08 20		09 20		09 45	10 20		11 20	11 45
Leominster	d	23p48			06 22	07 00		07 27	07 53	08 31		09 31			10 31		11 31	
Hereford [7]	a	00 03			06 36	07 14		07 45	08 08	08 45		09 45		10 08	10 45		11 45	12 08
	d	00 04	05 42		06 49	07 16	07 22	07 48	08 10	08 48		09 47		10 09	10 48		11 48	12 09
Abergavenny	d	00 27	06 07		07 12	07 39		08 11	08 33	09 11		10 10		10 33	11 11		12 11	12 32
Pontypool and New Inn	d	00 37	06 18		07 22	07 49			08 43			10 20						12 42
Cwmbran	d	00 42	06 23		07 27	07 54		08 24	08 48	09 23		10 24		10 46	11 23		12 23	12 47
Newport (South Wales)	a	00 53	06 34		07 39	08 04		08 34	08 58	09 34		10 34		10 58	11 34		12 34	12 58
Bristol Temple Meads [10]	a																	
Reading [7]	a		*08 02*			*09 33*	10 20	*10 01*		*10 59*		*12 02*			*13 01*		*14 01*	
London Paddington [15] ⊖	a		*08 30*			*10 00*	10 54	*10 31*		*11 31*		*12 32*			*13 36*		*14 30*	
Cardiff Central [7]	a	01 14	06 54	10 17	07 57	08 25		08 51	09 18	09 53		10 54		11 20	11 54		12 54	13 20
Swansea [7]	a		*08 48*	09 07	08 55			09 56	*10 43*	11 01		11 56	13 01	*12 43*	12 56		13 56	*14 42*

For general notes see front of timetable
For details of catering facilities see Directory of Train Operators

- **A** To Milford Haven (Table 128)
- **B** To Carmarthen (Table 128)
- **C** To Barry Island (Table 130)
- **b** Change at Chester and Crewe
- **c** Fridays arr. 2342
- **e** Previous night.
- **x** Stops on request, passengers wishing to alight must inform the guard and those wishing to join must give a hand signal to the driver

Table 131

Saturdays

Manchester, Liverpool and Crewe → Cardiff

Route Diagram - see first page of Table 129

		AW	AW	GW	GW	AW	AW	AW	AW	AW	GW	AW	AW	AW	AW	AW	AW
								R				R		R	R		R
		◇		1 ◇	1 ◇	◇	◇		◇		1 ◇		◇				
		A		B	C	D		A				D		E	G		D
		🛒		☕	☕	🛒	🛒	🛒			☕	🛒	🛒	🛒	🛒		🛒
Manchester Piccadilly 10 ⛴	d	10 34				11 34		12 34				13 34		14 34	14 34		15 34
Stockport	d	10 43				11 42		12 42				13 42		14 42	14 42		15 42
Wilmslow	d	10 51				11 51		12 51				13 54		14 51	14 51		15 51
Liverpool Lime Street 10	d													14 15			
Runcorn	d													14 31			
Holyhead	d					09 50	10 30					11 40	12 35				13 35
Bangor (Gwynedd)	d					10 18	11 03					12 19	13 04				14 14
Llandudno Junction	d					10 36	11 26					12 42	13 27				14 37
Chester	d	10 29				11 28	12 20	12 29				13 33	14 20	14 30	14 49		15 30
Crewe 10	d	11 18	11 26			12 18		13 18		13 26		14 18		15 18	15 18	15 26	16 15
Nantwich	d		11 34							13 34						15 34	16 23
Wrenbury	d		11x41							13x41						15x41	
Whitchurch (Shrops)	d		11 49							13 49						15 49	16 33
Prees	d		11x55							13x55						15x55	
Wem	d		12 01							14 01						16 01	16 41
Yorton	d		12x06							14x06						16x06	
Shrewsbury	a	11 46	12 19			12 46	13 15	13 46		14 19		14 46	15 15	15 46	15 46	16 19	16 54
	d	11 49				12 49	13 18	13 49	14 05			14 49	15 18	15 49	15 49		16 55
Church Stretton	d	12 04				13 04		14 04	14 23			15 04		16 04	16 04		17 10
Craven Arms	d	12 12				13 12		14 12	14 36			15 12		16 12	16 12		17 18
Ludlow	d	12 20				13 20	13 45	14 20				15 20	15 45	16 20	16 20		17 26
Leominster	d	12 31				13 31		14 31				15 31		16 31	16 31		17 36
Hereford 7	a	12 45				13 45	14 08	14 45				15 45	16 08	16 45	16 45		17 51
	d	12 48		13 20	13 20	13 48	14 09	14 48			15 23	15 48	16 09	16 48	16 48		17 53
Abergavenny	d	13 11				14 11	14 32	15 11				16 11	16 32	17 11	17 11		18 16
Pontypool and New Inn	d						14 42						16 42				
Cwmbran	d	13 23				14 23	14 47	15 23				16 23	16 47	17 23	17 23		18 29
Newport (South Wales)	a	13 34				14 34	14 58	15 34				16 34	16 58	17 34	17 34		18 39
Bristol Temple Meads 10	a													18 18			
Reading 7	a			16 25	16 28	16 01		17 01			18 25	18 01		19 01	19 01		
London Paddington 15	⊖ a			16 58	17 06	16 30		17 31			18 58	18 29		19 31	19 31		
Cardiff Central 7	a	13 53				14 54	15 20	15 53				16 54	17 20	17 54	17 55		18 54
Swansea 7	a	14 56				15 56	16 43	16 56	18 06			18 06	18 44	18 56	18 56		19 56

		AW	AW	AW	AW	AW	AW	AW	GW	AW	AW	AW	AW	AW	AW	AW	AW
			R			R	R										
		◇		◇				◇	1 ◇	◇	◇		◇	◇	◇		
			A			H	J			K	L					C	B
		🛒	🛒			🛒	🛒	🛒	☕	🛒	🛒		🛒				
Manchester Piccadilly 10 ⛴	d		16 34			17 34	17 34			18 34	18 34		19 34	20 34	21 34	22 34	22 34
Stockport	d		16 43			17 42	17 42			18 43	18 43		19 42	20 46	21 45	22 42	22 43
Wilmslow	d		16 51			17 51	17 51			18 51	18 53		19 54	20 54	21 54	22 50	22 51
Liverpool Lime Street 10	d						17 15				18 15						
Runcorn	d						17 31				18 31						
Holyhead	d	14 35				15 39	15 39	16 35					17 35	18e35	19 35	20e35	20e35
Bangor (Gwynedd)	d	15 04				16 17	16 17	17 04					18 14	19e14	20 14	21e03	21e03
Llandudno Junction	d	15 27				16 40	16 40	17 27					18 37	19e32	20 37	21e28	21e28
Chester	d	16 20				17 31	17 31	18 20		18 30	18 30		19 34	20 30	21 33	22 33	22 33
Crewe 10	d		17 18		17 26	18 18	18 18			19 18	19 18	19 28	20 18	21 18	22 18	23 16	23 16
Nantwich	d				17 34	18 25	18 25					19 34		21 25	22 25	23 23	23 23
Wrenbury	d				17x41							19x41		21x32	22x31	23x30	23x30
Whitchurch (Shrops)	d				17 49	18 36	18 36					19 49		21 39	22 38	23 38	23 38
Prees	d				17x55							19x55		21x45	22x44	23x44	23x44
Wem	d				18 01	18 45	18 45					20 01		21 50	22 48	23 50	23 50
Yorton	d				18x06							20x06		21x56	22x54	23x55	23x55
Shrewsbury	a	17 15	17 46		18 19	18 54	18 57	19 15		19 46	19 46	20 19	20 46	22 04	23 04	00 07	00 07
	d	17 18	17 49	18 05		18 56	18 59	19 18		19 49	19 49		20 49	22 07	23 06		
Church Stretton	d		18 04	18 23		19 11	19 14			20 04	20 04		21 04	22 22	23 22		
Craven Arms	d		18 12	18 35		19 22	19 22			20 12	20 12		21 12	22 30	23 30		
Ludlow	d	17 47	18 20			19 30	19 30	19 45		20 20	20 20		21 20	22 38	23 38		
Leominster	d		18 31			19 41	19 41			20 31	20 31		21 31	22 49	23 48		
Hereford 7	a	18 10	18 45			19 55	19 55	20 08		20 45	20 45		21 45	23 03	00 03		
	d	18 11	18 48			19 57	19 57	20 09	20 22	20 48	20 48		21 48	23 05	00 04		
Abergavenny	d	18 34	19 13			20 20	20 20	20 33		21 11	21 11		22 11	23 28	00 27		
Pontypool and New Inn	d	18 44						20 42					22 21		00 37		
Cwmbran	d	18 48	19 25			20 32	20 32	20 47		21 23	21 23		22 23	23 40	00 42		
Newport (South Wales)	a	19 00	19 40			20 45	20 45	20 59		21 35	21 35		22 40	23 52	00 53		
Bristol Temple Meads 10	a										23 00						
Reading 7	a		21 58						23 28								
London Paddington 15	⊖ a		22 31						00 09								
Cardiff Central 7	a	19 22	19 58			21 01	21 01	21 20		22 00	22 00		23 01	00 17	01 19		
Swansea 7	a	20 44	21 47	22 13		22 03	22 03	22 46		23 00	23 00						

For general notes see front of timetable
For details of catering facilities see Directory of Train Operators

- **A** To Milford Haven (Table 128)
- **B** From 13 September
- **C** Until 6 September
- **D** To Carmarthen (Table 128)
- **E** Until 6 September. To Milford Haven (Table 128)
- **G** From 13 September. To Milford Haven (Table 128)
- **H** From 13 September. To Haverfordwest (Table 128)
- **J** Until 6 September. To Haverfordwest (Table 128)
- **K** From 13 September. To Carmarthen (Table 128)
- **L** Until 6 September. To Carmarthen (Table 128)
- **c** Until 6 September only

Table 131

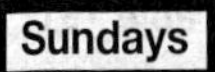

until 13 July

Manchester, Liverpool and Crewe → Cardiff

Route Diagram - see first page of Table 129

		AW	AW	AW	AW	AW	GW	AW	GW	AW	GW	AW	AW	AW	GW	AW	AW	AW	AW	AW	AW	AW
												R		R			R	R	R	R		
		◇			◇	◇	1 ◇	◇	1 ◇	◇	1 ◇		◇		1 ◇						◇	
			🚌	A	B					C		D					C					
Manchester Piccadilly 10	d	21p34			10 04					12 29		14 34		15 39			16 36	17 04		18 40	20 46	22 46
Stockport	d	21p45			10 13					12 40		14 42		15 47			16 44			18 48	20 54	22 54
Wilmslow	d	21p54			10 20					12 55		14 54		15 57			16 54	17 32		18 56	21 02	23 02
Liverpool Lime Street 10	d				09 15					12 18		14 18		15 31			16 18	17 18		18 18	20 18	21 47
Runcorn	d				09 32					12 34		14 34		15 49			16 34	17 38		18 34	20 34	22 05
Holyhead	d							10 35				13 15		13b30				16 32	17 23	17 00	18b40	
Bangor (Gwynedd)	d				07 42			11 04				13 42		13b58			14 41	16 59	17 51	17 27	19b09	20 11
Llandudno Junction	d				08 00			11 22				14 00		14b16			15 04	17 22	18 09	17 45	19b27	20 34
Chester	d				08 57			12 20		12 43		14 46		15 15			16 48	18 21	19 07	18 41	20 23	22 25
Crewe 10	d	22p18			10 50					13 23		15 24		16 21			17 22	19 00		19 20	21 35	23 26
Nantwich	d	22p25			10 57					13 30							17 29			19 26		23 33
Wrenbury	d	22c31			11x03					13x36							17x35			19x32		23x39
Whitchurch (Shrops)	d	22p38			11 10					13 44							17 43			19 39		23 46
Prees	d	22c44			11x15					13x49							17x48			19x44		23x51
Wem	d	22p48			11 20					13 55							17 54			19 49		23 56
Yorton	d	22c54			11x25					13x59							17x58			19x54		00x01
Shrewsbury	a	23p04			11 33			13 13		14 09		15 52		16 54			18 08	19 33	19 56	20 07	22 09	00 13
	d	23p06	07 50		11 45	12 07		13 17		14 10		16 11	16 24	16 57			18 09	19 35	20 13		22 13	
Church Stretton	d	23p22	08 15		12 00	12 24		13 33		14 26		16 26	16 42				18 25		20 28		22 28	
Craven Arms	d	23p30	08 35		12 08	12 36		13 41		14 35		16 34	16 53				18 34		20 36		22 36	
Ludlow	d	23p38	08 55		12 16			13 49		14 43		16 42		17 26			18 42	20 04	20 44		22 44	
Leominster	d	23p48	09 20		12 27			13 59		14 55		16 53					18 54		20 55		22 55	
Hereford 7	a	00 03	09 50		12 41			14 14		15 09		17 07		17 49			19 08	20 27	21 09		23 09	
	d	00 04		10 00	12 44		13 30	14 15	14 30	15 11	16 30	17 09		17 51	18 30	18 44	19 10	20 29	21 11		23 14	
Abergavenny	d	00 27		10 23	13 07			14 38		15 34		17 32		18 14		19 07	19 33	20 52	21 34		23 37	
Pontypool and New Inn	d	00 37		10 34	13 17			14 48		15 44		17 42				19 18	19 44		21 44		23 47	
Cwmbran	d	00 42		10 39	13 22			14 53		15 49		17 47		18 27		19 23	19 49	21 05	21 49		23 52	
Newport (South Wales)	a	00 53		10 54	13 37			15 09		15 59		17 59		18 38		19 36	19 59	21 16	22 01		00 02	
Bristol Temple Meads 10	a																		23e42			
Reading 7	a			13 44	16 29		16 18	17 29	17 18	18 49	19 07	20 50		21 45	21 19		23 23					
London Paddington 15 ⊖	a			14 24	17 10		17 07	18 15	18 08	19 30	19 52	21 30		22 28	22 03		00 05					
Cardiff Central 7	a	01 19		11 15	13 53			15 35		16 15		18 13	21 30	18 55		19 55	20 15	21 37	22 27		00 25	
Swansea 7	a			13 34	14 58	16 13				17 12		19 17	20 13	20 33			21 16		23 26		01 33	

Sundays

20 July to 7 September

		AW	AW	AW	AW	AW	GW	AW	GW	AW	GW	AW	AW	AW	GW	AW	AW	AW	AW	AW	AW	AW
										R		R		R			R	R	R	R		
		◇			◇	◇	1 ◇	◇	1 ◇		1 ◇		◇		1 ◇						◇	
			🚌	A	B					C		D					C					
Manchester Piccadilly 10	d	21p34			09 14					12 33		14 34		15 39			16 36	17 06		18 40	20 46	22 46
Stockport	d	21p45								12 42		14 42		15 47			16 44	16 44		18 48	20 54	22 55
Wilmslow	d	21p54			09 41					12 56		14 54		15 57			16 54	17 28		18 56	21 02	23 03
Liverpool Lime Street 10	d				09 15					12 15		14 15		15 31			16 15	17 25		18 15	20 15	21 47
Runcorn	d				09 32					12 32		14 31		15 49			16 31	17 43		18 31	20 31	22 05
Holyhead	d							10 35				13 15		13b30				16 32	17 23	17 00	18b40	
Bangor (Gwynedd)	d				07 42			11 04				13 42		13b58			14 41	16 59	17 51	17 27	19b09	20 11
Llandudno Junction	d				08 00			11 22				14 00		14b16			15 04	17 22	18 09	17 45	19b27	20 34
Chester	d				08 57			12 20		12 43		14 46		15 15			16 48	18 21	19 06	18 41	20 23	22 25
Crewe 10	d	22p18			10 50					13 23		15 24		16 21			17 22	19 00		19 21	21 35	23 26
Nantwich	d	22p25			10 57					13 30							17 29			19 26		23 33
Wrenbury	d	22c31			11x03					13x36							17x35			19x32		23x39
Whitchurch (Shrops)	d	22p38			11 10					13 44							17 43			19 39		23 46
Prees	d	22c44			11x15					13x49							17x48			19x44		23x51
Wem	d	22p48			11 20					13 55							17 54			19 49		23 56
Yorton	d	22c54			11x25					13x59							17x58			19x54		00x01
Shrewsbury	a	23p04			11 33			13 13		14 09		15 52		16 54			18 08	19 33	19 56	20 07	22 09	00 13
	d	23p06	07 50		11 45	12 07		13 17		14 10		16 11	16 24	16 57			18 09	19 35	20 13		22 13	
Church Stretton	d	23p22	08 15		12 00	12 24		13 33		14 26		16 26	16 42				18 25		20 28		22 28	
Craven Arms	d	23p30	08 35		12 08	12 36		13 41		14 35		16 34	16 53				18 34		20 36		22 36	
Ludlow	d	23p38	08 55		12 16			13 49		14 43		16 42		17 26			18 42	20 04	20 44		22 44	
Leominster	d	23p48	09 20		12 27			13 59		14 55		16 53					18 54		20 55		22 55	
Hereford 7	a	00 03	09 50		12 41			14 14		15 09		17 07		17 49			19 08	20 27	21 09		23 09	
	d	00 04		10 00	12 44		13 30	14 15	14 30	15 11	16 30	17 09		17 51	18 30	18 44	19 10	20 29	21 11		23 14	
Abergavenny	d	00 27		10 23	13 07			14 38		15 33		17 32		18 14		19 07	19 33	20 52	21 34		23 37	
Pontypool and New Inn	d	00 37		10 34	13 17			14 48		15 44		17 42				19 18	19 44		21 44		23 47	
Cwmbran	d	00 42		10 39	13 22			14 53		15 49		17 47		18 27		19 23	19 49	21 05	21 49		23 52	
Newport (South Wales)	a	00 53		10 54	13 37			15 09		15 59		17 59		18 38		19 36	19 59	21 16	22 01		00 02	
Bristol Temple Meads 10	a																		23e42			
Reading 7	a			13 44	16 29		16 18	17 29	17 18	18 49	19 07	20 50		21 45	21 19		23 23					
London Paddington 15 ⊖	a			14 24	17 10		17 07	18 15	18 08	19 30	19 52	21 30		22 28	22 03		00 05					
Cardiff Central 7	a	01 19		11 15	13 53			15 35		16 15		18 13	21 30	18 55		19 55	20 15	21 37	22 27		00 25	
Swansea 7	a			13 34	14 58	16 13				17 12		19 17	20 13	20 33			21 16		23 26		01 33	

For general notes see front of timetable
For details of catering facilities see Directory of Train Operators

A To Barry Island (Table 130)
B To Carmarthen (Table 128)
C To Milford Haven (Table 128)
D To Pembroke Dock and Millford Haven (Table 128)
b Change at Chester and Crewe
c Previous night.
Stops on request, passengers wishing to alight must inform the guard and those wishing to join must give a hand signal to the driver
e By bus

Sundays

from 14 September

Manchester, Liverpool and Crewe → Cardiff

Route Diagram - see first page of Table 129

		AW	AW	AW	AW	AW	GW	AW	GW	AW	AW	GW	AW	AW	AW	AW	GW	AW	AW	AW	AW	AW	AW	AW	AW
										R			R		R				R	R	R	R			
		◇	🚌	◇	◇	◇	1 ◇	◇	1 ◇			1 ◇		◇			1 ◇							◇	
				A	B					C			D						C						
					🍴		☕	🍴	☕	🍴		☕	🍴		🍴		☕		🍴	🍴	🍴	🍴			
Manchester Piccadilly 10 🚢	d	21p34								12 33			14 34		15 48				16 36			18 40		20 46	22 46
Stockport	d	21p45								12 42			14 42		15 59				16 44			18 49		20 54	22 54
Wilmslow	d	21p54								12 56			14 54		16 08				16 54			18 57		21 02	23 02
Liverpool Lime Street 10	d																								
Runcorn	d																								
Holyhead	d							10b17							13c30					16 21	17 23			18c40	
Bangor (Gwynedd)	d							10b47					13 00		13c58					16 50	17 51			19c09	19c55
Llandudno Junction	d							11 22					13 23		14c16					17 10	18 09			19c27	20c18
Chester	d				09 55			12 20		12 25			14 19		15 25				16 25	18 25	19 06	18 35		20 55	22 25
Crewe 10	d	22p18			10 50					13 23	14 05		15 24		16 32	16 44			17 22	19 00		19 18	20 25	21 35	23 26
Nantwich	d	22p25			10 57					13 30									17 29			19 26			23 33
Wrenbury	d	22e31			11x03					13x36									17x35			19x32			23x39
Whitchurch (Shrops)	d	22p38			11 10					13 44									17 43			19 39			23 46
Prees	d	22e44			11x15					13x49									17x48			19x44			23x51
Wem	d	22p48			11 20					13 55									17 54			19 49			23 56
Yorton	d	22e54			11x25					13x59									17x58			19x54			00x01
Shrewsbury	a	23p04			11 33			13 13		14 09	14 33		15 52		17 05	17 12			18 08	19 33	19 56	20 07	20 53	22 09	00 13
	d	23p06	07 50		11 45	12 07		13 17		14 10			16 11	16 24	17 08				18 09	19 35	20 13			22 13	
Church Stretton	d	23p22	08 15		12 00	12 24		13 33		14 26			16 25	16 42					18 25		20 28			22 28	
Craven Arms	d	23p30	08 35		12 08	12 36		13 41		14 35			16 34	16 53					18 34		20 36			22 36	
Ludlow	d	23p38	08 55		12 16			13 49		14 43			16 42		17 37				18 42	20 04	20 44			22 44	
Leominster	d	23p48	09 20		12 27			13 59		14 55			16 53						18 54		20 55			22 55	
Hereford 7	a	00 03	09 50		12 41			14 14		15 09			17 07		18 00				19 08	20 27	21 09			23 09	
	d	00 04		10 11	12 44		13 30	14 15	14 30	15 11		16 30	17 09		18 02		18 30	18 35	19 10	20 29	21 11			23 14	
Abergavenny	d	00 27		10 34	13 07			14 38		15 34			17 32		18 25			18 58	19 33	20 52	21 34			23 37	
Pontypool and New Inn	d	00 37		10 45	13 17			14 48		15 44			17 42					19 08	19 44		21 44			23 47	
Cwmbran	d	00 42		10 50	13 22			14 54		15 49			17 47		18 38			19 13	19 49	21 05	21 49			23 52	
Newport (South Wales)	a	00 53		11 00	13 37			15 09		15 59			17 59		18 51			19 25	19 59	21 16	22 01			00 02	
Bristol Temple Meads 10	a																								
Reading 7	a			12 27	15 27		16 18		17 18	17 27		19 07	19 58				21 19	20 57	22 35						
London Paddington 15 ⊖	a			13 05	16 05		17 00		18 06	18 08		19 53	20 42				22 03	21 42	23 15						
Cardiff Central 7	a	01 19		11 17	13 53			15 31		16 15			18 13	21 30	19 08			19 45	20 15	21 37	22 27			00 25	
Swansea 7	a			12 14	14 58	16 13		16 42		17 12			19 12	20 13	20 44				21 16	22 44	23 26				

For general notes see front of timetable
For details of catering facilities see Directory of Train Operators

A To Fishguard Harbour (Table 128)
B To Carmarthen (Table 128)
C To Milford Haven (Table 128)
D To Pembroke Dock and Milford Haven (Table 128)
b By bus
c Change at Chester and Crewe
e Previous night.
Stops on request, passengers wishing to alight must inform the guard and those wishing to join must give a hand signal to the driver

Network Diagram for Tables 132, 133 ,134

DM-26/05
Design BAJS

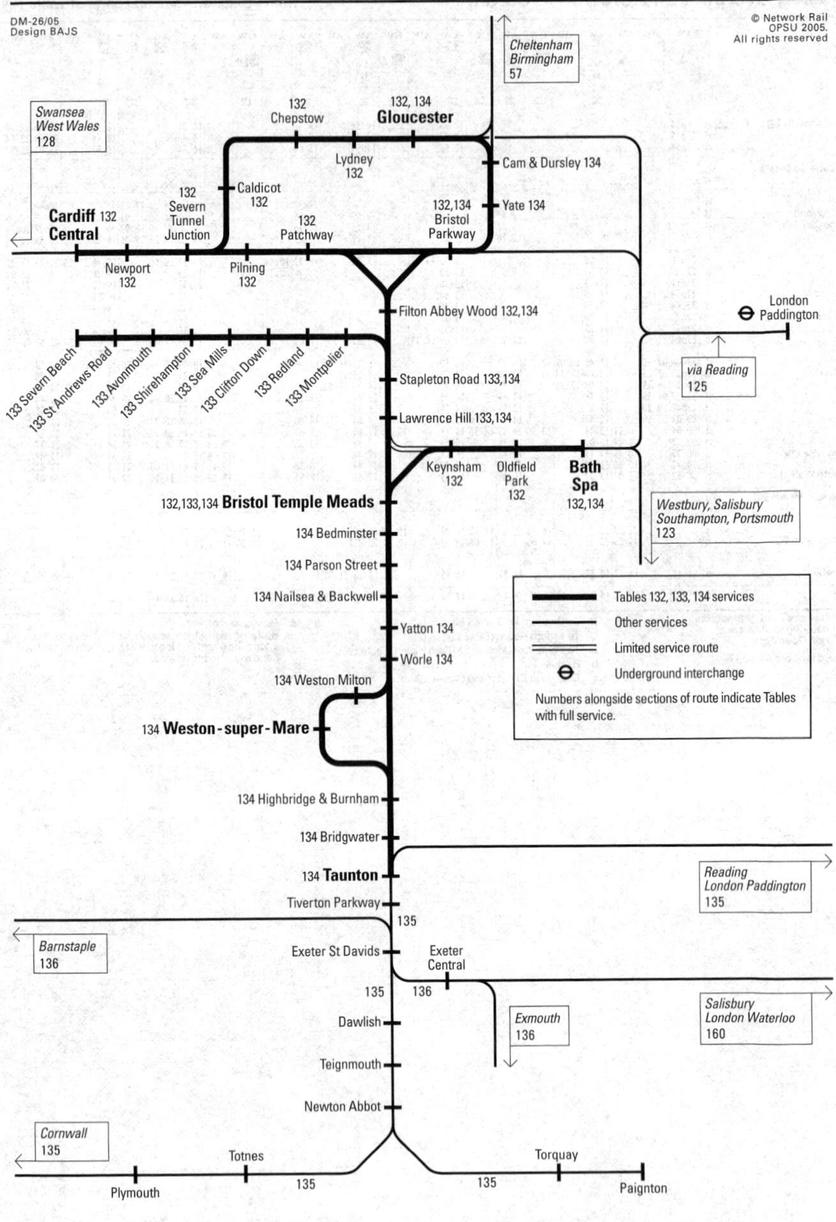
Cheltenham
Birmingham
57
Swansea
West Wales
128
132
Chepstow
132, 134
Gloucester
Lydney
132
Cam & Dursley 134
Caldicot
132
132
Severn
Tunnel
Junction
Yate 134
132,134
Bristol
Parkway
Cardiff 132
Central
132
Patchway
Newport
132
Pilning
132
Filton Abbey Wood 132,134
London
Paddington
133 Severn Beach
133 St Andrews Road
133 Avonmouth
133 Shirehampton
133 Sea Mills
133 Clifton Down
133 Redland
133 Montpelier
Stapleton Road 133,134
via Reading
125
Lawrence Hill 133,134
Keynsham
132
Oldfield
Park
132
Bath
Spa
132,134
132,133,134 Bristol Temple Meads
Westbury, Salisbury
Southampton, Portsmouth
123
134 Bedminster
134 Parson Street
134 Nailsea & Backwell
Yatton 134
Worle 134
134 Weston Milton
134 Weston-super-Mare
Tables 132, 133, 134 services
Other services
Limited service route
Underground interchange
Numbers alongside sections of route indicate Tables with full service.
134 Highbridge & Burnham
134 Bridgwater
134 Taunton
Reading
London Paddington
135
Tiverton Parkway
135
Barnstaple
136
Exeter St Davids
Exeter
Central
135
136
Exmouth
136
Salisbury
London Waterloo
160
Dawlish
Teignmouth
Newton Abbot
Cornwall
135
Totnes
Torquay
Plymouth
135
135
Paignton

Cardiff → Gloucester, Bristol and Bath Spa

Network Diagram - see first page of Table 132

Miles	Miles	Miles			AW	AW	AW	AW	GW	GW	GW	GW	AW		GW	GW	GW	GW	GW	AW	GW	GW	GW		AW	GW
					MX	MX	◇	◇	■1 ◇	◇	◇	■1 ◇	◇		■1 ◇	■1 ◇	■1 ◇	■1 ◇			■1 ◇	■1 ◇	◇		◇	■1 ◇
					A													B		C			D			E
								🛒	☕	🛒		🛒	🛒		☕	⊠	☕	☕			⊠	☕	🛒		🛒	⊠
0	0	0	**Cardiff Central 7**	d	23p20	00 30	04 00	05 10				05 15	05 35			05 54				06 12	06 20		06 25		06 50	
11¾	11¾	11¾	Newport (South Wales)	a	23p37	00 48	04 16	05 26				05 32	05 51			06 07				06 25	06 33		06 38		07 02	
—	—	—		d	23p39							05 33				06 08				06 27	06 34		06 39			
21¾	21¾	21¾	Severn Tunnel Jn	d	23p57															06 38			06 50			
—	—	22½	Caldicot	d	23p59															06 40						
—	—	29¾	Chepstow	d	00 08															06 49						
—	—	37	Lydney	d	00 17															06 58						
—	—	56½	**Gloucester 7**	a	00 38															07 20						
28¾	28¾	—	Pilning	d																						
32¼	32¼	—	Patchway	d																			07 03			
—	33½	—	**Bristol Parkway 7**	a								06 00				06 29					06 55					
—	—	—		d																						
33¾	—	—	Filton Abbey Wood	d																			07 09			
38¼	—	—	**Bristol Temple Meads 10**	a																			07 18			
—	—	—		d					05 30	05 44	05 50				06 00		06 30	06 40	06 44			07 00	07 22			07 30
42¾	—	—	Keynsham	d						05 51	05 57							⌇	06 51							
48¾	—	—	Oldfield Park	d						05 58	06 04							⌇	06 58							
49¾	—	—	**Bath Spa 7**	a					05 41	05 59	06 06				06 11		06 41	06 51	07 00			07 11	07 35			07 41

		GW	GW	XC	AW	AW	GW	GW	GW	GW		GW	XC	AW	GW	GW	SW	GW	GW	GW		GW	GW	GW	XC	AW
			■1 ◇	■1 ◇		◇	■1 ◇	■1 ◇		◇		■1 ◇	◇	◇	◇	■1 ◇	■1 ◇		■1 ◇	■1 ◇			◇	■1 ◇	◇	◇
		G		H	C		J		K						L		N	Q								
			☕	☕			✕	⊠		🛒		☕	🛒	🛒		☕			☕	☕			🛒	☕	🛒	🛒
Cardiff Central 7	d		06 55	07 00	07 12	07 20	07 25			07 30			07 45	07 50		07 55		08 00		08 25			08 30		08 45	08 50
Newport (South Wales)	a		07 08	07 13	07 25	07 32	07 38			07 43			07 57	08 03		08 08		08 13		08 38			08 43		08 58	09 03
	d		07 09	07 15	07 27		07 39			07 44			07 59			08 09		08 15		08 39			08 44		08 59	
Severn Tunnel Jn	d			07 25	07 38					07 55								08 25								
Caldicot	d				07 40																					
Chepstow	d				07 49																					
Lydney	d				07 58																					
Gloucester 7	a				08 20								08 43												09 43	
Pilning	d																									
Patchway	d			07 39														08 39								
Bristol Parkway 7	a		07 30				08 00									08 30				09 00						
	d	07 25													08 24											
Filton Abbey Wood	d	07 28		07 47						08 09					08 27			08 42					09 09			
Bristol Temple Meads 10	a	07 40		07 53						08 18					08 36			08 52					09 18			
	d	07 49						08 00	08 13	08 22		08 30			08 40		08 50		09 00			09 09	09 22	09 30		
Keynsham	d	07 56							08 20						08 47		08 57					09 16				
Oldfield Park	d	08 03							08 27						08 54							09 23				
Bath Spa 7	a	08 05						08 11	08 29	08 35		08 41			08 56		09 04		09 11			09 25	09 34	09 41		

		GW	GW	GW	GW	AW	AW		GW	GW	GW	XC	AW	GW	GW	GW	GW		AW	GW	GW	GW	XC	AW	GW	GW
		◇	■1 ◇		■1 ◇		◇		■1 ◇	◇	■1 ◇	◇	◇		■1 ◇		■1 ◇			■1 ◇	◇	■1 ◇	◇	◇	◇	■1 ◇
		U		V		C								X		V			A						U	
			⊠		☕		🛒		⊠	🛒	☕	🛒	🛒		☕		☕			☕	🛒	☕	🛒	🛒		☕
Cardiff Central 7	d		08 55	09 00		09 12	09 20		09 25	09 30		09 45	09 50		09 55	10 00			10 12	10 25	10 30		10 45	10 50		10 55
Newport (South Wales)	a		09 08	09 13		09 25	09 32		09 38	09 43		09 58	10 03		10 08	10 13			10 25	10 38	10 43		10 58	11 03		11 08
	d		09 09	09 15		09 27			09 39	09 44		09 59			10 09	10 15			10 27	10 39	10 44		10 59			11 09
Severn Tunnel Jn	d			09 25		09 38										10 25			10 38							
Caldicot	d					09 40													10 40							
Chepstow	d					09 49													10 49							
Lydney	d					09 58													10 58							
Gloucester 7	a					10 20						10 43							11 20				11 43			
Pilning	d																									
Patchway	d			09 39												10 39										
Bristol Parkway 7	a		09 30						10 00						10 30					11 00						11 30
	d	09 19												10 19											11 19	
Filton Abbey Wood	d	09 22		09 42						10 09				10 22		10 42					11 09				11 22	
Bristol Temple Meads 10	a	09 35		09 52						10 18				10 34		10 52					11 18				11 35	
	d	09 49			10 00					10 22	10 30			10 49			11 00				11 22	11 30			11 49	
Keynsham	d	09 56												10 56											11 56	
Oldfield Park	d	10 03												11 03											12 03	
Bath Spa 7	a	10 05			10 11					10 35	10 41			11 05			11 11				11 35	11 41			12 05	

For general notes see front of timetable
For details of catering facilities see Directory of Train Operators

- **A** From Maesteg (Table 128) to Cheltenham Spa (Table 57)
- **B** Until 27 June and from 8 September
- **C** To Cheltenham Spa (Table 57)
- **D** To Portsmouth Harbour (Table 123)
- **E** **The Bristolian**
- **G** To Westbury (Table 123)
- **H** Until 5 September to Newcastle, from 8 September to Edinburgh (Table 51)
- **J** **The Red Dragon**
- **K** To Swindon (Table 125)
- **L** From Worcester Shrub Hill (Table 57) to Weymouth (Table 123)
- **N** To London Waterloo (Table 160)
- **Q** To Weston-super-Mare (Table 134)
- **U** From Gloucester (Table 134) to Weymouth (Table 123)
- **V** To Taunton (Table 134)
- **X** From Great Malvern (Table 71) to Westbury (Table 123)

Cardiff → Gloucester, Bristol and Bath Spa

Network Diagram - see first page of Table 132

		GW	AW	GW		GW	GW	GW	XC	AW	GW	GW	GW	GW		AW	GW	SW	GW	GW	XC	AW	GW	GW		GW
			◇	1 ◇		1 ◇	◇	1 ◇	◇	◇	◇	1 ◇		1 ◇		◇	1 ◇	1 ◇	◇	1 ◇	◇	◇		1 ◇		
		A									B		A			C	D						E			A
			⊥	⊡		⊡	⊥	⊥	⊥	⊥		⊡		⊥			⊠		⊥	⊥	⊥	⊥		⊡		
Cardiff Central 7	d	11 00	11 20			11 25	11 30		11 45	11 50		11 55	12 00			12 12	12 25		12 30		12 45	12 50		12 55		13 00
Newport (South Wales)	a	11 13	11 32			11 38	11 43		11 58	12 03		12 08	12 13			12 25	12 38		12 43		12 58	13 03		13 08		13 13
	d	11 15				11 39	11 44		11 59			12 09	12 15			12 27	12 39		12 44		12 59			13 09		13 15
Severn Tunnel Jn	d	11 25											12 25			12 38										13 25
Caldicot	d															12 40										
Chepstow	d															12 49										
Lydney	d															12 58										
Gloucester 7	a								12 45							13 20					13 45					
Pilning	d																									
Patchway	d	11 39											12 39													13 39
Bristol Parkway 7	a					12 00						12 30					13 00							13 30		
	d										12 19												13 19			
Filton Abbey Wood	d	11 42					12 09				12 22		12 42						13 09				13 22			13 42
Bristol Temple Meads 10	a	11 52					12 18				12 35		12 52						13 17				13 36			13 52
	d			12 00			12 22	12 30			12 39			13 00				13 10	13 22	13 30			13 49			
Keynsham	d										12 46												13 56			
Oldfield Park	d										12 53												14 03			
Bath Spa 7	a			12 11			12 35	12 41			12 56			13 11				13 21	13 35	13 41			14 05			

		GW	AW	AW	GW	GW	GW	XC	AW	GW		GW	GW	GW	GW	GW	GW	XC	AW	GW		GW	GW	SW	GW	AW
																			R							
		1 ◇		◇	1 ◇	◇	1 ◇	◇	◇	◇		1 ◇		1 ◇	1 ◇	◇	1 ◇	◇				1 ◇		1 ◇	1 ◇	
			C							G			A							E			A			C
		⊥		⊥	⊡	⊥	⊡	⊥	⊥			⊡		⊡	⊡	⊥	⊡	⊥	⊥			⊡			⊡	
Cardiff Central 7	d		13 12	13 20	13 25	13 30		13 45	13 50			13 55	14 00		14 25	14 30		14 45	14 50			14 55	15 00			15 12
Newport (South Wales)	a		13 25	13 32	13 38	13 43		13 58	14 03			14 08	14 13		14 38	14 43		14 58	15 03			15 08	15 13			15 25
	d		13 27		13 39	13 44		13 59				14 09	14 15		14 39	14 44		14 59				15 09	15 15			15 27
Severn Tunnel Jn	d		13 39										14 25										15 25			15 38
Caldicot	d		13 41																							15 40
Chepstow	d		13 50																							15 49
Lydney	d		13 59																							15 58
Gloucester 7	a		14 20					14 45										15 45								16 21
Pilning	d																									
Patchway	d												14 39										15 39			
Bristol Parkway 7	a				14 00							14 30			15 00							15 30				
	d									14 19										15 19						
Filton Abbey Wood	d					14 09				14 22			14 42			15 09				15 22			15 42			
Bristol Temple Meads 10	a					14 19				14 34			14 52			15 18				15 36			15 51			
	d	14 00				14 22	14 30			14 49				15 00		15 22	15 30			15 43				15 52	16 00	
Keynsham	d									14 56										15 50						
Oldfield Park	d									15 03										15 57						
Bath Spa 7	a	14 11				14 35	14 41			15 05				15 11		15 35	15 41			15 59				16 05	16 11	

		AW	GW	GW	XC	AW	GW		GW	GW	GW	AW	GW	GW	AW	GW	GW		GW	XC	AW	GW	GW	GW	GW	GW
						R															R					
		◇	1 ◇	◇	◇		1 ◇		◇	1 ◇			1 ◇			1 ◇	◇		1 ◇	◇		◇	1 ◇		1 ◇	
									G		A			H	C							J		A		H
		⊥	⊡	⊥		⊥	⊡			⊡			⊡			⊡	⊥		⊡		⊥		⊡		⊡	
Cardiff Central 7	d	15 20	15 25	15 30	15 45	15 50				15 55	16 00	16 06			16 12	16 25	16 30			16 45	16 50		16 55	17 00		
Newport (South Wales)	a	15 32	15 38	15 43	15 58	16 03				16 08	16 13	16 21			16 25	16 38	16 43			16 58	17 03		17 08	17 13		
	d		15 39	15 44	15 59					16 09	16 15				16 27	16 39	16 44			16 59			17 09	17 15		
Severn Tunnel Jn	d										16 25				16 39		16 55							17 25		
Caldicot	d														16 41											
Chepstow	d														16 50											
Lydney	d														16 59											
Gloucester 7	a				16 44										17 21					17 45						
Pilning	d																									
Patchway	d										16 39													17 39		
Bristol Parkway 7	a		16 00							16 30						17 00							17 30			
	d								16 19					16 46								17 19				17 46
Filton Abbey Wood	d			16 09					16 22		16 42			16 49			17 09					17 22		17 42		17 49
Bristol Temple Meads 10	a			16 18					16 34		16 51			17 02			17 18					17 36		17 52		18 02
	d			16 22			16 30		16 49				17 00	17 07			17 22		17 30			17 49			18 00	18 07
Keynsham	d								16 56					17 14								17 56				18 14
Oldfield Park	d								17 03					17 21			17 32					18 03				18 21
Bath Spa 7	a			16 35			16 41		17 05				17 11	17 24			17 35		17 41			18 05			18 11	18 24

For general notes see front of timetable
For details of catering facilities see Directory of Train Operators

A To Taunton (Table 134)
B From Great Malvern (Table 71) to Brighton (Table 123)
C From Maesteg (Table 128) to Cheltenham Spa (Table 57)
D **The St David**
E From Gloucester (Table 134) to Westbury (Table 123)
G From Great Malvern (Table 71) to Weymouth (Table 123)
H To Westbury (Table 123)
J From Gloucester (Table 134) to Weymouth (Table 123)

Cardiff → Gloucester, Bristol and Bath Spa

Network Diagram - see first page of Table 132

		AW	AW	GW		GW	GW	XC	AW	GW	GW	GW	AW	GW		GW	GW	XC	AW	GW	GW	GW	GW	AW		GW
			R	1 ◇		◇	1 ◇	◇	R		1 ◇			1 ◇		◇	1 ◇	◇	◇			1 ◇	◇	◇		1 ◇
		A								B		C	A							D	C					
			🛒	☕		🛒	☕		🛒		☕			☕		🛒	☕		🛒			☕	🛒			☕
Cardiff Central [7]	d	17 12	17 20	17 25		17 30		17 45	17 50		17 55	18 00	18 12	18 25		18 30		18 45	18 50		19 00	19 25	19 30	19 34		
Newport (South Wales)	a	17 27	17 32	17 38		17 43		17 58	18 03		18 08	18 13	18 25	18 38		18 42		18 58	19 05		19 13	19 38	19 43	19 47		
	d	17 27		17 39		17 44		17 59			18 09	18 15	18 27	18 39		18 44		18 59			19 15	19 39	19 44			
Severn Tunnel Jn	d	17 38				17 55						18 25	18 38			18 54					19 25					
Caldicot	d	17 40											18 40													
Chepstow	d	17 49											18 49													
Lydney	d	17 58											18 58													
Gloucester [7]	a	18 20						18 44					19 20					19 46								
Pilning	d																									
Patchway	d											18 39									19 39					
Bristol Parkway [7]	a			18 00							18 30			19 00								20 00				
	d									18 19										19 19						
Filton Abbey Wood	d					18 09				18 22		18 42				19 09				19 22	19 42		20 09			
Bristol Temple Meads [10]	a					18 18				18 37		18 52				19 18				19 35	19 52		20 18			
	d					18 22	18 30			18 49						19 22	19 30			19 49			20 22			20 30
Keynsham	d									18 56										19 56						
Oldfield Park	d									19 03										20 03						
Bath Spa [7]	a					18 34	18 41			19 06						19 35	19 41			20 05			20 35			20 41

		GW	GW	XC	AW	AW	GW	GW	XC	AW		GW	GW	AW	GW	AW	SW	GW	GW	GW		GW	AW			
		◇		◇	◇		1 ◇	◇	◇	◇		1 ◇			1 ◇	◇	1	1 ◇								
		E	C			A							G	A					C				A			
							☕	🛒				☕			☕			🛒								
Cardiff Central [7]	d		19 55	20 00	20 10	20 15	20 25	20 30	20 50	20 53			21 00	21 14	21 25	21 56			22 00			23 00	23 20			
Newport (South Wales)	a		20 08	20 13	20 22	20 28	20 38	20 43	21 02	21 08			21 12	21 27	21 38	22 13			22 14			23 15	23 37			
	d		20 10	20 15		20 30	20 39	20 44	21 04				21 14	21 29	21 39				22 17			23 16	23 39			
Severn Tunnel Jn	d		20 21			20 41							21 24	21 40					22 32			23 32	23 57			
Caldicot	d					20 43								21 42									23 59			
Chepstow	d					20 52								21 51									00 08			
Lydney	d					21 01								22 01									00 17			
Gloucester [7]	a			20 56		21 22			21 46					22 22									00 38			
Pilning	d																									
Patchway	d		20 35										21 37						22 48			23 46				
Bristol Parkway [7]	a						21 00								22 00											
	d	20 19																								
Filton Abbey Wood	d	20 22	20 38					21 09					21 41						22 52			23 50				
Bristol Temple Meads [10]	a	20 34	20 48					21 18					21 53						23 03			00 04				
	d	20 49						21 22				21 40	22 00				22 25	22 33		23 16						
Keynsham	d	20 56											22 08							23 23						
Oldfield Park	d	21 03											22 15							23 29						
Bath Spa [7]	a	21 05						21 35				21 55	22 17				22 36	22 44		23 32						

Saturdays

until 6 September

		AW	AW	AW	GW	GW	GW	GW	AW	AW	GW	GW		GW	GW	AW	GW	GW	AW	GW	GW	GW	GW	GW		AW
				◇	1 ◇	◇	◇	1 ◇	◇	◇	1 ◇	1 ◇			1 ◇		1 ◇	◇	◇	1 ◇	1 ◇			1 ◇		
		A						H								J							K			J
					☕			☕	🛒	🛒	☕	☕			☕		☕		🛒	☕	☕			☕		
Cardiff Central [7]	d	23p20	00 30	04 00				04 54	05 10	05 35		05 55				06 12	06 25	06 30	06 50		06 55		07 00			07 12
Newport (South Wales)	a	23p37	00 48	04 16				05 08	05 23	05 51		06 08				06 25	06 38	06 43	07 02		07 08		07 13			07 25
	d	23p39						05 08				06 09				06 27	06 39	06 44			07 09		07 15			07 27
Severn Tunnel Jn	d	23p57														06 38		06 55					07 25			07 38
Caldicot	d	23p59														06 40										07 40
Chepstow	d	00 08														06 49										07 49
Lydney	d	00 17														06 58										07 58
Gloucester [7]	a	00 38														07 20										08 21
Pilning	d																									
Patchway	d																						07 39			
Bristol Parkway [7]	a							05 36				06 30					07 00				07 30					
	d							05 41																		
Filton Abbey Wood	d																	07 09					07 42			
Bristol Temple Meads [10]	a							05 52										07 18					07 52			
	d				05 30	05 45	05 50	06 00			06 30			06 43	07 00			07 22		07 30		07 49		08 00		
Keynsham	d					05 52	05 57							06 50								07 56				
Oldfield Park	d					05 59	06 04							06 56								08 02				
Bath Spa [7]	a				05 41	06 01	06 06	06 11			06 41			06 59	07 11			07 35		07 41		08 05		08 11		

For general notes see front of timetable
For details of catering facilities see Directory of Train Operators

- **A** From Maesteg (Table 128) to Cheltenham Spa (Table 57)
- **B** From Cheltenham Spa (Table 57) to Westbury (Table 123)
- **C** To Taunton (Table 134)
- **D** From Gloucester (Table 134) to Frome (Table 123)
- **E** From Great Malvern (Table 71) to Weymouth (Table 123)
- **G** To Westbury (Table 123)
- **H** From Swansea (Table 125)
- **J** To Cheltenham Spa (Table 57)
- **K** To Weston-super-Mare (Table 134)

Due to Engineering Operations, services from Saturday 13 September on this Table had not been confirmed at time of going to press. These services will be issued in a special Supplement as soon as exact timings have been confirmed

Table 132

Saturdays

until 6 September

Cardiff → Gloucester, Bristol and Bath Spa

Network Diagram - see first page of Table 132

		AW ◇ [trolley]	GW 1◇ [buffet]	GW ◇ [trolley]	GW 1◇ [buffet]	XC ◇	AW ◇ [trolley]	GW A	GW 1◇ [buffet]	SW 1◇ B	GW C	GW 1◇ [buffet]		GW 1◇ [buffet]	GW D	GW ◇ [trolley]	XC ◇	AW ◇ [trolley]	GW 1◇ [buffet]	GW ◇ E	XC 1◇ [buffet]	AW G	AW ◇ [trolley]	GW 1◇ [buffet]		GW 1◇ [buffet]
Cardiff Central 7	d	07 20	07 25	07 30		07 45	07 50		07 55		08 00			08 25		08 30	08 45	08 50			09 00	09 12	09 20	09 25		
Newport (South Wales)	a	07 32	07 38	07 43		07 57	08 02		08 08		08 13			08 38		08 43	08 58	09 02			09 13	09 25	09 32	09 38		
	d		07 39	07 44		07 59			08 09		08 15			08 39		08 44	08 59				09 15	09 27		09 39		
Severn Tunnel Jn	d			07 55							08 25											09 38				
Caldicot	d																					09 40				
Chepstow	d																					09 49				
Lydney	d																					09 58				
Gloucester 7	a					08 45											09 45					10 20				
Pilning	d										08 32															
Patchway	d										08 40															
Bristol Parkway 7	a		08 00						08 30					09 00										10 00		
	d							08 20												09 19						
Filton Abbey Wood	d			08 09				08 23			08 43					09 09				09 23						
Bristol Temple Meads 10	a			08 18				08 34			08 52					09 18				09 35	09 52					
	d			08 22	08 30			08 40		08 50		09 00			09 09	09 22			09 30	09 49						10 00
Keynsham	d							08 47		08 57					09 16					09 56						
Oldfield Park	d							08 54							09 23					10 03						
Bath Spa 7	a			08 35	08 41			08 56		09 04		09 11			09 26	09 35			09 41	10 05						10 11

		GW ◇ [trolley]	GW 1◇ [buffet]	XC ◇	AW ◇ [trolley]	GW H	GW C	GW 1◇ [buffet]	AW J	GW 1◇ [buffet]	GW ◇ [trolley]	GW 1◇ [buffet]		XC ◇	AW ◇ [trolley]	GW ◇ E	GW C	AW ◇ [trolley]	GW 1 [buffet]	GW 1◇ [buffet]	GW ◇ [trolley]	GW 1◇ [buffet]	XC ◇	AW ◇ [trolley]		GW ◇ K
Cardiff Central 7	d	09 30		09 45	09 50		10 00		10 12	10 25	10 30			10 45	10 50		11 00	11 20		11 25	11 30		11 45	11 50		
Newport (South Wales)	a	09 43		09 58	10 03		10 13		10 25	10 38	10 43			10 58	11 03		11 13	11 32		11 38	11 43		11 58	12 03		
	d	09 44		09 59			10 15		10 27	10 39	10 44			10 59			11 15			11 39	11 44		11 59			
Severn Tunnel Jn	d						10 25		10 38								11 25									
Caldicot	d								10 40																	
Chepstow	d								10 49																	
Lydney	d								10 58																	
Gloucester 7	a			10 45					11 21					11 45									12 45			
Pilning	d																									
Patchway	d						10 39										11 39									
Bristol Parkway 7	a									11 00										12 00						
	d					10 22										11 19										12 22
Filton Abbey Wood	d	10 09				10 25	10 42				11 09					11 23	11 42				12 09					12 25
Bristol Temple Meads 10	a	10 18				10 36	10 52				11 18					11 35	11 52				12 18					12 36
	d	10 22	10 30			10 49		11 00			11 22	11 30				11 49			12 00		12 22	12 30				12 40
Keynsham	d					10 56										11 56										12 47
Oldfield Park	d					11 03										12 03										12 54
Bath Spa 7	a	10 35	10 41			11 05		11 11			11 35	11 41				12 05			12 11		12 35	12 41				12 57

		GW C	GW 1◇ [buffet]	AW J	GW 1◇ [buffet]	SW 1◇	GW ◇ [trolley]	GW 1◇ [buffet]	XC ◇	AW ◇ [trolley]	GW L	GW C		GW 1◇ [buffet]	AW J	AW ◇ [trolley]	GW 1 N [restaurant]	GW ◇ [trolley]	GW 1◇ [buffet]	XC ◇	AW ◇ [trolley]	GW ◇ Q [trolley]	GW C	GW 1◇ [buffet]		GW 1◇ [buffet]
Cardiff Central 7	d	12 00		12 12	12 25		12 30		12 45	12 50		13 00			13 12	13 20	13 25	13 30		13 45	13 50		14 00			14 25
Newport (South Wales)	a	12 13		12 25	12 38		12 43		12 58	13 03		13 13			13 25	13 32	13 38	13 43		13 58	14 03		14 13			14 38
	d	12 15		12 27	12 39		12 44		12 59			13 15			13 27		13 39	13 44		13 59			14 15			14 39
Severn Tunnel Jn	d	12 25		12 38								13 26			13 38								14 25			
Caldicot	d			12 40											13 40											
Chepstow	d			12 49											13 49											
Lydney	d			12 58											13 58											
Gloucester 7	a			13 20					13 45						14 20					14 45						
Pilning	d																									
Patchway	d	12 39										13 39											14 39			
Bristol Parkway 7	a				13 00												14 00									15 00
	d										13 19											14 23				
Filton Abbey Wood	d	12 42					13 09				13 23	13 43						14 09				14 27	14 42			
Bristol Temple Meads 10	a	12 52					13 18				13 35	13 52						14 18				14 39	14 52			
	d		13 00			13 10	13 22	13 30			13 49			14 00				14 22	14 30			14 49		15 00		
Keynsham	d										13 56											14 56				
Oldfield Park	d										14 03											15 03				
Bath Spa 7	a		13 11			13 21	13 35	13 41			14 05			14 11				14 35	14 41			15 06		15 11		

For general notes see front of timetable
For details of catering facilities see Directory of Train Operators

- **A** From Worcester Shrub Hill (Table 57) to Weymouth (Table 123)
- **B** To London Waterloo (Table 160)
- **C** To Taunton (Table 134)
- **D** From 5 July
- **E** From Gloucester (Table 134) to Weymouth (Table 123)
- **G** To Cheltenham Spa (Table 57)
- **H** From Great Malvern (Table 71) to Westbury (Table 123)
- **J** From Maesteg (Table 128) to Cheltenham Spa (Table 57)
- **K** From Great Malvern (Table 71) to Brighton (Table 123)
- **L** From Gloucester (Table 134) to Westbury (Table 123)
- **N** **Pembroke Coast Express**
- **Q** From Great Malvern (Table 71) to Weymouth (Table 123)

Due to Engineering Operations, services from Saturday 13 September on this Table had not been confirmed at time of going to press. These services will be issued in a special Supplement as soon as exact timings have been confirmed

Table 132

Saturdays
until 6 September

Cardiff → Gloucester, Bristol and Bath Spa

Network Diagram - see first page of Table 132

		GW	GW	XC	AW	GW	SW	GW	GW	AW	AW	GW		GW	XC	AW	GW	GW	GW	AW	GW	AW	GW	GW		GW
					R											R										
		◇	1◇	◇			1◇		1◇		◇	1◇		◇	◇		1◇	◇			1◇		1◇	◇		1◇
						A		B		C								D	B			C				
		🛒	☕		🛒				☕		🛒	☕		🛒		🛒	☕				☕		☕	🛒		☕
Cardiff Central [7]	d	14 30		14 45	14 50			15 00		15 12	15 20	15 25		15 30	15 45	15 50			16 00	16 06		16 12	16 25	16 30		
Newport (South Wales)	a	14 43		14 58	15 03			15 13		15 25	15 32	15 38		15 43	15 58	16 03			16 13	16 19		16 23	16 38	16 43		
	d	14 44		14 59				15 15		15 27		15 39		15 44	15 59				16 15			16 26	16 39	16 44		
Severn Tunnel Jn	d							15 25		15 38									16 25			16 37		16 55		
Caldicot	d									15 40												16 38				
Chepstow	d									15 49												16 47				
Lydney	d									15 58												16 56				
Gloucester [7]	a			15 45						16 20					16 45							17 20				
Pilning	d																									
Patchway	d							15 39											16 39							
Bristol Parkway [7]	a											16 00											17 00			
	d					15 19												16 19								
Filton Abbey Wood	d	15 09				15 23		15 42						16 09				16 23	16 42					17 09		
Bristol Temple Meads [10]	a	15 18				15 35		15 52						16 18				16 34	16 52					17 18		
	d	15 22	15 30			15 43	15 52		16 00					16 22			16 30	16 49			17 00			17 22		17 30
Keynsham	d					15 50												16 56								
Oldfield Park	d					15 57												17 02								
Bath Spa [7]	a	15 35	15 41			15 59	16 05		16 11					16 35			16 41	17 05			17 11			17 35		17 41

		XC	AW	GW	GW	GW	AW	AW	GW	GW	GW	XC		AW	GW	GW	AW	GW	GW	GW	XC	AW	GW	GW		GW
			R											R												
		◇		◇		1◇		◇	1◇	◇	1◇	◇						1◇	◇	1◇	◇	◇				1◇
				E	B		C								G	B	C						H	B		
			🛒			☕		🛒	☕	🛒	☕			🛒				☕	🛒	☕		🛒				☕
Cardiff Central [7]	d	16 45	16 50		17 00		17 12	17 20	17 25	17 30		17 45		17 50		18 00	18 12	18 25	18 30		18 45	18 50		19 00		19 25
Newport (South Wales)	a	16 58	17 03		17 13		17 27	17 32	17 38	17 43		17 58		18 03		18 13	18 25	18 38	18 43		18 59	19 05		19 13		19 38
	d	16 59			17 15		17 27		17 39	17 44		17 59				18 15	18 27	18 39	18 44		18 59			19 15		19 39
Severn Tunnel Jn	d				17 25		17 38			17 55						18 25	18 38							19 25		
Caldicot	d						17 40										18 40									
Chepstow	d						17 49										18 49									
Lydney	d						17 58										18 58									
Gloucester [7]	a	17 45					18 20					18 45					19 20				19 45					
Pilning	d																									
Patchway	d				17 39											18 39								19 39		
Bristol Parkway [7]	a								18 00									19 00								20 00
	d			17 19											18 23								19 19			
Filton Abbey Wood	d			17 23	17 42					18 09					18 27	18 42			19 09				19 22	19 42		
Bristol Temple Meads [10]	a			17 35	17 52					18 18					18 39	18 52			19 18				19 36	19 52		
	d			17 49		18 00				18 22	18 30				18 49				19 22	19 30			19 49			
Keynsham	d			17 56											18 56								19 56			
Oldfield Park	d			18 03											19 03								20 03			
Bath Spa [7]	a			18 05		18 11				18 35	18 41				19 06				19 35	19 41			20 05			

		GW	AW	GW	GW	GW	XC	AW	AW	GW	GW	XC		AW	GW	GW	GW	AW	AW	SW	GW	GW	GW	AW		
		◇	◇	1◇	◇		◇	◇		1◇	◇	◇		◇	1◇				◇	1	1◇					
					J	K			C								K	L						L		
		🛒	🛒	☕				🛒		☕	🛒			🛒	☕											
Cardiff Central [7]	d	19 30	19 34			19 50	20 00	20 10	20 15	20 25	20 30	20 50		20 53			21 00	21 15	21 50			22 00		23 20		
Newport (South Wales)	a	19 43	19 48			20 03	20 13	20 23	20 28	20 38	20 43	21 02		21 07			21 13	21 28	22 06			22 13		23 37		
	d	19 44				20 05	20 15		20 30	20 39	20 44	21 04					21 15	21 30				22 16		23 40		
Severn Tunnel Jn	d					20 15			20 41								21 25	21 41				22 33		23 57		
Caldicot	d								20 43									21 43						23 59		
Chepstow	d								20 52									21 52						00 08		
Lydney	d								21 01									22 01						00 17		
Gloucester [7]	a						20 56		21 22			21 48						22 22						00 42		
Pilning	d																									
Patchway	d					20 29											21 39					22 48				
Bristol Parkway [7]	a									21 00																
	d				20 23																					
Filton Abbey Wood	d	20 09			20 27	20 34					21 09						21 42					22 52				
Bristol Temple Meads [10]	a	20 18			20 40	20 45					21 18						21 52					23 00				
	d	20 22		20 33	20 49						21 22				21 44	21 51				22 23	22 33		23 10			
Keynsham	d				20 56											21 58							23 17			
Oldfield Park	d				21 03											22 04							23 23			
Bath Spa [7]	a	20 35		20 44	21 05						21 35				21 58	22 07				22 34	22 44		23 26			

For general notes see front of timetable
For details of catering facilities see Directory of Train Operators

A From Gloucester (Table 134) to Westbury (Table 123)
B To Taunton (Table 134)
C From Maesteg (Table 128) to Cheltenham Spa (Table 57)
D From Worcester Foregate Street (Table 71) to Weymouth (Table 123)
E From Gloucester (Table 134) to Weymouth (Table 123)
G From Great Malvern (Table 71) to Westbury (Table 123)
H From Gloucester (Table 134) to Frome (Table 123)
J From Worcester Shrub Hill (Table 57) to Weymouth (Table 123)
K To Exeter St Davids (Table 135)
L From Maesteg (Table 128)

Due to Engineering Operations, services from Saturday 13 September on this Table had not been confirmed at time of going to press. These services will be issued in a special Supplement as soon as exact timings have been confirmed

Table 132

Sundays

until 7 September

Cardiff → Gloucester, Bristol and Bath Spa

Network Diagram - see first page of Table 132

		AW	GW	GW	GW	GW	GW	GW	GW	AW	GW	GW	GW	GW		GW	GW	GW	GW	GW	GW	GW	GW	AW	GW	GW
		A	1◇	1◇		1◇	1◇	◇ B			◇			1◇		◇ B	1◇			1◇	1◇	1◇	◇ C	D		
			☕	☕	🚌	☕	☕	🛒	🚌			🚌	🚌	☕		🛒	☕	🚌	🚌	☕	☕	☕	🛒		🚌	🚌
Cardiff Central 7	d	23p20			07 23	07 55				08 34		08 23					09 25		09 18			10 25		10 30		10 18
Newport (South Wales)	a	23p37				08 11				08 48							09 38					10 38		10 43		
	d	23p40			07u53	08 13			08 18			08u53					09 39	09 45	09u48			10 39		10 45	10 45	10u48
Severn Tunnel Jn	d	23p57			08 13							09 13							10 08					10 56		11 08
Caldicot	d	23p59																						10 58		
Chepstow	d	00 08																						11 07		
Lydney	d	00 17																						11 16		
Gloucester 7	a	00 42				09 03											10 21					11 21		11 43		
Pilning	d																									
Patchway	d												09 38													
Bristol Parkway 7	a				08 43				08 58			09 43	09 43					10 25	10 43						11 25	11 43
	d							08 51								09 50							10 50			
Filton Abbey Wood	d							08 55								09 55							10 53			
Bristol Temple Meads 10	a							09 05								10 05							11 02			
	d		07 40	08 10			09 00	09 10			09 15			10 00		10 10				10 30	11 00		11 10			
Keynsham	d							09 17			09 22												11 17			
Oldfield Park	d							09 24			09 30												11 24			
Bath Spa 7	a		07 52	08 21			09 12	09 26			09 32			10 11		10 21				10 42	11 12		11 26			

		GW	GW	GW	GW		GW	AW	XC	GW	GW	GW	AW	GW	GW	GW	AW	GW	GW		GW	GW	GW	XC	GW	GW
		1◇	1◇	◇ B				◇	◇		1◇	1◇	D	◇ C			◇	1◇	◇ B		1◇			◇		1◇
		☕	☕	🛒	🚌		🚌	🛒		🚌	☕	☕		🛒	🚌	🚌		☕	🛒		☕	🚌	🚌		🚌	☕
Cardiff Central 7	d		11 25				11 18	11 35	11 50		12 25		12 30			12 18	12 39				13 25		13 18	13 50		14 25
Newport (South Wales)	a		11 38					11 48	12 02		12 38		12 43				12 48				13 38			14 02		14 38
	d		11 39		11 45		11u48		12 04		12 39		12 45		12 45	12u48					13 39	13 45	13u48	14 04		14 39
Severn Tunnel Jn	d						12 08						12 56			13 08							14 08			
Caldicot	d												12 58													
Chepstow	d												13 07													
Lydney	d												13 16													
Gloucester 7	a		12 21						12 45		13 21		13 42								14 21			14 45		15 21
Pilning	d																									
Patchway	d									12 38															14 38	
Bristol Parkway 7	a				12 25		12 43			12 43					13 25	13 43						14 25	14 43		14 43	
	d			11 50										12 50					13 50							
Filton Abbey Wood	d			11 54										12 57					13 54							
Bristol Temple Meads 10	a			12 04										13 05					14 04							
	d	12 00		12 10								13 00		13 10				14 00	14 10							
Keynsham	d													13 17												
Oldfield Park	d													13 24												
Bath Spa 7	a	12 12		12 21								13 12		13 26				14 11	14 23							

		GW	AW	GW	GW	GW	AW	XC	GW	GW		GW	SW	GW	AW	XC	GW	GW	GW	GW	AW	GW	GW	AW		GW
		1◇	D	◇ B			◇	◇	1◇	1◇			1◇ E		◇	◇	1◇	1◇	1◇	◇ B	D			R		1◇
		☕		🛒	🚌	🚌	🛒		☕	☕		🚌		🚌	🛒		☕	☕	☕	🛒		🚌	🚌	🛒		☕
Cardiff Central 7	d		14 30			14 18	14 35	14 50		15 25				15 18	15 35	15 50		16 25			16 30		16 18	16 35		
Newport (South Wales)	a		14 43				14 48	15 02		15 38					15 47	16 02		16 38			16 43			16 48		
	d		14 45		14 45	14u48		15 04		15 39		15 45		15u48		16 04		16 39			16 45	16 45	16u48			
Severn Tunnel Jn	d		14 56			15 08								16 08							16 56		17 08			
Caldicot	d		14 58																		16 58					
Chepstow	d		15 07																		17 07					
Lydney	d		15 16																		17 16					
Gloucester 7	a		15 37					15 45		16 21						16 45		17 21			17 37					
Pilning	d																									
Patchway	d																									
Bristol Parkway 7	a				15 25	15 43						16 25		16 43								17 25	17 43			
	d			14 50																16 50						
Filton Abbey Wood	d			14 54																16 53						
Bristol Temple Meads 10	a			15 04																17 02						
	d	15 00		15 10					16 00				16 04				16 30		17 00	17 10						17 30
Keynsham	d			15 17									16 11							17 17						
Oldfield Park	d			15 24																17 24						
Bath Spa 7	a	15 12		15 26					16 12				16 18				16 41		17 12	17 26						17 42

For general notes see front of timetable
For details of catering facilities see Directory of Train Operators

A From Maesteg (Table 128)
B To Portsmouth Harbour (Table 123)
C To Brighton (Table 123)
D To Cheltenham Spa (Table 57)
E To London Waterloo (Table 160)

Due to Engineering Operations, services from Sunday 14 September on this Table had not been confirmed at time of going to press. These services will be issued in a special Supplement as soon as exact timings have been confirmed

until 7 September

Cardiff → Gloucester, Bristol and Bath Spa

Network Diagram - see first page of Table 132

		GW	XC	GW	GW	AW	GW	GW	GW	GW	GW	GW	XC	GW		GW	GW	GW	GW	GW	AW	GW	GW	AW	GW	XC
		◇ A	◇	1 ◇ ☕	◇ B 🛒	C	🚌	1 ◇ ☕	1 ◇ ☕	◇ D 🛒	🚌	🚌	◇	1 ◇ ☕		◇ D 🛒	🚌	1 ◇ ☕	1 ◇ ☕	◇ D 🛒	E	🚌	🚌	R	🚌	◇
Cardiff Central 7	d		16 50			17 05	16 50	17 25				17 18	17 50				17 48	18 25			18 30		18 20	18 35		18 50
Newport (South Wales)	a		17 02			17 17		17 38					18 02					18 38			18 43			18 48		19 02
	d		17u04				17 20	17 39			17 45	17u48	18 04				18u18	18 39			18 45	18 45	18u50			19 04
Severn Tunnel Jn	d											18 08					18 38				18 56					
Caldicot	d																				18 58					
Chepstow	d																				19 07					
Lydney	d																				19 16					
Gloucester 7	a		17 45					18 21					18 45					19 21			19 38					19 46
Pilning	d																									
Patchway	d																								19 38	
Bristol Parkway 7	a						18 10				18 25	18 43					19 13					19 25	19 40		19 43	
	d				17 50					18 20						18 50				19 20						
Filton Abbey Wood	d				17 54					18 23						18 53				19 23						
Bristol Temple Meads 10	a				18 02					18 33						19 02				19 33						
	d	17 42		18 00	18 10				18 30	18 50				19 00		19 10			19 30	19 50						
Keynsham	d	17 49			18 17											19 17										
Oldfield Park	d	17 56			18 24											19 24										
Bath Spa 7	a	17 58		18 11	18 26				18 43	19 01				19 12		19 26			19 42	20 01						

		GW	GW	GW	GW		GW	XC	GW	GW	GW	AW	AW	SW	GW	GW	GW	GW	GW	GW	XC	GW	AW	AW		
		1 ◇ ☕	◇ D 🛒	1 ◇ ☕	🚌		🚌	◇	◇	1 ◇	◇ D 🛒		R 🛒	1	1 ◇ ☕	🚌	1 ◇ ☕	🚌	🚌	◇ G 🛒		🚌		◇		
Cardiff Central 7	d			19 25			19 18	19 50				20 30	20 35		20 55			21 23			21 50	22 04	22 30	22 47		
Newport (South Wales)	a			19 38				20 02				20 43	20 48		21 08						22 07		22 47	23 08		
	d			19 39	19 45		19u48	20 04				20 45			21 09	21 15		21u53			22 09	22u34	22 49			
Severn Tunnel Jn	d						20 08					20 56						22 13				22 54	23 06			
Caldicot	d											20 58											23 08			
Chepstow	d											21 07											23 17			
Lydney	d											21 16											23 26			
Gloucester 7	a			20 21				20 45				21 38			21 51						22 57		23 48			
Pilning	d																									
Patchway	d																		22 38							
Bristol Parkway 7	a				20 25		20 43									21 55		22 43	22 43			23 19				
	d		19 50								20 50									22 53		23 20				
Filton Abbey Wood	d		19 53								20 53									22 56		23 25				
Bristol Temple Meads 10	a		20 02								21 02									23 05		23 42				
	d	20 00	20 10						20 50	21 00	21 10			21 35			22 05			23 10						
Keynsham	d								20 57																	
Oldfield Park	d								21 04																	
Bath Spa 7	a	20 11	20 21						21 07	21 13	21 21			21 47			22 18			23 21						

For general notes see front of timetable
For details of catering facilities see Directory of Train Operators

A From Weston-super-Mare (Table 134)
B To Brighton (Table 123)
C From Barry Island (Table 130)
D To Portsmouth Harbour (Table 123)
E To Cheltenham Spa (Table 57)
G To Warminster (Table 123)

Due to Engineering Operations, services from Sunday 14 September on this Table had not been confirmed at time of going to press. These services will be issued in a special Supplement as soon as exact timings have been confirmed

Bath Spa, Bristol and Gloucester → Cardiff

Network Diagram - see first page of Table 132

Miles	Miles	Miles			AW	AW	GW	GW	AW	GW	GW	AW	AW	GW		XC	GW	AW	GW	XC	GW	GW	AW	GW	SW	GW
					MX	MO	MO	MX	MX	MX																
						◇	1◇	1◇	◇	1◇								◇	1◇				◇			1◇
					A		B						C			D			E	G	H	J		K		
							⊏P	⊏P		⊤								⊤	⊏P							⊏P
0	—	—	**Bath Spa 7**	d						01 13							06 28		06 56			07 12		07 28	07 34	
1	—	—	Oldfield Park	d													06 31					07 14		07 31	07 37	
7	—	—	Keynsham	d													06 38					07 22		07 38	07 44	
11½	—	—	**Bristol Temple Meads 10**	a						01s29							06 46		07 08			07 29		07 45	07 52	
—	—	—		d							05 54			06 22			06 50		07 15		07 19	07 41		07 54		
16	—	—	Filton Abbey Wood	d							06 01			06 33			07 02		07 22		07 30	07 48		08 00		
—	0	—	**Bristol Parkway 7**	a																	07 33	07 52				
—	—	—		d				00 22													07 39					08 07
17½	—	—	Patchway	d							06 05			06 37							07 44			08 04		
21	4¾	—	Pilning	d																						
—	—	0	**Gloucester 7**	d	22p58		23p28						05 50			06 16				07 00						
—	—	19¼	Lydney	d	23p17								06 09			06 35				07 19						
—	—	27¼	Chepstow	d	23p27								06 19			06 44				07 28						
—	—	34	Caldicot	d	23p35								06 26			06 53				07 37						
28	11¾	34¾	Severn Tunnel Jn	d	23p38						06 16		06 29	06 49			07 15			07 40	07 55					
38	21¾	44¾	Newport (South Wales)	a	23p59		00 18	00 52		02s10	06 27		06 41	07 01		07 06	07 26		07 44	07 50	08 08			08 24		08 29
—	—	—		d	00 01	00 04	00 20	00 52	00 58		06 29	06 41	06 44	07 02		07 07	07 28	07 35	07 45	07 52	08 11		08 08	08 26		08 31
49¾	33½	56½	**Cardiff Central 7**	a	00 24	00 25	00 40	01 12	01 22	02 31	06 45	06 59	07 00	07 18		07 27	07 44	07 50	08 01	08 12	08 28		08 29	08 42		08 48

		GW		GW	AW	AW	AW	GW	GW	XC	GW	GW	GW		GW	GW	GW	AW	AW	GW	GW	XC	GW	GW		GW
		◇		1◇	◇		◇	1◇		◇		◇	1◇		1◇	◇	1◇	◇			1◇	◇		◇		1◇
		L		N		C			Q		U				V	L			C	Q			X			
				⊏P	⊤		⊤	⊏P		⊤		⊤	⊏P		☒		☒	⊤			⊏P	⊤		⊤		⊏P
Bath Spa 7	d	07 48		08 00							08 08	08 22	08 30			08 47	08 55						09 15	09 24		09 30
Oldfield Park	d	07 51									08 10	08 24				08 49							09 17			
Keynsham	d	07 58		08 09							08 17	08 32				08 57							09 25	09 32		
Bristol Temple Meads 10	a	08 06		08 17							08 29	08 39	08 45			09 04	09 10						09 32	09 39		09 45
	d	08 10							08 22		08 41	08 54				09 10				09 19			09 41	09 54		
Filton Abbey Wood	d	08 21							08 30		08 48	09 01				09 20				09 30			09 48	10 01		
Bristol Parkway 7	a	08 28									08 52					09 27							09 51			
	d							08 42							09 07						09 42					
Patchway	d								08 34											09 34						
Pilning	d																									
Gloucester 7	d					07 58				08 25									08 58			09 22				
Lydney	d					08 17													09 17							
Chepstow	d					08 27													09 27							
Caldicot	d					08 34													09 35							
Severn Tunnel Jn	d					08 37			08 46										09 38	09 46						
Newport (South Wales)	a					08 49		09 04	08 59	09 07		09 23			09 29				09 50	09 58	10 04	10 09		10 23		
	d				08 37	08 51	08 59	09 05	09 03	09 07		09 25			09 31			09 37	09 52	09 59	10 05	10 09		10 25		
Cardiff Central 7	a				08 53	09 10	09 18	09 22	09 24	09 29		09 41			09 48			09 53	10 10	10 17	10 22	10 30		10 41		

		GW	GW	AW	AW	GW	GW	XC	GW	GW	GW		GW	GW	AW	AW	GW	GW	XC	GW	GW	GW		SW	GW	GW
		1◇	1◇	◇	◇	1◇		◇	◇	1◇	◇		1◇	1◇	◇			1◇	◇		1◇	◇		1◇	1◇	1◇
							Q		Y							C	H			Z	AA					
		⊏P	⊏P	⊤		⊏P		⊤		⊏P	⊤		☒	⊏P	⊤			⊏P	⊤		⊏P	⊤			☒	⊏P
Bath Spa 7	d		10 00						10 08	10 25	10 35			11 00						11 08	11 25	11 35		11 46		12 00
Oldfield Park	d								10 10											11 10						
Keynsham	d								10 17											11 17						
Bristol Temple Meads 10	a		10 15						10 29	10 42	10 47			11 15						11 29	11 42	11 47		12 05		12 15
	d						10 19		10 41		10 54						11 19			11 41		11 54				
Filton Abbey Wood	d						10 30		10 48		11 01						11 30			11 48		12 01				
Bristol Parkway 7	a								10 52											11 51						
	d	10 07				10 42							11 07					11 42							12 07	
Patchway	d						10 35										11 34									
Pilning	d																									
Gloucester 7	d							10 22								10 58			11 22							
Lydney	d															11 18										
Chepstow	d															11 27										
Caldicot	d															11 35										
Severn Tunnel Jn	d						10 46									11 38	11 46									
Newport (South Wales)	a	10 29				11 04	11 05	11 10			11 24		11 29			11 50	11 58	12 04	12 09			12 24			12 29	
	d	10 32		10 38	10 58	11 05	11 07	11 10			11 25		11 31		11 38	11 52	11 59	12 05	12 09			12 25			12 31	
Cardiff Central 7	a	10 48		10 54	11 20	11 23	11 25	11 32			11 43		11 48		11 54	12 10	12 17	12 22	12 32			12 43			12 48	

For general notes see front of timetable
For details of catering facilities see Directory of Train Operators

- **A** From Cheltenham Spa (Table 57)
- **B** Until 8 September
- **C** From Cheltenham Spa (Table 57) to Maesteg (Table 128)
- **D** From Worcester Shrub Hill (Table 57)
- **E** From London Paddington to Swansea (Table 125)
- **G** From Birmingham New Street (Table 57)
- **H** From Taunton (Table 134)
- **J** From Salisbury (Table 123) to Gloucester (Table 134)
- **K** From Frome (Table 123)
- **L** From Weymouth (Table 123)
- **N** From London Paddington (Table 125)
- **Q** From Weston-super-Mare (Table 134)
- **U** From Warminster (Table 123) to Great Malvern (Table 71)
- **V** **The St David**
- **X** From Westbury (Table 123) to Gloucester (Table 134)
- **Y** From Westbury (Table 123) to Great Malvern (Table 71)
- **Z** From Weymouth (Table 123) to Gloucester (Table 134)
- **AA** **Torbay Express**

Bath Spa, Bristol and Gloucester → Cardiff

Network Diagram - see first page of Table 132

Station		AW ◇	AW A	AW ◇	GW 1◇	GW B	XC ◇	GW ◇ C	GW 1◇	GW ◇		GW 1◇ ⊠	GW 1◇	AW ◇	GW B	GW 1◇	XC ◇	GW ◇ D	GW 1◇	GW ◇	GW 1◇ ⊠		GW 1◇	AW ◇	AW A	AW ◇
Bath Spa 7	d							12 08	12 25	12 35			13 00					13 19	13 25	13 35			14 00			
Oldfield Park	d							12 10										13 21								
Keynsham	d							12 17										13 28								
Bristol Temple Meads 10	a							12 29	12 42	12 47			13 15					13 36	13 42	13 47			14 15			
	d					12 19		12 41		12 54					13 19			13 41		13 54						
Filton Abbey Wood	d					12 30		12 48		13 01					13 30			13 48		14 01						
Bristol Parkway 7	a							12 51										13 51								
	d				12 42							13 07				13 42					14 07					
Patchway	d					12 34									13 34											
Pilning	d																									
Gloucester 7	d		11 58				12 22										13 22								13 58	
Lydney	d		12 17																						14 17	
Chepstow	d		12 27																						14 27	
Caldicot	d		12 35																						14 35	
Severn Tunnel Jn	d		12 38			12 46									13 46										14 38	
Newport (South Wales)	a		12 50		13 04	13 04	13 09			13 24		13 29			13 58	14 05	14 09			14 24	14 29				14 50	
	d	12 38	12 52	12 58	13 05	13 04	13 09			13 25		13 31		13 38	13 59	14 05	14 09			14 25	14 31			14 38	14 52	14 58
Cardiff Central 7	a	12 54	13 10	13 20	13 22	13 27	13 32			13 45		13 48		13 54	14 17	14 23	14 32			14 43	14 48			14 54	15 10	15 20

Station		GW B	GW 1◇	XC ◇	GW E	GW 1◇	GW ◇	SW 1◇	GW 1◇		GW 1◇	AW R	AW A	GW B	GW 1◇	XC ◇	GW ◇ D	GW 1◇	GW ◇	GW 1◇		GW 1◇	AW R	AW ◇	GW 1◇	GW B
Bath Spa 7	d				14 15	14 25	14 35	14 46			15 00						15 15	15 25	15 35			16 00				
Oldfield Park	d				14 17												15 17									
Keynsham	d				14 25												15 25									
Bristol Temple Meads 10	a				14 31	14 42	14 47	15 05			15 15						15 32	15 42	15 47			16 15				
	d	14 19			14 41		14 54							15 19			15 41		15 54							16 19
Filton Abbey Wood	d	14 30			14 48		15 01							15 30			15 48		16 01							16 30
Bristol Parkway 7	a				14 51												15 51									
	d		14 42						15 07						15 42					16 07					16 42	
Patchway	d	14 34												15 34												16 36
Pilning	d																									
Gloucester 7	d			14 22									14 58			15 22										
Lydney	d												15 17													
Chepstow	d												15 27													
Caldicot	d												15 35													
Severn Tunnel Jn	d	14 46											15 39	15 46												16 48
Newport (South Wales)	a	14 58	15 04	15 09			15 24		15 29				15 51	15 58	16 04	16 09			16 24	16 29					17 04	17 00
	d	15 02	15 05	15 09			15 25		15 31			15 38	15 52	15 59	16 05	16 09			16 25	16 31			16 38	16 57	17 05	17 02
Cardiff Central 7	a	15 24	15 24	15 32			15 43		15 48			15 54	16 09	16 17	16 22	16 32			16 43	16 48			16 54	17 15	17 22	17 24

Station		XC ◇	GW G	GW 1◇	GW ◇	GW 1◇	GW 1◇	AW R		AW A	GW B	GW 1◇	XC ◇	GW ◇ D	GW 1◇	GW ◇	GW 1◇	GW 1◇	AW R		AW A	AW ◇	GW B	GW 1◇	XC ◇	GW G
Bath Spa 7	d		16 08	16 25	16 35		17 00							17 08	17 25	17 35		18 00								18 08
Oldfield Park	d		16 10											17 10												18 10
Keynsham	d		16 17											17 17												18 17
Bristol Temple Meads 10	a		16 29	16 42	16 47		17 15							17 29	17 42	17 47		18 15								18 28
	d		16 41		16 54						17 19			17 41		17 54							18 19			18 41
Filton Abbey Wood	d		16 48		17 01						17 30			17 48		18 01							18 30			18 48
Bristol Parkway 7	a		16 51											17 51												18 51
	d					17 07						17 42					18 13							18 42		
Patchway	d										17 34												18 34			
Pilning	d																									
Gloucester 7	d	16 26								16 58			17 25								17 58				18 29	
Lydney	d									17 17											18 17					
Chepstow	d									17 27											18 27					
Caldicot	d									17 36											18 35					
Severn Tunnel Jn	d				17 15					17 39	17 46					18 15					18 38		18 46			
Newport (South Wales)	a	17 09			17 26	17 29				17 51	17 58	18 04	18 09			18 26	18 36				18 50		19 03	19 08	19 14	
	d	17 09			17 27	17 31		17 38		17 52	18 00	18 05	18 09			18 27	18 38		18 47		18 52	18 57	19 04	19 10	19 15	
Cardiff Central 7	a	17 32			17 47	17 48		17 54		18 10	18 16	18 22	18 32			18 45	18 53		19 01		19 09	19 20	19 20	19 23	19 32	

For general notes see front of timetable
For details of catering facilities see Directory of Train Operators

- **A** From Cheltenham Spa (Table 57) to Maesteg (Table 128)
- **B** From Taunton (Table 134)
- **C** From Brighton (Table 123) to Great Malvern (Table 71)
- **D** From Weymouth (Table 123) to Gloucester (Table 134)
- **E** From Southampton Central (Table 123) to Worcester Foregate Street (Table 71)
- **G** From Warminster (Table 123) to Great Malvern (Table 71)

Bath Spa, Bristol and Gloucester → Cardiff

Network Diagram - see first page of Table 132

		GW	GW	GW	GW	AW	AW	XC	GW	XC	GW	GW	GW	GW	GW	AW	AW	AW	GW	GW	XC	GW	GW	GW
		1 ◇	◇	1 ◇	1 ◇	R	A	R 1 B	1 ◇ C	◇	1 ◇ D	◇	◇	1 ◇	1 ◇	R	A	◇	1 ◇	E	◇	◇ G	1 ◇	◇
		☕	🛒	☕	☕	🛒		☕	☕		☕	🛒		☕	☕	🛒		🛒	☕				☕	🛒
Bath Spa 7	d	18 30	18 35	19 00							19 30	19 35	19 44		20 00							20 08	20 30	20 35
Oldfield Park	d												19 47									20 10		
Keynsham	d												19 54									20 17		
Bristol Temple Meads 10	a	18 45	18 50	19 15							19 45	19 49	20 03		20 15							20 29	20 45	20 50
	d		18 54					19 25				19 54								20 19		20 41		20 54
Filton Abbey Wood	d		19 01					19 31				20 01								20 30		20 48		21 01
Bristol Parkway 7	a																					20 51		
	d				19 11				19 42					20 07					20 42					
Patchway	d							19 37												20 34				
Pilning	d																							
Gloucester 7	d						18 58			19 25							19 58				20 26			
Lydney	d						19 17										20 17							
Chepstow	d						19 27										20 27							
Caldicot	d						19 34										20 35							
Severn Tunnel Jn	d		19 15				19 37	19 49									20 38			20 46				
Newport (South Wales)	a		19 27		19 34		19 51	19 59	20 04	20 09		20 23		20 29			20 50		21 04	21 00	21 09			21 28
	d		19 27		19 34	19 40	19 51	20 01	20 05	20 09		20 25		20 31		20 46	20 52	20 58	21 05	21 00	21 12			21 30
Cardiff Central 7	a		19 45		19 50	19 54	20 11	20 19	20 21	20 32		20 43		20 48		21 01	21 10	21 19	21 22	21 26	21 32			21 47

		GW	AW	GW	GW	GW	GW	GW	SW	GW	GW	AW	AW	GW	GW	GW	GW	AW	AW	GW	GW
								FX												FO	FX
		1 ◇	◇			1 ◇	1 ◇	◇ H	1 ◇	◇	1 ◇	◇	J	1 ◇	◇ H		1 ◇	◇	J	1 ◇	1 ◇
		☕	🛒			☕	☕	🛒			☕			☕	🛒		☕			☕	☕
Bath Spa 7	d	20 55			21 08		21 30	21 35	21 51	22 08	22 15				22 35	23 10	23 21			23 48	23 55
Oldfield Park	d				21 10					22 10						23 13					
Keynsham	d				21 17				21 59	22 17						23 20					
Bristol Temple Meads 10	a	21 10			21 29		21 45	21 50	22 06	22 27	22 30				22 47	23 29	23 33			00 05	00 11
	d			21 19				21 54							22 54						
Filton Abbey Wood	d			21 30				22 01							23 01						
Bristol Parkway 7	a																				
	d					21 42								22 46							
Patchway	d			21 34				22 05							23 05						
Pilning	d																				
Gloucester 7	d												21 58						22 58		
Lydney	d												22 17						23 17		
Chepstow	d												22 27						23 27		
Caldicot	d												22 35						23 35		
Severn Tunnel Jn	d			21 45				22 16					22 38		23 16				23 38		
Newport (South Wales)	a			21 57		22 04		22 35					22 57	23 15	23 35				23 59		
	d		21 38	21 58		22 05		22 35				22 41	22 58	23 16	23 35			23 52	00 01		
Cardiff Central 7	a		21 57	22 18		22 25		22 54				23 04	23 18	23 37	23 55			00 17	00 24		

Saturdays

until 6 September

		AW	GW	AW	GW	AW	AW	XC	GW	GW	AW	XC	GW	AW	GW	SW	GW	AW	AW	AW	GW	XC	GW	GW
		J	1 ◇	◇	1 ◇	K	L	N		1 ◇ Q	◇	U	V	◇		1	1 ◇	◇	A	◇	X	◇	Y	1 ◇
					🛒					☕	🛒						☕	🛒		🛒				☕
Bath Spa 7	d				01 13								07 07		07 18	07 34	08 01						08 09	08 25
Oldfield Park	d												07 10		07 21	07 37							08 11	
Keynsham	d												07 17		07 28	07 44							08 18	
Bristol Temple Meads 10	a				01s29								07 29		07 35	07 52	08 15						08 29	08 40
	d								06 50	06 58			07 41		07 54						08 21		08 41	
Filton Abbey Wood	d								07 01				07 48		08 01						08 30		08 48	
Bristol Parkway 7	a									07 06			07 51										08 51	
	d		00 17							07 13														
Patchway	d																				08 34			
Pilning	d																							
Gloucester 7	d	22p58					05 50	06 16				07 00							07 58			08 22		
Lydney	d	23p17					06 09	06 35				07 19							08 17					
Chepstow	d	23p27					06 19	06 44				07 28							08 27					
Caldicot	d	23p35					06 27	06 53				07 37							08 35					
Severn Tunnel Jn	d	23p38					06 30		07 17			07 40							08 38		08 46			
Newport (South Wales)	a	23p59	00 48		02s06		06 42	07 05	07 28	07 34		07 50			08 24				08 50		09 00	09 05		
	d	00 01	00 48	00 55		06 38	06 44	07 06	07 30	07 36	07 40	07 52		08 06	08 26			08 37	08 52	09 01	09 03	09 05		
Cardiff Central 7	a	00 24	01 04	01 14	02 23	06 54	07 00	07 26	07 44	07 51	07 57	08 12		08 25	08 42			08 51	09 10	09 18	09 21	09 25		

For general notes see front of timetable
For details of catering facilities see Directory of Train Operators

- **A** From Cheltenham Spa (Table 57) to Maesteg (Table 128)
- **B** Until 5 September from Newcastle, from 8 September from Edinburgh (Table 51)
- **C** The Red Dragon
- **D** The Bristolian
- **E** From Taunton (Table 134)
- **G** From Brighton (Table 123) to Worcester Shrub Hill (Table 57)
- **H** From Portsmouth Harbour (Table 123)
- **J** From Cheltenham Spa (Table 57)
- **K** To Barry Island (Table 130)
- **L** To Maesteg (Table 128)
- **N** From Worcester Shrub Hill (Table 57)
- **Q** To Swansea (Table 125)
- **U** From Birmingham New Street (Table 57)
- **V** From Salisbury (Table 123) to Gloucester (Table 134)
- **X** From Weston-super-Mare (Table 134)
- **Y** From Warminster (Table 123) to Great Malvern (Table 71)

Due to Engineering Operations, services from Saturday 13 September on this Table had not been confirmed at time of going to press. These services will be issued in a special Supplement as soon as exact timings have been confirmed

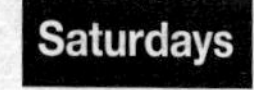

Saturdays

until 6 September

Bath Spa, Bristol and Gloucester → Cardiff

Network Diagram - see first page of Table 132

		GW	GW	GW		GW	AW	AW	GW	XC	GW	GW	GW		GW	AW	GW	GW	GW	AW	XC	GW		GW	GW	AW
		◇	1 ◇	◇		1 ◇	◇			◇	1 ◇	◇	1 ◇		1 ◇	◇		◇	1 ◇	◇	◇	◇		1 ◇	1 ◇	◇
				A				B	C				D				C	E								
Bath Spa 7	d	08 33		08 47		08 56					09 25	09 35			10 01			10 08	10 25			10 35			11 00	
Oldfield Park	d			08 49														10 10								
Keynsham	d			08 57														10 17								
Bristol Temple Meads 10	a	08 45		09 04		09 10					09 40	09 47			10 15			10 28	10 39			10 48			11 15	
	d	08 54		09 10					09 21			09 54					10 21	10 41				10 54				
Filton Abbey Wood	d	09 01		09 17					09 30			10 01					10 30	10 48				11 01				
Bristol Parkway 7	a			09 20														10 51								
	d		09 07										10 07											11 07		
Patchway	d								09 34								10 34									
Pilning	d																									
Gloucester 7	d							08 58		09 22											10 22					
Lydney	d							09 17																		
Chepstow	d							09 27																		
Caldicot	d							09 35																		
Severn Tunnel Jn	d							09 38	09 46								10 46									
Newport (South Wales)	a	09 23	09 30					09 50	09 58	10 05		10 23	10 31				10 58				11 05	11 22		11 29		
	d	09 23	09 32				09 36	09 52	09 59	10 05		10 23	10 31			10 36	10 59			10 58	11 05	11 22		11 32		11 38
Cardiff Central 7	a	09 41	09 48				09 53	10 09	10 16	10 25		10 41	10 47			10 54	11 18			11 20	11 25	11 41		11 48		11 54

		AW	GW	XC	GW	GW	GW	SW		GW	GW	AW	AW	GW	GW	GW	AW		XC	GW	GW	GW	AW	GW	XC	GW
				◇		1 ◇	◇	1 ◇		1 ◇	1 ◇	◇			◇	1 ◇	◇		◇	◇	1 ◇	1 ◇	◇		◇	◇
		B	G		A								B	G	H									G		A
Bath Spa 7	d				11 08	11 25	11 35	11 46			12 00				12 08	12 25				12 35		13 01				13 18
Oldfield Park	d				11 10										12 10											13 21
Keynsham	d				11 17										12 17											13 28
Bristol Temple Meads 10	a				11 29	11 42	11 47	12 00			12 15				12 29	12 42				12 47		13 15				13 36
	d		11 21		11 41		11 54							12 21	12 41					12 54				13 21		13 41
Filton Abbey Wood	d		11 30		11 48		12 01							12 30	12 48					13 01				13 30		13 48
Bristol Parkway 7	a				11 51										12 51											13 51
	d									12 07											13 07					
Patchway	d		11 34											12 34										13 34		
Pilning	d																									
Gloucester 7	d	10 58		11 22									11 58						12 22						13 22	
Lydney	d	11 17											12 17													
Chepstow	d	11 27											12 27													
Caldicot	d	11 35											12 35													
Severn Tunnel Jn	d	11 38	11 46										12 38	12 46										13 46		
Newport (South Wales)	a	11 50	11 58	12 05			12 22			12 31			12 50	12 58					13 05	13 22	13 29			13 58	14 05	
	d	11 52	11 59	12 05			12 22			12 31		12 38	12 52	12 59			12 58		13 05	13 22	13 31		13 38	13 59	14 05	
Cardiff Central 7	a	12 10	12 15	12 25			12 41			12 47		12 54	13 10	13 18			13 20		13 25	13 41	13 47		13 53	14 15	14 25	

		GW	GW		GW	GW	AW	AW	AW	GW	XC	GW		GW	GW	SW	GW	GW	AW	AW	GW		XC	GW	GW	GW
		1 ◇	◇		1 ◇	1 ◇	◇		◇		◇			1 ◇	◇	1 ◇	1 ◇	1 ◇	R				◇	◇	1 ◇	◇
								B		G		J								B	G			A		
Bath Spa 7	d	13 25	13 35			14 02						14 10		14 25	14 35	14 46		15 02						15 18	15 25	15 35
Oldfield Park	d											14 13												15 21		
Keynsham	d											14 20												15 28		
Bristol Temple Meads 10	a	13 42	13 47			14 15						14 29		14 42	14 47	15 05		15 16						15 35	15 42	15 47
	d		13 54							14 21		14 41			14 54						15 21			15 41		15 54
Filton Abbey Wood	d		14 01							14 30		14 48			15 01						15 30			15 48		16 01
Bristol Parkway 7	a											14 51												15 51		
	d				14 07												15 07									
Patchway	d									14 34											15 34					
Pilning	d																				15 40					
Gloucester 7	d							13 58			14 22									14 58			15 22			
Lydney	d							14 17												15 17						
Chepstow	d							14 27												15 27						
Caldicot	d							14 35												15 35						
Severn Tunnel Jn	d							14 38		14 46										15 38	15 48					
Newport (South Wales)	a		14 22		14 32			14 50		14 58	15 05				15 22		15 29			15 50	16 00		16 05			16 24
	d		14 22		14 32		14 38	14 52	14 58	15 02	15 05				15 22		15 32		15 38	15 52	16 02		16 05			16 24
Cardiff Central 7	a		14 41		14 48		14 54	15 09	15 20	15 24	15 25				15 41		15 48		15 53	16 07	16 17		16 25			16 41

For general notes see front of timetable
For details of catering facilities see Directory of Train Operators

A From Weymouth (Table 123) to Gloucester (Table 134)

B From Cheltenham Spa (Table 57) to Maesteg (Table 128)

C From Weston-super-Mare (Table 134)

D **Pembroke Coast Express**

E From Westbury (Table 123) to Great Malvern (Table 71)

G From Taunton (Table 134)

H From Brighton (Table 123) to Worcester Foregate Street (Table 71)

J From Southampton Central (Table 123) to Great Malvern (Table 71)

Due to Engineering Operations, services from Saturday 13 September on this Table had not been confirmed at time of going to press. These services will be issued in a special Supplement as soon as exact timings have been confirmed

Table 132

Saturdays

until 6 September

Bath Spa, Bristol and Gloucester → Cardiff

Network Diagram - see first page of Table 132

		GW	GW	AW	AW	GW	XC		GW	GW	GW	GW	GW	AW	AW	GW		XC	GW	GW	GW	GW	GW	AW	AW	GW
		1 ◇	1 ◇	R	◇		◇			1 ◇	◇	1 ◇	1 ◇	R				◇	◇	1 ◇	◇	1 ◇	1 ◇	R		
						A			B						C	A			D						C	A
		🍴	🍴	🛒	🛒					🍴		🍴	🍴	🛒						🍴		🍴	🍴	🛒		
Bath Spa 7	d		16 01						16 08	16 25	16 35		17 01						17 08	17 25	17 35		18 01			
Oldfield Park	d								16 10										17 10							
Keynsham	d								16 17										17 17							
Bristol Temple Meads 10	a		16 15						16 29	16 42	16 47		17 15						17 29	17 42	17 47		18 15			
	d					16 21			16 41		16 54					17 21			17 41		17 54					18 21
Filton Abbey Wood	d					16 30			16 48		17 01					17 30			17 48		18 01					18 30
Bristol Parkway 7	a								16 51										17 51							
	d	16 07										17 07										18 07				
Patchway	d					16 34										17 34										18 34
Pilning	d																									
Gloucester 7	d						16 25								16 58			17 25							17 58	
Lydney	d														17 17										18 17	
Chepstow	d														17 27										18 27	
Caldicot	d														17 35										18 35	
Severn Tunnel Jn	d					16 46					17 14				17 38	17 46					18 14				18 38	18 46
Newport (South Wales)	a	16 32				17 01	17 05				17 25	17 29			17 50	17 58		18 05			18 25	18 31			18 50	18 58
	d	16 32		16 38	16 58	17 02	17 05				17 25	17 31		17 38	17 52	17 59		18 05			18 25	18 31		18 40	18 52	18 59
Cardiff Central 7	a	16 48		16 54	17 20	17 21	17 25				17 45	17 47		17 54	18 10	18 17		18 25			18 41	18 47		18 54	19 10	19 15

		GW		AW	XC	GW	GW	GW	GW	AW	AW		XC	XC	GW	GW	GW	GW	GW	GW		AW	AW	AW	GW	GW
				◇	◇	1 ◇	◇	1 ◇	1 ◇	R			1 ◇	◇	◇	1 ◇	◇	◇	1 ◇	1 ◇		R		◇		
		E									C		G		H								C		A	J
				🛒		🍴		🍴	🍴				🍴			🍴			🍴	🍴		🛒		🛒		
Bath Spa 7	d	18 08				18 25	18 35	19 01							19 09	19 25	19 35	19 47		20 01						20 09
Oldfield Park	d	18 10													19 12			19 50								20 11
Keynsham	d	18 17													19 19			19 57								20 18
Bristol Temple Meads 10	a	18 29				18 42	18 47	19 16							19 26	19 42	19 47	20 04		20 15						20 27
	d	18 41					18 54						19 26				19 54								20 21	20 41
Filton Abbey Wood	d	18 48					19 01						19 33				20 01								20 30	20 48
Bristol Parkway 7	a	18 51																								20 51
	d								19 12										20 07							
Patchway	d												19 37												20 34	
Pilning	d																									
Gloucester 7	d				18 30						18 58			19 25									19 58			
Lydney	d										19 17												20 17			
Chepstow	d										19 27												20 27			
Caldicot	d										19 34												20 35			
Severn Tunnel Jn	d										19 37		19 48										20 38		20 46	
Newport (South Wales)	a				19 12		19 24		19 35		19 50		19 59	20 05			20 22		20 31				20 50		20 58	
	d			19 00	19 14		19 24		19 35	19 43	19 52		20 00	20 05			20 22		20 32			20 47	20 52	20 59	21 03	
Cardiff Central 7	a			19 22	19 33		19 41		19 52	19 58	20 10		20 19	20 25			20 41		20 48			21 01	21 10	21 20	21 24	

		GW	GW	GW	GW	AW		GW	GW	GW	GW	SW	GW	AW	GW		AW	GW	GW	GW	GW	AW	AW	GW		
		1 ◇	◇	1 ◇	1 ◇	◇				1 ◇	◇	1 ◇	1 ◇	◇	1 ◇			◇	◇	1 ◇		◇		1 ◇		
								A			K	L					N		K							
		🍴		🍴	🍴	🛒				🍴			🍴	🛒	🍴					🍴						
Bath Spa 7	d	20 25	20 35		21 02				21 08	21 30	21 39	21 51	21 59					22 08	22 38	23 03	23 10					
Oldfield Park	d								21 10									22 10			23 13					
Keynsham	d								21 18			21 59						22 18			23 20					
Bristol Temple Meads 10	a	20 42	20 47		21 16				21 29	21 47	21 51	22 06	22 16					22 31	22 50	23 18	23 27					
	d		20 54					21 28			21 54								22 54							
Filton Abbey Wood	d		21 01					21 35			22 01								23 01							
Bristol Parkway 7	a																									
	d			21 06											22 14									23 29		
Patchway	d							21 40			22 07								23 05							
Pilning	d																									
Gloucester 7	d																21 58						22 58			
Lydney	d																22 17						23 17			
Chepstow	d																22 27						23 27			
Caldicot	d																22 35						23 35			
Severn Tunnel Jn	d							21 51			22 18						22 38		23 16				23 38			
Newport (South Wales)	a		21 23	21 31				22 08			22 35				22 45		22 55		23 33				23 57	00 01		
	d		21 23	21 31		21 37		22 10			22 36			22 42	22 46		22 57		23 35			23 53	23 58	00 01		
Cardiff Central 7	a		21 41	21 47		22 00		22 28			22 56			23 01	23 06		23 18		23 54			00 17	00 19	00 23		

For general notes see front of timetable
For details of catering facilities see Directory of Train Operators

A From Taunton (Table 134)
B From Warminster (Table 123) to Great Malvern (Table 71)
C From Cheltenham Spa (Table 57) to Maesteg (Table 128)
D From Warminster (Table 123) to Gloucester (Table 134)
E From Weymouth (Table 123) to Great Malvern (Table 71)
G From Newcastle (Table 51)
H From 5 July
J From Brighton (Table 123) to Cheltenham Spa (Table 57)
K From Portsmouth Harbour (Table 123)
L From London Waterloo (Table 160)
N From Cheltenham Spa (Table 57)

Due to Engineering Operations, services from Saturday 13 September on this Table had not been confirmed at time of going to press. These services will be issued in a special Supplement as soon as exact timings have been confirmed

until 7 September

Bath Spa, Bristol and Gloucester → Cardiff

Network Diagram - see first page of Table 132

		GW	GW	AW	GW	AW	GW	GW		GW	XC	GW	AW	GW	GW	AW		XC	GW	GW	GW	GW	GW	GW		GW
		1 ◇	1 ◇	◇	1 ◇	◇	1 ◇			1 ◇		1 ◇	A	🚌	🚌			◇	1 ◇	🚌	◇ B	1 ◇	🚌	🚌		1 ◇
Bath Spa 7	d		00 10		01 06		09 47	10 25		10 47											11 25	11 48				
Oldfield Park	d							10 27													11 28					
Keynsham	d							10 35													11 35					
Bristol Temple Meads 10	a		00 26		01 21		10 00	10 43		11 00											11 43	12 04				
	d																				11 47					
Filton Abbey Wood	d																				11 54					
Bristol Parkway 7	a																				11 58					
	d	23p29												10 07	10 10					11 30			12 06	12 07		
Patchway	d																						12a11			
Pilning	d																									
Gloucester 7	d										10 09	10 14				10 33		11 22	11 27							12 23
Lydney	d															10 52										
Chepstow	d															11 02										
Caldicot	d															11 10										
Severn Tunnel Jn	d													10 32		11 13								12 32		
Newport (South Wales)	a	00 01									10 51	10 57		10 52	10 50	11 25		12 05	12 09	12 10				12 52		13 05
	d	00 01		00 55		08 07					10 52	10 59	10 56	10 52		11 27		12 05	12 10					12 52		13 06
Cardiff Central 7	a	00 23		01 19		08 26					11 12	11 14	11 15	11 22		11 45		12 25	12 25					13 22		13 22

		GW	AW	GW	AW	XC	GW	GW		GW	GW	GW	XC	GW	GW	GW		GW	AW	AW	SW	AW	GW	XC		GW
		🚌	C	1 ◇	◇	◇	🚌	1 ◇		◇ B	1 ◇	🚌	◇	1 ◇	🚌	◇ D		1 ◇	◇	C	1 ◇	R	🚌	◇		🚌
Bath Spa 7	d			12 48						13 27	13 47					14 25		14 47			14 54					
Oldfield Park	d									13 30						14 27										
Keynsham	d									13 37						14 35										
Bristol Temple Meads 10	a			13 01						13 44	14 01					14 42		15 00			15 06					
	d									13 49						14 48										
Filton Abbey Wood	d									13 56						14 56										
Bristol Parkway 7	a									13 59						14 59										
	d	12 30					13 30					14 07			14 30								15 07			15 30
Patchway	d																									
Pilning	d																									
Gloucester 7	d		12 33			13 22		13 28					14 22	14 26						14 33				15 26		
Lydney	d		12 52																	14 52						
Chepstow	d		13 02																	15 02						
Caldicot	d		13 10																	15 10						
Severn Tunnel Jn	d		13 13									14 32								15 13			15 32			
Newport (South Wales)	a	13 10	13 25			14 05	14 10	14 10				14 52	15 05	15 09	15 10					15 25			15 52	16 08		16 10
	d		13 27		13 38	14 05		14 12				14 52	15 05	15 09					15 16	15 27		16 01	15 52	16 08		
Cardiff Central 7	a		13 45		13 53	14 25		14 27				15 22	15 25	15 25					15 35	15 45		16 15	16 22	16 29		

		GW	GW	GW	GW	XC	GW	GW		GW	AW	GW	GW	GW	AW	GW		XC	GW	GW	GW	GW	AW	GW		XC
		1 ◇	◇ B	1 ◇	🚌	◇		🚌		1 ◇	C	◇ B	1 ◇	🚌	R	🚌		◇	🚌	1 ◇	◇ B	1 ◇	R	🚌		◇
Bath Spa 7	d		15 28	15 47			16 10					16 28	16 47								17 27	17 47				
Oldfield Park	d						16 12														17 30					
Keynsham	d						16 20														17 37					
Bristol Temple Meads 10	a		15 40	16 00			16 28					16 41	17 00								17 44	18 00				
	d		15 48									16 48									17 49					
Filton Abbey Wood	d		15 55									16 56									17 56					
Bristol Parkway 7	a		15 58									16 59									17 59					
	d				16 07			16 30						17 06		17 07			17 30					18 07		
Patchway	d													17a11												
Pilning	d																									
Gloucester 7	d	15 30				16 26				16 30	16 33							17 22		17 33						18 22
Lydney	d										16 52															
Chepstow	d										17 02															
Caldicot	d										17 10															
Severn Tunnel Jn	d				16 32						17 13					17 32								18 32		
Newport (South Wales)	a	16 13			16 52	17 05		17 10		17 12	17 25					17 52		18 05	18 10	18 15				18 52		19 05
	d	16 14			16 52	17 05				17 13	17 27				18 01	17 52		18 05		18 15			18 39	18 52		19 05
Cardiff Central 7	a	16 29			17 22	17 25				17 29	17 45				18 13	18 22		18 25		18 31			18 55	19 22		19 25

For general notes see front of timetable
For details of catering facilities see Directory of Train Operators

A To Barry Island (Table 130)
B From Portsmouth Harbour (Table 123)
C From Cheltenham Spa (Table 57)
D From Brighton (Table 123)

Due to Engineering Operations, services from Sunday 14 September on this Table had not been confirmed at time of going to press. These services will be issued in a special Supplement as soon as exact timings have been confirmed

Sundays

until 7 September

Bath Spa, Bristol and Gloucester → Cardiff

Network Diagram - see first page of Table 132

		GW	GW	GW	AW	GW	GW	AW		GW	AW	GW	XC	GW	GW	GW		GW	GW	GW	GW	GW	GW	GW		GW
		1 ◇				◇	1 ◇			◇	R		◇		1 ◇	1 ◇		◇	1 ◇				◇	1 ◇		◇
					A	B												B								B
		☕		🚌		🛒	☕				🛒	🚌		🚌	☕	☕		🛒	☕	🚌	🚌	🚌		☕		🛒
Bath Spa 7	d		18 10			18 27	18 47			19 04						19 17		19 28	19 47				20 02			20 28
Oldfield Park	d		18 13							19 06													20 04			
Keynsham	d		18 20							19 14													20 13			
Bristol Temple Meads 10	a		18 28			18 40	19 01			19 22						19 38		19 40	20 00				20 20			20 40
	d					18 49												19 49								20 49
Filton Abbey Wood	d					18 56												19 56								20 56
Bristol Parkway 7	a					18 59												19 59								20 59
	d			18 30								19 07		19 30						20 06	20 07	20 20				
Patchway	d																			20a11						
Pilning	d																									
Gloucester 7	d	18 27			18 33								19 22		19 29									20 26		
Lydney	d				18 52																					
Chepstow	d				19 02																					
Caldicot	d				19 10																					
Severn Tunnel Jn	d				19 13							19 32									20 32					
Newport (South Wales)	a	19 09		19 10	19 25							19 52	20 05	20 10	20 11						20 52	21 00		21 08		
	d	19 09			19 27			19 38			20 01	19 52	20 05		20 12						20 52			21 10		
Cardiff Central 7	a	19 27			19 48			19 55			20 15	20 22	20 25		20 28						21 22			21 25		

		GW	AW	AW	GW	SW	GW	AW		GW	GW	GW	GW	GW	GW	GW		AW	GW	GW	GW	GW	GW	GW		
		1 ◇	R			1 ◇	◇	R			1 ◇	◇	1 ◇			1 ◇			◇	◇	1 ◇		1 ◇	1 ◇		
				A		C						B								B						
		☕	🛒		🚌			🛒		🚌	☕	🛒	☕	🚌	🚌	☕				🛒		🚌	☕	☕		
Bath Spa 7	d	20 47				21 01	21 11					21 28	21 47						22 16	22 29	22 47			23 52		
Oldfield Park	d						21 13												22 18							
Keynsham	d					21 08	21 21												22 27							
Bristol Temple Meads 10	a	21 00				21 16	21 28					21 44	22 02						22 34	22 42	23 03			00 06		
	d											21 47								22 49						
Filton Abbey Wood	d											21 56								22 56						
Bristol Parkway 7	a											21 59								22 59						
	d				21 07					21 35				22 06	22 07							23 07				
Patchway	d													22a11												
Pilning	d																									
Gloucester 7	d			20 33							21 31					22 26		22 37					23 28			
Lydney	d			20 52														22 56								
Chepstow	d			21 02														23 06								
Caldicot	d			21 10														23 14								
Severn Tunnel Jn	d			21 13	21 32										22 32			23 17				23 32				
Newport (South Wales)	a			21 25	21 52					22 15	22 21				22 52	23 16		23 34				23 52	00 18			
	d		21 18	21 27	21 52			22 03			22 22				22 52	23 17		23 36				23 52	00 20			
Cardiff Central 7	a		21 37	21 45	22 22			22 27			22 41				23 22	23 36		23 57				00 22	00 40			

For general notes see front of timetable
For details of catering facilities see
Directory of Train Operators

A From Cheltenham Spa (Table 57)
B From Portsmouth Harbour (Table 123)
C From London Waterloo (Table 160)

Due to Engineering Operations, services from Sunday 14 September on this Table had not been confirmed at time of going to press. These services will be issued in a special Supplement as soon as exact timings have been confirmed

Bristol → Avonmouth and Severn Beach

Network Diagram - see first page of Table 132

Miles			GW	GW	GW	GW	GW	GW	GW	GW	GW	GW ◇	GW	GW	GW ◇	GW	GW	GW		GW	GW	GW	GW	GW	GW	GW
0	**Bristol Temple Meads** 10	d	05 25	05 25	06 22	06 31	06 50	07 05	07 19	07 46	08 03	08 10	08 36	08 44	09 10	09 15	09 46	10 03		10 34	10 46	11 16	11 46	12 03	12 19	12 34
1	Lawrence Hill	d	05 28		06 25	06 34	06 54	07 07	07 22	07 49	08 05	08 13	08 38	08 49	09 13	09 17	09 49			10 36	10 49	11 18	11 49		12 22	12 36
1½	Stapleton Road	d	05 30	05 52	06a27	06 36	06a56	07 09	07a24	07a51	08 07	08a15	08 40	08a50	09a15	09 19	09a51	10 07		10 38	10a51	11 20	11a51	12 07	12a24	12 38
2¾	Montpelier	d	05 34	05 56		06 40		07 14			08 12		08 45			09 24		10 11		10 43		11 24		12 11		12 43
3¼	Redland	d	05 36	05 58		06 42		07 16			08 14		08 47			09 26		10 13		10 45		11 26		12 13		12 45
4	Clifton Down	d	05 39	06 01		06 46		07 19			08 18		08b52			09 30		10 18		10 49		11 29		12 18		12 49
6	Sea Mills	d	05 43	06 05		06 50		07 23			08 22		08 56			09 34		10 22		10 53		11 33		12 22		12 53
7¼	Shirehampton	d	05 46	06 09		06 53		07 26			08 25		08 59			09 37		10 25		10 56		11 37		12 25		12 56
9	Avonmouth 2	d	05 50	06a12		06 57		07 31			08a30		09a05			09 41		10a30		11a01		11 40		12a30		13a01
10	St Andrews Road	d	05x53			07x00		07x34								09x44						11x44				
13½	**Severn Beach**	a	06 02			07 08		07 42								09 52						11 52				

		GW	GW	GW	GW	GW	GW	GW	GW	GW	GW	GW	GW	GW	GW	GW	GW	GW	GW	GW	GW	GW	GW	GW		
Bristol Temple Meads 10	d	12 46	13 15	13 46	14 03	14 34	14 46	15 16	15 46	16 03	16 34	16 46	17 10	17 16	17 46	18 04	18 19	18 46	19 33	19 46	20 34	20 19	21 19	22 15		
Lawrence Hill	d	12 49	13 18	13 49		14 36	14 49	15 19	15 49		16 36	16 49	17 13	17 18	17 49	18 07	18 22	18 48	19 36	19 49	20 37	20 22	21 22	22 18		
Stapleton Road	d	12a51	13 19	13a51	14 07	14 38	14a51	15 20	15a51	16 07	16 38	16a51	17a15	17 20	17a51	18 09	18a24	18a51	19 38	19a51	20 39	20a24	21a24	22 19		
Montpelier	d		13 23		14 11	14 43		15 24		16 11	16 43			17 24		18 13			19 41		20 42			22 23		
Redland	d		13 25		14 13	14 45		15 26		16 13	16 45			17 26		18 15			19 43		20 44			22 25		
Clifton Down	d		13 29		14 18	14 49		15 29		16 18	16 49			17 29		18 18			19 46		20 47			22 29		
Sea Mills	d		13 33		14 22	14 53		15 33		16 22	16 53			17 33		18 22			19 50		20 51			22 33		
Shirehampton	d		13 37		14 25	14 56		15 37		16 25	16 56			17 37		18 26			19 54		20 55			22 36		
Avonmouth 2	d		13 40		14a29	15a01		15 40		16a30	17a01			17 40		18 30			19a58		20 59			22 40		
St Andrews Road	d		13x44					15x44						17x44		18 33					21 02			22x43		
Severn Beach	a		13 52					15 52						17 52		18 41					21 10			22 51		

Saturdays

		GW	GW	GW		GW	GW	GW		GW	GW	GW		GW	GW	GW		GW	GW	GW		GW	GW	GW		GW
Bristol Temple Meads 10	d	06 03	06 34	06 50		07 16	07 46	08 03		08 34	09 16	09 19		09 46	10 03	10 34		10 46	11 16	11 46		12 03	12 46	12 34		13 16
Lawrence Hill	d		06 36	06 53		07 18	07 49	08 05		08 36	09 19	09 22		09 49		10 37		10 49	11 19	11 49			12 49	12 37		13 19
Stapleton Road	d	06 07	06 38	06a55		07 20	07a51	08 07		08 38	09 21	09a24		09a51	10 06	10 39		10a51	11 21	11a51		12 06	12a51	12 39		13 21
Montpelier	d	06 11	06 43			07 24		08 11		08 43	09 24				10 10	10 42			11 24			12 10		12 42		13 24
Redland	d	06 13	06 45			07 26		08 13		08 45	09 26				10 12	10 44			11 26			12 12		12 44		13 26
Clifton Down	d	06 18	06 49			07 29		08 18		08 49	09 29				10c17	10 47			11 29			12 15		12 47		13 29
Sea Mills	d	06 22	06 53			07 33		08 22		08 53	09 33				10 21	10 51			11 33			12 19		12 51		13 33
Shirehampton	d	06 25	06 56			07 37		08 25		08 56	09 37				10 24	10 55			11 37			12 22		12 55		13 37
Avonmouth 2	d	06a30	07a01			07 40		08a30		09a01	09 41				10a28	10a58			11 41			12a26		12a58		13 41
St Andrews Road	d					07x44					09x44								11x44							13x44
Severn Beach	a					07 52					09 51								11 51							13 51

		GW	GW	GW		GW	GW	GW		GW	GW	GW		GW	GW	GW		GW	GW	GW		GW	GW			
Bristol Temple Meads 10	d	13 46	14 03	14 34		14 46	15 16	15 46		16 03	16 34	16 46		17 16	17 46	18 16		18 46	19 16	19 46		20 16	22 25			
Lawrence Hill	d	13 49		14 37		14 49	15 19	15 49			16 37	16 49		17 19	17 49	18 19		18 49	19 19	19 49		20 19	22 28			
Stapleton Road	d	13a51	14 06	14 39		14a51	15 21	15a51		16 06	16 39	16a51		17 21	17a51	18 21		18a51	19 21	19a51		20 21	22 30			
Montpelier	d		14 10	14 42			15 24			16 10	16 42			17 24		18 24			19 24			20 24	22 33			
Redland	d		14 12	14 44			15 26			16 12	16 44			17 26		18 26			19 26			20 26	22 35			
Clifton Down	d		14 15	14 47			15 29			16 15	16 47			17 29		18 29			19 29			20 29	22 38			
Sea Mills	d		14 19	14 51			15 33			16 19	16 51			17 33		18 33			19 33			20 33	22 42			
Shirehampton	d		14 22	14 55			15 37			16 22	16 55			17 37		18 37			19 37			20 37	22 46			
Avonmouth 2	d		14a26	14a58			15 41			16a26	16a58			17 41		18 41			19 41			20 41	22 50			
St Andrews Road	d						15x44							17x44		18x44			19x44			20x44	22x53			
Severn Beach	a						15 51							17 51		18 51			19 51			20 51	23 00			

Sundays

until 7 September

		GW			GW			GW			GW			GW			GW			GW			GW		
Bristol Temple Meads 10	d	10 23			11 23			12 23			13 23			14 23			15 23			16 23			17 23		
Lawrence Hill	d	10 25			11 25			12 25			13 25			14 25			15 25			16 25			17 25		
Stapleton Road	d	10 27			11 27			12 27			13 27			14 27			15 27			16 27			17 27		
Montpelier	d	10 31			11 31			12 31			13 31			14 31			15 31			16 31			17 31		
Redland	d	10 33			11 33			12 33			13 33			14 33			15 33			16 33			17 33		
Clifton Down	d	10 36			11 36			12 36			13 36			14 36			15 36			16 36			17 36		
Sea Mills	d	10 40			11 40			12 40			13 40			14 40			15 40			16 40			17 40		
Shirehampton	d	10 44			11 44			12 44			13 44			14 44			15 44			16 44			17 44		
Avonmouth 2	d	10a49			11a49			12a49			13a49			14a49			15a49			16a49			17a49		
St Andrews Road	d																								
Severn Beach	a																								

For general notes see front of timetable
For details of catering facilities see Directory of Train Operators

b Arr. 0849
c Arr. 1014

No Sunday Service from 14 September

Severn Beach and Avonmouth → Bristol

Network Diagram - see first page of Table 132

Mondays to Fridays

Miles	Station		GW	GW	GW	GW	GW	GW	GW	GW	GW	GW	GW	GW	GW	GW	GW	GW	GW	GW	GW	GW	GW
											◇					◇							◇
0	**Severn Beach**	d	06 03				07 20	07 54					09 54					11 54				13 54	
3½	St Andrews Road	d	06x09				07x26	08x00					10x00					12x00				14x00	
4½	Avonmouth 2	d	06 14	06 32			07 31	08 04		08 38		09 17	10 04		10 35		11 15	12 04	12 35		13 15	14 04	
6	Shirehampton	d	06 17	06 35			07 34	08 07		08 41		09 20	10 07		10 38		11 18	12 07	12 38		13 18	14 07	
7½	Sea Mills	d	06 21	06 39			07 38	08 11		08 45		09 24	10 11		10 42		11 22	12 11	12 42		13 22	14 11	
9½	Clifton Down	d	06 26	06 45			07 43	08 17		08 52		09 29	10 16		10 48		11 31	12 16	12 48		13 31	14 16	
10¼	Redland	d	06 29	06 47			07 46	08 19		08 54		09 32	10 19		10 50		11 34	12 19	12 50		13 34	14 19	
10¾	Montpelier	d	06 31	06 49			07 48	08 21		08 56		09 34	10 21		10 52		11 36	12 21	12 52		13 36	14 21	
12	Stapleton Road	d	06 35	06 53	07 07	07 33	07 52	08 25	08 54	09 00	09 28	09 38	10 25	10 28	10 56	11 28	11 40	12 25	12 56	13 28	13 40	14 25	14 27
12½	Lawrence Hill	d	06 37	06 56	07 09	07 35	07 55	08 27	08 56	09 02	09 30	09 40		10 30	10 58	11 30	11 42		12 58	13 30	13 42		14 29
13½	**Bristol Temple Meads 10**	a	06 41	07 02	07 15	07 40	07 58	08 32	09 02	09 09	09 35	09 46	10 32	10 36	11 05	11 35	11 48	12 32	13 05	13 36	13 48	14 32	14 35

Station		GW	GW	GW	GW	GW	GW	GW	GW	GW	GW	GW	GW	GW	GW	GW	GW	GW	GW	GW	GW	GW
							◇			◇								◇				FX
Severn Beach	d					15 54								17 54		18 50			21 29		22 54	
St Andrews Road	d					16x00								18x00		18 56			21 35		23x00	
Avonmouth 2	d	14 35			15 15	16 04			16 35		17 15			18 04		19 00	20 02		21 39		23 04	
Shirehampton	d	14 38			15 18	16 07			16 38		17 18			18 07		19 04	20 05		21 43		23 07	
Sea Mills	d	14 42			15 22	16 11			16 42		17 22			18 11		19 08	20 09		21 47		23 11	
Clifton Down	d	14 48			15 31	16 16			16 48		17 31			18 29		19 13	20 14		21 52		23 16	
Redland	d	14 50			15 34	16 19			16 50		17 34			18 31		19 15	20 17		21 54		23 19	
Montpelier	d	14 52			15 36	16 21			16 52		17 36			18 33		19 17	20 19		21 56		23 21	
Stapleton Road	d	14 56	14 58	15 28	15 40	16 25	16 24	16 54	17 00	17 28	17 40	17 54	18 18	18 37	18 28	19 22	20 24	20 28	22 01	21 45	23 25	23 57
Lawrence Hill	d	14 58	15 00	15 30	15 42		16 30	16 56	17 02	17 30	17 42	17 56	18 20	18 40	18 31	19 24	20 26	20 30	22 03	21 48	23 27	23 59
Bristol Temple Meads 10	a	15 05	15 07	15 36	15 48	16 32	16 36	17 02	17 08	17 36	17 48	18 02	18 25	18 44	18 37	19 28	20 31	20 37	22 08	21 53	23 32	00 04

Saturdays

Station		GW	GW	GW	GW	GW	GW	GW	GW	GW	GW	GW	GW	GW	GW	GW	GW	GW	GW	GW
							◇					◇			◇					◇ 🛒
Severn Beach	d			07 54					09 54					11 54					13 54	
St Andrews Road	d			08x00					10x00					12x00					14x00	
Avonmouth 2	d	06 35	07 15	08 04		08 35		09 16	10 04		10 34		11 18	12 04		12 36		13 18	14 04	
Shirehampton	d	06 38	07 18	08 07		08 38		09 19	10 08		10 37		11 21	12 08		12 39		13 21	14 08	
Sea Mills	d	06 42	07 22	08 11		08 42		09 23	10 12		10 41		11 25	12 12		12 43		13 25	14 12	
Clifton Down	d	06 48	07 31	08 16		08b48		09c31	10 18		10e49		11 31	12 18		12 49		13 31	14 18	
Redland	d	06 50	07 34	08 19		08 50		09 34	10 20		10 52		11 34	12 20		12 52		13 34	14 20	
Montpelier	d	06 52	07 36	08 21		08 52		09 36	10 22		10 54		11 36	12 22		12 54		13 36	14 22	
Stapleton Road	d	06 56	07 40	08 25	08 29	08 56	09 27	09 40	10 27	10 29	10 58	11 29	11 40	12 27	12 29	12 58	13 27	13 40	14 27	14 28
Lawrence Hill	d	07 06	07 42	08 27	08 31	08 58	09 29	09 42		10 31	11 00	11 31	11 42		12 31	13 00	13 29	13 42		14 30
Bristol Temple Meads 10	a	07 05	07 48	08 32	08 35	09 05	09 35	09 46	10 31	10 36	11 04	11 35	11 46	12 31	12 36	13 04	13 35	13 46	14 31	14 34

Station		GW	GW	GW	GW	GW	GW	GW	GW	GW	GW	GW	GW	GW	GW	GW	GW	GW
		🛒					◇		◇						◇			
Severn Beach	d					15 54						18 03		19 03		20 03	21 03	23 03
St Andrews Road	d					16x00						18x09		19x09		20x09	21x09	23x09
Avonmouth 2	d		14 36		15 18	16 04		16 36		17 18		18 13		19 13		20 13	21 13	23 13
Shirehampton	d		14 39		15 21	16 08		16 39		17 21		18 17		19 17		20 17	21 17	23 17
Sea Mills	d		14 43		15 25	16 12		16 43		17 25		18 21		19 21		20 21	21 21	23 21
Clifton Down	d		14 49		15 31	16 18		16 49		17 31		18 27		19 27		20 27	21 27	23 27
Redland	d		14 52		15 34	16 20		16 52		17 34		18 29		19 29		20 29	21 29	23 29
Montpelier	d		14 54		15 36	16 22		16 54		17 36		18 31		19 31		20 31	21 31	23 31
Stapleton Road	d	14 32	14 58	15 27	15 40	16 27	16 27	16 58	17 28	17 40	18 29	18 36	19 28	19 36	20 31	20 36	21 36	23 36
Lawrence Hill	d	14 34	15 00	15 29	15 42		16 29	17 00	17 30	17 42	18 31	18 38	19 30	19 38	20 33	20 38	21 38	23 38
Bristol Temple Meads 10	a	14 39	15 04	15 35	15 46	16 31	16 34	17 04	17 35	17 46	18 35	18 41	19 36	19 41	20 40	20 41	21 41	23 41

For general notes see front of timetable
For details of catering facilities see Directory of Train Operators

b Arr. 0846
c Arr. 0928
e Arr. 1046

Table 133

Sundays

until 7 September

Severn Beach and Avonmouth → Bristol

Network Diagram - see first page of Table 132

		GW			GW			GW			GW			GW			GW			GW			GW		
Severn Beach	d																								
St Andrews Road	d																								
Avonmouth 2	d	10 52			11 52			12 52			13 52			14 52			15 52			16 52			17 52		
Shirehampton	d	10 55			11 55			12 55			13 55			14 55			15 55			16 55			17 55		
Sea Mills	d	10 59			11 59			12 59			13 59			14 59			15 59			16 59			17 59		
Clifton Down	d	11 04			12 04			13 04			14 04			15 04			16 04			17 04			18 04		
Redland	d	11 07			12 07			13 07			14 07			15 07			16 07			17 07			18 07		
Montpelier	d	11 09			12 09			13 09			14 09			15 09			16 09			17 09			18 09		
Stapleton Road	d	11 13			12 13			13 13			14 13			15 13			16 13			17 13			18 13		
Lawrence Hill	d	11 15			12 15			13 15			14 15			15 15			16 15			17 15			18 15		
Bristol Temple Meads 10	a	11 20			12 20			13 20			14 20			15 20			16 20			17 20			18 20		

For general notes see front of timetable
For details of catering facilities see Directory of Train Operators

No Sunday Service from 14 September

Table 134

Gloucester → Taunton

Mondays to Fridays

Network Diagram - see first page of Table 132

Miles			GW	GW	GW	GW	GW	GW	GW	GW	GW	XC	GW	XC	GW	GW	GW	XC	GW	GW	GW	XC	GW	GW	GW	XC
			MX																							
				◇		◇			◇			1 ◇		1 ◇	◇		◇	1 ◇			1 ◇	1 ◇	◇		◇	1 ◇
			A			B	C			D			E				G		A						H	
									⊼			⊡		⊡	⊼			⊡			⊠	⊡	⊼			⊡
0	**Gloucester 7**	d						06 21					07 12				07 48								08 42	
13	Cam & Dursley	d						06 35					07 25				08 02								08 57	
28	Yate	d						06 48					07 39				08 15								09 10	
—	London Paddington 15 ⊖	d																			07 30					
—	Bath Spa 7	d																			08 55					
34	**Bristol Parkway 7**	a						06 58					07 47				08 24								09 19	
—		d						06 58		07 25			07 48	07 55		08 12	08 24	08 25		08 46		08 55		09 12	09 19	09 25
35¼	Filton Abbey Wood	d	22p52					07 02	07 09	07 28		07 47	07 51		08 09	08 15	08 27		08 42	08 49			09 09	09 15	09 22	
38¼	Stapleton Road	d					06 43	07 07		07 33										08 53					09 28	
38¾	Lawrence Hill	d					06 45	07 09		07 35										08 55					09 30	
39¾	**Bristol Temple Meads 10**	a	23p03				06 49	07 15	07 18	07 40		07 53	08 02	08 11	08 18	08 23	08 36	08 41	08 52	09 02	09 10	09 11	09 18	09 23	09 35	09 41
—		d	23p06	05 30	06 19	06 46	06 51	07 19			07 51			08 11		08 25		08 44	08 55		09 13			09 25		09 44
40¾	Bedminster	d	23p10				06 54				07 54					08 28								09 28		
41½	Parson Street	d	23p13				06 57				07 56					08 30								09 30		
47¾	Nailsea & Backwell	d	23p20		06 29		07 05	07 29			08 04					08 38			09 05					09 38		
51¾	Yatton	d	23p26		06 35		07 10	07 35			08 10					08 44			09 11					09 44		
55¾	Worle	d	23p32		06 41		07 16	07 41			08 16					08 50			09 17					09 50		
58½	Weston Milton	d	23p37				07 20				08 21					08 55								09 55		
59¾	**Weston-super-Mare**	a	23p40	05 49	06 46	07 05	07 25	07 46			08 25					08 59			09 23					09 59		
—		d	23p42	05 51	06 50	07 07		07 48																		
67¼	Highbridge & Burnham	d	23p53		07 00	07 17		07 59																		
73½	Bridgwater	d	00 02		07 08	07 25		08 07																		
85¼	**Taunton**	a	00 14	06 17	07 25	07 38		08 23						08 42				09 15			09 45					10 15

		GW	GW	XC	GW	GW	GW	XC	GW		XC	GW	GW	GW	XC	GW	GW	XC	GW	GW	GW	XC	GW	XC	GW	GW
				1 ◇	◇			R 1			R 1	◇		◇	1 ◇	1 ◇		1 ◇	◇		◇	1 ◇		1 ◇	◇	
			A				J		A					H		K	A				L		A			A
				⊡	⊼			⊡			⊡	⊼			⊡	⊡		⊡	⊼			⊡		⊡	⊼	
Gloucester 7	d						09 42							10 42							11 42					
Cam & Dursley	d						09 57							10 57							11 57					
Yate	d						10 10							11 10							12 10					
London Paddington 15 ⊖	d															10 00										
Bath Spa 7	d															11 25										
Bristol Parkway 7	a						10 19							11 19							12 19					
	d	09 34		09 55		10 12	10 19	10 25			10 55		11 12	11 19	11 25			11 55		12 12	12 19	12 25		12 55		
Filton Abbey Wood	d	09 37	09 42		10 09	10 15	10 22		10 42			11 09	11 15	11 22			11 42		12 09	12 15	12 22		12 42		13 09	
Stapleton Road	d	09 42					10 27							11 28												
Lawrence Hill	d						10 29							11 30												
Bristol Temple Meads 10	a	09 49	09 52	10 11	10 18	10 23	10 35	10 41	10 52		11 11	11 18	11 23	11 35	11 41	11 42	11 52	12 11	12 18	12 23	12 35	12 41	12 52	13 11	13 17	
	d		09 55			10 25		10 44	10 53		11 14		11 25		11 44	11 45	11 53			12 25		12 44	12 53	13 11		
Bedminster	d					10 28							11 28							12 28						
Parson Street	d					10 30							11 30							12 30						
Nailsea & Backwell	d		10 05			10 38			11 04				11 38				12 04			12 38			13 04			←
Yatton	d		10 11			10 44			11 10				11 44				12 10			12 44			13 10			
Worle	d		10 17			10 50			11 16				11 50				12 16			12 50			13 16			13 16
Weston Milton	d					10 55							11 55							12 55			→			
Weston-super-Mare	a		10 22			10 59			11 21		11 32		11 59			12 06	12 21			12 59						13 21
	d		10 23						11 23		11 42					12 07	12 23									13 23
Highbridge & Burnham	d		10 34						11 34								12 34									13 34
Bridgwater	d		10 42						11 42								12 42									13 42
Taunton	a		10 59					11 15	11 59		12 03				12 15	12 29	12 59					13 15		13 42		13 59

		GW	GW	XC	GW	XC	GW	GW	GW	XC	GW	GW	XC	GW	GW	GW	GW		XC	GW	XC	GW	GW	GW	GW	XC
				R 1 ◇		1 ◇	◇		◇	1 ◇			R 1	◇					R 1		1 ◇	1 ◇	◇		◇	R 1
			D		A				N		A				A		D			A					N	
				⊡		⊡	⊼			⊡			⊡	⊼					⊡		⊡	⊡	⊼			⊡
Gloucester 7	d		12 42						13 42								14 42								15 42	
Cam & Dursley	d		12 57						13 57								14 57								15 57	
Yate	d		13 10						14 10								15 10								16 10	
London Paddington 15 ⊖	d																					14 30				
Bath Spa 7	d																					16 00				
Bristol Parkway 7	a		13 19						14 19								15 19								16 19	
	d	13 12	13 19	13 25		13 55		14 12	14 19	14 25		14 47	14 55			15 12	15 19		15 25		15 55			16 12	16 19	16 25
Filton Abbey Wood	d	13 15	13 22		13 42		14 09	14 15	14 22		14 42	14 50		15 09		15 15	15 22			15 42			16 09	16 15	16 22	
Stapleton Road	d		13 28						14 27			14 58					15 28								16 27	
Lawrence Hill	d		13 30						14 29			15 00					15 30								16 29	
Bristol Temple Meads 10	a	13 23	13 36	13 41	13 52	14 11	14 19	14 23	14 35	14 41	14 52	15 07	15 11	15 18		15 23	15 36		15 41	15 51	16 11	16 15	16 18	16 23	16 35	16 41
	d	13 25		13 44	13 53			14 25		14 44	14 53		15 11			15 25			15 44	15 53		16 18		16 25		16 44
Bedminster	d	13 28						14 28								15 28				15 56				16 28		
Parson Street	d	13 30						14 30								15 30				15 58				16 30		
Nailsea & Backwell	d	13 38			14 04			14 38			15 04					15 38				16 06		16 26		16 38		
Yatton	d	13 44			14 10			14 44			15 10				←	15 44				16 12		16 32		16 44		
Worle	d	13 50			14 16			14 50			15 16				15 16	15 50				16 18		16 38		16 50		
Weston Milton	d	13 55						14 55			→					15 55				16 22				16 55		
Weston-super-Mare	a	13 59			14 21			14 59							15 22	15 59				16 25		16 48		16 59		
	d				14 23										15 23					16 25						
Highbridge & Burnham	d				14 34										15 34					16 37						
Bridgwater	d				14 42										15 42					16 45						
Taunton	a			14 15	14 59					15 15			15 42		16 01				16 15	17 00						17 15

For general notes see front of timetable
For details of catering facilities see Directory of Train Operators

- **A** From Cardiff Central (Table 132)
- **B** To Penzance (Table 135)
- **C** From Severn Beach (Table 133)
- **D** To Westbury (Table 123)
- **E** From Cheltenham Spa (Table 57)
- **G** From Worcester Shrub Hill (Table 57) to Weymouth (Table 123)
- **H** To Weymouth (Table 123)
- **J** From Great Malvern (Table 71) to Westbury (Table 123)
- **K** **Torbay Express**
- **L** From Great Malvern (Table 71) to Brighton (Table 123)
- **N** From Great Malvern (Table 71) to Weymouth (Table 123)

Gloucester → Taunton

Network Diagram - see first page of Table 132

		GW	GW	XC	GW	GW	GW	GW	GW	XC	GW	GW	XC	GW	GW	GW	GW	XC	GW	GW	GW	GW	XC	GW	XC	GW
				1 ◇		1 ◇	◇		◇	R 1			1 ◇	1 ◇	◇			R 1	1 ◇		1 ◇	◇	R 1		1 ◇	
		A	B		A				C		A	B					D			A				E		
				☕		☕	🛒			☕			☕	☕	🛒			☕	☕		☕	🛒	☕		☕	
Gloucester 7	d								16 42								17 40						18 38	18 42		
Cam & Dursley	d								16 57								17 55							18 57		
Yate	d								17 10								18 09							19 10		
London Paddington 15 ⊖	d					15 30								16 30							17 30					
Bath Spa 7	d					17 00								18 00							19 00					
Bristol Parkway 7	a								17 19								18 18						19 05	19 19		
	d		16 46	16 55				17 12	17 19	17 25		17 46	17 55			18 11	18 19	18 25					19 06	19 19	19 25	19 31
Filton Abbey Wood	d	16 42	16 49				17 09	17 15	17 22		17 42	17 49			18 09	18 14	18 22			18 42		19 09		19 22		19 34
Stapleton Road	d		16 54						17 28			17 54				18 18	18 28							19 28		
Lawrence Hill	d		16 56						17 30			17 56				18 20	18 31									
Bristol Temple Meads 10	a	16 51	17 02	17 11		17 15	17 18	17 23	17 36	17 41	17 52	18 02	18 11	18 15	18 18	18 25	18 37	18 41		18 52	19 15	19 18	19 22	19 35	19 41	19 45
	d	16 53		17 11		17 18		17 25		17 44	17 53			18 22		18 25		18 44		18 55	19 15				19 44	
Bedminster	d	16 56						17 28			17 56					18 28				18 59						
Parson Street	d	16 58						17 30			17 58					18 30				19 02						
Nailsea & Backwell	d	17 06				17 28		17 38			18 06			18 32		18 38				19 10	19 25					
Yatton	d	17 12			←	17 34		17 44			18 12			18 38		18 44				19 15	19 32					
Worle	d	17 18			17 18	17 40		17 50			18 18			18 44		18 50				19 21	19 38					
Weston Milton	d	→			17 22			17 55			18 22					18 55				19 25	19 43					
Weston-super-Mare	a				17 25	17 51		18 00			18 24			18 52		18 59				19 29	→					
	d				17 27						18 27			18 56						19 30						
Highbridge & Burnham	d				17 37						18 37			19 06					←	19 41						
Bridgwater	d				17 45						18 45			19 14					19 14	19 49						
Taunton	a			17 42	18 01					18 15	19 01			→				19 15	19 30	20 04					20 15	

		GW	GW	XC	GW	GW	GW	GW	XC	GW	GW	XC	GW	XC	GW	GW	GW	XC	GW FO	GW FX	GW	GW	XC	GW
		1 ◇		R 1	1 ◇	◇		◇	1 ◇		1 ◇	R 1	◇	1 ◇				1 ◇			1 ◇	1 ◇	1 ◇	
			A					G		A					H		J		A	A				A
		☕			☕	🛒					☕	☕	🛒								☕	☕		
Gloucester 7	d							19 42									21 15					22 49		
Cam & Dursley	d							19 57									21 28							
Yate	d							20 10									21 41							
London Paddington 15 ⊖	d				18 30						19 30										21 45			
Bath Spa 7	d				20 00						20 55										23 21			
Bristol Parkway 7	a							20 19									21 50					23 16		
	d			19 55			20 11	20 19	20 25			20 55		21 25			21 50	22 25				23 18	23 25	
Filton Abbey Wood	d		19 42			20 09	20 14	20 22		20 38			21 09		21 41				22 52	22 52				23 50
Stapleton Road	d							20 28							21 45									23 57
Lawrence Hill	d							20 30							21 48									23 59
Bristol Temple Meads 10	a		19 52	20 11	20 15	20 18	20 25	20 34	20 41	20 48	21 10	21 11	21 18	21 41	21 53		22 02	22 41	23 03	23 03	23 33	23 37	23 41	00 04
	d		19 55	20 14	20 15				20 44	20 55	21 13			21 44		21 55			23 06	23 06	23 36			
Bedminster	d		19 59							20 59						21 59			23 10	23 10				
Parson Street	d		20 02							21 01						22 01			23 12	23 13				
Nailsea & Backwell	d		20 10		20 28					21 09	21 21					22 09			23 19	23 20	23s45			
Yatton	d		20 15		20 34					21 15	21 27					22 15			23 26	23 26	23s51			
Worle	d	←	20 21		20 42					21 21	21 33					22 21			23 32	23 32	23s57			
Weston Milton	d	19 43	20 25		20 47					21 25						22 25			23 37	23 37				
Weston-super-Mare	a	19 47	20 29	20 39	20 53					21 28	21 44					22 28			23 40	23 40	00s04			
	d	19 57	20 30							21 30						22 30			23 42	23 42				
Highbridge & Burnham	d	20 07	20 41							21 41						22 41			23 52	23 53	00s15			
Bridgwater	d	20 14	20 49							21 49						22 49			00 01	00 02	00s23			
Taunton	a	20 27	21 04						21 15	22 03				22 15		23 03			00 14	00 14	00s35			

Saturdays

until 6 September

		GW	GW	GW	GW	GW	GW	GW	GW	XC	GW	GW	GW	GW	GW	XC	GW	GW	GW	GW	GW	GW
			◇	1 ◇		◇			◇	1 ◇			◇			1 ◇		1 ◇	◇			◇
		A	K								A	J			L		A			A		C
			🛒	☕		🛒				☕			🛒			☕		☕	🛒			
Gloucester 7	d							06 21				07 15			07 40							08 42
Cam & Dursley	d							06 36				07 29			07 55							08 56
Yate	d							06 50				07 43			08 09							09 10
London Paddington 15 ⊖	d																	07 30				
Bath Spa 7	d																	08 56				
Bristol Parkway 7	a							07 00				07 53			08 18							09 19
	d			05 41				07 00				07 53		08 12	08 20	08 25					09 12	09 19
Filton Abbey Wood	d	22p52						07 03	07 09		07 42	07 57	08 09	08 15	08 23		08 43		09 09		09 15	09 23
Stapleton Road	d														08 29							09 27
Lawrence Hill	d														08 31							09 29
Bristol Temple Meads 10	a	23p03		05 52				07 13	07 18		07 52	08 05	08 18	08 23	08 35	08 41	08 52	09 10	09 18		09 23	09 35
	d	23p06	05 31		06 20	06 48	06 53	07 22		07 35	07 53			08 25		08 44	08 53	09 17			09 25	
Bedminster	d	23p10					06 56				07 56			08 28							09 28	
Parson Street	d	23p12					06 58				07 59			08 30							09 30	
Nailsea & Backwell	d	23p19			06 30		07 06	07 32			08 07			08 38			09 04				09 38	
Yatton	d	23p26			06 36		07 12	07 38			08 13			08 44			09 10			←	09 44	
Worle	d	23p32			06 42		07 18	07 44			08 19			08 50			09 16			09 16	09 50	
Weston Milton	d	23p37					07 23							08 55			→				09 55	
Weston-super-Mare	a	23p40	05 50		06 47	07 07	07 28	07 49			08 24			08 59						09 21	09 59	
	d	23p42	05 51		06 49	07 08		07 51												09 30		
Highbridge & Burnham	d	23p52	06 02		07 00			08 02												09 44		
Bridgwater	d	00 01	06 10		07 08			08 10												09 52		
Taunton	a	00 14	06 23		07 22	07 34		08 25		08 41						09 15		09 53		10 06		

For general notes see front of timetable
For details of catering facilities see Directory of Train Operators

A From Cardiff Central (Table 132)
B To Westbury (Table 123)
C To Weymouth (Table 123)
D From Cheltenham Spa (Table 57) to Westbury (Table 123)
E To Frome (Table 123)
G From Great Malvern (Table 71) to Weymouth (Table 123)
H From Cardiff Central (Table 132) to Westbury (Table 123)
J From Cheltenham Spa (Table 57)
K To Penzance (Table 135)
L From Worcester Shrub Hill (Table 57) to Weymouth (Table 123)

Due to Engineering Operations, services from Saturday 13 September on this Table had not been confirmed at time of going to press. These services will be issued in a special Supplement as soon as exact timings have been confirmed

Gloucester → Taunton

Network Diagram - see first page of Table 132

		XC	GW	GW	GW	GW	GW	XC	GW	XC	GW	GW	GW	XC	GW	XC	GW	GW	GW	GW	XC	GW
		1 ◇		◇			1 ◇	R 1		R 1	◇		◇	R 1		1 ◇	1 ◇	◇		◇	R 1	
						A			B				C		B					E		B
Gloucester 7	d					09 42							10 42							11 42		
Cam & Dursley	d					09 57							10 56							11 57		
Yate	d					10 13							11 10							12 13		
London Paddington 15 ⊖	d						09 00										10 30					
Bath Spa 7	d						10 25										12 00					
Bristol Parkway 7	a					10 21							11 19							12 21		
	d	09 25			10 12	10 22		10 25		10 55		11 12	11 19	11 25		11 55			12 12	12 22	12 25	
Filton Abbey Wood	d			10 09	10 15	10 25			10 42		11 09	11 15	11 23		11 42			12 09	12 15	12 25		12 42
Stapleton Road	d					10 29							11 29							12 29		
Lawrence Hill	d					10 31							11 31							12 31		
Bristol Temple Meads 10	a	09 41		10 18	10 23	10 36	10 39	10 41	10 52	11 11	11 18	11 23	11 35	11 41	11 52	12 11	12 15	12 18	12 23	12 36	12 41	12 52
	d	09 44	09 56		10 25		10 48		10 53	11 11		11 25		11 44	11 53		12 18		12 25		12 44	12 53
Bedminster	d				10 28							11 28							12 28			
Parson Street	d				10 30							11 30							12 30			
Nailsea & Backwell	d		10 07		10 38				11 04			11 38			12 04				12 38			13 04
Yatton	d		10 13		10 44				11 10			11 44			12 10				12 44			13 10
Worle	d		10 19		10 50				11 16			11 50			12 16				12 50			13 16
Weston Milton	d				10 55							11 55							12 55			
Weston-super-Mare	a		10 24		10 59		11 05		11 21	11 28		11 59			12 21		12 35		12 59			13 21
	d		10 26						11 23	11 29					12 23							13 23
Highbridge & Burnham	d		10 37						11 34						12 34							13 34
Bridgwater	d		10 45						11 42						12 42							13 42
Taunton	a	10 15	10 59						11 56	12 00				12 15	12 56						13 15	13 56

		XC	GW	GW	GW	XC	GW	XC	GW	GW	GW	GW	GW	XC	GW	GW	GW	XC	GW	XC	GW	GW
		1 ◇	◇			R 1		1 ◇	1 ◇	◇		◇		R 1	◇			R 1		1 ◇	1 ◇	◇
					G		B					H	B				G		B			
Gloucester 7	d				12 42							13 43					14 42					
Cam & Dursley	d				12 56							13 59					14 56					
Yate	d				13 10							14 14					15 10					
London Paddington 15 ⊖	d								12 30												14 30	
Bath Spa 7	d								14 02												16 01	
Bristol Parkway 7	a				13 19							14 23					15 19					
	d	12 55		13 12	13 19	13 25		13 55			14 12	14 23		14 55		15 12	15 19	15 25		15 55		
Filton Abbey Wood	d		13 09	13 15	13 23		13 43			14 09	14 15	14 27	14 42		15 09	15 15	15 23		15 42			16 09
Stapleton Road	d				13 27							14 32					15 27					
Lawrence Hill	d				13 29							14 34					15 29					
Bristol Temple Meads 10	a	13 11	13 18	13 23	13 35	13 41	13 52	14 11	14 15	14 18	14 23	14 39	14 52	15 11	15 18	15 23	15 35	15 41	15 52	16 11	16 15	16 18
	d			13 25		13 44	13 53		14 19		14 25		14 53			15 25		15 44	15 53		16 18	
Bedminster	d			13 28							14 28					15 28						
Parson Street	d			13 30							14 30					15 30						
Nailsea & Backwell	d			13 38			14 04				14 38		15 04			15 38			16 04			
Yatton	d			13 44			14 10				14 44		15 10			15 44			16 10			
Worle	d			13 50			14 16				14 50		15 16			15 50			16 16			
Weston Milton	d			13 55							14 55					15 55						
Weston-super-Mare	a			13 59		14 01	14 21		14 36		14 59		15 21			15 59			16 21		16 35	
	d					14 07	14 23						15 26						16 23			
Highbridge & Burnham	d						14 34						15 37						16 34			
Bridgwater	d						14 42						15 45						16 42			
Taunton	a					14 27	14 57						15 59					16 15	16 56			

		GW	GW	XC	GW	XC	GW	GW	GW	GW	XC	GW	XC	GW	GW	GW	GW	XC	GW	GW	GW	XC
			◇	R 1		1 ◇	1 ◇	◇		◇	1 ◇		1 ◇	1 ◇	◇			1 ◇		1 ◇	◇	1 ◇
			K		B					C		B					A		B			
Gloucester 7	d		15 42							16 42							17 43					18 37
Cam & Dursley	d		15 56							16 56							17 59					
Yate	d		16 10							17 10							18 14					
London Paddington 15 ⊖	d						15 30							16 30						17 30		
Bath Spa 7	d						17 01							18 01						19 01		
Bristol Parkway 7	a		16 19							17 19							18 23					19 09
	d	16 12	16 19	16 25		16 55			17 12	17 19	17 25		17 55			18 12	18 23	18 25				19 11
Filton Abbey Wood	d	16 15	16 23		16 42			17 09	17 15	17 23		17 42			18 09	18 14	18 27		18 42		19 09	
Stapleton Road	d		16 27							17 28							18 33					
Lawrence Hill	d		16 29							17 30							18 36					
Bristol Temple Meads 10	a	16 23	16 34	16 41	16 52	17 11	17 16	17 18	17 23	17 35	17 41	17 52	18 11	18 16	18 18	18 23	18 39	18 41	18 52	19 16	19 18	19 26
	d	16 25		16 44	16 53		17 18		17 25		17 44	17 53		18 16		18 25		18 44	18 53	19 17		
Bedminster	d	16 28							17 28							18 28						
Parson Street	d	16 30							17 30							18 30						
Nailsea & Backwell	d	16 38			17 04				17 38			18 04				18 38			19 04	19 29		
Yatton	d	16 44			17 10				17 44			18 10				18 44			19 10	19 35		
Worle	d	16 50			17 16				17 50			18 16				18 50			19 16	19 41		
Weston Milton	d	16 55							17 55							18 55			19 20			
Weston-super-Mare	a	16 59			17 21		17 35		17 59			18 21		18 36		18 59		19 04	19 23	19 52		
	d				17 23							18 23		18 40				19 06	19 25			
Highbridge & Burnham	d				17 34							18 34							19 36			
Bridgwater	d				17 42							18 42							19 44			
Taunton	a			17 15	17 56						18 15	18 56		19 06				19 26	19 58			

For general notes see front of timetable
For details of catering facilities see Directory of Train Operators

- **A** From Great Malvern (Table 71) to Westbury (Table 123)
- **B** From Cardiff Central (Table 132)
- **C** To Weymouth (Table 123)
- **E** From Great Malvern (Table 71) to Brighton (Table 123)
- **G** To Westbury (Table 123)
- **H** From Great Malvern (Table 71) to Weymouth (Table 123)
- **K** From Worcester Foregate Street (Table 71) to Weymouth (Table 123)

Due to Engineering Operations, services from Saturday 13 September on this Table had not been confirmed at time of going to press. These services will be issued in a special Supplement as soon as exact timings have been confirmed

Table 134

Gloucester → Taunton

Saturdays

until 6 September

Network Diagram - see first page of Table 132

		GW	GW	XC	GW	XC	GW	GW	GW	GW	XC	GW	GW	XC	GW	XC	GW	GW	GW	XC	GW
				1 ◇		1 ◇	1 ◇	◇		◇	1 ◇	1 ◇		1 ◇	◇	1 ◇			1 ◇	1 ◇	
			A		B					C		D					E	G	D		
				☕		☕	☕	🛒			☕	☕		☕	🛒	☕			☕	☕	
Gloucester 7	d		18 42							19 45								21 16			
Cam & Dursley	d		18 56							19 58								21 30			
Yate	d		19 10							20 14								21 44			
London Paddington 15 ⊖	d						18 30					19 00							20 30		
Bath Spa 7	d						20 01					20 25							21 59		
Bristol Parkway 7	a		19 19							20 23								21 53			
	d	19 16	19 19	19 26		19 55			20 17	20 23	20 25			20 55		21 25		21 53		22 25	
Filton Abbey Wood	d	19 19	19 22		19 42			20 09	20 20	20 27			20 34		21 09		21 42	21 57			22 52
Stapleton Road	d		19 28							20 31											
Lawrence Hill	d		19 30							20 33											
Bristol Temple Meads 10	a	19 28	19 36	19 41	19 52	20 11	20 15	20 18	20 29	20 40	20 41	20 42	20 45	21 11	21 18	21 41	21 52	22 05	22 16	22 41	23 00
	d			19 44	19 53		20 15				20 44	20 55				21 44	21 53		22 16		
Bedminster	d				19 56																
Parson Street	d				19 59																
Nailsea & Backwell	d				20 07							21 03									
Yatton	d				20 12							21 09					22 04		22s27		
Worle	d				20 18							21 15					22 10		22s33		
Weston Milton	d				20 22							21 20					22 16		22s39		
Weston-super-Mare	a				20 26		20 37					21 24					22 25		22s45		
	d				20 26		20 39					21 24					22 27				
Highbridge & Burnham	d				20 37							21 36					22 38		22s57		
Bridgwater	d				20 45							21 43					22 46		23s05		
Taunton	a			20 15	20 59		21 06				21 15	21 55				22 15	23 00		23s16		

Sundays

until 7 September

		GW	GW	GW	GW	GW	GW	GW	GW	GW	GW	GW	XC	GW	GW	GW	XC	GW	GW	GW	XC	GW	XC
		◇	◇	◇	1	1 ◇	◇		◇		◇	1 ◇	1 ◇	1 ◇	◇		1 ◇	1 ◇	◇		R 1	◇	1 ◇
		H	H				J			G				K		G						J	N
				🛒		☕	🛒		🛒		🛒	☕	☕	☕	🛒		☕	☕	🛒		☕	🛒	☕
Gloucester 7	d									10 19						12 14							
Cam & Dursley	d									10 32						12 28							
Yate	d									10 46						12 43							
London Paddington 15 ⊖	d					07 57						10 07		11 07				12 07					
Bath Spa 7	d					09 47						11 48		12 48				13 47					
Bristol Parkway 7	a									10 55						12 52							
	d			08 51			09 50		10 50	10 55	11 50		12 25		12 50	12 54	13 25		13 50		14 25	14 50	14 58
Filton Abbey Wood	d			08 55			09 55		10 53	10 59	11 54				12 53	12 58			13 54			14 54	
Stapleton Road	d																						
Lawrence Hill	d																						
Bristol Temple Meads 10	a			09 05		10 00	10 05		11 02	11 07	12 04	12 04	12 38	13 01	13 01	13 06	13 38	14 01	14 04		14 38	15 04	15 11
	d	07 45	08 30		09 30	10 01		10 10		11 10		12 04	12 44	13 04			13 44	14 01		14 10	14 44		15 12
Bedminster	d																						
Parson Street	d																						
Nailsea & Backwell	d		08 40		09 41			10 20		11 21		12 15		13 13						14 20			
Yatton	d	07 58	08 45		09 47			10 25		11 26		12 21		13 19						14 25			
Worle	d		08 51		09 53			10 31		11 32		12 26		13 25						14 31			
Weston Milton	d																						
Weston-super-Mare	a	08 07	08 57		10 02			10 38		11 37		12 34		13 31						14 37			
	d	08 08	08 58					10 40		11 39				13 32						14 38			
Highbridge & Burnham	d		09 09					10 50		11 49										14 49			
Bridgwater	d	08 24	09 17					10 58		11 57										14 57			
Taunton	a	08 37	09 30			10 34		11 11		12 11			13 15	13 54			14 15	14 35		15 11	15 15		15 43

For general notes see front of timetable
For details of catering facilities see Directory of Train Operators

- **A** To Frome (Table 123)
- **B** From Cardiff Central (Table 132)
- **C** From Worcester Shrub Hill (Table 57) to Weymouth (Table 123)
- **D** To Exeter St Davids (Table 135)
- **E** From Cardiff Central (Table 132) to Exeter St Davids (Table 135)
- **G** From Cheltenham Spa (Table 57)
- **H** To Penzance (Table 135)
- **K** To Paignton (Table 135)
- **N** From 20 July

Due to Engineering Operations, services from Saturday 13 September on this Table had not been confirmed at time of going to press. These services will be issued in a special Supplement as soon as exact timings have been confirmed

Due to Engineering Operations, services from Sunday 14 September on this Table had not been confirmed at time of going to press. These services will be issued in a special Supplement as soon as exact timings have been confirmed

Table 134

Sundays

until 7 September

Gloucester → Taunton

Network Diagram - see first page of Table 132

		GW	XC	GW	GW	XC	XC	GW		GW	XC	GW	XC	GW	GW	XC		GW	GW	XC	GW	GW	GW	XC		GW
			R 1			1 ◇	R 1	1 ◇		◇	1 ◇		R 1	◇		1 ◇			◇	R 1		1 ◇	◇	R 1		
					A	B					B				A	B		C			C			B		
			☕			☕	☕	☕		🛒	☕		☕	🛒		☕			🛒	☕		☕	🛒	☕		
Gloucester 7	d				15 15										17 18									18 39		
Cam & Dursley	d				15 29										17 32											
Yate	d				15 43										17 47											
London Paddington 15	⊖ d							15 07														17 07				
Bath Spa 7	d							16 47														18 47				
Bristol Parkway 7	a				15 51										17 55									19 07		
	d		15 25		15 53	15 58	16 25			16 50	16 58		17 25	17 50	17 57	17 58			18 20	18 25			18 50	19 08		
Filton Abbey Wood	d				15 58					16 53				17 54	18 00				18 23				18 53			
Stapleton Road	d																									
Lawrence Hill	d																									
Bristol Temple Meads 10	a		15 38		16 06	16 14	16 38	17 00		17 02	17 13		17 38	18 02	18 09	18 13			18 33	18 38		19 01	19 02	19 24		
	d	15 16	15 44	15 50	16 16		16 44	17 05				17 16	17 44					18 15		18 44		19 02				19 25
Bedminster	d	15 19		15 53								17 19														19 28
Parson Street	d			15 56																						19 30
Nailsea & Backwell	d	15 28		16 04	16 26			17 15				17 28						18 25				19 11				19 38
Yatton	d	15 34		16 10	16 31			17 21				17 34						18 30			←	19 18				19 44
Worle	d	15 40		16 19	16 37			17 27				17 40						18 36 →			18 36	19 24				19 50 →
Weston Milton	d	15 45			16 43							17 45														
Weston-super-Mare	a	15 48		16 26	16 47			17 38				17 48									18 42	19 32				
	d			16 27				17 39													18 59					
Highbridge & Burnham	d			16 38																	19 10					
Bridgwater	d			16 46																	19 18					
Taunton	a		16 15	17 02			17 15	18 01					18 15							19 15	19 32					

		GW	XC	GW		GW	GW	XC		GW	XC	GW	GW	GW	XC	XC		GW	GW	XC	GW	GW	GW	XC		
		◇	R 1			◇		1 ◇			R 1		1 ◇	◇	1 ◇	R 1				1 ◇	1 ◇	◇		1 ◇		
		D					A	B					C		B			A					🚌			
		🛒	☕			🛒		☕			☕		☕	🛒	☕	☕				☕		🛒		☕		
Gloucester 7	d						19 18											21 15								
Cam & Dursley	d						19 32											21 31								
Yate	d						19 46											21 45								
London Paddington 15	⊖ d												19 07								21 07					
Bath Spa 7	d												20 47								22 47					
Bristol Parkway 7	a						19 55											21 53								
	d	19 20	19 25			19 50	19 55	19 58			20 25			20 50	20 58	21 25		21 55		22 25		22 53	23 20	23 25		
Filton Abbey Wood	d	19 23				19 53	19 59							20 53				21 58				22 56	23 25			
Stapleton Road	d																									
Lawrence Hill	d																									
Bristol Temple Meads 10	a	19 33	19 38			20 02	20 08	20 13			20 38		21 00	21 02	21 13	21 38		22 07		22 41	23 03	23 05	23 42	23 41		
	d		19 44							20 25	20 44		21 02			21 44			22 30		23 03					
Bedminster	d									20 28									22 33							
Parson Street	d																		22 35							
Nailsea & Backwell	d									20 36			21 11						22 43		23 15					
Yatton	d			←						20 42		←	21 17						22 49		23 21					
Worle	d			19 50						20 48 →		20 48	21 23						22 55		23 26					
Weston Milton	d			19 54															23 00							
Weston-super-Mare	a			19 57								20 53	21 31						23 03		23 33					
	d			19 59								20 58	21 32													
Highbridge & Burnham	d			20 09								21 09														
Bridgwater	d			20 17								21 17														
Taunton	a		20 15	20 32							21 15	21 33	21 54			22 15										

For general notes see front of timetable
For details of catering facilities see
Directory of Train Operators

A From Worcester Shrub Hill (Table 57)
B From 20 July
C To Exeter St Davids (Table 135)

Due to Engineering Operations, services from Sunday 14 September on this Table had not been confirmed at time of going to press. These services will be issued in a special Supplement as soon as exact timings have been confirmed

Taunton → Gloucester

Network Diagram - see first page of Table 132

Miles			GW	XC R 1 ☕	GW A	GW	GW B	GW 1◇ ☕	XC 1◇ ☕	GW 1◇ ☕	GW A	GW 1◇ C ⊠	GW D	XC 1◇ ☕	GW E	GW D	GW	GW 1◇ G ⊠	XC 1◇ ☕	GW ◇ H	GW A	GW 1◇ D ☕		GW	XC 1◇ ☕	GW J
0	**Taunton**	d				05 30					06 02		06 34	06 51				06 55				07 15		07 32	07 51	
11¾	Bridgwater	d				05 41					06 14		06 47					07 05				07 25		07 44		
18	Highbridge & Burnham	d				05 48					06 22		06 55					07 13				07 33		07 52		
25¾	**Weston-super-Mare**	a				06 01					06 33		07 06					07 23				07 44		08 03		
—		d				06 03		06 23			06 34	06 48	07 07					07 25			07 33	07 50		08 08		
27	Weston Milton	d						06 27			06 38	06 52	07 11			←					07 36	07 54		08 11		
29½	Worle	d				06 08		06 33			06 43	06 57	07 16			07 16		07 31			07 41	07 59		08 16		
33½	Yatton	d				06 13		06 39			06 48	07 03	→			07 21		07 37			07 46	08 04		→		
37½	Nailsea & Backwell	d				06 19		06 45			06 54	07 10				07 27		07 44			07 52	08 11				
43½	Parson Street	d									07 02					07 35					08 00					
44½	Bedminster	d									07 04					07 37					08 02					
45½	**Bristol Temple Meads** 10	a				06 31		06 57			07 09	07 21		07 25		07 42		07 57			08 07	08 23			08 25	
—		d	05 54	06 15	06 22		06 50	07 00	07 00	07 15	07 19	07 30		07 30	07 41	07 46	07 54	08 00	08 00	08 10	08 22	08 30			08 30	08 41
46½	Lawrence Hill	d			06 25		06 54				07 22					07 49				08 13						
47	Stapleton Road	d			06 27		06 56				07 24					07 52				08 15						
50	Filton Abbey Wood	d	06a00		06a32		07a01			07a21	07 30				07 48	07 58	08a00			08 21	08a30					08 48
51¼	**Bristol Parkway** 7	a		06 23					07 08		07 33			07 38	07 52	08 03			08 08	08 28					08 38	08 52
—		d		06 25											07 52											08 52
—	Bath Spa 7	a						07 11				07 41						08 11				08 41				
—	London Paddington 15	⊖ a						08 44				09 14						09 44				10 14				
57½	Yate	d													08 01											09 02
72¼	Cam & Dursley	d													08 13											09 13
85¼	**Gloucester** 7	a		06 55											08 32											09 31

		GW	GW ◇ 🛒	XC 1◇ ☕	GW ◇ H	GW A	GW	XC R 1 ☕	GW K	GW	GW ◇ 🛒	GW 1◇ L ☕	XC 1◇ ☕	GW A	XC 1◇ ☕	GW ◇ N	GW	GW ◇ 🛒	XC 1◇ ☕	GW A		XC R 1 ☕	GW H	GW	GW A	GW ◇ 🛒
Taunton	d			08 06			08 36	08 51				09 05			09 51					10 07		10 51			11 04	
Bridgwater	d						08 48													10 19					11 16	
Highbridge & Burnham	d						08 56													10 27					11 24	
Weston-super-Mare	a			08 29			09 08					09 26								10 39					11 35	
	d			08 30		08 40	09 09					09 28		09 40			10 10			10 40				11 10	11 40	
Weston Milton	d	←				08 43	09 13			←				09 43			10 13							11 13	→	
Worle	d	08 16				08 48	09 17			09 17		09 34		09 48			10 18			10 46				11 18		
Yatton	d	08 22				08 53	→			09 23		09 40		09 53			10 23			10 52				11 23		
Nailsea & Backwell	d	08 28				08 59				09 29		09 46		09 59			10 29			10 58				11 29		
Parson Street	d	08 36				09 07				09 36				10 07			10 37							11 37		
Bedminster	d	08 39				09 09				09 39				10 09			10 39							11 39		
Bristol Temple Meads 10	a	08 44		08 50		09 14		09 25		09 44		09 57		10 14	10 25		10 44			11 11		11 25		11 44		
	d	08 44	08 54	09 00	09 10	09 19		09 30	09 41	09 46	09 54	10 00	10 00	10 19	10 30	10 41	10 46	10 54	11 00	11 19		11 30	11 41	11 46		11 54
Lawrence Hill	d	08 49			09 13									10 22												
Stapleton Road	d	08 50			09 15									10 26												
Filton Abbey Wood	d	08 55	09a01		09 20	09a29			09 48	09 53	10a01			10a30		10 48	10 53	11a01		11a29			11 48	11 53		12a01
Bristol Parkway 7	a	09 03		09 08	09 27			09 38	09 51	09 56			10 08		10 38	10 52	10 58		11 08			11 38	11 51	11 58		
	d								09 52							10 52							11 52			
Bath Spa 7	a											10 11														
London Paddington 15	⊖ a											11 42														
Yate	d								10 01							11 01							12 01			
Cam & Dursley	d								10 13							11 13							12 13			
Gloucester 7	a								10 31							11 30							12 30			

		XC 1◇ ☕	GW 1◇ ☕	GW A	XC R 1 ☕	GW ◇ Q	GW	GW ◇ 🛒	XC R 1 ☕	GW A	XC R 1 ☕	GW ◇ H	GW	GW A	GW ◇ 🛒	XC R 1 ☕	GW A	XC R 1 ☕		GW U	GW	GW ◇ 🛒	XC R 1 ☕	GW A	XC R 1 ☕	GW ◇ H
Taunton	d	11 16	11 26		11 51					12 07	12 51			13 07		13 16		13 51						14 07	14 51	
Bridgwater	d									12 19				13 19										14 19		
Highbridge & Burnham	d									12 27				13 27										14 27		
Weston-super-Mare	a			←						12 38				13 38			←							14 38		
	d			11 40			12 10			12 40			13 10	13 40			13 40				14 10			14 40		
Weston Milton	d						12 13						13 13	→							14 13					
Worle	d			11 50			12 18			12 46			13 18				13 46				14 18			14 46		
Yatton	d			11 56			12 23			12 52			13 23				13 52				14 23			14 52		
Nailsea & Backwell	d			12 02			12 29			12 58			13 29				13 58				14 29			14 58		
Parson Street	d						12 37						13 37								14 37					
Bedminster	d						12 39						13 39								14 39					
Bristol Temple Meads 10	a	11 53	11 59	12 15	12 25		12 44			13 13	13 25		13 44			13 55	14 11	14 25			14 44			15 11	15 25	
	d	12 00	12 00	12 19	12 30	12 41	12 46	12 54	13 00	13 19	13 30	13 41	13 46		13 54	14 00	14 19	14 30		14 41	14 46	14 54	15 00	15 19	15 30	15 41
Lawrence Hill	d			12 22													14 22									
Stapleton Road	d			12 24													14 24									
Filton Abbey Wood	d			12a29		12 48	12 53	13a01		13a29		13 48	13 53		14a01		14a29			14 48	14 53	15a01		15a29		15 48
Bristol Parkway 7	a	12 08			12 38	12 51	12 58		13 08		13 38	13 51	13 58			14 08		14 38		14 51	14 58		15 08		15 38	15 51
	d					12 52						13 52								14 53						15 52
Bath Spa 7	a		12 11																							
London Paddington 15	⊖ a		13 42																							
Yate	d					13 01						14 01								15 02						16 01
Cam & Dursley	d					13 13						14 13								15 14						16 13
Gloucester 7	a					13 29						14 30								15 32						16 31

For general notes see front of timetable
For details of catering facilities see Directory of Train Operators

- **A** To Cardiff Central (Table 132)
- **B** From Westbury to Cardiff Central (Table 123)
- **C** **The Bristolian**
- **D** From Exeter St Davids (Table 135)
- **E** From Salisbury (Table 123)
- **G** From Plymouth (Table 135)
- **H** From Weymouth (Table 123)
- **J** From Warminster (Table 123) to Great Malvern (Table 71)
- **K** From Westbury (Table 123)
- **L** From Paignton (Table 135)
- **N** From Westbury (Table 123) to Great Malvern (Table 71)
- **Q** From Brighton (Table 123) to Great Malvern (Table 71)
- **U** From Southampton Central (Table 123) to Worcester Foregate Street (Table 71)

Taunton → Gloucester

Network Diagram - see first page of Table 132

		GW	GW	XC	GW	XC	GW	GW	GW	XC	GW	GW	XC	GW	GW	GW		GW	GW	XC	GW	XC	GW	GW	GW	GW
			◇	R 1		R 1			◇	R 1			R 1	1 ◇	◇				◇	1 ◇		1 ◇	1 ◇			◇
					A		B					A			C			A			A			B		
			🚲	☕		☕			🚲	☕			☕	☕					🚲	☕		☕	☕			🚲
Taunton	d			15 12	15 15	15 51						16 05	16 51					17 05		17 21		17 51				
Bridgwater	d				15 27							16 17						17 17								
Highbridge & Burnham	d				15 35							16 25						17 25								
Weston-super-Mare	a			15 35	15 46							16 36						17 36								
	d	15 10		15 36	15 46			16 10				16 37		17 08		17 14		17 38					18 09		18 14	
Weston Milton	d	15 13						16 13										17 41			←					
Worle	d	15 18			15 52			16 18				16 44				17 20		17 46 →			17 46				18 20	
Yatton	d	15 23			15 58			16 23				16 50				17 25					17 52				18 25	
Nailsea & Backwell	d	15 29			16 04			16 29				16 56				17 31					17 58				18 31	
Parson Street	d	15 37						16 37													18 06					
Bedminster	d	15 39						16 39													18 08					
Bristol Temple Meads 10	a	15 44		15 56	16 17	16 25		16 44				17 08	17 25	17 29		17 44				17 55	18 14	18 25	18 29		18 45	
	d	15 46	15 54	16 00	16 19	16 30	16 41	16 46	16 54	17 00	17 10	17 19	17 30	17 30	17 41	17 46			17 54	18 00	18 19	18 30	18 30	18 41	18 47	18 54
Lawrence Hill	d										17 13					17 49					18 22					
Stapleton Road	d										17 15										18 24					
Filton Abbey Wood	d	15 53	16a01		16a24		16 48	16 53	17a01		17 21	17a29			17 48	17 55			18a01		18a29			18 48	18 54	19a01
Bristol Parkway 7	a	15 58		16 08		16 38	16 51	16 58		17 08	17 27		17 38		17 51	18 01				18 08		18 38		18 51	18 58	
	d						16 52								17 52									18 52		
Bath Spa 7	a													17 41									18 41			
London Paddington 15 ⊖	a													19 15									20 15			
Yate	d						17 01								18 01									19 01		
Cam & Dursley	d						17 13								18 13									19 13		
Gloucester 7	a						17 29								18 31									19 29		

		XC	GW	XC	XC	GW	GW	GW	XC	GW	GW	GW	GW	GW	GW	GW	XC	GW	GW	GW	GW	GW	GW	GW
														FO	FX	FX				FO	FX			
		1 ◇		R 1	1 ◇		◇		1 ◇	◇	◇			1 ◇	1 ◇	◇	1 ◇	1		1 ◇	1 ◇	◇		
								A	D	E		A												
		☕		☕	☕		🚲		☕		🚲			☕	☕	🚲				🚲	🚲	🚲		
Taunton	d		18 07		18 51			19 11	19 51				20 28	21 08	21 08					21 30	21 30		22 20	22 45
Bridgwater	d		18 19					19 23					20 41							21 40	21 40			22 57
Highbridge & Burnham	d		18 27					19 31					20 48							21 47	21 47			23 05
Weston-super-Mare	a		18 38					19 42					20 59							21 58	21 58		22 44	23 16
	d		18 40			19 10		19 48					21 01					21 30		22 00	22 00		22 46	23 18
Weston Milton	d		18 43			19 13							21 04					21 34						23 21
Worle	d		18 48			19 18		19 54					21 09					21 38		22 06	22 06			23 26
Yatton	d		18 54			19 23		20 00					21 15					21 44		22 11	22 11			23 32
Nailsea & Backwell	d		19 00			19 29		20 06					21 21					21 50		22 17	22 17			23 38
Parson Street	d		19 07			19 37							21 28											23 46
Bedminster	d		19 10			19 39							21 31											23 49
Bristol Temple Meads 10	a		19 15		19 25	19 44		20 18	20 25				21 36	21 40	21 40			22 01		22 29	22 29		23 08	23 54
	d	19 00		19 25	19 30	19 46	19 54	20 19	20 30	20 41	20 54	21 19		21 40	21 40	21 54	22 00		22 11	22 33	22 33	22 54		
Lawrence Hill	d					19 49		20 22				21 22												
Stapleton Road	d					19 51		20 24				21 24												
Filton Abbey Wood	d			19a31		19 57	20a00	20a30		20 48	21a01	21a29				22a00			22 18			23a00		
Bristol Parkway 7	a	19 08			19 38	20 03			20 38	20 51							22 08		22 21					
	d									20 52									22 22					
Bath Spa 7	a													21 55	21 55					22 44	22 44			
London Paddington 15 ⊖	a													23 29	23 36					00 25	00 32			
Yate	d									21 01									22 31					
Cam & Dursley	d									21 13									22 44					
Gloucester 7	a									21 29									23 02					

Saturdays

until 6 September

		XC	GW	GW	GW	GW	XC		GW	GW	GW	GW	XC	GW		GW	XC	GW	GW	GW	GW		XC	GW	GW	XC
		1 ◇		1 ◇	1 ◇		1 ◇					1 ◇	1 ◇				1 ◇			◇	1 ◇		1 ◇	◇		1 ◇
						G			H	G				A				B			G			C	A	
		☕		☕	☕		☕					☕	☕				☕				☕		☕			☕
Taunton	d		05 30			06 13						06 58				07 32	07 51				08 00					08 51
Bridgwater	d		05 41			06 26						07 08				07 44					08 11					
Highbridge & Burnham	d		05 48			06 34						07 16				07 52					08 18					
Weston-super-Mare	a		06 00			06 45						07 26				08 03					08 28					
	d		06 03		06 24	06 49						07 28		07 40		08 10					08 30				08 40	
Weston Milton	d					06 52										08 13			←							
Worle	d		06 08		06 31	06 57						07 34		07 46		08 18 →			08 18						08 48	
Yatton	d		06 14		06 37	07 03						07 40		07 51					08 23		08 39				08 51	
Nailsea & Backwell	d		06 20		06 43	07 09						07 46		07 57					08 29		08 45				08 57	
Parson Street	d					07 19													08 37							
Bedminster	d					07 21													08 39							
Bristol Temple Meads 10	a		06 32		06 54	07 24				←		07 58		08 10			08 25		08 44		08 57				09 10	09 25
	d	06 15		06 58	07 00	07 46 →	07 30		07 41	07 46	07 54	08 00	08 00	08 21			08 30	08 41	08 46	08 54	09 00		09 00	09 10	09 21	09 30
Lawrence Hill	d									07 49									08 49							
Stapleton Road	d									07 51									08 51							
Filton Abbey Wood	d								07 48	07 57	08a00			08a29				08 48	08 57	09a00				09 17	09a29	
Bristol Parkway 7	a	06 23		07 06			07 38		07 51	08 03			08 08				08 38	08 51	09 03				09 08	09 20		09 38
	d	06 25							07 52									08 52						09 21		
Bath Spa 7	a				07 11							08 11									09 11					
London Paddington 15 ⊖	a				08 45							09 44									10 43					
Yate	d								08 01									09 01						09 30		
Cam & Dursley	d								08 15									09 15						09 44		
Gloucester 7	a	06 54							08 31									09 32						10 00		

For general notes see front of timetable
For details of catering facilities see Directory of Train Operators

- **A** To Cardiff Central (Table 132)
- **B** From Warminster (Table 123) to Great Malvern (Table 71)
- **C** From Weymouth (Table 123)
- **D** ☕ to Bristol Temple Meads
- **E** From Brighton (Table 123) to Worcester Shrub Hill (Table 57)
- **G** From Exeter St Davids (Table 135)
- **H** From Salisbury (Table 123)

Due to Engineering Operations, services from Saturday 13 September on this Table had not been confirmed at time of going to press. These services will be issued in a special Supplement as soon as exact timings have been confirmed

Table 134

Taunton → Gloucester

Network Diagram - see first page of Table 132

		GW	GW	XC			GW	XC	GW	GW	GW	XC		GW	GW	XC	GW	GW	GW		GW	XC	GW	XC	GW	GW
			◇	1 ◇ ☕			B	1 ◇ ☕	◇ C		◇	1 ◇ ☕		B	1 ◇ ☕	1 ◇ ☕	D		◇		1 ☕	R 1 ☕	B	R 1 ☕	◇ E	
Taunton	d						08 58	09 51						10 11	10 45								11 07	11 33		
Bridgwater	d						09 10							10 23									11 19			
Highbridge & Burnham	d						09 18							10 31									11 27			
Weston-super-Mare	a						09 29							10 42									11 38	11 58		
	d	09 10					09 40			10 10		10 27		10 43				11 10			11 30		11 40	12 00		12 10
Weston Milton	d	09 13								10 13								11 13								12 13
Worle	d	09 18					09 46			10 18				10 49				11 18					11 46			12 18
Yatton	d	09 23					09 51			10 23				10 55				11 23					11 51			12 23
Nailsea & Backwell	d	09 29					09 57			10 29				11 01				11 29					11 57			12 29
Parson Street	d	09 37								10 37								11 37								12 37
Bedminster	d	09 39								10 39								11 39								12 39
Bristol Temple Meads 10	a	09 44					10 10	10 25		10 44		10 55		11 13	11 19			11 44			11 50		12 10	12 25		12 44
	d	09 46	09 54	10 00			10 21	10 30	10 41	10 46	10 54	11 00		11 21	11 30	11 30	11 41	11 46	11 54		12 00	12 00	12 21	12 30	12 41	12 46
Lawrence Hill	d	09 49								10 49								11 49								12 49
Stapleton Road	d	09 51								10 51								11 51								12 51
Filton Abbey Wood	d	09 57	10a00				10a29		10 48	10 57	11a00			11a29			11 48	11 57	12a00				12a29		12 48	12 57
Bristol Parkway 7	a	10 03		10 08				10 38	10 51	11 03		11 08				11 38	11 51	12 03				12 08		12 38	12 51	13 03
	d								10 52								11 52								12 52	
Bath Spa 7	a														11 41						12 11					
London Paddington 15 ⊖	a														13 17						13 41					
Yate	d								11 01								12 01								13 01	
Cam & Dursley	d								11 29								12 15								13 15	
Gloucester 7	a								11 29								12 31								13 33	

		GW	XC		GW	GW	GW	GW	GW	XC		GW	XC	GW	GW	GW	XC		GW	GW	XC	GW	GW	GW		GW
		◇	R 1 ☕		B	1 ◇ ☕	◇ D		◇	R 1 ☕		B	R 1 ☕	G		◇	R 1 ☕		B	1 ◇ ☕	R 1 ☕	◇ D		B		◇
Taunton	d				12 11							13 07	13 51						14 07					15 07		
Bridgwater	d				12 23							13 19							14 19					15 19		
Highbridge & Burnham	d				12 31							13 27							14 27					15 27		
Weston-super-Mare	a				12 42							13 38							14 38					15 38		
	d				12 44	13 01		13 10				13 40			14 10				14 40	15 01			15 10	15 40		
Weston Milton	d							13 13							14 13								15 13	→		
Worle	d				12 50			13 18				13 46			14 18				14 46				15 18			
Yatton	d				12 55			13 23				13 51			14 23				14 51				15 23			
Nailsea & Backwell	d				13 01			13 29				13 57			14 29				14 57				15 29			
Parson Street	d							13 37							14 37								15 37			
Bedminster	d							13 39							14 39								15 39			
Bristol Temple Meads 10	a				13 14	13 19		13 44				14 10	14 25		14 44				15 10	15 20			15 44			
	d	12 54	13 00		13 21	13 30	13 41	13 46	13 54	14 00		14 21	14 30	14 41	14 46	14 54	15 00		15 21	15 30	15 30	15 41	15 46			15 54
Lawrence Hill	d							13 49							14 49								15 49			
Stapleton Road	d							13 51							14 51								15 51			
Filton Abbey Wood	d	13a00			13a29		13 48	13 57	14a00			14a29		14 48	14 57	15a00			15a29			15 48	15 57			16a00
Bristol Parkway 7	a		13 08				13 51	14 03		14 08			14 38	14 51	15 03		15 08				15 38	15 51	16 03			
	d						13 52							14 52								15 52				
Bath Spa 7	a					13 41														15 41						
London Paddington 15 ⊖	a					15 14														17 16						
Yate	d						14 01							15 01								16 01				
Cam & Dursley	d						14 13							15 13								16 13				
Gloucester 7	a						14 29							15 31								16 29				

		XC	GW	XC	GW	GW	GW		XC	GW	GW	XC	GW	GW		GW	XC	GW	GW	XC			GW	GW	GW	XC
		1 ◇ ☕	B	R 1 ☕	J		◇		R 1 ☕	B	1 ◇ ☕	R 1 ☕	◇ K			◇	1 ◇ ☕	B	1 ◇ ☕	R 1 ☕			L		◇	1 ◇ ☕
Taunton	d	15 23		15 51						16 07		16 51						17 07		17 51						
Bridgwater	d									16 19								17 19								
Highbridge & Burnham	d									16 27								17 27								
Weston-super-Mare	a		←							16 38								17 38								
	d		15 40			16 10				16 40	17 01			17 10				17 40	18 01					18 10		
Weston Milton	d					16 13								17 13										18 13		
Worle	d		15 46			16 18				16 46				17 18				17 46						18 18		
Yatton	d		15 51			16 23				16 51				17 23				17 51						18 23		
Nailsea & Backwell	d		15 57			16 29				16 57				17 29				17 57						18 29		
Parson Street	d					16 37								17 37										18 37		
Bedminster	d					16 39								17 39										18 39		
Bristol Temple Meads 10	a	15 57	16 10	16 25		16 44				17 10	17 19	17 26		17 44				18 10	18 20	18 25				18 44		
	d	16 00	16 21	16 30	16 41	16 46	16 54		17 00	17 21	17 30	17 30	17 41	17 46		17 54	18 00	18 21	18 30	18 30			18 41	18 46	18 54	19 00
Lawrence Hill	d					16 49								17 51										18 49		
Stapleton Road	d					16 51								17 57										18 51		
Filton Abbey Wood	d		16a29		16 48	16 57	17a00			17a29			17 48	17 57		18a00		18a29					18 48	18 57	19a00	
Bristol Parkway 7	a	16 08		16 38	16 51	17 03			17 08			17 38	17 51	18 03			18 08			18 38			18 51	19 03		19 08
	d				16 52								17 52										18 52			
Bath Spa 7	a										17 41								18 41							
London Paddington 15 ⊖	a										19 14								20 14							
Yate	d				17 01								18 01										19 01			
Cam & Dursley	d				17 13								18 13										19 13			
Gloucester 7	a				17 33								18 31										19 31			

For general notes see front of timetable
For details of catering facilities see Directory of Train Operators

B To Cardiff Central (Table 132)
C From Westbury (Table 123) to Great Malvern (Table 71)
D From Weymouth (Table 123)
E From Brighton (Table 123) to Worcester Foregate Street (Table 71)
G From Southampton Central (Table 123) to Great Malvern (Table 71)
J From Warminster (Table 123) to Great Malvern (Table 71)
K From Warminster (Table 123)
L From Weymouth (Table 123) to Great Malvern (Table 71)

Due to Engineering Operations, services from Saturday 13 September on this Table had not been confirmed at time of going to press. These services will be issued in a special Supplement as soon as exact timings have been confirmed

Table 134

Taunton → Gloucester

Saturdays
until 6 September

Network Diagram - see first page of Table 132

		GW	XC	XC	GW	GW	GW	GW	XC	GW	GW	GW	XC	GW	GW	GW	GW	GW	GW	GW
			1 ◇	R 1	◇		◇		1 ◇	1 ◇		◇	1 ◇		1 ◇	◇		1 ◇		◇
					A			B			C		D							
			⊡	⊡					⊡	⊡			⊡		⊡					
Taunton	d	18 07						19 07	19 51				20 13	20 18	21 11			21 30	21 39	
Bridgwater	d	18 19						19 19						20 30				21 41	21 51	
Highbridge & Burnham	d	18 27						19 27						20 38				21 48	21 59	
Weston-super-Mare	a	18 38						19 38					20 34	20 50				21 58	22 10	
	d	18 40				19 10		19 40		20 10			20 39	20 51				22 01	22 12	
Weston Milton	d					19 13								20 55					22 15	
Worle	d	18 46				19 18		19 46						21 00				22 08	22 20	
Yatton	d	18 51				19 23		19 51						21 06				22 13	22 26	
Nailsea & Backwell	d	18 57				19 29		19 57						21 12				22 18	22 32	
Parson Street	d					19 37								21 21					22 40	
Bedminster	d					19 39								21 24					22 43	
Bristol Temple Meads 10	a	19 10				19 44		20 10	20 25	20 30			20 55	21 27	21 44			22 30	22 50	
	d		19 26	19 30	19 40	19 46	19 54	20 21	20 30	20 33	20 41	20 54	21 00	21 28	21 44	21 54	22 06	22 33		22 54
Lawrence Hill	d					19 49														
Stapleton Road	d					19 51														
Filton Abbey Wood	d		19a32		19 48	19 57	20a00	20a29			20 48	21a00		21a35		22a00	22 14			23a00
Bristol Parkway 7	a			19 38	19 51	20 03			20 38		20 51		21 08				22 17			
	d				19 52						20 52						22 18			
Bath Spa 7	a									20 44					21 58			22 44		
London Paddington 15 ⊖	a									22 16					23 38			00 32		
Yate	d				20 01						21 01						22 28			
Cam & Dursley	d				20 15						21 13						22 43			
Gloucester 7	a				20 33						21 30						23 01			

Sundays
until 7 September

		GW	XC	GW	GW	XC	GW	GW	XC	GW	XC	GW	GW	XC	GW	GW	GW	XC	XC	GW	GW	XC	GW
		1 ◇	1 ◇		◇	1 ◇	1 ◇		1 ◇	◇	1 ◇	1 ◇		R 1			1 ◇	1 ◇	R 1	◇	1 ◇	1 ◇	
				A	G			G			K					J	E	K				K	
		⊡	⊡		trolley	⊡	⊡		⊡	trolley	⊡	⊡		⊡			⊡	⊡	⊡	trolley	⊡	⊡	
Taunton	d				08 43			10 19	10 51		11 16	11 21	11 31	11 51			12 22		12 51				13 20
Bridgwater	d				08 55			10 31					11 43										13 32
Highbridge & Burnham	d				09 02			10 38					11 50										13 39
Weston-super-Mare	a				09 12			10 48					12 00										13 49
	d	08 28			09 14		10 28	10 50					12 09		←						13 32		13 51
Weston Milton	d				09 17								12 12 →		12 12								13 56
Worle	d	08 34			09 21		10 34	10 56													13 40		14 02
Yatton	d	08 40			09 27		10 40	11 01							12 19						13 46		14 08
Nailsea & Backwell	d	08 46			09 33		10 46	11 07							12 25								
Parson Street	d																						
Bedminster	d														12 36								
Bristol Temple Meads 10	a	08 57			09 45		10 57	11 19	11 25		11 55	11 57		12 25	12 39		12 57		13 25		13 57		14 20
	d	09 00	09 15	09 44	09 50	10 30	11 00		11 30	11 48	12 00	12 00		12 30		12 44	13 00	13 00	13 30	13 49	14 00	14 00	
Lawrence Hill	d																						
Stapleton Road	d																						
Filton Abbey Wood	d			09 51	09 57					11 55						12 51				13 56			
Bristol Parkway 7	a		09 23	09 54	10 00	10 38			11 38	11 58	12 08			12 38		12 54		13 08	13 38	13 59		14 08	
	d		09 25	09 55												12 55							
Bath Spa 7	a	09 12					11 12					12 12					13 12				14 11		
London Paddington 15 ⊖	a	10 54					12 55					13 55					14 54				15 55		
Yate	d			10 04												13 04							
Cam & Dursley	d			10 17												13 18							
Gloucester 7	a		09 55	10 34												13 34							

For general notes see front of timetable
For details of catering facilities see Directory of Train Operators

A To Cheltenham Spa (Table 57)
B To Cardiff Central (Table 132)
C From Brighton (Table 123) to Cheltenham Spa (Table 57)
D ⊡ to Bristol Temple Meads
G From Exeter St Davids (Table 135)
J To Worcester Shrub Hill (Table 57)
K From 20 July

Due to Engineering Operations, services from Saturday 13 September on this Table had not been confirmed at time of going to press. These services will be issued in a special Supplement as soon as exact timings have been confirmed

Due to Engineering Operations, services from Sunday 14 September on this Table had not been confirmed at time of going to press. These services will be issued in a special Supplement as soon as exact timings have been confirmed

until 7 September

Taunton → Gloucester

Network Diagram - see first page of Table 132

	XC R 1	GW	GW ◇	GW 1 ◇		XC 1 ◇	XC R 1	GW ◇	XC R 1	GW	XC R 1		XC R 1	GW	GW ◇	GW	XC R 1	GW 1 ◇		XC R 1	GW ◇	GW ◇	GW 1 ◇	XC 1 ◇	GW
		A				B			B		C		B	A			B				D		E	B	
	☕			☕		☕	☕	🛒	☕		☕		☕		🛒		☕	☕		☕		🛒	☕	☕	
Taunton d	13 51						14 51		15 07	15 19	15 36		15 51					16 37		16 51			17 03		17 19
Bridgwater d										15 31															17 30
Highbridge & Burnham d										15 38															17 37
Weston-super-Mare a									15 28	15 48	15 56							16 58					17 24		17 48
d				14 26					15 30	15 50	16 05					16 14		16 59			17 07		17 25		17 50
Weston Milton d										15 53						16 17					17 10				
Worle d				14 32						15 57						16 22					17 15		17 32		17 55
Yatton d				14 38						16 02						16 27					17 20		17 38		18 01
Nailsea & Backwell d				14 44						16 08						16 33					17 26		17 46		18 07
Parson Street d																16 43									
Bedminster d																16 45					17 37				
Bristol Temple Meads 10 a	14 25			14 55			15 25		15 55	16 20	16 25		16 25			16 48		17 20		17 25	17 40		17 57		18 19
d	14 30	14 43	14 48	15 00		15 00	15 30	15 48	16 00		16 30		16 30	16 44	16 48		17 00	17 30		17 30	17 42	17 49	18 00	18 00	
Lawrence Hill d																									
Stapleton Road d																									
Filton Abbey Wood d		14 50	14 56					15 55						16 54	16 56							17 56			
Bristol Parkway 7 a	14 38	14 53	14 59			15 08	15 38	15 58	16 08		16 38		16 38	16 55	16 59		17 08			17 38		17 59		18 08	
d		14 55																							
Bath Spa 7 a				15 12														17 42			17 58		18 11		
London Paddington 15 ⊖ a				16 54														19 24					19 58		
Yate d		15 04												17 04											
Cam & Dursley d		15 18												17 18											
Gloucester 7 a		15 37												17 37											

	GW 1 ◇	XC R 1		GW	GW ◇	XC 1 ◇	GW 1 ◇	XC 1 ◇	GW ◇		GW ◇	XC 1 ◇	GW	GW ◇	GW 1 ◇	GW ◇		GW	GW 1 ◇	XC 1 ◇	GW	GW ◇	GW		
				A		B					H		J												
	☕	☕			🛒	☕	☕	☕	🛒		🛒	☕		🛒		🛒			☕	☕		🛒			
Taunton d	17 46	17 51					18 24	18 51			19 07	19 51						20 44	21 23		21 35				
Bridgwater d							18 35				19 19							20 56			21 47				
Highbridge & Burnham d							18 42				19 26							21 04			21 54				
Weston-super-Mare a							18 52				19 37							21 15			22 05				
d							18 54				19 40				20 38			21 17			22 07		23 15		
Weston Milton d																		21 20			22 10		23 18		
Worle d							19 00				19 45							21 25					23 23		
Yatton d							19 05				19 51							21 30			22 17		23 28		
Nailsea & Backwell d							19 11				19 57							21 36			22 23		23 34		
Parson Street d																									
Bedminster d																		21 47					23 45		
Bristol Temple Meads 10 a	18 25	18 25					19 26	19 25			20 09	20 25			20 58			21 50	21 58		22 35		23 48		
d	18 30	18 30		18 41	18 49	19 00	19 30	19 30	19 49			20 30	20 43	20 49	21 00	21 49			22 05	22 10		22 49			
Lawrence Hill d																									
Stapleton Road d																									
Filton Abbey Wood d				18 51	18 56				19 56				20 50	20 56		21 56						22 56			
Bristol Parkway 7 a		18 38		18 54	18 59	19 08		19 38	19 59			20 38	20 53	20 59		21 59				22 18		22 59			
d				18 55									20 55												
Bath Spa 7 a	18 43						19 42								21 13				22 18						
London Paddington 15 ⊖ a	20 21						21 22								22 59				00 17						
Yate d				19 04									21 04												
Cam & Dursley d				19 18									21 18												
Gloucester 7 a				19 35									21 34												

For general notes see front of timetable
For details of catering facilities see Directory of Train Operators

A To Worcester Shrub Hill (Table 57)
B From 20 July
C Until 13 July
D To Weymouth (Table 123)
E From Paignton (Table 135)
H From Penzance (Table 135)
J To Cheltenham Spa (Table 57)

Due to Engineering Operations, services from Sunday 14 September on this Table had not been confirmed at time of going to press. These services will be issued in a special Supplement as soon as exact timings have been confirmed

Route Diagram for Tables 135, 136, 139, 140, 142, 143, 144

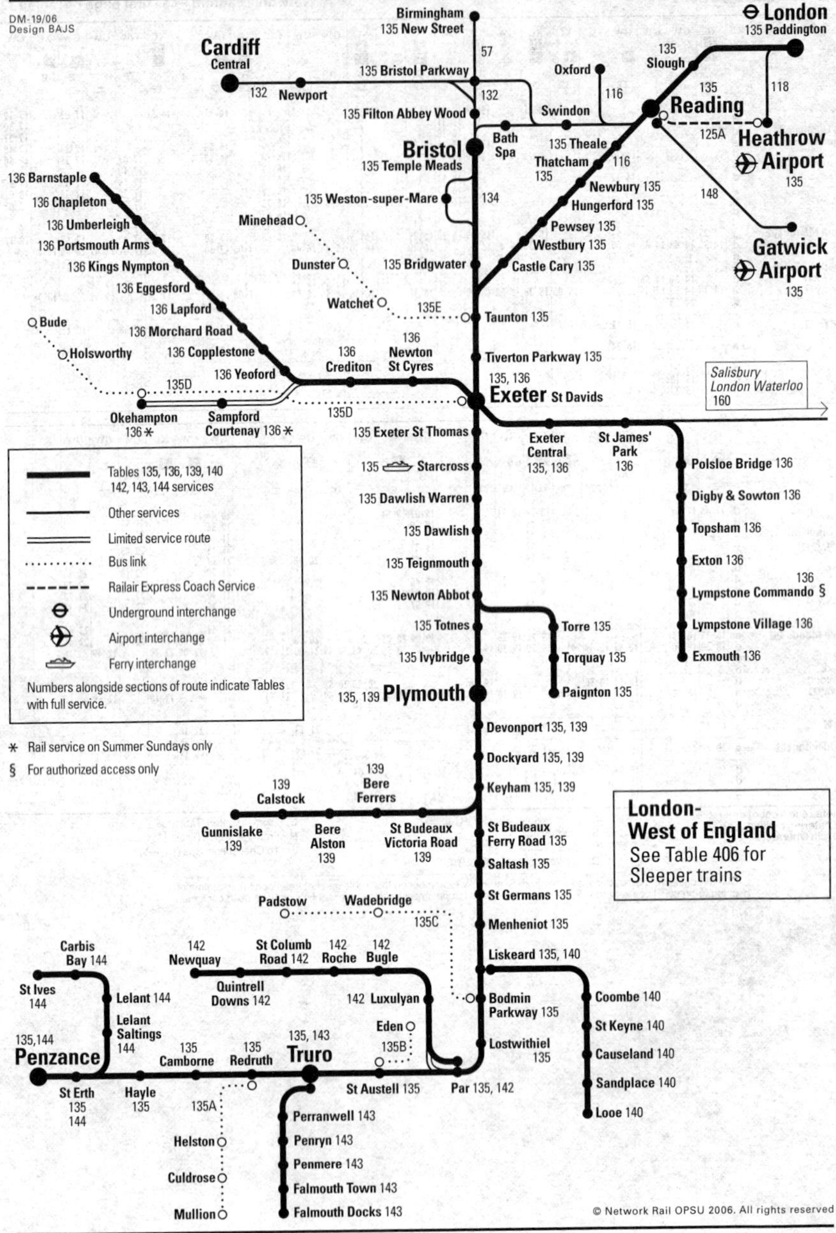

Sleeper services are published in Table 406

London and Birmingham → Devon and Cornwall

Network Diagram - see first page of Table 135

Miles	Miles		GW	GW	GW	GW	GW	XC	GW		XC	GW	GW	GW	GW	GW	GW		GW	GW	GW	GW	XC	GW
			MX	MX	MX	MX	MO	MO			MX	MO												
			1	1 ◇	1 ◇	1 ◇	1 ◇	1 ◇			1 ◇	1 ◇			1		◇				◇		1 ◇	
						A	A					A							B					
			✕	☕	☕	☕	☕	☕			☕	☕											☕	
0	—	**London Paddington** 15 ⊖ d	19p03	20p35	21p45	23p45	23p50																	
—	—	**London Waterloo** 15 ⊖ d																						
18½	—	Slough 3 d																						
—	—	Heathrow Terminal 1 Bus 🚌 d																						
—	—	Gatwick Airport 10 d																						
—	—	Oxford d																						
36	—	**Reading** 7 d	19p32	21p02	22p11	00u37	00u37																	
41¼	—	Theale d																						
49½	—	Thatcham d																						
53	—	Newbury d	19p49	21p18																				
61½	—	Hungerford d																						
75¼	—	Pewsey d		21p39																				
95½	—	Westbury d		21p57																				
115¼	—	Castle Cary d		22p15																				
—	0	**Birmingham New Street** 12 d																					06 10	
—	—	Cardiff Central 7 d																						
—	—	Newport (South Wales) d																						
—	—	Swindon d			22p52																			
—	87	Bristol Parkway 7 d																					07 55	
—	88¼	Filton Abbey Wood d																						
—	—	Bath Spa 7 d			23p21																			
—	92¾	**Bristol Temple Meads** 10 d			23p36												05 29				06 46		08 11	
—	112¾	Weston-super-Mare d			00 06												05 50				07 07			
—	126½	Bridgwater d			00 24																07 25			
143	138¼	Taunton d	20p55	22p38	00 36	03 34											06 18				07 40		08 43	
157¼	—	Tiverton Parkway d		22p50	00 49												06 33				07 55			
173¾	—	**Exeter St Davids** 6 a	21p20	23p48	00 59	04 45	04 03										06 51				08 13		09 07	
—	—	Exeter Central a															*07 13*				*08 29*		*09 21*	
—	—	Exmouth a															*07 40*						*09 45*	
—	—	Barnstaple a																			*09 32*		*10 24*	
—	—	Exmouth d															*06 03*			07 15	*07 15*	07 50	*08 20*	
—	—	Exeter Central d															*06 32*			07 39	*07 54*	08 16	*08 44*	09 00
—	—	**Exeter St Davids** 6 d	21p22	23p51		04 47	04 35						05 42	06 12			06 53			07 48	08 15	08 24	09 07	09 10
174¾	—	Exeter St Thomas d											05 45	06 15			06 55			07 51		08 27		09 13
182¼	—	Starcross d											05 53	06 23			07 04			07 59				09 21
184¼	—	Dawlish Warren d											05 58	06 28			07 08			08 04				09 26
185¾	—	Dawlish d											06 02	06 32			07 12			08 08	08 28	08 39		09 30
188¾	—	Teignmouth d											06 07	06 37			07 17			08 13	08 33	08 44		09 35
193¾	—	Newton Abbot a	21p42	00 09		05 07	04 55						06 13	06 43			07 24			08 19	08 39	08 51		09 41
—	0	d	21p43	00 12		05 09	04 56		05 42				06 15	06 45		07 06	07 24			08 21	08 40	08 52		09 45
—	5¼	Torre d							05 50				06 23	06 53		07 15				08 29		09 01		
—	6	Torquay d							05 53				06 26	06 56		07 20				08 32		09 04	09 36	
—	8¼	Paignton a							06 00				06 33	07 02		07 28				08 39		09 13	09 47	
202½	—	Totnes d	21p57	00 23													07 38				08 53			09 58
214	—	Ivybridge d															07 54				09 10			10 15
225¾	—	**Plymouth** a	22p24	00 52		05 47	05 35					←					08 08				09 24			10 29
—	—	d	22p26			05 50	06 30 →	05 50			06 30	06 30			07 05		08 13		08 23		09 25			
227	—	Devonport d													07 10				08 26					
227½	—	Dockyard d																						
228	—	Keyham d																						
228¾	—	St Budeaux Ferry Road d																						
230	—	Saltash d	22p36												07 18		08 21		08 33					
235	—	St Germans d	22p43												07 25		08 28		08 41					
240¼	—	Menheniot d																	08 49					
243½	—	Liskeard 3 d	22p55			06 16		06 16			06 53	06 58			07 37		08 40		08 55		09 48			
—	—	Looe a						*07 44*			*07 44*						*09b14*				*10 23*			
252½	—	Bodmin Parkway d	23p07			06 30		06 30			07 06	07 15			07 49		08 54				10 00			
256	—	Lostwithiel d	23p12			06 36		06 36			07 11	07 22			07 55		08 59				10 05			
260½	—	Par 3 d	23p19			06 43		06 42			07 18	07 29			08 02		09 06		09 18		10 12			
—	—	Newquay a																	10 10					
265	—	St Austell d	23p27			06 51		06 49			07 25	07 38			08 10		09 13				10 23			
279½	—	Truro d	23p44			07 10		07 10			07 42	07 58			08 28		09 32				10 41			
—	—	Falmouth Docks a						*07 50*							*08 55*		*10 08*				*11 10*			
288½	—	Redruth d	23p57			07 24		07 24			07 53	08 11			08 40		09 45				10 54			
292	—	Camborne d	00 04			07 31		07 31			08 00	08 19			08 47		09 51				11 00			
298	—	Hayle d	00 12			07 40		07 40			08 08	08 31			08 56		09 58				11 07			
299½	—	St Erth 2 d	00 17			07 45		07 45			08 12	08 42			09 00		10 02				11 10			
—	—	St Ives a						*08 16*							*09 19*		*10 22*				*11 53*			
305¼	—	**Penzance** a	00 35			08 00		08 00			08 27	08 59			09 14		10 14				11 24			

For general notes see front of timetable
For details of catering facilities see Directory of Train Operators

A **Night Riviera**
B From Gunnislake (Table 139)
b Until 5 September only

Sleeper services are published in Table 406

London and Birmingham → Devon and Cornwall

Network Diagram - see first page of Table 135

		GW	GW	XC	GW	GW	SW	XC	SW	GW	GW	GW	GW	GW	XC	GW	GW	GW	GW	GW	XC	SW
				1 ◇		1 ◇	1 ◇	1 ◇	1 ◇		1 ◇	1 ◇	1 ◇		R 1			1 ◇	1 ◇		R 1	1 ◇
												A	B C	A			D	E	G	H		
				☕		⊠	☕	☕	☕		☕	☕	☕		☕			☕	☕		☕	☕
London Paddington 15 ⊖	d					07 30					08 18	09 06	09 06					10 00	10 06			
London Waterloo 15 ⊖	d						07 10															09 20
Slough 3	d																					
Heathrow Terminal 1 Bus	d																					
Gatwick Airport 10	d					06b02					06 59	07 58	07 58					08b14				
Oxford	d					07 15					08 15	08 50	08 50					09 43	10 01			
Reading 7	d					07 57					08 47	09 32	09 32					10 27	10 32			
Theale	d										08 55											
Thatcham	d										09 04											
Newbury	d										09 10											
Hungerford	d										09 20											
Pewsey	d										09 38											
Westbury	d										10 00											
Castle Cary	d										10 16											
Birmingham New Street 12	d			07 10				08 10							09 10						09 40	
Cardiff Central 7	d																					
Newport (South Wales)	d																					
Swindon	d					08 26												10 56				
Bristol Parkway 7	d			08 25				09 25							10 25						10 55	
Filton Abbey Wood	d																					
Bath Spa 7	d					08 55												11 25				
Bristol Temple Meads 10	d			08 44		09 13		09 44							10 44			11 45 →			11 14	
Weston-super-Mare	d																				11 42	
Bridgwater	d																					
Taunton	d			09 17		09 46		10 17			10 39	10 48	10 48		11 17						12 05	
Tiverton Parkway	d			09 29				10 29			10 52	11 01	11 01		11 29						12 17	
Exeter St Davids 6	a			09 43		10 12		10 43			11 12	11 18	11 18		11 43				12 10		12 31	
Exeter Central	a			*10 13*		*10 21*					*11 21*	*11 48*			*12 13*				*12 21*		*12 48*	
Exmouth	a					*10 45*					*11 45*	*12 15*							*12 45*		*13 15*	
Barnstaple	a											*12 30*	*12 30*									
Exmouth	d			*08 50*	09 20		*09 50*			10 20			*10 20*		*10 50*	11 20					*11 50*	
Exeter Central	d			*09 24*	09 44		10 30			10 43			*10 43*		*11 14*	11 43				12 08	*12 24*	12 24
Exeter St Davids 6	d			09 45	09 51	10 13	10 39	10 45		10 51		11 19	11 19		11 45	11 51			12 10	12 15	12 33	12 39
Exeter St Thomas	d				09 54					10 54						11 54						
Starcross	d				10 02				←	11 02						12 02						
Dawlish Warren	d				10 07		10c57 →		10 57	11 07						12 07						12e57 →
Dawlish	d				10 11				11 01	11 11						12 11				12 28	12 45	
Teignmouth	d				10 16				11 06	11 16						12 16				12 33	12 50	
Newton Abbot	a			10 02	10 22	10 33		11 02	11 12	11 22		11 39	11 39		12 02	12 22			12 31	12 39	12 56	
	d	09 51		10 04	10 24	10 34		11 04	11 14	11 24		11 40	11 40		12 04	12 24			12 31	12 40	12 57	
Torre	d	09 59			10 32					11 32						12 32						
Torquay	d	10 02			10 35				11 25	11 35						12 35					13 08	
Paignton	a	10 08			10 41				11 31	11 42						12 43					13 20	
Totnes	d			10 17		10 47		11 17				11 53	11 53		12 17					12 52		
Ivybridge	d																			13 09		
Plymouth	a			10 48		11 15		11 48				12 23	12 23		12 48				13 10	13 25		
	d		10 35			11 17							12 25	12 44					13 10	13 33		
Devonport	d																			13 36		
Dockyard	d																			13x38		
Keyham	d																			13x40		
St Budeaux Ferry Road	d		10 40										12 35	12 52								
Saltash	d		10 45										12 42	12 59								
St Germans	d		10 52																			
Menheniot	d																					
Liskeard 3	d		11 04			11 41							12 54	13 11					13 34			
Looe	a		*11f37*			*12g37*							*13 47*	*13h47*					*14j15*			
Bodmin Parkway	d		11 16			11 53							13 06	13 23					13 48			
Lostwithiel	d		11 21										13 15	13 28								
Par 3	d		11 28			12 05							13 26	13 35			13 35		13 58			
Newquay	a		*12 23*										14 32						*14k50*			
St Austell	d		11 35			12 12								13 43			13 43		14 06			
Truro	d		11 53			12 29								14 00			14 01		14 22			
Falmouth Docks	a					*13 02*													*14 52*			
Redruth	d		12 06			12 42								14 13			14 14		14 36			
Camborne	d		12 12			12 49								14 19			14 20		14 42			
Hayle	d		12 19			12 58													14 51			
St Erth 2	d		12 22			13 02								14 29			14 30		14 55			
St Ives	a		*12 53*			*13 22*								*14 53*			*14 53*		*15 22*			
Penzance	a		12 35			13 21								14 42			14 41		15 13			

For general notes see front of timetable
For details of catering facilities see Directory of Train Operators

- **A** Until 27 June and from 8 September
- **B** 30 June to 5 September
- **C** **Atlantic Coast Express**
- **D** 30 June to 5 September. From Newquay (Table 142)
- **E** **Torbay Express**
- **G** **Cornish Riviera**
- **H** To Gunnislake (Table 139)
- **b** Change at Redhill
- **c** Arr. 1050
- **e** Arr. 1250
- **f** Until 5 September only
- **g** From 8 September arr. 1219
- **h** Until 27 June only
- **j** From 8 September only
- **k** Until 27 June and from 8 September only

Sleeper services are published in Table 406

London and Birmingham → Devon and Cornwall

Network Diagram - see first page of Table 135

Station		XC	SW	GW	GW	GW	GW	XC	GW	GW	XC	XC	GW	GW	GW	GW	GW	GW	XC	SW	GW	GW
		1 ◇	1 ◇	1 ◇			1 ◇	1 ◇		1 ◇	1 ◇	1 ◇		1 ◇		1 ◇	1 ◇		1 ◇	1 ◇		
				A			B			C D						E	G					
London Paddington 15	⊖ d						11 06			12 06				12 18		13 06	13 06					
London Waterloo 15	⊖ d																			12 20		
Slough 3	d																					
Heathrow Terminal 1 Bus	d																					
Gatwick Airport 10	d						10 03			11 03						12 03	12 03					
Oxford	d						11 01			12 01				12 15		13 01	13 01					
Reading 7	d						11 32			12 32				12 47		13 32	13 32					
Theale	d													12 55								
Thatcham	d													13 04								
Newbury	d													13 10								
Hungerford	d													13 20								
Pewsey	d						12 03							13 39								
Westbury	d						12 22							13 58								
Castle Cary	d						12 39							14 22								
Birmingham New Street 12	d	10 10						11 10			11 40	12 10							13 10			
Cardiff Central 7	d																					
Newport (South Wales)	d																					
Swindon	d																					
Bristol Parkway 7	d	11 25						12 25			12 55	13 25							14 25			
Filton Abbey Wood	d																					
Bath Spa 7	d			←																		
Bristol Temple Meads 10	d	11 44		11 45				12 44			13 11	13 44							14 44			
Weston-super-Mare	d			12 07																		
Bridgwater	d																					
Taunton	d	12 17		12 29			13 02	13 17			13b50	14 17		14a44		14 50	14 50		15 17			
Tiverton Parkway	d	12 29					13 15	13 29			14 02	14 29				15 03	15 03		15 29			
Exeter St Davids 6	a	12 43		12 56			13 32	13 43		14 10	14 16	14 43				15 20	15 20		15 43			
Exeter Central	a			13 21			13 48	14 13		14 21	14 48	15 21				15 33	15 33		16 13			
Exmouth	a			13 45			14 15			14 45	15 15	15 45				16 15	16 15		16 45			
Barnstaple	a			14 25						15 22						16 30	16 30					
Exmouth	d			12 20			12 50		13 20			13 50	14 20						14 50		15 20	
Exeter Central	d			12 43			13 14		13 42			14 14	14 42						15 24	15 39	15 44	
Exeter St Davids 6	d	12 45		12 57	13 02		13 33	13 45	13 51	14 11	14 18	14 45	14 51			15 21	15 21		15 45	15 49	15 52	
Exeter St Thomas	d				13 05				13 54				14 54								15 55	
Starcross	d		←		13 14				14 02				15 02								16 03	
Dawlish Warren	d		12 57		13 18				14 07				15 07								16 08	
Dawlish	d		13 01	13 10	13 22				14 11		14 30		15 11							16 01	16 12	
Teignmouth	d		13 06	13 16	13 27				14 16		14 35		15 16							16 06	16 17	
Newton Abbot	a	13 02	13 13	13 23	13 34		13 53	14 02	14 22		14 41	15 02	15 22			15 41	15 41		16 02	16 13	16 23	
	d	13 04	13 13	13 24	13 35		13 54	14 04	14 24		14 42	15 04	15 24			15 42	15 42	15 56	16 04	16 13	16 25	
Torre	d				13 43				14 32				15 32								16 33	
Torquay	d			13 35	13 46				14 35		14 53		15 35								16 36	
Paignton	a			13 48	13 53				14 42		15 05		15 40								16 43	
Totnes	d	13 17	13 26				14 07	14 17				15 17				15 55	15 55	16 08	16 17	16 25		
Ivybridge	d		13 41															16 24		16 41		
Plymouth	a	13 48	13 56				14 36	14 48		15 06		15 48				16 26	16 28	16 40	16 48	16 56		
	d					14 01				15 08					15 55	16 27						17 06
Devonport	d														15 58							17 09
Dockyard	d														16x00							17x11
Keyham	d														16x02							17x13
St Budeaux Ferry Road	d														16 04							17 15
Saltash	d					14 09									16 09							17 20
St Germans	d					14 16									16 16							17 27
Menheniot	d														16 24							17 35
Liskeard 3	d					14 28				15 32					16 30	16 51						17a41
Looe	a					15c01				17 05					17 05							
Bodmin Parkway	d					14 40				15 44					16 45	17 03						
Lostwithiel	d														16 50	17 09						
Par 3	d					14 51				15 54					16 57	17 16						
Newquay	a									16e54						19 21						
St Austell	d					14 58				16 02					17 05	17 24						
Truro	d					15 17				16 21					17 23	17 42						
Falmouth Docks	a									16 32					17 49	18 45						
Redruth	d					15 30				16 32					17 36	17 55						
Camborne	d					15 36				16 41					17 42	18 02						
Hayle	d					15 43									17 49	18 10						
St Erth 2	d					15 47				16 50					17 53	18 15						
St Ives	a					16 22				17 24					18 12	18 49						
Penzance	a					15 59				17 05					18 05	18 27						

For general notes see front of timetable
For details of catering facilities see Directory of Train Operators

A **Torbay Express**
B **The Mayflower**
C ✕ to Plymouth, ☕ from Plymouth
D **The Royal Duchy**
E 30 June to 5 September
G Until 27 June and from 8 September
b Arr. 1342
c From 8 September arr. 1544
e 30 June to 5 September only

Sleeper services are published in Table 406

London and Birmingham → Devon and Cornwall

Network Diagram - see first page of Table 135

		XC	GW	GW	XC	GW	GW	GW		GW	GW	GW	XC	SW	XC	GW		GW	XC	GW	GW	GW	GW	XC	GW
		R 1	1 ◇		R 1							1 ◇	R 1	1 ◇	1 ◇	1 ◇			R 1	1 ◇		1 ◇		R 1	1 ◇
							A	B		C			D						E						
		⊏P	⊠		⊏P							⊏P	⊏P	⊏P	⊏P	⊏P			⊏P	⊏P		⊏P		⊏P	⊏P
London Paddington 15 ⊖	d		14 06									15 06				16 06				16 33		17 03			17 06
London Waterloo 15 ⊖	d													14 20											
Slough 3	d																			16 48					
Heathrow Terminal 1 Bus	d																								
Gatwick Airport 10	d		13 03									14 03				15 03						16 03			
Oxford	d		14 01									15 01				16 01				16 31		17 01			
Reading 7	d		14 32									15 32				16 32				17 04		17 32			17 37
Theale	d																								17 45
Thatcham	d																								17 54
Newbury	d																			17 20		17 48			18 01
Hungerford	d																			17 30					18 14
Pewsey	d											16 03								17 45					18 32
Westbury	d											16 22								18 04					18a51
Castle Cary	d											16 39								18 22					
Birmingham New Street 12	d	13 40			14 10								15 10		15 40				16 10					17 10	
Cardiff Central 7	d																								
Newport (South Wales)	d																								
Swindon	d																								
Bristol Parkway 7	d	14 55			15 25								16 25		16 55				17 25					18 25	
Filton Abbey Wood	d																								
Bath Spa 7	d																								
Bristol Temple Meads 10	d	15 11			15 44								16 44		17 11				17 44					18 44	
Weston-super-Mare	d																								
Bridgwater	d																								
Taunton	d	15 43	15 48		16 17							17 04	17 17		17 44	17 48			18 17	18 44		18 53		19 17	
Tiverton Parkway	d	15 55	16 01		16 29							17 17	17 29		17 56	18 01			18 29	18 57		19 06		19 29	
Exeter St Davids 6	a	16 10	16 17		16 43							17 33	17 43		18 10	18 18			18 43	19 17		19 22		19 43	
Exeter Central	a	16 21	16 39		17 21							17 43	18 13		18 21	18 27			19 13	19 30				19 51	
Exmouth	a	16 45	17 15		17 48										18 48	19 18								20 18	
Barnstaple	a				18 03								19 07						20 10						
Exmouth	d			15 50							16 50				17 20			17 50				18 23	18 50		
Exeter Central	d			16 14	16 23						17 14		17 35	17 35	17 56			18 19				19 01	19 14		
Exeter St Davids 6	d	16 12	16 19	16 24	16 45	16 53					17 21	17 33	17 45	17 49	18 12	18 21		18 25	18 45			19 23	19 28	19 45	
Exeter St Thomas	d			16 27		16 56					17 24			17 52				18 28					19 31		
Starcross	d			16 35		17 04					17 32			18 00				18 36					19 39		
Dawlish Warren	d			16 40		17 09					17 37			18 04				18 41					19 44		
Dawlish	d			16 44		17 13					17 41			18 08	18 24			18 45					19 48		
Teignmouth	d			16 49		17 18					17 46			18 13	18 29			18 50					19 53		
Newton Abbot	a	16 30	16 39	16 55	17 02	17 24					17 52	17 57	18 08	18 20	18 35	18 42		18 56	19 02		⟵	19 43	19 59	20 02	
	d	16 31	16 40	16 57	17 04	17 26				17 29	17 54	17 58	18 09	18 21	18 36	18 42		19 08	19 04		19 08	19 44	20 08	20 04	
Torre	d			17 05		17 34					18 02			18 30				⟶			19 16		⟶		
Torquay	d			17 08		17 37					18 05			18 34							19 19				
Paignton	a			17 15		17 44					18 12			18 40							19 25				
Totnes	d	16 44	16 53		17 17					17 41		18 11	18 22		18 49	18 56			19 17			19 58		20 17	
Ivybridge	d									17 58															
Plymouth	a	17 15	17 21		17 48					18 13		18 39	18 48		19 20	19 24			19 48			20 25		20 48	
	d		17 25		17 55		18⟆12	18⟆12		18 16		18 40	19 00			19 26			19 50			20 27			
Devonport	d						18⟆15	18⟆15		18 19															
Dockyard	d						18x17	18x17		18x21															
Keyham	d						18x19	18x19		18x23															
St Budeaux Ferry Road	d						18⟆21	18⟆21																	
Saltash	d		17 35				18⟆26	18⟆26								19 36						20 37			
St Germans	d		17 42				18⟆33	18⟆33								19 43						20 44			
Menheniot	d						18⟆41	18⟆41																	
Liskeard 3	d		17 54		18 18		18⟆47	18a46				19 04	19 23			19 55			20 13			20 56			
Looe	a		18 32				⟆					19 40													
Bodmin Parkway	d		18 07		18 31		18⟆59					19 16	19 35			20 07			20 26			21 09			
Lostwithiel	d		18 12				19⟆04						19 41									21 14			
Par 3	d		18 18		18 41		19b33					19 26	19 47			20 17			20 36			21 20			
Newquay	a		19c16				20⟆23												21c31						
St Austell	d		18 26		18 48							19 34	19 54			20 25			20 42			21 28			
Truro	d		18 44		19 05							19 53	20 11			20 43			21 00			21 47			
Falmouth Docks	a											20 23							21 27						
Redruth	d		18 56		19 17							20 05	20 22			20 55			21 14			21 59			
Camborne	d		19 04		19 24							20 13	20 29			21 03			21 21			22 07			
Hayle	d		19 13										20 36			21 12						22 15			
St Erth 2	d		19 17		19 34							20 23	20 41			21 16			21 31			22 20			
St Ives	a				19 53							20 43							21 47						
Penzance	a		19 34		19 49							20 41	20 56			21 30			21 47			22 35			

For general notes see front of timetable
For details of catering facilities see Directory of Train Operators

A Until 27 June and from 8 September. From Gunnislake (Table 139)
B 30 June to 5 September. From Gunnislake (Table 139)
C To Gunnislake (Table 139)
D Until 5 September from Glasgow Central, from 8 September from Newcastle (Table 51)
E ⊏P to Plymouth
b Arr. 1913
c 30 June to 5 September only

Sleeper services are published in Table 406

London and Birmingham → Devon and Cornwall

Network Diagram - see first page of Table 135

		GW	GW	GW	GW	XC	GW	GW	GW	GW	GW	XC	GW	GW	GW	XC	GW	GW	GW
		[1] ◇		[1] ◇	[1] ◇	[1] ◇	[1] ◇	[1] ◇	[1] ◇	[1]		[1] ◇		[1] ◇		[1] ◇	[1] ◇	[1] ◇	[1] ◇
				A			B	C	D			E							G
		☐		✕	☐	☐	☐	☐	☐	✕		☐		☐			☐	☐	☐
London Paddington [15]	⊖ d	17 33		18 03			18 06	18 33	18 36	19 03				19 45			20 35	21 45	23 45
London Waterloo [15]	⊖ d																		
Slough [3]	d																		
Heathrow Terminal 1 Bus	🚌 d																		
Gatwick Airport [10]	d	*16b08*		*17 03*						*18 03*							*19 16*		
Oxford	d	*17 15*		*18 01*				*18 31*	*18 31*	*18 43*				*19 30*			*20 31*		
Reading [7]	d	18 02		18 32			18 36	19 03	19 03	19 32				20 11			21 02	22 11	00u37
Theale	d						18 45												
Thatcham	d						18 54												
Newbury	d	18 18					19 01	19 19	19 19	19 49				20 26			21 18		
Hungerford	d						19 15	19 29	19 29										
Pewsey	d	18 39					19 34	19 44	19 44					20 47			21 39		
Westbury	d	18 58					19a52	20 05	20 05					21 06			21 57		
Castle Cary	d	19 16						20 22	20 22					21 24			22 15		
Birmingham New Street [12]	d					18 10						19 10				20 10			
Cardiff Central [7]	d																		
Newport (South Wales)	d																		
Swindon	d																	22 52	
Bristol Parkway [7]	d					19 25						20 25				21 25			
Filton Abbey Wood	d																		
Bath Spa [7]	d																	23 21	
Bristol Temple Meads [10]	d					19 44						20 44				21 44		23 36	
Weston-super-Mare	d																	00 06	
Bridgwater	d																	00 24	
Taunton	d	19 38		19 47		20 17		20 45	20 45	20 55		21 17		21 46		22 17	22 38	00 36	03 34
Tiverton Parkway	d	19 51				20 29		20 58	20 58			21 29		21 59		22 29	22 50	00 49	
Exeter St Davids [6]	a	20 07		20 13		20 43		21 16	21 16	21 20		21 43		22 16		23 24	23 48	01 59	04 45
Exeter Central	a	*20 18*				*20 51*						*21 51*		*22c33*					
Exmouth	a					*21 18*						*22 18*		*23 52*					
Barnstaple	a					*22 08*													
Exmouth	d			*19 20*						*20 20*				*21 20*		*22 20*			
Exeter Central	d			*19 52*	←	*20 31*				*20 44*				*21 50*		*22 44*			
Exeter St Davids [6]	d	20 19 →		20 15	20 19	20 45				21 22	21 28	21 45		22 17	22 30	23 25	23 51		04 47
Exeter St Thomas	d				20 23						21 31				22 33				
Starcross	d				20 32						21 39				22 41				
Dawlish Warren	d				20 36						21 44				22 46				
Dawlish	d				20 41						21 48				22 50				
Teignmouth	d				20 47						21 53				22 55				
Newton Abbot	a		←	20 35	20 54	21 02				21 42	21 59	22 02	←	22 38	23 01	23 44	00 09		05 07
	d		20 08	20 36	20 54	21 04				21 43	22 08	22 04	22 08	22 38	23 03	23 45	00 12		05 09
Torre	d		20 16		21 04						→		22 16		23 11				
Torquay	d		20 19		21 07								22 19		23 14				
Paignton	a		20 25		21 20								22 26		23 21				
Totnes	d			20 49		21 17				21 57		22 17		22 52		23 58	00 23		
Ivybridge	d																		
Plymouth	a			21 17		21 48				22 24		22 48		23 22		00 29	00 52		05 47
	d			21 19						22 26									05 50
Devonport	d																		
Dockyard	d																		
Keyham	d																		
St Budeaux Ferry Road	d																		
Saltash	d									22 36									
St Germans	d									22 43									
Menheniot	d																		
Liskeard [3]	d			21 43						22 55									06 16
Looe	a																		
Bodmin Parkway	d			21 55						23 07									06 30
Lostwithiel	d									23 12									06 36
Par [3]	d			22 05						23 19									06 43
Newquay	a																		
St Austell	d			22 13						23 27									06 51
Truro	d			22 31						23 44									07 10
Falmouth Docks	a																		
Redruth	d			22 43						23 57									07 24
Camborne	d									00 04									07 31
Hayle	d									00 12									07 40
St Erth [2]	d									00 17									07 45
St Ives	a																		
Penzance	a			23 10						00 35									08 00

For general notes see front of timetable
For details of catering facilities see Directory of Train Operators

A **The Golden Hind**
B To Frome (Table 123)
C 30 June to 5 September
D Until 27 June and from 8 September
E ☐ to Bristol Temple Meads
G **Night Riviera**
b Change at Redhill
c Fridays arr. 2300

Sleeper services are published in Table 406

London and Birmingham → Devon and Cornwall

Network Diagram - see first page of Table 135

		GW	GW	GW	GW	GW	GW	XC	GW	GW	GW	GW	GW	XC	GW	GW	SW	GW		XC	GW	GW	XC	GW	GW
		1	1 ◇		1 ◇ A			1 ◇		◇			1 ◇	1 ◇		◇	1		1 ◇	1 ◇			1 ◇	1 ◇	
		✕	⊡		⊡			⊡		⊼			⊡	⊡		⊼			⊡	⊡	⊼	⊼	⊡	⊡	
London Paddington 15	⊖ d	19p03	20p35		23p45																			07 30	
London Waterloo 15	⊖ d																								
Slough 3	d																								
Heathrow Terminal 1 Bus	d																								
Gatwick Airport 10	d																							*06 03*	
Oxford	d																							*07 15*	
Reading 7	d	19p32	21p02		00u37																			07 56	
Theale	d																								
Thatcham	d																								
Newbury	d	19p49	21p18																						
Hungerford	d																								
Pewsey	d		21p39																						
Westbury	d		21p57																						
Castle Cary	d		22p15																						
Birmingham New Street 12	d																						07 10		
Cardiff Central 7	d																								
Newport (South Wales)	d																								
Swindon	d																							08 26	
Bristol Parkway 7	d																						08 25		
Filton Abbey Wood	d																								
Bath Spa 7	d																							08 56	
Bristol Temple Meads 10	d									05 31						06 48				07 35			08 44	09 17 →	
Weston-super-Mare	d									05 51						07 08									
Bridgwater	d									06 10															
Taunton	d	20p55	22p38		03 34					06 25						07 34				08 42			09 17		
Tiverton Parkway	d		22p50							06 40						07 51				08 55			09 29		
Exeter St Davids 6	a	21p20	23p48		04 45					06 58						08 09				09 10			09 43		
Exeter Central	a									*07 17*						*08 21*				*09 21*			*10 13*		
Exmouth	a									*07 43*						*08 47*				*09 45*			*10 45*		
Barnstaple	a															*09 30*				*10 23*					
Exmouth	d									*06 15*		07 18					07 50	08 20				08 50	*08 50*		09 20
Exeter Central	d									*06 39*		07 42					08 27	08 44				09 14	*09 24*		09 44
Exeter St Davids 6	d	21p22	23p51		04 47	05 29	06 00		06 14	07 00		07 48			08 15		08 37	08 50		09 12		09 20	09 46		09 52
Exeter St Thomas	d					05 32	06 03		06 17	07 02		07 51						08 53							09 55
Starcross	d					05 40	06 11		06 25	07 11		07 59						09 02							10 04
Dawlish Warren	d					05 45	06 16		06 30	07 15		08 04						09 07							10 09
Dawlish	d					05 49	06 20		06 34	07 19		08 08					08 50	09 11		09 25		09 33	09 58		10 13
Teignmouth	d					05 54	06 25		06 39	07 24		08 13					08 55	09 17		09 31		09 38	10 04		10 19
Newton Abbot	a	21p42	00 09		05 07	06 00	06 31		06 45	07 31		08 19			08 37		09 01	09 24		09 40		09 44	10 10		10 25
	d	21p43	00 12		05 09	06 02	06 33		06 47	07 31	07 37	08 21			08 38		09 06	09 28		09 42		09 46	10 11		10 27
Torre	d					06 10	06 41		06 55		07 45	08 29						09 36							10 35
Torquay	d					06 13	06 44		06 58		07 48	08 32					09 17	09 39		09 54			10 23		10 38
Paignton	a					06 19	06 50		07 04		07 55	08 38					09 23	09 45		10 05			10 34		10 44
Totnes	d	21p57	00 23							07 45					08 51							09 59			
Ivybridge	d									08 01					09 08							10 16			
Plymouth	a	22p24	00 52		05 47					08 15					09 22							10 30			
	d	22p26			05 50			06 53		08 17			08 58	09 18					09 30		10 00	10 36			
Devonport	d																				10 03				
Dockyard	d																								
Keyham	d																								
St Budeaux Ferry Road	d																								
Saltash	d	22p36								08 25											10 10	10 45			
St Germans	d	22p43								08 32											10 17				
Menheniot	d																				10 25				
Liskeard 3	d	22p55			06 16			07 16		08 44			09 22	09 41					09 53		10 31	11 02			
Looe	a																		*10 24*			*11 33*			
Bodmin Parkway	d	23p07			06 30			07 29		08 58			09 34	09 54					10 05		10 43	11 14			
Lostwithiel	d	23p12			06 36					09 03									10 12		10 48				
Par 3	d	23p19		06 10	06 43					09 10			09 47	10 04					10 19		10a55	11 24			
Newquay	a							08 41					11 10												
St Austell	d	23p27		06 17	06 51					09 18				10 10					10 26			11 32			
Truro	d	23p44		06 35	07 10					09 36				10 28					10 44			11 49			
Falmouth Docks	a			*07 53*						*10 06*									*11 48*						
Redruth	d	23p57		06 48	07 24					09 49				10 39					10 56			12 02			
Camborne	d	00 04		06 54	07 31					09 55				10 45					11 04			12 08			
Hayle	d	00 12		07 01	07 40					10 02									11 15						
St Erth 2	d	00 17		07 04	07 45					10 06				10 55					11 21			12 18			
St Ives	a			*07 43*						*10 22*				*11 22*					*11 53*			*12 53*			
Penzance	a	00 35		07 17	08 00					10 17				11 11					11 32			12 31			

For general notes see front of timetable
For details of catering facilities see Directory of Train Operators

A Night Riviera

Due to Engineering Operations, services from Saturday 13 September on this Table had not been confirmed at time of going to press. These services will be issued in a special Supplement as soon as exact timings have been confirmed

Saturdays

until 6 September

Sleeper services are published in Table 406

London and Birmingham → Devon and Cornwall

Network Diagram - see first page of Table 135

		GW	GW	GW	SW	XC	SW	GW	GW	GW	XC	GW	GW	GW	XC	XC	SW	GW	GW	GW	XC	GW	GW	GW	SW
		1	1 ◇		1 ◇	1 ◇	1 ◇		1	1	R 1		1		R 1	R 1	1 ◇		1	1	R 1	1		1	1 ◇
				A							B		C	A					D			E		G	
		🍴	🍴		🍴	🍴	🍴		🍴	🍴	🍴		🍴		🍴	🍴	🍴		🍴	🍴	🍴	🍴		🍴	🍴
London Paddington 15	⊖ d	08 06							08 35	09 06			10 06						10 35	11 06		11 35		12 06	
London Waterloo 15	⊖ d				07 10												09 20								11 20
Slough 3	d																								
Heathrow Terminal 1 Bus	🚌 d																								
Gatwick Airport 10	d	*07 03*							*07b08*	*08 03*			*09 03*						*09b08*	*10 03*		*10b08*		*11 03*	
Oxford	d	*08 00*							*08 30*	*09 00*			*09 57*						*10 30*	*10 43*		*11 31*		*11 43*	
Reading 7	d	08 33							09 03	09 33			10 32						11 03	11 31		12u04		12 32	
Theale	d																								
Thatcham	d																								
Newbury	d								09 19																
Hungerford	d																								
Pewsey	d								09 39										11 35						
Westbury	d								09 56										11 54						
Castle Cary	d								10 14										12 12						
Birmingham New Street 12	d					08 10					09 10				09 40	10 10					11 10				
Cardiff Central 7	d																								
Newport (South Wales)	d																								
Swindon	d																								
Bristol Parkway 7	d					09 25					10 25				10 55	11 25					12 25				
Filton Abbey Wood	d																								
Bath Spa 7	d		←																						
Bristol Temple Meads 10	d		09 17			09 44					10 44				11 11	11 44					12 44				
Weston-super-Mare	d														11 29										
Bridgwater	d																								
Taunton	d		09 54			10 17			10 36	10 50					12 02	12 17			12 34	12 52	13 17				
Tiverton Parkway	d					10 29				11 03					12 14				12 47		13 29				
Exeter St Davids 6	a	10 11	10 20			10 43			11 01	11 20	11 43		12 10		12 28	12 43			13 03	13 18	13 43			14 10	
Exeter Central	a								*11 11*	*11 49*	*12 13*		*12 21*						*13 21*	*13 38*	*14 13*			*14 21*	
Exmouth	a								*11 42*	*12 16*			*12 45*						*13 45*	*14 16*				*14 45*	
Barnstaple	a								*12 24*										*14 27*					*15 33*	
Exmouth	d		*09 20*	*09 50*				10 20			*10 50*	11 20			*11 50*			12 20			*12 50*	*13 20*	13 20		*13 50*
Exeter Central	d		*09 44*	*10 14*	10 29			10 43			*11 14*	11 43	*11 53*		*12 14*	*12 27*	12 27	12 43			*13 14*	*13 46*	13 46		14 20
Exeter St Davids 6	d	10 12	10 22	10 27	10 38	10 45		10 50	11 04	11 22	11 45	11 50	12 12		12 30	12 45	12 39	12 50	13 06	13 20	13 45	13u55	13 57	14 12	14 28
Exeter St Thomas	d							10 53				11 53						12 53					14 00		
Starcross	d						←	11 02				12 02						13 01					14 08		
Dawlish Warren	d				10c57		10 57	11 07	11 16			12 07					13e00	13 06					14 13		14 39
Dawlish	d				→		11 01	11 11	11 22			12 11			12 44	12 59	13 04	13 10	13 19				14 17		14 43
Teignmouth	d						11 06	11 17	11 28			12 17			12 50	13 04	13 09	13 15	13 26				14 22		14 48
Newton Abbot	a		10 42	10 51		11 03	11 12	11 23	11 35	11 42		12 23	12 31		12 56	13 10	13 15	13 21	13 32	13 40	14 03		14 28		14 55
	d		10 43	10 51		11 04	11 14	11 25	11 35	11 43		12 25	12 34	12 40	12 58	13 14	13 16	13 23	13 34	13 41	14 04		14 30		14 56
Torre	d							11 33				12 33						13 31					14 38		15 05
Torquay	d						11 25	11 36	11 48			12 38			13 10	13 27		13 34	13 46				14 41		15 09
Paignton	a						11 31	11 42	11 53			12 44			13 21	13 38		13 41	13 55				14 48		15 15
Totnes	d		10 56	11 02		11 17				11 56				12 52			13 28			13 54	14 17				
Ivybridge	d			11 19										13 09			13 44								
Plymouth	a	11 09	11 24	11 34		11 48				12 26	12 48		13 11	13 25			13 59			14 23	14 48			15 07	
	d	11 09	11 27	11 35						12 28	12 48		13 18	13 35						14 26		14u55		15 09	
Devonport	d			11 38										13 38											
Dockyard	d			11x40										13x39											
Keyham	d			11x42										13x41											
St Budeaux Ferry Road	d																								
Saltash	d									12 38															
St Germans	d									12 45															
Menheniot	d																								
Liskeard 3	d		11 51							12 58	13 11		13 43							14 49				15 33	
Looe	a		*12 39*										*14 15*							*15 44*					
Bodmin Parkway	d		12 06							13 11	13 24		13 55							15 02				15 46	
Lostwithiel	d									13 17												15 31			
Par 3	d	11 53											14 06									15 40		15 56	
Newquay	a	13 00									14 49											16 50			
St Austell	d		12 22							13 28			14 14							15 17				16 04	
Truro	d		12 39							13 46			14 31							15 38				16 22	
Falmouth Docks	a		*13 10*										*15 00*							*16 21*				*17 14*	
Redruth	d		12 52							13 58			14 44							15 49				16 34	
Camborne	d		12 59							14 06			14 51							15 57				16 42	
Hayle	d		13 09							14 16			15 01							16 08					
St Erth 2	d		13 14							14 21			15 06							16 12				16 53	
St Ives	a		*13 53*							*14 53*			*15 22*							*16 54*				*17 24*	
Penzance	a		13 28							14 34			15 20							16 26				17 09	

For general notes see front of timetable
For details of catering facilities see Directory of Train Operators

- **A** To Gunnislake (Table 139)
- **B** From Manchester Piccadilly (Tab le 51)
- **C** **Cornish Riviera**
- **D** **Torbay Express**
- **E** **Atlantic Coast Express**
- **G** **The Royal Duchy**
- **b** Change at Redhill
- **c** Arr. 1049
- **e** Arr. 1250

Due to Engineering Operations, services from Saturday 13 September on this Table had not been confirmed at time of going to press. These services will be issued in a special Supplement as soon as exact timings have been confirmed

Sleeper services are published in Table 406

London and Birmingham → Devon and Cornwall

Network Diagram - see first page of Table 135

		GW	XC	GW	GW	GW	XC	GW	SW	GW	XC	GW	XC	GW	GW	GW	GW	GW	GW		XC	SW	SW	GW	GW
			R 1		1	1	R 1		1 ◇		R 1	1 ◇	R 1					1 ◇			R 1	1 ◇	1	1 ◇	
							A	B								B									
			🛒	🍴	🛒	🛒	🛒		🛒		🛒	🛒	🛒		🍴			🛒			🛒	🛒		🛒	
London Paddington 15	⊖ d				12 35	13 06						14 06						15 06						16 06	
London Waterloo 15	⊖ d								12 20													14 20			
Slough 3	d																								
Heathrow Terminal 1 Bus	🚌 d																								
Gatwick Airport 10	d				*11b08*	*12 03*						*13 03*						*14 03*						*15 03*	
Oxford	d				*12 30*	*12 43*						*14 00*						*15 00*						*15 43*	
Reading 7	d				13 05	13 32						14 32						15 32						16 32	
Theale	d																								
Thatcham	d																								
Newbury	d				13 21																				
Hungerford	d																								
Pewsey	d				13 42													16 03							
Westbury	d				14 00													16 22							
Castle Cary	d				14 18													16 40							
Birmingham New Street 12	d		12 10				13 10				13 40		14 10								15 10				
Cardiff Central 7	d																								
Newport (South Wales)	d																								
Swindon	d																								
Bristol Parkway 7	d		13 25								14 55		15 25								16 25				
Filton Abbey Wood	d																								
Bath Spa 7	d																								
Bristol Temple Meads 10	d		13 44				14 44				15 11		15 44								16 44				
Weston-super-Mare	d		14 07																						
Bridgwater	d																								
Taunton	d		14 29		14 41	14 49						15 50	16 17					17 03			17 17			17 48	
Tiverton Parkway	d		14 41			15 02						16 03	16 29					17 16			17 29			18 01	
Exeter St Davids 6	a		14 55		15 06	15 19					16 03	16 20	16 43					17 32			17 43			18 18	
Exeter Central	a				*15 21*	*15 33*					*16 13*	*16 43*	*17 21*					*17 43*			*17 55*				
Exmouth	a				*15 45*	*16 14*					*16 45*	*17 17*	*17 45*								*18 21*				
Barnstaple	a					*16 38*						*17 48*									*19 05*				
Exmouth	d	14 20							*14 50*	15 20			*15 50*	16 20			16 50						*17 20*		17 50
Exeter Central	d	14 41							15 39	15 47			*16 24*	16 42			17 14				*17 33*	17 33	17 54		18 19
Exeter St Davids 6	d	14 46	14 58		15 09	15 20			15 49	15 54	16 10	16 22	16 45	16 51			17 21	17 34			17 45	17 43	18 02	18 20	18 26
Exeter St Thomas	d	14 49								15 57				16 54			17 24								18 29
Starcross	d	14 58								16 05				17 02			17 32								18 38
Dawlish Warren	d	15 02			15 21					16 10				17 07			17 37					18c02	18 15		18 42
Dawlish	d	15 06	15 14		15 27				16 01	16 14				17 11			17 41				17 59	18 06	18 19		18 46
Teignmouth	d	15 11	15 20		15 33				16 06	16 19				17 16			17 46				18 05	18 11	18 24		18 51
Newton Abbot	a	15 18	15 26		15 40	15 43			16 13	16 25		16 41		17 22			17 52	17 57	←		18 11	18 17	18 30	18 39	18 58
	d	15 19	15 28		15 43	15 44		16 06	16 13	16 27		16 43		17 24		17 29	18 02	17 59	18 02		18 15	18 20	18 32	18 40	18 59
Torre	d	15 27								16 35				17 32			→		18 10						19 07
Torquay	d	15 30	15 43		15 56					16 38			17 18	17 35					18 13		18 27		18 43		19 10
Paignton	a	15 37	15 52		16 03					16 44			17 29	17 41					18 19		18 39		18 50		19 17
Totnes	d					15 56		16 18	16 25			16 55				17 41		18 11				18 32		18 53	
Ivybridge	d							16 34	16 41							17 58						18 48			
Plymouth	a					16 26	16 43	16 50	16 57		17 07	17 23				18 13		18 39				19 02		19 21	
	d			15 55		16 28	16 45	16 50			17 15				17 59	18 16		18 40				19 11		19 25	
Devonport	d							16 53							18 02	18 19									
Dockyard	d							16x54							18 04	18x21									
Keyham	d							16x56							18 06	18x23									
St Budeaux Ferry Road	d														18 08										
Saltash	d			16 03											18 13							19 19			
St Germans	d			16 10											18 19							19 26			
Menheniot	d			16 18											18 27										
Liskeard 3	d			16 24		16 53	17 08								18 33			19 03				19 38		19 51	
Looe	a			*17 00*			*18 27*											*19 40*							
Bodmin Parkway	d			16 36		17 08	17 21								18 45			19 15				19 50		20 05	
Lostwithiel	d			16 41											18 51							19 56			
Par 3	d			16a48							17 56				18 58			19 26				20 03		20 16	
Newquay	a						18 40																		
St Austell	d					17 23					18 03				19 05			19 34				20 11		20 24	
Truro	d					17 41					18 21				19 23			19 52				20 29		20 41	
Falmouth Docks	a					*18 25*												*20 19*							
Redruth	d					17 53					18 32				19 36			20 04				20 41		20 57	
Camborne	d					18 01					18 39				19 42			20 11				20 47		21 04	
Hayle	d					18 12									19 49									21 14	
St Erth 2	d					18 16					18 49				19 53			20 22						21 18	
St Ives	a										*19 11*							*20 38*						*21 45*	
Penzance	a					18 29					19 05				20 04			20 40				21 05		21 31	

For general notes see front of timetable
For details of catering facilities see Directory of Train Operators

A From Newcastle (Table 51)
B To Gunnislake (Table 139)
b Change at Redhill
c Arr. 1754
e Arr. 2008

Due to Engineering Operations, services from Saturday 13 September on this Table had not been confirmed at time of going to press. These services will be issued in a special Supplement as soon as exact timings have been confirmed

until 6 September

Sleeper services are published in Table 406

London and Birmingham → Devon and Cornwall

Network Diagram - see first page of Table 135

Station		XC	GW	GW	GW	GW	GW	GW	XC	GW	GW	XC	GW	GW	GW	GW	XC	GW	GW	XC	GW	GW
		1 ◇	1 ◇		1 ◇	1 ◇			1 ◇		1 ◇	1 ◇	1 ◇		1 ◇	1 ◇	1 ◇	1 ◇	1 ◇	1 ◇		1 ◇
				A							B											
		☕	☕		☕	☕			☕		☕	☕	☕		☕	☕	☕	☕	☕	☕		☕
London Paddington 15 ⊖	d		16 30		17 06						18 06		18 30		19 00	19 06			20 06			20 30
London Waterloo 15 ⊖	d																					
Slough 3	d																					
Heathrow Terminal 1 Bus	d																					
Gatwick Airport 10	d				*16 03*						*17 03*				*18 03*				*19 03*			
Oxford	d		*16 15*		*17 00*						*18 00*		*18 15*		*18 43*	*19 00*			*19 43*			*20 15*
Reading 7	d		16 58		17 32						18 32		18 57		19 27	19 32			20 31			20 58
Theale	d																					
Thatcham	d																					
Newbury	d															19 49			20 46			
Hungerford	d																					
Pewsey	d				18 03											20 10			21 05			
Westbury	d				18 22											20 28			21 24			
Castle Cary	d				18 40											20 45			21 43			
Birmingham New Street 12	d	16 10							17 10			18 10					19 10			20 10		
Cardiff Central 7	d																				21 00	
Newport (South Wales)	d																				21 15	
Swindon	d		17 32										19 31		19 56							21 31
Bristol Parkway 7	d	17 25							18 25			19 26					20 25			21 25		
Filton Abbey Wood	d					←															21 42	
Bath Spa 7	d		18 01 →			18 01							20 01		20 25			←				21 59
Bristol Temple Meads 10	d	17 44				18 16			18 44			19 44	20 15		20 55 →		20 44	20 55		21 44	21 53	22 16
Weston-super-Mare	d					18 40			19 06				20 39					21 24			22 27	
Bridgwater	d																	21 43			22 46	
Taunton	d	18 17			19 02	19 07			19 28		19 47	20 17	21a06			21 07	21 17	21 55	22 05	22 17	23 01	23s16
Tiverton Parkway	d	18 29			19 15	19 21			19 40			20 29				21 20	21 29	22 09	22 18	22 29	23 16	23s29
Exeter St Davids 6	a	18 43			19 32	19 37			19 54		20 14	20 43				21 38	21 43	22 30	22 35	22 43	23 35	23 50
Exeter Central	a	*18 52*				*19 52*			*20 18*		*20 24*	*20 53*				*21 49*				*23 00*		
Exmouth	a	*19 18*				*20 18*						*21 20*				*22 16*						
Barnstaple	a	*20 24*										*22 08*										
Exmouth	d			*18 20*	*18 54*			19 20								*20 26*			*21 20*			
Exeter Central	d			*19 02*	*19 18*			19 44			*19 52*					*20 50*			*21 48*			
Exeter St Davids 6	d	18 45		19 11	19 34	19 38		19 54	19 56		20 15	20 45		20 53		21 39	21 45		22 37	22 45		
Exeter St Thomas	d			19 14				19 57		←				20 56								
Starcross	d			19 22				20 05 →		20 05				21 04								
Dawlish Warren	d			19 27						20 11				21 09								
Dawlish	d			19 31						20 15				21 13					22 49			
Teignmouth	d			19 36						20 20				21 18					22 55			
Newton Abbot	a	19 03		19 42	19 53	19 58			20 14	20 26	20 36	21 03		21 24		21 59	22 03		23 02	23 11		
	d	19 04		19 44	19 54	19 59			20 15	20 28	20 36	21 04		21 26		22 00	22 05		23 03	23 12		
Torre	d			19 52		20 09				20 36				21 34								
Torquay	d			19 55		20 12				20 39				21 37								
Paignton	a			20 02		20 24				20 45				21 43								
Totnes	d	19 17			20 07				20 28		20 50	21 17				22 13	22 21		23 16	23 27		
Ivybridge	d																					
Plymouth	a	19 48			20 36				20 54		21 18	21 48				22 43	22 55		23 47	23 59		
	d	19 55					20 41		21 01		21 19											
Devonport	d																					
Dockyard	d																					
Keyham	d																					
St Budeaux Ferry Road	d																					
Saltash	d						20 51															
St Germans	d						20 57															
Menheniot	d																					
Liskeard 3	d	20 18					21 10				21 43											
Looe	a	*21 09*																				
Bodmin Parkway	d	20 31					21 23				21 56											
Lostwithiel	d						21 29															
Par 3	d	20 41					21 37		21 47		22 06											
Newquay	a																					
St Austell	d	20 47					21 44		21 54		22 14											
Truro	d	21 05					22 02		22 13		22 32											
Falmouth Docks	a	*21 32*																				
Redruth	d	21 16					22 15		22 30		22 44											
Camborne	d	21 22					22 21		22 37		22 52											
Hayle	d						22 28															
St Erth 2	d	21 32					22 32		22 47		23 04											
St Ives	a																					
Penzance	a	21 48					22 43		23 03		23 19											

For general notes see front of timetable
For details of catering facilities see Directory of Train Operators

A From Barnstaple (Table 136)
B **The Golden Hind**

Due to Engineering Operations, services from Saturday 13 September on this Table had not been confirmed at time of going to press. These services will be issued in a special Supplement as soon as exact timings have been confirmed

Sundays

until 7 September

Sleeper services are published in Table 406

London and Birmingham → Devon and Cornwall

Network Diagram - see first page of Table 135

	GW	XC	GW	GW	GW	GW	SW	GW	GW	SW	GW	GW	GW	GW	GW	XC	SW	GW	XC	GW	GW
		1 ◇	◇			◇	1 ◇	1 ◇		1 ◇	1 ◇			1 ◇		1 ◇	1 ◇	1 ◇	1 ◇		
														C							
		🍴						🍴		🍴	🍴			🍴		🍴	🍴	🍴	🍴		
London Paddington 15 ⊖ d								07 57			08 57			09 57				10 57			
London Waterloo 15 ⊖ d										08 15							09 15				
Slough 3 d																					
Heathrow Terminal 1 Bus 🚌 d																					
Gatwick Airport 10 d								*07 07*						*08 07*				*09 07*			
Oxford d											*08 38*			*09 38*				*10 38*			
Reading 7 d								08 42			09 32			10 30				11 32			
Theale d																					
Thatcham d																					
Newbury d																					
Hungerford d																					
Pewsey d																					
Westbury d											10 36										
Castle Cary d														11 52							
Birmingham New Street 12 d																10 10			11 10		
Cardiff Central 7 d																					
Newport (South Wales) d																					
Swindon d								09 17						11 03							
Bristol Parkway 7 d																11 25			12 25		
Filton Abbey Wood d																					
Bath Spa 7 d								09 47													
Bristol Temple Meads 10 d			07 45			08 30		10 01								11 44			12 44		
Weston-super-Mare d			08 08			08 58										12 02					
Bridgwater d			08 24			09 17															
Taunton d			08 39			09b37		10 34			11 17			12 16		12 24		13 05	13 17		
Tiverton Parkway d			08 54			09 54		10 48			11 30					12 36			13 29		
Exeter St Davids 6 a			09 12			10 12		11 05			11 46			12 43		12 51		13 33	13 43		
Exeter Central a			*09 23*			*10 35*		*11 23*			*12 28*					*13 21*					
Exmouth a			*09 57*			*11 00*		*11 54*			*12 54*					*13 53*					
Barnstaple a			*10 55*								*13 02*								*15 10*		
Exmouth d					*09 10*		*10 00*				*11 10*		12 05						*13 05*		
Exeter Central d			*09 06*	*09 06*	*09 34*		10 46			11 29	*11 37*		12 30				12 46	*13 06*	*13 29*		
Exeter St Davids 6 d			09 17	09 25	10 10	10 17	10 56	11 07		11 40	11 47		12 34	12 44		12 52	13 01	13 34	13 45	13 54	
Exeter St Thomas d				09 28	10 13								12 38		←					13 57	
Starcross d				09 36	10 21								12 47 →		12 47					14 05	
Dawlish Warren d				09 41	10 26		11 07								12c56					14 10	
Dawlish d			09 30	09 45	10 30	10 35	11 11	11 20							13 00	13 06	13 14			14 14	
Teignmouth d			09 35	09 50	10 35	10 40	11 16	11 26							13 05	13 12	13 20			14 19	
Newton Abbot a			09 41	09 56	10 41	10 46	11 23	11 32		12 00	12 07			13 04	13 12	13 21	13 27	13 54	14 03	14 25	
Newton Abbot d			09 42	09 58	10 43	10 47	11 24	11 33	11 38	12 01	12 08	12 30		13 05	13 13	13 22	13 32	13 55	14 04	14 28	
Torre d				10 06	10 51				11 46			12 38			13 21					14 36	
Torquay d				10 09	10 54		11 35		11 49			12 41			13 24	13 34	13 44			14 39	
Paignton a				10 15	11 00		11 42		11 55			12 47			13 31	13 46	13 50			14 45	
Totnes d			09 55			11 00		11 46		12 14	12 21			13 19					14 17		
Ivybridge d			10 12							12 30											
Plymouth a			10 26			11 29		12 14		12 44	12 52			13 49				14 32	14 48		
Plymouth d	09 10	09 30	10 30			11 30		12 16			12 54			13 50				14 35			14 55
Devonport d			10 34																		
Dockyard d																					
Keyham d																					
St Budeaux Ferry Road d	09 15																				
Saltash d	09 20		10 41			11 39															
St Germans d	09 27		10 48			11 46															
Menheniot d			10 56			11 54															
Liskeard 3 d	09 39	09 53	11 02			12 00		12 40			13 16			14 14				14 59			15 19
Looe a																					
Bodmin Parkway d	09 51	10 07	11 14			12 12		12 55			13 30			14 26				15 11			15 32
Lostwithiel d	09 56		11 19			12 17															15 38
Par 3 d	10 03	10 18	11 26			12 24		13 06			13 40			14 40							15 45
Newquay a		11 19												15 46							
St Austell d	10 11		11 34			12 32		13 13			13 47							15 27			15 52
Truro d	10 29		11 52			12 50		13 30			14 07							15 44			16 11
Falmouth Docks a	*11 34*		*12 50*					*13 59*			*14 53*										
Redruth d	10 42		12 06			13 04		13 43			14 18							15 57			16 24
Camborne d	10 48		12 12			13 10		13 50			14 27							16 04			16 30
Hayle d	10 56		12 19			13 17															16 37
St Erth 2 d	10 59		12 22			13 20		14 03			14 41							16 17			16 41
St Ives a	*11 37*		*12 37*			*13 37*		*14 37*			*15 06*							*16 38*			*17 07*
Penzance a	11 17		12 37			13 33		14 17			15 00							16 31			16 56

For general notes see front of timetable
For details of catering facilities see
Directory of Train Operators

C **Atlantic Coast Express**
b Arr. 0930
c Arr. 1251

Due to Engineering Operations, services from Sunday 14 September on this Table had not been confirmed at time of going to press. These services will be issued in a special Supplement as soon as exact timings have been confirmed

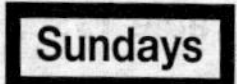

Until 7 September

Sleeper services are published in Table 406

London and Birmingham → Devon and Cornwall

Network Diagram - see first page of Table 135

Station		GW	GW	XC	SW	GW	GW	GW	XC	GW	XC	GW	GW	XC	GW	SW	GW	XC	GW	GW	GW
		1◇	1◇	1◇	1◇	1◇		1◇	R 1		1◇			R 1	1◇	1◇	1◇	R 1	1◇		
											B										
		☕	☕	☕	☕	☕		☕	☕		☕			☕	☕	☕	☕	☕	☕		
London Paddington 15 ⊖	d	11 07	11 57			12 07		12 57							13 57		14 57		15 07		
London Waterloo 15 ⊖	d				11 15											13 15					
Slough 3	d																				
Heathrow Terminal 1 Bus	d																				
Gatwick Airport 10	d	*10 12*				*11 07*									*12 07*		*13 07*		*14 07*		
Oxford	d		*11b38*					*12 50*							*13c38*		*14e38*				
Reading 7	d	11 44	12 31			12 42		13 32							14 30		15 32		15 42		
Theale	d																				
Thatcham	d																				
Newbury	d																				
Hungerford	d																				
Pewsey	d																				
Westbury	d														15 36						
Castle Cary	d														15 54						
Birmingham New Street 12	d			12 10					13 10		13 40			14 10				15 10			
Cardiff Central 7	d																				
Newport (South Wales)	d																				
Swindon	d	12 19				13 17													16 17		
Bristol Parkway 7	d			13 25					14 25		14 58			15 25				16 25			
Filton Abbey Wood	d																				
Bath Spa 7	d	12 48				13 47													16 47		
Bristol Temple Meads 10	d	13 04		13 44		14 01			14 44		15 12			15 44				16 44	17 05		
Weston-super-Mare	d	13 32																	17 39		
Bridgwater	d																				
Taunton	d	13 54	14 03	14 17		14 35		15 06	15 17		15 44			16 17	16 20		17 06	17 17	18a01		
Tiverton Parkway	d		14 18	14 29					15 29		15 56			16 29			17 20	17 29			
Exeter St Davids 6	a	14 20	14 35	14 43		15 02		15 34	15 43		16 10			16 43	16 49		17 37	17 43			
Exeter Central	a	*14 29*	*14 47*			*15 23*			*16 28*		*16 28*							*18 38*			
Exmouth	a	*14 54*				*15 54*			*16 54*		*16 54*							*19 03*			
Barnstaple	a								*17 09*									*19 07*			
Exmouth	d				*13 05*				*15 10*					*16 10*				*17 10*			
Exeter Central	d				14 43			*15 06*	*15 34*					*16 34*		16 47	*17 06*	*17 34*			
Exeter St Davids 6	d	14 22	14 35	14 45	14 52	15 02	15 06	15 35	15 45	15 59	16 12			16 45	16 51	16 57	17 37	17 45		17 50	
Exeter St Thomas	d						15 09			16 02										17 53	
Starcross	d						15 17													18 01	
Dawlish Warren	d	14 35					15 22													18 06	
Dawlish	d	14 40					15 26			16 14						17 10				18 10	
Teignmouth	d	14 46					15 31			16 19						17 15				18 15	
Newton Abbot	a	14 53	14 57	15 03	15 13	15 23	15 37	15 54	16 03	16 26	16 30	←		17 03	17 10	17 22	17 57	18 03		18 21	
	d	14 53	14 57	15 04	15 15	15 24	15 39	15 54	16 04	16 36	16 31	16 36	17 00	17 04	17 10	17 26	17 57	18 04		18 23	
Torre	d						15 47			→										18 31	
Torquay	d	15 06			15 26		15 50						17 10			17 37				18 34	
Paignton	a	15 12			15 32		15 57						17 16			17 43				18 40	
Totnes	d		15 10	15 17				16 09	16 17		16 44	16 52		17 17	17 25		18 12	18 17			
Ivybridge	d											17 08									
Plymouth	a		15 38	15 48		16 03		16 37	16 48		17 16	17 22		17 48	17 58		18 39	18 48			
	d		15 39					16 39				17 24		17 55			18 40	18 55			19 25
Devonport	d																				
Dockyard	d																				
Keyham	d																				
St Budeaux Ferry Road	d																				
Saltash	d											17 32									
St Germans	d											17 39									
Menheniot	d											17 48									
Liskeard 3	d		16 03					17 01				17 54		18 19			19 04	19 18			19 49
Looe	a																				
Bodmin Parkway	d		16 16					17 14				18 06		18 31			19 17	19 31			20 01
Lostwithiel	d											18 11									20 06
Par 3	d		16 27					17 26				18 18		18 41			19 28	19 41			20 13
Newquay	a																				
St Austell	d		16 35					17 34				18 25		18 48			19 35	19 48			20 21
Truro	d		16 52					17 54				18 43		19 06			19 53	20 05			20 39
Falmouth Docks	a		*17 23*									*19 13*					*20 23*				*21 23*
Redruth	d		17 05					18 05				18 57		19 17			20 05	20 21			20 52
Camborne	d		17 12					18 13				19 03		19 23			20 13	20 28			20 58
Hayle	d											19 10									21 06
St Erth 2	d		17 23					18 25				19 14		19 33			20 25	20 38			21 09
St Ives	a		*17 40*					*18 39*				*19 33*									
Penzance	a		17 39					18 42				19 28		19 49			20 38	20 53			21 29

For general notes see front of timetable
For details of catering facilities see Directory of Train Operators

B From 20 July
b From 20 July dep. 1145
c From 20 July dep. 1343
e From 20 July dep. 1443

Due to Engineering Operations, services from Sunday 14 September on this Table had not been confirmed at time of going to press. These services will be issued in a special Supplement as soon as exact timings have been confirmed

Table 135

Sundays

Until 7 September

Sleeper services are published in Table 406

London and Birmingham → Devon and Cornwall

Network Diagram - see first page of Table 135

		XC R 1	GW 1 ◇	GW		GW 1 ◇	XC R 1	GW	GW	XC R 1		GW 1 ◇	SW 1 ◇	GW 1 ◇	XC R 1	GW		GW 1 ◇	XC R 1	GW 1 ◇	GW 1 ◇	GW 1 ◇ A			
London Paddington 15	⊖ d		15 57			16 57						17 57		18 57				19 07		19 57	20 57	23 50			
London Waterloo 15	⊖ d												17 15												
Slough 3	d																								
Heathrow Terminal 1 Bus	d																								
Gatwick Airport 10	d					15 07						16 07		17 07				18 07			19 07				
Oxford	d		15 50			16 50						17 50		18 46						19 50	20 50				
Reading 7	d		16 30			17 32						18 31		19 33				19 42		20 33	21 33	00u37			
Theale	d																								
Thatcham	d																								
Newbury	d																								
Hungerford	d																								
Pewsey	d																								
Westbury	d		17 36									19 39								21 43					
Castle Cary	d		17 54									19 57								22 01					
Birmingham New Street 12	d	16 10					17 10			18 10					19 10				20 10						
Cardiff Central 7	d																								
Newport (South Wales)	d																								
Swindon	d											19 03						20 17		21 03					
Bristol Parkway 7	d	17 25					18 25			19 25					20 25				21 25						
Filton Abbey Wood	d																								
Bath Spa 7	d																	20 47							
Bristol Temple Meads 10	d	17 44					18 44		18 15	19 44					20 44			21 02	21 44						
Weston-super-Mare	d								18 59									21 32							
Bridgwater	d								19 18																
Taunton	d	18 17	18 21			19 05	19 17		19 32	20 17		20 19		21 05	21 17			21 55	22 17	22 21	23s09				
Tiverton Parkway	d	18 29	18 34			19 18	19 29		19 48	20 29		20 33		21 19	21 29			22 08	22 29	22 34	23s22				
Exeter St Davids 6	a	18 43	18 51			19 36	19 43		20 06	20 43		20 50		21 36	21 43			22 24	22 43	22 52	23 39	04 03			
Exeter Central	a		19 01			19 45			20 38			21 23		21 45				22 33		23 13					
Exmouth	a					20 10			21 06					22 10				22 58		23 47					
Barnstaple	a					21 11	21 11																		
Exmouth	d	18 10	18 10	18 10			19 10					20 15			21 11	21 11				22 15					
Exeter Central	d	18 35	18 43	18 35			19 34					20 39	20 46		21 35	21 35				22 43					
Exeter St Davids 6	d	18 45	18 53	18 56		19 37	19 45	20 05		20 45		20 52	20 56	21 38	21 45	21 49			22 45	22 54		04 35			
Exeter St Thomas	d			18 59				20 08								21 53									
Starcross	d			19 07				20 16								22 01									
Dawlish Warren	d			19 12				20 21								22 06									
Dawlish	d			19 16				20 25					21 09			22 10				23 06					
Teignmouth	d			19 21				20 30					21 14			22 15				23 13					
Newton Abbot	a	19 03	19 12	19 27		19 56	20 03	20 36		21 03		21 11	21 20	21 57	22 03	22 21			23 03	23 19		04 55			
	d	19 04	19 14	19 29		19 57	20 04	20 38		21 04		21 12	21 22	21 58	22 04	22 24			23 04	23 19		04 56			
Torre	d			19 37				20 46								22 32									
Torquay	d			19 40				20 49					21 33			22 35									
Paignton	a			19 46				20 55					21 39			22 41									
Totnes	d	19 17				20 11	20 17			21 17		21 27		22 12	22 17				23 17	23 33					
Ivybridge	d																								
Plymouth	a	19 48	19 54			20 39	20 48			21 48		21 54		22 40	22 48				23 48	00 06		05 35			
	d	19 54				20 40						21 56										06 30			
Devonport	d																								
Dockyard	d																								
Keyham	d																								
St Budeaux Ferry Road	d																								
Saltash	d																								
St Germans	d																								
Menheniot	d																								
Liskeard 3	d	20 18				21 04						22 19										06 58			
Looe	a																								
Bodmin Parkway	d	20 31				21 17						22 31										07 15			
Lostwithiel	d																					07 22			
Par 3	d	20 41				21 28						22 43										07 29			
Newquay	a																								
St Austell	d	20 48				21 37						22 51										07 38			
Truro	d	21 05				21 55						23 08										07 58			
Falmouth Docks	a					22 23																			
Redruth	d	21 16				22 07						23 21										08 11			
Camborne	d	21 23				22 15						23 28										08 19			
Hayle	d																					08 31			
St Erth 2	d	21 33				22 27						23 39										08 42			
St Ives	a																								
Penzance	a	21 48				22 40						23 55										08 59			

For general notes see front of timetable
For details of catering facilities see Directory of Train Operators

A Night Riviera

Due to Engineering Operations, services from Sunday 14 September on this Table had not been confirmed at time of going to press. These services will be issued in a special Supplement as soon as exact timings have been confirmed

Sleeper services are published in Table 406

Cornwall and Devon → Birmingham and London

Network Diagram - see first page of Table 135

Miles	Miles			GW MX	GW MO	GW MO	GW MX	GW	GW	GW	GW	XC	GW	GW	GW	GW	GW	GW	GW	GW	GW	XC	GW	XC	GW
					1◇	1◇	1◇	1◇	1◇	1◇		1◇	1◇	1◇	1◇		1◇			1◇	1◇	1◇		1◇	
					A B	B C	B		D										E				E		E
					⊡	⊡	⊡	⊡	⊡	⊡		⊡	☒	⊡	⊡		⊡			⊡	☒	⊡		⊡	
0	—	**Penzance**	d		21p15	21p15	22p00																		
—	—	St Ives	d																						
5¾	—	St Erth [2]	d		21p25	21p25	22p10																		
7¼	—	Hayle	d				22p14																		
13½	—	Camborne	d		21p37	21p37	22p24																		
16¾	—	Redruth	d		21p44	21p44	22p32																		
—	—	Falmouth Docks	d																						
25¾	—	Truro	d		21p57	21p57	22p44																		
40¼	—	St Austell	d		22p15	22p15	23p02																		
—	—	Newquay	d																						
44¾	—	Par [3]	d				23p11																		
49½	—	Lostwithiel	d				23p19																		
52¾	—	Bodmin Parkway	d		22p32	22p32	23p26																		
—	—	Looe	d																						
61¾	—	Liskeard [3]	d		22p47	22p47	23p41																		
65	—	Menheniot	d																						
70¼	—	St Germans	d																						
75¼	—	Saltash	d																						
76½	—	St Budeaux Ferry Road	d																						
77¼	—	Keyham	d																						
77¾	—	Dockyard	d																						
78¼	—	Devonport	d																						
79½	—	**Plymouth**	a		23p13	23p13	00 07																		
—			d		23p20	23p20	00 20						05 22	05 35			06 00					06 25		06 40	
90¼	—	Ivybridge	d																						
102¾	—	Totnes	d		23p48	23p48	00 48						05 49	06 02								06 50		07 05	
—	0	Paignton	d	23p30												06 07			06 36						07 09
—	2¼	Torquay	d	23p35												06 12			06 41						07 14
—	3	Torre	d	23p38												06 15			06 44						07 17
111½	8¼	Newton Abbot	a	23p46	23p59	23p59	01 00						06 00	06 14		06 23	06 34		06 52			07 01		07 16	07 25
—	—		d	23p48	00 01	00 01	01 01						06 02	06 15		06 25	06 35		06 54			07 03		07 18	07 34 →
116½	—	Teignmouth	d	23p55									06 09			06 32			07 01						
119¾	—	Dawlish	d	23p59									06 15			06 37		←	07 06				←		
121	—	Dawlish Warren	d	00 04												06b46		06 46	07c16				07 16		
123	—	Starcross	d	00 07												→		06 49	→				07 19		
130½	—	Exeter St Thomas	d	00 16														06 58					07 28		
131½	—	**Exeter St Davids** [6]	a	00 20	00 26	00 26	01 23						06 28	06 35			06 54	07 02				07 21	07 32	07 36	
—	—	Exeter Central	a										*06 39*	*06 44*				07 13				*07 38*	07 38	*07 48*	
—	—	Exmouth	a										*07 05*					07 40						*08 15*	
—	—	Barnstaple	d																						
—	—	Exmouth	d											*06 03*								*06 40*			
—	—	Exeter Central	d											*06 28*	*06 32*							*07 04*			
—	—	**Exeter St Davids** [6]	d		01 27	01 27	01 27			05 46	05 58	06 23	06 29	06 38	06 45		06 55					07 23		07 38	
148	—	Tiverton Parkway	d							06 06	06 17	06 37		06 54	07 00							07 37		07 52	
162¼	—	Taunton	d				02 48			06 21	06 34	06 51	06 55	07 08	07 15		07 19					07 51		08 06	
—	11¾	Bridgwater	a								06 46		07 05		07 24										
—	25¾	Weston-super-Mare	a								07 06		07 24		07 44									08 29	
—	45½	**Bristol Temple Meads** [10]	a								07 42	07 25	07 57		08 23						←	08 25		08 50	
—	—	Bath Spa [7]	a										08 13		08 41						08 13				
—	—	Filton Abbey Wood	a								07 57		→		→										
—	51¼	Bristol Parkway [7]	a								08 03	07 38										08 38		09 08	
—	—	Swindon	a																		08 42				
—	—	Newport (South Wales)	a																						
—	—	Cardiff Central [7]	a																						
—	138¼	**Birmingham New Street** [12]	a									09 00										09 57		10 26	
190	—	Castle Cary	d							06 43				07 30						←					
209¾	—	Westbury	d					06 08	06 21	07 05				07 51						07 51					
230	—	Pewsey	d					06 25	06 39	07 23				→						08 09					
243¾	—	Hungerford	a					06 38	06 56	07 36															
252¼	—	Newbury	a					06 49	07 11	07 46										08 30					
255¾	—	Thatcham	a					06 56	07 18																
264½	—	Theale	a					07 06	07 27																
269¼	—	**Reading** [7]	a		03s54	04s19	04s50	07 17	07 41	08 07							08 33			08 51	09 16				
—	—	Oxford	a					*08e00*	*08 20*								*09 06*			*09 34*	*09 51*				
—	—	Gatwick Airport [10]	a					*09 02*	*09f47*	*09 59*										*10f39*	*10 50*				
—	—	Heathrow Terminal 1 Bus	a					*08 37*	*08 57*	*09 37*							*09 45*			*10 05*	*10 25*				
286¾	—	Slough [3]	a																						
—	—	**London Waterloo** [15]	⊖ a																						
305¼	—	**London Paddington** [15]	⊖ a		05 40	05 40	05 40	07 52	08 09	08 38							09 00			09 22	09 44				

For general notes see front of timetable
For details of catering facilities see Directory of Train Operators

A Unitl 8 September
B **Night Riviera**
C From 15 September
D From Frome (Table 123)
E To St James' Park (Table 136)

b Arr. 0640
c Arr. 0709
e Change at Reading and Didcot Parkway
f Change at Reading and Redhill

Sleeper services are published in Table 406

Cornwall and Devon → Birmingham and London

Network Diagram - see first page of Table 135

		GW	GW	GW		GW	GW	XC	GW	GW	GW	GW	XC	GW	GW	GW	GW	GW	XC	XC	GW	GW	XC	GW	GW
		1◇				1◇	1◇	R 1	1◇	1◇			1◇			1◇	1◇		R 1	1◇	1◇		R 1	1	1◇
		A ✕		B		☕	☕	☕	☕	⊠			☕			☕	⊠		☕	☕	☕		☕	C ☕	☕
Penzance	d	05 05	05 23							05 41	06 04						06 40		07 30		07 43		08 30	08 42	
St Ives	d																				07 38		08 19		
St Erth 2	d										06 12						06 51		07 38		07 53		08 38	08 53	
Hayle	d		05 32								06 15						06 54				07 57			08 57	
Camborne	d		05 42							06 00	06 25						07 04		07 48		08 08		08 48	09 07	
Redruth	d	05 26	05 48							06 07	06 31						07 11		07 54		08 15		08 54	09 14	
Falmouth Docks	d																06 55				07 55			08 58	
Truro	d	05 39	05a58							06 19	06 43						07 24		08 06		08 27		09 06	09 27	
St Austell	d	05 56								06 37	07 00						07 41		08 22		08 45		09 22	09 44	
Newquay	d																								
Par 3	d									06 44	07 07						07 48		08 29				09 29	09 52	
Lostwithiel	d									06 51	07 14						07 55								
Bodmin Parkway	d	06 12								06 58	07 20						08 01		08 40		09 01		09 40	10 04	
Looe	d									06 41							07 45						09b17		
Liskeard 3	d	06 24								07 11	07 34						08 14		08 52		09 14		09 52	10 17	
Menheniot	d									07 17	07 39						08 21								
St Germans	d									07 26	07 46						08 29				09 25				
Saltash	d									07 33	07 53						08 36				09 33				
St Budeaux Ferry Road	d										07 57														
Keyham	d										07x59														
Dockyard	d										08x01														
Devonport	d										08 03														
Plymouth	a									07 44	08 09						08 48		09 14		09 45		10 18	10 42	
	d							07 25		07 47	08 12		08 25				08 55		09 25		09 47		10 25	10 45	
Ivybridge	d										08 27														
Totnes	d							07 50		08 14	08 41		08 50				09 22		09 50		10 14		10 50		
Paignton	d					07 38						08 43			09 14					10 04		10 25			
Torquay	d					07 44						08 48			09 19					10 10		10 30			
Torre	d					07 48						08 51			09 22							10 33			
Newton Abbot	a	07 29		←		07 56		08 01	←	08 25	08 55	08 59	09 01	←	09 30		09 33	←	10 01	10 19	10 26	10 41	11 01		
	d	07 30		07 34		08 06 →		08 03	08 06	08 27		09 07 →	09 03	09 07	09 43 →		09 35	09 43	10 03	10 21	10 27	10 43	11 03		
Teignmouth	d			07 40					08 13					09 14				09 50		10 28	10 35	10 50			
Dawlish	d			07 45					08 19					09 19				09 55		10 33	10 41	10 55			
Dawlish Warren	d			07 49										09 23				09 59				10 59			
Starcross	d			07 52					08 25					09 26				10 02				11 02			
Exeter St Thomas	d			08 01					08 34					09 35				10 11				11 11			
Exeter St Davids 6	a	07 50		08 05				08 21	08 39	08 47			09 21	09 39			09 55	10 17	10 21	10 45	10 54	11 15	11 21	11 38	
Exeter Central	a	08 03		08 11					08 48	09 21				09 48			10 13	10 21				11 21		11 48	
Exmouth	a			08 43					09 15	09 45				10 15				10 45				11 45		12 15	
Barnstaple	d							07 01									08 35			09 32				10 30	
Exmouth	d	07 15							07 50				08 50				09 20			09 50	10 20		10 50		11 20
Exeter Central	d	07 39						08 12	08 16				09 14				09 44			10 30	10 43		11 14		11 43
Exeter St Davids 6	d	07 52						08 23	08 40	08 49			09 23				09 57		10 23	10 48	10 56		11 23	11 40	11 54
Tiverton Parkway	d							08 37		09 04			09 37				10 12		10 37	11 01	11 11		11 37		12 09
Taunton	d	08 17						08 51	09 05	09 19			09 51				10 27		10 51	11 16	11 26		11 51		12 24
Bridgwater	a																								
Weston-super-Mare	a								09 26							←									
Bristol Temple Meads 10	a						←	09 25	09 57				10 25			09 57			11 25	11 53	11 59		12 25		
Bath Spa 7	a						08 41		→							10 11					12 11				
Filton Abbey Wood	a																								
Bristol Parkway 7	a							09 38					10 38						11 38	12 08			12 38		
Swindon	a						09 10									10 39					12 40				
Newport (South Wales)	a																								
Cardiff Central 7	a																								
Birmingham New Street 12	a							10 57					11 57						12 57	13 26			13 57		
Castle Cary	d									09 40															12 45
Westbury	d									09 59							11 03								13 04
Pewsey	d									10 16															13 22
Hungerford	a																								13 38
Newbury	a																								13 48
Thatcham	a																								13 55
Theale	a																								14 04
Reading 7	a	09 33					09 44			10 51						11 09	11 51				13 11			13 17	14 17
Oxford	a	10 06					10 18			11 34						11 51	12 34				13 51			14 06	15 06
Gatwick Airport 10	a						11c39			12c39						12 50	13c39							14 50	15 50
Heathrow Terminal 1 Bus	a						10 45									12 05	13 05				14 05			14 25	15 25
Slough 3	a																								
London Waterloo 15	⊖ a																								
London Paddington 15	⊖ a	10 03					10 14			11 23						11 42	12 23				13 42			13 44	14 44

For general notes see front of timetable
For details of catering facilities see Directory of Train Operators

A **The Golden Hind**
B To St James' Park (Table 136)
C **Cornish Riviera**

b Until 5 September only
c Change at Reading and Redhill

Sleeper services are published in Table 406

Cornwall and Devon → Birmingham and London

Network Diagram - see first page of Table 135

		GW	XC	XC	GW	GW		GW	SW	XC	GW	SW	GW	GW	GW	GW	XC	GW	XC	GW	GW	GW	XC	SW	GW
			R 1	R 1		1			1 ◇	R 1		1 ◇		1 ◇	1 ◇		R 1		R 1	1 ◇	1 ◇		R 1	1 ◇	
														A	B			C							
			⊐P	⊐P		✕			⊐P	⊐P		⊐P		⊠	⊠		⊐P		⊐P	⊤	⊐P		⊐P	⊐P	
Penzance	d		09 30			10 00					10 36				10 55			11 42							12 55
St Ives	d		*09 22*			*09 55*					*10 25*				*10 25*			*11 25*							*12 25*
St Erth 2	d		09 38			10 11					10 44				11 05			11 50							13 03
Hayle	d										10 47							11 54							13 06
Camborne	d		09 48			10 22					10 57				11 16			12 03							13 16
Redruth	d		09 54			10 29					11 03				11 23			12 09							13 22
Falmouth Docks	d					*10 11*									*10 11*			*11 50*							*13 05*
Truro	d		10 06			10 41					11 15				11 36			12 21							13 34
St Austell	d		10 22			10 59					11 32				11 53			12 38							13 51
Newquay	d					*10b18*									*10 41*										*13c02*
Par 3	d		10 29			11 08					11 39				12 01			12 46							13 58
Lostwithiel	d										11 46							12 52							14 05
Bodmin Parkway	d		10 40			11 17					11 52				12 12			12 58							14 11
Looe	d					*10 24*									*11 38*			*12 33*							*13e50*
Liskeard 3	d		10 52			11 30					12 05				12 25			13 11							14 24
Menheniot	d										12 10														
St Germans	d										12 17							13 22							14 35
Saltash	d										12 24							13 29							14 42
St Budeaux Ferry Road	d																								
Keyham	d																								
Dockyard	d																								
Devonport	d																								
Plymouth	a		11 17			11 57					12 37				12 50			13 40							14 52
	d		11 25	11 50		12 00				12 25				12 55	12 55		13 25						14 25	14 47	
Ivybridge	d																							15 02	
Totnes	d		11 50	12 15		12 27				12 50				13 22	13 22		13 50						14 50	15 16	
Paignton	d	11 25			12 19				12 35				13 14						14 01		14 15	14 25			
Torquay	d	11 30			12 24				12 41				13 19						14 07		14 21	14 30			
Torre	d	11 33			12 27								13 22									14 33			
Newton Abbot	a	11 41	12 01	12 26	12 35	12 39		←	12 51	13 01			13 30	13 33	13 33	←	14 01		14 17		14 31	14 41	15 01	15 27	
	d	11 42	12 03	12 28	12 44	12 40		12 44	12 53	13 03			13 43	13 35	13 35	13 43	14 03		14 18		14 33	14 43	15 03	15 29	
Teignmouth	d	11 49			→			12 51	13 00			←	→			13 50			14 25		14 40	14 50		15 36	
Dawlish	d	11 54						12 56	13 05			13 05				13 55			14 30		14 46	14 55		15 41	
Dawlish Warren	d	11 58						13 00	→			13f16				13 59						14 59		15 45	
Starcross	d	12 02						13 03								14 02						15 02			
Exeter St Thomas	d	12 11						13 12								14 11						15 11			
Exeter St Davids 6	a	12 14	12 21	12 46		13 00		13 16		13 21		13 27		13 55	13 55	14 15	14 21		14 42		14 59	15 15	15 21	15 56	
Exeter Central	a	12 21	*12 48*			*13 21*		13 21				13 38		*14 13*	*14 13*	14 21	*14 48*					15 21	*15 33*	16 13	
Exmouth	a	12 45	*13 15*			*13 45*		13 45				*14 15*				14 45	*15 15*					15 45	*16 15*		
Barnstaple	d													*12 40*	*12 40*										
Exmouth	d			*11 50*		*12 20*				*12 50*				*13 20*	*13 20*		*13 50*				*14 20*		*14 50*		
Exeter Central	d		*12 08*	*12 24*		*12 43*				*13 14*				*13 42*	*13 42*		*14 14*				*14 42*		*15 14*		
Exeter St Davids 6	d		12 23	12 48		13 00				13 23				13 57	13 57		14 23		14 44		15 00		15 23		
Tiverton Parkway	d		12 37	13 02		13 16				13 37							14 37		14 57		15 16		15 37		
Taunton	d		12 51	13 16		13 30				13 51				14 23	14 23		14 51		15 12	15 19	15 30		15 51		
Bridgwater	a																								
Weston-super-Mare	a																		15 35						
Bristol Temple Meads 10	a		13 25	13 55						14 25							15 25		15 56				16 25		
Bath Spa 7	a																								
Filton Abbey Wood	a																								
Bristol Parkway 7	a		13 38	14 08						14 38							15 38		16 08				16 38		
Swindon	a																								
Newport (South Wales)	a																								
Cardiff Central 7	a																								
Birmingham New Street 12	a		14 57	15 26						15 57							16 57		17 26				17 57		
Castle Cary	d													14 44	14 44					15 40					
Westbury	d													15 03	15 03					16 07					
Pewsey	d																			16 27					
Hungerford	a																			→					
Newbury	a																								
Thatcham	a																								
Theale	a																								
Reading 7	a					14 51								15 51	15 51						16 51				
Oxford	a					*15 34*								*16 34*	*16 34*						*17 34*				
Gatwick Airport 10	a					*16g56*								*17 50*	*17 50*						*18g58*				
Heathrow Terminal 1 Bus	a					*16 05*								*17 05*	*17 05*						*18 05*				
Slough 3	a																								
London Waterloo 15 ⊖	a											16 49												19 49	
London Paddington 15 ⊖	a					15 21								16 22	16 22						17 24				

For general notes see front of timetable
For details of catering facilities see Directory of Train Operators

A Until 27 June and from 8 September
B 30 June to 5 September
C From 8 September
b Until 27 June and from 8 September only
c 30 June to 5 September dep. 1240
e Until 5 September only
f Arr. 1308
g Change at Reading and Redhill

Sleeper services are published in Table 406

Cornwall and Devon → Birmingham and London

Network Diagram - see first page of Table 135

		GW	GW	GW	GW	GW	XC	GW		XC	GW	XC	GW	GW	GW	GW	GW	GW	GW	GW	XC	GW	SW	GW	GW
			1 ◇	1 ◇			R 1			1 ◇	1 ◇	1 ◇						1 ◇	1 ◇		1 ◇		1 ◇		1 ◇
				A		B							C					D E	G						
			⊥	✕			☕			☕	☕	☕						☕	☕		☕				☕
Penzance	d										14 00					14 50									
St Ives	d										13 55					14 25									
St Erth 2	d										14 11					14 58									
Hayle	d															15 01									
Camborne	d										14 22					15 11									
Redruth	d										14 29					15 17									
Falmouth Docks	d															14 59									
Truro	d										14 41					15 28									
St Austell	d										14 59					15 45									
Newquay	d												14 54					15 04							
Par 3	d										15 06		15 42			15 52		16 01							
Lostwithiel	d															15 59									
Bodmin Parkway	d										15 18					16 05		16 13							
Looe	d										15b02					15c46									
Liskeard 3	d										15 32					16 18		16 31							
Menheniot	d															16 23									
St Germans	d															16 30									
Saltash	d															16 37									
St Budeaux Ferry Road	d															16 44									
Keyham	d					15x01										16x46									
Dockyard	d					15x03										16x48									
Devonport	d					15 05										16 51									
Plymouth	a					15 09					15 57		16 26			16 55		16 57							
	d			15 00		15 11	15 25				16 00	16 25			16 44			16 59	17 00		17 25		17 48		
Ivybridge	d					15 26									16 59								18 03		
Totnes	d			15 27		15 39	15 50				16 27	16 50			17 13			17 27	17 27		17 50		18 17		
Paignton	d	15 19						15 56		16 15				16 50			17 19					17 50		18 21	
Torquay	d	15 24						16 01		16 21				16 55			17 24					17 55		18 26	
Torre	d	15 27						16 03						16 58			17 27					17 58		18 29	
Newton Abbot	a	15 35		15 38	←	15 53	16 01	16 12		16 31	16 38	17 01		17 06	17 27		17 35	17 38	17 38	←	18 01	18 06	18 28	18 37	
	d	15 43 →		15 40	15 43		16 03	16 13		16 33	16 40	17 03		17 08			17 43 →	17 40	17 40	17 43	18 03	18 08	18 30	18 45 →	
Teignmouth	d				15 50			16 20						17 15						17 50		18 15	18 37		
Dawlish	d				15 55			16 25						17 20						17 55		18 20	18 42		
Dawlish Warren	d				15 59			16 29						17 24						17 59		18 24	18 46		
Starcross	d				16 03			16 33						17 27						18 03		18 27			
Exeter St Thomas	d				16 12			16 42						17 36						18 12		18 36			
Exeter St Davids 6	a			16 00	16 15		16 21	16 47		16 51	17 00	17 21		17 40				18 00	18 00	18 15	18 21	18 40	18 57		
Exeter Central	a			16 13	16 21		16 39				17 21	17 43		17 48				18 13	18 13	18 21		18 51	19 13		
Exmouth	a				16 45		17 15				17 48			18 15						18 48		19 18			
Barnstaple	d			14 29						15 37															
Exmouth	d			15 20			15 50				16 20	16 50						17 20	17 20						
Exeter Central	d			15 44			16 14			16 23	16 44	17 14						17 49	17 49		17 56				
Exeter St Davids 6	d			16 00			16 23			16 53	17 00	17 23						18 00	18 00		18 23				
Tiverton Parkway	d			16 16			16 37			17 07	17 16	17 37						18 16	18 16		18 37				
Taunton	d			16 30			16 51			17 21	17 30	17 51						18 30	18 30		18 51				
Bridgwater	a																								
Weston-super-Mare	a																								
Bristol Temple Meads 10	a						17 25			17 55		18 25									19 25				
Bath Spa 7	a																								
Filton Abbey Wood	a																								
Bristol Parkway 7	a						17 38			18 08		18 38									19 38				
Swindon	a																								
Newport (South Wales)	a																								
Cardiff Central 7	a																								
Birmingham New Street 12	a						18 57			19 26		19 57									20 57				
Castle Cary	d																	18 53	18 53						
Westbury	d		←															19 11	19 11						19 17
Pewsey	d		16 27																						19 34
Hungerford	a		16 40																						19 51
Newbury	a		16 50															19 44	19 44						20 05
Thatcham	a		16 56																						20 11
Theale	a		17 05																						20 20
Reading 7	a		17 17	17 51							18 51							20 07	20 07						20 33
Oxford	a		18 06	18 34							19 34							20 49	20 49						21 16
Gatwick Airport 10	a		19 07	19 50							21 47							22 04	22 04						
Heathrow Terminal 1 Bus	a		18 25	19 15							20 15							21 15	21 15						21 45
Slough 3	a		17 31																						
London Waterloo 15	⊖ a																						22 57		
London Paddington 15	⊖ a		17 53	18 21							19 24							20 39	20 39						21 02

For general notes see front of timetable
For details of catering facilities see Directory of Train Operators

A The Mayflower
B From Gunnislake (Table 139)
C Until 27 June and from 8 September. To Gunnislake (Table 139)
D 30 June to 5 September
E Atlantic Coast Express
G Until 27 June and from 8 September
b From 8 September dep. 1440
c Arr. 1625

Sleeper services are published in Table 406

Cornwall and Devon → Birmingham and London

Network Diagram - see first page of Table 135

		GW	GW	GW	XC	GW	GW	SW	GW	GW	GW	GW	GW	GW	GW	GW	GW	GW	GW	XC	GW	GW	GW
										FO	FX		FO	FX								FX	FO
		1 ◇			1 ◇		1 ◇	1		1 ◇	1 ◇		1 ◇	1 ◇	1			1		1 ◇		1 ◇	1 ◇
					A									B								C	C
		⊠			🍽		🍽			🍽	🍽		🛒	🛒								🍽	🍽
Penzance	d	16 00				16 40				17 35	17 35						19 05	20 11		20 55		22 00	22 00
St Ives	d	*15 55*				*16 25*				*17 27*	*17 27*						*18 55*	*20 00*		*20 46*			*21 50*
St Erth 2	d	16 11				16 48				17 45	17 45						19 13	20 21		21 03		22 10	22 10
Hayle	d					16 51				17 49	17 49						19 16	20 25		21 06		22 14	22 14
Camborne	d	16 22				17 01				17 59	17 59						19 26	20 35		21 16		22 24	22 24
Redruth	d	16 29				17 07				18 06	18 06						19 32	20 42		21 22		22 32	22 32
Falmouth Docks	d									*16 54*	*16 54*						*19 12*	*20 26*					*21 30*
Truro	d	16 41				17 19				18 19	18 19						19 44	20 56		21 34		22 44	22 44
St Austell	d	16 59				17 36				18 36	18 36						20 01	21 13		21 50		23 02	23 02
Newquay	d									*17b35*	*17c35*							*20e25*				*21c55*	*21b55*
Par 3	d	17 06				17 43				18 44	18 44						20 08	21 21		21 57		23 11	23 11
Lostwithiel	d	17 15				17 50											20 15	21 28				23 19	23 19
Bodmin Parkway	d	17 21				17 56				18 55	18 55						20 21	21 35		22 08		23 26	23 26
Looe	d	*16b06*	*17 06*							*18 35*	*18 35*						*19 43*						
Liskeard 3	d	17 34	17 49			18 11				19 08	19 08						20 34	21 48		22 20		23 41	23 41
Menheniot	d		17 54														20 39						
St Germans	d		18 01			18 22											20 46	21 59					
Saltash	d		18 08			18 29											20 53	22 06					
St Budeaux Ferry Road	d																20 58						
Keyham	d																21x00						
Dockyard	d																21x02						
Devonport	d																21 04						
Plymouth	a	17 59	18 19			18 39				19 33	19 33						21 09	22 17		22 51		00 07	00 07
	d	18 00			18 25	18 43				19 35	19 35						21 13					00 20	00 20
Ivybridge	d					18 58											21 29						
Totnes	d	18 29			18 50	19 12				20 03	20 03						21 43					00 48	00 48
Paignton	d							19 10	19 30			20 30			21 30				22 30		23 30		
Torquay	d							19 16	19 35			20 35			21 36				22 35		23 35		
Torre	d								19 38			20 38			21 40				22 38		23 38		
Newton Abbot	a	18 40		←	19 01	19 24		19 26	19 46	20 14	20 14	20 46			21 50		21 55		22 46		23 46	01 00	01 00
	d	18 42		18 45	19 03	19 25		19 28	19 48	20 16	20 16	20 48					21 55		22 48		23 48	01 01	01 01
Teignmouth	d			18 52				19 35	19 55			20 55					22 02		22 55		23 55		
Dawlish	d			18 57				19 40	20 00			21 00					22 07		23 00		23 59		
Dawlish Warren	d			19 01				19 44	20 04			21 04					22 11		23 04		00 04		
Starcross	d			19 05					20 07			21 07					22 15		23 07		00 07		
Exeter St Thomas	d			19 14					20 16			21 16					22 24		23 16		00 16		
Exeter St Davids 6	a	19 02		19 17	19 21	19 46		19 59	20 20	20 36	20 36	21 20					22 28		23 20		00 20	01 23	01 23
Exeter Central	a	*19 13*		*19 30*	*19 51*			20 18		*20 51*	*20 51*	*21 51*					*23g25*						
Exmouth	a				*20 18*					*21 18*	*21 18*	*22 18*					*23 52*						
Barnstaple	d	*17 06*					*18 06*			*19 15*	*19 15*					*20 20*							
Exmouth	d	*18 23*					*19 20*									*20 20*							
Exeter Central	d	*18 50*					*19 44*			*19 52*	*19 52*					*20 44*							*23 51*
Exeter St Davids 6	d	19 04			19 23		19 53			20 38	20 38					21 45						01 27	01 27
Tiverton Parkway	d	19 19			19 37		20 08			20 53	20 53					22 01							
Taunton	d	19 34			19 51		20 23			21 08	21 08		21 30	21 30		22 20						02 48	02 48
Bridgwater	a												21 40	21 40									
Weston-super-Mare	a												21 58	21 58		22 44							
Bristol Temple Meads 10	a				20 25					21 40	21 40		22 29	22 29		23 08							
Bath Spa 7	a									21 55	21 55		22 44	22 44									
Filton Abbey Wood	a																						
Bristol Parkway 7	a				20 38																		
Swindon	a									22 23	22 23		23 13	23 13									
Newport (South Wales)	a																						
Cardiff Central 7	a																						
Birmingham New Street 12	a				21 57																		
Castle Cary	d						20 44																
Westbury	d						21 04																
Pewsey	d						21 22																
Hungerford	a																						
Newbury	a						21 42																
Thatcham	a																						
Theale	a																						
Reading 7	a	20 51					22 00			22 55	22 55		23 55	23 55								04s50	04s53
Oxford	a	*21 34*					*22 50*			*00 23*	*23 37*		*01 08*	*01 08*									
Gatwick Airport 10	a	*23 04*					*00h11*			*01 01*	*01 01*												
Heathrow Terminal 1 Bus 🚌	a	*22 45*					*23 45*																
Slough 3	a																						
London Waterloo 15 ⊖	a																						
London Paddington 15 ⊖	a	21 21					22 30			23 29	23 36		00 25	00 32								05 40	05 41

For general notes see front of timetable
For details of catering facilities see Directory of Train Operators

A 🍽 to Bristol Temple Meads
B 🛒 to Reading
C **Night Riviera**
b Until 5 September only
c Until 4 September only
e 30 June to 5 September dep. 1924
g Fridays arr. 2300
h Change at Reading and Redhill

Saturdays

until 6 September

Sleeper services are published in Table 406

Cornwall and Devon → Birmingham and London

Network Diagram - see first page of Table 135

		GW	GW 1 ◇ A ⊡	GW	GW	GW 1 ◇ ⊡	GW 1 ◇ ⊡	GW	GW 1 ◇ ⊡	XC 1 ◇ ⊡	GW 1 ◇ ⊡	GW	GW	GW 1 ◇ ⊡	GW 1 ◇ ⊡	XC 1 ◇ ⊡	GW	GW 1 ◇ ⊡	GW	GW 1 ◇ C 🍴	XC 1 ◇ ⊡	GW	GW 1 ⊡	GW	GW 1 ◇ ⊡
Penzance	d		22p00	05 30																06 00			06 45		
St Ives	d																								
St Erth 2	d		22p10																	06 09			06 56		
Hayle	d		22p14																	06 11			07 00		
Camborne	d		22p24	05 47																06 22			07 10		
Redruth	d		22p32	05 53																06 29			07 17		
Falmouth Docks	d																						*06 53*		
Truro	d		22p44	06a04																06 41			07 29		
St Austell	d		23p02																	06 59			07 47		
Newquay	d																								
Par 3	d		23p11																	07 06			07 54		
Lostwithiel	d		23p19																	07 13			08 01		
Bodmin Parkway	d		23p26																	07 19			08 08		
Looe	d																			*06 45*			*07 46*		
Liskeard 3	d		23p41																	07 34			08 21		
Menheniot	d																			07 39					
St Germans	d																			07 46					
Saltash	d																			07 53					
St Budeaux Ferry Road	d																			07 58					
Keyham	d																			08 03					
Dockyard	d																			08 05					
Devonport	d																			08 07					
Plymouth	a		00 07																	08 10			08 46		
	d		00 20				05 40			06 25				06 55		07 25		07 54		08 11	08 25		08 52		
Ivybridge	d																			08 27					
Totnes	d		00 48				06 07			06 50						07 50		08 21		08 42	08 50		09 19		
Paignton	d	23p30						06 23				06 54	07 08				08 13					09 05			09 20
Torquay	d	23p35						06 28				06 59	07 13				08 18					09 10			09 27
Torre	d	23p38						06 31				07 02	07 16				08 21					09 13			
Newton Abbot	a	23p46	01 00				06 18	06 39		07 01		07 10	07 25	07 30		08 01	08 29	08 33	←	08 55	09 01	09 21	09 31		09 37
	d	23p48	01 01				06 20	06 41		07 03		07 11		07 31		08 03	08 39 →	08 34	08 39	08 55	09 03	09 24	09 32		09 39
Teignmouth	d	23p55						06 48				07 18							08 46			09 31			09 48
Dawlish	d	23p59						06 53				07 23							08 51			09 36		←	09 55
Dawlish Warren	d	00 04						06 57				07 27							08 55			09b49		09 49	10 01
Starcross	d	00 07						07 00				07 30							08 58			→		09 52	
Exeter St Thomas	d	00 16						07 09				07 39							09 07					10 01	
Exeter St Davids 6	a	00 20	01 23				06 40	07 11		07 21		07 43		07 51		08 21		08 54	09 11	09 16	09 21		09 52	10 05	10 13
Exeter Central	a							07 17				07 49		*08 03*		*08 49*			09 21		*09 48*		*10 13*	10 21	
Exmouth	a							07 43				08 15		*08 47*		*09 15*			09 45		*10 14*			10 45	
Barnstaple	d															*07 03*							*08 38*		*08 38*
Exmouth	d									*06 15*				*07 18*		*07 50*		*08 20*			*08 50*		*09 20*		*09 20*
Exeter Central	d						*06 32*			*06 39*				*07 42*		*08 14*		*08 44*			*09 14*		*09 44*		*09 44*
Exeter St Davids 6	d		01 27	05 23			06 41			07 23	07 30			07 53		08 23		08 56			09 23		09 54		10 15
Tiverton Parkway	d			05 56			06 56			07 37	07 45					08 37		09 11			09 37		10 09		10 30
Taunton	d		02 48	06 13		06 58	07 11			07 51	08 00			08 19		08 51		09 26			09 51		10 24		10 45
Bridgwater	a			06 25		07 07			←		08 10				←										
Weston-super-Mare	a			06 45		07 26			07 26		08 28				08 28										
Bristol Temple Meads 10	a			07 24		→			07 58	08 25	→				08 57	09 25					10 25				11 19
Bath Spa 7	a								08 11						09 11										11 41
Filton Abbey Wood	a			07 56																					→
Bristol Parkway 7	a			08 03						08 38						09 38					10 38				
Swindon	a								08 39						09 39										
Newport (South Wales)	a																								
Cardiff Central 7	a																								
Birmingham New Street 12	a									09 57						10 57					11 57				
Castle Cary	d						07 33											09 47							
Westbury	d						07c56											10e11					11 00		
Pewsey	d						08 13											10 27							
Hungerford	a																								
Newbury	a						08 33																		
Thatcham	a																								
Theale	a																								
Reading 7	a		04s53				08 52		09 14					09 35	10 09			11 08					11 50		
Oxford	a						*09 34*		*09 47*					*10 21*	*10 47*			*11 47*					*12f30*		
Gatwick Airport 10	a						*10g39*		*10 50*					*11 39*	*11 50*			*12 50*					*13g39*		
Heathrow Terminal 1 Bus	a						*09 55*		*10 25*					*10 55*	*11 25*			*12 25*					*12 55*		
Slough 3	a																								
London Waterloo 15	⊖ a																								
London Paddington 15	⊖ a		05 41				09 21		09 44					10 06	10 43			11 45					12 21		

For general notes see front of timetable
For details of catering facilities see Directory of Train Operators

A **Night Riviera**
C To Barnstaple (Table 136)
b Arr. 0939
c Arr. 0751
e Arr. 1005
f Change at Reading and Didcot Parkway
g Change at Reading and Redhill

Due to Engineering Operations, services from Saturday 13 September on this Table had not been confirmed at time of going to press. These services will be issued in a special Supplement as soon as exact timings have been confirmed

Table 135

Saturdays

until 6 September

Sleeper services are published in Table 406

Cornwall and Devon → Birmingham and London

Network Diagram - see first page of Table 135

		XC		GW	XC	SW	GW	GW	XC	GW	GW	GW	GW	XC	GW	GW	GW	SW	XC	SW	GW	GW	GW	GW	GW
		1 ◇		1	R 1	1 ◇		1 ◇	R 1		1			R 1		1		1 ◇	R 1	1 ◇	1			1	
											A		B	C											
		☕		☕	☕	☕		☕	☕		☕			☕		☕		☕	☕	☕	☕	trolley		☕	
Penzance	d			07 18	08 05						08 42					09 55								10 55	
St Ives	d			*07 17*	*07 46*						*08 18*														
St Erth 2	d			07 30	08 14						08 54					10 07								11 07	
Hayle	d			07 34							08 58					10 11								11 11	
Camborne	d			07 44	08 24						09 08					10 21								11 21	
Redruth	d			07 51	08 31						09 15					10 28								11 28	
Falmouth Docks	d				*07 56*						*08 56*					*10 09*									
Truro	d			08 05	08 44						09 29					10 42								11 42	
St Austell	d			08 22	09 00						09 46					10 59								11 59	
Newquay	d													09 40											
Par 3	d			08 30												11 07						11 37			
Lostwithiel	d			08 37																		11 44			
Bodmin Parkway	d			08 43	09 16						10 03					11 18						11 50		12 16	
Looe	d										*09 12*					*10 25*						*11 34*		*11 34*	
Liskeard 3	d			08 56	09 29						10 16					11 31						12 03		12 29	
Menheniot	d																					12 08			
St Germans	d			09 07																		12 15			
Saltash	d			09 16																		12 24			
St Budeaux Ferry Road	d																								
Keyham	d												11x00												
Dockyard	d												11x02												
Devonport	d												11 04												
Plymouth	a			09 26	09 53						10 41		11 09	11 18		11 56						12 33		12 54	
	d			09 28	09 57						10 43		11 10	11 25		11 59						12 33		12 56	
Ivybridge	d												11 25									12 48			
Totnes	d			09 55									11 39			12 27						13 02		13 24	
Paignton	d	09 30				10 01	10 20		10 32			11 17			12 12			12 23	12 30		12 40		13 15		
Torquay	d	09 37				10 07	10 25		10 39			11 22			12 17			12 29	12 39		12 47		13 20		
Torre	d					10 10	10 28					11 25			12 20								13 23		
Newton Abbot	a	09 49		10 07		10 18	10 36				11 18	11 33	11 53		12 28	12 38		12 42	12 49		12 58	13 14	13 31	13 35	←
	d	09 51		10 08		10 20	10 38				11 20	11 35			12 30	12 40		12 44	12 50		12 59	13 15	13 43	13 37	13 43
Teignmouth	d	09 59				10 27	10 45					11 42			12 37			12 51	12 59		13 08		→		13 50
Dawlish	d	10 06				10 32	10 50			←		11 47			12 42		←	12 56	13 05	←	13 16				13 55
Dawlish Warren	d					10c43	10e59			10 59		11 51			12f53		12 53	13g10		13 10	13 22				13 59
Starcross	d						→			11 02		11 54			→		12 56	→							14 02
Exeter St Thomas	d									11 11		12 03					13 05								14 11
Exeter St Davids 6	a	10 18		10 32	10 48	10 54			11 07	11 14	11 40	12 07		12 16		13 00	13 09		13 17	13 21	13 34	13 37		13 57	14 15
Exeter Central	a			*10 48*		11 11				11 21	*11 49*	12 21		*12 48*		*13 21*	13 21			13 38		*13 49*		*14 13*	14 21
Exmouth	a			*11 15*						11 42	*12 16*	12 45		*13 14*		*13 45*	13 45					*14 16*			14 45
Barnstaple	d				*09 32*									*10 40*										*12 41*	
Exmouth	d			*09 50*	*10 20*						*10 50*			*11 20*		*12 20*			*12 50*					*13 20*	
Exeter Central	d			*10 14*	*10 43*						*11 14*			*11 53*		*12 43*			*13 14*					*13 46*	
Exeter St Davids 6	d	10 23		10 35	11 00				11 10		11 42			12 23		13 02			13 23		13 36			13 59	
Tiverton Parkway	d															13 17			13 37						
Taunton	d			11 00					11 33							13 32			13 51		14 02			14 25	
Bridgwater	a																								
Weston-super-Mare	a								11 58																
Bristol Temple Meads 10	a	11 25			11 56			←	12 25					13 25					14 25						
Bath Spa 7	a							11 41																	
Filton Abbey Wood	a																								
Bristol Parkway 7	a	11 38			12 08				12 38										14 38						
Swindon	a							12 09																	
Newport (South Wales)	a																								
Cardiff Central 7	a																								
Birmingham New Street 12	a	12 57			13 26				13 57					14 57					15 57						
Castle Cary	d			11 21																	14 24				
Westbury	d			11 40																	14 44				
Pewsey	d			11 57																	15 01				
Hungerford	a																								
Newbury	a																				15 21				
Thatcham	a																								
Theale	a																								
Reading 7	a			12 35				12 46			13 19					14 50					15 42			15 49	
Oxford	a							*13 21*			*14 05*					*15 30*					*16 21*			*16h30*	
Gatwick Airport 10	a							*14j39*			*14 50*					*16h39*								*17j39*	
Heathrow Terminal 1 Bus	a							*13 55*			*14 25*					*15j55*								*16 55*	
Slough 3	a																								
London Waterloo 15	⊖ a					14 49														16 49					
London Paddington 15	⊖ a			13 13				13 17			13 54					15 24					16 13			16 24	

For general notes see front of timetable
For details of catering facilities see Directory of Train Operators

- **A** **Cornish Riviera**
- **B** From Gunnislake (Table 139)
- **C** To Newcastle (Table 51)
- **c** Arr. 1035
- **e** Arr. 1053
- **f** Arr. 1245
- **g** Arr. 1259
- **h** Change at Reading and Didcot Parkway
- **j** Change at Reading and Redhill

Due to Engineering Operations, services from Saturday 13 September on this Table had not been confirmed at time of going to press. These services will be issued in a special Supplement as soon as exact timings have been confirmed

Table 135

Saturdays

until 6 September

Sleeper services are published in Table 406

Cornwall and Devon → Birmingham and London

Network Diagram - see first page of Table 135

		XC	GW	XC		GW	GW	GW	XC	GW	GW	SW	GW	GW	XC	SW	GW	GW	GW	XC	GW	GW	GW	XC	GW
		R 1 ☕	1 A ☕	1◇ ☕		1 ☕		1 ☕	R 1 ☕	1 ☕		1◇ ☕	1 ☕	B	R 1 ☕	1		1◇ C ☕		R 1 ☕		1◇ ☕		R 1 D ☕	
Penzance	d	11 37				11 58												14 00							
St Ives	d	11 25				11 56												13 56							
St Erth 2	d	11 46				12 10												14 11							
Hayle	d					12 14																			
Camborne	d	11 56				12 24												14 22							
Redruth	d	12 03				12 31												14 29							
Falmouth Docks	d					11 51												13 13							
Truro	d	12 15				12 45												14 41							
St Austell	d	12 31				13 02												14 59							
Newquay	d		11 35										13 22											15 22	
Par 3	d	12 39	12 51										14 20					15 06							
Lostwithiel	d																								
Bodmin Parkway	d	12 50				13 19												15 18						16 29	
Looe	d					12 40												14 30						15 49	
Liskeard 3	d	13 02				13 32												15 32						16 44	
Menheniot	d																								
St Germans	d																								
Saltash	d																								
St Budeaux Ferry Road	d																								
Keyham	d													15x01											
Dockyard	d													15x03											
Devonport	d													15 05											
Plymouth	a	13 26	13s40			13 57							15 04	15 09				15 56						17 11	
	d	13 30				14 00			14 25			14 50	15 05	15 14				16 00			16 34			17 25	
Ivybridge	d											15 05		15 29							16 49				
Totnes	d								14 50			15 19	15 34	15 43				16 27			17 03			17 50	
Paignton	d			14 10			14 25	14 31			14 51				15 39	15 52	16 10			16 35		17 03	17 22		17 50
Torquay	d			14 17			14 30	14 37			14 56				15 46	15 58	16 15			16 42		17 10	17 27		17 55
Torre	d						14 33				14 59						16 18						17 30		17 58
Newton Abbot	a					14 36	14 41	14 48	15 01		15 07	15 30	15 46	15 56	15 56	16 08	16 26	16 39		16 52	17 17	17 21	17 38		18 06
	d					14 37	14 42	14 50	15 03	←	15 09	15 32	15 47		15 59	16 10	16 28	16 40		16 53		17 22	17 39		18 08
Teignmouth	d			14 34			14 49	14 58		14 58	15 16	15 39			16 07	16 17	16 35			17 02		17 30	17 46		18 15
Dawlish	d			14 41			14 54	→		15 04	15 22	15 44			16 12	16 22	16 41		←	17 08		17 37	17 52		18 21
Dawlish Warren	d						14 58				15 26	15 48					16b53		16 53			17 42	17 56		18 25
Starcross	d						15 02				15 30						→		16 57				18 00		18 29
Exeter St Thomas	d						15 11				15 39								17 06				18 09		18 38
Exeter St Davids 6	a	14 21	14s36	14 52		14 57	15 14		15 21	15 27	15 42	15 59	16 07		16 23	16 35		17 00	17 09	17 20		17 54	18 13	18 22	18 42
Exeter Central	a		14 48				15 21		15 33	15 47		16 13	16 21			16 43			17 21	17 43		18 13	18 21	18 52	18 52
Exmouth	a		15 14				15 45			16 14			16 45			17 17			17 45	18 21			18 47	19 18	19 18
Barnstaple	d			12 41									14 35					15 42				16 48			
Exmouth	d			14 20						14 50			15 20		15 50			16 20		16 50		17 20			
Exeter Central	d			14 41						15 14			15 47		16 14			16 42		17 14		17 45		17 54	
Exeter St Davids 6	d	14 23		14 55		15 00			15 23	15 30			16 10		16 26			17 01		17 23		17 56		18 23	
Tiverton Parkway	d			15 08		15 15			15 37									17 17		17 37					
Taunton	d			15 23		15 30			15 51	15 55			16 35		16 50			17 31		17 51		18 22			
Bridgwater	a																								
Weston-super-Mare	a																								
Bristol Temple Meads 10	a	15 25		15 57					16 25						17 25					18 25				19 25	
Bath Spa 7	a																								
Filton Abbey Wood	a																								
Bristol Parkway 7	a	15 38		16 08					16 38						17 38					18 38				19 38	
Swindon	a																								
Newport (South Wales)	a																								
Cardiff Central 7	a																								
Birmingham New Street 12	a	16 57		17 26					17 57						18 57					19 57				20 57	
Castle Cary	d									16 16												18 43			
Westbury	d									16 36												19 02			
Pewsey	d									16 51															
Hungerford	a																								
Newbury	a																					19 35			
Thatcham	a																								
Theale	a																								
Reading 7	a		16 27			16 49				17 34			17 51					18 47				19 56			
Oxford	a		17 05			17c30				18 21			18c30					19c30				20 34			
Gatwick Airport 10	a		17 50			18e39							19e39									21 47			
Heathrow Terminal 1 Bus	a		17 25			17 55							18 55					19 55				21 05			
Slough 3	a																								
London Waterloo 15 ⊖	a											19 49													
London Paddington 15 ⊖	a		16 58			17 23				18 05			18 24					19 23				20 36			

For general notes see front of timetable
For details of catering facilities see Directory of Train Operators

- **A** **Atlantic Coast Express**
- **B** From Gunnislake (Table 139)
- **C** **The Royal Duchy**
- **D** To Manchester Piccadilly (Table 51)
- **b** Arr. 1644
- **c** Change at Reading and Didcot Parkway
- **e** Change at Reading and Redhill

Due to Engineering Operations, services from Saturday 13 September on this Table had not been confirmed at time of going to press. These services will be issued in a special Supplement as soon as exact timings have been confirmed

Saturdays

until 6 September

Sleeper services are published in Table 406

Cornwall and Devon → Birmingham and London

Network Diagram - see first page of Table 135

		SW	GW	SW	XC	GW	GW	XC	GW	SW	GW	SW	GW	GW	GW	GW	GW	GW	GW	XC	GW	GW	XC
		1 ◇	1 ◇	1 ◇	1 ◇	1 ◇		1 ◇		1	1	1		1 ◇			1 ◇		◇	1 ◇			1 ◇
								A															
			☕		☕	☕		☕	☕		☕			☕					[symbol]				
Penzance	d		15 53			16 32								17 35					19 08				20 45
St Ives	d		*15 25*			*16 25*								*17 27*					*18 17*				*20 00*
St Erth 2	d		16 04			16 43								17 46					19 16				20 53
Hayle	d					16 47								17 50					19 20				
Camborne	d		16 15			16 57								18 00					19 29				21 03
Redruth	d		16 22			17 04								18 07					19 35				21 10
Falmouth Docks	d		*15 03*			*16 24*								*17 25*					*18 28*				*20 26*
Truro	d		16 34			17 16								18 19					19 47				21 22
St Austell	d		16 52			17 34								18 37					20 04				21 38
Newquay	d										17 15									19 55			
Par 3	d		16 59			17 41					18 13			18 44	18 55				20 12				21 46
Lostwithiel	d		17 07			17 48									19 02				20 19				
Bodmin Parkway	d		17 13			17 54					18 25			18 56	19 08				20 25	21 02			21 57
Looe	d					*17 10*								*18 30*					*19 43*			*21 10*	*21 10*
Liskeard 3	d		17 26			18 07					18 38			19 09	19 21				20 38	21 15		21 53	22 10
Menheniot	d																		20 43				
St Germans	d					18 18									19 32				20 50				
Saltash	d					18 27									19 41				20 59				
St Budeaux Ferry Road	d																		21 03				
Keyham	d																		21x05				
Dockyard	d																		21x07				
Devonport	d																		21 09				
Plymouth	a		17 51			18 36					19 03			19 34	19 57				21 12	21 45		22 18	22 39
	d	17 42	17 54		18 25				18 42		19 04			19 36					21 18				
Ivybridge	d	17 57							18 59										21 33				
Totnes	d	18 11	18 21		18 50				19 13					20 03					21 47				
Paignton	d						18 52	19 03		19 14			19 28			20 06		21 07			21 50		
Torquay	d						18 57	19 09		19 20			19 33			20 11		21 12			21 55		
Torre	d						19 00						19 36			20 14		21 15			21 58		
Newton Abbot	a	18 22	18 33		19 01		19 08	19 19	19 25	19 30	19 41		19 44	20 15		20 22		21 23	21 59		22 06		
	d	18 24	18 34		19 03		19 10	19 20	19 26	19 32	19 43		19 47	20 16		20 24		21 25	21 59		22 08		
Teignmouth	d	18 31		←			19 17	19 27	19 33	19 39		←	19 54			20 31		21 32	22 06		22 15		
Dawlish	d	18 36		18 36			19 22	19 32	19 39	19 44		19 44	19 59			20 36		21 37	22 11		22 20		
Dawlish Warren	d	→		18b48			19 26			→		19c56	20 03			20 40		21 41	22 15		22 24		
Starcross	d						19 29						20 06			20 43		21 44	22 19		22 27		
Exeter St Thomas	d						19 38						20 15			20 52		21 53	22 27		22 36		
Exeter St Davids 6	a		18 54	19 00	19 21		19 42	19 44	19 53		20 03	20 07	20 19	20 36		20 56		21 57	22 30		22 40		
Exeter Central	a			19 13			19 52					20 18	20 24	*20 53*		*21 49*					*23 00*		
Exmouth	a						20 18							*21 20*		*22 16*					*23 44*		
Barnstaple	d				*18 00*									*19 24*									
Exmouth	d		*17 50*		*18 20*			*18 54*			*19 20*												
Exeter Central	d		*18 19*		*19 02*			*19 18*			*19 52*												
Exeter St Davids 6	d		18 56		19 23			19 45			20 05			20 38									
Tiverton Parkway	d		19 11		19 36			19 59						20 53									
Taunton	d		19 26		19 51			20 13			20 31			21 11			21 30						
Bridgwater	a																21 40						
Weston-super-Mare	a							20 34									21 57						
Bristol Temple Meads 10	a				20 25			20 55						21 44			22 29						
Bath Spa 7	a													21 58			22 44						
Filton Abbey Wood	a																						
Bristol Parkway 7	a				20 38			21 08															
Swindon	a													22 27			23 13						
Newport (South Wales)	a																						
Cardiff Central 7	a																						
Birmingham New Street 12	a				22 03			22 26															
Castle Cary	d		19 47																				
Westbury	d		20 06																				
Pewsey	d		20 23																				
Hungerford	a																						
Newbury	a																						
Thatcham	a																						
Theale	a																						
Reading 7	a		20 57								21 57			23 07			23 52						
Oxford	a		*21 34*								*22 46*						*00 39*						
Gatwick Airport 10	a		*23 03*											*01e02*									
Heathrow Terminal 1 Bus 🚌	a		*22 45*								*23 45*												
Slough 3	a																						
London Waterloo 15 ⊖	a			22 57																			
London Paddington 15 ⊖	a		21 30								22 37			23 38			00 32						

For general notes see front of timetable
For details of catering facilities see Directory of Train Operators

A ☕ to Bristol Temple Meads
b Arr. 1840
c Arr. 1947
e Change at Reading and Redhill

Due to Engineering Operations, services from Saturday 13 September on this Table had not been confirmed at time of going to press. These services will be issued in a special Supplement as soon as exact timings have been confirmed

Table 135

Until 7 September

Sleeper services are published in Table 406

Cornwall and Devon → Birmingham and London

Network Diagram - see first page of Table 135

		GW	GW	GW	GW	GW	XC	XC	GW		GW	XC	GW	GW	GW	XC	GW	GW		SW	XC	GW	GW	XC	XC
		◇	1 ◇		1 ◇		1 ◇	1 ◇	1 ◇			R 1	1 ◇		1 ◇	R 1		1 ◇		1 ◇	R 1		1 ◇	R 1	R 1
								A																C	A
		🛒	☕		☕		☕	☕	☕			☕	☕		☕	☕		☕		☕	☕		☕	☕	☕
Penzance	d												08 30			09 30		09 50			10 30		10 50		
St Ives	d															*09 20*		*09 20*			*10 09*		*10 40*		
St Erth 2	d												08 40			09 38		10 00			10 38		11 00		
Hayle	d												08 45												
Camborne	d												08 55			09 48		10 12			10 48		11 12		
Redruth	d												09 01			09 54		10 18			10 54		11 18		
Falmouth Docks	d																								
Truro	d												09 15			10 06		10 30			11 06		11 30		
St Austell	d												09 31			10 22		10 48			11 22		11 48		
Newquay	d																							11 34	
Par 3	d												09 40			10 29		10 55			11 29		11 55	12 29	
Lostwithiel	d																								
Bodmin Parkway	d												09 51			10 40		11 08			11 40		12 08	12 40	
Looe	d																								
Liskeard 3	d												10 04			10 52		11 21			11 52		12 21	12 52	
Menheniot	d																								
St Germans	d												10 15												
Saltash	d												10 24												
St Budeaux Ferry Road	d																								
Keyham	d																								
Dockyard	d																								
Devonport	d																								
Plymouth	a												10 34			11 18		11 45			12 16		12 46	13 16	
	d				08 40		09 25		09 50			10 25	10 35		10 50	11 25		11 45			12 25		12 50	13 25	
Ivybridge	d																								
Totnes	d				09 07		09 50		10 17			10 50	11 04		11 18	11 50		12 15			12 50		13 17	13 50	
Paignton	d										10 25			11 04			12 08			12 25		12 52			13{59
Torquay	d										10 30			11 09			12 13			12 31		12 57			14{05
Torre	d										10 33			11 12			12 16					13 00			
Newton Abbot	a				09 20		10 01		10 29		10 41	11 01	11 15	11 20	11 29	12 01	12 24	12 28		12 41	13 01	13 09	13 29	14 01	14{15
	d				09 22		10 03		10 30		10 43	11 03	11 17		11 31	12 03		12 29		12 44	13 03	13 10	13 30	14 03	14{16
Teignmouth	d				09 29						10 50									12 51		13 17			14{24
Dawlish	d				09 35						10 55									12 58		13 22			14{29
Dawlish Warren	d										10 59											13 26			
Starcross	d										11 02											13 30			
Exeter St Thomas	d										11 11											13 39			
Exeter St Davids 6	a				09 48		10 21		10 50		11 15	11 21	11 37		11 51	12 21		12 49		13 13	13 21	13 42	13 50	14 21	14{41
Exeter Central	a						*10 35*		*11 23*		11 28				*12 28*	*12 50*				*13 21*			*14 29*	*14 47*	
Exmouth	a						*11 00*				11 54				*12 54*			*13 53*		*13 53*			*14 54*		
Barnstaple	d																	*11 10*							*13{19*
Exmouth	d				*09 10*			*10{00*	*10 00*						*11 10*			*12 05*					*13 05*		
Exeter Central	d			*09 06*	*09 34*			*10{24*	*10 24*			*11 06*	*11 29*		*11 37*			*12 30*			*13 06*		*13 29*		
Exeter St Davids 6	d	08 10	08 30	09 38	09 50		10 23	10{48	10 52			11 23	11 38		11 53	12 23		12 50			13 23		13 52	14 23	14{43
Tiverton Parkway	d	08 26	08 45	09 54		←	10 37	11{01	11 06			11 37	11 54		12 08	12 37					13 37		14 06	14 37	
Taunton	d	08 43	08 59	10b19	10 14	10 19	10 51	11{16	11 21			11 51	12 08		12 22	12 51		13 16			13 51		14 21	14 51	15{07
Bridgwater	a	08 54		→		10 30																			
Weston-super-Mare	a	09 12				10 48																			15{28
Bristol Temple Meads 10	a	09 45				11 19	11 25	11{55	11 57			12 25			12 57	13 25					14 25			15 25	15{55
Bath Spa 7	a								12 12						13 12										
Filton Abbey Wood	a	09 56																							
Bristol Parkway 7	a	10 00					11 38	12{08				12 38				13 38					14 38			15 38	16{08
Swindon	a		10 13						12 40				13 22		13 40										
Newport (South Wales)	a																								
Cardiff Central 7	a																								
Birmingham New Street 12	a						12 51	13{26				13 51				14 57					15 51			16 57	17{26
Castle Cary	d		09 21										12 30												
Westbury	d		09 40		10 54								12 48												
Pewsey	d																								
Hungerford	a																								
Newbury	a																								
Thatcham	a																								
Theale	a																								
Reading 7	a		10 43		11 54				13 13				13 52		14 14			14 50					15 52		
Oxford	a		*11c49*		*12 34*				*13 49*				*14 34*		*15e27*			*15 34*					*16 34*		
Gatwick Airport 10	a		*12 30*		*13 31*								*15 31*					*16 30*					*17 33*		
Heathrow Terminal 1 Bus 🚌	a		*11 55*		*12 55*				*14 25*				*14 55*		*15 25*			*15 55*					*16 55*		
Slough 3	a																								
London Waterloo 15 ⊖	a																			16 58					
London Paddington 15 ⊖	a		11 26		12 41				13 55				14 30		14 54			15 31					16 31		

For general notes see front of timetable
For details of catering facilities see Directory of Train Operators

A From 20 July
B Until 7 September
C To Manchester Piccadilly (Table 51)
b Arr. 1010
c From 20 July arr. 1134
e From 20 July arr. 1505

Due to Engineering Operations, services from Sunday 14 September on this Table had not been confirmed at time of going to press. These services will be issued in a special Supplement as soon as exact timings have been confirmed

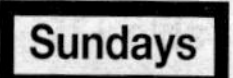

Sundays

Until 7 September

Sleeper services are published in Table 406

Cornwall and Devon → Birmingham and London

Network Diagram - see first page of Table 135

		GW	XC	GW	SW	GW	XC	GW	GW	GW	GW	SW	XC	GW	GW	GW	SW	SW	GW	GW	XC	GW
		1 ◇	R 1		1 ◇		R 1		1 ◇		1 ◇	1 ◇	R 1	1 ◇	1 ◇	1 ◇	1 ◇	1 ◇		1 ◇	R 1	1 ◇
			A				B															
		☕	☕		☕		☕		☕		☕	☕	☕	☕	☕	☕		☕		☕	☕	☕
Penzance	d	11 42				12 25			12 47									13 50				14 44
St Ives	d	11 09				12 09			12 40									13 40				14 40
St Erth 2	d	11 53				12 32			12 57									14 00				14 55
Hayle	d																	14 03				
Camborne	d	12 04				12 44			13 09									14 13				15 06
Redruth	d	12 11				12 50			13 15									14 19				15 13
Falmouth Docks	d	11 37							12 58									14 02				14 56
Truro	d	12 23				13 02			13 27									14 31				15 25
St Austell	d	12 41				13 20			13 46									14 48				15 43
Newquay	d																					
Par 3	d	12 48				13 28			13 52									14 56				15 50
Lostwithiel	d					13 35												15 03				
Bodmin Parkway	d	13 00				13 42			14 05									15 08				16 02
Looe	d																					
Liskeard 3	d	13 13				13 56			14 18									15 22				16 16
Menheniot	d																	15 29				
St Germans	d																	15 37				
Saltash	d																	15 51				
St Budeaux Ferry Road	d																					
Keyham	d																					
Dockyard	d																					
Devonport	d																					
Plymouth	a	13 38				14 20			14 43									16 00				16 41
	d	13 44			14 06		14 25		14 50		15 05		15 25		15 43			16 02		16 10	16 25	16 45
Ivybridge	d				14 21													16 17				
Totnes	d	14 10			14 35		14 50		15 17		15 32		15 50		16 10			16 31		16 42	16 50	17 12
Paignton	d		14 11	14 20				15 02				15 27		15 46			16 10		16 31			
Torquay	d		14 17	14 25				15 07				15 33		15 51			16 16		16 36			
Torre	d			14 28				15 10						15 56					16 39			
Newton Abbot	a	14 23	14 27	14 36	14 46		15 51	15 18	15 29		15 44	15 48	16 01	16 04	16 22		16 30	16 42	16 47	16 53	17 01	17 24
	d	14 24	14 28	14 38	14 47		15 53	15 20	15 30		15 45	15 49	16 03	16 05	16 23		16 32	16 43		16 55	17 03	17 25
Teignmouth	d		14 35	14 45	14 54			15 27				15 56		16 13								
Dawlish	d		14 40	14 50	14 59			15 32		←		16 01		16 18								
Dawlish Warren	d			14 54				15b43 →		15 43		16 06		16 25								
Starcross	d			14 57						15 46												
Exeter St Thomas	d			15 08						15 55												
Exeter St Davids 6	a	14 44	14 52	15 11	15 15		15 21		15 50	16 00	16 05	16 17	16 21	16 36	16 43		16 54	17 05		17 15	17 21	17 45
Exeter Central	a			15 28	15 23						16 28	16 36	16 36	16 47			17 21	17 21		17 28		
Exmouth	a			15 54	15 54							16 54								17 54		
Barnstaple	d	13 19																				
Exmouth	d								15 10						16 10							17 10
Exeter Central	d						14 43		15 34						16 34					17 06		17 34
Exeter St Davids 6	d	14 45	15 08				15 23		15 50		16 07		16 23	16 38	16 45					17 17	17 23	17 47
Tiverton Parkway	d		15 22				15 37		16 06		16 22		16 37		16 59					17 32	17 37	18 01
Taunton	d	15 11	15 36				15 51		16 21		16 37		16 51	17 03	17 14					17 46	17 51	18 16
Bridgwater	a																					
Weston-super-Mare	a		15 56								16 58			17 24								
Bristol Temple Meads 10	a		16 25				16 25				17 20		17 25	17 57		←				18 25	18 25	
Bath Spa 7	a										17 42			18 11 →		18 11				18 43		
Filton Abbey Wood	a																					
Bristol Parkway 7	a		16 38				16 38						17 38								18 38	
Swindon	a	16 25									18 10					18 40				19 11		
Newport (South Wales)	a																					
Cardiff Central 7	a																					
Birmingham New Street 12	a		17 51				17 51						18 57								19 51	
Castle Cary	d	15 33													17 37							
Westbury	d	15 51													17 57							
Pewsey	d																					
Hungerford	a																					
Newbury	a																					
Thatcham	a																					
Theale	a																					
Reading 7	a	16 54							17 56		18 44				18 56	19 14				19 43		19 56
Oxford	a	17 35							18 34						19 35	20 25						20 34
Gatwick Airport 10	a	18 29							19 33						20 30							21 31
Heathrow Terminal 1 Bus	a	17 55							18 55						19 55	20 25						21 05
Slough 3	a																					
London Waterloo 15	⊖ a				18 58							20 04					20 58					
London Paddington 15	⊖ a	17 34							18 36		19 24				19 39	19 58				20 21		20 38

For general notes see front of timetable
For details of catering facilities see Directory of Train Operators

A Until 13 July
B From 20 July
b Arr. 1535

Due to Engineering Operations, services from Sunday 14 September on this Table had not been confirmed at time of going to press. These services will be issued in a special Supplement as soon as exact timings have been confirmed

Table 135

Sundays

Until 7 September

Sleeper services are published in Table 406

Cornwall and Devon → Birmingham and London

Network Diagram - see first page of Table 135

		GW	GW ◇	GW 1 ◇	XC 1 ◇	GW ◇	GW 1 ◇	SW 1 ◇	GW 1 ◇		XC 1 ◇	GW	GW 1 ◇	GW ◇	GW	GW 1 ◇	GW	GW ◇	GW	SW 1	XC 1 ◇	GW	GW 1 ◇
									A														B
Penzance	d		15 08				15 48						17 20	17 50				18 57	20 00		20 55		21 15
St Ives	d						15 40						17 10	17 43				18 43	19 40				
St Erth 2	d		15 17				16 01						17 30	17 59				19 05	20 09				21 25
Hayle	d		15 20											18 02				19 08	20 12				
Camborne	d		15 30				16 12						17 42	18 11				19 19	20 21		21 11		21 37
Redruth	d		15 36				16 19						17 49	18 17				19 25	20 27		21 17		21 44
Falmouth Docks	d						16 04						17 26						19 25		20 31		
Truro	d		15 48				16 32						18 00	18 29				19 37	20 40		21 29		21 57
St Austell	d		16 05				16 50						18 19	18 46				19 54	20 57		21 45		22 15
Newquay	d								16 11														
Par 3	d		16 13				16 56		17 10				18 25	18 54				20 01	21 04		21 53		
Lostwithiel	d		16 19						17 18					19 00				20 08					
Bodmin Parkway	d		16 25				17 09		17 25				18 38	19 06				20 14	21 16		22 04		22 32
Looe	d																						
Liskeard 3	d		16 38				17 22		17 38				18 51	19 22				20 27	21 30		22 16		22 47
Menheniot	d		16 43															20 32					
St Germans	d		16 50															20 39					
Saltash	d		16 59															20b52					
St Budeaux Ferry Road	d																						
Keyham	d																						
Dockyard	d																						
Devonport	d													19 43				20 58					
Plymouth	a		17 07				17 46		18 04				19 15	19 46				21 01	21 59		22 45		23 13
	d		17 08		17 25		17 47		18 10		18 25		19 15			19 55		21 08					23 20
Ivybridge	d		17 24																				
Totnes	d		17 39		17 50		18 17		18 39		18 50		19 46					21 37					23 48
Paignton	d	17 20						18 23				18 55			19 50		21 00			22 10		23 00	
Torquay	d	17 25						18 29				19 00			19 55		21 05			22 16		23 05	
Torre	d	17 28										19 03			19 58		21 08					23 08	
Newton Abbot	a	17 36	17 51		18 01		18 28	18 39	18 50		19 01	19 11	19 57		20 06	20 31	21 16	21 49		22 26		23 16	23 59
	d	17 38	17 52		18 03		18 29	18 41	18 52		19 03	19 13	19 59		20 08	20 32	21 18	21 49		22 28		23 18	00 01
Teignmouth	d	17 45	17 59					18 48				19 20			20 15		21 25	21 56		22 35		23 25	
Dawlish	d	17 50	18 04					18 53				19 25			20 20		21 30	22 01		22 40		23 30	
Dawlish Warren	d	17 54						18 57				19 29			20 24		21 34			22 44		23 34	
Starcross	d	17 57										19 32			20 27		21 37					23 37	
Exeter St Thomas	d	18 06										19 41			20 36		21 46					23 46	
Exeter St Davids 6	a	18 10	18 17		18 21		18 50	19 08	19 12		19 21	19 48	20 19		20 40	20 53	21 50	22 15		22 55		23 50	00 26
Exeter Central	a				18 38		19 01	19 23	19 23		19 45		20 38			21 23		22 33		23 13			
Exmouth	a				19 03				20 10		20 10		21 06			22 10		22 58		23 47			
Barnstaple	d						17 17									19 15							
Exmouth	d						18 10						19 10			20 15							
Exeter Central	d					←	18 43						19 34			20 46							
Exeter St Davids 6	d		18 33 →		18 23	18 33	18 52		19 14		19 23		20 20			20 55							01 27
Tiverton Parkway	d				18 37	18 49			19 29		19 37		20 36			21 10							
Taunton	d			18 24	18 51	19 07	19 18		19 43		19 51		20 49			21 23							
Bridgwater	a			18 34		19 18																	
Weston-super-Mare	a			18 52		19 37																	
Bristol Temple Meads 10	a			19 26	19 25	20 09					20 25					21 58							
Bath Spa 7	a			19 42												22 18							
Filton Abbey Wood	a																						
Bristol Parkway 7	a				19 38						20 38												
Swindon	a			20 10									22 06			22 46							
Newport (South Wales)	a																						
Cardiff Central 7	a																						
Birmingham New Street 12	a				20 57						21 51												
Castle Cary	d								20 06				21 12										
Westbury	d								20 25				21 30										
Pewsey	d																						
Hungerford	a																						
Newbury	a																						
Thatcham	a																						
Theale	a																						
Reading 7	a			20 43			20 56		21 25				22 41			23 29							03 54
Oxford	a						21 34		22 29				23 30			00 35							
Gatwick Airport 10	a						22 30		23 31				00c59										
Heathrow Terminal 1 Bus	a						21 55		22 45				23 45										
Slough 3	a																						
London Waterloo 15	⊖ a							22 58															
London Paddington 15	⊖ a			21 22			21 37		22 25				23 23			00 17							05 40

For general notes see front of timetable
For details of catering facilities see Directory of Train Operators

A **Atlantic Coast Express**
B **Night Riviera**
b Arr. 2047
c Change at Reading and Redhill

Due to Engineering Operations, services from Sunday 14 September on this Table had not been confirmed at time of going to press. These services will be issued in a special Supplement as soon as exact timings have been confirmed

Table 135A

Mondays to Fridays

Redruth — Helston and Culdrose
Bus Service

Mondays to Fridays

		GW 🚌	GW 🚌	GW 🚌	GW 🚌	GW 🚌	GW 🚌	GW 🚌	GW 🚌	GW 🚌	GW 🚌	GW 🚌	GW 🚌	GW 🚌	GW 🚌
Redruth	d	08 00	09 15	10 15	11 15	12 15	13 15	14 15	15 15	16 15	17 00	18 15	19 15	21 15	23 15
Helston (Woolworths)	a	08 47	09 47	10 47	11 47	12 47	13 47	14 47	15 47	16 47	17 32	18 47	19 47	21 47	23 41
Culdrose (R.N.A.S.)	a	08 56	10 00	11 00	12 00	13 00	14 00	15 00	16 00	17 00	17 50	18 55	19 55	21 55	
Mullion Holiday Park	a														

Saturdays

		GW 🚌	GW 🚌	GW 🚌	GW 🚌	GW 🚌	GW 🚌	GW 🚌	GW 🚌	GW 🚌	GW 🚌	GW 🚌	GW 🚌	GW 🚌	GW 🚌
Redruth	d	08 15	09 15	10 15	11 15	12 15	13 15	14 15	15 15	16 15	17 15	18 15	19 15	21 15	23 15
Helston (Woolworths)	a	08 47	09 47	10 47	11 47	12 47	13 47	14 47	15 47	16 47	17 47	18 47	19 47	21 47	23 41
Culdrose (R.N.A.S.)	a	08 55	10 00	11 00	12 00	13 00	14 00	15 00	16 00	17 00	18 00	18 55	19 55	21 55	
Mullion Holiday Park	a														

Sundays

		GW 🚌	GW 🚌	GW 🚌	GW 🚌	GW 🚌	GW 🚌
Redruth	d	09 50	11 50	13 50	15 50	17 50	23 00
Helston (Woolworths)	a	10 19	12 19	14 19	16 19	18s19	23s29
Culdrose (R.N.A.S.)	a	10 35	12 35	14 35	16 35	18 35	23 45
Mullion Holiday Park	a						

Mondays to Fridays

		GW 🚌	GW 🚌	GW 🚌	GW 🚌	GW 🚌	GW 🚌	GW 🚌	GW 🚌	GW 🚌	GW 🚌	GW 🚌	GW 🚌	GW 🚌	GW 🚌	GW 🚌
Mullion Holiday Park	d															
Culdrose (R.N.A.S.)	d	06 55	08 01	09 21	10 14	11 14	12 14	13 00	14 14	15 09	16 14	17 14	17 14	18 14	18 14	19 39
Helston (Woolworths)	d	07 05	08 06	09 27	10 27	11 27	12 27	13 10	14 27	15 15	16 27	17 27	17 27	18 27	18 27	19 47
Redruth	a	07 39	08 55	10 01	11 01	12 01	13 01	13 40	15 01	16 01	17 01	18 01	18 01	18 59	18 59	20 19

Saturdays

		GW 🚌	GW 🚌	GW 🚌	GW 🚌	GW 🚌	GW 🚌	GW 🚌	GW 🚌	GW 🚌	GW 🚌	GW 🚌	GW 🚌
Mullion Holiday Park	d												
Culdrose (R.N.A.S.)	d	07 19	08 19	09 19	10 14	11 14	12 14	13 14	14 14	15 14	16 14	18 14	19 39
Helston (Woolworths)	d	07 27	08 27	09 27	10 27	11 27	12 27	13 27	14 27	15 27	16 27	18 27	19 47
Redruth	a	08 01	09 01	10 01	11 01	12 01	13 01	14 01	15 01	16 01	17 01	18 59	20 19

Sundays

		GW 🚌	GW 🚌	GW 🚌	GW 🚌	GW 🚌
Mullion Holiday Park	d					
Culdrose (R.N.A.S.)	d		10 35	12 35	14 35	16 35
Helston (Woolworths)	d	08 50	10 50	12 50	14 50	16 50
Redruth	a	09 21	11 21	13 21	15 21	17 21

For general notes see front of timetable
For details of catering facilities see Directory of Train Operators

Table 135B

Mondays to Fridays

St. Austell — Eden Project
Bus Service

		GW	GW	GW	GW	GW	GW	GW	GW	GW	GW	GW	GW	GW	GW
St Austell	d	08 50	08 50	09 30	10 30	10 55	11 40	12 40	13 10	13 50	15 15	15 50	16 50	17 30	17 30
Eden Project	a	09 10	09 10	09 50	10 50	11 15	12 00	13 00	13 30	14 10	15 35	16 10	17 10	17 50	17 50

Saturdays

		GW	GW	GW	GW	GW	GW	GW	GW	GW	GW	GW	GW	GW	GW
St Austell	d	08 50	09 30	10 30	11 40	12 40	12 50	13 50	15 35	15 50	15 55	16 35	16 50	17 20	17 30
Eden Project	a	09 10	09 50	10 50	12 00	13 00	13 10	14 10	15 55	16 10	16 15	16 55	17 10	17 40	17 50

Sundays

		GW	GW	GW	GW	GW	GW	GW	GW	GW	GW	GW	GW	GW
St Austell	d	08 50	10 00	10 40	11 35	12 30	13 35	15 00	15 20	15 40	16 30	16 35	17 20	17 35
Eden Project	a	09 10	10 20	11 00	11 55	12 50	13 55	15 20	15 40	16 00	16 50	16 55	17 40	17 55

Mondays to Fridays

		GW	GW	GW	GW	GW	GW	GW	GW	GW	GW	GW	GW	GW
Eden Project	d	09 10	09 50	11 00	12 10	13 10	15 05	16 00	16 30	16 30	17 00	17 10	18 00	18 00
St Austell	a	09 30	10 10	11 20	12 30	13 30	15 25	16 20	16 50	16 50	17 20	17 30	18 20	18 20

Saturdays

		GW	GW	GW	GW	GW	GW	GW	GW	GW	GW	GW	GW
Eden Project	d	09 10	09 50	11 00	12 10	13 10	14 20	15 05	16 30	17 00	17 10	18 00	18 00
St Austell	a	09 30	10 10	11 20	12 30	13 30	14 40	15 25	16 50	17 20	17 30	18 20	18 20

Sundays

		GW	GW	GW	GW	GW	GW	GW	GW	GW	GW	GW	GW	GW
Eden Project	d	10 10	10 20	11 00	11 55	12 50	14 40	15 20	16 15	16 35	17 00	17 10	17 50	18 00
St Austell	a	10 30	10 40	11 20	12 15	13 10	15 00	15 40	16 35	16 55	17 20	17 30	18 10	18 20

For general notes see front of timetable
For details of catering facilities see
Directory of Train Operators

Table 135C

Mondays to Saturdays

Bodmin — Wadebridge and Padstow

Bus Service

		GW 🚌	GW 🚌	GW 🚌	GW 🚌	GW 🚌	GW 🚌	GW 🚌	GW 🚌	GW 🚌	GW 🚌	GW 🚌	GW 🚌	GW 🚌	GW 🚌
Bodmin Parkway	d	07 25	08 30	09 30	10 30	11 30	12 30	13 30	14 30	15 30	16 30	17 30	18 30	19 30	22 00
Bodmin Tsb Bus Stop	a														
Bodmin Mount Folly	a	07 35	08 40	09 40	10 40	11 40	12 40	13 40	14 40	15 40	16 40	17 40	18 40	19 40	22 10
Wadebridge Bus Station	a	07 55	09 00	10 00	11 00	12 00	13 00	14 00	15 00	16 00	17 00	18 00	19 00	20 00	22 30
Padstow Old Rly Station	a	08 27	09 27	10 27	11 27	12 27	13 27	14 27	15 27	16 27	17 27	18 27	19 27	20 27	22 57

Sundays

		GW 🚌	GW 🚌	GW 🚌	GW 🚌	GW 🚌	GW 🚌
Bodmin Parkway	d	09 30	11 30	13 30	15 30	17 30	19 30
Bodmin Tsb Bus Stop	a						
Bodmin Mount Folly	a	09 40	11 40	13 40	15 40	17 40	19 40
Wadebridge Bus Station	a	10 00	12 00	14 00	16 00	18 00	20 00
Padstow Old Rly Station	a	10 27	12 27	14 27	16 27	18 27	20 27

Mondays to Saturdays

		GW 🚌	GW 🚌	GW 🚌	GW 🚌	GW 🚌	GW 🚌	GW 🚌	GW 🚌	GW 🚌	GW 🚌	GW 🚌	GW 🚌	GW 🚌	GW 🚌
Padstow Old Rly Station	d	06 30	07 30	08 30	09 30	10 30	11 30	12 30	13 30	14 30	15 30	16 30	17 30	18 30	20 30
Wadebridge Bus Station	d	06 55	07 55	08 55	09 55	10 55	11 55	12 55	13 55	14 55	15 55	16 55	17 55	18 55	20 55
Bodmin Mount Folly	d														
Bodmin Tsb Bus Stop	d	07 17	08 17	09 17	10 17	11 17	12 17	13 17	14 17	15 17	16 17	17 17	18 17	19 17	21 17
Bodmin Parkway	a	07 25	08 25	09 25	10 25	11 25	12 25	13 25	14 25	15 25	16 25	17 25	18 25	19 25	21 25

Sundays

		GW 🚌	GW 🚌	GW 🚌	GW 🚌	GW 🚌	GW 🚌
Padstow Old Rly Station	d	08 30	10 30	12 30	14 30	16 30	18 30
Wadebridge Bus Station	d	08 55	10 55	12 55	14 55	16 55	18 55
Bodmin Mount Folly	d						
Bodmin Tsb Bus Stop	d	09 17	11 17	13 17	15 17	17 17	19 17
Bodmin Parkway	a	09 25	11 25	13 25	15 25	17 25	19 25

For general notes see front of timetable
For details of catering facilities see Directory of Train Operators

Table 135D

Mondays to Fridays

Exeter — Okehampton, Holsworthy and Bude
Bus Service

		GW	GW	GW	GW	GW
Exeter St Davids	d	09 50	11 50	13 50	15 40	17 55
Okehampton West Street	a	10 25	12 25	14 25	16 25	18 30
Okehampton Fore Street	a					
Holsworthy Library	a					
Holsworthy Church	a	10 58	12 58	14 58	16 58	19 03
Bude Strand	a	11 20	13 20	15 20	17 20	19 25

Saturdays

		GW	GW	GW	GW	GW	GW	GW	GW	GW	GW	GW	GW	GW	GW	GW	GW
Exeter St Davids	d	09 25	10 25	11 25	12 25	13 25	13 55	14 25	15 25	15 55	16 25	16 55	17 25	17 55	18 25	19 40	20 40
Okehampton West Street	a	10 00	11 10	12 00	13 10	14 00	14 40	15 00	16 10	16 30	17 00	17 45	18 15	18 45	19 15	20 30	21 30
Okehampton Fore Street	a																
Holsworthy Library	a																
Holsworthy Church	a	10 33		12 33		14 33					17 33		18 48		19 48	21 03	22 03
Bude Strand	a	10 55		12 55		14 55					17 55		19 10	20 00	20 10	21 25	22 25

Sundays

		GW	GW
Exeter St Davids	d	12 25	17 25
Okehampton West Street	a	13 15	18 15
Okehampton Fore Street	a		
Holsworthy Library	a		
Holsworthy Church	a	13 48	18 48
Bude Strand	a	14 10	19 10

Mondays to Fridays

		GW	GW	GW	GW	GW	GW
Bude Strand	d	06 40	09 00	11 30	13 30	15 25	15 30
Holsworthy Library	d						
Holsworthy Church	d	07 02	09 22	11 52	13 52	15 57	15 57
Okehampton West Street	d	07 40	10 00	12 30	14 30	16 35	16 35
Okehampton Fore Street	d						
Exeter St Davids	a	08 15	10 35	13 05	15 05	17 15	17 15

Saturdays

		GW	GW	GW	GW	GW	GW	GW	GW	GW	GW	GW	GW	GW	GW	GW
Bude Strand	d	05 45	06 40	08 15	09 15			11 15		13 15				15 30	17 15	17 30
Holsworthy Library	d															
Holsworthy Church	d		07 02	08 37	09 37			11 37		13 37				15 57	17 37	17 52
Okehampton West Street	d	07 00	07 40	09 15	10 15	10 45	11 15	12 15	13 15	14 15	14 45	15 15	16 15	16 35	18 10	18 25
Okehampton Fore Street	d															
Exeter St Davids	a	07 40	08 20	10 00	10 50	11 20	12 00	12 50	14 00	14 50	15 30	15 50	17 00	17 10	18 50	19 07

Sundays

		GW	GW
Bude Strand	d	10 10	15 10
Holsworthy Library	d		
Holsworthy Church	d	10 32	15 32
Okehampton West Street	d	11 10	16 10
Okehampton Fore Street	d		
Exeter St Davids	a	12 00	17 00

For general notes see front of timetable
For details of catering facilities see Directory of Train Operators

Table 135E

Mondays to Saturdays

Taunton — Watchet, Dunster and Minehead
Bus Service

		GW MO	GW MX	GW	GW	GW	GW	GW	GW	GW	GW	GW	GW	GW	GW	GW	GW	GW
Taunton	d	23p15	23p16	05 41	07 14	07 44	08 14	08 44	09 14	09 44	10 14	10 44	11 14	11 44	12 14	12 44	13 14	13 44
Watchet (West Somerset Ry)	a	23p58	23p59	06 25	07 58	08 28	08 58	09 32	10 02	10 32	11 02	11 32	12 02	12 32	13 02	13 32	14 02	14 32
Dunster Steep	a	00 12	00 14	06 39	08 15	08 45	09 15	09 49	10 19	10 49	11 19	11 49	12 19	12 49	13 19	13 49	14 19	14 49
Minehead Parade	a	00 20	00 22	06 47	08 23	08 53	09 23	09 57	10 27	10 57	11 27	11 57	12 27	12 57	13 27	13 57	14 27	14 57
Minehead Bancks Street	a																	

		GW	GW	GW	GW	GW	GW	GW SX	GW SO	GW	GW	GW	GW	GW	GW	GW	GW
Taunton	d	14 14	14 44	15 14	15 44	16 14	16 44	17 09	17 09	17 29	17 59	18 29	19 16	20 16	21 16	22 16	23 16
Watchet (West Somerset Ry)	a	15 02	15 32	16 02	16 32	16 58	17 28	17 51	17 53	18 13	18 43	19 13	20 00	21 00	22 00	23 00	23 59
Dunster Steep	a	15 19	15 49	16 19	16 49	17 15	17 45	18 08	18 10	18 30	19 00	19 30	20 14	21 14	22 14	23 14	00 14
Minehead Parade	a	15 27	15 57	16 27	16 57	17 23	17 53	18 16	18 18	18 38	19 08	19 38	20 22	21 22	22 22	23 22	00 22
Minehead Bancks Street	a																

Sundays

		GW	GW	GW	GW	GW	GW	GW	GW	GW	GW	GW
Taunton	d	23p16	09 35	11 35	12 35	13 35	14 35	15 35	16 35	17 35	19 35	23 15
Watchet (West Somerset Ry)	a	23p59	10 18	12 18	13 18	14 18	15 18	16 18	17 18	18 18	20 18	23 58
Dunster Steep	a	00 14	10 32	12 32	13 32	14 32	15 32	16 32	17 32	18 32	20 32	00 12
Minehead Parade	a	00 22	10 40	12 40	13 40	14 40	15 40	16 40	17 40	18 40	20 40	00 20
Minehead Bancks Street	a											

Mondays to Saturdays

		GW	GW SX	GW SO	GW SX	GW SO	GW	GW	GW	GW	GW	GW	GW	GW	GW	GW	GW	GW
Minehead Bancks Street	d	05 50	07 00	07 10	07 20	07 42	08 17	08 47	09 17	09 47	10 17	10 47	11 17	11 47	12 17	12 47	13 17	13 47
Minehead Parade	d																	
Dunster Steep	d	05 58	07 08	07 18	07 28	07 50	08 25	08 55	09 25	09 55	10 25	10 55	11 25	11 55	12 25	12 55	13 25	13 55
Watchet (West Somerset Ry)	d	06 13	07 26	07 36	07 46	08 08	08 43	09 13	09 43	10 13	10 43	11 13	11 43	12 13	12 43	13 13	13 43	14 13
Taunton	a	06 55	08 14	08 18	08 33	08 50	09 25	09 55	10 25	10 55	11 25	11 59	12 29	12 59	13 29	14 00	14 29	14 59

		GW	GW	GW	GW	GW	GW	GW	GW	GW SX	GW SO	GW	GW	GW	GW	GW
Minehead Bancks Street	d	14 17	14 47	15 17	15 47	16 17	16 47	17 17	17 47	18 17	18 17	18 45	19 45	20 35	21 35	22 35
Minehead Parade	d															
Dunster Steep	d	14 25	14 55	15 25	15 55	16 25	16 55	17 25	17 55	18 25	18 25	18 53	19 53	20 43	21 43	22 43
Watchet (West Somerset Ry)	d	14 43	15 13	15 43	16 13	16 43	17 13	17 43	18 13	18 43	18 43	19 08	20 08	20 58	21 58	22 58
Taunton	a	15 29	15 59	16 29	16 59	17 29	17 59	18 29	19 00	19 25	19 29	19 50	20 50	21 40	22 40	23 40

Sundays

		GW	GW	GW	GW	GW	GW	GW	GW	GW
Minehead Bancks Street	d	08 55	10 55	12 55	13 55	14 55	15 55	16 55	17 55	18 55
Minehead Parade	d									
Dunster Steep	d	09 03	11 03	13 03	14 03	15 03	16 03	17 03	18 03	19 03
Watchet (West Somerset Ry)	d	09 18	11 18	13 18	14 18	15 18	16 18	17 18	18 18	19 18
Taunton	a	10 00	12 00	14 00	15 00	16 00	17 00	18 00	19 00	20 00

For general notes see front of timetable
For details of catering facilities see Directory of Train Operators

Exmouth → Exeter → Barnstaple

Network Diagram - see first page of Table 135

Miles			GW	GW	GW	SW	GW	GW	SW	GW	GW	SW	GW	GW	GW	GW	SW	GW	GW	SW	GW
			MO			■1			■1			■1					■1			■1 ◇	
			A							B			B					B		⊏P	B
0	**Exmouth**	d	23p50		06 05			06 40		07 15			07 50		08 20	08 50		09 20	09 50		10 20
2	Lympstone Village	d	23p54		06 09			06 44		07 19			07 54		08 24	08 54		09 24	09 54		10 24
3	Lympstone Commando	d	23b56		06x11			06x46		07x20			07x55		08x25	08x55		09x25	09x55		
3½	Exton	d	23b57		06x13			06x48		07x22			07x57		08x27	08x57		09x27	09x57		
5	Topsham	d	00 01		06 17			06 54		07 27			08 02		08 32	09 02		09 32	10 02		10 32
7	Digby & Sowton	d	00 05		06 21			06 58		07 31			08 06		08 36	09 06		09 36	10 06		10 36
9	Polsloe Bridge	d	00 08		06 24			07 01		07 34			08 09		08 39	09 09		09 39	10 09		
10	St James' Park	d	00 11		06 27			07 04		07 37	07 52		08 12		08 42	09 12		09 42	10 12		
10½	**Exeter Central**	a	00 13		06 29			07 06		07 39	07 54		08 14		08 44	09 14		09 44	10 14		10 42
—		d	00 13		06 29	06 32		07 06	07 32	07 39	07 54	08 12	08 15		08 44	09 14	09 24	09 44	10 14	10 30	10 43
11¼	**Exeter St Davids** ■3	a	00 16		06 33	06 36		07 12	07 35	07 42	07 59	08 15	08 20		08 49	09 17	09 27	09 47	10 17	10 33	10 46
—		d		05 53			06 50							08 27		09 19					
15½	Newton St Cyres	d																			
18¼	Crediton	d		06 05			07 01							08 38		09 32					
—	Sampford Courtenay	d																			
—	Okehampton	a																			
21¾	Yeoford	d		06 11			07 07							08 45		09 39					
24½	Copplestone	d		06x16			07x12							08x49		09x44					
26¼	Morchard Road	d					07x15									09x47					
28¾	Lapford	d					07x19														
32½	Eggesford	d		06 30			07c48							09 04		10 00					
36¼	Kings Nympton	d					07x53														
39¼	Portsmouth Arms	d					07x58														
43½	Umberleigh	d		06x45			08x04							09x18		10x15					
45¾	Chapelton	d					08x08														
50¼	**Barnstaple**	a		06 57			08 16							09 31		10 22					

		GW	SW	GW	GW	SW	GW	GW	SW	GW	GW	GW	GW	GW	SW	GW	GW	SW	GW	GW
			■1 ◇			■1 ◇			■1 ◇						■1 ◇			■1		
				B						B			B			B	B			B
			⊏P			⊏P			⊏P						⊏P					
Exmouth	d	10 50		11 20	11 50		12 20	12 50		13 20		13 50	14 20	14 50		15 20	15 50		16 20	16 50
Lympstone Village	d	10 54		11 24	11 54		12 24	12 54		13 24		13 54	14 24	14 54		15 24	15 54		16 24	16 54
Lympstone Commando	d	10x55			11x55			12x55				13x55		14 55		15x25	15x55		16x25	16x55
Exton	d	10x57			11x57			12x57				13x57		14 57		15x27	15x57		16x27	16x57
Topsham	d	11 02		11 32	12 02		12 32	13 02		13 32		14 02	14 32	15 02		15 32	16 02		16 32	17 02
Digby & Sowton	d	11 06		11 36	12 06		12 36	13 06		13 36		14 06	14 36	15 06		15 36	16 06		16 36	17 06
Polsloe Bridge	d	11 09			12 09			13 09				14 09		15 09		15 39	16 09		16 39	17 09
St James' Park	d	11 12			12 12			13 12				14 12		15 12		15 42	16 12		16 42	17 12
Exeter Central	a	11 14		11 42	12 14		12 42	13 14		13 42		14 14	14 42	15 14		15 44	16 14		16 44	17 14
	d	11 16	11 38	11 43	12 17	12 24	12 43	13 14	13 38	13 42	14 00	14 17	14 42	15 14	15 39	15 44	16 14	16 23	16 44	17 14
Exeter St Davids ■6	a	11 19	11 42	11 48	12 23	12 27	12 49	13 17	13 41	13 48	14 05	14 23	14 46	15 17	15 42	15 49	16 17	16 26	16 50	17 17
	d	11 27						13 19						15 19					16 57	
Newton St Cyres	d																			
Crediton	d	11 37						13 29						15 32					17 07	
Sampford Courtenay	d																			
Okehampton	a																			
Yeoford	d	11 44						13 36						15 39					17 14	
Copplestone	d	11x49						13x41						15x44					17x20	
Morchard Road	d							13x44											17x23	
Lapford	d							13x49											17x27	
Eggesford	d	12 03						13 57						16 05					17 38	
Kings Nympton	d							14x04											17x43	
Portsmouth Arms	d																			
Umberleigh	d	12x18						14x14						16x20					17x53	
Chapelton	d																			
Barnstaple	a	12 30						14 25						16 30					18 03	

		SW	GW	SW	GW	GW	GW	SW	GW	GW	SW	SW	GW	GW	SW	SW	GW	SW	SW
																FO		FO	FX
		■1 ◇		■1				■1			■1 ◇	■1			■1 ◇	■1 ◇		■1 ◇	■1 ◇
					B				B										
		⊏P									⊏P	▼ ⊏P			⊏P	⊏P		⊏P	⊏P
Exmouth	d		17 20		17 50		18 20		18 50	19 20			20 20	21 20			22 20		
Lympstone Village	d		17 24		17 54		18 24		18 54	19 24			20 24	21 24			22 24		
Lympstone Commando	d		17x25		17x55		18 25		18x55	19x25			20x25	21x25			22x25		
Exton	d		17x27		17x57		18 27		18x57	19x27			20x27	21x27			22x27		
Topsham	d		17 32		18 06		18 33		19 02	19 32			20 32	21 32			22 32		
Digby & Sowton	d		17 36		18 10		18 36		19 06	19 36			20 36	21 36			22 36		
Polsloe Bridge	d		17 39		18 13		18 39		19 09	19 39			20 39	21 39			22 39		
St James' Park	d		17 42		18 16		18 42		19 12	19 42			20 42	21 42			22 42		
Exeter Central	a		17 44		18 19		18 47		19 14	19 44			20 44	21 44			22 44		
	d	17 35	17 48	17 56	18 19	18 30	18 47	19 01	19 14	19 44	19 52	20 31	20 44	21 44	21 50	22 38	22 44	23 51	23 58
Exeter St Davids ■6	a	17 38	17 52	17 59	18 22	18 35	18 51	19 04	19 21	19 47	19 57	20 36	20 47	21 50	21 55	22 41	22 50	23 54	00 01
	d		17 54				18 58						20 51						
Newton St Cyres	d		18x01				19x06						20x58						
Crediton	d		18 07				19 11						21 04						
Sampford Courtenay	d																		
Okehampton	a																		
Yeoford	d		18 14				19 18						21 11						
Copplestone	d		18x19				19x23						21x16						
Morchard Road	d		18x22				19x26						21x19						
Lapford	d		18x26				19x30						21x23						
Eggesford	d		18 40				19 41						21 34						
Kings Nympton	d		18x45				19x47						21x40						
Portsmouth Arms	d		18x50				19x52						21x48						
Umberleigh	d		18x56				19x58						21x51						
Chapelton	d		19x00				20x02						21x55						
Barnstaple	a		19 08				20 10						22 03						

For general notes see front of timetable
For details of catering facilities see Directory of Train Operators

A Until 8 September
B To Paignton (Table 135)

b Previous night.
x Stops on request, passengers wishing to alight must inform the guard and those wishing to join must give a hand signal to the driver
c Arr. 0729

Table 136

Saturdays

Exmouth → Exeter → Barnstaple

Network Diagram - see first page of Table 135

		GW	GW	SW	GW	SW	GW	GW	GW	SW	GW	GW	GW	GW	SW	GW	GW	GW	SW	GW
				1		1				1			1◇	1◇	1			1◇	1◇	
							A				A	B	C	D		A		C		A
												🍴	🍴	🍴				🍴	☕	
Exmouth	d		06 05				07 15	07 50			08 20	08 50				09 20	09 50			10 20
Lympstone Village	d		06 09				07 19	07 54			08 24	08 54				09 24	09 54			10 24
Lympstone Commando	d		06x11				07x20	07x56			08x26	08x55				09x26	09x55			
Exton	d		06x13				07x22	07x58			08x28	08x57				09x28	09x57			
Topsham	d		06 17				07 29	08 01			08 32	09 02				09 32	10 02			10 32
Digby & Sowton	d		06 21				07 33	08 05			08 36	09 06				09 36	10 06			10 36
Polsloe Bridge	d		06 24				07 37	08 08			08 39	09 09				09 39	10 09			
St James' Park	d		06 27				07 39	08 11			08 42	09 12				09 42	10 12			
Exeter Central	a		06 29				07 41	08 14			08 44	09 14				09 44	10 14			10 41
	d		06 29	06 32		07 33	07 42	08 14		08 27	08 44	09 14			09 24	09 44	10 14		10 29	10 43
Exeter St Davids 6	a		06 32	06 35		07 36	07 45	08 17		08 30	08 47	09 17			09 27	09 47	10 17		10 32	10 46
	d	05 53			06 50				08 25				09 18	09 19						
Newton St Cyres	d																			
Crediton	d	06 05			07 01				08 36				09 31	09 31						
Sampford Courtenay	d																			
Okehampton	a																			
Yeoford	d	06x11			07 07				08 43				09x38	09 38						
Copplestone	d	06x16			07x12				08x48				09x43	09x43						
Morchard Road	d				07x15								09x46	09x46						
Lapford	d				07x19															
Eggesford	d	06 30			07b48				09 03				09 59	09 59						
Kings Nympton	d				07x53															
Portsmouth Arms	d				07x58															
Umberleigh	d	06x45			08x04				09x18				10x14 →	10x14				← 10x14		
Chapelton	d				08x08															
Barnstaple	a	06 57			08 16				09 30					10 23				10 26		

		GW	GW	SW	GW	SW	GW	GW	SW	GW	GW	SW	GW	GW	GW	SW	GW	GW	SW	GW
				1◇		1◇			1◇			1◇				1◇			1	
			A				A			A			A				A			A
				☕		☕			☕			☕				☕				
Exmouth	d	10 50	11 20		11 50		12 20	12 50		13 20	13 50		14 20	14 50			15 20	15 50		16 20
Lympstone Village	d	10 54	11 24		11 54		12 24	12 54		13 24	13 54		14 24	14 54			15 24	15 54		16 24
Lympstone Commando	d	10x55			11x55			12x56			13x55			14x56			15x25	15x55		16 25
Exton	d	10x57			11x57			12x57			13x57			14x58			15x27	15x57		16 27
Topsham	d	11 02	11 32		12 02		12 33	13 02		13 32	14 02		14 22	15 02			15 32	16 02		16 32
Digby & Sowton	d	11 06	11 36		12 06		12 36	13 06		13 36	14 06		14 36	15 06			15 36	16 06		16 36
Polsloe Bridge	d	11 09			12 09			13 09			14 09			15 09			15 39	16 09		16 39
St James' Park	d	11 12			12 12			13 12			14 12			15 12			15 42	16 12		16 42
Exeter Central	a	11 14	11 41		12 14		12 41	13 14		13 43	14 14		14 41	15 14			15 44	16 14		16 44
	d	11 16	11 43	11 53	12 17	12 27	12 43	13 14	13 39	13 46	14 14	14 20	14 42	15 14	15 31	15 39	15 44	16 14	16 24	16 44
Exeter St Davids 6	a	11 19	11 46	11 56	12 20	12 30	12 46	13 17	13 42	13 49	14 17	14 23	14 45	15 18	15 34	15 42	15 48	16 17	16 27	16 47
	d	11 27						13 19			14 19				15 35			16 21		
Newton St Cyres	d																			
Crediton	d	11 37						13 29			14 29				15 47			16 32		
Sampford Courtenay	d																			
Okehampton	a																			
Yeoford	d	11x44						13x36			14 36				15 54			16x38		
Copplestone	d	11x49						13x41			14x41				15x59			16x43		
Morchard Road	d							13x44			14x44							16x46		
Lapford	d							13 48										16x50		
Eggesford	d	12 03						13 57			15 05				16 13			17 09		
Kings Nympton	d							14 04										17x15		
Portsmouth Arms	d																			
Umberleigh	d	12x18						14x14			15x20				16x28			17x25		
Chapelton	d																			
Barnstaple	a	12 30						14 25			15 31				16 38			17 36		

		GW	SW	GW	SW	GW	GW	SW	GW	GW	SW	GW	GW	SW	SW	GW	GW
			1◇		1			1			1◇			1◇	1◇		
		A				A				A							
			☕								☕			☕	☕		
Exmouth	d	16 50		17 20		17 50	18 19		18 50	19 20			21 20			22 26	23 41
Lympstone Village	d	16 54		17 24		17 54	18 23		18 54	19 24			21 24			22 30	23 45
Lympstone Commando	d	16x56		17x25		17x55	18x25		18x55	19x25			21x26			22x31	23x46
Exton	d	16x58		17x27		17x57	18x27		18x57	19x27			21x28			22x33	23x48
Topsham	d	17 02		17 32		18 04	18 33		19 02	19 32			21 32			22 38	23 53
Digby & Sowton	d	17 06		17 36		18 08	18 36		19 06	19 36			21 36			22 42	23 57
Polsloe Bridge	d	17 09		17 39		18 11	18 39		19 10	19 39			21 39			22 45	24 00
St James' Park	d	17 12		17 42		18 14	18 42		19 12	19 42			21 42			22 48	00 03
Exeter Central	a	17 14		17 44		18 16	18 45		19 15	19 44			21 44			22 50	00 05
	d	17 14	17 33	17 44	17 54	18 19	18 47	19 02	19 16	19 44	19 52	20 29	21 44	21 48	22 38	22 50	00 05
Exeter St Davids 6	a	17 17	17 36	17 47	17 57	18 22	18 50	19 05	19 19	19 47	19 57	20 32	21 48	21 53	22 41	22 54	00 09
	d			17 49			19 06					20 40					
Newton St Cyres	d			17 57			19 15					20x47					
Crediton	d			18 03			19 20					21 09					
Sampford Courtenay	d																
Okehampton	a																
Yeoford	d			18x10			19x27					20x53					
Copplestone	d			18x15			19x32					20x59					
Morchard Road	d			18x18			19x35					21x02					
Lapford	d			18x22			19x39					21x06					
Eggesford	d			18 35			19 50					21 17					
Kings Nympton	d			18x41			19x56					21x23					
Portsmouth Arms	d			18x46			20x01					21x27					
Umberleigh	d			18x52			20x07					21x34					
Chapelton	d			18x56			20x11					21x38					
Barnstaple	a			19 05			20 20					21 48					

For general notes see front of timetable
For details of catering facilities see Directory of Train Operators

A To Paignton (Table 135)
B To Penzance (Table 135)
C From 13 September. From Penzance (Table 135)
D Until 6 September. From Penzance (Table 135)
b Arr. 0730

Table 136

Sundays

Exmouth → Exeter → Barnstaple

Network Diagram - see first page of Table 135

		GW	SW 1	GW A	GW B	GW A	GW B	GW E	GW A	SW 1 ◇	GW D	SW 1 ◇ cater.	GW	GW E	GW G	SW 1 ◇ cater.	GW D	GW	GW E	GW	SW 1 ◇ cater.	GW D
Exmouth	d	23p41				09 10			10 00				11 10		12 05			13 05		14 10		
Lympstone Village	d	23p45				09 14			10 04				11 14		12 09			13 09		14 14		
Lympstone Commando	d	23b47				09x15			10x05				11x15		12x10			13x10		14 15		
Exton	d	23b49				09x17			10x07				11x17		12x12			13x12		14 17		
Topsham	d	23p53				09 22			10 12				11 23		12 17			13 18		14 22		
Digby & Sowton	d	23p57				09 26			10 16				11 27		12 21			13 22		14 26		
Polsloe Bridge	d	00 01				09 29			10 19				11 30		12 24			13 25		14 29		
St James' Park	d	00 03		09 03	09 03	09 32			10 22		11 03		11 33		12 27		13 03	13 28		14 32		15 03
Exeter Central	a	00 05		09 05	09 05	09 34			10 24		11 05		11 35		12 29		13 06	13 30		14 34		15 05
	d	00 05	08 56	09 06	09 06	09 34			10 24	10 46	11 06	11 29	11 37		12 30	12 46	13 06	13 30		14 34	14 43	15 06
Exeter St Davids 6	a	00 09	08 59	09 09	09 09	09 37			10 27	10 49	11 09	11 32	11 40		12 33	12 49	13 10	13 33		14 37	14 46	15 09
	d			09 13	09 13	09 42	09 42				11 12		11 55				13 12	13 55				15 12
Newton St Cyres	d					09x49	09x49											14x02				
Crediton	d			09 23	09 24	09 57	09 57				11 22		12 11				13 22	14 11				15 22
Sampford Courtenay	d			09 44	09 45			10 09			11 43			12 09			13 43		14 09			15 43
Okehampton	a			09 51	09 52						11 50						13 50					15 50
Yeoford	d					10 04	10 04	10a22					12 18	12a22				14 18	14a22			
Copplestone	d					10x08	10x08						12x22					14x23				
Morchard Road	d					10x11	10x11						12x25					14x26				
Lapford	d					10x15	10x15											14x30				
Eggesford	d					10 28	10 28						12 39					14 42				
Kings Nympton	d					10x33	10x33											14x48				
Portsmouth Arms	d					10x38	10x38											14x52				
Umberleigh	d					10x44	10x44						12x53					14x59				
Chapelton	d					10x48	10x48											15x03				
Barnstaple	a					10 57	10 57						13 04					15 11				

		GW	GW E	GW	SW 1 ◇ cater.	GW D	GW	GW E	GW J	GW K	SW 1 ◇ cater.	GW	GW B	GW A	SW 1 ◇ cater.	GW G	GW B	GW A	SW 1 ◇ cater.	GW	GW
Exmouth	d	15 10		16 10			17 10		18 10	18 10		19 10	20 10	20 15		21 10	22 10	22 15		23 04	23 51
Lympstone Village	d	15 14		16 14			17 14		18 14	18 14		19 14	20 14	20 19		21 14	22 14	22 19		23 08	23 55
Lympstone Commando	d	15x15		16x15			17x16		18x15	18x16		19x15	20x15	20x21		21x15	22x16	22x21		23x09	23x56
Exton	d	15x17		16x17			17x17		18x17	18x17		19x17	20x17	20x22		21x17	22x17	22x22		23x11	23x58
Topsham	d	15 23		16 22			17 22		18 23	18 22		19 23	20 22	20 27		21 22	22 22	22 27		23 17	00 03
Digby & Sowton	d	15 27		16 26			17 26		18 27	18 26		19 27	20 26	20 31		21 26	22 26	22 31		23 21	00 07
Polsloe Bridge	d	15 30		16 29			17 29		18 30	18 29		19 30	20 29	20 34		21 29	22 29	22 34		23 24	00 10
St James' Park	d	15 33		16 32		17 03	17 32		18 33	18 32		19 33	20 32	20 37		21 32	22 32	22 37		23 27	00 13
Exeter Central	a	15 35		16 34		17 05	17 34		18 35	18 34		19 35	20 34	20 39		21 34	22 34	22 39		23 29	00 15
	d	15 35		16 34	16 47	17 06	17 34		18 36	18 37	18 43	19 35	20 34	20 39	20 46	21 35	22 34	22 39	22 43	23 29	00 15
Exeter St Davids 6	a	15 38		16 37	16 50	17 09	17 37		18 39	18 41	18 46	19 38	20 39	20 44	20 49	21 38	22 37	22 42	22 46	23 32	00 18
	d	15 55				17 12	18 00					19 56									
Newton St Cyres	d	16x04										20x04									
Crediton	d	16 11				17 22	18 15					20 13									
Sampford Courtenay	d		16 08			17 43		18 23													
Okehampton	a					17 50															
Yeoford	d	16 18	16a21				18 22	18a36				20 19									
Copplestone	d	16x23					18x28					20x24									
Morchard Road	d	16x26					18x30					20x27									
Lapford	d	16x30										20x31									
Eggesford	d	16 40					18 44					20 44									
Kings Nympton	d	16x47										20x49									
Portsmouth Arms	d	16x51										20x54									
Umberleigh	d	16x58					18x58					21x00									
Chapelton	d	17x02										21x04									
Barnstaple	a	17 11					19 09					21 14									

For general notes see front of timetable
For details of catering facilities see Directory of Train Operators

A Until 7 September
B From 14 September
D Until 21 September
E Until 21 September. From Okehampton
G To Paignton (Table 135)
J Until 7 September. To Paignton (Table 135)
K From 14 September. To Paignton (Table 135)
b Previous night.
Stops on request, passengers wishing to alight must inform the guard and those wishing to join must give a hand signal to the driver

Barnstaple → Exeter → Exmouth

Network Diagram - see first page of Table 135

Miles			SW 1◇ ☕	GW	GW	GW	SW 1◇ ☕	GW A	GW A	GW	SW 1	GW A	GW	SW 1◇ ☕	GW	GW	GW	GW	SW 1◇ ☕	GW A	GW
0	**Barnstaple**	d											07 01					08 35			09 33
4¼	Chapelton	d											07x06								
6¾	Umberleigh	d											07x10					08x42			09 40
10¾	Portsmouth Arms	d											07x17								
13¾	Kings Nympton	d											07x22					08x53			
17¼	Eggesford	d											07 31					09 04			10 01
21¼	Lapford	d											07x37								
23¾	Morchard Road	d											07x41					09x14			10 09
25½	Copplestone	d											07x45					09x16			10x13
28½	Yeoford	d											07 49					09 21			10 18
—	Okehampton	d																			
—	Sampford Courtenay	d																			
32	Crediton	d											07 57					09 30			10 26
34¾	Newton St Cyres	d											08x01								
39	**Exeter St Davids** 6	a											08 09					09 41			10 37
—		d	05 10	05 35	06 00	06 37	06 42	07 10	07 35	07 45	08 00	08 06	08 12	08 25	08 45	08 54	09 18	09 45	10 10	10 18	10 45
39½	**Exeter Central**	a	05 13	05 38	06 03	06 40	06 45	07 13	07 38	07 48	08 03	08 11	08 15	08 29	08 48	08 59	09 21	09 48	10 13	10 21	10 48
—		d		05 38	06 03	06 40		07 13	07 38	07 48		08 12	08 18		08 48		09 21	09 48		10 21	10 48
40¼	St James' Park	d		05 40	06 05	06 42		07 15	07a42	07 50		08a16	08 20		08 50			09 50			10 50
41¼	Polsloe Bridge	d		05 43	06 08	06 45		07 18		07 53			08 23		08 53			09 53			10 53
43¾	Digby & Sowton	d		05 47	06 12	06 49		07 22		07 57			08 27		08 57		09 27	09 57		10 27	10 57
45¼	Topsham	d		05 51	06 18	06 53		07 28		08 02			08 32		09 02		09 32	10 02		10 32	11 02
46¾	Exton	d		05x53	06x20	06x56		07x31		08x05			08x35		09x05			10x05			11x05
47¼	Lympstone Commando	d		05x55	06x22	06x58		07x33		08x07			08x37		09x07			10x07			11x07
48¼	Lympstone Village	d		05 57	06 24	07 00		07 35		08 09			08 39		09 09		09 37	10 09		10 37	11 09
50¼	**Exmouth**	a		06 04	06 32	07 07		07 42		08 17			08 47		09 17		09 45	10 17		10 46	11 17

		GW A	GW	SW 1◇ ☕	GW A	GW	GW A	SW 1◇ ☕	GW	GW	SW 1◇ ☕	GW A	GW 1◇	GW A	SW 1	GW	SW 1◇ ☕	GW A	SW 1	GW
Barnstaple	d		10 32							12 40						14 39				15 39
Chapelton	d																			
Umberleigh	d		10x39							12 47						14x46				15x46
Portsmouth Arms	d																			
Kings Nympton	d																			
Eggesford	d		10 57							13 05						15b06				16 04
Lapford	d																			
Morchard Road	d															15x15				
Copplestone	d		11x07							13 15						15x19				16x14
Yeoford	d		11 12							13 20						15 23				16 19
Okehampton	d																			
Sampford Courtenay	d																			
Crediton	d		11 20							13 31						15 31				16 28
Newton St Cyres	d																			
Exeter St Davids 6	a		11 31							13 41						15 41				16 41
	d	11 18	11 45	12 10	12 18	12 45	13 18	13 35	13 45	13 50	14 10	14 18	14 45	15 18	15 30	15 43	16 10	16 18	16 36	16 45
Exeter Central	a	11 21	11 48	12 13	12 21	12 48	13 21	13 38	13 48	13 53	14 13	14 21	14 48	15 21	15 33	15 46	16 13	16 21	16 39	16 48
	d	11 21	11 48		12 21	12 48	13 21		13 48			14 21	14 48	15 21		15 48		16 22		16 48
St James' Park	d		11 50			12 50			13 50				14 50			15 50				16 50
Polsloe Bridge	d		11 53			12 53			13 53				14 53			15 53				16 53
Digby & Sowton	d	11 27	11 57		12 27	12 57	13 27		13 57			14 27	14 57	15 27		15 57		16 27		16 57
Topsham	d	11 32	12 02		12 32	13 02	13 32		14 02			14 32	15 02	15 32		16 02		16 32		17 02
Exton	d		12x05			13x05			14x05				15x05			16x05				17x04
Lympstone Commando	d		12x07			13x07			14x07				15x07			16x07				17x06
Lympstone Village	d	11 37	12 09		12 37	13 09	13 37		14 09			14 37	15 09	15 37		16 09		16 37		17 08
Exmouth	a	11 46	12 17		12 46	13 17	13 47		14 17			14 46	15 17	15 46		16 17		16 45		17 17

		GW	SW 1	GW A	SW 1◇ ☕	GW A	GW	GW A	SW 1◇	GW	GW	SW 1	GW	GW	SW 1	GW	SW FX 1	SW FO 1	GW
Barnstaple	d						17 06			18 08			19 15			20 15			22 08
Chapelton	d						17x11			18x13									22x13
Umberleigh	d						17 15			18x17			19 22			20x22			22x17
Portsmouth Arms	d						17x22			18x24									22x24
Kings Nympton	d						17x27			18x29									22x29
Eggesford	d						17 38			18 38			19 42			20 40			22 37
Lapford	d						17x44			18x44									22x43
Morchard Road	d						17 48			18x48									22x48
Copplestone	d						17x52			18x52			19x52			20x50			22x51
Yeoford	d						17 56			18 56			19 57			20 55			22 59
Okehampton	d																		
Sampford Courtenay	d																		
Crediton	d						18 09			19c13			20 05			21 08			23 04
Newton St Cyres	d									19x17			20 09			21x12			23x08
Exeter St Davids 6	a						18 22			19 26			20 23			21 25			23 16
	d	17 15	17 40	17 45	18 10	18 18	18 24	18 48	19 10	19 27	19 49	20 15		20 49	21 00	21 49	22 30	22 57	23 22
Exeter Central	a	17 18	17 43	17 48	18 13	18 21	18 29	18 51	19 13	19 32	19 51	20 18		20 51	21 03	21 51	22 33	23 00	23 25
	d	17 18		17 48		18 21		18 51			19 51			20 51		21 51			23 26
St James' Park	d	17 20		17 50		18 23		18 53			19 53			20 53		21 53			23 28
Polsloe Bridge	d	17 23		17 53		18 26		18 56			19 56			20 56		21 56			23 31
Digby & Sowton	d	17 27		17 57		18 30		19 00			20 00			21 00		22 00			23 34
Topsham	d	17 32		18 02		18 35		19 04			20 04			21 04		22 04			23 38
Exton	d	17x34		18x04		18x37		19x07			20x07			21x07		22x07			23x40
Lympstone Commando	d	17x36		18x06		18x39		19x09			20x09			21x09		22x09			23x42
Lympstone Village	d	17 38		18 08		18 41		19 11			20 11			21 11		22 11			23 46
Exmouth	a	17 47		18 16		18 50		19 19			20 19			21 19		22 19			23 53

For general notes see front of timetable
For details of catering facilities see Directory of Train Operators

A From Paignton (Table 135)
b Arr. 1453
c Arr. 1905

Barnstaple → Exeter → Exmouth

Network Diagram - see first page of Table 135

		SW	GW	SW	GW	GW	GW	SW	GW	SW	GW	GW	GW	SW	GW	GW	SW	GW
		1 ◇		1 ◇				1		1 ◇				1 ◇			1 ◇	
						A	A					A			A			A
		☕		☕						☕				☕				
Barnstaple	d								07 01				08 35			09 33		
Chapelton	d								07x07									
Umberleigh	d								07x11				08x42			09 41		
Portsmouth Arms	d								07x18									
Kings Nympton	d								07x23				08 54					
Eggesford	d								07 34				09 03			10 01		
Lapford	d								07x39									
Morchard Road	d								07x43				09 12			10 09		
Copplestone	d								07x47				09x16			10x13		
Yeoford	d								07 51				09x20			10 18		
Okehampton	d																	
Sampford Courtenay	d																	
Crediton	d								07 59				09 28			10 26		
Newton St Cyres	d								08x03									
Exeter St Davids 6	a								08 12				09 40			10 37		
	d	05 10	05 35	06 41	06 45	07 14	07 45	08 00	08 15	08 25	08 45	09 18	09 45	10 10	10 18	10 45	11 08	11 18
Exeter Central	a	05 13	05 38	06 44	06 48	07 17	07 48	08 03	08 18	08 29	08 48	09 21	09 48	10 13	10 21	10 48	11 11	11 21
	d		05 38		06 48	07 17	07 49		08 18		08 48	09 21	09 48		10 21	10 48		11 21
St James' Park	d		05 40		06 50	07 19	07 50		08 20		08 50		09 50			10 50		
Polsloe Bridge	d		05 43		06 53	07 22	07 53		08 23		08 53		09 53			10 53		
Digby & Sowton	d		05 47		06 57	07 26	07 57		08 27		08 57	09 27	09 57		10 27	10 57		11 27
Topsham	d		05 51		07 01	07 31	08 02		08 32		09 02	09 32	10 02		10 32	11 02		11 32
Exton	d		05x53		07x03	07x33	08x05		08x35		09x05		10x05			11x05		
Lympstone Commando	d		05x55		07x05	07x35	08x07		08x37		09x07		10x07			11x07		
Lympstone Village	d		05 57		07 07	07 37	08 09		08 39		09 09	09 37	10 09		10 37	11 09		11 37
Exmouth	a		06 03		07 15	07 45	08 15		08 45		09 15	09 45	10 15		10 45	11 15		11 45

		GW	SW	GW	GW	GW	SW	GW	SW	GW	GW	GW	SW	GW	SW	GW	SW	GW
			1 ◇				1 ◇		1 ◇				1		1 ◇		1	
				A		A				A		A						
			☕				☕		☕						☕			
Barnstaple	d	10 31						12 40						14 39				15 39
Chapelton	d																	
Umberleigh	d	10x39						12x47						14x46				15x46
Portsmouth Arms	d																	
Kings Nympton	d																	
Eggesford	d	10 57						13 05						15 04				16 04
Lapford	d																	
Morchard Road	d													15x13				
Copplestone	d	11x07						13x15						15x16				16x14
Yeoford	d	11 12						13x20						15x21				16 19
Okehampton	d																	
Sampford Courtenay	d																	
Crediton	d	11 20						13 30						15 29				16 33
Newton St Cyres	d																	
Exeter St Davids 6	a	11 30						13 40						15 40				16 43
	d	11 45	12 10	12 18	12 45	13 18	13 35	13 45	14 10	14 18	14 45	15 18	15 30	15 41	16 10	16 18	16 40	16 45
Exeter Central	a	11 48	12 13	12 21	12 48	13 21	13 38	13 48	14 13	14 21	14 48	15 21	15 33	15 44	16 13	16 21	16 43	16 48
	d	11 48		12 21	12 48	13 21		13 48		14 21	14 48	15 21		15 48		16 21		16 48
St James' Park	d	11 50			12 50			13 50			14 50			15 50				16 50
Polsloe Bridge	d	11 53			12 53			13 53			14 53			15 53				16 53
Digby & Sowton	d	11 57		12 27	12 57	13 27		13 57		14 27	14 57	15 27		15 57		16 27		16 57
Topsham	d	12 03		12 32	13 02	13 32		14 02		14 32	15 02	15 32		16 02		16 32		17 02
Exton	d	12x06			13x05			14x05			15x05			16x05				17x04
Lympstone Commando	d	12x08			13x07			14x07			15x07			16x07				17x06
Lympstone Village	d	12 10		12 37	13 09	13 37		14 09		14 37	15 09	15 37		16 09		16 37		17 08
Exmouth	a	12 15		12 45	13 15	13 45		14 15		14 45	15 15	15 45		16 15		16 45		17 15

		GW	SW	GW	SW	GW	GW	GW	SW	GW	SW	GW	GW	SW	GW	SW	GW
			1		1 ◇				1 ◇		1			1		1	
		A				A	A	B		A							
					☕												
Barnstaple	d			16 38				18 00					19 24		20 50		22 00
Chapelton	d			16 43				18x05									22x05
Umberleigh	d			16x47				18x09					19x31		20x57		22x09
Portsmouth Arms	d			16 54				18x16									22x16
Kings Nympton	d			16x59				18x21									22x21
Eggesford	d			17 08				18 33					19 52		21 18		22 30
Lapford	d			17 13				18x38									22x35
Morchard Road	d			17 18				18x42									22x40
Copplestone	d			17x21				18x46					20x01		21x28		22x43
Yeoford	d			17x26				18 50					20x06		21x32		22 48
Okehampton	d																
Sampford Courtenay	d																
Crediton	d			17 35				18 59					20 15		21 41		22 57
Newton St Cyres	d			17 38				19x02					20x18		21x44		23x00
Exeter St Davids 6	a			17 45				19 10					20 27		21 53		23 08
	d	17 15	17 40	17 47	18 10	18 18	18 48		19 10	19 49	20 15	20 21	20 49	21 00	21 55	22 57	23 10
Exeter Central	a	17 18	17 43	17 51	18 13	18 21	18 51		19 13	19 51	20 18	20 24	20 51	21 03	21 58	23 00	23 13
	d	17 18		17 52		18 21	18 51			19 51			20 51		21 58		23 14
St James' Park	d	17 20		17 54		18 23	18 53			19 53			20 53		22 00		23 16
Polsloe Bridge	d	17 23		17 57		18 26	18 56			19 56			20 56		22 03		23 19
Digby & Sowton	d	17 27		18 00		18 30	19 00			20 00			21 00		22 07		23 22
Topsham	d	17 32		18 04		18 35	19 04			20 05			21 04		22 11		23 26
Exton	d	17x34		18x03		18x37	19x07			20x07			21x07		22x13		23x28
Lympstone Commando	d	17x36		18x09		18x39	19x09			20x09			21x09		22x15		23x30
Lympstone Village	d	17 38		18 12		18 41	19 11			20 11			21 11		22 17		23 33
Exmouth	a	17 45		18 16		18 48	19 18			20 19			21 17		22 25		23 40

For general notes see front of timetable
For details of catering facilities see
Directory of Train Operators

A From Paignton (Table 135)
B To Paignton (Table 135)

Table 136

Sundays

Barnstaple → Exeter → Exmouth

Network Diagram - see first page of Table 135

Station		GW A	SW 1 ◇	GW A			GW	GW C	SW 1 ◇	GW D			GW	GW C	SW 1 ◇		GW		GW G	GW A		GW C	SW 1 ◇	GW D		GW
Barnstaple	d												11 10						13 19	13 19						15 13
Chapelton	d												11x15													15x18
Umberleigh	d												11x19						13x26	13x26						15x22
Portsmouth Arms	d												11x26													15x29
Kings Nympton	d												11x31													15x34
Eggesford	d												11 41						13 45	13 45						15 43
Lapford	d												11x46													15x48
Morchard Road	d												11x51						13x53	13x53						15x53
Copplestone	d												11x54						13x56	13x56						15x56
Yeoford	d												12 00						14 02	14 01						16 02
Okehampton	d							10 02						12 02								14 02				
Sampford Courtenay	d							10 09						12 09								14 09				
Crediton	d							10 29					12 10	12 29					14 11	14 12		14 29				16 12
Newton St Cyres	d												12x13													16x16
Exeter St Davids 6	a							10 39					12 24	12 46					14 24	14 26		14 39				16 26
	d	08 25	09 20	09 26			10 32	10 43	11 20	11 25			12 25	12 48	13 18		13 25		14 25	14 26		14 43	15 20	15 25		16 28
Exeter Central	a	08 28	09 23	09 29			10 35	10 47	11 23	11 28			12 28	12 51	13 21		13 28		14 28	14 29		14 47	15 23	15 28		16 31
	d	08 28		09 29			10 36	10 47		11 29			12 29	12 51			13 29		14 29	14 30		14 47		15 29		16 32
St James' Park	d	08 30		09 34			10 38	10a49		11 31			12 31	12a53			13 31		14 31	14 32		14a49		15 31		16 34
Polsloe Bridge	d	08 33		09 37			10 41			11 35			12 34				13 34		14 34	14 35				15 35		16 37
Digby & Sowton	d	08 37		09 40			10 44			11 39			12 38				13 37		14 38	14 38				15 39		16 40
Topsham	d	08 42		09 45			10 49			11 43			12 42				13 42		14 42	14 43				15 43		16 45
Exton	d	08x44		09x48			10x52			11x45			12x44				13x44		14x44	14x45				15x45		16x47
Lympstone Commando	d	08x46		09x49			10x54			11x47			12x46				13x46		14x46	14x47				15x47		16x49
Lympstone Village	d	08 48		09 52			10 56			11 51			12 50				13 49		14 50	14 50				15 51		16 52
Exmouth	a	08 53		09 57			11 00			11 55			12 54				13 54		14 54	14 54				15 55		16 56

Station		SW 1 ◇		GW H	GW A	SW 1 ◇	GW			GW	GW A	GW H		SW 1 ◇	GW G	GW A	GW		SW 1	GW G	GW A	GW	SW 1	GW		
Barnstaple	d									17 17							19 15					21 28				
Chapelton	d									17x22							19x21									
Umberleigh	d									17x26							19x25					21x35				
Portsmouth Arms	d									17x33							19x32									
Kings Nympton	d									17x38							19x37									
Eggesford	d									17 48							19 46					21 54				
Lapford	d									17x53							19x52									
Morchard Road	d									17x58							19x57									
Copplestone	d									18x01							20x00					22x04				
Yeoford	d									18 07							20 05					22 09				
Okehampton	d			16 01	16 02						18 02	18 16														
Sampford Courtenay	d			16 08	16 09						18 11	18 23														
Crediton	d			16 28	16 29					18 18	18 31	18 43					20 15					22 17				
Newton St Cyres	d									18x22							20x18									
Exeter St Davids 6	a			16 37	16 40					18 33	18 47	18 53					20 30					22 28				
	d	16 33		16 43	16 43	17 18	17 25			18 35	18 58	18 58		19 20	19 35	19 42	20 35		21 20	21 35	21 42	22 28	23 10	23 16		
Exeter Central	a	16 36		16 47	16 47	17 21	17 28			18 38	19 01	19 01		19 23	19 38	19 45	20 38		21 23	21 38	21 45	22 32	23 13	23 19		
	d			16 47	16 47		17 29			18 39	19 01	19 01			19 39	19 46	20 39			21 39	21 46	22 32		23 20		
St James' Park	d			16 49	16a49		17 31			18 41	19a03	19 03			19 41	19 48	20 41			21 41	21 48	22 34		23 22		
Polsloe Bridge	d						17 35			18 44					19 44	19 51	20 46			21 44	21 51	22 37		23 29		
Digby & Sowton	d						17 39			18 47					19 47	19 54	20 50			21 47	21 54	22 41		23 33		
Topsham	d						17 43			18 52					19 52	19 59	20 54			21 52	21 59	22 45		23 37		
Exton	d						17x45			18x54					19x54	20x02	20x56			21x54	22x01	22x47		23x39		
Lympstone Commando	d						17x47			18x56					19x57	20x04	20x58			21x56	22x03	22x49		23x41		
Lympstone Village	d						17 51			18 59					19 59	20 06	21 02			21 59	22 06	22 53		23 44		
Exmouth	a						17 55			19 03					20 03	20 10	21 06			22 03	22 10	22 58		23 48		

For general notes see front of timetable
For details of catering facilities see
Directory of Train Operators

A Until 7 September
B Until 21 September. To Okehampton
C Until 21 September
D From Paignton (Table 135)
G From 14 September
H 14 and 21 September

Table 139

Plymouth → Gunnislake

Mondays to Fridays

Network Diagram - see first page of Table 135

Miles			GW	GW	GW 1	GW	GW	GW	GW	GW	GW	GW	GW	GW	GW	GW
0	**Plymouth**	d	05 12	06 42	07 05	08 23	09 34	10 35	11 30	13 33	15 55	16 34	17 06	18 12	18 16	21 24
1½	Devonport	d		06 45	07a09	08a26	09 37		11 33	13 36	15 58	16 38	17 09	18 15	18 19	21 27
1¾	Dockyard	d		06x47			09x39		11x35	13x38	16x00	16x39	17x11	18x17	18x21	21x29
2¼	Keyham	d		06x49			09x41		11x37	13x40	16x02	16x41	17x13	18x19	18x23	21x31
—	St Budeaux Ferry Road	a						10 40			16 04		17 15	18 21		
3¼	St Budeaux Victoria Road	d	05 18	06 52			09 44		11 40	13 43		16 44			18 26	21 34
7½	Bere Ferrers	d		07x00			09x52		11x47	13x51		16x51			18x34	21x42
10¼	Bere Alston	a	05 30	07 06			09 58		11 53	13 57		16 57			18 40	21 48
—		d	05 33	07 08			10 00		11 55	13 59		17 00			18 42	21 50
12	Calstock	d	05 39	07x15			10x07		12x03	14x06		17x06			18x49	21x57
15	**Gunnislake**	a	05 52	07 27			10 20		12 15	14 18		17 19			19 02	22 09

Saturdays

		GW	GW	GW ⚲	GW A	GW B	GW	GW A	GW B	GW ⚲	GW	GW
Plymouth	d	06 45	09 34	10 00	11⌇30	11⌇35	13 35	16⌇44	16⌇50	17 59	18 16	21 24
Devonport	d	06 48	09 37	10a03	11⌇33	11⌇38	13 38	16⌇47	16⌇53	18 02	18 19	21 27
Dockyard	d	06x49	09x39		11x35	11x40	13x39	16x48	16x54	18 04	18x21	21x29
Keyham	d	06x51	09x41		11x37	11x42	13x41	16x50	16x56	18 06	18x23	21x31
St Budeaux Ferry Road	a				⌇	⌇		⌇	⌇	18 07		
St Budeaux Victoria Road	d	06 55	09 44		11⌇40	11⌇46	13 45	16⌇54	17⌇00		18 26	21 34
Bere Ferrers	d	07x02	09x52		11x47	11x53	13x52	17x01	17x07		18x34	21x42
Bere Alston	a	07 09	09 58		11⌇53	11⌇59	13 59	17⌇08	17⌇14		18 40	21 48
	d	07 10	10 00		11⌇55	12⌇01	14 00	17⌇09	17⌇15		18 42	21 50
Calstock	d	07x18	10x07		12x03	12x09	14x08	17x17	17x23		18x49	21x57
Gunnislake	a	07 30	10 20		12⌇15	12⌇21	14 20	17⌇29	17⌇35		19 02	22 09

Sundays

		GW C	GW D	GW E	GW ◇	GW C	GW G	GW E	GW D	GW E	GW D	GW E	GW D	GW
Plymouth	d	09⌇10	09⌇17	09⌇35	10 30	11⌇15	11⌇20	11⌇40	13⌇18	13⌇45	15⌇17	15⌇46	17⌇41	17⌇45
Devonport	d	⌇	09⌇20	09⌇38	10a33	11⌇18	11⌇23	11⌇43	13⌇21	13⌇48	15⌇20	15⌇49	17⌇44	17⌇48
Dockyard	d	⌇	09x22	09⌇40		11x20	11x25	11⌇45	13x23	13⌇50	15x22	15⌇51	17x46	17⌇50
Keyham	d	⌇	09x24	09⌇42		11x22	11x27	11⌇47	13x25	13⌇52	15x24	15⌇53	17x48	17⌇52
St Budeaux Ferry Road	a	09⌇15	⌇	⌇		⌇	⌇	⌇	⌇	⌇	⌇	⌇	⌇	⌇
St Budeaux Victoria Road	d		09⌇27	09⌇45		11⌇25	11⌇30	11⌇50	13⌇28	13⌇55	15⌇27	15⌇56	17⌇51	17⌇55
Bere Ferrers	d		09x35	09⌇53		11x33	11x38	11⌇58	13x36	14⌇03	15x35	16⌇04	17x59	18⌇03
Bere Alston	a		09⌇41	09⌇59		11⌇39	11⌇44	12⌇04	13⌇42	14⌇09	15⌇41	16⌇10	18⌇05	18⌇09
	d		09⌇44	10⌇02		11⌇42	11⌇47	12⌇07	13⌇45	14⌇12	15⌇44	16⌇13	18⌇08	18⌇12
Calstock	d		09x51	10⌇09		11x49	11x54	12⌇14	13x52	14⌇19	15x51	16⌇20	18x15	18⌇19
Gunnislake	a		10⌇03	10⌇21		12⌇01	12⌇06	12⌇26	14⌇04	14⌇31	16⌇03	16⌇32	18⌇27	18⌇31

For general notes see front of timetable
For details of catering facilities see Directory of Train Operators

A From 13 September
B Until 6 September
C Until 7 September
D Until 21 September
E From 28 September.
G 14 and 21 September

Table 139

Mondays to Fridays

Gunnislake → Plymouth

Network Diagram - see first page of Table 135

Miles			GW	GW	GW	GW	GW	GW	GW	GW	GW	GW	GW
									A				
0	**Gunnislake**	d	05 56		07 34	10 23	12 19	14 24		17 24	19 07		22 15
3	Calstock	d	06 07		07x46	10x35	12x31	14x36		17x36	19x19		22x27
4¾	Bere Alston	a	06 14		07 52	10 41	12 37	14 42		17 43	19 25		22 33
—		d	06 17		07 55	10 44	12 40	14 45		17 45	19 28		22 36
7½	Bere Ferrers	d	06x22		08x00	10x49	12x45	14x50		17x50	19x33		22x41
11¾	St Budeaux Victoria Road	d	06 30		08 09	10 58	12 54	14 59		17 59	19 42		22 50
—	St Budeaux Ferry Road	d		07 57					16 43			20 58	
12¾	Keyham	d	06x32	07x59	08x11	11x00	12x56	15x01	16x45	18x01	19x44	21x00	22x52
13¼	Dockyard	d	06x34	08x01	08x13	11x02	12x58	15x03	16x47	18x03	19x46	21x02	22x54
13¾	Devonport	d	06 36	08 03	08 15	11 04	13 00	15 05	16 50	18 05	19 48	21 04	22 56
15	**Plymouth**	a	06 39	08 09	08 19	11 08	13 04	15 09	16 54	18 09	19 52	21 09	23 00

Saturdays

		GW	GW	GW	GW	GW	GW	GW	GW
		1 ◇	1 ◇						◇
		B	C				B	C	
Gunnislake	d			07 42	10 24	14 24	17§33	17§38	
Calstock	d			07x54	10x36	14x36	17x45	17x50	
Bere Alston	a			08 00	10 42	14 42	17§51	17§56	
	d			08 02	10 45	14 44	17§53	17§58	
Bere Ferrers	d			08x07	10x50	14x49	17x58	18x03	
St Budeaux Victoria Road	d			08 16	10 59	14 58	18§07	18§12	
St Budeaux Ferry Road	d	07§57	07§58						21 03
Keyham	d	07§59	08§03	08x19	11x00	15x01	18x10	18x15	21x05
Dockyard	d	08§01	08§05	08x21	11x02	15x03	18x12	18x17	21x07
Devonport	d	08§03	08§07	08 23	11 04	15 05	18§14	18§19	21 09
Plymouth	a	08§09	08§10	08 27	11 09	15 09	18§18	18§23	21 12

Sundays

		GW	GW	GW	GW	GW	GW	GW	GW	GW	GW	GW	GW
											◇	◇	◇
			D	E	G	D	H	D	H	D	E	E	G
Gunnislake	d	10 18	10§25	12§07	12§10	12§45	14§07	14§45	16§07	16§55			
Calstock	d	10x30	10x37	12x19	12§22	12x57	14x19	14x57	16x19	17§07			
Bere Alston	a	10 36	10§43	12§25	12§28	13§03	14§25	15§03	16§25	17§13			
	d	10 38	10§45	12§27	12§30	13§05	14§27	15§05	16§27	17§15			
Bere Ferrers	d	10x44	10x51	12x33	12§36	13x11	14x33	15x11	16x33	17§21			
St Budeaux Victoria Road	d	10 52	10§59	12§41	12§44	13§19	14§41	15§19	16§42	17§29			
St Budeaux Ferry Road	d												
Keyham	d	10x56	11x02	12x44	12§47	13x22	14x44	15x22	16x44	17§32			
Dockyard	d	10x58	11x04	12x46	12§49	13x24	14x46	15x24	16x46	17§34			
Devonport	d	11 00	11§06	12§48	12§51	13§26	14§48	15§26	16§48	17§36	19§43	20§58	21§01
Plymouth	a	11 04	11§10	12§52	12§55	13§30	14§53	15§30	16§53	17§40	19§46	21§01	21§04

For general notes see front of timetable
For details of catering facilities see Directory of Train Operators

A Until 27 June and from 8 September
B From 13 September
C Until 6 September
D From 28 September
E Until 7 September
G From 14 September
H Until 21 September

Liskeard — Looe

Network Diagram - see first page of Table 135

Mondays to Fridays

Miles			GW	GW	GW A	GW	GW A	GW B	GW A	GW A	GW B	GW A	GW B	GW A	GW	GW	GW
0	**Liskeard** 3	d	06 10	07 15	08∫48	09 54	11∫09	11∫50	12∫08	13∫17	13∫45	14∫33	15∫15	15∫36	16 36	18 02	19 11
2	Coombe	a			⌇		⌇	⌇	⌇	13∫23	13∫51	⌇	⌇	⌇		18 08	
—		d			⌇		⌇	⌇	⌇	13∫26	13∫54	⌇	⌇	⌇		18 11	
3¾	St Keyne	d	06x23	07x28	09x01	10x07	⌇	12x03	12x21	13x33	14x01	⌇	15x28	15x49	16x49	18x18	19x24
5	Causeland	d	06x26	07x31	09x05	10x10	⌇	12x06	12x24	13x37	14x05	⌇	15x31	15x52	16x52	18x22	19x27
6½	Sandplace	d	06x30	07x35	09x08	10x14	⌇	12x10	12x28	13x40	14x08	⌇	15x35	15x56	16x56	18x25	19x31
8¾	**Looe**	a	06 39	07 44	09∫17	10 23	11∫37	12∫19	12∫37	13∫47	14∫15	15∫01	15∫44	16∫05	17 05	18 32	19 40

Saturdays

		GW	GW	GW C	GW	GW C	GW	GW	GW	GW	GW	GW	GW C
Liskeard 3	d	06 12	07 15	08∫41	09 56	11∫04	12 10	13 45	15 15	16 31	17 57	19 11	20∫40
Coombe	a			⌇		⌇		13 51			18 03		⌇
	d			⌇		⌇		13 54			18 06		⌇
St Keyne	d	06x25	07x28	08x54		11x17	12x23	14x01	15x28	16x44	18x13	19x24	20x53
Causeland	d	06x28	07x31	08x57		11x20	12x26	14x05	15x31	16x47	18x17	19x27	20x56
Sandplace	d	06x32	07x35	09x01		11x24	12x30	14x08	15x35	16x51	18x20	19x31	21x00
Looe	a	06 41	07 44	09∫10	10 24	11∫33	12 39	14 15	15 44	17 00	18 27	19 40	21∫09

Mondays to Fridays

Miles			GW	GW	GW A	GW	GW A	GW B	GW A	GW A	GW B	GW A	GW B	GW A	GW	GW	GW
0	**Looe**	d	06 41	07 45	09∫18	10 24	11∫38	12∫33	12∫38	13∫50	14∫40	15∫02	15∫46	16∫06	17 06	18 35	19 43
2¼	Sandplace	d	06x46	07x50	09x23	10x29	⌇	12x38	12x43	13x55	14x45	15x07	15x51	16x11	17x11	18x40	19x48
3¾	Causeland	d	06x50	07x54	09x27	10x33	⌇	12x42	12x47	13x59	14x49	15x11	15x55	16x15	17x15	18x44	19x52
5	St Keyne	d	06x54	07x58	09x31	10x37	⌇	12x46	12x51	14x03	14x53	15x15	15x59	16x19	17x19	18x48	19x56
6¾	Coombe	a			⌇		⌇	12∫54	12∫59	14∫11	15∫01	⌇	⌇	⌇			
—		d			⌇		⌇	12∫57	13∫02	14∫14	15∫04	⌇	⌇	⌇			
8¾	**Liskeard** 3	a	07 07	08 11	09∫44	10 50	12∫03	13∫03	13∫08	14∫20	15∫10	15∫28	16∫12	16∫32	17 32	19 01	20 09

Saturdays

		GW	GW	GW C	GW	GW C	GW	GW	GW	GW	GW	GW	GW C
Looe	d	06 45	07 46	09∫12	10 25	11∫34	12 40	14 30	15 49	17 10	18 30	19 43	21∫10
Sandplace	d		07x51	09x17		11x39	12x45	14x35	15x54	17x15	18x35	19x48	21x15
Causeland	d		07x55	09x21		11x43	12x49	14x39	15x58	17x19	18x39	19x52	21x19
St Keyne	d		07x59	09x25		11x47	12x53	14x43	16x02	17x23	18x43	19x56	21x23
Coombe	a		08 07	⌇		⌇		14 51					⌇
	d		08 10	⌇		⌇		14 54					⌇
Liskeard 3	a	07 10	08 16	09∫38	10 50	12∫00	13 07	15 00	16 16	17 37	18 57	20 10	21∫36

For general notes see front of timetable
For details of catering facilities see Directory of Train Operators

A Until 5 September
B From 8 September
C Until 6 September

No Sunday Service

Par — Newquay

Mondays to Fridays

Network Diagram - see first page of Table 135

Miles			GW	GW	GW 1 ◇ A B ☕	GW C	GW A	GW A	GW C	GW A
0	Par 3	d	09 18	11 33	13ʃ13	14ʃ02	15ʃ57	18ʃ28	19ʃ33	20ʃ40
4¼	Luxulyan	d	09x30	11x44	⌇	14x13	16ʃ08	⌇	19x44	20x51
6¼	Bugle	d	09x36	11x50	⌇	14x19	16ʃ14	⌇	19x50	20x57
8¾	Roche	d	09x40	11x55	⌇	14x24	16ʃ19	⌇	19x55	21x02
14¼	St Columb Road	d	09x52	12x06	⌇	14x35	16ʃ30	⌇	20x06	21x13
18¼	Quintrell Downs	d	10x00	12x14	⌇	14x43	16ʃ38	⌇	20x14	21x21
20¾	Newquay	a	10 10	12 23	14ʃ20	14ʃ52	16ʃ49	19ʃ16	20ʃ23	21ʃ31

Saturdays

		GW D	GW 1 ◇ E ☕	GW D	GW 1 E ☕	GW D	GW 1 B E ☕	GW D
Par 3	d	09ʃ19	09ʃ47	11ʃ28	11ʃ53	14ʃ03	15ʃ40	18ʃ45
Luxulyan	d	09x31	⌇	11x39	⌇	14x14	⌇	18x56
Bugle	d	09x37	⌇	11x45	⌇	14x20	⌇	19x02
Roche	d	09x41	⌇	11x50	⌇	14x25	⌇	19x07
St Columb Road	d	09x53	⌇	12x01	⌇	14x36	⌇	19x18
Quintrell Downs	d	10x01	⌇	12x09	⌇	14x44	⌇	19x26
Newquay	a	10ʃ11	11ʃ10	12ʃ20	13ʃ00	14ʃ55	16ʃ50	19ʃ37

Mondays to Fridays

Miles			GW C	GW A	GW	GW C	GW 1 ◇ A B ☕	GW A	GW A	GW C	GW A
0	Newquay	d	10ʃ16	10ʃ41	12 59	14ʃ54	15ʃ04	17ʃ35	19ʃ20	20ʃ25	21ʃ55
2½	Quintrell Downs	d	10ʃ22	10ʃ47	13 05	15ʃ00	⌇	17ʃ41	19ʃ26	20ʃ31	22ʃ01
6½	St Columb Road	d	⌇	10x55	13 13	15x08	⌇	17ʃ49	⌇	20x39	22x09
12	Roche	d	⌇	11x06	13 24	15x19	⌇	18ʃ00	⌇	20x50	22x20
14½	Bugle	d	⌇	11x11	13 29	15x24	⌇	18ʃ05	⌇	20x55	22x25
16½	Luxulyan	d	⌇	11x16	13 38	15x29	⌇	18ʃ10	⌇	21x00	22x30
20¾	Par 3	a	11ʃ01	11ʃ28	13 51	15ʃ41	16ʃ00	18ʃ23	20ʃ05	21ʃ13	22ʃ41

Saturdays

		GW D	GW 1 B E ☕	GW D	GW 1 E ☕	GW D	GW 1 E ☕	GW D
Newquay	d	10ʃ13	11ʃ35	12ʃ42	13ʃ22	15ʃ10	17ʃ15	19ʃ57
Quintrell Downs	d	10ʃ19	⌇	12x48	⌇	15x16	⌇	20x03
St Columb Road	d	10x27	⌇	12x56	⌇	15x24	⌇	20x11
Roche	d	10x38	⌇	13x07	⌇	15x35	⌇	20x22
Bugle	d	10x43	⌇	13x12	⌇	15x40	⌇	20x27
Luxulyan	d	10x48	⌇	13x17	⌇	15x45	⌇	20x32
Par 3	a	11ʃ01	12ʃ47	13ʃ30	14ʃ19	15ʃ58	18ʃ12	20ʃ44

For general notes see front of timetable
For details of catering facilities see Directory of Train Operators

A 30 June to 5 September
B Atlantic Coast Express
C Until 27 June and from 8 September
D From 13 September
E Until 6 September

No Sunday Service

Truro — Falmouth

Mondays to Fridays

Network Diagram - see first page of Table 135

Miles			GW	GW	GW	GW	GW	GW	GW	GW	GW	GW	GW	GW
0	**Truro**	d	06 27	07 28	08 32	09 43	10 47	12 37	14 29	16 25	17 26	18 22	20 00	21 04
4¼	Perranwell	d	06 34	07 35	08 39	09 50	10 54	12 44	14 36	16 32	17 33	18 29	20 07	21 11
8¼	Penryn	d	06 41	07 42	08 46	09 57	11 01	12 51	14 43	16 38	17 40	18 36	20 14	21 18
10¼	Penmere	d	06 45	07 46	08 50	10 01	11 05	12 55	14 47	16 43	17 44	18 40	20 18	21 22
11¾	Falmouth Town	d	06 47	07 48	08 52	10 03	11 07	12 57	14 49	16 44	17 47	18 42	20 20	21 24
12¼	**Falmouth Docks**	a	06 50	07 51	08 55	10 06	11 10	13 00	14 52	16 48	17 49	18 45	20 23	21 27

Saturdays

		GW	GW	GW	GW	GW	GW	GW	GW	GW	GW	GW	GW
Truro	d	06 25	07 30	08 30	09 43	11 25	12 47	14 37	15 58	16 51	18 02	19 56	21 09
Perranwell	d	06 32	07 37	08 37	09 50	11 32	12 54	14 44	16 05	16 58	18 09	20 03	21 16
Penryn	d	06 39	07 44	08 44	09 57	11 39	13 01	14 51	16 12	17 05	18 16	20 10	21 23
Penmere	d	06 43	07 48	08 48	10 01	11 43	13 05	14 55	16 16	17 09	18 20	20 14	21 27
Falmouth Town	d	06 45	07 50	08 50	10 03	11 45	13 07	14 57	16 18	17 11	18 22	20 16	21 29
Falmouth Docks	a	06 48	07 53	08 53	10 06	11 48	13 10	15 00	16 21	17 14	18 25	20 19	21 32

Sundays

		GW	GW	GW	GW	GW	GW A	GW B	GW	GW	GW	GW
Truro	d	11 11	12 27	13 36	14 30	15 35	17 00	17 04	18 50	20 00	21 00	22 00
Perranwell	d	11 18	12 34	13 43	14 37	15 42	17 07	17 11	18 57	20 07	21 07	22 07
Penryn	d	11 25	12 41	13 50	14 44	15 49	17 14	17 18	19 04	20 14	21 14	22 14
Penmere	d	11 29	12 45	13 54	14 48	15 52	17 18	17 22	19 08	20 18	21 18	22 18
Falmouth Town	d	11 31	12 47	13 56	14 50	15 55	17 20	17 24	19 10	20 20	21 20	22 20
Falmouth Docks	a	11 34	12 50	13 59	14 53	15 58	17 23	17 27	19 13	20 23	21 23	22 23

Mondays to Fridays

Miles			GW	GW	GW	GW	GW	GW	GW	GW	GW	GW	GW	GW
0	**Falmouth Docks**	d	06 55	07 55	08 58	10 11	11 50	13 05	14 59	16 51	17 52	19 12	20 27	21 30
½	Falmouth Town	d	06 57	07 57	09 00	10 13	11 52	13 07	15 01	16 53	17 54	19 14	20 29	21 32
2	Penmere	d	07 00	08 00	09 03	10 16	11 55	13 10	15 04	16 56	17 57	19 17	20 32	21 35
4	Penryn	d	07 05	08 05	09 08	10 21	12 00	13 15	15 09	17 01	18 02	19 22	20 37	21 40
8	Perranwell	d	07 12	08 12	09 15	10 28	12 07	13 22	15 16	17 08	18 09	19 29	20 44	21 47
12¼	**Truro**	a	07 19	08 19	09 22	10 35	12 14	13 29	15 23	17 15	18 16	19 36	20 51	21 54

Saturdays

		GW	GW	GW	GW	GW	GW	GW	GW	GW	GW	GW
Falmouth Docks	d	06 53	07 56	08 56	10 09	11 51	13 13	15 03	16 24	17 25	18 28	20 26
Falmouth Town	d	06 55	07 58	08 58	10 11	11 53	13 15	15 05	16 26	17 27	18 30	20 28
Penmere	d	06 58	08 01	09 01	10 14	11 56	13 18	15 08	16 29	17 30	18 33	20 31
Penryn	d	07 03	08 06	09 06	10 19	12 01	13 23	15 13	16 34	17 35	18 38	20 36
Perranwell	d	07 10	08 13	09 13	10 26	12 08	13 30	15 20	16 41	17 42	18 45	20 43
Truro	a	07 17	08 20	09 20	10 33	12 15	13 37	15 27	16 48	17 49	18 52	20 50

Sundays

		GW	GW	GW	GW	GW	GW A	GW B	GW	GW	GW	GW
Falmouth Docks	d	11 37	12 58	14 02	14 56	16 04	17 26	17 32	19 25	20 31	21 28	22 26
Falmouth Town	d	11 39	13 00	14 04	14 58	16 06	17 28	17 34	19 27	20 33	21 30	22 28
Penmere	d	11 42	13 03	14 07	15 01	16 09	17 31	17 37	19 30	20 36	21 33	22 31
Penryn	d	11 47	13 08	14 12	15 06	16 13	17 36	17 42	19 35	20 41	21 38	22 36
Perranwell	d	11 54	13 15	14 19	15 13	16 20	17 43	17 49	19 42	20 48	21 45	22 43
Truro	a	12 01	13 22	14 26	15 20	16 27	17 50	17 56	19 49	20 55	21 52	22 50

For general notes see front of timetable
For details of catering facilities see
Directory of Train Operators

A Until 7 September
B From 14 September

Table 144

Mondays to Fridays

St. Erth → St. Ives

Network Diagram - see first page of Table 135

Miles			GW	GW	GW	GW	GW	GW	GW	GW	GW	GW	GW	GW	GW
—	Penzance	d	06 34	06 40	07 43	08 57	09 30	09 59	.....	.....	.....	11 42	.....	12 55	.....
0	St Erth 2	d	06 42	07 24	08 05	09 05	09 41	10 11	10 41	11 11	11 41	12 11	12 41	13 11	13 41
¾	Lelant Saltings	d	.....	.....	.....	09 08	09 44	10 14	10 44	11 14	11 44	12 14	12 44	13 14	13 44
1	Lelant	d	06x45	07x27	08x08	09x10	.	.	.	.	.	.	.	.	.
3	Carbis Bay	d	06 50	07 32	08 13	09 15	09 50	.....	10 50	.....	11 50	.....	12 50	.....	13 50
4¼	St Ives	a	06 55	07 36	08 18	09 19	09 55	10 24	10 55	11 24	11 53	12 22	12 53	13 24	13 53

Miles			GW	GW	GW	GW	GW	GW	GW	GW	GW	GW	GW	GW
—	Penzance	d	14 00	.....	14 50	.....	16 00	.....	16 55	17 36	.....	.....	20 11	20 55
0	St Erth 2	d	14 11	14 41	15 11	15 41	16 11	16 41	17 12	17 59	18 36	19 40	20 30	21 34
¾	Lelant Saltings	d	14 14	14 44	15 14	15 44	16 14	16 44	17 15	18 02	18 39	19 43	20 33	21 37
1	Lelant	d	.	.	.	.	.	16x46	.	18x04	18x41	19x45	20x35	21x39
3	Carbis Bay	d	.....	14 50	.....	15 50	.....	16 51	17 21	18 09	18 46	19 50	20 40	21 44
4¼	St Ives	a	14 24	14 53	15 24	15 53	16 24	16 54	17 26	18 12	18 49	19 53	20 43	21 47

Saturdays

		GW	GW	GW	GW	GW	GW	GW	GW		GW	GW	GW	GW
Penzance	d	06 55	.....	.....	08 58	.....	.....	.....	.....	.....	.....	.....	.....	.....
St Erth 2	d	07 03	07 32	08 00	09 06	10 11	10 41	11 11	11 41	.	12 11	12 41	13 11	13 41
Lelant Saltings	d	.....	.....	.....	09 09	10 14	10 44	11 14	11 44	.....	12 14	12 44	13 14	13 44
Lelant	d	07x06	07x35	08x03	09x11	.	.	.	.	.	.	.	.	.
Carbis Bay	d	07 11	07 40	08 08	09 16	.....	10 50	.....	11 50	.....	.....	12 50	.....	13 50
St Ives	a	07 16	07 45	08 13	09 20	10 24	10 55	11 24	11 55	.	12 24	12 55	13 22	13 53

		GW	GW	GW	GW	GW	GW	GW	GW	GW	GW	GW	GW
Penzance	d	14 00	.....	.....	.....	15 54	.....	.....	17 35	18 50	19 08	.....	20 45
St Erth 2	d	14 11	14 41	15 11	15 41	16 11	16 41	17 12	17 59	18 58	19 37	20 25	21 32
Lelant Saltings	d	14 14	14 44	15 14	15 44	16 14	16 44	17 15	18 02	19 01	19 40	20 28	21 35
Lelant	d	.	.	.	.	.	16x46	.	18x04	19x03	19x42	20x30	21x37
Carbis Bay	d	.....	14 50	.....	15 50	.....	16 51	17 21	18 09	19 08	19 47	20 35	21 42
St Ives	a	14 22	14 53	15 22	15 53	16 22	16 54	17 24	18 12	19 11	19 50	20 38	21 45

Sundays

Until 7 September

		GW	GW	GW	GW	GW	GW	GW	GW	GW	GW
Penzance	d	08 30	09 30	09 50	.....	10 50	11 42	.....	12 25	12 47	.....
St Erth 2	d	09 02	09 55	10 25	10 55	11 25	11 55	12 25	12 55	13 25	13 55
Lelant Saltings	d	09x05	09 58	10 28	10 58	11 28	11 58	12 28	12 58	13 28	13 58
Lelant	d	09 07	.	.	.	.	.	.	.	.	.
Carbis Bay	d	09 12	10a12	10 34	11a12	11 34	12a12	12 34	13a12	13 34	14a12
St Ives	a	09 16	10 06	10 37	11 06	11 37	12 06	12 37	13 06	13 37	14 06

		GW	GW	GW	GW	GW	GW	GW	GW	GW
Penzance	d	13 50	14 44	15 08	.....	15 48	.....	.....	.....	.....
St Erth 2	d	14 25	14 55	15 25	15 55	16 25	16 55	17 27	18 26	19 20
Lelant Saltings	d	14 28	14 58	15 28	15 58	16 28	16 58	17 30	18 29	19 23
Lelant	d	.	.	.	.	16x30	17x18	17x32	18x31	19x25
Carbis Bay	d	14 34	15a12	15 34	16a12	16 35	17 04	17 37	18 36	19 30
St Ives	a	14 37	15 06	15 37	16 06	16 38	17 07	17 40	18 39	19 33

Sundays

From 14 September

		GW	GW	GW	GW	GW	GW	GW	GW	GW
Penzance	d	11 50	12 50	13 50	14 44	15 08	16 15	.....	.....	.....
St Erth 2	d	12 00	13 15	14 06	15 06	16 06	16 46	17 22	18 26	19 20
Lelant Saltings	d	12 03	13 18	14 09	15 09	16 09	16 49	17 25	18 29	19 23
Lelant	d	12x05	13x20	14x11	15x11	16x11	16x51	17x27	18x31	19x25
Carbis Bay	d	12 10	13 25	14 16	15 16	16 16	16 56	17 32	18 36	19 30
St Ives	a	12 13	13 28	14 19	15 19	16 19	16 59	17 35	18 39	19 33

For general notes see front of timetable
For details of catering facilities see Directory of Train Operators

St. Ives → St. Erth

Network Diagram - see first page of Table 135

Mondays to Fridays

Miles			GW	GW	GW	GW	GW	GW	GW	GW	GW	GW	GW	GW	GW	GW	GW	GW	GW	GW	GW	GW	GW	GW	GW	GW	GW	
0	**St Ives**	d	07 08	07 38	08 19	09 22	09 55	10 25	10 55	11 25	11 55	12 25	12 55	13 25	13 55	14 25	14 55	15 25	15 55	16 25	16 57	17 27	18 17	18 55	20 00	20 46	21 50	.....
1¼	Carbis Bay	d	07 11	07 41	08 22	09 25	.	10 28	.	11 28	.	12 28	.	13 28	.	14 28	.	15 28	.	16 28	17 00	17 30	18 20	18 58	20 03	20 49	21 53	.
3¼	Lelant	d	07x16	07x46	08x27	09x30	.....	.....	.....	.....	.....	.....	.....	.....	.....	.....	.....	.....	.....	.....	.....	17x35	18x25	19x03	20x08	20x54	21x58	.....
3½	Lelant Saltings	d	.	.	.	09 33	10 05	10 35	11 05	11 35	12 05	12 35	13 05	13 35	14 05	14 35	15 05	15 35	16 05	16 35	17 07	17 38	18 28	19 06	20 11	20 57	22 01	.
4¼	**St Erth** 2	a	07 19	07 49	08 30	09 35	10 08	10 38	11 08	11 38	12 08	12 38	13 08	13 38	14 08	14 38	15 08	15 38	16 08	16 38	17 10	17 40	18 31	19 09	20 13	21 00	22 03	.....
—	Penzance	a	.	.	08 41	*10 15*	.	.	*11 24*	.	*12 35*	*13 21*	.	.	.	*15 13*	.	*15 59*	.	*17 11*	.	.	.	*19 34*	*20 41*	*21 30*	22 14	.

Saturdays

		GW	GW	GW	GW	GW	GW	GW	GW		GW	GW	GW	GW	GW	GW	GW	GW	GW	GW	GW	GW	GW	GW	GW	GW		
St Ives	d	07 17	07 46	08 18	09 23	10 25	10 55	11 25	11 56	.....	12 25	12 55	13 25	13 55	14 25	14 55	15 25	15 56	16 25	16 57	17 27	18 17	19 15	20 00	20 45	21 50	.....	.....
Carbis Bay	d	07 20	07 49	08 21	09 26	10 28	.	11 28	.	.	12 28	.	.	.	14 28	.	15 28	15 50	16 28	.	17 30	18 20	19 18	20 03	20 48	21 53	.	.
Lelant	d	07x25	07x54	08x26	09x31	.....	.....	.....	.....	.....	.....	.....	.....	.....	.....	.....	.....	.....	.....	.....	17x35	18x25	19x23	20x08	20 53	21x58	.....	.....
Lelant Saltings	d	.	.	.	09 34	10 35	11 05	11 35	12 05	.	12 35	13 05	13 35	14 05	14 35	15 05	15 35	16 05	16 35	17 06	17 38	18 28	19 26	20 11	20 56	22 01	.	.
St Erth 2	a	07 28	07 57	08 30	09 37	10 39	11 07	11 39	12 07	.....	12 39	13 07	13 38	14 08	14 38	15 08	15 38	16 08	16 38	17 09	17 40	18 30	19 28	20 13	20 58	22 04	.....	.....
Penzance	a	.	.	08 41	*10 16*	.	.	.	.	.	.	.	.	.	.	.	.	.	.	.	.	18 39	.	*20 41*	*21 31*	22 13	.	.

Sundays

Until 7 September

		GW	GW		GW	GW		GW	GW		GW	GW		GW	GW		GW	GW		GW	GW	GW	GW	GW	GW	GW		
St Ives	d	09 20	10 09	.....	10 40	11 09	.....	11 40	12 09	.....	12 40	13 09	.....	13 40	14 09	.....	14 40	15 09	.....	15 40	16 09	16 41	17 10	17 43	18 43	19 40	.....	.....
Carbis Bay	d	09 24	10 12	.	.	11 12	.	.	12 12	.	.	13 12	.	.	14 12	.	.	15 12	.	.	16 12	.	17 13	17 46	18 46	19 43	.	.
Lelant	d	09 29	.....	.....	.....	.....	.....	.....	.....	.....	.....	.....	.....	.....	.....	.....	.....	.....	.....	.....	.....	.....	17x18	17x51	18x51	19 48	.....	.....
Lelant Saltings	d	09 31	10 19	.	10 49	11 19	.	11 49	12 19	.	12 49	13 19	.	13 49	14 19	.	14 49	15 19	.	15 49	16 19	16 50	17 20	17 54	18 54	19 51	.	.
St Erth 2	a	09 36	10 23	.....	10 53	11 23	.....	11 53	12 23	.....	12 53	13 23	.....	13 53	14 23	.....	14 53	15 23	.....	15 53	16 23	16 54	17 22	17 58	18 58	19 53	.....	.....
Penzance	a	.	.	.	*11 17*	.	.	*12 37*	.	.	*13 33*	.	.	*14 17*	*15 00*	.	.	.	.	*16 31*	*16 56*	*17 39*	.	*18 42*	*19 28*	20 11	.	.

Sundays

From 14 September

		GW			GW			GW			GW			GW			GW			GW			GW					
St Ives	d	12 40	.....	.....	13 40	.....	.....	14 39	.....	.....	15 40	.....	.....	16 30	.....	.....	17 48	.....	.....	18 45	.....	.....	19 40	.....	.....	.....	.....	.....
Carbis Bay	d	12 43	.	.	13 43	.	.	14 42	.	.	15 43	.	.	16 33	.	.	17 51	.	.	18 48	.	.	19 43	.	.	.	.	.
Lelant	d	12x48	.....	.....	13x48	.....	.....	14x47	.....	.....	15x48	.....	.....	16x38	.....	.....	17x56	.....	.....	18x53	.....	.....	19x48	.....	.....	.....	.....	.....
Lelant Saltings	d	12 51	.	.	13 51	.	.	14 50	.	.	15 51	.	.	16 41	.	.	17 59	.	.	18 56	.	.	19 51	.	.	.	.	.
St Erth 2	a	12 55	.....	.....	13 55	.....	.....	14 54	.....	.....	15 53	.....	.....	16 45	.....	.....	18 03	.....	.....	19 00	.....	.....	19 53	.....	.....	.....	.....	.....
Penzance	a	*13 20*	.	.	*14 12*	.	.	.	.	.	*16 10*	.	.	*17 37*	.	.	*18 34*	.	.	*19 29*	.	.	20 06	.	.	.	.	.

For general notes see front of timetable
For details of catering facilities see
Directory of Train Operators

Network Diagram for Tables 148, 149

DM-36/04
Design BAJS

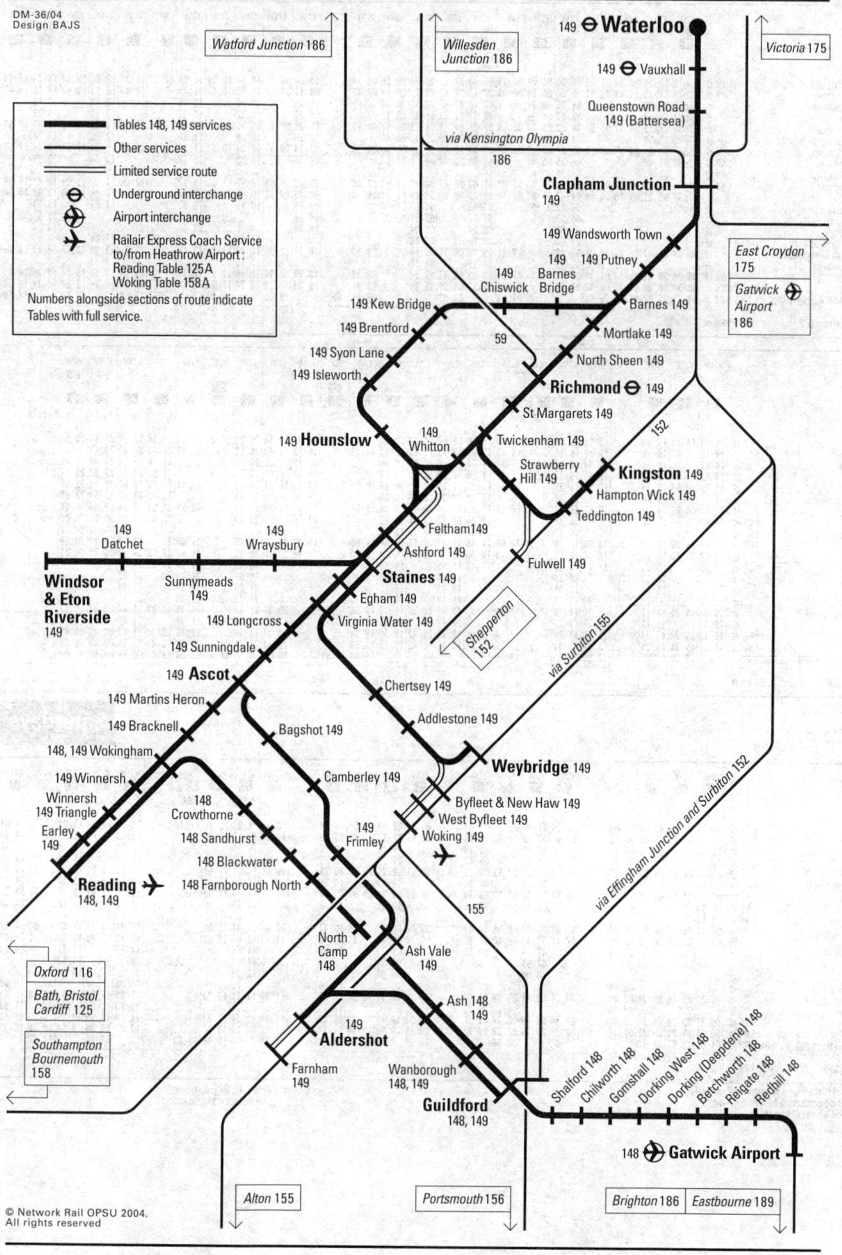

Watford Junction 186
Willesden Junction 186
149 Waterloo
Victoria 175
149 Vauxhall
Queenstown Road 149 (Battersea)
via Kensington Olympia
186
Clapham Junction 149
Tables 148, 149 services
Other services
Limited service route
Underground interchange
Airport interchange
Railair Express Coach Service to/from Heathrow Airport: Reading Table 125A Woking Table 158A
Numbers alongside sections of route indicate Tables with full service.
149 Wandsworth Town
East Croydon 175
Gatwick Airport 186
149 Putney
149 Barnes Bridge
149 Chiswick
149 Kew Bridge
Barnes 149
149 Brentford
Mortlake 149
59
149 Syon Lane
North Sheen 149
149 Isleworth
Richmond 149
St Margarets 149
152
149 Hounslow
149 Whitton
Twickenham 149
Strawberry Hill 149
Kingston 149
Hampton Wick 149
Teddington 149
Feltham 149
149 Datchet
149 Wraysbury
Ashford 149
Fulwell 149
Windsor & Eton Riverside 149
Sunnymeads 149
Staines 149
Egham 149
149 Longcross
Virginia Water 149
Shepperton 152
149 Sunningdale
via Surbiton 155
149 Ascot
Chertsey 149
149 Martins Heron
Addlestone 149
149 Bracknell
Bagshot 149
148, 149 Wokingham
Weybridge 149
149 Winnersh
Camberley 149
Byfleet & New Haw 149
Winnersh 149 Triangle
148 Crowthorne
West Byfleet 149
via Effingham Junction and Surbiton 152
Earley 149
148 Sandhurst
149 Frimley
Woking 149
148 Blackwater
Reading 148, 149
148 Farnborough North
155
North Camp 148
Ash Vale 149
Oxford 116
Bath, Bristol Cardiff 125
Ash 148 149
149 Aldershot
Southampton Bournemouth 158
Farnham 149
Wanborough 148, 149
Shalford 148
Chilworth 148
Gomshall 148
Dorking West 148
Dorking (Deepdene) 148
Betchworth 148
Reigate 148
Redhill 148
Guildford 148, 149
148 Gatwick Airport
Alton 155
Portsmouth 156
Brighton 186
Eastbourne 189

Reading → Guildford, Redhill, and Gatwick Airport

Network Diagram - see first page of Table 148

Miles			GW MO 1	GW MX 1	GW 1	GW 1	GW 1	GW 1	GW 1	GW 1	GW 1	GW 1	GW 1	GW 1	GW 1	GW 1	GW 1	GW 1	GW 1	XC 1 ◇	GW 1	GW 1	GW 1	GW 1	GW 1
0	**Reading 7**	149 d	23p15	23p34	04 34	05 34	05 50	06 07	06 34	07 04	07 34	08 04	08 20	08 34	09 04	09 34	10 04	10 34	11 04	11 09	11 34	12 04	12 34	13 04	13 34
6¾	Wokingham	149 d	23p24	23p43	04 43	05 43	06 00	06 16	06 43	07 13	07 43	08 13	08 29	08 43	09 13	09 43	10 13	10 43	11 13	.	11 43	12 13	12 43	13 13	13 43
10	Crowthorne	d	23p29	23p48			06 05	06 21		07 18	07 48	08 18	08 34		09 18		10 18		11 18			12 18		13 18	
11½	Sandhurst	d	23p33	23p52			06 09	06 25		07 22	07 52	08 22	08 38		09 22		10 22		11 22			12 22		13 22	
13¼	Blackwater	d	23p36	23p55	04 51	05 51	06 12	06 28	06 51	07 25	07 55	08 25	08 41	08 51	09 25	09 51	10 25	10 51	11 25		11 51	12 25	12 51	13 25	13 51
15½	Farnborough North	d	23p41	23p59			06 17	06 33		07 30	08 00	08 30	08 46		09 30		10 30		11 30			12 30		13 30	
17¼	North Camp	d	23p45	00 04	04 57	05 57	06 21	06 37	06 57	07 34	08 04	08 34	08 50	08 58	09 34	09 57	10 34	10 57	11 34		11 57	12 34	12 57	13 34	13 57
19¾	Ash 3	149 d	23p49	00 08			06 25	06 41		07 38	08 08	08 38	08 54		09 38		10 38		11 38			12 38		13 38	
21¾	Wanborough	149 d		00 12			06 29																		
25¾	**Guildford**	149 a	23p58	00 19	05 08	06 08	06 36	06 50	07 08	07 47	08 17	08 47	09 03	09 08	09 47	10 08	10 47	11 08	11 47		12 08	12 47	13 08	13 47	14 08
—		d	23p59	00 21	05 10	06 10	06 43	06 57	07 10	07 48	08 18	08 48	09 04	09 10	09 48	10 10	10 48	11 10	11 48		12 10	12 48	13 10	13 48	14 10
27¾	Shalford	d					06 48	07a02		07 53		08 53	09a10		09 53		10 53		11 53			12 53		13 53	
29¾	Chilworth	d					06 52			07 57		08 57			09 57				11 57					13 57	
33¾	Gomshall	d					06 58			08 04		09 04			10 04				12 04					14 04	
38¼	Dorking West	d					07 06			08 11		09 12					11 06					13 06			
39	Dorking Deepdene	d	00 19	00 37	05 26	06 26	07 08		07 26	08 14	08 35	09 14		09 30	10 11	10 26	11 08	11 26	12 11		12 26	13 08	13 26	14 11	14 26
41¾	Betchworth	d					07 13			08 19		09 19					11 13					13 13			
44½	Reigate	186 d	00 26	00 45	05 34	06 34	07 18		07 34	08 24	08 42	09 24		09 37	10 19	10 34	11 18	11 34	12 19		12 34	13 18	13 34	14 19	14 34
46½	**Redhill**	186 a	00 30	00 49	05 39	06 38	07 23		07 38	08 29	08 51	09 29		09 41	10 24	10 38	11 24	11 38	12 24		12 38	13 24	13 38	14 24	14 38
52¼	**Gatwick Airport 10**	186 ✈ a	00 41	01 01	05 54	06 56			07 54		09 02			09 59		10 50		11 50		12 33	12 50		13 50		14 50
—	Brighton 10	186 a																		13 15					

		GW 1	GW 1	GW 1	GW 1	GW 1	XC 1 ◇	GW 1	GW 1	GW 1	GW 1	GW 1	GW 1	XC R 1	GW 1	GW 1	GW 1	XC R 1	GW 1	GW 1	GW 1	GW FX 1	GW FO 1
Reading 7	149 d	14 04	14 34	15 04	15 28	16 04	16 11	16 34	16 50	17 04	17 34	18 04	18 34	18 11	19 04	19 34	20 04	20 09	20 34	21 34	22 34	23 34	23 34
Wokingham	149 d	14 13	14 43	15 13	15 39	16 13	.	16 43	17 00	17 13	17 43	18 13	18 43	.	19 13	19 43	20 13	.	20 43	21 43	22 43	23 43	.
Crowthorne	d	14 18		15 18	15 44	16 18			17 06	17 18	17 48	18 18			19 18		20 18			21 48	22 48	23 48	23 48
Sandhurst	d	14 22		15 22	15 48	16 22			17 10	17 22	17 52	18 22			19 22		20 22			21 52	22 52	23 52	23 52
Blackwater	d	14 25	14 51	15 25	15 51	16 25		16 51	17 13	17 25	17 55	18 25	18 51		19 25	19 51	20 25		20 51	21 55	22 55	23 55	23 55
Farnborough North	d	14 30		15 30		16 30			17 18	17 30	18 00	18 30			19 30		20 30			22 00	23 00	23 59	23 59
North Camp	d	14 34	14 57	15 34	15 57	16 34		16 57	17 22	17 34	18 04	18 34	18 57		19 34	19 57	20 34		20 57	22 04	23 04	00 04	00 04
Ash 3	149 d	14 38		15 38		16 38			17 26	17 38	18 08	18 38			19 38		20 38			22 08	23 08	00 08	00 08
Wanborough	149 d					16 42				17 42		18 42										00 12	00 12
Guildford	149 a	14 47	15 08	15 47	16 08	16 49	16 59	17 08	17 35	17 49	18 17	18 49	19 08		19 47	20 08	20 47		21 08	22 17	23 17	00 19	00 19
	d	14 48	15 10	15 48	16 10	16 50		17 10	17 40	17 50	18 18	18 54	19 10		19 48	20 10	20 48		21 10	22 18	23 18	00 21	00 21
Shalford	d	14 53		15 53	16 15	16 55			17a48	17 55		18 59			19a54		20 53		21 15	22 23	23 23		
Chilworth	d			15 57		16 59				17 59		19 03					20 58		21 19		23 27		
Gomshall	d			16 04		17 06				18 06		19 10					21 04		21 25		23 34		
Dorking West	d	15 06			16 28	17 13				18 13		19 17					21 12		21 33		23 41		
Dorking Deepdene	d	15 08	15 26	16 11	16 30	17 16		17 26		18 16	18 35	19 20	19 26			20 26	21 14		21 35	22 37	23 44	00 37	00 37
Betchworth	d	15 13		16 16	16 35	17 21				18 21		19 25					21 19		21 40		23 49		
Reigate	186 d	15 18	15 34	16 21	16 40	17 26		17 34		18 26	18 42	19 30	19 34			20 34	21 24		21 45	22 44	23 54	00 45	00 45
Redhill	186 a	15 24	15 38	16 26	16 47	17 31		17 38		18 31	18 52	19 35	19 38			20 38	21 28	21 34	21 53	22 48	23 58	00 49	00 49
Gatwick Airport 10	186 ✈ a	.	15 50	.	17 00			17 50			19 07		19 50	19 52		20 50		21 47	22 04	23 04	00 11	01 01	01 01
Brighton 10	186 a													20 30									

Saturdays

		GW 1	GW 1	GW 1	GW 1	GW 1	GW 1	GW 1	GW 1	GW 1	GW 1	GW 1	GW 1	GW 1	GW 1	GW 1	XC 1 ◇	GW 1	GW 1	GW 1	GW 1	GW 1
Reading 7	149 d	23p34	04 34	05 34	06 04	06 34	07 04	07 34	08 04	08 34	09 04	09 34	10 04	10 34	11 04	11 34	11b13	12 04	12 34	13 04	13 34	14 04
Wokingham	149 d	.	04 43	05 43	06 13	06 43	07 13	07 43	08 13	08 43	09 13	09 43	10 13	10 43	11 13	11 43	.	12 13	12 43	13 13	13 43	14 13
Crowthorne	d	23p48			06 18		07 18		08 18		09 18		10 18		11 18			12 18		13 18		14 18
Sandhurst	d	23p52			06 22		07 22		08 22		09 22		10 22		11 22			12 22		13 22		14 22
Blackwater	d	23p55	04 51	05 51	06 25	06 51	07 25	07 51	08 25	08 51	09 25	09 51	10 25	10 51	11 25	11 51		12 25	12 51	13 25	13 51	14 25
Farnborough North	d	23p59			06 30		07 30		08 30		09 30		10 30		11 30			12 30		13 30		14 30
North Camp	d	00 04	04 57	05 57	06 34	06 57	07 34	07 57	08 34	08 57	09 34	09 57	10 34	10 57	11 34	11 57		12 34	12 57	13 34	13 57	14 34
Ash 3	149 d	00 08			06 38		07 38		08 38		09 38		10 38		11 38			12 38		13 38		14 38
Wanborough	149 d	00 12																				
Guildford	149 a	00 19	05 08	06 08	06 47	07 08	07 47	08 08	08 47	09 08	09 47	10 08	10 47	11 08	11 47	12 08		12 47	13 08	13 47	14 08	14 47
	d	00 21	05 10	06 10	06 48	07 10	07 48	08 10	08 48	09 10	09 48	10 10	10 48	11 10	11 48	12 10		12 48	13 10	13 48	14 10	14 48
Shalford	d				06 53		07 53		08 53		09 53		10 53		11 53			12 53		13 53		14 53
Chilworth	d						07 57				09 57				11 57					13 57		
Gomshall	d						08 04				10 04				12 04					14 04		
Dorking West	d				07 06				09 06				11 06					13 06				15 06
Dorking Deepdene	d	00 37	05 26	06 26	07 08	07 26	08 11	08 26	09 08	09 26	10 11	10 26	11 08	11 26	12 11	12 26		13 08	13 26	14 11	14 26	15 08
Betchworth	d				07 13				09 13				11 13					13 13				15 13
Reigate	186 d	00 45	05 34	06 34	07 18	07 34	08 19	08 34	09 18	09 34	10 19	10 34	11 18	11 34	12 19	12 34		13 18	13 34	14 19	14 34	15 18
Redhill	186 a	00 49	05 38	06 38	07 23	07 38	08 24	08 38	09 23	09 38	10 24	10 38	11 24	11 38	12 24	12 38		13 23	13 38	14 24	14 38	15 23
Gatwick Airport 10	186 ✈ a	01 01	05 53	06 50	.	07 50	.	08 50	.	09 50	.	10 50	.	11 50	.	12 50	12 53	.	13 50	.	14 50	.
Brighton 10	186 a																13 37					

For general notes see front of timetable
For details of catering facilities see
Directory of Train Operators

b From 13 September. Departs 1 minute later.

Table 148

Reading → Guildford, Redhill, and Gatwick Airport

Saturdays

Network Diagram - see first page of Table 148

Station		GW 1	GW 1	GW 1	GW 1	XC 1 ◇	GW 1	GW 1	GW 1	GW 1	GW 1	XC 1 ◇	GW 1	GW 1	GW 1	XC 1 ◇	GW 1	GW 1	GW 1	GW 1
						⊡						⊡				⊡				
Reading 7	149 d	14 34	15 04	15 34	16 04	16b13	16 34	17 04	17 34	18 04	18 34	18b13	19 04	19 34	20 04	20b13	20 34	21 34	22 34	23 34
Wokingham	149 d	14 43	15 13	15 43	16 13	.	16 43	17 13	17 43	18 13	18 43	.	19 13	19 43	20 13	.	20 43	21 43	22 43	.
Crowthorne	d	.	15 18	.	16 18	.	.	17 18	.	18 18	.	.	19 18	.	20 18	.	.	21 48	22 48	23 48
Sandhurst	d	.	15 22	.	16 22	.	.	17 22	.	18 22	.	.	19 22	.	20 22	.	.	21 52	22 52	23 52
Blackwater	d	14 51	15 25	15 51	16 25	.	16 51	17 25	17 51	18 25	18 51	.	19 25	19 51	20 25	.	20 51	21 55	22 55	23 55
Farnborough North	d	.	15 30	.	16 30	.	.	17 30	.	18 30	.	.	19 30	.	20 30	.	.	22 00	23 00	23 59
North Camp	d	14 57	15 34	15 57	16 34	.	16 57	17 34	17 57	18 34	18 57	.	19 34	19 57	20 34	.	20 57	22 04	23 04	00 04
Ash 3	149 d	.	15 38	.	16 38	.	.	17 38	.	18 38	.	.	19 38	.	20 38	.	.	22 08	23 08	00 08
Wanborough	149 d	.	.	.	.	.	.	.	.	.	.	.	.	.	.	.	.	.	.	00 12
Guildford	149 a	15 08	15 47	16 08	16 47	16 58	17 08	17 47	18 08	18 47	19 08	.	19 47	20 08	20 47	20 58	21 08	22 17	23 17	00 19
	d	15 10	15 48	16 10	16 48	.	17 10	17 48	18 10	18 48	19 10	.	19 48	20 10	20 48	21 00	21 10	22 18	23 18	00 21
Shalford	d	.	15 53	.	16 53	.	.	17 53	.	18 53	.	.	19 53	.	20 53	.	21 15	22 23	23 23	.
Chilworth	d	.	15 57	.	.	.	.	17 57	.	.	.	.	19 57	.	.	.	21 19	.	23 27	.
Gomshall	d	.	16 04	.	.	.	.	18 04	.	.	.	.	20 04	.	.	.	21 25	.	23 34	.
Dorking West	d	.	.	.	17 06	.	.	.	.	19 06	.	.	.	.	21 06	.	.	22 36	23 41	.
Dorking Deepdene	d	15 26	16 11	16 26	17 08	.	17 26	18 11	18 26	19 08	19 26	.	20 11	20 26	21 08	.	21 33	22 38	23 44	00 37
Betchworth	d	.	.	.	17 13	.	.	.	.	19 13	.	.	.	.	21 13	.	.	22 43	23 49	.
Reigate	186 d	15 34	16 19	16 34	17 18	.	17 34	18 19	18 34	19 18	19 34	.	20 19	20 34	21 18	.	21 40	22 48	23 54	00 45
Redhill	186 a	15 38	16 24	16 38	17 23	.	17 38	18 24	18 38	19 23	19 38	.	20 24	20 38	21 23	21 28	21 44	22 52	23 58	00 49
Gatwick Airport 10	186 ✈ a	15 50	.	16 50	.	.	17 50	.	18 50	.	19 50	19 52	.	20 50	.	21 47	21 59	23 03	00 10	01 02
Brighton 10	186 a	.	.	.	.	.	.	.	.	.	.	20 28	.	.	.	.	.	.	.	.

Sundays

Station		GW 1	GW 1	GW 1	GW 1	GW 1	GW 1	GW 1	GW 1	GW 1	GW 1	GW 1	GW 1	GW 1	GW 1	GW 1	XC 1 ◇	GW 1	XC 1 ◇	XC 1 ◇	GW 1	GW 1	GW 1	XC R 1
																			A	B				
																	⊡		⊡	⊡				
Reading 7	149 d	23p34	06 03	07 03	08 03	09 03	10 03	11 03	12 03	13 03	14 03	15 03	16 03	17 03	18 03	19 03	19 14	20 03	20 14	20 15	21 03	22 03	23 15	21 06
Wokingham	149 d	.	06 11	07 11	08 11	09 11	10 11	11 11	12 11	13 11	14 11	15 11	16 11	17 11	18 11	19 11	.	20 11	⌇	⌇	21 11	22 11	23 24	.
Crowthorne	d	23p48	.	07 17	.	09 18	.	11 18	.	13 18	.	15 18	.	17 18	.	19 18	.	.	⌇	⌇	21 18	.	23 29	.
Sandhurst	d	23p52	.	07 21	.	09 21	.	11 21	.	13 21	.	15 21	.	17 21	.	19 21	.	.	⌇	⌇	21 21	.	23 33	.
Blackwater	d	23p55	06 20	07 24	08 19	09 25	10 19	11 25	12 19	13 25	14 19	15 25	16 19	17 25	18 19	19 25	.	20 19	⌇	⌇	21 25	22 19	23 36	.
Farnborough North	d	23p59	.	07 29	.	09 29	.	11 29	.	13 29	.	15 29	.	17 29	.	19 29	.	.	⌇	⌇	21 29	.	23 41	.
North Camp	d	00 04	06 26	07 33	08 26	09 33	10 26	11 33	12 26	13 33	14 26	15 33	16 26	17 33	18 26	19 33	.	20 26	⌇	⌇	21 33	22 26	23 45	.
Ash 3	149 d	00 08	.	07 37	.	09 37	.	11 37	.	13 37	.	15 37	.	17 37	.	19 37	.	.	⌇	⌇	21 37	.	23 49	.
Wanborough	149 d	00 12	.	.	.	.	.	.	.	.	.	.	.	.	.	.	.	.	⌇	⌇	.	.	.	.
Guildford	149 a	00 19	06 37	07 46	08 37	09 46	10 37	11 46	12 37	13 46	14 37	15 46	16 37	17 46	18 37	19 46	19 54	20 37	20 50	20 50	21 46	22 37	23 58	21 33
	d	00 21	06 39	07 49	08 39	09 49	10 39	11 49	12 39	13 49	14 39	15 49	16 39	17 49	18 39	19 49	19 57	20 39	20 52	20 55	21 49	22 39	23 59	21 43
Shalford	d	.	.	.	08 44	.	10 44	.	12 44	.	14 44	.	16 44	.	18 44	.	.	20 44	⌇	⌇	.	22 44	.	.
Chilworth	d	.	.	.	08 48	.	10 48	.	12 48	.	14 48	.	16 48	.	18 48	.	.	20 48	⌇	⌇	.	22 48	.	.
Gomshall	d	.	.	.	08 54	.	10 54	.	12 54	.	14 54	.	16 54	.	18 54	.	.	20 54	⌇	⌇	.	22 54	.	.
Dorking West	d	.	.	.	09 02	.	11 02	.	13 02	.	15 02	.	17 02	.	19 02	.	.	21 02	⌇	⌇	.	23 02	.	.
Dorking Deepdene	d	00 37	06 56	08 06	09 04	10 06	11 04	12 06	13 04	14 06	15 04	16 06	17 04	18 06	19 04	20 06	.	21 04	⌇	⌇	22 06	23 04	00 19	.
Betchworth	d	.	.	.	09 09	.	11 09	.	13 09	.	15 09	.	17 09	.	19 09	.	.	21 09	⌇	⌇	.	23 09	.	.
Reigate	186 d	00 45	07 03	08 13	09 14	10 13	11 14	12 13	13 14	14 13	15 14	16 13	17 14	18 13	19 14	20 13	.	21 14	⌇	⌇	22 13	23 14	00 26	.
Redhill	186 a	00 49	07 09	08 17	09 18	10 17	11 18	12 17	13 18	14 17	15 18	16 17	17 20	18 17	19 20	20 17	20 27	21 18	21 31	21 31	22 18	23 18	00 30	22 11
Gatwick Airport 10	186 ✈ a	01 02	07 27	08 32	09 31	10 30	11 31	12 30	13 31	14 30	15 31	16 30	17 33	18 29	19 33	20 30	20 44	21 31	21 47	21 47	22 30	23 31	00 41	22 37
Brighton 10	186 a	.	.	.	.	.	.	.	.	.	.	.	.	.	.	.	21 13	.	⌇	⌇	.	.	.	.

For general notes see front of timetable
For details of catering facilities see
Directory of Train Operators

A 20 July to 7 September
B From 14 September.

b From 13 September. Departs 1 minute later.

Gatwick Airport, Redhill and Guildford → Reading

Network Diagram - see first page of Table 148

Miles			GW MO 1	GW MX 1	XC 1 ◇	GW 1	XC 1 ◇	GW 1	XC 1 ◇	GW 1	GW 1	GW 1	GW 1	GW 1	GW 1	GW 1	GW 1	GW 1	XC 1 ◇	GW 1	GW 1	GW 1	GW 1	GW 1	GW 1
—	Brighton 10	186 d																	09 21						
0	**Gatwick Airport 10**	186 ✈ d	23p07	23p18	05 15	05 31	05 45	05 57				06 59		07 58			09 17		09 46	10 03		11 03		12 03	
5¾	**Redhill**	186 d	23p20	23p29	05 33	05 44	06 04	06 14		06 24		07 11	07 28	08 09	08 33		09 29	09 34		10 14	10 34	11 14	11 34	12 14	12 34
7¼	Reigate	186 d	23p24	23p33		05 49		06 18		06 28		07 15	07 32	08 13	08 37		09 33	09 38		10 18	10 38	11 18	11 38	12 18	12 38
10½	Betchworth	d								06 33			07 37		08 42			09 43			10 43				12 43
13¼	Dorking Deepdene	d	23p31	23p40		05 56		06 25		06 37		07 22	07 41	08 20	08 46		09 40	09 47		10 25	10 47	11 25	11 45	12 25	12 47
14	Dorking West	d								06 40			07 44		08 49			09 50			10 50				12 50
18¾	Gomshall	d								06 48		07 30	07 52		08 57			09 58					11 53		
22¼	Chilworth	d								06 54			07 58		09 03			10 04					11 59		
24¼	Shalford	d								06 58	07 21		08 02		09 07	09 31		10 08			11 03		12 03		13 03
26½	**Guildford**	a	23p48	23p59	05 59	06 11	06 36	06 41	←	07 02	07 25	07 40	08 06	08 36	09 11	09 35	09 56	10 12		10 42	11 07	11 42	12 07	12 42	13 07
—		d	23p50	00 01	06 00	06 12	06 51	06 42	06 51	07 04	07 26	07 42	08 12	08 37	09 12	09 36	09 57	10 13		10 43	11 09	11 43	12 09	12 43	13 09
30¾	Wanborough	149 d				06 20	→			07 11			08 20		09 20										
32¾	Ash 3	149 d	23p59			06 24		06 52		07 16	07 36	07 52	08 24		09 24	09 46		10 23			11 18		12 18		13 18
34¾	North Camp	d	00 03	00 13		06 28		06 56		07 20	07 41	07 56	08 28	08 49	09 28	09 50		10 27		10 55	11 22	11 55	12 22	12 55	13 22
36¾	Farnborough North	d	00 07			06 32		07 00		07 24	07 45	08 00	08 32		09 32			10 31			11 26		12 26		13 26
38¾	Blackwater	d	00 12	00 20		06 37		07 04		07 28	07 49	08 04	08 37	08 56	09 37	09 56		10 35		11 02	11 31	12 02	12 31	13 02	13 31
40¾	Sandhurst	d	00 15			06 40		07 08		07 32	07 53	08 08	08 40		09 40			10 39			11 34		12 34		13 34
42¼	Crowthorne	d	00 19			06 44		07 12		07 36	07 57	08 12	08 44		09 44			10 43			11 38		12 38		13 38
45½	Wokingham	149 d	00 24	00 28		06 49		07 17		07 41	08 02	08 17	08 49	09 04	09 51	10 04		10 48		11 10	11 43	12 10	12 43	13 10	13 43
52¼	**Reading 7**	149 a	00 36	00 38	06 30	06 59		07 28	07 37	07 50	08 16	08 28	08 59	09 16	10 00	10 16	10 27	10 57	11 35	11 19	11 53	12 19	12 53	13 19	13 53

		GW 1	GW 1	GW 1	GW 1	XC R 1	GW 1	GW 1	GW 1	GW 1	GW 1	XC 1 ◇	GW 1	GW 1	GW 1	GW 1	GW 1	GW 1	GW 1	GW 1	GW 1	GW 1	GW 1	GW 1
Brighton 10	186 d					14 22																		
Gatwick Airport 10	186 ✈ d	13 03		14 03		14 51	15 03		16 03		17 03				18 03		19 16		20 03		21 03		22 22	23 18
Redhill	186 d	13 14	13 34	14 14	14 34		15 14	15 29	16 14	16 32	17 14			17 44	18 14	18 43	19 27		20 14	20 34	21 14	21 35	22 33	23 29
Reigate	186 d	13 18	13 38	14 18	14 38		15 18	15 34	16 18	16 36	17 18			17 49	18 18	18 47	19 31		20 18	20 40	21 18	21 39	22 38	23 33
Betchworth	d				14 43			15 38		16 41				17 53		18 52				20 45		21 44	22 43	
Dorking Deepdene	d	13 25	13 45	14 25	14 47		15 25	15 43	16 25	16 45	17 25			17 58	18 25	18 56	19 38		20 25	20 49	21 25	21 48	22 47	23 40
Dorking West	d				14 50			15 45						18 00		18 59				20 52		21 51	22 50	
Gomshall	d		13 53					15 53		16 53				18 08		19 07				21 00		21 59	22 58	
Chilworth	d		13 59					15 59		16 59				18 14		19 13				21 06		22 05	23 04	
Shalford	d		14 03		15 03			16 03		17 03			18 08	18 18		19 17		20 08		21 10		22 09	23 08	
Guildford	a	13 42	14 07	14 42	15 07		15 42	16 07	16 42	17 07	17 44		18 12	18 22	18 42	19 21	19 54	20 12	20 42	21 14	21 42	22 13	23 12	23 59
	d	13 43	14 09	14 43	15 09		15 43	16 14	16 43	17 09	17 44	17 57	18 13	18 24	18 49	19 36	19 55	20 13	20 43	21 15	21 43	22 14	23 14	00 01
Wanborough	149 d																						23 21	
Ash 3	149 d		14 18		15 18			16 23		17 18	17 54		18 23	18 33		19 45		20 23		21 25		22 23	23 26	
North Camp	d	13 55	14 22	14 55	15 22		15 55	16 27	16 55	17 22	17 58		18 27	18 38	19 01	19 49	20 07	20 27	20 55	21 29	21 55	22 27	23 30	00 13
Farnborough North	d		14 26		15 26			16 31		17 26	18 02		18 31	18 42		19 53		20 31		21 33		22 31	23 34	
Blackwater	d	14 02	14 31	15 02	15 31		16 02	16 36	17 02	17 31	18 07		18 35	18 46	19 06	19 58	20 14	20 35	21 02	21 37	22 02	22 36	23 38	00 20
Sandhurst	d		14 34		15 34			16 39		17 34			18 39	18 51		20 01		20 39		21 41		22 39	23 42	
Crowthorne	d		14 38		15 38			16 43		17 38			18 43	18 59		20 05		20 43		21 45		22 43	23 46	
Wokingham	149 d	14 10	14 43	15 10	15 43		16 10	16 48	17 10	17 43	18 15		18 51	19 04	19 15	20 10	20 22	20 48	21 10	21 50	22 10	22 48	23 51	00 28
Reading 7	149 a	14 19	14 53	15 19	15 54	16 35	16 23	16 59	17 19	17 53	18 24	18 38	19 01	19 15	19 25	20 20	20 37	20 58	21 19	22 00	22 19	23 00	00 01	00 38

Saturdays

		GW 1	XC 1 ◇ A	XC 1 ◇ B	GW 1	XC 1 ◇	GW 1	GW 1	GW 1	GW 1	GW 1	GW 1	GW 1	GW 1	XC 1 ◇ A	XC 1 ◇ B	GW 1	GW 1	GW 1	GW 1	GW 1	GW 1	GW 1
Brighton 10	186 d														09 15	09 15							
Gatwick Airport 10	186 ✈ d	23p18	05 15	05 15	05 31	05 45	06 03		07 03		08 03		09 03		09 46	09 47	10 03		11 03		12 03		13 03
Redhill	186 d	23p29	05 33	05 33	05 43	05 52	06 14	06 34	07 14	07 34	08 14	08 34	09 14	09 34			10 14	10 34	11 14	11 34	12 14	12 34	13 14
Reigate	186 d	23p33			05 47		06 18	06 38	07 18	07 38	08 18	08 38	09 18	09 38			10 18	10 38	11 18	11 38	12 18	12 38	13 18
Betchworth	d							06 43				08 43						10 43				12 43	
Dorking Deepdene	d	23p40			05 54		06 25	06 47	07 25	07 45	08 25	08 47	09 25	09 45			10 25	10 47	11 25	11 45	12 25	12 47	13 25
Dorking West	d							06 50				08 50						10 50				12 50	
Gomshall	d									07 52				09 53						11 53			
Chilworth	d									07 58				09 59						11 59			
Shalford	d							07 03		08 02		09 03		10 03				11 03		12 03		13 03	
Guildford	a	23p59	05 54	05 54	06 10		06 41	07 07	07 41	08 06	08 42	09 07	09 42	10 07			10 42	11 07	11 42	12 07	12 42	13 07	13 42
	d	00 01	06 00	06 00	06 12		06 43	07 09	07 43	08 09	08 43	09 09	09 43	10 09			10 43	11 09	11 43	12 09	12 43	13 09	13 43
Wanborough	149 d				06 20																		
Ash 3	149 d				06 24			07 18		08 18		09 18		10 18				11 18		12 18		13 18	
North Camp	d	00 13			06 28		06 55	07 22	07 55	08 22	08 55	09 22	09 55	10 22			10 55	11 22	11 55	12 22	12 55	13 22	13 55
Farnborough North	d				06 32			07 26		08 26		09 26		10 26				11 26		12 26		13 26	
Blackwater	d	00 20			06 37		07 02	07 31	08 02	08 31	09 02	09 31	10 02	10 31			11 02	11 31	12 02	12 31	13 02	13 31	14 02
Sandhurst	d				06 40			07 34		08 34		09 34		10 34				11 34		12 34		13 34	
Crowthorne	d				06 44			07 38		08 38		09 38		10 38				11 38		12 38		13 38	
Wokingham	149 d	00 28			06 49		07 10	07 43	08 10	08 43	09 10	09 43	10 10	10 43			11 10	11 43	12 10	12 43	13 10	13 43	14 10
Reading 7	149 a	00 38	06 33	06 35	07 02	07 35	07 19	07 53	08 19	08 53	09 19	09 53	10 19	10 53	11 35	11 35	11 19	11 53	12 19	12 53	13 19	13 53	14 19

For general notes see front of timetable
For details of catering facilities see Directory of Train Operators

A Until 6 September
B From 13 September.

Saturdays

Gatwick Airport, Redhill and Guildford → Reading

Network Diagram - see first page of Table 148

Station		GW 1	GW 1	GW 1	XC 1 ◇	GW 1	GW 1	GW 1	GW 1	GW 1	XC 1 ◇	GW 1	GW 1	GW 1	GW 1	GW 1	GW 1	GW 1	GW 1	GW 1	GW 1	GW 1
Brighton 10	186 d				14 22																	
Gatwick Airport 10	186 ✈ d		14 03		14 52	15 03		16 03		17 03			18 03		19 03		20 03		21 03		22 22	23 18
Redhill	186 d	13 34	14 14	14 34		15 14	15 34	16 14	16 34	17 14		17 34	18 14	18 34	19 14	19 34	20 14	20 34	21 14	21 36	22 33	23 29
Reigate	186 d	13 38	14 18	14 38		15 18	15 38	16 18	16 38	17 18		17 38	18 18	18 38	19 18	19 38	20 18	20 38	21 18	21 40	22 38	23 33
Betchworth	d			14 43					16 43					18 43				20 43			22 43	
Dorking Deepdene	d	13 45	14 25	14 47		15 25	15 45	16 25	16 47	17 25		17 45	18 25	18 47	19 25	19 45	20 25	20 47	21 25	21 47	22 47	23 40
Dorking West	d			14 50					16 50					18 50				20 50			22 50	
Gomshall	d	13 53					15 53					17 53				19 53				21 55	22 58	
Chilworth	d	13 59					15 59					17 59				19 59				22 01	23 04	
Shalford	d	14 03		15 03			16 03		17 03			18 03		19 03		20 03		21 03		22 05	23 08	
Guildford	a	14 07	14 42	15 07		15 42	16 07	16 42	17 07	17 42		18 07	18 42	19 07	19 42	20 07	20 42	21 07	21 42	22 12	23 12	23 59
	d	14 09	14 43	15 09		15 43	16 09	16 43	17 09	17 43	17 58	18 09	18 43	19 09	19 43	20 09	20 43	21 09	21 43	22 14	23 14	00 01
Wanborough	149 d																				23 21	
Ash 3	149 d	14 18		15 18			16 18		17 18			18 18		19 18		20 18		21 18		22 23	23 26	
North Camp	d	14 22	14 55	15 22		15 55	16 22	16 55	17 22	17 55		18 22	18 55	19 22	19 55	20 22	20 55	21 22	21 55	22 27	23 30	00 13
Farnborough North	d	14 26		15 26			16 26		17 26			18 26		19 26		20 26		21 26		22 31	23 34	
Blackwater	d	14 31	15 02	15 31		16 02	16 31	17 02	17 31	18 02		18 31	19 02	19 31	20 02	20 31	21 02	21 31	22 02	22 36	23 38	00 20
Sandhurst	d	14 34		15 34			16 34		17 34			18 34		19 34		20 34		21 34		22 39	23 42	
Crowthorne	d	14 38		15 38			16 38		17 38			18 38		19 38		20 38		21 38		22 43	23 46	
Wokingham	149 d	14 43	15 10	15 43		16 10	16 43	17 10	17 43	18 10		18 43	19 10	19 43	20 10	20 43	21 10	21 43	22 10	22 48	23 51	00 28
Reading 7	149 a	14 53	15 19	15 53	16 35	16 19	16 53	17 19	17 53	18 19	18 35	18 53	19 19	19 53	20 19	20 53	21 19	21 53	22 19	22 57	23 59	00 37

Sundays

Station		GW 1	GW 1	GW 1	GW 1	GW 1	GW 1	XC 1 ◇ A	XC 1 ◇ B	GW 1	GW 1	GW 1	GW 1	GW 1	GW 1	GW 1	GW 1	GW 1	GW 1	GW 1	GW 1	GW 1	GW 1
Brighton 10	186 d							09 40	09 40														
Gatwick Airport 10	186 ✈ d	23p18	06 09	07 07	08 07	09 07	10 07	10 11	10 12		11 07	12 07	13 07	14 07	15 07	16 07	17 07	18 07	19 07	20 07	21 07	22 07	23 07
Redhill	186 d	23p29	06 20	07 21	08 19	09 20	10 19	10 33	10 33		11 20	12 19	13 20	14 19	15 20	16 19	17 21	18 19	19 21	20 19	21 20	22 20	23 20
Reigate	186 d	23p33	06 25	07 26	08 23	09 24	10 23				11 24	12 23	13 24	14 23	15 24	16 23	17 26	18 23	19 26	20 23	21 25	22 24	23 24
Betchworth	d				08 28		10 28					12 28		14 28		16 28		18 28		20 28		22 29	
Dorking Deepdene	d	23p40	06 32	07 33	08 32	09 31	10 32				11 31	12 32	13 31	14 32	15 31	16 32	17 33	18 32	19 33	20 32	21 32	22 33	23 31
Dorking West	d				08 35		10 35					12 35		14 35		16 35		18 35		20 35		22 36	
Gomshall	d				08 43		10 43					12 43		14 43		16 43		18 43		20 43		22 44	
Chilworth	d				08 49		10 49					12 49		14 49		16 49		18 49		20 49		22 50	
Shalford	d				08 53		10 53					12 53		14 53		16 53		18 53		20 53		22 54	
Guildford	a	23p59	06 47	07 48	08 57	09 48	10 57	11 02	11 02	←	11 48	12 57	13 48	14 57	15 48	16 57	17 48	18 57	19 48	20 57	21 47	22 58	23 48
	d	00 01	06 49	07 50	08 58	09 50	11 06 →	11 03	11 03	11 06	11 50	12 58	13 50	14 58	15 50	16 58	17 50	18 58	19 50	20 57	21 49	22 59	23 50
Wanborough	149 d																						
Ash 3	149 d			07 59		09 59					11 59		13 59		16 00		17 59		19 59		21 58		23 59
North Camp	d	00 13	07 01	08 03	09 10	10 03				11 18	12 03	13 10	14 03	15 10	16 04	17 10	18 03	19 10	20 03	21 10	22 02	23 11	00 03
Farnborough North	d			08 07		10 07					12 07		14 07		16 08		18 07		20 07		22 06		00 07
Blackwater	d	00 20	07 07	08 12	09 17	10 12				11 24	12 12	13 17	14 12	15 17	16 12	17 17	18 12	19 17	20 12	21 17	22 11	23 18	00 12
Sandhurst	d			08 15		10 15					12 15		14 15		16 16		18 15		20 15		22 14		00 15
Crowthorne	d			08 19		10 19					12 19		14 19		16 20		18 19		20 19		22 18		00 19
Wokingham	149 d	00 28	07 15	08 24	09 25	10 24				11 32	12 24	13 25	14 24	15 25	16 25	17 25	18 24	19 25	20 24	21 25	22 23	23 26	00 24
Reading 7	149 a	00 37	07 24	08 34	09 34	10 34		11 36	11 36	11 41	12 34	13 34	14 34	15 34	16 34	17 34	18 34	19 34	20 34	21 34	22 37	23 37	00 36

For general notes see front of timetable
For details of catering facilities see
Directory of Train Operators

A From 14 September.
B Until 7 September.

South West Trains
A Stagecoach Company

These notes apply to Tables 149 to 156, 158, 160, 165 and 167

Spring Holiday

Saturday 24 May — A normal Saturday service will operate
Sunday 25 May — A normal Sunday service will operate
Monday 26 May — A normal Saturday service will operate
Engineering Works will be taking place between
Poole and Wareham Saturday – Monday
Basingstoke and Salisbury Saturday – Monday
Woking and Haslemere/Aldershot Sunday

Late Summer Holiday

Saturday 23 August — A normal Saturday service will operate
Sunday 24 August — A normal Sunday service will operate
Monday 25 August — A normal Saturday service will operate
Engineering Works will be taking place between
New Malden and Strawberry Hill Saturday – Monday

For details of Bank Holiday service alterations, please see first page of this Table

London → Hounslow, Richmond, Kingston, Windsor, Weybridge, Ascot, Guildford and Reading

Network Diagram - see first page of Table 148

Miles	Miles	Miles			SW	SW	SW	SW	SW	SW	SW	SW	SW	SW	SW	SW	SW	SW	SW	SW	SW		SW	SW	SW
					MO	MO	MO	MO	MO	MX	MX	MX	MX	MX	MX	MX	MX	MX	MX	MX	MX		MX		
						1	1			1			1				1								A
0	—	0	**London Waterloo** [15]	⊖ d	22p50	23p09	23p39		23p44	22p50	22p52	23p13	23p20	23p22	23p35	23p37				23p52	23p58			00 18	
1¼	—	1¼	Vauxhall	⊖ d	22p54	23p13	23p43		23p48		22p56	23p17		23p26		23p41				23p56	00 02			00 22	
2¾	—	2¾	Queenstown Rd.(Battersea)	d	22p57				23p51		22p59			23p29		23p44				23p59				00 25	
4	—	4	**Clapham Junction** [10]	d	23p00	23p19	23p49		23p54	22p58	23p02	23p23	23p28	23p32	23p43	23p47				00 02	00 08			00 28	
4¾	—	4¾	Wandsworth Town	d	23p03				23p57		23p05			23p35		23p50				00 05				00 31	
5¾	—	5¾	Putney	d	23p06	23p23	23p53		23p59		23p08	23p27		23p38		23p53			←	00 08	00 12			00 34	
7	0	7	Barnes	d	23p09				00 03		23p12			23p42		23p56			23p56	00 12				00 37	
—	½	—	Barnes Bridge	d	23p11						23p14			23p44		↦		←		00 14					
—	1½	—	Chiswick	d	23p13						23p17			23p47				23p47		00 17			←		
—	2½	—	Kew Bridge	d	23p16						23p20			↦				23p50		00 20			00 20		
—	3½	—	Brentford	d	23p19						23p23							23p53		↦			00 23		
—	4¼	—	Syon Lane	d	23p21						23p25							23p55					00 25		
—	5	—	Isleworth	d	23p23						23p27							23p57					00 27		
—	6½	—	**Hounslow**	d	23p27						23p31							00 01					00 31		
8¼	—	8¼	Mortlake	d					00 05										23p58					00 39	
9	—	9	North Sheen	d					00 07										00 01					00 41	
9¾	—	9¾	**Richmond**	⊖ d		23p29	23p59		00 10	23p06		23p33	23p37		23p51				00 03		00 18			00 44	
10¾	—	10¾	St Margarets	d					00 12										00 06					00 46	
11¼	—	11¼	Twickenham	a		23p32	00 02		00 14	23p10		23p36	23p41		23p55				00 08		00 21			00 48	
—	—	—		d		23p33	00 03		00 15	23p10		23p37	23p41		23p55				00 08		00 22			00 49	04 52
12¼	—	—	Strawberry Hill	d															00 12					00s52	04 55
12½	—	—	Fulwell	a																					
13½	—	—	Teddington	a															00 15					00s55	04 58
14¾	—	—	Hampton Wick	a															00 17					00s58	05 01
15¼	—	—	**Kingston**	a															00 19					01 00	05 03
—	—	12½	Whitton	d					00 18			23p40									00 25				
—	—	14¾	Feltham	d	23p33	23p39	00 09		00 22	23p16	23p36	23p44	23p48		00 01			00 06			00 29		00 36		
—	—	17½	Ashford (Surrey)	d	23p37				00 26		23p40	23p48						00 10			00 33		00 40		
0	—	19	**Staines**	d	23p41	23p45	00 15	00 21	00a30	23p23	23p45	23p52	23p56		00 08			00 15			00a37		00a46		
2½	—	—	Wraysbury	d								23p56													
3¾	—	—	Sunnymeads	d								23p59													
4¾	—	—	Datchet	d								00 02													
6¾	—	—	**Windsor & Eton Riverside**	a								00 06													
—	—	21	Egham	d	23p45	23p50	00 20	00s25		23p27	23p50		00 01		00 12			00 20							
0	—	23¼	Virginia Water	a	23p49	23p54	00 24	00s29		23p31	23p54		00 05		00 16			00 24							
—	—	—		d	23p49	23p54	00 24			23p31	23p54		00 05		00 16			00 24							
2½	—	—	Chertsey §	d	23p55			00s34			23p59							00 29							
4	—	—	Addlestone §	d	23p58			00s38			00 02							00 32							
5¾	—	—	**Weybridge**	a														00 37							
7¼	—	—	Byfleet & New Haw	d	00 02			00s42			00 07														
8½	—	—	West Byfleet	d	00 05			00s45			00 10														
11	—	—	Woking	a	00 10			00 50			00 16														
—	—	25¼	Longcross	d																					
—	—	27	Sunningdale	d		23p59	00 29			23p37			00 10		00 22										
—	0	29	**Ascot** [3]	d		00 04	00 34			23p43			00 15		00 27		00 29								
—	3¼	—	Bagshot	d													00 35								
—	6½	—	Camberley	a													00 41								
—	—	—		d													00 41								
—	8¾	—	Frimley	d													00 45								
—	12	—	Ash Vale	d													00 52								
—	14½	—	**Aldershot**	a													00 57								
—	—	—		d																					
—	17¼	—	Ash [3]	d																					
—	19¼	—	Wanborough	d																					
—	23½	—	**Guildford**	a																					
—	—	31¼	Martins Heron	d		00 08	00 38			23p47			00 19		00 31										
—	—	32¼	Bracknell	d		00 11	00 41			23p50			00 23		00 34										
—	—	36¾	**Wokingham**	d		00 18	00 48			23p57			00 32		00 41										
—	—	38¾	Winnersh	d		00 21	00 51			00 01			00 36												
—	—	39¼	Winnersh Triangle	d		00 23	00 53			00 02			00 38												
—	—	40½	Earley	d		00 26	00 56			00 05			00 40												
—	—	43½	**Reading** [7]	a		00 31	01 01			00 10			00 45		00 49										

For general notes see front of timetable
For details of catering facilities see Directory of Train Operators

§ Passengers to/from London may travel via Weybridge. See Table 155.

A To London Waterloo (Table 152)

For details of Bank Holiday service alterations, please see first page of this Table

London → Hounslow, Richmond, Kingston, Windsor, Weybridge, Ascot, Guildford and Reading

Network Diagram - see first page of Table 148

		SW 1	SW	SW 1	SW 1	SW	SW	SW	SW 1	SW 1	SW 1	SW	SW	SW	SW	SW 1	SW 1		SW	SW	SW	SW	SW	SW	SW 1
							A						A	B						B		A	B		
London Waterloo 15 ⊖	d				05 05		05 33				05 50	05 58	06 03	06 15			06 20		06 22		06 28	06 33	06 45		
Vauxhall ⊖	d				05 09		05 37					06 02	06 07	06 19					06 26		06 32	06 37	06 49		
Queenstown Rd.(Battersea)	d				05 12		05 40						06 10	06 22					06 29			06 40	06 52		
Clapham Junction 10	d				05 15		05 43				05 58	06 08	06 13	06 25			06 28		06 32		06 38	06 43	06 55		
Wandsworth Town	d				05 18		05 46						06 16	06 28					06 35			06 46	06 58		
Putney	d				05 21		05 49					06 12	06 19	06 31					06 38	←	06 42	06 49	07 01		
Barnes	d				05 24		05 52						06 22	06 35					06 42	06 35		06 52	07 05		
Barnes Bridge	d													→					06 44				→		
Chiswick	d																		06 47					←	
Kew Bridge	d																		06 50 →					06 50	
Brentford	d																							06 53	
Syon Lane	d																							06 55	
Isleworth	d																							06 57	
Hounslow	d																							07 01	
Mortlake	d				05 26		05 54						06 24							06 37		06 54			
North Sheen	d				05 28		05 56						06 26							06 39		06 56			
Richmond ⊖	d				05 31		05 59				06 06	06 18	06 29				06 36			06 42	06 48	06 59			
St Margarets	d				05 33		06 01						06 31							06 44		07 01			
Twickenham	a				05 35		06 03				06 10	06 21	06 33				06 40			06 46	06 51	07 03			
	d				05 36	05 52	06 04				06 10	06 22	06 34				06 40			06 47	06 52	07 04			
Strawberry Hill	d						06 07						06 37									07 07			
Fulwell	a																								
Teddington	a						06 10						06 40									07 10			
Hampton Wick	a						06 14						06 44									07 14			
Kingston	a						06 16						06 46									07 16			
Whitton	d				05 39	05 55						06 25								06a50	06 55				
Feltham	d				05 43	05 59					06 16	06 29					06 46				06 59			07 06	
Ashford (Surrey)	d				05 47	06 03						06 33									07 03			07 10	
Staines	d	05 23	05 45		05 53	06 07		06 15			06 23	06 37			06 45		06 53				07 07			07 15	
Wraysbury	d					06 11						06 41									07 11				
Sunnymeads	d					06 14						06 44									07 14				
Datchet	d					06 17						06 47									07 17				
Windsor & Eton Riverside	a					06 24						06 51									07 21				
Egham	d	05 27	05 50		05 57			06 20			06 27				06 50		06 57							07 20	
Virginia Water	a	05 31	05 54		06 01			06 24			06 31				06 54		07 01							07 24	
	d	05 31	05 54		06 01			06 24			06 31				06 54		07 01							07 24	
Chertsey §	d		05 59					06 29							06 59									07 29	
Addlestone §	d		06 02					06 32							07 02									07 32	
Weybridge	a		06 07					06 37							07 07									07 37	
Byfleet & New Haw	d																								
West Byfleet	d																								
Woking	a																								
Longcross	d										06 35						07 05								
Sunningdale	d	05 37			06 07						06 37						07 07								
Ascot 3	d	05 43			06 13					06 23	06 43					06 53	07 13								07 23
Bagshot	d									06 29						06 59									07 29
Camberley	a									06 35						07 05									07 35
	d									06 39						07 09									07 39
Frimley	d									06 43						07 13									07 43
Ash Vale	d									06 49						07 19									07 49
Aldershot	a									06 56						07 26									07 54
	d			06 08					06 38	07 08						07 38									08 08
Ash 3	d			06 15					06 45	07 15						07 45									08 15
Wanborough	d			06 18					06 48	07 18						07 48									08 18
Guildford	a			06 25					06 55	07 25						07 55									08 25
Martins Heron	d	05 47			06 17						06 47						07 17								
Bracknell	d	05 50			06 20						06 50						07 20								
Wokingham	d	05 57			06 27						06 57						07 27								
Winnersh	d	06 00			06 30						07 00						07 30								
Winnersh Triangle	d	06 02			06 32						07 02						07 32								
Earley	d	06 05			06 35						07 05						07 35								
Reading 7	a	06 10			06 40						07 10						07 40								

For general notes see front of timetable
For details of catering facilities see Directory of Train Operators

§ Passengers to/from London may travel via Weybridge. See Table 155.

A To London Waterloo (Table 152)
B To London Waterloo

For details of Bank Holiday service alterations, please see first page of this Table

London → Hounslow, Richmond, Kingston, Windsor, Weybridge, Ascot, Guildford and Reading

Network Diagram - see first page of Table 148

		SW ■1	SW	GW ■1	SW ■1	SW	SW	SW	SW	SW	SW	SW ■1	SW		SW ■1	SW	SW	SW	SW	SW	SW	SW	SW ■1	SW	SW ■1
				A		B		C		B	C					B		C			B	C			
London Waterloo 15	⊖ d	06 50	06 52				06 58	07 03		07 15		07 20	07 22				07 28	07 33		07 37	07 45		07 50	07 52	
Vauxhall	⊖ d		06 56				07 02	07 07		07 19			07 26				07 32	07 37		07 41	07 49			07 56	
Queenstown Rd.(Battersea)	d		06 59					07 10		07 22			07 29					07 40		07 44	07 52			07 59	
Clapham Junction 10	d	06 58	07 02				07 08	07 13		07 25		07 28	07 32				07 38	07 43		07 47	07 55		07 58	08 02	
Wandsworth Town	d		07 05					07 16		07 28			07 35					07 46		07 50	07 58			08 05	
Putney	d		07 08			←	07 12	07 19		07 31			07 38			←	07 42	07 49		07 53	08 01			08 08	
Barnes	d		07 12			07 05		07 22		07 35			07 42			07 35		07 52		07 57	08 05			08 12	
Barnes Bridge	d		07 14							→			07 44							07 59	→			08 14	
Chiswick	d		07 17						←				07 47						←	08 02				08 17	
Kew Bridge	d		07 20						07 20				07 50						07 50	08 05				08 20	
Brentford	d		→						07 23				→						07 53	08 08				→	
Syon Lane	d								07 25										07 55	08 10					
Isleworth	d								07 27										07 57	08 12					
Hounslow	d								07 31										08 01	08a18					
Mortlake	d					07 07		07 24								07 37		07 54							
North Sheen	d					07 09		07 26								07 39		07 56							
Richmond	⊖ d	07 06				07 12	07 18	07 29				07 36				07 42	07 48	07 59					08 06		
St Margarets	d					07 14		07 31								07 44		08 01							
Twickenham	a	07 10				07 16	07 21	07 33				07 40				07 46	07 51	08 03					08 10		
	d	07 10				07 17	07 22	07 34			07 37	07 40				07 47	07 52	08 04				08 07	08 10		
Strawberry Hill	d							07 37			07b47							08 07				08c17			
Fulwell	a																								
Teddington	a							07 40			07 50							08 10				08 20			
Hampton Wick	a							07 44			07 52							08 14				08 22			
Kingston	a							07 46			07 54							08 16				08 24			
Whitton	d					07a20	07 25									07a50	07 55								
Feltham	d	07 16					07 29		07 36			07 46					07 59		08 06				08 16		
Ashford (Surrey)	d						07 33		07 40								08 03		08 10						
Staines	d	07 23					07 37		07 45			07 53					08 07		08 15				08 23		
Wraysbury	d						07 41										08 11								
Sunnymeads	d						07 44										08 14								
Datchet	d						07 47										08 17								
Windsor & Eton Riverside	a						07 51										08 21								
Egham	d	07 27							07 50			07 57							08 20				08 27		
Virginia Water	a	07 31							07 54			08 01							08 24				08 31		
	d	07 31							07 54			08 01							08 24				08 31		
Chertsey §	d								07 59										08 29						
Addlestone §	d								08 02										08 32						
Weybridge	a								08 07										08 37						
Byfleet & New Haw	d																								
West Byfleet	d																								
Woking	a																								
Longcross	d	07 35										08 05											08 35		
Sunningdale	d	07 37										08 07											08 37		
Ascot 3	d	07 43			07 53							08 13			08 23								08 43		08 53
Bagshot	d				07 59										08 29										08 59
Camberley	a				08 05										08 37										09 05
	d				08 09										08 39										09 09
Frimley	d				08 13										08 43										09 13
Ash Vale	d				08 19										08 49										09 19
Aldershot	a				08 24										08 54										09 25
	d				08 38										09 08										09 38
Ash 3	d				08 45										09 15										09 45
Wanborough	d				08 48										09 18										09 48
Guildford	a				08 55										09 25										09 55
Martins Heron	d	07 47										08 17											08 47		
Bracknell	d	07 50										08 20											08 50		
Wokingham	d	07 57		08 17								08 27											08 57		
Winnersh	d	08 00		08 21								08 30											09 00		
Winnersh Triangle	d	08 02										08 32											09 02		
Earley	d	08 05										08 35											09 05		
Reading 7	a	08 10		08 28								08 40											09 10		

For general notes see front of timetable
For details of catering facilities see Directory of Train Operators

§ Passengers to/from London may travel via Weybridge. See Table 155.

A From Gatwick Airport (Table 148)
B To London Waterloo
C To London Waterloo (Table 152)

b Arr. 0740
c Arr. 0810

Table 149

Mondays to Fridays

until 26 September

For details of Bank Holiday service alterations, please see first page of this Table

London → Hounslow, Richmond, Kingston, Windsor, Weybridge, Ascot, Guildford and Reading

Network Diagram - see first page of Table 148

		SW	SW	SW	SW 1	SW	SW	SW	SW		SW 1	SW	SW 1	SW	SW	SW 1	SW	SW	SW	SW	SW 1	SW	SW 1	SW
		A		B		B		A	A					A		B		B		A	A			A
London Waterloo 15	⊖ d		07 58	08 03	08 07			08 10	08 15		08 20	08 22			08 28	08 33	08 37			08 40	08 43	08 50	08 52	
Vauxhall	⊖ d		08 02	08 07				08 14	08 19			08 26			08 32	08 37				08 44	08 47		08 56	
Queenstown Rd.(Battersea)	d			08 10				08 17	08 22			08 29				08 40				08 47	08 50		08 59	
Clapham Junction 10	d		08 08	08 13	08 15			08 20	08 25		08 28	08 32			08 38	08 43	08 45			08 50	08 55	08 58	09 02	
Wandsworth Town	d			08 16				08 23	08 28			08 35				08 46				08 53	08 58		09 05	
Putney	d	⟵	08 12	08 19		⟵		08 26	08 31			08 38		⟵	08 42	08 49		⟵		08 56	09 01		09 08	⟵
Barnes	d	08 05		08 22		08 22		08 28	08 35			08 42		08 35		08 52		08 52		08 58	09 05		09 12	09 05
Barnes Bridge	d			⟶				08 30	⟶			08 44				⟶				09 00	⟶		09 14	
Chiswick	d						⟵	08 33				08 47							⟵	09 02			09 17	
Kew Bridge	d						08 20	08 35				08 50							08 50	09 05			09 20	
Brentford	d						08 23	08 38				⟶							08 53	09 08			⟶	
Syon Lane	d						08 25	08 40											08 55	09 10				
Isleworth	d						08 27	08 42											08 57	09 12				
Hounslow	d						08 31	08 48											09 01	09 18				
Mortlake	d	08 07				08 24								08 37				08 54						09 07
North Sheen	d	08 09				08 26								08 39				08 56						09 09
Richmond	⊖ d	08 12	08 18		08 23	08 29					08 36			08 42	08 48		08 53	08 59				09 06		09 12
St Margarets	d	08 14				08 31								08 44				09 01						09 14
Twickenham	a	08 16	08 21		08 27	08 33					08 40			08 46	08 51		08 57	09 03				09 10		09 16
	d	08 17	08 22		08 27	08 34					08 40			08 47	08 52		08 57	09 04				09 10		09 17
Strawberry Hill	d					08 37												09 07						
Fulwell	a																							
Teddington	a					08 40												09 10						
Hampton Wick	a					08 44												09 14						
Kingston	a					08 46												09 16						
Whitton	d	08a20	08 25					08a53						08a50	08 55					09a23				09a20
Feltham	d		08 29		08 33		08 36				08 46				08 59		09 03		09 07			09 16		
Ashford (Surrey)	d		08 33		08 37		08 40								09 03		09 07		09 10					
Staines	d		08 37		08 41		08 45				08 53				09 07		09 11		09 15			09 23		
Wraysbury	d		08 41												09 11									
Sunnymeads	d		08 44												09 14									
Datchet	d		08 47												09 17									
Windsor & Eton Riverside	a		08 51												09 21									
Egham	d				08 46		08 50				08 57						09 16		09 20			09 27		
Virginia Water	a				08 50		08 54				09 01						09 20		09 24			09 31		
	d				08 50		08 54				09 01						09 20		09 24			09 31		
Chertsey §	d						08 59												09 29					
Addlestone §	d						09 02												09 32					
Weybridge	a						09 07												09 37					
Byfleet & New Haw	d																							
West Byfleet	d																							
Woking	a																							
Longcross	d				08 53																			
Sunningdale	d				08 57						09 07						09 25					09 37		
Ascot 3	d				09 01						09 13		09 23				09 30					09 43		09 53
Bagshot	d												09 29											09 59
Camberley	a												09 35											10 05
	d												09 39											10 09
Frimley	d												09 43											10 13
Ash Vale	d												09 49											10 19
Aldershot	a												09 54											10 24
	d												10 08											10 38
Ash 3	d												10 15											10 45
Wanborough	d												10 18											10 48
Guildford	a												10 25											10 55
Martins Heron	d				09 05						09 17						09 34					09 47		
Bracknell	d				09 09						09 20						09 37					09 50		
Wokingham	d				09 17						09 27						09 46					09 57		
Winnersh	d				09 20						09 30											10 00		
Winnersh Triangle	d				09 22						09 32											10 02		
Earley	d				09 25						09 35											10 05		
Reading 7	a				09 30						09 40						09 55					10 10		

For general notes see front of timetable
For details of catering facilities see Directory of Train Operators

A To London Waterloo
B To London Waterloo (Table 152)

§ Passengers to/from London may travel via Weybridge. See Table 155.

For details of Bank Holiday service alterations, please see first page of this Table

London → Hounslow, Richmond, Kingston, Windsor, Weybridge, Ascot, Guildford and Reading

Network Diagram - see first page of Table 148

		SW	SW	SW	SW	SW	SW	SW	SW	SW	SW	SW	SW	SW	SW	SW	SW	SW	SW	SW	SW	SW
							1		1							1		1				
			A		B	B				B		A		B	B				B		A	
London Waterloo 15	⊖ d	08 58	09 03		09 07	09 15	09 20	09 22			09 28	09 33		09 37	09 45	09 50	09 52			09 58	10 03	
Vauxhall	⊖ d	09 02	09 07		09 11	09 19		09 26			09 32	09 37		09 41	09 49		09 56			10 02	10 07	
Queenstown Rd.(Battersea)	d		09 10		09 14	09 22		09 29				09 40		09 44	09 52		09 59				10 10	
Clapham Junction 10	d	09 08	09 13		09 17	09 25	09 28	09 32			09 38	09 43		09 47	09 55	09 58	10 02			10 08	10 13	
Wandsworth Town	d		09 16		09 20	09 28		09 35				09 46		09 50	09 58		10 05				10 16	
Putney	d	09 12	09 19		09 23	09 31		09 38		←	09 42	09 49		09 53	10 01		10 08		←	10 12	10 19	
Barnes	d		09 22		09 27	09 35		09 42		09 35		09 52		09 57	10 05		10 12		10 05		10 22	
Barnes Bridge	d				09 29	→		09 44						09 59	→		10 14					
Chiswick	d			←	09 32			09 47					←	10 02			10 17					←
Kew Bridge	d			09 20	09 35			09 50					09 50	10 05			10 20					10 20
Brentford	d			09 23	09 38			→					09 53	10 08			→					10 23
Syon Lane	d			09 25	09 40								09 55	10 10								10 25
Isleworth	d			09 27	09 42								09 57	10 12								10 27
Hounslow	d			09 31	09b48								10 01	10c18								10 31
Mortlake	d		09 24							09 37		09 54							10 07		10 24	
North Sheen	d		09 26							09 39		09 56							10 09		10 26	
Richmond	⊖ d	09 18	09 29				09 36			09 42	09 48	09 59				10 06			10 12	10 18	10 29	
St Margarets	d		09 31							09 44		10 01							10 14		10 31	
Twickenham	a	09 21	09 33				09 40			09 46	09 51	10 03				10 10			10 16	10 21	10 33	
	d	09 22	09 34				09 40			09 47	09 52	10 04				10 10			10 17	10 22	10 34	
Strawberry Hill	d		09 37									10 07									10 37	
Fulwell	a																					
Teddington	a		09 40									10 10									10 40	
Hampton Wick	a		09 44									10 14									10 44	
Kingston	a		09 46									10 16									10 46	
Whitton	d	09 25			09a53					09a50	09 55			10a26					10a20	10 25		
Feltham	d	09 29		09 36			09 46				09 59		10 06			10 16				10 29		10 36
Ashford (Surrey)	d	09 33		09 40							10 03		10 10							10 33		10 40
Staines	d	09 37		09 45			09 53				10 07		10 15			10 23				10 37		10 45
Wraysbury	d	09 41									10 11									10 41		
Sunnymeads	d	09 44									10 14									10 44		
Datchet	d	09 47									10 17									10 47		
Windsor & Eton Riverside	a	09 51									10 21									10 51		
Egham	d			09 50			09 57						10 20			10 27						10 50
Virginia Water	a			09 54			10 01						10 24			10 31						10 54
	d			09 54			10 01						10 24			10 31						10 54
Chertsey §	d			09 59									10 29									10 59
Addlestone §	d			10 02									10 32									11 02
Weybridge	a			10 07									10 37									11 07
Byfleet & New Haw	d																					
West Byfleet	d																					
Woking	a																					
Longcross	d																					
Sunningdale	d						10 07									10 37						
Ascot 3	d						10 13		10 23							10 43		10 53				
Bagshot	d								10 29									10 59				
Camberley	a								10 35									11 05				
	d								10 39									11 09				
Frimley	d								10 43									11 13				
Ash Vale	d								10 49									11 19				
Aldershot	a								10 54									11 24				
	d								11 08									11 38				
Ash 3	d								11 15									11 45				
Wanborough	d								11 18									11 48				
Guildford	a								11 25									11 55				
Martins Heron	d						10 17									10 47						
Bracknell	d						10 20									10 50						
Wokingham	d						10 27									10 57						
Winnersh	d						10 30									11 00						
Winnersh Triangle	d						10 32									11 02						
Earley	d						10 35									11 05						
Reading 7	a						10 40									11 10						

For general notes see front of timetable
For details of catering facilities see Directory of Train Operators

§ Passengers to/from London may travel via Weybridge. See Table 155.

A To London Waterloo (Table 152)
B To London Waterloo
b Arr. 0945
c Arr. 1015

For details of Bank Holiday service alterations, please see first page of this Table

London → Hounslow, Richmond, Kingston, Windsor, Weybridge, Ascot, Guildford and Reading

Network Diagram - see first page of Table 148

		SW	SW	SW ■1	SW	SW ■1	SW	SW	SW	SW	SW	SW	SW ■1	SW	SW ■1	SW	SW	SW	SW		SW ■1	SW
		A	A				A		B		A	A				A		B		C		
London Waterloo 15	⊖ d	10 07	10 15	10 20	10 22			10 28	10 33		10 37	10 45	10 50	10 52			10 58	11 03			15 20	15 22
Vauxhall	⊖ d	10 11	10 19		10 26			10 32	10 37		10 41	10 49		10 56			11 02	11 07				15 26
Queenstown Rd.(Battersea)	d	10 14	10 22		10 29				10 40		10 44	10 52		10 59				11 10				15 29
Clapham Junction 10	d	10 17	10 25	10 28	10 32			10 38	10 43		10 47	10 55	10 58	11 02			11 08	11 13			15 28	15 32
Wandsworth Town	d	10 20	10 28		10 35				10 46		10 50	10 58		11 05				11 16				15 35
Putney	d	10 23	10 31		10 38		←	10 42	10 49		10 53	11 01		11 08		←	11 12	11 19				15 38
Barnes	d	10 27	10 35		10 42		10 35		10 52		10 57	11 05		11 12		11 05		11 22				15 42
Barnes Bridge	d	10 29	→		10 44						10 59	→		11 14								15 44
Chiswick	d	10 32			10 47					←	11 02			11 17					←			15 47
Kew Bridge	d	10 35			10 50					10 50	11 05			11 20					11 20			15 50
Brentford	d	10 38			→					10 53	11 08			→					11 23			→
Syon Lane	d	10 40								10 55	11 10								11 25			
Isleworth	d	10 42								10 57	11 12								11 27			
Hounslow	d	10b48								11 01	11c18								11 31			
Mortlake	d						10 37		10 54							11 07		11 24				
North Sheen	d						10 39		10 56							11 09		11 26				
Richmond	⊖ d			10 36			10 42	10 48	10 59				11 06			11 12	11 18	11 29			15 36	
St Margarets	d						10 44		11 01							11 14		11 31				
Twickenham	a			10 40			10 46	10 51	11 03				11 10			11 17	11 21	11 33			15 40	
	d			10 40			10 47	10 52	11 04				11 10			11 17	11 22	11 34			15 40	
Strawberry Hill	d								11 07									11 37				
Fulwell	a																					
Teddington	a								11 10									11 40				
Hampton Wick	a								11 14									11 44				
Kingston	a								11 16									11 46		and at		
Whitton	d	10a56					10a50	10 55			11a23					11a20	11 25			the same		
Feltham	d			10 46				10 59		11 06			11 16				11 29		11 36		15 46	
Ashford (Surrey)	d							11 03		11 10							11 33		11 40	minutes		
Staines	d			10 53				11 07		11 15			11 23				11 37		11 45		15 53	
Wraysbury	d							11 11									11 41			past		
Sunnymeads	d							11 14									11 44			each		
Datchet	d							11 17									11 47					
Windsor & Eton Riverside	a							11 21									11 51			hour until		
Egham	d			10 57						11 20			11 27						11 50		15 57	
Virginia Water	a			11 01						11 24			11 31						11 54		16 01	
	d			11 01						11 24			11 31						11 54		16 01	
Chertsey §	d									11 29									11 59			
Addlestone §	d									11 32									12 02			
Weybridge	a									11 37									12 07			
Byfleet & New Haw	d																					
West Byfleet	d																					
Woking	a																					
Longcross	d																					
Sunningdale	d			11 07									11 37								16 07	
Ascot 3	d			11 13		11 23							11 43		11 53						16 13	
Bagshot	d					11 29									11 59							
Camberley	a					11 35									12 05							
	d					11 39									12 09							
Frimley	d					11 43									12 13							
Ash Vale	d					11 49									12 19							
Aldershot	a					11 54									12 24							
	d					12 08									12 38							
Ash 3	d					12 15									12 45							
Wanborough	d					12 18									12 48							
Guildford	a					12 25									12 55							
Martins Heron	d			11 17									11 47								16 17	
Bracknell	d			11 20									11 50								16 20	
Wokingham	d			11 27									11 57								16 27	
Winnersh	d			11 30									12 00								16 30	
Winnersh Triangle	d			11 32									12 02								16 32	
Earley	d			11 35									12 05								16 35	
Reading 7	a			11 40									12 10								16 40	

For general notes see front of timetable
For details of catering facilities see Directory of Train Operators

§ Passengers to/from London may travel via Weybridge. See Table 155.

A To London Waterloo
B To London Waterloo (Table 152)
C 1250 from London Waterloo calls Longcross 1335

b Arr. 1045
c Arr. 1115

For details of Bank Holiday service alterations, please see first page of this Table

London → Hounslow, Richmond, Kingston, Windsor, Weybridge, Ascot, Guildford and Reading

Network Diagram - see first page of Table 148

		SW 1	SW	SW	SW	SW	SW	SW	SW 1	SW	SW 1	SW	SW	SW	SW 1	SW	SW	SW		SW	SW 1	SW	SW 1	SW	SW
			A		B		A	A				A		B		B		A		A				A	
London Waterloo 15	⊖ d			15 28	15 33		15 37	15 45	15 50	15 52			15 58	16 01	16 05			16 07		16 15	16 20	16 22			16 28
Vauxhall	⊖ d			15 32	15 37		15 41	15 49		15 56			16 02	16 05	16 09			16 11		16 19		16 26			16 32
Queenstown Rd.(Battersea)	d				15 40		15 44	15 52		15 59				16 08				16 14		16 22		16 29			
Clapham Junction 10	d			15 38	15 43		15 47	15 55	15 58	16 02			16 08	16 11	16 15			16 17		16 25	16 28	16 32			16 38
Wandsworth Town	d				15 46		15 50	15 58		16 05				16 14				16 20		16 28		16 35			
Putney	d		←	15 42	15 49		15 53	16 01		16 08		←	16 12	16 17		←		16 23		16 31		16 38		←	16 42
Barnes	d		15 35		15 52		15 57	16 05		16 12		16 05		16 22		16 22		16 27		16 35		16 42		16 35	
Barnes Bridge	d						15 59	→		16 14				→				16 29		→		16 44			
Chiswick	d					←	16 02			16 17							←	16 32				16 47			
Kew Bridge	d					15 50	16 05			16 20							16 20	16 35				16 50			
Brentford	d					15 53	16 08			→							16 23	16 38				→			
Syon Lane	d					15 55	16 10										16 25	16 40							
Isleworth	d					15 57	16 12										16 27	16 42							
Hounslow	d					16 01	16b18										16 31	16c48							
Mortlake	d		15 37		15 54							16 07				16 24								16 37	
North Sheen	d		15 39		15 56							16 09				16 26								16 39	
Richmond	⊖ d		15 42	15 48	15 59				16 06			16 12	16 18		16 23	16 29					16 36			16 42	16 48
St Margarets	d		15 44		16 01							16 14				16 31								16 44	
Twickenham	a		15 46	15 51	16 03				16 10			16 16	16 21		16 27	16 33					16 40			16 46	16 51
	d		15 47	15 52	16 04				16 10			16 17	16 22		16 27	16 34					16 40			16 47	16 52
Strawberry Hill	d				16 07											16 37									
Fulwell	a																								
Teddington	a				16 10											16 42									
Hampton Wick	a				16 14											16 46									
Kingston	a				16 16											16 48									
Whitton	d		15a50	15 55			16a23					16a20	16 25					16a53						16a50	16 55
Feltham	d			15 59		16 06			16 16				16 29		16 33		16 36				16 46				16 59
Ashford (Surrey)	d			16 03		16 10							16 33		16 37		16 40								17 03
Staines	d			16 07		16 15			16 23				16 37		16 41		16 45				16 53				17 07
Wraysbury	d			16 11									16 41												17 11
Sunnymeads	d			16 14									16 44												17 14
Datchet	d			16 17									16 47												17 17
Windsor & Eton Riverside	a			16 21									16 51												17 23
Egham	d					16 20			16 27						16 46		16 50				16 57				
Virginia Water	a					16 24			16 31						16 50		16 54				17 01				
	d					16 24			16 31						16 50		16 54				17 01				
Chertsey §	d					16 29											16 59								
Addlestone §	d					16 32											17 02								
Weybridge	a					16 37											17 07								
Byfleet & New Haw	d																								
West Byfleet	d																								
Woking	a																								
Longcross	d																								
Sunningdale	d								16 37						16 55						17 07				
Ascot 3	d	16 23							16 43		16 53				17 00						17 13		17 23		
Bagshot	d	16 29									16 59												17 29		
Camberley	a	16 35									17 05												17 35		
	d	16 39									17 09												17 39		
Frimley	d	16 43									17 13												17 43		
Ash Vale	d	16 49									17 19												17 49		
Aldershot	a	16 54									17 24												17 54		
	d	17 08									17 38												18 08		
Ash 3	d	17 15									17 45												18 15		
Wanborough	d	17 18									17 48												18 18		
Guildford	a	17 25									17 55												18 25		
Martins Heron	d								16 47						17 04						17 17				
Bracknell	d								16 50						17 07						17 20				
Wokingham	d								16 57						17 17						17 27				
Winnersh	d								17 00												17 30				
Winnersh Triangle	d								17 02												17 32				
Earley	d								17 05												17 35				
Reading 7	a								17 10						17 27						17 42				

For general notes see front of timetable
For details of catering facilities see Directory of Train Operators

§ Passengers to/from London may travel via Weybridge. See Table 155.

A To London Waterloo
B To London Waterloo (Table 152)
b Arr. 1615
c Arr. 1645

For details of Bank Holiday service alterations, please see first page of this Table

London → Hounslow, Richmond, Kingston, Windsor, Weybridge, Ascot, Guildford and Reading

Network Diagram - see first page of Table 148

		SW	SW	SW	SW	SW	SW	SW 1	SW	SW	SW	SW	SW 1	SW		SW	SW 1	SW	SW	SW	SW 1	SW	SW 1	SW	SW
		A		A		B	B			B		A		A				B		B				B	
London Waterloo 15 ⊖	d	16 31	16 35			16 37	16 45	16 50	16 52		16 58	17 01	17 05					17 07	17 13	17 15	17 20	17 22			17 28
Vauxhall ⊖	d	16 35	16 39			16 41	16 49		16 56		17 02	17 05	17 09					17 11	17 17	17 19		17 26			17 32
Queenstown Rd.(Battersea)	d	16 38				16 44	16 52		16 59			17 08						17 14		17 22		17 29			
Clapham Junction 10	d	16 41	16 45			16 47	16 55	16 58	17 02		17 08	17 11	17 15					17 17	17 23	17 25	17 28	17 32			17 38
Wandsworth Town	d	16 44				16 50	16 58		17 05			17 14						17 20		17 28		17 35			
Putney	d	16 47		←		16 53	17 01		17 08	←	17 12	17 17		←				17 23	17 27	17 31		17 38		←	17 42
Barnes	d	16 52		16 52		16 57	17 05		17 12	17 05		17 22		17 22				17 27		17 35		17 42		17 35	
Barnes Bridge	d	→				16 59	→		17 14			→						17 29		→		17 44			
Chiswick	d				←	17 02			17 17							←		17 32				17 47			
Kew Bridge	d				16 50	17 05			17 20							17 20		17 35				17 50			
Brentford	d				16 53	17 08			→							17 23		17 38				→			
Syon Lane	d				16 55	17 10										17 25		17 40							
Isleworth	d				16 57	17 12										17 27		17 42							
Hounslow	d				17 01	17b18										17 31		17c48							
Mortlake	d			16 54						17 07				17 24				18a08						17 37	
North Sheen	d			16 56						17 09				17 26										17 39	
Richmond ⊖	d		16 53	16 59				17 06		17 12	17 18		17 23	17 29					17 33		17 36			17 42	17 48
St Margarets	d			17 01						17 14				17 31										17 44	
Twickenham	a		16 57	17 03				17 10		17 16	17 21		17 27	17 33					17 37		17 40			17 46	17 51
	d		16 57	17 04				17 10		17 17	17 22		17 27	17 34					17 37		17 40			17 47	17 52
Strawberry Hill	d			17 07										17 37					17 41						
Fulwell	a																								
Teddington	a			17 12										17 42					17 46						
Hampton Wick	a			17 16										17 46											
Kingston	a			17 18										17 48											
Whitton	d					17a23				17a20	17 25							17a53						17a50	17 55
Feltham	d		17 03		17 06			17 16			17 29		17 33			17 36					17 46				17 59
Ashford (Surrey)	d		17 07		17 10						17 33		17 37			17 40									18 03
Staines	d		17 11		17 15			17 23			17 37		17 41			17 45					17 53				18 07
Wraysbury	d										17 41														18 11
Sunnymeads	d										17 44														18 14
Datchet	d										17 47														18 17
Windsor & Eton Riverside	a										17 53														18 23
Egham	d		17 16		17 20			17 27					17 46			17 50					17 57				
Virginia Water	a		17 20		17 24			17 31					17 50			17 54					18 01				
	d		17 20		17 24			17 31					17 50			17 54					18 01				
Chertsey §	d				17 29											17 59									
Addlestone §	d				17 32											18 02									
Weybridge	a				17 40											18 10									
Byfleet & New Haw	d																								
West Byfleet	d																								
Woking	a																								
Longcross	d		17 23																		18 07				
Sunningdale	d		17 27					17 37					17 55								18 13				
Ascot 3	d		17 31					17 43					18 00										18 23		
Bagshot	d												18 06										18 29		
Camberley	a												18 12										18 35		
	d												18 13										18 39		
Frimley	d												18 17										18 43		
Ash Vale	d												18 24										18 49		
Aldershot	a												18 31										18 54		
	d																18 38						19 08		
Ash 3	d																18 45						19 15		
Wanborough	d																18 48						19 18		
Guildford	a																18 55						19 25		
Martins Heron	d		17 35					17 47													18 17				
Bracknell	d		17 39					17 50													18 20				
Wokingham	d		17 47					17 57													18 27				
Winnersh	d							18 00													18 30				
Winnersh Triangle	d							18 02													18 32				
Earley	d							18 05													18 35				
Reading 7	a		17 58					18 12													18 43				

For general notes see front of timetable
For details of catering facilities see
Directory of Train Operators

§ Passengers to/from London may travel via Weybridge. See Table 155.

A To London Waterloo (Table 152)
B To London Waterloo
b Arr. 1715
c Arr. 1745

For details of Bank Holiday service alterations, please see first page of this Table

London → Hounslow, Richmond, Kingston, Windsor, Weybridge, Ascot, Guildford and Reading

Network Diagram - see first page of Table 148

		SW	SW [1]	SW	SW	SW	SW	SW	SW [1]	SW	SW	SW	SW	SW [1]	SW	SW	SW [1]	SW	SW	SW	SW [1]	SW	SW [1]	SW
		A		A		B	C	B			B		A		A			B	C	B				B
London Waterloo [15]	⊖ d	17 31	17 35			17 37	17 43	17 45	17 50	17 52		17 58	18 01	18 05				18 07	18 13	18 15	18 20	18 22		
Vauxhall	⊖ d	17 35	17 39			17 41	17 47	17 49		17 56		18 02	18 05	18 09				18 11	18 17	18 19		18 26		
Queenstown Rd.(Battersea)	d	17 38				17 44		17 52		17 59			18 08					18 14		18 22		18 29		
Clapham Junction [10]	d	17 41	17 45			17 47	17 53	17 55	17 58	18 02		18 08	18 11	18 15				18 17	18 23	18 25	18 28	18 32		
Wandsworth Town	d	17 44				17 50		17 58		18 05			18 14					18 20		18 28		18 35		
Putney	d	17 47		←		17 53	17 57	18 01		18 08	←	18 12	18 17		←			18 23	18 27	18 31		18 38		←
Barnes	d	17 52		17 52		17 57		18 05		18 12	18 05		18 22		18 22			18 27		18 35		18 42		18 35
Barnes Bridge	d	→				17 59		→		18 14			→					18 29		→		18 44		
Chiswick	d				←	18 02				18 17						←		18 32				18 47		
Kew Bridge	d				17 50	18 05				18 20						18 20		18 35				18 50		
Brentford	d				17 53	18 08				→						18 23		18 38				→		
Syon Lane	d				17 55	18 10										18 25		18 40						
Isleworth	d				17 57	18 12										18 27		18 42						
Hounslow	d				18 01	18b18										18 31		18c48						
Mortlake	d			17 54							18 07				18 24									18 37
North Sheen	d			17 56							18 09				18 26									18 39
Richmond	⊖ d		17 53	17 59			18 03		18 06		18 12	18 18		18 23	18 29				18 33		18 36			18 42
St Margarets	d			18 01							18 14				18 31									18 44
Twickenham	a		17 57	18 03			18 07		18 10		18 16	18 21		18 27	18 33				18 37		18 40			18 46
	d		17 57	18 04			18 07		18 10		18 17	18 22		18 27	18 34				18 37		18 40			18 47
Strawberry Hill	d			18 07			18 11								18 37				18 41					
Fulwell	a						18 13												18 43					
Teddington	a			18 12											18 42									
Hampton Wick	a			18 16											18 46									
Kingston	a			18 18											18 48									
Whitton	d					18a23					18a20	18 25						18a53						18a50
Feltham	d		18 03		18 06				18 16			18 29		18 33		18 36					18 46			
Ashford (Surrey)	d		18 07		18 10							18 33		18 37		18 40								
Staines	d		18 11		18 15				18 23			18 37		18 41		18 45					18 53			
Wraysbury	d											18 41												
Sunnymeads	d											18 44												
Datchet	d											18 47												
Windsor & Eton Riverside	a											18 53												
Egham	d		18 16		18 20				18 27					18 46		18 50					18 57			
Virginia Water	a		18 20		18 24				18 31					18 50		18 54					19 01			
	d		18 20		18 24				18 31					18 50		18 54					19 01			
Chertsey §	d				18 29											18 59								
Addlestone §	d				18 32											19 02								
Weybridge	a				18 40											19 10								
Byfleet & New Haw	d																							
West Byfleet	d																							
Woking	a																							
Longcross	d								18 35															
Sunningdale	d		18 25						18 37					18 55							19 07			
Ascot [3]	d		18 30						18 43					19 02							19 13		19 23	
Bagshot	d													19 08									19 29	
Camberley	a													19 14									19 35	
	d													19 15									19 39	
Frimley	d													19 19									19 43	
Ash Vale	d													19 26									19 49	
Aldershot	a													19 35									19 54	
	d															19 38							20 08	
Ash [3]	d															19 45							20 15	
Wanborough	d															19 48							20 18	
Guildford	a															19 55							20 25	
Martins Heron	d		18 34						18 47												19 17			
Bracknell	d		18 37						18 50												19 20			
Wokingham	d		18 47						18 57												19 27			
Winnersh	d								19 00												19 30			
Winnersh Triangle	d								19 02												19 32			
Earley	d								19 05												19 35			
Reading [7]	a		18 57						19 12												19 42			

For general notes see front of timetable
For details of catering facilities see Directory of Train Operators

§ Passengers to/from London may travel via Weybridge. See Table 155.

A To London Waterloo (Table 152)
B To London Waterloo
C To Shepperton (Table 152)

b Arr. 1815
c Arr. 1845

For details of Bank Holiday service alterations, please see first page of this Table

London → Hounslow, Richmond, Kingston, Windsor, Weybridge, Ascot, Guildford and Reading

Network Diagram - see first page of Table 148

		SW	SW	SW 1	SW	SW		SW	SW	SW	SW 1	SW	SW 1	SW	SW	SW	SW 1	SW	SW	SW	SW	SW 1	SW	SW 1	SW
			A		A			B	C	B				B		A		A		B	B				B
London Waterloo 15 ⊖	d	18 28	18 31	18 35				18 37	18 43	18 45	18 50	18 52			18 58	19 01	19 05			19 07	19 15	19 20	19 22		
Vauxhall ⊖	d	18 32	18 35	18 39				18 41	18 47	18 49		18 56			19 02	19 05	19 09			19 11	19 19		19 26		
Queenstown Rd.(Battersea)	d		18 38					18 44		18 52		18 59				19 08				19 14	19 22		19 29		
Clapham Junction 10	d	18 38	18 41	18 45				18 47	18 53	18 55	18 58	19 02			19 08	19 11	19 15			19 17	19 25	19 28	19 32		
Wandsworth Town	d		18 44					18 50		18 58		19 05				19 14				19 20	19 28		19 35		
Putney	d	18 42	18 47		←			18 53	18 57	19 01		19 08		←	19 12	19 17		←		19 23	19 31		19 38		←
Barnes	d		18 52		18 52			18 57		19 05		19 12		19 05		19 22		19 22		19 27	19 35		19 42		19 35
Barnes Bridge	d		→					18 59		→		19 14				→				19 29	→		19 44		
Chiswick	d					←		19 02				19 17							←	19 32			19 47		
Kew Bridge	d					18 50		19 05				19 20 →							19 20	19 35			19 50 →		
Brentford	d					18 53		19 08											19 23	19 38					
Syon Lane	d					18 55		19 10											19 25	19 40					
Isleworth	d					18 57		19 12											19 27	19 42					
Hounslow	d					19 01		19b18											19 31	19c48					
Mortlake	d				18 54									19 07				19 24							19 37
North Sheen	d				18 56									19 09				19 26							19 39
Richmond ⊖	d	18 48		18 53	18 59				19 03		19 06			19 12	19 18		19 23	19 29				19 36			19 42
St Margarets	d				19 01									19 14				19 31							19 44
Twickenham	a	18 51		18 57	19 03				19 07		19 10			19 16	19 21		19 27	19 33				19 40			19 46
	d	18 52		18 57	19 04				19 07		19 10			19 17	19 22		19 27	19 34				19 40			19 47
Strawberry Hill	d				19 07				19 11									19 37							
Fulwell	a								19 13																
Teddington	a				19 12													19 42							
Hampton Wick	a				19 16													19 46							
Kingston	a				19 18													19 48							
Whitton	d	18 55						19a23						19a20	19 25					19a53					19a50
Feltham	d	18 59		19 03		19 06					19 16				19 29		19 33		19 36			19 46			
Ashford (Surrey)	d	19 03		19 07		19 10									19 33		19 37		19 40						
Staines	d	19 07		19 11		19 15					19 23				19 37		19 41		19 45			19 53			
Wraysbury	d	19 11													19 41										
Sunnymeads	d	19 14													19 44										
Datchet	d	19 17													19 47										
Windsor & Eton Riverside	a	19 23													19 53										
Egham	d			19 16		19 20					19 27						19 46		19 50			19 57			
Virginia Water	a			19 20		19 24					19 31						19 50		19 54			20 01			
	d			19 20		19 24					19 31						19 50		19 54			20 01			
Chertsey §	d					19 29													19 59						
Addlestone §	d					19 31													20 02						
Weybridge	a					19 40													20 10						
Byfleet & New Haw	d																								
West Byfleet	d																								
Woking	a																								
Longcross	d																								
Sunningdale	d			19 25							19 37						19 55					20 07			
Ascot 3	d			19 30							19 43		19 53				20 00					20 13		20 23	
Bagshot	d												19 59											20 29	
Camberley	a												20 05											20 35	
	d												20 09											20 39	
Frimley	d												20 13											20 43	
Ash Vale	d												20 19											20 49	
Aldershot	a												20 24											20 54	
	d												20 38											21 08	
Ash 3	d												20 45											21 15	
Wanborough	d												20 48											21 18	
Guildford	a												20 55											21 25	
Martins Heron	d			19 34							19 47						20 04					20 17			
Bracknell	d			19 37							19 50						20 07					20 20			
Wokingham	d			19 47							19 57						20 17					20 27			
Winnersh	d										20 00											20 30			
Winnersh Triangle	d										20 02											20 32			
Earley	d										20 05											20 35			
Reading 7	a			19 57							20 12						20 25					20 40			

For general notes see front of timetable
For details of catering facilities see Directory of Train Operators

§ Passengers to/from London may travel via Weybridge. See Table 155.

A To London Waterloo (Table 152)
B To London Waterloo
C To Shepperton (Table 152)

b Arr. 1915
c Arr. 1945

For details of Bank Holiday service alterations, please see first page of this Table

London → Hounslow, Richmond, Kingston, Windsor, Weybridge, Ascot, Guildford and Reading

Network Diagram - see first page of Table 148

		SW		SW	SW	SW	SW	SW	SW	SW	SW	SW	SW	SW	SW	SW	SW	SW	SW	SW		SW	SW	SW	SW
								1		1							1		1	1					
				A		B	B				B		A		B	B						B		A	
London Waterloo 15 ⊖	d	19 28		19 33		19 37	19 45	19 50	19 52			19 58	20 03		20 07	20 15	20 20	20 22					20 28	20 33	
Vauxhall ⊖	d	19 32		19 37		19 41	19 49		19 56			20 02	20 07		20 11	20 19		20 26					20 32	20 37	
Queenstown Rd.(Battersea)	d			19 40		19 44	19 52		19 59				20 10		20 14	20 22		20 29						20 40	
Clapham Junction 10	d	19 38		19 43		19 47	19 55	19 58	20 02			20 08	20 13		20 17	20 25	20 28	20 32					20 38	20 43	
Wandsworth Town	d			19 46		19 50	19 58		20 05				20 16		20 20	20 28		20 35						20 46	
Putney	d	19 42		19 49		19 53	20 01		20 08		←	20 12	20 19		20 23	20 31		20 38				←	20 42	20 49	
Barnes	d			19 52		19 57	20 05		20 12		20 05		20 22		20 27	20 35		20 42				20 35		20 52	
Barnes Bridge	d					19 59	→		20 14						20 29	→		20 44							
Chiswick	d				←	20 02			20 17					←	20 32			20 47							←
Kew Bridge	d				19 50	20 05			20 20 →					20 20	20 35			20 50 →							20 50
Brentford	d				19 53	20 08								20 23	20 38										20 53
Syon Lane	d				19 55	20 10								20 25	20 40										20 55
Isleworth	d				19 57	20 12								20 27	20 42										20 57
Hounslow	d				20 01	20b18								20 31	20c48										21 01
Mortlake	d			19 54							20 07		20 24									20 37		20 54	
North Sheen	d			19 56							20 09		20 26									20 39		20 56	
Richmond ⊖	d	19 48		19 59				20 06			20 12	20 18	20 29				20 36					20 42	20 48	20 59	
St Margarets	d			20 01							20 14		20 31									20 44		21 01	
Twickenham	a	19 51		20 03				20 10			20 16	20 21	20 33				20 40					20 46	20 51	21 03	
	d	19 52		20 04				20 10			20 17	20 22	20 34				20 40					20 47	20 52	21 04	
Strawberry Hill	d			20 07									20 37											21 07	
Fulwell	a																								
Teddington	a			20 10									20 40											21 10	
Hampton Wick	a			20 14									20 44											21 14	
Kingston	a			20 16									20 46											21 16	
Whitton	d	19 55				20a23					20a20	20 25			20a53							20a50	20 55		
Feltham	d	19 59			20 06			20 16				20 29		20 36			20 46						20 59		21 06
Ashford (Surrey)	d	20 03			20 10							20 33		20 40									21 03		21 10
Staines	d	20 07			20 15			20 23				20 37		20 45			20 53						21 07		21 15
Wraysbury	d	20 11										20 41											21 11		
Sunnymeads	d	20 14										20 44											21 14		
Datchet	d	20 17										20 47											21 17		
Windsor & Eton Riverside	a	20 21										20 51											21 21		
Egham	d				20 20			20 27						20 50			20 57								21 20
Virginia Water	a				20 24			20 31						20 54			21 01								21 24
	d				20 24			20 31						20 54			21 01								21 24
Chertsey §	d				20 29									20 59											21 29
Addlestone §	d				20 32									21 02											21 32
Weybridge	a				20 37									21 07											21 37
Byfleet & New Haw	d																								
West Byfleet	d																								
Woking	a																								
Longcross	d																								
Sunningdale	d							20 37									21 07								
Ascot 3	d							20 43		20 53							21 13		21 23						
Bagshot	d									20 59									21 29						
Camberley	a									21 05									21 35						
	d									21 09									21 39						
Frimley	d									21 13									21 43						
Ash Vale	d									21 19									21 49						
Aldershot	a									21 24									21 54						
	d									21 38									22 08	22 38					
Ash 3	d									21 45									22 15	22 45					
Wanborough	d									21 48									22 18	22 48					
Guildford	a									21 55									22 25	22 55					
Martins Heron	d							20 47									21 17								
Bracknell	d							20 50									21 20								
Wokingham	d							20 57									21 27								
Winnersh	d							21 00									21 30								
Winnersh Triangle	d							21 02									21 32								
Earley	d							21 05									21 35								
Reading 7	a							21 10									21 40								

For general notes see front of timetable
For details of catering facilities see Directory of Train Operators

§ Passengers to/from London may travel via Weybridge. See Table 155.

A To London Waterloo (Table 152)
B To London Waterloo
b Arr. 2015
c Arr. 2045

For details of Bank Holiday service alterations, please see first page of this Table

London → Hounslow, Richmond, Kingston, Windsor, Weybridge, Ascot, Guildford and Reading

Network Diagram - see first page of Table 148

		SW	SW	SW	SW	SW	SW	SW	SW	SW	SW	SW	SW	SW	SW	SW		SW	SW	SW	SW	SW	SW	SW	SW
				1								1		1								1			
		A	A			A		B		A	A				A			B		A					
London Waterloo 15 ⊖	d	20 37	20 45	20 50	20 52		20 58	21 03		21 07	21 15	21 20	21 22			21 28		21 33		21 37	21 45	21 50		21 52	21 58
Vauxhall ⊖	d	20 41	20 49		20 56		21 02	21 07		21 11	21 19		21 26			21 32		21 37		21 41	21 49			21 56	22 02
Queenstown Rd.(Battersea)	d	20 44	20 52		20 59			21 10		21 14	21 22		21 29					21 40		21 44	21 52			21 59	
Clapham Junction 10	d	20 47	20 55	20 58	21 02		21 08	21 13		21 17	21 25	21 28	21 32			21 38		21 43		21 47	21 55	21 58		22 02	22 08
Wandsworth Town	d	20 50	20 58		21 05			21 16		21 20	21 28		21 35					21 46		21 50	21 58			22 05	
Putney	d	20 53	21 01		21 08	←	21 12	21 19		21 23	21 31		21 38		←	21 42		21 49		21 53	22 01		←	22 08	22 12
Barnes	d	20 57	21 05		21 12	21 05		21 22		21 27	21 35		21 42		21 35			21 52		21 57	22 05		22 05	22 12	
Barnes Bridge	d	20 59	→		21 14					21 29	→		21 44							21 59	→			22 14	
Chiswick	d	21 02			21 17				←	21 32			21 47						←	22 02				22 17	
Kew Bridge	d	21 05			21 20				21 20	21 35			21 50						21 50	22 05				22 20	
Brentford	d	21 08			→				21 23	21 38			→						21 53	22 08				→	
Syon Lane	d	21 10							21 25	21 40									21 55	22 10					
Isleworth	d	21 12							21 27	21 42									21 57	22 12					
Hounslow	d	21b18							21 31	21c48									22 01	22e18					
Mortlake	d					21 07		21 24							21 37			21 54					22 07		
North Sheen	d					21 09		21 26							21 39			21 56					22 09		
Richmond ⊖	d			21 06		21 12	21 18	21 29				21 36			21 42	21 48		21 59				22 06	22 12		22 18
St Margarets	d					21 14		21 31							21 44			22 01					22 14		
Twickenham	a			21 10		21 16	21 21	21 33				21 40			21 46	21 51		22 03				22 10	22 17		22 21
	d			21 10		21 17	21 22	21 34				21 40			21 47	21 52		22 04				22 10			22 22
Strawberry Hill	d							21 37										22 07							
Fulwell	a																								
Teddington	a							21 40										22 10							
Hampton Wick	a							21 44										22 14							
Kingston	a							21 46										22 16							
Whitton	d	21a23				21a20	21 25			21a53					21a50	21 55				22a23					22 25
Feltham	d			21 16			21 29		21 36			21 46				21 59			22 06			22 16			22 29
Ashford (Surrey)	d						21 33		21 40							22 03			22 10						22 33
Staines	d			21 23			21 37		21 45			21 53				22 07			22 15			22 23			22 37
Wraysbury	d						21 41									22 11									22 41
Sunnymeads	d						21 44									22 14									22 44
Datchet	d						21 47									22 17									22 47
Windsor & Eton Riverside	a						21 51									22 21									22 51
Egham	d			21 27					21 50			21 57							22 20			22 27			
Virginia Water	a			21 31					21 54			22 01							22 24			22 31			
	d			21 31					21 54			22 01							22 24			22 31			
Chertsey §	d								21 59										22 29						
Addlestone §	d								22 02										22 32						
Weybridge	a								22 07										22 37						
Byfleet & New Haw	d																								
West Byfleet	d																								
Woking	a																								
Longcross	d																								
Sunningdale	d			21 37								22 07										22 37			
Ascot 3	d			21 43								22 13		22 23								22 43			
Bagshot	d													22 29											
Camberley	a													22 35											
	d													22 39											
Frimley	d													22 43											
Ash Vale	d													22 49											
Aldershot	a													22 54											
	d													23 08											
Ash 3	d													23 15											
Wanborough	d													23 18											
Guildford	a													23 25											
Martins Heron	d			21 47								22 17										22 47			
Bracknell	d			21 50								22 20										22 50			
Wokingham	d			21 57								22 27										22 57			
Winnersh	d			22 00								22 30										23 00			
Winnersh Triangle	d			22 02								22 32										23 02			
Earley	d			22 05								22 35										23 05			
Reading 7	a			22 10								22 40										23 10			

For general notes see front of timetable
For details of catering facilities see Directory of Train Operators

§ Passengers to/from London may travel via Weybridge. See Table 155.

A To London Waterloo
B To London Waterloo (Table 152)
b Arr. 2115
c Arr. 2145
e Arr. 2215

Table 149

Mondays to Fridays

until 26 September

London → Hounslow, Richmond, Kingston, Windsor, Weybridge, Ascot, Guildford and Reading

For details of Bank Holiday service alterations, please see first page of this Table

Network Diagram - see first page of Table 148

		SW	SW	SW	SW	SW	SW	SW	SW	SW	SW	SW	SW	SW	SW	SW	SW	SW	SW	SW	SW	SW	SW
				1				1		1						1							
		A					A	B					A										
London Waterloo 15	⊖ d	22 03		22 20	22 22	22 28	22 33			22 50	22 52	22 58	23 03		23 13	23 20	23 22	23 35		23 37	23 52	23 58	
Vauxhall	⊖ d	22 07			22 26	22 32	22 37				22 56	23 02	23 07		23 17		23 26			23 41	23 56	00 02	
Queenstown Rd.(Battersea)	d	22 10			22 29		22 40				22 59		23 10				23 29			23 44	23 59		
Clapham Junction 10	d	22 13		22 28	22 32	22 38	22 43			22 58	23 02	23 08	23 13		23 23	23 28	23 32	23 43		23 47	00 02	00 08	
Wandsworth Town	d	22 16			22 35		22 46				23 05		23 16				23 35			23 50	00 05		
Putney	d	22 19			22 38	22 42	22 49				23 08	23 12	23 19		23 27		23 38			23 53	00 08	00 12	
Barnes	d	22 22			22 42		22 52				23 12		23 22				23 42			23 56	00 12		
Barnes Bridge	d				22 44						23 14						23 44		←		00 14		
Chiswick	d		←		22 47				←		23 17			←			23 47		23 47		00 17		←
Kew Bridge	d		22 20		22 50				22 50		23 20			23 20			→		23 50		00 20		00 20
Brentford	d		22 23		→				22 53		→			23 23					23 53		→		00 23
Syon Lane	d		22 25						22 55					23 25					23 55				00 25
Isleworth	d		22 27						22 57					23 27					23 57				00 27
Hounslow	d		22 31						23 01					23 31					00 01				00 31
Mortlake	d	22 24					22 54						23 24							23 58			
North Sheen	d	22 26					22 56						23 26							00 01			
Richmond	⊖ d	22 29		22 36		22 48	22 59			23 06		23 18	23 29		23 33	23 37		23 51		00 03		00 18	
St Margarets	d	22 31					23 01						23 31							00 06			
Twickenham	a	22 33		22 40		22 51	23 03			23 10		23 21	23 33		23 36	23 41		23 55		00 08		00 21	
	d	22 34		22 40		22 52	23 04			23 10		23 22	23 34		23 37	23 41		23 55		00 08		00 22	
Strawberry Hill	d	22 37					23 07						23 37							00 12			
Fulwell	a																						
Teddington	a	22 40					23 10						23 40							00 15			
Hampton Wick	a	22 44					23 14						23 44							00 17			
Kingston	a	22 46					23 16						23 46							00 19			
Whitton	d					22 55						23 25			23 40							00 25	
Feltham	d		22 36	22 46		22 59			23 06	23 16		23 29		23 36	23 44	23 48		00 01	00 06			00 29	00 36
Ashford (Surrey)	d		22 40			23 03			23 10			23 33		23 40	23 48				00 10			00 33	00 40
Staines	d		22 45	22 53		23 07			23 15	23 23		23 37		23 45	23 52	23 56		00 08	00 15			00a37	00a46
Wraysbury	d					23 11						23 41			23 56								
Sunnymeads	d					23 14						23 44			23 59								
Datchet	d					23 17						23 47			00 02								
Windsor & Eton Riverside	a					23 21						23 51			00 06								
Egham	d		22 50	22 57					23 20	23 27				23 50		00 01		00 12	00 20				
Virginia Water	a		22 54	23 01					23 24	23 31				23 54		00 05		00 16	00 24				
	d		22 54	23 01					23 24	23 31				23 54		00 05		00 16	00 24				
Chertsey §	d		22 59						23 29					23 59					00 29				
Addlestone §	d		23 02						23 32					00 02					00 32				
Weybridge	a		23 07						23 37										00 37				
Byfleet & New Haw	d													00 07									
West Byfleet	d													00 10									
Woking	a													00 16									
Longcross	d																						
Sunningdale	d			23 07						23 37						00 10		00 22					
Ascot 3	d			23 13				23 23		23 43						00 15		00 27					
Bagshot	d							23 29															
Camberley	a							23 35															
	d							23 39															
Frimley	d							23 43															
Ash Vale	d							23 49															
Aldershot	a							23 54															
	d																						
Ash 3	d																						
Wanborough	d																						
Guildford	a																						
Martins Heron	d			23 17						23 47						00 19		00 31					
Bracknell	d			23 20						23 50						00 23		00 34					
Wokingham	d			23 27						23 57						00 32		00 41					
Winnersh	d			23 30						00 01						00 36							
Winnersh Triangle	d			23 32						00 02						00 38							
Earley	d			23 35						00 05						00 40							
Reading 7	a			23 40						00 10						00 45		00 49					

For general notes see front of timetable
For details of catering facilities see Directory of Train Operators

§ Passengers to/from London may travel via Weybridge. See Table 155.

A To London Waterloo (Table 152)
B To Farnham (Table 155)

Table 149

Mondays to Fridays

from 29 September

London → Hounslow, Richmond, Kingston, Windsor, Weybridge, Ascot, Guildford and Reading

Network Diagram - see first page of Table 148

		SW	SW	SW	SW	SW	SW	SW	SW	SW	SW	SW	SW	SW	SW	SW	SW	SW	SW	SW	SW	SW	SW	SW	SW
		MO	MO	MO	MO	MO	MX	MX	MX	MX	MX	MX	MX	MX	MX	MX	MX	MX	MX						
			1	1			1			1				1								1		1	1
																					A				
London Waterloo 15 ⊖	d	22p50	23p09	23p39		23p44	22p50	22p52	23p13	23p20	23p22	23p35	23p37				23p52	23p58		00 18					05 05
Vauxhall ⊖	d	22p54	23p13	23p43		23p48		22p56	23p17		23p26		23p41				23p56	00 02		00 22					05 09
Queenstown Rd.(Battersea)	d	22p57				23p51		22p59			23p29		23p44				23p59			00 25					05 12
Clapham Junction 10	d	23p00	23p19	23p49		23p54	22p58	23p02	23p23	23p28	23p32	23p43	23p47				00 02	00 08		00 28					05 15
Wandsworth Town	d	23p03				23p57		23p05			23p35		23p50				00 05			00 31					05 18
Putney	d	23p06	23p23	23p53		23p59		23p08	23p27		23p38		23p53			←	00 08	00 12		00 34					05 21
Barnes	d	23p09				00 03		23p12			23p42		23p56			23p56	00 12			00 37					05 24
Barnes Bridge	d	23p11						23p14			23p44		→		←		00 14								
Chiswick	d	23p13						23p17			23p47 →				23p47		00 17		←						
Kew Bridge	d	23p16						23p20							23p50		00 20 →		00 20						
Brentford	d	23p19						23p23							23p53				00 23						
Syon Lane	d	23p21						23p25							23p55				00 25						
Isleworth	d	23p23						23p27							23p57				00 27						
Hounslow	d	23p27						23p31							00 01				00 31						
Mortlake	d					00 05										23p58				00 39					05 26
North Sheen	d					00 07										00 01				00 41					05 28
Richmond ⊖	d		23p29	23p59		00 10	23p06		23p33	23p37		23p51				00 03		00 18		00 44					05 31
St Margarets	d					00 12										00 06				00 46					05 33
Twickenham	a		23p32	00 02		00 14	23p10		23p36	23p41		23p55				00 08		00 21		00 48					05 35
	d		23p33	00 03		00 15	23p10		23p37	23p41		23p55				00 08		00 22		00 49	04 52				05 36
Strawberry Hill	d															00 12				00s52	04 55				
Fulwell	a																								
Teddington	a															00 15				00s55	04 58				
Hampton Wick	a															00 17				00s58	05 01				
Kingston	a															00 19				01 00	05 03				
Whitton	d					00 18			23p40									00 25							05 39
Feltham	d	23p33	23p39	00 09		00 22	23p16	23p36	23p44	23p48		00 01			00 06			00 29	00 36						05 43
Ashford (Surrey)	d	23p37				00 26		23p40	23p48						00 10			00 33	00 40						05 47
Staines	d	23p41	23p45	00 15	00 21	00a30	23p23	23p45	23p52	23p56		00 08			00 15			00a37	00a46			05 23	05 45		05 53
Wraysbury	d								23p56																
Sunnymeads	d								23p59																
Datchet	d								00 02																
Windsor & Eton Riverside	a								00 09																
Egham	d	23p45	23p50	00 20	00s25		23p27	23p50		00 01		00 12			00 20							05 27	05 50		05 57
Virginia Water	a	23p49	23p54	00 24	00s29		23p31	23p54		00 05		00 16			00 24							05 31	05 54		06 01
	d	23p49	23p54	00 24			23p31	23p54		00 05		00 16			00 24							05 31	05 54		06 01
Chertsey §	d	23p55			00s34			23p59							00 29								05 59		
Addlestone §	d	23p58			00s38			00 02							00 32								06 02		
Weybridge	a														00 37								06 07		
Byfleet & New Haw	d	00 02			00s42			00 07																	
West Byfleet	d	00 05			00s45			00 10																	
Woking	a	00 10			00 50			00 16																	
Longcross	d																								
Sunningdale	d		23p59	00 29			23p37			00 10		00 22										05 37			06 07
Ascot 3	d		00 04	00 34			23p43			00 15		00 27		00 29								05 43			06 13
Bagshot	d													00 35											
Camberley	a													00 41											
	d													00 41											
Frimley	d													00 45											
Ash Vale	d													00 52											
Aldershot	a													00 57											
	d																							06 08	
Ash 3	d																							06 15	
Wanborough	d																							06 18	
Guildford	a																							06 25	
Martins Heron	d		00 08	00 38			23p47			00 19		00 31										05 47			06 17
Bracknell	d		00 11	00 41			23p50			00 23		00 34										05 50			06 20
Wokingham	d		00 18	00 48			23p57			00 32		00 41										05 57			06 27
Winnersh	d		00 21	00 51			00 01			00 36												06 00			06 30
Winnersh Triangle	d		00 23	00 53			00 02			00 38												06 02			06 32
Earley	d		00 26	00 56			00 05			00 40												06 05			06 35
Reading 7	a		00 34	01 04			00 13			00 48		00 52										06 13			06 43

For general notes see front of timetable
For details of catering facilities see
Directory of Train Operators

§ Passengers to/from London may travel via Weybridge. See Table 155.

A To London Waterloo (Table 152)

London → Hounslow, Richmond, Kingston, Windsor, Weybridge, Ascot, Guildford and Reading

Network Diagram - see first page of Table 148

		SW	SW	SW	SW	SW	SW	SW	SW	SW	SW	SW	SW	SW	SW	SW	SW	SW	SW	SW	SW	SW		GW	SW
					1	1	1					1	1							1	1			1	1
			A						A	B					B		A	B						C	
London Waterloo 15 ⊖	d		05 33				05 50	05 58	06 03	06 15			06 20	06 22		06 28	06 33	06 45			06 50	06 52			
Vauxhall ⊖	d		05 37					06 02	06 07	06 19				06 26		06 32	06 37	06 49				06 56			
Queenstown Rd.(Battersea)	d		05 40						06 10	06 22				06 29			06 40	06 52				06 59			
Clapham Junction 10	d		05 43				05 58	06 08	06 13	06 25			06 28	06 32		06 38	06 43	06 55			06 58	07 02			
Wandsworth Town	d		05 46						06 16	06 28				06 35			06 46	06 58				07 05			
Putney	d		05 49					06 12	06 19	06 31				06 38	←	06 42	06 49	07 01				07 08			
Barnes	d		05 52						06 22	06 35				06 42	06 35		06 52	07 05				07 12			
Barnes Bridge	d									→				06 44				→				07 14			
Chiswick	d													06 47					←			07 17			
Kew Bridge	d													06 50					06 50			07 20			
Brentford	d													→					06 53			→			
Syon Lane	d																		06 55						
Isleworth	d																		06 57						
Hounslow	d																		07 01						
Mortlake	d		05 54						06 24						06 37		06 54								
North Sheen	d		05 56						06 26						06 39		06 56								
Richmond ⊖	d		05 59				06 06	06 18	06 29				06 36		06 42	06 48	06 59				07 06				
St Margarets	d		06 01						06 31						06 44		07 01								
Twickenham	a		06 03				06 10	06 21	06 33				06 40		06 46	06 51	07 03				07 10				
	d	05 52	06 04				06 10	06 22	06 34				06 40		06 47	06 52	07 04				07 10				
Strawberry Hill	d		06 07						06 37								07 07								
Fulwell	a																								
Teddington	a		06 10						06 40								07 10								
Hampton Wick	a		06 14						06 44								07 14								
Kingston	a		06 16						06 46								07 16								
Whitton	d	05 55						06 25							06a50	06 55									
Feltham	d	05 59					06 16	06 29					06 46			06 59			07 06		07 16				
Ashford (Surrey)	d	06 03						06 33								07 03			07 10						
Staines	d	06 07		06 15			06 23	06 37			06 45		06 53			07 07			07 15		07 23				
Wraysbury	d	06 11						06 41								07 11									
Sunnymeads	d	06 14						06 44								07 14									
Datchet	d	06 17						06 47								07 17									
Windsor & Eton Riverside	a	06 25						06 54								07 24									
Egham	d			06 20			06 27				06 50		06 57						07 20		07 27				
Virginia Water	a			06 24			06 31				06 54		07 01						07 24		07 31				
	d			06 24			06 31				06 54		07 01						07 24		07 31				
Chertsey §	d			06 29							06 59								07 29						
Addlestone §	d			06 32							07 02								07 32						
Weybridge	a			06 37							07 07								07 37						
Byfleet & New Haw	d																								
West Byfleet	d																								
Woking	a																								
Longcross	d						06 35						07 05								07 35				
Sunningdale	d						06 37						07 07								07 37				
Ascot 3	d					06 23	06 43					06 53	07 13							07 23	07 43				07 53
Bagshot	d					06 29						06 59								07 29					07 59
Camberley	a					06 35						07 05								07 35					08 05
	d					06 39						07 09								07 39					08 09
Frimley	d					06 43						07 13								07 43					08 13
Ash Vale	d					06 49						07 19								07 49					08 19
Aldershot	a					06 56						07 26								07 54					08 24
	d				06 38	07 08						07 38								08 08					08 38
Ash 3	d				06 45	07 15						07 45								08 15					08 45
Wanborough	d				06 48	07 18						07 48								08 18					08 48
Guildford	a				06 55	07 25						07 55								08 25					08 55
Martins Heron	d						06 47						07 17								07 47				
Bracknell	d						06 50						07 20								07 50				
Wokingham	d						06 57						07 27								07 57			08 17	
Winnersh	d						07 00						07 30								08 00			08 21	
Winnersh Triangle	d						07 02						07 32								08 02				
Earley	d						07 05						07 35								08 05				
Reading 7	a						07 13						07 43								08 13			08 28	

For general notes see front of timetable
For details of catering facilities see Directory of Train Operators

§ Passengers to/from London may travel via Weybridge. See Table 155.

A To London Waterloo (Table 152)
B To London Waterloo
C From Gatwick Airport (Table 148)

Table 149

Mondays to Fridays

from 29 September

London → Hounslow, Richmond, Kingston, Windsor, Weybridge, Ascot, Guildford and Reading

Network Diagram - see first page of Table 148

		SW	SW	SW	SW	SW	SW	SW ■1	SW	SW ■1	SW	SW	SW	SW	SW	SW	SW	SW ■1	SW	SW ■1	SW	SW	SW	SW ■1	SW
		A		B		A	B				A		B			A	B				A		B		B
London Waterloo 15 ⊖	d		06 58	07 03		07 15		07 20	07 22			07 28	07 33		07 37	07 45		07 50	07 52			07 58	08 03	08 07	
Vauxhall ⊖	d		07 02	07 07		07 19			07 26			07 32	07 37		07 41	07 49			07 56			08 02	08 07		
Queenstown Rd.(Battersea)	d			07 10		07 22			07 29				07 40		07 44	07 52			07 59				08 10		
Clapham Junction 10	d		07 08	07 13		07 25		07 28	07 32			07 38	07 43		07 47	07 55		07 58	08 02			08 08	08 13	08 15	
Wandsworth Town	d			07 16		07 28			07 35				07 46		07 50	07 58			08 05				08 16		
Putney	d	←	07 12	07 19		07 31			07 38		←	07 42	07 49		07 53	08 01			08 08		←	08 12	08 19		←
Barnes	d	07 05		07 22		07 35			07 42		07 35		07 52		07 57	08 05			08 12		08 05		08 22		08 22
Barnes Bridge	d					→			07 44						07 59	→			08 14				→		
Chiswick	d				←				07 47					←	08 02				08 17						
Kew Bridge	d				07 20				07 50					07 50	08 05				08 20						
Brentford	d				07 23				→					07 53	08 08				→						
Syon Lane	d				07 25									07 55	08 10										
Isleworth	d				07 27									07 57	08 12										
Hounslow	d				07 31									08 01	08a18										
Mortlake	d	07 07		07 24							07 37		07 54								08 07				08 24
North Sheen	d	07 09		07 26							07 39		07 56								08 09				08 26
Richmond ⊖	d	07 12	07 18	07 29				07 36			07 42	07 48	07 59					08 06			08 12	08 18		08 23	08 29
St Margarets	d	07 14		07 31							07 44		08 01								08 14				08 31
Twickenham	a	07 16	07 21	07 33				07 40			07 46	07 51	08 03					08 10			08 16	08 21		08 27	08 33
	d	07 17	07 22	07 34			07 37	07 40			07 47	07 52	08 04				08 07	08 10			08 17	08 22		08 27	08 34
Strawberry Hill	d			07 37			07b47						08 07				08c17								08 37
Fulwell	a																								
Teddington	a			07 40			07 50						08 10				08 20								08 40
Hampton Wick	a			07 44			07 52						08 14				08 22								08 44
Kingston	a			07 46			07 54						08 16				08 24								08 46
Whitton	d	07a20	07 25								07a50	07 55									08a20	08 25			
Feltham	d		07 29		07 36			07 46				07 59		08 06				08 16				08 29		08 33	
Ashford (Surrey)	d		07 33		07 40							08 03		08 10								08 33		08 37	
Staines	d		07 37		07 45			07 53				08 07		08 15				08 23				08 37		08 41	
Wraysbury	d		07 41									08 11										08 41			
Sunnymeads	d		07 44									08 14										08 44			
Datchet	d		07 47									08 17										08 47			
Windsor & Eton Riverside	a		07 54									08 24										08 54			
Egham	d				07 50			07 57						08 20				08 27						08 46	
Virginia Water	a				07 54			08 01						08 24				08 31						08 50	
	d				07 54			08 01						08 24				08 31						08 50	
Chertsey §	d				07 59									08 29											
Addlestone §	d				08 02									08 32											
Weybridge	a				08 07									08 37											
Byfleet & New Haw	d																								
West Byfleet	d																								
Woking	a																								
Longcross	d							08 05										08 35						08 53	
Sunningdale	d							08 07										08 37						08 57	
Ascot 3	d							08 13		08 23								08 43		08 53				09 01	
Bagshot	d									08 29										08 59					
Camberley	a									08 37										09 05					
	d									08 39										09 09					
Frimley	d									08 43										09 13					
Ash Vale	d									08 49										09 19					
Aldershot	a									08 54										09 25					
	d									09 08										09 38					
Ash 3	d									09 15										09 45					
Wanborough	d									09 18										09 48					
Guildford	a									09 25										09 55					
Martins Heron	d							08 17										08 47						09 05	
Bracknell	d							08 20										08 50						09 09	
Wokingham	d							08 27										08 57						09 17	
Winnersh	d							08 30										09 00						09 20	
Winnersh Triangle	d							08 32										09 02						09 22	
Earley	d							08 35										09 05						09 25	
Reading 7	a							08 43										09 13						09 33	

For general notes see front of timetable
For details of catering facilities see Directory of Train Operators

§ Passengers to/from London may travel via Weybridge. See Table 155.

A To London Waterloo

B To London Waterloo (Table 152)

b Arr. 0740

c Arr. 0810

Table 149

Mondays to Fridays

from 29 September

London → Hounslow, Richmond, Kingston, Windsor, Weybridge, Ascot, Guildford and Reading

Network Diagram - see first page of Table 148

		SW	SW	SW	SW 1	SW	SW 1	SW	SW	SW	SW 1	SW	SW	SW	SW	SW 1	SW	SW 1	SW	SW	SW	SW	SW	SW
			A	A				A		B		B		A	A				A		B		A	A
London Waterloo 15	⊖ d		08 10	08 15	08 20	08 22			08 28	08 33	08 37			08 40	08 43	08 50	08 52			08 58	09 03		09 07	09 15
Vauxhall	⊖ d		08 14	08 19		08 26			08 32	08 37				08 44	08 47		08 56			09 02	09 07		09 11	09 19
Queenstown Rd.(Battersea)	d		08 17	08 22		08 29				08 40				08 47	08 50		08 59				09 10		09 14	09 22
Clapham Junction 10	d		08 20	08 25	08 28	08 32			08 38	08 43	08 45			08 50	08 55	08 58	09 02			09 08	09 13		09 17	09 25
Wandsworth Town	d		08 23	08 28		08 35				08 46				08 53	08 58		09 05				09 16		09 20	09 28
Putney	d		08 26	08 31		08 38		←	08 42	08 49		←		08 56	09 01		09 08		←	09 12	09 19		09 23	09 31
Barnes	d		08 28	08 35		08 42		08 35		08 52		08 52		08 58	09 05		09 12		09 05		09 22		09 27	09 35
Barnes Bridge	d		08 30	→		08 44				→				09 00	→		09 14						09 29	→
Chiswick	d	←	08 33			08 47							←	09 02			09 17					←	09 32	
Kew Bridge	d	08 20	08 35			08 50							08 50	09 05			09 20					09 20	09 35	
Brentford	d	08 23	08 38			→							08 53	09 08			→					09 23	09 38	
Syon Lane	d	08 25	08 40										08 55	09 10								09 25	09 40	
Isleworth	d	08 27	08 42										08 57	09 12								09 27	09 42	
Hounslow	d	08 31	08 48										09 01	09 18								09 31	09b48	
Mortlake	d							08 37				08 54							09 07		09 24			
North Sheen	d							08 39				08 56							09 09		09 26			
Richmond	⊖ d				08 36			08 42	08 48		08 53	08 59				09 06			09 12	09 18	09 29			
St Margarets	d							08 44				09 01							09 14		09 31			
Twickenham	a				08 40			08 46	08 51		08 57	09 03				09 10			09 16	09 21	09 33			
	d				08 40			08 47	08 52		08 57	09 04				09 10			09 17	09 22	09 34			
Strawberry Hill	d											09 07									09 37			
Fulwell	a																							
Teddington	a											09 10									09 40			
Hampton Wick	a											09 14									09 44			
Kingston	a											09 16									09 46			
Whitton	d		08a53					08a50	08 55					09a23					09a20	09 25			09a53	
Feltham	d	08 36			08 46				08 59		09 03		09 07			09 16				09 29		09 36		
Ashford (Surrey)	d	08 40							09 03		09 07		09 10							09 33		09 40		
Staines	d	08 45			08 53				09 07		09 11		09 15			09 23				09 37		09 45		
Wraysbury	d								09 11											09 41				
Sunnymeads	d								09 14											09 44				
Datchet	d								09 17											09 47				
Windsor & Eton Riverside	a								09 24											09 54				
Egham	d	08 50			08 57						09 16		09 20			09 27						09 50		
Virginia Water	a	08 54			09 01						09 20		09 24			09 31						09 54		
	d	08 54			09 01						09 20		09 24			09 31						09 54		
Chertsey §	d	08 59											09 29									09 59		
Addlestone §	d	09 02											09 32									10 02		
Weybridge	a	09 07											09 37									10 07		
Byfleet & New Haw	d																							
West Byfleet	d																							
Woking	a																							
Longcross	d																							
Sunningdale	d				09 07						09 25					09 37								
Ascot 3	d				09 13		09 23				09 30					09 43		09 53						
Bagshot	d						09 29											09 59						
Camberley	a						09 35											10 05						
	d						09 39											10 09						
Frimley	d						09 43											10 13						
Ash Vale	d						09 49											10 19						
Aldershot	a						09 54											10 24						
	d						10 08											10 38						
Ash 3	d						10 15											10 45						
Wanborough	d						10 18											10 48						
Guildford	a						10 25											10 55						
Martins Heron	d				09 17						09 34					09 47								
Bracknell	d				09 20						09 37					09 50								
Wokingham	d				09 27						09 46					09 57								
Winnersh	d				09 30											10 00								
Winnersh Triangle	d				09 32											10 02								
Earley	d				09 35											10 05								
Reading 7	a				09 43						09 58					10 13								

For general notes see front of timetable
For details of catering facilities see Directory of Train Operators

§ Passengers to/from London may travel via Weybridge. See Table 155.

A To London Waterloo
B To London Waterloo (Table 152)
b Arr. 0945

from 29 September

London → Hounslow, Richmond, Kingston, Windsor, Weybridge, Ascot, Guildford and Reading

Network Diagram - see first page of Table 148

		SW 1	SW	SW 1	SW	SW	SW	SW	SW	SW	SW 1	SW	SW 1	SW	SW			SW	SW 1	SW	SW	SW	SW	SW 1
					A		B		A	A				A		C		B		B		A	A	
London Waterloo 15	⊖ d	09 20	09 22			09 28	09 33		09 37	09 45	09 50	09 52			09 58			16 01	16 05			16 07	16 15	16 20
Vauxhall	⊖ d		09 26			09 32	09 37		09 41	09 49		09 56			10 02			16 05	16 09			16 11	16 19	
Queenstown Rd.(Battersea)	d		09 29				09 40		09 44	09 52		09 59						16 08				16 14	16 22	
Clapham Junction 10	d	09 28	09 32			09 38	09 43		09 47	09 55	09 58	10 02			10 08			16 11	16 15			16 17	16 25	16 28
Wandsworth Town	d		09 35				09 46		09 50	09 58		10 05						16 14				16 20	16 28	
Putney	d		09 38		←	09 42	09 49		09 53	10 01		10 08		←	10 12			16 17		←		16 23	16 31	
Barnes	d		09 42		09 35		09 52		09 57	10 05		10 12		10 05				16 22		16 22		16 27	16 35	
Barnes Bridge	d		09 44						09 59	→		10 14						→				16 29	→	
Chiswick	d		09 47					←	10 02			10 17									←	16 32		
Kew Bridge	d		09 50 →					09 50	10 05			10 20 →									16 20	16 35		
Brentford	d							09 53	10 08												16 23	16 38		
Syon Lane	d							09 55	10 10												16 25	16 40		
Isleworth	d							09 57	10 12												16 27	16 42		
Hounslow	d							10 01	10b18												16 31	16c48		
Mortlake	d				09 37		09 54							10 07						16 24				
North Sheen	d				09 39		09 56							10 09						16 26				
Richmond	⊖ d	09 36			09 42	09 48	09 59				10 06			10 12	10 18				16 23	16 29				16 36
St Margarets	d				09 44		10 01							10 14						16 31				
Twickenham	a	09 40			09 46	09 51	10 03				10 10			10 16	10 21				16 27	16 33				16 40
	d	09 40			09 47	09 52	10 04				10 10			10 17	10 22				16 27	16 34				16 40
Strawberry Hill	d						10 07													16 37				
Fulwell	a																							
Teddington	a						10 10													16 42				
Hampton Wick	a						10 14													16 46				
Kingston	a						10 16									and at				16 48				
Whitton	d				09a50	09 55			10a26					10a20	10 25	the same						16a53		
Feltham	d	09 46				09 59		10 06			10 16				10 29				16 33		16 36			16 46
Ashford (Surrey)	d					10 03		10 10							10 33	minutes			16 37		16 40			
Staines	d	09 53				10 07		10 15			10 23				10 37				16 41		16 45			16 53
Wraysbury	d					10 11									10 41	past								
Sunnymeads	d					10 14									10 44	each								
Datchet	d					10 17									10 47									
Windsor & Eton Riverside	a					10 24									10 54	hour until								
Egham	d	09 57						10 20			10 27								16 46		16 50			16 57
Virginia Water	a	10 01						10 24			10 31								16 50		16 54			17 01
	d	10 01						10 24			10 31								16 50		16 54			17 01
Chertsey §	d							10 29													16 59			
Addlestone §	d							10 32													17 02			
Weybridge	a							10 37													17 07			
Byfleet & New Haw	d																							
West Byfleet	d																							
Woking	a																							
Longcross	d																							
Sunningdale	d	10 07									10 37								16 55					17 07
Ascot 3	d	10 13		10 23							10 43		10 53						17 00					17 13
Bagshot	d			10 29									10 59											
Camberley	a			10 35									11 05											
	d			10 39									11 09											
Frimley	d			10 43									11 13											
Ash Vale	d			10 49									11 19											
Aldershot	a			10 54									11 24											
	d			11 08									11 38											
Ash 3	d			11 15									11 45											
Wanborough	d			11 18									11 48											
Guildford	a			11 25									11 55											
Martins Heron	d	10 17									10 47								17 04					17 17
Bracknell	d	10 20									10 50								17 07					17 20
Wokingham	d	10 27									10 57								17 17					17 27
Winnersh	d	10 30									11 00													17 30
Winnersh Triangle	d	10 32									11 02													17 32
Earley	d	10 35									11 05													17 35
Reading 7	a	10 43									11 13								17 30					17 45

For general notes see front of timetable
For details of catering facilities see Directory of Train Operators

§ Passengers to/from London may travel via Weybridge. See Table 155.

A To London Waterloo
B To London Waterloo (Table 152)
C 1250 from London Waterloo calls Longcross 1335

b Arr. 1015
c Arr. 1645

Table 149

London → Hounslow, Richmond, Kingston, Windsor, Weybridge, Ascot, Guildford and Reading

Mondays to Fridays
from 29 September

Network Diagram - see first page of Table 148

		SW	SW [1]	SW A	SW	SW B	SW	SW B	SW	SW A	SW A	SW [1]	SW	SW A	SW	SW B	SW [1]	SW B	SW	SW [1]	SW A	SW	SW A	SW [1]	SW
London Waterloo [15] ⊖	d	16 22			16 28	16 31	16 35			16 37	16 45	16 50	16 52		16 58	17 01	17 05				17 07	17 13	17 15	17 20	17 22
Vauxhall ⊖	d	16 26			16 32	16 35	16 39			16 41	16 49		16 56		17 02	17 05	17 09				17 11	17 17	17 19		17 26
Queenstown Rd.(Battersea)	d	16 29				16 38				16 44	16 52		16 59			17 08					17 14		17 22		17 29
Clapham Junction [10]	d	16 32			16 38	16 41	16 45			16 47	16 55	16 58	17 02		17 08	17 11	17 15				17 17	17 23	17 25	17 28	17 32
Wandsworth Town	d	16 35				16 44				16 50	16 58		17 05			17 14					17 20		17 28		17 35
Putney	d	16 38		←	16 42	16 47		←		16 53	17 01		17 08	←	17 12	17 17		←			17 23	17 27	17 31		17 38
Barnes	d	16 42		16 35		16 52		16 52		16 57	17 05		17 12	17 05		17 22		17 22			17 27		17 35		17 42
Barnes Bridge	d	16 44				→				16 59	→		17 14			→					17 29		→		17 44
Chiswick	d	16 47							←	17 02			17 17						←		17 32				17 47
Kew Bridge	d	16 50							16 50	17 05			17 20						17 20		17 35				17 50
Brentford	d	→							16 53	17 08			→						17 23		17 38				→
Syon Lane	d								16 55	17 10									17 25		17 40				
Isleworth	d								16 57	17 12									17 27		17 42				
Hounslow	d								17 01	17b18									17 31		17c48				
Mortlake	d			16 37				16 54						17 07				17 24							
North Sheen	d			16 39				16 56						17 09				17 26							
Richmond ⊖	d			16 42	16 48		16 53	16 59				17 06		17 12	17 18		17 23	17 29				17 33		17 36	
St Margarets	d			16 44				17 01						17 14				17 31							
Twickenham	a			16 46	16 51		16 57	17 03				17 10		17 16	17 21		17 27	17 33				17 37		17 40	
	d			16 47	16 52		16 57	17 04				17 10		17 17	17 22		17 27	17 34				17 37		17 40	
Strawberry Hill	d							17 07										17 37				17 41			
Fulwell	a																								
Teddington	a							17 12										17 42				17 46			
Hampton Wick	a							17 16										17 46							
Kingston	a							17 18										17 48							
Whitton	d			16a50	16 55					17a23				17a20	17 25						17a53				
Feltham	d				16 59		17 03		17 06			17 16			17 29		17 33		17 36					17 46	
Ashford (Surrey)	d				17 03		17 07		17 10						17 33		17 37		17 40						
Staines	d				17 07		17 11		17 15			17 23			17 37		17 41		17 45					17 53	
Wraysbury	d				17 11										17 41										
Sunnymeads	d				17 14										17 44										
Datchet	d				17 17										17 47										
Windsor & Eton Riverside	a				17 26										17 56										
Egham	d						17 16		17 20			17 27					17 46		17 50					17 57	
Virginia Water	a						17 20		17 24			17 31					17 50		17 54					18 01	
	d						17 20		17 24			17 31					17 50		17 54					18 01	
Chertsey §	d								17 29										17 59						
Addlestone §	d								17 32										18 02						
Weybridge	a								17 40										18 10						
Byfleet & New Haw	d																								
West Byfleet	d																								
Woking	a																								
Longcross	d						17 23																		
Sunningdale	d						17 27					17 37					17 55							18 07	
Ascot [3]	d		17 23				17 31					17 43					18 00							18 13	
Bagshot	d		17 29														18 06								
Camberley	a		17 35														18 12								
	d		17 39														18 13								
Frimley	d		17 43														18 17								
Ash Vale	d		17 49														18 24								
Aldershot	a		17 54														18 34								
	d		18 08																	18 38					
Ash [3]	d		18 15																	18 45					
Wanborough	d		18 18																	18 48					
Guildford	a		18 25																	18 55					
Martins Heron	d						17 35					17 47												18 17	
Bracknell	d						17 39					17 50												18 20	
Wokingham	d						17 47					17 57												18 27	
Winnersh	d											18 00												18 30	
Winnersh Triangle	d											18 02												18 32	
Earley	d											18 05												18 35	
Reading [7]	a						18 01					18 15												18 46	

For general notes see front of timetable
For details of catering facilities see Directory of Train Operators

§ Passengers to/from London may travel via Weybridge. See Table 155.

A To London Waterloo
B To London Waterloo (Table 152)
b Arr. 1715
c Arr. 1745

from 29 September

London → Hounslow, Richmond, Kingston, Windsor, Weybridge, Ascot, Guildford and Reading

Network Diagram - see first page of Table 148

		SW 1	SW	SW	SW	SW 1	SW	SW	SW	SW	SW	SW 1	SW	SW	SW	SW	SW 1		SW	SW	SW 1	SW	SW	SW	SW 1
			A		B		B		A	C	A			A		B			B			A	C	A	
London Waterloo 15 ⊖	d			17 28	17 31	17 35			17 37	17 43	17 45	17 50	17 52		17 58	18 01	18 05					18 07	18 13	18 15	18 20
Vauxhall ⊖	d			17 32	17 35	17 39			17 41	17 47	17 49		17 56		18 02	18 05	18 09					18 11	18 17	18 19	
Queenstown Rd.(Battersea)	d				17 38				17 44		17 52		17 59			18 08						18 14		18 22	
Clapham Junction 10	d			17 38	17 41	17 45			17 47	17 53	17 55	17 58	18 02		18 08	18 11	18 15					18 17	18 23	18 25	18 28
Wandsworth Town	d				17 44				17 50		17 58		18 05			18 14						18 20		18 28	
Putney	d		←	17 42	17 47		←		17 53	17 57	18 01		18 08	←	18 12	18 17			←			18 23	18 27	18 31	
Barnes	d		17 35		17 52		17 52		17 57		18 05		18 12	18 05		18 22			18 22			18 27		18 35	
Barnes Bridge	d				↪				17 59		↪		18 14			↪						18 29		↪	
Chiswick	d							←	18 02				18 17							←		18 32			
Kew Bridge	d							17 50	18 05				18 20							18 20		18 35			
Brentford	d							17 53	18 08				↪							18 23		18 38			
Syon Lane	d							17 55	18 10											18 25		18 40			
Isleworth	d							17 57	18 12											18 27		18 42			
Hounslow	d							18 01	18b18											18 31		18c48			
Mortlake	d		17 37				17 54							18 07					18 24						
North Sheen	d		17 39				17 56							18 09					18 26						
Richmond ⊖	d		17 42	17 48		17 53	17 59			18 03		18 06		18 12	18 18		18 23		18 29				18 33		18 36
St Margarets	d		17 44				18 01							18 14					18 31						
Twickenham	a		17 46	17 51		17 57	18 03			18 07		18 10		18 16	18 21		18 27		18 33				18 37		18 40
	d		17 47	17 52		17 57	18 04			18 07		18 10		18 17	18 22		18 27		18 34				18 37		18 40
Strawberry Hill	d						18 07			18 11									18 37				18 41		
Fulwell	a									18 13													18 43		
Teddington	a						18 12												18 42						
Hampton Wick	a						18 16												18 46						
Kingston	a						18 18												18 48						
Whitton	d		17a50	17 55					18a23					18a20	18 25							18a53			
Feltham	d			17 59		18 03		18 06				18 16			18 29		18 33			18 36					18 46
Ashford (Surrey)	d			18 03		18 07		18 10							18 33		18 37			18 40					
Staines	d			18 07		18 11		18 15				18 23			18 37		18 41			18 45					18 53
Wraysbury	d			18 11											18 41										
Sunnymeads	d			18 14											18 44										
Datchet	d			18 17											18 47										
Windsor & Eton Riverside	a			18 26											18 56										
Egham	d					18 16		18 20				18 27					18 46			18 50					18 57
Virginia Water	a					18 20		18 24				18 31					18 50			18 54					19 01
	d					18 20		18 24				18 31					18 50			18 54					19 01
Chertsey §	d							18 29												18 59					
Addlestone §	d							18 32												19 02					
Weybridge	a							18 40												19 10					
Byfleet & New Haw	d																								
West Byfleet	d																								
Woking	a																								
Longcross	d											18 35													19 07
Sunningdale	d					18 25						18 37					18 55								19 13
Ascot 3	d	18 23				18 30						18 43					19 02								
Bagshot	d	18 29															19 08								
Camberley	a	18 35															19 14								
	d	18 39															19 15								
Frimley	d	18 43															19 19								
Ash Vale	d	18 49															19 26								
Aldershot	a	18 54															19 36								
	d	19 08																			19 38				
Ash 3	d	19 15																			19 45				
Wanborough	d	19 18																			19 48				
Guildford	a	19 25																			19 55				
Martins Heron	d					18 34						18 47													19 17
Bracknell	d					18 37						18 50													19 20
Wokingham	d					18 47						18 57													19 27
Winnersh	d											19 00													19 30
Winnersh Triangle	d											19 02													19 32
Earley	d											19 05													19 35
Reading 7	a					19 00						19 15													19 45

For general notes see front of timetable
For details of catering facilities see Directory of Train Operators

§ Passengers to/from London may travel via Weybridge. See Table 155.

A To London Waterloo
B To London Waterloo (Table 152)
C To Shepperton (Table 152)

b Arr. 1815
c Arr. 1845

Table 149

Mondays to Fridays

from 29 September

London → Hounslow, Richmond, Kingston, Windsor, Weybridge, Ascot, Guildford and Reading

Network Diagram - see first page of Table 148

	SW	SW 1	SW	SW	SW	SW 1	SW	SW	SW	SW	SW	SW 1	SW	SW 1	SW	SW	SW	SW 1	SW	SW	SW	SW	SW 1	SW
			A		B		B		A	C	A				A		B		B		A	A		
London Waterloo 15 ⊖ d	18 22			18 28	18 31	18 35			18 37	18 43	18 45	18 50	18 52			18 58	19 01	19 05			19 07	19 15	19 20	19 22
Vauxhall ⊖ d	18 26			18 32	18 35	18 39			18 41	18 47	18 49		18 56			19 02	19 05	19 09			19 11	19 19		19 26
Queenstown Rd.(Battersea) d	18 29				18 38				18 44		18 52		18 59				19 08				19 14	19 22		19 29
Clapham Junction 10 d	18 32			18 38	18 41	18 45			18 47	18 53	18 55	18 58	19 02			19 08	19 11	19 15			19 17	19 25	19 28	19 32
Wandsworth Town d	18 35				18 44				18 50		18 58		19 05				19 14				19 20	19 28		19 35
Putney d	18 38		←	18 42	18 47		←		18 53	18 57	19 01		19 08		←	19 12	19 17		←		19 23	19 31		19 38
Barnes d	18 42		18 35		18 52		18 52		18 57		19 05		19 12		19 05		19 22		19 22		19 27	19 35		19 42
Barnes Bridge d	18 44				→				18 59		→		19 14				→				19 29	→		19 44
Chiswick d	18 47							←	19 02				19 17							←	19 32			19 47
Kew Bridge d	18 50							18 50	19 05				19 20							19 20	19 35			19 50
Brentford d	→							18 53	19 08				→							19 23	19 38			→
Syon Lane d								18 55	19 10											19 25	19 40			
Isleworth d								18 57	19 12											19 27	19 42			
Hounslow d								19 01	19b18											19 31	19c48			
Mortlake d			18 37				18 54								19 07				19 24					
North Sheen d			18 39				18 56								19 09				19 26					
Richmond ⊖ d			18 42	18 48		18 53	18 59			19 03		19 06			19 12	19 18		19 23	19 29				19 36	
St Margarets d			18 44				19 01								19 14				19 31					
Twickenham a			18 46	18 51		18 57	19 03			19 07		19 10			19 16	19 21		19 27	19 33				19 40	
d			18 47	18 52		18 57	19 04			19 07		19 10			19 17	19 22		19 27	19 34				19 40	
Strawberry Hill d							19 07			19 11									19 37					
Fulwell a										19 13														
Teddington a							19 12												19 42					
Hampton Wick a							19 16												19 46					
Kingston a							19 18												19 48					
Whitton d			18a50	18 55					19a23						19a20	19 25					19a53			
Feltham d				18 59		19 03		19 06				19 16				19 29		19 33		19 36			19 46	
Ashford (Surrey) d				19 03		19 07		19 10								19 33		19 37		19 40				
Staines d				19 07		19 11		19 15				19 23				19 37		19 41		19 45			19 53	
Wraysbury d				19 11												19 41								
Sunnymeads d				19 14												19 44								
Datchet d				19 17												19 47								
Windsor & Eton Riverside a				19 26												19 56								
Egham d						19 16		19 20				19 27						19 46		19 50			19 57	
Virginia Water a						19 20		19 24				19 31						19 50		19 54			20 01	
d						19 20		19 24				19 31						19 50		19 54			20 01	
Chertsey § d								19 29												19 59				
Addlestone § d								19 31												20 02				
Weybridge a								19 40												20 10				
Byfleet & New Haw d																								
West Byfleet d																								
Woking a																								
Longcross d																								
Sunningdale d						19 25						19 37						19 55					20 07	
Ascot 3 d		19 23				19 30						19 43		19 53				20 00					20 13	
Bagshot d		19 29												19 59										
Camberley a		19 35												20 05										
d		19 39												20 09										
Frimley d		19 43												20 13										
Ash Vale d		19 49												20 19										
Aldershot a		19 54												20 24										
d		20 08												20 38										
Ash 3 d		20 15												20 45										
Wanborough d		20 18												20 48										
Guildford a		20 25												20 55										
Martins Heron d						19 34						19 47						20 04					20 17	
Bracknell d						19 37						19 50						20 07					20 20	
Wokingham d						19 47						19 57						20 17					20 27	
Winnersh d												20 00											20 30	
Winnersh Triangle d												20 02											20 32	
Earley d												20 05											20 35	
Reading 7 a						20 00						20 15						20 28					20 43	

For general notes see front of timetable
For details of catering facilities see Directory of Train Operators

§ Passengers to/from London may travel via Weybridge. See Table 155.

A To London Waterloo
B To London Waterloo (Table 152)
C To Shepperton (Table 152)

b Arr. 1915
c Arr. 1945

London → Hounslow, Richmond, Kingston, Windsor, Weybridge, Ascot, Guildford and Reading

Network Diagram - see first page of Table 148

		SW 1	SW	SW	SW	SW	SW	SW	SW 1	SW	SW 1	SW	SW	SW	SW	SW	SW		SW 1	SW	SW 1	SW 1	SW	SW	SW
			A		B		A	A				A		B		A	A						A		B
London Waterloo 15 ⊖	d			19 28	19 33		19 37	19 45	19 50	19 52			19 58	20 03		20 07	20 15		20 20	20 22				20 28	20 33
Vauxhall ⊖	d			19 32	19 37		19 41	19 49		19 56			20 02	20 07		20 11	20 19			20 26				20 32	20 37
Queenstown Rd.(Battersea)	d				19 40		19 44	19 52		19 59				20 10		20 14	20 22			20 29					20 40
Clapham Junction 10	d			19 38	19 43		19 47	19 55	19 58	20 02			20 08	20 13		20 17	20 25		20 28	20 32				20 38	20 43
Wandsworth Town	d				19 46		19 50	19 58		20 05				20 16		20 20	20 28			20 35					20 46
Putney	d		←	19 42	19 49		19 53	20 01		20 08		←	20 12	20 19		20 23	20 31			20 38			←	20 42	20 49
Barnes	d		19 35		19 52		19 57	20 05		20 12		20 05		20 22		20 27	20 35			20 42			20 35		20 52
Barnes Bridge	d						19 59	→		20 14						20 29	→			20 44					
Chiswick	d					←	20 02			20 17					←	20 32				20 47					
Kew Bridge	d					19 50	20 05			20 20 →					20 20	20 35				20 50 →					
Brentford	d					19 53	20 08								20 23	20 38									
Syon Lane	d					19 55	20 10								20 25	20 40									
Isleworth	d					19 57	20 12								20 27	20 42									
Hounslow	d					20 01	20b18								20 31	20c48									
Mortlake	d		19 37		19 54							20 07		20 24									20 37		20 54
North Sheen	d		19 39		19 56							20 09		20 26									20 39		20 56
Richmond ⊖	d		19 42	19 48	19 59				20 06			20 12	20 18	20 29					20 36				20 42	20 48	20 59
St Margarets	d		19 44		20 01							20 14		20 31									20 44		21 01
Twickenham	a		19 46	19 51	20 03				20 10			20 16	20 21	20 33					20 40				20 46	20 51	21 03
	d		19 47	19 52	20 04				20 10			20 17	20 22	20 34					20 40				20 47	20 52	21 04
Strawberry Hill	d				20 07									20 37											21 07
Fulwell	a																								
Teddington	a				20 10									20 40											21 10
Hampton Wick	a				20 14									20 44											21 14
Kingston	a				20 16									20 46											21 16
Whitton	d		19a50	19 55			20a23					20a20	20 25			20a53							20a50	20 55	
Feltham	d			19 59		20 06			20 16				20 29		20 36				20 46					20 59	
Ashford (Surrey)	d			20 03		20 10							20 33		20 40									21 03	
Staines	d			20 07		20 15			20 23				20 37		20 45				20 53					21 07	
Wraysbury	d			20 11									20 41											21 11	
Sunnymeads	d			20 14									20 44											21 14	
Datchet	d			20 17									20 47											21 17	
Windsor & Eton Riverside	a			20 24									20 54											21 24	
Egham	d					20 20			20 27						20 50				20 57						
Virginia Water	a					20 24			20 31						20 54				21 01						
	d					20 24			20 31						20 54				21 01						
Chertsey §	d					20 29									20 59										
Addlestone §	d					20 32									21 02										
Weybridge	a					20 37									21 07										
Byfleet & New Haw	d																								
West Byfleet	d																								
Woking	a																								
Longcross	d																								
Sunningdale	d								20 37										21 07						
Ascot 3	d	20 23							20 43		20 53								21 13		21 23				
Bagshot	d	20 29									20 59										21 29				
Camberley	a	20 35									21 05										21 35				
	d	20 39									21 09										21 39				
Frimley	d	20 43									21 13										21 43				
Ash Vale	d	20 49									21 19										21 49				
Aldershot	a	20 54									21 24										21 54				
	d	21 08									21 38										22 08	22 38			
Ash 3	d	21 15									21 45										22 15	22 45			
Wanborough	d	21 18									21 48										22 18	22 48			
Guildford	a	21 25									21 55										22 25	22 55			
Martins Heron	d								20 47										21 17						
Bracknell	d								20 50										21 20						
Wokingham	d								20 57										21 27						
Winnersh	d								21 00										21 30						
Winnersh Triangle	d								21 02										21 32						
Earley	d								21 05										21 35						
Reading 7	a								21 13										21 43						

For general notes see front of timetable
For details of catering facilities see Directory of Train Operators

§ Passengers to/from London may travel via Weybridge. See Table 155.

A To London Waterloo
B To London Waterloo (Table 152)
b Arr. 2015
c Arr. 2045

from 29 September

London → Hounslow, Richmond, Kingston, Windsor, Weybridge, Ascot, Guildford and Reading

Network Diagram - see first page of Table 148

		SW	SW	SW	SW	SW	SW	SW	SW	SW	SW	SW	SW	SW	SW	SW	SW	SW	SW	SW	SW	SW	SW	SW	SW
					1								1		1							1			
			A	A			A		B		A	A				A		B		A					
London Waterloo 15	⊖ d		20 37	20 45	20 50	20 52		20 58	21 03		21 07	21 15	21 20	21 22			21 28	21 33		21 37	21 45	21 50		21 52	21 58
Vauxhall	⊖ d		20 41	20 49		20 56		21 02	21 07		21 11	21 19		21 26			21 32	21 37		21 41	21 49			21 56	22 02
Queenstown Rd.(Battersea)	d		20 44	20 52		20 59			21 10		21 14	21 22		21 29				21 40		21 44	21 52			21 59	
Clapham Junction 10	d		20 47	20 55	20 58	21 02		21 08	21 13		21 17	21 25	21 28	21 32			21 38	21 43		21 47	21 55	21 58		22 02	22 08
Wandsworth Town	d		20 50	20 58		21 05			21 16		21 20	21 28		21 35				21 46		21 50	21 58			22 05	
Putney	d		20 53	21 01		21 08	←	21 12	21 19		21 23	21 31		21 38		←	21 42	21 49		21 53	22 01		←	22 08	22 12
Barnes	d		20 57	21 05		21 12	21 05		21 22		21 27	21 35		21 42		21 35		21 52		21 57	22 05		22 05	22 12	
Barnes Bridge	d		20 59	→		21 14					21 29	→		21 44						21 59	→			22 14	
Chiswick	d	←	21 02			21 17				←	21 32			21 47					←	22 02				22 17	
Kew Bridge	d	20 50	21 05			21 20				21 20	21 35			21 50					21 50	22 05				22 20	
Brentford	d	20 53	21 08			→				21 23	21 38			→					21 53	22 08				→	
Syon Lane	d	20 55	21 10							21 25	21 40								21 55	22 10					
Isleworth	d	20 57	21 12							21 27	21 42								21 57	22 12					
Hounslow	d	21 01	21b18							21 31	21c48								22 01	22e18					
Mortlake	d						21 07		21 24							21 37		21 54					22 07		
North Sheen	d						21 09		21 26							21 39		21 56					22 09		
Richmond	⊖ d				21 06		21 12	21 18	21 29				21 36			21 42	21 48	21 59				22 06	22 12		22 18
St Margarets	d						21 14		21 31							21 44		22 01					22 14		
Twickenham	a				21 10		21 16	21 21	21 33				21 40			21 46	21 51	22 03				22 10	22 17		22 21
	d				21 10		21 17	21 22	21 34				21 40			21 47	21 52	22 04				22 10			22 22
Strawberry Hill	d								21 37									22 07							
Fulwell	a																								
Teddington	a								21 40									22 10							
Hampton Wick	a								21 44									22 14							
Kingston	a								21 46									22 16							
Whitton	d		21a23				21a20	21 25			21a53					21a50	21 55			22a23					22 25
Feltham	d	21 06			21 16			21 29		21 36			21 46				21 59		22 06			22 16			22 29
Ashford (Surrey)	d	21 10						21 33		21 40							22 03		22 10						22 33
Staines	d	21 15			21 23			21 37		21 45			21 53				22 07		22 15			22 23			22 37
Wraysbury	d							21 41									22 11								22 41
Sunnymeads	d							21 44									22 14								22 44
Datchet	d							21 47									22 17								22 47
Windsor & Eton Riverside	a							21 54									22 24								22 54
Egham	d	21 20			21 27					21 50			21 57						22 20			22 27			
Virginia Water	a	21 24			21 31					21 54			22 01						22 24			22 31			
	d	21 24			21 31					21 54			22 01						22 24			22 31			
Chertsey §	d	21 29								21 59									22 29						
Addlestone §	d	21 32								22 02									22 32						
Weybridge	a	21 37								22 07									22 37						
Byfleet & New Haw	d																								
West Byfleet	d																								
Woking	a																								
Longcross	d																								
Sunningdale	d				21 37								22 07									22 37			
Ascot 3	d				21 43								22 13		22 23							22 43			
Bagshot	d														22 29										
Camberley	a														22 35										
	d														22 39										
Frimley	d														22 43										
Ash Vale	d														22 49										
Aldershot	a														22 54										
	d														23 08										
Ash 3	d														23 15										
Wanborough	d														23 18										
Guildford	a														23 25										
Martins Heron	d				21 47								22 17									22 47			
Bracknell	d				21 50								22 20									22 50			
Wokingham	d				21 57								22 27									22 57			
Winnersh	d				22 00								22 30									23 00			
Winnersh Triangle	d				22 02								22 32									23 02			
Earley	d				22 05								22 35									23 05			
Reading 7	a				22 13								22 43									23 13			

For general notes see front of timetable
For details of catering facilities see Directory of Train Operators

§ Passengers to/from London may travel via Weybridge. See Table 155.

A To London Waterloo
B To London Waterloo (Table 152)
b Arr. 2115
c Arr. 2145
e Arr. 2215

London → Hounslow, Richmond, Kingston, Windsor, Weybridge, Ascot, Guildford and Reading

Network Diagram - see first page of Table 148

Station		SW	SW	SW	SW	SW	SW	SW	SW	SW	SW	SW	SW	SW	SW	SW	SW	SW	SW	SW	SW	SW	SW
				1		1				1						1							
		A				B		A					A										
London Waterloo 15 ⊖	d	22 03		22 20	22 22		22 28	22 33		22 50	22 52	22 58	23 03		23 13	23 20	23 22	23 35		23 37	23 52	23 58	
Vauxhall ⊖	d	22 07			22 26		22 32	22 37			22 56	23 02	23 07		23 17		23 26			23 41	23 56	00 02	
Queenstown Rd.(Battersea)	d	22 10			22 29			22 40			22 59		23 10				23 29			23 44	23 59		
Clapham Junction 10	d	22 13		22 28	22 32		22 38	22 43		22 58	23 02	23 08	23 13		23 23	23 28	23 32	23 43		23 47	00 02	00 08	
Wandsworth Town	d	22 16			22 35			22 46			23 05		23 16				23 35			23 50	00 05		
Putney	d	22 19			22 38		22 42	22 49			23 08	23 12	23 19		23 27		23 38			23 53	00 08	00 12	
Barnes	d	22 22			22 42			22 52			23 12		23 22				23 42			23 56	00 12		
Barnes Bridge	d				22 44						23 14						23 44		←		00 14		
Chiswick	d		←		22 47				←		23 17			←			23 47		23 47		00 17		←
Kew Bridge	d		22 20		22 50				22 50		23 20			23 20			→		23 50		00 20		00 20
Brentford	d		22 23		→				22 53		→			23 23					23 53		→		00 23
Syon Lane	d		22 25						22 55					23 25					23 55				00 25
Isleworth	d		22 27						22 57					23 27					23 57				00 27
Hounslow	d		22 31						23 01					23 31					00 01				00 31
Mortlake	d	22 24						22 54					23 24							23 58			
North Sheen	d	22 26						22 56					23 26							00 01			
Richmond ⊖	d	22 29		22 36			22 48	22 59		23 06		23 18	23 29		23 33	23 37		23 51		00 03		00 18	
St Margarets	d	22 31						23 01					23 31							00 06			
Twickenham	a	22 33		22 40			22 51	23 03		23 10		23 21	23 33		23 36	23 41		23 55		00 08		00 21	
	d	22 34		22 40			22 52	23 04		23 10		23 22	23 34		23 37	23 41		23 55		00 08		00 22	
Strawberry Hill	d	22 37						23 07					23 37							00 12			
Fulwell	a																						
Teddington	a	22 40						23 10					23 40							00 15			
Hampton Wick	a	22 44						23 14					23 44							00 17			
Kingston	a	22 46						23 16					23 46							00 19			
Whitton	d						22 55					23 25			23 40							00 25	
Feltham	d		22 36	22 46			22 59		23 06	23 16		23 29		23 36	23 44	23 48		00 01	00 06			00 29	00 36
Ashford (Surrey)	d		22 40				23 03		23 10			23 33		23 40	23 48				00 10			00 33	00 40
Staines	d		22 45	22 53			23 07		23 15	23 23		23 37		23 45	23 52	23 56		00 08	00 15			00a37	00a46
Wraysbury	d						23 11					23 41			23 56								
Sunnymeads	d						23 14					23 44			23 59								
Datchet	d						23 17					23 47			00 02								
Windsor & Eton Riverside	a						23 24					23 54			00 09								
Egham	d		22 50	22 57					23 20	23 27				23 50		00 01		00 12	00 20				
Virginia Water	a		22 54	23 01					23 24	23 31				23 54		00 05		00 16	00 24				
	d		22 54	23 01					23 24	23 31				23 54		00 05		00 16	00 24				
Chertsey §	d		22 59						23 29					23 59					00 29				
Addlestone §	d		23 02						23 32					00 02					00 32				
Weybridge	a		23 07						23 37										00 37				
Byfleet & New Haw	d													00 07									
West Byfleet	d													00 10									
Woking	a													00 16									
Longcross	d																						
Sunningdale	d			23 07						23 37						00 10		00 22					
Ascot 3	d			23 13		23 23				23 43						00 15		00 27					
Bagshot	d					23 29																	
Camberley	a					23 35																	
	d					23 39																	
Frimley	d					23 43																	
Ash Vale	d					23 49																	
Aldershot	a					23 54																	
	d																						
Ash 3	d																						
Wanborough	d																						
Guildford	a																						
Martins Heron	d			23 17						23 47						00 19		00 31					
Bracknell	d			23 20						23 50						00 23		00 34					
Wokingham	d			23 27						23 57						00 32		00 41					
Winnersh	d			23 30						00 01						00 36							
Winnersh Triangle	d			23 32						00 02						00 38							
Earley	d			23 35						00 05						00 40							
Reading 7	a			23 43						00 13						00 48		00 52					

For general notes see front of timetable
For details of catering facilities see Directory of Train Operators

§ Passengers to/from London may travel via Weybridge. See Table 155.

A To London Waterloo (Table 152)
B To Farnham (Table 155)

until 27 September

London → Hounslow, Richmond, Kingston, Windsor, Weybridge, Ascot, Guildford and Reading

Network Diagram - see first page of Table 148

		SW 1	SW	SW	SW 1	SW	SW	SW	SW 1	SW	SW	SW	SW	SW	SW	SW 1	SW	SW 1	SW	SW 1	SW	SW	SW
															A				B				A
London Waterloo 15 ⊖	d	22p50	22p52	23p13	23p20	23p22	23p35	23p37			23p52	23p58		00 18				05 05					05 33
Vauxhall ⊖	d		22p56	23p17		23p26		23p41			23p56	00 02		00 22				05 09					05 37
Queenstown Rd.(Battersea)	d		22p59			23p29		23p44			23p59			00 25				05 12					05 40
Clapham Junction 10	d	22p58	23p02	23p23	23p28	23p32	23p43	23p47			00 02	00 08		00 28				05 15					05 43
Wandsworth Town	d		23p05			23p35		23p50			00 05			00 31				05 18					05 46
Putney	d		23p08	23p27		23p38		23p53			00 08	00 12		00 34				05 21					05 49
Barnes	d		23p12			23p42		23p56			00 12			00 37				05 24					05 52
Barnes Bridge	d		23p14			23p44				←	00 14												
Chiswick	d		23p17			23p47				23p47	00 17		←										
Kew Bridge	d		23p20			→				23p50	00 20		00 20										
Brentford	d		23p23							23p53	→		00 23										
Syon Lane	d		23p25							23p55			00 25										
Isleworth	d		23p27							23p57			00 27										
Hounslow	d		23p31							00 01			00 31										
Mortlake	d							23p58						00 39				05 26					05 54
North Sheen	d							00 01						00 41				05 28					05 56
Richmond ⊖	d	23p06		23p33	23p37		23p51	00 03				00 18		00 44				05 31					05 59
St Margarets	d							00 06						00 46				05 33					06 01
Twickenham	a	23p10		23p36	23p41		23p55	00 08				00 21		00 48				05 35					06 03
	d	23p10		23p37	23p41		23p55	00 08				00 22		00 49	04 52			05 36	05 38		05 52		06 04
Strawberry Hill	d							00 12						00s52	04 55								06 07
Fulwell	a																						
Teddington	a							00 15						00s55	04 58								06 10
Hampton Wick	a							00 17						00s58	05 01								06 14
Kingston	a							00 19						01 00	05 03								06 16
Whitton	d			23p40								00 25						05 39	05a41		05 55		
Feltham	d	23p16	23p36	23p44	23p48		00 01			00 06		00 29	00 36					05 43			05 59		
Ashford (Surrey)	d		23p40	23p48						00 10		00 33	00 40					05 47			06 03		
Staines	d	23p23	23p45	23p52	23p56		00 08			00 15		00a37	00a46			05 23	05 45	05 53			06 07	06 15	
Wraysbury	d			23p56																	06 11		
Sunnymeads	d			23p59																	06 14		
Datchet	d			00 02																	06 17		
Windsor & Eton Riverside	a			00 06																	06 23		
Egham	d	23p27	23p50		00 01		00 12			00 20						05 27	05 50	05 57				06 20	
Virginia Water	a	23p31	23p54		00 05		00 16			00 24						05 31	05 54	06 01				06 24	
	d	23p31	23p54		00 05		00 16			00 24						05 31	05 54	06 01				06 24	
Chertsey §	d		23p59							00 29							05 59					06 29	
Addlestone §	d		00 02							00 32							06 02					06 32	
Weybridge	a									00 37							06 07					06 37	
Byfleet & New Haw	d		00 07																				
West Byfleet	d		00 10																				
Woking	a		00 16																				
Longcross	d																						
Sunningdale	d	23p37			00 10		00 22									05 38		06 07					
Ascot 3	d	23p43			00 15		00 27		00 29							05 43		06 13					
Bagshot	d								00 35														
Camberley	a								00 41														
	d								00 41														
Frimley	d								00 45														
Ash Vale	d								00 52														
Aldershot	a								00 57														
	d																			06 08			
Ash 3	d																			06 15			
Wanborough	d																			06 18			
Guildford	a																			06 25			
Martins Heron	d	23p47			00 19		00 31									05 47		06 17					
Bracknell	d	23p50			00 23		00 34									05 50		06 20					
Wokingham	d	23p57			00 32		00 41									05 57		06 27					
Winnersh	d	00 01			00 36											06 00		06 30					
Winnersh Triangle	d	00 02			00 38											06 03		06 32					
Earley	d	00 05			00 40											06 05		06 35					
Reading 7	a	00 10			00 45		00 49									06 10		06 40					

For general notes see front of timetable
For details of catering facilities see Directory of Train Operators

§ Passengers to/from London may travel via Weybridge. See Table 155.

A To London Waterloo (Table 152)
B To London Waterloo

Table 149

until 27 September

London → Hounslow, Richmond, Kingston, Windsor, Weybridge, Ascot, Guildford and Reading

Network Diagram - see first page of Table 148

Station		SW 1		SW 1	SW	SW	SW	SW 1	SW 1	SW 1		SW	SW	SW	SW	SW 1	SW	SW		SW	SW	SW	SW 1	SW 1	SW 1
						A								A						A	B				
London Waterloo 15	⊖ d			05 50	05 58	06 03				06 20		06 22	06 28	06 33		06 50	06 52	06 58		07 03	07 15				07 20
Vauxhall	⊖ d				06 02	06 07						06 26	06 32	06 37			06 56	07 02		07 07	07 19				
Queenstown Rd.(Battersea)	d					06 10						06 29		06 40			06 59			07 10	07 22				
Clapham Junction 10	d			05 58	06 08	06 13				06 28		06 32	06 38	06 43		06 58	07 02	07 08		07 13	07 25				07 28
Wandsworth Town	d					06 16						06 35		06 46			07 05			07 16	07 28				
Putney	d				06 12	06 19						06 38	06 42	06 49			07 08	07 12		07 19	07 31				
Barnes	d					06 22						06 42		06 52			07 12			07 22	07 35				
Barnes Bridge	d											06 44					07 14				→				
Chiswick	d											06 47			←		07 17					←			
Kew Bridge	d											06 50 →			06 50		07 20 →					07 20			
Brentford	d														06 53							07 23			
Syon Lane	d														06 55							07 25			
Isleworth	d														06 57							07 27			
Hounslow	d														07 01							07 31			
Mortlake	d					06 24								06 54						07 24					
North Sheen	d					06 26								06 56						07 26					
Richmond	⊖ d			06 06	06 18	06 29				06 36			06 48	06 59		07 06		07 18		07 29					07 36
St Margarets	d					06 31								07 01						07 31					
Twickenham	a			06 10	06 21	06 33				06 40			06 51	07 03		07 10		07 21		07 33					07 40
	d			06 10	06 22	06 34				06 40			06 52	07 04		07 10		07 22		07 34					07 40
Strawberry Hill	d					06 37								07 07						07 37					
Fulwell	a																								
Teddington	a					06 40								07 10						07 40					
Hampton Wick	a					06 44								07 14						07 44					
Kingston	a					06 46								07 16						07 46					
Whitton	d				06 25								06 55					07 25							
Feltham	d			06 16	06 29					06 46			06 59		07 06	07 16		07 29				07 36			07 46
Ashford (Surrey)	d				06 33								07 03		07 10			07 33				07 40			
Staines	d			06 23	06 37		06 45			06 53			07 07		07 15	07 23		07 37				07 45			07 53
Wraysbury	d				06 41								07 11					07 41							
Sunnymeads	d				06 44								07 14					07 44							
Datchet	d				06 47								07 17					07 47							
Windsor & Eton Riverside	a				06 51								07 21					07 51							
Egham	d			06 27			06 50			06 57					07 20	07 27						07 50			07 57
Virginia Water	a			06 31			06 54			07 01					07 24	07 31						07 54			08 01
	d			06 31			06 54			07 01					07 24	07 31						07 54			08 01
Chertsey §	d						06 59								07 29							07 59			
Addlestone §	d						07 02								07 32							08 02			
Weybridge	a						07 07								07 37							08 07			
Byfleet & New Haw	d																								
West Byfleet	d																								
Woking	a																								
Longcross	d																								
Sunningdale	d			06 37						07 07						07 37									08 07
Ascot 3	d			06 43					06 53	07 13						07 43								07 53	08 13
Bagshot	d								06 59															07 59	
Camberley	a								07 05															08 05	
	d								07 09															08 09	
Frimley	d								07 13															08 13	
Ash Vale	d								07 19															08 19	
Aldershot	a								07 24															08 24	
	d	06 38						07 08	07 38														08 08	08 38	
Ash 3	d	06 45						07 15	07 45														08 15	08 45	
Wanborough	d	06 48						07 18	07 48														08 18	08 48	
Guildford	a	06 55						07 25	07 55														08 25	08 55	
Martins Heron	d			06 47						07 17						07 47									08 17
Bracknell	d			06 50						07 20						07 50									08 20
Wokingham	d			06 57						07 27						07 57									08 27
Winnersh	d			07 00						07 30						08 00									08 30
Winnersh Triangle	d			07 02						07 32						08 02									08 32
Earley	d			07 05						07 35						08 05									08 35
Reading 7	a			07 10						07 40						08 10									08 40

For general notes see front of timetable
For details of catering facilities see Directory of Train Operators

§ Passengers to/from London may travel via Weybridge. See Table 155.

A To London Waterloo (Table 152)
B To London Waterloo

Table 149

until 27 September

London → Hounslow, Richmond, Kingston, Windsor, Weybridge, Ascot, Guildford and Reading

Network Diagram - see first page of Table 148

		SW	SW	SW	SW	SW	SW	SW	SW	SW	SW	SW	SW	SW	SW	SW	SW	SW	SW	SW	SW	SW
			■1							■1		■1							■1		■1	
				A		B		A	A				A		B		A	A				A
London Waterloo ■15	⊖ d	07 22			07 28	07 33		07 37	07 45	07 50	07 52			07 58	08 03		08 07	08 15	08 20	08 22		
Vauxhall	⊖ d	07 26			07 32	07 37		07 41	07 49		07 56			08 02	08 07		08 11	08 19		08 26		
Queenstown Rd.(Battersea)	d	07 29				07 40		07 44	07 52		07 59				08 10		08 14	08 22		08 29		
Clapham Junction ■10	d	07 32			07 38	07 43		07 47	07 55	07 58	08 02			08 08	08 13		08 17	08 25	08 28	08 32		
Wandsworth Town	d	07 35				07 46		07 50	07 58		08 05				08 16		08 20	08 28		08 35		
Putney	d	07 38		←	07 42	07 49		07 53	08 01		08 08		←	08 12	08 19		08 23	08 31		08 38		←
Barnes	d	07 42		07 35		07 52		07 57	08 05		08 12		08 05		08 22		08 27	08 35		08 42		08 35
Barnes Bridge	d	07 44						07 59	→		08 14						08 29	→		08 44		
Chiswick	d	07 47					←	08 02			08 17					←	08 32			08 47		
Kew Bridge	d	07 50					07 50	08 05			08 20					08 20	08 35			08 50		
Brentford	d	→					07 53	08 08			→					08 23	08 38			→		
Syon Lane	d						07 55	08 10								08 25	08 40					
Isleworth	d						07 57	08 12								08 27	08 42					
Hounslow	d						08 01	08b18								08 31	08c48					
Mortlake	d			07 37		07 54							08 07		08 24							08 37
North Sheen	d			07 39		07 56							08 09		08 26							08 39
Richmond	⊖ d			07 42	07 48	07 59				08 06			08 12	08 18	08 29				08 36			08 42
St Margarets	d			07 44		08 01							08 14		08 31							08 44
Twickenham	a			07 46	07 51	08 03				08 10			08 16	08 21	08 33				08 40			08 46
	d			07 47	07 52	08 04				08 10			08 17	08 22	08 34				08 40			08 47
Strawberry Hill	d					08 07									08 37							
Fulwell	a																					
Teddington	a					08 10									08 40							
Hampton Wick	a					08 14									08 44							
Kingston	a					08 16									08 46							
Whitton	d			07a50	07 55			08a23					08a20	08 25			08a53					08a50
Feltham	d				07 59		08 06			08 16				08 29		08 36			08 46			
Ashford (Surrey)	d				08 03		08 10							08 33		08 40						
Staines	d				08 07		08 15			08 23				08 37		08 45			08 53			
Wraysbury	d				08 11									08 41								
Sunnymeads	d				08 14									08 44								
Datchet	d				08 17									08 47								
Windsor & Eton Riverside	a				08 21									08 51								
Egham	d						08 20			08 27						08 50			08 57			
Virginia Water	a						08 24			08 31						08 54			09 01			
	d						08 24			08 31						08 54			09 01			
Chertsey §	d						08 29									08 59						
Addlestone §	d						08 32									09 02						
Weybridge	a						08 37									09 07						
Byfleet & New Haw	d																					
West Byfleet	d																					
Woking	a																					
Longcross	d																					
Sunningdale	d									08 37									09 07			
Ascot ■3	d		08 23							08 43		08 53							09 13		09 23	
Bagshot	d		08 29									08 59									09 29	
Camberley	a		08 35									09 05									09 35	
	d		08 39									09 09									09 39	
Frimley	d		08 43									09 13									09 43	
Ash Vale	d		08 49									09 19									09 49	
Aldershot	a		08 54									09 24									09 54	
	d		09 08									09 38									10 08	
Ash ■3	d		09 15									09 45									10 15	
Wanborough	d		09 18									09 48									10 18	
Guildford	a		09 25									09 55									10 25	
Martins Heron	d									08 47									09 17			
Bracknell	d									08 50									09 20			
Wokingham	d									08 57									09 27			
Winnersh	d									09 00									09 30			
Winnersh Triangle	d									09 02									09 32			
Earley	d									09 05									09 35			
Reading ■7	a									09 10									09 40			

For general notes see front of timetable
For details of catering facilities see Directory of Train Operators

§ Passengers to/from London may travel via Weybridge. See Table 155.

A To London Waterloo
B To London Waterloo (Table 152)
b Arr. 0815
c Arr. 0845

Table 149

Saturdays

until 27 September

London → Hounslow, Richmond, Kingston, Windsor, Weybridge, Ascot, Guildford and Reading

Network Diagram - see first page of Table 148

Station		SW	SW	SW	SW	SW		SW	SW	SW	SW	SW		SW	SW	SW	SW	SW	SW	SW	SW	SW	SW	SW	SW
			A		B	B		1		1	B			A		B	B	1		1	B		A		B
London Waterloo 15	⊖ d	08 28	08 33		08 37	08 45		08 50	08 52			08 58		09 03		09 07	09 15	09 20	09 22			09 28	09 33		09 37
Vauxhall	⊖ d	08 32	08 37		08 41	08 49			08 56			09 02		09 07		09 11	09 19		09 26			09 32	09 37		09 41
Queenstown Rd.(Battersea)	d		08 40		08 44	08 52			08 59					09 10		09 14	09 22		09 29				09 40		09 44
Clapham Junction 10	d	08 38	08 43		08 47	08 55		08 58	09 02			09 08		09 13		09 17	09 25	09 28	09 32			09 38	09 43		09 47
Wandsworth Town	d		08 46		08 50	08 58			09 05					09 16		09 20	09 28		09 35				09 46		09 50
Putney	d	08 42	08 49		08 53	09 01			09 08		⟵	09 12		09 19		09 23	09 31		09 38		⟵	09 42	09 49		09 53
Barnes	d		08 52		08 57	09 05			09 12		09 05			09 22		09 27	09 35		09 42		09 35		09 52		09 57
Barnes Bridge	d				08 59	⟶			09 14							09 29	⟶		09 44						09 59
Chiswick	d			⟵	09 02				09 17						⟵	09 32			09 47					⟵	10 02
Kew Bridge	d			08 50	09 05				09 20						09 20	09 35			09 50					09 50	10 05
Brentford	d			08 53	09 08				⟶						09 23	09 38			⟶					09 53	10 08
Syon Lane	d			08 55	09 10										09 25	09 40								09 55	10 10
Isleworth	d			08 57	09 12										09 27	09 42								09 57	10 12
Hounslow	d			09 01	09b18										09 31	09c48								10 01	10e18
Mortlake	d		08 54								09 07			09 24							09 37		09 54		
North Sheen	d		08 56								09 09			09 26							09 39		09 56		
Richmond	⊖ d	08 48	08 59					09 06			09 12	09 18		09 29				09 36			09 42	09 48	09 59		
St Margarets	d		09 01								09 14			09 31							09 44		10 01		
Twickenham	a	08 51	09 03					09 10			09 16	09 21		09 33				09 40			09 46	09 51	10 03		
	d	08 52	09 04					09 10			09 17	09 22		09 34				09 40			09 47	09 52	10 04		
Strawberry Hill	d		09 07											09 37									10 07		
Fulwell	a																								
Teddington	a		09 10											09 40									10 10		
Hampton Wick	a		09 14											09 44									10 14		
Kingston	a		09 16											09 46									10 16		
Whitton	d	08 55			09a23						09a20	09 25				09a53					09a50	09 55			10a23
Feltham	d	08 59		09 06				09 16				09 29			09 36			09 46				09 59		10 06	
Ashford (Surrey)	d	09 03		09 10								09 33			09 40							10 03		10 10	
Staines	d	09 07		09 15				09 23				09 37			09 45			09 53				10 07		10 15	
Wraysbury	d	09 11										09 41										10 11			
Sunnymeads	d	09 14										09 44										10 14			
Datchet	d	09 17										09 47										10 17			
Windsor & Eton Riverside	a	09 21										09 51										10 21			
Egham	d			09 20				09 27							09 50			09 57						10 20	
Virginia Water	a			09 24				09 31							09 54			10 01						10 24	
	d			09 24				09 31							09 54			10 01						10 24	
Chertsey §	d			09 29											09 59									10 29	
Addlestone §	d			09 32											10 02									10 32	
Weybridge	a			09 37											10 07									10 37	
Byfleet & New Haw	d																								
West Byfleet	d																								
Woking	a																								
Longcross	d																								
Sunningdale	d							09 37										10 07							
Ascot 3	d							09 43		09 53								10 13		10 23					
Bagshot	d									09 59										10 29					
Camberley	a									10 05										10 35					
	d									10 09										10 39					
Frimley	d									10 13										10 43					
Ash Vale	d									10 19										10 49					
Aldershot	a									10 24										10 54					
	d									10 38										11 08					
Ash 3	d									10 45										11 15					
Wanborough	d									10 48										11 18					
Guildford	a									10 55										11 25					
Martins Heron	d							09 47										10 17							
Bracknell	d							09 50										10 20							
Wokingham	d							09 57										10 27							
Winnersh	d							10 00										10 30							
Winnersh Triangle	d							10 02										10 32							
Earley	d							10 05										10 35							
Reading 7	a							10 10										10 40							

For general notes see front of timetable
For details of catering facilities see Directory of Train Operators

§ Passengers to/from London may travel via Weybridge. See Table 155.

A To London Waterloo (Table 152)
B To London Waterloo
b Arr. 0915
c Arr. 0945
e Arr. 1015

Table 149

Saturdays

London → Hounslow, Richmond, Kingston, Windsor, Weybridge, Ascot, Guildford and Reading

until 27 September

Network Diagram - see first page of Table 148

		SW A	SW 1	SW	SW 1	SW A	SW		SW A	SW A	SW 1	SW	SW 1	SW A	SW	SW B	SW	SW A	SW A	SW 1	SW	SW 1
London Waterloo 15	⊖ d	09 45	09 50	09 52			09 58		19 07	19 15	19 20	19 22			19 28	19 33		19 37	19 45	19 50	19 52	
Vauxhall	⊖ d	09 49		09 56			10 02		19 11	19 19		19 26			19 32	19 37		19 41	19 49		19 56	
Queenstown Rd.(Battersea)	d	09 52		09 59					19 14	19 22		19 29				19 40		19 44	19 52		19 59	
Clapham Junction 10	d	09 55	09 58	10 02			10 08		19 17	19 25	19 28	19 32			19 38	19 43		19 47	19 55	19 58	20 02	
Wandsworth Town	d	09 58		10 05					19 20	19 28		19 35				19 46		19 50	19 58		20 05	
Putney	d	10 01		10 08		←	10 12		19 23	19 31		19 38		←	19 42	19 49		19 53	20 01		20 08	
Barnes	d	10 05		10 12		10 05			19 27	19 35		19 42		19 35		19 52		19 57	20 05		20 12	
Barnes Bridge	d	→		10 14					19 29	→		19 44						19 59	→		20 14	
Chiswick	d			10 17					19 32			19 47					←	20 02			20 17	
Kew Bridge	d			10 20 →					19 35			19 50 →					19 50	20 05			20 20 →	
Brentford	d								19 38								19 53	20 08				
Syon Lane	d								19 40								19 55	20 10				
Isleworth	d								19 42								19 57	20 12				
Hounslow	d								19b48								20 01	20c18				
Mortlake	d					10 07								19 37		19 54						
North Sheen	d					10 09								19 39		19 56						
Richmond	⊖ d		10 06			10 12	10 18				19 36			19 42	19 48	19 59				20 06		
St Margarets	d					10 14								19 44		20 01						
Twickenham	a		10 10			10 16	10 21				19 40			19 46	19 51	20 03				20 10		
	d		10 10			10 17	10 22				19 40			19 47	19 52	20 04				20 10		
Strawberry Hill	d															20 07						
Fulwell	a																					
Teddington	a															20 10						
Hampton Wick	a															20 14						
Kingston	a							and at								20 16						
Whitton	d					10a20	10 25		19a53					19a50	19 55			20a23				
Feltham	d		10 16				10 29	the same			19 46				19 59		20 06			20 16		
Ashford (Surrey)	d						10 33								20 03		20 10					
Staines	d		10 23				10 37	minutes			19 53				20 07		20 15			20 23		
Wraysbury	d						10 41	past							20 11							
Sunnymeads	d						10 44								20 14							
Datchet	d						10 47	each							20 17							
Windsor & Eton Riverside	a						10 51								20 21							
Egham	d		10 27					hour until			19 57						20 20			20 27		
Virginia Water	a		10 31								20 01						20 24			20 31		
	d		10 31								20 01						20 24			20 31		
Chertsey §	d																20 29					
Addlestone §	d																20 32					
Weybridge	a																20 37					
Byfleet & New Haw	d																					
West Byfleet	d																					
Woking	a																					
Longcross	d																					
Sunningdale	d		10 37								20 07									20 37		
Ascot 3	d		10 43		10 53						20 13		20 23							20 43		20 53
Bagshot	d				10 59								20 29									20 59
Camberley	a				11 05								20 35									21 05
	d				11 09								20 39									21 09
Frimley	d				11 13								20 43									21 13
Ash Vale	d				11 19								20 49									21 19
Aldershot	a				11 24								20 54									21 24
	d				11 38								21 08									21 38
Ash 3	d				11 45								21 15									21 45
Wanborough	d				11 48								21 18									21 48
Guildford	a				11 55								21 25									21 55
Martins Heron	d		10 47								20 17									20 47		
Bracknell	d		10 50								20 20									20 50		
Wokingham	d		10 57								20 27									20 57		
Winnersh	d		11 00								20 30									21 00		
Winnersh Triangle	d		11 02								20 32									21 02		
Earley	d		11 05								20 35									21 05		
Reading 7	a		11 10								20 40									21 10		

For general notes see front of timetable
For details of catering facilities see Directory of Train Operators

§ Passengers to/from London may travel via Weybridge. See Table 155.

A To London Waterloo
B To London Waterloo (Table 152)
b Arr. 1945
c Arr. 2015

until 27 September

London → Hounslow, Richmond, Kingston, Windsor, Weybridge, Ascot, Guildford and Reading

Network Diagram - see first page of Table 148

		SW	SW		SW	SW	SW	SW	SW	SW	SW		SW	SW	SW	SW	SW	SW	SW		SW	SW	SW	SW	SW
									1		1		1								1				
		A			B		A	A						A		B		A	A				A		B
London Waterloo 15	⊖ d		19 58		20 03		20 07	20 15	20 20	20 22					20 28	20 33		20 37	20 45		20 50	20 52		20 58	21 03
Vauxhall	⊖ d		20 02		20 07		20 11	20 19		20 26					20 32	20 37		20 41	20 49			20 56		21 02	21 07
Queenstown Rd.(Battersea)	d				20 10		20 14	20 22		20 29						20 40		20 44	20 52			20 59			21 10
Clapham Junction 10	d		20 08		20 13		20 17	20 25	20 28	20 32					20 38	20 43		20 47	20 55		20 58	21 02		21 08	21 13
Wandsworth Town	d				20 16		20 20	20 28		20 35						20 46		20 50	20 58			21 05			21 16
Putney	d	←	20 12		20 19		20 23	20 31		20 38				←	20 42	20 49		20 53	21 01			21 08	←	21 12	21 19
Barnes	d	20 05			20 22		20 27	20 35		20 42				20 35		20 52		20 57	21 05			21 12	21 05		21 22
Barnes Bridge	d						20 29	→		20 44								20 59	→			21 14			
Chiswick	d					←	20 32			20 47							←	21 02				21 17			
Kew Bridge	d					20 20	20 35			20 50							20 50	21 05				21 20			
Brentford	d					20 23	20 38			→							20 53	21 08				→			
Syon Lane	d					20 25	20 40										20 55	21 10							
Isleworth	d					20 27	20 42										20 57	21 12							
Hounslow	d					20 31	20b48										21 01	21c18							
Mortlake	d	20 07			20 24									20 37		20 54							21 07		21 24
North Sheen	d	20 09			20 26									20 39		20 56							21 09		21 26
Richmond	⊖ d	20 12	20 18		20 29				20 36					20 42	20 48	20 59					21 06		21 12	21 18	21 29
St Margarets	d	20 14			20 31									20 44		21 01							21 14		21 31
Twickenham	a	20 16	20 21		20 33				20 40					20 46	20 51	21 03					21 10		21 16	21 21	21 33
	d	20 17	20 22		20 34				20 40					20 47	20 52	21 04					21 10		21 17	21 22	21 34
Strawberry Hill	d				20 37											21 07									21 37
Fulwell	a																								
Teddington	a				20 40											21 10									21 40
Hampton Wick	a				20 44											21 14									21 44
Kingston	a				20 46											21 16									21 46
Whitton	d	20a20	20 25				20a53							20a50	20 55			21a23					21a20	21 25	
Feltham	d		20 29			20 36			20 46						20 59		21 06				21 16			21 29	
Ashford (Surrey)	d		20 33			20 40									21 03		21 10							21 33	
Staines	d		20 37			20 45			20 53						21 07		21 15				21 23			21 37	
Wraysbury	d		20 41												21 11									21 41	
Sunnymeads	d		20 44												21 14									21 44	
Datchet	d		20 47												21 17									21 47	
Windsor & Eton Riverside	a		20 51												21 21									21 51	
Egham	d					20 50			20 57								21 20				21 27				
Virginia Water	a					20 54			21 01								21 24				21 31				
	d					20 54			21 01								21 24				21 31				
Chertsey §	d					20 59											21 29								
Addlestone §	d					21 02											21 32								
Weybridge	a					21 07											21 37								
Byfleet & New Haw	d																								
West Byfleet	d																								
Woking	a																								
Longcross	d																								
Sunningdale	d								21 07												21 37				
Ascot 3	d								21 13		21 23										21 43				
Bagshot	d										21 29														
Camberley	a										21 35														
	d										21 39														
Frimley	d										21 43														
Ash Vale	d										21 49														
Aldershot	a										21 54														
	d										22 08		22 38												
Ash 3	d										22 15		22 45												
Wanborough	d										22 18		22 48												
Guildford	a										22 25		22 55												
Martins Heron	d								21 17												21 47				
Bracknell	d								21 20												21 50				
Wokingham	d								21 27												21 57				
Winnersh	d								21 30												22 00				
Winnersh Triangle	d								21 32												22 02				
Earley	d								21 35												22 05				
Reading 7	a								21 40												22 10				

For general notes see front of timetable
For details of catering facilities see Directory of Train Operators

§ Passengers to/from London may travel via Weybridge. See Table 155.

A To London Waterloo
B To London Waterloo (Table 152)
b Arr. 2045
c Arr. 2115

Table 149

Saturdays

London → Hounslow, Richmond, Kingston, Windsor, Weybridge, Ascot, Guildford and Reading

until 27 September

Network Diagram - see first page of Table 148

		SW	SW	SW	SW ■1		SW	SW ■1	SW	SW	SW	SW	SW		SW	SW ■1	SW	SW	SW	SW	SW		SW ■1	SW	SW
			A	A					A		B		A							B					
London Waterloo [15] ⊖	d		21 07	21 15	21 20		21 22			21 28	21 33		21 37		21 45	21 50		21 52	21 58	22 03			22 20	22 22	22 28
Vauxhall ⊖	d		21 11	21 19			21 26			21 32	21 37		21 41		21 49			21 56	22 02	22 07				22 26	22 32
Queenstown Rd.(Battersea)	d		21 14	21 22			21 29				21 40		21 44		21 52			21 59		22 10				22 29	
Clapham Junction [10]	d		21 17	21 25	21 28		21 32			21 38	21 43		21 47		21 55	21 58		22 02	22 08	22 13			22 28	22 32	22 38
Wandsworth Town	d		21 20	21 28			21 35				21 46		21 50		21 58			22 05		22 16				22 35	
Putney	d		21 23	21 31			21 38		←	21 42	21 49		21 53		22 01		←	22 08	22 12	22 19				22 38	22 42
Barnes	d		21 27	21 35			21 42		21 35		21 52		21 57		22 05		22 05	22 12		22 22				22 42	
Barnes Bridge	d		21 29	→			21 44						21 59		→			22 14						22 44	
Chiswick	d	←	21 32				21 47					←	22 02					22 17			←			22 47	
Kew Bridge	d	21 20	21 35				21 50 →					21 50	22 05					22 20 →			22 20			22 50 →	
Brentford	d	21 23	21 38									21 53	22 08								22 23				
Syon Lane	d	21 25	21 40									21 55	22 10								22 25				
Isleworth	d	21 27	21 42									21 57	22 12								22 27				
Hounslow	d	21 31	21b48									22 01	22c18								22 31				
Mortlake	d								21 37		21 54						22 07			22 24					
North Sheen	d								21 39		21 56						22 09			22 26					
Richmond ⊖	d				21 36				21 42	21 48	21 59					22 06	22 12		22 18	22 29			22 36		22 48
St Margarets	d								21 44		22 01						22 14			22 31					
Twickenham	a				21 40				21 46	21 51	22 03					22 10	22 16		22 21	22 33			22 40		22 51
	d				21 40				21 47	21 52	22 04					22 10			22 22	22 34			22 40		22 52
Strawberry Hill	d										22 07									22 37					
Fulwell	a																								
Teddington	a										22 10									22 40					
Hampton Wick	a										22 14									22 44					
Kingston	a										22 16									22 46					
Whitton	d		21a53						21a50	21 55			22a23						22 25						22 55
Feltham	d	21 36			21 46					21 59		22 06				22 16			22 29		22 36		22 46		22 59
Ashford (Surrey)	d	21 40								22 03		22 10							22 33		22 40				23 03
Staines	d	21 45			21 53					22 07		22 15				22 23			22 37		22 45		22 53		23 07
Wraysbury	d									22 11									22 41						23 11
Sunnymeads	d									22 14									22 44						23 14
Datchet	d									22 17									22 47						23 17
Windsor & Eton Riverside	a									22 21									22 51						23 21
Egham	d	21 50			21 57							22 20				22 27					22 50		22 57		
Virginia Water	a	21 54			22 01							22 24				22 31					22 54		23 01		
	d	21 54			22 01							22 24				22 31					22 54		23 01		
Chertsey §	d	21 59										22 29									22 59				
Addlestone §	d	22 02										22 32									23 02				
Weybridge	a	22 07										22 37									23 07				
Byfleet & New Haw	d																								
West Byfleet	d																								
Woking	a																								
Longcross	d																								
Sunningdale	d				22 07											22 37							23 07		
Ascot [3]	d				22 13			22 23								22 43							23 13		
Bagshot	d							22 29																	
Camberley	a							22 35																	
	d							22 39																	
Frimley	d							22 43																	
Ash Vale	d							22 49																	
Aldershot	a							22 54																	
	d							23 08																	
Ash [3]	d							23 15																	
Wanborough	d							23 18																	
Guildford	a							23 25																	
Martins Heron	d				22 17											22 47							23 17		
Bracknell	d				22 20											22 50							23 20		
Wokingham	d				22 27											22 57							23 27		
Winnersh	d				22 30											23 00							23 30		
Winnersh Triangle	d				22 32											23 02							23 32		
Earley	d				22 35											23 05							23 35		
Reading [7]	a				22 40											23 10							23 40		

For general notes see front of timetable
For details of catering facilities see Directory of Train Operators

§ Passengers to/from London may travel via Weybridge. See Table 155.

A To London Waterloo

B To London Waterloo (Table 152)

b Arr. 2145

c Arr. 2215

Table 149

Saturdays

until 27 September

London → Hounslow, Richmond, Kingston, Windsor, Weybridge, Ascot, Guildford and Reading

Network Diagram - see first page of Table 148

Station		SW	SW 1	SW	SW 1	SW	SW	SW	SW	SW	SW 1	SW	SW 1	SW	SW	SW	SW	SW
		A						A										
London Waterloo 15	⊖ d	22 33			22 50	22 52	22 58	23 03		23 13	23 20	23 22	23 35		23 37	23 52	23 58	
Vauxhall	⊖ d	22 37				22 56	23 02	23 07		23 17		23 26			23 41	23 56	00 02	
Queenstown Rd.(Battersea)	d	22 40				22 59		23 10				23 29			23 44	23 59		
Clapham Junction 10	d	22 43			22 58	23 02	23 08	23 13		23 23	23 28	23 32	23 43		23 47	00 02	00 08	
Wandsworth Town	d	22 46				23 05		23 16				23 35			23 50	00 05		
Putney	d	22 49				23 08	23 12	23 19		23 27		23 38			23 53	00 08	00 12	
Barnes	d	22 52				23 12		23 22				23 42			23 56	00 12		
Barnes Bridge	d					23 14						23 44		←		00 14		
Chiswick	d			←		23 17			←			23 47		23 47		00 17		←
Kew Bridge	d			22 50		23 20			23 20			→		23 50		00 20		00 20
Brentford	d			22 53		→			23 23					23 53		→		00 23
Syon Lane	d			22 55					23 25					23 55				00 25
Isleworth	d			22 57					23 27					23 57				00 27
Hounslow	d			23 01					23 31					00 01				00 31
Mortlake	d	22 54						23 24							23 58			
North Sheen	d	22 56						23 26							00 01			
Richmond	⊖ d	22 59			23 06		23 18	23 29		23 33	23 37		23 51		00 03		00 18	
St Margarets	d	23 01						23 31							00 06			
Twickenham	a	23 03			23 10		23 21	23 33		23 36	23 41		23 55		00 08		00 21	
	d	23 04			23 10		23 22	23 34		23 37	23 41		23 55		00 08		00 22	
Strawberry Hill	d	23 07						23 37							00 12			
Fulwell	a																	
Teddington	a	23 10						23 40							00 15			
Hampton Wick	a	23 14						23 44							00 17			
Kingston	a	23 16						23 46							00 19			
Whitton	d						23 25			23 40							00 25	
Feltham	d			23 06	23 16		23 29		23 36	23 44	23 48		00 01	00 06			00 29	00 36
Ashford (Surrey)	d			23 10			23 33		23 40	23 48				00 10			00 33	00 40
Staines	d			23 15	23 23		23 37		23 45	23 52	23 56		00 08	00 15			00a37	00a46
Wraysbury	d						23 41			23 56								
Sunnymeads	d						23 44			23 59								
Datchet	d						23 47			00 02								
Windsor & Eton Riverside	a						23 51			00 06								
Egham	d			23 20	23 27				23 50		00 01		00 12	00 20				
Virginia Water	a			23 24	23 31				23 54		00 05		00 16	00 24				
	d			23 24	23 31				23 54		00 05		00 16	00 24				
Chertsey §	d			23 29					23 59					00 29				
Addlestone §	d			23 32					00 02					00 32				
Weybridge	a			23 37										00 37				
Byfleet & New Haw	d								00 07									
West Byfleet	d								00 10									
Woking	a								00 16									
Longcross	d																	
Sunningdale	d				23 37						00 10		00 22					
Ascot 3	d		23 23		23 43						00 15		00 27					
Bagshot	d		23 29															
Camberley	a		23 35															
	d		23 39															
Frimley	d		23 43															
Ash Vale	d		23 49															
Aldershot	a		23 54															
	d																	
Ash 3	d																	
Wanborough	d																	
Guildford	a																	
Martins Heron	d				23 47						00 19		00 31					
Bracknell	d				23 50						00 23		00 34					
Wokingham	d				23 57						00 31		00 41					
Winnersh	d				00 01						00 35							
Winnersh Triangle	d				00 02						00 37							
Earley	d				00 05						00 39							
Reading 7	a				00 10						00 44		00 49					

For general notes see front of timetable
For details of catering facilities see Directory of Train Operators

§ Passengers to/from London may travel via Weybridge. See Table 155.

A To London Waterloo (Table 152)

Table 149

Saturdays

London → Hounslow, Richmond, Kingston, Windsor, Weybridge, Ascot, Guildford and Reading

from 4 October

Network Diagram - see first page of Table 148

Station		SW 1	SW	SW	SW 1	SW	SW	SW		SW 1	SW	SW	SW	SW	SW	SW A		SW 1	SW	SW 1	SW B	SW 1	SW	SW	SW A
London Waterloo 15 ⊖	d	22p50	22p52	23p13	23p20	23p22	23p35	23p37				23p52	23p58		00 18					05 05					05 33
Vauxhall ⊖	d		22p56	23p17		23p26		23p41				23p56	00 02		00 22					05 09					05 37
Queenstown Rd.(Battersea)	d		22p59			23p29		23p44				23p59			00 25					05 12					05 40
Clapham Junction 10	d	22p58	23p02	23p23	23p28	23p32	23p43	23p47				00 02	00 08		00 28					05 15					05 43
Wandsworth Town	d		23p05			23p35		23p50				00 05			00 31					05 18					05 46
Putney	d		23p08	23p27		23p38		23p53				00 08	00 12		00 34					05 21					05 49
Barnes	d		23p12			23p42		23p56				00 12			00 37					05 24					05 52
Barnes Bridge	d		23p14			23p44					←	00 14													
Chiswick	d		23p17			23p47 →					23p47	00 17		←											
Kew Bridge	d		23p20								23p50	00 20 →		00 20											
Brentford	d		23p23								23p53			00 23											
Syon Lane	d		23p25								23p55			00 25											
Isleworth	d		23p27								23p57			00 27											
Hounslow	d		23p31								00 01			00 31											
Mortlake	d							23p58							00 39					05 26					05 54
North Sheen	d							00 01							00 41					05 28					05 56
Richmond ⊖	d	23p06		23p33	23p37		23p51	00 03					00 18		00 44					05 31					05 59
St Margarets	d							00 06							00 46					05 33					06 01
Twickenham	a	23p10		23p36	23p41		23p55	00 08					00 21		00 48					05 35					06 03
	d	23p10		23p37	23p41		23p55	00 08					00 22		00 49	04 52				05 36	05 38		05 52		06 04
Strawberry Hill	d							00 12							00s52	04 55									06 07
Fulwell	a																								
Teddington	a							00 15							00s55	04 58									06 10
Hampton Wick	a							00 17							00s58	05 01									06 14
Kingston	a							00 19							01 00	05 03									06 16
Whitton	d			23p40									00 25							05 39	05a41		05 55		
Feltham	d	23p16	23p36	23p44	23p48		00 01				00 06		00 29	00 36						05 43			05 59		
Ashford (Surrey)	d		23p40	23p48							00 10		00 33	00 40						05 47			06 03		
Staines	d	23p23	23p45	23p52	23p56		00 08				00 15		00a37	00a46				05 23	05 45	05 53			06 07	06 15	
Wraysbury	d			23p56																			06 11		
Sunnymeads	d			23p59																			06 14		
Datchet	d			00 02																			06 17		
Windsor & Eton Riverside	a			00 09																			06 24		
Egham	d	23p27	23p50		00 01		00 12				00 20							05 27	05 50	05 57				06 20	
Virginia Water	a	23p31	23p54		00 05		00 16				00 24							05 31	05 54	06 01				06 24	
	d	23p31	23p54		00 05		00 16				00 24							05 31	05 54	06 01				06 24	
Chertsey §	d		23p59								00 29								05 59					06 29	
Addlestone §	d		00 02								00 32								06 02					06 32	
Weybridge	a										00 37								06 07					06 37	
Byfleet & New Haw	d		00 07																						
West Byfleet	d		00 10																						
Woking	a		00 16																						
Longcross	d																								
Sunningdale	d	23p37			00 10		00 22											05 38		06 07					
Ascot 3	d	23p43			00 15		00 27			00 29								05 43		06 13					
Bagshot	d									00 35															
Camberley	a									00 41															
	d									00 41															
Frimley	d									00 45															
Ash Vale	d									00 52															
Aldershot	a									00 57															
	d																					06 08			
Ash 3	d																					06 15			
Wanborough	d																					06 18			
Guildford	a																					06 25			
Martins Heron	d	23p47			00 19		00 31											05 47		06 17					
Bracknell	d	23p50			00 23		00 34											05 50		06 20					
Wokingham	d	23p57			00 32		00 41											05 57		06 27					
Winnersh	d	00 01			00 36													06 00		06 30					
Winnersh Triangle	d	00 02			00 38													06 03		06 32					
Earley	d	00 05			00 40													06 05		06 35					
Reading 7	a	00 13			00 48		00 52											06 13		06 43					

For general notes see front of timetable
For details of catering facilities see
Directory of Train Operators

§ Passengers to/from London may travel via Weybridge. See Table 155.

A To London Waterloo (Table 152)
B To London Waterloo

Table 149

Saturdays

from 4 October

London → Hounslow, Richmond, Kingston, Windsor, Weybridge, Ascot, Guildford and Reading

Network Diagram - see first page of Table 148

Station		SW 1		SW 1	SW	SW A	SW	SW 1	SW 1	SW 1		SW	SW	SW A	SW	SW 1	SW	SW		SW A	SW B	SW	SW 1	SW 1	SW 1
London Waterloo 15 ⊖	d			05 50	05 58	06 03				06 20		06 22	06 28	06 33		06 50	06 52	06 58		07 03	07 15				07 20
Vauxhall ⊖	d				06 02	06 07						06 26	06 32	06 37			06 56	07 02		07 07	07 19				
Queenstown Rd.(Battersea)	d					06 10						06 29		06 40			06 59			07 10	07 22				
Clapham Junction 10	d			05 58	06 08	06 13				06 28		06 32	06 38	06 43		06 58	07 02	07 08		07 13	07 25				07 28
Wandsworth Town	d					06 16						06 35		06 46			07 05			07 16	07 28				
Putney	d				06 12	06 19						06 38	06 42	06 49			07 08	07 12		07 19	07 31				
Barnes	d					06 22						06 42		06 52			07 12			07 22	07 35				
Barnes Bridge	d											06 44					07 14				→				
Chiswick	d											06 47			←		07 17					←			
Kew Bridge	d											06 50			06 50		07 20					07 20			
Brentford	d											→			06 53		→					07 23			
Syon Lane	d														06 55							07 25			
Isleworth	d														06 57							07 27			
Hounslow	d														07 01							07 31			
Mortlake	d					06 24								06 54						07 24					
North Sheen	d					06 26								06 56						07 26					
Richmond ⊖	d			06 06	06 18	06 29				06 36			06 48	06 59		07 06		07 18		07 29					07 36
St Margarets	d					06 31								07 01						07 31					
Twickenham	a			06 10	06 21	06 33				06 40			06 51	07 03		07 10		07 21		07 33					07 40
	d			06 10	06 22	06 34				06 40			06 52	07 04		07 10		07 22		07 34					07 40
Strawberry Hill	d					06 37								07 07						07 37					
Fulwell	a																								
Teddington	a					06 40								07 10						07 40					
Hampton Wick	a					06 44								07 14						07 44					
Kingston	a					06 46								07 16						07 46					
Whitton	d				06 25								06 55					07 25							
Feltham	d			06 16	06 29					06 46			06 59		07 06	07 16		07 29				07 36			07 46
Ashford (Surrey)	d				06 33								07 03		07 10			07 33				07 40			
Staines	d			06 23	06 37		06 45			06 53			07 07		07 15	07 23		07 37				07 45			07 53
Wraysbury	d				06 41								07 11					07 41							
Sunnymeads	d				06 44								07 14					07 44							
Datchet	d				06 47								07 17					07 47							
Windsor & Eton Riverside	a				06 54								07 24					07 54							
Egham	d			06 27			06 50			06 57					07 20	07 27						07 50			07 57
Virginia Water	a			06 31			06 54			07 01					07 24	07 31						07 54			08 01
	d			06 31			06 54			07 01					07 24	07 31						07 54			08 01
Chertsey §	d						06 59								07 29							07 59			
Addlestone §	d						07 02								07 32							08 02			
Weybridge	a						07 07								07 37							08 07			
Byfleet & New Haw	d																								
West Byfleet	d																								
Woking	a																								
Longcross	d																								
Sunningdale	d			06 37						07 07						07 37									08 07
Ascot 3	d			06 43					06 53	07 13						07 43								07 53	08 13
Bagshot	d								06 59															07 59	
Camberley	a								07 05															08 05	
	d								07 09															08 09	
Frimley	d								07 13															08 13	
Ash Vale	d								07 19															08 19	
Aldershot	a								07 24															08 24	
	d	06 38						07 08	07 38														08 08	08 38	
Ash 3	d	06 45						07 15	07 45														08 15	08 45	
Wanborough	d	06 48						07 18	07 48														08 18	08 48	
Guildford	a	06 55						07 25	07 55														08 25	08 55	
Martins Heron	d			06 47						07 17						07 47									08 17
Bracknell	d			06 50						07 20						07 50									08 20
Wokingham	d			06 57						07 27						07 57									08 27
Winnersh	d			07 00						07 30						08 00									08 30
Winnersh Triangle	d			07 02						07 32						08 02									08 32
Earley	d			07 05						07 35						08 05									08 35
Reading 7	a			07 13						07 43						08 13									08 43

For general notes see front of timetable
For details of catering facilities see Directory of Train Operators

§ Passengers to/from London may travel via Weybridge. See Table 155.

A To London Waterloo (Table 152)
B To London Waterloo

Table 149

from 4 October

London → Hounslow, Richmond, Kingston, Windsor, Weybridge, Ascot, Guildford and Reading

Network Diagram - see first page of Table 148

		SW	SW 1	SW	SW	SW	SW	SW	SW	SW 1	SW	SW 1	SW	SW	SW	SW	SW	SW	SW 1	SW	SW 1	SW
				A		B		A	A				A		B		A	A				A
London Waterloo 15	⊖ d	07 22			07 28	07 33		07 37	07 45	07 50	07 52			07 58	08 03		08 07	08 15	08 20	08 22		
Vauxhall	⊖ d	07 26			07 32	07 37		07 41	07 49		07 56			08 02	08 07		08 11	08 19		08 26		
Queenstown Rd.(Battersea)	d	07 29				07 40		07 44	07 52		07 59				08 10		08 14	08 22		08 29		
Clapham Junction 10	d	07 32			07 38	07 43		07 47	07 55	07 58	08 02			08 08	08 13		08 17	08 25	08 28	08 32		
Wandsworth Town	d	07 35				07 46		07 50	07 58		08 05				08 16		08 20	08 28		08 35		
Putney	d	07 38		←	07 42	07 49		07 53	08 01		08 08		←	08 12	08 19		08 23	08 31		08 38		←
Barnes	d	07 42		07 35		07 52		07 57	08 05		08 12		08 05		08 22		08 27	08 35		08 42		08 35
Barnes Bridge	d	07 44						07 59	→		08 14						08 29	→		08 44		
Chiswick	d	07 47					←	08 02			08 17					←	08 32			08 47		
Kew Bridge	d	07 50					07 50	08 05			08 20					08 20	08 35			08 50		
Brentford	d	→					07 53	08 08			→					08 23	08 38			→		
Syon Lane	d						07 55	08 10								08 25	08 40					
Isleworth	d						07 57	08 12								08 27	08 42					
Hounslow	d						08 01	08b18								08 31	08c48					
Mortlake	d			07 37		07 54							08 07		08 24							08 37
North Sheen	d			07 39		07 56							08 09		08 26							08 39
Richmond	⊖ d			07 42	07 48	07 59				08 06			08 12	08 18	08 29				08 36			08 42
St Margarets	d			07 44		08 01							08 14		08 31							08 44
Twickenham	a			07 46	07 51	08 03				08 10			08 16	08 21	08 33				08 40			08 46
	d			07 47	07 52	08 04				08 10			08 17	08 22	08 34				08 40			08 47
Strawberry Hill	d					08 07									08 37							
Fulwell	a																					
Teddington	a					08 10									08 40							
Hampton Wick	a					08 14									08 44							
Kingston	a					08 16									08 46							
Whitton	d			07a50	07 55			08a23					08a20	08 25			00a53					08a50
Feltham	d				07 59		08 06			08 16				08 29		08 36			08 46			
Ashford (Surrey)	d				08 03		08 10							08 33		08 40						
Staines	d				08 07		08 15			08 23				08 37		08 45			08 53			
Wraysbury	d				08 11									08 41								
Sunnymeads	d				08 14									08 44								
Datchet	d				08 17									08 47								
Windsor & Eton Riverside	a				08 24									08 54								
Egham	d						08 20			08 27						08 50			08 57			
Virginia Water	a						08 24			08 31						08 54			09 01			
	d						08 24			08 31						08 54			09 01			
Chertsey §	d						08 29									08 59						
Addlestone §	d						08 32									09 02						
Weybridge	a						08 37									09 07						
Byfleet & New Haw	d																					
West Byfleet	d																					
Woking	a																					
Longcross	d																					
Sunningdale	d									08 37									09 07			
Ascot 3	d		08 23							08 43		08 53							09 13		09 23	
Bagshot	d		08 29									08 59									09 29	
Camberley	a		08 35									09 05									09 35	
	d		08 39									09 09									09 39	
Frimley	d		08 43									09 13									09 43	
Ash Vale	d		08 49									09 19									09 49	
Aldershot	a		08 54									09 24									09 54	
	d		09 08									09 38									10 08	
Ash 3	d		09 15									09 45									10 15	
Wanborough	d		09 18									09 48									10 18	
Guildford	a		09 25									09 55									10 25	
Martins Heron	d									08 47									09 17			
Bracknell	d									08 50									09 20			
Wokingham	d									08 57									09 27			
Winnersh	d									09 00									09 30			
Winnersh Triangle	d									09 02									09 32			
Earley	d									09 05									09 35			
Reading 7	a									09 13									09 43			

For general notes see front of timetable
For details of catering facilities see Directory of Train Operators

§ Passengers to/from London may travel via Weybridge. See Table 155.

A To London Waterloo

B To London Waterloo (Table 152)

b Arr. 0815

c Arr. 0845

Table 149

London → Hounslow, Richmond, Kingston, Windsor, Weybridge, Ascot, Guildford and Reading

Network Diagram - see first page of Table 148

		SW	SW	SW	SW	SW		SW	SW	SW	SW	SW		SW	SW	SW	SW	SW	SW	SW	SW	SW	SW	SW	SW
			A		B	B		1		1	B			A		B	B	1		1	B		A		B
London Waterloo 15 ⊖	d	08 28	08 33		08 37	08 45		08 50	08 52			08 58		09 03		09 07	09 15	09 20	09 22			09 28	09 33		09 37
Vauxhall ⊖	d	08 32	08 37		08 41	08 49			08 56			09 02		09 07		09 11	09 19		09 26			09 32	09 37		09 41
Queenstown Rd.(Battersea)	d		08 40		08 44	08 52			08 59					09 10		09 14	09 22		09 29				09 40		09 44
Clapham Junction 10	d	08 38	08 43		08 47	08 55		08 58	09 02			09 08		09 13		09 17	09 25	09 28	09 32			09 38	09 43		09 47
Wandsworth Town	d		08 46		08 50	08 58			09 05					09 16		09 20	09 28		09 35				09 46		09 50
Putney	d	08 42	08 49		08 53	09 01			09 08		←	09 12		09 19		09 23	09 31		09 38		←	09 42	09 49		09 53
Barnes	d		08 52		08 57	09 05			09 12		09 05			09 22		09 27	09 35		09 42		09 35		09 52		09 57
Barnes Bridge	d				08 59	→			09 14							09 29	→		09 44						09 59
Chiswick	d			←	09 02				09 17						←	09 32			09 47					←	10 02
Kew Bridge	d			08 50	09 05				09 20						09 20	09 35			09 50					09 50	10 05
Brentford	d			08 53	09 08				→						09 23	09 38			→					09 53	10 08
Syon Lane	d			08 55	09 10										09 25	09 40								09 55	10 10
Isleworth	d			08 57	09 12										09 27	09 42								09 57	10 12
Hounslow	d			09 01	09b18										09 31	09c48								10 01	10e18
Mortlake	d		08 54								09 07			09 24							09 37		09 54		
North Sheen	d		08 56								09 09			09 26							09 39		09 56		
Richmond ⊖	d	08 48	08 59					09 06			09 12	09 18		09 29				09 36			09 42	09 48	09 59		
St Margarets	d		09 01								09 14			09 31							09 44		10 01		
Twickenham	a	08 51	09 03					09 10			09 16	09 21		09 33				09 40			09 46	09 51	10 03		
	d	08 52	09 04					09 10			09 17	09 22		09 34				09 40			09 47	09 52	10 04		
Strawberry Hill	d		09 07											09 37									10 07		
Fulwell	a																								
Teddington	a		09 10											09 40									10 10		
Hampton Wick	a		09 14											09 44									10 14		
Kingston	a		09 16											09 46									10 16		
Whitton	d	08 55			09a23						09a20	09 25				09a53					09a50	09 55			10a23
Feltham	d	08 59		09 06				09 16				09 29			09 36			09 46				09 59		10 06	
Ashford (Surrey)	d	09 03		09 10								09 33			09 40							10 03		10 10	
Staines	d	09 07		09 15				09 23				09 37			09 45			09 53				10 07		10 15	
Wraysbury	d	09 11										09 41										10 11			
Sunnymeads	d	09 14										09 44										10 14			
Datchet	d	09 17										09 47										10 17			
Windsor & Eton Riverside	a	09 24										09 54										10 24			
Egham	d			09 20				09 27							09 50			09 57						10 20	
Virginia Water	a			09 24				09 31							09 54			10 01						10 24	
	d			09 24				09 31							09 54			10 01						10 24	
Chertsey §	d			09 29											09 59									10 29	
Addlestone §	d			09 32											10 02									10 32	
Weybridge	a			09 37											10 07									10 37	
Byfleet & New Haw	d																								
West Byfleet	d																								
Woking	a																								
Longcross	d																								
Sunningdale	d							09 37										10 07							
Ascot 3	d							09 43		09 53								10 13		10 23					
Bagshot	d									09 59										10 29					
Camberley	a									10 05										10 35					
	d									10 09										10 39					
Frimley	d									10 13										10 43					
Ash Vale	d									10 19										10 49					
Aldershot	a									10 24										10 54					
	d									10 38										11 08					
Ash 3	d									10 45										11 15					
Wanborough	d									10 48										11 18					
Guildford	a									10 55										11 25					
Martins Heron	d							09 47										10 17							
Bracknell	d							09 50										10 20							
Wokingham	d							09 57										10 27							
Winnersh	d							10 00										10 30							
Winnersh Triangle	d							10 02										10 32							
Earley	d							10 05										10 35							
Reading 7	a							10 13										10 43							

For general notes see front of timetable
For details of catering facilities see Directory of Train Operators

§ Passengers to/from London may travel via Weybridge. See Table 155.

A To London Waterloo (Table 152)
B To London Waterloo
b Arr. 0915
c Arr. 0945
e Arr. 1015

from 4 October

London → Hounslow, Richmond, Kingston, Windsor, Weybridge, Ascot, Guildford and Reading

Network Diagram - see first page of Table 148

		SW	SW 1	SW	SW 1	SW	SW			SW	SW	SW 1	SW	SW 1	SW	SW		SW	SW	SW	SW	SW 1	SW	SW 1
		A				A				A	A				A			B		A	A			
London Waterloo 15	⊖ d	09 45	09 50	09 52			09 58			19 07	19 15	19 20	19 22			19 28		19 33		19 37	19 45	19 50	19 52	
Vauxhall	⊖ d	09 49		09 56			10 02			19 11	19 19		19 26			19 32		19 37		19 41	19 49		19 56	
Queenstown Rd.(Battersea)	d	09 52		09 59						19 14	19 22		19 29					19 40		19 44	19 52		19 59	
Clapham Junction 10	d	09 55	09 58	10 02			10 08			19 17	19 25	19 28	19 32			19 38		19 43		19 47	19 55	19 58	20 02	
Wandsworth Town	d	09 58		10 05						19 20	19 28		19 35					19 46		19 50	19 58		20 05	
Putney	d	10 01		10 08		←	10 12			19 23	19 31		19 38		←	19 42		19 49		19 53	20 01		20 08	
Barnes	d	10 05		10 12		10 05				19 27	19 35		19 42		19 35			19 52		19 57	20 05		20 12	
Barnes Bridge	d	→		10 14						19 29	→		19 44							19 59	→		20 14	
Chiswick	d			10 17						19 32			19 47						←	20 02			20 17	
Kew Bridge	d			10 20						19 35			19 50						19 50	20 05			20 20	
Brentford	d			→						19 38			→						19 53	20 08			→	
Syon Lane	d									19 40									19 55	20 10				
Isleworth	d									19 42									19 57	20 12				
Hounslow	d									19b48									20 01	20c18				
Mortlake	d					10 07									19 37			19 54						
North Sheen	d					10 09									19 39			19 56						
Richmond	⊖ d		10 06			10 12	10 18					19 36			19 42	19 48		19 59				20 06		
St Margarets	d					10 14									19 44			20 01						
Twickenham	a		10 10			10 16	10 21					19 40			19 46	19 51		20 03				20 10		
	d		10 10			10 17	10 22					19 40			19 47	19 52		20 04				20 10		
Strawberry Hill	d																	20 07						
Fulwell	a																							
Teddington	a																	20 10						
Hampton Wick	a																	20 14						
Kingston	a							and at										20 16						
Whitton	d					10a20	10 25			19a53					19a50	19 55				20a23				
Feltham	d		10 16				10 29	the same				19 46				19 59			20 06			20 16		
Ashford (Surrey)	d						10 33									20 03			20 10					
Staines	d		10 23				10 37	minutes				19 53				20 07			20 15			20 23		
Wraysbury	d						10 41	past								20 11								
Sunnymeads	d						10 44									20 14								
Datchet	d						10 47	each								20 17								
Windsor & Eton Riverside	a						10 54									20 24								
Egham	d		10 27					hour until				19 57							20 20			20 27		
Virginia Water	a		10 31									20 01							20 24			20 31		
	d		10 31									20 01							20 24			20 31		
Chertsey §	d																		20 29					
Addlestone §	d																		20 32					
Weybridge	a																		20 37					
Byfleet & New Haw	d																							
West Byfleet	d																							
Woking	a																							
Longcross	d																							
Sunningdale	d		10 37									20 07										20 37		
Ascot 3	d		10 43		10 53							20 13		20 23								20 43		20 53
Bagshot	d				10 59									20 29										20 59
Camberley	a				11 05									20 35										21 05
	d				11 09									20 39										21 09
Frimley	d				11 13									20 43										21 13
Ash Vale	d				11 19									20 49										21 19
Aldershot	a				11 24									20 54										21 24
	d				11 38									21 08										21 38
Ash 3	d				11 45									21 15										21 45
Wanborough	d				11 48									21 18										21 48
Guildford	a				11 55									21 25										21 55
Martins Heron	d		10 47									20 17										20 47		
Bracknell	d		10 50									20 20										20 50		
Wokingham	d		10 57									20 27										20 57		
Winnersh	d		11 00									20 30										21 00		
Winnersh Triangle	d		11 02									20 32										21 02		
Earley	d		11 05									20 35										21 05		
Reading 7	a		11 13									20 43										21 13		

For general notes see front of timetable
For details of catering facilities see
Directory of Train Operators

§ Passengers to/from London may travel via Weybridge. See Table 155.

A To London Waterloo
B To London Waterloo (Table 152)
b Arr. 1945
c Arr. 2015

Table 149

from 4 October

London → Hounslow, Richmond, Kingston, Windsor, Weybridge, Ascot, Guildford and Reading

Network Diagram - see first page of Table 148

Station		SW	SW		SW	SW	SW	SW	SW	SW	SW		SW	SW	SW	SW	SW	SW	SW		SW	SW	SW	SW	SW
									1		1		1								1				
		A			B		A	A						A		B		A	A				A		B
London Waterloo 15	⊖ d		19 58		20 03		20 07	20 15	20 20	20 22					20 28	20 33		20 37	20 45		20 50	20 52		20 58	21 03
Vauxhall	⊖ d		20 02		20 07		20 11	20 19		20 26					20 32	20 37		20 41	20 49			20 56		21 02	21 07
Queenstown Rd.(Battersea)	d				20 10		20 14	20 22		20 29						20 40		20 44	20 52			20 59			21 10
Clapham Junction 10	d		20 08		20 13		20 17	20 25	20 28	20 32					20 38	20 43		20 47	20 55		20 58	21 02		21 08	21 13
Wandsworth Town	d				20 16		20 20	20 28		20 35						20 46		20 50	20 58			21 05			21 16
Putney	d	←	20 12		20 19		20 23	20 31		20 38				←	20 42	20 49		20 53	21 01			21 08	←	21 12	21 19
Barnes	d	20 05			20 22		20 27	20 35		20 42				20 35		20 52		20 57	21 05			21 12	21 05		21 22
Barnes Bridge	d						20 29	→		20 44								20 59	→			21 14			
Chiswick	d					←	20 32			20 47							←	21 02				21 17			
Kew Bridge	d					20 20	20 35			20 50							20 50	21 05				21 20			
Brentford	d					20 23	20 38			→							20 53	21 08				→			
Syon Lane	d					20 25	20 40										20 55	21 10							
Isleworth	d					20 27	20 42										20 57	21 12							
Hounslow	d					20 31	20b48										21 01	21c18							
Mortlake	d	20 07			20 24									20 37		20 54							21 07		21 24
North Sheen	d	20 09			20 26									20 39		20 56							21 09		21 26
Richmond	⊖ d	20 12	20 18		20 29				20 36					20 42	20 48	20 59					21 06		21 12	21 18	21 29
St Margarets	d	20 14			20 31									20 44		21 01							21 14		21 31
Twickenham	a	20 16	20 21		20 33				20 40					20 46	20 51	21 03					21 10		21 16	21 21	21 33
	d	20 17	20 22		20 34				20 40					20 47	20 52	21 04					21 10		21 17	21 22	21 34
Strawberry Hill	d				20 37											21 07									21 37
Fulwell	a																								
Teddington	a				20 40											21 10									21 40
Hampton Wick	a				20 44											21 14									21 44
Kingston	a				20 46											21 16									21 46
Whitton	d	20a20	20 25				20a53							20a50	20 55			21a23					21a20	21 25	
Feltham	d		20 29			20 36			20 46						20 59		21 06				21 16			21 29	
Ashford (Surrey)	d		20 33			20 40									21 03		21 10							21 33	
Staines	d		20 37			20 45			20 53						21 07		21 15				21 23			21 37	
Wraysbury	d		20 41												21 11									21 41	
Sunnymeads	d		20 44												21 14									21 44	
Datchet	d		20 47												21 17									21 47	
Windsor & Eton Riverside	a		20 54												21 24									21 54	
Egham	d					20 50			20 57								21 20				21 27				
Virginia Water	a					20 54			21 01								21 24				21 31				
	d					20 54			21 01								21 24				21 31				
Chertsey §	d					20 59											21 29								
Addlestone §	d					21 02											21 32								
Weybridge	a					21 07											21 37								
Byfleet & New Haw	d																								
West Byfleet	d																								
Woking	a																								
Longcross	d																								
Sunningdale	d								21 07												21 37				
Ascot 3	d								21 13		21 23										21 43				
Bagshot	d										21 29														
Camberley	a										21 35														
	d										21 39														
Frimley	d										21 43														
Ash Vale	d										21 49														
Aldershot	a										21 54														
	d										22 08		22 38												
Ash 3	d										22 15		22 45												
Wanborough	d										22 18		22 48												
Guildford	a										22 25		22 55												
Martins Heron	d								21 17												21 47				
Bracknell	d								21 20												21 50				
Wokingham	d								21 27												21 57				
Winnersh	d								21 30												22 00				
Winnersh Triangle	d								21 32												22 02				
Earley	d								21 35												22 05				
Reading 7	a								21 43												22 13				

For general notes see front of timetable
For details of catering facilities see Directory of Train Operators

§ Passengers to/from London may travel via Weybridge. See Table 155.

A To London Waterloo
B To London Waterloo (Table 152)
b Arr. 2045
c Arr. 2115

Table 149

Saturdays
from 4 October

London → Hounslow, Richmond, Kingston, Windsor, Weybridge, Ascot, Guildford and Reading

Network Diagram - see first page of Table 148

		SW	SW A	SW A	SW [1]		SW	SW [1]	SW A	SW	SW B	SW	SW A		SW	SW [1]	SW	SW	SW	SW B	SW		SW [1]	SW	SW [1]
London Waterloo [15]	⊖ d		21 07	21 15	21 20		21 22			21 28	21 33		21 37		21 45	21 50		21 52	21 58	22 03			22 20	22 22	
Vauxhall	⊖ d		21 11	21 19			21 26			21 32	21 37		21 41		21 49			21 56	22 02	22 07				22 26	
Queenstown Rd.(Battersea)	d		21 14	21 22			21 29				21 40		21 44		21 52			21 59		22 10				22 29	
Clapham Junction [10]	d		21 17	21 25	21 28		21 32			21 38	21 43		21 47		21 55	21 58		22 02	22 08	22 13			22 28	22 32	
Wandsworth Town	d		21 20	21 28			21 35				21 46		21 50		21 58			22 05		22 16				22 35	
Putney	d		21 23	21 31			21 38		←	21 42	21 49		21 53		22 01		←	22 08	22 12	22 19				22 38	
Barnes	d		21 27	21 35			21 42		21 35		21 52		21 57		22 05		22 05	22 12		22 22				22 42	
Barnes Bridge	d		21 29	→			21 44						21 59		→			22 14						22 44	
Chiswick	d	←	21 32				21 47					←	22 02					22 17			←			22 47	
Kew Bridge	d	21 20	21 35				21 50					21 50	22 05					22 20			22 20			22 50	
Brentford	d	21 23	21 38				→					21 53	22 08					→			22 23			→	
Syon Lane	d	21 25	21 40									21 55	22 10								22 25				
Isleworth	d	21 27	21 42									21 57	22 12								22 27				
Hounslow	d	21 31	21b48									22 01	22c18								22 31				
Mortlake	d								21 37		21 54						22 07			22 24					
North Sheen	d								21 39		21 56						22 09			22 26					
Richmond	⊖ d				21 36				21 42	21 48	21 59					22 06	22 12		22 18	22 29			22 36		
St Margarets	d								21 44		22 01						22 14			22 31					
Twickenham	a				21 40				21 46	21 51	22 03					22 10	22 16		22 21	22 33			22 40		
	d				21 40				21 47	21 52	22 04					22 10			22 22	22 34			22 40		
Strawberry Hill	d										22 07									22 37					
Fulwell	a																								
Teddington	a										22 10									22 40					
Hampton Wick	a										22 14									22 44					
Kingston	a										22 16									22 46					
Whitton	d		21a53						21a50	21 55			22a23						22 25						
Feltham	d	21 36			21 46					21 59		22 06				22 16			22 29		22 36		22 46		
Ashford (Surrey)	d	21 40								22 03		22 10							22 33		22 40				
Staines	d	21 45			21 53					22 07		22 15				22 23			22 37		22 45		22 53		
Wraysbury	d									22 11									22 41						
Sunnymeads	d									22 14									22 44						
Datchet	d									22 17									22 47						
Windsor & Eton Riverside	a									22 24									22 54						
Egham	d	21 50			21 57							22 20				22 27					22 50		22 57		
Virginia Water	a	21 54			22 01							22 24				22 31					22 54		23 01		
	d	21 54			22 01							22 24				22 31					22 54		23 01		
Chertsey §	d	21 59										22 29									22 59				
Addlestone §	d	22 02										22 32									23 02				
Weybridge	a	22 07										22 37									23 07				
Byfleet & New Haw	d																								
West Byfleet	d																								
Woking	a																								
Longcross	d																								
Sunningdale	d				22 07											22 37							23 07		
Ascot [3]	d				22 13			22 23								22 43							23 13		23 23
Bagshot	d							22 29																	23 29
Camberley	a							22 35																	23 35
	d							22 39																	23 39
Frimley	d							22 43																	23 43
Ash Vale	d							22 49																	23 49
Aldershot	a							22 54																	23 54
	d							23 08																	
Ash [3]	d							23 15																	
Wanborough	d							23 18																	
Guildford	a							23 25																	
Martins Heron	d				22 17											22 47							23 17		
Bracknell	d				22 20											22 50							23 20		
Wokingham	d				22 27											22 57							23 27		
Winnersh	d				22 30											23 00							23 30		
Winnersh Triangle	d				22 32											23 02							23 32		
Earley	d				22 35											23 05							23 35		
Reading [7]	a				22 43											23 13							23 43		

For general notes see front of timetable
For details of catering facilities see Directory of Train Operators

§ Passengers to/from London may travel via Weybridge. See Table 155.

A To London Waterloo
B To London Waterloo (Table 152)
b Arr. 2145
c Arr. 2215

Table 149

Saturdays

from 4 October

London → Hounslow, Richmond, Kingston, Windsor, Weybridge, Ascot, Guildford and Reading

Network Diagram - see first page of Table 148

		SW	SW	SW	SW	SW	SW	SW	SW	SW	SW	SW	SW	SW	SW	SW	SW	SW
					1						1		1					
			A					A										
London Waterloo 15	⊖ d	22 28	22 33		22 50	22 52	22 58	23 03		23 13	23 20	23 22	23 35		23 37	23 52	23 58	
Vauxhall	⊖ d	22 32	22 37			22 56	23 02	23 07		23 17		23 26			23 41	23 56	00 02	
Queenstown Rd.(Battersea)	d		22 40			22 59		23 10				23 29			23 44	23 59		
Clapham Junction 10	d	22 38	22 43		22 58	23 02	23 08	23 13		23 23	23 28	23 32	23 43		23 47	00 02	00 08	
Wandsworth Town	d		22 46			23 05		23 16				23 35			23 50	00 05		
Putney	d	22 42	22 49			23 08	23 12	23 19		23 27		23 38			23 53	00 08	00 12	
Barnes	d		22 52			23 12		23 22				23 42			23 56	00 12		
Barnes Bridge	d					23 14						23 44		←		00 14		
Chiswick	d			←		23 17			←			23 47 →		23 47		00 17		←
Kew Bridge	d			22 50		23 20 →			23 20					23 50		00 20 →		00 20
Brentford	d			22 53					23 23					23 53				00 23
Syon Lane	d			22 55					23 25					23 55				00 25
Isleworth	d			22 57					23 27					23 57				00 27
Hounslow	d			23 01					23 31					00 01				00 31
Mortlake	d		22 54					23 24							23 58			
North Sheen	d		22 56					23 26							00 01			
Richmond	⊖ d	22 48	22 59		23 06		23 18	23 29		23 33	23 37		23 51		00 03		00 18	
St Margarets	d		23 01					23 31							00 06			
Twickenham	a	22 51	23 03		23 10		23 21	23 33		23 36	23 41		23 55		00 08		00 21	
	d	22 52	23 04		23 10		23 22	23 34		23 37	23 41		23 55		00 08		00 22	
Strawberry Hill	d		23 07					23 37							00 12			
Fulwell	a																	
Teddington	a		23 10					23 40							00 15			
Hampton Wick	a		23 14					23 44							00 17			
Kingston	a		23 16					23 46							00 19			
Whitton	d	22 55					23 25			23 40							00 25	
Feltham	d	22 59		23 06	23 16		23 29		23 36	23 44	23 48		00 01	00 06			00 29	00 36
Ashford (Surrey)	d	23 03		23 10			23 33		23 40	23 48				00 10			00 33	00 40
Staines	d	23 07		23 15	23 23		23 37		23 45	23 52	23 56		00 08	00 15			00a37	00a46
Wraysbury	d	23 11					23 41			23 56								
Sunnymeads	d	23 14					23 44			23 59								
Datchet	d	23 17					23 47			00 02								
Windsor & Eton Riverside	a	23 24					23 54			00 09								
Egham	d			23 20	23 27				23 50		00 01		00 12	00 20				
Virginia Water	a			23 24	23 31				23 54		00 05		00 16	00 24				
	d			23 24	23 31				23 54		00 05		00 16	00 24				
Chertsey §	d			23 29					23 59					00 29				
Addlestone §	d			23 32					00 02					00 32				
Weybridge	a			23 37										00 37				
Byfleet & New Haw	d								00 07									
West Byfleet	d								00 10									
Woking	a								00 16									
Longcross	d																	
Sunningdale	d				23 37						00 10		00 22					
Ascot 3	d				23 43						00 15		00 27					
Bagshot	d																	
Camberley	a																	
	d																	
Frimley	d																	
Ash Vale	d																	
Aldershot	a																	
	d																	
Ash 3	d																	
Wanborough	d																	
Guildford	a																	
Martins Heron	d				23 47						00 19		00 31					
Bracknell	d				23 50						00 23		00 34					
Wokingham	d				23 57						00 31		00 41					
Winnersh	d				00 01						00 35							
Winnersh Triangle	d				00 02						00 37							
Earley	d				00 05						00 39							
Reading 7	a				00 13						00 47		00 52					

For general notes see front of timetable
For details of catering facilities see Directory of Train Operators

§ Passengers to/from London may travel via Weybridge. See Table 155.

A To London Waterloo (Table 152)

Table 149

Sundays

London → Hounslow, Richmond, Kingston, Windsor, Weybridge, Ascot, Guildford and Reading

until 21 September

Network Diagram - see first page of Table 148

		SW 1	SW	SW	SW 1	SW	SW 1	SW	SW 1	SW	SW	SW	SW	SW	SW 1	SW	SW	SW 1	SW	SW 1	SW	SW 1
																A					A	
London Waterloo 15	⊖ d	22p50	22p52	23p13	23p20	23p22	23p35	23p37			23p52	23p58		00 18		06 14	06 44			07 09	07 14	
Vauxhall	⊖ d		22p56	23p17		23p26		23p41			23p56	00 02		00 22		06 18	06 48			07 13	07 18	
Queenstown Rd.(Battersea)	d		22p59			23p29		23p44			23p59			00 25		06 21	06 51				07 21	
Clapham Junction 10	d	22p58	23p02	23p23	23p28	23p32	23p43	23p47			00 02	00 08		00 28		06 24	06 54			07 19	07 24	
Wandsworth Town	d		23p05			23p35		23p50			00 05			00 31		06 27	06 57				07 27	
Putney	d		23p08	23p27		23p38		23p53			00 08	00 12		00 34		06 30	07 00			07 23	07 30	
Barnes	d		23p12			23p42		23p56			00 12			00 37		06 33	07 03				07 33	
Barnes Bridge	d		23p14			23p44				←	00 14											
Chiswick	d		23p17			23p47				23p47	00 17		←									
Kew Bridge	d		23p20			→				23p50	00 20		00 20									
Brentford	d		23p23							23p53	→		00 23									
Syon Lane	d		23p25							23p55			00 25									
Isleworth	d		23p27							23p57			00 27									
Hounslow	d		23p31							00 01			00 31									
Mortlake	d							23p58						00 39		06 35	07 05				07 35	
North Sheen	d							00 01						00 41		06 37	07 07				07 37	
Richmond	⊖ d	23p06		23p33	23p37		23p51	00 03				00 18		00 44		06 40	07 10			07 29	07 40	
St Margarets	d							00 06						00 46		06 42	07 12				07 42	
Twickenham	a	23p10		23p36	23p41		23p55	00 08				00 21		00 48		06 44	07 14			07 32	07 44	
	d	23p10		23p37	23p41		23p55	00 08				00 22		00 49		06 45	07 15			07 33	07 45	
Strawberry Hill	d							00 12						00s52		06 49					07 49	
Fulwell	a																					
Teddington	a							00 15						00s55		06 52					07 52	
Hampton Wick	a							00 17						00s58		06 57					07 57	
Kingston	a							00 19						01 00		06 59					07 59	
Whitton	d			23p40								00 25					07 18					
Feltham	d	23p16	23p36	23p44	23p48		00 01			00 06		00 29	00 36				07 22			07 39		
Ashford (Surrey)	d		23p40	23p48						00 10		00 33	00 40				07 26					
Staines	d	23p23	23p45	23p52	23p56		00 08			00 15		00a37	00a46		06 32		07 30		07 41	07 45		
Wraysbury	d			23p56													07 34					
Sunnymeads	d			23p59													07 37					
Datchet	d			00 02													07 40					
Windsor & Eton Riverside	a			00 06													07 44					
Egham	d	23p27	23p50		00 01		00 12			00 20					06 37				07 45	07 50		
Virginia Water	a	23p31	23p54		00 05		00 16			00 24					06 41				07 49	07 54		
	d	23p31	23p54		00 05		00 16			00 24					06 41				07 49	07 54		
Chertsey §	d		23p59							00 29					06 46				07 55			
Addlestone §	d		00 02							00 32					06 49				07 58			
Weybridge	a									00 37					06 53							
Byfleet & New Haw	d		00 07																08 02			
West Byfleet	d		00 10																08 05			
Woking	a		00 16																08 10			
Longcross	d																					
Sunningdale	d	23p37			00 10		00 22													07 59		
Ascot 3	d	23p43			00 15		00 27		00 29											08 04		08 13
Bagshot	d								00 35													08 19
Camberley	a								00 41													08 25
	d								00 41													08 25
Frimley	d								00 45													08 29
Ash Vale	d								00 52													08 36
Aldershot	a								00 57													08 41
	d																	07 48				08 48
Ash 3	d																	07 55				08 55
Wanborough	d																	07 58				08 58
Guildford	a																	08 05				09 05
Martins Heron	d	23p47			00 19		00 31													08 08		
Bracknell	d	23p50			00 23		00 34													08 11		
Wokingham	d	23p57			00 31		00 41													08 18		
Winnersh	d	00 01			00 35															08 21		
Winnersh Triangle	d	00 02			00 37															08 23		
Earley	d	00 05			00 39															08 26		
Reading 7	a	00 10			00 44		00 49													08 31		

For general notes see front of timetable
For details of catering facilities see Directory of Train Operators

A To London Waterloo (Table 152)

§ Passengers to/from London may travel via Weybridge. See Table 155.

Table 149

Sundays

until 21 September

London → Hounslow, Richmond, Kingston, Windsor, Weybridge, Ascot, Guildford and Reading

Network Diagram - see first page of Table 148

		SW 1	SW	SW	SW 1	SW	SW 1	SW 1	SW	SW	SW 1	SW	SW 1	SW	SW 1	SW	SW	SW 1	SW	SW 1	SW	SW 1
						A						A							A			
London Waterloo 15 ⊖	d		07 44	07 50	08 09	08 14		08 39	08 44	08 50	09 09	09 14		09 25	09 39	09 44	09 50	10 09	10 14		10 25	10 39
Vauxhall ⊖	d		07 48	07 54	08 13	08 18		08 43	08 48	08 54	09 13	09 18		09 29	09 43	09 48	09 54	10 13	10 18		10 29	10 43
Queenstown Rd.(Battersea)	d		07 51	07 57		08 21			08 51	08 57		09 21				09 51	09 57		10 21			
Clapham Junction 10	d		07 54	08 00	08 19	08 24		08 49	08 54	09 00	09 19	09 24		09 35	09 49	09 54	10 00	10 19	10 24		10 35	10 49
Wandsworth Town	d		07 57	08 03		08 27			08 57	09 03		09 27				09 57	10 03		10 27			
Putney	d		08 00	08 06	08 23	08 30		08 53	09 00	09 06	09 23	09 30		09 39	09 53	10 00	10 06	10 23	10 30		10 39	10 53
Barnes	d		08 03	08 09		08 33			09 03	09 09		09 33				10 03	10 09		10 33			
Barnes Bridge	d			08 11						09 11							10 11					
Chiswick	d			08 13						09 13							10 13					
Kew Bridge	d			08 16						09 16							10 16					
Brentford	d			08 19						09 19							10 19					
Syon Lane	d			08 21						09 21							10 21					
Isleworth	d			08 23						09 23							10 23					
Hounslow	d			08 27						09 27							10 27					
Mortlake	d		08 05			08 35			09 05			09 35				10 05			10 35			
North Sheen	d		08 07			08 37			09 07			09 37				10 07			10 37			
Richmond ⊖	d		08 10		08 29	08 40		08 59	09 10		09 29	09 40		09 45	09 59	10 10		10 29	10 40		10 45	10 59
St Margarets	d		08 12			08 42			09 12			09 42				10 12			10 42			
Twickenham	a		08 14		08 32	08 44		09 02	09 14		09 32	09 44		09 48	10 02	10 14		10 32	10 44		10 48	11 02
	d		08 15		08 33	08 45		09 03	09 15		09 33	09 45		09 49	10 03	10 15		10 33	10 45		10 49	11 03
Strawberry Hill	d					08 49						09 49							10 49			
Fulwell	a																					
Teddington	a					08 52						09 52							10 52			
Hampton Wick	a					08 57						09 57							10 57			
Kingston	a					08 59						09 59							10 59			
Whitton	d		08 18						09 18					09 52		10 18					10 52	
Feltham	d		08 22	08 33	08 39			09 09	09 22	09 33	09 39			09 56	10 09	10 22	10 33	10 39			10 56	11 09
Ashford (Surrey)	d		08 26	08 37					09 26	09 37				10 00		10 26	10 37				11 00	
Staines	d	08 15	08 30	08 41	08 45			09 15	09 30	09 41	09 45			10 04	10 15	10 30	10 41	10 45			11 04	11 15
Wraysbury	d		08 34						09 34							10 34						
Sunnymeads	d		08 37						09 37							10 37						
Datchet	d		08 40						09 40					10 12		10 40					11 12	
Windsor & Eton Riverside	a		08 44						09 44					10 16		10 44					11 16	
Egham	d	08 20		08 45	08 50			09 20		09 45	09 50				10 20		10 45	10 50				11 20
Virginia Water	a	08 24		08 49	08 54			09 24		09 49	09 54				10 24		10 49	10 54				11 24
	d	08 24		08 49	08 54			09 24		09 49	09 54				10 24		10 49	10 54				11 24
Chertsey §	d			08 55						09 55							10 55					
Addlestone §	d			08 58						09 58							10 58					
Weybridge	a																					
Byfleet & New Haw	d			09 02						10 02							11 02					
West Byfleet	d			09 05						10 05							11 05					
Woking	a			09 10						10 10							11 10					
Longcross	d																					
Sunningdale	d	08 29			08 59			09 29			09 59				10 29			10 59				11 29
Ascot 3	d	08 34			09 04		09 13	09 34			10 04		10 13		10 34			11 04		11 13		11 34
Bagshot	d						09 19						10 19							11 19		
Camberley	a						09 25						10 25							11 25		
	d						09 25						10 25							11 25		
Frimley	d						09 29						10 29							11 29		
Ash Vale	d						09 36						10 36							11 36		
Aldershot	a						09 41						10 41							11 41		
	d						09 48						10 48							11 48		
Ash 3	d						09 55						10 55							11 55		
Wanborough	d						09 58						10 58							11 58		
Guildford	a						10 05						11 05							12 05		
Martins Heron	d	08 38			09 08			09 38			10 08				10 38			11 08				11 38
Bracknell	d	08 41			09 11			09 41			10 11				10 41			11 11				11 41
Wokingham	d	08 48			09 18			09 48			10 18				10 48			11 18				11 48
Winnersh	d	08 51			09 21			09 51			10 21				10 51			11 21				11 51
Winnersh Triangle	d	08 53			09 23			09 53			10 23				10 53			11 23				11 53
Earley	d	08 56			09 26			09 56			10 26				10 56			11 26				11 56
Reading 7	a	09 01			09 31			10 01			10 31				11 01			11 31				12 01

For general notes see front of timetable
For details of catering facilities see Directory of Train Operators

§ Passengers to/from London may travel via Weybridge. See Table 155.

A To London Waterloo (Table 152)

Table 149

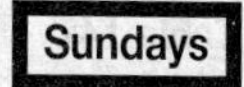

Sundays

until 21 September

London → Hounslow, Richmond, Kingston, Windsor, Weybridge, Ascot, Guildford and Reading

Network Diagram - see first page of Table 148

Station		SW	SW	SW 1	SW A		SW 1	SW	SW 1	SW	SW	SW 1		SW A	SW 1	SW	SW 1	SW	SW		SW 1	SW A	SW 1	SW	SW 1
London Waterloo 15 ⊖	d	10 44	10 50	11 09	11 14			11 25	11 39	11 44	11 50	12 09		12 14		12 25	12 39	12 44	12 50		13 09	13 14		13 25	13 39
Vauxhall ⊖	d	10 48	10 54	11 13	11 18			11 29	11 43	11 48	11 54	12 13		12 18		12 29	12 43	12 48	12 54		13 13	13 18		13 29	13 43
Queenstown Rd.(Battersea)	d	10 51	10 57		11 21					11 51	11 57			12 21				12 51	12 57			13 21			
Clapham Junction 10	d	10 54	11 00	11 19	11 24			11 35	11 49	11 54	12 00	12 19		12 24		12 35	12 49	12 54	13 00		13 19	13 24		13 35	13 49
Wandsworth Town	d	10 57	11 03		11 27					11 57	12 03			12 27				12 57	13 03			13 27			
Putney	d	11 00	11 06	11 23	11 30			11 39	11 53	12 00	12 06	12 23		12 30		12 39	12 53	13 00	13 06		13 23	13 30		13 39	13 53
Barnes	d	11 03	11 09		11 33					12 03	12 09			12 33				13 03	13 09			13 33			
Barnes Bridge	d		11 11								12 11								13 11						
Chiswick	d		11 13								12 13								13 13						
Kew Bridge	d		11 16								12 16								13 16						
Brentford	d		11 19								12 19								13 19						
Syon Lane	d		11 21								12 21								13 21						
Isleworth	d		11 23								12 23								13 23						
Hounslow	d		11 27								12 27								13 27						
Mortlake	d	11 05			11 35					12 05				12 35				13 05				13 35			
North Sheen	d	11 07			11 37					12 07				12 37				13 07				13 37			
Richmond ⊖	d	11 10		11 29	11 40			11 45	11 59	12 10		12 29		12 40		12 45	12 59	13 10			13 29	13 40		13 45	13 59
St Margarets	d	11 12			11 42					12 12				12 42				13 12				13 42			
Twickenham	a	11 14		11 32	11 44			11 48	12 02	12 14		12 32		12 44		12 48	13 02	13 14			13 32	13 44		13 48	14 02
	d	11 15		11 33	11 45			11 49	12 03	12 15		12 33		12 45		12 49	13 03	13 15			13 33	13 45		13 49	14 03
Strawberry Hill	d				11 49									12 49								13 49			
Fulwell	a																								
Teddington	a				11 52									12 52								13 52			
Hampton Wick	a				11 57									12 57								13 57			
Kingston	a				11 59									12 59								13 59			
Whitton	d	11 18						11 52		12 18						12 52		13 18						13 52	
Feltham	d	11 22	11 33	11 39				11 56	12 09	12 22	12 33	12 39				12 56	13 09	13 22	13 33		13 39			13 56	14 09
Ashford (Surrey)	d	11 26	11 37					12 00		12 26	12 37					13 00		13 26	13 37					14 00	
Staines	d	11 30	11 41	11 45				12 04	12 15	12 30	12 41	12 45				13 04	13 15	13 30	13 41		13 45			14 04	14 15
Wraysbury	d	11 34								12 34								13 34							
Sunnymeads	d	11 37								12 37								13 37							
Datchet	d	11 40						12 12		12 40						13 12		13 40						14 12	
Windsor & Eton Riverside	a	11 44						12 16		12 44						13 16		13 44						14 16	
Egham	d		11 45	11 50					12 20		12 45	12 50					13 20		13 45		13 50				14 20
Virginia Water	a		11 49	11 54					12 24		12 49	12 54					13 24		13 49		13 54				14 24
	d		11 49	11 54					12 24		12 49	12 54					13 24		13 49		13 54				14 24
Chertsey §	d		11 55								12 55								13 55						
Addlestone §	d		11 58								12 58								13 58						
Weybridge	a																								
Byfleet & New Haw	d		12 02								13 02								14 02						
West Byfleet	d		12 05								13 05								14 05						
Woking	a		12 10								13 10								14 10						
Longcross	d																								
Sunningdale	d			11 59					12 29			12 59					13 29				13 59				14 29
Ascot 3	d			12 04			12 13		12 34			13 04			13 13		13 34				14 04		14 13		14 34
Bagshot	d						12 19								13 19								14 19		
Camberley	a						12 25								13 25								14 25		
	d						12 25								13 25								14 25		
Frimley	d						12 29								13 29								14 29		
Ash Vale	d						12 36								13 36								14 36		
Aldershot	a						12 41								13 41								14 41		
	d						12 48								13 48								14 48		
Ash 3	d						12 55								13 55								14 55		
Wanborough	d						12 58								13 58								14 58		
Guildford	a						13 05								14 05								15 05		
Martins Heron	d			12 08					12 38			13 08					13 38				14 08				14 38
Bracknell	d			12 11					12 41			13 11					13 41				14 11				14 41
Wokingham	d			12 18					12 48			13 18					13 48				14 18				14 48
Winnersh	d			12 21					12 51			13 21					13 51				14 21				14 51
Winnersh Triangle	d			12 23					12 53			13 23					13 53				14 23				14 53
Earley	d			12 26					12 56			13 26					13 56				14 26				14 56
Reading 7	a			12 31					13 01			13 31					14 01				14 31				15 01

For general notes see front of timetable
For details of catering facilities see Directory of Train Operators

§ Passengers to/from London may travel via Weybridge. See Table 155.

A To London Waterloo (Table 152)

Sundays

until 21 September

London → Hounslow, Richmond, Kingston, Windsor, Weybridge, Ascot, Guildford and Reading

Network Diagram - see first page of Table 148

	SW	SW	SW			SW 1	SW A	SW 1	SW	SW 1	SW	SW	SW			SW 1	SW A	SW 1	SW 1	SW	SW		SW
London Waterloo 15 ⊖ d	13 44	13 50	13 56			14 09	14 14		14 25	14 39	14 44	14 50	14 56			20 09	20 14		20 39	20 44	20 50		20 56
Vauxhall ⊖ d	13 48	13 54	14 00			14 13	14 18		14 29	14 43	14 48	14 54	15 00			20 13	20 18		20 43	20 48	20 54		21 00
Queenstown Rd.(Battersea) d	13 51	13 57	14 03				14 21				14 51	14 57	15 03				20 21			20 51	20 57		21 03
Clapham Junction 10 d	13 54	14 00	14 06			14 19	14 24		14 35	14 49	14 54	15 00	15 06			20 19	20 24		20 49	20 54	21 00		21 06
Wandsworth Town d	13 57	14 03	14 09				14 27				14 57	15 03	15 09				20 27			20 57	21 03		21 09
Putney d	14 00	14 06	14 12			14 23	14 30		14 39	14 53	15 00	15 06	15 12			20 23	20 30		20 53	21 00	21 06		21 12
Barnes d	14 03	14 09	14 15				14 33				15 03	15 09	15 15				20 33			21 03	21 09		21 15
Barnes Bridge d		14 11										15 11									21 11		
Chiswick d		14 13										15 13									21 13		
Kew Bridge d		14 16										15 16									21 16		
Brentford d		14 19										15 19									21 19		
Syon Lane d		14 21										15 21									21 21		
Isleworth d		14 23										15 23									21 23		
Hounslow d		14 27										15 27									21 27		
Mortlake d	14 05		14 17				14 35				15 05		15 17				20 35			21 05			21 17
North Sheen d	14 07		14 19				14 37				15 07		15 19				20 37			21 07			21 19
Richmond ⊖ d	14 10		14 22			14 29	14 40		14 45	14 59	15 10		15 22			20 29	20 40		20 59	21 10			21 22
St Margarets d	14 12		14 24				14 42				15 12		15 24				20 42			21 12			21 24
Twickenham a	14 14		14 26			14 32	14 44		14 48	15 02	15 14		15 26			20 32	20 44		21 02	21 14			21 26
Twickenham d	14 15		14 27			14 33	14 45		14 49	15 03	15 15		15 27			20 33	20 45		21 03	21 15			21 27
Strawberry Hill d			14 30				14 49						15 30				20 49						21 30
Fulwell a																							
Teddington a			14 33				14 52						15 33				20 52						21 33
Hampton Wick a			14 36				14 57						15 36				20 57						21 36
Kingston a			14 38				14 59						15 38	and at			20 59						21 38
Whitton d	14 18								14 52		15 18									21 18			
Feltham d	14 22	14 33				14 39			14 56	15 09	15 22	15 33		the same		20 39			21 09	21 22	21 33		
Ashford (Surrey) d	14 26	14 37							15 00		15 26	15 37								21 26	21 37		
Staines d	14 30	14 41				14 45			15 04	15 15	15 30	15 41		minutes		20 45			21 15	21 30	21 41		
Wraysbury d	14 34										15 34			past						21 34			
Sunnymeads d	14 37										15 37									21 37			
Datchet d	14 40								15 12		15 40			each						21 40			
Windsor & Eton Riverside a	14 44								15 16		15 44			hour until						21 44			
Egham d		14 45				14 50				15 20		15 45				20 50			21 20		21 45		
Virginia Water a		14 49				14 54				15 24		15 49				20 54			21 24		21 49		
Virginia Water d		14 49				14 54				15 24		15 49				20 54			21 24		21 49		
Chertsey § d		14 55										15 55									21 55		
Addlestone § d		14 58										15 58									21 58		
Weybridge a																							
Byfleet & New Haw d		15 02										16 02									22 02		
West Byfleet d		15 05										16 05									22 05		
Woking a		15 10										16 10									22 10		
Longcross d																							
Sunningdale d						14 59				15 29						20 59			21 29				
Ascot 3 d						15 04		15 13		15 34						21 04		21 13	21 34				
Bagshot d								15 19										21 19					
Camberley a								15 25										21 25					
Camberley d								15 25										21 25					
Frimley d								15 29										21 29					
Ash Vale d								15 36										21 36					
Aldershot a								15 41										21 41					
Aldershot d								15 48										21 48					
Ash 3 d								15 55										21 55					
Wanborough d								15 58										21 58					
Guildford a								16 05										22 05					
Martins Heron d						15 08				15 38						21 08			21 38				
Bracknell d						15 11				15 41						21 11			21 41				
Wokingham d						15 18				15 48						21 18			21 48				
Winnersh d						15 21				15 51						21 21			21 51				
Winnersh Triangle d						15 23				15 53						21 23			21 53				
Earley d						15 26				15 56						21 26			21 56				
Reading 7 a						15 31				16 01						21 31			22 01				

For general notes see front of timetable
For details of catering facilities see
Directory of Train Operators

§ Passengers to/from London may travel via Weybridge. See Table 155.

A To London Waterloo (Table 152)

Table 149

until 21 September

London → Hounslow, Richmond, Kingston, Windsor, Weybridge, Ascot, Guildford and Reading

Network Diagram - see first page of Table 148

		SW 1	SW	SW 1	SW 1	SW	SW	SW	SW 1	SW	SW 1	SW 1	SW	SW	SW	SW 1	SW	SW 1	SW
			A							A	B								
London Waterloo 15 ⊖	d	21 09	21 14		21 39	21 44	21 50	21 56	22 09	22 14		22 39	22 44	22 50	22 56	23 09	23 14	23 39	23 44
Vauxhall ⊖	d	21 13	21 18		21 43	21 48	21 54	22 00	22 13	22 18		22 43	22 48	22 54	23 00	23 13	23 18	23 43	23 48
Queenstown Rd.(Battersea)	d		21 21			21 51	21 57	22 03		22 21			22 51	22 57	23 03		23 21		23 51
Clapham Junction 10	d	21 19	21 24		21 49	21 54	22 00	22 06	22 19	22 24		22 49	22 54	23 00	23 06	23 19	23 24	23 49	23 54
Wandsworth Town	d		21 27			21 57	22 03	22 09		22 27			22 57	23 03	23 09		23 27		23 57
Putney	d	21 23	21 30		21 53	22 00	22 06	22 12	22 23	22 30		22 53	23 00	23 06	23 12	23 23	23 30	23 53	23 59
Barnes	d		21 33			22 03	22 09	22 15		22 33			23 03	23 09	23 15		23 33		00 03
Barnes Bridge	d						22 11							23 11					
Chiswick	d						22 13							23 13					
Kew Bridge	d						22 16							23 16					
Brentford	d						22 19							23 19					
Syon Lane	d						22 21							23 21					
Isleworth	d						22 23							23 23					
Hounslow	d						22 27							23 27					
Mortlake	d		21 35			22 05		22 17		22 35			23 05		23 17		23 35		00 05
North Sheen	d		21 37			22 07		22 19		22 37			23 07		23 19		23 37		00 07
Richmond ⊖	d	21 29	21 40		21 59	22 10		22 22	22 29	22 40		22 59	23 10		23 22	23 29	23 40	23 59	00 10
St Margarets	d		21 42			22 12		22 24		22 42			23 12		23 24		23 42		00 12
Twickenham	a	21 32	21 44		22 02	22 14		22 26	22 32	22 44		23 02	23 14		23 26	23 32	23 44	00 02	00 14
	d	21 33	21 45		22 03	22 15		22 27	22 33	22 45		23 03	23 15		23 27	23 33	23 45	00 03	00 15
Strawberry Hill	d		21 49					22 30		22 49					23 30		23 48		
Fulwell	a																		
Teddington	a		21 52					22 33		22 52					23 33		23 51		
Hampton Wick	a		21 57					22 36		22 57					23 36		23 54		
Kingston	a		21 59					22 38		22 59					23 38		23 56		
Whitton	d					22 18							23 18						00 18
Feltham	d	21 39			22 09	22 22	22 33		22 39			23 09	23 22	23 33		23 39		00 09	00 22
Ashford (Surrey)	d					22 26	22 37						23 26	23 37					00 26
Staines	d	21 45			22 15	22 30	22 41		22 45			23 15	23 30	23 41		23 45		00 15	00a30
Wraysbury	d					22 34							23 34						
Sunnymeads	d					22 37							23 37						
Datchet	d					22 40							23 40						
Windsor & Eton Riverside	a					22 44							23 44						
Egham	d	21 50			22 20		22 45		22 50			23 20		23 45		23 50		00 20	
Virginia Water	a	21 54			22 24		22 49		22 54			23 24		23 49		23 54		00 24	
	d	21 54			22 24		22 49		22 54			23 24		23 49		23 54		00 24	
Chertsey §	d						22 55							23 55					
Addlestone §	d						22 58							23 58					
Weybridge	a																		
Byfleet & New Haw	d						23 02							00 02					
West Byfleet	d						23 05							00 05					
Woking	a						23 10							00 10					
Longcross	d																		
Sunningdale	d	21 59			22 29				22 59			23 29				23 59		00 29	
Ascot 3	d	22 04		22 13	22 34				23 04		23 13	23 34				00 04		00 34	
Bagshot	d			22 19							23 19								
Camberley	a			22 25							23 25								
	d			22 25							23 25								
Frimley	d			22 29							23 29								
Ash Vale	d			22 36							23 36								
Aldershot	a			22 41							23 41								
	d			22 48															
Ash 3	d			22 55															
Wanborough	d			22 58															
Guildford	a			23 05															
Martins Heron	d	22 08			22 38				23 08			23 38				00 08		00 38	
Bracknell	d	22 11			22 41				23 11			23 41				00 11		00 41	
Wokingham	d	22 18			22 48				23 20			23 48				00 18		00 48	
Winnersh	d	22 21			22 51				23 24			23 51				00 21		00 51	
Winnersh Triangle	d	22 23			22 53				23 26			23 53				00 23		00 53	
Earley	d	22 26			22 56				23 28			23 56				00 26		00 56	
Reading 7	a	22 31			23 01				23 33			00 01				00 31		01 01	

For general notes see front of timetable
For details of catering facilities see Directory of Train Operators

A To London Waterloo (Table 152)
B To Farnham (Table 155)

§ Passengers to/from London may travel via Weybridge. See Table 155.

Table 149

Sundays

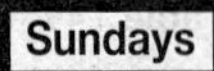

from 28 September

London → Hounslow, Richmond, Kingston, Windsor, Weybridge, Ascot, Guildford and Reading

Network Diagram - see first page of Table 148

		SW	SW	SW	SW	SW	SW	SW	SW		SW	SW	SW	SW	SW	SW	SW	SW		SW	SW	SW	SW	SW	SW
		1	1				1	1			1	1		1							1			1	
		A	B		A	B	A	B			A	B										C			
London Waterloo [15]	⊖ d	22p50	22p50	22p52	23p13	23p13	23p20	23p20	23p22		23p35	23p35	23p37			23p52	23p58			00 18		06 14	06 44		
Vauxhall	⊖ d			22p56	23p17	23p17			23p26				23p41			23p56	00 02			00 22		06 18	06 48		
Queenstown Rd.(Battersea)	d			22p59					23p29				23p44			23p59				00 25		06 21	06 51		
Clapham Junction [10]	d	22p58	22p58	23p02	23p23	23p23	23p28	23p28	23p32		23p43	23p43	23p47			00 02	00 08			00 28		06 24	06 54		
Wandsworth Town	d			23p05					23p35				23p50			00 05				00 31		06 27	06 57		
Putney	d			23p08	23p27	23p27			23p38				23p53			00 08	00 12			00 34		06 30	07 00		
Barnes	d			23p12					23p42				23p56			00 12				00 37		06 33	07 03		
Barnes Bridge	d			23p14					23p44						⟵	00 14									
Chiswick	d			23p17					23p47						23p47	00 17		⟵							
Kew Bridge	d			23p20					⟶						23p50	00 20		00 20							
Brentford	d			23p23											23p53	⟶		00 23							
Syon Lane	d			23p25											23p55			00 25							
Isleworth	d			23p27											23p57			00 27							
Hounslow	d			23p31											00 01			00 31							
Mortlake	d												23p58							00 39		06 35	07 05		
North Sheen	d												00 01							00 41		06 37	07 07		
Richmond	⊖ d	23p06	23p06		23p33	23p33	23p37	23p37			23p51	23p51	00 03				00 18			00 44		06 40	07 10		
St Margarets	d												00 06							00 46		06 42	07 12		
Twickenham	a	23p10	23p10		23p36	23p36	23p41	23p41			23p55	23p55	00 08				00 21			00 48		06 44	07 14		
	d	23p10	23p10		23p37	23p37	23p41	23p41			23p55	23p55	00 08				00 22			00 49		06 45	07 15		
Strawberry Hill	d												00 12							00s52		06 49			
Fulwell	a																								
Teddington	a												00 15							00s55		06 52			
Hampton Wick	a												00 17							00s58		06 57			
Kingston	a												00 19							01 00		06 59			
Whitton	d				23p40	23p40											00 25						07 18		
Feltham	d	23p16	23p16	23p36	23p44	23p44	23p48	23p48			00 01	00 01			00 06		00 29	00 36					07 22		
Ashford (Surrey)	d			23p40	23p48	23p48									00 10		00 33	00 40					07 26		
Staines	d	23p23	23p23	23p45	23p52	23p52	23p56	23p56			00 08	00 08			00 15		00a37	00a46			06 32		07 30		07 41
Wraysbury	d				23p56	23p56																	07 34		
Sunnymeads	d				23p59	23p59																	07 37		
Datchet	d				00 02	00 02																	07 40		
Windsor & Eton Riverside	a				00 06	00 09																	07 46		
Egham	d	23p27	23p27	23p50			00 01	00 01			00 12	00 12			00 20						06 37				07 45
Virginia Water	a	23p31	23p31	23p54			00 05	00 05			00 16	00 16			00 24						06 41				07 49
	d	23p31	23p31	23p54			00 05	00 05			00 16	00 16			00 24						06 41				07 49
Chertsey §	d			23p59											00 29						06 46				07 55
Addlestone §	d			00 02											00 32						06 49				07 58
Weybridge	a														00 37						06 53				
Byfleet & New Haw	d			00 07																					08 02
West Byfleet	d			00 10																					08 05
Woking	a			00 16																					08 10
Longcross	d																								
Sunningdale	d	23p37	23p37				00 10	00 10			00 22	00 22													
Ascot [3]	d	23p43	23p43				00 15	00 15			00 27	00 27		00 29											
Bagshot	d													00 35											
Camberley	a													00 41											
	d													00 41											
Frimley	d													00 45											
Ash Vale	d													00 52											
Aldershot	a													00 57											
	d																							07 48	
Ash [3]	d																							07 55	
Wanborough	d																							07 58	
Guildford	a																							08 05	
Martins Heron	d	23p47	23p47				00 19	00 19			00 31	00 31													
Bracknell	d	23p50	23p50				00 23	00 23			00 34	00 34													
Wokingham	d	23p57	23p57				00 31	00 31			00 41	00 41													
Winnersh	d	00 01	00 01				00 35	00 35																	
Winnersh Triangle	d	00 02	00 02				00 37	00 37																	
Earley	d	00 05	00 05				00 39	00 39																	
Reading [7]	a	00 10	00 13				00 44	00 47			00 49	00 52													

For general notes see front of timetable
For details of catering facilities see Directory of Train Operators

§ Passengers to/from London may travel via Weybridge. See Table 155.

A 28 September
B From 5 October
C To London Waterloo (Table 152)

Table 149

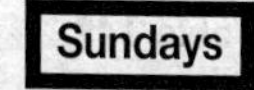

London → Hounslow, Richmond, Kingston, Windsor, Weybridge, Ascot, Guildford and Reading

Sundays from 28 September

Network Diagram - see first page of Table 148

		SW	SW	SW	SW		SW	SW	SW	SW	SW	SW	SW	SW		SW	SW	SW	SW	SW	SW	SW	SW		SW
		1		1	1				1		1	1				1		1		1			1		
			A							A							A								A
London Waterloo 15 ⊖	d	07 09	07 14				07 44	07 50	08 09	08 14		08 39	08 44	08 50		09 09	09 14		09 25	09 39	09 44	09 50	10 09		10 14
Vauxhall ⊖	d	07 13	07 18				07 48	07 54	08 13	08 18		08 43	08 48	08 54		09 13	09 18		09 29	09 43	09 48	09 54	10 13		10 18
Queenstown Rd.(Battersea)	d		07 21				07 51	07 57		08 21			08 51	08 57			09 21				09 51	09 57			10 21
Clapham Junction 10	d	07 19	07 24				07 54	08 00	08 19	08 24		08 49	08 54	09 00		09 19	09 24		09 35	09 49	09 54	10 00	10 19		10 24
Wandsworth Town	d		07 27				07 57	08 03		08 27			08 57	09 03			09 27				09 57	10 03			10 27
Putney	d	07 23	07 30				08 00	08 06	08 23	08 30		08 53	09 00	09 06		09 23	09 30		09 39	09 53	10 00	10 06	10 23		10 30
Barnes	d		07 33				08 03	08 09		08 33			09 03	09 09			09 33				10 03	10 09			10 33
Barnes Bridge	d							08 11						09 11								10 11			
Chiswick	d							08 13						09 13								10 13			
Kew Bridge	d							08 16						09 16								10 16			
Brentford	d							08 19						09 19								10 19			
Syon Lane	d							08 21						09 21								10 21			
Isleworth	d							08 23						09 23								10 23			
Hounslow	d							08 27						09 27								10 27			
Mortlake	d		07 35				08 05			08 35			09 05				09 35				10 05				10 35
North Sheen	d		07 37				08 07			08 37			09 07				09 37				10 07				10 37
Richmond ⊖	d	07 29	07 40				08 10		08 29	08 40		08 59	09 10			09 29	09 40		09 45	09 59	10 10		10 29		10 40
St Margarets	d		07 42				08 12			08 42			09 12				09 42				10 12				10 42
Twickenham	a	07 32	07 44				08 14		08 32	08 44		09 02	09 14			09 32	09 44		09 48	10 02	10 14		10 32		10 44
	d	07 33	07 45				08 15		08 33	08 45		09 03	09 15			09 33	09 45		09 49	10 03	10 15		10 33		10 45
Strawberry Hill	d		07 49							08 49							09 49								10 49
Fulwell	a																								
Teddington	a		07 52							08 52							09 52								10 52
Hampton Wick	a		07 57							08 57							09 57								10 57
Kingston	a		07 59							08 59							09 59								10 59
Whitton	d						08 18						09 18						09 52		10 18				
Feltham	d	07 39					08 22	08 33	08 39			09 09	09 22	09 33		09 39			09 56	10 09	10 22	10 33	10 39		
Ashford (Surrey)	d						08 26	08 37					09 26	09 37					10 00		10 26	10 37			
Staines	d	07 45			08 15		08 30	08 41	08 45			09 15	09 30	09 41		09 45			10 04	10 15	10 30	10 41	10 45		
Wraysbury	d						08 34						09 34								10 34				
Sunnymeads	d						08 37						09 37								10 37				
Datchet	d						08 40						09 40						10 12		10 40				
Windsor & Eton Riverside	a						08 46						09 46						10 18		10 46				
Egham	d	07 50			08 20			08 45	08 50			09 20		09 45		09 50				10 20		10 45	10 50		
Virginia Water	a	07 54			08 24			08 49	08 54			09 24		09 49		09 54				10 24		10 49	10 54		
	d	07 54			08 24			08 49	08 54			09 24		09 49		09 54				10 24		10 49	10 54		
Chertsey §	d							08 55						09 55								10 55			
Addlestone §	d							08 58						09 58								10 58			
Weybridge	a																								
Byfleet & New Haw	d							09 02						10 02								11 02			
West Byfleet	d							09 05						10 05								11 05			
Woking	a							09 10						10 10								11 10			
Longcross	d																								
Sunningdale	d	07 59			08 29				08 59			09 29				09 59				10 29			10 59		
Ascot 3	d	08 04		08 13	08 34				09 04		09 13	09 34				10 04		10 13		10 34			11 04		
Bagshot	d			08 19							09 19							10 19							
Camberley	a			08 25							09 25							10 25							
	d			08 25							09 25							10 25							
Frimley	d			08 29							09 29							10 29							
Ash Vale	d			08 36							09 36							10 36							
Aldershot	a			08 41							09 41							10 41							
	d			08 48							09 48							10 48							
Ash 3	d			08 55							09 55							10 55							
Wanborough	d			08 58							09 58							10 58							
Guildford	a			09 05							10 05							11 05							
Martins Heron	d	08 08			08 38				09 08			09 38				10 08				10 38			11 08		
Bracknell	d	08 11			08 41				09 11			09 41				10 11				10 41			11 11		
Wokingham	d	08 18			08 48				09 18			09 48				10 18				10 48			11 18		
Winnersh	d	08 21			08 51				09 21			09 51				10 21				10 51			11 21		
Winnersh Triangle	d	08 23			08 53				09 23			09 53				10 23				10 53			11 23		
Earley	d	08 26			08 56				09 26			09 56				10 26				10 56			11 26		
Reading 7	a	08 34			09 04				09 34			10 04				10 34				11 04			11 34		

For general notes see front of timetable
For details of catering facilities see Directory of Train Operators

§ Passengers to/from London may travel via Weybridge. See Table 155.

A To London Waterloo (Table 152)

Table 149

Sundays
from 28 September

London → Hounslow, Richmond, Kingston, Windsor, Weybridge, Ascot, Guildford and Reading

Network Diagram - see first page of Table 148

Station		SW 1	SW	SW 1	SW	SW	SW 1	SW A	SW 1	SW	SW 1	SW	SW	SW 1	SW A	SW 1	SW	SW 1	SW	SW	SW 1	SW A	SW 1
London Waterloo 15 ⊖	d		10 25	10 39	10 44	10 50	11 09	11 14		11 25	11 39	11 44	11 50	12 09	12 14		12 25	12 39	12 44	12 50	13 09	13 14	
Vauxhall ⊖	d		10 29	10 43	10 48	10 54	11 13	11 18		11 29	11 43	11 48	11 54	12 13	12 18		12 29	12 43	12 48	12 54	13 13	13 18	
Queenstown Rd.(Battersea)	d				10 51	10 57		11 21				11 51	11 57		12 21				12 51	12 57		13 21	
Clapham Junction 10	d		10 35	10 49	10 54	11 00	11 19	11 24		11 35	11 49	11 54	12 00	12 19	12 24		12 35	12 49	12 54	13 00	13 19	13 24	
Wandsworth Town	d				10 57	11 03		11 27				11 57	12 03		12 27				12 57	13 03		13 27	
Putney	d		10 39	10 53	11 00	11 06	11 23	11 30		11 39	11 53	12 00	12 06	12 23	12 30		12 39	12 53	13 00	13 06	13 23	13 30	
Barnes	d				11 03	11 09		11 33				12 03	12 09		12 33				13 03	13 09		13 33	
Barnes Bridge	d					11 11							12 11							13 11			
Chiswick	d					11 13							12 13							13 13			
Kew Bridge	d					11 16							12 16							13 16			
Brentford	d					11 19							12 19							13 19			
Syon Lane	d					11 21							12 21							13 21			
Isleworth	d					11 23							12 23							13 23			
Hounslow	d					11 27							12 27							13 27			
Mortlake	d				11 05			11 35				12 05			12 35				13 05			13 35	
North Sheen	d				11 07			11 37				12 07			12 37				13 07			13 37	
Richmond ⊖	d		10 45	10 59	11 10		11 29	11 40		11 45	11 59	12 10		12 29	12 40		12 45	12 59	13 10		13 29	13 40	
St Margarets	d				11 12			11 42				12 12			12 42				13 12			13 42	
Twickenham	a		10 48	11 02	11 14		11 32	11 44		11 48	12 02	12 14		12 32	12 44		12 48	13 02	13 14		13 32	13 44	
	d		10 49	11 03	11 15		11 33	11 45		11 49	12 03	12 15		12 33	12 45		12 49	13 03	13 15		13 33	13 45	
Strawberry Hill	d							11 49							12 49							13 49	
Fulwell	a																						
Teddington	a							11 52							12 52							13 52	
Hampton Wick	a							11 57							12 57							13 57	
Kingston	a							11 59							12 59							13 59	
Whitton	d		10 52		11 18					11 52		12 18					12 52		13 18				
Feltham	d		10 56	11 09	11 22	11 33	11 39			11 56	12 09	12 22	12 33	12 39			12 56	13 09	13 22	13 33	13 39		
Ashford (Surrey)	d		11 00		11 26	11 37				12 00		12 26	12 37				13 00		13 26	13 37			
Staines	d		11 04	11 15	11 30	11 41	11 45			12 04	12 15	12 30	12 41	12 45			13 04	13 15	13 30	13 41	13 45		
Wraysbury	d				11 34							12 34							13 34				
Sunnymeads	d				11 37							12 37							13 37				
Datchet	d		11 12		11 40					12 12		12 40					13 12		13 40				
Windsor & Eton Riverside	a		11 18		11 46					12 18		12 46					13 18		13 46				
Egham	d			11 20		11 45	11 50				12 20		12 45	12 50				13 20		13 45	13 50		
Virginia Water	a			11 24		11 49	11 54				12 24		12 49	12 54				13 24		13 49	13 54		
	d			11 24		11 49	11 54				12 24		12 49	12 54				13 24		13 49	13 54		
Chertsey §	d					11 55							12 55							13 55			
Addlestone §	d					11 58							12 58							13 58			
Weybridge	a																						
Byfleet & New Haw	d					12 02							13 02							14 02			
West Byfleet	d					12 05							13 05							14 05			
Woking	a					12 10							13 10							14 10			
Longcross	d																						
Sunningdale	d			11 29			11 59				12 29			12 59				13 29			13 59		
Ascot 3	d	11 13		11 34			12 04		12 13		12 34			13 04		13 13		13 34			14 04		14 13
Bagshot	d	11 19							12 19							13 19							14 19
Camberley	a	11 25							12 25							13 25							14 25
	d	11 25							12 25							13 25							14 25
Frimley	d	11 29							12 29							13 29							14 29
Ash Vale	d	11 36							12 36							13 36							14 36
Aldershot	a	11 41							12 41							13 41							14 41
	d	11 48							12 48							13 48							14 48
Ash 3	d	11 55							12 55							13 55							14 55
Wanborough	d	11 58							12 58							13 58							14 58
Guildford	a	12 05							13 05							14 05							15 05
Martins Heron	d			11 38			12 08				12 38			13 08				13 38			14 08		
Bracknell	d			11 41			12 11				12 41			13 11				13 41			14 11		
Wokingham	d			11 48			12 18				12 48			13 18				13 48			14 18		
Winnersh	d			11 51			12 21				12 51			13 21				13 51			14 21		
Winnersh Triangle	d			11 53			12 23				12 53			13 23				13 53			14 23		
Earley	d			11 56			12 26				12 56			13 26				13 56			14 26		
Reading 7	a			12 04			12 34				13 04			13 34				14 04			14 34		

For general notes see front of timetable
For details of catering facilities see Directory of Train Operators

§ Passengers to/from London may travel via Weybridge. See Table 155.

A To London Waterloo (Table 152)

Table 149

from 28 September

London → Hounslow, Richmond, Kingston, Windsor, Weybridge, Ascot, Guildford and Reading

Network Diagram - see first page of Table 148

		SW	SW 1	SW	SW		SW		SW 1	SW A	SW 1	SW	SW 1	SW	SW	SW			SW 1	SW A	SW 1	SW 1	SW	SW
London Waterloo 15 ⊖	d	13 25	13 39	13 44	13 50		13 56		14 09	14 14		14 25	14 39	14 44	14 50	14 56			20 09	20 14		20 39	20 44	20 50
Vauxhall ⊖	d	13 29	13 43	13 48	13 54		14 00		14 13	14 18		14 29	14 43	14 48	14 54	15 00			20 13	20 18		20 43	20 48	20 54
Queenstown Rd.(Battersea)	d			13 51	13 57		14 03			14 21				14 51	14 57	15 03				20 21			20 51	20 57
Clapham Junction 10	d	13 35	13 49	13 54	14 00		14 06		14 19	14 24		14 35	14 49	14 54	15 00	15 06			20 19	20 24		20 49	20 54	21 00
Wandsworth Town	d			13 57	14 03		14 09			14 27				14 57	15 03	15 09				20 27			20 57	21 03
Putney	d	13 39	13 53	14 00	14 06		14 12		14 23	14 30		14 39	14 53	15 00	15 06	15 12			20 23	20 30		20 53	21 00	21 06
Barnes	d			14 03	14 09		14 15			14 33				15 03	15 09	15 15				20 33			21 03	21 09
Barnes Bridge	d				14 11										15 11									21 11
Chiswick	d				14 13										15 13									21 13
Kew Bridge	d				14 16										15 16									21 16
Brentford	d				14 19										15 19									21 19
Syon Lane	d				14 21										15 21									21 21
Isleworth	d				14 23										15 23									21 23
Hounslow	d				14 27										15 27									21 27
Mortlake	d			14 05			14 17			14 35				15 05		15 17				20 35			21 05	
North Sheen	d			14 07			14 19			14 37				15 07		15 19				20 37			21 07	
Richmond ⊖	d	13 45	13 59	14 10			14 22		14 29	14 40		14 45	14 59	15 10		15 22			20 29	20 40		20 59	21 10	
St Margarets	d			14 12			14 24			14 42				15 12		15 24				20 42			21 12	
Twickenham	a	13 48	14 02	14 14			14 26		14 32	14 44		14 48	15 02	15 14		15 26			20 32	20 44		21 02	21 14	
	d	13 49	14 03	14 15			14 27		14 33	14 45		14 49	15 03	15 15		15 27			20 33	20 45		21 03	21 15	
Strawberry Hill	d						14 30			14 49						15 30				20 49				
Fulwell	a																							
Teddington	a						14 33			14 52						15 33				20 52				
Hampton Wick	a						14 36			14 57						15 36				20 57				
Kingston	a						14 38			14 59						15 38				20 59				
Whitton	d	13 52		14 18								14 52		15 18			and at						21 18	
Feltham	d	13 56	14 09	14 22	14 33				14 39			14 56	15 09	15 22	15 33		the same		20 39			21 09	21 22	21 33
Ashford (Surrey)	d	14 00		14 26	14 37							15 00		15 26	15 37								21 26	21 37
Staines	d	14 04	14 15	14 30	14 41				14 45			15 04	15 15	15 30	15 41		minutes		20 45			21 15	21 30	21 41
Wraysbury	d			14 34										15 34			past						21 34	
Sunnymeads	d			14 37										15 37									21 37	
Datchet	d	14 12		14 40								15 12		15 40			each						21 40	
Windsor & Eton Riverside	a	14 18		14 46								15 18		15 46									21 46	
Egham	d		14 20		14 45				14 50				15 20		15 45		hour until		20 50			21 20		21 45
Virginia Water	a		14 24		14 49				14 54				15 24		15 49				20 54			21 24		21 49
	d		14 24		14 49				14 54				15 24		15 49				20 54			21 24		21 49
Chertsey §	d				14 55										15 55									21 55
Addlestone §	d				14 58										15 58									21 58
Weybridge	a																							
Byfleet & New Haw	d				15 02										16 02									22 02
West Byfleet	d				15 05										16 05									22 05
Woking	a				15 10										16 10									22 10
Longcross	d																							
Sunningdale	d		14 29						14 59				15 29						20 59			21 29		
Ascot 3	d		14 34						15 04		15 13		15 34						21 04		21 13	21 34		
Bagshot	d										15 19										21 19			
Camberley	a										15 25										21 25			
	d										15 25										21 25			
Frimley	d										15 29										21 29			
Ash Vale	d										15 36										21 36			
Aldershot	a										15 41										21 41			
	d										15 48										21 48			
Ash 3	d										15 55										21 55			
Wanborough	d										15 58										21 58			
Guildford	a										16 05										22 05			
Martins Heron	d		14 38						15 08				15 38						21 08			21 38		
Bracknell	d		14 41						15 11				15 41						21 11			21 41		
Wokingham	d		14 48						15 18				15 48						21 18			21 48		
Winnersh	d		14 51						15 21				15 51						21 21			21 51		
Winnersh Triangle	d		14 53						15 23				15 53						21 23			21 53		
Earley	d		14 56						15 26				15 56						21 26			21 56		
Reading 7	a		15 04						15 34				16 04						21 34			22 04		

For general notes see front of timetable
For details of catering facilities see Directory of Train Operators

§ Passengers to/from London may travel via Weybridge. See Table 155.

A To London Waterloo (Table 152)

Table 149

Sundays

from 28 September

London → Hounslow, Richmond, Kingston, Windsor, Weybridge, Ascot, Guildford and Reading

Network Diagram - see first page of Table 148

		SW	SW 1	SW	SW 1	SW 1	SW	SW	SW	SW 1	SW	SW 1	SW 1	SW	SW	SW	SW 1	SW	SW 1	SW
				A							A	B								
London Waterloo 15 ⊖	d	20 56	21 09	21 14		21 39	21 44	21 50	21 56	22 09	22 14		22 39	22 44	22 50	22 56	23 09	23 14	23 39	23 44
Vauxhall ⊖	d	21 00	21 13	21 18		21 43	21 48	21 54	22 00	22 13	22 18		22 43	22 48	22 54	23 00	23 13	23 18	23 43	23 48
Queenstown Rd.(Battersea)	d	21 03		21 21			21 51	21 57	22 03		22 21			22 51	22 57	23 03		23 21		23 51
Clapham Junction 10	d	21 06	21 19	21 24		21 49	21 54	22 00	22 06	22 19	22 24		22 49	22 54	23 00	23 06	23 19	23 24	23 49	23 54
Wandsworth Town	d	21 09		21 27			21 57	22 03	22 09		22 27			22 57	23 03	23 09		23 27		23 57
Putney	d	21 12	21 23	21 30		21 53	22 00	22 06	22 12	22 23	22 30		22 53	23 00	23 06	23 12	23 23	23 30	23 53	23 59
Barnes	d	21 15		21 33			22 03	22 09	22 15		22 33			23 03	23 09	23 15		23 33		00 03
Barnes Bridge	d							22 11							23 11					
Chiswick	d							22 13							23 13					
Kew Bridge	d							22 16							23 16					
Brentford	d							22 19							23 19					
Syon Lane	d							22 21							23 21					
Isleworth	d							22 23							23 23					
Hounslow	d							22 27							23 27					
Mortlake	d	21 17		21 35			22 05		22 17		22 35			23 05		23 17		23 35		00 05
North Sheen	d	21 19		21 37			22 07		22 19		22 37			23 07		23 19		23 37		00 07
Richmond ⊖	d	21 22	21 29	21 40		21 59	22 10		22 22	22 29	22 40		22 59	23 10		23 22	23 29	23 40	23 59	00 10
St Margarets	d	21 24		21 42			22 12		22 24		22 42			23 12		23 24		23 42		00 12
Twickenham	a	21 26	21 32	21 44		22 02	22 14		22 26	22 32	22 44		23 02	23 14		23 26	23 32	23 44	00 02	00 14
	d	21 27	21 33	21 45		22 03	22 15		22 27	22 33	22 45		23 03	23 15		23 27	23 33	23 45	00 03	00 15
Strawberry Hill	d	21 30		21 49					22 30		22 49					23 30		23 48		
Fulwell	a																			
Teddington	a	21 33		21 52					22 33		22 52					23 33		23 51		
Hampton Wick	a	21 36		21 57					22 36		22 57					23 36		23 54		
Kingston	a	21 38		21 59					22 38		22 59					23 38		23 56		
Whitton	d						22 18							23 18						00 18
Feltham	d		21 39			22 09	22 22	22 33		22 39			23 09	23 22	23 33		23 39		00 09	00 22
Ashford (Surrey)	d						22 26	22 37						23 26	23 37					00 26
Staines	d		21 45			22 15	22 30	22 41		22 45			23 15	23 30	23 41		23 45		00 15	00a30
Wraysbury	d						22 34							23 34						
Sunnymeads	d						22 37							23 37						
Datchet	d						22 40							23 40						
Windsor & Eton Riverside	a						22 46							23 46						
Egham	d		21 50			22 20		22 45		22 50			23 20		23 45		23 50		00 20	
Virginia Water	a		21 54			22 24		22 49		22 54			23 24		23 49		23 54		00 24	
	d		21 54			22 24		22 49		22 54			23 24		23 49		23 54		00 24	
Chertsey §	d							22 55							23 55					
Addlestone §	d							22 58							23 58					
Weybridge	a																			
Byfleet & New Haw	d							23 02							00 02					
West Byfleet	d							23 05							00 05					
Woking	a							23 10							00 10					
Longcross	d																			
Sunningdale	d		21 59			22 29				22 59			23 29				23 59		00 29	
Ascot 3	d		22 04		22 13	22 34				23 04		23 13	23 34				00 04		00 34	
Bagshot	d				22 19							23 19								
Camberley	a				22 25							23 25								
	d				22 25							23 25								
Frimley	d				22 29							23 29								
Ash Vale	d				22 36							23 36								
Aldershot	a				22 41							23 41								
	d				22 48															
Ash 3	d				22 55															
Wanborough	d				22 58															
Guildford	a				23 05															
Martins Heron	d		22 08			22 38				23 08			23 38				00 08		00 38	
Bracknell	d		22 11			22 41				23 11			23 41				00 11		00 41	
Wokingham	d		22 18			22 48				23 20			23 48				00 18		00 48	
Winnersh	d		22 21			22 51				23 24			23 51				00 21		00 51	
Winnersh Triangle	d		22 23			22 53				23 26			23 53				00 23		00 53	
Earley	d		22 26			22 56				23 28			23 56				00 26		00 56	
Reading 7	a		22 34			23 04				23 36			00 04				00 34		01 04	

For general notes see front of timetable
For details of catering facilities see Directory of Train Operators

§ Passengers to/from London may travel via Weybridge. See Table 155.

A To London Waterloo (Table 152)
B To Farnham (Table 155)

Mondays to Fridays

until 26 September

For details of Bank Holiday service alterations, please see first page of this Table

Reading, Guildford, Ascot, Weybridge, Windsor, Kingston, Richmond and Hounslow → London

Network Diagram - see first page of Table 148

Miles	Miles	Miles	Miles			SW MO	SW MO	SW MO 1	SW MX A	SW MX A	SW MX 1	SW A	SW	SW	SW B	SW	SW	SW	SW	SW	SW	SW 1	SW		SW
—	—	0	—	**Reading** 7	d			22p54			23p12											05 42			
—	—	3	—	Earley	d			22p59			23p17											05 47			
—	—	4¼	—	Winnersh Triangle	d			23p01			23p19											05 49			
—	—	4¾	—	Winnersh	d			23p03			23p21											05 51			
—	—	6¾	—	**Wokingham**	d			23p08			23p26											05 56			
—	—	11¼	—	Bracknell	d			23p14			23p32											06 02			
—	—	12¼	—	Martins Heron	d			23p17			23p35											06 05			
—	0	—	—	**Guildford**	d																				
—	4¼	—	—	Wanborough	d																				
—	6¼	—	—	Ash 3	d																				
—	9	—	—	**Aldershot**	a																				
—	—	—	—		d																				
—	11½	—	—	Ash Vale	d																				
—	14¾	—	—	Frimley	d																				
—	17	—	—	Camberley	a																				
—	—	—	—		d																				
—	20¼	—	—	Bagshot	d																				
—	23½	14½	—	**Ascot** 3	d			23p22			23p40											06 10			
—	—	16½	—	Sunningdale	d			23p25			23p43											06 13			
—	—	18¼	—	Longcross	d																				
0	—	—	—	Woking	d		22p52												05 25						
2½	—	—	—	West Byfleet	d		22p56												05 30						
3¾	—	—	—	Byfleet & New Haw	d		23p00												05 33						
5¼	—	—	—	**Weybridge**	d																				
7	—	—	—	Addlestone §	d		23p04												05 37						
8½	—	—	—	Chertsey §	d		23p07												05 40						
11	—	20¼	—	Virginia Water	a		23p12	23p30			23p49								05 45			06 19			
—	—	—	—		d		23p12	23p30			23p49								05 54			06 19			
—	—	22½	—	Egham	d		23p16	23p34			23p53								05 57			06 23			
—	—	—	0	**Windsor & Eton Riverside**	d	23p01														05 53					
—	—	—	2	Datchet	d	23p04														05 56					
—	—	—	3	Sunnymeads	d	23p07														05 59					
—	—	—	4¼	Wraysbury	d	23p10														06 02					
—	—	24½	6¾	**Staines**	d	23p16	23p21	23p39			23p59		04 58			05 38			06 03	06 08		06 29			
—	—	26	—	Ashford (Surrey)	d	23p19	23p24						05 01			05 41			06 06	06 11					
—	—	28¾	—	Feltham	d	23p24	23p29	23p46			00 05		05 06			05 46			06 11	06 16		06 35			
—	—	31	—	Whitton	d	23p28							05 10			05 50				06 20			06 20		
0	—	—	—	**Kingston**	d				23p29	23p55		01 17						05 59							06 29
½	—	—	—	Hampton Wick	d				23p31	23p57		01s22						06 01							06 31
1¾	—	—	—	Teddington	d				23p35	23p59		01s25						06 05							06 35
2¾	—	—	—	Fulwell	d										05 36										
3	—	—	—	Strawberry Hill	d				23p38	00 03		01a28			05 38			06 08							06 38
4	—	32¼	—	Twickenham	a	23p31		23p51	23p42	00 07	00 10		05 13		05 42	05 53		06 12		06 23		06 40			06 42
—	—	—	—		d	23p32		23p51	23p43		00 11		05 13		05 43	05 53		06 13		06 23		06 41			06 43
4½	—	32¾	—	St Margarets	d	23p34			23p45				05 15		05 45			06 15							06 45
5½	—	33¾	—	**Richmond**	⊖ d	23p37		23p56	23p49		00 15		05 19		05 49	05 58		06 19		06 28		06 45			06 49
6¼	—	34½	—	North Sheen	d	23p39			23p51				05 21		05 51			06 21							06 51
7	—	35¼	—	Mortlake	d	23p42			23p53				05 23		05 53			06 23							06 53
—	0	—	—	**Hounslow**	d		23p35							05 31			06 01		06 16				06 31		
—	—	—	—	Isleworth	d		23p38							05 34			06 04		06 19				06 34		
—	2¼	—	—	Syon Lane	d		23p40							05 36			06 06		06 21		←		06 36		
—	3	—	—	Brentford	d		23p42							05 39			06 09		06 24		06 24		06 39		
—	4	—	—	Kew Bridge	d		23p45							05 41			06 11		→		06 26		06 41		
—	5	—	—	Chiswick	d		23p47							05 44			06 14				06 29		06 44		
—	6	—	—	Barnes Bridge	d		23p50							05 46			06 16				06 31		06 46		
8¼	6½	36½	—	Barnes	d	23p45	23p53		23p56				05 26	05 48	05 56		06 19	06 26			06 34		06 49		06 56
9½	—	37¾	—	Putney	d	23p48	23p56	00 02	23p59				05 29	05 51	05 59	06 04	06 22	06 29		06 34	06 37	06 52	06 52		06 59
10½	—	38¾	—	Wandsworth Town	d	23p51	23p59		00 02				05 32	05 54	06 02		06 25	06 32			06 40		06 55		07 02
11¼	—	39¾	—	**Clapham Junction** 10	d	23p54	00 02	00 07	00 05		00 24		05 35	05 57	06 05	06 09	06 28	06 35		06 39	06 43	06 56	06 58		07 05
12½	—	41¼	—	Queenstown Rd.(Battersea)	d	23p57	00 05		00 08				05 38	06 00	06 08		06 31	06 38			06 46		07 01		07 08
14	—	42½	—	Vauxhall	⊖ d	00 01	00 08	00 12	00 12				05 42	06 04	06 12	06 15	06 35	06 42		06 45	06 50		07 05		07 12
15¼	—	43½	—	**London Waterloo** 15	⊖ a	00 05	00 13	00 17	00 16		00 32		05 46	06 08	06 16	06 19	06 39	06 46		06 49	06 56	07 07	07 11		07 18

For general notes see front of timetable
For details of catering facilities see Directory of Train Operators

§ Passengers to/from London may travel via Weybridge. See Table 155.

A From London Waterloo (Table 152)

B From Shepperton (Table 152)

For details of Bank Holiday service alterations, please see first page of this Table

Reading, Guildford, Ascot, Weybridge, Windsor, Kingston, Richmond and Hounslow → London

Network Diagram - see first page of Table 148

Station		SW	SW	SW 1	SW	SW	SW 1	SW A	SW	SW B	SW	SW	SW C	SW 1	SW 1	SW C	SW 1	SW A	SW		SW B	SW	SW	SW C	SW 1
Reading 7	d						06 12										06 42								
Earley	d						06 17										06 47								
Winnersh Triangle	d						06 19										06 49								
Winnersh	d						06 21										06 51								
Wokingham	d						06 26										06 56								
Bracknell	d						06 32										07 02								
Martins Heron	d						06 35										07 05								
Guildford	d														06 30										
Wanborough	d														06 36										
Ash 3	d														06 40										
Aldershot	a														06 47										
	d			06 00										06 30											07 00
Ash Vale	d			06 04										06 34											07 04
Frimley	d			06 10										06 40											07 10
Camberley	a			06 14										06 44											07 14
	d			06 18										06 47											07 17
Bagshot	d			06 23										06 52											07 22
Ascot 3	d			06a30			06 40							06 59			07 10								07 29
Sunningdale	d						06 43							07 02			07 13								07 32
Longcross	d																								
Woking	d																								
West Byfleet	d																								
Byfleet & New Haw	d																								
Weybridge	d								06 33										07 03						
Addlestone §	d								06 37										07 07						
Chertsey §	d								06 40										07 10						
Virginia Water	a						06 49		06 45					07 08			07 19		07 15						07 38
	d						06 49		06 54					07 08			07 19		07 24						07 38
Egham	d						06 53		06 57					07 12			07 23		07 27						07 42
Windsor & Eton Riverside	d		06 23								06 53											07 23			
Datchet	d		06 26								06 56											07 26			
Sunnymeads	d		06 29								06 59											07 29			
Wraysbury	d		06 32								07 02											07 32			
Staines	d	06 33	06 38				06 59		07 03		07 08			07 18			07 29		07 33			07 38			07 48
Ashford (Surrey)	d	06 36	06 41						07 06		07 11			07 21					07 36			07 41			07 51
Feltham	d	06 41	06 46				07 05		07 11		07 16			07 26			07 35		07 41			07 46			07 56
Whitton	d		06 50			06 53		06 50			07 20			07 30				07 20				07 50			08 00
Kingston	d									06 59											07 29				
Hampton Wick	d									07 01											07 31				
Teddington	d									07 05											07 35				
Fulwell	d												07 12											07 42	
Strawberry Hill	d									07 08			07 14								07 38			07 44	
Twickenham	a		06 53			06 56	07 10			07 12	07 23		07 18	07 33			07 40				07 42	07 53		07 48	08 03
	d		06 53			06 58	07 11			07 13	07 23		07 27	07 33			07 41				07 43	07 53		07 57	08 03
St Margarets	d					07 00				07 15			07 29								07 45			07 59	
Richmond	⊖ d		06 58			07 04	07 15			07 19	07 28		07 32	07 38			07 45				07 49	07 58		08 02	08 08
North Sheen	d					07 06				07 21			07 34								07 51			08 04	
Mortlake	d					07 08				07 23			07 37								07 53			08 07	
Hounslow	d	06 46						07 01	07 16									07 31	07 46						
Isleworth	d	06 49						07 04	07 19									07 34	07 49						
Syon Lane	d	06 51			←			07 06	07 21			←						07 36	07 51				←		
Brentford	d	06 54			06 54			07 09	07 24			07 24						07 39	07 54				07 54		
Kew Bridge	d	→			06 56			07 11	→			07 26						07 41	→				07 56		
Chiswick	d				06 59			07 14				07 29						07 44					07 59		
Barnes Bridge	d				07 01			07 16				07 31				←		07 46					08 01		
Barnes	d				07 04	07 11		07 19		07 26		07 34	07 40			07 40		07 49			07 56		08 04	08 10	
Putney	d		07 04		07 07	07 14	07 22	07 22		07 29	07 34	07 37	→			07 43		07 52			07 59	08 04	08 07	→	
Wandsworth Town	d				07 10	07 17		07 25		07 32		07 40				07 46		07 55			08 02		08 10		
Clapham Junction 10	d		07 09		07 13	07 20	07 26	07 28		07 35	07 39	07 43		07 47		07 49	07 54	07 58			08 05	08 09	08 13		08 17
Queenstown Rd.(Battersea)	d				07 16	07 23		07 31		07 38		07 46				07 52		08 01			08 08		08 16		
Vauxhall	⊖ d		07 15		07 20	07 27		07 35		07 42	07 45	07 50		07 53		07 56		08 05			08 12	08 15	08 20		08 23
London Waterloo 15	⊖ a		07 21		07 28	07 34	07 37	07 43		07 48	07 51	07 58		07 59		08 04	08 06	08 11			08 18	08 21	08 28		08 29

For general notes see front of timetable
For details of catering facilities see Directory of Train Operators

§ Passengers to/from London may travel via Weybridge. See Table 155.

A From London Waterloo.
B From London Waterloo (Table 152)
C From Shepperton (Table 152)

For details of Bank Holiday service alterations, please see first page of this Table

Reading, Guildford, Ascot, Weybridge, Windsor, Kingston, Richmond and Hounslow → London

Network Diagram - see first page of Table 148

		SW	SW	SW	SW	SW	SW	SW	SW	SW	SW	SW	SW	SW	SW	SW		SW	SW	SW	SW	SW	SW	SW	SW
		1		1				1					1		1								1	1	
			A		B		C		C			A		A		B		C				B			B
Reading 7	d			07 12				07 24							07 42									08 12	
Earley	d			07 17											07 47									08 17	
Winnersh Triangle	d			07 19											07 49									08 19	
Winnersh	d			07 21											07 51									08 21	
Wokingham	d			07 26				07 33							07 56									08 26	
Bracknell	d			07 32				07 39							08 02									08 32	
Martins Heron	d			07 35				07 42							08 05									08 35	
Guildford	d	07 00																					07 30		
Wanborough	d	07 06																					07 36		
Ash 3	d	07 10																					07 40		
Aldershot	a	07 17																					07 47		
	d												07 30										08 00		
Ash Vale	d												07 34										08 04		
Frimley	d												07 40										08 10		
Camberley	a												07 44										08 14		
	d												07 47										08 18		
Bagshot	d												07 52										08 23		
Ascot 3	d			07 40				07 47					07 59		08 10								08a30	08 40	
Sunningdale	d			07 43				07 50					08 02		08 13									08 43	
Longcross	d														08 16									08 46	
Woking	d																								
West Byfleet	d																								
Byfleet & New Haw	d																								
Weybridge	d					07 33													08 03						
Addlestone §	d					07 37													08 07						
Chertsey §	d					07 40													08 10						
Virginia Water	a					07 45		07 55					08 08		08 19				08 15					08 49	
	d					07 51		07 55					08 08		08 19				08 24					08 49	
Egham	d			07 50		07 54		07 58					08 12		08 23				08 27					08 53	
Windsor & Eton Riverside	d									07 53										08 23					
Datchet	d									07 56										08 26					
Sunnymeads	d									07 59										08 29					
Wraysbury	d									08 02										08 32					
Staines	d			07 56		08 00		08 04		08 08			08 18		08 29				08 33	08 38				08 59	
Ashford (Surrey)	d					08 03				08 11			08 21						08 36	08 41					
Feltham	d			08 03		08 08		08 12		08 16			08 26		08 35				08 41	08 46				09 05	
Whitton	d				07 50					08 20			08 30			08 20				08 50		08 53			08 50
Kingston	d						07 59											08 29							
Hampton Wick	d						08 01											08 31							
Teddington	d						08 05											08 35							
Fulwell	d											08 12													
Strawberry Hill	d						08 08					08 14						08 38							
Twickenham	a			08 09			08 12	08 17		08 23		08 18	08 33		08 40			08 42		08 53		08 56		09 10	
	d			08 09			08 13	08 18		08 23		08 27	08 33		08 41			08 43		08 53		08 58		09 11	
St Margarets	d						08 15					08 29						08 45				09 00			
Richmond	⊖ d			08 14			08 19	08 24		08 28		08 32	08 38		08 45			08 49		08 58		09 04		09 15	
North Sheen	d						08 21					08 34						08 51				09 06			
Mortlake	d						08 23					08 37						08 53				09 08			
Hounslow	d				08 01	08 16										08 31			08 46						09 01
Isleworth	d				08 04	08 19										08 34			08 49						09 04
Syon Lane	d				08 06	08 21										08 36			08 51		←				09 06
Brentford	d				08 09	08 24					←					08 39			08 54		08 54				09 09
Kew Bridge	d				08 11	08 26					08 26					08 41			→		08 56				09 11
Chiswick	d				08 14	→					08 29					08 44					08 59				09 14
Barnes Bridge	d		←		08 16				←		08 31			←		08 46					09 01				09 16
Barnes	d		08 10		08 19		08 26		08 26		08 34	08 40		08 40		08 49		08 56			09 04	09 11			09 19
Putney	d		08 13		08 22		→		08 29	08 34	08 37	→		08 43		08 52		08 59		09 04	09 07	09 14			09 22
Wandsworth Town	d		08 16		08 25				08 32		08 40			08 46		08 55		09 02			09 10	09 17			09 25
Clapham Junction 10	d		08 19	08 22	08 28			08 33	08 35	08 39	08 43		08 47	08 49	08 54	08 58		09 05		09 09	09 13	09 20		09 24	09 28
Queenstown Rd.(Battersea)	d		08 22		08 31				08 38		08 46			08 52		09 01		09 08			09 16	09 23			09 31
Vauxhall	⊖ d		08 26		08 35			08 38	08 42	08 45	08 50		08 53	08 56		09 05		09 12		09 15	09 20	09 27			09 35
London Waterloo 15	⊖ a		08 34	08 36	08 43			08 46	08 49	08 51	08 58		09 00	09 04	09 06	09 13		09 18		09 21	09 28	09 34		09 34	09 43

For general notes see front of timetable
For details of catering facilities see Directory of Train Operators

§ Passengers to/from London may travel via Weybridge. See Table 155.

A From Shepperton (Table 152)
B From London Waterloo.
C From London Waterloo (Table 152)

For details of Bank Holiday service alterations, please see first page of this Table

Reading, Guildford, Ascot, Weybridge, Windsor, Kingston, Richmond and Hounslow → London

Network Diagram - see first page of Table 148

Station		SW A	SW	SW	SW	SW B	SW 1	SW 1	SW B	SW A	SW	SW	SW	SW B	SW 1	SW 1	SW B	SW A	SW	SW	SW 1	SW	SW B	SW 1
Reading 7	d							08 42								09 12					09 25			
Earley	d							08 47								09 17					09 30			
Winnersh Triangle	d							08 49								09 19					09 32			
Winnersh	d							08 51								09 21					09 34			
Wokingham	d							08 56								09 26					09 39			
Bracknell	d							09 02								09 32					09 46			
Martins Heron	d							09 05								09 35					09 49			
Guildford	d						08 00								08 30									09 00
Wanborough	d						08 06								08 36									09 06
Ash 3	d						08 10								08 40									09 10
Aldershot	a						08 17								08 47									09 17
	d						08 30								09 00									09 30
Ash Vale	d						08 34								09 04									09 34
Frimley	d						08 40								09 10									09 40
Camberley	a						08 44								09 14									09 44
	d						08 48								09 18									09 48
Bagshot	d						08 53								09 23									09 53
Ascot 3	d						09a00	09 10							09a30	09 40					09 55			10a00
Sunningdale	d							09 13								09 43					09 58			
Longcross	d							09 16																
Woking	d																							
West Byfleet	d																							
Byfleet & New Haw	d																							
Weybridge	d		08 33								09 03								09 33					
Addlestone §	d		08 37								09 07								09 37					
Chertsey §	d		08 40								09 10								09 40					
Virginia Water	a		08 45					09 19			09 15					09 49			09 45		10 03			
	d		08 54					09 19			09 24					09 49			09 54		10 03			
Egham	d		08 57					09 23			09 27					09 53			09 57		10 06			
Windsor & Eton Riverside	d			08 53								09 23								09 53				
Datchet	d			08 56								09 26								09 56				
Sunnymeads	d			08 59								09 29								09 59				
Wraysbury	d			09 02								09 32								10 02				
Staines	d		09 03	09 08				09 29			09 33	09 38				09 59			10 03	10 08	10 14			
Ashford (Surrey)	d		09 06	09 11							09 36	09 41							10 06	10 11				
Feltham	d		09 11	09 16				09 35			09 41	09 46				10 05			10 11	10 16	10 20			
Whitton	d			09 20		09 23			09 20			09 50		09 53			09 50			10 20			10 26	
Kingston	d	08 59								09 29								09 59						
Hampton Wick	d	09 01								09 31								10 01						
Teddington	d	09 05								09 35								10 05						
Fulwell	d																							
Strawberry Hill	d	09 08								09 38								10 08						
Twickenham	a	09 12		09 23		09 26		09 40		09 42		09 53		09 56		10 10		10 12		10 23	10 27		10 28	
	d	09 13		09 23		09 28		09 41		09 43		09 53		09 58		10 11		10 13		10 23	10 27		10 28	
St Margarets	d	09 15				09 30				09 45				10 00				10 15					10 30	
Richmond	⊖ d	09 19		09 28		09 34		09 45		09 49		09 58		10 04		10 15		10 19		10 28	10 32		10 34	
North Sheen	d	09 21				09 36				09 51				10 06				10 21					10 36	
Mortlake	d	09 23				09 38				09 53				10 08				10 23					10 38	
Hounslow	d		09 16						09 31		09 46						10 01		10 16					
Isleworth	d		09 19						09 34		09 49						10 04		10 19					
Syon Lane	d		09 21		←				09 36		09 51		←				10 06		10 21			←		
Brentford	d		09 24 →		09 24				09 39		09 54 →		09 54				10 09		10 24					
Kew Bridge	d				09 26				09 41				09 56				10 11		10 26 →			10 26		
Chiswick	d				09 29				09 44				09 59				10 14					10 29		
Barnes Bridge	d				09 31				09 46				10 01				10 16					10 31		
Barnes	d	09 26			09 34	09 41			09 49	09 56			10 04	10 11			10 19	10 26				10 34	10 41	
Putney	d	09 29		09 34	09 37	09 44			09 52	09 59		10 04	10 07	10 14			10 22	10 29		10 34		10 37	10 44	
Wandsworth Town	d	09 32			09 40	09 47			09 55	10 02			10 10	10 17			10 25	10 32				10 40	10 47	
Clapham Junction 10	d	09 35		09 39	09 43	09 50		09 54	09 58	10 05		10 09	10 13	10 20		10 24	10 28	10 35		10 39	10 42	10 43	10 50	
Queenstown Rd.(Battersea)	d	09 38			09 46	09 53			10 01	10 08			10 16	10 23			10 31	10 38				10 46	10 53	
Vauxhall	⊖ d	09 42		09 45	09 50	09 57			10 05	10 12		10 15	10 20	10 27			10 35	10 42		10 45		10 50	10 57	
London Waterloo 15	⊖ a	09 48		09 51	09 58	10 02		10 04	10 11	10 16		10 19	10 26	10 32		10 34	10 41	10 46		10 49	10 53	10 56	11 02	

For general notes see front of timetable
For details of catering facilities see Directory of Train Operators

A From London Waterloo (Table 152)
B From London Waterloo.

§ Passengers to/from London may travel via Weybridge. See Table 155.

For details of Bank Holiday service alterations, please see first page of this Table

Reading, Guildford, Ascot, Weybridge, Windsor, Kingston, Richmond and Hounslow → London

Network Diagram - see first page of Table 148

		SW 1	SW	SW	SW	SW	SW 1	SW	SW	SW 1			SW 1	SW	SW	SW	SW	SW	SW	SW 1	SW 1	SW	SW	SW	SW
			A	B					A					A	B				A			A	B		
Reading 7	d	09 42					09 56						10 12								10 42				
Earley	d	09 47					10 01						10 17								10 47				
Winnersh Triangle	d	09 49					10 03						10 19								10 49				
Winnersh	d	09 51					10 05						10 21								10 51				
Wokingham	d	09 56					10 10						10 26								10 56				
Bracknell	d	10 02					10 16						10 32								11 02				
Martins Heron	d	10 05					10 19						10 35								11 05				
Guildford	d									09 30										10 00					
Wanborough	d									09 36										10 06					
Ash 3	d									09 40										10 10					
Aldershot	a									09 47										10 17					
	d									10 00										10 30					
Ash Vale	d									10 04										10 34					
Frimley	d									10 10										10 40					
Camberley	a									10 14										10 44					
	d									10 18										10 48					
Bagshot	d									10 23										10 53					
Ascot 3	d	10 10					10 25			10a30			10 40							11a00	11 10				
Sunningdale	d	10 13					10 28						10 43								11 13				
Longcross	d																								
Woking	d																								
West Byfleet	d																								
Byfleet & New Haw	d																								
Weybridge	d				10 03											10 33								11 03	
Addlestone §	d				10 07											10 37								11 07	
Chertsey §	d				10 10											10 40								11 10	
Virginia Water	a	10 19			10 15		10 33						10 49			10 45					11 19			11 15	
	d	10 19			10 24		10 33						10 49			10 54					11 19			11 24	
Egham	d	10 23			10 27		10 36						10 53			10 57					11 23			11 27	
Windsor & Eton Riverside	d					10 23											10 53								11 23
Datchet	d					10 26											10 56								11 26
Sunnymeads	d					10 29											10 59								11 29
Wraysbury	d					10 32											11 02								11 32
Staines	d	10 29			10 33	10 38	10 44						10 59			11 03	11 08				11 29			11 33	11 38
Ashford (Surrey)	d				10 36	10 41										11 06	11 11							11 36	11 41
Feltham	d	10 35			10 41	10 46	10 50						11 05			11 11	11 16				11 35			11 41	11 46
Whitton	d		10 20			10 50			10 56					10 50			11 20		11 23			11 20			11 50
Kingston	d			10 29											10 59								11 29		
Hampton Wick	d			10 31											11 01								11 31		
Teddington	d			10 35											11 05								11 35		
Fulwell	d																								
Strawberry Hill	d			10 38											11 08								11 38		
Twickenham	a	10 40		10 42		10 53	10 57		10 58				11 10		11 12		11 23		11 26		11 40		11 42		11 53
	d	10 41		10 43		10 53	10 57		10 58				11 11		11 13		11 23		11 28		11 41		11 43		11 53
St Margarets	d			10 45					11 00						11 15				11 30				11 45		
Richmond	⊖ d	10 45		10 49		10 58	11 02		11 04				11 15		11 19		11 28		11 34		11 45		11 49		11 58
North Sheen	d			10 51					11 06						11 21				11 36				11 51		
Mortlake	d			10 53					11 08						11 23				11 38				11 53		
Hounslow	d		10 31		10 46									11 01		11 16						11 31		11 46	
Isleworth	d		10 34		10 49									11 04		11 19						11 34		11 49	
Syon Lane	d		10 36		10 51									11 06		11 21		←				11 36		11 51	
Brentford	d		10 39		10 54			←						11 09		11 24		11 24				11 39		11 54	
Kew Bridge	d		10 41		10 56			10 56						11 11		→		11 26				11 41		→	
Chiswick	d		10 44		→			10 59						11 14				11 29				11 44			
Barnes Bridge	d		10 46					11 01						11 16				11 31				11 46			
Barnes	d		10 49	10 56				11 04	11 11					11 19	11 26			11 34	11 41			11 49	11 56		
Putney	d		10 52	10 59		11 04		11 07	11 14					11 22	11 29		11 34	11 37	11 44			11 52	11 59		12 04
Wandsworth Town	d		10 55	11 02				11 10	11 17					11 25	11 32			11 40	11 47			11 55	12 02		
Clapham Junction 10	d	10 54	10 58	11 05		11 09	11 12	11 13	11 20				11 24	11 29	11 35		11 39	11 43	11 50		11 54	11 58	12 05		12 09
Queenstown Rd.(Battersea)	d		11 01	11 08				11 16	11 23					11 31	11 38			11 46	11 53			12 01	12 08		
Vauxhall	⊖ d		11 05	11 12		11 15		11 20	11 27					11 35	11 42		11 45	11 50	11 57			12 05	12 12		12 15
London Waterloo 15	⊖ a	11 04	11 11	11 16		11 19	11 26	11 27	11 32				11 34	11 41	11 46		11 49	11 56	12 02		12 04	12 11	12 16		12 19

For general notes see front of timetable
For details of catering facilities see Directory of Train Operators

§ Passengers to/from London may travel via Weybridge. See Table 155.

A From London Waterloo.
B From London Waterloo (Table 152)

For details of Bank Holiday service alterations, please see first page of this Table

Reading, Guildford, Ascot, Weybridge, Windsor, Kingston, Richmond and Hounslow → London

Network Diagram - see first page of Table 148

		SW	SW	SW		SW	SW	SW	SW		SW	SW	GW	SW	SW	SW	SW	SW	SW	SW	SW	SW	SW	SW
				[1]		[1]						[1]	[1]			[1]							[1]	[1]
			A		B		A		C				D		E		A	C				A		
Reading [7]	d					15 12							15 28			15 42								16 12
Earley	d					15 17										15 47								16 17
Winnersh Triangle	d					15 19										15 49								16 19
Winnersh	d					15 21							15 35			15 51								16 21
Wokingham	d					15 26							15a38			15 56								16 26
Bracknell	d					15 32										16 02								16 32
Martins Heron	d					15 35										16 05								16 35
Guildford	d			10 30								15 00											15 30	
Wanborough	d			10 36								15 06											15 36	
Ash [3]	d			10 40								15 10											15 40	
Aldershot	a			10 47								15 17											15 47	
	d			11 00								15 30											16 00	
Ash Vale	d			11 04								15 34											16 04	
Frimley	d			11 10								15 40											16 10	
Camberley	a			11 14								15 44											16 14	
	d			11 18								15 48											16 18	
Bagshot	d			11 23								15 53											16 23	
Ascot [3]	d			11a30		15 40						16a00				16 10							16a30	16 40
Sunningdale	d					15 43										16 13								16 43
Longcross	d																							
Woking	d																							
West Byfleet	d																							
Byfleet & New Haw	d																							
Weybridge	d							15 33											16 03					
Addlestone §	d				and at			15 37											16 07					
Chertsey §	d							15 40											16 10					
Virginia Water	a				the same	15 49		15 45								16 19			16 15					16 49
	d				minutes	15 49		15 54								16 19			16 24					16 49
Egham	d					15 53		15 57								16 23			16 27					16 53
Windsor & Eton Riverside	d				past						15 53									16 23				
Datchet	d										15 56									16 26				
Sunnymeads	d				each						15 59									16 29				
Wraysbury	d				hour until						16 02									16 32				
Staines	d					15 59		16 03			16 08					16 29			16 33	16 38				16 59
Ashford (Surrey)	d							16 06			16 11								16 36	16 41				
Feltham	d					16 05		16 11			16 16					16 35			16 41	16 46				17 05
Whitton	d		11 53				15 50				16 20				16 23		16 20			16 50		16 53		
Kingston	d								15 59									16 29						
Hampton Wick	d								16 01									16 31						
Teddington	d								16 05									16 35						
Fulwell	d																							
Strawberry Hill	d								16 08									16 38						
Twickenham	a		11 56			16 10			16 12		16 23				16 26	16 40		16 42		16 53		16 56		17 10
	d		11 58			16 11			16 13		16 23				16 28	16 41		16 43		16 53		16 58		17 11
St Margarets	d		12 00						16 15						16 30			16 45				17 00		
Richmond	⊖ d		12 04			16 15			16 19		16 28				16 34	16 45		16 49		16 58		17 04		17 15
North Sheen	d		12 06						16 21						16 36			16 51				17 06		
Mortlake	d		12 08						16 23						16 38			16 53				17 08		
Hounslow	d						16 01	16 16									16 31		16 46					
Isleworth	d						16 04	16 19									16 34		16 49					
Syon Lane	d	←					16 06	16 21						←			16 36		16 51		←			
Brentford	d	11 54					16 09	16 24						16 24			16 39		16 54		16 54			
Kew Bridge	d	11 56					16 11	→						16 26			16 41		→		16 56			
Chiswick	d	11 59					16 14							16 29			16 44				16 59			
Barnes Bridge	d	12 01					16 16							16 31			16 46				17 01			
Barnes	d	12 04	12 11				16 19		16 26					16 34	16 41		16 49	16 56			17 04	17 11		
Putney	d	12 07	12 14				16 22		16 29		16 34			16 37	16 44		16 52	16 59		17 04	17 07	17 14		
Wandsworth Town	d	12 10	12 17				16 25		16 32					16 40	16 47		16 55	17 02			17 10	17 17		
Clapham Junction [10]	d	12 13	12 20			16 24	16 28		16 35		16 39			16 43	16 50	16 54	16 58	17 05		17 09	17 13	17 20		17 24
Queenstown Rd.(Battersea)	d	12 16	12 23				16 31		16 38					16 46	16 53		17 01	17 08			17 16	17 23		
Vauxhall	⊖ d	12 20	12 27				16 35		16 42		16 45			16 50	16 57		17 05	17 12		17 15	17 20	17 27		
London Waterloo [15]	⊖ a	12 26	12 32			16 34	16 41		16 49		16 49			16 54	17 02	17 04	17 11	17 19		17 19	17 24	17 32		17 34

For general notes see front of timetable
For details of catering facilities see Directory of Train Operators

§ Passengers to/from London may travel via Weybridge. See Table 155.

A From London Waterloo.
B 1242 from Reading calls at Longcross 1316.
C From London Waterloo (Table 152)
D To Gatwick Airport (Table 148)
E From London Waterloo. Also stops at Queenstown Rd.(Battersea) 1653

For details of Bank Holiday service alterations, please see first page of this Table

Reading, Guildford, Ascot, Weybridge, Windsor, Kingston, Richmond and Hounslow → London

Network Diagram - see first page of Table 148

	SW	SW	SW	SW	SW	SW		SW 1	SW 1	SW	SW	SW	SW	SW	SW	SW 1	SW 1	SW	SW	SW	SW	SW	SW 1	SW
	A	B				A				A	B				A			A	B					A
Reading 7 d									16 42								17 12						17 22	
Earley d									16 47								17 17						17 27	
Winnersh Triangle d									16 49								17 19						17 29	
Winnersh d									16 51								17 21						17 31	
Wokingham d									16 56								17 26						17 36	
Bracknell d									17 02								17 32						17 42	
Martins Heron d									17 05								17 35						17 45	
Guildford d								16 00								16 30								
Wanborough d								16 06								16 36								
Ash 3 d								16 10								16 40								
Aldershot a								16 17								16 47								
d								16 30								17 00								
Ash Vale d								16 34								17 04								
Frimley d								16 40								17 10								
Camberley a								16 44								17 14								
d								16 48								17 18								
Bagshot d								16 53								17 23								
Ascot 3 d								17a00	17 10							17a30	17 40						17b55	
Sunningdale d									17 13								17 43						17 58	
Longcross d									17 16															
Woking d																								
West Byfleet d																								
Byfleet & New Haw d																								
Weybridge d			16 33									17 03								17 37				
Addlestone § d			16 37									17 07								17 41				
Chertsey § d			16 40									17 10								17 44				
Virginia Water a			16 45						17 19			17 15					17 49			17 49			18 03	
d			16 54						17 19			17 24					17 49			17 54			18 03	
Egham d			16 57						17 23			17 27					17 53			17 57			18 06	
Windsor & Eton Riverside d				16 53									17 23								17 53			
Datchet d				16 56									17 26								17 56			
Sunnymeads d				16 59									17 29								17 59			
Wraysbury d				17 02									17 32								18 02			
Staines d			17 03	17 08					17 29			17 33	17 38				17 59			18 03	18 08		18 14	
Ashford (Surrey) d			17 06	17 11								17 36	17 41							18 06	18 11			
Feltham d			17 11	17 16					17 35			17 41	17 46				18 05			18 11	18 16		18 20	
Whitton d	16 50			17 20		17 23				17 20			17 50		17 53			17 50			18 20			18 23
Kingston d		16 59									17 29								17 59					
Hampton Wick d		17 01									17 31								18 01					
Teddington d		17 05									17 35								18 05					
Fulwell d																								
Strawberry Hill d		17 08									17 38								18 08					
Twickenham a		17 12		17 23		17 26			17 40		17 42		17 53		17 56		18 10		18 12		18 23			18 26
d		17 13		17 23		17 28			17 41		17 43		17 53		17 58		18 11		18 13		18 23			18 28
St Margarets d		17 15				17 30					17 45				18 00				18 15					18 30
Richmond ⊖ d		17 19		17 28		17 34			17 45		17 49		17 58		18 04		18 15		18 19		18 28			18 34
North Sheen d		17 21				17 36					17 51				18 06				18 21					18 36
Mortlake d		17 23				17 38					17 53				18 08				18 23					18 38
Hounslow d	17 01		17 16							17 31		17 46						18 01		18 16			18 26	
Isleworth d	17 04		17 19							17 34		17 49						18 04		18 19				
Syon Lane d	17 06		17 21		←					17 36		17 51		←				18 06		18 21		←		
Brentford d	17 09		17 24		17 24					17 39		17 54		17 54				18 09		18 24		18 24	18 31	
Kew Bridge d	17 11		→		17 26					17 41		→		17 56				18 11		→		18 26		
Chiswick d	17 14				17 29					17 44				17 59				18 14				18 29		
Barnes Bridge d	17 16				17 31					17 46				18 01				18 16				18 31		
Barnes d	17 19	17 26			17 34	17 41				17 49	17 56			18 04	18 11			18 19	18 26			18 34		18 41
Putney d	17 22	17 29		17 34	17 37	17 44				17 52	17 59		18 04	18 07	18 14			18 22	18 29		18 34	18 37	18 39	18 44
Wandsworth Town d	17 25	17 32			17 40	17 47				17 55	18 02			18 10	18 17			18 25	18 32			18 40		18 47
Clapham Junction 10 d	17 28	17 35		17 39	17 43	17 50			17 54	17 58	18 05		18 09	18 13	18 20		18 24	18 28	18 35		18 39	18 43	18 44	18 51
Queenstown Rd.(Battersea) d	17 31	17 38			17 46	17 53				18 01	18 08			18 16	18 23			18 31	18 38			18 46		18 53
Vauxhall ⊖ d	17 35	17 42		17 45	17 50	17 57				18 05	18 12		18 15	18 20	18 27			18 35	18 42		18 45	18 50		18 57
London Waterloo 15 ⊖ a	17 41	17 49		17 49	17 55	18 02			18 04	18 11	18 19		18 19	18 24	18 32		18 34	18 41	18 49		18 49	18 54	18 56	19 02

For general notes see front of timetable
For details of catering facilities see Directory of Train Operators

§ Passengers to/from London may travel via Weybridge. See Table 155.

A From London Waterloo.
B From London Waterloo (Table 152)
b Arr. 1749

For details of Bank Holiday service alterations, please see first page of this Table

Reading, Guildford, Ascot, Weybridge, Windsor, Kingston, Richmond and Hounslow → London

Network Diagram - see first page of Table 148

		SW 1	SW 1	SW		SW	SW	SW	SW	SW 1	SW	SW 1	SW	SW	SW	SW	SW	SW 1	SW	SW	SW 1	SW	SW		SW 1
				A		B					A			A	B					A		A			
Reading 7	d		17 42							17 52			18 12								18 42				18 52
Earley	d		17 47							17 57			18 17								18 47				18 57
Winnersh Triangle	d		17 49							17 59			18 19								18 49				18 59
Winnersh	d		17 51							18 01			18 21								18 51				19 01
Wokingham	d		17 56							18 06			18 26								18 56				19 06
Bracknell	d		18 02							18 12			18 32								19 02				19 12
Martins Heron	d		18 05							18 15			18 35								19 05				19 15
Guildford	d	17 00										17 30						18 00							
Wanborough	d	17 06										17 36						18 06							
Ash 3	d	17 10										17 40						18 10							
Aldershot	a	17 17										17 47						18 17							
	d	17 30										18 00						18 30							
Ash Vale	d	17 34										18 04						18 34							
Frimley	d	17 40										18 10						18 40							
Camberley	a	17 44										18 14						18 44							
	d	17 48										18 18						18 48							
Bagshot	d	17 53										18 23						18 53							
Ascot 3	d	18a00	18 10							18b25		18a30	18 40					19a00			19 10				19a19
Sunningdale	d		18 13							18 28			18 43								19 13				
Longcross	d		18 16										18 46								19 16				
Woking	d																								
West Byfleet	d																								
Byfleet & New Haw	d																								
Weybridge	d						18 07									18 37							19 07		
Addlestone §	d						18 11									18 41							19 11		
Chertsey §	d						18 14									18 44							19 14		
Virginia Water	a		18 19				18 19			18 33			18 49			18 49					19 19		19 19		
	d		18 19				18 24			18 33			18 49			18 54					19 19		19 24		
Egham	d		18 23				18 27			18 36			18 53			18 57					19 23		19 27		
Windsor & Eton Riverside	d							18 23									18 53								
Datchet	d							18 26									18 56								
Sunnymeads	d							18 29									18 59								
Wraysbury	d							18 32									19 02								
Staines	d		18 29				18 33	18 38		18 44			18 59			19 03	19 08				19 29		19 33		
Ashford (Surrey)	d						18 36	18 41								19 06	19 11						19 36		
Feltham	d		18 35				18 41	18 46		18 50			19 05			19 11	19 16				19 35		19 41		
Whitton	d			18 20				18 50			18 53			18 50			19 20			19 23		19 20			
Kingston	d					18 29									18 59										
Hampton Wick	d					18 31									19 01										
Teddington	d					18 35									19 05										
Fulwell	d																								
Strawberry Hill	d					18 38									19 08										
Twickenham	a		18 40			18 42		18 53			18 56		19 10		19 12		19 23			19 26	19 40				
	d		18 41			18 43		18 53			18 58		19 11		19 13		19 23			19 28	19 41				
St Margarets	d					18 45					19 00				19 15					19 30					
Richmond	⊖ d		18 45			18 49		18 58			19 04		19 15		19 19		19 28			19 34	19 45				
North Sheen	d					18 51					19 06				19 21					19 36					
Mortlake	d					18 53					19 08				19 23					19 38					
Hounslow	d			18 31			18 46			18 56				19 01		19 16						19 31	19 46		
Isleworth	d			18 34			18 49							19 04		19 19						19 34	19 49		
Syon Lane	d			18 36			18 51		←					19 06		19 21			←			19 36	19 51		
Brentford	d			18 39			18 54 →		18 54	19 01				19 09		19 24 →			19 24			19 39	19 54 →		
Kew Bridge	d			18 41					18 56					19 11					19 26			19 41			
Chiswick	d			18 44					18 59					19 14					19 29			19 44			
Barnes Bridge	d			18 46					19 01					19 16					19 31			19 46			
Barnes	d			18 49		18 56			19 04		19 11			19 19	19 26				19 34	19 41		19 49			
Putney	d			18 52		18 59		19 04	19 07	19 09	19 14			19 22	19 29		19 34		19 37	19 44		19 52			
Wandsworth Town	d			18 55		19 02			19 10		19 17			19 25	19 32				19 40	19 47		19 55			
Clapham Junction 10	d		18 54	18 58		19 05		19 09	19 13	19 14	19 20		19 24	19 28	19 35		19 39		19 43	19 50	19 54	19 58			
Queenstown Rd.(Battersea)	d			19 01		19 08			19 16		19 23			19 31	19 38				19 46	19 53		20 01			
Vauxhall	⊖ d			19 05		19 12		19 15	19 20		19 27			19 35	19 42		19 45		19 50	19 57		20 05			
London Waterloo 15	⊖ a		19 04	19 09		19 16		19 19	19 26	19 28	19 32		19 34	19 41	19 46		19 49		19 56	20 02	20 04	20 10			

For general notes see front of timetable
For details of catering facilities see Directory of Train Operators

§ Passengers to/from London may travel via Weybridge. See Table 155.

A From London Waterloo.
B From London Waterloo (Table 152)
b Arr. 1820

For details of Bank Holiday service alterations, please see first page of this Table

Reading, Guildford, Ascot, Weybridge, Windsor, Kingston, Richmond and Hounslow → London

Network Diagram - see first page of Table 148

Station		SW A	SW	SW	SW B	SW 1	SW 1	SW B	SW A	SW	SW	SW	SW B	SW 1	SW 1	SW B	SW A	SW	SW		SW 1	SW	SW B	SW 1	SW B
Reading 7	d						19 12								19 42									20 12	
Earley	d						19 17								19 47									20 17	
Winnersh Triangle	d						19 19								19 49									20 19	
Winnersh	d						19 21								19 51									20 21	
Wokingham	d						19 26								19 56									20 26	
Bracknell	d						19 32								20 02									20 32	
Martins Heron	d						19 35								20 05									20 35	
Guildford	d					18 30								19 00							19 30				
Wanborough	d					18 36								19 06							19 36				
Ash 3	d					18 40								19 10							19 40				
Aldershot	a					18 47								19 17							19 47				
	d					19 00								19 30							20 00				
Ash Vale	d					19 04								19 34							20 04				
Frimley	d					19 10								19 40							20 10				
Camberley	a					19 14								19 44							20 14				
	d					19 18								19 48							20 18				
Bagshot	d					19 23								19 53							20 23				
Ascot 3	d					19a30	19 40							20a00	20 10						20a30			20 40	
Sunningdale	d						19 43								20 13									20 43	
Longcross	d						19 46								20 16									20 46	
Woking	d																								
West Byfleet	d																								
Byfleet & New Haw	d																								
Weybridge	d									19 37								20 03							
Addlestone §	d									19 41								20 07							
Chertsey §	d									19 44								20 10							
Virginia Water	a						19 49			19 49					20 19			20 15						20 49	
	d						19 49			19 54					20 19			20 24						20 49	
Egham	d						19 53			19 57					20 23			20 27						20 53	
Windsor & Eton Riverside	d		19 23								19 53								20 23						
Datchet	d		19 26								19 56								20 26						
Sunnymeads	d		19 29								19 59								20 29						
Wraysbury	d		19 32								20 02								20 32						
Staines	d		19 38				19 59			20 03	20 08				20 29			20 33	20 38					20 59	
Ashford (Surrey)	d		19 41							20 06	20 11							20 36	20 41						
Feltham	d		19 46				20 05			20 11	20 16				20 35			20 41	20 46					21 05	
Whitton	d		19 50		19 53			19 50			20 20		20 23			20 20			20 50				20 53		20 50
Kingston	d	19 29							19 59								20 29								
Hampton Wick	d	19 31							20 01								20 31								
Teddington	d	19 35							20 05								20 35								
Fulwell	d																								
Strawberry Hill	d	19 38							20 08								20 38								
Twickenham	a	19 42	19 53		19 56		20 10		20 12		20 23		20 26		20 40		20 42		20 53				20 56	21 10	
	d	19 43	19 53		19 58		20 11		20 13		20 23		20 28		20 41		20 43		20 53				20 58	21 11	
St Margarets	d	19 45			20 00				20 15				20 30				20 45						21 00		
Richmond ⊖	d	19 49	19 58		20 04		20 15		20 19		20 28		20 34		20 45		20 49		20 58				21 04	21 15	
North Sheen	d	19 51			20 06				20 21				20 36				20 51						21 06		
Mortlake	d	19 53			20 08				20 23				20 38				20 53						21 08		
Hounslow	d							20 01		20 16						20 31		20 46							21 01
Isleworth	d							20 04		20 19						20 34		20 49							21 04
Syon Lane	d			←				20 06		20 21		←				20 36		20 51				←			21 06
Brentford	d			19 54				20 09		20 24		20 24				20 39		20 54				20 54			21 09
Kew Bridge	d			19 56				20 11		→		20 26				20 41		→				20 56			21 11
Chiswick	d			19 59				20 14				20 29				20 44						20 59			21 14
Barnes Bridge	d			20 01				20 16				20 31				20 46						21 01			21 16
Barnes	d	19 56		20 04	20 11			20 19	20 26			20 34	20 41			20 49	20 56					21 04	21 11		21 19
Putney	d	19 59	20 05	20 07	20 14			20 22	20 29		20 34	20 37	20 44			20 52	20 59		21 04			21 07	21 14		21 22
Wandsworth Town	d	20 02		20 10	20 17			20 25	20 32			20 40	20 47			20 55	21 02					21 10	21 17		21 25
Clapham Junction 10	d	20 05	20 09	20 13	20 20		20 24	20 28	20 35		20 39	20 43	20 50		20 54	20 58	21 05		21 09			21 13	21 20	21 24	21 28
Queenstown Rd.(Battersea)	d	20 08		20 16	20 23			20 31	20 38			20 46	20 53			21 01	21 08					21 16	21 23		21 31
Vauxhall ⊖	d	20 12	20 15	20 20	20 27			20 35	20 42		20 45	20 50	20 57			21 05	21 12		21 15			21 20	21 27		21 35
London Waterloo 15 ⊖	a	20 16	20 19	20 26	20 32		20 34	20 41	20 46		20 49	20 56	21 02		21 04	21 11	21 16		21 19			21 26	21 32	21 34	21 41

For general notes see front of timetable
For details of catering facilities see Directory of Train Operators

§ Passengers to/from London may travel via Weybridge. See Table 155.

A From London Waterloo (Table 152)
B From London Waterloo.

For details of Bank Holiday service alterations, please see first page of this Table

Reading, Guildford, Ascot, Weybridge, Windsor, Kingston, Richmond and Hounslow → London

Network Diagram - see first page of Table 148

		SW	SW A	SW	SW ■1	SW ■1	SW	SW B	SW ■1	SW B	SW A	SW	SW	SW	SW B	SW ■1		SW B	SW	SW A	SW	SW ■1	SW ■1	SW	SW B
Reading ■7	d								20 42							21 12									
Earley	d								20 47							21 17									
Winnersh Triangle	d								20 49							21 19									
Winnersh	d								20 51							21 21									
Wokingham	d								20 56							21 26									
Bracknell	d								21 02							21 32									
Martins Heron	d								21 05							21 35									
Guildford	d				20 00	20 30																21 00	21 30		
Wanborough	d				20 06	20 36																21 06	21 36		
Ash ■3	d				20 10	20 40																21 10	21 40		
Aldershot	a				20 17	20 47																21 17	21 47		
	d				20 30																	21 30			
Ash Vale	d				20 34																	21 34			
Frimley	d				20 40																	21 40			
Camberley	a				20 44																	21 44			
	d				20 48																	21 48			
Bagshot	d				20 53																	21 53			
Ascot ■3	d				21a00				21 10							21 40						22a00			
Sunningdale	d								21 13							21 43									
Longcross	d																								
Woking	d																								
West Byfleet	d																								
Byfleet & New Haw	d																								
Weybridge	d	20 33										21 03							21 33						
Addlestone §	d	20 37										21 07							21 37						
Chertsey §	d	20 40										21 10							21 40						
Virginia Water	a	20 45							21 19			21 15				21 49			21 45						
	d	20 54							21 19			21 24				21 49			21 54						
Egham	d	20 57							21 23			21 27				21 53			21 57						
Windsor & Eton Riverside	d			20 53									21 23								21 53				
Datchet	d			20 56									21 26								21 56				
Sunnymeads	d			20 59									21 29								21 59				
Wraysbury	d			21 02									21 32								22 02				
Staines	d	21 03		21 08					21 29			21 33	21 38			21 59			22 03		22 08				
Ashford (Surrey)	d	21 06		21 11								21 36	21 41						22 06		22 11				
Feltham	d	21 11		21 16					21 35			21 41	21 46			22 05			22 11		22 16				
Whitton	d			21 20				21 23		21 20			21 50		21 53			21 50			22 20				22 23
Kingston	d		20 59								21 29									21 59					
Hampton Wick	d		21 01								21 31									22 01					
Teddington	d		21 05								21 35									22 05					
Fulwell	d																								
Strawberry Hill	d		21 08								21 38									22 08					
Twickenham	a		21 12	21 23				21 26	21 40		21 42		21 53		21 56	22 10				22 12	22 23				22 26
	d		21 13	21 23				21 28	21 41		21 43		21 53		21 58	22 11				22 13	22 23				22 28
St Margarets	d		21 15					21 30			21 45				22 00					22 15					22 30
Richmond	⊖ d		21 19	21 28				21 34	21 45		21 49		21 58		22 04	22 15				22 19	22 28				22 34
North Sheen	d		21 21					21 36			21 51				22 06					22 21					22 36
Mortlake	d		21 23					21 38			21 53				22 08					22 23					22 38
Hounslow	d	21 16								21 31		21 46						22 01	22 16						
Isleworth	d	21 19								21 34		21 49						22 04	22 19						
Syon Lane	d	21 21					←			21 36		21 51		←				22 06	22 21					←	
Brentford	d	21 24					21 24			21 39		21 54		21 54				22 09	22 24					22 24	
Kew Bridge	d	→					21 26			21 41		→		21 56				22 11	→					22 26	
Chiswick	d						21 29			21 44				21 59				22 14						22 29	
Barnes Bridge	d						21 31			21 46				22 01				22 16						22 31	
Barnes	d		21 26				21 34	21 41		21 49	21 56			22 04	22 11			22 19		22 26				22 34	22 41
Putney	d		21 29	21 34			21 37	21 44		21 52	21 59		22 04	22 07	22 14			22 22		22 29	22 34			22 37	22 44
Wandsworth Town	d		21 32				21 40	21 47		21 55	22 02			22 10	22 17			22 25		22 32				22 40	22 47
Clapham Junction ■10	d		21 35	21 39			21 43	21 50	21 54	21 58	22 05		22 09	22 13	22 20	22 24		22 28		22 35	22 39			22 43	22 50
Queenstown Rd.(Battersea)	d		21 38				21 46	21 53		22 01	22 08			22 16	22 23			22 31		22 38				22 46	22 53
Vauxhall	⊖ d		21 42	21 45			21 50	21 57		22 05	22 12		22 15	22 20	22 27			22 35		22 42	22 45			22 50	22 57
London Waterloo ■15	⊖ a		21 46	21 49			21 56	22 02	22 04	22 11	22 16		22 19	22 26	22 32	22 34		22 41		22 46	22 49			22 56	23 01

For general notes see front of timetable
For details of catering facilities see Directory of Train Operators

§ Passengers to/from London may travel via Weybridge. See Table 155.

A From London Waterloo (Table 152)

B From London Waterloo.

For details of Bank Holiday service alterations, please see first page of this Table

Reading, Guildford, Ascot, Weybridge, Windsor, Kingston, Richmond and Hounslow → London

Network Diagram - see first page of Table 148

		SW 1	SW	SW	SW	SW	SW 1	SW	SW	SW 1	SW 1	SW	SW		SW 1	SW	SW	SW	SW	SW 1	SW	SW 1	SW 1		
			A						A							A			A						
Reading 7	d	21 42					22 12								22 42					23 12					
Earley	d	21 47					22 17								22 47					23 17					
Winnersh Triangle	d	21 49					22 19								22 49					23 19					
Winnersh	d	21 51					22 21								22 51					23 21					
Wokingham	d	21 56					22 26								22 56					23 26					
Bracknell	d	22 02					22 32								23 02					23 32					
Martins Heron	d	22 05					22 35								23 05					23 35					
Guildford	d									22 00	22 30											23 00	23 30		
Wanborough	d									22 06	22 36											23 06	23 36		
Ash 3	d									22 10	22 40											23 10	23 40		
Aldershot	a									22 17	22 47											23 17	23 47		
	d									22 30												23 30			
Ash Vale	d									22 34												23 34			
Frimley	d									22 40												23 40			
Camberley	a									22 44												23 44			
	d									22 48												23 48			
Bagshot	d									22 53												23 53			
Ascot 3	d	22 10					22 40			23a00					23 10					23 40		00a01			
Sunningdale	d	22 13					22 43								23 13					23 43					
Longcross	d																								
Woking	d																								
West Byfleet	d																								
Byfleet & New Haw	d																								
Weybridge	d			22 03				22 33									23 03				23 33				
Addlestone §	d			22 07				22 37									23 07				23 37				
Chertsey §	d			22 10				22 40									23 10				23 40				
Virginia Water	a	22 19		22 15			22 49	22 45							23 19		23 15			23 49	23 45				
	d	22 19		22 24			22 49	22 54							23 19		23 24			23 49	23 54				
Egham	d	22 23		22 27			22 53	22 57							23 23		23 27			23 53	23 57				
Windsor & Eton Riverside	d				22 23							22 53						23 23							
Datchet	d				22 26							22 56						23 26							
Sunnymeads	d				22 29							22 59						23 29							
Wraysbury	d				22 32							23 02						23 32							
Staines	d	22 29		22 33	22 38		22 59	23 03				23 08			23 29		23a32	23a37		23 59	00a02				
Ashford (Surrey)	d			22 36	22 41			23 06				23 11													
Feltham	d	22 35		22 41	22 46		23 05	23 11				23 16			23 35					00 05					
Whitton	d				22 50							23 20													
Kingston	d		22 29						22 59							23 29			23 55						
Hampton Wick	d		22 31						23 01							23 31			23 57						
Teddington	d		22 35						23 05							23 35			23 59						
Fulwell	d																								
Strawberry Hill	d		22 38						23 08							23 38			00 03						
Twickenham	a	22 40	22 42		22 53		23 10		23 12			23 23			23 40	23 42			00 07	00 10					
	d	22 41	22 43		22 53		23 11		23 13			23 23			23 41	23 43				00 11					
St Margarets	d		22 45						23 15							23 45									
Richmond	⊖ d	22 45	22 49		22 58		23 15		23 19			23 28			23 45	23 49				00 15					
North Sheen	d		22 51						23 21							23 51									
Mortlake	d		22 53						23 23							23 53									
Hounslow	d			22 46				23 16																	
Isleworth	d			22 49				23 19																	
Syon Lane	d			22 51		←		23 21					←												
Brentford	d			22 54		22 54		23 24					23 24												
Kew Bridge	d			→		22 56		→					23 26												
Chiswick	d					22 59							23 29												
Barnes Bridge	d					23 01							23 31												
Barnes	d		22 56			23 04			23 26				23 34			23 56									
Putney	d		22 59		23 04	23 07			23 29			23 34	23 37			23 59									
Wandsworth Town	d		23 02			23 10			23 32				23 40			00 02									
Clapham Junction 10	d	22 54	23 05		23 09	23 13	23 24		23 35			23 39	23 43		23 54	00 05				00 24					
Queenstown Rd.(Battersea)	d		23 08			23 16			23 38				23 46			00 08									
Vauxhall	⊖ d		23 12		23 15	23 20			23 42			23 45	23 50			00 12									
London Waterloo 15	⊖ a	23 04	23 16		23 19	23 26	23 34		23 46			23 49	23 56		00 03	00 16				00 32					

For general notes see front of timetable
For details of catering facilities see Directory of Train Operators

§ Passengers to/from London may travel via Weybridge. See Table 155.

A From London Waterloo (Table 152)

Table 149

Mondays to Fridays
from 29 September

Reading, Guildford, Ascot, Weybridge, Windsor, Kingston, Richmond and Hounslow → London

Network Diagram - see first page of Table 148

		SW MO	SW MO	SW MO [1]	SW MX	SW MX	SW MX [1]	SW	SW	SW	SW	SW	SW	SW		SW	SW	SW	SW [1]	SW	SW	SW	SW	SW [1]	SW
					A	A		A			B														
Reading 7	d			22p54			23p12												05 39						
Earley	d			22p59			23p17												05 44						
Winnersh Triangle	d			23p01			23p19												05 46						
Winnersh	d			23p03			23p21												05 48						
Wokingham	d			23p08			23p26												05 53						
Bracknell	d			23p14			23p32												05 59						
Martins Heron	d			23p17			23p35												06 02						
Guildford	d																								
Wanborough	d																								
Ash 3	d																								
Aldershot	a																								
	d																							06 00	
Ash Vale	d																							06 04	
Frimley	d																							06 10	
Camberley	a																							06 14	
	d																							06 18	
Bagshot	d																							06 23	
Ascot 3	d			23p22			23p40												06 07					06a30	
Sunningdale	d			23p25			23p43												06 10						
Longcross	d																								
Woking	d		22p52													05 25									
West Byfleet	d		22p56													05 30									
Byfleet & New Haw	d		23p00													05 33									
Weybridge	d																								
Addlestone §	d		23p04													05 37									
Chertsey §	d		23p07													05 40									
Virginia Water	a		23p12	23p30			23p49									05 45			06 19						
	d		23p12	23p30			23p49									05 54			06 19						
Egham	d		23p16	23p34			23p53									05 57			06 23						
Windsor & Eton Riverside	d	23p01															05 51						06 21		
Datchet	d	23p04															05 54						06 24		
Sunnymeads	d	23p07															05 57						06 27		
Wraysbury	d	23p10															06 00						06 30		
Staines	d	23p16	23p21	23p39			23p59		04 58		05 38					06 03	06 08		06 29			06 33	06 38		
Ashford (Surrey)	d	23p19	23p24						05 01		05 41					06 06	06 11					06 36	06 41		
Feltham	d	23p24	23p29	23p46			00 05		05 06		05 46					06 11	06 16		06 35			06 41	06 46		
Whitton	d	23p28							05 10		05 50						06 20			06 20			06 50		
Kingston	d				23p29	23p55		01 17						05 59							06 29				
Hampton Wick	d				23p31	23p57		01s22						06 01							06 31				
Teddington	d				23p35	23p59		01s25						06 05							06 35				
Fulwell	d										05 36														
Strawberry Hill	d				23p38	00 03		01a28			05 38			06 08							06 38				
Twickenham	a	23p31		23p51	23p42	00 07	00 10		05 13		05 42	05 53		06 12			06 23		06 40		06 42		06 53		
	d	23p32		23p51	23p43		00 11		05 13		05 43	05 53		06 13			06 23		06 41		06 43		06 53		
St Margarets	d	23p34			23p45				05 15		05 45			06 15							06 45				
Richmond	⊖ d	23p37		23p56	23p49		00 15		05 19		05 49	05 58		06 19			06 28		06 45		06 49		06 58		
North Sheen	d	23p39			23p51				05 21		05 51			06 21							06 51				
Mortlake	d	23p42			23p53				05 23		05 53			06 23							06 53				
Hounslow	d		23p35							05 31			06 01			06 16				06 31		06 46			
Isleworth	d		23p38							05 34			06 04			06 19				06 34		06 49			
Syon Lane	d		23p40							05 36			06 06			06 21		←		06 36		06 51			←
Brentford	d		23p42							05 39			06 09			06 24		06 24		06 39		06 54			06 54
Kew Bridge	d		23p45							05 41			06 11			→		06 26		06 41		→			06 56
Chiswick	d		23p47							05 44			06 14					06 29		06 44					06 59
Barnes Bridge	d		23p50							05 46			06 16					06 31		06 46					07 01
Barnes	d	23p45	23p53		23p56				05 26	05 48	05 56		06 19	06 26				06 34		06 49	06 56				07 04
Putney	d	23p48	23p56	00 02	23p59				05 29	05 51	05 59	06 04	06 22	06 29			06 34	06 37	06 52	06 52	06 59		07 04		07 07
Wandsworth Town	d	23p51	23p59		00 02				05 32	05 54	06 02		06 25	06 32				06 40		06 55	07 02				07 10
Clapham Junction 10	d	23p54	00 02	00 07	00 05		00 24		05 35	05 57	06 05	06 09	06 28	06 35			06 39	06 43	06 56	06 58	07 05		07 09		07 13
Queenstown Rd.(Battersea)	d	23p57	00 05		00 08				05 38	06 00	06 08		06 31	06 38				06 46		07 01	07 08				07 16
Vauxhall	⊖ d	00 01	00 08	00 12	00 12				05 42	06 04	06 12	06 15	06 35	06 42			06 45	06 50		07 05	07 12		07 15		07 20
London Waterloo 15	⊖ a	00 05	00 13	00 17	00 16		00 32		05 46	06 08	06 16	06 19	06 39	06 46			06 49	06 56	07 07	07 11	07 18		07 21		07 28

For general notes see front of timetable
For details of catering facilities see
Directory of Train Operators

§ Passengers to/from London may travel via Weybridge. See Table 155.

A From London Waterloo (Table 152)
B From Shepperton (Table 152)

Table 149

Mondays to Fridays

from 29 September

Reading, Guildford, Ascot, Weybridge, Windsor, Kingston, Richmond and Hounslow → London

Network Diagram - see first page of Table 148

Station		SW	SW	SW	SW	SW		SW	SW	SW	SW	SW	SW	SW	SW	SW	SW	SW	SW	SW		SW	SW	SW	SW
			1	A		B				C	1	1	C	1	A		B			C		1	1	C	1
Reading 7	d		06 09											06 39											07 09
Earley	d		06 14											06 44											07 14
Winnersh Triangle	d		06 16											06 46											07 16
Winnersh	d		06 18											06 48											07 18
Wokingham	d		06 23											06 53											07 23
Bracknell	d		06 29											06 59											07 29
Martins Heron	d		06 32											07 02											07 32
Guildford	d											06 30											07 00		
Wanborough	d											06 36											07 06		
Ash 3	d											06 40											07 10		
Aldershot	a											06 47											07 17		
	d										06 29											06 59			
Ash Vale	d										06 33											07 03			
Frimley	d										06 39											07 09			
Camberley	a										06 43											07 13			
	d										06 44											07 14			
Bagshot	d										06 49											07 19			
Ascot 3	d		06 37								06 56			07 07								07 26			07 37
Sunningdale	d		06 40								06 59			07 10								07 29			07 40
Longcross	d																								
Woking	d																								
West Byfleet	d																								
Byfleet & New Haw	d																								
Weybridge	d				06 33											07 03									
Addlestone §	d				06 37											07 07									
Chertsey §	d				06 40											07 10									
Virginia Water	a		06 49		06 45						07 08			07 19		07 15						07 38			
	d		06 49		06 54						07 08			07 19		07 24						07 38			
Egham	d		06 53		06 57						07 12			07 23		07 27						07 42			07 50
Windsor & Eton Riverside	d							06 51										07 21							
Datchet	d							06 54										07 24							
Sunnymeads	d							06 57										07 27							
Wraysbury	d							07 00										07 30							
Staines	d		06 59		07 03			07 08			07 18			07 29		07 33		07 38				07 48			07 56
Ashford (Surrey)	d				07 06			07 11			07 21					07 36		07 41				07 51			
Feltham	d		07 05		07 11			07 16			07 26			07 35		07 41		07 46				07 56			08 03
Whitton	d	06 53		06 50				07 20			07 30				07 20			07 50				08 00			
Kingston	d					06 59											07 29								
Hampton Wick	d					07 01											07 31								
Teddington	d					07 05											07 35								
Fulwell	d									07 12										07 42					
Strawberry Hill	d					07 08				07 14							07 38			07 44					
Twickenham	a	06 56	07 10			07 12		07 23		07 18	07 33			07 40			07 42	07 53		07 48		08 03			08 09
	d	06 58	07 11			07 13		07 23		07 27	07 33			07 41			07 43	07 53		07 57		08 03			08 09
St Margarets	d	07 00				07 15				07 29							07 45			07 59					
Richmond	⊖ d	07 04	07 15			07 19		07 28		07 32	07 38			07 45			07 49	07 58		08 02		08 08			08 14
North Sheen	d	07 06				07 21				07 34							07 51			08 04					
Mortlake	d	07 08				07 23				07 37							07 53			08 07					
Hounslow	d	06 48		07 01	07 16										07 31	07 46									
Isleworth	d			07 04	07 19										07 34	07 49									
Syon Lane	d			07 06	07 21				←						07 36	07 51			←						
Brentford	d			07 09	07 24				07 24						07 39	07 54			07 54						
Kew Bridge	d			07 11	→				07 26						07 41	→			07 56						
Chiswick	d			07 14					07 29						07 44				07 59						
Barnes Bridge	d			07 16					07 31				←		07 46				08 01					←	
Barnes	d	07 11		07 19		07 26			07 34	07 40			07 40		07 49		07 56		08 04	08 10				08 10	
Putney	d	07 14	07 22	07 22		07 29		07 34	07 37	→			07 43		07 52		07 59	08 04	08 07	→				08 13	
Wandsworth Town	d	07 17		07 25		07 32			07 40				07 46		07 55		08 02		08 10					08 16	
Clapham Junction 10	d	07 20	07 26	07 28		07 35		07 39	07 43		07 47		07 49	07 54	07 58		08 05	08 09	08 13			08 17		08 19	08 22
Queenstown Rd.(Battersea)	d	07 23		07 31		07 38			07 46				07 52		08 01		08 08		08 16					08 22	
Vauxhall	⊖ d	07 27		07 35		07 42		07 45	07 50		07 53		07 56		08 05		08 12	08 15	08 20			08 23		08 26	
London Waterloo 15	⊖ a	07 34	07 37	07 43		07 48		07 51	07 58		07 59		08 04	08 06	08 11		08 18	08 21	08 28			08 29		08 34	08 36

For general notes see front of timetable
For details of catering facilities see Directory of Train Operators

§ Passengers to/from London may travel via Weybridge. See Table 155.

A From London Waterloo.
B From London Waterloo (Table 152)
C From Shepperton (Table 152)

Table 149

Mondays to Fridays

from 29 September

Reading, Guildford, Ascot, Weybridge, Windsor, Kingston, Richmond and Hounslow → London

Network Diagram - see first page of Table 148

	SW A	SW	SW B	SW 1	SW B	SW	SW	SW C	SW 1	SW C	SW 1		SW A	SW B	SW	SW	SW	SW A	SW 1	SW 1	SW A	SW B	SW	SW
Reading 7 d				07 21							07 39									08 09				
Earley d											07 44									08 14				
Winnersh Triangle d											07 46									08 16				
Winnersh d											07 48									08 18				
Wokingham d				07 30							07 53									08 23				
Bracknell d				07 36							07 59									08 29				
Martins Heron d				07 39							08 02									08 32				
Guildford d																			07 30					
Wanborough d																			07 36					
Ash 3 d																			07 40					
Aldershot a																			07 47					
d									07 29										08 00					
Ash Vale d									07 33										08 04					
Frimley d									07 39										08 10					
Camberley a									07 43										08 14					
d									07 44										08 18					
Bagshot d									07 49										08 23					
Ascot 3 d				07 44					07 56		08 07								08a30	08 37				
Sunningdale d				07 47					07 59		08 10									08 40				
Longcross d											08 13									08 43				
Woking d																								
West Byfleet d																								
Byfleet & New Haw d																								
Weybridge d		07 33													08 03								08 33	
Addlestone § d		07 37													08 07								08 37	
Chertsey § d		07 40													08 10								08 40	
Virginia Water a		07 45		07 55					08 08		08 19				08 15					08 49			08 45	
d		07 51		07 55					08 08		08 19				08 24					08 49			08 54	
Egham d		07 54		07 58					08 12		08 23				08 27					08 53			08 57	
Windsor & Eton Riverside d						07 51										08 21								08 51
Datchet d						07 54										08 24								08 54
Sunnymeads d						07 57										08 27								08 57
Wraysbury d						08 00										08 30								09 00
Staines d		08 00		08 04		08 08			08 18		08 29				08 33	08 38				08 59			09 03	09 08
Ashford (Surrey) d		08 03				08 11			08 21						08 36	08 41							09 06	09 11
Feltham d		08 08		08 12		08 16			08 26		08 35				08 41	08 46				09 05			09 11	09 16
Whitton d	07 50					08 20			08 30				08 20			08 50		08 53			08 50			09 20
Kingston d			07 59											08 29								08 59		
Hampton Wick d			08 01											08 31								09 01		
Teddington d			08 05											08 35								09 05		
Fulwell d								08 12																
Strawberry Hill d			08 08					08 14						08 38								09 08		
Twickenham a			08 12	08 17		08 23		08 18	08 33		08 40			08 42		08 53		08 56		09 10		09 12		09 23
d			08 13	08 18		08 23		08 27	08 33		08 41			08 43		08 53		08 58		09 11		09 13		09 23
St Margarets d			08 15					08 29						08 45				09 00				09 15		
Richmond ⊖ d			08 19	08 24		08 28		08 32	08 38		08 45			08 49		08 58		09 04		09 15		09 19		09 28
North Sheen d			08 21					08 34						08 51				09 06				09 21		
Mortlake d			08 23					08 37						08 53				09 08				09 23		
Hounslow d	08 01	08 16											08 31		08 46						09 01		09 16	
Isleworth d	08 04	08 19											08 34		08 49						09 04		09 19	
Syon Lane d	08 06	08 21											08 36		08 51		←				09 06		09 21	
Brentford d	08 09	08 24					←						08 39		08 54 →		08 54				09 09		09 24 →	
Kew Bridge d	08 11	08 26 →					08 26						08 41				08 56				09 11			
Chiswick d	08 14						08 29						08 44				08 59				09 14			
Barnes Bridge d	08 16				←		08 31			←			08 46				09 01				09 16			
Barnes d	08 19		08 26 →		08 26		08 34	08 40 →		08 40			08 49	08 56			09 04	09 11			09 19	09 26		
Putney d	08 22				08 29	08 34	08 37			08 43			08 52	08 59		09 04	09 07	09 14			09 22	09 29		09 34
Wandsworth Town d	08 25				08 32		08 40			08 46			08 55	09 02			09 10	09 17			09 25	09 32		
Clapham Junction 10 d	08 28			08 33	08 35	08 39	08 43		08 47	08 49	08 54		08 58	09 05		09 09	09 13	09 20		09 24	09 28	09 35		09 39
Queenstown Rd.(Battersea) d	08 31				08 38		08 46			08 52			09 01	09 08			09 16	09 23			09 31	09 38		
Vauxhall ⊖ d	08 35			08 38	08 42	08 45	08 50		08 53	08 56			09 05	09 12		09 15	09 20	09 27			09 35	09 42		09 45
London Waterloo 15 ⊖ a	08 43			08 46	08 49	08 51	08 58		09 00	09 04	09 06		09 13	09 18		09 21	09 28	09 34		09 34	09 43	09 48		09 51

For general notes see front of timetable
For details of catering facilities see Directory of Train Operators

§ Passengers to/from London may travel via Weybridge. See Table 155.

A From London Waterloo.
B From London Waterloo (Table 152)
C From Shepperton (Table 152)

Table 149

Mondays to Fridays

from 29 September

Reading, Guildford, Ascot, Weybridge, Windsor, Kingston, Richmond and Hounslow → London

Network Diagram - see first page of Table 148

Station		SW	SW A	SW 1		SW 1	SW A	SW B	SW	SW	SW	SW A	SW 1	SW 1	SW A	SW B	SW	SW		SW 1	SW	SW A	SW 1	SW 1	SW A
Reading 7	d					08 39								09 09						09 22				09 39	
Earley	d					08 44								09 14						09 27				09 44	
Winnersh Triangle	d					08 46								09 16						09 29				09 46	
Winnersh	d					08 48								09 18						09 31				09 48	
Wokingham	d					08 53								09 23						09 36				09 53	
Bracknell	d					08 59								09 29						09 43				09 59	
Martins Heron	d					09 02								09 32						09 46				10 02	
Guildford	d			08 00									08 30										09 00		
Wanborough	d			08 06									08 36										09 06		
Ash 3	d			08 10									08 40										09 10		
Aldershot	a			08 17									08 47										09 17		
	d			08 30									09 00										09 30		
Ash Vale	d			08 34									09 04										09 34		
Frimley	d			08 40									09 10										09 40		
Camberley	a			08 44									09 14										09 44		
	d			08 48									09 18										09 48		
Bagshot	d			08 53									09 23										09 53		
Ascot 3	d			09a00		09 07							09a30	09 37						09 52			10a00	10 07	
Sunningdale	d					09 10								09 40						09 55				10 10	
Longcross	d					09 13																			
Woking	d																								
West Byfleet	d																								
Byfleet & New Haw	d																								
Weybridge	d								09 03								09 33								
Addlestone §	d								09 07								09 37								
Chertsey §	d								09 10								09 40								
Virginia Water	a					09 19			09 15					09 49			09 45			10 03				10 19	
	d					09 19			09 24					09 49			09 54			10 03				10 19	
Egham	d					09 23			09 27					09 53			09 57			10 06				10 23	
Windsor & Eton Riverside	d									09 21								09 51							
Datchet	d									09 24								09 54							
Sunnymeads	d									09 27								09 57							
Wraysbury	d									09 30								10 00							
Staines	d					09 29			09 33	09 38				09 59			10 03	10 08		10 14				10 29	
Ashford (Surrey)	d								09 36	09 41							10 06	10 11							
Feltham	d					09 35			09 41	09 46				10 05			10 11	10 16		10 20				10 35	
Whitton	d		09 23				09 20			09 50		09 53			09 50			10 20				10 26			10 20
Kingston	d							09 29								09 59									
Hampton Wick	d							09 31								10 01									
Teddington	d							09 35								10 05									
Fulwell	d																								
Strawberry Hill	d							09 38								10 08									
Twickenham	a		09 26			09 40		09 42		09 53		09 56		10 10		10 12		10 23		10 27		10 28		10 40	
	d		09 28			09 41		09 43		09 53		09 58		10 11		10 13		10 23		10 27		10 28		10 41	
St Margarets	d		09 30					09 45				10 00				10 15						10 30			
Richmond	⊖ d		09 34			09 45		09 49		09 58		10 04		10 15		10 19		10 28		10 32		10 34		10 45	
North Sheen	d		09 36					09 51				10 06				10 21						10 36			
Mortlake	d		09 38					09 53				10 08				10 23						10 38			
Hounslow	d						09 31		09 46						10 01		10 16								10 31
Isleworth	d						09 34		09 49						10 04		10 19								10 34
Syon Lane	d	←					09 36		09 51		←				10 06		10 21								10 36
Brentford	d	09 24					09 39		09 54		09 54				10 09		10 24				←				10 39
Kew Bridge	d	09 26					09 41		→		09 56				10 11		10 26				10 26				10 41
Chiswick	d	09 29					09 44				09 59				10 14		→				10 29				10 44
Barnes Bridge	d	09 31					09 46				10 01				10 16						10 31				10 46
Barnes	d	09 34	09 41				09 49	09 56			10 04	10 11			10 19	10 26					10 34	10 41			10 49
Putney	d	09 37	09 44				09 52	09 59		10 04	10 07	10 14			10 22	10 29		10 34			10 37	10 44			10 52
Wandsworth Town	d	09 40	09 47				09 55	10 02			10 10	10 17			10 25	10 32					10 40	10 47			10 55
Clapham Junction 10	d	09 43	09 50			09 54	09 58	10 05		10 09	10 13	10 20		10 24	10 28	10 35		10 39		10 42	10 43	10 50		10 54	10 58
Queenstown Rd.(Battersea)	d	09 46	09 53				10 01	10 08			10 16	10 23			10 31	10 38					10 46	10 53			11 01
Vauxhall	⊖ d	09 50	09 57				10 05	10 12		10 15	10 20	10 27			10 35	10 42		10 45			10 50	10 57			11 05
London Waterloo 15	⊖ a	09 58	10 02			10 04	10 11	10 16		10 19	10 26	10 32		10 34	10 41	10 46		10 49		10 53	10 56	11 02		11 04	11 11

For general notes see front of timetable
For details of catering facilities see Directory of Train Operators

§ Passengers to/from London may travel via Weybridge. See Table 155.

A From London Waterloo.
B From London Waterloo (Table 152)

from 29 September

Reading, Guildford, Ascot, Weybridge, Windsor, Kingston, Richmond and Hounslow → London

Network Diagram - see first page of Table 148

		SW	SW	SW	SW	SW	SW	SW	SW	SW	SW	SW	SW	SW	SW	SW	SW	SW	SW	SW	SW	SW	SW
					1			1	1							1	1						
		A					B			B	A				B			B	A				
Reading 7	d				09 53				10 09								10 39						
Earley	d				09 58				10 14								10 44						
Winnersh Triangle	d				10 00				10 16								10 46						
Winnersh	d				10 02				10 18								10 48						
Wokingham	d				10 07				10 23								10 53						
Bracknell	d				10 13				10 29								10 59						
Martins Heron	d				10 16				10 32								11 02						
Guildford	d							09 30								10 00							
Wanborough	d							09 36								10 06							
Ash 3	d							09 40								10 10							
Aldershot	a							09 47								10 17							
	d							10 00								10 30							
Ash Vale	d							10 04								10 34							
Frimley	d							10 10								10 40							
Camberley	a							10 14								10 44							
	d							10 18								10 48							
Bagshot	d							10 23								10 53							
Ascot 3	d				10 22			10a30	10 37							11a00	11 07						
Sunningdale	d				10 25				10 40								11 10						
Longcross	d																						
Woking	d																						
West Byfleet	d																						
Byfleet & New Haw	d																						
Weybridge	d		10 03									10 33								11 03			
Addlestone §	d		10 07									10 37								11 07			
Chertsey §	d		10 10									10 40								11 10			
Virginia Water	a		10 15		10 33				10 49			10 45					11 19			11 15			
	d		10 24		10 33				10 49			10 54					11 19			11 24			
Egham	d		10 27		10 36				10 53			10 57					11 23			11 27			
Windsor & Eton Riverside	d			10 21									10 51								11 21		
Datchet	d			10 24									10 54								11 24		
Sunnymeads	d			10 27									10 57								11 27		
Wraysbury	d			10 30									11 00								11 30		
Staines	d		10 33	10 38	10 44				10 59			11 03	11 08				11 29			11 33	11 38		
Ashford (Surrey)	d		10 36	10 41								11 06	11 11							11 36	11 41		
Feltham	d		10 41	10 46	10 50				11 05			11 11	11 16				11 35			11 41	11 46		
Whitton	d			10 50			10 56			10 50			11 20		11 23			11 20			11 50		
Kingston	d	10 29									10 59								11 29				
Hampton Wick	d	10 31									11 01								11 31				
Teddington	d	10 35									11 05								11 35				
Fulwell	d																						
Strawberry Hill	d	10 38									11 08								11 38				
Twickenham	a	10 42		10 53	10 57		10 58		11 10		11 12		11 23		11 26		11 40		11 42		11 53		
	d	10 43		10 53	10 57		10 58		11 11		11 13		11 23		11 28		11 41		11 43		11 53		
St Margarets	d	10 45					11 00				11 15				11 30				11 45				
Richmond	⊖ d	10 49		10 58	11 02		11 04		11 15		11 19		11 28		11 34		11 45		11 49		11 58		
North Sheen	d	10 51					11 06				11 21				11 36				11 51				
Mortlake	d	10 53					11 08				11 23				11 38				11 53				
Hounslow	d		10 46							11 01		11 16						11 31		11 46			
Isleworth	d		10 49							11 04		11 19						11 34		11 49			
Syon Lane	d		10 51							11 06		11 21		←				11 36		11 51			←
Brentford	d		10 54			←				11 09		11 24		11 24				11 39		11 54			11 54
Kew Bridge	d		10 56			10 56				11 11		→		11 26				11 41		→			11 56
Chiswick	d		→			10 59				11 14				11 29				11 44					11 59
Barnes Bridge	d					11 01				11 16				11 31				11 46					12 01
Barnes	d	10 56				11 04	11 11			11 19	11 26			11 34	11 41			11 49	11 56				12 04
Putney	d	10 59		11 04		11 07	11 14			11 22	11 29		11 34	11 37	11 44			11 52	11 59			12 04	12 07
Wandsworth Town	d	11 02				11 10	11 17			11 25	11 32			11 40	11 47			11 55	12 02				12 10
Clapham Junction 10	d	11 05		11 09	11 12	11 13	11 20		11 24	11 29	11 35		11 39	11 43	11 50		11 54	11 58	12 05			12 09	12 13
Queenstown Rd.(Battersea)	d	11 08				11 16	11 23			11 31	11 38			11 46	11 53			12 01	12 08				12 16
Vauxhall	⊖ d	11 12		11 15		11 20	11 27			11 35	11 42		11 45	11 50	11 57			12 05	12 12			12 15	12 20
London Waterloo 15	⊖ a	11 16		11 19	11 26	11 27	11 32		11 34	11 41	11 46		11 49	11 56	12 02		12 04	12 11	12 16			12 19	12 26

For general notes see front of timetable
For details of catering facilities see Directory of Train Operators

§ Passengers to/from London may travel via Weybridge. See Table 155.

A From London Waterloo (Table 152)
B From London Waterloo.

Table 149

Mondays to Fridays

from 29 September

Reading, Guildford, Ascot, Weybridge, Windsor, Kingston, Richmond and Hounslow → London

Network Diagram - see first page of Table 148

		SW		SW	SW	SW	SW	SW	SW	GW	SW	SW	SW	SW	SW	SW	SW	SW	SW	SW	SW	SW
				1					1	1			1							1	1	
		A			A		B			C		A		A	B				A			A
Reading 7	d			15 09						15 28			15 39								16 09	
Earley	d			15 14									15 44								16 14	
Winnersh Triangle	d			15 16									15 46								16 16	
Winnersh	d			15 18						15 35			15 48								16 18	
Wokingham	d			15 23						15a38			15 53								16 23	
Bracknell	d			15 29									15 59								16 29	
Martins Heron	d			15 32									16 02								16 32	
Guildford	d								15 00											15 30		
Wanborough	d								15 06											15 36		
Ash 3	d								15 10											15 40		
Aldershot	a								15 17											15 47		
	d								15 30											16 00		
Ash Vale	d								15 34											16 04		
Frimley	d								15 40											16 10		
Camberley	a								15 44											16 14		
	d								15 48											16 18		
Bagshot	d								15 53											16 23		
Ascot 3	d			15 37					16a00				16 07							16a30	16 37	
Sunningdale	d			15 40									16 10								16 40	
Longcross	d																					
Woking	d																					
West Byfleet	d																					
Byfleet & New Haw	d																					
Weybridge	d					15 33										16 03						
Addlestone §	d					15 37										16 07						
Chertsey §	d		and at			15 40										16 10						
Virginia Water	a		the same	15 49		15 45							16 19			16 15					16 49	
	d			15 49		15 54							16 19			16 24					16 49	
Egham	d		minutes	15 53		15 57							16 23			16 27					16 53	
Windsor & Eton Riverside	d		past					15 51									16 21					
Datchet	d							15 54									16 24					
Sunnymeads	d		each					15 57									16 27					
Wraysbury	d							16 00									16 30					
Staines	d		hour until	15 59		16 03		16 08					16 29			16 33	16 38				16 59	
Ashford (Surrey)	d					16 06		16 11								16 36	16 41					
Feltham	d			16 05		16 11		16 16					16 35			16 41	16 46				17 05	
Whitton	d	11 53			15 50			16 20				16 23		16 20			16 50		16 53			16 50
Kingston	d						15 59								16 29							
Hampton Wick	d						16 01								16 31							
Teddington	d						16 05								16 35							
Fulwell	d																					
Strawberry Hill	d						16 08								16 38							
Twickenham	a	11 56		16 10			16 12	16 23				16 26	16 40		16 42		16 53		16 56		17 10	
	d	11 58		16 11			16 13	16 23				16 28	16 41		16 43		16 53		16 58		17 11	
St Margarets	d	12 00					16 15					16 30			16 45				17 00			
Richmond ⊖	d	12 04		16 15			16 19	16 28				16 34	16 45		16 49		16 58		17 04		17 15	
North Sheen	d	12 06					16 21					16 36			16 51				17 06			
Mortlake	d	12 08					16 23					16 38			16 53				17 08			
Hounslow	d				16 01	16 16								16 31		16 46						17 01
Isleworth	d				16 04	16 19								16 34		16 49						17 04
Syon Lane	d				16 06	16 21					←			16 36		16 51		←				17 06
Brentford	d				16 09	16 24					16 24			16 39		16 54		16 54				17 09
Kew Bridge	d				16 11	→					16 26			16 41		→		16 56				17 11
Chiswick	d				16 14						16 29			16 44				16 59				17 14
Barnes Bridge	d				16 16						16 31			16 46				17 01				17 16
Barnes	d	12 11			16 19		16 26				16 34	16 41		16 49	16 56			17 04	17 11			17 19
Putney	d	12 14			16 22		16 29	16 34			16 37	16 44		16 52	16 59		17 04	17 07	17 14			17 22
Wandsworth Town	d	12 17			16 25		16 32				16 40	16 47		16 55	17 02			17 10	17 17			17 25
Clapham Junction 10	d	12 20		16 24	16 28		16 35	16 39			16 43	16 50	16 54	16 58	17 05		17 09	17 13	17 20		17 24	17 28
Queenstown Rd.(Battersea)	d	12 23			16 31		16 38				16 46	16 53		17 01	17 08			17 16	17 23			17 31
Vauxhall ⊖	d	12 27			16 35		16 42	16 45			16 50	16 57		17 05	17 12		17 15	17 20	17 27			17 35
London Waterloo 15 ⊖	a	12 32		16 34	16 41		16 49	16 49			16 54	17 02	17 04	17 11	17 19		17 19	17 24	17 32		17 34	17 41

For general notes see front of timetable
For details of catering facilities see
Directory of Train Operators

§ Passengers to/from London may travel via Weybridge. See Table 155.

A From London Waterloo.
B From London Waterloo (Table 152)
C To Gatwick Airport (Table 148)

Table 149

Mondays to Fridays

from 29 September

Reading, Guildford, Ascot, Weybridge, Windsor, Kingston, Richmond and Hounslow → London

Network Diagram - see first page of Table 148

Station		SW	SW	SW	SW	SW	SW	SW	SW	SW	SW	SW	SW	SW	SW	SW	SW	SW	SW	SW	SW	SW	SW	SW
		A				B	1	1	B	A				B	1	1	B	A				1	B	1
Reading 7	d							16 39								17 09						17 19		
Earley	d							16 44								17 14						17 24		
Winnersh Triangle	d							16 46								17 16						17 26		
Winnersh	d							16 48								17 18						17 28		
Wokingham	d							16 53								17 23						17 33		
Bracknell	d							16 59								17 29						17 39		
Martins Heron	d							17 02								17 32						17 42		
Guildford	d						16 00								16 30									17 00
Wanborough	d						16 06								16 36									17 06
Ash 3	d						16 10								16 40									17 10
Aldershot	a						16 17								16 47									17 17
	d						16 30								17 00									17 30
Ash Vale	d						16 34								17 04									17 34
Frimley	d						16 40								17 10									17 40
Camberley	a						16 44								17 14									17 44
	d						16 48								17 18									17 48
Bagshot	d						16 53								17 23									17 53
Ascot 3	d						17a00	17 07							17a30	17 37						17b55		18a00
Sunningdale	d							17 10								17 40						17 58		
Longcross	d							17 13																
Woking	d																							
West Byfleet	d																							
Byfleet & New Haw	d																							
Weybridge	d		16 33								17 03								17 37					
Addlestone §	d		16 37								17 07								17 41					
Chertsey §	d		16 40								17 10								17 44					
Virginia Water	a		16 45					17 19			17 15					17 49			17 49			18 03		
	d		16 54					17 19			17 24					17 49			17 54			18 03		
Egham	d		16 57					17 23			17 27					17 53			17 57			18 06		
Windsor & Eton Riverside	d			16 51								17 21								17 51				
Datchet	d			16 54								17 24								17 54				
Sunnymeads	d			16 57								17 27								17 57				
Wraysbury	d			17 00								17 30								18 00				
Staines	d		17 03	17 08				17 29			17 33	17 38				17 59			18 03	18 08		18 14		
Ashford (Surrey)	d		17 06	17 11							17 36	17 41							18 06	18 11				
Feltham	d		17 11	17 16				17 35			17 41	17 46				18 05			18 11	18 16		18 20		
Whitton	d			17 20		17 23			17 20			17 50		17 53			17 50			18 20			18 23	
Kingston	d	16 59								17 29								17 59						
Hampton Wick	d	17 01								17 31								18 01						
Teddington	d	17 05								17 35								18 05						
Fulwell	d																							
Strawberry Hill	d	17 08								17 38								18 08						
Twickenham	a	17 12		17 23		17 26		17 40		17 42		17 53		17 56		18 10		18 12		18 23			18 26	
	d	17 13		17 23		17 28		17 41		17 43		17 53		17 58		18 11		18 13		18 23			18 28	
St Margarets	d	17 15				17 30				17 45				18 00				18 15					18 30	
Richmond	⊖ d	17 19		17 28		17 34		17 45		17 49		17 58		18 04		18 15		18 19		18 28			18 34	
North Sheen	d	17 21				17 36				17 51				18 06				18 21					18 36	
Mortlake	d	17 23				17 38				17 53				18 08				18 23					18 38	
Hounslow	d		17 16						17 31		17 46						18 01		18 16			18 26		
Isleworth	d		17 19						17 34		17 49						18 04		18 19					
Syon Lane	d		17 21		←				17 36		17 51		←				18 06		18 21		←			
Brentford	d		17 24 →		17 24				17 39		17 54 →		17 54				18 09		18 24 →		18 24	18 31		
Kew Bridge	d				17 26				17 41				17 56				18 11				18 26			
Chiswick	d				17 29				17 44				17 59				18 14				18 29			
Barnes Bridge	d				17 31				17 46				18 01				18 16				18 31			
Barnes	d	17 26			17 34	17 41			17 49	17 56			18 04	18 11			18 19	18 26			18 34		18 41	
Putney	d	17 29		17 34	17 37	17 44			17 52	17 59		18 04	18 07	18 14			18 22	18 29		18 34	18 37	18 39	18 44	
Wandsworth Town	d	17 32			17 40	17 47			17 55	18 02			18 10	18 17			18 25	18 32			18 40		18 47	
Clapham Junction 10	d	17 35		17 39	17 43	17 50		17 54	17 58	18 05		18 09	18 13	18 20		18 24	18 28	18 35		18 39	18 43	18 44	18 51	
Queenstown Rd.(Battersea)	d	17 38			17 46	17 53			18 01	18 08			18 16	18 23			18 31	18 38			18 46		18 53	
Vauxhall	⊖ d	17 42		17 45	17 50	17 57			18 05	18 12		18 15	18 20	18 27			18 35	18 42		18 45	18 50		18 57	
London Waterloo 15	⊖ a	17 49		17 49	17 55	18 02		18 04	18 11	18 19		18 19	18 24	18 32		18 34	18 41	18 49		18 49	18 54	18 56	19 02	

For general notes see front of timetable
For details of catering facilities see Directory of Train Operators

§ Passengers to/from London may travel via Weybridge. See Table 155.

A From London Waterloo (Table 152)

B From London Waterloo.

b Arr. 1749

Table 149

Mondays to Fridays

from 29 September

Reading, Guildford, Ascot, Weybridge, Windsor, Kingston, Richmond and Hounslow → London

Network Diagram - see first page of Table 148

		SW 1		SW	SW	SW	SW	SW	SW 1	SW	SW 1	SW	SW	SW	SW	SW		SW 1	SW	SW	SW 1	SW	SW	SW 1	SW
				A	B					A			A	B						A		A			B
Reading 7	d	17 39							17 49			18 09									18 39			18 52	
Earley	d	17 44							17 54			18 14									18 44			18 57	
Winnersh Triangle	d	17 46							17 56			18 16									18 46			18 59	
Winnersh	d	17 48							17 58			18 18									18 48			19 01	
Wokingham	d	17 53							18 03			18 23									18 53			19 06	
Bracknell	d	17 59							18 09			18 29									18 59			19 12	
Martins Heron	d	18 02							18 12			18 32									19 02			19 15	
Guildford	d										17 30							18 00							
Wanborough	d										17 36							18 06							
Ash 3	d										17 40							18 10							
Aldershot	a										17 47							18 17							
	d										18 00							18 30							
Ash Vale	d										18 04							18 34							
Frimley	d										18 10							18 40							
Camberley	a										18 14							18 44							
	d										18 18							18 48							
Bagshot	d										18 23							18 53							
Ascot 3	d	18 07							18b25		18a30	18 37						19a00			19 07			19a19	
Sunningdale	d	18 10							18 28			18 40									19 10				
Longcross	d	18 13										18 43									19 13				
Woking	d																								
West Byfleet	d																								
Byfleet & New Haw	d																								
Weybridge	d					18 07									18 37								19 07		
Addlestone §	d					18 11									18 41								19 11		
Chertsey §	d					18 14									18 44								19 14		
Virginia Water	a	18 19				18 19			18 33			18 49			18 49						19 19		19 19		
	d	18 19				18 24			18 33			18 49			18 54						19 19		19 24		
Egham	d	18 23				18 27			18 36			18 53			18 57						19 23		19 27		
Windsor & Eton Riverside	d						18 21									18 51									
Datchet	d						18 24									18 54									
Sunnymeads	d						18 27									18 57									
Wraysbury	d						18 30									19 00									
Staines	d	18 29				18 33	18 38		18 44			18 59			19 03	19 08					19 29		19 33		
Ashford (Surrey)	d					18 36	18 41								19 06	19 11							19 36		
Feltham	d	18 35				18 41	18 46		18 50			19 05			19 11	19 16					19 35		19 41		
Whitton	d			18 20			18 50			18 53			18 50			19 20				19 23		19 20			
Kingston	d				18 29									18 59											19 29
Hampton Wick	d				18 31									19 01											19 31
Teddington	d				18 35									19 05											19 35
Fulwell	d																								
Strawberry Hill	d				18 38									19 08											19 38
Twickenham	a	18 40			18 42		18 53			18 56		19 10		19 12		19 23				19 26	19 40				19 42
	d	18 41			18 43		18 53			18 58		19 11		19 13		19 23				19 28	19 41				19 43
St Margarets	d				18 45					19 00				19 15						19 30					19 45
Richmond	⊖ d	18 45			18 49		18 58			19 04		19 15		19 19		19 28				19 34	19 45				19 49
North Sheen	d				18 51					19 06				19 21						19 36					19 51
Mortlake	d				18 53					19 08				19 23						19 38					19 53
Hounslow	d			18 31		18 46			18 56				19 01		19 16							19 31	19 46		
Isleworth	d			18 34		18 49							19 04		19 19							19 34	19 49		
Syon Lane	d			18 36		18 51		←					19 06		19 21				←			19 36	19 51		
Brentford	d			18 39		18 54 →		18 54	19 01				19 09		19 24 →				19 24			19 39	19 54 →		
Kew Bridge	d			18 41				18 56					19 11						19 26			19 41			
Chiswick	d			18 44				18 59					19 14						19 29			19 44			
Barnes Bridge	d			18 46				19 01					19 16						19 31			19 46			
Barnes	d			18 49	18 56			19 04		19 11			19 19	19 26					19 34	19 41		19 49			19 56
Putney	d			18 52	18 59		19 04	19 07	19 09	19 14			19 22	19 29		19 34			19 37	19 44		19 52			19 59
Wandsworth Town	d			18 55	19 02			19 10		19 17			19 25	19 32					19 40	19 47		19 55			20 02
Clapham Junction 10	d	18 54		18 58	19 05		19 09	19 13	19 14	19 20		19 24	19 28	19 35		19 39			19 43	19 50	19 54	19 58			20 05
Queenstown Rd.(Battersea)	d			19 01	19 08			19 16		19 23			19 31	19 38					19 46	19 53		20 01			20 08
Vauxhall	⊖ d			19 05	19 12		19 15	19 20		19 27			19 35	19 42		19 45			19 50	19 57		20 05			20 12
London Waterloo 15	⊖ a	19 04		19 09	19 16		19 19	19 26	19 28	19 32		19 34	19 41	19 46		19 49			19 56	20 02	20 04	20 10			20 16

For general notes see front of timetable
For details of catering facilities see
Directory of Train Operators

§ Passengers to/from London may travel via Weybridge. See Table 155.

A From London Waterloo.
B From London Waterloo (Table 152)
b Arr. 1820

Table 149

Mondays to Fridays

from 29 September

Reading, Guildford, Ascot, Weybridge, Windsor, Kingston, Richmond and Hounslow → London

Network Diagram - see first page of Table 148

		SW	SW	SW A	SW 1	SW 1	SW A	SW B		SW	SW	SW	SW A	SW 1	SW 1	SW A	SW B	SW	SW	SW 1	SW	SW A		SW 1	SW A
Reading 7	d					19 09									19 39									20 09	
Earley	d					19 14									19 44									20 14	
Winnersh Triangle	d					19 16									19 46									20 16	
Winnersh	d					19 18									19 48									20 18	
Wokingham	d					19 23									19 53									20 23	
Bracknell	d					19 29									19 59									20 29	
Martins Heron	d					19 32									20 02									20 32	
Guildford	d				18 30									19 00						19 30					
Wanborough	d				18 36									19 06						19 36					
Ash 3	d				18 40									19 10						19 40					
Aldershot	a				18 47									19 17						19 47					
	d				19 00									19 30						20 00					
Ash Vale	d				19 04									19 34						20 04					
Frimley	d				19 10									19 40						20 10					
Camberley	a				19 14									19 44						20 14					
	d				19 18									19 48						20 18					
Bagshot	d				19 23									19 53						20 23					
Ascot 3	d				19a30	19 37								20a00	20 07					20a30				20 37	
Sunningdale	d					19 40									20 10									20 40	
Longcross	d					19 43									20 13									20 43	
Woking	d																								
West Byfleet	d																								
Byfleet & New Haw	d																								
Weybridge	d									19 37								20 03							
Addlestone §	d									19 41								20 07							
Chertsey §	d									19 44								20 10							
Virginia Water	a					19 49				19 49					20 19			20 15						20 49	
	d					19 49				19 54					20 19			20 24						20 49	
Egham	d					19 53				19 57					20 23			20 27						20 53	
Windsor & Eton Riverside	d	19 21									19 51								20 21						
Datchet	d	19 24									19 54								20 24						
Sunnymeads	d	19 27									19 57								20 27						
Wraysbury	d	19 30									20 00								20 30						
Staines	d	19 38				19 59				20 03	20 08				20 29			20 33	20 38					20 59	
Ashford (Surrey)	d	19 41								20 06	20 11							20 36	20 41						
Feltham	d	19 46				20 05				20 11	20 16				20 35			20 41	20 46					21 05	
Whitton	d	19 50		19 53			19 50				20 20		20 23			20 20			20 50			20 53			20 50
Kingston	d							19 59									20 29								
Hampton Wick	d							20 01									20 31								
Teddington	d							20 05									20 35								
Fulwell	d																								
Strawberry Hill	d							20 08									20 38								
Twickenham	a	19 53		19 56		20 10		20 12			20 23		20 26		20 40		20 42		20 53			20 56		21 10	
	d	19 53		19 58		20 11		20 13			20 23		20 28		20 41		20 43		20 53			20 58		21 11	
St Margarets	d			20 00				20 15					20 30				20 45					21 00			
Richmond	⊖ d	19 58		20 04		20 15		20 19			20 28		20 34		20 45		20 49		20 58			21 04		21 15	
North Sheen	d			20 06				20 21					20 36				20 51					21 06			
Mortlake	d			20 08				20 23					20 38				20 53					21 08			
Hounslow	d						20 01			20 16						20 31		20 46							21 01
Isleworth	d						20 04			20 19						20 34		20 49							21 04
Syon Lane	d		←				20 06			20 21		←				20 36		20 51			←				21 06
Brentford	d		19 54				20 09			20 24 →		20 24				20 39		20 54 →			20 54				21 09
Kew Bridge	d		19 56				20 11					20 26				20 41					20 56				21 11
Chiswick	d		19 59				20 14					20 29				20 44					20 59				21 14
Barnes Bridge	d		20 01				20 16					20 31				20 46					21 01				21 16
Barnes	d		20 04	20 11			20 19	20 26				20 34	20 41			20 49	20 56				21 04	21 11			21 19
Putney	d	20 05	20 07	20 14			20 22	20 29			20 34	20 37	20 44			20 52	20 59		21 04		21 07	21 14			21 22
Wandsworth Town	d		20 10	20 17			20 25	20 32				20 40	20 47			20 55	21 02				21 10	21 17			21 25
Clapham Junction 10	d	20 09	20 13	20 20		20 24	20 28	20 35			20 39	20 43	20 50		20 54	20 58	21 05		21 09		21 13	21 20		21 24	21 28
Queenstown Rd.(Battersea)	d		20 16	20 23			20 31	20 38				20 46	20 53			21 01	21 08				21 16	21 23			21 31
Vauxhall	⊖ d	20 15	20 20	20 27			20 35	20 42			20 45	20 50	20 57			21 05	21 12		21 15		21 20	21 27			21 35
London Waterloo 15	⊖ a	20 19	20 26	20 32		20 34	20 41	20 46			20 49	20 56	21 02		21 04	21 11	21 16		21 19		21 26	21 32		21 34	21 41

For general notes see front of timetable
For details of catering facilities see Directory of Train Operators

§ Passengers to/from London may travel via Weybridge. See Table 155.

A From London Waterloo.
B From London Waterloo (Table 152)

Table 149

Mondays to Fridays
from 29 September

Reading, Guildford, Ascot, Weybridge, Windsor, Kingston, Richmond and Hounslow → London

Network Diagram - see first page of Table 148

Station		SW	SW	SW	SW	SW	SW	SW	SW	SW	SW	SW	SW	SW		SW	SW	SW	SW	SW	SW	SW	SW	SW	SW
			A		[1]	[1]		B	[1]	B	A					B	[1]	B		A		[1]	[1]		B
Reading [7]	d								20 39								21 09								
Earley	d								20 44								21 14								
Winnersh Triangle	d								20 46								21 16								
Winnersh	d								20 48								21 18								
Wokingham	d								20 53								21 23								
Bracknell	d								20 59								21 29								
Martins Heron	d								21 02								21 32								
Guildford	d				20 00	20 30																21 00	21 30		
Wanborough	d				20 06	20 36																21 06	21 36		
Ash [3]	d				20 10	20 40																21 10	21 40		
Aldershot	a				20 17	20 47																21 17	21 47		
	d				20 30																	21 30			
Ash Vale	d				20 34																	21 34			
Frimley	d				20 40																	21 40			
Camberley	a				20 44																	21 44			
	d				20 48																	21 48			
Bagshot	d				20 53																	21 53			
Ascot [3]	d				21a00				21 07								21 37					22a00			
Sunningdale	d								21 10								21 40								
Longcross	d																								
Woking	d																								
West Byfleet	d																								
Byfleet & New Haw	d																								
Weybridge	d	20 33										21 03							21 33						
Addlestone §	d	20 37										21 07							21 37						
Chertsey §	d	20 40										21 10							21 40						
Virginia Water	a	20 45							21 19			21 15					21 49		21 45						
	d	20 54							21 19			21 24					21 49		21 54						
Egham	d	20 57							21 23			21 27					21 53		21 57						
Windsor & Eton Riverside	d			20 51									21 21								21 51				
Datchet	d			20 54									21 24								21 54				
Sunnymeads	d			20 57									21 27								21 57				
Wraysbury	d			21 00									21 30								22 00				
Staines	d	21 03		21 08					21 29			21 33	21 38				21 59		22 03		22 08				
Ashford (Surrey)	d	21 06		21 11								21 36	21 41						22 06		22 11				
Feltham	d	21 11		21 16					21 35			21 41	21 46				22 05		22 11		22 16				
Whitton	d			21 20				21 23		21 20			21 50			21 53		21 50			22 20				22 23
Kingston	d		20 59								21 29									21 59					
Hampton Wick	d		21 01								21 31									22 01					
Teddington	d		21 05								21 35									22 05					
Fulwell	d																								
Strawberry Hill	d		21 08								21 38									22 08					
Twickenham	a		21 12	21 23				21 26	21 40		21 42		21 53			21 56	22 10			22 12	22 23				22 26
	d		21 13	21 23				21 28	21 41		21 43		21 53			21 58	22 11			22 13	22 23				22 28
St Margarets	d		21 15					21 30			21 45					22 00				22 15					22 30
Richmond ⊖	d		21 19	21 28				21 34	21 45		21 49		21 58			22 04	22 15			22 19	22 28				22 34
North Sheen	d		21 21					21 36			21 51					22 06				22 21					22 36
Mortlake	d		21 23					21 38			21 53					22 08				22 23					22 38
Hounslow	d	21 16								21 31		21 46						22 01	22 16						
Isleworth	d	21 19								21 34		21 49						22 04	22 19						
Syon Lane	d	21 21					←			21 36		21 51		←				22 06	22 21					←	
Brentford	d	21 24 →					21 24			21 39		21 54 →		21 54				22 09	22 24 →					22 24	
Kew Bridge	d						21 26			21 41				21 56				22 11						22 26	
Chiswick	d						21 29			21 44				21 59				22 14						22 29	
Barnes Bridge	d						21 31			21 46				22 01				22 16						22 31	
Barnes	d		21 26				21 34	21 41		21 49	21 56			22 04		22 11		22 19		22 26				22 34	22 41
Putney	d		21 29	21 34			21 37	21 44		21 52	21 59		22 04	22 07		22 14		22 22		22 29	22 34			22 37	22 44
Wandsworth Town	d		21 32				21 40	21 47		21 55	22 02			22 10		22 17		22 25		22 32				22 40	22 47
Clapham Junction [10]	d		21 35	21 39			21 43	21 50	21 54	21 58	22 05		22 09	22 13		22 20	22 24	22 28		22 35	22 39			22 43	22 50
Queenstown Rd.(Battersea)	d		21 38				21 46	21 53		22 01	22 08			22 16		22 23		22 31		22 38				22 46	22 53
Vauxhall ⊖	d		21 42	21 45			21 50	21 57		22 05	22 12		22 15	22 20		22 27		22 35		22 42	22 45			22 50	22 57
London Waterloo [15] ⊖	a		21 46	21 49			21 56	22 02	22 04	22 11	22 16		22 19	22 26		22 32	22 34	22 41		22 46	22 49			22 56	23 01

For general notes see front of timetable
For details of catering facilities see Directory of Train Operators

§ Passengers to/from London may travel via Weybridge. See Table 155.

A From London Waterloo (Table 152)
B From London Waterloo.

Table 149

Mondays to Fridays
from 29 September

Reading, Guildford, Ascot, Weybridge, Windsor, Kingston, Richmond and Hounslow → London

Network Diagram - see first page of Table 148

		SW 1	SW	SW	SW	SW		SW 1	SW	SW	SW 1	SW 1	SW	SW	SW 1	SW	SW	SW	SW	SW 1		SW	SW 1	SW 1	
			A							A						A			A						
Reading 7	d	21 39						22 09							22 39					23 12					
Earley	d	21 44						22 14							22 44					23 17					
Winnersh Triangle	d	21 46						22 16							22 46					23 19					
Winnersh	d	21 48						22 18							22 48					23 21					
Wokingham	d	21 53						22 23							22 53					23 26					
Bracknell	d	21 59						22 29							22 59					23 32					
Martins Heron	d	22 02						22 32							23 02					23 35					
Guildford	d										22 00	22 30											23 00	23 30	
Wanborough	d										22 06	22 36											23 06	23 36	
Ash 3	d										22 10	22 40											23 10	23 40	
Aldershot	a										22 17	22 47											23 17	23 47	
	d										22 30												23 30		
Ash Vale	d										22 34												23 34		
Frimley	d										22 40												23 40		
Camberley	a										22 44												23 44		
	d										22 48												23 48		
Bagshot	d										22 53												23 53		
Ascot 3	d	22 07						22 37			23a00				23 07					23 40			00a01		
Sunningdale	d	22 10						22 40							23 10					23 43					
Longcross	d																								
Woking	d																								
West Byfleet	d																								
Byfleet & New Haw	d																								
Weybridge	d			22 03					22 33								23 03					23 33			
Addlestone §	d			22 07					22 37								23 07					23 37			
Chertsey §	d			22 10					22 40								23 10					23 40			
Virginia Water	a	22 19		22 15				22 49	22 45						23 19		23 15			23 49		23 45			
	d	22 19		22 24				22 49	22 54						23 19		23 24			23 49		23 54			
Egham	d	22 23		22 27				22 53	22 57						23 23		23 27			23 53		23 57			
Windsor & Eton Riverside	d				22 21								22 53					23 23							
Datchet	d				22 24								22 56					23 26							
Sunnymeads	d				22 27								22 59					23 29							
Wraysbury	d				22 30								23 02					23 32							
Staines	d	22 29		22 33	22 38			22 59	23 03				23 08		23 29		23a32	23a37		23 59		00a02			
Ashford (Surrey)	d			22 36	22 41				23 06				23 11												
Feltham	d	22 35		22 41	22 46			23 05	23 11				23 16		23 35					00 05					
Whitton	d				22 50								23 20												
Kingston	d		22 29							22 59						23 29			23 55						
Hampton Wick	d		22 31							23 01						23 31			23 57						
Teddington	d		22 35							23 05						23 35			23 59						
Fulwell	d																								
Strawberry Hill	d		22 38							23 08						23 38			00 03						
Twickenham	a	22 40	22 42		22 53			23 10		23 12			23 23		23 40	23 42			00 07	00 10					
	d	22 41	22 43		22 53			23 11		23 13			23 23		23 41	23 43				00 11					
St Margarets	d		22 45							23 15						23 45									
Richmond	⊖ d	22 45	22 49		22 58			23 15		23 19			23 28		23 45	23 49				00 15					
North Sheen	d		22 51							23 21						23 51									
Mortlake	d		22 53							23 23						23 53									
Hounslow	d			22 46					23 16																
Isleworth	d			22 49					23 19																
Syon Lane	d			22 51		←			23 21					←											
Brentford	d			22 54 →		22 54			23 24 →					23 24											
Kew Bridge	d					22 56								23 26											
Chiswick	d					22 59								23 29											
Barnes Bridge	d					23 01								23 31											
Barnes	d		22 56			23 04				23 26				23 34		23 56									
Putney	d		22 59		23 04	23 07				23 29			23 34	23 37		23 59									
Wandsworth Town	d		23 02			23 10				23 32				23 40		00 02									
Clapham Junction 10	d	22 54	23 05		23 09	23 13		23 24		23 35			23 39	23 43	23 54	00 05				00 24					
Queenstown Rd.(Battersea)	d		23 08			23 16				23 38				23 46		00 08									
Vauxhall	⊖ d		23 12		23 15	23 20				23 42			23 45	23 50		00 12									
London Waterloo 15	⊖ a	23 04	23 16		23 19	23 26		23 34		23 46			23 49	23 56	00 03	00 16				00 32					

For general notes see front of timetable
For details of catering facilities see Directory of Train Operators

§ Passengers to/from London may travel via Weybridge. See Table 155.

A From London Waterloo (Table 152)

Saturdays until 27 September

Reading, Guildford, Ascot, Weybridge, Windsor, Kingston, Richmond and Hounslow → London

Network Diagram - see first page of Table 148

		SW A	SW A	SW 1	SW A	SW	SW	SW	SW	SW	SW	SW	SW	SW 1	SW	SW 1	SW	SW	SW	SW 1	SW A	SW
Reading 7	d			23p12										05 42						06 12		
Earley	d			23p17										05 47						06 17		
Winnersh Triangle	d			23p19										05 49						06 19		
Winnersh	d			23p21										05 51						06 21		
Wokingham	d			23p26										05 56						06 26		
Bracknell	d			23p32										06 02						06 32		
Martins Heron	d			23p35										06 05						06 35		
Guildford	d																					
Wanborough	d																					
Ash 3	d																					
Aldershot	a																					
	d															06 00						
Ash Vale	d															06 04						
Frimley	d															06 10						
Camberley	a															06 14						
	d															06 18						
Bagshot	d															06 23						
Ascot 3	d			23p40										06 10		06a30				06 40		
Sunningdale	d			23p43										06 13						06 43		
Longcross	d																					
Woking	d										05 25											
West Byfleet	d										05 30											
Byfleet & New Haw	d										05 33											
Weybridge	d																					06 33
Addlestone §	d										05 37											06 37
Chertsey §	d										05 40											06 40
Virginia Water	a			23p49							05 45			06 19						06 49		06 45
	d			23p49							05 54			06 19						06 49		06 54
Egham	d			23p53							05 57			06 23						06 53		06 57
Windsor & Eton Riverside	d											05 53						06 23				
Datchet	d											05 56						06 26				
Sunnymeads	d											05 59						06 29				
Wraysbury	d											06 02						06 32				
Staines	d			23p59		04 58		05 38			06 03	06 08		06 29			06 33	06 38		06 59		07 03
Ashford (Surrey)	d					05 01		05 41			06 06	06 11					06 36	06 41				07 06
Feltham	d			00 05		05 06		05 46			06 11	06 16		06 35			06 41	06 46		07 05		07 11
Whitton	d					05 10		05 50	05 41			06 20						06 50				
Kingston	d	23p29	23p55		01 17					05 59					06 29						06 59	
Hampton Wick	d	23p31	23p57		01s22					06 01					06 31						07 01	
Teddington	d	23p35	23p59		01s25					06 05					06 35						07 05	
Fulwell	d																					
Strawberry Hill	d	23p38	00 03		01a28		05 38			06 08					06 38						07 08	
Twickenham	a	23p42	00 07	00 10		05 13	05 41	05 53		06 12		06 23		06 40	06 42			06 53		07 10	07 12	
	d	23p43		00 11		05 13	05 43	05 53		06 13		06 23		06 41	06 43			06 53		07 11	07 13	
St Margarets	d	23p45				05 15	05 45			06 15					06 45						07 15	
Richmond	⊖ d	23p49		00 15		05 19	05 49	05 58		06 19		06 28		06 45	06 49			06 58		07 15	07 19	
North Sheen	d	23p51				05 21	05 51			06 21					06 51						07 21	
Mortlake	d	23p53				05 23	05 53			06 23					06 53						07 23	
Hounslow	d								05 46		06 16						06 46					07 16
Isleworth	d								05 49		06 19						06 49					07 19
Syon Lane	d								05 51		06 21		←				06 51		←			07 21
Brentford	d								05 54		06 24		06 24				06 54		06 54			07 24
Kew Bridge	d								05 56		→		06 26				→		06 56			→
Chiswick	d								05 59				06 29						06 59			
Barnes Bridge	d								06 01				06 31						07 01			
Barnes	d	23p56				05 26	05 56		06 04	06 26			06 34		06 56				07 04		07 26	
Putney	d	23p59				05 29	05 59	06 04	06 07	06 29		06 34	06 37		06 59			07 04	07 07		07 29	
Wandsworth Town	d	00 02				05 32	06 02		06 10	06 32			06 40		07 02				07 10		07 32	
Clapham Junction 10	d	00 05		00 24		05 35	06 05	06 09	06 13	06 35		06 39	06 43	06 54	07 05			07 09	07 13	07 24	07 35	
Queenstown Rd.(Battersea)	d	00 08				05 38	06 08		06 16	06 38			06 46		07 08				07 16		07 38	
Vauxhall	⊖ d	00 12				05 42	06 12	06 15	06 20	06 42		06 45	06 50		07 12			07 15	07 20		07 42	
London Waterloo 15	⊖ a	00 16		00 32		05 46	06 16	06 19	06 26	06 46		06 51	06 56	07 04	07 16			07 19	07 26	07 34	07 46	

For general notes see front of timetable
For details of catering facilities see
Directory of Train Operators

§ Passengers to/from London may travel via Weybridge. See Table 155.

A From London Waterloo (Table 152)

Table 149

Saturdays

until 27 September

Reading, Guildford, Ascot, Weybridge, Windsor, Kingston, Richmond and Hounslow → London

Network Diagram - see first page of Table 148

Station		SW	SW	SW	SW	SW	SW	SW	SW	SW	SW	SW	SW	SW	SW	SW	SW	SW	SW	SW	SW	SW
				1		A			1			1	B	A				B	1	1	B	A
Reading 7	d			06 42								07 12								07 42		
Earley	d			06 47								07 17								07 47		
Winnersh Triangle	d			06 49								07 19								07 49		
Winnersh	d			06 51								07 21								07 51		
Wokingham	d			06 56								07 26								07 56		
Bracknell	d			07 02								07 32								08 02		
Martins Heron	d			07 05								07 35								08 05		
Guildford	d								06 30										07 00			
Wanborough	d								06 36										07 06			
Ash 3	d								06 40										07 10			
Aldershot	a								06 47										07 17			
	d								07 00										07 30			
Ash Vale	d								07 04										07 34			
Frimley	d								07 10										07 40			
Camberley	a								07 14										07 44			
	d								07 18										07 48			
Bagshot	d								07 23										07 53			
Ascot 3	d			07 10					07a30			07 40							08a00	08 10		
Sunningdale	d			07 13								07 43								08 13		
Longcross	d																					
Woking	d																					
West Byfleet	d																					
Byfleet & New Haw	d																					
Weybridge	d						07 03								07 33							
Addlestone §	d						07 07								07 37							
Chertsey §	d						07 10								07 40							
Virginia Water	a			07 19			07 15					07 49			07 45					08 19		
	d			07 19			07 24					07 49			07 54					08 19		
Egham	d			07 23			07 27					07 53			07 57					08 23		
Windsor & Eton Riverside	d	06 53						07 23								07 53						
Datchet	d	06 56						07 26								07 56						
Sunnymeads	d	06 59						07 29								07 59						
Wraysbury	d	07 02						07 32								08 02						
Staines	d	07 08		07 29			07 33	07 38				07 59			08 03	08 08				08 29		
Ashford (Surrey)	d	07 11					07 36	07 41							08 06	08 11						
Feltham	d	07 16		07 35			07 41	07 46				08 05			08 11	08 16				08 35		
Whitton	d	07 20						07 50					07 50			08 20		08 23			08 20	
Kingston	d					07 29								07 59								08 29
Hampton Wick	d					07 31								08 01								08 31
Teddington	d					07 35								08 05								08 35
Fulwell	d																					
Strawberry Hill	d					07 38								08 08								08 38
Twickenham	a	07 23		07 40		07 42		07 53				08 10		08 12		08 23		08 26		08 40		08 42
	d	07 23		07 41		07 43		07 53			07 58	08 11		08 13		08 23		08 28		08 41		08 43
St Margarets	d					07 45					08 00			08 15				08 30				08 45
Richmond	⊖ d	07 28		07 45		07 49		07 58			08 04	08 15		08 19		08 28		08 34		08 45		08 49
North Sheen	d					07 51					08 06			08 21				08 36				08 51
Mortlake	d					07 53					08 08			08 23				08 38				08 53
Hounslow	d				07 31		07 46						08 01		08 16						08 31	
Isleworth	d				07 34		07 49						08 04		08 19						08 34	
Syon Lane	d		←		07 36		07 51			←			08 06		08 21		←				08 36	
Brentford	d		07 24		07 39		07 54 →			07 54			08 09		08 24 →		08 24				08 39	
Kew Bridge	d		07 26		07 41					07 56			08 11				08 26				08 41	
Chiswick	d		07 29		07 44					07 59			08 14				08 29				08 44	
Barnes Bridge	d		07 31		07 46					08 01			08 16				08 31				08 46	
Barnes	d		07 34		07 49	07 56				08 04	08 11		08 19	08 26			08 34	08 41			08 49	08 56
Putney	d	07 34	07 37		07 52	07 59		08 04		08 07	08 14		08 22	08 29		08 34	08 37	08 44			08 52	08 59
Wandsworth Town	d		07 40		07 55	08 02				08 10	08 17		08 25	08 32			08 40	08 47			08 55	09 02
Clapham Junction 10	d	07 39	07 43	07 54	07 58	08 05		08 09		08 13	08 20	08 24	08 28	08 35		08 39	08 43	08 50		08 54	08 58	09 05
Queenstown Rd.(Battersea)	d		07 46		08 01	08 08				08 16	08 23		08 31	08 38			08 46	08 53			09 01	09 08
Vauxhall	⊖ d	07 45	07 50		08 05	08 12		08 15		08 20	08 27		08 35	08 42		08 45	08 50	08 57			09 05	09 12
London Waterloo 15	⊖ a	07 49	07 56	08 04	08 11	08 16		08 19		08 26	08 32	08 34	08 41	08 46		08 49	08 56	09 02		09 04	09 11	09 16

For general notes see front of timetable
For details of catering facilities see Directory of Train Operators

A From London Waterloo (Table 152)
B From London Waterloo.

§ Passengers to/from London may travel via Weybridge. See Table 155.

Table 149

Saturdays

until 27 September

Reading, Guildford, Ascot, Weybridge, Windsor, Kingston, Richmond and Hounslow → London

Network Diagram - see first page of Table 148

	SW	SW	SW	SW A	SW 1	SW 1	SW A	SW B	SW	SW	SW	SW A	SW 1	SW 1	SW A	SW B	SW	SW	SW	SW A
Reading 7 d						08 12								08 42						
Earley d						08 17								08 47						
Winnersh Triangle d						08 19								08 49						
Winnersh d						08 21								08 51						
Wokingham d						08 26								08 56						
Bracknell d						08 32								09 02						
Martins Heron d						08 35								09 05						
Guildford d					07 30								08 00							
Wanborough d					07 36								08 06							
Ash 3 d					07 40								08 10							
Aldershot a					07 47								08 17							
d					08 00								08 30							
Ash Vale d					08 04								08 34							
Frimley d					08 10								08 40							
Camberley a					08 14								08 44							
d					08 18								08 48							
Bagshot d					08 23								08 53							
Ascot 3 d					08a30	08 40							09a00	09 10						
Sunningdale d						08 43								09 13						
Longcross d																				
Woking d																				
West Byfleet d																				
Byfleet & New Haw d																				
Weybridge d	08 03								08 33								09 03			
Addlestone § d	08 07								08 37								09 07			
Chertsey § d	08 10								08 40								09 10			
Virginia Water a	08 15					08 49			08 45					09 19			09 15			
d	08 24					08 49			08 54					09 19			09 24			
Egham d	08 27					08 53			08 57					09 24			09 27			
Windsor & Eton Riverside d		08 23								08 53								09 23		
Datchet d		08 26								08 56								09 26		
Sunnymeads d		08 29								08 59								09 29		
Wraysbury d		08 32								09 02								09 32		
Staines d	08 33	08 38				08 59			09 03	09 08				09 29			09 33	09 38		
Ashford (Surrey) d	08 36	08 41							09 06	09 11							09 36	09 41		
Feltham d	08 41	08 46				09 05			09 11	09 16				09 35			09 41	09 46		
Whitton d		08 50		08 53			08 50			09 20		09 23			09 20			09 50		09 53
Kingston d								08 59								09 29				
Hampton Wick d								09 01								09 31				
Teddington d								09 05								09 35				
Fulwell d																				
Strawberry Hill d								09 08								09 38				
Twickenham a		08 53		08 56		09 10		09 12		09 23		09 26		09 40		09 42		09 53		09 56
d		08 53		08 58		09 11		09 13		09 23		09 28		09 41		09 43		09 53		09 58
St Margarets d				09 00				09 15				09 30				09 45				10 00
Richmond ⊖ d		08 58		09 04		09 15		09 19		09 28		09 34		09 45		09 49		09 58		10 04
North Sheen d				09 06				09 21				09 36				09 51				10 06
Mortlake d				09 08				09 23				09 38				09 53				10 08
Hounslow d	08 46						09 01		09 16						09 31		09 46			
Isleworth d	08 49						09 04		09 19						09 34		09 49			
Syon Lane d	08 51		←				09 06		09 21		←				09 36		09 51		←	
Brentford d	08 54 →		08 54				09 09		09 24 →		09 24				09 39		09 54 →		09 54	
Kew Bridge d			08 56				09 11				09 26				09 41				09 56	
Chiswick d			08 59				09 14				09 29				09 44				09 59	
Barnes Bridge d			09 01				09 16				09 31				09 46				10 01	
Barnes d			09 04	09 11			09 19	09 26			09 34	09 41			09 49	09 56			10 04	10 11
Putney d		09 04	09 07	09 14			09 22	09 29		09 34	09 37	09 44			09 52	09 59		10 04	10 07	10 14
Wandsworth Town d			09 10	09 17			09 25	09 32			09 40	09 47			09 55	10 02			10 10	10 17
Clapham Junction 10 d		09 09	09 13	09 20		09 24	09 28	09 35		09 39	09 43	09 50		09 54	09 58	10 05		10 09	10 13	10 20
Queenstown Rd.(Battersea) d			09 16	09 23			09 31	09 38			09 46	09 53			10 01	10 08			10 16	10 23
Vauxhall ⊖ d		09 15	09 20	09 27			09 35	09 42		09 45	09 50	09 57			10 05	10 12		10 15	10 20	10 27
London Waterloo 15 ⊖ a		09 19	09 26	09 32		09 34	09 41	09 46		09 49	09 56	10 02		10 04	10 11	10 16		10 19	10 26	10 32

For general notes see front of timetable
For details of catering facilities see Directory of Train Operators

§ Passengers to/from London may travel via Weybridge. See Table 155.

A From London Waterloo.
B From London Waterloo (Table 152)

Table 149

Saturdays

until 27 September

Reading, Guildford, Ascot, Weybridge, Windsor, Kingston, Richmond and Hounslow → London

Network Diagram - see first page of Table 148

Station		SW 1	SW 1	SW	SW	SW	SW	SW	SW	SW 1	SW 1	SW	SW	SW	SW	SW	SW		SW 1	SW 1	SW	SW
				A	B				A			A	B				A				A	B
Reading 7	d		09 12								09 42									19 12		
Earley	d		09 17								09 47									19 17		
Winnersh Triangle	d		09 19								09 49									19 19		
Winnersh	d		09 21								09 51									19 21		
Wokingham	d		09 26								09 56									19 26		
Bracknell	d		09 32								10 02									19 32		
Martins Heron	d		09 35								10 05									19 35		
Guildford	d	08 30								09 00									18 30			
Wanborough	d	08 36								09 06									18 36			
Ash 3	d	08 40								09 10									18 40			
Aldershot	a	08 47								09 17									18 47			
	d	09 00								09 30									19 00			
Ash Vale	d	09 04								09 34									19 04			
Frimley	d	09 10								09 40									19 10			
Camberley	a	09 14								09 44									19 14			
	d	09 18								09 48									19 18			
Bagshot	d	09 23								09 53									19 23			
Ascot 3	d	09a30	09 40							10a00	10 10								19a30	19 40		
Sunningdale	d		09 43								10 13									19 43		
Longcross	d																					
Woking	d																					
West Byfleet	d																					
Byfleet & New Haw	d																					
Weybridge	d					09 33								10 03								
Addlestone §	d					09 37								10 07				and at				
Chertsey §	d					09 40								10 10								
Virginia Water	a		09 49			09 45					10 19			10 15				the same		19 49		
	d		09 49			09 54					10 19			10 24						19 49		
Egham	d		09 53			09 57					10 23			10 27				minutes		19 53		
Windsor & Eton Riverside	d						09 53								10 23			past				
Datchet	d						09 56								10 26							
Sunnymeads	d						09 59								10 29			each				
Wraysbury	d						10 02								10 32			hour until				
Staines	d		09 59			10 03	10 08				10 29			10 33	10 38					19 59		
Ashford (Surrey)	d					10 06	10 11							10 36	10 41							
Feltham	d		10 05			10 11	10 16				10 35			10 41	10 46					20 05		
Whitton	d			09 50			10 20		10 23			10 20			10 50		10 53				19 50	
Kingston	d				09 59								10 29									19 59
Hampton Wick	d				10 01								10 31									20 01
Teddington	d				10 05								10 35									20 05
Fulwell	d																					
Strawberry Hill	d				10 08								10 38									20 08
Twickenham	a		10 10		10 12		10 23		10 26		10 40		10 42		10 53		10 56			20 10		20 12
	d		10 11		10 13		10 23		10 28		10 41		10 43		10 53		10 58			20 11		20 13
St Margarets	d				10 15				10 30				10 45				11 00					20 15
Richmond	⊖ d		10 15		10 19		10 28		10 34		10 45		10 49		10 58		11 04			20 15		20 19
North Sheen	d				10 21				10 36				10 51				11 06					20 21
Mortlake	d				10 23				10 38				10 53				11 08					20 23
Hounslow	d			10 01		10 16						10 31		10 46							20 01	
Isleworth	d			10 04		10 19						10 34		10 49							20 04	
Syon Lane	d			10 06		10 21		←				10 36		10 51		←					20 06	
Brentford	d			10 09		10 24 →		10 24				10 39		10 54 →		10 54					20 09	
Kew Bridge	d			10 11				10 26				10 41				10 56					20 11	
Chiswick	d			10 14				10 29				10 44				10 59					20 14	
Barnes Bridge	d			10 16				10 31				10 46				11 01					20 16	
Barnes	d			10 19	10 26			10 34	10 41			10 49	10 56			11 04	11 11				20 19	20 26
Putney	d			10 22	10 29		10 34	10 37	10 44			10 52	10 59		11 04	11 07	11 14				20 22	20 29
Wandsworth Town	d			10 25	10 32			10 40	10 47			10 55	11 02			11 10	11 17				20 25	20 32
Clapham Junction 10	d		10 24	10 28	10 35		10 39	10 43	10 50		10 54	10 58	11 05		11 09	11 13	11 20			20 24	20 28	20 35
Queenstown Rd.(Battersea)	d			10 31	10 38			10 46	10 53			11 01	11 08			11 16	11 23				20 31	20 38
Vauxhall	⊖ d			10 35	10 42		10 45	10 50	10 57			11 05	11 12		11 15	11 20	11 27				20 35	20 42
London Waterloo 15	⊖ a		10 34	10 41	10 46		10 49	10 56	11 02		11 04	11 11	11 16		11 19	11 26	11 32			20 34	20 41	20 46

For general notes see front of timetable
For details of catering facilities see Directory of Train Operators

§ Passengers to/from London may travel via Weybridge. See Table 155.

A From London Waterloo.
B From London Waterloo (Table 152)

Table 149

Saturdays

until 27 September

Reading, Guildford, Ascot, Weybridge, Windsor, Kingston, Richmond and Hounslow → London

Network Diagram - see first page of Table 148

		SW	SW	SW	SW	SW [1]	SW [1]	SW	SW	SW	SW	SW [1]	SW	SW	SW [1]	SW	SW	SW	SW	SW [1]	SW [1]	SW
					A			A	B					A		A		B				
Reading [7]	d						19 42								20 12							
Earley	d						19 47								20 17							
Winnersh Triangle	d						19 49								20 19							
Winnersh	d						19 51								20 21							
Wokingham	d						19 56								20 26							
Bracknell	d						20 02								20 32							
Martins Heron	d						20 05								20 35							
Guildford	d					19 00						19 30								20 00	20 30	
Wanborough	d					19 06						19 36								20 06	20 36	
Ash [3]	d					19 10						19 40								20 10	20 40	
Aldershot	a					19 17						19 47								20 17	20 47	
	d					19 30						20 00								20 30		
Ash Vale	d					19 34						20 04								20 34		
Frimley	d					19 40						20 10								20 40		
Camberley	a					19 44						20 14								20 44		
	d					19 48						20 18								20 48		
Bagshot	d					19 53						20 23								20 53		
Ascot [3]	d					20a00	20 10					20a30			20 40					21a00		
Sunningdale	d						20 13								20 43							
Longcross	d																					
Woking	d																					
West Byfleet	d																					
Byfleet & New Haw	d																					
Weybridge	d	19 33								20 03							20 33					
Addlestone §	d	19 37								20 07							20 37					
Chertsey §	d	19 40								20 10							20 40					
Virginia Water	a	19 45					20 19			20 15					20 49		20 45					
	d	19 54					20 19			20 24					20 49		20 54					
Egham	d	19 57					20 23			20 27					20 53		20 57					
Windsor & Eton Riverside	d		19 53								20 23								20 53			
Datchet	d		19 56								20 26								20 56			
Sunnymeads	d		19 59								20 29								20 59			
Wraysbury	d		20 02								20 32								21 02			
Staines	d	20 03	20 08				20 29			20 33	20 38				20 59		21 03		21 08			
Ashford (Surrey)	d	20 06	20 11							20 36	20 41						21 06		21 11			
Feltham	d	20 11	20 16				20 35			20 41	20 46				21 05		21 11		21 16			
Whitton	d		20 20		20 23			20 20			20 50			20 53		20 50			21 20			
Kingston	d								20 29									20 59				
Hampton Wick	d								20 31									21 01				
Teddington	d								20 35									21 05				
Fulwell	d																					
Strawberry Hill	d								20 38									21 08				
Twickenham	a		20 23		20 26		20 40		20 42		20 53			20 56	21 10			21 12	21 23			
	d		20 23		20 28		20 41		20 43		20 53			20 58	21 11			21 13	21 23			
St Margarets	d				20 30				20 45					21 00				21 15				
Richmond	⊖ d		20 28		20 34		20 45		20 49		20 58			21 04	21 15			21 19	21 28			
North Sheen	d				20 36				20 51					21 06				21 21				
Mortlake	d				20 38				20 53					21 08				21 23				
Hounslow	d	20 16						20 31		20 46						21 01	21 16					
Isleworth	d	20 19						20 34		20 49						21 04	21 19					
Syon Lane	d	20 21		←				20 36		20 51			←			21 06	21 21					←
Brentford	d	20 24		20 24				20 39		20 54			20 54			21 09	21 24					21 24
Kew Bridge	d	→		20 26				20 41		→			20 56			21 11	→					21 26
Chiswick	d			20 29				20 44					20 59			21 14						21 29
Barnes Bridge	d			20 31	19 59			20 46					21 01			21 16						21 31
Barnes	d			20 34	20 41			20 49	20 56				21 04	21 11		21 19		21 26				21 34
Putney	d		20 34	20 37	20 44			20 52	20 59		21 04		21 07	21 14		21 22		21 29	21 34			21 37
Wandsworth Town	d			20 40	20 47			20 55	21 02				21 10	21 17		21 25		21 32				21 40
Clapham Junction [10]	d		20 39	20 43	20 50		20 54	20 58	21 05		21 09		21 13	21 20	21 24	21 28		21 35	21 39			21 43
Queenstown Rd.(Battersea)	d			20 46	20 53			21 01	21 08				21 16	21 23		21 31		21 38				21 46
Vauxhall	⊖ d		20 45	20 50	20 57			21 05	21 12		21 15		21 20	21 27		21 35		21 42	21 45			21 50
London Waterloo [15]	⊖ a		20 49	20 56	21 02		21 04	21 11	21 16		21 19		21 26	21 32	21 34	21 41		21 46	21 49			21 56

For general notes see front of timetable
For details of catering facilities see Directory of Train Operators

§ Passengers to/from London may travel via Weybridge. See Table 155.

A From London Waterloo.
B From London Waterloo (Table 152)

Saturdays

until 27 September

Reading, Guildford, Ascot, Weybridge, Windsor, Kingston, Richmond and Hounslow → London

Network Diagram - see first page of Table 148

		SW	SW 1	SW	SW	SW	SW	SW	SW	SW 1	SW	SW	SW	SW	SW 1	SW 1	SW	SW	SW 1	SW	SW	SW
		A		A	B				A		A		B					A		B		
Reading 7	d		20 42							21 12									21 42			
Earley	d		20 47							21 17									21 47			
Winnersh Triangle	d		20 49							21 19									21 49			
Winnersh	d		20 51							21 21									21 51			
Wokingham	d		20 56							21 26									21 56			
Bracknell	d		21 02							21 32									22 02			
Martins Heron	d		21 05							21 35									22 05			
Guildford	d														21 00	21 30						
Wanborough	d														21 06	21 36						
Ash 3	d														21 10	21 40						
Aldershot	a														21 17	21 47						
	d														21 30							
Ash Vale	d														21 34							
Frimley	d														21 40							
Camberley	a														21 44							
	d														21 48							
Bagshot	d														21 53							
Ascot 3	d		21 10							21 40					22a00				22 10			
Sunningdale	d		21 13							21 43									22 13			
Longcross	d																					
Woking	d																					
West Byfleet	d																					
Byfleet & New Haw	d																					
Weybridge	d					21 03						21 33									22 03	
Addlestone §	d					21 07						21 37									22 07	
Chertsey §	d					21 10						21 40									22 10	
Virginia Water	a		21 19			21 15				21 49		21 45							22 19		22 15	
	d		21 19			21 24				21 49		21 54							22 19		22 24	
Egham	d		21 23			21 27				21 53		21 57							22 23		22 27	
Windsor & Eton Riverside	d						21 23							21 53								22 23
Datchet	d						21 26							21 56								22 26
Sunnymeads	d						21 29							21 59								22 29
Wraysbury	d						21 32							22 02								22 32
Staines	d		21 29			21 33	21 38			21 59		22 03		22 08					22 29		22 33	22 38
Ashford (Surrey)	d					21 36	21 41					22 06		22 11							22 36	22 41
Feltham	d		21 35			21 41	21 46			22 05		22 11		22 16					22 35		22 41	22 46
Whitton	d	21 23		21 20			21 50		21 53		21 50			22 20				22 23				22 50
Kingston	d				21 29								21 59							22 29		
Hampton Wick	d				21 31								22 01							22 31		
Teddington	d				21 35								22 05							22 35		
Fulwell	d																					
Strawberry Hill	d				21 38								22 08							22 38		
Twickenham	a	21 26	21 40		21 42		21 53		21 56	22 10			22 12	22 23				22 26	22 40	22 42		22 53
	d	21 28	21 41		21 43		21 53		21 58	22 11			22 13	22 23				22 28	22 41	22 43		22 53
St Margarets	d	21 30			21 45				22 00				22 15					22 30		22 45		
Richmond	⊖ d	21 34	21 45		21 49		21 58		22 04	22 15			22 19	22 28				22 34	22 45	22 49		22 58
North Sheen	d	21 36			21 51				22 06				22 21					22 36		22 51		
Mortlake	d	21 38			21 53				22 08				22 23					22 38		22 53		
Hounslow	d			21 31		21 46					22 01	22 16									22 46	
Isleworth	d			21 34		21 49					22 04	22 19									22 49	
Syon Lane	d			21 36		21 51		←			22 06	22 21					←				22 51	
Brentford	d			21 39		21 54		21 54			22 09	22 24					22 24				22 54	
Kew Bridge	d			21 41		→		21 56			22 11	→					22 26				→	
Chiswick	d			21 44				21 59			22 14						22 29					
Barnes Bridge	d			21 46				22 01			22 16						22 31					
Barnes	d	21 41		21 49	21 56			22 04	22 11		22 19		22 26				22 34	22 41		22 56		
Putney	d	21 44		21 52	21 59		22 04	22 07	22 14		22 22		22 29	22 34			22 37	22 44		22 59		23 04
Wandsworth Town	d	21 47		21 55	22 02			22 10	22 18		22 25		22 32				22 40	22 47		23 02		
Clapham Junction 10	d	21 50	21 54	21 58	22 05		22 09	22 13	22 20	22 24	22 28		22 35	22 39			22 43	22 50	22 54	23 05		23 09
Queenstown Rd.(Battersea)	d	21 53		22 01	22 08			22 16	22 23		22 31		22 38				22 46	22 53		23 08		
Vauxhall	⊖ d	21 57		22 05	22 12		22 15	22 20	22 27		22 35		22 42	22 45			22 50	22 57		23 12		23 15
London Waterloo 15	⊖ a	22 02	22 04	22 11	22 16		22 19	22 26	22 32	22 34	22 41		22 46	22 49			22 56	23 02	23 04	23 17		23 19

For general notes see front of timetable
For details of catering facilities see Directory of Train Operators

§ Passengers to/from London may travel via Weybridge. See Table 155.

A From London Waterloo.
B From London Waterloo (Table 152)

Table 149

until 27 September

Reading, Guildford, Ascot, Weybridge, Windsor, Kingston, Richmond and Hounslow → London

Network Diagram - see first page of Table 148

		SW	SW 1		SW	SW A	SW 1	SW 1	SW	SW		SW 1	SW A	SW	SW	SW A	SW 1		SW	SW 1	SW 1 B				
Reading [7]	d		22 12									22 42					23 12								
Earley	d		22 17									22 47					23 17								
Winnersh Triangle	d		22 19									22 49					23 19								
Winnersh	d		22 21									22 51					23 21								
Wokingham	d		22 26									22 56					23 26								
Bracknell	d		22 32									23 02					23 32								
Martins Heron	d		22 35									23 05					23 35								
Guildford	d						22 00	22 30												23 00	23 30				
Wanborough	d						22 06	22 36												23 06	23 36				
Ash [3]	d						22 10	22 40												23 10	23 40				
Aldershot	a						22 17	22 47												23 17	23 47				
	d						22 30													23 30					
Ash Vale	d						22 34													23 34					
Frimley	d						22 40													23 40					
Camberley	a						22 44													23 44					
	d						22 48													23 48					
Bagshot	d						22 53													23 53					
Ascot [3]	d		22 40				23a00					23 10					23 40			00a01					
Sunningdale	d		22 43									23 13					23 43								
Longcross	d																								
Woking	d																								
West Byfleet	d																								
Byfleet & New Haw	d																								
Weybridge	d				22 33									23 03					23 33						
Addlestone §	d				22 37									23 07					23 37						
Chertsey §	d				22 40									23 10					23 40						
Virginia Water	a		22 49		22 45							23 19		23 15			23 49		23 45						
	d		22 49		22 54							23 19		23 24			23 49		23 54						
Egham	d		22 53		22 57							23 23		23 27			23 53		23 57						
Windsor & Eton Riverside	d								22 53						23 23										
Datchet	d								22 56						23 26										
Sunnymeads	d								22 59						23 29										
Wraysbury	d								23 02						23 32										
Staines	d		22 59		23 03				23 08			23 29		23a32	23a37		23 59		00a02						
Ashford (Surrey)	d				23 06				23 11																
Feltham	d		23 05		23 11				23 16			23 35					00 05								
Whitton	d								23 20																
Kingston	d					22 59							23 29			23 55									
Hampton Wick	d					23 01							23 31			23 57									
Teddington	d					23 05							23 35			23 59									
Fulwell	d																								
Strawberry Hill	d					23 08							23 38			00 03									
Twickenham	a		23 10			23 12			23 23			23 40	23 42			00 07	00 10								
	d		23 11			23 13			23 23			23 41	23 43				00 12								
St Margarets	d					23 15							23 45												
Richmond	⊖ d		23 15			23 19			23 28			23 45	23 49				00 16								
North Sheen	d					23 21							23 51												
Mortlake	d					23 23							23 53												
Hounslow	d				23 16																				
Isleworth	d				23 19																				
Syon Lane	d	←			23 21					←															
Brentford	d	22 54			23 24 →					23 24															
Kew Bridge	d	22 56								23 26															
Chiswick	d	22 59								23 29															
Barnes Bridge	d	23 01								23 31															
Barnes	d	23 04				23 26				23 34			23 56												
Putney	d	23 07				23 29			23 34	23 37			23 59												
Wandsworth Town	d	23 10				23 32				23 40			00 02												
Clapham Junction [10]	d	23 13	23 24			23 35			23 39	23 43		23 54	00 05				00 25								
Queenstown Rd.(Battersea)	d	23 16				23 38				23 46			00 08												
Vauxhall	⊖ d	23 20				23 42			23 45	23 50			00 12												
London Waterloo [15]	⊖ a	23 26	23 34			23 47			23 49	23 56		00 02	00 16				00 33								

For general notes see front of timetable
For details of catering facilities see Directory of Train Operators

§ Passengers to/from London may travel via Weybridge. See Table 155.

A From London Waterloo (Table 152)
B To Farnham (Table 155)

Saturdays

from 4 October

Reading, Guildford, Ascot, Weybridge, Windsor, Kingston, Richmond and Hounslow → London

Network Diagram - see first page of Table 148

		SW	SW	SW	SW	SW	SW		SW	SW	SW	SW	SW	SW		SW	SW	SW	SW	SW	SW		SW	SW	SW
				1												1		1					1		
		A	A		A																			A	
Reading 7	d			23p12												05 39							06 09		
Earley	d			23p17												05 44							06 14		
Winnersh Triangle	d			23p19												05 46							06 16		
Winnersh	d			23p21												05 48							06 18		
Wokingham	d			23p26												05 53							06 23		
Bracknell	d			23p32												05 59							06 29		
Martins Heron	d			23p35												06 02							06 32		
Guildford	d																								
Wanborough	d																								
Ash 3	d																								
Aldershot	a																								
	d																	06 00							
Ash Vale	d																	06 04							
Frimley	d																	06 10							
Camberley	a																	06 14							
	d																	06 18							
Bagshot	d																	06 23							
Ascot 3	d			23p40												06 07		06a30					06 37		
Sunningdale	d			23p43												06 10							06 40		
Longcross	d																								
Woking	d											05 25													
West Byfleet	d											05 30													
Byfleet & New Haw	d											05 33													
Weybridge	d																								06 33
Addlestone §	d											05 37													06 37
Chertsey §	d											05 40													06 40
Virginia Water	a			23p49								05 45				06 19							06 49		06 45
	d			23p49								05 54				06 19							06 49		06 54
Egham	d			23p53								05 57				06 23							06 53		06 57
Windsor & Eton Riverside	d												05 51							06 21					
Datchet	d												05 54							06 24					
Sunnymeads	d												05 57							06 27					
Wraysbury	d												06 00							06 30					
Staines	d			23p59		04 58			05 38			06 03	06 08			06 29			06 33	06 38			06 59		07 03
Ashford (Surrey)	d					05 01			05 41			06 06	06 11						06 36	06 41					07 06
Feltham	d			00 05		05 06			05 46			06 11	06 16			06 35			06 41	06 46			07 05		07 11
Whitton	d					05 10			05 50	05 41			06 20							06 50					
Kingston	d	23p29	23p55		01 17						05 59						06 29							06 59	
Hampton Wick	d	23p31	23p57		01s22						06 01						06 31							07 01	
Teddington	d	23p35	23p59		01s25						06 05						06 35							07 05	
Fulwell	d																								
Strawberry Hill	d	23p38	00 03		01a28		05 38				06 08						06 38							07 08	
Twickenham	a	23p42	00 07	00 10		05 13	05 41		05 53		06 12		06 23			06 40	06 42			06 53			07 10	07 12	
	d	23p43		00 11		05 13	05 43		05 53		06 13		06 23			06 41	06 43			06 53			07 11	07 13	
St Margarets	d	23p45				05 15	05 45				06 15						06 45							07 15	
Richmond	⊖ d	23p49		00 15		05 19	05 49		05 58		06 19		06 28			06 45	06 49			06 58			07 15	07 19	
North Sheen	d	23p51				05 21	05 51				06 21						06 51							07 21	
Mortlake	d	23p53				05 23	05 53				06 23						06 53							07 23	
Hounslow	d									05 46		06 16							06 46						07 16
Isleworth	d									05 49		06 19							06 49						07 19
Syon Lane	d									05 51		06 21		←					06 51		←				07 21
Brentford	d									05 54		06 24 →		06 24					06 54 →		06 54				07 24 →
Kew Bridge	d									05 56				06 26							06 56				
Chiswick	d									05 59				06 29							06 59				
Barnes Bridge	d									06 01				06 31							07 01				
Barnes	d	23p56				05 26	05 56			06 04	06 26			06 34			06 56				07 04			07 26	
Putney	d	23p59				05 29	05 59		06 04	06 07	06 29		06 34	06 37			06 59			07 04	07 07			07 29	
Wandsworth Town	d	00 02				05 32	06 02			06 10	06 32			06 40			07 02				07 10			07 32	
Clapham Junction 10	d	00 05		00 24		05 35	06 05		06 09	06 13	06 35		06 39	06 43		06 54	07 05			07 09	07 13		07 24	07 35	
Queenstown Rd.(Battersea)	d	00 08				05 38	06 08			06 16	06 38			06 46			07 08				07 16			07 38	
Vauxhall	⊖ d	00 12				05 42	06 12		06 15	06 20	06 42		06 45	06 50			07 12			07 15	07 20			07 42	
London Waterloo 15	⊖ a	00 16		00 32		05 46	06 16		06 19	06 26	06 46		06 51	06 56		07 04	07 16			07 19	07 26		07 34	07 46	

For general notes see front of timetable
For details of catering facilities see Directory of Train Operators

§ Passengers to/from London may travel via Weybridge. See Table 155.

A From London Waterloo (Table 152)

from 4 October

Reading, Guildford, Ascot, Weybridge, Windsor, Kingston, Richmond and Hounslow → London

Network Diagram - see first page of Table 148

		SW	SW	SW	SW	SW	SW	SW	SW	SW	SW	SW	SW	SW	SW	SW	SW	SW	SW	SW	SW	SW
				1		A			1			1	B	A				B	1	1	B	A
Reading 7	d			06 39								07 09								07 39		
Earley	d			06 44								07 14								07 44		
Winnersh Triangle	d			06 46								07 16								07 46		
Winnersh	d			06 48								07 18								07 48		
Wokingham	d			06 53								07 23								07 53		
Bracknell	d			06 59								07 29								07 59		
Martins Heron	d			07 02								07 32								08 02		
Guildford	d								06 30										07 00			
Wanborough	d								06 36										07 06			
Ash 3	d								06 40										07 10			
Aldershot	a								06 47										07 17			
	d								07 00										07 30			
Ash Vale	d								07 04										07 34			
Frimley	d								07 10										07 40			
Camberley	a								07 14										07 44			
	d								07 18										07 48			
Bagshot	d								07 23										07 53			
Ascot 3	d			07 07					07a30			07 37							08a00	08 07		
Sunningdale	d			07 10								07 40								08 10		
Longcross	d																					
Woking	d																					
West Byfleet	d																					
Byfleet & New Haw	d																					
Weybridge	d						07 03								07 33							
Addlestone §	d						07 07								07 37							
Chertsey §	d						07 10								07 40							
Virginia Water	a			07 19			07 15					07 49			07 45					08 19		
	d			07 19			07 24					07 49			07 54					08 19		
Egham	d			07 23			07 27					07 53			07 57					08 23		
Windsor & Eton Riverside	d	06 51						07 21								07 51						
Datchet	d	06 54						07 24								07 54						
Sunnymeads	d	06 57						07 27								07 57						
Wraysbury	d	07 00						07 30								08 00						
Staines	d	07 08		07 29			07 33	07 38				07 59			08 03	08 08				08 29		
Ashford (Surrey)	d	07 11					07 36	07 41							08 06	08 11						
Feltham	d	07 16		07 35			07 41	07 46				08 05			08 11	08 16				08 35		
Whitton	d	07 20						07 50					07 50			08 20		08 23			08 20	
Kingston	d					07 29								07 59								08 29
Hampton Wick	d					07 31								08 01								08 31
Teddington	d					07 35								08 05								08 35
Fulwell	d																					
Strawberry Hill	d					07 38								08 08								08 38
Twickenham	a	07 23		07 40		07 42		07 53				08 10		08 12		08 23		08 26		08 40		08 42
	d	07 23		07 41		07 43		07 53			07 58	08 11		08 13		08 23		08 28		08 41		08 43
St Margarets	d					07 45					08 00			08 15				08 30				08 45
Richmond	⊖ d	07 28		07 45		07 49		07 58			08 04	08 15		08 19		08 28		08 34		08 45		08 49
North Sheen	d					07 51					08 06			08 21				08 36				08 51
Mortlake	d					07 53					08 08			08 23				08 38				08 53
Hounslow	d				07 31		07 46						08 01		08 16						08 31	
Isleworth	d				07 34		07 49						08 04		08 19						08 34	
Syon Lane	d		←		07 36		07 51			←			08 06		08 21		←				08 36	
Brentford	d		07 24		07 39		07 54 →			07 54			08 09		08 24 →		08 24				08 39	
Kew Bridge	d		07 26		07 41					07 56			08 11				08 26				08 41	
Chiswick	d		07 29		07 44					07 59			08 14				08 29				08 44	
Barnes Bridge	d		07 31		07 46					08 01			08 16				08 31				08 46	
Barnes	d		07 34		07 49	07 56				08 04	08 11		08 19	08 26			08 34	08 41			08 49	08 56
Putney	d	07 34	07 37		07 52	07 59		08 04		08 07	08 14		08 22	08 29		08 34	08 37	08 44			08 52	08 59
Wandsworth Town	d		07 40		07 55	08 02				08 10	08 17		08 25	08 32			08 40	08 47			08 55	09 02
Clapham Junction 10	d	07 39	07 43	07 54	07 58	08 05		08 09		08 13	08 20	08 24	08 28	08 35		08 39	08 43	08 50		08 54	08 58	09 05
Queenstown Rd.(Battersea)	d		07 46		08 01	08 08				08 16	08 23		08 31	08 38			08 46	08 53			09 01	09 08
Vauxhall	⊖ d	07 45	07 50		08 05	08 12		08 15		08 20	08 27		08 35	08 42		08 45	08 50	08 57			09 05	09 12
London Waterloo 15	⊖ a	07 49	07 56	08 04	08 11	08 16		08 19		08 26	08 32	08 34	08 41	08 46		08 49	08 56	09 02		09 04	09 11	09 16

For general notes see front of timetable
For details of catering facilities see Directory of Train Operators

§ Passengers to/from London may travel via Weybridge. See Table 155.

A From London Waterloo (Table 152)
B From London Waterloo.

Table 149

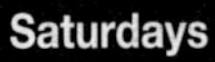

Saturdays

from 4 October

Reading, Guildford, Ascot, Weybridge, Windsor, Kingston, Richmond and Hounslow → London

Network Diagram - see first page of Table 148

		SW	SW	SW	SW	SW 1	SW 1	SW	SW	SW	SW	SW	SW	SW 1	SW 1	SW	SW	SW	SW	SW	SW
					A			A	B				A			A	B				A
Reading 7	d						08 09								08 39						
Earley	d						08 14								08 44						
Winnersh Triangle	d						08 16								08 46						
Winnersh	d						08 18								08 48						
Wokingham	d						08 23								08 53						
Bracknell	d						08 29								08 59						
Martins Heron	d						08 32								09 02						
Guildford	d					07 30								08 00							
Wanborough	d					07 36								08 06							
Ash 3	d					07 40								08 10							
Aldershot	a					07 47								08 17							
	d					08 00								08 30							
Ash Vale	d					08 04								08 34							
Frimley	d					08 10								08 40							
Camberley	a					08 14								08 44							
	d					08 18								08 48							
Bagshot	d					08 23								08 53							
Ascot 3	d					08a30	08 37							09a00	09 07						
Sunningdale	d						08 40								09 10						
Longcross	d																				
Woking	d																				
West Byfleet	d																				
Byfleet & New Haw	d																				
Weybridge	d	08 03								08 33								09 03			
Addlestone §	d	08 07								08 37								09 07			
Chertsey §	d	08 10								08 40								09 10			
Virginia Water	a	08 15					08 49			08 45					09 19			09 15			
	d	08 24					08 49			08 54					09 19			09 24			
Egham	d	08 27					08 53			08 57					09 24			09 27			
Windsor & Eton Riverside	d		08 21								08 51								09 21		
Datchet	d		08 24								08 54								09 24		
Sunnymeads	d		08 27								08 57								09 27		
Wraysbury	d		08 30								09 00								09 30		
Staines	d	08 33	08 38				08 59			09 03	09 08				09 29			09 33	09 38		
Ashford (Surrey)	d	08 36	08 41							09 06	09 11							09 36	09 41		
Feltham	d	08 41	08 46				09 05			09 11	09 16				09 35			09 41	09 46		
Whitton	d		08 50		08 53			08 50			09 20		09 23			09 20			09 50		09 53
Kingston	d								08 59								09 29				
Hampton Wick	d								09 01								09 31				
Teddington	d								09 05								09 35				
Fulwell	d																				
Strawberry Hill	d								09 08								09 38				
Twickenham	a		08 53		08 56		09 10		09 12		09 23		09 26		09 40		09 42		09 53		09 56
	d		08 53		08 58		09 11		09 13		09 23		09 28		09 41		09 43		09 53		09 58
St Margarets	d				09 00				09 15				09 30				09 45				10 00
Richmond ⊖	d		08 58		09 04		09 15		09 19		09 28		09 34		09 45		09 49		09 58		10 04
North Sheen	d				09 06				09 21				09 36				09 51				10 06
Mortlake	d				09 08				09 23				09 38				09 53				10 08
Hounslow	d	08 46						09 01		09 16						09 31		09 46			
Isleworth	d	08 49						09 04		09 19						09 34		09 49			
Syon Lane	d	08 51		←				09 06		09 21		←				09 36		09 51		←	
Brentford	d	08 54		08 54				09 09		09 24		09 24				09 39		09 54		09 54	
Kew Bridge	d	→		08 56				09 11		→		09 26				09 41		→		09 56	
Chiswick	d			08 59				09 14				09 29				09 44				09 59	
Barnes Bridge	d			09 01				09 16				09 31				09 46				10 01	
Barnes	d			09 04	09 11			09 19	09 26			09 34	09 41			09 49	09 56			10 04	10 11
Putney	d		09 04	09 07	09 14			09 22	09 29		09 34	09 37	09 44			09 52	09 59		10 04	10 07	10 14
Wandsworth Town	d			09 10	09 17			09 25	09 32			09 40	09 47			09 55	10 02			10 10	10 17
Clapham Junction 10	d		09 09	09 13	09 20		09 24	09 28	09 35		09 39	09 43	09 50		09 54	09 58	10 05		10 09	10 13	10 20
Queenstown Rd.(Battersea)	d			09 16	09 23			09 31	09 38			09 46	09 53			10 01	10 08			10 16	10 23
Vauxhall ⊖	d		09 15	09 20	09 27			09 35	09 42		09 45	09 50	09 57			10 05	10 12		10 15	10 20	10 27
London Waterloo 15 ⊖	a		09 19	09 26	09 32		09 34	09 41	09 46		09 49	09 56	10 02		10 04	10 11	10 16		10 19	10 26	10 32

For general notes see front of timetable
For details of catering facilities see Directory of Train Operators

§ Passengers to/from London may travel via Weybridge. See Table 155.

A From London Waterloo.
B From London Waterloo (Table 152)

Saturdays from 4 October

Reading, Guildford, Ascot, Weybridge, Windsor, Kingston, Richmond and Hounslow → London

Network Diagram - see first page of Table 148

	SW [1]	SW [1]	SW A	SW B	SW	SW	SW	SW A	SW [1]	SW [1]	SW A	SW B	SW	SW	SW	SW A		SW [1]	SW [1]	SW A	SW B
Reading [7] d		09 09								09 39									19 09		
Earley d		09 14								09 44									19 14		
Winnersh Triangle d		09 16								09 46									19 16		
Winnersh d		09 18								09 48									19 18		
Wokingham d		09 23								09 53									19 23		
Bracknell d		09 29								09 59									19 29		
Martins Heron d		09 32								10 02									19 32		
Guildford d	08 30								09 00									18 30			
Wanborough d	08 36								09 06									18 36			
Ash [3] d	08 40								09 10									18 40			
Aldershot a	08 47								09 17									18 47			
d	09 00								09 30									19 00			
Ash Vale d	09 04								09 34									19 04			
Frimley d	09 10								09 40									19 10			
Camberley a	09 14								09 44									19 14			
d	09 18								09 48									19 18			
Bagshot d	09 23								09 53									19 23			
Ascot [3] d	09a30	09 37							10a00	10 07								19a30	19 37		
Sunningdale d		09 40								10 10									19 40		
Longcross d																					
Woking d																					
West Byfleet d																					
Byfleet & New Haw d																					
Weybridge d					09 33								10 03								
Addlestone § d					09 37								10 07								
Chertsey § d					09 40								10 10				and at				
Virginia Water a		09 49			09 45					10 19			10 15				the same		19 49		
d		09 49			09 54					10 19			10 24						19 49		
Egham d		09 53			09 57					10 23			10 27				minutes		19 53		
Windsor & Eton Riverside d						09 51								10 21			past				
Datchet d						09 54								10 24							
Sunnymeads d						09 57								10 27			each				
Wraysbury d						10 00								10 30							
Staines d		09 59			10 03	10 08				10 29			10 33	10 38			hour until		19 59		
Ashford (Surrey) d					10 06	10 11							10 36	10 41							
Feltham d		10 05			10 11	10 16				10 35			10 41	10 46					20 05		
Whitton d			09 50			10 20		10 23			10 20			10 50		10 53				19 50	
Kingston d				09 59								10 29									19 59
Hampton Wick d				10 01								10 31									20 01
Teddington d				10 05								10 35									20 05
Fulwell d																					
Strawberry Hill d				10 08								10 38									20 08
Twickenham a		10 10		10 12		10 23		10 26		10 40		10 42		10 53		10 56			20 10		20 12
d		10 11		10 13		10 23		10 28		10 41		10 43		10 53		10 58			20 11		20 13
St Margarets d				10 15				10 30				10 45				11 00					20 15
Richmond ⊖ d		10 15		10 19		10 28		10 34		10 45		10 49		10 58		11 04			20 15		20 19
North Sheen d				10 21				10 36				10 51				11 06					20 21
Mortlake d				10 23				10 38				10 53				11 08					20 23
Hounslow d			10 01		10 16						10 31		10 46							20 01	
Isleworth d			10 04		10 19						10 34		10 49							20 04	
Syon Lane d			10 06		10 21		←				10 36		10 51		←					20 06	
Brentford d			10 09		10 24 →		10 24				10 39		10 54 →		10 54					20 09	
Kew Bridge d			10 11				10 26				10 41				10 56					20 11	
Chiswick d			10 14				10 29				10 44				10 59					20 14	
Barnes Bridge d			10 16				10 31				10 46				11 01					20 16	
Barnes d			10 19	10 26			10 34	10 41			10 49	10 56			11 04	11 11				20 19	20 26
Putney d			10 22	10 29		10 34	10 37	10 44			10 52	10 59		11 04	11 07	11 14				20 22	20 29
Wandsworth Town d			10 25	10 32			10 40	10 47			10 55	11 02			11 10	11 17				20 25	20 32
Clapham Junction [10] d		10 24	10 28	10 35		10 39	10 43	10 50		10 54	10 58	11 05		11 09	11 13	11 20			20 24	20 28	20 35
Queenstown Rd.(Battersea) d			10 31	10 38			10 46	10 53			11 01	11 08			11 16	11 23				20 31	20 38
Vauxhall ⊖ d			10 35	10 42		10 45	10 50	10 57			11 05	11 12		11 15	11 20	11 27				20 35	20 42
London Waterloo [15] ⊖ a		10 34	10 41	10 46		10 49	10 56	11 02		11 04	11 11	11 16		11 19	11 26	11 32			20 34	20 41	20 46

For general notes see front of timetable
For details of catering facilities see Directory of Train Operators

§ Passengers to/from London may travel via Weybridge. See Table 155.

A From London Waterloo.
B From London Waterloo (Table 152)

Table 149

Saturdays

from 4 October

Reading, Guildford, Ascot, Weybridge, Windsor, Kingston, Richmond and Hounslow → London

Network Diagram - see first page of Table 148

Station		SW	SW	SW	SW	SW	SW	SW	SW	SW	SW	SW	SW	SW	SW	SW	SW	SW	SW	SW	SW	SW
					A	1	1	A	B			1		A	1	A		B		1	1	
Reading 7	d						19 39								20 09							
Earley	d						19 44								20 14							
Winnersh Triangle	d						19 46								20 16							
Winnersh	d						19 48								20 18							
Wokingham	d						19 53								20 23							
Bracknell	d						19 59								20 29							
Martins Heron	d						20 02								20 32							
Guildford	d					19 00						19 30								20 00	20 30	
Wanborough	d					19 06						19 36								20 06	20 36	
Ash 3	d					19 10						19 40								20 10	20 40	
Aldershot	a					19 17						19 47								20 17	20 47	
	d					19 30						20 00								20 30		
Ash Vale	d					19 34						20 04								20 34		
Frimley	d					19 40						20 10								20 40		
Camberley	a					19 44						20 14								20 44		
	d					19 48						20 18								20 48		
Bagshot	d					19 53						20 23								20 53		
Ascot 3	d					20a00	20 07					20a30			20 37					21a00		
Sunningdale	d						20 10								20 40							
Longcross	d																					
Woking	d																					
West Byfleet	d																					
Byfleet & New Haw	d																					
Weybridge	d	19 33								20 03							20 33					
Addlestone §	d	19 37								20 07							20 37					
Chertsey §	d	19 40								20 10							20 40					
Virginia Water	a	19 45					20 19			20 15					20 49		20 45					
	d	19 54					20 19			20 24					20 49		20 54					
Egham	d	19 57					20 23			20 27					20 53		20 57					
Windsor & Eton Riverside	d		19 51								20 21								20 51			
Datchet	d		19 54								20 24								20 54			
Sunnymeads	d		19 57								20 27								20 57			
Wraysbury	d		20 00								20 30								21 00			
Staines	d	20 03	20 08				20 29			20 33	20 38				20 59		21 03		21 08			
Ashford (Surrey)	d	20 06	20 11							20 36	20 41						21 06		21 11			
Feltham	d	20 11	20 16				20 35			20 41	20 46				21 05		21 11		21 16			
Whitton	d		20 20		20 23			20 20			20 50			20 53		20 50			21 20			
Kingston	d								20 29									20 59				
Hampton Wick	d								20 31									21 01				
Teddington	d								20 35									21 05				
Fulwell	d																					
Strawberry Hill	d								20 38									21 08				
Twickenham	a		20 23		20 26		20 40		20 42		20 53			20 56	21 10			21 12	21 23			
	d		20 23		20 28		20 41		20 43		20 53			20 58	21 11			21 13	21 23			
St Margarets	d				20 30				20 45					21 00				21 15				
Richmond ⊖	d		20 28		20 34		20 45		20 49		20 58			21 04	21 15			21 19	21 28			
North Sheen	d				20 36				20 51					21 06				21 21				
Mortlake	d				20 38				20 53					21 08				21 23				
Hounslow	d	20 16						20 31		20 46						21 01	21 16					
Isleworth	d	20 19						20 34		20 49						21 04	21 19					
Syon Lane	d	20 21		←				20 36		20 51			←			21 06	21 21					←
Brentford	d	20 24		20 24				20 39		20 54			20 54			21 09	21 24					21 24
Kew Bridge	d	→		20 26				20 41		→			20 56			21 11	→					21 26
Chiswick	d			20 29				20 44					20 59			21 14						21 29
Barnes Bridge	d			20 31				20 46					21 01			21 16						21 31
Barnes	d			20 34	20 41			20 49	20 56				21 04	21 11		21 19		21 26				21 34
Putney	d		20 34	20 37	20 44			20 52	20 59		21 04		21 07	21 14		21 22		21 29	21 34			21 37
Wandsworth Town	d			20 40	20 47			20 55	21 02				21 10	21 17		21 25		21 32				21 40
Clapham Junction 10	d		20 39	20 43	20 50		20 54	20 58	21 05		21 09		21 13	21 20	21 24	21 28		21 35	21 39			21 43
Queenstown Rd.(Battersea)	d			20 46	20 53			21 01	21 08				21 16	21 23		21 31		21 38				21 46
Vauxhall ⊖	d		20 45	20 50	20 57			21 05	21 12		21 15		21 20	21 27		21 35		21 42	21 45			21 50
London Waterloo 15 ⊖	a		20 49	20 56	21 02		21 04	21 11	21 16		21 19		21 26	21 32	21 34	21 41		21 46	21 49			21 56

For general notes see front of timetable
For details of catering facilities see Directory of Train Operators

§ Passengers to/from London may travel via Weybridge. See Table 155.

A From London Waterloo.
B From London Waterloo (Table 152)

Reading, Guildford, Ascot, Weybridge, Windsor, Kingston, Richmond and Hounslow → London

Saturdays from 4 October

Network Diagram - see first page of Table 148

		SW	SW 1	SW		SW	SW	SW	SW	SW	SW 1		SW	SW	SW	SW	SW 1	SW 1		SW	SW	SW 1	SW	SW	SW
		A		A		B				A			A		B						A		B		
Reading 7	d		20 39								21 09											21 39			
Earley	d		20 44								21 14											21 44			
Winnersh Triangle	d		20 46								21 16											21 46			
Winnersh	d		20 48								21 18											21 48			
Wokingham	d		20 53								21 23											21 53			
Bracknell	d		20 59								21 29											21 59			
Martins Heron	d		21 02								21 32											22 02			
Guildford	d																21 00	21 30							
Wanborough	d																21 06	21 36							
Ash 3	d																21 10	21 40							
Aldershot	a																21 17	21 47							
	d																21 30								
Ash Vale	d																21 34								
Frimley	d																21 40								
Camberley	a																21 44								
	d																21 48								
Bagshot	d																21 53								
Ascot 3	d		21 07								21 37						22a00					22 07			
Sunningdale	d		21 10								21 40											22 10			
Longcross	d																								
Woking	d																								
West Byfleet	d																								
Byfleet & New Haw	d																								
Weybridge	d						21 03							21 33										22 03	
Addlestone §	d						21 07							21 37										22 07	
Chertsey §	d						21 10							21 40										22 10	
Virginia Water	a		21 19				21 15				21 49			21 45								22 19		22 15	
	d		21 19				21 24				21 49			21 54								22 19		22 24	
Egham	d		21 23				21 27				21 53			21 57								22 23		22 27	
Windsor & Eton Riverside	d							21 21								21 51									22 21
Datchet	d							21 24								21 54									22 24
Sunnymeads	d							21 27								21 57									22 27
Wraysbury	d							21 30								22 00									22 30
Staines	d		21 29				21 33	21 38			21 59			22 03		22 08						22 29		22 33	22 38
Ashford (Surrey)	d						21 36	21 41						22 06		22 11								22 36	22 41
Feltham	d		21 35				21 41	21 46			22 05			22 11		22 16						22 35		22 41	22 46
Whitton	d	21 23		21 20				21 50		21 53			21 50			22 20					22 23				22 50
Kingston	d					21 29									21 59								22 29		
Hampton Wick	d					21 31									22 01								22 31		
Teddington	d					21 35									22 05								22 35		
Fulwell	d																								
Strawberry Hill	d					21 38									22 08								22 38		
Twickenham	a	21 26	21 40			21 42		21 53		21 56	22 10				22 12	22 23					22 26	22 40	22 42		22 53
	d	21 28	21 41			21 43		21 53		21 58	22 11				22 13	22 23					22 28	22 41	22 43		22 53
St Margarets	d	21 30				21 45				22 00					22 15						22 30		22 45		
Richmond	⊖ d	21 34	21 45			21 49		21 58		22 04	22 15				22 19	22 28					22 34	22 45	22 49		22 58
North Sheen	d	21 36				21 51				22 06					22 21						22 36		22 51		
Mortlake	d	21 38				21 53				22 08					22 23						22 38		22 53		
Hounslow	d			21 31			21 46						22 01	22 16										22 46	
Isleworth	d			21 34			21 49						22 04	22 19										22 49	
Syon Lane	d			21 36			21 51		←				22 06	22 21						←				22 51	
Brentford	d			21 39			21 54		21 54				22 09	22 24						22 24				22 54	
Kew Bridge	d			21 41			→		21 56				22 11	→						22 26				→	
Chiswick	d			21 44					21 59				22 14							22 29					
Barnes Bridge	d			21 46					22 01				22 16							22 31					
Barnes	d	21 41		21 49		21 56			22 04	22 11			22 19		22 26					22 34	22 41		22 56		
Putney	d	21 44		21 52		21 59		22 04	22 07	22 14			22 22		22 29	22 34				22 37	22 44		22 59		23 04
Wandsworth Town	d	21 47		21 55		22 02			22 10	22 18			22 25		22 32					22 40	22 47		23 02		
Clapham Junction 10	d	21 50	21 54	21 58		22 05		22 09	22 13	22 20	22 24		22 28		22 35	22 39				22 43	22 50	22 54	23 05		23 09
Queenstown Rd.(Battersea)	d	21 53		22 01		22 08			22 16	22 23			22 31		22 38					22 46	22 53		23 08		
Vauxhall	⊖ d	21 57		22 05		22 12		22 15	22 20	22 27			22 35		22 42	22 45				22 50	22 57		23 12		23 15
London Waterloo 15	⊖ a	22 02	22 04	22 11		22 16		22 19	22 26	22 32	22 34		22 41		22 46	22 49				22 56	23 02	23 04	23 17		23 19

For general notes see front of timetable
For details of catering facilities see Directory of Train Operators

§ Passengers to/from London may travel via Weybridge. See Table 155.

A From London Waterloo.
B From London Waterloo (Table 152)

Table 149

from 4 October

Reading, Guildford, Ascot, Weybridge, Windsor, Kingston, Richmond and Hounslow → London

Network Diagram - see first page of Table 148

		SW	SW 1		SW	SW	SW 1	SW 1	SW	SW		SW 1	SW	SW	SW	SW	SW 1		SW	SW 1	SW 1				
						A							A			A					B				
Reading 7	d		22 09									22 39					23 12								
Earley	d		22 14									22 44					23 17								
Winnersh Triangle	d		22 16									22 46					23 19								
Winnersh	d		22 18									22 48					23 21								
Wokingham	d		22 23									22 53					23 26								
Bracknell	d		22 29									22 59					23 32								
Martins Heron	d		22 32									23 02					23 35								
Guildford	d						22 00	22 30												23 00	23 30				
Wanborough	d						22 06	22 36												23 06	23 36				
Ash 3	d						22 10	22 40												23 10	23 40				
Aldershot	a						22 17	22 47												23 17	23 47				
	d						22 30													23 30					
Ash Vale	d						22 34													23 34					
Frimley	d						22 40													23 40					
Camberley	a						22 44													23 44					
	d						22 48													23 48					
Bagshot	d						22 53													23 53					
Ascot 3	d		22 37				23a00					23 07					23 40			00a01					
Sunningdale	d		22 40									23 10					23 43								
Longcross	d																								
Woking	d																								
West Byfleet	d																								
Byfleet & New Haw	d																								
Weybridge	d				22 33									23 03					23 33						
Addlestone §	d				22 37									23 07					23 37						
Chertsey §	d				22 40									23 10					23 40						
Virginia Water	a		22 49		22 45							23 19		23 15			23 49		23 45						
	d		22 49		22 54							23 19		23 24			23 49		23 54						
Egham	d		22 53		22 57							23 23		23 27			23 53		23 57						
Windsor & Eton Riverside	d								22 53						23 23										
Datchet	d								22 56						23 26										
Sunnymeads	d								22 59						23 29										
Wraysbury	d								23 02						23 32										
Staines	d		22 59		23 03				23 08			23 29		23a32	23a37		23 59		00a02						
Ashford (Surrey)	d				23 06				23 11																
Feltham	d		23 05		23 11				23 16			23 35					00 05								
Whitton	d								23 20																
Kingston	d					22 59							23 29			23 55									
Hampton Wick	d					23 01							23 31			23 57									
Teddington	d					23 05							23 35			23 59									
Fulwell	d																								
Strawberry Hill	d					23 08							23 38			00 03									
Twickenham	a		23 10			23 12			23 23			23 40	23 42			00 07	00 10								
	d		23 11			23 13			23 23			23 41	23 43				00 12								
St Margarets	d					23 15							23 45												
Richmond	⊖ d		23 15			23 19			23 28			23 45	23 49				00 16								
North Sheen	d					23 21							23 51												
Mortlake	d					23 23							23 53												
Hounslow	d				23 16																				
Isleworth	d				23 19																				
Syon Lane	d	←			23 21					←															
Brentford	d	22 54			23 24 →					23 24															
Kew Bridge	d	22 56								23 26															
Chiswick	d	22 59								23 29															
Barnes Bridge	d	23 01								23 31															
Barnes	d	23 04				23 26				23 34			23 56												
Putney	d	23 07				23 29			23 34	23 37			23 59												
Wandsworth Town	d	23 10				23 32				23 40			00 02												
Clapham Junction 10	d	23 13	23 24			23 35			23 39	23 43		23 54	00 05				00 25								
Queenstown Rd.(Battersea)	d	23 16				23 38				23 46			00 08												
Vauxhall	⊖ d	23 20				23 42			23 45	23 50			00 12												
London Waterloo 15	⊖ a	23 26	23 34			23 47			23 49	23 56		00 02	00 16				00 33								

For general notes see front of timetable
For details of catering facilities see Directory of Train Operators

§ Passengers to/from London may travel via Weybridge. See Table 155.

A From London Waterloo (Table 152)
B To Farnham (Table 155)

Table 149

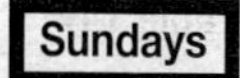

Sundays

Reading, Guildford, Ascot, Weybridge, Windsor, Kingston, Richmond and Hounslow → London

until 21 September

Network Diagram - see first page of Table 148

		SW	SW	SW	SW	SW	SW	SW	SW	SW	SW	SW	SW	SW	SW	SW	SW	SW	SW	SW	SW	SW	SW
				1									1	1		1			1	1		1	
		A	A		A	A	A			A					A						A		
Reading 7	d			23p12										07 54		08 24				08 54		09 24	
Earley	d			23p17										07 59		08 29				08 59		09 29	
Winnersh Triangle	d			23p19										08 01		08 31				09 01		09 31	
Winnersh	d			23p21										08 03		08 33				09 03		09 33	
Wokingham	d			23p26										08 08		08 38				09 08		09 38	
Bracknell	d			23p32										08 14		08 44				09 14		09 44	
Martins Heron	d			23p35										08 17		08 47				09 17		09 47	
Guildford	d												07 17						08 17				
Wanborough	d												07 23						08 23				
Ash 3	d												07 27						08 27				
Aldershot	a												07 34						08 34				
	d												07 40						08 40				
Ash Vale	d												07 45						08 45				
Frimley	d												07 51						08 51				
Camberley	a												07 55						08 55				
	d												07 55						08 55				
Bagshot	d												08 01						09 01				
Ascot 3	d			23p40									08a07	08 22		08 52			09a07	09 22		09 52	
Sunningdale	d			23p43										08 25		08 55				09 25		09 55	
Longcross	d																						
Woking	d											07 52						08 52					
West Byfleet	d											07 56						08 56					
Byfleet & New Haw	d											08 00						09 00					
Weybridge	d								07 00														
Addlestone §	d								07 04			08 04						09 04					
Chertsey §	d								07 07			08 07						09 07					
Virginia Water	a			23p49					07 12			08 12		08 30		09 00		09 12		09 30		10 00	
	d			23p49					07 12			08 12		08 30		09 00		09 12		09 30		10 00	
Egham	d			23p53					07 16			08 16		08 34		09 04		09 16		09 34		10 04	
Windsor & Eton Riverside	d							07 01			08 01						09 01						10 01
Datchet	d							07 04			08 04						09 04						10 04
Sunnymeads	d							07 07			08 07						09 07						10 07
Wraysbury	d							07 10			08 10						09 10						10 10
Staines	d			23p59				07 16	07 21		08 16	08 21		08 39		09 09	09 16	09 21		09 39		10 09	10 16
Ashford (Surrey)	d							07 19	07 24		08 19	08 24					09 19	09 24					10 19
Feltham	d			00 05				07 24	07 29		08 24	08 29		08 46		09 16	09 24	09 29		09 46		10 16	10 24
Whitton	d							07 28			08 28						09 28						10 28
Kingston	d	23p29	23p55		01 17	02 16	06 49			07 49					08 49						09 49		
Hampton Wick	d	23p31	23p57		01s22	02s21	06 51			07 51					08 51						09 51		
Teddington	d	23p35	23p59		01s25	02s23	06 56			07 56					08 56						09 56		
Fulwell	d																						
Strawberry Hill	d	23p38	00 03		01a28	02s26	06 59			07 59					08 59						09 59		
Twickenham	a	23p42	00 07	00 10		02 30	07 02	07 31		08 02	08 31			08 51	09 02	09 21	09 31			09 51	10 02	10 21	10 31
	d	23p43		00 12			07 03	07 32		08 03	08 32			08 51	09 03	09 21	09 32			09 51	10 03	10 21	10 32
St Margarets	d	23p45					07 05	07 34		08 05	08 34				09 05		09 34				10 05		10 34
Richmond	⊖ d	23p49		00 16			07 09	07 37		08 09	08 37			08 56	09 09	09 26	09 37			09 56	10 09	10 26	10 37
North Sheen	d	23p51					07 11	07 39		08 11	08 39				09 11		09 39				10 11		10 39
Mortlake	d	23p53					07 13	07 42		08 13	08 42				09 13		09 42				10 13		10 42
Hounslow	d								07 35			08 35						09 35					
Isleworth	d								07 38			08 38						09 38					
Syon Lane	d								07 40			08 40						09 40					
Brentford	d								07 42			08 42						09 42					
Kew Bridge	d								07 45			08 45						09 45					
Chiswick	d								07 47			08 47						09 47					
Barnes Bridge	d								07 50			08 50						09 50					
Barnes	d	23p56					07 16	07 45	07 53	08 16	08 45	08 53			09 16		09 45	09 53			10 16		10 45
Putney	d	23p59					07 19	07 48	07 56	08 19	08 48	08 56		09 02	09 19	09 32	09 48	09 56		10 02	10 19	10 32	10 48
Wandsworth Town	d	00 02					07 22	07 51	07 59	08 22	08 51	08 59			09 22		09 51	09 59			10 22		10 51
Clapham Junction 10	d	00 05		00 25			07 25	07 54	08 02	08 25	08 54	09 02		09 07	09 25	09 37	09 54	10 02		10 07	10 25	10 37	10 54
Queenstown Rd.(Battersea)	d	00 08					07 28	07 57	08 05	08 28	08 57	09 05			09 28		09 57	10 05			10 28		10 58
Vauxhall	⊖ d	00 12					07 32	08 00	08 08	08 32	09 00	09 08		09 12	09 32	09 42	10 00	10 08		10 12	10 32	10 42	11 02
London Waterloo 15	⊖ a	00 16		00 33			07 41	08 10	08 13	08 41	09 10	09 13		09 23	09 41	09 53	10 10	10 13		10 23	10 41	10 53	11 10

For general notes see front of timetable
For details of catering facilities see Directory of Train Operators

§ Passengers to/from London may travel via Weybridge. See Table 155.

A From London Waterloo (Table 152)

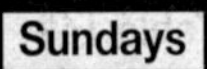

until 21 September

Reading, Guildford, Ascot, Weybridge, Windsor, Kingston, Richmond and Hounslow → London

Network Diagram - see first page of Table 148

		SW		SW 1	SW 1	SW	SW A	SW 1	SW	SW		SW 1	SW 1	SW	SW A	SW 1	SW	SW		SW 1	SW 1	SW	SW A	SW 1	SW
Reading 7	d				09 54			10 24					10 54			11 24					11 54			12 24	
Earley	d				09 59			10 29					10 59			11 29					11 59			12 29	
Winnersh Triangle	d				10 01			10 31					11 01			11 31					12 01			12 31	
Winnersh	d				10 03			10 33					11 03			11 33					12 03			12 33	
Wokingham	d				10 08			10 38					11 08			11 38					12 08			12 38	
Bracknell	d				10 14			10 44					11 14			11 44					12 14			12 44	
Martins Heron	d				10 17			10 47					11 17			11 47					12 17			12 47	
Guildford	d			09 17								10 17								11 17					
Wanborough	d			09 23								10 23								11 23					
Ash 3	d			09 27								10 27								11 27					
Aldershot	a			09 34								10 34								11 34					
	d			09 40								10 40								11 40					
Ash Vale	d			09 45								10 45								11 45					
Frimley	d			09 51								10 51								11 51					
Camberley	a			09 55								10 55								11 55					
	d			09 55								10 55								11 55					
Bagshot	d			10 01								11 01								12 01					
Ascot 3	d			10a07	10 22			10 52				11a07	11 22			11 52				12a07	12 22			12 52	
Sunningdale	d				10 25			10 55					11 25			11 55					12 25			12 55	
Longcross	d																								
Woking	d	09 52								10 52								11 52							
West Byfleet	d	09 56								10 56								11 56							
Byfleet & New Haw	d	10 00								11 00								12 00							
Weybridge	d																								
Addlestone §	d	10 04								11 04								12 04							
Chertsey §	d	10 07								11 07								12 07							
Virginia Water	a	10 12			10 30			11 00		11 12			11 30			12 00		12 12			12 30			13 00	
	d	10 12			10 30			11 00		11 12			11 30			12 00		12 12			12 30			13 00	
Egham	d	10 16			10 34			11 04		11 16			11 34			12 04		12 16			12 34			13 04	
Windsor & Eton Riverside	d					10 34			11 01					11 34			12 01					12 34			
Datchet	d					10 37			11 04					11 37			12 04					12 37			
Sunnymeads	d								11 07								12 07								
Wraysbury	d								11 10								12 10								
Staines	d	10 21			10 39	10 45		11 09	11 16	11 21			11 39	11 45		12 09	12 16	12 21			12 39	12 45		13 09	
Ashford (Surrey)	d	10 24				10 48			11 19	11 24				11 48			12 19	12 24				12 48			
Feltham	d	10 29			10 46	10 53		11 16	11 24	11 29			11 46	11 53		12 16	12 24	12 29			12 46	12 53		13 16	
Whitton	d					10 57			11 28					11 57			12 28					12 57			
Kingston	d						10 49								11 49								12 49		13 11
Hampton Wick	d						10 51								11 51								12 51		13 13
Teddington	d						10 56								11 56								12 56		13 16
Fulwell	d																								
Strawberry Hill	d						10 59								11 59								12 59		13 19
Twickenham	a				10 51	11 00	11 02	11 21	11 31				11 51	12 00	12 02	12 21	12 31				12 51	13 00	13 02	13 21	13 22
	d				10 51	11 01	11 03	11 21	11 32				11 51	12 01	12 03	12 21	12 32				12 51	13 01	13 03	13 21	13 23
St Margarets	d						11 05		11 34						12 05		12 34						13 05		13 25
Richmond	⊖ d				10 56	11 05	11 09	11 26	11 37				11 56	12 05	12 09	12 26	12 37				12 56	13 05	13 09	13 26	13 29
North Sheen	d						11 11		11 39						12 11		12 39						13 11		13 31
Mortlake	d						11 13		11 42						12 13		12 42						13 13		13 33
Hounslow	d	10 35								11 35								12 35							
Isleworth	d	10 38								11 38								12 38							
Syon Lane	d	10 40								11 40								12 40							
Brentford	d	10 42								11 42								12 42							
Kew Bridge	d	10 45								11 45								12 45							
Chiswick	d	10 47								11 47								12 47							
Barnes Bridge	d	10 50								11 50								12 50							
Barnes	d	10 53					11 16		11 45	11 53					12 16		12 45	12 53					13 16		13 36
Putney	d	10 56			11 02	11 14	11 19	11 32	11 48	11 56			12 02	12 14	12 19	12 32	12 48	12 56			13 02	13 14	13 19	13 32	13 39
Wandsworth Town	d	10 59					11 22		11 51	11 59					12 22		12 51	12 59					13 22		13 42
Clapham Junction 10	d	11 04			11 07	11 18	11 25	11 37	11 54	12 04			12 07	12 18	12 25	12 37	12 54	13 02			13 07	13 18	13 25	13 37	13 45
Queenstown Rd.(Battersea)	d	11 09					11 33		11 58	12 09					12 33		12 58	13 05					13 28		13 48
Vauxhall	⊖ d	11 13			11 16	11 26	11 37	11 45	12 02	12 13			12 16	12 26	12 37	12 45	13 02	13 08			13 12	13 24	13 32	13 42	13 52
London Waterloo 15	⊖ a	11 19			11 23	11 34	11 41	11 53	12 10	12 19			12 23	12 34	12 41	12 53	13 10	13 13			13 23	13 34	13 41	13 53	14 00

For general notes see front of timetable
For details of catering facilities see
Directory of Train Operators

§ Passengers to/from London may travel via Weybridge. See Table 155.

A From London Waterloo (Table 152)

Table 149

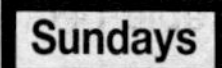

Sundays

until 21 September

Reading, Guildford, Ascot, Weybridge, Windsor, Kingston, Richmond and Hounslow → London

Network Diagram - see first page of Table 148

		SW	SW	SW 1	SW 1	SW	SW	SW 1	SW	SW	SW	SW 1	SW 1	SW	SW	SW 1	SW	SW	SW	SW 1	SW 1	SW
							A								A							
Reading 7	d				12 54			13 24					13 54			14 24					14 54	
Earley	d				12 59			13 29					13 59			14 29					14 59	
Winnersh Triangle	d				13 01			13 31					14 01			14 31					15 01	
Winnersh	d				13 03			13 33					14 03			14 33					15 03	
Wokingham	d				13 08			13 38					14 08			14 38					15 08	
Bracknell	d				13 14			13 44					14 14			14 44					15 14	
Martins Heron	d				13 17			13 47					14 17			14 47					15 17	
Guildford	d			12 17								13 17								14 17		
Wanborough	d			12 23								13 23								14 23		
Ash 3	d			12 27								13 27								14 27		
Aldershot	a			12 34								13 34								14 34		
	d			12 40								13 40								14 40		
Ash Vale	d			12 45								13 45								14 45		
Frimley	d			12 51								13 51								14 51		
Camberley	a			12 55								13 55								14 55		
	d			12 55								13 55								14 55		
Bagshot	d			13 01								14 01								15 01		
Ascot 3	d			13a07	13 22			13 52				14a07	14 22			14 52				15a07	15 22	
Sunningdale	d				13 25			13 55					14 25			14 55					15 25	
Longcross	d																					
Woking	d		12 52								13 52								14 52			
West Byfleet	d		12 56								13 56								14 56			
Byfleet & New Haw	d		13 00								14 00								15 00			
Weybridge	d																					
Addlestone §	d		13 04								14 04								15 04			
Chertsey §	d		13 07								14 07								15 07			
Virginia Water	a		13 12		13 30			14 00			14 12		14 30			15 00			15 12		15 30	
	d		13 12		13 30			14 00			14 12		14 30			15 00			15 12		15 30	
Egham	d		13 16		13 34			14 04			14 16		14 34			15 04			15 16		15 34	
Windsor & Eton Riverside	d	13 01				13 34				14 01				14 34				15 01				15 34
Datchet	d	13 04				13 37				14 04				14 37				15 04				15 37
Sunnymeads	d	13 07								14 07								15 07				
Wraysbury	d	13 10								14 10								15 10				
Staines	d	13 16	13 21		13 39	13 45		14 09		14 16	14 21		14 39	14 45		15 09		15 16	15 21		15 39	15 45
Ashford (Surrey)	d	13 19	13 24			13 48				14 19	14 24			14 48				15 19	15 24			15 48
Feltham	d	13 24	13 29		13 46	13 53		14 16		14 24	14 29		14 46	14 53		15 16		15 24	15 29		15 46	15 53
Whitton	d	13 28				13 57				14 28				14 57				15 28				15 57
Kingston	d						13 49		14 11						14 49		15 11					
Hampton Wick	d						13 51		14 13						14 51		15 13					
Teddington	d						13 56		14 16						14 56		15 16					
Fulwell	d																					
Strawberry Hill	d						13 59		14 19						14 59		15 19					
Twickenham	a	13 31			13 51	14 00	14 02	14 21	14 22	14 31			14 51	15 00	15 02	15 21	15 22	15 31			15 51	16 00
	d	13 32			13 51	14 01	14 03	14 21	14 23	14 32			14 51	15 01	15 03	15 21	15 23	15 32			15 51	16 01
St Margarets	d	13 34					14 05		14 25	14 34					15 05		15 25	15 34				
Richmond	⊖ d	13 37			13 56	14 05	14 09	14 26	14 29	14 37			14 56	15 05	15 09	15 26	15 29	15 37			15 56	16 05
North Sheen	d	13 39					14 11		14 31	14 39					15 11		15 31	15 39				
Mortlake	d	13 42					14 13		14 33	14 42					15 13		15 33	15 42				
Hounslow	d		13 35								14 35								15 35			
Isleworth	d		13 38								14 38								15 38			
Syon Lane	d		13 40								14 40								15 40			
Brentford	d		13 42								14 42								15 42			
Kew Bridge	d		13 45								14 45								15 45			
Chiswick	d		13 47								14 47								15 47			
Barnes Bridge	d		13 50								14 50								15 50			
Barnes	d	13 45	13 53				14 16		14 36	14 45	14 53				15 16		15 36	15 45	15 53			
Putney	d	13 48	13 56		14 02	14 14	14 19	14 32	14 39	14 48	14 56		15 02	15 14	15 19	15 32	15 39	15 48	15 56		16 02	16 14
Wandsworth Town	d	13 51	13 59				14 22		14 42	14 51	14 59				15 22		15 42	15 51	15 59			
Clapham Junction 10	d	13 54	14 02		14 07	14 18	14 25	14 37	14 45	14 54	15 02		15 07	15 18	15 25	15 37	15 45	15 54	16 02		16 07	16 18
Queenstown Rd.(Battersea)	d	13 57	14 05				14 28		14 48	14 57	15 05				15 28		15 48	15 57	16 05			
Vauxhall	⊖ d	14 00	14 08		14 12	14 24	14 32	14 42	14 52	15 00	15 08		15 12	15 24	15 32	15 42	15 52	16 00	16 08		16 12	16 24
London Waterloo 15	⊖ a	14 10	14 13		14 23	14 29	14 36	14 48	15 00	15 05	15 13		15 18	15 29	15 36	15 48	16 00	16 05	16 13		16 18	16 29

For general notes see front of timetable
For details of catering facilities see
Directory of Train Operators

§ Passengers to/from London may travel via Weybridge. See Table 155.

A From London Waterloo (Table 152)

Table 149

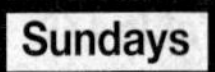

Sundays

until 21 September

Reading, Guildford, Ascot, Weybridge, Windsor, Kingston, Richmond and Hounslow → London

Network Diagram - see first page of Table 148

		SW	SW 1	SW	SW	SW		SW 1	SW 1	SW	SW	SW 1	SW	SW		SW	SW 1	SW 1	SW	SW	SW 1	SW		SW	SW
		A									A									A					
Reading 7	d		15 24						15 54			16 24						16 54			17 24				
Earley	d		15 29						15 59			16 29						16 59			17 29				
Winnersh Triangle	d		15 31						16 01			16 31						17 01			17 31				
Winnersh	d		15 33						16 03			16 33						17 03			17 33				
Wokingham	d		15 38						16 08			16 38						17 08			17 38				
Bracknell	d		15 44						16 14			16 44						17 14			17 44				
Martins Heron	d		15 47						16 17			16 47						17 17			17 47				
Guildford	d							15 17									16 17								
Wanborough	d							15 23									16 23								
Ash 3	d							15 27									16 27								
Aldershot	a							15 34									16 34								
	d							15 40									16 40								
Ash Vale	d							15 45									16 45								
Frimley	d							15 51									16 51								
Camberley	a							15 55									16 55								
	d							15 55									16 55								
Bagshot	d							16 01									17 01								
Ascot 3	d		15 52					16a07	16 22			16 52					17a07	17 22			17 52				
Sunningdale	d		15 55						16 25			16 55						17 25			17 55				
Longcross	d																								
Woking	d					15 52										16 52									17 52
West Byfleet	d					15 56										16 56									17 56
Byfleet & New Haw	d					16 00										17 00									18 00
Weybridge	d																								
Addlestone §	d					16 04										17 04									18 04
Chertsey §	d					16 07										17 07									18 07
Virginia Water	a		16 00			16 12			16 30			17 00				17 12		17 30			18 00				18 12
	d		16 00			16 12			16 30			17 00				17 12		17 30			18 00				18 12
Egham	d		16 04			16 16			16 34			17 04				17 16		17 34			18 04				18 16
Windsor & Eton Riverside	d				16 01					16 34				17 01					17 34					18 01	
Datchet	d				16 04					16 37				17 04					17 37					18 04	
Sunnymeads	d				16 07									17 07										18 07	
Wraysbury	d				16 10									17 10										18 10	
Staines	d		16 09		16 16	16 21			16 39	16 45		17 09		17 16		17 21		17 39	17 45		18 09			18 16	18 21
Ashford (Surrey)	d				16 19	16 24				16 48				17 19		17 24			17 48					18 19	18 24
Feltham	d		16 16		16 24	16 29			16 46	16 53		17 16		17 24		17 29		17 46	17 53		18 16			18 24	18 29
Whitton	d				16 28					16 57				17 28					17 57					18 28	
Kingston	d	15 49		16 11							16 49		17 11							17 49		18 11			
Hampton Wick	d	15 51		16 13							16 51		17 13							17 51		18 13			
Teddington	d	15 56		16 16							16 56		17 16							17 56		18 16			
Fulwell	d																								
Strawberry Hill	d	15 59		16 19							16 59		17 19							17 59		18 19			
Twickenham	a	16 02	16 21	16 22	16 31				16 51	17 00	17 02	17 21	17 22	17 31				17 51	18 00	18 02	18 21	18 22		18 31	
	d	16 03	16 21	16 23	16 32				16 51	17 01	17 03	17 21	17 23	17 32				17 51	18 01	18 03	18 21	18 23		18 32	
St Margarets	d	16 05		16 25	16 34						17 05		17 25	17 34						18 05		18 25		18 34	
Richmond	⊖ d	16 09	16 26	16 29	16 37				16 56	17 05	17 09	17 26	17 29	17 37				17 56	18 05	18 09	18 26	18 29		18 37	
North Sheen	d	16 11		16 31	16 39						17 11		17 31	17 39						18 11		18 31		18 39	
Mortlake	d	16 13		16 33	16 42						17 13		17 33	17 42						18 13		18 33		18 42	
Hounslow	d					16 35										17 35									18 35
Isleworth	d					16 38										17 38									18 38
Syon Lane	d					16 40										17 40									18 40
Brentford	d					16 42										17 42									18 42
Kew Bridge	d					16 45										17 45									18 45
Chiswick	d					16 47										17 47									18 47
Barnes Bridge	d					16 50										17 50									18 50
Barnes	d	16 16		16 36	16 45	16 53					17 16		17 36	17 45		17 53				18 16		18 36		18 45	18 53
Putney	d	16 19	16 32	16 39	16 48	16 56			17 02	17 14	17 19	17 32	17 39	17 48		17 56		18 02	18 14	18 19	18 32	18 39		18 48	18 56
Wandsworth Town	d	16 22		16 42	16 51	16 59					17 22		17 42	17 51		17 59				18 22		18 42		18 51	18 59
Clapham Junction 10	d	16 25	16 37	16 45	16 54	17 02			17 07	17 18	17 25	17 37	17 45	17 54		18 02		18 07	18 18	18 25	18 37	18 45		18 54	19 02
Queenstown Rd.(Battersea)	d	16 28		16 48	16 57	17 05					17 28		17 48	17 57		18 05				18 28		18 48		18 57	19 05
Vauxhall	⊖ d	16 32	16 42	16 52	17 00	17 08			17 12	17 24	17 32	17 42	17 52	18 00		18 08		18 12	18 24	18 32	18 42	18 52		19 00	19 08
London Waterloo 15	⊖ a	16 36	16 48	17 00	17 05	17 13			17 18	17 29	17 36	17 48	18 00	18 05		18 13		18 18	18 29	18 36	18 48	19 00		19 05	19 13

For general notes see front of timetable
For details of catering facilities see Directory of Train Operators

§ Passengers to/from London may travel via Weybridge. See Table 155.

A From London Waterloo (Table 152)

Table 149

Sundays

until 21 September

Reading, Guildford, Ascot, Weybridge, Windsor, Kingston, Richmond and Hounslow → London

Network Diagram - see first page of Table 148

		SW 1	SW 1	SW	SW	SW 1	SW	SW	SW	SW 1	SW 1	SW	SW	SW 1	SW	SW	SW	SW 1	SW 1	SW	SW	SW 1	SW
					A								A								A		
Reading 7	d		17 54			18 24					18 54			19 24					19 54			20 24	
Earley	d		17 59			18 29					18 59			19 29					19 59			20 29	
Winnersh Triangle	d		18 01			18 31					19 01			19 31					20 01			20 31	
Winnersh	d		18 03			18 33					19 03			19 33					20 03			20 33	
Wokingham	d		18 08			18 38					19 08			19 38					20 08			20 38	
Bracknell	d		18 14			18 44					19 14			19 44					20 14			20 44	
Martins Heron	d		18 17			18 47					19 17			19 47					20 17			20 47	
Guildford	d	17 17								18 17								19 17					
Wanborough	d	17 23								18 23								19 23					
Ash 3	d	17 27								18 27								19 27					
Aldershot	a	17 34								18 34								19 34					
	d	17 40								18 40								19 40					
Ash Vale	d	17 45								18 45								19 45					
Frimley	d	17 51								18 51								19 51					
Camberley	a	17 55								18 55								19 55					
	d	17 55								18 55								19 55					
Bagshot	d	18 01								19 01								20 01					
Ascot 3	d	18a07	18 22			18 52				19a07	19 22			19 52				20a07	20 22			20 52	
Sunningdale	d		18 25			18 55					19 25			19 55					20 25			20 55	
Longcross	d																						
Woking	d								18 52								19 52						
West Byfleet	d								18 56								19 56						
Byfleet & New Haw	d								19 00								20 00						
Weybridge	d																						
Addlestone §	d								19 04								20 04						
Chertsey §	d								19 07								20 07						
Virginia Water	a		18 30			19 00			19 12		19 30			20 00			20 12		20 30			21 00	
	d		18 30			19 00			19 12		19 30			20 00			20 12		20 30			21 00	
Egham	d		18 34			19 04			19 16		19 34			20 04			20 16		20 34			21 04	
Windsor & Eton Riverside	d			18 34				19 01				19 34				20 01				20 34			
Datchet	d			18 37				19 04				19 37				20 04				20 37			
Sunnymeads	d							19 07								20 07							
Wraysbury	d							19 10								20 10							
Staines	d		18 39	18 45		19 09		19 16	19 21		19 39	19 45		20 09		20 16	20 21		20 39	20 45		21 09	
Ashford (Surrey)	d			18 48				19 19	19 24			19 48				20 19	20 24			20 48			
Feltham	d		18 46	18 53		19 16		19 24	19 29		19 46	19 53		20 16		20 24	20 29		20 46	20 53		21 16	
Whitton	d			18 57				19 28				19 57				20 28				20 57			
Kingston	d				18 49		19 11						19 49		20 11						20 49		21 11
Hampton Wick	d				18 51		19 13						19 51		20 13						20 51		21 13
Teddington	d				18 56		19 16						19 56		20 16						20 56		21 16
Fulwell	d																						
Strawberry Hill	d				18 59		19 19						19 59		20 19						20 59		21 19
Twickenham	a		18 51	19 00	19 02	19 21	19 22	19 31			19 51	20 00	20 02	20 21	20 22	20 31			20 51	21 00	21 02	21 21	21 22
	d		18 51	19 01	19 03	19 21	19 23	19 32			19 51	20 01	20 03	20 21	20 23	20 32			20 51	21 01	21 03	21 21	21 23
St Margarets	d				19 05		19 25	19 34					20 05		20 25	20 34					21 05		21 25
Richmond	⊖ d		18 56	19 05	19 09	19 26	19 29	19 37			19 56	20 05	20 09	20 26	20 29	20 37			20 56	21 05	21 09	21 26	21 29
North Sheen	d				19 11		19 31	19 39					20 11		20 31	20 39					21 11		21 31
Mortlake	d				19 13		19 33	19 42					20 13		20 33	20 42					21 13		21 33
Hounslow	d								19 35								20 35						
Isleworth	d								19 38								20 38						
Syon Lane	d								19 40								20 40						
Brentford	d								19 42								20 42						
Kew Bridge	d								19 45								20 45						
Chiswick	d								19 47								20 47						
Barnes Bridge	d								19 50								20 50						
Barnes	d				19 16		19 36	19 45	19 53				20 16		20 36	20 45	20 53				21 16		21 36
Putney	d		19 02	19 14	19 19	19 32	19 39	19 48	19 56		20 02	20 14	20 19	20 32	20 39	20 48	20 56		21 02	21 14	21 19	21 32	21 39
Wandsworth Town	d				19 22		19 42	19 51	19 59				20 22		20 42	20 51	20 59				21 22		21 42
Clapham Junction 10	d		19 07	19 18	19 25	19 37	19 45	19 54	20 02		20 07	20 18	20 25	20 37	20 45	20 54	21 02		21 07	21 18	21 25	21 37	21 45
Queenstown Rd.(Battersea)	d				19 28		19 48	19 57	20 05				20 28		20 48	20 57	21 05				21 28		21 48
Vauxhall	⊖ d		19 12	19 24	19 32	19 42	19 52	20 00	20 08		20 12	20 24	20 32	20 42	20 52	21 00	21 08		21 12	21 24	21 32	21 42	21 52
London Waterloo 15	⊖ a		19 18	19 29	19 36	19 48	20 00	20 05	20 13		20 18	20 29	20 36	20 48	21 00	21 05	21 13		21 18	21 29	21 36	21 48	22 00

For general notes see front of timetable
For details of catering facilities see Directory of Train Operators

§ Passengers to/from London may travel via Weybridge. See Table 155.

A From London Waterloo (Table 152)

Reading, Guildford, Ascot, Weybridge, Windsor, Kingston, Richmond and Hounslow → London

until 21 September

Network Diagram - see first page of Table 148

		SW	SW	SW [1]	SW [1]	SW A	SW [1]	SW	SW	SW	SW [1]	SW [1]	SW A	SW [1]	SW	SW	SW	SW [1]	SW [1]	SW [1]	SW A
Reading [7]	d				20 54		21 24					21 54		22 24						22 54	
Earley	d				20 59		21 29					21 59		22 29						22 59	
Winnersh Triangle	d				21 01		21 31					22 01		22 31						23 01	
Winnersh	d				21 03		21 33					22 03		22 33						23 03	
Wokingham	d				21 08		21 38					22 08		22 38						23 08	
Bracknell	d				21 14		21 44					22 14		22 44						23 14	
Martins Heron	d				21 17		21 47					22 17		22 47						23 17	
Guildford	d			20 17							21 17							22 17	23 17		
Wanborough	d			20 23							21 23							22 23	23 23		
Ash [3]	d			20 27							21 27							22 27	23 27		
Aldershot	a			20 34							21 34							22 34	23 34		
	d			20 40							21 40							22 40			
Ash Vale	d			20 45							21 45							22 45			
Frimley	d			20 51							21 51							22 51			
Camberley	a			20 55							21 55							22 55			
	d			20 55							21 55							22 55			
Bagshot	d			21 01							22 01							23 01			
Ascot [3]	d			21a07	21 22		21 52				22a07	22 22		22 52				23a07		23 22	
Sunningdale	d				21 25		21 55					22 25		22 55						23 25	
Longcross	d																				
Woking	d		20 52							21 52							22 52				
West Byfleet	d		20 56							21 56							22 56				
Byfleet & New Haw	d		21 00							22 00							23 00				
Weybridge	d																				
Addlestone §	d		21 04							22 04							23 04				
Chertsey §	d		21 07							22 07							23 07				
Virginia Water	a		21 12		21 30		22 00			22 12		22 30		23 00			23 12			23 30	
	d		21 12		21 30		22 00			22 12		22 30		23 00			23 12			23 30	
Egham	d		21 16		21 34		22 04			22 16		22 34		23 04			23 16			23 34	
Windsor & Eton Riverside	d	21 01							22 01							23 01					
Datchet	d	21 04							22 04							23 04					
Sunnymeads	d	21 07							22 07							23 07					
Wraysbury	d	21 10							22 10							23 10					
Staines	d	21 16	21 21		21 39		22 09		22 16	22 21		22 39		23 09		23 16	23 21			23 39	
Ashford (Surrey)	d	21 19	21 24						22 19	22 24						23 19	23 24				
Feltham	d	21 24	21 29		21 46		22 16		22 24	22 29		22 46		23 16		23 24	23 29			23 46	
Whitton	d	21 28							22 28							23 28					
Kingston	d					21 49		22 11					22 49		23 11						23 47
Hampton Wick	d					21 51		22 13					22 51		23 13						23 49
Teddington	d					21 56		22 16					22 56		23 16						23 51
Fulwell	d																				
Strawberry Hill	d					21 59		22 19					22 59		23 19						23a54
Twickenham	a	21 31			21 51	22 02	22 21	22 22	22 31			22 51	23 02	23 21	23 22	23 31				23 51	
	d	21 32			21 51	22 03	22 21	22 23	22 32			22 51	23 03	23 21	23 23	23 32				23 51	
St Margarets	d	21 34				22 05		22 25	22 34				23 05		23 25	23 34					
Richmond	⊖ d	21 37			21 56	22 09	22 26	22 29	22 37			22 56	23 09	23 26	23 29	23 37				23 56	
North Sheen	d	21 39				22 11		22 31	22 39				23 11		23 31	23 39					
Mortlake	d	21 42				22 13		22 33	22 42				23 13		23 33	23 42					
Hounslow	d		21 35							22 35							23 35				
Isleworth	d		21 38							22 38							23 38				
Syon Lane	d		21 40							22 40							23 40				
Brentford	d		21 42							22 42							23 42				
Kew Bridge	d		21 45							22 45							23 45				
Chiswick	d		21 47							22 47							23 47				
Barnes Bridge	d		21 50							22 50							23 50				
Barnes	d	21 45	21 53			22 16		22 36	22 45	22 53			23 16		23 36	23 45	23 53				
Putney	d	21 48	21 56		22 02	22 19	22 32	22 39	22 48	22 56		23 02	23 19	23 32	23 39	23 48	23 56			00 02	
Wandsworth Town	d	21 51	21 59			22 22		22 42	22 51	22 59			23 22		23 42	23 51	23 59				
Clapham Junction [10]	d	21 54	22 02		22 07	22 25	22 37	22 45	22 54	23 02		23 07	23 25	23 37	23 45	23 54	00 02			00 07	
Queenstown Rd.(Battersea)	d	21 57	22 05			22 28		22 48	22 57	23 05			23 28		23 48	23 57	00 05				
Vauxhall	⊖ d	22 00	22 08		22 12	22 32	22 42	22 52	23 00	23 08		23 12	23 32	23 42	23 52	00 01	00 08			00 12	
London Waterloo [15]	⊖ a	22 05	22 13		22 18	22 36	22 48	23 00	23 05	23 13		23 18	23 36	23 48	23 59	00 05	00 13			00 17	

For general notes see front of timetable
For details of catering facilities see Directory of Train Operators

§ Passengers to/from London may travel via Weybridge. See Table 155.

A From London Waterloo (Table 152)

Table 149

Sundays

Reading, Guildford, Ascot, Weybridge, Windsor, Kingston, Richmond and Hounslow → London

from 28 September

Network Diagram - see first page of Table 148

		SW	SW	SW	SW	SW	SW	SW	SW	SW	SW	SW	SW	SW	SW	SW	SW	SW	SW	SW	SW	SW	SW
				1									1	1		1			1	1		1	
		A	A		A	A	A			A					A						A		
Reading 7	d			23p12										07 51		08 21				08 51		09 21	
Earley	d			23p17										07 56		08 26				08 56		09 26	
Winnersh Triangle	d			23p19										07 58		08 28				08 58		09 28	
Winnersh	d			23p21										08 00		08 30				09 00		09 30	
Wokingham	d			23p26										08 05		08 35				09 05		09 35	
Bracknell	d			23p32										08 11		08 41				09 11		09 41	
Martins Heron	d			23p35										08 14		08 44				09 14		09 44	
Guildford	d												07 17						08 17				
Wanborough	d												07 23						08 23				
Ash 3	d												07 27						08 27				
Aldershot	a												07 34						08 34				
	d												07 40						08 40				
Ash Vale	d												07 45						08 45				
Frimley	d												07 51						08 51				
Camberley	a												07 55						08 55				
	d												07 55						08 55				
Bagshot	d												08 01						09 01				
Ascot 3	d			23p40									08a07	08 19		08 49			09a07	09 19		09 49	
Sunningdale	d			23p43										08 22		08 52				09 25		09 52	
Longcross	d																						
Woking	d											07 52						08 52					
West Byfleet	d											07 56						08 56					
Byfleet & New Haw	d											08 00						09 00					
Weybridge	d								07 00														
Addlestone §	d								07 04			08 04						09 04					
Chertsey §	d								07 07			08 07						09 07					
Virginia Water	a			23p49					07 12			08 12		08 30		09 00		09 12		09 30		10 00	
	d			23p49					07 12			08 12		08 30		09 00		09 12		09 30		10 00	
Egham	d			23p53					07 16			08 16		08 34		09 04		09 16		09 34		10 04	
Windsor & Eton Riverside	d							06 59			07 59						08 59						09 59
Datchet	d							07 02			08 02						09 02						10 02
Sunnymeads	d							07 05			08 05						09 05						10 05
Wraysbury	d							07 08			08 08						09 08						10 08
Staines	d			23p59				07 16	07 21		08 16	08 21		08 39		09 09	09 16	09 21		09 39		10 09	10 16
Ashford (Surrey)	d							07 19	07 24		08 19	08 24					09 19	09 24					10 19
Feltham	d			00 05				07 24	07 29		08 24	08 29		08 46		09 16	09 24	09 29		09 46		10 16	10 24
Whitton	d							07 28			08 28						09 28						10 28
Kingston	d	23p29	23p55		01 17	02 16	06 49			07 49					08 49						09 49		
Hampton Wick	d	23p31	23p57		01s22	02s21	06 51			07 51					08 51						09 51		
Teddington	d	23p35	23p59		01s25	02s23	06 56			07 56					08 56						09 56		
Fulwell	d																						
Strawberry Hill	d	23p38	00 03		01a28	02s26	06 59			07 59					08 59						09 59		
Twickenham	a	23p42	00 07	00 10		02 30	07 02	07 31		08 02	08 31			08 51	09 02	09 21	09 31			09 51	10 02	10 21	10 31
	d	23p43		00 12			07 03	07 32		08 03	08 32			08 51	09 03	09 21	09 32			09 51	10 03	10 21	10 32
St Margarets	d	23p45					07 05	07 34		08 05	08 34				09 05		09 34				10 05		10 34
Richmond	⊖ d	23p49		00 16			07 09	07 37		08 09	08 37			08 56	09 09	09 26	09 37			09 56	10 09	10 26	10 37
North Sheen	d	23p51					07 11	07 39		08 11	08 39				09 11		09 39				10 11		10 39
Mortlake	d	23p53					07 13	07 42		08 13	08 42				09 13		09 42				10 13		10 42
Hounslow	d								07 35			08 35						09 35					
Isleworth	d								07 38			08 38						09 38					
Syon Lane	d								07 40			08 40						09 40					
Brentford	d								07 42			08 42						09 42					
Kew Bridge	d								07 45			08 45						09 45					
Chiswick	d								07 47			08 47						09 47					
Barnes Bridge	d								07 50			08 50						09 50					
Barnes	d	23p56					07 16	07 45	07 53	08 16	08 45	08 53			09 16		09 45	09 53			10 16		10 45
Putney	d	23p59					07 19	07 48	07 56	08 19	08 48	08 56		09 02	09 19	09 32	09 48	09 56		10 02	10 19	10 32	10 48
Wandsworth Town	d	00 02					07 22	07 51	07 59	08 22	08 51	08 59			09 22		09 51	09 59			10 22		10 51
Clapham Junction 10	d	00 05		00 25			07 25	07 54	08 02	08 25	08 54	09 02		09 07	09 25	09 37	09 54	10 02		10 07	10 25	10 37	10 54
Queenstown Rd.(Battersea)	d	00 08					07 28	07 57	08 05	08 28	08 57	09 05			09 28		09 57	10 05			10 28		10 58
Vauxhall	⊖ d	00 12					07 32	08 00	08 08	08 32	09 00	09 08		09 12	09 32	09 42	10 00	10 08		10 12	10 32	10 42	11 02
London Waterloo 15	⊖ a	00 16		00 33			07 41	08 10	08 13	08 41	09 10	09 13		09 23	09 41	09 53	10 10	10 13		10 23	10 41	10 53	11 10

For general notes see front of timetable
For details of catering facilities see
Directory of Train Operators

§ Passengers to/from London may travel via Weybridge. See Table 155.

A From London Waterloo (Table 152)

Table 149

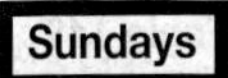

Sundays

from 28 September

Reading, Guildford, Ascot, Weybridge, Windsor, Kingston, Richmond and Hounslow → London

Network Diagram - see first page of Table 148

		SW	SW 1	SW 1	SW	SW A	SW 1	SW	SW	SW 1	SW 1	SW	SW A	SW 1	SW	SW	SW 1	SW 1	SW	SW A	SW 1	SW
Reading 7	d			09 51			10 21				10 51			11 21				11 51			12 21	
Earley	d			09 56			10 26				10 56			11 26				11 56			12 26	
Winnersh Triangle	d			09 58			10 28				10 58			11 28				11 58			12 28	
Winnersh	d			10 00			10 30				11 00			11 30				12 00			12 30	
Wokingham	d			10 05			10 35				11 05			11 35				12 05			12 35	
Bracknell	d			10 11			10 41				11 11			11 41				12 11			12 41	
Martins Heron	d			10 14			10 44				11 14			11 44				12 14			12 44	
Guildford	d		09 17							10 17							11 17					
Wanborough	d		09 23							10 23							11 23					
Ash 3	d		09 27							10 27							11 27					
Aldershot	a		09 34							10 34							11 34					
	d		09 40							10 40							11 40					
Ash Vale	d		09 45							10 45							11 45					
Frimley	d		09 51							10 51							11 51					
Camberley	a		09 55							10 55							11 55					
	d		09 55							10 55							11 55					
Bagshot	d		10 01							11 01							12 01					
Ascot 3	d		10a07	10 19			10 49			11a07	11 19			11 49			12a07	12 19			12 49	
Sunningdale	d			10 22			10 52				11 22			11 52				12 22			12 52	
Longcross	d																					
Woking	d	09 52							10 52							11 52						
West Byfleet	d	09 56							10 56							11 56						
Byfleet & New Haw	d	10 00							11 00							12 00						
Weybridge	d																					
Addlestone §	d	10 04							11 04							12 04						
Chertsey §	d	10 07							11 07							12 07						
Virginia Water	a	10 12		10 30			11 00		11 12		11 30			12 00		12 12		12 30			13 00	
	d	10 12		10 30			11 00		11 12		11 30			12 00		12 12		12 30			13 00	
Egham	d	10 16		10 34			11 04		11 16		11 34			12 04		12 16		12 34			13 04	
Windsor & Eton Riverside	d				10 32			10 59				11 32			11 59				12 32			
Datchet	d				10 35			11 02				11 35			12 02				12 35			
Sunnymeads	d							11 05							12 05							
Wraysbury	d							11 08							12 08							
Staines	d	10 21		10 39	10 45		11 09	11 16	11 21		11 39	11 45		12 09	12 16	12 21		12 39	12 45		13 09	
Ashford (Surrey)	d	10 24			10 48			11 19	11 24			11 48			12 19	12 24			12 48			
Feltham	d	10 29		10 46	10 53		11 16	11 24	11 29		11 46	11 53		12 16	12 24	12 29		12 46	12 53		13 16	
Whitton	d				10 57			11 28				11 57			12 28				12 57			
Kingston	d					10 49							11 49							12 49		13 11
Hampton Wick	d					10 51							11 51							12 51		13 13
Teddington	d					10 56							11 56							12 56		13 16
Fulwell	d																					
Strawberry Hill	d					10 59							11 59							12 59		13 19
Twickenham	a			10 51	11 00	11 02	11 21	11 31			11 51	12 00	12 02	12 21	12 31			12 51	13 00	13 02	13 21	13 22
	d			10 51	11 01	11 03	11 21	11 32			11 51	12 01	12 03	12 21	12 32			12 51	13 01	13 03	13 21	13 23
St Margarets	d					11 05		11 34					12 05		12 34					13 05		13 25
Richmond	⊖ d			10 56	11 05	11 09	11 26	11 37			11 56	12 05	12 09	12 26	12 37			12 56	13 05	13 09	13 26	13 29
North Sheen	d					11 11		11 39					12 11		12 39					13 11		13 31
Mortlake	d					11 13		11 42					12 13		12 42					13 13		13 33
Hounslow	d	10 35							11 35							12 35						
Isleworth	d	10 38							11 38							12 38						
Syon Lane	d	10 40							11 40							12 40						
Brentford	d	10 42							11 42							12 42						
Kew Bridge	d	10 45							11 45							12 45						
Chiswick	d	10 47							11 47							12 47						
Barnes Bridge	d	10 50							11 50							12 50						
Barnes	d	10 53				11 16		11 45	11 53				12 16		12 45	12 53				13 16		13 36
Putney	d	10 56		11 02	11 14	11 19	11 32	11 48	11 56		12 02	12 14	12 19	12 32	12 48	12 56		13 02	13 14	13 19	13 32	13 39
Wandsworth Town	d	10 59				11 22		11 51	11 59				12 22		12 51	12 59				13 22		13 42
Clapham Junction 10	d	11 04		11 07	11 18	11 25	11 37	11 54	12 04		12 07	12 18	12 25	12 37	12 54	13 02		13 07	13 18	13 25	13 37	13 45
Queenstown Rd.(Battersea)	d	11 09				11 33		11 58	12 09				12 33		12 58	13 05				13 28		13 48
Vauxhall	⊖ d	11 13		11 16	11 26	11 37	11 45	12 02	12 13		12 16	12 26	12 37	12 45	13 02	13 08		13 12	13 24	13 32	13 42	13 52
London Waterloo 15	⊖ a	11 19		11 23	11 34	11 41	11 53	12 10	12 19		12 23	12 34	12 41	12 53	13 10	13 13		13 23	13 34	13 41	13 53	14 00

For general notes see front of timetable
For details of catering facilities see
Directory of Train Operators

§ Passengers to/from London may travel via Weybridge. See Table 155.

A From London Waterloo (Table 152)

Table 149

Sundays

Reading, Guildford, Ascot, Weybridge, Windsor, Kingston, Richmond and Hounslow → London

from 28 September

Network Diagram - see first page of Table 148

		SW	SW	SW	SW	SW	SW	SW	SW	SW	SW	SW	SW	SW	SW	SW	SW	SW	SW	SW	SW	SW
				1	1			1				1	1			1				1	1	
							A								A							
Reading 7	d				12 51			13 21					13 51			14 21					14 51	
Earley	d				12 56			13 26					13 56			14 26					14 56	
Winnersh Triangle	d				12 58			13 28					13 58			14 28					14 58	
Winnersh	d				13 00			13 30					14 00			14 30					15 00	
Wokingham	d				13 05			13 35					14 05			14 35					15 05	
Bracknell	d				13 11			13 41					14 11			14 41					15 11	
Martins Heron	d				13 14			13 44					14 14			14 44					15 14	
Guildford	d			12 17								13 17								14 17		
Wanborough	d			12 23								13 23								14 23		
Ash 3	d			12 27								13 27								14 27		
Aldershot	a			12 34								13 34								14 34		
	d			12 40								13 40								14 40		
Ash Vale	d			12 45								13 45								14 45		
Frimley	d			12 51								13 51								14 51		
Camberley	a			12 55								13 55								14 55		
	d			12 55								13 55								14 55		
Bagshot	d			13 01								14 01								15 01		
Ascot 3	d			13a07	13 19			13 49				14a07	14 19			14 49				15a07	15 19	
Sunningdale	d				13 22			13 52					14 22			14 52					15 22	
Longcross	d																					
Woking	d		12 52								13 52								14 52			
West Byfleet	d		12 56								13 56								14 56			
Byfleet & New Haw	d		13 00								14 00								15 00			
Weybridge	d																					
Addlestone §	d		13 04								14 04								15 04			
Chertsey §	d		13 07								14 07								15 07			
Virginia Water	a		13 12		13 30			14 00			14 12		14 30			15 00			15 12		15 30	
	d		13 12		13 30			14 00			14 12		14 30			15 00			15 12		15 30	
Egham	d		13 16		13 34			14 04			14 16		14 34			15 04			15 16		15 34	
Windsor & Eton Riverside	d	12 59				13 32				13 59				14 32				14 59				15 32
Datchet	d	13 02				13 35				14 02				14 35				15 02				15 35
Sunnymeads	d	13 05								14 05								15 05				
Wraysbury	d	13 08								14 08								15 08				
Staines	d	13 16	13 21		13 39	13 45		14 09		14 16	14 21		14 39	14 45		15 09		15 16	15 21		15 39	15 45
Ashford (Surrey)	d	13 19	13 24			13 48				14 19	14 24			14 48				15 19	15 24			15 48
Feltham	d	13 24	13 29		13 46	13 53		14 16		14 24	14 29		14 46	14 53		15 16		15 24	15 29		15 46	15 53
Whitton	d	13 28				13 57				14 28				14 57				15 28				15 57
Kingston	d						13 49		14 11						14 49		15 11					
Hampton Wick	d						13 51		14 13						14 51		15 13					
Teddington	d						13 56		14 16						14 56		15 16					
Fulwell	d																					
Strawberry Hill	d						13 59		14 19						14 59		15 19					
Twickenham	a	13 31			13 51	14 00	14 02	14 21	14 22	14 31			14 51	15 00	15 02	15 21	15 22	15 31			15 51	16 00
	d	13 32			13 51	14 01	14 03	14 21	14 23	14 32			14 51	15 01	15 03	15 21	15 23	15 32			15 51	16 01
St Margarets	d	13 34					14 05		14 25	14 34					15 05		15 25	15 34				
Richmond	⊖ d	13 37			13 56	14 05	14 09	14 26	14 29	14 37			14 56	15 05	15 09	15 26	15 29	15 37			15 56	16 05
North Sheen	d	13 39					14 11		14 31	14 39					15 11		15 31	15 39				
Mortlake	d	13 42					14 13		14 33	14 42					15 13		15 33	15 42				
Hounslow	d		13 35								14 35								15 35			
Isleworth	d		13 38								14 38								15 38			
Syon Lane	d		13 40								14 40								15 40			
Brentford	d		13 42								14 42								15 42			
Kew Bridge	d		13 45								14 45								15 45			
Chiswick	d		13 47								14 47								15 47			
Barnes Bridge	d		13 50								14 50								15 50			
Barnes	d	13 45	13 53				14 16		14 36	14 45	14 53				15 16		15 36	15 45	15 53			
Putney	d	13 48	13 56		14 02	14 14	14 19	14 32	14 39	14 48	14 56		15 02	15 14	15 19	15 32	15 39	15 48	15 56		16 02	16 14
Wandsworth Town	d	13 51	13 59				14 22		14 42	14 51	14 59				15 22		15 42	15 51	15 59			
Clapham Junction 10	d	13 54	14 02		14 07	14 18	14 25	14 37	14 45	14 54	15 02		15 07	15 18	15 25	15 37	15 45	15 54	16 02		16 07	16 18
Queenstown Rd.(Battersea)	d	13 57	14 05				14 28		14 48	14 57	15 05				15 28		15 48	15 57	16 05			
Vauxhall	⊖ d	14 00	14 08		14 12	14 24	14 32	14 42	14 52	15 00	15 08		15 12	15 24	15 32	15 42	15 52	16 00	16 08		16 12	16 24
London Waterloo 15	⊖ a	14 10	14 13		14 23	14 29	14 36	14 48	15 00	15 05	15 13		15 18	15 29	15 36	15 48	16 00	16 05	16 13		16 18	16 29

For general notes see front of timetable
For details of catering facilities see Directory of Train Operators

§ Passengers to/from London may travel via Weybridge. See Table 155.

A From London Waterloo (Table 152)

Table 149

from 28 September

Reading, Guildford, Ascot, Weybridge, Windsor, Kingston, Richmond and Hounslow → London

Network Diagram - see first page of Table 148

		SW	SW	SW	SW	SW		SW	SW	SW	SW	SW	SW	SW		SW	SW	SW	SW	SW	SW	SW		SW	SW
			1					1	1			1					1	1			1				
		A									A									A					
Reading 7	d		15 21						15 51			16 21						16 51			17 21				
Earley	d		15 26						15 56			16 26						16 56			17 26				
Winnersh Triangle	d		15 28						15 58			16 28						16 58			17 28				
Winnersh	d		15 30						16 00			16 30						17 00			17 30				
Wokingham	d		15 35						16 05			16 35						17 05			17 35				
Bracknell	d		15 41						16 11			16 41						17 11			17 41				
Martins Heron	d		15 44						16 14			16 44						17 14			17 44				
Guildford	d							15 17									16 17								
Wanborough	d							15 23									16 23								
Ash 3	d							15 27									16 27								
Aldershot	a							15 34									16 34								
	d							15 40									16 40								
Ash Vale	d							15 45									16 45								
Frimley	d							15 51									16 51								
Camberley	a							15 55									16 55								
	d							15 55									16 55								
Bagshot	d							16 01									17 01								
Ascot 3	d		15 49					16a07	16 19			16 49					17a07	17 19			17 49				
Sunningdale	d		15 52						16 22			16 52						17 25			17 55				
Longcross	d																								
Woking	d					15 52										16 52									17 52
West Byfleet	d					15 56										16 56									17 56
Byfleet & New Haw	d					16 00										17 00									18 00
Weybridge	d																								
Addlestone §	d					16 04										17 04									18 04
Chertsey §	d					16 07										17 07									18 07
Virginia Water	a		16 00			16 12			16 30			17 00				17 12		17 30			18 00				18 12
	d		16 00			16 12			16 30			17 00				17 12		17 30			18 00				18 12
Egham	d		16 04			16 16			16 34			17 04				17 16		17 34			18 04				18 16
Windsor & Eton Riverside	d				15 59					16 32				16 59					17 32					17 59	
Datchet	d				16 02					16 35				17 02					17 35					18 02	
Sunnymeads	d				16 05									17 05										18 05	
Wraysbury	d				16 08									17 08										18 08	
Staines	d		16 09		16 16	16 21			16 39	16 45		17 09		17 16		17 21		17 39	17 45		18 09			18 16	18 21
Ashford (Surrey)	d				16 19	16 24				16 48				17 19		17 24			17 48					18 19	18 24
Feltham	d		16 16		16 24	16 29			16 46	16 53		17 16		17 24		17 29		17 46	17 53		18 16			18 24	18 29
Whitton	d				16 28					16 57				17 28					17 57					18 28	
Kingston	d	15 49		16 11							16 49		17 11							17 49		18 11			
Hampton Wick	d	15 51		16 13							16 51		17 13							17 51		18 13			
Teddington	d	15 56		16 16							16 56		17 16							17 56		18 16			
Fulwell	d																								
Strawberry Hill	d	15 59		16 19							16 59		17 19							17 59		18 19			
Twickenham	a	16 02	16 21	16 22	16 31				16 51	17 00	17 02	17 21	17 22	17 31				17 51	18 00	18 02	18 21	18 22		18 31	
	d	16 03	16 21	16 23	16 32				16 51	17 01	17 03	17 21	17 23	17 32				17 51	18 01	18 03	18 21	18 23		18 32	
St Margarets	d	16 05		16 25	16 34						17 05		17 25	17 34						18 05		18 25		18 34	
Richmond	⊖ d	16 09	16 26	16 29	16 37				16 56	17 05	17 09	17 26	17 29	17 37				17 56	18 05	18 09	18 26	18 29		18 37	
North Sheen	d	16 11		16 31	16 39						17 11		17 31	17 39						18 11		18 31		18 39	
Mortlake	d	16 13		16 33	16 42						17 13		17 33	17 42						18 13		18 33		18 42	
Hounslow	d					16 35										17 35									18 35
Isleworth	d					16 38										17 38									18 38
Syon Lane	d					16 40										17 40									18 40
Brentford	d					16 42										17 42									18 42
Kew Bridge	d					16 45										17 45									18 45
Chiswick	d					16 47										17 47									18 47
Barnes Bridge	d					16 50										17 50									18 50
Barnes	d	16 16		16 36	16 45	16 53					17 16		17 36	17 45		17 53				18 16		18 36		18 45	18 53
Putney	d	16 19	16 32	16 39	16 48	16 56			17 02	17 14	17 19	17 32	17 39	17 48		17 56		18 02	18 14	18 19	18 32	18 39		18 48	18 56
Wandsworth Town	d	16 22		16 42	16 51	16 59					17 22		17 42	17 51		17 59				18 22		18 42		18 51	18 59
Clapham Junction 10	d	16 25	16 37	16 45	16 54	17 02			17 07	17 18	17 25	17 37	17 45	17 54		18 02		18 07	18 18	18 25	18 37	18 45		18 54	19 02
Queenstown Rd.(Battersea)	d	16 28		16 48	16 57	17 05					17 28		17 48	17 57		18 05				18 28		18 48		18 57	19 05
Vauxhall	⊖ d	16 32	16 42	16 52	17 00	17 08			17 12	17 24	17 32	17 42	17 52	18 00		18 08		18 12	18 24	18 32	18 42	18 52		19 00	19 08
London Waterloo 15	⊖ a	16 36	16 48	17 00	17 05	17 13			17 18	17 29	17 36	17 48	18 00	18 05		18 13		18 18	18 29	18 36	18 48	19 00		19 05	19 13

For general notes see front of timetable
For details of catering facilities see
Directory of Train Operators

§ Passengers to/from London may travel via Weybridge. See Table 155.

A From London Waterloo (Table 152)

Reading, Guildford, Ascot, Weybridge, Windsor, Kingston, Richmond and Hounslow → London

from 28 September

Network Diagram - see first page of Table 148

		SW [1]	SW [1]	SW	SW	SW [1]	SW	SW		SW	SW [1]	SW [1]	SW	SW	SW [1]	SW		SW	SW	SW [1]	SW [1]	SW	SW	SW [1]	SW
					A									A									A		
Reading 7	d		17 51			18 21						18 51			19 21						19 51			20 21	
Earley	d		17 56			18 26						18 56			19 26						19 56			20 26	
Winnersh Triangle	d		17 58			18 28						18 58			19 28						19 58			20 28	
Winnersh	d		18 00			18 30						19 00			19 30						20 00			20 30	
Wokingham	d		18 05			18 35						19 05			19 35						20 05			20 35	
Bracknell	d		18 11			18 41						19 11			19 41						20 11			20 41	
Martins Heron	d		18 14			18 44						19 14			19 44						20 14			20 44	
Guildford	d	17 17									18 17									19 17					
Wanborough	d	17 23									18 23									19 23					
Ash 3	d	17 27									18 27									19 27					
Aldershot	a	17 34									18 34									19 34					
	d	17 40									18 40									19 40					
Ash Vale	d	17 45									18 45									19 45					
Frimley	d	17 51									18 51									19 51					
Camberley	a	17 55									18 55									19 55					
	d	17 55									18 55									19 55					
Bagshot	d	18 01									19 01									20 01					
Ascot 3	d	18a07	18 19			18 49					19a07	19 19			19 49					20a07	20 19			20 49	
Sunningdale	d		18 22			18 52						19 22			19 52						20 22			20 52	
Longcross	d																								
Woking	d									18 52									19 52						
West Byfleet	d									18 56									19 56						
Byfleet & New Haw	d									19 00									20 00						
Weybridge	d																								
Addlestone §	d									19 04									20 04						
Chertsey §	d									19 07									20 07						
Virginia Water	a		18 30			19 00				19 12		19 30			20 00				20 12		20 30			21 00	
	d		18 30			19 00				19 12		19 30			20 00				20 12		20 30			21 00	
Egham	d		18 34			19 04				19 16		19 34			20 04				20 16		20 34			21 04	
Windsor & Eton Riverside	d			18 32				18 59					19 32					19 59				20 32			
Datchet	d			18 35				19 02					19 35					20 02				20 35			
Sunnymeads	d							19 05										20 05							
Wraysbury	d							19 08										20 08							
Staines	d		18 39	18 45		19 09		19 16		19 21		19 39	19 45		20 09			20 16	20 21		20 39	20 45		21 09	
Ashford (Surrey)	d			18 48				19 19		19 24			19 48					20 19	20 24			20 48			
Feltham	d		18 46	18 53		19 16		19 24		19 29		19 46	19 53		20 16			20 24	20 29		20 46	20 53		21 16	
Whitton	d			18 57				19 28					19 57					20 28				20 57			
Kingston	d				18 49		19 11							19 49		20 11							20 49		21 11
Hampton Wick	d				18 51		19 13							19 51		20 13							20 51		21 13
Teddington	d				18 56		19 16							19 56		20 16							20 56		21 16
Fulwell	d																								
Strawberry Hill	d				18 59		19 19							19 59		20 19							20 59		21 19
Twickenham	a		18 51	19 00	19 02	19 21	19 22	19 31				19 51	20 00	20 02	20 21	20 22		20 31			20 51	21 00	21 02	21 21	21 22
	d		18 51	19 01	19 03	19 21	19 23	19 32				19 51	20 01	20 03	20 21	20 23		20 32			20 51	21 01	21 03	21 21	21 23
St Margarets	d				19 05		19 25	19 34						20 05		20 25		20 34					21 05		21 25
Richmond	⊖ d		18 56	19 05	19 09	19 26	19 29	19 37				19 56	20 05	20 09	20 26	20 29		20 37			20 56	21 05	21 09	21 26	21 29
North Sheen	d				19 11		19 31	19 39						20 11		20 31		20 39					21 11		21 31
Mortlake	d				19 13		19 33	19 42						20 13		20 33		20 42					21 13		21 33
Hounslow	d									19 35									20 35						
Isleworth	d									19 38									20 38						
Syon Lane	d									19 40									20 40						
Brentford	d									19 42									20 42						
Kew Bridge	d									19 45									20 45						
Chiswick	d									19 47									20 47						
Barnes Bridge	d									19 50									20 50						
Barnes	d				19 16		19 36	19 45		19 53				20 16		20 36		20 45	20 53				21 16		21 36
Putney	d		19 02	19 14	19 19	19 32	19 39	19 48		19 56		20 02	20 14	20 19	20 32	20 39		20 48	20 56		21 02	21 14	21 19	21 32	21 39
Wandsworth Town	d				19 22		19 42	19 51		19 59				20 22		20 42		20 51	20 59				21 22		21 42
Clapham Junction 10	d		19 07	19 18	19 25	19 37	19 45	19 54		20 02		20 07	20 18	20 25	20 37	20 45		20 54	21 02		21 07	21 18	21 25	21 37	21 45
Queenstown Rd.(Battersea)	d				19 28		19 48	19 57		20 05				20 28		20 48		20 57	21 05				21 28		21 48
Vauxhall	⊖ d		19 12	19 24	19 32	19 42	19 52	20 00		20 08		20 12	20 24	20 32	20 42	20 52		21 00	21 08		21 12	21 24	21 32	21 42	21 52
London Waterloo 15	⊖ a		19 18	19 29	19 36	19 48	20 00	20 05		20 13		20 18	20 29	20 36	20 48	21 00		21 05	21 13		21 18	21 29	21 36	21 48	22 00

For general notes see front of timetable
For details of catering facilities see
Directory of Train Operators

§ Passengers to/from London may travel via Weybridge. See Table 155.

A From London Waterloo (Table 152)

Table 149

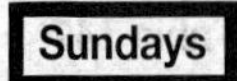

from 28 September

Reading, Guildford, Ascot, Weybridge, Windsor, Kingston, Richmond and Hounslow → London

Network Diagram - see first page of Table 148

Station		SW	SW	SW 1	SW 1	SW A	SW 1	SW	SW	SW	SW 1	SW 1	SW A	SW 1	SW	SW	SW	SW 1	SW 1	SW 1	SW A
Reading 7	d				20 51		21 21					21 51		22 21						22 54	
Earley	d				20 56		21 26					21 56		22 26						22 59	
Winnersh Triangle	d				20 58		21 28					21 58		22 28						23 01	
Winnersh	d				21 00		21 30					22 00		22 30						23 03	
Wokingham	d				21 05		21 35					22 05		22 35						23 08	
Bracknell	d				21 11		21 41					22 11		22 41						23 14	
Martins Heron	d				21 14		21 44					22 14		22 44						23 17	
Guildford	d			20 17							21 17							22 17	23 17		
Wanborough	d			20 23							21 23							22 23	23 23		
Ash 3	d			20 27							21 27							22 27	23 27		
Aldershot	a			20 34							21 34							22 34	23 34		
	d			20 40							21 40							22 40			
Ash Vale	d			20 45							21 45							22 45			
Frimley	d			20 51							21 51							22 51			
Camberley	a			20 55							21 55							22 55			
	d			20 55							21 55							22 55			
Bagshot	d			21 01							22 01							23 01			
Ascot 3	d			21a07	21 19		21 49				22a07	22 19		22 49				23a07		23 22	
Sunningdale	d				21 22		21 52					22 22		22 52						23 25	
Longcross	d																				
Woking	d		20 52							21 52							22 52				
West Byfleet	d		20 56							21 56							22 56				
Byfleet & New Haw	d		21 00							22 00							23 00				
Weybridge	d																				
Addlestone §	d		21 04							22 04							23 04				
Chertsey §	d		21 07							22 07							23 07				
Virginia Water	a		21 12		21 30		22 00			22 12		22 30		23 00			23 12			23 30	
	d		21 12		21 30		22 00			22 12		22 30		23 00			23 12			23 30	
Egham	d		21 16		21 34		22 04			22 16		22 34		23 04			23 16			23 34	
Windsor & Eton Riverside	d	20 59							21 59							23 01					
Datchet	d	21 02							22 02							23 04					
Sunnymeads	d	21 05							22 05							23 07					
Wraysbury	d	21 08							22 08							23 10					
Staines	d	21 16	21 21		21 39		22 09		22 16	22 21		22 39		23 09		23 16	23 21			23 39	
Ashford (Surrey)	d	21 19	21 24						22 19	22 24						23 19	23 24				
Feltham	d	21 24	21 29		21 46		22 16		22 24	22 29		22 46		23 16		23 24	23 29			23 46	
Whitton	d	21 28							22 28							23 28					
Kingston	d					21 49		22 11					22 49		23 11						23 47
Hampton Wick	d					21 51		22 13					22 51		23 13						23 49
Teddington	d					21 56		22 16					22 56		23 16						23 51
Fulwell	d																				
Strawberry Hill	d					21 59		22 19					22 59		23 19						23a54
Twickenham	a	21 31			21 51	22 02	22 21	22 22	22 31			22 51	23 02	23 21	23 22	23 31				23 51	
	d	21 32			21 51	22 03	22 21	22 23	22 32			22 51	23 03	23 21	23 23	23 32				23 51	
St Margarets	d	21 34				22 05		22 25	22 34				23 05		23 25	23 34					
Richmond ⊖	d	21 37			21 56	22 09	22 26	22 29	22 37			22 56	23 09	23 26	23 29	23 37				23 56	
North Sheen	d	21 39				22 11		22 31	22 39				23 11		23 31	23 39					
Mortlake	d	21 42				22 13		22 33	22 42				23 13		23 33	23 42					
Hounslow	d		21 35							22 35							23 35				
Isleworth	d		21 38							22 38							23 38				
Syon Lane	d		21 40							22 40							23 40				
Brentford	d		21 42							22 42							23 42				
Kew Bridge	d		21 45							22 45							23 45				
Chiswick	d		21 47							22 47							23 47				
Barnes Bridge	d		21 50							22 50							23 50				
Barnes	d	21 45	21 53			22 16		22 36	22 45	22 53			23 16		23 36	23 45	23 53				
Putney	d	21 48	21 56		22 02	22 19	22 32	22 39	22 48	22 56		23 02	23 19	23 32	23 39	23 48	23 56			00 02	
Wandsworth Town	d	21 51	21 59			22 22		22 42	22 51	22 59			23 22		23 42	23 51	23 59				
Clapham Junction 10	d	21 54	22 02		22 07	22 25	22 37	22 45	22 54	23 02		23 07	23 25	23 37	23 45	23 54	00 02			00 07	
Queenstown Rd.(Battersea)	d	21 57	22 05			22 28		22 48	22 57	23 05			23 28		23 48	23 57	00 05				
Vauxhall ⊖	d	22 00	22 08		22 12	22 32	22 42	22 52	23 00	23 08		23 12	23 32	23 42	23 52	00 01	00 08			00 12	
London Waterloo 15 ⊖	a	22 05	22 13		22 18	22 36	22 48	23 00	23 05	23 13		23 18	23 36	23 48	23 59	00 05	00 13			00 17	

For general notes see front of timetable
For details of catering facilities see Directory of Train Operators

§ Passengers to/from London may travel via Weybridge. See Table 155.

A From London Waterloo (Table 152)

Network Diagram for Table 152

DM-16/06
Design BAJS

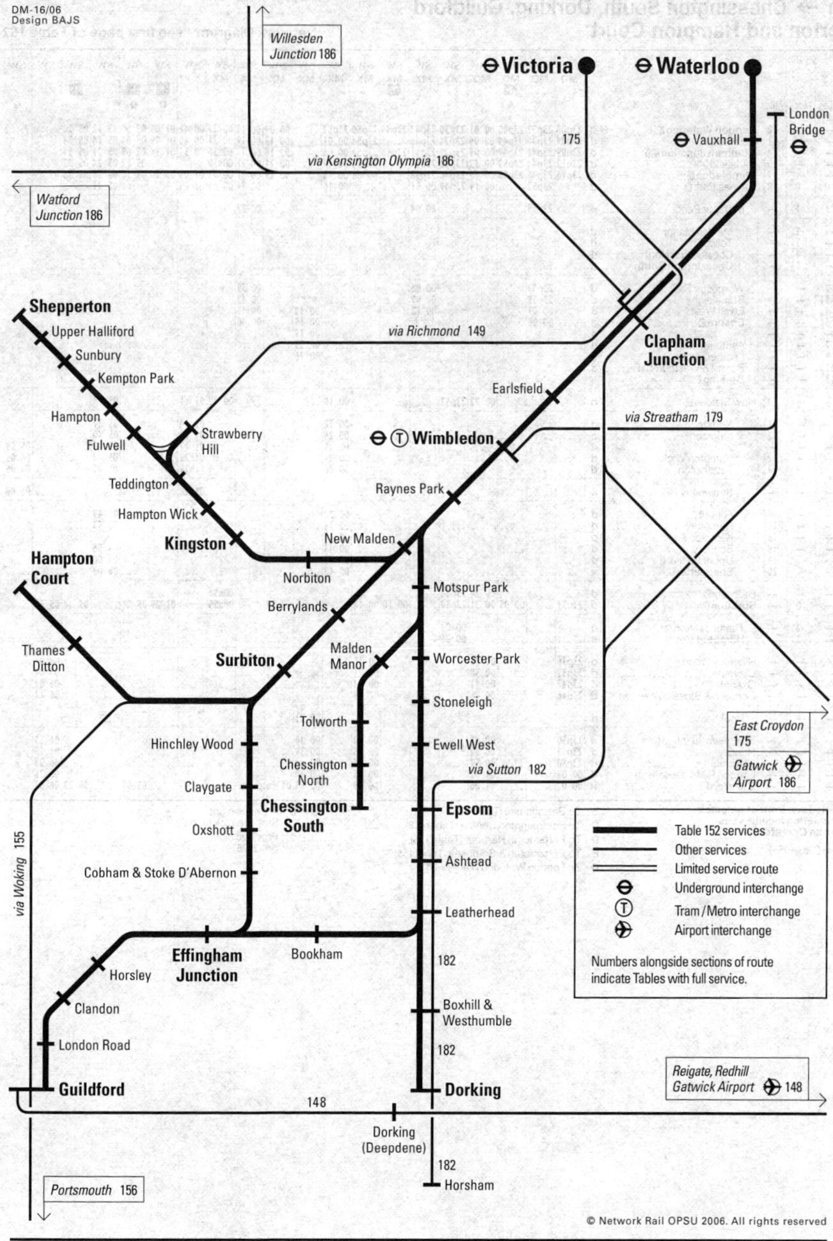

Willesden Junction 186
Victoria
Waterloo
London Bridge
175
Vauxhall
via Kensington Olympia 186
Watford Junction 186
Shepperton
Upper Halliford
Sunbury
Kempton Park
Hampton
Fulwell
Strawberry Hill
Teddington
Hampton Wick
Kingston
via Richmond 149
Clapham Junction
Earlsfield
via Streatham 179
Wimbledon
Raynes Park
New Malden
Norbiton
Hampton Court
Thames Ditton
Berrylands
Surbiton
Malden Manor
Motspur Park
Worcester Park
Stoneleigh
Tolworth
Hinchley Wood
Ewell West
Chessington North
Claygate
Chessington South
via Sutton 182
Epsom
East Croydon 175
Gatwick Airport 186
Oxshott
Cobham & Stoke D'Abernon
Ashtead
Leatherhead
via Woking 155
Effingham Junction
Bookham
Horsley
Clandon
London Road
Guildford
182
Boxhill & Westhumble
182
Dorking
148
Reigate, Redhill Gatwick Airport 148
Dorking (Deepdene)
182
Horsham
Portsmouth 156
Table 152 services
Other services
Limited service route
Underground interchange
Tram/Metro interchange
Airport interchange
Numbers alongside sections of route indicate Tables with full service.

For details of Bank Holiday service alterations, please see first page of Table 149

London → Chessington South, Dorking, Guildford Shepperton and Hampton Court

Network Diagram - see first page of Table 152

Miles	Miles	Miles	Miles	Miles			SW MO	SW MO	SW MO [1] A	SW MO	SW MX	SW MX	SW MX [1] B	SW MX	SW MX	SW MX	SW MX	SW MX	SW MX	SW	SW [1] C	SW [1] D	SW	SW [1] E	SW	SW G
0	—	—	—	0	**London Waterloo** [15] ⊖	d	23p00	23p32	23p40	00 01	23p30	23p42	23p48	23p50	23p57		00 09	00 15	00 27	00 42	01 05	05 00	05 12	05 20		
1¼	—	—	—	1¼	Vauxhall ⊖	d	23p04	23p36	23p44	00 04	23p34	23p46		23p54	00 01		00 13	00 19	00 31	00 46	01 09	05 04	05 16	05 24		
4	—	—	—	4	**Clapham Junction** [10]	d	23p09	23p41	23p49	00 09	23p39	23p51	23b56	23p59	00 06		00 18	00 24	00 36	00 51	01 14	05 09	05 21	05 29		
5½	—	—	—	5½	Earlsfield	d	23p12	23p44	23p52	00 12	23p42	23p54		00 02	00 09		00 21	00 27	00s39			05 12	05 24	05 32		
7¼	—	—	—	7¼	**Wimbledon** [6] ⊖	d	23p16	23p48	23p56	00 16	23p46	23p58		00 06	00 13		00 25	00 31	00 43	01 05	01 20	05 16	05 28	05 36	05 49	
8¾	—	0	0	8¾	Raynes Park [6]	d		23p52		00 19	23p49	00 01			00 16			00 34	00 46	01 08			05 31			
—	—	1	1	—	Motspur Park	d		23p55				00 04						00 37								
—	—	—	2½	—	Malden Manor	d																				
—	—	—	3½	—	Tolworth	d																				
—	—	—	4¼	—	Chessington North	d																				
—	—	—	5¼	—	**Chessington South**	a																				
—	—	2	—	—	Worcester Park	d		23p57				00 06						00 39								
—	—	3¼	—	—	Stoneleigh	d		23p59				00 09				←		00 42								
—	—	4¼	—	—	Ewell West	d		00 03				00 12				00 12		00 45								
—	—	5½	—	—	**Epsom** [3]	a		00 06				→				00 15		00 48								
—	—	—	—	—		d										00 19										
—	—	7½	—	—	Ashtead	d										00 23										
—	0	9¼	—	—	Leatherhead	d										00 26										
—	—	12½	—	—	Boxhill & Westhumble	d																				
—	—	13¼	—	—	**Dorking** [4]	a																				
9¾	—	—	—	9¾	New Malden [6]	d				00 22	23p52				00 19				00 49	01 11			05 34			
—	—	—	—	11¼	Norbiton	d									00 22					01 14			05 37			
—	—	—	—	12	Kingston	a									00 25					01 17			05 40			
—	—	—	—	—		d									00 25					01 17			05 40			05 59
—	—	—	—	12½	Hampton Wick	d									00 27					01s22			05 42			06 01
—	—	—	—	13¾	Teddington	d									00 30					01s25			05 45			06 05
—	—	—	—	—	Strawberry Hill	a														01 28						06 08
—	—	—	—	14¾	Fulwell	d									00 34								05 49			
—	—	—	—	16½	Hampton	d									00 38								05 53			
—	—	—	—	18¼	Kempton Park	d									00 41											
—	—	—	—	18¾	Sunbury	d									00 43								05 58			
—	—	—	—	19¼	Upper Halliford	d									00 45								06 00			
—	—	—	—	20¾	**Shepperton**	a									00 48								06 03			
11	—	—	—	—	Berrylands	d				00 24	23p54								00s51							
12	—	—	0	—	**Surbiton** [6]	d	23c32		00 05	00 31	23p59		00 10	00 14			00 33		00a55		01 29	05 24		05 44	05 57	
—	—	—	2	—	Thames Ditton	d					00 03															
—	—	—	3	—	**Hampton Court**	a					00 06															
14	—	—	—	—	Hinchley Wood	d	23p36			00 35				00 18											06 01	
15¼	—	—	—	—	Claygate	d	23p39			00 38				00 21											06 04	
17	—	—	—	—	Oxshott	d	23p42			00 41				00 24											06 07	
19	—	—	—	—	Cobham & Stoke d'Abernon	d	23p46			00 45				00 28											06 11	
—	2½	—	—	—	Bookham	d										00 31										
21¼	4¼	—	—	—	Effingham Junction [6]	d	23p50			00 49				00 32		00 36									06 15	
22¼	—	—	—	—	Horsley	d	23p53			00 52				00 35		00 39									06 18	
25½	—	—	—	—	Clandon	d	23p58			00 57				00 40		00 44									06 23	
28¾	—	—	—	—	London Road (Guildford)	d	00 03			01 02				00 45		00 49									06 28	
30	—	—	—	—	**Guildford**	a	00 07			01 06				00 49		00 53	01 06					05 59		06 23	06 32	

For general notes see front of timetable
For details of catering facilities see Directory of Train Operators

A To Farnham (Table 155)

B To Basingstoke (Table 155)
C To Southampton Central (Table 158)
D To Portsmouth Harbour (Table 156)
E To Portsmouth & Southsea (Table 156)
G To London Waterloo (Table 149)

b Previous night. Stops to pick up only
c Previous night. Arr. 2328

For details of Bank Holiday service alterations, please see first page of Table 149

London → Chessington South, Dorking, Guildford Shepperton and Hampton Court

Network Diagram - see first page of Table 152

		SW	SW	SW	SW		SW 1	SW	SW	SW	SW	SN	SW	SW	SW	SW	SW 1	SW	SW	SW	SW	SW 1	SW	SW	SW	SW
			A				B		C			D			C		E					G			C	
London Waterloo 15 ⊖	d	05 47	05 50		06 03		06 12	06 06		06 12	06 16		06 20	06 24	06 27	06 33	06 42	06 36	06 39	06 42	06 46	06 53	06 50	06 54	06 57	07 03
Vauxhall ⊖	d	05 51	05 54		06 07			06 10		06 16	06 20		06 24	06 28	06 31	06 37		06 40	06 43	06 46	06 50		06 54	06 58	07 01	07 07
Clapham Junction 10	d	05 56	05 59		06 12		06u19	06 15		06 21	06 25		06 29	06 33	06 36	06 42	06u49	06 45	06 48	06 51	06 55	07u00	06 59	07 03	07 06	07 12
Earlsfield	d	05 59	06 02		06 15			06 18		06 24	06 28		06 32	06 36	06 39	06 45		06 48	06 51	06 54	06 58		07 02	07 06	07 09	07 15
Wimbledon 6 ⊖	d	06 03	06 06	06 15	06 19			06 22		06 28	06 32		06 36	06 40	06 43	06 49		06 52	06 55	06 58	07 02		07 06	07 10	07 13	07 19
Raynes Park 6	d	06 06		06 18				06 25		06 31	06 35			06 43	06 46			06 55		07 01	07 05			07 13	07 16	
Motspur Park	d	06 09		06 20							06 38			06 46							07 08			07 16		
Malden Manor	d			06 24							06 41										07 11					
Tolworth	d			06 26							06 44										07 14					
Chessington North	d			06 29							06 47										07 17					
Chessington South	a			06 31							06 49										07 19					
Worcester Park	d	06 11												06 48					07 01					07 18		
Stoneleigh	d	06 14												06 51										07 21		
Ewell West	d	06 17												06 54										07 24		
Epsom 3	a	06 20												06 57					07 08					07 27		
	d	06 21										06 49		06 58					07 08					07 28		
Ashtead	d	06 25												07 02					07 12					07 32		
Leatherhead	d	06 28										06 56		07 05					07 15					07 35		
Boxhill & Westhumble	d																									
Dorking 4	a													07 11										07 41		
New Malden 6	d							06 28		06 34					06 49			06 58		07 04					07 19	
Norbiton	d									06 37					06 52					07 07					07 22	
Kingston	a									06 40					06 55					07 10					07 25	
	d								06 29	06 40					06 59					07 10					07 29	
Hampton Wick	d								06 31	06 42					07 01					07 12					07 31	
Teddington	d								06 35	06 45					07 05					07 15					07 35	
Strawberry Hill	a								06 38						07 08										07 38	
Fulwell	d									06 49										07 19						
Hampton	d									06 53										07 23						
Kempton Park	d																									
Sunbury	d									06 58										07 28						
Upper Halliford	d									07 00										07 30						
Shepperton	a									07 03										07 33						
Berrylands	d							06 30										07 00								
Surbiton 6	d		06 14		06 27		06 30	06 35					06 44			06 57	07 00	07 05				07 11	07 14			07 27
Thames Ditton	d							06 39										07 09								
Hampton Court	a							06 42										07 12								
Hinchley Wood	d				06 31											07 01										07 31
Claygate	d				06 34											07 04										07 34
Oxshott	d				06 37											07 07										07 37
Cobham & Stoke d'Abernon	d				06 41											07 11										07 41
Bookham	d	06 33										07 01							07 21							
Effingham Junction 6	d	06 37			06 45							07 05				07 15			07a24							07 45
Horsley	d				06 48											07 18										07 48
Clandon	d				06 53											07 23										07 53
London Road (Guildford)	d	06 46			06 58											07 28										07 58
Guildford	a	06 50			07 02							07 17	07 20			07 32							07 47			08 02

For general notes see front of timetable
For details of catering facilities see Directory of Train Operators

A To Woking (Table 155)
B To Weymouth (Table 158)
C To London Waterloo (Table 149)
D From Sutton (Surrey) (Table 182)
E To Portsmouth Harbour (Table 158)
G To Alton (Table 155)

For details of Bank Holiday service alterations, please see first page of Table 149

London → Chessington South, Dorking, Guildford Shepperton and Hampton Court

Network Diagram - see first page of Table 152

		SW 1 A	SW	SN B	SW		SW	SW	SW 1 C	SW D	SW	SW E	SW	SW 1 A	SW	SW	SW	SW	SW 1 C	SW	SW	SW E	SW	SW 1 A	SW	SW
London Waterloo 15 ⊖	d	07 12	07 06		07 09		07 12	07 16	07 23	07 20	07 24	07 27	07 33	07 42	07 36	07 39	07 42	07 46	07 53	07 50	07 54	07 57	08 03	08 12	08 06	08 09
Vauxhall ⊖	d		07 10		07 13		07 16	07 20		07 24	07 28	07 31	07 37		07 40	07 43	07 46	07 50		07 54	07 58	08 01	08 07		08 10	08 13
Clapham Junction 10	d	07u20	07 15		07 18		07 21	07 25	07u30	07 29	07 33	07 36	07 42		07 45	07 48	07 51	07 55	08u00	07 59	08 03	08 06	08 12	08u19	08 15	08 18
Earlsfield	d		07 18		07 21		07 24	07 28		07 32	07 36	07 39	07 45		07 48	07 51	07 54	07 58		08 02	08 06	08 09	08 15		08 18	08 21
Wimbledon 6 ⊖	d		07 22		07 25		07 28	07 32		07 36	07 40	07 43	07 49		07 52	07 55	07 58	08 02		08 06	08 10	08 13	08 19		08 22	08 25
Raynes Park 6	d		07 25		07 28		07 31	07 35			07 43	07 46			07 55	07 58	08 01	08 05			08 13	08 16			08 25	08 28
Motspur Park	d				07 31			07 38			07 46					08 01		08 08			08 16					08 31
Malden Manor	d							07 41										08 11								
Tolworth	d							07 44										08 14								
Chessington North	d							07 47										08 17								
Chessington South	a							07 49										08 19								
Worcester Park	d				07 33						07 48					08 03					08 18					08 33
Stoneleigh	d				07 36						07 51					08 06					08 21					08 36
Ewell West	d				07 39						07 54					08 09					08 24					08 39
Epsom 3	a				07 42						07 58					08 15					08 27					08 42
	d			07 38							07 58					08 15					08 28					08 47
Ashtead	d			07 42							08 02					08 19					08 32					08 51
Leatherhead	d			07 45							08 05					08 22					08 35					08 54
Boxhill & Westhumble	d																									
Dorking 4	a										08 12										08 41					
New Malden 6	d		07 28				07 34					07 49			07 58		08 04					08 19			08 28	
Norbiton	d						07 37					07 52					08 07					08 22				
Kingston	a						07 40					07 55					08 10					08 25				
	d						07 40					07 59					08 10					08 29				
Hampton Wick	d						07 42					08 01					08 12					08 31				
Teddington	d						07 45					08 05					08 15					08 35				
Strawberry Hill	a											08 08										08 38				
Fulwell	d						07 49										08 19									
Hampton	d						07 53										08 23									
Kempton Park	d						07 56										08 26									
Sunbury	d						07 58										08 28									
Upper Halliford	d						08 00										08 30									
Shepperton	a						08 03										08 33									
Berrylands	d		07 30												08 00										08 30	
Surbiton 6	d	07 30	07 35						07 41	07 44			07 57	08 00	08 05				08 11	08 14			08 27	08 30	08 35	
Thames Ditton	d		07 39												08 09										08 39	
Hampton Court	a		07 42												08 12										08 42	
Hinchley Wood	d												08 01										08 31			
Claygate	d												08 04										08 34			
Oxshott	d												08 07										08 37			
Cobham & Stoke d'Abernon	d												08 11										08 41			
Bookham	d			07 50												08 28										08 59
Effingham Junction 6	d			07 54									08 15			08 32							08 45			09 03
Horsley	d												08 18			08 34							08 48			09 06
Clandon	d												08 23			08 39							08 53			09 11
London Road (Guildford)	d			08 03									08 28			08 44							08 58			09 16
Guildford	a			08 07									08 32			08 48				08 50			09 04			09 20

For general notes see front of timetable
For details of catering facilities see Directory of Train Operators

A To Basingstoke (Table 155)
B From London Bridge (Table 182)
C To Alton (Table 155)
D To Woking (Table 155)
E To London Waterloo (Table 149)

For details of Bank Holiday service alterations, please see first page of Table 149

London → Chessington South, Dorking, Guildford Shepperton and Hampton Court

Network Diagram - see first page of Table 152

		SW	SW	SW 1 A	SW B		SW	SW C	SW	SW 1 D	SW	SW	SW	SW	SW 1 A	SW B	SW	SW C	SW	SW 1 D	SW	SW	SW	SW	SW 1 A	SW B
London Waterloo 15 ⊖	d	08 12	08 16	08 23	08 20		08 24	08 27	08 33	08 42	08 36	08 39	08 42	08 46	08 53	08 50	08 54	08 57	09 03	09 12	09 06	09 09	09 12	09 16	09 23	09 20
Vauxhall ⊖	d	08 16	08 20		08 24		08 28	08 31	08 37		08 40	08 43	08 46	08 50		08 54	08 58	09 01	09 07		09 10	09 13	09 16	09 20		09 24
Clapham Junction 10	d	08 21	08 25		08 29		08 33	08 36	08 42		08 45	08 48	08 51	08 55	09u00	08 59	09 03	09 06	09 12	09u19	09 15	09 18	09 21	09 25		09 29
Earlsfield	d	08 24	08 28		08 32		08 36	08 39	08 45		08 48	08 51	08 54	08 58		09 02	09 06	09 09	09 15		09 18	09 21	09 24	09 28		09 32
Wimbledon 6 ⊖	d	08 28	08 32		08 36		08 40	08 43	08 49		08 52	08 55	08 58	09 02		09 06	09 10	09 13	09 19		09 22	09 25	09 28	09 32		09 36
Raynes Park 6	d	08 31	08 35				08 43	08 46			08 55	08 58	09 01	09 05			09 13	09 16			09 25	09 28	09 31	09 35		
Motspur Park	d		08 38				08 46					09 01		09 08			09 16					09 31		09 38		
Malden Manor	d		08 41											09 11										09 41		
Tolworth	d		08 44											09 14										09 44		
Chessington North	d		08 47											09 17										09 47		
Chessington South	a		08 49											09 19										09 49		
Worcester Park	d						08 48					09 03					09 18					09 33				
Stoneleigh	d						08 51					09 06					09 21					09 36				
Ewell West	d						08 54					09 09					09 24					09 39				
Epsom 3	a						08 57					09 16					09 27					09 42				
	d						08 58					09 17					09 28					09 47				
Ashtead	d						09 02					09 21					09 32					09 51				
Leatherhead	d						09 05					09 24					09 35					09 54				
Boxhill & Westhumble	d																									
Dorking 4	a						09 11										09 41									
New Malden 6	d	08 34						08 49			08 58		09 04					09 19			09 28		09 34			
Norbiton	d	08 37						08 52					09 07					09 22					09 37			
Kingston	a	08 40						08 55					09 10					09 25					09 40			
	d	08 40						08 59					09 10					09 29					09 40			
Hampton Wick	d	08 42						09 01					09 12					09 31					09 42			
Teddington	d	08 45						09 05					09 15					09 35					09 45			
Strawberry Hill	a							09 08										09 38								
Fulwell	d	08 49											09 19										09 49			
Hampton	d	08 53											09 23										09 53			
Kempton Park	d	08 56											09 26										09 56			
Sunbury	d	08 58											09 28										09 58			
Upper Halliford	d	09 00											09 30										10 00			
Shepperton	a	09 03											09 33										10 03			
Berrylands	d										09 00										09 30					
Surbiton 6	d			08 41	08 44				08 57	09 00	09 05				09 11	09 14			09 27	09 30	09 35				09 41	09 44
Thames Ditton	d										09 09										09 39					
Hampton Court	a										09 12										09 42					
Hinchley Wood	d								09 01										09 31							
Claygate	d								09 04										09 34							
Oxshott	d								09 07										09 37							
Cobham & Stoke d'Abernon	d								09 11										09 41							
Bookham	d											09 29										09 59				
Effingham Junction 6	d								09 15			09 33							09 45			10 03				
Horsley	d								09 18			09 36							09 48			10 06				
Clandon	d								09 23			09 41							09 53			10 11				
London Road (Guildford)	d								09 28			09 46							09 58			10 16				
Guildford	a								09 32			09 50							10 02			10 20				

For general notes see front of timetable
For details of catering facilities see Directory of Train Operators

A To Alton (Table 155)
B To Woking (Table 155)
C To London Waterloo (Table 149)
D To Basingstoke (Table 155)

For details of Bank Holiday service alterations, please see first page of Table 149

London → Chessington South, Dorking, Guildford Shepperton and Hampton Court

Network Diagram - see first page of Table 152

		SW	SW	SW	SW	SW	SW	SW	SW	SW	SW	SW	SW	SW	SW	SW	SW	SW	SW	SW	SW	SW	SW	SW
					1					1					1					1				
			A		B					C	D		A		B					E	D		A	
London Waterloo 15 ⊖	d	09 24	09 27	09 33	09 42	09 36	09 39	09 42	09 46	09 53	09 50	09 54	09 57	10 03	10 12	10 06	10 09	10 12	10 16	10 23	10 20	10 24	10 27	10 33
Vauxhall ⊖	d	09 28	09 31	09 37		09 40	09 43	09 46	09 50		09 54	09 58	10 01	10 07		10 10	10 13	10 16	10 20		10 24	10 28	10 31	10 37
Clapham Junction 10	d	09 33	09 36	09 42		09 45	09 48	09 51	09 55	10u00	09 59	10 03	10 06	10 12	10u19	10 15	10 18	10 21	10 25		10 29	10 33	10 36	10 42
Earlsfield	d	09 36	09 39	09 45		09 48	09 51	09 54	09 58		10 02	10 06	10 09	10 15		10 18	10 21	10 24	10 28		10 32	10 36	10 39	10 45
Wimbledon 6 ⊖	d	09 40	09 43	09 49		09 52	09 55	09 58	10 02		10 06	10 10	10 13	10 19		10 22	10 25	10 28	10 32		10 36	10 40	10 43	10 49
Raynes Park 6	d	09 43	09 46			09 55	09 58	10 01	10 05			10 13	10 16			10 25	10 28	10 31	10 35			10 43	10 46	
Motspur Park	d	09 46					10 01		10 08			10 16					10 31		10 38			10 46		
Malden Manor	d								10 11										10 41					
Tolworth	d								10 14										10 44					
Chessington North	d								10 17										10 47					
Chessington South	a								10 19										10 49					
Worcester Park	d	09 48					10 03					10 18					10 33					10 48		
Stoneleigh	d	09 51					10 06					10 21					10 36					10 51		
Ewell West	d	09 54					10 09					10 24					10 39					10 54		
Epsom 3	a	09 57					10 16					10 27					10 46					10 57		
	d	09 58					10 17					10 28					10 47					10 58		
Ashtead	d	10 02					10 21					10 32					10 51					11 02		
Leatherhead	d	10 05					10 24					10 35					10 54					11 05		
Boxhill & Westhumble	d																							
Dorking 4	a	10 11										10 41										11 11		
New Malden 6	d		09 49			09 58		10 04					10 19			10 28		10 34					10 49	
Norbiton	d		09 52					10 07					10 22					10 37					10 52	
Kingston	a		09 55					10 10					10 25					10 40					10 55	
	d		09 59					10 10					10 29					10 40					10 59	
Hampton Wick	d		10 01					10 12					10 31					10 42					11 01	
Teddington	d		10 05					10 15					10 35					10 45					11 05	
Strawberry Hill	a		10 08										10 38										11 08	
Fulwell	d							10 19										10 49						
Hampton	d							10 23										10 53						
Kempton Park	d							10 26										10 56						
Sunbury	d							10 28										10 58						
Upper Halliford	d							10 30										11 00						
Shepperton	a							10 33										11 03						
Berrylands	d					10 00										10 30								
Surbiton 6	d			09 57	10 00	10 05				10 11	10 14			10 27	10 30	10 35				10 41	10 44			10 57
Thames Ditton	d					10 09										10 39								
Hampton Court	a					10 12										10 42								
Hinchley Wood	d			10 01										10 31										11 01
Claygate	d			10 04										10 34										11 04
Oxshott	d			10 07										10 37										11 07
Cobham & Stoke d'Abernon	d			10 11										10 41										11 11
Bookham	d						10 29										10 59							
Effingham Junction 6	d			10 15			10 33							10 45			11 03							11 15
Horsley	d			10 18			10 36							10 48			11 06							11 18
Clandon	d			10 23			10 41							10 53			11 11							11 23
London Road (Guildford)	d			10 28			10 46							10 58			11 16							11 28
Guildford	a			10 32			10 50							11 02			11 20							11 32

For general notes see front of timetable
For details of catering facilities see Directory of Train Operators

A To London Waterloo (Table 149)
B To Basingstoke (Table 155)
C To Alton (Table 155)
D To Woking (Table 155)
E To Farnham (Table 155)

For details of Bank Holiday service alterations, please see first page of Table 149

London → Chessington South, Dorking, Guildford Shepperton and Hampton Court

Network Diagram - see first page of Table 152

		SW 1 A		SW	SW	SW	SW	SW 1 B	SW C	SW	SW D	SW	SW 1 A	SW	SW	SW	SW	SW 1 B	SW C	SW	SW D	SW	SW 1 A	SW
London Waterloo 15 ⊖	d	10 42	and at the same minutes past each hour until	15 36	15 39	15 42	15 46	15 53	15 50	15 54	15 57	16 03	16 12	16 06	16 09	16 12	16 16	16 25	16 20	16 24	16 27	16 33	16 42	16 36
Vauxhall ⊖	d			15 40	15 43	15 46	15 50		15 54	15 58	16 01	16 07		16 10	16 13	16 16	16 20		16 24	16 28	16 31	16 37		16 40
Clapham Junction 10	d			15 45	15 48	15 51	15 55	16u00	15 59	16 03	16 06	16 12	16u19	16 15	16 18	16 21	16 25		16 29	16 33	16 36	16 42		16 45
Earlsfield	d			15 48	15 51	15 54	15 58		16 02	16 06	16 09	16 15		16 18	16 21	16 24	16 28		16 32	16 36	16 39	16 45		16 48
Wimbledon 6 ⊖	d			15 52	15 55	15 58	16 02		16 06	16 10	16 13	16 19		16 22	16 25	16 28	16 32		16 36	16 40	16 43	16 49		16 52
Raynes Park 6	d			15 55	15 58	16 01	16 05			16 13	16 16			16 25	16 28	16 31	16 35			16 43	16 46			16 55
Motspur Park	d				16 01		16 08			16 16					16 31		16 38			16 46				
Malden Manor	d						16 11										16 41							
Tolworth	d						16 14										16 44							
Chessington North	d						16 17										16 47							
Chessington South	a						16 19										16 51							
Worcester Park	d				16 03					16 18					16 33					16 48				
Stoneleigh	d				16 06					16 21					16 36					16 51				
Ewell West	d				16 09					16 24					16 39					16 54				
Epsom 3	a				16 16					16 27					16 46					16 57				
	d				16 17					16 28					16 47					17 01				
Ashtead	d				16 21					16 32					16 51					17 05				
Leatherhead	d				16 24					16 35					16 54					17 08				
Boxhill & Westhumble	d																			17 13				
Dorking 4	a									16 41										17 18				
New Malden 6	d			15 58		16 04					16 19			16 28		16 34					16 49			16 58
Norbiton	d					16 07					16 22					16 37					16 52			
Kingston	a					16 10					16 25					16 40					16 55			
	d					16 10					16 29					16 40					16 59			
Hampton Wick	d					16 12					16 31					16 42					17 01			
Teddington	d					16 15					16 35					16 45					17 05			
Strawberry Hill	a										16 38										17 08			
Fulwell	d					16 19										16 49								
Hampton	d					16 23										16 53								
Kempton Park	d					16 26										16 56								
Sunbury	d					16 28										16 58								
Upper Halliford	d					16 30										17 00								
Shepperton	a					16 33										17 05								
Berrylands	d			16 00										16 30										17 00
Surbiton 6	d	11 00		16 05				16 11	16 14			16 27	16 30	16 35				16 41	16 44			16 57	17 00	17 05
Thames Ditton	d			16 09										16 39										17 09
Hampton Court	a			16 12										16 44										17 14
Hinchley Wood	d											16 31										17 01		
Claygate	d											16 34										17 04		
Oxshott	d											16 37										17 07		
Cobham & Stoke d'Abernon	d											16 41										17 11		
Bookham	d				16 29										16 59									
Effingham Junction 6	d				16 33							16 45			17 03							17 15		
Horsley	d				16 36							16 48			17 06							17 18		
Clandon	d				16 41							16 53			17 11							17 23		
London Road (Guildford)	d				16 46							16 58			17 16							17 28		
Guildford	a				16 50							17 04			17 22							17 34		

For general notes see front of timetable
For details of catering facilities see Directory of Train Operators

A To Basingstoke (Table 155)
B To Alton (Table 155)
C To Woking (Table 155)
D To London Waterloo (Table 149)

For details of Bank Holiday service alterations, please see first page of Table 149

London → Chessington South, Dorking, Guildford Shepperton and Hampton Court

Network Diagram - see first page of Table 152

		SN	SW	SW	SW	SW	SW	SW	SW 1	SW	SW	SN	SW	SW	SW	SW 1	SW	SW	SW	SW	SW 1	SW	SW	SN	SW
		A				B		C				A				D	B		C					A	
London Waterloo 15 ⊖	d		16 39	16 42	16 46	16 50	16 54	16 57	17 02	17 02	17 06		17 09	17 12	17 16	17 23	17 20	17 24	17 27	17 30	17 32	17 32	17 36		17 39
Vauxhall ⊖	d		16 43	16 46	16 50	16 54	16 58	17 01		17 07	17 10		17 13	17 16	17 20		17 24	17 28	17 31	17 34		17 37	17 40		17 43
Clapham Junction 10	d		16 48	16 51	16 55	16 59	17 03	17 06		17 12	17 15		17 18	17 22	17 25		17 29	17 33	17 36	17 39		17 42	17 45		17 48
Earlsfield	d		16 51	16 54	16 58	17 02	17 06	17 09		17 15	17 18		17 21	17 25	17 28		17 32	17 36	17 39	17 42		17 45	17 48		17 51
Wimbledon 6 ⊖	d		16 55	16 58	17 02	17 06	17 10	17 13		17 19	17 22		17 25	17 29	17 32		17 36	17 40	17 43	17 46		17 49	17 52		17 55
Raynes Park 6	d		16 58	17 01	17 05		17 13	17 16			17 25		17 28	17 32	17 35			17 43	17 46	17 49			17 55		17 58
Motspur Park	d		17 01		17 08		17 16						17 31		17 38					17 52					18 01
Malden Manor	d				17 11										17 41										
Tolworth	d				17 14										17 44										
Chessington North	d				17 17										17 47										
Chessington South	a				17 21										17 51										
Worcester Park	d		17 03				17 18						17 33					17 47		17 54					18 03
Stoneleigh	d		17 06				17 21						17 36							17 57					18 06
Ewell West	d		17 09				17 24						17 39							18 00					18 09
Epsom 3	a		17 12				17 27						17 42					17 54		18 06					18 20
	d	17 07	17 17				17 31					17 38	17 47					17 54						18 13	18 20
Ashtead	d	17 11	17 21				17 35					17 42	17 51					17 58						18 17	18 24
Leatherhead	d	17 14	17 24				17 38					17 45	17 54					18 01						18 20	18 28
Boxhill & Westhumble	d						17 43											18 06							
Dorking 4	a						17 48											18 11							
New Malden 6	d			17 04				17 19			17 28			17 35					17 49				17 58		
Norbiton	d			17 07				17 22						17 38					17 52						
Kingston	a			17 10				17 25						17 41					17 55						
	d			17 10				17 29						17 41					17 59						
Hampton Wick	d			17 12				17 31						17 43					18 01						
Teddington	d			17 15				17 35						17 46					18 05						
Strawberry Hill	a							17 38											18 08						
Fulwell	d			17 19										17 50											
Hampton	d			17 23										17 54											
Kempton Park	d			17 26										17 57											
Sunbury	d			17 28										17 59											
Upper Halliford	d			17 30										18 01											
Shepperton	a			17 35										18 06											
Berrylands	d										17 30												18 00		
Surbiton 6	d					17 14			17 18	17 27	17 35					17 39	17 44				17 48	17 57	18 05		
Thames Ditton	d										17 39												18 09		
Hampton Court	a										17 44												18 14		
Hinchley Wood	d									17 31												18 05			
Claygate	d									17 34												18 07			
Oxshott	d									17 37												18 11			
Cobham & Stoke d'Abernon	d									17 41												18 14			
Bookham	d	17 19	17 29									17 50	17 59											18 25	18 33
Effingham Junction 6	d	17 23	17 33							17 45		17 54	18a05									18 19		18 29	18a44
Horsley	d		17 36							17 48		17 56										18 21		18 31	
Clandon	d		17 41							17 53		18 01										18 26		18 36	
London Road (Guildford)	d		17 46							17 58		18 06										18 31		18 41	
Guildford	a	17 38	17 52						17 56	18 04		18 13									18 29	18 38		18 47	

For general notes see front of timetable
For details of catering facilities see Directory of Train Operators

A From London Bridge (Table 182)
B To Woking (Table 155)
C To London Waterloo (Table 149)
D To Basingstoke (Table 155)

For details of Bank Holiday service alterations, please see first page of Table 149

London → Chessington South, Dorking, Guildford Shepperton and Hampton Court

Network Diagram - see first page of Table 152

		SW	SW	SW	SW 1 A	SW B	SW	SW C	SW	SW 1 B	SW	SW	SW	SW	SW	SW	SW 1 A	SW B	SW	SW C	SW	SW 1 A	SW	SW	SW
London Waterloo 15	d	17 43	17 42	17 46	17 53	17 50	17 54	17 57	18 00	18 02	18 02	18 06	18 09	18 13	18 12	18 16	18 23	18 20	18 24	18 27	18 30	18 32	18 32	18 36	18 43
Vauxhall	d	17 47	17 46	17 50		17 54	17 58	18 01	18 04		18 07	18 10	18 13	18 17	18 16	18 20		18 24	18 28	18 31	18 34		18 37	18 40	18 47
Clapham Junction 10	d	17 53	17 52	17 55		17 59	18 03	18 06	18 09		18 12	18 15	18 18	18 23	18 22	18 25		18 29	18 33	18 36	18 39		18 42	18 45	18 53
Earlsfield	d		17 55	17 58		18 02	18 06	18 09	18 12		18 15	18 18	18 21		18 25	18 28		18 32	18 36	18 39	18 42		18 45	18 48	
Wimbledon 6	d		17 59	18 02		18 06	18 10	18 13	18 16		18 19	18 22	18 25		18 29	18 32		18 36	18 40	18 43	18 46		18 49	18 52	
Raynes Park 6	d		18 02	18 05			18 13	18 16	18 19			18 25	18 28		18 32	18 35			18 43	18 46	18 49			18 55	
Motspur Park	d			18 08					18 22				18 31			18 38					18 52				
Malden Manor	d			18 11												18 41									
Tolworth	d			18 14												18 44									
Chessington North	d			18 17												18 47									
Chessington South	a			18 21												18 51									
Worcester Park	d						18 17		18 24				18 33						18 47		18 54				
Stoneleigh	d								18 27				18 36								18 57				
Ewell West	d								18 30				18 39								19 00				
Epsom 3	a						18 24		18 35				18 43						18 54		19 05				
	d						18 24						18 47						18 54						
Ashtead	d						18 28						18 51						18 58						
Leatherhead	d						18 31						18 54						19 01						
Boxhill & Westhumble	d						18 36												19 06						
Dorking 4	a						18 41												19 11						
New Malden 6	d		18 05					18 19				18 28			18 35					18 49				18 58	
Norbiton	d		18 08					18 22							18 38					18 52					
Kingston	a		18 11					18 25							18 41					18 55					
	d		18 11					18 29							18 41					18 59					
Hampton Wick	d		18 13					18 31							18 43					19 01					
Teddington	d		18 16					18 35							18 46					19 05					
Strawberry Hill	a	18 11						18 38						18 41						19 08					19 11
Fulwell	d	18 13	18 20											18 43	18 50										19 13
Hampton	d	18 17	18 24											18 47	18 54										19 17
Kempton Park	d		18 27												18 57										
Sunbury	d	18 21	18 29											18 51	18 59										19 21
Upper Halliford	d	18 23	18 31											18 53	19 01										19 23
Shepperton	a	18 28	18 40											18 58	19 10										19 28
Berrylands	d											18 30												19 00	
Surbiton 6	d				18 09	18 14				18 18	18 27	18 35					18 40	18 44				18 48	18 57	19 05	
Thames Ditton	d											18 39												19 09	
Hampton Court	a											18 44												19 14	
Hinchley Wood	d										18 35												19 01		
Claygate	d										18 37												19 04		
Oxshott	d										18 41												19 07		
Cobham & Stoke d'Abernon	d										18 44												19 11		
Bookham	d												18 59												
Effingham Junction 6	d										18 49		19 03										19 15		
Horsley	d										18 51		19 06										19 18		
Clandon	d										18 56		19 11										19 23		
London Road (Guildford)	d										19 01		19 16										19 28		
Guildford	a										19 07		19 22										19 34		

For general notes see front of timetable
For details of catering facilities see Directory of Train Operators

A To Basingstoke (Table 155)
B To Woking (Table 155)
C To London Waterloo (Table 149)

For details of Bank Holiday service alterations, please see first page of Table 149

London → Chessington South, Dorking, Guildford Shepperton and Hampton Court

Network Diagram - see first page of Table 152

		SW	SW	SW	SW	SW	SW	SW		SW	SW 1	SW	SW	SW	SW	SW	SW	SW	SW	SW	SW	SW 1	SW	SW	SW	SW
						A		B			A							A		B		C				
London Waterloo 15 ⊖	d	18 48	18 39	18 42	18 46	18 50	18 54	18 57		19 00	19 02	19 02	19 06	19 09	19 12	19 16	19 23	19 20	19 24	19 27	19 33	19 42	19 36	19 39	19 42	19 46
Vauxhall ⊖	d		18 43	18 46	18 50	18 54	18 58	19 01		19 04		19 07	19 10	19 13	19 16	19 20		19 24	19 28	19 31	19 37		19 40	19 43	19 46	19 50
Clapham Junction 10	d		18 48	18 52	18 55	18 59	19 03	19 06		19 09		19 12	19 15	19 18	19 22	19 25		19 29	19 33	19 36	19 42		19 45	19 48	19 51	19 55
Earlsfield	d		18 51	18 55	18 58	19 02	19 06	19 09		19 12		19 15	19 18	19 21	19 25	19 28		19 32	19 36	19 39	19 45		19 48	19 51	19 54	19 58
Wimbledon 6 ⊖	d		18 55	18 59	19 02	19 06	19 10	19 13		19 16		19 19	19 22	19 25	19 29	19 32		19 36	19 40	19 43	19 49		19 52	19 55	19 58	20 02
Raynes Park 6	d		18 58	19 02	19 05		19 13	19 16		19 19			19 25	19 28	19 32	19 35			19 43	19 46			19 55	19 58	20 01	20 05
Motspur Park	d		19 01		19 08					19 22				19 31		19 38			19 46					20 01		20 08
Malden Manor	d				19 11											19 41										20 11
Tolworth	d				19 14											19 44										20 14
Chessington North	d				19 17											19 47										20 17
Chessington South	a				19 21											19 49										20 19
Worcester Park	d		19 03				19 17			19 24				19 33					19 48					20 03		
Stoneleigh	d		19 06							19 27				19 36					19 51					20 06		
Ewell West	d		19 09							19 30				19 39					19 54					20 09		
Epsom 3	a		19 13				19 29			19 33				19 43					19 57					20 12		
	d		19 17				19 30							19 47					19 58					20 17		
Ashtead	d		19 21				19 34							19 51					20 02					20 21		
Leatherhead	d		19 24				19 37							19 54					20 05					20 24		
Boxhill & Westhumble	d						19 42												20 10							
Dorking 4	a						19 46												20 12							
New Malden 6	d			19 05				19 19					19 28		19 35					19 49			19 58		20 04	
Norbiton	d			19 08				19 22							19 38					19 52					20 07	
Kingston	a			19 11				19 25							19 41					19 55					20 10	
	d			19 11				19 29							19 41					19 59					20 10	
Hampton Wick	d			19 13				19 31							19 43					20 01					20 12	
Teddington	d			19 16				19 35							19 46					20 05					20 15	
Strawberry Hill	a							19 38												20 08						
Fulwell	d			19 20											19 50										20 19	
Hampton	d			19 24											19 54										20 23	
Kempton Park	d			19 27											19 57										20 26	
Sunbury	d			19 29											19 59										20 28	
Upper Halliford	d			19 31											20 01										20 30	
Shepperton	a			19 37											20 04										20 33	
Berrylands	d												19 30										20 00			
Surbiton 6	d	19 06				19 14					19 18	19 27	19 35				19a39	19 44			19 57	20 00	20 05			
Thames Ditton	d												19 39										20 09			
Hampton Court	a												19 42										20 12			
Hinchley Wood	d	19 10										19 31									20 01					
Claygate	d	19 13										19 34									20 04					
Oxshott	d	19 16										19 37									20 07					
Cobham & Stoke d'Abernon	d	19 20										19 41									20 11					
Bookham	d		19 29											19 59										20 29		
Effingham Junction 6	d	19 24	19 33									19 45		20 03							20 15			20 33		
Horsley	d	19 27	19 36									19 48		20 06							20 18			20 36		
Clandon	d	19 32	19 41									19 53		20 11							20 23			20 41		
London Road (Guildford)	d	19 37	19 46									19 58		20 16							20 28			20 46		
Guildford	a	19 43	19 52									20 02		20 20							20 32			20 50		

For general notes see front of timetable
For details of catering facilities see Directory of Train Operators

A To Woking (Table 155)
B To London Waterloo (Table 149)
C To Basingstoke (Table 155)

For details of Bank Holiday service alterations, please see first page of Table 149

London → Chessington South, Dorking, Guildford Shepperton and Hampton Court

Network Diagram - see first page of Table 152

		SW 1 A	SW B	SW	SW C	SW	SW 1 D	SW		SW	SW	SW	SW 1 A	SW B	SW	SW C	SW	SW 1 D	SW	SW	SW	SW	SW 1 A	SW B	SW	SW C
London Waterloo 15 ⊖	d	19 53	19 50	19 54	19 57	20 03	20 12	20 06		20 09	20 12	20 16	20 23	20 20	20 24	20 27	20 33	20 42	20 36	20 39	20 42	20 46	20 53	20 50	20 54	20 57
Vauxhall ⊖	d		19 54	19 58	20 01	20 07		20 10		20 13	20 16	20 20		20 24	20 28	20 31	20 37		20 40	20 43	20 46	20 50		20 54	20 58	21 01
Clapham Junction 10	d	20u00	19 59	20 03	20 06	20 12	20u19	20 15		20 18	20 21	20 25		20 29	20 33	20 36	20 42		20 45	20 48	20 51	20 55	21u00	20 59	21 03	21 06
Earlsfield	d		20 02	20 06	20 09	20 15		20 18		20 21	20 24	20 28		20 32	20 36	20 39	20 45		20 48	20 51	20 54	20 58		21 02	21 06	21 09
Wimbledon 6 ⊖	d		20 06	20 10	20 13	20 19		20 22		20 25	20 28	20 32		20 36	20 40	20 43	20 49		20 52	20 55	20 58	21 02		21 06	21 10	21 13
Raynes Park 6	d			20 13	20 16			20 25		20 28	20 31	20 35			20 43	20 46			20 55	20 58	21 01	21 05			21 13	21 16
Motspur Park	d			20 16						20 31		20 38			20 46					21 01		21 08			21 16	
Malden Manor	d											20 41										21 11				
Tolworth	d											20 44										21 14				
Chessington North	d											20 47										21 17				
Chessington South	a											20 49										21 19				
Worcester Park	d			20 18						20 33					20 48					21 03					21 18	
Stoneleigh	d			20 21						20 36					20 51					21 06					21 21	
Ewell West	d			20 24						20 39					20 54					21 09					21 24	
Epsom 3	a			20 27						20 42					20 57					21 12					21 27	
	d									20 47										21 17						
Ashtead	d									20 51										21 21						
Leatherhead	d									20 54										21 24						
Boxhill & Westhumble	d									20 59																
Dorking 4	a									21 01																
New Malden 6	d				20 19			20 28			20 34					20 49			20 58		21 04					21 19
Norbiton	d				20 22						20 37					20 52					21 07					21 22
Kingston	a				20 25						20 40					20 55					21 10					21 25
	d				20 29						20 40					20 59					21 10					21 29
Hampton Wick	d				20 31						20 42					21 01					21 12					21 31
Teddington	d				20 35						20 45					21 05					21 15					21 35
Strawberry Hill	a				20 38											21 08										21 38
Fulwell	d										20 49										21 19					
Hampton	d										20 53										21 23					
Kempton Park	d										20 56										21 26					
Sunbury	d										20 58										21 28					
Upper Halliford	d										21 00										21 30					
Shepperton	a										21 03										21 33					
Berrylands	d							20 30											21 00							
Surbiton 6	d	20 11	20 14			20 27	20 30	20 35					20 41	20 44			20 57	21 00	21 05				21 11	21 14		
Thames Ditton	d							20 39											21 09							
Hampton Court	a							20 42											21 12							
Hinchley Wood	d					20 31											21 01									
Claygate	d					20 34											21 04									
Oxshott	d					20 37											21 07									
Cobham & Stoke d'Abernon	d					20 41											21 11									
Bookham	d																			21 29						
Effingham Junction 6	d					20 45											21 15			21 33						
Horsley	d					20 48											21 18			21 36						
Clandon	d					20 53											21 23			21 41						
London Road (Guildford)	d					20 58											21 28			21 46						
Guildford	a					21 02											21 32			21 50						

For general notes see front of timetable
For details of catering facilities see Directory of Train Operators

A To Alton (Table 155)
B To Woking (Table 155)
C To London Waterloo (Table 149)
D To Basingstoke (Table 155)

Table 152

Mondays to Fridays

until 26 September

For details of Bank Holiday service alterations, please see first page of Table 149

London → Chessington South, Dorking, Guildford Shepperton and Hampton Court

Network Diagram - see first page of Table 152

		SW	SW	SW	SW	SW	SW	SW	SW	SW	SW	SW	SW	SW	SW	SW	SW	SW	SW	SW	SW	SW	SW	SW	SW
				1		1					1					1							1		
				A		B	C		D		E					B			D				B	C	D
London Waterloo 15	⊖ d	21 03	21 09	21 12	21 12	21 23	21 20	21 24	21 27	21 33	21 42	21 36	21 39	21 42	21 46	21 53	21 50	21 54	21 57	22 03	22 09	22 12	22 23	22 20	22 27
Vauxhall	⊖ d	21 07	21 13		21 16		21 24	21 28	21 31	21 37		21 40	21 43	21 46	21 50		21 54	21 58	22 01	22 07	22 13	22 16		22 24	22 31
Clapham Junction 10	d	21 12	21 18	21u19	21 21		21 29	21 33	21 36	21 42		21 45	21 48	21 51	21 55	22u00	21 59	22 03	22 06	22 12	22 18	22 21	22u30	22 29	22 36
Earlsfield	d	21 15	21 21		21 24		21 32	21 36	21 39	21 45		21 48	21 51	21 54	21 58		22 02	22 06	22 09	22 15	22 21	22 24		22 32	22 39
Wimbledon 6	⊖ d	21 19	21 25		21 28		21 36	21 40	21 43	21 49		21 52	21 55	21 58	22 02		22 06	22 10	22 13	22 19	22 25	22 28		22 36	22 43
Raynes Park 6	d		21 28		21 31			21 43	21 46			21 55	21 58	22 01	22 05			22 13	22 16		22 28	22 31			22 46
Motspur Park	d		21 31					21 46					22 01		22 08			22 16			22 31				
Malden Manor	d														22 11										
Tolworth	d														22 14										
Chessington North	d														22 17										
Chessington South	a														22 19										
Worcester Park	d		21 33					21 48					22 03					22 18			22 33				
Stoneleigh	d		21 36					21 51					22 06					22 21			22 36				
Ewell West	d		21 39					21 54					22 09					22 24			22 39				
Epsom 3	a		21 42					21 57					22 12					22 27			22 42				
	d		21 47										22 17								22 47				
Ashtead	d		21 51										22 21								22 51				
Leatherhead	d		21 54										22 24								22 54				
Boxhill & Westhumble	d		21 59																		22 59				
Dorking 4	a		22 01																		23 01				
New Malden 6	d				21 34				21 49			21 58		22 04					22 19			22 34			22 49
Norbiton	d				21 37				21 52					22 07					22 22			22 37			22 52
Kingston	a				21 40				21 55					22 10					22 25			22 40			22 55
	d				21 40				21 59					22 10					22 29			22 40			22 59
Hampton Wick	d				21 42				22 01					22 12					22 31			22 42			23 01
Teddington	d				21 45				22 05					22 15					22 35			22 45			23 05
Strawberry Hill	a								22 08										22 38						23 08
Fulwell	d				21 49									22 19								22 49			
Hampton	d				21 53									22 23								22 53			
Kempton Park	d				21 56									22 26								22 56			
Sunbury	d				21 58									22 28								22 58			
Upper Halliford	d				22 00									22 30								23 00			
Shepperton	a				22 03									22 33								23 03			
Berrylands	d											22 00													
Surbiton 6	d	21 27		21 30		21 41	21 44			21 57	22 00	22 05				22 11	22 14			22 27			22 41	22 44	
Thames Ditton	d											22 09													
Hampton Court	a											22 12													
Hinchley Wood	d	21 31								22 01										22 31					
Claygate	d	21 34								22 04										22 34					
Oxshott	d	21 37								22 07										22 37					
Cobham & Stoke d'Abernon	d	21 41								22 11										22 41					
Bookham	d												22 29												
Effingham Junction 6	d	21 45								22 15			22 33							22 45					
Horsley	d	21 48								22 18			22 36							22 48					
Clandon	d	21 53								22 23			22 41							22 53					
London Road (Guildford)	d	21 58								22 28			22 46							22 58					
Guildford	a	22 02								22 32			22 50				22 47			23 06					

For general notes see front of timetable
For details of catering facilities see Directory of Train Operators

A To Basingstoke (Table 155)
B To Alton (Table 155)
C To Woking (Table 155)
D To London Waterloo (Table 149)
E To Portsmouth Harbour (Table 158)

For details of Bank Holiday service alterations, please see first page of Table 149

London → Chessington South, Dorking, Guildford Shepperton and Hampton Court

Network Diagram - see first page of Table 152

		SW	SW	SW	SW	SW	SW	SW	SW	SW	SW	SW	SW	SW	SW	SW	SW	SW	SW	SW	SW	SW	SW
				1				1							1					1			
			A	B				C	D	E					C	D	G			B			
London Waterloo 15 ⊖	d	22 33	22 33	22 42	22 36	22 39	22 42	22 53	22 50	22 57	23 00	23 03	23 09	23 12	23 23	23 20	23 27	23 30	23 42	23 48	23 50	23 57	
Vauxhall ⊖	d	22 37	22 37		22 40	22 43	22 46		22 54	23 01	23 04	23 07	23 13	23 16		23 24	23 31	23 34	23 46		23 54	00 01	
Clapham Junction 10	d	22 42	22 43	22u49	22 45	22 48	22 51	23u00	22 59	23 06	23 09	23 12	23 18	23 21	23u30	23 29	23 36	23 39	23 51	23u56	23 59	00 06	
Earlsfield	d	22 45	23a35		22 48	22 51	22 54		23 02	23 09	23 12	23 15	23 21	23 24		23 32	23 39	23 42	23 54		00 02	00 09	
Wimbledon 6 ⊖	d	22 49			22 52	22 55	22 58		23 06	23 13	23 16	23 19	23 25	23 28		23 36	23 43	23 46	23 58		00 06	00 13	
Raynes Park 6	d				22 55	22 58	23 01			23 16	23 19		23 28	23 31			23 46	23 49	00 01			00 16	
Motspur Park	d					23 01					23 22		23 31						00 04				
Malden Manor	d										23 25												
Tolworth	d										23 28												
Chessington North	d										23 31												
Chessington South	a										23 33												
Worcester Park	d					23 03							23 33						00 06				
Stoneleigh	d					23 06							23 36						00 09				←
Ewell West	d					23 09							23 39						00 12				00 12
Epsom 3	a					23 12							23 42						→				00 15
	d					23 17							23 47										00 19
Ashtead	d					23 21							23 51										00 23
Leatherhead	d					23 24							23 54										00 26
Boxhill & Westhumble	d												23 59										
Dorking 4	a												00 01										
New Malden 6	d				22 58		23 04			23 19				23 34			23 49	23 52				00 19	
Norbiton	d						23 07			23 22				23 37			23 52					00 22	
Kingston	a						23 10			23 25				23 40			23 55					00 25	
	d						23 10			23 29				23 40			23 55					00 25	
Hampton Wick	d						23 12			23 31				23 42			23 57					00 27	
Teddington	d						23 15			23 35				23 45			23 59					00 30	
Strawberry Hill	a		23 07							23 38							00 03						
Fulwell	d						23 19							23 49								00 34	
Hampton	d						23 23							23 53								00 38	
Kempton Park	d						23 26							23 56								00 41	
Sunbury	d						23 28							23 58								00 43	
Upper Halliford	d						23 30							23 59								00 45	
Shepperton	a						23 33							00 03								00 48	
Berrylands	d				23 00													23 54					
Surbiton 6	d	22 57		23 00	23 05			23 11	23 14			23 27			23 41	23 44		23 59		00 10	00 14		
Thames Ditton	d				23 09													00 03					
Hampton Court	a				23 12													00 06					
Hinchley Wood	d	23 01										23 31									00 18		
Claygate	d	23 04										23 34									00 21		
Oxshott	d	23 07										23 37									00 24		
Cobham & Stoke d'Abernon	d	23 11										23 41									00 28		
Bookham	d					23 29																	00 31
Effingham Junction 6	d	23 15				23 33						23 45									00 32		00 36
Horsley	d	23 18				23 36						23 48									00 35		00 39
Clandon	d	23 23				23 41						23 53									00 40		00 44
London Road (Guildford)	d	23 28				23 46						23 58									00 45		00 49
Guildford	a	23 32				23 54						00 02									00 49		00 53

For general notes see front of timetable
For details of catering facilities see Directory of Train Operators

A To London Waterloo
B To Basingstoke (Table 155)
C To Alton (Table 155)
D To Woking (Table 155)
E To London Waterloo (Table 149)
G To Twickenham (Table 149)

Table 152

Mondays to Fridays

from 29 September

For details of Bank Holiday service alterations, please see first page of Table 149

London → Chessington South, Dorking, Guildford Shepperton and Hampton Court

Network Diagram - see first page of Table 152

		SW MO	SW MO	SW MO 1 A	SW MO	SW MX B	SW MX	SW MX	SW MX 1 C	SW MX	SW MX	SW MX	SW MX	SW MX	SW MX	SW	SW 1 D	SW 1 E		SW	SW 1 G	SW 1 H	SW	SW J	SW	SW K
London Waterloo 15 ⊖	d	23p00	23p32	23p40	00 01	23p03	23p30	23p42	23p48	23p50	23p57		00 09	00 15	00 27	00 42	01 05	05 00		05 12	05 20	05 30			05 47	05 50
Vauxhall ⊖	d	23p04	23p36	23p44	00 04	23p07	23p34	23p46		23p54	00 01		00 13	00 19	00 31	00 46	01 09	05 04		05 16	05 24				05 51	05 54
Clapham Junction 10	d	23p09	23p41	23p49	00 09	23p13	23p39	23p51	23b56	23p59	00 06		00 18	00 24	00 36	00 51	01 14	05 09		05 21	05 29	05u37			05 56	05 59
Earlsfield	d	23p12	23p44	23p52	00 12	00a08	23p42	23p54		00 02	00 09		00 21	00 27	00s39			05 12		05 24	05 32				05 59	06 02
Wimbledon 6 ⊖	d	23p16	23p48	23p56	00 16		23p46	23p58		00 06	00 13		00 25	00 31	00 43	01 05	01 20	05 16		05 28	05 36	05 43	05 49		06 03	06 06
Raynes Park 6	d		23p52		00 19		23p49	00 01			00 16			00 34	00 46	01 08				05 31					06 06	
Motspur Park	d		23p55					00 04						00 37											06 09	
Malden Manor	d																									
Tolworth	d																									
Chessington North	d																									
Chessington South	a																									
Worcester Park	d		23p57					00 06						00 39											06 11	
Stoneleigh	d		23p59					00 09						00 42											06 14	
Ewell West	d		00 03					00 12 →				← 00 12		00 45											06 17	
Epsom 3	a		00 06									00 15		00 48											06 20	
	d											00 19													06 21	
Ashtead	d											00 23													06 25	
Leatherhead	d											00 26													06 28	
Boxhill & Westhumble	d																									
Dorking 4	a																									
New Malden 6	d				00 22		23p52				00 19				00 49	01 11				05 34						
Norbiton	d										00 22					01 14				05 37						
Kingston	a										00 25					01 17				05 40						
	d										00 25					01 17				05 40				05 59		
Hampton Wick	d										00 27					01s22				05 42				06 01		
Teddington	d										00 30					01s25				05 45				06 05		
Strawberry Hill	a					23p37										01 28								06 08		
Fulwell	d										00 34									05 49						
Hampton	d										00 38									05 53						
Kempton Park	d										00 41															
Sunbury	d										00 43									05 58						
Upper Halliford	d										00 45									06 00						
Shepperton	a										00 50									06 05						
Berrylands	d				00 24		23p54								00s51											
Surbiton 6	d	23c32		00 05	00 31		23p59		00 10	00 14			00 33		00a55		01 29	05 24			05 44		05 57			06 14
Thames Ditton	d						00 03																			
Hampton Court	a						00 06																			
Hinchley Wood	d	23p36			00 35					00 18													06 01			
Claygate	d	23p39			00 38					00 21													06 04			
Oxshott	d	23p42			00 41					00 24													06 07			
Cobham & Stoke d'Abernon	d	23p46			00 45					00 28													06 11			
Bookham	d											00 31													06 33	
Effingham Junction 6	d	23p50			00 49					00 32		00 36											06 15		06 37	
Horsley	d	23p53			00 52					00 35		00 39											06 18			
Clandon	d	23p58			00 57					00 40		00 44											06 23			
London Road (Guildford)	d	00 03			01 02					00 45		00 49											06 28		06 46	
Guildford	a	00 10			01 09					00 52		00 56	01 06					05 59			06 23		06 35		06 53	

For general notes see front of timetable
For details of catering facilities see Directory of Train Operators

A To Farnham (Table 155)
B To London Waterloo
C To Basingstoke (Table 155)
D To Southampton Central (Table 158)
E To Portsmouth Harbour (Table 156)
G To Portsmouth & Southsea (Table 156)
H To Weymouth (Table 158)
J To London Waterloo (Table 149)
K To Woking (Table 155)
b Previous night. Stops to pick up only
c Previous night. Arr. 2328

Table 152

Mondays to Fridays

from 29 September

For details of Bank Holiday service alterations, please see first page of Table 149

London → Chessington South, Dorking, Guildford Shepperton and Hampton Court

Network Diagram - see first page of Table 152

		SW	SW	SW 1 A	SW	SW B	SW	SW	SN C	SW	SW	SW B	SW		SW 1 D	SW	SW	SW	SW	SW 1 E	SW	SW	SW B	SW	SW 1 G	SW
London Waterloo 15 ⊖	d		06 03	06 12	06 06		06 12	06 16		06 20	06 24	06 27	06 33		06 42	06 36	06 39	06 42	06 46	06 53	06 50	06 54	06 57	07 03	07 12	07 06
Vauxhall ⊖	d		06 07		06 10		06 16	06 20		06 24	06 28	06 31	06 37			06 40	06 43	06 46	06 50		06 54	06 58	07 01	07 07		07 10
Clapham Junction 10	d		06 12	06u19	06 15		06 21	06 25		06 29	06 33	06 36	06 42		06u49	06 45	06 48	06 51	06 55	07u00	06 59	07 03	07 06	07 12	07u20	07 15
Earlsfield	d		06 15		06 18		06 24	06 28		06 32	06 36	06 39	06 45			06 48	06 51	06 54	06 58		07 02	07 06	07 09	07 15		07 18
Wimbledon 6 ⊖	d	06 15	06 19		06 22		06 28	06 32		06 36	06 40	06 43	06 49			06 52	06 55	06 58	07 02		07 06	07 10	07 13	07 19		07 22
Raynes Park 6	d	06 18			06 25		06 31	06 35			06 43	06 46				06 55		07 01	07 05			07 13	07 16			07 25
Motspur Park	d	06 20						06 38			06 46								07 08			07 16				
Malden Manor	d	06 24						06 41											07 11							
Tolworth	d	06 26						06 44											07 14							
Chessington North	d	06 29						06 47											07 17							
Chessington South	a	06 31						06 49											07 19							
Worcester Park	d										06 48						07 01					07 18				
Stoneleigh	d										06 51											07 21				
Ewell West	d										06 54											07 24				
Epsom 3	a										06 57						07 08					07 27				
	d								06 49		06 58						07 08					07 28				
Ashtead	d										07 02						07 12					07 32				
Leatherhead	d								06 56		07 05						07 15					07 35				
Boxhill & Westhumble	d																									
Dorking 4	a										07 13											07 43				
New Malden 6	d				06 28		06 34					06 49				06 58		07 04					07 19			07 28
Norbiton	d						06 37					06 52						07 07					07 22			
Kingston	a						06 40					06 55						07 10					07 25			
	d					06 29	06 40					06 59						07 10					07 29			
Hampton Wick	d					06 31	06 42					07 01						07 12					07 31			
Teddington	d					06 35	06 45					07 05						07 15					07 35			
Strawberry Hill	a					06 38						07 08											07 38			
Fulwell	d						06 49											07 19								
Hampton	d						06 53											07 23								
Kempton Park	d																									
Sunbury	d						06 58											07 28								
Upper Halliford	d						07 00											07 30								
Shepperton	a						07 05											07 35								
Berrylands	d				06 30											07 00										07 30
Surbiton 6	d		06 27	06 30	06 35					06 44			06 57		07 00	07 05				07 11	07 14			07 27	07 30	07 35
Thames Ditton	d				06 39											07 09										07 39
Hampton Court	a				06 42											07 12										07 42
Hinchley Wood	d		06 31										07 01											07 31		
Claygate	d		06 34										07 04											07 34		
Oxshott	d		06 37										07 07											07 37		
Cobham & Stoke d'Abernon	d		06 41										07 11											07 41		
Bookham	d								07 01								07 21									
Effingham Junction 6	d		06 45						07 05				07 15				07a24							07 45		
Horsley	d		06 48										07 18											07 48		
Clandon	d		06 53										07 23											07 53		
London Road (Guildford)	d		06 58										07 28											07 58		
Guildford	a		07 05						07 17	07 20			07 35								07 47			08 05		

For general notes see front of timetable
For details of catering facilities see Directory of Train Operators

A To Weymouth (Table 158)
B To London Waterloo (Table 149)
C From Sutton (Surrey) (Table 182)
D To Portsmouth Harbour (Table 158)
E To Alton (Table 155)
G To Basingstoke (Table 155)

For details of Bank Holiday service alterations, please see first page of Table 149

London → Chessington South, Dorking, Guildford Shepperton and Hampton Court

Network Diagram - see first page of Table 152

		SN	SW	SW	SW	SW	SW	SW	SW	SW	SW	SW	SW	SW	SW	SW	SW	SW	SW	SW	SW	SW	SW	SW	SW
						1					1					1					1				
		A				B	C		D		E					B			D		E				
London Waterloo 15 ⊖	d		07 09	07 12	07 16	07 23	07 20	07 24	07 27	07 33	07 42	07 36	07 39	07 42	07 46	07 53	07 50	07 54	07 57	08 03	08 12	08 06	08 09	08 12	08 16
Vauxhall ⊖	d		07 13	07 16	07 20		07 24	07 28	07 31	07 37		07 40	07 43	07 46	07 50		07 54	07 58	08 01	08 07		08 10	08 13	08 16	08 20
Clapham Junction 10	d		07 18	07 21	07 25	07u30	07 29	07 33	07 36	07 42		07 45	07 48	07 51	07 55	08u00	07 59	08 03	08 06	08 12	08u19	08 15	08 18	08 21	08 25
Earlsfield	d		07 21	07 24	07 28		07 32	07 36	07 39	07 45		07 48	07 51	07 54	07 58		08 02	08 06	08 09	08 15		08 18	08 21	08 24	08 28
Wimbledon 6 ⊖	d		07 25	07 28	07 32		07 36	07 40	07 43	07 49		07 52	07 55	07 58	08 02		08 06	08 10	08 13	08 19		08 22	08 25	08 28	08 32
Raynes Park 6	d		07 28	07 31	07 35			07 43	07 46			07 55	07 58	08 01	08 05			08 13	08 16			08 25	08 28	08 31	08 35
Motspur Park	d		07 31		07 38			07 46					08 01		08 08			08 16					08 31		08 38
Malden Manor	d				07 41										08 11										08 41
Tolworth	d				07 44										08 14										08 44
Chessington North	d				07 47										08 17										08 47
Chessington South	a				07 49										08 19										08 49
Worcester Park	d		07 33					07 48					08 03					08 18					08 33		
Stoneleigh	d		07 36					07 51					08 06					08 21					08 36		
Ewell West	d		07 39					07 54					08 09					08 24					08 39		
Epsom 3	a		07 42					07 58					08 15					08 27					08 42		
	d	07 38						07 58					08 15					08 28					08 47		
Ashtead	d	07 42						08 02					08 19					08 32					08 51		
Leatherhead	d	07 45						08 05					08 22					08 35					08 54		
Boxhill & Westhumble	d																								
Dorking 4	a							08 14										08 43							
New Malden 6	d			07 34					07 49			07 58		08 04					08 19			08 28		08 34	
Norbiton	d			07 37					07 52					08 07					08 22					08 37	
Kingston	a			07 40					07 55					08 10					08 25					08 40	
	d			07 40					07 59					08 10					08 29					08 40	
Hampton Wick	d			07 42					08 01					08 12					08 31					08 42	
Teddington	d			07 45					08 05					08 15					08 35					08 45	
Strawberry Hill	a								08 08										08 38						
Fulwell	d			07 49										08 19										08 49	
Hampton	d			07 53										08 23										08 53	
Kempton Park	d			07 56										08 26										08 56	
Sunbury	d			07 58										08 28										08 58	
Upper Halliford	d			08 00										08 30										09 00	
Shepperton	a			08 05										08 35										09 05	
Berrylands	d											08 00										08 30			
Surbiton 6	d					07 41	07 44			07 57	08 00	08 05				08 11	08 14			08 27	08 30	08 35			
Thames Ditton	d											08 09										08 39			
Hampton Court	a											08 12										08 42			
Hinchley Wood	d									08 01										08 31					
Claygate	d									08 04										08 34					
Oxshott	d									08 07										08 37					
Cobham & Stoke d'Abernon	d									08 11										08 41					
Bookham	d	07 50											08 28										08 59		
Effingham Junction 6	d	07 54								08 15			08 32							08 45			09 03		
Horsley	d									08 18			08 34							08 48			09 06		
Clandon	d									08 23			08 39							08 53			09 11		
London Road (Guildford)	d	08 03								08 28			08 44							08 58			09 16		
Guildford	a	08 07								08 35			08 51				08 50			09 07			09 23		

For general notes see front of timetable
For details of catering facilities see Directory of Train Operators

A From London Bridge (Table 182)
B To Alton (Table 155)
C To Woking (Table 155)
D To London Waterloo (Table 149)
E To Basingstoke (Table 155)

For details of Bank Holiday service alterations, please see first page of Table 149

London → Chessington South, Dorking, Guildford Shepperton and Hampton Court

Network Diagram - see first page of Table 152

	SW 1 A	SW B	SW	SW C	SW	SW 1 D	SW	SW	SW	SW	SW 1 A	SW B	SW	SW C	SW	SW 1 D	SW	SW	SW	SW	SW 1 A	SW B	SW
London Waterloo 15 ⊖ d	08 23	08 20	08 24	08 27	08 33	08 42	08 36	08 39	08 42	08 46	08 53	08 50	08 54	08 57	09 03	09 12	09 06	09 09	09 12	09 16	09 23	09 20	09 24
Vauxhall ⊖ d		08 24	08 28	08 31	08 37		08 40	08 43	08 46	08 50		08 54	08 58	09 01	09 07		09 10	09 13	09 16	09 20		09 24	09 28
Clapham Junction 10 d		08 29	08 33	08 36	08 42		08 45	08 48	08 51	08 55	09u00	08 59	09 03	09 06	09 12	09u19	09 15	09 18	09 21	09 25		09 29	09 33
Earlsfield d		08 32	08 36	08 39	08 45		08 48	08 51	08 54	08 58		09 02	09 06	09 09	09 15		09 18	09 21	09 24	09 28		09 32	09 36
Wimbledon 6 ⊖ d		08 36	08 40	08 43	08 49		08 52	08 55	08 58	09 02		09 06	09 10	09 13	09 19		09 22	09 25	09 28	09 32		09 36	09 40
Raynes Park 6 d			08 43	08 46			08 55	08 58	09 01	09 05			09 13	09 16			09 25	09 28	09 31	09 35			09 43
Motspur Park d			08 46					09 01		09 08			09 16					09 31		09 38			09 46
Malden Manor d										09 11										09 41			
Tolworth d										09 14										09 44			
Chessington North d										09 17										09 47			
Chessington South a										09 19										09 49			
Worcester Park d			08 48					09 03					09 18					09 33					09 48
Stoneleigh d			08 51					09 06					09 21					09 36					09 51
Ewell West d			08 54					09 09					09 24					09 39					09 54
Epsom 3 a			08 57					09 16					09 27					09 42					09 57
d			08 58					09 17					09 28					09 47					09 58
Ashtead d			09 02					09 21					09 32					09 51					10 02
Leatherhead d			09 05					09 24					09 35					09 54					10 05
Boxhill & Westhumble d																							
Dorking 4 a			09 13										09 43										10 13
New Malden 6 d				08 49			08 58		09 04					09 19			09 28		09 34				
Norbiton d				08 52					09 07					09 22					09 37				
Kingston a				08 55					09 10					09 25					09 40				
d				08 59					09 10					09 29					09 40				
Hampton Wick d				09 01					09 12					09 31					09 42				
Teddington d				09 05					09 15					09 35					09 45				
Strawberry Hill a				09 08										09 38									
Fulwell d									09 19										09 49				
Hampton d									09 23										09 53				
Kempton Park d									09 26										09 56				
Sunbury d									09 28										09 58				
Upper Halliford d									09 30										10 00				
Shepperton a									09 35										10 05				
Berrylands d							09 00										09 30						
Surbiton 6 d	08 41	08 44			08 57	09 00	09 05				09 11	09 14			09 27	09 30	09 35				09 41	09 44	
Thames Ditton d							09 09										09 39						
Hampton Court a							09 12										09 42						
Hinchley Wood d					09 01										09 31								
Claygate d					09 04										09 34								
Oxshott d					09 07										09 37								
Cobham & Stoke d'Abernon d					09 11										09 41								
Bookham d								09 29										09 59					
Effingham Junction 6 d					09 15			09 33							09 45			10 03					
Horsley d					09 18			09 36							09 48			10 06					
Clandon d					09 23			09 41							09 53			10 11					
London Road (Guildford) d					09 28			09 46							09 58			10 16					
Guildford a					09 35			09 53							10 05			10 23					

For general notes see front of timetable
For details of catering facilities see Directory of Train Operators

A To Alton (Table 155)
B To Woking (Table 155)
C To London Waterloo (Table 149)
D To Basingstoke (Table 155)

Table 152

Mondays to Fridays
from 29 September

For details of Bank Holiday service alterations, please see first page of Table 149

London → Chessington South, Dorking, Guildford Shepperton and Hampton Court

Network Diagram - see first page of Table 152

	SW	SW	SW 1	SW	SW	SW	SW	SW 1	SW	SW	SW	SW	SW 1	SW	SW	SW	SW	SW 1	SW	SW	SW	SW
	A		B					C	D		A		B					E	D		A	
London Waterloo 15 ⊖ d	09 27	09 33	09 42	09 36	09 39	09 42	09 46	09 53	09 50	09 54	09 57	10 03	10 12	10 06	10 09	10 12	10 16	10 23	10 20	10 24	10 27	10 33
Vauxhall ⊖ d	09 31	09 37		09 40	09 43	09 46	09 50		09 54	09 58	10 01	10 07		10 10	10 13	10 16	10 20		10 24	10 28	10 31	10 37
Clapham Junction 10 d	09 36	09 42		09 45	09 48	09 51	09 55	10u00	09 59	10 03	10 06	10 12	10u19	10 15	10 18	10 21	10 25		10 29	10 33	10 36	10 42
Earlsfield d	09 39	09 45		09 48	09 51	09 54	09 58		10 02	10 06	10 09	10 15		10 18	10 21	10 24	10 28		10 32	10 36	10 39	10 45
Wimbledon 6 ⊖ d	09 43	09 49		09 52	09 55	09 58	10 02		10 06	10 10	10 13	10 19		10 22	10 25	10 28	10 32		10 36	10 40	10 43	10 49
Raynes Park 6 d	09 46			09 55	09 58	10 01	10 05			10 13	10 16			10 25	10 28	10 31	10 35			10 43	10 46	
Motspur Park d					10 01		10 08			10 16					10 31		10 38			10 46		
Malden Manor d							10 11										10 41					
Tolworth d							10 14										10 44					
Chessington North d							10 17										10 47					
Chessington South a							10 19										10 49					
Worcester Park d					10 03					10 18					10 33					10 48		
Stoneleigh d					10 06					10 21					10 36					10 51		
Ewell West d					10 09					10 24					10 39					10 54		
Epsom 3 a					10 16					10 27					10 46					10 57		
d					10 17					10 28					10 47					10 58		
Ashtead d					10 21					10 32					10 51					11 02		
Leatherhead d					10 24					10 35					10 54					11 05		
Boxhill & Westhumble d																						
Dorking 4 a										10 43										11 13		
New Malden 6 d	09 49			09 58		10 04					10 19			10 28		10 34					10 49	
Norbiton d	09 52					10 07					10 22					10 37					10 52	
Kingston a	09 55					10 10					10 25					10 40					10 55	
d	09 59					10 10					10 29					10 40					10 59	
Hampton Wick d	10 01					10 12					10 31					10 42					11 01	
Teddington d	10 05					10 15					10 35					10 45					11 05	
Strawberry Hill a	10 08										10 38										11 08	
Fulwell d						10 19										10 49						
Hampton d						10 23										10 53						
Kempton Park d						10 26										10 56						
Sunbury d						10 28										10 58						
Upper Halliford d						10 30										11 00						
Shepperton a						10 35										11 05						
Berrylands d				10 00										10 30								
Surbiton 6 d		09 57	10 00	10 05				10 11	10 14			10 27	10 30	10 35				10 41	10 44			10 57
Thames Ditton d				10 09										10 39								
Hampton Court a				10 12										10 42								
Hinchley Wood d		10 01										10 31										11 01
Claygate d		10 04										10 34										11 04
Oxshott d		10 07										10 37										11 07
Cobham & Stoke d'Abernon d		10 11										10 41										11 11
Bookham d					10 29										10 59							
Effingham Junction 6 d		10 15			10 33							10 45			11 03							11 15
Horsley d		10 18			10 36							10 48			11 06							11 18
Clandon d		10 23			10 41							10 53			11 11							11 23
London Road (Guildford) d		10 28			10 46							10 58			11 16							11 28
Guildford a		10 35			10 53							11 05			11 23							11 35

For general notes see front of timetable
For details of catering facilities see Directory of Train Operators

A To London Waterloo (Table 149)
B To Basingstoke (Table 155)
C To Alton (Table 155)
D To Woking (Table 155)
E To Farnham (Table 155)

For details of Bank Holiday service alterations, please see first page of Table 149

London → Chessington South, Dorking, Guildford Shepperton and Hampton Court

Network Diagram - see first page of Table 152

		SW 1 A		SW	SW	SW	SW	SW 1 B	SW C	SW	SW D	SW	SW 1 A	SW	SW	SW	SW	SW 1 B	SW C	SW	SW D	SW	SW 1 A
London Waterloo 15 ⊖	d	10 42	and at the same minutes past each hour until	15 36	15 39	15 42	15 46	15 53	15 50	15 54	15 57	16 03	16 12	16 06	16 09	16 12	16 16	16 25	16 20	16 24	16 27	16 33	16 42
Vauxhall ⊖	d			15 40	15 43	15 46	15 50		15 54	15 58	16 01	16 07		16 10	16 13	16 16	16 20		16 24	16 28	16 31	16 37	
Clapham Junction 10	d			15 45	15 48	15 51	15 55	16u00	15 59	16 03	16 06	16 12	16u19	16 15	16 18	16 21	16 25		16 29	16 33	16 36	16 42	
Earlsfield	d			15 48	15 51	15 54	15 58		16 02	16 06	16 09	16 15		16 18	16 21	16 24	16 28		16 32	16 36	16 39	16 45	
Wimbledon 6 ⊖	d			15 52	15 55	15 58	16 02		16 06	16 10	16 13	16 19		16 22	16 25	16 28	16 32		16 36	16 40	16 43	16 49	
Raynes Park 6	d			15 55	15 58	16 01	16 05			16 13	16 16			16 25	16 28	16 31	16 35			16 43	16 46		
Motspur Park	d				16 01		16 08			16 16					16 31		16 38			16 46			
Malden Manor	d						16 11										16 41						
Tolworth	d						16 14										16 44						
Chessington North	d						16 17										16 47						
Chessington South	a						16 19										16 51						
Worcester Park	d				16 03					16 18					16 33					16 48			
Stoneleigh	d				16 06					16 21					16 36					16 51			
Ewell West	d				16 09					16 24					16 39					16 54			
Epsom 3	a				16 16					16 27					16 46					16 57			
	d				16 17					16 28					16 47					17 01			
Ashtead	d				16 21					16 32					16 51					17 05			
Leatherhead	d				16 24					16 35					16 54					17 08			
Boxhill & Westhumble	d																			17 13			
Dorking 4	a									16 43										17 20			
New Malden 6	d			15 58		16 04					16 19			16 28		16 34					16 49		
Norbiton	d					16 07					16 22					16 37					16 52		
Kingston	a					16 10					16 25					16 40					16 55		
	d					16 10					16 29					16 40					16 59		
Hampton Wick	d					16 12					16 31					16 42					17 01		
Teddington	d					16 15					16 35					16 45					17 05		
Strawberry Hill	a										16 38										17 08		
Fulwell	d					16 19										16 49							
Hampton	d					16 23										16 53							
Kempton Park	d					16 26										16 56							
Sunbury	d					16 28										16 58							
Upper Halliford	d					16 30										17 00							
Shepperton	a					16 35										17 07							
Berrylands	d			16 00										16 30									
Surbiton 6	d	11 00		16 05				16 11	16 14			16 27	16 30	16 35				16 41	16 44			16 57	17 00
Thames Ditton	d			16 09										16 39									
Hampton Court	a			16 12										16 44									
Hinchley Wood	d											16 31										17 01	
Claygate	d											16 34										17 04	
Oxshott	d											16 37										17 07	
Cobham & Stoke d'Abernon	d											16 41										17 11	
Bookham	d				16 29										16 59								
Effingham Junction 6	d				16 33							16 45			17 03							17 15	
Horsley	d				16 36							16 48			17 06							17 18	
Clandon	d				16 41							16 53			17 11							17 23	
London Road (Guildford)	d				16 46							16 58			17 16							17 28	
Guildford	a				16 53							17 07			17 25							17 37	

For general notes see front of timetable
For details of catering facilities see Directory of Train Operators

A To Basingstoke (Table 155)
B To Alton (Table 155)
C To Woking (Table 155)
D To London Waterloo (Table 149)

Table 152

Mondays to Fridays

from 29 September

For details of Bank Holiday service alterations, please see first page of Table 149

London → Chessington South, Dorking, Guildford Shepperton and Hampton Court

Network Diagram - see first page of Table 152

		SW	SN A	SW	SW	SW	SW B	SW	SW C	SW 1	SW	SW	SN A	SW	SW	SW	SW 1 D		SW B	SW	SW C	SW	SW 1	SW	SW	SN A
London Waterloo 15 ⊖	d	16 36		16 39	16 42	16 46	16 50	16 54	16 57	17 02	17 02	17 06		17 09	17 12	17 16	17 23		17 20	17 24	17 27	17 30	17 32	17 32	17 36	
Vauxhall ⊖	d	16 40		16 43	16 46	16 50	16 54	16 58	17 01		17 07	17 10		17 13	17 16	17 20			17 24	17 28	17 31	17 34		17 37	17 40	
Clapham Junction 10	d	16 45		16 48	16 51	16 55	16 59	17 03	17 06		17 12	17 15		17 18	17 22	17 25			17 29	17 33	17 36	17 39		17 42	17 45	
Earlsfield	d	16 48		16 51	16 54	16 58	17 02	17 06	17 09		17 15	17 18		17 21	17 25	17 28			17 32	17 36	17 39	17 42		17 45	17 48	
Wimbledon 6 ⊖	d	16 52		16 55	16 58	17 02	17 06	17 10	17 13		17 19	17 22		17 25	17 29	17 32			17 36	17 40	17 43	17 46		17 49	17 52	
Raynes Park 6	d	16 55		16 58	17 01	17 05		17 13	17 16			17 25		17 28	17 32	17 35				17 43	17 46	17 49			17 55	
Motspur Park	d			17 01		17 08		17 16						17 31		17 38						17 52				
Malden Manor	d					17 11										17 41										
Tolworth	d					17 14										17 44										
Chessington North	d					17 17										17 47										
Chessington South	a					17 21										17 51										
Worcester Park	d			17 03				17 18						17 33						17 47		17 54				
Stoneleigh	d			17 06				17 21						17 36								17 57				
Ewell West	d			17 09				17 24						17 39								18 00				
Epsom 3	a			17 12				17 27						17 42						17 54		18 06				
	d		17 07	17 17				17 31					17 38	17 47						17 54						18 13
Ashtead	d		17 11	17 21				17 35					17 42	17 51						17 58						18 17
Leatherhead	d		17 14	17 24				17 38					17 45	17 54						18 01						18 20
Boxhill & Westhumble	d							17 43												18 06						
Dorking 4	a							17 50												18 13						
New Malden 6	d	16 58			17 04				17 19			17 28			17 35						17 49				17 58	
Norbiton	d				17 07				17 22						17 38						17 52					
Kingston	a				17 10				17 25						17 41						17 55					
	d				17 10				17 29						17 41						17 59					
Hampton Wick	d				17 12				17 31						17 43						18 01					
Teddington	d				17 15				17 35						17 46						18 05					
Strawberry Hill	a								17 38												18 08					
Fulwell	d				17 19										17 50											
Hampton	d				17 23										17 54											
Kempton Park	d				17 26										17 57											
Sunbury	d				17 28										17 59											
Upper Halliford	d				17 30										18 01											
Shepperton	a				17 37										18 08											
Berrylands	d	17 00										17 30													18 00	
Surbiton 6	d	17 05					17 14			17 18	17 27	17 35					17 39		17 44				17 48	17 57	18 05	
Thames Ditton	d	17 09										17 39													18 09	
Hampton Court	a	17 14										17 44													18 14	
Hinchley Wood	d										17 31													18 05		
Claygate	d										17 34													18 07		
Oxshott	d										17 37													18 11		
Cobham & Stoke d'Abernon	d										17 41													18 14		
Bookham	d		17 19	17 29									17 50	17 59												18 25
Effingham Junction 6	d		17 23	17 33							17 45		17 54	18a05										18 19		18 29
Horsley	d			17 36							17 48		17 56											18 21		18 31
Clandon	d			17 41							17 53		18 01											18 26		18 36
London Road (Guildford)	d			17 46							17 58		18 06											18 31		18 41
Guildford	a		17 38	17 55						17 56	18 07		18 13										18 29	18 41		18 47

For general notes see front of timetable
For details of catering facilities see Directory of Train Operators

A From London Bridge (Table 182)
B To Woking (Table 155)
C To London Waterloo (Table 149)
D To Basingstoke (Table 155)

For details of Bank Holiday service alterations, please see first page of Table 149

London → Chessington South, Dorking, Guildford Shepperton and Hampton Court

Network Diagram - see first page of Table 152

		SW	SW	SW	SW	SW	SW	SW	SW	SW	SW	SW	SW	SW	SW	SW	SW	SW	SW	SW	SW	SW	SW	SW	SW
						1											1								
						A	B		C								A	B		C					
London Waterloo 15 ⊖	d	17 39	17 43	17 42	17 46	17 53	17 50	17 54	17 57	18 00	18 02	18 06	18 09	18 13	18 12	18 16	18 23	18 20	18 24	18 27	18 30	18 32	18 36	18 43	18 48
Vauxhall ⊖	d	17 43	17 47	17 46	17 50		17 54	17 58	18 01	18 04	18 07	18 10	18 13	18 17	18 16	18 20		18 24	18 28	18 31	18 34	18 37	18 40	18 47	
Clapham Junction 10	d	17 48	17 53	17 52	17 55		17 59	18 03	18 06	18 09	18 12	18 15	18 18	18 23	18 22	18 25		18 29	18 33	18 36	18 39	18 42	18 45	18 53	
Earlsfield	d	17 51		17 55	17 58		18 02	18 06	18 09	18 12	18 15	18 18	18 21		18 25	18 28		18 32	18 36	18 39	18 42	18 45	18 48		
Wimbledon 6 ⊖	d	17 55		17 59	18 02		18 06	18 10	18 13	18 16	18 19	18 22	18 25		18 29	18 32		18 36	18 40	18 43	18 46	18 49	18 52		
Raynes Park 6	d	17 58		18 02	18 05			18 13	18 16	18 19		18 25	18 28		18 32	18 35			18 43	18 46	18 49		18 55		
Motspur Park	d	18 01			18 08					18 22			18 31			18 38					18 52				
Malden Manor	d				18 11											18 41									
Tolworth	d				18 14											18 44									
Chessington North	d				18 17											18 47									
Chessington South	a				18 21											18 51									
Worcester Park	d	18 03						18 17		18 24			18 33						18 47		18 54				
Stoneleigh	d	18 06								18 27			18 36								18 57				
Ewell West	d	18 09								18 30			18 39								19 00				
Epsom 3	a	18 20						18 24		18 35			18 43						18 54		19 05				
	d	18 20						18 24					18 47						18 54						
Ashtead	d	18 24						18 28					18 51						18 58						
Leatherhead	d	18 28						18 31					18 54						19 01						
Boxhill & Westhumble	d							18 36											19 06						
Dorking 4	a							18 43											19 13						
New Malden 6	d			18 05					18 19			18 28			18 35					18 49			18 58		
Norbiton	d			18 08					18 22						18 38					18 52					
Kingston	a			18 11					18 25						18 41					18 55					
	d			18 11					18 29						18 41					18 59					
Hampton Wick	d			18 13					18 31						18 43					19 01					
Teddington	d			18 16					18 35						18 46					19 05					
Strawberry Hill	a		18 11						18 38					18 41						19 08				19 11	
Fulwell	d		18 13	18 20										18 43	18 50									19 13	
Hampton	d		18 17	18 24										18 47	18 54									19 17	
Kempton Park	d			18 27											18 57										
Sunbury	d		18 21	18 29										18 51	18 59									19 21	
Upper Halliford	d		18 23	18 31										18 53	19 01									19 23	
Shepperton	a		18 30	18 40										19 00	19 10									19 30	
Berrylands	d											18 30											19 00		
Surbiton 6	d					18 09	18 14				18 27	18 35					18 40	18 44				18 57	19 05		19 06
Thames Ditton	d											18 39											19 09		
Hampton Court	a											18 44											19 14		
Hinchley Wood	d										18 35											19 01			19 10
Claygate	d										18 37											19 04			19 13
Oxshott	d										18 41											19 07			19 16
Cobham & Stoke d'Abernon	d										18 44											19 11			19 20
Bookham	d	18 33											18 59												
Effingham Junction 6	d	18a44									18 49		19 03									19 15			19 24
Horsley	d										18 51		19 06									19 18			19 27
Clandon	d										18 56		19 11									19 23			19 32
London Road (Guildford)	d										19 01		19 16									19 28			19 37
Guildford	a										19 10		19 25									19 37			19 46

For general notes see front of timetable
For details of catering facilities see Directory of Train Operators

A To Basingstoke (Table 155)
B To Woking (Table 155)
C To London Waterloo (Table 149)

Table 152

Mondays to Fridays

from 29 September

For details of Bank Holiday service alterations, please see first page of Table 149

London → Chessington South, Dorking, Guildford Shepperton and Hampton Court

Network Diagram - see first page of Table 152

		SW	SW	SW	SW	SW	SW		SW	SW	SW	SW	SW	SW	SW	SW	SW	SW	SW	SW	SW	SW	SW	SW	SW	SW
										1											1					1
					A		B			A							A		B		C					D
London Waterloo 15 ⊖	d	18 39	18 42	18 46	18 50	18 54	18 57		19 00	19 02	19 02	19 06	19 09	19 12	19 16	19 23	19 20	19 24	19 27	19 33	19 42	19 36	19 39	19 42	19 46	19 53
Vauxhall ⊖	d	18 43	18 46	18 50	18 54	18 58	19 01		19 04		19 07	19 10	19 13	19 16	19 20		19 24	19 28	19 31	19 37		19 40	19 43	19 46	19 50	
Clapham Junction 10	d	18 48	18 52	18 55	18 59	19 03	19 06		19 09		19 12	19 15	19 18	19 22	19 25		19 29	19 33	19 36	19 42		19 45	19 48	19 51	19 55	20u00
Earlsfield	d	18 51	18 55	18 58	19 02	19 06	19 09		19 12		19 15	19 18	19 21	19 25	19 28		19 32	19 36	19 39	19 45		19 48	19 51	19 54	19 58	
Wimbledon 6 ⊖	d	18 55	18 59	19 02	19 06	19 10	19 13		19 16		19 19	19 22	19 25	19 29	19 32		19 36	19 40	19 43	19 49		19 52	19 55	19 58	20 02	
Raynes Park 6	d	18 58	19 02	19 05		19 13	19 16		19 19			19 25	19 28	19 32	19 35			19 43	19 46			19 55	19 58	20 01	20 05	
Motspur Park	d	19 01		19 08					19 22				19 31		19 38			19 46					20 01		20 08	
Malden Manor	d			19 11											19 41										20 11	
Tolworth	d			19 14											19 44										20 14	
Chessington North	d			19 17											19 47										20 17	
Chessington South	a			19 21											19 49										20 19	
Worcester Park	d	19 03				19 17			19 24				19 33					19 48					20 03			
Stoneleigh	d	19 06							19 27				19 36					19 51					20 06			
Ewell West	d	19 09							19 30				19 39					19 54					20 09			
Epsom 3	a	19 13				19 29			19 33				19 43					19 57					20 12			
	d	19 17				19 30							19 47					19 58					20 17			
Ashtead	d	19 21				19 34							19 51					20 02					20 21			
Leatherhead	d	19 24				19 37							19 54					20 05					20 24			
Boxhill & Westhumble	d					19 42												20 10								
Dorking 4	a					19 48												20 14								
New Malden 6	d		19 05				19 19					19 28		19 35					19 49			19 58		20 04		
Norbiton	d		19 08				19 22							19 38					19 52					20 07		
Kingston	a		19 11				19 25							19 41					19 55					20 10		
	d		19 11				19 29							19 41					19 59					20 10		
Hampton Wick	d		19 13				19 31							19 43					20 01					20 12		
Teddington	d		19 16				19 35							19 46					20 05					20 15		
Strawberry Hill	a						19 38												20 08							
Fulwell	d		19 20											19 50										20 19		
Hampton	d		19 24											19 54										20 23		
Kempton Park	d		19 27											19 57										20 26		
Sunbury	d		19 29											19 59										20 28		
Upper Halliford	d		19 31											20 01										20 30		
Shepperton	a		19 39											20 06										20 35		
Berrylands	d											19 30										20 00				
Surbiton 6	d				19 14					19 18	19 27	19 35				19a39	19 44			19 57	20 00	20 05				20 11
Thames Ditton	d											19 39										20 09				
Hampton Court	a											19 42										20 12				
Hinchley Wood	d										19 31									20 01						
Claygate	d										19 34									20 04						
Oxshott	d										19 37									20 07						
Cobham & Stoke d'Abernon	d										19 41									20 11						
Bookham	d	19 29											19 59										20 29			
Effingham Junction 6	d	19 33									19 45		20 03							20 15			20 33			
Horsley	d	19 36									19 48		20 06							20 18			20 36			
Clandon	d	19 41									19 53		20 11							20 23			20 41			
London Road (Guildford)	d	19 46									19 58		20 16							20 28			20 46			
Guildford	a	19 55									20 05		20 23							20 35			20 53			

For general notes see front of timetable
For details of catering facilities see Directory of Train Operators

A To Woking (Table 155)
B To London Waterloo (Table 149)
C To Basingstoke (Table 155)
D To Alton (Table 155)

For details of Bank Holiday service alterations, please see first page of Table 149

London → Chessington South, Dorking, Guildford Shepperton and Hampton Court

Network Diagram - see first page of Table 152

Station		SW	SW	SW	SW	SW 1	SW	SW	SW	SW	SW 1	SW	SW	SW	SW	SW 1	SW	SW	SW	SW	SW 1	SW	SW	SW
		A		B		C					D	A		B		C					D	A		B
London Waterloo 15 ⊖	d	19 50	19 54	19 57	20 03	20 12	20 06	20 09	20 12	20 16	20 23	20 20	20 24	20 27	20 33	20 42	20 36	20 39	20 42	20 46	20 53	20 50	20 54	20 57
Vauxhall ⊖	d	19 54	19 58	20 01	20 07	.	20 10	20 13	20 16	20 20	.	20 24	20 28	20 31	20 37	.	20 40	20 43	20 46	20 50	.	20 54	20 58	21 01
Clapham Junction 10	d	19 59	20 03	20 06	20 12	20u19	20 15	20 18	20 21	20 25	.	20 29	20 33	20 36	20 42	.	20 45	20 48	20 51	20 55	21u00	20 59	21 03	21 06
Earlsfield	d	20 02	20 06	20 09	20 15	.	20 18	20 21	20 24	20 28	.	20 32	20 36	20 39	20 45	.	20 48	20 51	20 54	20 58	.	21 02	21 06	21 09
Wimbledon 6 ⊖	d	20 06	20 10	20 13	20 19	.	20 22	20 25	20 28	20 32	.	20 36	20 40	20 43	20 49	.	20 52	20 55	20 58	21 02	.	21 06	21 10	21 13
Raynes Park 6	d	.	20 13	20 16	.	.	20 25	20 28	20 31	20 35	.	.	20 43	20 46	.	.	20 55	20 58	21 01	21 05	.	.	21 13	21 16
Motspur Park	d	.	20 16	.	.	.	.	20 31	.	20 38	.	.	20 46	.	.	.	.	21 01	.	21 08	.	.	21 16	.
Malden Manor	d	.	.	.	.	.	.	.	.	20 41	.	.	.	.	.	.	.	.	.	21 11	.	.	.	.
Tolworth	d	.	.	.	.	.	.	.	.	20 44	.	.	.	.	.	.	.	.	.	21 14	.	.	.	.
Chessington North	d	.	.	.	.	.	.	.	.	20 47	.	.	.	.	.	.	.	.	.	21 17	.	.	.	.
Chessington South	a	.	.	.	.	.	.	.	.	20 49	.	.	.	.	.	.	.	.	.	21 19	.	.	.	.
Worcester Park	d	.	20 18	.	.	.	.	20 33	.	.	.	.	20 48	.	.	.	.	21 03	.	.	.	.	21 18	.
Stoneleigh	d	.	20 21	.	.	.	.	20 36	.	.	.	.	20 51	.	.	.	.	21 06	.	.	.	.	21 21	.
Ewell West	d	.	20 24	.	.	.	.	20 39	.	.	.	.	20 54	.	.	.	.	21 09	.	.	.	.	21 24	.
Epsom 3	a	.	20 27	.	.	.	.	20 42	.	.	.	.	20 57	.	.	.	.	21 12	.	.	.	.	21 27	.
	d	.	.	.	.	.	.	20 47	.	.	.	.	.	.	.	.	.	21 17	.	.	.	.	.	.
Ashtead	d	.	.	.	.	.	.	20 51	.	.	.	.	.	.	.	.	.	21 21	.	.	.	.	.	.
Leatherhead	d	.	.	.	.	.	.	20 54	.	.	.	.	.	.	.	.	.	21 24	.	.	.	.	.	.
Boxhill & Westhumble	d	.	.	.	.	.	.	20 59	.	.	.	.	.	.	.	.	.	.	.	.	.	.	.	.
Dorking 4	a	.	.	.	.	.	.	21 03	.	.	.	.	.	.	.	.	.	.	.	.	.	.	.	.
New Malden 6	d	.	.	20 19	.	.	20 28	.	20 34	.	.	.	.	20 49	.	.	20 58	.	21 04	.	.	.	.	21 19
Norbiton	d	.	.	20 22	.	.	.	.	20 37	.	.	.	.	20 52	.	.	.	.	21 07	.	.	.	.	21 22
Kingston	a	.	.	20 25	.	.	.	.	20 40	.	.	.	.	20 55	.	.	.	.	21 10	.	.	.	.	21 25
	d	.	.	20 29	.	.	.	.	20 40	.	.	.	.	20 59	.	.	.	.	21 10	.	.	.	.	21 29
Hampton Wick	d	.	.	20 31	.	.	.	.	20 42	.	.	.	.	21 01	.	.	.	.	21 12	.	.	.	.	21 31
Teddington	d	.	.	20 35	.	.	.	.	20 45	.	.	.	.	21 05	.	.	.	.	21 15	.	.	.	.	21 35
Strawberry Hill	a	.	.	20 38	.	.	.	.	.	.	.	.	.	21 08	.	.	.	.	.	.	.	.	.	21 38
Fulwell	d	.	.	.	.	.	.	.	20 49	.	.	.	.	.	.	.	.	.	21 19	.	.	.	.	.
Hampton	d	.	.	.	.	.	.	.	20 53	.	.	.	.	.	.	.	.	.	21 23	.	.	.	.	.
Kempton Park	d	.	.	.	.	.	.	.	20 56	.	.	.	.	.	.	.	.	.	21 26	.	.	.	.	.
Sunbury	d	.	.	.	.	.	.	.	20 58	.	.	.	.	.	.	.	.	.	21 28	.	.	.	.	.
Upper Halliford	d	.	.	.	.	.	.	.	21 00	.	.	.	.	.	.	.	.	.	21 30	.	.	.	.	.
Shepperton	a	.	.	.	.	.	.	.	21 05	.	.	.	.	.	.	.	.	.	21 35	.	.	.	.	.
Berrylands	d	.	.	.	.	.	20 30	.	.	.	.	.	.	.	.	.	21 00	.	.	.	.	.	.	.
Surbiton 6	d	20 14	.	.	20 27	20 30	20 35	.	.	.	20 41	20 44	.	.	20 57	21 00	21 05	.	.	.	21 11	21 14	.	.
Thames Ditton	d	.	.	.	.	.	20 39	.	.	.	.	.	.	.	.	.	21 09	.	.	.	.	.	.	.
Hampton Court	a	.	.	.	.	.	20 42	.	.	.	.	.	.	.	.	.	21 12	.	.	.	.	.	.	.
Hinchley Wood	d	.	.	.	20 31	.	.	.	.	.	.	.	.	.	21 01	.	.	.	.	.	.	.	.	.
Claygate	d	.	.	.	20 34	.	.	.	.	.	.	.	.	.	21 04	.	.	.	.	.	.	.	.	.
Oxshott	d	.	.	.	20 37	.	.	.	.	.	.	.	.	.	21 07	.	.	.	.	.	.	.	.	.
Cobham & Stoke d'Abernon	d	.	.	.	20 41	.	.	.	.	.	.	.	.	.	21 11	.	.	.	.	.	.	.	.	.
Bookham	d	.	.	.	.	.	.	.	.	.	.	.	.	.	.	.	.	21 29	.	.	.	.	.	.
Effingham Junction 6	d	.	.	.	20 45	.	.	.	.	.	.	.	.	.	21 15	.	.	21 33	.	.	.	.	.	.
Horsley	d	.	.	.	20 48	.	.	.	.	.	.	.	.	.	21 18	.	.	21 36	.	.	.	.	.	.
Clandon	d	.	.	.	20 53	.	.	.	.	.	.	.	.	.	21 23	.	.	21 41	.	.	.	.	.	.
London Road (Guildford)	d	.	.	.	20 58	.	.	.	.	.	.	.	.	.	21 28	.	.	21 46	.	.	.	.	.	.
Guildford	a	.	.	.	21 05	.	.	.	.	.	.	.	.	.	21 35	.	.	21 53	.	.	.	.	.	.

For general notes see front of timetable
For details of catering facilities see Directory of Train Operators

A To Woking (Table 155)
B To London Waterloo (Table 149)
C To Basingstoke (Table 155)
D To Alton (Table 155)

For details of Bank Holiday service alterations, please see first page of Table 149

London → Chessington South, Dorking, Guildford Shepperton and Hampton Court

Network Diagram - see first page of Table 152

		SW	SW	SW	SW	SW	SW	SW	SW	SW	SW	SW	SW	SW	SW		SW	SW	SW	SW	SW	SW	SW	SW	SW	SW
				1		1					1						1						1		1	
				A		B	C		D		E						B			D			A		B	C
London Waterloo [15] ⊖	d	21 03	21 09	21 12	21 12	21 23	21 20	21 24	21 27	21 33	21 42	21 36	21 39	21 42	21 46		21 53	21 50	21 54	21 57	22 03	22 09	22 12	22 12	22 23	22 20
Vauxhall ⊖	d	21 07	21 13		21 16		21 24	21 28	21 31	21 37		21 40	21 43	21 46	21 50			21 54	21 58	22 01	22 07	22 13		22 16		22 24
Clapham Junction [10]	d	21 12	21 18	21u19	21 21		21 29	21 33	21 36	21 42		21 45	21 48	21 51	21 55		22u00	21 59	22 03	22 06	22 12	22 18	22u19	22 21	22u30	22 29
Earlsfield	d	21 15	21 21		21 24		21 32	21 36	21 39	21 45		21 48	21 51	21 54	21 58			22 02	22 06	22 09	22 15	22 21		22 24		22 32
Wimbledon [6] ⊖ 🚊	d	21 19	21 25		21 28		21 36	21 40	21 43	21 49		21 52	21 55	21 58	22 02			22 06	22 10	22 13	22 19	22 25		22 28		22 36
Raynes Park [6]	d		21 28		21 31			21 43	21 46			21 55	21 58	22 01	22 05				22 13	22 16		22 28		22 31		
Motspur Park	d		21 31					21 46					22 01		22 08				22 16			22 31				
Malden Manor	d														22 11											
Tolworth	d														22 14											
Chessington North	d														22 17											
Chessington South	a														22 19											
Worcester Park	d		21 33					21 48					22 03						22 18			22 33				
Stoneleigh	d		21 36					21 51					22 06						22 21			22 36				
Ewell West	d		21 39					21 54					22 09						22 24			22 39				
Epsom [3]	a		21 42					21 57					22 12						22 27			22 42				
	d		21 47										22 17									22 47				
Ashtead	d		21 51										22 21									22 51				
Leatherhead	d		21 54										22 24									22 54				
Boxhill & Westhumble	d		21 59																			22 59				
Dorking [4]	a		22 03																			23 03				
New Malden [6]	d				21 34				21 49			21 58		22 04						22 19				22 34		
Norbiton	d				21 37				21 52					22 07						22 22				22 37		
Kingston	a				21 40				21 55					22 10						22 25				22 40		
	d				21 40				21 59					22 10						22 29				22 40		
Hampton Wick	d				21 42				22 01					22 12						22 31				22 42		
Teddington	d				21 45				22 05					22 15						22 35				22 45		
Strawberry Hill	a								22 08											22 38						
Fulwell	d				21 49									22 19										22 49		
Hampton	d				21 53									22 23										22 53		
Kempton Park	d				21 56									22 26										22 56		
Sunbury	d				21 58									22 28										22 58		
Upper Halliford	d				22 00									22 30										23 00		
Shepperton	a				22 05									22 35										23 05		
Berrylands	d											22 00														
Surbiton [6]	d	21 27		21 30		21 41	21 44			21 57	22 00	22 05					22 11	22 14			22 27		22 30		22 41	22 44
Thames Ditton	d											22 09														
Hampton Court	a											22 12														
Hinchley Wood	d	21 31								22 01											22 31					
Claygate	d	21 34								22 04											22 34					
Oxshott	d	21 37								22 07											22 37					
Cobham & Stoke d'Abernon	d	21 41								22 11											22 41					
Bookham	d												22 29													
Effingham Junction [6]	d	21 45								22 15			22 33								22 45					
Horsley	d	21 48								22 18			22 36								22 48					
Clandon	d	21 53								22 23			22 41								22 53					
London Road (Guildford)	d	21 58								22 28			22 46								22 58					
Guildford	a	22 05								22 35			22 53					22 47			23 06					

For general notes see front of timetable
For details of catering facilities see Directory of Train Operators

A To Basingstoke (Table 155)
B To Alton (Table 155)
C To Woking (Table 155)
D To London Waterloo (Table 149)
E To Portsmouth Harbour (Table 158)

For details of Bank Holiday service alterations, please see first page of Table 149

London → Chessington South, Dorking, Guildford Shepperton and Hampton Court

Network Diagram - see first page of Table 152

		SW	SW	SW	SW	SW	SW	SW	SW	SW	SW	SW	SW	SW	SW	SW	SW	SW	SW	SW	SW	SW	SW	SW
				1				1						1		1					1			
		A		B				C	D	A				B		C	D	E			B			
London Waterloo 15	⊖ d	22 27	22 33	22 42	22 36	22 39	22 42	22 53	22 50	22 57	23 00	23 03	23 09	23 12	23 12	23 23	23 20	23 27	23 30	23 42	23 48	23 50	23 57	
Vauxhall	⊖ d	22 31	22 37		22 40	22 43	22 46		22 54	23 01	23 04	23 07	23 13		23 16		23 24	23 31	23 34	23 46		23 54	00 01	
Clapham Junction 10	d	22 36	22 42	22u49	22 45	22 48	22 51	23u00	22 59	23 06	23 09	23 12	23 18	23u19	23 21	23u30	23 29	23 36	23 39	23 51	23u56	23 59	00 06	
Earlsfield	d	22 39	22 45		22 48	22 51	22 54		23 02	23 09	23 12	23 15	23 21		23 24		23 32	23 39	23 42	23 54		00 02	00 09	
Wimbledon 6	⊖ ⛴ d	22 43	22 49		22 52	22 55	22 58		23 06	23 13	23 16	23 19	23 25		23 28		23 36	23 43	23 46	23 58		00 06	00 13	
Raynes Park 6	d	22 46			22 55	22 58	23 01			23 16	23 19		23 28		23 31			23 46	23 49	00 01			00 16	
Motspur Park	d					23 01					23 22		23 31							00 04				
Malden Manor	d										23 25													
Tolworth	d										23 28													
Chessington North	d										23 31													
Chessington South	a										23 33													
Worcester Park	d					23 03							23 33							00 06				
Stoneleigh	d					23 06							23 36							00 09				←
Ewell West	d					23 09							23 39							00 12 →				00 12
Epsom 3	a					23 12							23 42											00 15
	d					23 17							23 47											00 19
Ashtead	d					23 21							23 51											00 23
Leatherhead	d					23 24							23 54											00 26
Boxhill & Westhumble	d												23 59											
Dorking 4	a												00 03											
New Malden 6	d	22 49			22 58		23 04			23 19					23 34			23 49	23 52				00 19	
Norbiton	d	22 52					23 07			23 22					23 37			23 52					00 22	
Kingston	a	22 55					23 10			23 25					23 40			23 55					00 25	
	d	22 59					23 10			23 29					23 40			23 55					00 25	
Hampton Wick	d	23 01					23 12			23 31					23 42			23 57					00 27	
Teddington	d	23 05					23 15			23 35					23 45			23 59					00 30	
Strawberry Hill	a	23 08								23 38								00 03						
Fulwell	d						23 19								23 49								00 34	
Hampton	d						23 23								23 53								00 38	
Kempton Park	d						23 26								23 56								00 41	
Sunbury	d						23 28								23 58								00 43	
Upper Halliford	d						23 30								23 59								00 45	
Shepperton	a						23 35								00 05								00 50	
Berrylands	d				23 00														23 54					
Surbiton 6	d		22 57	23 00	23 05			23 11	23 14			23 27		23 30		23 41	23 44		23 59		00 10	00 14		
Thames Ditton	d				23 09														00 03					
Hampton Court	a				23 12														00 06					
Hinchley Wood	d		23 01									23 31										00 18		
Claygate	d		23 04									23 34										00 21		
Oxshott	d		23 07									23 37										00 24		
Cobham & Stoke d'Abernon	d		23 11									23 41										00 28		
Bookham	d					23 29																		00 31
Effingham Junction 6	d		23 15			23 33						23 45										00 32		00 36
Horsley	d		23 18			23 36						23 48										00 35		00 39
Clandon	d		23 23			23 41						23 53										00 40		00 44
London Road (Guildford)	d		23 28			23 46						23 58										00 45		00 49
Guildford	a		23 35			23 54						00 05										00 52		00 56

For general notes see front of timetable
For details of catering facilities see Directory of Train Operators

A To London Waterloo (Table 149)
B To Basingstoke (Table 155)
C To Alton (Table 155)
D To Woking (Table 155)
E To Twickenham (Table 149)

Saturdays

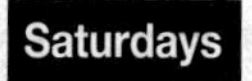

until 27 September

For details of Bank Holiday service alterations, please see first page of Table 149

London → Chessington South, Dorking, Guildford Shepperton and Hampton Court

Network Diagram - see first page of Table 152

		SW	SW	SW	SW	SW	SW	SW	SW	SW	SW	SW	SW	SW	SW	SW		SW	SW	SW	SW	SW	SW	SW	SW	SW
		A			1 B								1 C	1 D		1 E		G	H	A	1 B		G			H
London Waterloo 15	⊖ d	23p03	23p30	23p42	23p48	23p50	23p57		00 09	00 15	00 27	00 42	01 05	05 00	05 12	05 20			05 50	06 03	06 12	06 06		06 12	06 16	06 20
Vauxhall	⊖ d	23p07	23p34	23p46		23p54	00 01		00 13	00 19	00 31	00 46	01 09	05 04	05 16	05 24			05 54	06 07		06 10		06 16	06 20	06 24
Clapham Junction 10	d	23p13	23p39	23p51	23b56	23p59	00 06		00 18	00 24	00 36	00 51	01 14	05 09	05 21	05 29			05 59	06 13	06u19	06 15		06 21	06 25	06 29
Earlsfield	d	00a08	23p42	23p54		00 02	00 09		00 21	00 27	00s39			05 12	05 24	05 32			06 02	07a05		06 18		06 24	06 28	06 32
Wimbledon 6	⊖ 🚋 d		23p46	23p58		00 06	00 13		00 25	00 31	00 43	01 05	01 20	05 16	05 28	05 36			06 06			06 22		06 28	06 32	06 36
Raynes Park 6	d		23p49	00 01			00 16			00 34	00 46	01 08			05 31							06 25		06 31	06 35	
Motspur Park	d			00 04						00 37															06 38	
Malden Manor	d																								06 41	
Tolworth	d																								06 44	
Chessington North	d																								06 47	
Chessington South	a																								06 49	
Worcester Park	d			00 06						00 39																
Stoneleigh	d			00 09				←		00 42																
Ewell West	d			00 12 →				00 12		00 45																
Epsom 3	a							00 15		00 48																
	d							00 19																		
Ashtead	d							00 23																		
Leatherhead	d							00 26																		
Boxhill & Westhumble	d																									
Dorking 4	a																									
New Malden 6	d		23p52				00 19				00 49	01 11			05 34							06 28		06 34		
Norbiton	d						00 22					01 14			05 37									06 37		
Kingston	a						00 25					01 17			05 40									06 40		
	d						00 25					01 17			05 40			05 59					06 29	06 40		
Hampton Wick	d						00 27					01s22			05 42			06 01					06 31	06 42		
Teddington	d						00 30					01s25			05 45			06 05					06 35	06 45		
Strawberry Hill	a	23p37										01 28						06 08		06 37			06 38			
Fulwell	d						00 34								05 49									06 49		
Hampton	d						00 38								05 53									06 53		
Kempton Park	d						00 41								05 56									06 56		
Sunbury	d						00 43								05 58									06 58		
Upper Halliford	d						00 45								06 00									07 00		
Shepperton	a						00 48								06 03									07 03		
Berrylands	d		23p54								00s51											06 30				
Surbiton 6	d		23p59		00 10	00 14			00 33		00a55		01 29	05 24		05 44			06 14		06 30	06 35				06 44
Thames Ditton	d		00 03																			06 39				
Hampton Court	a		00 06																			06 42				
Hinchley Wood	d					00 18																				
Claygate	d					00 21																				
Oxshott	d					00 24																				
Cobham & Stoke d'Abernon	d					00 28																				
Bookham	d							00 31																		
Effingham Junction 6	d					00 32		00 36																		
Horsley	d					00 35		00 39																		
Clandon	d					00 40		00 44																		
London Road (Guildford)	d					00 45		00 49																		
Guildford	a					00 49		00 53	01 06					05 59		06 23										

For general notes see front of timetable
For details of catering facilities see Directory of Train Operators

- **A** To London Waterloo
- **B** To Basingstoke (Table 155)
- **C** To Southampton Central (Table 158)
- **D** To Haslemere (Table 156)
- **E** To Portsmouth Harbour (Table 156)
- **G** To London Waterloo (Table 149)
- **H** To Woking (Table 155)
- **b** Previous night.
  Stops to pick up only

Saturdays

until 27 September

For details of Bank Holiday service alterations, please see first page of Table 149

London → Chessington South, Dorking, Guildford Shepperton and Hampton Court

Network Diagram - see first page of Table 152

	SW A	SW	SW 1 B	SW	SW	SW	SW	SW 1 C		SW D	SW A	SW	SW 1 E	SW	SW	SW	SW	SW 1 C	SW D	SW	SW A	SW	SW 1 E	SW	SW
London Waterloo 15 ⊖ d	06 27	06 33	06 42	06 36	06 39	06 42	06 46	06 53		06 50	06 57	07 03	07 12	07 06	07 09	07 12	07 16	07 23	07 20	07 24	07 27	07 33	07 42	07 36	07 39
Vauxhall ⊖ d	06 31	06 37		06 40	06 43	06 46	06 50			06 54	07 01	07 07		07 10	07 13	07 16	07 20		07 24	07 28	07 31	07 37		07 40	07 43
Clapham Junction 10 d	06 36	06 42	06u49	06 45	06 48	06 51	06 55	07u00		06 59	07 06	07 12	07u19	07 15	07 18	07 21	07 25	07u30	07 29	07 33	07 36	07 42		07 45	07 48
Earlsfield d	06 39	06 45		06 48	06 51	06 54	06 58			07 02	07 09	07 15		07 18	07 21	07 24	07 28		07 32	07 36	07 39	07 45		07 48	07 51
Wimbledon 6 ⊖ d	06 43	06 49		06 52	06 55	06 58	07 02			07 06	07 13	07 19		07 22	07 25	07 28	07 32		07 36	07 40	07 43	07 49		07 52	07 55
Raynes Park 6 d	06 46			06 55	06 58	07 01	07 05				07 16			07 25	07 28	07 31	07 35			07 43	07 46			07 55	07 58
Motspur Park d					07 01		07 08								07 31		07 38			07 46					08 01
Malden Manor d							07 11										07 41								
Tolworth d							07 14										07 44								
Chessington North d							07 17										07 47								
Chessington South a							07 19										07 49								
Worcester Park d					07 03										07 33					07 48					08 03
Stoneleigh d					07 06										07 36					07 51					08 06
Ewell West d					07 09										07 39					07 54					08 09
Epsom 3 a					07 16										07 46					07 57					08 16
d					07 17										07 47					07 58					08 17
Ashtead d					07 21										07 51					08 02					08 21
Leatherhead d					07 24										07 54					08 05					08 24
Boxhill & Westhumble d																									
Dorking 4 a																				08 11					
New Malden 6 d	06 49			06 58		07 04					07 19			07 28		07 34					07 49			07 58	
Norbiton d	06 52					07 07					07 22					07 37					07 52				
Kingston a	06 55					07 10					07 25					07 40					07 55				
d	06 59					07 10					07 29					07 40					07 59				
Hampton Wick d	07 01					07 12					07 31					07 42					08 01				
Teddington d	07 05					07 15					07 35					07 45					08 05				
Strawberry Hill a	07 08										07 38										08 08				
Fulwell d						07 19										07 49									
Hampton d						07 23										07 53									
Kempton Park d						07 26										07 56									
Sunbury d						07 28										07 58									
Upper Halliford d						07 30										08 00									
Shepperton a						07 33										08 03									
Berrylands d				07 00										07 30										08 00	
Surbiton 6 d		06 57	07 00	07 05				07 11		07 14		07 27	07 30	07 35				07 41	07 44			07 57	08 00	08 05	
Thames Ditton d				07 09										07 39										08 09	
Hampton Court a				07 12										07 42										08 12	
Hinchley Wood d		07 01										07 31										08 01			
Claygate d		07 04										07 34										08 04			
Oxshott d		07 07										07 37										08 07			
Cobham & Stoke d'Abernon d		07 11										07 41										08 11			
Bookham d					07 29										07 59										08 29
Effingham Junction 6 d		07 15			07 33							07 45			08 03							08 15			08 33
Horsley d		07 18			07 36							07 48			08 06							08 18			08 36
Clandon d		07 23			07 41							07 53			08 11							08 23			08 41
London Road (Guildford) d		07 28			07 46							07 58			08 16							08 28			08 46
Guildford a		07 32			07 50							08 02			08 20							08 32			08 50

For general notes see front of timetable
For details of catering facilities see Directory of Train Operators

- **A** To London Waterloo (Table 149)
- **B** To Portsmouth Harbour (Table 158)
- **C** To Alton (Table 155)
- **D** To Woking (Table 155)
- **E** To Basingstoke (Table 155)

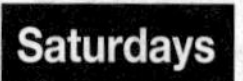

Saturdays

until 27 September

For details of Bank Holiday service alterations, please see first page of Table 149

London → Chessington South, Dorking, Guildford Shepperton and Hampton Court

Network Diagram - see first page of Table 152

		SW		SW	SW	SW	SW	SW		SW	SW	SW	SW	SW	SW	SW	SW	SW	SW	SW	SW	SW	SW	SW	SW	SW
					1										1					1					1	
					A	B		C							A	B		C		D					A	B
London Waterloo 15 ⊖	d	07 42		07 46	07 53	07 50	07 54	07 57		08 03	08 06	08 09	08 12	08 16	08 23	08 20	08 24	08 27	08 33	08 42	08 36	08 39	08 42	08 46	08 53	08 50
Vauxhall ⊖	d	07 46		07 50		07 54	07 58	08 01		08 07	08 10	08 13	08 16	08 20		08 24	08 28	08 31	08 37		08 40	08 43	08 46	08 50		08 54
Clapham Junction 10	d	07 51		07 55	08u00	07 59	08 03	08 06		08 12	08 15	08 18	08 21	08 25		08 29	08 33	08 36	08 42		08 45	08 48	08 51	08 55	09u00	08 59
Earlsfield	d	07 54		07 58		08 02	08 06	08 09		08 15	08 18	08 21	08 24	08 28		08 32	08 36	08 39	08 45		08 48	08 51	08 54	08 58		09 02
Wimbledon 6 ⊖	d	07 58		08 02		08 06	08 10	08 13		08 19	08 22	08 25	08 28	08 32		08 36	08 40	08 43	08 49		08 52	08 55	08 58	09 02		09 06
Raynes Park 6	d	08 01		08 05			08 13	08 16			08 25	08 28	08 31	08 35			08 43	08 46			08 55	08 58	09 01	09 05		
Motspur Park	d			08 08			08 16					08 31		08 38			08 46					09 01		09 08		
Malden Manor	d			08 11										08 41										09 11		
Tolworth	d			08 14										08 44										09 14		
Chessington North	d			08 17										08 47										09 17		
Chessington South	a			08 19										08 49										09 19		
Worcester Park	d						08 18					08 33					08 48					09 03				
Stoneleigh	d						08 21					08 36					08 51					09 06				
Ewell West	d						08 24					08 39					08 54					09 09				
Epsom 3	a						08 27					08 46					08 57					09 16				
	d						08 28					08 47					08 58					09 17				
Ashtead	d						08 32					08 51					09 02					09 21				
Leatherhead	d						08 35					08 54					09 05					09 24				
Boxhill & Westhumble	d																									
Dorking 4	a						08 41										09 11									
New Malden 6	d	08 04						08 19			08 28		08 34					08 49			08 58		09 04			
Norbiton	d	08 07						08 22					08 37					08 52					09 07			
Kingston	a	08 10						08 25					08 40					08 55					09 10			
	d	08 10						08 29					08 40					08 59					09 10			
Hampton Wick	d	08 12						08 31					08 42					09 01					09 12			
Teddington	d	08 15						08 35					08 45					09 05					09 15			
Strawberry Hill	a							08 38										09 08								
Fulwell	d	08 19											08 49										09 19			
Hampton	d	08 23											08 53										09 23			
Kempton Park	d	08 26											08 56										09 26			
Sunbury	d	08 28											08 58										09 28			
Upper Halliford	d	08 30											09 00										09 30			
Shepperton	a	08 33											09 03										09 33			
Berrylands	d										08 30										09 00					
Surbiton 6	d				08 11	08 14				08 27	08 35				08 41	08 44			08 57	09 00	09 05				09 11	09 14
Thames Ditton	d										08 39										09 09					
Hampton Court	a										08 42										09 12					
Hinchley Wood	d									08 31									09 01							
Claygate	d									08 34									09 04							
Oxshott	d									08 37									09 07							
Cobham & Stoke d'Abernon	d									08 41									09 11							
Bookham	d											08 59										09 29				
Effingham Junction 6	d									08 45		09 03							09 15			09 33				
Horsley	d									08 48		09 06							09 18			09 36				
Clandon	d									08 53		09 11							09 23			09 41				
London Road (Guildford)	d									08 58		09 16							09 28			09 46				
Guildford	a									09 02		09 20							09 32			09 50				

For general notes see front of timetable
For details of catering facilities see Directory of Train Operators

A To Alton (Table 155)
B To Woking (Table 155)
C To London Waterloo (Table 149)
D To Basingstoke (Table 155)

Table 152

Saturdays

until 27 September

For details of Bank Holiday service alterations, please see first page of Table 149

London → Chessington South, Dorking, Guildford Shepperton and Hampton Court

Network Diagram - see first page of Table 152

		SW	SW A		SW	SW 1 B	SW	SW	SW	SW	SW 1 C	SW D	SW	SW A	SW	SW 1 B	SW	SW	SW	SW	SW 1 C	SW D	SW
London Waterloo 15 ⊖	d	08 54	08 57	and at the same minutes past each hour until	19 03	19 12	19 06	19 09	19 12	19 16	19 23	19 20	19 24	19 27	19 33	19 42	19 36	19 39	19 42	19 46	19 53	19 50	19 54
Vauxhall ⊖	d	08 58	09 01		19 07	.	19 10	19 13	19 16	19 20	.	19 24	19 28	19 31	19 37	.	19 40	19 43	19 46	19 50	.	19 54	19 58
Clapham Junction 10	d	09 03	09 06		19 12	19u19	19 15	19 18	19 21	19 25	.	19 29	19 33	19 36	19 42	.	19 45	19 48	19 51	19 55	20u00	19 59	20 03
Earlsfield	d	09 06	09 09		19 15	.	19 18	19 21	19 24	19 28	.	19 32	19 36	19 39	19 45	.	19 48	19 51	19 54	19 58	.	20 02	20 06
Wimbledon 6 ⊖	d	09 10	09 13		19 19	.	19 22	19 25	19 28	19 32	.	19 36	19 40	19 43	19 49	.	19 52	19 55	19 58	20 02	.	20 06	20 10
Raynes Park 6	d	09 13	09 16		.	.	19 25	19 28	19 31	19 35	.	.	19 43	19 46	.	.	19 55	19 58	20 01	20 05	.	.	20 13
Motspur Park	d	09 16	.		.	.	.	19 31	.	19 38	.	.	19 46	.	.	.	.	20 01	.	20 08	.	.	20 16
Malden Manor	d	.	.		.	.	.	.	.	19 41	.	.	.	.	.	.	.	.	.	20 11	.	.	.
Tolworth	d	.	.		.	.	.	.	.	19 44	.	.	.	.	.	.	.	.	.	20 14	.	.	.
Chessington North	d	.	.		.	.	.	.	.	19 47	.	.	.	.	.	.	.	.	.	20 17	.	.	.
Chessington South	a	.	.		.	.	.	.	.	19 49	.	.	.	.	.	.	.	.	.	20 19	.	.	.
Worcester Park	d	09 18	.		.	.	.	19 33	.	.	.	.	19 48	.	.	.	.	20 03	.	.	.	.	20 18
Stoneleigh	d	09 21	.		.	.	.	19 36	.	.	.	.	19 51	.	.	.	.	20 06	.	.	.	.	20 21
Ewell West	d	09 24	.		.	.	.	19 39	.	.	.	.	19 54	.	.	.	.	20 09	.	.	.	.	20 24
Epsom 3	a	09 27	.		.	.	.	19 42	.	.	.	.	19 57	.	.	.	.	20 12	.	.	.	.	20 27
	d	09 28	.		.	.	.	19 47	.	.	.	.	19 58	.	.	.	.	20 17	.	.	.	.	.
Ashtead	d	09 32	.		.	.	.	19 51	.	.	.	.	20 02	.	.	.	.	20 21	.	.	.	.	.
Leatherhead	d	09 35	.		.	.	.	19 54	.	.	.	.	20 05	.	.	.	.	20 24	.	.	.	.	.
Boxhill & Westhumble	d	.	.		.	.	.	.	.	.	.	.	.	.	.	.	.	.	.	.	.	.	.
Dorking 4	a	09 41	.		.	.	.	.	.	.	.	.	20 11	.	.	.	.	.	.	.	.	.	.
New Malden 6	d	.	09 19		.	.	19 28	.	19 34	.	.	.	.	19 49	.	.	19 58	.	20 04	.	.	.	.
Norbiton	d	.	09 22		.	.	.	.	19 37	.	.	.	.	19 52	.	.	.	.	20 07	.	.	.	.
Kingston	a	.	09 25		.	.	.	.	19 40	.	.	.	.	19 55	.	.	.	.	20 10	.	.	.	.
	d	.	09 29		.	.	.	.	19 40	.	.	.	.	19 59	.	.	.	.	20 10	.	.	.	.
Hampton Wick	d	.	09 31		.	.	.	.	19 42	.	.	.	.	20 01	.	.	.	.	20 12	.	.	.	.
Teddington	d	.	09 35		.	.	.	.	19 45	.	.	.	.	20 05	.	.	.	.	20 15	.	.	.	.
Strawberry Hill	a	.	09 38		.	.	.	.	.	.	.	.	.	20 08	.	.	.	.	.	.	.	.	.
Fulwell	d	.	.		.	.	.	.	19 49	.	.	.	.	.	.	.	.	.	20 19	.	.	.	.
Hampton	d	.	.		.	.	.	.	19 53	.	.	.	.	.	.	.	.	.	20 23	.	.	.	.
Kempton Park	d	.	.		.	.	.	.	19 56	.	.	.	.	.	.	.	.	.	20 26	.	.	.	.
Sunbury	d	.	.		.	.	.	.	19 58	.	.	.	.	.	.	.	.	.	20 28	.	.	.	.
Upper Halliford	d	.	.		.	.	.	.	20 00	.	.	.	.	.	.	.	.	.	20 30	.	.	.	.
Shepperton	a	.	.		.	.	.	.	20 03	.	.	.	.	.	.	.	.	.	20 33	.	.	.	.
Berrylands	d	.	.		.	.	19 30	.	.	.	.	.	.	.	.	.	20 00	.	.	.	.	.	.
Surbiton 6	d	.	.		19 27	19 30	19 35	.	.	.	19 41	19 44	.	.	19 57	20 00	20 05	.	.	.	20 11	20 14	.
Thames Ditton	d	.	.		.	.	19 39	.	.	.	.	.	.	.	.	.	20 09	.	.	.	.	.	.
Hampton Court	a	.	.		.	.	19 42	.	.	.	.	.	.	.	.	.	20 12	.	.	.	.	.	.
Hinchley Wood	d	.	.		19 31	.	.	.	.	.	.	.	.	.	20 01	.	.	.	.	.	.	.	.
Claygate	d	.	.		19 34	.	.	.	.	.	.	.	.	.	20 04	.	.	.	.	.	.	.	.
Oxshott	d	.	.		19 37	.	.	.	.	.	.	.	.	.	20 07	.	.	.	.	.	.	.	.
Cobham & Stoke d'Abernon	d	.	.		19 41	.	.	.	.	.	.	.	.	.	20 11	.	.	.	.	.	.	.	.
Bookham	d	.	.		.	.	.	19 59	.	.	.	.	.	.	.	.	.	20 29	.	.	.	.	.
Effingham Junction 6	d	.	.		19 45	.	.	20 03	.	.	.	.	.	.	20 15	.	.	20 33	.	.	.	.	.
Horsley	d	.	.		19 48	.	.	20 06	.	.	.	.	.	.	20 18	.	.	20 36	.	.	.	.	.
Clandon	d	.	.		19 53	.	.	20 11	.	.	.	.	.	.	20 23	.	.	20 41	.	.	.	.	.
London Road (Guildford)	d	.	.		19 58	.	.	20 16	.	.	.	.	.	.	20 28	.	.	20 46	.	.	.	.	.
Guildford	a	.	.		20 02	.	.	20 20	.	.	.	.	.	.	20 32	.	.	20 50	.	.	.	.	.

For general notes see front of timetable
For details of catering facilities see Directory of Train Operators

A To London Waterloo (Table 149)
B To Basingstoke (Table 155)
C To Alton (Table 155)
D To Woking (Table 155)

Table 152

Saturdays

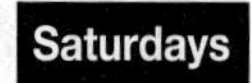

until 27 September

For details of Bank Holiday service alterations, please see first page of Table 149

London → Chessington South, Dorking, Guildford Shepperton and Hampton Court

Network Diagram - see first page of Table 152

		SW	SW	SW	SW	SW	SW	SW	SW	SW	SW	SW	SW	SW		SW	SW	SW	SW	SW	SW	SW	SW	SW	SW	SW
				1					1 ◇	1						1					1					
		A		B					C	D	E		A			G					D	E		A		
									☕																	
London Waterloo 15 ⊖	d	19 57	20 03	20 12	20 06	20 09	20 12	20 16	20 20	20 23	20 20	20 24	20 27	20 33		20 42	20 36	20 39	20 42	20 46	20 53	20 50	20 54	20 57	21 03	21 09
Vauxhall ⊖	d	20 01	20 07		20 10	20 13	20 16	20 20			20 24	20 28	20 31	20 37			20 40	20 43	20 46	20 50		20 54	20 58	21 01	21 07	21 13
Clapham Junction 10	d	20 06	20 12	20u19	20 15	20 18	20 21	20 25	20u27		20 29	20 33	20 36	20 42			20 45	20 48	20 51	20 55	21u00	20 59	21 03	21 06	21 12	21 18
Earlsfield	d	20 09	20 15		20 18	20 21	20 24	20 28			20 32	20 36	20 39	20 45			20 48	20 51	20 54	20 58		21 02	21 06	21 09	21 15	21 21
Wimbledon 6 ⊖	d	20 13	20 19		20 22	20 25	20 28	20 32			20 36	20 40	20 43	20 49			20 52	20 55	20 58	21 02		21 06	21 10	21 13	21 19	21 25
Raynes Park 6	d	20 16			20 25	20 28	20 31	20 35				20 43	20 46				20 55	20 58	21 01	21 05			21 13	21 16		21 28
Motspur Park	d					20 31		20 38				20 46						21 01		21 08			21 16			21 31
Malden Manor	d							20 41												21 11						
Tolworth	d							20 44												21 14						
Chessington North	d							20 47												21 17						
Chessington South	a							20 49												21 19						
Worcester Park	d					20 33						20 48						21 03					21 18			21 33
Stoneleigh	d					20 36						20 51						21 06					21 21			21 36
Ewell West	d					20 39						20 54						21 09					21 24			21 39
Epsom 3	a					20 42						20 57						21 12					21 27			21 42
	d					20 47												21 17								21 47
Ashtead	d					20 51												21 21								21 51
Leatherhead	d					20 54												21 24								21 54
Boxhill & Westhumble	d																									
Dorking 4	a					21 00																				22 00
New Malden 6	d	20 19			20 28		20 34						20 49				20 58		21 04					21 19		
Norbiton	d	20 22					20 37						20 52						21 07					21 22		
Kingston	a	20 25					20 40						20 55						21 10					21 25		
	d	20 29					20 40						20 59						21 10					21 29		
Hampton Wick	d	20 31					20 42						21 01						21 12					21 31		
Teddington	d	20 35					20 45						21 05						21 15					21 35		
Strawberry Hill	a	20 38											21 08											21 38		
Fulwell	d						20 49												21 19							
Hampton	d						20 53												21 23							
Kempton Park	d						20 56												21 26							
Sunbury	d						20 58												21 28							
Upper Halliford	d						21 00												21 30							
Shepperton	a						21 03												21 33							
Berrylands	d				20 30												21 00									
Surbiton 6	d		20 27	20 30	20 35					20 41	20 44			20 57		21 00	21 05				21 11	21 14			21 27	
Thames Ditton	d				20 39												21 09									
Hampton Court	a				20 42												21 12									
Hinchley Wood	d		20 31											21 01											21 31	
Claygate	d		20 34											21 04											21 34	
Oxshott	d		20 37											21 07											21 37	
Cobham & Stoke d'Abernon	d		20 41											21 11											21 41	
Bookham	d																	21 29								
Effingham Junction 6	d		20 45											21 15				21 33							21 45	
Horsley	d		20 48											21 18				21 36							21 48	
Clandon	d		20 53											21 23				21 41							21 53	
London Road (Guildford)	d		20 58											21 28				21 46							21 58	
Guildford	a		21 02											21 32				21 50							22 02	

For general notes see front of timetable
For details of catering facilities see Directory of Train Operators

A To London Waterloo (Table 149)
B To Basingstoke (Table 155)
C To Yeovil Junction (Table 160)
D To Alton (Table 155)
E To Woking (Table 155)
G To Portsmouth Harbour (Table 158)

Saturdays

until 27 September

For details of Bank Holiday service alterations, please see first page of Table 149

London → Chessington South, Dorking, Guildford Shepperton and Hampton Court

Network Diagram - see first page of Table 152

		SW 1	SW	SW 1	SW	SW	SW		SW	SW 1	SW	SW	SW	SW	SW 1	SW	SW	SW	SW	SW	SW 1	SW	SW 1		SW	SW
		A		B	C		D			E					B			D			A		B		C	D
London Waterloo 15 ⊖	d	21 12	21 12	21 23	21 20	21 24	21 27		21 33	21 42	21 36	21 39	21 42	21 46	21 53	21 50	21 54	21 57	22 03	22 09	22 12	22 12	22 23		22 20	22 27
Vauxhall ⊖	d		21 16		21 24	21 28	21 31		21 37		21 40	21 43	21 46	21 50		21 54	21 58	22 01	22 07	22 13		22 16			22 24	22 31
Clapham Junction 10	d	21u19	21 21		21 29	21 33	21 36		21 42		21 45	21 48	21 51	21 55	22u00	21 59	22 03	22 06	22 12	22 18	22u19	22 21	22u30		22 29	22 36
Earlsfield	d		21 24		21 32	21 36	21 39		21 45		21 48	21 51	21 54	21 58		22 02	22 06	22 09	22 15	22 21		22 24			22 32	22 39
Wimbledon 6 ⊖	d		21 28		21 36	21 40	21 43		21 49		21 52	21 55	21 58	22 02		22 06	22 10	22 13	22 19	22 25		22 28			22 36	22 43
Raynes Park 6	d		21 31			21 43	21 46				21 55	21 58	22 01	22 05			22 13	22 16		22 28		22 31				22 46
Motspur Park	d					21 46						22 01		22 08			22 16			22 31						
Malden Manor	d													22 11												
Tolworth	d													22 14												
Chessington North	d													22 17												
Chessington South	a													22 19												
Worcester Park	d					21 48						22 03					22 18			22 33						
Stoneleigh	d					21 51						22 06					22 21			22 36						
Ewell West	d					21 54						22 09					22 24			22 39						
Epsom 3	a					21 57						22 12					22 27			22 42						
	d											22 17								22 47						
Ashtead	d											22 21								22 51						
Leatherhead	d											22 24								22 54						
Boxhill & Westhumble	d																									
Dorking 4	a																			23 00						
New Malden 6	d		21 34				21 49				21 58		22 04					22 19				22 34				22 49
Norbiton	d		21 37				21 52						22 07					22 22				22 37				22 52
Kingston	a		21 40				21 55						22 10					22 25				22 40				22 55
	d		21 40				21 59						22 10					22 29				22 40				22 59
Hampton Wick	d		21 42				22 01						22 12					22 31				22 42				23 01
Teddington	d		21 45				22 05						22 15					22 35				22 45				23 05
Strawberry Hill	a						22 08											22 38								23 08
Fulwell	d		21 49										22 19									22 49				
Hampton	d		21 53										22 23									22 53				
Kempton Park	d		21 56										22 26									22 56				
Sunbury	d		21 58										22 28									22 58				
Upper Halliford	d		22 00										22 30									23 00				
Shepperton	a		22 03										22 33									23 03				
Berrylands	d										22 00															
Surbiton 6	d	21 30		21 41	21 44				21 57	22 00	22 05				22 11	22 14			22 27		22 30		22 41		22 44	
Thames Ditton	d										22 09															
Hampton Court	a										22 12															
Hinchley Wood	d								22 01										22 31							
Claygate	d								22 04										22 34							
Oxshott	d								22 07										22 37							
Cobham & Stoke d'Abernon	d								22 11										22 41							
Bookham	d											22 29														
Effingham Junction 6	d								22 15			22 33							22 45							
Horsley	d								22 18			22 36							22 48							
Clandon	d								22 23			22 41							22 53							
London Road (Guildford)	d								22 28			22 46							22 58							
Guildford	a								22 32			22 50				22 47			23 02							

For general notes see front of timetable
For details of catering facilities see Directory of Train Operators

A To Basingstoke (Table 155)
B To Alton (Table 155)
C To Woking (Table 155)
D To London Waterloo (Table 149)
E To Portsmouth Harbour (Table 158)

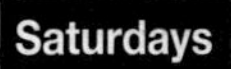

until 27 September

For details of Bank Holiday service alterations, please see first page of Table 149

London → Chessington South, Dorking, Guildford Shepperton and Hampton Court

Network Diagram - see first page of Table 152

		SW	SW 1	SW	SW	SW	SW 1	SW	SW	SW	SW	SW	SW 1	SW	SW 1	SW		SW	SW	SW	SW 1	SW	SW	SW
			A				B	C	D				A		B	C		E			A			
London Waterloo 15 ⊖	d	22 33	22 42	22 36	22 39	22 42	22 53	22 50	22 57	23 00	23 03	23 09	23 12	23 12	23 23	23 20		23 27	23 30	23 42	23 48	23 50	23 57	
Vauxhall ⊖	d	22 37		22 40	22 43	22 46		22 54	23 01	23 04	23 07	23 13		23 16		23 24		23 31	23 34	23 46		23 54	00 01	
Clapham Junction 10	d	22 42	22u49	22 45	22 48	22 51	23u00	22 59	23 06	23 09	23 12	23 18	23u19	23 21	23u30	23 29		23 36	23 39	23 51	23u56	23 59	00 06	
Earlsfield	d	22 45		22 48	22 51	22 54		23 02	23 09	23 12	23 15	23 21		23 24		23 32		23 39	23 42	23 54		00 02	00 09	
Wimbledon 6 ⊖	d	22 49		22 52	22 55	22 58		23 06	23 13	23 16	23 19	23 25		23 28		23 36		23 43	23 46	23 58		00 06	00 13	
Raynes Park 6	d			22 55	22 58	23 01			23 16	23 19		23 28		23 31				23 46	23 49	00 01			00 16	
Motspur Park	d				23 01					23 22		23 31								00 04				
Malden Manor	d									23 25														
Tolworth	d									23 28														
Chessington North	d									23 31														
Chessington South	a									23 33														
Worcester Park	d				23 03							23 33								00 06				
Stoneleigh	d				23 06							23 36								00 09				←
Ewell West	d				23 09							23 39								00 12				00 12
Epsom 3	a				23 12							23 42								→				00 15
	d				23 17							23 47												00 19
Ashtead	d				23 21							23 51												00 23
Leatherhead	d				23 24							23 54												00 26
Boxhill & Westhumble	d																							
Dorking 4	a											00 01												
New Malden 6	d			22 58		23 04			23 19					23 34				23 49	23 52				00 19	
Norbiton	d					23 07			23 22					23 37				23 52					00 22	
Kingston	a					23 10			23 25					23 40				23 55					00 25	
	d					23 10			23 29					23 40				23 55					00 25	
Hampton Wick	d					23 12			23 31					23 42				23 57					00 27	
Teddington	d					23 15			23 35					23 45				23 59					00 30	
Strawberry Hill	a								23 38									00 03						
Fulwell	d					23 19								23 49									00 34	
Hampton	d					23 23								23 53									00 38	
Kempton Park	d					23 26								23 56									00 41	
Sunbury	d					23 28								23 58									00 43	
Upper Halliford	d					23 30								23 59									00 45	
Shepperton	a					23 33								00 03									00 48	
Berrylands	d			23 00															23 54					
Surbiton 6	d	22 57	23 00	23 05			23 11	23 14			23 27		23 30		23 41	23 44			23 59		00 10	00 14		
Thames Ditton	d			23 09															00 03					
Hampton Court	a			23 12															00 06					
Hinchley Wood	d	23 01									23 31											00 18		
Claygate	d	23 04									23 34											00 21		
Oxshott	d	23 07									23 37											00 24		
Cobham & Stoke d'Abernon	d	23 11									23 41											00 28		
Bookham	d				23 29																			00 31
Effingham Junction 6	d	23 15			23 33						23 45											00 32		00 36
Horsley	d	23 18			23 36						23 48											00 35		00 39
Clandon	d	23 23			23 41						23 53											00 40		00 44
London Road (Guildford)	d	23 28			23 46						23 58											00 45		00 49
Guildford	a	23 32			23 54						00 02											00 49		00 53

For general notes see front of timetable
For details of catering facilities see Directory of Train Operators

A To Basingstoke (Table 155)
B To Alton (Table 155)
C To Woking (Table 155)
D To London Waterloo (Table 149)
E To Twickenham (Table 149)

Table 152

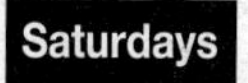

from 4 October

For details of Bank Holiday service alterations, please see first page of Table 149

London → Chessington South, Dorking, Guildford Shepperton and Hampton Court

Network Diagram - see first page of Table 152

	SW	SW	SW 1 A	SW	SW	SW	SW	SW	SW	SW	SW 1 B	SW 1 C		SW	SW 1 D	SW E	SW G	SW 1 A	SW	SW E	SW	SW	SW G	SW E	SW
London Waterloo 15 ⊖ d	23p30	23p42	23p48	23p50	23p57		00 09	00 15	00 27	00 42	01 05	05 00		05 12	05 20		05 50	06 12	06 06		06 12	06 16	06 20	06 27	06 33
Vauxhall ⊖ d	23p34	23p46		23p54	00 01		00 13	00 19	00 31	00 46	01 09	05 04		05 16	05 24		05 54		06 10		06 16	06 20	06 24	06 31	06 37
Clapham Junction 10 d	23p39	23p51	23b56	23p59	00 06		00 18	00 24	00 36	00 51	01 14	05 09		05 21	05 29		05 59	06u19	06 15		06 21	06 25	06 29	06 36	06 42
Earlsfield d	23p42	23p54		00 02	00 09		00 21	00 27	00s39			05 12		05 24	05 32		06 02		06 18		06 24	06 28	06 32	06 39	06 45
Wimbledon 6 ⊖ d	23p46	23p58		00 06	00 13		00 25	00 31	00 43	01 05	01 20	05 16		05 28	05 36		06 06		06 22		06 28	06 32	06 36	06 43	06 49
Raynes Park 6 d	23p49	00 01			00 16			00 34	00 46	01 08				05 31					06 25		06 31	06 35		06 46	
Motspur Park d		00 04						00 37														06 38			
Malden Manor d																						06 41			
Tolworth d																						06 44			
Chessington North d																						06 47			
Chessington South a																						06 49			
Worcester Park d		00 06						00 39																	
Stoneleigh d		00 09				←		00 42																	
Ewell West d		00 12 →				00 12		00 45																	
Epsom 3 a						00 15		00 48																	
Epsom d						00 19																			
Ashtead d						00 23																			
Leatherhead d						00 26																			
Boxhill & Westhumble d																									
Dorking 4 a																									
New Malden 6 d	23p52				00 19				00 49	01 11				05 34					06 28		06 34			06 49	
Norbiton d					00 22					01 14				05 37							06 37			06 52	
Kingston a					00 25					01 17				05 40							06 40			06 55	
Kingston d					00 25					01 17				05 40		05 59				06 29	06 40			06 59	
Hampton Wick d					00 27					01s22				05 42		06 01				06 31	06 42			07 01	
Teddington d					00 30					01s25				05 45		06 05				06 35	06 45			07 05	
Strawberry Hill a										01 28						06 08				06 38				07 08	
Fulwell d					00 34									05 49							06 49				
Hampton d					00 38									05 53							06 53				
Kempton Park d					00 41									05 56							06 56				
Sunbury d					00 43									05 58							06 58				
Upper Halliford d					00 45									06 00							07 00				
Shepperton a					00 50									06 05							07 05				
Berrylands d	23p54								00s51										06 30						
Surbiton 6 d	23p59		00 10	00 14			00 33		00a55		01 29	05 24			05 44		06 14	06 30	06 35				06 44		06 57
Thames Ditton d	00 03																		06 39						
Hampton Court a	00 06																		06 42						
Hinchley Wood d				00 18																					07 01
Claygate d				00 21																					07 04
Oxshott d				00 24																					07 07
Cobham & Stoke d'Abernon d				00 28																					07 11
Bookham d						00 31																			
Effingham Junction 6 d				00 32		00 36																			07 15
Horsley d				00 35		00 39																			07 18
Clandon d				00 40		00 44																			07 23
London Road (Guildford) d				00 45		00 49																			07 28
Guildford a				00 52		00 56	01 06					05 59			06 23										07 35

For general notes see front of timetable
For details of catering facilities see Directory of Train Operators

A To Basingstoke (Table 155)
B To Southampton Central (Table 158)
C To Haslemere (Table 156)
D To Portsmouth Harbour (Table 156)
E To London Waterloo (Table 149)
G To Woking (Table 155)
b Previous night.
Stops to pick up only

Saturdays
from 4 October

For details of Bank Holiday service alterations, please see first page of Table 149

London → Chessington South, Dorking, Guildford Shepperton and Hampton Court

Network Diagram - see first page of Table 152

		SW 1 A	SW		SW	SW	SW	SW 1 B	SW C	SW D	SW	SW 1 E	SW	SW	SW	SW		SW 1 B	SW C	SW	SW D	SW	SW 1 E	SW	SW	SW
London Waterloo 15 ⊖	d	06 42	06 36		06 39	06 42	06 46	06 53	06 50	06 57	07 03	07 12	07 06	07 09	07 12	07 16		07 23	07 20	07 24	07 27	07 33	07 42	07 36	07 39	07 42
Vauxhall ⊖	d		06 40		06 43	06 46	06 50		06 54	07 01	07 07		07 10	07 13	07 16	07 20			07 24	07 28	07 31	07 37		07 40	07 43	07 46
Clapham Junction 10	d	06u49	06 45		06 48	06 51	06 55	07u00	06 59	07 06	07 12	07u19	07 15	07 18	07 21	07 25		07u30	07 29	07 33	07 36	07 42		07 45	07 48	07 51
Earlsfield	d		06 48		06 51	06 54	06 58		07 02	07 09	07 15		07 18	07 21	07 24	07 28			07 32	07 36	07 39	07 45		07 48	07 51	07 54
Wimbledon 6 ⊖	d		06 52		06 55	06 58	07 02		07 06	07 13	07 19		07 22	07 25	07 28	07 32			07 36	07 40	07 43	07 49		07 52	07 55	07 58
Raynes Park 6	d		06 55		06 58	07 01	07 05			07 16			07 25	07 28	07 31	07 35				07 43	07 46			07 55	07 58	08 01
Motspur Park	d				07 01		07 08							07 31		07 38				07 46					08 01	
Malden Manor	d						07 11									07 41										
Tolworth	d						07 14									07 44										
Chessington North	d						07 17									07 47										
Chessington South	a						07 19									07 49										
Worcester Park	d				07 03									07 33						07 48					08 03	
Stoneleigh	d				07 06									07 36						07 51					08 06	
Ewell West	d				07 09									07 39						07 54					08 09	
Epsom 3	a				07 16									07 46						07 57					08 16	
	d				07 17									07 47						07 58					08 17	
Ashtead	d				07 21									07 51						08 02					08 21	
Leatherhead	d				07 24									07 54						08 05					08 24	
Boxhill & Westhumble	d																									
Dorking 4	a																			08 13						
New Malden 6	d		06 58			07 04				07 19			07 28		07 34						07 49			07 58		08 04
Norbiton	d					07 07				07 22					07 37						07 52					08 07
Kingston	a					07 10				07 25					07 40						07 55					08 10
	d					07 10				07 29					07 40						07 59					08 10
Hampton Wick	d					07 12				07 31					07 42						08 01					08 12
Teddington	d					07 15				07 35					07 45						08 05					08 15
Strawberry Hill	a									07 38											08 08					
Fulwell	d					07 19									07 49											08 19
Hampton	d					07 23									07 53											08 23
Kempton Park	d					07 26									07 56											08 26
Sunbury	d					07 28									07 58											08 28
Upper Halliford	d					07 30									08 00											08 30
Shepperton	a					07 35									08 05											08 35
Berrylands	d		07 00										07 30											08 00		
Surbiton 6	d	07 00	07 05					07 11	07 14		07 27	07 30	07 35					07 41	07 44			07 57	08 00	08 05		
Thames Ditton	d		07 09										07 39											08 09		
Hampton Court	a		07 12										07 42											08 12		
Hinchley Wood	d										07 31											08 01				
Claygate	d										07 34											08 04				
Oxshott	d										07 37											08 07				
Cobham & Stoke d'Abernon	d										07 41											08 11				
Bookham	d				07 29									07 59											08 29	
Effingham Junction 6	d				07 33						07 45			08 03								08 15			08 33	
Horsley	d				07 36						07 48			08 06								08 18			08 36	
Clandon	d				07 41						07 53			08 11								08 23			08 41	
London Road (Guildford)	d				07 46						07 58			08 16								08 28			08 46	
Guildford	a				07 53						08 05			08 23								08 35			08 53	

For general notes see front of timetable
For details of catering facilities see Directory of Train Operators

- **A** To Portsmouth Harbour (Table 158)
- **B** To Alton (Table 155)
- **C** To Woking (Table 155)
- **D** To London Waterloo (Table 149)
- **E** To Basingstoke (Table 155)

Table 152

from 4 October

For details of Bank Holiday service alterations, please see first page of Table 149

London → Chessington South, Dorking, Guildford Shepperton and Hampton Court

Network Diagram - see first page of Table 152

Station		SW	SW 1 A	SW B	SW	SW C			SW	SW 1 D	SW	SW	SW	SW	SW 1 A	SW B	SW	SW C	SW	SW 1 D	SW	SW	SW	SW	SW 1 A	SW B
London Waterloo 15 ⊖	d	07 46	07 53	07 50	07 54	07 57			08 03	08 12	08 06	08 09	08 12	08 16	08 23	08 20	08 24	08 27	08 33	08 42	08 36	08 39	08 42	08 46	08 53	08 50
Vauxhall ⊖	d	07 50		07 54	07 58	08 01			08 07		08 10	08 13	08 16	08 20		08 24	08 28	08 31	08 37		08 40	08 43	08 46	08 50		08 54
Clapham Junction 10	d	07 55	08u00	07 59	08 03	08 06			08 12	08u19	08 15	08 18	08 21	08 25		08 29	08 33	08 36	08 42		08 45	08 48	08 51	08 55	09u00	08 59
Earlsfield	d	07 58		08 02	08 06	08 09			08 15		08 18	08 21	08 24	08 28		08 32	08 36	08 39	08 45		08 48	08 51	08 54	08 58		09 02
Wimbledon 6 ⊖	d	08 02		08 06	08 10	08 13			08 19		08 22	08 25	08 28	08 32		08 36	08 40	08 43	08 49		08 52	08 55	08 58	09 02		09 06
Raynes Park 6	d	08 05			08 13	08 16					08 25	08 28	08 31	08 35			08 43	08 46			08 55	08 58	09 01	09 05		
Motspur Park	d	08 08			08 16							08 31		08 38			08 46					09 01		09 08		
Malden Manor	d	08 11												08 41										09 11		
Tolworth	d	08 14												08 44										09 14		
Chessington North	d	08 17												08 47										09 17		
Chessington South	a	08 19												08 49										09 19		
Worcester Park	d				08 18							08 33					08 48					09 03				
Stoneleigh	d				08 21							08 36					08 51					09 06				
Ewell West	d				08 24							08 39					08 54					09 09				
Epsom 3	a				08 27							08 46					08 57					09 16				
	d				08 28							08 47					08 58					09 17				
Ashtead	d				08 32							08 51					09 02					09 21				
Leatherhead	d				08 35							08 54					09 05					09 24				
Boxhill & Westhumble	d																									
Dorking 4	a				08 43												09 13									
New Malden 6	d					08 19					08 28		08 34					08 49			08 58		09 04			
Norbiton	d					08 22							08 37					08 52					09 07			
Kingston	a					08 25							08 40					08 55					09 10			
	d					08 29							08 40					08 59					09 10			
Hampton Wick	d					08 31							08 42					09 01					09 12			
Teddington	d					08 35							08 45					09 05					09 15			
Strawberry Hill	a					08 38												09 08								
Fulwell	d												08 49										09 19			
Hampton	d												08 53										09 23			
Kempton Park	d												08 56										09 26			
Sunbury	d												08 58										09 28			
Upper Halliford	d												09 00										09 30			
Shepperton	a												09 05										09 35			
Berrylands	d										08 30										09 00					
Surbiton 6	d		08 11	08 14					08 27	08 30	08 35				08 41	08 44			08 57	09 00	09 05				09 11	09 14
Thames Ditton	d										08 39										09 09					
Hampton Court	a										08 42										09 12					
Hinchley Wood	d								08 31										09 01							
Claygate	d								08 34										09 04							
Oxshott	d								08 37										09 07							
Cobham & Stoke d'Abernon	d								08 41										09 11							
Bookham	d											08 59										09 29				
Effingham Junction 6	d								08 45			09 03							09 15			09 33				
Horsley	d								08 48			09 06							09 18			09 36				
Clandon	d								08 53			09 11							09 23			09 41				
London Road (Guildford)	d								08 58			09 16							09 28			09 46				
Guildford	a								09 05			09 23							09 35			09 53				

For general notes see front of timetable
For details of catering facilities see Directory of Train Operators

A To Alton (Table 155)
B To Woking (Table 155)
C To London Waterloo (Table 149)
D To Basingstoke (Table 155)

Table 152

Saturdays

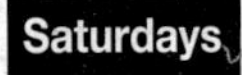

from 4 October

For details of Bank Holiday service alterations, please see first page of Table 149

London → Chessington South, Dorking, Guildford Shepperton and Hampton Court

Network Diagram - see first page of Table 152

		SW	SW		SW 1	SW	SW	SW	SW	SW 1	SW	SW	SW	SW	SW 1	SW	SW	SW	SW	SW 1	SW	SW	SW
			A		B					C	D		A		B					C	D		A
London Waterloo 15 ⊖	d	08 54	08 57		19 12	19 06	19 09	19 12	19 16	19 23	19 20	19 24	19 27	19 33	19 42	19 36	19 39	19 42	19 46	19 53	19 50	19 54	19 57
Vauxhall ⊖	d	08 58	09 01			19 10	19 13	19 16	19 20		19 24	19 28	19 31	19 37		19 40	19 43	19 46	19 50		19 54	19 58	20 01
Clapham Junction 10	d	09 03	09 06		19u19	19 15	19 18	19 21	19 25		19 29	19 33	19 36	19 42		19 45	19 48	19 51	19 55	20u00	19 59	20 03	20 06
Earlsfield	d	09 06	09 09			19 18	19 21	19 24	19 28		19 32	19 36	19 39	19 45		19 48	19 51	19 54	19 58		20 02	20 06	20 09
Wimbledon 6 ⊖	d	09 10	09 13			19 22	19 25	19 28	19 32		19 36	19 40	19 43	19 49		19 52	19 55	19 58	20 02		20 06	20 10	20 13
Raynes Park 6	d	09 13	09 16			19 25	19 28	19 31	19 35			19 43	19 46			19 55	19 58	20 01	20 05			20 13	20 16
Motspur Park	d	09 16					19 31		19 38			19 46					20 01		20 08			20 16	
Malden Manor	d								19 41										20 11				
Tolworth	d								19 44										20 14				
Chessington North	d								19 47										20 17				
Chessington South	a								19 49										20 19				
Worcester Park	d	09 18					19 33					19 48					20 03					20 18	
Stoneleigh	d	09 21					19 36					19 51					20 06					20 21	
Ewell West	d	09 24					19 39					19 54					20 09					20 24	
Epsom 3	a	09 27					19 42					19 57					20 12					20 27	
	d	09 28					19 47					19 58					20 17						
Ashtead	d	09 32					19 51					20 02					20 21						
Leatherhead	d	09 35					19 54					20 05					20 24						
Boxhill & Westhumble	d			and at																			
Dorking 4	a	09 43		the same								20 13											
New Malden 6	d		09 19	minutes		19 28		19 34					19 49			19 58		20 04					20 19
Norbiton	d		09 22	past				19 37					19 52					20 07					20 22
Kingston	a		09 25	each				19 40					19 55					20 10					20 25
	d		09 29	hour until				19 40					19 59					20 10					20 29
Hampton Wick	d		09 31					19 42					20 01					20 12					20 31
Teddington	d		09 35					19 45					20 05					20 15					20 35
Strawberry Hill	a		09 38										20 08										20 38
Fulwell	d							19 49										20 19					
Hampton	d							19 53										20 23					
Kempton Park	d							19 56										20 26					
Sunbury	d							19 58										20 28					
Upper Halliford	d							20 00										20 30					
Shepperton	a							20 05										20 35					
Berrylands	d					19 30										20 00							
Surbiton 6	d				19 30	19 35				19 41	19 44			19 57	20 00	20 05				20 11	20 14		
Thames Ditton	d					19 39										20 09							
Hampton Court	a					19 42										20 12							
Hinchley Wood	d													20 01									
Claygate	d													20 04									
Oxshott	d													20 07									
Cobham & Stoke d'Abernon	d													20 11									
Bookham	d						19 59										20 29						
Effingham Junction 6	d						20 03							20 15			20 33						
Horsley	d						20 06							20 18			20 36						
Clandon	d						20 11							20 23			20 41						
London Road (Guildford)	d						20 16							20 28			20 46						
Guildford	a						20 23							20 35			20 53						

For general notes see front of timetable
For details of catering facilities see Directory of Train Operators

A To London Waterloo (Table 149)
B To Basingstoke (Table 155)
C To Alton (Table 155)
D To Woking (Table 155)

Table 152

Saturdays

from 4 October

For details of Bank Holiday service alterations, please see first page of Table 149

London → Chessington South, Dorking, Guildford Shepperton and Hampton Court

Network Diagram - see first page of Table 152

		SW	SW 1 A	SW	SW	SW	SW	SW 1 B		SW C	SW	SW D	SW	SW 1 E	SW	SW	SW	SW	SW 1 B	SW C	SW		SW D	SW	SW	SW 1 A
London Waterloo 15 ⊖	d	20 03	20 12	20 06	20 09	20 12	20 16	20 23		20 20	20 24	20 27	20 33	20 42	20 36	20 39	20 42	20 46	20 53	20 50	20 54		20 57	21 03	21 09	21 12
Vauxhall ⊖	d	20 07		20 10	20 13	20 16	20 20			20 24	20 28	20 31	20 37		20 40	20 43	20 46	20 50		20 54	20 58		21 01	21 07	21 13	
Clapham Junction 10	d	20 12	20u19	20 15	20 18	20 21	20 25			20 29	20 33	20 36	20 42		20 45	20 48	20 51	20 55	21u00	20 59	21 03		21 06	21 12	21 18	21u19
Earlsfield	d	20 15		20 18	20 21	20 24	20 28			20 32	20 36	20 39	20 45		20 48	20 51	20 54	20 58		21 02	21 06		21 09	21 15	21 21	
Wimbledon 6 ⊖ 🚋	d	20 19		20 22	20 25	20 28	20 32			20 36	20 40	20 43	20 49		20 52	20 55	20 58	21 02		21 06	21 10		21 13	21 19	21 25	
Raynes Park 6	d			20 25	20 28	20 31	20 35				20 43	20 46			20 55	20 58	21 01	21 05			21 13		21 16		21 28	
Motspur Park	d				20 31		20 38				20 46					21 01		21 08			21 16				21 31	
Malden Manor	d						20 41											21 11								
Tolworth	d						20 44											21 14								
Chessington North	d						20 47											21 17								
Chessington South	a						20 49											21 19								
Worcester Park	d				20 33						20 48					21 03					21 18				21 33	
Stoneleigh	d				20 36						20 51					21 06					21 21				21 36	
Ewell West	d				20 39						20 54					21 09					21 24				21 39	
Epsom 3	a				20 42						20 57					21 12					21 27				21 42	
	d				20 47											21 17									21 47	
Ashtead	d				20 51											21 21									21 51	
Leatherhead	d				20 54											21 24									21 54	
Boxhill & Westhumble	d																									
Dorking 4	a				21 02																				22 02	
New Malden 6	d			20 28		20 34						20 49			20 58		21 04						21 19			
Norbiton	d					20 37						20 52					21 07						21 22			
Kingston	a					20 40						20 55					21 10						21 25			
	d					20 40						20 59					21 10						21 29			
Hampton Wick	d					20 42						21 01					21 12						21 31			
Teddington	d					20 45						21 05					21 15						21 35			
Strawberry Hill	a											21 08											21 38			
Fulwell	d					20 49											21 19									
Hampton	d					20 53											21 23									
Kempton Park	d					20 56											21 26									
Sunbury	d					20 58											21 28									
Upper Halliford	d					21 00											21 30									
Shepperton	a					21 05											21 35									
Berrylands	d			20 30											21 00											
Surbiton 6	d	20 27	20 30	20 35				20 41		20 44			20 57	21 00	21 05				21 11	21 14				21 27		21 30
Thames Ditton	d			20 39											21 09											
Hampton Court	a			20 42											21 12											
Hinchley Wood	d	20 31											21 01											21 31		
Claygate	d	20 34											21 04											21 34		
Oxshott	d	20 37											21 07											21 37		
Cobham & Stoke d'Abernon	d	20 41											21 11											21 41		
Bookham	d															21 29										
Effingham Junction 6	d	20 45											21 15			21 33								21 45		
Horsley	d	20 48											21 18			21 36								21 48		
Clandon	d	20 53											21 23			21 41								21 53		
London Road (Guildford)	d	20 58											21 28			21 46								21 58		
Guildford	a	21 05											21 35			21 53								22 05		

For general notes see front of timetable
For details of catering facilities see Directory of Train Operators

A To Basingstoke (Table 155)
B To Alton (Table 155)
C To Woking (Table 155)
D To London Waterloo (Table 149)
E To Portsmouth Harbour (Table 158)

Table 152

Saturdays

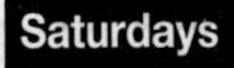

from 4 October

For details of Bank Holiday service alterations, please see first page of Table 149

London → Chessington South, Dorking, Guildford Shepperton and Hampton Court

Network Diagram - see first page of Table 152

Station		SW	SW 1 A	SW B	SW	SW C	SW	SW 1 D	SW	SW	SW	SW	SW 1 A	SW	SW	SW C	SW	SW	SW 1 E	SW	SW 1 A	SW B	SW C	SW
London Waterloo 15 ⊖	d	21 12	21 23	21 20	21 24	21 27	21 33	21 42	21 36	21 39	21 42	21 46	21 53	21 50	21 54	21 57	22 03	22 09	22 12	22 12	22 23	22 20	22 27	22 33
Vauxhall ⊖	d	21 16		21 24	21 28	21 31	21 37		21 40	21 43	21 46	21 50		21 54	21 58	22 01	22 07	22 13		22 16		22 24	22 31	22 37
Clapham Junction 10	d	21 21		21 29	21 33	21 36	21 42		21 45	21 48	21 51	21 55	22u00	21 59	22 03	22 06	22 12	22 18	22u19	22 21	22u30	22 29	22 36	22 42
Earlsfield	d	21 24		21 32	21 36	21 39	21 45		21 48	21 51	21 54	21 58		22 02	22 06	22 09	22 15	22 21		22 24		22 32	22 39	22 45
Wimbledon 6 ⊖	d	21 28		21 36	21 40	21 43	21 49		21 52	21 55	21 58	22 02		22 06	22 10	22 13	22 19	22 25		22 28		22 36	22 43	22 49
Raynes Park 6	d	21 31			21 43	21 46			21 55	21 58	22 01	22 05			22 13	22 16		22 28		22 31			22 46	
Motspur Park	d				21 46					22 01		22 08			22 16			22 31						
Malden Manor	d											22 11												
Tolworth	d											22 14												
Chessington North	d											22 17												
Chessington South	a											22 19												
Worcester Park	d				21 48					22 03					22 18			22 33						
Stoneleigh	d				21 51					22 06					22 21			22 36						
Ewell West	d				21 54					22 09					22 24			22 39						
Epsom 3	a				21 57					22 12					22 27			22 42						
	d									22 17								22 47						
Ashtead	d									22 21								22 51						
Leatherhead	d									22 24								22 54						
Boxhill & Westhumble	d																							
Dorking 4	a																	23 02						
New Malden 6	d	21 34				21 49			21 58		22 04					22 19				22 34			22 49	
Norbiton	d	21 37				21 52					22 07					22 22				22 37			22 52	
Kingston	a	21 40				21 55					22 10					22 25				22 40			22 55	
	d	21 40				21 59					22 10					22 29				22 40			22 59	
Hampton Wick	d	21 42				22 01					22 12					22 31				22 42			23 01	
Teddington	d	21 45				22 05					22 15					22 35				22 45			23 05	
Strawberry Hill	a					22 08										22 38							23 08	
Fulwell	d	21 49									22 19									22 49				
Hampton	d	21 53									22 23									22 53				
Kempton Park	d	21 56									22 26									22 56				
Sunbury	d	21 58									22 28									22 58				
Upper Halliford	d	22 00									22 30									23 00				
Shepperton	a	22 05									22 35									23 05				
Berrylands	d								22 00															
Surbiton 6	d		21 41	21 44			21 57	22 00	22 05				22 11	22 14			22 27		22 30		22 41	22 44		22 57
Thames Ditton	d								22 09															
Hampton Court	a								22 12															
Hinchley Wood	d						22 01										22 31							23 01
Claygate	d						22 04										22 34							23 04
Oxshott	d						22 07										22 37							23 07
Cobham & Stoke d'Abernon	d						22 11										22 41							23 11
Bookham	d									22 29														
Effingham Junction 6	d						22 15			22 33							22 45							23 15
Horsley	d						22 18			22 36							22 48							23 18
Clandon	d						22 23			22 41							22 53							23 23
London Road (Guildford)	d						22 28			22 46							22 58							23 28
Guildford	a						22 35			22 53				22 47			23 05							23 35

For general notes see front of timetable
For details of catering facilities see Directory of Train Operators

A To Alton (Table 155)
B To Woking (Table 155)
C To London Waterloo (Table 149)
D To Portsmouth Harbour (Table 158)
E To Basingstoke (Table 155)

Table 152

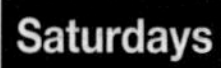

Saturdays

from 4 October

For details of Bank Holiday service alterations, please see first page of Table 149

London → Chessington South, Dorking, Guildford Shepperton and Hampton Court

Network Diagram - see first page of Table 152

		SW 1 A	SW	SW	SW	SW 1 B	SW C	SW D	SW	SW	SW	SW 1 A	SW	SW 1 B	SW C	SW E	SW	SW	SW 1 A	SW	SW	SW
London Waterloo 15 ⊖	d	22 42	22 36	22 39	22 42	22 53	22 50	22 57	23 00	23 03	23 09	23 12	23 12	23 23	23 20	23 27	23 30	23 42	23 48	23 50	23 57	
Vauxhall ⊖	d		22 40	22 43	22 46		22 54	23 01	23 04	23 07	23 13		23 16		23 24	23 31	23 34	23 46		23 54	00 01	
Clapham Junction 10	d	22u49	22 45	22 48	22 51	23u00	22 59	23 06	23 09	23 12	23 18	23u19	23 21	23u30	23 29	23 36	23 39	23 51	23u56	23 59	00 06	
Earlsfield	d		22 48	22 51	22 54		23 02	23 09	23 12	23 15	23 21		23 24		23 32	23 39	23 42	23 54		00 02	00 09	
Wimbledon 6 ⊖ 🚊	d		22 52	22 55	22 58		23 06	23 13	23 16	23 19	23 25		23 28		23 36	23 43	23 46	23 58		00 06	00 13	
Raynes Park 6	d		22 55	22 58	23 01			23 16	23 19		23 28		23 31			23 46	23 49	00 01			00 16	
Motspur Park	d			23 01					23 22		23 31							00 04				
Malden Manor	d								23 25													
Tolworth	d								23 28													
Chessington North	d								23 31													
Chessington South	a								23 33													
Worcester Park	d			23 03							23 33							00 06				
Stoneleigh	d			23 06							23 36							00 09				←
Ewell West	d			23 09							23 39							00 12 →				00 12
Epsom 3	a			23 12							23 42											00 15
	d			23 17							23 47											00 19
Ashtead	d			23 21							23 51											00 23
Leatherhead	d			23 24							23 54											00 26
Boxhill & Westhumble	d																					
Dorking 4	a										00 03											
New Malden 6	d		22 58		23 04			23 19					23 34			23 49	23 52				00 19	
Norbiton	d				23 07			23 22					23 37			23 52					00 22	
Kingston	a				23 10			23 25					23 40			23 55					00 25	
	d				23 10			23 29					23 40			23 55					00 25	
Hampton Wick	d				23 12			23 31					23 42			23 57					00 27	
Teddington	d				23 15			23 35					23 45			23 59					00 30	
Strawberry Hill	a							23 38								00 03						
Fulwell	d				23 19								23 49								00 34	
Hampton	d				23 23								23 53								00 38	
Kempton Park	d				23 26								23 56								00 41	
Sunbury	d				23 28								23 58								00 43	
Upper Halliford	d				23 30								23 59								00 45	
Shepperton	a				23 35								00 05								00 50	
Berrylands	d		23 00														23 54					
Surbiton 6	d	23 00	23 05			23 11	23 14			23 27		23 30		23 41	23 44		23 59		00 10	00 14		
Thames Ditton	d		23 09														00 03					
Hampton Court	a		23 12														00 06					
Hinchley Wood	d									23 31										00 18		
Claygate	d									23 34										00 21		
Oxshott	d									23 37										00 24		
Cobham & Stoke d'Abernon	d									23 41										00 28		
Bookham	d			23 29																		00 31
Effingham Junction 6	d			23 33						23 45										00 32		00 36
Horsley	d			23 36						23 48										00 35		00 39
Clandon	d			23 41						23 53										00 40		00 44
London Road (Guildford)	d			23 46						23 58										00 45		00 49
Guildford	a			23 54						00 05										00 52		00 56

For general notes see front of timetable
For details of catering facilities see Directory of Train Operators

A To Basingstoke (Table 155)
B To Alton (Table 155)
C To Woking (Table 155)
D To London Waterloo (Table 149)
E To Twickenham (Table 149)

Table 152

Sundays

until 21 September

For details of Bank Holiday service alterations, please see first page of Table 149

London → Chessington South, Dorking, Guildford Shepperton and Hampton Court

Network Diagram - see first page of Table 152

		SW	SW	SW	SW	SW	SW	SW	SW	SW	SW	SW	SW	SW	SW	SW	SW	SW	SW	SW	SW	SW	SW	SW	SW	SW
				1								1														
				A								B	C	D						D						
London Waterloo 15 ⊖	d	23p30	23p42	23p48	23p50	23p57		00 09	00 15	00 27	00 42	01 05	01 42	06 18		06 57			07 10	07 18		07 27		07 40	07 48	
Vauxhall ⊖	d	23p34	23p46		23p54	00 01		00 13	00 19	00 31	00 46	01 09	01 46	06 22		07 01			07 14	07 22		07 31		07 44	07 52	
Clapham Junction 10	d	23p39	23p51	23b56	23p59	00 06		00 18	00 24	00 36	00 51	01 14	01 51	06 27		07 06			07 19	07 27		07 36		07 49	07 57	
Earlsfield	d	23p42	23p54		00 02	00 09		00 21	00 27	00s39						07 09			07 22	07 30		07 39		07 52	08 00	
Wimbledon 6 ⊖	d	23p46	23p58		00 06	00 13		00 25	00 31	00 43	01 05	01 20	02c04	06 34	06 48	07 13	07 16	07 18	07 26	07 34	07 37	07 43	07 48	07 56	08 04	08 07
Raynes Park 6	d	23p49	00 01			00 16			00 34	00 46	01 08		02 07	06 37	06 52	07 16		07 22		07 37	07 40	07 46	07 52		08 07	08 10
Motspur Park	d		00 04						00 37						06 55			07 25			07 43		07 55			08 13
Malden Manor	d																				07 46					08 16
Tolworth	d																				07 49					08 19
Chessington North	d																				07 52					08 22
Chessington South	a																				07 54					08 24
Worcester Park	d		00 06						00 39						06 57			07 27					07 57			
Stoneleigh	d		00 09				←		00 42						07 00			07 30					08 00			
Ewell West	d		00 12				00 12		00 45						07 03			07 33					08 03			
Epsom 3	a		→				00 15		00 48						07 06			07 36					08 06			
	d						00 19																08 08			
Ashtead	d						00 23																08 12			
Leatherhead	d						00 26																08 15			
Boxhill & Westhumble	d																									
Dorking 4	a																									
New Malden 6	d	23p52				00 19				00 49	01 11		02 09	06 40		07 19				07 40		07 49			08 10	
Norbiton	d					00 22					01 14		02 13	06 43						07 43					08 13	
Kingston	a					00 25					01 17		02 15	06 46						07 46					08 16	
	d					00 25					01 17		02 16	06 49						07 49					08 16	
Hampton Wick	d					00 27					01s22		02s21	06 51						07 51					08 18	
Teddington	d					00 30					01s25		02s23	06 56						07 56					08 21	
Strawberry Hill	a										01 28		02s26	06 59						07 59						
Fulwell	d					00 34																			08 25	
Hampton	d					00 38																			08 29	
Kempton Park	d					00 41																			08 32	
Sunbury	d					00 43																			08 34	
Upper Halliford	d					00 45																			08 36	
Shepperton	a					00 48																			08 39	
Berrylands	d	23p54								00s51						07 21						07 51				
Surbiton 6	d	23p59		00 10	00 14			00 33		00a55		01 29				07 25	07e32		07 35			07 55		08 05		
Thames Ditton	d	00 03														07 30						08 00				
Hampton Court	a	00 06														07 33						08 03				
Hinchley Wood	d				00 18												07 36									
Claygate	d				00 21												07 39									
Oxshott	d				00 24												07 42									
Cobham & Stoke d'Abernon	d				00 28												07 46									
Bookham	d						00 31																08 20			
Effingham Junction 6	d				00 32		00 36										07 50						08 24			
Horsley	d				00 35		00 39										07 53						08 27			
Clandon	d				00 40		00 44										07 58						08 32			
London Road (Guildford)	d				00 45		00 49										08 03						08 37			
Guildford	a				00 49		00 53	01 06									08 07		08 13				08 41	08 40		

For general notes see front of timetable
For details of catering facilities see Directory of Train Operators

A To Basingstoke (Table 155)
B To Southampton Central (Table 158)
C To Twickenham (Table 149)
D To London Waterloo (Table 149)

b Previous night.
Stops to pick up only
c Arr. 0156
e Arr. 0728

Table 152

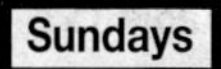

Sundays

until 21 September

For details of Bank Holiday service alterations, please see first page of Table 149

London → Chessington South, Dorking, Guildford Shepperton and Hampton Court

Network Diagram - see first page of Table 152

		SW			SW	SW	SW	SW	SW	SW	SW	SW	SW	SW	SW	SW	SW	SW		SW	SW	SW	SW	SW	SW
							1															1			
							A			B	C											A			C
London Waterloo 15	⊖ d	07 57				08 02	08 07		08 10	08 14	08 18	08 21	08 27	08 32	08 40	08 48	08 51	08 57	and at the same minutes past each hour until		12 02	12 07		12 10	12 18
Vauxhall	⊖ d	08 01				08 06			08 14	08 18	08 22	08 25	08 31	08 36	08 44	08 52	08 55	09 01			12 06			12 14	12 22
Clapham Junction 10	d	08 06				08 11	08 15		08 19	08 24	08 27	08 30	08 36	08 41	08 49	08 57	09 00	09 06			12 11	12 15		12 19	12 27
Earlsfield	d	08 09				08 14			08 22	09a20	08 30	08 33	08 39	08 44	08 52	09 00	09 03	09 09			12 14			12 22	12 30
Wimbledon 6	⊖ d	08 13			08 16	08 18	08 22		08 26		08 34	08 37	08 43	08 48	08 56	09 04	09 07	09 13		12 16	12 18	12 22		12 26	12 34
Raynes Park 6	d	08 16				08 22					08 37	08 40	08 46	08 52		09 07	09 10	09 16			12 22				12 37
Motspur Park	d					08 25						08 43		08 55			09 13				12 25				
Malden Manor	d											08 46					09 16								
Tolworth	d											08 49					09 19								
Chessington North	d											08 52					09 22								
Chessington South	a											08 54					09 24								
Worcester Park	d					08 27								08 57							12 27				
Stoneleigh	d					08 30								09 00							12 30				
Ewell West	d					08 33								09 03							12 33				
Epsom 3	a					08 36								09 06							12 36				
	d					08 38								09 08							12 38				
Ashtead	d					08 42								09 12							12 42				
Leatherhead	d					08 45								09 15							12 45				
Boxhill & Westhumble	d																								
Dorking 4	a					08 51															12 51				
New Malden 6	d	08 19									08 40		08 49			09 10		09 19							12 40
Norbiton	d										08 43					09 13									12 43
Kingston	a										08 46					09 16									12 46
	d										08 49					09 16									12 49
Hampton Wick	d										08 51					09 18									12 51
Teddington	d										08 56					09 21									12 56
Strawberry Hill	a									08 48	08 59														12 59
Fulwell	d															09 25									
Hampton	d															09 29									
Kempton Park	d															09 32									
Sunbury	d															09 34									
Upper Halliford	d															09 36									
Shepperton	a															09 39									
Berrylands	d	08 21						←					08 51					09 21					←		
Surbiton 6	d	08 25			08b32		08 30	08 32	08 35				08 55		09 05			09 25		12 32		12 30	12 32	12 35	
Thames Ditton	d	08 30			↪								09 00					09 30		↪					
Hampton Court	a	08 33											09 03					09 33							
Hinchley Wood	d							08 36															12 36		
Claygate	d							08 39															12 39		
Oxshott	d							08 42															12 42		
Cobham & Stoke d'Abernon	d							08 46															12 46		
Bookham	d													09 20											
Effingham Junction 6	d							08 50						09 24									12 50		
Horsley	d							08 53						09 27									12 53		
Clandon	d							08 58						09 32									12 58		
London Road (Guildford)	d							09 03						09 37									13 03		
Guildford	a							09 07	09 10					09 41	09 40								13 07	13 13	

For general notes see front of timetable
For details of catering facilities see Directory of Train Operators

A To Alton (Table 155) and to Basingstoke (Table 155)
B To London Waterloo
C To London Waterloo (Table 149)
b Arr. 0828

Table 152

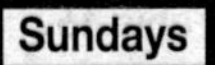

Sundays

until 21 September

For details of Bank Holiday service alterations, please see first page of Table 149

London → Chessington South, Dorking, Guildford Shepperton and Hampton Court

Network Diagram - see first page of Table 152

		SW	SW	SW	SW	SW	SW		SW	SW	SW	SW	SW	SW	SW	SW	SW	SW	SW	SW	SW	SW	SW	SW	SW	SW
						A							1 B			A					A					
London Waterloo 15 ⊖	d	12 21	12 27	12 32	12 40		12 48		12 51	12 57	13 00	13 02	13 07		13 10	13 18	13 21	13 27	13 32	13 40		13 48	13 51	13 57	14 00	14 02
Vauxhall ⊖	d	12 25	12 31	12 36	12 44		12 52		12 55	13 01	13 04	13 06			13 14	13 22	13 25	13 31	13 36	13 44		13 52	13 55	14 01	14 04	14 06
Clapham Junction 10	d	12 30	12 36	12 41	12 49		12 57		13 00	13 06	13 09	13 11	13 15		13 19	13 27	13 30	13 36	13 41	13 49		13 57	14 00	14 06	14 09	14 11
Earlsfield	d	12 33	12 39	12 44	12 52		13 00		13 03	13 09	13 12	13 14			13 22	13 30	13 33	13 39	13 44	13 52		14 00	14 03	14 09	14 12	14 14
Wimbledon 6 ⊖ 🚋	d	12 37	12 43	12 48	12 56		13 04		13 07	13 13	13 16	13 18	13 22		13 26	13 34	13 37	13 43	13 48	13 56		14 04	14 07	14 13	14 16	14 18
Raynes Park 6	d	12 40	12 46	12 52			13 07		13 10	13 16		13 22				13 37	13 40	13 46	13 52			14 07	14 10	14 16		14 22
Motspur Park	d	12 43		12 55					13 13			13 25					13 43		13 55				14 13			14 25
Malden Manor	d	12 46							13 16								13 46						14 16			
Tolworth	d	12 49							13 19								13 49						14 19			
Chessington North	d	12 52							13 22								13 52						14 22			
Chessington South	a	12 54							13 24								13 54						14 24			
Worcester Park	d			12 57								13 27							13 57							14 27
Stoneleigh	d			13 00								13 30							14 00							14 30
Ewell West	d			13 03								13 33							14 03							14 33
Epsom 3	a			13 06								13 36							14 06							14 36
	d			13 08								13 38							14 08							14 38
Ashtead	d			13 12								13 42							14 12							14 42
Leatherhead	d			13 15								13 45							14 15							14 45
Boxhill & Westhumble	d																									
Dorking 4	a											13 51														14 51
New Malden 6	d		12 49				13 10			13 19						13 40		13 49				14 10		14 19		
Norbiton	d						13 13									13 43						14 13				
Kingston	a						13 16									13 46						14 16				
	d					13 11	13 16									13 49					14 11	14 16				
Hampton Wick	d					13 13	13 18									13 51					14 13	14 18				
Teddington	d					13 16	13 21									13 56					14 16	14 21				
Strawberry Hill	a					13 19										13 59					14 19					
Fulwell	d						13 25															14 25				
Hampton	d						13 29															14 29				
Kempton Park	d						13 32															14 32				
Sunbury	d						13 34															14 34				
Upper Halliford	d						13 36															14 36				
Shepperton	a						13 39															14 39				
Berrylands	d		12 51							13 21								13 51						14 21		
Surbiton 6	d		12 55		13 05					13 25	13b32		13 30	← 13 32	13 35			13 55		14 05				14 25	14c32	
Thames Ditton	d		13 00							13 30	→							14 00						14 30	→	
Hampton Court	a		13 03							13 33								14 03						14 33		
Hinchley Wood	d													13 36												
Claygate	d													13 39												
Oxshott	d													13 42												
Cobham & Stoke d'Abernon	d													13 46												
Bookham	d			13 20															14 20							
Effingham Junction 6	d			13 24										13 50					14 24							
Horsley	d			13 27										13 53					14 27							
Clandon	d			13 32										13 58					14 32							
London Road (Guildford)	d			13 37										14 03					14 37							
Guildford	a			13 41	13 43									14 07	14 13				14 41	14 43						

For general notes see front of timetable
For details of catering facilities see Directory of Train Operators

A To London Waterloo (Table 149)
B To Alton (Table 155) and to Basingstoke (Table 155)
b Arr. 1328
c Arr. 1428

Table 152

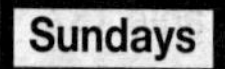

until 21 September

For details of Bank Holiday service alterations, please see first page of Table 149

London → Chessington South, Dorking, Guildford Shepperton and Hampton Court

Network Diagram - see first page of Table 152

		SW	SW	SW	SW	SW	SW	SW	SW		SW	SW	SW	SW		SW	SW	SW	SW	SW	SW	SW	SW	SW	SW	SW
		[1]																[1]							[1]	
		A			B						B							A			B				A	
London Waterloo [15] ⊖	d	14 07		14 10	14 18	14 21	14 27	14 32	14 40			14 48	14 51	14 57		15 00	15 02	15 07		15 10	15 18	15 21	15 27	15 32	15 37	15 40
Vauxhall ⊖	d			14 14	14 22	14 25	14 31	14 36	14 44			14 52	14 55	15 01		15 04	15 06			15 14	15 22	15 25	15 31	15 36		15 44
Clapham Junction [10]	d	14 15		14 19	14 27	14 30	14 36	14 41	14 49			14 57	15 00	15 06		15 09	15 11	15 15		15 19	15 27	15 30	15 36	15 41	15 46	15 49
Earlsfield	d			14 22	14 30	14 33	14 39	14 44	14 52			15 00	15 03	15 09		15 12	15 14			15 22	15 30	15 33	15 39	15 44		15 52
Wimbledon [6] ⊖ 🚊	d	14 22		14 26	14 34	14 37	14 43	14 48	14 56			15 04	15 07	15 13		15 16	15 18	15 22		15 26	15 34	15 37	15 43	15 48	15 53	15 56
Raynes Park [6]	d				14 37	14 40	14 46	14 52				15 07	15 10	15 16			15 22				15 37	15 40	15 46	15 52		
Motspur Park	d					14 43		14 55					15 13				15 25					15 43		15 55		
Malden Manor	d					14 46							15 16									15 46				
Tolworth	d					14 49							15 19									15 49				
Chessington North	d					14 52							15 22									15 52				
Chessington South	a					14 54							15 24									15 54				
Worcester Park	d							14 57									15 27							15 57		
Stoneleigh	d							15 00									15 30							16 00		
Ewell West	d							15 03									15 33							16 03		
Epsom [3]	a							15 06									15 36							16 06		
	d							15 08									15 38							16 08		
Ashtead	d							15 12									15 42							16 12		
Leatherhead	d							15 15									15 45							16 15		
Boxhill & Westhumble	d																									
Dorking [4]	a																15 51									
New Malden [6]	d				14 40		14 49					15 10		15 19							15 40		15 49			
Norbiton	d				14 43							15 13									15 43					
Kingston	a				14 46							15 16									15 46					
	d				14 49						15 11	15 16									15 49					
Hampton Wick	d				14 51						15 13	15 18									15 51					
Teddington	d				14 56						15 16	15 21									15 56					
Strawberry Hill	a				14 59						15 19										15 59					
Fulwell	d											15 25														
Hampton	d											15 29														
Kempton Park	d											15 32														
Sunbury	d											15 34														
Upper Halliford	d											15 36														
Shepperton	a											15 39														
Berrylands	d		←				14 51							15 21					←				15 51			
Surbiton [6]	d	14 30	14 32	14 35			14 55		15 05					15 25		15b32		15 30	15 32	15 35			15 55		16 02	16 05
Thames Ditton	d						15 00							15 30		→							16 00			
Hampton Court	a						15 03							15 33									16 03			
Hinchley Wood	d		14 36																15 36							
Claygate	d		14 39																15 39							
Oxshott	d		14 42																15 42							
Cobham & Stoke d'Abernon	d		14 46																15 46							
Bookham	d							15 20																16 20		
Effingham Junction [6]	d		14 50					15 24											15 50					16 24		
Horsley	d		14 53					15 27											15 53					16 27		
Clandon	d		14 58					15 32											15 58					16 32		
London Road (Guildford)	d		15 03					15 37											16 03					16 37		
Guildford	a		15 07	15 13				15 41	15 43										16 07	16 13				16 41		16 43

For general notes see front of timetable
For details of catering facilities see Directory of Train Operators

A To Alton (Table 155) and to Basingstoke (Table 155)
B To London Waterloo (Table 149)
b Arr. 1528

Table 152

Sundays

until 21 September

For details of Bank Holiday service alterations, please see first page of Table 149

London → Chessington South, Dorking, Guildford Shepperton and Hampton Court

Network Diagram - see first page of Table 152

		SW	SW	SW	SW		SW	SW	SW 1	SW	SW	SW	SW		SW	SW	SW 1	SW	SW	SW	SW	SW	SW	SW	SW 1
		A							B			A					B		A						B
London Waterloo 15 ⊖	d		15 48	15 51	15 57	and at the same minutes past each hour until	19 00	19 02	19 07		19 10	19 18	19 21		19 27	19 32	19 37	19 40		19 48	19 56	19 57	20 00	20 02	20 07
Vauxhall ⊖	d		15 52	15 55	16 01		19 04	19 06			19 14	19 22	19 25		19 31	19 36		19 44		19 52	20 00	20 01	20 04	20 06	
Clapham Junction 10	d		15 57	16 00	16 06		19 09	19 11	19 15		19 19	19 27	19 30		19 36	19 41	19 46	19 49		19 57	20 06	20 06	20 09	20 11	20 15
Earlsfield	d		16 00	16 03	16 09		19 12	19 14			19 22	19 30	19 33		19 39	19 44		19 52		20 00		20 09	20 12	20 14	
Wimbledon 6 ⊖	d		16 04	16 07	16 13		19 16	19 18	19 22		19 26	19 34	19 37		19 43	19 48	19 53	19 56		20 04		20 13	20 16	20 18	20 22
Raynes Park 6	d		16 07	16 10	16 16			19 22				19 37	19 40		19 46	19 52				20 07		20 16		20 22	
Motspur Park	d			16 13				19 25					19 43			19 55								20 25	
Malden Manor	d			16 16									19 46												
Tolworth	d			16 19									19 49												
Chessington North	d			16 22									19 52												
Chessington South	a			16 24									19 54												
Worcester Park	d							19 27								19 57								20 27	
Stoneleigh	d							19 30								20 00								20 30	
Ewell West	d							19 33								20 03								20 33	
Epsom 3	a							19 36								20 06								20 36	
	d							19 38								20 08								20 38	
Ashtead	d							19 42								20 12								20 42	
Leatherhead	d							19 45								20 15								20 45	
Boxhill & Westhumble	d																								
Dorking 4	a							19 51																20 51	
New Malden 6	d		16 10		16 19							19 40			19 49					20 10		20 19			
Norbiton	d		16 13									19 43								20 13					
Kingston	a		16 16									19 46								20 16	20 38				
	d	16 11	16 16									19 49							20 11	20 16					
Hampton Wick	d	16 13	16 18									19 51							20 13	20 18					
Teddington	d	16 16	16 21									19 56							20 16	20 21					
Strawberry Hill	a	16 19										19 59							20 19		20 30				
Fulwell	d		16 25																	20 25					
Hampton	d		16 29																	20 29					
Kempton Park	d		16 32																	20 32					
Sunbury	d		16 34																	20 34					
Upper Halliford	d		16 36																	20 36					
Shepperton	a		16 39																	20 39					
Berrylands	d				16 21					←					19 51							20 21			
Surbiton 6	d				16 25		19b32		19 30	19 32	19 35				19 55		20 02	20 05				20 25	20c32		20 30
Thames Ditton	d				16 30		→								20 00							20 30	→		
Hampton Court	a				16 33										20 03							20 33			
Hinchley Wood	d									19 36															
Claygate	d									19 39															
Oxshott	d									19 42															
Cobham & Stoke d'Abernon	d									19 46															
Bookham	d															20 20									
Effingham Junction 6	d									19 50						20 24									
Horsley	d									19 53						20 27									
Clandon	d									19 58						20 32									
London Road (Guildford)	d									20 03						20 37									
Guildford	a									20 07	20 13					20 41		20 43							

For general notes see front of timetable
For details of catering facilities see Directory of Train Operators

A To London Waterloo (Table 149)
B To Alton (Table 155) and to Basingstoke (Table 155)
b Arr. 1928
c Arr. 2028

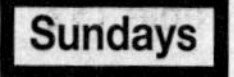

until 21 September

For details of Bank Holiday service alterations, please see first page of Table 149

London → Chessington South, Dorking, Guildford Shepperton and Hampton Court

Network Diagram - see first page of Table 152

		SW	SW	SW	SW	SW	SW	SW	SW	SW	SW	SW	SW	SW	SW	SW		SW	SW	SW	SW	SW	SW	SW	SW	SW
								1							1							1				
				A				B		A					B				A			B		A		
London Waterloo 15 ⊖	d		20 10	20 18	20 21	20 27	20 32	20 37	20 40		20 48	20 57	21 00	21 02	21 07			21 10	21 18	21 21	21 32	21 37	21 40		21 48	21 56
Vauxhall ⊖	d		20 14	20 22	20 25	20 31	20 36		20 44		20 52	21 01	21 04	21 06				21 14	21 22	21 25	21 36		21 44		21 52	22 00
Clapham Junction 10	d		20 19	20 27	20 30	20 36	20 41	20 46	20 49		20 57	21 06	21 09	21 11	21 15			21 19	21 27	21 30	21 41	21 46	21 49		21 57	22 06
Earlsfield	d		20 22	20 30	20 33	20 39	20 44		20 52		21 00	21 09	21 12	21 14				21 22	21 30	21 33	21 44		21 52		22 00	
Wimbledon 6 ⊖	d		20 26	20 34	20 37	20 43	20 48	20 53	20 56		21 04	21 13	21 16	21 18	21 22			21 26	21 34	21 37	21 48	21 53	21 56		22 04	
Raynes Park 6	d			20 37	20 40	20 46	20 52				21 07	21 16		21 22					21 37	21 40	21 52				22 07	
Motspur Park	d				20 43		20 55							21 25						21 43	21 55					
Malden Manor	d				20 46															21 46						
Tolworth	d				20 49															21 49						
Chessington North	d				20 52															21 52						
Chessington South	a				20 54															21 54						
Worcester Park	d						20 57							21 27							21 57					
Stoneleigh	d						21 00							21 30							22 00					
Ewell West	d						21 03							21 33							22 03					
Epsom 3	a						21 06							21 36							22 06					
	d						21 08							21 38							22 08					
Ashtead	d						21 12							21 42							22 12					
Leatherhead	d						21 15							21 45							22 15					
Boxhill & Westhumble	d																									
Dorking 4	a													21 51												
New Malden 6	d			20 40		20 49					21 10	21 19							21 40						22 10	
Norbiton	d			20 43							21 13								21 43						22 13	
Kingston	a			20 46							21 16								21 46						22 16	22 38
	d			20 49						21 11	21 16								21 49					22 11	22 16	
Hampton Wick	d			20 51						21 13	21 18								21 51					22 13	22 18	
Teddington	d			20 56						21 16	21 21								21 56					22 16	22 21	
Strawberry Hill	a			20 59						21 19									21 59					22 19		22 30
Fulwell	d										21 25														22 25	
Hampton	d										21 29														22 29	
Kempton Park	d										21 32														22 32	
Sunbury	d										21 34														22 34	
Upper Halliford	d										21 36														22 36	
Shepperton	a										21 39														22 39	
Berrylands	d	⟵				20 51						21 21				⟵										
Surbiton 6	d	20 32	20 35			20 55		21 02	21 05			21 25	21b32		21 30	21 32		21 35				22 02	22 05			
Thames Ditton	d					21 00						21 30	⟶													
Hampton Court	a					21 03						21 33														
Hinchley Wood	d	20 36														21 36										
Claygate	d	20 39														21 39										
Oxshott	d	20 42														21 42										
Cobham & Stoke d'Abernon	d	20 46														21 46										
Bookham	d						21 20														22 20					
Effingham Junction 6	d	20 50					21 24									21 50					22 24					
Horsley	d	20 53					21 27									21 53					22 27					
Clandon	d	20 58					21 32									21 58					22 32					
London Road (Guildford)	d	21 03					21 37									22 03					22 37					
Guildford	a	21 07	21 13				21 41		21 43							22 07		22 13			22 41		22 43			

For general notes see front of timetable
For details of catering facilities see Directory of Train Operators

A To London Waterloo (Table 149)
B To Alton (Table 155) and to Basingstoke (Table 155)
b Arr. 2128

Table 152

Sundays

until 21 September

For details of Bank Holiday service alterations, please see first page of Table 149

London → Chessington South, Dorking, Guildford Shepperton and Hampton Court

Network Diagram - see first page of Table 152

		SW	SW	SW	SW 1 A	SW	SW	SW B	SW	SW	SW 1 A	SW	SW B	SW	SW	SW	SW	SW	SW 1 A	SW	SW	SW	SW	SW 1 C		
London Waterloo 15 ⊖	d	21 57	22 00	22 02	22 07		22 10	22 18	22 21	22 32	22 37	22 40		22 48	22 51	22 57	23 00	23 02	23 07		23 10	23 18	23 32	23 40		
Vauxhall ⊖	d	22 01	22 04	22 06			22 14	22 22	22 25	22 36		22 44		22 52	22 55	23 01	23 04	23 06			23 14	23 22	23 36	23 44		
Clapham Junction 10	d	22 06	22 09	22 11	22 15		22 19	22 27	22 30	22 41	22 46	22 49		22 57	23 00	23 06	23 09	23 11	23 15		23 19	23 27	23 41	23 49		
Earlsfield	d	22 09	22 12	22 14			22 22	22 30	22 33	22 44		22 52		23 00	23 03	23 09	23 12	23 14			23 22	23 30	23 44	23 52		
Wimbledon 6 ⊖	d	22 13	22 16	22 18	22 22		22 26	22 34	22 37	22 48	22 53	22 56		23 04	23 07	23 13	23 16	23 18	23 22		23 26	23 34	23 48	23 56		
Raynes Park 6	d	22 16		22 22				22 37	22 40	22 52				23 07	23 10	23 16		23 22				23 37	23 52			
Motspur Park	d			22 25					22 43	22 55					23 13			23 25					23 55			
Malden Manor	d								22 46						23 16											
Tolworth	d								22 49						23 19											
Chessington North	d								22 52						23 22											
Chessington South	a								22 54						23 24											
Worcester Park	d			22 27						22 57								23 27					23 57			
Stoneleigh	d			22 30						23 00								23 30					23 59			
Ewell West	d			22 33						23 03								23 33					00 03			
Epsom 3	a			22 36						23 06								23 36					00 06			
	d			22 38						23 08																
Ashtead	d			22 42						23 12																
Leatherhead	d			22 45						23 15																
Boxhill & Westhumble	d																									
Dorking 4	a			22 51																						
New Malden 6	d	22 19						22 40						23 10		23 19						23 40				
Norbiton	d							22 43						23 13								23 43				
Kingston	a							22 46						23 16								23 46				
	d							22 49					23 11	23 16								23 47				
Hampton Wick	d							22 51					23 13	23 18								23 49				
Teddington	d							22 56					23 16	23 21								23 51				
Strawberry Hill	a							22 59					23 19									23 54				
Fulwell	d													23 25												
Hampton	d													23 29												
Kempton Park	d													23 32												
Sunbury	d													23 34												
Upper Halliford	d													23 36												
Shepperton	a													23 39												
Berrylands	d	22 21				←										23 21				←						
Surbiton 6	d	22 25	22b32		22 30	22 32	22 35				23 02	23 05				23 25	23c32		23 30	23 32	23 35			00 05		
Thames Ditton	d	22 30	→													23 30	→									
Hampton Court	a	22 33														23 33										
Hinchley Wood	d					22 36														23 36						
Claygate	d					22 39														23 39						
Oxshott	d					22 42														23 42						
Cobham & Stoke d'Abernon	d					22 46														23 46						
Bookham	d									23 20																
Effingham Junction 6	d					22 50				23 24										23 50						
Horsley	d					22 53				23 27										23 53						
Clandon	d					22 58				23 32										23 58						
London Road (Guildford)	d					23 03				23 37										00 03						
Guildford	a					23 07	23 13			23 41		23 43								00 07	00 13					

For general notes see front of timetable
For details of catering facilities see Directory of Train Operators

A To Alton (Table 155) and to Basingstoke (Table 155)
B To London Waterloo (Table 149)
C To Farnham (Table 155)

b Arr. 2228
c Arr. 2328

Table 152

Sundays

from 28 September

For details of Bank Holiday service alterations, please see first page of Table 149

London → Chessington South, Dorking, Guildford Shepperton and Hampton Court

Network Diagram - see first page of Table 152

	SW	SW	SW	SW	SW	SW	SW	SW	SW	SW	SW	SW	SW	SW	SW	SW	SW	SW	SW	SW	SW	SW	SW	SW	SW
				1											1										
		A	B	C	A	B	A	B	A	B					D	E	G						G		
London Waterloo 15 ⊖ d	23p30	23p42	23p42	23p48	23p50	23p50	23p57	23p57			00 09	00 15	00 27	00 42	01 05	01 42	06 18		06 57			07 10	07 18		07 27
Vauxhall ⊖ d	23p34	23p46	23p46		23p54	23p54	00 01	00 01			00 13	00 19	00 31	00 46	01 09	01 46	06 22		07 01			07 14	07 22		07 31
Clapham Junction 10 d	23p39	23p51	23p51	23b56	23p59	23p59	00 06	00 06			00 18	00 24	00 36	00 51	01 14	01 51	06 27		07 06			07 19	07 27		07 36
Earlsfield d	23p42	23p54	23p54		00 02	00 02	00 09	00 09			00 21	00 27	00s39						07 09			07 22	07 30		07 39
Wimbledon 6 ⊖ d	23p46	23p58	23p58		00 06	00 06	00 13	00 13			00 25	00 31	00 43	01 05	01 20	02c04	06 34	06 48	07 13	07 16	07 18	07 26	07 34	07 37	07 43
Raynes Park 6 d	23p49	00 01	00 01				00 16	00 16				00 34	00 46	01 08		02 07	06 37	06 52	07 16		07 22		07 37	07 40	07 46
Motspur Park d		00 04	00 04									00 37						06 55			07 25			07 43	
Malden Manor d																								07 46	
Tolworth d																								07 49	
Chessington North d																								07 52	
Chessington South a																								07 54	
Worcester Park d		00 06	00 06									00 39						06 57			07 27				
Stoneleigh d		00 09	00 09						←	←		00 42						07 00			07 30				
Ewell West d		00 12	00 12						00 12	00 12		00 45						07 03			07 33				
Epsom 3 a		→	→						00 15	00 15		00 48						07 06			07 36				
d									00 19	00 19															
Ashtead d									00 23	00 23															
Leatherhead d									00 26	00 26															
Boxhill & Westhumble d																									
Dorking 4 a																									
New Malden 6 d	23p52						00 19	00 19					00 49	01 11		02 09	06 40		07 19				07 40		07 49
Norbiton d							00 22	00 22						01 14		02 13	06 43						07 43		
Kingston a							00 25	00 25						01 17		02 15	06 46						07 46		
d							00 25	00 25						01 17		02 16	06 49						07 49		
Hampton Wick d							00 27	00 27						01s22		02s21	06 51						07 51		
Teddington d							00 30	00 30						01s25		02s23	06 56						07 56		
Strawberry Hill a														01 28		02s26	06 59						07 59		
Fulwell d							00 34	00 34																	
Hampton d							00 38	00 38																	
Kempton Park d							00 41	00 41																	
Sunbury d							00 43	00 43																	
Upper Halliford d							00 45	00 45																	
Shepperton a							00 48	00 50																	
Berrylands d	23p54												00s51						07 21						07 51
Surbiton 6 d	23p59			00 10	00 14	00 14					00 33		00a55		01 29				07 25	07e32		07 35			07 55
Thames Ditton d	00 03																		07 30						08 00
Hampton Court a	00 06																		07 33						08 03
Hinchley Wood d					00 18	00 18														07 36					
Claygate d					00 21	00 21														07 39					
Oxshott d					00 24	00 24														07 42					
Cobham & Stoke d'Abernon d					00 28	00 28														07 46					
Bookham d									00 31	00 31															
Effingham Junction 6 d					00 32	00 32			00 36	00 36										07 50					
Horsley d					00 35	00 35			00 39	00 39										07 53					
Clandon d					00 40	00 40			00 44	00 44										07 58					
London Road (Guildford) d					00 45	00 45			00 49	00 49										08 03					
Guildford a					00 49	00 52			00 53	00 56	01 06									08 10		08 13			

For general notes see front of timetable
For details of catering facilities see Directory of Train Operators

A 28 September
B From 5 October
C To Basingstoke (Table 155)
D To Southampton Central (Table 158)
E To Twickenham (Table 149)
G To London Waterloo (Table 149)

b Previous night. Stops to pick up only
c Arr. 0156
e Arr. 0728

from 28 September

For details of Bank Holiday service alterations, please see first page of Table 149

London → Chessington South, Dorking, Guildford Shepperton and Hampton Court

Network Diagram - see first page of Table 152

		SW	SW	SW	SW	SW			SW	SW	SW 1 A	SW	SW	SW B	SW	SW	SW	SW	SW	SW	SW		SW	SW	SW 1 A
London Waterloo 15 ⊖	d		07 40	07 48		07 57				08 02	08 07		08 10	08 18	08 21	08 27	08 32	08 40	08 48	08 51	08 57	and at the same minutes past each hour until		12 02	12 07
Vauxhall ⊖	d		07 44	07 52		08 01				08 06			08 14	08 22	08 25	08 31	08 36	08 44	08 52	08 55	09 01			12 06	
Clapham Junction 10	d		07 49	07 57		08 06				08 11	08 15		08 19	08 27	08 30	08 36	08 41	08 49	08 57	09 00	09 06			12 11	12 15
Earlsfield	d		07 52	08 00		08 09				08 14			08 22	08 30	08 33	08 39	08 44	08 52	09 00	09 03	09 09			12 14	
Wimbledon 6 ⊖ 🚋	d	07 48	07 56	08 04	08 07	08 13			08 16	08 18	08 22		08 26	08 34	08 37	08 43	08 48	08 56	09 04	09 07	09 13		12 16	12 18	12 22
Raynes Park 6	d	07 52		08 07	08 10	08 16				08 22				08 37	08 40	08 46	08 52		09 07	09 10	09 16			12 22	
Motspur Park	d	07 55			08 13					08 25					08 43		08 55			09 13				12 25	
Malden Manor	d				08 16										08 46					09 16					
Tolworth	d				08 19										08 49					09 19					
Chessington North	d				08 22										08 52					09 22					
Chessington South	a				08 24										08 54					09 24					
Worcester Park	d	07 57								08 27							08 57							12 27	
Stoneleigh	d	08 00								08 30							09 00							12 30	
Ewell West	d	08 03								08 33							09 03							12 33	
Epsom 3	a	08 06								08 36							09 06							12 36	
	d	08 08								08 38							09 08							12 38	
Ashtead	d	08 12								08 42							09 12							12 42	
Leatherhead	d	08 15								08 45							09 15							12 45	
Boxhill & Westhumble	d																								
Dorking 4	a									08 51														12 51	
New Malden 6	d			08 10		08 19								08 40		08 49			09 10		09 19				
Norbiton	d			08 13										08 43					09 13						
Kingston	a			08 16										08 46					09 16						
	d			08 16										08 49					09 16						
Hampton Wick	d			08 18										08 51					09 18						
Teddington	d			08 21										08 56					09 21						
Strawberry Hill	a													08 59											
Fulwell	d			08 25															09 25						
Hampton	d			08 29															09 29						
Kempton Park	d			08 32															09 32						
Sunbury	d			08 34															09 34						
Upper Halliford	d			08 36															09 36						
Shepperton	a			08 41															09 41						
Berrylands	d					08 21						⟵				08 51					09 21				
Surbiton 6	d		08 05			08 25			08b32		08 30	08 32	08 35			08 55		09 05			09 25		12c32		12 30
Thames Ditton	d					08 30			⟶							09 00					09 30		⟶		
Hampton Court	a					08 33										09 03					09 33				
Hinchley Wood	d											08 36													
Claygate	d											08 39													
Oxshott	d											08 42													
Cobham & Stoke d'Abernon	d											08 46													
Bookham	d	08 20															09 20								
Effingham Junction 6	d	08 24										08 50					09 24								
Horsley	d	08 27										08 53					09 27								
Clandon	d	08 32										08 58					09 32								
London Road (Guildford)	d	08 37										09 03					09 37								
Guildford	a	08 44	08 40									09 10	09 10				09 44	09 40							

For general notes see front of timetable
For details of catering facilities see Directory of Train Operators

A To Alton (Table 155) and to Basingstoke (Table 155)
B To London Waterloo (Table 149)
b Arr. 0828
c Arr. 1228

Sundays

from 28 September

For details of Bank Holiday service alterations, please see first page of Table 149

London → Chessington South, Dorking, Guildford Shepperton and Hampton Court

Network Diagram - see first page of Table 152

Station		SW	SW	SW	SW	SW	SW	SW	SW	SW	SW	SW	SW	SW	SW		SW	SW	SW	SW	SW	SW	SW	SW	SW	SW
				A					A						[1] B				A					A		
London Waterloo [15] ⊖	d		12 10	12 18	12 21	12 27	12 32	12 40		12 48	12 51	12 57	13 00	13 02	13 07			13 10	13 18	13 21	13 27	13 32	13 40		13 48	13 51
Vauxhall ⊖	d		12 14	12 22	12 25	12 31	12 36	12 44		12 52	12 55	13 01	13 04	13 06				13 14	13 22	13 25	13 31	13 36	13 44		13 52	13 55
Clapham Junction [10]	d		12 19	12 27	12 30	12 36	12 41	12 49		12 57	13 00	13 06	13 09	13 11	13 15			13 19	13 27	13 30	13 36	13 41	13 49		13 57	14 00
Earlsfield	d		12 22	12 30	12 33	12 39	12 44	12 52		13 00	13 03	13 09	13 12	13 14				13 22	13 30	13 33	13 39	13 44	13 52		14 00	14 03
Wimbledon [6] ⊖ 🚋	d		12 26	12 34	12 37	12 43	12 48	12 56		13 04	13 07	13 13	13 16	13 18	13 22			13 26	13 34	13 37	13 43	13 48	13 56		14 04	14 07
Raynes Park [6]	d			12 37	12 40	12 46	12 52			13 07	13 10	13 16		13 22					13 37	13 40	13 46	13 52			14 07	14 10
Motspur Park	d				12 43		12 55				13 13			13 25						13 43		13 55				14 13
Malden Manor	d				12 46						13 16									13 46						14 16
Tolworth	d				12 49						13 19									13 49						14 19
Chessington North	d				12 52						13 22									13 52						14 22
Chessington South	a				12 54						13 24									13 54						14 24
Worcester Park	d						12 57							13 27								13 57				
Stoneleigh	d						13 00							13 30								14 00				
Ewell West	d						13 03							13 33								14 03				
Epsom [3]	a						13 06							13 36								14 06				
	d						13 08							13 38								14 08				
Ashtead	d						13 12							13 42								14 12				
Leatherhead	d						13 15							13 45								14 15				
Boxhill & Westhumble	d																									
Dorking [4]	a													13 51												
New Malden [6]	d			12 40		12 49				13 10		13 19							13 40		13 49				14 10	
Norbiton	d			12 43						13 13									13 43						14 13	
Kingston	a			12 46						13 16									13 46						14 16	
	d			12 49					13 11	13 16									13 49					14 11	14 16	
Hampton Wick	d			12 51					13 13	13 18									13 51					14 13	14 18	
Teddington	d			12 56					13 16	13 21									13 56					14 16	14 21	
Strawberry Hill	a			12 59					13 19										13 59					14 19		
Fulwell	d									13 25															14 25	
Hampton	d									13 29															14 29	
Kempton Park	d									13 32															14 32	
Sunbury	d									13 34															14 34	
Upper Halliford	d									13 36															14 36	
Shepperton	a									13 41															14 41	
Berrylands	d	⟵				12 51						13 21					⟵				13 51					
Surbiton [6]	d	12 32	12 35			12 55		13 05				13 25	13b32		13 30		13 32	13 35			13 55		14 05			
Thames Ditton	d					13 00						13 30	⟶								14 00					
Hampton Court	a					13 03						13 33									14 03					
Hinchley Wood	d	12 36															13 36									
Claygate	d	12 39															13 39									
Oxshott	d	12 42															13 42									
Cobham & Stoke d'Abernon	d	12 46															13 46									
Bookham	d						13 20															14 20				
Effingham Junction [6]	d	12 50					13 24										13 50					14 24				
Horsley	d	12 53					13 27										13 53					14 27				
Clandon	d	12 58					13 32										13 58					14 32				
London Road (Guildford)	d	13 03					13 37										14 03					14 37				
Guildford	a	13 10	13 13				13 44	13 43									14 10	14 13				14 44	14 43			

For general notes see front of timetable
For details of catering facilities see Directory of Train Operators

A To London Waterloo (Table 149)
B To Alton (Table 155) and to Basingstoke (Table 155)
b Arr. 1328

Table 152

Sundays

from 28 September

For details of Bank Holiday service alterations, please see first page of Table 149

London → Chessington South, Dorking, Guildford Shepperton and Hampton Court

Network Diagram - see first page of Table 152

		SW	SW	SW	SW	SW	SW	SW	SW	SW	SW	SW	SW	SW	SW	SW		SW	SW	SW	SW	SW	SW	SW	SW	SW
					1 A			B					B							1 A			B			
London Waterloo 15 ⊖	d	13 57	14 00	14 02	14 07		14 10	14 18	14 21	14 27	14 32	14 40		14 48	14 51	14 57		15 00	15 02	15 07		15 10	15 18	15 21	15 27	15 32
Vauxhall ⊖	d	14 01	14 04	14 06			14 14	14 22	14 25	14 31	14 36	14 44		14 52	14 55	15 01		15 04	15 06			15 14	15 22	15 25	15 31	15 36
Clapham Junction 10	d	14 06	14 09	14 11	14 15		14 19	14 27	14 30	14 36	14 41	14 49		14 57	15 00	15 06		15 09	15 11	15 15		15 19	15 27	15 30	15 36	15 41
Earlsfield	d	14 09	14 12	14 14			14 22	14 30	14 33	14 39	14 44	14 52		15 00	15 03	15 09		15 12	15 14			15 22	15 30	15 33	15 39	15 44
Wimbledon 6 ⊖ 🚋	d	14 13	14 16	14 18	14 22		14 26	14 34	14 37	14 43	14 48	14 56		15 04	15 07	15 13		15 16	15 18	15 22		15 26	15 34	15 37	15 43	15 48
Raynes Park 6	d	14 16		14 22				14 37	14 40	14 46	14 52			15 07	15 10	15 16			15 22				15 37	15 40	15 46	15 52
Motspur Park	d			14 25					14 43		14 55				15 13				15 25					15 43		15 55
Malden Manor	d								14 46						15 16									15 46		
Tolworth	d								14 49						15 19									15 49		
Chessington North	d								14 52						15 22									15 52		
Chessington South	a								14 54						15 24									15 54		
Worcester Park	d			14 27							14 57								15 27							15 57
Stoneleigh	d			14 30							15 00								15 30							16 00
Ewell West	d			14 33							15 03								15 33							16 03
Epsom 3	a			14 36							15 06								15 36							16 06
	d			14 38							15 08								15 38							16 08
Ashtead	d			14 42							15 12								15 42							16 12
Leatherhead	d			14 45							15 15								15 45							16 15
Boxhill & Westhumble	d																									
Dorking 4	a			14 51															15 51							
New Malden 6	d	14 19						14 40		14 49				15 10		15 19							15 40		15 49	
Norbiton	d							14 43						15 13									15 43			
Kingston	a							14 46						15 16									15 46			
	d							14 49					15 11	15 16									15 49			
Hampton Wick	d							14 51					15 13	15 18									15 51			
Teddington	d							14 56					15 16	15 21									15 56			
Strawberry Hill	a							14 59					15 19										15 59			
Fulwell	d													15 25												
Hampton	d													15 29												
Kempton Park	d													15 32												
Sunbury	d													15 34												
Upper Halliford	d													15 36												
Shepperton	a													15 41												
Berrylands	d	14 21				⟵				14 51						15 21					⟵				15 51	
Surbiton 6	d	14 25	14b32		14 30	14 32	14 35			14 55		15 05				15 25		15c32		15 30	15 32	15 35			15 55	
Thames Ditton	d	14 30	⟶							15 00						15 30		⟶							16 00	
Hampton Court	a	14 33								15 03						15 33									16 03	
Hinchley Wood	d					14 36															15 36					
Claygate	d					14 39															15 39					
Oxshott	d					14 42															15 42					
Cobham & Stoke d'Abernon	d					14 46															15 46					
Bookham	d										15 20															16 20
Effingham Junction 6	d					14 50					15 24										15 50					16 24
Horsley	d					14 53					15 27										15 53					16 27
Clandon	d					14 58					15 32										15 58					16 32
London Road (Guildford)	d					15 03					15 37										16 03					16 37
Guildford	a					15 10	15 13				15 44	15 43									16 10	16 13				16 44

For general notes see front of timetable
For details of catering facilities see Directory of Train Operators

A To Alton (Table 155) and to Basingstoke (Table 155)
B To London Waterloo (Table 149)
b Arr. 1428
c Arr. 1528

from 28 September

For details of Bank Holiday service alterations, please see first page of Table 149

London → Chessington South, Dorking, Guildford Shepperton and Hampton Court

Network Diagram - see first page of Table 152

Station		SW 1 A	SW	SW B	SW	SW	SW		SW	SW	SW 1 A	SW	SW	SW B	SW	SW	SW	SW 1 A	SW	SW B	SW	SW	SW	SW
London Waterloo 15 ⊖	d	15 37	15 40		15 48	15 51	15 57	and at the same minutes past each hour until	19 00	19 02	19 07		19 10	19 18	19 21	19 27	19 32	19 37	19 40		19 48	19 57	20 00	20 02
Vauxhall ⊖	d		15 44		15 52	15 55	16 01		19 04	19 06			19 14	19 22	19 25	19 31	19 36		19 44		19 52	20 01	20 04	20 06
Clapham Junction 10	d	15 46	15 49		15 57	16 00	16 06		19 09	19 11	19 15		19 19	19 27	19 30	19 36	19 41	19 46	19 49		19 57	20 06	20 09	20 11
Earlsfield	d		15 52		16 00	16 03	16 09		19 12	19 14			19 22	19 30	19 33	19 39	19 44		19 52		20 00	20 09	20 12	20 14
Wimbledon 6 ⊖	d	15 53	15 56		16 04	16 07	16 13		19 16	19 18	19 22		19 26	19 34	19 37	19 43	19 48	19 53	19 56		20 04	20 13	20 16	20 18
Raynes Park 6	d				16 07	16 10	16 16			19 22				19 37	19 40	19 46	19 52				20 07	20 16		20 22
Motspur Park	d					16 13				19 25					19 43		19 55							20 25
Malden Manor	d					16 16									19 46									
Tolworth	d					16 19									19 49									
Chessington North	d					16 22									19 52									
Chessington South	a					16 24									19 54									
Worcester Park	d									19 27							19 57							20 27
Stoneleigh	d									19 30							20 00							20 30
Ewell West	d									19 33							20 03							20 33
Epsom 3	a									19 36							20 06							20 36
	d									19 38							20 08							20 38
Ashtead	d									19 42							20 12							20 42
Leatherhead	d									19 45							20 15							20 45
Boxhill & Westhumble	d																							
Dorking 4	a									19 51														20 51
New Malden 6	d				16 10		16 19							19 40		19 49					20 10	20 19		
Norbiton	d				16 13									19 43							20 13			
Kingston	a				16 16									19 46							20 16			
	d			16 11	16 16									19 49						20 11	20 16			
Hampton Wick	d			16 13	16 18									19 51						20 13	20 18			
Teddington	d			16 16	16 21									19 56						20 16	20 21			
Strawberry Hill	a			16 19										19 59						20 19				
Fulwell	d				16 25																20 25			
Hampton	d				16 29																20 29			
Kempton Park	d				16 32																20 32			
Sunbury	d				16 34																20 34			
Upper Halliford	d				16 36																20 36			
Shepperton	a				16 41																20 41			
Berrylands	d						16 21					←				19 51						20 21		
Surbiton 6	d	16 02	16 05				16 25		19b32		19 30	19 32	19 35			19 55		20 02	20 05			20 25	20c32	
Thames Ditton	d						16 30		→							20 00						20 30	→	
Hampton Court	a						16 33									20 03						20 33		
Hinchley Wood	d											19 36												
Claygate	d											19 39												
Oxshott	d											19 42												
Cobham & Stoke d'Abernon	d											19 46												
Bookham	d																20 20							
Effingham Junction 6	d											19 50					20 24							
Horsley	d											19 53					20 27							
Clandon	d											19 58					20 32							
London Road (Guildford)	d											20 03					20 37							
Guildford	a		16 43									20 10	20 13				20 44		20 43					

For general notes see front of timetable
For details of catering facilities see Directory of Train Operators

A To Alton (Table 155) and to Basingstoke (Table 155)
B To London Waterloo (Table 149)
b Arr. 1928
c Arr. 2028

Table 152

Sundays

from 28 September

For details of Bank Holiday service alterations, please see first page of Table 149

London → Chessington South, Dorking, Guildford Shepperton and Hampton Court

Network Diagram - see first page of Table 152

		SW	SW	SW	SW	SW	SW	SW	SW	SW	SW	SW	SW	SW	SW		SW	SW	SW	SW	SW	SW	SW	SW	SW	SW
		1							1								1						1			
		A			B				A		B						A			B			A		B	
London Waterloo 15 ⊖	d	20 07		20 10	20 18	20 21	20 27	20 32	20 37	20 40		20 48	20 57	21 00	21 02		21 07		21 10	21 18	21 21	21 32	21 37	21 40		21 48
Vauxhall ⊖	d			20 14	20 22	20 25	20 31	20 36		20 44		20 52	21 01	21 04	21 06				21 14	21 22	21 25	21 36		21 44		21 52
Clapham Junction 10	d	20 15		20 19	20 27	20 30	20 36	20 41	20 46	20 49		20 57	21 06	21 09	21 11		21 15		21 19	21 27	21 30	21 41	21 46	21 49		21 57
Earlsfield	d			20 22	20 30	20 33	20 39	20 44		20 52		21 00	21 09	21 12	21 14				21 22	21 30	21 33	21 44		21 52		22 00
Wimbledon 6 ⊖	d	20 22		20 26	20 34	20 37	20 43	20 48	20 53	20 56		21 04	21 13	21 16	21 18		21 22		21 26	21 34	21 37	21 48	21 53	21 56		22 04
Raynes Park 6	d				20 37	20 40	20 46	20 52				21 07	21 16		21 22					21 37	21 40	21 52				22 07
Motspur Park	d					20 43		20 55							21 25						21 43	21 55				
Malden Manor	d					20 46															21 46					
Tolworth	d					20 49															21 49					
Chessington North	d					20 52															21 52					
Chessington South	a					20 54															21 54					
Worcester Park	d							20 57							21 27							21 57				
Stoneleigh	d							21 00							21 30							22 00				
Ewell West	d							21 03							21 33							22 03				
Epsom 3	a							21 06							21 36							22 06				
	d							21 08							21 38							22 08				
Ashtead	d							21 12							21 42							22 12				
Leatherhead	d							21 15							21 45							22 15				
Boxhill & Westhumble	d																									
Dorking 4	a														21 51											
New Malden 6	d				20 40		20 49					21 10	21 19							21 40						22 10
Norbiton	d				20 43							21 13								21 43						22 13
Kingston	a				20 46							21 16								21 46						22 16
	d				20 49						21 11	21 16								21 49					22 11	22 16
Hampton Wick	d				20 51						21 13	21 18								21 51					22 13	22 18
Teddington	d				20 56						21 16	21 21								21 56					22 16	22 21
Strawberry Hill	a				20 59						21 19									21 59					22 19	
Fulwell	d											21 25														22 25
Hampton	d											21 29														22 29
Kempton Park	d											21 32														22 32
Sunbury	d											21 34														22 34
Upper Halliford	d											21 36														22 36
Shepperton	a											21 41														22 41
Berrylands	d		←				20 51						21 21					←								
Surbiton 6	d	20 30	20 32	20 35			20 55		21 02	21 05			21 25	21b32			21 30	21 32	21 35				22 02	22 05		
Thames Ditton	d						21 00						21 30	→												
Hampton Court	a						21 03						21 33													
Hinchley Wood	d		20 36															21 36								
Claygate	d		20 39															21 39								
Oxshott	d		20 42															21 42								
Cobham & Stoke d'Abernon	d		20 46															21 46								
Bookham	d							21 20														22 20				
Effingham Junction 6	d		20 50					21 24										21 50				22 24				
Horsley	d		20 53					21 27										21 53				22 27				
Clandon	d		20 58					21 32										21 58				22 32				
London Road (Guildford)	d		21 03					21 37										22 03				22 37				
Guildford	a		21 10	21 13				21 44		21 43								22 10	22 13			22 44		22 43		

For general notes see front of timetable
For details of catering facilities see
Directory of Train Operators

A To Alton (Table 155) and to Basingstoke (Table 155)
B To London Waterloo (Table 149)
b Arr. 2128

Sundays

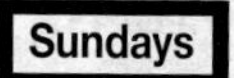

from 28 September

For details of Bank Holiday service alterations, please see first page of Table 149

London → Chessington South, Dorking, Guildford Shepperton and Hampton Court

Network Diagram - see first page of Table 152

		SW	SW	SW	SW 1 A	SW	SW	SW B	SW	SW	SW 1 A	SW	SW B	SW	SW	SW	SW	SW	SW 1 A	SW	SW	SW	SW	SW 1 C		
London Waterloo 15 ⊖	d	21 57	22 00	22 02	22 07		22 10	22 18	22 21	22 32	22 37	22 40		22 48	22 51	22 57	23 00	23 02	23 07		23 10	23 18	23 32	23 40		
Vauxhall ⊖	d	22 01	22 04	22 06			22 14	22 22	22 25	22 36		22 44		22 52	22 55	23 01	23 04	23 06			23 14	23 22	23 36	23 44		
Clapham Junction 10	d	22 06	22 09	22 11	22 15		22 19	22 27	22 30	22 41	22 46	22 49		22 57	23 00	23 06	23 09	23 11	23 15		23 19	23 27	23 41	23 49		
Earlsfield	d	22 09	22 12	22 14			22 22	22 30	22 33	22 44		22 52		23 00	23 03	23 09	23 12	23 14			23 22	23 30	23 44	23 52		
Wimbledon 6 ⊖	d	22 13	22 16	22 18	22 22		22 26	22 34	22 37	22 48	22 53	22 56		23 04	23 07	23 13	23 16	23 18	23 22		23 26	23 34	23 48	23 56		
Raynes Park 6	d	22 16		22 22				22 37	22 40	22 52				23 07	23 10	23 16		23 22				23 37	23 52			
Motspur Park	d			22 25					22 43	22 55					23 13			23 25					23 55			
Malden Manor	d								22 46						23 16											
Tolworth	d								22 49						23 19											
Chessington North	d								22 52						23 22											
Chessington South	a								22 54						23 24											
Worcester Park	d			22 27						22 57								23 27					23 57			
Stoneleigh	d			22 30						23 00								23 30					23 59			
Ewell West	d			22 33						23 03								23 33					00 03			
Epsom 3	a			22 36						23 06								23 36					00 06			
	d			22 38						23 08																
Ashtead	d			22 42						23 12																
Leatherhead	d			22 45						23 15																
Boxhill & Westhumble	d																									
Dorking 4	a			22 51																						
New Malden 6	d	22 19						22 40						23 10		23 19						23 40				
Norbiton	d							22 43						23 13								23 43				
Kingston	a							22 46						23 16								23 46				
	d							22 49					23 11	23 16								23 47				
Hampton Wick	d							22 51					23 13	23 18								23 49				
Teddington	d							22 56					23 16	23 21								23 51				
Strawberry Hill	a							22 59					23 19									23 54				
Fulwell	d													23 25												
Hampton	d													23 29												
Kempton Park	d													23 32												
Sunbury	d													23 34												
Upper Halliford	d													23 36												
Shepperton	a													23 41												
Berrylands	d	22 21				←										23 21				←						
Surbiton 6	d	22 25	22b32		22 30	22 32	22 35				23 02	23 05				23 25	23c32		23 30	23 32	23 35			00 05		
Thames Ditton	d	22 30	→													23 30	→									
Hampton Court	a	22 33														23 33										
Hinchley Wood	d					22 36														23 36						
Claygate	d					22 39														23 39						
Oxshott	d					22 42														23 42						
Cobham & Stoke d'Abernon	d					22 46														23 46						
Bookham	d									23 20																
Effingham Junction 6	d					22 50				23 24										23 50						
Horsley	d					22 53				23 27										23 53						
Clandon	d					22 58				23 32										23 58						
London Road (Guildford)	d					23 03				23 37										00 03						
Guildford	a					23 10	23 13			23 44		23 43								00 10	00 13					

For general notes see front of timetable
For details of catering facilities see Directory of Train Operators

A To Alton (Table 155) and to Basingstoke (Table 155)
B To London Waterloo (Table 149)
C To Farnham (Table 155)

b Arr. 2228
c Arr. 2328

Table 152

Mondays to Fridays

until 26 September

For details of Bank Holiday service alterations, please see first page of Table 149

Hampton Court, Shepperton, Guildford, Dorking and Chessington South → London

Network Diagram - see first page of Table 152

Miles	Miles	Miles	Miles	Miles	Station		SW MO	SW MX	SW MX	SW MX A	SW MX ■1 B	SW MX A	SW MX ■1 C	SW	SW D	SW ■1 B	SW	SW	SW	SW	SW E	SW	SW	SW	SW A
0	—	—	—	—	**Guildford**	d			23p08					04 00			04 58			05 12			05 38		
1¼	—	—	—	—	London Road (Guildford)	d			23p12								05 02						05 42		
4½	—	—	—	—	Clandon	d			23p17								05 07						05 47		
7½	—	—	—	—	Horsley	d			23p21								05 11						05 51		
8¾	0	—	—	—	Effingham Junction ■6	d			23p24								05 16						05 54		
—	1¾	—	—	—	Bookham	d											05 19								
11	—	—	—	—	Cobham & Stoke d'Abernon	d			23p28														05 58		
13	—	—	—	—	Oxshott	d			23p31														06 01		
14¾	—	—	—	—	Claygate	d			23p34														06 04		
16	—	—	—	—	Hinchley Wood	d			23p37														06 07		
—	—	—	0	—	**Hampton Court**	d	23p45															05 54			
—	—	—	1	—	Thames Ditton	d	23p47															05 56			
18	—	—	3	—	**Surbiton** ■6	d	23p53		23p42		23p57		00 40	04 24		05 40				05 57	06 01	06 02	06 12		
19	—	—	—	—	Berrylands	d	23p55															06 04			
—	—	—	—	0	**Shepperton**	d		23p11										05 23							
—	—	—	—	1½	Upper Halliford	d		23p14										05 26							
—	—	—	—	2	Sunbury	d		23p16										05 28							
—	—	—	—	2½	Kempton Park	d		23p18																	
—	—	—	—	4¼	Hampton	d		23p21										05 33							
—	—	—	—	6	Fulwell	d		23p24										05 36							
—	—	—	0	—	Strawberry Hill	d				23p37		00 12			04 55			05 38							06 07
—	—	—	1¼	7	Teddington	d		23p29		23p41		00 15			04 59				05 44						06 11
—	—	—	—	8½	Hampton Wick	d		23p31		23p44		00 17			05 01				05 46						06 14
—	—	—	—	8¾	Kingston	a		23p33		23p46		00 19			05 03				05 48						06 16
—	—	—	—	—		d		23p34		23p49					05 04				05 49						06 19
—	—	—	—	9½	Norbiton	d		23p36		23p51					05 06				05 51						06 21
20	—	—	—	11	New Malden ■6	d	23p58	23p40		23p55					05 10				05 55			06 07			06 25
—	—	0	—	—	**Dorking** ■4	d																		05 48	
—	—	¾	—	—	Boxhill & Westhumble	d																		05 50	
—	4¼	4	—	—	Leatherhead	d											05 24							05 56	
—	—	5¾	—	—	Ashtead	d											05 28							05 59	
—	—	7¾	—	—	**Epsom** ■3	a											05 32							06 04	
—	—	—	—	—		d											05 34							06 04	
—	—	9	—	—	Ewell West	d											05 37							06 07	
—	—	10	—	—	Stoneleigh	d											05 40							06 10	
—	—	11¼	—	—	Worcester Park	d											05 42							06 12	
—	0	—	—	—	**Chessington South**	d																			
—	¾	—	—	—	Chessington North	d																			
—	1¾	—	—	—	Tolworth	d																			
—	2¾	—	—	—	Malden Manor	d																			
—	3¾	12¼	—	—	Motspur Park	d											05 46							06 16	
21½	5½	13½	—	12	Raynes Park ■6	d	00 01	23p43		23p58					05 13		05 49		05 58			06 10		06 19	06 28
22¾	6¾	14¾	—	13½	**Wimbledon** ■6 ⊖	d	00a04	23p49	23p55	00 05	00 08		00 48	04 32	05 17	05 49	05 53		06 02	06 05		06 14	06 20	06 23	06 32
24½	8½	16½	—	15¼	Earlsfield	d		23p55	23p58	00 08	00 10				05 21		05 57		06 05	06 08		06 17	06 24	06 27	06 35
26	10	18	—	16¾	**Clapham Junction** ■10	d		23p59	00 02	23p13	00 14		00 55	04 44	05 25	06 01	06 01	06 05	06 09	06 12		06 21	06 28	06 31	05 43
28¾	12¾	20¾	—	19½	Vauxhall ⊖	d		00 04	00 07	00 17	00 19				05 30	06 08	06 06	06 12	06 14	06 17		06 26	06 33	06 36	06 44
30	14	22	—	20¾	**London Waterloo** ■15 ⊖	a		00 09	00 13	00 22	00 27		01 02	04 53	05 35	06 12	06 11	06 16	06 19	06 22	06 20	06 31	06 37	06 40	06 49

For general notes see front of timetable
For details of catering facilities see Directory of Train Operators

A From London Waterloo (Table 149)
B From Basingstoke (Table 155)
C From Weymouth (Table 158)
D From Twickenham (Table 149)
E From Woking (Table 155)

For details of Bank Holiday service alterations, please see first page of Table 149

Hampton Court, Shepperton, Guildford, Dorking and Chessington South → London

Network Diagram - see first page of Table 152

		SW	SW	SW	SW	SW 1	SW	SW 1		SW	SW	SW	SW	SW	SW	SW	SW 1	SW	SW 1	SW	SW		SW	SW 1	SW	SW
		A				B		C					D	A			E 🍴		A					A		D
Guildford	d			05 58						06 07						06 28					06 37					
London Road (Guildford)	d			06 02						06 11						06 32					06 41					
Clandon	d			06 07						06 16						06 37					06 46					
Horsley	d			06 11						06 20						06 41					06 50					
Effingham Junction 6	d			06 16						06 24						06b48					06 54					
Bookham	d			06 19												06 51										
Cobham & Stoke d'Abernon	d									06 27											06 57					
Oxshott	d									06 31											07 01					
Claygate	d									06 34											07 04					
Hinchley Wood	d									06 37											07 07					
Hampton Court	d				06 24													06 54								
Thames Ditton	d				06 26													06 56								
Surbiton 6	d	06 28			06 32	06 34		06 41		06 42				06 57				07 02	07 08		07 12			07 27		
Berrylands	d				06 34													07 04								
Shepperton	d						06 11													06 41						
Upper Halliford	d						06 14													06 44						
Sunbury	d						06 16													06 46						
Kempton Park	d																									
Hampton	d						06 21													06 51						
Fulwell	d						06 24													06 54						
Strawberry Hill	d												06 37													07 07
Teddington	d						06 29						06 41							06 59						07 11
Hampton Wick	d						06 31						06 44							07 01						07 14
Kingston	a						06 33						06 46							07 03						07 16
	d						06 34						06 49							07 04						07 19
Norbiton	d						06 36						06 51							07 06						07 21
New Malden 6	d				06 37		06 40						06 55					07 07		07 10						07 25
Dorking 4	d														06 32											
Boxhill & Westhumble	d														06 34											
Leatherhead	d			06 24											06 39	06 56										
Ashtead	d			06 28											06 43	06 59										
Epsom 3	a			06 32											06 47	07 04										
	d		06 18	06 33							←				06 48	07 04							←			
Ewell West	d		06 21	06 36							06 36				06 51	07 07							07 07			
Stoneleigh	d		06 24	→							06 38				06 53	→							07 10			
Worcester Park	d		06 27								06 41				06 56								07 12			
Chessington South	d											06 40													07 10	
Chessington North	d											06 42													07 12	
Tolworth	d											06 44													07 14	
Malden Manor	d											06 47													07 17	
Motspur Park	d		06 30								06 46	06 50			07 00								07 16		07 20	
Raynes Park 6	d		06 34		06 40		06 43				06 49	06 54	06 58		07 04			07 10		07 13			07 19		07 24	07 28
Wimbledon 6 ⊖	d	06 35	06 38		06 44		06 47	06 47		06 50	06 53	06 58	07 02	07 05	07 08			07 14		07 17	07 20		07 23		07 28	07 32
Earlsfield	d	06 39	06 42		06 47		06 50			06 54	06 57	07 01	07 05	07 08	07 11			07 17		07 20	07 24		07 27		07 31	07 35
Clapham Junction 10	d	06 43	06 46		06 51	06 46	06 54	06 54		06 58	07 01	07 05	06 13	07 12	07 15			07 21		07 24	07 28		07 31		07 35	06 43
Vauxhall ⊖	d	06 48	06 51		06 56		06 59			07 03	07 06	07 10	07 14	07 17	07 20			07 26		07 29	07 33		07 36		07 40	07 44
London Waterloo 15 ⊖	a	06 52	06 55		07 03	06 54	07 06	07 04		07 09	07 12	07 17	07 21	07 24	07 27		07 18	07 33	07 28	07 36	07 39		07 42	07 49	07 47	07 51

For general notes see front of timetable
For details of catering facilities see Directory of Train Operators

A From Woking (Table 155)
B From Alton (Table 155)
C From Basingstoke (Table 155)
D From London Waterloo (Table 149)
E From Salisbury (Table 160)
b Arr. 0644

For details of Bank Holiday service alterations, please see first page of Table 149

Hampton Court, Shepperton, Guildford, Dorking and Chessington South → London

Network Diagram - see first page of Table 152

Station		SW	SW	SW	SW	SW	SW	SW	SW	SW	SW		SW	SW	SW	SW	SW	SW	SW	SN	SW	SW	SW	SW		SW
								1							1									1		
								A							A	B		C		D				E		
Guildford	d				06 58					07 07	07 17									07 26						
London Road (Guildford)	d				07 02					07 11	07 21									07 29						
Clandon	d				07 07					07 16	07 26															
Horsley	d				07 11					07 20	07 30															
Effingham Junction 6	d				07 16					07 24	07 34									07 38	07 46					
Bookham	d				07 19															07 41	07 49					
Cobham & Stoke d'Abernon	d									07 27	07 37															
Oxshott	d									07 31	07 41															
Claygate	d									07 34	07 44															
Hinchley Wood	d									07 37	07 47															
Hampton Court	d						07 24																07 54			
Thames Ditton	d						07 26																07 56			
Surbiton 6	d						07 32	07 38		07 42	07 53				07 57								08 02	08 08		
Berrylands	d						07 34																08 04			
Shepperton	d					07 00			07 11													07 30				07 41
Upper Halliford	d					07 03			07 14													07 33				07 44
Sunbury	d					07 05			07 16													07 35				07 46
Kempton Park	d																									
Hampton	d					07 09			07 21													07 39				07 51
Fulwell	d					07 12			07 24													07 42				07 54
Strawberry Hill	d					07 14										07 37		07 47				07 44				
Teddington	d		07 20						07 29							07 41		07 50								07 59
Hampton Wick	d		07 22						07 31							07 44		07 52								08 01
Kingston	a		07 24						07 33							07 46		07 54								08 03
	d		07 26						07 34							07 49		07 56								08 04
Norbiton	d		07 28						07 36							07 51		07 58								08 06
New Malden 6	d		07 32				07 37		07 40	07 46						07 55		08 02					08 07			08 10
Dorking 4	d	07 02															07 32									
Boxhill & Westhumble	d	07 04															07 34									
Leatherhead	d	07 09			07 24												07 39			07 46	07 54					
Ashtead	d	07 13			07 27												07 43			07 50	07 57					
Epsom 3	a	07 17			07 32												07 47			07 54	08 02					
	d	07 18		07 22	07 34								←				07 48		07 52		08 04					
Ewell West	d			07 25	07 37								07 37						07 55		08 07					
Stoneleigh	d			07 27	→								07 40						07 57		→					
Worcester Park	d	07 25		07 30									07 43				07 55		08 00							
Chessington South	d													07 40												
Chessington North	d													07 42												
Tolworth	d													07 44												
Malden Manor	d													07 47												
Motspur Park	d			07 34									07 46	07 50					08 04							
Raynes Park 6	d	07 31	07 34	07 37			07 40		07 43				07 50	07 54		07 58	08 01	08 04	08 07				08 10			08 13
Wimbledon 6 ⊖	d	07 35	07 38	07 41			07 44		07 47	07 51			07 54	07 58		08 02	08 05	08 08	08 11				08 14			08 17
Earlsfield	d	07 38	07 42	07 45			07 48		07 51	07 54			07 58	08 01		08 05	08 08	08 12	08 15				08 18			08 21
Clapham Junction 10	d	07 42	07 46	07 49		07 49	07 52		07 55	07 58			08 02	08 05		07 13	08 12	08 16	08 19			08 19	08 22			08 25
Vauxhall ⊖	d	07 47	07 51	07 54		07 56	07 57		08 00	08 03			08 07	08 10		08 14	08 17	08 21	08 24			08 26	08 27			08 30
London Waterloo 15 ⊖	a	07 54	07 57	08 00		08 04	08 04	07 56	08 06	08 11	08 13		08 13	08 17	08 19	08 21	08 24	08 27	08 30			08 34	08 33	08 26		08 36

For general notes see front of timetable
For details of catering facilities see Directory of Train Operators

A From Woking (Table 155)
B From London Waterloo (Table 149)
C From Twickenham (Table 149)
D To London Bridge (Table 182)
E From West Byfleet (Table 155)

For details of Bank Holiday service alterations, please see first page of Table 149

Hampton Court, Shepperton, Guildford, Dorking and Chessington South → London

Network Diagram - see first page of Table 152

		SW	SW	SW	SW	SW	SW	SW	SW	SW	SW	SW	SW		SW	SW	SW	SW	SW	SW	SW	SW	SW	SN	SW	SW
			1 A	1 A			B		1 ◊ C 🍴	D			1 E						A		B			G		
Guildford	d	07 37															07 58	08 07				08 20		08 16		
London Road (Guildford)	d	07 41															08 02	08 11						08 19		
Clandon	d	07 46															08 07	08 16						08 24		
Horsley	d	07 50															08 11	08 20						08 29		
Effingham Junction 6	d	07 54															08 15	08 24						08 32	08 48	
Bookham	d																08 18							08 35	08 51	
Cobham & Stoke d'Abernon	d	07 57																08 27								
Oxshott	d	08 01																08 31								
Claygate	d	08 04																08 34								
Hinchley Wood	d	08 07																08 37								
Hampton Court	d											08 24														08 54
Thames Ditton	d											08 26														08 56
Surbiton 6	d	08 12	08 19	08 25								08 32	08 38					08 42	08 48			08 57				09 02
Berrylands	d											08 34														09 04
Shepperton	d														08 00	08 11										
Upper Halliford	d														08 03	08 14										
Sunbury	d														08 05	08 16										
Kempton Park	d																									
Hampton	d														08 09	08 21										
Fulwell	d														08 12	08 24										
Strawberry Hill	d						08 07			08 17					08 14						08 37					
Teddington	d						08 11			08 20						08 29					08 41					
Hampton Wick	d						08 14			08 22						08 31					08 44					
Kingston	a						08 16			08 24						08 33					08 46					
	d						08 19			08 26						08 34					08 49					
Norbiton	d						08 21			08 28						08 36					08 51					
New Malden 6	d	08 16					08 25			08 32		08 37				08 40					08 55					09 07
Dorking 4	d							08 02															08 31			
Boxhill & Westhumble	d							08 04															08 33			
Leatherhead	d							08 09									08 23						08 38	08 41	08 56	
Ashtead	d							08 13									08 27						08 42	08 45	08 59	
Epsom 3	a							08 17									08 31						08 46	08 49	09 04	
	d				←			08 18			08 22						08 34						08 48		09 04	
Ewell West	d				08 07						08 25						08 37						08 51		09 07 →	
Stoneleigh	d				08 10						08 27						08 40						08 54			
Worcester Park	d				08 13			08 25			08 30						08 42						08 57			
Chessington South	d					08 10														08 40						
Chessington North	d					08 12														08 42						
Tolworth	d					08 14														08 44						
Malden Manor	d					08 17														08 47						
Motspur Park	d				08 16	08 20					08 34						08 46			08 50			09 00			
Raynes Park 6	d				08 20	08 24	08 28	08 31		08 34	08 37	08 40				08 43	08 49			08 54	08 58		09 04			09 10
Wimbledon 6 ⊖	d	08 21			08 24	08 28	08 32	08 35		08 38	08 41	08 44				08 47	08 53			08 58	09 02	09 05	09 08			09 14
Earlsfield	d	08 24			08 28	08 31	08 35	08 38		08 42	08 45	08 48				08 51	08 57			09 01	09 05	09 08	09 12			09 17
Clapham Junction 10	d	08 28			08 32	08 35	07 43	08 42		08 46	08 49	08 52			08 49	08 55	09 01			09 05	08 13	09 12	09 16			09 21
Vauxhall ⊖	d	08 33			08 37	08 40	08 44	08 47		08 51	08 54	08 57			08 56	09 00	09 06			09 10	09 14	09 17	09 21			09 26
London Waterloo 15 ⊖	a	08 40	08 36	08 46	08 43	08 47	08 51	08 54	08 46	08 57	09 00	09 03	08 59		09 04	09 06	09 12	09 01	09 06	09 17	09 21	09 24	09 27			09 33

For general notes see front of timetable
For details of catering facilities see Directory of Train Operators

A From Woking (Table 155)
B From London Waterloo (Table 149)
C From Exeter St Davids (Table 160)
D From Twickenham (Table 149)
E From Farnham (Table 155)
G To London Bridge (Table 178)

For details of Bank Holiday service alterations, please see first page of Table 149

Hampton Court, Shepperton, Guildford, Dorking and Chessington South → London

Network Diagram - see first page of Table 152

		SW 1	SW		SW	SW 1	SW	SW	SW	SW	SW	SW	SW	SW 1	SW	SW		SW 1	SW	SW	SW	SW	SW	SW	SW	SW 1
		A				B			C					D				E			C	B				D
Guildford	d				08 37					08 46		08 58				09 08								09 28		
London Road (Guildford)	d				08 41							09 02				09 12								09 32		
Clandon	d				08 46							09 07				09 17								09 37		
Horsley	d				08 50							09 11				09 21								09 41		
Effingham Junction 6	d				08 54							09 16				09 24								09 46		
Bookham	d											09 19												09 49		
Cobham & Stoke d'Abernon	d				08 57											09 28										
Oxshott	d				09 01											09 31										
Claygate	d				09 04											09 34										
Hinchley Wood	d				09 07											09 37										
Hampton Court	d												09 24												09 54	
Thames Ditton	d												09 26												09 56	
Surbiton 6	d	09 11			09 12	09 19				09 27			09 32	09 38		09 42		09 47				09 57			10 02	10 08
Berrylands	d												09 34												10 04	
Shepperton	d		08 41												09 11											
Upper Halliford	d		08 44												09 14											
Sunbury	d		08 46												09 16											
Kempton Park	d														09 18											
Hampton	d		08 51												09 21											
Fulwell	d		08 54												09 24											
Strawberry Hill	d								09 07												09 37					
Teddington	d		08 59						09 11						09 29						09 41					
Hampton Wick	d		09 01						09 14						09 31						09 44					
Kingston	a		09 03						09 16						09 33						09 46					
	d		09 04						09 19						09 34						09 49					
Norbiton	d		09 06						09 21						09 36						09 51					
New Malden 6	d		09 10						09 25				09 37		09 40						09 55				10 07	
Dorking 4	d										09 02												09 35			
Boxhill & Westhumble	d										09 04															
Leatherhead	d										09 09	09 24											09 41	09 54		
Ashtead	d										09 13	09 28											09 44	09 58		
Epsom 3	a										09 17	09 32											09 49	10 02		
	d						⟵				09 18	09 35							⟵				09 50	10 05		
Ewell West	d						09 07				09 21	09 38							09 38				09 53	10 08		
Stoneleigh	d						09 10				09 24	⟶							09 40				09 55	⟶		
Worcester Park	d						09 12				09 27								09 43				09 58			
Chessington South	d							09 10												09 40						
Chessington North	d							09 12												09 42						
Tolworth	d							09 14												09 44						
Malden Manor	d							09 17												09 47						
Motspur Park	d						09 16	09 20			09 30								09 46	09 50			10 01			
Raynes Park 6	d		09 13				09 19	09 24	09 28		09 34		09 40		09 43				09 49	09 53	09 58		10 04		10 10	
Wimbledon 6	⊖ d		09 17		09 20		09 23	09 28	09 32	09 35	09 38		09 44		09 47	09 50			09 53	09 57	10 02	10 05	10 08		10 14	
Earlsfield	d		09 20		09 24		09 27	09 31	09 35	09 38	09 42		09 47		09 50	09 54			09 57	10 01	10 05	10 08	10 12		10 17	
Clapham Junction 10	d		09 24		09 28		09 31	09 35	08 43	09 42	09 46		09 51	09 51	09 54	09 58		09 59	10 01	10 05	09 13	10 12	10 16		10 21	
Vauxhall	⊖ d		09 29		09 33		09 36	09 40	09 44	09 47	09 51		09 56		09 59	10 03			10 06	10 10	10 14	10 17	10 21		10 26	
London Waterloo 15	⊖ a	09 29	09 36		09 39	09 40	09 42	09 47	09 51	09 54	09 57		10 01	09 59	10 04	10 07		10 06	10 10	10 15	10 19	10 22	10 25		10 31	10 25

For general notes see front of timetable
For details of catering facilities see Directory of Train Operators

A From Southampton Central (Table 158)
B From Woking (Table 155)
C From London Waterloo (Table 149)
D From Alton (Table 155)
E From Basingstoke (Table 155)

Mondays to Fridays
until 26 September

For details of Bank Holiday service alterations, please see first page of Table 149

Hampton Court, Shepperton, Guildford, Dorking and Chessington South → London

Network Diagram - see first page of Table 152

		SW	SW	SW 1 A	SW	SW		SW B	SW C	SW	SW	SW	SW 1 D	SW	SW	SW 1 A	SW	SW		SW B	SW C	SW	SW	SW	SW 1 D	SW
Guildford	d		09 38								09 58				10 08								10 28			
London Road (Guildford)	d		09 42								10 02				10 12								10 32			
Clandon	d		09 47								10 07				10 17								10 37			
Horsley	d		09 51								10 11				10 21								10 41			
Effingham Junction 6	d		09 54								10 16				10 24								10 46			
Bookham	d										10 19												10 49			
Cobham & Stoke d'Abernon	d		09 58												10 28											
Oxshott	d		10 01												10 31											
Claygate	d		10 04												10 34											
Hinchley Wood	d		10 07												10 37											
Hampton Court	d											10 24												10 54		
Thames Ditton	d											10 26												10 56		
Surbiton 6	d		10 12	10 17					10 27			10 32	10 38		10 42	10 47					10 57			11 02	11 08	
Berrylands	d											10 34												11 04		
Shepperton	d	09 41												10 11												10 41
Upper Halliford	d	09 44												10 14												10 44
Sunbury	d	09 46												10 16												10 46
Kempton Park	d	09 48												10 18												10 48
Hampton	d	09 51												10 21												10 51
Fulwell	d	09 54												10 24												10 54
Strawberry Hill	d							10 07												10 37						
Teddington	d	09 59						10 11						10 29						10 41						10 59
Hampton Wick	d	10 01						10 14						10 31						10 44						11 01
Kingston	a	10 03						10 16						10 33						10 46						11 03
	d	10 04						10 19						10 34						10 49						11 04
Norbiton	d	10 06						10 21						10 36						10 51						11 06
New Malden 6	d	10 10						10 25				10 37		10 40						10 55				11 07		11 10
Dorking 4	d									10 05												10 35				
Boxhill & Westhumble	d																									
Leatherhead	d									10 11	10 24											10 41	10 54			
Ashtead	d									10 14	10 28											10 44	10 58			
Epsom 3	a									10 19	10 32											10 49	11 02			
	d				←					10 20	10 35						←					10 50	11 05			
Ewell West	d				10 08					10 23	10 38						10 38					10 53	11 08			
Stoneleigh	d				10 10					10 25	→						10 40					10 55	→			
Worcester Park	d				10 13					10 28							10 43					10 58				
Chessington South	d					10 10												10 40								
Chessington North	d					10 12												10 42								
Tolworth	d					10 14												10 44								
Malden Manor	d					10 17												10 47								
Motspur Park	d				10 16	10 20				10 31							10 46	10 50				11 01				
Raynes Park 6	d	10 13			10 19	10 23		10 28		10 34		10 40		10 43			10 49	10 53		10 58		11 04		11 10		11 13
Wimbledon 6 ⊖ ⛴	d	10 17	10 20		10 23	10 27		10 32	10 35	10 38		10 44		10 47	10 50		10 53	10 57		11 02	11 05	11 08		11 14		11 17
Earlsfield	d	10 20	10 24		10 27	10 31		10 35	10 38	10 42		10 47		10 50	10 54		10 57	11 01		11 05	11 08	11 12		11 17		11 20
Clapham Junction 10	d	10 24	10 28		10 31	10 35		09 43	10 42	10 46		10 51	10 49	10 54	10 58	10 59	11 01	11 05		10 13	11 12	11 16		11 21		11 24
Vauxhall ⊖	d	10 29	10 33		10 36	10 40		10 44	10 47	10 51		10 56		10 59	11 03		11 06	11 10		11 14	11 17	11 21		11 26		11 29
London Waterloo 15 ⊖	a	10 34	10 37	10 35	10 40	10 45		10 49	10 52	10 55		11 01	10 57	11 04	11 07	11 06	11 10	11 15		11 19	11 22	11 25		11 31	11 27	11 34

For general notes see front of timetable
For details of catering facilities see Directory of Train Operators

A From Basingstoke (Table 155)
B From London Waterloo (Table 149)
C From Woking (Table 155)
D From Alton (Table 155)

For details of Bank Holiday service alterations, please see first page of Table 149

Hampton Court, Shepperton, Guildford, Dorking and Chessington South → London

Network Diagram - see first page of Table 152

		SW	SW 1	SW	SW	SW	SW	SW	SW	SW	SW 1	SW	SW	SW 1	SW	SW		SW	SW	SW	SW	SW	SW 1	SW
			A			B	C				D			A				B	C				D	
Guildford	d	10 38							10 58				11 08				and at the same minutes past each hour until				16 28			
London Road (Guildford)	d	10 42							11 02				11 12								16 32			
Clandon	d	10 47							11 07				11 17								16 37			
Horsley	d	10 51							11 11				11 21								16 41			
Effingham Junction 6	d	10 54							11 16				11 24								16 46			
Bookham	d								11 19												16 49			
Cobham & Stoke d'Abernon	d	10 58											11 28											
Oxshott	d	11 01											11 31											
Claygate	d	11 04											11 34											
Hinchley Wood	d	11 07											11 37											
Hampton Court	d									11 24												16 54		
Thames Ditton	d									11 26												16 56		
Surbiton 6	d	11 12	11 17				11 27			11 32	11 38		11 42	11 47					16 57			17 02	17 08	
Berrylands	d									11 34												17 04		
Shepperton	d											11 11												16 41
Upper Halliford	d											11 14												16 44
Sunbury	d											11 16												16 46
Kempton Park	d											11 18												16 48
Hampton	d											11 21												16 51
Fulwell	d											11 24												16 54
Strawberry Hill	d					11 07												16 37						
Teddington	d					11 11						11 29						16 43						16 59
Hampton Wick	d					11 14						11 31						16 46						17 01
Kingston	a					11 16						11 33						16 48						17 03
	d					11 19						11 34						16 49						17 04
Norbiton	d					11 21						11 36						16 51						17 06
New Malden 6	d					11 25				11 37		11 40						16 55				17 07		17 10
Dorking 4	d							11 05												16 35				
Boxhill & Westhumble	d																							
Leatherhead	d							11 11	11 24											16 41	16 54			
Ashtead	d							11 14	11 28											16 44	16 58			
Epsom 3	a							11 19	11 32											16 49	17 02			
	d			←				11 20	11 35						←					16 50	17 05			
Ewell West	d			11 08				11 23	11 38						11 38					16 53	17 08			
Stoneleigh	d			11 10				11 25	→						11 40					16 55	→			
Worcester Park	d			11 13				11 28							11 43					16 58				
Chessington South	d				11 10											11 40								
Chessington North	d				11 12											11 42								
Tolworth	d				11 14											11 44								
Malden Manor	d				11 17											11 47								
Motspur Park	d			11 16	11 20			11 31							11 46	11 50				17 01				
Raynes Park 6	d			11 19	11 23	11 28		11 34		11 40		11 43			11 49	11 53		16 58		17 04		17 10		17 13
Wimbledon 6 ⊖ 🚋	d	11 20		11 23	11 27	11 32	11 35	11 38		11 44		11 47	11 50		11 54	11 57		17 02	17 05	17 08		17 14		17 17
Earlsfield	d	11 24		11 27	11 31	11 35	11 38	11 42		11 47		11 50	11 54		11 57	12 01		17 05	17 08	17 12		17 17		17 20
Clapham Junction 10	d	11 28		11 31	11 35	10 43	11 42	11 46		11 51	11 49	11 54	11 58	11 59	12 01	12 05		16 11	17 12	17 16		17 21		17 24
Vauxhall ⊖	d	11 33		11 36	11 40	11 44	11 47	11 51		11 56		11 59	12 03		12 06	12 10		17 14	17 17	17 21		17 26		17 29
London Waterloo 15 ⊖	a	11 37	11 36	11 40	11 45	11 49	11 52	11 55		12 01	11 57	12 04	12 08	12 06	12 11	12 15		17 21	17 22	17 25		17 31	17 29	17 35

For general notes see front of timetable
For details of catering facilities see Directory of Train Operators

A From Basingstoke (Table 155)
B From London Waterloo (Table 149)
C From Woking (Table 155)
D From Alton (Table 155)

For details of Bank Holiday service alterations, please see first page of Table 149

Hampton Court, Shepperton, Guildford, Dorking and Chessington South → London

Network Diagram - see first page of Table 152

		SW	SW 1 A	SW	SW	SW B	SW C	SW		SW	SW	SW 1 D	SW	SW	SW 1 A	SW	SW	SW B	SW C	SW	SW		SW	SW 1 D	SW	SW
Guildford	d	16 38								16 58				17 08							17 28					17 34
London Road (Guildford)	d	16 42								17 02				17 12							17 32					17 38
Clandon	d	16 47								17 07				17 17							17 37					17 43
Horsley	d	16 51								17 11				17 21							17 41					17 47
Effingham Junction 6	d	16 54								17 16				17 24							17 46					17 50
Bookham	d									17 19											17 49					
Cobham & Stoke d'Abernon	d	16 58												17 28												17 54
Oxshott	d	17 01												17 31												17 57
Claygate	d	17 04												17 34												18 00
Hinchley Wood	d	17 07												17 37												18 03
Hampton Court	d										17 24												17 54			
Thames Ditton	d										17 26												17 56			
Surbiton 6	d	17 12	17 17				17 27				17 32	17 38		17 42	17 47				17 57				18 02	18 08		18 12
Berrylands	d										17 34												18 04			
Shepperton	d												17 11												17 41	
Upper Halliford	d												17 14												17 44	
Sunbury	d												17 16												17 46	
Kempton Park	d												17 18												17 48	
Hampton	d												17 21												17 51	
Fulwell	d												17 24												17 54	
Strawberry Hill	d					17 07												17 37								
Teddington	d					17 13							17 29					17 43							17 59	
Hampton Wick	d					17 16							17 31					17 46							18 01	
Kingston	a					17 18							17 33					17 48							18 03	
	d					17 19							17 34					17 49							18 04	
Norbiton	d					17 21							17 36					17 51							18 06	
New Malden 6	d					17 25					17 37		17 40					17 55					18 07		18 10	
Dorking 4	d							17 05												17 35						
Boxhill & Westhumble	d																									
Leatherhead	d							17 11		17 24										17 41	17 54					
Ashtead	d							17 14		17 28										17 44	17 58					
Epsom 3	a							17 19		17 32										17 49	18 02					
	d			←				17 20		17 35						←				17 50	18 05					
Ewell West	d			17 08				17 23		17 38						17 38				17 53	18 08					
Stoneleigh	d			17 10				17 25		→						17 40				17 55	→					
Worcester Park	d			17 13				17 28								17 43				17 58						
Chessington South	d				17 10												17 40									
Chessington North	d				17 12												17 42									
Tolworth	d				17 14												17 44									
Malden Manor	d				17 17												17 47									
Motspur Park	d			17 16	17 20			17 31								17 46	17 50			18 01						
Raynes Park 6	d			17 19	17 23	17 28		17 34			17 40		17 43			17 49	17 53	17 58		18 04			18 10		18 13	
Wimbledon 6 ⊖	d	17 20		17 23	17 27	17 32	17 35	17 38			17 44		17 47	17 50		17 53	17 57	18 02	18 05	18 08			18 14		18 17	18 20
Earlsfield	d	17 24		17 27	17 31	17 35	17 38	17 42			17 47		17 50	17 54		17 57	18 01	18 05	18 08	18 12			18 17		18 20	18 24
Clapham Junction 10	d	17 28		17 31	17 35	16 41	17 42	17 46			17 51	17 49	17 54	17 58	17 59	18 01	18 05	17 11	18 12	18 16			18 21		18 24	18 28
Vauxhall ⊖	d	17 33		17 36	17 40	17 44	17 47	17 51			17 56		17 59	18 03		18 06	18 10	18 14	18 17	18 21			18 26		18 29	18 33
London Waterloo 15 ⊖	a	17 37	17 34	17 40	17 44	17 49	17 52	17 55			18 01	17 59	18 05	18 07	18 09	18 10	18 15	18 19	18 23	18 25			18 31	18 29	18 35	18 37

For general notes see front of timetable
For details of catering facilities see Directory of Train Operators

A From Basingstoke (Table 155)
B From London Waterloo (Table 149)
C From Woking (Table 155)
D From Alton (Table 155)

Mondays to Fridays
until 26 September

For details of Bank Holiday service alterations, please see first page of Table 149

Hampton Court, Shepperton, Guildford, Dorking and Chessington South → London

Network Diagram - see first page of Table 152

		SN	SW 1	SW	SW	SW	SW	SW	SW	SW	SW 1		SW	SW	SW 1	SW	SW	SW	SW	SW	SN	SW	SW 1	SW		SW
		A	B			C	D				E				B			C	D		G		E			
Guildford	d	17 42							17 58					18 08							18 22					18 38
London Road (Guildford)	d								18 02					18 12							18 25					18 42
Clandon	d								18 07					18 17							18 30					18 47
Horsley	d								18 11					18 21							18 35					18 51
Effingham Junction 6	d	17 55							18 16					18 24							18 39					18 54
Bookham	d								18 19												18 42					
Cobham & Stoke d'Abernon	d													18 28												18 58
Oxshott	d													18 31												19 01
Claygate	d													18 34												19 04
Hinchley Wood	d													18 37												19 07
Hampton Court	d									18 24												18 54				
Thames Ditton	d									18 26												18 56				
Surbiton 6	d		18 17				18 27			18 32	18 38			18 42	18 47				18 57			19 02	19 08			19 12
Berrylands	d									18 34												19 04				
Shepperton	d												18 11											18 36		
Upper Halliford	d												18 14											18 39		
Sunbury	d												18 16											18 41		
Kempton Park	d												18 18											18 43		
Hampton	d												18 21											18b51		
Fulwell	d												18 24											18 54		
Strawberry Hill	d					18 07												18 37								
Teddington	d					18 13							18 29					18 43						18 59		
Hampton Wick	d					18 16							18 31					18 46						19 01		
Kingston	a					18 18							18 33					18 48						19 03		
	d					18 19							18 34					18 49						19 04		
Norbiton	d					18 21							18 36					18 51						19 06		
New Malden 6	d					18 25				18 37			18 40					18 55				19 07		19 10		
Dorking 4	d							18 05												18 35						
Boxhill & Westhumble	d																									
Leatherhead	d	18 02						18 11	18 24											18 41	18 47					
Ashtead	d	18 06						18 14	18 28											18 44	18 50					
Epsom 3	a	18 10						18 19	18 32											18 50	18 58					
	d			←				18 20	18 35							←				18 50						
Ewell West	d			18 08				18 23	18 38							18 38				18 53						
Stoneleigh	d			18 10				18 25	→							18 40				18 55						
Worcester Park	d			18 13				18 28								18 43				18 58						
Chessington South	d				18 10												18 40									
Chessington North	d				18 12												18 42									
Tolworth	d				18 14												18 44									
Malden Manor	d				18 17												18 47									
Motspur Park	d			18 16	18 20			18 31								18 46	18 50			19 01						
Raynes Park 6	d			18 19	18 23	18 28		18 34		18 40			18 43			18 49	18 53	18 58		19 04		19 10		19 13		
Wimbledon 6 ⊖ (tram)	d			18 23	18 27	18 32	18 35	18 38		18 44			18 47	18 50		18 53	18 57	19 02	19 05	19 08		19 14		19 17		19 20
Earlsfield	d			18 27	18 31	18 35	18 38	18 42		18 47			18 50	18 54		18 57	19 01	19 05	19 08	19 12		19 17		19 20		19 24
Clapham Junction 10	d			18 31	18 35	17 41	18 42	18 46		18 51	18 49		18 54	18 58	18 59	19 01	19 05	18 11	19 12	19 16		19 21		19 24		19 28
Vauxhall ⊖	d			18 36	18 40	18 44	18 47	18 51		18 56			18 59	19 03		19 06	19 10	19 14	19 17	19 21		19 26		19 29		19 33
London Waterloo 15 ⊖	a		18 39	18 40	18 47	18 49	18 52	18 55		19 01	18 57		19 05	19 07	19 06	19 10	19 14	19 19	19 23	19 27		19 31	19 25	19 34		19 37

For general notes see front of timetable
For details of catering facilities see Directory of Train Operators

A To London Victoria (Table 177)
B From Basingstoke (Table 155)
C From London Waterloo (Table 149)
D From Woking (Table 155)
E From Alton (Table 155)
G To London Bridge (Table 182)
b Arr. 1846

For details of Bank Holiday service alterations, please see first page of Table 149

Hampton Court, Shepperton, Guildford, Dorking and Chessington South → London

Network Diagram - see first page of Table 152

		SW 1 A	SW	SW	SW B	SW C	SW	SN D	SW	SW 1 E	SW	SW	SW 1 A		SW	SW	SW B	SW C	SW	SW	SW	SW 1 E	SW	SW	SW 1 A	SW
Guildford	d							18 52				19 08								19 28				19 38		
London Road (Guildford)	d							18 55				19 12								19 32				19 42		
Clandon	d							19 00				19 17								19 37				19 47		
Horsley	d							19 05				19 21								19 41				19 51		
Effingham Junction 6	d						18 59	19 08				19 24								19 46				19 54		
Bookham	d						19 02	19 11												19 49						
Cobham & Stoke d'Abernon	d											19 28												19 58		
Oxshott	d											19 31												20 01		
Claygate	d											19 34												20 04		
Hinchley Wood	d											19 37												20 07		
Hampton Court	d								19 24												19 54					
Thames Ditton	d								19 26												19 56					
Surbiton 6	d	19 17				19 27			19 32	19 38		19 42	19 47					19 57			20 02	20 08		20 12	20 17	
Berrylands	d								19 34												20 04					
Shepperton	d										19 06												19 42			
Upper Halliford	d										19 09												19 45			
Sunbury	d										19 11												19 47			
Kempton Park	d										19 13												19 49			
Hampton	d										19b21												19 52			
Fulwell	d										19 24												19 54			
Strawberry Hill	d				19 07												19 37									
Teddington	d				19 13						19 29						19 43						19 59			
Hampton Wick	d				19 16						19 31						19 46						20 01			
Kingston	a				19 18						19 33						19 48						20 04			
	d				19 19						19 34						19 49						20 04			
Norbiton	d				19 21						19 36						19 51						20 06			
New Malden 6	d				19 25				19 37		19 40						19 55				20 07		20 10			
Dorking 4	d		18 50																19 33							
Boxhill & Westhumble	d																									
Leatherhead	d		18 56				19 07	19 16											19 39	19 54						
Ashtead	d		18 59				19 10	19 20											19 42	19 58						
Epsom 3	a		19 04				19 15	19 24											19 47	20 02						
	d		19 05				19 20								19 35				19 50	20 05						←
Ewell West	d		19 08				19 23								19 38				19 53	20 08						20 08
Stoneleigh	d		19 10				19 25								19 40				19 55	→						20 10
Worcester Park	d		19 13				19 28								19 43				19 58							20 13
Chessington South	d			19 10												19 40										
Chessington North	d			19 12												19 42										
Tolworth	d			19 14												19 44										
Malden Manor	d			19 17												19 47										
Motspur Park	d		19 16	19 20			19 31								19 46	19 50			20 01							20 16
Raynes Park 6	d		19 19	19 23	19 28		19 34		19 40		19 43				19 49	19 53	19 58		20 04		20 10		20 13			20 19
Wimbledon 6 ⊖ 🚋	d		19 23	19 27	19 32	19 35	19 38		19 44		19 47	19 50			19 53	19 57	20 02	20 05	20 08		20 14		20 17	20 20		20 23
Earlsfield	d		19 27	19 31	19 35	19 38	19 42		19 47		19 50	19 54			19 57	20 01	20 05	20 08	20 12		20 17		20 20	20 24		20 27
Clapham Junction 10	d		19 31	19 35	18 41	19 42	19 46		19 51	19 49	19 54	19 58	19 59		20 01	20 05	19 11	20 12	20 16		20 21		20 24	20 28		20 31
Vauxhall ⊖	d		19 36	19 40	19 44	19 47	19 51		19 56		19 59	20 03			20 06	20 10	20 14	20 17	20 21		20 26		20 29	20 33		20 36
London Waterloo 15 ⊖	a	19 39	19 41	19 45	19 49	19 52	19 55		20 01	19 57	20 04	20 07	20 06		20 10	20 15	20 19	20 22	20 25		20 31	20 25	20 35	20 38	20 36	20 41

For general notes see front of timetable
For details of catering facilities see Directory of Train Operators

A From Basingstoke (Table 155)
B From London Waterloo (Table 149)
C From Woking (Table 155)
D To London Bridge (Table 178)
E From Alton (Table 155)
b Arr. 1916

For details of Bank Holiday service alterations, please see first page of Table 149

Hampton Court, Shepperton, Guildford, Dorking and Chessington South → London

Network Diagram - see first page of Table 152

		SW	SW		SW	SW	SW	SW	SW 1	SW	SW	SW 1	SW	SW	SW	SW		SW	SW	SW 1	SW	SW	SW 1	SW	SW	SW
			A		B				C			D			A	B				C			D			A
Guildford	d						19 58				20 08											20 38				
London Road (Guildford)	d						20 02				20 12											20 42				
Clandon	d						20 07				20 17											20 47				
Horsley	d						20 11				20 21											20 51				
Effingham Junction 6	d						20 16				20 24											20 54				
Bookham	d						20 19																			
Cobham & Stoke d'Abernon	d										20 28											20 58				
Oxshott	d										20 31											21 01				
Claygate	d										20 34											21 04				
Hinchley Wood	d										20 37											21 07				
Hampton Court	d							20 24											20 54							
Thames Ditton	d							20 26											20 56							
Surbiton 6	d				20 27			20 32	20 38		20 42	20 47				20 57			21 02	21 08		21 12	21 17			
Berrylands	d							20 34											21 04							
Shepperton	d									20 11											20 41					
Upper Halliford	d									20 14											20 44					
Sunbury	d									20 16											20 46					
Kempton Park	d									20 18											20 48					
Hampton	d									20 21											20 51					
Fulwell	d									20 24											20 54					
Strawberry Hill	d		20 07												20 37											21 07
Teddington	d		20 11							20 29					20 41						20 59					21 11
Hampton Wick	d		20 14							20 31					20 44						21 01					21 14
Kingston	a		20 16							20 33					20 46						21 03					21 16
	d		20 19							20 34					20 49						21 04					21 19
Norbiton	d		20 21							20 36					20 51						21 06					21 21
New Malden 6	d		20 25					20 37		20 40					20 55				21 07		21 10					21 25
Dorking 4	d					20 05												20 35								
Boxhill & Westhumble	d																									
Leatherhead	d					20 11	20 24											20 41								
Ashtead	d					20 14	20 28											20 44								
Epsom 3	a					20 19	20 32											20 49								
	d					20 20	20 35						←					20 50						21 05		
Ewell West	d					20 23	20 38						20 38					20 53						21 08		
Stoneleigh	d					20 25	→						20 40					20 55						21 10		
Worcester Park	d					20 28							20 43					20 58						21 13		
Chessington South	d	20 10												20 40											21 10	
Chessington North	d	20 12												20 42											21 12	
Tolworth	d	20 14												20 44											21 14	
Malden Manor	d	20 17												20 47											21 17	
Motspur Park	d	20 20				20 31							20 46	20 50				21 01						21 16	21 20	
Raynes Park 6	d	20 23	20 28			20 34		20 40		20 43			20 49	20 53	20 58			21 04	21 10		21 13			21 19	21 23	21 28
Wimbledon 6 ⊖ 🚋	d	20 27	20 32		20 35	20 38		20 44		20 47	20 50		20 53	20 57	21 02	21 05		21 08	21 14		21 17	21 20		21 23	21 27	21 32
Earlsfield	d	20 31	20 35		20 38	20 42		20 47		20 50	20 54		20 57	21 01	21 05	21 08		21 12	21 17		21 20	21 24		21 27	21 31	21 35
Clapham Junction 10	d	20 35	19 43		20 42	20 46		20 51	20 49	20 54	20 58	20 59	21 01	21 05	20 13	21 12		21 16	21 21		21 24	21 28		21 31	21 35	20 43
Vauxhall ⊖	d	20 40	20 44		20 47	20 51		20 56		20 59	21 03		21 06	21 10	21 14	21 17		21 21	21 26		21 29	21 33		21 36	21 40	21 44
London Waterloo 15 ⊖	a	20 46	20 49		20 52	20 55		21 01	20 57	21 04	21 07	21 06	21 10	21 15	21 19	21 22		21 25	21 31	21 29	21 34	21 37	21 34	21 40	21 45	21 49

For general notes see front of timetable
For details of catering facilities see Directory of Train Operators

A From London Waterloo (Table 149)
B From Woking (Table 155)
C From Alton (Table 155)
D From Basingstoke (Table 155)

For details of Bank Holiday service alterations, please see first page of Table 149

Hampton Court, Shepperton, Guildford, Dorking and Chessington South → London

Network Diagram - see first page of Table 152

		SW	SW	SW	SW	SW		SW	SW	SW	SW	SW	SW	SW	SW	SW	SW	SW	SW		SW	SW	SW	SW	SW	SW
					1				1						1			1						1		
		A			B				C			D	A		B			E	D		A			B		
Guildford	d		20 46					21 08									21 38					21 46				22 08
London Road (Guildford)	d		20 50					21 12									21 42					21 50				22 12
Clandon	d		20 55					21 17									21 47					21 55				22 17
Horsley	d		20 59					21 21									21 51					21 59				22 21
Effingham Junction 6	d		21 03					21 24									21 54					22 03				22 24
Bookham	d		21 06																			22 06				
Cobham & Stoke d'Abernon	d							21 28									21 58									22 28
Oxshott	d							21 31									22 01									22 31
Claygate	d							21 34									22 04									22 34
Hinchley Wood	d							21 37									22 07									22 37
Hampton Court	d			21 24																			22 24			
Thames Ditton	d			21 26																			22 26			
Surbiton 6	d	21 27		21 32	21 38			21 42	21 47				21 57		22 08		22 12	22 17			22 27		22 32	22 38		22 42
Berrylands	d			21 34																			22 34			
Shepperton	d					21 11										21 41									22 11	
Upper Halliford	d					21 14										21 44									22 14	
Sunbury	d					21 16										21 46									22 16	
Kempton Park	d					21 18										21 48									22 18	
Hampton	d					21 21										21 51									22 21	
Fulwell	d					21 24										21 54									22 24	
Strawberry Hill	d											21 37							22 07							
Teddington	d					21 29						21 41				21 59			22 11						22 29	
Hampton Wick	d					21 31						21 44				22 01			22 14						22 31	
Kingston	a					21 33						21 46				22 03			22 16						22 33	
	d					21 34						21 49				22 04			22 19						22 34	
Norbiton	d					21 36						21 51				22 06			22 21						22 36	
New Malden 6	d			21 37		21 40						21 55				22 10			22 25				22 37		22 40	
Dorking 4	d													21 35												
Boxhill & Westhumble	d																									
Leatherhead	d		21 11											21 41								22 11				
Ashtead	d		21 14											21 44								22 14				
Epsom 3	a		21 19											21 49								22 19				
	d		21 20							21 35				21 50								22 20				
Ewell West	d		21 23							21 38				21 53								22 23				
Stoneleigh	d		21 25							21 40				21 55								22 25				
Worcester Park	d		21 28							21 43				21 58								22 28				
Chessington South	d										21 40															
Chessington North	d										21 42															
Tolworth	d										21 44															
Malden Manor	d										21 47															
Motspur Park	d		21 31							21 46	21 50			22 01								22 31				
Raynes Park 6	d		21 34	21 40		21 43				21 49	21 53	21 58		22 04		22 13			22 28			22 34	22 40		22 43	
Wimbledon 6 ⊖	d	21 35	21 38	21 44		21 47		21 50		21 53	21 57	22 02	22 05	22 08		22 17	22 20		22 32		22 35	22 38	22 44		22 47	22 50
Earlsfield	d	21 38	21 42	21 47		21 50		21 54		21 57	22 01	22 05	22 08	22 12		22 20	22 24		22 35		22 38	22 42	22 47		22 50	22 54
Clapham Junction 10	d	21 42	21 46	21 51	21 49	21 54		21 58	21 59	22 01	22 05	21 13	22 12	22 16		22 24	22 28		21 43		22 42	22 46	22 51	22 53	22 54	22 58
Vauxhall ⊖	d	21 47	21 51	21 56		21 59		22 03		22 06	22 10	22 14	22 17	22 21		22 29	22 33		22 44		22 47	22 51	22 56		22 59	23 03
London Waterloo 15 ⊖	a	21 52	21 55	22 01	21 57	22 04		22 07	22 06	22 10	22 16	22 19	22 22	22 25	22 26	22 34	22 39	22 34	22 49		22 52	22 55	23 01	23 01	23 04	23 07

For general notes see front of timetable
For details of catering facilities see Directory of Train Operators

A From Woking (Table 155)
B From Alton (Table 155)
C From Basingstoke (Table 155)
D From London Waterloo (Table 149)
E From Portsmouth Harbour (Table 158)

For details of Bank Holiday service alterations, please see first page of Table 149

Hampton Court, Shepperton, Guildford, Dorking and Chessington South → London

Network Diagram - see first page of Table 152

		SW 1	SW	SW	SW	SW	SW 1	SW	SW		SW 1	SW	SW	SW	SW	SW 1	SW	SW	SW	SW	SW 1
		A		B			C				D	B				C				B	A
Guildford	d				22 20				22 38				22 55	22 46				23 08			
London Road (Guildford)	d								22 42					22 50				23 12			
Clandon	d								22 47					22 55				23 17			
Horsley	d								22 51					22 59				23 21			
Effingham Junction 6	d								22 54					23 03				23 24			
Bookham	d													23 06							
Cobham & Stoke d'Abernon	d								22 58									23 28			
Oxshott	d								23 01									23 31			
Claygate	d								23 04									23 34			
Hinchley Wood	d								23 07									23 37			
Hampton Court	d														23 24						
Thames Ditton	d														23 26						
Surbiton 6	d	22 47			22 57		23 08		23 12		23 17		23 30		23 33	23 38		23 42			23 57
Berrylands	d														23 35						
Shepperton	d							22 41									23 11				
Upper Halliford	d							22 44									23 14				
Sunbury	d							22 46									23 16				
Kempton Park	d							22 48									23 18				
Hampton	d							22 51									23 21				
Fulwell	d							22 54									23 24				
Strawberry Hill	d			22 37								23 07								23 37	
Teddington	d			22 41				22 59				23 11					23 29			23 41	
Hampton Wick	d			22 44				23 01				23 14					23 31			23 44	
Kingston	a			22 46				23 03				23 16					23 33			23 46	
	d			22 49				23 04				23 19					23 34			23 49	
Norbiton	d			22 51				23 06				23 21					23 36			23 51	
New Malden 6	d			22 55				23 10				23 25			23 38		23 40			23 55	
Dorking 4	d					22 35															
Boxhill & Westhumble	d																				
Leatherhead	d					22 41								23 11							
Ashtead	d					22 44								23 14							
Epsom 3	a					22 49								23 19							
	d					22 50								23 20							
Ewell West	d					22 53								23 23							
Stoneleigh	d					22 55								23 25							
Worcester Park	d					22 58								23 28							
Chessington South	d		22 40																23 40		
Chessington North	d		22 42																23 42		
Tolworth	d		22 44																23 44		
Malden Manor	d		22 47																23 47		
Motspur Park	d		22 50			23 01								23 31					23 50		
Raynes Park 6	d		22 53	22 58		23 04		23 13				23 28		23b37	23 41		23 43		23 54	23 58	
Wimbledon 6 ⊖ ⛴	d		22 57	23 02	23 05	23 08		23 17	23 20			23 32	23 37	23 41	23a44		23 49	23 55	23a59	00 05	00 08
Earlsfield	d		23 01	23 05	23 08	23 12		23 20	23 24			23 35	23 41	23 44			23 55	23 58		00 08	00 10
Clapham Junction 10	d	22 59	23 05	22 13	23 12	23 16		23 24	23 28			22 43	23 45	23 48		23 53	23 59	00 02		23 13	00 14
Vauxhall ⊖	d		23 10	23 14	23 17	23 21		23 29	23 33			23 44	23 50	23 53			00 04	00 07		00 17	00 19
London Waterloo 15 ⊖	a	23 08	23 15	23 19	23 23	23 25	23 26	23 34	23 37		23 33	23 49	23 54	23 58		00 01	00 09	00 13		00 22	00 27

For general notes see front of timetable
For details of catering facilities see Directory of Train Operators

A From Basingstoke (Table 155)
B From London Waterloo (Table 149)
C From Alton (Table 155)
D From Portsmouth Harbour (Table 158)
b Arr. 2334

Table 152

Mondays to Fridays

from 29 September

For details of Bank Holiday service alterations, please see first page of Table 149

Hampton Court, Shepperton, Guildford, Dorking and Chessington South → London

Network Diagram - see first page of Table 152

		SW	SW	SW	SW	SW	SW	SW	SW	SW	SW	SW	SW	SW	SW	SW	SW	SW	SW	SW	SW	SW	SW	SW	SW	SW
		MO	MX	MX	MX	MX	MX	MX																		
						1		1			1														1	
					A	B	A	C		D	B					E				A	E				G	
Guildford	d			23p08					04 00			04 58			05 12			05 35					05 58			
London Road (Guildford)	d			23p12								05 02						05 39					06 02			
Clandon	d			23p17								05 07						05 44					06 07			
Horsley	d			23p21								05 11						05 48					06 11			
Effingham Junction 6	d			23p24								05 16						05 51					06 16			
Bookham	d											05 19											06 19			
Cobham & Stoke d'Abernon	d			23p28														05 55								
Oxshott	d			23p31														05 58								
Claygate	d			23p34														06 01								
Hinchley Wood	d			23p37														06 04								
Hampton Court	d	23p45															05 54							06 24		
Thames Ditton	d	23p47															05 56							06 26		
Surbiton 6	d	23p53		23p42		23p57		00 40	04 24		05 40				05 57	06 01	06 02	06 12			06 28			06 32	06 34	
Berrylands	d	23p55															06 04							06 34		
Shepperton	d		23p11										05 23													06 11
Upper Halliford	d		23p14										05 26													06 14
Sunbury	d		23p16										05 28													06 16
Kempton Park	d		23p18																							
Hampton	d		23p21										05 33													06 21
Fulwell	d		23p24										05 36													06 24
Strawberry Hill	d				23p37		00 12			04 55			05 38							06 07						
Teddington	d		23p29		23p41		00 15			04 59				05 44						06 11						06 29
Hampton Wick	d		23p31		23p44		00 17			05 01				05 46						06 14						06 31
Kingston	a		23p33		23p46		00 19			05 03				05 48						06 16						06 33
	d		23p34		23p49					05 04				05 49						06 19						06 34
Norbiton	d		23p36		23p51					05 06				05 51						06 21						06 36
New Malden 6	d	23p58	23p40		23p55					05 10				05 55			06 07			06 25				06 37		06 40
Dorking 4	d																		05 48							
Boxhill & Westhumble	d																		05 50							
Leatherhead	d											05 24							05 56				06 24			
Ashtead	d											05 28							05 59				06 28			
Epsom 3	a											05 32							06 04				06 32			
	d											05 34							06 04			06 18	06 33			
Ewell West	d											05 37							06 07			06 21	06 36			
Stoneleigh	d											05 40							06 10			06 24	→			
Worcester Park	d											05 42							06 12			06 27				
Chessington South	d																									
Chessington North	d																									
Tolworth	d																									
Malden Manor	d																									
Motspur Park	d											05 46							06 16			06 30				
Raynes Park 6	d	00 01	23p43		23p58					05 13		05 49		05 58			06 10		06 19	06 28		06 34		06 40		06 43
Wimbledon 6 ⊖	d	00a04	23p49	23p55	00 05	00 08		00 48	04 32	05 17	05 49	05 53		06 02	06 05		06 14	06 20	06 23	06 32	06 35	06 38		06 44		06 47
Earlsfield	d		23p55	23p58	00 08	00 10				05 21		05 57		06 05	06 08		06 17	06 24	06 27	06 35	06 39	06 42		06 47		06 50
Clapham Junction 10	d		23p59	00 02	23p13	00 14		00 55	04 44	05 25	06 01	06 01	06 05	06 09	06 12		06 21	06 28	06 31	05 43	06 43	06 46		06 51	06 46	06 54
Vauxhall ⊖	d		00 04	00 07	00 17	00 19				05 30	06 08	06 06	06 12	06 14	06 17		06 26	06 33	06 36	06 44	06 48	06 51		06 56		06 59
London Waterloo 15 ⊖	a		00 09	00 13	00 22	00 27		01 02	04 53	05 35	06 15	06 11	06 16	06 19	06 22	06 20	06 31	06 37	06 40	06 49	06 52	06 55		07 03	06 56	07 06

For general notes see front of timetable
For details of catering facilities see Directory of Train Operators

- **A** From London Waterloo (Table 149)
- **B** From Basingstoke (Table 155)
- **C** From Weymouth (Table 158)
- **D** From Twickenham (Table 149)
- **E** From Woking (Table 155)
- **G** From Alton (Table 155)

Table 152

Mondays to Fridays

from 29 September

For details of Bank Holiday service alterations, please see first page of Table 149

Hampton Court, Shepperton, Guildford, Dorking and Chessington South → London

Network Diagram - see first page of Table 152

		SW 1 A	SW	SW	SW	SW B	SW C	SW	SW	SW	SW 1 C	SW	SW	SW	SW 1 C	SW	SW B	SW	SW 1 D	SW	SW	SW	SW	SW	SW 1 C	SW
Guildford	d		06 04						06 28				06 34									06 58				
London Road (Guildford)	d		06 08						06 32				06 38									07 02				
Clandon	d		06 13						06 37				06 43									07 07				
Horsley	d		06 17						06 41				06 47									07 11				
Effingham Junction 6	d		06 21						06b48				06 51									07 16				
Bookham	d								06 51													07 19				
Cobham & Stoke d'Abernon	d		06 24										06 54													
Oxshott	d		06 28										06 58													
Claygate	d		06 31										07 01													
Hinchley Wood	d		06 34										07 04													
Hampton Court	d									06 54														07 24		
Thames Ditton	d									06 56														07 26		
Surbiton 6	d	06 41	06 42				06 57			07 02	07 08		07 12		07 27									07 32	07 38	
Berrylands	d									07 04														07 34		
Shepperton	d											06 41											07 00			07 11
Upper Halliford	d											06 44											07 03			07 14
Sunbury	d											06 46											07 05			07 16
Kempton Park	d																									
Hampton	d											06 51											07 09			07 21
Fulwell	d											06 54											07 12			07 24
Strawberry Hill	d					06 37											07 07						07 14			
Teddington	d					06 41						06 59					07 11			07 20						07 29
Hampton Wick	d					06 44						07 01					07 14			07 22						07 31
Kingston	a					06 46						07 03					07 16			07 24						07 33
	d					06 49						07 04					07 19			07 26						07 34
Norbiton	d					06 51						07 06					07 21			07 28						07 36
New Malden 6	d					06 55				07 07		07 10					07 25			07 32				07 37		07 40
Dorking 4	d							06 32										07 02								
Boxhill & Westhumble	d							06 34										07 04								
Leatherhead	d							06 39	06 56									07 09				07 24				
Ashtead	d							06 43	06 59									07 13				07 27				
Epsom 3	a							06 47	07 04									07 17				07 32				
	d			←				06 48	07 04					←				07 18			07 22	07 34				
Ewell West	d			06 36				06 51	07 07 →					07 07							07 25	07 37 →				
Stoneleigh	d			06 38				06 53						07 10							07 27					
Worcester Park	d			06 41				06 56						07 12				07 25			07 30					
Chessington South	d				06 40											07 10										
Chessington North	d				06 42											07 12										
Tolworth	d				06 44											07 14										
Malden Manor	d				06 47											07 17										
Motspur Park	d			06 46	06 50			07 00						07 16		07 20					07 34					
Raynes Park 6	d			06 49	06 54	06 58		07 04		07 10		07 13		07 19		07 24	07 28	07 31		07 34	07 37			07 40		07 43
Wimbledon 6 ⊖	d	06 47	06 50	06 53	06 58	07 02	07 05	07 08		07 14		07 17	07 20	07 23		07 28	07 32	07 35		07 38	07 41			07 44		07 47
Earlsfield	d		06 54	06 57	07 01	07 05	07 08	07 11		07 17		07 20	07 24	07 27		07 31	07 35	07 38		07 42	07 45			07 48		07 51
Clapham Junction 10	d	06 54	06 58	07 01	07 05	06 13	07 12	07 15		07 21		07 24	07 28	07 31		07 35	06 43	07 42		07 46	07 49		07 49	07 52		07 55
Vauxhall ⊖	d		07 03	07 06	07 10	07 14	07 17	07 20		07 26		07 29	07 33	07 36		07 40	07 44	07 47		07 51	07 54		07 56	07 57		08 00
London Waterloo 15 ⊖	a	07 04	07 09	07 12	07 17	07 21	07 24	07 27		07 33	07 28	07 36	07 39	07 42	07 49	07 47	07 51	07 54	07 51	07 57	08 00		08 04	08 04	07 56	08 06

For general notes see front of timetable
For details of catering facilities see Directory of Train Operators

A From Basingstoke (Table 155)
B From London Waterloo (Table 149)
C From Woking (Table 155)
D From Alton (Table 155)
b Arr. 0644

Mondays to Fridays

from 29 September

For details of Bank Holiday service alterations, please see first page of Table 149

Hampton Court, Shepperton, Guildford, Dorking and Chessington South → London

Network Diagram - see first page of Table 152

		SW	SW	SW	SW	SW	SW	SW	SW	SW	SW	SN	SW	SW	SW	SW	SW	SW	SW	SW	SW	SW	SW	SW	SW	SW
						1			1							1			1	1	1					
						A	B		C	D		E				G			A	A	H			B		D
Guildford	d	07 04	07 14									07 26						07 34								
London Road (Guildford)	d	07 08	07 18									07 29						07 38								
Clandon	d	07 13	07 23															07 43								
Horsley	d	07 17	07 27															07 47								
Effingham Junction 6	d	07 21	07 31									07 38	07 46					07 51								
Bookham	d											07 41	07 49													
Cobham & Stoke d'Abernon	d	07 24	07 34															07 54								
Oxshott	d	07 28	07 38															07 58								
Claygate	d	07 31	07 41															08 01								
Hinchley Wood	d	07 34	07 44															08 04								
Hampton Court	d														07 54											
Thames Ditton	d														07 56											
Surbiton 6	d	07 42	07 53			07 57									08 02	08 08		08 12	08 19	08 25						
Berrylands	d														08 04											
Shepperton	d													07 30			07 41									
Upper Halliford	d													07 33			07 44									
Sunbury	d													07 35			07 46									
Kempton Park	d																									
Hampton	d													07 39			07 51									
Fulwell	d													07 42			07 54									
Strawberry Hill	d						07 37			07 47				07 44										08 07		08 17
Teddington	d						07 41			07 50							07 59							08 11		08 20
Hampton Wick	d						07 44			07 52							08 01							08 14		08 22
Kingston	a						07 46			07 54							08 03							08 16		08 24
	d						07 49			07 56							08 04							08 19		08 26
Norbiton	d						07 51			07 58							08 06							08 21		08 28
New Malden 6	d	07 46					07 55			08 02					08 07		08 10	08 16						08 25		08 32
Dorking 4	d							07 32																	08 02	
Boxhill & Westhumble	d							07 34																	08 04	
Leatherhead	d							07 39				07 46	07 54												08 09	
Ashtead	d							07 43				07 50	07 57												08 13	
Epsom 3	a							07 47				07 54	08 02												08 17	
	d			←				07 48			07 52		08 04									←			08 18	
Ewell West	d			07 37							07 55		08 07									08 07				
Stoneleigh	d			07 40							07 57		→									08 10				
Worcester Park	d			07 43				07 55			08 00											08 13			08 25	
Chessington South	d				07 40																		08 10			
Chessington North	d				07 42																		08 12			
Tolworth	d				07 44																		08 14			
Malden Manor	d				07 47																		08 17			
Motspur Park	d			07 46	07 50						08 04											08 16	08 20			
Raynes Park 6	d			07 50	07 54		07 58	08 01		08 04	08 07				08 10		08 13					08 20	08 24	08 28	08 31	08 34
Wimbledon 6 ⊖ ⛴	d	07 51		07 54	07 58		08 02	08 05		08 08	08 11				08 14		08 17	08 21				08 24	08 28	08 32	08 35	08 38
Earlsfield	d	07 54		07 58	08 01		08 05	08 08		08 12	08 15				08 18		08 21	08 24				08 28	08 31	08 35	08 38	08 42
Clapham Junction 10	d	07 58		08 02	08 05		07 13	08 12		08 16	08 19			08 19	08 22		08 25	08 28				08 32	08 35	07 43	08 42	08 46
Vauxhall ⊖	d	08 03		08 07	08 10		08 14	08 17		08 21	08 24			08 26	08 27		08 30	08 33				08 37	08 40	08 44	08 47	08 51
London Waterloo 15 ⊖	a	08 11	08 13	08 13	08 17	08 19	08 21	08 24	08 22	08 27	08 30			08 34	08 33	08 26	08 36	08 40	08 36	08 46	08 34	08 43	08 47	08 51	08 54	08 57

For general notes see front of timetable
For details of catering facilities see Directory of Train Operators

A From Woking (Table 155)
B From London Waterloo (Table 149)
C From Alton (Table 155)
D From Twickenham (Table 149)
E To London Bridge (Table 182)
G From West Byfleet (Table 155)
H From Portsmouth Harbour (Table 158)

Table 152

Mondays to Fridays
from 29 September

For details of Bank Holiday service alterations, please see first page of Table 149

Hampton Court, Shepperton, Guildford, Dorking and Chessington South → London

Network Diagram - see first page of Table 152

		SW	SW	SW	SW	SW	SW	SW	SW	SW	SW	SW	SW	SN	SW	SW	SW	SW	SW	SW	SW	SW	SW	SW	SW	SW
				1													1			1						
				A					B		C			D			E			B			C			
Guildford	d						07 58	08 04				08 20		08 16					08 34					08 46		08 58
London Road (Guildford)	d						08 02	08 08						08 19					08 38							09 02
Clandon	d						08 07	08 13						08 24					08 43							09 07
Horsley	d						08 11	08 17						08 29					08 47							09 11
Effingham Junction 6	d						08 15	08 21						08 32	08 48				08 51							09 16
Bookham	d						08 18							08 35	08 51											09 19
Cobham & Stoke d'Abernon	d							08 24											08 54							
Oxshott	d							08 28											08 58							
Claygate	d							08 31											09 01							
Hinchley Wood	d							08 34											09 04							
Hampton Court	d		08 24													08 54										
Thames Ditton	d		08 26													08 56										
Surbiton 6	d		08 32	08 38				08 42	08 48			08 57				09 02	09 11		09 12	09 19				09 27		
Berrylands	d		08 34													09 04										
Shepperton	d				08 00	08 11												08 41								
Upper Halliford	d				08 03	08 14												08 44								
Sunbury	d				08 05	08 16												08 46								
Kempton Park	d																									
Hampton	d				08 09	08 21												08 51								
Fulwell	d				08 12	08 24												08 54								
Strawberry Hill	d				08 14						08 37												09 07			
Teddington	d					08 29					08 41							08 59					09 11			
Hampton Wick	d					08 31					08 44							09 01					09 14			
Kingston	a					08 33					08 46							09 03					09 16			
	d					08 34					08 49							09 04					09 19			
Norbiton	d					08 36					08 51							09 06					09 21			
New Malden 6	d		08 37			08 40					08 55					09 07		09 10					09 25			
Dorking 4	d												08 31												09 02	
Boxhill & Westhumble	d												08 33												09 04	
Leatherhead	d						08 23						08 38	08 41	08 56										09 09	09 24
Ashtead	d						08 27						08 42	08 45	08 59										09 13	09 28
Epsom 3	a						08 31						08 46	08 49	09 04						←				09 17	09 32
	d	08 22					08 34						08 48		09 04										09 18	09 35
Ewell West	d	08 25					08 37						08 51		09 07						09 07				09 21	09 38
Stoneleigh	d	08 27					08 40						08 54		→						09 10				09 24	→
Worcester Park	d	08 30					08 42						08 57								09 12				09 27	
Chessington South	d									08 40												09 10				
Chessington North	d									08 42												09 12				
Tolworth	d									08 44												09 14				
Malden Manor	d									08 47												09 17				
Motspur Park	d	08 34					08 46			08 50			09 00								09 16	09 20			09 30	
Raynes Park 6	d	08 37	08 40			08 43	08 49			08 54	08 58		09 04			09 10		09 13			09 19	09 24	09 28		09 34	
Wimbledon 6 ⊖	d	08 41	08 44			08 47	08 53			08 58	09 02	09 05	09 08			09 14		09 17	09 20		09 23	09 28	09 32	09 35	09 38	
Earlsfield	d	08 45	08 48			08 51	08 57			09 01	09 05	09 08	09 12			09 17		09 20	09 24		09 27	09 31	09 35	09 38	09 42	
Clapham Junction 10	d	08 49	08 52		08 49	08 55	09 01			09 05	08 13	09 12	09 16			09 21		09 24	09 28		09 31	09 35	08 43	09 42	09 46	
Vauxhall ⊖	d	08 54	08 57		08 56	09 00	09 06			09 10	09 14	09 17	09 21			09 26		09 29	09 33		09 36	09 40	09 44	09 47	09 51	
London Waterloo 15 ⊖	a	09 00	09 03	08 59	09 04	09 06	09 12	09 01	09 06	09 17	09 21	09 24	09 27			09 33	09 29	09 36	09 39	09 40	09 42	09 47	09 51	09 54	09 57	

For general notes see front of timetable
For details of catering facilities see Directory of Train Operators

A From Farnham (Table 155)
B From Woking (Table 155)
C From London Waterloo (Table 149)
D To London Bridge (Table 178)
E From Southampton Central (Table 158)

For details of Bank Holiday service alterations, please see first page of Table 149

Hampton Court, Shepperton, Guildford, Dorking and Chessington South → London

Network Diagram - see first page of Table 152

		SW	SW 1 A	SW	SW	SW 1 B	SW	SW		SW C	SW D	SW	SW	SW	SW 1 A	SW	SW	SW 1 B	SW	SW	SW C	SW D	SW	SW	SW	SW 1 A
Guildford	d				09 05								09 28				09 35							09 58		
London Road (Guildford)	d				09 09								09 32				09 39							10 02		
Clandon	d				09 14								09 37				09 44							10 07		
Horsley	d				09 18								09 41				09 48							10 11		
Effingham Junction 6	d				09 21								09 46				09 51							10 16		
Bookham	d												09 49											10 19		
Cobham & Stoke d'Abernon	d				09 25												09 55									
Oxshott	d				09 28												09 58									
Claygate	d				09 31												10 01									
Hinchley Wood	d				09 34												10 04									
Hampton Court	d	09 24												09 54											10 24	
Thames Ditton	d	09 26												09 56											10 26	
Surbiton 6	d	09 32	09 38		09 42	09 47					09 57			10 02	10 08		10 12	10 17				10 27			10 32	10 38
Berrylands	d	09 34												10 04											10 34	
Shepperton	d			09 11												09 41										
Upper Halliford	d			09 14												09 44										
Sunbury	d			09 16												09 46										
Kempton Park	d			09 18												09 48										
Hampton	d			09 21												09 51										
Fulwell	d			09 24												09 54										
Strawberry Hill	d									09 37											10 07					
Teddington	d			09 29						09 41						09 59					10 11					
Hampton Wick	d			09 31						09 44						10 01					10 14					
Kingston	a			09 33						09 46						10 03					10 16					
	d			09 34						09 49						10 04					10 19					
Norbiton	d			09 36						09 51						10 06					10 21					
New Malden 6	d	09 37		09 40						09 55				10 07		10 10					10 25				10 37	
Dorking 4	d											09 35											10 05			
Boxhill & Westhumble	d																									
Leatherhead	d											09 41	09 54										10 11	10 24		
Ashtead	d											09 44	09 58										10 14	10 28		
Epsom 3	a											09 49	10 02										10 19	10 32		
	d						←					09 50	10 05						←				10 20	10 35		
Ewell West	d						09 38					09 53	10 08						10 08				10 23	10 38		
Stoneleigh	d						09 40					09 55	→						10 10				10 25	→		
Worcester Park	d						09 43					09 58							10 13				10 28			
Chessington South	d							09 40												10 10						
Chessington North	d							09 42												10 12						
Tolworth	d							09 44												10 14						
Malden Manor	d							09 47												10 17						
Motspur Park	d						09 46	09 50				10 01							10 16	10 20			10 31			
Raynes Park 6	d	09 40		09 43			09 49	09 53		09 58		10 04		10 10		10 13			10 19	10 23	10 28		10 34		10 40	
Wimbledon 6 ⊖	d	09 44		09 47	09 50		09 53	09 57		10 02	10 05	10 08		10 14		10 17	10 20		10 23	10 27	10 32	10 35	10 38		10 44	
Earlsfield	d	09 47		09 50	09 54		09 57	10 01		10 05	10 08	10 12		10 17		10 20	10 24		10 27	10 31	10 35	10 38	10 42		10 47	
Clapham Junction 10	d	09 51	09 51	09 54	09 58	09 59	10 01	10 05		09 13	10 12	10 16		10 21		10 24	10 28		10 31	10 35	09 43	10 42	10 46		10 51	10 49
Vauxhall ⊖	d	09 56		09 59	10 03		10 06	10 10		10 14	10 17	10 21		10 26		10 29	10 33		10 36	10 40	10 44	10 47	10 51		10 56	
London Waterloo 15 ⊖	a	10 01	09 59	10 04	10 07	10 06	10 10	10 15		10 19	10 22	10 25		10 31	10 25	10 34	10 37	10 35	10 40	10 45	10 49	10 52	10 55		11 01	10 57

For general notes see front of timetable
For details of catering facilities see Directory of Train Operators

A From Alton (Table 155)
B From Basingstoke (Table 155)
C From London Waterloo (Table 149)
D From Woking (Table 155)

For details of Bank Holiday service alterations, please see first page of Table 149

Hampton Court, Shepperton, Guildford, Dorking and Chessington South → London

Network Diagram - see first page of Table 152

		SW	SW	SW 1 A	SW	SW	SW B	SW C	SW	SW	SW	SW 1 D	SW	SW	SW 1 A	SW	SW	SW B	SW C	SW	SW	SW	SW 1 D	SW	SW
Guildford	d		10 05							10 28				10 35							10 58				11 05
London Road (Guildford)	d		10 09							10 32				10 39							11 02				11 09
Clandon	d		10 14							10 37				10 44							11 07				11 14
Horsley	d		10 18							10 41				10 48							11 11				11 18
Effingham Junction 6	d		10 21							10 46				10 51							11 16				11 21
Bookham	d									10 49											11 19				
Cobham & Stoke d'Abernon	d		10 25											10 55											11 25
Oxshott	d		10 28											10 58											11 28
Claygate	d		10 31											11 01											11 31
Hinchley Wood	d		10 34											11 04											11 34
Hampton Court	d										10 54											11 24			
Thames Ditton	d										10 56											11 26			
Surbiton 6	d		10 42	10 47				10 57			11 02	11 08		11 12	11 17				11 27			11 32	11 38		11 42
Berrylands	d										11 04											11 34			
Shepperton	d	10 11											10 41											11 11	
Upper Halliford	d	10 14											10 44											11 14	
Sunbury	d	10 16											10 46											11 16	
Kempton Park	d	10 18											10 48											11 18	
Hampton	d	10 21											10 51											11 21	
Fulwell	d	10 24											10 54											11 24	
Strawberry Hill	d						10 37											11 07							
Teddington	d	10 29					10 41						10 59					11 11						11 29	
Hampton Wick	d	10 31					10 44						11 01					11 14						11 31	
Kingston	a	10 33					10 46						11 03					11 16						11 33	
	d	10 34					10 49						11 04					11 19						11 34	
Norbiton	d	10 36					10 51						11 06					11 21						11 36	
New Malden 6	d	10 40					10 55				11 07		11 10					11 25				11 37		11 40	
Dorking 4	d								10 35											11 05					
Boxhill & Westhumble	d																								
Leatherhead	d								10 41	10 54										11 11	11 24				
Ashtead	d								10 44	10 58										11 14	11 28				
Epsom 3	a								10 49	11 02										11 19	11 32				
	d				←				10 50	11 05						←				11 20	11 35				
Ewell West	d				10 38				10 53	11 08						11 08				11 23	11 38				
Stoneleigh	d				10 40				10 55	→						11 10				11 25	→				
Worcester Park	d				10 43				10 58							11 13				11 28					
Chessington South	d					10 40											11 10								
Chessington North	d					10 42											11 12								
Tolworth	d					10 44											11 14								
Malden Manor	d					10 47											11 17								
Motspur Park	d				10 46	10 50			11 01							11 16	11 20			11 31					
Raynes Park 6	d	10 43			10 49	10 53	10 58		11 04		11 10		11 13			11 19	11 23	11 28		11 34		11 40		11 43	
Wimbledon 6 ⊖ 🚋	d	10 47	10 50		10 53	10 57	11 02	11 05	11 08		11 14		11 17	11 20		11 23	11 27	11 32	11 35	11 38		11 44		11 47	11 50
Earlsfield	d	10 50	10 54		10 57	11 01	11 05	11 08	11 12		11 17		11 20	11 24		11 27	11 31	11 35	11 38	11 42		11 47		11 50	11 54
Clapham Junction 10	d	10 54	10 58	10 59	11 01	11 05	10 13	11 12	11 16		11 21		11 24	11 28		11 31	11 35	10 43	11 42	11 46		11 51	11 49	11 54	11 58
Vauxhall ⊖	d	10 59	11 03		11 06	11 10	11 14	11 17	11 21		11 26		11 29	11 33		11 36	11 40	11 44	11 47	11 51		11 56		11 59	12 03
London Waterloo 15 ⊖	a	11 04	11 07	11 06	11 10	11 15	11 19	11 22	11 25		11 31	11 27	11 34	11 37	11 36	11 40	11 45	11 49	11 52	11 55		12 01	11 57	12 04	12 08

For general notes see front of timetable
For details of catering facilities see Directory of Train Operators

A From Basingstoke (Table 155)
B From London Waterloo (Table 149)
C From Woking (Table 155)
D From Alton (Table 155)

For details of Bank Holiday service alterations, please see first page of Table 149

Hampton Court, Shepperton, Guildford, Dorking and Chessington South → London

Network Diagram - see first page of Table 152

		SW [1] A	SW	SW		SW B	SW C	SW	SW	SW	SW [1] D	SW	SW	SW [1] A	SW	SW	SW B	SW C	SW	SW	SW	SW [1] D	SW	SW	SW [1] A
Guildford	d								16 28				16 35							16 58				17 05	
London Road (Guildford)	d								16 32				16 39							17 02				17 09	
Clandon	d								16 37				16 44							17 07				17 14	
Horsley	d								16 41				16 48							17 11				17 18	
Effingham Junction [6]	d								16 46				16 51							17 16				17 21	
Bookham	d								16 49											17 19					
Cobham & Stoke d'Abernon	d												16 55											17 25	
Oxshott	d												16 58											17 28	
Claygate	d												17 01											17 31	
Hinchley Wood	d												17 04											17 34	
Hampton Court	d									16 54											17 24				
Thames Ditton	d									16 56											17 26				
Surbiton [6]	d	11 47					16 57			17 02	17 08		17 12	17 17				17 27			17 32	17 38		17 42	17 47
Berrylands	d									17 04											17 34				
Shepperton	d											16 41											17 11		
Upper Halliford	d											16 44											17 14		
Sunbury	d											16 46											17 16		
Kempton Park	d				and at							16 48											17 18		
Hampton	d				the same							16 51											17 21		
Fulwell	d											16 54											17 24		
Strawberry Hill	d				minutes	16 37											17 07								
Teddington	d				past	16 43						16 59					17 13						17 29		
Hampton Wick	d					16 46						17 01					17 16						17 31		
Kingston	a				each	16 48						17 03					17 18						17 33		
	d				hour until	16 49						17 04					17 19						17 34		
Norbiton	d					16 51						17 06					17 21						17 36		
New Malden [6]	d					16 55				17 07		17 10					17 25				17 37		17 40		
Dorking [4]	d							16 35											17 05						
Boxhill & Westhumble	d																								
Leatherhead	d							16 41	16 54										17 11	17 24					
Ashtead	d							16 44	16 58										17 14	17 28					
Epsom [3]	a							16 49	17 02										17 19	17 32					
	d		←					16 50	17 05						←				17 20	17 35					
Ewell West	d		11 38					16 53	17 08						17 08				17 23	17 38					
Stoneleigh	d		11 40					16 55	→						17 10				17 25	→					
Worcester Park	d		11 43					16 58							17 13				17 28						
Chessington South	d			11 40												17 10									
Chessington North	d			11 42												17 12									
Tolworth	d			11 44												17 14									
Malden Manor	d			11 47												17 17									
Motspur Park	d		11 46	11 50				17 01							17 16	17 20			17 31						
Raynes Park [6]	d		11 49	11 53		16 58		17 04		17 10		17 13			17 19	17 23	17 28		17 34		17 40		17 43		
Wimbledon [6] ⊖ ⛴	d		11 54	11 57		17 02	17 05	17 08		17 14		17 17	17 20		17 23	17 27	17 32	17 35	17 38		17 44		17 47	17 50	
Earlsfield	d		11 57	12 01		17 05	17 08	17 12		17 17		17 20	17 24		17 27	17 31	17 35	17 38	17 42		17 47		17 50	17 54	
Clapham Junction [10]	d	11 59	12 01	12 05		16 11	17 12	17 16		17 21		17 24	17 28		17 31	17 35	16 41	17 42	17 46		17 51	17 49	17 54	17 58	17 59
Vauxhall ⊖	d		12 06	12 10		17 14	17 17	17 21		17 26		17 29	17 33		17 36	17 40	17 44	17 47	17 51		17 56		17 59	18 03	
London Waterloo [15] ⊖	a	12 06	12 11	12 15		17 21	17 22	17 25		17 31	17 29	17 35	17 37	17 34	17 40	17 44	17 49	17 52	17 55		18 01	17 59	18 05	18 07	18 09

For general notes see front of timetable
For details of catering facilities see Directory of Train Operators

A From Basingstoke (Table 155)
B From London Waterloo (Table 149)
C From Woking (Table 155)
D From Alton (Table 155)

For details of Bank Holiday service alterations, please see first page of Table 149

Hampton Court, Shepperton, Guildford, Dorking and Chessington South → London

Network Diagram - see first page of Table 152

		SW	SW	SW	SW	SW	SW	SW	SW	SW	SW	SN	SW	SW	SW	SW	SW	SW	SW	SW	SW	SW	SW	SW	SW	SW
				A	B				1 C			D	1 E			A	B				1 C			1 E		
Guildford	d						17 28				17 34	17 42							17 58				18 05			
London Road (Guildford)	d						17 32				17 38								18 02				18 09			
Clandon	d						17 37				17 43								18 07				18 14			
Horsley	d						17 41				17 47								18 11				18 18			
Effingham Junction 6	d						17 46				17 50	17 55							18 16				18 21			
Bookham	d						17 49												18 19							
Cobham & Stoke d'Abernon	d										17 54												18 25			
Oxshott	d										17 57												18 28			
Claygate	d										18 00												18 31			
Hinchley Wood	d										18 03												18 34			
Hampton Court	d							17 54												18 24						
Thames Ditton	d							17 56												18 26						
Surbiton 6	d				17 57			18 02	18 08		18 12		18 17				18 27			18 32	18 38		18 42	18 47		
Berrylands	d							18 04												18 34						
Shepperton	d									17 41												18 11				
Upper Halliford	d									17 44												18 14				
Sunbury	d									17 46												18 16				
Kempton Park	d									17 48												18 18				
Hampton	d									17 51												18 21				
Fulwell	d									17 54												18 24				
Strawberry Hill	d			17 37												18 07										
Teddington	d			17 43						17 59						18 13						18 29				
Hampton Wick	d			17 46						18 01						18 16						18 31				
Kingston	a			17 48						18 03						18 18						18 33				
	d			17 49						18 04						18 19						18 34				
Norbiton	d			17 51						18 06						18 21						18 36				
New Malden 6	d			17 55				18 07		18 10						18 25				18 37		18 40				
Dorking 4	d					17 35												18 05								
Boxhill & Westhumble	d																									
Leatherhead	d					17 41	17 54					18 02						18 11	18 24							
Ashtead	d					17 44	17 58					18 06						18 14	18 28							
Epsom 3	a					17 49	18 02					18 10						18 19	18 32							
	d	←				17 50	18 05							←				18 20	18 35						←	
Ewell West	d	17 38				17 53	18 08							18 08				18 23	18 38						18 38	
Stoneleigh	d	17 40				17 55	→							18 10				18 25	→						18 40	
Worcester Park	d	17 43				17 58								18 13				18 28							18 43	
Chessington South	d		17 40												18 10											18 40
Chessington North	d		17 42												18 12											18 42
Tolworth	d		17 44												18 14											18 44
Malden Manor	d		17 47												18 17											18 47
Motspur Park	d	17 46	17 50			18 01								18 16	18 20			18 31							18 46	18 50
Raynes Park 6	d	17 49	17 53	17 58		18 04		18 10		18 13				18 19	18 23	18 28		18 34		18 40		18 43			18 49	18 53
Wimbledon 6 ⊖ 🚋	d	17 53	17 57	18 02	18 05	18 08		18 14		18 17	18 20			18 23	18 27	18 32	18 35	18 38		18 44		18 47	18 50		18 53	18 57
Earlsfield	d	17 57	18 01	18 05	18 08	18 12		18 17		18 20	18 24			18 27	18 31	18 35	18 38	18 42		18 47		18 50	18 54		18 57	19 01
Clapham Junction 10	d	18 01	18 05	17 11	18 12	18 16		18 21		18 24	18 28			18 31	18 35	17 41	18 42	18 46		18 51	18 49	18 54	18 58	18 59	19 01	19 05
Vauxhall ⊖	d	18 06	18 10	18 14	18 17	18 21		18 26		18 29	18 33			18 36	18 40	18 44	18 47	18 51		18 56		18 59	19 03		19 06	19 10
London Waterloo 15 ⊖	a	18 10	18 15	18 19	18 23	18 25		18 31	18 29	18 35	18 37		18 39	18 40	18 47	18 49	18 52	18 55		19 01	18 57	19 05	19 07	19 06	19 10	19 14

For general notes see front of timetable
For details of catering facilities see Directory of Train Operators

A From London Waterloo (Table 149)
B From Woking (Table 155)
C From Alton (Table 155)
D To London Victoria (Table 177)
E From Basingstoke (Table 155)

Table 152

Mondays to Fridays
from 29 September

For details of Bank Holiday service alterations, please see first page of Table 149

Hampton Court, Shepperton, Guildford, Dorking and Chessington South → London

Network Diagram - see first page of Table 152

		SW	SW	SW	SN	SW	SW 1	SW	SW	SW 1	SW	SW	SW	SW	SW	SN	SW	SW 1	SW	SW	SW 1	SW	SW	SW	SW	SW
		A	B		C		D			E			A	B		G		D			E			A	B	
Guildford	d				18 22				18 35							18 52				19 05						
London Road (Guildford)	d				18 25				18 39							18 55				19 09						
Clandon	d				18 30				18 44							19 00				19 14						
Horsley	d				18 35				18 48							19 05				19 18						
Effingham Junction 6	d				18 39				18 51						18 59	19 08				19 21						
Bookham	d				18 42										19 02	19 11										
Cobham & Stoke d'Abernon	d								18 55											19 25						
Oxshott	d								18 58											19 28						
Claygate	d								19 01											19 31						
Hinchley Wood	d								19 04											19 34						
Hampton Court	d					18 54											19 24									
Thames Ditton	d					18 56											19 26									
Surbiton 6	d		18 57			19 02	19 08		19 12	19 17				19 27			19 32	19 38		19 42	19 47				19 57	
Berrylands	d					19 04											19 34									
Shepperton	d							18 36											19 06							
Upper Halliford	d							18 39											19 09							
Sunbury	d							18 41											19 11							
Kempton Park	d							18 43											19 13							
Hampton	d							18b51											19c21							
Fulwell	d							18 54											19 24							
Strawberry Hill	d	18 37											19 07											19 37		
Teddington	d	18 43						18 59					19 13						19 29					19 43		
Hampton Wick	d	18 46						19 01					19 16						19 31					19 46		
Kingston	a	18 48						19 03					19 18						19 33					19 48		
	d	18 49						19 04					19 19						19 34					19 49		
Norbiton	d	18 51						19 06					19 21						19 36					19 51		
New Malden 6	d	18 55				19 07		19 10					19 25				19 37		19 40					19 55		
Dorking 4	d			18 35							18 50															19 33
Boxhill & Westhumble	d																									
Leatherhead	d			18 41	18 47						18 56				19 07	19 16										19 39
Ashtead	d			18 44	18 50						18 59				19 10	19 20										19 42
Epsom 3	a			18 50	18 58						19 04				19 15	19 24										19 47
	d			18 50							19 05				19 20							19 35				19 50
Ewell West	d			18 53							19 08				19 23							19 38				19 53
Stoneleigh	d			18 55							19 10				19 25							19 40				19 55
Worcester Park	d			18 58							19 13				19 28							19 43				19 58
Chessington South	d											19 10											19 40			
Chessington North	d											19 12											19 42			
Tolworth	d											19 14											19 44			
Malden Manor	d											19 17											19 47			
Motspur Park	d			19 01							19 16	19 20			19 31							19 46	19 50			20 01
Raynes Park 6	d	18 58		19 04		19 10		19 13			19 19	19 23	19 28		19 34		19 40		19 43			19 49	19 53	19 58		20 04
Wimbledon 6 ⊖ ⛴	d	19 02	19 05	19 08		19 14		19 17	19 20		19 23	19 27	19 32	19 35	19 38		19 44		19 47	19 50		19 53	19 57	20 02	20 05	20 08
Earlsfield	d	19 05	19 08	19 12		19 17		19 20	19 24		19 27	19 31	19 35	19 38	19 42		19 47		19 50	19 54		19 57	20 01	20 05	20 08	20 12
Clapham Junction 10	d	18 11	19 12	19 16		19 21		19 24	19 28		19 31	19 35	18 41	19 42	19 46		19 51	19 49	19 54	19 58	19 59	20 01	20 05	19 11	20 12	20 16
Vauxhall ⊖	d	19 14	19 17	19 21		19 26		19 29	19 33		19 36	19 40	19 44	19 47	19 51		19 56		19 59	20 03		20 06	20 10	20 14	20 17	20 21
London Waterloo 15 ⊖	a	19 19	19 23	19 27		19 31	19 25	19 34	19 37	19 39	19 41	19 45	19 49	19 52	19 55		20 01	19 57	20 04	20 07	20 06	20 10	20 15	20 19	20 22	20 25

For general notes see front of timetable
For details of catering facilities see Directory of Train Operators

- **A** From London Waterloo (Table 149)
- **B** From Woking (Table 155)
- **C** To London Bridge (Table 182)
- **D** From Alton (Table 155)
- **E** From Basingstoke (Table 155)
- **G** To London Bridge (Table 178)
- **b** Arr. 1846
- **c** Arr. 1916

For details of Bank Holiday service alterations, please see first page of Table 149

Hampton Court, Shepperton, Guildford, Dorking and Chessington South → London

Network Diagram - see first page of Table 152

		SW	SW	SW 1 A	SW	SW	SW 1 B	SW	SW	SW C	SW D	SW	SW	SW	SW 1 A	SW	SW	SW 1 B	SW	SW	SW C	SW D	SW	SW	SW 1 A	SW
Guildford	d	19 28				19 35							19 58				20 05									
London Road (Guildford)	d	19 32				19 39							20 02				20 09									
Clandon	d	19 37				19 44							20 07				20 14									
Horsley	d	19 41				19 48							20 11				20 18									
Effingham Junction 6	d	19 46				19 51							20 16				20 21									
Bookham	d	19 49											20 19													
Cobham & Stoke d'Abernon	d					19 55											20 25									
Oxshott	d					19 58											20 28									
Claygate	d					20 01											20 31									
Hinchley Wood	d					20 04											20 34									
Hampton Court	d		19 54											20 24										20 54		
Thames Ditton	d		19 56											20 26										20 56		
Surbiton 6	d		20 02	20 08		20 12	20 17				20 27			20 32	20 38		20 42	20 47				20 57		21 02	21 08	
Berrylands	d		20 04											20 34										21 04		
Shepperton	d				19 42											20 11										20 41
Upper Halliford	d				19 45											20 14										20 44
Sunbury	d				19 47											20 16										20 46
Kempton Park	d				19 49											20 18										20 48
Hampton	d				19 52											20 21										20 51
Fulwell	d				19 54											20 24										20 54
Strawberry Hill	d									20 07											20 37					
Teddington	d				19 59					20 11						20 29					20 41					20 59
Hampton Wick	d				20 01					20 14						20 31					20 44					21 01
Kingston	a				20 04					20 16						20 33					20 46					21 03
	d				20 04					20 19						20 34					20 49					21 04
Norbiton	d				20 06					20 21						20 36					20 51					21 06
New Malden 6	d		20 07		20 10					20 25				20 37		20 40					20 55			21 07		21 10
Dorking 4	d											20 05											20 35			
Boxhill & Westhumble	d																									
Leatherhead	d	19 54										20 11	20 24										20 41			
Ashtead	d	19 58										20 14	20 28										20 44			
Epsom 3	a	20 02										20 19	20 32										20 49			
	d	20 05						←				20 20	20 35						←				20 50			
Ewell West	d	20 08						20 08				20 23	20 38						20 38				20 53			
Stoneleigh	d	→						20 10				20 25	→						20 40				20 55			
Worcester Park	d							20 13				20 28							20 43				20 58			
Chessington South	d								20 10											20 40						
Chessington North	d								20 12											20 42						
Tolworth	d								20 14											20 44						
Malden Manor	d								20 17											20 47						
Motspur Park	d							20 16	20 20			20 31							20 46	20 50			21 01			
Raynes Park 6	d		20 10		20 13			20 19	20 23	20 28		20 34		20 40		20 43			20 49	20 53	20 58		21 04	21 10		21 13
Wimbledon 6 ⊖ 🚋	d		20 14		20 17	20 20		20 23	20 27	20 32	20 35	20 38		20 44		20 47	20 50		20 53	20 57	21 02	21 05	21 08	21 14		21 17
Earlsfield	d		20 17		20 20	20 24		20 27	20 31	20 35	20 38	20 42		20 47		20 50	20 54		20 57	21 01	21 05	21 08	21 12	21 17		21 20
Clapham Junction 10	d		20 21		20 24	20 28		20 31	20 35	19 43	20 42	20 46		20 51	20 49	20 54	20 58	20 59	21 01	21 05	20 13	21 12	21 16	21 21		21 24
Vauxhall ⊖	d		20 26		20 29	20 33		20 36	20 40	20 44	20 47	20 51		20 56		20 59	21 03		21 06	21 10	21 14	21 17	21 21	21 26		21 29
London Waterloo 15 ⊖	a		20 31	20 25	20 35	20 38	20 36	20 41	20 46	20 49	20 52	20 55		21 01	20 57	21 04	21 07	21 06	21 10	21 15	21 19	21 22	21 25	21 31	21 29	21 34

For general notes see front of timetable
For details of catering facilities see Directory of Train Operators

A From Alton (Table 155)
B From Basingstoke (Table 155)
C From London Waterloo (Table 149)
D From Woking (Table 155)

For details of Bank Holiday service alterations, please see first page of Table 149

Hampton Court, Shepperton, Guildford, Dorking and Chessington South → London

Network Diagram - see first page of Table 152

		SW	SW 1 A	SW 1 B	SW	SW	SW C	SW D	SW	SW	SW 1 E	SW	SW	SW 1 B	SW	SW	SW C	SW D	SW	SW 1 E	SW	SW	SW 1 G	SW C	SW D	SW
Guildford	d	20 35	20 47						20 46				21 05									21 35				21 46
London Road (Guildford)	d	20 39							20 50				21 09									21 39				21 50
Clandon	d	20 44							20 55				21 14									21 44				21 55
Horsley	d	20 48							20 59				21 18									21 48				21 59
Effingham Junction 6	d	20 51							21 03				21 21									21 51				22 03
Bookham	d								21 06																	22 06
Cobham & Stoke d'Abernon	d	20 55											21 25									21 55				
Oxshott	d	20 58											21 28									21 58				
Claygate	d	21 01											21 31									22 01				
Hinchley Wood	d	21 04											21 34									22 04				
Hampton Court	d									21 24																
Thames Ditton	d									21 26																
Surbiton 6	d	21 12		21 17				21 27		21 32	21 38		21 42	21 47				21 57		22 08		22 12	22 17		22 27	
Berrylands	d									21 34																
Shepperton	d											21 11									21 41					
Upper Halliford	d											21 14									21 44					
Sunbury	d											21 16									21 46					
Kempton Park	d											21 18									21 48					
Hampton	d											21 21									21 51					
Fulwell	d											21 24									21 54					
Strawberry Hill	d						21 07										21 37							22 07		
Teddington	d						21 11					21 29					21 41				21 59			22 11		
Hampton Wick	d						21 14					21 31					21 44				22 01			22 14		
Kingston	a						21 16					21 33					21 46				22 03			22 16		
	d						21 19					21 34					21 49				22 04			22 19		
Norbiton	d						21 21					21 36					21 51				22 06			22 21		
New Malden 6	d						21 25			21 37		21 40					21 55				22 10			22 25		
Dorking 4	d																		21 35							
Boxhill & Westhumble	d																									
Leatherhead	d								21 11										21 41							22 11
Ashtead	d								21 14										21 44							22 14
Epsom 3	a								21 19										21 49							22 19
	d				21 05				21 20						21 35				21 50							22 20
Ewell West	d				21 08				21 23						21 38				21 53							22 23
Stoneleigh	d				21 10				21 25						21 40				21 55							22 25
Worcester Park	d				21 13				21 28						21 43				21 58							22 28
Chessington South	d					21 10										21 40										
Chessington North	d					21 12										21 42										
Tolworth	d					21 14										21 44										
Malden Manor	d					21 17										21 47										
Motspur Park	d				21 16	21 20			21 31						21 46	21 50			22 01							22 31
Raynes Park 6	d				21 19	21 23	21 28		21 34	21 40		21 43			21 49	21 53	21 58		22 04		22 13			22 28		22 34
Wimbledon 6 ⊖	d	21 20			21 23	21 27	21 32	21 35	21 38	21 44		21 47	21 50		21 53	21 57	22 02	22 05	22 08		22 17	22 20		22 32	22 35	22 38
Earlsfield	d	21 24			21 27	21 31	21 35	21 38	21 42	21 47		21 50	21 54		21 57	22 01	22 05	22 08	22 12		22 20	22 24		22 35	22 38	22 42
Clapham Junction 10	d	21 28			21 31	21 35	20 43	21 42	21 46	21 51	21 49	21 54	21 58	21 59	22 01	22 05	21 13	22 12	22 16		22 24	22 28		21 43	22 42	22 46
Vauxhall ⊖	d	21 33			21 36	21 40	21 44	21 47	21 51	21 56		21 59	22 03		22 06	22 10	22 14	22 17	22 21		22 29	22 33		22 44	22 47	22 51
London Waterloo 15 ⊖	a	21 37	21 27	21 34	21 40	21 45	21 49	21 52	21 55	22 01	21 57	22 04	22 07	22 06	22 10	22 16	22 19	22 22	22 25	22 26	22 34	22 39	22 34	22 49	22 52	22 55

For general notes see front of timetable
For details of catering facilities see Directory of Train Operators

A From Portsmouth Harbour (Table 156)
B From Basingstoke (Table 155)
C From London Waterloo (Table 149)
D From Woking (Table 155)
E From Alton (Table 155)
G From Portsmouth Harbour (Table 158)

For details of Bank Holiday service alterations, please see first page of Table 149

Hampton Court, Shepperton, Guildford, Dorking and Chessington South → London

Network Diagram - see first page of Table 152

		SW	SW 1 A	SW	SW	SW 1 B	SW	SW C	SW	SW	SW 1 A	SW	SW	SW 1 D	SW C	SW	SW	SW	SW 1 A	SW	SW	SW	SW C	SW 1 B
Guildford	d				22 05				22 20				22 35			22 55	22 46				23 08			
London Road (Guildford)	d				22 09								22 39				22 50				23 12			
Clandon	d				22 14								22 44				22 55				23 17			
Horsley	d				22 18								22 48				22 59				23 21			
Effingham Junction 6	d				22 21								22 51				23 03				23 24			
Bookham	d																23 06							
Cobham & Stoke d'Abernon	d				22 25								22 55								23 28			
Oxshott	d				22 28								22 58								23 31			
Claygate	d				22 31								23 01								23 34			
Hinchley Wood	d				22 34								23 04								23 37			
Hampton Court	d	22 24																23 24						
Thames Ditton	d	22 26																23 26						
Surbiton 6	d	22 32	22 38		22 42	22 47			22 57		23 08		23 12	23 17		23 30		23 33	23 38		23 42			23 57
Berrylands	d	22 34																23 35						
Shepperton	d			22 11								22 41								23 11				
Upper Halliford	d			22 14								22 44								23 14				
Sunbury	d			22 16								22 46								23 16				
Kempton Park	d			22 18								22 48								23 18				
Hampton	d			22 21								22 51								23 21				
Fulwell	d			22 24								22 54								23 24				
Strawberry Hill	d							22 37							23 07								23 37	
Teddington	d			22 29				22 41				22 59			23 11					23 29			23 41	
Hampton Wick	d			22 31				22 44				23 01			23 14					23 31			23 44	
Kingston	a			22 33				22 46				23 03			23 16					23 33			23 46	
	d			22 34				22 49				23 04			23 19					23 34			23 49	
Norbiton	d			22 36				22 51				23 06			23 21					23 36			23 51	
New Malden 6	d	22 37		22 40				22 55				23 10			23 25			23 38		23 40			23 55	
Dorking 4	d									22 35														
Boxhill & Westhumble	d																							
Leatherhead	d									22 41							23 11							
Ashtead	d									22 44							23 14							
Epsom 3	a									22 49							23 19							
	d									22 50							23 20							
Ewell West	d									22 53							23 23							
Stoneleigh	d									22 55							23 25							
Worcester Park	d									22 58							23 28							
Chessington South	d						22 40															23 40		
Chessington North	d						22 42															23 42		
Tolworth	d						22 44															23 44		
Malden Manor	d						22 47															23 47		
Motspur Park	d						22 50			23 01							23 31					23 50		
Raynes Park 6	d	22 40		22 43			22 53	22 58		23 04		23 13			23 28		23b37	23 41		23 43		23 54	23 58	
Wimbledon 6 ⊖	d	22 44		22 47	22 50		22 57	23 02	23 05	23 08		23 17	23 20		23 32	23 37	23 41	23a44		23 49	23 55	23a59	00 05	00 08
Earlsfield	d	22 47		22 50	22 54		23 01	23 05	23 08	23 12		23 20	23 24		23 35	23 41	23 44			23 55	23 58		00 08	00 10
Clapham Junction 10	d	22 51	22 53	22 54	22 58	22 59	23 05	22 13	23 12	23 16		23 24	23 28		22 43	23 45	23 48		23 53	23 59	00 02		23 13	00 14
Vauxhall ⊖	d	22 56		22 59	23 03		23 10	23 14	23 17	23 21		23 29	23 33		23 44	23 50	23 53			00 04	00 07		00 17	00 19
London Waterloo 15 ⊖	a	23 01	23 01	23 04	23 07	23 08	23 15	23 19	23 23	23 25	23 26	23 34	23 37	23 33	23 49	23 54	23 58		00 01	00 09	00 13		00 22	00 27

For general notes see front of timetable
For details of catering facilities see Directory of Train Operators

A From Alton (Table 155)
B From Basingstoke (Table 155)
C From London Waterloo (Table 149)
D From Portsmouth Harbour (Table 158)
b Arr. 2334

Saturdays

until 27 September

Hampton Court, Shepperton, Guildford, Dorking and Chessington South → London

For details of Bank Holiday service alterations, please see first page of Table 149

Network Diagram - see first page of Table 152

		SW	SW	SW	SW	SW	SW	SW	SW	SW	SW	SW	SW	SW	SW	SW	SW	SW	SW	SW	SW	SW	SW	SW	SW
					1		1			1									1						
				A	B	A	C		D	B						A	E		G				A	E	
Guildford	d		23p08					04 00					05 12												06 28
London Road (Guildford)	d		23p12																						06 32
Clandon	d		23p17																						06 37
Horsley	d		23p21																						06 41
Effingham Junction 6	d		23p24																						06 46
Bookham	d																								06 49
Cobham & Stoke d'Abernon	d		23p28																						
Oxshott	d		23p31																						
Claygate	d		23p34																						
Hinchley Wood	d		23p37																						
Hampton Court	d													05 54				06 24							
Thames Ditton	d													05 56				06 26							
Surbiton 6	d		23p42		23p57		00 40	04 24		05 40			05 57	06 02			06 27	06 32	06 47					06 57	
Berrylands	d													06 04				06 34							
Shepperton	d	23p11																		06 11					
Upper Halliford	d	23p14																		06 14					
Sunbury	d	23p16																		06 16					
Kempton Park	d	23p18																		06 18					
Hampton	d	23p21																		06 21					
Fulwell	d	23p24																		06 24					
Strawberry Hill	d			23p37		00 12			04 55							06 07							06 37		
Teddington	d	23p29		23p41		00 15			04 59			05 44				06 11				06 29			06 41		
Hampton Wick	d	23p31		23p44		00 17			05 01			05 46				06 14				06 31			06 44		
Kingston	a	23p33		23p46		00 19			05 03			05 48				06 16				06 33			06 46		
	d	23p34		23p49					05 04			05 49				06 19				06 34			06 49		
Norbiton	d	23p36		23p51					05 06			05 51				06 21				06 36			06 51		
New Malden 6	d	23p40		23p55					05 10			05 55		06 07		06 25		06 37		06 40			06 55		
Dorking 4	d																								
Boxhill & Westhumble	d																								
Leatherhead	d																								06 54
Ashtead	d																								06 58
Epsom 3	a																								07 02
	d										05 35				06 05						06 35				07 05
Ewell West	d										05 38				06 08						06 38				07 08
Stoneleigh	d										05 40				06 10						06 40				→
Worcester Park	d										05 43				06 13						06 43				
Chessington South	d																					06 40			
Chessington North	d																					06 42			
Tolworth	d																					06 44			
Malden Manor	d																					06 47			
Motspur Park	d										05 46				06 16						06 46	06 50			
Raynes Park 6	d	23p43		23p58					05 13		05 49	05 58		06 10	06 19	06 28		06 40		06 43	06 49	06 53	06 58		
Wimbledon 6 ⊖ ⛴	d	23p49	23p55	00 05	00 08		00 48	04 32	05 17	05 49	05 53	06 02	06 05	06 14	06 23	06 32	06 35	06 44		06 47	06 53	06 57	07 02	07 05	
Earlsfield	d	23p55	23p58	00 08	00 10				05 21		05 57	06 05	06 08	06 17	06 27	06 35	06 38	06 47		06 50	06 57	07 01	07 05	07 08	
Clapham Junction 10	d	23p59	00 02	23p13	00 14		00 55	04 44	05 25	06 01	06 01	06 09	06 12	06 21	06 31	05 43	06 42	06 51	06 59	06 54	07 01	07 05	06 13	07 12	
Vauxhall ⊖	d	00 04	00 07	00 17	00 19				05 30	06 08	06 06	06 14	06 17	06 26	06 36	06 44	06 47	06 56		06 59	07 06	07 10	07 14	07 17	
London Waterloo 15 ⊖	a	00 09	00 13	00 22	00 27		01 02	04 53	05 35	06 12	06 11	06 19	06 22	06 31	06 40	06 49	06 52	07 01	07 06	07 04	07 10	07 15	07 19	07 22	

For general notes see front of timetable
For details of catering facilities see
Directory of Train Operators

A From London Waterloo (Table 149)
B From Basingstoke (Table 155)
C From Weymouth (Table 158)
D From Twickenham (Table 149)
E From Woking (Table 155)
G From Southampton Central (Table 158)

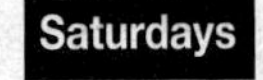

Saturdays

until 27 September

For details of Bank Holiday service alterations, please see first page of Table 149

Hampton Court, Shepperton, Guildford, Dorking and Chessington South → London

Network Diagram - see first page of Table 152

		SW	SW	SW	SW	SW	SW		SW	SW	SW	SW	SW	SW	SW	SW	SW	SW	SW	SW	SW	SW		SW	SW	SW
			1			1								1			1								1	
			A			B				C	D			A			E			C	D				A	
Guildford	d				06 38							06 58				07 08						07 28				
London Road (Guildford)	d				06 42							07 02				07 12						07 32				
Clandon	d				06 47							07 07				07 17						07 37				
Horsley	d				06 51							07 11				07 21						07 41				
Effingham Junction 6	d				06 54							07 16				07 24						07 46				
Bookham	d											07 19										07 49				
Cobham & Stoke d'Abernon	d				06 58											07 28										
Oxshott	d				07 01											07 31										
Claygate	d				07 04											07 34										
Hinchley Wood	d				07 07											07 37										
Hampton Court	d	06 54											07 24											07 54		
Thames Ditton	d	06 56											07 26											07 56		
Surbiton 6	d	07 02	07 08		07 12	07 17					07 27		07 32	07 38		07 42	07 47				07 57			08 02	08 08	
Berrylands	d	07 04											07 34											08 04		
Shepperton	d			06 41											07 11											07 41
Upper Halliford	d			06 44											07 14											07 44
Sunbury	d			06 46											07 16											07 46
Kempton Park	d			06 48											07 18											07 48
Hampton	d			06 51											07 21											07 51
Fulwell	d			06 54											07 24											07 54
Strawberry Hill	d									07 07										07 37						
Teddington	d			06 59						07 11					07 29					07 41						07 59
Hampton Wick	d			07 01						07 14					07 31					07 44						08 01
Kingston	a			07 03						07 16					07 33					07 46						08 03
	d			07 04						07 19					07 34					07 49						08 04
Norbiton	d			07 06						07 21					07 36					07 51						08 06
New Malden 6	d	07 07		07 10						07 25			07 37		07 40					07 55				08 07		08 10
Dorking 4	d																									
Boxhill & Westhumble	d																									
Leatherhead	d											07 24										07 54				
Ashtead	d											07 28										07 58				
Epsom 3	a											07 32										08 02				
	d						←					07 35						←				08 05				
Ewell West	d						07 08					07 38 →						07 38				08 08 →				
Stoneleigh	d						07 10											07 40								
Worcester Park	d						07 13											07 43								
Chessington South	d								07 10										07 40							
Chessington North	d								07 12										07 42							
Tolworth	d								07 14										07 44							
Malden Manor	d								07 17										07 47							
Motspur Park	d						07 16		07 20									07 46	07 50							
Raynes Park 6	d	07 10		07 13			07 19		07 23	07 28			07 40		07 43			07 49	07 53	07 58				08 10		08 13
Wimbledon 6 ⊖ 🚋	d	07 14		07 17	07 20		07 23		07 27	07 32	07 35		07 44		07 47	07 50		07 53	07 57	08 02	08 05			08 14		08 17
Earlsfield	d	07 17		07 20	07 24		07 27		07 31	07 35	07 38		07 47		07 50	07 54		07 57	08 01	08 05	08 08			08 17		08 20
Clapham Junction 10	d	07 21	07 19	07 24	07 28		07 31		07 35	06 43	07 42		07 51	07 51	07 54	07 58	07 59	08 01	08 05	07 13	08 12			08 21		08 24
Vauxhall ⊖	d	07 26		07 29	07 33		07 36		07 40	07 44	07 47		07 56		07 59	08 03		08 06	08 10	08 14	08 17			08 26		08 29
London Waterloo 15 ⊖	a	07 31	07 27	07 34	07 37	07 33	07 40		07 45	07 49	07 52		08 01	07 58	08 04	08 07	08 06	08 10	08 15	08 19	08 22			08 31	08 25	08 34

For general notes see front of timetable
For details of catering facilities see Directory of Train Operators

A From Alton (Table 155)
B From Southampton Central (Table 158)
C From London Waterloo (Table 149)
D From Woking (Table 155)
E From Basingstoke (Table 155)

Table 152

until 27 September

For details of Bank Holiday service alterations, please see first page of Table 149

Hampton Court, Shepperton, Guildford, Dorking and Chessington South → London

Network Diagram - see first page of Table 152

		SW	SW	SW	SW	SW	SW	SW	SW	SW	SW	SW	SW	SW	SW	SW	SW	SW	SW	SW	SW	SW	SW	SW	SW
			1 A			B	C				1 D			1 E			B	C				1 D			1 E
Guildford	d	07 38							07 58				08 08							08 28				08 38	
London Road (Guildford)	d	07 42							08 02				08 12							08 32				08 42	
Clandon	d	07 47							08 07				08 17							08 37				08 47	
Horsley	d	07 51							08 11				08 21							08 41				08 51	
Effingham Junction 6	d	07 54							08 16				08 24							08 46				08 54	
Bookham	d								08 19											08 49					
Cobham & Stoke d'Abernon	d	07 58											08 28											08 58	
Oxshott	d	08 01											08 31											09 01	
Claygate	d	08 04											08 34											09 04	
Hinchley Wood	d	08 07											08 37											09 07	
Hampton Court	d									08 24											08 54				
Thames Ditton	d									08 26											08 56				
Surbiton 6	d	08 12	08 17				08 27			08 32	08 38		08 42	08 47				08 57			09 02	09 08		09 12	09 17
Berrylands	d									08 34											09 04				
Shepperton	d											08 11											08 41		
Upper Halliford	d											08 14											08 44		
Sunbury	d											08 16											08 46		
Kempton Park	d											08 18											08 48		
Hampton	d											08 21											08 51		
Fulwell	d											08 24											08 54		
Strawberry Hill	d					08 07											08 37								
Teddington	d					08 11						08 29					08 41						08 59		
Hampton Wick	d					08 14						08 31					08 44						09 01		
Kingston	a					08 16						08 33					08 46						09 03		
	d					08 19						08 34					08 49						09 04		
Norbiton	d					08 21						08 36					08 51						09 06		
New Malden 6	d					08 25				08 37		08 40					08 55				09 07		09 10		
Dorking 4	d							08 05											08 35						
Boxhill & Westhumble	d																								
Leatherhead	d							08 11	08 24										08 41	08 54					
Ashtead	d							08 14	08 28										08 44	08 58					
Epsom 3	a							08 19	08 32										08 49	09 02					
	d			←				08 20	08 35						←				08 50	09 05					
Ewell West	d			08 08				08 23	08 38						08 38				08 53	09 08					
Stoneleigh	d			08 10				08 25	→						08 40				08 55	→					
Worcester Park	d			08 13				08 28							08 43				08 58						
Chessington South	d				08 10											08 40									
Chessington North	d				08 12											08 42									
Tolworth	d				08 14											08 44									
Malden Manor	d				08 17											08 47									
Motspur Park	d			08 16	08 20			08 31							08 46	08 50			09 01						
Raynes Park 6	d			08 19	08 23	08 28		08 34		08 40		08 43			08 49	08 53	08 58		09 04		09 10		09 13		
Wimbledon 6 ⊖ 🚋	d	08 20		08 23	08 27	08 32	08 35	08 38		08 44		08 47	08 50		08 53	08 57	09 02	09 05	09 08		09 14		09 17	09 20	
Earlsfield	d	08 24		08 27	08 31	08 35	08 38	08 42		08 47		08 50	08 54		08 57	09 01	09 05	09 08	09 12		09 17		09 20	09 24	
Clapham Junction 10	d	08 28		08 31	08 35	07 43	08 42	08 46		08 51	08 50	08 54	08 58	08 59	09 01	09 05	08 13	09 12	09 16		09 21		09 24	09 28	
Vauxhall ⊖	d	08 33		08 36	08 40	08 44	08 47	08 51		08 56		08 59	09 03		09 06	09 10	09 14	09 17	09 21		09 26		09 29	09 33	
London Waterloo 15 ⊖	a	08 37	08 34	08 40	08 45	08 49	08 52	08 55		09 01	08 58	09 04	09 07	09 06	09 10	09 15	09 19	09 22	09 25		09 31	09 25	09 34	09 37	09 35

For general notes see front of timetable
For details of catering facilities see Directory of Train Operators

A From Portsmouth Harbour (Table 158)
B From London Waterloo (Table 149)
C From Woking (Table 155)
D From Alton (Table 155)
E From Basingstoke (Table 155)

For details of Bank Holiday service alterations, please see first page of Table 149

Hampton Court, Shepperton, Guildford, Dorking and Chessington South → London

Network Diagram - see first page of Table 152

		SW	SW	SW	SW	SW	SW	SW	SW	SW		SW	SW	SW	SW	SW	SW	SW	SW	SW	SW	SW	SW	SW
									1				1							1			1	
				A	B				C				D			A	B			C			D	
Guildford	d						08 58				and at the same minutes past each hour until	20 08										20 38		
London Road (Guildford)	d						09 02					20 12										20 42		
Clandon	d						09 07					20 17										20 47		
Horsley	d						09 11					20 21										20 51		
Effingham Junction 6	d						09 16					20 24										20 54		
Bookham	d						09 19																	
Cobham & Stoke d'Abernon	d											20 28										20 58		
Oxshott	d											20 31										21 01		
Claygate	d											20 34										21 04		
Hinchley Wood	d											20 37										21 07		
Hampton Court	d							09 24											20 54					
Thames Ditton	d							09 26											20 56					
Surbiton 6	d				09 27			09 32	09 38			20 42	20 47				20 57		21 02	21 08		21 12	21 17	
Berrylands	d							09 34											21 04					
Shepperton	d									09 11											20 41			
Upper Halliford	d									09 14											20 44			
Sunbury	d									09 16											20 46			
Kempton Park	d									09 18											20 48			
Hampton	d									09 21											20 51			
Fulwell	d									09 24											20 54			
Strawberry Hill	d			09 07												20 37								
Teddington	d			09 11						09 29						20 41					20 59			
Hampton Wick	d			09 14						09 31						20 44					21 01			
Kingston	a			09 16						09 33						20 46					21 03			
	d			09 19						09 34						20 49					21 04			
Norbiton	d			09 21						09 36						20 51					21 06			
New Malden 6	d			09 25				09 37		09 40						20 55			21 07		21 10			
Dorking 4	d					09 05												20 35						
Boxhill & Westhumble	d																							
Leatherhead	d					09 11	09 24											20 41						
Ashtead	d					09 14	09 28											20 44						
Epsom 3	a					09 19	09 32											20 49						
	d	←				09 20	09 35							←				20 50						21 05
Ewell West	d	09 08				09 23	09 38							20 38				20 53						21 08
Stoneleigh	d	09 10				09 25	→							20 40				20 55						21 10
Worcester Park	d	09 13				09 28								20 43				20 58						21 13
Chessington South	d		09 10												20 40									
Chessington North	d		09 12												20 42									
Tolworth	d		09 14												20 44									
Malden Manor	d		09 17												20 47									
Motspur Park	d	09 16	09 20			09 31								20 46	20 50			21 01						21 16
Raynes Park 6	d	09 19	09 23	09 28		09 34		09 40		09 43				20 49	20 53	20 58		21 04	21 10		21 13			21 19
Wimbledon 6 ⊖	d	09 23	09 27	09 32	09 35	09 38		09 44		09 47		20 50		20 53	20 57	21 02	21 05	21 08	21 14		21 17	21 20		21 23
Earlsfield	d	09 27	09 31	09 35	09 38	09 42		09 47		09 50		20 54		20 57	21 01	21 05	21 08	21 12	21 17		21 20	21 24		21 27
Clapham Junction 10	d	09 31	09 35	08 43	09 42	09 46		09 51	09 49	09 54		20 58	20 59	21 01	21 05	20 13	21 12	21 16	21 21		21 24	21 28		21 31
Vauxhall ⊖	d	09 36	09 40	09 44	09 47	09 51		09 56		09 59		21 03		21 06	21 10	21 14	21 17	21 21	21 26		21 29	21 33		21 36
London Waterloo 15 ⊖	a	09 40	09 45	09 49	09 52	09 55		10 01	09 57	10 04		21 07	21 06	21 10	21 15	21 19	21 23	21 25	21 31	21 29	21 34	21 37	21 34	21 40

For general notes see front of timetable
For details of catering facilities see Directory of Train Operators

A From London Waterloo (Table 149)
B From Woking (Table 155)
C From Alton (Table 155)
D From Basingstoke (Table 155)

Table 152

Saturdays

until 27 September

For details of Bank Holiday service alterations, please see first page of Table 149

Hampton Court, Shepperton, Guildford, Dorking and Chessington South → London

Network Diagram - see first page of Table 152

Station		SW	SW A	SW B		SW	SW	SW 1 C	SW	SW	SW 1 D	SW	SW	SW A	SW B	SW	SW 1 C	SW	SW		SW 1 E	SW A	SW B	SW	SW	SW 1 C
Guildford	d					20 46				21 08									21 38					21 46		
London Road (Guildford)	d					20 50				21 12									21 42					21 50		
Clandon	d					20 55				21 17									21 47					21 55		
Horsley	d					20 59				21 21									21 51					21 59		
Effingham Junction 6	d					21 03				21 24									21 54					22 03		
Bookham	d					21 06																		22 06		
Cobham & Stoke d'Abernon	d									21 28									21 58							
Oxshott	d									21 31									22 01							
Claygate	d									21 34									22 04							
Hinchley Wood	d									21 37									22 07							
Hampton Court	d						21 24																		22 24	
Thames Ditton	d						21 26																		22 26	
Surbiton 6	d			21 27			21 32	21 38		21 42	21 47				21 57		22 08		22 12		22 17		22 27		22 32	22 38
Berrylands	d						21 34																		22 34	
Shepperton	d								21 11									21 41								
Upper Halliford	d								21 14									21 44								
Sunbury	d								21 16									21 46								
Kempton Park	d								21 18									21 48								
Hampton	d								21 21									21 51								
Fulwell	d								21 24									21 54								
Strawberry Hill	d		21 07											21 37								22 07				
Teddington	d		21 11						21 29					21 41				21 59				22 11				
Hampton Wick	d		21 14						21 31					21 44				22 01				22 14				
Kingston	a		21 16						21 33					21 46				22 03				22 16				
	d		21 19						21 34					21 49				22 04				22 19				
Norbiton	d		21 21						21 36					21 51				22 06				22 21				
New Malden 6	d		21 25				21 37		21 40					21 55				22 10				22 25			22 37	
Dorking 4	d															21 35										
Boxhill & Westhumble	d																									
Leatherhead	d					21 11										21 41								22 11		
Ashtead	d					21 14										21 44								22 14		
Epsom 3	a					21 19										21 49								22 19		
	d					21 20						21 35				21 50								22 20		
Ewell West	d					21 23						21 38				21 53								22 23		
Stoneleigh	d					21 25						21 40				21 55								22 25		
Worcester Park	d					21 28						21 43				21 58								22 28		
Chessington South	d	21 10											21 40													
Chessington North	d	21 12											21 42													
Tolworth	d	21 14											21 44													
Malden Manor	d	21 17											21 47													
Motspur Park	d	21 20				21 31						21 46	21 50			22 01								22 31		
Raynes Park 6	d	21 23	21 28			21 34	21 40		21 43			21 49	21 53	21 58		22 04		22 13				22 28		22 34	22 40	
Wimbledon 6 ⊖	d	21 27	21 32	21 35		21 38	21 44		21 47	21 50		21 53	21 57	22 02	22 05	22 08		22 17	22 20			22 32	22 35	22 38	22 44	
Earlsfield	d	21 31	21 35	21 38		21 42	21 47		21 50	21 54		21 57	22 01	22 05	22 08	22 12		22 20	22 24			22 35	22 38	22 42	22 47	
Clapham Junction 10	d	21 35	20 43	21 42		21 46	21 51	21 49	21 54	21 58	21 59	22 01	22 05	21 13	22 12	22 16		22 24	22 28			21 43	22 42	22 46	22 51	22 53
Vauxhall ⊖	d	21 40	21 44	21 47		21 51	21 56		21 59	22 03		22 06	22 10	22 14	22 17	22 21		22 29	22 33			22 44	22 47	22 51	22 56	
London Waterloo 15 ⊖	a	21 45	21 49	21 52		21 55	22 01	21 57	22 04	22 07	22 07	22 10	22 15	22 19	22 22	22 25	22 26	22 34	22 39		22 34	22 49	22 52	22 55	23 01	23 01

For general notes see front of timetable
For details of catering facilities see Directory of Train Operators

A From London Waterloo (Table 149)
B From Woking (Table 155)
C From Alton (Table 155)
D From Basingstoke (Table 155)
E From Portsmouth Harbour (Table 158)

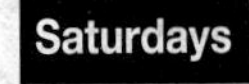

Saturdays

until 27 September

For details of Bank Holiday service alterations, please see first page of Table 149

Hampton Court, Shepperton, Guildford, Dorking and Chessington South → London

Network Diagram - see first page of Table 152

		SW	SW	SW ■1 A	SW	SW B	SW	SW	SW ■1 C	SW	SW	SW ■1 D	SW B	SW	SW	SW	SW ■1 C	SW	SW	SW	SW B	SW ■1 A
Guildford	d		22 08				22 20				22 38			22 55	22 46				23 08			
London Road (Guildford)	d		22 12								22 42				22 50				23 12			
Clandon	d		22 17								22 47				22 55				23 17			
Horsley	d		22 21								22 51				22 59				23 21			
Effingham Junction [6]	d		22 24								22 54				23 03				23 24			
Bookham	d														23 06							
Cobham & Stoke d'Abernon	d		22 28								22 58								23 28			
Oxshott	d		22 31								23 01								23 31			
Claygate	d		22 34								23 04								23 34			
Hinchley Wood	d		22 37								23 07								23 37			
Hampton Court	d															23 24						
Thames Ditton	d															23 26						
Surbiton [6]	d		22 42	22 47			22 57		23 08		23 12	23 17		23 30		23 33	23 38		23 42			23 57
Berrylands	d															23 35						
Shepperton	d	22 11								22 41								23 11				
Upper Halliford	d	22 14								22 44								23 14				
Sunbury	d	22 16								22 46								23 16				
Kempton Park	d	22 18								22 48								23 18				
Hampton	d	22 21								22 51								23 21				
Fulwell	d	22 24								22 54								23 24				
Strawberry Hill	d					22 37							23 07								23 37	
Teddington	d	22 29				22 41				22 59			23 11					23 29			23 41	
Hampton Wick	d	22 31				22 44				23 01			23 14					23 31			23 44	
Kingston	a	22 33				22 46				23 03			23 16					23 33			23 46	
	d	22 34				22 49				23 04			23 19					23 34			23 49	
Norbiton	d	22 36				22 51				23 06			23 21					23 36			23 51	
New Malden [6]	d	22 40				22 55				23 10			23 25			23 38		23 41			23 55	
Dorking [4]	d							22 35														
Boxhill & Westhumble	d																					
Leatherhead	d							22 41							23 11							
Ashtead	d							22 44							23 14							
Epsom [3]	a							22 49							23 19							
	d							22 50							23 20							
Ewell West	d							22 53							23 23							
Stoneleigh	d							22 55							23 25							
Worcester Park	d							22 58							23 28							
Chessington South	d				22 40															23 40		
Chessington North	d				22 42															23 42		
Tolworth	d				22 44															23 44		
Malden Manor	d				22 47															23 47		
Motspur Park	d				22 50			23 01							23 31					23 50		
Raynes Park [6]	d	22 43			22 53	22 58		23 04		23 13			23 28		23b37	23 41		23 43		23 54	23 58	
Wimbledon [6]	d	22 47	22 50		22 57	23 02	23 05	23 08		23 17	23 20		23 32	23 37	23 41	23 45		23 52	23 58	00a02	00 07	00 08
Earlsfield	d	22 50	22 54		23 01	23 06	23 08	23 12		23 20	23 24		23 35	23 41	23 44	23 48		23 55	00 01		00 10	00 10
Clapham Junction [10]	d	22 54	22 58	22 59	23 05	22 13	23 12	23 16		23 24	23 28		22 43	23 45	23 48	23 52	23 53	23 59	00 05		23 13	00 14
Vauxhall	d	22 59	23 03		23 10	23 15	23 17	23 21		23 29	23 33		23 44	23 50	23 53	23 58		00 04	00 10		00 19	00 19
London Waterloo [15]	a	23 04	23 07	23 06	23 15	23 19	23 22	23 25	23 25	23 34	23 37	23 37	23 49	23 54	23 58	00 02	00 03	00 09	00 14		00 24	00 29

For general notes see front of timetable
For details of catering facilities see Directory of Train Operators

- **A** From Basingstoke (Table 155)
- **B** From London Waterloo (Table 149)
- **C** From Alton (Table 155)
- **D** From Portsmouth Harbour (Table 158)
- **b** Arr. 2334

Table 152

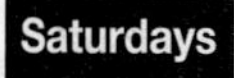

from 4 October

For details of Bank Holiday service alterations, please see first page of Table 149

Hampton Court, Shepperton, Guildford, Dorking and Chessington South → London

Network Diagram - see first page of Table 152

		SW	SW	SW	SW 1	SW	SW 1	SW	SW	SW 1	SW	SW	SW	SW	SW		SW	SW	SW	SW 1	SW	SW	SW	SW	SW	SW
				A	B	A	C		D	B							A	E		G				A	E	
Guildford	d		23p08					04 00					05 12													06 28
London Road (Guildford)	d		23p12																							06 32
Clandon	d		23p17																							06 37
Horsley	d		23p21																							06 41
Effingham Junction 6	d		23p24																							06 46
Bookham	d																									06 49
Cobham & Stoke d'Abernon	d		23p28																							
Oxshott	d		23p31																							
Claygate	d		23p34																							
Hinchley Wood	d		23p37																							
Hampton Court	d													05 54					06 24							
Thames Ditton	d													05 56					06 26							
Surbiton 6	d		23p42		23p57		00 40	04 24		05 40			05 57	06 02				06 27	06 32	06 47					06 57	
Berrylands	d													06 04					06 34							
Shepperton	d	23p11																			06 11					
Upper Halliford	d	23p14																			06 14					
Sunbury	d	23p16																			06 16					
Kempton Park	d	23p18																			06 18					
Hampton	d	23p21																			06 21					
Fulwell	d	23p24																			06 24					
Strawberry Hill	d			23p37		00 12			04 55								06 07							06 37		
Teddington	d	23p29		23p41		00 15			04 59			05 44					06 11				06 29			06 41		
Hampton Wick	d	23p31		23p44		00 17			05 01			05 46					06 14				06 31			06 44		
Kingston	a	23p33		23p46		00 19			05 03			05 48					06 16				06 33			06 46		
	d	23p34		23p49					05 04			05 49					06 19				06 34			06 49		
Norbiton	d	23p36		23p51					05 06			05 51					06 21				06 36			06 51		
New Malden 6	d	23p40		23p55					05 10			05 55		06 07			06 25		06 37		06 40			06 55		
Dorking 4	d																									
Boxhill & Westhumble	d																									
Leatherhead	d																									
Ashtead	d																									06 54
Epsom 3	a																									06 58
	d										05 35				06 05							06 35				07 02
Ewell West	d										05 38				06 08							06 38				07 05
Stoneleigh	d										05 40				06 10							06 40				07 08 →
Worcester Park	d										05 43				06 13							06 43				
Chessington South	d																						06 40			
Chessington North	d																						06 42			
Tolworth	d																						06 44			
Malden Manor	d																						06 47			
Motspur Park	d										05 46				06 16							06 46	06 50			
Raynes Park 6	d	23p43		23p58					05 13		05 49	05 58		06 10	06 19		06 28		06 40		06 43	06 49	06 53	06 58		
Wimbledon 6 ⊖	d	23p49	23p55	00 05	00 08		00 48	04 32	05 17	05 49	05 53	06 02	06 05	06 14	06 23		06 32	06 35	06 44		06 47	06 53	06 57	07 02	07 05	
Earlsfield	d	23p55	23p58	00 08	00 10				05 21		05 57	06 05	06 08	06 17	06 27		06 35	06 38	06 47		06 50	06 57	07 01	07 05	07 08	
Clapham Junction 10	d	23p59	00 02	23p13	00 14		00 55	04 44	05 25	06 01	06 01	06 09	06 12	06 21	06 31		05 43	06 42	06 51	06 59	06 54	07 01	07 05	06 13	07 12	
Vauxhall ⊖	d	00 04	00 07	00 17	00 19				05 30	06 08	06 06	06 14	06 17	06 26	06 36		06 44	06 47	06 56		06 59	07 06	07 10	07 14	07 17	
London Waterloo 15 ⊖	a	00 09	00 13	00 22	00 27		01 02	04 53	05 35	06 15	06 11	06 19	06 22	06 31	06 40		06 49	06 52	07 01	07 09	07 04	07 10	07 15	07 19	07 22	

For general notes see front of timetable
For details of catering facilities see Directory of Train Operators

A From London Waterloo (Table 149)
B From Basingstoke (Table 155)
C From Weymouth (Table 158)
D From Twickenham (Table 149)
E From Woking (Table 155)
G From Southampton Central (Table 158)

Table 152

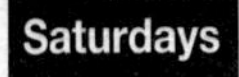

Saturdays

from 4 October

For details of Bank Holiday service alterations, please see first page of Table 149

Hampton Court, Shepperton, Guildford, Dorking and Chessington South → London

Network Diagram - see first page of Table 152

		SW	SW [1] A	SW	SW	SW [1] B	SW		SW	SW C	SW D	SW	SW	SW [1] A	SW	SW	SW [1] E	SW	SW	SW C	SW D	SW		SW	SW [1] A	SW
Guildford	d				06 35							06 58				07 05						07 28				
London Road (Guildford)	d				06 39							07 02				07 09						07 32				
Clandon	d				06 44							07 07				07 14						07 37				
Horsley	d				06 48							07 11				07 18						07 41				
Effingham Junction [6]	d				06 51							07 16				07 21						07 46				
Bookham	d											07 19										07 49				
Cobham & Stoke d'Abernon	d				06 55											07 25										
Oxshott	d				06 58											07 28										
Claygate	d				07 01											07 31										
Hinchley Wood	d				07 04											07 34										
Hampton Court	d	06 54											07 24											07 54		
Thames Ditton	d	06 56											07 26											07 56		
Surbiton [6]	d	07 02	07 08		07 12	07 17					07 27		07 32	07 38		07 42	07 47				07 57			08 02	08 08	
Berrylands	d	07 04											07 34											08 04		
Shepperton	d			06 41											07 11											07 41
Upper Halliford	d			06 44											07 14											07 44
Sunbury	d			06 46											07 16											07 46
Kempton Park	d			06 48											07 18											07 48
Hampton	d			06 51											07 21											07 51
Fulwell	d			06 54											07 24											07 54
Strawberry Hill	d									07 07										07 37						
Teddington	d			06 59						07 11					07 29					07 41						07 59
Hampton Wick	d			07 01						07 14					07 31					07 44						08 01
Kingston	a			07 03						07 16					07 33					07 46						08 03
	d			07 04						07 19					07 34					07 49						08 04
Norbiton	d			07 06						07 21					07 36					07 51						08 06
New Malden [6]	d	07 07		07 10						07 25			07 37		07 40					07 55				08 07		08 10
Dorking [4]	d																									
Boxhill & Westhumble	d																									
Leatherhead	d											07 24										07 54				
Ashtead	d											07 28										07 58				
Epsom [3]	a											07 32										08 02				
	d						←					07 35						←				08 05				
Ewell West	d						07 08					07 38 →						07 38				08 08 →				
Stoneleigh	d						07 10											07 40								
Worcester Park	d						07 13											07 43								
Chessington South	d								07 10										07 40							
Chessington North	d								07 12										07 42							
Tolworth	d								07 14										07 44							
Malden Manor	d								07 17										07 47							
Motspur Park	d						07 16		07 20									07 46	07 50							
Raynes Park [6]	d	07 10		07 13			07 19		07 23	07 28			07 40		07 43			07 49	07 53	07 58				08 10		08 13
Wimbledon [6] ⊖ ⛴	d	07 14		07 17	07 20		07 23		07 27	07 32	07 35		07 44		07 47	07 50		07 53	07 57	08 02	08 05			08 14		08 17
Earlsfield	d	07 17		07 20	07 24		07 27		07 31	07 35	07 38		07 47		07 50	07 54		07 57	08 01	08 05	08 08			08 17		08 20
Clapham Junction [10]	d	07 21	07 19	07 24	07 28		07 31		07 35	06 43	07 42		07 51	07 51	07 54	07 58	07 59	08 01	08 05	07 13	08 12			08 21		08 24
Vauxhall ⊖	d	07 26		07 29	07 33		07 36		07 40	07 44	07 47		07 56		07 59	08 03		08 06	08 10	08 14	08 17			08 26		08 29
London Waterloo [15] ⊖	a	07 31	07 30	07 34	07 37	07 33	07 40		07 45	07 49	07 52		08 01	07 58	08 04	08 07	08 06	08 10	08 15	08 19	08 22			08 31	08 25	08 34

For general notes see front of timetable
For details of catering facilities see Directory of Train Operators

A From Alton (Table 155)
B From Southampton Central (Table 158)
C From London Waterloo (Table 149)
D From Woking (Table 155)
E From Basingstoke (Table 155)

Table 152

from 4 October

For details of Bank Holiday service alterations, please see first page of Table 149

Hampton Court, Shepperton, Guildford, Dorking and Chessington South → London

Network Diagram - see first page of Table 152

Station		SW	SW 1 A	SW	SW	SW B	SW C	SW	SW	SW	SW 1 D	SW
Guildford	d	07 35							07 58			
London Road (Guildford)	d	07 39							08 02			
Clandon	d	07 44							08 07			
Horsley	d	07 48							08 11			
Effingham Junction 6	d	07 51							08 16			
Bookham	d								08 19			
Cobham & Stoke d'Abernon	d	07 55										
Oxshott	d	07 58										
Claygate	d	08 01										
Hinchley Wood	d	08 04										
Hampton Court	d									08 24		
Thames Ditton	d									08 26		
Surbiton 6	d	08 12	08 17				08 27			08 32	08 38	
Berrylands	d									08 34		
Shepperton	d											08 11
Upper Halliford	d											08 14
Sunbury	d											08 16
Kempton Park	d											08 18
Hampton	d											08 21
Fulwell	d											08 24
Strawberry Hill	d					08 07						
Teddington	d					08 11						08 29
Hampton Wick	d					08 14						08 31
Kingston	a					08 16						08 33
	d					08 19						08 34
Norbiton	d					08 21						08 36
New Malden 6	d					08 25				08 37		08 40
Dorking 4	d							08 05				
Boxhill & Westhumble	d											
Leatherhead	d							08 11	08 24			
Ashtead	d							08 14	08 28			
Epsom 3	a							08 19	08 32			
	d			←				08 20	08 35			
Ewell West	d			08 08				08 23	08 38			
Stoneleigh	d			08 10				08 25	→			
Worcester Park	d			08 13				08 28				
Chessington South	d				08 10							
Chessington North	d				08 12							
Tolworth	d				08 14							
Malden Manor	d				08 17							
Motspur Park	d			08 16	08 20			08 31				
Raynes Park 6	d			08 19	08 23	08 28		08 34		08 40		08 43
Wimbledon 6 ⊖ 🚋	d	08 20		08 23	08 27	08 32	08 35	08 38		08 44		08 47
Earlsfield	d	08 24		08 27	08 31	08 35	08 38	08 42		08 47		08 50
Clapham Junction 10	d	08 28		08 31	08 35	07 43	08 42	08 46		08 51	08 50	08 54
Vauxhall ⊖	d	08 33		08 36	08 40	08 44	08 47	08 51		08 56		08 59
London Waterloo 15 ⊖	a	08 37	08 34	08 40	08 45	08 49	08 52	08 55		09 01	08 58	09 04

Station		SW	SW 1 E	SW	SW	SW B	SW C	SW	SW	SW	SW 1 D	SW	SW	SW 1 E
Guildford	d	08 05							08 28				08 35	
London Road (Guildford)	d	08 09							08 32				08 39	
Clandon	d	08 14							08 37				08 44	
Horsley	d	08 18							08 41				08 48	
Effingham Junction 6	d	08 21							08 46				08 51	
Bookham	d								08 49					
Cobham & Stoke d'Abernon	d	08 25											08 55	
Oxshott	d	08 28											08 58	
Claygate	d	08 31											09 01	
Hinchley Wood	d	08 34											09 04	
Hampton Court	d									08 54				
Thames Ditton	d									08 56				
Surbiton 6	d	08 42	08 47				08 57			09 02	09 08		09 12	09 17
Berrylands	d									09 04				
Shepperton	d											08 41		
Upper Halliford	d											08 44		
Sunbury	d											08 46		
Kempton Park	d											08 48		
Hampton	d											08 51		
Fulwell	d											08 54		
Strawberry Hill	d					08 37								
Teddington	d					08 41						08 59		
Hampton Wick	d					08 44						09 01		
Kingston	a					08 46						09 03		
	d					08 49						09 04		
Norbiton	d					08 51						09 06		
New Malden 6	d					08 55				09 07		09 10		
Dorking 4	d							08 35						
Boxhill & Westhumble	d													
Leatherhead	d							08 41	08 54					
Ashtead	d							08 44	08 58					
Epsom 3	a							08 49	09 02					
	d			←				08 50	09 05					
Ewell West	d			08 38				08 53	09 08					
Stoneleigh	d			08 40				08 55	→					
Worcester Park	d			08 43				08 58						
Chessington South	d				08 40									
Chessington North	d				08 42									
Tolworth	d				08 44									
Malden Manor	d				08 47									
Motspur Park	d			08 46	08 50			09 01						
Raynes Park 6	d			08 49	08 53	08 58		09 04		09 10		09 13		
Wimbledon 6 ⊖ 🚋	d	08 50		08 53	08 57	09 02	09 05	09 08		09 14		09 17	09 20	
Earlsfield	d	08 54		08 57	09 01	09 05	09 08	09 12		09 17		09 20	09 24	
Clapham Junction 10	d	08 58	08 59	09 01	09 05	08 13	09 12	09 16		09 21		09 24	09 28	
Vauxhall ⊖	d	09 03		09 06	09 10	09 14	09 17	09 21		09 26		09 29	09 33	
London Waterloo 15 ⊖	a	09 07	09 06	09 10	09 15	09 19	09 22	09 25		09 31	09 25	09 34	09 37	09 35

For general notes see front of timetable
For details of catering facilities see Directory of Train Operators

A From Portsmouth Harbour (Table 158)
B From London Waterloo (Table 149)
C From Woking (Table 155)
D From Alton (Table 155)
E From Basingstoke (Table 155)

from 4 October

For details of Bank Holiday service alterations, please see first page of Table 149

Hampton Court, Shepperton, Guildford, Dorking and Chessington South → London

Network Diagram - see first page of Table 152

Station		SW	SW	SW	SW	SW	SW	SW	SW 1	SW		SW	SW 1	SW	SW	SW	SW	SW	SW	SW 1	SW	SW	SW 1	SW
				A	B				C				D			A	B			C			D	
Guildford	d						08 58					20 05										20 35		
London Road (Guildford)	d						09 02					20 09										20 39		
Clandon	d						09 07					20 14										20 44		
Horsley	d						09 11					20 18										20 48		
Effingham Junction 6	d						09 16					20 21										20 51		
Bookham	d						09 19																	
Cobham & Stoke d'Abernon	d											20 25										20 55		
Oxshott	d											20 28										20 58		
Claygate	d											20 31										21 01		
Hinchley Wood	d											20 34										21 04		
Hampton Court	d							09 24											20 54					
Thames Ditton	d							09 26											20 56					
Surbiton 6	d				09 27			09 32	09 38			20 42	20 47				20 57		21 02	21 08		21 12	21 17	
Berrylands	d							09 34											21 04					
Shepperton	d									09 11											20 41			
Upper Halliford	d									09 14											20 44			
Sunbury	d									09 16	and at										20 46			
Kempton Park	d									09 18											20 48			
Hampton	d									09 21	the same										20 51			
Fulwell	d									09 24											20 54			
Strawberry Hill	d			09 07							minutes					20 37								
Teddington	d			09 11						09 29	past					20 41					20 59			
Hampton Wick	d			09 14						09 31						20 44					21 01			
Kingston	a			09 16						09 33	each					20 46					21 03			
	d			09 19						09 34	hour until					20 49					21 04			
Norbiton	d			09 21						09 36						20 51					21 06			
New Malden 6	d			09 25				09 37		09 40						20 55			21 07		21 10			
Dorking 4	d					09 05												20 35						
Boxhill & Westhumble	d																							
Leatherhead	d					09 11	09 24											20 41						
Ashtead	d					09 14	09 28											20 44						
Epsom 3	a					09 19	09 32											20 49						
	d	⟵				09 20	09 35							⟵				20 50						21 05
Ewell West	d	09 08				09 23	09 38							20 38				20 53						21 08
Stoneleigh	d	09 10				09 25	⟶							20 40				20 55						21 10
Worcester Park	d	09 13				09 28								20 43				20 58						21 13
Chessington South	d		09 10												20 40									
Chessington North	d		09 12												20 42									
Tolworth	d		09 14												20 44									
Malden Manor	d		09 17												20 47									
Motspur Park	d	09 16	09 20			09 31								20 46	20 50			21 01						21 16
Raynes Park 6	d	09 19	09 23	09 28		09 34		09 40		09 43				20 49	20 53	20 58		21 04	21 10		21 13			21 19
Wimbledon 6 ⊖	d	09 23	09 27	09 32	09 35	09 38		09 44		09 47		20 50		20 53	20 57	21 02	21 05	21 08	21 14		21 17	21 20		21 23
Earlsfield	d	09 27	09 31	09 35	09 38	09 42		09 47		09 50		20 54		20 57	21 01	21 05	21 08	21 12	21 17		21 20	21 24		21 27
Clapham Junction 10	d	09 31	09 35	08 43	09 42	09 46		09 51	09 49	09 54		20 58	20 59	21 01	21 05	20 13	21 12	21 16	21 21		21 24	21 28		21 31
Vauxhall ⊖	d	09 36	09 40	09 44	09 47	09 51		09 56		09 59		21 03		21 06	21 10	21 14	21 17	21 21	21 26		21 29	21 33		21 36
London Waterloo 15 ⊖	a	09 40	09 45	09 49	09 52	09 55		10 01	09 57	10 04		21 07	21 06	21 10	21 15	21 19	21 23	21 25	21 31	21 29	21 34	21 37	21 34	21 40

For general notes see front of timetable
For details of catering facilities see Directory of Train Operators

A From London Waterloo (Table 149)
B From Woking (Table 155)
C From Alton (Table 155)
D From Basingstoke (Table 155)

Saturdays

from 4 October

For details of Bank Holiday service alterations, please see first page of Table 149

Hampton Court, Shepperton, Guildford, Dorking and Chessington South → London

Network Diagram - see first page of Table 152

		SW	SW	SW		SW	SW	SW 1	SW	SW	SW 1	SW	SW	SW	SW	SW	SW 1	SW	SW		SW 1	SW	SW	SW	SW	SW 1
			A	B				C			D			A	B		C				E	A	B			C
Guildford	d					20 46				21 05									21 35					21 46		
London Road (Guildford)	d					20 50				21 09									21 39					21 50		
Clandon	d					20 55				21 14									21 44					21 55		
Horsley	d					20 59				21 18									21 48					21 59		
Effingham Junction 6	d					21 03				21 21									21 51					22 03		
Bookham	d					21 06																		22 06		
Cobham & Stoke d'Abernon	d									21 25									21 55							
Oxshott	d									21 28									21 58							
Claygate	d									21 31									22 01							
Hinchley Wood	d									21 34									22 04							
Hampton Court	d						21 24																		22 24	
Thames Ditton	d						21 26																		22 26	
Surbiton 6	d			21 27			21 32	21 38		21 42	21 47				21 57		22 08		22 12		22 17		22 27		22 32	22 38
Berrylands	d						21 34																		22 34	
Shepperton	d								21 11									21 41								
Upper Halliford	d								21 14									21 44								
Sunbury	d								21 16									21 46								
Kempton Park	d								21 18									21 48								
Hampton	d								21 21									21 51								
Fulwell	d								21 24									21 54								
Strawberry Hill	d		21 07											21 37								22 07				
Teddington	d		21 11						21 29					21 41				21 59				22 11				
Hampton Wick	d		21 14						21 31					21 44				22 01				22 14				
Kingston	a		21 16						21 33					21 46				22 03				22 16				
	d		21 19						21 34					21 49				22 04				22 19				
Norbiton	d		21 21						21 36					21 51				22 06				22 21				
New Malden 6	d		21 25				21 37		21 40					21 55				22 10				22 25			22 37	
Dorking 4	d															21 35										
Boxhill & Westhumble	d																									
Leatherhead	d					21 11										21 41								22 11		
Ashtead	d					21 14										21 44								22 14		
Epsom 3	a					21 19										21 49								22 19		
	d					21 20						21 35				21 50								22 20		
Ewell West	d					21 23						21 38				21 53								22 23		
Stoneleigh	d					21 25						21 40				21 55								22 25		
Worcester Park	d					21 28						21 43				21 58								22 28		
Chessington South	d	21 10											21 40													
Chessington North	d	21 12											21 42													
Tolworth	d	21 14											21 44													
Malden Manor	d	21 17											21 47													
Motspur Park	d	21 20				21 31						21 46	21 50			22 01								22 31		
Raynes Park 6	d	21 23	21 28			21 34	21 40		21 43			21 49	21 53	21 58		22 04		22 13				22 28		22 34	22 40	
Wimbledon 6 ⊖ ⛴	d	21 27	21 32	21 35		21 38	21 44		21 47	21 50		21 53	21 57	22 02	22 05	22 08		22 17	22 20			22 32	22 35	22 38	22 44	
Earlsfield	d	21 31	21 35	21 38		21 42	21 47		21 50	21 54		21 57	22 01	22 05	22 08	22 12		22 20	22 24			22 35	22 38	22 42	22 47	
Clapham Junction 10	d	21 35	20 43	21 42		21 46	21 51	21 49	21 54	21 58	21 59	22 01	22 05	21 13	22 12	22 16		22 24	22 28			21 43	22 42	22 46	22 51	22 53
Vauxhall ⊖	d	21 40	21 44	21 47		21 51	21 56		21 59	22 03		22 06	22 10	22 14	22 17	22 21		22 29	22 33			22 44	22 47	22 51	22 56	
London Waterloo 15 ⊖	a	21 45	21 49	21 52		21 55	22 01	21 57	22 04	22 07	22 07	22 10	22 15	22 19	22 22	22 25	22 26	22 34	22 39		22 34	22 49	22 52	22 55	23 01	23 01

For general notes see front of timetable
For details of catering facilities see Directory of Train Operators

A From London Waterloo (Table 149)
B From Woking (Table 155)
C From Alton (Table 155)
D From Basingstoke (Table 155)
E From Portsmouth Harbour (Table 158)

Table 152

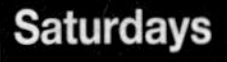

Saturdays

from 4 October

For details of Bank Holiday service alterations, please see first page of Table 149

Hampton Court, Shepperton, Guildford, Dorking and Chessington South → London

Network Diagram - see first page of Table 152

		SW	SW	SW 1 A	SW	SW B	SW	SW	SW 1 C	SW	SW		SW 1 D	SW B	SW	SW	SW	SW 1 C	SW	SW	SW	SW B	SW 1 A
Guildford	d		22 05				22 20				22 35				22 55	22 46				23 08			
London Road (Guildford)	d		22 09								22 39					22 50				23 12			
Clandon	d		22 14								22 44					22 55				23 17			
Horsley	d		22 18								22 48					22 59				23 21			
Effingham Junction 6	d		22 21								22 51					23 03				23 24			
Bookham	d															23 06							
Cobham & Stoke d'Abernon	d		22 25								22 55									23 28			
Oxshott	d		22 28								22 58									23 31			
Claygate	d		22 31								23 01									23 34			
Hinchley Wood	d		22 34								23 04									23 37			
Hampton Court	d																23 24						
Thames Ditton	d																23 26						
Surbiton 6	d		22 42	22 47			22 57		23 08		23 12		23 17		23 30		23 33	23 38		23 42			23 57
Berrylands	d																23 35						
Shepperton	d	22 11								22 41									23 11				
Upper Halliford	d	22 14								22 44									23 14				
Sunbury	d	22 16								22 46									23 16				
Kempton Park	d	22 18								22 48									23 18				
Hampton	d	22 21								22 51									23 21				
Fulwell	d	22 24								22 54									23 24				
Strawberry Hill	d					22 37								23 07								23 37	
Teddington	d	22 29				22 41				22 59				23 11					23 29			23 41	
Hampton Wick	d	22 31				22 44				23 01				23 14					23 31			23 44	
Kingston	a	22 33				22 46				23 03				23 16					23 33			23 46	
	d	22 34				22 49				23 04				23 19					23 34			23 49	
Norbiton	d	22 36				22 51				23 06				23 21					23 36			23 51	
New Malden 6	d	22 40				22 55				23 10				23 25			23 38		23 41			23 55	
Dorking 4	d							22 35															
Boxhill & Westhumble	d																						
Leatherhead	d							22 41								23 11							
Ashtead	d							22 44								23 14							
Epsom 3	a							22 49								23 19							
	d							22 50								23 20							
Ewell West	d							22 53								23 23							
Stoneleigh	d							22 55								23 25							
Worcester Park	d							22 58								23 28							
Chessington South	d				22 40																23 40		
Chessington North	d				22 42																23 42		
Tolworth	d				22 44																23 44		
Malden Manor	d				22 47																23 47		
Motspur Park	d				22 50			23 01								23 31					23 50		
Raynes Park 6	d	22 43			22 53	22 58		23 04		23 13				23 28		23b37	23 41		23 43		23 54	23 58	
Wimbledon 6 ⊖ 🚋	d	22 47	22 50		22 57	23 02	23 05	23 08		23 17	23 20			23 32	23 37	23 41	23 45		23 52	23 58	00a02	00 07	00 08
Earlsfield	d	22 50	22 54		23 01	23 06	23 08	23 12		23 20	23 24			23 35	23 41	23 44	23 48		23 55	00 01		00 10	00 10
Clapham Junction 10	d	22 54	22 58	22 59	23 05	22 13	23 12	23 16		23 24	23 28			22 43	23 45	23 48	23 52	23 53	23 59	00 05		23 13	00 14
Vauxhall ⊖	d	22 59	23 03		23 10	23 15	23 17	23 21		23 29	23 33			23 44	23 50	23 53	23 58		00 04	00 10		00 19	00 19
London Waterloo 15 ⊖	a	23 04	23 07	23 06	23 15	23 19	23 22	23 25	23 25	23 34	23 37		23 37	23 49	23 54	23 58	00 02	00 03	00 09	00 14		00 24	00 29

For general notes see front of timetable
For details of catering facilities see Directory of Train Operators

A From Basingstoke (Table 155)
B From London Waterloo (Table 149)
C From Alton (Table 155)
D From Portsmouth Harbour (Table 158)
b Arr. 2334

Table 152

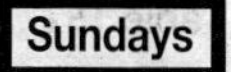

until 21 September

For details of Bank Holiday service alterations, please see first page of Table 149

Hampton Court, Shepperton, Guildford, Dorking and Chessington South → London

Network Diagram - see first page of Table 152

		SW	SW	SW	SW 1	SW	SW 1	SW	SW	SW	SW	SW	SW	SW	SW	SW	SW	SW	SW	SW	SW 1	SW	SW	SW	SW
				A	B	A	C				D	A								A	E				
Guildford	d		23p08											06 57				07 27						07 50	07 57
London Road (Guildford)	d		23p12																					07 54	
Clandon	d		23p17																					07 59	
Horsley	d		23p21																					08 03	
Effingham Junction 6	d		23p24																					08 06	
Bookham	d																								
Cobham & Stoke d'Abernon	d		23p28																					08 10	
Oxshott	d		23p31																					08 13	
Claygate	d		23p34																					08 16	
Hinchley Wood	d		23p37																					08 19	
Hampton Court	d																07 35					08 05			
Thames Ditton	d																07 37					08 07			
Surbiton 6	d		23p42		23p57		00 40				07 00			07 30			07 43	08 00			08 10	08 13		08 24	08 30
Berrylands	d																07 45					08 15			
Shepperton	d	23p11														07 11									
Upper Halliford	d	23p14														07 14									
Sunbury	d	23p16														07 16									
Kempton Park	d	23p18														07 18									
Hampton	d	23p21														07 21									
Fulwell	d	23p24														07 24									
Strawberry Hill	d			23p37		00 12						06 49								07 49					
Teddington	d	23p29		23p41		00 15						06b55				07 29				07c55					
Hampton Wick	d	23p31		23p44		00 17						06 57				07 31				07 57					
Kingston	a	23p33		23p46		00 19						06 59				07 33				07 59					
	d	23p34		23p49								07 04				07 34				08 04					
Norbiton	d	23p36		23p51								07 06				07 36				08 06					
New Malden 6	d	23p41		23p55								07 10				07 40	07 48			08 10		08 18			
Dorking 4	d																								
Boxhill & Westhumble	d																								
Leatherhead	d																								
Ashtead	d																								
Epsom 3	a																								
	d														07 24				07 54						
Ewell West	d														07 27				07 57						
Stoneleigh	d														07 29				07 59						
Worcester Park	d														07 32				08 02						
Chessington South	d																						08 10		
Chessington North	d																						08 12		
Tolworth	d																						08 14		
Malden Manor	d																						08 17		
Motspur Park	d														07 35				08 05				08 20		
Raynes Park 6	d	23p43		23p58								07 13			07 38	07 43	07 51		08 08	08 13		08 21	08 24		
Wimbledon 6 ⊖ ⛴	d	23p52	23p58	00 07	00 08		00 48	05 31	06 12	06 42	07 08	07e19	07 31	07 38	07 42	07 47	07 55	08 08	08 12	08 17	08 17	08 25	08 28	08a33	08 38
Earlsfield	d	23p55	00 01	00 10	00 10					06 46	07 11	07 22	07 34	07 41	07 46	07 50	07 58	08 11	08 16	08 20		08 28	08 31		08 41
Clapham Junction 10	d	23p59	00 05	23p13	00 14		00 55	05 38	06 20	06 50	07 15	06 24	07 38	07 45	07 50	07 54	08 02	08 15	08 20	07 24	08 24	08 34	08 37		08 45
Vauxhall ⊖	d	00 04	00 10	00 19	00 19			05 43	06 25	06 55	07 20	07 31	07 43	07 50	07 55	07 59	08 07	08 20	08 25	08 29		08 39	08 42		08 50
London Waterloo 15 ⊖	a	00 09	00 14	00 24	00 29		01 02	05 54	06 34	07 04	07 30	07 41	07 53	08 00	08 04	08 07	08 17	08 30	08 34	08 39	08 39	08 47	08 50		09 00

For general notes see front of timetable
For details of catering facilities see Directory of Train Operators

A From London Waterloo (Table 149)
B From Basingstoke (Table 155)
C From Weymouth (Table 158)
D From Woking (Table 155)
E From Farnham (Table 155) and from Basingstoke (Table 155)
b Arr. 0652
c Arr. 0752
e Arr. 0716

Table 152

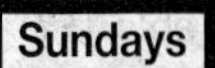

Sundays

until 21 September

For details of Bank Holiday service alterations, please see first page of Table 149

Hampton Court, Shepperton, Guildford, Dorking and Chessington South → London

Network Diagram - see first page of Table 152

		SW	SW		SW	SW	SW	SW	SW	SW	SW	SW	SW	SW	SW	SW		SW	SW	SW	SW	SW	SW	SW	SW	SW
										1													1			
									A	B												A	B			
Guildford	d						08 27	08 20					08 50	08 57						09 27	09 20					09 50
London Road (Guildford)	d							08 24					08 54								09 24					09 54
Clandon	d							08 29					08 59								09 29					09 59
Horsley	d							08 33					09 03								09 33					10 03
Effingham Junction 6	d							08 36					09 06								09 36					10 06
Bookham	d							08 39													09 39					
Cobham & Stoke d'Abernon	d												09 10													10 10
Oxshott	d												09 13													10 13
Claygate	d												09 16													10 16
Hinchley Wood	d												09 19													10 19
Hampton Court	d				08 35						09 05							09 35						10 05		
Thames Ditton	d				08 37						09 07							09 37						10 07		
Surbiton 6	d				08 43		09 00			09 10	09 13		09 24	09 30				09 43		10 00			10 10	10 13		10 24
Berrylands	d				08 45						09 15							09 45						10 15		
Shepperton	d		08 11													09 11										
Upper Halliford	d		08 14													09 14										
Sunbury	d		08 16													09 16										
Kempton Park	d		08 18													09 18										
Hampton	d		08 21													09 21										
Fulwell	d		08 24													09 24										
Strawberry Hill	d								08 49													09 49				
Teddington	d		08 29						08b55							09 29						09c55				
Hampton Wick	d		08 31						08 57							09 31						09 57				
Kingston	a		08 33						08 59							09 33						09 59				
	d		08 34						09 04							09 34						10 04				
Norbiton	d		08 36						09 06							09 36						10 06				
New Malden 6	d		08 40		08 48				09 10		09 18					09 40		09 48				10 10		10 18		
Dorking 4	d														09 08											
Boxhill & Westhumble	d																									
Leatherhead	d							08 45							09 15						09 45					
Ashtead	d							08 48							09 18						09 48					
Epsom 3	a							08 53							09 23						09 53					
	d	08 24						08 54							09 24						09 54					
Ewell West	d	08 27						08 57							09 27						09 57					
Stoneleigh	d	08 29						08 59							09 29						09 59					
Worcester Park	d	08 32						09 02							09 32						10 02					
Chessington South	d					08 40						09 10							09 40						10 10	
Chessington North	d					08 42						09 12							09 42						10 12	
Tolworth	d					08 44						09 14							09 44						10 14	
Malden Manor	d					08 47						09 17							09 47						10 17	
Motspur Park	d	08 35				08 50		09 05				09 20			09 35				09 50		10 05				10 20	
Raynes Park 6	d	08 38	08 43		08 51	08 54		09 08	09 13		09 21	09 24			09 38	09 43		09 51	09 54		10 08	10 13		10 21	10 24	
Wimbledon 6 ⊖	d	08 42	08 47		08 55	08 58	09 08	09 12	09 17	09 17	09 25	09 28	09a33	09 38	09 42	09 47		09 55	09 58	10 08	10 12	10 17	10 17	10 25	10 28	10a33
Earlsfield	d	08 46	08 50		08 58	09 01	09 11	09 16	09 20		09 28	09 31		09 41	09 46	09 50		09 58	10 01	10 11	10 16	10 20		10 28	10 31	
Clapham Junction 10	d	08 50	08 54		09 02	09 09	09 15	09 20	08 24	09 24	09 32	09 36		09 45	09 50	09 54		10 02	10 05	10 15	10 20	09 24	10 24	10 32	10 36	
Vauxhall ⊖	d	08 55	08 59		09 07	09 14	09 20	09 25	09 29		09 37	09 41		09 50	09 55	09 59		10 07	10 10	10 20	10 25	10 29		10 37	10 41	
London Waterloo 15 ⊖	a	09 04	09 07		09 17	09 20	09 30	09 34	09 39	09 39	09 47	09 50		10 00	10 04	10 07		10 17	10 20	10 30	10 34	10 39	10 39	10 47	10 50	

For general notes see front of timetable
For details of catering facilities see Directory of Train Operators

A From London Waterloo (Table 149)
B From Alton (Table 155) and from Basingstoke (Table 155)
b Arr. 0852
c Arr. 0952

until 21 September

For details of Bank Holiday service alterations, please see first page of Table 149

Hampton Court, Shepperton, Guildford, Dorking and Chessington South → London

Network Diagram - see first page of Table 152

		SW	SW	SW	SW	SW		SW	SW	SW	SW	SW	SW	SW	SW	SW	SW	SW	SW		SW	SW	SW	SW	SW	SW
											1													1		
										A	B												A	B		
Guildford	d	09 57						10 27	10 20					10 50	10 57						11 27	11 20				
London Road (Guildford)	d								10 24					10 54								11 24				
Clandon	d								10 29					10 59								11 29				
Horsley	d								10 33					11 03								11 33				
Effingham Junction 6	d								10 36					11 06								11 36				
Bookham	d								10 39													11 39				
Cobham & Stoke d'Abernon	d													11 10												
Oxshott	d													11 13												
Claygate	d													11 16												
Hinchley Wood	d													11 19												
Hampton Court	d				10 35							11 05						11 35							12 05	
Thames Ditton	d				10 37							11 07						11 37							12 07	
Surbiton 6	d	10 30			10 43			11 00			11 10	11 13		11 24	11 30			11 43			12 00			12 10	12 13	
Berrylands	d				10 45							11 15						11 45							12 15	
Shepperton	d			10 11													11 11									
Upper Halliford	d			10 14													11 14									
Sunbury	d			10 16													11 16									
Kempton Park	d			10 18													11 18									
Hampton	d			10 21													11 21									
Fulwell	d			10 24													11 24									
Strawberry Hill	d									10 49													11 49			
Teddington	d			10 29						10b55							11 29						11c55			
Hampton Wick	d			10 31						10 57							11 31						11 57			
Kingston	a			10 33						10 59							11 33						11 59			
	d			10 34						11 04							11 34						12 04			
Norbiton	d			10 36						11 06							11 36						12 06			
New Malden 6	d			10 40	10 48					11 10		11 18					11 40	11 48					12 10		12 18	
Dorking 4	d		10 08													11 08										
Boxhill & Westhumble	d																									
Leatherhead	d		10 15						10 45							11 15						11 45				
Ashtead	d		10 18						10 48							11 18						11 48				
Epsom 3	a		10 23						10 53							11 23						11 53				
	d		10 24						10 54							11 24						11 54				
Ewell West	d		10 27						10 57							11 27						11 57				
Stoneleigh	d		10 29						10 59							11 29						11 59				
Worcester Park	d		10 32						11 02							11 32						12 02				
Chessington South	d					10 40							11 10						11 40							12 10
Chessington North	d					10 42							11 12						11 42							12 12
Tolworth	d					10 44							11 14						11 44							12 14
Malden Manor	d					10 47							11 17						11 47							12 17
Motspur Park	d		10 35			10 50			11 05				11 20			11 35			11 50			12 05				12 20
Raynes Park 6	d		10 38	10 43	10 51	10 54			11 08	11 13		11 21	11 24			11 38	11 43	11 51	11 54			12 08	12 13		12 21	12 24
Wimbledon 6 ⊖	d	10 38	10 42	10 47	10 55	10 58		11 08	11 12	11 17	11 17	11 25	11 28	11a33	11 38	11 42	11 47	11 55	11 58		12 08	12 12	12 17	12 17	12 25	12 28
Earlsfield	d	10 41	10 46	10 50	10 58	11 01		11 11	11 16	11 20		11 28	11 31		11 41	11 46	11 50	11 58	12 01		12 11	12 16	12 20		12 28	12 31
Clapham Junction 10	d	10 45	10 50	10 54	11 02	11 05		11 15	11 20	10 24	11 24	11 32	11 35		11 45	11 50	11 54	12 02	12 05		12 15	12 20	11 24	12 24	12 32	12 35
Vauxhall ⊖	d	10 50	10 55	10 59	11 07	11 10		11 20	11 25	11 29		11 37	11 40		11 50	11 55	11 59	12 07	12 10		12 20	12 25	12 29		12 37	12 40
London Waterloo 15 ⊖	a	11 00	11 04	11 07	11 17	11 20		11 30	11 34	11 39	11 39	11 47	11 50		12 00	12 04	12 07	12 17	12 20		12 30	12 34	12 39	12 39	12 47	12 50

For general notes see front of timetable
For details of catering facilities see Directory of Train Operators

A From London Waterloo (Table 149)

B From Alton (Table 155) and from Basingstoke (Table 155)

b Arr. 1052

c Arr. 1152

until 21 September

For details of Bank Holiday service alterations, please see first page of Table 149

Hampton Court, Shepperton, Guildford, Dorking and Chessington South → London

Network Diagram - see first page of Table 152

		SW	SW	SW	SW	SW	SW	SW	SW	SW	SW 1	SW	SW	SW	SW	SW	SW	SW	SW	SW	SW	SW	SW 1	SW
										A	B											A	B	
Guildford	d	11 50	11 57					12 27	12 20					12 50	12 57					13 27	13 20			
London Road (Guildford)	d	11 54							12 24					12 54							13 24			
Clandon	d	11 59							12 29					12 59							13 29			
Horsley	d	12 03							12 33					13 03							13 33			
Effingham Junction 6	d	12 06							12 36					13 06							13 36			
Bookham	d								12 39												13 39			
Cobham & Stoke d'Abernon	d	12 10												13 10										
Oxshott	d	12 13												13 13										
Claygate	d	12 16												13 16										
Hinchley Wood	d	12 19												13 19										
Hampton Court	d					12 35						13 05						13 35						14 05
Thames Ditton	d					12 37						13 07						13 37						14 07
Surbiton 6	d	12 24	12 30			12 43		13 00			13 10	13 13		13 24	13 30			13 43		14 00			14 10	14 13
Berrylands	d					12 45						13 15						13 45						14 15
Shepperton	d				12 11												13 11							
Upper Halliford	d				12 14												13 14							
Sunbury	d				12 16												13 16							
Kempton Park	d				12 18												13 18							
Hampton	d				12 21												13 21							
Fulwell	d				12 24												13 24							
Strawberry Hill	d									12 49												13 49		
Teddington	d				12 29					12b55							13 29					13c55		
Hampton Wick	d				12 31					12 57							13 31					13 57		
Kingston	a				12 33					12 59							13 33					13 59		
	d				12 34					13 04							13 34					14 04		
Norbiton	d				12 36					13 06							13 36					14 06		
New Malden 6	d				12 40	12 48				13 10		13 18					13 40	13 48				14 10		14 18
Dorking 4	d			12 08												13 08								
Boxhill & Westhumble	d																							
Leatherhead	d			12 15					12 45							13 15					13 45			
Ashtead	d			12 18					12 48							13 18					13 48			
Epsom 3	a			12 23					12 53							13 23					13 53			
	d			12 24					12 54							13 24					13 54			
Ewell West	d			12 27					12 57							13 27					13 57			
Stoneleigh	d			12 29					12 59							13 29					13 59			
Worcester Park	d			12 32					13 02							13 32					14 02			
Chessington South	d						12 40						13 10						13 40					
Chessington North	d						12 42						13 12						13 42					
Tolworth	d						12 44						13 14						13 44					
Malden Manor	d						12 47						13 17						13 47					
Motspur Park	d			12 35			12 50		13 05				13 20			13 35			13 50		14 05			
Raynes Park 6	d			12 38	12 43	12 51	12 54		13 08	13 13		13 21	13 24			13 38	13 43	13 51	13 54		14 08	14 13		14 21
Wimbledon 6 ⊖	d	12 31	12 38	12 42	12 47	12 55	12 58	13 08	13 12	13 17	13 17	13 25	13 28	13 31	13 38	13 42	13 47	13 55	13 58	14 08	14 12	14 17	14 17	14 25
Earlsfield	d	12 35	12 41	12 46	12 50	12 58	13 01	13 11	13 16	13 20		13 28	13 31	13 35	13 41	13 46	13 50	13 58	14 01	14 11	14 16	14 20		14 28
Clapham Junction 10	d	12 39	12 45	12 50	12 54	13 02	13 05	13 15	13 20	12 24	13 24	13 32	13 35	13 39	13 45	13 50	13 54	14 02	14 05	14 15	14 20	13 24	14 24	14 32
Vauxhall ⊖	d	12 44	12 50	12 55	12 59	13 07	13 10	13 20	13 25	13 29		13 37	13 40	13 44	13 50	13 55	13 59	14 07	14 10	14 20	14 25	14 29		14 37
London Waterloo 15 ⊖	a	12 53	13 00	13 04	13 07	13 17	13 20	13 30	13 34	13 39	13 39	13 47	13 50	13 53	14 00	14 04	14 07	14 17	14 20	14 30	14 34	14 34	14 34	14 42

For general notes see front of timetable
For details of catering facilities see Directory of Train Operators

A From London Waterloo (Table 149)

B From Alton (Table 155) and from Basingstoke (Table 155)

b Arr. 1252

c Arr. 1352

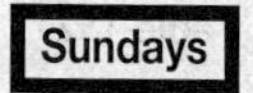

until 21 September

For details of Bank Holiday service alterations, please see first page of Table 149

Hampton Court, Shepperton, Guildford, Dorking and Chessington South → London

Network Diagram - see first page of Table 152

		SW	SW	SW	SW	SW	SW	SW	SW 1	SW	SW	SW	SW	SW	SW 1	SW	SW		SW	SW	SW	SW	SW
							A		B					A	B								A
Guildford	d		13 50	13 57								14 27	14 20						19 50	19 57			
London Road (Guildford)	d		13 54										14 24						19 54				
Clandon	d		13 59										14 29						19 59				
Horsley	d		14 03										14 33						20 03				
Effingham Junction 6	d		14 06										14 36						20 06				
Bookham	d												14 39										
Cobham & Stoke d'Abernon	d		14 10																20 10				
Oxshott	d		14 13																20 13				
Claygate	d		14 16																20 16				
Hinchley Wood	d		14 19																20 19				
Hampton Court	d							14 35								15 05							
Thames Ditton	d							14 37								15 07							
Surbiton 6	d		14 24	14 30				14 43	14 46			15 00			15 10	15 13			20 24	20 30			
Berrylands	d							14 45								15 15							
Shepperton	d					14 11												and at				20 11	
Upper Halliford	d					14 14												the same				20 14	
Sunbury	d					14 16												minutes				20 16	
Kempton Park	d					14 18												past				20 18	
Hampton	d					14 21												each				20 21	
Fulwell	d					14 24												hour until				20 24	
Strawberry Hill	d						14 30							14 49									20 30
Teddington	d					14 29	14 33							14b55								20 29	20 33
Hampton Wick	d					14 31	14 36							14 57								20 31	20 36
Kingston	a					14 33	14 38							14 59								20 33	20 38
	d					14 34								15 04								20 34	
Norbiton	d					14 36				←				15 06								20 36	
New Malden 6	d					14 40		14 48		14 48				15 10		15 18						20 40	
Dorking 4	d				14 08			↪													20 08		
Boxhill & Westhumble	d																						
Leatherhead	d				14 15								14 45								20 15		
Ashtead	d				14 18								14 48								20 18		
Epsom 3	a				14 23								14 53								20 23		
	d				14 24								14 54								20 24		
Ewell West	d				14 27								14 57								20 27		
Stoneleigh	d				14 29								14 59								20 29		
Worcester Park	d				14 32								15 02								20 32		
Chessington South	d	14 10									14 40						15 10						
Chessington North	d	14 12									14 42						15 12						
Tolworth	d	14 14									14 44						15 14						
Malden Manor	d	14 17									14 47						15 17						
Motspur Park	d	14 20			14 35						14 50		15 05				15 20				20 35		
Raynes Park 6	d	14 24			14 38	14 43				14 51	14 54		15 08	15 13		15 21	15 24				20 38	20 43	
Wimbledon 6 ⊖	d	14 28	14 31	14 38	14 42	14 47			14 54	14 55	14 58	15 08	15 12	15 17	15 17	15 25	15 28		20 31	20 38	20 42	20 47	
Earlsfield	d	14 31	14 35	14 41	14 46	14 50				14 58	15 01	15 11	15 16	15 20		15 28	15 31		20 35	20 41	20 46	20 50	
Clapham Junction 10	d	14 35	14 39	14 45	14 50	14 54			15 00	15 02	15 05	15 15	15 20	14 24	15 24	15 32	15 35		20 39	20 45	20 50	20 54	
Vauxhall ⊖	d	14 40	14 44	14 50	14 55	14 59				15 07	15 10	15 20	15 25	15 29		15 37	15 40		20 44	20 50	20 55	20 59	
London Waterloo 15 ⊖	a	14 45	14 48	14 55	14 59	15 04			15 10	15 12	15 15	15 25	15 29	15 34	15 34	15 42	15 45		20 48	20 55	21 00	21 04	

For general notes see front of timetable
For details of catering facilities see Directory of Train Operators

A From London Waterloo (Table 149)
B From Alton (Table 155) and from Basingstoke (Table 155)
b Arr. 1452

Table 152

until 21 September

For details of Bank Holiday service alterations, please see first page of Table 149

Hampton Court, Shepperton, Guildford, Dorking and Chessington South → London

Network Diagram - see first page of Table 152

		SW	SW 1 A	SW	SW	SW	SW B	SW 1 A	SW	SW		SW	SW	SW	SW	SW B	SW	SW 1 A	SW	SW	SW	SW B	SW 1 A		SW	SW
Guildford	d				20 27	20 20						20 50	20 57							21 27	21 20					
London Road (Guildford)	d					20 24						20 54									21 24					
Clandon	d					20 29						20 59									21 29					
Horsley	d					20 33						21 03									21 33					
Effingham Junction 6	d					20 36						21 06									21 36					
Bookham	d					20 39															21 39					
Cobham & Stoke d'Abernon	d											21 10														
Oxshott	d											21 13														
Claygate	d											21 16														
Hinchley Wood	d											21 19														
Hampton Court	d	20 35							21 05								21 35								22 05	
Thames Ditton	d	20 37							21 07								21 37								22 07	
Surbiton 6	d	20 43	20 46		21 00			21 10	21 13			21 24	21 30				21 43	21 46		22 00			22 10		22 13	
Berrylands	d	20 45							21 15								21 45								22 15	
Shepperton	d														21 11											
Upper Halliford	d														21 14											
Sunbury	d														21 16											
Kempton Park	d														21 18											
Hampton	d														21 21											
Fulwell	d														21 24											
Strawberry Hill	d						20 49									21 30						21 49				
Teddington	d						20b55								21 29	21 33						21c55				
Hampton Wick	d						20 57								21 31	21 36						21 57				
Kingston	a						20 59								21 33	21 38						21 59				
	d						21 04								21 34							22 04				
Norbiton	d			←			21 06								21 36				←			22 06				
New Malden 6	d	20 48		20 48			21 10		21 18						21 40		21 48		21 48			22 10			22 18	
Dorking 4	d	→												21 08			→									
Boxhill & Westhumble	d																									
Leatherhead	d					20 45								21 15							21 45					
Ashtead	d					20 48								21 18							21 48					
Epsom 3	a					20 53								21 23							21 53					
	d					20 54								21 24							21 54					
Ewell West	d					20 57								21 27							21 57					
Stoneleigh	d					20 59								21 29							21 59					
Worcester Park	d					21 02								21 32							22 02					
Chessington South	d									21 10																22 10
Chessington North	d									21 12																22 12
Tolworth	d									21 14																22 14
Malden Manor	d									21 17																22 17
Motspur Park	d					21 05				21 20				21 35							22 05					22 20
Raynes Park 6	d			20 51		21 08	21 13		21 21	21 24				21 38	21 43				21 51		22 08	22 13			22 21	22 24
Wimbledon 6 ⊖	d		20 54	20 55	21 08	21 12	21 17	21 17	21 25	21 28		21 31	21 38	21 42	21 47			21 54	21 55	22 08	22 12	22 17	22 17		22 25	22 28
Earlsfield	d			20 58	21 11	21 16	21 20		21 28	21 31		21 35	21 41	21 46	21 50				21 58	22 11	22 16	22 20			22 28	22 31
Clapham Junction 10	d		21 00	21 02	21 15	21 20	20 24	21 24	21 32	21 35		21 39	21 45	21 50	21 54			22 00	22 02	22 15	22 20	21 24	22 24		22 32	22 35
Vauxhall ⊖	d			21 07	21 20	21 25	21 29		21 37	21 40		21 44	21 50	21 55	21 59				22 07	22 20	22 25	22 29			22 37	22 40
London Waterloo 15 ⊖	a		21 10	21 13	21 25	21 29	21 35	21 34	21 42	21 45		21 48	21 55	22 00	22 04			22 10	22 12	22 25	22 29	22 35	22 34		22 42	22 45

For general notes see front of timetable
For details of catering facilities see Directory of Train Operators

A From Alton (Table 155) and from Basingstoke (Table 155)
B From London Waterloo (Table 149)
b Arr. 2052
c Arr. 2152

Table 152

until 21 September

For details of Bank Holiday service alterations, please see first page of Table 149

Hampton Court, Shepperton, Guildford, Dorking and Chessington South → London

Network Diagram - see first page of Table 152

		SW	SW	SW	SW	SW	SW	SW	SW	SW	SW	SW	SW	SW	SW	SW	SW	SW	SW	SW	SW	SW
						A	1 B			A	1 B							A	1 C		A	
Guildford	d	21 50	21 57					22 27	22 20					22 50	22 57							
London Road (Guildford)	d	21 54							22 24					22 54								
Clandon	d	21 59							22 29					22 59								
Horsley	d	22 03							22 33					23 03								
Effingham Junction 6	d	22 06							22 36					23 06								
Bookham	d								22 39													
Cobham & Stoke d'Abernon	d	22 10												23 10								
Oxshott	d	22 13												23 13								
Claygate	d	22 16												23 16								
Hinchley Wood	d	22 19												23 19								
Hampton Court	d											23 05										23 45
Thames Ditton	d											23 07										23 47
Surbiton 6	d	22 24	22 30				22 46	23 00			23 10	23 13		23 24	23 30				23 46			23 53
Berrylands	d											23 15										23 55
Shepperton	d				22 11												23 11					
Upper Halliford	d				22 14												23 14					
Sunbury	d				22 16												23 16					
Kempton Park	d				22 18												23 18					
Hampton	d				22 21												23 21					
Fulwell	d				22 24												23 24					
Strawberry Hill	d					22 30				22 49								23 30			23 48	
Teddington	d				22 29	22 33				22b55							23 29	23 33			23 51	
Hampton Wick	d				22 31	22 36				22 57							23 31	23 36			23 54	
Kingston	a				22 33	22 38				22 59							23 33	23 38			23 56	
	d				22 34					23 04							23 34					
Norbiton	d				22 36					23 06							23 36					
New Malden 6	d				22 40					23 10		23 18					23 40					23 58
Dorking 4	d			22 08												23 08						
Boxhill & Westhumble	d																					
Leatherhead	d			22 15					22 44							23 15						
Ashtead	d			22 18					22 48							23 18						
Epsom 3	a			22 23					22 52							23 23						
	d			22 24					22 54							23 24						
Ewell West	d			22 27					22 57							23 27						
Stoneleigh	d			22 29					22 59							23 29						
Worcester Park	d			22 32					23 02							23 32						
Chessington South	d												23 10							23 40		
Chessington North	d												23 12							23 42		
Tolworth	d												23 14							23 44		
Malden Manor	d												23 17							23 47		
Motspur Park	d			22 35					23 05				23 20			23 35				23 50		
Raynes Park 6	d			22 38	22 43				23 08	23 13		23 21	23 24			23 38	23 43			23 53		00 01
Wimbledon 6 ⊖	d	22 31	22 38	22 42	22 47		22 54	23 08	23 12	23 17	23 17	23 25	23 28	23 31	23 38	23 42	23 47		23 54	23a58		00a04
Earlsfield	d	22 35	22 41	22 46	22 50			23 11	23 16	23 20		23 28	23 31	23 35	23 41	23 46	23 50					
Clapham Junction 10	d	22 39	22 45	22 50	22 54		23 00	23 15	23 20	22 24	23 24	23 32	23 35	23 39	23 45	23 50	23 54		23 59			
Vauxhall ⊖	d	22 44	22 50	22 55	22 59			23 20	23 25	23 29		23 37	23 40	23 44	23 50	23 55	23 59					
London Waterloo 15 ⊖	a	22 48	22 55	23 00	23 04		23 11	23 25	23 29	23 34	23 34	23 42	23 45	23 48	23 55	23 59	00 04		00 10			

For general notes see front of timetable
For details of catering facilities see Directory of Train Operators

A From London Waterloo (Table 149)
B From Alton (Table 155) and from Basingstoke (Table 155)
C From Alton (Table 155)
b Arr. 2252

Table 152

from 28 September

For details of Bank Holiday service alterations, please see first page of Table 149

Hampton Court, Shepperton, Guildford, Dorking and Chessington South → London

Network Diagram - see first page of Table 152

		SW	SW	SW	SW 1	SW	SW 1	SW	SW	SW	SW	SW	SW	SW	SW	SW	SW	SW	SW	SW	SW 1	SW	SW	SW	SW
				A	B	A	C				D	A								A	E				
Guildford	d		23p08											06 57				07 27						07 48	07 57
London Road (Guildford)	d		23p12																					07 52	
Clandon	d		23p17																					07 57	
Horsley	d		23p21																					08 01	
Effingham Junction 6	d		23p24																					08 04	
Bookham	d																								
Cobham & Stoke d'Abernon	d		23p28																					08 08	
Oxshott	d		23p31																					08 11	
Claygate	d		23p34																					08 14	
Hinchley Wood	d		23p37																					08 17	
Hampton Court	d																07 35					08 05			
Thames Ditton	d																07 37					08 07			
Surbiton 6	d		23p42		23p57		00 40				07 00			07 30			07 43	08 00			08 10	08 13		08 24	08 30
Berrylands	d																07 45					08 15			
Shepperton	d	23p11														07 11									
Upper Halliford	d	23p14														07 14									
Sunbury	d	23p16														07 16									
Kempton Park	d	23p18														07 18									
Hampton	d	23p21														07 21									
Fulwell	d	23p24														07 24									
Strawberry Hill	d			23p37		00 12						06 49								07 49					
Teddington	d	23p29		23p41		00 15						06b55				07 29				07c55					
Hampton Wick	d	23p31		23p44		00 17						06 57				07 31				07 57					
Kingston	a	23p33		23p46		00 19						06 59				07 33				07 59					
	d	23p34		23p49								07 04				07 34				08 04					
Norbiton	d	23p36		23p51								07 06				07 36				08 06					
New Malden 6	d	23p41		23p55								07 10				07 40	07 48			08 10		08 18			
Dorking 4	d																								
Boxhill & Westhumble	d																								
Leatherhead	d																								
Ashtead	d																								
Epsom 3	a																								
	d														07 24				07 54						
Ewell West	d														07 27				07 57						
Stoneleigh	d														07 29				07 59						
Worcester Park	d														07 32				08 02						
Chessington South	d																						08 10		
Chessington North	d																						08 12		
Tolworth	d																						08 14		
Malden Manor	d																						08 17		
Motspur Park	d														07 35				08 05				08 20		
Raynes Park 6	d	23p43		23p58								07 13			07 38	07 43	07 51		08 08	08 13		08 21	08 24		
Wimbledon 6	d	23p52	23p58	00 07	00 08		00 48	05 31	06 12	06 42	07 08	07e19	07 31	07 38	07 42	07 47	07 55	08 08	08 12	08 17	08 17	08 25	08 28	08a33	08 38
Earlsfield	d	23p55	00 01	00 10	00 10					06 46	07 11	07 22	07 34	07 41	07 46	07 50	07 58	08 11	08 16	08 20		08 28	08 31		08 41
Clapham Junction 10	d	23p59	00 05	23p13	00 14		00 55	05 38	06 20	06 50	07 15	06 24	07 38	07 45	07 50	07 54	08 02	08 15	08 20	07 24	08 24	08 34	08 37		08 45
Vauxhall	d	00 04	00 10	00 19	00 19			05 43	06 25	06 55	07 20	07 31	07 43	07 50	07 55	07 59	08 07	08 20	08 25	08 29		08 39	08 42		08 50
London Waterloo 15	a	00 09	00 14	00 24	00 29		01 02	05 54	06 34	07 04	07 30	07 41	07 53	08 00	08 04	08 07	08 17	08 30	08 34	08 39	08 42	08 47	08 50		09 00

For general notes see front of timetable
For details of catering facilities see Directory of Train Operators

A From London Waterloo (Table 149)
B From Basingstoke (Table 155)
C From Weymouth (Table 158)
D From Woking (Table 155)
E From Farnham (Table 155) and from Basingstoke (Table 155)
b Arr. 0652
c Arr. 0752
e Arr. 0716

Sundays

from 28 September

For details of Bank Holiday service alterations, please see first page of Table 149

Hampton Court, Shepperton, Guildford, Dorking and Chessington South → London

Network Diagram - see first page of Table 152

		SW	SW		SW	SW	SW	SW	SW	SW 1	SW	SW	SW	SW	SW	SW		SW	SW	SW	SW	SW	SW 1	SW	SW	SW
									A	B												A	B			
Guildford	d						08 27	08 18					08 48	08 57						09 27	09 18					09 48
London Road (Guildford)	d							08 22					08 52								09 22					09 52
Clandon	d							08 27					08 57								09 27					09 57
Horsley	d							08 31					09 01								09 31					10 01
Effingham Junction 6	d							08 34					09 04								09 34					10 04
Bookham	d							08 37													09 37					
Cobham & Stoke d'Abernon	d												09 08													10 08
Oxshott	d												09 11													10 11
Claygate	d												09 14													10 14
Hinchley Wood	d												09 17													10 17
Hampton Court	d				08 35						09 05							09 35						10 05		
Thames Ditton	d				08 37						09 07							09 37						10 07		
Surbiton 6	d				08 43		09 00			09 10	09 13		09 24	09 30				09 43		10 00			10 10	10 13		10 24
Berrylands	d				08 45						09 15							09 45						10 15		
Shepperton	d		08 11													09 11										
Upper Halliford	d		08 14													09 14										
Sunbury	d		08 16													09 16										
Kempton Park	d		08 18													09 18										
Hampton	d		08 21													09 21										
Fulwell	d		08 24													09 24										
Strawberry Hill	d								08 49													09 49				
Teddington	d		08 29						08b55							09 29						09c55				
Hampton Wick	d		08 31						08 57							09 31						09 57				
Kingston	a		08 33						08 59							09 33						09 59				
	d		08 34						09 04							09 34						10 04				
Norbiton	d		08 36						09 06							09 36						10 06				
New Malden 6	d		08 40		08 48				09 10		09 18					09 40		09 48				10 10		10 18		
Dorking 4	d														09 08											
Boxhill & Westhumble	d																									
Leatherhead	d							08 45							09 15						09 45					
Ashtead	d							08 48							09 18						09 48					
Epsom 3	a							08 53							09 23						09 53					
	d	08 24						08 54							09 24						09 54					
Ewell West	d	08 27						08 57							09 27						09 57					
Stoneleigh	d	08 29						08 59							09 29						09 59					
Worcester Park	d	08 32						09 02							09 32						10 02					
Chessington South	d					08 40						09 10							09 40						10 10	
Chessington North	d					08 42						09 12							09 42						10 12	
Tolworth	d					08 44						09 14							09 44						10 14	
Malden Manor	d					08 47						09 17							09 47						10 17	
Motspur Park	d	08 35				08 50		09 05				09 20			09 35				09 50		10 05				10 20	
Raynes Park 6	d	08 38	08 43		08 51	08 54		09 08	09 13		09 21	09 24			09 38	09 43		09 51	09 54		10 08	10 13		10 21	10 24	
Wimbledon 6 ⊖	d	08 42	08 47		08 55	08 58	09 08	09 12	09 17	09 17	09 25	09 28	09a33	09 38	09 42	09 47		09 55	09 58	10 08	10 12	10 17	10 17	10 25	10 28	10a33
Earlsfield	d	08 46	08 50		08 58	09 01	09 11	09 16	09 20		09 28	09 31		09 41	09 46	09 50		09 58	10 01	10 11	10 16	10 20		10 28	10 31	
Clapham Junction 10	d	08 50	08 54		09 02	09 09	09 15	09 20	08 24	09 24	09 32	09 36		09 45	09 50	09 54		10 02	10 05	10 15	10 20	09 24	10 24	10 32	10 36	
Vauxhall ⊖	d	08 55	08 59		09 07	09 14	09 20	09 25	09 29		09 37	09 41		09 50	09 55	09 59		10 07	10 10	10 20	10 25	10 29		10 37	10 41	
London Waterloo 15 ⊖	a	09 04	09 07		09 17	09 20	09 30	09 34	09 39	09 42	09 47	09 50		10 00	10 04	10 07		10 17	10 20	10 30	10 34	10 39	10 39	10 47	10 50	

For general notes see front of timetable
For details of catering facilities see Directory of Train Operators

A From London Waterloo (Table 149)
B From Alton (Table 155) and from Basingstoke (Table 155)
b Arr. 0852
c Arr. 0952

Table 152

from 28 September

For details of Bank Holiday service alterations, please see first page of Table 149

Hampton Court, Shepperton, Guildford, Dorking and Chessington South → London

Network Diagram - see first page of Table 152

		SW	SW	SW	SW	SW		SW	SW	SW	SW	SW	SW	SW	SW	SW	SW	SW	SW		SW	SW	SW	SW	SW	SW
										A	1 B												A	1 B		
Guildford	d	09 57						10 27	10 18					10 48	10 57						11 27	11 18				
London Road (Guildford)	d								10 22					10 52								11 22				
Clandon	d								10 27					10 57								11 27				
Horsley	d								10 31					11 01								11 31				
Effingham Junction 6	d								10 34					11 04								11 34				
Bookham	d								10 37													11 37				
Cobham & Stoke d'Abernon	d													11 08												
Oxshott	d													11 11												
Claygate	d													11 14												
Hinchley Wood	d													11 17												
Hampton Court	d				10 35							11 05						11 35							12 05	
Thames Ditton	d				10 37							11 07						11 37							12 07	
Surbiton 6	d	10 30			10 43			11 00			11 10	11 13		11 24	11 30			11 43			12 00			12 10	12 13	
Berrylands	d				10 45							11 15						11 45							12 15	
Shepperton	d			10 11													11 11									
Upper Halliford	d			10 14													11 14									
Sunbury	d			10 16													11 16									
Kempton Park	d			10 18													11 18									
Hampton	d			10 21													11 21									
Fulwell	d			10 24													11 24									
Strawberry Hill	d									10 49													11 49			
Teddington	d			10 29						10b55							11 29						11c55			
Hampton Wick	d			10 31						10 57							11 31						11 57			
Kingston	a			10 33						10 59							11 33						11 59			
	d			10 34						11 04							11 34						12 04			
Norbiton	d			10 36						11 06							11 36						12 06			
New Malden 6	d			10 40	10 48					11 10		11 18					11 40	11 48					12 10		12 18	
Dorking 4	d		10 08													11 08										
Boxhill & Westhumble	d																									
Leatherhead	d		10 15						10 45							11 15						11 45				
Ashtead	d		10 18						10 48							11 18						11 48				
Epsom 3	a		10 23						10 53							11 23						11 53				
	d		10 24						10 54							11 24						11 54				
Ewell West	d		10 27						10 57							11 27						11 57				
Stoneleigh	d		10 29						10 59							11 29						11 59				
Worcester Park	d		10 32						11 02							11 32						12 02				
Chessington South	d					10 40							11 10						11 40							12 10
Chessington North	d					10 42							11 12						11 42							12 12
Tolworth	d					10 44							11 14						11 44							12 14
Malden Manor	d					10 47							11 17						11 47							12 17
Motspur Park	d		10 35			10 50			11 05				11 20			11 35			11 50			12 05				12 20
Raynes Park 6	d		10 38	10 43	10 51	10 54			11 08	11 13		11 21	11 24			11 38	11 43	11 51	11 54			12 08	12 13		12 21	12 24
Wimbledon 6 ⊖	d	10 38	10 42	10 47	10 55	10 58		11 08	11 12	11 17	11 17	11 25	11 28	11a33	11 38	11 42	11 47	11 55	11 58		12 08	12 12	12 17	12 17	12 25	12 28
Earlsfield	d	10 41	10 46	10 50	10 58	11 01		11 11	11 16	11 20		11 28	11 31		11 41	11 46	11 50	11 58	12 01		12 11	12 16	12 20		12 28	12 31
Clapham Junction 10	d	10 45	10 50	10 54	11 02	11 05		11 15	11 20	10 24	11 24	11 32	11 35		11 45	11 50	11 54	12 02	12 05		12 15	12 20	11 24	12 24	12 32	12 35
Vauxhall ⊖	d	10 50	10 55	10 59	11 07	11 10		11 20	11 25	11 29		11 37	11 40		11 50	11 55	11 59	12 07	12 10		12 20	12 25	12 29		12 37	12 40
London Waterloo 15 ⊖	a	11 00	11 04	11 07	11 17	11 20		11 30	11 34	11 39	11 39	11 47	11 50		12 00	12 04	12 07	12 17	12 20		12 30	12 34	12 39	12 39	12 47	12 50

For general notes see front of timetable
For details of catering facilities see Directory of Train Operators

A From London Waterloo (Table 149)
B From Alton (Table 155) and from Basingstoke (Table 155)
b Arr. 1052
c Arr. 1152

Table 152

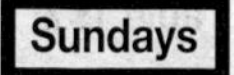

Sundays

from 28 September

For details of Bank Holiday service alterations, please see first page of Table 149

Hampton Court, Shepperton, Guildford, Dorking and Chessington South → London

Network Diagram - see first page of Table 152

		SW	SW	SW	SW	SW	SW	SW	SW	SW	SW 1	SW	SW	SW	SW	SW	SW	SW	SW	SW	SW	SW	SW 1	SW
										A	B											A	B	
Guildford	d	11 48	11 57					12 27	12 18					12 48	12 57					13 27	13 18			
London Road (Guildford)	d	11 52							12 22					12 52							13 22			
Clandon	d	11 57							12 27					12 57							13 27			
Horsley	d	12 01							12 31					13 01							13 31			
Effingham Junction 6	d	12 04							12 34					13 04							13 34			
Bookham	d								12 37												13 37			
Cobham & Stoke d'Abernon	d	12 08												13 08										
Oxshott	d	12 11												13 11										
Claygate	d	12 14												13 14										
Hinchley Wood	d	12 17												13 17										
Hampton Court	d					12 35						13 05						13 35						14 05
Thames Ditton	d					12 37						13 07						13 37						14 07
Surbiton 6	d	12 24	12 30			12 43		13 00			13 10	13 13		13 24	13 30			13 43		14 00			14 10	14 13
Berrylands	d					12 45						13 15						13 45						14 15
Shepperton	d				12 11												13 11							
Upper Halliford	d				12 14												13 14							
Sunbury	d				12 16												13 16							
Kempton Park	d				12 18												13 18							
Hampton	d				12 21												13 21							
Fulwell	d				12 24												13 24							
Strawberry Hill	d									12 49												13 49		
Teddington	d				12 29					12b55							13 29					13c55		
Hampton Wick	d				12 31					12 57							13 31					13 57		
Kingston	a				12 33					12 59							13 33					13 59		
	d				12 34					13 04							13 34					14 04		
Norbiton	d				12 36					13 06							13 36					14 06		
New Malden 6	d				12 40	12 48				13 10		13 18					13 40	13 48				14 10		14 18
Dorking 4	d			12 08												13 08								
Boxhill & Westhumble	d																							
Leatherhead	d			12 15					12 45							13 15					13 45			
Ashtead	d			12 18					12 48							13 18					13 48			
Epsom 3	a			12 23					12 53							13 23					13 53			
	d			12 24					12 54							13 24					13 54			
Ewell West	d			12 27					12 57							13 27					13 57			
Stoneleigh	d			12 29					12 59							13 29					13 59			
Worcester Park	d			12 32					13 02							13 32					14 02			
Chessington South	d						12 40						13 10						13 40					
Chessington North	d						12 42						13 12						13 42					
Tolworth	d						12 44						13 14						13 44					
Malden Manor	d						12 47						13 17						13 47					
Motspur Park	d			12 35			12 50		13 05				13 20			13 35			13 50		14 05			
Raynes Park 6	d			12 38	12 43	12 51	12 54		13 08	13 13		13 21	13 24			13 38	13 43	13 51	13 54		14 08	14 13		14 21
Wimbledon 6 ⊖ ⛴	d	12 31	12 38	12 42	12 47	12 55	12 58	13 08	13 12	13 17	13 17	13 25	13 28	13 31	13 38	13 42	13 47	13 55	13 58	14 08	14 12	14 17	14 17	14 25
Earlsfield	d	12 35	12 41	12 46	12 50	12 58	13 01	13 11	13 16	13 20		13 28	13 31	13 35	13 41	13 46	13 50	13 58	14 01	14 11	14 16	14 20		14 28
Clapham Junction 10	d	12 39	12 45	12 50	12 54	13 02	13 05	13 15	13 20	12 24	13 24	13 32	13 35	13 39	13 45	13 50	13 54	14 02	14 05	14 15	14 20	13 24	14 24	14 32
Vauxhall ⊖	d	12 44	12 50	12 55	12 59	13 07	13 10	13 20	13 25	13 29		13 37	13 40	13 44	13 50	13 55	13 59	14 07	14 10	14 20	14 25	14 29		14 37
London Waterloo 15 ⊖	a	12 53	13 00	13 04	13 07	13 17	13 20	13 30	13 34	13 39	13 39	13 47	13 50	13 53	14 00	14 04	14 07	14 17	14 20	14 30	14 34	14 34	14 34	14 42

For general notes see front of timetable
For details of catering facilities see Directory of Train Operators

A From London Waterloo (Table 149)
B From Alton (Table 155) and from Basingstoke (Table 155)
b Arr. 1252
c Arr. 1352

Table 152

Sundays

from 28 September

For details of Bank Holiday service alterations, please see first page of Table 149

Hampton Court, Shepperton, Guildford, Dorking and Chessington South → London

Network Diagram - see first page of Table 152

		SW	SW	SW	SW	SW	SW	SW	SW [1]	SW	SW	SW	SW	SW	SW [1]	SW	SW		SW	SW	SW	SW	SW
							A		B					A	B								A
Guildford	d		13 48	13 57								14 27	14 18						19 48	19 57			
London Road (Guildford)	d		13 52										14 22						19 52				
Clandon	d		13 57										14 27						19 57				
Horsley	d		14 01										14 31						20 01				
Effingham Junction [6]	d		14 04										14 34						20 04				
Bookham	d												14 37										
Cobham & Stoke d'Abernon	d		14 08																20 08				
Oxshott	d		14 11																20 11				
Claygate	d		14 14																20 14				
Hinchley Wood	d		14 17																20 17				
Hampton Court	d							14 35								15 05							
Thames Ditton	d							14 37								15 07							
Surbiton [6]	d		14 24	14 30				14 43	14 46			15 00			15 10	15 13			20 24	20 30			
Berrylands	d							14 45								15 15							
Shepperton	d					14 11												and at				20 11	
Upper Halliford	d					14 14												the same				20 14	
Sunbury	d					14 16												minutes				20 16	
Kempton Park	d					14 18												past				20 18	
Hampton	d					14 21												each				20 21	
Fulwell	d					14 24												hour until				20 24	
Strawberry Hill	d						14 30							14 49									20 30
Teddington	d					14 29	14 33							14b55								20 29	20 33
Hampton Wick	d					14 31	14 36							14 57								20 31	20 36
Kingston	a					14 33	14 38							14 59								20 33	20 38
	d					14 34								15 04								20 34	
Norbiton	d					14 36				←				15 06								20 36	
New Malden [6]	d					14 40		14 48		14 48				15 10		15 18						20 40	
Dorking [4]	d				14 08			→													20 08		
Boxhill & Westhumble	d																						
Leatherhead	d				14 15								14 45								20 15		
Ashtead	d				14 18								14 48								20 18		
Epsom [3]	a				14 23								14 53								20 23		
	d				14 24								14 54								20 24		
Ewell West	d				14 27								14 57								20 27		
Stoneleigh	d				14 29								14 59								20 29		
Worcester Park	d				14 32								15 02								20 32		
Chessington South	d	14 10									14 40						15 10						
Chessington North	d	14 12									14 42						15 12						
Tolworth	d	14 14									14 44						15 14						
Malden Manor	d	14 17									14 47						15 17						
Motspur Park	d	14 20			14 35						14 50		15 05				15 20				20 35		
Raynes Park [6]	d	14 24			14 38	14 43				14 51	14 54		15 08	15 13		15 21	15 24				20 38	20 43	
Wimbledon [6] ⊖	d	14 28	14 31	14 38	14 42	14 47			14 54	14 55	14 58	15 08	15 12	15 17	15 17	15 25	15 28		20 31	20 38	20 42	20 47	
Earlsfield	d	14 31	14 35	14 41	14 46	14 50				14 58	15 01	15 11	15 16	15 20		15 28	15 31		20 35	20 41	20 46	20 50	
Clapham Junction [10]	d	14 35	14 39	14 45	14 50	14 54			15 00	15 02	15 05	15 15	15 20	14 24	15 24	15 32	15 35		20 39	20 45	20 50	20 54	
Vauxhall ⊖	d	14 40	14 44	14 50	14 55	14 59				15 07	15 10	15 20	15 25	15 29		15 37	15 40		20 44	20 50	20 55	20 59	
London Waterloo [15] ⊖	a	14 45	14 48	14 55	14 59	15 04			15 10	15 12	15 15	15 25	15 29	15 34	15 34	15 42	15 45		20 48	20 55	21 00	21 04	

For general notes see front of timetable
For details of catering facilities see Directory of Train Operators

A From London Waterloo (Table 149)
B From Alton (Table 155) and from Basingstoke (Table 155)
b Arr. 1452

Table 152

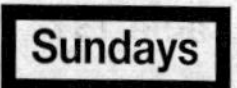

from 28 September

For details of Bank Holiday service alterations, please see first page of Table 149

Hampton Court, Shepperton, Guildford, Dorking and Chessington South → London

Network Diagram - see first page of Table 152

		SW	SW	SW	SW	SW	SW	SW	SW	SW		SW	SW	SW	SW	SW	SW	SW	SW	SW	SW	SW	SW		SW	SW
			1					1										1					1			
			A				B	A								B		A				B	A			
Guildford	d				20 27	20 18						20 48	20 57							21 27	21 18					
London Road (Guildford)	d					20 22						20 52									21 22					
Clandon	d					20 27						20 57									21 27					
Horsley	d					20 31						21 01									21 31					
Effingham Junction 6	d					20 34						21 04									21 34					
Bookham	d					20 37															21 37					
Cobham & Stoke d'Abernon	d											21 08														
Oxshott	d											21 11														
Claygate	d											21 14														
Hinchley Wood	d											21 17														
Hampton Court	d	20 35							21 05								21 35								22 05	
Thames Ditton	d	20 37							21 07								21 37								22 07	
Surbiton 6	d	20 43	20 46		21 00			21 10	21 13			21 24	21 30				21 43	21 46		22 00			22 10		22 13	
Berrylands	d	20 45							21 15								21 45								22 15	
Shepperton	d														21 11											
Upper Halliford	d														21 14											
Sunbury	d														21 16											
Kempton Park	d														21 18											
Hampton	d														21 21											
Fulwell	d														21 24											
Strawberry Hill	d						20 49									21 30						21 49				
Teddington	d						20b55								21 29	21 33						21c55				
Hampton Wick	d						20 57								21 31	21 36						21 57				
Kingston	a						20 59								21 33	21 38						21 59				
	d						21 04								21 34							22 04				
Norbiton	d			←			21 06								21 36				←			22 06				
New Malden 6	d	20 48		20 48			21 10		21 18						21 40		21 48		21 48			22 10			22 18	
Dorking 4	d	→												21 08			→									
Boxhill & Westhumble	d																									
Leatherhead	d					20 45								21 15							21 45					
Ashtead	d					20 48								21 18							21 48					
Epsom 3	a					20 53								21 23							21 53					
	d					20 54								21 24							21 54					
Ewell West	d					20 57								21 27							21 57					
Stoneleigh	d					20 59								21 29							21 59					
Worcester Park	d					21 02								21 32							22 02					
Chessington South	d									21 10																22 10
Chessington North	d									21 12																22 12
Tolworth	d									21 14																22 14
Malden Manor	d									21 17																22 17
Motspur Park	d					21 05				21 20				21 35							22 05					22 20
Raynes Park 6	d			20 51		21 08	21 13		21 21	21 24				21 38	21 43				21 51		22 08	22 13			22 21	22 24
Wimbledon 6 ⊖ ⛴	d		20 54	20 55	21 08	21 12	21 17	21 17	21 25	21 28		21 31	21 38	21 42	21 47			21 54	21 55	22 08	22 12	22 17	22 17		22 25	22 28
Earlsfield	d			20 58	21 11	21 16	21 20		21 28	21 31		21 35	21 41	21 46	21 50				21 58	22 11	22 16	22 20			22 28	22 31
Clapham Junction 10	d		21 00	21 02	21 15	21 20	20 24	21 24	21 32	21 35		21 39	21 45	21 50	21 54			22 00	22 02	22 15	22 20	21 24	22 24		22 32	22 35
Vauxhall ⊖	d			21 07	21 20	21 25	21 29		21 37	21 40		21 44	21 50	21 55	21 59				22 07	22 20	22 25	22 29			22 37	22 40
London Waterloo 15 ⊖	a		21 10	21 13	21 25	21 29	21 35	21 34	21 42	21 45		21 48	21 55	22 00	22 04			22 10	22 12	22 25	22 29	22 35	22 34		22 42	22 45

For general notes see front of timetable
For details of catering facilities see Directory of Train Operators

A From Alton (Table 155) and from Basingstoke (Table 155)
B From London Waterloo (Table 149)
b Arr. 2052
c Arr. 2152

Table 152

from 28 September

For details of Bank Holiday service alterations, please see first page of Table 149

Hampton Court, Shepperton, Guildford, Dorking and Chessington South → London

Network Diagram - see first page of Table 152

		SW	SW	SW	SW	SW	SW	SW	SW	SW	SW	SW	SW	SW	SW	SW	SW	SW	SW	SW	SW	SW
							1				1								1			
						A	B			A	B							A	C		A	
Guildford	d	21 48	21 57					22 27	22 20					22 50	22 57							
London Road (Guildford)	d	21 52							22 24					22 54								
Clandon	d	21 57							22 29					22 59								
Horsley	d	22 01							22 33					23 03								
Effingham Junction 6	d	22 04							22 36					23 06								
Bookham	d								22 39													
Cobham & Stoke d'Abernon	d	22 08												23 10								
Oxshott	d	22 11												23 13								
Claygate	d	22 14												23 16								
Hinchley Wood	d	22 17												23 19								
Hampton Court	d											23 05										23 45
Thames Ditton	d											23 07										23 47
Surbiton 6	d	22 24	22 30				22 46	23 00			23 10	23 13		23 24	23 30				23 46			23 53
Berrylands	d											23 15										23 55
Shepperton	d				22 11												23 11					
Upper Halliford	d				22 14												23 14					
Sunbury	d				22 16												23 16					
Kempton Park	d				22 18												23 18					
Hampton	d				22 21												23 21					
Fulwell	d				22 24												23 24					
Strawberry Hill	d					22 30				22 49								23 30			23 48	
Teddington	d				22 29	22 33				22b55							23 29	23 33			23 51	
Hampton Wick	d				22 31	22 36				22 57							23 31	23 36			23 54	
Kingston	a				22 33	22 38				22 59							23 33	23 38			23 56	
	d				22 34					23 04							23 34					
Norbiton	d				22 36					23 06							23 36					
New Malden 6	d				22 40					23 10		23 18					23 40					23 58
Dorking 4	d			22 08												23 08						
Boxhill & Westhumble	d																					
Leatherhead	d			22 15					22 44							23 15						
Ashtead	d			22 18					22 48							23 18						
Epsom 3	a			22 23					22 52							23 23						
	d			22 24					22 54							23 24						
Ewell West	d			22 27					22 57							23 27						
Stoneleigh	d			22 29					22 59							23 29						
Worcester Park	d			22 32					23 02							23 32						
Chessington South	d												23 10							23 40		
Chessington North	d												23 12							23 42		
Tolworth	d												23 14							23 44		
Malden Manor	d												23 17							23 47		
Motspur Park	d			22 35					23 05				23 20			23 35				23 50		
Raynes Park 6	d			22 38	22 43				23 08	23 13		23 21	23 24			23 38	23 43			23 53		00 01
Wimbledon 6 ⊖	d	22 31	22 38	22 42	22 47		22 54	23 08	23 12	23 17	23 17	23 25	23 28	23 31	23 38	23 42	23 47		23 54	23a58		00a04
Earlsfield	d	22 35	22 41	22 46	22 50			23 11	23 16	23 20		23 28	23 31	23 35	23 41	23 46	23 50					
Clapham Junction 10	d	22 39	22 45	22 50	22 54		23 00	23 15	23 20	22 24	23 24	23 32	23 35	23 39	23 45	23 50	23 54		23 59			
Vauxhall ⊖	d	22 44	22 50	22 55	22 59			23 20	23 25	23 29		23 37	23 40	23 44	23 50	23 55	23 59					
London Waterloo 15 ⊖	a	22 48	22 55	23 00	23 04		23 11	23 25	23 29	23 34	23 34	23 42	23 45	23 48	23 55	23 59	00 04		00 10			

For general notes see front of timetable
For details of catering facilities see Directory of Train Operators

A From London Waterloo (Table 149)
B From Alton (Table 155) and from Basingstoke (Table 155)
C From Alton (Table 155)
b Arr. 2252

Network Diagram for Tables 155, 156, 157

DM-17/08
Design BAJS

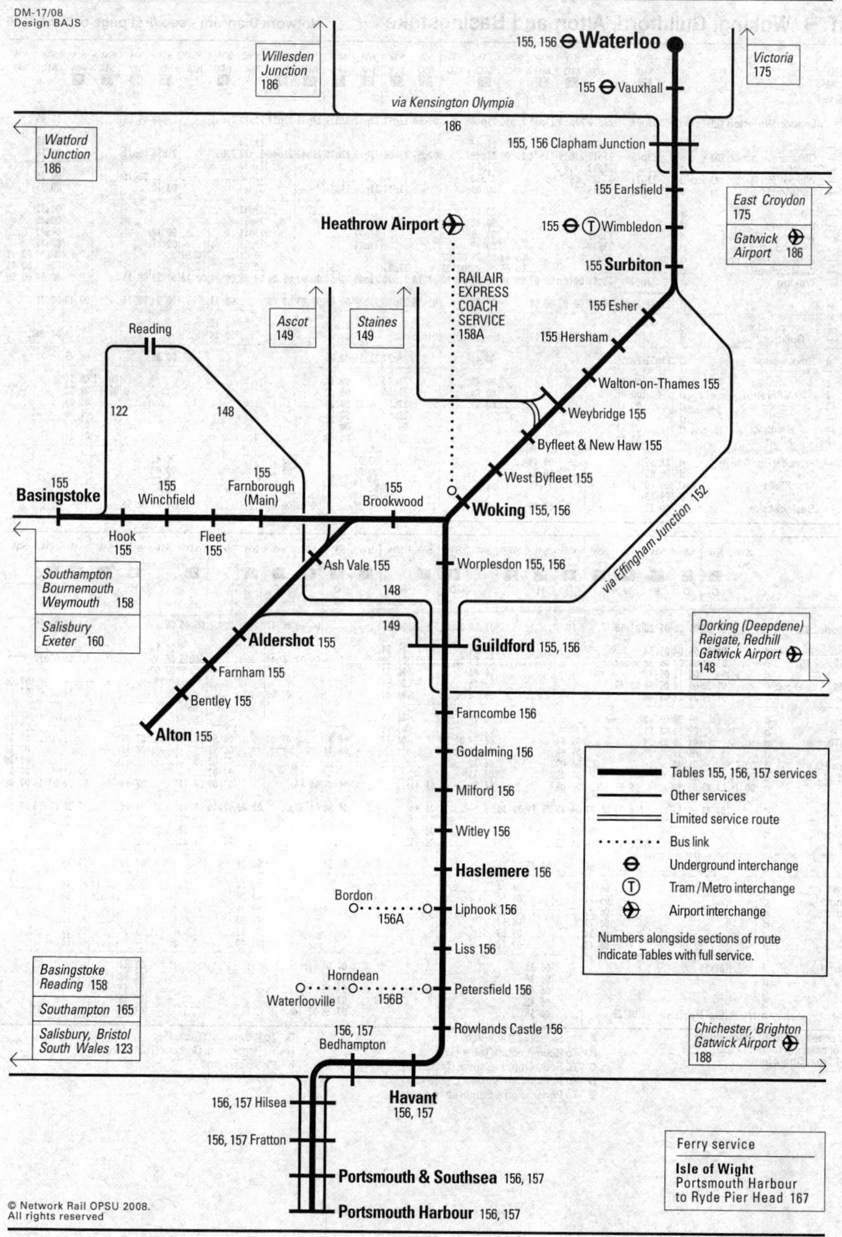

155, 156 Waterloo
155 Vauxhall
155, 156 Clapham Junction
155 Earlsfield
155 Wimbledon
155 Surbiton
155 Esher
155 Hersham
Walton-on-Thames 155
Weybridge 155
Byfleet & New Haw 155
West Byfleet 155
Woking 155, 156
Worplesdon 155, 156
Guildford 155, 156
Farncombe 156
Godalming 156
Milford 156
Witley 156
Haslemere 156
Liphook 156
Liss 156
Petersfield 156
Rowlands Castle 156
156, 157 Bedhampton
Havant 156, 157
156, 157 Hilsea
156, 157 Fratton
Portsmouth & Southsea 156, 157
Portsmouth Harbour 156, 157
Bordon
156A
Horndean
Waterlooville
156B
155 Basingstoke
Hook 155
155 Winchfield
Fleet 155
155 Farnborough (Main)
155 Brookwood
Ash Vale 155
Aldershot 155
Farnham 155
Bentley 155
Alton 155
Reading
122
148
149
Willesden Junction 186
via Kensington Olympia
186
Watford Junction 186
Victoria 175
East Croydon 175
Gatwick Airport 186
Heathrow Airport
RAILAIR EXPRESS COACH SERVICE 158A
Ascot 149
Staines 149
via Effingham Junction 152
Southampton Bournemouth Weymouth 158
Salisbury Exeter 160
Dorking (Deepdene) Reigate, Redhill Gatwick Airport 148
Basingstoke Reading 158
Southampton 165
Salisbury, Bristol South Wales 123
Chichester, Brighton Gatwick Airport 188
Tables 155, 156, 157 services
Other services
Limited service route
Bus link
Underground interchange
Tram / Metro interchange
Airport interchange
Numbers alongside sections of route indicate Tables with full service.
Ferry service
Isle of Wight
Portsmouth Harbour to Ryde Pier Head 167

For details of Bank Holiday service alterations, please see first page of Table 149

London → Woking, Guildford, Alton and Basingstoke

Network Diagram - see first page of Table 155

Miles	Miles	Miles			SW MO 1		SW MO	SW MO 1	SW MO 1 A	SW MO	SW MO 1	SW MO	SW MO 1	SW MX 1	SW MX 1	SW MX 1	SW MX 1	SW MX 1	SW MX	SW MX 1	SW MX	SW MX 1	SW MX 1 B	SW MX 1	SW MX 1	SW MX	SW MX
0	—	—	**London Waterloo 15** ⊖	d	23p07		23p10	23p30	23p35	22p50	23p40		00 50	22p53	23p12	23p23	23p35	23p39	23p20	23p45		23p48	00 05			00 09	
1¼	—	—	Vauxhall ⊖	d			23p14			22p54	23p44								23p24							00 13	
4	—	—	Clapham Junction 10	d	23p15		23p19	23b39	23b44	23p00	23p49		00u57	23b00	23b19	23b30	23b42	23b46	23p29	23b52		23b56	00u12			00 18	
5½	—	—	Earlsfield	d			23p22				23p52								23p32							00 21	
7¼	—	—	Wimbledon 6 ⊖	d	23p22		23p26				23p56								23p36				00u18			00 25	
12	—	—	**Surbiton 6**	d	23p30		23p35				00 05			23p11	23p30	23p41			23p44			00 10				00 33	
14½	—	—	Esher	d			23p39				00 09								23p48							00s37	
16½	—	—	Hersham	d			23p42				00 12								23p51							00s40	
17	—	—	Walton-on-Thames	d			23p45				00 15				23p37				23p54			00 17				00s43	
19	—	—	Weybridge	d			23p49				00 19				23p41				23p58			00 21				00s46	
20½	—	—	Byfleet & New Haw	d			23p51			00 02	00 21	00 02							00 01		00 07					00s49	00 42
21½	—	—	West Byfleet	d			23p54			00 05	00 24	00 05		23p21		23p51			00 03		00 10					00s52	00 45
24¼	0	—	**Woking**	a	23p42		23p59	00 01	00 07	00 10	00 30	00 10	01 16	23p28	23p48	23p59	00 02	00 06	00 08	00 11	00 16	00 27	00 35			00 57	00 50
—	—	—		d	23p46	23p49	00 05	00 02	00 08		00 35		01 18	23p30	23p49	00 01	00 03	00 08		00 13		00 29	00 36		00 40	00 58	
—	2½	—	Worplesdon	d																00 18							
—	6	—	**Guildford**	a			00 13	00 10					01s26							00 24						01 06	
28	—	0	Brookwood	d	23p52	23p56					00 41			23p37	23p55	00 06						00 35			00 45		
—	—	4½	Ash Vale	d		00 04					00 48			23p44		00 14								00 52	00 56		
—	—	7	**Aldershot**	d		00 09					00 54			23p50		00 20								00a57	01 02		
—	—	10	Farnham	a		00 15					00 59			23p56		00 25									01 07		
—	—	—		d		00 15								23p57		00 26									01 08		
—	—	14	Bentley	d		00 23								00 04		00 32									01s14		
—	—	18¾	**Alton**	a		00 30								00 11		00 40									01 21		
33¼	—	—	Farnborough (Main)	d	23p59				00 18						00 03			00 18				00 42					
36½	—	—	Fleet	d	00 05				00 24						00 08			00 23				00 48					
40	—	—	Winchfield	d	00 10										00 14							00s53					
42¼	—	—	Hook	d	00 15										00 18							00s58					
47¾	—	—	**Basingstoke**	a	00 22				00 39						00 25		00 22	00 35				01 07	00 55				

		SW MX	SW 1 C	SW 1 D	SW 1 E	SW 1 G	SW 1	SW 1 E	SW 1 H	SW 1	SW	SW 1 G	SW 1	SW	SW 1	SW 1 G	SW 1	SW 1 H	SW 1	SW	SW 1	SW	SW 1 H	SW 1	SW 1	SW 1 ◇ ☐	SW
London Waterloo 15 ⊖	d		01 05	05 00	05 20	05 30					05 50	06 12	06 15	06 20			06 30	06 42			06 45	06 50			06 53	07 10	
Vauxhall ⊖	d		01 09	05 04	05 24						05 54			06 24								06 54					
Clapham Junction 10	d		01 14	05 09	05 29	05u37					05 59	06u19	06u22	06 29			06u37	06u49			06u52	06 59			07u00	07u17	←
Earlsfield	d			05 12	05 32						06 02			06 32								07 02					07 02
Wimbledon 6 ⊖	d		01 20	05 16	05 36	05 43					06 06			06 36								→					07 06
Surbiton 6	d		01 29	05 24	05 44						06 14	06 30		06 44				07 00							07 11		07 14
Esher	d			05 28	05 48						06 18			06 48													07 18
Hersham	d			05 32	05 51			←			06 21			06 51		←				←			←				07 21
Walton-on-Thames	d			05 35	05 54			05 54			06 24	06 37		06 54		06 37		07 07		06 54			07 07				07 24
Weybridge	d			05 39	→			05 58			06 28	→		→		06 41		→		06 58			07 11				07 28
Byfleet & New Haw	d	00 07		05 42				06 00			06 30									07 00							07 30
West Byfleet	d	00 10		05 45				06 03			06 33									07 03					07 21		07 33
Woking	a	00 16	01 42	05 50		05 59		06 08			06 38		06 41			06 48	06 56			07 08	07 11		07 18		07 26	07 35	07 38
	d		01 42	05 51		06 01	06 02	06 13	06 19	06 30			06 43			06 50	06 57		07 00	07 10	07 13		07 19		07 30	07 36	07 39
Worplesdon	d							06 18					06 48								07 18						
Guildford	a			05 59				06 23					06 53							07 20	07 23						07 47
Brookwood	d						06 08		06 25	06 36						06 56			07 06				07 25		07 36		
Ash Vale	d						06 16			06 44					06 49				07 14					07 19	07 44		
Aldershot	d						06 21			06 50					06a56				07 20					07a26	07 50		
Farnham	a						06 27			06 55									07 25						07 55		
	d						06 27			06 57									07 26						07 57		
Bentley	d						06 34			07 03									07 32						08 03		
Alton	a						06 41			07 10									07 40						08 10		
Farnborough (Main)	d		01s58						06 33							07 04							07 33				
Fleet	d								06 38							07 09							07 38				
Winchfield	d								06 44							07 15							07 44				
Hook	d								06 48							07 19							07 48				
Basingstoke	a		02s12			06 20			06 58							07 28	07 16						07 56			07 55	

For general notes see front of timetable
For details of catering facilities see Directory of Train Operators

- **A** To Salisbury (Table 160)
- **B** To Bournemouth (Table 158)
- **C** To Southampton Central (Table 158)
- **D** To Portsmouth Harbour (Table 156)
- **E** To Portsmouth & Southsea (Table 156)
- **G** To Weymouth (Table 158)
- **H** To Portsmouth Harbour (Table 158)
- **b** Previous night. Stops to pick up only

For details of Bank Holiday service alterations, please see first page of Table 149

London → Woking, Guildford, Alton and Basingstoke

Network Diagram - see first page of Table 155

	SW 1	SW 1	SW	SW 1	SW 1	SW 1 ☕	SW 1	SW 1◊	SW	SW 1	SW 1	SW 1	SW 1◊ ☕	SW 1	SW	SW 1	SW 1	SW 1◊ ☕	SW 1	SW	SW 1	SW 1	SW 1◊ ☕	SW 1	SW 1	SW 1 ☕
London Waterloo 15 ⊖ d	07 12	07 15	07 20			07 30	07 23	07 35		07 38	07 45		07 50	07 42	07 50	08 00	07 53	08 05	08 09		08 12	08 15	08 20			08 30
Vauxhall ⊖ d			07 24												07 54											
Clapham Junction 10 d	07u20	07u22	07 29				07u30		←	07u45	07u52		07u57		07 59		08u00	08u12		←	08u19	08u22	08u27			
Earlsfield d			07 32						07 32						08 02					08 02						
Wimbledon 6 ⊖ ⛴ d			→						07 36						→					08 06						
Surbiton 6 d	07 30						07 41		07 44					08 00			08 11			08 14	08 30					
Esher d									07 48											08 18						
Hersham d				←					07 51											08 21				←		
Walton-on-Thames d	07 37			07 37					07 54					08 07						08 24	08 37			08 37		
Weybridge d	→			07 41					07 58					08 11						08 28	→			08 41		
Byfleet & New Haw d									08 00											08 30						
West Byfleet d							07 51		08 03								08 21			08 33						
Woking a		07 42		07 48		07 55	07 59	07 59	08 08		08 12		08 15	08 18		08 24	08 29		08 34	08 38		08 42	08 45	08 49		08 55
d		07 44		07 49		07 55	08 00	08 00			08 14		08 16	08 19		08 25	08 30		08 35	08 39		08 44	08 46	08 49		08 55
Worplesdon d		07 49									08 19											08 49				
Guildford a		07 54				08 04					08 24					08 35				08 50		08 54				09 04
Brookwood d				07 55			08 06							08 25			08 36							08 55		
Ash Vale d					07 49		08 14					08 19					08 44								08 49	
Aldershot d					07a54		08 20					08a24					08 50								08a54	
Farnham a							08 26										08 55									
d							08 26										08 57									
Bentley d							08 32										09 03									
Alton a							08 40										09 10									
Farnborough (Main) d				08 03						08 13				08 33					08 45					09 03		
Fleet d				08 08						08 19				08 38										09 08		
Winchfield d				08 14										08 44										09 14		
Hook d				08 18										08 48										09 18		
Basingstoke a				08 25				08 20		08 34			08 35	08 58				08 48	08 59				09 06	09 28		

	SW 1◊ ☕	SW 1	SW	SW 1	SW 1	SW 1	SW 1◊ ☕	SW 1	SW	SW 1 ☕	SW 1	SW 1◊ ☕	SW 1	SW	SW 1	SW 1	SW 1◊ ☕	SW 1	SW 1	SW 1 ☕	SW 1◊ ☕	SW 1 A	SW 1 B	SW	SW 1	SW 1
London Waterloo 15 ⊖ d	08 35	08 23	08 20	08 39		08 45	08 50	08 42	08 50	09 00	08 53	09 05	09 09		09 12	09 15	09 20			09 30	09 35	09§23	09§23	09 20	09 39	09 45
Vauxhall ⊖ d			08 24						08 54															09 24		
Clapham Junction 10 d			08 29	08u46		08u52			08 59		09u00	09u12		←	09u19	09u22	09u27							09 29	09u46	09u52
Earlsfield d			08 32						09 02					09 02										09 32		
Wimbledon 6 ⊖ ⛴ d			08 36						→					09 06										09 36		
Surbiton 6 d		08 41	08 44					09 00			09 11			09 14	09 30							09§41	09§41	09 44		
Esher d			08 48											09 18										09 48		
Hersham d			08 51											09 21				←						09 51		
Walton-on-Thames d			08 54					09 07						09 24	09 37			09 37						09 54		
Weybridge d			08 58					09 11						09 28	→			09 41						09 58		
Byfleet & New Haw d			09 00											09 30										10 00		
West Byfleet d		08 51	09 03								09 21			09 33								09§51	09§51	10 03		
Woking a	08 58	09 00	09 08			09 11	09 15	09 18		09 24	09 29		09 33	09 38		09 42	09 45	09 48		09 54	09 58	09§59	09§59	10 08		10 11
d	09 00	09 00				09 13	09 16	09 19		09 25	09 30		09 35			09 43	09 46	09 49		09 55	10 00	10§00	10§00			10 13
Worplesdon d						09 18																				10 18
Guildford a						09 23				09 33						09 52				10 03						10 23
Brookwood d		09 06						09 25			09 36							09 55				10§06	10§06			
Ash Vale d		09 14			09 19						09 44								09 49			10§14	10§14			
Aldershot d		09 20			09a25						09 50								09a54			10§20	10§20			
Farnham a		09 26									09 55											10§25	10§25			
d		09 26									09 57											10§26	10§26			
Bentley d											10 03															
Alton a		09 39									10 10											10§38	10§58			
Farnborough (Main) d				09 13				09 33					09 45					10 03							10 13	
Fleet d				09 19				09 38										10 08							10 19	
Winchfield d								09 44										10 14								
Hook d								09 48										10 18								
Basingstoke a				09 34			09 35	09 58				09 48	09 58				10 05	10 28							10 34	

For general notes see front of timetable
For details of catering facilities see
Directory of Train Operators

A Until 26 September
B From 29 September

For details of Bank Holiday service alterations, please see first page of Table 149

London → Woking, Guildford, Alton and Basingstoke

Network Diagram - see first page of Table 155

		SW 1	SW 1◇ ☕	SW 1	SW	SW 1 ☕	SW 1	SW 1◇ ☕	SW 1	SW	SW 1	SW 1	SW 1◇ ☕	SW 1	SW 1	SW 1 ☕	SW 1◇ ☕	SW 1	SW	SW 1	SW 1	SW 1	SW 1◇ ☕	SW 1	SW	SW 1 ☕	SW 1
London Waterloo 15 ⊖	d		09 50	09 42	09 50	10 00	09 53	10 05	10 09		10 12	10 15	10 20			10 30	10 35	10 23	10 20	10 39	10 45		10 50	10 42	10 50	11 00	10 53
Vauxhall ⊖	d				09 54														10 24						10 54		
Clapham Junction 10	d				09 59		10u00	10u12		←	10u19	10u22	10u27						10 29	10u46	10u52				10 59		11u00
Earlsfield	d				10 02 →					10 02									10 32						11 02 →		
Wimbledon 6 ⊖	d									10 06									10 36								
Surbiton 6	d			10 00			10 11			10 14	10 30							10 41	10 44					11 00			11 11
Esher	d									10 18									10 48								
Hersham	d									10 21				←					10 51								
Walton-on-Thames	d			10 07						10 24	10 37 →			10 37					10 54					11 07			
Weybridge	d			10 11						10 28				10 41					10 58					11 11			
Byfleet & New Haw	d									10 30									11 00								
West Byfleet	d						10 21			10 33								10 51	11 03								11 21
Woking	a		10 14	10 18		10 24	10 29		10 33	10 38		10 41	10 45	10 48		10 54	10 58	10 59	11 08		11 11		11 14	11 18		11 24	11 29
	d		10 16	10 19		10 25	10 30		10 35			10 43	10 46	10 49		10 55	11 00	11 01			11 13		11 16	11 19		11 25	11 30
Worplesdon	d																				11 18						
Guildford	a					10 33						10 50				11 03					11 23					11 33	
Brookwood	d			10 25			10 36							10 55				11 06						11 25			11 36
Ash Vale	d	10 19					10 44								10 49			11 14				11 19					11 44
Aldershot	d	10a24					10 50								10a54			11 20				11a24					11 50
Farnham	a						10 55											11 25									11 55
	d						10 57																				11 57
Bentley	d						11 03																				12 03
Alton	a						11 10																				12 10
Farnborough (Main)	d			10 33					10 45					11 03						11 13				11 33			
Fleet	d			10 38										11 08						11 19				11 38			
Winchfield	d			10 44										11 14										11 44			
Hook	d			10 48										11 18										11 48			
Basingstoke	a		10 35	10 58				10 48	10 58				11 05	11 28						11 34			11 35	11 58			

		SW 1◇ ☕	SW 1	SW	SW 1	SW 1	SW 1◇ ☕	SW 1	SW 1	SW 1 ☕	SW 1◇ ☕	SW 1	SW		SW 1	SW 1	SW 1	SW 1◇ ☕	SW 1	SW	SW 1 ☕	SW 1	SW 1◇ ☕	SW 1	SW	SW 1	SW 1
London Waterloo 15 ⊖	d	11 05	11 09		11 12	11 15	11 20			11 30	11 35	11 23	11 20		11 39	11 45		11 50	11 42	11 50	12 00	11 53	12 05	12 09		12 12	12 15
Vauxhall ⊖	d												11 24							11 54							
Clapham Junction 10	d	11u12		←	11u19	11u22	11u27						11 29		11u46	11u52				11 59		12u00	12u12		←	12u19	12u22
Earlsfield	d			11 02									11 32							12 02 →					12 02		
Wimbledon 6 ⊖	d			11 06									11 36												12 06		
Surbiton 6	d			11 14	11 30							11 41	11 44						12 00			12 11			12 14	12 30	
Esher	d			11 18									11 48												12 18		
Hersham	d			11 21				←					11 51												12 21		
Walton-on-Thames	d			11 24	11 37 →			11 37					11 54						12 07						12 24	12 37 →	
Weybridge	d			11 28				11 41					11 58						12 11						12 28		
Byfleet & New Haw	d			11 30									12 00												12 30		
West Byfleet	d			11 33								11 51	12 03									12 21			12 33		
Woking	a		11 33	11 38		11 41	11 45	11 48		11 54	11 58	11 59	12 08			12 11		12 14	12 18		12 24	12 29		12 33	12 38		12 41
	d		11 35			11 43	11 46	11 49		11 55	12 00	12 00				12 13		12 16	12 19		12 25	12 30		12 35			12 43
Worplesdon	d															12 18											
Guildford	a					11 50				12 03						12 23					12 33						12 50
Brookwood	d							11 55				12 06							12 25			12 36					
Ash Vale	d								11 49			12 14					12 19					12 44					
Aldershot	d								11a54			12 20					12a24					12 50					
Farnham	a											12 25										12 55					
	d											12 26										12 57					
Bentley	d																					13 03					
Alton	a											12 37										13 10					
Farnborough (Main)	d		11 45					12 03							12 13				12 33					12 45			
Fleet	d							12 08							12 19				12 38								
Winchfield	d							12 14											12 44								
Hook	d							12 18											12 48								
Basingstoke	a	11 48	11 58				12 05	12 28							12 34			12 35	12 58				12 48	12 58			

For general notes see front of timetable
For details of catering facilities see
Directory of Train Operators

For details of Bank Holiday service alterations, please see first page of Table 149

London → Woking, Guildford, Alton and Basingstoke

Network Diagram - see first page of Table 155

	SW	SW	SW	SW	SW	SW	SW	SW	SW	SW	SW	SW	SW	SW	SW	SW	SW	SW	SW	SW	SW	SW	SW	SW	SW	SW
	1 ◇ ☕	1	1	1 ☕	1 ◇ ☕	1		1	1	1	1 ◇ ☕	1		1 ☕	1	1 ◇ ☕	1		1	1	1 ◇ ☕	1	1	1 ☕	1 ◇ ☕	1
London Waterloo 15 ⊖ d	12 20			12 30	12 35	12 23	12 20	12 39	12 45		12 50	12 42	12 50	13 00	12 53	13 05	13 09		13 12	13 15	13 20			13 30	13 35	13 23
Vauxhall ⊖ d							12 24						12 54													
Clapham Junction 10 d	12u27						12 29	12u46	12u52				12 59		13u00	13u12		←	13u19	13u22	13u27					
Earlsfield d							12 32						13 02 →					13 02								
Wimbledon 6 ⊖ d							12 36											13 06								
Surbiton 6 d						12 41	12 44					13 00			13 11			13 14	13 30							13 41
Esher d							12 48											13 18								
Hersham d		←					12 51											13 21				←				
Walton-on-Thames d		12 37					12 54					13 07						13 24	13 37 →			13 37				
Weybridge d		12 41					12 58					13 11						13 28				13 41				
Byfleet & New Haw d							13 00											13 30								
West Byfleet d						12 50	13 03								13 21			13 33								13 51
Woking a	12 45	12 48		12 54	12 58	12 59	13 08		13 11		13 14	13 18		13 24	13 29		13 33	13 38		13 41	13 45	13 48		13 54	13 58	13 59
d	12 46	12 49		12 55	13 00	13 00			13 13		13 16	13 19		13 25	13 30		13 35			13 43	13 46	13 49		13 55	14 00	14 00
Worplesdon d									13 18																	
Guildford a				13 03					13 23					13 33						13 50				14 03		
Brookwood d		12 55				13 06						13 25			13 36							13 55				14 06
Ash Vale d			12 49			13 14				13 19					13 44								13 49			14 14
Aldershot d			12a54			13 20				13a24					13 50								13a54			14 20
Farnham a						13 25									13 55											14 25
d						13 26									13 57											14 26
Bentley d															14 03											
Alton a						13 37									14 11											14 37
Farnborough (Main) d		13 03						13 13				13 33					13 45					14 03				
Fleet d		13 08						13 19				13 38										14 08				
Winchfield d		13 14										13 47										14 14				
Hook d		13 18										13 51										14 18				
Basingstoke a	13 05	13 28						13 34			13 35	13 58				13 48	13 59				14 05	14 28				

	SW	SW	SW	SW	SW	SW	SW	SW	SW	SW	SW	SW	SW	SW	SW	SW	SW	SW	SW	SW	SW	SW	SW	SW	SW	SW
		1	1	1	1 ◇ ☕	1		1 ☕	1	1 ◇ ☕	1		1	1	1 ◇ ☕	1	1	1 ☕	1 ◇ ☕	1		1	1	1	1 ◇ ☕	1
London Waterloo 15 ⊖ d	13 20	13 39	13 45		13 50	13 42	13 50	14 00	13 53	14 05	14 09		14 12	14 15	14 20			14 30	14 35	14 23	14 20	14 39	14 45		14 50	14 42
Vauxhall ⊖ d	13 24						13 54														14 24					
Clapham Junction 10 d	13 29	13u46	13u52				13 59		14u00	14u12		←	14u19	14u22	14u27						14 29	14u46	14u52			
Earlsfield d	13 32						14 02 →					14 02									14 32					
Wimbledon 6 ⊖ d	13 36											14 06									14 36					
Surbiton 6 d	13 44					14 00			14 11			14 14	14 30							14 41	14 44					15 00
Esher d	13 48											14 18									14 48					
Hersham d	13 51											14 21				←					14 51					
Walton-on-Thames d	13 54					14 07						14 24	14 37 →			14 37					14 54					15 07
Weybridge d	13 58					14 11						14 28				14 41					14 58					15 11
Byfleet & New Haw d	14 00											14 30									15 00					
West Byfleet d	14 03								14 21			14 33								14 51	15 03					
Woking a	14 08		14 11		14 14	14 18		14 24	14 29		14 33	14 38		14 41	14 45	14 48		14 54	14 58	14 59	15 08		15 11		15 14	15 18
d			14 13		14 16	14 19		14 25	14 30		14 35			14 43	14 46	14 49		14 55	15 00	15 00			15 13		15 16	15 19
Worplesdon d			14 18																				15 18			
Guildford a			14 23					14 33						14 50				15 03					15 23			
Brookwood d						14 25			14 36							14 55				15 06						15 25
Ash Vale d				14 19					14 44								14 49			15 14				15 19		
Aldershot d				14a24					14 50								14a54			15 20				15a24		
Farnham a									14 55											15 25						
d									14 57											15 26						
Bentley d									15 03																	
Alton a									15 10											15 37						
Farnborough (Main) d		14 13				14 33					14 45					15 03						15 13				15 33
Fleet d		14 19				14 38										15 08						15 19				15 38
Winchfield d						14 44										15 14										15 44
Hook d						14 48										15 18										15 48
Basingstoke a		14 34			14 35	14 58				14 48	14 58				15 05	15 28						15 34			15 35	15 58

For general notes see front of timetable
For details of catering facilities see Directory of Train Operators

For details of Bank Holiday service alterations, please see first page of Table 149

London → Woking, Guildford, Alton and Basingstoke

Network Diagram - see first page of Table 155

		SW	SW 1 ☕	SW 1	SW 1 ◇ ☕	SW 1	SW	SW 1	SW 1	SW 1 ◇ ☕	SW 1	SW 1	SW 1 ☕	SW 1 ◇ ☕	SW 1	SW	SW 1	SW 1	SW 1	SW 1 ◇ ☕	SW 1	SW	SW 1 ☕	SW 1	SW 1 ◇	SW 1	SW
London Waterloo 15 ⊖	d	14 50	15 00	14 53	15 05	15 09		15 12	15 15	15 20			15 30	15 35	15 23	15 20	15 39	15 45		15 50	15 42	15 50	16 00	15 53	16 05	16 09	
Vauxhall ⊖	d	14 54														15 24						15 54					
Clapham Junction 10	d	14 59		15u00	15u12		←	15u19	15u22	15u27						15 29	15u46	15u52		15u57		15 59		16u00	16u12		←
Earlsfield	d	15 02 →					15 02									15 32						16 02 →					16 02
Wimbledon 6 ⊖	d						15 06									15 36											16 06
Surbiton 6	d			15 11			15 14	15 30							15 41	15 44					16 00			16 11			16 14
Esher	d						15 18									15 48											16 18
Hersham	d						15 21				←					15 51											16 21
Walton-on-Thames	d						15 24	15 37 →			15 37					15 54					16 07						16 24
Weybridge	d						15 28				15 41					15 58					16 11						16 28
Byfleet & New Haw	d						15 30									16 00											16 30
West Byfleet	d			15 21			15 33								15 51	16 03								16 21			16 33
Woking	a		15 23	15 29		15 33	15 38		15 41	15 45	15 48		15 54	15 58	15 59	16 08		16 11		16 15	16 18		16 24	16 29		16 33	16 38
	d		15 25	15 30		15 35			15 43	15 46	15 49		15 55	16 00	16 00			16 13		16 16	16 19		16 25	16 30		16 35	
Worplesdon	d								15 48																		
Guildford	a		15 32						15 53				16 03					16 20					16 33				
Brookwood	d			15 36							15 55				16 06						16 25			16 36			
Ash Vale	d			15 44								15 49			16 14				16 19					16 44			
Aldershot	d			15 50								15a54			16 20				16a24					16 50			
Farnham	a			15 55											16 25									16 55			
	d			15 57											16 26									16 57			
Bentley	d			16 03																				17 03			
Alton	a			16 10											16 37									17 10			
Farnborough (Main)	d					15 45					16 03						16 13				16 33					16 45	
Fleet	d										16 08						16 19				16 38						
Winchfield	d										16 14										16 44						
Hook	d										16 18										16 48						
Basingstoke	a				15 48	15 58				16 05	16 28						16 34			16 35	16 58				16 48	16 58	

		SW 1	SW 1	SW 1 ◇ ☕	SW 1	SW 1	SW 1 ☕	SW 1	SW 1	SW 1 ◇	SW	SW 1	SW 1	SW 1 ◇ ☕	SW 1	SW	SW 1 ☕	SW 1	SW 1	SW 1	SW 1	SW 1	SW	SW 1	SW 1 ▼ ☕	SW 1	SW 1 A
London Waterloo 15 ⊖	d	16 12	16 15	16 20			16 30	16 25		16 35	16 20	16 39	16 45	16 50	16 42	16 50	17 00	16 55		17 09	17 12	17 15		17 02	17 20	17 25	17 05
Vauxhall ⊖	d										16 24					16 54											17 09
Clapham Junction 10	d	16u19	16u22	16u27							16 29	16u46	16u52	16u57		16 59		17u02									17 15
Earlsfield	d										16 32					17 02											
Wimbledon 6 ⊖	d										16 36					17 06											
Surbiton 6	d	16 30						16 41			16 44				17 00	17 14								17 18			
Esher	d										16 48					17 18							←	17 22			
Hersham	d				←						16 51					17 21 →							17 21	17 25			
Walton-on-Thames	d	16 37 →			16 37						16 54				17 07								17 24	17 29			
Weybridge	d				16 41						16 58				17 11								17 28	17 33			
Byfleet & New Haw	d										17 00												17 30	17 36			
West Byfleet	d							16 51			17 03							17 21					17 33	17 39			
Woking	a		16 41	16 45	16 48		16 54	16 59			17 10		17 11		17 18		17 24	17 29		17 32	17 36	17 38	17 43	17 44		17 50	
	d		16 43	16 46	16 49		16 55	17 00		17u00			17 13	17u16	17 19		17 25	17 30		17 34	17 37	17 40		17 46	17u46	17 51	
Worplesdon	d		16 48														17 30					17 45					
Guildford	a		16 53				17 03						17 20				17 36					17 51		17 56			
Brookwood	d				16 55			17 06							17 25			17 36			17 43						
Ash Vale	d					16 49		17 14	17 19									17 44	17 49							18 03	18 24
Aldershot	d					16a54		17 20	17a24									17 50	17a54							18 09	18a31
Farnham	a							17 25										17 55								18 14	
	d							17 26										17 57								18 15	
Bentley	d							17 32										18 03								18 23	
Alton	a							17 41										18 12								18 32	
Farnborough (Main)	d				17 03							17 13			17 33						17 51						
Fleet	d				17 08							17 19			17 38						17 56						
Winchfield	d				17 14										17 44						18 02						
Hook	d				17 18										17 48						18 06						
Basingstoke	a			17 05	17 30							17 34		17 35	18 00					17 53	18 16				18 05		

For general notes see front of timetable
For details of catering facilities see
Directory of Train Operators

A Until 26 September

For details of Bank Holiday service alterations, please see first page of Table 149

London → Woking, Guildford, Alton and Basingstoke

Network Diagram - see first page of Table 155

		SW 1 A	SW 1	SW 1 🍴	SW 1	SW 1	SW	SW 1	SW 1	SW 1	SW 1	SW 1 ▼ 🍴	SW 1 B	SW 1 A	SW 1	SW 1	SW 1	SW 1 🍴	SW 1	SW	SW 1	SW 1	SW 1	SW 1 ◇ 🍴	SW 1	SW 1	SW 1
London Waterloo 15 ⊖	d	17§05	17 23	17 30	17 35	17 39	17 20	17 41	17 45	17 48	17 32	17 50			17 55	17 53		18 00	18 09	17 50	18 11	18 15	18 18	18 20	18 02	18 41	18 23
Vauxhall ⊖	d	17§09					17 24													17 54							
Clapham Junction 10	d	17§15					17 29													17 59				18u27			
Earlsfield	d						17 32													18 02							
Wimbledon 6 ⊖ 🚊	d						17 36													18 06							
Surbiton 6	d		17 39				17 44				17 48					18 09				18 14					18 18		18 40
Esher	d						17 48				17 52									18 18					18 22		→
Hersham	d						17 51				17 55									18 21					18 25		
Walton-on-Thames	d						17 54				17 59									18 24					18 29		
Weybridge	d						17 58				18 03									18 28					18 33		
Byfleet & New Haw	d						18 00				18 06									18 30					18 36		
West Byfleet	d						18 03				18 09					18 19				18 33					18 39		
Woking	a		17 51	17 54		18 02	18 10			18 11	18 14				18 20	18 23			18 32	18 40			18 42	18 45	18 48		
	d		17 52	17 56		18 04				18 13	18 16				18 21	18 26			18 34				18 43	18 46			
Worplesdon	d			18 00							18 21												18 48				
Guildford	a			18 06					18 21		18 29							18 31				18 50	18 54				
Brookwood	d		18 00					18 11							18 27						18 41					19 13	
Ash Vale	d	18§24											18§24	18§24	18 35		18 49										
Aldershot	d	18a34											18a34	18a31	18 41		18a54										
Farnham	a														18 46												
	d														18 48												
Bentley	d														18 54												
Alton	a														19 03												
Farnborough (Main)	d		18 08					18 19								18 38					18 48					19 20	
Fleet	d		18 13					18 24								18 44					18 54					19 26	
Winchfield	d		18 19					18 30								18 49					18 59					19 31	
Hook	d		18 23					18 34								18 54					19 04					19 36	
Basingstoke	a		18 32			18 23		18 45		18 32		18 37				19 03			18 53		19 16			19 05		19 47	

		SW	SW 1	SW 1	SW 1 B	SW 1 A	SW 1 🍴	SW 1	SW	SW 1 C	SW 1 ◇ 🍴	SW 1	SW	SW 1	SW 1 🍴	SW 1	SW 1 ◇ 🍴	SW 1	SW 1	SW	SW 1	SW 1 ◇ 🍴	SW 1	SW	SW 1 🍴	SW 1 ◇ 🍴	SW 1
London Waterloo 15 ⊖	d	18 20	18 25				18 30	18 39		18 45	18 50	18 32	18 50	18 55	19 00		19 05	19 09	19 12		19 15	19 20	19 02	19 20	19 30	19 35	19 25
Vauxhall ⊖	d	18 24											18 54											19 24			
Clapham Junction 10	d	18 29	18u33					18u46					18 59	19u02			19u12		19u19		19u22	19u27		19 29			19u32
Earlsfield	d	18 32											19 02											19 32			
Wimbledon 6 ⊖ 🚊	d	18 36		←									19 06											19 36			
Surbiton 6	d	18 44		18 40								18 48	19 14										19 18	19 44			
Esher	d	18 48										18 52	19 18										19 22	19 48			
Hersham	d	18 51							←			18 55	19 21							←			19 25	19 51			
Walton-on-Thames	d	18 54							18 54			18 59	19 24							19 24			19 29	→			
Weybridge	d	→							18 58			19 03	→							19 28			19 33				
Byfleet & New Haw	d								19 00			19 06								19 30			19 36				
West Byfleet	d								19 03	19 08		19 09								19 33			19 39				19 51
Woking	a		18 52	18 52			18 57	19 05	19 12	19 13	19 17	19 18		19 21	19 24			19 33	19 38	19 42	19 43	19 45	19 48		19 54	19 58	19 59
	d		18 53	18 54			18 58	19 06		19 14	19 18	19 20		19 23	19 25			19 35	19 39		19 45	19 46			19 55	20 00	20 00
Worplesdon	d														19 30												
Guildford	a						19 06			19 23					19 36						19 52				20 03		
Brookwood	d			19 02										19 30					19 45								20 06
Ash Vale	d		19 05		19§24	19§24								19 37		19 49											20 14
Aldershot	d		19 11		19a35	19a36								19 43		19a54											20 20
Farnham	a		19 16											19 48													20 25
	d		19 17											19 49													20 26
Bentley	d		19 23											19 55													20 32
Alton	a		19 32											20 04													20 39
Farnborough (Main)	d			19 10								19 31						19 45	19 53								
Fleet	d			19 15								19 37							19 58								
Winchfield	d			19 21								19 42							20 04								
Hook	d			19 25								19 47							20 08								
Basingstoke	a			19 34				19 28			19 37	20 00					19 48	19 58	20 15			20 06					

For general notes see front of timetable
For details of catering facilities see Directory of Train Operators

A From 29 September
B Until 26 September
C To Portsmouth Harbour (Table 156)

For details of Bank Holiday service alterations, please see first page of Table 149

London → Woking, Guildford, Alton and Basingstoke

Network Diagram - see first page of Table 155

	SW 1	SW	SW 1	SW 1 ◇ ☕	SW 1	SW	SW 1 ☕	SW 1	SW 1	SW 1 ◇ ☕	SW 1	SW	SW 1	SW 1	SW 1 ◇ ☕	SW 1	SW 1	SW 1 ☕	SW 1 ◇ ☕	SW 1	SW	SW 1	SW 1	SW 1	SW	SW 1
London Waterloo 15 ⊖ d	19 39		19 45	19 50	19 42	19 50	20 00		19 53	20 05	20 09		20 12	20 15	20 20			20 30	20 35	20 23	20 20	20 39	20 45	20 42	20 50	
Vauxhall ⊖ d						19 54															20 24				20 54	
Clapham Junction 10 d	19u46		19u52			19 59			20u00	20u12		←	20u19	20u22	20u27						20 29	20u46	20u52		20 59	
Earlsfield d						20 02 →						20 02									20 32				21 02 →	
Wimbledon 6 ⊖ d												20 06									20 36					
Surbiton 6 d					20 00				20 11			20 14	20 30							20 41	20 44			21 00		
Esher d		←										20 18									20 48					
Hersham d		19 51										20 21					←				20 51					
Walton-on-Thames d		19 54			20 07							20 24	20 37 →				20 37				20 54			21 07		
Weybridge d		19 58			20 11							20 28					20 41				20 58			21 11		
Byfleet & New Haw d		20 00										20 30									21 00					
West Byfleet d		20 03							20 21			20 33								20 51	21 03					
Woking a		20 08	20 11	20 14	20 18		20 25		20 29		20 33	20 38		20 41	20 45		20 48	20 54	20 58	20 59	21 08		21 11	21 18		
d			20 13	20 16	20 19		20 25		20 30		20 35			20 43	20 46		20 49	20 55	21 00	21 00			21 13	21 19		
Worplesdon d			20 18																				21 18			
Guildford a			20 23				20 34							20 50				21 03					21 23			
Brookwood d					20 25				20 37								20 55			21 06				21 25		
Ash Vale d								20 19	20 44							20 49				21 14						21 19
Aldershot d								20a24	20 50							20a54				21 20						21a24
Farnham a									20 56											21 25						
d									20 57											21 26						
Bentley d									21 03											21 32						
Alton a									21 17											21 42						
Farnborough (Main) d	20 13				20 33						20 45						21 03					21 13		21 33		
Fleet d	20 19				20 38												21 08					21 19		21 38		
Winchfield d					20 44												21 14							21 44		
Hook d					20 48												21 18							21 48		
Basingstoke a	20 34			20 35	20 58					20 48	20 58				21 05		21 28					21 34		21 58		

	SW 1 ☕	SW 1	SW 1 ◇ ☕	SW	SW 1	SW 1 ◇ ☕	SW 1	SW 1	SW 1	SW 1 ◇ ☕	SW 1	SW	SW 1	SW 1	SW 1 A	SW	SW 1	SW 1	SW 1 ☕	SW	SW 1	SW 1 ☕	SW	SW 1	SW 1	SW 1
London Waterloo 15 ⊖ d	21 00	20 53	21 05		21 12	21 20			21 30	21 35	21 23	21 20	21 39	21 45	21 42	21 50	22 00	21 53	22 05		22 12	22 20	22 20			22 30
Vauxhall ⊖ d												21 24				21 54							22 24			
Clapham Junction 10 d		21u00	21u12	←	21u19	21u27						21 29	21u46	21u52		21 59		22u00	22u12	←	22u19	22u27	22 29			
Earlsfield d				21 02								21 32				22 02 →				22 02			22 32 →			
Wimbledon 6 ⊖ d				21 06								21 36								22 06						
Surbiton 6 d		21 11		21 14	21 30						21 41	21 44			22 00			22 11		22 14	22 30					
Esher d				21 18								21 48								22 18						
Hersham d				21 21				←				21 51								22 21					←	
Walton-on-Thames d				21 24	21 37 →			21 37				21 54			22 07					22 24	22 37 →				22 37	
Weybridge d				21 28				21 41				21 58			22 11					22 28					22 41	
Byfleet & New Haw d				21 30								22 00								22 30						
West Byfleet d		21 21		21 33							21 51	22 03						22 21		22 33						
Woking a	21 24	21 29	21 31	21 38		21 45		21 48	21 54	21 58	21 59	22 08		22 11	22 18		22 24	22 29	22 31	22 38		22 45			22 48	22 54
d	21 25	21 30	21 32			21 49		21 49	21 55	22 00	22 00			22 13	22 19		22 25	22 30	22 32	22 39		22 49			22 49	22 55
Worplesdon d														22 18												
Guildford a	21 33								22 03					22 23			22 33			22 47						23 03
Brookwood d		21 36						21 55			22 06				22 25			22 36							22 55	
Ash Vale d		21 44					21 49				22 14							22 44						22 49		
Aldershot d		21 50					21a54				22 20							22 50						22a54		
Farnham a		21 55									22 25							22 56								
d		21 57									22 26							22 57								
Bentley d		22 03									22 32							23 03								
Alton a		22 10									22 39							23 10								
Farnborough (Main) d								22 03					22 13		22 33										23 03	
Fleet d								22 08					22 19		22 38										23 08	
Winchfield d								22 14							22 44										23 14	
Hook d								22 18							22 48										23 18	
Basingstoke a			21 51			22 08		22 28					22 34		22 58				22 51			23 10			23 27	

For general notes see front of timetable
For details of catering facilities see Directory of Train Operators

A To Portsmouth Harbour (Table 158)

For details of Bank Holiday service alterations, please see first page of Table 149

London → Woking, Guildford, Alton and Basingstoke

Network Diagram - see first page of Table 155

Mondays to Fridays

		SW 1	SW 1	SW	SW 1	SW 1	SW 1	SW 1	SW	SW 1	SW	SW 1	SW 1	SW	SW 1	SW 1	SW 1	SW	SW 1	SW 1	SW 1	SW	SW 1	SW	SW 1
		🍴										A													
London Waterloo 15 ⊖	d	22 35	22 23		22 39	22 42	22 45		22 50	22 53			23 05		23 12	23 15		23 20	23 23	23 35	23 39		23 45		23 48
Vauxhall ⊖	d								22 54									23 24							
Clapham Junction 10	d		22u30	←	22u46	22u49	22u52		22 59	23u00	←		23u12		23u19	23u22		23 29	23u30	23u42	23u46	←	23u52		23u56
Earlsfield	d			22 32					23 02 →		23 02							23 32 →				23 32			
Wimbledon 6 ⊖	d			22 36							23 06											23 36			
Surbiton 6	d		22 41	22 44		23 00				23 11	23 14				23 30				23 41			23 44			00 10
Esher	d			22 48							23 18											23 48			
Hersham	d			22 51				←			23 21			←			←					23 51			
Walton-on-Thames	d			22 54		23 07 →		23 07			23 24 →			23 24	23 37 →		23 37					23 54			00 17
Weybridge	d			22 58				23 11						23 28			23 41					23 58			00 21
Byfleet & New Haw	d			23 00										23 30								00 01		00 07	
West Byfleet	d		22 51	23 03						23 21				23 33					23 51			00 03		00 10	
Woking	a	22 58	22 59	23 08			23 11	23 18		23 28			23 31	23 38		23 41	23 48		23 59	00 02	00 06	00 08	00 11	00 16	00 27
	d	23 00	23 00				23 13	23 19		23 30			23 32			23 43	23 49		00 01	00 03	00 08		00 13		00 29
Worplesdon	d						23 18																00 18		
Guildford	a						23 23									23 51							00 24		
Brookwood	d		23 06					23 25		23 37							23 55		00 06						00 35
Ash Vale	d		23 14							23 44		23 49							00 14						
Aldershot	d		23 20							23 50		23 55							00 20						
Farnham	a		23 25							23 56		00 03							00 25						
	d		23 26							23 57									00 26						
Bentley	d		23 32							00 04									00 32						
Alton	a		23 39							00 11									00 40						
Farnborough (Main)	d				23 13			23 33									00 03				00 18				00 42
Fleet	d				23 19			23 38									00 08				00 23				00 48
Winchfield	d							23 44									00 14								00s53
Hook	d							23 48									00 18								00s58
Basingstoke	a				23 33			23 57					23 51				00 25			00 22	00 35				01 07

Saturdays

		SW 1	SW 1	SW	SW 1	SW 1	SW 1	SW	SW 1	SW	SW 1	SW 1	SW 1	SW 1		SW	SW 1	SW 1	SW 1	SW 1	SW 1	SW 1	SW 1	SW 1	SW	SW 1	SW 1
												B					C	D	E	G		E	H				
London Waterloo 15 ⊖	d	22p53	23p12	23p20	23p23	23p35	23p39		23p45		23p48	00 05				00 09	01 05	05 00	05 20	05 30					05 50	06 12	06 15
Vauxhall ⊖	d			23p24												00 13	01 09	05 04	05 24						05 54		
Clapham Junction 10	d	23b00	23b19	23p29	23b30	23b42	23b46	←	23b52		23b56	00u12				00 18	01 14	05 09	05 29	05u37					05 59	06u19	06u22
Earlsfield	d			23p32 →				23p32								00 21		05 12	05 32						06 02		
Wimbledon 6 ⊖	d							23p36				00u18				00 25	01 20	05 16	05 36	05 43					06 06		
Surbiton 6	d	23p11	23p30		23p41			23p44			00 10					00 33	01 29	05 24	05 44						06 14	06 30	
Esher	d							23p48								00s37		05 28	05 48						06 18		
Hersham	d							23p51								00s40		05 32	05 51			←			06 21		
Walton-on-Thames	d		23p37					23p54			00 17					00s43		05 35	05 54 →			05 54			06 24	06 37 →	
Weybridge	d		23p41					23p58			00 21					00s46		05 39				05 58			06 28		
Byfleet & New Haw	d							00 01		00 07						00s49		05 42				06 00			06 30		
West Byfleet	d	23p21			23p51			00 03		00 10						00s52		05 45				06 03			06 33		
Woking	a	23p28	23p48		23p59	00 02	00 06	00 08	00 11	00 16	00 27	00 35				00 57	01 42	05 50		05 59		06 08			06 38		06 41
	d	23p30	23p49		00 01	00 03	00 08		00 13		00 29	00 36		00 40		00 58	01 42	05 51		06 01	06 02	06 13	06 19	06 30			06 43
Worplesdon	d								00 18													06 18					
Guildford	a								00 24							01 06		05 59				06 23					06 50
Brookwood	d	23p37	23p55		00 06						00 35			00 45							06 08		06 25	06 36			
Ash Vale	d	23p44			00 14								00 52	00 56							06 16			06 44			
Aldershot	d	23p50			00 20								00a57	01 02							06 21			06 50			
Farnham	a	23p56			00 25									01 07							06 27			06 55			
	d	23p57			00 26									01 08							06 27			06 57			
Bentley	d	00 04			00 32									01s14							06 34			07 03			
Alton	a	00 11			00 40									01 21							06 41			07 10			
Farnborough (Main)	d		00 03				00 18				00 42						01s58						06 33				
Fleet	d		00 08				00 23				00 48												06 38				
Winchfield	d		00 14								00s53												06 43				
Hook	d		00 18								00s58												06 48				
Basingstoke	a		00 25			00 22	00 35				01 07	00 55					02s12			06 20			06 58				

For general notes see front of timetable
For details of catering facilities see Directory of Train Operators

- **A** From Ascot (Table 149)
- **B** To Bournemouth (Table 158)
- **C** To Southampton Central (Table 158)
- **D** To Haslemere (Table 156)
- **E** To Portsmouth Harbour (Table 156)
- **G** To Weymouth (Table 158)
- **H** To Portsmouth Harbour (Table 158)
- **b** Previous night. Stops to pick up only

London → Woking, Guildford, Alton and Basingstoke

Network Diagram - see first page of Table 155

Station		SW	SW 1	SW 1		SW 1 A	SW 1	SW	SW 1	SW	SW 1	SW 1 A	SW 1	SW 1 ◇ ☕	SW	SW 1	SW 1	SW		SW 1	SW 1	SW 1 ◇	SW 1	SW	SW 1	SW 1	SW 1
London Waterloo 15 ⊖	d	06 20		06 30		06 42			06 45	06 50			06 53	07 10		07 12	07 15	07 20			07 30	07 35	07 23		07 39	07 45	
Vauxhall ⊖	d	06 24								06 54								07 24									
Clapham Junction 10	d	06 29		06u37		06u49			06u52	06 59			07u00	07u17	←	07u19	07u22	07 29					07u30	←	07u46	07u52	
Earlsfield	d	06 32								07 02 →					07 02			07 32 →						07 32			
Wimbledon 6 ⊖	d	06 36													07 06									07 36			
Surbiton 6	d	06 44				07 00							07 11		07 14	07 30							07 41	07 44			
Esher	d	06 48													07 18									07 48			
Hersham	d	06 51	←					←				←			07 21					←				07 51			
Walton-on-Thames	d	06 54 →	06 37			07 07 →		06 54				07 07			07 24	07 37 →				07 37				07 54			
Weybridge	d		06 41					06 58				07 11			07 28					07 41				07 58			
Byfleet & New Haw	d							07 00							07 30									08 00			
West Byfleet	d							07 03					07 21		07 33								07 51	08 03			
Woking	a		06 48	06 56				07 08	07 11			07 18	07 26	07 35	07 38		07 41			07 48	07 54	07 58	07 59	08 08		08 11	
	d		06 49	06 57			07 00		07 13			07 19	07 30	07 36			07 43			07 49	07 55	08 00	08 00			08 13	
Worplesdon	d								07 18																	08 18	
Guildford	a								07 23								07 50				08 03					08 23	
Brookwood	d		06 55				07 06					07 25	07 36							07 55			08 06				
Ash Vale	d						07 14				07 19		07 44										08 14				08 19
Aldershot	d						07 20				07a24		07 50										08 20				08a24
Farnham	a						07 25						07 55										08 25				
	d						07 26						07 57										08 26				
Bentley	d						07 32						08 03										08 32				
Alton	a						07 40						08 10										08 40				
Farnborough (Main)	d		07 03									07 33								08 03					08 13		
Fleet	d		07 08									07 38								08 08					08 19		
Winchfield	d		07 14									07 44								08 14							
Hook	d		07 18									07 48								08 18							
Basingstoke	a		07 28	07 16								07 58		07 57						08 28		08 20			08 34		

Station		SW 1 ◇ ☕	SW 1	SW	SW 1	SW 1	SW 1 ◇	SW 1		SW	SW 1	SW 1	SW 1 ◇ ☕	SW 1	SW 1	SW 1	SW 1 ◇ ☕	SW 1	SW	SW 1	SW 1	SW 1		SW 1 ◇ ☕	SW 1	SW	SW 1 ☕
London Waterloo 15 ⊖	d	07 50	07 42	07 50	08 00	07 53	08 05	08 09			08 12	08 15	08 20			08 30	08 35	08 23	08 20	08 39	08 45			08 50	08 42	08 50	09 00
Vauxhall ⊖	d			07 54															08 24							08 54	
Clapham Junction 10	d	07u57		07 59		08u00	08u12			←	08u19	08u22	08u27						08 29	08u46	08u52					08 59	
Earlsfield	d			08 02 →						08 02									08 32							09 02 →	
Wimbledon 6 ⊖	d									08 06									08 36								
Surbiton 6	d		08 00			08 11				08 14	08 30							08 41	08 44						09 00		
Esher	d									08 18									08 48								
Hersham	d									08 21				←					08 51								
Walton-on-Thames	d		08 07							08 24	08 37 →			08 37					08 54						09 07		
Weybridge	d		08 11							08 28				08 41					08 58						09 11		
Byfleet & New Haw	d									08 30									09 00								
West Byfleet	d					08 21				08 33								08 51	09 03								
Woking	a	08 15	08 18		08 24	08 29		08 33		08 38		08 41	08 45	08 48		08 54	08 58	08 59	09 08		09 11			09 14	09 18		09 24
	d	08 16	08 19		08 25	08 30		08 35				08 43	08 46	08 49		08 55	09 00	09 00			09 13			09 16	09 19		09 25
Worplesdon	d																				09 18						
Guildford	a				08 33							08 50				09 03					09 23						09 33
Brookwood	d		08 25			08 36								08 55				09 06							09 25		
Ash Vale	d					08 44									08 49			09 14				09 19					
Aldershot	d					08 50									08a54			09 20				09a24					
Farnham	a					08 55												09 25									
	d					08 57												09 26									
Bentley	d					09 03																					
Alton	a					09 10												09 38									
Farnborough (Main)	d		08 33					08 45						09 03						09 13					09 33		
Fleet	d		08 38											09 08						09 19					09 38		
Winchfield	d		08 44											09 14											09 44		
Hook	d		08 48											09 18											09 48		
Basingstoke	a	08 35	08 58				08 48	08 58					09 05	09 28						09 34				09 35	09 58		

Station		SW 1	SW 1 ◇ ☕	SW 1	SW	SW 1	SW 1	SW 1 ◇ ☕	SW 1	SW 1	SW 1 ☕	SW 1 ◇ ☕		SW 1	SW	SW 1	SW 1	SW 1	SW 1 ◇ ☕	SW 1	SW	SW 1 ☕	SW 1 B	SW 1 C	SW 1 ◇ ☕	SW 1	SW
London Waterloo 15 ⊖	d	08 53	09 05	09 09		09 12	09 15	09 20			09 30	09 35		09 23	09 20	09 39	09 45		09 50	09 42	09 50	10 00	09 53	09 53	10 05	10 09	
Vauxhall ⊖	d														09 24						09 54						
Clapham Junction 10	d	09u00	09u12		←	09u19	09u22	09u27							09 29	09u46	09u52				09 59		10u00	10u00	10u12		←
Earlsfield	d				09 02										09 32						10 02 →						10 02
Wimbledon 6 ⊖	d				09 06										09 36												10 06
Surbiton 6	d	09 11			09 14	09 30								09 41	09 44					10 00			10 11	10 11			10 14
Esher	d				09 18										09 48												10 18
Hersham	d				09 21				←						09 51												10 21
Walton-on-Thames	d				09 24	09 37 →			09 37						09 54					10 07							10 24
Weybridge	d				09 28				09 41						09 58					10 11							10 28
Byfleet & New Haw	d				09 30										10 00												10 30
West Byfleet	d	09 21			09 33									09 51	10 03								10 21	10 21			10 33
Woking	a	09 29		09 33	09 38		09 41	09 45	09 48		09 54	09 58		09 59	10 08		10 11		10 14	10 18		10 24	10 29	10 29		10 33	10 38
	d	09 30		09 35			09 43	09 46	09 49		09 55	10 00		10 00			10 13		10 16	10 19		10 25	10 30	10 30		10 35	
Worplesdon	d																10 18										
Guildford	a						09 50				10 03						10 23					10 33					
Brookwood	d	09 36							09 55					10 06						10 25			10 36	10 36			
Ash Vale	d	09 44								09 49				10 14				10 19					10 44	10 44			
Aldershot	d	09 50								09a54				10 20				10a24					10 50	10 50			
Farnham	a	09 55												10 25									10 55	10 55			
	d	09 57												10 26									10 57	10 57			
Bentley	d	10 03																					11 03	11b09			
Alton	a	10 10												10 38									11 10	11 16			
Farnborough (Main)	d			09 45					10 03							10 13				10 33						10 45	
Fleet	d								10 08							10 19				10 38							
Winchfield	d								10 14											10 44							
Hook	d								10 18											10 48							
Basingstoke	a		09 48	09 58				10 05	10 28							10 34			10 35	10 58					10 48	10 58	

For general notes see front of timetable
For details of catering facilities see Directory of Train Operators

A To Portsmouth Harbour (Table 158)
B Until 27 September
C From 4 October
b Arr. 1103

Table 155

Saturdays

London → Woking, Guildford, Alton and Basingstoke

Network Diagram - see first page of Table 155

Station		SW 1		SW 1	SW 1 ◇ ☕	SW 1	SW 1		SW 1 ☕	SW 1 ◇ ☕	SW 1	SW	SW 1	SW 1	SW 1	SW 1 ◇ ☕	SW 1	SW	SW 1 ☕	SW 1	SW 1 ◇ ☕	SW 1	SW	SW 1	SW 1	SW 1 ◇ ☕	SW 1
London Waterloo 15 ⊖	d	10 12		10 15	10 20				10 30	10 35	10 23	10 20	10 39	10 45		10 50	10 42	10 50	11 00	10 53	11 05	11 09		11 12	11 15	11 20	
Vauxhall ⊖	d											10 24						10 54									
Clapham Junction 10	d	10u19		10u22	10u27							10 29	10u46	10u52				10 59		11u00	11u12		←	11u19	11u22	11u27	
Earlsfield	d											10 32						11 02 →					11 02				
Wimbledon 6 ⊖ 🚊	d											10 36											11 06				
Surbiton 6	d	10 30									10 41	10 44					11 00			11 11			11 14	11 30			
Esher	d											10 48											11 18				
Hersham	d					←						10 51											11 21				←
Walton-on-Thames	d	10 37 →				10 37						10 54					11 07						11 24	11 37 →			11 37
Weybridge	d					10 41						10 58					11 11						11 28				11 41
Byfleet & New Haw	d											11 00											11 30				
West Byfleet	d										10 51	11 03								11 21			11 33				
Woking	a			10 41	10 45	10 48			10 54	10 58	10 59	11 08		11 11		11 14	11 18		11 24	11 29		11 33	11 38		11 41	11 45	11 48
	d			10 43	10 46	10 49			10 55	11 00	11 00			11 13		11 16	11 19		11 25	11 30		11 35			11 43	11 46	11 49
Worplesdon	d													11 18													
Guildford	a			10 50					11 03					11 23					11 33						11 50		
Brookwood	d					10 55					11 06						11 25			11 36							11 55
Ash Vale	d						10 49				11 14				11 19					11 44							
Aldershot	d						10a54				11 20				11a24					11 50							
Farnham	a										11 25									11 55							
	d										11 27									11 57							
Bentley	d																			12 03							
Alton	a										11 38									12 10							
Farnborough (Main)	d					11 03							11 13				11 33					11 45					12 03
Fleet	d					11 08							11 19				11 38										12 08
Winchfield	d					11 14											11 44										12 14
Hook	d					11 18											11 48										12 18
Basingstoke	a				11 05	11 28							11 34			11 35	11 58				11 48	11 58				12 05	12 28

Station		SW 1	and at the same minutes past each hour until		SW 1 ☕	SW 1 ◇ ☕	SW 1	SW	SW 1	SW 1	SW 1	SW 1 ◇ ☕	SW 1	SW	SW 1 ☕	SW 1	SW 1 ◇ ☕		SW 1	SW	SW 1	SW 1	SW 1 ◇ ☕	SW 1	SW 1	SW 1 ☕
London Waterloo 15 ⊖	d				16 30	16 35	16 23	16 20	16 39	16 45		16 50	16 42	16 50	17 00	16 53	17 05		17 09		17 12	17 15	17 20			17 30
Vauxhall ⊖	d							16 24						16 54												
Clapham Junction 10	d							16 29	16u46	16u52				16 59		17u00	17u12			←	17u19	17u22	17u27			
Earlsfield	d							16 32						17 02 →						17 02						
Wimbledon 6 ⊖ 🚊	d							16 36												17 06						
Surbiton 6	d						16 41	16 44					17 00			17 11				17 14	17 30					
Esher	d							16 48												17 18						
Hersham	d							16 51												17 21				←		
Walton-on-Thames	d							16 54					17 07							17 24	17 37 →			17 37		
Weybridge	d							16 58					17 11							17 28				17 41		
Byfleet & New Haw	d							17 00												17 30						
West Byfleet	d						16 51	17 03								17 21				17 33						
Woking	a				16 54	16 58	16 59	17 08		17 11		17 14	17 18		17 24	17 29			17 33	17 38		17 41	17 45	17 48		17 54
	d				16 55	17 00	17 00			17 13		17 16	17 19		17 25	17 30			17 35			17 43	17 46	17 49		17 55
Worplesdon	d									17 18																
Guildford	a				17 03					17 23					17 33							17 50				18 03
Brookwood	d						17 06						17 25			17 36								17 55		
Ash Vale	d	11 49					17 14				17 19					17 44									17 49	
Aldershot	d	11a54					17 20				17a24					17 50									17a54	
Farnham	a						17 25									17 55										
	d						17 26									17 57										
Bentley	d						17 32									18 03										
Alton	a						17 42									18 10										
Farnborough (Main)	d								17 13				17 33						17 45					18 03		
Fleet	d								17 19				17 38											18 08		
Winchfield	d												17 44											18 14		
Hook	d												17 48											18 18		
Basingstoke	a								17 34			17 35	17 58				17 48		17 58				18 05	18 28		

Station		SW 1 ◇ ☕	SW 1	SW	SW 1	SW 1	SW 1	SW 1 ◇ ☕		SW 1	SW	SW 1 ☕	SW 1	SW 1 ◇ ☕	SW 1	SW	SW 1	SW 1	SW 1 ◇ ☕	SW 1	SW 1	SW 1 ☕		SW 1 ◇ ☕	SW 1	SW	SW 1
London Waterloo 15 ⊖	d	17 35	17 23	17 20	17 39	17 45		17 50		17 42	17 50	18 00	17 53	18 05	18 09		18 12	18 15	18 20			18 30		18 35	18 23	18 20	18 39
Vauxhall ⊖	d			17 24							17 54															18 24	
Clapham Junction 10	d			17 29	17u46	17u52					17 59		18u00	18 12		←	18u19	18u22	18u27							18 29	18u46
Earlsfield	d			17 32							18 02 →					18 02										18 32	
Wimbledon 6 ⊖ 🚊	d			17 36												18 06										18 36	
Surbiton 6	d		17 41	17 44						18 00			18 11			18 14	18 30								18 41	18 44	
Esher	d			17 48												18 18										18 48	
Hersham	d			17 51												18 21				←						18 51	
Walton-on-Thames	d			17 54						18 07						18 24	18 37 →			18 37						18 54	
Weybridge	d			17 58						18 11						18 28				18 41						18 58	
Byfleet & New Haw	d			18 00												18 30										19 00	
West Byfleet	d		17 51	18 03									18 21			18 33									18 51	19 03	
Woking	a	17 58	17 59	18 08		18 11		18 14		18 18		18 24	18 29		18 33	18 38		18 41	18 45	18 48		18 54		18 58	18 59	19 08	
	d	18 00	18 00			18 13		18 16		18 19		18 25	18 30		18 35			18 43	18 46	18 49		18 55		19 00	19 00		
Worplesdon	d					18 18																					
Guildford	a					18 23						18 33						18 50				19 03					
Brookwood	d		18 06							18 25			18 36							18 55					19 06		
Ash Vale	d		18 14				18 19						18 44								18 49				19 14		
Aldershot	d		18 20				18a24						18 50								18a54				19 20		
Farnham	a		18 26										18 55												19 25		
	d		18 26										18 57												19 26		
Bentley	d		18 32										19 03												19 32		
Alton	a		18 40										19 10												19 39		
Farnborough (Main)	d				18 13					18 33					18 45					19 03							19 13
Fleet	d				18 19					18 38										19 08							19 19
Winchfield	d									18 44										19 14							
Hook	d									18 48										19 18							
Basingstoke	a				18 34			18 35		18 58				18 48	18 58				19 05	19 28							19 34

For general notes see front of timetable
For details of catering facilities see
Directory of Train Operators

London → Woking, Guildford, Alton and Basingstoke

Network Diagram - see first page of Table 155

Station																											
		SW 1	SW 1	SW 1 ◇ ☕	SW 1	SW	SW 1 ☕	SW 1	SW 1 ◇ ☕	SW 1	SW	SW 1		SW 1	SW 1 ◇ ☕	SW 1	SW 1	SW 1 ☕	SW 1 ◇ ☕	SW 1	SW	SW 1	SW 1	SW 1	SW 1 ◇ ☕	SW 1	SW
London Waterloo 15 ⊖	d	18 45		18 50	18 42	18 50	19 00	18 53	19 05	19 09		19 12		19 15	19 20			19 30	19 35	19 23	19 20	19 39	19 45		19 50	19 42	19 50
Vauxhall ⊖	d					18 54															19 24						19 54
Clapham Junction 10	d	18u52				18 59		19u00	19u12		←	19u19		19u22	19u27						19 29	19u46	19u52				19 59
Earlsfield	d					19 02 →					19 02										19 32						20 02 →
Wimbledon 6 ⊖	d										19 06										19 36						
Surbiton 6	d				19 00			19 11			19 14	19 30								19 41	19 44					20 00	
Esher	d										19 18										19 48						
Hersham	d										19 21					←					19 51						
Walton-on-Thames	d				19 07						19 24	19 37 →				19 37					19 54					20 07	
Weybridge	d				19 11						19 28					19 41					19 58					20 11	
Byfleet & New Haw	d										19 30										20 00						
West Byfleet	d							19 21			19 33									19 51	20 03						
Woking	a	19 11		19 15	19 18		19 24	19 29		19 33	19 38			19 41	19 45	19 48		19 54	19 58	19 59	20 08		20 11		20 14	20 18	
	d	19 13		19 16	19 19		19 25	19 30		19 35				19 43	19 46	19 49		19 55	20 00	20 00			20 13		20 16	20 19	
Worplesdon	d	19 18																					20 18				
Guildford	a	19 23					19 33							19 50				20 03					20 23				
Brookwood	d				19 25			19 36								19 55				20 06						20 25	
Ash Vale	d		19 19					19 44									19 49			20 14				20 19			
Aldershot	d		19a24					19 50									19a54			20 20				20a24			
Farnham	a							19 55												20 25							
	d							19 57												20 26							
Bentley	d							20 03												20 32							
Alton	a							20 10												20 39							
Farnborough (Main)	d				19 33					19 45						20 03						20 13				20 33	
Fleet	d				19 38											20 08						20 19				20 38	
Winchfield	d				19 44											20 14										20 44	
Hook	d				19 48											20 18										20 48	
Basingstoke	a			19 35	19 58				19 48	19 58					20 05	20 28						20 34			20 35	20 58	

Station																											
		SW 1		SW 1	SW 1 ◇ ☕	SW 1	SW	SW 1	SW 1	SW 1 ◇ ☕	SW 1	SW 1	SW 1	SW 1 ◇ ☕	SW 1	SW		SW 1	SW 1	SW 1 A	SW	SW 1	SW 1	SW 1	SW 1 ◇ ☕	SW	SW 1
London Waterloo 15 ⊖	d	20 00		19 53	20 05	20 09		20 12	20 15	20 20			20 30	20 35	20 23	20 20		20 39	20 45	20 42	20 50		21 00	20 53	21 05		21 12
Vauxhall ⊖	d															20 24					20 54						
Clapham Junction 10	d			20u00	20u12		←	20u19	20u22	20u27						20 29		20u46	20u52		20 59			21u00	21u12	←	21u19
Earlsfield	d						20 02									20 32					21 02 →					21 02	
Wimbledon 6 ⊖	d						20 06									20 36										21 06	
Surbiton 6	d			20 11			20 14	20 30							20 41	20 44				21 00				21 11		21 14	21 30
Esher	d						20 18									20 48										21 18	
Hersham	d						20 21				←					20 51										21 21	
Walton-on-Thames	d						20 24	20 37 →			20 37					20 54				21 07						21 24	21 37 →
Weybridge	d						20 28				20 41					20 58				21 11						21 28	
Byfleet & New Haw	d						20 30									21 00										21 30	
West Byfleet	d			20 21			20 33								20 51	21 03								21 21		21 33	
Woking	a	20 24		20 29		20 33	20 38		20 41	20 45	20 48		20 54	20 58	20 59	21 08			21 11	21 18			21 24	21 29	21 31	21 38	
	d	20 25		20 30		20 35			20 43	20 46	20 49		20 55	21 00	21 00				21 13	21 19			21 25	21 30	21 32		
Worplesdon	d																		21 18								
Guildford	a	20 33							20 50				21 03						21 23				21 33				
Brookwood	d			20 36							20 55				21 06					21 25				21 36			
Ash Vale	d			20 44								20 49			21 14							21 19		21 44			
Aldershot	d			20 50								20a54			21 20							21a24		21 50			
Farnham	a			20 55											21 25									21 55			
	d			20 57											21 26									21 57			
Bentley	d			21 03											21 32									22 03			
Alton	a			21 10											21 39									22 10			
Farnborough (Main)	d					20 45					21 03							21 13		21 33							
Fleet	d										21 08							21 19		21 38							
Winchfield	d										21 14									21 44							
Hook	d										21 18									21 48							
Basingstoke	a				20 48	20 58				21 05	21 28							21 34		21 58					21 51		

Station																											
		SW 1 ◇ ☕	SW 1	SW 1	SW 1	SW 1 ◇ ☕		SW 1	SW	SW 1	SW 1	SW 1 A	SW	SW 1	SW 1	SW 1 ☕	SW	SW 1	SW 1 ☕	SW		SW 1	SW 1	SW 1	SW 1 ☕	SW 1	SW
London Waterloo 15 ⊖	d	21 20			21 30	21 35		21 23	21 20	21 39	21 45	21 42	21 50	22 00	21 53	22 05		22 12	22 20	22 20				22 30	22 35	22 23	
Vauxhall ⊖	d								21 24				21 54							22 24							
Clapham Junction 10	d	21u27							21 29	21u46	21u52		21 59		22u00	22u12	←	22u19	22u27	22 29						22u30	←
Earlsfield	d								21 32				22 02 →				22 02			22 32 →							22 32
Wimbledon 6 ⊖	d								21 36								22 06										22 36
Surbiton 6	d							21 41	21 44			22 00			22 11		22 14	22 30								22 41	22 44
Esher	d								21 48								22 18										22 48
Hersham	d		←						21 51								22 21					←					22 51
Walton-on-Thames	d		21 37						21 54			22 07					22 24	22 37 →				22 37					22 54
Weybridge	d		21 41						21 58			22 11					22 28					22 41					22 58
Byfleet & New Haw	d								22 00								22 30										23 00
West Byfleet	d							21 51	22 03						22 21		22 33									22 51	23 03
Woking	a	21 45	21 48		21 54	21 58		21 59	22 08		22 11	22 18		22 24	22 29	22 31	22 38		22 45			22 48		22 54	22 58	22 59	23 08
	d	21 49	21 49		21 55	22 00		22 00			22 13	22 19		22 25	22 30	22 32	22 39		22 49			22 49		22 55	23 00	23 00	
Worplesdon	d										22 18																
Guildford	a				22 03						22 23			22 33			22 47							23 03			
Brookwood	d		21 55					22 06				22 25			22 36							22 55				23 06	
Ash Vale	d			21 49				22 14							22 44								22 49			23 14	
Aldershot	d			21a54				22 20							22 50								22a54			23 20	
Farnham	a							22 25							22 56											23 25	
	d							22 26							22 57											23 26	
Bentley	d							22 32							23 03											23 32	
Alton	a							22 39							23 10											23 39	
Farnborough (Main)	d		22 03							22 13		22 33										23 03					
Fleet	d		22 08							22 19		22 38										23 08					
Winchfield	d		22 14									22 44										23 14					
Hook	d		22 18									22 48										23 18					
Basingstoke	a	22 10	22 25							22 34		22 58				22 51			23 10			23 25					

For general notes see front of timetable
For details of catering facilities see
Directory of Train Operators

A To Portsmouth Harbour (Table 158)

Table 155

Saturdays

London → Woking, Guildford, Alton and Basingstoke

Network Diagram - see first page of Table 155

		SW 1	SW 1	SW 1	SW 1	SW	SW 1	SW 1	SW 1	SW 1		SW	SW 1	SW 1	SW 1	SW	SW 1	SW 1	SW 1	SW	SW 1	SW	SW 1
									A														
London Waterloo 15	⊖ d	22 39	22 42	22 45		22 50	22 53			23 05			23 12	23 15		23 20	23 23	23 35	23 39		23 45		23 48
Vauxhall	⊖ d					22 54										23 24							
Clapham Junction 10	d	22u46	22u49	22u52		22 59	23u00			23u12		←	23u19	23u22		23 29	23u30	23u42	23u46	←	23u52		23u56
Earlsfield	d					23 02 →						23 02				23 32 →				23 32			
Wimbledon 6	⊖ ⛴ d											23 06								23 36			
Surbiton 6	d		23 00				23 11					23 14	23 30				23 41			23 44			00 10
Esher	d											23 18								23 48			
Hersham	d				←							23 21			←					23 51			
Walton-on-Thames	d		23 07 →		23 07							23 24	23 37 →		23 37					23 54			00 17
Weybridge	d				23 11							23 28			23 41					23 58			00 21
Byfleet & New Haw	d											23 30								23 59		00 07	
West Byfleet	d						23 21					23 33					23 51			00 03		00 10	
Woking	a			23 11	23 18		23 29			23 31		23 38		23 41	23 48		23 59	00 02	00 06	00 08	00 12	00 16	00 27
	d			23 13	23 19		23 30			23 32				23 43	23 49		00 01	00 03	00 08		00 13		00 29
Worplesdon	d			23 18																	00 18		
Guildford	a			23 23										23 51							00 23		
Brookwood	d				23 25		23 36								23 55		00 06						00 35
Ash Vale	d						23 44	23 49									00 14						
Aldershot	d						23 50	23a54	23 58								00 20						
Farnham	a						23 55		00 03								00 25						
	d						23 57										00 26						
Bentley	d						00 04										00 33						
Alton	a						00 11										00 40						
Farnborough (Main)	d	23 13			23 33										00 03				00 18				00 42
Fleet	d	23 19			23 38										00 08				00 23				00 48
Winchfield	d				23 44										00 14								00s53
Hook	d				23 48										00 18								00s58
Basingstoke	a	23 34			23 55					23 51					00 25			00 22	00 35				01 07

Sundays

		SW 1	SW 1	SW	SW 1	SW 1	SW 1	SW	SW 1	SW	SW 1	SW 1	SW 1	SW 1	SW	SW 1	SW 1	SW 1	SW 1	SW	SW	SW	SW 1 ◇	SW	SW 1	SW 1
												B				C						D				
London Waterloo 15	⊖ d	22p53	23p12	23p20	23p23	23p35	23p39		23p45		23p48	00 05			00 09	01 05				07 10	07 40		07 54			08 00
Vauxhall	⊖ d			23p24											00 13	01 09				07 14	07 44					
Clapham Junction 10	d	23b00	23b19	23p29	23b30	23b42	23b46	←	23b52		23b56	00u12			00 18	01 14				07 19	07 49		08u03			08u09
Earlsfield	d			23p32 →				23p32							00 21					07 22	07 52					
Wimbledon 6	⊖ ⛴ d							23p36				00u18			00 25	01 20				07 26	07 56					
Surbiton 6	d	23p11	23p30		23p41			23p44			00 10				00 33	01 29				07 35	08 05					
Esher	d							23p48							00s37					07 39	08 09					
Hersham	d							23p51							00s40					07 42	08 12			←		
Walton-on-Thames	d		23p37					23p54			00 17				00s43					07 45	08 15 →			08 15		
Weybridge	d		23p41					23p58			00 21				00s46					07 49				08 19		
Byfleet & New Haw	d							23p59		00 07					00s49					07 51		08 02		08 21		
West Byfleet	d	23p21			23p51			00 03		00 10					00s52					07 54		08 05		08 24		
Woking	a	23p29	23p48		23p59	00 02	00 06	00 08	00 12	00 16	00 27	00 35			00 57	01 42				07 59		08 10	08 27	08 29		08 34
	d	23p30	23p49		00 01	00 03	00 08		00 13		00 29	00 36		00 40	00 58	01 42	07 32	07 46	07 49	08 05			08 28	08 32		08 35
Worplesdon	d								00 18																	
Guildford	a								00 23						01 06		07 40			08 13				08 40		08 43
Brookwood	d	23p36	23p55		00 06						00 35			00 45				07 52	07 56							
Ash Vale	d	23p44			00 14								00 52	00 56					08 04						08 36	
Aldershot	d	23p50			00 20								00a57	01 02					08 09						08a41	
Farnham	a	23p55			00 25									01 07					08 15							
	d	23p57			00 26									01 08					08 15							
Bentley	d	00 04			00 33									01s14					08 24							
Alton	a	00 11			00 40									01 21					08 31							
Farnborough (Main)	d		00 03				00 18				00 42					01s58		07 59								
Fleet	d		00 08				00 23				00 48							08 05								
Winchfield	d		00 14								00s53							08 10								
Hook	d		00 18								00s58							08 15								
Basingstoke	a		00 25			00 22	00 35				01 07	00 55				02s12		08 22					08 47			

For general notes see front of timetable
For details of catering facilities see
Directory of Train Operators

- **A** From Guildford (Table 149)
- **B** To Bournemouth (Table 158)
- **C** To Southampton Central (Table 158)
- **D** From Staines (Table 149)

- **b** Previous night.
  Stops to pick up only

Table 155

Sundays

London → Woking, Guildford, Alton and Basingstoke

Network Diagram - see first page of Table 155

		SW		SW	SW	SW	SW	SW	SW	SW	SW	SW	SW	SW	SW	SW		SW	SW	SW	SW	SW		SW	SW	SW	SW
		■1			■1 ◇ ☕	■1		■1	■1	■1 ◇			■1 ◇		■1	■1			■1 ◇ ☕	■1		■1		■1	■1 ◇		
London Waterloo 15 ⊖	d	08 07		08 10	08 15				08 30	08 35		08 40	08 54		09 00	09 07		09 10	09 15					09 30	09 35		09 40
Vauxhall ⊖	d			08 14								08 44						09 14									09 44
Clapham Junction 10	d	08 15		08 19	08u22				08u39	08u42		08 49	09u03		09u09	09 15		09 19	09u22					09u39	09u42		09 49
Earlsfield	d			08 22								08 52						09 22									09 52
Wimbledon 6 ⊖	d	08 22		08 26								08 56				09 22		09 26									09 56
Surbiton 6	d	08 30		08 35								09 05				09 30		09 35									10 05
Esher	d			08 39								09 09						09 39									10 09
Hersham	d			08 42			←					09 12		←				09 43			←						10 12
Walton-on-Thames	d			08 45 →			08 45					09 15 →		09 15				09 45 →			09 45						10 15 →
Weybridge	d						08 49							09 19							09 49						
Byfleet & New Haw	d						08 51				09 02			09 21							09 51					10 02	
West Byfleet	d						08 54				09 05			09 24							09 54					10 05	
Woking	a	08 42			08 46	←	08 59		09 03	09 08	09 10		09 27	09 29	09 34	09 42			09 46	←	09 59			10 03	10 08	10 10	
	d	08 49	08 46		08 47	08 49	09 02		09 04	09 09			09 28	09 32	09 35	09 49	09 46		09 47	09 49	10 02			10 04	10 09		
Worplesdon	d	→														→											
Guildford	a						09 10		09 12					09 40	09 43						10 10			10 12			
Brookwood	d		08 52			08 56											09 52			09 56							
Ash Vale	d					09 04		09 36												10 04		10 36					
Aldershot	d					09 09		09a41												10 09		10a41					
Farnham	a					09 15														10 15							
	d					09 15														10 15							
Bentley	d					09 24														10 24							
Alton	a					09 31														10 31							
Farnborough (Main)	d		08 59														09 59										
Fleet	d		09 05														10 05										
Winchfield	d		09 10														10 10										
Hook	d		09 15														10 15										
Basingstoke	a		09 22		09 06					09 28			09 47				10 22		10 06						10 28		

		SW	SW	SW	SW	SW		SW	SW	SW	SW	SW		SW	SW	SW	SW		SW	SW	SW	SW	SW	SW		SW
		■1 ◇		■1		■1			■1 ◇ ☕	■1		■1		■1 ☕	■1 ◇ ☕		■1			■1 ◇		■1		■1		
London Waterloo 15 ⊖	d	09 54		10 00		10 07		10 10	10 15					15 30	15 35		15 37		15 40	15 54		16 00		16 07		16 10
Vauxhall ⊖	d							10 14											15 44							16 14
Clapham Junction 10	d	10u03		10u09		10 15		10 19	10u22					15u39	15u42		15 46		15 49	16u03		16u09		16 15		16 19
Earlsfield	d							10 22											15 52							16 22
Wimbledon 6 ⊖	d					10 22		10 26									15 53		15 56					16 22		16 26
Surbiton 6	d					10 30		10 35									16 02		16 05					16 30		16 35
Esher	d							10 39											16 09							16 39
Hersham	d		←					10 42			←		and at						16 12		←					16 42
Walton-on-Thames	d		10 15					10 45 →			10 45						16 09		16 15 →		16 15					16 45 →
Weybridge	d		10 19								10 49		the same				16 13				16 19					
Byfleet & New Haw	d		10 21								10 51					16 02					16 21					
West Byfleet	d		10 24								10 54		minutes			16 05					16 24					
Woking	a	10 26	10 29	10 31	←	10 42			10 45	←	10 59			16 01	16 06	16 10	16 19			16 26	16 29	16 31	←	16 42		
	d	10 28	10 35	10 32	10 35	10 49	10 46		10 46	10 49	11 05		past	16 02	16 07		16 23	16 26		16 28	16 35	16 32	16 35	16 49	16 46	
Worplesdon	d		→			→							each								→			→		
Guildford	a			10 40	10 43						11 13		hour until	16 10								16 40	16 43			
Brookwood	d						10 52			10 56							16 29	16 33							16 52	
Ash Vale	d									11 04		11 36						16 41								
Aldershot	d									11 09		11a41						16 46								
Farnham	a									11 15								16 52								
	d									11 15								16 56								
Bentley	d									11 24																
Alton	a									11 31								17 07								
Farnborough (Main)	d						10 59										16 36								16 59	
Fleet	d						11 05										16 42								17 05	
Winchfield	d						11 10																		17 10	
Hook	d						11 15																		17 15	
Basingstoke	a	10 47					11 22		11 05						16 26		16 54			16 47					17 22	

For general notes see front of timetable
For details of catering facilities see
Directory of Train Operators

London → Woking, Guildford, Alton and Basingstoke

Network Diagram - see first page of Table 155

		SW 1 ◇ ☕	SW 1	SW	SW 1	SW 1 ☕	SW	SW 1 ◇ ☕	SW	SW 1		SW	SW 1 ◇	SW	SW 1	SW	SW 1		SW	SW 1 ◇ ☕	SW 1	SW	SW 1	SW 1 ☕	SW	SW 1 ◇ ☕	SW
London Waterloo 15 ⊖	d	16 15				16 30		16 35		16 37		16 40	16 54		17 00		17 07		17 10	17 15				17 30		17 35	
Vauxhall ⊖	d											16 44							17 14								
Clapham Junction 10	d	16u22				16u39		16u42		16 46		16 49	17u03		17u09		17 15		17 19	17u22				17u39		17u42	
Earlsfield	d											16 52							17 22								
Wimbledon 6 ⊖ 🚊	d									16 53		16 56					17 22		17 26								
Surbiton 6	d									17 02		17 05					17 30		17 35								
Esher	d											17 09							17 39								
Hersham	d			←								17 12		←					17 42			←					
Walton-on-Thames	d			16 45						17 09		17 15		17 15					17 45			17 45					
Weybridge	d			16 49						17 13		→		17 19					→			17 49					
Byfleet & New Haw	d			16 51					17 02					17 21								17 51					18 02
West Byfleet	d			16 54					17 05					17 24								17 54					18 05
Woking	a	16 45		16 59		17 01		17 06	17 10	17 19			17 26	17 29	17 31		17 42			17 45		17 59		18 01		18 06	18 10
			←				←									←					←				←		
	d	16 46	16 49	17 05		17 02	17 05	17 07		17 23	17 26		17 28	17 35	17 32	17 35	17 49	17 46		17 46	17 49	18 05		18 02	18 05	18 07	
Worplesdon	d			→										→			→					→					
Guildford	a					17 10	17 13								17 40	17 43								18 10	18 13		
Brookwood	d		16 56							17 29	17 33							17 52			17 56						
Ash Vale	d		17 04		17 36						17 41										18 04		18 36				
Aldershot	d		17 09		17a41						17 46										18 09		18a41				
Farnham	a		17 15								17 52										18 15						
	d		17 15								17 56										18 15						
Bentley	d		17 24																		18 24						
Alton	a		17 31								18 07										18 31						
Farnborough (Main)	d									17 36								17 59									
Fleet	d									17 42								18 05									
Winchfield	d																	18 10									
Hook	d																	18 15									
Basingstoke	a	17 05						17 26		17 54			17 47					18 22		18 05						18 26	

		SW 1		SW	SW 1 ◇	SW	SW 1	SW	SW 1		SW	SW 1 ◇ ☕	SW 1	SW	SW 1	SW 1 ☕	SW	SW 1 ◇ ☕	SW	SW 1		SW	SW 1 ◇	SW	SW 1	SW
London Waterloo 15 ⊖	d	17 37		17 40	17 54		18 00		18 07		18 10	18 15				18 30		18 35		18 37		18 40	18 54		19 00	
Vauxhall ⊖	d			17 44							18 14											18 44				
Clapham Junction 10	d	17 46		17 49	18u03		18u09		18 15		18 19	18u22				18u39		18u42		18 46		18 49	19u03		19u09	
Earlsfield	d			17 52							18 22											18 52				
Wimbledon 6 ⊖ 🚊	d	17 53		17 56					18 22		18 26									18 53		18 56				
Surbiton 6	d	18 02		18 05					18 30		18 35									19 02		19 05				
Esher	d			18 09							18 39											19 09				
Hersham	d			18 12		←					18 42			←								19 12		←		
Walton-on-Thames	d	18 09		18 15		18 15					18 45			18 45						19 09		19 15		19 15		
Weybridge	d	18 13		→		18 19					→			18 49						19 13		→		19 19		
Byfleet & New Haw	d					18 21								18 51					19 02					19 21		
West Byfleet	d					18 24								18 54					19 05					19 24		
Woking	a	18 19			18 26	18 29	18 31		18 42			18 45		18 59		19 01		19 06	19 10	19 19			19 26	19 29	19 31	
								←					←				←									←
	d	18 23	18 26		18 28	18 35	18 32	18 35	18 49	18 46		18 46	18 49	19 05		19 02	19 05	19 07		19 23	19 26		19 28	19 35	19 32	19 35
Worplesdon	d					→			→					→										→		
Guildford	a						18 40	18 43								19 10	19 13								19 40	19 43
Brookwood	d	18 29	18 33							18 52			18 56							19 29	19 33					
Ash Vale	d		18 41										19 04		19 36						19 41					
Aldershot	d		18 46										19 09		19a41						19 46					
Farnham	a		18 52										19 15								19 52					
	d		18 56										19 15								19 56					
Bentley	d												19 24													
Alton	a		19 07										19 31								20 07					
Farnborough (Main)	d	18 36								18 59										19 36						
Fleet	d	18 42								19 05										19 42						
Winchfield	d									19 10																
Hook	d									19 15																
Basingstoke	a	18 54			18 47					19 22		19 05						19 26		19 54			19 47			

For general notes see front of timetable
For details of catering facilities see
Directory of Train Operators

London → Woking, Guildford, Alton and Basingstoke

Network Diagram - see first page of Table 155

	SW 1		SW	SW 1 ◇ ⊡	SW 1	SW	SW 1	SW 1 ⊡	SW	SW 1 ◇ ⊡	SW	SW 1		SW	SW 1 ◇	SW	SW 1	SW	SW 1		SW	SW 1 ◇ ⊡	SW 1	SW	SW 1	SW 1 ⊡
London Waterloo 15 ⊖ d	19 07		19 10	19 15				19 30		19 35		19 37		19 40	19 54		20 00		20 07		20 10	20 15				20 30
Vauxhall ⊖ d			19 14											19 44							20 14					
Clapham Junction 10 d	19 15		19 19	19u22				19u39		19u42		19 46		19 49	20u03		20u09		20 15		20 19	20u22				20u39
Earlsfield d			19 22											19 52							20 22					
Wimbledon 6 ⊖ d	19 22		19 26									19 53		19 56					20 22		20 26					
Surbiton 6 d	19 30		19 35									20 02		20 05					20 30		20 35					
Esher d			19 39											20 09							20 39					
Hersham d			19 42			←								20 12		←					20 42			←		
Walton-on-Thames d			19 45 →			19 45						20 09		20 15 →		20 15					20 45 →			20 45		
Weybridge d						19 49						20 13				20 19								20 49		
Byfleet & New Haw d						19 51					20 02					20 21								20 51		
West Byfleet d						19 54					20 05					20 24								20 54		
Woking a	19 42			19 45	←	19 59		20 01	←	20 06	20 10	20 19			20 26	20 29	20 31	←	20 42			20 45	←	20 59		21 01
d	19 49	19 46		19 46	19 49	20 05		20 02	20 05	20 07		20 23	20 26		20 28	20 35	20 32	20 35	20 49	20 46		20 46	20 49	21 05		21 02
Worplesdon d	→					→										→			→					→		
Guildford a								20 10	20 13								20 40	20 43								21 10
Brookwood d		19 52			19 56							20 29	20 33							20 52			20 56			
Ash Vale d					20 04		20 36						20 41										21 04		21 36	
Aldershot d					20 09		20a41						20 46										21 09		21a41	
Farnham a					20 15								20 52										21 15			
d					20 15								20 56										21 15			
Bentley d					20 24																		21 24			
Alton a					20 31								21 07										21 31			
Farnborough (Main) d		19 59										20 36								20 59						
Fleet d		20 05										20 42								21 05						
Winchfield d		20 10																		21 10						
Hook d		20 15																		21 15						
Basingstoke a		20 22		20 05						20 26		20 54			20 47					21 22		21 05				

	SW	SW 1 ◇ ⊡	SW	SW 1		SW	SW 1 ◇	SW	SW 1	SW	SW 1		SW	SW 1 ◇ ⊡	SW 1	SW	SW 1	SW 1	SW	SW 1 ◇ ⊡	SW	SW 1		SW	SW 1 ◇	SW
London Waterloo 15 ⊖ d		20 35		20 37		20 40	20 54		21 00		21 07		21 10	21 15				21 30		21 35		21 37		21 40	21 54	
Vauxhall ⊖ d						20 44							21 14											21 44		
Clapham Junction 10 d		20u42		20 46		20 49	21u03		21u09		21 15		21 19	21u22				21u39		21u42		21 46		21 49	22u03	
Earlsfield d						20 52							21 22											21 52		
Wimbledon 6 ⊖ d				20 53		20 56					21 22		21 26									21 53		21 56		
Surbiton 6 d				21 02		21 05					21 30		21 35									22 02		22 05		
Esher d						21 09							21 39											22 09		
Hersham d						21 12		←					21 42			←								22 12		←
Walton-on-Thames d				21 09		21 15 →		21 15					21 45 →			21 45						22 09		22 15 →		22 15
Weybridge d				21 13				21 19								21 49						22 13				22 19
Byfleet & New Haw d			21 02					21 21								21 51					22 02					22 21
West Byfleet d			21 05					21 24								21 54					22 05					22 24
Woking a	←	21 06	21 10	21 19			21 26	21 29	21 31	←	21 42			21 45	←	21 59		22 01	←	22 06	22 10	22 19			22 26	22 29
d	21 05	21 07		21 23	21 26		21 28	21 35	21 32	21 35	21 49	21 46		21 46	21 49	22 05		22 02	22 05	22 07		22 23	22 26		22 28	22 35
Worplesdon d								→			→					→										→
Guildford a	21 13								21 40	21 43								22 10	22 13							
Brookwood d				21 29	21 33							21 52			21 56							22 29	22 33			
Ash Vale d					21 41										22 04		22 36						22 41			
Aldershot d					21 46										22 09		22a41						22 46			
Farnham a					21 52										22 15								22 52			
d					21 56										22 15								22 56			
Bentley d															22 24											
Alton a					22 07										22 31								23 07			
Farnborough (Main) d				21 36								21 59										22 36				
Fleet d				21 42								22 05										22 42				
Winchfield d												22 10														
Hook d												22 15														
Basingstoke a		21 26		21 54			21 47					22 22		22 05						22 26		22 54			22 47	

For general notes see front of timetable
For details of catering facilities see
Directory of Train Operators

Table 155

Sundays

London → Woking, Guildford, Alton and Basingstoke

Network Diagram - see first page of Table 155

		SW 1	SW	SW 1		SW	SW 1	SW 1	SW	SW 1	SW 1	SW	SW	SW 1		SW	SW 1	SW	SW 1	SW	SW 1		SW	SW 1	SW	SW 1	SW
							☕			A							☕									B	
London Waterloo 15 ⊖	d	22 00		22 07		22 10	22 15				22 30			22 37		22 40	22 54		23 00		23 07		23 10	23 30		23 35	22 50
Vauxhall ⊖	d					22 14										22 44							23 14				22 54
Clapham Junction 10	d	22u09		22 15		22 19	22u22				22u39			22 46		22 49	23u03		23u09		23 15		23 19	23u39		23u44	23 00
Earlsfield	d					22 22										22 52							23 22				
Wimbledon 6 ⊖ ⛴	d			22 22		22 26								22 53		22 56					23 22		23 26				
Surbiton 6	d			22 30		22 35								23 02		23 05					23 30		23 35				
Esher	d					22 39										23 09							23 39				
Hersham	d					22 42			←							23 12		←					23 42				
Walton-on-Thames	d					22 45			22 45					23 09		23 15		23 15					23 45				
Weybridge	d					→			22 49					23 13		→		23 19					23 49				
Byfleet & New Haw	d								22 51				23 02					23 21					23 51				00 02
West Byfleet	d								22 54				23 05					23 24					23 54				00 05
Woking	a	22 31	←	22 42			22 45	←	22 59		23 01	←	23 10	23 19			23 26	23 29	23 31	←	23 42		23 59	00 01	←	00 07	00 10
	d	22 32	22 35	22 49	22 46		22 46	22 49	23 05		23 02	23 05		23 23	23 26		23 28	23 35	23 32	23 35	23 46	23 49	00 05	00 02	00 05	00 08	
Worplesdon	d			→					→									→					→				
Guildford	a	22 40	22 43								23 10	23 13							23 40	23 43				00 10	00 13		
Brookwood	d				22 52			22 56						23 29	23 33						23 52	23 56					
Ash Vale	d							23 04		23 36					23 41							00 04					
Aldershot	d							23 09		23 42					23 47							00 09					
Farnham	a							23 15		23 47					23 54							00 15					
	d							23 15							23 56							00 15					
Bentley	d							23 24														00 23					
Alton	a							23 31							00 07							00 30					
Farnborough (Main)	d				22 59									23 36							23 59					00 18	
Fleet	d				23 05									23 42							00 05					00 24	
Winchfield	d				23 10																00 10						
Hook	d				23 15																00 15						
Basingstoke	a				23 22		23 05							23 54			23 47				00 22					00 39	

		SW 1
London Waterloo 15 ⊖	d	23 40
Vauxhall ⊖	d	23 44
Clapham Junction 10	d	23 49
Earlsfield	d	23 52
Wimbledon 6 ⊖ ⛴	d	23 56
Surbiton 6	d	00 05
Esher	d	00 09
Hersham	d	00 12
Walton-on-Thames	d	00 15
Weybridge	d	00 19
Byfleet & New Haw	d	00 21
West Byfleet	d	00 24
Woking	a	00 30
	d	00 35
Worplesdon	d	
Guildford	a	
Brookwood	d	00 41
Ash Vale	d	00 48
Aldershot	d	00 54
Farnham	a	00 59
	d	
Bentley	d	
Alton	a	
Farnborough (Main)	d	
Fleet	d	
Winchfield	d	
Hook	d	
Basingstoke	a	

For general notes see front of timetable
For details of catering facilities see Directory of Train Operators

A From Ascot (Table 149)
B To Salisbury (Table 160)

For details of Bank Holiday service alterations, please see first page of Table 149

Basingstoke, Alton, Guildford and Woking → Waterloo

Network Diagram - see first page of Table 155

Miles	Miles	Miles			SW	SW	SW	SW	SW	SW	SW	SW	SW	SW	SW	SW	SW	SW	SW	SW	SW	SW	SW	SW	SW	SW	SW
					MO	MO	MO	MO	MX	MX	MX	MX															
						1	1	1	1	1	1	1			1		1	1			1		1	1	1		1
												A					B	C							catering		B
0	—	—	**Basingstoke**	d			23p43		22p54			23p44					04 54	04 54					05 39	05 54	05 59		
5½	—	—	Hook	d					23p01			23p51					05 01	05 01						06 01			
7¾	—	—	Winchfield	d					23p05			23p55					05 05	05 05						06 05			
11¼	—	—	Fleet	d					23p10			00 01					05 10	05 10					05 50	06 10			
14½	—	—	Farnborough (Main)	d					23p16			00 06					05 16	05 16					05 56	→			
—	0	—	**Alton**	d																							05 44
—	4¾	—	Bentley	d																							05 51
—	8¾	—	Farnham	a																							05 56
—	—	—		d																							05 58
—	11¾	—	**Aldershot**	d											06 00												06 04
—	14¾	—	Ash Vale	d											06a04												06 09
19¾	18¾	—	Brookwood	d					23p23			00 13					05 23	05 23									06 16
—	—	0	**Guildford**	d		23p35		00 05			23p39		04 00	05 12							05 50						
—	—	3½	Worplesdon	d							23p44			05 17							05 55						
23½	—	6	**Woking**	a		23p42	00 02	00 13	23p28		23p49	00 18	04 08	05 22			05 28	05 28	←		06 00		06 05		06 18		06 21
—	—	—		d	22p52	23p45	00 03		23p33		23p56	00 20	04 10	05 33		05 25	05 29	05 29	05 33	05 43	06 01	06 04	06 06		06 19		06 22
26	—	—	West Byfleet	d	22p56				23p37			00 25		→		05 30			05 37	05 47		06 08					
27¼	—	—	Byfleet & New Haw	d	23p00				23p40							05 33			05 40			06 11					
28¾	—	—	Weybridge	d					23p43	←		00 29							05 43	05 51		06 14				←	
30¾	—	—	Walton-on-Thames	d					23p47	23p47		00 34							05 47	05 55		06 18				06 18	
31¾	—	—	Hersham	d					→	23p49									05 49			→				06 20	
33¼	—	—	Esher	d						23p52									05 52							06 23	
35¾	—	—	**Surbiton** 6	a						23p57		00 40	04 24				05 40	05 40	05 56	06 01						06 27	06 33
40½	—	—	Wimbledon 6 ⊖ 🚊	a						00 07		00 48	04 31				05 48	05 48	06 04							06 35	
42¼	—	—	Earlsfield	a						00 10									06 08							06 39	
43¾	—	—	Clapham Junction 10	a		00 04	00 22			00 14	00 20	00 54	04 43				06 00	06 00	06 12		06 20		06 25		06 38	06 42	06 45
46½	—	—	Vauxhall ⊖	a						00 19							06 07	06 07	06 17							06 47	
47¾	—	—	**London Waterloo** 15 ⊖	a		00 14	00 33			00 27	00 29	01 02	04 53				06 12	06 15	06 22	06 20	06 29		06 34		06 49	06 52	06 54

		SW	SW	SW	SW	SW	SW		SW	SW	SW	SW	SW	SW	SW	SW	SW	SW	SW	SW	SW	SW	SW	SW	SW	SW	SW
		1	1		1	1	1		1	1		1	1	1		1	1	1	1	1	1	1	1	1	1	1	1
		C							C	B									C	B				C	B		
						catering							catering			catering						▼ catering					catering
Basingstoke	d						06 24						06 29			06 36						06 52					
Hook	d						06 31																				
Winchfield	d		←				06 35										←										
Fleet	d		06 10				06 40										06 40										
Farnborough (Main)	d		06 16				→										06 46										
Alton	d	05 44												06 14												06 44	
Bentley	d	05 51												06 21												06 51	
Farnham	a	05 56												06 26												06 56	
	d	05 58												06 28												06 58	
Aldershot	d	06 04							06 29	06 30				06 34										06 59	07 00	07 04	
Ash Vale	d	06 09							06 33	06 34				06 39										07 03	07 04	07 09	
Brookwood	d	06 16	06 23											06 46			06 53									07 16	
Guildford	d				06 24	06 31													06 52	06 55			07 07				07 17
Worplesdon	d				06 30														06 58	07 01							
Woking	a	06 21	06 28		06 35	06 39							06 48	06 51		06 54	06 58		07 05	07 05		07 11	07 15			07 21	07 25
	d	06 22	06 29	06 32	06 37	06 41						06 41	06 49	06 52		06 55	06 59	07 02	07 07	07 07	07 11	07 12	07 17			07 22	07 26
West Byfleet	d			06 36								06 46						07 07			07 16						
Byfleet & New Haw	d			06 39								06 49									07 19						
Weybridge	d			06 43							←	06 52						07 11			07 22						
Walton-on-Thames	d			06 47							06 47	06 57						07 16			07 27						
Hersham	d			→							06 49	07 00						07 19			07 30						
Esher	d										06 52	07 03						07 22			07 33						
Surbiton 6	a	06 33	06 40								06 56	07 07						07 26			07 37						
Wimbledon 6 ⊖ 🚊	a		06 47								07 04				←												
Earlsfield	a										07 08				07 08												
Clapham Junction 10	a	06 45	06 54		06 58	07 02			07 46	07 46	→			07 11	07 12	07 16	07 22		07 26	07 26		07 31		08 16	08 16		
Vauxhall ⊖	a								07 52	07 52					07 17									08 22	08 22		
London Waterloo 15 ⊖	a	06 56	07 04		07 08	07 12			07 59	07 59		07 28	07 18	07 22	07 24	07 26	07 32	07 49	07 37	07 37	07 56	07 44	07 44	08 29	08 29	07 51	07 54

For general notes see front of timetable
For details of catering facilities see Directory of Train Operators

A From Weymouth (Table 158)
B Until 26 September
C From 29 September

For details of Bank Holiday service alterations, please see first page of Table 149

Basingstoke, Alton, Guildford and Woking → Waterloo

Network Diagram - see first page of Table 155

		SW 1	SW 1	SW 1	SW 1	SW 1	SW 1	SW 1	SW 1	SW 1 A	SW 1 B		SW 1	SW 1	SW 1	SW 1 ▼ 🍽	SW 1 🍽	SW 1	SW 1	SW 1 C	SW 1	SW 1 C	SW 1	SW 1	SW 1	SW	SW 1 ◇ 🍽
Basingstoke	d	06 54	07 06	07 17											07 24	07 29				07 36	07 47				07 52		07 59
Hook	d	07 01	07 13												07 31					07 43		←			07 59		
Winchfield	d	07 05	07 17												07 35					07 47		07 47			08 04		
Fleet	d	07 10	07 22												07 40					→		07 52			08 09		
Farnborough (Main)	d	07 16	07 28												07 46							07 58			→		
Alton	d												07 14														
Bentley	d												07 21														
Farnham	a												07 26														
	d												07 28						07 39								
Aldershot	d									07 29	07 30		07 34						07 46					08 00			
Ash Vale	d									07 33	07 34		07 39						07 50					08a04			
Brookwood	d	07 23											07 46		07 53				07 57								
Guildford	d				07 32									07 45			07 54						08 03				
Worplesdon	d				07 40									07 50													
Woking	a	07 28					07 38						07 51	07 54	07 58				08 03		08 05	08 08	08 11				08 18
	d	07 29				07 32	07 40		07 47				07 52	07 56	07 59			08 02	08 05		08 06	08 09	08 12			08 17	08 19
West Byfleet	d					07 37		07 46	07b54									08 06	08c16							08e26	
Byfleet & New Haw	d							07 49	07 57										08 19							08 29	
Weybridge	d					07 41		07 52	08 01									08 11	08 22							08 32	
Walton-on-Thames	d					07 46		07 57	08 06									08 15	08 27							08 36	
Hersham	d					07 49		08 00	08 09									08 17	08 30							08 39	
Esher	d					07 52		08 03	08 13									08 20	08 33							08 43	
Surbiton 6	a					07 56		08 07	08 18									08 24	08 37							08 47	
Wimbledon 6 ⊖	a																										
Earlsfield	a																										
Clapham Junction 10	a									08 46	08 46																
Vauxhall	⊖ a									08 52	08 52																
London Waterloo 15	⊖ a	07 59	08 06	08 01	08 11	08 19	08 08	08 26	08 36	09 00	09 00		08 22	08 24	08 29	08 14	08 32	08 46	08 59		08 34	08 39	08 41			09 06	08 46

		SW 1	SW 1 🍽	SW 1	SW	SW 1 C	SW 1	SW 1 C	SW 1	SW 1	SW 1 C	SW 1	SW 1 ◇ 🍽	SW 1	SW		SW 1 🍽	SW 1 C	SW 1	SW 1	SW 1	SW	SW 1 🍽	SW 1	SW 1 ◇ 🍽	SW 1	SW
Basingstoke	d					08 05	08 16				08 24		08 29				08 35		08 42	08 54					08 59		
Hook	d					08 12		←			08 31									09 01							
Winchfield	d			←		08 16		08 16			08 35							←		09 05							
Fleet	d			08 09		→		08 22			08 40							08 40	08 54	09 10							
Farnborough (Main)	d			08 16				08 28			→							08 46	08 59	→							
Alton	d	07 44												08 14													
Bentley	d	07 51												08 21													
Farnham	a	07 56												08 26													
	d	07 58												08 28													
Aldershot	d	08 04								08 30				08 34												09 00	
Ash Vale	d	08 09								08a34				08 39												09a04	
Brookwood	d	08 16		08 23										08 46				08 53									
Guildford	d		08 15		08 20				08 31													08 46	08 54	09 03			
Worplesdon	d		08 20						08 37													08 51					
Woking	a	08 21	08 26	08 28	08 30		08 34	08 38	08 41				08 48	08 51			08 53	08 58				08 59		09 11	09 18		
	d	08 23	08 27	08 29	08 32		08 36	08 39	08 43			08 47	08 49	08 52			08 55	08 59				09 02		09 13	09 19		
West Byfleet	d				08 36							08f54										09 06					
Byfleet & New Haw	d				08 39							08 57									←	09 09					
Weybridge	d				08 43							09 02			←						09 02	09 13					←
Walton-on-Thames	d				08 47							→			08 47						09 07	09 17					09 17
Hersham	d				→										08 49						09 10	→					09 19
Esher	d														08 52						09 13						09 22
Surbiton 6	a														08 56			09 10			09 18						09 26
Wimbledon 6 ⊖	a														09 04												09 34
Earlsfield	a														09 08												09 38
Clapham Junction 10	a								09 03						09 12		09 14		09 26					09 32	09 38		09 42
Vauxhall	⊖ a														09 17												09 47
London Waterloo 15	⊖ a	08 51	08 55	09 00			09 03	09 10	09 13				09 17	09 21	09 24		09 25	09 29	09 38		09 40		09 31	09 43	09 51		09 54

For general notes see front of timetable
For details of catering facilities see Directory of Train Operators

A From 29 September
B Until 26 September
C From Southampton Central (Table 158)
b Arr. 0751
c Arr. 0809
e Arr. 0821
f Arr. 0851

For details of Bank Holiday service alterations, please see first page of Table 149

Basingstoke, Alton, Guildford and Woking → Waterloo

Network Diagram - see first page of Table 155

		SW 1	SW 1◇ ☕	SW 1 ☕	SW 1	SW 1	SW	SW 1	SW 1	SW 1	SW 1	SW 1◇ ☕	SW	SW 1	SW 1◇ ☕	SW 1	SW 1 ☕	SW 1	SW		SW 1	SW 1	SW 1	SW 1◇ ☕	SW 1◇ ☕	SW	SW 1
Basingstoke	d								09 17		09 24	09 31			09 36			09 41					09 54	09 57			
Hook	d										09 31												10 01				
Winchfield	d					←					09 35					←							10 05				
Fleet	d					09 10					09 40 →					09 40		09 53					10 10 →				
Farnborough (Main)	d					09 16			09 31							09 46		09 58									
Alton	d	08 44												09 14													09 44
Bentley	d	08 51												09 21													09 51
Farnham	a	08 56												09 26													09 56
	d	08 58												09 28													09 58
Aldershot	d	09 04						09 30						09 34								10 00					10 04
Ash Vale	d	09 09						09a34						09 39								10a04					10 09
Brookwood	d	09 16				09 23								09 46		09 53											10 16
Guildford	d			09 17						09 32							09 47				10 02						
Worplesdon	d									09 40																	
Woking	a	09 21	09 22	09 27		09 28			09 40	09 44		09 49		09 51	09 54	09 58	09 59				10 11			10 15	10 20		10 21
	d	09 22	09 24	09 28	←	09 29	09 33		09 41	09 46		09 51		09 52	09 55	09 59	09 59		10 03		10 12			10 17	10 21		10 22
West Byfleet	d	09 27 →			09 27		09 37							09 57					10 07								10 27
Byfleet & New Haw	d						09 40												10 10								
Weybridge	d					09 36	09 43						←			10 06			10 13							←	
Walton-on-Thames	d					09 41	09 47 →						09 47			10 11			10 17 →							10 17	
Hersham	d												09 49													10 19	
Esher	d												09 52													10 22	
Surbiton 6	a				09 37	09 47							09 56	10 07		10 17										10 26	10 37
Wimbledon 6 ⊖	a												10 04													10 34	
Earlsfield	a												10 08													10 38	
Clapham Junction 10	a		09 43		09 50	09 58				10 05		10 10	10 12		10 14			10 24			10 31			10 36		10 42	10 48
Vauxhall ⊖	a												10 17													10 47	
London Waterloo 15 ⊖	a		09 53	09 55	09 59	10 06			10 08	10 13		10 19	10 22	10 25	10 23	10 35	10 27	10 34			10 40			10 49	10 49	10 52	10 57

		SW 1 ☕	SW 1	SW	SW 1	SW 1	SW 1	SW 1	SW 1◇ ☕	SW 1	SW	SW 1	SW 1 ☕	SW 1	SW 1	SW	SW 1	SW 1	SW 1	SW 1◇ ☕	SW 1◇ ☕	SW	SW 1		SW 1 ☕	SW 1	SW
Basingstoke	d					10 17		10 24	10 31	10 36					10 41				10 54	10 57							
Hook	d							10 31											11 01								
Winchfield	d		←					10 35						←					11 05							←	
Fleet	d		10 10					10 40 →						10 40	10 53				11 10 →							11 10	
Farnborough (Main)	d		10 16			10 31								10 46	10 58											11 16	
Alton	d											10 14											10 44				
Bentley	d											10 21											10 51				
Farnham	a											10 26											10 56				
	d											10 28											10 58				
Aldershot	d				10 30							10 34						11 00					11 04				
Ash Vale	d				10a34							10 39						11a04					11 09				
Brookwood	d		10 23									10 46		10 53									11 16			11 23	
Guildford	d	10 17					10 32						10 47				11 02								11 17		
Worplesdon	d						10 40																				
Woking	a	10 25	10 28			10 40	10 44		10 49			10 51	10 57	10 58			11 11			11 15	11 19		11 21		11 25	11 28	
	d	10 26	10 29	10 33		10 41	10 46		10 51			10 52	10 59	10 59		11 03	11 12			11 17	11 21		11 22		11 26	11 29	11 33
West Byfleet	d			10 37								10 57				11 07							11 27				11 37
Byfleet & New Haw	d			10 40												11 10											11 40
Weybridge	d		10 36	10 43							←			11 06		11 13						←				11 36	11 43
Walton-on-Thames	d		10 41	10 47 →							10 47			11 11		11 17 →						11 17				11 41	11 47 →
Hersham	d										10 49											11 19					
Esher	d										10 52											11 22					
Surbiton 6	a		10 47								10 56	11 07		11 17								11 26	11 37			11 47	
Wimbledon 6 ⊖	a										11 04											11 34					
Earlsfield	a										11 08											11 38					
Clapham Junction 10	a		10 58				11 05			11 12	11 12				11 24		11 31			11 36		11 42	11 48			11 58	
Vauxhall ⊖	a										11 17											11 47					
London Waterloo 15 ⊖	a	10 51	11 06			11 08	11 13		11 19	11 20	11 22	11 27	11 24	11 36	11 34		11 40			11 49	11 49	11 52	11 57		11 51	12 06	

For general notes see front of timetable
For details of catering facilities see Directory of Train Operators

For details of Bank Holiday service alterations, please see first page of Table 149

Basingstoke, Alton, Guildford and Woking → Waterloo

Network Diagram - see first page of Table 155

	SW 1	SW 1	SW 1	SW 1	SW 1 ◇ ☕	SW 1 ◇ ☕	SW	SW 1	SW 1 ☕	SW 1	SW 1	SW	SW 1	SW 1	SW 1	SW 1 ◇ ☕	SW 1 ◇ ☕	SW	SW 1	SW 1 ☕	SW 1	SW	SW 1	SW 1	SW 1	SW 1
Basingstoke d		11 17		11 24	11 31	11 36					11 41				11 54	11 57								12 17		12 24
Hook d				11 31											12 01											12 31
Winchfield d				11 35						←					12 05						←					12 35
Fleet d				11 40						11 40	11 53				12 10						12 10					12 40
Farnborough (Main) d		11 31		→						11 46	11 58				→						12 16			12 31		→
Alton d								11 15											11 44							
Bentley d																			11 51							
Farnham a								11 25											11 56							
d								11 28											11 58							
Aldershot d	11 30							11 34						12 00					12 04				12 30			
Ash Vale d	11a34							11 39						12a04					12 09				12a34			
Brookwood d								11 46		11 53									12 16		12 23					
Guildford d			11 32						11 47				12 02							12 17					12 32	
Worplesdon d			11 40																						12 40	
Woking a		11 40	11 44		11 49			11 51	11 57	11 58			12 11			12 15	12 19		12 21	12 25	12 28			12 40	12 44	
d		11 41	11 46		11 51			11 52	11 59	11 59		12 03	12 12			12 17	12 21		12 22	12 26	12 29	12 33		12 41	12 46	
West Byfleet d								11 57				12 07							12 27			12 37				
Byfleet & New Haw d												12 10										12 40				
Weybridge d							←			12 06		12 13						←			12 36	12 43				
Walton-on-Thames d							11 47			12 11		12 17						12 17			12 41	12 47				
Hersham d							11 49					→						12 19				→				
Esher d							11 52											12 22								
Surbiton 6 a							11 56	12 07		12 17								12 26	12 37		12 47					
Wimbledon 6 ⊖ a							12 04											12 34								
Earlsfield a							12 08											12 38								
Clapham Junction 10 a			12 05			12 12	12 12				12 24		12 31			12 36		12 42	12 48		12 58				13 05	
Vauxhall ⊖ a							12 17											12 47								
London Waterloo 15 ⊖ a		12 08	12 13		12 19	12 20	12 22	12 27	12 23	12 36	12 34		12 40			12 49	12 49	12 52	12 57	12 51	13 06			13 08	13 13	

	SW 1 ◇ ☕	SW 1 ◇ ☕		SW	SW 1	SW 1 ☕	SW 1	SW 1	SW	SW 1	SW 1	SW 1	SW 1 ◇ ☕	SW 1 ◇ ☕	SW	SW 1	SW 1 ☕	SW 1	SW	SW 1	SW 1	SW 1	SW 1	SW 1 ◇ ☕	SW 1 ◇ ☕	SW
Basingstoke d	12 31	12 36						12 41				12 54	12 57								13 17		13 24	13 31	13 36	
Hook d												13 01											13 31			
Winchfield d							←					13 05						←					13 35			
Fleet d							12 40	12 53				13 10						13 10					13 40			
Farnborough (Main) d							12 46	12 58				→						13 16			13 31		→			
Alton d																12 44										
Bentley d																12 51										
Farnham a																12 56										
d					12 28											12 58										
Aldershot d					12 34						13 00					13 04				13 30						
Ash Vale d					12 39						13a04					13 09				13a34						
Brookwood d					12 46		12 53									13 16		13 23								
Guildford d						12 47				13 02							13 17					13 32				
Worplesdon d																						13 40				
Woking a	12 49				12 51	12 57	12 58			13 11			13 15	13 19		13 21	13 25	13 28			13 40	13 44		13 49		
d	12 51				12 52	12 59	12 59		13 03	13 12			13 17	13 21		13 22	13 26	13 29	13 33		13 41	13 46		13 51		
West Byfleet d					12 57				13 07							13 27			13 37							
Byfleet & New Haw d									13 10										13 40							
Weybridge d				←			13 06		13 13						←			13 36	13 43							←
Walton-on-Thames d				12 47			13 11		13 17						13 17			13 41	13 47							13 47
Hersham d				12 49					→						13 19				→							13 49
Esher d				12 52											13 22											13 52
Surbiton 6 a				12 56	13 07		13 17								13 26	13 37		13 47								13 56
Wimbledon 6 ⊖ a				13 04											13 34											14 04
Earlsfield a				13 08											13 38											14 08
Clapham Junction 10 a		13 12		13 12				13 24		13 31			13 36		13 42	13 48		13 58				14 05			14 12	14 12
Vauxhall ⊖ a				13 17											13 47											14 17
London Waterloo 15 ⊖ a	13 19	13 20		13 22	13 25	13 23	13 35	13 34		13 40			13 49	13 49	13 52	13 57	13 51	14 06			14 08	14 13		14 19	14 20	14 22

For general notes see front of timetable
For details of catering facilities see Directory of Train Operators

For details of Bank Holiday service alterations, please see first page of Table 149

Basingstoke, Alton, Guildford and Woking → Waterloo

Network Diagram - see first page of Table 155

		SW	SW	SW	SW	SW	SW		SW	SW	SW	SW	SW	SW	SW	SW	SW	SW	SW	SW	SW	SW	SW	SW	SW	SW	SW
		[1]	[1] ☕	[1]	[1]		[1]		[1]	[1]	[1] ◇ ☕	[1] ◇ ☕		[1]	[1] ☕	[1]		[1]	[1]	[1]	[1]	[1] ◇ ☕	[1] ◇ ☕		[1]	[1] ☕	[1]
Basingstoke	d				13 41					13 54	13 57								14 17		14 24	14 31	14 36				
Hook	d									14 01											14 31						
Winchfield	d			←						14 05						←					14 35						←
Fleet	d			13 40	13 53					14 10						14 10					14 40						14 40
Farnborough (Main)	d			13 46	13 58					→						14 16			14 31		→						14 46
Alton	d	13 15												13 44											14 15		
Bentley	d													13 51													
Farnham	a	13 25												13 56											14 25		
	d	13 28												13 58											14 28		
Aldershot	d	13 34							14 00					14 04				14 30							14 34		
Ash Vale	d	13 39							14a04					14 09				14a34							14 39		
Brookwood	d	13 46		13 53										14 16		14 23									14 46		14 53
Guildford	d		13 47				14 02								14 17					14 32						14 47	
Worplesdon	d																			14 40							
Woking	a	13 51	13 57	13 58			14 11				14 15	14 19		14 21	14 25	14 28			14 40	14 44		14 49			14 51	14 57	14 58
	d	13 52	13 59	13 59		14 03	14 12				14 17	14 21		14 22	14 26	14 29	14 33		14 41	14 46		14 51			14 52	14 59	14 59
West Byfleet	d	13 57				14 07								14 27			14 37								14 57		
Byfleet & New Haw	d					14 10											14 40										
Weybridge	d			14 06		14 13							←			14 36	14 43							←			15 06
Walton-on-Thames	d			14 11		14 17							14 17			14 41	14 47							14 47			15 11
Hersham	d					→							14 19				→							14 49			
Esher	d												14 22											14 52			
Surbiton [6]	a	14 07		14 17									14 26	14 37		14 47								14 56	15 07		15 17
Wimbledon [6] ⊖ 🚊	a												14 34											15 04			
Earlsfield	a												14 38											15 08			
Clapham Junction [10]	a				14 24		14 31				14 36		14 42	14 48		14 58				15 05			15 12	15 12			
Vauxhall ⊖	a												14 47											15 17			
London Waterloo [15] ⊖	a	14 25	14 23	14 35	14 34		14 40				14 49	14 49	14 52	14 57	14 51	15 06			15 08	15 13		15 19	15 20	15 22	15 25	15 23	15 35

		SW	SW	SW	SW	SW	SW	SW	SW	SW	SW		SW	SW	SW	SW	SW	SW	SW	SW	SW	SW	SW	SW	SW	SW	SW
		[1]		[1]	[1]	[1]	[1] ◇ ☕	[1] ◇ ☕		[1]	[1] ☕		[1]		[1]	[1]	[1]	[1]	[1] ◇ ☕	[1] ◇ ☕		[1]	[1] ☕	[1]	[1]		[1]
Basingstoke	d	14 41				14 54	14 57									15 17		15 24	15 31	15 36					15 41		
Hook	d					15 01												15 31									
Winchfield	d					15 05							←					15 35						←			
Fleet	d	14 53				15 10							15 10					15 40						15 40	15 53		
Farnborough (Main)	d	14 58				→							15 16			15 31		→						15 46	15 58		
Alton	d									14 44												15 15					
Bentley	d									14 51																	
Farnham	a									14 56												15 25					
	d									14 58												15 28					
Aldershot	d				15 00					15 04					15 30							15 34					
Ash Vale	d				15a04					15 09					15a34							15 39					
Brookwood	d									15 16			15 23									15 46		15 53			
Guildford	d			15 02							15 17						15 32						15 47				16 00
Worplesdon	d																15 40										16 06
Woking	a			15 11			15 15	15 19		15 21	15 25		15 28			15 40	15 44		15 49			15 51	15 57	15 58			16 11
	d		15 03	15 12			15 17	15 21		15 22	15 26		15 29	15 33		15 41	15 46		15 51			15 52	15 59	15 59		16 03	16 12
West Byfleet	d		15 07							15 27				15 37								15 57				16 07	
Byfleet & New Haw	d		15 10											15 40												16 10	
Weybridge	d		15 13						←				15 36	15 43							←			16 06		16 13	
Walton-on-Thames	d		15 17						15 17				15 41	15 47							15 47			16 11		16 17	
Hersham	d		→						15 19					→							15 49					→	
Esher	d								15 22												15 52						
Surbiton [6]	a								15 26	15 37			15 47								15 56	16 07		16 17			
Wimbledon [6] ⊖ 🚊	a								15 34												16 04						
Earlsfield	a								15 38												16 08						
Clapham Junction [10]	a	15 24		15 31			15 36		15 42	15 48			15 58				16 05			16 12	16 12				16 24		16 31
Vauxhall ⊖	a								15 47												16 17						
London Waterloo [15] ⊖	a	15 34		15 40			15 49	15 49	15 52	15 58	15 51		16 06			16 08	16 13		16 19	16 20	16 22	16 29	16 23	16 36	16 34		16 40

For general notes see front of timetable
For details of catering facilities see
Directory of Train Operators

For details of Bank Holiday service alterations, please see first page of Table 149

Basingstoke, Alton, Guildford and Woking → Waterloo

Network Diagram - see first page of Table 155

	SW 1	SW 1	SW 1 ◇ ☕	SW 1 ◇ ☕	SW	SW 1	SW 1 ☕	SW 1	SW	SW 1	SW 1	SW 1	SW 1	SW 1 ◇ ☕		SW 1 ◇ ☕	SW	SW 1	SW 1	SW 1	SW 1	SW	SW 1 ☕	SW 1	SW 1	SW 1 ◇ ☕
Basingstoke d		15 54	15 57								16 17		16 24	16 31		16 36					16 41				16 54	16 57
Hook d		16 01											16 31												17 01	
Winchfield d		16 05						←					16 35							←					17 05	
Fleet d		16 10						16 10					16 40							16 40	16 53				17 10	
Farnborough (Main) d		→						16 16			16 31		→							16 46	16 58				→	
Alton d						15 44												16 15								
Bentley d						15 51																				
Farnham a						15 56												16 25								
Farnham d						15 58												16 28								
Aldershot d	16 00					16 04				16 30								16 34						17 00		
Ash Vale d	16a04					16 09				16a34								16 39						17a04		
Brookwood d						16 16		16 23										16 46		16 53						
Guildford d							16 17					16 32							16 47				17 00			
Worplesdon d												16 40											17 06			
Woking a			16 15	16 19		16 21	16 25	16 28			16 40	16 44		16 49				16 51	16 57	16 58			17 11			17 16
Woking d			16 17	16 21		16 22	16 26	16 29	16 33		16 41	16 46		16 51				16 52	16 59	16 59		17 03	17 12			17 17
West Byfleet d						16 27			16 37									16 57				17 07				
Byfleet & New Haw d									16 40													17 10				
Weybridge d					←			16 36	16 43								←			17 06		17 13				
Walton-on-Thames d					16 17			16 41	16 47								16 47			17 11		17 17				
Hersham d					16 19				→								16 49					→				
Esher d					16 22												16 52									
Surbiton 6 a					16 26	16 37		16 47									16 56	17 07		17 17						
Wimbledon 6 ⊖ 🚋 a					16 35												17 04									
Earlsfield a					16 38												17 08									
Clapham Junction 10 a			16 36		16 42	16 48		16 58				17 05				17 12	17 12				17 24		17 31			17 36
Vauxhall ⊖ a					16 47												17 17									
London Waterloo 15 ⊖ a			16 49	16 49	16 53	16 59	16 51	17 08			17 08	17 14		17 19		17 20	17 22	17 29	17 24	17 34	17 36		17 43			17 45

	SW 1 ◇ ☕	SW	SW 1	SW 1 ☕	SW 1	SW	SW 1	SW 1	SW 1	SW 1	SW 1 ◇ ☕	SW	SW 1 ◇ ☕	SW 1	SW 1	SW 1	SW 1	SW		SW 1 ☕	SW 1	SW 1	SW 1 ◇ ☕	SW 1 ◇ ☕	SW	SW 1
Basingstoke d								17 17		17 24	17 31		17 36				17 41					17 54	17 57			
Hook d										17 31												18 01				
Winchfield d					←					17 35						←						18 05				
Fleet d					17 10					17 40						17 40	17 53					18 10				
Farnborough (Main) d					17 16			17 31		→						17 46	17 58					→				
Alton d			16 44											17 15												17 44
Bentley d			16 51																							17 51
Farnham a			16 56											17 25												17 56
Farnham d			16 58											17 28												17 58
Aldershot d			17 04				17 30							17 34							18 00					18 04
Ash Vale d			17 09				17a34							17 39							18a04					18 09
Brookwood d			17 16		17 23									17 46		17 53										18 16
Guildford d				17 17					17 32						17 47					18 00						
Worplesdon d									17 40											18 06						
Woking a	17 20		17 21	17 25	17 28			17 40	17 44		17 49			17 51	17 58	17 58				18 11			18 15	18 19		18 21
Woking d	17 21		17 22	17 26	17 29	17 33		17 41	17 46		17 51			17 52	17 59	17 59		18 03		18 12			18 17	18 21		18 22
West Byfleet d			17 27			17 37								17 57				18 07								18 27
Byfleet & New Haw d						17 40												18 10								
Weybridge d		←			17 36	17 43						←				18 06		18 13							←	
Walton-on-Thames d		17 17			17 41	17 47						17 47				18 11		18 17							18 17	
Hersham d		17 19				→						17 49						→							18 19	
Esher d		17 22										17 52													18 22	
Surbiton 6 a		17 26	17 37		17 47							17 56		18 07		18 17									18 26	18 37
Wimbledon 6 ⊖ 🚋 a		17 34										18 04													18 34	
Earlsfield a		17 38										18 08													18 38	
Clapham Junction 10 a		17 42	17 48		17 58				18 05			18 12	18 12				18 24			18 31			18 36		18 42	18 48
Vauxhall ⊖ a		17 47										18 17													18 47	
London Waterloo 15 ⊖ a	17 50	17 52	17 59	17 52	18 09			18 08	18 14		18 21	18 23	18 23	18 29	18 27	18 39	18 34			18 43			18 45	18 47	18 52	18 57

For general notes see front of timetable
For details of catering facilities see Directory of Train Operators

For details of Bank Holiday service alterations, please see first page of Table 149

Basingstoke, Alton, Guildford and Woking → Waterloo

Network Diagram - see first page of Table 155

		SW 1 ☕	SW 1	SW	SW 1	SW 1	SW 1	SW 1	SW 1 ◇ ☕	SW 1 ◇ ☕	SW	SW 1	SW 1	SW	SW 1 ☕	SW 1	SW 1	SW 1	SW 1 ◇ ☕	SW	SW 1	SW 1 ◇ ☕	SW 1		SW 1 ☕	SW	SW 1
Basingstoke	d				18 17			18 24	18 31	18 36						18 38		18 54	19 01								19 17
Hook	d							18 31										19 01									
Winchfield	d		←					18 35					←					19 05					←				
Fleet	d		18 10					18 40 →					18 40			18 50		19 10 →					19 10				
Farnborough (Main)	d		18 16		18 31								18 46			18 55							19 16				19 31
Alton	d											18 14									18 35						
Bentley	d											18b23									18 42						
Farnham	a											18 28									18 47						
	d											18 28									18 58						
Aldershot	d						18 30					18 34					19 00				19 04						
Ash Vale	d						18a34					18 39					19a04				19 09						
Brookwood	d		18 23									18 46	18 53								19 16		19 23				
Guildford	d	18 17				18 32									18 55										19 21		
Worplesdon	d					18 40																					
Woking	a		18 28		18 40	18 44			18 49			18 52	18 58		19 03				19 19		19 21	19 24	19 28		19 28		19 40
	d		18 29	18 33	18 41	18 46			18 51			18 52	18 59	19 03	19 05				19 21		19 22	19 25	19 29		19 30	19 33	19 41
West Byfleet	d			18 37								18 57		19 07							19 27					19 37	
Byfleet & New Haw	d			18 40										19 10												19 40	
Weybridge	d		18 36	18 43							←		19 06	19 13						←			19 36			19 43	
Walton-on-Thames	d		18 41	18 47 →							18 47		19 11	19 17 →						19 17			19 41			19 47 →	
Hersham	d										18 49									19 19							
Esher	d										18 52									19 22							
Surbiton 6	a		18 47								18 56	19 08	19 17							19 26	19 37		19 47				
Wimbledon 6 ⊖ 🚋	a										19 05									19 34							
Earlsfield	a										19 08									19 38							
Clapham Junction 10	a		18 58			19 05				19 12	19 12					19 26			19 40	19 42	19 48		19 58				
Vauxhall ⊖	a										19 17									19 47							
London Waterloo 15 ⊖	a	18 59	19 06		19 08	19 14			19 19	19 20	19 23	19 25	19 39		19 29	19 38			19 49	19 52	19 57	19 51	20 06		19 59		20 08

		SW 1	SW 1	SW 1	SW 1 ◇ ☕	SW 1 ◇ ☕	SW	SW 1	SW 1 ☕	SW 1	SW 1	SW	SW 1	SW 1 ◇ ☕	SW 1	SW	SW 1	SW 1	SW 1	SW 1 ◇ ☕	SW 1	SW 1	SW	SW 1	SW 1	SW 1	SW 1
Basingstoke	d			19 24	19 31	19 36					19 41								19 54	20 09				20 17			
Hook	d			19 31															20 01								
Winchfield	d			19 35						←									20 05								
Fleet	d			19 40 →						19 40	19 53								20 10								
Farnborough (Main)	d									19 46	19 58								20 16					20 31			
Alton	d							19 07									19 35								20 15		
Bentley	d																19 42										
Farnham	a							19 17									19 47								20 25		
	d							19 28									19 58								20 28		
Aldershot	d		19 30					19 34							20 00		20 04				20 30				20 34		
Ash Vale	d		19a34					19 39							20a04		20 09				20a34				20 39		
Brookwood	d							19 46		19 53							20 16		20 23						20 46		
Guildford	d	19 32							19 47				20 02					20 17								20 39	20 47
Worplesdon	d	19 40																								20 44	
Woking	a	19 45			19 49			19 51	19 57	19 58			20 11	20 19			20 21	20 25	20 28	20 29				20 40	20 51	20 52	20 58
	d	19 46			19 51			19 52	19 59	19 59		20 03	20 12	20 21			20 22	20 26	20 29	20 30			20 33	20 41	20 52	20 53	20 59
West Byfleet	d							19 57				20 07					20 27						20 37		20 57		
Byfleet & New Haw	d											20 10										←	20 40				
Weybridge	d						←			20 06		20 13				←			20 36 →			20 36	20 43				
Walton-on-Thames	d						19 47			20 11		20 17 →				20 17						20 41	20 47				
Hersham	d						19 49									20 19							20 49				
Esher	d						19 52									20 22							20 52				
Surbiton 6	a						19 56	20 07		20 17						20 26	20 37					20 47	20 56		21 07		
Wimbledon 6 ⊖ 🚋	a						20 04									20 35							21 05				
Earlsfield	a						20 08									20 38							21 08				
Clapham Junction 10	a	20 05				20 12	20 12				20 25		20 31			20 41	20 48			20 52		20 58	21 11			21 12	
Vauxhall ⊖	a						20 17									20 46							21 16				
London Waterloo 15 ⊖	a	20 14			20 19	20 20	20 22	20 25	20 23	20 36	20 34		20 40	20 49		20 52	20 57	20 50		21 00		21 06	21 22	21 08	21 29	21 21	21 27

For general notes see front of timetable
For details of catering facilities see Directory of Train Operators

b Arr. 1820

For details of Bank Holiday service alterations, please see first page of Table 149

Basingstoke, Alton, Guildford and Woking → Waterloo

Network Diagram - see first page of Table 155

		SW	SW		SW	SW	SW	SW	SW	SW	SW	SW	SW	SW	SW	SW	SW	SW	SW	SW	SW	SW	SW	SW	SW	SW	SW
		1	1◇			1	1◇		1	1	1	1◇	1	1		1		1	1	1	1◇		1	1		1	1
																				A							
			🛒				🛒					🛒															
Basingstoke	d	20 24	20 36			20 41					20 54	21 09								21 24	21 36		21 41				21 54
Hook	d	20 31									21 01									21 31							22 01
Winchfield	d	20 35									21 05									21 35							22 05
Fleet	d	20 40				20 53					21 10									21 40			21 53				22 10
Farnborough (Main)	d	20 46				20 58					21 16									21 46			21 58				22 16
Alton	d								20 44									21 15								21 44	
Bentley	d								20 51																	21 51	
Farnham	a								20 56									21 28								21 56	
	d								20 58									21 28								21 58	
Aldershot	d								21 04				21 30					21 34								22 04	
Ash Vale	d								21 09				21a34					21 39								22 09	
Brookwood	d	20 53							21 16		21 23							21 46		21 53						22 16	22 23
Guildford	d									21 17						21 39			21 47								→
Worplesdon	d															21 44											
Woking	a	20 58				21 07	21 19		21 21	21 25	21 28	21 29				21 49		21 51	21 57	21 58			22 07	22 19		22 21	
	d	20 59			21 03	21 09	21 21		21 22	21 26	21 29	21 30			21 33	21 50		21 52	21 59	21 59		22 03	22 09	22 21		22 22	
West Byfleet	d				21 07				21 27						21 37			21 57				22 07				22 27	
Byfleet & New Haw	d				21 10									←	21 40							22 10				→	
Weybridge	d	21 06			21 13			←			21 36			21 36	21 43		←			22 06		22 13			←		
Walton-on-Thames	d	21 11			21 17			21 17			→			21 41	21 47		21 47			22 11		22 17			22 17		
Hersham	d				→			21 19							→		21 49					→			22 19		
Esher	d							21 22									21 52								22 22		
Surbiton 6	a	21 17						21 26	21 37					21 47			21 56	22 07		22 17					22 26		
Wimbledon 6 ⊖	a							21 34									22 04								22 34		
Earlsfield	a							21 38									22 08								22 38		
Clapham Junction 10	a		21 16			21 33		21 42	21 48			21 52		21 58		22 09	22 12				22 14		22 33		22 42		
Vauxhall ⊖	a							21 47									22 17								22 47		
London Waterloo 15 ⊖	a	21 34	21 24			21 43	21 49	21 52	21 57	21 50		22 04		22 06		22 18	22 22	22 26	22 27	22 34	22 22		22 43	22 49	22 52		

		SW	SW	SW	SW	SW	SW		SW	SW	SW	SW	SW	SW	SW	SW	SW	SW	SW	SW	SW	SW	SW	SW	SW		
		1◇	1	1		1	1			1	1	1◇	1		1		1	1	1	1	1	1	1	1	1		
											A		A												B		
Basingstoke	d	22 09									22 24	22 36			22 41			22 54	23 12						23 44		
Hook	d										22 31							23 01							23 51		
Winchfield	d										22 35		←					23 05							23 55		
Fleet	d										22 40		22 40		22 53			23 10							00 01		
Farnborough (Main)	d										→		22 46		22 58			23 16							00 06		
Alton	d									22 15							22 44						23 15	23 44			
Bentley	d																22 51							23 51			
Farnham	a									22 25							22 56						23 25	23 56			
	d									22 28							22 58						23 28				
Aldershot	d					22 30				22 34							23 04			23 30			23 34				
Ash Vale	d			←		22a34				22 39							23 09			23a34			23 39				
Brookwood	d			22 23						22 46			22 53				23 16	23 23					23 46		00 13		
Guildford	d				22 20		22 39							22 55								23 39					
Worplesdon	d						22 44															23 44					
Woking	a	22 28		22 28	22 32		22 49			22 51		22 54	22 58	23 05	23 07		23 21	23 28	23 30			23 49	23 51		00 18		
	d	22 29	←	22 29	22 33		22 50			22 52		22 55	22 59	23 06	23 09		23 22	23 33	23 33			23 56			00 20		
West Byfleet	d		22 27		22 37					22 57				23 10			23 27	23 37							00 25		
Byfleet & New Haw	d				22 40									23 13				23 40									
Weybridge	d			22 36	22 43				←				23 06	23 16		←		23 43			←				00 29		
Walton-on-Thames	d			22 41	22 47				22 47				23 11	23 20		23 20		23 47			23 47				00 34		
Hersham	d				→				22 49					→		23 22		→			23 49						
Esher	d								22 52							23 25					23 52						
Surbiton 6	a		22 37	22 47					22 56	23 07			23 17			23 29	23 37				23 57				00 40		
Wimbledon 6 ⊖	a								23 04							23 37					00 07				00 48		
Earlsfield	a								23 08							23 41					00 10						
Clapham Junction 10	a	22 48	22 52	22 58			23 09		23 12			23 14			23 32	23 44	23 52		23 55		00 14	00 20			00 54		
Vauxhall ⊖	a								23 17							23 49					00 19						
London Waterloo 15 ⊖	a	22 57	23 01	23 08			23 18		23 23	23 26		23 23	23 33		23 43	23 54	00 01		00 04		00 27	00 29			01 02		

For general notes see front of timetable
For details of catering facilities see Directory of Train Operators

A From Portsmouth Harbour (Table 158)
B From Weymouth (Table 158)

Basingstoke, Alton, Guildford and Woking → Waterloo

Network Diagram - see first page of Table 155

		SW 1	SW 1	SW 1 A	SW	SW	SW 1	SW	SW 1 B	SW 1 C	SW	SW	SW 1	SW 1 D	SW 1 E	SW 1 ☕	SW	SW 1 D	SW 1 E		SW	SW 1	SW 1 G	SW 1 ◇ ☕	SW	SW 1 B	SW 1 C
Basingstoke	d	22p54		23p44					04 54	04 54				05 54	05 54	05 59							06 24	06 31			
Hook	d	23p01		23p51					05 01	05 01				06 01	06 01								06 31				
Winchfield	d	23p05		23p55					05 05	05 05				06 05	06 05			←	←				06 35				
Fleet	d	23p10		00 01					05 10	05 10				06 10	06 10			06 10	06 10				06 40				
Farnborough (Main)	d	23p16		00 06					05 16	05 16				→	→			06 16	06 16				→				
Alton	d																									06 14	06 14
Bentley	d																									06 21	06 21
Farnham	a																									06 26	06 26
	d																									06 28	06 28
Aldershot	d						06 00																			06 34	06 34
Ash Vale	d						06a04																			06 39	06 39
Brookwood	d	23p23		00 13					05 23	05 23								06 23	06 23							06 46	06 46
Guildford	d		23p39		04 00	05 12							06 02									06 32					
Worplesdon	d		23p44			05 17																06 40					
Woking	a	23p28	23p49	00 18	04 08	05 22			05 28	05 28	←		06 11			06 18		06 28	06 28			06 44		06 49		06 51	06 51
	d	23p33	23p56	00 20	04 10	05 33		05 25	05 29	05 29	05 33	06 03	06 13			06 19		06 29	06 29		06 33	06 46		06 51		06 52	06 52
West Byfleet	d	23p37		00 25		→		05 30			05 37	06 07									06 37					06 57	06 57
Byfleet & New Haw	d	23p40						05 33			05 40	06 10									06 40						
Weybridge	d	23p43		00 29							05 43	06 13					←	06 36	06 36		06 43				←		
Walton-on-Thames	d	23p47		00 34							05 47	06 17					06 17	06 41	06 41		06 47				06 47		
Hersham	d	23p49									05 49	→					06 19				→				06 49		
Esher	d	23p52									05 52						06 22								06 52		
Surbiton 6	a	23p57		00 40	04 24				05 40	05 40	05 56						06 26	06 47	06 47						06 56	07 07	07 07
Wimbledon 6 ⊖	a	00 07		00 48	04 31				05 48	05 48	06 04						06 34								07 04		
Earlsfield	a	00 10									06 08						06 38								07 08		
Clapham Junction 10	a	00 14	00 20	00 54	04 43			06 43	06 00	06 00	06 12		06 32			06 38	06 42	06 58	06 58			07 05			07 12	07 18	07 18
Vauxhall ⊖	a	00 19						06 49	06 07	06 07	06 17						06 47								07 17		
London Waterloo 15 ⊖	a	00 27	00 29	01 02	04 53			06 56	06 12	06 15	06 22		06 40			06 49	06 52	07 06	07 09			07 13		07 19	07 22	07 27	07 30

		SW 1 G	SW 1	SW	SW 1	SW 1	SW 1	SW 1 ◇ ☕	SW	SW 1	SW 1 ☕	SW 1	SW	SW 1		SW 1	SW 1 H	SW 1 ◇ ☕	SW	SW 1	SW 1 ☕	SW 1 H	SW	SW 1	SW 1	SW 1	SW 1
Basingstoke	d		06 40				06 54	06 57			07 09						07 24	07 31						07 42			07 54
Hook	d						07 01										07 31										08 01
Winchfield	d	←					07 05					←					07 35					←					08 05
Fleet	d	06 40					07 10					07 10					07 40					07 40		07 53			08 10
Farnborough (Main)	d	06 46					→					07 16					→					07 46		07 59			→
Alton	d									06 44										07 14							
Bentley	d									06 51										07 21							
Farnham	a									06 56										07 26							
	d									06 58										07 28							
Aldershot	d					07 00				07 04						07 30				07 34						08 00	
Ash Vale	d					07a04				07 09						07a34				07 39						08a04	
Brookwood	d	06 53								07 16		07 23								07 46		07 53					
Guildford	d				07 02									07 32							07 47				08 02		
Worplesdon	d													07 40													
Woking	a	06 58	06 58		07 11			07 15		07 21	07 27	07 28		07 44				07 49		07 51	07 57	07 58		08 08	08 12		
	d	06 59	07 00	07 03	07 12			07 17		07 22	07 29	07 29	07 33	07 46				07 51		07 52	07 59	07 59	08 03	08 09	08 14		
West Byfleet	d			07 07						07 27			07 37							07 57			08 07				
Byfleet & New Haw	d			07 10									07 40										08 10				
Weybridge	d	07 06		07 13					←			07 36	07 43						←			08 06	08 13				
Walton-on-Thames	d	07 11		07 17					07 17			07 41	07 47						07 47			08 11	08 17				
Hersham	d			→					07 19				→						07 49				→				
Esher	d								07 22										07 52								
Surbiton 6	a	07 17							07 27	07 37		07 47							07 56	08 07		08 17					
Wimbledon 6 ⊖	a								07 35										08 04								
Earlsfield	a								07 38										08 08								
Clapham Junction 10	a		07 23		07 31			07 36	07 42	07 50		07 58		08 05					08 12					08 30	08 33		
Vauxhall ⊖	a								07 47										08 17								
London Waterloo 15 ⊖	a	07 33	07 31		07 40			07 49	07 52	07 58	07 53	08 06		08 13				08 19	08 22	08 25	08 23	08 34		08 38	08 42		

		SW 1 ◇ ☕	SW	SW 1	SW 1 ◇ ☕	SW 1 ☕	SW 1	SW	SW 1		SW 1	SW 1	SW 1	SW 1 ◇ ☕	SW 1 ☕	SW	SW 1	SW 1 ☕	SW 1	SW 1	SW	SW 1	SW 1	SW 1	SW 1 ◇ ☕	SW 1 ◇ ☕	SW
Basingstoke	d	07 57							08 17				08 24	08 28	08 36					08 41				08 54	08 57		
Hook	d												08 31											09 01			
Winchfield	d						←						08 35						←					09 05			
Fleet	d						08 10						08 40						08 40	08 53				09 10			
Farnborough (Main)	d						08 16		08 31				→						08 46	08 58				→			
Alton	d			07 44													08 14										
Bentley	d			07 51													08 21										
Farnham	a			07 56													08 26										
	d			07 58													08 28										
Aldershot	d			08 04								08 30					08 34						09 00				
Ash Vale	d			08 09								08a34					08 39						09a04				
Brookwood	d			08 16			08 23										08 46		08 53								
Guildford	d					08 17					08 32							08 47				09 02					
Worplesdon	d										08 40																
Woking	a	08 17		08 21	08 21	08 26	08 28		08 40		08 44			08 49			08 51	08 57	08 58			09 11			09 15	09 19	
	d	08 18		08 22	08 23	08 27	08 29	08 33	08 41		08 46			08 51			08 52	08 59	08 59		09 03	09 12			09 17	09 21	
West Byfleet	d			08 27				08 37									08 57				09 07						
Byfleet & New Haw	d							08 40													09 10						
Weybridge	d		←				08 36	08 43								←			09 06		09 13						←
Walton-on-Thames	d		08 17				08 41	08 47								08 47			09 11		09 17						09 17
Hersham	d		08 19					→								08 49					→						09 19
Esher	d		08 22													08 52											09 22
Surbiton 6	a		08 26	08 37			08 47									08 56	09 07		09 17								09 26
Wimbledon 6 ⊖	a		08 34													09 04											09 34
Earlsfield	a		08 38													09 08											09 38
Clapham Junction 10	a	08 37	08 42	08 49			08 58				09 05				09 12	09 12				09 24		09 31			09 36		09 42
Vauxhall ⊖	a		08 47													09 17											09 47
London Waterloo 15 ⊖	a	08 49	08 52	08 58	08 49	08 51	09 06		09 08		09 13			09 19	09 20	09 22	09 25	09 23	09 35	09 34		09 40			09 49	09 49	09 52

For general notes see front of timetable
For details of catering facilities see Directory of Train Operators

- **A** From Weymouth (Table 158)
- **B** Until 27 September
- **C** From 4 October
- **D** Until 27 September. From Southampton Central (Table 158)
- **E** From 4 October. From Southampton Central (Table 158)
- **G** From Southampton Central (Table 158)
- **H** From Portsmouth Harbour (Table 158)

Basingstoke, Alton, Guildford and Woking → Waterloo

Network Diagram - see first page of Table 155

	SW 1	SW 1	SW 1		SW	SW 1	SW 1	SW 1	SW 1	SW 1 ◇	SW 1 ◇	SW	SW 1	SW 1	SW 1	SW 1	SW	SW 1	SW 1	SW 1	SW 1 ◇	SW 1 ◇		SW	SW 1	SW 1
		☕								☕	☕			☕							☕	☕				☕
Basingstoke d							09 17		09 24	09 31	09 36					09 41				09 54	09 57					
Hook d									09 31											10 01						
Winchfield d			←						09 35						←					10 05						
Fleet d			09 10						09 40						09 40	09 53				10 10						
Farnborough (Main) d			09 16				09 31		→						09 46	09 58				→						
Alton d	08 44												09 14												09 44	
Bentley d	08 51												09 21												09 51	
Farnham a	08 56												09 26												09 56	
Farnham d	08 58												09 28												09 58	
Aldershot d	09 04					09 30							09 34						10 00						10 04	
Ash Vale d	09 09					09a34							09 39						10a04						10 09	
Brookwood d	09 16		09 23										09 46		09 53										10 16	
Guildford d		09 17						09 32						09 47				10 02								10 17
Worplesdon d								09 40																		
Woking a	09 21	09 25	09 28				09 40	09 44		09 49			09 51	09 57	09 58			10 11			10 15	10 19			10 21	10 25
Woking d	09 22	09 26	09 29		09 33		09 41	09 46		09 51			09 52	09 59	09 59		10 03	10 12			10 17	10 21			10 22	10 26
West Byfleet d	09 27				09 37								09 57				10 07								10 27	
Byfleet & New Haw d					09 40												10 10									
Weybridge d			09 36		09 43							←			10 06		10 13							←		
Walton-on-Thames d			09 41		09 47							09 47			10 11		10 17							10 17		
Hersham d					→							09 49					→							10 19		
Esher d												09 52												10 22		
Surbiton 6 a	09 37		09 47									09 56	10 07		10 17									10 26	10 37	
Wimbledon 6 ⊖ a												10 04												10 34		
Earlsfield a												10 08												10 38		
Clapham Junction 10 a	09 48		09 58					10 05			10 12	10 12				10 24		10 31			10 36			10 42	10 48	
Vauxhall ⊖ a												10 17												10 47		
London Waterloo 15 ⊖ a	09 57	09 52	10 06				10 08	10 13		10 19	10 20	10 22	10 25	10 23	10 35	10 34		10 40			10 49	10 49		10 52	10 57	10 51

	SW 1	SW	SW 1	SW 1	SW 1	SW 1	SW 1 ◇	SW 1 ◇	SW	SW 1	SW 1	SW 1	SW 1	SW	SW 1	SW 1	SW 1		SW 1 ◇	SW 1 ◇	SW	SW 1	SW 1	SW 1	SW	SW 1
							☕	☕			☕								☕	☕			☕			
Basingstoke d				10 17		10 24	10 31	10 36					10 41				10 54		10 57							
Hook d						10 31											11 01									
Winchfield d	←					10 35						←					11 05							←		
Fleet d	10 10					10 40						10 40	10 53				11 10							11 10		
Farnborough (Main) d	10 16			10 31		→						10 46	10 58				→							11 16		
Alton d										10 14												10 44				
Bentley d										10 21												10 51				
Farnham a										10 26												10 56				
Farnham d										10 28												10 58				
Aldershot d			10 30							10 34						11 00						11 04				11 30
Ash Vale d			10a34							10 39						11a04						11 09				11a34
Brookwood d	10 23									10 46		10 53										11 16		11 23		
Guildford d					10 32						10 47				11 02								11 17			
Worplesdon d					10 40																					
Woking a	10 28			10 40	10 44		10 49			10 51	10 57	10 58			11 11				11 15	11 19		11 21	11 25	11 28		
Woking d	10 29	10 33		10 41	10 46		10 51			10 52	10 59	10 59		11 03	11 12				11 17	11 21		11 22	11 26	11 29	11 33	
West Byfleet d		10 37								10 57				11 07								11 27			11 37	
Byfleet & New Haw d		10 40												11 10											11 40	
Weybridge d	10 36	10 43							←			11 06		11 13							←			11 36	11 43	
Walton-on-Thames d	10 41	10 47							10 47			11 11		11 17							11 17			11 41	11 47	
Hersham d		→							10 49					→							11 19				→	
Esher d									10 52												11 22					
Surbiton 6 a	10 47								10 56	11 07		11 17									11 26	11 37		11 47		
Wimbledon 6 ⊖ a									11 04												11 34					
Earlsfield a									11 08												11 38					
Clapham Junction 10 a	10 58				11 05			11 12	11 12				11 24		11 31				11 36		11 42	11 48		11 58		
Vauxhall ⊖ a									11 17												11 47					
London Waterloo 15 ⊖ a	11 06			11 08	11 13		11 19	11 20	11 22	11 25	11 23	11 35	11 34		11 40				11 49	11 49	11 52	11 57	11 51	12 06		

	SW 1	SW 1	SW 1	SW 1 ◇	SW 1 ◇	SW	SW 1 A	SW 1 B	SW 1	SW 1		SW 1	SW	SW 1	SW 1	SW 1	SW 1 ◇	SW 1 ◇	SW	SW 1	SW 1	SW 1	SW	SW 1	SW 1	SW 1
				☕	☕				☕								☕	☕			☕					
Basingstoke d	11 17		11 24	11 31	11 36							11 41				11 54	11 57								12 17	
Hook d			11 31													12 01										
Winchfield d			11 35							←						12 05						←				
Fleet d			11 40							11 40		11 53				12 10						12 10				
Farnborough (Main) d	11 31		→							11 46		11 58				→						12 16			12 31	
Alton d							11 15	11 15												11 44						
Bentley d																				11 51						
Farnham a							11 25	11 27												11 56						
Farnham d							11 28	11 28												11 58						
Aldershot d							11 34	11 34							12 00					12 04				12 30		
Ash Vale d							11 39	11 39							12a04					12 09				12a34		
Brookwood d							11 46	11 46		11 53										12 16		12 23				
Guildford d		11 32							11 47					12 02							12 17					12 32
Worplesdon d		11 40																								12 40
Woking a	11 40	11 44		11 49			11 51	11 51	11 57	11 58				12 11			12 15	12 19		12 21	12 25	12 28			12 40	12 44
Woking d	11 41	11 46		11 51			11 52	11 52	11 59	11 59			12 03	12 12			12 17	12 21		12 22	12 26	12 29	12 33		12 41	12 46
West Byfleet d							11 57	11 57					12 07							12 27			12 37			
Byfleet & New Haw d													12 10										12 40			
Weybridge d						←				12 06			12 13						←			12 36	12 43			
Walton-on-Thames d						11 47				12 11			12 17						12 17			12 41	12 47			
Hersham d						11 49							→						12 19				→			
Esher d						11 52													12 22							
Surbiton 6 a						11 56	12 07	12 07		12 17									12 26	12 37		12 47				
Wimbledon 6 ⊖ a						12 04													12 34							
Earlsfield a						12 08													12 38							
Clapham Junction 10 a		12 05			12 12	12 12						12 24		12 31			12 36		12 42	12 48		12 58				13 05
Vauxhall ⊖ a						12 17													12 47							
London Waterloo 15 ⊖ a	12 08	12 13		12 19	12 20	12 22	12 27	12 27	12 23	12 35		12 34		12 40			12 49	12 49	12 52	12 57	12 52	13 06			13 08	13 13

For general notes see front of timetable
For details of catering facilities see
Directory of Train Operators

A Until 27 September
B From 4 October

Table 155

Saturdays

Basingstoke, Alton, Guildford and Woking → Waterloo

Network Diagram - see first page of Table 155

Station		SW 1	SW 1 ◇ ☕	SW 1 ◇ ☕	SW	SW 1	SW 1 ☕	SW 1	and at the same minutes past each hour until		SW 1	SW	SW 1	SW 1	SW 1	SW 1 ◇ ☕	SW 1 ◇ ☕	SW	SW 1	SW 1	SW 1	SW	SW 1	SW 1	SW 1	SW 1
Basingstoke	d	12 24	12 31	12 36							18 41				18 54	18 57								19 17		19 24
Hook	d	12 31													19 01											19 31
Winchfield	d	12 35						←							19 05						←					19 35
Fleet	d	12 40						12 40			18 53				19 10						19 10					19 40
Farnborough (Main)	d	→						12 46			18 58				→						19 16			19 31		→
Alton	d					12 15													18 44							
Bentley	d																		18 51							
Farnham	a					12 25													18 56							
	d					12 28													18 58							
Aldershot	d					12 34								19 00					19 04				19 30			
Ash Vale	d					12 39								19a04					19 09				19a34			
Brookwood	d					12 46		12 53											19 16		19 23					
Guildford	d						12 47						19 02							19 17					19 32	
Worplesdon	d																								19 40	
Woking	a		12 49			12 51	12 57	12 58					19 11			19 15	19 19		19 21	19 25	19 28			19 40	19 44	
	d		12 51			12 52	12 59	12 59				19 03	19 12			19 17	19 21		19 22	19 26	19 29	19 33		19 41	19 46	
West Byfleet	d					12 57						19 07							19 27			19 37				
Byfleet & New Haw	d											19 10										19 40				
Weybridge	d				←			13 06				19 13						←			19 36	19 43				
Walton-on-Thames	d				12 47			13 11				19 17						19 17			19 41	19 47				
Hersham	d				12 49							→						19 19				→				
Esher	d				12 52													19 22								
Surbiton 6	a				12 56	13 07		13 17										19 26	19 37		19 47					
Wimbledon 6 ⊖	a				13 04													19 34								
Earlsfield	a				13 08													19 38								
Clapham Junction 10	a			13 12	13 12						19 24		19 31			19 36		19 42	19 48		19 58				20 05	
Vauxhall ⊖	a				13 17													19 47								
London Waterloo 15 ⊖	a		13 19	13 20	13 22	13 25	13 23	13 35			19 34		19 40			19 49	19 49	19 52	19 57	19 51	20 06			20 08	20 13	

Station		SW	SW 1 ◇ ☕	SW 1 ◇ ☕	SW 1		SW 1	SW 1	SW 1	SW	SW 1	SW 1 ◇ ☕	SW 1	SW	SW 1	SW 1	SW 1	SW 1 ◇ ☕	SW 1	SW 1	SW	SW 1	SW 1	SW 1		SW 1	SW 1
Basingstoke	d		19 31	19 36					19 41								19 54	20 09				20 17					20 24
Hook	d																20 01										20 31
Winchfield	d							←									20 05										20 35
Fleet	d							19 40	19 53								20 10										20 40
Farnborough (Main)	d							19 46	19 58								20 16					20 31					20 46
Alton	d				19 15										19 44								20 15				
Bentley	d														19 51												
Farnham	a				19 25										19 56								20 25				
	d				19 28										19 58								20 28				
Aldershot	d				19 34								20 00		20 04				20 30				20 34				
Ash Vale	d				19 39								20a04		20 09				20a34				20 39				
Brookwood	d				19 46			19 53							20 16		20 23						20 46				20 53
Guildford	d						19 47				20 02					20 17								20 39		20 49	
Worplesdon	d																							20 44			
Woking	a		19 49		19 51		19 57	19 58			20 11	20 19			20 21	20 25	20 28	20 29				20 40	20 51	20 52		20 58	20 58
	d		19 51		19 52		19 59	19 59		20 03	20 12	20 21			20 22	20 26	20 29	20 30			20 33	20 41	20 52	20 53		20 59	20 59
West Byfleet	d				19 57					20 07					20 27						20 37		20 57				
Byfleet & New Haw	d									20 10										←	20 40						
Weybridge	d	←						20 06		20 13				←			20 36 →			20 36	20 43						21 06
Walton-on-Thames	d	19 47						20 11		20 17 →				20 17						20 41	20 47						21 11
Hersham	d	19 49												20 19							20 49						
Esher	d	19 52												20 22							20 52						
Surbiton 6	a	19 56			20 07			20 17						20 26	20 37					20 47	20 56		21 07				21 17
Wimbledon 6 ⊖	a	20 04												20 34							21 04						
Earlsfield	a	20 08												20 38							21 08						
Clapham Junction 10	a	20 12		20 12					20 24		20 31			20 42	20 48			20 52		20 58	21 12			21 12			
Vauxhall ⊖	a	20 17												20 47							21 17						
London Waterloo 15 ⊖	a	20 22	20 26	20 20	20 25		20 23	20 35	20 34		20 40	20 49		20 52	20 57	20 50		21 04		21 06	21 23	21 08	21 29	21 21		21 27	21 34

Station		SW 1 ◇ ☕	SW	SW 1	SW 1 ◇ ☕	SW	SW 1	SW 1	SW 1	SW 1 ◇ ☕	SW 1	SW 1	SW	SW 1	SW	SW 1	SW 1	SW 1 A	SW 1 ◇		SW	SW 1	SW 1	SW	SW 1	SW 1	SW 1 ◇
Basingstoke	d	20 36		20 41					20 54	21 09								21 24	21 36			21 41				21 54	22 09
Hook	d								21 01									21 31								22 01	
Winchfield	d								21 05									21 35								22 05	
Fleet	d			20 53					21 10									21 40				21 53				22 10	
Farnborough (Main)	d			20 58					21 16									21 46				21 58				22 16	
Alton	d						20 44									21 15									21 44		
Bentley	d						20 51																		21 51		
Farnham	a						20 56									21 25									21 56		
	d						20 58									21 28									21 58		
Aldershot	d						21 04				21 30					21 34									22 04		
Ash Vale	d						21 09				21a34					21 39									22 09		
Brookwood	d						21 16		21 23							21 46		21 53							22 16	22 23 →	
Guildford	d							21 17						21 39			21 49										
Worplesdon	d													21 44													
Woking	a			21 07	21 19		21 21	21 25	21 28	21 29				21 49		21 51	21 57	21 58				22 07	22 19		22 21		22 28
	d		21 03	21 09	21 21		21 22	21 26	21 29	21 30			21 33	21 50		21 52	21 59	21 59			22 03	22 09	22 21		22 22		22 29
West Byfleet	d		21 07				21 27						21 37			21 57					22 07				22 27 →		
Byfleet & New Haw	d		21 10									←	21 40								22 10						
Weybridge	d		21 13			←			21 36 →			21 36	21 43		←			22 06			22 13			←			
Walton-on-Thames	d		21 17 →			21 17						21 41	21 47 →		21 47			22 11			22 17 →			22 17			
Hersham	d					21 19									21 49									22 19			
Esher	d					21 22									21 52									22 22			
Surbiton 6	a					21 26	21 37					21 47			21 56	22 07		22 17						22 26			
Wimbledon 6 ⊖	a					21 34									22 04									22 34			
Earlsfield	a					21 38									22 08									22 38			
Clapham Junction 10	a	21 16		21 30		21 42	21 48			21 52		21 58		22 09	22 12				22 14			22 30		22 42			22 48
Vauxhall ⊖	a					21 47									22 17									22 47			
London Waterloo 15 ⊖	a	21 27		21 38	21 49	21 52	21 57	21 50		22 04		22 07		22 18	22 22	22 26	22 24	22 34	22 22			22 38	22 49	22 52			22 57

For general notes see front of timetable
For details of catering facilities see
Directory of Train Operators

A From Portsmouth Harbour (Table 158)

Table 155

Saturdays

Basingstoke, Alton, Guildford and Woking → Waterloo

Network Diagram - see first page of Table 155

		SW 1	SW 1	SW	SW 1	SW 1	SW	SW 1	SW 1 A	SW 1 ◇	SW 1 A	SW	SW 1	SW		SW 1	SW 1	SW 1	SW 1	SW 1	SW 1	SW 1	SW 1	SW 1 B
Basingstoke	d								22 24	22 36			22 41				22 54	23 14						23 44
Hook	d								22 31								23 01							23 51
Winchfield	d								22 35		←						23 05							23 55
Fleet	d								22 40		22 40		22 53				23 10							00 01
Farnborough (Main)	d								→		22 46		22 58				23 16							00 06
Alton	d							22 15								22 44						23 15	23 44	
Bentley	d															22 51							23 51	
Farnham	a							22 25								22 56						23 25	23 56	
	d							22 28								22 58						23 28		
Aldershot	d				22 30			22 34								23 04			23 30			23 34		
Ash Vale	d		←		22a34			22 39								23 09			23a34			23 39		
Brookwood	d		22 23					22 46			22 53					23 16	23 23					23 46		00 13
Guildford	d			22 20		22 39						22 55									23 39			
Worplesdon	d					22 44															23 44			
Woking	a		22 28	22 32		22 49		22 51		22 54	22 58	23 05	23 07			23 21	23 28	23 32			23 49	23 51		00 18
	d	←	22 29	22 33		22 50		22 52		22 56	22 59	23 06	23 09			23 22	23 33	23 33			23 56			00 20
West Byfleet	d	22 27		22 37				22 57				23 10				23 27	23 37							00 25
Byfleet & New Haw	d			22 40								23 13					23 40							
Weybridge	d		22 36	22 43			←				23 06	23 16		←			23 43			←				00 29
Walton-on-Thames	d		22 41	22 47			22 47				23 11	23 20		23 20			23 47			23 47				00 34
Hersham	d			→			22 49					→		23 22			→			23 49				
Esher	d						22 52							23 25						23 52				
Surbiton 6	a	22 37	22 47				22 56	23 07			23 17			23 29		23 37				23 57				00 40
Wimbledon 6 ⊖	a						23 04							23 37						00 08				00 48
Earlsfield	a						23 08							23 41						00 10				
Clapham Junction 10	a	22 52	22 58			23 09	23 12			23 15			23 30	23 44		23 52		23 57		00 14	00 22			00 54
Vauxhall ⊖	a						23 17							23 49						00 19				
London Waterloo 15 ⊖	a	23 01	23 06			23 18	23 22	23 25		23 23	23 37		23 38	23 54		00 03		00 05		00 29	00 31			01 02

Sundays

		SW 1	SW 1	SW 1 B	SW	SW	SW	SW 1 C	SW 1 D	SW 1 ◇	SW	SW	SW 1 D	SW 1 C	SW 1 C	SW 1 D	SW 1 D	SW 1	SW 1	SW	SW 1	SW	SW 1 ◇	SW	SW 1	SW	SW
Basingstoke	d	22p54		23p44				07 16	07 16	07 20									07 44				08 05				
Hook	d	23p01		23p51				07 23	07 23																		
Winchfield	d	23p05		23p55				07 27	07 27				←	←													
Fleet	d	23p10		00 01				07 32	07 32				07 32	07 32													
Farnborough (Main)	d	23p16		00 06				→	→				07 38	07 38													
Alton	d																										
Bentley	d																										
Farnham	a																										
	d														07 30		07 30										
Aldershot	d														07 36		07 36	07 40									
Ash Vale	d														07 41	←	07 41	07a44									
Brookwood	d	23p23		00 13									07 45	07 45	07 48	07 45	07 48										
Guildford	d		23p39			06 57	07 27						→							07 57	08 05			08 27	08 35		
Worplesdon	d		23p44																								
Woking	a	23p28	23p49	00 18		07 05	07 35			07 39				07 50	07 54	07 50	07 54		08 02	08 05	08 13		08 23	08 35	08 42		
	d	23p33	23p56	00 20	06 36	07 06	07 36			07 40		07 52		07 58		07 58			08 04	08 06	08 15		08 25	08 36	08 45		08 52
West Byfleet	d	23p37		00 25	06 40	07 10	07 40					07 56								08 10				08 40			08 56
Byfleet & New Haw	d	23p40			06 43	07 13	07 43					08 00								08 13				08 43			09 00
Weybridge	d	23p43		00 29	06 46	07 16	07 46				←									08 16		←		08 46		←	
Walton-on-Thames	d	23p47		00 34	06 50	07 20	07 50				07 50									08 20		08 20		08 50		08 50	
Hersham	d	23p49			06 52	07 22	→				07 52									→		08 22		→		08 52	
Esher	d	23p52			06 55	07 25					07 55											08 25				08 55	
Surbiton 6	a	23p57		00 40	06 59	07 29					07 59			08 09		08 09						08 29				08 59	
Wimbledon 6 ⊖	a	00 08		00 48	07 07	07 37					08 07			08 16		08 16						08 37				09 07	
Earlsfield	a	00 10			07 11	07 41					08 11											08 41				09 11	
Clapham Junction 10	a	00 14	00 22	00 54	07 15	07 45				08 03	08 15			08 23		08 23			08 27		08 37	08 45	08 55		09 06	09 15	
Vauxhall ⊖	a	00 19			07 20	07 50					08 20											08 50				09 20	
London Waterloo 15 ⊖	a	00 29	00 31	01 02	07 30	08 00				08 19	08 30			08 39		08 42			08 42		08 49	09 00	09 09		09 19	09 30	

For general notes see front of timetable
For details of catering facilities see Directory of Train Operators

A From Portsmouth Harbour (Table 158)
B From Weymouth (Table 158)
C Until 21 September
D From 28 September

Table 155

Sundays

Basingstoke, Alton, Guildford and Woking → Waterloo

Network Diagram - see first page of Table 155

		SW 1 A	SW 1 B	SW 1 B	SW 1 A	SW 1 A	SW 1	SW 1◇ ☕	SW	SW 1	SW	SW 1◇ ☕	SW	SW 1	SW	SW	SW 1	SW 1	SW 1	SW 1◇	SW	SW 1	SW 1◇ ☕	SW 1◇ ☕	SW	SW	SW 1 ☕
Basingstoke	d	08 16	08 16					08 44				09 11					09 16			09 44			10 00	10 05			
Hook	d	08 23	08 23														09 23										
Winchfield	d	08 27	08 27														09 27										
Fleet	d	08 32	08 32														09 32										
Farnborough (Main)	d	08 38	08 38														09 38										
Alton	d			08 15		08 15												09 15									
Bentley	d			08b24		08b24												09c24									
Farnham	a			08 29		08 29												09 29									
	d			08 30		08 30												09 30									
Aldershot	d			08 36		08 36	08 40											09 36	09 40								
Ash Vale	d			08 41	←	08 41	08a44											09 41	09a44								
Brookwood	d	08 45	08 45	08 48	08 45	08 48											09 45	09 48									
Guildford	d	→							08 57	09 05			09 27	09 35							09 57	10 05				10 27	10 35
Worplesdon	d																										
Woking	a		08 50	08 54	08 50	08 54		09 02	09 05	09 15		09 30	09 35	09 42			09 50	09 54		10 02	10 05	10 15	10 19	10 23		10 35	10 42
	d			08 58		08 58		09 04	09 06	09 15		09 31	09 36	09 45		09 52		09 58		10 04	10 06	10 15	10 20	10 25		10 36	10 45
West Byfleet	d								09 10				09 40			09 56					10 10					10 40	
Byfleet & New Haw	d								09 13				09 43			10 00					10 13					10 43	
Weybridge	d								09 16		←		09 46		←						10 16				←	10 46	
Walton-on-Thames	d								09 20 →		09 20		09 50 →		09 50						10 20 →				10 20	10 50 →	
Hersham	d										09 22				09 52										10 22		
Esher	d										09 25				09 55										10 25		
Surbiton 6	a			09 09		09 09					09 29				09 59			10 09							10 29		
Wimbledon 6 ⊖ 🚋	a			09 16		09 16					09 37				10 07			10 17							10 37		
Earlsfield	a										09 41				10 11										10 41		
Clapham Junction 10	a			09 24		09 24		09 27		09 35	09 45	09 55		10 06	10 15			10 22		10 27		10 35	10 39	10 44	10 45		11 04
Vauxhall ⊖	a										09 50				10 20										10 50		
London Waterloo 15 ⊖	a			09 39		09 42		09 42		09 49	10 00	10 08		10 21	10 30			10 39		10 42		10 49	10 54	11 03	11 00		11 19

		SW	SW	SW 1	SW 1	SW 1	SW 1◇	SW	SW 1	SW 1◇ ☕	SW	SW 1◇ ☕	SW	SW 1 ☕	SW	SW	SW 1	SW 1		SW 1	SW 1◇	SW	SW 1	SW 1◇ ☕	SW 1◇ ☕	SW	SW
Basingstoke	d			10 16			10 44			11 00		11 11					11 16				11 44			12 00	12 05		
Hook	d			10 23													11 23										
Winchfield	d			10 27													11 27										
Fleet	d			10 32													11 32										
Farnborough (Main)	d			10 38													11 38										
Alton	d				10 15													11 15									
Bentley	d				10e24													11f24									
Farnham	a				10 29													11 29									
	d				10 30													11 30									
Aldershot	d				10 36	10 40												11 36		11 40							
Ash Vale	d				10 41	10a44												11 41		11a44							
Brookwood	d			10 45	10 48												11 45	11 48									
Guildford	d							10 57	11 05				11 27	11 35								11 57	12 05				12 27
Worplesdon	d																										
Woking	a			10 50	10 54		11 02	11 05	11 14	11 18		11 30	11 35	11 42			11 50	11 54			12 02	12 05	12 13	12 18	12 23		12 35
	d		10 52		10 58		11 04	11 06	11 15	11 20		11 31	11 36	11 45		11 52		11 58			12 04	12 06	12 15	12 20	12 25		12 36
West Byfleet	d		10 56					11 10					11 40			11 56						12 10					12 40
Byfleet & New Haw	d		11 00					11 13					11 43			12 00						12 13					12 43
Weybridge	d	←						11 16			←		11 46		←							12 16				←	12 46
Walton-on-Thames	d	10 50						11 20 →			11 20		11 50 →		11 50							12 20 →				12 20	12 50 →
Hersham	d	10 52									11 22				11 52											12 22	
Esher	d	10 55									11 25				11 55											12 25	
Surbiton 6	a	10 59			11 09						11 29				11 59			12 09								12 29	
Wimbledon 6 ⊖ 🚋	a	11 07			11 16						11 37				12 07			12 17								12 37	
Earlsfield	a	11 11									11 41				12 11											12 41	
Clapham Junction 10	a	11 15			11 22		11 27		11 34	11 39	11 45	11 50		12 04	12 15			12 23			12 27		12 34	12 39	12 44	12 45	
Vauxhall ⊖	a	11 20									11 50				12 20											12 50	
London Waterloo 15 ⊖	a	11 30			11 39		11 40		11 49	11 52	12 00	12 03		12 19	12 30			12 39			12 40		12 47	12 52	13 03	13 00	

For general notes see front of timetable
For details of catering facilities see Directory of Train Operators

A From 28 September
B Until 21 September
b Arr. 0821
c Arr. 0921
e Arr. 1021
f Arr. 1121

Table 155

Sundays

Basingstoke, Alton, Guildford and Woking → Waterloo

Network Diagram - see first page of Table 155

		SW 1 ☕	SW	SW	SW 1	SW 1	SW 1	SW 1◇	SW	SW 1	SW 1◇ ☕	SW	SW 1◇ ☕	SW	SW 1 ☕	SW	SW	SW 1	SW 1	SW 1	SW 1◇	SW	SW 1	SW 1	SW 1◇ ☕	SW 1	SW 1◇ ☕
Basingstoke	d				12 16			12 44			13 00		13 11					13 16			13 44			13 50	14 00		14 05
Hook	d				12 23													13 23									
Winchfield	d				12 27													13 27									
Fleet	d				12 32													13 32						14 02		←	
Farnborough (Main)	d				12 38													13 38						14 08		14 08	
Alton	d					12 15													13 15					→			
Bentley	d					12b24													13c24								
Farnham	a					12 29													13 29								
	d					12 30													13 30								
Aldershot	d					12 36	12 40												13 36	13 40							
Ash Vale	d					12 41	12a44												13 41	13a44							
Brookwood	d				12 45	12 48												13 45	13 48							14 15	
Guildford	d	12 35							12 57	13 05				13 27	13 35							13 57	14 05				
Worplesdon	d																										
Woking	a	12 42			12 50	12 54		13 02	13 05	13 13	13 18		13 30	13 35	13 42			13 50	13 54		14 02	14 05	14 13		14 18	14 20 →	14 23
	d	12 45		12 52	12 58			13 04	13 06	13 15	13 20		13 31	13 36	13 45		13 52	13 58			14 04	14 06	14 15		14 20		14 25
West Byfleet	d			12 56					13 10					13 40			13 56					14 10					
Byfleet & New Haw	d			13 00					13 13					13 43			14 00					14 13					
Weybridge	d		←						13 16			←		13 46		←						14 16					
Walton-on-Thames	d		12 50						13 20 →			13 20		13 50 →		13 50						14 20 →					
Hersham	d		12 52									13 22				13 52											
Esher	d		12 55									13 25				13 55											
Surbiton 6	a		12 59		13 09							13 29				13 59		14 09									
Wimbledon 6 ⊖ 🚊	a		13 07		13 17							13 37				14 07		14 17									
Earlsfield	a		13 11									13 41				14 11											
Clapham Junction 10	a	13 04	13 15		13 23			13 27		13 34	13 39	13 45	13 50		14 04	14 15		14 23			14 27		14 34		14 39		14 44
Vauxhall	⊖ a		13 20									13 50				14 20											
London Waterloo 15	⊖ a	13 14	13 30		13 39			13 40		13 44	13 49	14 00	14 04		14 14	14 30		14 34			14 37		14 44		14 49		14 58

		SW	SW 1	SW 1	SW	SW 1 ☕	SW	SW	SW 1	SW 1	SW 1	SW 1◇	SW	SW 1	SW 1	SW 1◇ ☕	SW	SW 1	SW 1	SW 1◇ ☕	SW	SW 1	SW 1 ☕	SW	SW	SW 1	SW 1
Basingstoke	d								14 16			14 44			14 50	15 00				15 11						15 16	
Hook	d								14 23																	15 23	
Winchfield	d								14 27																	15 27	
Fleet	d								14 32						15 02			←								15 32	
Farnborough (Main)	d								14 38						15 08			15 08								15 38	
Alton	d			13 45						14 15					→				14 45								15 15
Bentley	d									14e24																	15f24
Farnham	a			13 55						14 29									14 55								15 29
	d			14 00						14 30									15 00								15 30
Aldershot	d			14 06						14 36	14 40								15 06								15 36
Ash Vale	d			14 11						14 41	14a44								15 11								15 41
Brookwood	d			14 18					14 45	14 48								15 15	15 18							15 45	15 48
Guildford	d				14 27	14 35							14 57	15 05							15 27		15 35				
Worplesdon	d		←																								
Woking	a		14 20	14 24	14 35	14 42			14 50	14 54		15 02	15 05	15 13		15 18		15 20	15 24	15 30	15 35		15 42			15 50	15 54
	d		14 28		14 36	14 45		14 52	14 58			15 04	15 06	15 15		15 20		15 28		15 31	15 36		15 45		15 52	15 58	
West Byfleet	d				14 40			14 56					15 10								15 40				15 56		
Byfleet & New Haw	d				14 43			15 00					15 13								15 43				16 00		
Weybridge	d	←	14 35		14 46		←						15 16				←	15 35			15 46			←			
Walton-on-Thames	d	14 20	14 39		14 50 →		14 50						15 20 →				15 20	15 39			15 50 →			15 50			
Hersham	d	14 22					14 52										15 22							15 52			
Esher	d	14 25					14 55										15 25					←		15 55			
Surbiton 6	a	14 29	14 45				14 59		15 09								15 29	15 45 →				15 45		15 59		16 09	
Wimbledon 6 ⊖ 🚊	a	14 37	14 53				15 07		15 17								15 37					15 53		16 07		16 17	
Earlsfield	a	14 41					15 11										15 41							16 11			
Clapham Junction 10	a	14 45	14 59			15 04	15 15		15 23			15 27		15 34		15 39	15 45			15 50		15 59	16 04	16 15		16 23	
Vauxhall	⊖ a	14 50					15 20										15 50							16 20			
London Waterloo 15	⊖ a	14 55	15 10			15 14	15 25		15 34			15 37		15 44		15 49	15 55			16 04		16 10	16 14	16 25		16 34	

For general notes see front of timetable
For details of catering facilities see Directory of Train Operators

b Arr. 1221
c Arr. 1321
e Arr. 1421
f Arr. 1521

Table 155

Sundays

Basingstoke, Alton, Guildford and Woking → Waterloo

Network Diagram - see first page of Table 155

	SW 1	SW 1◇	SW	SW 1	SW 1	SW 1◇ ☕	SW 1	SW 1◇ ☕	SW	SW 1	SW 1		SW	SW 1 ☕	SW	SW	SW 1	SW 1	SW 1	SW 1◇	SW	SW 1	SW 1	SW 1◇ ☕	SW	
Basingstoke d		15 44			15 50	16 00		16 05									16 16			16 44			16 50	17 00		
Hook d																	16 23									
Winchfield d																	16 27									
Fleet d					16 02		←										16 32						17 02			
Farnborough (Main) d					16 08		16 08										16 38						17 08			
Alton d					→						15 45							16 15					→			
Bentley d																		16b24								
Farnham a											15 55							16 29								
d											16 00							16 30								
Aldershot d	15 40										16 06							16 36	16 40							
Ash Vale d	15a44										16 11							16 41	16a44							
Brookwood d							16 15				16 18						16 45	16 48								
Guildford d			15 57	16 05									16 27	16 35							16 57	17 05				
Worplesdon d										←																
Woking a		16 02	16 05	16 13		16 18	16 20 →	16 23		16 20	16 24		16 35	16 42			16 50	16 54		17 02	17 05	17 13		17 18		
d		16 04	16 06	16 15		16 20		16 25			16 28		16 36	16 45		16 52		16 58		17 04	17 06	17 15		17 20		
West Byfleet d			16 10										16 40			16 56					17 10					
Byfleet & New Haw d			16 13										16 43			17 00					17 13					
Weybridge d			16 16						←		16 35		16 46		←						17 16				←	
Walton-on-Thames d			16 20 →						16 20		16 39		16 50 →		16 50						17 20 →				17 20	
Hersham d									16 22						16 52										17 22	
Esher d									16 25						16 55										17 25	
Surbiton 6 a									16 29		16 45				16 59			17 09							17 29	
Wimbledon 6 ⊖ a									16 37		16 53				17 07			17 17							17 37	
Earlsfield a									16 41						17 11										17 41	
Clapham Junction 10 a		16 27		16 34		16 39		16 44	16 45		16 59			17 04	17 15			17 23		17 27		17 34		17 39	17 45	
Vauxhall ⊖ a									16 50						17 20										17 50	
London Waterloo 15 ⊖ a		16 37		16 44		16 49		16 58	16 55		17 10			17 14	17 25			17 34		17 37		17 44		17 49	17 55	

	SW 1	SW 1	SW 1◇ ☕	SW	SW 1	SW 1 ☕	SW	SW	SW 1	SW 1	SW 1	SW 1◇	SW	SW 1	SW 1	SW 1◇ ☕	SW 1	SW 1◇ ☕	SW	SW 1	SW 1	SW	SW 1 ☕	SW	SW	
Basingstoke d			17 11						17 16			17 44			17 50	18 00		18 05								
Hook d									17 23																	
Winchfield d									17 27																	
Fleet d	←								17 32						18 02		←									
Farnborough (Main) d	17 08								17 38						18 08		18 08									
Alton d		16 45								17 15					→						17 45					
Bentley d										17c24																
Farnham a		16 55								17 29											17 55					
d		17 00								17 30											18 00					
Aldershot d		17 06								17 36	17 40										18 06					
Ash Vale d		17 11								17 41	17a44										18 11					
Brookwood d	17 15	17 18							17 45	17 48							18 15				18 18					
Guildford d				17 27		17 35							17 57	18 05								18 27	18 35			
Worplesdon d																				←						
Woking a	17 20	17 24	17 30	17 35		17 42			17 50	17 54		18 02	18 05	18 13		18 18	18 20 →	18 23		18 20	18 24	18 35	18 42			
d		17 28	17 31	17 36		17 45		17 52		17 58		18 04	18 06	18 15		18 20		18 25			18 28	18 36	18 45		18 52	
West Byfleet d				17 40				17 56					18 10									18 40			18 56	
Byfleet & New Haw d				17 43				18 00					18 13									18 43			19 00	
Weybridge d		17 35		17 46			←						18 16						←		18 35	18 46		←		
Walton-on-Thames d		17 39		17 50 →			17 50						18 20 →						18 20		18 39	18 50 →		18 50		
Hersham d							17 52												18 22					18 52		
Esher d					←		17 55												18 25					18 55		
Surbiton 6 a		17 45 →			17 45		17 59			18 09									18 29		18 45			18 59		
Wimbledon 6 ⊖ a					17 53		18 07			18 17									18 37		18 53			19 07		
Earlsfield a							18 11												18 41					19 11		
Clapham Junction 10 a			17 50		17 59	18 04	18 15			18 23		18 27		18 34		18 39		18 44	18 45		18 59		19 04	19 15		
Vauxhall ⊖ a							18 20												18 50					19 20		
London Waterloo 15 ⊖ a			18 04		18 10	18 14	18 25			18 34		18 37		18 44		18 49		18 58	18 55		19 10		19 14	19 25		

For general notes see front of timetable
For details of catering facilities see
Directory of Train Operators

b Arr. 1621
c Arr. 1721

Sundays

Basingstoke, Alton, Guildford and Woking → Waterloo

Network Diagram - see first page of Table 155

		SW 1	SW 1	SW 1	SW 1 ◇	SW	SW 1	SW 1	SW 1 ◇ ☕	SW	SW 1	SW 1	SW 1 ◇ ☕	SW	SW 1	SW 1 ☕	SW	SW	SW 1	SW 1	SW 1	SW 1 ◇	SW	SW 1	SW 1	SW 1 ◇ ☕	SW 1
Basingstoke	d	18 16			18 44			18 50	19 00				19 11						19 16			19 44			19 50	20 00	
Hook	d	18 23																	19 23								
Winchfield	d	18 27																	19 27								
Fleet	d	18 32						19 02			←								19 32						20 02		←
Farnborough (Main)	d	18 38						19 08			19 08								19 38						20 08		20 08
Alton	d		18 15					→				18 45								19 15					→		
Bentley	d		18b24																	19c24							
Farnham	a		18 29									18 55								19 29							
	d		18 30									19 00								19 30							
Aldershot	d		18 36	18 40								19 06								19 36	19 40						
Ash Vale	d		18 41	18a44								19 11								19 41	19a44						
Brookwood	d	18 45	18 48								19 15	19 18							19 45	19 48							20 15
Guildford	d					18 57	19 05							19 27		19 35							19 57	20 05			
Worplesdon	d																										
Woking	a	18 50	18 54		19 02	19 05	19 13		19 18		19 20	19 24	19 30	19 35		19 42			19 50	19 54		20 02	20 05	20 13		20 18	20 20 →
	d	18 58			19 04	19 06	19 15		19 20		19 28		19 31	19 36		19 45		19 52	19 58			20 04	20 06	20 15		20 20	
West Byfleet	d					19 10								19 40				19 56					20 10				
Byfleet & New Haw	d					19 13								19 43				20 00					20 13				
Weybridge	d					19 16				←	19 35			19 46			←						20 16				
Walton-on-Thames	d					19 20 →				19 20	19 39			19 50 →			19 50						20 20 →				
Hersham	d									19 22							19 52										
Esher	d									19 25					←		19 55										
Surbiton 6	a	19 09								19 29	19 45 →				19 45		19 59		20 09								
Wimbledon 6 ⊖	a	19 17								19 37					19 53		20 07		20 17								
Earlsfield	a									19 41							20 11										
Clapham Junction 10	a	19 23			19 27		19 34		19 39	19 45			19 50		19 59	20 04	20 15		20 23			20 27		20 34		20 39	
Vauxhall ⊖	a									19 50							20 20										
London Waterloo 15 ⊖	a	19 34			19 37		19 44		19 49	19 55			20 04		20 10	20 14	20 25		20 34			20 37		20 44		20 49	

		SW 1 ◇ A ☕	SW	SW 1	SW 1	SW	SW 1	SW	SW	SW 1	SW 1	SW 1	SW 1 ◇	SW	SW 1	SW 1	SW 1 ◇ ☕	SW	SW 1	SW 1	SW 1 ◇ ☕	SW	SW 1	SW 1	SW	SW
Basingstoke	d	20 05								20 16			20 44			20 50	21 00				21 11					
Hook	d									20 23																
Winchfield	d									20 27																
Fleet	d									20 32						21 02			←							
Farnborough (Main)	d									20 38						21 08			21 08							
Alton	d				19 45						20 15					→				20 45						
Bentley	d										20e24															
Farnham	a				19 55						20 29									20 55						
	d				20 00						20 30									21 00						
Aldershot	d				20 06						20 36	20 40								21 06						
Ash Vale	d				20 11						20 41	20a44								21 11						
Brookwood	d				20 18					20 45	20 48								21 15	21 18						
Guildford	d					20 27	20 35							20 57	21 05							21 27		21 35		
Worplesdon	d			←																						
Woking	a	20 23		20 20	20 24	20 35	20 42			20 50	20 54		21 02	21 05	21 13		21 18		21 20	21 24	21 30	21 35		21 42		
	d	20 25		20 28		20 36	20 45		20 52	20 58			21 04	21 06	21 15		21 20		21 28		21 31	21 36		21 45		21 52
West Byfleet	d					20 40			20 56					21 10								21 40				21 56
Byfleet & New Haw	d					20 43			21 00					21 13								21 43				22 00
Weybridge	d		←	20 35		20 46		←						21 16				←	21 35			21 46			←	
Walton-on-Thames	d		20 20	20 39		20 50 →		20 50						21 20 →				21 20	21 39			21 50 →			21 50	
Hersham	d		20 22					20 52										21 22							21 52	
Esher	d		20 25					20 55										21 25					←		21 55	
Surbiton 6	a		20 29	20 45				20 59		21 09								21 29	21 45 →				21 45		21 59	
Wimbledon 6 ⊖	a		20 37	20 53				21 07		21 17								21 37					21 53		22 07	
Earlsfield	a		20 41					21 11										21 41							22 11	
Clapham Junction 10	a	20 44	20 45	20 59			21 04	21 15		21 23			21 27		21 34		21 39	21 45			21 50		21 59	22 04	22 15	
Vauxhall ⊖	a		20 50					21 20										21 50							22 20	
London Waterloo 15 ⊖	a	20 58	20 55	21 10			21 14	21 25		21 34			21 37		21 44		21 49	21 55			22 04		22 10	22 14	22 25	

For general notes see front of timetable
For details of catering facilities see Directory of Train Operators

A From Penzance (Table 135)
b Arr. 1821
c Arr. 1921
e Arr. 2021

Basingstoke, Alton, Guildford and Woking → Waterloo

Network Diagram - see first page of Table 155

		SW 1	SW 1	SW 1	SW 1 ◇	SW	SW 1	SW 1	SW 1 ◇ 🍴	SW	SW 1	SW 1	SW	SW 1	SW	SW	SW 1	SW 1	SW 1	SW 1	SW	SW 1	SW	SW 1	SW 1	SW 1	SW 1
Basingstoke	d	21 16			21 44			21 50	22 05								22 16			22 44						23 16	
Hook	d	21 23															22 23									23 23	
Winchfield	d	21 27															22 27									23 27	
Fleet	d	21 32						22 02									22 32									23 32	
Farnborough (Main)	d	21 38						22 08									22 38									23 38	
Alton	d		21 15									21 45						22 15						22 45			23 15
Bentley	d		21b24															22c24									23e24
Farnham	a		21 29									21 55						22 29						22 55			23 29
	d		21 30									22 00						22 30						23 00			23 30
Aldershot	d		21 36	21 40								22 06						22 36	22 40					23 06			23 36
Ash Vale	d		21 41	21a44								22 11						22 41	22a44					23 11			23 41
Brookwood	d	21 45	21 48					22 15				22 18					22 45	22 48						23 18		23 45	23 48
Guildford	d					21 57	22 05				←		22 27	22 35							22 57	23 05			23 35		
Worplesdon	d																										
Woking	a	21 50	21 54		22 02	22 05	22 13	22 21 →	22 23		22 21	22 24	22 35	22 42			22 50	22 54		23 02	23 05	23 13		23 24	23 42	23 50	23 54
	d	21 58			22 04	22 06	22 15		22 25		22 28		22 36	22 45		22 52	22 58			23 04	23 06	23 15		23 28	23 45		
West Byfleet	d					22 10							22 40			22 56					23 10						
Byfleet & New Haw	d					22 13							22 43			23 00					23 13						
Weybridge	d					22 16				←	22 35		22 46		←						23 16		←	23 35			
Walton-on-Thames	d					22 20 →				22 20	22 39		22 50 →		22 50						23 20 →		23 20	23 39			
Hersham	d									22 22					22 52								23 22				
Esher	d									22 25					22 55								23 25				
Surbiton 6	a	22 09								22 29	22 45				22 59		23 09						23 29	23 45			
Wimbledon 6 ⊖ 🚋	a	22 17								22 37	22 53				23 07		23 17						23 37	23 53			
Earlsfield	a									22 41					23 11								23 41				
Clapham Junction 10	a	22 23			22 27		22 34		22 44	22 45	22 59			23 04	23 15		23 23			23 27		23 34	23 45	23 58	00 04		
Vauxhall ⊖	a									22 50					23 20								23 50				
London Waterloo 15 ⊖	a	22 34			22 37		22 44		22 58	22 55	23 11			23 14	23 25		23 34			23 37		23 44	23 55	00 10	00 14		

		SW 1
Basingstoke	d	23 43
Hook	d	
Winchfield	d	
Fleet	d	
Farnborough (Main)	d	
Alton	d	
Bentley	d	
Farnham	a	
	d	
Aldershot	d	
Ash Vale	d	
Brookwood	d	
Guildford	d	
Worplesdon	d	
Woking	a	00 02
	d	00 03
West Byfleet	d	
Byfleet & New Haw	d	
Weybridge	d	
Walton-on-Thames	d	
Hersham	d	
Esher	d	
Surbiton 6	a	
Wimbledon 6 ⊖ 🚋	a	
Earlsfield	a	
Clapham Junction 10	a	00 22
Vauxhall ⊖	a	
London Waterloo 15 ⊖	a	00 33

For general notes see front of timetable
For details of catering facilities see Directory of Train Operators

b Arr. 2121
c Arr. 2221
e Arr. 2321

London → Guildford, Haslemere and Portsmouth

Network Diagram - see first page of Table 155

Miles			SW MO 1	SW MX 1	SW MO 1	SW MO 1	SW MO 1	SW MO 1	SW MX 1	SW MX 1	SW MX 1	SW 1	SW 1	SW 1	SW 1	SW 1	SW 1	SW 1 ☕	SW 1	SW 1	SW 1	SW 1	SW 1	SW 1 ☕	SW 1	SW 1 ☕
0	**London Waterloo** 15 ⊖	d	22p30	22p45	23p00		23p30	00 50	22p30	23p15	23p45		05 00	05 20	06 15	06 45	07 15	07 30		07 45	08 00		08 15	08 30	08 45	09 00
4	Clapham Junction 10	d	22b39	22b52	23b09		23b39	00u57		23b22	23b52		05 09	05 29	06u22	06u52	07u22			07u52			08u22		08u52	
24¼	**Woking**	a	23p01	23p11	23p31		00 01	01 16	22p54	23p41	00 11		05 50	06 08	06 41	07 11	07 42	07 55		08 12	08 24		08 42	08 55	09 11	09 24
—		d	23p02	23p13	23p32		00 02	01 18	22p55	23p43	00 13		05 51	06 13	06 43	07 13	07 44	07 55		08 14	08 25		08 44	08 55	09 13	09 25
26¾	Worplesdon	d		23p18							00 18			06 18	06 48	07 18	07 49			08 19			08 49		09 18	
30¼	**Guildford**	a	23p10	23p23	23p40		00 10	01s26	23p03	23p51	00 24		05 59	06 23	06 53	07 23	07 54	08 04		08 24	08 35		08 54	09 04	09 23	09 33
—		d	23p12	23p25	23p46		00 12		23p04	23p52	00 25	05 15	06 00	06 25	06 55	07 25	07 56	08 04		08 26	08 39		08 56	09 04	09 25	09 34
33½	Farncombe	d		23p31	23p53				23p10	23p58	00 31		06 06	06 31	07 01	07 31	08 02			08 32			09 02		09 31	
34¾	Godalming	d		23p34	23p56				23p13	00 01	00 34		06 09	06 34	07 04	07 34	08 05			08 35			09 05		09 34	
36¾	Milford (Surrey)	d		23p38	00 01						00s38		06 13	06 38	07 08	07 38	08 09			08 39			09 09			
38½	Witley	d		23p42	00 04						00s43		06 18	06 42	07 12	07 42	08 13			08 43			09 13			
43	**Haslemere** 4	a	23p26	23p49	00 11		00 26		23p24	00 12	00 49	05 29	06 24	06 49	07 19	07 49	08 20	08 24	←	08 50	08 54	←	09 20	09 24	09 45	09 49
		d	23p27	23p50	00 12	←	00 27		23p25	00 13	00 50	05 30	06 25	06 55	07 20	07 55	08 30 →	08 25	08 30	09 00 →	08 55	09 00		09 25	09 55 →	09 50
46¾	Liphook	d		23p55	00 17 →	00 17					00s55	05 35	06 30	07 00	07 25	08 00			08 35			09 05				
51½	Liss	d		00 01		00 23					01s01	05 41	06 36	07 06	07 31	08 06			08 41			09 11				
55	Petersfield	d	23p38	00 06		00 28	00 38		23p36	00 24	01 06	05 46	06 41	07 11	07 36	08 11		08 36	08 46		09 06	09 16		09 36		10 01
63¼	Rowlands Castle	d		00 16		00 38					01s16	05 56	06 51	07 21	07 46	08 21			08 56			09 26				
66½	**Havant**	a	23p50	00 21		00 44	00 50	02s00	23p48	00 36	01 21	06 01	06 57	07 27	07 51	08 26		08 49	09 04		09 18	09 34		09 49		10 14
66½		d	23p51	00 22		00 45	00 51		23p49	00 37	01 22	06 02	06 58	07 28	07 52	08 27		08 50	09 05		09 19	09 35		09 50		10 15
67¾	Bedhampton	a		00 24		00 47					01s24	06 04	07 00	07 30	07 54	08 29			09 07			09 37				
70½	Hilsea	a		00 30							01s30	06 10	07 07	07 37	08 00	08 35			09 13			09 44				
72¾	Fratton	a	23p59	00 34		00 55	01 00	02s10	23p58	00 46	01s34	06 14	07 11	07 41	08 04	08 39		08 58	09 17		09 28	09 48		09 58		10 23
73¾	**Portsmouth & Southsea**	a	00 04	00 38		00 59	01 04	02s14	00 02	00 50	01 38	06 18	07 16	07 46	08 07	08 43		09 02	09 20		09 32	09 53		10 02		10 27
74½	**Portsmouth Harbour**	a	00 09			01 04	01 09	02 19	00 07	00 55		06 22	07 20		08 12	08 48		09 07	09 26		09 37			10 07		10 32

		SW 1	SW 1	SW 1 ☕	SW 1	SW 1 ☕	SW 1	SW 1	SW 1 ☕	SW 1	SW 1 ☕	SW 1	SW 1	SW 1 ☕	SW 1	SW 1 ☕	SW 1	SW 1	SW 1 ☕	SW 1	SW 1 ☕	SW 1	SW 1	SW 1 ☕	SW 1	SW 1 ☕
London Waterloo 15 ⊖	d		09 15	09 30	09 45	10 00		10 15	10 30	10 45	11 00		11 15	11 30	11 45	12 00		12 15	12 30	12 45	13 00		13 15	13 30	13 45	14 00
Clapham Junction 10	d		09u22		09u52			10u22		10u52			11u22		11u52			12u22		12u52			13u22		13u52	
Woking	a		09 42	09 54	10 11	10 24		10 41	10 54	11 11	11 24		11 41	11 54	12 11	12 24		12 41	12 54	13 11	13 24		13 41	13 54	14 11	14 24
	d		09 43	09 55	10 13	10 25		10 43	10 55	11 13	11 25		11 43	11 55	12 13	12 25		12 43	12 55	13 13	13 25		13 43	13 55	14 13	14 25
Worplesdon	d				10 18					11 18					12 18					13 18					14 18	
Guildford	a		09 52	10 03	10 23	10 33		10 50	11 03	11 23	11 33		11 50	12 03	12 23	12 33		12 50	13 03	13 23	13 33		13 50	14 03	14 23	14 33
	d		09 54	10 04	10 25	10 34		10 52	11 04	11 25	11 34		11 52	12 04	12 25	12 34		12 52	13 04	13 25	13 34		13 52	14 04	14 25	14 34
Farncombe	d		10 00		10 31			10 58		11 31			11 58		12 31			12 58		13 31			13 58		14 31	
Godalming	d		10 03		10 34			11 01		11 34			12 01		12 34			13 01		13 34			14 01		14 34	
Milford (Surrey)	d		10 07					11 05					12 05					13 05					14 05			
Witley	d		10 11					11 09					12 09					13 09					14 09			
Haslemere 4	a	←	10 19	10 22	10 45	10 49	←	11 16	11 20	11 45	11 49	←	12 16	12 20	12 45	12 49	←	13 16	13 20	13 45	13 49	←	14 16	14 20	14 45	14 49
	d	09 55		10 23	10 55 →	10 50	10 55		11 21	11 55 →	11 50	11 55		12 21	12 55 →	12 50	12 55		13 21	13 55 →	13 50	13 55		14 21	14 55 →	14 50
Liphook	d	10 00					11 00					12 00					13 00					14 00				
Liss	d	10 06					11 06					12 06					13 06					14 06				
Petersfield	d	10 11		10 34		11 01	11 11		11 32		12 01	12 11		12 32		13 01	13 11		13 32		14 01	14 11		14 32		15 01
Rowlands Castle	d	10 21					11 21					12 21					13 21					14 21				
Havant	a	10 26		10 48		11 14	11 26		11 49		12 14	12 26		12 49		13 14	13 26		13 49		14 14	14 26		14 49		15 15
	d	10 27		10 50		11 15	11 27		11 50		12 15	12 27		12 50		13 15	13 27		13 50		14 15	14 27		14 50		15 15
Bedhampton	a	10 29					11 29					12 29					13 29					14 29				
Hilsea	a	10 35					11 35					12 35					13 35					14 35				
Fratton	a	10 39		10 58		11 23	11 39		11 58		12 23	12 39		12 58		13 23	13 39		13 58		14 23	14 39		14 58		15 24
Portsmouth & Southsea	a	10 43		11 02		11 27	11 43		12 02		12 27	12 43		13 02		13 27	13 43		14 03		14 27	14 43		15 02		15 28
Portsmouth Harbour	a			11 07		11 32			12 07		12 32			13 07		13 32			14 07		14 32			15 07		15 32

		SW 1	SW 1	SW 1 ☕	SW 1	SW 1 ☕	SW 1	SW 1	SW 1 ☕	SW 1	SW 1	SW 1 ☕	SW 1	SW 1	SW 1 ☕	SW 1	SW 1	SW 1 ☕	SW 1	SW 1	SW 1 ☕	SW 1	SW 1	SW 1 ☕	SW 1	SW 1
London Waterloo 15 ⊖	d		14 15	14 30	14 45	15 00		15 15	15 30		15 45	16 00		16 15	16 30		16 45	17 00		17 15	17 30		17 45	18 00		18 15
Clapham Junction 10	d		14u22		14u52			15u22			15u52			16u22			16u52									
Woking	a		14 41	14 54	15 11	15 23		15 41	15 54		16 11	16 24		16 41	16 54		17 11	17 24		17 38	17 54					
	d		14 43	14 55	15 13	15 25		15 43	15 55		16 13	16 25		16 43	16 55		17 13	17 25		17 40	17 56					
Worplesdon	d				15 18			15 48						16 48				17 30		17 45	18 00					
Guildford	a		14 50	15 03	15 23	15 32		15 53	16 03		16 20	16 33		16 53	17 03		17 20	17 36		17 51	18 06		18 21	18 31		18 50
	d		14 52	15 04	15 25	15 34		15 55	16 04		16 22	16 34		16 55	17 04		17 22	17 37		17 54	18 08		18 23	18 33		18 51
Farncombe	d		14 58		15 31			16 01			16 28			17 01			17 28			18 00			18 29			
Godalming	d		15 01		15 34			16 04			16 31			17 04			17 31			18 03	18 15		18 32	18 39		
Milford (Surrey)	d		15 05					16 08			16 35			17 08			17 35			18 07			18 36			
Witley	d		15 09					16 12			16 39			17 12			17 39			18 11			18 40			
Haslemere 4	a	←	15 16	15 20	15 45	15 49	←	16 19	16 23	←	16 46	16 50	←	17 19	17 23	←	17 46	17 51	←	18 18	18 25	←	18 49	18 51	←	19 05
	d	14 55		15 21	15 55 →	15 50	15 55	16 29 →	16 24	16 29	16 55 →	16 51	16 55	17 29 →	17 24	17 29	17 56 →	17 52	17 56	18 31 →	18 26	18 31	18 56 →	18 52	18 56	19 06
Liphook	d	15 00					16 00			16 34			17 00			17 34			18 01			18 36			19 01	19 11
Liss	d	15 06					16 06			16 40			17 06			17 40			18 07			18 42			19 07	19 17
Petersfield	d	15 11		15 32		16 01	16 11		16 35	16 45		17 02	17 11		17 35	17 45		18 03	18 12		18 37	18 47		19 03	19 12	19 23
Rowlands Castle	d	15 21					16 21			16 55			17 21			17 55			18 22			18 57			19 22	19 32
Havant	a	15 26		15 49		16 14	16 26		16 49	17 03		17 15	17 26		17 48	18 03		18 18	18 29		18 50	19 03		19 16	19 29	19 41
	d	15 27		15 50		16 15	16 27		16 50	17 04		17 16	17 27		17 49	18 04		18 19	18 30		18 51	19 04		19 17		19 42
Bedhampton	a	15 29					16 29			17 06			17 29			18 07			18 32			19 07				19 44
Hilsea	a	15 35					16 35			17 11			17 35			18 12			18 38			19 12				19 50
Fratton	a	15 39		15 58		16 23	16 39		16 58	17 15		17 24	17 39		17 58	18 16		18 28	18 42		18 59	19 16		19 25		19 56
Portsmouth & Southsea	a	15 43		16 02		16 27	16 43		17 02	17 22		17 28	17 43		18 02	18 20		18 32	18 46		19 03			19 29		
Portsmouth Harbour	a			16 07		16 32	16 49		17 07	17 27		17 35			18 09	18 28		18 39			19 10			19 36		

For general notes see front of timetable
For details of catering facilities see
Directory of Train Operators

b Previous night.
Stops to pick up only

London → Guildford, Haslemere and Portsmouth

Network Diagram - see first page of Table 155

Mondays to Fridays

		SW 1	SW 1 ☕	SW 1	SW 1 ☕	SW 1	SW 1	SW 1 ☕	SW 1	SW 1	SW 1 ☕	SW 1	SW 1	SW 1 ☕	SW 1	SW 1 ☕	SW 1	SW 1	SW 1	SW 1	SW 1	SW 1	SW 1	SW 1	SW 1
London Waterloo 15 ⊖	d	18 18	18 30	18 45	19 00		19 15	19 30		19 45	20 00		20 15	20 30	20 45	21 00		21 30	21 45	22 00		22 30	22 45	23 15	23 45
Clapham Junction 10	d						19u22			19u52			20u22		20u52				21u52				22u52	23u22	23u52
Woking	a	18 42	18 57	19 13	19 24		19 43	19 54		20 11	20 25		20 41	20 54	21 11	21 24		21 54	22 11	22 24		22 54	23 11	23 41	00 11
	d	18 43	18 58	19 14	19 25		19 45	19 55		20 13	20 25		20 43	20 55	21 13	21 25		21 55	22 13	22 25		22 55	23 13	23 43	00 13
Worplesdon	d	18 48			19 30					20 18					21 18				22 18				23 18		00 18
Guildford	a	18 54	19 06	19 23	19 36		19 52	20 03		20 23	20 34		20 50	21 03	21 23	21 33		22 03	22 23	22 33		23 03	23 23	23 51	00 24
	d	18 57	19 08	19 24	19 37		19 54	20 04		20 25	20 34		20 52	21 04	21 25	21 34		22 04	22 25	22 34		23 04	23 25	23 52	00 25
Farncombe	d	19 03		19 30			20 00			20 31	20 41		20 58		21 31	21 40		22 10	22 31	22 40		23 10	23 31	23 58	00 31
Godalming	d	19 06	19 14	19 33			20 03	20 11		20 34	20 44		21 01	21 11	21 34	21 43		22 13	22 34	22 43		23 13	23 34	00 01	00 34
Milford (Surrey)	d	19 10		19 37			20 07			20 38			21 05		21 38				22 38				23 38		00s38
Witley	d	19 14		19 41			20 11			20 42			21 09		21 42				22 42				23 42		00s43
Haslemere 4	a	19 23	19 25	19 49	19 52	←	20 18	20 22	←	20 49	20 55	←	21 16	21 21	21 49	21 54	←	22 24	22 49	22 54	←	23 24	23 49	00 12	00 49
	d		19 26	19 57 →	19 53	19 57	20 27 →	20 22	20 27	20 59 →	20 55	20 59		21 22	21 59 →	21 55	21 59	22 25	22 59 →	22 55	22 59	23 25	23 50	00 13	00 50
Liphook	d					20 02			20 32			21 04					22 04				23 04		23 55		00s55
Liss	d					20 08			20 38			21 10					22 10				23 10		00 01		01s01
Petersfield	d		19 37		20 04	20 13		20 33	20 43		21 06	21 16		21 33		22 06	22 16	22 36		23 06	23 15	23 36	00 06	00 24	01 06
Rowlands Castle	d					20 23			20 53			21 25					22 25				23 25		00 16		01s16
Havant	a		19 50		20 18	20 28		20 48	21 00		21 19	21 30		21 46		22 18	22 30	22 48		23 18	23 30	23 48	00 21	00 36	01 21
	d		19 51		20 19	20 29		20 49			21 20	21 31		21 46		22 19	22 31	22 49		23 19	23 31	23 49	00 22	00 37	01 22
Bedhampton	a					20 31						21 34					22 34				23 33		00 24		01s24
Hilsea	a					20 37						21 40					22 39				23 39		00 30		01s30
Fratton	a		19 59		20 27	20 41		20 58			21 29	21 44		21 55		22 28	22 43	22 58		23 28	23 43	23 58	00 34	00 46	01s34
Portsmouth & Southsea	a		20 03		20 31	20 44		21 02			21 33	21 47		21 58		22 32	22 47	23 03		23 32	23 47	00 02	00 38	00 50	01 38
Portsmouth Harbour	a		20 10		20 36	20 52		21 07			21 38			22 02		22 38		23 08		23 37		00 07		00 55	

Saturdays

		SW 1	SW 1	SW 1	SW 1	SW 1	SW 1	SW 1	SW 1	SW 1	SW 1	SW 1	SW 1	SW 1	SW 1	SW 1		SW 1 ☕	SW 1	SW 1 ☕	SW 1
London Waterloo 15 ⊖	d	22p30	22p45	23p15	23p45		05 00	05 20	06 15	06 45	07 15	07 30	07 45	08 00		08 15		18 30	18 45	19 00	
Clapham Junction 10	d		22b52	23b22	23b52		05 09	05 29	06u22	06u52	07u22		07u52			08u22			18u52		
Woking	a	22p54	23p11	23p41	00 11		05 50	06 08	06 41	07 11	07 41	07 54	08 11	08 24		08 41		18 54	19 11	19 24	
	d	22p55	23p13	23p43	00 13		05 51	06 13	06 43	07 13	07 43	07 55	08 13	08 25		08 43		18 55	19 13	19 25	
Worplesdon	d		23p18		00 18			06 18		07 18			08 18						19 18		
Guildford	a	23p03	23p23	23p51	00 24		05 59	06 23	06 50	07 23	07 50	08 03	08 23	08 33		08 50	and at	19 03	19 23	19 33	
	d	23p04	23p25	23p52	00 25	05 15	06 00	06 25	06 52	07 25	07 52	08 04	08 25	08 34		08 52	the same	19 04	19 25	19 34	
Farncombe	d	23p10	23p31	23p58	00 31		06 06	06 31	06 58	07 31	07 58		08 31			08 58			19 31		
Godalming	d	23p13	23p34	00 01	00 34		06 09	06 34	07 01	07 34	08 01		08 34			09 01	minutes		19 34		
Milford (Surrey)	d		23p38		00s38		06 13		07 05		08 05					09 05					
Witley	d		23p42		00s43		06 18		07 09		08 09					09 09	past				
Haslemere 4	a	23p24	23p49	00 12	00 49	05 29	06 25	06 44	07 16	07 44	08 16	08 20	08 45	08 49	←	09 16		19 20	19 45	19 49	←
	d	23p25	23p50	00 13	00 50	05 29		06 45		07 45		08 21	08 55 →	08 50	08 55		each	19 21	19 55 →	19 50	19 55
Liphook	d		23p55		00s55	05 34		06 50		07 50					09 00						20 00
Liss	d		00 01		01s01	05 40		06 56		07 56					09 06		hour until				20 06
Petersfield	d	23p36	00 06	00 24	01 06	05 46		07 01		08 01		08 32		09 01	09 11			19 32		20 01	20 11
Rowlands Castle	d		00 16		01s16	05 55		07 11		08 11					09 21						20 21
Havant	a	23p48	00 21	00 36	01 21	06 00		07 18		08 16		08 49		09 14	09 26			19 49		20 14	20 29
	d	23p49	00 22	00 37	01 22	06 01		07 19		08 17		08 50		09 15	09 27			19 50		20 15	20 30
Bedhampton	a		00 24		01s24	06 03		07 21		08 19					09 29						20 32
Hilsea	a		00 30		01s30	06 09		07 27		08 25					09 35						20 38
Fratton	a	23p58	00 34	00 46	01s34	06 13		07 31		08 29		08 59		09 23	09 39			19 58		20 23	20 43
Portsmouth & Southsea	a	00 02	00 38	00 50	01 38	06 17		07 34		08 32		09 02		09 27	09 43			20 02		20 27	20 48
Portsmouth Harbour	a	00 07		00 55		06 22		07 39		08 37		09 07		09 32				20 07		20 32	

		SW 1	SW 1 ☕	SW 1	SW 1	SW 1	SW 1	SW 1	SW 1	SW 1	SW 1	SW 1	SW 1	SW 1	SW 1	SW 1	SW 1	SW 1	SW 1
London Waterloo 15 ⊖	d	19 15	19 30	19 45	20 00		20 15	20 30	20 45	21 00		21 30	21 45	22 00		22 30	22 45	23 15	23 45
Clapham Junction 10	d	19u22		19u52			20u22		20u52				21u52				22u52	23u22	23u52
Woking	a	19 41	19 54	20 11	20 24		20 41	20 54	21 11	21 24		21 54	22 11	22 24		22 54	23 11	23 41	00 12
	d	19 43	19 55	20 13	20 25		20 43	20 55	21 13	21 25		21 55	22 13	22 25		22 55	23 13	23 43	00 13
Worplesdon	d			20 18					21 18				22 18				23 18		00 18
Guildford	a	19 50	20 03	20 23	20 33		20 50	21 03	21 23	21 33		22 03	22 23	22 33		23 03	23 23	23 51	00 23
	d	19 52	20 04	20 25	20 34		20 52	21 04	21 25	21 34		22 04	22 25	22 34		23 04	23 25	23 52	00 25
Farncombe	d	19 58		20 31			20 58		21 31	21 40		22 10	22 31	22 40		23 10	23 31	23 58	00 31
Godalming	d	20 01		20 34			21 01		21 34	21 43		22 13	22 34	22 43		23 13	23 34	00 01	00 34
Milford (Surrey)	d	20 05					21 05		21 38				22 38				23 38		00s38
Witley	d	20 09					21 09		21 42				22 42				23 42		00s43
Haslemere 4	a	20 16	20 20	20 45	20 49	←	21 16	21 20	21 49	21 54	←	22 24	22 49	22 54	←	23 24	23 49	00 12	00 49
	d		20 21	20 55 →	20 50	20 55		21 21	21 59 →	21 55	21 59	22 25	22 59 →	22 55	22 59	23 25	23 50	00 13	00 50
Liphook	d					21 00					22 04				23 04		23 55		00s55
Liss	d					21 06					22 10				23 10		00 01		01s01
Petersfield	d		20 32		21 01	21 11		21 32		22 06	22 16	22 36		23 06	23 15	23 36	00 06	00 24	01 06
Rowlands Castle	d					21 21					22 25				23 25		00 16		01s16
Havant	a		20 49		21 14	21 26		21 45		22 18	22 30	22 48		23 18	23 30	23 48	00 21	00 36	01 21
	d		20 50		21 15	21 27		21 46		22 19	22 31	22 49		23 19	23 31	23 49	00 22	00 37	01 22
Bedhampton	a					21 29					22 34				23 33		00 24		01s24
Hilsea	a					21 35					22 39				23 39		00 30		01s30
Fratton	a		20 58		21 23	21 39		21 54		22 28	22 43	22 58		23 28	23 43	23 58	00 34	00 46	01s34
Portsmouth & Southsea	a		21 02		21 27	21 43		21 58		22 32	22 48	23 02		23 32	23 47	00 02	00 38	00 50	01 38
Portsmouth Harbour	a		21 07		21 32			22 03		22 36	22 52	23 08		23 37	23 52	00 07		00 55	

For general notes see front of timetable
For details of catering facilities see
Directory of Train Operators

b Previous night.
Stops to pick up only

Table 156

Sundays

London → Guildford, Haslemere and Portsmouth

Network Diagram - see first page of Table 155

		SW 1	SW 1	SW 1	SW 1	SW 1	SW 1	SW 1	SW 1	SW 1	SW 1	SW 1	SW 1
London Waterloo [15] ⊖	d	22p30	22p45	23p15	23p45		08 00	08 30	09 00	09 30	10 00	10 30	11 00
Clapham Junction [10]	d		22b52	23b22	23b52		08u09	08u39	09u09	09u39	10u09	10u39	11u09
Woking	a	22p54	23p11	23p41	00 12		08 34	09 03	09 34	10 03	10 31	11 01	11 31
	d	22p55	23p13	23p43	00 13	07 32	08 35	09 04	09 35	10 04	10 32	11 02	11 32
Worplesdon	d		23p18		00 18								
Guildford	a	23p03	23p23	23p51	00 23	07 40	08 43	09 12	09 43	10 12	10 40	11 10	11 40
	d	23p04	23p25	23p52	00 25	07 46	08 46	09 14	09 46	10 14	10 46	11 12	11 46
Farncombe	d	23p10	23p31	23p58	00 31	07 53	08 53		09 53		10 53		11 53
Godalming	d	23p13	23p34	00 01	00 34	07 56	08 56		09 56		10 56		11 56
Milford (Surrey)	d		23p38		00s38	08 00	09 00		10 00		11 00		12 00
Witley	d		23p42		00s43	08 04	09 04		10 04		11 04		12 04
Haslemere [4]	a	23p24	23p49	00 12	00 49	08 11	09 11	09 28	10 11	10 28	11 11	11 26	12 11
	d	23p25	23p50	00 13	00 50	08 12	09 12	09 29	10 12	10 29	11 12	11 27	12 12
Liphook	d		23p55		00s55	08 17	09 17		10 17		11 17		12 17
Liss	d		00 01		01s01	08 23	09 23		10 23		11 23		12 23
Petersfield	d	23p36	00 06	00 24	01 06	08 28	09 28	09 40	10 28	10 40	11 28	11 38	12 28
Rowlands Castle	d		00 16		01s16	08 38	09 38		10 38		11 38		12 38
Havant	a	23p48	00 21	00 36	01 21	08 44	09 44	09 50	10 44	10 52	11 44	11 50	12 44
	d	23p49	00 22	00 37	01 22	08 45	09 45	09 52	10 45	10 53	11 45	11 51	12 45
Bedhampton	a		00 24		01s24	08 47	09 47		10 47		11 47		12 47
Hilsea	a		00 30		01s30								
Fratton	a	23p58	00 34	00 46	01s34	08 55	09 55	10 00	10 55	11 01	11 55	12 00	12 55
Portsmouth & Southsea	a	00 02	00 38	00 50	01 38	08 59	09 59	10 05	10 59	11 05	11 59	12 05	12 59
Portsmouth Harbour	a	00 07		00 55		09 04	10 04	10 11	11 04	11 11	12 04	12 09	13 04

		SW 1 ☕		SW 1	SW 1 ☕	SW 1	SW 1 ☕	SW 1	SW 1	SW 1	SW 1	SW 1	SW 1
London Waterloo [15] ⊖	d	11 30		19 00	19 30	20 00	20 30	21 00	21 30	22 00	22 30	23 00	23 30
Clapham Junction [10]	d	11u39		19u09	19u39	20u09	20u39	21u09	21u39	22u09	22u39	23u09	23u39
Woking	a	12 01		19 31	20 01	20 31	21 01	21 31	22 01	22 31	23 01	23 31	00 01
	d	12 02		19 32	20 02	20 32	21 02	21 32	22 02	22 32	23 02	23 32	00 02
Worplesdon	d												
Guildford	a	12 10	and at	19 40	20 10	20 40	21 10	21 40	22 10	22 40	23 10	23 40	00 10
	d	12 12	the same	19 46	20 12	20 46	21 12	21 46	22 12	22 46	23 12	23 46	00 12
Farncombe	d			19 53		20 53		21 53		22 53		23 53	
Godalming	d		minutes	19 56		20 56		21 56		22 56		23 56	
Milford (Surrey)	d			20 00		21 00		22 00		23 00		00 01	
Witley	d		past	20 04		21 04		22 04		23 04		00 04	
Haslemere [4]	a	12 26		20 11	20 26	21 11	21 26	22 11	22 26	23 11	23 26	00 11	00 26
	d	12 27	each	20 12	20 27	21 12	21 27	22 12	22 27	23 12	23 27	00 12	00 27
Liphook	d			20 17		21 17		22 17		23 17		00 17	
Liss	d		hour until	20 23		21 23		22 23		23 23		00 23	
Petersfield	d	12 38		20 28	20 38	21 28	21 38	22 28	22 38	23 28	23 38	00 28	00 38
Rowlands Castle	d			20 38		21 38		22 38		23 38		00 38	
Havant	a	12 50		20 44	20 50	21 44	21 50	22 44	22 50	23 44	23 50	00 44	00 50
	d	12 51		20 45	20 51	21 45	21 51	22 45	22 51	23 45	23 51	00 45	00 51
Bedhampton	a			20 47		21 47		22 47		23 47		00 47	
Hilsea	a												
Fratton	a	13 00		20 55	21 00	21 55	22 00	22 55	23 00	23 55	23 59	00 55	01 00
Portsmouth & Southsea	a	13 04		20 59	21 04	21 59	22 04	22 59	23 04	23 59	00 04	00 59	01 04
Portsmouth Harbour	a	13 11		21 04	21 09	22 04	22 11	23 04	23 09	00 04	00 09	01 04	01 09

For general notes see front of timetable
For details of catering facilities see Directory of Train Operators

b Previous night.
Stops to pick up only

Portsmouth, Haslemere and Guildford → London

Network diagram - see first page of Table 155

Miles			SW MO [1]	SW MX [1]	SW MX [1]	SW MO [1]	SW MX [1]	SW [1] A	SW [1] B	SW [1] A	SW [1] B	SW [1] A ☕	SW [1] B ☕	SW [1] A	SW [1] B	SW [1]	SW [1] ☕	SW [1]	SW [1]	SW [1] ☕	SW [1]	SW [1]
0	**Portsmouth Harbour**	d	22p32	22p17		22p48	23p17	04 25	04 30			05 14	05 19			05 50	06 15			06 42		06 55
¾	**Portsmouth & Southsea**	d	22p37	22p24		22p53	23p24	04 30	04 35			05 19	05 24			05 55	06 20			06 47		07 00
1¾	Fratton	d	22p41	22p28		22p57	23p28	04 34	04 39			05 23	05 28			05 59	06 24			06 51		07 04
4	Hilsea	d		22p32			23p32	04 38	04 43			05 27	05 32			06 03			06 42			07 08
7¼	Bedhampton	d		22p37		23p04	23p37	04 43	04 48			05 32	05 37			06 08			06 47			07 13
8	**Havant**	a	22p49	22p39		23p07	23p39	04 45	04 50			05 34	05 40			06 10	06 33		06 49	06 59		07 15
—		d	22p50	22p40		23p07	23p40	04 46	04 51			05 35	05 41			06 11	06 34		06 50	07 00	07 11	07 16
11¼	Rowlands Castle	d		22p46		23p13	23p46	04 52	04 57			05 41	05 46			06 16			06 56			07 22
19½	Petersfield	d	23p04	22p57		23p24	23p57	05 03	05 08			05 52	05 57			06 29	06 48		07 07	07 14	07 25	07 33
23	Liss	d		23p02		23p29	00 02	05 08	05 13			05 57	06 02			06 34			07 12	07 20		07 38
27¾	Liphook	d		23p09		23p36	00 09	05 15	05 20			06 04	06 09			06 41			07 19	07 27		07 45
31½	**Haslemere [4]**	a	23p16	23p15		23p41	00 15	05 20	05 25			06 10	06 15			06 46	07 01		07 25	07 33	07 38	07 51
—		d	23p17	23p15		23p42	00 15	05 21	05 26	05 57	06 00	06 11	06 16	06 29	06 32	06 47	07 02	07 10	07 26	07 35	07 40	08 07 →
36	Witley	d		23p21	←	23p48	00 21	05 27	05 32	06 03	06 06			06 35	06 38			07 16			07 46	
38¼	Milford (Surrey)	d		23p25	23p25	23p52	00 25	05 31	05 36	06 08	06 11			06 39	06 42			07 21			07 50	
40	Godalming	d		→	23p29	23p56	00 29	05 35	05 40	06 12	06 15			06 43	06 46	06 57		07 25	07 35	07 45	07 54	
41	Farncombe	d			23p32	23p59	00 32	05 38	05 43	06 15	06 18			06 46	06 49	07 00		07 28	07 38		07 57	
44¼	**Guildford**	a	23p31		23p37	00 04	00 37	05 48	05 48	06 23	06 23	06 29	06 29	06 51	06 54	07 05	07 15	07 32	07 43	07 52	08 02	
—		d	23p35		23p39	00 05		05 50	05 50	06 24	06 24	06 31	06 31	06 52	06 55	07 07	07 17	07 32	07 45	07 54	08 03	
47¾	Worplesdon	d			23p44			05 55	05 55	06 30	06 30			06 58	07 01			07 40	07 50			
50½	**Woking**	a	23p42		23p49	00 13		06 00	06 00	06 35	06 35	06 39	06 39	07 05	07 05	07 15	07 25		07 54		08 11	
—		d	23p45		23p56			06 01	06 01	06 37	06 37	06 41	06 41	07 07	07 07	07 17	07 26		07 56		08 12	
70½	Clapham Junction [10]	a	00 04		00 20			06 20	06 20	06 58	06 58	07 02	07 02	07 26	07 26							
74½	**London Waterloo [15]**	⊖ a	00 14		00 29			06 29	06 29	07 08	07 08	07 12	07 12	07 37	07 37	07 44	07 54	08 11	08 24	08 32	08 41	

		SW [1] ☕	SW [1]	SW [1]	SW [1] ☕	SW [1]	SW [1] ☕	SW [1]	SW [1] ☕	SW [1]	SW [1] ☕	SW [1]	SW [1] ☕	SW [1]	SW [1] ☕	SW [1]	SW [1] ☕	SW [1]	SW [1] ☕	SW [1]	SW [1] ☕
Portsmouth Harbour	d	07 13		07 29	07 45		08 15		08 45		09 15	09 17	09 45		10 15		10 45		11 15		11 45
Portsmouth & Southsea	d	07 18		07 33	07 50		08 20	08 24	08 50		09 20	09 24	09 50		10 20	10 24	10 50		11 20	11 24	11 50
Fratton	d	07 22		07 37	07 54		08 24	08 28	08 54		09 24	09 28	09 54		10 24	10 28	10 54		11 24	11 28	11 54
Hilsea	d			07 41				08 32				09 32				10 32				11 32	
Bedhampton	d			07 49				08 37				09 37				10 37				11 37	
Havant	a	07 30		07 51	08 02		08 32	08 40	09 03		09 33	09 39	10 03		10 33	10 39	11 03		11 33	11 39	12 03
	d	07 32		07 52	08 03		08 34	08 40	09 04		09 34	09 40	10 04		10 34	10 40	11 04		11 34	11 40	12 04
Rowlands Castle	d			07 58				08 46				09 46				10 46				11 46	
Petersfield	d	07 46		08 09	08 17		08 48	08 57	09 18		09 48	09 57	10 18		10 48	10 57	11 18		11 48	11 57	12 18
Liss	d			08 14				09 02				10 02				11 02				12 02	
Liphook	d			08 21				09 09				10 09				11 09				12 09	
Haslemere [4]	a	07 59	←	08 27	08 31	←	09 01	09 15	09 31		10 01	10 15	10 31		11 01	11 15	11 31		12 01	12 15	12 31
	d	08 00	08 07	08 39	08 32	08 39	09 02	09 15	09 32	09 39	10 02	10 15	10 32	10 39	11 02	11 15	11 32	11 39	12 02	12 15	12 32
Witley	d		08 13	→		08 45				09 45				10 45				11 45			
Milford (Surrey)	d		08 17			08 49				09 49				10 49				11 49			
Godalming	d		08 21			08 53		09 25		09 53		10 25		10 53		11 25		11 53		12 25	
Farncombe	d		08 25			08 57		09 28		09 56		10 28		10 56		11 28		11 56		12 28	
Guildford	a	08 13	08 30		08 47	09 02	09 15	09 32	09 45	10 01	10 15	10 32	10 46	11 01	11 15	11 32	11 45	12 01	12 15	12 32	12 45
	d	08 15	08 31		08 54	09 03	09 17	09 32	09 47	10 02	10 17	10 32	10 47	11 02	11 17	11 32	11 47	12 02	12 17	12 32	12 47
Worplesdon	d	08 20	08 37					09 40				10 40				11 40				12 40	
Woking	a	08 26	08 41			09 11	09 27	09 44	09 59	10 11	10 25	10 44	10 57	11 11	11 25	11 44	11 57	12 11	12 25	12 44	12 57
	d	08 27	08 43			09 13	09 28	09 46	09 59	10 12	10 26	10 46	10 59	11 12	11 26	11 46	11 59	12 12	12 26	12 46	12 59
Clapham Junction [10]	a		09 03			09 32		10 05		10 31		11 05		11 31		12 05		12 31		13 05	
London Waterloo [15]	⊖ a	08 55	09 13		09 31	09 43	09 55	10 13	10 27	10 40	10 51	11 13	11 24	11 40	11 51	12 13	12 23	12 40	12 51	13 13	13 23

		SW [1]	SW [1] ☕	SW [1]	SW [1] ☕	SW [1]	SW [1] ☕	SW [1]	SW [1] ☕	SW [1]	SW [1] ☕	SW [1]	SW [1] ☕	SW [1]	SW [1] ☕	SW [1]	SW [1]	SW [1] ☕	SW [1] ☕	SW [1]	SW [1]	SW [1] ☕
Portsmouth Harbour	d		12 15		12 45		13 15		13 45		14 15		14 45		15 15			15 45	16 15			16 45
Portsmouth & Southsea	d		12 20	12 24	12 50		13 20	13 24	13 50		14 20	14 24	14 50		15 20	15 24		15 50	16 20	16 24		16 50
Fratton	d		12 24	12 28	12 54		13 24	13 28	13 54		14 24	14 28	14 54		15 24	15 28		15 54	16 24	16 28		16 54
Hilsea	d			12 32				13 32				14 32				15 32				16 32		
Bedhampton	d			12 37				13 37				14 37				15 37				16 37		
Havant	a		12 33	12 39	13 03		13 33	13 39	14 03		14 33	14 39	15 03		15 33	15 40		16 03	16 33	16 39		17 03
	d		12 34	12 40	13 04		13 34	13 40	14 04		14 34	14 40	15 04		15 34	15 40	15 56	16 04	16 34	16 40	16 56	17 04
Rowlands Castle	d			12 46				13 46				14 46				15 46				16 46		
Petersfield	d		12 48	12 57	13 18		13 48	13 57	14 18		14 48	14 57	15 18		15 48	15 57	16 10	16 18	16 48	16 57	17 10	17 18
Liss	d			13 02				14 02				15 02				16 02		16 23		17 02		17 23
Liphook	d			13 09				14 09				15 09				16 09		16 30		17 09		17 30
Haslemere [4]	a		13 01	13 15	13 31		14 01	14 15	14 31		15 01	15 15	15 31		16 01	16 15	16 23	16 36	17 01	17 15	17 23	17 36
	d	12 39	13 02	13 15	13 32	13 39	14 02	14 15	14 32	14 39	15 02	15 15	15 32	15 37	16 02	16 15	16 24	16 37	17 02	17 15	17 32	17 37
Witley	d	12 45				13 45				14 45				15 43			16 30	16 43				17 43
Milford (Surrey)	d	12 49				13 49				14 49				15 47			16 34	16 47				17 47
Godalming	d	12 53		13 25		13 53		14 25		14 53		15 25		15 51		16 25	16 38	16 51		17 25		17 51
Farncombe	d	12 56		13 28		13 56		14 28		14 56		15 28		15 54		16 28	16 41	16 54		17 28		17 54
Guildford	a	13 01	13 15	13 32	13 45	14 01	14 15	14 32	14 45	15 01	15 15	15 32	15 45	15 59	16 15	16 32	16 46	16 59	17 15	17 32	17 45	17 59
	d	13 02	13 17	13 32	13 47	14 02	14 17	14 32	14 47	15 02	15 17	15 32	15 47	16 00	16 17	16 32	16 47	17 00	17 17	17 32	17 47	18 00
Worplesdon	d			13 40				14 40				15 40		16 06		16 40		17 06		17 40		18 06
Woking	a	13 11	13 25	13 44	13 57	14 11	14 25	14 44	14 57	15 11	15 25	15 44	15 57	16 11	16 25	16 44	16 57	17 11	17 25	17 44	17 58	18 11
	d	13 12	13 26	13 46	13 59	14 12	14 26	14 46	14 59	15 12	15 26	15 46	15 59	16 12	16 26	16 46	16 59	17 12	17 26	17 46	17 59	18 12
Clapham Junction [10]	a	13 31		14 05		14 31		15 05		15 31		16 05		16 31		17 05		17 31		18 05		18 31
London Waterloo [15]	⊖ a	13 40	13 51	14 13	14 23	14 40	14 51	15 13	15 23	15 40	15 51	16 13	16 23	16 40	16 51	17 14	17 24	17 43	17 52	18 14	18 27	18 43

For general notes see front of timetable
For details of catering facilities see Directory of Train Operators

A From 29 September
B Until 26 September

Portsmouth, Haslemere and Guildford → London

Network diagram - see first page of Table 155

Mondays to Fridays

		SW 1 ☕	SW 1	SW 1 ☕	SW 1 ☕	SW 1	SW 1 ☕	SW 1	SW 1	SW 1	SW 1	SW 1	SW 1	SW 1	SW 1	SW 1	SW 1
Portsmouth Harbour	d	17 15	17 17	17 45	18 15		18 45		19 15		19 45	20 15	20 17	20 45	21 17	22 17	23 17
Portsmouth & Southsea	d	17 20	17 24	17 50	18 20	18 24	18 50		19 20	19 24	19 50	20 20	20 24	20 50	21 24	22 24	23 24
Fratton	d	17 24	17 28	17 54	18 24	18 28	18 54		19 24	19 28	19 54	20 24	20 28	20 54	21 28	22 28	23 28
Hilsea	d		17 32			18 32				19 32			20 32		21 32	22 32	23 32
Bedhampton	d		17 37			18 37				19 37			20 37		21 37	22 37	23 37
Havant	a	17 33	17 39	18 03	18 33	18 39	19 03		19 33	19 39	20 03	20 33	20 39	21 03	21 39	22 39	23 39
	d	17 34	17 40	18 04	18 34	18 40	19 04		19 34	19 40	20 04	20 34	20 40	21 04	21 40	22 40	23 40
Rowlands Castle	d		17 46			18 46				19 46			20 46		21 46	22 46	23 46
Petersfield	d	17 48	17 57	18 18	18 48	18 57	19 18		19 48	19 57	20 18	20 48	20 57	21 18	21 57	22 57	23 57
Liss	d		18 02			19 02				20 02			21 02		22 02	23 02	00 02
Liphook	d		18 09			19 09				20 09			21 09		22 09	23 09	00 09
Haslemere 4	a	18 01	18 15	18 31	19 01	19 15	19 31		20 01	20 15	20 31	21 01	21 15	21 31	22 15	23 15	00 15
	d	18 02	18 15	18 32	19 02	19 15	19 32	19 39	20 02	20 15	20 32	21 02	21 15	21 32	22 15	23 15	00 15
Witley	d			18 38				19 45		20 21			21 21		22 21	23 21	00 21
Milford (Surrey)	d			18 42				19 49		20 25			21 25		22 25	23 25	00 25
Godalming	d		18 25	18 46	19 11	19 25		19 53		20 29			21 29		22 29	23 29	00 29
Farncombe	d		18 28	18 49	19 14	19 28		19 56		20 32			21 32		22 32	23 32	00 32
Guildford	a	18 15	18 32	18 54	19 19	19 32	19 47	20 01	20 15	20 37	20 45	21 16	21 37	21 46	22 37	23 37	00 37
	d	18 17	18 32	18 55	19 21	19 32	19 47	20 02	20 17	20 39	20 47	21 17	21 39	21 47	22 39	23 39	
Worplesdon	d		18 40			19 40				20 44			21 44		22 44	23 44	
Woking	a		18 44	19 03	19 28	19 45	19 57	20 11	20 25	20 52	20 58	21 25	21 49	21 57	22 49	23 49	
	d		18 46	19 05	19 30	19 46	19 59	20 12	20 26	20 53	20 59	21 26	21 50	21 59	22 50	23 56	
Clapham Junction 10	a		19 05			20 05		20 31		21 12			22 09		23 09	00 20	
London Waterloo 15	⊖ a	18 59	19 14	19 29	19 59	20 14	20 23	20 40	20 50	21 21	21 27	21 50	22 18	22 27	23 18	00 29	

Saturdays

		SW 1	SW 1	SW 1 A	SW 1 B	SW 1 A	SW 1 B	SW 1	SW 1	SW 1 ☕	SW 1	SW 1 ☕	SW 1	SW 1 ☕	SW 1	SW 1 ☕	SW 1		SW 1 ☕
Portsmouth Harbour	d	22p17	23p17	04 38	04 43	05 13	05 18		06 18	06 45		07 15		07 45		08 15			16 45
Portsmouth & Southsea	d	22p24	23p24	04 43	04 48	05 19	05 24		06 24	06 50		07 20	07 24	07 50		08 20	08 24		16 50
Fratton	d	22p28	23p28	04 47	04 52	05 23	05 28		06 28	06 54		07 24	07 28	07 54		08 24	08 28		16 54
Hilsea	d	22p32	23p32	04 51	04 56	05 27	05 32		06 32				07 32				08 32		
Bedhampton	d	22p37	23p37	04 56	05 01	05 32	05 37		06 37				07 37				08 37	and at	
Havant	a	22p39	23p39	04 58	05 03	05 34	05 39		06 39	07 03		07 33	07 39	08 03		08 33	08 39		17 03
	d	22p40	23p40	04 59	05 04	05 35	05 40		06 40	07 04		07 34	07 40	08 04		08 34	08 40	the same	17 04
Rowlands Castle	d	22p46	23p46	05 04	05 09	05 41	05 46		06 46				07 46				08 46		
Petersfield	d	22p57	23p57	05 15	05 20	05 52	05 57		06 57	07 18		07 48	07 57	08 18		08 48	08 57	minutes	17 18
Liss	d	23p02	00 02	05 20	05 25	05 57	06 02		07 02				08 02				09 02		
Liphook	d	23p09	00 09	05 27	05 32	06 04	06 09		07 09				08 09				09 09	past	
Haslemere 4	a	23p15	00 15	05 33	05 38	06 10	06 15		07 15	07 31		08 01	08 15	08 31		09 01	09 15		17 31
	d	23p15	00 15	05 34	05 39	06 10	06 15	06 39	07 15	07 32	07 39	08 02	08 15	08 32	08 39	09 02	09 15	each	17 32
Witley	d	23p21	00 21	05 40	05 45			06 45			07 45				08 45				
Milford (Surrey)	d	23p25	00 25	05 44	05 49			06 49			07 49				08 49			hour until	
Godalming	d	23p29	00 29	05 48	05 53	06 20	06 25	06 53	07 25		07 53		08 25		08 53		09 25		
Farncombe	d	23p32	00 32	05 51	05 56	06 23	06 28	06 56	07 28		07 56		08 28		08 56		09 28		
Guildford	a	23p37	00 37	06 01	06 01	06 32	06 32	07 01	07 32	07 46	08 01	08 16	08 32	08 46	09 01	09 16	09 32		17 45
	d	23p39		06 02	06 02	06 32	06 32	07 02	07 32	07 47	08 02	08 17	08 32	08 47	09 02	09 17	09 32		17 47
Worplesdon	d	23p44				06 40	06 40		07 40				08 40				09 40		
Woking	a	23p49		06 11	06 11	06 44	06 44	07 11	07 44	07 57	08 12	08 26	08 44	08 57	09 11	09 25	09 44		17 57
	d	23p56		06 13	06 13	06 46	06 46	07 12	07 46	07 59	08 14	08 27	08 46	08 59	09 12	09 26	09 46		17 59
Clapham Junction 10	a	00 20		06 32	06 32	07 05	07 05	07 31	08 05		08 33		09 05		09 31		10 05		
London Waterloo 15	⊖ a	00 29		06 40	06 40	07 13	07 13	07 40	08 13	08 23	08 42	08 51	09 13	09 23	09 40	09 52	10 13		18 23

		SW 1	SW 1	SW 1	SW 1 ☕	SW 1	SW 1	SW 1	SW 1	SW 1	SW 1	SW 1	SW 1	SW 1	SW 1	SW 1	SW 1	SW 1	SW 1
Portsmouth Harbour	d			17 16	17 45		18 15		18 45		19 15		19 45	20 15		20 45	21 17	22 17	23 17
Portsmouth & Southsea	d		17 10	17 24	17 50		18 20	18 24	18 50		19 20	19 24	19 50	20 20	20 24	20 50	21 24	22 24	23 24
Fratton	d		17 14	17 28	17 54		18 24	18 28	18 54		19 24	19 28	19 54	20 24	20 28	20 54	21 28	22 28	23 28
Hilsea	d		17 18	17 32				18 32				19 32			20 32		21 32	22 32	23 32
Bedhampton	d		17 23	17 37				18 37				19 37			20 37		21 37	22 37	23 37
Havant	a		17 25	17 39	18 03		18 33	18 39	19 03		19 33	19 39	20 03	20 33	20 39	21 03	21 39	22 39	23 39
	d		17 26	17 40	18 04		18 34	18 40	19 04		19 34	19 40	20 04	20 34	20 40	21 04	21 40	22 40	23 40
Rowlands Castle	d		17 32	17 46				18 46				19 46			20 46		21 46	22 46	23 46
Petersfield	d		17 43	17 57	18 18		18 48	18 57	19 18		19 48	19 57	20 18	20 48	20 57	21 18	21 57	22 57	23 57
Liss	d		17 48	18 02				19 02				20 02			21 02		22 02	23 02	00 02
Liphook	d		17 55	18 09				19 09				20 09			21 09		22 09	23 09	00 09
Haslemere 4	a		18 01	18 15	18 31		19 01	19 15	19 31		20 01	20 15	20 31	21 01	21 15	21 31	22 15	23 15	00 15
	d	17 39	18 02	18 15	18 32	18 39	19 02	19 15	19 32	19 39	20 02	20 15	20 32	21 02	21 15	21 32	22 15	23 15	00 15
Witley	d	17 45				18 45				19 45		20 21			21 21		22 21	23 21	00 21
Milford (Surrey)	d	17 49				18 49				19 49		20 25			21 25		22 25	23 25	00 25
Godalming	d	17 53		18 25		18 53		19 25		19 53		20 29			21 29		22 29	23 29	00 29
Farncombe	d	17 56		18 28		18 56		19 28		19 56		20 32			21 32		22 32	23 32	00 32
Guildford	a	18 01	18 15	18 32	18 45	19 01	19 15	19 32	19 46	20 01	20 15	20 37	20 47	21 15	21 37	21 47	22 37	23 37	00 37
	d	18 02	18 17	18 32	18 47	19 02	19 17	19 32	19 47	20 02	20 17	20 39	20 49	21 17	21 39	21 49	22 39	23 39	
Worplesdon	d			18 40				19 40				20 44			21 44		22 44	23 44	
Woking	a	18 11	18 25	18 44	18 57	19 11	19 25	19 44	19 57	20 11	20 25	20 52	20 58	21 25	21 49	21 57	22 49	23 49	
	d	18 12	18 26	18 46	18 59	19 12	19 26	19 46	19 59	20 12	20 26	20 53	20 59	21 26	21 50	21 59	22 50	23 56	
Clapham Junction 10	a	18 31		19 05		19 31		20 05		20 31		21 12			22 09		23 09	00 22	
London Waterloo 15	⊖ a	18 40	18 51	19 13	19 23	19 40	19 51	20 13	20 23	20 40	20 50	21 21	21 27	21 50	22 18	22 24	23 18	00 31	

For general notes see front of timetable
For details of catering facilities see
Directory of Train Operators

A From 4 October
B Until 27 September

Table 156

Sundays

Portsmouth, Haslemere and Guildford → London

Network diagram - see first page of Table 155

Station		SW 1	SW 1	SW 1 A	SW 1 B	SW 1 A	SW 1 B	SW 1	SW 1 A	SW 1 B	SW 1	SW 1 ☕	SW 1
Portsmouth Harbour	d	22p17	23p17	06 43	06 48	07 29	07 32	07 48	08 29	08 32	08 48	09 32	09 48
Portsmouth & Southsea	d	22p24	23p24	06 48	06 53	07 34	07 37	07 53	08 34	08 37	08 53	09 37	09 53
Fratton	d	22p28	23p28	06 52	06 57	07 38	07 41	07 57	08 38	08 41	08 57	09 41	09 57
Hilsea	d	22p32	23p32										
Bedhampton	d	22p37	23p37	06 59	07 04			08 04			09 04		10 04
Havant	a	22p39	23p39	07 02	07 07	07 46	07 49	08 07	08 46	08 49	09 07	09 49	10 07
	d	22p40	23p40	07 02	07 07	07 47	07 50	08 07	08 47	08 50	09 07	09 50	10 07
Rowlands Castle	d	22p46	23p46	07 08	07 13			08 13			09 13		10 13
Petersfield	d	22p57	23p57	07 19	07 24	08 01	08 04	08 24	09 01	09 04	09 24	10 04	10 24
Liss	d	23p02	00 02	07 24	07 29			08 29			09 29		10 29
Liphook	d	23p09	00 09	07 31	07 36			08 36			09 36		10 36
Haslemere 4	a	23p15	00 15	07 36	07 41	08 13	08 16	08 41	09 13	09 16	09 41	10 16	10 41
	d	23p15	00 15	07 37	07 42	08 14	08 17	08 42	09 14	09 17	09 42	10 17	10 42
Witley	d	23p21	00 21	07 43	07 48			08 48			09 48		10 48
Milford (Surrey)	d	23p25	00 25	07 47	07 52			08 52			09 52		10 52
Godalming	d	23p29	00 29	07 51	07 56			08 56			09 56		10 56
Farncombe	d	23p32	00 32	07 54	07 59			08 59			09 59		10 59
Guildford	a	23p37	00 37	08 04	08 04	08 31	08 31	09 04	09 31	09 31	10 03	10 31	11 04
	d	23p39		08 05	08 05	08 35	08 35	09 05	09 35	09 35	10 05	10 35	11 05
Worplesdon	d	23p44											
Woking	a	23p49		08 13	08 13	08 42	08 42	09 15	09 42	09 42	10 15	10 42	11 14
	d	23p56		08 15	08 15	08 45	08 45	09 15	09 45	09 45	10 15	10 45	11 15
Clapham Junction 10	a	00 22		08 37	08 37	09 06	09 06	09 35	10 06	10 06	10 35	11 04	11 34
London Waterloo 15 ⊖	a	00 31		08 49	08 49	09 19	09 19	09 49	10 21	10 21	10 49	11 19	11 49

Station		SW 1 ☕	SW 1		SW 1 ☕	SW 1	SW 1	SW 1	SW 1	SW 1	SW 1	SW 1	SW 1	SW 1
Portsmouth Harbour	d	10 32	10 48	and at	18 32	18 48	19 32	19 48	20 32	20 48	21 32	21 48	22 32	22 48
Portsmouth & Southsea	d	10 37	10 53	the same	18 37	18 53	19 37	19 53	20 37	20 53	21 37	21 53	22 37	22 53
Fratton	d	10 41	10 57	minutes	18 41	18 57	19 41	19 57	20 41	20 57	21 41	21 57	22 41	22 57
Hilsea	d			past										
Bedhampton	d		11 04	each		19 04		20 04		21 04		22 04		23 04
Havant	a	10 49	11 06	hour until	18 49	19 07	19 49	20 07	20 49	21 07	21 49	22 07	22 49	23 07
	d	10 50	11 07		18 50	19 07	19 50	20 07	20 50	21 07	21 50	22 07	22 50	23 07
Rowlands Castle	d		11 13			19 13		20 13		21 13		22 13		23 13
Petersfield	d	11 04	11 24		19 04	19 24	20 04	20 24	21 04	21 24	22 04	22 24	23 04	23 24
Liss	d		11 29			19 29		20 29		21 29		22 29		23 29
Liphook	d		11 36			19 36		20 36		21 36		22 36		23 36
Haslemere 4	a	11 16	11 41		19 16	19 41	20 16	20 41	21 16	21 41	22 17	22 41	23 16	23 41
	d	11 17	11 42		19 17	19 42	20 17	20 42	21 17	21 42	22 17	22 42	23 17	23 42
Witley	d		11 48			19 48		20 48		21 48		22 48		23 48
Milford (Surrey)	d		11 52			19 52		20 52		21 52		22 52		23 52
Godalming	d		11 56			19 56		20 56		21 56		22 56		23 56
Farncombe	d		11 59			19 59		20 59		21 59		22 59		23 59
Guildford	a	11 31	12 04		19 31	20 04	20 31	21 04	21 31	22 04	22 31	23 04	23 31	00 04
	d	11 35	12 05		19 35	20 05	20 35	21 05	21 35	22 05	22 35	23 05	23 35	00 05
Worplesdon	d													
Woking	a	11 42	12 13		19 42	20 13	20 42	21 13	21 42	22 13	22 42	23 13	23 42	00 13
	d	11 45	12 15		19 45	20 15	20 45	21 15	21 45	22 15	22 45	23 15	23 45	
Clapham Junction 10	a	12 04	12 34		20 04	20 34	21 04	21 34	22 04	22 34	23 04	23 34	00 04	
London Waterloo 15 ⊖	a	12 19	12 47		20 14	20 44	21 14	21 44	22 14	22 44	23 14	23 44	00 14	

For general notes see front of timetable
For details of catering facilities see Directory of Train Operators

A From 28 September
B Until 21 September

Table 156A

Mondays to Fridays

Liphook → Liphook via Lindford, Bordon and Whitehill (circular service)

Bus Service

Station		SW	SW	SW	SW	SW	SW	SW	SW	SW	SW	SW	SW	SW	SW	SW	SW	SW	SW	SW	SW	SW
		MX	MX																			
London Waterloo 15	⊖ 156 d	22 45	23 45		05 00	06 15	06 45	07 45	08 45	09 45	10 45	11 45	12 45	13 45	15 15	16 15	16 45	17 45	18 45	19 45	20 45	21 45
Woking	156 d	23 13	00 13		05 51	06 43	07 13	08 14	09 13	10 13	11 13	12 13	13 13	14 13	15 43	16 43	17 13	17b56	19 14	20 13	21 13	22 13
Guildford	156 d	23 25	00 25		06 00	06 55	07 25	08 26	09 25	10 25	11 25	12 25	13 25	14 25	15 55	16 55	17 22	18 23	19 24	20 25	21 25	22 25
Portsmouth Harbour	156 d	23 17			05c19	06 42	06 55	07 29	09 17	10e15	11e15	12 15	13e15	14e15	15 45	16 45	17 17	18e15	19e15	20 17	21 17	22 17
Portsmouth & Southsea	156 d	23 24			05f24	06 47	07 00	08 24	09 24	10 24	11 24	12 24	13 24	14 24	15 50	16 50	17 24	18 24	19 24	20 24	21 24	22 24
Liphook	d	**00 15**	**01 01**		**06 35**	**07 35**	**08 25**	**09 15**	**10 15**	**11 15**	**12 15**	**13 15**	**14 15**	**15 15**	**16 40**	**17 40**	**18 40**	**19 15**	**20 15**	**21 15**	**22 15**	**23 15**
Lindford (Liphook Road)	d	**00 23**	**01 10**	**06 04**	**06 44**	**07 44**	**08 34**	**09 24**	**10 24**	**11 24**	**12 24**	**13 24**	**14 24**	**15 24**	**16 49**	**17 49**	**18 49**	**19 24**	**20 23**	**21 23**	**22 23**	**23 23**
Bordon Camp (Fire Station)	d	**00 26**	**01 14**	**06 08**	**06 48**	**07 48**	**08 38**	**09 28**	**10 28**	**11 28**	**12 28**	**13 28**	**14 28**	**15 28**	**16 53**	**17 53**	**18 53**	**19 28**	**20 26**	**21 26**	**22 26**	**23 26**
Whitehill, Prince of Wales	d	**00 34**	**01a23**	**06 17**	**06 57**	**07 57**	**08 47**	**09 37**	**10 37**	**11 37**	**12 37**	**13 37**	**14 37**	**15 37**	**17 02**	**18 02**	**19 02**	**19 37**	**20 32**	**21 32**	**22 32**	**23 32**
Liphook	a	**00 47**		**06 30**	**07 10**	**08 10**	**09 00**	**09 50**	**10 50**	**11 50**	**12 50**	**13 50**	**14 50**	**15 50**	**17 15**	**18 15**	**19 15**	**19 50**	**20 45**	**21 45**	**22 45**	**23 45**
Portsmouth & Southsea	156 a			07 46	08 07	09 20	09 53	10 43	11 43	12 43	13 43	14 43	15 43	16 43	18 20	19e29		20 44	21 47	22 47	23 47	00 38
Portsmouth Harbour	156 a				08 12	09 26	10e07	11e07	12e07	13e07	14 07	15e07	16e07	16 49	18 28	19e36		20 52	22e02	23e08	00e07	00e55
Guildford	156 a			07 05	07 43	09 02	09 32	10 32	11 32	12 32	13 32	14 32	15 32	16 32	17 59	19 32		20 37	21 37	22 37	23 37	00 37
Woking	156 a			07 15	07 54	09 11	09 44	10 44	11 44	12 44	13 44	14 44	15 44	16 44	18 11	19 45		20 52	21 49	22 49	23 49	
London Waterloo 15	⊖ 156 a			07 44	08 24	09 43	10 13	11 13	12 13	13 13	14 13	15 13	16 13	17 14	18 43	20 14		21 21	22 18	23 18	00 29	

Saturdays

Station		SW	SW	SW	SW	SW	SW	SW	SW	SW	SW	SW	SW	SW	SW	SW	SW	SW	SW	SW
London Waterloo 15	⊖ 156 d	22 45	23 45		06 45	07 45	08 45	09 45	10 45	11 45	12 45	13 45	14 45	15 45	16 45	17 45	18 45	19 45	20 45	21 45
Woking	156 d	23 13	00 13		07 13	08 13	09 13	10 13	11 13	12 13	13 13	14 13	15 13	16 13	17 13	18 13	19 13	20 13	21 13	22 13
Guildford	156 d	23 25	00 25		07 25	08 25	09 25	10 25	11 25	12 25	13 25	14 25	15 25	16 25	17 25	18 25	19 25	20 25	21 25	22 25
Portsmouth Harbour	156 d	23 17			06 18	08e15	09e15	10e15	11e15	12e15	13e15	14e15	15e15	16e15	17 16	18e15	19e15	20e15	21 17	22 17
Portsmouth & Southsea	156 d	23 24			07 24	08 24	09 24	10 24	11 24	12 24	13 24	14 24	15 24	16 24	17 24	18 24	19 24	20 24	21 24	22 24
Liphook	d	**00 15**	**01 01**		**08 15**	**09 15**	**10 15**	**11 15**	**12 15**	**13 15**	**14 15**	**15 15**	**16 15**	**17 15**	**18 15**	**19 15**	**20 15**	**21 15**	**22 15**	**23 15**
Lindford (Liphook Road)	d	**00 23**	**01 10**	**07 19**	**08 24**	**09 24**	**10 24**	**11 24**	**12 24**	**13 24**	**14 24**	**15 24**	**16 24**	**17 24**	**18 23**	**19 23**	**20 23**	**21 23**	**22 23**	**23 23**
Bordon Camp (Fire Station)	d	**00 26**	**01 14**	**07 23**	**08 28**	**09 28**	**10 28**	**11 28**	**12 28**	**13 28**	**14 28**	**15 28**	**16 28**	**17 28**	**18 26**	**19 26**	**20 26**	**21 26**	**22 26**	**23 26**
Whitehill, Prince of Wales	d	**00 32**	**01a23**	**07 32**	**08 37**	**09 37**	**10 37**	**11 37**	**12 37**	**13 37**	**14 37**	**15 37**	**16 37**	**17 37**	**18 32**	**19 32**	**20 32**	**21 32**	**22 32**	**23 32**
Liphook	a	**00 45**		**07 45**	**08 50**	**09 50**	**10 50**	**11 50**	**12 50**	**13 50**	**14 50**	**15 50**	**16 50**	**17 50**	**18 45**	**19 45**	**20 45**	**21 45**	**22 45**	**23 45**
Portsmouth & Southsea	156 a			08 32	09 43	10 43	11 43	12 43	13 43	14 43	15 43	16 43	17 43	18 43	19 43	20 48	21 43	22 48	23 47	00 38
Portsmouth Harbour	156 a			08 37	10e07	11e07	12e07	13e07	14e07	15e07	16e07	17e07	18e07	19e07	20e07	21e07	22e03	22 52	23 52	00e55
Guildford	156 a			08 32	09 32	10 32	11 32	12 32	13 32	14 32	15 32	16 32	17 32	18 15	19 32	20 37	21 37	22 37	23 37	00 37
Woking	156 a			08 44	09 44	10 44	11 44	12 44	13 44	14 44	15 44	16 44	17 44	18 25	19 44	20 52	21 49	22 49	23 49	
London Waterloo 15	⊖ 156 a			09 13	10 13	11 13	12 13	13 13	14 13	15 13	16 13	17 13	18 13	18 51	20 13	21 21	22 18	23 18	00 31	

Sundays

Station		SW	SW	SW	SW	SW	SW	SW	SW	SW	SW	SW	SW	SW	SW	SW	SW	SW	SW	SW
London Waterloo 15	⊖ 156 d	22 45	23 45			08 00	09 00	10 00	11 00	12 00	13 00	14 00	15 00	16 00	17 00	18 00	19 00	20 00	21 00	22 00
Woking	156 d	23 13	00 13		07 32	08 35	09 35	10 32	11 32	12 32	13 32	14 32	15 32	16 32	17 32	18 32	19 32	20 32	21 32	22 32
Guildford	156 d	23 25	00 25		07 46	08 46	09 46	10 46	11 46	12 46	13 46	14 46	15 46	16 46	17 46	18 46	19 46	20 46	21 46	22 46
Portsmouth Harbour	156 d	23 17			07 48	08 48	09 48	10 48	11 48	12 48	13 48	14 48		15 48	16 48	17 48	18 48	19 48	20 48	21 48
Portsmouth & Southsea	156 d	23 24			07 53	08 53	09 53	10 53	11 53	12 53	13 53	14 53		15 53	16 53	17 53	18 53	19 53	20 53	21 53
Liphook	d	**00 15**	**01 01**		**08 50**	**09 50**	**10 50**	**11 50**	**12 50**	**13 50**	**14 50**	**15 50**	**16 30**	**17 30**	**18 30**	**19 30**	**20 30**	**21 30**	**22 30**	**23 30**
Lindford (Liphook Road)	d	**00 23**	**01 10**	**07 59**	**08 59**	**09 59**	**10 59**	**11 59**	**12 59**	**13 59**	**14 59**	**15 59**	**16 39**	**17 39**	**18 39**	**19 39**	**20 39**	**21 39**	**22 39**	**23 39**
Bordon Camp (Fire Station)	d	**00 26**	**01 14**	**08 03**	**09 03**	**10 03**	**11 03**	**12 03**	**13 03**	**14 03**	**15 03**	**16 03**	**16 43**	**17 43**	**18 43**	**19 43**	**20 43**	**21 43**	**22 43**	**23 43**
Whitehill, Prince of Wales	d	**00 32**	**01a23**	**08 12**	**09 12**	**10 12**	**11 12**	**12 12**	**13 12**	**14 12**	**15 12**	**16 12**	**16 52**	**17 52**	**18 52**	**19 52**	**20 52**	**21 52**	**22 52**	**23a52**
Liphook	a	**00 45**		**08 25**	**09 25**	**10 25**	**11 25**	**12 25**	**13 25**	**14 25**	**15 25**	**16 25**	**17 05**	**18 05**	**19 05**	**20 05**	**21 05**	**22 05**	**23 05**	
Portsmouth & Southsea	156 a			09 59	10 59	11 59	12 59	13 59	14 59	15 59	16 59		17 59	18 59	19 59	20 59	21 59	22 59	23 59	
Portsmouth Harbour	156 a			10 04	11 04	12 04	13 04	14 04	15 04	16 04	17 05		18 04	19 04	20 04	21 04	22 04	23 04	00 04	
Guildford	156 a			09 04	10 03	11 04	12 04	13 04	14 04	15 04	16 04	17 04	18 04	19 04	20 04	21 04	22 04	23 04	00 04	
Woking	156 a			09 15	10 15	11 14	12 13	13 13	14 13	15 13	16 13	17 13	18 13	19 13	20 13	21 13	22 13	23 13	00 13	
London Waterloo 15	⊖ 156 a			09 49	10 49	11 49	12 47	13 44	14 44	15 44	16 44	17 44	18 44	19 44	20 44	21 44	22 44	23 44	01g02	

For general notes see front of timetable
For details of catering facilities see Directory of Train Operators

b Change at Guildford and Liphook
c From 29 September dep. 0514
e Change at Fratton.
f From 29 September dep. 0519
g Change at Liphook and Woking

Table 156B

Mondays to Fridays

Petersfield—Waterlooville

Bus Service

Miles			SW 🚌	SW 🚌	SW 🚌	SW 🚌	SW 🚌	SW 🚌	SW 🚌	SW 🚌	SW 🚌	SW 🚌	SW 🚌	SW 🚌	SW 🚌	SW 🚌	SW 🚌
	London Waterloo 15	⊖ 156 d	05 00	06 15	07 30	08 30	09 30	10 30	11 30	12 30	13 30	14 30	15 30	16 30	17 30	18 30	19 30
	Woking	156 d	05 51	06 43	07 55	08 55	09 55	10 55	11 55	12 55	13 55	14 55	15 55	16 55	17 56	18 58	19 55
	Guildford	156 d	06 00	06 55	08 04	09 04	10 04	11 04	12 04	13 04	14 04	15 04	16 04	17 04	18 08	19 08	20 04
	Haslemere	156 d	06 25	07 20	08 25	09 25	10 23	11 21	12 21	13 21	14 21	15 21	16 24	17 24	18 26	19 26	20 22
	Petersfield	156 a	06 41	07 36	08 36	09 36	10 34	11 32	12 32	13 32	14 32	15 32	16 35	17 35	18 37	19 37	20 33
	Petersfield	d	06 42	07 40	08 45	09 45	10 42	11 42	12 42	13 42	14 42	15 42	16 42	17 42	18 42	19 45	20 45
	Horndean Precinct	d	06 57	07 55	09 00	10 00	10 57	11 57	12 57	13 57	14 57	15 57	16 57	17 57	18 57	20 00	21 00
	Cowplain (Shops)	d	07 01	07 59	09 04	10 04	11 01	12 01	13 01	14 01	15 01	16 01	17 01	18 01	19 01	20 04	21 04
	Waterlooville (Precinct)	a	07 06	08 04	09 09	10 09	11 06	12 06	13 06	14 06	15 06	16 06	17 06	18 06	19 06	20 09	21 09

Saturdays

Network Diagram - see first page of Table 155

		SW 🚌	SW 🚌	SW 🚌	SW 🚌	SW 🚌	SW 🚌	SW 🚌	SW 🚌	SW 🚌	SW 🚌	SW 🚌	SW 🚌	SW 🚌	SW 🚌
London Waterloo 15	⊖ 156 d	05 20	07 30	08 30	09 30	10 30	11 30	12 30	13 30	14 30	15 30	16 30	17 30	18 30	19 30
Woking	156 d	06 13	07 55	08 55	09 55	10 55	11 55	12 55	13 55	14 55	15 55	16 55	17 55	18 55	19 55
Guildford	156 d	06 25	08 04	09 04	10 04	11 04	12 04	13 04	14 04	15 04	16 04	17 04	18 04	19 04	20 04
Haslemere	156 d	06 45	08 21	09 21	10 21	11 21	12 21	13 21	14 21	15 21	16 21	17 21	18 21	19 21	20 21
Petersfield	156 a	07 01	08 32	09 32	10 32	11 32	12 32	13 32	14 32	15 32	16 32	17 32	18 32	19 32	20 32
Petersfield	d	07 42	08 45	09 45	10 42	11 42	12 42	13 42	14 42	15 42	16 42	17 42	18 42	19 42	20 42
Horndean Precinct	d	07 57	09 00	10 00	10 57	11 57	12 57	13 57	14 57	15 57	16 57	17 57	18 57	19 57	20 57
Cowplain (Shops)	d	08 01	09 04	10 04	11 01	12 01	13 01	14 01	15 01	16 01	17 01	18 01	19 01	20 01	21 01
Waterlooville (Precinct)	a	08 06	09 09	10 09	11 06	12 06	13 06	14 06	15 06	16 06	17 06	18 06	19 06	20 06	21 06

Mondays to Fridays

		SW 🚌	SW 🚌	SW 🚌	SW 🚌	SW 🚌	SW 🚌	SW 🚌	SW 🚌	SW 🚌	SW 🚌	SW 🚌	SW 🚌	SW 🚌	SW 🚌	SW 🚌
Waterlooville (Precinct)	d	06 15	07 10	08 05	09 15	10 15	11 15	12 15	13 15	14 15	15 15	16 15	17 15	18 15	19 15	20 15
Cowplain (Shops)	d	06 20	07 15	08 10	09 20	10 20	11 20	12 20	13 20	14 20	15 20	16 20	17 20	18 20	19 20	20 20
Horndean Precinct	d	06 24	07 19	08 14	09 24	10 24	11 24	12 24	13 24	14 24	15 24	16 24	17 24	18 24	19 24	20 24
Petersfield	a	06 39	07 34	08 39	09 39	10 39	11 39	12 39	13 39	14 39	15 39	16 39	17 39	18 39	19 39	20 39
Petersfield	156 d	06 48	07 46	08 48	09 48	10 48	11 48	12 48	13 48	14 48	15 48	16 48	17 48	18 48	19 48	20 48
Haslemere	156 d	07 02	08 00	09 02	10 02	11 02	12 02	13 02	14 02	15 02	16 02	17 02	18 02	19 02	20 02	21 02
Guildford	156 d	07 17	08 15	09 17	10 17	11 17	12 17	13 17	14 17	15 17	16 17	17 17	18 17	19 21	20 17	21 17
Woking	156 d	07 26	08 27	09 28	10 26	11 26	12 26	13 26	14 26	15 26	16 26	17 26	.	19 30	20 26	21 26
London Waterloo 15	⊖ 156 a	07 54	08 55	09 55	10 51	11 51	12 51	13 51	14 51	15 51	16 51	17 52	18 59	19 59	20 50	21 50

Saturdays

		SW 🚌	SW 🚌	SW 🚌	SW 🚌	SW 🚌	SW 🚌	SW 🚌	SW 🚌	SW 🚌	SW 🚌	SW 🚌	SW 🚌	SW 🚌	SW 🚌
Waterlooville (Precinct)	d	07 15	08 15	09 15	10 15	11 15	12 15	13 15	14 15	15 15	16 15	17 15	18 15	19 15	20 15
Cowplain (Shops)	d	07 20	08 20	09 20	10 20	11 20	12 20	13 20	14 20	15 20	16 20	17 20	18 20	19 20	20 20
Horndean Precinct	d	07 24	08 24	09 24	10 24	11 24	12 24	13 24	14 24	15 24	16 24	17 24	18 24	19 24	20 24
Petersfield	a	07 39	08 39	09 39	10 39	11 39	12 39	13 39	14 39	15 39	16 39	17 39	18 39	19 39	20 39
Petersfield	156 d	07 48	08 48	09 48	10 48	11 48	12 48	13 48	14 48	15 48	16 48	17 43	18 48	19 48	20 48
Haslemere	156 d	08 02	09 02	10 02	11 02	12 02	13 02	14 02	15 02	16 02	17 02	18 02	19 02	20 02	21 02
Guildford	156 d	08 17	09 17	10 17	11 17	12 17	13 17	14 17	15 17	16 17	17 17	18 17	19 17	20 17	21 17
Woking	156 d	08 27	09 26	10 26	11 26	12 26	13 26	14 26	15 26	16 26	17 26	18 26	19 26	20 26	21 26
London Waterloo 15	⊖ 156 a	08 51	09 52	10 51	11 51	12 52	13 51	14 51	15 51	16 51	17 51	18 51	19 51	20 50	21 50

For general notes see front of timetable
For details of catering facilities see
Directory of Train Operators

No Sunday Service

Havant → Portsmouth Harbour

(Complete service)

Network Diagram - see first page of Table 155

		SW	SW	SW	SW	SW	SW	SW	SW		SW	SW	SW	SN	SN	SW	SN	SW		SN	SW	SW	SW	GW	SW	SW
		MO	MO	MO	MO	MO	MX	MX	MX		MX	MX														
		1	1	1	1	1	1	1	1		1	1	1	1	1	1	1	1		1	1	1	1		1	1
Havant	d	23p45	23p51		00 45	00 51	23p49		00 22		00 37	01 22	04 40	05 24	05 39	06 02	06 13			06 53		06 58				07 28
Bedhampton	d	23p47			00 47				00 25			01s24	04 43			06 05	06 15			06 56		07 01				07 31
Hilsea	d			23p59				00 04	00 30			01s30	04 48			06 10	06 20	06 33		07 01	07 05	07 07	07 13		07 35	07 37
Fratton	d	23p56	00 01	00 04	00 56	01 01	23p59	00 08	00 34		00 47	01s34	04 52	05 33	05 48	06 15	06 25	06 38		07 05	07 09	07 12	07 17	07 35	07 39	07 42
Portsmouth & Southsea	a	23p59	00 04	00 08	00 59	01 04	00 02	00 11	00 38		00 50	01 38	04 55	05 36	05 51	06 18	06 28	06 44		07 08	07 12	07 16	07 22	07 38	07 42	07 46
	d	00 01	00 05	00 09	01 00	01 05	00 03	00 13			00 51		04 56	05 36	05 51	06 19	06 28	06 45		07 09	07 13	07 17		07 39	07 43	
Portsmouth Harbour	a	00 04	00 09	00 13	01 04	01 09	00 07	00 16			00 55		04 59	05 40	05 55	06 22	06 32	06 49		07 12	07 17	07 20		07 45	07 48	

		SN	SN	SW		SW	SN	SW	GW	SN	SW	SW	SN		SW	SW	SN	SW	SW	SW	GW	SN		SW	SN	SW
		1	1	1		1	1	1	◇	1	1	1	1		1	1	1	1	1	1	◇	1		1	1	1
Havant	d	07 35	07 41	07 52			07 57			08 22	08 27		08 44		08 50		09 01	09 05	09 19			09 31		09 35	09 46	09 50
Bedhampton	d	07 37		07 55			08 00			08 24	08 30							09 08				09 34		09 38		
Hilsea	d	07 42		08 00		08 03	08 06	08 09		08 29	08 35	08 43				09 05		09 13		09 31		09 41		09 44		
Fratton	d	07 47	07 50	08 04		08 07	08 11	08 13	08 21	08 34	08 40	08 48	08 53		08 59	09 10	09 13	09 17	09 29	09 36	09 41	09 46		09 49	09 55	09 59
Portsmouth & Southsea	a	07 50	07 53	08 07		08 11	08 15	08 18	08 24	08 37	08 43	08 51	08 56		09 02	09 13	09 16	09 20	09 32	09 40	09 45	09 49		09 53	09 58	10 02
	d		07 53	08 09		08 13	08 16	08 20	08 25	08 37	08 45	08 52	08 57		09 04	09 14	09 17	09 22	09 34		09 45				09 58	10 04
Portsmouth Harbour	a		07 57	08 12		08 16	08 19	08 23	08 30	08 41	08 48	08 55	09 00		09 07	09 18	09 21	09 26	09 37		09 54				10 02	10 07

		SW	SN	SW	SW	SW	GW	SN		SN	SW	SW	SN	SW	SW	SW	GW		SN	SN	SW	SW	SN	SW	SW	SW
		1	1	1	1	1	◇	1		1	1	1	1	1	1	1	◇		1	1	1	1	1	1	1	1
Havant	d		10 04	10 15		10 27		10 33		10 46	10 50		11 04	11 15		11 27			11 33	11 46	11 50		12 04	12 15		12 27
Bedhampton	d					10 30		10 35								11 30			11 35							12 30
Hilsea	d	10 03			10 32	10 35		10 42				11 03			11 32	11 35			11 42			12 03			12 32	12 35
Fratton	d	10 08	10 13	10 24	10 37	10 40	10 41	10 46		10 55	10 59	11 08	11 13	11 24	11 37	11 40	11 41		11 46	11 55	11 59	12 08	12 13	12 24	12 37	12 40
Portsmouth & Southsea	a	10 12	10 16	10 27	10 41	10 43	10 45	10 49		10 58	11 02	11 12	11 16	11 27	11 40	11 43	11 45		11 49	11 58	12 02	12 12	12 16	12 27	12 40	12 43
	d	10 13	10 16	10 29			10 45			10 58	11 04	11 13	11 16	11 29			11 45			11 58	12 04	12 13	12 16	12 29		
Portsmouth Harbour	a	10 18	10 20	10 32			10 54			11 02	11 07	11 18	11 20	11 32			11 54			12 02	12 07	12 18	12 20	12 32		

		GW	SN		SN	SW	SW	SN	SW	SW	SW	GW		SN	SN	SW	SW	SN	SW	SW	SW		GW	SN	SN	SW
		◇	1		1	1	1	1	1	1	1	◇		1	1	1	1	1	1	1	1		◇	1	1	1
Havant	d		12 33		12 46	12 50		13 04	13 15		13 27			13 33	13 46	13 50		14 04	14 15		14 27			14 33	14 46	14 50
Bedhampton	d		12 35								13 30			13 35							14 30			14 35		
Hilsea	d		12 41				13 03			13 32	13 35			13 42			14 03			14 32	14 35			14 42		
Fratton	d	12 41	12 46		12 55	12 59	13 08	13 13	13 24	13 37	13 40	13 41		13 46	13 55	13 59	14 08	14 13	14 24	14 37	14 40		14 41	14 46	14 55	14 59
Portsmouth & Southsea	a	12 45	12 49		12 58	13 02	13 12	13 16	13 27	13 40	13 43	13 45		13 49	13 58	14 03	14 12	14 16	14 27	14 40	14 43		14 45	14 49	14 58	15 02
	d	12 45			12 58	13 04	13 13	13 16	13 29			13 45			13 58	14 04	14 13	14 16	14 29				14 46		14 58	15 04
Portsmouth Harbour	a	12 54			13 02	13 07	13 18	13 20	13 32			13 54			14 02	14 07	14 18	14 20	14 32				14 54		15 02	15 07

		SW	SN	SW	SW	SW	GW		SN	SN	SW	SW	SN	SN	SW	SW		SW	SN	GW	SN	SW	SN	SW	SN	SW
		1	1	1	1	1	◇		1	1	1	1	1	1	1	1		1	1	◇	1	1	1	1	1	1
Havant	d		15 04	15 15		15 27			15 32	15 46	15 50		16 02	16 06	16 15			16 27	16 32		16 46	16 50	17 00		17 08	17 04
Bedhampton	d					15 30			15 34				16 04					16 30	16 34				17 02			17 06
Hilsea	d	15 03			15 32	15 35			15 41			16 03				16 32		16 35	16 39				17 07	17 03		17 11
Fratton	d	15 08	15 13	15 24	15 37	15 40	15 41		15 46	15 55	15 59	16 08	16 12	16 16	16 24	16 37		16 35	16 45	16 47	16 55	16 59	17 12	17 08	17 19	17 16
Portsmouth & Southsea	a	15 12	15 16	15 28	15 40	15 43	15 45		15 49	15 58	16 02	16 12	16 15	16 19	16 27	16 40		16 43	16 49	16 51	16 58	17 02	17 15	17 18	17 22	17 22
	d	15 13	15 16	15 29			15 45			15 58	16 04	16 13	16 16	16 20	16 29	16 41		16 45		16 51	16 58	17 04	17 15	17 19		17 23
Portsmouth Harbour	a	15 18	15 20	15 32			15 54			16 02	16 07	16 18	16 20	16 25	16 32	16 44		16 49		16 59	17 02	17 07	17 19	17 25		17 27

		SW		SW	SW	SW	GW	SN	SW	SN	SW		SW	SN	SW	SW	SW	SW	SN	GW		SW	SW	SN	SW	SN
		1		1	1	1	◇	1	1	1	1		1	1	1	1	1	1	1	◇		1	1	1	1	1
Havant	d	17 16				17 27		17 32	17 49	17 53			18 04	18 13	18 19			18 30	18 34			18 51		19 00	19 04	19 11
Bedhampton	d					17 30		17 34		17 55			18 07					18 33	18 36					19 02	19 07	
Hilsea	d				17 32	17 35		17 41		18 00	18 03		18 12			18 32		18 38	18 41				19 05	19 07	19 12	
Fratton	d	17 25		17 27	17 37	17 40	17 41	17 46	17 59	18 05	18 08		18 17	18 22	18 29	18 37	18 40	18 43	18 46	18 47		19 00	19 09	19 13	19a16	19 20
Portsmouth & Southsea	a	17 28		17 31	17 40	17 43	17 45	17 49	18 02	18 08	18 11		18 20	18 25	18 32	18 40	18 43	18 46	18 49	18 51		19 03	19 12	19 16		19 23
	d	17 30					17 45		18 03	18 08	18 12		18 22	18 26	18 33		18 45			18 51		19 05	19 14	19 17		19 23
Portsmouth Harbour	a	17 35					17 54		18 09	18 14	18 20		18 28	18 31	18 39		18 51			18 59		19 10	19 20	19 21		19 27

		SW	SW	SW	GW	SN		SW	SW	SW	SN	SN	SW	SW	SW		GW	SW	SN	SW	SN	SW	SW	GW		SW
		1	1	1	◇	1		1	1	1	1	1	1	1	1		◇	1	1	1	1	1	1	◇		1
Havant	d	19 17				19 35		19 42	19 51		20 05	20 11	20 19		20 29			20 49	20 52		21 10	21 20				21 31
Bedhampton	d					19 37		19 45							20 32											21 34
Hilsea	d		19 28	19 32		19 43		19 50		20 08				20 32	20 37					20 59			21 32			21 40
Fratton	d	19 26	19 33	19 37	19 41	19 49		19a56	20 00	20 13	20 16	20 20	20 28	20 37	20 41		20 47	20 59	21 02	21 08	21 19	21 30	21 37	21 41		21 44
Portsmouth & Southsea	a	19 29	19 36	19 42	19 45	19 53			20 03	20 16	20 20	20 23	20 31	20 41	20 44		20 51	21 02	21 06	21 11	21 23	21 33	21 40	21 45		21 47
	d	19 31	19 38		19 45				20 05	20 17		20 23	20 33		20 46		20 51	21 03		21 13	21 23	21 34		21 46		
Portsmouth Harbour	a	19 36	19 43		19 54				20 10	20 23		20 27	20 36		20 52		20 59	21 07		21 21	21 27	21 38		21 52		

		SW	SN	SW	SW	SN	SW	SW	SW		SN	GW	SW	SW	SN	SW	SW	SW		GW	SW	SN	SW			
		1	1	1	1	1	1	1	1		1	◇	1	1	1	1	1	1		◇	1	1	1			
Havant	d	21 46	21 49		22 05	22 10	22 19		22 31		22 43		22 49	22 59	23 11	23 19					23 31	23 36	23 49			
Bedhampton	d				22a07				22 34					23a01							23 34					
Hilsea	d			22 06				22 32	22 39								23 24	23 32			23 39					
Fratton	d	21 55	21 59	22 10		22 19	22 29	22 37	22 44		22 53	22 55	22 59		23 20	23 29	23 33	23 37		23 41	23 44	23 50	23 59			
Portsmouth & Southsea	a	21 58	22 02	22 13		22 22	22 32	22 41	22 47		22 56	22 59	23 03		23 23	23 32	23 36	23 40		23 45	23 47	23 53	00 02			
	d	21 59	22 02	22 15		22 22	22 33				22 57	22 59	23 04		23 24	23 33	23 36			23 45			00 03			
Portsmouth Harbour	a	22 02	22 06	22 18		22 26	22 38				23 00	23 04	23 08		23 27	23 37	23 40			23 54			00 07			

For general notes see front of timetable
For details of catering facilities see
Directory of Train Operators

Table 157

Saturdays

Havant → Portsmouth Harbour
(Complete service)

Network Diagram - see first page of Table 155

		SW 1	SW 1	SW 1	SW 1	SW 1	SW 1	SN 1	SN 1	SN 1		SW 1	SW 1	SN 1	SN 1	SW 1	SN 1	SW 1	SW 1	SN 1		SN 1	SW 1	SN 1	SW 1	SW 1
Havant	d	23p49		00 22	00 37	01 22	04 40	05 34	05 49	05 57		06 01		06 33	06 46		07 04	07 19		07 33		07 46		08 04	08 17	
Bedhampton	d			00 25		01s24	04 43					06 04		06 35				07 22		07 35					08 20	
Hilsea	d		00 04	00 30		01s30	04 48					06 09	06 32	06 41		07 03		07 27	07 32	07 41			08 04		08 25	08 32
Fratton	d	23p59	00 08	00 34	00 47	01s34	04 52	05 43	05 58	06 06		06 14	06 37	06 46	06 55	07 07	07 13	07 31	07 37	07 46		07 55	08 08	08 14	08 29	08 37
Portsmouth & Southsea	a	00 02	00 11	00 38	00 50	01 38	04 55	05 46	06 01	06 09		06 17	06 40	06 49	06 58	07 10	07 17	07 34	07 40	07 49		07 58	08 11	08 18	08 32	08 40
	d	00 03	00 13		00 51		04 57		06 01	06 09		06 18			06 58	07 12	07 17	07 36				07 59	08 12	08 18	08 34	
Portsmouth Harbour	a	00 07	00 16		00 55		05 00		06 05	06 16		06 22			07 02	07 17	07 21	07 39				08 02	08 18	08 22	08 37	

		GW ◇	SN 1	SN 1	SW 1	SW 1	SN 1		SW 1	SW 1	SW 1	GW ◇	SN 1	SN 1	SW 1	SW 1	SN 1		SW 1	SW 1	SW 1	GW ◇	SN 1	SN 1	SW 1	SW 1
Havant	d		08 33	08 46	08 50		09 04		09 15		09 27		09 33	09 46	09 50		10 04		10 15		10 27		10 33	10 46	10 50	
Bedhampton	d		08 35								09 30		09 35								10 30		10 35			
Hilsea	d		08 41			09 03				09 32	09 35		09 41			10 03				10 32	10 35		10 41			11 03
Fratton	d	08 41	08 46	08 55	08 59	09 08	09 13		09 24	09 37	09 40	09 41	09 46	09 55	09 59	10 08	10 13		10 24	10 37	10 40	10 41	10 46	10 55	10 59	11 08
Portsmouth & Southsea	a	08 45	08 49	08 58	09 02	09 11	09 16		09 27	09 40	09 43	09 45	09 49	09 58	10 02	10 11	10 16		10 27	10 40	10 43	10 45	10 49	10 58	11 02	11 11
	d	08 45		08 59	09 04	09 12	09 16		09 29			09 45		09 58	10 04	10 12	10 16		10 29			10 45		10 58	11 04	11 12
Portsmouth Harbour	a	08 49		09 02	09 07	09 18	09 20		09 32			09 51		10 02	10 07	10 18	10 20		10 32			10 51		11 02	11 07	11 18

		SN 1	SW 1	SW 1		SW 1	GW ◇	SN 1	SN 1	SW 1	SW 1	SN 1	SW 1	SW 1		SW 1	GW ◇	SN 1	SN 1	SW 1	SW 1	SN 1	SW 1	SW 1		SW 1
Havant	d	11 04	11 15			11 27		11 33	11 46	11 50		12 04	12 15			12 27		12 33	12 46	12 50		13 04	13 15			13 27
Bedhampton	d					11 30		11 35								12 30		12 35								13 30
Hilsea	d			11 32		11 35		11 41			12 03			12 32		12 35		12 41			13 03			13 32		13 35
Fratton	d	11 13	11 24	11 37		11 40	11 41	11 46	11 55	11 59	12 08	12 13	12 24	12 37		12 40	12 41	12 46	12 55	12 59	13 08	13 13	13 24	13 37		13 40
Portsmouth & Southsea	a	11 16	11 27	11 40		11 43	11 45	11 49	11 58	12 02	12 11	12 16	12 27	12 40		12 43	12 45	12 49	12 58	13 02	13 11	13 16	13 27	13 40		13 43
	d	11 16	11 29				11 45		11 58	12 04	12 12	12 16	12 29				12 45		12 58	13 04	13 12	13 16	13 29			
Portsmouth Harbour	a	11 20	11 32				11 51		12 02	12 07	12 18	12 20	12 32				12 51		13 02	13 07	13 18	13 20	13 32			

		GW ◇	SN 1	SN 1	SW 1	SW 1	SN 1	SW 1	SW 1	SW 1		GW ◇	SN 1	SN 1 ◇	SW 1	SW 1	SN 1	SW 1	SW 1	SW 1		GW ◇	SN 1	SN 1	SW 1	SW 1
Havant	d		13 33	13 46	13 50		14 04	14 15		14 27			14 33	14 46	14 50		15 04	15 15		15 27			15 33	15 46	15 50	
Bedhampton	d		13 35							14 30			14 35							15 30			15 35			
Hilsea	d		13 41			14 03			14 32	14 35			14 41			15 03			15 32	15 35			15 41			16 03
Fratton	d	13 41	13 46	13 55	13 59	14 08	14 13	14 24	14 37	14 40		14 41	14 46	14 55	14 59	15 08	15 13	15 24	15 37	15 40		15 41	15 46	15 55	15 59	16 08
Portsmouth & Southsea	a	13 45	13 49	13 58	14 02	14 11	14 16	14 27	14 40	14 43		14 45	14 49	14 58	15 02	15 11	15 16	15 27	15 40	15 43		15 45	15 49	15 58	16 02	16 11
	d	13 45		13 58	14 04	14 12	14 16	14 29				14 45		14 58	15 04	15 12	15 16	15 29				15 45		15 58	16 04	16 12
Portsmouth Harbour	a	13 51		14 02	14 07	14 18	14 20	14 32				14 51		15 02	15 07	15 18	15 20	15 32				15 51		16 02	16 07	16 18

		SN 1	SW 1	SW 1	SW 1	GW ◇	SN 1		SN 1	SW 1	SW 1	SN 1	SW 1	SW 1	SW 1	GW ◇	SN 1		SN 1	SW 1	SW 1	SN 1	SW 1	SW 1	SW 1	GW ◇
Havant	d	16 04	16 15		16 27		16 33		16 46	16 50		17 04	17 15		17 27		17 33		17 46	17 50		18 04	18 15		18 27	
Bedhampton	d				16 30		16 35								17 30		17 35								18 30	
Hilsea	d			16 32	16 35		16 41				17 03			17 32	17 35		17 41				18 03			18 32	18 35	
Fratton	d	16 13	16 24	16 37	16 40	16 41	16 46		16 55	16 59	17 08	17 13	17 24	17 37	17 40	17 41	17 46		17 55	17 59	18 08	18 13	18 24	18 37	18 40	18 41
Portsmouth & Southsea	a	16 16	16 27	16 40	16 43	16 45	16 49		16 58	17 02	17 11	17 16	17 27	17 40	17 43	17 45	17 49		17 58	18 02	18 11	18 16	18 27	18 40	18 43	18 45
	d	16 16	16 29	16 41		16 45			16 58	17 04	17 12	17 16	17 29			17 45			17 58	18 04	18 12	18 16	18 29			18 45
Portsmouth Harbour	a	16 20	16 32	16 44		16 51			17 02	17 07	17 18	17 20	17 32			17 51			18 02	18 07	18 18	18 20	18 32			18 51

		SN 1	SN 1	SW 1		SW 1	SN 1	SW 1	SW 1	SW 1	GW ◇	SN 1	SN 1	SW 1		SW 1	SN 1	SW 1	SW 1	GW ◇	SW 1	SN 1	SW 1	SW 1		SN 1
Havant	d	18 33	18 46	18 50			19 04	19 15		19 27		19 33	19 46	19 50			20 10	20 15			20 30	20 46	20 50			21 10
Bedhampton	d	18 35								19 30		19 35									20 33					
Hilsea	d	18 41				19 03			19 32	19 35		19 41				20 03			20 32		20 38			21 03		
Fratton	d	18 46	18 55	18 59		19 08	19 13	19 24	19 37	19 40	19 41	19 46	19 55	19 59		20 08	20 19	20 24	20 37	20 41	20 43	20 55	20 59	21 08		21 19
Portsmouth & Southsea	a	18 49	18 58	19 02		19 11	19 16	19 27	19 40	19 43	19 45	19 49	19 58	20 02		20 11	20 22	20 27	20 40	20 44	20 48	20 58	21 02	21 11		21 22
	d		18 58	19 04		19 12	19 16	19 29			19 45		19 58	20 04		20 12	20 22	20 29		20 45		20 58	21 04	21 12		21 22
Portsmouth Harbour	a		19 02	19 07		19 18	19 20	19 32			19 51		20 02	20 07		20 18	20 26	20 32		20 51		21 02	21 07	21 18		21 26

		SW 1	SW 1	SW 1	GW ◇	SW 1	SN 1	SW 1	SN 1	SW 1		SW 1	GW ◇	SW 1	SN 1	SW 1	SW 1	SN 1	SW 1	SW 1	GW ◇	SW 1	SN 1	SW 1		
Havant	d	21 15		21 27		21 46	21 49		22 10	22 19				22 31	22 43	22 49		23 10	23 19			23 31	23 36	23 49		
Bedhampton	d			21 30										22 34								23 34				
Hilsea	d		21 32	21 35				22 03				22 32		22 39			23 03			23 32		23 39				
Fratton	d	21 24	21 37	21 40	21 41	21 55	21 59	22 08	22 19	22 29		22 37	22 41	22 44	22 52	22 59	23 08	23 19	23 29	23 37	23 41	23 44	23 48	23 59		
Portsmouth & Southsea	a	21 27	21 40	21 43	21 45	21 58	22 02	22 11	22 22	22 32		22 40	22 43	22 48	22 55	23 02	23 11	23 22	23 32	23 40	23 44	23 47	23 51	00 02		
	d	21 29			21 45	22 00	22 03	22 12	22 22	22 33		22 41	22 43	22 49	22 56	23 03	23 12	23 22	23 33		23 45	23 49		00 03		
Portsmouth Harbour	a	21 32			21 51	22 03	22 06	22 18	22 26	22 36		22 47	22 50	22 52	22 59	23 08	23 16	23 26	23 37		23 49	23 52		00 07		

Sundays

		SW 1	SW 1	SW 1	SW 1	SW 1	SN 1	SW 1	SW 1	SN 1	SW 1	SW 1	SN 1		SW 1	SN 1	SW 1	SW 1	SN 1	SW 1	SW 1	SN 1	SW 1	SN 1	SW 1	SW 1
Havant	d	23p49		00 22	00 37	01 22	07 10			08 10		08 45	08 49			09 10		09 45	09 49	09 52		10 17		10 41	10 45	10 53
Bedhampton	d			00 25		01s24						08 47	08 51					09 47	09 51					10 43	10 47	
Hilsea	d		00 03	00 30		01s30		07 26	08 00		08 26				09 00		09 26				10 00		10 26			
Fratton	d	23p59	00 07	00 34	00 47	01s34	07 19	07 30	08 05	08 19	08 30	08 56	08 59		09 05	09 19	09 30	09 56	09 59	10 01	10 05	10 26	10 30	10 51	10 56	11 02
Portsmouth & Southsea	a	00 02	00 11	00 38	00 50	01 38	07 22	07 33	08 08	08 22	08 33	08 59	09 03		09 08	09 22	09 33	09 59	10 03	10 05	10 10	10 29	10 33	10 54	10 59	11 05
	d	00 03	00 12		00 51		07 22		08 09	08 22		09 00	09 04		09 09	09 22		10 00	10 04	10 06	10 12	10 30		10 55	11 00	11 07
Portsmouth Harbour	a	00 07	00 16		00 55		07 26		08 13	08 26		09 04	09 07		09 13	09 26		10 04	10 07	10 11	10 15	10 35		10 58	11 04	11 11

For general notes see front of timetable
For details of catering facilities see
Directory of Train Operators

Table 157

Sundays

Havant → Portsmouth Harbour
(Complete service)

Network Diagram - see first page of Table 155

		SW	SN		SW	GW	SN	SW	SW	SW	SN	SW	GW	SN	SW	SW		SW	SN	SW	SN	SW	SW	SW	SN	SW
		1	1		1	◇	1	1	1	1	1	1	◇	1	1	1		1	1	1	1	1	1	1	1	1
Havant	d		11 17				11 41	11 45	11 51		12 17			12 41	12 45	12 51			13 17		13 41	13 45	13 51		14 17	
Bedhampton	d						11 43	11 47						12 43	12 47						13 43	13 47				
Hilsea	d	11 00			11 26					12 00		12 26						13 00		13 26				14 00		14 26
Fratton	d	11 05	11 26		11 30	11 41	11 52	11 56	12 01	12 04	12 26	12 30	12 44	12 51	12 56	13 01		13 04	13 26	13 30	13 51	13 56	14 01	14 04	14 26	14 30
Portsmouth & Southsea	a	11 08	11 29		11 33	11 44	11 55	11 59	12 05	12 08	12 29	12 33	12 47	12 54	12 59	13 04		13 08	13 29	13 33	13 54	13 59	14 04	14 08	14 29	14 33
	d	11 09	11 30			11 44	11 56	12 00	12 06	12 09	12 30		12 48	12 55	13 00	13 05		13 09	13 30		13 55	14 00	14 05	14 09	14 30	
Portsmouth Harbour	a	11 14	11 35			11 51	11 59	12 04	12 09	12 13	12 35		12 51	12 58	13 04	13 11		13 13	13 35		13 58	14 04	14 11	14 13	14 35	

		GW	SN	SW	SW	SW		SN	SW	SN	SW	SW	SW	SN	SW	GW	GW	SN	SW		SW	SW	SN	SW	GW	SN
		◇	1	1	1	1		1	1	1	1	1	1	1	1	◇	◇	1	1		1	1	1	1	◇	1
																A	B									
Havant	d		14 41	14 45	14 51			15 17		15 41	15 45	15 51		16 17				16 41	16 44		16 51		17 17			17 41
Bedhampton	d		14 43	14 47						15 43	15 47							16 43	16 47							17 43
Hilsea	d					15 00			15 26				16 00		16 26							17 00		17 26		
Fratton	d	14 38	14 51	14 56	15 01	15 04		15 26	15 30	15 51	15 56	16 01	16 04	16 26	16 30	16 41	16 42	16 51	16 56		17 01	17 05	17 26	17 30	17 44	17 51
Portsmouth & Southsea	a	14 41	14 54	14 59	15 04	15 08		15 29	15 33	15 54	15 59	16 04	16 08	16 29	16 33	16 45	16 45	16 54	16 59		17 04	17 08	17 29	17 33	17 47	17 54
	d	14 42	14 55	15 00	15 05	15 09		15 30		15 55	16 00	16 05	16 09	16 30		16 45	16 46	16 55	17 00		17 05	17 09	17 30		17 48	17 55
Portsmouth Harbour	a	14 46	14 58	15 04	15 11	15 13		15 35		15 58	16 04	16 11	16 13	16 35		16 51	16 51	16 58	17 05		17 11	17 13	17 35		17 51	17 58

		SW	SW	SW	SN	SW	GW	SN	SW		SW	SW	SN	SW	GW	SN	SW	SW	SW	SN	SW	SN		SW	SW	SW
		1	1	1	1	1	◇	1	1		1	1	1	1	◇	1	1	1	1	1	1	1		1	1	1
							A																			
Havant	d	17 45	17 51		18 17			18 41	18 44		18 51		19 17			19 41	19 45	19 51		20 17		20 41		20 45	20 51	
Bedhampton	d	17 47						18 43	18 47							19 43	19 47					20 43		20 47		
Hilsea	d			18 00		18 26						19 00		19 26					20 00		20 26					21 00
Fratton	d	17 56	18 01	18 04	18 26	18 30	18 44	18 51	18 56		19 01	19 05	19 26	19 30	19 44	19 51	19 56	20 01	20 04	20 26	20 30	20 51		20 56	21 01	21 04
Portsmouth & Southsea	a	17 59	18 04	18 08	18 29	18 33	18 47	18 54	18 59		19 03	19 08	19 29	19 33	19 47	19 54	19 59	20 04	20 08	20 29	20 33	20 54		20 59	21 04	21 08
	d	18 00	18 05	18 09	18 30		18 48	18 55	19 00		19 06	19 09	19 30		19 48	19 55	20 00	20 05	20 09	20 30		20 55		21 00	21 05	21 09
Portsmouth Harbour	a	18 04	18 11	18 13	18 35		18 51	18 58	19 04		19 11	19 13	19 35		19 51	19 58	20 04	20 11	20 13	20 35		20 58		21 04	21 09	21 13

		GW	SN	SW	GW	SN	SW	SW	SW	GW	SN	SW		GW	SN	SW	SW	SW	SW	SN	GW	SW	SW	SW		
		◇	1	1	◇	1	1	1	1	◇	1	1		◇	1	1	1	1	1	1	◇	1	1	1		
Havant	d		21 17			21 41	21 45	21 51			22 17				22 41	22 45	22 51			23 21		23 45	23 51			
Bedhampton	d					21 43	21 47								22 43	22 47						23 47				
Hilsea	d			21 26					22 00			22 26						23 00	23 24					23 59		
Fratton	d	21 10	21 26	21 30	21 36	21 51	21 56	22 01	22 04	22 08	22 26	22 30		22 36	22 51	22 56	23 01	23 04	23 29	23 31	23 37	23 56	00 01	00 04		
Portsmouth & Southsea	a	21 15	21 29	21 33	21 39	21 54	21 59	22 04	22 08	22 13	22 29	22 33		22 39	22 54	22 59	23 04	23 08	23 32	23 34	23 40	23 59	00 04	00 08		
	d	21 15	21 30		21 40	21 55	22 00	22 05	22 09	22 13	22 30			22 40	22 55	23 00	23 05	23 09		23 35	23 41	00 01	00 05	00 09		
Portsmouth Harbour	a	21 23	21 35		21 46	21 58	22 04	22 11	22 13	22 20	22 35			22 46	22 58	23 04	23 09	23 13		23 38	23 44	00 04	00 09	00 13		

For general notes see front of timetable
For details of catering facilities see
Directory of Train Operators

A From 14 September
B Until 7 September

Portsmouth Harbour → Havant

(Complete service)

Network Diagram - see first page of Table 155

		SW [1] A	SW [1] B	SW [1]	SW [1]	SW [1] A	SW [1] B	SN [1]	SW [1]	SN [1]	SW [1]	GW ◇	SN [1]	SW [1]	SW [1]	SW [1]	SW [1]	SW [1]	SN [1]		SW [1]	SN [1]	GW ◇	SW [1]	GW	SW [1]
Portsmouth Harbour	d	04 25	04 30	05 00		05 14	05 19	05 34	05 43	05 47	05 50	06 00	06 04	06 15		06 23		06 38			06 42	06 46	06 51	06 55	07 01	07 13
Portsmouth & Southsea	a	04 28	04 33	05 03		05 17	05 22	05 37	05 46	05 50	05 53	06 03	06 07	06 18		06 26		06 41			06 45	06 49	06 54	06 58	07 04	07 16
	d	04 30	04 35	05 05	05 16	05 19	05 24	05 38	05 48	05 51	05 55	06 04	06 08	06 20	06 23	06 28		06 43			06 47	06 50	06 55	07 00	07 05	07 18
Fratton	d	04 34	04 39	05 09	05 20	05 23	05 28	05 42	05 52	05 55	05 59	06a07	06 12	06 24	06 27	06 32		06 47			06 51	06 54	06a59	07 04	07 10	07 22
Hilsea	d	04 38	04 43	05a13	05a24	05 27	05 32	05 46	05a56	05 59	06 03				06a31	06a36	06 42	06a51				06 58		07 08		
Bedhampton	d	04 43	04 48			05 32	05 37	05 51		06 04	06 08						06 47		06 34			07 03		07 13		
Havant	a	04 45	04 50			05 34	05 40	05 53		06 06	06 10		06 20	06 33			06 49		06 37		06 59	07 05		07 15	07 19	07 30

		SN [1]	SW [1]	SW [1]	SW [1]	SW [1]	SW [1]	SN [1]	SW [1]	SN [1]	SW [1]	SW [1]	GW ◇	SN [1]	SW [1]		SW [1]	SW [1]	SN [1]	SN [1]	SW [1]	SW [1]	GW ◇	SN [1]	SW [1]	SW [1]
Portsmouth Harbour	d	07 20	07 24	07 29		07 45	07 52		08 05	08 10	08 15		08 22	08 26	08 32		08 45	08 51	08 59	09 12	09 15	09 17	09 22	09 28	09 32	09 45
Portsmouth & Southsea	a	07 23	07 27	07 32		07 48	07 55		08 08	08 13	08 18		08 26	08 29	08 35		08 48	08 54	09 02	09 15	09 18	09 22	09 26	09 31	09 35	09 48
	d	07 24	07 29	07 33	07 36	07 50	07 57	08 03	08 10	08 14	08 20	08 24	08 27	08 30	08 36		08 50	08 56	09 03	09 16	09 20	09 24	09 27	09 32	09 36	09 50
Fratton	d	07 28	07 33	07 37	07 40	07 54	08 01	08 07	08 14	08 18	08 24	08 28	08a31	08 35	08 40		08 54	09 01	09 07	09 20	09 24	09 28	09a31	09 36	09 40	09 54
Hilsea	d		07a37	07 41	07a44		08a05	08 11	08a18			08 32			08a44			09a05	09 11			09 32			09a44	
Bedhampton	d			07 49				08 16				08 37							09 16			09 37				
Havant	a	07 36		07 51		08 02		08 18		08 26	08 32	08 40		08 44			09 03		09 18	09 28	09 33	09 39		09 44		10 03

		SW [1]	SN [1]	SN [1]	SW [1]	SW [1]	GW ◇	SN [1]	SW [1]	SW [1]	SW [1]		SN [1]	SN [1]	SW [1]	SW [1]	GW ◇	SN [1]	SW [1]	SW [1]	SW [1]	SN [1]	SN [1]	SW [1]	SW [1]	GW ◇
Portsmouth Harbour	d	09 54		10 12	10 15		10 22	10 28	10 31	10 45	10 54			11 12	11 15		11 22	11 28		11 45	11 54		12 12	12 15		12 22
Portsmouth & Southsea	a	09 57		10 15	10 18		10 26	10 31	10 34	10 48	10 57			11 15	11 18		11 26	11 31		11 48	11 57		12 15	12 18		12 26
	d	09 59	10 03	10 16	10 20	10 24	10 27	10 32	10 36	10 50	10 59		11 03	11 16	11 20	11 24	11 27	11 32	11 36	11 50	11 59	12 03	12 16	12 20	12 24	12 27
Fratton	d	10 03	10 07	10 20	10 24	10 28	10a31	10 36	10 40	10 54	11 03		11 07	11 20	11 24	11 28	11a31	11 36	11 40	11 54	12 03	12 07	12 20	12 24	12 28	12a31
Hilsea	d	10a07	10 11			10 32			10a44		11a07		11 11			11 32			11a44		12a07	12 11			12 32	
Bedhampton	d		10 16			10 37							11 16			11 37						12 16			12 37	
Havant	a		10 18	10 28	10 33	10 39		10 44		11 03			11 18	11 29	11 33	11 39		11 44		12 03		12 19	12 29	12 33	12 39	

		SN [1]	SW [1]	SW [1]	SW [1]	SN [1]	SN [1]		SW [1]	SW [1]	GW ◇	SN [1]	SW [1]	SW [1]	SW [1]	SN [1]	SN [1]	SW [1]	SW [1]	GW ◇	SN [1]	SW [1]	SW [1]	SW [1]	SN [1]	SN [1]
Portsmouth Harbour	d	12 28		12 45	12 54		13 12		13 15		13 22	13 28		13 45	13 54		14 12	14 15		14 22	14 28		14 45	14 54		15 12
Portsmouth & Southsea	a	12 31		12 48	12 57		13 15		13 18		13 26	13 31		13 48	13 57		14 15	14 18		14 26	14 31		14 48	14 57		15 15
	d	12 32	12 36	12 50	12 59	13 03	13 16		13 20	13 24	13 27	13 32	13 36	13 50	13 59	14 03	14 16	14 20	14 24	14 27	14 32	14 36	14 50	14 59	15 03	15 16
Fratton	d	12 36	12 40	12 54	13 03	13 07	13 20		13 24	13 28	13a31	13 36	13 40	13 54	14 03	14 07	14 20	14 24	14 28	14a31	14 36	14 40	14 54	15 03	15 07	15 20
Hilsea	d		12a44		13a07	13 11				13 32			13a44		14a07	14 11			14 32			14a44		15a07	15 11	
Bedhampton	d					13 16				13 37						14 16			14 37						15 16	
Havant	a	12 44		13 03		13 18	13 29		13 33	13 39		13 44		14 03		14 18	14 29	14 33	14 39		14 44		15 03		15 18	15 29

		SW [1]	SW [1]		GW ◇	SN [1]	SW [1]	SW [1]	SW [1]	SN [1]	SN [1]	SW [1]	SW [1]	GW ◇	SN [1]	SW [1]	SN [1]	SW [1]	SW [1]	SN [1]	SW [1]	SN [1]		SW [1]	SW [1]	GW ◇
Portsmouth Harbour	d	15 15			15 22	15 28		15 45	15 54		16 12	16 15		16 22	16 28		16 40	16 45	16 54		17 03	17 12		17 15	17 17	17 22
Portsmouth & Southsea	a	15 18			15 26	15 31		15 48	15 57		16 15	16 18		16 26	16 31		16 44	16 47	16 57		17 06	17 15		17 18	17 22	17 26
	d	15 20	15 24		15 27	15 32	15 36	15 50	15 59	16 03	16 16	16 20	16 24	16 27	16 32	16 36	16 46	16 50	16 59	17 03	17 07	17 16		17 20	17 24	17 27
Fratton	d	15 24	15 28		15a31	15 36	15 40	15 54	16 03	16 07	16 20	16 24	16 28	16a31	16 36	16 40	16 50	16 54	17 03	17 07	17 11	17 20		17 24	17 28	17a31
Hilsea	d		15 32				15a44		16a07	16 11			16 32			16a44	16 54		17a07	17 11	17a15				17 32	
Bedhampton	d		15 37							16 16			16 37							17 16					17 37	
Havant	a	15 33	15 40			15 44		16 03		16 18	16 29	16 33	16 39		16 44		16 59	17 03		17 18		17 30		17 33	17 39	

		SN [1]	SW [1]	SN [1]	SW [1]	SW [1]	SN [1]	SW [1]	SW [1]	GW ◇	SN [1]	SW [1]	SN [1]	SW [1]	SW [1]	SN [1]	SW [1]	SW [1]		GW ◇	SN [1]	SW [1]	SN [1]	SW [1]	SW [1]	SN [1]
Portsmouth Harbour	d	17 28			17 45	17 54		18 15		18 22	18 28		18 36	18 45	18 54		19 15			19 22	19 28		19 40	19 45	19 54	
Portsmouth & Southsea	a	17 31			17 48	17 57		18 18		18 26	18 31		18 39	18 48	18 57		19 18			19 26	19 31		19 43	19 48	19 57	
	d	17 32	17 36	17 46	17 50	17 59	18 03	18 20	18 24	18 27	18 32	18 36	18 41	18 50	18 59	19 03	19 20	19 24		19 27	19 32	19 36	19 44	19 50	19 59	20 03
Fratton	d	17 36	17 40	17 50	17 54	18 03	18 07	18 24	18 28	18a31	18 36	18 40	18 45	18 54	19 03	19 07	19 24	19 28		19a31	19 36	19 40	19 48	19 54	20 03	20 07
Hilsea	d		17a44	17 54		18a07	18 11		18 32			18a44	18 49		19a07	19 11		19 32				19a44			20a07	20 11
Bedhampton	d						18 16		18 37							19 16		19 37								20 16
Havant	a	17 44		17 59	18 03		18 18	18 33	18 39		18 44		18 54	19 03		19 18	19 33	19 39			19 44		19 56	20 03		20 18

		SW [1]	SW [1]	GW ◇	SN [1]	SW [1]	SN [1]	SW [1]	SW [1]	SN [1]	SW [1]	GW	SW [1]	SW [1]	SN [1]	SW [1]	SN [1]	SW [1]	SW [1]	SW [1]	SN [1]	SN [1]	SW [1]	SW [1]		
Portsmouth Harbour	d	20 15	20 17	20 22			20 40	20 45	20 54		21 17	21 22	21 28		21 40	21 54	22 15	22 17	22 28		22 44	23 15	23 17	23 24		
Portsmouth & Southsea	a	20 18	20 22	20 26			20 43	20 48	20 57		21 20	21 26	21 31		21 43	21 57	22 18	22 22	22 31		22 47	23 18	23 22	23 27		
	d	20 20	20 24	20 27	20 32	20 36	20 44	20 50	20 59	21 15	21 24	21 27	21 33	21 36	21 44	21 59	22 19	22 24	22 33	22 36	22 48	23 19	23 24	23 29		
Fratton	d	20 24	20 28	20a31	20 36	20 40	20 48	20 54	21 03	21 19	21 28	21a31	21 37	21 40	21 48	22 03	22 23	22 28	22 37	22 40	22 52	23 23	23 28	23 33		
Hilsea	d		20 32			20a44			21a07	21 23	21 32		21 41	21a44	21 52	22a07	22 27	22 32	22 41	22a44	22 56	23 27	23 32	23a37		
Bedhampton	d		20 37							21 28	21 37		21 47		21 57		22 32	22 37	22 46		23 01	23 33	23 37			
Havant	a	20 33	20 39		20 44		20 56	21 03		21 30	21 39		21 49		21 59		22 34	22 39	22 53		23 05	23 36	23 39			

For general notes see front of timetable
For details of catering facilities see Directory of Train Operators

A From 29 September
B Until 26 September

Table 157

Saturdays

Portsmouth Harbour → Havant

(Complete service)

Network Diagram - see first page of Table 155

		SW 1 A	SW 1 B	SN 1	SW 1	SW 1 A	SW 1 B	SN 1	SW 1		GW ◇	SN 1	SW 1	SN 1	SW 1	SW 1	GW	SW 1		SN 1	GW ◇	SN 1	SW 1	SW 1	SN 1	SW 1
Portsmouth Harbour	d	04 38	04 43			05 13	05 18		05 54		06 00	06 12	06 18	06 28		06 45	06 48	06 54			07 04	07 12	07 15		07 28	
Portsmouth & Southsea	a	04 41	04 46			05 17	05 22		05 57		06 03	06 15	06 22	06 31		06 48	06 52	06 57			07 07	07 15	07 18		07 31	
	d	04 43	04 48	04 56	05 16	05 19	05 24	05 56	05 59		06 04	06 16	06 24	06 32	06 36	06 50	06 53	06 59		07 03	07 08	07 16	07 20	07 24	07 32	07 36
Fratton	d	04 47	04 52	05 00	05 20	05 23	05 28	06 00	06 03		06a07	06 20	06 28	06 36	06 40	06 54	06 57	07 03		07 07	07a12	07 20	07 24	07 28	07 36	07 40
Hilsea	d	04 51	04 56		05a24	05 27	05 32	06 04	06a07				06 32		06a44			07a07		07 11				07 32		07a44
Bedhampton	d	04 56	05 01			05 32	05 37	06 09					06 37							07 16				07 37		
Havant	a	04 58	05 03	05 08		05 34	05 39	06 13				06 29	06 39	06 44		07 03	07 09			07 18		07 29	07 33	07 39	07 44	

		SW 1	SW 1	SN 1		SN 1	SW 1	SW 1	GW ◇	SN 1	SW 1	SW 1	SW 1		SN 1	SN 1	SW 1	SW 1	GW ◇	SN 1	SW 1	SW 1		SW 1	SN 1	SN 1
Portsmouth Harbour	d	07 45	07 54			08 12	08 15		08 22	08 28		08 45	08 54			09 12	09 15		09 22	09 28		09 45		09 54		10 12
Portsmouth & Southsea	a	07 48	07 57			08 15	08 18		08 25	08 31		08 48	08 57			09 15	09 18		09 25	09 31		09 48		09 57		10 15
	d	07 50	07 59	08 03		08 16	08 20	08 24	08 27	08 32	08 36	08 50	08 59		09 03	09 16	09 20	09 24	09 27	09 32	09 36	09 50		09 59	10 03	10 16
Fratton	d	07 54	08 03	08 07		08 20	08 24	08 28	08a30	08 36	08 40	08 54	09 03		09 07	09 20	09 24	09 28	09a30	09 36	09 40	09 54		10 03	10 07	10 20
Hilsea	d		08a07	08 11				08 32			08a44		09a07		09 11			09 32			09a44			10a07	10 11	
Bedhampton	d			08 16				08 37							09 16			09 37							10 16	
Havant	a	08 03		08 19		08 29	08 33	08 39		08 44		09 03			09 18	09 29	09 33	09 39		09 44		10 03			10 18	10 28

		SW 1	SW 1	GW ◇	SN 1	SW 1	SW 1	SW 1		SN 1	SN 1	SW 1	SW 1	GW ◇	SN 1	SW 1	SW 1		SW 1	SN 1	SN 1	SW 1	SW 1	GW ◇	SN 1	SW 1
Portsmouth Harbour	d	10 15		10 22	10 28		10 45	10 54			11 12	11 15		11 22	11 28		11 45		11 54		12 12	12 15		12 22	12 28	
Portsmouth & Southsea	a	10 18		10 25	10 31		10 48	10 57			11 15	11 18		11 25	11 31		11 48		11 57		12 15	12 18		12 25	12 31	
	d	10 20	10 24	10 27	10 32	10 36	10 50	10 59		11 03	11 16	11 20	11 24	11 27	11 32	11 36	11 50		11 59	12 03	12 16	12 20	12 24	12 27	12 32	12 36
Fratton	d	10 24	10 28	10a30	10 36	10 40	10 54	11 03		11 07	11 20	11 24	11 28	11a30	11 36	11 40	11 54		12 03	12 07	12 20	12 24	12 28	12a30	12 36	12 40
Hilsea	d		10 32			10a44		11a07		11 11			11 32			11a44			12a07	12 11			12 32			12a44
Bedhampton	d		10 37							11 16			11 37							12 16			12 37			
Havant	a	10 33	10 39		10 44		11 03			11 18	11 29	11 33	11 39		11 44		12 03			12 18	12 29	12 33	12 39		12 44	

		SW 1	SW 1		SN 1	SN 1	SW 1	SW 1	GW ◇	SN 1	SW 1	SW 1		SW 1	SN 1	SN 1	SW 1	SW 1	GW ◇	SN 1	SW 1		SW 1	SW 1	SN 1	SN 1
Portsmouth Harbour	d	12 45	12 54			13 12	13 15		13 22	13 28		13 45		13 54		14 12	14 15		14 22	14 28			14 45	14 54		15 12
Portsmouth & Southsea	a	12 48	12 57			13 15	13 18		13 25	13 31		13 48		13 57		14 15	14 18		14 25	14 31			14 48	14 57		15 15
	d	12 50	12 59		13 03	13 16	13 20	13 24	13 27	13 32	13 36	13 50		13 59	14 03	14 16	14 20	14 24	14 27	14 32	14 36		14 50	14 59	15 03	15 16
Fratton	d	12 54	13 03		13 07	13 20	13 24	13 28	13a30	13 36	13 40	13 54		14 03	14 07	14 20	14 24	14 28	14a30	14 36	14 40		14 54	15 03	15 07	15 20
Hilsea	d		13a07		13 11			13 32			13a44			14a07	14 11			14 32			14a44			15a07	15 11	
Bedhampton	d				13 16			13 37							14 16			14 37							15 16	
Havant	a	13 03			13 18	13 29	13 33	13 39		13 44		14 03			14 18	14 29	14 33	14 39		14 44			15 03		15 18	15 29

		SW 1	SW 1	GW ◇	SN 1	SW 1	SW 1		SW 1	SN 1	SN 1	SW 1	SW 1	GW ◇	SN 1	SW 1		SW 1	SW 1	SN 1	SW 1	SW 1	SN 1	SW 1	GW ◇	SN 1
Portsmouth Harbour	d	15 15		15 22	15 28		15 45		15 54		16 12	16 15		16 22	16 28			16 45	16 54		17 01		17 12	17 16	17 22	17 28
Portsmouth & Southsea	a	15 18		15 25	15 31		15 48		15 57		16 15	16 18		16 25	16 31			16 48	16 57		17 04		17 15	17 22	17 26	17 31
	d	15 20	15 24	15 27	15 32	15 36	15 50		15 59	16 03	16 16	16 20	16 24	16 27	16 32	16 36		16 50	16 59	17 03	17 06	17 10	17 16	17 24	17 27	17 32
Fratton	d	15 24	15 28	15a30	15 36	15 40	15 54		16 03	16 07	16 20	16 24	16 28	16a31	16 36	16 40		16 54	17 03	17 07	17 10	17 14	17 20	17 28	17a31	17 36
Hilsea	d		15 32			15a44			16a07	16 11			16 32			16a44			17a07	17 11	17a14	17 18		17 32		
Bedhampton	d		15 37							16 16			16 37							17 16		17 23		17 37		
Havant	a	15 33	15 39		15 44		16 03			16 18	16 29	16 33	16 39		16 44			17 03		17 18		17 25	17 29	17 39		17 44

		SW 1		SW 1	SW 1	SN 1	SN 1	SW 1	SW 1	GW ◇	SN 1		SW 1	SW 1	SW 1	SN 1	SN 1	SW 1	SW 1	GW ◇		SN 1	SW 1	SW 1	SW 1	SN 1
Portsmouth Harbour	d	17 32		17 45	17 54		18 12	18 15		18 22	18 28			18 45	18 54		19 12	19 15		19 22		19 28		19 45	19 54	
Portsmouth & Southsea	a	17 35		17 48	17 57		18 15	18 18		18 26	18 31			18 48	18 57		19 15	19 18		19 25		19 31		19 48	19 57	
	d	17 36		17 50	17 59	18 03	18 16	18 20	18 24	18 27	18 32		18 36	18 50	18 59	19 03	19 16	19 20	19 24	19 27		19 32	19 36	19 50	19 59	20 03
Fratton	d	17 40		17 54	18 03	18 07	18 20	18 24	18 28	18a31	18 36		18 40	18 54	19 03	19 07	19 20	19 24	19 28	19a30		19 36	19 40	19 54	20 03	20 07
Hilsea	d	17a44			18a07	18 11			18 32				18a44		19a07	19 11			19 32				19a44		20a07	20 11
Bedhampton	d					18 16			18 37							19 16			19 37							20 16
Havant	a			18 03		18 18	18 28	18 33	18 39		18 44			19 03		19 18	19 28	19 33	19 39			19 44		20 03		20 18

		SW 1	SW 1	GW ◇	SN 1	SW 1		SN 1	SW 1	SW 1	SN 1	SW 1	SW 1	SN 1	SW 1		SN 1	SW 1	SW 1	SN 1	SN 1	SW 1	SW 1			
Portsmouth Harbour	d	20 15		20 22	20 28			20 40	20 45	20 54	21 11	21 17		21 40	21 54		22 15	22 17		22 44	23 15	23 17	23 24			
Portsmouth & Southsea	a	20 18		20 25	20 31			20 43	20 48	20 57	21 14	21 20		21 43	21 57		22 18	22 22		22 47	23 18	23 22	23 28			
	d	20 20	20 24	20 27	20 32	20 36		20 44	20 50	20 59	21 15	21 24	21 36	21 44	21 59		22 19	22 24	22 36	22 48	23 19	23 24	23 29			
Fratton	d	20 24	20 28	20a30	20 36	20 40		20 48	20 54	21 03	21 19	21 28	21 40	21 48	22 03		22 23	22 28	22 40	22 52	23 23	23 28	23 33			
Hilsea	d		20 32			20a44				21a07	21 23	21 32	21a44	21 52	22a07		22 27	22 32	22a44	22 56	23 27	23 32	23a37			
Bedhampton	d		20 37								21 28	21 37		21 57			22 32	22 37		23 01	23 33	23 37				
Havant	a	20 33	20 39		20 44			20 56	21 03		21 30	21 39		21 59			22 34	22 39		23 03	23 36	23 39				

For general notes see front of timetable
For details of catering facilities see Directory of Train Operators

A From 4 October
B Until 27 September

Table 157 | **Sundays**

Portsmouth Harbour → Havant
(Complete service)

Network Diagram - see first page of Table 155

		SW 1	SW 1 A	SW 1 B	GW 1	SN 1	SW 1	SW 1 A	SW 1 B	SW 1	SN 1		SW 1	SN 1	SW 1	SW 1 A	SW 1 B	SW 1	SN 1	SW 1	GW ◇	SN 1		SW 1	SW 1	SW 1
Portsmouth Harbour	d	06 37	06 43	06 48	07 08	07 14	07 17	07 29	07 32		07 43		07 48	08 14	08 17	08 29	08 32		08 43	08 48	09 08	09 14		09 17	09 32	
Portsmouth & Southsea	a	06 40	06 46	06 51	07 11	07 17	07 20	07 32	07 35		07 46		07 51	08 17	08 20	08 32	08 35		08 46	08 51	09 11	09 17		09 20	09 35	
	d	06 42	06 48	06 53	07 12	07 18	07 22	07 34	07 37	07 42	07 47		07 53	08 18	08 22	08 34	08 37	08 42	08 47	08 53	09 12	09 18		09 22	09 37	09 42
Fratton	d	06 46	06 52	06 57	07a15	07 22	07 26	07 38	07 41	07 46	07 51		07 57	08 22	08 26	08 38	08 41	08 46	08 51	08 57	09a15	09 22		09 26	09 41	09 46
Hilsea	d	06a50					07a30			07a50					08a30			08a50						09a30		09a50
Bedhampton	d		06 59	07 04		07 30							08 04	08 30						09 04		09 30				
Havant	a		07 02	07 07		07 32		07 46	07 49		07 59		08 07	08 32		08 46	08 49		08 59	09 07		09 32			09 49	

		SN 1	SW 1	SN 1	SW 1	SW 1	SW 1	SN 1	SW 1	GW ◇		SN 1	SW 1	SW 1	SW 1	SN 1	SW 1	SN 1	SW 1	SW 1	SW 1		SN 1	SW 1	GW ◇	SN 1
Portsmouth Harbour	d	09 43	09 48	10 14	10 17	10 32		10 43	10 48	11 08		11 14	11 17	11 32		11 43	11 48	12 14	12 17	12 32			12 43	12 48	13 08	13 14
Portsmouth & Southsea	a	09 46	09 51	10 17	10 20	10 35		10 46	10 51	11 11		11 17	11 20	11 35		11 46	11 51	12 17	12 20	12 35			12 46	12 51	13 11	13 17
	d	09 47	09 53	10 18	10 22	10 37	10 42	10 47	10 53	11 12		11 18	11 22	11 37	11 42	11 47	11 53	12 18	12 22	12 37	12 42		12 47	12 53	13 12	13 18
Fratton	d	09 51	09 57	10 22	10 26	10 41	10 46	10 51	10 57	11a15		11 22	11 26	11 41	11 46	11 51	11 57	12 22	12 26	12 41	12 46		12 51	12 57	13a15	13 22
Hilsea	d				10a30		10a50						11a30		11a50				12a30		12a50					
Bedhampton	d		10 04	10 30					11 04			11 30					12 04	12 30						13 04		13 30
Havant	a	09 59	10 07	10 32		10 49		10 59	11 06			11 32		11 49		11 59	12 07	12 32		12 49			12 59	13 07		13 32

		SW 1	SW 1	SW 1	SN 1	SW 1	GW ◇	SN 1	SW 1		SW 1	SW 1	SN 1	SW 1	GW ◇	SN 1	SW 1	SW 1	SW 1	SN 1		SW 1	GW ◇	SN 1	SW 1	SW 1
Portsmouth Harbour	d	13 17	13 32		13 43	13 48	14 08	14 14	14 17		14 32		14 43	14 48	15 08	15 14	15 17	15 32		15 43		15 48	16 08	16 14	16 17	16 32
Portsmouth & Southsea	a	13 20	13 35		13 46	13 51	14 11	14 17	14 20		14 35		14 46	14 51	15 11	15 17	15 20	15 35		15 46		15 51	16 11	16 17	16 20	16 35
	d	13 22	13 37	13 42	13 47	13 53	14 12	14 18	14 22		14 37	14 42	14 47	14 53	15 12	15 18	15 22	15 37	15 42	15 47		15 53	16 12	16 18	16 22	16 37
Fratton	d	13 26	13 41	13 46	13 51	13 57	14a15	14 22	14 26		14 41	14 46	14 51	14 57	15a15	15 22	15 26	15 41	15 46	15 51		15 57	16a15	16 22	16 26	16 41
Hilsea	d	13a30		13a50					14a30			14a50					15a30		15a50						16a30	
Bedhampton	d					14 04		14 30						15 04		15 30						16 04		16 30		
Havant	a		13 49		13 59	14 07		14 32			14 49		14 59	15 07		15 32		15 49		15 59		16 07		16 32		16 49

		SW 1	SN 1	SW 1	GW ◇	SN 1	SW 1	SW 1		SW 1	SN 1	SW 1	GW ◇	SN 1	SW 1	SW 1	SW 1	SN 1	SW 1		GW ◇	SN 1	SW 1	SW 1	SW 1	SN 1
Portsmouth Harbour	d		16 43	16 48	17 08	17 14	17 17	17 32			17 43	17 48	18 08	18 14	18 17	18 32		18 43	18 48		19 08	19 14	19 17	19 32		19 43
Portsmouth & Southsea	a		16 46	16 51	17 11	17 17	17 20	17 35			17 46	17 51	18 11	18 17	18 20	18 35		18 46	18 51		19 11	19 17	19 20	19 35		19 46
	d	16 42	16 47	16 53	17 12	17 18	17 22	17 37		17 42	17 47	17 53	18 12	18 18	18 22	18 37	18 42	18 47	18 53		19 12	19 18	19 22	19 37	19 42	19 47
Fratton	d	16 46	16 51	16 57	17a15	17 22	17 26	17 41		17 46	17 51	17 57	18a15	18 22	18 26	18 41	18 46	18 51	18 57		19a15	19 22	19 26	19 41	19 46	19 51
Hilsea	d	16a50					17a30			17a50					18a30		18a50						19a30		19a50	
Bedhampton	d			17 04		17 30						18 04		18 30					19 04			19 30				
Havant	a		16 59	17 07		17 32		17 49			17 59	18 07		18 32		18 49		18 59	19 07			19 32		19 49		19 59

		SW 1	GW ◇	SN 1	SW 1	SW 1	SW 1		SN 1	SW 1	SN 1	SW 1	SW 1	SW 1	SN 1	SW 1	GW ◇	SN 1	SW 1	SW 1	SW 1	SN 1	SW 1	SW 1		
Portsmouth Harbour	d	19 48	20 08	20 14	20 17	20 32			20 43	20 48	21 14	21 17	21 32		21 43	21 48	22 07	22 14	22 17	22 32		22 43	22 48	23 17		
Portsmouth & Southsea	a	19 51	20 11	20 17	20 20	20 35			20 46	20 51	21 17	21 20	21 35		21 46	21 51	22 11	22 17	22 20	22 34		22 46	22 51	23 20		
	d	19 53	20 12	20 18	20 22	20 37	20 42		20 47	20 53	21 18	21 22	21 37	21 42	21 47	21 53	22 12	22 18	22 22	22 37	22 42	22 47	22 53	23 22		
Fratton	d	19 57	20a15	20 22	20 26	20 41	20 46		20 51	20 57	21 22	21 26	21 41	21 46	21 51	21 57	22a15	22 22	22 26	22 41	22 46	22 51	22 57	23 26		
Hilsea	d				20a30		20a50					21a30		21a50					22a30		22a50			23a30		
Bedhampton	d	20 04		20 30						21 04	21 30					22 04		22 30					23 04			
Havant	a	20 07		20 32		20 49			20 59	21 07	21 32		21 49		21 59	22 07		22 32		22 49		22 59	23 07			

For general notes see front of timetable
For details of catering facilities see
Directory of Train Operators

A From 28 September
B Until 21 September

Network Diagram for Table 158

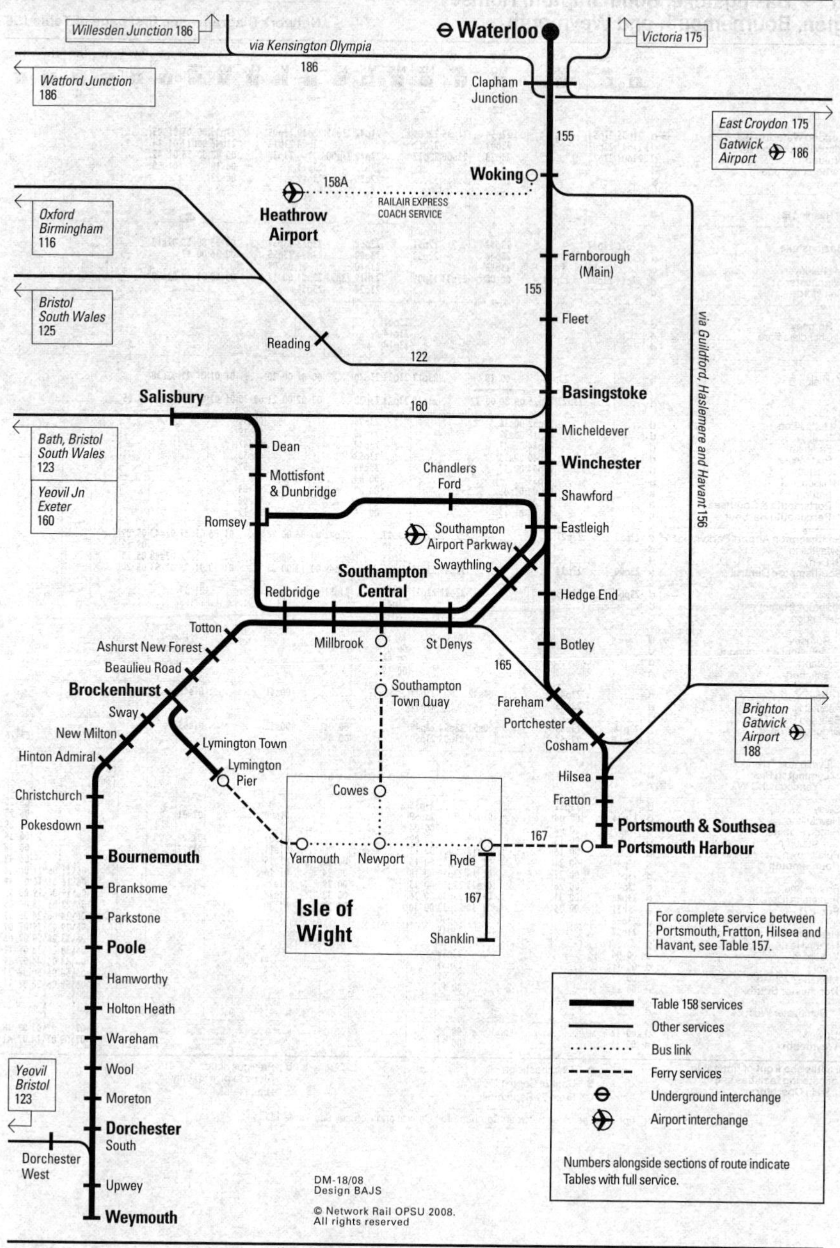

Waterloo
Willesden Junction 186
via Kensington Olympia
186
Victoria 175
Watford Junction 186
Clapham Junction
155
East Croydon 175
Gatwick Airport 186
Woking
158A
Heathrow Airport
RAILAIR EXPRESS COACH SERVICE
Oxford Birmingham 116
Farnborough (Main)
155
Bristol South Wales 125
Fleet
via Guildford, Haslemere and Havant 156
Reading
122
Basingstoke
Salisbury
160
Bath, Bristol South Wales 123
Yeovil Jn Exeter 160
Dean
Micheldever
Winchester
Mottisfont & Dunbridge
Chandlers Ford
Shawford
Romsey
Eastleigh
Southampton Airport Parkway
Swaythling
Southampton Central
Redbridge
Hedge End
Totton
Millbrook
St Denys
Botley
Ashurst New Forest
Beaulieu Road
165
Brockenhurst
Southampton Town Quay
Fareham
Sway
Portchester
New Milton
Lymington Town
Cosham
Hinton Admiral
Lymington Pier
Brighton Gatwick Airport 188
Hilsea
Christchurch
Cowes
Fratton
Pokesdown
167
Portsmouth & Southsea
Portsmouth Harbour
Yarmouth
Newport
Ryde
Bournemouth
Branksome
167
Parkstone
Isle of Wight
Shanklin
For complete service between Portsmouth, Fratton, Hilsea and Havant, see Table 157.
Poole
Hamworthy
Holton Heath
Table 158 services
Other services
Bus link
Ferry services
Underground interchange
Airport interchange
Wareham
Wool
Yeovil Bristol 123
Moreton
Dorchester South
Dorchester West
Numbers alongside sections of route indicate Tables with full service.
Upwey
Weymouth
DM-18/08
Design BAJS
© Network Rail OPSU 2008. All rights reserved

For details of Bank Holiday service alterations, please see first page of Table 149

London → Basingstoke, Southampton, Romsey Lymington, Bournemouth and Weymouth

Network Diagram - see first page of Table 158

Miles	Miles																								
				SW	SW	SW		SW		SW	SW	SW	SW	SW	SW	SW	SW	SW	SW	SW	SW	SW	SW	SW	SW
				MO	MO	MO		MO		MX	MX	MX	MX	MX	MX	MX	MX	MX	MX						
				1 ◇	1 ◇	1 ◇		1		1 ◇	1	1	1	1	1	1	1	1	1	1	1	1	1	1	1
								A															B	C	
								☕			☕			☕											
0	—	**London Waterloo** [15] ⊖	d	21p35	21p54			22p54		21p35	22p05		21p42	22p35	22p39	23p05		23p39	00 05	01 05					
4	—	Clapham Junction [10]	d	21b42	22b03			23b03			22b12				22b46	23b12		23b46	00u12	01 14					
24¼	—	**Woking**	d	22p07	22p28			23p28		22p00	22p32		22p19	23p00		23p32		00 08	00 36	01 42					
33¾	—	Farnborough (Main)	d										22p33		23p13			00 18		01s58					
36½	—	Fleet	d										22p38		23p19			00 23							
—	—	Reading [7]	d																						
47¾	—	**Basingstoke**	a	22p26	22p47			23p47			22p51		22p58		23p33	23p51		00 35	00 55	02s12					
—	—		d	22p28	22p48			23p48			22p53		23p00		23p34	23p53		00 36	00 57						
58	—	Micheldever	d		22p58	←		23p58					23p10			00 03									
66½	—	**Winchester**	d	22p44	23p08 →	23p08		00 08		22p33	23p09		23p19	23p33	23p51	00 12		00 53	01 13	02s29					
69¾	—	Shawford	d										23p24		23p55										
—	0	**Romsey**	d									23p07													
—	5¼	Chandlers Ford	a									23p14													
—	—		d									23p14													
73½	—	Eastleigh [3]	a			23p18		00 18			23p17	23p22	23p30		00 01	00 20		01 01	01 21	02s38					
—	0		d			23p22	23p26	00 30	00 22		23p18	23p23	23p30		00 02	00 21	00 30	01 02	01 22		05 05				
—	4½	Hedge End	d				23p32	00s36	→				23p36				00s36								
—	5½	Botley	d				23p36	00s39					23p40				00s39								
—	11	Fareham	d				23p44	00s47					23p48				00s47								
—	14¼	Portchester	d				23p49	00s53					23p53				00s53								
—	16¾	Cosham	d				23p54	00s57					23p59				00s57								
—	18¼	Hilsea	a				23p59						00 04												
—	20½	Fratton	a				00 04	01s05					00 08				01s05								
—	21½	**Portsmouth & Southsea**	a				00 08	01s08					00 11				01s08								
—	22¼	**Portsmouth Harbour**	a				00 13	01 12					00 16				01 12								
75	—	**Southampton Airport Parkwy** ✈	d	22p53		23p27				22p42	23p23	23p27		23p42	00 06	00 26		01 06	01 27	02s43	05 09				
75¾	—	Swaythling	d									23p30									05 12				
77¼	—	St Denys	d									23p33				00s30				02s48	05 15				
79¼	—	**Southampton Central**	a	23p00		23p34				22p49	23p30	23p38		23p49	00 13	00 35		01 13	01 36	02 53	05 20				
—	—		d	23p03		23p35				22p51	23p31	23p39		23p51		00 36			01 37						
80¼	—	Millbrook (Hants)	d									23p42													
82	0	Redbridge	d									23p45													
—	6	**Romsey**	d									23p56													
—	9¾	Mottisfont & Dunbridge	d									00 01													
—	13½	Dean	d									00 06													
—	22½	**Salisbury**	a									00 19													
82½	—	Totton	d			23p41			00s42		23p37					00s41			01s42						
85½	—	Ashurst New Forest	d			23p45					23p41														
88	—	Beaulieu Road	d																						
92¾	—	**Brockenhurst** [3]	a	23p16		23p53			00s53	23p04	23p49			00 04		00s52			01s53						
—	0		d	23p17		23p54				23p05	23p50			00 05								05 59			06 16
—	4¾	Lymington Town	d																			06 07			
—	5¼	**Lymington Pier**	a																			06 09			
—	—	Yarmouth (I.O.W.) ⛴	a																			*06c45*			
95½	—	Sway	d			23p59					23p55														06 20
98½	—	New Milton	d	23p24		00 04			01s01		23p59					01s00			02s01						06 25
101	—	Hinton Admiral	d			00 08					00 04														06 29
104¼	—	Christchurch	d			00 13			01s08		00 09					01s07			02s08						06 34
106¼	—	Pokesdown	d			00 16			01s12		00 12					01s11			02s12						06 38
108	—	**Bournemouth**	a	23p35		00 21			01 16	23p23	00 16			00 22		01 15			02 16						06 42
—	—		d	23p40		00 22			01 18	23p28	00 18			00 24		01 16							06 11	06 11	06 44
110¾	—	Branksome	d	23p45		00 28			01s23	23p33	00 23			00 29		01s21							06 16	06 16	06 49
112	—	Parkstone (Dorset)	d	23p48		00 31			01s26	23p36	00 26			00 32		01s24							06 19	06 19	06 52
113¾	—	**Poole** [4]	a	23p51		00 35			01 30	23p39	00 30			00 36		01 30							06 23	06 23	06 55
—	—		d	23p52						23p40													06 24	06 24	06 57
116	—	Hamworthy	d	23p57						23p45													06 29	06 29	07 02
118¾	—	Holton Heath	d																				06 33	06 33	07 06
120¾	—	Wareham	d	00 04						23p52													06 38	06 38	07 11
125¾	—	Wool	d	00 11						23p59													06 44	06 44	07 17
130¼	—	Moreton (Dorset)	d	00 17						00 05													06 50	06 50	07 23
135¾	—	**Dorchester South**	d	00 25						00 13													06 58	06 58	07 31
—	—	Dorchester West	d																						
140½	—	Upwey	d	00 32						00 19													07 05	07 05	07 38
142¾	—	**Weymouth**	a	00 36						00 24													07 09	07 14	07 42

For general notes see front of timetable
For details of catering facilities see Directory of Train Operators

A ☕ to Eastleigh
B Until 26 September
C From 29 September

b Previous night.
Stops to pick up only
c Until 11 July.

For other services between Southampton Central and Romsey see Table 123.

For details of Bank Holiday service alterations, please see first page of Table 149

London → Basingstoke, Southampton, Romsey Lymington, Bournemouth and Weymouth

Network Diagram - see first page of Table 158

		SW 1	SW 1	SW 1	SW 1	SW 1	SW 1	SW 1	GW ◇	SW 1	SW 1		SW 1	SW 1	SW 1	SW 1	SW 1	SW 1	SW 1	SW 1	SW 1	SW 1	SW 1	XC 1 ◇	SW 1
				A	B		C																		
London Waterloo 15 ⊖	d									05 30									06 30		06 12		06 42		
Clapham Junction 10	d									05u37									06u37		06u19		06u49		
Woking	d									06 01								06 19	06 57		06 50		07 19		
Farnborough (Main)	d																	06 33			07 04		07 33		
Fleet	d																	06 38			07 09		07 38		
Reading 7	d																							07 45	
Basingstoke	a									06 20								06 58	07 16		07 28		07 56	08 08	
	d			05 40	05 40					06 21						06 55		07 00	07 18		07 30		08 00	08 10	
Micheldever	d			05 50	05 50													07 10			07 41		08 10		
Winchester	d			05 59	05 59			06 18		06 38						07 11		07 19	07 34		07 50		08 19	08 25	
Shawford	d							06 23								07 16					07 55		08 24		
Romsey	d						05 58								07 07							08 07			
Chandlers Ford	a						06 06								07 14							08 14			
	d						06 06								07 14							08 14			
Eastleigh 3	a			06 07	06 07		06 11	06 28		06 47					07 20	07 22		07 29	07 43		08 00	08 20	08 30		
	d		06 00	06 08	06 08		06 13	06 30		06 48			07 02		07 21	07 25		07 30	07 44		08 02	08 21	08 30		
Hedge End	d		06 06					06 36					07 08					07 36					08 36		
Botley	d		06 10					06 40					07 12					07 40					08 41		
Fareham	d		06 18					06 50					07 20					07 48					08 50		
Portchester	d		06 23					06 55					07 25					07 53					08 55		
Cosham	d		06 28					07 00					07 29					07 58					09 00		
Hilsea	a		06 33					07 05					07 35					08 03					09 05		
Fratton	a		06 38					07 09					07 39					08 07					09 09		
Portsmouth & Southsea	a		06 44					07 12					07 42					08 11					09 13		
Portsmouth Harbour	a		06 49					07 17					07 48					08 16					09 18		
Southampton Airport Parkwy ✈	d			06 13	06 13		06 17			06 53					07 25	07 29			07 49		08 06	08 25		08 34	
Swaythling	d			06 15	06 15		06 20								07 28	07 32					08 09	08 28			
St Denys	d			06 18	06 18		06 23								07 31	07 35					08 12	08 31			
Southampton Central	a			06 23	06 23		06 28			07 00					07 36	07 40			07 57		08 17	08 38		08 40	
	d			06 25	06 25		06 30			07 01				07 18	07 37				08 00		08 19	08 40		08 42	
Millbrook (Hants)	d						06 32							07 20	07 40						08 21	08 42			
Redbridge	d						06 36							07 24	07 43						08 25	08 46			
Romsey	d						06 44								07 51							08 54			
Mottisfont & Dunbridge	d						06 49								07 56							08 59			
Dean	d						06 54								08 02							09 04			
Salisbury	a						07 07								08 14							09 20			
Totton	d			06 30	06 30					07 07				07 27					08 05		08 28				
Ashurst New Forest	d			06 35	06 35									07 31							08 32				
Beaulieu Road	d													07 36							08 37				
Brockenhurst 3	a			06 43	06 43					07 17				07 42					08 16		08 43			08 56	
	d	06 29		06 44	06 44	06 59				07 18	07 29			07 44			07 59		08 17	08 29	08 44			08 57	08 59
Lymington Town	d	06 37				07 07					07 37						08 07			08 37					09 07
Lymington Pier	a	06 39				07 09					07 39						08 09			08 39					09 09
Yarmouth (I.O.W.) ⛴	a	*07 15*				*07 45*					*08b15*						*08 45*			*09 15*					*09b45*
Sway	d			06 48	06 48					07 23				07 48					08 21		08 48				
New Milton	d			06 53	06 53					07 28				07 53					08 26		08 53				
Hinton Admiral	d			06 57	06 57					07 32				07 57					08 30		08 57				
Christchurch	d			07 02	07 02					07 37				08 02					08 35		09 02				
Pokesdown	d			07 06	07 06					07 41				08 06					08 39		09 06				
Bournemouth	a			07 10	07 10					07 45				08 10					08 43		09 10			09 15	
	d			07 11	07 11					07 49				08 11					08 44		09 11				
Branksome	d			07 16	07 16					07 54				08 16					08 49		09 16				
Parkstone (Dorset)	d			07 19	07 19					07 57				08 19					08 52		09 19				
Poole 4	a			07 23	07 23					08 01				08 23					08 56		09 23				
	d			07 24	07 24					08 02				08 24					08 57		09 24				
Hamworthy	d			07 29	07 29					08 07				08 29					09 02		09 29				
Holton Heath	d			07 33	07 33					08 11				08 33							09 33				
Wareham	d			07 38	07 38					08 16				08 38					09 09		09 38				
Wool	d			07 44	07 44					08 22				08 44					09 15		09 44				
Moreton (Dorset)	d			07 50	07 50					08 28				08 50					09 21		09 50				
Dorchester South	d			07 58	07 58					08 36				08 58					09 29		09 58				
Dorchester West	d								08 08																
Upwey	d			08 05	08 05				08 15	08 43				09 05					09 36		10 05				
Weymouth	a			08 09	08 14				08 20	08 47				09 09					09 40		10 09				

For general notes see front of timetable
For details of catering facilities see Directory of Train Operators

A Until 26 September
B From 29 September
C From Salisbury

b Until 11 July.

For other services between Southampton Central and Romsey see Table 123.

For details of Bank Holiday service alterations, please see first page of Table 149

London → Basingstoke, Southampton, Romsey Lymington, Bournemouth and Weymouth

Network Diagram - see first page of Table 158

Station		SW	SW	SW	GW	SW	SW	SW	SW	XC	SW	SW	SW
		1 ◇	1	1	◇	1 ◇	1	1	1	1 ◇	1	1 ◇	1
						A						A	
						☕				☕		☕	
London Waterloo 15 ⊖	d	07 35	07 38			08 05			08 09			08 35	08 39
Clapham Junction 10	d		07u45			08u12							08u46
Woking	d	08 00							08 35			09 00	
Farnborough (Main)	d		08 13						08 45				09 13
Fleet	d		08 19										09 19
Reading 7	d									08 45			
Basingstoke	a	08 20	08 34			08 48			08 59	09 08			09 34
	d	08 21	08 36			08 50			09 00	09 10			09 36
Micheldever	d								09 10				
Winchester	d	08 38	08 52			09 06			09 19	09 25		09 33	09 52
Shawford	d		08 57										09 57
Romsey	d							09 05					
Chandlers Ford	a							09 12					
	d							09 12					
Eastleigh 3	a	08 46	09 02					09 18	09 29				10 02
	d	08 47	09 03					09 19	09 30				10 03
Hedge End	d								09 36				
Botley	d								09 40				
Fareham	d								09 48				
Portchester	d								09 53				
Cosham	d								09 58				
Hilsea	a								10 03				
Fratton	a								10 07				
Portsmouth & Southsea	a								10 12				
Portsmouth Harbour	a								10 18				
Southampton Airport Parkwy ✈	d	08 51	09 08			09 15		09 23		09 34		09 42	10 08
Swaythling	d							09 26					
St Denys	d							09 29					
Southampton Central	a	08 58	09 15			09 22	←	09 34		09 40		09 49	10 15
	d	09 00	09 30 →			09 24	09 30	09 38		09 42		09 51	10 30 →
Millbrook (Hants)	d							09 40					
Redbridge	d							09 44					
Romsey	d							09 52					
Mottisfont & Dunbridge	d							09 57					
Dean	d							10 02					
Salisbury	a							10 15					
Totton	d	09 05					09 35						
Ashurst New Forest	d						09 40						
Beaulieu Road	d												
Brockenhurst 3	a	09 16				09 37	09 49			09 56		10 04	
	d	09 17		09 29		09 38	10 16			09 57	09 59	10 05	
Lymington Town	d			09 37			→				10 07		
Lymington Pier	a			09 39							10 09		
Yarmouth (I.O.W.) ⛴	a			*10 15*							*10 45*		
Sway	d	09 21											
New Milton	d	09 26				09 45							
Hinton Admiral	d	09 30											
Christchurch	d	09 35				09 52							
Pokesdown	d	09 39				09 56							
Bournemouth	a	09 43				10 00				10 15		10 20	
	d	09 44				10 04						10 24	
Branksome	d	09 49										10 29	
Parkstone (Dorset)	d	09 52										10 32	
Poole 4	a	09 56				10 13						10 36	
	d	09 57				10 14						10 37	
Hamworthy	d	10 02				10 20						10 42	
Holton Heath	d					10 27							
Wareham	d	10 09				10c35						10 49	
Wool	d					10 42							
Moreton (Dorset)	d					10 48							
Dorchester South	d	10 27				10 56						11 05	
Dorchester West	d				10 42								
Upwey	d				10 49	11 02							
Weymouth	a	10 35			10 55	11 07						11 13	

Station		SW	SW	SW	SW	SW	SW	XC		SW	GW	SW	SW
		1	1	1 ◇	1	1	1	1 ◇		1	◇	1 ◇	1
				A								A	
				☕				☕				☕	
London Waterloo 15 ⊖	d			09 05			09 09					09 35	09 39
Clapham Junction 10	d			09u12									09u46
Woking	d						09 35					10 00	
Farnborough (Main)	d						09 45						10 13
Fleet	d												10 19
Reading 7	d							09 45					
Basingstoke	a			09 48			09 58	10 08					10 34
	d			09 50			10 00	10 10					10 36
Micheldever	d						10 10						
Winchester	d			10 06			10 19	10 25				10 33	10 52
Shawford	d												10 57
Romsey	d					10 05							
Chandlers Ford	a					10 12							
	d					10 12							
Eastleigh 3	a					10 18	10 29						11 02
	d					10 19	10 30						11 03
Hedge End	d						10 36						
Botley	d						10 40						
Fareham	d						10 48						
Portchester	d						10 53						
Cosham	d						10 58						
Hilsea	a						11 03						
Fratton	a						11 07						
Portsmouth & Southsea	a						11 12						
Portsmouth Harbour	a						11 18						
Southampton Airport Parkwy ✈	d			10 15		10 23		10 34				10 42	11 08
Swaythling	d					10 26							
St Denys	d					10 29							
Southampton Central	a			10 22	←	10 34		10 40				10 49	11 14
	d			10 24	10 30	10 38		10 42				10 51	11 30 →
Millbrook (Hants)	d					10 40							
Redbridge	d					10 44							
Romsey	d					10 57							
Mottisfont & Dunbridge	d												
Dean	d												
Salisbury	a					11 15							
Totton	d				10 35								
Ashurst New Forest	d				10 40								
Beaulieu Road	d												
Brockenhurst 3	a	←		10 37	10 51			10 56				11 04	
	d	10 16	10 29	10 38	11 16			10 57		10 59		11 05	
Lymington Town	d		10 37		→					11 07			
Lymington Pier	a		10 39							11 09			
Yarmouth (I.O.W.) ⛴	a		*11b15*							*11 45*			
Sway	d	10 20											
New Milton	d	10 25		10 45									
Hinton Admiral	d	10 29											
Christchurch	d	10 34		10 52									
Pokesdown	d	10 38		10 56									
Bournemouth	a	10 42		11 00				11 15				11 20	
	d	10 43		11 04								11 24	
Branksome	d	10 48										11 29	
Parkstone (Dorset)	d	10 51										11 32	
Poole 4	a	10 55		11 13								11 36	
	d			11 14								11 37	
Hamworthy	d			11 19								11 42	
Holton Heath	d			11 23									
Wareham	d			11 28								11 49	
Wool	d			11 35									
Moreton (Dorset)	d			11 41									
Dorchester South	d			11 49								12 05	
Dorchester West	d										11 50		
Upwey	d			11 55							12 02		
Weymouth	a			12 00							12 08	12 13	

For general notes see front of timetable
For details of catering facilities see Directory of Train Operators

A ☕ to Bournemouth
b Until 11 July.
c Arr. 1031

For other services between Southampton Central and Romsey see Table 123.

London → Basingstoke, Southampton, Romsey Lymington, Bournemouth and Weymouth

For details of Bank Holiday service alterations, please see first page of Table 149

Network Diagram - see first page of Table 158

Station		SW	SW	SW	SW	SW	SW	XC	SW	SW	SW	SW	SW	SW	SW	SW	SW	XC	SW	GW	SW	SW	SW	SW	SW
		1	1	1 ◇	1	1	1	R 1	1	1 ◇	1	1	1	1 ◇	1	1	1	R 1	1	◇	1 ◇	1	1	1	1 ◇
				A						A				A							A				A
London Waterloo 15 ⊖	d			10 05			10 09			10 35	10 39			11 05			11 09				11 35	11 39			12 05
Clapham Junction 10	d			10u12							10u46			11u12								11u46			12u12
Woking	d						10 35			11 00							11 35				12 00				
Farnborough (Main)	d						10 45				11 13						11 45					12 13			
Fleet	d										11 19											12 19			
Reading 7	d							10 45										11 45							
Basingstoke	a			10 48			10 58	11 08			11 34			11 48			11 58	12 08				12 34			12 48
	d			10 50			11 00	11 10			11 36			11 50			12 00	12 10				12 36			12 50
Micheldever	d						11 10										12 10								
Winchester	d			11 06			11 19	11 25		11 33	11 52			12 06			12 19	12 25			12 33	12 52			13 06
Shawford	d										11 57											12 57			
Romsey	d					11 05										12 05									
Chandlers Ford	a					11 12										12 12									
	d					11 12										12 12									
Eastleigh 3	a					11 18	11 29				12 02					12 18	12 29					13 02			
	d					11 19	11 30				12 03					12 19	12 30					13 03			
Hedge End	d						11 36										12 36								
Botley	d						11 40										12 40								
Fareham	d						11 48										12 48								
Portchester	d						11 53										12 53								
Cosham	d						11 58										12 58								
Hilsea	a						12 03										13 03								
Fratton	a						12 07										13 07								
Portsmouth & Southsea	a						12 12										13 12								
Portsmouth Harbour	a						12 18										13 18								
Southampton Airport Parkway ✈	d			11 15		11 23		11 34		11 42	12 08			12 15		12 23		12 34			12 42	13 08			13 15
Swaythling	d					11 26										12 26									
St Denys	d					11 29										12 29									
Southampton Central	a			11 22	←	11 34		11 40		11 49	12 15			12 22	←	12 34		12 40			12 49	13 15			13 22
	d			11 24	11 30	11 38		11 42		11 51	12 30			12 24	12 30	12 38		12 42			12 51	13 30			13 24
Millbrook (Hants)	d					11 40					→					12 40						→			
Redbridge	d					11 44										12 44									
Romsey	d					11 52										12 52									
Mottisfont & Dunbridge	d					11 57																			
Dean	d					12 02																			
Salisbury	a					12 15										13 10									
Totton	d				11 35										12 35										
Ashurst New Forest	d				11 40										12 40										
Beaulieu Road	d				11 44																				
Brockenhurst 3	a	←		11 37	11 51			11 56		12 04		←		12 37	12 51			12 56			13 04		←		13 37
	d	11 16	11 29	11 38	12 16			11 57	11 59	12 05		12 16	12 29	12 38	13 16			12 57	12 59		13 05		13 16	13 29	13 38
Lymington Town	d		11 37		→				12 07				12 37		→				13 07					13 37	
Lymington Pier	a		11 39						12 09				12 39						13 09					13 39	
Yarmouth (I.O.W.) ⛴	a		*12b15*						*12c45*				*13e15*						*13 45*					*14f15*	
Sway	d	11 20										12 20											13 20		
New Milton	d	11 25		11 45								12 25		12 45									13 25		13 45
Hinton Admiral	d	11 29										12 29											13 29		
Christchurch	d	11 34		11 52								12 34		12 52									13 34		13 52
Pokesdown	d	11 38		11 56								12 38		12 56									13 38		13 56
Bournemouth	a	11 42		12 00				12 15		12 20		12 42		13 00				13 15			13 20		13 42		14 00
	d	11 43		12 04						12 24		12 43		13 04							13 24		13 43		14 04
Branksome	d	11 48								12 29		12 48									13 29		13 48		
Parkstone (Dorset)	d	11 51								12 32		12 51									13 32		13 51		
Poole 4	a	11 55		12 13						12 36		12 55		13 13							13 36		13 55		14 13
	d			12 14						12 37				13 14							13 37				14 14
Hamworthy	d			12 19						12 42				13 19							13 42				14 19
Holton Heath	d			12 23										13 23											14 23
Wareham	d			12 28						12 49				13 28							13 49				14 28
Wool	d			12 35										13 35											14 35
Moreton (Dorset)	d			12 41										13 41											14 41
Dorchester South	d			12 49						13 05				13 49							14 05				14 49
Dorchester West	d																			13 54					
Upwey	d			12 55										13 55						14 02					14 55
Weymouth	a			13 00						13 13				14 00						14 09	14 13				15 00

For general notes see front of timetable
For details of catering facilities see Directory of Train Operators

A — to Bournemouth
b — Until 5 September.
c — Until 11 July and from 8 September until 31 October.
e — Until 5 September and from 3 November.
f — Until 11 July and from 8 September but excluding Tuesdays 18 May to 11 September.

For other services between Southampton Central and Romsey see Table 123.

For details of Bank Holiday service alterations, please see first page of Table 149

London → Basingstoke, Southampton, Romsey Lymington, Bournemouth and Weymouth

Network Diagram - see first page of Table 158

		SW	SW	SW	XC	SW	SW		SW	SW	SW	SW	SW	SW	SW	XC	SW	SW	SN	SW	SW	SW	SW	SW	SW
					R											R									
		1	1	1	1	1	1◇		1	1	1	1◇	1	1	1	1	1	1◇	1	1	1	1	1◇	1	1
							A					A						A					A		
					🍴		🍴					🍴				🍴		🍴					🍴		
London Waterloo 15 ⊖	d			12 09			12 35		12 39			13 05			13 09			13 35			13 39		14 05		
Clapham Junction 10	d								12u46			13u12									13u46		14u12		
Woking	d			12 35			13 00								13 35			14 00							
Farnborough (Main)	d			12 45					13 13						13 45						14 13				
Fleet	d								13 19												14 19				
Reading 7	d				12 45											13 45									
Basingstoke	a			12 58	13 08				13 34			13 48			13 59	14 08					14 34		14 48		
	d			13 00	13 10				13 36			13 50			14 00	14 10					14 36		14 50		
Micheldever	d			13 10											14 10										
Winchester	d			13 19	13 25		13 33		13 52			14 06			14 20	14 25		14 33			14 52		15 06		
Shawford	d								13 57												14 57				
Romsey	d		13 05											14 05											15 05
Chandlers Ford	a		13 12											14 12											15 12
	d		13 12											14 12											15 12
Eastleigh 3	a		13 18	13 29					14 02					14 18	14 29						15 02				15 18
	d		13 19	13 30					14 03					14 19	14 30				14 48		15 03				15 19
Hedge End	d			13 36											14 36										
Botley	d			13 40											14 40										
Fareham	d			13 48											14 48				15a02						
Portchester	d			13 53											14 53										
Cosham	d			13 58											14 58										
Hilsea	a			14 03											15 03										
Fratton	a			14 07											15 07										
Portsmouth & Southsea	a			14 12											15 12										
Portsmouth Harbour	a			14 18											15 18										
Southampton Airport Parkwy ✈	d		13 23		13 34		13 42		14 08			14 15		14 23		14 34		14 42			15 08		15 15		15 23
Swaythling	d		13 26											14 26											15 26
St Denys	d		13 29											14 29											15 29
Southampton Central	a	←	13 34		13 40		13 49		14 13			14 22	←	14 34		14 40		14 49			15 16		15 22	←	15 34
	d	13 30	13 38		13 42		13 51		14 30 →			14 24	14 30	14 38		14 42		14 51			15 30 →		15 24	15 30	15 38
Millbrook (Hants)	d		13 40											14 40											15 40
Redbridge	d		13 44											14 44											15 44
Romsey	d		13 52											14 52											15 52
Mottisfont & Dunbridge	d		13 57											14 57											15 57
Dean	d		14 02											15 02											16 02
Salisbury	a		14 15											15 15											16 15
Totton	d	13 35											14 35											15 35	
Ashurst New Forest	d	13 40											14 40											15 40	
Beaulieu Road	d																								
Brockenhurst 3	a	13 51			13 56		14 04			←		14 37	14 51			14 56		15 04		←			15 37	15 51	
	d	14 16			13 57	13 59	14 05			14 16	14 29	14 38	15 16			14 57	14 59	15 05		15 16		15 29	15 38	16 28	
Lymington Town	d	→				14 07					14 37		→				15 07					15 37		→	
Lymington Pier	a					14 09					14 39						15 09					15 39			
Yarmouth (I.O.W.) ⛴	a					*14b45*					*15c15*						*15e45*					*16f15*			
Sway	d									14 20										15 20					
New Milton	d									14 25		14 45								15 25			15 45		
Hinton Admiral	d									14 29										15 29					
Christchurch	d									14 34		14 52								15 34			15 52		
Pokesdown	d									14 38		14 56								15 38			15 56		
Bournemouth	a				14 15		14 20			14 42		15 00				15 15		15 20		15 42			16 00		
	d						14 24			14 43		15 04						15 24		15 43			16 04		
Branksome	d						14 29			14 48								15 29		15 48					
Parkstone (Dorset)	d						14 32			14 51								15 32		15 51					
Poole 4	a						14 36			14 55		15 13						15 36		15 55			16 13		
	d						14 37					15 14						15 37					16 14		
Hamworthy	d						14 42					15 19						15 42					16 19		
Holton Heath	d											15 23											16 23		
Wareham	d						14 49					15 28						15 49					16 28		
Wool	d											15 35											16 35		
Moreton (Dorset)	d											15 41											16 41		
Dorchester South	d						15 05					15 49						16 05					16 49		
Dorchester West	d																								
Upwey	d											15 55											16 55		
Weymouth	a						15 13					16 00						16 13					17 00		

For general notes see front of timetable
For details of catering facilities see Directory of Train Operators

A 🍴 to Bournemouth
b Until 5 September except Wednesdays.
c Until 5 September except Thursdays and Daily from 3 November.
e Until 11 July and from 8 September until 31 October.
f Until 5 September.

For other services between Southampton Central and Romsey see Table 123.

For details of Bank Holiday service alterations, please see first page of Table 149

London → Basingstoke, Southampton, Romsey Lymington, Bournemouth and Weymouth

Network Diagram - see first page of Table 158

		SW	XC	SW	GW	SW	SW	SW	SW	SW	SW	SW	SW	XC	SW	SW			SW	SW	SW	SW	SW	SN	SW
		1	R 1	1	◇	1 ◇	1	1	1	1 ◇	1	1	1	R 1	1	1 ◇			1	1	1	1	1 ◇	1	1
						A				A						A									
			🍴			🍴				🍴				🍴		🍴									
London Waterloo 15 ⊖	d	14 09				14 35	14 39			15 05			15 09			15 35					15 39		16 05		
Clapham Junction 10	d						14u46			15u12											15u46		16u12		
Woking	d	14 35				15 00							15 35			16 00									
Farnborough (Main)	d	14 45					15 13						15 45								16 13				
Fleet	d						15 19														16 19				
Reading 7	d		14 45											15 45											
Basingstoke	a	14 58	15 08				15 34			15 48			15 58	16 08							16 34		16 48		
	d	15 00	15 10				15 36			15 50			16 00	16 10						16 24	16 36		16 50		
Micheldever	d	15 10											16 10												
Winchester	d	15 19	15 25			15 33	15 52			16 06			16 19	16 25		16 33			16 38	16 43	16 52		17 06		
Shawford	d						15 57												16 42		16 57				
Romsey	d											16 05													
Chandlers Ford	a											16 12													
	d											16 12													
Eastleigh 3	a	15 29					16 02					16 18	16 29						16 48	16 51	17 02				
	d	15 30					16 03					16 19	16 30						16 49	16 52	17 03			17 16	
Hedge End	d	15 36											16 36							16 58					
Botley	d	15 40											16 40							17 02					
Fareham	d	15 48											16 48							17 10					
Portchester	d	15 53											16 53							17 15					
Cosham	d	15 58											16 58							17 20				16 44	
Hilsea	a	16 03											17 03												
Fratton	a	16 07											17 07							17 27					
Portsmouth & Southsea	a	16 12											17 18							17 31					
Portsmouth Harbour	a	16 18											17 25												
Southampton Airport Parkwy ✈	d		15 34			15 42	16 08			16 15		16 23		16 34		16 42			16 53		17 08		17 15		
Swaythling	d											16 26							16 56						
St Denys	d											16 29							16 59						
Southampton Central	a		15 40			15 49	16 15			16 22	←	16 34		16 40		16 49			17 04		17 15		17 22	17 28	←
	d		15 42			15 51	16 30 →			16 24	16 30	16 38		16 42		16 53	16 56		17 06		17 30 →		17 24		17 30
Millbrook (Hants)	d											16 40													
Redbridge	d											16 44													
Romsey	d											16 52													
Mottisfont & Dunbridge	d											16 57													
Dean	d											17 02													
Salisbury	a											17 15													
Totton	d										16 35						17 01		17a11						17 35
Ashurst New Forest	d										16 40						17 06								17 40
Beaulieu Road	d										16 44														17 44
Brockenhurst 3	a		15 56			16 04		←		16 37	16 51			16 56		17 07	17 14						17 37		17 51
	d		15 57	15 59		16 05		16 28	16 29	16 38				16 57	16 59	17 08	17 16					17 29	17 38		
Lymington Town	d			16 07					16 37						17 07							17 37			
Lymington Pier	a			16 09					16 39						17 09							17 39			
Yarmouth (I.O.W.) ⛴	a			*16 45*					*17b15*						*17c45*							*18 15*			
Sway	d							16 32		16 43							17 20						17 43		
New Milton	d							16 37		16 48							17 25						17 48		
Hinton Admiral	d							16 41		16 52							17 29						17 52		
Christchurch	d							16 46		16 57							17 34						17 57		
Pokesdown	d							16 50		17 00							17 38						18 00		
Bournemouth	a		16 15			16 20		16 54		17 04				17 15		17 22	17 42						18 04		
	d					16 24		16 55		17 06						17 24	17 43						18 09		
Branksome	d					16 29		17 00								17 29	17 48								
Parkstone (Dorset)	d					16 32		17 03								17 32	17 51								
Poole 4	a					16 36		17 07		17 15						17 36	17 55						18 18		
	d					16 37				17 16						17 37							18 19		
Hamworthy	d					16 42				17 21						17 42							18 24		
Holton Heath	d									17 25													18 28		
Wareham	d					16 49				17 30						17 49							18 33		
Wool	d									17 36													18 39		
Moreton (Dorset)	d									17 42													18 45		
Dorchester South	d					17 05				17 50						18 05							18 53		
Dorchester West	d				16 55																				
Upwey	d				17 02					17 57													19 00		
Weymouth	a				17 08	17 13				18 01						18 13							19 06		

For general notes see front of timetable
For details of catering facilities see
Directory of Train Operators

A 🍴 to Bournemouth

b Until 11 July and from 8 September until 31 October.

c Until 5 September.

For other services between Southampton Central and Romsey see Table 123.

For details of Bank Holiday service alterations, please see first page of Table 149

London → Basingstoke, Southampton, Romsey Lymington, Bournemouth and Weymouth

Network Diagram - see first page of Table 158

		SW	SW	XC	SW	GW	SW		SW	SW	SW	SW		SW	SW	XC	SW	GW	SW		SW	SW	SW	SW	SW
		[1]	[1]	[1] ◇	[1]	◇	[1] ◇		[1]	[1]	[1]	[1]		[1]	[1]	R [1]	[1]	◇	[1]		[1]	[1]	[1]	[1]	[1]
							A					A							A					A	
				[trolley]			[trolley]					[trolley]				[trolley]			[trolley]					[trolley]	
London Waterloo [15] ⊖	d		16 09				16 35			16 39		17 05			17 09				17 35		17 39	17 48		18 05	
Clapham Junction [10]	d									16u46															
Woking	d		16 35				17u00								17 34						18 04	18 13			
Farnborough (Main)	d		16 45							17 13															
Fleet	d									17 19															
Reading [7]	d			16 45												17 45									
Basingstoke	a		16 58	17 08						17 34					17 53	18 08					18 23	18 32			
	d		17 00	17 10					17 24	17 36					17 54	18 10					18 24	18 33			
Micheldever	d		17 10						17 34						18 04						18 34				
Winchester	d		17 19	17 25			17 33		17 44	17 52		18 01			18 14	18 25			18 31		18 44	18 50		19b01	19 05
Shawford	d								17 48						18 19						18 49				19 09
Romsey	d	17 05												18 05											
Chandlers Ford	a	17 12												18 12											
	d	17 12												18 12											
Eastleigh [3]	a	17 18	17 29						17 53	18 00				18 18	18 24						18 54	18 58			19 15
	d	17 19	17 30						17 54	18 01				18 19	18 27						18 55	18 59			19 16
Hedge End	d		17 36							18 07					18 33						19 01				
Botley	d		17 40							18 11					18 37						19 05				
Fareham	d		17 48							18 21					18 50						19 14				
Portchester	d		17 53							18 26					18 55						19 19				
Cosham	d		17 58							18 31					19 00						19 24				
Hilsea	a		18 03												19 05						19 28				
Fratton	a		18 07							18 39					19 09						19 32				
Portsmouth & Southsea	a		18 11							18 43					19 12						19 36				
Portsmouth Harbour	a		18 20							18 51					19 20						19 43				
Southampton Airport Parkwy ✈	d	17 23		17 34			17 42		17 59			18 10		18 23		18 34			18 40			19 03		19 10	19 20
Swaythling	d	17 26							18 01					18 26								19 06			19 23
St Denys	d	17 29							18 04					18 29								19 10			19 26
Southampton Central	a	17 34		17 40			17 49		18 10			18 17		18 34		18 40			18 48			19 17		19 17	19 33
	d	17 38		17 42			17 53	17 56				18 22	18 25	18 38		18 42			18 52	18 55				19 19	
Millbrook (Hants)	d	17 40												18 40											
Redbridge	d	17 44												18 44											
Romsey	d	17 52												18 58											
Mottisfont & Dunbridge	d	17 57												19 04											
Dean	d	18 02												19 09											
Salisbury	a	18 15												19 23											
Totton	d							18 01					18 30							19 00				19 24	
Ashurst New Forest	d							18 06					18 35							19 05					
Beaulieu Road	d																								
Brockenhurst [3]	a			17 56			18 07	18 14					18 43			18 56				19 13				19 35	
	d			17 57	17 59		18 08	18 16			18 29		18 44			18 57	18 59			19 14			19 29	19 36	
Lymington Town	d				18 07						18 37						19 07						19 37		
Lymington Pier	a				18 09						18 39						19 09						19 39		
Yarmouth (I.O.W.) ⛴	a				*18c45*						*19e15*						*19 45*						*20f15*		
Sway	d							18 20					18 48							19 18				19 40	
New Milton	d							18 25					18 53							19 23				19 45	
Hinton Admiral	d							18 29					18 58							19 26				19 49	
Christchurch	d							18 34					19 02							19 32				19 54	
Pokesdown	d							18 38					19 06							19 36				19 58	
Bournemouth	a			18 15			18 22	18 44				18 49	19 10			19 15			19 20	19 40				20 02	
	d						18 24					18 50	19 11						19 21	19 41				20 06	
Branksome	d						18 29					18 55	19 16						19 26	19 46				20 11	
Parkstone (Dorset)	d						18 32					18 58	19 19						19 29	19 49				20 14	
Poole [4]	a						18 36					19 02	19 26						19 33	19 56				20 18	
	d						18 37					19 03							19 34					20 19	
Hamworthy	d						18 42					19 08							19 39					20 24	
Holton Heath	d											19 12												20 28	
Wareham	d						18 49					19 17							19 46					20 33	
Wool	d											19 23												20 39	
Moreton (Dorset)	d											19 30												20 45	
Dorchester South	d						19 05					19 38							20 02					20 53	
Dorchester West	d					18 58												19 52							
Upwey	d					19 07						19 44						19 59						21 00	
Weymouth	a					19 13	19 17					19 51						20 06	20 15					21 06	

For general notes see front of timetable
For details of catering facilities see Directory of Train Operators

A [trolley] to Bournemouth
b Arr. 1858
c Until 11 July and from 8 September until 31 October.
e Until 5 September and from 3 November.
f Until 11 July.

For other services between Southampton Central and Romsey see Table 123.

London → Basingstoke, Southampton, Romsey Lymington, Bournemouth and Weymouth

For details of Bank Holiday service alterations, please see first page of Table 149

Network Diagram - see first page of Table 158

		SW	SW	XC		SW		SW	XC	SW	SW	SW	SW	SW	SW	SW	SW	XC	SW	SW	SW	XC	SW	SW	SW
		1	1	R 1		1		1	R 1	1	1	1	1	1 ◇	1	1	1	R 1	1	1 ◇	1	R 1	1	1	1 ◇
						B								B						B					
				⊏P		⊏P			⊏P	⊏P				⊏P				⊏P		⊏P		⊏P			⊏P
London Waterloo 15 ⊖	d		18 09			18 35						18 39		19 05			19 09			19 35	19 39				20 05
Clapham Junction 10	d											18u46		19u12							19u46				20u12
Woking	d		18 34									19 06					19 35			20 00					
Farnborough (Main)	d																19 45				20 13				
Fleet	d																				20 19				
Reading 7	d			18 45														19 45							
Basingstoke	a		18 53	19 08								19 28		19 48			19 58	20 08			20 34				20 48
	d		18 54	19 10							19 24	19 30		19 50			20 00	20 10			20 36				20 50
Micheldever	d		19 04									19 40					20 10								
Winchester	d		19 14	19 25		19 31					19 40	19 49		20 06			20 19	20 25		20 33	20 52				21 06
Shawford	d		19 19								19 45	19 54					20 24				20 57				
Romsey	d	19 05														20 05									
Chandlers Ford	a	19 12														20 12									
	d	19 12														20 12									
Eastleigh 3	a	19 18	19 24								19 50	19 59				20 18	20 30				21 02				
	d	19 19	19 29								19 51	20 00				20 19	20 30				21 03				
Hedge End	d		19 35								19 57						20 36								
Botley	d		19 39								20 01						20 40								
Fareham	d		19 50								20a09						20 48								
Portchester	d		19 55														20 53								
Cosham	d		20 00														20 58								
Hilsea	a		20 08														20 59								
Fratton	a		20 12														21 08								
Portsmouth & Southsea	a		20 16														21 11								
Portsmouth Harbour	a		20 23														21 21								
Southampton Airport Parkway ✈	d	19 24		19 34		19 40						20 05		20 15		20 23		20 34		20 42	21 08				21 15
Swaythling	d	19 26														20 26									
St Denys	d	19 29														20 29									
Southampton Central	a	19 34		19 40		19 47						20 15		20 22		20 34		20 40		20 49	21 15				21 22
	d	19 38		19 42		19 52	19 55 →			← 19 55		20 30 →		20 24	← 20 30	20 38		20 42		20 51					21 24
Millbrook (Hants)	d	19 40														20 40									
Redbridge	d	19 44														20 44									
Romsey	d	19 52														20 52									
Mottisfont & Dunbridge	d	19 57																							
Dean	d	20 02																							
Salisbury	a	20 15														21 10									
Totton	d									20 00					20 35					20 56					21 29
Ashurst New Forest	d									20 05					20 40										21 34
Beaulieu Road	d																								
Brockenhurst 3	a			19 56					←	20 13				20 37	20 51			20 56		21 07			←	←	21 42
	d			19 57				19 59	19 57	20 14			20 29	20 38	21 16			20 57	20 59	21 08		20 57	21 16	21 29	21 43
Lymington Town	d			→				20 07					20 37		→			→	21 07					21 37	
Lymington Pier	a							20 09					20 39						21 09					21 39	
Yarmouth (I.O.W.) ⛴	a							*20 45*					*21b15*						*22c00*					*22 45*	
Sway	d									20 18													21 20		21 47
New Milton	d									20 23				20 45									21 25		21 52
Hinton Admiral	d									20 27													21 29		21 56
Christchurch	d									20 32				20 52									21 34		22 01
Pokesdown	d									20 36				20 56									21 38		22 05
Bournemouth	a					20 20			20 24	20 40				21 00						21 22		21 26	21 42		22 09
	d					20 21				20 41				21 04						21 27			21 43		22 10
Branksome	d					20 26				20 46										21 32			21 48		22 15
Parkstone (Dorset)	d					20 29				20 49										21 35			21 51		22 18
Poole 4	a					20 33				20 56				21 13						21 38			21 57		22 23
	d					20 34								21 14						21 39					
Hamworthy	d					20 39								21 19						21 44					
Holton Heath	d																								
Wareham	d					20 46								21 26						21 51					
Wool	d													21 33						21 58					
Moreton (Dorset)	d													21 39						22 04					
Dorchester South	d					21 02								21 47						22 12					
Dorchester West	d																								
Upwey	d													21 53						22 18					
Weymouth	a					21 13								21 58						22 23					

For general notes see front of timetable
For details of catering facilities see Directory of Train Operators

B ⊏P to Bournemouth
b Until 5 September.
c Until 11 July.

For other services between Southampton Central and Romsey see Table 123.

For details of Bank Holiday service alterations, please see first page of Table 149

London → Basingstoke, Southampton, Romsey Lymington, Bournemouth and Weymouth

Network Diagram - see first page of Table 158

		SW	SW	XC	SW	GW	SW	SW	XC	SW	SW	XC	SW	SW	SW	SW	SW	SW	XC	SW	SW	SW	SW
		1	1	R 1	1	◇	1 ◇	1	R 1	1 ◇	1	R 1	1 ◇	1	1	1	1	1	1 ◇	1	1	1	1
							A ☕			☕			A ☕			☕				☕			
London Waterloo 15 ⊖	d		20 09				20 35	20 39		21 05			21 35		21 39	22 05		21 42		22 35	22 39	23 05	23 39
Clapham Junction 10	d							20u46		21u12					21u46	22u12					22u46	23u12	23u46
Woking	d		20 35				21 00			21 32			22 00			22 32		22 19		23 00		23 32	00 08
Farnborough (Main)	d		20 45					21 13							22 13			22 33			23 13		00 18
Fleet	d							21 19							22 19			22 38			23 19		00 23
Reading 7	d			20 45								21 45							22 45				
Basingstoke	a		20 58	21 08				21 34		21 51		22 08			22 34	22 51		22 58	23 08		23 33	23 51	00 35
	d		21 00	21 10				21 36		21 53		22 10		22 21	22 36	22 53		23 00	23 10		23 34	23 53	00 36
Micheldever	d		21 10											22 31	22s46			23 10				00 03	
Winchester	d		21 19	21 25			21 33	21 52		22 09		22 25	22 33	22 40	22 55	23 09		23 19	23 25	23 33	23 51	00 12	00 53
Shawford	d		21 24					21 57						22 45	23 00			23 24			23 55		
Romsey	d	21 05									22 07						23 07						
Chandlers Ford	a	21 12									22 14						23 14						
	d	21 12									22 14						23 14						
Eastleigh 3	a	21 18	21 30					22 02		22 17	22 22			22 50	23 05	23 17	23 22	23 30			00 01	00 20	01 01
	d	21 19	21 30					22 03		22 18	22 23			22 51	23 06	23 18	23 23	23 30			00 02	00 21	01 02
Hedge End	d		21 36											22 57				23 36					
Botley	d		21 40											23 01				23 40					
Fareham	d		21 48											23 10				23 48					
Portchester	d		21 53											23 15				23 53					
Cosham	d		21 58											23 20				23 59					
Hilsea	a		22 06											23 24				00 04					
Fratton	a		22 10											23 32				00 08					
Portsmouth & Southsea	a		22 13											23 36				00 11					
Portsmouth Harbour	a		22 18											23 40				00 16					
Southampton Airport Parkwy ✈	d	21 23		21 34			21 42	22 08		22 23	22 27	22 34	22 42		23 11	23 23	23 27		23 34	23 42	00 06	00 26	01 06
Swaythling	d	21 26									22 30						23 30					00s30	
St Denys	d	21 29									22 33						23 33						
Southampton Central	a	21 34		21 40			21 49	22 15		22 30	22 38	22 46	22 49		23 18	23 30	23 38		23 47	23 49	00 13	00 35	01 13
	d	21 38		21 42			21 51			22 31	22 39		22 51			23 31	23 39			23 51		00 36	
Millbrook (Hants)	d	21 40									22 42						23 42						
Redbridge	d	21 44									22 45						23 45						
Romsey	d	21 52									22a53						23 56						
Mottisfont & Dunbridge	d	21 57															00 01						
Dean	d	22 02															00 06						
Salisbury	a	22 15															00 19						
Totton	d									22 37						23 37						00s41	
Ashurst New Forest	d									22 41						23 41							
Beaulieu Road	d																						
Brockenhurst 3	a			21 56			22 04		←	22 49			23 04			23 49				00 04		00s52	
	d			21 57	21 59		22 05		21 57	22 50			23 05			23 50				00 05			
Lymington Town	d			→	22 07																		
Lymington Pier	a				22 09																		
Yarmouth (I.O.W.) ⛴	a				22 45																		
Sway	d									22 55						23 55							
New Milton	d									23 00						23 59						01s00	
Hinton Admiral	d									23 04						00 04							
Christchurch	d									23 09						00 09						01s07	
Pokesdown	d									23 12						00 12						01s11	
Bournemouth	a						22 20		22 26	23 16			23 23			00 16				00 22		01 15	
	d						22 24			23 18			23 28			00 18				00 24		01 16	
Branksome	d						22 29			23 23			23 33			00 23				00 29		01s21	
Parkstone (Dorset)	d						22 32			23 26			23 36			00 26				00 32		01s24	
Poole 4	a						22 36			23 30			23 39			00 30				00 36		01 30	
	d						22 37						23 40										
Hamworthy	d						22 42						23 45										
Holton Heath	d																						
Wareham	d						22 49						23 52										
Wool	d						22 55						23 59										
Moreton (Dorset)	d						23 01						00 05										
Dorchester South	d						23 09						00 13										
Dorchester West	d					22 50																	
Upwey	d					22 57	23 16						00 19										
Weymouth	a					23 05	23 20						00 24										

For general notes see front of timetable
For details of catering facilities see Directory of Train Operators

A ☕ to Bournemouth

For other services between Southampton Central and Romsey see Table 123.

London → Basingstoke, Southampton, Romsey Lymington, Bournemouth and Weymouth

Network Diagram - see first page of Table 158

		SW	SW	SW	SW	SW	SW	SW	SW	SW	SW	SW	SW	SW	SW	SW	SW	SW	SW	SW	GW	SW	SW	SW	SW
		1 ◇	1 ☕	1	1	1 ☕	1	1	1	1	1	1	1	1	1	1	1	1	1	1	◇	1	1	1	1
London Waterloo 15 ⊖	d	21p35	22p05		21p42	22p35	22p39	23p05		23p39	00 05	01 05										05 30			
Clapham Junction 10	d		22b12				22b46	23b12		23b46	00u12	01 14										05u37			
Woking	d	22p00	22p32		22p19	23p00		23p32		00 08	00 36	01 42										06 01			
Farnborough (Main)	d				22p33		23p13			00 18		01s58													
Fleet	d				22p38		23p19			00 23															
Reading 7	d																								
Basingstoke	a		22p51		22p58		23p33	23p51		00 35	00 55	02s12										06 20			
	d		22p53		23p00		23p34	23p53		00 36	00 57											06 21			
Micheldever	d				23p10			00 03														06 31			
Winchester	d	22p33	23p09		23p19	23p33	23p51	00 12		00 53	01 13	02s29										06 41			
Shawford	d				23p24		23p55																		
Romsey	d			23p07															05 58						07 07
Chandlers Ford	a			23p14															06 06						07 14
	d			23p14															06 06						07 14
Eastleigh 3	a		23p17	23p22	23p30		00 01	00 20		01 01	01 21	02s38							06 11			06 50			07 20
	d		23p18	23p23	23p30		00 02	00 21	00 30	01 02	01 22								06 13	06 30		06 51			07 21
Hedge End	d				23p36				00s36											06 36					
Botley	d				23p40				00s39											06 40					
Fareham	d				23p48				00s47											06 48					
Portchester	d				23p53				00s53											06 53					
Cosham	d				23p59				00s57											06 58					
Hilsea	a				00 04															07 03					
Fratton	a				00 08				01s05											07 06					
Portsmouth & Southsea	a				00 11				01s08											07 10					
Portsmouth Harbour	a				00 16				01 12											07 17					
Southampton Airport Parkwy ✈	d	22p42	23p23	23p27		23p42	00 06	00 26		01 06	01 27	02s43							06 17			06 56			07 25
Swaythling	d			23p30															06 20						07 28
St Denys	d			23p33				00s30				02s48							06 23						07 31
Southampton Central	a	22p49	23p30	23p38		23p49	00 13	00 35		01 13	01 36	02 53							06 28			07 03			07 36
	d	22p51	23p31	23p39		23p51		00 36			01 37						06 25		06 30			07 05		07 25	07 37
Millbrook (Hants)	d			23p42															06 32						07 40
Redbridge	d			23p45															06 36						07 43
Romsey	d			23p56															06 44						07 51
Mottisfont & Dunbridge	d			00 01															06 49						07 56
Dean	d			00 06															06 54						08 02
Salisbury	a			00 19															07 07						08 14
Totton	d		23p37					00s41			01s42						06 30					07 10		07 30	
Ashurst New Forest	d		23p41														06 35							07 35	
Beaulieu Road	d																								
Brockenhurst 3	a	23p04	23p49			00 04		00s52			01s53						06 43					07 21		07 43	
	d	23p05	23p50			00 05							05 59		06 16	06 29	06 44	06 59				07 22	07 29	07 44	
Lymington Town	d												06 07			06 37		07 07					07 37		
Lymington Pier	a												06 09			06 39		07 09					07 39		
Yarmouth (I.O.W.) ⛴	a												*06c45*			*07 15*		*07 45*					*08c15*		
Sway	d		23p55												06 20		06 48					07 26		07 48	
New Milton	d		23p59					01s00			02s01				06 25		06 53					07 31		07 53	
Hinton Admiral	d		00 04												06 29		06 57					07 35		07 57	
Christchurch	d		00 09					01s07			02s08				06 34		07 02					07 40		08 02	
Pokesdown	d		00 12					01s11			02s12				06 38		07 06					07 44		08 06	
Bournemouth	a	23p23	00 16			00 22		01 15			02 16				06 42		07 10					07 48		08 10	
	d	23p28	00 18			00 24		01 16						06 11	06 44		07 11					07 49		08 11	
Branksome	d	23p33	00 23			00 29		01s21						06 16	06 49		07 16					07 54		08 16	
Parkstone (Dorset)	d	23p36	00 26			00 32		01s24						06 19	06 52		07 19					07 57		08 19	
Poole 4	a	23p39	00 30			00 36		01 30						06 23	06 55		07 23					08 01		08 23	
	d	23p40												06 24	06 57		07 24					08 02		08 24	
Hamworthy	d	23p45												06 29	07 02		07 29					08 07		08 29	
Holton Heath	d													06 33	07 06		07 33							08 33	
Wareham	d	23p52												06 38	07 11		07 38					08 14		08 38	
Wool	d	23p59												06 44	07 17		07 44					08 20		08 44	
Moreton (Dorset)	d	00 05												06 50	07 23		07 50					08 26		08 50	
Dorchester South	d	00 13												06 58	07 31		07 58					08 34		08 58	
Dorchester West	d																				08 14				
Upwey	d	00 19												07 05	07 38		08 05				08 20	08 41		09 05	
Weymouth	a	00 24												07 09	07 42		08 09				08 26	08 45		09 09	

For general notes see front of timetable
For details of catering facilities see Directory of Train Operators

b Previous night.
Stops to pick up only
c Until 12 July.

For other services between Southampton Central and Romsey see Table 123.

Table 158

Saturdays

London → Basingstoke, Southampton, Romsey Lymington, Bournemouth and Weymouth

Network Diagram - see first page of Table 158

		SW 1	SW 1	SW 1	SW 1	SW 1	SW 1	SW 1	SW 1	SW 1 ◇	SW 1	SW 1	GW	SW 1 ◇	SW 1	SW 1	SW 1	XC 1 ◇	SW 1	SW 1 ◇	SW 1	SW 1	SW 1	GW	SW 1 ◇
																				A				B	A
																		⊡		⊡					⊡
London Waterloo 15 ⊖	d			06 30					06 42	07 35	07 39			08 05			08 09			08 35	08 39				09 05
Clapham Junction 10	d			06u37					06u49		07u46			08u12							08u46				09u12
Woking	d		06 19	06 57					07 19	08 00							08 35			09 00					
Farnborough (Main)	d		06 33						07 33		08 13						08 45				09 13				
Fleet	d		06 38						07 38		08 19										09 19				
Reading 7	d																	08 45							
Basingstoke	a		06 58	07 16					07 58	08 20	08 34			08 48			08 58	09 08			09 34				09 48
	d		07 00	07 18					08 00	08 21	08 36			08 50			09 00	09 10			09 36				09 50
Micheldever	d		07 10						08 10								09 10								
Winchester	d		07 19	07 34					08 19	08 38	08 52			09 06			09 19	09 25		09 33	09 52				10 06
Shawford	d		07 24						08 24		08 57										09 57				
Romsey	d						08 05									09 05									
Chandlers Ford	a						08 12									09 12									
	d						08 12									09 12									
Eastleigh 3	a		07 30	07 42			08 18		08 30	08 46	09 02					09 18	09 29				10 02				
	d		07 30	07 43			08 19		08 30	08 47	09 03					09 19	09 30				10 03				
Hedge End	d		07 36						08 36								09 36								
Botley	d		07 40						08 40								09 40								
Fareham	d		07 48						08 48								09 48								
Portchester	d		07 53						08 53								09 53								
Cosham	d		07 58						08 58								09 58								
Hilsea	a		08 04						09 03								10 03								
Fratton	a		08 07						09 07								10 07								
Portsmouth & Southsea	a		08 11						09 11								10 11								
Portsmouth Harbour	a		08 18						09 18								10 18								
Southampton Airport Parkwy ✈	d			07 48			08 23			08 51	09 08			09 15		09 23		09 34		09 42	10 08				10 15
Swaythling	d						08 26									09 26									
St Denys	d						08 29									09 29									
Southampton Central	a			07 55			08 34			08 58	09 15			09 22	←	09 34		09 40		09 49	10 15				10 22
	d			08 00		08 22	08 38			09 00	09 30			09 24	09 30	09 38		09 42		09 51	10 30				10 24
Millbrook (Hants)	d						08 40				→					09 40					→				
Redbridge	d						08 44									09 44									
Romsey	d						08 52									09 52									
Mottisfont & Dunbridge	d						08 57									09 57									
Dean	d						09 02									10 02									
Salisbury	a						09 15									10 15									
Totton	d			08 05		08 27				09 05					09 35										
Ashurst New Forest	d					08 31									09 40										
Beaulieu Road	d					08 36									09 44										
Brockenhurst 3	a			08 16		08 42				09 16				09 37	09 51			09 56		10 04		←			10 37
	d	07 59		08 17	08 29	08 44		08 59		09 16		09 29		09 38	10 16			09 57	09 59	10 05		10 16	10 29		10 38
Lymington Town	d	08 07			08 37			09 07				09 37			→				10 07				10 37		
Lymington Pier	a	08 09			08 39			09 09				09 39							10 09				10 39		
Yarmouth (I.O.W.) ⛴	a	*08 45*			*09 15*			*09b45*				*10 15*							*10 45*				*11b15*		
Sway	d			08 21		08 48				09 20												10 20			
New Milton	d			08 26		08 53				09 25				09 45								10 25			10 45
Hinton Admiral	d			08 30		08 57				09 29												10 29			
Christchurch	d			08 35		09 02				09 34				09 52								10 34			10 52
Pokesdown	d			08 39		09 06				09 38				09 56								10 38			10 56
Bournemouth	a			08 43		09 10				09 43				10 00				10 15		10 20		10 42			11 00
	d			08 44		09 11				09 43				10 04						10 24		10 43			11 04
Branksome	d			08 49		09 16				09 48										10 29		10 49			
Parkstone (Dorset)	d			08 52		09 19				09 51										10 32		10 52			
Poole 4	a			08 56		09 23				09 56				10 13						10 36		10 55			11 13
	d			08 57		09 24				09 56				10 14						10 37					11 14
Hamworthy	d			09 02		09 29				10 02				10 19						10 42					11 19
Holton Heath	d					09 33								10 23											11 23
Wareham	d			09 09		09 38				10 11				10 28						10 49					11 28
Wool	d			09 15		09 44								10 35											11 35
Moreton (Dorset)	d			09 21		09 50								10 41											11 41
Dorchester South	d			09 29		09 58				10 27				10 49						11 05					11 49
Dorchester West	d												10 42											11{29	
Upwey	d			09 36		10 05							10 49	10 55										}	11 55
Weymouth	a			09 40		10 09				10 35			10 55	11 00						11 13				11{42	12 00

For general notes see front of timetable
For details of catering facilities see Directory of Train Operators

A ⊡ to Bournemouth
B 5 July to 6 September
b Until 12 July.

For other services between Southampton Central and Romsey see Table 123.

London → Basingstoke, Southampton, Romsey Lymington, Bournemouth and Weymouth

Network Diagram - see first page of Table 158

		SW	SW	SW	XC	SW	GW	SW	SW	SW	SW	SW	SW	SW	SW	XC	SW	SW	SW	SW	SW	SW	SW	SW	SW
		1	1	1	1 ◇	1	◇	1 ◇	1	1	1	1 ◇	1	1	1	R 1	1	1 ◇	1	1	1	1 ◇	1	1	1
					☕			A ☕				A ☕				☕		A ☕				A ☕			
London Waterloo 15 ⊖	d			09 09				09 35	09 39			10 05			10 09			10 35	10 39			11 05			11 09
Clapham Junction 10	d								09u46			10u12							10u46			11u12			
Woking	d			09 35				10 00							10 35			11 00							11 35
Farnborough (Main)	d			09 45					10 13						10 45				11 13						11 45
Fleet	d								10 19										11 19						
Reading 7	d				09 45											10 45									
Basingstoke	a			09 58	10 08				10 34			10 48			10 58	11 08			11 34			11 48			11 58
	d			10 00	10 10				10 36			10 50			11 00	11 10			11 36			11 50			12 00
Micheldever	d			10 10											11 10										12 10
Winchester	d			10 19	10 25			10 33	10 52			11 06			11 19	11 25		11 33	11 52			12 06			12 19
Shawford	d								10 57										11 57						
Romsey	d		10 05											11 05										12 05	
Chandlers Ford	a		10 12											11 12										12 12	
	d		10 12											11 12										12 12	
Eastleigh 3	a		10 18	10 29					11 02					11 18	11 29				12 02					12 18	12 29
	d		10 19	10 30					11 03					11 19	11 30				12 03					12 19	12 30
Hedge End	d			10 36											11 36										12 36
Botley	d			10 40											11 40										12 40
Fareham	d			10 48											11 48										12 48
Portchester	d			10 53											11 53										12 53
Cosham	d			10 58											11 58										12 58
Hilsea	a			11 03											12 03										13 03
Fratton	a			11 07											12 07										13 07
Portsmouth & Southsea	a			11 11											12 11										13 11
Portsmouth Harbour	a			11 18											12 18										13 18
Southampton Airport Parkwy ✈	d		10 23		10 34			10 42	11 08			11 15		11 23		11 34		11 42	12 08			12 15		12 23	
Swaythling	d		10 26											11 26										12 26	
St Denys	d		10 29											11 29										12 29	
Southampton Central	a	←	10 34		10 40			10 49	11 15			11 22	←	11 34		11 40		11 49	12 15			12 22	←	12 34	
	d	10 30	10 38		10 42			10 51	11 30			11 24	11 30	11 38		11 42		11 51	12 30			12 24	12 30	12 38	
Millbrook (Hants)	d		10 40						→					11 40					→					12 40	
Redbridge	d		10 44											11 44										12 44	
Romsey	d		10 57											11 52										12 57	
Mottisfont & Dunbridge	d													11 57											
Dean	d													12 02											
Salisbury	a		11 15											12 15										13 15	
Totton	d	10 35											11 35										12 35		
Ashurst New Forest	d	10 40											11 40										12 40		
Beaulieu Road	d												11 44												
Brockenhurst 3	a	10 51			10 56			11 04		←		11 37	11 51			11 56		12 04		←		12 37	12 51		
	d	11 16			10 57	10 59		11 05		11 16	11 29	11 38	12 16			11 57	11 59	12 05		12 16	12 29	12 38	13 16		
Lymington Town	d	→				11 07					11 37		→				12 07				12 37		→		
Lymington Pier	a					11 09					11 39						12 09				12 39				
Yarmouth (I.O.W.) ⛴	a					*11 45*					*12b15*						*12c45*				*13e15*				
Sway	d									11 20										12 20					
New Milton	d									11 25		11 45								12 25		12 45			
Hinton Admiral	d									11 29										12 29					
Christchurch	d									11 34		11 52								12 34		12 52			
Pokesdown	d									11 38		11 56								12 38		12 56			
Bournemouth	a				11 15			11 20		11 42		12 00				12 15		12 20		12 42		13 00			
	d							11 24		11 43		12 04						12 24		12 43		13 04			
Branksome	d							11 29		11 48								12 29		12 48					
Parkstone (Dorset)	d							11 32		11 51								12 32		12 51					
Poole 4	a							11 36		11 55		12 13						12 36		12 55		13 13			
	d							11 37				12 14						12 37				13 14			
Hamworthy	d							11 42				12 19						12 42				13 19			
Holton Heath	d											12 23										13 23			
Wareham	d							11 49				12 28						12 49				13 28			
Wool	d											12 35										13 35			
Moreton (Dorset)	d											12 41										13 41			
Dorchester South	d							12 05				12 49						13 05				13 49			
Dorchester West	d						11 56																		
Upwey	d						12 03					12 55										13 55			
Weymouth	a						12 08	12 13				13 00						13 13				14 00			

For general notes see front of timetable
For details of catering facilities see Directory of Train Operators

A ☕ to Bournemouth
b Until 6 September.
c Until 12 July then from 13 September until 1 November.
e Until 6 September and from 8 November.

For other services between Southampton Central and Romsey see Table 123.

Table 158

Saturdays

London → Basingstoke, Southampton, Romsey Lymington, Bournemouth and Weymouth

Network Diagram - see first page of Table 158

		XC	XC	SW	GW	SW	SW	SW	SW	SW	SW	SW	SW	XC	SW	SW	SW	SW	SW	SW	SW	SW	SW	XC	SW
		1 ◇	R 1	1	◇	1 ◇	1	1	1	1 ◇	1	1	1	1 ◇	1	1 ◇	1	1	1	1 ◇	1	1	1	1 ◇	1
		A ☕	B ☕			C ☕				C ☕				☕		C ☕				C ☕				☕	
London Waterloo 15 ⊖	d					11 35	11 39			12 05			12 09			12 35	12 39			13 05			13 09		
Clapham Junction 10	d						11u46			12u12							12u46			13u12					
Woking	d					12 00							12 35			13 00							13 35		
Farnborough (Main)	d						12 13						12 45				13 13						13 45		
Fleet	d						12 19										13 19								
Reading 7	d	11 45	11 45											12 45										13 45	
Basingstoke	a	12 08	12 08				12 34			12 48			12 58	13 08			13 34			13 48			13 58	14 08	
	d	12 10	12 10				12 36			12 50			13 00	13 10			13 36			13 50			14 00	14 10	
Micheldever	d												13 10										14 10		
Winchester	d	12 25	12 25			12 33	12 52			13 06			13 19	13 25		13 33	13 52			14 06			14 19	14 25	
Shawford	d						12 57										13 57								
Romsey	d											13 05										14 05			
Chandlers Ford	a											13 12										14 12			
	d											13 12										14 12			
Eastleigh 3	a						13 02					13 18	13 29				14 02					14 18	14 29		
	d						13 03					13 19	13 30				14 03					14 19	14 30		
Hedge End	d												13 36										14 36		
Botley	d												13 40										14 40		
Fareham	d												13 48										14 48		
Portchester	d												13 53										14 53		
Cosham	d												13 58										14 58		
Hilsea	a												14 03										15 03		
Fratton	a												14 07										15 07		
Portsmouth & Southsea	a												14 11										15 11		
Portsmouth Harbour	a												14 18										15 18		
Southampton Airport Parkwy ✈	d	12 34	12 34			12 42	13 08			13 15		13 23		13 34		13 42	14 08			14 15		14 23		14 34	
Swaythling	d											13 26										14 26			
St Denys	d											13 29										14 29			
Southampton Central	a	12 40	12 40			12 49	13 15			13 22	←	13 34		13 40		13 49	14 15			14 22	←	14 34		14 40	
	d	12 42	12 42			12 51	13 30 →			13 24	13 30	13 38		13 42		13 51	14 30 →			14 24	14 30	14 38		14 42	
Millbrook (Hants)	d											13 40										14 40			
Redbridge	d											13 44										14 44			
Romsey	d											13 52										14 52			
Mottisfont & Dunbridge	d											13 57										14 57			
Dean	d											14 02										15 02			
Salisbury	a											14 15										15 15			
Totton	d										13 35										14 35				
Ashurst New Forest	d										13 40										14 40				
Beaulieu Road	d										13 44														
Brockenhurst 3	a	12 55	12 56			13 04		←		13 37	13 51			13 56		14 04		←		14 37	14 51			14 56	
	d	12 56	12 57	12 59		13 05		13 16	13 29	13 38	14 16			13 57	13 59	14 05		14 16	14 29	14 38	15 16			14 57	14 59
Lymington Town	d			13 07					13 37		→				14 07				14 37		→				15 07
Lymington Pier	a			13 09					13 39						14 09				14 39						15 09
Yarmouth (I.O.W.) ⛴	a			*13 45*					*14b15*						*14c45*				*15 15*						*15b45*
Sway	d							13 20										14 20							
New Milton	d							13 25		13 45								14 25		14 45					
Hinton Admiral	d							13 29										14 29							
Christchurch	d							13 34		13 52								14 34		14 52					
Pokesdown	d							13 38		13 56								14 38		14 56					
Bournemouth	a	13 14	13 15			13 20		13 42		14 00				14 15		14 20		14 42		15 00				15 15	
	d					13 24		13 43		14 04						14 24		14 43		15 04					
Branksome	d					13 29		13 48								14 29		14 48							
Parkstone (Dorset)	d					13 32		13 51								14 32		14 51							
Poole 4	a					13 36		13 55		14 13						14 36		14 55		15 13					
	d					13 37				14 14						14 37				15 14					
Hamworthy	d					13 42				14 19						14 42				15 19					
Holton Heath	d									14 23										15 23					
Wareham	d					13 49				14 28						14 49				15 28					
Wool	d									14 35										15 35					
Moreton (Dorset)	d									14 41										15 41					
Dorchester South	d					14 05				14 49						15 05				15 49					
Dorchester West	d				13 55																				
Upwey	d				14 03					14 55										15 55					
Weymouth	a				14 08	14 13				15 00						15 13				16 00					

For general notes see front of timetable
For details of catering facilities see Directory of Train Operators

A From 13 September.
B Until 6 September.
C ☕ to Bournemouth

b Until 12 July and from 13 September.

For other services between Southampton Central and Romsey see Table 123.

Table 158

Saturdays

London → Basingstoke, Southampton, Romsey Lymington, Bournemouth and Weymouth

Network Diagram - see first page of Table 158

		SW	SN	SW	SW	SW	SW	SW	SW	SW	XC	SW	GW	GW	SW	SW	SW	SW	SW	SW	SW	SW	XC	SW	SW
		1 ◇	1	1	1	1	1 ◇	1	1	1	1 ◇	1	◇	◇	1 ◇	1	1	1	1 ◇	1	1	1	R 1	1	1 ◇
		A											B	C	A				A						A
		☕					☕				☕		🍴	🍴	☕				☕				☕		☕
London Waterloo 15 ⊖	d	13 35		13 39			14 05			14 09					14 35	14 39			15 05			15 09			15 35
Clapham Junction 10	d			13u46			14u12									14u46			15u12						
Woking	d	14 00								14 35					15 00							15 35			16 00
Farnborough (Main)	d			14 13						14 45						15 13						15 45			
Fleet	d			14 19												15 19									
Reading 7	d										14 45												15 45		
Basingstoke	a			14 34			14 48			14 58	15 08					15 34			15 48			15 58	16 08		
	d			14 36			14 50			15 00	15 10					15 36			15 50			16 00	16 10		
Micheldever	d									15 10												16 10			
Winchester	d	14 33		14 52			15 06			15 19	15 25				15 33	15 52			16 06			16 19	16 25		16 33
Shawford	d			14 57												15 57									
Romsey	d								15 05												16 05				
Chandlers Ford	a								15 12												16 12				
	d								15 12												16 12				
Eastleigh 3	a			15 02					15 18	15 29						16 02					16 18	16 29			
	d		14 42	15 03					15 19	15 30						16 03					16 19	16 30			
Hedge End	d									15 36												16 36			
Botley	d									15 40												16 40			
Fareham	d		15a01							15 48												16 48			
Portchester	d									15 53												16 53			
Cosham	d									15 58												16 58			
Hilsea	a									16 03												17 03			
Fratton	a									16 07												17 07			
Portsmouth & Southsea	a									16 11												17 11			
Portsmouth Harbour	a									16 18												17 18			
Southampton Airport Parkway ✈	d	14 42		15 08			15 15		15 23		15 34				15 42	16 08			16 15		16 23		16 34		16 42
Swaythling	d								15 26												16 26				
St Denys	d								15 29												16 29				
Southampton Central	a	14 49		15 15			15 22	←	15 34		15 40				15 49	16 15			16 22	←	16 34		16 40		16 49
	d	14 51		15 30			15 24	15 30	15 38		15 42				15 51	16 30			16 24	16 30	16 38		16 42		16 51
Millbrook (Hants)	d			→					15 40							→					16 40				
Redbridge	d								15 44												16 44				
Romsey	d								15 52												16 52				
Mottisfont & Dunbridge	d								15 57												16 57				
Dean	d								16 02												17 02				
Salisbury	a								16 15												17 15				
Totton	d							15 35												16 35					
Ashurst New Forest	d							15 40												16 40					
Beaulieu Road	d							15 44																	
Brockenhurst 3	a	15 04			←		15 37	15 51			15 56				16 04		←		16 37	16 51			16 56		17 04
	d	15 05			15 16	15 29	15 38	16 16			15 57	15 59			16 05		16 16	16 29	16 38	17 16			16 57	16 59	17 05
Lymington Town	d					15 37		→				16 07						16 37		→				17 07	
Lymington Pier	a					15 39						16 09						16 39						17 09	
Yarmouth (I.O.W.) ⛴	a					*16b15*						*16 45*						*17c15*						*17b45*	
Sway	d				15 20												16 20								
New Milton	d				15 25		15 45										16 25		16 45						
Hinton Admiral	d				15 29												16 29								
Christchurch	d				15 34		15 52										16 34		16 52						
Pokesdown	d				15 38		15 56										16 38		16 56						
Bournemouth	a	15 20			15 42		16 00				16 15				16 20		16 42		17 00				17 15		17 20
	d	15 24			15 43		16 04								16 24		16 43		17 04						17 24
Branksome	d	15 29			15 48										16 29		16 48								17 29
Parkstone (Dorset)	d	15 32			15 51										16 32		16 51								17 32
Poole 4	a	15 36			15 55		16 13								16 36		16 55		17 13						17 36
	d	15 37					16 14								16 37				17 14						17 37
Hamworthy	d	15 42					16 19								16 42				17 19						17 42
Holton Heath	d						16 23												17 23						
Wareham	d	15 49					16 28								16 49				17 28						17 49
Wool	d						16 35												17 35						
Moreton (Dorset)	d						16 41												17 41						
Dorchester South	d	16 05					16 49								17 05				17 49						18 05
Dorchester West	d												16 54	16 55											
Upwey	d						16 55						17 02	17 02					17 55						
Weymouth	a	16 13					17 00						17 08	17 08	17 13				18 00						18 13

For general notes see front of timetable
For details of catering facilities see Directory of Train Operators

A ☕ to Bournemouth
B Until 6 September.
C From 13 September.
c Until 12 July and from 13 September.

For other services between Southampton Central and Romsey see Table 123.

Table 158

Saturdays

London → Basingstoke, Southampton, Romsey Lymington, Bournemouth and Weymouth

Network Diagram - see first page of Table 158

		SW	SW	SW	SW	SW	SW	SW	XC	SW	SW	SW	SW	SW	SW	GW	SW	SW	SW	SW	XC	SW	GW	SW	SW
		1	1	1	1 ◇	1	1	1	1 ◇	1	1 ◇	1	1	1	1	◇	1 ◇	1	1	1	1 ◇	1	◇	1 ◇	1
					A ⊡				⊡		A ⊡						A ⊡				⊡			A ⊡	
London Waterloo 15 ⊖	d	15 39			16 05			16 09			16 35		16 39				17 05			17 09				17 35	17 39
Clapham Junction 10	d	15u46			16u12								16u46				17u12								17u46
Woking	d							16 35			17 00									17 35				18 00	
Farnborough (Main)	d	16 13						16 45					17 13							17 45					18 13
Fleet	d	16 19											17 19												18 19
Reading 7	d								16 45												17 45				
Basingstoke	a	16 34			16 48			16 58	17 08				17 34				17 48			17 58	18 08				18 34
	d	16 36			16 50			17 00	17 10			17 24	17 36				17 50			18 00	18 10				18 36
Micheldever	d							17 10				17 34								18 10					
Winchester	d	16 52			17 06			17 19	17 25		17 33	17 43	17 52				18 06			18 19	18 25			18 33	18 52
Shawford	d	16 57										17 48	17 57												18 57
Romsey	d						17 05												18 05						
Chandlers Ford	a						17 12												18 12						
	d						17 12												18 12						
Eastleigh 3	a	17 02					17 18	17 29				17 53	18 02						18 18	18 29					19 02
	d	17 03					17 19	17 30				17 54	18 03						18 19	18 30					19 03
Hedge End	d							17 36												18 36					
Botley	d							17 40												18 40					
Fareham	d							17 48												18 48					
Portchester	d							17 53												18 53					
Cosham	d							17 58												18 58					
Hilsea	a							18 03												19 03					
Fratton	a							18 07												19 07					
Portsmouth & Southsea	a							18 11												19 11					
Portsmouth Harbour	a							18 18												19 18					
Southampton Airport Parkwy ✈	d	17 08			17 15		17 23		17 34		17 42	17 59	18 08				18 15		18 23		18 34			18 42	19 08
Swaythling	d						17 26					18 01							18 26						
St Denys	d						17 29					18 04							18 29						
Southampton Central	a	17 15			17 22	←	17 34		17 40		17 49	18 10	18 15				18 22	←	18 34		18 40			18 49	19 15
	d	17 30			17 24	17 30	17 38		17 42		17 51		18 30				18 24	18 30	18 38		18 42			18 51	19 30
Millbrook (Hants)	d	→					17 40						→						18 40						→
Redbridge	d						17 44												18 44						
Romsey	d						17 52												18 57						
Mottisfont & Dunbridge	d						17 57												19 04						
Dean	d						18 02												19 09						
Salisbury	a						18 15												19 23						
Totton	d					17 35												18 35							
Ashurst New Forest	d					17 40												18 40							
Beaulieu Road	d					17 44																			
Brockenhurst 3	a		←		17 37	17 51			17 56		18 04			←			18 37	18 51			18 56			19 04	
	d		17 16	17 29	17 38	18 16			17 57	17 59	18 05			18 16	18 29		18 38	19 16			18 57	18 59		19 05	
Lymington Town	d			17 37		→				18 07					18 37			→				19 07			
Lymington Pier	a			17 39						18 09					18 39							19 09			
Yarmouth (I.O.W.) ⛴	a			*18 15*						*18b45*					*19c15*							*19 45*			
Sway	d		17 20											18 20											
New Milton	d		17 25		17 45									18 25			18 45								
Hinton Admiral	d		17 29											18 29											
Christchurch	d		17 34		17 52									18 34			18 52								
Pokesdown	d		17 38		17 56									18 38			18 56								
Bournemouth	a		17 42		18 00				18 15		18 20			18 42			19 00				19 15			19 20	
	d		17 43		18 04						18 24			18 43			19 04							19 24	
Branksome	d		17 48								18 29			18 48										19 29	
Parkstone (Dorset)	d		17 51								18 32			18 51										19 32	
Poole 4	a		17 55		18 13						18 36			18 55			19 13							19 36	
	d				18 14						18 37						19 14							19 37	
Hamworthy	d				18 19						18 42						19 19							19 42	
Holton Heath	d				18 23												19 23								
Wareham	d				18 28						18 49						19 28							19 49	
Wool	d				18 35												19 35								
Moreton (Dorset)	d				18 41												19 41								
Dorchester South	d				18 49						19 05						19 49							20 05	
Dorchester West	d															19 12							19 54		
Upwey	d				18 55											19 21	19 55						20 02		
Weymouth	a				19 00						19 13					19 26	20 01						20 08	20 13	

For general notes see front of timetable
For details of catering facilities see Directory of Train Operators

A ⊡ to Bournemouth

b Until 12 July then from 13 September until 1 November.

c Until 12 July and from 13 September.

For other services between Southampton Central and Romsey see Table 123.

Saturdays

London → Basingstoke, Southampton, Romsey Lymington, Bournemouth and Weymouth

Network Diagram - see first page of Table 158

		SW	SW	SW	SW	SW	SW	XC	SW	SW	SW	SW	SW	SW	SW	SW	SW	XC	SW	SW	SW	SW	SW	SW	SW
		1	1	1 ◇	1	1	1	1 ◇	1	1 ◇	1	1	1	1 ◇	1	1	1	1 ◇	1	1 ◇	1	1	1	1 ◇	1
				A						A				A						A					
				🛒				🛒		🛒				🛒				🛒		🛒				🛒	
London Waterloo 15 ⊖	d			18 05			18 09			18 35	18 39			19 05			19 09			19 35	19 39			20 05	
Clapham Junction 10	d			18 12							18u46			19u12							19u46			20u12	
Woking	d						18 35			19 00							19 35			20 00					
Farnborough (Main)	d						18 45				19 13						19 45				20 13				
Fleet	d										19 19										20 19				
Reading 7	d							18 45										19 45							
Basingstoke	a			18 48			18 58	19 08			19 34			19 48			19 58	20 08			20 34			20 48	
	d			18 50			19 00	19 10			19 36			19 50			20 00	20 10			20 36			20 50	
Micheldever	d						19 10										20 10								
Winchester	d			19 06			19 19	19 25		19 33	19 52			20 06			20 19	20 25		20 33	20 52			21 06	
Shawford	d										19 57										20 57				
Romsey	d					19 05										20 05									21 05
Chandlers Ford	a					19 12										20 12									21 12
	d					19 12										20 12									21 12
Eastleigh 3	a					19 18	19 29				20 02					20 18	20 29				21 02				21 18
	d					19 19	19 30				20 03					20 19	20 30				21 03				21 19
Hedge End	d						19 36										20 36								
Botley	d						19 40										20 40								
Fareham	d						19 48										20 48								
Portchester	d						19 53										20 53								
Cosham	d						19 58										20 58								
Hilsea	a						20 03										21 03								
Fratton	a						20 07										21 07								
Portsmouth & Southsea	a						20 11										21 11								
Portsmouth Harbour	a						20 18										21 18								
Southampton Airport Parkway ✈	d			19 15		19 23		19 34		19 42	20 08			20 15		20 23		20 34		20 42	21 08			21 15	21 23
Swaythling	d					19 26										20 26									21 26
St Denys	d					19 29										20 29									21 29
Southampton Central	a			19 22	←	19 34		19 40		19 49	20 15			20 22	←	20 34		20 40		20 49	21 15			21 22	21 35
	d			19 24	19 30	19 38		19 42		19 51	20 30			20 24	20 30	20 38		20 42		20 51				21 24	21 38
Millbrook (Hants)	d					19 40					→					20 40									21 40
Redbridge	d					19 44										20 44									21 44
Romsey	d					19 52										20 57									21 52
Mottisfont & Dunbridge	d					19 57																			21 57
Dean	d					20 02																			22 02
Salisbury	a					20 15										21 15									22 15
Totton	d				19 35										20 35									21 29	
Ashurst New Forest	d				19 40										20 40									21 34	
Beaulieu Road	d																								
Brockenhurst 3	a	←		19 37	19 51			19 56		20 04		←		20 37	20 51			20 56		21 04		←		21 42	
	d	19 16	19 29	19 38	20 16			19 57	19 59	20 05		20 16	20 29	20 38	21 16			20 57	20 59	21 05		21 16	21 29	21 43	
Lymington Town	d		19 37		→				20 07				20 37		→				21 07				21 37		
Lymington Pier	a		19 39						20 09				20 39						21 09				21 39		
Yarmouth (I.O.W.) ⛴	a		*20b15*						*20 45*				*21c15*						*22b00*				*22 45*		
Sway	d	19 20										20 20										21 20		21 47	
New Milton	d	19 25		19 45								20 25		20 45								21 25		21 52	
Hinton Admiral	d	19 29										20 29										21 29		21 56	
Christchurch	d	19 34		19 52								20 34		20 52								21 34		22 01	
Pokesdown	d	19 38		19 56								20 38		20 56								21 38		22 05	
Bournemouth	a	19 42		20 00				20 15		20 20		20 42		21 00				21 15		21 20		21 42		22 09	
	d	19 43		20 04						20 24		20 43		21 04						21 24		21 43		22 10	
Branksome	d	19 48								20 29		20 48								21 29		21 48		22 15	
Parkstone (Dorset)	d	19 51								20 32		20 51								21 32		21 51		22 18	
Poole 4	a	19 55		20 13						20 36		20 55		21 13						21 36		21 55		22 23	
	d			20 14						20 37				21 14						21 37					
Hamworthy	d			20 19						20 42				21 19						21 42					
Holton Heath	d			20 23																					
Wareham	d			20 28						20 49				21 28						21 49					
Wool	d			20 35										21 35						21 55					
Moreton (Dorset)	d			20 41										21 42						22 01					
Dorchester South	d			20 49						21 05				21 49						22 10					
Dorchester West	d																								
Upwey	d			20 55										21 56						22 16					
Weymouth	a			21 00						21 13				22 00						22 21					

For general notes see front of timetable
For details of catering facilities see Directory of Train Operators

A 🛒 to Bournemouth
b Until 12 July.
c Until 6 September.

For other services between Southampton Central and Romsey see Table 123.

Table 158

Saturdays

London → Basingstoke, Southampton, Romsey Lymington, Bournemouth and Weymouth

Network Diagram - see first page of Table 158

		SW	XC	XC	SW	GW	SW	SW	SW	SW	SW	XC	SW	XC	SW	SW	SW	SW	XC	XC	SW	SW	SW	SW
		■1	■1 ◇	■1 ◇	■1	◇	■1 ◇	■1	■1 ◇	■1	■1	■1 ◇	■1 ◇	■1 ◇	■1	■1	■1	■1	■1 ◇	■1 ◇	■1	■1	■1	■1
			A	B			C						C						A	B				
			🍴	🍴			🍴		🍴			🍴	🍴	🍴		🍴					🍴			
London Waterloo 15 ⊖	d	20 09					20 35	20 39	21 05		20 42		21 35		21 39	22 05		21 42			22 35	22 39	23 05	23 39
Clapham Junction 10	d							20u46	21u12						21u46	22u12						22u46	23u12	23u46
Woking	d	20 35					21 00		21 32		21 19		22 00			22 32		22 19			23 00		23 32	00 08
Farnborough (Main)	d	20 45						21 13			21 33				22 13			22 33				23 13		00 18
Fleet	d							21 19			21 38				22 19			22 38				23 19		00 23
Reading 7	d		20 45	20 45								21 45							22 45	22 45				
Basingstoke	a	20 58	21 09	21 08				21 34	21 51		21 58	22 08			22 34	22 51		22 58	23 08	23 08		23 34	23 51	00 35
	d	21 00	21 10	21 10				21 36	21 53		22 00	22 10			22 36	22 53		23 00	23 08	23 10		23 36	23 53	00 36
Micheldever	d	21 10									22 10				22s46			23 10					00 03	
Winchester	d	21 19	21 25	21 25			21 33	21 52	22 09		22 19	22 25	22 33		22 56	23 09		23 19	23 23	23 25	23 33	23 52	00 12	00 53
Shawford	d							21 57							23 00							23 57		
Romsey	d									22 07							23 08							
Chandlers Ford	a									22 14							23 16							
	d									22 14							23 16							
Eastleigh 3	a	21 29						22 02	22 17	22 23	22 29				23 06	23 17	23 22	23 29				00 02	00 20	01 01
	d	21 30						22 03	22 18	22 24	22 30				23 07	23 18	23 23	23 30				00 03	00 21	01 02
Hedge End	d	21 36									22 36							23 36						
Botley	d	21 40									22 40							23 40						
Fareham	d	21 48									22 48							23 48						
Portchester	d	21 53									22 53							23 53						
Cosham	d	21 58									22 58							23 58						
Hilsea	a	22 03									23 03							00 03						
Fratton	a	22 07									23 07							00 07						
Portsmouth & Southsea	a	22 11									23 11							00 11						
Portsmouth Harbour	a	22 18									23 16			←				00 16						
Southampton Airport Parkwy ✈	d		21 34	21 34			21 42	22 08	22 23	22 28		22 34 →	22 42	22 34	23 11	23 23	23 27		23 34	23 34	23 42	00 08	00 26	01 06
Swaythling	d									22 31							23 30							
St Denys	d									22 34							23 33						00s30	
Southampton Central	a		21 40	21 40			21 49	22 15	22 30	22 39			22 49	22 50	23 18	23 30	23 38		23 45	23 45	23 49	00 15	00 35	01 13
	d		21 42	21 42			21 51		22 31	22 40			22 51			23 31	23 40				23 51		00 36	
Millbrook (Hants)	d									22 43							23 42							
Redbridge	d									22 46							23 49							
Romsey	d									22a55							23 57							
Mottisfont & Dunbridge	d																00 02							
Dean	d																00 08							
Salisbury	a																00 20							
Totton	d								22 37							23 37							00s41	
Ashurst New Forest	d								22 41							23 41								
Beaulieu Road	d																							
Brockenhurst 3	a		21 56	21 56			22 04		22 49				23 04			23 49					00 04		00s52	
	d		21 57	21 57	21 59		22 05		22 50				23 05			23 50					00 05			
Lymington Town	d				22 07																			
Lymington Pier	a				22 09																			
Yarmouth (I.O.W.) ⛴	a				22 45																			
Sway	d								22 55							23 55								
New Milton	d								23 00							23 59							01s00	
Hinton Admiral	d								23 04							00 04								
Christchurch	d								23 09							00 09							01s07	
Pokesdown	d								23 12							00 12							01s11	
Bournemouth	a		22 15	22 15			22 20		23 16				23 23			00 16					00 22		01 15	
	d						22 24		23 18				23 28			00 18					00 24		01 16	
Branksome	d						22 29		23 23				23 33			00 23					00 29		01s21	
Parkstone (Dorset)	d						22 32		23 26				23 36			00 26					00 32		01s24	
Poole 4	a						22 36		23 30				23 39			00 30					00 36		01 29	
	d						22 37						23 40											
Hamworthy	d						22 42						23 45											
Holton Heath	d																							
Wareham	d						22 49						23 52											
Wool	d						22 55						23 59											
Moreton (Dorset)	d						23 01						00 05											
Dorchester South	d						23 09						00 13											
Dorchester West	d					22 47																		
Upwey	d					22 54	23 16						00 19											
Weymouth	a					22 59	23 20						00 24											

For general notes see front of timetable
For details of catering facilities see Directory of Train Operators

A From 13 September.
B Until 6 September.
C 🍴 to Bournemouth

For other services between Southampton Central and Romsey see Table 123.

Table 158

Sundays

London → Basingstoke, Southampton, Romsey Lymington, Bournemouth and Weymouth

Network Diagram - see first page of Table 158

		SW 1 ◇	SW 1 (trolley)	SW 1	SW 1	SW 1 (trolley)	SW 1	SW 1	SW 1	SW 1	SW 1	SW 1	SW 1	SW 1	SW 1	SW 1	GW ◇ A	SW 1	SW 1	SW 1	SW 1 ◇	SW 1 ◇
London Waterloo 15 ⊖	d	21p35	22p05		21p42	22p35	22p39	23p05		23p39	00 05	01 05									07 54	
Clapham Junction 10	d		22b12				22b46	23b12		23b46	00u12	01 14									08u03	
Woking	d	22p00	22p32		22p19	23p00		23p32		00 08	00 36	01 42									08 28	
Farnborough (Main)	d				22p33		23p13			00 18		01s58										
Fleet	d				22p38		23p19			00 23												
Reading 7	d																					
Basingstoke	a		22p51		22p58		23p34	23p51		00 35	00 55	02s12									08 47	
	d		22p53		23p00		23p36	23p53		00 36	00 57			07 48							08 49	
Micheldever	d				23p10			00 03						07 58							08 59	
Winchester	d	22p33	23p09		23p19	23p33	23p52	00 12		00 53	01 13	02s29		08 08							09 08	
Shawford	d						23p57							08 12								
Romsey	d			23p08															08 35			
Chandlers Ford	a			23p16															08 42			
	d			23p16															08 42			
Eastleigh 8	a		23p17	23p22	23p29		00 02	00 20		01 01	01 21	02s38		08 18					08 48		09 18	
	d		23p18	23p23	23p30		00 03	00 21	00 30	01 02	01 22			08 22	08 26				08 54		09 22	09 26
Hedge End	d				23p36				00s36						08 32							09 32
Botley	d				23p40				00s39						08 36							09 36
Fareham	d				23p48				00s47						08 44							09 44
Portchester	d				23p53				00s53						08 49							09 49
Cosham	d				23p58				00s57						08 54							09 54
Hilsea	a				00 03										09 00							10 00
Fratton	a				00 07				01s05						09 04							10 04
Portsmouth & Southsea	a				00 11				01s08						09 08							10 10
Portsmouth Harbour	a				00 16				01 12						09 13							10 15
Southampton Airport Parkwy ✈	d	22p42	23p23	23p27		23p42	00 08	00 26		01 06	01 27	02s43		08 27					08 58		09 27	
Swaythling	d			23p30															09 01			
St Denys	d			23p33				00s30				02s48							09 04			
Southampton Central	a	22p49	23p30	23p38		23p49	00 15	00 35		01 13	01 36	02 53		08 34					09 09		09 34	
	d	22p51	23p31	23p40		23p51		00 36			01 37			08 35				09 03	09 10		09 35	
Millbrook (Hants)	d			23p42															09 13			
Redbridge	d			23p49															09 16			
Romsey	d			23p57															09 24			
Mottisfont & Dunbridge	d			00 02															09 29			
Dean	d			00 08															09 35			
Salisbury	a			00 20															09 47			
Totton	d		23p37					00s41			01s42			08 41							09 41	
Ashurst New Forest	d		23p41											08 45							09 45	
Beaulieu Road	d													08 50							09 50	
Brockenhurst 3	a	23p04	23p49			00 04		00s52			01s53			08 56				09 16			09 56	
	d	23p05	23p50			00 05								08 57		08 59		09 17		09 29	09 57	
Lymington Town	d															09 07				09 37		
Lymington Pier	a															09 09				09 39		
Yarmouth (I.O.W.) ⛴	a															*09c45*				*10 15*		
Sway	d		23p55											09 01							10 01	
New Milton	d		23p59					01s00			02s01			09 06				09 24			10 06	
Hinton Admiral	d		00 04											09 10							10 10	
Christchurch	d		00 09					01s07			02s08			09 15							10 15	
Pokesdown	d		00 12					01s11			02s12			09 19							10 19	
Bournemouth	a	23p23	00 16			00 22		01 15			02 16			09 23				09 35			10 23	
	d	23p28	00 18			00 24		01 16					08 40	09 25				09 40			10 25	
Branksome	d	23p33	00 23			00 29		01s21					08 45					09 45				
Parkstone (Dorset)	d	23p36	00 26			00 32		01s24					08 48					09 48				
Poole 4	a	23p39	00 30			00 36		01 29					08 51	09 34				09 51			10 34	
	d	23p40											08 52					09 52				
Hamworthy	d	23p45											08 57					09 57				
Holton Heath	d																					
Wareham	d	23p52											09 04					10 04				
Wool	d	23p59											09 11					10 11				
Moreton (Dorset)	d	00 05											09 17					10 17				
Dorchester South	d	00 13											09 25					10 25				
Dorchester West	d																10 13					
Upwey	d	00 19											09 32				10 20	10 32				
Weymouth	a	00 24											09 36				10 25	10 36				

For general notes see front of timetable
For details of catering facilities see Directory of Train Operators

A Until 7 September
b Previous night. Stops to pick up only
c Until 13 July.

For other services between Southampton Central and Romsey see Table 123.

Table 158

Sundays

London → Basingstoke, Southampton, Romsey Lymington, Bournemouth and Weymouth

Network Diagram - see first page of Table 158

		SW	GW	SW	SW	SW	SW		SW	SW	SW	SW	SW		SW	XC	SW	SW	SW	SW		SW
		1	◇	1 ◇	1	1	1 ◇		1	1 ◇	1	1	1 ◇		1	1 ◇	1 ◇	1	1	1 ◇		1
			A													🍽	B 🍽					
London Waterloo 15 ⊖	d			08 35			08 54			09 35			09 54				10 35			10 54		
Clapham Junction 10	d			08u42			09u03			09u42			10u03				10u42			11u03		
Woking	d			09 09			09 28			10 09			10 28				11 07			11 28		
Farnborough (Main)	d																					
Fleet	d																					
Reading 7	d															10 50						
Basingstoke	a			09 28			09 47			10 28			10 47			11 08	11 26			11 47		
	d			09 30			09 48			10 30			10 48			11 10	11 28			11 48		
Micheldever	d						09 58						10 58							11 58		
Winchester	d			09 46			10 08			10 46			11 08			11 25	11 44			12 08		
Shawford	d						10 12													12 12		
Romsey	d					09 35						10 35							11 35			
Chandlers Ford	a					09 42						10 42							11 42			
	d					09 42						10 42							11 42			
Eastleigh 3	a					09 48	10 18					10 48	11 18						11 48	12 18		
	d					09 54	10 22	10 26				10 54	11 22	11 26					11 54	12 22	12 26	
Hedge End	d							10 32						11 32							12 32	
Botley	d							10 36						11 36							12 36	
Fareham	d							10 44						11 44							12 44	
Portchester	d							10 49						11 49							12 49	
Cosham	d							10 54						11 54							12 54	
Hilsea	a							11 00						12 00							13 00	
Fratton	a							11 04						12 04							13 04	
Portsmouth & Southsea	a							11 08						12 08							13 08	
Portsmouth Harbour	a							11 14						12 13							13 13	
Southampton Airport Parkwy ✈	d			09 55		09 58	10 27			10 55		10 58	11 27			11 34	11 53		11 58	12 27		
Swaythling	d					10 01						11 01							12 01			
St Denys	d					10 04						11 04							12 04			
Southampton Central	a			10 02		10 09	10 34			11 02		11 09	11 34			11 42	12 00		12 09	12 34		
	d			10 04		10 10	10 35			11 04		11 10	11 35			11 44	12 03		12 10	12 35		
Millbrook (Hants)	d					10 13						11 13							12 13			
Redbridge	d					10 16						11 16							12 16			
Romsey	d					10 24						11 24							12 24			
Mottisfont & Dunbridge	d											11 29										
Dean	d											11 35										
Salisbury	a					10 44						11 50							12 43			
Totton	d						10 41						11 41							12 41		
Ashurst New Forest	d						10 45						11 45							12 45		
Beaulieu Road	d						10 50						11 50							12 50		
Brockenhurst 3	a			10 17			10 56			11 17			11 56			12 02	12 16			12 56		
	d	09 59		10 18	10 29		10 57		10 59	11 18	11 29		11 57		11 59	12 03	12 17	12 29		12 57		12 59
Lymington Town	d	10 07			10 37				11 07		11 37				12 07			12 37				13 07
Lymington Pier	a	10 09			10 39				11 09		11 39				12 09			12 39				13 09
Yarmouth (I.O.W.) ⛴	a	*10 45*			*11b15*				*11 45*		*12c15*				*12e45*			*13f15*				*13 45*
Sway	d						11 01						12 01							13 01		
New Milton	d			10 25			11 06			11 25			12 06				12 24			13 06		
Hinton Admiral	d						11 10						12 10							13 10		
Christchurch	d						11 15						12 15							13 15		
Pokesdown	d						11 19						12 19							13 19		
Bournemouth	a			10 35			11 23			11 35			12 23			12 32	12 35			13 23		
	d			10 40			11 25			11 40			12 25				12 40			13 25		
Branksome	d			10 45						11 45							12 45					
Parkstone (Dorset)	d			10 48						11 48							12 48					
Poole 4	a			10 51			11 34			11 51			12 34				12 51			13 34		
	d			10 52						11 52							12 52					
Hamworthy	d			10 57						11 57							12 57					
Holton Heath	d																					
Wareham	d			11 04						12 04							13 04					
Wool	d			11 11						12 11							13 11					
Moreton (Dorset)	d			11 17						12 17							13 17					
Dorchester South	d			11 25						12 25							13 25					
Dorchester West	d		11 17																			
Upwey	d		11 24	11 32						12 32							13 32					
Weymouth	a		11 29	11 36						12 36							13 36					

For general notes see front of timetable
For details of catering facilities see
Directory of Train Operators

A Until 7 September
B 🍽 to Bournemouth
b Until 13 July.
e Until 13 July then from 14 September until 2 November.
f Until 7 September then from 9 November.

For other services between Southampton Central and Romsey see Table 123.

Table 158

Sundays

London → Basingstoke, Southampton, Romsey Lymington, Bournemouth and Weymouth

Network Diagram - see first page of Table 158

		XC	SW	SW	SW	SW		SW	XC	SW	SW	SW	SW		SW	XC	GW	GW	SW	SW	SW
		1 ◇	1 ◇	1	1	1 ◇		1	1 ◇	1 ◇	1	1	1 ◇		1	1 ◇	◇	◇	1 ◇	1	1
			A							A							B	C	A		
		[catering]	[catering]						[catering]	[catering]						[catering]			[catering]		
London Waterloo 15 ⊖	d		11 35			11 54				12 35			12 54						13 35		
Clapham Junction 10	d		11u42			12u03				12u42			13u03						13u42		
Woking	d		12 07			12 28				13 07			13 28						14 07		
Farnborough (Main)	d																				
Fleet	d																				
Reading 7	d	11 50							12 50							13 50					
Basingstoke	a	12 08	12 26			12 47			13 08	13 26			13 47			14 08			14 26		
	d	12 10	12 28			12 48			13 10	13 28			13 48			14 10			14 28		
Micheldever	d					12 58							13 58								
Winchester	d	12 25	12 44			13 08			13 25	13 44			14 08			14 25			14 44		
Shawford	d												14 12								
Romsey	d				12 35							13 35									14 35
Chandlers Ford	a				12 42							13 42									14 42
	d				12 42							13 42									14 42
Eastleigh 3	a				12 48	13 18						13 48	14 18								14 48
	d				12 54	13 22	13 26					13 54	14 22	14 26							14 54
Hedge End	d						13 32							14 32							
Botley	d						13 36							14 36							
Fareham	d						13 44							14 44							
Portchester	d						13 49							14 49							
Cosham	d						13 54							14 54							
Hilsea	a						14 00							15 00							
Fratton	a						14 04							15 04							
Portsmouth & Southsea	a						14 08							15 08							
Portsmouth Harbour	a						14 13							15 13							
Southampton Airport Parkwy ✈	d	12 34	12 53		12 58	13 27			13 34	13 53		13 58	14 27			14 34			14 53		14 58
Swaythling	d				13 01							14 01									15 01
St Denys	d				13 04							14 04									15 04
Southampton Central	a	12 42	13 00		13 09	13 34			13 42	14 00		14 09	14 34			14 42			15 00		15 09
	d	12 44	13 03		13 10	13 35			13 44	14 03		14 10	14 35			14 44			15 03		15 10
Millbrook (Hants)	d				13 13							14 13									15 13
Redbridge	d				13 16							14 16									15 16
Romsey	d				13 24							14 24									15 24
Mottisfont & Dunbridge	d				13 29																15 29
Dean	d				13 38																15 35
Salisbury	a				13 50							14 43									15 50
Totton	d					13 41							14 41								
Ashurst New Forest	d					13 45							14 45								
Beaulieu Road	d					13 50							14 50								
Brockenhurst 3	a	13 02	13 16			13 56			14 02	14 16			14 56			15 02			15 16		
	d	13 03	13 17	13 29		13 57		13 59	14 03	14 17	14 29		14 57		14 59	15 03			15 17	15 29	
Lymington Town	d			13 37				14 07			14 37				15 07					15 37	
Lymington Pier	a			13 39				14 09			14 39				15 09					15 39	
Yarmouth (I.O.W.) ⛴	a			*14b15*				*14c45*			*15 15*				*15b45*					*16c15*	
Sway	d					14 01							15 01								
New Milton	d		13 24			14 06				14 24			15 06						15 24		
Hinton Admiral	d					14 10							15 10								
Christchurch	d					14 15							15 15								
Pokesdown	d					14 19							15 19								
Bournemouth	a	13 32	13 35			14 23			14 32	14 35			15 23			15 32			15 35		
	d		13 40			14 25				14 40			15 25						15 40		
Branksome	d		13 45							14 45									15 45		
Parkstone (Dorset)	d		13 48							14 48									15 48		
Poole 4	a		13 51			14 34				14 51			15 34						15 51		
	d		13 52							14 52									15 52		
Hamworthy	d		13 57							14 57									15 57		
Holton Heath	d																				
Wareham	d		14 04							15 04									16 04		
Wool	d		14 11							15 11									16 11		
Moreton (Dorset)	d		14 17							15 17									16 17		
Dorchester South	d		14 25							15 25									16 25		
Dorchester West	d																15⟆33	15⟆53			
Upwey	d		14 32							15 32							15⟆40	16⟆00	16 32		
Weymouth	a		14 36							15 36							15⟆45	16⟆05	16 36		

For general notes see front of timetable
For details of catering facilities see Directory of Train Operators

A [catering] to Bournemouth
B Until 7 September
C From 14 September
b Until 13 July then from 14 September.

For other services between Southampton Central and Romsey see Table 123.

Table 158

Sundays

London → Basingstoke, Southampton, Romsey Lymington, Bournemouth and Weymouth

Network Diagram - see first page of Table 158

Station		SW		SW	XC	SW	SW	SW	SW		SW	XC	SW	SW	SW	SW		SW	XC	SW	SW	SW
		[1] ◇		[1]	[1] ◇	[1] ◇	[1]	[1]	[1] ◇		[1]	[R] [1]	[1] ◇	[1]	[1]	[1] ◇		[1]	[R] [1]	[1] ◇	[1]	[1]
						A							A							A		
					☕	☕						☕	☕						☕	☕		
London Waterloo [15] ⊖	d	13 54				14 35			14 54				15 35			15 54				16 35		
Clapham Junction [10]	d	14u03				14u42			15u03				15u42			16u03				16u42		
Woking	d	14 28				15 07			15 28				16 07			16 28				17 07		
Farnborough (Main)	d																					
Fleet	d																					
Reading [7]	d				14 50							15 50							16 50			
Basingstoke	a	14 47			15 08	15 26			15 47			16 08	16 26			16 47			17 08	17 26		
	d	14 48			15 10	15 28			15 48			16 10	16 28			16 48			17 10	17 28		
Micheldever	d	14 58							15 58							16 58						
Winchester	d	15 08			15 25	15 44			16 08			16 25	16 44			17 08			17 25	17 44		
Shawford	d								16 12													
Romsey	d							15 35							16 35							17 35
Chandlers Ford	a							15 42							16 42							17 42
	d							15 42							16 42							17 42
Eastleigh [3]	a	15 18						15 48	16 18						16 48	17 18						17 48
	d	15 22	15 26					15 54	16 22	16 26					16 54	17 22	17 26					17 54
Hedge End	d		15 32							16 32							17 32					
Botley	d		15 36							16 36							17 36					
Fareham	d		15 45							16 44							17 44					
Portchester	d		15 50							16 49							17 49					
Cosham	d		15 55							16 54							17 54					
Hilsea	a		16 00							17 00							18 00					
Fratton	a		16 04							17 04							18 04					
Portsmouth & Southsea	a		16 08							17 08							18 08					
Portsmouth Harbour	a		16 13							17 13							18 13					
Southampton Airport Parkwy ✈	d	15 27			15 34	15 53		15 58	16 27			16 34	16 53		16 58	17 27			17 34	17 53		17 58
Swaythling	d							16 01							17 01							18 01
St Denys	d							16 04							17 04							18 04
Southampton Central	a	15 34			15 42	16 00		16 09	16 34			16 42	17 00		17 09	17 34			17 42	18 00		18 09
	d	15 35			15 44	16 03		16 10	16 35			16 44	17 03		17 10	17 35			17 44	18 03		18 10
Millbrook (Hants)	d							16 13							17 13							18 13
Redbridge	d							16 16							17 16							18 16
Romsey	d							16 24							17 24							18 24
Mottisfont & Dunbridge	d														17 29							
Dean	d														17 35							
Salisbury	a							16 43							17 50							18 43
Totton	d	15 41							16 41							17 41						
Ashurst New Forest	d	15 45							16 45							17 45						
Beaulieu Road	d	15 50							16 50							17 50						
Brockenhurst [3]	a	15 56			16 02	16 16			16 56			17 02	17 16			17 56			18 02	18 16		
	d	15 57		15 59	16 03	16 17	16 29		16 57		16 59	17 03	17 17	17 29		17 57		17 59	18 03	18 17	18 29	
Lymington Town	d			16 07			16 37				17 07			17 37				18 07			18 37	
Lymington Pier	a			16 09			16 39				17 09			17 39				18 09			18 39	
Yarmouth (I.O.W.) ⛴	a			*16 45*			*17b15*				*17c45*			*18 15*				*18e45*			*19f15*	
Sway	d	16 01							17 01							18 01						
New Milton	d	16 06				16 24			17 06				17 24			18 06				18 24		
Hinton Admiral	d	16 10							17 10							18 10						
Christchurch	d	16 15							17 15							18 15						
Pokesdown	d	16 19							17 19							18 19						
Bournemouth	a	16 23			16 32	16 35			17 23			17 32	17 35			18 23			18 32	18 35		
	d	16 25				16 40			17 25				17 40			18 25				18 40		
Branksome	d					16 45							17 45							18 45		
Parkstone (Dorset)	d					16 48							17 48							18 48		
Poole [4]	a	16 34				16 51			17 34				17 51			18 34				18 51		
	d					16 52							17 52							18 52		
Hamworthy	d					16 57							17 57							18 57		
Holton Heath	d																					
Wareham	d					17 04							18 04							19 04		
Wool	d					17 11							18 11							19 11		
Moreton (Dorset)	d					17 17							18 17							19 17		
Dorchester South	d					17 25							18 25							19 25		
Dorchester West	d																					
Upwey	d					17 32							18 32							19 32		
Weymouth	a					17 36							18 36							19 36		

For general notes see front of timetable
For details of catering facilities see Directory of Train Operators

A ☕ to Bournemouth
b Until 13 July then from 14 September.
c Until 7 September
e Until 13 July then from 14 September until 2 November.
f Until 7 September then from 9 November.

For other services between Southampton Central and Romsey see Table 123.

Table 158

Sundays

London → Basingstoke, Southampton, Romsey Lymington, Bournemouth and Weymouth

Network Diagram - see first page of Table 158

		SW		SW		XC	GW	SW	SW	SW	SW			SW	XC	SW	SW	SW	SW			SW	XC	SW	SW
		[1] ◇		[1]		[R] [1]	◇	[1] ◇	[1]	[1]	[1] ◇			[1]	[R] [1]	[1] ◇	[1]	[1]	[1] ◇			[1]	[R] [1]	[1] ◇	[1]
						[catering]		A [catering]							[catering]	A [catering]							[catering]	A [catering]	
London Waterloo [15] ⊖	d	16 54						17 35			17 54					18 35			18 54					19 35	
Clapham Junction [10]	d	17u03						17u42			18u03					18u42			19u03					19u42	
Woking	d	17 28						18 07			18 28					19 07			19 28					20 07	
Farnborough (Main)	d																								
Fleet	d																								
Reading [7]	d					17 50									18 50								19 50		
Basingstoke	a	17 47				18 08		18 26			18 47				19 08	19 26			19 47				20 08	20 26	
	d	17 48				18 10		18 28			18 48				19 10	19 28			19 48				20 10	20 28	
Micheldever	d	17 58									18 58								19 58						
Winchester	d	18 08				18 25		18 44			19 08				19 25	19 44			20 08				20 25	20 44	
Shawford	d	18 12																	20 12						
Romsey	d									18 35								19 35							
Chandlers Ford	a									18 42								19 42							
	d									18 42								19 42							
Eastleigh [3]	a	18 18								18 48	19 18							19 48	20 18						
	d	18 22	18 26							18 54	19 22	19 26						19 54	20 22	20 26					
Hedge End	d		18 32									19 32								20 32					
Botley	d		18 36									19 36								20 36					
Fareham	d		18 44									19 44								20 44					
Portchester	d		18 49									19 49								20 49					
Cosham	d		18 54									19 54								20 54					
Hilsea	a		19 00									20 00								21 00					
Fratton	a		19 04									20 04								21 04					
Portsmouth & Southsea	a		19 08									20 08								21 08					
Portsmouth Harbour	a		19 13									20 13								21 13					
Southampton Airport Parkwy ✈	d	18 27				18 34		18 53		18 58	19 27				19 34	19 53		19 58	20 27				20 34	20 53	
Swaythling	d									19 01								20 01							
St Denys	d									19 04								20 04							
Southampton Central	a	18 34				18 42		19 00		19 09	19 34				19 42	20 00		20 09	20 34				20 42	21 00	
	d	18 35				18 44		19 03		19 10	19 35				19 44	20 03		20 10	20 35				20 44	21 03	
Millbrook (Hants)	d									19 13								20 13							
Redbridge	d									19 16								20 16							
Romsey	d									19 24								20 24							
Mottisfont & Dunbridge	d									19 29															
Dean	d									19 35															
Salisbury	a									19 50								20 43							
Totton	d	18 41									19 41								20 41						
Ashurst New Forest	d	18 45									19 45								20 45						
Beaulieu Road	d	18 50									19 50								20 50						
Brockenhurst [3]	a	18 56				19 02		19 16			19 56				20 02	20 16			20 56				21 02	21 16	
	d	18 57		18 59		19 03		19 17	19 29		19 57			19 59	20 03	20 17	20 29		20 57			20 59	21 03	21 17	21 29
Lymington Town	d			19 07					19 37					20 07			20 37					21 07			21 37
Lymington Pier	a			19 09					19 39					20 09			20 39					21 09			21 39
Yarmouth (I.O.W.) ⛴	a			*19 45*					*20b15*					*20 45*			*21c15*					*22b00*			*22 45*
Sway	d	19 01									20 01								21 01						
New Milton	d	19 06						19 24			20 06					20 24			21 06					21 24	
Hinton Admiral	d	19 10									20 10								21 10						
Christchurch	d	19 15									20 15								21 15						
Pokesdown	d	19 19									20 19								21 19						
Bournemouth	a	19 23				19 32		19 35			20 23				20 32	20 35			21 23				21 32	21 35	
	d	19 25						19 40			20 25					20 40			21 25					21 40	
Branksome	d							19 45								20 45								21 45	
Parkstone (Dorset)	d							19 48								20 48								21 48	
Poole [4]	a	19 34						19 51			20 34					20 51			21 34					21 51	
	d							19 52								20 52								21 52	
Hamworthy	d							19 57								20 57								21 57	
Holton Heath	d																								
Wareham	d							20 04								21 04								22 04	
Wool	d							20 11								21 11								22 11	
Moreton (Dorset)	d							20 17								21 17								22 17	
Dorchester South	d							20 25								21 25								22 25	
Dorchester West	d						19 48																		
Upwey	d						19 55	20 32								21 32								22 32	
Weymouth	a						20 01	20 36								21 36								22 36	

For general notes see front of timetable
For details of catering facilities see Directory of Train Operators

A [catering] to Bournemouth
b Until 13 July.
c Until 7 September

For other services between Southampton Central and Romsey see Table 123.

London → Basingstoke, Southampton, Romsey Lymington, Bournemouth and Weymouth

Network Diagram - see first page of Table 158

		SW	SW		SW		XC	GW	SW	SW	SW			XC	SW	SW	SW		XC		SW				
		1	1 ◇		1		R 1	◇	1 ◇	1	1 ◇			R 1	1 ◇	1	1 ◇		1 ◇		1				
									A						A						B				
							🛒		🛒					🛒	🛒						🛒				
London Waterloo 15 ⊖	d		19 54						20 35		20 54				21 35		21 54				22 54				
Clapham Junction 10	d		20u03						20u42		21u03				21u42		22u03				23u03				
Woking	d		20 28						21 07		21 28				22 07		22 28				23 28				
Farnborough (Main)	d																								
Fleet	d																								
Reading 7	d						20 50							21 50					22 50						
Basingstoke	a		20 47				21 08		21 26		21 47			22 08	22 26		22 47		23 08		23 47				
	d		20 48				21 10		21 28		21 48			22 10	22 28		22 48		23 10		23 48				
Micheldever	d		20 58								21 58						22 58				23 58				
Winchester	d		21 08				21 25		21 44		22 08				22 44		23 08		23 25		00 08				
Shawford	d										22 12														
Romsey	d	20 35								21 35						22 35									
Chandlers Ford	a	20 40								21 42						22 42									
	d	20 42								21 42						22 42									
Eastleigh 3	a	20 48	21 18							21 48	22 18					22 48	23 18				00 18				
	d	20 54	21 22	21 26						21 54	22 22	22 26				22 54	23 22	23 26			00 22	00 30			
Hedge End	d			21 32								22 32						23 32				00s36			
Botley	d			21 36								22 36						23 36				00s39			
Fareham	d			21 44								22 44						23 44				00s47			
Portchester	d			21 49								22 49						23 49				00s53			
Cosham	d			21 54								22 54						23 54				00s57			
Hilsea	a			22 00								23 00						23 59							
Fratton	a			22 04								23 04						00 04				01s05			
Portsmouth & Southsea	a			22 08								23 08						00 08				01s08			
Portsmouth Harbour	a			22 13								23 13						00 13				01 12			
Southampton Airport Parkwy ✈	d	20 58	21 27				21 34		21 53	21 58	22 27			23 19	22 53	22 58	23 27		23 34		00 27				
Swaythling	d	21 01								22 01						23 01									
St Denys	d	21 04								22 04						23 04					00s31				
Southampton Central	a	21 09	21 34				21 42		22 00	22 09	22 34			23 31	23 00	23 09	23 34		23 45		00 36				
	d	21 10	21 35				21 44		22 03	22 10	22 35				23 03	23 10	23 35				00 37				
Millbrook (Hants)	d	21 13								22 13						23 13									
Redbridge	d	21 16								22 16						23 16									
Romsey	d	21 24								22a24						23 24									
Mottisfont & Dunbridge	d	21 29														23 29									
Dean	d	21 35														23 35									
Salisbury	a	21 50														23 50									
Totton	d		21 41								22 41						23 41				00s42				
Ashurst New Forest	d		21 45								22 45						23 45								
Beaulieu Road	d		21 50								22 50														
Brockenhurst 3	a		21 56				22 02		22 16		22 56				23 16		23 53				00s53				
	d		21 57		21 59		22 03		22 17		22 57				23 17		23 54								
Lymington Town	d				22 07																				
Lymington Pier	a				22 09																				
Yarmouth (I.O.W.) ⛴	a				22 45																				
Sway	d		22 01								23 01						23 59								
New Milton	d		22 06						22 24		23 06				23 24		00 04				01s01				
Hinton Admiral	d		22 10								23 10						00 08								
Christchurch	d		22 15								23 15						00 13				01s08				
Pokesdown	d		22 19								23 19						00 16				01s12				
Bournemouth	a		22 23				22 32		22 35		23 23				23 35		00 21				01 16				
	d		22 25						22 40		23 25				23 40		00 22				01 18				
Branksome	d								22 45						23 45		00 28				01s23				
Parkstone (Dorset)	d								22 48						23 48		00 31				01s26				
Poole 4	a		22 34						22 51		23 34				23 51		00 35				01 30				
	d								22 52						23 52										
Hamworthy	d								22 57						23 57										
Holton Heath	d																								
Wareham	d								23 04						00 04										
Wool	d								23 11						00 11										
Moreton (Dorset)	d								23 17						00 17										
Dorchester South	d								23 25						00 25										
Dorchester West	d							22 52																	
Upwey	d							22 59	23 32						00 32										
Weymouth	a							23 03	23 36						00 36										

For general notes see front of timetable
For details of catering facilities see
Directory of Train Operators

A 🛒 to Bournemouth
B 🛒 to Poole

For other services between Southampton Central and Romsey see Table 123.

Weymouth, Bournemouth, Lymington, Romsey, Southampton and Basingstoke → London

For details of Bank Holiday service alterations, please see first page of Table 149

Network Diagram - see first page of Table 158

Miles	Miles			SW	SW	SW	SW	SW	SW	XC	SW	SW	SW	SW	SW	SW	XC	SW	SW	SW	SW	GW	SW	SW	SW
				MO	MX	MX	MX																		
				1	1	1	1 ◇	1	1	1 ◇	1	1	1	1	1	1	1 ◇	1	1	1	1	◇	1	1	1
													A	B	A	B			A	B					
										☕			☕	☕			☕		☕	☕					
0	—	**Weymouth**	d	20p58	21p10		22p10															05 40			
2¼	—	Upwey	d	21p02	21p14		22p14															05 45			
—	—	Dorchester West	a																			05 53			
7	—	**Dorchester South**	d	21p10	21p22		22p22																		
12½	—	Moreton (Dorset)	d	21p17	21p28		22p28																		
17	—	Wool	d	21p23	21p34		22p34																		
22	—	Wareham	d	21p30	21p42		22p42																		
24	—	Holton Heath	d																						
26¾	—	Hamworthy	d	21p37	21p48		22p48																		
29	—	**Poole** 4	a	21p41	21p53		22p53																		
—	—		d	21p50	21p54		22p54						04 57	05 00	05 23	05 26			05 42	05 45					
30¾	—	Parkstone (Dorset)	d	21p54	21p58		22p58						05 01	05 04	05 27	05 30									
32	—	Branksome	d	21p57	22p01		23p01						05 04	05 07	05 30	05 33									
34¾	—	**Bournemouth**	a	22p03	22p07		23p07						05 09	05 12	05 36	05 38			05 51	05 54					
—	—		d	22p06	22p12		23p12						05 12	05 15	05 38	05 40			05 54	05 57					
36½	—	Pokesdown	d	22p10	22p16		23p16						05 16	05 19	05 42	05 44									
38¼	—	Christchurch	d	22p14	22p20		23p20						05 20	05 23	05 46	05 48									
41¾	—	Hinton Admiral	d	22p19	22p25		23p25								05 51	05 53									
44¼	—	New Milton	d	22p23	22p29		23p29						05 27	05 30	05 55	05 57									
47¼	—	Sway	d	22p28	22p34		23p34								06 00	06 02									
—	—	Yarmouth (I.O.W.) ⛴	d																				*04 40*		
—	0	**Lymington Pier** ⛴	d																				06 14		
—	½	Lymington Town	d																				06 16		
50	5¼	**Brockenhurst** 3	a	22p33	22p39		23p39						05 37	05 37	06 07	06 07			06 12	06 12			06 24		
—	—		d	22p34	22p40		23p40						05 38	05 38					06 14	06 14					
54¾	—	Beaulieu Road	d	22p39																					
57¼	—	Ashurst New Forest	d	22p43	22p47		23p47																		
60¼	—	Totton	d	22p48	22p52		23p52						05 49	05 49				06 12							
—	0	**Salisbury**	d																						
—	9	Dean	d																						
—	12¾	Mottisfont & Dunbridge	d																						
—	16½	**Romsey**	d																						
60¾	22½	Redbridge	d															06 14							
62½	—	Millbrook (Hants)	d															06 17							
63½	—	**Southampton Central**	a	22p53	22p57		23p57						05 54	05 54				06 20	06 27	06 27				←	
—	—		d	22p55	23p00		23p59	04 40	04 55	05 15		05 42	05 55	05 55			06 15	06 33 →	06 30	06 30				06 33	
65½	—	St Denys	d				00 04	04 45				05 47												06 38	
67	—	Swaythling	d				00 07	04 48				05 50												06 41	
67¾	—	**Southampton Airport Parkwy** ✈	d	23p03	23p08		00 10	04 51	05 02	05 22		05 53	06 03	06 03			06 22		06 38	06 38				06 44	06 50
—	0	**Portsmouth Harbour**	d			23p24					05 00										05 43				
—	¾	**Portsmouth & Southsea**	d			23p29					05 05										05 48				
—	1¾	Fratton	d			23p33					05 09										05 52				
—	4	Hilsea	d			23p37					05 13										05 56				
—	5½	Cosham	d			23p42					05 18										06 03				
—	8	Portchester	d			23p47					05 23										06 08				
—	11½	Fareham	d			23p53					05 29										06 19				
—	16¾	Botley	d			23p59					05 36										06 27				
—	17¾	Hedge End	d			00 05					05 40										06 31				
69¼	22¼	Eastleigh 3	a	23p09	23p11	00 11	00 14	04 56	05 06		05 48	05 56	06 07	06 07							06 37			06 47	06 53
—	—		d	23p11	23p12	00 19			05 06		05 49		06 08	06 08							06 42			06 48	06 54
—	24¼	Chandlers Ford	a																					06 53	
—	—		d																					06 53	
—	29½	**Romsey**	a																					07 03	
73	—	Shawford	d		23p18				05 12		05 55										06 49				
76¼	—	**Winchester**	d	23p23	23p24	00a28			05 18	05 31	06 01		06 18	06 18			06 31		06 48	06 48	06 55				07 05
84¾	—	Micheldever	d	23p32	23p33				05 27		06 10										07 04				
95	—	**Basingstoke**	a	23p42	23p43				05 37	05 45	06 21		06 34	06 34			06 46				07 14				
—	—		d	23p43	23p44				05 39	05 47			06 36	06 36			06 47				07 17				
—	—	Reading 7	a							06 04							07 04								
106¼	—	Fleet	d		00 01				05 50																
109½	—	Farnborough (Main)	d		00 06				05 56																
118¼	—	**Woking**	a	00 02	00 18				06 05				06 54	06 54											
138¾	—	Clapham Junction 10	a	00 22	00 54				06 25				07 16	07 16											07 38
142¾	—	**London Waterloo** 15 ⊖	a	00 33	01 02				06 34				07 26	07 26					07 46	07 46	08 01				08 08

For general notes see front of timetable
For details of catering facilities see Directory of Train Operators

A From 29 September
B Until 26 September

For other services between Romsey and Southampton Central see Table 123.

For details of Bank Holiday service alterations, please see first page of Table 149

Weymouth, Bournemouth, Lymington, Romsey, Southampton and Basingstoke → London

Network Diagram - see first page of Table 158

Station		SW 1	SW 1	SW 1	SW 1	SW 1	SW 1	SW 1	SW 1	XC 1 ◇	SW 1	SW 1	SW 1	SW 1	SW 1	SW 1	SW 1	SW 1	SW 1	SW 1	SW 1	SW 1	SW 1	SW 1
			A	B	B	A	A						A	B	C	A	D					A	B	C
			☕	☕	☕	☕	☕			☕			☕	☕	☕	☕	☕					☕	☕	☕
Weymouth	d														05 50		05 55							06 20
Upwey	d														05 54		05 59							06 24
Dorchester West	a																							
Dorchester South	d														06 02		06 07							06 32
Moreton (Dorset)	d														06 09		06 14							06 39
Wool	d														06 15		06 20							06 45
Wareham	d														06 22		06 27							06 52
Holton Heath	d														06 26		06 31							
Hamworthy	d														06 31		06 36							06 59
Poole 4	a														06 35		06 40							07 03
	d				06 08		06 11								06 36		06 41							07 06
Parkstone (Dorset)	d				06 12		06 15								06 40		06 45							07 10
Branksome	d				06 15		06 18								06 46		06 49							07 14
Bournemouth	a				06 23		06 23								06 54		06 54							07 24
	d		06 04	06 04	06 25		06 25			06 30			06 34	06 34	06 56		06 56					07 04	07 04	07 26
Pokesdown	d		06 08	06 08									06 38	06 38								07 08	07 08	
Christchurch	d		06 12	06 12									06 42	06 42								07 12	07 12	
Hinton Admiral	d		06 17	06 17									06 47	06 47								07 17	07 17	
New Milton	d		06 21	06 21									06 51	06 51								07 21	07 21	
Sway	d		06 26	06 26									06 56	06 56								07 26	07 26	
Yarmouth (I.O.W.) ⛴	d										*06 00*									*06 35*				
Lymington Pier ⛴	d										06 44									07 14				
Lymington Town	d										06 46									07 16				
Brockenhurst 3	a		06 31	06 31						06 46	06 54		07 01	07 01						07 24		07 31	07 31	
	d		06 32	06 32						06 48			07 02	07 02								07 32	07 32	
Beaulieu Road	d																							
Ashurst New Forest	d		06 40	06 40		←							07 10	07 10		←						07 40	07 40	
Totton	d		06 45	06 45		06 45							07 15	07 15		07 15						07 45	07 45	
Salisbury	d		→										→						06 50			→		
Dean	d																		07 02					
Mottisfont & Dunbridge	d																		07 08					
Romsey	d																		07 13					
Redbridge	d																		07 21					
Millbrook (Hants)	d																		07 24					
Southampton Central	a			06 51	06 55	06 51	06 55			07 00				07 20	07 25	07 20	07 25		07 29				07 50	07 55
	d	06 43		07 00		07 00			07 10	07 15				07 30		07 30			07 33		07 38		08 00	
St Denys	d	06 48																	07 38		07 43			
Swaythling	d	06 51																	07 41		07 46			
Southampton Airport Parkwy ✈	d	06 54		07 08		07 08			07 18	07 22				07 38		07 38			07 44		07 49		08 08	
Portsmouth Harbour	d							06 23										06 38						
Portsmouth & Southsea	d							06 28										06 43						
Fratton	d							06 32										06 47						
Hilsea	d							06 36										06 51						
Cosham	d							06 42										06 58						
Portchester	d							06 46										07 03						
Fareham	d							06 53										07 11						
Botley	d							07 01										07 25						
Hedge End	d							07 05										07 29						
Eastleigh 3	a	06 58						07 11	07 21			←						07 35	07 47		07 53			
	d	06 59						07 12	07 30			07 30						07 42	07 48		07 54			
Chandlers Ford	a								→										07 53					
	d																		07 53					
Romsey	a																		08 02					
Shawford	d	07 05										07 36						07 49			08 00			
Winchester	d	07 11		07 18		07 18		07 22		07 31		07 42		07 48		07 48		07 55			08 06		08 18	
Micheldever	d							07 31										08 02						
Basingstoke	a	07 27						07 41		07 46		07 58						08 14			08 22		08 34	
	d	07 36						07 47		07 47		08 05						08 16			08 24		08 35	
Reading 7	a									08 04														
Fleet	d	07 52										08 22									08 40			
Farnborough (Main)	d	07 58										08 28									08 46			
Woking	a	08 08						08 05				08 38						08 34			08 58		08 53	
Clapham Junction 10	a																						09 14	
London Waterloo 15 ⊖	a	08 39		08 16		08 16		08 34				09 10		08 48		08 48		09 03			09 29		09 25	

For general notes see front of timetable
For details of catering facilities see Directory of Train Operators

A Until 26 September
B From 29 September
C From 29 September. ☕ from Bournemouth
D Until 26 September. ☕ from Bournemouth

For other services between Romsey and Southampton Central see Table 123.

For details of Bank Holiday service alterations, please see first page of Table 149

Weymouth, Bournemouth, Lymington, Romsey, Southampton and Basingstoke → London

Network Diagram - see first page of Table 158

		SW	SW	GW	SW	XC	SW	SW	SW	SW	SW	SW	SW	SW	SW	SW	SW	SW	SW	SW	XC	SW	SW	SW	SW
		1	1	◇	1	1 ◇	1	1	1	1 ◇	1 ◇	1	1	1	1	1	1 ◇	1	1	1	R 1	1	1 ◇	1	1
		A 🍴	B 🍴			🍴				C 🍴	B 🍴						🍴				🍴		D 🍴		
Weymouth	d		06 25	06 40						06 50	06 55							07 25					07 55		
Upwey	d		06 29	06 45						06 54	06 59							07 29					07 59		
Dorchester West	a			06 53																					
Dorchester South	d		06 37							07 02	07 07							07 37					08 07		
Moreton (Dorset)	d		06 44							07 09	07 14							07 44					08 14		
Wool	d		06 50							07 15	07 20							07 50					08 20		
Wareham	d		06 57							07 22	07 27							07 57					08 27		
Holton Heath	d									07 26	07 31							08 01					08 31		
Hamworthy	d		07 04							07 31	07 36							08 06					08 36		
Poole 4	a		07 08							07 35	07 40							08 10					08 40		
	d		07 11					07 20		07 36	07 41						07 55	08 11					08 41		
Parkstone (Dorset)	d		07 15					07 24		07 40	07 45						07 59	08 15					08 45		
Branksome	d		07 19					07 27		07 46	07 49						08 02	08 19					08 49		
Bournemouth	a		07 24					07 32		07 54	07 54						08 07	08 24					08 54		
	d		07 26			07 30		07 34		07 59	07 59						08 10	08 26			08 45		08 59		
Pokesdown	d							07 38									08 14	08 30							
Christchurch	d							07 42									08 18	08 34							
Hinton Admiral	d							07 47									08 24	08 39							
New Milton	d							07 51									08 29	08 43							
Sway	d							07 56									08 34	08 48							
Yarmouth (I.O.W.) ⛴	d						*07b00*						*07 30*						*08 00*						*08b30*
Lymington Pier ⛴	d						07 44						08 14						08 44						09 14
Lymington Town	d						07 46						08 16						08 46						09 16
Brockenhurst 3	a					07 45	07 54	08 01		08 14	08 14		08 24				08 39	08 53	08 54		08 58		09 14		09 24
	d					07 47		08 02		08 15	08 15						08 41				09 00		09 15		
Beaulieu Road	d							08 08																	
Ashurst New Forest	d	←						08 12									08 48								
Totton	d	07 45						08 17									08 53								
Salisbury	d								07 48													08 48			
Dean	d								08 00													09 00			
Mottisfont & Dunbridge	d								08 06													09 06			
Romsey	d								08 11													09 11			
Redbridge	d								08 21													09 19			
Millbrook (Hants)	d								08 24													09 22			
Southampton Central	a	07 50	07 55			08 03		08 22	08 27	08 28	08 28						08 58				09 12	09 25	09 28		
	d		08 00			08 15		08 45 →	08 33 →	08 30	08 30			← 08 33		← 08 45	09 00				09 15	09 33 →	09 30		
St Denys	d													08 38		08 50									
Swaythling	d													08 41		08 53									
Southampton Airport Parkwy ✈	d		08 08			08 22				08 38	08 38			08 44		08 57	09 08				09 22		09 38		
Portsmouth Harbour	d				07 24							07 52			08 05									08 51	
Portsmouth & Southsea	d				07 29							07 57			08 10									08 56	
Fratton	d				07 33							08 01			08 14									09 01	
Hilsea	d				07 37							08 05			08 18									09 05	
Cosham	d				07 43							08 10			08 23									09 10	
Portchester	d				07 48							08 15			08 28									09 15	
Fareham	d				07 54							08 21			08 34									09 23	
Botley	d				08 01							08 29			08 42									09 30	
Hedge End	d				08 06							08 34			08 46									09 35	
Eastleigh 3	a				08 12							08 41		08 47	08 52	09 03				←				09 41	
	d				08 12							08 42		08 48	08 53	09 12				09 12				09 42	
Chandlers Ford	a													08 53		→									
	d													08 53											
Romsey	a													09 01											
Shawford	d				08 19							08 49								09 18					
Winchester	d		08 18		08 25	08 31				08 48	08 48	08 54			09 03		09 18			09 24	09 31		09 48	09 54	
Micheldever	d											09 02												10 02	
Basingstoke	a		08 34		08 41	08 46						09 15			09 19		09 34			09 40	09 46			10 15	
	d		08 35		08 42	08 47						09 17					09 36			09 41	09 47			10 17	
Reading 7	a					09 04															10 04				
Fleet	d				08 54															09 53					
Farnborough (Main)	d				08 59							09 31								09 58				10 31	
Woking	a		08 53							09 22	09 22	09 40					09 54						10 20	10 40	
Clapham Junction 10	a		09 14		09 26					09 43	09 43						10 14			10 24					
London Waterloo 15 ⊖	a		09 25		09 38					09 53	09 53	10 08					10 23			10 34			10 49	11 08	

For general notes see front of timetable
For details of catering facilities see Directory of Train Operators

A Until 26 September
B Until 26 September. 🍴 from Bournemouth
C From 29 September. 🍴 from Bournemouth
D 🍴 from Bournemouth
b Until 11 July.

For other services between Romsey and Southampton Central see Table 123.

For details of Bank Holiday service alterations, please see first page of Table 149

Weymouth, Bournemouth, Lymington, Romsey, Southampton and Basingstoke → London

Network Diagram - see first page of Table 158

		SW	SW	SW	SW	GW	SW	SW	XC	SW	SW	SW	SW	SW	SW	SW	SW	SW	XC	SW	SW	SW	SW	SW	SW
		1	1	1	1		1	1	R 1	1	1 ◇	1	1	1	1	1 ◇	1	1	R 1	1 ◇	1	1	1	1	1
											A					A				A					
									☕		☕					☕			☕	☕					
Weymouth	d				08 25	08 50					09 03					09 20				10 03					
Upwey	d				08 29	08 55										09 24									
Dorchester West	a					09 03																			
Dorchester South	d				08 37						09 13					09 32				10 13					
Moreton (Dorset)	d				08 44											09 39									
Wool	d				08 50											09 45									
Wareham	d				08 57						09 28					09 52				10 28					
Holton Heath	d				09 01											09 56									
Hamworthy	d				09 06						09 35					10 01				10 35					
Poole 4	a				09 10						09 39					10 05				10 39					
	d		08 50	09 06	09 11						09 40				09 50	10 06				10 40					10 50
Parkstone (Dorset)	d		08 54		09 15						09 44				09 54					10 44					10 54
Branksome	d		08 57		09 19						09 48				09 57					10 48					10 57
Bournemouth	a		09 02	09 16	09 24						09 53				10 02	10 16				10 54					11 02
	d		09 05	09 18	09 26				09 45		09 55				10 05	10 21			10 45	10 59					11 05
Pokesdown	d		09 09	09 22	09 30										10 09	10 25									11 09
Christchurch	d		09 13	09 26	09 34										10 13	10 29									11 13
Hinton Admiral	d		09 18		09 39										10 18										11 18
New Milton	d		09 22	09 33	09 43										10 22	10 36									11 22
Sway	d		09 27		09 48										10 27										11 27
Yarmouth (I.O.W.) ⛴	d							*09 00*					*09 30*					*10b00*						*10 30*	
Lymington Pier ⛴	d							09 44					10 14					10 44						11 14	
Lymington Town	d							09 46					10 16					10 46						11 16	
Brockenhurst 3	a		09 32	09 40	09 52			09 54	09 58		10 10		10 24		10 32	10 43		10 54	10 58	11 14				11 24	11 32
	d		09 33	09 41	09 53				10 00		10 11				10 33	10 44			11 00	11 15					11 33
Beaulieu Road	d																								11 38
Ashurst New Forest	d		09 40												10 40										11 42
Totton	d		09 45												10 45										11 47
Salisbury	d									09 48													10 50		
Dean	d									10 00													11 02		
Mottisfont & Dunbridge	d									10 06													11 09		
Romsey	d									10 11												11 05	11 14		
Redbridge	d									10 19												11 44	11 21		
Millbrook (Hants)	d									10 22													11 25		
Southampton Central	a	←	09 51	09 55	10 08				10 12	10 25	10 26			←	10 51	10 57			11 12	11 28			11 29		11 53
	d	09 33	09 55	10 00					10 15	10 33 →	10 30			10 33	10 55	11 00			11 15	11 30			11 33		11 55
St Denys	d	09 38												10 38									11 38		
Swaythling	d	09 41												10 41									11 41		
Southampton Airport Parkwy ✈	d	09 44	10 03	10 08					10 22		10 38			10 44	11 03	11 08			11 22	11 38			11 44		12 03
Portsmouth Harbour	d											09 54									10 54				
Portsmouth & Southsea	d											09 59									10 59				
Fratton	d											10 03									11 03				
Hilsea	d											10 07									11 07				
Cosham	d											10 12									11 12				
Portchester	d											10 17									11 17				
Fareham	d											10 23									11 23				
Botley	d											10 30									11 30				
Hedge End	d											10 35									11 35				
Eastleigh 3	a	09 47	10 06				←					10 41		10 47	11 06		←				11 41		11 47		12 06
	d	09 48	10 12				10 12					10 42		10 48	11 12		11 12				11 42		11 48		12 12
Chandlers Ford	a	09 53	→											10 53	→							11 12	11 53		→
	d	09 53												10 53								11 12	11 53		
Romsey	a	10 01												11 01								11 51	12 01		
Shawford	d						10 18										11 18								
Winchester	d			10 18			10 24		10 31		10 48	10 54				11 18	11 24		11 31	11 48	11 54				
Micheldever	d											11 02									12 02				
Basingstoke	a			10 34			10 40		10 46			11 15				11 34	11 40		11 46		12 15				
	d			10 36			10 41		10 47			11 17				11 36	11 41		11 47		12 17				
Reading 7	a								11 04										12 04						
Fleet	d						10 53										11 53								
Farnborough (Main)	d						10 58					11 31					11 58				12 31				
Woking	a										11 19	11 40								12 19	12 40				
Clapham Junction 10	a			11 12			11 24									12 12	12 24								
London Waterloo 15 ⊖	a			11 20			11 34				11 49	12 08				12 20	12 34			12 49	13 08				

For general notes see front of timetable
For details of catering facilities see
Directory of Train Operators

A ☕ from Bournemouth
b Until 11 July.

For other services between Romsey and Southampton Central see Table 123.

For details of Bank Holiday service alterations, please see first page of Table 149

Weymouth, Bournemouth, Lymington, Romsey, Southampton and Basingstoke → London

Network Diagram - see first page of Table 158

		SW	SW	SW	XC	SW	SW	GW	SW	SW	SW	SW	SW	SW	SW	XC	SW	SW	SW	SW	SW	SW	SW	SW	SW
		1 ◇	1	1	R 1	1	1 ◇	◇	1	1	1	1	1 ◇	1	1	R 1	1	1 ◇	1	1	1	1	1 ◇	1	1
		A ☕			☕		A ☕						A ☕			☕		A ☕					A ☕		
Weymouth	d	10 20					11 03	11 10					11 20					12 03					12 20		
Upwey	d	10 24						11 16					11 24										12 24		
Dorchester West	a							11 23																	
Dorchester South	d	10 32					11 13						11 32					12 13					12 32		
Moreton (Dorset)	d	10 39											11 39										12 39		
Wool	d	10 45											11 45										12 45		
Wareham	d	10 52					11 28						11 52					12 28					12 52		
Holton Heath	d	10 56											11 56										12 56		
Hamworthy	d	11 01					11 35						12 01					12 35					13 01		
Poole 4	a	11 05					11 39						12 05					12 39					13 05		
	d	11 06					11 40					11 50	12 06					12 40				12 50	13 06		
Parkstone (Dorset)	d						11 44					11 54						12 44				12 54			
Branksome	d						11 48					11 57						12 48				12 57			
Bournemouth	a	11 16					11 54					12 02	12 16					12 54				13 02	13 16		
	d	11 21			11 45		11 59					12 05	12 21			12 45		12 59				13 05	13 21		
Pokesdown	d	11 25										12 09	12 25									13 09	13 25		
Christchurch	d	11 29										12 13	12 29									13 13	13 29		
Hinton Admiral	d											12 18										13 18			
New Milton	d	11 36										12 22	12 36									13 22	13 36		
Sway	d											12 27										13 27			
Yarmouth (I.O.W.) ⛴	d			*11 00*						*11b30*					*12 00*					*12c30*					*13e00*
Lymington Pier ⛴	d			11 44						12 14					12 44					13 14					13 44
Lymington Town	d			11 46						12 16					12 46					13 16					13 46
Brockenhurst 3	a	11 43		11 54	11 58		12 14			12 24		12 32	12 43		12 54	12 58		13 14		13 24		13 32	13 43		13 54
	d	11 44			12 00		12 15					12 33	12 44			13 00		13 15				13 33	13 44		
Beaulieu Road	d																								
Ashurst New Forest	d											12 40										13 40			
Totton	d											12 45										13 45			
Salisbury	d					11 53											12 48								
Dean	d																13 00								
Mottisfont & Dunbridge	d																13 06								
Romsey	d					12 11											13 11								
Redbridge	d					12 19											13 19								
Millbrook (Hants)	d					12 22											13 22								
Southampton Central	a	11 57			12 12	12 25	12 28				←	12 52	12 57			13 12	13 25	13 28			←	13 52	13 57		
	d	12 00			12 15	12 33 →	12 30				12 33	12 55	13 00			13 15	13 33 →	13 30			13 33	13 55	14 00		
St Denys	d										12 38										13 38				
Swaythling	d										12 41										13 41				
Southampton Airport Parkwy ✈	d	12 08			12 22		12 38				12 44	13 03	13 08			13 22		13 38			13 44	14 03	14 08		
Portsmouth Harbour	d								11 54										12 54						
Portsmouth & Southsea	d								11 59										12 59						
Fratton	d								12 03										13 03						
Hilsea	d								12 07										13 07						
Cosham	d								12 12										13 12						
Portchester	d								12 17										13 17						
Fareham	d								12 23										13 23						
Botley	d								12 30										13 30						
Hedge End	d								12 35										13 35						
Eastleigh 3	a		←						12 41		12 47	13 06		←					13 41		13 47	14 05		←	
	d		12 12						12 42		12 48	13 12		13 12					13 42		13 48	14 12		14 12	
Chandlers Ford	a										12 53	→									13 53	→			
	d										12 53										13 53				
Romsey	a										13 01										14 01				
Shawford	d		12 18											13 18										14 18	
Winchester	d	12 18	12 24		12 31		12 48		12 54				13 18	13 24		13 31		13 48	13 54				14 18	14 24	
Micheldever	d								13 02										14 02						
Basingstoke	a	12 34	12 40		12 46				13 15				13 34	13 40		13 46			14 15				14 34	14 40	
	d	12 36	12 41		12 47				13 17				13 36	13 41		13 47			14 17				14 36	14 41	
Reading 7	a				13 04											14 04									
Fleet	d		12 53											13 53										14 53	
Farnborough (Main)	d		12 58						13 31					13 58					14 31					14 58	
Woking	a						13 19		13 40									14 19	14 40						
Clapham Junction 10	a	13 12	13 24										14 12	14 24									15 12	15 25	
London Waterloo 15 ⊖	a	13 20	13 34				13 49		14 08				14 20	14 34				14 49	15 08				15 20	15 34	

For general notes see front of timetable
For details of catering facilities see Directory of Train Operators

A ☕ from Bournemouth
b Until 11 July.
c Until 5 September.
e Until 11 July and from 8 September.

For other services between Romsey and Southampton Central see Table 123.

For details of Bank Holiday service alterations, please see first page of Table 149

Weymouth, Bournemouth, Lymington, Romsey, Southampton and Basingstoke → London

Network Diagram - see first page of Table 158

		XC	SW	SW	SN	SW	GW	SW	SW	SW	SW	SW	SW	XC	SW	SW	SW	SW	SW	SW	SW	SW	SW	XC	SW
		R 1	1	1	1	1 ◇	◇	1	1	1	1 ◇	1	1	R 1	1	1 ◇	1	1	1	1	1 ◇	1	1	R 1	1
						A					A					A					A				
		🛒				🛒					🛒			🛒		🛒					🛒			🛒	
Weymouth	d					13 03	13 10				13 20					14 03					14 20				
Upwey	d						13 16				13 24										14 24				
Dorchester West	a						13 24																		
Dorchester South	d					13 13					13 32					14 13					14 32				
Moreton (Dorset)	d										13 39										14 39				
Wool	d										13 45										14 45				
Wareham	d					13 28					13 52					14 28					14 52				
Holton Heath	d										13 56										14 56				
Hamworthy	d					13 35					14 01					14 35					15 01				
Poole 4	a					13 39					14 05					14 39					15 05				
	d					13 40				13 50	14 06					14 40				14 50	15 06				
Parkstone (Dorset)	d					13 44				13 54						14 44				14 54					
Branksome	d					13 48				13 57						14 48				14 57					
Bournemouth	a					13 54				14 02	14 16					14 54				15 02	15 16				
	d	13 45				13 59				14 05	14 21			14 45		14 59				15 05	15 21			15 45	
Pokesdown	d									14 09	14 25									15 09	15 25				
Christchurch	d									14 13	14 29									15 13	15 29				
Hinton Admiral	d									14 18										15 18					
New Milton	d									14 22	14 36									15 22	15 36				
Sway	d									14 27										15 27					
Yarmouth (I.O.W.)	⛴ d							*13b30*					*14 00*					*14c30*					*15e00*		
Lymington Pier	⛴ d							14 14					14 44					15 14					15 44		
Lymington Town	d							14 16					14 46					15 16					15 46		
Brockenhurst 3	a	13 58				14 14		14 24		14 32	14 43		14 54	14 58		15 14		15 24		15 32	15 43		15 54	15 58	
	d	14 00				14 15				14 33	14 44			15 00		15 15				15 33	15 44			16 00	
Beaulieu Road	d																								
Ashurst New Forest	d									14 40										15 40					
Totton	d									14 45										15 45					
Salisbury	d		13 53												14 48										15 48
Dean	d														15 00										16 00
Mottisfont & Dunbridge	d														15 06										16 06
Romsey	d		14 11												15 11										16 11
Redbridge	d		14 19												15 19										16 19
Millbrook (Hants)	d		14 22												15 22										16 22
Southampton Central	a	14 12	14 25			14 28				14 52	14 57			15 12	15 25	15 28				15 51	15 57			16 12	16 25
	d	14 15	14 33 →		14 26	14 30			← 14 33	14 55	15 00			15 15	15 33 →	15 30			← 15 33	15 56	16 00			16 15	16 33 →
St Denys	d								14 38										15 38						
Swaythling	d								14 41										15 41						
Southampton Airport Parkwy	✈ d	14 22				14 38			14 44	15 03	15 08			15 22		15 38			15 44	16 04	16 08			16 22	
Portsmouth Harbour	d			13 54													14 54								
Portsmouth & Southsea	d			13 59													14 59								
Fratton	d			14 03													15 03								
Hilsea	d			14 07													15 07								
Cosham	d			14 12													15 12								
Portchester	d			14 17													15 17								
Fareham	d			14 23													15 23								
Botley	d			14 30													15 30								
Hedge End	d			14 35													15 35								
Eastleigh 3	a			14 41	14 44				14 47	15 06		←					15 41		15 47	16 07		←			
	d			14 42					14 49	15 12		15 12					15 42		15 48	16 12		16 12			
Chandlers Ford	a								14 53	→									15 53	→					
	d								14 53										15 53						
Romsey	a								15 01										16 01						
Shawford	d											15 18										16 18			
Winchester	d	14 31		14 54		14 48					15 18	15 24		15 31		15 48	15 54				16 18	16 24		16 31	
Micheldever	d			15 02													16 02								
Basingstoke	a	14 46		15 15							15 34	15 40		15 46			16 15				16 34	16 40		16 46	
	d	14 47		15 17							15 36	15 41		15 47			16 17				16 36	16 41		16 47	
Reading 7	a	15 04												16 04										17 04	
Fleet	d											15 53										16 53			
Farnborough (Main)	d			15 31								15 58					16 31					16 58			
Woking	a			15 40		15 19										16 19	16 40								
Clapham Junction 10	a										16 12	16 24									17 12	17 24			
London Waterloo 15	⊖ a			16 08		15 49					16 20	16 34				16 49	17 08				17 20	17 36			

For general notes see front of timetable
For details of catering facilities see
Directory of Train Operators

A 🛒 from Bournemouth
b Until 5 September.
c Until 11 July and from 8 September excluding Tuesdays 18 May to 11 September.
e Until 5 September not Wednesdays.

For other services between Romsey and Southampton Central see Table 123.

For details of Bank Holiday service alterations, please see first page of Table 149

Weymouth, Bournemouth, Lymington, Romsey, Southampton and Basingstoke → London

Network Diagram - see first page of Table 158

		SW	GW	SW	SW	SW	SW	SN	SW	SW	SW	XC	SW	SW	SW	SW	SW	SW	SW	SW	SW	SW	XC	SW	SW
		1 ◇	◇	1	1	1	1	1	1 ◇	1	1	R 1	1	1 ◇	1	1	1	1	1	1 ◇	1	1	1 ◇	1	1
		A							A					A						A					
		🍴							🍴			🍴		🍴						🍴			🍴		
Weymouth	d	15 03	15 10						15 20					16 03						16 20					
Upwey	d		15 16						15 24											16 24					
Dorchester West	a		15 24																						
Dorchester South	d	15 13							15 32					16 13						16 32					
Moreton (Dorset)	d								15 39											16 39					
Wool	d								15 45											16 45					
Wareham	d	15 28							15 52					16 28						16 52					
Holton Heath	d								15 56											16 56					
Hamworthy	d	15 35							16 01					16 35						17 01					
Poole 4	a	15 39							16 05					16 39						17 05					
	d	15 40					15 50		16 06					16 40					16 50	17 06					
Parkstone (Dorset)	d	15 44					15 54							16 44					16 54						
Branksome	d	15 48					15 57							16 48					16 57						
Bournemouth	a	15 54					16 02		16 16					16 54					17 02	17 16					
	d	15 59					16 05		16 21			16 45		16 59					17 05	17 21			17 45		
Pokesdown	d						16 09		16 25										17 09	17 25					
Christchurch	d						16 13		16 29										17 13	17 29					
Hinton Admiral	d						16 18												17 18						
New Milton	d						16 22		16 36										17 22	17 36					
Sway	d						16 27												17 27						
Yarmouth (I.O.W.) ⛴	d				*15b30*						*16c00*							*16e30*				*17 00*			
Lymington Pier ⛴	d				16 14						16 44							17 14				17 44			
Lymington Town	d				16 16						16 46							17 16				17 46			
Brockenhurst 3	a	16 14			16 24		16 32		16 43		16 54	16 58		17 14				17 24	17 32	17 43		17 54	17 58		
	d	16 15					16 33		16 44			17 00		17 15			17 20		17 33	17 44			18 00		
Beaulieu Road	d																								
Ashurst New Forest	d						16 40										17 27		17 40						
Totton	d						16 45										17 32		17 45						
Salisbury	d												16 48												17 48
Dean	d												17 00												18 00
Mottisfont & Dunbridge	d												17 06												18 06
Romsey	d												17 11												18 11
Redbridge	d												17 19												18 19
Millbrook (Hants)	d												17 22												18 22
Southampton Central	a	16 28				←	16 50		16 57			17 12	17 25	17 28		←	17 39		17 51	17 57			18 12		18 25
	d	16 30				16 33	16 52		17 00			17 15	17 33 →	17 30		17 33			17 56	18 00			18 15	18 17	18 33 →
St Denys	d					16 38	16 57									17 38								18 22	
Swaythling	d					16 41	17 00									17 41								18 25	
Southampton Airport Parkwy ✈	d	16 38				16 44	17 03		17 08			17 22		17 38		17 44			18 04	18 08			18 22	18 28	
Portsmouth Harbour	d			15 54											16 54										
Portsmouth & Southsea	d			15 59											16 59										
Fratton	d			16 03											17 03										
Hilsea	d			16 07											17 07										
Cosham	d			16 12				16 44							17 12										
Portchester	d			16 17											17 17										
Fareham	d			16 23				16 53							17 23										
Botley	d			16 30											17 30										
Hedge End	d			16 35											17 35										
Eastleigh 3	a			16 41		16 47	17 07	17 08		←					17 41	17 47			18 07		←			18 32	
	d			16 42		16 48	17 12			17 12					17 42	17 48			18 12		18 12			18 33	
Chandlers Ford	a					16 53	→									17 53			→						
	d					16 53										17 53									
Romsey	a					17 01										18 01									
Shawford	d									17 18											18 18				
Winchester	d	16 48		16 54					17 18	17 24		17 31		17 48	17 54					18 18	18 24		18 31	18a41	
Micheldever	d			17 02											18 02										
Basingstoke	a			17 15					17 34	17 40		17 46			18 15					18 34	18 38		18 46		
	d			17 17					17 36	17 41		17 47			18 17					18 36	18 38		18 47		
Reading 7	a											18 04											19 04		
Fleet	d									17 53											18 50				
Farnborough (Main)	d			17 31						17 58					18 31						18 55				
Woking	a	17 20		17 40										18 19	18 40										
Clapham Junction 10	a								18 12	18 24										19 12	19 26				
London Waterloo 15 ⊖	a	17 50		18 08					18 23	18 34				18 47	19 08					19 20	19 38				

For general notes see front of timetable
For details of catering facilities see Directory of Train Operators

A 🍴 from Bournemouth
b Until 5 September not Thursdays.
c Until 11 July and from 8 September.
e Until 5 September.

For other services between Romsey and Southampton Central see Table 123.

For details of Bank Holiday service alterations, please see first page of Table 149

Weymouth, Bournemouth, Lymington, Romsey, Southampton and Basingstoke → London

Network Diagram - see first page of Table 158

		SW	SW	SW	SW	SW	SW	GW	SW	SW	XC	SW	SW	SW	SW	SW	SW	SW	SW	SW	XC	SW	SW	SW	SW
		1◇	1	1	1	1	1◇	◇	1	1	1◇	1	1◇	1	1	1	1	1◇	1	1	1◇	1	1◇	1	1
		A					A						A					A					A		
		🍴					🍴				🍴		🍴					🍴			🍴		🍴		
Weymouth	d	17 03					17 20	17 30					18 03					18 20					19 03		
Upwey	d						17 24	17 35										18 24							
Dorchester West	a							17 43																	
Dorchester South	d	17 13					17 32						18 13					18 32					19 13		
Moreton (Dorset)	d						17 39											18 39							
Wool	d						17 45											18 45							
Wareham	d	17 28					17 52						18 28					18 52					19 28		
Holton Heath	d						17 56											18 56							
Hamworthy	d	17 35					18 01						18 35					19 01					19 35		
Poole 4	a	17 39					18 05						18 39					19 05					19 39		
	d	17 40				17 50	18 06						18 40				18 50	19 06					19 40		
Parkstone (Dorset)	d	17 44				17 54							18 44				18 54						19 44		
Branksome	d	17 48				17 57							18 48				18 57						19 48		
Bournemouth	a	17 54				18 02	18 16						18 54				19 02	19 16					19 55		
	d	17 59				18 05	18 21				18 45		18 59				19 05	19 21			19 45		19 59		
Pokesdown	d					18 09	18 25										19 09	19 25							
Christchurch	d					18 13	18 29										19 13	19 29							
Hinton Admiral	d					18 18											19 18								
New Milton	d					18 22	18 36										19 22	19 36							
Sway	d					18 27											19 27								
Yarmouth (I.O.W.) ⛴	d			17b30						18c00					18 30				19b00						19c30
Lymington Pier ⛴	d			18 14						18 44					19 14				19 44						20 14
Lymington Town	d			18 16						18 46					19 16				19 46						20 16
Brockenhurst 3	a	18 14		18 24		18 32	18 43			18 54	18 58		19 14		19 24		19 32	19 43	19 54		19 58		20 14		20 24
	d	18 15				18 33	18 44				19 00		19 15				19 33	19 44			20 00		20 15		
Beaulieu Road	d					18 38																			
Ashurst New Forest	d					18 42											19 40								
Totton	d					18 47											19 45								
Salisbury	d											18 48										19 53			
Dean	d											19 00													
Mottisfont & Dunbridge	d											19 06													
Romsey	d											19 11										20 11			
Redbridge	d											19 19										20 19			
Millbrook (Hants)	d											19 22										20 22			
Southampton Central	a	18 28				18 53	18 57				19 13	19 25	19 28				19 51	19 57			20 12	20 25	20 28		
	d	18 30			← 18 33	18 55	19 00				19 15	19 33 →	19 30			← 19 33	19 55	20 00			20 15	20 33 →	20 30		
St Denys	d				18 38											19 38									
Swaythling	d				18 41											19 41									
Southampton Airport Parkwy ✈	d	18 38			18 44	19 03	19 08				19 22		19 38			19 44	20 03	20 08			20 22		20 38		
Portsmouth Harbour	d		17 54											18 54										19 54	
Portsmouth & Southsea	d		17 59											18 59										19 59	
Fratton	d		18 03											19 03										20 03	
Hilsea	d		18 07											19 07										20 07	
Cosham	d		18 12											19 12										20 12	
Portchester	d		18 17											19 17										20 17	
Fareham	d		18 23											19 23										20 23	
Botley	d		18 30											19 30										20 30	
Hedge End	d		18 35											19 35										20 35	
Eastleigh 3	a		18 41		18 47	19 06								19 41		19 47	20 06							20 41	
	d		18 42		18 48	19 12			← 19 12					19 42		19 48	20 12			← 20 12				20 42	
Chandlers Ford	a				18 53	→										19 53	→								
	d				18 53											19 53									
Romsey	a				19 01											20 01									
Shawford	d								19 18											20 18				20 49	
Winchester	d	18 48	18 54				19 18		19 24		19 31		19 48	19 54				20 18		20 24	20 31		20 48	20 54	
Micheldever	d		19 02											20 02										21 04	
Basingstoke	a		19 15				19 34		19 40		19 46			20 15				20 34		20 40	20 46			21 19	
	d		19 17				19 36		19 41		19 47			20 17				20 36		20 41	20 47			21 24	
Reading 7	a										20 04										21 04				
Fleet	d								19 53											20 53				21 40	
Farnborough (Main)	d		19 31						19 58					20 31						20 58				21 46	
Woking	a	19 24	19 40										20 19	20 40						21 07			21 19	21 58	
Clapham Junction 10	a						20 12		20 25									21 16		21 33					
London Waterloo 15 ⊖	a	19 51	20 08				20 20		20 34				20 49	21 08				21 24		21 43			21 49	22 34	

For general notes see front of timetable
For details of catering facilities see Directory of Train Operators

A 🍴 from Bournemouth
b Until 11 July and from 8 September.
c Until 5 September.

For other services between Romsey and Southampton Central see Table 123.

For details of Bank Holiday service alterations, please see first page of Table 149

Weymouth, Bournemouth, Lymington, Romsey, Southampton and Basingstoke → London

Network Diagram - see first page of Table 158

		SW	SW	SW	GW	SW	SW	SW	SW	SW	SW	SW	SW	SW	SW	SW	SW	SW	SW	SW	SW	SW	SW	SW
		1	1	1 ◇	◇	1	1	1	1	1	1	1	1 ◇	1	1	1	1	1	1	1	1	1	1 ◇	1
Weymouth	d			19 20	20 01								20 10							21 10			22 10	23 10
Upwey	d			19 24	20 06								20 14							21 14			22 14	23 14
Dorchester West	a				20 14																			
Dorchester South	d			19b37									20 22							21 22			22 22	23 22
Moreton (Dorset)	d			19 43									20 28							21 28			22 28	23 28
Wool	d			19 49									20 34							21 34			22 34	23 34
Wareham	d			19 57									20 42							21 42			22 42	23 42
Holton Heath	d																							
Hamworthy	d			20 03									20 48							21 48			22 48	23 48
Poole 4	a			20 08									20 53							21 53			22 53	23 53
	d		19 50	20 09									20 54							21 54			22 54	23 54
Parkstone (Dorset)	d		19 54										20 58							21 58			22 58	
Branksome	d		19 57										21 01							22 01			23 01	
Bournemouth	a		20 02	20 18									21 07							22 07			23 07	00 03
	d		20 05	20 21									21 12							22 12			23 12	
Pokesdown	d		20 09	20 25									21 16							22 16			23 16	
Christchurch	d		20 13	20 29									21 20							22 20			23 20	
Hinton Admiral	d		20 18										21 25							22 25			23 25	
New Milton	d		20 22	20 36									21 29							22 29			23 29	
Sway	d		20 27										21 34							22 34			23 34	
Yarmouth (I.O.W.) ⛴	d						*20 00*				*20c30*				*21 00*		*21e30*							
Lymington Pier ⛴	d						20 44				21 14				21 44		22 14							
Lymington Town	d						20 46				21 16				21 46		22 16							
Brockenhurst 3	a		20 32	20 43			20 54				21 24		21 39		21 54		22 24			22 39			23 39	
	d		20 33	20 44									21 40							22 40			23 40	
Beaulieu Road	d																							
Ashurst New Forest	d		20 40										21 47							22 47			23 47	
Totton	d		20 45										21 52							22 52			23 52	
Salisbury	d									20 48									21 48					
Dean	d									21 00									22 00					
Mottisfont & Dunbridge	d									21 06									22 06					
Romsey	d									21 11									22 11		22 58			
Redbridge	d									21 19									22 19		23 05			
Millbrook (Hants)	d									21 22									22 22		23 09			
Southampton Central	a	←	20 51	20 58						21 25			21 57						22 25	22 57	23 12		23 57	
	d	20 33	20 55	21 00				21 30		21 33		21 55	22 00					22 30	22 33	23 00	23 20		23 59	
St Denys	d	20 38								21 38									22 38		23 25		00 04	
Swaythling	d	20 41								21 41									22 41		23 28		00 07	
Southampton Airport Parkwy ✈	d	20 44	21 03	21 08				21 38		21 44		22 03	22 08					22 38	22 44	23 08	23 31		00 10	
Portsmouth Harbour	d								20 54					21 54								23 24		
Portsmouth & Southsea	d								20 59					21 59								23 29		
Fratton	d								21 03					22 03								23 33		
Hilsea	d								21 07					22 07								23 37		
Cosham	d								21 12					22 12								23 42		
Portchester	d								21 17					22 17								23 47		
Fareham	d								21 23					22 23								23 53		
Botley	d								21 30					22 30								23 59		
Hedge End	d								21 35					22 35								00 05		
Eastleigh 3	a	20 47	21 06			←			21 41	21 47		22 06		22 41		←		22 41	22 47	23 11	23 34	00 11	00 14	
	d	20 48	21 12			21 12			21 42	21 48		22 12				22 12		22 44	22 48	23 12	23 36	00 19		
Chandlers Ford	a	20 53	→							21 53		→							22 53		23 41			
	d	20 53								21 53									22 53		23 41			
Romsey	a	21 01								22 01									23 01		23 48			
Shawford	d					21 18										22 18				23 18				
Winchester	d			21 18		21 24		21 48	21f54				22 18			22 24		22 54		23 24		00a28		
Micheldever	d								22 02											23 33				
Basingstoke	a			21 34		21 40			22 15				22 34			22 40		23 10		23 43				
	d			21 36		21 41			22 24				22 36			22 41		23 12		23 44				
Reading 7	a																							
Fleet	d					21 53			22 40							22 53				00 01				
Farnborough (Main)	d					21 58			22 46							22 58				00 06				
Woking	a					22 07		22 19	22 58				22 54			23 07		23 30		00 18				
Clapham Junction 10	a			22 14		22 33							23 14			23 32		23 55		00 54				
London Waterloo 15 ⊖	a			22 22		22 43		22 49	23 33				23 23			23 43		00 04		01 02				

For general notes see front of timetable
For details of catering facilities see Directory of Train Operators

b Arr. 1931
c Until 11 July.
e Until 5 September.
f Arr. 2151

For other services between Romsey and Southampton Central see Table 123.

Table 158

Saturdays

Weymouth, Bournemouth, Lymington, Romsey, Southampton and Basingstoke → London

Network Diagram - see first page of Table 158

Station		SW	SW	SW	SW	SW	SW	SW	SW	XC	XC	SW	SW	SW	SW	SW	SW	XC	SW	SW	SW	SW	SW	SW	SW
		1	1	1 ◇	1	1	1	1	1	1 ◇	1 ◇	1	1	1	1	1	1	1 ◇	1	1	1 ◇	1	1	1	1
					A	B				C	D														
										☕	☕		☕					☕			☕				
Weymouth	d	21p10		22p10																					
Upwey	d	21p14		22p14																					
Dorchester West	a																								
Dorchester South	d	21p22		22p22																					
Moreton (Dorset)	d	21p28		22p28																					
Wool	d	21p34		22p34																					
Wareham	d	21p42		22p42																					
Holton Heath	d																								
Hamworthy	d	21p48		22p48																					
Poole 4	a	21p53		22p53																					
	d	21p54		22p54									05 28								06 28				06 50
Parkstone (Dorset)	d	21p58		22p58									05 32								06 32				06 54
Branksome	d	22p01		23p01									05 35								06 35				06 57
Bournemouth	a	22p07		23p07									05 40								06 40				07 02
	d	22p12		23p12									05 42					06 37			06 42				07 05
Pokesdown	d	22p16		23p16									05 46								06 46				07 09
Christchurch	d	22p20		23p20									05 50								06 50				07 13
Hinton Admiral	d	22p25		23p25									05 55								06 55				07 18
New Milton	d	22p29		23p29									05 59								06 59				07 22
Sway	d	22p34		23p34									06 04								07 04				07 27
Yarmouth (I.O.W.) ⛴	d														*04 40*				*06 00*				*06 35*		
Lymington Pier ⛴	d														06 14				06 44				07 14		
Lymington Town	d														06 16				06 46				07 16		
Brockenhurst 3	a	22p39		23p39									06 09		06 24			06 52	06 54		07 09		07 24		07 32
	d	22p40		23p40									06 10					06 54			07 10				07 33
Beaulieu Road	d																								
Ashurst New Forest	d	22p47		23p47									06 17								07 17				07 40
Totton	d	22p52		23p52								06 12	06 22								07 22				07 45
Salisbury	d																			06 48					
Dean	d																			07 00					
Mottisfont & Dunbridge	d																			07 06					
Romsey	d																			07 11					
Redbridge	d											06 14								07 19					
Millbrook (Hants)	d											06 18								07 22					
Southampton Central	a	22p57		23p57								06 20	06 27			←		07 06		07 25	07 27			←	07 51
	d	23p00		23p59	05 12	05 12		05 30	06 00	06 15	06 15	06 33 →	06 30			06 33	07 00	07 15		07 33 →	07 30			07 33	07 55
St Denys	d			00 04				05 35								06 38								07 38	
Swaythling	d			00 07				05 38								06 41								07 41	
Southampton Airport Parkwy ✈	d	23p08		00 10	05 20	05 20		05 41	06 08	06 22	06 22		06 38			06 44	07 08	07 22			07 38			07 44	08 03
Portsmouth Harbour	d		23p24											05 54								06 54			
Portsmouth & Southsea	d		23p29											05 59								06 59			
Fratton	d		23p33											06 03								07 03			
Hilsea	d		23p37											06 07								07 07			
Cosham	d		23p42				05 09							06 12								07 12			
Portchester	d		23p47				05 14							06 17								07 17			
Fareham	d		23p53				05 20							06 23								07 23			
Botley	d		23p59				05 27							06 30								07 30			
Hedge End	d		00 05				05 32							06 35								07 35			
Eastleigh 3	a	23p11	00 11	00 14	05 23	05 23	05 38	05 45	06 11				06 41	06 41		06 47	07 11					07 41		07 47	08 06
	d	23p12	00 19		05 24	05 24		05 46	06 13				06 42	06 46		06 48	07 12					07 42		07 48	08 12
Chandlers Ford	a															06 53								07 53	→
	d															06 53								07 53	
Romsey	a															07 03								08 01	
Shawford	d	23p18						05 52						06 52			07 18								
Winchester	d	23p24	00a28		05 34	05 34		06b00	06 23	06 31	06 31		06 52	07 00			07 24	07 31			07 48	07 54			
Micheldever	d	23p33						06 08						07 08								08 02			
Basingstoke	a	23p43			05 50	05 50		06 19	06 39	06 46	06 46		07 08	07 19			07 40	07 46				08 15			
	d	23p44			05 54	05 54		06 24	06 40	06 47	06 47		07 09	07 24			07 42	07 47				08 17			
Reading 7	a									07 04	07 05							08 05							
Fleet	d	00 01			06 10	06 10		06 40						07 40			07 53								
Farnborough (Main)	d	00 06			06 16	06 16		06 46						07 46			07 59					08 31			
Woking	a	00 18			06 28	06 28		06 58	06 58				07 27	07 58			08 08				08 21	08 40			
Clapham Junction 10	a	00 54			06 58	06 58			07 23								08 30								
London Waterloo 15 ⊖	a	01 02			07 06	07 09		07 33	07 31				07 53	08 34			08 38				08 49	09 08			

For general notes see front of timetable
For details of catering facilities see Directory of Train Operators

A Until 27 September
B From 4 October
C From 13 September.
D Until 6 September
b Arr. 0557

For other services between Romsey and Southampton Central see Table 123.

Saturdays

Weymouth, Bournemouth, Lymington, Romsey, Southampton and Basingstoke → London

Network Diagram - see first page of Table 158

Station		SW	GW	SW	SW	XC	XC	SW	SW	SW	SW	SW	SW	SW	SW	SW	SW	XC	SW	SW	SW	SW	SW	SW	SW
		1	◇	1	1	1 ◇	R 1	1	1 ◇	1 ◇	1	1	1	1	1 ◇	1	1	R 1	1	1 ◇	1 ◇	1	1	1	1
		A				B	C		D	E					A					D	E				
		🛒				🛒	🛒		🛒	🛒					🛒			🛒		🛒	🛒				
Weymouth	d		06 40						06 50	06 55					07 20					07 58	08 03				
Upwey	d		06 45						06 54	06 59					07 24										
Dorchester West	a		06 53																						
Dorchester South	d								07 02	07 07					07 32					08 08	08 13				
Moreton (Dorset)	d								07 08	07 14					07 39										
Wool	d								07 15	07 20					07 45										
Wareham	d	06 52							07 23	07 27					07 52					08 23	08 28				
Holton Heath	d	06 56							07 25	07 31					07 56										
Hamworthy	d	07 01							07 30	07 36					08 01					08 30	08 35				
Poole 4	a	07 05							07 35	07 40					08 05					08 34	08 39				
	d	07 06							07 36	07 41				07 50	08 06					08 35	08 40				08 50
Parkstone (Dorset)	d								07 41	07 45				07 54						08 39	08 44				08 54
Branksome	d								07 43	07 49				07 57						08 43	08 48				08 57
Bournemouth	a	07 16							07 54	07 54				08 02	08 16					08 54	08 54				09 02
	d	07 21				07 45	07 45		07 59	07 59				08 05	08 21			08 45		08 59	08 59				09 05
Pokesdown	d	07 25												08 09	08 25										09 09
Christchurch	d	07 29												08 13	08 29										09 13
Hinton Admiral	d													08 18											09 18
New Milton	d	07 36												08 22	08 36										09 22
Sway	d													08 27											09 27
Yarmouth (I.O.W.) ⛴	d				07b00							07 30				08 00							08b30		
Lymington Pier ⛴	d				07 44							08 14				08 44							09 14		
Lymington Town	d				07 46							08 16				08 46							09 16		
Brockenhurst 3	a	07 43			07 54	07 58	07 58		08 14	08 14		08 24		08 32	08 43	08 54		08 58		09 14	09 14		09 24		09 32
	d	07 44				08 00	08 00		08 15	08 15				08 33	08 44			09 00		09 15	09 15				09 33
Beaulieu Road	d																								09 38
Ashurst New Forest	d													08 40											09 42
Totton	d													08 45											09 47
Salisbury	d							07 48											08 48						
Dean	d							08 00											09 00						
Mottisfont & Dunbridge	d							08 06											09 06						
Romsey	d							08 11											09 11						
Redbridge	d							08 19											09 19						
Millbrook (Hants)	d							08 22											09 22						
Southampton Central	a	07 57				08 12	08 12	08 25	08 28	08 28			←	08 52	08 57			09 12	09 25	09 28	09 28			←	09 53
	d	08 00				08 15	08 15	08 33 →	08 30	08 30			08 33	08 55	09 00			09 15	09 33 →	09 30	09 30			09 33	09 55
St Denys	d												08 38											09 38	
Swaythling	d												08 41											09 41	
Southampton Airport Parkwy ✈	d	08 08				08 22	08 22		08 38	08 38			08 44	09 03	09 08			09 22		09 38	09 38			09 44	10 03
Portsmouth Harbour	d										07 54											08 54			
Portsmouth & Southsea	d										07 59											08 59			
Fratton	d										08 03											09 03			
Hilsea	d										08 07											09 07			
Cosham	d										08 12											09 12			
Portchester	d										08 17											09 17			
Fareham	d										08 23											09 23			
Botley	d										08 30											09 30			
Hedge End	d										08 35											09 35			
Eastleigh 3	a			←							08 41		08 47	09 06			←					09 41		09 47	10 06
	d			08 12							08 42		08 48	09 12			09 12					09 42		09 48	10 12
Chandlers Ford	a												08 53	→										09 53	→
	d												08 53											09 53	
Romsey	a												09 01											10 01	
Shawford	d			08 18													09 18								
Winchester	d	08 18		08 24		08 31	08 31		08 48	08 48	08 54				09 18		09 24	09 31		09 48	09 48	09 54			
Micheldever	d										09 02											10 02			
Basingstoke	a	08 34		08 40		08 45	08 46				09 15				09 34		09 40	09 46				10 15			
	d	08 36		08 41		08 47	08 47				09 17				09 36		09 41	09 47				10 17			
Reading 7	a					09 04	09 05											10 05							
Fleet	d			08 53													09 53								
Farnborough (Main)	d			08 58							09 31						09 58					10 31			
Woking	a								09 19	09 19	09 40									10 19	10 19	10 40			
Clapham Junction 10	a	09 12		09 24											10 12		10 24								
London Waterloo 15 ⊖	a	09 20		09 34					09 49	09 49	10 08				10 20		10 34			10 49	10 49	11 08			

For general notes see front of timetable
For details of catering facilities see Directory of Train Operators

A 🛒 from Bournemouth
B From 13 September.
C Until 6 September
D From 4 October. 🛒 from Bournemouth
E Until 27 September. 🛒 from Bournemouth
b Until 12 July.

For other services between Romsey and Southampton Central see Table 123.

Table 158

Saturdays

Weymouth, Bournemouth, Lymington, Romsey, Southampton and Basingstoke → London

Network Diagram - see first page of Table 158

		SW	GW	SW	SW	XC	XC	SW	SW	SW	SW	SW	SW	SW	SW	SW	XC	SW	SW	SW	SW	SW	SW	SW	SW
		1 ◇		1	1	1 ◇	1 ◇	1	1 ◇	1	1	1	1	1 ◇	1	1	1 ◇	1	1 ◇	1	1	1	1	1 ◇	1
		A				B	C		A					A					A					A	
		☕				☕	☕		☕					☕			☕		☕					☕	
Weymouth	d	08 20	08 53						09 03					09 20					10 03					10 20	
Upwey	d	08 24	08 58											09 24										10 24	
Dorchester West	a		09 05																						
Dorchester South	d	08 32							09 13					09 32					10 13					10 32	
Moreton (Dorset)	d	08 39												09 39										10 39	
Wool	d	08 45												09 45										10 45	
Wareham	d	08 52							09 28					09 52					10 28					10 52	
Holton Heath	d	08 56												09 56										10 56	
Hamworthy	d	09 01							09 35					10 01					10 35					11 01	
Poole 4	a	09 06							09 39					10 05					10 39					11 05	
	d	09 06							09 40				09 50	10 06					10 40				10 50	11 06	
Parkstone (Dorset)	d								09 44				09 54						10 44				10 54		
Branksome	d								09 48				09 57						10 48				10 57		
Bournemouth	a	09 17							09 54				10 02	10 16					10 54				11 03	11 16	
	d	09 21				09 45	09 45		09 59				10 05	10 21			10 45		10 59				11 05	11 21	
Pokesdown	d	09 25											10 09	10 25									11 09	11 25	
Christchurch	d	09 29											10 13	10 29									11 12	11 29	
Hinton Admiral	d												10 18										11 18		
New Milton	d	09 36											10 22	10 36									11 22	11 36	
Sway	d												10 27										11 27		
Yarmouth (I.O.W.)	⛴ d				*09 00*						*09 30*					*10b00*					*10 30*				
Lymington Pier	⛴ d				09 44						10 14					10 44					11 14				
Lymington Town	d				09 46						10 16					10 46					11 16				
Brockenhurst 3	a	09 44			09 54	09 58	09 58		10 14		10 24		10 32	10 43		10 54	10 58		11 14		11 24		11 32	11 43	
	d	09 44				10 00	10 00		10 15				10 33	10 44			11 00		11 15				11 33	11 44	
Beaulieu Road	d																						11 38		
Ashurst New Forest	d												10 40										11 42		
Totton	d												10 45										11 47		
Salisbury	d							09 48										10 48							
Dean	d							10 00										11 00							
Mottisfont & Dunbridge	d							10 06										11 06							
Romsey	d							10 11										11 11							
Redbridge	d							10 19										11 19							
Millbrook (Hants)	d							10 22										11 22							
Southampton Central	a	09 58				10 12	10 12	10 25	10 28			←	10 51	10 57			11 12	11 25	11 28			←	11 54	11 57	
	d	10 00				10 15	10 15	10 33 →	10 30			10 33	10 55	11 00			11 15	11 33 →	11 30			11 33	11 55	12 00	
St Denys	d											10 38										11 38			
Swaythling	d											10 41										11 41			
Southampton Airport Parkwy	✈ d	10 08				10 22	10 22		10 38			10 44	11 03	11 08			11 22		11 38			11 44	12 03	12 08	
Portsmouth Harbour	d									09 54										10 54					
Portsmouth & Southsea	d									09 59										10 59					
Fratton	d									10 03										11 03					
Hilsea	d									10 07										11 07					
Cosham	d									10 12										11 12					
Portchester	d									10 17										11 17					
Fareham	d									10 23										11 23					
Botley	d									10 30										11 30					
Hedge End	d									10 35										11 35					
Eastleigh 3	a			←						10 41		10 47	11 06		←					11 41		11 47	12 07		←
	d			10 12						10 42		10 48	11 12		11 12					11 42		11 48	12 12		12 12
Chandlers Ford	a											10 53	→									11 53	→		
	d											10 53										11 53			
Romsey	a											11 01										12 01			
Shawford	d			10 18											11 18										12 18
Winchester	d	10 18		10 24		10 31	10 31		10 48	10 54				11 18	11 24		11 31		11 48	11 54				12 18	12 24
Micheldever	d									11 02										12 02					
Basingstoke	a	10 34		10 40		10 46	10 46			11 15				11 34	11 40		11 46			12 15				12 34	12 40
	d	10 36		10 41			10 47			11 17				11 36	11 41					12 17				12 36	12 41
Reading 7	a						11 04																		
Fleet	d			10 53											11 53										12 53
Farnborough (Main)	d			10 58						11 31					11 58					12 31					12 58
Woking	a								11 19	11 40									12 19	12 40					
Clapham Junction 10	a	11 12		11 24										12 12	12 24									13 12	13 24
London Waterloo 15	⊖ a	11 20		11 34					11 49	12 08				12 20	12 34				12 49	13 08				13 20	13 34

For general notes see front of timetable
For details of catering facilities see Directory of Train Operators

A ☕ from Bournemouth
B Until 6 September
C From 13 September.
b Until 12 July.

For other services between Romsey and Southampton Central see Table 123.

Table 158

Saturdays

Weymouth, Bournemouth, Lymington, Romsey, Southampton and Basingstoke → London

Network Diagram - see first page of Table 158

		SW	XC	SW	SW	GW	SW	SW	SW	SW	SW	SW	SW	XC	SW	SW	SW	SW	SW	SW	SW	SW	SW	XC	XC
		1	1 ◇	1	1 ◇	◇	1	1	1	1	1 ◇	1	1	R 1	1	1 ◇	1	1	1	1	1 ◇	1	1	1 ◇	1 ◇
					A						A					A					A			B	C
			🛒		🛒						🛒			🛒		🛒					🛒			🛒	🛒
Weymouth	d				11 03	11 10					11 20					12 03					12 20				
Upwey	d					11 15					11 24										12 24				
Dorchester West	a					11 23																			
Dorchester South	d				11 13						11 32					12 13					12 32				
Moreton (Dorset)	d										11 39										12 39				
Wool	d										11 45										12 45				
Wareham	d				11 28						11 52					12 28					12 52				
Holton Heath	d										11 56										12 56				
Hamworthy	d				11 35						12 01					12 35					13 01				
Poole 4	a				11 39						12 05					12 39					13 05				
	d				11 40					11 50	12 06					12 40				12 50	13 06				
Parkstone (Dorset)	d				11 44					11 54						12 44				12 54					
Branksome	d				11 48					11 57						12 48				12 57					
Bournemouth	a				11 54					12 02	12 16					12 54				13 02	13 16				
	d		11 45		11 59					12 05	12 21			12 45		12 59				13 05	13 21			13 45	13 45
Pokesdown	d									12 09	12 25									13 09	13 25				
Christchurch	d									12 13	12 29									13 13	13 29				
Hinton Admiral	d									12 18										13 18					
New Milton	d									12 22	12 36									13 22	13 36				
Sway	d									12 27										13 27					
Yarmouth (I.O.W.) ⛴	d	*11 00*						*11b30*					*12 00*					*12c30*					*13e00*		
Lymington Pier ⛴	d	11 44						12 14					12 44					13 14					13 44		
Lymington Town	d	11 46						12 16					12 46					13 16					13 46		
Brockenhurst 3	a	11 54	11 58		12 14			12 24		12 32	12 43		12 54	12 58		13 14		13 24		13 32	13 43		13 54	13 58	13 58
	d		12 00		12 15					12 33	12 44			13 00		13 15				13 33	13 44			14 00	14 00
Beaulieu Road	d																			13 38					
Ashurst New Forest	d									12 40										13 42					
Totton	d									12 45										13 47					
Salisbury	d			11 53											12 48										
Dean	d														13 00										
Mottisfont & Dunbridge	d														13 06										
Romsey	d			12 11											13 11										
Redbridge	d			12 19											13 19										
Millbrook (Hants)	d			12 22											13 22										
Southampton Central	a		12 12	12 25	12 28				←	12 51	12 57			13 12	13 25	13 28			←	13 53	13 57			14 12	14 12
	d		12 15	12 33 →	12 30				12 33	12 55	13 00			13 15	13 33 →	13 30			13 33	13 55	14 00			14 15	14 15
St Denys	d								12 38										13 38						
Swaythling	d								12 41										13 41						
Southampton Airport Parkwy ✈	d		12 22		12 38				12 44	13 03	13 08			13 22		13 38			13 44	14 03	14 08			14 22	14 22
Portsmouth Harbour	d						11 54										12 54								
Portsmouth & Southsea	d						11 59										12 59								
Fratton	d						12 03										13 03								
Hilsea	d						12 07										13 07								
Cosham	d						12 12										13 12								
Portchester	d						12 17										13 17								
Fareham	d						12 23										13 23								
Botley	d						12 30										13 30								
Hedge End	d						12 35										13 35								
Eastleigh 3	a						12 41		12 47	13 06		←					13 41		13 47	14 06		←			
	d						12 42		12 48	13 12		13 12					13 42		13 48	14 12		14 12			
Chandlers Ford	a								12 53	→									13 53	→					
	d								12 53										13 53						
Romsey	a								13 01										14 01						
Shawford	d											13 18										14 18			
Winchester	d		12 31		12 48		12 54				13 18	13 24		13 31		13 48	13 54				14 18	14 24		14 31	14 31
Micheldever	d						13 02										14 02								
Basingstoke	a		12 46				13 15				13 34	13 40		13 46			14 15				14 34	14 40		14 46	14 46
	d		12 47				13 17				13 36	13 41		13 47			14 17				14 36	14 41		14 47	14 47
Reading 7	a		13 05											14 05										15 04	15 05
Fleet	d											13 53										14 53			
Farnborough (Main)	d						13 31					13 58					14 31					14 58			
Woking	a				13 19		13 40									14 19	14 40								
Clapham Junction 10	a										14 12	14 24									15 12	15 24			
London Waterloo 15 ⊖	a				13 49		14 08				14 20	14 34				14 49	15 08				15 20	15 34			

For general notes see front of timetable
For details of catering facilities see Directory of Train Operators

A 🛒 from Bournemouth
B From 13 September.
C Until 6 September
b Until 12 July.
e Until 12 July then from 13 September.

For other services between Romsey and Southampton Central see Table 123.

Table 158

Saturdays

Weymouth, Bournemouth, Lymington, Romsey, Southampton and Basingstoke → London

Network Diagram - see first page of Table 158

		SW	SN	SW	GW	SW	SW	SW	SW	SW	SW	SW	XC	SW	SW	SW	SW	SW	SW	SW	SW	SW	XC	XC	SW
		1	1	1 ◇	◇	1	1	1	1	1 ◇	1	1	1 ◇	1	1 ◇	1	1	1	1	1 ◇	1	1	1 ◇	1 ◇	1
				A						A					A					A			B	C	
				☕						☕			☕		☕					☕			☕	☕	
Weymouth	d			13 03	13 10					13 20					14 03					14 20					
Upwey	d				13 15					13 24										14 24					
Dorchester West	a				13 23																				
Dorchester South	d			13 13						13 32					14 13					14 32					
Moreton (Dorset)	d									13 39										14 39					
Wool	d									13 45										14 45					
Wareham	d			13 28						13 52					14 28					14 52					
Holton Heath	d									13 56										14 56					
Hamworthy	d			13 35						14 01					14 35					15 01					
Poole 4	a			13 39						14 05					14 39					15 05					
	d			13 40					13 50	14 06					14 40				14 50	15 06					
Parkstone (Dorset)	d			13 44					13 54						14 44				14 54						
Branksome	d			13 48					13 57						14 48				14 57						
Bournemouth	a			13 54					14 02	14 16					14 54				15 02	15 16					
	d			13 59					14 05	14 21			14 45		14 59				15 05	15 21			15 45	15 45	
Pokesdown	d								14 09	14 25									15 09	15 25					
Christchurch	d								14 13	14 29									15 13	15 29					
Hinton Admiral	d								14 18										15 18						
New Milton	d								14 22	14 36									15 22	15 36					
Sway	d								14 27										15 27						
Yarmouth (I.O.W.) ⛴	d						*13b30*					*14 00*					*14c30*					*15b00*			
Lymington Pier ⛴	d						14 14					14 44					15 14					15 44			
Lymington Town	d						14 16					14 46					15 16					15 46			
Brockenhurst 3	a			14 14			14 24		14 32	14 43		14 54	14 58		15 14		15 24		15 32	15 43		15 54	15 58	15 58	
	d			14 15					14 33	14 44			15 00		15 15				15 33	15 44			16 00	16 00	
Beaulieu Road	d																		15 38						
Ashurst New Forest	d								14 40										15 42						
Totton	d								14 45										15 47						
Salisbury	d	13 53												14 48											15 48
Dean	d													15 00											16 00
Mottisfont & Dunbridge	d													15 06											16 06
Romsey	d	14 11												15 11											16 11
Redbridge	d	14 19												15 19											16 19
Millbrook (Hants)	d	14 22												15 22											16 22
Southampton Central	a	14 25		14 28				←	14 51	14 57			15 12	15 25	15 28			←	15 53	15 57			16 12	16 12	16 25
	d	14 33 →	14 26	14 30				14 33	14 55	15 00			15 15	15 33 →	15 30			15 33	15 55	16 00			16 15	16 15	16 33 →
St Denys	d							14 38										15 38							
Swaythling	d							14 41										15 41							
Southampton Airport Parkway ✈	d			14 38				14 44	15 03	15 08			15 22		15 38			15 44	16 03	16 08			16 22	16 22	
Portsmouth Harbour	d					13 54										14 54									
Portsmouth & Southsea	d					13 59										14 59									
Fratton	d					14 03										15 03									
Hilsea	d					14 07										15 07									
Cosham	d					14 12										15 12									
Portchester	d					14 17										15 17									
Fareham	d					14 23										15 23									
Botley	d					14 30										15 30									
Hedge End	d					14 35										15 35									
Eastleigh 3	a		14 36			14 41		14 47	15 06		←					15 41		15 47	16 06		←				
	d					14 42		14 48	15 12		15 12					15 42		15 48	16 12		16 12				
Chandlers Ford	a							14 53	→									15 53	→						
	d							14 53										15 53							
Romsey	a							15 01										16 01							
Shawford	d										15 18										16 18				
Winchester	d			14 48		14 54				15 18	15 24		15 31		15 48	15 54				16 18	16 24		16 31	16 31	
Micheldever	d					15 02										16 02									
Basingstoke	a					15 15				15 34	15 40		15 46			16 15				16 34	16 40		16 46	16 46	
	d					15 17				15 36	15 41		15 47			16 17				16 36	16 41		16 47	16 47	
Reading 7	a												16 05										17 04	17 05	
Fleet	d										15 53										16 53				
Farnborough (Main)	d					15 31					15 58					16 31					16 58				
Woking	a			15 19		15 40									16 19	16 40									
Clapham Junction 10	a									16 12	16 24									17 12	17 24				
London Waterloo 15 ⊖	a			15 49		16 08				16 20	16 34				16 49	17 08				17 20	17 34				

For general notes see front of timetable
For details of catering facilities see Directory of Train Operators

A ☕ from Bournemouth
B From 13 September.
C Until 6 September
c Until 12 July then from 13 September.

For other services between Romsey and Southampton Central see Table 123.

Table 158

Saturdays

Weymouth, Bournemouth, Lymington, Romsey, Southampton and Basingstoke → London

Network Diagram - see first page of Table 158

		SW	GW	SW	SW	SW	SW	SW	SW	SW	XC	SW	SW	GW	SW	SW	SW	SW	SW	GW	SW	SW	XC	XC	SW
		1 ◇		1	1	1	1	1 ◇	1	1	1 ◇	1	1 ◇		1	1	1	1	1 ◇	◇	1	1	1 ◇	1 ◇	1
		A	B					A					A	C					A	D			B	C	
		☕						☕			☕		☕						☕				☕	☕	
Weymouth	d	15 03	15 10					15 20					16 03	16 10					16 20	16 55					
Upwey	d		15 15					15 24						16 15					16 24						
Dorchester West	a		15 22											16 22						17 06					
Dorchester South	d	15 13						15 32					16 13						16 32						
Moreton (Dorset)	d							15 39											16 39						
Wool	d							15 45											16 45						
Wareham	d	15 28						15 52					16 28						16 52						
Holton Heath	d							15 56											16 56						
Hamworthy	d	15 35						16 01					16 35						17 01						
Poole 4	a	15 39						16 05					16 39						17 05						
	d	15 40					15 50	16 06					16 40					16 50	17 06						
Parkstone (Dorset)	d	15 44					15 54						16 44					16 54							
Branksome	d	15 48					15 57						16 48					16 57							
Bournemouth	a	15 54					16 02	16 16					16 54					17 02	17 16						
	d	15 59					16 05	16 21			16 45		16 59					17 05	17 21				17 45	17 45	
Pokesdown	d						16 09	16 25										17 09	17 25						
Christchurch	d						16 13	16 29										17 13	17 29						
Hinton Admiral	d						16 18											17 18							
New Milton	d						16 22	16 36										17 22	17 36						
Sway	d						16 27											17 27							
Yarmouth (I.O.W.) ⛴	d				*15 30*				*16b00*							*16c30*						*17 00*			
Lymington Pier ⛴	d				16 14				16 44							17 14						17 44			
Lymington Town	d				16 16				16 46							17 16						17 46			
Brockenhurst 3	a	16 14			16 24		16 32	16 43	16 54		16 58		17 14			17 24		17 32	17 43			17 54	17 58	17 58	
	d	16 15					16 33	16 44			17 00		17 15					17 33	17 44				18 00	18 00	
Beaulieu Road	d																	17 38							
Ashurst New Forest	d						16 40											17 42							
Totton	d						16 45											17 47							
Salisbury	d											16 48													17 48
Dean	d											17 00													18 00
Mottisfont & Dunbridge	d											17 06													18 06
Romsey	d											17 11													18 11
Redbridge	d											17 19													18 19
Millbrook (Hants)	d											17 22													18 22
Southampton Central	a	16 28				←	16 51	16 57			17 12	17 25	17 28				←	17 53	17 57				18 12	18 12	18 25
	d	16 30				16 33	16 55	17 00			17 15	17 33	17 30				17 33	17 55	18 00				18 15	18 15	18 33
St Denys	d					16 38						→					17 38								→
Swaythling	d					16 41											17 41								
Southampton Airport Parkwy ✈	d	16 38				16 44	17 03	17 08			17 22		17 38				17 44	18 03	18 08				18 22	18 22	
Portsmouth Harbour	d			15 54											16 54										
Portsmouth & Southsea	d			15 59											16 59										
Fratton	d			16 03											17 03										
Hilsea	d			16 07											17 07										
Cosham	d			16 12											17 12										
Portchester	d			16 17											17 17										
Fareham	d			16 23											17 23										
Botley	d			16 30											17 30										
Hedge End	d			16 35											17 35										
Eastleigh 3	a			16 41		16 47	17 06			←					17 41		17 47	18 06			←				
	d			16 42		16 48	17 12			17 12					17 42		17 48	18 12			18 12				
Chandlers Ford	a					16 53	→										17 53	→							
	d					16 53											17 53								
Romsey	a					17 01											18 01								
Shawford	d									17 18											18 18				
Winchester	d	16 48		16 54				17 18		17 24	17 31		17 48		17 54				18 18		18 24		18 31	18 31	
Micheldever	d			17 02											18 02										
Basingstoke	a			17 15				17 34		17 40	17 46				18 15				18 34		18 40		18 46	18 46	
	d			17 17				17 36		17 41	17 47				18 17				18 36		18 41		18 47	18 47	
Reading 7	a										18 05												19 04	19 05	
Fleet	d									17 53											18 53				
Farnborough (Main)	d			17 31						17 58					18 31						18 58				
Woking	a	17 19		17 40									18 19		18 40										
Clapham Junction 10	a							18 12		18 24									19 12		19 24				
London Waterloo 15 ⊖	a	17 49		18 08				18 20		18 34			18 49		19 08				19 20		19 34				

For general notes see front of timetable
For details of catering facilities see Directory of Train Operators

A ☕ from Bournemouth
B From 13 September.
C Until 6 September
D 5 July to 6 September
b Until 12 July then from 13 September.

For other services between Romsey and Southampton Central see Table 123.

Table 158

Saturdays

Weymouth, Bournemouth, Lymington, Romsey, Southampton and Basingstoke → London

Network Diagram - see first page of Table 158

		SW	SW	SW	SW	SW	SW	GW	SW	SW	XC	SW	SW	SW	SW	SW	SW	SW	SW	SW	XC	SW	SW	SW	SW
		1 ◇	1	1	1	1	1 ◇	◇	1	1	1 ◇	1	1 ◇	1	1	1	1	1 ◇	1	1	1 ◇	1	1 ◇	1	1
		A					A						A					A					A		
		☕					☕				☕		☕					☕					☕		
Weymouth	d	17 03					17 20	17 30					18 03					18 20					19 03		
Upwey	d						17 24	17 35										18 24							
Dorchester West	a							17 42																	
Dorchester South	d	17 13					17 32						18 13					18 32					19 13		
Moreton (Dorset)	d						17 39											18 39							
Wool	d						17 45											18 45							
Wareham	d	17 28					17 52						18 28					18 52					19 28		
Holton Heath	d						17 56											18 56							
Hamworthy	d	17 35					18 01						18 35					19 01					19 35		
Poole 4	a	17 39					18 05						18 39					19 05					19 39		
	d	17 40				17 50	18 06						18 40				18 50	19 06					19 40		
Parkstone (Dorset)	d	17 44				17 54							18 44				18 54						19 44		
Branksome	d	17 48				17 57							18 48				18 57						19 48		
Bournemouth	a	17 54				18 02	18 16						18 54				19 02	19 16					19 54		
	d	17 59				18 05	18 21				18 45		18 59				19 05	19 21			19 45		19 59		
Pokesdown	d					18 09	18 25										19 09	19 25							
Christchurch	d					18 13	18 29										19 13	19 29							
Hinton Admiral	d					18 18											19 18								
New Milton	d					18 22	18 36										19 22	19 36							
Sway	d					18 27											19 27								
Yarmouth (I.O.W.) ⛴	d			17b30						18c00					18 30				19b00						19c30
Lymington Pier ⛴	d			18 14						18 44					19 14				19 44						20 14
Lymington Town	d			18 16						18 46					19 16				19 46						20 16
Brockenhurst 3	a	18 14		18 24		18 32	18 43			18 54	18 58		19 14		19 24		19 32	19 43	19 54		19 58		20 14		20 24
	d	18 15				18 33	18 44				19 00		19 15				19 33	19 44			20 00		20 15		
Beaulieu Road	d																								
Ashurst New Forest	d					18 40											19 40								
Totton	d					18 45											19 45								
Salisbury	d											18 48										19 53			
Dean	d											19 00													
Mottisfont & Dunbridge	d											19 06													
Romsey	d											19 11										20 11			
Redbridge	d											19 19										20 19			
Millbrook (Hants)	d											19 22										20 22			
Southampton Central	a	18 28			←	18 51	18 57				19 12	19 25	19 28			←	19 51	19 57			20 12	20 25	20 28		
	d	18 30			18 33	18 55	19 00				19 15	19 33 →	19 30			19 33	19 55	20 00			20 15	20 33 →	20 30		
St Denys	d				18 38											19 38									
Swaythling	d				18 41											19 41									
Southampton Airport Parkwy ✈	d	18 38			18 44	19 03	19 08				19 22		19 38			19 44	20 03	20 08			20 22		20 38		
Portsmouth Harbour	d		17 54											18 54										19 54	
Portsmouth & Southsea	d		17 59											18 59										19 59	
Fratton	d		18 03											19 03										20 03	
Hilsea	d		18 07											19 07										20 07	
Cosham	d		18 12											19 12										20 12	
Portchester	d		18 17											19 17										20 17	
Fareham	d		18 23											19 23										20 23	
Botley	d		18 30											19 30										20 30	
Hedge End	d		18 35											19 35										20 35	
Eastleigh 3	a		18 41		18 47	19 06			←					19 41		19 47	20 06			←				20 41	
	d		18 42		18 48	19 12			19 12					19 42		19 48	20 12			20 12				20 42	
Chandlers Ford	a				18 53	→										19 53	→								
	d				18 53											19 53									
Romsey	a				19 01											20 01									
Shawford	d								19 18											20 18					
Winchester	d	18 48	18 54				19 18		19 24		19 31		19 48	19 54				20 18		20 24	20 31		20 48	20 54	
Micheldever	d		19 02											20 02										21 02	
Basingstoke	a		19 15				19 34		19 40		19 46			20 15				20 34		20 40	20 46			21 15	
	d		19 17				19 36		19 41		19 47			20 17				20 36		20 41	20 47			21 24	
Reading 7	a										20 05										21 05				
Fleet	d								19 53											20 53				21 40	
Farnborough (Main)	d		19 31						19 58					20 31						20 58				21 46	
Woking	a	19 19	19 40										20 19	20 40						21 07			21 19	21 58	
Clapham Junction 10	a						20 12		20 24									21 16		21 30					
London Waterloo 15 ⊖	a	19 49	20 08				20 20		20 34				20 49	21 08				21 27		21 38			21 49	22 34	

For general notes see front of timetable
For details of catering facilities see Directory of Train Operators

A ☕ from Bournemouth
b Until 12 July then from 13 September.
c Until 6 September

For other services between Romsey and Southampton Central see Table 123.

Table 158

Saturdays

Weymouth, Bournemouth, Lymington, Romsey, Southampton and Basingstoke → London

Network Diagram - see first page of Table 158

		SW 1	SW 1	SW 1 ◇	GW ◇	SW 1	SW 1	SW 1	SW 1	SW 1	SW 1	SW 1	SW 1 ◇	SW 1	SW 1	SW 1	SW 1	SW 1	SW 1	SW 1	SW 1	SW 1	SW 1	SW 1
Weymouth	d			19 20	19 58								20 10							21 10			22 10	23 10
Upwey	d			19 24	20 03								20 14							21 14			22 14	23 14
Dorchester West	a				20 11																			
Dorchester South	d			19 32									20 22							21 22			22 22	23 22
Moreton (Dorset)	d			19 39									20 28							21 28			22 28	23 28
Wool	d			19 45									20 34							21 34			22 34	23 34
Wareham	d			19 52									20 42							21 42			22 42	23 42
Holton Heath	d																							
Hamworthy	d			20 01									20 48							21 48			22 48	23 48
Poole 4	a			20 05									20 53							21 53			22 53	23 53
	d		19 50	20 06									20 54							21 54			22 54	23 54
Parkstone (Dorset)	d		19 54										20 58							21 58			22 58	
Branksome	d		19 57										21 01							22 01			23 01	
Bournemouth	a		20 02	20 16									21 07							22 07			23 07	00 03
	d		20 05	20 21									21 12							22 12			23 12	
Pokesdown	d		20 09	20 25									21 16							22 16			23 16	
Christchurch	d		20 13	20 29									21 20							22 20			23 20	
Hinton Admiral	d		20 18										21 25							22 25			23 25	
New Milton	d		20 22	20 36									21 29							22 29			23 29	
Sway	d		20 27										21 34							22 34			23 34	
Yarmouth (I.O.W.) ⛴	d						*20 00*				*20b30*				*21 00*		*21c30*							
Lymington Pier ⛴	d						20 44				21 14				21 44		22 14							
Lymington Town	d						20 46				21 16				21 46		22 16							
Brockenhurst 3	a		20 32	20 43			20 54				21 24		21 39		21 54		22 24			22 39			23 39	
	d		20 33	20 44									21 40							22 40			23 40	
Beaulieu Road	d																							
Ashurst New Forest	d		20 40										21 47							22 47			23 47	
Totton	d		20 45										21 52							22 52			23 52	
Salisbury	d									20 48									21 48					
Dean	d									21 00									22 00					
Mottisfont & Dunbridge	d									21 06									22 06					
Romsey	d									21 11									22 11		23 00			
Redbridge	d									21 19									22 19		23 08			
Millbrook (Hants)	d									21 22									22 22		23 12			
Southampton Central	a	←	20 51	20 57						21 25			21 57						22 25	22 57	23 15		23 57	
	d	20 33	20 55	21 00				21 30		21 33		21 55	22 00					22 30	22 33	23 00	23 21		23 59	
St Denys	d	20 38								21 38									22 38		23 26		00 04	
Swaythling	d	20 41								21 41									22 41		23 29		00 07	
Southampton Airport Parkwy ✈	d	20 44	21 03	21 08				21 38		21 44		22 03	22 08					22 38	22 44	23 08	23 32		00 10	
Portsmouth Harbour	d								20 54					21 54								23 24		
Portsmouth & Southsea	d								20 59					21 59								23 29		
Fratton	d								21 03					22 03								23 33		
Hilsea	d								21 07					22 07								23 37		
Cosham	d								21 12					22 12								23 42		
Portchester	d								21 17					22 17								23 47		
Fareham	d								21 23					22 23								23 53		
Botley	d								21 30					22 30								23 59		
Hedge End	d								21 35					22 35								00 05		
Eastleigh 3	a	20 47	21 06			←			21 41	21 47		22 06		22 41		←		22 41	22 47	23 11	23 35	00 11	00 14	
	d	20 48	21 12			21 12			21 42	21 48		22 12				22 12		22 44	22 48	23 12	23 37	00 21		
Chandlers Ford	a	20 53	→							21 53		→							22 53		23 42			
	d	20 53								21 53									22 53		23 42			
Romsey	a	21 01								22 01									23 03		23 49			
Shawford	d					21 18										22 18				23 18				
Winchester	d			21 18		21 24		21 48	21 54				22 18			22 24		22 54		23 24		00a30		
Micheldever	d								22 02											23 33				
Basingstoke	a			21 34		21 40			22 15				22 34			22 40		23 10		23 43				
	d			21 36		21 41			22 24				22 36			22 41		23 14		23 44				
Reading 7	a																							
Fleet	d					21 53			22 40							22 53				00 01				
Farnborough (Main)	d					21 58			22 46							22 58				00 06				
Woking	a					22 07		22 19	22 58				22 54			23 07		23 32		00 18				
Clapham Junction 10	a			22 14		22 30							23 15			23 30		23 57		00 54				
London Waterloo 15 ⊖	a			22 22		22 38		22 49	23 37				23 23			23 38		00 05		01 02				

For general notes see front of timetable
For details of catering facilities see
Directory of Train Operators

b Until 12 July.
c 5 minutes later from 13 September.

For other services between Romsey and Southampton Central see Table 123.

Table 158

Sundays

Weymouth, Bournemouth, Lymington, Romsey, Southampton and Basingstoke → London

Network Diagram - see first page of Table 158

		SW	SW	SW	SW	SW	SW	XC	SW	SW	SW	SW	XC		SW	SW	SW	SW	SW	SW	SW	XC	SW	SW	SW
		1	1	1	1	1◇	1◇	1◇	1	1◇	1◇	1	1◇		1◇	1◇	1	1	1◇	1◇	1	1◇	1	1◇	1◇
															A	B								A	B
							☕	☕					☕		☕	☕						☕		☕	☕
Weymouth	d	21p10		22p10											07 43	07 48								08 43	08 48
Upwey	d	21p14		22p14											07 47	07 52								08 47	08 52
Dorchester West	a																								
Dorchester South	d	21p22		22p22											07 55	08 00								08 55	09 00
Moreton (Dorset)	d	21p28		22p28											08 02	08 07								09 02	09 07
Wool	d	21p34		22p34											08 08	08 13								09 08	09 13
Wareham	d	21p42		22p42											08 15	08 20								09 15	09 20
Holton Heath	d																								
Hamworthy	d	21p48		22p48											08 22	08 27								09 22	09 27
Poole 4	a	21p53		22p53											08 26	08 31								09 26	09 31
	d	21p54		22p54			06 50				07 50				08 27	08 32				08 55				09 27	09 32
Parkstone (Dorset)	d	21p58		22p58			06 54				07 54				08 31	08 36								09 31	09 36
Branksome	d	22p01		23p01			06 57				07 57				08 35	08 40								09 40	09 40
Bournemouth	a	22p07		23p07			07 02				08 02				08 46	08 46				09 04				09 46	09 46
	d	22p12		23p12			07 06				08 06				08 50	08 50				09 06		09 40		09 50	09 50
Pokesdown	d	22p16		23p16			07 10				08 10									09 10					
Christchurch	d	22p20		23p20			07 14				08 14									09 14					
Hinton Admiral	d	22p25		23p25			07 19				08 19									09 19					
New Milton	d	22p29		23p29			07 23				08 23				09 01	09 01				09 23				10 01	10 01
Sway	d	22p34		23p34			07 28				08 28									09 28					
Yarmouth (I.O.W.) ⛴	d																	08b30					09 00		
Lymington Pier ⛴	d																	09 14					09 44		
Lymington Town	d																	09 16					09 46		
Brockenhurst 3	a	22p39		23p39			07 33				08 33				09 08	09 08		09 24		09 33		09 53	09 54	10 08	10 08
	d	22p40		23p40			07 34				08 34				09 09	09 09				09 34		09 57		10 09	10 09
Beaulieu Road	d										08 39									09 39					
Ashurst New Forest	d	22p47		23p47			07 43				08 43									09 43					
Totton	d	22p52		23p52			07 48				08 48									09 48					
Salisbury	d								08 20								09 08								
Dean	d																09 20								
Mottisfont & Dunbridge	d																09 26								
Romsey	d								08 39								09 32								
Redbridge	d								08 46								09 39								
Millbrook (Hants)	d								08 50								09 43								
Southampton Central	a	22p57		23p57			07 53		08 52		08 53	←			09 23	09 23	09 45			09 53	←	10 10		10 23	10 23
	d	23p00		23p59	06 55		07 55	08 39	08 59 →		08 55	08 59			09 25	09 25	09 59 →			09 55	09 59	10 15		10 25	10 25
St Denys	d			00 04								09 04									10 04				
Swaythling	d			00 07								09 07	←								10 07				
Southampton Airport Parkway ✈	d	23p08		00 10	07 03		08 03	08 46			09 03	09 10	08 46		09 33	09 33				10 03	10 10	10 22		10 33	10 33
Portsmouth Harbour	d		23p24			07 17		→		08 17									09 17						
Portsmouth & Southsea	d		23p29			07 22				08 22									09 22						
Fratton	d		23p33			07 26				08 26									09 26						
Hilsea	d		23p37			07 30				08 30									09 30						
Cosham	d		23p42			07 35				08 35									09 35						
Portchester	d		23p47			07 40				08 40									09 40						
Fareham	d		23p53			07 46				08 46									09 46						
Botley	d		23p59			07 54				08 54									09 54						
Hedge End	d		00 05			07 58				08 58									09 58						
Eastleigh 3	a	23p11	00 11	00 14	07 07	08 04	08 07			09 04	09 07	09 13							10 04	10 07	10 13				
	d	23p12	00 21		07 11		08 11				09 11	09 15								10 11	10 15				
Chandlers Ford	a											09 20									10 20				
	d											09 20									10 20				
Romsey	a											09 28									10 28				
Shawford	d	23p18									09 17														
Winchester	d	23p24	00a30		07 23		08 23				09 23				09 42	09 42				10 23		10 31		10 42	10 42
Micheldever	d	23p33			07 32		08 32				09 32									10 32					
Basingstoke	a	23p43			07 42		08 42				09 42		09 46		09 58	09 58				10 42		10 46		10 58	10 58
	d	23p44			07 44		08 44				09 44		09 47		10 00	10 00				10 44		10 47		11 00	11 00
Reading 7	a												10 05									11 05			
Fleet	d	00 01																							
Farnborough (Main)	d	00 06																							
Woking	a	00 18			08 02		09 02				10 02				10 19	10 19				11 02				11 18	11 18
Clapham Junction 10	a	00 54			08 27		09 27				10 27				10 39	10 39				11 27				11 39	11 39
London Waterloo 15	⊖ a	01 02			08 42		09 42				10 42				10 54	10 54				11 40				11 52	11 52

For general notes see front of timetable
For details of catering facilities see Directory of Train Operators

A From 28 September. ☕ from Bournemouth

B Until 21 September. ☕ from Bournemouth

b Until 13 July.

For other services between Romsey and Southampton Central see Table 123.

Table 158

Sundays

Weymouth, Bournemouth, Lymington, Romsey, Southampton and Basingstoke → London

Network Diagram - see first page of Table 158

Station		SW	SW	SW	SW		SW	XC	SW	SW	SW	SW	SW
		1	1	1 ◇	1 ◇		1	R 1 ⊡	1	1 ◇ A ⊡	1	1	1 ◇
Weymouth	d									09 48			
Upwey	d									09 52			
Dorchester West	a												
Dorchester South	d									10 00			
Moreton (Dorset)	d									10 07			
Wool	d									10 13			
Wareham	d									10 20			
Holton Heath	d												
Hamworthy	d									10 27			
Poole 4	a									10 31			
	d				09 55					10 32			
Parkstone (Dorset)	d									10 36			
Branksome	d									10 40			
Bournemouth	a				10 04					10 46			
	d				10 06			10 40		10 50			
Pokesdown	d				10 10								
Christchurch	d				10 14								
Hinton Admiral	d				10 19								
New Milton	d				10 23					11 01			
Sway	d				10 28								
Yarmouth (I.O.W.) ⛴	d		*09 30*						*10b00*			*10 30*	
Lymington Pier ⛴	d		10 14						10 44			11 14	
Lymington Town	d		10 16						10 46			11 16	
Brockenhurst 3	a		10 24		10 33			10 53	10 54	11 08		11 24	
	d				10 34			10 55		11 09			
Beaulieu Road	d				10 39								
Ashurst New Forest	d				10 43								
Totton	d				10 48								
Salisbury	d	10 13									11 08		
Dean	d										11 20		
Mottisfont & Dunbridge	d										11 26		
Romsey	d	10 32									11 32		
Redbridge	d	10 39									11 39		
Millbrook (Hants)	d	10 43									11 43		
Southampton Central	a	10 45			10 53		←	11 10		11 23	11 45		
	d	10 59 →			10 55		10 59	11 15		11 25	11 59 →		
St Denys	d						11 04						
Swaythling	d						11 07						
Southampton Airport Parkwy ✈	d				11 03		11 10	11 22		11 33			
Portsmouth Harbour	d			10 17									11 17
Portsmouth & Southsea	d			10 22									11 22
Fratton	d			10 26									11 26
Hilsea	d			10 30									11 30
Cosham	d			10 35									11 35
Portchester	d			10 40									11 40
Fareham	d			10 46									11 46
Botley	d			10 54									11 54
Hedge End	d			10 58									11 58
Eastleigh 3	a			11 04	11 07		11 13						12 04
	d			11 11			11 15						12 11
Chandlers Ford	a						11 20						
	d						11 20						
Romsey	a						11 28						
Shawford	d			11 17									
Winchester	d			11 23				11 31		11 42			12 23
Micheldever	d			11 32									12 32
Basingstoke	a			11 42				11 46		11 58			12 42
	d			11 44				11 47		12 00			12 44
Reading 7	a							12 05					
Fleet	d												
Farnborough (Main)	d												
Woking	a			12 02						12 18			13 02
Clapham Junction 10	a			12 27						12 39			13 27
London Waterloo 15 ⊖	a			12 40						12 52			13 40

Station		SW	SW	XC	SW	SW		GW	SW	SW	SW	SW	SW
		1 ◇	1	R 1 ⊡	1	1 ◇ A ⊡		B	1	1	1 ◇	1 ◇	1
Weymouth	d					10 48		11 11					
Upwey	d					10 52		11 16					
Dorchester West	a							11 24					
Dorchester South	d					11 00							
Moreton (Dorset)	d					11 07							
Wool	d					11 13							
Wareham	d					11 20							
Holton Heath	d												
Hamworthy	d					11 27							
Poole 4	a					11 31							
	d	10 55				11 32						11 55	
Parkstone (Dorset)	d					11 36							
Branksome	d					11 40							
Bournemouth	a	11 04				11 46						12 04	
	d	11 06		11 40		11 50						12 06	
Pokesdown	d	11 10										12 10	
Christchurch	d	11 14										12 14	
Hinton Admiral	d	11 19										12 19	
New Milton	d	11 23				12 01						12 23	
Sway	d	11 28										12 28	
Yarmouth (I.O.W.) ⛴	d				*11b00*					*11c30*			
Lymington Pier ⛴	d				11 44					12 14			
Lymington Town	d				11 46					12 16			
Brockenhurst 3	a	11 33		11 53	11 54	12 08				12 24		12 33	
	d	11 34		11 57		12 09						12 34	
Beaulieu Road	d	11 39										12 39	
Ashurst New Forest	d	11 43										12 43	
Totton	d	11 48										12 48	
Salisbury	d								12 13				
Dean	d												
Mottisfont & Dunbridge	d												
Romsey	d								12 32				
Redbridge	d								12 39				
Millbrook (Hants)	d								12 43				
Southampton Central	a	11 53	←	12 10		12 23			12 45			12 53	←
	d	11 55	11 59	12 15		12 25			12 59 →			12 55	12 59
St Denys	d		12 04										13 04
Swaythling	d		12 07										13 07
Southampton Airport Parkwy ✈	d	12 03	12 10	12 22		12 33						13 03	13 10
Portsmouth Harbour	d										12 17		
Portsmouth & Southsea	d										12 22		
Fratton	d										12 26		
Hilsea	d										12 30		
Cosham	d										12 35		
Portchester	d										12 40		
Fareham	d										12 46		
Botley	d										12 54		
Hedge End	d										12 58		
Eastleigh 3	a	12 07	12 13								13 04	13 07	13 13
	d		12 15								13 11		13 15
Chandlers Ford	a		12 20										13 20
	d		12 20										13 20
Romsey	a		12 28										13 28
Shawford	d										13 17		
Winchester	d			12 31		12 42					13 23		
Micheldever	d										13 32		
Basingstoke	a			12 46		12 58					13 42		
	d			12 47		13 00					13 44		
Reading 7	a			13 05									
Fleet	d												
Farnborough (Main)	d												
Woking	a					13 18					14 02		
Clapham Junction 10	a					13 39					14 27		
London Waterloo 15 ⊖	a					13 49					14 37		

For general notes see front of timetable
For details of catering facilities see Directory of Train Operators

A ⊡ from Bournemouth
B Until 7 September
b Until 13 July.
c Until 2 November.

For other services between Romsey and Southampton Central see Table 123.

Table 158

Sundays

Weymouth, Bournemouth, Lymington, Romsey, Southampton and Basingstoke → London

Network Diagram - see first page of Table 158

		XC	SW	SW	SW	SW	SW	SW	SW	XC	SW	SW	SW	SW	SW	SW	SW	XC	XC	SW	SW	GW	GW
		R 1	1	1 ◇	1	1	1 ◇	1 ◇	1	R 1	1	1 ◇	1	1	1 ◇	1 ◇	1	R 1	R 1	1	1 ◇	◇	
				A								A						B	C		A	D	B
		⊏P		⊏P						⊏P		⊏P						⊏P	⊏P		⊏P		
Weymouth	d			11 48								12 48									13 48	14 00	14 08
Upwey	d			11 52								12 52									13 52	14 05	14 13
Dorchester West	a																					14 13	14 21
Dorchester South	d			12 00								13 00									14 00		
Moreton (Dorset)	d			12 07								13 07									14 07		
Wool	d			12 13								13 13									14 13		
Wareham	d			12 20								13 20									14 20		
Holton Heath	d																						
Hamworthy	d			12 27								13 27									14 27		
Poole 4	a			12 31								13 31									14 31		
	d			12 32				12 55				13 32				13 55					14 32		
Parkstone (Dorset)	d			12 36								13 36									14 36		
Branksome	d			12 40								13 40									14 40		
Bournemouth	a			12 46				13 04				13 46				14 04					14 46		
	d	12 40		12 50				13 06		13 40		13 50				14 06		14 40	14 40		14 50		
Pokesdown	d							13 10								14 10							
Christchurch	d							13 14								14 14							
Hinton Admiral	d							13 19								14 19							
New Milton	d			13 01				13 23				14 01				14 23					15 01		
Sway	d							13 28								14 28							
Yarmouth (I.O.W.) ⛴	d		*12 00*			*12b30*					*13c00*			*13b30*						*14 00*			
Lymington Pier ⛴	d		12 44			13 14					13 44			14 14						14 44			
Lymington Town	d		12 46			13 16					13 46			14 16						14 46			
Brockenhurst 3	a	12 53	12 54	13 08		13 24		13 33		13 53	13 54	14 08		14 24		14 33		14 53	14 53	14 54	15 08		
	d	12 57		13 09				13 34		13 57		14 09				14 34		14 57	14 57		15 09		
Beaulieu Road	d							13 39								14 39							
Ashurst New Forest	d							13 43								14 43							
Totton	d							13 48								14 48							
Salisbury	d				13 08								14 13										
Dean	d				13 20																		
Mottisfont & Dunbridge	d				13 26																		
Romsey	d				13 32								14 32										
Redbridge	d				13 39								14 39										
Millbrook (Hants)	d				13 43								14 43										
Southampton Central	a	13 10		13 23	13 45			13 53	←	14 10		14 23	14 45			14 53	←	15 10	15 10		15 23		
	d	13 15		13 25	13 59 →			13 55	13 59	14 15		14 25	14 59 →			14 55	14 59	15 15	15 15		15 25		
St Denys	d								14 04								15 04						
Swaythling	d								14 07								15 07						
Southampton Airport Parkwy ✈	d	13 22		13 33				14 03	14 10	14 22		14 33				15 03	15 10	15 22	15 22		15 33		
Portsmouth Harbour	d						13 17								14 17								
Portsmouth & Southsea	d						13 22								14 22								
Fratton	d						13 26								14 26								
Hilsea	d						13 30								14 30								
Cosham	d						13 35								14 35								
Portchester	d						13 40								14 40								
Fareham	d						13 46								14 46								
Botley	d						13 54								14 54								
Hedge End	d						13 58								14 58								
Eastleigh 3	a						14 04	14 07	14 13						15 04	15 07	15 13						
	d						14 11		14 15						15 11		15 15						
Chandlers Ford	a								14 20								15 20						
	d								14 20								15 20						
Romsey	a								14 28								15 28						
Shawford	d														15 17								
Winchester	d	13 31		13 42			14 23			14 31		14 42			15 23			15 31	15 31		15 42		
Micheldever	d						14 32								15 32								
Basingstoke	a	13 46		13 58			14 42			14 46		14 58			15 42			15 46	15 46		15 58		
	d	13 47		14 00			14 44			14 47		15 00			15 44			15 47	15 47		16 00		
Reading 7	a	14 05								15 05								16 05	16 07				
Fleet	d																						
Farnborough (Main)	d																						
Woking	a			14 18			15 02					15 18			16 02						16 18		
Clapham Junction 10	a			14 39			15 27					15 39			16 27						16 39		
London Waterloo 15 ⊖	a			14 49			15 37					15 49			16 37						16 49		

For general notes see front of timetable
For details of catering facilities see Directory of Train Operators

A ⊏P from Bournemouth
B Until 7 September
C From 14 September. To Manchester Piccadilly
D From 14 September
c Until 13 July then from 14 September.

For other services between Romsey and Southampton Central see Table 123.

Table 158

Sundays

Weymouth, Bournemouth, Lymington, Romsey, Southampton and Basingstoke → London

Network Diagram - see first page of Table 158

		SW	SW	SW	SW	SW	XC	SW	SW	SW	SW	SW	SW		SW	XC	SW	SW	GW	SW	SW	SW	SW	SW	XC
		1	1	1 ◊	1 ◊	1	R 1	1	1 ◊	1	1	1 ◊	1 ◊		1	R 1	1	1 ◊		1	1	1 ◊	1 ◊	1	1 ◊
									A									A	B						
							☕		☕							☕		☕							☕
Weymouth	d								14 48									15 48	16 15						
Upwey	d								14 52									15 52	16 20						
Dorchester West	a																		16 28						
Dorchester South	d								15 00									16 00							
Moreton (Dorset)	d								15 07									16 07							
Wool	d								15 13									16 13							
Wareham	d								15 20									16 20							
Holton Heath	d																								
Hamworthy	d								15 27									16 27							
Poole 4	a								15 31									16 31							
	d				14 55				15 32				15 55					16 32					16 55		
Parkstone (Dorset)	d								15 36									16 36							
Branksome	d								15 40									16 40							
Bournemouth	a				15 04				15 46				16 04					16 46					17 04		
	d				15 06		15 40		15 50				16 06			16 40		16 50					17 06		17 40
Pokesdown	d				15 10								16 10										17 10		
Christchurch	d				15 14								16 14										17 14		
Hinton Admiral	d				15 19								16 19										17 19		
New Milton	d				15 23				16 01				16 23					17 01					17 23		
Sway	d				15 28								16 28										17 28		
Yarmouth (I.O.W.) ⛴	d		14b30					15c00			15 30						16c00				16c30				
Lymington Pier ⛴	d		15 14					15 44			16 14						16 44				17 14				
Lymington Town	d		15 16					15 46			16 16						16 46				17 16				
Brockenhurst 3	a		15 24		15 33		15 53	15 54	16 08		16 24		16 33			16 53	16 54	17 08			17 24		17 33		17 53
	d				15 34		15 57		16 09				16 34			16 57		17 09					17 34		17 57
Beaulieu Road	d				15 39								16 39										17 39		
Ashurst New Forest	d				15 43								16 43										17 43		
Totton	d				15 48								16 48										17 48		
Salisbury	d	15 08								16 13										17 08					
Dean	d	15 20																		17 20					
Mottisfont & Dunbridge	d	15 26																		17 26					
Romsey	d	15 32								16 32										17 32					
Redbridge	d	15 39								16 39										17 39					
Millbrook (Hants)	d	15 43								16 43										17 43					
Southampton Central	a	15 45			15 53	←	16 10		16 23	16 45			16 53		←	17 10		17 23		17 45			17 53	←	18 10
	d	15 59 →			15 55	15 59	16 15		16 25	16 59 →			16 55		16 59	17 15		17 25		17 59 →			17 55	17 59	18 15
St Denys	d					16 04									17 04									18 04	
Swaythling	d					16 07									17 07									18 07	
Southampton Airport Parkwy ✈	d				16 03	16 10	16 22		16 33				17 03		17 10	17 22		17 33					18 03	18 10	18 22
Portsmouth Harbour	d			15 17								16 17										17 17			
Portsmouth & Southsea	d			15 22								16 22										17 22			
Fratton	d			15 26								16 26										17 26			
Hilsea	d			15 30								16 30										17 30			
Cosham	d			15 35								16 35										17 35			
Portchester	d			15 40								16 40										17 40			
Fareham	d			15 46								16 46										17 46			
Botley	d			15 54								16 54										17 54			
Hedge End	d			15 58								16 58										17 58			
Eastleigh 3	a			16 04	16 07	16 13						17 04	17 07		17 13							18 04	18 07	18 13	
	d			16 11		16 15						17 11			17 15							18 11		18 15	
Chandlers Ford	a					16 20									17 20									18 20	
	d					16 20									17 20									18 20	
Romsey	a					16 28									17 28									18 28	
Shawford	d											17 17													
Winchester	d			16 23			16 31		16 42			17 23				17 31		17 42				18 23			18 31
Micheldever	d			16 32								17 32										18 32			
Basingstoke	a			16 42			16 46		16 58			17 42				17 46		17 58				18 42			18 46
	d			16 44			16 47		17 00			17 44				17 47		18 00				18 44			18 47
Reading 7	a						17 05									18 05									19 05
Fleet	d																								
Farnborough (Main)	d																								
Woking	a			17 02					17 18			18 02						18 18				19 02			
Clapham Junction 10	a			17 27					17 39			18 27						18 39				19 27			
London Waterloo 15 ⊖	a			17 37					17 49			18 37						18 49				19 37			

For general notes see front of timetable
For details of catering facilities see
Directory of Train Operators

A ☕ from Bournemouth
B Until 7 September
b Until 13 July then from 14 September.

For other services between Romsey and Southampton Central see Table 123.

Table 158

Sundays

Weymouth, Bournemouth, Lymington, Romsey, Southampton and Basingstoke → London

Network Diagram - see first page of Table 158

		SW	SW	SW	SW	SW	SW	SW	XC	XC	SW	SW	GW	SW	SW	SW	SW	SW	XC	SW	SW	SW	SW
		1	1 ◇	1	1	1 ◇	1 ◇	1	1 ◇	1 ◇	1	1 ◇	◇	1	1	1 ◇	1 ◇	1	1 ◇	1	1 ◇	1	1
			A						B	C		A									A		
			⊏P						⊏P	⊏P		⊏P									⊏P		
Weymouth	d		16 48									17 48	18 00								18 48		
Upwey	d		16 52									17 52	18 05								18 52		
Dorchester West	a												18 13										
Dorchester South	d		17 00									18 00									19 00		
Moreton (Dorset)	d		17 07									18 07									19 07		
Wool	d		17 13									18 13									19 13		
Wareham	d		17 20									18 20									19 20		
Holton Heath	d																						
Hamworthy	d		17 27									18 27									19 27		
Poole 4	a		17 31									18 31									19 31		
	d		17 32				17 55					18 32					18 55				19 32		
Parkstone (Dorset)	d		17 36									18 36									19 36		
Branksome	d		17 40									18 40									19 40		
Bournemouth	a		17 46				18 04					18 46					19 04				19 46		
	d		17 50				18 06		18 40	18 40		18 50					19 06		19 40		19 50		
Pokesdown	d						18 10										19 10						
Christchurch	d						18 14										19 14						
Hinton Admiral	d						18 19										19 19						
New Milton	d		18 01				18 23					19 01					19 23				20 01		
Sway	d						18 28										19 28						
Yarmouth (I.O.W.) ⛴	d	*17 00*			*17b30*						*18c00*				*18 30*					*19b00*			*19c30*
Lymington Pier ⛴	d	17 44			18 14						18 44				19 14					19 44			20 14
Lymington Town	d	17 46			18 16						18 46				19 16					19 46			20 16
Brockenhurst 3	a	17 54	18 08		18 24		18 33		18 53	18 53	18 54	19 08			19 24		19 33		19 53	19 54	20 08		20 24
	d		18 09				18 34		18 55	18 57		19 09					19 34		19 57		20 09		
Beaulieu Road	d						18 39										19 39						
Ashurst New Forest	d						18 43										19 43						
Totton	d						18 48										19 48						
Salisbury	d			18 13										19 08								20 13	
Dean	d													19 20									
Mottisfont & Dunbridge	d													19 26									
Romsey	d			18 32										19 32								20 32	
Redbridge	d			18 39										19 39								20 39	
Millbrook (Hants)	d			18 43										19 43								20 43	
Southampton Central	a		18 23	18 45			18 53	←	19 10	19 10		19 23		19 45			19 53	←	20 10		20 23	20 45	
	d		18 25	18 59 →			18 55	18 59	19 15	19 15		19 25		19 59 →			19 55	19 59	20 15		20 25	20 59 →	
St Denys	d							19 04										20 04					
Swaythling	d							19 07										20 07					
Southampton Airport Parkwy ✈	d		18 33				19 03	19 10	19 22	19 22		19 33					20 03	20 10	20 22		20 33		
Portsmouth Harbour	d					18 17										19 17							
Portsmouth & Southsea	d					18 22										19 22							
Fratton	d					18 26										19 26							
Hilsea	d					18 30										19 30							
Cosham	d					18 35										19 35							
Portchester	d					18 40										19 40							
Fareham	d					18 46										19 46							
Botley	d					18 54										19 54							
Hedge End	d					18 58										19 58							
Eastleigh 3	a					19 04	19 07	19 13								20 04	20 07	20 13					
	d						19 11	19 15									20 11	20 15					
Chandlers Ford	a							19 20										20 20					
	d							19 20										20 20					
Romsey	a							19 28										20 28					
Shawford	d						19 17																
Winchester	d		18 42				19 23		19 31	19 31		19 42					20 23		20 31		20 42		
Micheldever	d						19 32										20 32						
Basingstoke	a		18 58				19 42		19 46	19 46		19 58					20 42		20 46		20 58		
	d		19 00				19 44		19 47	19 47		20 00					20 44		20 47		21 00		
Reading 7	a								20 05	20 05									21 05				
Fleet	d																						
Farnborough (Main)	d																						
Woking	a		19 18				20 02					20 18					21 02				21 18		
Clapham Junction 10	a		19 39				20 27					20 39					21 27				21 39		
London Waterloo 15 ⊖	a		19 49				20 37					20 49					21 37				21 49		

For general notes see front of timetable
For details of catering facilities see Directory of Train Operators

A ⊏P from Bournemouth
B 20 July to 7 September
C Until 13 July and from 14 September.
b Until 13 July then from 14 September.
c Until 7 September

For other services between Romsey and Southampton Central see Table 123.

Table 158

Sundays

Weymouth, Bournemouth, Lymington, Romsey, Southampton and Basingstoke → London

Network Diagram - see first page of Table 158

Station		SW 1 ◇	SW 1 ◇	SW 1	XC 1 ◇ A	XC 1 ◇ B	SW 1	SW 1	SW 1		SW 1	SW 1	GW ◇	SW 1	SW 1	SW 1	SW 1	SW 1	SW 1	SW 1	SW 1	SW 1	SW 1		
Weymouth	d											19 58	20 09						20 58			21 58	22 58		
Upwey	d											20 02	20 14						21 02			22 02	23 02		
Dorchester West	a												20 22												
Dorchester South	d											20 10							21 10			22 10	23 10		
Moreton (Dorset)	d											20 17							21 17			22 17	23 17		
Wool	d											20 23							21 23			22 23	23 23		
Wareham	d											20 30							21 30			22 30	23 30		
Holton Heath	d																								
Hamworthy	d											20 37							21 37			22 37	23 37		
Poole 4	a											20 41							21 41			22 41	23 41		
	d		19 55									20 50							21 50			22 50	23 50		
Parkstone (Dorset)	d											20 54							21 54			22 54	23 54		
Branksome	d											20 57							21 57			22 57	23 57		
Bournemouth	a		20 04									21 03							22 03			23 03	00 03		
	d		20 06		20 40	20 40						21 06							22 06			23 06			
Pokesdown	d		20 10									21 10							22 10			23 10			
Christchurch	d		20 14									21 14							22 14			23 14			
Hinton Admiral	d		20 19									21 19							22 19			23 19			
New Milton	d		20 23									21 23							22 23			23 23			
Sway	d		20 28									21 28							22 28			23 28			
Yarmouth (I.O.W.) ⛴	d						*20 00*		*20b30*					*21 00*			*21c30*								
Lymington Pier ⛴	d						20 44		21 14					21 44			22 14								
Lymington Town	d						20 46		21 16					21 46			22 16								
Brockenhurst 3	a		20 33		20 53	20 53	20 54		21 24			21 33		21 54			22 24		22 33			23 33			
	d		20 34		20 57	20 57						21 34							22 34			23 34			
Beaulieu Road	d		20 39									21 39							22 39						
Ashurst New Forest	d		20 43									21 43							22 43			23 43			
Totton	d		20 48									21 48							22 48			23 48			
Salisbury	d							21 08																	
Dean	d							21 20																	
Mottisfont & Dunbridge	d							21 26																	
Romsey	d							21 32										22 28							
Redbridge	d							21 39										22 35							
Millbrook (Hants)	d							21 43										22 39							
Southampton Central	a		20 53	←	21 10	21 11		21 45				21 53			←			22 41	22 53	←		23 53			
	d		20 55	20 59	21 15	21 15		21 59 →				21 55			21 59			23 05 →	22 55	23 05					
St Denys	d			21 04											22 04					23 10					
Swaythling	d			21 07											22 07					23 13					
Southampton Airport Parkwy ✈	d		21 03	21 10	21 22	21 22						22 03			22 10				23 03	23 16					
Portsmouth Harbour	d	20 17									21 17					22 17					23 17				
Portsmouth & Southsea	d	20 22									21 22					22 22					23 22				
Fratton	d	20 26									21 26					22 26					23 26				
Hilsea	d	20 30									21 30					22 30					23 30				
Cosham	d	20 35									21 35					22 35					23 35				
Portchester	d	20 40									21 40					22 40					23 40				
Fareham	d	20 46									21 46					22 46					23 46				
Botley	d	20 54									21 54					22 54					23 54				
Hedge End	d	20 58									21 58					22 58					23 58				
Eastleigh 3	a	21 04	21 07	21 13							22 04	22 07			22 13	23 04			23 09	23 19	00 04				
	d	21 11		21 15							22 11				22 15				23 11	23 21					
Chandlers Ford	a			21 20											22 20					23 26					
	d			21 20											22 20					23 26					
Romsey	a			21 28											22 31					23 33					
Shawford	d	21 17																							
Winchester	d	21 23			21 31	21 31					22 23								23 23						
Micheldever	d	21 32									22 32								23 32						
Basingstoke	a	21 42			21 46	21 46					22 42								23 42						
	d	21 44			21 47	21 47					22 44								23 43						
Reading 7	a				22 05	22 05																			
Fleet	d																								
Farnborough (Main)	d																								
Woking	a	22 02									23 02								00 02						
Clapham Junction 10	a	22 27									23 27								00 22						
London Waterloo 15 ⊖	a	22 37									23 37								00 33						

For general notes see front of timetable
For details of catering facilities see Directory of Train Operators

A Until 7 September
B From 14 September
b Until 13 July.
c 5 minutes later from 14 September.

For other services between Romsey and Southampton Central see Table 123.

Woking → Heathrow Railair

Express Coach Service

		SW SX	SW SX	SW SX	SW SX	SW	SW	SW	SW SO	SW SX	SW	SW SO	SW SX	SW	SW SO	SW SX	SW	SW SO	SW SX	SW	SW SO	SW SX
		🚌	🚌	🚌	🚌	🚌	🚌	🚌	🚌	🚌	🚌	🚌	🚌	🚌	🚌	🚌	🚌	🚌	🚌	🚌	🚌	🚌
Woking §	d		05 20		05 50		06 20		06 50	06 50		07 20	07 20		07 50	07 50		08 20	08 20		08 50	08 50
Heathrow Terminal 5	d		05 45		06 15		06 45		07 15	07 25		07 45	08 05		08 15	08 35		08 45	09 05		09 15	09 35
Heathrow Central Bus Stn	a		06 00		06 30		07 00		07 30	07 40		08 00	08 20		08 30	08 50		09 00	09 20		09 30	09 50
	d	05 45		06 15		06 45		07 15			07 45			08 30			09 00			09 30		
Heathrow Terminal 5	a	06 00		06 30		07 00		07 30			08 00			08 45			09 15			09 45		
Woking	a	06 30		07 00		07 30		08 05			08 40			09 25			09 55			10 25		

		SW	SW SO	SW SX	SW	SW	SW	SW	SW	SW	SW	SW	SW	SW	SW	SW	SW	SW	SW	SW	SW	SW
		🚌	🚌	🚌	🚌	🚌	🚌	🚌	🚌	🚌	🚌	🚌	🚌	🚌	🚌	🚌	🚌	🚌	🚌	🚌	🚌	🚌
Woking §	d		09 35	09 35		10 05		10 35		11 05		11 35		12 05		12 35		13 05		13 35		14 05
Heathrow Terminal 5	d		10 00	10 10		10 30		11 00		11 30		12 00		12 30		13 00		13 30		14 00		14 30
Heathrow Central Bus Stn	a		10 15	10 25		10 45		11 15		11 45		12 15		12 45		13 15		13 45		14 15		14 45
	d	10 00			10 30		11 00		11 30		12 00		12 30		13 00		13 30		14 00		14 30	
Heathrow Terminal 5	a	10 15			10 45		11 15		11 45		12 15		12 45		13 15		13 45		14 15		14 45	
Woking	a	10 50			11 15		11 45		12 15		12 45		13 15		13 45		14 15		14 45		15 15	

		SW	SW	SW	SW	SW	SW	SW	SW SO	SW SX	SW	SW SO	SW SX	SW	SW SO	SW SX	SW	SW SO	SW SX	SW	SW SO	SW SX
		🚌	🚌	🚌	🚌	🚌	🚌	🚌	🚌	🚌	🚌	🚌	🚌	🚌	🚌	🚌	🚌	🚌	🚌	🚌	🚌	🚌
Woking §	d		14 35		15 05		15 35		16 05	16 05		16 35	16 35		17 05	17 05		17 35	17 35		18 05	18 05
Heathrow Terminal 5	d		15 00		15 30		16 00		16 30	16 35		17 00	17 10		17 30	17 40		18 00	18 10		18 30	18 40
Heathrow Central Bus Stn	a		15 15		15 45		16 15		16 45	16 50		17 15	17 25		17 45	17 55		18 15	18 25		18 45	18 55
	d	15 00		15 30		16 00		16 30			17 00			17 30			18 00			18 30		
Heathrow Terminal 5	a	15 15		15 45		16 15		16 45			17 15			17 45			18 15			18 45		
Woking	a	15 45		16 15		16 45		17 25			18 05			18 35			19 05			19 35		

		SW	SW	SW	SW SO	SW SX	SW	SW SO	SW SX	SW	SW SO	SW SX	SW	SW SO	SW SX	SW SO	SW SX	SW	SW SO	SW SX	SW	
		🚌	🚌	🚌	🚌	🚌	🚌	🚌	🚌	🚌	🚌	🚌	🚌	🚌	🚌	🚌	🚌	🚌	🚌	🚌	🚌	
Woking §	d		18 35		19 05	19 05		19 35	19 35		20 05	20 05		20 35	20 35	21 05	21 05		22 05	22 05		
Heathrow Terminal 5	d		19 00		19 30	19 35		20 00	20 05		20 30	20 35		21 00	21 05	21 30	21 35		22 30	22 35		
Heathrow Central Bus Stn	a		19 15		19 45	19 45		20 15	20 15		20 45	20 45		21 15	21 15	21 45	21 45		22 45	22 45		
	d	19 00		19 30			20 00			20 30			21 15					22 15			23 15	
Heathrow Terminal 5	a	19 15		19 45			20 15			20 45			21 30					22 30			23 30	
Woking	a	19 55		20 15			20 45			21 15			22 00					23 00			23 59	

Sundays

		SW	SW	SW	SW	SW	SW	SW	SW	SW	SW	SW	SW	SW	SW	SW	SW	SW	SW	SW	SW	SW
		🚌	🚌	🚌	🚌	🚌	🚌	🚌	🚌	🚌	🚌	🚌	🚌	🚌	🚌	🚌	🚌	🚌	🚌	🚌	🚌	🚌
Woking §	d		06 20		06 50		07 20		07 50		08 20		08 50		09 35		10 05		10 35		11 05	
Heathrow Terminal 5	d		06 45		07 15		07 45		08 15		08 45		09 15		10 00		10 30		11 00		11 30	
Heathrow Central Bus Stn	a		07 00		07 30		08 00		08 30		09 00		09 30		10 15		10 45		11 15		11 45	
	d	06 45		07 15		07 45		08 30		09 00		09 30		10 00		10 30		11 00		11 30		12 00
Heathrow Terminal 5	a	07 00		07 30		08 00		08 45		09 15		09 45		10 15		10 45		11 15		11 45		12 15
Woking	a	07 30		08 00		08 30		09 15		09 45		10 15		10 45		11 15		11 45		12 15		12 45

		SW	SW	SW	SW	SW	SW	SW	SW	SW	SW	SW	SW	SW	SW	SW	SW	SW	SW	SW	SW	SW
		🚌	🚌	🚌	🚌	🚌	🚌	🚌	🚌	🚌	🚌	🚌	🚌	🚌	🚌	🚌	🚌	🚌	🚌	🚌	🚌	🚌
Woking §	d	11 35		12 05		12 35		13 05		13 35		14 05		14 35		15 05		15 35		16 05		16 35
Heathrow Terminal 5	d	12 00		12 30		13 00		13 30		14 00		14 30		15 00		15 30		16 00		16 30		17 00
Heathrow Central Bus Stn	a	12 15		12 45		13 15		13 45		14 15		14 45		15 15		15 45		16 15		16 45		17 15
	d		12 30		13 00		13 30		14 00		14 30		15 00		15 30		16 00		16 30		17 00	
Heathrow Terminal 5	a		12 45		13 15		13 45		14 15		14 45		15 15		15 45		16 15		16 45		17 15	
Woking	a		13 15		13 45		14 15		14 45		15 15		15 45		16 15		16 45		17 15		17 45	

		SW	SW	SW	SW	SW	SW	SW	SW	SW	SW	SW	SW	SW	SW	SW	SW	SW	SW	SW	SW	
		🚌	🚌	🚌	🚌	🚌	🚌	🚌	🚌	🚌	🚌	🚌	🚌	🚌	🚌	🚌	🚌	🚌	🚌	🚌	🚌	
Woking §	d		17 05		17 35		18 05		18 35		19 05		19 35		20 05		20 35	21 05		22 05		
Heathrow Terminal 5	d		17 30		18 00		18 30		19 00		19 30		20 00		20 30		21 00	21 30		22 30		
Heathrow Central Bus Stn	a		17 45		18 15		18 45		19 15		19 45		20 15		20 45		21 15	21 45		22 45		
	d	17 30		18 00		18 30		19 00		19 30		20 00		20 30		21 15			22 15		23 15	
Heathrow Terminal 5	a	17 45		18 15		18 45		19 15		19 45		20 15		20 45		21 30			22 30		23 30	
Woking	a	18 15		18 45		19 15		19 45		20 15		20 45		21 15		22 00			23 00		23 59	

For general notes see front of timetable
For details of catering facilities see
Directory of Train Operators

§ On arrival at Woking passengers should proceed to the exit on platform 5, the coach leaves from immediately outside the station.

Network Diagram for Table 160

DM-19/08
Design BAJS

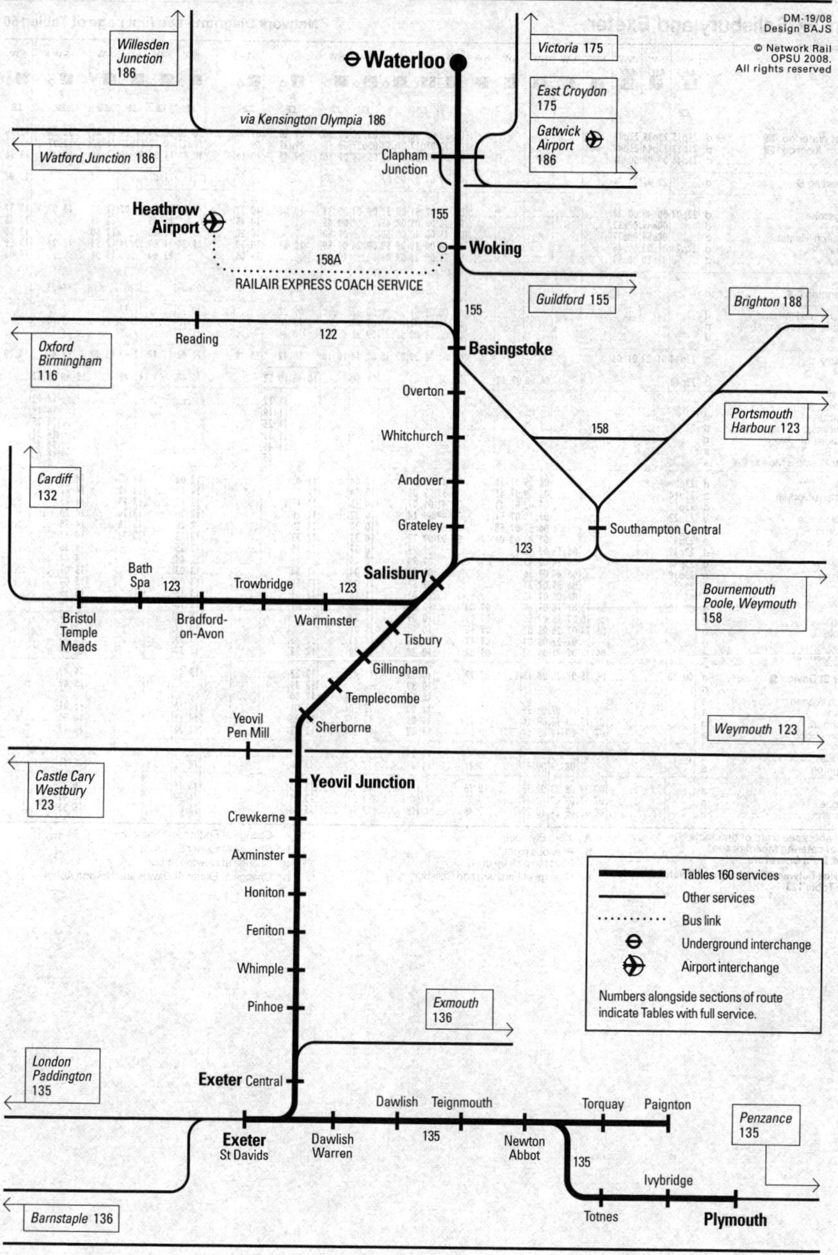
Waterloo
Willesden Junction 186
Victoria 175
East Croydon 175
Gatwick Airport 186
via Kensington Olympia 186
Watford Junction 186
Clapham Junction
Heathrow Airport
155
Woking
158A
RAILAIR EXPRESS COACH SERVICE
Guildford 155
155
Brighton 188
Reading
122
Oxford Birmingham 116
Basingstoke
Overton
Whitchurch
158
Portsmouth Harbour 123
Andover
Cardiff 132
Grateley
Southampton Central
123
Salisbury
Bath Spa
123
Trowbridge
123
Bournemouth Poole, Weymouth 158
Bristol Temple Meads
Bradford-on-Avon
Warminster
Tisbury
Gillingham
Templecombe
Yeovil Pen Mill
Sherborne
Weymouth 123
Castle Cary Westbury 123
Yeovil Junction
Crewkerne
Axminster
Honiton
Feniton
Whimple
Pinhoe
Exmouth 136
London Paddington 135
Exeter Central
Dawlish
Teignmouth
Torquay
Paignton
Penzance 135
Exeter St Davids
Dawlish Warren
135
Newton Abbot
135
Ivybridge
Totnes
Plymouth
Barnstaple 136
Tables 160 services
Other services
Bus link
Underground interchange
Airport interchange
Numbers alongside sections of route indicate Tables with full service.

For details of Bank Holiday service alterations, please see first page of Table 149

London → Salisbury and Exeter

Network Diagram - see first page of Table 160

Miles			SW	SW	SW	SW	SW	SW	SW	SW	SW	SW	SW	SW	SW	SW		SW		SW	SW	SW	SW	SW		SW
			MO	MO	MX																					
			1 ◇	1	1	1	1	1	1	1	1	1 ◇	1 ◇	1 ◇	1 ◇	1 ◇		1 ◇		1 ◇	1 ◇	1 ◇	1 ◇	1 ◇		1 ◇
																A								A		
			☕									☕	☕	☕	☕	☕		☕		☕	☕	☕	☕	☕		☕
0	**London Waterloo** 15 ⊖	d	21p15	23p35	23p35						06 30	07 10	07 50	08 20	08 50	09 20		09 50		10 20	10 50	11 20	11 50	12 20		12 50
4	Clapham Junction 10	d	21b22	23b44	23b42						06 37	07u17	07u57	08u27	08 52	09u27		09 52		10u27	10 52	11u27	11 52	12u27		12 52
24¼	Woking	d	21p46	00 08	00 03						06 57	07 36	08 16	08 46	09 16	09 46		10 16		10 46	11 16	11 46	12 16	12 46		13 16
—	Reading 7	d		23 37	23 34						06 39	07 07	08 07		09 07			10 07			11 07		12 07			13 07
47¾	**Basingstoke**	d	22p07	00 40	00 24						07 22	07 57	08 37	09 07	09 37	10 07		10 37		11 07	11 37	12 07	12 37	13 07		13 37
55½	Overton	d		00s49	00s32						07 30	08 05	08 45		09 45			10 45			11 45		12 45			13 45
59¼	Whitchurch (Hants)	d		00s54	00s37						07 35	08 10	08 50		09 50			10 50			11 50		12 50			13 50
66½	Andover	d	22p24	01 02	00 46						07 44	08 19	08 59	09 24	09 59	10 24		10 59		11 24	11 59	12 24	12 59	13 24		13 59
72¾	Grateley	d		01s10	00s53						07 51	08 26	09 06		10 06			11 06			12 06		13 06			14 06
—	Brighton 10	d										05c30		07c06		08e03				09e03		10e03		11e03		
—	Portsmouth Harbour	d									06 00	06 51		08 22		09 22				10 22		11 22		12 22		
—	Southampton Central	d									06 46	07 47		09 10		10 10				11 10		12 10		13 10		
—	Romsey	d									07 00	08 00		09 21		10 21				11 21		12 21		13 21		
83¾	**Salisbury**	a	22p44	01 22	01 05						08 03	08 39	09 18	09 44	10 18	10 42		11 18		11 42	12 18	12 42	13 18	13 43		14 20
—		d	22p48					06 08	07 12		08 08	08 45		09 50		10 48	10 52			11 48		12 48		13 48	13 52	
—	Warminster	d															11 12								14 12	
—	Westbury	d															11 19								14 19	
—	Trowbridge	d															11 25								14 25	
—	Bradford-on-Avon	d															11 31								14 31	
—	Bath Spa 7	a															11 45								14 45	
—	Bristol Temple Meads 10	a															12 05								15 05	
96½	Tisbury	d	23p04					06 29	07 31		08 27			10 04		11 02				12 02		13 02		14 02		
105¼	Gillingham (Dorset)	a	23p14					06 39	07 41		08 37	09 06		10 14		11 12				12 12		13 12		14 12		
—		d	23p15					06 42	07 43		08 41	09 07		10 15		11 13				12 13		13 13		14 13		
112¼	Templecombe	d	23p22					06 50	07 51		08 49	09 14		10 22		11 20				12 20		13 20		14 20		
118¼	Sherborne	d	23p30					06 57	07 58		08 56	09 22		10 30		11 28				12 28		13 28		14 28		
122¾	Yeovil Junction	a	23p35					07 03	08 04		09 02	09 27		10 35		11 33				12 33		13 33		14 33		
—		d	23p37				06 15	07 08				09 29		10 37		11 35				12 35				14 35		
131¾	Crewkerne	d	23p46				06 24	07 17				09 38		10 46						12 44				14 44		
144¾	Axminster	a	23p58				06 44	07 36				09 51		11 04		11 54				13 03				15 03		
—		d	23p58				06 55	07 37				09 52		11 04		11 55				13 04				15 04		
155	Honiton	a	00 09				07 06	07 48				10 03		11 16		12 06				13 15				15 15		
—		d	00 10			06 13	07 10	07 49		09 00		10 04		11 16		12 07				13 16				15 16		
159½	Feniton	d				06 18	07 15	07 55		09 05		10 09		11 22						13 22				15 22		
163¼	Whimple	d				06 23	07 20	08 01		09 10		10 14		11 27						13 27				15 27		
169	Pinhoe	d					07 27	08 07		09 17		10 21		11 33						13 33				15 33		
171¾	**Exeter Central**	a				06 32	07 31	08 12		09 23		10 29		11 38		12 22				13 38				15 38		
172½	**Exeter St Davids** 3	a	00 30			06 35	07 35	08 15		09 27		10 33		11 42		12 27				13 41				15 42		
—		d										10 39				12 39								15 49		
—	Dawlish Warren	a										10 50				12 50										
—	Dawlish	a				07 13	08 07	08 39		10 10		11 00		12 10		13 01				14 10				16 01		
—	Teignmouth	a				07 18	08 12	08 44		10 15		11 05		12 15		13 06				14 15				16 06		
—	Newton Abbot	a				07 25	08 19	08 51		10 02		11 12		12 22		13 13				14 22				16 13		
—	Torquay	a										11 23														
—	Paignton	a					08 39	09 13		10 41		11 31		12 43		13 48				14 42				16 43		
—	Totnes	a				07 39	08 53	09 58		10 16		11f16		12 52		13 25				15 16				16 25		
—	Ivybridge	a				07 55	09 09	10 14				13g09		13 09		13 41				16h24				16 41		
—	Plymouth	a				08 10	09 24	10 29		10 48		11f48		13 10		13 56				15 09				16 56		

For general notes see front of timetable
For details of catering facilities see Directory of Train Operators

For full service between Salisbury and Bristol Temple Meads see Table 123

A ☕ to Plymouth
b Previous night. Stops to pick up only
c Change at Fareham and Salisbury
e Change at Fratton and Salisbury
f Change at Exeter St Davids
g Change at Newton Abbot
h Change at Exeter St Davids and Newton Abbot

For details of Bank Holiday service alterations, please see first page of Table 149

London → Salisbury and Exeter

Network Diagram - see first page of Table 160

		SW	SW	SW	SW	SW	SW	SW	SW	SW	SW	SW	SW	SW	SW	SW	SW	SW	SW	SW	SW	SW	SW	SW
																	FX	FO		FO	FX			
		1 ◇ ☕	1 ◇ ☕	1	1 ◇ ☕	1 ◇ ☕	1	1 ◇ ☕	1 ◇ ☕	1	1 ◇ ☕	1 ◇ ☕	1 ▼ ☕	1 ▼ ☕	1 ◇ ☕	1 ◇ ☕	1 ◇ ☕	1 ◇ ☕	1 ◇ ☕	1 ◇ ☕	1 ◇ ☕	1 ◇ ☕	1 ☕	1
London Waterloo 15 ⊖	d	13 20	13 50		14 20	14 50		15 20	15 50		16 20	16 50	17 20	17 50	18 20	18 50	19 20	19 20	19 50	20 20	20 20	21 20	22 20	23 35
Clapham Junction 10	d	13u27	13 52		14u27	14 52		15u27	15u57		16u27	16u57	17 02		18u27	18 46	19u27	19u27	19 52	20u27	20u27	21u27	22u27	23u42
Woking	d	13 46	14 16		14 46	15 16		15 46	16 16		16 46	17u16	17u46	18 13	18 46	19 18	19 46	19 46	20 16	20 46	20 46	21 49	22 49	00 03
Reading 7	d		14 07			15 07			16 07			17 07		18 07		19 07	19 37	19 37	20 07			21 41	22 10	23 34
Basingstoke	d	14 07	14 37		15 07	15 37		16 07	16 37		17 07	17 37	18 07	18 38	19 07	19 39	20 07	20 07	20 37	21 07	21 07	22 10	23 10	00 24
Overton	d		14 45			15 45			16 45		17 15	17 45	18 15	18 47	19 15	19 47	20 15	20 15	20 45	21 15	21 15	22 18	23 18	00s32
Whitchurch (Hants)	d		14 50			15 50			16 50		17 20	17 50	18 20	18 52	19 20	19 52	20 20	20 20	20 50	21 20	21 20	22 23	23 23	00s37
Andover	d	14 24	14 59		15 24	15 59		16 24	16 59		17 29	17 59	18 29	19 00	19 29	20 01	20 29	20 29	20 59	21 29	21 29	22 32	23 32	00 46
Grateley	d		15 06			16 06			17 06		17 36	18 06	18 36	19 08	19 36	20 08	20 36	20 36	21 06	21 36	21 36	22 39	23 39	00s53
Brighton 10	d	12b03			13b03			14b03			15b03		16b03	17 00	17b03		18b08			18c35	19b03	20c30		
Portsmouth Harbour	d	13 22			14 22			15 22			16 22		17 22		18 22		19 22				20 22	21 22		
Southampton Central	d	14 10			15 10			16 10			17 10		18 10	18 40	19 10		20 10			21 20	21 20	22 22		
Romsey	d	14 21			15 21			16 21			17 21		18 21	18 51	19 21		20 21			21 31	21 31	22 33		
Salisbury	a	14 42	15 18		15 42	16 18		16 42	17 18		17 48	18 18	18 48	19 20	19 48	20 22	20 49	20 49	21 18	21 51	21 51	22 55	23 53	01 05
	d	14 48	15 21		15 48			16 48	17 23		17 53	18 23	18 53	19 23	19 53		20 53	20 53		22 04	22 04	23 04		
Warminster	d																							
Westbury	d																							
Trowbridge	d																							
Bradford-on-Avon	d																							
Bath Spa 7	a																							
Bristol Temple Meads 10	a																							
Tisbury	d	15 02			16 02			17 02	17 37		18 07	18 37	19 07	19 37	20 07		21 07	21 07		22 18	22 18	23s19		
Gillingham (Dorset)	a	15 12	15 44		16 12			17 12	17 47		18 17	18 47	19 17	19 47	20 17		21 17	21 17		22 28	22 28	23s30		
	d	15 13			16 13			17 13			18 18	18 48	19 18	19 48	20 18		21 18	21 18		22 29	22 29			
Templecombe	d	15 20			16 20			17 20			18 25	18 55	19 25	19 55	20 25		21 25	21 25		22 36	22 36	23s38		
Sherborne	d	15 28			16 28			17 28			18 33	19 03	19 33	20 03	20 33		21 33	21 33		22 44	22 44	23s45		
Yeovil Junction	a	15 33			16 33			17 33			18 38	19 10	19 38	20 11	20 38		21 38	21 38		22 49	22 49	23 51		
	d				16 37						18 40		19 40		20 40		21 40	21 40		22 51	22 51			
Crewkerne	d				16 46						18 49		19 49		20 49		21 49	21 49		23 00	23 00			
Axminster	a				17 05						19 04		20 02		21 10		22 02	22 02		23 13	23 22			
	d				17 06					18 23	19 05		20 03		21 11		22 03	22 03		23 14	23 23			
Honiton	a				17 17					18 34	19 16		20 14		21 22		22 14	22 14		23 27	23 34			
	d			16 01	17 18		17 32			18 38	19 30		20 15		21 23			22 15		23 28	23 35			
Feniton	d			16 06			17 37			18 44	19 36				21 29			22 20		23 33	23 41			
Whimple	d			16 11			17 42			18 49	19 41				21 34			22 25		23 38	23 46			
Pinhoe	d			16 18			17 49			18 55	19 47				21 40			22 32		23 45	23 52			
Exeter Central	a			16 22	17 33		17 55			19 00	19 52		20 30		21 49			22 36		23 49	23 57			
Exeter St Davids 6	a			16 26	17 38		17 59			19 04	19 57		20 36		21 55			22 41		23 54	00 01			
	d				17 49																			
Dawlish Warren	a				18 04																			
Dawlish	a			17 12	18 08		18e23			19 47	20 41		21 47		22 49									
Teignmouth	a			17 17	18 13		18f28			19 52	20 47		21 52		22 54									
Newton Abbot	a			17 02	18 20		18g35			19 43	20 35		21 02		22 38			23 44						
Torquay	a				18 32																			
Paignton	a			17 44	18 40		19 25			20 25	21 20		22 26		23 21									
Totnes	a			17 16	18h21		18j48			19 57	20 49		21 16		22 52			23 57						
Ivybridge	a			17k58																				
Plymouth	a			17 48	18h48		19m20			20 25	21 17		21 48		23 22			00 29						

For general notes see front of timetable
For details of catering facilities see Directory of Train Operators

For full service between Salisbury and Bristol Temple Meads see Table 123

- **b** Change at Fratton and Salisbury
- **c** Change at Southampton Central and Salisbury
- **e** From 8 September arr. 1844
- **f** From 8 September arr. 1849
- **g** From 8 September arr. 1842
- **h** Change at Exeter St Davids
- **j** From 8 September arr. 1856
- **k** Change at Exeter St Davids and Newton Abbot
- **m** From 8 September arr. 1924

London → Salisbury and Exeter

Network Diagram - see first page of Table 160

		SW 1	SW 1	SW 1	SW 1	SW 1	SW 1		SW 1	SW 1 ◇	SW 1 ◇	SW 1 ◇	SW 1 ◇	SW 1 ◇ A			SW 1 ◇	SW 1 ◇	SW 1 ◇	SW 1 ◇	SW 1 ◇	SW 1 ◇ A			SW 1 ◇	SW 1 ◇
										⊏P	⊏P	⊏P	⊏P	⊏P			⊏P	⊏P	⊏P	⊏P	⊏P	⊏P			⊏P	⊏P
London Waterloo 15 ⊖	d	23p35							06 30	07 10	07 50	08 20	08 50	09 20			09 50	10 20	10 50	11 20	11 50	12 20			12 50	13 20
Clapham Junction 10	d	23b42							06 37	07u17	07u57	08u27	08 52	09u27			09 52	10u27	10 52	11u27	11 52	12u27			12 52	13u27
Woking	d	00 03							06 57	07 36	08 16	08 46	09 16	09 46			10 16	10 46	11 16	11 46	12 16	12 46			13 16	13 46
Reading 7	d	23 34							06 39	07 07	08 07		09 07				10 07		11 07		12 07				12 45	13 10
Basingstoke	d	00 24							07 22	07 59	08 37	09 07	09 37	10 07			10 37	11 07	11 37	12 07	12 37	13 07			13 37	14 07
Overton	d	00s32							07 30	08 07	08 45		09 45				10 45		11 45		12 45				13 45	
Whitchurch (Hants)	d	00s37							07 35	08 12	08 50		09 50				10 50		11 50		12 50				13 50	
Andover	d	00 46							07 44	08 21	08 59	09 24	09 59	10 24			10 59	11 24	11 59	12 24	12 59	13 24			13 59	14 24
Grateley	d	00s53							07 51	08 28	09 06		10 06				11 06		12 06		13 06				14 06	
Brighton 10	d									05c27		07e03		08e03				09e03		10e03		11e03				12e03
Portsmouth Harbour	d								06 00	07 04		08 22		09 22				10 22		11 22		12 22				13 22
Southampton Central	d								06 52	07 52		09 10		10 10				11 10		12 10		13 10				14 10
Romsey	d								07 11	08 09		09 21		10 21				11 21		12 21		13 21				14 21
Salisbury	a	01 05							08 03	08 42	09 18	09 42	10 18	10 42			11 18	11 42	12 18	12 42	13 18	13 42			14 18	14 42
	d				06 15	07 12			08 08	08 45		09 48		10 48	10 52			11 48		12 48		13 48	13 52			14 48
Warminster	d														11 12								14 12			
Westbury	d														11 19								14 19			
Trowbridge	d														11 25								14 25			
Bradford-on-Avon	d														11 31								14 31			
Bath Spa 7	a														11 45								14 45			
Bristol Temple Meads 10	a														12 00								15 05			
Tisbury	d				06 29	07 31			08 27			10 02		11 02				12 02				14 02				15 02
Gillingham (Dorset)	a				06 39	07 41			08 37	09 06		10 12		11 12				12 12		13 09		14 12				15 12
	d				06 42	07 43			08 41	09 07		10 13		11 13				12 13		13 10		14 13				15 13
Templecombe	d				06 50	07 51			08 49	09 14		10 20		11 20				12 20				14 20				15 20
Sherborne	d				06 57	07 58			08 56	09 22		10 28		11 28				12 28				14 28				15 28
Yeovil Junction	a				07 03	08 04			09 02	09 27		10 33		11 33				12 33		13 27		14 33				15 33
	d			06 15	07 08					09 29		10 35		11 35				12 35		13 28		14 35				
Crewkerne	d			06 24	07 17					09 38		10 44						12 44				14 44				
Axminster	a			06 44	07 36					09 51		11 04		11 54				13 03				15 03				
	d			06 55	07 37					09 52		11 05		11 55				13 04				15 04				
Honiton	a			07 06	07 48					10 03		11 16		12 06				13 15		13 56		15 15				
	d		06 13	07 10	07 49		09 00			10 04		11 30		12 07				13 16		14 00		15 16				
Feniton	d		06 18	07 15	07 55		09 05			10 09		11 35						13 22				15 22				
Whimple	d		06 23	07 20	08 01		09 10			10 14		11 40						13 27				15 27				
Pinhoe	d			07 27	08f16		09 17			10 21		11 47						13 33				15 33				
Exeter Central	a		06 32	07 31	08 20		09 23			10 28		11 51		12 25				13 38		14 19		15 38				
Exeter St Davids 6	a		06 35	07 36	08 30		09 27			10 32		11 56		12 30				13 42		14 23		15 42				
	d				08 37					10 38				12 39						14 28		15 49				
Dawlish Warren	a									10 49				12 50						14 39						
Dawlish	a		07 19	08 07	08 49		09g57			11 00		12 41		13 03				14h17		14 43		16 01				
Teignmouth	a		07 24	08 12	08 54		10j02			11 05		12 48		13 08				14k22		14 48		16 06				
Newton Abbot	a		07 31	08 19	09 01		10m10			11 12		12n32		13 15				14q28		14 55		16 13				
Torquay	a				09 15					11 23										15 07						
Paignton	a		07r55	08 38	09 23		10t34			11 31		13 21		13v41				14w48		15 15		16 44				
Totnes	a		07 44	08y57	09z59		10j56			11B16		13C16		13 28				15D56		15E56		16 25				
Ivybridge	a		08 01	09y13	10z15		11G19			13H08		13J43		13 43				16K34		16L34		16 41				
Plymouth	a		08 15	09y28	10z30		11N12			11B48		13Q11		13 59				15U11		16V26		16 57				

For general notes see front of timetable
For details of catering facilities see Directory of Train Operators

For full service between Salisbury and Bristol Temple Meads see Table 123

- **A** ⊏P to Plymouth
- **B** Change at Exeter St Davids
- **C** Until 6 September arr. 1252, change at Exeter St Davids and Newton Abbot
- **D** From 13 September arr. 1516
- **E** Change at Newton Abbot. From 13 September arr. 1516
- **G** Until 6 September only
- **H** Until 6 September change at Newton Abbot. From 13 September arr. 1343, change at Exeter St Davids and Newton Abbot
- **J** Until 6 September arr. 1308, change at Exeter St Davids and Newton Abbot
- **K** Change at Exeter St Davids and Newton Abbot. From 13 September arr. 1624
- **L** Change at Newton Abbot. From 13 September arr. 1624
- **N** From 13 September arr. 1048
- **Q** From 13 September arr. 1310
- **U** From 13 September arr. 1510
- **V** Change at Newton Abbot. From 13 September arr. 1548
- **b** Previous night. Stops to pick up only
- **c** Change at Fareham and Salisbury
- **e** Change at Fratton and Salisbury
- **f** Arr. 0807
- **g** From 13 September arr. 1011
- **h** From 13 September arr. 1411
- **j** From 13 September arr. 1016
- **k** From 13 September arr. 1416
- **m** From 13 September arr. 1003
- **n** From 13 September arr. 1230
- **q** From 13 September arr. 1422
- **r** Change at Exeter St Davids and Newton Abbot
- **t** From 13 September arr. 1042
- **v** Until 6 September arr. 1338, change at Exeter St Davids
- **w** From 13 September arr. 1442
- **y** From 13 September only
- **z** Change at Newton Abbot

Table 160

London → Salisbury and Exeter

Saturdays

Network Diagram - see first page of Table 160

		SW	SW	SW	SW	SW	SW		SW	SW	SW	SW	SW	SW		SW	SW	SW		SW	SW	SW	SW	SW		
		1◇	1	1◇	1◇	1◇	1◇		1	1	1◇	1◇	1◇	1◇		1◇	1◇	1◇		1◇	1◇	1◇	1	1		
				A														B								
		⊡		⊡	⊡	⊡	⊡				⊡	⊡	⊡	⊡		⊡	⊡	⊡		⊡	⊡	⊡	⊡			
London Waterloo 15 ⊖	d	13 50		14 20	14 50	15 20	15 50				16 20	16 50	17 20	17 50		18 20	18 50	19 20		19 50	20 20	21 20	22 20	23 35		
Clapham Junction 10	d	13 52		14u27	14 52	15u27	15 52				16u27	16 52	17u27	17 52		18u27	18 52	19u27		19 52	20u27	21u27	22u27	23u42		
Woking	d	14 16		14 46	15 16	15 46	16 16				16 46	17 16	17 46	18 16		18 46	19 16	19 46		20 16	20 46	21 49	22 49	00 03		
Reading 7	d	14 07			15 07		16 07					17 07		18 08			19 07			20 07		21 39	22 39	23 07		
Basingstoke	d	14 37		15 07	15 37	16 07	16 37				17 07	17 37	18 07	18 37		19 07	19 37	20 07		20 37	21 07	22 12	23 12	00 24		
Overton	d	14 45			15 45		16 45					17 45		18 45			19 45			20 45	21 15	22 20	23 20	00s32		
Whitchurch (Hants)	d	14 50			15 50		16 50					17 50		18 50			19 50			20 50	21 20	22 25	23 25	00s37		
Andover	d	14 59		15 24	15 59	16 24	16 59				17 24	17 59	18 24	18 59		19 24	19 59	20 24		20 59	21 29	22 34	23 34	00 46		
Grateley	d	15 06			16 06		17 06					18 06		19 06			20 06			21 06	21 36	22 41	23 41	00s53		
Brighton 10	d			13b03		14b03					15b03		16b03			17b03		18b03			19b03	19c27				
Portsmouth Harbour	d			14 22		15 22					16 22		17 22			18 22		19 22			20 22					
Southampton Central	d			15 10		16 10					17 10		18 10			19 10		20 10			21 12	21 27				
Romsey	d			15 21		16 21					17 21		18 21			19 21		20 21			21 23	21 38				
Salisbury	a	15 18		15 42	16 18	16 42	17 18				17 42	18 18	18 43	19 18		19 45	20 18	20 42		21 18	21 48	22 53	23 53	01 05		
	d			15 48		16 48					17 48		18 53			19 53		20 53	20 57		22 00	23 04				
Warminster	d																		21 17							
Westbury	d																		21 24							
Trowbridge	d																		21 30							
Bradford-on-Avon	d																		21 36							
Bath Spa 7	a																		21 50							
Bristol Temple Meads 10	a																		22 06							
Tisbury	d			16 02		17 02					18 02		19 07			20 07		21 07			22 15	23s18				
Gillingham (Dorset)	a			16 12		17 12					18 12		19 17			20 17		21 17			22 25	23s29				
	d			16 13		17 13					18 13		19 18			20 18		21 18			22 26					
Templecombe	d			16 20		17 20					18 20		19 25			20 25		21 25			22 33	23s37				
Sherborne	d			16 28		17 28					18 28		19 33			20 33		21 33			22 41	23s44				
Yeovil Junction	a			16 33		17 33					18 33		19 38			20 38		21 38			22 46	23 50				
	d			16 35							18 35					20 40		21 40								
Crewkerne	d			16 44							18 44					20 49		21 49								
Axminster	a			17 03							19 03					21 10		22 02								
	d			17 04						18 23	19 04					21 11		22 03								
Honiton	a			17 15						18 34	19 15					21 22		22 14								
	d		16 01	17 16					17 30	18 38	19 30					21 23		22 15								
Feniton	d		16 06						17 35	18 43	19 35					21 29		22 20								
Whimple	d		16 11						17 40	18 48	19 40					21 34		22 25								
Pinhoe	d		16 18						17 47	18 55	19 47					21 40		22 32								
Exeter Central	a		16 23	17 32					17 52	19 00	19 51					21 48		22 36								
Exeter St Davids 6	a		16 27	17 36					17 57	19 05	19 57					21 53		22 41								
	d			17 43					18 02																	
Dawlish Warren	a			17 54					18 13																	
Dawlish	a		17 10	18 05					18 18	20 14	21 12					22 49										
Teignmouth	a		17 15	18 10					18 23	20 19	21 17					22 55										
Newton Abbot	a		17e22	18 17					18 30	19 53	20 36					23 02										
Torquay	a								18 41																	
Paignton	a		17f29	18g50					18 50	20 24	21 43															
Totnes	a		17 16	18 32					18h53	20 07	20 50					23 16										
Ivybridge	a		17j57	18 47																						
Plymouth	a		17 48	19 02					19h21	20 36	21 18					23 47										

For general notes see front of timetable
For details of catering facilities see Directory of Train Operators

For full service between Salisbury and Bristol Temple Meads see Table 123

- **A** To Penzance (Table 135)
- **B** ⊡ to Exeter St Davids
- **b** Change at Fratton and Salisbury
- **c** Change at Southampton Central and Salisbury
- **e** From 13 September arr. 1703
- **f** From 13 September arr. 1741
- **g** Until 6 September arr. 1839, change at Exeter St Davids
- **h** Change at Newton Abbot
- **j** Change at Exeter St Davids and Newton Abbot

Sundays

London → Salisbury and Exeter

Network Diagram - see first page of Table 160

Station		SW [1]	SW [1]	SW [1]◇	SW [1]◇ 🍴	SW [1]◇ 🍴	SW [1]◇ 🍴	SW [1]◇ 🍴	SW [1]◇ A 🍴		SW [1]◇ 🍴	SW [1]◇ 🍴	SW [1]◇ 🍴	SW [1]◇ 🍴	SW [1]◇ 🍴	SW [1]◇ A 🍴		SW [1]◇ 🍴	SW [1]◇ 🍴	SW [1]◇ 🍴	SW [1] 🍴	SW [1]
London Waterloo [15] ⊖	d	23p35			08 15	09 15	10 15	11 15	12 15		13 15	14 15	15 15	16 15	17 15	18 15		19 15	20 15	21 15	22 15	23 35
Clapham Junction [10]	d	23b42			08u22	09u22	10u22	11u22	12u22		13u22	14u22	15u22	16u22	17u22	18u22		19u22	20u22	21u22	22u22	23u44
Woking	d	00 03			08 47	09 47	10 46	11 46	12 46		13 46	14 46	15 46	16 46	17 46	18 46		19 46	20 46	21 46	22 46	00 08
Reading [7]	d	23 07		07 37	08 37	09 37	10 37	11 37	12 37		13 37	14 37	15 37	16 37	17 37	18 37		19 37	20 37	21 37	22 37	23 37
Basingstoke	d	00 24		08 08	09 08	10 08	11 07	12 07	13 07		14 07	15 07	16 07	17 07	18 07	19 07		20 07	21 07	22 07	23 07	00 40
Overton	d	00s32		08 16	09 16		11 15		13 15			15 15		17 15		19 15			21 15		23 15	00s49
Whitchurch (Hants)	d	00s37		08 21	09 21		11 20		13 20			15 20		17 20		19 20			21 20		23 20	00s54
Andover	d	00 46		08 30	09 30	10 25	11 29	12 24	13 29		14 24	15 29	16 24	17 29	18 24	19 29		20 24	21 29	22 24	23 29	01 02
Grateley	d	00s53		08 37	09 37		11 36		13 36			15 36		17 36		19 36			21 36		23 36	01s10
Brighton [10]	d					07c23		09c17	11 10		11c17	12c17	13c17	14c17	15 47	16c17		17 47	18c17			
Portsmouth Harbour	d					09 08		11 08			13 08	14 08	15 08	16 08	17 08	18 08		19 08	20 08			
Southampton Central	d					09 54		11 54	12 54		13 54	14 54	15 54	16 54	17 54	18 54		19 54	20 54			
Romsey	d					10 05		12 06	13 06		14 06	15 06	16 06	17 06	18 06	19 06		20 06	21 06			
Salisbury	a	01 05		08 49	09 50	10 41	11 48	12 40	13 48		14 40	15 48	16 40	17 48	18 40	19 48		20 40	21 48	22 44	23 48	01 22
	d		07 10	08 54	09 54	10 50	11 54	12 50	13 54	13 58	14 50	15 54	16 54	17 54	18 50	19 54	19 58	20 54	21 54	22 48		
Warminster	d									14 18							20 18					
Westbury	d									14 25							20 32					
Trowbridge	d									14 32							20 38					
Bradford-on-Avon	d									14 38							20 44					
Bath Spa [7]	a									14 52							20 59					
Bristol Temple Meads [10]	a									15 06							21 16					
Tisbury	d		07 24	09 08	10 08	11 04	12 08	13 04	14 08		15 04	16 08	17 08	18 08	19 04	20 08		21 08	22 08	23 04		
Gillingham (Dorset)	a		07 34	09 18	10 18	11 14	12 18	13 14	14 18		15 14	16 18	17 18	18 18	19 14	20 18		21 18	22 18	23 14		
	d		07 35	09 19	10 19	11 15	12 19	13 15	14 19		15 15	16 19	17 19	18 19	19 15	20 19		21 19	22 19	23 15		
Templecombe	d		07 42	09 26	10 26	11 22	12 26	13 22	14 26		15 22	16 26	17 26	18 26	19 22	20 26		21 26	22 26	23 22		
Sherborne	d		07 50	09 34	10 34	11 30	12 34	13 30	14 34		15 30	16 34	17 34	18 34	19 30	20 34		21 34	22 34	23 30		
Yeovil Junction	a		07 55	09 39	10 39	11 35	12 39	13 35	14 39		15 35	16 39	17 39	18 40	19 35	20 39		21 40	22 39	23 35		
	d		07 57	09 41	10 41	11 40		13 40			15 40		17 40		19 40			21 40		23 37		
Crewkerne	d		08 06	09 50		11 49		13 49			15 49		17 49		19 49			21 49		23 46		
Axminster	a		08 19	10 10	11 00	12 10		14 10			16 10		18 10		20 12			22 10		23 58		
	d		08 20	10 11	11 01	12 11		14 11			16 11		18 11		20 13			22 11		23 58		
Honiton	a		08 31	10 22	11 12	12 22		14 22			16 22		18 22		20 24			22 22		00 09		
	d		08 35	10 23	11 13	12 23		14 23			16 23		18 23		20 25			22 23		00 10		
Feniton	d		08 41	10 28		12 28		14 28			16 28		18 28		20 31			22 28				
Whimple	d		08 46	10 33		12 33		14 33			16 33		18 33		20 36			22 33				
Pinhoe	d			10 40		12 40																
Exeter Central	a		08 54	10 44	11 28	12 44		14 42			16 42		18 42		20 44			22 42				
Exeter St Davids [6]	a		08 59	10 49	11 32	12 49		14 46			16 50		18 46		20 49			22 46		00 30		
	d			10 56	11 40	13 01		14 52			16 57				20 56							
Dawlish Warren	a			11 07																		
Dawlish	a		09e29	11 11	13 00	13 13		15 25			17 09		19f15		21 08			23 06				
Teignmouth	a		09g34	11 16	13 05	13 19		15 30			17 14		19h20		21 13			23 12				
Newton Abbot	a		09j41	11 23	12 00	13 27		15 13			17 22		19k12		21 20			23 19				
Torquay	a			11 34		13 42		15 24			17 35				21 31							
Paignton	a		10 15	11 42	12 47	13 50		15 32			17 43		19m46		21 39							
Totnes	a		09n55	11q46	12 14	14r16		16t09			18v11		20w10		22y11			23 33				
Ivybridge	a		10z11		12 29	17B08		17C08														
Plymouth	a		10D26	12E14	12 44	14G29		16t03			18H39		19J54		22K40			00 06				

For general notes see front of timetable
For details of catering facilities see Directory of Train Operators

For full service between Salisbury and Bristol Temple Meads see Table 123

- **A** 🍴 to Yeovil Junction
- **B** Until 7 September only. Change at Dawlish and Teignmouth
- **C** Change at Newton Abbot. From 14 September arr. 1709
- **D** From 14 September arr. 1023
- **E** Change at Newton Abbot. From 14 September arr. 1211
- **G** Change at Exeter St Davids. From 14 September arr. 1411
- **H** Change at Newton Abbot. From 14 September arr. 1822
- **J** From 14 September arr. 2021
- **K** Change at Newton Abbot. From 14 September arr. 2231
- **b** Previous night. Stops to pick up only
- **c** Change at Fratton and Salisbury
- **e** From 14 September arr. 0926
- **f** From 14 September arr. 2024
- **g** From 14 September arr. 0931
- **h** From 14 September arr. 2029
- **j** From 14 September arr. 0938
- **k** From 14 September arr. 1939
- **m** From 14 September arr. 2055
- **n** From 14 September arr. 0952
- **q** Change at Newton Abbot. From 14 September arr. 1143
- **r** Change at Newton Abbot. From 14 September arr. 1415
- **t** Change at Newton Abbot. From 14 September arr. 1600
- **v** Change at Newton Abbot. From 14 September arr. 1754
- **w** From 14 September arr. 1953
- **y** Change at Newton Abbot. From 14 September arr. 2202
- **z** From 14 September arr. 1008

For details of Bank Holiday service alterations, please see first page of Table 149

Exeter and Salisbury → London

Network Diagram - see first page of Table 160

Miles			SW	SW	SW	SW	SW	SW	SW	SW	SW	SW	SW	SW	SW	SW	SW	SW	SW	SW	SW	SW	SW	SW	SW
			MO																						
			1	1	1	1	1	1	1	1	1 ◇	1 ◇	1 ◇	1 ◇	1 ◇	1	1 ◇	1 ◇	1 ◇	1 ◇	1 ◇	1 ◇	1 ◇	1 ◇	1 ◇
				A	B	A	B	A	B																
				⊡	⊡	⊡	⊡	▼	▼	▼	⊡	⊡	⊡	⊡	⊡		⊡		⊡	⊡	⊡	⊡	⊡	⊡	⊡
								⊡	⊡	⊡															
—	Plymouth	d												05 24		06 40							08 55		
—	Ivybridge	d																					08b27		
—	Totnes	d												05 51		07 05							09 22		
—	Paignton	d	22p10													07b09							09b14		
—	Torquay	d	22p16													07b14							09b19		
—	Newton Abbot	d	22p28											06 04		07 30			07 34				09 35		
—	Teignmouth	d	22p35											06 11		07 01							09 14		
—	Dawlish	d	22p40											06 17		07 06							09 19		
—	Dawlish Warren	d	22p44																						
0	**Exeter St Davids** 5	a	22p55																						
—		d	23p10								05 10			06 41		08 00			08 25				10 10		
¾	**Exeter Central**	d	23p14								05 14			06 44		08 05			08 30				10 14		
3½	Pinhoe	d									05 19			06 50		08 11							10 21		
9¼	Whimple	d									05 26			06 57		08 18							10 28		
13	Feniton	d									05 31			07 02		08 23							10 33		
17½	Honiton	a	23c29								05 37			07 09		08 29			08 45				10 39		
—		d									05 38	06 20		07 12					08 46				10 40		
27¾	Axminster	a	23c40								05 48	06 30		07 22					08 56				10 50		
—		d									05 49	06 31		07 23					08 57				10 51		
40¾	Crewkerne	d	00s04								06 02	06 44		07 36					09 10				11 04		
49¾	Yeovil Junction	a	00s13								06 11	06 52		07 45					09 19				11 13		
—		d						05 12	05 15	05 50	06 20	06 54	07 20	07 50	08 20				09 20		10 20		11 20		12 20
54½	Sherborne	d						05 18	05 21	05 56	06 26	07 00	07 26	07 56	08 26				09 26		10 26		11 26		12 26
60¾	Templecombe	d						05 26	05 29	06 04	06 34	07 08	07 34	08 04	08 34				09 34		10 34		11 34		12 34
67¼	Gillingham (Dorset)	a						05 33	05 36	06 11	06 41	07 15	07 43	08 11	08 41				09 41		10 41		11 41		12 41
—		d						05 34	05 37	06 12	06 42	07 16	07 44	08 12	08 42				09 42		10 42		11 42		12 42
76¼	Tisbury	d						05 44	05 47	06 24	06 52	07 26	07 54	08 22	08 52				09 52		10 52		11 52		12 52
—	Bristol Temple Meads 10	d																08 50							
—	Bath Spa 7	d																09 05							
—	Bradford-on-Avon	d																09 20							
—	Trowbridge	d																09 27							
—	Westbury	d																09 39							
—	Warminster	d																09 46							
88¾	**Salisbury**	a	00 50					05 59	06 02	06 39	07 07	07 40	08 09	08 37	09 15			10 09	10 15		11 15		12 15		13 15
—		d		05 12	05 15	05 42	05 45	06 05	06 08	06 45	07 15	07 45	08 15	08 45	09 20		09 45	10 20		10 45	11 20	11 45	12 20	12 45	13 20
—	Romsey	a						06 38	06 38	07 30	07 56		08 50		09 50			10 50			11 50		12 50		13 50
—	Southampton Central	a						06 49	06 49	07 41	08 09		09 03		10 02			11 02			12 02		13 02		14 02
—	Portsmouth Harbour	a						07 45	07 45	08 30			09 54		10 54			11 54			12 54		13 54		14 54
—	Brighton 10	a						09e19	09e19	09f48	10g18		11e18		12e18			13e18			14e18		15e18		16 14
99¾	Grateley	d		05 25	05 27	05 54	05 57	06 17	06 20	06 57	07 27	07 57	08 27	08 57			09 57			10 57		11 57		12 57	
106	Andover	d		05 32	05 35	06 02	06 05	06 25	06 28	07 05	07 35	08 05	08 35	09 04	09 37		10 04	10 37		11 04	11 37	12 04	12 37	13 04	13 37
113½	Whitchurch (Hants)	d		05 41	05 43	06 10	06 13	06 33	06 36	07 13	07 43	08 13	08 43	09 12			10 12			11 12		12 12		13 12	
117	Overton	d		05 47	05 49	06 16	06 19	06 39	06 42	07 19	07 49	08 19	08 49	09 18			10 18			11 18		12 18		13 18	
124¾	**Basingstoke**	a		05 58	05 58	06 28	06 28	06 51	06 51	07 28	07 58	08 28	08 58	09 27	09 54		10 27	10 55		11 27	11 54	12 27	12 54	13 27	13 54
—	Reading 7	a		06 30	06 30	07 00	07 00	07 30	07 30	08 00	08 30	09 00	09 30	10 00	10 30		11 00	11 30			12 31	13 00	13 30	14 00	14 30
148½	Woking	a		06 18	06 18	06 48	06 48	07 11	07 11	08 05	08 18	08 48	09 18	09 49	10 15		10 49	11 15		11 49	12 15	12 49	13 15	13 49	14 15
168¼	Clapham Junction 10	a		06 38	06 38	07 16	07 16	07 31	07 31	09 14	09 03	09 14	09 38	10 10	10 36		11h12	11 36			12 36	13h12	13 36	14h12	14 36
172½	**London Waterloo** 15 ⊖	a		06 49	06 49	07 18	07 18	07 44	07 44	08 14	08 46	09 17	09 51	10 19	10 49		11 19	11 49		12 19	12 49	13 19	13 49	14 19	14 49

For general notes see front of timetable
For details of catering facilities see Directory of Train Operators

For full service between Bristol Temple Meads and Salisbury see Table 123

A From 29 September
B Until 26 September
b Change at Newton Abbot and Exeter St Davids
c Previous night. Stops to set down only
e Change at Salisbury and Fareham
f Change at Salisbury and Fratton
g Change at Salisbury and Southampton Central
h Change at Basingstoke

For details of Bank Holiday service alterations, please see first page of Table 149

Exeter and Salisbury → London

Network Diagram - see first page of Table 160

		SW	SW	SW	SW	SW	SW	SW	SW	SW	SW	SW	SW	SW	SW	SW	SW	SW	SW	SW	SW	SW	SW FX	SW FO
		1 ◇ ☕	1 ◇ ☕	1 ◇	1 ◇ ☕	1 ◇ ☕	1 ◇ ☕	1 ◇ ☕	1	1 ◇ ☕	1 ◇	1 ◇ ☕	1 ◇ ☕	1 ◇ ☕	1	1	1 ◇ ☕	1 ◇ ☕	1 ◇ ☕	1 ◇	1	1	1	1
Plymouth	d		10 45			12b25		12 55	14c25					14 47	15 25	16 25			17 00	17 48	18b43	19 35	19e35	21f13
Ivybridge	d					11g25		11 25						15 02	15h26				16h59	18 03	18b58		18j58	21k29
Totnes	d		10 50			12b50		13 22	14m50					15 16	15 50	16 50			17 27	18 17	19b12	20 03	20n03	21q43
Paignton	d		10 25			12 35		13h14	14 25					15h19		16 15			17h19	18h21	19 10	19 30	20 30	21r28
Torquay	d		10 30			12 41		13h19	14 30					15h24		16 21			17h24	18h26	19 16	19 35	20 35	21t35
Newton Abbot	d		11 03			12 53		13 35	15v03					15 29	16 03	17 03			17 40	18 30	19 28	20 16	20w48	21y55
Teignmouth	d		10 50			13 00			14 50					15 36	15 50	16 20			17 15	18 37	19 35	19 55	20z55	22A02
Dawlish	d		10 55			13 05			14 55					15 41	15 55	16 25			17 20	18 42	19 40	20 00	21B00	22C07
Dawlish Warren	d					13 16								15 45						18 46	19 44			
Exeter St Davids 6	a					13 25								15 56						18 57	19 59			
	d		12 10			13 35		14 10	15 30					16 10	16 36	17 40			18 10	19 10	20 15	21 00	22 30	22 57
Exeter Central	d		12 14			13 39		14 14	15 34					16 14	16 40	17 44			18 14	19 14	20 19	21 04	22 34	23 01
Pinhoe	d		12 19					14 19	15 39					16 19	16 49	17 49			18 19		20D27		22 39	23 06
Whimple	d		12 26					14 26	15 46					16 26	16 56	17 56			18 26		20 34		22 46	23 13
Feniton	d		12 31					14 31	15 51					16 31	17 01	18 01			18 31		20 39		22 51	23 18
Honiton	a		12 37			13 54		14 37	15 57					16 37	17 07	18 07			18 38	19 30	20 45	21 20	22 57	23 25
	d		12 38			13 57		14 38						16 38		18 08			18 39	19 31	20 46	21 23	22 58	23 27
Axminster	a		12 48			14 07		14 48						16 48		18 18			18 49	19 41	20 56	21 33	23 08	23 37
	d		12 49			14 08		14 49						16 49					18 50	19 42	20 57	21 45	23 09	23 38
Crewkerne	d		13 03					15 03						17 05					19 10	20 08	21 10	22 08	23 22	23 51
Yeovil Junction	a		13 12			14 27		15 12						17 14					19 18	20 16	21 19	22 16	23 31	23 59
	d		13 20		13 50	14 28		15 20				16 20		17 22				18 20	19 20	20 20	21 20	22 24	23 34	00 01
Sherborne	d		13 26		13 56			15 26				16 26		17 28				18 26	19 26	20 26	21 26	22 30		
Templecombe	d		13 34					15 34				16 34		17 36				18 34	19 34	20 34	21 34	22 41		
Gillingham (Dorset)	a		13 41		14 09	14 44		15 41				16 41		17 43				18 41	19 41	20 41	21 41	22 48		
	d		13 42		14 13	14 45		15 45		16 15		16 42		17 48				18 48	19 48	20 42	21 42	22 49		
Tisbury	d		13 52			14 55		15 55		16 25		16 52		17 58				18 58	19 59	20 52	21 52	22 59		
Bristol Temple Meads 10	d			13 10							15 52													
Bath Spa 7	d			13 22							16 06													
Bradford-on-Avon	d			13 35							16 22													
Trowbridge	d			13 42							16 28													
Westbury	d			13 53							16 39													
Warminster	d			14 00							16 47													
Salisbury	a		14 15	14 24	14 35	15 15		16 15		16 40	17 09	17 15		18 20				19 21	20 20	21 20	22 08	23 13	00 29	00 35
	d	13 45	14 20		14 45	15 20	15 45	16 20		16 45		17 20	17 45	18 25			18 45	19 25	20 25	21 25	22 25			
Romsey	a				14 50	15 50		16 50				17 50		18 50				19 50	20 49	21 50	22 50			
Southampton Central	a				15 02	16 02		17 02				18 02		19 01				20 02	21 02	22 02	23 03			
Portsmouth Harbour	a				15 54	16 59		17 54				18 59		19 54				20 59	21 52	23 04	23 54			
Brighton 10	a				17E18	18E18		19E18				20E18		21E18				22E22	23G18					
Grateley	d	13 57			14 57		15 57	16 32		16 57			17 57				18 57	19 37	20 37	21 37	22 37			
Andover	d	14 04	14 37		15 04	15 37	16 04	16 39		17 04		17 37	18 04	18 42			19 04	19 44	20 44	21 44	22 44			
Whitchurch (Hants)	d	14 12			15 12		16 12			17 12			18 12				19 12	19 52	20 52	21 52	22 52			
Overton	d	14 18			15 18		16 18			17 18			18 18				19 18	19 58	20 58	21 58	22 58			
Basingstoke	a	14 28	14 54		15 27	15 54	16 27	16 56		17 27		17 54	18 27	18 59			19 27	20 08	21 08	22 08	23 07			
Reading 7	a	15 00	15 31		16 00	16 30	17 00	17 30		18 00		18 31	19 00	19 31			20 00	21 01	22 04	22 45	23 53			
Woking	a	14 49	15 15		15 49	16 15	16 49	17 16		17 49		18 15	18 49	19 19			19 49	20 29	21 29	22 28	23 30			
Clapham Junction 10	a	15H12	15 36		16H12	16 36	17H12	17 36		18H12		18 36	19H12	19 40			20H12	20 52	21 52	22 48	23 55			
London Waterloo 15 ⊖	a	15 19	15 49		16 19	16 49	17 19	17 45		18 21		18 45	19 19	19 49			20 19	21 00	22 04	22 57	00 04			

For general notes see front of timetable
For details of catering facilities see Directory of Train Operators
For full service between Bristol Temple Meads and Salisbury see Table 123

- **A** 4 July to 5 September dep. 2159
- **B** 30 June to 4 September dep. 2204
- **C** 4 July to 5 September dep. 2204
- **D** Arr. 2024
- **E** Change at Salisbury and Fareham
- **G** Change at Salisbury and Fratton
- **H** Change at Basingstoke
- **b** Change at Exeter St Davids
- **c** From 8 September dep. 1325
- **e** 30 June to 4 September dep. 2110
- **f** 4 July to 5 September dep. 2110
- **g** Change at Newton Abbot
- **h** Change at Newton Abbot and Exeter St Davids
- **j** 30 June to 4 September dep. 2125
- **k** 4 July to 5 September dep. 2125
- **m** From 8 September dep. 1350
- **n** 30 June to 4 September dep. 2139
- **q** 4 July to 5 September dep. 2139
- **r** 4 July to 5 September dep. 2030
- **t** 4 July to 5 September dep. 2035
- **v** From 8 September dep. 1443
- **w** 30 June to 4 September dep. 2152
- **y** 4 July to 5 September dep. 2152
- **z** 30 June to 4 September dep. 2159

Table 160

Saturdays

Exeter and Salisbury → London

Network Diagram - see first page of Table 160

Station		SW	SW	SW	SW	SW	SW	SW	SW	SW	SW	SW	SW	SW	SW	SW	SW	SW		SW	SW	SW	SW	SW	SW	SW
		1	1	1	1 ◇	1 ◇	1 ◇	1 ◇	1 ◇	1 ◇	1 ◇	1 ◇	1 ◇	1 ◇	1	1 ◇	1 ◇	1 ◇		1 ◇	1 ◇	1 ◇	1 ◇	1 ◇	1 ◇	1 ◇
			A	B	A	B	A	B																	C	D
			⊡	⊡	⊡	⊡	⊡	⊡	⊡	⊡	⊡	⊡	⊡	⊡		⊡		⊡		⊡	⊡	⊡	⊡	⊡	⊡	⊡
Plymouth	d														06 55								08 52		09b57	09c25
Ivybridge	d																						08e27		08c27	08c25
Totnes	d														06 50								09 19		09c55	09c50
Paignton	d														07f08			07g16					09h05		10 01	10 12
Torquay	d														07f13								09j10		10 07	10 18
Newton Abbot	d														07 31								09 32		10 20	10 31
Teignmouth	d														07 18								08 46		10 27	10 38
Dawlish	d														07 23								08 51		10 32	10 43
Dawlish Warren	d																								10 43	10 47
Exeter St Davids 6	a																								10 54	10 58
	d	22p57								05 10			06 41		08 00			08 25					10 10		11 08	11 08
Exeter Central	d	23p01								05 14			06 45		08 08			08 30					10 14		11 12	11 12
Pinhoe	d	23p06								05 19			06 50		08 13								10 21			
Whimple	d	23p13								05 26			06 57		08 20								10 28			
Feniton	d	23p18								05 31			07 02		08 25								10 33			
Honiton	a	23p25								05 37			07 08		08 31			08 45					10 39		11 27	11 27
	d	23p27								05 38	06 20		07 12					08 46					10 40		11 28	11 28
Axminster	a	23p37								05 48	06 30		07 22					08 56					10 50		11 38	11 38
	d	23p38								05 49	06 31		07 23					08 57					10 51		11 39	11 39
Crewkerne	d	23p51								06 02	06 44		07 36					09 10					11 04		12 00	12 00
Yeovil Junction	a	23p59								06 11	06 52		07 45					09 19					11 13		12 09	12 09
	d	00 01								06 20	06 54		07 50	08 20				09 20			10 20		11 20		12 20	12 20
Sherborne	d									06 26	07 00		07 56	08 26				09 26			10 26		11 26		12 26	12 26
Templecombe	d									06 34	07 08		08 04	08 34				09 34			10 34		11 34		12 34	12 34
Gillingham (Dorset)	a									06 41	07 15		08 11	08 41				09 41			10 41		11 41		12 41	12 41
	d									06 42	07 16		08 12	08 42				09 42			10 42		11 42		12 42	12 42
Tisbury	d									06 52	07 26		08 22	08 52				09 52			10 52		11 52		12 52	12 52
Bristol Temple Meads 10	d																08 50									
Bath Spa 7	d																09 05									
Bradford-on-Avon	d																09 20									
Trowbridge	d																09 27									
Westbury	d																09 39									
Warminster	d																09 46									
Salisbury	a	00 35								07 10	07 40		08 37	09 15			10 09	10 15			11 15		12 15		13 15	13 15
	d		05 12	05 15	05 42	05 45	06 17	06 20	06 45	07 20	07 45	08 20	08 45	09 20		09 45		10 20		10 45	11 20	11 45	12 20	12 45	13 20	13 20
Romsey	a									07 42	08 50			09 50				10 50			11 50		12 50		13 50	13 50
Southampton Central	a									08 02	09 02			10 02				11 02			12 02		13 02		14 02	14 02
Portsmouth Harbour	a									08 49	09 51			10 51				11 51			12 51		13 51		14 51	14 51
Brighton 10	a									10k18	11k18			12k18				13k18			14k18		15k18		16 14	16 14
Grateley	d		05 24	05 27	05 54	05 57			06 57		07 57		08 57			09 57				10 57		11 57		12 57		
Andover	d		05 32	05 35	06 01	06 04	06 34	06 37	07 04	07 37	08 04	08 37	09 04	09 37		10 04		10 37		11 04	11 37	12 04	12 37	13 04	13 37	13 37
Whitchurch (Hants)	d		05 40	05 43	06 09	06 12			07 12		08 12		09 12			10 12				11 12		12 12		13 12		
Overton	d		05 46	05 49	06 15	06 18			07 18		08 18		09 18			10 18				11 18		12 18		13 18		
Basingstoke	a		05 58	05 58	06 27	06 27	06 54	06 54	07 27	07 54	08 27	08 54	09 27	09 54		10 27		10 55		11 27	11 54	12 27	12 54	13 27	13 54	13 54
Reading 7	a					07 00		07 31	08 00	08 31	09 00	09 31	10 00	10 31		11 00		11 31			12 31	13 00	13 31	14 00	14 31	
Woking	a		06 18	06 18	06 49	06 49	07 15	07 15	07 49	08 17	08 49	09 15	09 49	10 15		10 49		11 15		11 49	12 15	12 49	13 15	13 49	14 15	14 15
Clapham Junction 10	a		06 38	06 38	07 23	07 23	07 36	07 36	08 30	08 37	09m12	09 36	10m12	10 36		11m12		11 36			12 36	13m12	13 36	14m12	14 36	14 36
London Waterloo 15 ⊖	a		06 49	06 49	07 19	07 19	07 49	07 49	08 19	08 49	09 19	09 49	10 19	10 49		11 19		11 49		12 19	12 49	13 19	13 49	14 19	14 49	14 49

For general notes see front of timetable
For details of catering facilities see Directory of Train Operators
For full service between Bristol Temple Meads and Salisbury see Table 123

- **A** From 4 October
- **B** Until 27 September
- **C** Until 6 September
- **D** From 13 September
- **b** Change at Exeter St Davids
- **c** Change at Newton Abbot
- **e** From 13 September dep. 0825
- **f** Change at Newton Abbot and Exeter St Davids
- **g** From 13 September only
- **h** Change at Newton Abbot and Exeter St Davids. From 13 September dep. 0911
- **j** Change at Newton Abbot and Exeter St Davids. From 13 September dep. 0916
- **k** Change at Salisbury and Fareham
- **m** Change at Basingstoke

Table 160

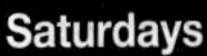

Saturdays

Exeter and Salisbury → London

Network Diagram - see first page of Table 160

		SW	SW	SW	SW	SW	SW	SW	SW	SW	SW	SW	SW	SW	SW	SW	SW	SW	SW	SW	SW	SW	SW	SW
		1◇	1◇	1◇	1◇	1◇	1◇	1◇	1	1◇	1◇	1◇	1◇	1◇	1	1	1◇	1◇	1◇	1◇	1	1	1	1
					A	B															B	A		
		☕	☕		☕	☕	☕	☕		☕		☕	☕	☕			☕	☕	☕					
Plymouth	d		10b43		11c59	12c00		12e56	14f25					14 50	15g11	16 00			16h34	17 42	18c45	19j04	19 35	21 18
Ivybridge	d				11c25	11c25		12k48						15 05	15m26	15n26			16q49	17 57	19c00	18c59	18r59	21 33
Totnes	d		09t55		12c27	12c27		13v24	14w50					15 19	15y40	16 27			17q03	18 11	19c14	19c13	20 02	21 47
Paignton	d		10b32		12 23	12 25		13z15	14C31					14D51	15 52	16E35			17E03	17G50	19 14	19 14	19H28	21 50
Torquay	d		10J39		12 29	12 31		13K20	14L37					14N56	15 58	16Q42			17Q10	17U55	19 20	19 20	19V33	21 55
Newton Abbot	d		11X20		12 44	12 44		13Y37	15Z03					15 32	16 10	16¡53			17$22	18 24	19 32	19 32	20 15	22 08
Teignmouth	d		10*45		12 51	12 51		13!08	14 49					15 39	16 17	17+02			17+30	18 31	19 39	19 39	19‡54	22 15
Dawlish	d		10†50		12 56	12 56		13∞16	14 54					15 44	16 22	17¶08			17¶37	18 36	19 44	19 44	19§59	22 20
Dawlish Warren	d				13 10	13 01								15 48						18 48	19 49	19 56		
Exeter St Davids 6	a				13 21	13 19								15 59	16 35					19 00	20 03	20 07		
	d		12 10		13 35	13 35		14 10	15 30					16 10	16 40	17 40			18 10	19 10	20 15	20 15	21 00	22 57
Exeter Central	d		12 14		13 39	13 39		14 14	15 34					16 14	16 44	17 44			18 14	19 14	20 19	20 19	21 04	23 01
Pinhoe	d		12 19					14 19	15 39					16 19	16 49	17 49			18 19		20 27	20 27		23 06
Whimple	d		12 26					14 26	15 46					16 26	16 56	17 56			18 26		20 34	20 34		23 13
Feniton	d		12 31					14 31	15 51					16 31	17 01	18 01			18 31		20 39	20 39		23 18
Honiton	a		12 37		13 54	13 54		14 37	15 57					16 37	17 07	18 07			18 37	19 29	20 45	20 45	21 19	23 24
	d		12 38		13 57	13 57		14 38						16 38		18 08			18 38	19 30	20 46	20 46	21 23	23 28
Axminster	a		12 48		14 07	14 07		14 48						16 48		18 18			18 48	19 40	20 56	20 56	21 33	23 38
	d		12 49		14 08	14 08		14 49						16 49					18 49	19 41	20 57	20 57	21 46	23 39
Crewkerne	d		13 03					15 03						17 03					19 03	19 54	21 10	21 10	22 09	23 52
Yeovil Junction	a		13 12		14 27	14 27		15 12						17 12					19 12	20 03	21 19	21 19	22 17	00 01
	d		13 20		14 28	14 28		15 20				16 20		17 20				18 20	19 20	20 20	21 20	21 20	22 24	00 02
Sherborne	d		13 26					15 26				16 26		17 26				18 26	19 26	20 26	21 26	21 26	22 30	
Templecombe	d		13 34					15 34				16 34		17 34				18 34	19 34	20 34	21 34	21 34	22 38	
Gillingham (Dorset)	a		13 41		14 44	14 44		15 41				16 41		17 41				18 41	19 41	20 41	21 41	21 41	22 45	
	d		13 42		14 45	14 45		15 42				16 42		17 42				18 42	19 42	20 42	21 42	21 42	22 46	
Tisbury	d		13 52		14 55	14 55		15 52				16 52		17 52				18 52	19 52	20 52	21 52	21 52	22 56	
Bristol Temple Meads 10	d			13 10							15 52													
Bath Spa 7	d			13 22							16 06													
Bradford-on-Avon	d			13 35							16 22													
Trowbridge	d			13 42							16 28													
Westbury	d			13 53							16 39													
Warminster	d			14 00							16 47													
Salisbury	a		14 15	14 24	15 15	15 15		16 15			17 09	17 15		18 15				19 21	20 20	21 20	22 07	22 07	23 12	00 36
	d	13 45	14 20	14 45	15 20	15 20	15 45	16 20		16 45		17 20	17 45	18 20			18 45	19 25	20 25	21 25	22 25	22 25		
Romsey	a			14 50	15 50	15 50		16 50				17 50		18 50				19 50	20 50	21 50	22 50	22 50		
Southampton Central	a			15 02	16 02	16 02		17 02				18 02		19 02				20 02	21 02	22 02	23 02	23 02		
Portsmouth Harbour	a			15 51	16 51	16 51		17 51				18 51		19 51				20 51	21 51	22 50	23 49	23 49		
Brighton 10	a			17 18	18 18	18 18		19 18				20 20		21 18				22 22	23 18	00 25				
Grateley	d	13 57		14 57			15 57			16 57			17 57				18 57	19 37	20 37	21 37	22 37	22 37		
Andover	d	14 04	14 37	15 04	15 37	15 37	16 04	16 37		17 04		17 37	18 04	18 37			19 04	19 44	20 44	21 44	22 44	22 44		
Whitchurch (Hants)	d	14 12		15 12			16 12			17 12			18 12				19 12	19 52	20 52	21 52	22 52	22 52		
Overton	d	14 18		15 18			16 18			17 18			18 18				19 18	19 58	20 58	21 58	22 58	22 58		
Basingstoke	a	14 27	14 54	15 27	15 54	15 54	16 27	16 54		17 27		17 54	18 27	18 54			19 27	20 08	21 08	22 08	23 07	23 07		
Reading 7	a	15 00	15 31	16 00	16 31		17 00	17 31		18 00		18 31	19 00	19 31			20 00	21 00	22 00	23 00		00 01		
Woking	a	14 49	15 15	15 49	16 15	16 15	16 49	17 15		17 49		18 15	18 49	19 15			19 49	20 29	21 29	22 28	23 32	23 32		
Clapham Junction 10	a	15 12	15 36	16 12	16 36	16 36	17 12	17 36		18 12		18 36	19 12	19 36			20 12	20 52	21 52	22 48	23 57	23 57		
London Waterloo 15 ⊖	a	15 19	15 49	16 19	16 49	16 49	17 19	17 49		18 19		18 49	19 19	19 49			20 26	21 04	22 04	22 57	00 05	00 05		

For general notes see front of timetable
For details of catering facilities see Directory of Train Operators

For full service between Bristol Temple Meads and Salisbury see Table 123

- **A** Until 6 September
- **B** From 13 September
- **C** From 13 September dep. 1425
- **D** From 13 September dep. 1453
- **E** From 13 September dep. 1612
- **G** From 13 September dep. 1752
- **H** From 13 September dep. 1922
- **J** From 13 September dep. 1051
- **K** From 13 September dep. 1231
- **L** From 13 September dep. 1430
- **N** From 13 September dep. 1458
- **Q** From 13 September dep. 1617
- **U** From 13 September dep. 1757
- **V** From 13 September dep. 1927
- **X** From 13 September dep. 1122
- **Y** From 13 September dep. 1335
- **Z** From 13 September dep. 1442
- **¡** From 13 September dep. 1640
- **$** From 13 September dep. 1731
- ***** From 13 September dep. 1114
- **!** From 13 September dep. 1251
- **+** From 13 September dep. 1637
- **‡** From 13 September dep. 1947
- **¶** From 13 September dep. 1642
- **§** From 13 September dep. 1952
- **b** From 13 September dep. 1046
- **c** Change at Newton Abbot
- **e** From 13 September dep. 1254
- **f** From 13 September dep. 1359
- **g** Change at Newton Abbot. From 13 September dep. 1525
- **h** From 13 September dep. 1654
- **j** Change at Exeter St Davids
- **k** From 13 September dep. 1125
- **m** Change at Newton Abbot. From 13 September dep. 1527
- **n** Change at Newton Abbot and Exeter St Davids. From 13 September dep. 1527
- **q** Change at Newton Abbot and Exeter St Davids
- **r** From 13 September dep. 1900
- **t** From 13 September dep. 1032
- **v** From 13 September dep. 1321
- **w** From 13 September dep. 1350
- **y** Change at Newton Abbot. From 13 September dep. 1550
- **z** From 13 September dep. 1225
- **†** From 13 September dep. 1119
- **∞** From 13 September dep. 1256

Table 160

Sundays

Exeter and Salisbury → London

Network Diagram - see first page of Table 160

Station		SW 1	SW 1 ◇ A ☕	SW 1 ◇ B ☕	SW 1 ◇ A ☕	SW 1 ◇ B ☕	SW 1 ◇ ☕	SW 1 ◇ ☕	SW 1 ◇ ☕	SW 1 ◇ ☕	SW 1 ◇ ☕	SW 1 ◇ ☕	SW 1 ◇ ☕	SW 1 ◇ ☕	SW 1 ◇ ☕	SW 1 ◇	SW 1 ◇ ☕	SW 1 ◇ ☕	SW 1 ◇	SW 1 ◇ C ☕	SW 1 ◇ ☕	SW 1 ◇ ☕	SW 1	SW 1	SW 1
Plymouth	d											09 50		11b45			14 06	15c25	16e02	16 02		18f10		19 55	21g08
Ivybridge	d																14 21		16h17	16 17		17b24		17j24	
Totnes	d											10 17		12b15			14 35		16h31	16 31		18k39		19m46	21n37
Paignton	d													12 25			14 20	15 27	16 10			18 23		19 50	22 10
Torquay	d													12 31				15 33	16 16			18 29		19 55	22 16
Newton Abbot	d											10 30		12 44			14 47	15 49	16 32	16 43		18 41		20 32	22 28
Teignmouth	d											09q29		12 51			14 54	15 56	16 13			18 48		20 15	22 35
Dawlish	d											09r35		12 58			14 59	16 01	16 18			18 53		20 20	22 40
Dawlish Warren	d																	16 06				18 57			22 44
Exeter St Davids 6	a													13 13			15 15	16 17	16 54	17 05		19 08			22 55
	d	22p57								09 20		11 20		13 18			15 20	16 33	17 18			19 20		21 20	23 10
Exeter Central	d	23p01								09 24		11 24		13 22			15 24	16 37	17 23			19 24		21 24	23 14
Pinhoe	d	23p06																16 42				19 29			
Whimple	d	23p13								09 33		11 33		13 33			15 33		17 33			19 36		21 33	
Feniton	d	23p18								09 39		11 39		13 39			15 39		17 39			19 41		21 39	
Honiton	a	23p24								09 45		11 45		13 45			15 45	16 54	17 45			19 47		21 45	23s29
	d	23p28							08 46	09 46		11 46		13 46			15 46	16 55	17 46			19 48		21 46	
Axminster	a	23p38							08 56	09 56		11 56		13 56			15 56	17 05	17 56			19 58		21 56	23s40
	d	23p39							08 57	09 57		11 57		13 57			15 57	17 06	17 57			19 59		21 57	
Crewkerne	d	23p52							09 10	10 10		12 10		14 10			16 10	17 19	18 10			20 12		22 10	00s04
Yeovil Junction	a	00 01							09 18	10 18		12 18		14 18			16 18	17 28	18 18			20 21		22 18	00s13
	d	00 02					07 32		09 25	10 25	11 25	12 25	13 25	14 25	15 25		16 25	17 29	18 25		19 25	20 25	21 25	22 25	
Sherborne	d						07 38		09 31	10 31	11 31	12 31	13 31	14 31	15 31		16 31	17 36	18 31		19 31	20 31	21 31	22 31	
Templecombe	d						07 47		09 39	10 39	11 39	12 39	13 39	14 39	15 39		16 39	17 43	18 39		19 39	20 39	21 39	22 39	
Gillingham (Dorset)	a						07 54		09 46	10 46	11 46	12 46	13 46	14 46	15 46		16 46	17 50	18 46		19 46	20 46	21 46	22 46	
	d						07 55		09 47	10 47	11 47	12 47	13 47	14 47	15 47		16 47	17 51	18 47		19 47	20 47	21 47	22 47	
Tisbury	d						08 05		09 57	10 57	11 57	12 57	13 57	14 57	15 57		16 57	18 02	18 57		19 57	20 57	21 57	22 57	
Bristol Temple Meads 10	d															16 04									
Bath Spa 7	d															16 20									
Bradford-on-Avon	d															16 31									
Trowbridge	d															16 37									
Westbury	d															16 46									
Warminster	d															16 53									
Salisbury	a	00 36					08 20		10 21	11 17	12 21	13 17	14 21	15 18	16 21	17 16	17 21	18 22	19 17		20 21	21 21	22 21	23 17	00 50
	d		06 42	06 45	07 23	07 26	08 26	09 26	10 26	11 26	12 26	13 26	14 26	15 26	16 26	17 26		18 26	19 26		20 26	21 26	22 26		
Romsey	a								10 49	11 49	12 55	13 47	15 09	15 51	16 49	18t49			19 55		20 48	21 47	22 48		
Southampton Central	a								11 00	12 04	13 06	13 58	15 20	16 02	17 04	19v04			20 06		20 59	21 58	22 59		
Portsmouth Harbour	a								11 51	12 51		14 46		16 51	17 51	19w51			21 23		21 46	22 46	23 44		
Brighton 10	a								14y00	15y00	15 06	17y00	17 05	19y00	20y00	21z55			22 01		23y25				
Grateley	d						08 38		10 38		12 38		14 38		16 38			18 38			20 38		22 38		
Andover	d		06 59	07 02	07 40	07 43	08 46	09 43	10 46	11 43	12 46	13 43	14 46	15 43	16 46	17 43		18 46	19 43		20 46	21 43	22 46		
Whitchurch (Hants)	d				07 48	07 51	08 54		10 54		12 54		14 54		16 54			18 54			20 54		22 54		
Overton	d						08 59		10 59		12 59		14 59		16 59			18 59			20 59		22 59		
Basingstoke	a		07 19	07 19	08 03	08 03	09 08	10 00	11 08	12 00	13 08	14 00	15 08	16 00	17 08	18 00		19 08	20 00		21 08	22 00	23 08		
Reading 7	a			08 30		09 30	10 05	10 30	12 05	12 30	14 05	14 30	16 05	16 30	18 05	18 30			20 30		22 05	22 33	00 30		
Woking	a		07 39	07 39	08 23	08 23	09 30	10 23	11 30	12 23	13 30	14 23	15 30	16 23	17 30	18 23		19 30	20 23		21 30	22 23	23 50		
Clapham Junction 10	a		08 03	08 03	08 55	08 55	09 55	10 44	11 50	12 44	13 50	14 44	15 50	16 44	17 50	18 44		19 50	20 44		21 50	22 44	00 22		
London Waterloo 15 ⊖	a		08 19	08 19	09 09	09 09	10 08	11 03	12 03	13 03	14 04	14 58	16 04	16 58	18 04	18 58		20 04	20 58		22 04	22 58	00 33		

For general notes see front of timetable
For details of catering facilities see Directory of Train Operators

For full service between Bristol Temple Meads and Salisbury see Table 123

- **A** From 28 September
- **B** Until 21 September
- **C** From Penzance (Table 135)
- **b** Change at Newton Abbot
- **c** 20 July to 7 September only. Change at Exeter St Davids
- **e** From 14 September only. Change at Exeter St Davids
- **f** Until 7 September change at Exeter St Davids. From 14 September dep. 1750, change at Newton Abbot
- **g** Until 30 November only. Change at Newton Abbot. 14 September to 30 November dep. 2115
- **h** Change at Exeter St Davids
- **j** Change at Newton Abbot and Exeter St Davids
- **k** Until 7 September change at Exeter St Davids. From 14 September dep. 1816, change at Newton Abbot
- **m** From 14 September dep. 1945
- **n** Until 30 November only. Change at Newton Abbot. 14 September to 30 November dep. 2142
- **q** From 14 September dep. 0928
- **r** From 14 September dep. 0934
- **t** From 14 September arr. 1749
- **v** From 14 September arr. 1804
- **w** From 14 September arr. 1851
- **y** Change at Salisbury and Fratton
- **z** Change at Salisbury and Fratton. From 14 September arr. 2100

Network Diagram for Tables 165, 167

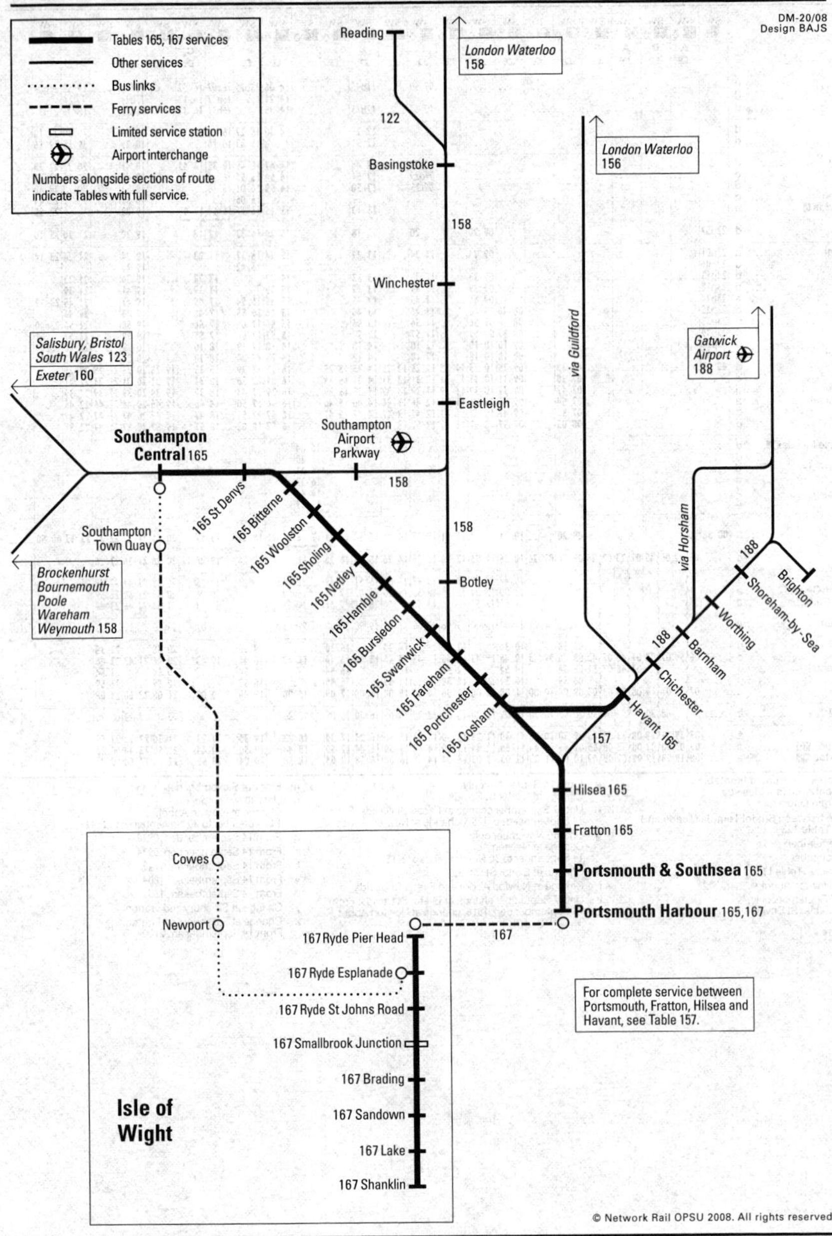

Tables 165, 167 services
Other services
Bus links
Ferry services
Limited service station
Airport interchange
Numbers alongside sections of route indicate Tables with full service.
DM-20/08
Design BAJS
Reading
London Waterloo 158
122
Basingstoke
158
Winchester
London Waterloo 156
via Guildford
Gatwick Airport 188
Salisbury, Bristol
South Wales 123
Exeter 160
Eastleigh
Southampton Airport Parkway
Southampton Central 165
158
158
Southampton Town Quay
Brockenhurst
Bournemouth
Poole
Wareham
Weymouth 158
165 St Denys
165 Bitterne
165 Woolston
165 Sholing
165 Netley
165 Hamble
165 Bursledon
165 Swanwick
165 Fareham
165 Portchester
165 Cosham
Botley
via Horsham
188
Brighton
Shoreham-by-Sea
Worthing
188
Barnham
Chichester
Havant 165
157
Hilsea 165
Fratton 165
Portsmouth & Southsea 165
Portsmouth Harbour 165,167
167
Cowes
Newport
167 Ryde Pier Head
167 Ryde Esplanade
167 Ryde St Johns Road
167 Smallbrook Junction
167 Brading
167 Sandown
167 Lake
167 Shanklin
Isle of Wight
For complete service between Portsmouth, Fratton, Hilsea and Havant, see Table 157.

Table 165

Mondays to Fridays

For details of Bank Holiday service alterations, please see first page of Table 149

Southampton → Fareham and Portsmouth

Network Diagram - see first page of Table 165

Miles	Miles			SW	SW	SN	SW	SN	SW	SW	GW	SW	SN	SW	SW	SN	GW	SW	SN	SW	SN	SW	GW	SN	SW	SN
				MO 1	MX 1	1	1	1	1	1		1	1	1	1	1	◇	1	1	1	1	1	◇	1	1	1
0	—	**Southampton Central**	d			05 48		06 10		06 21	06 53		07 06		07 17	07 36	07 42	07 51	08 10		08 36	08 42	09 03	09 11		09 36
2	—	St Denys	d							06 27					07 23			07 57	08 15			08 48				
2½	—	Bitterne	d							06 29					07 25			07 59				08 50				
4¼	—	Woolston	d			05 57		06 19		06 33			07 15		07 29			08 03				08 54				
5	—	Sholing	d							06 35					07 31			08 05				08 56				
6¾	—	Netley	d							06 39					07 35			08 09				09 00				
7¾	—	Hamble	d							06 41					07 37			08 11				09 02				
8¾	—	Bursledon	d							06 44					07 40			08 14				09 05				
10¾	—	Swanwick	d			06 06		06 27		06 48			07 24		07 44	07 53		08 18	08 28		08 53	09 09		09 28		09 53
14½	—	**Fareham**	a			06 12		06 33		06 57	07 14		07 30		07 52	07 59	08 05	08 25	08 34		08 59	09 16	09 26	09 35		09 59
—	—		d	23p44	23p48	06 13	06 18	06 34	06 50	06 58	07 15	07 20	07 31	07 48	07 53	08 00	08 06	08 26	08 35	08 50	09 00	09 17	09 26	09 36	09 48	10 00
17¾	—	Portchester	d	23p49	23p53	06 18	06 23	06 40	06 55	07 03		07 25	07 36	07 53	07 58			08 31	08 40	08 55		09 22		09 41	09 53	
20¼	0	Cosham	d	23p54	23p59	06 23	06 28	06 44	07 00	07 08	07 23	07 29	07 40	07 58	08 03	08 08	08 14	08 36	08 44	09 00	09 08	09 27	09 34	09 45	09 58	10 08
—	4	Havant	a			06 37		06 53					07 46			08 14			08 50		09 14			09 51		10 14
21¾	—	Hilsea	a	23p59	00 04		06 33		07 05	07 13		07 35		08 03	08 09			08 43		09 05		09 31			10 03	
24	—	Fratton	a	00 04	00 08		06 38		07 09	07 17	07 34	07 39		08 07	08 13		08 21	08 47		09 09		09 35	09 41		10 07	
25	—	**Portsmouth & Southsea**	a	00 08	00 11		06 44		07 12	07 22	07 38	07 42		08 11	08 18		08 24	08 51		09 13		09 40	09 45		10 12	
25¾	—	**Portsmouth Harbour**	a	00 13	00 16		06 49		07 17		07 45	07 48		08 16	08 23		08 30	08 55		09 18			09 54		10 18	

		SW	GW	SN	SW	SN	SW	GW	SN	SW	SN	SW		GW	SN	SW	SN	SW	GW	SN	SW	SN	SW	GW	SN	SW
		1	◇	1	1	1	1	◇	1	1	1	1		◇	1	1	1	1	◇	1	1	1	1	◇	1	1
Southampton Central	d	09 42	10 03	10 11		10 36	10 42	11 03	11 11		11 36	11 42		12 03	12 11		12 36	12 42	13 03	13 11		13 36	13 42	14 03	14 11	
St Denys	d	09 48					10 48					11 48						12 48					13 48			
Bitterne	d	09 50					10 50					11 50						12 50					13 50			
Woolston	d	09 54					10 54					11 54						12 54					13 54			
Sholing	d	09 56					10 56					11 56						12 56					13 56			
Netley	d	10 00					11 00					12 00						13 00					14 00			
Hamble	d	10 02					11 02					12 02						13 02					14 02			
Bursledon	d	10 05					11 05					12 05						13 05					14 05			
Swanwick	d	10 09		10 28		10 53	11 09		11 28		11 53	12 09			12 28		12 53	13 09		13 28		13 53	14 09		14 28	
Fareham	a	10 16	10 26	10 34		10 59	11 16	11 26	11 34		11 59	12 16		12 26	12 34		12 59	13 16	13 26	13 34		13 59	14 16	14 26	14 34	
	d	10 17	10 26	10 35	10 48	11 00	11 17	11 26	11 35	11 48	12 00	12 17		12 26	12 35	12 48	13 00	13 17	13 26	13 35	13 48	14 00	14 17	14 26	14 35	14 48
Portchester	d	10 22		10 40	10 53		11 22		11 40	11 53		12 22			12 40	12 53		13 22		13 40	13 53		14 22		14 40	14 53
Cosham	d	10 27	10 34	10 45	10 58	11 08	11 27	11 34	11 45	11 58	12 09	12 27		12 34	12 44	12 58	13 08	13 27	13 34	13 45	13 58	14 08	14 27	14 34	14 45	14 58
Havant	a			10 51		11 14			11 51		12 15				12 50		13 14			13 51		14 14			14 51	
Hilsea	a	10 32			11 03		11 32			12 03		12 32				13 03		13 32			14 03		14 32			15 03
Fratton	a	10 36	10 41		11 07		11 36	11 41		12 07		12 36		12 41		13 07		13 36	13 41		14 07		14 36	14 41		15 07
Portsmouth & Southsea	a	10 41	10 45		11 12		11 40	11 45		12 12		12 40		12 45		13 12		13 40	13 45		14 12		14 40	14 45		15 12
Portsmouth Harbour	a		10 54		11 18			11 54		12 18				12 54		13 18			13 54		14 18			14 54		15 18

		GW	SN	SW	GW	SN	SW	SN	SW	GW	SN	SW	SN	SW	SW	GW	SN	SW	SN	SW	SW	GW	SN	SW	SN	SW
		◇	1	1	◇	1	1	1	1	◇	1	1	1	1	1	◇	1	1	1	1	1	◇	1	1	1	1
Southampton Central	d	14 35	14 26	14 42	15 03	15 11		15 36	15 42	16 03	16 11		16 36		16 42	17 03	17 11		17 36	17 42		18 03	18 11		18 27	
St Denys	d			14 48					15 48						16 48					17 48						
Bitterne	d			14 50					15 50						16 50					17 50						
Woolston	d			14 54					15 54						16 54					17 54						
Sholing	d			14 56					15 56						16 56					17 56						
Netley	d			15 00					16 00						17 00					18 00						
Hamble	d			15 02					16 02						17 02					18 02						
Bursledon	d			15 05					16 05						17 05					18 05						
Swanwick	d			15 09		15 28		15 53	16 09		16 28		16 53		17 09		17 28		17 53	18 09			18 28		18 47	
Fareham	a	14 55	15 02	15 16	15 26	15 34		15 59	16 16	16 26	16 35		16 59		17 16	17 26	17 34		17 59	18 16		18 26	18 34		18 55	
	d	14 56	15 02	15 17	15 26	15 35	15 48	16 00	16 17	16 26	16 36	16 48	17 00	17 10	17 17	17 26	17 35	17 48	18 00	18 17	18 21	18 26	18 35	18 50	18 56	19 14
Portchester	d			15 22		15 40	15 53		16 22		16 41	16 53		17 15	17 22		17 40	17 53		18 22	18 26		18 40	18 55		19 19
Cosham	d	15 04		15 27	15 34	15 44	15 58	16 08	16 27	16 34	16 45	16 58	17 08	17 20	17 27	17 34	17 44	17 58	18 08	18 27	18 31	18 34	18 44	19 00	19 04	19 24
Havant	a	15 10	15 14			15 50		16 14			16 51		17 14				17 50		18 14				18 50		19 10	
Hilsea	a			15 32			16 03		16 32			17 03			17 32			18 03		18 32				19 05		19 28
Fratton	a			15 36	15 41		16 07		16 36	16 47		17 07		17 27	17 36	17 41		18 07		18 36	18 39	18 47		19 09		19 32
Portsmouth & Southsea	a			15 40	15 45		16 12		16 40	16 51		17 18		17 31	17 40	17 45		18 11		18 40	18 43	18 51		19 12		19 36
Portsmouth Harbour	a				15 54		16 18		16 44	16 59		17 25				17 54		18 20			18 51	18 59		19 20		19 43

		SW	GW	SN	SW	SN	SW	GW	SN	SW	SN	SW	GW	SN	SW	SN	SW	SN	GW	SN	SW	SW	GW	SW		
		1	◇	1	1	1	1	◇	1	1	1	1	◇	1	1	1	1	1	◇	1	1	1	◇	1		
Southampton Central	d	18 42	19 03	19 11		19 36	19 42	20 03	20 11		20 36	20 42	21 03	21 11		21 23	21 42	22 12	22 03	22 36		22 42	23 03			
St Denys	d	18 48					19 48					20 48					21 48					22 48				
Bitterne	d	18 50					19 50					20 50					21 50					22 50				
Woolston	d	18 54					19 54					20 54					21 54					22 54				
Sholing	d	18 56					19 56					20 56					21 56					22 56				
Netley	d	19 00					20 00					21 00					22 00					23 00				
Hamble	d	19 02					20 02					21 02					22 02					23 02				
Bursledon	d	19 05					20 05					21 05					22 05					23 05				
Swanwick	d	19 09		19 28		19 53	20 09		20 28		20 53	21 09		21 28			22 09	22 29		22 53		23 09				
Fareham	a	19 17	19 26	19 34		19 59	20 16	20 26	20 34		20 59	21 16	21 26	21 38		21 55	22 16	22 35	22 39	22 59		23 16	23 26			
	d	19 18	19 26	19 35	19 50	20 00	20 17	20 26	20 35	20 48	21 00	21 17	21 26	21 39	21 48	21 56	22 17	22 36	22 39	23 00	23 10	23 17	23 26	23 48		
Portchester	d	19 23		19 40	19 55		20 22		20 40	20 53		21 22		21 44	21 53	22 01	22 22	22 41			23 15	23 22		23 53		
Cosham	d	19 28	19 34	19 44	20 00	20 08	20 27		20 44	20 58	21 08	21 27		21 48	21 58	22 06	22 27	22 45		23 08	23 20	23 27		23 59		
Havant	a			19 51		20 14			20 50		21 14			21 54		22 13		22 57		23 14						
Hilsea	a	19 32			20 08		20 32			20 59		21 32			22 06		22 32				23 24	23 32		00 04		
Fratton	a	19 37	19 41		20 12		20 36	20 47		21 08		21 36	21 40		22 10		22 36		22 55		23 32	23 36	23 41	00 08		
Portsmouth & Southsea	a	19 42	19 45		20 16		20 41	20 51		21 11		21 40	21 45		22 13		22 41		22 59		23 36	23 40	23 45	00 11		
Portsmouth Harbour	a		19 54		20 23			20 59		21 21			21 52		22 18				23 04		23 40		23 54	00 16		

For general notes see front of timetable
For details of catering facilities see Directory of Train Operators

Southampton → Fareham and Portsmouth

Network Diagram - see first page of Table 165

		SW	SW	SN	SW	SN	SW	SN	SW	SN	SW	GW	SN	SW	SN	SW	GW	SN	SW	SN	SW	GW	SN
		1	1	1	1	1	1	1	1	1	1	◇	1	1	1	1	◇	1	1	1	1	◇ 🛒	1
Southampton Central	d		05 42	06 11		06 36	06 42	07 11		07 36	07 42	08 03	08 11		08 36	08 42	09 03	09 11		09 36	09 42	10 03	10 11
St Denys	d		05 48				06 48				07 48					08 48					09 48		
Bitterne	d		05 50				06 50				07 50					08 50					09 50		
Woolston	d		05 54				06 54				07 54					08 54					09 54		
Sholing	d		05 56				06 56				07 56					08 56					09 56		
Netley	d		06 00				07 00				08 00					09 00					10 00		
Hamble	d		06 02				07 02				08 02					09 02					10 02		
Bursledon	d		06 05				07 05				08 05					09 05					10 05		
Swanwick	d		06 09	06 28		06 53	07 09	07 28		07 53	08 09		08 28		08 53	09 09		09 28		09 53	10 09		10 28
Fareham	a		06 16	06 34		06 59	07 16	07 34		07 59	08 16	08 26	08 34		08 59	09 16	09 26	09 34		09 59	10 16	10 26	10 34
	d	23p48	06 17	06 35	06 48	07 00	07 17	07 35	07 48	08 00	08 17	08 26	08 35	08 48	09 00	09 17	09 26	09 35	09 48	10 00	10 17	10 26	10 35
Portchester	d	23p53	06 22	06 40	06 53		07 22	07 40	07 53		08 22		08 40	08 53		09 22		09 40	09 53		10 22		10 40
Cosham	d	23p59	06 27	06 44	06 58	07 08	07 27	07 44	07 58	08 09	08 27	08 34	08 44	08 58	09 08	09 27	09 34	09 44	09 58	10 08	10 27	10 34	10 44
Havant	a			06 50		07 14		07 50		08 15			08 50		09 14			09 50		10 14			10 50
Hilsea	a	00 04	06 32		07 03		07 32		08 04		08 32			09 03		09 32			10 03		10 32		
Fratton	a	00 08	06 36		07 06		07 36		08 07		08 36	08 41		09 07		09 36	09 41		10 07		10 36	10 41	
Portsmouth & Southsea	a	00 11	06 40		07 10		07 40		08 11		08 40	08 45		09 11		09 40	09 45		10 11		10 40	10 45	
Portsmouth Harbour	a	00 16			07 17				08 18			08 49		09 18			09 51		10 18			10 51	

		SW	SN	SW	GW	SN	SW	SN	SW	GW	SN	SW	SN	SW	GW	SN	SW	SN	SW	GW	SN	SW	GW
		1	1	1	◇ 🛒	1	1	1	1	◇ 🛒	1	1	1	1	◇ 🛒	1	1	1	1	◇ 🛒	1	1	◇
Southampton Central	d		10 36	10 42	11 03	11 11		11 36	11 42	12 03	12 11		12 36	12 42	13 03	13 11		13 36	13 42	14 03	14 11		14 35
St Denys	d			10 48					11 48					12 48					13 48				
Bitterne	d			10 50					11 50					12 50					13 50				
Woolston	d			10 54					11 54					12 54					13 54				
Sholing	d			10 56					11 56					12 56					13 56				
Netley	d			11 00					12 00					13 00					14 00				
Hamble	d			11 02					12 02					13 02					14 02				
Bursledon	d			11 05					12 05					13 05					14 05				
Swanwick	d		10 53	11 09		11 28		11 53	12 09		12 28		12 53	13 09		13 28		13 53	14 09		14 28		
Fareham	a		10 59	11 16	11 26	11 34		11 59	12 16	12 26	12 34		12 59	13 16	13 26	13 34		13 59	14 16	14 26	14 34		14 55
	d	10 48	11 00	11 17	11 26	11 35	11 48	12 00	12 17	12 26	12 35	12 48	13 00	13 17	13 26	13 35	13 48	14 00	14 17	14 26	14 35	14 48	14 56
Portchester	d	10 53		11 22		11 40	11 53		12 22		12 40	12 53		13 22		13 40	13 53		14 22		14 40	14 53	
Cosham	d	10 58	11 08	11 27	11 34	11 44	11 58	12 08	12 27	12 34	12 44	12 58	13 08	13 27	13 34	13 44	13 58	14 08	14 27	14 34	14 44	14 58	15 04
Havant	a		11 14			11 50		12 14			12 50		13 14			13 50		14 14			14 50		15 11
Hilsea	a	11 03		11 32			12 03		12 32			13 03		13 32			14 03		14 32			15 03	
Fratton	a	11 07		11 36	11 41		12 07		12 36	12 41		13 07		13 36	13 41		14 07		14 36	14 41		15 07	
Portsmouth & Southsea	a	11 11		11 40	11 45		12 11		12 40	12 45		13 11		13 40	13 45		14 11		14 40	14 45		15 11	
Portsmouth Harbour	a	11 18			11 51		12 18			12 51		13 18			13 51		14 18			14 51		15 18	

		SN	SW	GW	SN	SW	SN	SW	GW	SN	SW	SN	SW	GW	SN	SW	SN	SW	GW	SN	SW	SN	SW
		1	1	◇ 🛒	1	1	1	1	◇ 🛒	1	1	1	1	◇ 🛒	1	1	1	1	◇ 🛒	1	1	1	1
Southampton Central	d	14 26	14 42	15 03	15 11		15 36	15 42	16 03	16 11		16 36	16 42	17 03	17 11		17 36	17 42	18 03	18 11		18 36	18 42
St Denys	d		14 48					15 48					16 48					17 48					18 48
Bitterne	d		14 50					15 50					16 50					17 50					18 50
Woolston	d		14 54					15 54					16 54					17 54					18 54
Sholing	d		14 56					15 56					16 56					17 56					18 56
Netley	d		15 00					16 00					17 00					18 00					19 00
Hamble	d		15 02					16 02					17 02					18 02					19 02
Bursledon	d		15 05					16 05					17 05					18 05					19 05
Swanwick	d		15 09		15 28		15 53	16 09		16 28		16 53	17 09		17 28		17 53	18 09		18 28		18 53	19 09
Fareham	a	15 01	15 16	15 26	15 34		15 59	16 16	16 26	16 34		16 59	17 16	17 26	17 34		17 59	18 16	18 26	18 34		18 59	19 16
	d	15 02	15 17	15 26	15 35	15 48	16 00	16 17	16 26	16 35	16 48	17 00	17 17	17 26	17 35	17 48	18 00	18 17	18 26	18 35	18 48	19 00	19 17
Portchester	d		15 22		15 40	15 53		16 22		16 40	16 53		17 22		17 40	17 53		18 22		18 40	18 53		19 22
Cosham	d		15 27	15 34	15 44	15 58	16 08	16 27	16 34	16 44	16 58	17 08	17 27	17 34	17 44	17 58	18 08	18 27	18 34	18 44	18 58	19 08	19 27
Havant	a	15 14			15 50		16 14			16 50		17 14			17 50		18 14			18 50		19 14	
Hilsea	a		15 32			16 03		16 32			17 03		17 32			18 03		18 32			19 03		19 32
Fratton	a		15 36	15 41		16 07		16 36	16 41		17 07		17 36	17 41		18 07		18 36	18 41		19 07		19 36
Portsmouth & Southsea	a		15 40	15 45		16 11		16 40	16 45		17 11		17 40	17 45		18 11		18 40	18 45		19 11		19 40
Portsmouth Harbour	a			15 51		16 18		16 44	16 51		17 18			17 51		18 18			18 51		19 18		

		GW	SN	SW	SN	SW	GW	SN	SW	SN	SW	GW	SN	SW	SN	SW	GW	SN	SW	SN	SW	GW	SW
		◇ 🛒	1	1	1	1	◇ 🛒	1	1	1	1	◇ 🛒	1	1	1	1	◇ 🛒	1	1	1	1	◇ 🛒	1
Southampton Central	d	19 03	19 11		19 36	19 42	20 03	20 11		20 36	20 42	21 03	21 11		21 23	21 42	22 03	22 11		22 36	22 42	23 04	
St Denys	d					19 48					20 48				21 28	21 48					22 48		
Bitterne	d					19 50					20 50					21 50					22 50		
Woolston	d					19 54					20 54				21 33	21 54					22 54		
Sholing	d					19 56					20 56					21 56					22 56		
Netley	d					20 00					21 00				21 37	22 00					23 00		
Hamble	d					20 02					21 02					22 02					23 02		
Bursledon	d					20 05					21 05					22 05					23 05		
Swanwick	d		19 28		19 53	20 09		20 28		20 53	21 09		21 28		21 45	22 09		22 28		22 53	23 09		
Fareham	a	19 26	19 34		19 59	20 16	20 26	20 34		20 59	21 16	21 26	21 38		21 54	22 16	22 25	22 38		22 59	23 16	23 25	
	d	19 26	19 35	19 48	20 00	20 17	20 26	20 35	20 48	21 00	21 17	21 26	21 39	21 48	21 55	22 17	22 26	22 39	22 48	23 00	23 17	23 26	23 48
Portchester	d		19 40	19 53		20 22		20 40	20 53		21 22		21 44	21 53	22 00	22 22		22 44	22 53		23 22		23 53
Cosham	d	19 34	19 44	19 58	20 08	20 27		20 44	20 58	21 08	21 27		21 48	21 58	22 04	22 27		22 48	22 58	23 08	23 27		23 58
Havant	a		19 51		20 14			20 50		21 14			21 54		22 12			22 54		23 14			
Hilsea	a			20 03		20 32			21 03		21 32			22 03		22 32			23 03		23 32		00 03
Fratton	a	19 41		20 07		20 36	20 40		21 07		21 36	21 41		22 07		22 36	22 39		23 07		23 36	23 40	00 07
Portsmouth & Southsea	a	19 45		20 11		20 40	20 44		21 11		21 40	21 45		22 11		22 40	22 43		23 11		23 40	23 44	00 11
Portsmouth Harbour	a	19 51		20 18			20 51		21 18			21 51		22 18		22 47	22 50		23 16			23 49	00 16

For general notes see front of timetable
For details of catering facilities see
Directory of Train Operators

Table 165

Sundays

Southampton → Fareham and Portsmouth

Network Diagram - see first page of Table 165

		SW	SW	SW	SW	SW	GW	SW	SW	SW	SW	SW	GW	SW	SW	GW	SW	SW
		1	1	1	1	1	1 🛒	1	1	1	1	1	◇ 🛒	1	1	◇ 🛒	1	1
Southampton Central	d		06 35		07 35		08 31	08 35		09 35		10 35	11 04		11 35	12 07		12 35
St Denys	d		06 41		07 41			08 41		09 41		10 41			11 41			12 41
Bitterne	d		06 43		07 43			08 43		09 43		10 43			11 43			12 43
Woolston	d		06 47		07 47			08 47		09 47		10 47			11 47			12 47
Sholing	d		06 49		07 49			08 49		09 49		10 49			11 49			12 49
Netley	d		06 53		07 53			08 53		09 53		10 53			11 53			12 53
Hamble	d		06 55		07 55			08 55		09 55		10 55			11 55			12 55
Bursledon	d		06 58		07 58			08 58		09 58		10 58			11 58			12 58
Swanwick	d		07 02		08 02			09 02		10 02		11 02			12 02			13 02
Fareham	a		07 09		08 09		08 51	09 09		10 09		11 09	11 25		12 09	12 28		13 09
	d	23p48	07 10	07 44	08 10	08 44	08 52	09 10	09 44	10 10	10 44	11 10	11 26	11 44	12 10	12 29	12 44	13 10
Portchester	d	23p53	07 15	07 49	08 15	08 49		09 15	09 49	10 15	10 49	11 15		11 49	12 15		12 49	13 15
Cosham	d	23p58	07 20	07 54	08 20	08 54	09 00	09 20	09 54	10 20	10 54	11 20	11 34	11 54	12 20	12 37	12 54	13 20
Havant	a						09 11											
Hilsea	a	00 03	07 26	08 00	08 26	09 00		09 26	10 00	10 26	11 00	11 26		12 00	12 26		13 00	13 26
Fratton	a	00 07	07 30	08 04	08 30	09 04		09 30	10 04	10 30	11 04	11 30	11 40	12 04	12 30	12 44	13 04	13 30
Portsmouth & Southsea	a	00 11	07 33	08 08	08 33	09 08		09 33	10 10	10 33	11 08	11 33	11 44	12 08	12 33	12 47	13 08	13 33
Portsmouth Harbour	a	00 16		08 13		09 13			10 15		11 14		11 51	12 13		12 51	13 13	

		GW	SW	SW	GW	SW	SW	SW	GW	SW	GW	GW	SW	SW	GW	SW	SW	GW
		◇ 🛒	1	1	◇ 🛒	1	1	1	◇ 🛒	1	◇ A 🛒	◇ B 🛒	1	1	◇ 🛒	1	1	◇ A 🛒
Southampton Central	d	13 08		13 35	14 01		14 35		15 22	15 35	16 03	16 04		16 35	17 07		17 35	18 07
St Denys	d			13 41			14 41			15 41				16 41			17 41	
Bitterne	d			13 43			14 43			15 43				16 43			17 43	
Woolston	d			13 47			14 47			15 47				16 47			17 47	
Sholing	d			13 49			14 49			15 49				16 49			17 49	
Netley	d			13 53			14 53			15 53				16 53			17 53	
Hamble	d			13 55			14 55			15 55				16 55			17 55	
Bursledon	d			13 58			14 58			15 58				16 58			17 58	
Swanwick	d			14 02			15 02			16 02				17 02			18 02	
Fareham	a	13 33		14 09	14 22		15 09		15 50	16 09	16 26	16 26		17 09	17 28		18 09	18 28
	d	13 34	13 44	14 10	14 23	14 44	15 10	15 45	15 51	16 10	16 26	16 27	16 44	17 10	17 29	17 44	18 10	18 29
Portchester	d		13 49	14 15		14 49	15 15	15 50		16 15			16 49	17 15		17 49	18 15	
Cosham	d	13 42	13 54	14 20	14 31	14 54	15 20	15 55	16 01	16 20	16 34	16 35	16 54	17 20	17 37	17 54	18 20	18 37
Havant	a	14 03							16 11									
Hilsea	a		14 00	14 26		15 00	15 26	16 00		16 26			17 00	17 26		18 00	18 26	
Fratton	a		14 04	14 30	14 38	15 04	15 30	16 04		16 30	16 41	16 42	17 04	17 30	17 44	18 04	18 30	18 44
Portsmouth & Southsea	a		14 08	14 33	14 41	15 08	15 33	16 08		16 33	16 45	16 45	17 08	17 33	17 47	18 08	18 33	18 47
Portsmouth Harbour	a		14 13		14 46	15 13		16 13			16 51	16 51	17 13		17 51	18 13		18 51

		SW	SW	GW	SW	SW	GW	SW	GW	SW	GW	SW	GW	SW	GW	SW	SW	GW	SW
		1	1	◇ 🛒	1	1	◇ 🛒	1	◇ 🛒	1	◇ 🛒	1	◇ 🛒	1	◇ 🛒	1	1	◇ 🛒	1
Southampton Central	d		18 35	19 07		19 35	20 07		20 33	20 35	21 01		21 29	21 35	22 01		22 35	23 00	
St Denys	d		18 41			19 41				20 41				21 41			22 41		
Bitterne	d		18 43			19 43				20 43				21 43			22 43		
Woolston	d		18 47			19 47				20 47				21 47			22 47		
Sholing	d		18 49			19 49				20 49				21 49			22 49		
Netley	d		18 53			19 53				20 53				21 53			22 53		
Hamble	d		18 55			19 55				20 55				21 55			22 55		
Bursledon	d		18 58			19 58				20 58				21 58			22 58		
Swanwick	d		19 02			20 02				21 02				22 02			23 02		
Fareham	a		19 09	19 28		20 09	20 28		20 54	21 09	21 22		21 50	22 09	22 22		23 09	23 21	
	d	18 44	19 10	19 29	19 44	20 10	20 29	20 44	20 55	21 10	21 23	21 44	21 51	22 10	22 23	22 44	23 10	23 22	23 44
Portchester	d	18 49	19 15		19 49	20 15		20 49		21 15		21 49		22 15		22 49	23 15		23 49
Cosham	d	18 54	19 20	19 37	19 54	20 20	20 44	20 54		21 20		21 54		22 20		22 54	23 20		23 54
Havant	a						20 52												
Hilsea	a	19 00	19 26		20 00	20 26		21 00		21 26		22 00		22 26		23 00	23 24		23 59
Fratton	a	19 04	19 30	19 44	20 04	20 30		21 04	21 09	21 30	21 36	22 04	22 08	22 30	22 36	23 04	23 28	23 37	00 04
Portsmouth & Southsea	a	19 08	19 33	19 47	20 08	20 33		21 08	21 15	21 33	21 39	22 08	22 13	22 33	22 39	23 08	23 32	23 40	00 08
Portsmouth Harbour	a	19 13		19 51	20 13			21 13	21 23		21 46	22 13	22 20		22 46	23 13		23 44	00 13

For general notes see front of timetable
For details of catering facilities see
Directory of Train Operators

A From 14 September
B Until 7 September.

For details of Bank Holiday service alterations, please see first page of Table 149

Portsmouth and Fareham → Southampton

Network Diagram - see first page of Table 165

Miles	Miles			SW 1	SN 1	SW 1	SW 1	GW ◇	SN 1	SW 1	SW 1	SN 1	SW 1	GW ◇	SN 1	SN 1	SW 1	SW 1	SW 1	SN 1	SW 1	GW ◇	SN 1	SW 1	SW 1	SN 1
0	—	**Portsmouth Harbour**	d	05 00			05 43	06 00			06 23		06 38	06 51			07 24		07 52		08 05	08 22		08 32	08 51	
¾	—	**Portsmouth & Southsea**	d	05 05		05 16	05 48	06 04		06 23	06 28		06 43	06 55			07 29	07 36	07 57		08 10	08 27		08 36	08 56	
1¾	—	Fratton	d	05 09		05 20	05 52	06 08		06 27	06 32		06 47	06 59			07 33	07 40	08 01		08 14	08 31		08 40	09 01	
4	—	Hilsea	d	05 13		05 24	05 56			06 31	06 36		06 51				07 37	07 44	08 05		08 18			08 44	09 05	
—	0	Havant	d		05 17				06 21			06 40			07 19	07 31				08 04			08 37			09 26
5½	4	Cosham	d	05 18	05 24	05 30	06 03	06 15	06 28	06 36	06 42	06 50	06 58	07 07	07 26	07 38	07 43	07 49	08 10	08 15	08 23	08 39	08 44	08 49	09 10	09 33
8	—	Portchester	d	05 23	05 28	05 35	06 08			06 41	06 46	06 54	07 03	07 12	07 30		07 48	07 54	08 15	08 19	08 28		08 48	08 54	09 15	
11¼	—	**Fareham**	a	05 28	05 33	05 40	06 13	06 23	06 37	06 46	06 51	06 59	07 08	07 17	07 35	07 46	07 53	07 59	08 20	08 24	08 33	08 46	08 53	08 59	09 20	09 41
—	—		d		05 34	05 41		06 24	06 38	06 47		07 00		07 18	07 36	07 47		08 00		08 25		08 47	08 54	09 00		09 42
15	—	Swanwick	d		05 40	05 47			06 44	06 53		07 06		07 24	07 42	07 53		08 06		08 31			09 00	09 06		
17	—	Bursledon	d			05 51				06 57								08 10		08 35				09 10		
18¼	—	Hamble	d			05 54				07 00								08 13		08 38				09 13		
19	—	Netley	d		05 46	05 56				07 02				07 30	07 48	07 59		08 15		08 40				09 15		
20¾	—	Sholing	d			06 00				07 06								08 19		08 43				09 19		
21½	—	Woolston	d		05 50	06 02				07 08				07 35	07 52	08 03		08 21		08 45				09 21		
23¼	—	Bitterne	d			06 06				07 12								08 25		08 49				09 25		
23¾	—	St Denys	d			06 09				07 15				07 40		08 08		08 28		08 51				09 28		
25¾	—	**Southampton Central**	a		05 59	06 14		06 45	07 02	07 21		07 26		07 45	08 01	08 13		08 36		08 56		09 08	09 19	09 36		10 03

		GW ◇	SN 1	SW 1	GW ◇	SW 1	SN 1	GW ◇	SN 1	SW 1	SW 1	SN 1		GW ◇	SN 1	SW 1	SW 1	SN 1	GW ◇	SN 1	SW 1	SW 1	SN 1	GW ◇	SN 1	SW 1
Portsmouth Harbour	d	09 22		09 32		09 54		10 22		10 31	10 54			11 22			11 54		12 22			12 54		13 22		
Portsmouth & Southsea	d	09 27		09 36		09 59		10 27		10 36	10 59			11 27		11 36	11 59		12 27		12 36	12 59		13 27		13 36
Fratton	d	09 31		09 40		10 03		10 31		10 40	11 03			11 31		11 40	12 03		12 31		12 40	13 03		13 31		13 40
Hilsea	d			09 44		10 07				10 44	11 07					11 44	12 07				12 44	13 07				13 44
Havant	d		09 38		09 59		10 22		10 37			11 23			11 37			12 23		12 37			13 23		13 37	
Cosham	d	09 39	09 45	09 49	10 05	10 12	10 29	10 39	10 45	10 49	11 12	11 29		11 39	11 45	11 49	12 12	12 29	12 39	12 45	12 49	13 12	13 29	13 39	13 45	13 49
Portchester	d			09 54		10 17	10 33			10 54	11 17	11 33				11 54	12 17	12 33			12 54	13 17	13 33			13 54
Fareham	a	09 46	09 53	09 59	10 13	10 22	10 38	10 46	10 52	10 59	11 22	11 38		11 46	11 52	11 59	12 22	12 38	12 46	12 52	12 59	13 22	13 38	13 46	13 52	13 59
	d	09 47	09 54	10 00	10 14		10 39	10 47	10 53	11 00		11 39		11 47	11 53	12 00		12 39	12 47	12 53	13 00		13 39	13 47	13 53	14 00
Swanwick	d		10 00	10 06			10 45		10 59	11 06		11 45			11 59	12 06		12 45		12 59	13 06		13 45		13 59	14 06
Bursledon	d			10 10						11 10						12 10					13 10					14 10
Hamble	d			10 13						11 13						12 13					13 13					14 13
Netley	d			10 15						11 15						12 15					13 15					14 15
Sholing	d			10 19						11 19						12 19					13 19					14 19
Woolston	d			10 21						11 21						12 21					13 21					14 21
Bitterne	d			10 25						11 25						12 25					13 25					14 25
St Denys	d			10 28						11 28						12 28					13 28					14 28
Southampton Central	a	10 08	10 19	10 36	10 38		11 02	11 08	11 18	11 36		12 02		12 08	12 18	12 36		13 02	13 08	13 18	13 36		14 02	14 08	14 18	14 36

		SW 1	SN 1	GW ◇	SN 1	SW 1	SW 1	SN 1	GW ◇	SN 1	SW 1	SW 1	SN 1	GW ◇	SN 1	SW 1	SW 1	SW 1	SN 1	GW ◇	SN 1	SW 1	GW ◇	SW 1	SN 1	GW ◇
Portsmouth Harbour	d	13 54		14 22			14 54		15 22			15 54		16 22			16 54	17 03		17 22				17 54		18 22
Portsmouth & Southsea	d	13 59		14 27		14 36	14 59		15 27		15 36	15 59		16 27		16 36	16 59	17 07		17 27		17 36		17 59		18 27
Fratton	d	14 03		14 31		14 40	15 03		15 31		15 40	16 03		16 31		16 40	17 03	17 11		17 31		17 40		18 03		18 31
Hilsea	d	14 07				14 44	15 07				15 44	16 07				16 44	17 07	17 15				17 44		18 07		
Havant	d		14 23		14 37			15 23		15 37			16 23		16 37				17 19		17 37		17 58		18 23	
Cosham	d	14 12	14 29	14 39	14 45	14 49	15 12	15 29	15 39	15 45	15 49	16 12	16 29	16 39	16 44	16 49	17 12	17 21	17 26	17 39	17 45	17 49	18 05	18 12	18 30	18 39
Portchester	d	14 17	14 33			14 54	15 17	15 33			15 54	16 17	16 33			16 54	17 17	17 25	17 30			17 54		18 17	18 34	
Fareham	a	14 22	14 38	14 46	14 52	14 59	15 22	15 38	15 46	15 52	15 59	16 22	16 38	16 46	16 52	16 59	17 22	17 30	17 35	17 46	17 52	17 59	18 12	18 22	18 39	18 46
	d		14 39	14 47	14 53	15 00		15 39	15 47	15 53	16 00		16 39	16 47	16 53	17 00			17 36	17 47	17 53	18 00	18 13		18 40	18 47
Swanwick	d		14 45		14 59	15 06		15 45		15 59	16 06		16 45			17 06			17 42		17 59	18 06			18 46	
Bursledon	d					15 10					16 10					17 10						18 10				
Hamble	d					15 13					16 13					17 13						18 13				
Netley	d					15 15					16 15					17 15			17 48			18 15				
Sholing	d					15 19					16 19					17 19						18 19				
Woolston	d					15 21					16 21					17 21			17 52			18 21				
Bitterne	d					15 25					16 25					17 25						18 25				
St Denys	d					15 28					16 28					17 28			17 57			18 28				
Southampton Central	a		15 02	15 08	15 18	15 36		16 02	16 08	16 18	16 36		17 02	17 08	17 28	17 36			18 03	18 08	18 19	18 36	18 38		19 05	19 08

		SN 1	SW 1	SW 1	SN 1	GW ◇	SN 1	SW 1	SW 1	SN 1	GW ◇	SN 1	SW 1	SW 1	SN 1	GW	SN 1	SW 1	SW 1	SW 1	SN 1	SW 1	SW 1	SW 1
Portsmouth Harbour	d			18 54		19 22			19 54		20 22			20 54		21 22			21 54					23 24
Portsmouth & Southsea	d		18 36	18 59		19 27		19 36	19 59		20 27		20 36	20 59		21 27		21 36	21 59			22 36		23 29
Fratton	d		18 40	19 03		19 31		19 40	20 03		20 31		20 40	21 03		21 31		21 40	22 03			22 40		23 33
Hilsea	d		18 44	19 07				19 44	20 07				20 44	21 07				21 44	22 07			22 44		23 37
Havant	d	18 37			19 22		19 38			20 25		20 37			21 26		21 37			22 05	22 26		22 59	
Cosham	d	18 44	18 49	19 12	19 30	19 39	19 45	19 49	20 12	20 33		20 44	20 49	21 12	21 33		21 44	21 49	22 12	22 16	22 33	22 49	23 08	23 42
Portchester	d		18 54	19 17	19 34			19 54	20 17			20 48	20 54	21 17	21 37			21 54	22 17	22 21		22 54	23 13	23 47
Fareham	a	18 52	18 59	19 22	19 39	19 46	19 52	19 59	20 22	20 41	20 46	20 53	20 59	21 22	21 42	21 46	21 52	21 59	22 22	22 26	22 42	22 59	23 18	23 52
	d	18 53	19 00		19 40	19 47	19 53	20 00		20 42	20 47	20 54	21 00		21 43	21 47	21 53	22 00			22 43	23 00		
Swanwick	d	18 59	19 06		19 46		19 59	20 06		20 48		21 00	21 06		21 49		21 59	22 06			22 49	23 06		
Bursledon	d		19 10					20 10					21 10					22 10				23 10		
Hamble	d		19 13					20 13					21 13					22 13				23 13		
Netley	d		19 15					20 15					21 15					22 15				23 15		
Sholing	d		19 19					20 19					21 19					22 19				23 19		
Woolston	d		19 21					20 21					21 21		21 58			22 21				23 21		
Bitterne	d		19 25					20 25					21 25					22 25				23 25		
St Denys	d		19 28					20 28					21 28		22 02			22 28				23 28		
Southampton Central	a	19 19	19 36		20 05	20 08	20 18	20 36		21 07	21 08	21 18	21 36		22 07	22 20	22 17	22 33			23 06	23 33		

For general notes see front of timetable
For details of catering facilities see Directory of Train Operators

Table 165

Saturdays

Portsmouth and Fareham → Southampton

Network Diagram - see first page of Table 165

		SW 1	SN 1	SW 1	SN 1	SW 1	GW ◇	SN 1	SN 1	SW 1		SW 1	GW ◇	SN 1	SN 1	SW 1	SW 1	SN 1	GW ◇	SN 1		SW 1	SW 1	SN 1	GW ◇	SN 1
Portsmouth Harbour	d					05 54	06 00					06 54	07 04				07 54		08 22				08 54		09 22	
Portsmouth & Southsea	d			05 16		05 59	06 04			06 36		06 59	07 08			07 36	07 59		08 27			08 36	08 59		09 27	
Fratton	d			05 20		06 03	06 08			06 40		07 03	07 13			07 40	08 03		08 31			08 40	09 03		09 31	
Hilsea	d			05 24		06 07				06 44		07 07				07 44	08 07					08 44	09 07			
Havant	d		05 14		05 39			06 23	06 37					07 23	07 37			08 23		08 37				09 23		09 37
Cosham	d	05 09	05 23	05 31	05 49	06 12	06 16	06 30	06 44	06 49		07 12	07 20	07 29	07 44	07 49	08 12	08 30	08 39	08 45		08 49	09 12	09 29	09 39	09 45
Portchester	d	05 14	05 27	05 35		06 17		06 34		06 54		07 17		07 33		07 54	08 17	08 34				08 54	09 17	09 33		
Fareham	a	05 19	05 32	05 40	05 57	06 22	06 26	06 39	06 52	06 59		07 22	07 28	07 38	07 52	07 59	08 22	08 39	08 46	08 52		08 59	09 22	09 38	09 46	09 52
	d		05 33	05 41	05 58		06 27	06 40	06 53	07 00			07 29	07 39	07 53	08 00		08 40	08 47	08 53		09 00		09 39	09 47	09 53
Swanwick	d		05 39	05 48	06 04			06 46	06 59	07 06				07 45	07 59	08 06		08 46		08 59		09 06		09 45		09 59
Bursledon	d			05 51						07 10						08 10						09 10				
Hamble	d			05 55						07 13						08 13						09 13				
Netley	d		05 45	05 57						07 15						08 15						09 15				
Sholing	d			06 01						07 19						08 19						09 19				
Woolston	d		05 49	06 03						07 21						08 21						09 21				
Bitterne	d			06 06						07 25						08 25						09 25				
St Denys	d			06 09						07 28						08 28						09 28				
Southampton Central	a		05 58	06 14	06 21		06 48	07 05	07 18	07 33			07 50	08 02	08 18	08 36		09 03	09 08	09 18		09 36		10 02	10 08	10 18

		SW 1	GW ◇	SW 1	SN 1	GW ◇	SN 1		SW 1	SW 1	SN 1	GW ◇	SN 1	SW 1	SW 1	SN 1	GW ◇		SN 1	SW 1	SW 1	SN 1	GW ◇	SN 1	SW 1	SW 1
Portsmouth Harbour	d			09 54		10 22				10 54		11 22			11 54		12 22				12 54		13 22			13 54
Portsmouth & Southsea	d	09 36		09 59		10 27			10 36	10 59		11 27		11 36	11 59		12 27			12 36	12 59		13 27		13 36	13 59
Fratton	d	09 40		10 03		10 31			10 40	11 03		11 31		11 40	12 03		12 31			12 40	13 03		13 31		13 40	14 03
Hilsea	d	09 44		10 07					10 44	11 07				11 44	12 07					12 44	13 07				13 44	14 07
Havant	d		10 00		10 23		10 37				11 23		11 37			12 23			12 37			13 23		13 37		
Cosham	d	09 49	10 06	10 12	10 29	10 39	10 45		10 49	11 12	11 29	11 39	11 45	11 49	12 12	12 29	12 39		12 45	12 49	13 12	13 29	13 39	13 45	13 49	14 12
Portchester	d	09 54		10 17	10 33				10 54	11 17	11 33			11 54	12 17	12 33				12 54	13 17	13 33			13 54	14 17
Fareham	a	09 59	10 14	10 22	10 38	10 46	10 52		10 59	11 22	11 38	11 46	11 52	11 59	12 22	12 38	12 46		12 52	12 59	13 22	13 38	13 46	13 52	13 59	14 22
	d	10 00	10 15		10 39	10 47	10 53		11 00		11 39	11 47	11 53	12 00		12 39	12 47		12 53	13 00		13 39	13 47	13 53	14 00	
Swanwick	d	10 06			10 45		10 59		11 06		11 45		11 59	12 06		12 45			12 59	13 06		13 45		13 59	14 06	
Bursledon	d	10 10							11 10					12 10						13 10					14 10	
Hamble	d	10 13							11 13					12 13						13 13					14 13	
Netley	d	10 15							11 15					12 15						13 15					14 15	
Sholing	d	10 19							11 19					12 19						13 19					14 19	
Woolston	d	10 21							11 21					12 21						13 21					14 21	
Bitterne	d	10 25							11 25					12 25						13 25					14 25	
St Denys	d	10 28							11 28					12 28						13 28					14 28	
Southampton Central	a	10 36	10 38		11 02	11 08	11 18		11 36		12 02	12 08	12 18	12 36		13 02	13 08		13 18	13 36		14 02	14 08	14 18	14 36	

		SN 1	GW ◇	SN 1		SW 1	SW 1	SN 1	GW ◇	SN 1	SW 1	SW 1	SN 1	GW ◇		SN 1	SW 1	SW 1	SW 1	SN 1	GW ◇	SN 1	SW 1	GW		SW 1
Portsmouth Harbour	d		14 22				14 54		15 22			15 54		16 22				16 54	17 01		17 22		17 32			17 54
Portsmouth & Southsea	d		14 27			14 36	14 59		15 27		15 36	15 59		16 27			16 36	16 59	17 06		17 27		17 36			17 59
Fratton	d		14 31			14 40	15 03		15 31		15 40	16 03		16 31			16 40	17 03	17 10		17 31		17 40			18 03
Hilsea	d					14 44	15 07				15 44	16 07					16 44	17 07	17 14				17 44			18 07
Havant	d	14 23		14 37				15 23		15 37			16 23			16 37				17 23		17 37		18 00		
Cosham	d	14 29	14 39	14 45		14 49	15 12	15 29	15 39	15 45	15 49	16 12	16 29	16 39		16 45	16 49	17 12	17 20	17 29	17 39	17 45	17 49	18 06		18 12
Portchester	d	14 33				14 54	15 17	15 33			15 54	16 17	16 33				16 54	17 17	17 25	17 33			17 54			18 17
Fareham	a	14 38	14 46	14 52		14 59	15 22	15 38	15 46	15 52	15 59	16 22	16 38	16 46		16 52	16 59	17 22	17 30	17 38	17 46	17 52	17 59	18 14		18 22
	d	14 39	14 47	14 53		15 00		15 39	15 47	15 53	16 00		16 39	16 47		16 53	17 00			17 39	17 47	17 53	18 00	18 15		
Swanwick	d	14 45		14 59		15 06		15 45		15 59	16 06		16 45			16 59	17 06			17 45		17 59	18 06			
Bursledon	d					15 10					16 10						17 10						18 10			
Hamble	d					15 13					16 13						17 13						18 13			
Netley	d					15 15					16 15						17 15						18 15			
Sholing	d					15 19					16 19						17 19						18 19			
Woolston	d					15 21					16 21						17 21						18 21			
Bitterne	d					15 25					16 25						17 25						18 25			
St Denys	d					15 28					16 28						17 28						18 28			
Southampton Central	a	15 02	15 08	15 18		15 36		16 02	16 08	16 18	16 36		17 02	17 08		17 18	17 36			18 02	18 08	18 18	18 36	18 38		

		SN 1	GW ◇	SN 1	SW 1	SW 1	SN 1	GW ◇	SN 1	SW 1		SW 1	SN 1	GW ◇	SN 1	SW 1	SW 1	SN 1	SN 1	SW 1	SW 1	SN 1	SW 1	SW 1		
Portsmouth Harbour	d		18 22			18 54		19 22				19 54		20 22			20 54				21 54			23 24		
Portsmouth & Southsea	d		18 27		18 36	18 59		19 27		19 36		19 59		20 27		20 36	20 59			21 36	21 59		22 36	23 29		
Fratton	d		18 31		18 40	19 03		19 31		19 40		20 03		20 31		20 40	21 03			21 40	22 03		22 40	23 33		
Hilsea	d				18 44	19 07				19 44		20 07				20 44	21 07			21 44	22 07		22 44	23 37		
Havant	d	18 23		18 37			19 23		19 37				20 26		20 37			21 23	21 37			22 26				
Cosham	d	18 29	18 39	18 45	18 49	19 12	19 29	19 39	19 45	19 49		20 12	20 32		20 45	20 49	21 12	21 29	21 45	21 49	22 12	22 33	22 49	23 42		
Portchester	d	18 33			18 54	19 17	19 33			19 54		20 17	20 36			20 54	21 17	21 33		21 54	22 17		22 54	23 47		
Fareham	a	18 38	18 46	18 52	18 59	19 22	19 38	19 46	19 52	19 59		20 22	20 41	20 45	20 52	20 59	21 22	21 38	21 52	21 59	22 22	22 41	22 59	23 52		
	d	18 39	18 47	18 53	19 00		19 39	19 47	19 53	20 00			20 42	20 48	20 53	21 00		21 39	21 53	22 00		22 42	23 00			
Swanwick	d	18 45		18 59	19 06		19 45		19 59	20 06			20 48		20 59	21 06		21 45	21 59	22 06		22 48	23 06			
Bursledon	d				19 10					20 10						21 10				22 10			23 10			
Hamble	d				19 13					20 13						21 13				22 13			23 13			
Netley	d				19 15					20 15						21 15				22 15			23 15			
Sholing	d				19 19					20 19						21 19				22 19			23 19			
Woolston	d				19 21					20 21						21 21				22 21			23 21			
Bitterne	d				19 25					20 25						21 25				22 25			23 25			
St Denys	d				19 28					20 28						21 28				22 28			23 28			
Southampton Central	a	19 02	19 08	19 18	19 36		20 02	20 08	20 18	20 36			21 05	21 10	21 18	21 37		22 02	22 18	22 34		23 05	23 33			

For general notes see front of timetable
For details of catering facilities see Directory of Train Operators

Table 165

Sundays

Portsmouth and Fareham → Southampton

Network Diagram - see first page of Table 165

		SW 1	GW 1 🛒	SW 1	SW 1	SW 1	SW 1	GW ◇ 🛒	SW 1	SW 1	SW 1	SW 1	GW ◇ 🛒	SW 1	SW 1	GW ◇	SW 1	SW 1	GW ◇ 🛒	SW 1	SW 1	GW ◇ 🛒	SW 1	SW 1	GW ◇ 🛒	SW 1
Portsmouth Harbour	d	06 37	07 08	07 17		08 17		09 08	09 17		10 17		11 08	11 17			12 17		13 08	13 17		14 08	14 17		15 08	15 17
Portsmouth & Southsea	d	06 42	07 12	07 22	07 42	08 22	08 42	09 12	09 22	09 42	10 22	10 42	11 12	11 22	11 42		12 22	12 42	13 12	13 22	13 42	14 12	14 22	14 42	15 12	15 22
Fratton	d	06 46	07 16	07 26	07 46	08 26	08 46	09 16	09 26	09 46	10 26	10 46	11 16	11 26	11 46		12 26	12 46	13 16	13 26	13 46	14 16	14 26	14 46	15 16	15 26
Hilsea	d	06 50		07 30	07 50	08 30	08 50		09 30	09 50	10 30	10 50		11 30	11 50		12 30	12 50		13 30	13 50		14 30	14 50		15 30
Havant	d															12 10										
Cosham	d	06 55	07 23	07 35	07 55	08 35	08 55	09 23	09 35	09 55	10 35	10 55	11 23	11 35	11 55	12b23	12 35	12 55	13 23	13 35	13 55	14 23	14 35	14 55	15 23	15 35
Portchester	d	07 00		07 40	08 00	08 40	09 00		09 40	10 00	10 40	11 00		11 40	12 00		12 40	13 00		13 40	14 00		14 40	15 00		15 40
Fareham	a	07 05	07 31	07 45	08 05	08 45	09 05	09 31	09 45	10 05	10 45	11 05	11 31	11 45	12 05	12 31	12 45	13 05	13 31	13 45	14 05	14 31	14 45	15 05	15 31	15 45
	d	07 06	07 32		08 06		09 06	09 32		10 06		11 06	11 32		12 06	12 32		13 06	13 32		14 06	14 32		15 06	15 32	
Swanwick	d	07 12			08 12		09 12			10 12		11 12			12 12			13 12			14 12			15 12		
Bursledon	d	07 16			08 16		09 16			10 16		11 16			12 16			13 16			14 16			15 16		
Hamble	d	07 19			08 19		09 19			10 19		11 19			12 19			13 19			14 19			15 19		
Netley	d	07 21			08 21		09 21			10 21		11 21			12 21			13 21			14 21			15 21		
Sholing	d	07 25			08 25		09 25			10 25		11 25			12 25			13 25			14 25			15 25		
Woolston	d	07 27			08 27		09 27			10 27		11 27			12 27			13 27			14 27			15 27		
Bitterne	d	07 31			08 31		09 31			10 31		11 31			12 31			13 31			14 31			15 31		
St Denys	d	07 34			08 34		09 34			10 34		11 34			12 34			13 34			14 34			15 34		
Southampton Central	a	07 40	07 53		08 40		09 40	09 53		10 40		11 40	11 53		12 40	12 53		13 40	13 53		14 40	14 53		15 40	15 53	

		SW 1	GW ◇ 🛒	SW 1	GW ◇	SW 1	GW ◇ 🛒	SW 1	SW 1	GW ◇ 🛒	SW 1	GW ◇	SW 1	GW ◇ 🛒	SW 1	SW 1	GW ◇ 🛒	SW 1	SW 1	SW 1	SW 1	GW ◇ 🛒	SW 1	SW 1	SW 1
Portsmouth Harbour	d		16 08	16 17			17 08	17 17		18 08	18 17			19 08	19 17		20 08	20 17		21 17		22 07	22 17		23 17
Portsmouth & Southsea	d	15 42	16 12	16 22		16 42	17 12	17 22	17 42	18 12	18 22		18 42	19 12	19 22	19 42	20 12	20 22	20 42	21 22	21 42	22 12	22 22	22 42	23 22
Fratton	d	15 46	16 16	16 26		16 46	17 16	17 26	17 46	18 16	18 26		18 46	19 16	19 26	19 46	20 16	20 26	20 46	21 26	21 46	22 16	22 26	22 46	23 26
Hilsea	d	15 50		16 30		16 50		17 30	17 50		18 30		18 50		19 30	19 50		20 30	20 50	21 30	21 50		22 30	22 50	23 30
Havant	d				16 48							18 48													
Cosham	d	15 55	16 23	16 35	16 55	16 58	17 23	17 35	17 55	18 23	18 35		18 55	19 23	19 35	19 55	20 23	20 35	20 55	21 35	21 55	22 23	22 35	22 55	23 35
Portchester	d	16 00		16 40		17 02		17 40	18 00		18 40		19 00		19 40	20 00		20 40	21 00	21 40	22 00		22 40	23 00	23 40
Fareham	a	16 05	16 31	16 45	17 02	17 07	17 31	17 45	18 05	18 31	18 45	19 00	19 05	19 31	19 45	20 05	20 31	20 45	21 05	21 45	22 05	22 31	22 45	23 05	23 45
	d	16 06	16 32		17 03	17 08	17 32		18 06	18 32		19 01	19 06	19 32		20 06	20 32		21 06		22 06	22 32		23 06	
Swanwick	d	16 12				17 14			18 12				19 12			20 12			21 12		22 12			23 12	
Bursledon	d	16 16				17 17			18 16				19 16			20 16			21 16		22 16			23 16	
Hamble	d	16 19				17 20			18 19				19 19			20 19			21 19		22 19			23 19	
Netley	d	16 21				17 22			18 21				19 21			20 21			21 21		22 21			23 21	
Sholing	d	16 25				17 26			18 25				19 25			20 25			21 25		22 25			23 25	
Woolston	d	16 27				17 28			18 27				19 27			20 27			21 27		22 27			23 27	
Bitterne	d	16 31				17 31			18 31				19 31			20 31			21 31		22 31			23 31	
St Denys	d	16 34				17 34			18 34				19 34			20 34			21 34		22 34			23 34	
Southampton Central	a	16 40	16 53		17 24	17 42	17 53		18 40	18 53		19 22	19 42	19 53		20 40	20 53		21 40		22 40	22 53		23 40	

For general notes see front of timetable
For details of catering facilities see
Directory of Train Operators

b Arr. 1216

To and from the Isle of Wight via Portsmouth and Ryde

Network Diagram - see first page of Table 165

Mondays to Fridays

Miles			IL	IL		IL	IL		IL	IL		IL	IL		IL	IL		IL	IL		IL	IL		IL	IL	IL
—	Portsmouth Harbour ⛴	d	05 15	05 45	.....	06 15	06 45	.....	07 15	07 45	.....	08 15	08 45	.....	09 15	09 45	.....	10 15	10 45	.....	11 15	11 45	.....	11 45	12 45	12 45
0	**Ryde Pier Head**	d	05 49	06 08		06 49	07 08		07 49	08 08		08 49	09 08		09 49	10 08		10 49	11 08		11 49	12 08		12 49	13 08	13 49
—	**Ryde Esplanade**	d	05 51	06 10		06 51	07 10		07 51	08 10		08 51	09 10		09 51	10 10		10 51	11 10		11 51	12 10		12 51	13 10	13 51
1¼	Ryde St Johns Road	d	05 54	06 13		06 54	07 13		07 54	08 13		08 54	09 13		09 54	10 13		10 54	11 13		11 54	12 13		12 54	13 13	13 54
2¼	Smallbrook Junction §	d																10 57	11 16		11 57	12 16		12 57	13 16	13 57
4½	Brading	d	06 02	06 21		07 02	07 21		08 02	08 21		09 02	09 21		10 02	10 21		11 02	11 21		12 02	12 21		13 02	13 21	14 02
6½	Sandown	d	06 06	06 25		07 06	07 25		08 06	08 25		09 06	09 25		10 06	10 25		11 06	11 25		12 06	12 25		13 06	13 25	14 06
7¼	Lake	d	06 09	06 28		07 09	07 28		08 09	08 28		09 09	09 28		10 09	10 28		11 09	11 28		12 09	12 28		13 09	13 28	14 09
8½	**Shanklin**	a	06 13	06 32		07 13	07 32		08 13	08 32		09 13	09 32		10 13	10 32		11 13	11 32		12 13	12 32		13 13	13 32	14 13

		IL		IL	IL		IL	IL		IL	IL		IL	IL		IL	IL		IL	IL	IL	IL	IL	IL		
Portsmouth Harbour ⛴	d	13 45	.....	13 45	14 45	.....	14 45	15 45	.....	16 15	16 45	.....	17 15	17 45	.....	18 15	18 45	.....	19 15	19 45	20 15	20 45	21 45	22 45	.....	
Ryde Pier Head	d	14 08		14 49	15 08		15 49	16 08		16 49	17 08		17 49	18 08		18 49	19 08		19 49	20 08	20 45	21 08	22 08	23 08		
Ryde Esplanade	d	14 10		14 51	15 10		15 51	16 10		16 51	17 10		17 51	18 10		18 51	19 10		19 51	20 10	20 47	21 10	22 10	23 10		
Ryde St Johns Road	d	14 13		14 54	15 13		15 54	16 13		16 54	17 13		17 54	18 13		18 54	19 13		19 54	20 13	20a50	21 13	22 13	23a13		
Smallbrook Junction §	d	14 16		14 57	15 16		15 57	16 16		16 57																
Brading	d	14 21		15 02	15 21		16 02	16 21		17 02	17 21		18 02	18 21		19 02	19 21		20 02	20 21		21 21	22 21			
Sandown	d	14 25		15 06	15 25		16 06	16 25		17 06	17 25		18 06	18 25		19 06	19 25		20 06	20 25		21 25	22 25			
Lake	d	14 28		15 09	15 28		16 09	16 28		17 09	17 28		18 09	18 28		19 09	19 28		20 09	20 28		21 28	22 28			
Shanklin	a	14 32		15 13	15 32		16 13	16 32		17 13	17 32		18 13	18 32		19 13	19 32		20 13	20 32		21 32	22 32			

Saturdays

		IL	IL		IL	IL		IL	IL		IL	IL		IL	IL		IL	IL		IL	IL		IL	IL		IL
Portsmouth Harbour ⛴	d	05 15	.....	.....	06 15	06 45	.....	07 15	07 45	.....	08 15	08 45	.....	09 15	09 45	.....	10 15	10 45	.....	11 15	11 45	.....	12 15	12 45	.....	13b15
Ryde Pier Head	d	05 49	06 08		06 49	07 08		07 49	08 08		08 49	09 08		09 49	10 08		10 49	11 08		11 49	12 08		12 49	13 08		13 49
Ryde Esplanade	d	05 51	06 10		06 51	07 10		07 51	08 10		08 51	09 10		09 51	10 10		10 51	11 10		11 51	12 10		12 51	13 10		13 51
Ryde St Johns Road	d	05 54	06 13		06 54	07 13		07 54	08 13		08 54	09 13		09 54	10 13		10 54	11 13		11 54	12 13		12 54	13 13		13 54
Smallbrook Junction §	d																10 57			11 57				13 16		13 57
Brading	d	06 02	06 21		07 02	07 21		08 02	08 21		09 02	09 21		10 02	10 21		11 02	11 21		12 02	12 21		13 02	13 21		14 02
Sandown	d	06 06	06 25		07 06	07 25		08 06	08 25		09 06	09 25		10 06	10 25		11 06	11 25		12 06	12 25		13 06	13 25		14 06
Lake	d	06 09	06 28		07 09	07 28		08 09	08 28		09 09	09 28		10 09	10 28		11 09	11 28		12 09	12 28		13 09	13 28		14 09
Shanklin	a	06 13	06 32		07 13	07 32		08 13	08 32		09 13	09 32		10 13	10 32		11 13	11 32		12 13	12 32		13 13	13 32		14 13

		IL	IL		IL	IL		IL	IL		IL	IL		IL	IL		IL	IL		IL	IL		IL	IL		
Portsmouth Harbour ⛴	d	13 45	14c15	.....	14 45	15 15	.....	15 45	16 15	.....	16 45	17 15	.....	17 45	18 15	.....	18 45	.....	.....	19 45	20 45	.....	21 45	22 45	.....	.....
Ryde Pier Head	d	14 08	14 49		15 08	15 49		16 08	16 49		17 08	17 49		18 08	18 49		19 08	19 49		20 08	21 08		22 08	23 08		
Ryde Esplanade	d	14 10	14 51		15 10	15 51		16 10	16 51		17 10	17 51		18 10	18 51		19 10	19 51		20 10	21 10		22 10	23 10		
Ryde St Johns Road	d	14 13	14 54		15 13	15 54		16 13	16 54		17 13	17 54		18 13	18 54		19 13	19 54		20 13	21 13		22 13	23a13		
Smallbrook Junction §	d	14 16	14 57			15 57		16 16																		
Brading	d	14 21	15 02		15 21	16 02		16 21	17 02		17 21	18 02		18 21	19 02		19 21	20 02		20 21	21 21		22 21			
Sandown	d	14 25	15 06		15 25	16 06		16 25	17 06		17 25	18 06		18 25	19 06		19 25	20 06		20 25	21 25		22 25			
Lake	d	14 28	15 09		15 28	16 09		16 28	17 09		17 28	18 09		18 28	19 09		19 28	20 09		20 28	21 28		22 28			
Shanklin	a	14 32	15 13		15 32	16 13		16 32	17 13		17 32	18 13		18 32	19 13		19 32	20 13		20 32	21 32		22 32			

Sundays

		IL	IL		IL A	IL		IL A	IL		IL A	IL		IL A	IL		IL A	IL		IL A	IL		IL A	IL		IL
Portsmouth Harbour ⛴	d	06 15	07 15	.....	.....	08 15	.....	08~45	09 15	.....	09~45	10 15	.....	10~45	11 15	.....	11~45	12 15	.....	12~45	13 15	.....	13~45	14 15	.....	14 45
Ryde Pier Head	d	06 49	07 49			08 49		09~08	09 49		10~08	10 49		11~08	11 49		12~08	12 49		13~08	13 49		14~08	14 49		15 08
Ryde Esplanade	d	06 51	07 51			08 51		09~10	09 51		10~10	10 51		11~10	11 51		12~10	12 51		13~10	13 51		14~10	14 51		15 10
Ryde St Johns Road	d	06 54	07 54		08~13	08 54		09~13	09 54		10~13	10 54		11~13	11 54		12~13	12 54		13~13	13 54		14~13	14 54		15 13
Smallbrook Junction §	d											10 57			11 57					13~16	13 57		14~16	14 57		
Brading	d	07 02	08 02		08~21	09 02		09~21	10 02		10~21	11 02		11~21	12 02		12~21	13 02		13~21	14 02		14~21	15 02		15 21
Sandown	d	07 06	08 06		08~25	09 06		09~25	10 06		10~25	11 06		11~25	12 06		12~25	13 06		13~25	14 06		14~25	15 06		15 25
Lake	d	07 09	08 09		08~28	09 09		09~28	10 09		10~28	11 09		11~28	12 09		12~28	13 09		13~28	14 09		14~28	15 09		15 28
Shanklin	a	07 13	08 14		08~32	09 13		09~32	10 13		10~32	11 13		11~32	12 13		12~32	13 13		13~32	14 13		14~32	15 13		15 32

		IL	IL		IL	IL		IL	IL		IL	IL		IL	IL		IL	IL		IL A
Portsmouth Harbour ⛴	d	15 15	15 45	.....	16 15	16 45	.....	17 15	17 45	.....	18 15	18 45	.....	19 15	19 45	.....	20 15	21 15	.....	22~15
Ryde Pier Head	d	15 49	16 08		16 49	17 08		17 49	18 08		18 49	19 08		19 49	20 08		20 49	21 49		22~46
Ryde Esplanade	d	15 51	16 10		16 51	17 10		17 51	18 10		18 51	19 10		19 51	20 10		20 51	21 51		22~48
Ryde St Johns Road	d	15 54	16 13		16 54	17 13		17 54	18 13		18 54	19 13		19 54	20a13		20 54	21 54		22a51
Smallbrook Junction §	d	15 57	16 16																	
Brading	d	16 02	16 21		17 02	17 21		18 02	18 21		19 02	19 21		20 02			21 02	22 02		
Sandown	d	16 06	16 25		17 06	17 25		18 06	18 25		19 06	19 25		20 06			21 06	22 06		
Lake	d	16 09	16 28		17 09	17 28		18 09	18 28		19 09	19 28		20 09			21 09	22 09		
Shanklin	a	16 13	16 32		17 13	17 32		18 13	18 32		19 13	19 32		20 13			21 13	22 13		

For general notes see front of timetable
For details of catering facilities see Directory of Train Operators

§ Smallbrook Jn is only open for access to The I.O.W. Steam Railway. For days of operation please enquire locally.

A Until 21 September
b From 27 September dep. 1245
c From 27 September dep. 1345

Mondays to Fridays

To and from the Isle of Wight via Portsmouth and Ryde

Network Diagram - see first page of Table 165

Miles			IL	IL		IL	IL		IL	IL		IL	IL		IL	IL		IL	IL		IL	IL		IL	IL	IL
0	**Shanklin**	d				06 17	06 36		07 17	07 36		08 17	08 36		09 17	09 36		10 17	10 36		11 17	11 36		12 17	12 36	13 17
1½	Lake	d				06 21	06 40		07 21	07 40		08 21	08 40		09 21	09 40		10 21	10 40		11 21	11 40		12 21	12 40	13 21
2	Sandown	d				06 24	06 43		07 24	07 43		08 24	08 43		09 24	09 43		10 24	10 43		11 24	11 43		12 24	12 43	13 24
3¾	Brading	d				06 28	06 47		07 28	07 47		08 28	08 47		09 28	09 47		10 28	10 47		11 28	11 47		12 28	12 47	13 28
6¼	Smallbrook Junction §	d																10 33	10 52		11 33	11 52		12 33	12 52	13 33
7¼	Ryde St Johns Road	d	05 36	05 55		06 36	06 55		07 36	07 55		08 36	08 55		09 36	09 55		10 36	10 55		11 36	11 55		12 36	12 55	13 36
8¼	**Ryde Esplanade**	d	05 39	05 58		06 39	06 58		07 39	07 58		08 39	08 58		09 39	09 58		10 39	10 58		11 39	11 58		12 39	12 58	13 39
8½	**Ryde Pier Head**	a	05 41	06 00		06 42	07 01		07 42	08 01		08 42	09 01		09 42	10 01		10 42	11 01		11 42	12 01		12 42	13 01	13 42
—	**Portsmouth Harbour**	⛴ a	*06 03*	*06 33*		*07 03*	*07 33*		*08 03*	*08 33*		*09 03*	*09 33*		*10 03*	*10 33*		*11 03*	*11 33*		*12 03*	*12 33*		*13 33*	*13 33*	*14 33*

		IL		IL	IL		IL	IL		IL	IL		IL	IL		IL	IL		IL	IL	IL	IL	IL	IL		
Shanklin	d	13 36		14 17	14 36		15 17	15 36		16 17	16 36		17 17	17 36		18 17	18 36		19 17	19 36	20 17	20 36	21 36	22 36		
Lake	d	13 40		14 21	14 40		15 21	15 40		16 21	16 40		17 21	17 40		18 21	18 40		19 21	19 40	20 21	20 40	21 40	22 40		
Sandown	d	13 43		14 24	14 43		15 24	15 43		16 24	16 43		17 24	17 43		18 24	18 43		19 24	19 43	20 24	20 43	21 43	22 43		
Brading	d	13 47		14 28	14 47		15 28	15 47		16 28	16 47		17 28	17 47		18 28	18 47		19 28	19 47	20 28	20 47	21 47	22 47		
Smallbrook Junction §	d	13 52		14 33	14 52		15 33	15 52		16 33	16 52															
Ryde St Johns Road	d	13 55		14 36	14 55		15 36	15 55		16 36	16 55		17 36	17 55		18 36	18 55		19 36	19 55	20 36	20 55	21 55	22 55		
Ryde Esplanade	d	13 58		14 39	14 58		15 39	15 58		16 39	16 58		17 39	17 58		18 39	18 58		19 39	19 58	20 39	20 58	21 58	22 58		
Ryde Pier Head	a	14 01		14 42	15 01		15 42	16 01		16 42	17 01		17 42	18 01		18 42	19 01		19 42	20 01	20 42	21 01	22 01	23 01		
Portsmouth Harbour	⛴ a	*14 33*		*15 33*	*15 33*		*16 33*	*16 33*		*17 03*	*17 33*		*18 03*	*18 33*		*19 03*	*19 33*		*20 03*	*20 33*	*21 03*	*21 33*	*22 33*	*23 33*		

Saturdays

		IL	IL		IL	IL		IL	IL		IL	IL		IL	IL		IL	IL		IL	IL		IL	IL		IL
Shanklin	d				06 17	06 36		07 17	07 36		08 17	08 36		09 17	09 36		10 17	10 36		11 17	11 36		12 17	12 36		13 17
Lake	d				06 21	06 40		07 21	07 40		08 21	08 40		09 21	09 40		10 21	10 40		11 21	11 40		12 21	12 40		13 21
Sandown	d				06 24	06 43		07 24	07 43		08 24	08 43		09 24	09 43		10 24	10 43		11 24	11 43		12 24	12 43		13 24
Brading	d				06 28	06 47		07 28	07 47		08 28	08 47		09 28	09 47		10 28	10 47		11 28	11 47		12 28	12 47		13 28
Smallbrook Junction §	d																	10 52			11 52			12 52		
Ryde St Johns Road	d	05 36	05 55		06 36	06 55		07 36	07 55		08 36	08 55		09 36	09 55		10 36	10 55		11 36	11 55		12 36	12 55		13 36
Ryde Esplanade	d	05 39	05 58		06 39	06 58		07 39	07 58		08 39	08 58		09 39	09 58		10 39	10 58		11 39	11 58		12 39	12 58		13 39
Ryde Pier Head	a	05 41	06 01		06 42	07 01		07 42	08 01		08 42	09 01		09 42	10 01		10 42	11 01		11 42	12 01		12 42	13 01		13 42
Portsmouth Harbour	⛴ a	*06 03*			*07 03*	*07 33*		*08 03*	*08 33*		*09 03*	*09 33*		*10 03*	*10 33*		*11 03*	*11 33*		*12 03*	*12 33*		*13 03*	*13 33*		*14b03*

		IL	IL		IL	IL		IL	IL		IL	IL		IL	IL		IL	IL		IL	IL	IL	IL	IL		
Shanklin	d	13 36	14 17		14 36	15 17		15 36	16 17		16 36	17 17		17 36	18 17		18 36	19 17		19 36	20 17	20 36	21 36	22 36		
Lake	d	13 40	14 21		14 40	15 21		15 40	16 21		16 40	17 21		17 40	18 21		18 40	19 21		19 40	20 21	20 40	21 40	22 40		
Sandown	d	13 43	14 24		14 43	15 24		15 43	16 24		16 43	17 24		17 43	18 24		18 43	19 24		19 43	20 24	20 43	21 43	22 43		
Brading	d	13 47	14 28		14 47	15 28		15 47	16 28		16 47	17 28		17 47	18 28		18 47	19 28		19 47	20 28	20 47	21 47	22 47		
Smallbrook Junction §	d							15 52																		
Ryde St Johns Road	d	13 55	14 36		14 55	15 36		15 55	16 36		16 55	17 36		17 55	18 36		18 55	19 36		19 55	20a36	20 55	21 55	22 55		
Ryde Esplanade	d	13 58	14 39		14 58	15 39		15 58	16 39		16 58	17 39		17 58	18 39		18 58	19 39		19 58		20 58	21 58	22 58		
Ryde Pier Head	a	14 01	14 42		15 01	15 42		16 01	16 42		17 01	17 42		18 01	18 42		19 01	19 42		20 01		21 01	22 01	23 01		
Portsmouth Harbour	⛴ a	*14 33*	*15c03*		*15 33*	*16 03*		*16 33*	*17 03*		*17 33*	*18 03*		*18 33*	*19 03*		*19 33*			*20 33*		*21 33*	*22 33*	*23 33*		

Sundays

		IL	IL		IL	IL A		IL	IL A		IL	IL A		IL	IL A		IL	IL A		IL	IL A		IL	IL A		IL A
Shanklin	d		07 17		08 17	08 36		09 17	09 36		10 17	10 36		11 17	11 36		12 17	12 36		13 17	13 36		14 17	14 36		
Lake	d		07 21		08 21	08 40		09 21	09 40		10 21	10 40		11 21	11 40		12 21	12 40		13 21	13 40		14 21	14 40		
Sandown	d		07 24		08 24	08 43		09 24	09 43		10 24	10 43		11 24	11 43		12 24	12 43		13 24	13 43		14 24	14 43		
Brading	d		07 28		08 28	08 47		09 28	09 47		10 28	10 47		11 28	11 47		12 28	12 47		13 28	13 47		14 28	14 47		
Smallbrook Junction §	d											10 52			11 52			12 52						14 52		
Ryde St Johns Road	d	06 36	07 36		08 36	08 55		09 36	09 55		10 36	10 55		11 36	11 55		12 36	12 55		13 36	13 55		14 36	14 55		14 55
Ryde Esplanade	d	06 39	07 39		08 39	08 58		09 39	09 58		10 39	10 58		11 39	11 58		12 39	12 58		13 39	13 58		14 39	14 58		14 58
Ryde Pier Head	a	06 42	07 42		08 42	09 01		09 42	10 01		10 42	11 01		11 42	12 01		12 42	13 01		13 42	14 01		14 42	15 01		15 01
Portsmouth Harbour	⛴ a	*07 03*	*08 03*		*09 03*	*09 33*		*10 03*	*10 33*		*11 03*	*11 33*		*12 03*	*12 33*		*13 03*	*13 33*		*14 03*	*14 33*		*15 03*			*15 33*

		IL	IL		IL	IL		IL	IL		IL	IL		IL	IL		IL	IL		IL						
Shanklin	d	15 17	15 36		16 17	16 36		17 17	17 36		18 17	18 36		19 17	19 36		20 17	21 17		22 17						
Lake	d	15 21	15 40		16 21	16 40		17 21	17 40		18 21	18 40		19 21	19 40		20 21	21 21		22 21						
Sandown	d	15 24	15 43		16 24	16 43		17 24	17 43		18 24	18 43		19 24	19 43		20 24	21 24		22 24						
Brading	d	15 28	15 47		16 28	16 47		17 28	17 47		18 28	18 47		19 28	19 47		20 28	21 28		22 28						
Smallbrook Junction §	d		15 52																							
Ryde St Johns Road	d	15 36	15 55		16 36	16 55		17 36	17 55		18 36	18 55		19 36	19 55		20 36	21 36		22 36						
Ryde Esplanade	d	15 39	15 58		16 39	16 58		17 39	17 58		18 39	18 58		19 39	19 58		20 39	21 39		22 39						
Ryde Pier Head	a	15 42	16 01		16 42	17 01		17 42	18 01		18 42	19 01		19 42	20 01		20 42	21 42		22 42						
Portsmouth Harbour	⛴ a	*16 03*	*16 33*		*17 03*	*17 33*		*18 03*	*18 33*		*19 03*	*19 33*		*20 03*	*20 33*		*21 03*	*22 03*		*23 03*						

For general notes see front of timetable
For details of catering facilities see Directory of Train Operators

§ Smallbrook Jn is only open for access to the I.O.W. Steam Railway. For days of operation please enquire locally.

A Until 21 September
b From 27 September arr. 1433
c From 27 September arr. 1533

London → East Croydon and Purley
COMPLETE SERVICE

		SN	SN	SN	SN	SN	FC	SN	SN	SN	FC	SN	SN	FC	FC	SN	FC	SN	FC	FC	SN		FC	FC	SN
		MX	MO	MO	MX	MX				MX	MX			MO	MX										
		1		1		1 ◇		1					1 ◇	1	1	1	1	1		1	1 ◇		1	1	1 ◇
London Victoria 15	⊖ d	23p47				00 05		00 14	00 17			00 42	01 00			02 00		03 00			04 00				05 02
Clapham Junction 10	d	23p53		00 02		00 11		00 20	00 23			00 49	01 08			02 08		03 08			04 08				05 08
London Charing Cross 4	⊖ d		23p36		23p45					00 12															
London Waterloo (East) 4	⊖ d		23p39		23p48					00 15															
St Pancras International 15	⊖ d						23p54				00 24			00 54	00 54		01 54		02 54	03 25			03 54	04 25	
Farringdon 3	⊖ d						23p59				00 29														
City Thameslink 3	d																								
London Blackfriars 3	⊖ d						00 04				00 34			01 04	01 04		02 04		03 04	03 34			04 04	04 34	
London Bridge 4	⊖ d		23p44		23p53		00 11			00 26	00 41														
Norwood Junction 2	a		00 09		00 16					00 49															
East Croydon	🚌 a	00 05	00 13	00 20	00 20	00 24	00 26	00 32	00 42	00 53	00 56	01 10	01 21	01 30	01 32	02 21	02 30	03 21	03 30	04 00	04 21		04 30	05 00	05 21
South Croydon 4	a		00 16		00 23																				
Purley Oaks	a		00 19		00 26																				
Purley 4	a	00 12	00 22		00 29			00 38					01 27			02 27		03 27			04 27				05 26

		FC	SN	FC	SN	FC	SN	SN	SN	FC	SN	SN	SN	SN	SN	FC	SN	SN	SN	FC		SN	SN	SN	FC
		1	1	1	1	1	1	1	1	1	1 ◇			1	1 ◇	1	1	1		1			1	1	1
London Victoria 15	⊖ d		05 32		05 23			06 02	06 17		06 21		06 15		06 32		06 47		06 45				07 02	07 06	
Clapham Junction 10	d		05 38		05 33			06 08	06 23		06 27		06 22		06 38		06 53		06 51				07 08	07 12	
London Charing Cross 4	⊖ d											06 05													
London Waterloo (East) 4	⊖ d											06 08													
St Pancras International 15	⊖ d	04 54		05 14		05 34				06 04						06 24				06 39					06 57
Farringdon 3	⊖ d	04 59		05 19		05 39				06 09						06 29				06 44					07 02
City Thameslink 3	d									06 11						06 31				06 47					07 07
London Blackfriars 3	⊖ d	05 04		05 24		05 44				06 14						06 36				06 50					07 10
London Bridge 4	⊖ d			05 31		05 50	05 55			06 21		06 13		06 30		06 43		06 56		07 00		06 54			07 16
Norwood Junction 2	a				05 49							06 37		06 44								07 14			
East Croydon	🚌 a	05 30	05 48	05 51	05 53	06 04	06 09	06 17	06 34	06 35	06 38	06 41	06 45	06 48	06 48	06 56	07 03	07 09	07 11	07 15		07 18	07 21	07 21	07 31
South Croydon 4	a				05 56							06 45										07 21			
Purley Oaks	a											06 48										07 24			
Purley 4	a		05 54					06 23			06 44	06 51	06 56		06 54							07 27		07 27	

		SN	SN	SN	SN	SN	SE	SN	SN	FC	SN	SN	SN	SN	SN	SN	SN	SN	SN		SN	SN	SN	FC	SN
							43																		
		1	1	1	1			1	1	1			1		1	1	1		1		1	1 ◇ 🍴	1	1	1
London Victoria 15	⊖ d	07 17		07 23		07 20			07 36				07 47		07 52			07 45	08 02			08 06			08 09
Clapham Junction 10	d	07 23		07 29		07 27			07 42				07 53		07 58			07 51	08 08			08 12			08 15
London Charing Cross 4	⊖ d																								
London Waterloo (East) 4	⊖ d																								
St Pancras International 15	⊖ d									07 17														07 48	
Farringdon 3	⊖ d									07 22														07 52	
City Thameslink 3	d									07 27														07 55	
London Blackfriars 3	⊖ d									07 32														08 00	
London Bridge 4	⊖ d		07 20		07 28		07 34	07 36		07 40	07 25	07 46		07 40		07 54	07 56				08 03		08 06		
Norwood Junction 2	a		07 32		07 41						07 48			08 00		08 06					08 14				
East Croydon	🚌 a	07 33	07 36	07 41	07 45	07 48	07 48	07 51	07 52	07 55	07 55	08 00	08 03	08 04	08 08	08 11	08 11	08 13	08 18		08 19	08 22	08 22	08 25	08 26
South Croydon 4	a					07 51								08 07				08 16							
Purley Oaks	a					07 54								08 10				08 19							
Purley 4	a					07 57			07 58		08 01			08 13				08 22			08 27				

		SN	SN	SN	FC	SN	SN	SN	SN	SN	SN	SN	SN	SN	SN	SN	SN	SN		SN	FC	SN	SN	SN	SN
				1	1	1	1	1			1 🍴	1	1 🍴		1 ◇			1 🍴		1	1	1		1	
London Victoria 15	⊖ d			08 17			08 20		08 15		08 32		08 36		08 38			08 47				08 53	08 45		
Clapham Junction 10	d			08 23			08 28		08 22		08 38		08 43		08 46			08 53				08 59	08 52		
London Charing Cross 4	⊖ d																								
London Waterloo (East) 4	⊖ d																								
St Pancras International 15	⊖ d				08 00																08 20				
Farringdon 3	⊖ d				08 04																08 24				
City Thameslink 3	d				08 09																08 27				
London Blackfriars 3	⊖ d				08 12																08 32				
London Bridge 4	⊖ d	08 05	08 09		08 19	08 23		08 25		08 27		08 30		08 21		08 41	08 36			08 49				09 00	08 37
Norwood Junction 2	a	08 25	08 28					08 37				08 44		08 49			08 56			09 01				09 11	09 13
East Croydon	🚌 a	08 29	08 32	08 33	08 36	08 37	08 39	08 41	08 43	08 45	08 48	08 49	08 52	08 53	08 56	08 57	09 00	09 03		09 05	09 06	09 09	09 13	09 15	09 17
South Croydon 4	a	08 32						08 44	08 47								09 03						09 16		
Purley Oaks	a	08 35							08 50								09 06						09 19		
Purley 4	a	08 38	08 41						08 53			08 58				09 04	09 09			09 12			09 22	09 27	09 25

For general notes see front of timetable
For details of catering facilities see Directory of Train Operators

London → East Croydon and Purley
COMPLETE SERVICE

		SN	SN	SN	FC	SE 13	SN	SN	SN	FC	SN	SN	SN	SN	SN	SN	FC		SN	SN	SN	SN	FC	SN	SN
		1 🛒	1	1 ◇ 🛒	1			1 🛒		1	1			1 🛒	1	1 ◇	1			1 🛒		1	1	1	
London Victoria 15	⊖ d	09 02		09 06				09 17			09 23	09 15		09 32		09 36				09 47				09 53	09 45
Clapham Junction 10	d	09 08		09 12				09 23			09 29	09 22		09 38		09 42				09 53		09 54		09 59	09 52
London Charing Cross 4	⊖ d																								
London Waterloo (East) 4	⊖ d																								
St Pancras International 15	⊖ d				08 47					09 04							09 20						09 39		
Farringdon 3	⊖ d				08 52					09 08							09 24						09 44		
City Thameslink 3	d				08 55					09 13							09 27						09 46		
London Blackfriars 3	⊖ d				08 58					09 17							09 34						09 49		
London Bridge 4	⊖ d		09 02		09 06	09 11	09 05		09 19	09 25			09 07		09 33		09 42		09 35		09 47		09 56		
Norwood Junction 2	a						09 25		09 31				09 43		09 45				09 55		09 59				
East Croydon	a	09 18	09 22	09 22	09 23	09 25	09 29	09 33	09 35	09 39	09 39	09 43	09 47	09 48	09 49	09 51	09 54		09 59	10 03	10 05	10 07	10 09	10 09	10 13
South Croydon 4	a						09 32					09 46							10 02						10 16
Purley Oaks	a						09 35					09 49							10 05						10 19
Purley 4	a						09 38		09 41			09 52	09 54		09 56				10 08		10 11				10 22

		SN	SN	SE 13	SN	SN	FC	SN	SN	SN		FC	SN	SN	SN	SN	SN	SN	FC	SN	SN	SN	SN	FC	SN
			1 🛒		1 ◇ 🛒	1	1		1 🛒			1	1			1 🛒	1	1 ◇ 🛒	1		1 🛒		1	1	1
London Victoria 15	⊖ d		10 02		10 06				10 17				10 23	10 15		10 32		10 36			10 47				10 53
Clapham Junction 10	d		10 08		10 12				10 23				10 29	10 22		10 38		10 42			10 53		10 54		10 59
London Charing Cross 4	⊖ d																					10 40			
London Waterloo (East) 4	⊖ d																					10 43			
St Pancras International 15	⊖ d						09 54					10 09							10 24					10 39	
Farringdon 3	⊖ d						09 59					10 14							10 29					10 44	
City Thameslink 3	d						10 01					10 16							10 31					10 46	
London Blackfriars 3	⊖ d						10 05					10 20							10 35					10 50	
London Bridge 4	⊖ d	09 37		10 03		10 08	10 11	10 05		10 17		10 26			10 08		10 33		10 41	10 35		10 48		10 56	
Norwood Junction 2	a	10 13		10 16				10 25		10 31					10 43		10 45			10 55					
East Croydon	a	10 17	10 18	10 19	10 22	10 22	10 24	10 29	10 33	10 35		10 39	10 39	10 43	10 47	10 48	10 49	10 52	10 54	10 59	11 03	11 05	11 07	11 09	11 09
South Croydon 4	a							10 32						10 46						11 02					
Purley Oaks	a							10 35						10 49						11 05					
Purley 4	a	10 24		10 26				10 38		10 41				10 52	10 54		10 56			11 08		11 11			

		SN	SN	SN	SE 13	SN	SN	FC	SN	SN	SN			FC	SN	SN	SN	SN	SN	SN	SN	FC	SN	SN
				1		1 ◇ 🛒	1	1		1 🛒				1	1			1	1	1 ◇ 🛒	1	1		1 🛒
London Victoria 15	⊖ d	10 45		11 02		11 06				11 17		and at			15 23	15 15		15 32		15 36				15 47
Clapham Junction 10	d	10 52		11 08		11 12				11 23					15 29	15 22		15 38		15 42				15 53
London Charing Cross 4	⊖ d										11 10	the same												
London Waterloo (East) 4	⊖ d										11 13	minutes												
St Pancras International 15	⊖ d							10 54				past		15 09								15 24		
Farringdon 3	⊖ d							10 59				each		15 14								15 29		
City Thameslink 3	d							11 01						15 16								15 31		
London Blackfriars 3	⊖ d							11 05				hour until		15 20								15 35		
London Bridge 4	⊖ d		10 38		11 03		11 08	11 11	11 05		11 18			15 26			15 08		15 33		15 38	15 41	15 35	
Norwood Junction 2	a		11 13		11 16				11 25								15 43		15 45				15 55	
East Croydon	a	11 13	11 17	11 18	11 19	11 22	11 22	11 24	11 29	11 33	11 35			15 39	15 39	15 43	15 47	15 48	15 49	15 52	15 52	15 54	15 59	16 03
South Croydon 4	a	11 16							11 32						15 42	15 46							16 02	
Purley Oaks	a	11 19							11 35							15 49							16 05	
Purley 4	a	11 22	11 24		11 26				11 38		11 41					15 52	15 54		15 56				16 08	

		SN	SN	FC	SN	SN	SN	SN	SE 13	SN	SN	FC		SN	SN	SN	SN	SN	FC	SN	SN	SN	SN	SN	SN
			1	1	1			1		1 🛒	1	1		1		1 🛒		1	1			1	1	1 🛒	1
London Victoria 15	⊖ d				15 53	15 45		16 02		16 06				16 10		16 17		16 23		16 15		16 32		16 36	
Clapham Junction 10	d		15 54		15 59	15 52		16 08		16 12				16 16		16 23		16 29		16 22		16 38		16 42	
London Charing Cross 4	⊖ d	15 40															16 08								
London Waterloo (East) 4	⊖ d	15 43															16 11								
St Pancras International 15	⊖ d			15 39								15 54							16 09						
Farringdon 3	⊖ d			15 44								15 59							16 14						
City Thameslink 3	d			15 46								16 01							16 16						
London Blackfriars 3	⊖ d			15 50								16 05							16 20						
London Bridge 4	⊖ d	15 48		15 56			15 38		16 03		16 08	16 11			16 05		16 16		16 26		16 07		16 33		16 38
Norwood Junction 2	a						16 13		16 16						16 25		16 29				16 43				16 50
East Croydon	a	16 05	16 07	16 09	16 09	16 13	16 17	16 18	16 19	16 22	16 23	16 24		16 28	16 29	16 33	16 34	16 39	16 40	16 43	16 47	16 48	16 50	16 52	16 54
South Croydon 4	a				16 12	16 16									16 32			16 42		16 46					
Purley Oaks	a					16 19									16 35					16 49					
Purley 4	a	16 11				16 22	16 24		16 26					16 34	16 38		16 41			16 52	16 54				17 00

For general notes see front of timetable
For details of catering facilities see Directory of Train Operators

London → East Croydon and Purley

COMPLETE SERVICE

		SN	FC	SN	SN	SN	SN	SE 13	SN	SN	SN		FC	SN	SN	SN	SN	SN	SN	SN	SN	SN	SN	SN	SN
		1 🍴	1		1 🍴	1	1				1		1	1	1	1	1	1	1 🍴		1 🍴	1	1	1	1
London Victoria 15	⊖ d	16 38			16 47		16 53		16 45		17 02			17 07		17 10			17 17		17 21	17 24			17 32
Clapham Junction 10	d	16 45			16 53		16 59		16 52		17 08			17 13		17 16			17 23		17 27	17 30			
London Charing Cross 4	⊖ d																								
London Waterloo (East) 4	⊖ d																								
St Pancras International 15	⊖ d		16 27																						
Farringdon 3	⊖ d		16 32																						
City Thameslink 3	d		16 34																						
London Blackfriars 3	⊖ d		16 37																						
London Bridge 4	⊖ d		16 46	16 35		16 53		16 57		16 59			17 08		17 10		17 13	17 17		17 19			17 30	17 32	
Norwood Junction 2	a			16 55						17 12										17 33					
East Croydon	a	16 55	16 59	16 59	17 03	17 07	17 09	17 11	17 13	17 16	17 18		17 20	17 23	17 24	17 26	17 27	17 31	17 33	17 37	17 37	17 40	17 44	17 46	17 47
South Croydon 4	a			17 02			17 12		17 22	17 19							17 30			17 40					
Purley Oaks	a			17 05					17 25	17 22										17 43					
Purley 4	a			17 08					17 28	17 25						17 33		17 37		17 46					

		FC	SN	SN	SN	SN	SN	SN	SN	SN		SN	FC	SN	SN	SN	SN	SN	FC	SN	SN	SN	SN	SN	SN
		1		1	1		1	1	1	1		1	1	1 🍴	1	1	1		1		1 🍴	1	1	1	1
London Victoria 15	⊖ d		17 34	17 37	17 40				17 47					17 53			18 02			18 04	18 07	18 10			
Clapham Junction 10	d		17 40	17 43	17 46		17 34		17 53					17 59						18 10	18 13	18 16		18 06	
London Charing Cross 4	⊖ d																								
London Waterloo (East) 4	⊖ d																								
St Pancras International 15	⊖ d	17 09											17 35						17 46						
Farringdon 3	⊖ d	17 14											17 40						17 50						
City Thameslink 3	d	17 16											17 42						17 53						
London Blackfriars 3	⊖ d	17 20											17 46						17 57						
London Bridge 4	⊖ d	17 32				17 39		17 46		17 50		17 52	17 52		17 59	18 03		18 01					18 12		18 16
Norwood Junction 2	a					17 53												18 15							
East Croydon	a	17 49	17 51	17 53	17 56	17 57	17 59	17 59	18 03	18 04		18 06	18 08	18 10	18 12	18 16	18 17	18 19	18 20	18 21	18 23	18 26	18 26	18 28	18 29
South Croydon 4	a		17 54			18 00												18 22		18 24					
Purley Oaks	a		17 57			18 03												18 25		18 27					
Purley 4	a		18 00		18 02	18 06												18 28		18 30		18 32			

		SN	SN	SN	FC	SN	SN	SN	SN		SN	FC	SN	SN	SN	SE 13	SN	SN	FC	SN	SN	SN	SN	FC	SN
		1 🍴	1		1	1	1		1 🍴		1	1	1		1 🍴		1	1	1		1 🍴	1 🍴	1	1	1
London Victoria 15	⊖ d	18 17	18 21			18 24		18 17	18 32				18 40		18 47					18 53	19 02	19 06			19 10
Clapham Junction 10	d	18 23	18 27			18 30		18 25	18 38				18 46		18 53		18 55			18 59	19 08	19 12			19 16
London Charing Cross 4	⊖ d																								
London Waterloo (East) 4	⊖ d																								
St Pancras International 15	⊖ d				18 09														18 39					18 54	
Farringdon 3	⊖ d				18 14														18 44					18 59	
City Thameslink 3	d				18 16														18 46					19 01	
London Blackfriars 3	⊖ d				18 20														18 49					19 04	
London Bridge 4	⊖ d			18 20	18 26		18 31				18 34	18 38		18 42		18 48		18 54	18 56				19 08	19 12	
Norwood Junction 2	a			18 35										18 56				19 05							
East Croydon	a	18 33	18 37	18 38	18 40	18 41	18 44	18 46	18 48		18 48	18 52	18 56	19 00	19 03	19 03	19 07	19 09	19 10	19 11	19 18	19 22	19 22	19 24	19 28
South Croydon 4	a			18 41			18 47	18 52						19 03				19 12		19 14					
Purley Oaks	a			18 44				18 55						19 06						19 17					
Purley 4	a			18 47				18 58			18 54		19 01	19 09						19 20					19 33

		SN	SN	FC	SN	SN	SN	SN		FC	SN	SN	SN	SN	SN	SN	SN	FC	SN	SN	SN	FC	SN	SN	SN
			1 🍴	1	1		1 🍴	1		1	1		1 🍴	1	1	1		1	1 🍴	1	1 ◇	1	1		1
London Victoria 15	⊖ d	19 00	19 17		19 23		19 32	19 36			19 40	19 31	19 47			19 53			20 02		20 06		20 10	20 01	20 17
Clapham Junction 10	d	19 08	19 23		19 29		19 38	19 42			19 46	19 38	19 53		19 54	19 59			20 08		20 12		20 16	20 08	20 23
London Charing Cross 4	⊖ d																19 37								
London Waterloo (East) 4	⊖ d																19 40								
St Pancras International 15	⊖ d			19 09						19 24								19 39				19 54			
Farringdon 3	⊖ d			19 14						19 29								19 44				19 59			
City Thameslink 3	d			19 16						19 31								19 47				20 01			
London Blackfriars 3	⊖ d			19 19						19 34								19 54				20 04			
London Bridge 4	⊖ d			19 27		19 15				19 41				19 52			19 45	20 01		20 05		20 11			
Norwood Junction 2	a					19 38								20 03			20 08			20 16					
East Croydon	a	19 30	19 33	19 39	19 39	19 42	19 48	19 52		19 54	19 58	19 59	20 03	20 06	20 07	20 09	20 12	20 14	20 19	20 19	20 22	20 23	20 28	20 29	20 33
South Croydon 4	a	19 34				19 45						20 02					20 15							20 32	
Purley Oaks	a	19 37				19 48						20 05					20 18							20 35	
Purley 4	a	19 41				19 51					20 03	20 08		20 11			20 21						20 33	20 38	

For general notes see front of timetable
For details of catering facilities see
Directory of Train Operators

London → East Croydon and Purley
COMPLETE SERVICE

		SN 1	SN 1	SN	SN 1	SN 1	SN 1 ◇		FC 1	SN 1	SN	SN 1	SN 1	SN 1	SN 1	SN	SN 1	SN 1	SN 1 ◇	FC 1	SN 1	SN	SN 1	SN 1	SN
London Victoria 15	⊖ d	20 23			20 32		20 36			20 40	20 30	20 47		20 53			21 02		21 06		21 10	21 00	21 17	21 23	
Clapham Junction 10	d	20 29			20 38		20 42			20 46	20 38	20 53	20 54	20 59			21 08		21 12		21 16	21 08	21 23	21 29	
London Charing Cross 4	⊖ d			20 07												20 37									21 07
London Waterloo (East) 4	⊖ d			20 10												20 40									21 10
St Pancras International 15	⊖ d								20 24											20 54					
Farringdon 3	⊖ d								20 29											20 59					
City Thameslink 3	d								20 31											21 01					
London Blackfriars 3	⊖ d								20 34											21 04					
London Bridge 4	⊖ d		20 28	20 15		20 35			20 41						20 58	20 45		21 05		21 11					21 15
Norwood Junction 2	a			20 38		20 46										21 08		21 16							21 38
East Croydon	a	20 39	20 40	20 42	20 48	20 49	20 52		20 54	20 58	20 59	21 03	21 07	21 09	21 10	21 12	21 18	21 19	21 22	21 24	21 28	21 29	21 33	21 39	21 42
South Croydon 4	a			20 45							21 02					21 15						21 32			21 45
Purley Oaks	a			20 48							21 05					21 18						21 35			21 48
Purley 4	a			20 51						21 03	21 08					21 21					21 33	21 38			21 51

		SN 1	SN 1	SN 1 ◇	FC 1	SN 1		SN	SN 1	SN 1	SN 1	SN	SN 1 ◇	SN 1	SN 1 ◇	FC 1	SN 1	SN	SN 1	SN 1	SN	SN 1	SN 1	SN 1	FC 1
London Victoria 15	⊖ d		21 32	21 36		21 40		21 30	21 47		21 53		22 02		22 06		22 10	22 00	22 17	22 23			22 32	22 36	
Clapham Junction 10	d		21 38	21 42		21 46		21 38	21 53	21 54	21 59		22 08		22 12		22 16	22 08	22 23	22 29			22 38	22 42	
London Charing Cross 4	⊖ d											21 37									22 07				
London Waterloo (East) 4	⊖ d											21 40									22 10				
St Pancras International 15	⊖ d				21 24											21 54									22 24
Farringdon 3	⊖ d				21 29											21 59									22 29
City Thameslink 3	d				21 31											22 01									22 31
London Blackfriars 3	⊖ d				21 34											22 04									22 34
London Bridge 4	⊖ d	21 28			21 41							21 45		22 05		22 11					22 15	22 28			22 41
Norwood Junction 2	a	21 39										22 08		22 16							22 38	22 40			
East Croydon	a	21 44	21 48	21 52	21 54	21 58		21 59	22 03	22 07	22 09	22 12	22 18	22 19	22 22	22 24	22 28	22 29	22 33	22 39	22 42	22 44	22 48	22 52	22 54
South Croydon 4	a							22 02				22 15						22 32			22 45				
Purley Oaks	a							22 05				22 18						22 35			22 48				
Purley 4	a					22 03		22 08				22 21					22 33	22 38			22 51				

		SN 1	SN	SN 1	SN 1		SN	SN 1	SN 1 ◇	SN 1 ◇	FC 1	SN 1	SN	SN 1	SN	SN 1	SN 1	FC 1	SN 1	SN 1	SN	FC			
London Victoria 15	⊖ d	22 40	22 30	22 47	22 53				23 02	23 06		23 10	23 00	23 17		23 24	23 32		23 47	23 49					
Clapham Junction 10	d	22 46	22 38	22 53	22 59				23 08	23 12		23 16	23 08	23 23		23 30	23 38		23 53	23 56					
London Charing Cross 4	⊖ d						22 37								23 07						23 45				
London Waterloo (East) 4	⊖ d						22 40								23 10						23 48				
St Pancras International 15	⊖ d										22 54							23 24				23 54			
Farringdon 3	⊖ d										22 59							23 29				23 59			
City Thameslink 3	d										23 01														
London Blackfriars 3	⊖ d										23 04							23 34				00 04			
London Bridge 4	⊖ d						22 45	23 00			23 11				23 15			23 41			23 53	00 11			
Norwood Junction 2	a						23 08	23 11							23 38						00 16				
East Croydon	a	22 58	22 59	23 03	23 09		23 12	23 16	23 18	23 22	23 24	23 28	23 29	23 33	23 42	23 42	23 51	23 56	00 05	00 09	00 20	00 26			
South Croydon 4	a		23 02				23 15						23 32		23 45						00 23				
Purley Oaks	a		23 05				23 18						23 35		23 48						00 26				
Purley 4	a	23 03	23 08				23 21					23 33	23 38		23 51				00 12		00 29				

Saturdays

		SN 1	SN	SN 1 ◇	FC	SN 1	SN	SN	FC	SN	SN 1 ◇		FC 1	SN 1	FC 1	SN 1	FC 1	SN 1 ◇	FC 1	FC 1	SN 1 ◇	FC 1		SN 1 ◇	SN 1
London Victoria 15	⊖ d	23p47		00 05		00 14	00 17			00 42	01 00			02 00		03 00		04 00			05 02			05 32	05 25
Clapham Junction 10	d	23p53		00 11		00 20	00 23			00 49	01 08			02 08		03 08		04 08			05 08			05 38	05 31
London Charing Cross 4	⊖ d		23p45					00 12																	
London Waterloo (East) 4	⊖ d		23p48					00 15																	
St Pancras International 15	⊖ d				23p54				00 24				00 54		01 54		02 54		03 54	04 23		04 54			
Farringdon 3	⊖ d				23p59				00 29													04 59			
City Thameslink 3	d																								
London Blackfriars 3	⊖ d				00 04				00 34				01 04		02 04		03 04		04 04	04 34		05 04			
London Bridge 4	⊖ d		23p53		00 11			00 26	00 41																
Norwood Junction 2	a		00 16					00 49																	05 47
East Croydon	a	00 05	00 20	00 24	00 26	00 32	00 42	00 53	00 56	01 10	01 21		01 32	02 21	02 30	03 21	03 30	04 21	04 30	05 00	05 21	05 32		05 48	05 51
South Croydon 4	a		00 23																						05 54
Purley Oaks	a		00 26																						
Purley 4	a	00 12	00 29			00 38					01 27			02 27		03 27		04 27			05 26			05 53	

For general notes see front of timetable
For details of catering facilities see Directory of Train Operators

Table 175

Saturdays

London → East Croydon and Purley
COMPLETE SERVICE

		FC	SN	SN	FC	SN	FC	SN	SN	SN	FC		SN	SN	SN	SN	FC	SN	SN	SN	FC	SN		SN	SN
		1	1	1	1	1	1	1		1	1		1		1 ◇	1	1	1			1	1			1
London Victoria 15	⊖ d			06 10		06 23		06 40						06 45	07 06			07 10				07 23		07 15	07 32
Clapham Junction 10	d			06 16		06 29		06 46		06 54				06 52	07 12			07 16				07 29		07 22	07 38
London Charing Cross 4	⊖ d																								
London Waterloo (East) 4	⊖ d																								
St Pancras International 15	⊖ d	05 34			06 04		06 24				06 39						06 54				07 09				
Farringdon 3	⊖ d	05 39			06 09		06 29				06 44						06 59				07 14				
City Thameslink 3	d																								
London Blackfriars 3	⊖ d	05 44			06 20		06 35				06 50						07 05				07 20				
London Bridge 4	⊖ d	05 50	06 08		06 26		06 41		06 47		06 56		06 50			07 08	07 11		07 05	07 18	07 26				
Norwood Junction 2	a								07 00										07 25	07 31					
East Croydon	a	06 04	06 22	06 27	06 39	06 39	06 54	06 57	07 05	07 07	07 09		07 09	07 13	07 22	07 22	07 24	07 28	07 29	07 34	07 39	07 39		07 43	07 48
South Croydon 4	a													07 16					07 32					07 46	
Purley Oaks	a													07 19					07 35					07 49	
Purley 4	a			06 33				07 03	07 11					07 22				07 36	07 38	07 41				07 52	

		SN	SN	FC	SN	SN	SN	SN	FC	SN	SN		SN	SN	SE 13	SN	SN	FC	SN	SN	SN	FC		SN	SN
		1	1 ◇	1		1		1	1	1				1		1 ◇	1	1		1		1		1	
London Victoria 15	⊖ d		07 36			07 47				07 53	07 45			08 02		08 06				08 17				08 23	08 15
Clapham Junction 10	d		07 42			07 53		07 54		07 59	07 52			08 08		08 12				08 23				08 29	08 22
London Charing Cross 4	⊖ d						07 40														08 10				
London Waterloo (East) 4	⊖ d						07 43														08 13				
St Pancras International 15	⊖ d			07 24					07 39									07 54				08 10			
Farringdon 3	⊖ d			07 29					07 44									07 59				08 14			
City Thameslink 3	d																								
London Blackfriars 3	⊖ d			07 35					07 50									08 05				08 20			
London Bridge 4	⊖ d	07 33		07 41	07 35		07 48		07 56				07 38		08 03		08 08	08 11	08 05		08 18	08 26			
Norwood Junction 2	a	07 45			07 55								08 13		08 16				08 25						
East Croydon	a	07 49	07 52	07 54	07 59	08 03	08 05	08 07	08 09	08 09	08 13		08 17	08 18	08 19	08 22	08 22	08 24	08 29	08 33	08 35	08 39		08 39	08 43
South Croydon 4	a				08 02						08 16								08 32						08 46
Purley Oaks	a				08 05						08 19								08 35						08 49
Purley 4	a	07 56			08 08		08 11				08 22		08 24		08 26				08 38		08 41				08 52

		SN	SN	SN	SN	FC	SN	SN	SN	SN	FC		SN	SN	SN	SN	SE 13	SN	SN	FC	SN	SN		SN	FC
			1	1	1 ◇	1		1 ⊥		1	1		1			1		1 ◇ ⊥	1	1		1 ⊥			1
London Victoria 15	⊖ d		08 32		08 36			08 47					08 53	08 45		09 02		09 06				09 17			
Clapham Junction 10	d		08 38		08 42			08 53		08 54			08 59	08 52		09 08		09 12				09 23			
London Charing Cross 4	⊖ d								08 40															09 10	
London Waterloo (East) 4	⊖ d								08 43															09 13	
St Pancras International 15	⊖ d					08 24					08 39									08 54					09 09
Farringdon 3	⊖ d					08 29					08 44									08 59					09 14
City Thameslink 3	d																			09 01					09 16
London Blackfriars 3	⊖ d					08 35					08 50									09 05					09 20
London Bridge 4	⊖ d	08 08		08 33		08 41	08 35		08 48		08 56				08 38		09 03		09 08	09 11	09 05			09 18	09 26
Norwood Junction 2	a	08 43		08 45			08 55								09 13		09 16				09 25				
East Croydon	a	08 47	08 48	08 49	08 52	08 54	08 59	09 03	09 05	09 07	09 09		09 09	09 13	09 17	09 18	09 19	09 22	09 22	09 24	09 29	09 33		09 35	09 39
South Croydon 4	a						09 02							09 16							09 32				
Purley Oaks	a						09 05							09 19							09 35				
Purley 4	a	08 54		08 56			09 08		09 11					09 22	09 24		09 26				09 38			09 41	

			SN	SN	SN	SN	SN	SN	FC	SN	SN	SN	SN	FC	SN	SN	SN	SN	SE 13	SN	SN	FC	SN	SN	SN
			1			1	1	1 ◇	1		1 ⊥		1	1	1			1 ⊥		1 ◇ ⊥	1	1		1 ⊥	
London Victoria 15	⊖ d		09 23	09 15		09 32		09 36			09 47				09 53	09 45		10 02		10 06				10 17	
Clapham Junction 10	d		09 29	09 22		09 38		09 42			09 53		09 54		09 59	09 52		10 08		10 12				10 23	
London Charing Cross 4	⊖ d											09 40													10 10
London Waterloo (East) 4	⊖ d											09 43													10 13
St Pancras International 15	⊖ d								09 24					09 39								09 54			
Farringdon 3	⊖ d								09 29					09 44								09 59			
City Thameslink 3	d								09 31					09 46								10 01			
London Blackfriars 3	⊖ d								09 35					09 50								10 05			
London Bridge 4	⊖ d				09 08		09 33		09 41	09 35		09 48		09 56			09 38		10 03		10 08	10 11	10 05		10 18
Norwood Junction 2	a				09 43		09 45			09 55							10 13		10 16				10 25		
East Croydon	a		09 39	09 43	09 47	09 48	09 49	09 52	09 54	09 59	10 03	10 05	10 07	10 09	10 09	10 13	10 17	10 18	10 19	10 22	10 22	10 24	10 29	10 33	10 35
South Croydon 4	a			09 46						10 02						10 16							10 32		
Purley Oaks	a			09 49						10 05						10 19							10 35		
Purley 4	a			09 52	09 54		09 56			10 08		10 11				10 22	10 24		10 26				10 38		10 41

		FC			SN	SN	SN	SN	SN	SN	FC	SN	SN	SN		SN	FC	SN	SN	SN	SE 13	SN	SN	FC
		1	and at		1			1	1	1 ◇ ⊥	1		1 ⊥			1	1	1		1 ⊥		1 ◇ ⊥	1	1
London Victoria 15	⊖ d		the same		18 23	18 15		18 32		18 36			18 47					18 53		19 02		19 06		
Clapham Junction 10	d				18 29	18 22		18 38		18 42			18 53			18 54		18 59		19 08		19 12		
London Charing Cross 4	⊖ d		minutes											18 40										
London Waterloo (East) 4	⊖ d													18 43										
St Pancras International 15	⊖ d	10 09	past								18 24						18 39							18 54
Farringdon 3	⊖ d	10 14									18 29						18 44							18 59
City Thameslink 3	d	10 16	each								18 31						18 46							19 01
London Blackfriars 3	⊖ d	10 20									18 35						18 50							19 04
London Bridge 4	⊖ d	10 26	hour until				18 08		18 33		18 41	18 35		18 48			18 56		18 45		19 03		19 08	19 11
Norwood Junction 2	a						18 43		18 45			18 55		19 03					19 08		19 16			
East Croydon	a	10 39			18 39	18 43	18 47	18 48	18 49	18 52	18 54	18 59	19 03	19 06		19 07	19 09	19 09	19 13	19 18	19 19	19 22	19 22	19 24
South Croydon 4	a					18 46						19 02		19 09					19 16					
Purley Oaks	a					18 49						19 05		19 12					19 19					
Purley 4	a					18 52	18 54		18 56			19 08		19 15					19 22		19 25			

For general notes see front of timetable
For details of catering facilities see
Directory of Train Operators

Table 175

London → East Croydon and Purley
COMPLETE SERVICE

		SN 1	SN	SN 1 🚲		FC 1	SN 1	SN	SN 1	SN 1	SN 1 ◇	FC 1	SN	SN 1 🚲	SN 1		FC 1	SN 1	SN	SN 1 🚲	SN 1 ◇	SN 1	FC 1	SN 1	SN
London Victoria 15	⊖ d	19 10	19 00	19 17			19 23		19 32		19 36		19 30	19 47				19 53		20 02	20 06			20 10	20 00
Clapham Junction 10	d	19 16	19 08	19 23			19 29		19 38		19 42		19 38	19 53	19 54			19 59		20 08	20 12			20 16	20 08
London Charing Cross 4	⊖ d							19 07											19 37						
London Waterloo (East) 4	⊖ d							19 10											19 39						
St Pancras International 15	⊖ d					19 09						19 24					19 39						19 54		
Farringdon 3	⊖ d					19 14						19 29					19 44						19 59		
City Thameslink 3	d					19 16						19 30					19 46						20 01		
London Blackfriars 3	⊖ d					19 20						19 35					19 50						20 04		
London Bridge 4	⊖ d					19 26		19 15		19 33		19 41					19 56		19 44			20 08	20 11		
Norwood Junction 2	a							19 38		19 45									20 08			20 19			
East Croydon	a	19 28	19 29	19 33		19 39	19 39	19 42	19 48	19 50	19 52	19 54	19 59	20 03	20 07		20 09	20 09	20 12	20 19	20 22	20 22	20 24	20 28	20 29
South Croydon 4	a		19 32					19 45					20 02						20 15						20 32
Purley Oaks	a		19 35					19 48					20 05						20 18						20 35
Purley 4	a	19 33	19 38					19 51		19 56			20 08						20 21					20 33	20 38

		SN 1	SN 1	SN		SN 1	SN 1 ◇	FC 1	SN 1	SN	SN 1	SN 1	SN 1	SN	SN 1 ◇		SN 1 ◇	SN 1	FC 1	SN 1	SN	SN 1	SN 1	SN	SN 1
London Victoria 15	⊖ d	20 17	20 23			20 32	20 36		20 40	20 30	20 47		20 53		21 02		21 06			21 10	21 00	21 17	21 23		21 32
Clapham Junction 10	d	20 23	20 29			20 38	20 42		20 46	20 38	20 53	20 54	20 59		21 08		21 12			21 16	21 08	21 23	21 29		21 38
London Charing Cross 4	⊖ d			20 07										20 37										21 07	
London Waterloo (East) 4	⊖ d			20 10										20 40										21 10	
St Pancras International 15	⊖ d							20 24											20 54						
Farringdon 3	⊖ d							20 29											20 59						
City Thameslink 3	d							20 31											21 01						
London Blackfriars 3	⊖ d							20 34											21 04						
London Bridge 4	⊖ d			20 15				20 41						20 45				21 08	21 11					21 15	
Norwood Junction 2	a			20 38										21 08				21 19						21 38	
East Croydon	a	20 33	20 39	20 42		20 48	20 52	20 54	20 58	20 59	21 03	21 07	21 09	21 12	21 18		21 22	21 22	21 24	21 28	21 29	21 33	21 39	21 42	21 48
South Croydon 4	a			20 45						21 02				21 15							21 32			21 45	
Purley Oaks	a			20 48						21 05				21 18							21 35			21 48	
Purley 4	a			20 51					21 03	21 08				21 21						21 33	21 38			21 51	

		SN 1 ◇	FC 1	SN 1		SN	SN 1	SN 1	SN 1	SN	SN 1 ◇	SN 1 ◇	SN 1	FC 1	SN 1		SN	SN 1	SN 1	SN	SN 1	SN 1 ◇	FC 1	SN 1	SN
London Victoria 15	⊖ d	21 36		21 40		21 30	21 47		21 53		22 02	22 06			22 10		22 00	22 17	22 23		22 32	22 36		22 40	22 30
Clapham Junction 10	d	21 42		21 46		21 38	21 53	21 54	21 59		22 08	22 12			22 16		22 08	22 23	22 29		22 38	22 42		22 46	22 38
London Charing Cross 4	⊖ d									21 37										22 07					
London Waterloo (East) 4	⊖ d									21 40										22 10					
St Pancras International 15	⊖ d		21 24											21 54									22 24		
Farringdon 3	⊖ d		21 29											21 59									22 29		
City Thameslink 3	d																								
London Blackfriars 3	⊖ d		21 34											22 04									22 34		
London Bridge 4	⊖ d		21 41							21 45			22 08	22 11						22 15			22 41		
Norwood Junction 2	a									22 08			22 19							22 38					
East Croydon	a	21 52	21 54	21 58		21 59	22 03	22 07	22 09	22 12	22 18	22 22	22 22	22 24	22 28		22 29	22 33	22 39	22 42	22 48	22 52	22 54	22 58	22 59
South Croydon 4	a					22 02				22 15							22 32			22 45					23 02
Purley Oaks	a					22 05				22 18							22 35			22 48					23 05
Purley 4	a			22 03		22 08				22 21					22 33		22 38			22 51				23 03	23 08

		SN 1	SN 1	SN		SN	SN 1 ◇	SN 1 ◇	FC 1	SN 1	SN	SN 1	SN 1	SN	SN 1		FC	SN 1	SN 1	SN	FC
London Victoria 15	⊖ d	22 47	22 53				23 02	23 06		23 10	23 00	23 17	23 24		23 32			23 47	23 49		
Clapham Junction 10	d	22 53	22 59				23 08	23 12		23 16	23 08	23 23	23 30		23 38			23 53	23 56		
London Charing Cross 4	⊖ d			22 37										23 07						23 45	
London Waterloo (East) 4	⊖ d			22 40										23 10						23 48	
St Pancras International 15	⊖ d								22 54								23 24				23 54
Farringdon 3	⊖ d								22 59								23 29				23 59
City Thameslink 3	d																				
London Blackfriars 3	⊖ d								23 04								23 34				00 04
London Bridge 4	⊖ d			22 45		23 00			23 11					23 15			23 41			23 53	00 16
Norwood Junction 2	a			23 08		23 11								23 38						00 16	
East Croydon	a	23 03	23 09	23 12		23 16	23 18	23 22	23 24	23 28	23 29	23 33	23 41	23 42	23 52		23 56	00 06	00 09	00 20	00 29
South Croydon 4	a			23 15							23 32			23 45						00 23	
Purley Oaks	a			23 18							23 35			23 48						00 26	
Purley 4	a			23 21						23 33	23 38			23 51				00 12		00 29	

For general notes see front of timetable
For details of catering facilities see
Directory of Train Operators

London → East Croydon and Purley
COMPLETE SERVICE

	SN 1	SN	SN 1	FC	SN 1	SN	SN		FC 1	SN	SN 1	SN 1	SN 1	SN 1	SN 1		SN 1 ◇	SN 1 ◇	SN 1	FC 1	SN A	SN 1	SN 1 ◇	SN 1
London Victoria 15 ⊖ d	23p47		00 05		00 14	00 17				00 42	01 00	02 00	03 00	04 00	05 02		05 47	06 32	07 02			07 22	07 32	07 34
Clapham Junction 10 d	23p53		00 11		00 20	00 23				00 49	01 08	02 08	03 08	04 08	05 08		05 53	06 38	07 08			07 28	07 38	07 40
London Charing Cross 4 ⊖ d		23p45					00 12																	
London Waterloo (East) 4 ⊖ d		23p48					00 15																	
St Pancras International 15 ⊖ d				23p54					00 24											06 54				
Farringdon 3 ⊖ d				23p59					00 29											06 59				
City Thameslink 3 d																								
London Blackfriars 3 ⊖ d				00 04					00 34											07 04				
London Bridge 4 ⊖ d		23p53		00 16			00 26		00 41											07 11	07 14			
Norwood Junction 2 a		00 16					00 49														07 26			
East Croydon a	00 06	00 20	00 24	00 29	00 32	00 42	00 53		00 56	01 10	01 21	02 21	03 21	04 21	05 22		06 05	06 51	07 23	07 26	07 30	07 42	07 50	07 53
South Croydon 4 a		00 23																						
Purley Oaks a		00 26																						
Purley 4 a	00 12	00 29			00 38						01 27	02 27	03 27	04 27	05 28			06 56	07 28		07 37			07 59

	FC 1		SN	SN 1	FC 1	SN A	SN 1	SN	SN 1		SN 1 ◇	SN 1	FC 1	SN 1 🚲	SN		SN 1	FC 1	SN A	SN 1	SN	SN 1	FC	SN 1 ◇ 🚲
London Victoria 15 ⊖ d				08 04			08 17		08 22		08 32	08 34		08 47			09 04			09 17		09 22		09 32
Clapham Junction 10 d				08 10			08 23		08 28		08 38	08 40		08 53			09 10			09 23		09 28		09 38
London Charing Cross 4 ⊖ d			07 34					08 04							08 34						09 04			
London Waterloo (East) 4 ⊖ d			07 37					08 07							08 37						09 07			
St Pancras International 15 ⊖ d	07 24				07 54								08 24					08 54					09 10	
Farringdon 3 ⊖ d	07 29				07 59								08 29					08 59					09 14	
City Thameslink 3 d																								
London Blackfriars 3 ⊖ d	07 34				08 04								08 34					09 04					09 19	
London Bridge 4 ⊖ d	07 41		07 44		08 11	08 14		08 14					08 41		08 44			09 11	09 14		09 14		09 26	
Norwood Junction 2 a			08 04			08 26		08 34							09 04				09 26		09 34			
East Croydon a	07 56		08 08	08 23	08 26	08 30	08 36	08 38	08 42		08 50	08 53	08 56	09 06	09 08		09 23	09 26	09 30	09 36	09 38	09 42	09 45	09 50
South Croydon 4 a			08 11					08 41							09 11						09 41			
Purley Oaks a			08 14					08 44							09 14						09 44			
Purley 4 a			08 17	08 29		08 37		08 47				08 59			09 17		09 29		09 37		09 47			

	SN 1	FC 1	SN 1 🚲	SN	FC 1	SN 1 ◇ A 🚲	and at the same minutes past each hour until		SN 1 🚲	FC 1	SN A	SN 1	SN	SN 1	FC 1		SN 1 ◇ 🚲	SN 1	FC 1	SN 1 🚲	SN	FC 1	SN 1 ◇
London Victoria 15 ⊖ d	09 34		09 47			10 02			16 04			16 17		16 22			16 32	16 34		16 47			17 02
Clapham Junction 10 d	09 40		09 53			10 07			16 10			16 23		16 28			16 38	16 40		16 53			17 07
London Charing Cross 4 ⊖ d				09 34									16 04								16 34		
London Waterloo (East) 4 ⊖ d				09 37									16 07								16 37		
St Pancras International 15 ⊖ d		09 24			09 40					15 54					16 10				16 24			16 40	
Farringdon 3 ⊖ d		09 29			09 44					15 59					16 14				16 29			16 44	
City Thameslink 3 d																							
London Blackfriars 3 ⊖ d		09 34			09 49					16 04					16 19				16 34			16 49	
London Bridge 4 ⊖ d		09 41		09 44	09 56					16 11	16 14		16 14		16 26				16 41		16 44	16 56	
Norwood Junction 2 a				10 04							16 26		16 34								17 04		
East Croydon a	09 53	09 56	10 06	10 08	10 15	10 20			16 23	16 26	16 30	16 36	16 38	16 42	16 45		16 50	16 53	16 56	17 06	17 08	17 15	17 20
South Croydon 4 a				10 11									16 41								17 11		
Purley Oaks a				10 14									16 44								17 14		
Purley 4 a	09 59			10 17					16 29		16 37		16 47					16 59			17 17		

	SN 1 🚲	FC 1		SN A	SN 1	SN	SN 1	FC	SN 1 ◇ 🚲	SN 1		FC 1	SN 1 🚲	SN	SN 1 ◇	SN 1 🚲	FC 1	SN A		SN 1	SN	SN 1	SN 1 ◇ 🚲	SN 1
London Victoria 15 ⊖ d	17 04				17 17		17 22		17 32	17 34			17 47		18 02	18 04				18 17		18 22	18 32	18 34
Clapham Junction 10 d	17 10				17 23		17 28		17 38	17 40			17 53		18 07	18 10				18 23		18 28	18 38	18 40
London Charing Cross 4 ⊖ d						17 04								17 34							18 04			
London Waterloo (East) 4 ⊖ d						17 07								17 37							18 07			
St Pancras International 15 ⊖ d		16 54						17 09				17 24					17 54							
Farringdon 3 ⊖ d		16 59						17 14				17 29					17 59							
City Thameslink 3 d																								
London Blackfriars 3 ⊖ d		17 04						17 19				17 34					18 04							
London Bridge 4 ⊖ d		17 11		17 14		17 14		17 26				17 41		17 44			18 11	18 14			18 14			
Norwood Junction 2 a				17 26		17 34								18 04				18 26			18 34			
East Croydon a	17 23	17 26		17 30	17 36	17 38	17 42	17 45	17 50	17 53		17 56	18 06	18 08	18 20	18 23	18 26	18 30		18 36	18 38	18 42	18 50	18 53
South Croydon 4 a						17 41								18 11							18 41			
Purley Oaks a						17 44								18 14							18 44			
Purley 4 a	17 29			17 37		17 47				17 59				18 17		18 29		18 37			18 47			18 59

For general notes see front of timetable
For details of catering facilities see
Directory of Train Operators

A Until 7 September

Table 175

Sundays

London → East Croydon and Purley
COMPLETE SERVICE

		FC 1	SN 1	SN	SN 1◇		SN 1	FC 1	SN	SN 1	SN	SN 1	SN 1◇		SN 1	FC 1	SN 1	SN	SN 1◇	SN 1	FC 1		SN	SN 1	SN
									A														A		
			🛒				🛒										🛒								
London Victoria 15	⊖ d		18 47		19 02		19 04			19 17		19 22	19 32		19 34		19 47		20 02	20 04				20 17	
Clapham Junction 10	d		18 53		19 07		19 10			19 23		19 28	19 38		19 40		19 53		20 07	20 10				20 23	
London Charing Cross 4	⊖ d			18 34							19 04							19 34							20 04
London Waterloo (East) 4	⊖ d			18 37							19 07							19 37							20 07
St Pancras International 15	⊖ d	18 24						18 54								19 24					19 54				
Farringdon 3	⊖ d	18 29						18 59								19 29					19 59				
City Thameslink 3	d																								
London Blackfriars 3	⊖ d	18 34						19 04								19 34					20 04				
London Bridge 4	⊖ d	18 41		18 44				19 11	19 14		19 14					19 41		19 44			20 11		20 14		20 14
Norwood Junction 2	a			19 04					19 26		19 34							20 04					20 26		20 34
East Croydon	a	18 56	19 06	19 08	19 20		19 23	19 26	19 30	19 36	19 38	19 42	19 50		19 53	19 56	20 06	20 08	20 20	20 23	20 26		20 30	20 36	20 38
South Croydon 4	a			19 11							19 41							20 11							20 41
Purley Oaks	a			19 14							19 44							20 14							20 44
Purley 4	a			19 17			19 29		19 37		19 47				19 59			20 17		20 29			20 37		20 47

		SN 1	SN 1◇	SN 1	FC 1	SN 1	SN		SN 1	FC 1	SN	SN 1	SN	SN 1	FC 1		SN 1◇	SN 1	FC 1	SN 1	SN	SN 1	FC 1		SN
											A														A
London Victoria 15	⊖ d	20 22	20 32	20 34		20 47			21 04			21 17		21 22			21 32	21 34		21 47		22 04			
Clapham Junction 10	d	20 28	20 38	20 40		20 53			21 10			21 23		21 28			21 38	21 40		21 53		22 10			
London Charing Cross 4	⊖ d						20 34						21 04								21 34				
London Waterloo (East) 4	⊖ d						20 37						21 07								21 37				
St Pancras International 15	⊖ d				20 24					20 54					21 10				21 24				21 54		
Farringdon 3	⊖ d				20 29					20 59					21 14				21 29				21 59		
City Thameslink 3	d																								
London Blackfriars 3	⊖ d				20 34					21 04					21 19				21 34				22 04		
London Bridge 4	⊖ d				20 41		20 44			21 11	21 14		21 14		21 26				21 41		21 44		22 11		22 14
Norwood Junction 2	a						21 04				21 26		21 34								22 04				22 26
East Croydon	a	20 42	20 50	20 53	20 56	21 06	21 08		21 23	21 26	21 30	21 36	21 38	21 42	21 47		21 50	21 53	21 56	22 06	22 08	22 23	22 26		22 30
South Croydon 4	a						21 11						21 41								22 11				
Purley Oaks	a						21 14						21 44								22 14				
Purley 4	a			20 59			21 17		21 29		21 37		21 47					21 59			22 17	22 29			22 37

		SN 1	SN	SN 1	SN 1◇	SN 1	FC 1	SN 1		SN	SN 1	FC 1	SN 1	SN	SN 1◇	FC		SN	SN	SN	FC				
London Victoria 15	⊖ d	22 17		22 22	22 32	22 34		22 47			23 04		23 17		23 32			23 47		23 49					
Clapham Junction 10	d	22 23		22 28	22 38	22 40		22 53			23 10		23 23		23 38			23 53		23 56					
London Charing Cross 4	⊖ d		22 04							22 34				23 04					23 34						
London Waterloo (East) 4	⊖ d		22 07							22 37				23 07					23 37						
St Pancras International 15	⊖ d						22 24					22 54				23 24					23 54				
Farringdon 3	⊖ d						22 29					22 59				23 29					23 59				
City Thameslink 3	d																								
London Blackfriars 3	⊖ d						22 34					23 04				23 34					00 04				
London Bridge 4	⊖ d		22 14				22 41			22 44		23 11		23 14		23 41			23 44		00 11				
Norwood Junction 2	a		22 37							23 07				23 37					00 09						
East Croydon	a	22 36	22 42	22 43	22 50	22 53	22 56	23 06		23 12	23 23	23 26	23 36	23 42	23 52	23 56		00 06	00 13	00 17	00 26				
South Croydon 4	a		22 45							23 15				23 45					00 16						
Purley Oaks	a		22 48							23 18				23 48					00 19						
Purley 4	a		22 51			22 59				23 21	23 28			23 51					00 22						

For general notes see front of timetable
For details of catering facilities see Directory of Train Operators

A Until 7 September

Purley and East Croydon → London
COMPLETE SERVICE

		SN	SN	SN	FC	SN	SN	SN	FC	SN	FC	SN	FC	SN	FC	SN	SN	SN	SN	FC	SN	SN	SN	SN	SN
		MO	MX																						
		1	1	1 ◇	1		1	1	1	1	1	1			1	1 ◇				1		1		1	
Purley [4]	d	23p50	23p49	00 11			01 22	02 22		03 22		04 22		05 07		05 23		05 39			06 00		06 03		
Purley Oaks	d																	05 42					06 06		
South Croydon [4]	d																	05 45					06 09		
East Croydon	d	23p56	23b58	00 17	00 36	00 49	01 28	02 28	02 47	03 28	03 47	04 28	04 47	05 13	05 17	05 29	05 34	05 48	05 51	06 02	06 07	06 10	06 12	06 15	06 17
Norwood Junction [2]	d													05 17			05 38		05 55				06 16		
London Bridge [4]	⊖ a				00 52									05 41	05 34				06 24	06 15			06 34		
London Blackfriars [3]	⊖ a				00 59				03 12		04 12		05 12		05 41					06 23					
City Thameslink [3]	a																			06 25					
Farringdon [3]	⊖ a												05 17		05 47					06 29					
St Pancras International [15]	⊖ a				01 07				03 21		04 21		05 21		05 51					06 33					
London Waterloo (East) [4]	⊖ a													05 46											
London Charing Cross [4]	⊖ a													05 49											
Clapham Junction [10]	a	00 10	00 11	00 29		01 02	01 40	02 40		03 40		04 47				05 48	05 58	06 08			06 17	06 25		06 25	06 37
London Victoria [15]	⊖ a	00 18	00 18	00 37		01 09	01 49	02 49		03 49		04 54				05 58	06 06	06 18			06 25			06 33	06 46

		SN	SN	SN	FC	SN	SN	SN	FC	SN	SN	SN	SE	FC	SN	SN	SN	SN	SN	SN	SN	SN	FC	SN	SN
													13												
		1		1	1	1		1	1		1	1		1		1	1		1			1	1	1	
Purley [4]	d		06 22	06 25			06 31						06 56				07 05	07 03			07 12				07 23
Purley Oaks	d						06 34											07 06			07 15				
South Croydon [4]	d						06 37			06 41								07 09			07 18				
East Croydon	d	06 23	06 28	06 31	06 32	06 34	06 40	06 42	06 44	06 45	06 57	06 59	07 02	07 02	07 05	07 08	07 10	07 12	07 16	07 17	07 21	07 21	07 24	07 26	07 29
Norwood Junction [2]	d		06 32				06 44											07 16							
London Bridge [4]	⊖ a	06 40	06 54		06 46		07 02		06 58			07 14	07 18	07 16	07 43	07 25		07 33				07 39		07 43	
London Blackfriars [3]	⊖ a				06 52				07 06					07 22									07 50		
City Thameslink [3]	a				06 55				07 09					07 25									07 55		
Farringdon [3]	⊖ a				06 59				07 12					07 28									07 58		
St Pancras International [15]	⊖ a				07 03				07 16					07 32									08 02		
London Waterloo (East) [4]	⊖ a																								
London Charing Cross [4]	⊖ a																								
Clapham Junction [10]	a			06 40		06 46		06 51		07 05	07 07						07 19		07 25	07 37	07 31				07 39
London Victoria [15]	⊖ a			06 47		06 54		07 00		07 16	07 17						07 28		07 34	07 47	07 40				07 48

		SN	SN	SN	SN	SN	SN	SN	SN	SN	SN	FC	SN	SN	SN	SN	SN	SN	SN	SN	SN	SN	SN	SN	SN
		1	1		1 [trolley]	1	1 [trolley]	1	1	1		1	1		1	1	1 [trolley]	1	1 [trolley]	1	1		1	1 [trolley]	1
Purley [4]	d			07 27				07 39			07 43			07 48						08 01		08 03			
Purley Oaks	d			07 30							07 46			07 51								08 06			
South Croydon [4]	d			07 33							07 49			07 54				08 01				08 09			
East Croydon	d	07 29	07 32	07 36	07 38	07 41	07 44	07 45	07 47	07 47	07 52	07 54	07 54	07 57	07 57	08 00	08 01	08 04	08 04	08 07	08 09	08 12	08 12	08 15	08 16
Norwood Junction [2]	d			07 41										08 01								08 17			
London Bridge [4]	⊖ a	07 46	07 48	08 01					08 03				08 11	08 16		08 18		08 20		08 24	08 26	08 31			08 35
London Blackfriars [3]	⊖ a											08 19													
City Thameslink [3]	a											08 25													
Farringdon [3]	⊖ a											08 29													
St Pancras International [15]	⊖ a											08 33													
London Waterloo (East) [4]	⊖ a																								
London Charing Cross [4]	⊖ a																								
Clapham Junction [10]	a				07 47	07 51	07 54	07 56		08 08	08 02				08 06		08 10		08 13				08 21	08 24	
London Victoria [15]	⊖ a				07 57	08 00	08 03	08 07			08 12				08 16		08 20		08 22				08 31	08 33	

		SN	SN	SN	SN	SN	SN	FC	SN	SN	SN	SN	SN	SN	FC	SN	SN	SN	SN	SE	SN	SN	FC	SN	SN
																				13					
				1	1 [trolley]	1	1	1	1	1	1		1 [trolley]	1	1	1	1 [trolley]		1 [trolley]			1	1	1	1
Purley [4]	d	08 08		08 16								08 25		08 32				08 36				08 48			
Purley Oaks	d	08 11										08 28						08 39							
South Croydon [4]	d	08 14				08 22						08 31				08 37		08 42						08 52	
East Croydon	d	08 17	08 18	08 22	08 24	08 25	08 27	08 28	08 30	08 30	08 32	08 34	08 34	08 37	08 38	08 40	08 44	08 45	08 47	08 48	08 50	08 53	08 54	08 56	09 00
Norwood Junction [2]	d											08 40						08 49							
London Bridge [4]	⊖ a			08 39	08 41		08 44		08 51		08 49	08 55				08 59		09 05		09 07		09 15	09 10		09 20
London Blackfriars [3]	⊖ a							08 52							09 08								09 18		
City Thameslink [3]	a							08 59							09 11								09 21		
Farringdon [3]	⊖ a							09 02							09 14								09 26		
St Pancras International [15]	⊖ a							09 06							09 18								09 33		
London Waterloo (East) [4]	⊖ a																								
London Charing Cross [4]	⊖ a																								
Clapham Junction [10]	a	08 27	08 38			08 37				08 40			08 43	08 49			08 53		08 56		09 10			09 07	
London Victoria [15]	⊖ a	08 35	08 48			08 46				08 49			08 52	08 58			09 02		09 07		09 20			09 16	

For general notes see front of timetable
For details of catering facilities see
Directory of Train Operators

b Previous night.
Arr. 2355

Purley and East Croydon → London

COMPLETE SERVICE

	SN	SN	SN	FC	SN	SN	SN	SN	SN	SN	SN	SN	SN	FC	SN	SN	SN	SE 13	SN	SN	SN	FC	SN	SN
	1			1	1	1	1			1	1	1		1	1		1		1	1		1		1
						🛒				🛒	🛒						🛒							
Purley [4] d			08 55		09 03			09 08	09 14				09 22			09 31		09 34			09 38		09 45	
Purley Oaks d			08 58					09 11					09 25								09 41			
South Croydon [4] d			09 01					09 14					09 28								09 44			
East Croydon 🚊 d	09 01	09 02	09 05	09 08	09 09	09 14	09 14	09 17	09 20	09 22	09 26	09 29	09 31	09 32	09 33	09 37	09 39	09 40	09 43	09 44	09 47	09 47	09 51	09 52
Norwood Junction [2] d			09 09						09 25				09 35										09 58	
London Bridge [4] ⊖ a		09 41	09 24						09 42				09 59	09 45	09 52	09 54		09 55				10 00	10 28	
London Blackfriars [3] ⊖ a				09 37										09 52								10 07		
City Thameslink [3] a				09 40										09 55								10 10		
Farringdon [3] ⊖ a				09 44										09 59								10 14		
St Pancras International [15] ⊖ a				09 48										10 03								10 18		
London Waterloo (East) [4] ⊖ a																								
London Charing Cross [4] ⊖ a																								
Clapham Junction [10] a	09 10				09 20	09 23	09 26	09 38		09 32	09 35	09 38					09 49		09 52	09 55	10 07			10 03
London Victoria [15] ⊖ a	09 19				09 29	09 33	09 37	09 48		09 42	09 44	09 48					09 58		10 00	10 05	10 14			

	SN	SN	FC	SN	SN	SN	SN	SN	SN	FC	SN	SE 13	SN	SN	SN	FC	SN	SN	SN	SN		SN	FC	SN
	1	1 ◇	1		1		1	1		1			1 ◇	1		1	1		1	1			1	
		🛒			🛒		🛒						🛒						🛒					
Purley [4] d	09 49			09 51		10 01			10 08		10 15	10 18			10 21			10 31				10 38		10 45
Purley Oaks d				09 54					10 11						10 24							10 41		
South Croydon [4] d				09 57					10 14						10 27							10 44		
East Croydon 🚊 d	09 55	09 56	09 57	10 00	10 00	10 07	10 12	10 14	10 17	10 17	10 21	10 24	10 24	10 29	10 30	10 32	10 33	10 37	10 40	10 44		10 47	10 47	10 51
Norwood Junction [2] d	09 59			10 04							10 28	10 28			10 34									10 58
London Bridge [4] ⊖ a	10 12		10 15	10 25		10 22				10 30	10 58	10 40			10 55	10 45	10 49	10 52					11 00	11 28
London Blackfriars [3] ⊖ a			10 22							10 37						10 52							11 07	
City Thameslink [3] a			10 25							10 40						10 55							11 10	
Farringdon [3] ⊖ a			10 29							10 44						10 59							11 14	
St Pancras International [15] ⊖ a			10 33							10 48						11 03							11 18	
London Waterloo (East) [4] ⊖ a						10 26												10 56						
London Charing Cross [4] ⊖ a						10 30												11 00						
Clapham Junction [10] a		10 05			10 09		10 21	10 25	10 37				10 33	10 38					10 49	10 55		11 07		
London Victoria [15] ⊖ a		10 13			10 16		10 28	10 35	10 44				10 40	10 45					10 58	11 05		11 14		

	SN	SN	SN	SN	SN	FC	SN	SN	SN	SN	FC	SN	SE 13	SN	SN	SN	FC	SN	SN	SN	SN		SN
	1	1	1 ◇		1	1		1	1		1			1 ◇	1		1	1		1	1		
			🛒					🛒						🛒	🛒					🛒			
Purley [4] d		10 49		10 51			11 01			11 08		11 15	11 18			11 21			11 31			and at	15 38
Purley Oaks d				10 54						11 11						11 24						the same	15 41
South Croydon [4] d				10 57						11 14						11 27						minutes	15 44
East Croydon 🚊 d	10 52	10 55	10 55	11 00	11 00	11 02	11 07	11 10	11 14	11 17	11 17	11 21	11 24	11 24	11 28	11 30	11 32	11 33	11 37	11 40	11 44	past	15 47
Norwood Junction [2] d		10 59		11 04								11 28	11 28			11 34						each	
London Bridge [4] ⊖ a		11 12		11 25		11 15	11 22				11 30	11 58	11 40			11 55	11 45	11 49	11 52			hour until	
London Blackfriars [3] ⊖ a						11 22					11 37						11 52						
City Thameslink [3] a						11 25					11 40						11 55						
Farringdon [3] ⊖ a						11 29					11 44						11 59						
St Pancras International [15] ⊖ a						11 33					11 48						12 03						
London Waterloo (East) [4] ⊖ a							11 26												11 56				
London Charing Cross [4] ⊖ a							11 30												12 00				
Clapham Junction [10] a	11 03		11 04		11 09			11 20	11 25	11 37				11 33	11 37					11 49	11 55		16 07
London Victoria [15] ⊖ a			11 11		11 16			11 27	11 35	11 44				11 40	11 44					11 58	12 02		16 14

	FC	SN	SN	SN	SN	SN	SN	FC	SN	SN	SN	SN	FC	SN	SE 13	SN	FC	SN	SN	SN	SN	SN	SN	SN
	1		1	1	1 ◇		1	1		1	1		1			1 ◇	1	1			1	1	1	1
					🛒		🛒			🛒						🛒		🛒					🛒	
Purley [4] d		15 45		15 49		15 51			16 01			16 08		16 15	16 18				16 21	16 31				
Purley Oaks d						15 54						16 11							16 24					
South Croydon [4] d						15 57						16 14							16 27					
East Croydon 🚊 d	15 47	15 51	15 52	15 55	15 55	16 00	16 00	16 02	16 07	16 12	16 14	16 17	16 17	16 21	16 24	16 24	16 27	16 30	16 31	16 37	16 38	16 39	16 42	16 44
Norwood Junction [2] d		15 58		15 59		16 04			16 11					16 28	16 28				16 35	16 41				16 48
London Bridge [4] ⊖ a	16 00	16 28		16 12		16 26		16 15	16 24					17 00	16 41		16 42		16 58	16 56		16 58		17 00
London Blackfriars [3] ⊖ a	16 07							16 24					16 48				16 53							
City Thameslink [3] a	16 10							16 28					16 52				16 56							
Farringdon [3] ⊖ a	16 14							16 31					16 56				17 01							
St Pancras International [15] ⊖ a	16 18							16 35					17 01				17 05							
London Waterloo (East) [4] ⊖ a																								
London Charing Cross [4] ⊖ a																								
Clapham Junction [10] a			16 03		16 04		16 11			16 21	16 25	16 37				16 33		16 39			16 47		16 51	
London Victoria [15] ⊖ a					16 11		16 20			16 29	16 32	16 44				16 41		16 46			16 56		16 58	

For general notes see front of timetable
For details of catering facilities see
Directory of Train Operators

Purley and East Croydon → London
COMPLETE SERVICE

	SN	FC 1	SN	SN 1	SN 1 🚲	SN 1	FC 1	SN	SN 1	SN	FC 1	SN 1 🚲	SN 1	SN	SN 1 🚲	SN 1	FC 1	SN 1 🚲	SN	SN	SN 1	SN 1	SN 1 🚲	SN 1
Purley 4 d	16 38		16 45			16 49		16 51		17 01				17 09		17 19			17 23	17 31				
Purley Oaks d	16 41							16 54						17 12					17 26					
South Croydon 4 d	16 44							16 57						17 15					17 29					
East Croydon d	16 47	16 47	16 51	16 52	16 55	16 55	16 57	17 00	17 01	17 07	17 09	17 12	17 14	17 18	17 25	17 25	17 27	17 30	17 32	17 37	17 38	17 39	17 41	17 44
Norwood Junction 2 d			16 56					17 04		17 11			17 18						17 36	17 41				17 49
London Bridge 4 ⊖ a		17 02	17 26					17 27		17 26	17 29		17 31						17 58	17 54		18 02		18 06
London Blackfriars 3 ⊖ a							17 25				17 36						17 56							
City Thameslink 3 a							17 28				17 38						18 08							
Farringdon 3 ⊖ a							17 31				17 41						18 11							
St Pancras International 15 ⊖ a							17 35				17 45						18 15							
London Waterloo (East) 4 ⊖ a																								
London Charing Cross 4 ⊖ a																								
Clapham Junction 10 a	17 07			17 03	17 04	17 07			17 10			17 21		17 38	17 34	17 37		17 40			17 47		17 50	
London Victoria 15 ⊖ a	17 14				17 11	17 14			17 20			17 28		17 48	17 43	17 45		17 50			17 56		17 57	

	FC 1	SN	SN 1	SN 1	SN 1 🚲	SN	SN 1 🚲	SN	SN 1	SE 13	SN 1 🚲	SN	FC 1	SN 1 🚲	SN 1	SN 1 🚲	FC 1	SN 1	SN	SN 1	SN 1	SN 1 🚲	SN	FC 1
Purley 4 d		17 39				17 49		17 56				18 08			18 19				18 26				18 38	
Purley Oaks d		17 42						17 59				18 11							18 29				18 41	
South Croydon 4 d		17 45						18 02				18 14							18 32				18 44	
East Croydon d	17 47	17 48	17 52	17 53	17 55	17 56	17 59	18 05	18 08	18 11	18 12	18 17	18 17	18 24	18 26	18 30	18 32	18 32	18 35	18 38	18 39	18 42	18 47	18 47
Norwood Junction 2 d				17 57				18 09											18 39					
London Bridge 4 ⊖ a	18 11			18 10				18 28	18 24	18 26							18 45	18 48	19 00	18 53				19 00
London Blackfriars 3 ⊖ a	18 19												18 49				18 55							19 07
City Thameslink 3 a	18 28												18 54				18 58							19 12
Farringdon 3 ⊖ a	18 31												18 57				19 01							19 15
St Pancras International 15 ⊖ a	18 35												19 01				19 05							19 19
London Waterloo (East) 4 ⊖ a																								
London Charing Cross 4 ⊖ a																								
Clapham Junction 10 a		18 08	18 02		18 04	18 07	18 10				18 21	18 38		18 33	18 37	18 41					18 48	18 51	19 07	
London Victoria 15 ⊖ a		18 15			18 11	18 14	18 20				18 28	18 45		18 40	18 45	18 50					18 56	18 59	19 14	

	SN 1	SN 1	SN 1	SN 1	SN 1	SN 1	FC 1	SN	SN 1 🚲	SN 1	SN	FC 1	SN 1	SN 1 ◇	SN 1	SN 1	FC 1	SN	SN 1	SN 1	SN	FC 1	SN 1	SN 1 ◇
Purley 4 d			18 49					19 01			19 08				19 19			19 29			19 38			
Purley Oaks d								19 04			19 11							19 32			19 41			
South Croydon 4 d								19 07			19 14							19 35			19 44			
East Croydon d	18 51	18 52	18 55	18 55	18 59	19 00	19 02	19 10	19 12	19 14	19 17	19 17	19 20	19 24	19 26	19 29	19 32	19 40	19 41	19 44	19 47	19 47	19 52	19 54
Norwood Junction 2 d			18 59					19 14										19 44						
London Bridge 4 ⊖ a			19 12		19 14		19 15	19 39				19 30	19 35				19 45	20 11				20 00		
London Blackfriars 3 ⊖ a							19 22					19 37					19 52					20 07		
City Thameslink 3 a							19 25					19 40					19 55					20 10		
Farringdon 3 ⊖ a							19 29					19 44					19 59					20 14		
St Pancras International 15 ⊖ a							19 33					19 48					20 03					20 18		
London Waterloo (East) 4 ⊖ a								19 45										20 16						
London Charing Cross 4 ⊖ a								19 49										20 20						
Clapham Junction 10 a	19 07	19 02		19 04		19 10			19 21	19 25	19 37			19 33	19 37	19 40			19 50	19 55	20 07		20 03	20 04
London Victoria 15 ⊖ a	19 14			19 11		19 17			19 29	19 33	19 45			19 40	19 44	19 47			19 59	20 02	20 14			20 11

	SN 1	SN 1 ◇	FC 1	SN 1	SN	SN 1	SN 1	SN	FC 1	SN 1 ◇	SN 1	SN	SN 1	FC 1	SN 1	SN	SN 1	SN 1	SN	FC 1	SN 1	SN 1	SN 1 ◇	SN 1
Purley 4 d	19 49				19 59			20 08			20 20	20 23				20 29			20 38					20 49
Purley Oaks d					20 02			20 11								20 32			20 41					
South Croydon 4 d					20 05			20 14								20 35			20 44					
East Croydon d	19 55	20 00	20 02	20 07	20 10	20 10	20 14	20 17	20 17	20 24	20 26	20 30	20 30	20 32	20 37	20 40	20 42	20 44	20 47	20 47	20 52	20 54	20 55	20 57
Norwood Junction 2 d					20 14							20 34				20 44								
London Bridge 4 ⊖ a			20 15	20 21	20 41				20 30			20 59		20 45	20 51	21 11				21 00		21 11		
London Blackfriars 3 ⊖ a			20 22						20 37					20 52						21 07				
City Thameslink 3 a			20 25						20 40					20 55						21 10				
Farringdon 3 ⊖ a			20 29						20 44					20 59						21 14				
St Pancras International 15 ⊖ a			20 33						20 48					21 03						21 18				
London Waterloo (East) 4 ⊖ a					20 46											21 16								
London Charing Cross 4 ⊖ a					20 50											21 20								
Clapham Junction 10 a	20 07	20 10				20 19	20 25	20 37		20 33	20 37		20 40				20 51	20 55	21 07		21 03		21 04	21 07
London Victoria 15 ⊖ a	20 14	20 20				20 28	20 32	20 45		20 40	20 46		20 50				20 59	21 05	21 14				21 11	21 14

For general notes see front of timetable
For details of catering facilities see Directory of Train Operators

Purley and East Croydon → London
COMPLETE SERVICE

	SN [1] ◇	FC [1]	SN	SN [1]	SN [1]	SN	FC [1]	SN [1] ◇	SN [1]	SN [1]	FC [1]	SN [1]
Purley [4] d			20 59			21 08			21 20			
Purley Oaks d			21 02			21 11						
South Croydon [4] d			21 05			21 14						
East Croydon d	21 00	21 02	21 10	21 10	21 14	21 17	21 17	21 24	21 26	21 30	21 32	21 33
Norwood Junction [2] d			21 14									
London Bridge [4] ⊖ a		21 15	21 41				21 30				21 45	21 49
London Blackfriars [3] ⊖ a		21 22					21 37				21 52	
City Thameslink [3] a		21 25					21 40				21 55	
Farringdon [3] ⊖ a		21 29					21 44				21 59	
St Pancras International [15] ⊖ a		21 33					21 48				22 03	
London Waterloo (East) [4] ⊖ a			21 46									
London Charing Cross [4] ⊖ a			21 50									
Clapham Junction [10] a	21 11			21 19	21 25	21 37		21 33	21 37	21 40		
London Victoria [15] ⊖ a	21 20			21 29	21 32	21 45		21 40	21 47	21 48		

	SN	SN [1]	SN [1]	SN	SN [1]	SN [1] ◇	SN [1]	SN [1] ◇	FC [1]	SN	SN [1]	SN [1]
Purley [4] d	21 29			21 38			21 49			21 59		
Purley Oaks d	21 32			21 41						22 02		
South Croydon [4] d	21 35			21 44						22 05		
East Croydon d	21 40	21 41	21 44	21 47	21 52	21 55	21b57	22 00	22 02	22 10	22 10	22 14
Norwood Junction [2] d	21 44									22 14		
London Bridge [4] ⊖ a	22 11								22 15	22 41		
London Blackfriars [3] ⊖ a									22 22			
City Thameslink [3] a									22 25			
Farringdon [3] ⊖ a									22 29			
St Pancras International [15] ⊖ a									22 33			
London Waterloo (East) [4] ⊖ a	22 16									22 46		
London Charing Cross [4] ⊖ a	22 20									22 50		
Clapham Junction [10] a		21 50	21 55	22 07	22 03	22 04	22 07	22 10			22 19	22 25
London Victoria [15] ⊖ a		21 58	22 05	22 14		22 11	22 14	22 20			22 27	22 35

	SN	SN [1]	SN [1] ◇	SN [1]	SN [1]	FC [1]	SN [1]	SN	SN [1]	SN [1]	SN	SN [1]
Purley [4] d	22 08			22 20				22 29			22 38	
Purley Oaks d	22 11							22 32			22 41	
South Croydon [4] d	22 14							22 35			22 44	
East Croydon d	22 17	22 17	22 24	22 26	22 30	22 32	22 33	22 40	22 41	22 44	22 47	22 52
Norwood Junction [2] d								22 44				
London Bridge [4] ⊖ a		22 32				22 45	22 49	23 11				
London Blackfriars [3] ⊖ a						22 52						
City Thameslink [3] a						22 55						
Farringdon [3] ⊖ a						22 59						
St Pancras International [15] ⊖ a						23 03						
London Waterloo (East) [4] ⊖ a								23 16				
London Charing Cross [4] ⊖ a								23 20				
Clapham Junction [10] a	22 37		22 33	22 37	22 40				22 50	22 55	23 07	23 03
London Victoria [15] ⊖ a	22 48		22 40	22 44	22 50				22 58	23 05	23 14	

	SN [1]	SN [1] ◇	FC [1]	SN	SN [1]	SN	SN [1]	FC [1]	SN	SN [1]		
Purley [4] d	22 52			22 59		23 08			23 34	23 49		
Purley Oaks d				23 02		23 11			23 37			
South Croydon [4] d				23 05		23 14			23 40			
East Croydon d	22 58	23 00	23 02	23 10	23 14	23 17	23 30	23 32	23a42	23c58		
Norwood Junction [2] d				23 14								
London Bridge [4] ⊖ a			23 15	23 38				23 45				
London Blackfriars [3] ⊖ a			23 22					23 52				
City Thameslink [3] a												
Farringdon [3] ⊖ a			23 28					23 58				
St Pancras International [15] ⊖ a			23 32					00 02				
London Waterloo (East) [4] ⊖ a				23 43								
London Charing Cross [4] ⊖ a				23 48								
Clapham Junction [10] a	23 07	23 10			23 25	23 37	23 42			00 11		
London Victoria [15] ⊖ a	23 14	23 20			23 35	23 45	23 52			00 18		

Saturdays

	SN [1]	SN [1] ◇	FC [1]	SN	SN [1]	SN [1]	FC [1]	SN [1]	FC [1]	SN [1]	FC [1]	FC [1]
Purley [4] d	23p49	00 11			01 22	02 22		03 22		04 22		
Purley Oaks d												
South Croydon [4] d												
East Croydon d	23e58	00 17	00 36	00 49	01 28	02 28	02 47	03 28	03 47	04 28	04 47	05 17
Norwood Junction [2] d												
London Bridge [4] ⊖ a			00 52									
London Blackfriars [3] ⊖ a			00 59				03 12		04 12		05 12	05 42
City Thameslink [3] a												
Farringdon [3] ⊖ a											05 17	05 47
St Pancras International [15] ⊖ a			01 07				03 21		04 21		05 21	05 51
London Waterloo (East) [4] ⊖ a												
London Charing Cross [4] ⊖ a												
Clapham Junction [10] a	00 11	00 29		01 02	01 40	02 40		03 40		04 41		
London Victoria [15] ⊖ a	00 18	00 37		01 09	01 49	02 49		03 49		04 49		

	SN [1] ◇	FC [1]	SN [1]	SN [1]	FC [1]	SN [1]	SN	SN [1] ◇	SN	SN	FC [1]	SN [1]
Purley [4] d	05 24		05 58			06 20	06 21			06 38		
Purley Oaks d							06 24			06 41		
South Croydon [4] d							06 27			06 44		
East Croydon d	05 29	05 42	06f07	06 10	06 17	06 27	06 30	06 41	06 43	06 47	06 47	06 53
Norwood Junction [2] d							06 34		06 49			
London Bridge [4] ⊖ a					06 31		06 55		07 14		07 01	
London Blackfriars [3] ⊖ a		06 07			06 37						07 07	
City Thameslink [3] a												
Farringdon [3] ⊖ a		06 13			06 41						07 13	
St Pancras International [15] ⊖ a		06 17			06 45						07 17	
London Waterloo (East) [4] ⊖ a												
London Charing Cross [4] ⊖ a												
Clapham Junction [10] a	05 49		06 18	06 22		06 37		06 50		07 07		07 03
London Victoria [15] ⊖ a	05 58		06 26			06 44		06 58		07 14		

	SN [1]	SN	SN	SN [1] ◇	SN [1]	SN		FC [1]	SE 13	SN [1] ◇	SN [1]	SN
Purley [4] d	06 49	06 51				07 08			07 18			07 21
Purley Oaks d		06 54				07 11						07 24
South Croydon [4] d		06 57				07 14						07 27
East Croydon d	06 55	07 00	07 05	07 10	07 14	07 17		07 17	07 24	07 24	07 28	07 30
Norwood Junction [2] d	06 59	07 04	07 10						07 28			07 34
London Bridge [4] ⊖ a	07 12	07 25	07 23					07 31	07 40			07 55
London Blackfriars [3] ⊖ a								07 37				
City Thameslink [3] a												
Farringdon [3] ⊖ a								07 43				
St Pancras International [15] ⊖ a								07 47				
London Waterloo (East) [4] ⊖ a			07 28									
London Charing Cross [4] ⊖ a			07 32									
Clapham Junction [10] a				07 19	07 25	07 37				07 33	07 37	
London Victoria [15] ⊖ a				07 27	07 32	07 44				07 40	07 44	

	FC [1]	SN [1]	SN	SN [1]	SN [1]	SN	FC [1]	SN [1]	SN [1]	SN [1] ◇	SN	SN [1]
Purley [4] d			07 31			07 38			07 49		07 51	
Purley Oaks d						07 41					07 54	
South Croydon [4] d						07 44					07 57	
East Croydon d	07 32	07 33	07 37	07 40	07 44	07 47	07 47	07 52	07 55	07 55	08 00	08 00
Norwood Junction [2] d									07 59		08 04	
London Bridge [4] ⊖ a	07 45	07 52	07 52				08 01		08 12		08 25	
London Blackfriars [3] ⊖ a	07 52						08 07					
City Thameslink [3] a												
Farringdon [3] ⊖ a	07 58						08 13					
St Pancras International [15] ⊖ a	08 02						08 17					
London Waterloo (East) [4] ⊖ a			07 56									
London Charing Cross [4] ⊖ a			08 00									
Clapham Junction [10] a				07 49	07 55	08 07		08 03		08 04		08 11
London Victoria [15] ⊖ a				07 57	08 02	08 14				08 11		08 18

For general notes see front of timetable
For details of catering facilities see
Directory of Train Operators

b Arr. 2154
c Arr. 2355
e Previous night. Arr. 2355
f Arr. 0602

Table 175

Saturdays

Purley and East Croydon → London

COMPLETE SERVICE

		FC	SN	SN	SN	SN	FC	SN	SE 13	SN	SN	SN	FC	SN		SN	SN	SN	SN	FC	SN	SN	SN	SN	SN
		1		1 trolley	1		1			1 ◇ trolley	1		1	1			1 trolley	1		1		1	1	1 ◇ trolley	
Purley 4	d		08 01			08 08		08 15	08 18			08 21				08 31			08 38		08 45		08 49		08 51
Purley Oaks	d					08 11						08 24							08 41						08 54
South Croydon 4	d					08 14						08 27							08 44						08 57
East Croydon	d	08 02	08 07	08 10	08 14	08 17	08 17	08 21	08 24	08 24	08 28	08 30	08 32	08 33	.	08 37	08 40	08 44	08 47	08 47	08 51	08 52	08 55	08 55	09 00
Norwood Junction 2	d							08 28	08 28			08 34									08 58		08 59		09 04
London Bridge 4	⊖ a	08 15	08 22				08 31	08 58	08 40			08 55	08 45	08 49		08 52				09 01	09 28		09 12		09 25
London Blackfriars 3	⊖ a	08 22					08 37						08 52							09 08					
City Thameslink 3	a																			09 10					
Farringdon 3	⊖ a	08 28					08 43						08 58							09 14					
St Pancras International 15	⊖ a	08 32					08 47						09 02							09 18					
London Waterloo (East) 4	⊖ a		08 26													08 56									
London Charing Cross 4	⊖ a		08 30													09 00									
Clapham Junction 10	a			08 19	08 25	08 37				08 33	08 37						08 49	08 55	09 07			09 03		09 04	
London Victoria 15	⊖ a			08 27	08 32	08 44				08 40	08 44						08 57	09 02	09 14					09 11	

		SN	FC	SN	SN	SN	SN	FC	SN	SE 13	SN	SN	SN	FC	SN	SN	SN	SN	SN	FC	SN		SN	SN	SN
		1	1		1 trolley	1		1			1 ◇ trolley	1 trolley		1	1		1 trolley	1		1			1	1	1 ◇ trolley
Purley 4	d			09 01			09 08		09 15	09 18			09 21			09 31			09 38		09 45			09 49	
Purley Oaks	d						09 11						09 24						09 41						
South Croydon 4	d						09 14						09 27						09 44						
East Croydon	d	09 00	09 02	09 07	09 10	09 14	09 17	09 17	09 21	09 24	09 24	09 28	09 30	09 32	09 33	09 37	09 40	09 44	09 47	09 47	09 51	.	09 52	09 55	09 55
Norwood Junction 2	d								09 28	09 28			09 34								09 58			09 59	
London Bridge 4	⊖ a		09 15	09 22				09 30	09 58	09 40			09 55	09 45	09 49	09 52				10 00	10 28			10 12	
London Blackfriars 3	⊖ a		09 22					09 37						09 52						10 07					
City Thameslink 3	a		09 25					09 40						09 55						10 10					
Farringdon 3	⊖ a		09 29					09 44						09 59						10 14					
St Pancras International 15	⊖ a		09 33					09 48						10 03						10 18					
London Waterloo (East) 4	⊖ a			09 26												09 56									
London Charing Cross 4	⊖ a			09 30												10 00									
Clapham Junction 10	a	09 11			09 19	09 25	09 37				09 33	09 37					09 49	09 55	10 07				10 03		10 04
London Victoria 15	⊖ a	09 18			09 27	09 32	09 44				09 40	09 44					09 57	10 02	10 14						10 11

		FC	SN	SN	SN	SN	SN	SN	FC	SN	SE 13	SN	SN	SN	FC	SN	SN	SN	SN	SN	SN	FC	SN	SN	SN
		1		1		1 trolley	1		1			1 ◇ trolley	1 trolley		1	1		1 trolley	1	1		1		1	1
Purley 4	d		09 51		10 01			10 08		10 15	10 18			10 21			10 31				10 38		10 45		10 49
Purley Oaks	d		09 54					10 11						10 24							10 41				
South Croydon 4	d		09 57					10 14						10 27							10 44				
East Croydon	d	09 57	10 00	10 00	10 07	10 10	10 14	10 17	10 17	10 21	10 24	10 24	10 28	10 30	10 32	10 33	10 37	10 38	10 42	10 44	10 47	10 47	10 51	10 52	10 55
Norwood Junction 2	d		10 04							10 28	10 28			10 34									10 58		10 59
London Bridge 4	⊖ a	10 15	10 25		10 22				10 30	10 58	10 40			10 55	10 45	10 49	10 52					11 00	11 28		11 12
London Blackfriars 3	⊖ a	10 22							10 37						10 52							11 07			
City Thameslink 3	a	10 25							10 40						10 55							11 10			
Farringdon 3	⊖ a	10 29							10 44						10 59							11 14			
St Pancras International 15	⊖ a	10 33							10 48						11 03							11 18			
London Waterloo (East) 4	⊖ a				10 26												10 56								
London Charing Cross 4	⊖ a				10 31												11 00								
Clapham Junction 10	a			10 11		10 19	10 25	10 37				10 33	10 37					10 47	10 51	10 55	11 07			11 03	
London Victoria 15	⊖ a			10 18		10 27	10 32	10 44				10 40	10 44					10 56	10 59	11 02	11 14				

		SN	SN	SN	FC		SN	SN	SN	SN	FC	SN	SE 13	SN	SN	SN	FC	SN	SN	SN	SN	SN	FC	SN	SN
		1 ◇ trolley		1	1			1 trolley	1		1			1 ◇ trolley	1 trolley		1	1		1 trolley	1		1		1
Purley 4	d		10 51				11 01			11 08		11 15	11 18			11 21			11 31			11 38		11 45	
Purley Oaks	d		10 54							11 11						11 24						11 41			
South Croydon 4	d		10 57							11 14						11 27						11 44			
East Croydon	d	10 55	11 00	11 00	11 02	.	11 07	11 10	11 14	11 17	11 17	11 21	11 24	11 24	11 28	11 30	11 32	11 33	11 37	11 40	11 44	11 47	11 47	11 51	11 52
Norwood Junction 2	d		11 04									11 28	11 28			11 34								11 58	
London Bridge 4	⊖ a		11 26		11 15		11 22				11 30	11 58	11 40			11 55	11 45	11 49	11 52				12 00	12 28	
London Blackfriars 3	⊖ a				11 22						11 37						11 52						12 07		
City Thameslink 3	a				11 25						11 40						11 55						12 10		
Farringdon 3	⊖ a				11 29						11 44						11 59						12 14		
St Pancras International 15	⊖ a				11 33						11 48						12 03						12 18		
London Waterloo (East) 4	⊖ a						11 26												11 56						
London Charing Cross 4	⊖ a						11 30												12 00						
Clapham Junction 10	a	11 04		11 11				11 19	11 25	11 37				11 33	11 37					11 49	11 55	12 07			12 03
London Victoria 15	⊖ a	11 11		11 18				11 27	11 32	11 44				11 40	11 44					11 57	12 02	12 14			

		SN	SN	SN	SN	FC			SN	SN	SN	SN	FC	SN	SE 13	SN	SN	SN	FC	SN	SN	SN	SN	SN
		1	1 ◇ trolley		1	1	and at			1 trolley	1		1			1 ◇ trolley	1 trolley		1	1		1 trolley	1	
Purley 4	d	11 49		11 51			the same		18 01			18 08		18 15	18 18			18 21			18 31			18 38
Purley Oaks	d			11 54								18 11						18 24						18 41
South Croydon 4	d			11 57			minutes					18 14						18 27						18 44
East Croydon	d	11 55	11 55	12 00	12 00	12 02		.	18 07	18 10	18 14	18 17	18 17	18 21	18 24	18 24	18 28	18 30	18 32	18 33	18 37	18 40	18 44	18 47
Norwood Junction 2	d	11 59		12 04			past							18 28	18 28			18 34						
London Bridge 4	⊖ a	12 12		12 25		12 15			18 22				18 30	18 58	18 40			18 55	18 45	18 49	18 52			
London Blackfriars 3	⊖ a					12 22	each						18 37						18 52					
City Thameslink 3	a					12 25							18 40						18 55					
Farringdon 3	⊖ a					12 29	hour until						18 44						18 59					
St Pancras International 15	⊖ a					12 33							18 48						19 03					
London Waterloo (East) 4	⊖ a								18 26												18 56			
London Charing Cross 4	⊖ a								18 30												19 00			
Clapham Junction 10	a		12 04		12 11					18 19	18 25	18 37				18 33	18 37					18 49	18 55	19 07
London Victoria 15	⊖ a		12 11		12 18					18 27	18 32	18 44				18 40	18 44					18 57	19 02	19 14

For general notes see front of timetable
For details of catering facilities see
Directory of Train Operators

Table 175

Saturdays

Purley and East Croydon → London
COMPLETE SERVICE

	FC 1	SN	SN 1	SN 1	SN 1 ◇	SN 1	FC 1	SN	SN	SN 1	SN 1	SN	FC 1	SN		SN 1 ◇	SN 1	SN 1	FC 1	SN 1	SN	SN 1	SN 1	SN
Purley 4 d		18 45		18 49				18 58	19 01			19 08		19 15			19 19				19 29			19 38
Purley Oaks d									19 04			19 11									19 32			19 41
South Croydon 4 d									19 07			19 14									19 35			19 44
East Croydon d	18 47	18 51	18 52	18 55	18 55	19 00	19 02	19 07	19 10	19 10	19 14	19 17	19 17	19 21		19 24	19 25	19 29	19 32	19 33	19 40	19 40	19 44	19 47
Norwood Junction 2 d		19 01		18 59					19 14					19 31							19 44			
London Bridge 4 ⊖ a	19 00	19 25		19 12			19 15	19 23	19 41				19 30	19 55					19 45	19 49	20 11			
London Blackfriars 3 ⊖ a	19 07						19 22						19 37						19 52					
City Thameslink 3 a	19 10						19 25						19 40						19 55					
Farringdon 3 ⊖ a	19 14						19 29						19 44						19 59					
St Pancras International 15 ⊖ a	19 18						19 33						19 48						20 03					
London Waterloo (East) 4 ⊖ a								19 28	19 46												20 16			
London Charing Cross 4 ⊖ a								19 31	19 51												20 21			
Clapham Junction 10 a			19 03		19 04	19 11				19 19	19 25	19 37				19 33	19 37	19 40				19 49	19 55	20 07
London Victoria 15 ⊖ a					19 11	19 18				19 27	19 32	19 45				19 40	19 44	19 48				19 57	20 02	20 15

	FC 1	SN 1	SN 1 ◇	SN 1	SN 1	FC 1	SN	SN 1	SN 1	SN	FC 1	SN 1 ◇	SN 1	SN 1	FC 1	SN 1	SN	SN 1	SN 1	SN	FC 1		SN 1	SN 1 ◇
Purley 4 d				19 49			19 59			20 08			20 20				20 29			20 38				
Purley Oaks d							20 02			20 11							20 32			20 41				
South Croydon 4 d							20 05			20 14							20 35			20 44				
East Croydon d	19 47	19 52	19 55	19 55	20 00	20 02	20 10	20 10	20 14	20 17	20 17	20 24	20 26	20 30	20 32	20 33	20 40	20 40	20 44	20 47	20 47		20 52	20 55
Norwood Junction 2 d							20 14										20 44							
London Bridge 4 ⊖ a	20 00					20 15	20 41				20 30				20 45	20 49	21 11				21 00			
London Blackfriars 3 ⊖ a	20 07					20 22					20 37				20 52						21 07			
City Thameslink 3 a	20 10					20 25					20 40				20 55									
Farringdon 3 ⊖ a	20 14					20 29					20 44				20 59						21 13			
St Pancras International 15 ⊖ a	20 18					20 33					20 48				21 03						21 17			
London Waterloo (East) 4 ⊖ a							20 46										21 16							
London Charing Cross 4 ⊖ a							20 51										21 21							
Clapham Junction 10 a		20 03	20 04	20 07	20 10			20 19	20 25	20 37		20 33	20 37	20 40				20 49	20 55	21 07			21 03	21 04
London Victoria 15 ⊖ a			20 11	20 14	20 17			20 27	20 32	20 45		20 40	20 44	20 50				20 57	21 02	21 15				21 11

	SN 1	SN 1 ◇	FC 1	SN	SN 1	SN 1	SN	FC 1	SN 1	SN 1	SN 1	FC 1	SN 1	SN	SN 1	SN 1	SN	SN 1	SN 1 ◇	SN 1	SN 1 ◇	FC 1	SN	SN 1
Purley 4 d	20 51			20 59			21 08			21 20				21 29			21 38			21 51			21 59	
Purley Oaks d				21 02			21 11							21 32			21 41						22 02	
South Croydon 4 d				21 05			21 14							21 35			21 44						22 05	
East Croydon d	20 57	21 00	21 02	21 10	21 10	21 14	21 17	21 17	21 24	21 26	21 30	21 32	21 33	21 40	21 40	21 44	21 47	21 52	21 55	21 57	22 00	22 02	22 10	22 10
Norwood Junction 2 d				21 14										21 44									22 14	
London Bridge 4 ⊖ a			21 15	21 41				21 30				21 45	21 49	22 11								22 15	22 41	
London Blackfriars 3 ⊖ a			21 22					21 37				21 52										22 22		
City Thameslink 3 a																								
Farringdon 3 ⊖ a			21 28					21 43				21 58										22 28		
St Pancras International 15 ⊖ a			21 32					21 47				22 02										22 32		
London Waterloo (East) 4 ⊖ a				21 46										22 16									22 46	
London Charing Cross 4 ⊖ a				21 51										22 21									22 51	
Clapham Junction 10 a	21 07	21 10			21 19	21 25	21 37		21 33	21 37	21 40				21 49	21 55	22 07	22 03	22 04	22 07	22 10			22 19
London Victoria 15 ⊖ a	21 14	21 20			21 27	21 32	21 45		21 40	21 44	21 48				21 57	22 02	22 15		22 11	22 14	22 18			22 27

	SN 1	SN	SN 1 ◇	SN 1	SN 1	FC 1		SN 1	SN	SN 1	SN 1	SN	SN 1	SN 1 ◇	FC 1	SN	SN 1	SN	SN 1	FC 1	SN	SN 1		
Purley 4 d		22 08		22 20					22 29			22 38	22 52			22 59		23 08			23 34	23 49		
Purley Oaks d		22 11							22 32			22 41				23 02		23 11			23 37			
South Croydon 4 d		22 14							22 35			22 44				23 05		23 14			23 40			
East Croydon d	22 14	22 17	22 24	22 26	22 30	22 32		22 33	22 40	22 40	22 44	22 47	22 58	23 00	23 02	23 10	23 14	23 17	23 30	23 32	23a42	23 56		
Norwood Junction 2 d									22 44							23 14								
London Bridge 4 ⊖ a						22 45		22 49	23 11						23 15	23 38				23 45				
London Blackfriars 3 ⊖ a						22 52									23 22					23 52				
City Thameslink 3 a																								
Farringdon 3 ⊖ a						22 58									23 28					23 58				
St Pancras International 15 ⊖ a						23 02									23 32					00 02				
London Waterloo (East) 4 ⊖ a									23 16							23 43								
London Charing Cross 4 ⊖ a									23 20							23 48								
Clapham Junction 10 a	22 25	22 37	22 33	22 37	22 40					22 49	22 55	23 07	23 07	23 10			23 25	23 37	23 42			00 11		
London Victoria 15 ⊖ a	22 32	22 45	22 40	22 44	22 48					22 57	23 02	23 14	23 14	23 17			23 32	23 45	23 52			00 18		

For general notes see front of timetable
For details of catering facilities see
Directory of Train Operators

Table 175

Sundays

Purley and East Croydon → London
COMPLETE SERVICE

		SN 1	SN 1 ◇	FC 1	SN	SN 1	SN 1	SN 1	SN 1	SN 1 ◇	FC 1	SN 1	FC 1	SN	SN	FC 1	SN 1 ◇	SN	SN	SN A	SN 1	FC 1	SN	SN 1
Purley 4	d	23p49	00 11			01 37	02 33	03 33	04 33	05 22		05 56			06 35					07 16	07 20		07 38	07 53
Purley Oaks	d														06 38								07 41	
South Croydon 4	d														06 41						07 24		07 44	
East Croydon	d	23p56	00 17	00 36	00 49	01 43	02 40	03 40	04 40	05 28	05 32	06 02	06 32	06 40	06 44	07 02	07 10	07 12	07 14	07 22	07 27	07 32	07 47	07 59
Norwood Junction 2	d														06 48			07 18		07 26			07 51	
London Bridge 4	⊖ a			00 52											07 12	07 15		07 42	07 48	07 38		07 45	08 12	
London Blackfriars 3	⊖ a			00 59							05 54		06 54			07 23						07 53		
City Thameslink 3	a																							
Farringdon 3	⊖ a												06 58			07 27						07 57		
St Pancras International 15	⊖ a			01 07							06 02		07 02			07 31						08 01		
London Waterloo (East) 4	⊖ a														07 17			07 47					08 17	
London Charing Cross 4	⊖ a														07 20			07 50					08 20	
Clapham Junction 10	a	00 11	00 29		01 02	01 53	02 52	03 52	04 52	05 48		06 14		07 00			07 24				07 40			08 08
London Victoria 15	⊖ a	00 18	00 37		01 09	02 05	03 05	04 05	05 05	05 58		06 22		07 08			07 31				07 48			08 16

		SN 1 ◇	FC 1	SN 1	SN	SN A	SN 1	SN 1	FC 1	SN 1	SN	SN 1 A	SN 1 ◇	FC 1	SN 1	SN	SN A	SN 1	SN 1	FC 1	SN 1 ◇ A	SN 1
Purley 4	d				08 08	08 16	08 18				08 38	08 53				09 08	09 16	09 18				
Purley Oaks	d				08 11						08 41					09 11						
South Croydon 4	d				08 14						08 44					09 14						
East Croydon	d	07 59	08 02	08 10	08 17	08 22	08 25	08 29	08 32	08 40	08 47	08 59	08 59	09 02	09 10	09 17	09 22	09 25	09 29	09 32	09 35	09 40
Norwood Junction 2	d				08 21	08 26					08 51					09 21	09 26					
London Bridge 4	⊖ a		08 15		08 42	08 38			08 45		09 12			09 15		09 42	09 38			09 45		
London Blackfriars 3	⊖ a		08 23						08 53					09 23						09 53		
City Thameslink 3	a																					
Farringdon 3	⊖ a		08 27						08 57					09 27						09 57		
St Pancras International 15	⊖ a		08 31						09 01					09 31						10 01		
London Waterloo (East) 4	⊖ a				08 47						09 17					09 47						
London Charing Cross 4	⊖ a				08 50						09 20					09 50						
Clapham Junction 10	a	08 11		08 24			08 37	08 41		08 54		09 08	09 11		09 24			09 37	09 41		09 47	09 54
London Victoria 15	⊖ a	08 18		08 31			08 46	08 48		09 01		09 16	09 18		09 31			09 46	09 48		09 53	10 01

		SN	SN 1	SN 1 ◇	FC 1	SN 1	FC	SN	SN A	SN 1	SN 1	FC 1	SN 1 ◇ A	SN 1	FC 1		SN	SN 1	SN 1 ◇	FC 1	SN 1	FC 1
Purley 4	d	09 38	09 53					10 08	10 16	10 18						and at	15 38	15 53				
Purley Oaks	d	09 41						10 11									15 41					
South Croydon 4	d	09 44						10 14									15 44					
East Croydon	d	09 47	09 59	09 59	10 02	10 10	10 12	10 17	10 22	10 25	10 29	10 32	10 35	10 40	10 42	the same	15 47	15 59	15 59	16 02	16 10	16 12
Norwood Junction 2	d	09 51						10 21	10 26							minutes	15 51					
London Bridge 4	⊖ a	10 12			10 15		10 30	10 42	10 38			10 45			11 00	past	16 12			16 15		16 30
London Blackfriars 3	⊖ a				10 23		10 37					10 53			11 07	each				16 23		16 37
City Thameslink 3	a																					
Farringdon 3	⊖ a				10 27		10 43					10 57			11 13	hour until				16 27		16 43
St Pancras International 15	⊖ a				10 31		10 47					11 01			11 17					16 31		16 47
London Waterloo (East) 4	⊖ a	10 17						10 47									16 17					
London Charing Cross 4	⊖ a	10 20						10 50									16 20					
Clapham Junction 10	a		10 08	10 11		10 24				10 37	10 41		10 47	10 54				16 08	16 11		16 24	
London Victoria 15	⊖ a		10 16	10 18		10 31				10 46	10 48		10 53	11 01				16 16	16 18		16 31	

		SN	SN A	SN 1	SN 1	FC 1	SN 1 ◇	SN 1	FC 1	SN	SN 1	SN 1 ◇	FC 1	SN 1	FC 1	SN	SN A	SN 1	SN 1	FC 1	SN 1 ◇	SN 1	FC 1	SN
Purley 4	d	16 08	16 16	16 18						16 38	16 53					17 08	17 16	17 18						
Purley Oaks	d	16 11								16 41						17 11								
South Croydon 4	d	16 14								16 44						17 14								
East Croydon	d	16 17	16 22	16 25	16 29	16 32	16 35	16 40	16 42	16 47	16 59	16 59	17 02	17 10	17 12	17 17	17 22	17 25	17 29	17 32	17 35	17 40	17 42	17 44
Norwood Junction 2	d	16 21	16 26							16 51						17 21	17 26							
London Bridge 4	⊖ a	16 42	16 38			16 45			17 00	17 12			17 15		17 30	17 42	17 38			17 45			18 00	18 18
London Blackfriars 3	⊖ a					16 53			17 07				17 23		17 37					17 53			18 07	
City Thameslink 3	a																							
Farringdon 3	⊖ a					16 57			17 13				17 27		17 43					17 57			18 13	
St Pancras International 15	⊖ a					17 01			17 17				17 31		17 47					18 01			18 17	
London Waterloo (East) 4	⊖ a	16 47								17 17						17 47								
London Charing Cross 4	⊖ a	16 50								17 20						17 50								
Clapham Junction 10	a			16 37	16 41		16 47	16 54			17 08	17 11		17 24				17 37	17 41		17 47	17 54		
London Victoria 15	⊖ a			16 46	16 48		16 53	17 01			17 16	17 18		17 31				17 46	17 48		17 53	18 01		

For general notes see front of timetable
For details of catering facilities see Directory of Train Operators

A Until 7 September

Table 175

Sundays

Purley and East Croydon → London
COMPLETE SERVICE

	SN	SN 1	SN 1 ◇ 🛒	FC 1	SN 1 🛒	FC	SN		SN A	SN 1 🛒	SN 1	FC 1	SN 1 ◇	SN 1	SN	SN 1	SN 1 ◇	FC 1	SN 1 🛒	SN	SN A	SN 1	SN 1	FC 1
Purley 4 d	17 38	17 53					18 08		18 16	18 18					18 38	18 53				19 08	19 16	19 18		
Purley Oaks d	17 41						18 11								18 41					19 11				
South Croydon 4 d	17 44						18 14								18 44					19 14				
East Croydon d	17 47	17 59	17 59	18 02	18 10	18 12	18 17		18 22	18 25	18 29	18 32	18 35	18 40	18 47	18 59	18 59	19 02	19 10	19 17	19 22	19 25	19 29	19 32
Norwood Junction 2 d	17 51						18 21		18 26						18 51					19 21	19 26			
London Bridge 4 ⊖ a	18 12			18 15		18 30	18 42		18 38			18 45			19 12			19 15		19 42	19 38			19 45
London Blackfriars 3 ⊖ a				18 23		18 37						18 53						19 23						19 53
City Thameslink 3 a																								
Farringdon 3 ⊖ a				18 27		18 43						18 57						19 27						19 57
St Pancras International 15 ⊖ a				18 31		18 47						19 01						19 31						20 01
London Waterloo (East) 4 ⊖ a	18 17						18 47								19 17					19 47				
London Charing Cross 4 ⊖ a	18 20						18 50								19 20					19 50				
Clapham Junction 10 a		18 08	18 11		18 24					18 37	18 41		18 47	18 54		19 08	19 11		19 24			19 37	19 41	
London Victoria 15 ⊖ a		18 16	18 18		18 31					18 46	18 48		18 53	19 01		19 16	19 18		19 31			19 46	19 48	

	SN 1 ◇	SN 1		SN	SN 1	SN 1 ◇	FC 1	SN 1	SN	SN A	SN 1	SN 1	FC 1	SN 1 ◇	SN 1	SN	SN 1	SN 1 ◇	FC 1		SN 1	SN	SN A	SN 1
Purley 4 d				19 38	19 53				20 08	20 16	20 18					20 38	20 53					21 08	21 16	21 23
Purley Oaks d				19 41					20 11							20 41						21 11		
South Croydon 4 d				19 44					20 14							20 44						21 14		
East Croydon d	19 35	19 40		19 47	19 59	19 59	20 02	20 10	20 17	20 22	20 25	20 29	20 32	20 35	20 40	20 47	20 59	20 59	21 02		21 10	21 17	21 22	21 28
Norwood Junction 2 d				19 51					20 21	20 26						20 51						21 21	21 26	
London Bridge 4 ⊖ a				20 12			20 15		20 42	20 38			20 45			21 12			21 15			21 42	21 39	
London Blackfriars 3 ⊖ a							20 23						20 53						21 23					
City Thameslink 3 a																								
Farringdon 3 ⊖ a							20 27						20 57						21 27					
St Pancras International 15 ⊖ a							20 31						21 01						21 31					
London Waterloo (East) 4 ⊖ a				20 17					20 47							21 17						21 47		
London Charing Cross 4 ⊖ a				20 20					20 50							21 20						21 50		
Clapham Junction 10 a	19 47	19 54			20 08	20 11		20 24			20 37	20 41		20 47	20 54		21 08	21 11			21 24			21 37
London Victoria 15 ⊖ a	19 53	20 01			20 16	20 18		20 31			20 46	20 48		20 53	21 01		21 16	21 18			21 31			21 46

	SN 1	FC 1	SN 1	SN	SN 1	SN 1 ◇	FC 1	SN 1	SN	SN A	SN 1	SN 1	FC 1	SN		SN 1	SN 1 ◇	FC 1	SN	SN 1	SN 1	SN	FC 1	SN 1
Purley 4 d				21 38	21 53				22 08	22 16	22 18			22 38		22 53			23 08	23 17		23 23		23 50
Purley Oaks d				21 41					22 11					22 41					23 11			23 26		
South Croydon 4 d				21 44					22 14					22 44					23 14			23 29		
East Croydon d	21 29	21 32	21 40	21 47	21 59	21 59	22 02	22 10	22 17	22 22	22 25	22 29	22 32	22 47		22 59	22 59	23 02	23a16	23 25	23 29	23a31	23 32	23 56
Norwood Junction 2 d				21 51					22 21	22 26				22 51										
London Bridge 4 ⊖ a		21 45		22 12			22 15		22 42	22 38			22 45	23 12				23 15					23 45	
London Blackfriars 3 ⊖ a		21 53					22 23						22 53					23 23					23 53	
City Thameslink 3 a																								
Farringdon 3 ⊖ a		21 57					22 27						22 57					23 27					23 57	
St Pancras International 15 ⊖ a		22 01					22 31						23 01					23 31					00 02	
London Waterloo (East) 4 ⊖ a				22 17					22 47					23 17										
London Charing Cross 4 ⊖ a				22 20					22 50					23 20										
Clapham Junction 10 a	21 41		21 54		22 08	22 11		22 24			22 37	22 41				23 10	23 13			23 37	23 41			00 10
London Victoria 15 ⊖ a	21 48		22 01		22 16	22 18		22 31			22 46	22 50				23 16	23 20			23 46	23 51			00 18

For general notes see front of timetable
For details of catering facilities see
Directory of Train Operators

A Until 7 September

Network Diagram for Tables 177, 178, 179, 181, 182 | also 175★

DM-24/08
Design BAJS

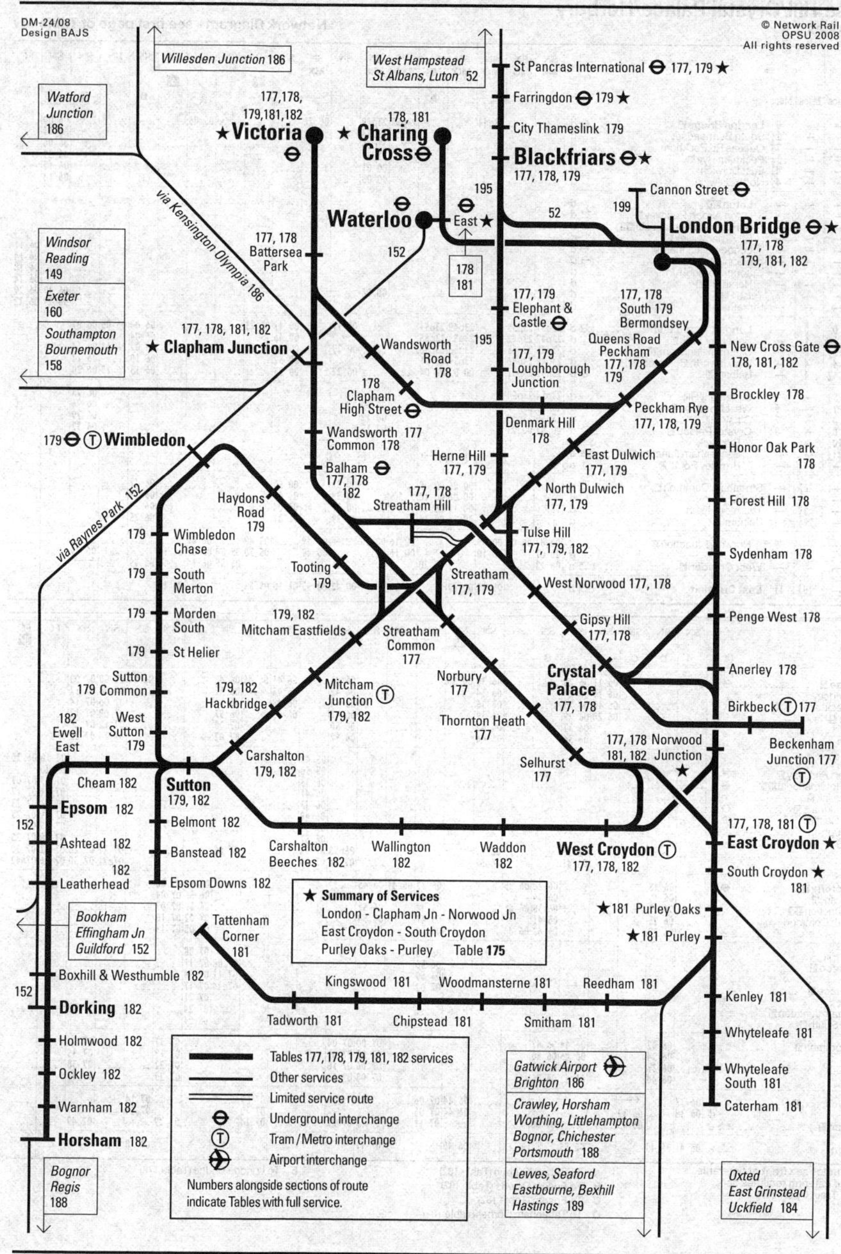

Table 177

Luton & London → East and West Croydon via Tulse Hill/Crystal Palace/Norbury

Local Services

Network Diagram - see first page of Table 177

Miles	Miles	Miles	Miles	Miles			SN MX	SN MO	SN MO	SN MO	SN MX A	SN MX	SN MX	SN	SN MX	SN	SN [1]	SN	SN	SN [1]	SN B	SN	SN C	SN	FC
—	0	—	—	0	**London Bridge [4]**	⊖ d			23p44			23p53	23p49		00 26				05 46					06 00	
—	1¾	—	—	1¾	South Bermondsey	d							23p53											06 04	
—	2¾	—	—	2¾	Queens Rd Peckham	d							23p55											06 06	
—	3½	—	—	3½	Peckham Rye [4]	d							23p58											06 09	
—	4¼	—	—	4¼	East Dulwich	d							00 01											06 12	
—	4¾	—	—	4¾	North Dulwich	d							00 03											06 14	
—	—	—	—	—	**Luton [10]**	d																			
—	—	—	—	—	Luton Airport Parkway [7]	d																			
—	—	—	—	—	St Pancras International [15]	⊖ d																			
—	—	—	—	—	City Thameslink [3]	d																			
—	—	—	—	—	London Blackfriars [3]	⊖ d																			06 11
—	—	—	—	—	Elephant & Castle	⊖ d																			06 14
—	—	—	—	—	Loughborough Jn	d																			06 18
—	—	—	—	—	Herne Hill [4]	d																			06 24
—	6	—	—	6	Tulse Hill [3]	d							00 06											06 17	06 29
—	7½	—	—	—	Streatham [4]	d																		06a21	06 32
0	—	0	0	—	**London Victoria [15]**	⊖ d	23p37	23p38		23p49	23p51			00 17		00 42	05 23				06 00	06 05	06 07		
1¼	—	1¼	1¼	—	Battersea Park [4]	d	23p42	23p42		23p53	23p55					00 46					06 04		06 11		
2¾	—	2¾	2¾	—	Clapham Junction [10]	d	23p45	23p45		23p56	23p58			00 23		00 49	05 33				06 07	06 11	06 14		
4	—	4	4	—	Wandsworth Common	d	23p48	23p48		23p59	00 01					00 52					06 10		06 17		
4¾	—	4¾	4¾	—	Balham [4]	⊖ d	23p51	23p51		00 02	00 04			00 27		00 55					06 13	06 15	06 20		
5¾	—	5¾	—	—	Streatham Hill	d	23p54	23p54															06 23		
7	—	7	—	6½	West Norwood [4]	d	23p57	23p57					00 09										06 26		
8	—	8	—	7½	Gipsy Hill	d	23p59	23p59					00 12										06 29		
8¾	—	8¾	—	8¼	**Crystal Palace [4]**	d	00 03	00 03					00 15										06 32		
—	—	10¼	—	—	Birkbeck	d																			
—	—	11¾	—	—	Beckenham Junction [4]	a																			
—	—	—	—	—	Bromley South [4]	a																			
—	8	—	6½	—	Streatham Common [4]	d				00 06	00 08			00 31		00 59					06 17				
—	9	—	7½	—	Norbury	d				00 08	00 10			00 34		01 01					06 19				
—	10¼	—	8¾	—	Thornton Heath	d				00 11	00 13			00 37		01 04					06 22				
—	11	—	9½	—	Selhurst [4]	d				00 14	00 16			00 39		01 07					06 25				
10¼	—	—	—	9¾	Norwood Junction [2]	a	00 07	00 07	00 09			00 16	00 19		00 49		05 49		06 09				06 36		
—	—	—	—	—		d	00 07		00 10			00 16			00 49		05 50	05 54	06 09	06 10			06 39		
—	12	—	—	—	**West Croydon [4]**	a	00 13				00 20							05 58	06 14		06 29		→		
11½	—	—	10½	11	**East Croydon**	a			00 13	00 17		00 20		00 42	00 53	01 10	05 53			06 13					

		SN	SN D	SN C	SN	SN	SN B	SN	SN	SN [1]	SN	SN	SN	SN	FC	SN	SN	SN E	SN	SN B	SN	SN	SN	FC	FC [1]
London Bridge [4]	⊖ d	06 13			06 11	06 20			06 30	06 30				06 38		06 41	06 46	06 48			06 54	07 00	07 08		
South Bermondsey	d				06 15	06 24			06 34					06 42		06 45		06 52				07 04	07 12		
Queens Rd Peckham	d				06 18	06 26			06 36					06 44		06 48		06 54				07 06	07 14		
Peckham Rye [4]	d				06 20	06 29			06 39					06 47		06 50		06 57				07 09	07 17		
East Dulwich	d					06 32			06 42					06 50				07 00				07 12	07 20		
North Dulwich	d					06 34			06 44					06 52				07 02				07 14	07 22		
Luton [10]	d														05 48									06 18	06 36
Luton Airport Parkway [7]	d														05 50									06 20	
St Pancras International [15]	⊖ d														06 33									07 03	07 07
City Thameslink [3]	d														06 41									07 11	07 17
London Blackfriars [3]	⊖ d														06 46									07 16	07 23
Elephant & Castle	⊖ d														06 49									07 19	07 27
Loughborough Jn	d														06 53									07 23	07 31
Herne Hill [4]	d														06 57									07 28	07 35
Tulse Hill [3]	d					06 37			06 47					06b58	07 02			07 05				07 17	07 26	07 32	07 38
Streatham [4]	d					06 41			06a51					07 01	07 06							07a21	07 30	07 36	07a42
London Victoria [15]	⊖ d		06 15				06 28	06 35			06 37	06 41	06 45						06 52	07 00					
Battersea Park [4]	d		06 19				06 34				06 41	06a45							06 56	07 04					
Clapham Junction [10]	d		06 22				06 38	06 41			06 44		06 51						06 59	07 07					
Wandsworth Common	d		06 25				06 41				06 47		06 54						07 02	07 10					
Balham [4]	⊖ d		06 28				06 43	06 46			06 50		06 56						07 05	07 13					
Streatham Hill	d										06 53								07 08						
West Norwood [4]	d										06 56							07 08	07 11						
Gipsy Hill	d										06 59							07 11	07 14						
Crystal Palace [4]	d										07 02							07a14	07 17						
Birkbeck	d																		07 21						
Beckenham Junction [4]	a																		07 24						
Bromley South [4]	a																		*08 04*						
Streatham Common [4]	d		06 32			06 44	06 47						07 00	07 04						07 17			07 33		
Norbury	d		06 34			06 46	06 50						07 03	07 07						07 19			07 35		
Thornton Heath	d		06 37			06 49	06 53						07 06	07 10						07 22			07 38		
Selhurst [4]	d		06 40			06 52	06 56						07 08	07 13						07 25			07 41		
Norwood Junction [2]	a	06 37		←						06 44	07 06						07 09				07 14				
	d	06 38		06 39						06 44	07 06						07 10				07 14				
West Croydon [4]	a			06 43			07 00				07 11			07 22			07 14			07 29			07 49		
East Croydon	a	06 41	06 45			06 55				06 48			07 11								07 18				

For general notes see front of timetable
For details of catering facilities see Directory of Train Operators

A To Sutton (Surrey) (Table 182)
B To Epsom Downs (Table 182)
C To Epsom (Table 182)
D To Tattenham Corner (Table 181)
E To London Bridge (Table 178)
b Arr. 0655

Luton & London → East and West Croydon via Tulse Hill/Crystal Palace/Norbury

Local Services

Network Diagram - see first page of Table 177

		SN [1]	SN	SN	SN	SN	SN	SN	SN	SN [1]	SN	SN	SN	SN	SN	SN	SN	FC	SN	SN	SN	SN	SN	SN	SN [1]
						A					B								C	D					
London Bridge [4]	⊖ d	07 20					07 11	07 15	07 22	07 28		07 25		07 31	07 40						07 47	07 41	07 53		07 54
South Bermondsey	d						07 15		07 26					07 35								07 45			
Queens Rd Peckham	d						07 18		07 28					07 37								07 48			
Peckham Rye [4]	d						07 20		07 31					07 40							07 53	07 50	07 59		
East Dulwich	d								07 34					07 43							07 56				
North Dulwich	d								07 36					07 45							07 58				
Luton [10]	d																	06 56							
Luton Airport Parkway [7]	✈ d																								
St Pancras International [15]	⊖ d																	07 28							
City Thameslink [3]	d																	07 37							
London Blackfriars [3]	⊖ d																	07 40							
Elephant & Castle	⊖ d																	07 43							
Loughborough Jn	d																	07 47							
Herne Hill [4]	d																	07 52							
Tulse Hill [3]	d								07 40					07 48				07 56			08 02		08 05		
Streatham [4]	d													07a52				07 59			08 05				
London Victoria [15]	⊖ d		07 06	07 11	07 15	07 20					07 30					07 36	07 41		07 45	07 47				07 51	
Battersea Park [4]	d		07 10	07a15		07 24					07 34					07 40	07a45			07 51				07 55	
Clapham Junction [10]	d		07 13		07 21	07 27					07 38					07 43			07 51	07 54				07 58	
Wandsworth Common	d		07 16			07 30					07 41					07 46			07 54	07 57				08 01	
Balham [4]	⊖ d		07 19		07 25	07 33					07 43					07 49			07 57	08 00				08 04	
Streatham Hill	d		07 22										07 45			07 52								08 07	
West Norwood [4]	d		07 25						07 43				07 48			07 55							08 08	08 10	
Gipsy Hill	d		07 28						07 46				07 51			07 58							08 11	08 13	
Crystal Palace [4]	d		07 31						07 49				07a54			08 01							08 14	08a16	
Birkbeck	d								07 53														08 18		
Beckenham Junction [4]	a								07 56														08 21		
Bromley South [4]	a																						08 32		
Streatham Common [4]	d					07 37					07 47								08 01		08 08				
Norbury	d					07 39					07 50								08 03		08 11				
Thornton Heath	d					07 42					07 53								08 06		08 14				
Selhurst [4]	d					07 45					07 56								08 09		08 17				
Norwood Junction [2]	a	07 32	07 35					07 38		07 41		07 48			08 00	08 05									08 06
	d	07 32	07 35					07 39		07 42		07 51			08 00	08 06									08 06
West Croydon [4]	a		07 40					07 43			08 02					08 11					08 22				
East Croydon	a	07 36				07 48				07 45		07 55			08 04				08 13						08 11

		SN	SN	SN		FC [1]	SN	SN [1]	SN	SN	SN	SN	FC	SN	SN	SN	SN	SN [1]	SN	SN [1]	SN	SN	SN	SN	SN
			B											C										E	B
London Bridge [4]	⊖ d	07 48					08 02	08 03	08 05	08 09						08 09	08 17	08 25	08 19	08 30	08 21				
South Bermondsey	d						08 06									08 13	09a05								
Queens Rd Peckham	d						08 08									08 15									
Peckham Rye [4]	d						08 11									08 18					08 27				
East Dulwich	d						08 14														08 30				
North Dulwich	d						08 16														08 32				
Luton [10]	d					07 16							07 08												
Luton Airport Parkway [7]	✈ d												07 10												
St Pancras International [15]	⊖ d					07 48							07 56												
City Thameslink [3]	d					07 55							08 03												
London Blackfriars [3]	⊖ d					08 00							08 08												
Elephant & Castle	⊖ d												08 11												
Loughborough Jn	d												08 15												
Herne Hill [4]	d					08 09							08 22												
Tulse Hill [3]	d					08 13	08 19						08 26								08 36				
Streatham [4]	d						08a23						08 29												
London Victoria [15]	⊖ d		08 03								08 07	08 11		08 15	08 20							08 22	08 26	08 31	08 34
Battersea Park [4]	d		08 07								08 11	08a15		08 19								08 26			08 38
Clapham Junction [10]	d		08 11								08 14			08 22	08 26							08 30		08 37	08 41
Wandsworth Common	d		08 14								08 17			08 25								08 33		08 40	08 44
Balham [4]	⊖ d		08 16								08 20			08 28	08 30							08 35		08 43	08 47
Streatham Hill	d			08 14							08 23											08 38			
West Norwood [4]	d			08 17							08 26										08 39	08 42			
Gipsy Hill	d			08 20							08 29										08 42	08 45			
Crystal Palace [4]	d			08a23							08 32						08a36				08 44	08a47			
Birkbeck	d																								
Beckenham Junction [4]	a																								
Bromley South [4]	a																								
Streatham Common [4]	d		08 20											08 32										08 47	08 51
Norbury	d		08 23											08 34										08 49	08 53
Thornton Heath	d		08 26											08 37										08 52	08 56
Selhurst [4]	d		08b32											08 40										08 55	09 00
Norwood Junction [2]	a	08 11						08 14	08 25	08 28	08 36							08 37	08 44	08 44	08 49				
	d	08 11						08 14	08 25	08 28	08 36							08 37	08 44	08 45	08 49				
West Croydon [4]	a	08 16	08 36								08 41								08 49				08 53	08 59	09 05
East Croydon	a					08 25		08 19	08 29	08 32				08 43				08 41		08 49	08 53				

For general notes see front of timetable
For details of catering facilities see Directory of Train Operators

A To Tattenham Corner (Table 181)
B To Epsom Downs (Table 182)
C To Caterham (Table 181)
D To Sutton (Surrey) (Table 182)
E To Epsom (Table 182)
b Arr. 0828

Luton & London → East and West Croydon via Tulse Hill/Crystal Palace/Norbury

Local Services

Network Diagram - see first page of Table 177

Station		SN	FC	SN	FC 1	SN	SN 1	SN	SN	SN	SN	SN	SN	SN 1	SN	SN	SN	FC	SN	SN	SN	FC	SN	FC	FC
										A					B					C	D				
London Bridge 4	⊖ d	08 24		08 36		08 29	08 49					08 45	08 41	09 00	08 37	08 54			08 47				08 57		
South Bermondsey	d	08 28				08 33							08 45		08 42				08 51				09 03		
Queens Rd Peckham	d	08 30				08 35							08 48		08 45				08 53				09 05		
Peckham Rye 4	d	08 33				08 38							08 50		08 47				08 56				09 08		
East Dulwich	d					08 41									08 51				08 59				09 11		
North Dulwich	d					08 43									08 53				09 01				09 13		
Luton 10	d				07 48													07 56						08 20	
Luton Airport Parkway 7	✈ d																	07 58							
St Pancras International 15	⊖ d		08 12		08 20													08 33				08 40		08 52	08 56
City Thameslink 3	d		08 19		08 27													08 40				08 47		08 59	09 03
London Blackfriars 3	⊖ d		08 24		08 32													08 45				08 52		09 03	09 08
Elephant & Castle	⊖ d		08 27		08 35																	08 55		09 06	09 11
Loughborough Jn	d		08 31		08 39																	08 59		09 10	09 15
Herne Hill 4	d		08 38		08 43													08 55				09 06		09 14	09 22
Tulse Hill 3	d	08 38	08 44		08 47	08 50									09b00			09c02	09 06			09 14	09 16	09 18	09 28
Streatham 4	d	08a42	08 47															09a05	09 10			09a19		09 22	09a31
London Victoria 15	⊖ d							08 37	08 41	08 45	08 50						08 52			08 57	09 05				
Battersea Park 4	d							08 41	08a45	08 49							08 56			09 01					
Clapham Junction 10	d							08 44		08 52	08 56						08 59			09 04	09 11				
Wandsworth Common	d							08 47		08 55							09 02			09 07	09 14				
Balham 4	⊖ d							08 50		08 58	09 02						09 05			09 10	09 17				
Streatham Hill	d							08 53									09 08								
West Norwood 4	d					08 53		08 56							09 03		09 11						09 19		
Gipsy Hill	d					08 56		08 59							09 06		09 14						09 22		
Crystal Palace 4	d					08 58		09 02							09 08	09a13	09a17						09 25		
Birkbeck	d					09 02																	09 29		
Beckenham Junction 4	a					09 06																	09 32		
Bromley South 4	a					*09 33*																	*09 48*		
Streatham Common 4	d									09 02									09 13	09 15	09 21				
Norbury	d									09 04									09 15	09 18	09 23				
Thornton Heath	d									09 07									09 18	09 21	09 26				
Selhurst 4	d									09 10									09 21	09 24	09 30				
Norwood Junction 2	a			08 56			09 01	09 06				09 09		09 11	09 13										
	d			08 56			09 02	09 06				09 09		09 11	09 13										
West Croydon 4	a							09 11				09 14							09 25	09 28	09 34				
East Croydon	a			09 00	09 06		09 05			09 13				09 15	09 17										

Station		SN	SN	SN	SN	SN	SN	SN	SN	SN	SN	SN	SN	SN	SN	FC	SN	SN 1	SN	SN	SN	SN	SN	SN	SN
						A			B					E	D								A		
London Bridge 4	⊖ d	09 05	09 19					09 15	09 07	09 24		09 11	09 17				09 30	09 33	09 35	09 47					09 45
South Bermondsey	d								09 12			09 15	09 23				09 34								
Queens Rd Peckham	d								09 14			09 18	09 25				09 36								
Peckham Rye 4	d								09 17			09 20	09 28				09 39								
East Dulwich	d								09 20				09 31				09 42								
North Dulwich	d								09 22				09 33				09 44								
Luton 10	d																								
Luton Airport Parkway 7	✈ d																								
St Pancras International 15	⊖ d															09 14									
City Thameslink 3	d															09 21									
London Blackfriars 3	⊖ d															09 26									
Elephant & Castle	⊖ d															09 29									
Loughborough Jn	d															09 33									
Herne Hill 4	d															09 38									
Tulse Hill 3	d								09e30				09 36			09 44	09 47								
Streatham 4	d												09 40			09 47									
London Victoria 15	⊖ d			09 07	09 11	09 15	09 20				09 22			09 28	09 35						09 37	09 41	09 45	09 50	
Battersea Park 4	d			09 11	09a15	09 19					09 26			09 32							09 41	09a45	09 49		
Clapham Junction 10	d			09 14		09 22	09 26				09 30			09 35	09 41						09 44		09 52	09 56	
Wandsworth Common	d			09 17		09 25					09 33			09 38	09 44						09 47		09 55		
Balham 4	⊖ d			09 20		09 28	09 32				09 35			09 41	09 47						09 50		09 58	10 02	
Streatham Hill	d			09 23							09 38										09 53				
West Norwood 4	d			09 26					09 33		09 42						09 50				09 56				
Gipsy Hill	d			09 29					09 36		09 45						09 53				09 59				
Crystal Palace 4	d			09 32					09 38	09a43	09a47						09 56				10 02				
Birkbeck	d																10 00								
Beckenham Junction 4	a																10 03								
Bromley South 4	a																*10 17*								
Streatham Common 4	d					09 32							09 43	09 45	09 51								10 02		
Norbury	d					09 34							09 45	09 48	09 53								10 04		
Thornton Heath	d					09 37							09 48	09 51	09 56								10 07		
Selhurst 4	d					09 40							09 51	09 54	09 59								10 10		
Norwood Junction 2	a	09 25	09 31	09 36				09 38	09 43									09 45	09 55	09 59	10 06				10 08
	d	09 25	09 31	09 36				09 39	09 43									09 46	09 55	09 59	10 06				10 09
West Croydon 4	a			09 41				09 44					09 55	09 58	10 03						10 11				10 14
East Croydon	a	09 29	09 35			09 43			09 47									09 49	09 59	10 05			10 13		

For general notes see front of timetable
For details of catering facilities see Directory of Train Operators

- **A** To Caterham (Table 181)
- **B** To Smitham (Table 181)
- **C** To Epsom (Table 182)
- **D** To Sutton (Surrey) (Table 182)
- **E** To Epsom Downs (Table 182)
- **b** Arr. 0857
- **c** Arr. 0859
- **e** Arr. 0926

Luton & London → East and West Croydon via Tulse Hill/Crystal Palace/Norbury

Local Services

Network Diagram - see first page of Table 177

		SN	SN		SN	FC	SN	SN	SN	SN	FC	SN	SE	SN	SN	SN	SN	SN	SN	SN	SN	SN	SN	FC	SN
													13												
		A						B	C				D						E			A			
London Bridge 4	⊖ d	09 37	09 54				09 47			09 41		10 00	10 03	10 05	10 24	10 17					10 15	10 08			10 11
South Bermondsey	d	09 42					09 53			09 45		10 04										10 12			10 15
Queens Rd Peckham	d	09 44					09 55			09 48		10 06										10 14			10 18
Peckham Rye 4	d	09 47					09 58			09 50		10 09										10 17			10 20
East Dulwich	d	09 50					10 01					10 12										10 20			
North Dulwich	d	09 52					10 03					10 14										10 22			
Luton 10	d																							09 14	
Luton Airport Parkway 7	✈ d																							09 16	
St Pancras International 15	⊖ d					09 32					09 48													10 02	
City Thameslink 3	d					09 39					09 55													10 09	
London Blackfriars 3	⊖ d					09 44					10 00													10 16	
Elephant & Castle	⊖ d					09 47					10 03													10 19	
Loughborough Jn	d					09 51					10 07													10 23	
Herne Hill 4	d					09 57					10 12													10 27	
Tulse Hill 3	d	10b00				10 02	10 06				10 16	10 17										10c30		10 32	
Streatham 4	d					10a05	10 10				10 19													10a35	
London Victoria 15	⊖ d				09 52			09 57	10 05								10 07	10 11	10 15	10 20			10 22		
Battersea Park 4	d				09 56			10 01									10 11	10a15	10 19				10 26		
Clapham Junction 10	d				09 59			10 04	10 11								10 14		10 22	10 26			10 29		
Wandsworth Common	d				10 02			10 07	10 14								10 17		10 25				10 32		
Balham 4	⊖ d				10 05			10 10	10 17								10 20		10 28	10 32			10 35		
Streatham Hill	d				10 08												10 23						10 38		
West Norwood 4	d	10 03			10 11							10 20					10 26					10 33	10 41		
Gipsy Hill	d	10 06			10 14							10 23					10 29					10 36	10 44		
Crystal Palace 4	d	10 08	10a14		10a17							10 26			10a43		10 32					10 38	10a47		
Birkbeck	d											10 30													
Beckenham Junction 4	a											10 33													
Bromley South 4	a											*10 47*													
Streatham Common 4	d						10 13	10 15	10 21										10 32						
Norbury	d						10 15	10 18	10 23										10 34						
Thornton Heath	d						10 18	10 21	10 26										10 37						
Selhurst 4	d						10 21	10 24	10 29										10 40						
Norwood Junction 2	a	10 13											10 16	10 25		10 31	10 36				10 38	10 43			
	d	10 13											10 16	10 25		10 31	10 36				10 39	10 43			
West Croydon 4	a						10 25	10 28	10 33								10 41				10 44				
East Croydon	a	10 17											10 19	10 29		10 35			10 43			10 47			

		SN	SN	SN	SN	FC	SN	SN	SN	SN	SN	SN	SN	SN	SN	SN	FC	SN	SN	SN	SN		SN	FC	SE
							1																		13
			G	C							E			A					B	C					D
London Bridge 4	⊖ d	10 19			10 29		10 33		10 35				10 45	10 38	10 54			10 49			10 41		10 59		11 03
South Bermondsey	d	10 23			10 33									10 42				10 53			10 45		11 03		
Queens Rd Peckham	d	10 25			10 35									10 44				10 55			10 48		11 05		
Peckham Rye 4	d	10 28			10 38									10 47				10 58			10 50		11 08		
East Dulwich	d	10 31			10 41									10 50				11 01					11 11		
North Dulwich	d	10 33			10 43									10 52				11 03					11 13		
Luton 10	d																09 44								
Luton Airport Parkway 7	✈ d																09 46								
St Pancras International 15	⊖ d					10 17											10 32							10 47	
City Thameslink 3	d					10 26											10 39							10 56	
London Blackfriars 3	⊖ d					10 30											10 46							11 00	
Elephant & Castle	⊖ d					10 33											10 49							11 03	
Loughborough Jn	d					10 37											10 53							11 07	
Herne Hill 4	d					10 42											10 57							11 12	
Tulse Hill 3	d	10 36			10 46	10 46								11e00			11 02	11 06					11 16	11 16	
Streatham 4	d	10 40				10 49											11a05	11 10						11 19	
London Victoria 15	⊖ d		10 28	10 35				10 41		10 37	10 45	10 50				10 52			10 55	11 05					
Battersea Park 4	d		10 32					10a45		10 41	10 49					10 56			10 59						
Clapham Junction 10	d		10 35	10 41						10 44	10 52	10 56				10 59			11 04	11 12					
Wandsworth Common	d		10 38	10 44						10 47	10 55					11 02			11 07	11 15					
Balham 4	⊖ d		10 41	10 47						10 50	10 58	11 02				11 05			11 10	11 17					
Streatham Hill	d									10 53						11 08									
West Norwood 4	d				10 49					10 56				11 03		11 11							11 19		
Gipsy Hill	d				10 52					10 59				11 06		11 14							11 22		
Crystal Palace 4	d				10 55					11 02				11 08	11a13	11a17							11 25		
Birkbeck	d				10 59																		11 29		
Beckenham Junction 4	a				11 02																		11 32		
Bromley South 4	a				*11 17*																		*11 47*		
Streatham Common 4	d	10 43	10 45	10 51							11 02							11 13	11 15	11 21					
Norbury	d	10 45	10 48	10 53							11 04							11 15	11 18	11 23					
Thornton Heath	d	10 48	10 51	10 56							11 07							11 18	11 21	11 26					
Selhurst 4	d	10 51	10 54	10 59							11 10							11 21	11 24	11 29					
Norwood Junction 2	a						10 45		10 55	11 06			11 08	11 13											11 16
	d						10 46		10 55	11 06			11 09	11 13											11 16
West Croydon 4	a	10 55	10 58	11 03						11 11			11 14					11 25	11 28	11 33					
East Croydon	a						10 49		10 59		11 13			11 17											11 19

For general notes see front of timetable
For details of catering facilities see Directory of Train Operators

- **A** To Smitham (Table 181)
- **B** To Epsom (Table 182)
- **C** To Sutton (Surrey) (Table 182)
- **D** To Tunbridge Wells (Table 209)
- **E** To Caterham (Table 181)
- **G** To Epsom Downs (Table 182)
- **b** Arr. 0956
- **c** Arr. 1026
- **e** Arr. 1056

Luton & London → East and West Croydon via Tulse Hill/Crystal Palace/Norbury

Local Services

Network Diagram - see first page of Table 177

	SN	SN	SN	SN	SN	SN	SN	SN	SN	FC	SN	SN	SN	SN	SN	FC	SN 1	SN	SN	SN	SN	SN	SN	SN
				A			B						C	D							A			B
London Bridge 4 ⊖ d		11 05				11 15	11 08	11 24			11 11	11 19			11 29		11 33		11 35				11 45	11 38
South Bermondsey d							11 12				11 15	11 23			11 33									11 42
Queens Rd Peckham d							11 14				11 18	11 25			11 35									11 44
Peckham Rye 4 d							11 17				11 20	11 28			11 38									11 47
East Dulwich d							11 20					11 31			11 41									11 50
North Dulwich d							11 22					11 33			11 43									11 52
Luton 10 d										10 14														
Luton Airport Parkway 7 ✈ d										10 16														
St Pancras International 15 ⊖ d										11 02						11 17								
City Thameslink 3 d										11 09						11 24								
London Blackfriars 3 ⊖ d										11 16						11 30								
Elephant & Castle ⊖ d										11 19						11 33								
Loughborough Jn d										11 23						11 37								
Herne Hill 4 d										11 27						11 42								
Tulse Hill 3 d							11b30			11 32		11 36			11 46	11 46								12c00
Streatham 4 d										11a35		11 40				11 49								
London Victoria 15 ⊖ d	11 11		11 07	11 15	11 20				11 22				11 25	11 35				11 41		11 37	11 45	11 50		
Battersea Park 4 d	11a15		11 11	11 19					11 26				11 29					11a45		11 41	11 49			
Clapham Junction 10 d			11 14	11 22	11 26				11 29				11 34	11 41						11 44	11 52	11 56		
Wandsworth Common d			11 17	11 25					11 32				11 37	11 44						11 47	11 55			
Balham 4 ⊖ d			11 20	11 28	11 32				11 35				11 40	11 47						11 50	11 58	12 02		
Streatham Hill d			11 23						11 38											11 53				
West Norwood 4 d			11 26				11 33		11 41						11 49					11 56				12 03
Gipsy Hill d			11 29				11 36		11 44						11 52					11 59				12 06
Crystal Palace 4 d			11 32				11 38	11a43	11a47						11 55					12 02				12 08
Birkbeck 🚊 d															11 59									
Beckenham Junction 4 🚊 a															12 02									
Bromley South 4 a															*12 17*									
Streatham Common 4 d				11 32								11 43	11 45	11 51							12 02			
Norbury d				11 34								11 45	11 48	11 53							12 04			
Thornton Heath d				11 37								11 48	11 51	11 56							12 07			
Selhurst 4 d				11 40								11 51	11 54	11 59							12 10			
Norwood Junction 2 a		11 25	11 36			11 38	11 43										11 45		11 55	12 06			12 08	12 13
d		11 25	11 36			11 39	11 43										11 46		11 55	12 06			12 09	12 13
West Croydon 4 🚊 a			11 41			11 44						11 55	11 58	12 03						12 11			12 14	
East Croydon 🚊 a		11 29		11 43			11 47										11 49		11 59		12 13			12 17

	SN	SN	FC	SN	SN	SN	SN			SN	FC	SE 13	SN	SN	SN	SN	SN	SN	SN	SN	SN	SN	FC
						E	D					G					A			H			
London Bridge 4 ⊖ d	11 54			11 41	11 49			and at the same minutes past each hour until		15 59		16 03	16 05	16 16					16 15	16 07	16 24		
South Bermondsey d				11 45	11 53					16 03										16 11			
Queens Rd Peckham d				11 48	11 55					16 05										16 13			
Peckham Rye 4 d				11 50	11 58					16 08										16 16			
East Dulwich d					12 01					16 11										16 19			
North Dulwich d					12 03					16 13										16 21			
Luton 10 d			10 44																				15 14
Luton Airport Parkway 7 ✈ d			10 46																				15 16
St Pancras International 15 ⊖ d			11 32								15 47												16 02
City Thameslink 3 d			11 39								15 54												16 09
London Blackfriars 3 ⊖ d			11 46								16 00												16 16
Elephant & Castle ⊖ d			11 49								16 03												16 19
Loughborough Jn d			11 53								16 07												16 23
Herne Hill 4 d			11 57								16 12												16 27
Tulse Hill 3 d			12 02		12 06					16 16	16 16									16e30			16 32
Streatham 4 d			12a05		12 10						16a19												16a35
London Victoria 15 ⊖ d		11 52				11 55	12 05								16 07	16 11	16 15	16 20				16 22	
Battersea Park 4 d		11 56				11 59									16 11	16a15	16 19					16 26	
Clapham Junction 10 d		11 59				12 04	12 11								16 14		16 22	16 26				16 29	
Wandsworth Common d		12 02				12 08	12 14								16 17		16 25					16 32	
Balham 4 ⊖ d		12 05				12 10	12 17								16 20		16 28	16 30				16 35	
Streatham Hill d		12 08													16 23							16 38	
West Norwood 4 d		12 11								16 19					16 26					16 33		16 41	
Gipsy Hill d		12 14								16 22					16 29					16 36		16 44	
Crystal Palace 4 d	12a13	12a17								16 25					16 32					16 38	16a43	16a47	
Birkbeck 🚊 d										16 29													
Beckenham Junction 4 🚊 a										16 32													
Bromley South 4 a										*16 52*													
Streatham Common 4 d					12 13	12 15	12 21										16 32						
Norbury d					12 15	12 18	12 23										16 34						
Thornton Heath d					12 18	12 21	12 26										16 37						
Selhurst 4 d					12 21	12 24	12 29										16 40						
Norwood Junction 2 a												16 16	16 25	16 29	16 36				16 38	16 43			
d												16 16	16 25	16 30	16 36				16 39	16 43			
West Croydon 4 🚊 a					12 25	12 27	12 33								16 43				16 43				
East Croydon 🚊 a												16 19	16 29	16 34			16 43			16 47			

For general notes see front of timetable
For details of catering facilities see Directory of Train Operators

A To Caterham (Table 181)
B To Smitham (Table 181)
C To Epsom Downs (Table 182)
D To Sutton (Surrey) (Table 182)
E To Epsom (Table 182)
G To Tonbridge (Table 209)
H To Tattenham Corner (Table 181)
b Arr. 1126
c Arr. 1156
e Arr. 1624

Luton & London → East and West Croydon via Tulse Hill/Crystal Palace/Norbury

Local Services

Network Diagram - see first page of Table 177

		SN	SN	SN	FC	SN	SN	SN	SN	SN	SN	SN	SN	SN	FC	FC	SN	SN	SN	SN	FC	SN	SN	SN	SN
							1									1									
				A							B								A						
London Bridge 4	⊖ d	16 11	16 19			16 29	16 38	16 35					16 37				16 41	16 44		16 53		16 59	17 05	16 55	17 19
South Bermondsey	d	16 15	16 23			16 33							16 41				16 45			16 57					
Queens Rd Peckham	d	16 18	16 25			16 35							16 43				16 48			16 59					
Peckham Rye 4	d	16 20	16 28			16 38							16 46				16 50			17 02					
East Dulwich	d		16 31			16 41							16 49							17 05					
North Dulwich	d		16 33			16 43							16 51							17 07					
Luton 10	d														15 44	15 55									
Luton Airport Parkway 7	✈ d														15 46	15 57									
St Pancras International 15	⊖ d				16 14										16 32	16 36					16 45				
City Thameslink 3	d				16 19										16 39	16 43					16 52				
London Blackfriars 3	⊖ d				16 26										16 42	16 46					16 58				
Elephant & Castle	⊖ d				16 30										16 45	16 50					17 02				
Loughborough Jn	d				16 34										16 49	16 54					17 06				
Herne Hill 4	d				16 38										16 53	16 58					17 11				
Tulse Hill 3	d		16 36		16 42	16 46							16 56		16 58	17b08				17 11	17 16				
Streatham 4	d		16 40		16 45	16 50									17a01	17a11				17 14	17 19				
London Victoria 15	⊖ d			16 30					16 37	16 41	16 45	16 50		16 52					17 01						
Battersea Park 4	d			16 34					16 41	16a45	16 49			16 56					17 05						
Clapham Junction 10	d			16 37					16 44		16 52	16 56		16 59					17 08						
Wandsworth Common	d			16 40					16 47		16 55			17 02					17 11						
Balham 4	⊖ d			16 43					16 50		16 58	17 00		17 05					17 14						
Streatham Hill	d								16 53					17 08											
West Norwood 4	d								16 56				16 59	17 11											
Gipsy Hill	d								16 59				17 02	17 14											
Crystal Palace 4	d								17 02				17 05	17a17										17a14	
Birkbeck	🚊 d												17 09												
Beckenham Junction 4	🚊 a												17 14												
Bromley South 4	a												*17 38*												
Streatham Common 4	d		16 43	16 47							17 02								17 18						
Norbury	d		16 45	16 49							17 04								17 20						
Thornton Heath	d		16 48	16 52							17 07								17 23						
Selhurst 4	d		16 51	16 55							17 10								17 26						
Norwood Junction 2	a						16 50	16 55	17 06									17 08				17 12	17 28		17 33
	d						16 51	16 55	17 06									17 09				17 12	17 28		17 33
West Croydon 4	🚊 a		16 57	16 59					17 13									17 14	17 30				17 35		
East Croydon	🚊 a						16 54	16 59			17 13											17 16			17 37

		SN	SN	SN	SN	SN	SN	SN	FC	SN	SN	SN	SN	SN	SN	FC	SN	SN	SN	SN	SN	SN	SN	FC	FC
												1													1
				C								D	A												
London Bridge 4	⊖ d				17 07	17 15				17 11	17 18			17 25	17 25		17 39	17 35					17 37		
South Bermondsey	d				17 11					17 15					17 29								17 41		
Queens Rd Peckham	d				17 13					17 18	17 23				17 31								17 43		
Peckham Rye 4	d				17 16					17 20	17 26				17 34								17 46		
East Dulwich	d				17 19						17 29				17 37								17 49		
North Dulwich	d				17 21						17 31				17 39								17 51		
Luton 10	d								16 14															16 44	17 18
Luton Airport Parkway 7	✈ d								16 16															16 46	
St Pancras International 15	⊖ d								17 01							17 17								17 31	17 46
City Thameslink 3	d								17 11							17 24								17 38	17 53
London Blackfriars 3	⊖ d								17 14							17 30								17 42	17 57
Elephant & Castle	⊖ d								17 17							17 34								17 45	
Loughborough Jn	d								17 21							17 38								17 49	
Herne Hill 4	d								17 25							17 42								17 53	18 06
Tulse Hill 3	d				17 26				17 29		17 34				17 42	17 46							17 56	17 58	
Streatham 4	d								17a33		17 38				17 46	17 50								18a01	
London Victoria 15	⊖ d	17 07	17 11	17 15			17 19	17 25					17 32						17 37	17 41	17 43	17 45			
Battersea Park 4	d	17 11	17a15				17 23						17 36						17 41	17a45		17 50			
Clapham Junction 10	d	17 14		17 21			17 26	17 31				17 34	17 39						17 44		17 49	17 53			
Wandsworth Common	d	17 17					17 29					17 37	17 42						17 47			17 56			
Balham 4	⊖ d	17 20		17 25			17 32	17 35				17 41	17 45						17 50		17 53	17 59			
Streatham Hill	d	17 23					17 35												17 53						
West Norwood 4	d	17 26			17 29		17 38												17 56				17 59		
Gipsy Hill	d	17 29			17 32		17 41												17 59				18 02		
Crystal Palace 4	d	17 32			17 35	17a34	17a44												18 02				18 05		
Birkbeck	🚊 d				17 39																		18 09		
Beckenham Junction 4	🚊 a				17 44																		18 14		
Bromley South 4	a				*18 02*																		*18 26*		
Streatham Common 4	d			17 29							17 41	17 45	17 49									18 03			
Norbury	d			17 32							17 43	17 48	17 51									18 05			
Thornton Heath	d			17 35							17 46	17 51	17 54									18 08			
Selhurst 4	d			17 38							17a51	17 54	17 57									18a13			
Norwood Junction 2	a	17 36												17 43			17 53	17 58	18 06						
	d	17 37												17 43			17 54	17 58	18 07						
West Croydon 4	🚊 a	17 46		17 42									18 01	17 48				18 05	18 14						
East Croydon	🚊 a											17 59					17 57								18 20

For general notes see front of timetable
For details of catering facilities see Directory of Train Operators

A To Epsom Downs (Table 182)
B To Tattenham Corner (Table 181)
C To Sutton (Surrey) (Table 182)
D From Kensington Olympia
b Arr. 1702

Luton & London → East and West Croydon via Tulse Hill/Crystal Palace/Norbury

Local Services

Network Diagram - see first page of Table 177

Station	SN	SN	SN	SN	SN	SN 1	SN	SN		SN	FC	SN	SN	SN	SN	SN	SN	SN	SN	SN	FC	SN	SN	SN
			A			B	C											D						
London Bridge 4 ⊖ d	17 41	17 45	17 47					17 55		17 58		18 01	18 05	18 20					18 08				18 11	18 18
South Bermondsey d	17 45									18 02									18 12				18 15	
Queens Rd Peckham d	17 48									18 04									18 14				18 18	
Peckham Rye 4 d	17 50		17 53							18 07									18 17				18 20	
East Dulwich d			17 56							18 10									18 20					
North Dulwich d			17 58							18 12									18 22					
Luton 10 d																					17 18			
Luton Airport Parkway 7 ✈ d																					17 20			
St Pancras International 15 ⊖ d											17 51										18 03			
City Thameslink 3 d											17 58										18 10			
London Blackfriars 3 ⊖ d											18 02										18 14			
Elephant & Castle ⊖ d											18 06										18 18			
Loughborough Jn d											18 10										18 21			
Herne Hill 4 d											18 14										18 26			
Tulse Hill 3 d			18 02							18 15	18 18								18 26		18 31			
Streatham 4 d										18a19	18 22										18a34			
London Victoria 15 ⊖ d				17 51	17 57		18 02								18 07	18 11	18 14	18 17		18 22		18 27		
Battersea Park 4 d				17 55			18 06								18 11	18a15		18 21		18 26				
Clapham Junction 10 d				17 59	18 03	18 06	18 09								18 14		18 20	18 25		18 29		18 33		
Wandsworth Common d				18 02		18 09	18 12								18 17			18 28		18 32				
Balham 4 ⊖ d				18 05	18 08	18 12	18 15								18 20		18 24	18 30		18 35		18 37		
Streatham Hill d				18 08											18 23					18 38				
West Norwood 4 d			18 05	18 15											18 26				18 29	18 41				
Gipsy Hill d			18 08	18 18											18 29				18 32	18 44				
Crystal Palace 4 d		18a09	18a12	18a21											18 32				18 35	18a47				18a39
Birkbeck d																			18 39					
Beckenham Junction 4 a																			18 44					
Bromley South 4 a																			*19 04*					
Streatham Common 4 d						18 16	18 19											18 34						
Norbury d						18 18	18 21											18 37						
Thornton Heath d						18 21	18 24											18 40						
Selhurst 4 d						18 24	18 27											18 43						
Norwood Junction 2 a								18 12				18 15	18 28	18 35	18 36									
Norwood Junction 2 d								18 13				18 15	18 28	18 35	18 37									
West Croydon 4 a							18 31	18 17					18 35		18 44									
East Croydon a						18 28						18 19		18 38				18 46						

Station	SN	FC	SN	SN	SN	SN	SN	SN 1	SN	SN	SN	SN	SN	SN	SN	FC	SN	SN	SN	FC	SN	SN	SN	SN
			C								E								G					
London Bridge 4 ⊖ d	18 21			18 25	18 31	18 42	18 36	18 54				18 38	18 51				18 41	18 51			19 05	19 00		
South Bermondsey d	18 25				18 35							18 42					18 45	18 55				19 04		
Queens Rd Peckham d	18 27				18 37							18 44					18 48	18 57				19 06		
Peckham Rye 4 d	18 30				18 40							18 47					18 50	19 00				19 09		
East Dulwich d	18 33				18 43							18 50						19 03				19 12		
North Dulwich d	18 35				18 45							18 52						19 05				19 14		
Luton 10 d																17 48								
Luton Airport Parkway 7 ✈ d																17 50								
St Pancras International 15 ⊖ d		18 15														18 33				18 45				
City Thameslink 3 d		18 22														18 40				18 52				
London Blackfriars 3 ⊖ d		18 26														18 44				18 56				
Elephant & Castle ⊖ d		18 30														18 48				19 00				
Loughborough Jn d		18 34														18 52				19 04				
Herne Hill 4 d		18 38														18 56				19 08				
Tulse Hill 3 d	18 38	18 44			18b51							18 56				19 02		19 09		19 14		19 17		
Streatham 4 d	18 42	18 47			18 54											19a05		19 12		19 17				
London Victoria 15 ⊖ d			18 33						18 37	18 41	18 45			18 52	18 57				19 00				19 05	19 11
Battersea Park 4 d			18 37						18 41	18a45	18 49			18 56					19 04				19 09	19a15
Clapham Junction 10 d			18 40						18 44		18 52			18 59	19 03				19 08				19 12	
Wandsworth Common d			18 43						18 47		18 55			19 02					19 11				19 15	
Balham 4 ⊖ d			18 46						18 50		18 58			19 05	19 07				19 14				19 18	
Streatham Hill d									18 53					19 08									19 21	
West Norwood 4 d									18 56			18 59		19 11								19 20	19 24	
Gipsy Hill d									18 59			19 02		19 14								19 23	19 27	
Crystal Palace 4 d									19 02			19 05	19a12	19 17								19 26	19a30	
Birkbeck d												19 09												
Beckenham Junction 4 a												19 14												
Bromley South 4 a												*19 33*												
Streatham Common 4 d	18 45		18 50								19 02							19 15	19 18					
Norbury d	18 47		18 52								19 04							19 18	19 20					
Thornton Heath d	18 50		18 55								19 07							19 21	19 23					
Selhurst 4 d	18a55		18 58								19 11							19a25	19 27					
Norwood Junction 2 a				18 41		18 56	18 59	19 05	19 06					19 21							19 28	19 30		
Norwood Junction 2 d				18 42		18 56	18 59	19 05	19 07					19 22							19 28	19 35		
West Croydon 4 a			19 02	18 46			19 06		19 15		19 15			19 29							19 33	19 41		
East Croydon a						19 00		19 09											19 30					

For general notes see front of timetable
For details of catering facilities see Directory of Train Operators

A To London Bridge (Table 178)
B From Watford Junction (Table 66)
C To Epsom Downs (Table 182)
D To Tattenham Corner (Table 181)
E To Epsom (Table 182)
G To Tattenham Corner (Table 181) and to Caterham (Table 181)
b Arr. 1848

Luton & London → East and West Croydon via Tulse Hill/Crystal Palace/Norbury

Local Services

Network Diagram - see first page of Table 177

		SN	SN	SN	FC	SN	SN	SN	SN	SN	SN	SN	SN	SN	SN	FC	SN	SN	SN	FC	SN	SN	SN	SN	SN
		A									B	C					D						1		
London Bridge 4	⊖ d			19 08		19 15	19 11	19 24	19 19	19 31			19 29						19 38		19 41	19 49	19 52	19 54	
South Bermondsey	d			19 12			19 15		19 23				19 33						19 42		19 45	19 53			
Queens Rd Peckham	d			19 14			19 18		19 25				19 35						19 44		19 48	19 55			
Peckham Rye 4	d			19 17			19 20		19 28				19 38						19 47		19 50	19 58			
East Dulwich	d			19 20					19 31				19 41						19 50			20 01			
North Dulwich	d			19 22					19 33				19 43						19 52			20 03			
Luton 10	d				18 20															18 50					
Luton Airport Parkway 7	✈ d				18 22															18 52					
St Pancras International 15	⊖ d				19 05											19 17				19 35					
City Thameslink 3	d				19 12											19 24				19 42					
London Blackfriars 3	⊖ d				19 16											19 30				19 46					
Elephant & Castle	⊖ d				19 19											19 33				19 49					
Loughborough Jn	d				19 23											19 37				19 53					
Herne Hill 4	d				19 28											19 42				19 58					
Tulse Hill 3	d			19 26	19 32				19 36				19 46			19 47			19 56	20 02		20 06			
Streatham 4	d				19a35				19 40							19 50				20a05		20 10			
London Victoria 15	⊖ d	19 15	19 20								19 22	19 31		19 35	19 41		19 45	19 50							
Battersea Park 4	d	19 19									19 26	19 35		19 39	19a45		19 49								
Clapham Junction 10	d	19 22	19 26								19 29	19 38		19 42			19 52	19 56							
Wandsworth Common	d	19 25									19 32	19 41		19 45			19 55								
Balham 4	⊖ d	19 28	19 32								19 35	19 44		19 48			19 58	20 02							
Streatham Hill	d										19 38			19 51											
West Norwood 4	d			19 29							19 41		19 49	19 54					19 59						
Gipsy Hill	d			19 32							19 44		19 52	19 57					20 02						
Crystal Palace 4	d			19 35				19a43			19 47		19 55	20a00					20 05					20a13	
Birkbeck	🚊 d			19 39															20 09						
Beckenham Junction 4	🚊 a			19 42															20 12						
Bromley South 4	a			*20 03*															*20 36*						
Streatham Common 4	d	19 32							19 43			19 48					20 02					20 13			
Norbury	d	19 34							19 45			19 50					20 04					20 15			
Thornton Heath	d	19 37							19 48			19 53					20 07					20 18			
Selhurst 4	d	19 40							19 51			19 56					20 10					20 21			
Norwood Junction 2	a					19 38				19 43	19 53		19 59										20 03		←
	d					19 39				19 44	19 54		20 05 →										20 03		20 05
West Croydon 4	🚊 a	19 44							19 56	19 48	19 59						20 14					20 26			20 10
East Croydon	🚊 a					19 42						19 59											20 06		

		SN	FC	FC	SN	SN	SN	SN		SN	SN	SN	SN	SN	FC	FC	SN	SN	SN	SN	SN	SN	SN	SN	SN
					1	A	C				D							1		B	C			D	
London Bridge 4	⊖ d	19 45			20 05								20 15	20 19			20 11	20 35	20 24						
South Bermondsey	d													20 23			20 15								
Queens Rd Peckham	d													20 25			20 18								
Peckham Rye 4	d													20 28			20 20								
East Dulwich	d													20 31											
North Dulwich	d													20 33											
Luton 10	d			19 20												19 50									
Luton Airport Parkway 7	✈ d			19 22												19 52									
St Pancras International 15	⊖ d		19 48	20 05											20 17	20 35									
City Thameslink 3	d		19 55	20 12											20 24	20 42									
London Blackfriars 3	⊖ d		20 00	20 16											20 30	20 46									
Elephant & Castle	⊖ d		20 03	20 19											20 33	20 49									
Loughborough Jn	d		20 07	20 23											20 37	20 53									
Herne Hill 4	d		20 12	20 27											20 42	20 57									
Tulse Hill 3	d		20 16	20 32										20 36	20 46	21 02									
Streatham 4	d		20 19	20a35										20 40	20 49	21a05									
London Victoria 15	⊖ d					19 52	20 01	20 05		20 11	20 15	20 20								20 22	20 30	20 35	20 41	20 45	20 50
Battersea Park 4	d					19 56	20 05	20 09		20a15	20 19									20 26	20 34	20 39	20a45	20 49	
Clapham Junction 10	d					19 59	20 08	20 12			20 22	20 26								20 29	20 38	20 42		20 52	20 56
Wandsworth Common	d					20 02	20 11	20 15			20 25									20 32	20 41	20 45		20 55	
Balham 4	⊖ d					20 05	20 14	20 18			20 28	20 31								20 35	20 43	20 48		20 58	21 02
Streatham Hill	d					20 08		20 21												20 38		20 51			
West Norwood 4	d					20 11		20 24												20 41		20 54			
Gipsy Hill	d					20 14		20 27												20 44		20 57			
Crystal Palace 4	d					20 17		20a30											20a43	20 47		21a00			
Birkbeck	🚊 d																								
Beckenham Junction 4	🚊 a																								
Bromley South 4	a																								
Streatham Common 4	d						20 18				20 32			20 43							20 47			21 02	
Norbury	d						20 20				20 34			20 45							20 50			21 04	
Thornton Heath	d						20 23				20 37			20 48							20 53			21 07	
Selhurst 4	d						20 26				20 40			20 51							20 56			21 10	
Norwood Junction 2	a	20 08			20 16	20 21							20 38					20 46		20 51					
	d	20 09			20 16	20 24							20 38					20 46		20 54					
West Croydon 4	🚊 a					20 29					20 44			20 56						20 59				21 14	
East Croydon	🚊 a	20 12			20 19		20 29						20 42					20 49			20 59				

For general notes see front of timetable
For details of catering facilities see Directory of Train Operators

A To Epsom (Table 182)
B To Epsom Downs (Table 182)
C To Tattenham Corner (Table 181)
D To Sutton (Surrey) (Table 182)

Luton & London → East and West Croydon via Tulse Hill/Crystal Palace/Norbury

Local Services

Network Diagram - see first page of Table 177

		SN	SN	SN	SN 1	SN	SN	SN	SN	SN	SN	SN	FC	SN	SN	SN	SN	SN 1	SN	SN	SN	SN	SN	SN	FC
							A	B			C								D	B			C		
London Bridge 4	⊖ d	20 45	20 49	20 41	21 05	20 54								21 24	21 15	21 11	21 19	21 28							
South Bermondsey	d		20 53	20 45												21 15	21 23								
Queens Rd Peckham	d		20 55	20 48												21 18	21 25								
Peckham Rye 4	d		20 58	20 50												21 20	21 28								
East Dulwich	d		21 01														21 31								
North Dulwich	d		21 03														21 33								
Luton 10	d												20 20												20 50
Luton Airport Parkway 7	✈ d												20 22												20 52
St Pancras International 15	⊖ d												21 05												21 35
City Thameslink 3	d												21 12												21 42
London Blackfriars 3	⊖ d												21 16												21 46
Elephant & Castle	⊖ d												21 19												21 49
Loughborough Jn	d												21 23												21 53
Herne Hill 4	d												21 27												21 57
Tulse Hill 3	d		21 06										21 32				21 36								22 02
Streatham 4	d		21 10										21a35				21 40								22a05
London Victoria 15	⊖ d						20 52	21 00	21 05	21 11	21 15	21 20							21 22	21 30	21 35	21 41	21 45	21 50	
Battersea Park 4	d						20 56	21 04	21 09	21a15	21 19								21 26	21 34	21 39	21a45	21 49		
Clapham Junction 10	d						20 59	21 08	21 12		21 22	21 26							21 29	21 38	21 42		21 52	21 56	
Wandsworth Common	d						21 02	21 11	21 15		21 25								21 32	21 41	21 45		21 55		
Balham 4	⊖ d						21 05	21 13	21 18		21 28	21 31							21 35	21 43	21 48		21 58	22 02	
Streatham Hill	d						21 08		21 21										21 38		21 51				
West Norwood 4	d						21 11		21 24										21 41		21 54				
Gipsy Hill	d						21 14		21 27										21 44		21 57				
Crystal Palace 4	d					21a13	21 17		21a30					21a43					21 47		22a00				
Birkbeck	🚋 d																								
Beckenham Junction 4	🚋 a																								
Bromley South 4	a																								
Streatham Common 4	d		21 13					21 17			21 32						21 43			21 47			22 02		
Norbury	d		21 15					21 20			21 34						21 45			21 50			22 04		
Thornton Heath	d		21 18					21 23			21 37						21 48			21 53			22 07		
Selhurst 4	d		21 21					21 26			21 40						21 51			21 56			22 10		
Norwood Junction 2	a	21 08			21 16		21 21								21 38			21 39	21 51						
	d	21 08			21 16		21 24								21 38			21 40	21 54						
West Croydon 4	🚋 a		21 26				21 29				21 44						21 56		21 59				22 14		
East Croydon	🚋 a	21 12			21 19			21 29							21 42			21 44		21 59					

		SN	SN	SN	FC	SN	SN 1	SN	SN	SN	SN	SN	SN	SN	SN	SN	SN	SN	SN 1	SN	SN	SN	SN	SN	FC
								A	B			C				D				B			C		
London Bridge 4	⊖ d	21 54	21 45	21 49		21 41	22 05							22 24	22 15		22 11	22 19	22 28						
South Bermondsey	d			21 53		21 45											22 15	22 23							
Queens Rd Peckham	d			21 55		21 48											22 18	22 25							
Peckham Rye 4	d			21 58		21 50											22 20	22 28							
East Dulwich	d			22 01														22 31							
North Dulwich	d			22 03														22 33							
Luton 10	d				21 20																				21 50
Luton Airport Parkway 7	✈ d				21 22																				21 52
St Pancras International 15	⊖ d				22 05																				22 36
City Thameslink 3	d				22 12																				22 42
London Blackfriars 3	⊖ d				22 16																				22 46
Elephant & Castle	⊖ d				22 19																				22 49
Loughborough Jn	d				22 23																				22 53
Herne Hill 4	d				22 27																				22 57
Tulse Hill 3	d			22 06	22 32													22 36							23 02
Streatham 4	d			22 10	22a35													22 40							23a04
London Victoria 15	⊖ d							21 52	22 00	22 05	22 11	22 15	22 20			22 22				22 30	22 35	22 41	22 45	22 50	
Battersea Park 4	d							21 56	22 04	22 09	22a15	22 19				22 26				22 34	22 39	22a45	22 49		
Clapham Junction 10	d							21 59	22 08	22 12		22 22	22 26			22 29				22 38	22 42		22 52	22 56	
Wandsworth Common	d							22 02	22 11	22 15		22 25				22 32				22 41	22 45		22 55		
Balham 4	⊖ d							22 05	22 13	22 18		22 28	22 32			22 35				22 43	22 48		22 58	23 00	
Streatham Hill	d							22 08		22 21						22 38					22 51				
West Norwood 4	d							22 11		22 24						22 41					22 54				
Gipsy Hill	d							22 14		22 27						22 44					22 57				
Crystal Palace 4	d	22a13						22 17		22a30				22a43		22 47					23a00				
Birkbeck	🚋 d																								
Beckenham Junction 4	🚋 a																								
Bromley South 4	a																								
Streatham Common 4	d			22 13					22 17			22 32						22 43		22 47			23 02		
Norbury	d			22 15					22 20			22 34						22 45		22 50			23 04		
Thornton Heath	d			22 18					22 23			22 37						22 48		22 53			23 07		
Selhurst 4	d			22 21					22 26			22 40						22 51		22 56			23 10		
Norwood Junction 2	a		22 08				22 16	22 21							22 38	22 51			22 40						
	d		22 08				22 16	22 24							22 38	22 54			22 40						
West Croydon 4	🚋 a			22 26				22 29				22 44				22 59		22 56					23 14		
East Croydon	🚋 a		22 12				22 19		22 29						22 42				22 44	22 59					

For general notes see front of timetable
For details of catering facilities see Directory of Train Operators

A To Epsom (Table 182)
B To Tattenham Corner (Table 181)
C To Sutton (Surrey) (Table 182)
D To Epsom Downs (Table 182)

Luton & London → East and West Croydon via Tulse Hill/Crystal Palace/Norbury

Local Services

Network Diagram - see first page of Table 177

		SN	SN	SN	SN	SN 1	SN A	SN B	SN	SN	SN C	FC	SN	SN	SN C	SN	SN	SN	SN	SN	SN C	SN	SN
London Bridge 4	⊖ d	22 54	22 45	22 41	22 49	23 00							23 15	23 24		23 11		23 19				23 53	23 49
South Bermondsey	d			22 45	22 53											23 15		23 23					23 53
Queens Rd Peckham	d			22 48	22 55											23 18		23 25					23 55
Peckham Rye 4	d			22 50	22 58											23 20		23 28					23 58
East Dulwich	d				23 01													23 31					00 01
North Dulwich	d				23 03													23 33					00 03
Luton 10	d											22 20											
Luton Airport Parkway 7	✈ d											22 22											
St Pancras International 15	⊖ d											23 06											
City Thameslink 3	d																						
London Blackfriars 3	⊖ d											23 16											
Elephant & Castle	⊖ d											23 19											
Loughborough Jn	d																						
Herne Hill 4	d											23 27											
Tulse Hill 3	d				23 06							23 32						23 36					00 06
Streatham 4	d				23 10							23a35						23 40					
London Victoria 15	⊖ d						22 52	23 00	23 05	23 11	23 15				23 22		23 26		23 34	23 37	23 51		
Battersea Park 4	d						22 56	23 04	23 09	23a15	23 19				23 26				23 38	23 42	23 55		
Clapham Junction 10	d						22 59	23 08	23 12		23 22				23 29		23 32		23 41	23 45	23 58		
Wandsworth Common	d						23 02	23 11	23 15		23 25				23 32				23 44	23 48	00 01		
Balham 4	⊖ d						23 05	23 13	23 18		23 28				23 35		23 37		23 47	23 51	00 04		
Streatham Hill	d						23 08		23 21						23 38					23 54			
West Norwood 4	d						23 11		23 24						23 41					23 57			00 09
Gipsy Hill	d						23 14		23 27						23 44					23 59			00 12
Crystal Palace 4	d	23a13					23 17		23a30					23a43	23 47					00 03			00 15
Birkbeck	🚊 d																						
Beckenham Junction 4	🚊 a																						
Bromley South 4	a																						
Streatham Common 4	d				23 13			23 17			23 32							23 43	23 51		00 08		
Norbury	d				23 15			23 20			23 34							23 45	23 53		00 10		
Thornton Heath	d				23 18			23 23			23 37							23 48	23 56		00 13		
Selhurst 4	d				23 21			23 26			23 40							23 51	23a59		00 16		
Norwood Junction 2	a		23 08			23 11	23 21						23 38		23 51					00 07		00 16	00 19
	d		23 08			23 11	23 24						23 38		23 54					00 07		00 16	
West Croydon 4	🚊 a				23 26		23 29				23 44				23 58			23 55		00 13	00 20		
East Croydon	🚊 a		23 12			23 16		23 29					23 42									00 20	

Saturdays

		SN	SN C	SN	SN	SN	SN	SN	SN 1	SN D	FC	SN	SN	FC	SN E	SN	SN	SN C	SN	SN	SN A	SN	FC	SN
London Bridge 4	⊖ d			23p53	23p49		00 26					06 11					06 47		06 41	06 49		07 05		07 18
South Bermondsey	d				23p53							06 15							06 45	06 53				
Queens Rd Peckham	d				23p55							06 18							06 48	06 55				
Peckham Rye 4	d				23p58							06 20							06 50	06 58				
East Dulwich	d				00 01															07 01				
North Dulwich	d				00 03															07 03				
Luton 10	d													05 50									06 20	
Luton Airport Parkway 7	✈ d													05 52									06 22	
St Pancras International 15	⊖ d													06 35									07 05	
City Thameslink 3	d																							
London Blackfriars 3	⊖ d										06 16			06 46									07 16	
Elephant & Castle	⊖ d										06 19			06 49									07 19	
Loughborough Jn	d													06 53									07 23	
Herne Hill 4	d										06 27			06 57									07 27	
Tulse Hill 3	d				00 06						06 32			07 02						07 06			07 32	
Streatham 4	d										06a35			07a05						07 10			07a35	
London Victoria 15	⊖ d	23p37	23p51			00 17		00 42	05 25	06 27			06 41		06 45	06 54					06 57			
Battersea Park 4	d	23p42	23p55					00 46		06 31			06a45		06 49						07 01			
Clapham Junction 10	d	23p45	23p58			00 23		00 49	05 31	06 34					06 52	07 00					07 04			
Wandsworth Common	d	23p48	00 01					00 52		06 37					06 55						07 07			
Balham 4	⊖ d	23p51	00 04			00 27		00 55		06 40					06 58	07 04					07 10			
Streatham Hill	d	23p54																06 53						
West Norwood 4	d	23p57			00 09													06 56						
Gipsy Hill	d	23p59			00 12													06 59						
Crystal Palace 4	d	00 03			00 15													07 02						
Birkbeck	🚊 d																							
Beckenham Junction 4	🚊 a																							
Bromley South 4	a																							
Streatham Common 4	d		00 08			00 31		00 59		06 44					07 02					07 13	07 15			
Norbury	d		00 10			00 34		01 01		06 46					07 04					07 15	07 18			
Thornton Heath	d		00 13			00 37		01 04		06 49					07 07					07 18	07 21			
Selhurst 4	d		00 16			00 39		01 07		06 52					07 10					07 21	07 24			
Norwood Junction 2	a	00 07		00 16	00 19		00 49		05 47								07 00	07 06				07 25		07 31
	d	00 07		00 16			00 49		05 48								07 00	07 06				07 25		07 31
West Croydon 4	🚊 a	00 13	00 20							06 56								07 11		07 25	07 28			
East Croydon	🚊 a			00 20		00 42	00 53	01 10	05 51						07 13		07 05					07 29		07 34

For general notes see front of timetable
For details of catering facilities see Directory of Train Operators

A To Epsom (Table 182)
B To Tattenham Corner (Table 181)
C To Sutton (Surrey) (Table 182)
D To Epsom Downs (Table 182)
E To Caterham (Table 181)

Table 177

Saturdays

Luton & London → East and West Croydon via Tulse Hill/Crystal Palace/Norbury

Local Services

Network Diagram - see first page of Table 177

Station		SN	SN	SN	SN	SN	SN	SN	SN	SN	SN	FC	SN	SN	SN	SN	SN	SN	SN	SN	SN	FC		SN	SN
				A					B	C			1				A			D					E
London Bridge 4	d					07 11	07 15	07 19			07 29		07 33	07 35					07 45	07 38				07 49	
South Bermondsey	d					07 15		07 23			07 33									07 42				07 53	
Queens Rd Peckham	d					07 18		07 25			07 35									07 44				07 55	
Peckham Rye 4	d					07 20		07 28			07 38									07 47				07 58	
East Dulwich	d							07 31			07 41									07 50				08 01	
North Dulwich	d							07 33			07 43									07 52				08 03	
Luton 10	d																					06 44			
Luton Airport Parkway 7	d																					06 46			
St Pancras International 15	d																					07 32			
City Thameslink 3	d																								
London Blackfriars 3	d											07 30										07 46			
Elephant & Castle	d											07 33										07 49			
Loughborough Jn	d											07 37										07 53			
Herne Hill 4	d											07 42										07 57			
Tulse Hill 3	d							07 36			07 46	07 46								08b00		08 02		08 06	
Streatham 4	d							07 40				07 49										08a05		08 10	
London Victoria 15	d	07 07	07 11	07 15	07 20				07 25	07 35					07 37	07 41	07 45	07 50			07 52				07 55
Battersea Park 4	d	07 11	07a15	07 19					07 29						07 41	07a45	07 49				07 56				07 59
Clapham Junction 10	d	07 14		07 22	07 26				07 34	07 41					07 44		07 52	07 56			07 59				08 04
Wandsworth Common	d	07 17		07 25					07 37	07 44					07 47		07 55				08 02				08 07
Balham 4	d	07 20		07 28	07 32				07 40	07 47					07 50		07 58	08 02			08 05				08 10
Streatham Hill	d	07 23													07 53						08 08				
West Norwood 4	d	07 26									07 49				07 56					08 03	08 11				
Gipsy Hill	d	07 29									07 52				07 59					08 06	08 14				
Crystal Palace 4	d	07 32									07 55				08 02					08 08	08a17				
Birkbeck	d										07 59														
Beckenham Junction 4	a										08 02														
Bromley South 4	a										*08 17*														
Streatham Common 4	d			07 32				07 43	07 45	07 51							08 02							08 13	08 15
Norbury	d			07 34				07 45	07 48	07 53							08 04							08 15	08 18
Thornton Heath	d			07 37				07 48	07 51	07 56							08 07							08 18	08 21
Selhurst 4	d			07 40				07 51	07 54	07 59							08 10							08 21	08 24
Norwood Junction 2	a	07 36					07 38						07 45	07 55	08 06				08 08	08 13					
	d	07 36					07 39						07 46	07 55	08 06				08 09	08 13					
West Croydon 4	a	07 41					07 44	07 55	07 58	08 03					08 11				08 14					08 25	08 28
East Croydon	a			07 43									07 49	07 59			08 13			08 17					

Station		SN	SN	SN	FC	SE	SN	SN	SN	SN	SN	SN	SN	SN	SN	FC	SN	SN	SN	SN	SN	FC		SN	SN
						13																		1	
		C				G				A				D				B	C						
London Bridge 4	d		07 41	07 59		08 03	08 05					08 15	08 24	08 08			08 19			08 11	08 29			08 33	08 35
South Bermondsey	d		07 45	08 03										08 12			08 23			08 15	08 33				
Queens Rd Peckham	d		07 48	08 05										08 14			08 25			08 18	08 35				
Peckham Rye 4	d		07 50	08 08										08 17			08 28			08 20	08 38				
East Dulwich	d			08 11										08 20			08 31				08 41				
North Dulwich	d			08 13										08 22			08 33				08 43				
Luton 10	d				06 59											07 14						07 26			
Luton Airport Parkway 7	d				07 01											07 16						07 28			
St Pancras International 15	d				07 47											08 02						08 17			
City Thameslink 3	d																								
London Blackfriars 3	d				08 00											08 16						08 30			
Elephant & Castle	d				08 03											08 19						08 33			
Loughborough Jn	d				08 07											08 23						08 37			
Herne Hill 4	d				08 12											08 27						08 42			
Tulse Hill 3	d			08 16	08 16									08c30		08 32	08 36				08 46	08 46			
Streatham 4	d				08 19											08a35	08 40					08 49			
London Victoria 15	d	08 05						08 07	08 11	08 15	08 20				08 22			08 25	08 35						
Battersea Park 4	d							08 11	08a15	08 19					08 26			08 29							
Clapham Junction 10	d	08 11						08 14		08 22	08 26				08 29			08 34	08 41						
Wandsworth Common	d	08 14						08 17		08 25					08 32			08 37	08 44						
Balham 4	d	08 17						08 20		08 28	08 32				08 35			08 40	08 47						
Streatham Hill	d							08 23							08 38										
West Norwood 4	d			08 19				08 26						08 33	08 41						08 49				
Gipsy Hill	d			08 22				08 29						08 36	08 44						08 52				
Crystal Palace 4	d			08 25				08 32					08a43	08 38	08a47						08 55				
Birkbeck	d			08 29																	08 59				
Beckenham Junction 4	a			08 32																	09 02				
Bromley South 4	a			*08 47*																	*09 17*				
Streatham Common 4	d	08 21								08 32							08 43	08 45	08 51						
Norbury	d	08 23								08 34							08 45	08 48	08 53						
Thornton Heath	d	08 26								08 37							08 48	08 51	08 56						
Selhurst 4	d	08 29								08 40							08 51	08 54	08 59						
Norwood Junction 2	a					08 16	08 25	08 36				08 38		08 43										08 45	08 55
	d					08 16	08 25	08 36				08 39		08 43										08 46	08 55
West Croydon 4	a	08 33						08 41				08 44					08 55	08 58	09 03						
East Croydon	a					08 19	08 29			08 43				08 47										08 49	08 59

For general notes see front of timetable
For details of catering facilities see Directory of Train Operators

- **A** To Caterham (Table 181)
- **B** To Epsom Downs (Table 182)
- **C** To Sutton (Surrey) (Table 182)
- **D** To Smitham (Table 181)
- **E** To Epsom (Table 182)
- **G** To Tunbridge Wells (Table 209)
- **b** Arr. 0756
- **c** Arr. 0826

Luton & London → East and West Croydon via Tulse Hill/Crystal Palace/Norbury

Local Services

Network Diagram - see first page of Table 177

Station	SN	SN	SN A	SN	SN	SN B	SN	SN	FC	SN	SN C	SN D	SN	SN	FC	SE 13 E	SN	SN	SN	SN A	SN		SN	SN B
London Bridge 4 ⊖ d					08 45	08 38	08 54			08 49			08 41	08 59		09 03		09 05					09 15	09 08
South Bermondsey d						08 42				08 53			08 45	09 03										09 12
Queens Rd Peckham d						08 44				08 55			08 48	09 05										09 14
Peckham Rye 4 d						08 47				08 58			08 50	09 08										09 17
East Dulwich d						08 50				09 01				09 11										09 20
North Dulwich d						08 52				09 03				09 13										09 22
Luton 10 d									07 44						07 59									
Luton Airport Parkway 7 ✈ d									07 46						08 01									
St Pancras International 15 ⊖ d									08 32						08 47									
City Thameslink 3 d																								
London Blackfriars 3 ⊖ d									08 46						09 00									
Elephant & Castle ⊖ d									08 49						09 03									
Loughborough Jn d									08 53						09 07									
Herne Hill 4 d									08 57						09 12									
Tulse Hill 3 d						09b00			09 02	09 06				09 16	09 16									09c30
Streatham 4 d									09a05	09 10					09 19									
London Victoria 15 ⊖ d	08 37	08 41	08 45	08 50				08 52			08 55	09 05					09 11		09 07	09 15	09 20			
Battersea Park 4 d	08 41	08a45	08 49					08 56			08 59						09a15		09 11	09 19				
Clapham Junction 10 d	08 44		08 52	08 56				08 59			09 04	09 11							09 14	09 22	09 26			
Wandsworth Common d	08 47		08 55					09 02			09 07	09 14							09 17	09 25				
Balham 4 ⊖ d	08 50		08 58	09 02				09 05			09 10	09 17							09 20	09 28	09 32			
Streatham Hill d	08 53							09 08											09 23					
West Norwood 4 d	08 56					09 03		09 11						09 19					09 26					09 33
Gipsy Hill d	08 59					09 06		09 14						09 22					09 29					09 36
Crystal Palace 4 d	09 02					09 08	09a13	09a17						09 25					09 32					09 38
Birkbeck d														09 29										
Beckenham Junction 4 a														09 32										
Bromley South 4 a														*09 47*										
Streatham Common 4 d			09 02							09 13	09 15	09 21								09 32				
Norbury d			09 04							09 15	09 18	09 23								09 34				
Thornton Heath d			09 07							09 18	09 21	09 26								09 37				
Selhurst 4 d			09 10							09 21	09 24	09 29								09 40				
Norwood Junction 2 a	09 06				09 08	09 13										09 16		09 25	09 36				09 38	09 43
Norwood Junction 2 d	09 06				09 09	09 13										09 16		09 25	09 36				09 39	09 43
West Croydon 4 a	09 11				09 14					09 25	09 28	09 33							09 41				09 44	
East Croydon a			09 13			09 17										09 19		09 29		09 43				09 47

Station	SN	SN	FC	SN	SN G	SN D	SN	SN	FC	SN 1		SN	SN	SN	SN A	SN	SN	SN B	SN	SN	FC	SN	SN C	SN D
London Bridge 4 ⊖ d	09 24			09 19			09 11	09 29		09 33		09 35					09 45	09 38	09 54			09 49		
South Bermondsey d				09 23			09 15	09 33										09 42				09 53		
Queens Rd Peckham d				09 25			09 18	09 35										09 44				09 55		
Peckham Rye 4 d				09 28			09 20	09 38										09 47				09 58		
East Dulwich d				09 31				09 41										09 50				10 01		
North Dulwich d				09 33				09 43										09 52				10 03		
Luton 10 d			08 14																		08 44			
Luton Airport Parkway 7 ✈ d			08 16																		08 46			
St Pancras International 15 ⊖ d			09 02						09 17												09 32			
City Thameslink 3 d			09 09						09 24												09 39			
London Blackfriars 3 ⊖ d			09 16						09 30												09 46			
Elephant & Castle ⊖ d			09 19						09 33												09 49			
Loughborough Jn d			09 23						09 37												09 53			
Herne Hill 4 d			09 27						09 42												09 57			
Tulse Hill 3 d			09 32	09 36				09 46	09 46									10e00			10 02	10 06		
Streatham 4 d			09a35	09 40					09 49												10a05	10 10		
London Victoria 15 ⊖ d		09 22			09 25	09 35							09 37	09 41	09 45	09 50				09 52			09 55	10 05
Battersea Park 4 d		09 26			09 29								09 41	09a45	09 49					09 56			09 59	
Clapham Junction 10 d		09 29			09 34	09 41							09 44		09 52	09 56				09 59			10 04	10 11
Wandsworth Common d		09 32			09 37	09 44							09 47		09 55					10 02			10 07	10 14
Balham 4 ⊖ d		09 35			09 40	09 47							09 50		09 58	10 02				10 05			10 10	10 17
Streatham Hill d		09 38											09 53							10 08				
West Norwood 4 d		09 41						09 49					09 56					10 03		10 11				
Gipsy Hill d		09 44						09 52					09 59					10 06		10 14				
Crystal Palace 4 d	09a43	09a47						09 55					10 02					10 08	10a13	10a17				
Birkbeck d								09 59																
Beckenham Junction 4 a								10 02																
Bromley South 4 a								*10 17*																
Streatham Common 4 d				09 43	09 45	09 51									10 02							10 13	10 15	10 21
Norbury d				09 45	09 48	09 53									10 04							10 15	10 18	10 23
Thornton Heath d				09 48	09 51	09 56									10 07							10 18	10 21	10 26
Selhurst 4 d				09 51	09 54	09 59									10 10							10 21	10 24	10 29
Norwood Junction 2 a										09 45		09 55	10 06				10 08	10 13						
Norwood Junction 2 d										09 46		09 55	10 06				10 09	10 13						
West Croydon 4 a				09 55	09 58	10 03							10 11				10 14					10 25	10 28	10 33
East Croydon a										09 49		09 59			10 13			10 17						

For general notes see front of timetable
For details of catering facilities see Directory of Train Operators

- **A** To Caterham (Table 181)
- **B** To Smitham (Table 181)
- **C** To Epsom (Table 182)
- **D** To Sutton (Surrey) (Table 182)
- **E** To Tunbridge Wells (Table 209)
- **G** To Epsom Downs (Table 182)
- **b** Arr. 0856
- **c** Arr. 0926
- **e** Arr. 0956

Table 177

Luton & London → East and West Croydon via Tulse Hill/Crystal Palace/Norbury

Local Services

Network Diagram - see first page of Table 177

Station		SN	SN	FC	SE	SN	SN	SN	SN	SN	SN	SN	SN	SN	FC	SN	SN	SN	SN	SN	FC	SN		SN
					13																	[1]	and at the same minutes past each hour until	
					A				B			C					D	E						
London Bridge [4]	⊖ d	09 41	09 59		10 03	10 05					10 15	10 08	10 24			10 19			10 11	10 29		10 33		17 35
South Bermondsey	d	09 45	10 03									10 12				10 23			10 15	10 33				
Queens Rd Peckham	d	09 48	10 05									10 14				10 25			10 18	10 35				
Peckham Rye [4]	d	09 50	10 08									10 17				10 28			10 20	10 38				
East Dulwich	d		10 11									10 20				10 31				10 41				
North Dulwich	d		10 13									10 22				10 33				10 43				
Luton [10]	d														09 14									
Luton Airport Parkway [7]	✈ d														09 16									
St Pancras International [15]	⊖ d			09 47											10 02						10 17			
City Thameslink [3]	d			09 54											10 09						10 24			
London Blackfriars [3]	⊖ d			10 00											10 16						10 30			
Elephant & Castle	⊖ d			10 03											10 19						10 33			
Loughborough Jn	d			10 07											10 23						10 37			
Herne Hill [4]	d			10 12											10 27						10 42			
Tulse Hill [3]	d		10 16	10 16								10b30			10 32	10 36				10 46	10 46			
Streatham [4]	d			10 19											10a35	10 40					10 49			
London Victoria [15]	⊖ d						10 07	10 11	10 15	10 20				10 22			10 25	10 35						
Battersea Park [4]	d						10 11	10a15	10 19					10 26			10 29							
Clapham Junction [10]	d						10 14		10 22	10 26				10 29			10 34	10 41						
Wandsworth Common	d						10 17		10 25					10 32			10 37	10 44						
Balham [4]	⊖ d						10 20		10 28	10 32				10 35			10 40	10 47						
Streatham Hill	d						10 23							10 38										
West Norwood [4]	d		10 19				10 26					10 33		10 41						10 49				
Gipsy Hill	d		10 22				10 29					10 36		10 44						10 52				
Crystal Palace [4]	d		10 25				10 32					10 38	10a43	10a47						10 55				
Birkbeck	🚊 d		10 29																	10 59				
Beckenham Junction [4]	🚊 a		10 32																	11 02				
Bromley South [4]	a		*10 47*																	*11 17*				
Streatham Common [4]	d								10 32							10 43	10 45	10 51						
Norbury	d								10 34							10 45	10 48	10 53						
Thornton Heath	d								10 37							10 48	10 51	10 56						
Selhurst [4]	d								10 40							10 51	10 54	10 59						
Norwood Junction [2]	a				10 16	10 25	10 36				10 38	10 43										10 45		17 55
	d				10 16	10 25	10 36				10 39	10 43										10 46		17 55
West Croydon [4]	🚊 a						10 41				10 44					10 55	10 58	11 03						
East Croydon	🚊 a				10 19	10 29			10 43			10 47										10 49		17 59

Station		SN		SN	SN	SN	SN	SN	SN	SN	FC	SN	SN	SN	SN	SN	FC	SE	SN	SN	SN	SN	SN	SN	SN
																		13							
					B			C						G				A				H			C
London Bridge [4]	⊖ d						17 45	17 38	17 54			17 41	17 49			17 59		18 03	18 05					18 15	18 08
South Bermondsey	d							17 42				17 45	17 53			18 03									18 12
Queens Rd Peckham	d							17 44				17 48	17 55			18 05									18 14
Peckham Rye [4]	d							17 47				17 50	17 58			18 08									18 17
East Dulwich	d							17 50					18 01			18 11									18 20
North Dulwich	d							17 52					18 03			18 13									18 22
Luton [10]	d										16 44														
Luton Airport Parkway [7]	✈ d										16 46														
St Pancras International [15]	⊖ d										17 32						17 47								
City Thameslink [3]	d										17 39						17 54								
London Blackfriars [3]	⊖ d										17 46						18 00								
Elephant & Castle	⊖ d										17 49						18 03								
Loughborough Jn	d										17 53						18 07								
Herne Hill [4]	d										17 57						18 12								
Tulse Hill [3]	d							18c00			18 02		18 06			18 16	18 16								18e30
Streatham [4]	d										18a05		18 10				18 19								
London Victoria [15]	⊖ d	17 37		17 41	17 45	17 50				17 52				17 55	18 05					18 07	18 11	18 15	18 20		
Battersea Park [4]	d	17 41		17a45	17 49					17 56				17 59						18 11	18a15	18 19			
Clapham Junction [10]	d	17 44			17 52	17 56				17 59				18 04	18 11					18 14		18 22	18 26		
Wandsworth Common	d	17 47			17 55					18 02				18 07	18 14					18 17		18 25			
Balham [4]	⊖ d	17 50			17 58	18 02				18 05				18 10	18 17					18 20		18 28	18 32		
Streatham Hill	d	17 53								18 08										18 23					
West Norwood [4]	d	17 56						18 03		18 11						18 19				18 26					18 33
Gipsy Hill	d	17 59						18 06		18 14						18 22				18 29					18 36
Crystal Palace [4]	d	18 02						18 08	18a13	18a17						18 25				18 32					18 38
Birkbeck	🚊 d															18 29									
Beckenham Junction [4]	🚊 a															18 32									
Bromley South [4]	a															*18 47*									
Streatham Common [4]	d				18 02								18 13	18 15	18 21							18 32			
Norbury	d				18 04								18 15	18 18	18 23							18 34			
Thornton Heath	d				18 07								18 18	18 21	18 26							18 37			
Selhurst [4]	d				18 10								18 21	18 24	18a29							18 40			
Norwood Junction [2]	a	18 06					18 08	18 13										18 16	18 25	18 36				18 38	18 43
	d	18 06					18 09	18 13										18 16	18 25	18 36				18 39	18 43
West Croydon [4]	🚊 a	18 11					18 14						18 25	18 28						18 41				18 44	
East Croydon	🚊 a				18 13			18 17										18 19	18 29			18 43			18 47

For general notes see front of timetable
For details of catering facilities see Directory of Train Operators

A To Tunbridge Wells (Table 209)
B To Caterham (Table 181)
C To Smitham (Table 181)
D To Epsom Downs (Table 182)
E To Sutton (Surrey) (Table 182)
G To Epsom (Table 182)
H To Purley (Table 175)
b Arr. 1026
c Arr. 1756
e Arr. 1826

Table 177

Saturdays

Luton & London → East and West Croydon via Tulse Hill/Crystal Palace/Norbury

Local Services

Network Diagram - see first page of Table 177

		SN		SN	SN	FC	SN	SN	SN	SN	FC	FC	SN	SN	SN	SN	SN	SN	SN	SN	SN	SN	SN	SE	SN
													1											13	
								A										B						C	D
London Bridge 4	⊖ d	18 24			18 11		18 19			18 29			18 33	18 35	18 48					18 41	18 45	18 49	18 54	19 03	
South Bermondsey	d				18 15		18 23			18 33										18 45		18 53			
Queens Rd Peckham	d				18 18		18 25			18 35										18 48		18 55			
Peckham Rye 4	d				18 20		18 28			18 38										18 50		18 58			
East Dulwich	d						18 31			18 41												19 01			
North Dulwich	d						18 33			18 43												19 03			
Luton 10	d					17 14						17 44													
Luton Airport Parkway 7	✈ d					17 16						17 46													
St Pancras International 15	⊖ d					18 02					18 17	18 32													
City Thameslink 3	d					18 09					18 24	18 39													
London Blackfriars 3	⊖ d					18 16					18 30	18 46													
Elephant & Castle	⊖ d					18 19					18 33	18 49													
Loughborough Jn	d					18 23					18 37	18 53													
Herne Hill 4	d					18 27					18 42	18 57													
Tulse Hill 3	d					18 32	18 36			18 46	18 46	19 02										19 06			
Streatham 4	d					18a35	18 40				18 49	19a05										19 10			
London Victoria 15	⊖ d			18 22				18 25	18 35							18 37	18 41	18 45	18 50						18 52
Battersea Park 4	d			18 26				18 29								18 41	18a45	18 49							18 56
Clapham Junction 10	d			18 29				18 34	18 41							18 44		18 52	18 56						18 59
Wandsworth Common	d			18 32				18 37	18 44							18 47		18 55							19 02
Balham 4	⊖ d			18 35				18 40	18 46							18 50		18 58	19 02						19 05
Streatham Hill	d			18 38												18 53									19 08
West Norwood 4	d			18 41						18 49						18 56									19 11
Gipsy Hill	d			18 44						18 52						18 59									19 14
Crystal Palace 4	d	18a43		18a47						18 55						19 02							19a13		19 17
Birkbeck	d									18 59															
Beckenham Junction 4	a									19 02															
Bromley South 4	a									*19 17*															
Streatham Common 4	d						18 43	18 45	18 50									19 02				19 13			
Norbury	d						18 45	18 48	18 53									19 04				19 15			
Thornton Heath	d						18 48	18 51	18 56									19 07				19 18			
Selhurst 4	d						18 51	18 53	18a58									19 10				19 21			
Norwood Junction 2	a												18 45	18 55	19 03	19 06					19 08			19 16	19 21
	d												18 46	18 55	19 03	19 06					19 09			19 16	19 24
West Croydon 4	a						18 55	18 57								19 11		19 14				19 25			19 29
East Croydon	a												18 49	18 59	19 06						19 13			19 19	

		SN		SN	SN	SN	SN	SN	FC	SN	FC	SN	SN	SN	SN	SN	SN	SN	SN	SN	SN	SN	SN	FC	SN
															1										
		E						B								A	E					B			
London Bridge 4	⊖ d			19 15	18 59							19 11	19 19	19 24	19 33			19 44	19 29						19 41
South Bermondsey	d				19 03							19 15	19 23						19 33						19 45
Queens Rd Peckham	d				19 05							19 18	19 25						19 35						19 48
Peckham Rye 4	d				19 08							19 20	19 28						19 38						19 50
East Dulwich	d				19 11								19 31						19 41						
North Dulwich	d				19 13								19 33						19 43						
Luton 10	d										18 20													18 50	
Luton Airport Parkway 7	✈ d										18 22													18 52	
St Pancras International 15	⊖ d								18 47		19 05													19 35	
City Thameslink 3	d								18 54		19 12													19 42	
London Blackfriars 3	⊖ d								19 00		19 16													19 46	
Elephant & Castle	⊖ d								19 03		19 19													19 49	
Loughborough Jn	d								19 07		19 23													19 53	
Herne Hill 4	d								19 12		19 27													19 57	
Tulse Hill 3	d				19 16				19 16		19 32		19 36						19 46					20 02	
Streatham 4	d								19 19		19a35		19 40											20a05	
London Victoria 15	⊖ d	19 00				19 05	19 11	19 15		19 20						19 22	19 30			19 35	19 41	19 45	19 50		
Battersea Park 4	d	19 04				19 09	19a15	19 19								19 26	19 34			19 39	19a45	19 49			
Clapham Junction 10	d	19 08				19 12		19 22		19 26						19 29	19 38			19 42		19 52	19 56		
Wandsworth Common	d	19 11				19 15		19 25								19 32	19 41			19 45		19 55			
Balham 4	⊖ d	19 13				19 18		19 28		19 32						19 35	19 43			19 48		19 58	20 02		
Streatham Hill	d					19 21										19 38				19 51					
West Norwood 4	d				19 19	19 24										19 41			19 49	19 54					
Gipsy Hill	d				19 22	19 27										19 44			19 52	19 57					
Crystal Palace 4	d				19 25	19a30								19a43		19 47			19 55	20a00					
Birkbeck	d				19 29														19 59						
Beckenham Junction 4	a				19 32														20 02						
Bromley South 4	a				*19 47*														*20 17*						
Streatham Common 4	d	19 18						19 32					19 43				19 47					20 02			
Norbury	d	19 20						19 34					19 45				19 50					20 04			
Thornton Heath	d	19 23						19 37					19 48				19 53					20 07			
Selhurst 4	d	19 26						19 40					19 51				19 55					20 10			
Norwood Junction 2	a			19 38											19 45	19 51		20 08							
	d			19 38											19 46	19 54		20 08							
West Croydon 4	a							19 44					19 55			19 59						20 14			
East Croydon	a	19 29		19 42											19 50		19 59	20 12							

For general notes see front of timetable
For details of catering facilities see Directory of Train Operators

A To Epsom Downs (Table 182)
B To Sutton (Surrey) (Table 182)
C To Tonbridge (Table 209)
D To Epsom (Table 182)
E To Tattenham Corner (Table 181)

Table 177

Luton & London → East and West Croydon via Tulse Hill/Crystal Palace/Norbury

Local Services

Network Diagram - see first page of Table 177

		SN		SN	SN	SN	SN	SN	SN	SN	SN	FC	SN	SN	SN	SN	SN	SN	SN	SN	SN	SN	FC	SN	SN
				1		A	B			C					D			B			C				
London Bridge 4	⊖ d	19 49		20 08	19 54								20 15	20 24		20 11	20 19							20 54	20 45
South Bermondsey	d	19 53														20 15	20 23								
Queens Rd Peckham	d	19 55														20 18	20 25								
Peckham Rye 4	d	19 58														20 20	20 28								
East Dulwich	d	20 01															20 31								
North Dulwich	d	20 03															20 33								
Luton 10	d											19 20											19 50		
Luton Airport Parkway 7	✈ d											19 22											19 52		
St Pancras International 15	⊖ d											20 05											20 35		
City Thameslink 3	d											20 12											20 42		
London Blackfriars 3	⊖ d											20 16											20 46		
Elephant & Castle	⊖ d											20 19											20 49		
Loughborough Jn	d											20 23											20 53		
Herne Hill 4	d											20 27											20 57		
Tulse Hill 3	d	20 06										20 32					20 36						21 02		
Streatham 4	d	20 10										20a35					20 40						21a05		
London Victoria 15	⊖ d					19 52	20 00	20 05	20 11	20 15	20 20				20 22			20 30	20 35	20 41	20 45	20 50			
Battersea Park 4	d					19 56	20 04	20 09	20a15	20 19					20 26			20 34	20 39	20a45	20 49				
Clapham Junction 10	d					19 59	20 08	20 12		20 22	20 26				20 29			20 38	20 42		20 52	20 56			
Wandsworth Common	d					20 02	20 11	20 15		20 25					20 32			20 41	20 45		20 55				
Balham 4	⊖ d					20 05	20 13	20 18		20 28	20 32				20 35			20 43	20 48		20 58	21 02			
Streatham Hill	d					20 08		20 21							20 38				20 51						
West Norwood 4	d					20 11		20 24							20 41				20 54						
Gipsy Hill	d					20 14		20 27							20 44				20 57						
Crystal Palace 4	d				20a13	20 17		20a30						20a43	20 47				21a00					21a13	
Birkbeck	🚋 d																								
Beckenham Junction 4	🚋 a																								
Bromley South 4	a																								
Streatham Common 4	d	20 13					20 17			20 32							20 43	20 47			21 02				
Norbury	d	20 15					20 20			20 34							20 45	20 50			21 04				
Thornton Heath	d	20 18					20 23			20 37							20 48	20 53			21 07				
Selhurst 4	d	20 21					20 25			20 40							20 51	20 55			21 10				
Norwood Junction 2	a			20 19		20 21							20 38		20 51										21 08
	d			20 19		20 24							20 38		20 54										21 08
West Croydon 4	🚋 a	20 26				20 29				20 44					20 59		20 56				21 14				
East Croydon	🚋 a			20 22			20 29						20 42					20 59							21 12

		SN		FC	SN	SN	SN	SN	SN	SN	SN	SN	SN	SN	SN	SN	SN	SN	SN	SN	SN	SN	FC	SN	SN
						1	A	B			C				D			B			C		1		
London Bridge 4	⊖ d	20 49			20 41	21 08							21 15	21 24		21 11	21 19							21 54	21 45
South Bermondsey	d	20 53			20 45											21 15	21 23								
Queens Rd Peckham	d	20 55			20 48											21 18	21 25								
Peckham Rye 4	d	20 58			20 50											21 20	21 28								
East Dulwich	d	21 01															21 31								
North Dulwich	d	21 03															21 33								
Luton 10	d			20 20																			20 50		
Luton Airport Parkway 7	✈ d			20 22																			20 52		
St Pancras International 15	⊖ d			21 05																			21 35		
City Thameslink 3	d																								
London Blackfriars 3	⊖ d			21 16																			21 46		
Elephant & Castle	⊖ d			21 19																			21 49		
Loughborough Jn	d			21 23																			21 53		
Herne Hill 4	d			21 27																			21 57		
Tulse Hill 3	d	21 06		21 32													21 36						22 02		
Streatham 4	d	21 10		21a35													21 40						22a05		
London Victoria 15	⊖ d						20 52	21 00	21 05	21 11	21 15	21 20			21 22			21 30	21 35	21 41	21 45	21 50			
Battersea Park 4	d						20 56	21 04	21 09	21a15	21 19				21 26			21 34	21 39	21a45	21 49				
Clapham Junction 10	d						20 59	21 08	21 12		21 22	21 26			21 29			21 38	21 42		21 52	21 56			
Wandsworth Common	d						21 02	21 11	21 15		21 25				21 32			21 41	21 45		21 55				
Balham 4	⊖ d						21 05	21 13	21 18		21 28	21 32			21 35			21 43	21 48		21 58	22 02			
Streatham Hill	d						21 08		21 21						21 38				21 51						
West Norwood 4	d						21 11		21 24						21 41				21 54						
Gipsy Hill	d						21 14		21 27						21 44				21 57						
Crystal Palace 4	d						21 17		21a30					21a43	21 47				22a00					22a13	
Birkbeck	🚋 d																								
Beckenham Junction 4	🚋 a																								
Bromley South 4	a																								
Streatham Common 4	d	21 13						21 17			21 32						21 43	21 47			22 02				
Norbury	d	21 15						21 20			21 34						21 45	21 50			22 04				
Thornton Heath	d	21 18						21 23			21 37						21 48	21 53			22 07				
Selhurst 4	d	21 21						21 25			21 40						21 51	21 55			22 10				
Norwood Junction 2	a					21 19	21 21						21 38		21 51										22 08
	d					21 19	21 24						21 38		21 54										22 08
West Croydon 4	🚋 a	21 26					21 29				21 44				21 59		21 56				22 14				
East Croydon	🚋 a					21 22		21 29					21 42					21 59							22 12

For general notes see front of timetable
For details of catering facilities see Directory of Train Operators

A To Epsom (Table 182)
B To Tattenham Corner (Table 181)
C To Sutton (Surrey) (Table 182)
D To Epsom Downs (Table 182)

Table 177

Saturdays

Luton & London → East and West Croydon via Tulse Hill/Crystal Palace/Norbury

Local Services

Network Diagram - see first page of Table 177

	SN		SN	SN 1	SN	SN	SN	SN	SN	SN	FC	SN	SN	SN	SN	SN	SN	SN	SN	SN	SN	FC	SN	SN
					A	B			C					D			B			C				
London Bridge 4 ⊖ d	21 41		21 49	22 08								22 24	22 15		22 11	22 19							22 54	22 45
South Bermondsey d	21 45		21 53												22 15	22 23								
Queens Rd Peckham d	21 48		21 55												22 18	22 25								
Peckham Rye 4 d	21 50		21 58												22 20	22 28								
East Dulwich d			22 01													22 31								
North Dulwich d			22 03													22 33								
Luton 10 d											21 20											21 50		
Luton Airport Parkway 7 ✈ d											21 22											21 52		
St Pancras International 15 ⊖ d											22 05											22 36		
City Thameslink 3 d																								
London Blackfriars 3 ⊖ d											22 16											22 46		
Elephant & Castle ⊖ d											22 19											22 49		
Loughborough Jn d											22 23											22 53		
Herne Hill 4 d											22 27											22 57		
Tulse Hill 3 d			22 06								22 32					22 36						23 02		
Streatham 4 d			22 10								22a35					22 40						23a05		
London Victoria 15 ⊖ d					21 52	22 00	22 05	22 11	22 15	22 20				22 22			22 30	22 35	22 41	22 45	22 50			
Battersea Park 4 d					21 56	22 04	22 09	22a15	22 19					22 26			22 34	22 39	22a45	22 49				
Clapham Junction 10 d					21 59	22 08	22 12		22 22	22 26				22 29			22 38	22 42		22 52	22 56			
Wandsworth Common d					22 02	22 11	22 15		22 25					22 32			22 41	22 45		22 55				
Balham 4 ⊖ d					22 05	22 13	22 18		22 28	22 32				22 35			22 43	22 48		22 58	23 00			
Streatham Hill d					22 08		22 21							22 38				22 51						
West Norwood 4 d					22 11		22 24							22 41				22 54						
Gipsy Hill d					22 14		22 27							22 44				22 57						
Crystal Palace 4 d					22 17		22a30					22a43		22 47				23a00					23a13	
Birkbeck d																								
Beckenham Junction 4 a																								
Bromley South 4 a																								
Streatham Common 4 d			22 13			22 17			22 32							22 43	22 47			23 02				
Norbury d			22 15			22 20			22 34							22 45	22 50			23 04				
Thornton Heath d			22 18			22 23			22 37							22 48	22 53			23 07				
Selhurst 4 d			22 21			22 25			22 40							22 51	22 55			23 10				
Norwood Junction 2 a				22 19	22 21								22 38	22 51										23 08
d				22 19	22 24								22 38	22 54										23 08
West Croydon 4 a			22 26		22 29				22 44					22 59		22 56				23 15				
East Croydon a				22 22		22 29							22 42				22 59							23 12

	SN		SN	FC	SN	SN	SN	SN	SN	SN	SN	SN	SN	SN	SN	SN	SN	SN	SN	SN	SN			
						A	B			C			C						C					
London Bridge 4 ⊖ d	22 41		22 49		23 00						23 24	23 15		23 11		23 19				23 53	23 49			
South Bermondsey d	22 45		22 53											23 15		23 23					23 53			
Queens Rd Peckham d	22 48		22 55											23 18		23 25					23 55			
Peckham Rye 4 d	22 50		22 58											23 20		23 28					23 58			
East Dulwich d			23 01													23 31					00 01			
North Dulwich d			23 03													23 33					00 03			
Luton 10 d				22 20																				
Luton Airport Parkway 7 ✈ d				22 22																				
St Pancras International 15 ⊖ d				23 06																				
City Thameslink 3 d																								
London Blackfriars 3 ⊖ d				23 16																				
Elephant & Castle ⊖ d				23 19																				
Loughborough Jn d																								
Herne Hill 4 d				23 27																				
Tulse Hill 3 d			23 06	23 32												23 36					00 06			
Streatham 4 d			23 10	23a35												23 40								
London Victoria 15 ⊖ d						22 52	23 00	23 05	23 11	23 15			23 22		23 26		23 34	23 37	23 51					
Battersea Park 4 d						22 56	23 04	23 09	23a15	23 19			23 26				23 38	23 42	23 55					
Clapham Junction 10 d						22 59	23 08	23 12		23 22			23 29		23 32		23 41	23 45	23 58					
Wandsworth Common d						23 02	23 11	23 15		23 25			23 32				23 44	23 48	00 01					
Balham 4 ⊖ d						23 05	23 13	23 18		23 28			23 35		23 37		23 47	23 51	00 04					
Streatham Hill d						23 08		23 21					23 38					23 54						
West Norwood 4 d						23 11		23 24					23 41					23 57			00 09			
Gipsy Hill d						23 14		23 27					23 44					23 59			00 12			
Crystal Palace 4 d						23 17		23a30			23a43		23 47					00 03			00 15			
Birkbeck d																								
Beckenham Junction 4 a																								
Bromley South 4 a																								
Streatham Common 4 d			23 13				23 17			23 32						23 43	23 51		00 08					
Norbury d			23 15				23 20			23 34						23 45	23 53		00 10					
Thornton Heath d			23 18				23 23			23 37						23 48	23 56		00 13					
Selhurst 4 d			23 21				23 25			23 40						23 51	23a59		00 16					
Norwood Junction 2 a					23 11	23 21						23 38	23 51					00 07		00 16	00 19			
d					23 11	23 24						23 38	23 54					00 07		00 16				
West Croydon 4 a			23 26			23 29				23 45			23 58			23 55		00 13	00 20					
East Croydon a					23 16		23 29					23 42								00 20				

For general notes see front of timetable
For details of catering facilities see Directory of Train Operators

A To Epsom (Table 182)
B To Tattenham Corner (Table 181)
C To Sutton (Surrey) (Table 182)
D To Epsom Downs (Table 182)

Table 177

Sundays

Luton & London → East and West Croydon via Tulse Hill/Crystal Palace/Norbury

Local Services

Network Diagram - see first page of Table 177

Station		SN	SN	SN	SN	SN	SN	SN	SN	SN	SN 1	SN	SN	SN	SN 1	SN	SN	SN	SN	SN	SN	SN	SN	SN	SN
			A							B	C	B		D	E			A		A					D
London Bridge 4	⊖ d			23p53	23p24	23p49		00 26					07 11	07 14		07 25	07 44				07 41		07 55	07 58	08 14
South Bermondsey	d					23p53							07 15			07 29					07 45		07 59		
Queens Rd Peckham	d					23p55							07 18			07 31					07 48		08 01		
Peckham Rye 4	d					23p58							07 20			07 34					07 50		08 04		
East Dulwich	d					00 01										07 37							08 07		
North Dulwich	d					00 03										07 39							08 09		
Luton 10	d																								
Luton Airport Parkway 7	✈ d																								
St Pancras International 15	⊖ d																								
City Thameslink 3	d																								
London Blackfriars 3	⊖ d																								
Elephant & Castle	⊖ d																								
Loughborough Jn	d																								
Herne Hill 4	d																								
Tulse Hill 3	d					00 06										07 42							08 12		
Streatham 4	d															07 46							08 16		
London Victoria 15	⊖ d	23p37	23p51				00 17		00 42	06 49	07 02	07 19			07 34			07 38	07 41	07 49		08 06			
Battersea Park 4	d	23p42	23p55						00 46	06 53		07 23						07 42	07a45	07 53					
Clapham Junction 10	d	23p45	23p58				00 23		00 49	06 56	07 08	07 26			07 40			07 45		07 56		08 12			
Wandsworth Common	d	23p48	00 01						00 52	06 59		07 29						07 48		07 59					
Balham 4	⊖ d	23p51	00 04				00 27		00 55	07 02		07 32						07 51		08 02		08 16			
Streatham Hill	d	23p54																07 54							
West Norwood 4	d	23p57				00 09												07 57							
Gipsy Hill	d	23p59				00 12												08 00							
Crystal Palace 4	d	00 03			23b43	00 15												08 03							
Birkbeck	🚊 d																								
Beckenham Junction 4	🚊 a																								
Bromley South 4	a																								
Streatham Common 4	d		00 08				00 31		00 59	07 06		07 36				07 49				08 06			08 19		
Norbury	d		00 10				00 34		01 01	07 08		07 38				07 51				08 08			08 21		
Thornton Heath	d		00 13				00 37		01 04	07 11		07 41				07 54				08 11			08 24		
Selhurst 4	d		00 16				00 39		01 07	07 14	07 18	07 44			07 50	07 58				08 14			08 27		
Norwood Junction 2	a	00 07		00 16		00 19		00 49						07 26			08 04	08 07						08 21	08 26
	d	00 07		00 16				00 49						07 26			08 04	08 07						08 21	08 26
West Croydon 4	🚊 a	00 13	00 20							07 18		07 48						08 12		08 18				08 26	
East Croydon	🚊 a			00 20			00 42	00 53	01 10		07 23			07 30	07 53	08 02	08 08						08 32		08 30

Station		SN	SN	SN	SN	SN	SN	SN	SN	SN	SN	SN	SN	SN	SN	SN	SN	FC	SN	SN	SN	SN	SN	SN	SN
			A		A						A		A						D		A		A		
London Bridge 4	⊖ d	08 14				08 11		08 25	08 28	08 44				08 41		08 55	08 58		09 14	09 14				09 11	
South Bermondsey	d					08 15		08 29						08 45		08 59								09 15	
Queens Rd Peckham	d					08 18		08 31						08 48		09 01								09 18	
Peckham Rye 4	d					08 20		08 34						08 50		09 04								09 20	
East Dulwich	d							08 37								09 07									
North Dulwich	d							08 39								09 09									
Luton 10	d																	08 20							
Luton Airport Parkway 7	✈ d																	08 22							
St Pancras International 15	⊖ d																	09 06							
City Thameslink 3	d																								
London Blackfriars 3	⊖ d																	09 16							
Elephant & Castle	⊖ d																	09 19							
Loughborough Jn	d																	09 23							
Herne Hill 4	d																	09 27							
Tulse Hill 3	d							08 42								09 12		09 31							
Streatham 4	d							08 46								09 16		09a34							
London Victoria 15	⊖ d		08 08	08 11	08 19		08 36				08 38	08 41	08 49		09 06						09 08	09 11	09 19		09 36
Battersea Park 4	d		08 12	08a15	08 23						08 42	08a45	08 53								09 12	09a15	09 23		
Clapham Junction 10	d		08 15		08 26		08 42				08 45		08 56		09 12						09 15		09 26		09 42
Wandsworth Common	d		08 18		08 29						08 48		08 59								09 18		09 29		
Balham 4	⊖ d		08 21		08 32		08 46				08 51		09 02		09 16						09 21		09 32		09 46
Streatham Hill	d		08 24								08 54										09 24				
West Norwood 4	d		08 27								08 57										09 27				
Gipsy Hill	d		08 30								09 00										09 30				
Crystal Palace 4	d		08 33								09 03										09 33				
Birkbeck	🚊 d																								
Beckenham Junction 4	🚊 a																								
Bromley South 4	a																								
Streatham Common 4	d				08 36			08 49					09 06			09 19							09 36		
Norbury	d				08 38			08 51					09 08			09 21							09 38		
Thornton Heath	d				08 41			08 54					09 11			09 24							09 41		
Selhurst 4	d				08 44			08 57					09 14			09 27							09 44		
Norwood Junction 2	a	08 34	08 37						08 51	09 04	09 07						09 21		09 26	09 34	09 37				
	d	08 34	08 37						08 51	09 04	09 07						09 21		09 26	09 34	09 37				
West Croydon 4	🚊 a		08 42		08 48				08 56		09 12		09 18				09 26				09 42		09 48		
East Croydon	🚊 a	08 38						09 00		09 08						09 32			09 30	09 38					

For general notes see front of timetable
For details of catering facilities see Directory of Train Operators

A To Sutton (Surrey) (Table 182)
B To Dorking (Table 182)
C To Bognor Regis (Table 188)
D Until 7 September
E To Horsham (Table 186)
b Previous night. Arrival time

Table 177

Sundays

Luton & London → East and West Croydon via Tulse Hill/Crystal Palace/Norbury

Local Services

Network Diagram - see first page of Table 177

		SN	SN	FC	SN	SN	SN	SN	SN	SN	SN	SN	FC	SN	SN	SN	SN	SN	SN	SN		SN	SN
						A		A						B		A		A					
London Bridge [4]	⊖ d	09 25	09 28		09 44				09 41		09 55	09 58		10 14	10 14				10 11			14 25	14 28
South Bermondsey	d	09 29							09 45		09 59								10 15			14 29	
Queens Rd Peckham	d	09 31							09 48		10 01								10 18			14 31	
Peckham Rye [4]	d	09 34							09 50		10 04								10 20			14 34	
East Dulwich	d	09 37									10 07											14 37	
North Dulwich	d	09 39									10 09											14 39	
Luton [10]	d			08 50									09 20										
Luton Airport Parkway [7]	✈ d			08 52									09 22										
St Pancras International [15]	⊖ d			09 36									10 06										
City Thameslink [3]	d																						
London Blackfriars [3]	⊖ d			09 46									10 16										
Elephant & Castle	⊖ d			09 49									10 19										
Loughborough Jn	d			09 53									10 23										
Herne Hill [4]	d			09 57									10 27								and at		
Tulse Hill [3]	d	09 42		10 01							10 12		10 31								the same	14 42	
Streatham [4]	d	09 46		10a04							10 16		10a34									14 46	
London Victoria [15]	⊖ d					09 38	09 41	09 49		10 06						10 08	10 11	10 19		10 36	minutes		
Battersea Park [4]	d					09 42	09a45	09 53								10 12	10a15	10 23					
Clapham Junction [10]	d					09 45		09 56		10 12						10 15		10 26		10 42	past		
Wandsworth Common	d					09 48		09 59								10 18		10 29					
Balham [4]	⊖ d					09 51		10 02		10 16						10 21		10 32		10 46	each		
Streatham Hill	d					09 54										10 24					hour until		
West Norwood [4]	d					09 57										10 27							
Gipsy Hill	d					10 00										10 30							
Crystal Palace [4]	d					10 03										10 33							
Birkbeck	d																						
Beckenham Junction [4]	a																						
Bromley South [4]	a																						
Streatham Common [4]	d	09 49						10 06			10 19							10 36				14 49	
Norbury	d	09 51						10 08			10 21							10 38				14 51	
Thornton Heath	d	09 54						10 11			10 24							10 41				14 54	
Selhurst [4]	d	09 57						10 14			10 27							10 44				14 57	
Norwood Junction [2]	a		09 51		10 04	10 07						10 21		10 26	10 34	10 37							14 51
	d		09 51		10 04	10 07						10 21		10 26	10 34	10 37							14 51
West Croydon [4]	a		09 56			10 12		10 18				10 26				10 42		10 48					14 56
East Croydon	a	10 02			10 08						10 34			10 30	10 38							15 02	

		FC	SN	SN	SN	SN	SN	SN	SN	SN	FC	SN	SN	SN	SN	SN	SN	SN	SN	SN	FC	SN	SN	SN
				A		A						B		A		A							A	
London Bridge [4]	⊖ d		14 44				14 41		14 55	14 58		15 14	15 14				15 11		15 25	15 28		15 44		
South Bermondsey	d						14 45		14 59								15 15		15 29					
Queens Rd Peckham	d						14 48		15 01								15 18		15 31					
Peckham Rye [4]	d						14 50		15 04								15 20		15 34					
East Dulwich	d								15 07										15 37					
North Dulwich	d								15 09										15 39					
Luton [10]	d	13 50									14 18										14 50			
Luton Airport Parkway [7]	✈ d	13 52									14 20										14 52			
St Pancras International [15]	⊖ d	14 36									15 06										15 36			
City Thameslink [3]	d																							
London Blackfriars [3]	⊖ d	14 46									15 16										15 46			
Elephant & Castle	⊖ d	14 49									15 19										15 49			
Loughborough Jn	d	14 53									15 23										15 53			
Herne Hill [4]	d	14 57									15 27										15 57			
Tulse Hill [3]	d	15 01							15 12		15 31								15 42		16 01			
Streatham [4]	d	15a04							15 16		15a34								15 46		16a04			
London Victoria [15]	⊖ d			14 38	14 41	14 49		15 06						15 08	15 11	15 19		15 36					15 38	15 41
Battersea Park [4]	d			14 42	14a45	14 53								15 12	15a15	15 23							15 42	15a45
Clapham Junction [10]	d			14 45		14 56		15 12						15 15		15 26		15 42					15 45	
Wandsworth Common	d			14 48		14 59								15 18		15 29							15 48	
Balham [4]	⊖ d			14 51		15 02		15 16						15 21		15 32		15 46					15 51	
Streatham Hill	d			14 54										15 24									15 54	
West Norwood [4]	d			14 57										15 27									15 57	
Gipsy Hill	d			15 00										15 30									16 00	
Crystal Palace [4]	d			15 03										15 33									16 03	
Birkbeck	d																							
Beckenham Junction [4]	a																							
Bromley South [4]	a																							
Streatham Common [4]	d					15 06			15 19							15 36			15 49					
Norbury	d					15 08			15 21							15 38			15 51					
Thornton Heath	d					15 11			15 24							15 41			15 54					
Selhurst [4]	d					15 14			15 27							15 44			15 57					
Norwood Junction [2]	a		15 04	15 07						15 21		15 26	15 34	15 37						15 51		16 04	16 07	
	d		15 04	15 07						15 21		15 26	15 34	15 37						15 51		16 04	16 07	
West Croydon [4]	a			15 12		15 18				15 26				15 42		15 48				15 56			16 12	
East Croydon	a		15 08						15 32			15 30	15 38						16 02			16 08		

For general notes see front of timetable
For details of catering facilities see Directory of Train Operators

A To Sutton (Surrey) (Table 182)
B Until 7 September

Sundays

Luton & London → East and West Croydon via Tulse Hill/Crystal Palace/Norbury

Local Services

Network Diagram - see first page of Table 177

		SN	SN	SN	SN	SN	FC	SN	SN	SN	SN	SN	SN	SN	SN	SN	FC	SN	SN	SN	SN	SN	SN	SN	SN
		A						B		A		A							A		A				
London Bridge 4	⊖ d		15 41		15 55	15 58		16 14	16 14				16 11		16 25	16 28		16 44				16 41		16 55	16 58
South Bermondsey	d		15 45		15 59								16 15		16 29							16 45		16 59	
Queens Rd Peckham	d		15 48		16 01								16 18		16 31							16 48		17 01	
Peckham Rye 4	d		15 50		16 04								16 20		16 34							16 50		17 04	
East Dulwich	d				16 07										16 37									17 07	
North Dulwich	d				16 09										16 39									17 09	
Luton 10	d						15 20										15 50								
Luton Airport Parkway 7	✈ d						15 22										15 52								
St Pancras International 15	⊖ d						16 06										16 36								
City Thameslink 3	d																								
London Blackfriars 3	⊖ d						16 16										16 46								
Elephant & Castle	⊖ d						16 19										16 49								
Loughborough Jn	d						16 23										16 53								
Herne Hill 4	d						16 27										16 57								
Tulse Hill 3	d				16 12		16 31								16 42		17 01							17 12	
Streatham 4	d				16 16		16a34								16 46		17a04							17 16	
London Victoria 15	⊖ d	15 49		16 06						16 08	16 11	16 19		16 36					16 38	16 41	16 49		17 06		
Battersea Park 4	d	15 53								16 12	16a15	16 23							16 42	16a45	16 53				
Clapham Junction 10	d	15 56		16 12						16 15		16 26		16 42					16 45		16 56		17 12		
Wandsworth Common	d	15 59								16 18		16 29							16 48		16 59				
Balham 4	⊖ d	16 02		16 16						16 21		16 32		16 46					16 51		17 02		17 16		
Streatham Hill	d									16 24									16 54						
West Norwood 4	d									16 27									16 57						
Gipsy Hill	d									16 30									17 00						
Crystal Palace 4	d									16 33									17 03						
Birkbeck	🚋 d																								
Beckenham Junction 4	🚋 a																								
Bromley South 4	a																								
Streatham Common 4	d	16 06			16 19							16 36			16 49						17 06			17 19	
Norbury	d	16 08			16 21							16 38			16 51						17 08			17 21	
Thornton Heath	d	16 11			16 24							16 41			16 54						17 11			17 24	
Selhurst 4	d	16 14			16 27							16 44			16 57						17 14			17 27	
Norwood Junction 2	a					16 21		16 26	16 34	16 37						16 51		17 04	17 07						17 21
	d					16 21		16 26	16 34	16 37						16 51		17 04	17 07						17 21
West Croydon 4	🚋 a	16 18				16 26				16 42		16 48				16 56			17 12		17 18				17 26
East Croydon	🚋 a				16 32			16 30	16 38						17 02			17 08						17 32	

		FC	SN	SN	SN	SN	SN	SN	SN	SN	SN	FC	SN	SN	SN	SN	SN	SN	SN	SN	FC	SN	SN	SN	SN
			B		A		A							A		A						B		A	
London Bridge 4	⊖ d		17 14	17 14				17 11		17 25	17 28		17 44				17 41		17 55	17 58		18 14	18 14		
South Bermondsey	d							17 15		17 29							17 45		17 59						
Queens Rd Peckham	d							17 18		17 31							17 48		18 01						
Peckham Rye 4	d							17 20		17 34							17 50		18 04						
East Dulwich	d									17 37									18 07						
North Dulwich	d									17 39									18 09						
Luton 10	d	16 20										16 50									17 20				
Luton Airport Parkway 7	✈ d	16 22										16 52									17 22				
St Pancras International 15	⊖ d	17 06										17 36									18 06				
City Thameslink 3	d																								
London Blackfriars 3	⊖ d	17 16										17 46									18 16				
Elephant & Castle	⊖ d	17 19										17 49									18 19				
Loughborough Jn	d	17 23										17 53									18 23				
Herne Hill 4	d	17 27										17 57									18 27				
Tulse Hill 3	d	17 31								17 42		18 01							18 12		18 31				
Streatham 4	d	17a34								17 46		18a04							18 16		18a34				
London Victoria 15	⊖ d				17 08	17 11	17 19		17 36					17 38	17 41	17 49		18 06						18 08	18 11
Battersea Park 4	d				17 12	17a15	17 23							17 42	17a45	17 53								18 12	18a15
Clapham Junction 10	d				17 15		17 26		17 42					17 45		17 56		18 12						18 15	
Wandsworth Common	d				17 18		17 29							17 48		17 59								18 18	
Balham 4	⊖ d				17 21		17 32		17 46					17 51		18 02		18 16						18 21	
Streatham Hill	d				17 24									17 54										18 24	
West Norwood 4	d				17 27									17 57										18 27	
Gipsy Hill	d				17 30									18 00										18 30	
Crystal Palace 4	d				17 33									18 03										18 33	
Birkbeck	🚋 d																								
Beckenham Junction 4	🚋 a																								
Bromley South 4	a																								
Streatham Common 4	d						17 36			17 49						18 06			18 19						
Norbury	d						17 38			17 51						18 08			18 21						
Thornton Heath	d						17 41			17 54						18 11			18 24						
Selhurst 4	d						17 44			17 57						18 14			18 27						
Norwood Junction 2	a		17 26	17 34	17 37						17 51		18 04	18 07						18 21		18 26	18 34	18 37	
	d		17 26	17 34	17 37						17 51		18 04	18 07						18 21		18 26	18 34	18 37	
West Croydon 4	🚋 a				17 42		17 48				17 56			18 12		18 18				18 26				18 42	
East Croydon	🚋 a		17 30	17 38						18 02			18 08						18 32			18 30	18 38		

For general notes see front of timetable
For details of catering facilities see
Directory of Train Operators

A To Sutton (Surrey) (Table 182)
B Until 7 September

Sundays

Luton & London → East and West Croydon via Tulse Hill/Crystal Palace/Norbury

Local Services

Network Diagram - see first page of Table 177

Station		SN A	SN	SN	SN	SN	FC	SN	SN A	SN	SN A	SN	SN	SN	SN	FC	SN B	SN	SN A	SN	SN A	SN	SN	SN	SN
London Bridge 4	⊖ d		18 11		18 25	18 28		18 44				18 41		18 55	18 58		19 14	19 14				19 11		19 25	19 28
South Bermondsey	d		18 15		18 29							18 45		18 59								19 15		19 29	
Queens Rd Peckham	d		18 18		18 31							18 48		19 01								19 18		19 31	
Peckham Rye 4	d		18 20		18 34							18 50		19 04								19 20		19 34	
East Dulwich	d				18 37									19 07										19 37	
North Dulwich	d				18 39									19 09										19 39	
Luton 10	d						17 50									18 20									
Luton Airport Parkway 7	✈ d						17 52									18 22									
St Pancras International 15	⊖ d						18 36									19 06									
City Thameslink 3	d																								
London Blackfriars 3	⊖ d						18 46									19 16									
Elephant & Castle	⊖ d						18 49									19 19									
Loughborough Jn	d						18 53									19 23									
Herne Hill 4	d						18 57									19 27									
Tulse Hill 3	d				18 42		19 01							19 12		19 31								19 42	
Streatham 4	d				18 46		19a04							19 16		19a34								19 46	
London Victoria 15	⊖ d	18 19		18 36					18 38	18 41	18 49		19 06						19 08	19 11	19 19		19 36		
Battersea Park 4	d	18 23							18 42	18a45	18 53								19 12	19a15	19 23				
Clapham Junction 10	d	18 26		18 42					18 45		18 56		19 12						19 15		19 26		19 42		
Wandsworth Common	d	18 29							18 48		18 59								19 18		19 29				
Balham 4	⊖ d	18 32		18 46					18 51		19 02		19 16						19 21		19 32		19 46		
Streatham Hill	d								18 54										19 24						
West Norwood 4	d								18 57										19 27						
Gipsy Hill	d								19 00										19 30						
Crystal Palace 4	d								19 03										19 33						
Birkbeck	🚋 d																								
Beckenham Junction 4	🚋 a																								
Bromley South 4	a																								
Streatham Common 4	d	18 36			18 49						19 06			19 19							19 36			19 49	
Norbury	d	18 38			18 51						19 08			19 21							19 38			19 51	
Thornton Heath	d	18 41			18 54						19 11			19 24							19 41			19 54	
Selhurst 4	d	18 44			18 57						19 14			19 27							19 44			19 57	
Norwood Junction 2	a					18 51		19 04	19 07						19 21		19 26	19 34	19 37						19 51
	d					18 51		19 04	19 07						19 21		19 26	19 34	19 37						19 51
West Croydon 4	🚋 a	18 48				18 56			19 12		19 18				19 26				19 42		19 48				19 56
East Croydon	🚋 a				19 02			19 08						19 32			19 30	19 38						20 02	

Station		FC	SN	SN A	SN	SN A	SN	SN	SN	SN	FC	SN B	SN	SN A	SN	SN A	SN	SN	SN	SN	FC	SN	SN A	SN	SN A
London Bridge 4	⊖ d		19 44				19 41		19 55	19 58		20 14	20 14				20 11		20 25	20 28		20 44			
South Bermondsey	d						19 45		19 59								20 15		20 29						
Queens Rd Peckham	d						19 48		20 01								20 18		20 31						
Peckham Rye 4	d						19 50		20 04								20 20		20 34						
East Dulwich	d								20 07										20 37						
North Dulwich	d								20 09										20 39						
Luton 10	d	18 50									19 20										19 50				
Luton Airport Parkway 7	✈ d	18 52									19 22										19 52				
St Pancras International 15	⊖ d	19 36									20 06										20 36				
City Thameslink 3	d																								
London Blackfriars 3	⊖ d	19 46									20 16										20 46				
Elephant & Castle	⊖ d	19 49									20 19										20 49				
Loughborough Jn	d	19 53									20 23										20 53				
Herne Hill 4	d	19 57									20 27										20 57				
Tulse Hill 3	d	20 01							20 12		20 31								20 42		21 01				
Streatham 4	d	20a04							20 16		20a34								20 46		21a04				
London Victoria 15	⊖ d			19 38	19 41	19 49		20 06						20 08	20 11	20 19		20 36					20 38	20 41	20 49
Battersea Park 4	d			19 42	19a45	19 53								20 12	20a15	20 23							20 42	20a45	20 53
Clapham Junction 10	d			19 45		19 56		20 12						20 15		20 26		20 42					20 45		20 56
Wandsworth Common	d			19 48		19 59								20 18		20 29							20 48		20 59
Balham 4	⊖ d			19 51		20 02		20 16						20 21		20 32		20 46					20 51		21 02
Streatham Hill	d			19 54										20 24									20 54		
West Norwood 4	d			19 57										20 27									20 57		
Gipsy Hill	d			20 00										20 30									21 00		
Crystal Palace 4	d			20 03										20 33									21 03		
Birkbeck	🚋 d																								
Beckenham Junction 4	🚋 a																								
Bromley South 4	a																								
Streatham Common 4	d					20 06			20 19							20 36			20 49						21 06
Norbury	d					20 08			20 21							20 38			20 51						21 08
Thornton Heath	d					20 11			20 24							20 41			20 54						21 11
Selhurst 4	d					20 14			20 27							20 44			20 57						21 14
Norwood Junction 2	a		20 04	20 07						20 21		20 26	20 34	20 37						20 51		21 04	21 07		
	d		20 04	20 07						20 21		20 26	20 34	20 37						20 51		21 04	21 07		
West Croydon 4	🚋 a			20 12		20 18				20 26				20 42		20 48				20 56			21 12		21 18
East Croydon	🚋 a		20 08						20 32			20 30	20 38						21 02			21 08			

For general notes see front of timetable
For details of catering facilities see
Directory of Train Operators

A To Sutton (Surrey) (Table 182)
B Until 7 September

Table 177

Sundays

Luton & London → East and West Croydon via Tulse Hill/Crystal Palace/Norbury

Local Services

Network Diagram - see first page of Table 177

Station		SN	SN	SN	SN	SN	SN	SN	SN	SN	SN	SN	SN	SN	SN	SN	SN	SN	SN	SN	SN	SN	SN	SN	SN
						A		B		B						B		B					A	B	
London Bridge 4	⊖ d	20 41		20 55	20 58	21 14	21 14				21 11		21 25	21 28	21 44				21 41		21 55	21 58	22 14		
South Bermondsey	d	20 45		20 59							21 15		21 29						21 45		21 59				
Queens Rd Peckham	d	20 48		21 01							21 18		21 31						21 48		22 01				
Peckham Rye 4	d	20 50		21 04							21 20		21 34						21 50		22 04				
East Dulwich	d			21 07									21 37								22 07				
North Dulwich	d			21 09									21 39								22 09				
Luton 10	d																								
Luton Airport Parkway 7	✈ d																								
St Pancras International 15	⊖ d																								
City Thameslink 3	d																								
London Blackfriars 3	⊖ d																								
Elephant & Castle	⊖ d																								
Loughborough Jn	d																								
Herne Hill 4	d																								
Tulse Hill 3	d			21 12									21 42								22 12				
Streatham 4	d			21 16									21 46								22 16				
London Victoria 15	⊖ d		21 06					21 08	21 11	21 19		21 36				21 38	21 41	21 49		22 06				22 08	22 11
Battersea Park 4	d							21 12	21a15	21 23						21 42	21a45	21 53						22 12	22a15
Clapham Junction 10	d		21 12					21 15		21 26		21 42				21 45		21 56		22 12				22 15	
Wandsworth Common	d							21 18		21 29						21 48		21 59						22 18	
Balham 4	⊖ d		21 16					21 21		21 32		21 46				21 51		22 02		22 16				22 21	
Streatham Hill	d							21 24								21 54								22 24	
West Norwood 4	d							21 27								21 57								22 27	
Gipsy Hill	d							21 30								22 00								22 30	
Crystal Palace 4	d							21 33								22 03								22 33	
Birkbeck	🚋 d																								
Beckenham Junction 4	🚋 a																								
Bromley South 4	a																								
Streatham Common 4	d			21 19						21 36			21 49					22 06			22 19				
Norbury	d			21 21						21 38			21 51					22 08			22 21				
Thornton Heath	d			21 24						21 41			21 54					22 11			22 24				
Selhurst 4	d			21 27						21 44			21 57					22 14			22 27				
Norwood Junction 2	a				21 21	21 26	21 34	21 37						21 51	22 04	22 07						22 21	22 26	22 37	
	d				21 21	21 26	21 34	21 37						21 51	22 04	22 07						22 21	22 26	22 39	
West Croydon 4	🚋 a				21 26			21 42		21 48				21 56		22 12		22 18				22 26		22 43	
East Croydon	🚋 a			21 32		21 30	21 38						22 00		22 08						22 32		22 30		

Station		SN	SN	SN	SN	SN	SN	SN	SN	SN	SN	SN	SN	SN	SN	SN	SN	SN	SN	SN	SN	SN	SN
																			1 ◇				
			B			B				B							C		D				
London Bridge 4	⊖ d	22 14		22 11				22 25	22 44		22 41				22 55	23 14		23 11			23 25	23 44	
South Bermondsey	d			22 15				22 29			22 45				22 59			23 15			23 29		
Queens Rd Peckham	d			22 18				22 31			22 48				23 01			23 18			23 31		
Peckham Rye 4	d			22 20				22 34			22 50				23 04			23 20			23 34		
East Dulwich	d							22 37							23 07						23 37		
North Dulwich	d							22 39							23 09						23 39		
Luton 10	d																						
Luton Airport Parkway 7	✈ d																						
St Pancras International 15	⊖ d																						
City Thameslink 3	d																						
London Blackfriars 3	⊖ d																						
Elephant & Castle	⊖ d																						
Loughborough Jn	d																						
Herne Hill 4	d																						
Tulse Hill 3	d							22 42							23 12						23 42		
Streatham 4	d							22 46							23 16						23 46		
London Victoria 15	⊖ d		22 19		22 36	22 38	22 41			22 49		23 06	23 08	23 11			23 19		23 32	23 38			23 49
Battersea Park 4	d		22 23			22 42	22a45			22 53			23 12	23a15			23 23			23 42			23 53
Clapham Junction 10	d		22 26		22 42	22 45				22 56		23 12	23 15				23 26		23 38	23 45			23 56
Wandsworth Common	d		22 29			22 48				22 59			23 18				23 29			23 48			23 59
Balham 4	⊖ d		22 32		22 46	22 51				23 02		23 16	23 21				23 32			23 51			00 02
Streatham Hill	d					22 54							23 24							23 54			
West Norwood 4	d					22 57							23 27							23 57			
Gipsy Hill	d					23 00							23 30							23 59			
Crystal Palace 4	d					23 03							23 33							00 03			
Birkbeck	🚋 d																						
Beckenham Junction 4	🚋 a																						
Bromley South 4	a																						
Streatham Common 4	d		22 36					22 49		23 06					23 19		23 36				23 49		00 06
Norbury	d		22 38					22 51		23 08					23 21		23 38				23 51		00 08
Thornton Heath	d		22 41					22 54		23 11					23 24		23 41				23 54		00 11
Selhurst 4	d		22 44					22 57		23 14					23 27		23 44		23 48		23 57		00 14
Norwood Junction 2	a	22 37				23 07			23 07				23 37			23 37				00 07		00 09	
	d	22 39				23 07			23 09				23 37			23 39						00 10	
West Croydon 4	🚋 a		22 48			23 12				23 18			23 42				23 48						
East Croydon	🚋 a	22 42						23 00	23 12						23 32	23 42			23 52		00 01	00 13	00 17

For general notes see front of timetable
For details of catering facilities see Directory of Train Operators

A Until 7 September
B To Sutton (Surrey) (Table 182)
C To Epsom (Table 182)
D To Brighton (Table 186)

East and West Croydon → London & Luton via Norbury/Crystal Palace/Tulse Hill

Local Services

Network Diagram - see first page of Table 177

Miles	Miles	Miles	Miles	Miles			SN MX	SN MO 1 A	SN	SN	SN 1 ◇ B	FC C	SN	SN	SN	SN D	SN	FC C	SN E	SN	SN	SN	SN	SN	SN
0	—	—	0	0	**East Croydon**	d		23p56		05 13	05 29			05 34		05 48	05 51			06 12					06 17
—	0	—	—	—	**West Croydon 4**	d									05 45				06 02		06 15				
1¼	—	—	—	1¼	Norwood Junction 2	a				05 17				05 38	05 50		05 55			06 16	06 19				
—	—	—	—	—		d				05 17				05 38	05 50		05 55			06 16	06 19				
—	1	—	1	—	Selhurst 4	d		00 01			05 32	05 36				05 51		05 56	06 06						06 20
—	1¾	—	1¾	—	Thornton Heath	d					05 35	05 38				05 53		05 58	06 08						06 22
—	3	—	3	—	Norbury	d					05 38	05 40				05 56		06 00	06 11						06 25
—	4	—	4	—	Streatham Common 4	d					05 40	05 43				05 59		06 03	06 14						06 27
—	—	—	—	—	Bromley South 4	d																			
—	—	0	—	—	Beckenham Junction 4	d																			
—	—	1½	—	—	Birkbeck	d																			
2¾	—	3	—	2¾	**Crystal Palace 4**	d	23p43							05 42			05 59								
3½	—	3¾	—	3½	Gipsy Hill	d	23p46							05 44			06 01								
4½	—	4¾	—	4½	West Norwood 4	d	23p49							05 47			06 04								
5¾	—	6	—	—	Streatham Hill	d	23p52							05 51											
6¾	—	7	5¾	—	Balham 4	⊖ d	23p55				05 44			05 54		06 03			06 18				06 27		06 31
7½	—	7¾	6½	—	Wandsworth Common	d	23p57									06 05			06 20						06 33
8¾	—	9	7¾	—	Clapham Junction 10	d	00 01	00 11	05 02		05 49			05 58		06 08			06 23				06 31		06 37
10¼	—	10½	9¼	—	Battersea Park 4	d	00 04				05 52			06 02		06 12			06 27			06 32			06 40
11½	—	11¾	10½	—	**London Victoria 15**	⊖ a	00 12	00 18	05 09		05 58			06 06		06 18			06 31			06 36	06 38		06 46
—	4½	—	—	—	Streatham 4	d						05 46	05 52					06 06						06 32	
—	6	—	—	5	Tulse Hill 3	d						05 50	05 55				06 07	06 10						06 35	
—	—	—	—	—	Herne Hill 4	a						05 53						06 13							
—	—	—	—	—	Loughborough Jn	a												06 17							
—	—	—	—	—	Elephant & Castle	⊖ a						06 01						06 22							
—	—	—	—	—	London Blackfriars 3	⊖ a						06 05						06 27							
—	—	—	—	—	City Thameslink 3	a						06 10						06 30							
—	—	—	—	—	St Pancras International 15	⊖ a						06 18						06 38							
—	—	—	—	—	Luton Airport Parkway 7	✈ a						07 01						07 21							
—	—	—	—	—	**Luton 10**	a						07 04						07 24							
—	7¼	—	—	6¼	North Dulwich	d											06 10							06 38	
—	7¾	—	—	6¾	East Dulwich	d											06 12							06 40	
—	8½	—	—	7½	Peckham Rye 4	d							06 00				06 15							06 43	
—	9¼	—	—	8¼	Queens Rd Peckham	d											06 17							06 45	
—	10¼	—	—	9¼	South Bermondsey	d											06 20							06 48	
—	12	—	—	11	**London Bridge 4**	⊖ a				05 41			06 07		06 14		06 24			06 34	06 45			06 52	

		FC	FC	SN	SN	SN G	SN	SN	FC H	SN	SN	SN	SN	SN	SN J	SN	SN	FC	SN K	SN	SN	SN	SN	SN	SN
East Croydon	d				06 28			06 40							06 45					07 12			07 05		
West Croydon 4	d					06 31					06 45								07 00					07 16	
Norwood Junction 2	a				06 32			06 44			06 50									07 16				07 21	
	d			06 24	06 32		06 42	06 44			06 50					06 54	07 03			07 16				07 21	
Selhurst 4	d					06 35			06 45						06 48				07 04				07 10		
Thornton Heath	d					06 37			06 47						06 50				07 06				07 12		
Norbury	d					06 40			06 49						06 53				07 09				07 15		
Streatham Common 4	d					06 43			06 52						06 56				07 12				07 17		
Bromley South 4	d																								
Beckenham Junction 4	d																								
Birkbeck	d																								
Crystal Palace 4	d			06 28			06 46									06 58	07 07				07 15				
Gipsy Hill	d			06 30			06 48									07 00	07 09								
West Norwood 4	d			06 33			06 51									07 03	07 12								
Streatham Hill	d			06 37												07 07									
Balham 4	⊖ d			06 40		06 47							06 57		07 00	07 10			07 16						
Wandsworth Common	d			06 42		06 49									07 02	07 12			07 18						
Clapham Junction 10	d			06 45		06 52							07 01		07 05	07 15			07 21						
Battersea Park 4	d			06 49		06 56						07 02			07 09	07 19			07 25						07 32
London Victoria 15	⊖ a			06 53		07 02						07 08	07 10		07 16	07 25			07 31						07 38
Streatham 4	d	06 36	06 50						06 56					07 06				07 16					07 20		
Tulse Hill 3	d	06 40	06 54				06b58		07 00					07 09			07 15	07 20					07 24		
Herne Hill 4	a	06 45	06 58						07 04									07 24							
Loughborough Jn	a	06 48	07 02						07 07									07 27							
Elephant & Castle	⊖ a	06 53	07 06						07 12									07 31							
London Blackfriars 3	⊖ a	06 56	07 11						07 17									07 37							
City Thameslink 3	a	07 00	07 14						07 20									07 40							
St Pancras International 15	⊖ a	07 08	07 21						07 28									07 48							
Luton Airport Parkway 7	✈ a	07 54																08 27							
Luton 10	a	07 56																08 30							
North Dulwich	d						07 01							07 12			07 18						07 27		
East Dulwich	d						07 03							07 14			07 20						07 29		
Peckham Rye 4	d						07 05			06 56				07 17			07 23					07 26	07 31		
Queens Rd Peckham	d						07 08			06 59							07 25					07 29	07 34		
South Bermondsey	d						07 10			07 01							07 28				06 52	07 31	07 36		
London Bridge 4	⊖ a				06 54		07 18	07 02		07 08	07 16			07 25			07 34			07 33	07 36	07 38	07 43	07 48	

For general notes see front of timetable
For details of catering facilities see Directory of Train Operators

- **A** From Horsham (Table 186)
- **B** From Brighton (Table 186)
- **C** To Bedford (Table 52)
- **D** From Redhill (Table 186)
- **E** From Epsom (Table 182)
- **G** From Sutton (Surrey) (Table 182)
- **H** To St Albans City (Table 52)
- **J** From Sanderstead (Table 184)
- **K** From Epsom Downs (Table 182)
- **b** Arr. 0654

East and West Croydon → London & Luton via Norbury/Crystal Palace/Tulse Hill

Local Services

Network Diagram - see first page of Table 177

	SN	SN	SN	SN	SN	SN	SN	SN	FC	SN	SN	SN	SN	SN		SN	SN	SN	SN	SN	SN	SN	SN	SN
										A							1 B							
East Croydon d		07 17				07 36											07 47						07 57	
West Croydon 4 d			07 19	07 28						07 30		07 43									07 46	07 56		
Norwood Junction 2 a			07 24	07 32		07 40						07 48									07 51	08 00	08 01	
d			07 24	07 32		07 41						07 48									07 51	08 01	08 01	
Selhurst 4 d		07 20								07 34	07 40						07 50			07 53				
Thornton Heath d		07 22								07 36	07 42						07 52			07 55				
Norbury d		07 25								07 39	07 45						07 55			07 58				
Streatham Common 4 d		07 27								07 42	07 47						07 58			08 01				
Bromley South 4 d														*07 16*										
Beckenham Junction 4 d														07 35										
Birkbeck d														07 38										
Crystal Palace 4 d			07 28											07 42				07 51	07 54		07 55			
Gipsy Hill d			07 30											07 45				07 53			07 57			
West Norwood 4 d			07 33											07 48				07 56			08 00			
Streatham Hill d			07 37											07 51					07 45		08 04			
Balham 4 ⊖ d	07 29	07 32	07 40		07 42					07 46	07 51			07 54		08 00	08 02			08 05	08 09			
Wandsworth Common d		07 34	07 42							07 48				07 56			08 04			08 07	08 11			
Clapham Junction 10 d	07 33	07 37	07 45		07 48					07 51	07 56			08 00		08 04	08a08			08 11	08 14			
Battersea Park 4 d		07 41	07 49							07 55			08 02	08 04						08 14	08 18			
London Victoria 15 ⊖ a	07 42	07 47	07 55		07 57					08 01	08 05		08 08	08 10		08 13				08 21	08 25			
Streatham 4 d							07 42		07 52															08 05
Tulse Hill 3 d							07 46		07 57									08 00						08 10
Herne Hill 4 a									08 01															
Loughborough Jn a									08 03															
Elephant & Castle ⊖ a									08 09															
London Blackfriars 3 ⊖ a									08 11															
City Thameslink 3 a									08 15															
St Pancras International 15 ⊖ a									08 23															
Luton Airport Parkway 7 ✈ a																								
Luton 10 a																								
North Dulwich d							07 49											08 03						08 13
East Dulwich d							07 51											08 05						08 15
Peckham Rye 4 d							07 53	07 56										08 08						08 17
Queens Rd Peckham d								07 59										08 10						08 20
South Bermondsey d								08 01										08 13						08 22
London Bridge 4 ⊖ a				07 58		08 01	08 02	08 08				08 08						08 21	08 16			08 27	08 16	08 30

	FC	FC	SN	SN	SN	SN	SN	SN	SN	SN	SN	SN	SN	SN	SN	FC	SN	SN	SN	SN	FC	SN	SN	SN
					C	A	D									1 E				G		D		
East Croydon d			08 12										08 09	08 18		08 28							08 34	08 45
West Croydon 4 d						08 01	08 07	08 16									08 19	08 23	08 28					
Norwood Junction 2 a			08 16					08 20									08 24	08 28	08 32				08 39	08 49
d			08 17					08 20									08 25	08 28	08 32				08 40	08 49
Selhurst 4 d						08 05	08 11						08 16	08 21										
Thornton Heath d						08 07	08 13						08 18	08 23										
Norbury d						08 10	08 16						08 21	08 26										
Streatham Common 4 d						08 12	08 18						08 23	08 28										
Bromley South 4 d										*07 37*														
Beckenham Junction 4 d										08 05														
Birkbeck d										08 08														
Crystal Palace 4 d										08 12	08 16	08 23					08 29			08 36				
Gipsy Hill d										08 14							08 31			08 38				
West Norwood 4 d										08 17							08 34			08 42				
Streatham Hill d										08 21					08 32		08 38							
Balham 4 ⊖ d					08 14	08 17	08 22			08 25				08 32			08 41					08 43		
Wandsworth Common d						08 19				08 27				08 34								08 45		
Clapham Junction 10 d					08 18	08 22	08 26			08 30				08 38			08 45					08 49		
Battersea Park 4 d					08 22	08 26			08 32	08 34				08 41			08 49							
London Victoria 15 ⊖ a					08 28	08 32	08 36		08 38	08 40				08 48			08 55					08 58		
Streatham 4 d	08 11	08 21											08 26								08 45			
Tulse Hill 3 d	08 15	08 27											08 30		08 36	08 39				08b51 →	08 49			
Herne Hill 4 a	08 19	08 31														08 43					08 53			
Loughborough Jn a	08 25	08 34																			08 56			
Elephant & Castle ⊖ a	08 29	08 39																			09 00			
London Blackfriars 3 ⊖ a	08 34	08 41														08 52					09 04			
City Thameslink 3 a	08 37	08 45														08 59					09 07			
St Pancras International 15 ⊖ a	08 46	08 54														09 06					09 14			
Luton Airport Parkway 7 ✈ a	09 20															09 40								
Luton 10 a	09 23															09 43								
North Dulwich d													08 33		08 39									
East Dulwich d													08 35		08 41									
Peckham Rye 4 d				08 26									08 38		08 43									
Queens Rd Peckham d				08 29									08 40		08 46									
South Bermondsey d				08 31									08 43		08 48									
London Bridge 4 ⊖ a			08 31	08 38				08 42			08 38	08 46	08 49		08 56			08 47	09 02				08 55	09 05

For general notes see front of timetable
For details of catering facilities see Directory of Train Operators

A From Epsom Downs (Table 182)
B To Kensington Olympia (Table 186)
C From Epsom (Table 182)
D From Sutton (Surrey) (Table 182)
E From Brighton (Table 52)
G From London Bridge (Table 178)
b Arr. 0846

East and West Croydon → London & Luton via Norbury/Crystal Palace/Tulse Hill

Local Services

Network Diagram - see first page of Table 177

Station		SN	SN	FC 1	SN	SN	SN	SN	SN	SN	SN	SN	SN	SN	SN	FC	SN	SN	SN	SN	SN	SN	SN	SN	SN
			A	B	C														D						
East Croydon	d			08 38								08 50					09 05				09 02				
West Croydon 4	d				08 32			08 44					08 49	08 59					08 57			09 15			
Norwood Junction 2	a							08 49					08 53	09 03			09 09					09 19			
	d							08 49					08 53	09 03			09 09					09 19			
Selhurst 4	d				08 36							08 53							09 01		09 05				
Thornton Heath	d				08 38							08 55							09 03		09 07				
Norbury	d				08 41							08 58							09 06		09 10				
Streatham Common 4	d				08 43							09 00							09 09		09 13				
Bromley South 4	d					*08 21*																			
Beckenham Junction 4	d					08 32																			
Birkbeck	d					08 35																			
Crystal Palace 4	d					08 39	08 48						08 57		09 06									09 13	09 17
Gipsy Hill	d					08 41							09 00		09 08									09 16	
West Norwood 4	d					08 44							09 03		09 12									09 19	
Streatham Hill	d					08 48							09 06											09 22	
Balham 4	⊖ d				08 48	08 51				09 02		09 05	09 09						09 13	09 23				09 26	
Wandsworth Common	d				08 50	08 53						09 07	09 11						09 15					09 28	
Clapham Junction 10	d				08 53	08 56				09 07		09 10	09 15						09 19	09 27				09 32	
Battersea Park 4	d				08 57	09 00			09 02			09 14	09 18						09 23				09 32	09 36	
London Victoria 15	⊖ a				09 03	09 06			09 08	09 16		09 20	09 25						09 29	09 36			09 39	09 42	
Streatham 4	d		←								09 06					09 15					09 18				
Tulse Hill 3	d		08 51	08 55							09 09				09 15	09 19					09 22				
Herne Hill 4	a			09 00												09 22									
Loughborough Jn	a															09 26									
Elephant & Castle	⊖ a															09 30									
London Blackfriars 3	⊖ a			09 08												09 33									
City Thameslink 3	a			09 11												09 36									
St Pancras International 15	⊖ a			09 18												09 44									
Luton Airport Parkway 7	✈ a			09 53																					
Luton 10	a			09 55																					
North Dulwich	d		08 54								09 12				09 18						09 25				
East Dulwich	d		08 56								09 14				09 20						09 27				
Peckham Rye 4	d	08 56	09 00								09 17				09 23			09 26			09 29				
Queens Rd Peckham	d	08 59	09 02								09 19				09 25			09 29			09 32				
South Bermondsey	d	09 01	09 05								09 22				09 28			09 31			09 34				
London Bridge 4	⊖ a	09 08	09 12				09 12	09 17			09 29			09 29	09 34		09 24	09 38			09 41	09 46			09 38

Station		SN	FC		SN	SN	SN	SN	SN	SN	SN	SN	SN	FC	SN	SN	SN	SN	FC	SN	SN	SN	SN	SN	SN 1
					E						C									D		E		G	
East Croydon	d				09 17		09 20	09 31														09 47		09 51	09 55
West Croydon 4	d					09 18					09 27		09 31				09 46			09 35			09 49		
Norwood Junction 2	a					09 23	09 24	09 35									09 51						09 53	09 57	09 59
	d					09 23	09 25	09 35									09 51						09 53	09 58	09 59
Selhurst 4	d				09 21						09 31		09 35							09 39		09 50			
Thornton Heath	d				09 23						09 33		09 37							09 41		09 52			
Norbury	d				09 26						09 36		09 40							09 44		09 55			
Streatham Common 4	d				09 28						09 39		09 43							09 47		09 58			
Bromley South 4	d	*09 03*																*09 33*							
Beckenham Junction 4	d	09 16																09 46							
Birkbeck	d	09 19																09 49							
Crystal Palace 4	d	09 23				09 27			09 33						09 43	09 47		09 53					09 57	10 02	
Gipsy Hill	d	09 25				09 29			09 35						09 46			09 55					10 00	10 05	
West Norwood 4	d	09 28				09 32			09 38						09 49			09 58					10 03	10 08	
Streatham Hill	d					09 36									09 52								10 06		
Balham 4	⊖ d				09 32	09 41					09 43	09 49			09 56					09 52		10 02	10 09		
Wandsworth Common	d				09 34	09 43					09 45				09 58					09 54		10 04	10 11		
Clapham Junction 10	d				09 38	09 47					09 48	09 53			10 01					09 57		10 07	10 15		
Battersea Park 4	d				09 41	09 50					09 52				10 05					10 01	10 03		10 18		
London Victoria 15	⊖ a				09 48	09 51					09 59	10 01			10 10					10 05	10 07	10 14	10 23		
Streatham 4	d		09 34										09 46	09 54					10 06						
Tulse Hill 3	d	09 31	09 38						09 41				09 51	09 58				10 01	10 12					10 11	
Herne Hill 4	a		09 42											10 02					10 16						
Loughborough Jn	a		09 45											10 05					10 19						
Elephant & Castle	⊖ a		09 49											10 10					10 24						
London Blackfriars 3	⊖ a		09 56											10 14					10 26						
City Thameslink 3	a		10 00											10 16					10 30						
St Pancras International 15	⊖ a		10 08											10 23					10 38						
Luton Airport Parkway 7	✈ a		10 57																11 25						
Luton 10	a		11 01																11 29						
North Dulwich	d	09 34							09 44				09 54					10 04						10 14	
East Dulwich	d	09 36							09 46				09 56					10 06						10 16	
Peckham Rye 4	d	09 39							09 49	09 56			09 59					10 09						10 19	
Queens Rd Peckham	d	09 41							09 51	09 59			10 02					10 11						10 21	
South Bermondsey	d	09 44							09 54	10 01			10 04					10 14						10 24	
London Bridge 4	⊖ a	09 52					09 42	09 59	09 59	10 06			10 09			10 08	10 15	10 18						10 28	10 12

For general notes see front of timetable
For details of catering facilities see Directory of Train Operators

- **A** From London Bridge (Table 178)
- **B** From Brighton (Table 52)
- **C** From Wimbledon (Table 52)
- **D** From Epsom Downs (Table 182)
- **E** From Caterham (Table 181)
- **G** From Smitham (Table 181)

East and West Croydon → London & Luton via Norbury/Crystal Palace/Tulse Hill

Local Services

Network Diagram - see first page of Table 177

Station		SN	SN	SN	SN	SN	FC	SN	SN	SN	SN	SN	SN	SN	FC	SN	SN	SE 13	SN	SN	SN	SN		SN	FC
				A					B				C				D	E				G			
East Croydon	d	10 00											10 17				10 21	10 24	10 30						
West Croydon [4]	d			09 57		10 01		10 15	10 05							10 18						10 27		10 31	
Norwood Junction [2]	a	10 04						10 19								10 23	10 27	10 28	10 34						
	d	10 04						10 19								10 23	10 28	10 28	10 34						
Selhurst [4]	d			10 01		10 05			10 09				10 20									10 31		10 35	
Thornton Heath	d			10 03		10 07			10 11				10 22									10 33		10 37	
Norbury	d			10 06		10 10			10 14				10 25									10 36		10 40	
Streatham Common [4]	d			10 09		10 13			10 17				10 27									10 39		10 43	
Bromley South [4]	d													*10 03*											
Beckenham Junction [4]	d													10 16											
Birkbeck	d													10 19											
Crystal Palace [4]	d										10 14	10 17		10 23		10 27	10 32								
Gipsy Hill	d										10 16			10 25		10 29	10 35								
West Norwood [4]	d										10 19			10 28		10 32	10 38								
Streatham Hill	d										10 23					10 36									
Balham [4]	⊖ d			10 13	10 18				10 21		10 26		10 31			10 39					10 48	10 43			
Wandsworth Common	d			10 15					10 23		10 28		10 33			10 41						10 45			
Clapham Junction [10]	d			10 18	10 22				10 26		10 31		10 37			10 45					10 52	10 48			
Battersea Park [4]	d			10 22					10 30	10 32	10 34					10 48						10 52			
London Victoria [15]	⊖ a			10 26	10 29				10 34	10 36	10 40		10 44			10 54					10 59	10 56			
Streatham [4]	d					10 16	10 23								10 33									10 47	10 53
Tulse Hill [3]	d					10 21	10 27							10 31	10 42		10 41							10 51	10 57
Herne Hill [4]	a						10 31								10 46										11 00
Loughborough Jn	a						10 34								10 49										11 04
Elephant & Castle	⊖ a						10 39								10 54										11 09
London Blackfriars [3]	⊖ a						10 41								10 56										11 11
City Thameslink [3]	a						10 45								11 00										11 15
St Pancras International [15]	⊖ a						10 53								11 08										11 23
Luton Airport Parkway [7]	✈ a														11 55										
Luton [10]	a														11 59										
North Dulwich	d					10 24								10 34			10 44							10 54	
East Dulwich	d					10 26								10 36			10 46							10 56	
Peckham Rye [4]	d		10 26			10 29								10 39			10 49			10 56				10 59	
Queens Rd Peckham	d		10 29			10 32								10 41			10 51			10 59				11 02	
South Bermondsey	d		10 31			10 34								10 44			10 54			11 01				11 04	
London Bridge [4]	⊖ a	10 25	10 36			10 39		10 44				10 38		10 50			10 58	10 40	10 55	11 06				11 09	

Station		SN	SN	SN	SN	SN	SN	FC	SN	SN	SN	SN [1]	SN	SN	SN	SN	SN	FC	SN	SN	SN	SN	SN	FC	SN
			B	C							D					A				B					
East Croydon	d			10 47							10 51	10 55	11 00												
West Croydon [4]	d	10 45	10 35							10 48						10 57	11 01		11 15	11 05					
Norwood Junction [2]	a	10 49								10 53	10 57	10 59	11 04						11 19						
	d	10 49								10 53	10 58	10 59	11 04						11 19						
Selhurst [4]	d		10 39	10 50												11 01	11 05			11 09					
Thornton Heath	d		10 41	10 52												11 03	11 07			11 11					
Norbury	d		10 44	10 55												11 06	11 10			11 14					
Streatham Common [4]	d		10 47	10 57												11 09	11 13			11 17					
Bromley South [4]	d						*10 33*																*11 03*		
Beckenham Junction [4]	d						10 46																11 16		
Birkbeck	d						10 49																11 19		
Crystal Palace [4]	d					10 47	10 53		10 43	10 57	11 02											11 17	11 23		11 13
Gipsy Hill	d						10 55		10 46	10 59	11 05												11 25		11 16
West Norwood [4]	d						10 58		10 49	11 02	11 08												11 28		11 19
Streatham Hill	d								10 52	11 06															11 22
Balham [4]	⊖ d		10 51	11 01					10 55	11 09					11 18	11 13				11 21					11 25
Wandsworth Common	d		10 53	11 03					10 57	11 11						11 15				11 23					11 27
Clapham Junction [10]	d		10 56	11 07					11 01	11 14					11 22	11 18				11 26					11 31
Battersea Park [4]	d		11 00		11 02				11 04	11 18						11 22				11 30	11 32				11 34
London Victoria [15]	⊖ a		11 04	11 14	11 06				11 09	11 23					11 29	11 26				11 34	11 36				11 39
Streatham [4]	d							11 06									11 16	11 23						11 36	
Tulse Hill [3]	d						11 01	11 12			11 11						11 21	11 27					11 31	11 42	
Herne Hill [4]	a							11 16										11 30						11 46	
Loughborough Jn	a							11 19										11 34						11 49	
Elephant & Castle	⊖ a							11 24										11 39						11 54	
London Blackfriars [3]	⊖ a							11 26										11 41						11 56	
City Thameslink [3]	a							11 30										11 45						12 00	
St Pancras International [15]	⊖ a							11 38										11 53						12 08	
Luton Airport Parkway [7]	✈ a							12 25																12 55	
Luton [10]	a							12 29																12 59	
North Dulwich	d						11 04				11 14						11 24						11 34		
East Dulwich	d						11 06				11 16						11 26						11 36		
Peckham Rye [4]	d						11 09				11 19			11 26			11 29						11 39		
Queens Rd Peckham	d						11 11				11 21			11 29			11 32						11 41		
South Bermondsey	d						11 14				11 24			11 31			11 34						11 44		
London Bridge [4]	⊖ a	11 14				11 06	11 18				11 28	11 12	11 25	11 36			11 39		11 44			11 36	11 48		

For general notes see front of timetable
For details of catering facilities see Directory of Train Operators

A From Epsom Downs (Table 182)
B From Sutton (Surrey) (Table 182)
C From Caterham (Table 181)
D From Smitham (Table 181)
E From Tonbridge (Table 209)
G From Epsom (Table 182)

East and West Croydon → London & Luton via Norbury/Crystal Palace/Tulse Hill

Local Services

Network Diagram - see first page of Table 177

Station		SN	SN	SN	SE 13	SN	SN	SN	SN		SN	FC	SN	SN	SN	SN	SN	SN	SN	SN	FC	SN	SN
		A		B	C				D						E				A				B
East Croydon	d	11 17		11 21	11 24	11 30													15 47				15 51
West Croydon 4	d		11 18						11 27		15 31			15 45	15 35							15 48	
Norwood Junction 2	a		11 23	11 27	11 28	11 34								15 49								15 53	15 57
	d		11 23	11 28	11 28	11 34								15 49								15 53	15 58
Selhurst 4	d	11 20							11 31		15 35				15 39				15 50				
Thornton Heath	d	11 22							11 33		15 37				15 41				15 52				
Norbury	d	11 25							11 36		15 40				15 44				15 55				
Streatham Common 4	d	11 27							11 39		15 43				15 47				15 57				
Bromley South 4	d																			*15 33*			
Beckenham Junction 4	d																			15 46			
Birkbeck	d									and at										15 49			
Crystal Palace 4	d		11 27	11 32													15 43	15 47		15 53		15 57	16 02
Gipsy Hill	d		11 29	11 35						the same							15 46			15 55		15 59	16 05
West Norwood 4	d		11 32	11 38													15 49			15 58		16 02	16 08
Streatham Hill	d		11 36							minutes			15 50				15 52					16 06	
Balham 4	⊖ d	11 31	11 39					11 48	11 43	past					15 52		15 55		16 01			16 09	
Wandsworth Common	d	11 33	11 41						11 45						15 54		15 57		16 03			16 11	
Clapham Junction 10	d	11 37	11 44					11 52	11 48	each					15 57		16 01		16 07			16 14	
Battersea Park 4	d		11 48						11 52						16 01	16 03	16 05					16 18	
London Victoria 15	⊖ a	11 44	11 53					11 59	11 56	hour until					16 05	16 07	16 10		16 14			16 23	
Streatham 4	d										15 46	15 53									16 06		
Tulse Hill 3	d			11 41							15 51	15 57	15b58							16 01	16 12		16 11
Herne Hill 4	a											16 00									16 16		
Loughborough Jn	a											16 04									16 19		
Elephant & Castle	⊖ a											16 09									16 24		
London Blackfriars 3	⊖ a											16 11									16 29		
City Thameslink 3	a											16 16									16 32		
St Pancras International 15	⊖ a											16 24									16 39		
Luton Airport Parkway 7	✈ a																				17 26		
Luton 10	a																				17 29		
North Dulwich	d			11 44							15 54									16 04			16 14
East Dulwich	d			11 46							15 56									16 06			16 16
Peckham Rye 4	d			11 49			11 56				15 59		16 03							16 09			16 19
Queens Rd Peckham	d			11 51			11 59				16 02									16 11			16 21
South Bermondsey	d			11 54			12 01				16 04									16 14			16 24
London Bridge 4	⊖ a			11 58	11 40	11 55	12 06				16 10		16 12	16 16				16 08		16 19			16 28

Station		SN	SN	SN	SN	SN	SN	SN	FC	SN	SN	SN	SN	SN	SN	SN	FC	FC	SN	SN	SE 13	SN	SN	SN	SN
		1															1							1	
						G					E				A		H			B	C				
East Croydon	d	15 55	16 00	16 07											16 17		16 17			16 21	16 24	16 31	16 37	16 44	
West Croydon 4	d					15 57		16 01		16 15	16 05								16 18						
Norwood Junction 2	a	15 59	16 04	16 11						16 19									16 23	16 27	16 28	16 35	16 41	16 48	
	d	15 59	16 04	16 11						16 19									16 23	16 28	16 28	16 35	16 41	16 48	
Selhurst 4	d					16 01		16 05			16 09				16 20										
Thornton Heath	d					16 03		16 07			16 11				16 22										
Norbury	d					16 06		16 10			16 14				16 25										
Streatham Common 4	d					16 09		16 13			16 17				16 27										
Bromley South 4	d															*16 03*									
Beckenham Junction 4	d															16 15									
Birkbeck	d															16 18									
Crystal Palace 4	d												16 13	16 17		16 22			16 27	16 32					
Gipsy Hill	d												16 16			16 24			16 29	16 35					
West Norwood 4	d												16 19			16 27			16 32	16 38					
Streatham Hill	d												16 22						16 36						
Balham 4	⊖ d					16 13	16 18				16 21		16 25		16 31				16 39						
Wandsworth Common	d					16 15					16 23		16 27		16 33				16 41						
Clapham Junction 10	d					16 18	16 22				16 26		16 31		16 37				16 44						
Battersea Park 4	d					16 22					16 30	16 32	16 34						16 48						
London Victoria 15	⊖ a					16 26	16 29				16 34	16 38	16 40		16 44				16 53						
Streatham 4	d							16 16	16 23									16 38							
Tulse Hill 3	d							16 21	16 27							16 31	16 33	16 41		16 41					
Herne Hill 4	a								16 31								16 37	16 46							
Loughborough Jn	a								16 34									16 49							
Elephant & Castle	⊖ a								16 40								16 43	16 54							
London Blackfriars 3	⊖ a								16 44								16 48	16 57							
City Thameslink 3	a								16 46								16 52	17 02							
St Pancras International 15	⊖ a								16 53								17 01	17 09							
Luton Airport Parkway 7	✈ a																17 34	17 50							
Luton 10	a																17 36	17 53							
North Dulwich	d							16 24								16 34				16 44					
East Dulwich	d							16 26								16 36				16 46					
Peckham Rye 4	d				16 26			16 29								16 39				16 49					16 56
Queens Rd Peckham	d				16 29			16 32								16 41				16 51					16 59
South Bermondsey	d				16 31			16 34								16 44				16 54					17 01
London Bridge 4	⊖ a	16 12	16 26	16 24	16 38			16 40		16 46				16 36		16 48				17 00	16 41	16 58	16 56	17 00	17 08

For general notes see front of timetable
For details of catering facilities see
Directory of Train Operators

- **A** From Caterham (Table 181)
- **B** From Smitham (Table 181)
- **C** From Tunbridge Wells (Table 209)
- **D** From Epsom (Table 182)
- **E** From Sutton (Surrey) (Table 182)
- **G** From Epsom Downs (Table 182)
- **H** From Brighton (Table 52)
- **b** Arr. 1555

East and West Croydon → London & Luton via Norbury/Crystal Palace/Tulse Hill

Local Services

Network Diagram - see first page of Table 177

Station		FC	SN	SN	SN	SN	SN	SN	SN	SN	SN	FC	SN	SN	SN	SN	SN	SN 1	SN	FC	SN		SN	SN	FC
			A				B						C		D						E				
East Croydon	d												16 47		16 51	17 00	17 07	17 14							
West Croydon 4	d		16 27		16 31	16 45	16 35							16 48							16 57			17 01	
Norwood Junction 2	a					16 49								16 53	16 56	17 04	17 11	17 18							
	d					16 49								16 53	16 56	17 04	17 11	17 18							
Selhurst 4	d		16 31		16 35		16 39						16 50								17 01			17 06	
Thornton Heath	d		16 33		16 37		16 41						16 52								17 03			17 08	
Norbury	d		16 36		16 40		16 44						16 55								17 06			17 11	
Streatham Common 4	d		16 39		16 43		16 47						16 57								17 09			17 14	
Bromley South 4	d										16 19														
Beckenham Junction 4	d										16 43														
Birkbeck	d										16 46														
Crystal Palace 4	d								16 43	16 47	16 50			16 57	17 00										
Gipsy Hill	d								16 46		16 52			16 59	17 03										
West Norwood 4	d								16 49		16 55			17 02	17 06										
Streatham Hill	d								16 52					17 06											
Balham 4	⊖ d		16 43	16 47			16 51		16 55				17 01	17 09							17 13		17 15		
Wandsworth Common	d		16 45				16 53						17 03	17 11							17 15				
Clapham Junction 10	d		16 48	16 51			16 56		17 01				17 07	17 14							17 18		17 21		
Battersea Park 4	d		16 52				17 00	17 02	17 04					17 18							17 22				
London Victoria 15	⊖ a		16 56	16 58			17 04	17 08	17 10				17 14	17 23							17 26		17 28		
Streatham 4	d	16 55			16 48							17 05								17 23				17 17	17 29
Tulse Hill 3	d	17 00			16 53						16 59	17 09			17 09					17 27				17 23	17 33
Herne Hill 4	a	17 06										17 14								17 31					17 37
Loughborough Jn	a	17 10										17 17								17 34					17 40
Elephant & Castle	⊖ a	17 14										17 22								17 39					17 44
London Blackfriars 3	⊖ a	17 18										17 32								17 44					17 47
City Thameslink 3	a	17 20										17 34								17 46					17 50
St Pancras International 15	⊖ a	17 28										17 42								17 53					17 57
Luton Airport Parkway 7	✈ a											18 28								18 33					
Luton 10	a											18 33								18 37					
North Dulwich	d				16 56						17 02				17 12									17 26	
East Dulwich	d				16 58						17 04				17 14									17 28	
Peckham Rye 4	d				17 01						17 06				17 16				17 26					17 30	
Queens Rd Peckham	d				17 04						17 09				17 19				17 29					17 33	
South Bermondsey	d				17 06						17 11				17 21				17 31					17 35	
London Bridge 4	⊖ a				17 11	17 14				17 10	17 16				17 26	17 27	17 26	17 31	17 38					17 40	

Station		SN	SN	SN	SN	SN	SN	SN	SN	SN	SN	FC	SN	SN	SN	SN 1	SN	SN	SN	SN	SN	SN	SN	SN	SN 1
		B						C							E							C			
East Croydon	d							17 18					17 32	17 37		17 44						17 48			17 53
West Croydon 4	d	17 05	17 13						17 19						17 30			17 47					17 38	17 50	
Norwood Junction 2	a		17 17						17 24				17 36	17 41		17 48		17 52						17 54	17 57
	d		17 19						17 24		17 29		17 36	17 41		17 49		17 52						17 55	17 57
Selhurst 4	d	17 09						17 21							17 36							17 51	17 42		
Thornton Heath	d	17 11						17 23							17 38							17 53	17 44		
Norbury	d	17 14						17 26							17 41							17 56	17 47		
Streatham Common 4	d	17 17						17 28							17 44							17 59	17 50		
Bromley South 4	d						16 47																		
Beckenham Junction 4	d						17 18																		
Birkbeck	d						17 21																		
Crystal Palace 4	d				17 14	17 17	17 25		17 28		17 33									17 43	17 45			17 59	
Gipsy Hill	d				17 16		17 27		17 30		17 35									17 46				18 01	
West Norwood 4	d				17 19		17 30		17 33		17 38									17 49				18 04	
Streatham Hill	d				17 23				17 37											17 52				18 08	
Balham 4	⊖ d	17 21			17 28			17 32	17 40	17 43					17 48					17 56		18 03		18 11	
Wandsworth Common	d	17 23			17 30			17 34	17 42						17 50							18 05		18 13	
Clapham Junction 10	d	17 26			17 33			17 38	17 45	17 48					17 53					18 01		18 08		18 16	
Battersea Park 4	d	17 30		17 32	17 37				17 49										18 02	18 05				18 20	
London Victoria 15	⊖ a	17 34		17 38	17 43			17 48	17 54	17 56					18 00				18 09	18 12		18 15		18 25	
Streatham 4	d											17 49											17 53		
Tulse Hill 3	d						17 33				17 42	17 54											17 57		
Herne Hill 4	a											17 57													
Loughborough Jn	a											18 01													
Elephant & Castle	⊖ a											18 06													
London Blackfriars 3	⊖ a											18 09													
City Thameslink 3	a											18 16													
St Pancras International 15	⊖ a											18 27													
Luton Airport Parkway 7	✈ a																								
Luton 10	a																								
North Dulwich	d						17 36				17 45												18 00		
East Dulwich	d						17 38				17 47												18 02		
Peckham Rye 4	d						17 41				17 49						17 56						18 04		
Queens Rd Peckham	d						17 43				17 52						17 59						18 07		
South Bermondsey	d						17 46				17 54						18 01						18 09		
London Bridge 4	⊖ a		17 43			17 38	17 50				17 59		17 58	17 54		18 06	18 08	18 19			18 10		18 14		18 10

For general notes see front of timetable
For details of catering facilities see Directory of Train Operators

A From Epsom (Table 182)
B From Sutton (Surrey) (Table 182)
C From Caterham (Table 181)
D From Smitham (Table 181)
E From Epsom Downs (Table 182)

East and West Croydon → London & Luton via Norbury/Crystal Palace/Tulse Hill

Local Services

Network Diagram - see first page of Table 177

		SN	FC	SN	SN	FC	SN	SN	SN	SN	FC [1]	SN	SN	FC	SN	SN	SN	SN	SN	SN	SN	SN	SN	SN	SN
								A			B								C						D
East Croydon	d			18 05							18 17								18 17			18 35			
West Croydon [4]	d							18 00		18 08		18 15								18 18					18 30
Norwood Junction [2]	a			18 09								18 19								18 23		18 39			
	d			18 09								18 19								18 24		18 39			
Selhurst [4]	d							18 04		18 13									18 21						18 36
Thornton Heath	d							18 06		18 15									18 23						18 38
Norbury	d							18 09		18 18									18 26						18 41
Streatham Common [4]	d							18 12		18 21									18 29						18 44
Bromley South [4]	d				17 47																				
Beckenham Junction [4]	d				17 57																		18 24		
Birkbeck	d				18 00																		18 27		
Crystal Palace [4]	d				18 05											18 10	18 14	18 21		18 28			18 31		
Gipsy Hill	d				18 07											18 13				18 30			18 34		
West Norwood [4]	d				18 10											18 16				18 33			18 37		
Streatham Hill	d															18 19				18 37					
Balham [4]	⊖ d							18 16	18 18							18 23			18 33	18 40	18 44				18 49
Wandsworth Common	d							18 18								18 25			18 35	18 42					18 51
Clapham Junction [10]	d							18 21	18 24							18 28			18 38	18 45	18 48				18 54
Battersea Park [4]	d							18 25							18 32	18 34				18 49					18 58
London Victoria [15]	⊖ a							18 30	18 34						18 38	18 40			18 45	18 53	18 55				19 03
Streatham [4]	d	18 01	18 08			18 20				18 25			18 32	18 38											
Tulse Hill [3]	d	18 05	18 12		18 15	18 24				18 28	18 32		18 36	18 42									18b45		
Herne Hill [4]	a		18 16			18 27					18 35			18 48											
Loughborough Jn	a		18 19			18 30					18 40			18 51											
Elephant & Castle	⊖ a		18 24			18 34					18 45			18 56											
London Blackfriars [3]	⊖ a		18 29			18 40					18 49			18 59											
City Thameslink [3]	a		18 34			18 48					18 54			19 04											
St Pancras International [15]	⊖ a		18 41			18 55					19 01			19 11											
Luton Airport Parkway [7]	✈ a		19 27											19 58											
Luton [10]	a		19 33								19 34			20 01											
North Dulwich	d	18 08			18 18					18 31			18 39										18 48		
East Dulwich	d	18 10			18 20					18 33			18 41										18 50		
Peckham Rye [4]	d	18 12			18 23		18 26			18 36			18 43				17 53						18 53	18 56	
Queens Rd Peckham	d	18 15			18 25		18 29			18 38			18 46										18 55	18 59	
South Bermondsey	d	18 17			18 28		18 31			18 41			18 48										18 58	19 01	
London Bridge [4]	⊖ a	18 24		18 28	18 32		18 38			18 45		18 44	18 53				18 34	18 42				19 00	19 02	19 08	

		SN	SN	SN	SN	SN	SN	SN	FC		SN	SN [1]	SN	SN	SN	FC	SN	SN	SN	SN	FC	SN	SN	SN	SN
							C												A					C	
East Croydon	d						18 47					18 55					19 10							19 17	
West Croydon [4]	d				18 39	18 48					18 50								19 01	19 10					19 19
Norwood Junction [2]	a					18 52					18 55	18 59					19 14								19 23
	d					18 52					18 55	18 59		19 06			19 14								19 23
Selhurst [4]	d				18 43		18 50												19 06	19 14				19 20	
Thornton Heath	d				18 45		18 52												19 08	19 16				19 22	
Norbury	d				18 48		18 55												19 11	19 19				19 25	
Streatham Common [4]	d				18 50		18 58												19 13	19 21				19 27	
Bromley South [4]	d														18 47										
Beckenham Junction [4]	d														19 02										
Birkbeck	d														19 05										
Crystal Palace [4]	d		18 43	18 47							18 59				19 09								19 13		19 27
Gipsy Hill	d		18 45								19 01				19 11								19 16		19 30
West Norwood [4]	d		18 48								19 04				19 14								19 19		19 33
Streatham Hill	d		18 52								19 08												19 22		19 36
Balham [4]	⊖ d		18 55				19 02				19 11		19 15						19 19				19 25	19 31	19 39
Wandsworth Common	d		18 57				19 04				19 13								19 21				19 27	19 33	19 41
Clapham Junction [10]	d		19 00				19 07				19 16		19 19						19 25				19 31	19 37	19 45
Battersea Park [4]	d	19 02	19 04								19 20								19 28			19 32	19 34	19 40	19 48
London Victoria [15]	⊖ a	19 08	19 11				19 14				19 24		19 27						19 34			19 36	19 41	19 45	19 53
Streatham [4]	d				18 53			18 59	19 08							19 21				19 24	19 36				
Tulse Hill [3]	d				18 57			19 05	19 12						19 17	19 27				19 28	19 42				
Herne Hill [4]	a								19 18							19 32					19 48				
Loughborough Jn	a								19 21							19 35					19 51				
Elephant & Castle	⊖ a								19 26							19 40					19 56				
London Blackfriars [3]	⊖ a								19 30							19 44					20 00				
City Thameslink [3]	a								19 32							19 46					20 02				
St Pancras International [15]	⊖ a								19 38							19 53					20 10				
Luton Airport Parkway [7]	✈ a								20 25							20 41					20 55				
Luton [10]	a								20 29							20 44					20 59				
North Dulwich	d				19 00			19 08							19 20					19 31					
East Dulwich	d				19 02			19 10							19 22					19 33					
Peckham Rye [4]	d				19 04			19 13							19 25			19 27		19 35					
Queens Rd Peckham	d				19 07			19 15										19 30		19 38					
South Bermondsey	d				19 09			19 18										19 32		19 40					
London Bridge [4]	⊖ a			19 08	19 14	19 18		19 22				19 12		19 27	19 31		19 39	19 37		19 45					

For general notes see front of timetable
For details of catering facilities see Directory of Train Operators

A From Epsom Downs (Table 182)
B From Brighton (Table 52)
C From Tattenham Corner (Table 181)
D From Guildford (Table 182)
b Arr. 1841

East and West Croydon → London & Luton via Norbury/Crystal Palace/Tulse Hill

Local Services

Network Diagram - see first page of Table 177

	SN	SN	SN	SN	SN	SN	SN A	SN	FC	SN	SN	SN B	SN	SN	SN	SN	SN	SN	SN	SN A	SN	FC	SN	SN
East Croydon d					19 40							19 47						20 10						
West Croydon d	19 22						19 31	19 36					19 47	19 49						20 01	20 06			
Norwood Junction a	19 27				19 44								19 52	19 54				20 14						
Norwood Junction d	19 27				19 44								19 52	19 54				20 14						
Selhurst d							19 36	19 40				19 50								20 05	20 10			
Thornton Heath d							19 38	19 42				19 52								20 07	20 12			
Norbury d							19 41	19 45				19 55								20 10	20 15			
Streatham Common d							19 44	19 48				19 57								20 12	20 18			
Bromley South d																*19 33*								
Beckenham Junction d				19 25												19 54								
Birkbeck d				19 28												19 57								
Crystal Palace d			19 32	19 32							19 43		19 56		20 01	20 01								20 13
Gipsy Hill d				19 34							19 46		19 58			20 03								20 16
West Norwood d				19 37							19 49		20 01			20 06								20 19
Streatham Hill d											19 52		20 05											20 22
Balham d		19 46					19 51				19 55	20 01	20 09				20 17			20 20				20 25
Wandsworth Common d							19 53				19 57	20 03	20 11							20 22				20 27
Clapham Junction d		19 50					19 56				20 01	20 07	20 14				20 21			20 25				20 31
Battersea Park d							20 00			20 02	20 04		20 18							20 29			20 32	20 34
London Victoria a		19 57					20 04			20 06	20 09	20 14	20 25				20 28			20 33			20 36	20 40
Streatham d								19 53	20 06												20 23	20 40		
Tulse Hill d				19 40				19 56	20 12							20 10					20 26	20 44		
Herne Hill a									20 16													20 48		
Loughborough Jn a									20 19													20 51		
Elephant & Castle a									20 24													20 56		
London Blackfriars a									20 30													21 00		
City Thameslink a									20 32													21 02		
St Pancras International a									20 40													21 10		
Luton Airport Parkway a									21 25													21 55		
Luton a									21 29													21 59		
North Dulwich d				19 43				19 59								20 13					20 29			
East Dulwich d				19 45				20 01								20 15					20 31			
Peckham Rye d				19 48		19 56		20 04								20 17			20 26		20 34			
Queens Rd Peckham d				19 50		19 59		20 06								20 20			20 29		20 36			
South Bermondsey d				19 53		20 01		20 09								20 22			20 31		20 39			
London Bridge a	19 49		19 52	19 57	20 11	20 06		20 14						20 19	20 22	20 27		20 41	20 36		20 44			

	SN B	SN C	SN	SN	SN	SN	SN	SN	SN A	SN	FC	SN	SN	SN B	SN D	SN	SN	SN		SN	SN A	SN	FC	SN
East Croydon d	20 17					20 30	20 40							20 47				21 10						
West Croydon d		20 18							20 31	20 36					20 48						21 01	21 06		
Norwood Junction a		20 23				20 34	20 44								20 53			21 14						
Norwood Junction d		20 23				20 34	20 44								20 53			21 14						
Selhurst d	20 20								20 36	20 40				20 50							21 06	21 10		
Thornton Heath d	20 22								20 38	20 42				20 52							21 08	21 12		
Norbury d	20 25								20 41	20 45				20 55							21 11	21 15		
Streatham Common d	20 27								20 44	20 47				20 57							21 14	21 18		
Bromley South d					*20 03*																			
Beckenham Junction d					20 24																			
Birkbeck d					20 27																			
Crystal Palace d		20 27		20 31	20 31								20 43		20 57		21 01							
Gipsy Hill d		20 29			20 33								20 46		20 59									
West Norwood d		20 32			20 36								20 49		21 02									
Streatham Hill d		20 36											20 52		21 06									
Balham d	20 31	20 39	20 44						20 48				20 55	21 01	21 09	21 14					21 18			
Wandsworth Common d	20 33	20 41							20 50				20 57	21 03	21 11						21 20			
Clapham Junction d	20 37	20 44	20 48						20 53				21 01	21 07	21 14	21 18					21 23			
Battersea Park d	20 41	20 48							20 57			21 02	21 04		21 18						21 27			21 32
London Victoria a	20 45	20 52	20 55						21 03			21 06	21 09	21 14	21 23	21 25					21 33			21 36
Streatham d										20 53	21 10											21 21	21 48	
Tulse Hill d					20 40					20 56	21 14											21 25	21 52	
Herne Hill a											21 18												21 56	
Loughborough Jn a											21 21												21 59	
Elephant & Castle a											21 26												22 04	
London Blackfriars a											21 32												22 08	
City Thameslink a											21 34												22 10	
St Pancras International a											21 43												22 18	
Luton Airport Parkway a											22 25												23 01	
Luton a											22 29												23 05	
North Dulwich d					20 43					20 59												21 28		
East Dulwich d					20 45					21 01												21 30		
Peckham Rye d					20 47			20 56		21 04										21 26		21 32		
Queens Rd Peckham d					20 50			20 59		21 06										21 29		21 35		
South Bermondsey d					20 52			21 01		21 09										21 31		21 37		
London Bridge a				20 53	20 57	20 59	21 11	21 06		21 14							21 22	21 41		21 36		21 44		

For general notes see front of timetable
For details of catering facilities see Directory of Train Operators

A From Epsom Downs (Table 182)
B From Tattenham Corner (Table 181)
C From Epsom (Table 182)
D From Sutton (Surrey) (Table 182)

East and West Croydon → London & Luton via Norbury/Crystal Palace/Tulse Hill

Local Services

Network Diagram - see first page of Table 177

		SN	SN A	SN B	SN	SN	SN	SN	SN C	SN	FC	SN	SN	SN A	SN B	SN	SN	SN	SN	SN D	SN	SN	SN	SN A	SN B
East Croydon	d		21 17				21 40							21 47				22 10						22 17	
West Croydon 4	d			21 18					21 32	21 36					21 48					22 01	22 06				22 18
Norwood Junction 2	a			21 23			21 44								21 53			22 14							22 23
	d			21 23			21 44								21 53			22 14							22 23
Selhurst 4	d		21 20						21 36	21 40				21 50						22 06	22 10			22 20	
Thornton Heath	d		21 22						21 38	21 42				21 52						22 08	22 12			22 22	
Norbury	d		21 25						21 41	21 45				21 55						22 11	22 15			22 25	
Streatham Common 4	d		21 27						21 44	21 48				21 57						22 14	22 18			22 27	
Bromley South 4	d																								
Beckenham Junction 4	d																								
Birkbeck	d																								
Crystal Palace 4	d	21 13		21 27		21 31							21 43		21 57		22 01						22 13		22 27
Gipsy Hill	d	21 16		21 29									21 46		21 59								22 16		22 29
West Norwood 4	d	21 19		21 32									21 49		22 02								22 19		22 32
Streatham Hill	d	21 22		21 36									21 52		22 06								22 22		22 36
Balham 4	⊖ d	21 25	21 31	21 39	21 44				21 48				21 55	22 01	22 09	22 14				22 18			22 25	22 31	22 39
Wandsworth Common	d	21 27	21 33	21 41					21 50				21 57	22 03	22 11					22 20			22 27	22 33	22 41
Clapham Junction 10	d	21 31	21 37	21 44	21 48				21 53				22 01	22 07	22 14	22 18				22 23			22 31	22 37	22 44
Battersea Park 4	d	21 34	21 40	21 48					21 57			22 02	22 04		22 18					22 27		22 32	22 34	22 40	22 48
London Victoria 15	⊖ a	21 39	21 45	21 53	21 55				22 03			22 06	22 09	22 14	22 25	22 27				22 33		22 36	22 39	22 48	22 53
Streatham 4	d									21 51	22 19										22 21				
Tulse Hill 3	d									21 55	22 23										22 25				
Herne Hill 4	a										22 26														
Loughborough Jn	a										22 30														
Elephant & Castle	⊖ a										22 34														
London Blackfriars 3	⊖ a										22 38														
City Thameslink 3	a										22 40														
St Pancras International 15	⊖ a										22 48														
Luton Airport Parkway 7	✈ a										23 31														
Luton 10	a										23 35														
North Dulwich	d									21 58											22 28				
East Dulwich	d									22 00											22 30				
Peckham Rye 4	d							21 56		22 02									22 26		22 32				
Queens Rd Peckham	d							21 59		22 05									22 29		22 35				
South Bermondsey	d							22 01		22 07									22 31		22 37				
London Bridge 4	⊖ a					21 52	22 11	22 06		22 14							22 22	22 41	22 36		22 44				

		SN	SN	SN	SN	SN C	SN	SN	SN	SN A	SN B	SN	SN	SN	SN	SN D	SN	SN	SN	SN A	SN B	SN	SN		
East Croydon	d			22 40						22 47				23 10						23 17					
West Croydon 4	d					22 32	22 36				22 48					23 01	23 06				23 18				
Norwood Junction 2	a			22 44							22 53			23 14							23 23				
	d			22 44							22 53			23 14							23 23				
Selhurst 4	d					22 36	22 40			22 50						23 06	23 10			23 20					
Thornton Heath	d					22 38	22 42			22 52						23 08	23 12			23 22					
Norbury	d					22 41	22 45			22 55						23 11	23 15			23 25					
Streatham Common 4	d					22 44	22 48			22 57						23 14	23 18			23 27					
Bromley South 4	d																								
Beckenham Junction 4	d																								
Birkbeck	d																								
Crystal Palace 4	d		22 31						22 43		22 57		23 01						23 13		23 27	23 31	23 43		
Gipsy Hill	d								22 46		22 59								23 16		23 29		23 46		
West Norwood 4	d								22 49		23 02								23 19		23 32		23 49		
Streatham Hill	d								22 52		23 06								23 22		23 36		23 52		
Balham 4	⊖ d	22 44				22 48			22 55	23 01	23 09	23 14				23 18			23 25	23 31	23 40		23 55		
Wandsworth Common	d					22 50			22 57	23 03	23 11					23 20			23 27	23 33	23 42		23 57		
Clapham Junction 10	d	22 48				22 53			23 01	23 07	23 15	23 18				23 23			23 31	23 37	23 45		00 01		
Battersea Park 4	d					22 57		23 02	23 04		23 18					23 27		23 32	23 34	23 40	23 49		00 04		
London Victoria 15	⊖ a	22 55				23 03		23 06	23 09	23 14	23 23	23 25				23 31		23 37	23 40	23 45	23 54		00 12		
Streatham 4	d						22 51										23 21								
Tulse Hill 3	d						22 55										23 25								
Herne Hill 4	a																								
Loughborough Jn	a																								
Elephant & Castle	⊖ a																								
London Blackfriars 3	⊖ a																								
City Thameslink 3	a																								
St Pancras International 15	⊖ a																								
Luton Airport Parkway 7	✈ a																								
Luton 10	a																								
North Dulwich	d						22 58										23 28								
East Dulwich	d						23 00										23 30								
Peckham Rye 4	d				22 56		23 02								23 26		23 32								
Queens Rd Peckham	d				22 59		23 05								23 29		23 35								
South Bermondsey	d				23 01		23 07								23 31		23 37								
London Bridge 4	⊖ a		22 52	23 11	23 06		23 14						23 22	23 38	23 36		23 44					23 52			

For general notes see front of timetable
For details of catering facilities see Directory of Train Operators

A From Tattenham Corner (Table 181)
B From Sutton (Surrey) (Table 182)
C From Epsom (Table 182)
D From Epsom Downs (Table 182)

Table 177

Saturdays

East and West Croydon → London & Luton via Norbury/Crystal Palace/Tulse Hill

Local Services

Network Diagram - see first page of Table 177

		SN	SN	FC	SN 1	SN	SN	FC	SN	FC A	SN	SN	SN	SN	SN	SN	FC	SN	SN B	SN	SN 1	SN	SN	SN C	SN
East Croydon	d				05 29							06 30				06 43			06 47		06 55	07 00			
West Croydon 4	d										06 18									06 48				06 57	
Norwood Junction 2	a										06 23	06 34				06 48				06 53	06 59	07 04			
	d					05 54					06 23	06 34	06 42	06 46		06 49				06 53	06 59	07 04			
Selhurst 4	d			05 39			06 01	06 09		06 39									06 50					07 01	
Thornton Heath	d			05 41			06 03	06 11		06 41									06 52					07 03	
Norbury	d			05 43			06 06	06 13		06 43									06 55					07 06	
Streatham Common 4	d			05 46			06 08	06 16		06 46									06 57					07 09	
Bromley South 4	d																								
Beckenham Junction 4	d																								
Birkbeck	d																								
Crystal Palace 4	d	23p43				05 58					06 27		06 46							06 57					
Gipsy Hill	d	23p46				06 00					06 29		06 48							06 59					
West Norwood 4	d	23p49				06 03					06 32		06 51							07 02					
Streatham Hill	d	23p52				06 07					06 36									07 06					
Balham 4	⊖ d	23p55			05 45	06 10	06 12				06 39								07 01	07 09				07 13	07 18
Wandsworth Common	d	23p57				06 12	06 14				06 41								07 03	07 11				07 15	
Clapham Junction 10	d	00 01	05 00		05 49	06 15	06 18				06 44								07 07	07 14				07 18	07 22
Battersea Park 4	d	00 04				06 19	06 21		06 32		06 48							07 02		07 18				07 22	
London Victoria 15	⊖ a	00 12	05 08		05 58	06 23	06 26		06 36		06 53							07 06	07 14	07 23				07 26	07 29
Streatham 4	d			05 49				06 19		06 49							07 06								
Tulse Hill 3	d			05b58				06 23		06 53			06 54				07 12								
Herne Hill 4	a			06 01				06 26		06 56							07 16								
Loughborough Jn	a							06 30		07 00							07 19								
Elephant & Castle	⊖ a			06 07				06 34		07 04							07 24								
London Blackfriars 3	⊖ a			06 11				06 41		07 11							07 26								
City Thameslink 3	a																								
St Pancras International 15	⊖ a			06 22				06 52		07 22							07 38								
Luton Airport Parkway 7	✈ a			07 06				07 36		08 08							08 25								
Luton 10	a			07 10				07 40		08 11							08 29								
North Dulwich	d												06 57												
East Dulwich	d												06 59												
Peckham Rye 4	d												07 02		06 56								07 26		
Queens Rd Peckham	d												07 04		06 59								07 29		
South Bermondsey	d												07 07		07 01								07 31		
London Bridge 4	⊖ a											06 55	07 11	07 00	07 06	07 14					07 12	07 25	07 36		

		SN	FC	SN	SN	FC		SN	SN B	SN	SE 13	SN	SN	SN D	SN	SN	FC	SN	FC	SN	SN	SN	SN E	SN	SN 1
East Croydon	d			07 05					07 17		07 24	07 30											07 47		07 55
West Croydon 4	d	07 01			07 15					07 18				07 27		07 31		07 45						07 48	
Norwood Junction 2	a			07 09	07 19					07 23	07 28	07 34						07 49						07 53	07 59
	d			07 10	07 19					07 23	07 28	07 34						07 49						07 53	07 59
Selhurst 4	d	07 05							07 20					07 31		07 35				07 39			07 50		
Thornton Heath	d	07 07							07 22					07 33		07 37				07 41			07 52		
Norbury	d	07 10							07 25					07 36		07 40				07 44			07 55		
Streatham Common 4	d	07 13							07 27					07 39		07 43				07 47			07 57		
Bromley South 4	d																								
Beckenham Junction 4	d																								
Birkbeck	d																								
Crystal Palace 4	d									07 27												07 43		07 57	
Gipsy Hill	d									07 29												07 45		07 59	
West Norwood 4	d									07 32												07 48		08 02	
Streatham Hill	d									07 36												07 52		08 06	
Balham 4	⊖ d								07 31	07 39				07 43	07 48					07 51		07 55	08 01	08 09	
Wandsworth Common	d								07 33	07 41				07 45						07 53		07 57	08 03	08 11	
Clapham Junction 10	d								07 37	07 44				07 48	07 52					07 56		08 00	08 07	08 14	
Battersea Park 4	d							07 32		07 48				07 52						08 00	08 02	08 04		08 18	
London Victoria 15	⊖ a							07 36	07 44	07 53				07 56	07 59					08 04	08 06	08 09	08 14	08 23	
Streatham 4	d	07 16	07 23			07 36										07 46	07 53		08 06						
Tulse Hill 3	d	07 21	07 27			07 42										07 51	07 57		08 12						
Herne Hill 4	a		07 30			07 46											08 00		08 16						
Loughborough Jn	a		07 34			07 49											08 04		08 19						
Elephant & Castle	⊖ a		07 39			07 54											08 09		08 24						
London Blackfriars 3	⊖ a		07 43			07 58											08 13		08 28						
City Thameslink 3	a																								
St Pancras International 15	⊖ a		07 53			08 08											08 23		08 38						
Luton Airport Parkway 7	✈ a					08 55													09 25						
Luton 10	a					08 59													09 29						
North Dulwich	d	07 24														07 54									
East Dulwich	d	07 26														07 56									
Peckham Rye 4	d	07 29											07 56			07 59									
Queens Rd Peckham	d	07 32											07 59			08 02									
South Bermondsey	d	07 34											08 01			08 04									
London Bridge 4	⊖ a	07 39		07 23	07 44						07 40	07 55	08 06			08 09		08 14							08 12

For general notes see front of timetable
For details of catering facilities see Directory of Train Operators

A To Bedford (Table 52)
B From Tattenham Corner (Table 181)
C From Sutton (Surrey) (Table 182)
D From Epsom (Table 182)
E From Caterham (Table 181)
b Arr. 0553

Saturdays

East and West Croydon → London & Luton via Norbury/Crystal Palace/Tulse Hill

Local Services

Network Diagram - see first page of Table 177

		SN	SN	SN	SN	SN	FC	SN	SN	SN	SN	SN		SN	SN	FC	SN	SN	SE	SN	SN	SN	SN	SN	FC
																			13						
				A						B								C	D				E		
East Croydon	d	08 00								08 17								08 21	08 24	08 30					
West Croydon [4]	d			07 57		08 01		08 15									08 18						08 27	08 31	
Norwood Junction [2]	a	08 04						08 19									08 23	08 27	08 28	08 34					
	d	08 04						08 19									08 23	08 28	08 28	08 34					
Selhurst [4]	d			08 01		08 05			08 09	08 20													08 31	08 35	
Thornton Heath	d			08 03		08 07			08 11	08 22													08 33	08 37	
Norbury	d			08 06		08 10			08 14	08 25													08 36	08 40	
Streatham Common [4]	d			08 09		08 13			08 17	08 27													08 39	08 43	
Bromley South [4]	d														*07 48*										
Beckenham Junction [4]	d														08 16										
Birkbeck	d														08 19										
Crystal Palace [4]	d											08 15		08 17	08 23		08 27	08 32							
Gipsy Hill	d											08 17			08 25		08 29	08 35							
West Norwood [4]	d											08 20			08 28		08 32	08 38							
Streatham Hill	d											08 24					08 36								
Balham [4]	⊖ d			08 13	08 18				08 21	08 31		08 27					08 39					08 48	08 43		
Wandsworth Common	d			08 15					08 23	08 33		08 29					08 41						08 45		
Clapham Junction [10]	d			08 18	08 22				08 26	08 37		08 32					08 44					08 52	08 48		
Battersea Park [4]	d			08 22					08 30		08 32	08 36					08 48						08 52		
London Victoria [15]	⊖ a			08 26	08 29				08 34	08 44	08 36	08 40					08 53					08 59	08 56		
Streatham [4]	d					08 16	08 23									08 36								08 46	08 53
Tulse Hill [3]	d					08 21	08 27								08 31	08 42		08 41						08 51	08 57
Herne Hill [4]	a						08 31									08 46									09 00
Loughborough Jn	a						08 34									08 49									09 04
Elephant & Castle	⊖ a						08 39									08 54									09 09
London Blackfriars [3]	⊖ a						08 43									08 58									09 13
City Thameslink [3]	a															09 00									09 15
St Pancras International [15]	⊖ a						08 53									09 08									09 23
Luton Airport Parkway [7]	✈ a															09 55									
Luton [10]	a															09 59									
North Dulwich	d					08 24									08 34			08 44						08 54	
East Dulwich	d					08 26									08 36			08 46						08 56	
Peckham Rye [4]	d		08 26			08 29									08 39			08 49			08 56			08 59	
Queens Rd Peckham	d		08 29			08 32									08 41			08 51			08 59			09 02	
South Bermondsey	d		08 31			08 34									08 44			08 54			09 01			09 04	
London Bridge [4]	⊖ a	08 25	08 36			08 39		08 44						08 36	08 48			08 58	08 40	08 55	09 06			09 09	

		SN	SN	SN	SN	SN	SN	SN	FC	SN	SN	SN	SN	SN	SN	SN	SN	FC		SN	SN	SN	SN	SN	SN
												[1]													
			G	B							C					A					G	B			
East Croydon	d			08 47							08 51	08 55	09 00									09 17			
West Croydon [4]	d	08 45	08 35							08 48						08 57	09 01			09 15	09 05				
Norwood Junction [2]	a	08 49								08 53	08 57	08 59	09 04							09 19					
	d	08 49								08 53	08 58	08 59	09 04							09 19					
Selhurst [4]	d		08 39	08 50												09 01	09 05				09 09	09 20			
Thornton Heath	d		08 41	08 52												09 03	09 07				09 11	09 22			
Norbury	d		08 44	08 55												09 06	09 10				09 14	09 25			
Streatham Common [4]	d		08 47	08 57												09 09	09 13				09 17	09 27			
Bromley South [4]	d							*08 33*																	
Beckenham Junction [4]	d							08 46																	
Birkbeck	d							08 49																	
Crystal Palace [4]	d					08 43	08 47	08 53		08 57	09 02													09 13	09 17
Gipsy Hill	d					08 46		08 55		08 59	09 05													09 16	
West Norwood [4]	d					08 49		08 58		09 02	09 08													09 19	
Streatham Hill	d					08 52				09 06														09 22	
Balham [4]	⊖ d		08 51	09 01		08 55				09 09					09 18	09 13					09 21	09 31		09 25	
Wandsworth Common	d		08 53	09 03		08 57				09 11						09 15					09 23	09 33		09 27	
Clapham Junction [10]	d		08 56	09 07		09 01				09 14					09 22	09 18					09 26	09 37		09 31	
Battersea Park [4]	d		09 00		09 02	09 04				09 18						09 22					09 30		09 32	09 34	
London Victoria [15]	⊖ a		09 04	09 14	09 06	09 09				09 23					09 29	09 26					09 34	09 44	09 36	09 39	
Streatham [4]	d								09 06								09 16	09 23							
Tulse Hill [3]	d							09 01	09 12		09 11						09 21	09 27							
Herne Hill [4]	a								09 16									09 30							
Loughborough Jn	a								09 19									09 34							
Elephant & Castle	⊖ a								09 24									09 39							
London Blackfriars [3]	⊖ a								09 28									09 43							
City Thameslink [3]	a								09 30									09 45							
St Pancras International [15]	⊖ a								09 38									09 53							
Luton Airport Parkway [7]	✈ a								10 25																
Luton [10]	a								10 29																
North Dulwich	d							09 04			09 14						09 24								
East Dulwich	d							09 06			09 16						09 26								
Peckham Rye [4]	d							09 09			09 19			09 26			09 29								
Queens Rd Peckham	d							09 11			09 21			09 29			09 32								
South Bermondsey	d							09 14			09 24			09 31			09 34								
London Bridge [4]	⊖ a	09 14					09 06	09 18			09 28	09 12	09 25	09 36			09 39			09 44					09 36

For general notes see front of timetable
For details of catering facilities see Directory of Train Operators

A From Epsom Downs (Table 182)
B From Caterham (Table 181)
C From Smitham (Table 181)
D From Tonbridge (Table 209)
E From Epsom (Table 182)
G From Sutton (Surrey) (Table 182)

Table 177

Saturdays

East and West Croydon → London & Luton via Norbury/Crystal Palace/Tulse Hill

Local Services

Network Diagram - see first page of Table 177

		SN	FC	SN	SN A	SE 13 B	SN	SN	SN	SN C	SN	FC	SN	SN D	SN E	SN	SN	SN	SN	FC	SN		SN A	SN 1	SN
East Croydon	d				09 21	09 24	09 30								09 47								09 51	09 55	10 00
West Croydon 4	d			09 18						09 27	09 31		09 45	09 35							09 48		09 57	09 59	10 04
Norwood Junction 2	a			09 23	09 27	09 28	09 34						09 49								09 53		09 57	09 59	10 04
	d			09 23	09 28	09 28	09 34						09 49								09 53		09 58	09 59	10 04
Selhurst 4	d									09 31	09 35			09 39	09 50										
Thornton Heath	d									09 33	09 37			09 41	09 52										
Norbury	d									09 36	09 40			09 44	09 55										
Streatham Common 4	d									09 39	09 43			09 47	09 57										
Bromley South 4	d	09 03																	09 33						
Beckenham Junction 4	d	09 16																	09 46						
Birkbeck	d	09 19																	09 49						
Crystal Palace 4	d	09 23		09 27	09 32												09 43	09 47	09 53		09 57		10 02		
Gipsy Hill	d	09 25		09 29	09 35												09 46		09 55		09 59		10 05		
West Norwood 4	d	09 28		09 32	09 38												09 49		09 58		10 02		10 08		
Streatham Hill	d			09 36													09 52				10 06				
Balham 4	⊖ d			09 39					09 48	09 43				09 51	10 01		09 55				10 09				
Wandsworth Common	d			09 41						09 45				09 53	10 03		09 57				10 11				
Clapham Junction 10	d			09 44					09 52	09 48				09 56	10 07		10 01				10 14				
Battersea Park 4	d			09 48						09 52				10 00		10 02	10 04				10 18				
London Victoria 15	⊖ a			09 53					09 59	09 56				10 04	10 14	10 06	10 09				10 23				
Streatham 4	d		09 36								09 46	09 53								10 06					
Tulse Hill 3	d	09 31	09 42		09 41						09 51	09 57							10 01	10 12			10 11		
Herne Hill 4	a		09 46									10 00								10 16					
Loughborough Jn	a		09 49									10 04								10 19					
Elephant & Castle	⊖ a		09 54									10 09								10 24					
London Blackfriars 3	⊖ a		09 58									10 13								10 28					
City Thameslink 3	a		10 00									10 15								10 30					
St Pancras International 15	⊖ a		10 08									10 23								10 38					
Luton Airport Parkway 7	✈ a		10 55																	11 25					
Luton 10	a		10 59																	11 29					
North Dulwich	d	09 34			09 44						09 54								10 04				10 14		
East Dulwich	d	09 36			09 46						09 56								10 06				10 16		
Peckham Rye 4	d	09 39			09 49			09 56			09 59								10 09				10 19		
Queens Rd Peckham	d	09 41			09 51			09 59			10 02								10 11				10 21		
South Bermondsey	d	09 44			09 54			10 01			10 04								10 14				10 24		
London Bridge 4	⊖ a	09 48			09 58	09 40	09 55	10 06			10 09		10 14					10 06	10 18				10 28	10 12	10 25

		SN	SN G	SN	SN	FC	SN	SN D	SN	SN	SN	SN	FC	SN E	SN	SN A	SE 13 H	SN	SN	SN C	SN	SN	FC	SN	SN D
East Croydon	d													10 17		10 21	10 24	10 30							
West Croydon 4	d		09 57		10 01		10 15	10 05							10 18					10 27		10 31		10 45	10 35
Norwood Junction 2	a						10 19								10 23	10 27	10 28	10 34						10 49	
	d						10 19								10 23	10 28	10 28	10 34						10 49	
Selhurst 4	d		10 01		10 05			10 09						10 20						10 31		10 35			10 39
Thornton Heath	d		10 03		10 07			10 11						10 22						10 33		10 37			10 41
Norbury	d		10 06		10 10			10 14						10 25						10 36		10 40			10 44
Streatham Common 4	d		10 09		10 13			10 17						10 27						10 39		10 43			10 47
Bromley South 4	d											10 03													
Beckenham Junction 4	d											10 16													
Birkbeck	d											10 19													
Crystal Palace 4	d									10 13	10 17	10 23			10 27	10 32									
Gipsy Hill	d									10 16		10 25			10 29	10 35									
West Norwood 4	d									10 19		10 28			10 32	10 38									
Streatham Hill	d									10 22					10 36										
Balham 4	⊖ d		10 13	10 18				10 21		10 25				10 31	10 39					10 43	10 48				10 51
Wandsworth Common	d		10 15					10 23		10 27				10 33	10 41					10 45					10 53
Clapham Junction 10	d		10 18	10 22				10 26		10 31				10 37	10 44					10 48	10 52				10 56
Battersea Park 4	d		10 22					10 30	10 32	10 34					10 48					10 52					11 00
London Victoria 15	⊖ a		10 26	10 29				10 34	10 36	10 39				10 44	10 53					10 56	10 59				11 04
Streatham 4	d				10 16	10 23							10 36									10 46	10 53		
Tulse Hill 3	d				10 21	10 27						10 31	10 42			10 41						10 51	10 57		
Herne Hill 4	a					10 30							10 46										11 00		
Loughborough Jn	a					10 34							10 49										11 04		
Elephant & Castle	⊖ a					10 39							10 54										11 09		
London Blackfriars 3	⊖ a					10 43							10 58										11 13		
City Thameslink 3	a					10 45							11 00										11 15		
St Pancras International 15	⊖ a					10 53							11 08										11 23		
Luton Airport Parkway 7	✈ a												11 55												
Luton 10	a												11 59												
North Dulwich	d				10 24							10 34				10 44						10 54			
East Dulwich	d				10 26							10 36				10 46						10 56			
Peckham Rye 4	d	10 26			10 29							10 39				10 49			10 56			10 59			
Queens Rd Peckham	d	10 29			10 32							10 41				10 51			10 59			11 02			
South Bermondsey	d	10 31			10 34							10 44				10 54			11 01			11 04			
London Bridge 4	⊖ a	10 36			10 39		10 44				10 36	10 48				10 58	10 40	10 55	11 06			11 09		11 14	

For general notes see front of timetable
For details of catering facilities see Directory of Train Operators

- **A** From Smitham (Table 181)
- **B** From Tonbridge (Table 209)
- **C** From Epsom (Table 182)
- **D** From Sutton (Surrey) (Table 182)
- **E** From Caterham (Table 181)
- **G** From Epsom Downs (Table 182)
- **H** From Tunbridge Wells (Table 209)

East and West Croydon → London & Luton via Norbury/Crystal Palace/Tulse Hill

Local Services

Network Diagram - see first page of Table 177

		SN	SN	SN	SN	SN	FC	SN		SN	SN	SN	SN	SN	SN	SN	FC	SN	SN	SN	SN	SN	SN
		A								B	1				C				D	A			
East Croydon	d	10 47								16 51	16 55	17 00								17 17			
West Croydon 4	d							10 48							16 57	17 01		17 15	17 05				
Norwood Junction 2	a							10 53		16 57	16 59	17 04						17 19					
	d							10 53		16 58	16 59	17 04						17 19					
Selhurst 4	d	10 50													17 01	17 05			17 09	17 20			
Thornton Heath	d	10 52													17 03	17 07			17 11	17 22			
Norbury	d	10 55													17 06	17 10			17 14	17 25			
Streatham Common 4	d	10 57													17 09	17 13			17 17	17 27			
Bromley South 4	d					*10 33*																	
Beckenham Junction 4	d					10 46																	
Birkbeck	d					10 49			and at														
Crystal Palace 4	d			10 43	10 47	10 53		10 57		17 02												17 13	17 17
Gipsy Hill	d			10 46		10 55		10 59	the same	17 05												17 16	
West Norwood 4	d			10 49		10 58		11 02		17 08												17 19	
Streatham Hill	d			10 52				11 06	minutes													17 22	
Balham 4	⊖ d	11 01		10 55				11 09	past					17 18	17 13				17 21	17 31		17 25	
Wandsworth Common	d	11 03		10 57				11 11							17 15				17 23	17 33		17 27	
Clapham Junction 10	d	11 07		11 01				11 14	each					17 22	17 18				17 26	17 37		17 31	
Battersea Park 4	d		11 02	11 04				11 18							17 22				17 30		17 32	17 34	
London Victoria 15	⊖ a	11 14	11 06	11 09				11 23	hour until					17 29	17 26				17 34	17 44	17 36	17 39	
Streatham 4	d						11 06									17 16	17 23						
Tulse Hill 3	d					11 01	11 12			17 11						17 21	17 27						
Herne Hill 4	a						11 16										17 30						
Loughborough Jn	a						11 19										17 34						
Elephant & Castle	⊖ a						11 24										17 39						
London Blackfriars 3	⊖ a						11 28										17 43						
City Thameslink 3	a						11 30										17 45						
St Pancras International 15	⊖ a						11 38										17 53						
Luton Airport Parkway 7	✈ a						12 25										18 40						
Luton 10	a						12 29										18 43						
North Dulwich	d					11 04				17 14						17 24							
East Dulwich	d					11 06				17 16						17 26							
Peckham Rye 4	d					11 09				17 19			17 26			17 29							
Queens Rd Peckham	d					11 11				17 21			17 29			17 32							
South Bermondsey	d					11 14				17 24			17 31			17 34							
London Bridge 4	⊖ a				11 06	11 18				17 28	17 12	17 25	17 36			17 39		17 44					17 36

		SN	FC	SN	SN	SE 13	SN	SN	SN	SN	SN	FC	SN	SN	SN	SN		SN	SN	SN	FC	SN	SN	SN	SN
					B	E				G				D	A								B	1	
East Croydon	d				17 21	17 24	17 30								17 47								17 51	17 55	18 00
West Croydon 4	d			17 18						17 27	17 31		17 45	17 35								17 48			
Norwood Junction 2	a			17 23	17 27	17 28	17 34						17 49									17 53	17 57	17 59	18 04
	d			17 23	17 28	17 28	17 34						17 49									17 53	17 58	17 59	18 04
Selhurst 4	d									17 31	17 35			17 39	17 50										
Thornton Heath	d									17 33	17 37			17 41	17 52										
Norbury	d									17 36	17 40			17 44	17 55										
Streatham Common 4	d									17 39	17 43			17 47	17 57										
Bromley South 4	d	*17 03*																		*17 33*					
Beckenham Junction 4	d	17 16																		17 46					
Birkbeck	d	17 19																		17 49					
Crystal Palace 4	d	17 23		17 27	17 32													17 43	17 47	17 53		17 57	18 02		
Gipsy Hill	d	17 25		17 29	17 35													17 46		17 55		17 59	18 05		
West Norwood 4	d	17 28		17 32	17 38													17 49		17 58		18 02	18 08		
Streatham Hill	d			17 36														17 52				18 06			
Balham 4	⊖ d			17 39					17 48	17 43				17 51	18 01			17 55				18 09			
Wandsworth Common	d			17 41						17 45				17 53	18 03			17 57				18 11			
Clapham Junction 10	d			17 44					17 52	17 48				17 56	18 07			18 01				18 14			
Battersea Park 4	d			17 48						17 52				18 00		18 02		18 04				18 18			
London Victoria 15	⊖ a			17 53					17 59	17 56				18 04	18 14	18 06		18 09				18 23			
Streatham 4	d		17 36								17 46	17 53									18 06				
Tulse Hill 3	d	17 31	17 42		17 41						17 51	17 57								18 01	18 12		18 11		
Herne Hill 4	a		17 46									18 00									18 16				
Loughborough Jn	a		17 49									18 04									18 19				
Elephant & Castle	⊖ a		17 54									18 09									18 24				
London Blackfriars 3	⊖ a		17 58									18 13									18 28				
City Thameslink 3	a		18 00									18 15									18 30				
St Pancras International 15	⊖ a		18 08									18 23									18 38				
Luton Airport Parkway 7	✈ a		18 55									19 10									19 25				
Luton 10	a		18 59									19 13									19 29				
North Dulwich	d	17 34			17 44						17 54									18 04			18 14		
East Dulwich	d	17 36			17 46						17 56									18 06			18 16		
Peckham Rye 4	d	17 39			17 49			17 56			17 59									18 09			18 19		
Queens Rd Peckham	d	17 41			17 51			17 59			18 02									18 11			18 21		
South Bermondsey	d	17 44			17 54			18 01			18 04									18 14			18 24		
London Bridge 4	⊖ a	17 48			17 58	17 40	17 55	18 06			18 09		18 14						18 06	18 18			18 28	18 12	18 25

For general notes see front of timetable
For details of catering facilities see Directory of Train Operators

A From Caterham (Table 181)
B From Smitham (Table 181)
C From Epsom Downs (Table 182)
D From Sutton (Surrey) (Table 182)
E From Tunbridge Wells (Table 209)
G From Epsom (Table 182)

Table 177

Saturdays

East and West Croydon → London & Luton via Norbury/Crystal Palace/Tulse Hill

Local Services

Network Diagram - see first page of Table 177

Station		SN	SN	SN A	SN	FC	SN	SN B	SN	SN	SN	SN C	SN	FC	SN	SN D	SE 13 E	SN	SN	SN G	SN	SN		FC	SN B
East Croydon	d											18 17				18 21	18 24	18 30							
West Croydon 4	d			17 57	18 01		18 15	18 05							18 18					18 27		18 31			18 35
Norwood Junction 2	a						18 19								18 23	18 27	18 28	18 34							
	d						18 19								18 23	18 28	18 28	18 34							
Selhurst 4	d			18 01	18 05			18 09				18 20								18 31		18 35			18 39
Thornton Heath	d			18 03	18 07			18 11				18 22								18 33		18 37			18 41
Norbury	d			18 06	18 10			18 14				18 25								18 36		18 40			18 44
Streatham Common 4	d			18 09	18 13			18 17				18 27								18 39		18 43			18 47
Bromley South 4	d												*18 03*												
Beckenham Junction 4	d												18 16												
Birkbeck	d												18 19												
Crystal Palace 4	d									18 13	18 17		18 23		18 27	18 32									
Gipsy Hill	d									18 16			18 25		18 29	18 35									
West Norwood 4	d									18 19			18 28		18 32	18 38									
Streatham Hill	d									18 22					18 36										
Balham 4	⊖ d		18 18	18 13				18 21		18 25		18 31			18 39					18 43	18 48				18 51
Wandsworth Common	d			18 15				18 23		18 27		18 33			18 41					18 45					18 53
Clapham Junction 10	d		18 22	18 18				18 26		18 31		18 37			18 44					18 48	18 52				18 56
Battersea Park 4	d			18 22				18 30	18 32	18 34					18 48					18 52					19 00
London Victoria 15	⊖ a		18 29	18 26				18 34	18 36	18 39		18 44			18 53					18 56	18 59				19 04
Streatham 4	d				18 16	18 23								18 36								18 46		18 53	
Tulse Hill 3	d				18 21	18 27							18 31	18 42		18 41						18b55		18 57	
Herne Hill 4	a					18 30								18 46										19 00	
Loughborough Jn	a					18 34								18 49										19 04	
Elephant & Castle	⊖ a					18 39								18 54										19 09	
London Blackfriars 3	⊖ a					18 43								18 58										19 13	
City Thameslink 3	a					18 45								19 00										19 15	
St Pancras International 15	⊖ a					18 53								19 08										19 23	
Luton Airport Parkway 7	✈ a					19 40								19 55										20 10	
Luton 10	a					19 43								19 59										20 13	
North Dulwich	d				18 24								18 34			18 44						18 58			
East Dulwich	d				18 26								18 36			18 46						19 00			
Peckham Rye 4	d	18 26			18 29								18 39			18 49			18 56			19 02			
Queens Rd Peckham	d	18 29			18 32								18 41			18 51			18 59			19 05			
South Bermondsey	d	18 31			18 34								18 44			18 54			19 01			19 07			
London Bridge 4	⊖ a	18 36			18 39		18 44				18 36		18 48			18 58	18 40	18 55	19 06			19 12			

Station		SN	SN	SN	SN	SN	SN C	FC	SN	SN	SN 1	SN	SN	SN	SN A	SN	SN	FC	SN	SN	SN	FC	SN H	SN	SN
East Croydon	d						18 47			18 51	18 55		19 10										19 17		
West Croydon 4	d	18 45							18 48						18 57		19 01							19 18	
Norwood Junction 2	a	18 49							18 53	18 56	18 59	←	19 14											19 23	
	d	18 49							18 53	19 01	18 59	19 01	19 14											19 23	
Selhurst 4	d						18 50			↪					19 01		19 05						19 20		
Thornton Heath	d						18 52								19 03		19 07						19 22		
Norbury	d						18 55								19 06		19 10						19 25		
Streatham Common 4	d						18 57								19 09		19 13						19 27		
Bromley South 4	d					*18 33*															*19 03*				
Beckenham Junction 4	d					18 46															19 16				
Birkbeck	d					18 49															19 19				
Crystal Palace 4	d			18 43	18 47	18 53			18 57											19 13	19 23			19 27	19 31
Gipsy Hill	d			18 46		18 55			18 59											19 16	19 25			19 29	
West Norwood 4	d			18 49		18 58			19 02											19 19	19 28			19 32	
Streatham Hill	d			18 52					19 06											19 22				19 36	
Balham 4	⊖ d			18 55			19 01		19 09						19 13	19 18				19 25			19 31	19 39	
Wandsworth Common	d			18 57			19 03		19 11						19 15					19 27			19 33	19 41	
Clapham Junction 10	d			19 01			19 07		19 14						19 18	19 22				19 31			19 37	19 44	
Battersea Park 4	d		19 02	19 04					19 18						19 22				19 32	19 34			19 40	19 48	
London Victoria 15	⊖ a		19 06	19 10			19 14		19 23						19 26	19 29			19 36	19 39			19 45	19 53	
Streatham 4	d							19 06									19 16	19 23				19 40			
Tulse Hill 3	d					19c10		19 12									19e25	19 27			19f40	19 44			
Herne Hill 4	a							19 16										19 30				19 47			
Loughborough Jn	a							19 19										19 34				19 51			
Elephant & Castle	⊖ a							19 24										19 39				19 56			
London Blackfriars 3	⊖ a							19 28										19 43				20 00			
City Thameslink 3	a							19 30										19 45				20 02			
St Pancras International 15	⊖ a							19 38										19 53				20 06			
Luton Airport Parkway 7	✈ a							20 25										20 41				20 55			
Luton 10	a							20 29										20 43				20 59			
North Dulwich	d					19 13											19 28				19 43				
East Dulwich	d					19 15											19 30				19 45				
Peckham Rye 4	d					19 17								19 26			19 32				19 47				
Queens Rd Peckham	d					19 20								19 29			19 35				19 50				
South Bermondsey	d					19 22								19 31			19 37				19 52				
London Bridge 4	⊖ a	19 14			19 06	19 27					19 12	19 25	19 41	19 36			19 44				19 58				19 52

For general notes see front of timetable
For details of catering facilities see Directory of Train Operators

A From Epsom Downs (Table 182)
B From Sutton (Surrey) (Table 182)
C From Caterham (Table 181)
D From Smitham (Table 181)
E From Tunbridge Wells (Table 209)
G From Epsom (Table 182)
H From Tattenham Corner (Table 181)
b Arr. 1850
c Arr. 1901
e Arr. 1920
f Arr. 1931

East and West Croydon → London & Luton via Norbury/Crystal Palace/Tulse Hill

Local Services

Network Diagram - see first page of Table 177

Station		SN	SN	SN	SN A	SN		SN	SN	SN	SN	FC	SN B	SN C	SN	SN	SN	SN	SN D	SN	SN	SN	SN	FC	SN B
East Croydon	d	19 21	19 40										19 47				20 10								20 17
West Croydon 4	d				19 27			19 36						19 48					20 01	20 06					
Norwood Junction 2	a	19 26	19 44											19 53			20 14								
	d	19 31	19 44											19 53			20 14								
Selhurst 4	d				19 31			19 40					19 50						20 06	20 10					20 20
Thornton Heath	d				19 33			19 42					19 52						20 08	20 12					20 22
Norbury	d				19 36			19 45					19 55						20 11	20 15					20 25
Streatham Common 4	d				19 39			19 48					19 57						20 14	20 18					20 27
Bromley South 4	d										*19 33*												*20 03*		
Beckenham Junction 4	d										19 46												20 16		
Birkbeck	d										19 49												20 19		
Crystal Palace 4	d									19 43	19 53			19 57		20 01						20 13	20 23		
Gipsy Hill	d									19 46	19 55			19 59								20 16	20 25		
West Norwood 4	d									19 49	19 58			20 02								20 19	20 28		
Streatham Hill	d									19 52				20 06								20 22			
Balham 4 ⊖	d				19 43	19 46				19 55			20 01	20 09	20 14				20 18			20 25			20 31
Wandsworth Common	d				19 45					19 57			20 03	20 11					20 20			20 27			20 33
Clapham Junction 10	d				19 48	19 51				20 01			20 07	20 14	20 18				20 23			20 31			20 37
Battersea Park 4	d				19 52				20 02	20 04			20 10	20 18					20 27		20 32	20 34			20 40
London Victoria 15 ⊖	a				19 56	19 58			20 06	20 09			20 15	20 23	20 25				20 33		20 36	20 39			20 45
Streatham 4	d							19 51				20 10								20 21				20 39	
Tulse Hill 3	d							19 55			20b10	20 14								20 25			20c40	20 43	
Herne Hill 4	a											20 17												20 47	
Loughborough Jn	a											20 21												20 51	
Elephant & Castle ⊖	a											20 26												20 56	
London Blackfriars 3 ⊖	a											20 30												21 00	
City Thameslink 3	a											20 32												21 02	
St Pancras International 15 ⊖	a											20 38												21 08	
Luton Airport Parkway 7 ✈	a											21 25												21 55	
Luton 10	a											21 29												21 59	
North Dulwich	d							19 58			20 13									20 28			20 43		
East Dulwich	d							20 00			20 15									20 30			20 45		
Peckham Rye 4	d			19 56				20 02			20 17							20 26		20 32			20 47		
Queens Rd Peckham	d			19 59				20 05			20 20							20 29		20 35			20 50		
South Bermondsey	d			20 01				20 07			20 22							20 31		20 37			20 52		
London Bridge 4 ⊖	a	19 55	20 11	20 06				20 12			20 27					20 22	20 41	20 36		20 42			20 57		

Station		SN C	SN	SN	SN	SN	SN A	SN	FC	SN	SN	SN B		SN C	SN	SN	SN	SN	SN D	SN	FC	SN	SN	SN B	SN C
East Croydon	d				20 40							20 47					21 10							21 17	
West Croydon 4	d	20 18					20 31	20 36						20 48					21 01	21 06					21 18
Norwood Junction 2	a	20 23			20 44									20 53			21 14								21 23
	d	20 23			20 44									20 53			21 14								21 23
Selhurst 4	d						20 36	20 40				20 50							21 06	21 10				21 20	
Thornton Heath	d						20 38	20 42				20 52							21 08	21 12				21 22	
Norbury	d						20 41	20 45				20 55							21 11	21 15				21 25	
Streatham Common 4	d						20 44	20 48				20 57							21 14	21 18				21 27	
Bromley South 4	d																								
Beckenham Junction 4	d																								
Birkbeck	d																								
Crystal Palace 4	d	20 27		20 31							20 43			20 57		21 01							21 13		21 27
Gipsy Hill	d	20 29									20 45			20 59									21 16		21 29
West Norwood 4	d	20 32									20 48			21 02									21 19		21 32
Streatham Hill	d	20 36									20 52			21 06									21 22		21 36
Balham 4 ⊖	d	20 39	20 44				20 48				20 55	21 01		21 09	21 14				21 18				21 25	21 31	21 39
Wandsworth Common	d	20 41					20 50				20 57	21 03		21 11					21 20				21 27	21 33	21 41
Clapham Junction 10	d	20 44	20 48				20 53				21 01	21 07		21 14	21 18				21 23				21 31	21 37	21 44
Battersea Park 4	d	20 48					20 57			21 02	21 04	21 10		21 18					21 27			21 32	21 34	21 40	21 48
London Victoria 15 ⊖	a	20 53	20 55				21 03			21 06	21 09	21 15		21 23	21 25				21 33			21 36	21 39	21 45	21 53
Streatham 4	d							20 51	21 09											21 21	21 48				
Tulse Hill 3	d							20 55	21 13											21 25	21 52				
Herne Hill 4	a								21 17												21 55				
Loughborough Jn	a								21 21												21 59				
Elephant & Castle ⊖	a								21 26												22 04				
London Blackfriars 3 ⊖	a								21 30												22 08				
City Thameslink 3	a																								
St Pancras International 15 ⊖	a								21 42												22 17				
Luton Airport Parkway 7 ✈	a								22 27												23 01				
Luton 10	a								22 30												23 05				
North Dulwich	d							20 58												21 28					
East Dulwich	d							21 00												21 30					
Peckham Rye 4	d					20 56		21 02										21 26		21 32					
Queens Rd Peckham	d					20 59		21 05										21 29		21 35					
South Bermondsey	d					21 01		21 07										21 31		21 37					
London Bridge 4 ⊖	a			20 52	21 11	21 06		21 14								21 22	21 41	21 36		21 42					

For general notes see front of timetable
For details of catering facilities see Directory of Train Operators

A From Epsom (Table 182)
B From Tattenham Corner (Table 181)
C From Sutton (Surrey) (Table 182)
D From Epsom Downs (Table 182)

b Arr. 2001
c Arr. 2031

Table 177

Saturdays

East and West Croydon → London & Luton via Norbury/Crystal Palace/Tulse Hill

Local Services

Network Diagram - see first page of Table 177

		SN	SN	SN	SN	SN A	SN	FC	SN	SN	SN B	SN C	SN	SN	SN	SN	SN D	SN		FC	SN	SN	SN B	SN C	SN
East Croydon	d			21 40							21 47				22 10								22 17		
West Croydon 4	d					21 31	21 36					21 48					22 01	22 06						22 18	
Norwood Junction 2	a			21 44								21 53			22 14									22 23	
	d			21 44								21 53			22 14									22 23	
Selhurst 4	d					21 36	21 40				21 50						22 06	22 10					22 20		
Thornton Heath	d					21 38	21 42				21 52						22 08	22 12					22 22		
Norbury	d					21 41	21 45				21 55						22 11	22 15					22 25		
Streatham Common 4	d					21 44	21 48				21 57						22 14	22 18					22 27		
Bromley South 4	d																								
Beckenham Junction 4	d																								
Birkbeck	d																								
Crystal Palace 4	d		21 31							21 43		21 57		22 01								22 13		22 27	
Gipsy Hill	d									21 46		21 59										22 16		22 29	
West Norwood 4	d									21 49		22 02										22 19		22 32	
Streatham Hill	d									21 52		22 06										22 22		22 36	
Balham 4	⊖ d	21 44				21 48				21 55	22 01	22 09	22 14				22 18					22 25	22 31	22 39	22 44
Wandsworth Common	d					21 50				21 57	22 03	22 11					22 20					22 27	22 33	22 41	
Clapham Junction 10	d	21 48				21 53				22 01	22 07	22 14	22 18				22 23					22 31	22 37	22 44	22 48
Battersea Park 4	d					21 57			22 02	22 04	22 10	22 18					22 27				22 32	22 34	22 40	22 48	
London Victoria 15	⊖ a	21 55				22 03			22 06	22 09	22 15	22 23	22 25				22 33				22 36	22 39	22 45	22 53	22 55
Streatham 4	d						21 51	22 18										22 21		22 48					
Tulse Hill 3	d						21 55	22 22										22 25		22 52					
Herne Hill 4	a							22 26												22 55					
Loughborough Jn	a							22 30																	
Elephant & Castle	⊖ a							22 34												23 04					
London Blackfriars 3	⊖ a							22 38												23 09					
City Thameslink 3	a																								
St Pancras International 15	⊖ a							22 47												23 17					
Luton Airport Parkway 7	✈ a							23 31												00 01					
Luton 10	a							23 35												00 05					
North Dulwich	d						21 58											22 28							
East Dulwich	d						22 00											22 30							
Peckham Rye 4	d				21 56		22 02									22 26		22 32							
Queens Rd Peckham	d				21 59		22 05									22 29		22 35							
South Bermondsey	d				22 01		22 07									22 31		22 37							
London Bridge 4	⊖ a		21 52	22 11	22 06		22 12							22 22	22 41	22 36		22 42							

		SN	SN	SN	SN A	SN	SN	SN	SN B	SN C	SN	SN	SN	SN	SN D	SN	SN	SN	SN B	SN C	SN	SN			
East Croydon	d		22 40						22 47				23 10						23 17						
West Croydon 4	d				22 31	22 36				22 48					23 01	23 06				23 18					
Norwood Junction 2	a		22 44							22 53			23 14							23 23					
	d		22 44							22 53			23 14							23 23					
Selhurst 4	d				22 36	22 40			22 50						23 06	23 10			23 20						
Thornton Heath	d				22 38	22 42			22 52						23 08	23 12			23 22						
Norbury	d				22 41	22 45			22 55						23 11	23 15			23 25						
Streatham Common 4	d				22 44	22 48			22 57						23 14	23 18			23 27						
Bromley South 4	d																								
Beckenham Junction 4	d																								
Birkbeck	d																								
Crystal Palace 4	d	22 31						22 43		22 57		23 01						23 13		23 27	23 31	23 43			
Gipsy Hill	d							22 46		22 59								23 16		23 29		23 46			
West Norwood 4	d							22 49		23 02								23 19		23 32		23 49			
Streatham Hill	d							22 52		23 06								23 22		23 36		23 52			
Balham 4	⊖ d				22 48			22 55	23 01	23 09	23 14				23 18			23 25	23 31	23 40		23 55			
Wandsworth Common	d				22 50			22 57	23 03	23 11					23 20			23 27	23 33	23 42		23 57			
Clapham Junction 10	d				22 53			23 01	23 07	23 14	23 18				23 23			23 31	23 37	23 45		00 01			
Battersea Park 4	d				22 57		23 02	23 04		23 18					23 27		23 32	23 34	23 40	23 49		00 04			
London Victoria 15	⊖ a				23 03		23 06	23 09	23 14	23 23	23 25				23 31		23 37	23 40	23 45	23 54		00 09			
Streatham 4	d					22 51										23 21									
Tulse Hill 3	d					22 55										23 25									
Herne Hill 4	a																								
Loughborough Jn	a																								
Elephant & Castle	⊖ a																								
London Blackfriars 3	⊖ a																								
City Thameslink 3	a																								
St Pancras International 15	⊖ a																								
Luton Airport Parkway 7	✈ a																								
Luton 10	a																								
North Dulwich	d					22 58										23 28									
East Dulwich	d					23 00										23 30									
Peckham Rye 4	d			22 56		23 02								23 26		23 32									
Queens Rd Peckham	d			22 59		23 05								23 29		23 35									
South Bermondsey	d			23 01		23 07								23 31		23 37									
London Bridge 4	⊖ a	22 52	23 11	23 06		23 12						23 22	23 38	23 36		23 42					23 52				

For general notes see front of timetable
For details of catering facilities see Directory of Train Operators

A From Epsom (Table 182)
B From Tattenham Corner (Table 181)
C From Sutton (Surrey) (Table 182)
D From Epsom Downs (Table 182)

Table 177

Sundays

East and West Croydon → London & Luton via Norbury/Crystal Palace/Tulse Hill

Local Services

Network Diagram - see first page of Table 177

		FC	SN	SN 1	SN	SN	SN	SN	SN	SN	SN	SN	SN 1	SN	SN	SN	SN	SN	SN	SN	SN	SN	SN	SN	SN
											A		B			C			D						
East Croydon	d			05 28	06 40		06 44		07 12			07 14	07 27			07 22				07 44	07 47				
West Croydon 4	d										07 09				07 18				07 39			07 48	08 01		
Norwood Junction 2	a						06 48		07 17						07 23	07 26					07 51	07 53	08 05		
	d						06 48	06 54	07 18						07 24	07 26					07 51	07 54	08 05		
Selhurst 4	d				06 43	06 47					07 13	07 17	07 31						07 43	07 47					
Thornton Heath	d				06 45	06 49					07 15	07 19							07 45	07 49					
Norbury	d				06 48	06 52					07 18	07 22							07 48	07 52					
Streatham Common 4	d				06 51	06 54					07 21	07 24							07 51	07 54					
Bromley South 4	d																								
Beckenham Junction 4	d																								
Birkbeck	d																								
Crystal Palace 4	d		23p43					06 58							07 28							07 58			
Gipsy Hill	d		23p46					07 00							07 30							08 00			
West Norwood 4	d		23p49					07 03							07 33							08 03			
Streatham Hill	d		23p52					07 07							07 37							08 07			
Balham 4	⊖ d		23p55	05 43	06 55			07 10			07 25				07 40		07 48		07 55			08 10			08 18
Wandsworth Common	d		23p57		06 57			07 12			07 27				07 42				07 57			08 12			
Clapham Junction 10	d		00 01	05 49	07 00			07 15			07 30		07 40		07 45		07 52		08 00			08 15			08 22
Battersea Park 4	d		00 04		07 04			07 19		07 32	07 34				07 49			08 02	08 04			08 19			
London Victoria 15	⊖ a		00 09	05 58	07 08			07 23		07 36	07 38		07 48		07 53		07 59	08 06	08 08			08 23			08 29
Streatham 4	d	22p49				06 57						07 27								07 57					
Tulse Hill 3	d	22p53				07 01						07 31								08 01					
Herne Hill 4	a	22p56																							
Loughborough Jn	a																								
Elephant & Castle	⊖ a	23p04																							
London Blackfriars 3	⊖ a	23p08																							
City Thameslink 3	a																								
St Pancras International 15	⊖ a	23p17																							
Luton Airport Parkway 7	✈ a	00 01																							
Luton 10	a	00 05																							
North Dulwich	d					07 04						07 34								08 04					
East Dulwich	d					07 06						07 36								08 06					
Peckham Rye 4	d					07 08						07 38		07 56						08 08				08 26	
Queens Rd Peckham	d					07 11						07 41		07 59						08 11				08 29	
South Bermondsey	d					07 13						07 43		08 01						08 13				08 31	
London Bridge 4	⊖ a					07 18	07 12		07 42			07 48		08 06		07 38				08 18	08 12		08 31	08 36	

		SN	SN	SN	SN	SN 1	SN	SN	SN	SN	SN	SN	SN	SN	SN	SN		SN	SN	SN	SN	SN	SN	SN	SN 1
			D			E		C					D			D						D			E
East Croydon	d			08 14	08 17	08 29		08 22						08 44	08 47								09 14	09 17	09 29
West Croydon 4	d		08 09				08 18		08 31				08 39			08 48		09 01				09 09			
Norwood Junction 2	a				08 21		08 23	08 26	08 35						08 51	08 53		09 05						09 21	
	d				08 21		08 24	08 26	08 35						08 51	08 54		09 05						09 21	
Selhurst 4	d		08 13	08 17		08 32							08 43	08 47								09 13	09 17		09 32
Thornton Heath	d		08 15	08 19									08 45	08 49								09 15	09 19		
Norbury	d		08 18	08 22									08 48	08 52								09 18	09 22		
Streatham Common 4	d		08 21	08 24									08 51	08 54								09 21	09 24		
Bromley South 4	d																								
Beckenham Junction 4	d																								
Birkbeck	d																								
Crystal Palace 4	d						08 28									08 58									
Gipsy Hill	d						08 30									09 00									
West Norwood 4	d						08 33									09 03									
Streatham Hill	d						08 37									09 07									
Balham 4	⊖ d		08 25				08 40				08 48		08 55			09 10				09 18		09 25			
Wandsworth Common	d		08 27				08 42						08 57			09 12						09 27			
Clapham Junction 10	d		08 30			08 41	08 45				08 52		09 00			09 15				09 22		09 30			09 41
Battersea Park 4	d	08 32	08 34				08 49					09 02	09 04			09 19					09 32	09 34			
London Victoria 15	⊖ a	08 36	08 38			08 48	08 53				08 59	09 06	09 08			09 23				09 29	09 36	09 38			09 48
Streatham 4	d			08 27										08 57									09 27		
Tulse Hill 3	d			08 31										09 01									09 31		
Herne Hill 4	a																								
Loughborough Jn	a																								
Elephant & Castle	⊖ a																								
London Blackfriars 3	⊖ a																								
City Thameslink 3	a																								
St Pancras International 15	⊖ a																								
Luton Airport Parkway 7	✈ a																								
Luton 10	a																								
North Dulwich	d			08 34										09 04									09 34		
East Dulwich	d			08 36										09 06									09 36		
Peckham Rye 4	d			08 38						08 56				09 08					09 26				09 38		
Queens Rd Peckham	d			08 41						08 59				09 11					09 29				09 41		
South Bermondsey	d			08 43						09 01				09 13					09 31				09 43		
London Bridge 4	⊖ a			08 48	08 42			08 38	09 01	09 06				09 18	09 12			09 31	09 36				09 48	09 42	

For general notes see front of timetable
For details of catering facilities see Directory of Train Operators

A From Epsom (Table 182)
B From Horsham (Table 186)
C Until 7 September
D From Sutton (Surrey) (Table 182)
E From East Grinstead (Table 184)

Table 177

Sundays

East and West Croydon → London & Luton via Norbury/Crystal Palace/Tulse Hill

Local Services

Network Diagram - see first page of Table 177

		SN	SN	SN	SN	SN	SN	SN	SN	SN	SN	SN	SN	SN	SN	SN	SN	SN	FC	SN 1	SN	SN	SN	SN
		A	B					A			A					A				C	A	B		
East Croydon	d		09 22						09 44	09 47							10 14	10 17		10 29		10 22		
West Croydon 4	d	09 18		09 31				09 39			09 48	10 01				10 09					10 18		10 31	
Norwood Junction 2	a	09 23	09 26	09 35						09 51	09 53	10 05						10 21			10 23	10 26	10 35	
	d	09 24	09 26	09 35						09 51	09 54	10 05						10 21			10 24	10 26	10 35	
Selhurst 4	d							09 43	09 47							10 13	10 17			10 32				
Thornton Heath	d							09 45	09 49							10 15	10 19							
Norbury	d							09 48	09 52							10 18	10 22							
Streatham Common 4	d							09 51	09 54							10 21	10 24							
Bromley South 4	d																							
Beckenham Junction 4	d																							
Birkbeck	d																							
Crystal Palace 4	d	09 28									09 58										10 28			
Gipsy Hill	d	09 30									10 00										10 30			
West Norwood 4	d	09 33									10 03										10 33			
Streatham Hill	d	09 37									10 07										10 37			
Balham 4	⊖ d	09 40				09 48		09 55			10 10			10 18		10 25					10 40			
Wandsworth Common	d	09 42						09 57			10 12					10 27					10 42			
Clapham Junction 10	d	09 45				09 52		10 00			10 15			10 22		10 30				10 41	10 45			
Battersea Park 4	d	09 49					10 02	10 04			10 19				10 32	10 34					10 49			
London Victoria 15	⊖ a	09 53				09 59	10 06	10 08			10 23			10 29	10 36	10 38				10 48	10 53			
Streatham 4	d								09 57								10 27		10 35					
Tulse Hill 3	d								10 01								10 31		10 38					
Herne Hill 4	a																		10 42					
Loughborough Jn	a																		10 45					
Elephant & Castle	⊖ a																		10 49					
London Blackfriars 3	⊖ a																		10 56					
City Thameslink 3	a																							
St Pancras International 15	⊖ a																		11 06					
Luton Airport Parkway 7	✈ a																		11 48					
Luton 10	a																		11 53					
North Dulwich	d								10 04								10 34							
East Dulwich	d								10 06								10 36							
Peckham Rye 4	d				09 56				10 08				10 26				10 38							10 56
Queens Rd Peckham	d				09 59				10 11				10 29				10 41							10 59
South Bermondsey	d				10 01				10 13				10 31				10 43							11 01
London Bridge 4	⊖ a		09 38	10 01	10 06				10 18	10 12		10 31	10 36				10 48	10 42				10 38	11 01	11 06

		SN	SN	SN	SN	SN	FC	SN	SN	SN	SN	SN	SN		SN	SN	FC	SN 1	SN	SN	SN	SN	SN
				A				A					A					C	A	B			
East Croydon	d				10 44	10 47									18 14	18 17		18 29		18 22			
West Croydon 4	d			10 39				10 48	11 01				11 09						18 18		18 31		
Norwood Junction 2	a					10 51		10 53	11 05							18 21			18 23	18 26	18 35		
	d					10 51		10 54	11 05							18 21			18 24	18 26	18 35		
Selhurst 4	d			10 43	10 47								11 13		18 17			18 32					
Thornton Heath	d			10 45	10 49								11 15		18 19								
Norbury	d			10 48	10 52								11 18		18 22								
Streatham Common 4	d			10 51	10 54								11 21		18 24								
Bromley South 4	d																						
Beckenham Junction 4	d													and at									
Birkbeck	d																						
Crystal Palace 4	d							10 58						the same					18 28				
Gipsy Hill	d							11 00											18 30				
West Norwood 4	d							11 03						minutes					18 33				
Streatham Hill	d							11 07											18 37				
Balham 4	⊖ d	10 48		10 55				11 10			11 18		11 25	past					18 40				18 48
Wandsworth Common	d			10 57				11 12					11 27						18 42				
Clapham Junction 10	d	10 52		11 00				11 15			11 22		11 30	each				18 41	18 45				18 52
Battersea Park 4	d		11 02	11 04				11 19				11 32	11 34						18 49				
London Victoria 15	⊖ a	10 59	11 06	11 08				11 23			11 29	11 36	11 38	hour until				18 48	18 53				18 59
Streatham 4	d				10 57		11 05								18 27		18 35						
Tulse Hill 3	d				11 01		11 08								18 31		18 38						
Herne Hill 4	a						11 12										18 42						
Loughborough Jn	a						11 15										18 44						
Elephant & Castle	⊖ a						11 19										18 49						
London Blackfriars 3	⊖ a						11 26										18 56						
City Thameslink 3	a																						
St Pancras International 15	⊖ a						11 36										19 06						
Luton Airport Parkway 7	✈ a						12 18										19 47						
Luton 10	a						12 23										19 52						
North Dulwich	d				11 04										18 34								
East Dulwich	d				11 06										18 36								
Peckham Rye 4	d				11 08					11 26					18 38							18 56	
Queens Rd Peckham	d				11 11					11 29					18 41							18 59	
South Bermondsey	d				11 13					11 31					18 43							19 01	
London Bridge 4	⊖ a				11 18	11 12			11 31	11 36					18 48	18 42				18 38	19 01	19 06	

For general notes see front of timetable
For details of catering facilities see Directory of Train Operators

A From Sutton (Surrey) (Table 182)
B Until 7 September
C From East Grinstead (Table 184)

Table 177

Sundays

East and West Croydon → London & Luton via Norbury/Crystal Palace/Tulse Hill

Local Services

Network Diagram - see first page of Table 177

Station		SN	SN	SN	SN	FC	SN	SN	SN	SN	SN	SN	SN	SN	FC	SN	SN	SN	SN	SN	SN	SN	SN	SN	SN
			A				A					A				1 B	A	C					A		
East Croydon	d			18 44	18 47								19 14	19 17		19 29		19 22						19 44	19 47
West Croydon [4]	d		18 39				18 48	19 01				19 09					19 18		19 31				19 39		
Norwood Junction [2]	a				18 51		18 53	19 05						19 21			19 23	19 26	19 35						19 51
	d				18 51		18 54	19 05						19 21			19 24	19 26	19 35						19 51
Selhurst [4]	d		18 43	18 47								19 13	19 17			19 32							19 43	19 47	
Thornton Heath	d		18 45	18 49								19 15	19 19										19 45	19 49	
Norbury	d		18 48	18 52								19 18	19 22										19 48	19 52	
Streatham Common [4]	d		18 51	18 54								19 21	19 24										19 51	19 54	
Bromley South [4]	d																								
Beckenham Junction [4]	d																								
Birkbeck	d																								
Crystal Palace [4]	d						18 58										19 28								
Gipsy Hill	d						19 00										19 30								
West Norwood [4]	d						19 03										19 33								
Streatham Hill	d						19 07										19 37								
Balham [4] ⊖	d		18 55				19 10			19 18		19 25					19 40				19 48		19 55		
Wandsworth Common	d		18 57				19 12					19 27					19 42						19 57		
Clapham Junction [10]	d		19 00				19 15			19 22		19 30				19 41	19 45				19 52		20 00		
Battersea Park [4]	d	19 02	19 04				19 19				19 32	19 34					19 49					20 02	20 04		
London Victoria [15] ⊖	a	19 06	19 08				19 23			19 29	19 36	19 38				19 48	19 53				19 59	20 06	20 08		
Streatham [4]	d			18 57		19 05							19 27		19 35									19 57	
Tulse Hill [3]	d			19 01		19 08							19 31		19 38									20 01	
Herne Hill [4]	a					19 12									19 42										
Loughborough Jn	a					19 14									19 44										
Elephant & Castle ⊖	a					19 19									19 49										
London Blackfriars [3] ⊖	a					19 26									19 56										
City Thameslink [3]	a																								
St Pancras International [15] ⊖	a					19 36									20 06										
Luton Airport Parkway [7] ✈	a					20 17									20 47										
Luton [10]	a					20 22									20 52										
North Dulwich	d			19 04									19 34											20 04	
East Dulwich	d			19 06									19 36											20 06	
Peckham Rye [4]	d			19 08					19 26				19 38							19 56				20 08	
Queens Rd Peckham	d			19 11					19 29				19 41							19 59				20 11	
South Bermondsey	d			19 13					19 31				19 43							20 01				20 13	
London Bridge [4] ⊖	a			19 18	19 12			19 31	19 36				19 48	19 42				19 38	20 01	20 06				20 18	20 12

Station		FC	SN	SN	SN	SN	SN	SN	SN		SN	FC	SN	SN	SN	SN	SN	SN	SN	SN	SN	SN	FC	SN	SN
			A					A					1 B	A	C					A				A	
East Croydon	d								20 14		20 17		20 29		20 22						20 44	20 47			
West Croydon [4]	d		19 48	20 01				20 09						20 18		20 31				20 39				20 48	21 01
Norwood Junction [2]	a		19 53	20 05							20 21			20 23	20 26	20 35						20 51		20 53	21 05
	d		19 54	20 05							20 21			20 24	20 26	20 35						20 51		20 54	21 05
Selhurst [4]	d							20 13	20 17				20 32							20 43	20 47				
Thornton Heath	d							20 15	20 19											20 45	20 49				
Norbury	d							20 18	20 22											20 48	20 52				
Streatham Common [4]	d							20 21	20 24											20 51	20 54				
Bromley South [4]	d																								
Beckenham Junction [4]	d																								
Birkbeck	d																								
Crystal Palace [4]	d		19 58											20 28										20 58	
Gipsy Hill	d		20 00											20 30										21 00	
West Norwood [4]	d		20 03											20 33										21 03	
Streatham Hill	d		20 07											20 37										21 07	
Balham [4] ⊖	d		20 10			20 18		20 25						20 40				20 48		20 55				21 10	
Wandsworth Common	d		20 12					20 27						20 42						20 57				21 12	
Clapham Junction [10]	d		20 15			20 22		20 30					20 41	20 45				20 52		21 00				21 15	
Battersea Park [4]	d		20 19				20 32	20 34						20 49					21 02	21 04				21 19	
London Victoria [15] ⊖	a		20 23			20 29	20 36	20 38					20 48	20 53				20 59	21 06	21 08				21 23	
Streatham [4]	d	20 05							20 27			20 35									20 57		21 05		
Tulse Hill [3]	d	20 08							20 31			20 38									21 01		21 08		
Herne Hill [4]	a	20 12										20 42											21 12		
Loughborough Jn	a	20 14										20 44											21 14		
Elephant & Castle ⊖	a	20 19										20 49											21 19		
London Blackfriars [3] ⊖	a	20 26										20 56											21 26		
City Thameslink [3]	a																								
St Pancras International [15] ⊖	a	20 36										21 06											21 36		
Luton Airport Parkway [7] ✈	a	21 17										21 47											22 17		
Luton [10]	a	21 22										21 50											22 22		
North Dulwich	d								20 34												21 04				
East Dulwich	d								20 36												21 06				
Peckham Rye [4]	d				20 26				20 38								20 56				21 08				
Queens Rd Peckham	d				20 29				20 41								20 59				21 11				
South Bermondsey	d				20 31				20 43								21 01				21 13				
London Bridge [4] ⊖	a			20 31	20 36				20 48		20 42				20 38	21 01	21 06				21 18	21 12			21 31

For general notes see front of timetable
For details of catering facilities see Directory of Train Operators

A From Sutton (Surrey) (Table 182)
B From East Grinstead (Table 184)
C Until 7 September

Table 177

Sundays

East and West Croydon → London & Luton via Norbury/Crystal Palace/Tulse Hill

Local Services

Network Diagram - see first page of Table 177

		SN	SN	SN	SN	SN	SN	FC	SN 1	SN	SN	SN	SN	SN	SN	SN	SN	SN	SN	SN	SN	SN	SN	SN	SN
					A				B	A	C					A			A					A	
East Croydon	d					21 14	21 17		21 29		21 22						21 44	21 47							22 14
West Croydon 4	d				21 09					21 18		21 31				21 39			21 48	22 01				22 09	
Norwood Junction 2	a						21 21			21 23	21 26	21 35						21 51	21 53	22 05					
	d						21 21			21 24	21 26	21 35						21 51	21 54	22 05					
Selhurst 4	d				21 13	21 17			21 32							21 43	21 47							22 13	22 17
Thornton Heath	d				21 15	21 19										21 45	21 49							22 15	22 19
Norbury	d				21 18	21 22										21 48	21 52							22 18	22 22
Streatham Common 4	d				21 21	21 24										21 51	21 54							22 21	22 24
Bromley South 4	d																								
Beckenham Junction 4	d																								
Birkbeck	d																								
Crystal Palace 4	d									21 28									21 58						
Gipsy Hill	d									21 30									22 00						
West Norwood 4	d									21 33									22 03						
Streatham Hill	d									21 37									22 07						
Balham 4 ⊖	d		21 18		21 25					21 40				21 48		21 55			22 10			22 18		22 25	
Wandsworth Common	d				21 27					21 42						21 57			22 12					22 27	
Clapham Junction 10	d		21 22		21 30				21 41	21 45				21 52		22 00			22 15			22 22		22 30	
Battersea Park 4	d			21 32	21 34					21 49					22 02	22 04			22 19				22 32	22 34	
London Victoria 15 ⊖	a		21 29	21 36	21 39				21 48	21 53				21 59	22 06	22 09			22 23			22 29	22 36	22 39	
Streatham 4	d					21 27		21 35									21 57								22 27
Tulse Hill 3	d					21 31		21 38									22 01								22 31
Herne Hill 4	a							21 42																	
Loughborough Jn	a							21 44																	
Elephant & Castle ⊖	a							21 49																	
London Blackfriars 3 ⊖	a							21 56																	
City Thameslink 3	a																								
St Pancras International 15 ⊖	a							22 06																	
Luton Airport Parkway 7 ✈	a							22 47																	
Luton 10	a							22 50																	
North Dulwich	d					21 34											22 04								22 34
East Dulwich	d					21 36											22 06								22 36
Peckham Rye 4	d	21 26				21 38							21 56				22 08				22 26				22 38
Queens Rd Peckham	d	21 29				21 41							21 59				22 11				22 29				22 41
South Bermondsey	d	21 31				21 43							22 01				22 13				22 31				22 43
London Bridge 4 ⊖	a	21 36				21 48	21 42				21 39	22 01	22 06				22 18	22 12		22 31	22 36				22 48

		SN	SN 1	SN	SN	SN	SN	SN	SN	SN	SN	SN	SN 1	SN	SN	SN	SN	SN	SN 1	SN	SN	SN	SN 1		
			B	A	C					A			D		A			A	B	A		A	D		
East Croydon	d	22 17	22 29		22 22						22 44	22 47	22 59						23 29				23 56		
West Croydon 4	d			22 18		22 31				22 39					22 48			23 09		23 18		23 43			
Norwood Junction 2	a	22 21		22 23	22 26	22 35						22 51			22 53					23 23					
	d	22 21		22 24	22 26	22 35						22 51			22 54					23 26					
Selhurst 4	d		22 32							22 43	22 47		23 02					23 13	23 32			23a47	00 01		
Thornton Heath	d									22 45	22 49							23 15							
Norbury	d									22 48	22 52							23 18							
Streatham Common 4	d									22 51	22 54							23 21							
Bromley South 4	d																								
Beckenham Junction 4	d																								
Birkbeck	d																								
Crystal Palace 4	d			22 28											22 58					23 30					
Gipsy Hill	d			22 30											23 00					23 32					
West Norwood 4	d			22 33											23 03					23 35					
Streatham Hill	d			22 37											23 07					23 39					
Balham 4 ⊖	d			22 40				22 48		22 55					23 10	23 18		23 25		23 42	23 48				
Wandsworth Common	d			22 42						22 57					23 12			23 27		23 44					
Clapham Junction 10	d		22 41	22 45				22 52		23 00			23 10		23 15	23 22		23 30	23 41	23 47	23 52		00 11		
Battersea Park 4	d			22 49					23 02	23 04					23 19		23 32	23 34		23 51					
London Victoria 15 ⊖	a		22 50	22 53				22 59	23 06	23 09			23 16		23 23	23 29	23 37	23 38	23 51	23 55	23 59		00 18		
Streatham 4	d										22 57														
Tulse Hill 3	d										23 01														
Herne Hill 4	a																								
Loughborough Jn	a																								
Elephant & Castle ⊖	a																								
London Blackfriars 3 ⊖	a																								
City Thameslink 3	a																								
St Pancras International 15 ⊖	a																								
Luton Airport Parkway 7 ✈	a																								
Luton 10	a																								
North Dulwich	d										23 04														
East Dulwich	d										23 06														
Peckham Rye 4	d						22 56				23 08			23 26											
Queens Rd Peckham	d						22 59				23 11			23 29											
South Bermondsey	d						23 01				23 13			23 31											
London Bridge 4 ⊖	a	22 42			22 38	23 01	23 06				23 18	23 12		23 36											

For general notes see front of timetable
For details of catering facilities see Directory of Train Operators

A From Sutton (Surrey) (Table 182)
B From East Grinstead (Table 184)
C Until 7 September
D From Horsham (Table 186)

Charing Cross and London Bridge → London Victoria and Croydon

Network Diagram - see first page of Table 177

Miles	Miles	Miles	Miles	Miles			SN MX	SN MO	SN MX	SN MX	SE	SN	SE	SN	SN	SE	SN	SN	SE	SN	SN	SN	SN	SN	SN	SE
											73		73			83	[1]		83						[1]	83
								A	A			B			A		C			D	E		G	A	H	
—	—	0	—	—	**London Charing Cross [4]**	⊖ d		23p36	23p45	00 12					06 05											
—	—	$\frac{3}{4}$	—	—	London Waterloo (East) [4]	⊖ d		23p39	23p48	00 15					06 08											
0	0	$1\frac{3}{4}$	—	—	**London Bridge [4]**	⊖ d	23p24	23p44	23p53	00 26		05 46		06 11	06 13		06 30	06 41		06 46	06 54	07 11	07 15	07 25	07 28	
—	$2\frac{3}{4}$	$4\frac{1}{2}$	—	—	New Cross Gate [4]	⊖ d	23p30	23p49	23p58	00 31		05 51			06 19		06 35			06 51	06 59		07 20	07 30	07 33	
—	$3\frac{3}{4}$	$5\frac{1}{2}$	—	—	Brockley	d	23p32	23p52	00 01	00 34		05 54			06 22					06 54	07 02		07 23	07 33		
—	$4\frac{3}{4}$	$6\frac{1}{2}$	—	—	Honor Oak Park	d	23p35	23p55	00 04	00 37		05 57			06 25					06 57	07 05		07 26	07 36		
—	$5\frac{3}{4}$	$7\frac{1}{2}$	—	—	Forest Hill [4]	d	23p38	23p57	00 06	00 39		05 59			06 27					06 59	07 07		07 28	07 38		
—	$6\frac{1}{2}$	$8\frac{1}{4}$	—	—	Sydenham	d	23p40	23p59	00 09	00 42		06 02			06 30					07 02	07 10		07 31	07 41		
—	$7\frac{3}{4}$	—	—	—	**Crystal Palace [4]**	d	23p43																			
—	$8\frac{1}{2}$	—	—	—	Gipsy Hill	d	23p46																			
—	$9\frac{1}{2}$	—	—	—	West Norwood [4]	d	23p49																			
—	$10\frac{3}{4}$	—	—	—	Streatham Hill	d	23p52																			
—	$11\frac{3}{4}$	—	—	—	Balham [4]	⊖ d	23p55																			
—	$12\frac{1}{2}$	—	—	—	Wandsworth Common	d	23p57																			
—	$13\frac{3}{4}$	—	—	—	Clapham Junction [10]	d	00 01																			
$1\frac{3}{4}$	—	—	—	—	South Bermondsey	d								06 15				06 45				07 15				
$2\frac{3}{4}$	—	—	—	—	Queens Rd Peckham	d								06 18				06 48				07 18				
$3\frac{1}{2}$	—	—	0	0	Peckham Rye [4]	d					05 04		06 04	06 20		06 33		06 50	07 02			07 20				07 34
$4\frac{1}{4}$	—	—	$\frac{3}{4}$	$\frac{3}{4}$	Denmark Hill [4]	d					05 06		06 07	06 23		06 35		06 53	07 05			07 23				07 36
—	—	—	—	$4\frac{1}{2}$	**London Blackfriars [3]**	⊖ a					05 16		06 18			06 45			07 15							07 46
$6\frac{1}{4}$	—	—	—	—	Clapham High Street	⊖ d								06 28				06 58				07 28				
$6\frac{3}{4}$	—	—	—	—	Wandsworth Road	d								06 29				06 59				07 29				
$7\frac{1}{2}$	$15\frac{1}{4}$	—	—	—	Battersea Park [4]	d	00 04							06 32				07 02				07 32				
$8\frac{3}{4}$	$16\frac{1}{2}$	—	5	—	**London Victoria [15]**	⊖ a	00 12							06 36				07 08				07 38				
—	—	9	—	—	Penge West	d		00 02	00 11	00 44		06 04			06 32					07 04			07 33	07 43		
—	—	$9\frac{1}{4}$	—	—	Anerley	d		00 04	00 13	00 46		06 06			06 34					07 06			07 35	07 45		
—	—	$10\frac{1}{2}$	—	0	Norwood Junction [2]	d		00 10	00 16	00 49		06 09			06 38		06 44			07 10	07 14		07 39	07b51	07 42	
—	—	—	—	$1\frac{3}{4}$	**West Croydon [4]**	a						06 14								07 14			07 43			
—	—	$11\frac{3}{4}$	—	—	**East Croydon**	a		00 13	00 20	00 53					06 41		06 48				07 18			07 55	07 45	

		SN	SN	SE	SE	SE	SN	SE	SE	SE	SE	SN	SN	SE	SE	SN	SE	SE	SE	SE	SN	SN	SN	SN	SE	SE
				18	18	83		96 [1]	78	78	73			83	20		78	78	9	83					18	18
		J		K	L		N		K	L		A				Q	K	L			B		A		K	L
London Charing Cross [4]	⊖ d																									
London Waterloo (East) [4]	⊖ d																									
London Bridge [4]	⊖ d	07 40	07 41				07 48					08 05	08 09			08 17					08 19	08 27	08 36	08 41		
New Cross Gate [4]	⊖ d	07 45					07 53					08 10				08 22					08 26	08 32	08 41			
Brockley	d	07 48					07 56					08 13				08 25					08 29		08 44			
Honor Oak Park	d	07 51					07 59					08 16				08 28					08 32		08 47			
Forest Hill [4]	d	07 53					08 01					08 18				08 30					08 34		08 49			
Sydenham	d	07 56					08 04					08 21				08 33					08 37		08 52			
Crystal Palace [4]	d															08 36										
Gipsy Hill	d															08 38										
West Norwood [4]	d															08a42										
Streatham Hill	d																									
Balham [4]	⊖ d																									
Wandsworth Common	d																									
Clapham Junction [10]	d																									
South Bermondsey	d		07 45										08 13											08 45		
Queens Rd Peckham	d		07 48										08 15											08 48		
Peckham Rye [4]	d		07 50	07 55	07 55	07 59			08 12	08 12	08 15		08 18				08 32	08 32	08 35	08 43				08 50	08 54	08 54
Denmark Hill [4]	d		07 53	07 59	07 59	08 03		08 06	08 15	08 15	08 18		08 21	08 22	08 27		08 35	08 35	08 38	08 45				08 53	08 59	08 59
London Blackfriars [3]	⊖ a					08 13					08 29			08 31					08 49	08 56						
Clapham High Street	⊖ d		07 58										08 26											08 58		
Wandsworth Road	d		07 59										08 28											08 59		
Battersea Park [4]	d		08 02										08 32											09 02		
London Victoria [15]	⊖ a		08 08	08 11	08 12			08 17	08 28	08 29			08 38		08 38		08 48	08 49						09 08	09 11	09 12
Penge West	d						08 06														08 39					
Anerley	d						08 08														08 41					
Norwood Junction [2]	d	08 00					08 11					08 25									08 44		08 56			
West Croydon [4]	a						08 16														08 49					
East Croydon	a	08 04										08 29										08 45	09 00			

For general notes see front of timetable
For details of catering facilities see Directory of Train Operators

- **A** To Caterham (Table 181)
- **B** To Sutton (Surrey) (Table 182)
- **C** To East Grinstead (Table 184)
- **D** To Guildford (Table 182)
- **E** To Tattenham Corner (Table 181) and to Caterham (Table 181)
- **G** To Epsom (Table 182)
- **H** To Brighton (Table 186)
- **J** To Tattenham Corner (Table 181)
- **K** Until 10 October
- **L** From 13 October
- **N** To Dorking (Table 182)
- **Q** To London Bridge (Table 177)
- **b** Arr. 0748

Charing Cross and London Bridge → London Victoria and Croydon

Network Diagram - see first page of Table 177

		SE 9	SN A	SE 83	SE 78 B	SE 78 C	SN	SN D	SN	SE 73	SN A	SE 83	SN	SN D	SN	SE 78 B	SE 78 C	SE 83	SN A	SN	SN D	SN	SE 83	SE 78
London Charing Cross 4	⊖ d																							
London Waterloo (East) 4	⊖ d																							
London Bridge 4	⊖ d		08 45				08 54	09 05	09 11		09 15		09 24	09 35	09 41				09 45	09 54	10 05	10 11		
New Cross Gate 4	⊖ d		08 50				09 00	09 10			09 20		09 30	09 40					09 50	10 00	10 10			
Brockley	d		08 53				09 02	09 13			09 23		09 32	09 43					09 53	10 03	10 13			
Honor Oak Park	d		08 56				09 05	09 16			09 26		09 35	09 46					09 56	10 06	10 16			
Forest Hill 4	d		08 58				09 08	09 18			09 28		09 38	09 48					09 58	10 08	10 18			
Sydenham	d		09 01				09 10	09 21			09 31		09 40	09 51					10 01	10 11	10 21			
Crystal Palace 4	d						09 13						09 43							10 14				
Gipsy Hill	d						09 16						09 46							10 16				
West Norwood 4	d						09 19						09 49							10 19				
Streatham Hill	d						09 22						09 52							10 23				
Balham 4	⊖ d						09 26						09 56							10 26				
Wandsworth Common	d						09 28						09 58							10 28				
Clapham Junction 10	d						09 32						10 01							10 31				
South Bermondsey	d								09 15						09 45							10 15		
Queens Rd Peckham	d								09 18						09 48							10 18		
Peckham Rye 4	d	09 04		09 08	09 18	09 18			09 20	09 25		09 34			09 50	09 58	09 58	10 01				10 20	10 22	10 28
Denmark Hill 4	d	09 06		09 10	09 20	09 20			09 23	09 27		09 36			09 53	10 01	10 01	10 04				10 23	10 25	10 31
London Blackfriars 3	⊖ a	09 17		09 21						09 37		09 46						10 12					10 33	
Clapham High Street	⊖ d								09 28						09 58							10 28		
Wandsworth Road	d								09 29						09 59							10 29		
Battersea Park 4	d						09 36		09 32				10 05		10 03					10 34		10 32		
London Victoria 15	⊖ a				09 32	09 33	09 42		09 39				10 10		10 07	10 12	10 14			10 40		10 36		10 42
Penge West	d		09 03								09 33								10 03					
Anerley	d		09 05								09 35								10 05					
Norwood Junction 2	d		09 09					09 25			09 39			09 55					10 09		10 25			
West Croydon 4	a		09 14								09 44								10 14					
East Croydon	a							09 29						09 59							10 29			

		SN A	SN	SN D	SN	SE 83	SE 78	SN A	SN	SN D	SN	SE 83	SE 78		SN A	SN	SN D	SN	SE 83	SE 78	SN A	SN	SN D	SN
London Charing Cross 4	⊖ d																							
London Waterloo (East) 4	⊖ d																							
London Bridge 4	⊖ d	10 15	10 24	10 35	10 41			10 45	10 54	11 05	11 11			and at the same minutes past each hour until	15 15	15 24	15 35	15 41			15 45	15 54	16 05	16 11
New Cross Gate 4	⊖ d	10 20	10 30	10 40				10 50	11 00	11 10					15 20	15 30	15 40				15 50	16 00	16 10	
Brockley	d	10 23	10 32	10 43				10 53	11 02	11 13					15 23	15 32	15 43				15 53	16 02	16 13	
Honor Oak Park	d	10 26	10 35	10 46				10 56	11 05	11 16					15 26	15 35	15 46				15 56	16 05	16 16	
Forest Hill 4	d	10 28	10 38	10 48				10 58	11 08	11 18					15 28	15 38	15 48				15 58	16 08	16 18	
Sydenham	d	10 31	10 40	10 51				11 01	11 10	11 21					15 31	15 40	15 51				16 01	16 10	16 21	
Crystal Palace 4	d		10 43						11 13							15 43						16 13		
Gipsy Hill	d		10 46						11 16							15 46						16 16		
West Norwood 4	d		10 49						11 19							15 49						16 19		
Streatham Hill	d		10 52						11 22							15 52						16 22		
Balham 4	⊖ d		10 55						11 25							15 55						16 25		
Wandsworth Common	d		10 57						11 27							15 57						16 27		
Clapham Junction 10	d		11 01						11 31							16 01						16 31		
South Bermondsey	d				10 45						11 15							15 45						16 15
Queens Rd Peckham	d				10 48						11 18							15 48						16 18
Peckham Rye 4	d				10 50	10 52	10 58				11 20	11 22	11 28					15 50	15 52	15 58				16 20
Denmark Hill 4	d				10 53	10 55	11 01				11 23	11 25	11 31					15 53	15 55	16 01				16 23
London Blackfriars 3	⊖ a					11 03						11 33							16 03					
Clapham High Street	⊖ d				10 58						11 28							15 58						16 28
Wandsworth Road	d				10 59						11 29							15 59						16 29
Battersea Park 4	d		11 04		11 02				11 34		11 32					16 05		16 03				16 34		16 32
London Victoria 15	⊖ a		11 09		11 06		11 12		11 39		11 36		11 42			16 10		16 07		16 12		16 40		16 38
Penge West	d	10 33						11 03							15 33						16 03			
Anerley	d	10 35						11 05							15 35						16 05			
Norwood Junction 2	d	10 39		10 55				11 09		11 25					15 39		15 55				16 10		16 25	
West Croydon 4	a	10 44						11 14							15 44						16 15			
East Croydon	a			10 59						11 29							15 59						16 29	

For general notes see front of timetable
For details of catering facilities see Directory of Train Operators

A To Sutton (Surrey) (Table 182)
B Until 10 October
C From 13 October
D To Caterham (Table 181)

Charing Cross and London Bridge → London Victoria and Croydon

Network Diagram - see first page of Table 177

	SE 83	SN A	SE 78	SN	SN B	SN	SE 83	SN A	SE 78	SN	SN	SN	SE 83	SN	SN	SN A	SN	SN	SN	SE 83	SE 78	SN	SN C	SN	SN
London Charing Cross 4 ⊖ d																									
London Waterloo (East) 4 ⊖ d																									
London Bridge 4 ⊖ d		16 15		16 24	16 35	16 41		16 44		16 55	17 05	17 11		17 15	17 19	17 25	17 35	17 39	17 41			17 45	17 55	18 01	18 05
New Cross Gate 4 ⊖ d		16 20		16 30	16 40			16 49		17 00	17 10			17 20	17 24	17 30	17 40	17 44				17 53		18 06	18 10
Brockley d		16 23		16 32	16 43			16 52		17 03	17 13			17 23			17 43					17 56			18 13
Honor Oak Park d		16 26		16 35	16 46			16 55		17 06	17 16			17 26			17 46					17 59			18 16
Forest Hill 4 d		16 28		16 38	16 48			16 57		17 08	17 18			17 28		17 36	17 48					18 01	18 05		18 18
Sydenham d		16 31		16 40	16 51			17 00		17 11	17 21			17 31		17 38	17 51					18 04	18 08		18 21
Crystal Palace 4 d				16 43						17 14				17b43								18 10			
Gipsy Hill d				16 46						17 16				17 46								18 13			
West Norwood 4 d				16 49						17 19				17 49								18 16			
Streatham Hill d				16 52						17 23				17 52								18 19			
Balham 4 ⊖ d				16 55						17 28				17 56								18 23			
Wandsworth Common d										17 30												18 25			
Clapham Junction 10 d				17 01						17 33				18 01								18 28			
South Bermondsey d						16 45						17 15							17 45						
Queens Rd Peckham d						16 48						17 18							17 48						
Peckham Rye 4 d	16 22		16 42			16 50	16 52		17 15			17 20	17 24						17 50	17 54	18 01				
Denmark Hill 4 d	16 25		16 46			16 53	16 55		17 18			17 23	17 27						17 53	17 57	18 04				
London Blackfriars 3 ⊖ a	16 33						17 05						17 39							18 08					
Clapham High Street ⊖ d						16 58						17 28							17 58						
Wandsworth Road d						16 59						17 29							17 59						
Battersea Park 4 d				17 04		17 02				17 37		17 32		18 05					18 02			18 34			
London Victoria 15 ⊖ a			17 03	17 10		17 08			17 28	17 43		17 38		18 12					18 09		18 16	18 40			
Penge West d		16 33						17 02			17 23						17 53								18 23
Anerley d		16 35						17 04			17 25						17 55								18 25
Norwood Junction 2 d		16 39			16 55			17 09			17 28				17 33	17 43	17 58	17 54					18 13	18 15	18 28
West Croydon 4 a		16 43						17 14			17 35					17 48	18 05						18 17		18 35
East Croydon a					16 59										17 37			17 57						18 19	

	SN	SE 83	SN	SN	SN C	SE 78	SN	SN	SN	SE 83	SE 78	SN	SN D	SN	SE 83	SN B	SN	SN	SN	SE 83	SN B	SN	SN	SE 83	SN B
London Charing Cross 4 ⊖ d																					19 37				20 07
London Waterloo (East) 4 ⊖ d																					19 40				20 10
London Bridge 4 ⊖ d	18 11		18 18	18 20	18 25		18 36	18 41	18 42			18 51	19 05	19 11		19 15	19 24	19 35	19 41		19 45	19 54	20 11		20 15
New Cross Gate 4 ⊖ d			18 23	18 26			18 41		18 47			18 56	19 10			19 20	19 30	19 40			19 50	20 00			20 20
Brockley d			18 26				18 44					18 59	19 13			19 23	19 32	19 43			19 53	20 02			20 23
Honor Oak Park d			18 29				18 47					19 02	19 16			19 26	19 35	19 46			19 56	20 05			20 26
Forest Hill 4 d			18 31		18 34		18 49					19 04	19 18			19 28	19 38	19 48			19 58	20 08			20 28
Sydenham d			18 34		18 37		18 52					19 07	19 21			19 31	19 40	19 51			20 01	20 10			20 31
Crystal Palace 4 d			18c43									19 13					19 43					20 13			
Gipsy Hill d			18 45									19 16					19 46					20 16			
West Norwood 4 d			18 48									19 19					19 49					20 19			
Streatham Hill d			18 52									19 22					19 52					20 22			
Balham 4 ⊖ d			18 55									19 25					19 55					20 25			
Wandsworth Common d			18 57									19 27					19 57					20 27			
Clapham Junction 10 d			19 00									19 31					20 01					20 31			
South Bermondsey d	18 15							18 45						19 15					19 45				20 15		
Queens Rd Peckham d	18 18							18 48						19 18					19 48				20 18		
Peckham Rye 4 d	18 20	18 23				18 47		18 50		18 52	19 12			19 20	19 28				19 50	19 53			20 20	20 22	
Denmark Hill 4 d	18 23	18 26				18 50		18 53		18 55	19 15			19 23	19 31				19 53	19 55			20 23	20 25	
London Blackfriars 3 ⊖ a		18 35								19 03					19 40					20 03				20 33	
Clapham High Street ⊖ d	18 28							18 58						19 28					19 58				20 28		
Wandsworth Road d	18 29							18 59						19 29					19 59				20 29		
Battersea Park 4 d	18 32		19 04					19 02				19 34		19 32			20 04		20 02			20 34	20 32		
London Victoria 15 ⊖ a	18 38		19 11			19 00		19 08			19 25	19 41		19 36			20 09		20 06			20 40	20 36		
Penge West d							18 54						19 23			19 33		19 53			20 03				20 33
Anerley d							18 56						19 25			19 35		19 55			20 05				20 35
Norwood Junction 2 d				18 35	18 42		18 59		18 56				19 28			19 39		19a58			20 09				20 38
West Croydon 4 a					18 46		19 06						19 33												
East Croydon a				18 38					19 00							19 42					20 12				20 42

For general notes see front of timetable
For details of catering facilities see Directory of Train Operators

A To Guildford (Table 182)
B To Caterham (Table 181)
C To Dorking (Table 182)
D To Epsom Downs (Table 182)

b Arr. 1734
c Arr. 1839

Charing Cross and London Bridge → London Victoria and Croydon

Network Diagram - see first page of Table 177

		SN	SN	SE 83	SN A	SN	SN	SE 83	SN A	SN	SN	SE 83	SN A	SN	SN	SE 83	SN A	SN	SN	SE 83	SN A	SN	SN	SE 83	SN A	SN
London Charing Cross 4	⊖ d				20 37				21 07				21 37				22 07				22 37				23 07	
London Waterloo (East) 4	⊖ d				20 40				21 10				21 40				22 10				22 40				23 10	
London Bridge 4	⊖ d	20 24	20 41		20 45	20 54	21 11		21 15	21 24	21 41		21 45	21 54	22 11		22 15	22 24	22 41		22 45	22 54	23 11		23 15	23 24
New Cross Gate 4	⊖ d	20 30			20 50	21 00			21 20	21 30			21 50	22 00			22 20	22 30			22 50	23 00			23 20	23 30
Brockley	d	20 32			20 53	21 02			21 23	21 32			21 53	22 02			22 23	22 32			22 53	23 02			23 23	23 32
Honor Oak Park	d	20 35			20 56	21 05			21 26	21 35			21 56	22 05			22 26	22 35			22 56	23 05			23 26	23 35
Forest Hill 4	d	20 38			20 58	21 08			21 28	21 38			21 58	22 08			22 28	22 38			22 58	23 08			23 28	23 38
Sydenham	d	20 40			21 01	21 10			21 31	21 40			22 01	22 10			22 31	22 40			23 01	23 10			23 31	23 40
Crystal Palace 4	d	20 43				21 13				21 43				22 13				22 43				23 13				23 43
Gipsy Hill	d	20 46				21 16				21 46				22 16				22 46				23 16				23 46
West Norwood 4	d	20 49				21 19				21 49				22 19				22 49				23 19				23 49
Streatham Hill	d	20 52				21 22				21 52				22 22				22 52				23 22				23 52
Balham 4	⊖ d	20 55				21 25				21 55				22 25				22 55				23 25				23 55
Wandsworth Common	d	20 57				21 27				21 57				22 27				22 57				23 27				23 57
Clapham Junction 10	d	21 01				21 31				22 01				22 31				23 01				23 31				00 01
South Bermondsey	d		20 45				21 15				21 45				22 15				22 45				23 15			
Queens Rd Peckham	d		20 48				21 18				21 48				22 18				22 48				23 18			
Peckham Rye 4	d		20 50	20 52			21 20	21 22			21 50	21 52			22 20	22 22			22 50	22 52			23 20	23 24		
Denmark Hill 4	d		20 53	20 55			21 23	21 25			21 53	21 55			22 23	22 25			22 53	22 55			23 23	23 26		
London Blackfriars 3	⊖ a			21 03				21 33				22 03				22 33				23 03				23 37		
Clapham High Street	⊖ d		20 58				21 28				21 58				22 28				22 58				23 28			
Wandsworth Road	d		20 59				21 29				21 59				22 29				22 59				23 29			
Battersea Park 4	d	21 04	21 02			21 34	21 32			22 04	22 02			22 34	22 32			23 04	23 02			23 34	23 32			00 04
London Victoria 15	⊖ a	21 09	21 06			21 39	21 36			22 09	22 06			22 39	22 36			23 09	23 06			23 40	23 37			00 12
Penge West	d				21 03				21 33				22 03				22 33				23 03				23 33	
Anerley	d				21 05				21 35				22 05				22 35				23 05				23 35	
Norwood Junction 2	d				21 08				21 38				22 08				22 38				23 08				23 38	
West Croydon 4	a																									
East Croydon	a				21 12				21 42				22 12				22 42				23 12				23 42	

		SN A
London Charing Cross 4	⊖ d	23 45
London Waterloo (East) 4	⊖ d	23 48
London Bridge 4	⊖ d	23 53
New Cross Gate 4	⊖ d	23 58
Brockley	d	00 01
Honor Oak Park	d	00 04
Forest Hill 4	d	00 06
Sydenham	d	00 09
Crystal Palace 4	d	
Gipsy Hill	d	
West Norwood 4	d	
Streatham Hill	d	
Balham 4	⊖ d	
Wandsworth Common	d	
Clapham Junction 10	d	
South Bermondsey	d	
Queens Rd Peckham	d	
Peckham Rye 4	d	
Denmark Hill 4	d	
London Blackfriars 3	⊖ a	
Clapham High Street	⊖ d	
Wandsworth Road	d	
Battersea Park 4	d	
London Victoria 15	⊖ a	
Penge West	d	00 11
Anerley	d	00 13
Norwood Junction 2	d	00 16
West Croydon 4	a	
East Croydon	a	00 20

For general notes see front of timetable
For details of catering facilities see Directory of Train Operators

A To Caterham (Table 181)

Table 178

Saturdays

Charing Cross and London Bridge → London Victoria and Croydon

Network Diagram - see first page of Table 177

	SN	SN A	SN	SN		SE 73	SN	SE 83	SN A		SN	SE 83	SE 78	SN B		SN A	SN	SE 83	SE 78		SN B	SN A	SN	SE 83	SE 78
London Charing Cross 4 ⊖ d		23p45	00 12																						
London Waterloo (East) 4 ⊖ d		23p48	00 15																						
London Bridge 4 ⊖ d	23p24	23p53	00 26	06 11			06 41		07 05		07 11			07 15		07 35	07 41				07 45	08 05	08 11		
New Cross Gate 4 ⊖ d	23p30	23p58	00 31						07 10					07 20		07 40					07 50	08 10			
Brockley d	23p32	00 01	00 34						07 13					07 23		07 43					07 53	08 13			
Honor Oak Park d	23p35	00 04	00 37						07 16					07 26		07 46					07 56	08 16			
Forest Hill 4 d	23p38	00 06	00 39						07 18					07 28		07 48					07 58	08 18			
Sydenham d	23p40	00 09	00 42						07 21					07 31		07 51					08 01	08 21			
Crystal Palace 4 d	23p43																								
Gipsy Hill d	23p46																								
West Norwood 4 d	23p49																								
Streatham Hill d	23p52																								
Balham 4 ⊖ d	23p55																								
Wandsworth Common d	23p57																								
Clapham Junction 10 d	00 01																								
South Bermondsey d				06 15			06 45				07 15						07 45						08 15		
Queens Rd Peckham d				06 18			06 48				07 18						07 48						08 18		
Peckham Rye 4 d				06 20		06 22	06 50	06 52			07 20	07 22	07 28				07 50	07 52	07 58				08 20	08 22	08 28
Denmark Hill 4 d				06 23		06 25	06 53	06 55			07 23	07 25	07 31				07 53	07 55	08 01				08 23	08 25	08 31
London Blackfriars 3 ⊖ a						06 33		07 03				07 33						08 03						08 33	
Clapham High Street ⊖ d				06 28			06 58				07 28						07 58						08 28		
Wandsworth Road d				06 29			06 59				07 29						07 59						08 29		
Battersea Park 4 d	00 04			06 32			07 02				07 32						08 02						08 32		
London Victoria 15 ⊖ a	00 12			06 36			07 06				07 36		07 42				08 06		08 12				08 36		08 42
Penge West d		00 11	00 44											07 33							08 03				
Anerley d		00 13	00 46											07 35							08 05				
Norwood Junction 2 d		00 16	00 49						07 25					07 39		07 55					08 09	08 25			
West Croydon 4 a														07 44							08 14				
East Croydon a		00 20	00 53						07 29							07 59						08 29			

		SN B	SN	SN A	SN	SE 83	SE 78	SN B	SN	SN A	SN	SE 83	SE 78	and at the same minutes past each hour until		SN B	SN	SN A	SN		SE 83	SE 78	SN A	SN
London Charing Cross 4 ⊖ d																								
London Waterloo (East) 4 ⊖ d																								
London Bridge 4 ⊖ d		08 15	08 24	08 35	08 41			08 45	08 54	09 05	09 11					18 15	18 24	18 35	18 41				18 45	18 54
New Cross Gate 4 ⊖ d		08 20	08 30	08 40				08 50	09 00	09 10						18 20	18 30	18 40					18 50	19 00
Brockley d		08 23	08 32	08 43				08 53	09 02	09 13						18 23	18 32	18 43					18 53	19 02
Honor Oak Park d		08 26	08 35	08 46				08 56	09 05	09 16						18 26	18 35	18 46					18 56	19 05
Forest Hill 4 d		08 28	08 38	08 48				08 58	09 08	09 18						18 28	18 38	18 48					18 58	19 08
Sydenham d		08 31	08 40	08 51				09 01	09 10	09 21						18 31	18 40	18 51					19 01	19 10
Crystal Palace 4 d			08 43						09 13								18 43							19 13
Gipsy Hill d			08 46						09 16								18 46							19 16
West Norwood 4 d			08 49						09 19								18 49							19 19
Streatham Hill d			08 52						09 22								18 52							19 22
Balham 4 ⊖ d			08 55						09 25								18 55							19 25
Wandsworth Common d			08 57						09 27								18 57							19 27
Clapham Junction 10 d			09 01						09 31								19 01							19 31
South Bermondsey d					08 45						09 15								18 45					
Queens Rd Peckham d					08 48						09 18								18 48					
Peckham Rye 4 d					08 50	08 52	08 58				09 20	09 22	09 28						18 50		18 52	18 58		
Denmark Hill 4 d					08 53	08 55	09 01				09 23	09 25	09 31						18 53		18 55	19 01		
London Blackfriars 3 ⊖ a						09 03						09 33									19 03			
Clapham High Street ⊖ d					08 58						09 28								18 58					
Wandsworth Road d					08 59						09 29								18 59					
Battersea Park 4 d			09 04		09 02				09 34		09 32						19 04		19 02					19 34
London Victoria 15 ⊖ a			09 09		09 06		09 12		09 39		09 36		09 42				19 10		19 06			19 12		19 39
Penge West d		08 33						09 03								18 33							19 03	
Anerley d		08 35						09 05								18 35							19 05	
Norwood Junction 2 d		08 39		08 55				09 09		09 25						18 39		18 55					19 09	
West Croydon 4 a		08 44						09 14								18 44								
East Croydon a				08 59						09 29								18 59					19 13	

	SN	SE 83		SN A	SN	SN	SE 83		SN A	SN	SN	SE 83		SN A	SN	SN	SE 83		SN A	SN	SN	SE 83		SN A	SN
London Charing Cross 4 ⊖ d				19 07					19 37					20 07					20 37					21 07	
London Waterloo (East) 4 ⊖ d				19 10					19 39					20 10					20 40					21 10	
London Bridge 4 ⊖ d	19 11			19 15	19 24	19 41			19 44	19 54	20 11			20 15	20 24	20 41			20 45	20 54	21 11			21 15	21 24
New Cross Gate 4 ⊖ d				19 20	19 30				19 50	20 00				20 20	20 29				20 50	21 00				21 20	21 30
Brockley d				19 23	19 32				19 52	20 02				20 23	20 32				20 53	21 02				21 23	21 32
Honor Oak Park d				19 26	19 35				19 55	20 05				20 26	20 35				20 56	21 05				21 26	21 35
Forest Hill 4 d				19 28	19 38				19 58	20 08				20 28	20 37				20 58	21 08				21 28	21 38
Sydenham d				19 31	19 40				20 00	20 10				20 31	20 40				21 01	21 10				21 31	21 40
Crystal Palace 4 d					19 43					20 13					20 43					21 13					21 43
Gipsy Hill d					19 46					20 16					20 45					21 16					21 46
West Norwood 4 d					19 49					20 19					20 48					21 19					21 49
Streatham Hill d					19 52					20 22					20 52					21 22					21 52
Balham 4 ⊖ d					19 55					20 25					20 55					21 25					21 55
Wandsworth Common d					19 57					20 27					20 57					21 27					21 57
Clapham Junction 10 d					20 01					20 31					21 01					21 31					22 01
South Bermondsey d	19 15					19 45					20 15					20 45					21 15				
Queens Rd Peckham d	19 18					19 48					20 18					20 48					21 18				
Peckham Rye 4 d	19 20	19 22				19 50	19 52				20 20	20 22				20 50	20 52				21 20	21 22			
Denmark Hill 4 d	19 23	19 25				19 53	19 55				20 23	20 25				20 53	20 55				21 23	21 25			
London Blackfriars 3 ⊖ a		19 33					20 03					20 33					21 03					21 33			
Clapham High Street ⊖ d	19 28					19 58					20 28					20 58					21 28				
Wandsworth Road d	19 29					19 59					20 29					20 59					21 29				
Battersea Park 4 d	19 32				20 04	20 02				20 34	20 32				21 04	21 02				21 34	21 32				22 04
London Victoria 15 ⊖ a	19 36				20 09	20 06				20 39	20 36				21 09	21 06				21 39	21 36				22 09
Penge West d				19 33					20 03					20 33					21 03					21 33	
Anerley d				19 35					20 05					20 35					21 05					21 35	
Norwood Junction 2 d				19 38					20 08					20 38					21 08					21 38	
West Croydon 4 a																									
East Croydon a				19 42					20 12					20 42					21 12					21 42	

For general notes see front of timetable
For details of catering facilities see Directory of Train Operators

A To Caterham (Table 181)
B To Sutton (Surrey) (Table 182)

Table 178

Saturdays

Charing Cross and London Bridge → London Victoria and Croydon

Network Diagram - see first page of Table 177

		SN	SE 83	SN A	SN	SN	SE 83	SN A	SN	SN	SE 83	SN A	SN	SN	SE 83	SN A	SN	SN A
London Charing Cross 4	⊖ d			21 37				22 07				22 37				23 07		23 45
London Waterloo (East) 4	⊖ d			21 40				22 10				22 40				23 10		23 48
London Bridge 4	⊖ d	21 41		21 45	21 54	22 11		22 15	22 24	22 41		22 45	22 54	23 11		23 15	23 24	23 53
New Cross Gate 4	⊖ d			21 50	22 00			22 20	22 30			22 50	23 00			23 20	23 30	23 58
Brockley	d			21 53	22 02			22 23	22 32			22 53	23 02			23 23	23 32	00 01
Honor Oak Park	d			21 56	22 05			22 26	22 35			22 56	23 05			23 26	23 35	00 04
Forest Hill 4	d			21 58	22 08			22 28	22 38			22 58	23 08			23 28	23 38	00 06
Sydenham	d			22 01	22 10			22 31	22 40			23 01	23 10			23 31	23 40	00 09
Crystal Palace 4	d				22 13				22 43				23 13				23 43	
Gipsy Hill	d				22 16				22 46				23 16				23 46	
West Norwood 4	d				22 19				22 49				23 19				23 49	
Streatham Hill	d				22 22				22 52				23 22				23 52	
Balham 4	⊖ d				22 25				22 55				23 25				23 55	
Wandsworth Common	d				22 27				22 57				23 27				23 57	
Clapham Junction 10	d				22 31				23 01				23 31				00 01	
South Bermondsey	d	21 45				22 15				22 45				23 15				
Queens Rd Peckham	d	21 48				22 18				22 48				23 18				
Peckham Rye 4	d	21 50	21 52			22 20	22 22			22 50	22 52			23 20	23 22			
Denmark Hill 4	d	21 53	21 55			22 23	22 25			22 53	22 55			23 23	23 25			
London Blackfriars 3	⊖ a		22 03				22 33				23 03				23 33			
Clapham High Street	⊖ d	21 58				22 28				22 58				23 28				
Wandsworth Road	d	21 59				22 29				22 59				23 29				
Battersea Park 4	d	22 02			22 34	22 32			23 04	23 02			23 34	23 32			00 04	
London Victoria 15	⊖ a	22 06			22 39	22 36			23 09	23 06			23 40	23 37			00 09	
Penge West	d			22 03				22 33				23 03				23 33		00 11
Anerley	d			22 05				22 35				23 05				23 35		00 13
Norwood Junction 2	d			22 08				22 38				23 08				23 38		00 16
West Croydon 4	🚌 a																	
East Croydon	🚌 a			22 12				22 42				23 12				23 42		00 20

Sundays

		SN	SN A	SN	SE 72	SN	SE 72	SN	SN B	SE 72	SN	SN	SN A	SE 72	SN	SN		SN B	SE 72	SN
London Charing Cross 4	⊖ d		23p45	00 12					07 36				08 06					21 36		
London Waterloo (East) 4	⊖ d		23p48	00 15					07 39				08 09					21 39		
London Bridge 4	⊖ d	23p24	23p53	00 26		07 11		07 41	07 44		07 58	08 11	08 14		08 28	08 41		21 44		21 58
New Cross Gate 4	⊖ d	23p30	23p58	00 31					07 49		08 03		08 19		08 33			21 49		22 03
Brockley	d	23p32	00 01	00 34					07 52		08 06		08 22		08 36			21 52		22 06
Honor Oak Park	d	23p35	00 04	00 37					07 55		08 09		08 25		08 39			21 55		22 09
Forest Hill 4	d	23p38	00 06	00 39					07 57		08 11		08 27		08 41			21 57		22 11
Sydenham	d	23p40	00 09	00 42					08 00		08 14		08 30		08 44		and at the same minutes past each hour until	22 00		22 14
Crystal Palace 4	d	23p43																		
Gipsy Hill	d	23p46																		
West Norwood 4	d	23p49																		
Streatham Hill	d	23p52																		
Balham 4	⊖ d	23p55																		
Wandsworth Common	d	23p57																		
Clapham Junction 10	d	00 01																		
South Bermondsey	d					07 15		07 45				08 15				08 45				
Queens Rd Peckham	d					07 18		07 48				08 18				08 48				
Peckham Rye 4	d				07 12	07 20	07 42	07 50		08 12		08 20		08 42		08 50			22 12	
Denmark Hill 4	d				07 14	07 23	07 44	07 53		08 14		08 23		08 44		08 53			22 14	
London Blackfriars 3	⊖ a																			
Clapham High Street	⊖ d					07 28		07 58				08 28				08 58				
Wandsworth Road	d					07 29		07 59				08 29				08 59				
Battersea Park 4	d	00 04				07 32		08 02				08 32				09 02				
London Victoria 15	⊖ a	00 09			07 23	07 36	07 53	08 06		08 23		08 36		08 53		09 06			22 23	
Penge West	d		00 11	00 44							08 16				08 46					22 16
Anerley	d		00 13	00 46							08 18				08 48					22 18
Norwood Junction 2	d		00 16	00 49					08 04		08 21		08 34		08 51			22 04		22 21
West Croydon 4	🚌 a										08 26				08 56					22 26
East Croydon	🚌 a		00 20	00 53					08 08				08 38					22 08		

For general notes see front of timetable
For details of catering facilities see Directory of Train Operators

A To Caterham (Table 181)
B To Tattenham Corner (Table 181)

Table 178

Sundays

Charing Cross and London Bridge → London Victoria and Croydon

Network Diagram - see first page of Table 177

		SN	SN A	SE 72	SN	SN B	SE 72	SN	SN A	SE 72	SN A
London Charing Cross 4	⊖ d		22 06			22 36			23 06		23 36
London Waterloo (East) 4	⊖ d		22 09			22 39			23 09		23 39
London Bridge 4	⊖ d	22 11	22 14		22 41	22 44		23 11	23 14		23 44
New Cross Gate 4	⊖ d		22 19			22 49			23 19		23 49
Brockley	d		22 22			22 52			23 22		23 52
Honor Oak Park	d		22 25			22 55			23 25		23 55
Forest Hill 4	d		22 27			22 57			23 27		23 57
Sydenham	d		22 30			23 00			23 30		23 59
Crystal Palace 4	d										
Gipsy Hill	d										
West Norwood 4	d										
Streatham Hill	d										
Balham 4	⊖ d										
Wandsworth Common	d										
Clapham Junction 10	d										
South Bermondsey	d	22 15			22 45			23 15			
Queens Rd Peckham	d	22 18			22 48			23 18			
Peckham Rye 4	d	22 20		22 42	22 50		23 12	23 20		23 42	
Denmark Hill 4	d	22 23		22 44	22 53		23 14	23 23		23 44	
London Blackfriars 3	⊖ a										
Clapham High Street	⊖ d	22 28			22 58			23 28			
Wandsworth Road	d	22 29			22 59			23 29			
Battersea Park 4	d	22 32			23 02			23 32			
London Victoria 15	⊖ a	22 36		22 53	23 06		23 24	23 37		23 53	
Penge West	d		22 32			23 02			23 32		00 02
Anerley	d		22 34			23 04			23 34		00 04
Norwood Junction 2	d		22 39			23 09			23 39		00 10
West Croydon 4	🚌 a										
East Croydon	🚌 a		22 42			23 12			23 42		00 13

For general notes see front of timetable
For details of catering facilities see Directory of Train Operators

A To Caterham (Table 181)
B To Tattenham Corner (Table 181)

Table 178

Mondays to Fridays

Croydon and London Victoria → London Bridge and Charing Cross

Network Diagram - see first page of Table 177

Miles	Miles	Miles	Miles	Miles		SN	SE 83	SN	SE 83	SN	SN	SN	SE 83	SN	SN	SN	SE 83	SN	SN	SN	SE 83	SN	SN		SN
						A		B		C	D	E				D			G			B			C
—	—	0	—	—	**East Croydon** d	05 13				06 12		06 28		06 40				07 12							07 36
—	—	—	—	0	**West Croydon 4** d			05 45			06 15					06 45						07 16	07 28		
—	—	1¼	—	1¾	Norwood Junction 2 d	05 17		05 50		06 16	06 19	06 32		06 44		06 50		07 16				07 21	07 32		07 41
—	—	2½	—	—	Anerley d	05 20		05 53			06 22					06 53						07 24	07 35		
—	—	2¾	—	—	Penge West d	05 22		05 55			06 24					06 55						07 26	07 37		
0	0	—	0	—	**London Victoria 15** ⊖ d										06 41					07 11					
1¼	1¼	—	—	—	Battersea Park 4 d										06 45					07 15					
2	—	—	—	—	Wandsworth Road d										06 47					07 17					
2½	—	—	—	—	Clapham High Street ⊖ d										06 49					07 19					
—	—	—	—	0	**London Blackfriars 3** ⊖ d		05 27		06 08				06 42				07 09				07 24				
4½	—	—	4¼	3¾	Denmark Hill 4 d		05 35		06b20				06 52		06 54		07 17			07 24	07 34				
5¼	—	—	5	4½	Peckham Rye 4 d		05a38		06a23				06a54		06 56		07a20			07 26	07a36				
6	—	—	—	—	Queens Rd Peckham d										06 59					07 29					
7	—	—	—	—	South Bermondsey d										07 01					07 31					
—	2¾	—	—	—	Clapham Junction 10 d																				
—	4	—	—	—	Wandsworth Common d																				
—	4¾	—	—	—	Balham 4 ⊖ d																				
—	5¾	—	—	—	Streatham Hill d																				
—	7	—	—	—	West Norwood 4 d														07 08						
—	8	—	—	—	Gipsy Hill d														07 11						
—	8¾	—	—	—	**Crystal Palace 4** d														07 15						
—	10	3½	—	—	Sydenham d	05 24		05 57		06 21	06 27	06 37				06 58			07 18			07 29	07 40		07 45
—	10¾	4¼	—	—	Forest Hill 4 d	05 27		06 00		06 23	06 29	06 39				07 00			07 20			07 31	07 42		07 48
—	11¾	5¼	—	—	Honor Oak Park d	05 29		06 02			06 32	06 42				07 03			07 23			07 34	07 45		
—	12¾	6¼	—	—	Brockley d	05 32		06 05			06 34	06 44				07 05			07 25			07 36	07 47		
—	13¾	7¼	—	—	New Cross Gate 4 ⊖ d	05 34		06 07		06 28	06 37	06 47		06 53		07 08		07 24	07 28			07 39	07 50		07 52
8¾	16½	10	—	—	**London Bridge 4** ⊖ a	05 41		06 14		06 34	06 45	06 54		07 02	07 08	07 16		07 33	07 36	07 38		07 48	07 58		08 01
—	—	11	—	—	London Waterloo (East) 4 ⊖ a	05 46																			
—	—	11¾	—	—	**London Charing Cross 4** ⊖ a	05 49																			

	SN	SN	SN	SE 83	SN	SN	SN	SN	SE 83	SE 78	SN	SN	SE 83	SN	SN	SN	SN	SN		SN	SE 78	SE 92 1	SE 83	SN	SE 92 1
		B									H						B					J			K
East Croydon d														08 45											
West Croydon 4 d		07 43			07 56						08 23	08 28					08 44	08 59							
Norwood Junction 2 d		07 48			08 01						08 28	08 32		08 49			08 49	09 03							
Anerley d					08 04							08 35					08 52	09 06							
Penge West d					08 06							08 37					08 54	09 08							
London Victoria 15 ⊖ d	07 41					07 51	08 11			08 21					08 41	08 22				08 52	09 01			09 11	09 15
Battersea Park 4 d	07 45					07 55	08 15								08 45	08 26				08 56				09 15	
Wandsworth Road d	07 47						08 17								08 47									09 17	
Clapham High Street ⊖ d	07 49						08 19								08 49									09 19	
London Blackfriars 3 ⊖ d				07 53					08 20				08 43										09 13		
Denmark Hill 4 d	07 54			08 02			08 24		08 29	08 31			08 52		08 54						09 12	09 20	09 22	09 24	09 25
Peckham Rye 4 d	07 56			08a04			08 26		08a31	08a35			08a55		08 56						09a14	09a22	09a25	09 26	09a28
Queens Rd Peckham d	07 59						08 29								08 59									09 29	
South Bermondsey d	08 01						08 31								09 01									09 31	
Clapham Junction 10 d						07 58										08 30				08 59					
Wandsworth Common d						08 01										08 33				09 02					
Balham 4 ⊖ d						08 04										08 35				09 05					
Streatham Hill d			07 45			08 07		08 14								08 38				09 08					
West Norwood 4 d			07 48			08 10		08 17								08 42				09 11					
Gipsy Hill d			07 51			08 13		08 20								08 45				09 14					
Crystal Palace 4 d			07 54			08 16		08 23								08 48				09 17					
Sydenham d		07 53	07 57		08 08	08 19		08 26			08 33	08 40				08 51	08 57	09 11		09 20					
Forest Hill 4 d		07 55	07 59		08 11	08 21		08 29			08 35	08 42				08 53	08 59	09 13		09 22					
Honor Oak Park d			08 02		08 13	08 24		08 31				08 45				08 56	09 02	09 16		09 25					
Brockley d			08 04		08 16	08 26		08 34				08 47				08 58	09 04	09 18		09 27					
New Cross Gate 4 ⊖ d		08 00	08 07		08 18	08 29		08 36				08 50		08 57		09 01	09 07	09 21		09 30					
London Bridge 4 ⊖ a	08 08	08 08	08 16		08 27	08 38	08 38	08 46			08 47	09 02		09 05	09 08	09 12	09 17	09 29		09 38				09 38	
London Waterloo (East) 4 ⊖ a																									
London Charing Cross 4 ⊖ a																									

For general notes see front of timetable
For details of catering facilities see Directory of Train Operators

A From Purley (Table 175)
B From Epsom (Table 182)
C From Caterham (Table 181)
D From Sutton (Surrey) (Table 182)
E From Tattenham Corner (Table 181)
G From London Bridge (Table 177)
H From Epsom Downs (Table 182)
J 21 July to 29 August
K Until 18 July and from 1 September
b Arr. 0617

Croydon and London Victoria → London Bridge and Charing Cross

Network Diagram - see first page of Table 177

	SN	SN	SE	SN	SE	SN	SN	SN		SN	SE	SE	SN	SN	SN	SN	SN	SE	SE	SN	SN			SN
			78		83						78	83						78	83					
		A		B				C		B					D	B					D			B
East Croydon d	09 20			09 31						10 00						10 30								15 00
West Croydon 4 d		09 15						09 46							10 15						10 45			
Norwood Junction 2 d	09 25	09 19		09 35				09 51		10 04					10 19	10 34					10 49			15 04
Anerley d		09 22						09 54							10 22						10 52			
Penge West d		09 24						09 56							10 24						10 54			
London Victoria 15 ⊖ d			09 31			09 41	09 22				10 01		10 11	09 52			10 22	10 31		10 41				
Battersea Park 4 d						09 45	09 26						10 15	09 56			10 26			10 45				
Wandsworth Road d						09 47							10 17							10 47				
Clapham High Street ⊖ d						09 49							10 19							10 49		and at		
London Blackfriars 3 ⊖ d					09 43							10 13							10 43			the same		
Denmark Hill 4 d			09 42		09 52	09 54					10 12	10 22	10 24					10 42	10 52	10 54				
Peckham Rye 4 d			09a44		09a55	09 56					10a14	10a25	10 26					10a44	10a55	10 56		minutes		
Queens Rd Peckham d						09 59							10 29							10 59				
South Bermondsey d						10 01							10 31							11 01		past		
Clapham Junction 10 d							09 30							09 59			10 29					each		
Wandsworth Common d							09 33							10 02			10 32							
Balham 4 ⊖ d							09 35							10 05			10 35					hour until		
Streatham Hill d							09 38							10 08			10 38							
West Norwood 4 d							09 42							10 11			10 41							
Gipsy Hill d							09 45							10 14			10 44							
Crystal Palace 4 d							09 47							10 17			10 47							
Sydenham d		09 27		09 40			09 50	09 58		10 09				10 20	10 27	10 39	10 50				10 57			15 09
Forest Hill 4 d		09 29		09 42			09 53	10 01		10 11				10 22	10 29	10 41	10 52				10 59			15 11
Honor Oak Park d		09 32		09 45			09 55	10 03		10 14				10 25	10 32	10 44	10 55				11 02			15 14
Brockley d		09 34		09 47			09 58	10 06		10 16				10 27	10 34	10 46	10 57				11 04			15 16
New Cross Gate 4 ⊖ d	09 33	09 37		09 50			10 00	10 08		10 19				10 30	10 37	10 49	11 00				11 07			15 19
London Bridge 4 ⊖ a	09 42	09 46		09 59		10 06	10 08	10 15		10 25			10 36	10 38	10 44	10 55	11 06			11 06	11 14			15 27
London Waterloo (East) 4 ⊖ a																								
London Charing Cross 4 ⊖ a																								

	SE	SE	SN	SN	SN	SN	SE	SE	SN	SN	SN	SN	SN	SE	SN	SE	SN	SE		SN	SE	SN	SN	SN	SE
	78	83					78	83						83		78		73			83				78
					D	B					D	B					D			B				D	
East Croydon d						15 30						16 00								16 31					
West Croydon 4 d					15 15						15 45						16 15							16 45	
Norwood Junction 2 d					15 19	15 34					15 49	16 04					16 19			16 35				16 49	
Anerley d					15 22						15 52						16 22							16 52	
Penge West d					15 24						15 54						16 24							16 54	
London Victoria 15 ⊖ d	15 01		15 11	14 52			15 31		15 41	15 22			15 52		16 11	16 14						16 41	16 22		17 00
Battersea Park 4 d			15 15	14 56					15 45	15 26			15 56		16 15							16 45	16 26		
Wandsworth Road d			15 17						15 47						16 17							16 47			
Clapham High Street ⊖ d			15 19						15 49						16 19							16 49			
London Blackfriars 3 ⊖ d		15 13						15 43						16 09				16 27			16 42				
Denmark Hill 4 d	15 12	15 22	15 24				15 42	15 52	15 54					16 18	16 24	16 27		16 36			16 51	16 54			17 09
Peckham Rye 4 d	15a14	15a25	15 26				15a44	15a55	15 56					16a21	16 26	16a29		16a40			16a54	16 56			17a13
Queens Rd Peckham d			15 29						15 59						16 29							16 59			
South Bermondsey d			15 31						16 01						16 31							17 01			
Clapham Junction 10 d				14 59						15 29			15 59										16 29		
Wandsworth Common d				15 02						15 32			16 02										16 32		
Balham 4 ⊖ d				15 05						15 35			16 05										16 35		
Streatham Hill d				15 08						15 38			16 08										16 38		
West Norwood 4 d				15 11						15 41			16 11										16 41		
Gipsy Hill d				15 14						15 44			16 14										16 44		
Crystal Palace 4 d				15 17						15 47			16 17										16 47		
Sydenham d				15 20	15 27	15 39				15 50	15 57	16 09	16 20				16 27			16 40			16 50	16 57	
Forest Hill 4 d				15 22	15 29	15 41				15 52	15 59	16 11	16 22				16 29			16 42			16 52	16 59	
Honor Oak Park d				15 25	15 32	15 44				15 55	16 02	16 14	16 25				16 32			16 45			16 55	17 02	
Brockley d				15 27	15 34	15 46				15 57	16 04	16 16	16 27				16 34			16 47			16 57	17 04	
New Cross Gate 4 ⊖ d				15 30	15 37	15 49				16 00	16 07	16 19	16 30				16 37			16 50			17 00	17 07	
London Bridge 4 ⊖ a			15 36	15 38	15 44	15 55			16 06	16 08	16 16	16 26	16 36		16 38		16 46			16 58		17 08	17 10	17 14	
London Waterloo (East) 4 ⊖ a																									
London Charing Cross 4 ⊖ a																									

For general notes see front of timetable
For details of catering facilities see Directory of Train Operators

A From Guildford (Table 182)
B From Caterham (Table 181)
C From Epsom (Table 182)
D From Sutton (Surrey) (Table 182)

Croydon and London Victoria → London Bridge and Charing Cross

Network Diagram - see first page of Table 177

	SN	SN	SE	SN	SE	SN	SN	SN	SE	SE	SN	SN	SN	SE		SN	SN	SN	SE	SN	SE	SN	SN	SN	SE
			83		78				83	78				83					78		83				83
	A					B	A						B			A	C					D	A		
East Croydon d	17 00						17 32									18 05							18 35		
West Croydon 4 d						17 14							17 47									18 15			
Norwood Junction 2 d	17 04					17 19	17 36						17 52			18 09						18 19	18 39		
Anerley d						17 22							17 55									18 22			
Penge West d						17 24							17 57									18 24			
London Victoria 15 ⊖ d		16 52		17 11	17 19			17 19		17 41	17 41							17 51	18 08	18 11				18 22	
Battersea Park 4 d		16 56		17 15				17 23			17 45							17 55		18 15				18 26	
Wandsworth Road d				17 17							17 47									18 17					
Clapham High Street ⊖ d				17 19							17 49									18 19					
London Blackfriars 3 ⊖ d			17 10						17 36					18 05							18 23				18 43
Denmark Hill 4 d			17 19	17 24	17 28				17 45	17 51	17 54			18 14					18 17	18 24	18 32				18 52
Peckham Rye 4 d			17a22	17 26	17a31				17a47	17a54	17 56			18a17					18a20	18 26	18a34				18a55
Queens Rd Peckham d				17 29							17 59									18 29					
South Bermondsey d				17 31							18 01									18 31					
Clapham Junction 10 d		16 59						17 26										17 59						18 29	
Wandsworth Common d		17 02						17 29										18 02						18 32	
Balham 4 ⊖ d		17 05						17 32										18 05						18 35	
Streatham Hill d		17 08						17 35										18 08						18 38	
West Norwood 4 d		17 11						17 38									18 05	18 15						18 41	
Gipsy Hill d		17 14						17 41									18 08	18 18						18 44	
Crystal Palace 4 d		17 17						17 45									18 14	18 21						18 47	
Sydenham d	17 09	17 20				17 27	17 40	17 49					17 59			18 14	18 17	18 24				18 27	18 44	18 50	
Forest Hill 4 d	17 11	17 22				17 29	17 43	17 51					18 02			18 16	18 19	18 26				18 29	18 46	18 52	
Honor Oak Park d	17 14	17 25				17 32	17 45	17 54					18 04				18 22	18 29				18 32	18 49	18 55	
Brockley d	17 16	17 27				17 34	17 48	17 56				←	18 07				18 24	18 31				18 34	18 51	18 57	
New Cross Gate 4 ⊖ d	17 19	17 30				17 37	17 50	17 59				17 59	18 09			18 21	18 27	18 34				18 37	18 54	19 00	
London Bridge 4 ⊖ a	17 27	17 38		17 38		17 43	17 58	→			18 08	18 10	18 19			18 28	18 34	18 42		18 38		18 44	19 00	19 08	
London Waterloo (East) 4 ⊖ a																									
London Charing Cross 4 ⊖ a																									

	SN	SE	SN	SN	SN	SE	SN	SE	SN	SN		SN	SE	SN	SE	SN	SN	SE	SN	SN	SN	SE	SN	SN	SN
		78				83		78					83		78			83				83			
			B				A		E					A		E				A			G		A
East Croydon d							19 10							19 40						20 10			20 30		20 40
West Croydon 4 d			18 48						19 22							19 49									
Norwood Junction 2 d			18 52	19 06			19 14		19 27					19 44		19 54				20 14			20 34		20 44
Anerley d			18 55				19 17							19 47		19 57				20 17			20 37		20 47
Penge West d			18 57				19 19							19 49		19 59				20 19			20 39		20 49
London Victoria 15 ⊖ d	18 41	18 46			19 11			19 16		19 05		19 41			19 46		19 35		20 11		20 05			20 41	
Battersea Park 4 d	18 45				19 15					19 09		19 45					19 39		20 15		20 09			20 45	
Wandsworth Road d	18 47				19 17							19 47							20 17					20 47	
Clapham High Street ⊖ d	18 49				19 19							19 49							20 19					20 49	
London Blackfriars 3 ⊖ d						19 17							19 47					20 13				20 43			
Denmark Hill 4 d	18 54	18 57			19 23	19 25		19 27				19 54	19 55		19 57			20 22	20 24			20 52		20 54	
Peckham Rye 4 d	18 56	19a00			19 27	19a28		19a31				19 56	19a58		20a01			20a25	20 26			20a55		20 56	
Queens Rd Peckham d	18 59				19 30							19 59							20 29					20 59	
South Bermondsey d	19 01				19 32							20 01							20 31					21 01	
Clapham Junction 10 d										19 12							19 42				20 12				
Wandsworth Common d										19 15							19 45				20 15				
Balham 4 ⊖ d										19 18							19 48				20 18				
Streatham Hill d										19 21							19 51				20 21				
West Norwood 4 d										19 24							19 54				20 24				
Gipsy Hill d										19 27							19 57				20 27				
Crystal Palace 4 d										19 32							20 01				20 31				
Sydenham d			19 00	19 10			19 22		19 32	19 35				19 52		20 02	20 05			20 22	20 34		20 41		20 52
Forest Hill 4 d			19 03	19 13			19 24		19 34	19 37				19 54		20 04	20 07			20 24	20 36		20 44		20 54
Honor Oak Park d			19 05	19 15			19 27		19 37	19 40				19 57		20 07	20 10			20 27	20 39		20 46		20 57
Brockley d			19 08	19 18			19 29		19 39	19 42				19 59		20 09	20 12			20 29	20 41		20 49		20 59
New Cross Gate 4 ⊖ d			19 11	19 20			19 32		19 42	19 45				20 02		20 12	20 15			20 32	20 44		20 51		21 02
London Bridge 4 ⊖ a	19 08		19 18	19 27	19 37		19 39		19 49	19 52		20 06		20 11		20 19	20 22		20 36	20 41	20 53		20 59	21 06	21 11
London Waterloo (East) 4 ⊖ a							19 45							20 16						20 46					21 16
London Charing Cross 4 ⊖ a							19 49							20 20						20 50					21 20

For general notes see front of timetable
For details of catering facilities see Directory of Train Operators

A From Caterham (Table 181)
B From Epsom (Table 182)
C From London Bridge (Table 177)
D From Sutton (Surrey) (Table 182)
E From Guildford (Table 182)
G From Tattenham Corner (Table 181)

Table 178

Mondays to Fridays

Croydon and London Victoria → London Bridge and Charing Cross

Network Diagram - see first page of Table 177

		SN	SE 83	SN	SN A	SN	SE 83		SN	SN A	SN	SE 83	SN	SN A	SN	SE 73	SN	SN A	SN	SE 73	SN	SN A	SN	SE 73		
East Croydon	d				21 10					21 40				22 10				22 40				23 10				
West Croydon 4	d																									
Norwood Junction 2	d				21 14					21 44				22 14				22 44				23 14				
Anerley	d				21 17					21 47				22 17				22 47				23 17				
Penge West	d				21 19					21 49				22 19				22 49				23 19				
London Victoria 15	⊖ d	20 35		21 11		21 05			21 41		21 35		22 11		22 05		22 41		22 35		23 11		23 05			
Battersea Park 4	d	20 39		21 15		21 09			21 45		21 39		22 15		22 09		22 45		22 39		23 15		23 09			
Wandsworth Road	d			21 17					21 47				22 17				22 47				23 17					
Clapham High Street	⊖ d			21 19					21 49				22 19				22 49				23 19					
London Blackfriars 3	⊖ d		21 13				21 43					22 13				22 43				23 13				23 43		
Denmark Hill 4	d		21 22	21 24			21 52		21 54			22 22	22 24			22 52	22 54			23 22	23 24			23 52		
Peckham Rye 4	d		21a25	21 26			21a55		21 56			22a25	22 26			22a55	22 56			23a25	23 26			23a55		
Queens Rd Peckham	d			21 29					21 59				22 29				22 59				23 29					
South Bermondsey	d			21 31					22 01				22 31				23 01				23 31					
Clapham Junction 10	d	20 42				21 12					21 42				22 12				22 42				23 12			
Wandsworth Common	d	20 45				21 15					21 45				22 15				22 45				23 15			
Balham 4	⊖ d	20 48				21 18					21 48				22 18				22 48				23 18			
Streatham Hill	d	20 51				21 21					21 51				22 21				22 51				23 21			
West Norwood 4	d	20 54				21 24					21 54				22 24				22 54				23 24			
Gipsy Hill	d	20 57				21 27					21 57				22 27				22 57				23 27			
Crystal Palace 4	d	21 01				21 31					22 01				22 31				23 01				23 31			
Sydenham	d	21 04			21 22	21 34				21 52	22 04			22 22	22 34			22 52	23 04			23 22	23 34			
Forest Hill 4	d	21 06			21 24	21 36				21 54	22 06			22 24	22 36			22 54	23 06			23 24	23 36			
Honor Oak Park	d	21 09			21 27	21 39				21 57	22 09			22 27	22 39			22 57	23 09			23 27	23 39			
Brockley	d	21 11			21 29	21 41				21 59	22 11			22 29	22 41			22 59	23 11			23 29	23 41			
New Cross Gate 4	⊖ d	21 14			21 32	21 44				22 02	22 14			22 32	22 44			23 02	23 14			23 32	23 44			
London Bridge 4	⊖ a	21 22		21 36	21 41	21 52			22 06	22 11	22 22		22 36	22 41	22 52		23 06	23 11	23 22		23 36	23 38	23 52			
London Waterloo (East) 4	⊖ a				21 46					22 16				22 46				23 16				23 43				
London Charing Cross 4	⊖ a				21 50					22 20				22 50				23 20				23 48				

Saturdays

		SE 82	SN A	SE 83	SN	SN	SN A		SE 83	SN	SN B	SN A	SE 83	SN		SN B	SN A	SN	SE 78	SE 83	SN		SN B	SN A	SN	SE 78
East Croydon	d		06 30			06 43	07 00					07 30					08 00							08 30		
West Croydon 4	d										07 15					07 45							08 15			
Norwood Junction 2	d		06 34			06 49	07 04				07 19	07 34				07 49	08 04						08 19	08 34		
Anerley	d					06 52					07 22					07 52							08 22			
Penge West	d					06 54					07 24					07 54							08 24			
London Victoria 15	⊖ d	06 13			06 41					07 11				07 41				07 52	08 01		08 11				08 22	08 31
Battersea Park 4	d				06 45					07 15				07 45				07 56			08 15				08 26	
Wandsworth Road	d				06 47					07 17				07 47							08 17					
Clapham High Street	⊖ d				06 49					07 19				07 49							08 19					
London Blackfriars 3	⊖ d			06 43					07 13				07 43							08 13						
Denmark Hill 4	d	06 22		06 52	06 54				07 22	07 24			07 52	07 54					08 12	08 22	08 24					08 42
Peckham Rye 4	d	06a25		06a55	06 56				07a25	07 26			07a55	07 56					08a14	08a25	08 26					08a44
Queens Rd Peckham	d				06 59					07 29				07 59							08 29					
South Bermondsey	d				07 01					07 31				08 01							08 31					
Clapham Junction 10	d																	07 59							08 29	
Wandsworth Common	d																	08 02							08 32	
Balham 4	⊖ d																	08 05							08 35	
Streatham Hill	d																	08 08							08 38	
West Norwood 4	d																	08 11							08 41	
Gipsy Hill	d																	08 14							08 44	
Crystal Palace 4	d																	08 17							08 47	
Sydenham	d		06 39			06 57	07 09				07 27	07 39				07 57	08 09	08 20					08 27	08 39	08 50	
Forest Hill 4	d		06 41			06 59	07 11				07 29	07 41				07 59	08 11	08 22					08 29	08 41	08 52	
Honor Oak Park	d		06 44			07 02	07 14				07 32	07 44				08 02	08 14	08 25					08 32	08 44	08 55	
Brockley	d		06 46			07 04	07 16				07 34	07 46				08 04	08 16	08 27					08 34	08 46	08 57	
New Cross Gate 4	⊖ d		06 49			07 07	07 19				07 37	07 49				08 07	08 19	08 30					08 37	08 49	09 00	
London Bridge 4	⊖ a		06 55		07 06	07 14	07 25			07 36	07 44	07 55		08 06		08 14	08 25	08 36			08 36		08 44	08 55	09 06	
London Waterloo (East) 4	⊖ a																									
London Charing Cross 4	⊖ a																									

For general notes see front of timetable
For details of catering facilities see Directory of Train Operators

A From Caterham (Table 181)
B From Sutton (Surrey) (Table 182)

Saturdays

Croydon and London Victoria → London Bridge and Charing Cross

Network Diagram - see first page of Table 177

Station		SE 83	SN	SN A	SN B		SN	SE 78	SN	SE 83	SN	SN A		SN B	SN	SE 78	SN	SE 83	SN		SN A		SN B	SN	SE 78	SE 83
East Croydon	d				09 00									09 30									10 00			
West Croydon 4	d			08 45								09 15									09 45					
Norwood Junction 2	d			08 49	09 04							09 19		09 34							09 49		10 04			
Anerley	d			08 52								09 22									09 52					
Penge West	d			08 54								09 24									09 54					
London Victoria 15	d		08 41				08 52	09 01	09 07		09 11				09 22	09 31	09 37		09 41					09 52	10 01	
Battersea Park 4	d		08 45				08 56		09 11		09 15				09 26		09 41		09 45					09 56		
Wandsworth Road	d		08 47								09 17								09 47							
Clapham High Street	d		08 49								09 19								09 49							
London Blackfriars 3	d	08 43								09 13								09 43								10 13
Denmark Hill 4	d	08 52	08 54					09 12		09 22	09 24					09 42		09 52	09 54						10 12	10 22
Peckham Rye 4	d	08a55	08 56					09a14		09a25	09 26					09a44		09a55	09 56						10a14	10a25
Queens Rd Peckham	d		08 59								09 29								09 59							
South Bermondsey	d		09 01								09 31								10 01							
Clapham Junction 10	d						08 59		09 14						09 29		09 44							09 59		
Wandsworth Common	d						09 02		09 17						09 32		09 47							10 02		
Balham 4	d						09 05		09 20						09 35		09 50							10 05		
Streatham Hill	d						09 08		09 23						09 38		09 53							10 08		
West Norwood 4	d						09 11		09 26						09 41		09 56							10 11		
Gipsy Hill	d						09 14		09 29						09 44		09 59							10 14		
Crystal Palace 4	d						09 17		09a32						09 47		10a02							10 17		
Sydenham	d			08 57	09 09		09 20					09 27		09 39	09 50						09 57		10 09	10 20		
Forest Hill 4	d			08 59	09 11		09 22					09 29		09 41	09 52						09 59		10 11	10 22		
Honor Oak Park	d			09 02	09 14		09 25					09 32		09 44	09 55						10 02		10 14	10 25		
Brockley	d			09 04	09 16		09 27					09 34		09 46	09 57						10 04		10 16	10 27		
New Cross Gate 4	d			09 07	09 19		09 30					09 37		09 49	10 00						10 07		10 19	10 30		
London Bridge 4	a		09 06	09 14	09 25		09 36				09 36	09 44		09 55	10 06				10 06		10 14		10 25	10 36		
London Waterloo (East) 4	a																									
London Charing Cross 4	a																									

Station		SN	SN A	SN B	SN	SE 78	SE 83	SN	SN A			SN B	SN	SE 78	SE 83	SN	SN A		SN B	SN	SE 78	SE 83	SN	SN A	SE 78
East Croydon	d			10 30								18 00							18 30						
West Croydon 4	d		10 15						10 45								18 15							18 45	
Norwood Junction 2	d		10 19	10 34					10 49			18 04					18 19		18 34					18 49	
Anerley	d		10 22						10 52								18 22							18 52	
Penge West	d		10 24						10 54								18 24							18 54	
London Victoria 15	d	10 11			10 22	10 31		10 41					17 52	18 01		18 11				18 22	18 31		18 41		19 01
Battersea Park 4	d	10 15			10 26			10 45		and at			17 56			18 15				18 26			18 45		
Wandsworth Road	d	10 17						10 47								18 17							18 47		
Clapham High Street	d	10 19						10 49		the same						18 19							18 49		
London Blackfriars 3	d						10 43								18 13							18 43			
Denmark Hill 4	d	10 24				10 42	10 52	10 54		minutes				18 12	18 22	18 24					18 42	18 52	18 54		19 12
Peckham Rye 4	d	10 26				10a44	10a55	10 56						18a14	18a25	18 26					18a44	18a55	18 56		19a14
Queens Rd Peckham	d	10 29						10 59		past						18 29							18 59		
South Bermondsey	d	10 31						11 01								18 31							19 01		
Clapham Junction 10	d				10 29					each			17 59							18 29					
Wandsworth Common	d				10 32								18 02							18 32					
Balham 4	d				10 35					hour until			18 05							18 35					
Streatham Hill	d				10 38								18 08							18 38					
West Norwood 4	d				10 41								18 11							18 41					
Gipsy Hill	d				10 44								18 14							18 44					
Crystal Palace 4	d				10 47								18 17							18 47					
Sydenham	d		10 27	10 39	10 50				10 57			18 09	18 20				18 27		18 39	18 50				18 57	
Forest Hill 4	d		10 29	10 41	10 52				10 59			18 11	18 22				18 29		18 41	18 52				18 59	
Honor Oak Park	d		10 32	10 44	10 55				11 02			18 14	18 25				18 32		18 44	18 55				19 02	
Brockley	d		10 34	10 46	10 57				11 04			18 16	18 27				18 34		18 46	18 57				19 04	
New Cross Gate 4	d		10 37	10 49	11 00				11 07			18 19	18 30				18 37		18 49	19 00				19 07	
London Bridge 4	a	10 36	10 44	10 55	11 06			11 06	11 14			18 25	18 36			18 36	18 44		18 55	19 06			19 06	19 14	
London Waterloo (East) 4	a																								
London Charing Cross 4	a																								

Station		SN C		SE 83	SN	SN D	SN	SE 78	SN C		SE 83	SN	SN B	SN	SE 83	SN		SN B	SN	SE 83	SN	SN B	SN		SE 83	SN
East Croydon	d	18 51				19 10			19 21				19 40					20 10				20 40				
West Croydon 4	d																									
Norwood Junction 2	d	19b01				19 14			19c31				19 44					20 14				20 44				
Anerley	d	19 04				19 17			19 34				19 47					20 17				20 47				
Penge West	d	19 06				19 19			19 36				19 49					20 19				20 49				
London Victoria 15	d				19 11		19 05	19 31				19 41		19 35		20 11			20 05		20 41		20 35			21 11
Battersea Park 4	d				19 15		19 09					19 45		19 39		20 15			20 09		20 45		20 39			21 15
Wandsworth Road	d				19 17							19 47				20 17					20 47					21 17
Clapham High Street	d				19 19							19 49				20 19					20 49					21 19
London Blackfriars 3	d			19 13							19 43				20 13					20 43					21 13	
Denmark Hill 4	d			19 22	19 24			19 42			19 52	19 54			20 22	20 24				20 52	20 54				21 22	21 24
Peckham Rye 4	d			19a25	19 26			19a44			19a55	19 56			20a25	20 26				20a55	20 56				21a25	21 26
Queens Rd Peckham	d				19 29							19 59				20 29					20 59					21 29
South Bermondsey	d				19 31							20 01				20 31					21 01					21 31
Clapham Junction 10	d						19 12							19 42					20 12				20 42			
Wandsworth Common	d						19 15							19 45					20 15				20 45			
Balham 4	d						19 18							19 48					20 18				20 48			
Streatham Hill	d						19 21							19 51					20 21				20 51			
West Norwood 4	d						19 24							19 54					20 24				20 54			
Gipsy Hill	d						19 27							19 57					20 27				20 57			
Crystal Palace 4	d						19 31							20 01					20 31				21 01			
Sydenham	d	19 08				19 22	19 34		19 38				19 52	20 04				20 22	20 34			20 52	21 04			
Forest Hill 4	d	19 11				19 24	19 36		19 41				19 54	20 06				20 24	20 36			20 54	21 06			
Honor Oak Park	d	19 13				19 27	19 39		19 43				19 57	20 09				20 27	20 39			20 57	21 09			
Brockley	d	19 16				19 29	19 41		19 46				19 59	20 11				20 29	20 41			20 59	21 11			
New Cross Gate 4	d	19 18				19 32	19 44		19 48				20 02	20 14				20 32	20 44			21 02	21 14			
London Bridge 4	a	19 25			19 36	19 41	19 52		19 55			20 06	20 11	20 22		20 36		20 41	20 52		21 06	21 11	21 22			21 36
London Waterloo (East) 4	a					19 46							20 16					20 46				21 16				
London Charing Cross 4	a					19 51							20 21					20 51				21 21				

For general notes see front of timetable
For details of catering facilities see Directory of Train Operators

A From Sutton (Surrey) (Table 182)
B From Caterham (Table 181)
C From Smitham (Table 181)
D From Purley (Table 175)

b Arr. 1856
c Arr. 1926

Table 178

Saturdays

Croydon and London Victoria → London Bridge and Charing Cross

Network Diagram - see first page of Table 177

	SN	SN	SE	SN	SN	SN	SE	SN	SN	SN	SE	SN	SN	SN	SE	SN	SN	SN	SE
			83				83				73				73				73
	A				A				A				A				A		
East Croydon d	21 10				21 40				22 10				22 40				23 10		
West Croydon 4 d																			
Norwood Junction 2 d	21 14				21 44				22 14				22 44				23 14		
Anerley d	21 17				21 47				22 17				22 47				23 17		
Penge West d	21 19				21 49				22 19				22 49				23 19		
London Victoria 15 ⊖ d		21 05		21 41		21 35		22 11		22 05		22 41		22 35		23 11		23 05	
Battersea Park 4 d		21 09		21 45		21 39		22 15		22 09		22 45		22 39		23 15		23 09	
Wandsworth Road d				21 47				22 17				22 47				23 17			
Clapham High Street ⊖ d				21 49				22 19				22 49				23 19			
London Blackfriars 3 ⊖ d			21 43				22 13				22 43				23 13				23 43
Denmark Hill 4 d			21 52	21 54			22 22	22 24			22 52	22 54			23 22	23 24			23 52
Peckham Rye 4 d			21a55	21 56			22a25	22 26			22a55	22 56			23a25	23 26			23a55
Queens Rd Peckham d				21 59				22 29				22 59				23 29			
South Bermondsey d				22 01				22 31				23 01				23 31			
Clapham Junction 10 d		21 12				21 42				22 12				22 42				23 12	
Wandsworth Common d		21 15				21 45				22 15				22 45				23 15	
Balham 4 ⊖ d		21 18				21 48				22 18				22 48				23 18	
Streatham Hill d		21 21				21 51				22 21				22 51				23 21	
West Norwood 4 d		21 24				21 54				22 24				22 54				23 24	
Gipsy Hill d		21 27				21 57				22 27				22 57				23 27	
Crystal Palace 4 d		21 31				22 01				22 31				23 01				23 31	
Sydenham d	21 22	21 34			21 52	22 04			22 22	22 34			22 52	23 04			23 22	23 34	
Forest Hill 4 d	21 24	21 36			21 54	22 06			22 24	22 36			22 54	23 06			23 24	23 36	
Honor Oak Park d	21 27	21 39			21 57	22 09			22 27	22 39			22 57	23 09			23 27	23 39	
Brockley d	21 29	21 41			21 59	22 11			22 29	22 41			22 59	23 11			23 29	23 41	
New Cross Gate 4 ⊖ d	21 32	21 44			22 02	22 14			22 32	22 44			23 02	23 14			23 32	23 44	
London Bridge 4 ⊖ a	21 41	21 52		22 06	22 11	22 22		22 36	22 41	22 52		23 06	23 11	23 22		23 36	23 38	23 52	
London Waterloo (East) 4 ⊖ a	21 46				22 16				22 46				23 16				23 43		
London Charing Cross 4 ⊖ a	21 51				22 21				22 51				23 20				23 48		

Sundays

	SN	SN	SE	SN	SN	SE	SN	SN	SN	SE	SN	SN	SN	SE
			72			72				72				72
	B				A				C				A	
East Croydon d	06 44	07 12			07 47				08 17				08 47	
West Croydon 4 d							08 01				08 31			
Norwood Junction 2 d	06 48	07 18			07 51		08 05		08 21		08 35		08 51	
Anerley d	06 51	07 21					08 08				08 38			
Penge West d	06 53	07 23					08 10				08 40			
London Victoria 15 ⊖ d			07 38	07 41		08 08		08 11		08 38		08 41		09 08
Battersea Park 4 d				07 45				08 15				08 45		
Wandsworth Road d				07 47				08 17				08 47		
Clapham High Street ⊖ d				07 49				08 19				08 49		
London Blackfriars 3 ⊖ d														
Denmark Hill 4 d			07 47	07 54		08 17		08 24		08 47		08 54		09 17
Peckham Rye 4 d			07a49	07 56		08a19		08 26		08a49		08 56		09a19
Queens Rd Peckham d				07 59				08 29				08 59		
South Bermondsey d				08 01				08 31				09 01		
Clapham Junction 10 d														
Wandsworth Common d														
Balham 4 ⊖ d														
Streatham Hill d														
West Norwood 4 d														
Gipsy Hill d														
Crystal Palace 4 d														
Sydenham d	06 55	07 25			07 55		08 13		08 25		08 43		08 55	
Forest Hill 4 d	06 58	07 28			07 58		08 15		08 28		08 45		08 58	
Honor Oak Park d	07 00	07 30			08 00		08 18		08 30		08 48		09 00	
Brockley d	07 03	07 33			08 03		08 20		08 33		08 50		09 03	
New Cross Gate 4 ⊖ d	07 05	07 35			08 05		08 23		08 35		08 53		09 05	
London Bridge 4 ⊖ a	07 12	07 42		08 06	08 12		08 31	08 36	08 42		09 01	09 06	09 12	
London Waterloo (East) 4 ⊖ a	07 16	07 46			08 16				08 46				09 16	
London Charing Cross 4 ⊖ a	07 20	07 50			08 20				08 50				09 20	

For general notes see front of timetable
For details of catering facilities see Directory of Train Operators

- **A** From Caterham (Table 181)
- **B** From Purley (Table 175)
- **C** From Tattenham Corner (Table 181)

Table 178

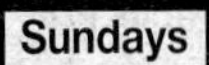

Croydon and London Victoria → London Bridge and Charing Cross

Network Diagram - see first page of Table 177

		SN	SN	SN A	SE 72	and at the same minutes past each hour until	SN	SN	SN B	SE 72	SN
East Croydon 🚊	d			09 17					22 47		
West Croydon 4 🚊	d	09 01					22 31				
Norwood Junction 2	d	09 05		09 21			22 35		22 51		
Anerley	d	09 08					22 38				
Penge West	d	09 10					22 40				
London Victoria 15 ⊖	d		09 11		09 38			22 41		23 08	23 11
Battersea Park 4	d		09 15					22 45			23 15
Wandsworth Road	d		09 17					22 47			23 17
Clapham High Street ⊖	d		09 19					22 49			23 19
London Blackfriars 3 ⊖	d										
Denmark Hill 4	d		09 24		09 47			22 54		23 17	23 24
Peckham Rye 4	d		09 26		09a49			22 56		23a19	23 26
Queens Rd Peckham	d		09 29					22 59			23 29
South Bermondsey	d		09 31					23 01			23 31
Clapham Junction 10	d										
Wandsworth Common	d										
Balham 4 ⊖	d										
Streatham Hill	d										
West Norwood 4	d										
Gipsy Hill	d										
Crystal Palace 4	d										
Sydenham	d	09 13		09 25			22 43		22 55		
Forest Hill 4	d	09 15		09 28			22 45		22 58		
Honor Oak Park	d	09 18		09 30			22 48		23 00		
Brockley	d	09 20		09 33			22 50		23 03		
New Cross Gate 4 ⊖	d	09 23		09 35			22 53		23 05		
London Bridge 4 ⊖	a	09 31	09 36	09 42			23 01	23 06	23 12		23 36
London Waterloo (East) 4 ⊖	a			09 46					23 16		
London Charing Cross 4 ⊖	a			09 52					23 20		

For general notes see front of timetable
For details of catering facilities see Directory of Train Operators

A From Tattenham Corner (Table 181)
B From Caterham (Table 181)

Luton and London → Wimbledon and Sutton via Streatham

Network Diagram - see first page of Table 177

Miles	Miles			SN	SN	FC	SN	FC	SN	FC	FC	SN	FC		SN	FC	SN	FC	FC	FC	FC	FC	FC	FC		FC
				A	A		A		A		1 B	C	B				C	D	B	D	B	D	D	D		D
—	—	**Luton** 10	d			04 44		05 48		06 18	06 36		06 56			07 08		07 30	07 56		08 20		08 28	08 54		09 04
—	—	Luton Airport Parkway 7 ✈	d			04 46		05 50		06 20			06 46			07 10		07 26	07 58		08 14		08 30	08 46		09 06
—	—	St Pancras International 15 ⊖	d			05 35		06 33		07 03	07 07		07 28			07 56		08 12	08 33	08 40	08 52	08 56	09 14	09 32		09 48
—	—	Farringdon 3 ⊖	d			05 39		06 38		07 08	07 12		07 32			08 00		08 16	08 37	08 44	08 56	09 00	09 18	09 36		09 52
—	0	City Thameslink 3	d					06 41		07 11	07 17		07 37			08 03		08 19	08 40	08 47	08 59	09 03	09 21	09 39		09 55
—	½	**London Blackfriars** 3 ⊖	d			06 11		06 46		07 16	07 23		07 40			08 08		08 24	08 45	08 52	09 03	09 08	09 26	09 44		10 00
—	1½	Elephant & Castle ⊖	d			06 14		06 49		07 19	07 27		07 43			08 11		08 27		08 55	09 06	09 11	09 29	09 47		10 03
—	3½	Loughborough Jn	d			06 18		06 53		07 23	07 31		07 47			08 15		08 31		08 59	09 10	09 15	09 33	09 51		10 07
—	4½	Herne Hill 4	d			06 24		06 57		07 28	07 35		07 52			08b22		08c38	08 55	09e06	09 14	09 22	09 38	09f57		10 12
0	—	**London Bridge** 4 ⊖	d		06 00		06 30	06 38	07 00	07 08	07 08	07 31	07 31		08 02	08 20	08 24	08 24	08 37		08 47	08 57	09 17	09 37		09 47
1¾	—	South Bermondsey	d		06 04		06 34	06 42	07 04	07 12	07 12	07 35			08 06	08 06	08 28	08 28	08 42		08 51	09 03	09 23	09 42		09 53
2¾	—	Queens Rd Peckham	d		06 06		06 36	06 44	07 06	07 14	07 14	07 37	07 37		08 08	08 08	08 30	08 30	08 45		08 53	09 05	09 25	09 44		09 55
3½	—	Peckham Rye 4	d		06 09		06 39	06 47	07 09	07 17	07 17	07 40	07 40		08 11	08 11	08 33		08 47		08 56	09 08	09 28	09 47		09 58
4½	—	East Dulwich	d		06 12		06 42	06 50	07 12	07 20	07 20	07 43	07 43		08 14	08 14		08 30	08 51		08 59	09 11	09 31	09 50		10 01
4¾	—	North Dulwich	d		06 14		06 44	06 52	07 14	07 22	07 22	07 45			08 16			08 32	08 53		09 01	09 13	09 33	09 52		10 03
6	5½	Tulse Hill 3	d		06 17	06 29	06 47	07 02	07 17	07 32	07 38	07 48	07 56		08 19	08 26	08 38	08g44	09h02	09 14	09 18	09 28	09 44	10 02		10 16
7½	7	Streatham 4	d		06 21	06 32	06 51	07 06	07 21	07 36	07 42	07 52	07 59		08 23	08 29	08 42	08 47	09 05	09 19	09 22	09 31	09 47	10 05		10 19
—	8	Mitcham Eastfields	d			06 36		07 10		07 40			08 03			08 33		08 51		09 23			09 51			10 23
—	9	Mitcham Junction 🚋	d			06 39		07 13		07 43			08 07			08 37		08 55		09 27			09 55			10 27
—	11	Hackbridge	d			06 43		07 17		07 47			08 10			08 40		08 58		09 30			09 58			10 30
—	11¾	Carshalton	d			06 45		07 19		07 49			08 13			08 43		09 01		09 33			10 01			10 33
9	—	Tooting	d		06 27		06 57		07 25		07 46	07 56			08 27		08 46		09 10		09 26	09 36		10 10		
10¼	—	Haydons Road	d		06 30		07 00		07 28		07 49	07 59			08 30		08 49		09 13		09 29	09 39		10 13		
11½	—	**Wimbledon** 6 ⊖ 🚋	a		06 32		07 02		07 31		07 54	08 01			08 32		08 51		09 16		09 32	09 44		10 20		
—	—		d	05 57	06 33		07 03		07 32			08 02			08 32		08 55		09 17			09 47		10 17		
12½	—	Wimbledon Chase	d	06 00	06 36		07j10		07 35			08 05			08 35		08 58		09 20			09 50		10 20		
13	—	South Merton	d	06 02	06 38		07 12		07 37			08 07			08 37		09 00		09 22			09 52		10 22		
13½	—	Morden South	d	06 04	06 40		07 14		07 39			08 09			08 39		09 02		09 24			09 54		10 24		
14	—	St Helier	d	06 06	06 42		07 16		07 41			08 11			08 41		09 04		09 26			09 56		10 26		
15	—	Sutton Common	d	06 08	06 44		07 18		07 43			08 13			08 43		09 06		09 28			09 58		10 28		
16	—	West Sutton	d	06 11	06 47		07 21		07 46			08 16			08 46		09 09		09 31			10 01		10 31		
17	13	**Sutton (Surrey)** 4	a	06 14	06 50	06 49	07 25	07 23	07 49	07 53		08 19	08 16		08 50	09 04	09 13	09 05	09 37	09 37	09 36	10 05	10 05	10 35		10 36

		FC	FC	FC	FC	FC	FC		FC	FC	FC	FC			FC	FC	FC	FC	SN	FC	FC	SN	FC	FC	SN
			D		D		D			D		D				D		D	E		1 B		D		
Luton 10	d	09 14	09 39	09 44	10 09	10 14	10 39		10 44	11 04	11 14	11 34			14 44	15 04	15 14	15 34		15 44	15 55		16 04	16 14	
Luton Airport Parkway 7 ✈	d	09 16	09 36	09 46	10 06	10 16	10 36		10 46	11 06	11 16	11 36			14 46	15 06	15 16	15 36		15 46	15 57		16 06	16 16	
St Pancras International 15 ⊖	d	10 02	10 17	10 32	10 47	11 02	11 18		11 32	11 47	12 02	12 17			15 32	15 47	16 02	16 14		16 32	16 36		16 45	17 01	
Farringdon 3 ⊖	d	10 07	10 22	10 37	10 52	11 07	11 22		11 37	11 52	12 07	12 22			15 37	15 52	16 07	16 19		16 37	16 40		16 50	17 06	
City Thameslink 3	d	10 09	10 26	10 39	10 56	11 09	11 26		11 39	11 54	12 09	12 24			15 39	15 54	16 09	16 21		16 39	16 43		16 52	17 11	
London Blackfriars 3 ⊖	d	10 16	10 30	10 46	11 00	11 16	11 30		11 46	12 00	12 16	12 30			15 46	16 00	16 16	16 26		16 42	16 46		16 58	17 14	
Elephant & Castle ⊖	d	10 19	10 33	10 49	11 03	11 19	11 33		11 49	12 03	12 19	12 33			15 49	16 03	16 19	16 30		16 45	16 50		17 02	17 17	
Loughborough Jn	d	10 23	10 37	10 53	11 07	11 23	11 37		11 53	12 07	12 23	12 37			15 53	16 07	16 23	16 34		16 49	16 54		17 06	17 21	
Herne Hill 4	d	10 27	10 42	10 57	11 12	11 27	11 42		11 57	12 12	12 27	12 42			15 57	16 12	16 27	16 38		16 53	16 58		17 11	17 25	
London Bridge 4 ⊖	d	10 08	10 19	10 38	10 49	11 08	11 19		11 38	11 49	12 08	12 19	and at		15 38	15 49	16 07	16 19	16 29	16 37		16 53	16 55		17 25
South Bermondsey	d	10 12	10 23	10 42	10 53	11 12	11 23		11 42	11 53	12 12	12 23			15 42	15 53	16 11	16 23	16 33	16 41		16 57	16 59		17 29
Queens Rd Peckham	d	10 14	10 25	10 44	10 55	11 14	11 25		11 44	11 55	12 14	12 25	the same		15 44	15 55	16 13	16 25	16 35	16 43		16 59	17 01		17 31
Peckham Rye 4	d	10 17	10 28	10 47	10 58	11 17	11 28		11 47	11 58	12 17	12 28			15 47	15 58	16 16	16 28	16 38	16 46		17 02	17 04		17 34
East Dulwich	d	10 20	10 31	10 50	11 01	11 20	11 31		11 50	12 01	12 20	12 31	minutes		15 50	16 01	16 19	16 31	16 41	16 49		17 05	17 07		17 37
North Dulwich	d	10 22	10 33	10 52	11 03	11 22	11 33		11 52	12 03	12 22	12 33			15 52	16 03	16 21	16 33	16 43	16 51		17 07			17 39
Tulse Hill 3	d	10 32	10 46	11 02	11 16	11 32	11 46		12 02	12 16	12 32	12 46	past		16 02	16 16	16 32	16 42	16 46	16 58	17k08	17 11	17 16	17 29	17 42
Streatham 4	d	10 35	10 49	11 05	11 19	11 35	11 49		12 05	12 19	12 35	12 49			16 05	16 19	16 35	16 45	16 50	17 01	17 11	17 14	17 19	17 33	17 46
Mitcham Eastfields	d		10 53		11 23		11 53			12 23		12 53	each			16 23		16 49	16 54			17 19	17 23		17 50
Mitcham Junction 🚋	d		10 57		11 27		11 57			12 27		12 57	hour until			16 27		16 52	16 58			17 22	17 27		17 54
Hackbridge	d		11 00		11 30		12 00			12 30		13 00				16 30		16 56	17 01			17 26	17 30		17 57
Carshalton	d		11 03		11 33		12 03			12 33		13 03				16 33		16 58	17 04			17 28	17 33		18 00
Tooting	d	10 40		11 10		11 40			12 10		12 40				16 10		16 39			17 06	17 16			17 38	
Haydons Road	d	10 43		11 13		11 43			12 13		12 43				16 13		16 42			17 09	17 19			17 41	
Wimbledon 6 ⊖ 🚋	a	10 46		11 16		11 46			12 16		12 46				16 16		16 46			17 12	17 23			17 44	
	d	10 47		11 17		11 47			12 17		12 47				16 17		16 46			17 13				17 45	
Wimbledon Chase	d	10 50		11 20		11 50			12 20		12 50				16 20		16 49			17 16				17 48	
South Merton	d	10 52		11 22		11 52			12 22		12 52				16 22		16 51			17 18				17 50	
Morden South	d	10 54		11 24		11 54			12 24		12 54				16 24		16 53			17 20				17 52	
St Helier	d	10 56		11 26		11 56			12 26		12 56				16 26		16 55			17 22				17 54	
Sutton Common	d	10 58		11 28		11 58			12 28		12 58				16 28		16 57			17 24				17 56	
West Sutton	d	11 01		11 31		12 01			12 31		13 01				16 31		17 00			17 27				17 59	
Sutton (Surrey) 4	a	11 05	11 06	11 35	11 36	12 05	12 06		12 35	12 36	13 05	13 06			16 35	16 36	17 05	17 02	17 07	17 31		17 32	17 38	18 03	18 03

For general notes see front of timetable
For details of catering facilities see Directory of Train Operators

- **A** To London Bridge
- **B** From Bedford (Table 52)
- **C** To London Victoria (Table 177)
- **D** From St Albans City (Table 52)
- **E** To Epsom (Table 182)
- **b** Arr. 0819
- **c** Arr. 0835
- **e** Arr. 0903
- **f** Arr. 0955
- **g** Arr. 0843
- **h** Arr. 0859
- **j** Arr. 0706
- **k** Arr. 1702

Luton and London → Wimbledon and Sutton via Streatham

Network Diagram - see first page of Table 177

Mondays to Fridays

		FC		FC	SN	FC	FC	FC	SN	FC	FC	FC	FC		FC	FC	FC	FC	FC	FC	FC	FC	FC	FC		
		A				A		A	B		A		A			A		A								
Luton	d	16 34		16 44		17 18	17 18	17 34		17 48	18 00	18 20			18 50	19 04	19 20	19 20	19 50	20 20	20 50	21 20	21 50	22 20		
Luton Airport Parkway	d	16 36		16 46		17 02	17 20	17 36		17 50	18 02	18 22			18 52	19 06	19 22		19 52	20 22	20 52	21 22	21 52	22 22		
St Pancras International	d	17 17		17 31		17 51	18 03	18 15		18 33	18 45	19 05	19 17		19 35	19 48	20 05	20 17	20 35	21 05	21 35	22 05	22 36	23 06		
Farringdon	d	17 22		17 36		17 56	18 08	18 20		18 38	18 50	19 10	19 22		19 40	19 52	20 10	20 22	20 40	21 10	21 40	22 10	22 40	23 10		
City Thameslink	d	17 24		17 38		17 58	18 10	18 22		18 40	18 52	19 12	19 24		19 42	19 55	20 12	20 24	20 42	21 12	21 42	22 12	22 42			
London Blackfriars	d	17 30		17 42		18 02	18 14	18 26		18 44	18 56	19 16	19 30		19 46	20 00	20 16	20 30	20 46	21 16	21 46	22 16	22 46	23 16		
Elephant & Castle	d	17 34		17 45		18 06	18 18	18 30		18 48	19 00	19 19	19 33		19 49	20 03	20 19	20 33	20 49	21 19	21 49	22 19	22 49	23 19		
Loughborough Jn	d	17 38		17 49		18 10	18 22	18 34		18 52	19 04	19 23	19 37		19 53	20 07	20 23	20 37	20 53	21 23	21 53	22 23	22 53	23s23		
Herne Hill	d	17 42		17 53		18 14	18 26	18 38		18 56	19 08	19 28	19 42		19 58	20 12	20 27	20 42	20 57	21 27	21 57	22 27	22 57	23 28		
London Bridge	d			17 37	17 58	17 58	18 08	18 21	18 31	18 38	18 51	19 19			19 38	19 49		20 19		20 49	21 19		22 19	22 48		
South Bermondsey	d			17 41	18 02	18 02	18 12	18 25	18 35	18 42	18 55	19 23			19 42	19 53		20 23		20 53	21 23		22 23	22 53		
Queens Rd Peckham	d			17 43	18 04	18 04	18 14	18 27	18 37	18 44	18 57	19 25			19 44	19 55		20 25		20 55	21 25		22 25	22 55		
Peckham Rye	d			17 46	18 07	18 07	18 17	18 30	18 40	18 47	19 00	19 28			19 47	19 58		20 28		20 58	21 28		22 28	22 58		
East Dulwich	d			17 49	18 10	18 10	18 20	18 33	18 43	18 50	19 03	19 31			19 50	20 01		20 31		21 01	21 31		22 31	23 01		
North Dulwich	d			17 51	18 12		18 22	18 35	18 45	18 52	19 05	19 33			19 52	20 03		20 33		21 03	21 33		22 33	23 03		
Tulse Hill	d	17 46		17 58	18 15	18 18	18 31	18 44	18 48	19 02	19 14	19 32	19 47		20 02	20 16	20 32	20 46	21 02	21 32	22 02	22 32	23 02	23 32		
Streatham	d	17 50		18 02	18 19	18 22	18 34	18 52	18 52	19 05	19 17	19 35	19 50		20 05	20 19	20 35	20 49	21 05	21 35	22 05	22 35	23 04	23 35		
Mitcham Eastfields	d	17 54				18 26		18 51	18 56		19 21		19 53			20 23		20 53								
Mitcham Junction	d	17 57				18 30		18 55	19 00		19 25		19 57			20 27		20 57								
Hackbridge	d	18 01				18 33		18 58	19 03		19 28		20 00			20 30		21 00								
Carshalton	d	18 03				18 36		19 01	19 06		19 31		20 04			20 33		21 03								
Tooting	d			18 06			18 38			19 10		19 40			20 10		20 40		21 10	21 40	22 10	22 40	23 10	23 40		
Haydons Road	d			18 09			18 41			19 13		19 43			20 13		20 43		21 13	21 43	22 13	22 43	23 13	23 43		
Wimbledon	a			18 12			18 44			19 16		19 46			20 16		20 46		21 16	21 46	22 16	22 46	23 16	23 46		
	d			18 13			18 45			19 17		19 47			20 17		20 47		21 17	21 47	22 17	22 47	23 17	23 47		
Wimbledon Chase	d			18 16			18 48			19 20		19 50			20 20		20 50		21 20	21 50	22 20	22 50	23 20	23 50		
South Merton	d			18 18			18 50			19 22		19 52			20 22		20 52		21 22	21 52	22 22	22 52	23 22	23 52		
Morden South	d			18 20			18 52			19 24		19 54			20 24		20 54		21 24	21 54	22 24	22 54	23 24	23 54		
St Helier	d			18 22			18 54			19 26		19 56			20 26		20 56		21 26	21 56	22 26	22 56	23 26	23 56		
Sutton Common	d			18 24			18 56			19 28		19 58			20 28		20 58		21 28	21 58	22 28	22 58	23 28	23 58		
West Sutton	d			18 27			18 59			19 31		20 01			20 31		21 01		21 31	22 01	22 10	23 01	23 31	00 01		
Sutton (Surrey)	a	18 07		18 31	18 30	18 39	19 03	19 04	19 09	19 38	19 34	20 08	20 08		20 38	20 38	21 05	21 08	21 38	22 05	22 38	23 05	23 35	00 05		

Saturdays

		FC	FC		FC	FC		FC	FC		FC	FC		FC	FC		FC	FC			FC	FC	FC			
																		A				A				
Luton	d	05 14	05 50		06 20	06 34		06 44	06 59		07 14	07 26		07 44	07 59		08 14	08 34			08 44	09 04	09 14			
Luton Airport Parkway	d	05 16	05 52		06 22	06 36		06 46	07 01		07 16	07 28		07 46	08 01		08 16	08 36			08 46	09 06	09 16			
St Pancras International	d	06 05	06 35		07 05	07 10		07 32	07 47		08 02	08 17		08 32	08 47		09 02	09 17			09 32	09 47	10 02			
Farringdon	d	06 09	06 40		07 10	07 14		07 37	07 52		08 07	08 22		08 37	08 52		09 07	09 22			09 37	09 52	10 07			
City Thameslink	d																09 09	09 24			09 39	09 54	10 09			
London Blackfriars	d	06 16	06 46		07 16	07 30		07b46	08 00		08c16	08 30		08e46	09 00		09 16	09 30			09 46	10 00	10 16			
Elephant & Castle	d	06 19	06 49		07 19	07 33		07 49	08 03		08 19	08 33		08 49	09 03		09 19	09 33			09 49	10 03	10 19			
Loughborough Jn	d		06 53		07 23	07 37		07 53	08 07		08 23	08 37		08 53	09 07		09 23	09 37			09 53	10 07	10 23			
Herne Hill	d	06 27	06 57		07 27	07 42		07 57	08 12		08 27	08 42		08 57	09 12		09 27	09 42			09 57	10 12	10 27			
London Bridge	d				06 49	07 18		07 38	07 49		08 08	08 19		08 38	08 49		09 08	09 18			09 38	09 49	10 08			
South Bermondsey	d				06 53	07 22		07 42	07 53		08 12	08 23		08 42	08 53		09 12	09 22			09 42	09 53	10 12			
Queens Rd Peckham	d				06 55	07 24		07 44	07 55		08 14	08 25		08 44	08 55		09 14	09 24			09 44	09 55	10 14			
Peckham Rye	d				06 58	07 27		07 47	07 58		08 17	08 28		08 47	08 58		09 17	09 27			09 47	09 38	10 17			
East Dulwich	d				07 01	07 30		07 50	08 01		08 20	08 31		08 50	09 01		09 20	09 30			09 50	10 01	10 20			
North Dulwich	d				07 03	07 32		07 52	08 03		08 22	08 33		08 52	09 03		09 22	09 32			09 52	10 03	10 22			
Tulse Hill	d	06 32	07 02		07 32	07 46		08 02	08 16		08 32	08 46		09 02	09 16		09 32	09 46			10 02	10 16	10 32			
Streatham	d	06 35	07 05		07 35	07 49		08 05	08 19		08 35	08 49		09 05	09 19		09 35	09 49			10 05	10 19	10 35			
Mitcham Eastfields	d					07 53			08 23			08 53			09 23			09 53				10 23				
Mitcham Junction	d					07 57			08 27			08 57			09 27			09 57				10 27				
Hackbridge	d					08 00			08 30			09 00			09 30			10 00				10 30				
Carshalton	d					08 03			08 33			09 03			09 33			10 03				10 33				
Tooting	d	06 40	07 10		07 40			08 10			08 40			09 10			09 40				10 10		10 40			
Haydons Road	d	06 43	07 13		07 43			08 13			08 43			09 13			09 43				10 13		10 43			
Wimbledon	a	06 46	07 16		07 46			08 16			08 46			09 16			09 46				10 16		10 46			
	d	06 47	07 17		07 47			08 17			08 47			09 17			09 47				10 17		10 47			
Wimbledon Chase	d	06 50	07 20		07 50			08 20			08 50			09 20			09 50				10 20		10 50			
South Merton	d	06 52	07 22		07 52			08 22			08 52			09 22			09 52				10 22		10 52			
Morden South	d	06 54	07 24		07 54			08 24			08 54			09 24			09 54				10 24		10 54			
St Helier	d	06 56	07 26		07 56			08 26			08 56			09 26			09 56				10 26		10 56			
Sutton Common	d	06 58	07 28		07 58			08 28			08 58			09 28			09 58				10 28		10 58			
West Sutton	d	07 01	07 31		08 01			08 31			09 01			09 31			10 01				10 31		11 01			
Sutton (Surrey)	a	07 05	07 35		08 05	08 06		08 35	08 36		09 05	09 06		09 35	09 36		10 05	10 06			10 35	10 36	11 05			

For general notes see front of timetable
For details of catering facilities see Directory of Train Operators

A From St Albans City (Table 52)
B To Epsom (Table 182)
b Arr. 0743
c Arr. 0813
e Arr. 0843

Luton and London → Wimbledon and Sutton via Streatham

Network Diagram - see first page of Table 177

Saturdays

	FC A		FC	FC A	FC	FC	FC	FC	FC	FC 1	FC	FC	FC
Luton 10 d	09 34		17 44	18 04	18 20	18 50	19 20	19 50	20 20	20 50	21 20	21 50	22 20
Luton Airport Parkway 7 ✈ d	09 36		17 46	18 06	18 22	18 52	19 22	19 52	20 22	20 52	21 22	21 52	22 22
St Pancras International 15 ⊖ d	10 17		18 32	18 47	19 05	19 35	20 05	20 35	21 05	21 35	22 05	22 36	23 06
Farringdon 3 ⊖ d	10 22		18 37	18 52	19 10	19 40	20 10	20 40	21 10	21 40	22 10	22 40	23 10
City Thameslink 3 d	10 24		18 39	18 54	19 12	19 42	20 12	20 42					
London Blackfriars 3 ⊖ d	10 30		18 46	19 00	19 16	19 46	20 16	20 46	21 16	21 46	22 16	22 46	23 16
Elephant & Castle ⊖ d	10 33		18 49	19 03	19 19	19 49	20 19	20 49	21 19	21 49	22 19	22 49	23 19
Loughborough Jn d	10 37		18 53	19 07	19 23	19 53	20 23	20 53	21 23	21 53	22 23	22 53	23s23
Herne Hill 4 d	10 42		18 57	19 12	19 27	19 57	20 27	20 57	21 27	21 57	22 27	22 57	23 27
London Bridge 4 ⊖ d	10 19	and at	18 29	18 49	18 59	19 29	19 49	20 19	20 49	21 19	21 49	22 19	22 49
South Bermondsey d	10 23		18 33	18 53	19 03	19 33	19 53	20 23	20 53	21 23	21 53	22 23	22 53
Queens Rd Peckham d	10 25	the same	18 35	18 55	19 05	19 35	19 55	20 25	20 55	21 25	21 55	22 25	22 55
Peckham Rye 4 d	10 28		18 38	18 58	19 08	19 38	19 58	20 28	20 58	21 28	21 58	22 28	22 58
East Dulwich d	10 31	minutes	18 41	19 01	19 11	19 41	20 01	20 31	21 01	21 30	22 01	22 31	23 01
North Dulwich d	10 33		18 43	19 03	19 13	19 43	20 03	20 33	21 03	21 33	22 03	22 33	23 03
Tulse Hill 3 d	10 46	past	19 02	19 16	19 32	20 02	20 32	21 02	21 32	22 02	22 32	23 02	23 32
Streatham 4 d	10 49		19 05	19 19	19 35	20 05	20 35	21 05	21 35	22 05	22 35	23 05	23 35
Mitcham Eastfields d	10 53	each		19 23									
Mitcham Junction 🚋 d	10 57	hour until		19 27									
Hackbridge d	11 00			19 30									
Carshalton d	11 03			19 33									
Tooting d			19 10		19 40	20 10	20 40	21 10	21 40	22 10	22 40	23 10	23 40
Haydons Road d			19 13		19 43	20 13	20 43	21 13	21 43	22 13	22 43	23 13	23 43
Wimbledon 6 ⊖ 🚋 a			19 16		19 46	20 16	20 46	21 16	21 46	22 16	22 46	23 16	23 46
d			19 17		19 47	20 17	20 47	21 17	21 47	22 17	22 47	23 17	23 47
Wimbledon Chase d			19 20		19 50	20 20	20 50	21 20	21 50	22 20	22 50	23 20	23 50
South Merton d			19 22		19 52	20 22	20 52	21 22	21 52	22 22	22 52	23 22	23 52
Morden South d			19 24		19 54	20 24	20 54	21 24	21 54	22 24	22 54	23 24	23 54
St Helier d			19 26		19 56	20 26	20 56	21 26	21 56	22 26	22 56	23 26	23 56
Sutton Common d			19 28		19 58	20 28	20 58	21 28	21 58	22 28	22 58	23 28	23 58
West Sutton d			19 31		20 01	20 31	21 01	21 31	22 01	22 31	23 01	23 31	00 01
Sutton (Surrey) 4 a	11 06		19 38	19 38	20 05	20 38	21 05	21 38	22 05	22 38	23 05	23 38	00 05

Sundays

	FC	FC	FC	FC	FC	FC	FC	FC	FC	FC	FC	FC B	FC B	FC B	FC B	FC B	FC B	FC B	FC B	FC B	FC	FC	FC	FC	FC
Luton 10 d	22p20	08 20	08 50	09 20	09 50	10 20	10 50	11 20	11 50	12 20	12 50	13 20	13 50	14 18	14 50	15 20	15 50	16 20	16 50	17 20	17 50	18 20	18 50	19 20	19 50
Luton Airport Parkway 7 ✈ d	22p22	08 22	08 52	09 22	09 52	10 22	10 52	11 22	11 52	12 22	12 52	13 22	13 52	14 20	14 52	15 22	15 52	16 22	16 52	17 22	17 52	18 22	18 52	19 22	19 52
St Pancras International 15 ⊖ d	23p06	09 06	09 36	10 06	10 36	11 06	11 36	12 06	12 36	13 06	13 36	14 06	14 36	15 06	15 36	16 06	16 36	17 06	17 36	18 06	18 36	19 06	19 36	20 06	20 36
Farringdon 3 ⊖ d	23p10	09 10	09 40	10 10	10 40	11 10	11 40	12 10	12 40	13 10	13 40	14 10	14 40	15 10	15 40	16 10	16 40	17 10	17 40	18 10	18 40	19 10	19 40	20 10	20 40
City Thameslink 3 d																									
London Blackfriars 3 ⊖ d	23p16	09 16	09 46	10 16	10 46	11 16	11 46	12 16	12 46	13 16	13 46	14 16	14 46	15 16	15 46	16 16	16 46	17 16	17 46	18 16	18 46	19 16	19 46	20 16	20 46
Elephant & Castle ⊖ d	23p19	09 19	09 49	10 19	10 49	11 19	11 49	12 19	12 49	13 19	13 49	14 19	14 49	15 19	15 49	16 19	16 49	17 19	17 49	18 19	18 49	19 19	19 49	20 19	20 49
Loughborough Jn d	23s23	09 23	09 53	10 23	10 53	11 23	11 53	12 23	12 53	13 23	13 53	14 23	14 53	15 23	15 53	16 23	16 53	17 23	17 53	18 23	18 53	19 23	19 53	20 23	20 53
Herne Hill 4 d	23p27	09 27	09 57	10 27	10 57	11 27	11 57	12 27	12 57	13 27	13 57	14 27	14 57	15 27	15 57	16 27	16 57	17 27	17 57	18 27	18 57	19 27	19 57	20 27	20 57
London Bridge 4 ⊖ d	22p49	08 55	09 25	09 55	10 25	10 55	11 25	11 55		12 55	13 25	13 55		14 55	15 25	15 55	16 25		17 25		18 25		19 25	19 55	20 25
South Bermondsey d	22p53	08 59	09 29	09 59	10 29	10 59	11 29	11 59		12 59	13 29	13 59		14 59	15 29	15 59	16 29		17 29		18 29		19 29	19 59	20 29
Queens Rd Peckham d	22p55	09 01	09 31	10 01	10 31	11 01	11 31	12 25		13 01	13 31	14 25		15 01	15 31	16 01	16 31		17 31		18 31		19 31	20 01	20 31
Peckham Rye 4 d	22p58	09 04	09 34	10 04	10 34	11 04	11 34	12 29		13 04	13 34	14 29		15 04	15 34	16 04	16 34		17 34		18 34		19 34	20 04	20 34
East Dulwich d	23p01	09 07	09 37	10 07	10 37	11 07	11 37	12 31		13 07	13 37	14 31		15 07	15 37	16 07	16 37		17 37		18 37		19 37	20 07	20 37
North Dulwich d	23p03	09 09	09 39	10 09	10 39	11 09	11 39	12 39		13 09	13 39	14 39		15 09	15 39	16 09	16 39		17 39		18 39		19 39	20 09	20 39
Tulse Hill 3 d	23p32	09 31	10 01	10 31	11 01	11 31	12 01	12 31	13 01	13 31	14 01	14 31	15 01	15 31	16 01	16 31	17 01	17 31	18 01	18 31	19 01	19 31	20 01	20 31	21 01
Streatham 4 d	23p35	09 34	10 04	10 34	11 04	11 34	12 04	12 34	13 04	13 34	14 04	14 34	15 04	15 34	16 04	16 34	17 04	17 34	18 04	18 34	19 04	19 34	20 04	20 34	21 04
Mitcham Eastfields d																									
Mitcham Junction 🚋 d																									
Hackbridge d																									
Carshalton d																									
Tooting d	23p40	09 38	10 08	10 38	11 08	11 38	12 08	12 38	13 08	13 38	14 08	14 38	15 08	15 38	16 08	16 38	17 08	17 38	18 08	18 38	19 08	19 38	20 08	20 38	21 08
Haydons Road d	23p43	09 41	10 11	10 41	11 11	11 41	12 11	12 41	13 11	13 41	14 11	14 41	15 11	15 41	16 11	16 41	17 11	17 41	18 11	18 41	19 11	19 41	20 11	20 41	21 11
Wimbledon 6 ⊖ 🚋 a	23p46	09 44	10 14	10 44	11 14	11 44	12 14	12 44	13 14	13 44	14 14	14 44	15 14	15 44	16 14	16 44	17 14	17 44	18 14	18 44	19 14	19 44	20 14	20 44	21 14
d	23p47	09 44	10 14	10 44	11 14	11 44	12 14	12 44	13 14	13 44	14 14	14 44	15 14	15 44	16 14	16 44	17 14	17 44	18 14	18 44	19 14	19 44	20 14	20 44	21 14
Wimbledon Chase d	23p50	09 47	10 17	10 47	11 17	11 47	12 17	12 47	13 17	13 47	14 17	14 47	15 17	15 47	16 17	16 47	17 17	17 47	18 17	18 47	19 17	19 47	20 17	20 47	21 17
South Merton d	23p52	09 49	10 19	10 49	11 19	11 49	12 19	12 49	13 19	13 49	14 19	14 49	15 19	15 49	16 19	16 49	17 19	17 49	18 19	18 49	19 19	19 49	20 19	20 49	21 19
Morden South d	23p54	09 51	10 21	10 51	11 21	11 51	12 21	12 51	13 21	13 51	14 21	14 51	15 21	15 51	16 21	16 51	17 21	17 51	18 21	18 51	19 21	19 51	20 21	20 51	21 21
St Helier d	23p56	09 53	10 23	10 53	11 23	11 53	12 23	12 53	13 23	13 53	14 23	14 53	15 23	15 53	16 23	16 53	17 23	17 53	18 23	18 53	19 23	19 53	20 23	20 53	21 23
Sutton Common d	23p58	09 55	10 25	10 55	11 25	11 55	12 25	12 55	13 25	13 55	14 25	14 55	15 25	15 55	16 25	16 55	17 25	17 55	18 25	18 55	19 25	19 55	20 25	20 55	21 25
West Sutton d	00 01	09 58	10 28	10 58	11 28	11 58	12 28	12 58	13 28	13 58	14 28	14 58	15 28	15 58	16 28	16 58	17 28	17 58	18 28	18 58	19 28	19 58	20 28	20 58	21 28
Sutton (Surrey) 4 a	00 05	10 01	10 31	11 01	11 31	12 01	12 31	13 01	13 31	14 01	14 31	15 01	15 31	16 01	16 31	17 01	17 31	18 01	18 31	19 01	19 31	20 01	20 31	21 01	21 31

For general notes see front of timetable
For details of catering facilities see Directory of Train Operators

A From St Albans City (Table 52)
B From Bedford (Table 52)

Table 179

Mondays to Fridays

Sutton and Wimbledon → London and Luton via Streatham

Network Diagram - see first page of Table 177

Miles	Miles			SN	SN	FC A	FC B	SN	FC A	SN	FC B	SN	FC A	FC B	FC B	SN	FC B	FC	FC B
0	0	**Sutton (Surrey)** 4	d	05 37	06 15		06 23	06 51	06 49	07 25	07 23	07 50		07 53	08 17	08 50	08 47	09 05	09 38
1	—	West Sutton	d				06 26		06 52		07 26			07 56	08 20		08 50	09 08	
2	—	Sutton Common	d				06 28		06 55		07 29			07 59	08 22		08 52	09 10	
3	—	St Helier	d				06 31		06 57		07 31			08 01	08 25		08 55	09 13	
3½	—	Morden South	d				06 33		06 59		07 33			08 03	08 27		08 57	09 15	
4	—	South Merton	d				06 35		07 01		07 35			08 05	08 29		08 59	09 17	
4½	—	Wimbledon Chase	d				06 37		07 03		07 37			08 07	08 31		09 01	09 19	
5½	—	**Wimbledon** 6 ⊖	a				06 40		07 06		07 41			08 11	08 35		09 04	09 23	
—	—		d			06 28	06 40		07 06		07 42		07 58	08 12	08 36		09 05	09 24	
6¾	—	Haydons Road	d			06 30	06 43		07 08		07 44		08 00	08 14	08 38		09 07	09 26	
8	—	Tooting	d			06 33	06 46		07 11		07 47		08 03	08 17	08 41		09 10	09 29	
—	1¼	Carshalton	d	05 40	06 18			06 54		07 28		07 53				08 53			09 41
—	2	Hackbridge	d	05 42	06 20			06 56		07 31		07 55				08 55			09 43
—	4	Mitcham Junction	d	05 46	06 24			07 00		07 34		07 59							09 46
—	5	Mitcham Eastfields	d	05 49	06 27					07 38						09 02			09 50
9½	6	Streatham 4	d	05 53	06 32	06 36	06 50	07 06	07 16	07 42	07 52	08 05	08 11	08 21	08 45	09 06	09 15	09 34	09 54
11	7½	Tulse Hill 3	d	05 57	06 35	06 40	06 54	07 09	07 20	07 46	07 57	08 10	08 15	08 27	08 49	09 09	09 19	09 38	09 58
12¼	—	North Dulwich	d	06 10	06 38		07 01	07 12	07 27	07 49	08 03	08 13		08 33		09 12	09 25	09 44	10 04
12½	—	East Dulwich	d	06 12	06 40		07 03	07 14	07 29	07 51	08 05	08 15		08 35		09 14	09 27	09 46	10 06
13½	—	Peckham Rye 4	d	06 02	06 43		07 05	07 17	07 31	07 53	08 07	08 17		08 38		09 17	09 29	09 49	10 09
14¼	—	Queens Rd Peckham	d	06 17	06 45		07 08	07 25	07 34	08 10	08 10	08 20		08 40	09 17	09 19	09 32	09 51	10 11
15¼	—	South Bermondsey	d	06 20	06 48		07 10	07 28	07 36	08 13	08 13	08 22		08 43	09 20	09 22	09 34	09 54	10 14
17	—	**London Bridge** 4 ⊖	a	06 08	06 52		07 18	07 25	07 43	08 02	08 21	08 30		08 49	09 29	09 29	09 41	09 59	10 18
—	8½	Herne Hill 4	d			06 45	06 59		07 24		08 01		08b22	08 31	08 53		09 23	09 42	10 02
—	9½	Loughborough Jn	d			06 48	07 02		07 27		08 03		08 25	08 34	08 56		09 26	09 45	10 05
—	11½	Elephant & Castle ⊖	d			06 53	07 07		07 32		08 09		08 30	08 40	09 00		09 30	09 50	10 10
—	12½	**London Blackfriars** 3 ⊖	a			06 57	07 11		07 37		08 13		08 34	08 45	09 04		09 33	09 56	10 13
—	13	City Thameslink 3	a			07 00	07 14		07 40		08 15		08 37	08 47	09 07		09 36	10 00	10 16
—	—	Farringdon 3 ⊖	a			07 04	07 16		07 44		08 19		08 41	08 50	09 10		09 40	10 04	10 19
—	—	St Pancras International 15 ⊖	a			07 08	07 21		07 48		08 23		08 46	08 54	09 14		09 44	10 08	10 23
—	—	Luton Airport Parkway 7 ✈	a			07 54	08 05		08 27		09 05		09 20	09 40	09 53		10 20	10 57	11 05
—	—	**Luton** 10	a			07 56	08 08		08 30		09 08		09 23	09 34	09 55		10 24	11 01	11 08

		FC	FC B	FC	FC B	FC	FC B	FC	FC B		FC	FC B	FC A	FC	FC B	FC A	FC B	FC B
Sutton (Surrey) 4	d	09 37	10 06	10 05	10 36	10 37	11 06	11 07	11 36		15 37	16 06	16 07	16 38	16 37	17 06	17 02	17 32
West Sutton	d	09 40		10 08		10 40		11 10			15 40		16 10		16 40		17 05	
Sutton Common	d	09 42		10 10		10 42		11 12			15 42		16 12		16 42		17 07	
St Helier	d	09 45		10 13		10 45		11 15			15 45		16 15		16 45		17 10	
Morden South	d	09 47		10 15		10 47		11 17			15 47		16 17		16 47		17 12	
South Merton	d	09 49		10 17		10 49		11 19			15 49		16 19		16 49		17 14	
Wimbledon Chase	d	09 51		10 19		10 51		11 21			15 51		16 21		16 51		17 16	
Wimbledon 6 ⊖	a	09 55		10 22		10 54		11 25			15 55		16 25		16 55		17 19	
	d	09 56		10 23		10 56		11 26			15 56		16 28		16 55		17 20	
Haydons Road	d	09 58		10 25		10 58		11 28		and at the same minutes past each hour until	15 58		16 30		16 57		17 22	
Tooting	d	10 01		10 28		11 01		11 31			16 01		16 33		17 00		17 25	
Carshalton	d		10 09		10 39		11 09		11 39			16 09		16 41		17 09		17 35
Hackbridge	d		10 11		10 41		11 11		11 41			16 11		16 43		17 11		17 37
Mitcham Junction	d		10 14		10 44		11 14		11 44			16 14		16 46		17 14		17 40
Mitcham Eastfields	d		10 18		10 48		11 18		11 48			16 18		16 50		17 18		17 44
Streatham 4	d	10 06	10 23	10 33	10 53	11 06	11 23	11 36	11 53		16 06	16 23	16 38	16 55	17 05	17 23	17 29	17 49
Tulse Hill 3	d	10 12	10 27	10 42	10 57	11 12	11 27	11 42	11 57		16 12	16 27	16 41	17 02	17 09	17 27	17 33	17 54
North Dulwich	d	10 24	10 34	10 54	11 04	11 24	11 34	11 54				16 34	16 56	17 12	17 26	17 36	17 45	18 00
East Dulwich	d	10 26	10 36	10 56	11 06	11 26	11 36	11 56				16 36	16 58	17 14	17 28	17 38	17 47	18 02
Peckham Rye 4	d	10 29	10 39	10 59	11 09	11 29	11 39	11 59				16 39	17 01	17 16	17 30	17 41	17 49	18 04
Queens Rd Peckham	d	10 31	10 41	11 01	11 11	11 31	11 41	12 01				16 41	17 04	17 19	17 33	17 43	17 52	18 07
South Bermondsey	d	10 34	10 44	11 04	11 14	11 34	11 44	12 04				16 44	17 06	17 21	17 35	17 46	17 54	18 09
London Bridge 4 ⊖	a	10 38	10 48	11 08	11 18	11 38	11 48	12 08				16 48	17 11	17 26	17 40	17 50	17 59	18 14
Herne Hill 4	d	10 16	10 31	10 46	11 00	11 16	11 30	11 46	12 00		16 16	16 31	16 46	17 06	17 14	17 31	17 37	17 57
Loughborough Jn	d	10 19	10 34	10 49	11 04	11 19	11 34	11 49	12 04		16 19	16 34	16 49	17 10	17 17	17 34	17 40	18 01
Elephant & Castle ⊖	d	10 24	10 39	10 54	11 08	11 23	11 38	11 53	12 09		16 24	16 40	16 54	17 14	17 22	17 39	17 44	18 06
London Blackfriars 3 ⊖	a	10 27	10 43	10 57	11 12	11 27	11 42	11 57	12 12		16 29	16 43	16 57	17 17	17 30	17 44	17 47	18 10
City Thameslink 3	a	10 30	10 45	11 00	11 15	11 30	11 45	12 00	12 15		16 32	16 46	17 02	17 20	17 34	17 46	17 50	18 16
Farringdon 3 ⊖	a	10 34	10 49	11 04	11 19	11 34	11 49	12 04	12 19		16 35	16 49	17 05	17 23	17 37	17 50	17 53	18 23
St Pancras International 15 ⊖	a	10 38	10 53	11 08	11 23	11 38	11 53	12 08	12 23		16 39	16 53	17 09	17 27	17 41	17 53	17 57	18 27
Luton Airport Parkway 7 ✈	a	11 25	11 35	11 55	12 04	12 25	12 35	12 55			17 26	17 39	17 50	18 09	18 28	18 33	18 39	19 09
Luton 10	a	11 29	11 38	11 59	12 08	12 29	12 38	12 59			17 29	17 34	17 53	18 04	18 33	18 37	18 34	19 04

For general notes see front of timetable
For details of catering facilities see Directory of Train Operators

A To Bedford (Table 52)
B To St Albans City (Table 52)
b Arr. 0819

Sutton and Wimbledon → London and Luton via Streatham

Network Diagram - see first page of Table 177

Station		SN	FC	FC A	SN	FC	SN	FC	FC B	FC	FC	FC B	FC B	FC B	FC B
Sutton (Surrey) 4	d	17 32	17 40	18 04	18 04	18 07	18 31	18 40	19 04	19 03	19 37	20 09	20 39	21 09	21 49
West Sutton	d	17 36	17 43		18 07	18 10	18 34	18 43		19 08	19 40	20 12	20 42	21 12	21 52
Sutton Common	d	17 38	17 45			18 12	18 37	18 45		19 10	19 42	20 14	20 44	21 14	21 54
St Helier	d	17 41	17 48			18 15	18 39	18 48		19 13	19 45	20 17	20 47	21 17	21 57
Morden South	d	17 43	17 50			18 17	18 41	18 50		19 15	19 47	20 19	20 49	21 19	21 59
South Merton	d	17 45	17 52			18 19	18 43	18 52		19 17	19 49	20 21	20 51	21 21	22 01
Wimbledon Chase	d	17 47	17 54			18 21	18 45	18 54		19 19	19 51	20 23	20 53	21 23	22 03
Wimbledon 6	a	17 51	17 57		18 18	18 25	18 50	18 57		19 22	19 55	20 27	20 57	21 27	22 07
	d	17 51	17 58		18 21	18 28	18 50	18 58		19 26	19 56	20 28	20 58	21 38	22 08
Haydons Road	d	17 53	18 00		18 23	18 30	18 52	19 00		19 28	19 58	20 30	21 00	21 40	22 10
Tooting	d	17 56	18 03		18 26	18 33	18 55	19 03		19 31	20 01	20 33	21 03	21 43	22 13
Carshalton	d			18 07					19 07						
Hackbridge	d			18 09					19 09						
Mitcham Junction	d			18 12					19 12						
Mitcham Eastfields	d			18 16					19 16						
Streatham 4	d	18 01	18 08	18 20	18 32	18 38	18 59	19 08	19 21	19 36	20 06	20 40	21 10	21 48	22 18
Tulse Hill 3	d	18 05	18 12	18 24	18 36	18 42	19 05	19 12	19 27	19 42	20 12	20 44	21 14	21 52	22 22
North Dulwich	d	18 08	*18 18*	*18 31*	18 39	*18 48*	19 08	*19 20*	*19 43*	*20 13*	*20 43*	*20 59*	*21 28*	*21 58*	*22 28*
East Dulwich	d	18 10	*18 20*	*18 33*	18 41	*18 50*	19 10	*19 22*	*19 45*	*20 15*	*20 45*	*21 01*	*21 30*	*22 00*	*22 30*
Peckham Rye 4	d	18 12	*18 23*	*18 36*	18 43	*18 53*	19 13	*19 25*	*19 48*	*20 17*	*20 47*	*21 04*	*21 32*	*22 02*	*22 32*
Queens Rd Peckham	d	18 15	*18 25*	*18 38*	18 46	*18 55*	19 15		*19 50*	*20 20*	*20 50*	*21 06*	*21 35*	*22 05*	*22 35*
South Bermondsey	d	18 17	*18 28*	*18 41*	18 48	*18 58*	19 18	*19 31*	*19 53*	*20 22*	*20 52*	*21 09*	*21 37*	*22 07*	*22 37*
London Bridge 4	⊖ a	18 24	*18 32*	*18 45*	18 53	*19 02*	19 22		*19 57*	*20 27*	*20 57*	*21 14*	*21 44*	*22 14*	*22 44*
Herne Hill 4	d		18 16	18 28		18 48		19 18	19 32	19 48	20 16	20 48	21 18	21 56	22 26
Loughborough Jn	d		18 19	18 31		18 51		19 21	19 35	19 51	20 19	20 51	21 21	21 59	22 29
Elephant & Castle	⊖ d		18 24	18 35		18 55		19 26	19 40	19 56	20 24	20 55	21 25	22 04	22 34
London Blackfriars 3	⊖ a		18 29	18 40		18 59		19 29	19 43	19 59	20 27	20 59	21 29	22 08	22 38
City Thameslink 3	a		18 34	18 48		19 04		19 32	19 46	20 02	20 32	21 02	21 34	22 10	22 40
Farringdon 3	⊖ a		18 37	18 51		19 07		19 36	19 49	20 06	20 36	21 06	21 38	22 14	22 44
St Pancras International 15	⊖ a		18 41	18 55		19 11		19 40	19 53	20 10	20 40	21 10	21 43	22 18	22 48
Luton Airport Parkway 7	✈ a		19 27	*19 40*		19 58		20 25	20 41	20 55	21 25	21 55	22 25	23 01	23 31
Luton 10	a		19 33	*19 34*		20 01		20 29	20 44	20 59	21 29	21 59	22 29	23 05	23 35

Saturdays

Station		FC	FC A	FC	FC A	FC	FC A	FC	FC A	FC	FC A	FC	FC A		FC	FC B	FC	FC B
Sutton (Surrey) 4	d		07 06	07 07	07 36	07 37	08 06	08 07	08 36	08 37	09 06	09 07	09 36	and at the same minutes past each hour until	16 37	17 06	17 07	17 36
West Sutton	d			07 10		07 40		08 10		08 40		09 10			16 40		17 10	
Sutton Common	d			07 12		07 42		08 12		08 42		09 12			16 42		17 12	
St Helier	d			07 15		07 45		08 15		08 45		09 15			16 45		17 15	
Morden South	d			07 17		07 47		08 17		08 47		09 17			16 47		17 17	
South Merton	d			07 19		07 49		08 19		08 49		09 19			16 49		17 19	
Wimbledon Chase	d			07 21		07 51		08 21		08 51		09 21			16 51		17 21	
Wimbledon 6	⊖ a			07 24		07 54		08 24		08 54		09 24			16 54		17 24	
	d	06 56		07 26		07 56		08 26		08 56		09 26			16 56		17 26	
Haydons Road	d	06 58		07 28		07 58		08 28		08 58		09 28			16 58		17 28	
Tooting	d	07 01		07 31		08 01		08 31		09 01		09 31			17 01		17 31	
Carshalton	d		07 09		07 39		08 09		08 39		09 09		09 39			17 09		17 39
Hackbridge	d		07 11		07 41		08 11		08 41		09 11		09 41			17 11		17 41
Mitcham Junction	d		07 14		07 44		08 14		08 44		09 14		09 44			17 14		17 44
Mitcham Eastfields	d		07 18		07 48		08 18		08 48		09 18		09 48			17 18		17 48
Streatham 4	d	07 06	07 23	07 36	07 53	08 06	08 23	08 36	08 53	09 06	09 23	09 36	09 53		17 06	17 23	17 36	17 53
Tulse Hill 3	d	07 12	07 27	07 42	07 57	08 12	08 27	08 42	08 57	09 12	09 27	09 42	09 57		17 12	17 27	17 42	17 57
North Dulwich	d	*07 24*		*07 54*		*08 24*	*08 34*	*08 54*	*09 04*	*09 24*	*09 34*	*09 54*	*10 04*		*17 24*	*17 34*	*17 54*	*18 04*
East Dulwich	d	*07 26*		*07 56*		*08 26*	*08 36*	*08 56*	*09 06*	*09 26*	*09 36*	*09 56*	*10 06*		*17 26*	*17 36*	*17 56*	*18 06*
Peckham Rye 4	d	*07 29*		*07 59*		*08 29*	*08 39*	*08 59*	*09 09*	*09 29*	*09 39*	*09 59*	*10 09*		*17 29*	*17 39*	*17 59*	*18 09*
Queens Rd Peckham	d	*07 32*		*08 02*		*08 32*	*08 41*	*09 01*	*09 11*	*09 31*	*09 41*	*10 01*	*10 11*		*17 31*	*17 41*	*18 01*	*18 11*
South Bermondsey	d	*07 34*		*08 04*		*08 34*	*08 44*	*09 04*	*09 14*	*09 34*	*09 44*	*10 04*	*10 14*		*17 34*	*17 44*	*18 04*	*18 14*
London Bridge 4	⊖ a	*07 39*		*08 09*		*08 39*	*08 48*	*09 08*	*09 18*	*09 38*	*09 48*	*10 08*	*10 18*		*17 38*	*17 48*	*18 08*	*18 18*
Herne Hill 4	d	07 16	07 30	07 46	08 00	08 16	08 31	08 46	09 00	09 16	09 30	09 46	10 00		17 16	17 30	17 46	18 00
Loughborough Jn	d	07 19	07 34	07 49	08 04	08 19	08 34	08 49	09 04	09 19	09 34	09 49	10 04		17 19	17 34	17 49	18 04
Elephant & Castle	⊖ d	07 24	07 39	07 54	08 09	08 24	08 39	08 54	09 09	09 24	09 39	09 54	10 09		17 24	17 39	17 54	18 09
London Blackfriars 3	⊖ a	07 28	07 43	07 58	08 13	08 28	08 43	08 58	09 13	09 28	09 43	09 58	10 13		17 28	17 43	17 58	18 13
City Thameslink 3	a							09 00	09 15	09 30	09 45	10 00	10 15		17 30	17 45	18 00	18 15
Farringdon 3	⊖ a	07 33	07 48	08 03	08 18	08 33	08 48	09 04	09 19	09 34	09 49	10 04	10 19		17 34	17 49	18 04	18 19
St Pancras International 15	⊖ a	07 38	07 53	08 08	08 23	08 38	08 53	09 08	09 23	09 38	09 53	10 08	10 23		17 38	17 53	18 08	18 23
Luton Airport Parkway 7	✈ a	08 25	*08 35*	08 55		09 25	*09 35*	09 55	*10 05*	10 25	*10 35*	10 55	*11 05*		18 25	18 40	18 55	19 10
Luton 10	a	08 29	*08 38*	08 59		09 29	*09 38*	09 59	*10 08*	10 29	*10 38*	10 59	*11 08*		18 29	18 43	18 59	19 13

For general notes see front of timetable
For details of catering facilities see Directory of Train Operators

A To St Albans City (Table 52)
B To Bedford (Table 52)

Table 179

Saturdays

Sutton and Wimbledon → London and Luton via Streatham

Network Diagram - see first page of Table 177

		FC	FC A	FC	FC A	FC	FC	FC	FC	FC A	FC A	FC A	FC A	FC A
Sutton (Surrey) 4	d	17 37	18 06	18 07	18 36	18 37	19 06	19 07	19 39	20 09	20 39	21 09	21 49	
West Sutton	d	17 40		18 10		18 40		19 10	19 42	20 12	20 42	21 12	21 52	
Sutton Common	d	17 42		18 12		18 42		19 12	19 44	20 14	20 44	21 14	21 54	
St Helier	d	17 45		18 15		18 45		19 15	19 47	20 17	20 47	21 17	21 57	
Morden South	d	17 47		18 17		18 47		19 17	19 49	20 19	20 49	21 19	21 59	
South Merton	d	17 49		18 19		18 49		19 19	19 51	20 21	20 51	21 21	22 01	
Wimbledon Chase	d	17 51		18 21		18 51		19 21	19 53	20 23	20 53	21 23	22 03	
Wimbledon 6 ⊖	a	17 54		18 24		18 54		19 24	19 56	20 24	20 54	21 27	22 08	
	d	17 56		18 26		18 56		19 28	19 58	20 27	20 57	21 38	22 08	22 38
Haydons Road	d	17 58		18 28		18 58		19 30	20 00	20 29	20 59	21 40	22 10	22 40
Tooting	d	18 01		18 31		19 01		19 33	20 03	20 32	21 02	21 43	22 13	22 43
Carshalton	d		18 09		18 39		19 09							
Hackbridge	d		18 11		18 41		19 11							
Mitcham Junction	d		18 14		18 44		19 14							
Mitcham Eastfields	d		18 18		18 48		19 18							
Streatham 4	d	18 06	18 23	18 36	18 53	19 06	19 23	19 40	20 10	20 39	21 09	21 48	22 18	22 48
Tulse Hill 3	d	18 12	18 27	18 42	18 57	19 12	19 27	19 44	20 14	20 43	21 13	21 52	22 22	22 52
North Dulwich	d	18 24	18 34	18 54	19 13		19 43	20 13	20 43	20 58	21 28	22 28	22 58	23 28
East Dulwich	d	18 26	18 36	18 56	19 15		19 45	20 15	20 45	21 00	21 30	22 30	23 00	23 30
Peckham Rye 4	d	18 29	18 39	18 59	19 17		19 47	20 17	20 47	21 03	21 32	22 32	23 02	23 32
Queens Rd Peckham	d	18 31	18 41	19 01	19 20		19 50	20 20	20 50	21 05	21 35	22 35	23 05	23 35
South Bermondsey	d	18 34	18 44	19 04	19 22		19 52	20 22	20 52	21 07	21 37	22 37	23 07	23 37
London Bridge 4 ⊖	a	18 38	18 48	19 08	19 27		19 58	20 27	20 57	21 12	21 42	22 42	23 12	23 42
Herne Hill 4	d	18 16	18 30	18 46	19 00	19 16	19 30	19 47	20 17	20 47	21 17	21 55	22 26	22 55
Loughborough Jn	d	18 19	18 34	18 49	19 04	19 19	19 34	19 51	20 21	20 51	21 21	21 59	22 30	
Elephant & Castle ⊖	d	18 24	18 39	18 54	19 09	19 24	19 39	19 56	20 26	20 56	21 26	22 04	22 34	23 04
London Blackfriars 3 ⊖	a	18 28	18 43	18 58	19 13	19 28	19 43	20 00	20 30	21 00	21 32	22 07	22 37	23 09
City Thameslink 3	a	18 30	18 45	19 00	19 15	19 30	19 45	20 02	20 32	21 02				
Farringdon 3 ⊖	a	18 34	18 49	19 04	19 19	19 34	19 49	20 06	20 36	21 06	21 38	22 13	22 43	23 13
St Pancras International 15 ⊖	a	18 38	18 53	19 08	19 23	19 38	19 53	20 10	20 40	21 10	21 42	22 17	22 47	23 17
Luton Airport Parkway 7 ✈	a	19 25	19 40	19 55	20 10	20 25	20 41	20 55	21 25	21 55	22 27	23 01	23 31	00 01
Luton 10	a	19 29	19 43	19 59	20 13	20 29	20 43	20 59	21 29	21 59	22 30	23 05	23 35	00 05

Sundays

		FC A	FC	FC	FC A	FC A	FC A	FC A	FC A	FC A	FC A	FC A	FC A
Sutton (Surrey) 4	d		10 10	10 40	11 10	11 40	12 10	12 40	13 10	13 40	14 10	14 40	15 10
West Sutton	d		10 13	10 43	11 13	11 43	12 13	12 43	13 13	13 43	14 13	14 43	15 13
Sutton Common	d		10 15	10 45	11 15	11 45	12 15	12 45	13 15	13 45	14 15	14 45	15 15
St Helier	d		10 17	10 47	11 17	11 47	12 17	12 47	13 17	13 47	14 17	14 47	15 17
Morden South	d		10 19	10 49	11 19	11 49	12 19	12 49	13 19	13 49	14 19	14 49	15 19
South Merton	d		10 21	10 51	11 21	11 51	12 21	12 51	13 21	13 51	14 21	14 51	15 21
Wimbledon Chase	d		10 22	10 52	11 22	11 52	12 22	12 52	13 22	13 52	14 22	14 52	15 22
Wimbledon 6 ⊖	a		10 25	10 55	11 25	11 55	12 25	12 55	13 25	13 55	14 25	14 55	15 25
	d	22p39	10 26	10 56	11 26	11 56	12 26	12 56	13 26	13 56	14 26	14 56	15 26
Haydons Road	d	22p41	10 28	10 58	11 28	11 58	12 28	12 58	13 28	13 58	14 28	14 58	15 28
Tooting	d	22p44	10 31	11 01	11 31	12 01	12 31	13 01	13 31	14 01	14 31	15 01	15 31
Carshalton	d												
Hackbridge	d												
Mitcham Junction	d												
Mitcham Eastfields	d												
Streatham 4	d	22p49	10 35	11 05	11 35	12 05	12 35	13 05	13 35	14 05	14 35	15 05	15 35
Tulse Hill 3	d	22p53	10 38	11 08	11 38	12 08	12 38	13 08	13 38	14 08	14 38	15 08	15 38
North Dulwich	d	23 28	11 04	11 34	12 04	12 34	13 04	13 34	14 34		15 04	15 34	16 04
East Dulwich	d	23 30	11 06	11 36	12 06	12 36	13 06	13 36	14 36		15 06	15 36	16 06
Peckham Rye 4	d	23 32	11 08	11 38	12 08	12 38	13 08	13 38	14 38		15 08	15 38	16 08
Queens Rd Peckham	d	23 35	11 11	11 41	12 11	12 41	13 11	13 43	14 41		15 11	15 41	16 11
South Bermondsey	d	23 37	11 13	11 43	12 13	12 43	13 13	13 48	14 43		15 13	15 43	16 13
London Bridge 4 ⊖	a	23 42	11 18	11 48	12 18	12 43	13 18	13 48	14 48		15 18	15 48	16 18
Herne Hill 4	d	22p56	10 42	11 12	11 42	12 14	12 44	13 12	13 42	14 12	14 42	15 12	15 42
Loughborough Jn	d		10 45	11 15	11 45	12 17	12 47	13 15	13 45	14 15	14 45	15 15	15 45
Elephant & Castle ⊖	d	23p05	10 50	11 20	11 50	12 22	12 52	13 20	13 50	14 20	14 50	15 20	15 50
London Blackfriars 3 ⊖	a	23p08	10 56	11 26	11 56	12 26	12 56	13 26	13 56	14 26	14 56	15 26	15 56
City Thameslink 3	a												
Farringdon 3 ⊖	a	23p13	11 02	11 32	12 02	12 32	13 02	13 32	14 02	14 32	15 02	15 32	16 02
St Pancras International 15 ⊖	a	23p17	11 06	11 36	12 06	12 36	13 06	13 36	14 06	14 36	15 06	15 36	16 06
Luton Airport Parkway 7 ✈	a	00 01	11 48	12 18	12 48	13 18	13 48	14 18	14 48	15 18	15 48	16 18	16 48
Luton 10	a	00 05	11 53	12 23	12 52	13 22	13 52	14 22	14 52	15 22	15 52	16 22	16 52

		FC	FC	FC	FC	FC	FC A	FC A	FC A	FC A	FC A	FC A	FC A
Sutton (Surrey) 4	d	15 40	16 10	16 40	17 10	17 40	18 10	18 40	19 10	19 40	20 10	20 40	21 10
West Sutton	d	15 43	16 13	16 43	17 13	17 43	18 13	18 43	19 13	19 43	20 13	20 43	21 13
Sutton Common	d	15 45	16 15	16 45	17 15	17 45	18 15	18 45	19 15	19 45	20 15	20 45	21 15
St Helier	d	15 47	16 17	16 47	17 17	17 47	18 17	18 47	19 17	19 47	20 17	20 47	21 17
Morden South	d	15 49	16 19	16 49	17 19	17 49	18 19	18 49	19 19	19 49	20 19	20 49	21 19
South Merton	d	15 51	16 21	16 51	17 21	17 51	18 21	18 51	19 21	19 51	20 21	20 51	21 21
Wimbledon Chase	d	15 52	16 22	16 52	17 22	17 52	18 22	18 52	19 22	19 52	20 22	20 52	21 22
Wimbledon 6 ⊖	a	15 55	16 25	16 55	17 25	17 55	18 25	18 55	19 25	19 55	20 25	20 55	21 25
	d	15 56	16 26	16 56	17 26	17 56	18 26	18 56	19 26	19 56	20 26	20 56	21 26
Haydons Road	d	15 58	16 28	16 58	17 28	17 58	18 28	18 58	19 28	19 58	20 28	20 58	21 28
Tooting	d	16 01	16 31	17 01	17 31	18 01	18 31	19 01	19 31	20 01	20 31	21 01	21 31
Carshalton	d												
Hackbridge	d												
Mitcham Junction	d												
Mitcham Eastfields	d												
Streatham 4	d	16 05	16 35	17 05	17 35	18 05	18 35	19 05	19 35	20 05	20 35	21 05	21 35
Tulse Hill 3	d	16 08	16 38	17 08	17 38	18 08	18 38	19 08	19 38	20 08	20 38	21 08	21 38
North Dulwich	d	16 34	17 04	17 34	18 04	18 34	19 04	20 04	20 04	20 34	21 04	21 34	22 04
East Dulwich	d	16 36	17 06	17 36	18 06	18 36	19 06	20 06	20 06	20 36	21 06	21 36	22 06
Peckham Rye 4	d	16 38	17 08	17 38	18 08	18 38	19 08	20 08	20 08	20 38	21 08	21 38	22 08
Queens Rd Peckham	d	16 41	17 11	17 43	18 11	18 41	19 11	21 11	20 11	20 41	21 11	21 41	22 11
South Bermondsey	d	16 43	17 13	17 48	18 13	18 43	19 13	21 13	20 13	20 43	21 13	21 43	22 13
London Bridge 4 ⊖	a	16 48	17 18	17 48	18 18	18 48	19 18	21 18	20 18	20 48	21 18	21 48	22 18
Herne Hill 4	d	16 14	16 42	17 14	17 42	18 12	18 42	19 12	19 42	20 12	20 42	21 12	21 42
Loughborough Jn	d	16 17	16 45	17 17	17 45	18 15	18 44	19 14	19 44	20 14	20 44	21 14	21 44
Elephant & Castle ⊖	d	16 22	16 50	17 22	17 50	18 20	18 50	19 20	19 50	20 20	20 50	21 20	21 50
London Blackfriars 3 ⊖	a	16 26	16 56	17 26	17 56	18 26	18 56	19 26	19 56	20 26	20 56	21 26	21 56
City Thameslink 3	a												
Farringdon 3 ⊖	a	16 32	17 02	17 32	18 02	18 32	19 02	19 32	20 02	20 32	21 02	21 32	22 02
St Pancras International 15 ⊖	a	16 36	17 06	17 36	18 06	18 36	19 06	19 36	20 06	20 36	21 06	21 36	22 06
Luton Airport Parkway 7 ✈	a	17 18	17 48	18 18	18 48	19 18	19 47	20 17	20 47	21 17	21 47	22 17	22 47
Luton 10	a	17 23	17 53	18 23	18 53	19 23	19 52	20 22	20 52	21 22	21 50	22 22	22 50

For general notes see front of timetable
For details of catering facilities see Directory of Train Operators

A To Bedford (Table 52)

London and Croydon → Caterham and Tattenham Corner

Network Diagram - see first page of Table 177

Miles	Miles			SN MX	SN MO	SN MX	SN	SN	SN		SN	SN	SN	SN		SN	SN	SN	SN	SN	SN	SN	SN	SN	SN
0	—	**London Victoria** [15]	⊖ d	23p00				06 15			07 20			07 45				08 15			08 45				09 15
2¾	—	Clapham Junction [10]	d	23p08				06 22			07 27			07 51				08 22			08 52				09 22
—	0	**London Charing Cross** [4]	⊖ d		23p36	23p45	06 05																		
—	¾	**London Waterloo (East)** [4]	⊖ d		23p39	23p48	06 08																		
—	1¾	**London Bridge** [4]	⊖ d		23p44	23p53	06 13		06 54			07 25	07 40			08 05	08 09		08 41	08 36		08 37	09 05	09 19	
—	4¼	New Cross Gate [4]	⊖ d		23p49	23p58	06 19		06 59			07 30	07 45			08 10				08 41			09 10		
—	10½	Norwood Junction [2]	d		00 10	00 16	06 38		07 14			07b51	08 00			08 25	08 28			08 56		09 13	09 25	09 31	
10½	11¾	**East Croydon**	d	23p29	00 14	00 20	06 42	06c49	07 18		07 48	07 55	08 04	08 14		08 29	08 33	08 45	08 57	09 00	09 13	09 18	09 29	09 35	09 43
11¼	12¾	South Croydon [4]	d	23p32	00 16	00 23	06 45		07 21		07 51		08 07	08 16		08 32		08 47		09 03	09 16		09 32		09 46
12¼	13¾	Purley Oaks	d	23p35	00 19	00 26	06 48		07 24		07 54		08 10	08 19		08 35		08 50		09 06	09 19		09 35		09 49
13½	14¾	Purley [4]	a	23p38	00 22	00 29	06 51	06 56	07 27		07 57	08 01	08 13	08 22		08 38	08 41	08 53	09 04	09 09	09 22	09 25	09 38	09 41	09 52
—	—		d	23p54	00 22	00 31	06 53	07 00	07 29	07 32	07 57	08 01	08 13	08 22		08 38	08 41	08 53	09 04	09 09	09 22	09 25	09 38	09 41	09 52
—	16	Kenley	d		00 25	00 34	06 56		07 32			08 04		08 25		08 41		08 56		09 12	09 25		09 41		09 55
—	17¼	Whyteleafe	d		00 29	00 38	07 00		07 36			08 08		08 29		08 44		09 00		09 15	09 28		09 44		09 58
—	17¾	Whyteleafe South	d		00 31	00 40	07 02		07 38			08 10		08 31		08 46		09 02		09 17	09 30		09 46		10 00
—	19½	**Caterham**	a		00 35	00 44	07 06		07 42			08 14		08 35		08 51		09 06		09 22	09 35		09 51		10 05
14¼	—	Reedham	d	23p56				07 02		07 34	07 59		08 15				08 43		09 07			09 28		09 44	
15	—	Smitham	d	23p59				07 05		07 37	08 02		08 18				08 46		09 09			09a30		09 46	
15¾	—	Woodmansterne	d	00 02				07 08		07 40	08 05		08 21				08 49		09 12					09 49	
16¾	—	Chipstead	d	00 05				07 11		07 43	08 08		08 24				08 52		09 15					09 52	
19¼	—	Kingswood	d	00 10				07 16		07 48	08 13		08 29				08 57		09 21					09 57	
20½	—	Tadworth	d	00 14				07 20		07 52	08 17		08 33				09 01		09 24					10 01	
21¾	—	**Tattenham Corner**	a	00 17				07 23		07 55	08 20		08 36				09 04		09 28					10 04	

		SN	SN	SN		SN	SN	SN	SN		SN	SN	SN	SN	SN	SN	SN	SN			SN	SN	SN	SN
London Victoria [15]	⊖ d					09 45					10 15				10 45						15 15			
Clapham Junction [10]	d					09 52					10 22				10 52						15 22			
London Charing Cross [4]	⊖ d													10 40				11 10						15 40
London Waterloo (East) [4]	⊖ d													10 43				11 13						15 43
London Bridge [4]	⊖ d	09 07	09 35	09 47			09 37	10 05	10 17			10 08	10 35	10 48		10 38	11 05	11 18				15 08	15 35	15 48
New Cross Gate [4]	⊖ d		09 40					10 10					10 40				11 10						15 40	
Norwood Junction [2]	d	09 43	09 55	09 59			10 13	10 25	10 31			10 43	10 55			11 13	11 25		and at			15 43	15 55	
East Croydon	d	09 48	09 59	10 05		10 13	10 18	10 29	10 35		10 43	10 48	10 59	11 05	11 13	11 18	11 29	11 35	the same		15 43	15 48	15 59	16 05
South Croydon [4]	d		10 02			10 16		10 32			10 46		11 02		11 16		11 32				15 46		16 02	
Purley Oaks	d		10 05			10 19		10 35			10 49		11 05		11 19		11 35		minutes		15 49		16 05	
Purley [4]	a	09 54	10 08	10 11		10 22	10 24	10 38	10 41		10 52	10 54	11 08	11 11	11 22	11 24	11 38	11 41			15 52	15 54	16 08	16 11
	d	09 55	10 08	10 11		10 22	10 25	10 38	10 41		10 52	10 55	11 08	11 11	11 22	11 25	11 38	11 41	past		15 52	15 55	16 08	16 11
Kenley	d		10 11			10 25		10 41			10 55		11 11		11 25		11 41		each		15 55		16 11	
Whyteleafe	d		10 14			10 28		10 44			10 58		11 14		11 28		11 44				15 58		16 14	
Whyteleafe South	d		10 16			10 30		10 46			11 00		11 16		11 30		11 46		hour until		16 00		16 16	
Caterham	a		10 21			10 35		10 51			11 05		11 21		11 35		11 51				16 05		16 21	
Reedham	d	09 57		10 14			10 27		10 44			10 57		11 14		11 27		11 44				15 57		16 14
Smitham	d	10a00		10 16			10a30		10 46			11a00		11 16		11a30		11 46				16a00		16 16
Woodmansterne	d			10 19					10 49					11 19				11 49						16 19
Chipstead	d			10 22					10 52					11 22				11 52						16 22
Kingswood	d			10 27					10 57					11 27				11 57						16 27
Tadworth	d			10 31					11 01					11 31				12 01						16 31
Tattenham Corner	a			10 34					11 04					11 34				12 04						16 34

		SN	SN	SN	SN	SN	SN	SN	SN	SN		SN	SN		SN	SN		SN	SN	SN	SN	SN			SN
London Victoria [15]	⊖ d	15 45				16 15			16 45						17 34				18 04		18 17				18 53
Clapham Junction [10]	d	15 52				16 22			16 52						17 40				18 10		18 25				18 59
London Charing Cross [4]	⊖ d				16 08																				
London Waterloo (East) [4]	⊖ d				16 11																				
London Bridge [4]	⊖ d		15 38	16 05	16 16		16 07	16 35		16 59			17 19			17 39		18 01		18 20		18 42			
New Cross Gate [4]	⊖ d			16 10				16 40					17 24			17 44		18 06		18 26		18 47			
Norwood Junction [2]	d		16 13	16 25	16 30		16 43	16 55		17 12		←	17 33			17 54		18 15		18 35		18 56			
East Croydon	d	16 13	16 18	16 29	16 35	16 43	16 48	16 59	17e19	17 17		17 19	17 37		17 52	17 58		18 19	18 22	18 39	18f50	19 00			19 12
South Croydon [4]	d	16 16		16 32		16 46		17 02	→	17 19		17 22	17 40		17 54	18 00		18 22	18 24	18 41	18 52	19 03			19 14
Purley Oaks	d	16 19		16 35		16 49		17 05		17 22		17 25	17 43		17 57	18 03		18 25	18 27	18 44	18 55	19 06			19 17
Purley [4]	a	16 22	16 24	16 38	16 41	16 52	16 54	17 08		17 25		17 28	17 46		18 00	18 06		18 28	18 30	18 47	18 58	19 09			19 20
	d	16 22	16 25	16 38	16 41	16 52	17 05	17 08		17 25		17 28	17 49	17 52	18 03	18 09	18 11	18 30	18 33	18 50	19 01	19 11	19 14		19 21
Kenley	d	16 25		16 41		16 55		17 11		17 28			17 52			18 12		18 33		18 53		19 14			
Whyteleafe	d	16 28		16 44		16 58		17 14		17 32			17 55			18 15		18 37		18 56		19 18			
Whyteleafe South	d	16 30		16 46		17 00		17 16		17 34			17 57			18 17		18 39		18 58		19 20			
Caterham	a	16 35		16 53		17 07		17 23		17 40			18 04			18 24		18 45		19 05		19 26			
Reedham	d		16 27		16 44		17 07					17 30		17 54	18 05		18 13		18 35		19 03		19 16		19 23
Smitham	d		16a30		16 46		17 10					17 33		17 57	18 08		18 16		18 38		19 06		19 19		19a28
Woodmansterne	d				16 49		17 13					17 36		18 00	18 11		18 19		18 41		19 09		19 22		
Chipstead	d				16 52		17 16					17 39		18 03	18 14		18 22		18 44		19 12		19 25		
Kingswood	d				16 57		17 21					17 44		18 08	18 19		18 27		18 49		19 17		19 30		
Tadworth	d				17 01		17 25					17 48		18 12	18 23		18 31		18 53		19 21		19 34		
Tattenham Corner	a				17 06		17 30					17 53		18 19	18 28		18 36		18 58		19 26		19 39		

For general notes see front of timetable
For details of catering facilities see Directory of Train Operators

b Arr. 0748
c Arr. 0645
e Arr. 1713
f Arr. 1846

London and Croydon → Caterham and Tattenham Corner

Network Diagram - see first page of Table 177

Mondays to Fridays

		SN		SN	SN	SN	SN	SN	SN	SN	SN	SN		SN	SN	SN	SN	SN	SN	SN	SN	SN	SN		
London Victoria 15	⊖ d	19 00			19 31		20 01		20 30		21 00			21 30		22 00		22 30		23 00					
Clapham Junction 10	d	19 08			19 38		20 08		20 38		21 08			21 38		22 08		22 38		23 08					
London Charing Cross 4	⊖ d					19 37		20 07		20 37		21 07			21 37		22 07		22 37		23 07		23 45		
London Waterloo (East) 4	⊖ d					19 40		20 10		20 40		21 10			21 40		22 10		22 40		23 10		23 48		
London Bridge 4	⊖ d			19 15		19 45		20 15		20 45		21 15			21 45		22 15		22 45		23 15		23 53		
New Cross Gate 4	⊖ d			19 20		19 50		20 20		20 50		21 20			21 50		22 20		22 50		23 20		23 58		
Norwood Junction 2	d			19 39		20 09		20 38		21 08		21 38			22 08		22 38		23 08		23 38		00 16		
East Croydon	⇌ d	19 32		19 43	19 59	20 13	20 30	20 43	20 59	21 13	21 29	21 43		21 59	22 13	22 29	22 43	22 59	23 13	23 29	23 42		00 20		
South Croydon 4	d	19 34		19 45	20 02	20 15	20 32	20 45	21 02	21 15	21 32	21 45		22 02	22 15	22 32	22 45	23 02	23 15	23 32	23 45		00 23		
Purley Oaks	d	19 37		19 48	20 05	20 18	20 35	20 48	21 05	21 18	21 35	21 48		22 05	22 18	22 35	22 48	23 05	23 18	23 35	23 48		00 26		
Purley 4	a	19 41		19 51	20 08	20 21	20 38	20 51	21 08	21 21	21 38	21 51		22 08	22 21	22 38	22 51	23 08	23 21	23 38	23 51	←	00 29		
	d	19 44	19 46	19 54	20 10	20 24	20 39	20 54	21 08	21 24	21 38	21 54		22 08	22 24	22 38	22 54	23 10	23 24	23 54	23 51	23 54	00 31		
Kenley	d	19 47		19 57		20 27		20 57		21 27		21 57			22 27		22 57		23 27	→	23 54		00 34		
Whyteleafe	d	19 50		20 00		20 30		21 00		21 30		22 00			22 30		23 00		23 30		23 57		00 38		
Whyteleafe South	d	19 52		20 02		20 32		21 02		21 32		22 02			22 32		23 02		23 32		23 59		00 40		
Caterham	a	19 57		20 07		20 37		21 07		21 37		22 07			22 37		23 07		23 37		00 04		00 44		
Reedham	d		19 48		20 13		20 41		21 10		21 40			22 10		22 40		23 13				23 56			
Smitham	d		19 51		20 15		20 44		21 13		21 43			22 13		22 43		23 15				23 59			
Woodmansterne	d		19 54		20 18		20 47		21 16		21 46			22 16		22 46		23 18				00 02			
Chipstead	d		19 57		20 21		20 50		21 19		21 49			22 19		22 49		23 21				00 05			
Kingswood	d		20 02		20 27		20 55		21 24		21 54			22 24		22 54		23 27				00 10			
Tadworth	d		20 06		20 30		20 59		21 28		21 58			22 28		22 58		23 30				00 14			
Tattenham Corner	a		20 09		20 34		21 02		21 31		22 01			22 31		23 01		23 34				00 17			

Saturdays

		SN	SN		SN	SN		SN	SN		SN		SN	SN	SN	SN	SN	SN	SN	SN			SN	SN
London Victoria 15	⊖ d	23p00				06 45					07 15				07 45				08 15		and at			
Clapham Junction 10	d	23p08				06 52					07 22				07 52				08 22		the same			
London Charing Cross 4	⊖ d		23p45											07 40				08 10			minutes			17 40
London Waterloo (East) 4	⊖ d		23p48											07 43				08 13			past			17 43
London Bridge 4	⊖ d		23p53		06 47			07 05	07 18				07 35	07 48		07 38	08 05	08 18		08 08	each		17 35	17 48
New Cross Gate 4	⊖ d		23p58					07 10					07 40				08 10				hour until		17 40	
Norwood Junction 2	d		00 16		07 00			07 25	07 31				07 55			08 13	08 25			08 43			17 55	
East Croydon	⇌ d	23p29	00 20		07 05	07 13		07 29	07 35		07 43		07 59	08 05	08 13	08 18	08 29	08 35	08 43	08 48			17 59	18 05
South Croydon 4	d	23p32	00 23			07 16		07 32			07 46		08 02		08 16		08 32		08 46				18 02	
Purley Oaks	d	23p35	00 26			07 19		07 35			07 49		08 05		08 19		08 35		08 49				18 05	
Purley 4	a	23p38	00 29		07 11	07 22		07 38	07 41		07 52		08 08	08 11	08 22	08 24	08 38	08 41	08 52	08 54			18 08	18 11
	d	23p54	00 31		07 11	07 22		07 38	07 41		07 52		08 08	08 11	08 22	08 25	08 38	08 41	08 52	08 55			18 08	18 11
Kenley	d		00 34			07 25		07 41			07 55		08 11		08 25		08 41		08 55				18 11	
Whyteleafe	d		00 38			07 28		07 44			07 58		08 14		08 28		08 44		08 58				18 14	
Whyteleafe South	d		00 40			07 30		07 46			08 00		08 16		08 30		08 46		09 00				18 16	
Caterham	a		00 44			07 35		07 51			08 05		08 21		08 35		08 51		09 05				18 21	
Reedham	d	23p56			07 14				07 43					08 14		08 27		08 44		08 57				18 14
Smitham	d	23p59			07 16				07 46					08 16		08a30		08 46		09a00				18 16
Woodmansterne	d	00 02			07 19				07 49					08 19				08 49						18 19
Chipstead	d	00 05			07 22				07 52					08 22				08 52						18 22
Kingswood	d	00 10			07 27				07 57					08 27				08 57						18 27
Tadworth	d	00 14			07 31				08 01					08 31				09 01						18 31
Tattenham Corner	a	00 17			07 34				08 04					08 34				09 04						18 34

		SN	SN		SN	SN		SN	SN		SN	SN		SN	SN		SN	SN		SN	SN		SN	SN	SN
London Victoria 15	⊖ d	17 45												19 00			19 30			20 00			20 30		21 00
Clapham Junction 10	d	17 52												19 08			19 38			20 08			20 38		21 08
London Charing Cross 4	⊖ d					18 10					18 40				19 07			19 37			20 07			20 37	
London Waterloo (East) 4	⊖ d					18 13					18 43				19 10			19 39			20 10			20 40	
London Bridge 4	⊖ d		17 38		18 05	18 18		18 08	18 35		18 48	18 45			19 15			19 44			20 15			20 45	
New Cross Gate 4	⊖ d				18 10				18 40			18 50			19 20			19 50			20 20			20 50	
Norwood Junction 2	d		18 13		18 25			18 43	18 55		19 03	19 09			19 38			20 08			20 38			21 08	
East Croydon	⇌ d	18 13	18 18		18 29	18 35		18 48	18 59		19 07	19 13		19 29	19 43		19 59	20 13		20 29	20 43		20 59	21 13	21 29
South Croydon 4	d	18 16			18 32				19 02		19 09	19 16		19 32	19 45		20 02	20 15		20 32	20 45		21 02	21 15	21 32
Purley Oaks	d	18 19			18 35				19 05		19 12	19 19		19 35	19 48		20 05	20 18		20 35	20 48		21 05	21 18	21 35
Purley 4	a	18 22	18 24		18 38	18 41		18 54	19 08		19 15	19 22		19 38	19 51		20 08	20 21		20 38	20 51		21 08	21 21	21 38
	d	18 22	18 25		18 38	18 41		18 55	19 10		19 15	19 22		19 38	19 51		20 08	20 21		20 38	20 51		21 08	21 21	21 38
Kenley	d	18 25			18 41				19 13			19 25			19 54			20 24			20 54			21 24	
Whyteleafe	d	18 28			18 44				19 17			19 28			19 58			20 28			20 58			21 28	
Whyteleafe South	d	18 30			18 46				19 19			19 30			20 00			20 30			21 00			21 30	
Caterham	a	18 35			18 51				19 23			19 35			20 04			20 34			21 04			21 34	
Reedham	d		18 27			18 44		18 57			19 18			19 40			20 10			20 40			21 10		21 40
Smitham	d		18a30			18 46		19a00			19 20			19 43			20 13			20 43			21 13		21 43
Woodmansterne	d					18 49					19 23			19 46			20 16			20 46			21 16		21 46
Chipstead	d					18 52					19 26			19 49			20 19			20 49			21 19		21 49
Kingswood	d					18 57					19 32			19 54			20 24			20 54			21 24		21 54
Tadworth	d					19 01					19 35			19 58			20 28			20 58			21 28		21 58
Tattenham Corner	a					19 04					19 39			20 01			20 31			21 01			21 31		22 01

For general notes see front of timetable
For details of catering facilities see Directory of Train Operators

Table 181

Saturdays

London and Croydon → Caterham and Tattenham Corner

Network Diagram - see first page of Table 177

		SN	SN	SN	SN	SN	SN	SN	SN	SN	SN	SN
London Victoria 15	⊖ d		21 30		22 00		22 30		23 00			
Clapham Junction 10	d		21 38		22 08		22 38		23 08			
London Charing Cross 4	⊖ d	21 07		21 37		22 07		22 37		23 07		23 45
London Waterloo (East) 4	⊖ d	21 10		21 40		22 10		22 40		23 10		23 48
London Bridge 4	⊖ d	21 15		21 45		22 15		22 45		23 15		23 53
New Cross Gate 4	⊖ d	21 20		21 50		22 20		22 50		23 20		23 58
Norwood Junction 2	d	21 38		22 08		22 38		23 08		23 38		00 16
East Croydon	d	21 43	21 59	22 13	22 29	22 43	22 59	23 13	23 29	23 42		00 20
South Croydon 4	d	21 45	22 02	22 15	22 32	22 45	23 02	23 15	23 32	23 45		00 23
Purley Oaks	d	21 48	22 05	22 18	22 35	22 48	23 05	23 18	23 35	23 48		00 26
Purley 4	a	21 51	22 08	22 21	22 38	22 51	23 08	23 21	23 38	23 51	←	00 29
	d	21 54	22 08	22 24	22 38	22 51	23 08	23 21	23 54	23 51	23 54	00 31
Kenley	d	21 57		22 27		22 54		23 24	→	23 54		00 34
Whyteleafe	d	22 00		22 30		22 58		23 28		23 57		00 38
Whyteleafe South	d	22 02		22 32		23 00		23 30		23 59		00 40
Caterham	a	22 07		22 37		23 04		23 34		00 04		00 44
Reedham	d		22 10		22 40		23 10				23 56	
Smitham	d		22 13		22 43		23 13				23 59	
Woodmansterne	d		22 16		22 46		23 16				00 02	
Chipstead	d		22 19		22 49		23 19				00 05	
Kingswood	d		22 24		22 54		23 24				00 10	
Tadworth	d		22 28		22 58		23 28				00 14	
Tattenham Corner	a		22 31		23 01		23 31				00 17	

Sundays

		SN	SN	SN	SN		SN	SN	SN	SN	SN
London Victoria 15	⊖ d	23p00									
Clapham Junction 10	d	23p08									
London Charing Cross 4	⊖ d		23p45	07 34	08 04		21 34	22 04	22 34	23 04	23 34
London Waterloo (East) 4	⊖ d		23p48	07 37	08 07		21 37	22 07	22 37	23 07	23 37
London Bridge 4	⊖ d		23p53	07 44	08 14		21 44	22 14	22 44	23 14	23 44
New Cross Gate 4	⊖ d		23p58	07 49	08 19		21 49	22 19	22 49	23 19	23 49
Norwood Junction 2	d		00 16	08 04	08 34	and at	22 04	22 39	23 09	23 39	00 10
East Croydon	d	23p29	00 20	08 09	08 39	the same	22 09	22 43	23 13	23 43	00 14
South Croydon 4	d	23p32	00 23	08 11	08 41	minutes	22 11	22 45	23 15	23 45	00 16
Purley Oaks	d	23p35	00 26	08 14	08 44	past	22 14	22 48	23 18	23 48	00 19
Purley 4	a	23p38	00 29	08 17	08 47	each	22 17	22 51	23 21	23 51	00 22
	d	23p54	00 31	08 17	08 47	hour until	22 17	22 51	23 32	23 51	00 22
Kenley	d		00 34		08 50			22 54		23 54	00 25
Whyteleafe	d		00 38		08 54			22 58		23 58	00 29
Whyteleafe South	d		00 40		08 56			23 00		23 59	00 31
Caterham	a		00 44		09 00			23 04		00 04	00 35
Reedham	d	23p56		08 20			22 20		23 34		
Smitham	d	23p59		08 22			22 22		23 37		
Woodmansterne	d	00 02		08 25			22 25		23 40		
Chipstead	d	00 05		08 28			22 28		23 43		
Kingswood	d	00 10		08 34			22 34		23 48		
Tadworth	d	00 14		08 37			22 37		23 52		
Tattenham Corner	a	00 17		08 41			22 41		23 55		

For general notes see front of timetable
For details of catering facilities see Directory of Train Operators

Tattenham Corner and Caterham → Croydon and London

Network Diagram - see first page of Table 177

Miles	Miles	Station		SN	SN	SN	SN	SN		SN	SN	SN	SN		SN	SN	SN	SN		SN	SN	SN	SN		
0	—	**Tattenham Corner**	d		05 56		06 34				06 58		07 17			07 34		07 42			07 58		08 08		
1¼	—	Tadworth	d		05 59		06 37				07 01		07 20			07 37		07 45			08 01		08 11		
2½	—	Kingswood	d		06 02		06 40				07 04		07 23			07 40		07 48			08 04		08 14		
5	—	Chipstead	d		06 08		06 46				07 10		07 29			07 46		07 54			08 10		08 20		
6	—	Woodmansterne	d		06 11		06 49				07 13		07 32			07 49		07 57			08 13		08 23		
6¾	—	Smitham	d		06 14		06 52				07 16		07 35			07 52		08 00			08 16		08 26		
7½	—	Reedham	d		06 16		06 54				07 18		07 37			07 54		08 02			08 18		08 28		
—	0	**Caterham**	d	05 52		06 20		06 47		07 00		07 14			07 36		07 47			08 08		08 19			
—	1¾	Whyteleafe South	d	05 55		06 23		06 50		07 03		07 17			07 39		07 50			08 11		08 22			
—	2¼	Whyteleafe	d	05 57		06 25		06 52		07 05		07 19			07 41		07 52			08 13		08 24			
—	3½	Kenley	d	06 00		06 28		06 55		07 08		07 22			07 44		07 55			08 16		08 27			
8¼	4¾	Purley 4	a	06 03	06 19	06 31	06 57	06 59		07 11	07 21	07 26	07 40		07 47	07 57	07 59	08 06		08 19	08 21	08 30	08 32		
—	—		d	06 03	06 22	06 31	07 03			07 12	07 23	07 27	07 43		07 48	08 03		08 08		08 25		08 36			
9¼	5¾	Purley Oaks	d	06 06		06 34	07 06			07 15		07 30	07 46		07 51	08 06		08 11		08 28		08 39			
10¼	6¾	South Croydon 4	d	06 09		06 37	07 09			07 18		07 33	07 49		07 54	08 09		08 14		08 31		08 42			
11¼	7¾	**East Croydon**	d	06 12	06 28	06 40	07 12			07 21	07 29	07 36	07 52		07 57	08 12		08 17		08 34		08 45			
—	9	Norwood Junction 2	d	06 16	06 32	06 44	07 16					07 41			08 01	08 17				08 40		08 49			
—	15	New Cross Gate 4	⊖ a	06 28	06 47	06 53	07 24					07 52										08 57			
—	17¾	**London Bridge 4**	⊖ a	06 34	06 54	07 02	07 33					08 01			08 16	08 31				08 55		09 05			
—	18¾	**London Waterloo (East) 4**	⊖ a																						
—	19½	**London Charing Cross 4**	⊖ a																						
19	—	Clapham Junction 10	a							07 31	07 39		08 02					08 27							
21¾	—	**London Victoria 15**	⊖ a							07 40	07 48		08 12					08 35							

Station		SN	SN	SN	SN		SN	SN	SN	SN			SN	SN	SN	SN	SN	SN	SN	SN			SN	SN
Tattenham Corner	d	08 26			08 51			09 09						09 39				10 09						15 39
Tadworth	d	08 29			08 54			09 12						09 42				10 12						15 42
Kingswood	d	08 32			08 57			09 15						09 45				10 15						15 45
Chipstead	d	08 38			09 03			09 20						09 50				10 20						15 50
Woodmansterne	d	08 41			09 06			09 23						09 53				10 23						15 53
Smitham	d	08 44			09 09			09 26		09 40				09 56		10 10		10 26		10 40				15 56
Reedham	d	08 46			09 11			09 28		09 42				09 58		10 12		10 28		10 42				15 58
Caterham	d		08 40	08 56			09 11		09 27				09 40		09 56		10 10		10 26		and at		15 40	
Whyteleafe South	d		08 43	08 59			09 14		09 30				09 43		09 59		10 13		10 29		the same		15 43	
Whyteleafe	d		08 45	09 01			09 16		09 32				09 45		10 01		10 15		10 31		minutes		15 45	
Kenley	d		08 48	09 04			09 19		09 35				09 48		10 04		10 18		10 34		past		15 48	
Purley 4	a	08 49	08 51	09 07	09 14		09 22	09 31	09 38	09 45			09 51	10 01	10 07	10 15	10 21	10 31	10 37	10 45	each		15 51	16 01
	d	08 55		09 08	09 14		09 22	09 31	09 38	09 45			09 51	10 01	10 08	10 15	10 21	10 31	10 38	10 45	hour until		15 51	16 01
Purley Oaks	d	08 58		09 11			09 25		09 41				09 54		10 11		10 24		10 41				15 54	
South Croydon 4	d	09 01		09 14			09 28		09 44				09 57		10 14		10 27		10 44				15 57	
East Croydon	d	09 05		09 17	09 20		09 31	09 37	09 47	09 51			10 00	10 07	10 17	10 21	10 30	10 37	10 47	10 51			16 00	16 07
Norwood Junction 2	d	09 09			09 25		09 35			09 58			10 04			10 28	10 34			10 58			16 04	16 11
New Cross Gate 4	⊖ a				09 32		09 50						10 19				10 49						16 19	
London Bridge 4	⊖ a	09 24			09 42		09 59	09 54		10 28			10 25	10 22		10 58	10 55	10 52		11 28			16 26	16 24
London Waterloo (East) 4	⊖ a													10 26				10 56						
London Charing Cross 4	⊖ a													10 30				11 00						
Clapham Junction 10	a			09 38					10 07						10 37				11 07					
London Victoria 15	⊖ a			09 48					10 14						10 44				11 14					

Station		SN	SN	SN	SN		SN	SN	SN	SN		SN	SN	SN	SN		SN	SN	SN	SN		SN	SN	SN	SN
Tattenham Corner	d				16 09					16 39				17 09				17 42		18 14			18 42		19 12
Tadworth	d				16 12					16 42				17 12				17 45		18 17			18 45		19 15
Kingswood	d				16 15					16 45				17 15				17 48		18 20			18 48		19 18
Chipstead	d				16 20					16 50				17 20				17 54		18 26			18 54		19 24
Woodmansterne	d				16 23					16 53				17 23				17 57		18 29			18 57		19 27
Smitham	d		16 10		16 26			16 40		16 56				17 26				18 00		18 32			19 00		19 30
Reedham	d		16 12		16 28			16 42		16 58				17 28				18 02		18 34			19 02		19 32
Caterham	d	15 56		16 10			16 26		16 40			16 57	17 10		17 27		17 45		18 13			18 49		19 15	
Whyteleafe South	d	15 59		16 13			16 29		16 43			17 00	17 13		17 30		17 48		18 16			18 52		19 18	
Whyteleafe	d	16 01		16 15			16 31		16 45			17 02	17 15		17 32		17 50		18 18			18 54		19 20	
Kenley	d	16 04		16 18			16 34		16 48			17 05	17 18		17 35		17 53		18 21			18 57		19 23	
Purley 4	a	16 07	16 15	16 21	16 31		16 37	16 45	16 51	17 01		17 08	17 21	17 31	17 38		17 56	18 05	18 24	18 38		19 00	19 05	19 26	19 35
	d	16 08	16 15	16 21	16 31		16 38	16 45	16 51	17 01		17 09	17 23	17 31	17 39		17 56	18 08	18 26	18 38		19 01	19 08	19 29	19 38
Purley Oaks	d	16 11		16 24			16 41		16 54			17 12	17 26		17 42		17 59	18 11	18 29	18 41		19 04	19 11	19 32	19 41
South Croydon 4	d	16 14		16 27			16 44		16 57			17 15	17 29		17 45		18 02	18 14	18 32	18 44		19 07	19 14	19 35	19 44
East Croydon	d	16 17	16 21	16 31	16 37		16 47	16 51	17 00	17 07		17 18	17 32	17 37	17 48		18 05	18 17	18 35	18 47		19 10	19 17	19 40	19 47
Norwood Junction 2	d		16 28	16 35	16 41			16 56	17 04	17 11			17 36	17 41			18 09		18 39			19 14		19 44	
New Cross Gate 4	⊖ a			16 50					17 19				17 50				18 21		18 54			19 32		20 02	
London Bridge 4	⊖ a		17 00	16 58	16 56			17 26	17 27	17 26			17 58	17 54			18 28		19 00			19 39		20 11	
London Waterloo (East) 4	⊖ a																					19 45		20 16	
London Charing Cross 4	⊖ a																					19 49		20 20	
Clapham Junction 10	a	16 37					17 07					17 38			18 08			18 38		19 07			19 37		20 07
London Victoria 15	⊖ a	16 44					17 14					17 48			18 15			18 45		19 14			19 45		20 14

For general notes see front of timetable
For details of catering facilities see Directory of Train Operators

Tattenham Corner and Caterham → Croydon and London

Network Diagram - see first page of Table 177

		SN	SN	SN	SN	SN	SN	SN	SN	SN	SN	SN	SN	SN	SN	SN	SN
Tattenham Corner	d		19 42	19 57		20 14		20 42		21 14		21 44		22 14		22 44	
Tadworth	d		19 45	20 00		20 17		20 45		21 17		21 47		22 17		22 47	
Kingswood	d		19 48	20 03		20 20		20 48		21 20		21 50		22 20		22 50	
Chipstead	d		19 54	20 09		20 26		20 54		21 26		21 56		22 26		22 56	
Woodmansterne	d		19 57	20 12		20 29		20 57		21 29		21 59		22 29		22 59	
Smitham	d		20 00	20 15		20 32		21 00		21 32		22 02		22 32		23 02	
Reedham	d		20 02	20 17		20 34		21 02		21 34		22 04		22 34		23 04	
Caterham	d	19 45			20 15		20 45		21 15		21 45		22 15		22 45		23 17
Whyteleafe South	d	19 48			20 18		20 48		21 18		21 48		22 18		22 48		23 20
Whyteleafe	d	19 50			20 20		20 50		21 20		21 50		22 20		22 50		23 22
Kenley	d	19 53			20 23		20 53		21 23		21 53		22 23		22 53		23 25
Purley 4	a	19 56	20 05	20 20	20 26	20 37	20 56	21 05	21 26	21 37	21 56	22 07	22 26	22 37	22 56	23 07	23 28
	d	19 59	20 08	20 23	20 29	20 38	20 59	21 08	21 29	21 38	21 59	22 08	22 29	22 38	22 59	23 08	23 34
Purley Oaks	d	20 02	20 11		20 32	20 41	21 02	21 11	21 32	21 41	22 02	22 11	22 32	22 41	23 02	23 11	23 37
South Croydon 4	d	20 05	20 14		20 35	20 44	21 05	21 14	21 35	21 44	22 05	22 14	22 35	22 44	23 05	23 14	23 40
East Croydon	d	20 10	20 17	20 30	20 40	20 47	21 10	21 17	21 40	21 47	22 10	22 17	22 40	22 47	23 10	23 17	23 43
Norwood Junction 2	d	20 14		20 34	20 44		21 14		21 44		22 14		22 44		23 14		23a47
New Cross Gate 4	⊖ a	20 32		20 51	21 02		21 32		22 02		22 32		23 02		23 32		
London Bridge 4	⊖ a	20 41		20 59	21 11		21 41		22 11		22 41		23 11		23 38		
London Waterloo (East) 4	⊖ a	20 46			21 16		21 46		22 16		22 46		23 16		23 43		
London Charing Cross 4	⊖ a	20 50			21 20		21 50		22 20		22 50		23 20		23 48		
Clapham Junction 10	a		20 37			21 07		21 37		22 07		22 37		23 07		23 37	
London Victoria 15	⊖ a		20 45			21 14		21 45		22 14		22 48		23 14		23 45	

Saturdays

		SN	SN	SN	SN	SN	SN	SN	SN	SN	SN	SN	SN	SN	SN	SN		SN	SN	SN	SN	SN	SN
Tattenham Corner	d		06 14		06 44		07 09			07 39				08 09					17 39				18 09
Tadworth	d		06 17		06 47		07 12			07 42				08 12					17 42				18 12
Kingswood	d		06 20		06 50		07 15			07 45				08 15					17 45				18 15
Chipstead	d		06 26		06 56		07 20			07 50				08 20					17 50				18 20
Woodmansterne	d		06 29		06 59		07 23			07 53				08 23					17 53				18 23
Smitham	d		06 32		07 02		07 26			07 56		08 10		08 26		08 40			17 56		18 10		18 26
Reedham	d		06 34		07 04		07 28			07 58		08 12		08 28		08 42	and at		17 58		18 12		18 28
Caterham	d	06 07		06 40		07 10		07 26	07 40		07 56		08 10		08 26			17 40		17 56		18 10	
Whyteleafe South	d	06 10		06 43		07 13		07 29	07 43		07 59		08 13		08 29		the same	17 43		17 59		18 13	
Whyteleafe	d	06 12		06 45		07 15		07 31	07 45		08 01		08 15		08 31			17 45		18 01		18 15	
Kenley	d	06 15		06 48		07 18		07 34	07 48		08 04		08 18		08 34		minutes	17 48		18 04		18 18	
Purley 4	a	06 18	06 37	06 51	07 07	07 21	07 31	07 37	07 51	08 01	08 07	08 15	08 21	08 31	08 37	08 45	past	17 51	18 01	18 07	18 15	18 21	18 31
	d	06 21	06 38	06 51	07 08	07 21	07 31	07 38	07 51	08 01	08 08	08 15	08 21	08 31	08 38	08 45		17 51	18 01	18 08	18 15	18 21	18 31
Purley Oaks	d	06 24	06 41	06 54	07 11	07 24		07 41	07 54		08 11		08 24		08 41		each	17 54		18 11		18 24	
South Croydon 4	d	06 27	06 44	06 57	07 14	07 27		07 44	07 57		08 14		08 27		08 44			17 57		18 14		18 27	
East Croydon	d	06 30	06 47	07 00	07 17	07 30	07 37	07 47	08 00	08 07	08 17	08 21	08 30	08 37	08 47	08 51	hour until	18 00	18 07	18 17	18 21	18 30	18 37
Norwood Junction 2	d	06 34		07 04		07 34			08 04			08 28	08 34			08 58		18 04			18 28	18 34	
New Cross Gate 4	⊖ a	06 49		07 19		07 49			08 19				08 49					18 19				18 49	
London Bridge 4	⊖ a	06 55		07 25		07 55	07 52		08 25	08 22		08 58	08 55	08 52		09 28		18 25	18 22		18 58	18 55	18 52
London Waterloo (East) 4	⊖ a						07 56			08 26				08 56					18 26				18 56
London Charing Cross 4	⊖ a						08 00			08 30				09 00					18 30				19 00
Clapham Junction 10	a		07 07		07 37			08 07			08 37				09 07					18 37			
London Victoria 15	⊖ a		07 14		07 44			08 14			08 44				09 14					18 44			

		SN	SN	SN	SN	SN	SN	SN	SN	SN	SN	SN	SN	SN	SN	SN	SN	SN	SN	SN	SN	SN	SN
Tattenham Corner	d				18 44			19 14		19 44		20 14		20 44		21 14		21 44		22 14		22 44	
Tadworth	d				18 47			19 17		19 47		20 17		20 47		21 17		21 47		22 17		22 47	
Kingswood	d				18 50			19 20		19 50		20 20		20 50		21 20		21 50		22 20		22 50	
Chipstead	d				18 56			19 26		19 56		20 26		20 56		21 26		21 56		22 26		22 56	
Woodmansterne	d				18 59			19 29		19 59		20 29		20 59		21 29		21 59		22 29		22 59	
Smitham	d		18 40		19 02	19 10		19 32		20 02		20 32		21 02		21 32		22 02		22 32		23 02	
Reedham	d		18 42		19 04	19 12		19 34		20 04		20 34		21 04		21 34		22 04		22 34		23 04	
Caterham	d	18 26		18 47			19 17		19 47		20 17		20 47		21 17		21 47		22 15		22 45		23 17
Whyteleafe South	d	18 29		18 50			19 20		19 50		20 20		20 50		21 20		21 50		22 18		22 48		23 20
Whyteleafe	d	18 31		18 52			19 22		19 52		20 22		20 52		21 22		21 52		22 20		22 50		23 22
Kenley	d	18 34		18 55			19 25		19 55		20 25		20 55		21 25		21 55		22 23		22 53		23 25
Purley 4	a	18 37	18 45	18 58	19 07	19 15	19 28	19 37	19 58	20 07	20 28	20 37	20 58	21 07	21 28	21 37	21 58	22 07	22 26	22 37	22 56	23 07	23 28
	d	18 38	18 45	18 58	19 08	19 15	19 29	19 38	19 59	20 08	20 29	20 38	20 59	21 08	21 29	21 38	21 59	22 08	22 29	22 38	22 59	23 08	23 34
Purley Oaks	d	18 41			19 11		19 32	19 41	20 02	20 11	20 32	20 41	21 02	21 11	21 32	21 41	22 02	22 11	22 32	22 41	23 02	23 11	23 37
South Croydon 4	d	18 44			19 14		19 35	19 44	20 05	20 14	20 35	20 44	21 05	21 14	21 35	21 44	22 05	22 14	22 35	22 44	23 05	23 14	23 40
East Croydon	d	18 47	18 51	19 07	19 17	19 21	19 40	19 47	20 10	20 17	20 40	20 47	21 10	21 17	21 40	21 47	22 10	22 17	22 40	22 47	23 10	23 17	23 43
Norwood Junction 2	d		19b01			19c31	19 44		20 14		20 44		21 14		21 44		22 14		22 44		23 14		23a47
New Cross Gate 4	⊖ a		19 18			19 48	20 02		20 32		21 02		21 32		22 02		22 32		23 02		23 32		
London Bridge 4	⊖ a		19 25	19 23		19 55	20 11		20 41		21 11		21 41		22 11		22 41		23 11		23 38		
London Waterloo (East) 4	⊖ a			19 28			20 16		20 46		21 16		21 46		22 16		22 46		23 16		23 43		
London Charing Cross 4	⊖ a			19 31			20 21		20 51		21 21		21 51		22 21		22 51		23 20		23 48		
Clapham Junction 10	a	19 07			19 37			20 07		20 37		21 07		21 37		22 07		22 37		23 07		23 37	
London Victoria 15	⊖ a	19 14			19 45			20 15		20 45		21 15		21 45		22 15		22 45		23 14		23 45	

For general notes see front of timetable
For details of catering facilities see Directory of Train Operators

b Arr. 1856
c Arr. 1926

Table 181

Sundays

Tattenham Corner and Caterham → Croydon and London

Network Diagram - see first page of Table 177

		SN	SN	SN		SN		SN	SN			SN	SN	SN		SN	SN	SN		SN	SN	SN		
Tattenham Corner	d		07 46			08 46			09 46				19 46			20 46		21 46			22 46			
Tadworth	d		07 49			08 49			09 49				19 49			20 49		21 49			22 49			
Kingswood	d		07 52			08 52			09 52				19 52			20 52		21 52			22 52			
Chipstead	d		07 57			08 57			09 57				19 57			20 57		21 57			22 57			
Woodmansterne	d		08 00			09 00			10 00				20 00			21 00		22 00			23 00			
Smitham	d		08 03			09 03			10 03				20 03			21 03		22 03			23 03			
Reedham	d		08 05			09 05			10 05	and at			20 05			21 05		22 05			23 05			
Caterham	d	07 26		08 26				09 26		the same		19 26		20 26			21 26			22 26		23 10		
Whyteleafe South	d	07 29		08 29				09 29				19 29		20 29			21 29			22 29		23 13		
Whyteleafe	d	07 31		08 31				09 31		minutes		19 31		20 31			21 31			22 31		23 15		
Kenley	d	07 34		08 34				09 34				19 34		20 34			21 34			22 34		23 18		
Purley 4	a	07 37	08 08	08 37		09 08		09 37	10 08	past		19 37	20 08	20 37		21 08	21 37	22 08		22 37	23 08	23 21		
	d	07 38	08 08	08 38		09 08		09 38	10 08	each		19 38	20 08	20 38		21 08	21 38	22 08		22 38	23 08	23 23		
Purley Oaks	d	07 41	08 11	08 41		09 11		09 41	10 11			19 41	20 11	20 41		21 11	21 41	22 11		22 41	23 11	23 26		
South Croydon 4	d	07 44	08 14	08 44		09 14		09 44	10 14	hour until		19 44	20 14	20 44		21 14	21 44	22 14		22 44	23 14	23 29		
East Croydon	d	07 47	08 17	08 47		09 17		09 47	10 17			19 47	20 17	20 47		21 17	21 47	22 17		22 47	23 17	23a31		
Norwood Junction 2	d	07 51	08 21	08 51		09 21		09 51	10 21			19 51	20 21	20 51		21 21	21 51	22 21		22 51	23a21			
New Cross Gate 4	⊖ a	08 05	08 35	09 05		09 35		10 05	10 35			20 05	20 35	21 05		21 35	22 05	22 35		23 05				
London Bridge 4	⊖ a	08 12	08 42	09 12		09 42		10 12	10 42			20 12	20 42	21 12		21 42	22 12	22 42		23 12				
London Waterloo (East) 4	⊖ a	08 17	08 47	09 17		09 47		10 17	10 47			20 17	20 47	21 17		21 47	22 17	22 47		23 17				
London Charing Cross 4	⊖ a	08 20	08 50	09 20		09 50		10 20	10 50			20 20	20 50	21 20		21 50	22 20	22 50		23 20				
Clapham Junction 10	a																							
London Victoria 15	⊖ a																							

For general notes see front of timetable
For details of catering facilities see
Directory of Train Operators

London → Sutton, Epsom, Guildford, Dorking and Horsham

Network Diagram - see first page of Table 177

Miles	Miles	Miles			SN MO	SN MX	SN MX	SN MO	SW MX	SN MX	SN MX	SW MX	SN	SN		SW	FC A	SN	SN	SN	SN	SN	SW	SN	FC B	SN
—	0	—	**London Victoria 15** ⊖	d	23p19	23p22	23p26				23p51									06 00	06 05					06 07
—	—	—	**London Waterloo 15** ⊖	d					23p42			00 15				05 47							06 24			
—	2¾	—	Clapham Junction 10	d	23p26	23p29	23p32		23p51		23p58	00 24				05 56				06 07	06 11		06 33			06 14
—	4¾	—	Balham 4 ⊖	d	23p32	23p35	23p37				00 04									06 13	06 15					06 20
0	—	0	**London Bridge 4** ⊖	d														05 46								
—	—	6	Tulse Hill 3	d																					06 29	
2¾	—	—	New Cross Gate 4 ⊖	d														05 51								
8¾	—	—	Norwood Junction 2	d		23b54								05 54				06 09								06c39
10½	—	12	**West Croydon 4**	d	23p50	00e01		←		←	00 20		05 46	05 59				06 14		06 30				←		06 44
11½	—	—	Waddon	d	23p52	00 03		23p52		00 03	00 22		05 48	06 02				06 17		06 32				06 32		06 46
13	—	—	Wallington	d	→	→		23p56		00 07	00 26		05 52	06 05				06 20		→				06 36		06 50
13¾	—	—	Carshalton Beeches	d				23p58		00 09	00 28		05 54	06 08				06 23						06 38		06 52
—	8	—	Mitcham Eastfields	d			23p44														06 22				06 36	
—	9	—	Mitcham Junction	d			23p48														06 26				06 39	
—	9¾	—	Hackbridge	d			23p51														06 29				06 43	
—	10¾	—	Carshalton	d			23p54														06 32				06 45	
14¾	12	0	**Sutton (Surrey) 4**	a			23p57	00 02		00 13	00 32		05 58	06 11				06 26			06 35			06 42	06 49	06 56
—	—	—		d			23p58	00 04						06 18			06 23		06 27		06 36	06 42		06 48	06 49	06 56
—	—	1	West Sutton	a													06 26								06 52	
—	—	5½	Wimbledon 6 ⊖	a													06 40								07 07	
—	13	—	Belmont	d										06 21										06 51		
—	14½	—	Banstead	d										06 25										06 55		
—	16	—	**Epsom Downs**	a										06 28										06 58		
15¾	—	—	Cheam	d			00 01	00 06											06 29		06 38					06 59
17¼	—	—	Ewell East	d			00 04	00 10													06 42					07 02
18¾	—	—	**Epsom 3**	a			00 08	00 14	00 15			00 48				06 20			06 35		06 46	06 48	06 57			07 06
—	—	—		d			00 09		00 19							06 21			06 35		06 46	06 49	06 58			
20½	—	—	Ashtead	d			00 13		00 23							06 25			06 39		06 50		07 02			
22½	—	0	Leatherhead	d			00 16		00 26							06 28			06 42		06 53	06 56	07 05			
25	—	—	Bookham	d					00 31							06 33						07 01				
26¾	—	—	Effingham Junction 6	d					00 36							06 37						07 05				
35	—	—	**Guildford**	a					00f56							06f53						07 17				
—	—	3¼	Boxhill & Westhumble	d			00 21														06 58					
—	—	4	**Dorking 4**	a			00 23												06 48		07 01		07g13			
—	—	—		d			00 23														07 01					
—	—	9	Holmwood	d			00s31														07 09					
—	—	11¼	Ockley	d			00s35														07 13					
—	—	15¾	Warnham	d			00s40														07 18					
—	—	17¾	**Horsham 4**	a			00 44														07 22					

		SN		SW	SN	SW	SN	FC C	SN	SN	SW	SN	SW		SN	FC C	SN	SN	SW	FC D	SN	SW	SN	SN		SN
London Victoria 15 ⊖	d	06 28			06 35					07 00		07 15						07 30			07 47		07 57			08 03
London Waterloo 15 ⊖	d			06 39		06 54					07 09		07 24						07 39			07 54				
Clapham Junction 10	d	06 38		06 48	06 41	07 03				07 07	07 18	07 21	07 33					07 38	07 48		07 54	08 03	08 03			08 11
Balham 4 ⊖	d	06 43			06 46					07 13		07 25						07 43			08 00					08 16
London Bridge 4 ⊖	d								06 46								07 15							07 48		
Tulse Hill 3	d							07 02								07 32				07 56						
New Cross Gate 4 ⊖	d								06 51								07 20							07 53		
Norwood Junction 2	d								07 10								07 39							08 11		
West Croydon 4	d	07 00					←		07 15	07 30							07 44	08 03						08 16		08 36
Waddon	d	07 03					07 03		07 17	07 32							07 46	08 05						08 19		08 39
Wallington	d	→					07 06		07 21	07 36							07 50	08 09						08 22		→
Carshalton Beeches	d						07 09		07 23	07 38							07 52	08 11						08 25		
Mitcham Eastfields	d							07 10								07 40				07 59			08 13			
Mitcham Junction	d				06 55			07 13				07 33				07 43				08 03	08 10					
Hackbridge	d				06 58			07 17				07 37				07 47				08 07	08 13					
Carshalton	d				07 01			07 19				07 39				07 49				08 10	08 16					
Sutton (Surrey) 4	a				07 04		07 12	07 23	07 27	07 42		07 43			←	07 53	07 58	08 15		08 13	08 19		08 22	08 28		
	d				07 05		07 18	07 23	07 27	07 45		07 43			07 45	07 53	07 58	08 16		08 17			08 23	08 29		
West Sutton	a							07 26		→						07 56				08 20						
Wimbledon 6 ⊖	a							07 42								08 11				08 35						
Belmont	d						07 21								07 48			08 19								
Banstead	d						07 25								07 52			08 23								
Epsom Downs	a						07 28								07 55			08 26								
Cheam	d				07 07				07 30			07 46					08 01						08 25	08 31		
Ewell East	d				07 11							07 49					08 04						08 29	08 35		
Epsom 3	a			07 08	07 15	07 27			07 35		07 42	07 53	07 58				08 08		08 15			08 27	08 33	08 39		
	d			07 08	07 15	07 28			07 36			07 54	07 58						08 15			08 28	08 33	08 39		
Ashtead	d			07 12	07 19	07 32			07 40			07 58	08 02						08 19			08 32	08 37	08 43		
Leatherhead	d			07 15	07 22	07 35			07 45			08 01	08 05						08 22			08 35	08 40	08 46		
Bookham	d			07 21					07 50										08 28							
Effingham Junction 6	d			07a24					07 54										08 32							
Guildford	a								08 07										08f51							
Boxhill & Westhumble	d											08 06											08 45			
Dorking 4	a				07 28	07g43						08 09	08g14									08g43	08 47	08 52		
	d				07 29							08 09											08 47			
Holmwood	d				07 36							08 16														
Ockley	d				07 40							08 20														
Warnham	d				07 46							08 26														
Horsham 4	a				07 50							08 30											09 03			

For general notes see front of timetable
For details of catering facilities see Directory of Train Operators

A To St Albans City (Table 52)
B From London Blackfriars (Table 52)
C From Luton (Table 52)
D From Bedford (Table 52)
b Previous night. Arr. 2351
c Arr. 0636
e Arr. 2358
f Until 26 September arr 3 minutes earlier
g Until 26 September arr 2 minutes earlier

London → Sutton, Epsom, Guildford, Dorking and Horsham

Network Diagram - see first page of Table 177

		SW	FC A	SW	SN	SN	SN	FC B	SW	SN	SN		SW	SN	SN	SN	SN	SW	FC C	SN	SN	SW		SN	SN	SN
London Victoria 15 ⊖	d				08 20					08 31	08 34			08 50		08 57	09 03				09 05			09 20		09 28
London Waterloo 15 ⊖	d	08 09		08 24					08 39				08 54					09 09				09 24				
Clapham Junction 10	d	08 18		08 33	08 26				08 48	08 37	08 41		09 03	08 56		09 04	09 09	09 18			09 11	09 33		09 26		09 35
Balham 4 ⊖	d				08 30					08 43	08 47			09 02		09 10					09 17			09 32		09 41
London Bridge 4 ⊖	d						08 19								08 45										09 15	
Tulse Hill 3	d		08 26					08 44											09 14							
New Cross Gate 4 ⊖	d						08 26								08 50										09 20	
Norwood Junction 2	d						08 44								09 09										09 39	
West Croydon 4	d					←	08 49			08 59	09 06				09 14	09 28				←	09 34				09 44	09 58
Waddon	d					08 39	08 52			09 02	09 08				09 17	09 31				09 31	09 37				09 47	10 01
Wallington	d					08 42	08 55			09 05	09 12				09 20	→				09 34	09 40				09 50	→
Carshalton Beeches	d					08 45	08 58			09 08	09 14				09 23					09 37	09 43				09 53	
Mitcham Eastfields	d		08 33		08 37			08 51						09 09					09 23					09 39		
Mitcham Junction	d		08 37		08 41			08 55						09 12					09 27					09 42		
Hackbridge	d		08 40		08 44			08 58						09 16					09 30					09 46		
Carshalton	d		08 43		08 47			09 01						09 18					09 33					09 48		
Sutton (Surrey) 4	a		08 46		08 50	08 48	09 01	09 05		09 11	09 18			09 22	09 26		09 27		09 37	09 40	09 46			09 52	09 56	
	d		08 47		08 52	08 53		09 05		09 12	09 19			09 22			09 27		09 37	09 41				09 52		
West Sutton	a		08 50					09 08											09 40							
Wimbledon 6 ⊖	a		09 04					09 24											09 55							
Belmont	d					08 56					09 22															
Banstead	d					09 00					09 26															
Epsom Downs	a					09 03					09 29															
Cheam	d				08 54									09 25			09 30			09 43				09 55		
Ewell East	d				08 58									09 28						09 47				09 58		
Epsom 3	a	08 42		08 57	09 02				09 16	09 18			09 27	09 32			09 36	09 42		09 51		09 57		10 02		
	d	08 47		08 58	09 02				09 17				09 28				09 37	09 47				09 58				
Ashtead	d	08 51		09 02	09 06				09 21				09 32				09 41	09 51				10 02				
Leatherhead	d	08 54		09 05	09 09				09 24				09 35				09 44	09 54				10 05				
Bookham	d	08 59							09 29									09 59								
Effingham Junction 6	d	09 03							09 33									10 03								
Guildford	a	09b23							09b53									10b23								
Boxhill & Westhumble	d				09 14												09 49									
Dorking 4	a			09c13	09 17								09c43				09 51					10c13				
	d				09 17																					
Holmwood	d				09 25																					
Ockley	d				09 29																					
Warnham	d				09 34																					
Horsham 4	a				09 38																					

		SN	FC B	SW	SN	SN	SW	SN	SN	SN		SN	FC B	SW	SN	SN	SW	SN	SN	SN	SN		FC B	SW	SN	SN
London Victoria 15 ⊖	d	09 31				09 35		09 50		09 57		10 03				10 05		10 20		10 28	10 33					10 35
London Waterloo 15 ⊖	d			09 39			09 54							10 09			10 24							10 39		
Clapham Junction 10	d	09 39		09 48		09 41	10 03	09 56		10 04		10 09		10 18		10 11	10 33	10 26		10 35	10 39			10 48		10 41
Balham 4 ⊖	d					09 47		10 02		10 10						10 17		10 32		10 41						10 47
London Bridge 4 ⊖	d								09 45										10 15							
Tulse Hill 3	d		09 44										10 16										10 46			
New Cross Gate 4 ⊖	d								09 50										10 20							
Norwood Junction 2	d								10 09										10 39							
West Croydon 4	d				←	10 04			10 14	10 28					←	10 34			10 44	10 58					←	11 04
Waddon	d				10 01	10 06			10 17	10 31					10 31	10 36			10 47	11 01					11 01	11 06
Wallington	d				10 04	10 10			10 20	→					10 34	10 40			10 50	→					11 04	11 10
Carshalton Beeches	d				10 07	10 12			10 23						10 37	10 42			10 53						11 07	11 12
Mitcham Eastfields	d		09 51					10 09					10 23					10 39					10 53			
Mitcham Junction	d		09 55					10 12					10 27					10 42					10 57			
Hackbridge	d		09 58					10 16					10 30					10 46					11 00			
Carshalton	d		10 01					10 18					10 33					10 48					11 03			
Sutton (Surrey) 4	a	09 58	10 05		10 10	10 16		10 22	10 26			10 28	10 37		10 40	10 46		10 52	10 56		10 58		11 06		11 10	11 16
	d	09 59	10 05		10 11			10 22				10 29	10 37		10 41			10 52			10 59		11 07		11 11	
West Sutton	a		10 08										10 40										11 10			
Wimbledon 6 ⊖	a		10 19										10 56										11 26			
Belmont	d				10 14																				11 14	
Banstead	d				10 18																				11 18	
Epsom Downs	a				10 21																				11 21	
Cheam	d	10 01						10 25				10 31			10 43			10 55			11 01					
Ewell East	d	10 05						10 28							10 47			10 58			11 05					
Epsom 3	a	10 09		10 16			10 27	10 32				10 38		10 46	10 51		10 57	11 02			11 09			11 16		
	d	10 09		10 17			10 28					10 38		10 47			10 58				11 09			11 17		
Ashtead	d	10 13		10 21			10 32					10 42		10 51			11 02				11 13			11 21		
Leatherhead	d	10 16		10 24			10 35					10 45		10 54			11 05				11 16			11 24		
Bookham	d			10 29										10 59										11 29		
Effingham Junction 6	d			10 33										11 03										11 33		
Guildford	a			10b53										11b23										11b53		
Boxhill & Westhumble	d	10 21																			11 21					
Dorking 4	a	10 24					10c43					10 51					11c13				11 24					
	d	10 24																			11 24					
Holmwood	d	10 32																			11 32					
Ockley	d	10 36																			11 36					
Warnham	d	10 41																			11 41					
Horsham 4	a	10 45																			11 45					

For general notes see front of timetable
For details of catering facilities see Directory of Train Operators

A From Luton (Table 52)
B From St Albans City (Table 52)
C From Bedford (Table 52)

b Until 26 September arr 3 minutes earlier
c Until 26 September arr 2 minutes earlier

London → Sutton, Epsom, Guildford, Dorking and Horsham

Network Diagram - see first page of Table 177

		SW	SN		SN	SN	SN	FC A	SW	SN	SN	SW	SN	SN	SN	SN	FC A	SW	SN	SN	SW	SN	and at the same minutes past each hour until		SN
London Victoria 15 ⊖	d		10 50			10 55	11 03				11 05		11 20		11 25	11 33				11 35		11 50			
London Waterloo 15 ⊖	d	10 54							11 09			11 24						11 39			11 54				
Clapham Junction 10	d	11 03	10 56			11 04	11 09		11 18		11 12	11 33	11 26		11 34	11 39		11 48		11 41	12 03	11 56			
Balham 4 ⊖	d		11 02			11 10					11 17		11 32		11 40					11 47		12 02			
London Bridge 4 ⊖	d				10 45									11 15											14 45
Tulse Hill 3	d							11 16									11 46								
New Cross Gate 4 ⊖	d				10 50									11 20											14 50
Norwood Junction 2	d				11 09									11 39											15 09
West Croydon 4	d				11 14	11 28				←	11 34			11 44	11 58				←	12 04					15 14
Waddon	d				11 17	11 31				11 31	11 36			11 47	12 01				12 01	12 06					15 17
Wallington	d				11 20	→				11 34	11 40			11 50	→				12 04	12 10					15 20
Carshalton Beeches	d				11 23					11 37	11 42			11 53					12 07	12 12					15 23
Mitcham Eastfields	d		11 09					11 23					11 39				11 53					12 09			
Mitcham Junction	d		11 12					11 27					11 42				11 57					12 12			
Hackbridge	d		11 16					11 30					11 46				12 00					12 16			
Carshalton	d		11 18					11 33					11 48				12 03					12 18			
Sutton (Surrey) 4	a		11 22		11 26		11 28	11 36		11 40	11 46		11 52	11 56		11 58	12 06		12 10	12 16		12 22			15 26
	d		11 22				11 29	11 37		11 41			11 52			11 59	12 07		12 11			12 22			
West Sutton	a							11 40									12 10								
Wimbledon 6 ⊖	a							11 54									12 24								
Belmont	d																		12 14						
Banstead	d																		12 18						
Epsom Downs	a																		12 21						
Cheam	d		11 25				11 31			11 43			11 55			12 01						12 25			
Ewell East	d		11 28							11 47			11 58			12 05						12 28			
Epsom 3	a	11 27	11 32				11 38		11 46	11 51		11 57	12 02			12 09		12 16			12 27	12 32			
	d	11 28					11 38		11 47			11 58				12 09		12 17			12 28				
Ashtead	d	11 32					11 42		11 51			12 02				12 13		12 21			12 32				
Leatherhead	d	11 35					11 45		11 54			12 05				12 16		12 24			12 35				
Bookham	d								11 59									12 29							
Effingham Junction 6	d								12 03									12 33							
Guildford	a								12b23									12b53							
Boxhill & Westhumble	d															12 21									
Dorking 4	a	11c43					11 51					12c13				12 24					12c43				
	d															12 24									
Holmwood	d															12 32									
Ockley	d															12 36									
Warnham	d															12 41									
Horsham 4	a															12 45									

		SN	SN	FC A	SW	SN	SN	SW	SN	SN	SN		SN	FC A	SW	SN	SN	SW	SN	SN	SN	SN		FC A	SW	SN
London Victoria 15 ⊖	d	14 55	15 03				15 05		15 20		15 25		15 33				15 35		15 50		15 55	16 02				
London Waterloo 15 ⊖	d				15 09			15 24							15 39			15 54							16 09	
Clapham Junction 10	d	15 04	15 09		15 18		15 11	15 33	15 26		15 34		15 39		15 48		15 41	16 03	15 56		16 04	16 09			16 18	
Balham 4 ⊖	d	15 10					15 17		15 32		15 40						15 47		16 02		16 10					
London Bridge 4 ⊖	d									15 15										15 45						
Tulse Hill 3	d			15 16										15 46										16 16		
New Cross Gate 4 ⊖	d									15 20										15 50						
Norwood Junction 2	d									15 39										16 10						
West Croydon 4	d	15 28				←	15 34			15 44	15 58					←	16 04			16 15	16 28					←
Waddon	d	15 31				15 31	15 36			15 47	16 01					16 01	16 06			16 18	16 31					16 31
Wallington	d	→				15 34	15 40			15 50	→					16 04	16 10			16 21	→					16 34
Carshalton Beeches	d					15 37	15 42			15 53						16 07	16 12			16 24						16 37
Mitcham Eastfields	d			15 23					15 39					15 53					16 09					16 23		
Mitcham Junction	d			15 27					15 42					15 57					16 12			16 20		16 27		
Hackbridge	d			15 30					15 46					16 00					16 16					16 30		
Carshalton	d			15 33					15 48					16 03					16 18					16 33		
Sutton (Surrey) 4	a		15 28	15 36		15 40	15 46		15 52	15 56			15 58	16 06		16 10	16 16		16 22	16 27		16 28		16 36		16 40
	d		15 29	15 37		15 41			15 52				15 59	16 07		16 11			16 22			16 29		16 37		16 41
West Sutton	a			15 40										16 10										16 40		
Wimbledon 6 ⊖	a			15 54										16 24										16 54		
Belmont	d															16 14										16 44
Banstead	d															16 18										16 48
Epsom Downs	a															16 21										16 51
Cheam	d		15 31			15 43			15 55				16 01						16 25			16 31				
Ewell East	d					15 47			15 58				16 05						16 28			16 35				
Epsom 3	a		15 38		15 46	15 51		15 57	16 02				16 09		16 16			16 27	16 32			16 39			16 46	
	d		15 38		15 47			15 58					16 09		16 17			16 28				16 39			16 47	
Ashtead	d		15 42		15 51			16 02					16 13		16 21			16 32				16 43			16 51	
Leatherhead	d		15 45		15 54			16 05					16 16		16 24			16 35				16 46			16 54	
Bookham	d				15 59										16 29										16 59	
Effingham Junction 6	d				16 03										16 33										17 03	
Guildford	a				16b23										16b53										17b25	
Boxhill & Westhumble	d												16 21									16 51				
Dorking 4	a		15 51					16c13					16 24					16c43				16 56				
	d												16 24													
Holmwood	d												16 32													
Ockley	d												16 36													
Warnham	d												16 41													
Horsham 4	a												16 45													

For general notes see front of timetable
For details of catering facilities see Directory of Train Operators

A From St Albans City (Table 52)
b Until 26 September arr 3 minutes earlier
c Until 26 September arr 2 minutes earlier

London → Sutton, Epsom, Guildford, Dorking and Horsham

Network Diagram - see first page of Table 177

Station		SN	SW	SN	SN	FC A	SW	SN	SN	SW		SN	SN	SN	FC A	SN	SW	SN	SW	SN	SN		SW	SN	SN	FC A
London Victoria 15 ⊖	d	16 05		16 20					16 30			16 50				17 01		17 15		17 25						
London Waterloo 15 ⊖	d		16 24				16 39			16 54							17 09		17 24				17 30			
Clapham Junction 10	d	16 11	16 33	16 26			16 48		16 37	17 03		16 56				17 08	17 18	17 21	17 33	17 31			17 39			
Balham 4 ⊖	d	16 17		16 30					16 43			17 00				17 14		17 25		17 35						
London Bridge 4 ⊖	d				16 15			16 29					16 44	16 53										17 25	17 25	
Tulse Hill 3	d					16 42		16 46						17 11	17 16										17 42	17 46
New Cross Gate 4 ⊖	d				16 20								16 49											17 30		
Norwood Junction 2	d				16 39								17 09											17 43		
West Croydon 4	d	16 34			16 44				16 59				17 15			17 30		17 42			←			17 48		
Waddon	d	16 36			16 46				17 02				17 17			17 33		17 45			17 45			17 51		
Wallington	d	16 40			16 50				17 05				17 21			17 36		→			17 48			17 54		
Carshalton Beeches	d	16 42			16 52				17 08				17 23			17 39					17 51			17 57		
Mitcham Eastfields	d			16 37		16 49		16 54				17 07		17 19	17 23					17 42					17 50	17 54
Mitcham Junction	d			16 41		16 52		16 58				17 11		17 22	17 27					17 46					17 54	17 57
Hackbridge	d			16 44		16 56		17 01				17 14		17 26	17 30					17 49					17 57	18 00
Carshalton	d			16 47		16 58		17 04				17 17		17 28	17 33					17 52					17 59	18 03
Sutton (Surrey) 4	a	16 48		16 50	16 56	17 02		17 07	17 11			17 20	17 27	17 32	17 38	17 42				17 55	17 56			18 00	18 03	18 07
	d			16 51	16 56	17 02		17 08	17 12			17 21	17 27	17 32	17 40	17 43				17 56				18 01	18 04	18 08
West Sutton	a					17 05								17 36	17 43										18 07	18 13
Wimbledon 6 ⊖	a					17 20								17 52	17 58										18 18	18 27
Belmont	d								17 15							17 46										
Banstead	d								17 19							17 50										
Epsom Downs	a								17 24							17 55										
Cheam	d			16 53	16 59			17 10				17 23	17 30							17 58				18 03		
Ewell East	d			16 57	17 02			17 14				17 27	17 33											18 07		
Epsom 3	a		16 57	17 01	17 06		17 12	17 20		17 27		17 31	17 37				17 42		17 54	18 04			18 06	18 11		
	d		16 58	17 01	17 07		17 17			17 28		17 31	17 38				17 47		17 54	18 04				18 13		
Ashtead	d		17 02	17 05	17 11		17 21			17 32		17 35	17 42				17 51		17 58	18 08				18 17		
Leatherhead	d		17 05	17 08	17 14		17 24			17 35		17 38	17 45				17 54		18 01	18 11				18 20		
Bookham	d				17 19		17 29						17 50				17 59							18 25		
Effingham Junction 6	d				17 23		17 33						17 54				18a05							18 29		
Guildford	a				17 38		17b55						18 13											18 47		
Boxhill & Westhumble	d		17 10	17 13						17 40									18 06	18 16						
Dorking 4	a		17 16	17 16						17 46		17 45							18c13	18 19						
	d			17 16								17 45								18 19						
Holmwood	d			17 24								17 53								18 27						
Ockley	d			17 28								17 57								18 31						
Warnham	d			17 33								18 02								18 36						
Horsham 4	a			17 39								18 08								18 42						

Station		SN	SW	SN	SN	SW	SN	SN	SW		SW	SN	SN	SW	FC A	SN	SW	SN	SN	SW		SN	FC A	SW	SN	SN
London Victoria 15 ⊖	d	17 32		17 43			17 57						18 02			18 14			18 27							18 33
London Waterloo 15 ⊖	d		17 39			17 54			18 00		18 09						18 24			18 30				18 39		
Clapham Junction 10	d	17 39	17 48	17 49		18 03	18 03		18 09		18 18		18 09			18 20	18 33		18 33	18 39				18 48		18 40
Balham 4 ⊖	d	17 45		17 53			18 08						18 15			18 24			18 37							18 46
London Bridge 4 ⊖	d							17 58				17 55										18 25			18 31	
Tulse Hill 3	d							18 15							18 18								18 44		18 48	
New Cross Gate 4 ⊖	d																									
Norwood Junction 2	d											18 13										18 42				
West Croydon 4	d	18 02			←							18 18	18 31					←				18 47				19 02
Waddon	d	18 04			18 04							18 20	18 34					18 34				18 49				19 05
Wallington	d	→			18 08							18 24	→					18 37				18 53				19 08
Carshalton Beeches	d				18 10							18 26						18 40				18 55				19 11
Mitcham Eastfields	d														18 26	18 31							18 51		18 56	
Mitcham Junction	d			18 01			18 16								18 30	18 35			18 45				18 55		19 00	
Hackbridge	d			18 05			18 19								18 33	18 38			18 49				18 58		19 03	
Carshalton	d			18 07			18 22								18 36	18 41			18 51				19 01		19 06	
Sutton (Surrey) 4	a			18 11	18 14		18 25	18 30				18 33			18 39	18 44		18 43	18 55			18 59	19 04		19 09	19 14
	d			18 11	18 15		18 26	18 31				18 34			18 40	18 45		18 46	18 55			18 59	19 05		19 10	19 15
West Sutton	a							18 34							18 43								19 08			
Wimbledon 6 ⊖	a							18 50							18 58								19 24			
Belmont	d				18 18													18 49								19 18
Banstead	d				18 22													18 53								19 22
Epsom Downs	a				18 27													18 58								19 27
Cheam	d			18 14			18 28					18 36				18 47			18 58			19 02			19 12	
Ewell East	d			18 17								18 40				18 51			19 01			19 05			19 16	
Epsom 3	a		18 20	18 23		18 24	18 34		18 35		18 43	18 44		←		18 57	18 54		19 05	19 05		19 09		19 13	19 22	
	d		18 20			18 24	18 34				18 47	18 44		18 47			18 54		19 06			19 10		19 17		
Ashtead	d		18 24			18 28	18 38				→	18 48		18 51			18 58		19 10			19 14		19 21		
Leatherhead	d		18 28			18 31	18 41					18 51		18 54			19 01		19 13			19 17		19 24		
Bookham	d		18 33											18 59										19 29		
Effingham Junction 6	d		18a44											19 03										19 33		
Guildford	a													19b25										19b55		
Boxhill & Westhumble	d					18 36						18 56					19 06		19 18			19 22				
Dorking 4	a					18c43	18 47					19 01					19c13		19 20			19 26				
	d						18 47												19 23							
Holmwood	d						18 55												19 30							
Ockley	d						18 59												19 34							
Warnham	d						19 04												19 40							
Horsham 4	a						19 10												19 46							

For general notes see front of timetable
For details of catering facilities see Directory of Train Operators

A From St Albans City (Table 52)
b Until 26 September arr 3 minutes earlier
c Until 26 September arr 2 minutes earlier

London → Sutton, Epsom, Guildford, Dorking and Horsham

Network Diagram - see first page of Table 177

Station		SN	SW	SW	SN	SN	FC A	SN		SW	SN	SW	SN	SN	SN	FC A	SN	SW	SN		SW	SN	SN	FC A	SW	SN
London Victoria [15] ⊖	d	18 45			18 57						19 15		19 20				19 22		19 45			19 50				19 52
London Waterloo [15] ⊖	d		18 54	19 00						19 09		19 24						19 39			19 54				20 09	
Clapham Junction [10]	d	18 52	19 03	19 09	19 03					19 18	19 22	19 33	19 26				19 29	19 48	19 52		20 03	19 56			20 18	19 59
Balham [4] ⊖	d	18 58			19 07						19 28		19 32				19 35		19 58			20 02				20 05
London Bridge [4] ⊖	d							19 05							19 31											
Tulse Hill [3]	d						19 14									19 47								20 16		
New Cross Gate [4] ⊖	d							19 10																		
Norwood Junction [2]	d							19 28							19 44		19 54									20b24
West Croydon [4]	d	19 16				←		19 33			19 45			←	19 49		20 00		20 15				←			20 30
Waddon	d	19 18				19 18		19 36			19 47			19 47	19 51		20 02		20 17				20 17			20 32
Wallington	d	→				19 22		19 39			→			19 51	19 55		20 06		→				20 21			20 36
Carshalton Beeches	d					19 24		19 42						19 53	19 57		20 08						20 23			20 38
Mitcham Eastfields	d				19 14		19 21						19 39			19 53						20 09		20 23		
Mitcham Junction	d				19 18		19 25						19 42			19 57						20 12		20 27		
Hackbridge	d				19 21		19 28						19 46			20 00						20 16		20 30		
Carshalton	d				19 24		19 31						19 48			20 04						20 18		20 33		
Sutton (Surrey) [4]	a				19 27	19 30	19 34	19 45					19 52	19 57	20 01	20 08	20 12					20 22	20 27	20 38		20 42
	d				19 28	19 31	19 37	19 46					19 52	19 58	20 02	20 09						20 22	20 28	20 39		
West Sutton	a						19 40									20 12								20 42		
Wimbledon [6] ⊖	a						19 54									20 26								20 56		
Belmont	d													20 01									20 31			
Banstead	d													20 05									20 35			
Epsom Downs	a													20 08									20 38			
Cheam	d				19 30	19 33		19 48					19 55		20 04							20 25				
Ewell East	d				19 34	19 37		19 52					19 58		20 08							20 28				
Epsom [3]	a		19 29	19 33	19 38	19 43		19 56		19 43		19 57	20 02		20 12			20 12			20 27	20 32			20 42	
	d		19 30		19 38					19 47		19 58	20 03		20 13			20 17				20 33			20 47	
Ashtead	d		19 34		19 42					19 51		20 02	20 07		20 17			20 21				20 37			20 51	
Leatherhead	d		19 37		19 45					19 54		20 05	20 10		20 20			20 24				20 40			20 54	
Bookham	d									19 59								20 29								
Effingham Junction [6]	d									20 03								20 33								
Guildford	a									20c23								20c53								
Boxhill & Westhumble	d		19 42		19 50							20 10	20 15									20 45			20 59	
Dorking [4]	a		19e48		19 55							20e14	20 17		20 26							20 47			21e03	
	d												20 18													
Holmwood	d												20 25													
Ockley	d												20 29													
Warnham	d												20 35													
Horsham [4]	a												20 39													

Station		SN	SW	SN	SN	FC A	SN		SW	SN	SW	SN	SW	SN	SN	SN	SW	SN		FC B	SN	SN	SW	SN	SW	SN
London Victoria [15] ⊖	d	20 15		20 20			20 22			20 45		20 50			20 52	21 15		21 20				21 22		21 45		21 50
London Waterloo [15] ⊖	d		20 24						20 39		20 54		21 09				21 24						21 39		21 54	
Clapham Junction [10]	d	20 22	20 33	20 26			20 29		20 48	20 52	21 03	20 56	21 18		20 59	21 22	21 33	21 26				21 29	21 48	21 52	22 03	21 56
Balham [4] ⊖	d	20 28		20 31			20 35			20 58		21 02			21 05	21 28		21 31				21 35		21 58		22 02
London Bridge [4] ⊖	d																									
Tulse Hill [3]	d					20 46																				
New Cross Gate [4] ⊖	d																									
Norwood Junction [2]	d						20f54								21g24							21h54				
West Croydon [4]	d	20 45			←		21 00			21 15				←	21 30	21 45					←	22 00		22 15		
Waddon	d	20 47			20 47		21 02			21 17				21 17	21 32	21 47					21 47	22 02		22 17		
Wallington	d	→			20 51		21 06			→				21 21	21 36	→					21 51	22 06		→		
Carshalton Beeches	d				20 53		21 08							21 23	21 38						21 53	22 08				
Mitcham Eastfields	d			20 39		20 53						21 09						21 39								22 09
Mitcham Junction	d			20 42		20 57						21 12						21 42								22 12
Hackbridge	d			20 46		21 00						21 16						21 46								22 16
Carshalton	d			20 48		21 03						21 18						21 48								22 18
Sutton (Surrey) [4]	a			20 52	20 57	21 08	21 12					21 22		21 27	21 42			21 52			21 57	22 12				22 22
	d			20 52		21 09						21 22		21 28				21 52		21 49	21 58					22 22
West Sutton	a					21 12														21 52						
Wimbledon [6] ⊖	a					21 27														22 07						
Belmont	d													21 31												
Banstead	d													21 35												
Epsom Downs	a													21 38												
Cheam	d			20 55								21 25						21 55			22 00					22 25
Ewell East	d			20 58								21 28						21 58			22 04					22 28
Epsom [3]	a		20 57	21 02					21 12		21 27	21 33	21 42				21 57	22 02			22 08		22 12		22 27	22 32
	d			21 03					21 17			21 33	21 47					22 03					22 17			22 33
Ashtead	d			21 07					21 21			21 37	21 51					22 07					22 21			22 37
Leatherhead	d			21 10					21 24			21 40	21 54					22 10					22 24			22 40
Bookham	d								21 29														22 29			
Effingham Junction [6]	d								21 33														22 33			
Guildford	a								21c53														22c53			
Boxhill & Westhumble	d			21 15								21 45	21 59													22 45
Dorking [4]	a			21 17								21 47	22e03					22 16								22 47
	d																									
Holmwood	d																									
Ockley	d																									
Warnham	d																									
Horsham [4]	a																									

For general notes see front of timetable
For details of catering facilities see Directory of Train Operators

A From St Albans City (Table 52)
B To Bedford (Table 52)
b Arr. 2021
c Until 26 September arr 3 minutes earlier
e Until 26 September arr 2 minutes earlier
f Arr. 2051
g Arr. 2121
h Arr. 2151

London → Sutton, Epsom, Guildford, Dorking and Horsham

Network Diagram - see first page of Table 177

Mondays to Fridays

Station		SW	SN	SN	SN	SN		SN	SN	SW	SN	SN	SW	SN	SN	SN	SN		SN	SN	SW	SN	SN			
London Victoria 15 ⊖	d			21 52	22 15	22 20			22 22		22 45	22 50			22 52	23 15	23 22		23 26				23 51			
London Waterloo 15 ⊖	d	22 09								22 39			23 09								23 42					
Clapham Junction 10	d	22 18		21 59	22 22	22 26			22 29	22 48	22 52	22 56	23 18		22 59	23 22	23 29		23 32		23 51		23 58			
Balham 4 ⊖	d			22 05	22 28	22 32			22 35		22 58	23 00			23 05	23 28	23 35		23 37				00 04			
London Bridge 4 ⊖	d																									
Tulse Hill 3	d																									
New Cross Gate 4 ⊖	d																									
Norwood Junction 2	d			22b24					22c54						23e24		23f54									
West Croydon 4	d		←	22 30	22 45			←	23 00		23 15			←	23 30	23 45	00g01			←		←	00 20			
Waddon	d		22 17	22 32	22 47			22 47	23 02		23 17			23 17	23 32	23 47	00 03			23 47		00 03	00 22			
Wallington	d		22 21	22 36	→			22 51	23 06		→			23 21	23 36	→	→			23 51		00 07	00 26			
Carshalton Beeches	d		22 23	22 38				22 53	23 08					23 23	23 38					23 53		00 09	00 28			
Mitcham Eastfields	d					22 39						23 07							23 44							
Mitcham Junction	d					22 42						23 11							23 48							
Hackbridge	d					22 46						23 14							23 51							
Carshalton	d					22 48						23 17							23 54							
Sutton (Surrey) 4	a		22 27	22 42		22 52		22 57	23 12			23 20		23 27	23 42				23 57	23 57		00 13	00 32			
	d		22 28	22 42		22 52		22 58				23 21		23 28	23 42				23 58							
West Sutton	a																									
Wimbledon 6 ⊖	a																									
Belmont	d		22 31											23 31												
Banstead	d		22 35											23 35												
Epsom Downs	a		22 38											23 38												
Cheam	d			22 45		22 55		23 00				23 23			23 45				00 01							
Ewell East	d			22 48		22 58		23 04				23 27			23 48				00 04							
Epsom 3	a	22 42		22 52		23 02		23 08		23 12		23 31	23 42		23 52				00 08		00 15					
	d	22 47				23 03				23 17		23 31	23 47						00 09		00 19					
Ashtead	d	22 51				23 07				23 21		23 35	23 51						00 13		00 23					
Leatherhead	d	22 54				23 10				23 24		23 38	23 54						00 16		00 26					
Bookham	d									23 29											00 31					
Effingham Junction 6	d									23 33											00 36					
Guildford	a									23 54											00h56					
Boxhill & Westhumble	d	22 59										23 43	23 59						00 21							
Dorking 4	a	23j03				23 16						23 46	00j03						00 23							
	d																		00 23							
Holmwood	d																		00s31							
Ockley	d																		00s35							
Warnham	d																		00s40							
Horsham 4	a																		00 44							

Saturdays

Station		SN	SN	SW	SN	SN	SW		SN	SW	FC A	SN	SN	SN B		SW	FC A	SN	SW	SN	SN		SN	SN	FC C	SW
London Victoria 15 ⊖	d	23p22	23p26			23p51						06 27	06 54					06 57		07 20			07 25	07 33		
London Waterloo 15 ⊖	d			23p42			00 15			06 39						07 09			07 24							07 39
Clapham Junction 10	d	23p29	23p32	23p51		23p58	00 24			06 48		06 34	07 00			07 18		07 04	07 33	07 26			07 34	07 39		07 48
Balham 4 ⊖	d	23p35	23p37			00 04						06 40	07 04					07 10		07 32			07 40			
London Bridge 4 ⊖	d																				07 15					
Tulse Hill 3	d																								07 46	
New Cross Gate 4 ⊖	d																				07 20					
Norwood Junction 2	d	23k54												07 06							07 39					
West Croydon 4	d	00g01			←	00 20			06 45			06 56		07m14				07 28			07 44		07 58			
Waddon	d	00 03			00 03	00 22			06 47			06 59		07 17				07 31			07 47		08 01			
Wallington	d	→			00 07	00 26			06 51			07 02		07 20				07 34			07 50		→			
Carshalton Beeches	d				00 09	00 28			06 53			07 05		07 23				07 37			07 53					
Mitcham Eastfields	d		23p44										07 12							07 39					07 53	
Mitcham Junction	d		23p48										07 16							07 42					07 57	
Hackbridge	d		23p51										07 19							07 46					08 00	
Carshalton	d		23p54										07 22							07 48					08 03	
Sutton (Surrey) 4	a		23p57		00 13	00 32			06 57			07 08	07 25	07 26				07 40		07 52	07 56			07 58	08 06	
	d		23p58						06 57		07 07	07 09	07 26				07 37	07 41		07 52				07 59	08 07	
West Sutton	a										07 10						07 40								08 10	
Wimbledon 6 ⊖	a										07 24						07 54								08 25	
Belmont	d											07 12														
Banstead	d											07 16														
Epsom Downs	a											07 19														
Cheam	d		00 01						07 00				07 28					07 43		07 55				08 01		
Ewell East	d		00 04						07 03				07 32					07 47		07 58				08 05		
Epsom 3	a		00 08	00 15			00 48		07 07	07 16			07 36			07 46		07 51	07 57	08 02				08 09		08 16
	d		00 09	00 19					07 08	07 17			07 36			07 47			07 58					08 09		08 17
Ashtead	d		00 13	00 23					07 12	07 21			07 40			07 51			08 02					08 13		08 21
Leatherhead	d		00 16	00 26					07 15	07 24			07 43			07 54			08 05					08 16		08 24
Bookham	d			00 31						07 29						07 59										08 29
Effingham Junction 6	d			00 36						07 33						08 03										08 33
Guildford	a			00n56						07n53						08n23										08n53
Boxhill & Westhumble	d		00 21										07 48											08 21		
Dorking 4	a		00 23						07 21				07 51						08q13					08 24		
	d		00 23																					08 24		
Holmwood	d		00s31																					08 32		
Ockley	d		00s35																					08 36		
Warnham	d		00s40																					08 41		
Horsham 4	a		00 44																					08 45		

For general notes see front of timetable
For details of catering facilities see Directory of Train Operators

A To Luton (Table 52)
B From Streatham Hill (Table 177)
C From London Blackfriars (Table 52)
b Arr. 2221
c Arr. 2251
e Arr. 2321
f Arr. 2351
g Arr. 2358
h Until 26 September arr 3 minutes earlier
j Until 26 September arr 2 minutes earlier
k Previous night. Arr. 2351
m Arr. 0711
n Until 27 September arr 3 minutes earlier
q Until 27 September arr 2 minutes earlier

Saturdays

London → Sutton, Epsom, Guildford, Dorking and Horsham

Network Diagram - see first page of Table 177

		SN		SN	SW	SN	SN	SN	SN	FC A	SW	SN	SN	SW	SN	SN	SN	SN	FC A	SW	SN			SN	SW
London Victoria 15 ⊖	d			07 35		07 50		07 55	08 03				08 05		08 20		08 25	08 33						17 35	
London Waterloo 15 ⊖	d				07 54						08 09			08 24						08 39					17 54
Clapham Junction 10	d			07 41	08 03	07 56		08 04	08 09		08 18		08 11	08 33	08 26		08 34	08 39		08 48				17 41	18 03
Balham 4 ⊖	d			07 47		08 02		08 10					08 17		08 32		08 40							17 47	
London Bridge 4 ⊖	d						07 45									08 15									
Tulse Hill 3	d									08 16									08 46						
New Cross Gate 4 ⊖	d						07 50									08 20									
Norwood Junction 2	d						08 09									08 39									
West Croydon 4	d	←		08 04			08 14	08 28				←	08 34			08 44	08 58				←			18 04	
Waddon	d	08 01		08 06			08 17	08 31				08 31	08 36			08 47	09 01				09 01			18 06	
Wallington	d	08 04		08 10			08 20	→				08 34	08 40			08 50	→				09 04			18 10	
Carshalton Beeches	d	08 07		08 12			08 23					08 37	08 42			08 53					09 07			18 12	
Mitcham Eastfields	d					08 09				08 23					08 39				08 53						
Mitcham Junction	d					08 12				08 27					08 42				08 57						
Hackbridge	d					08 16				08 30					08 46				09 00			and at			
Carshalton	d					08 18				08 33					08 48				09 03						
Sutton (Surrey) 4	a	08 10		08 16		08 22	08 26		08 28	08 36		08 40	08 46		08 52	08 56		08 58	09 06		09 10	the same		18 16	
	d	08 11				08 22			08 29	08 37		08 41			08 52			08 59	09 07		09 11	minutes			
West Sutton	a									08 40									09 10						
Wimbledon 6 ⊖	a									08 55									09 25			past			
Belmont	d	08 14																			09 14	each			
Banstead	d	08 18																			09 18				
Epsom Downs	a	08 21																			09 21	hour until			
Cheam	d					08 25			08 31			08 43			08 55			09 01							
Ewell East	d					08 28						08 47			08 58			09 05							
Epsom 3	a				08 27	08 32			08 38		08 46	08 51		08 57	09 02			09 09		09 16					18 27
	d				08 28				08 38		08 47			08 58				09 09		09 17					18 28
Ashtead	d				08 32				08 42		08 51			09 02				09 13		09 21					18 32
Leatherhead	d				08 35				08 45		08 54			09 05				09 16		09 24					18 35
Bookham	d										08 59									09 29					
Effingham Junction 6	d										09 03									09 33					
Guildford	a										09b23									09b53					
Boxhill & Westhumble	d																	09 21							
Dorking 4	a				08c43				08 51					09c13				09 24							18c43
	d																	09 24							
Holmwood	d																	09 32							
Ockley	d																	09 36							
Warnham	d																	09 41							
Horsham 4	a																	09 45							

		SN	SN	SN	SN	FC B	SW		SN	SW	SN	SN	FC B	SN		SW	SN	SW	SN	SN	FC B		SW	SN	SN	SW
London Victoria 15 ⊖	d	17 50		17 55	18 03						18 20			18 25			18 45		18 50					18 52	19 15	
London Waterloo 15 ⊖	d						18 09			18 24						18 39		18 54					19 09			19 24
Clapham Junction 10	d	17 56		18 04	18 09		18 18			18 33	18 26			18 34		18 48	18 52	19 03	18 56				19 18	18 59	19 22	19 33
Balham 4 ⊖	d	18 02		18 10							18 32			18 40			18 58		19 02					19 05	19 28	
London Bridge 4 ⊖	d		17 45									18 15														
Tulse Hill 3	d					18 16							18 46								19 16					
New Cross Gate 4 ⊖	d		17 50									18 20														
Norwood Junction 2	d		18 09									18 39												19e24		
West Croydon 4	d		18 14	18 28					←			18 44		18 58			19 14			←				19 30	19 45	
Waddon	d		18 17	18 31					18 31			18 47		19 00			19 17			19 17				19 32	19 47	
Wallington	d		18 20	→					18 34			18 50		19 04			→			19 20				19 36	→	
Carshalton Beeches	d		18 23						18 37			18 53		19 06						19 23				19 38		
Mitcham Eastfields	d	18 09				18 23					18 39		18 53						19 09		19 23					
Mitcham Junction	d	18 12				18 27					18 42		18 57						19 12		19 27					
Hackbridge	d	18 16				18 30					18 46		19 00						19 16		19 30					
Carshalton	d	18 18				18 33					18 48		19 03						19 18		19 33					
Sutton (Surrey) 4	a	18 22	18 26		18 28	18 36			18 40		18 52	18 56	19 06	19 10					19 22	19 26	19 38			19 42		
	d	18 22			18 29	18 37			18 41		18 52		19 07	19 10					19 22		19 39			19 42		
West Sutton	a					18 40							19 10								19 42					
Wimbledon 6 ⊖	a					18 55							19 25								19 57					
Belmont	d													19 14												
Banstead	d													19 17												
Epsom Downs	a													19 21												
Cheam	d	18 25			18 31				18 43		18 55								19 25					19 45		
Ewell East	d	18 28							18 47		18 58								19 28					19 48		
Epsom 3	a	18 32			18 38		18 46		18 51	18 57	19 02					19 12		19 27	19 32				19 42	19 52		19 57
	d				18 38		18 47			18 58	19 03					19 17		19 28	19 33				19 47			19 58
Ashtead	d				18 42		18 51			19 02	19 07					19 21		19 32	19 37				19 51			20 02
Leatherhead	d				18 45		18 54			19 05	19 10					19 24		19 35	19 40				19 54			20 05
Bookham	d						18 59									19 29							19 59			
Effingham Junction 6	d						19 03									19 33							20 03			
Guildford	a						19b23									19b53							20b23			
Boxhill & Westhumble	d										19 15								19 45							
Dorking 4	a				18 51					19c13	19 17							19c43	19 47							20c13
	d																									
Holmwood	d																									
Ockley	d																									
Warnham	d																									
Horsham 4	a																									

For general notes see front of timetable
For details of catering facilities see Directory of Train Operators

A From Luton (Table 52)
B From St Albans City (Table 52)
b Until 27 September arr 3 minutes earlier
c Until 27 September arr 2 minutes earlier
e Arr. 1921

Table 182

Saturdays

London → Sutton, Epsom, Guildford, Dorking and Horsham

Network Diagram - see first page of Table 177

Station		SN	SN	SW	FC A		SN	SN	SW	SN	SW	SN		SN	FC A	SN	SN	SW	SN		SN	SW	FC A	SN	SN	SW
London Victoria 15 ⊖	d	19 20					19 22	19 45		19 50						19 52	20 15		20 20					20 22	20 45	
London Waterloo 15 ⊖	d			19 39					19 54		20 09							20 24				20 39				20 54
Clapham Junction 10	d	19 26		19 48			19 29	19 52	20 03	19 56	20 18					19 59	20 22	20 33	20 26			20 48		20 29	20 52	21 03
Balham 4 ⊖	d	19 32					19 35	19 58		20 02						20 05	20 28		20 32					20 35	20 58	
London Bridge 4 ⊖	d																									
Tulse Hill 3	d																									
New Cross Gate 4 ⊖	d																									
Norwood Junction 2	d						19b54									20c24								20e54		
West Croydon 4	d		←				20 00	20 15						←		20 30	20 45				←			21 00	21 15	
Waddon	d		19 47				20 02	20 17						20 17		20 32	20 47				20 47			21 02	21 17	
Wallington	d		19 51				20 06	→						20 21		20 36	→				20 51			21 06	→	
Carshalton Beeches	d		19 53				20 08							20 23		20 38					20 53			21 08		
Mitcham Eastfields	d	19 39								20 09									20 39							
Mitcham Junction	d	19 42								20 12									20 42							
Hackbridge	d	19 46								20 16									20 46							
Carshalton	d	19 48								20 18									20 48							
Sutton (Surrey) 4	a	19 52	19 57				20 12			20 22		←		20 27		20 42			20 51		20 57			21 12		
	d	19 52			20 09		20 23			20 22		20 23			20 39	20 42			20 52				21 09	21 23		
West Sutton	a				20 12		→								20 42								21 12	→		
Wimbledon 6 ⊖	a				20 27										20 57								21 27			
Belmont	d											20 26														
Banstead	d											20 30														
Epsom Downs	a											20 33														
Cheam	d	19 55								20 25						20 45			20 55							
Ewell East	d	19 58								20 28						20 48			20 58							
Epsom 3	a	20 02		20 12					20 27	20 32	20 42					20 52		20 57	21 02			21 12				21 27
	d	20 03		20 17						20 33	20 47								21 03			21 17				
Ashtead	d	20 07		20 21						20 37	20 51								21 07			21 21				
Leatherhead	d	20 10		20 24						20 40	20 54								21 10			21 24				
Bookham	d			20 29																		21 29				
Effingham Junction 6	d			20 33																		21 33				
Guildford	a			20f53																		21f53				
Boxhill & Westhumble	d									20 45																
Dorking 4	a	20 16								20 47	21g02								21 16							
	d																									
Holmwood	d																									
Ockley	d																									
Warnham	d																									
Horsham 4	a																									

Station		SN	SW		SN	SN	SN	SN	SW	SN		FC A	SN	SN	SW	SN	SW		SN	SW	SN	SN	SN	SN		SN
London Victoria 15 ⊖	d	20 50					20 52	21 15		21 20				21 22		21 45			21 50				21 52	22 15		22 20
London Waterloo 15 ⊖	d		21 09						21 24						21 39		21 54			22 09						
Clapham Junction 10	d	20 56	21 18				20 59	21 22	21 33	21 26				21 29	21 48	21 52	22 03		21 56	22 18			21 59	22 22		22 26
Balham 4 ⊖	d	21 02					21 05	21 28		21 32				21 35		21 58			22 02				22 05	22 28		22 32
London Bridge 4 ⊖	d																									
Tulse Hill 3	d																									
New Cross Gate 4 ⊖	d																									
Norwood Junction 2	d						21h24							21j54									22k24			
West Croydon 4	d					←	21 30	21 45					←	22 00		22 15						←	22 30	22 45		
Waddon	d					21 17	21 32	21 47					21 47	22 02		22 17						22 17	22 32	22 47		
Wallington	d					21 21	21 36	→					21 51	22 06		→						22 21	22 36	→		
Carshalton Beeches	d					21 23	21 38						21 53	22 08								22 23	22 38			
Mitcham Eastfields	d	21 09								21 39									22 09							22 39
Mitcham Junction	d	21 12								21 42									22 12							22 42
Hackbridge	d	21 16								21 46									22 16							22 46
Carshalton	d	21 18								21 48									22 18							22 48
Sutton (Surrey) 4	a	21 22			←	21 27	21 42			21 52			21 57	22 12					22 22		←	22 27	22 42			22 52
	d	21 22			21 23		21 42			21 52		21 49		22 23					22 22		22 23		22 42			22 52
West Sutton	a											21 52		→												
Wimbledon 6 ⊖	a											22 07														
Belmont	d				21 26																22 26					
Banstead	d				21 30																22 30					
Epsom Downs	a				21 33																22 33					
Cheam	d	21 25					21 45			21 55									22 25				22 45			22 55
Ewell East	d	21 28					21 48			21 58									22 28				22 48			22 58
Epsom 3	a	21 32	21 42				21 52		21 57	22 02					22 12		22 27		22 33	22 42			22 52			23 02
	d	21 33	21 47							22 03					22 17				22 33	22 47						23 03
Ashtead	d	21 37	21 51							22 07					22 21				22 37	22 51						23 07
Leatherhead	d	21 40	21 54							22 10					22 24				22 40	22 54						23 10
Bookham	d														22 29											
Effingham Junction 6	d														22 33											
Guildford	a														22f53											
Boxhill & Westhumble	d	21 45																	22 45							
Dorking 4	a	21 47	22g02							22 16									22 47	23g02						23 16
	d																									
Holmwood	d																									
Ockley	d																									
Warnham	d																									
Horsham 4	a																									

For general notes see front of timetable
For details of catering facilities see Directory of Train Operators

A To Bedford (Table 52)
b Arr. 1951
c Arr. 2021
e Arr. 2051
f Until 27 September arr 3 minutes earlier
g Until 27 September arr 2 minutes earlier
h Arr. 2121
j Arr. 2151
k Arr. 2221

Table 182

London → Sutton, Epsom, Guildford, Dorking and Horsham

Saturdays

Network Diagram - see first page of Table 177

Station		SN	SN	SW	SN	SN	SW		SN	SN	SN	SN	SN	SN		SN	SW	SN	SN
London Victoria 15 ⊖	d		22 22		22 45	22 50					22 52	23 15	23 22	23 26					23 51
London Waterloo 15 ⊖	d			22 39			23 09										23 42		
Clapham Junction 10	d		22 29	22 48	22 52	22 56	23 18				22 59	23 22	23 29	23 32			23 51		23 58
Balham 4 ⊖	d		22 35		22 58	23 00					23 05	23 28	23 35	23 37					00 04
London Bridge 4 ⊖	d																		
Tulse Hill 3	d																		
New Cross Gate 4 ⊖	d																		
Norwood Junction 2	d		22b54								23c24		23e54						
West Croydon 4	d	←	23 00		23 15					←	23 30	23 45	00f01			←		←	00 20
Waddon	d	22 47	23 02		23 18					23 18	23 32	23 48	00 03			23 48		00 03	00 22
Wallington	d	22 51	23 06		→					23 21	23 36	→	→			23 51		00 07	00 26
Carshalton Beeches	d	22 53	23 08							23 24	23 38					23 54		00 09	00 28
Mitcham Eastfields	d					23 07								23 44					
Mitcham Junction	d					23 11								23 48					
Hackbridge	d					23 14								23 51					
Carshalton	d					23 17								23 54					
Sutton (Surrey) 4	a	22 57	23 12			23 20			←	23 27	23 42			23 58		23 57		00 13	00 32
	d		23 23			23 21			23 23		23 42			23 58					
West Sutton	a		→																
Wimbledon 6 ⊖	a																		
Belmont	d								23 26										
Banstead	d								23 30										
Epsom Downs	a								23 33										
Cheam	d					23 23					23 45			00 01					
Ewell East	d					23 27					23 48			00 04					
Epsom 3	a			23 12		23 31	23 42				23 52			00 08			00 15		
	d			23 17		23 31	23 47							00 09			00 19		
Ashtead	d			23 21		23 35	23 51							00 13			00 23		
Leatherhead	d			23 24		23 38	23 54							00 16			00 26		
Bookham	d			23 29													00 31		
Effingham Junction 6	d			23 33													00 36		
Guildford	a			23 54													00g56		
Boxhill & Westhumble	d					23 43								00 21					
Dorking 4	a					23 46	00h03							00 23					
	d																		
Holmwood	d																		
Ockley	d																		
Warnham	d																		
Horsham 4	a																		

Sundays

Station		SN	SN	SW	SN		SN	SW	SN	SW A		SN	SN	SN	SW
London Victoria 15 ⊖	d	23p22	23p26				23p51		06 49			07 19	07 38	07 49	
London Waterloo 15 ⊖	d			23p42				00 15							08 02
Clapham Junction 10	d	23p29	23p32	23p51			23p58	00 24	06 56			07 26	07 45	07 56	08 11
Balham 4 ⊖	d	23p35	23p37				00 04		07 02			07 32	07 51	08 02	
London Bridge 4 ⊖	d														
Tulse Hill 3	d														
New Cross Gate 4 ⊖	d														
Norwood Junction 2	d	23j54											08 07		
West Croydon 4	d	00f01			←		00 20		07 20			07 50	08 13	08 20	
Waddon	d	00 03			00 03		00 22		07 22			07 52		08 22	
Wallington	d	→			00 07		00 26		07 26			07 56	08 18	08 26	
Carshalton Beeches	d				00 09		00 28		07 28			07 58		08 28	
Mitcham Eastfields	d		23p44												
Mitcham Junction	d		23p48												
Hackbridge	d		23p51												
Carshalton	d		23p54												
Sutton (Surrey) 4	a		23p57		00 13		00 32		07 32			08 02	08 22	08 32	
	d		23p58						07 37			08 07			
West Sutton	a														
Wimbledon 6 ⊖	a														
Belmont	d														
Banstead	d														
Epsom Downs	a														
Cheam	d		00 01						07 39			08 09			
Ewell East	d		00 04						07 43			08 13			
Epsom 3	a		00 08	00 15				00 48	07 47	08 06		08 17			08 36
	d		00 09	00 19					07 47	08 08		08 17			08 38
Ashtead	d		00 13	00 23					07 51	08 12		08 21			08 42
Leatherhead	d		00 16	00 26					07 54	08 15		08 24			08 45
Bookham	d			00 31						08 20					
Effingham Junction 6	d			00 36						08 24					
Guildford	a			00g56						08g44					
Boxhill & Westhumble	d		00 21						07 59			08 29			
Dorking 4	a		00 23						08 02			08 32			08 51
	d														
Holmwood	d														
Ockley	d														
Warnham	d														
Horsham 4	a														

Station			SN	SN	SN	SW		SN	SN	SN	SW	SN
London Victoria 15 ⊖	d		08 06	08 08	08 19			08 36	08 38	08 49		09 06
London Waterloo 15 ⊖	d					08 32					09 02	
Clapham Junction 10	d		08 12	08 15	08 26	08 41		08 42	08 45	08 56	09 11	09 12
Balham 4 ⊖	d		08 16	08 21	08 32			08 46	08 51	09 02		09 16
London Bridge 4 ⊖	d											
Tulse Hill 3	d											
New Cross Gate 4 ⊖	d											
Norwood Junction 2	d			08 37					09 07			
West Croydon 4	d			08 43	08 50				09 13	09 20		
Waddon	d				08 52					09 22		
Wallington	d			08 48	08 56				09 18	09 26		
Carshalton Beeches	d				08 58					09 28		
Mitcham Eastfields	d		08 23					08 53				09 23
Mitcham Junction	d		08 27					08 57				09 27
Hackbridge	d		08 30					09 00				09 30
Carshalton	d		08 33					09 03				09 33
Sutton (Surrey) 4	a		08 36	08 52	09 02			09 06	09 22	09 32		09 36
	d		08 37					09 07				09 37
West Sutton	a											
Wimbledon 6 ⊖	a											
Belmont	d											
Banstead	d											
Epsom Downs	a											
Cheam	d		08 39					09 09				09 39
Ewell East	d		08 43					09 13				09 43
Epsom 3	a		08 47			09 06		09 17			09 36	09 47
	d		08 47			09 08		09 17			09 38	09 47
Ashtead	d		08 51			09 12		09 21			09 42	09 51
Leatherhead	d		08 54			09 15		09 24			09 45	09 54
Bookham	d					09 20						
Effingham Junction 6	d					09 24						
Guildford	a					09g44						
Boxhill & Westhumble	d		08 59					09 29				09 59
Dorking 4	a		09 02					09 32			09 51	10 02
	d											
Holmwood	d											
Ockley	d											
Warnham	d											
Horsham 4	a											

For general notes see front of timetable
For details of catering facilities see Directory of Train Operators

- **A** From Wimbledon (Table 152)
- **b** Arr. 2251
- **c** Arr. 2321
- **e** Arr. 2351
- **f** Arr. 2358
- **g** Until 27 September arr 3 minutes earlier
- **h** Until 27 September arr 2 minutes earlier
- **j** Previous night. Arr. 2351

Table 182

Sundays

London → Sutton, Epsom, Guildford, Dorking and Horsham

Network Diagram - see first page of Table 177

Station		SN	SN	SW	SN	FC A	SN	SN	SW	SN	FC A	SN	SN	SW	SN	and at the same minutes past each hour until	FC B	SN	SN	SW	SN
London Victoria 15 ⊖	d	09 08	09 19		09 36		09 38	09 49		10 06		10 08	10 19		10 36			20 38	20 49		21 06
London Waterloo 15 ⊖	d			09 32					10 02					10 32						21 02	
Clapham Junction 10	d	09 15	09 26	09 41	09 42		09 45	09 56	10 11	10 12		10 15	10 26	10 41	10 42			20 45	20 56	21 11	21 12
Balham 4 ⊖	d	09 21	09 32		09 46		09 51	10 02		10 16		10 21	10 32		10 46			20 51	21 02		21 16
London Bridge 4 ⊖	d																				
Tulse Hill 3	d																				
New Cross Gate 4 ⊖	d																				
Norwood Junction 2	d	09 37					10 07					10 37						21 07			
West Croydon 4	d	09 43	09 50				10 13	10 20				10 43	10 50					21 13	21 20		
Waddon	d		09 52					10 22					10 52						21 22		
Wallington	d	09 48	09 56				10 18	10 26				10 48	10 56					21 18	21 26		
Carshalton Beeches	d		09 58					10 28					10 58						21 28		
Mitcham Eastfields	d				09 53					10 23					10 53						21 23
Mitcham Junction	d				09 57					10 27					10 57						21 27
Hackbridge	d				10 00					10 30					11 00						21 30
Carshalton	d				10 03					10 33					11 03						21 33
Sutton (Surrey) 4	a	09 52	10 02		10 06		10 22	10 32		10 36		10 52	11 02		11 06			21 22	21 32		21 36
	d				10 07	10 10				10 37	10 40				11 07		21 10				21 37
West Sutton	a					10 13					10 43						21 13				
Wimbledon 6 ⊖	a					10 25					10 55						21 25				
Belmont	d																				
Banstead	d																				
Epsom Downs	a																				
Cheam	d				10 09					10 39					11 09						21 39
Ewell East	d				10 13					10 43					11 13						21 43
Epsom 3	a			10 06	10 17				10 36	10 47				11 06	11 17					21 36	21 47
	d			10 08	10 17				10 38	10 47				11 08	11 17					21 38	21 47
Ashtead	d			10 12	10 21				10 42	10 51				11 12	11 21					21 42	21 51
Leatherhead	d			10 15	10 24				10 45	10 54				11 15	11 24					21 45	21 54
Bookham	d			10 20										11 20							
Effingham Junction 6	d			10 24										11 24							
Guildford	a			10b44										11b44							
Boxhill & Westhumble	d				10 29					10 59					11 29						21 59
Dorking 4	a				10 32				10 51	11 02					11 32					21 51	22 02
	d																				
Holmwood	d																				
Ockley	d																				
Warnham	d																				
Horsham 4	a																				

Station		SN	SN	SW	SN	SN	SN	SW	SN	SN	SN	SW	SN	SN	SN	SW	SN	SW	SN
London Victoria 15 ⊖	d	21 08	21 19		21 36	21 38	21 49		22 06	22 08	22 19		22 36	22 38	22 49		23 06		23 19
London Waterloo 15 ⊖	d			21 32				22 02				22 32				23 02		23 32	
Clapham Junction 10	d	21 15	21 26	21 41	21 42	21 45	21 56	22 11	22 12	22 15	22 26	22 41	22 42	22 45	22 56	23 11	23 12	23 41	23 26
Balham 4 ⊖	d	21 21	21 32		21 46	21 51	22 02		22 16	22 21	22 32		22 46	22 51	23 02		23 16		23 32
London Bridge 4 ⊖	d																		
Tulse Hill 3	d																		
New Cross Gate 4 ⊖	d																		
Norwood Junction 2	d	21 37				22 07				22 39				23 07					
West Croydon 4	d	21 43	21 50			22 13	22 20			22 43	22 50			23 13	23 20				23 50
Waddon	d		21 52				22 22				22 52				23 22				23 52
Wallington	d	21 48	21 56			22 18	22 26			22 48	22 56			23 18	23 26				23 56
Carshalton Beeches	d		21 58				22 28				22 58				23 28				23 58
Mitcham Eastfields	d				21 53				22 23				22 53				23 23		
Mitcham Junction	d				21 57				22 27				22 57				23 27		
Hackbridge	d				22 00				22 30				23 00				23 30		
Carshalton	d				22 03				22 33				23 03				23 33		
Sutton (Surrey) 4	a	21 52	22 02		22 06	22 22	22 32		22 36	22 53	23 02		23 06	23 22	23 32		23 36		00 02
	d				22 07				22 37				23 07				23 37		00 04
West Sutton	a																		
Wimbledon 6 ⊖	a																		
Belmont	d																		
Banstead	d																		
Epsom Downs	a																		
Cheam	d				22 09				22 39				23 09				23 39		00 06
Ewell East	d				22 13				22 43				23 13				23 43		00 10
Epsom 3	a			22 06	22 17			22 36	22 47			23 06	23 17			23 36	23 47	00 06	00 14
	d			22 08	22 17			22 38	22 47			23 08	23 17				23 47		
Ashtead	d			22 12	22 21			22 42	22 51			23 12	23 21				23 51		
Leatherhead	d			22 15	22 24			22 45	22 54			23 15	23 24				23 54		
Bookham	d			22 20								23 20							
Effingham Junction 6	d			22 24								23 24							
Guildford	a			22b44								23b44							
Boxhill & Westhumble	d				22 29				22 59				23 29				23 59		
Dorking 4	a				22 32			22 51	23 02				23 32				00 02		
	d																		
Holmwood	d																		
Ockley	d																		
Warnham	d																		
Horsham 4	a																		

For general notes see front of timetable
For details of catering facilities see Directory of Train Operators

A To Luton (Table 52)
B To Bedford (Table 52)
b Until 27 September arr 3 minutes earlier

Horsham, Dorking, Guildford, Epsom and Sutton → London

Network Diagram - see first page of Table 177

Miles	Miles	Miles		SN MX	SN	SN	SW	SN	SN	SN	SN	SW		SN	SW	SN	SN	SN	SN	SW	SW	SN		SN	SN
—	—	0	**Horsham 4** d														05 49							06 20	
—	—	2	Warnham d														05 53							06 24	
—	—	6½	Ockley d														06 00							06 31	
—	—	8¾	Holmwood d														06 04							06 35	
—	—	13¾	**Dorking 4** a														06 10							06 41	
—	—	—	d									05 48					06 11				06 32			06 44	
—	—	14½	Boxhill & Westhumble d									05 50					06 13				06 34			06 46	
0	—	—	**Guildford** d				04 58													05 58					
8¼	—	—	Effingham Junction 6 d				05 16													06 16					
10	—	—	Bookham d				05 19													06 19					
12½	—	17¾	Leatherhead d				05 24					05 56					06 18			06 24	06 39			06 51	
14½	—	—	Ashtead d				05 28					05 59					06 22			06 28	06 43			06 55	
16¼	—	—	**Epsom 3** a				05 32					06 04					06 26			06 32	06 47			06 59	
—	—	—	d		05 23		05 34	05 40		05 57		06 04			06 18		06 27			06 33	06 48	06 54		07 00	
17¾	—	—	Ewell East d		05 27			05 44		06 01							06 31					06 58		07 04	
19¼	—	—	Cheam d		05 30			05 47		06 04							06 34					07 01		07 07	
—	0	—	**Epsom Downs** d	23p44														06 38							07 08
—	1½	—	Banstead d	23p47														06 41							07 11
—	3	—	Belmont d	23p50														06 44							07 14
—	—	0	Wimbledon 6 ⊖ ⛴ d								05 57								06 33						
—	—	4½	West Sutton d								06 11								06 47						
20¼	4	5½	**Sutton (Surrey) 4** a	23p53	05 33			05 50		06 07	06 14						06 37	06 47	06 50			07 04		07 10	07 17
—	—	—	d	23p54	05 33	05 37		05 50	06 03	06 07	06 15			06 19		06 33	06 37	06 48	06 51			07 04		07 10	07 18
—	5¼	—	Carshalton d			05 40				06 10	06 18						06 40		06 54					07 13	
—	6¼	—	Hackbridge d			05 42				06 13	06 20						06 43		06 56					07 16	
—	7	—	Mitcham Junction ⛴ d			05 46				06 16	06 24						06 46		07 00					07 19	
—	8	—	Mitcham Eastfields d			05 49				06 20	06 27						06 50							07 23	
21¼	—	—	Carshalton Beeches d	23p57	05 36			05 53	06 06					06 22		06 36		06 51				07 07			07 21
22	—	—	Wallington d	23p59	05 39			05 56	06 08					06 24		06 38		06 54				07 10			07 23
23½	—	—	Waddon d	00 02	05 42			05 59	06 11					06 27		06 41		06 57				07 13			07 26
24½	—	0	**West Croydon 4** ⛴ d	00a05	05 45			06 02	06 15					06 31		06 45		07 00				07 16			07 30
26¼	—	—	Norwood Junction 2 d		05 50				06 19							06 50						07 21			
32¼	—	—	New Cross Gate 4 ⊖ d		06 07				06 37							07 08						07 39			
—	—	6	Tulse Hill 3 d			05 57					06 35								07 09						
35	—	12	**London Bridge 4** ⊖ a		06 14	06 08			06 45		06 52					07 16			07 25			07 48			
—	11¼	—	Balham 4 ⊖ d					06 18		06 27				06 47			06 57	07 16						07 29	07 46
—	13¼	—	Clapham Junction 10 a				06 00	06 23		06 31		06 30		06 52	06 45		07 01	07 21		07 00	07 15			07 33	07 51
—	—	—	**London Waterloo 15** ⊖ a				06 11					06 40			06 55					07 12	07 27				
—	16	—	**London Victoria 15** ⊖ a					06 31		06 38				07 02			07 10	07 31						07 42	08 01

	SW	SN	SN	SW	SN	SW	SW	SN	SN		SN	SN	SN	SW	SW	SN	SN	SW	SN		SN	SW	SN	SN	SW
Horsham 4 d								06 58											07 28						
Warnham d								07 02											07 32						
Ockley d								07 09											07 39						
Holmwood d								07 13											07 43						
Dorking 4 a								07 19											07 49						
d		06 55		07 02				07 20						07 32					07 50			08 02			
Boxhill & Westhumble d		06 57		07 04										07 34								08 04			
Guildford d	06 28						06 58									07 26									
Effingham Junction 6 d	06b48						07 16									07 38		07 46							
Bookham d	06 51						07 19									07 41		07 49							
Leatherhead d	06 56	07 02		07 09			07 24	07 26						07 39		07 46		07 54	07 56			08 09			
Ashtead d	06 59	07 06		07 13			07 27	07 30						07 43		07 50		07 57	08 00			08 13			
Epsom 3 a	07 04	07 10		07 17			07 32	07 34						07 47		07 54		08 02	08 04			08 17			
d	07 04	07 11		07 18	07 21	07 22	07 34	07 35					07 44	07 48	07 52	07 55		08 04	08 05			08 18		08 22	08 22
Ewell East d		07 15			07 25								07 48			07 59			08 09					08 26	
Cheam d		07 18			07 28			07 40					07 51			08 02			08 12					08 29	
Epsom Downs d									07 34								08 00								
Banstead d									07 37								08 03								
Belmont d									07 40								08 06								
Wimbledon 6 ⊖ ⛴ d			07 03								07 32										08 02				
West Sutton d			07 21								07 46										08 16				
Sutton (Surrey) 4 a		07 21	07 25		07 31			07 43	07 43		07 49		07 54			08 05	08 09		08 15		08 19			08 32	
d		07 21	07 25		07 31			07 44	07 48		07 50	07 55	07 54			08 05	08 10		08 15		08 20		08 25	08 32	
Carshalton d		07 24	07 28					07 47			07 53		07 57						08 18				08 28		
Hackbridge d		07 27	07 31								07 55		08 00						08 21				08 30		
Mitcham Junction ⛴ d		07 30	07 34					07 51			07 59		08 03						08 24				08 34		
Mitcham Eastfields d		07 34	07 38										08 07										08 37		
Carshalton Beeches d					07 34				07 51			07 58				08 08	08 13				08 23			08 35	
Wallington d					07 37				07 53			08 00				08 11	08 15				08 25			08 38	
Waddon d					07 40				07 56			08 03					08 18				08 28			08 41	
West Croydon 4 ⛴ d					07 43				08 01			08 07				08 16	08 23				08 32			08 44	
Norwood Junction 2 d					07 48											08 20	08 28							08 49	
New Cross Gate 4 ⊖ d					08 00																			09 07	
Tulse Hill 3 d			07 46								08 10														
London Bridge 4 ⊖ a			08 02		08 08						08 30					08 42	08 47							09 17	
Balham 4 ⊖ d		07 42						08 00	08 17			08 22	08 14								08 48		08 44		
Clapham Junction 10 a	07 30	07 48		07 42		07 48	08 01	08 04	08 22			08 26	08 18	08 12	08 18			08 31	08 34		08 53	08 42	08 50		08 48
London Waterloo 15 ⊖ a	07 42			07 54		08 00	08 13							08 24	08 30			08 43				08 54			09 00
London Victoria 15 ⊖ a		07 57						08 13	08 32			08 36	08 28						08 43		09 03		08 59		

For general notes see front of timetable
For details of catering facilities see
Directory of Train Operators

b Arr. 0644

Horsham, Dorking, Guildford, Epsom and Sutton → London

Network Diagram - see first page of Table 177

		SN	SW	SN	SN	SW	SN	SN	SN	SN	SW	SN	SW	SN	SN	SW	FC A	SN	SN	SN	SN	SW	SN	FC A
Horsham 4	d			07 56																09 08				
Warnham	d			08 00																09 12				
Ockley	d			08 07																09 19				
Holmwood	d			08 11																09 23				
Dorking 4	a			08 17																09 29				
	d			08 18		08 31						08 57	09 02							09 29		09 35		
Boxhill & Westhumble	d			08 20		08 33						08 59	09 04							09 32				
Guildford	d		07 58				08 16									08 58								
Effingham Junction 6	d		08 15				08 32				08 48					09 16								
Bookham	d		08 18				08 35				08 51					09 19								
Leatherhead	d		08 23	08 26		08 38	08 41				08 56	09 04	09 09			09 24				09 37		09 41		
Ashtead	d		08 27	08 29		08 42	08 45				08 59	09 08	09 13			09 28				09 40		09 44		
Epsom 3	a		08 31	08 34		08 46	08 49				09 04	09 12	09 17			09 32				09 45		09 49		
	d		08 34	08 34		08 48	08 50				09 04	09 13	09 18		09 24	09 35				09 45	09 48	09 50		
Ewell East	d			08 38			08 54					09 17			09 28					09 49	09 52			
Cheam	d			08 41			08 57					09 20			09 31					09 52	09 55			
Epsom Downs	d	08 32								09 09								09 35						
Banstead	d	08 35								09 12								09 38						
Belmont	d	08 38								09 15								09 41						
Wimbledon 6 ⊖	d				08 32				08 55								09 17							09 47
West Sutton	d				08 46				09 09								09 31							10 01
Sutton (Surrey) 4	a	08 41		08 44	08 49		09 00		09 13	09 18		09 23			09 34		09 37	09 44		09 55	09 58			10 05
	d	08 45		08 45	08 50		09 02	09 06	09 15	09 23		09 23		09 32	09 34		09 38	09 45	09 53	09 56	09 59		10 03	10 06
Carshalton	d			08 48	08 53			09 09						09 35			09 41				10 02			10 09
Hackbridge	d			08 50	08 55			09 11						09 37			09 43				10 04			10 11
Mitcham Junction	d			08 54				09 15						09 41			09 46			10 02	10 08			10 14
Mitcham Eastfields	d			09 02	09 02							09 32					09 50				10 11			10 18
Carshalton Beeches	d	08 48					09 05		09 18	09 26					09 37			09 48	09 56				10 06	
Wallington	d	08 50					09 07		09 20	09 28					09 40			09 51	09 58				10 08	
Waddon	d	08 53					09 10		09 23	09 31					09 43			09 54	10 01				10 11	
West Croydon 4	d	08 57					09 15		09 27	09 35					09 46			09 57	10 05				10 15	
Norwood Junction 2	d						09 19								09 51								10 19	
New Cross Gate 4 ⊖	d						09 37								10 08								10 37	
Tulse Hill 3	d				09 09												09a58							10a27
London Bridge 4 ⊖	a				09 29		09 46								10 15								10 44	
Balham 4 ⊖	d	09 13		09 02				09 23	09 43	09 52				09 49				10 13	10 21		10 18			
Clapham Junction 10	a	09 18	09 00	09 06		09 15		09 27	09 49	09 57	09 30	09 42	09 45	09 53		10 00		10 18	10 26	10 12	10 22	10 15		
London Waterloo 15 ⊖	a		09 12			09 27					09 42		09 57			10 10						10 25		
London Victoria 15 ⊖	a	09 29		09 16				09 36	10 00	10 05		09 51		10 01				10 26	10 34	10 19	10 29			

		SW	SN	SN	SN	SN	SW	SN	FC A	SN	SW	SN	SN	SN	SW	SN	FC A	SW	SN	SN	SN	SN	SW
Horsham 4	d											10 04											
Warnham	d											10 08											
Ockley	d											10 15											
Holmwood	d											10 19											
Dorking 4	a											10 25											
	d			09 57			10 05					10 26			10 35					10 58			11 05
Boxhill & Westhumble	d			09 59								10 28											
Guildford	d	09 28									09 58							10 28					
Effingham Junction 6	d	09 46									10 16							10 46					
Bookham	d	09 49									10 19							10 49					
Leatherhead	d	09 54		10 04			10 11				10 24	10 33			10 41			10 54		11 04			11 11
Ashtead	d	09 58		10 08			10 14				10 28	10 37			10 44			10 58		11 07			11 14
Epsom 3	a	10 02		10 12			10 19				10 32	10 41			10 49			11 02		11 12			11 19
	d	10 05	10 05	10 13		10 18	10 20				10 35	10 42		10 48	10 50			11 05	11 05	11 12		11 18	11 20
Ewell East	d		10 09	10 17		10 22						10 46		10 52					11 09			11 22	
Cheam	d		10 12	10 20		10 25						10 49		10 55					11 12	11 18		11 25	
Epsom Downs	d									10 35													
Banstead	d									10 38													
Belmont	d									10 41													
Wimbledon 6 ⊖	d								10 17								10 47						
West Sutton	d								10 31								11 01						
Sutton (Surrey) 4	a		10 15	10 23		10 28			10 35	10 44		10 52		10 58			11 05		11 15	11 22		11 28	
	d		10 15	10 23	10 23	10 28		10 33	10 36	10 45		10 52	10 53	10 58		11 03	11 06		11 15	11 22	11 23	11 28	
Carshalton	d					10 31			10 39					11 01			11 09					11 31	
Hackbridge	d					10 34			10 41					11 04			11 11					11 34	
Mitcham Junction	d					10 37			10 44					11 07			11 14					11 37	
Mitcham Eastfields	d					10 41			10 48					11 11			11 18					11 41	
Carshalton Beeches	d		10 18		10 26			10 36		10 48			10 56			11 06			11 18		11 26		
Wallington	d		10 21		10 28			10 38		10 51			10 58			11 08			11 21		11 28		
Waddon	d		10 24		10 31			10 41		10 54			11 01			11 11			11 24		11 31		
West Croydon 4	d		10 27		10 35			10 45		10 57			11 05			11 15			11 27		11 35		
Norwood Junction 2	d							10 49								11 19							
New Cross Gate 4 ⊖	d							11 07								11 37							
Tulse Hill 3	d								10a57								11a27						
London Bridge 4 ⊖	a							11 14								11 44							
Balham 4 ⊖	d		10 43		10 51	10 48				11 13			11 21	11 18					11 43		11 51	11 48	
Clapham Junction 10	a	10 30	10 48	10 40	10 56	10 52	10 45			11 18	11 00	11 10	11 26	11 22	11 15			11 30	11 48	11 40	11 56	11 52	11 45
London Waterloo 15 ⊖	a	10 40					10 55				11 10				11 25			11 40					11 55
London Victoria 15 ⊖	a		10 56	10 48	11 04	10 59				11 26		11 18	11 34	11 29					11 56	11 48	12 04	11 59	

For general notes see front of timetable
For details of catering facilities see
Directory of Train Operators

A To St Albans City (Table 52)

Horsham, Dorking, Guildford, Epsom and Sutton → London

Network Diagram - see first page of Table 177

		SN	FC A	SN	SW	SN	SN	SN	SW	SN	FC A	SW			SN	SN	SN	SN	SW	SN	SW	FC B	SN		SN
Horsham 4	d					11 04																			16 00
Warnham	d					11 08																			16 04
Ockley	d					11 15																			16 11
Holmwood	d					11 19																			16 15
Dorking 4	a					11 25																			16 21
	d					11 26			11 35							15 57			16 05						16 26
Boxhill & Westhumble	d					11 28										15 59									16 28
Guildford	d				10 58							11 28									15 58				
Effingham Junction 6	d				11 16							11 46									16 16				
Bookham	d				11 19							11 49									16 19				
Leatherhead	d				11 24	11 33			11 41			11 54				16 04			16 11		16 24				16 33
Ashtead	d				11 28	11 37			11 44			11 58				16 08			16 14		16 28				16 37
Epsom 3	a				11 32	11 41			11 49			12 02				16 12			16 19		16 32				16 41
	d				11 35	11 42		11 48	11 50			12 05	and at the same minutes past each hour until		16 05	16 13		16 18	16 20		16 35				16 42
Ewell East	d					11 46		11 52							16 09	16 17		16 22							
Cheam	d					11 49		11 55							16 12	16 20		16 25							
Epsom Downs	d			11 35																			16 30		
Banstead	d			11 38																			16 33		
Belmont	d			11 41																			16 36		
Wimbledon 6 ⊖	d		11 17								11 47											16 17			
West Sutton	d		11 31								12 01											16 31			
Sutton (Surrey) 4	a		11 35	11 44		11 52		11 58			12 05				16 15	16 23		16 28				16 35	16 39		16 49
	d	11 33	11 36	11 45		11 52	11 53	11 58		12 03	12 06				16 15	16 23	16 23	16 28		16 33		16 38	16 45		16 49
Carshalton	d		11 39					12 01			12 09							16 31				16 41			
Hackbridge	d		11 41					12 04			12 11							16 34				16 43			
Mitcham Junction	d		11 44					12 07			12 14							16 37				16 46			16 55
Mitcham Eastfields	d		11 48					12 11			12 18							16 41				16 50			
Carshalton Beeches	d	11 36		11 48			11 56			12 06					16 18		16 26			16 36			16 48		
Wallington	d	11 38		11 51			11 58			12 08					16 21		16 28			16 38			16 51		
Waddon	d	11 41		11 54			12 01			12 11					16 24		16 31			16 41			16 54		
West Croydon 4	d	11 45		11 57			12 05			12 15					16 27		16 35			16 45			16 57		
Norwood Junction 2	d	11 49								12 19										16 49					
New Cross Gate 4 ⊖	d	12 07								12 37										17 07					
Tulse Hill 3	d		11a57								12a27											16a59			
London Bridge 4 ⊖	a	12 14								12 44										17 14					
Balham 4 ⊖	d			12 13			12 21	12 18							16 43		16 51	16 47					17 13		
Clapham Junction 10	a			12 18	12 01	12 10	12 26	12 22	12 15			12 30			16 48	16 40	16 56	16 51	16 45		17 00		17 18		17 10
London Waterloo 15 ⊖	a				12 11				12 25			12 40							16 55		17 10				
London Victoria 15 ⊖	a			12 26		12 18	12 34	12 29							16 56	16 48	17 04	16 58					17 26		17 18

		SN	SN	SW	SN	FC C	SN	SW	SN	SW		FC A	SN	SN	SW	SN	SW	SW	SN	FC A		SN	SN	SN	FC D	SW
Horsham 4	d															17 08								17 44		
Warnham	d															17 12										
Ockley	d															17 19										
Holmwood	d															17 23										
Dorking 4	a															17 29								18 00		
	d			16 35					17 00	17 05						17 30	17 35							18 00		18 05
Boxhill & Westhumble	d								17 02							17 33								18 03		
Guildford	d							16 28							16 58			17 28					17 42			
Effingham Junction 6	d							16 46							17 16			17 46					17 55			
Bookham	d							16 49							17 19			17 49								
Leatherhead	d			16 41				16 54	17 07	17 11					17 24	17 38	17 41	17 54					18 02	18 08		18 11
Ashtead	d			16 44				16 58	17 11	17 14					17 28	17 41	17 44	17 58					18 06	18 11		18 14
Epsom 3	a			16 49				17 02	17 15	17 19					17 32	17 46	17 49	18 02					18 10	18 16		18 19
	d		16 45	16 50	16 53			17 05	17 16	17 20			17 25		17 35	17 47	17 50	18 05					18 11	18 16		18 20
Ewell East	d		16 49										17 29			17 51								18 20		
Cheam	d		16 52		16 58				17 21				17 32			17 54								18 23		
Epsom Downs	d						17 00							17 30								18 00				
Banstead	d						17 03							17 33								18 03				
Belmont	d						17 06							17 36								18 06				
Wimbledon 6 ⊖	d					16 46						17 13								17 45					18 14	
West Sutton	d					17 00						17 27								17 59					18 28	
Sutton (Surrey) 4	a		16 55		17 01	17 05	17 09		17 24			17 31	17 35	17 39		17 57				18 03		18 09	18 18	18 26	18 31	
	d	16 53	16 55		17 02	17 06	17 18		17 25			17 32	17 35	17 48		17 58			18 03	18 04		18 10	18 18	18 27		
Carshalton	d		16 58			17 09			17 28			17 35				18 01				18 07				18 30		
Hackbridge	d		17 01			17 11			17 30			17 37				18 03				18 09				18 32		
Mitcham Junction	d		17 04			17 14			17 34			17 40				18 07				18 12				18 36		
Mitcham Eastfields	d		17 08			17 18			17 37			17 44				18 10				18 16				18 39		
Carshalton Beeches	d	16 56			17 05		17 21						17 38	17 51					18 06			18 13	18 21			
Wallington	d	16 58			17 08		17 23						17 41	17 53					18 08			18 15	18 24			
Waddon	d	17 01			17 11		17 26						17 44	17 56					18 11			18 18	18 27			
West Croydon 4	d	17 05			17 14		17 30						17 47	18 00					18 15			18a21	18 30			
Norwood Junction 2	d				17 19								17 52						18 19							
New Cross Gate 4 ⊖	d				17 37								18 09						18 37							
Tulse Hill 3	d					17a27						17a54								18a24						
London Bridge 4 ⊖	a				17 43								18 19						18 44							
Balham 4 ⊖	d	17 21	17 15				17 48		17 44					18 16		18 18							18 49	18 46		
Clapham Junction 10	a	17 26	17 21	17 15			17 53	17 30	17 48	17 45				18 21	18 00	18 24	18 15	18 30					18 54	18 50		18 45
London Waterloo 15 ⊖	a			17 25				17 40		17 55					18 10		18 25	18 40								18 55
London Victoria 15 ⊖	a	17 34	17 28				18 00		17 56					18 30		18 34							19 03	18 57		

For general notes see front of timetable
For details of catering facilities see Directory of Train Operators

- **A** To St Albans City (Table 52)
- **B** To Luton (Table 52)
- **C** To Bedford (Table 52)
- **D** From Luton (Table 52)

Horsham, Dorking, Guildford, Epsom and Sutton → London

Network Diagram - see first page of Table 177

		SN	SN	SW	SN	SW	FC A		SN	SN	SW	SW	SN	SW	SN	FC B	SN		SW	SW	SN	SW	SN	FC B	SN	SN
Horsham 4	d				18 11								18 45								19 14					
Warnham	d				18 15																19 18					
Ockley	d				18 22																19 25					
Holmwood	d				18 26								18 56								19 29					
Dorking 4	a				18 32								19 03								19 35					
	d				18 33	18 35					18 50		19 03							19 33	19 36					
Boxhill & Westhumble	d												19 05													
Guildford	d			17 58					18 22						18 52											
Effingham Junction 6	d			18 16					18 39			18 59			19 08											
Bookham	d			18 19					18 42			19 02			19 11											
Leatherhead	d			18 24	18 39	18 41			18 47		18 56	19 07	19 10		19 16					19 39	19 42					
Ashtead	d			18 28	18 42	18 44			18 50		18 59	19 10	19 14		19 20					19 42	19 45					
Epsom 3	a			18 32	18 47	18 50			18 58		19 04	19 15	19 18	←	19 24					19 47	19 50	←				
	d	18 27		18 35	18 47	18 50			18 58		19 05	19 20 →	19 18	19 20	19 25				19 35	19 50 →	19 50	19 50	19 55			
Ewell East	d				18 51				19 02				19 22		19 29						19 54		19 59			
Cheam	d	18 32			18 54				19 05				19 25		19 32						19 57		20 02			
Epsom Downs	d		18 32							19 02							19 39									20 15
Banstead	d		18 35							19 05							19 42									20 18
Belmont	d		18 38							19 08							19 45									20 21
Wimbledon 6 ⊖ ⛴	d						18 45									19 17								19 47		
West Sutton	d						18 59									19 31								20 01		
Sutton (Surrey) 4	a	18 35	18 41		18 57		19 03		19 08	19 11			19 28		19 35	19 38	19 48				20 00		20 05	20 08		20 24
	d	18 36	18 49		18 58		19 04		19 10	19 19			19 29		19 35		19 49				20 01		20 06		20 19	20 27
Carshalton	d				19 01		19 07						19 32								20 04					
Hackbridge	d				19 03		19 09						19 34								20 06					
Mitcham Junction ⛴	d				19 07		19 12						19 38								20 10					
Mitcham Eastfields	d				19 10		19 16						19 41								20 13					
Carshalton Beeches	d	18 39	18 52						19 13	19 22					19 38		19 52						20 09		20 22	20 30
Wallington	d	18 41	18 54						19 15	19 24					19 41		19 54						20 11		20 24	20 32
Waddon	d	18 44	18 57						19 18	19 27					19 44		19 57						20 14		20 27	20 35
West Croydon 4 ⛴	d	18 48	19 01						19 22	19 31					19 49		20 01						20 18		20 31	20a38
Norwood Junction 2	d	18 52							19 27						19 54								20 23			
New Cross Gate 4 ⊖	d	19 11							19 42						20 12											
Tulse Hill 3	d						19a27																			
London Bridge 4 ⊖	a	19 18							19 49						20 19											
Balham 4 ⊖	d		19 19		19 17					19 51			19 48				20 16				20 20		20 39		20 48	
Clapham Junction 10	a		19 24	19 00	19 21	19 16				19 56	19 30		19 52	19 45			20 22		20 00		20 25	20 15	20 44		20 53	
London Waterloo 15 ⊖	a			19 10		19 27					19 41			19 55					20 10			20 25				
London Victoria 15 ⊖	a		19 34		19 28					20 04			19 59				20 30				20 33		20 52		21 03	

		SW	SN	FC B		SW	SN	SN	SW	SN	FC B	SW	SN	SW		SN	SN	FC B	SW	SN	SN	SW	SN	FC B		SW
Horsham 4	d									20 07																
Warnham	d									20 11																
Ockley	d									20 18																
Holmwood	d									20 22																
Dorking 4	a									20 28																
	d		19 59			20 05				20 31		20 35					20 59						21 30			21 35
Boxhill & Westhumble	d		20 01														21 01									
Guildford	d	19 28							19 58										20 46							
Effingham Junction 6	d	19 46							20 16										21 03							
Bookham	d	19 49							20 19										21 06							
Leatherhead	d	19 54	20 06			20 11			20 24	20 37		20 41					21 06		21 11				21 36			21 41
Ashtead	d	19 58	20 10			20 14			20 28	20 41		20 44					21 10		21 14				21 40			21 44
Epsom 3	a	20 02	20 14			20 19			20 32	20 45		20 49					21 14		21 19				21 45			21 49
	d	20 05	20 15			20 20	20 25		20 35	20 46		20 50		21 05			21 15		21 20	21 25		21 35	21 45			21 50
Ewell East	d		20 19				20 29			20 50							21 19			21 29			21 49			
Cheam	d		20 22				20 32			20 53							21 22			21 32			21 52			
Epsom Downs	d												20 55													
Banstead	d												20 58													
Belmont	d												21 01													
Wimbledon 6 ⊖ ⛴	d			20 17							20 47							21 17						21 47		
West Sutton	d			20 31							21 01							21 31						22 01		
Sutton (Surrey) 4	a		20 25	20 38			20 35			20 56	21 05		21 04				21 25	21 38		21 35			21 55	22 05		
	d		20 25				20 36	20 49		20 56			21 06			21 19	21 25			21 36	21 49		21 55			
Carshalton	d		20 28							20 59							21 28						21 58			
Hackbridge	d		20 31							21 02							21 31						22 01			
Mitcham Junction ⛴	d		20 34							21 05							21 34						22 04			
Mitcham Eastfields	d		20 38							21 09							21 38						22 08			
Carshalton Beeches	d						20 39	20 52					21 09			21 22				21 39	21 52					
Wallington	d						20 41	20 54					21 11			21 24				21 41	21 54					
Waddon	d						20 44	20 57					21 14			21 27				21 44	21 57					
West Croydon 4 ⛴	d						20 48	21 01					21 18			21 31				21 48	22 01					
Norwood Junction 2	d						20 53						21 23							21 53						
New Cross Gate 4 ⊖	d																									
Tulse Hill 3	d																									
London Bridge 4 ⊖	a																									
Balham 4 ⊖	d		20 44				21 09	21 18		21 15			21 39			21 48	21 44			22 09	22 18		22 14			
Clapham Junction 10	a	20 30	20 48			20 45	21 14	21 23	21 00	21 20		21 15	21 44	21 30		21 53	21 48		21 45	22 14	22 23	22 00	22 18			22 15
London Waterloo 15 ⊖	a	20 41				20 55			21 10			21 25		21 40					21 55			22 10				22 25
London Victoria 15 ⊖	a		20 55				21 23	21 33		21 27			21 53			22 03	21 55			22 25	22 33		22 27			

For general notes see front of timetable
For details of catering facilities see
Directory of Train Operators

A To Bedford (Table 52)
B From Luton (Table 52)

Horsham, Dorking, Guildford, Epsom and Sutton → London

Network Diagram - see first page of Table 177

		SN	SN	SN	FC A	SW	SN	SN	SN	FC A		SW	SN	SN	SN	FC A	SW	SN	SN	SN		SN	FC A			
Horsham 4	d																									
Warnham	d																									
Ockley	d																									
Holmwood	d																									
Dorking 4	a																									
	d			21 59					22 30			22 35			23 00							23 30				
Boxhill & Westhumble	d			22 01											23 02											
Guildford	d					21 46											22 46									
Effingham Junction 6	d					22 03											23 03									
Bookham	d					22 06											23 06									
Leatherhead	d			22 06		22 11			22 36			22 41			23 07		23 11					23 36				
Ashtead	d			22 10		22 14			22 40			22 44			23 11		23 14					23 39				
Epsom 3	a			22 14		22 19			22 44			22 49			23 15		23 19					23 45				
	d			22 15		22 20	22 25		22 45			22 50			23 16		23 20	23 25								
Ewell East	d			22 19			22 29		22 49						23 20			23 29								
Cheam	d			22 22			22 32		22 52						23 23			23 32								
Epsom Downs	d	21 55											22 55							23 44						
Banstead	d	21 58											22 58							23 47						
Belmont	d	22 01											23 01							23 50						
Wimbledon 6 ⊖	d				22 17					22 47						23 17							23 46			
West Sutton	d				22 31					23 01						23 31							23 59			
Sutton (Surrey) 4	a	22 04		22 25	22 38		22 35		22 55	23 05			23 04		23 26	23 35		23 39		23 53			00 03			
	d	22 06	22 19	22 25			22 35	22 49	22 55				23 06	23 19	23 27			23 40	23 35	23 54						
Carshalton	d			22 28					22 58																	
Hackbridge	d			22 31					23 01																	
Mitcham Junction	d			22 34					23 04																	
Mitcham Eastfields	d			22 38					23 08																	
Carshalton Beeches	d	22 09	22 22				22 39	22 52					23 09	23 22	23 30			23 43	23 38	23 57						
Wallington	d	22 11	22 24				22 41	22 54					23 11	23 24	23 32			23 45	23 40	23 59						
Waddon	d	22 14	22 27				22 44	22 57					23 14	23 27	23 35			23 48	23 43	00 02						
West Croydon 4	d	22 18	22 31				22 48	23 01					23 18	23a36	23a38			23a51	23a46	00a05						
Norwood Junction 2	d	22 23					22 53						23 23													
New Cross Gate 4 ⊖	d																									
Tulse Hill 3	d																									
London Bridge 4 ⊖	a																									
Balham 4 ⊖	d	22 39	22 48	22 44			23 09	23 18	23 14				23 40													
Clapham Junction 10	a	22 44	22 53	22 48		22 45	23 15	23 23	23 18			23 15	23 45				23 48									
London Waterloo 15 ⊖	a					22 55						23 25					23 58									
London Victoria 15 ⊖	a	22 53	23 03	22 55			23 23	23 31	23 25				23 54													

Saturdays

		SN	SW	SW	SW	SN		SN	SN	SN	FC B	SW		SN	SN	SN	SN	FC B		SN	SW	SN	SN	SN		FC B
Horsham 4	d																									
Warnham	d																									
Ockley	d																									
Holmwood	d																									
Dorking 4	a																									
	d							06 26							06 57							07 26				
Boxhill & Westhumble	d														06 59							07 28				
Guildford	d											06 28									06 58					
Effingham Junction 6	d											06 46									07 16					
Bookham	d											06 49									07 19					
Leatherhead	d							06 33				06 54			07 04						07 24	07 33				
Ashtead	d							06 37				06 58			07 08						07 28	07 37				
Epsom 3	a							06 41				07 02			07 12						07 32	07 41				
	d		05 35	06 05	06 35			06 42	06 48			07 05		07 05	07 13	07 18					07 35	07 42	07 48			
Ewell East	d							06 46	06 52					07 09		07 22						07 46	07 52			
Cheam	d							06 49	06 55					07 12	07 18	07 25						07 49	07 55			
Epsom Downs	d	23p44																		07 35						
Banstead	d	23p47																		07 38						
Belmont	d	23p50																		07 41						
Wimbledon 6 ⊖	d										06 47							07 17								07 47
West Sutton	d										07 01							07 31								08 01
Sutton (Surrey) 4	a	23p53						06 52	06 58		07 05			07 15	07 22	07 28		07 35		07 44		07 52	07 58			08 05
	d	23p54				06 45		06 52	06 58	07 03	07 06			07 15	07 22	07 28	07 33	07 36		07 45		07 52	07 58	08 03		08 06
Carshalton	d								07 01		07 09					07 31		07 39					08 01			08 09
Hackbridge	d								07 04		07 11					07 34		07 41					08 04			08 11
Mitcham Junction	d								07 07		07 14					07 37		07 44					08 07			08 14
Mitcham Eastfields	d								07 11		07 18					07 41		07 48					08 11			08 18
Carshalton Beeches	d	23p57				06 48				07 06				07 18			07 36			07 48				08 06		
Wallington	d	23p59				06 51				07 08				07 21			07 38			07 51				08 08		
Waddon	d	00 02				06 54				07 11				07 24			07 41			07 54				08 11		
West Croydon 4	d	00a05				06 57				07 15				07 27			07 45			07 57				08 15		
Norwood Junction 2	d									07 19							07 49							08 19		
New Cross Gate 4 ⊖	d									07 37							08 07							08 37		
Tulse Hill 3	d										07a27							07a57								08a27
London Bridge 4 ⊖	a									07 44							08 14							08 44		
Balham 4 ⊖	d					07 13			07 18					07 43		07 48				08 13			08 18			
Clapham Junction 10	a		06 01	06 30	07 00	07 18		07 10	07 22			07 30		07 48	07 40	07 52				08 18	08 00	08 10	08 22			
London Waterloo 15 ⊖	a		06 11	06 40	07 10							07 40									08 10					
London Victoria 15 ⊖	a					07 26		07 18	07 29					07 56	07 48	07 59				08 26		08 18	08 29			

For general notes see front of timetable
For details of catering facilities see Directory of Train Operators

A From Luton (Table 52)
B To St Albans City (Table 52)

Saturdays

Horsham, Dorking, Guildford, Epsom and Sutton → London

Network Diagram - see first page of Table 177

	SW	SN	SN	SN	SN	SW	SN	FC A	SN	SW	SN	SN	SN	SW	SN	FC A	SW	SN	SN	SN	SN
Horsham 4 d											08 04										
Warnham d											08 08										
Ockley d											08 15										
Holmwood d											08 19										
Dorking 4 a											08 25										
d			07 58			08 05					08 26			08 35					08 58		
Boxhill & Westhumble d											08 28										
Guildford d	07 28									07 58							08 28				
Effingham Junction 6 d	07 46									08 16							08 46				
Bookham d	07 49									08 19							08 49				
Leatherhead d	07 54		08 04			08 11				08 24	08 33			08 41			08 54		09 04		
Ashtead d	07 58		08 07			08 14				08 28	08 37			08 44			08 58		09 07		
Epsom 3 a	08 02		08 12			08 19				08 32	08 41			08 49			09 02		09 12		
d	08 05	08 05	08 12		08 18	08 20				08 35	08 42		08 48	08 50			09 05	09 05	09 12		09 18
Ewell East d		08 09			08 22						08 46		08 52					09 09			09 22
Cheam d		08 12	08 18		08 25						08 49		08 55					09 12	09 18		09 25
Epsom Downs d									08 35												
Banstead d									08 38												
Belmont d									08 41												
Wimbledon 6 ⊖ d								08 17								08 47					
West Sutton d								08 31								09 01					
Sutton (Surrey) 4 a		08 15	08 22		08 28			08 35	08 44		08 52		08 58			09 05		09 15	09 22		09 28
d		08 15	08 22	08 23	08 28		08 33	08 36	08 45		08 52	08 53	08 58		09 03	09 06		09 15	09 22	09 23	09 38
Carshalton d					08 31			08 39					09 01			09 09					09 31
Hackbridge d					08 34			08 41					09 04			09 11					09 34
Mitcham Junction d					08 37			08 44					09 07			09 14					09 37
Mitcham Eastfields d					08 41			08 48					09 11			09 18					09 41
Carshalton Beeches d		08 18		08 26			08 36		08 48			08 56			09 06			09 18		09 26	
Wallington d		08 21		08 28			08 38		08 51			08 58			09 08			09 21		09 28	
Waddon d		08 24		08 31			08 41		08 54			09 01			09 11			09 24		09 31	
West Croydon 4 d		08 27		08 35			08 45		08 57			09 05			09 15			09 27		09 35	
Norwood Junction 2 d							08 49								09 19						
New Cross Gate 4 ⊖ d							09 07								09 37						
Tulse Hill 3 d								08a57								09a27					
London Bridge 4 ⊖ a							09 14								09 44						
Balham 4 ⊖ d		08 43		08 51	08 48				09 13			09 21	09 18					09 43		09 51	09 48
Clapham Junction 10 a	08 30	08 48	08 40	08 56	08 52	08 45			09 18	09 00	09 10	09 26	09 22	09 15			09 30	09 48	09 40	09 56	09 52
London Waterloo 15 ⊖ a	08 40					08 55				09 10				09 25			09 40				
London Victoria 15 ⊖ a		08 56	08 48	09 04	08 59				09 26		09 18	09 34	09 29					09 56	09 48	10 04	09 59

	SW	SN	FC A	SN	SW	SN	SN	SN	SW	SN	FC A	SW	SN		SN	SN	SN	SW	SN	FC B	SN	SW
Horsham 4 d						09 04																
Warnham d						09 08																
Ockley d						09 15																
Holmwood d						09 19																
Dorking 4 a						09 25																
d	09 05					09 26			09 35						17 58			18 05				
Boxhill & Westhumble d						09 28																
Guildford d					08 58							09 28										17 58
Effingham Junction 6 d					09 16							09 46										18 16
Bookham d					09 19							09 49										18 19
Leatherhead d	09 11				09 24	09 33			09 41			09 54			18 04			18 11				18 24
Ashtead d	09 14				09 28	09 37			09 44			09 58			18 07			18 14				18 28
Epsom 3 a	09 19				09 32	09 41			09 49			10 02			18 12			18 19				18 32
d	09 20				09 35	09 42		09 48	09 50			10 05	10 05	and at	18 12		18 18	18 20				18 35
Ewell East d						09 46		09 52					10 09				18 22					
Cheam d						09 49		09 55					10 12	the same	18 18		18 25					
Epsom Downs d				09 35										minutes							18 35	
Banstead d				09 38																	18 38	
Belmont d				09 41										past							18 41	
Wimbledon 6 ⊖ d			09 17								09 47			each						18 17		
West Sutton d			09 31								10 01									18 31		
Sutton (Surrey) 4 a			09 35	09 44		09 52		09 58			10 05		10 15	hour until	18 22		18 28			18 35	18 44	
d		09 33	09 36	09 45		09 52	09 53	09 58		10 03	10 06		10 15		18 22	18 23	18 28		18 33	18 36	18 45	
Carshalton d			09 39					10 01			10 09						18 31			18 39		
Hackbridge d			09 41					10 04			10 11						18 34			18 41		
Mitcham Junction d			09 44					10 07			10 14						18 37			18 44		
Mitcham Eastfields d			09 48					10 11			10 18						18 41			18 48		
Carshalton Beeches d		09 36		09 48			09 56			10 06			10 18			18 26			18 36		18 48	
Wallington d		09 38		09 51			09 58			10 08			10 21			18 28			18 38		18 51	
Waddon d		09 41		09 54			10 01			10 11			10 24			18 31			18 41		18 54	
West Croydon 4 d		09 45		09 57			10 05			10 15			10 27			18 35			18 45		18 57	
Norwood Junction 2 d		09 49								10 19									18 49			
New Cross Gate 4 ⊖ d		10 07								10 37									19 07			
Tulse Hill 3 d			09a57								10a27									18a57		
London Bridge 4 ⊖ a		10 14								10 44									19 14			
Balham 4 ⊖ d				10 13			10 21	10 18					10 43			18 51	18 48				19 13	
Clapham Junction 10 a	09 45			10 18	10 00	10 10	10 26	10 22	10 15			10 30	10 48		18 40	18 56	18 52	18 45			19 18	19 00
London Waterloo 15 ⊖ a	09 55				10 10				10 25			10 40						18 55				19 10
London Victoria 15 ⊖ a				10 26		10 18	10 34	10 29					10 56		18 48	19 04	18 59				19 26	

For general notes see front of timetable
For details of catering facilities see
Directory of Train Operators

A To St Albans City (Table 52)
B To Bedford (Table 52)

Table 182

Saturdays

Horsham, Dorking, Guildford, Epsom and Sutton → London

Network Diagram - see first page of Table 177

		SN	SN	SW	FC A		SN	SW	SN	SN	FC B		SW	SN	SN	SW	SN		FC B	SW	SN	SW	SN		SN	FC B
Horsham 4	d	18 04																								
Warnham	d	18 08																								
Ockley	d	18 15																								
Holmwood	d	18 19																								
Dorking 4	a	18 25																								
	d	18 26		18 35						19 00			19 05				19 30			19 35					19 59	
Boxhill & Westhumble	d	18 28								19 02															20 01	
Guildford	d							18 28								18 58						19 28				
Effingham Junction 6	d							18 46								19 16						19 46				
Bookham	d							18 49								19 19						19 49				
Leatherhead	d	18 33		18 41				18 54		19 07			19 11			19 24	19 36			19 41		19 54			20 06	
Ashtead	d	18 37		18 44				18 58		19 11			19 14			19 28	19 40			19 44		19 58			20 10	
Epsom 3	a	18 41		18 49				19 02		19 15			19 19			19 32	19 44			19 49		20 02			20 14	
	d	18 42	18 48	18 50				19 05	19 05	19 16			19 20			19 35	19 45			19 50		20 05	20 07		20 15	
Ewell East	d	18 46	18 52						19 09	19 20							19 49						20 11		20 19	
Cheam	d	18 49	18 55						19 12	19 23							19 52						20 14		20 22	
Epsom Downs	d														19 39											
Banstead	d														19 42											
Belmont	d														19 45											
Wimbledon 6 ⊖	d				18 47						19 17								19 47							20 17
West Sutton	d				19 01						19 31								20 01							20 31
Sutton (Surrey) 4	a	18 52	18 58		19 05				19 15	19 26	19 37				19 48		19 55		20 05				20 17		20 25	20 38
	d	18 52	18 58		19 06		19 05		19 15	19 26				19 35	19 49		19 55				20 05		20 19		20 25	
Carshalton	d		19 01		19 09					19 29							19 58								20 28	
Hackbridge	d		19 04		19 11					19 32							20 01								20 31	
Mitcham Junction	d		19 07		19 14					19 35							20 04								20 34	
Mitcham Eastfields	d		19 11		19 18					19 39							20 08								20 38	
Carshalton Beeches	d						19 08		19 18					19 38	19 52						20 08		20 22			
Wallington	d						19 10		19 21					19 41	19 54						20 11		20 24			
Waddon	d						19 13		19 24					19 44	19 57						20 14		20 27			
West Croydon 4	d						19a16		19 27					19 48	20 01						20 18		20 31			
Norwood Junction 2	d													19 53							20 23					
New Cross Gate 4 ⊖	d																									
Tulse Hill 3	d				19a27																					
London Bridge 4 ⊖	a																									
Balham 4 ⊖	d		19 18						19 43	19 46				20 09	20 18		20 14				20 39		20 48		20 44	
Clapham Junction 10	a	19 10	19 22	19 15				19 30	19 48	19 51			19 45	20 14	20 23	20 00	20 18			20 15	20 44	20 30	20 53		20 48	
London Waterloo 15 ⊖	a			19 25				19 40					19 55			20 10				20 25		20 40				
London Victoria 15 ⊖	a	19 18	19 29						19 56	19 58				20 23	20 33		20 26				20 53		21 03		20 56	

		SW	SN	SN	SW	SN		FC B	SW	SN	SW	SN		SN	FC B	SW	SN	SN		SW	SN	FC B	SW	SN		SN
Horsham 4	d																									
Warnham	d																									
Ockley	d																									
Holmwood	d																									
Dorking 4	a																									
	d	20 05				20 30			20 35					20 59							21 30		21 35			
Boxhill & Westhumble	d													21 01												
Guildford	d				19 58											20 46										
Effingham Junction 6	d				20 16											21 03										
Bookham	d				20 19											21 06										
Leatherhead	d	20 11			20 24	20 36			20 41					21 06		21 11					21 36		21 41			
Ashtead	d	20 14			20 28	20 40			20 44					21 10		21 14					21 40		21 44			
Epsom 3	a	20 19			20 32	20 44			20 49					21 14		21 19					21 44		21 49			
	d	20 20			20 35	20 45			20 50		21 05	21 07		21 15		21 20				21 35	21 45		21 50			22 07
Ewell East	d					20 49						21 11		21 19							21 49					22 11
Cheam	d					20 52						21 14		21 22							21 52					22 14
Epsom Downs	d			20 39														21 39								
Banstead	d			20 42														21 42								
Belmont	d			20 45														21 45								
Wimbledon 6 ⊖	d							20 47							21 17							21 46				
West Sutton	d							21 01							21 31							22 00				
Sutton (Surrey) 4	a			20 48		20 55		21 05				21 17		21 25	21 38			21 48			21 55	22 03				22 17
	d		20 35	20 49		20 55				21 05		21 19		21 25			21 35	21 49			21 55			22 05		22 19
Carshalton	d					20 58								21 28							21 58					
Hackbridge	d					21 01								21 31							22 01					
Mitcham Junction	d					21 04								21 34							22 04					
Mitcham Eastfields	d					21 08								21 38							22 08					
Carshalton Beeches	d		20 38	20 52						21 08		21 22					21 38	21 52						22 08		22 22
Wallington	d		20 41	20 54						21 11		21 24					21 41	21 54						22 11		22 24
Waddon	d		20 44	20 57						21 14		21 27					21 44	21 57						22 14		22 27
West Croydon 4	d		20 48	21 01						21 18		21 31					21 48	22 01						22 18		22 31
Norwood Junction 2	d		20 53							21 23							21 53							22 23		
New Cross Gate 4 ⊖	d																									
Tulse Hill 3	d																									
London Bridge 4 ⊖	a																									
Balham 4 ⊖	d		21 09	21 18		21 14				21 39		21 48		21 44			22 09	22 18			22 14			22 39		22 48
Clapham Junction 10	a	20 45	21 14	21 23	21 00	21 18			21 15	21 44	21 30	21 53		21 48		21 45	22 14	22 23		22 00	22 18		22 15	22 44		22 53
London Waterloo 15 ⊖	a	20 55			21 10				21 25		21 40					21 55				22 10			22 25			
London Victoria 15 ⊖	a		21 23	21 33		21 26				21 53		22 03		21 56			22 23	22 33			22 26			22 53		23 03

For general notes see front of timetable
For details of catering facilities see Directory of Train Operators

A To Luton (Table 52)
B From Luton (Table 52)

Table 182

Saturdays

Horsham, Dorking, Guildford, Epsom and Sutton → London

Network Diagram - see first page of Table 177

		SN	FC 1 A	SW	SN	SN	SN	FC A	SW	SN	SN	SN	FC A	SW	SN	SN	SN	FC A
Horsham 4	d																	
Warnham	d																	
Ockley	d																	
Holmwood	d																	
Dorking 4	a																	
	d	21 59					22 30		22 35			23 00					23 30	
Boxhill & Westhumble	d	22 01										23 02						
Guildford	d			21 46										22 46				
Effingham Junction 6	d			22 03										23 03				
Bookham	d			22 06										23 06				
Leatherhead	d	22 06		22 11			22 36		22 41			23 07		23 11			23 36	
Ashtead	d	22 10		22 14			22 40		22 44			23 11		23 14			23 39	
Epsom 3	a	22 14		22 19			22 44		22 49			23 15		23 19			23 45	
	d	22 15		22 20			22 45		22 50		23 07	23 20		23 20				
Ewell East	d	22 19					22 49				23 11	23 24						
Cheam	d	22 22					22 52				23 14	23 27						
Epsom Downs	d					22 39										23 39		
Banstead	d					22 42										23 42		
Belmont	d					22 45										23 45		
Wimbledon 6 ⊖	d		22 17					22 47					23 17					23 47
West Sutton	d		22 31					23 01					23 31					00 01
Sutton (Surrey) 4	a	22 25	22 38			22 48	22 55	23 05			23 17	23 30	23 38			23 48		00 05
	d	22 25			22 35	22 49	22 55			23 05	23 20				23 35	23 49		
Carshalton	d	22 28					22 58											
Hackbridge	d	22 31					23 01											
Mitcham Junction	d	22 34					23 04											
Mitcham Eastfields	d	22 38					23 08											
Carshalton Beeches	d				22 38	22 52				23 08	23 23				23 38	23 52		
Wallington	d				22 41	22 54				23 11	23 25				23 40	23 54		
Waddon	d				22 44	22 57				23 14	23 28				23 43	23 57		
West Croydon 4	d				22 48	23 01				23 18	23a31				23a46	00a01		
Norwood Junction 2	d				22 53					23 23								
New Cross Gate 4 ⊖	d																	
Tulse Hill 3	d																	
London Bridge 4 ⊖	a																	
Balham 4 ⊖	d	22 44			23 09	23 18	23 14			23 40								
Clapham Junction 10	a	22 48		22 45	23 14	23 23	23 18		23 15	23 45				23 48				
London Waterloo 15 ⊖	a			22 55					23 25					23 58				
London Victoria 15 ⊖	a	22 56			23 23	23 31	23 26			23 54								

Sundays

		FC	SN	SN	SN	SW	SN	SN	SW	SN	SN	SW	SN	SN	SN	SW B	SW C	SN	SN	SN	SW	SN
Horsham 4	d																					
Warnham	d																					
Ockley	d																					
Holmwood	d																					
Dorking 4	a																					
	d				06 56			07 26			07 56				08 26					08 56	09 08	
Boxhill & Westhumble	d				06 58			07 28			07 58				08 28					08 58		
Guildford	d															08 18	08 20					
Effingham Junction 6	d															08 34	08 36					
Bookham	d															08 37	08 39					
Leatherhead	d				07 03			07 33			08 03				08 33	08 45	08 45			09 03	09 15	
Ashtead	d				07 07			07 37			08 07				08 37	08 48	08 48			09 07	09 18	
Epsom 3	a				07 12			07 42			08 12				08 42	08 53	08 53			09 12	09 23	
	d		06 47		07 12	07 24		07 42	07 54		08 12	08 24			08 42	08 54	08 54			09 12	09 24	
Ewell East	d		06 51		07 16			07 46			08 16				08 46					09 16		
Cheam	d		06 54		07 19			07 49			08 19				08 49					09 19		
Epsom Downs	d																					
Banstead	d																					
Belmont	d																					
Wimbledon 6 ⊖	d	23p47																				
West Sutton	d	00 01																				
Sutton (Surrey) 4	a	00 05	06 57		07 22			07 52			08 22				08 52					09 22		
	d		06 57	07 28	07 29		07 58	07 59		08 27	08 29		08 39	08 57	08 59			09 09	09 27	09 29		09 39
Carshalton	d				07 32			08 02			08 32				09 02					09 32		
Hackbridge	d				07 34			08 04			08 34				09 04					09 34		
Mitcham Junction	d				07 38			08 08			08 38				09 08					09 38		
Mitcham Eastfields	d				07 41			08 11			08 41				09 11					09 41		
Carshalton Beeches	d		07 00	07 31			08 01			08 30				09 00					09 30			
Wallington	d		07 02	07 33			08 03			08 32			08 43	09 02				09 13	09 32			09 43
Waddon	d		07 05	07 36			08 06			08 35				09 05					09 35			
West Croydon 4	d		07 09	07 39			08 09			08 39			08 48	09 09				09 18	09 39			09 48
Norwood Junction 2	d												08 54					09 24				09 54
New Cross Gate 4 ⊖	d																					
Tulse Hill 3	d																					
London Bridge 4 ⊖	a																					
Balham 4 ⊖	d		07 25	07 55	07 48		08 25	08 18		08 55	08 48		09 10	09 25	09 18			09 40	09 55	09 48		10 10
Clapham Junction 10	a		07 30	08 00	07 52	07 49	08 30	08 22	08 19	09 00	08 52	08 49	09 15	09 30	09 22	09 19	09 19	09 45	10 00	09 52	09 49	10 15
London Waterloo 15 ⊖	a					08 04			08 34			09 04				09 34	09 34				10 04	
London Victoria 15 ⊖	a		07 38	08 08	07 59		08 38	08 29		09 08	08 59		09 23	09 38	09 29			09 53	10 08	09 59		10 23

For general notes see front of timetable
For details of catering facilities see Directory of Train Operators

A From Luton (Table 52)
B From 28 September
C Until 21 September

Table 182

Sundays

Horsham, Dorking, Guildford, Epsom and Sutton → London

Network Diagram - see first page of Table 177

Station		SN	SN		FC A	SW B	SW C	SN	SN	SN	FC A	SW	SN	SN	SN		FC A	SW B	SW C	SN	SN		SN	FC A
Horsham 4	d																							
Warnham	d																							
Ockley	d																							
Holmwood	d																							
Dorking 4	a																							
	d		09 26							09 56		10 08			10 26								20 56	
Boxhill & Westhumble	d		09 28							09 58					10 28								20 58	
Guildford	d					09 18	09 20											20 18	20 20					
Effingham Junction 6	d					09 34	09 36											20 34	20 36					
Bookham	d					09 37	09 39											20 37	20 39					
Leatherhead	d		09 33			09 45	09 45			10 03		10 15			10 33			20 45	20 45				21 03	
Ashtead	d		09 37			09 48	09 48			10 07		10 18			10 37			20 48	20 48				21 07	
Epsom 3	a		09 42			09 53	09 53			10 12		10 23			10 42			20 53	20 53				21 12	
	d		09 42			09 54	09 54			10 12		10 24			10 42			20 54	20 54				21 12	
Ewell East	d		09 46							10 16					10 46	and at the same minutes past each hour until							21 16	
Cheam	d		09 49							10 19					10 49								21 19	
Epsom Downs	d																							
Banstead	d																							
Belmont	d																							
Wimbledon 6 ⊖	d				09 44						10 14						20 44							21 14
West Sutton	d				09 58						10 28						20 58							21 28
Sutton (Surrey) 4	a		09 52		10 01					10 22	10 31				10 52		21 01						21 22	21 31
	d	09 57	09 59					10 09	10 27	10 29			10 39	10 57	10 59					21 09	21 27		21 29	
Carshalton	d		10 02							10 32					11 02								21 32	
Hackbridge	d		10 04							10 34					11 04								21 34	
Mitcham Junction	d		10 08							10 38					11 08								21 38	
Mitcham Eastfields	d		10 11							10 41					11 11								21 41	
Carshalton Beeches	d	10 00							10 30					11 00							21 30			
Wallington	d	10 02						10 13	10 32				10 43	11 02						21 13	21 32			
Waddon	d	10 05							10 35					11 05							21 35			
West Croydon 4	d	10 09						10 18	10 39				10 48	11 09						21 18	21 39			
Norwood Junction 2	d							10 24					10 54							21 24				
New Cross Gate 4 ⊖	d																							
Tulse Hill 3	d																							
London Bridge 4 ⊖	a																							
Balham 4 ⊖	d	10 25	10 18					10 40	10 55	10 48			11 10	11 25	11 18					21 40	21 55		21 48	
Clapham Junction 10	a	10 30	10 22			10 19	10 19	10 45	11 00	10 52		10 49	11 15	11 30	11 22			21 19	21 19	21 45	22 00		21 52	
London Waterloo 15 ⊖	a					10 34	10 34					11 04						21 29	21 29					
London Victoria 15 ⊖	a	10 38	10 29					10 53	11 08	10 59			11 23	11 38	11 29					21 53	22 09		21 59	

Station		SW	SN	SN	SN	SW B		SW C	SN	SN	SN	SW		SN	SN	SN	SW	SN		SN D	SN	SW	SN
Horsham 4	d																						
Warnham	d																						
Ockley	d																						
Holmwood	d																						
Dorking 4	a																						
	d	21 08			21 26						21 56	22 08				22 26					22 56	23 08	
Boxhill & Westhumble	d				21 28						21 58					22 28					22 58		
Guildford	d					21 18		21 20									22 20						
Effingham Junction 6	d					21 34		21 36									22 36						
Bookham	d					21 37		21 39									22 39						
Leatherhead	d	21 15			21 33	21 45		21 45			22 03	22 15				22 33	22 44				23 03	23 15	
Ashtead	d	21 18			21 37	21 48		21 48			22 07	22 18				22 37	22 48				23 07	23 18	
Epsom 3	a	21 23			21 42	21 53		21 53			22 12	22 23				22 42	22 52				23 12	23 23	
	d	21 24			21 42	21 54		21 54			22 12	22 24				22 42	22 54				23 12	23 24	
Ewell East	d				21 46						22 16					22 46					23 16		
Cheam	d				21 49						22 19					22 49					23 19		
Epsom Downs	d																						
Banstead	d																						
Belmont	d																						
Wimbledon 6 ⊖	d																						
West Sutton	d																						
Sutton (Surrey) 4	a				21 52						22 22					22 52					23 22		
	d		21 39	21 57	21 59				22 09	22 27	22 29			22 39	22 57	22 59		23 09		23 27	23 29		23 39
Carshalton	d				22 02						22 32					23 02					23 32		
Hackbridge	d				22 04						22 34					23 04					23 34		
Mitcham Junction	d				22 08						22 38					23 08					23 38		
Mitcham Eastfields	d				22 11						22 41					23 11					23 41		
Carshalton Beeches	d			22 00						22 30					23 00					23 30			23 42
Wallington	d		21 43	22 02					22 13	22 32				22 43	23 02			23 13		23 32			23 44
Waddon	d			22 05						22 35					23 05					23 35			23 47
West Croydon 4	d		21 48	22 09					22 18	22 39				22 48	23 09			23 18		23a38			23a50
Norwood Junction 2	d		21 54						22 24					22 54				23b26					
New Cross Gate 4 ⊖	d																						
Tulse Hill 3	d																						
London Bridge 4 ⊖	a																						
Balham 4 ⊖	d		22 10	22 25	22 18				22 40	22 55	22 48			23 10	23 25	23 18		23 42			23 48		
Clapham Junction 10	a	21 49	22 15	22 30	22 22	22 19		22 19	22 45	23 00	22 52	22 49		23 15	23 30	23 22	23 19	23 47			23 52	23 49	
London Waterloo 15 ⊖	a	22 00				22 29		22 29				23 00					23 29					23 59	
London Victoria 15 ⊖	a		22 23	22 39	22 29				22 53	23 09	22 59			23 23	23 38	23 29		23 55			23 59		

For general notes see front of timetable
For details of catering facilities see Directory of Train Operators

A From Luton (Table 52)
B From 28 September
C Until 21 September
D To Selhurst (Table 177)
b Arr. 2323

Network Diagram for Tables 184, 189

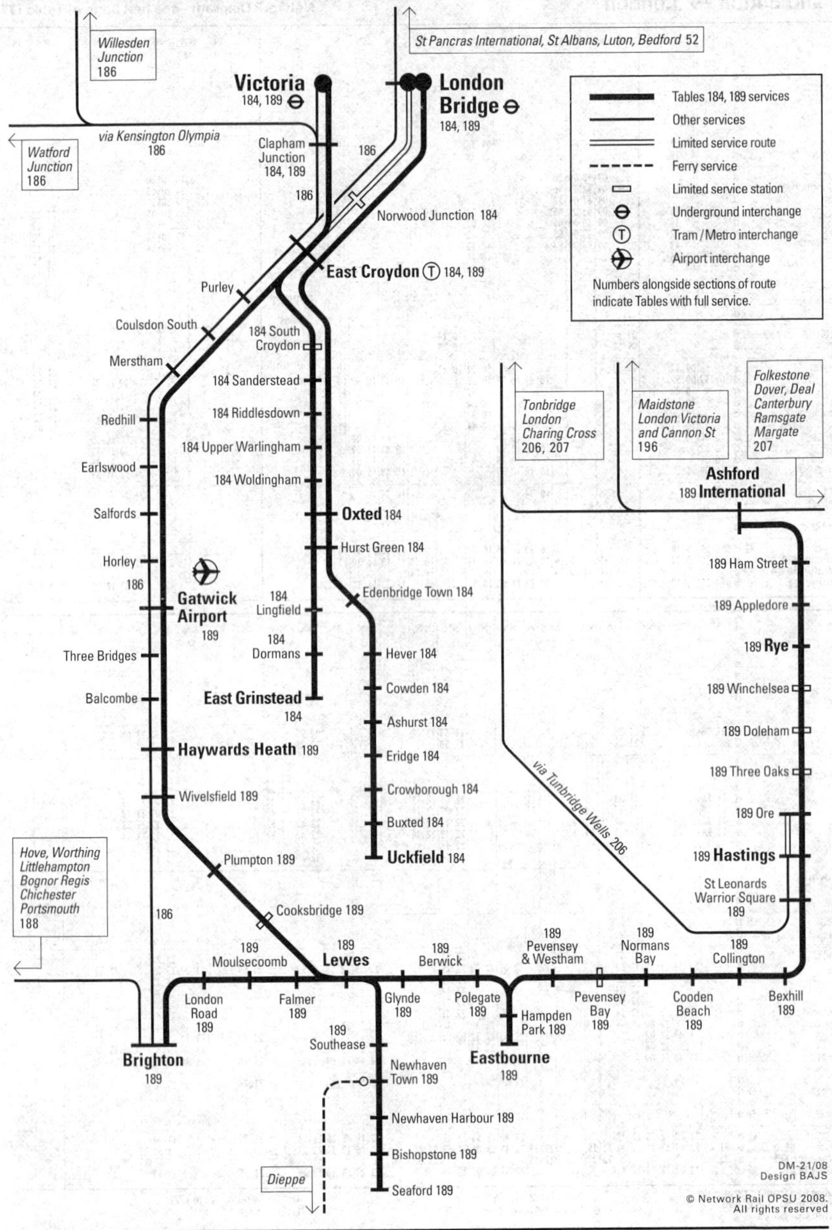

Willesden Junction 186
St Pancras International, St Albans, Luton, Bedford 52
Victoria 184, 189
London Bridge 184, 189
Tables 184, 189 services
Other services
Limited service route
Ferry service
Limited service station
Underground interchange
Tram / Metro interchange
Airport interchange
Numbers alongside sections of route indicate Tables with full service.
via Kensington Olympia 186
Watford Junction 186
Clapham Junction 184, 189
186
Norwood Junction 184
East Croydon 184, 189
Purley
Coulsdon South
Merstham
184 South Croydon
184 Sanderstead
184 Riddlesdown
184 Upper Warlingham
184 Woldingham
Oxted 184
Hurst Green 184
Edenbridge Town 184
Redhill
Earlswood
Salfords
Horley
Gatwick Airport 189
184 Lingfield
184 Dormans
Three Bridges
Balcombe
East Grinstead 184
Haywards Heath 189
Wivelsfield 189
Plumpton 189
Cooksbridge 189
Hever 184
Cowden 184
Ashurst 184
Eridge 184
Crowborough 184
Buxted 184
Uckfield 184
Tonbridge London Charing Cross 206, 207
Maidstone London Victoria and Cannon St 196
Folkestone Dover, Deal Canterbury Ramsgate Margate 207
Ashford 189 International
189 Ham Street
189 Appledore
189 Rye
189 Winchelsea
189 Doleham
189 Three Oaks
189 Ore
189 Hastings
St Leonards Warrior Square 189
via Tunbridge Wells 206
Hove, Worthing Littlehampton Bognor Regis Chichester Portsmouth 188
189 Moulsecoomb
189 Lewes
189 Berwick
189 Pevensey & Westham
189 Normans Bay
189 Collington
London Road 189
Falmer 189
Glynde 189
Polegate 189
Hampden Park 189
Pevensey Bay 189
Cooden Beach 189
Bexhill 189
Brighton 189
189 Southease
Newhaven Town 189
Eastbourne 189
Newhaven Harbour 189
Bishopstone 189
Seaford 189
Dieppe
DM-21/08
Design BAJS
© Network Rail OPSU 2008. All rights reserved

London → Oxted, East Grinstead and Uckfield

Network Diagram - see first page of Table 184

Miles	Miles			SN MX 1	SN MX 1	SN 1	SN 1	SN 1	SN 1	SN 1	SN 1	SN 1	SN 1	SN 1	SN 1	SN 1	SN 1	SN 1	SN 1	SN 1	SN 1
0	—	**London Victoria** 15	⊖ 175, 177 d	23p24	23p49		05 23			06 17				07 02	07 23			08 09		08 53	
2¾	—	Clapham Junction 10	175, 177 d	23p30	23p56		05 33			06 23				07 08	07 29			08 15		08 59	
—	0	**London Bridge** 4	⊖ 175, 177 d					05 55				06 30	06 56			07 36	08 06		08 25		09 02
—	8¾	Norwood Junction 2	175, 177 d				05 50		06 10			06 44							08 37		
10½	10¼	**East Croydon**	175, 177 ⛴ d	23p43	00 10	05 26	05 54	06 10	06 14	06 34		06 48	07 10	07 21	07 41	07 51	08 23	08 26	08 41	09 10	09 23
11½	—	South Croydon 4	175 d				05 56												08 44		
12½	—	Sanderstead	d	23p47	00s14				06 18	06 39		06 52	07 14	07 26		07 56			08 47	09 14	
13¾	—	Riddlesdown	d	23p50	00s17				06 21	06 42		06 55	07 17			07 59			08 50	09 17	
15½	—	Upper Warlingham	d	23p54	00s21				06 25	06 46		06 59	07 21			08 03		08 34	08 54	09 21	
17¼	—	Woldingham	d	23p58	00s25				06 29	06 50		07 03	07 25			08 07		08 38	08 58	09 25	
20½	—	**Oxted** 3	a	00 03	00 30	05 41	06 08	06 25	06 34	06 55		07 08	07 30	07 36	07 55	08 12	08 36	08 43	09 03	09 30	09 36
—	—		d	00 03		05 41	06 08	06 30	06 34	06 57	07 01	07 08	07 31	07 36	07 55	08 12	08 37	08 43	09 03	09 30	09 37
21½	0	Hurst Green	d	00 06		05 44	06 10	06 32	06 37	06 59	07 04	07 12	07 33	07 39		08 14	08 39	08 45	09 06	09 33	09 39
26¼	—	Lingfield	d	00 12			06 16		06 43	07 05		07 18		07 45		08 20		08 51	09 12	09 39	
28	—	Dormans	d	00 15			06 20		06 46	07 09		07 21		07 48		08 24		08 55	09 15	09 42	
30¼	—	**East Grinstead**	a	00 20			06 24		06 51	07 13		07 29		07 53	08 07	08 28		09 00	09 20	09 47	
—	4¼	Edenbridge Town	d			05 50		06 38			07 10		07 39				08 45				09 45
—	6	Hever	d					06 42					07 43				08 49				09 49
—	8	Cowden	d					06 46					07 47				08 53				09 53
—	10¾	Ashurst	d					06 50			07 19		07 51				08 57				09 57
—	14½	Eridge	d			06 02		06 56			07 26		07 58				09 03				10 03
—	17¾	Crowborough	d			06b12		07c07			07e37		08f09				09 09				10 09
—	22½	Buxted	d			06 18		07 13			07 43		08 15				09 15				10 15
—	25	**Uckfield**	a			06 24		07 19			07 49		08 21				09 21				10 21

		SN 1	SN 1	SN 1		SN 1	SN 1	SN 1	SN 1	SN 1	SN 1	SN 1	SN 1	SN 1	SN 1	SN 1	SN 1	SN 1	SN 1	SN 1
London Victoria 15	⊖ 175, 177 d	09 23	09 53			15 23		15 53		16 23		16 53					17 32		18 02	
Clapham Junction 10	175, 177 d	09 29	09 59			15 29		15 59		16 29		16 59								
London Bridge 4	⊖ 175, 177 d			10 08			15 38		16 08		16 33		17 10	17 13	17 30			17 50		18 12
Norwood Junction 2	175, 177 d																			
East Croydon	175, 177 ⛴ d	09 40	10 10	10 23		15 40	15 53	16 10	16 23	16 40	16 52	17 10	17 24	17 28	17 44		17 48	18 05	18 17	18 27
South Croydon 4	175 d				and at	15 42		16 12		16 42		17 12		17 30						
Sanderstead	d	09 44	10 14			15 45		16 15		16 45		17 15		17 33			17 52	18 09	18 22	18 31
Riddlesdown	d	09 47	10 17		the same	15 48		16 18		16 48		17 18		17 36			17 55	18 12	18 25	
Upper Warlingham	d	09 51	10 21			15 52		16 22		16 52		17 22		17 40			17 59	18 16	18 29	18 37
Woldingham	d	09 55	10 25		minutes	15 56		16 26		16 56		17 26		17 44			18 03	18 20	18 33	18 41
Oxted 3	a	10 00	10 30	10 36		16 01	16 06	16 31	16 36	17 01	17 06	17 31	17 37	17 49	17 58		18 08	18 25	18 38	18 46
	d	10 00	10 30	10 37	past	16 01	16 07	16 31	16 37	17 01	17 07	17 31	17 37	17 49	17 59	18 04	18 08	18 25	18 38	18 47
Hurst Green	d	10 03	10 33	10 39	each	16 04	16 09	16 34	16 39	17 04	17 09	17 34	17 40	17 52	18 01	18 06	18 11	18 28	18 41	18 49
Lingfield	d	10 09	10 39			16 10		16 40		17 10		17 40		17 58	18 07		18 17	18 34	18 47	
Dormans	d	10 12	10 42		hour until	16 13		16 43		17 13		17 43		18 01	18 11		18 20	18 37	18 50	
East Grinstead	a	10 17	10 47			16 18		16 48		17 20		17 50		18 08	18 17		18 27	18 44	18 57	
Edenbridge Town	d			10 45			16 15		16 45		17 15		17 46			18 12				18 55
Hever	d			10 49			16 19		16 49		17 19					18 16				
Cowden	d			10 53			16 23		16 53		17 23					18 20				
Ashurst	d			10 57			16 27		16 57		17 27					18 24				
Eridge	d			11 03			16 33		17 03		17 33		18 00			18 30				19 07
Crowborough	d			11 09			16 39		17 09		17 39		18 06			18 36				19 13
Buxted	d			11 15			16 46		17 16		17 46		18 12			18 42				19 19
Uckfield	a			11 21			16 52		17 22		17 52		18 20			18 48				19 27

		SN 1	SN 1	SN 1	SN 1	SN 1	SN 1	SN 1	SN 1	SN 1	SN 1	SN 1	SN 1	SN 1	SN 1	SN 1	SN 1	SN 1	SN 1
London Victoria 15	⊖ 175, 177 d	18 24					19 23	19 53		20 23	20 53		21 23	21 53		22 23	22 53	23 24	23 49
Clapham Junction 10	175, 177 d	18 30					19 29	19 59		20 29	20 59		21 29	21 59		22 29	22 59	23 30	23 56
London Bridge 4	⊖ 175, 177 d			18 31	18 54	19 08			20 05			21 05			22 05				
Norwood Junction 2	175, 177 d				19 05				20 16			21 16			22 16				
East Croydon	175, 177 ⛴ d	18 42		18 45	19 10	19 23	19 40	20 10	20 20	20 40	21 10	21 20	21 40	22 10	22 20	22 40	23 10	23 43	00 10
South Croydon 4	175 d			18 47	19 12														
Sanderstead	d	18 46		18 52	19 15		19 44	20 14	20 24	20 44	21 14	21 24	21 44	22 14	22 24	22 44	23 14	23 47	00s14
Riddlesdown	d	18 49		18 55	19 18		19 47	20 17		20 47	21 17		21 47	22 17		22 47	23 17	23 50	00s17
Upper Warlingham	d	18 53		18 59	19 22		19 51	20 21	20 30	20 51	21 21	21 30	21 51	22 21	22 30	22 51	23 21	23 54	00s21
Woldingham	d	18 57		19 03	19 26		19 55	20 25		20 55	21 25		21 55	22 25		22 55	23 25	23 58	00s25
Oxted 3	a	19 02		19 10	19 31	19 36	20 00	20 30	20 37	21 00	21 30	21 37	22 00	22 30	22 37	23 00	23 30	00 03	00 30
	d	19 03	19 07	19 11	19 32	19 37	20 00	20 30	20 37	21 00	21 30	21 37	22 00	22 30	22 37	23 00	23 30	00 03	
Hurst Green	d	19 05	19 09	19 13	19 34	19 39	20 03	20 33	20 40	21 03	21 33	21 40	22 03	22 33	22 40	23 03	23 33	00 06	
Lingfield	d	19 11		19 19	19 40		20 09	20 39		21 09	21 39		22 09	22 39		23 09	23 39	00 12	
Dormans	d	19 15		19 23	19 44		20 12	20 42		21 12	21 42		22 12	22 42		23 12	23 42	00 15	
East Grinstead	a	19 21		19 29	19 50		20 17	20 47		21 17	21 47		22 17	22 47		23 17	23 47	00 20	
Edenbridge Town	d		19 15			19 45			20 46			21 46			22 46				
Hever	d		19 19			19 49			20 49			21 49							
Cowden	d		19 23			19 53			20 53			21 53							
Ashurst	d		19 27			19 57			20 58			21 58							
Eridge	d		19 33			20 03			21 03			22 03			22 58				
Crowborough	d		19 39			20 09			21 09			22 09			23 04				
Buxted	d		19 46			20 15			21 15			22 15			23 10				
Uckfield	a		19 52			20 21			21 21			22 21			23 16				

For general notes see front of timetable
For details of catering facilities see Directory of Train Operators

b Arr. 0608
c Arr. 0702
e Arr. 0732
f Arr. 0804

Saturdays

London → Oxted, East Grinstead and Uckfield

Network Diagram - see first page of Table 184

Station		SN 1	SN 1	SN 1	SN 1	SN 1	SN 1	SN 1	SN 1	SN 1	SN 1		SN 1	SN 1
London Victoria 15	⊖ 175, 177 d	23p24	23p49	05 25		06 23			07 23	07 53			19 23	19 53
Clapham Junction 10	175, 177 d	23p30	23p56	05 31		06 29			07 29	07 59			19 29	19 59
London Bridge 4	⊖ 175, 177 d				06 08		06 50	07 08			08 08			
Norwood Junction 2	175, 177 d			05 48										
East Croydon	175, 177 ⇌ d	23p43	00 10	05 52	06 23	06 40	07 10	07 23	07 40	08 10	08 23	and at	19 40	20 10
South Croydon 4	175 d			05 54										
Sanderstead	d	23p47	00s14			06 44	07 14		07 44	08 14		the same	19 44	20 14
Riddlesdown	d	23p50	00s17			06 47	07 17		07 47	08 17			19 47	20 17
Upper Warlingham	d	23p54	00s21			06 51	07 21		07 51	08 21		minutes	19 51	20 21
Woldingham	d	23p58	00s25			06 55	07 25		07 55	08 25			19 55	20 25
Oxted 3	a	00 03	00 30	06 06	06 36	07 00	07 30	07 36	08 00	08 30	08 36	past	20 00	20 30
	d	00 03		06 06	06 37	07 00	07 30	07 37	08 00	08 30	08 37		20 00	20 30
Hurst Green	d	00 06		06 09	06 39	07 03	07 33	07 39	08 03	08 33	08 39	each	20 03	20 33
Lingfield	d	00 12		06 15		07 09	07 39		08 09	08 39			20 09	20 39
Dormans	d	00 15		06 18		07 12	07 42		08 12	08 42		hour until	20 12	20 42
East Grinstead	a	00 20		06 23		07 17	07 47		08 17	08 47			20 17	20 47
Edenbridge Town	d				06 45			07 45			08 45			
Hever	d				06 49			07 49			08 49			
Cowden	d				06 53			07 53			08 53			
Ashurst	d				06 57			07 57			08 57			
Eridge	d				07 03			08 03			09 03			
Crowborough	d				07 09			08 09			09 09			
Buxted	d				07 15			08 15			09 15			
Uckfield	a				07 21			08 21			09 21			

Station		SN 1	SN 1	SN 1	SN 1	SN 1	SN 1	SN 1	SN 1	SN 1	SN 1	SN 1
London Victoria 15	⊖ 175, 177 d		20 23	20 53		21 23	21 53		22 23	22 53	23 24	23 49
Clapham Junction 10	175, 177 d		20 29	20 59		21 29	21 59		22 29	22 59	23 30	23 56
London Bridge 4	⊖ 175, 177 d	20 08			21 08			22 08				
Norwood Junction 2	175, 177 d	20 19			21 19			22 19				
East Croydon	175, 177 ⇌ d	20 23	20 40	21 10	21 23	21 40	22 10	22 23	22 40	23 10	23 43	00 10
South Croydon 4	175 d											
Sanderstead	d		20 44	21 14		21 44	22 14		22 44	23 14	23 47	00s14
Riddlesdown	d		20 47	21 17		21 47	22 17		22 47	23 17	23 50	00s17
Upper Warlingham	d		20 51	21 21		21 51	22 21		22 51	23 21	23 54	00s21
Woldingham	d		20 55	21 25		21 55	22 25		22 55	23 25	23 58	00s25
Oxted 3	a	20 36	21 00	21 30	21 36	22 00	22 30	22 36	23 00	23 30	00 03	00 30
	d	20 37	21 00	21 30	21 37	22 00	22 30	22 37	23 00	23 30	00 03	
Hurst Green	d	20 39	21 03	21 33	21 39	22 03	22 33	22 39	23 03	23 33	00 06	
Lingfield	d		21 09	21 39		22 09	22 39		23 09	23 39	00 12	
Dormans	d		21 12	21 42		22 12	22 42		23 12	23 42	00 15	
East Grinstead	a		21 17	21 47		22 17	22 47		23 17	23 47	00 20	
Edenbridge Town	d	20 45			21 45			22 45				
Hever	d	20 49			21 49							
Cowden	d	20 53			21 53							
Ashurst	d	20 57			21 57							
Eridge	d	21 03			22 03			22 57				
Crowborough	d	21 09			22 09			23 03				
Buxted	d	21 15			22 15			23 09				
Uckfield	a	21 21			22 21			23 15				

Sundays

Station		SN 1	SN 1	SN 1	SN 1	SN 1	SN 1	SN 1	SN 1	SN 1		SN 1	SN 1	SN 1
London Victoria 15	⊖ 175, 177 d	23p24	23p49	07 22	08 22		09 22		10 22			21 22		22 22
Clapham Junction 10	175, 177 d	23p30	23p56	07 28	08 28		09 28		10 28			21 28		22 28
London Bridge 4	⊖ 175, 177 d													
Norwood Junction 2	175, 177 d													
East Croydon	175, 177 ⇌ d	23p43	00 10	07 43	08 43	09 05	09 43	10 05	10 43			21 43		22 44
South Croydon 4	175 d										and at			
Sanderstead	d	23p47	00s14	07 47	08 47		09 47		10 47			21 47		22 48
Riddlesdown	d	23p50	00s17	07 50	08 50		09 50		10 50		the same	21 50		22 51
Upper Warlingham	d	23p54	00s21	07 54	08 54		09 54		10 54			21 54		22 55
Woldingham	d	23p58	00s25	07 58	08 58		09 58		10 58		minutes	21 58		22 59
Oxted 3	a	00 03	00 30	08 03	09 03	09 17	10 03	10 17	11 03			22 03		23 04
	d	00 03		08 03	09 03	09 18	10 03	10 18	11 03	11 18	past	22 03	22 18	23 04
Hurst Green	d	00 06		08 06	09 06	09 21	10 06	10 21	11 06	11 21	each	22 06	22 21	23 07
Lingfield	d	00 12		08 12	09 12		10 12		11 12			22 12		23 13
Dormans	d	00 15		08 15	09 15		10 15		11 15		hour until	22 15		23 16
East Grinstead	a	00 20		08 20	09 20		10 20		11 20			22 20		23 21
Edenbridge Town	d					09 27		10 27		11 27			22 27	
Hever	d					09 31		10 31		11 31			22 31	
Cowden	d					09 35		10 35		11 35			22 35	
Ashurst	d					09 39		10 39		11 39			22 39	
Eridge	d					09 45		10 45		11 45			22 45	
Crowborough	d					09 51		10 51		11 51			22 51	
Buxted	d					09 57		10 57		11 57			22 57	
Uckfield	a					10 03		11 03		12 03			23 03	

For general notes see front of timetable
For details of catering facilities see Directory of Train Operators

Uckfield, East Grinstead and Oxted → London

Network Diagram - see first page of Table 184

Miles	Miles			SN 1	SN 1	SN	SN 1	SN 1	SN 1		SN 1	SN 1	SN 1	SN 1	SN 1	SN 1		SN 1	SN 1	SN 1	SN 1	SN 1	SN 1		SN 1
—	0	**Uckfield**	d					06 00				06 30		06 58					07 30			08 02			08 34
—	2¼	Buxted	d					06 05				06 35		07 03					07 35			08 07			08 39
—	7¼	Crowborough	d					06 12				06 42		07 10					07 42			08 14			08 46
—	10½	Eridge	d					06 17				06 47		07 15					07 47			08 19			08 51
—	14¼	Ashurst	d					06 22				06 52							07 52			08 24			08 56
—	17	Cowden	d					06 27				06 57							07 57			08 29			09 01
—	19	Hever	d					06 31				07 01							08 01			08 33			09 05
—	20¾	Edenbridge Town	d					06 34				07 04		07 28					08 04			08 36			09 08
0	—	**East Grinstead**	d		06 05		06 20		06 37		06 44		07 04		07 26	07 39		07 47		08 02	08 17		08 37		
2¼	—	Dormans	d		06 09		06 24		06 41		06 48		07 08		07 30	07 43		07 51		08 06	08 21		08 41		
4	—	Lingfield	d		06 12		06 27		06 44		06 51		07 11		07 33	07 46		07 54		08 09	08 24		08 44		
8¾	—	Hurst Green	d	06 00	06 19		06 34	06 41	06 51		06 58	07 11	07 18	07 35	07 40	07 55		08 01	08 11	08 16	08 31	08 43	08 51		09 15
9¾	25	**Oxted 3**	a	06 02	06 21		06 36	06 44	06 53		07 00	07 13	07 20	07 38	07 42	07 57		08 03	08 13	08 18	08 33	08 45	08 53		09 18
—	—		d	06 03	06 22		06 36		06 54		07 00	07 14	07 20	07 39	07 42	07 58		08 03	08 15	08 18	08 33	08 46	08 53		09 19
13	—	Woldingham	d	06 08			06 42				07 06		07 26		07 48			08 09		08 24	08 39		08 59		
14¾	—	Upper Warlingham	d	06 12			06 45				07 09		07 29		07 51			08 12		08 27	08 42		09 02		
16½	—	Riddlesdown	d	06 15			06 49				07 13		07 33		07 55			08 16		08 31	08 46		09 06		
17¾	—	Sanderstead	d	06 18		06 38	06 52		07 03		07 16		07 36		07 58	08 08		08 19		08 34	08 49		09 09		
18¾	—	South Croydon 4	175 d			06 41									08 01			08 22		08 37	08 52				
19¾	0	**East Croydon**	175, 177 a	06 23	06 34	06 44	06 56		07 08		07 20	07 25	07 40	07 53	08 03	08 15		08 24	08 29	08 40	08 56	08 59	09 13		09 32
—	1½	Norwood Junction 2	175, 177 a																						
—	10¼	**London Bridge 4**	⊖ 175, 177 a	06 40					07 25		07 39	07 43		08 11	08 20	08 35			08 51	08 59		09 20			09 52
27½	—	Clapham Junction 10	175, 177 a		06 46	07 05	07 07						07 51					08 37			09 07		09 26		
30¼	—	**London Victoria 15**	⊖ 175, 177 a		06 54	07 16	07 17						08 00					08 46			09 16		09 37		

		SN 1	SN 1	SN 1	SN 1		SN 1	SN 1	SN 1	and at the same minutes past each hour until		SN 1	SN 1	SN 1	SN 1	SN 1	SN 1		SN 1	SN 1	SN 1	SN 1	SN 1	SN 1
Uckfield	d			09 34				10 34					15 34			16 34				17 04		17 34		
Buxted	d			09 39				10 39					15 39			16 39				17 09		17 39		
Crowborough	d			09 46				10 46					15 46			16 46				17 16		17 46		
Eridge	d			09 51				10 51					15 51			16 51				17 21		17 51		
Ashurst	d			09 56				10 56					15 56			16 56				17 26		17 56		
Cowden	d			10 01				11 01					16 01			17 01				17 31		18 01		
Hever	d			10 05				11 05					16 05			17 05				17 35		18 05		
Edenbridge Town	d			10 08				11 08					16 08			17 08				17 38		18 08		
East Grinstead	d	09 07	09 37		10 07		10 37		11 07			15 37		16 07	16 37		17 07		17 24		17 55		18 12	18 22
Dormans	d	09 11	09 41		10 11		10 41		11 11			15 41		16 11	16 41		17 11		17 28		17 59		18 16	18 26
Lingfield	d	09 14	09 44		10 14		10 44		11 14			15 44		16 14	16 44		17 14		17 31		18 02		18 19	18 29
Hurst Green	d	09 21	09 51	10 15	10 21		10 51	11 15	11 21			15 51	16 15	16 21	16 51	17 15	17 21		17 38	17 45	18 09	18 15	18 26	18 36
Oxted 3	a	09 23	09 53	10 17	10 23		10 53	11 17	11 23			15 53	16 17	16 23	16 53	17 17	17 23		17 40	17 48	18 11	18 17	18 28	18 38
	d	09 23	09 53	10 18	10 23		10 53	11 18	11 23			15 53	16 18	16 23	16 53	17 18	17 23		17 40		18 11	18 18	18 28	18 39
Woldingham	d	09 29	09 59		10 29		10 59		11 29			15 59		16 29	16 59		17 29				18 17		18 34	
Upper Warlingham	d	09 32	10 02		10 32		11 02		11 32			16 02		16 32	17 02		17 32				18 20		18 37	18 46
Riddlesdown	d	09 36	10 06		10 36		11 06		11 36			16 06		16 36	17 06		17 36				18 24		18 41	
Sanderstead	d	09 39	10 09		10 39		11 09		11 39			16 09		16 39	17 09		17 39				18 27		18 44	18 52
South Croydon 4	175 d																							
East Croydon	175, 177 a	09 43	10 13	10 32	10 43		11 13	11 32	11 43			16 13	16 38	16 43	17 13	17 32	17 44		17 52		18 32	18 38	18 50	18 59
Norwood Junction 2	175, 177 a													16 48	17 18		17 48		17 57					
London Bridge 4	⊖ 175, 177 a			10 49				11 49					16 58	17 00	17 31	18 02	18 06		18 10		18 48	18 53		19 14
Clapham Junction 10	175, 177 a	09 55	10 25		10 55		11 25		11 55			16 25											19 07	
London Victoria 15	⊖ 175, 177 a	10 05	10 35		11 05		11 35		12 05			16 32											19 14	

		SN 1	SN 1		SN 1	SN 1	SN 1	SN 1	SN 1	SN 1		SN 1	SN 1	SN 1	SN 1	SN 1	SN 1		SN 1	SN 1	SN 1	SN 1	SN 1		
Uckfield	d	18 00			18 25			19 04				19 34		20 04		20 34				21 34			22 32		
Buxted	d	18 05			18 30			19 09				19 39		20 09		20 39				21 39			22 37		
Crowborough	d	18b16			18 38			19 16				19 46		20 16		20 46				21 46			22 44		
Eridge	d	18 21			18 43			19 21				19 51		20 21		20 51				21 51			22 49		
Ashurst	d	18 26						19 26				19 56				20 56				21 56					
Cowden	d	18 31						19 31				20 01				21 01				22 01					
Hever	d	18 35			18 54			19 35				20 05				21 05				22 05					
Edenbridge Town	d	18 38			18 57			19 38				20 08		20 33		21 08				22 08			23 01		
East Grinstead	d		18 37			19 07	19 20		19 37	19 45			20 07		20 37		21 07		21 37		22 07	22 37			
Dormans	d		18 41			19 11	19 24		19 41	19 49			20 11		20 41		21 11		21 41		22 11	22 41			
Lingfield	d		18 44			19 14	19 27		19 44	19 52			20 14		20 44		21 14		21 44		22 14	22 44			
Hurst Green	d	18 45	18 51		19 04	19 21	19 34	19 45	19 51	19 59		20 15	20 21	20 39	20 51	21 15	21 21		21 51	22 15	22 21	22 51	23 08		
Oxted 3	a	18 48	18 53		19 06	19 23	19 36	19 48	19 53	20 01		20 18	20 23	20 42	20 53	21 17	21 23		21 53	22 17	22 23	22 53	23 10		
	d		18 53		19 07	19 23	19 37	19 49	19 53	20 02		20 19	20 23	20 42	20 53	21 18	21 23		21 53	22 18	22 23	22 53	23 11		
Woldingham	d		18 59			19 29	19 42		19 59	20 07			20 29		20 59		21 29		21 59		22 29	22 59			
Upper Warlingham	d		19 02			19 32	19 46		20 02	20 11		20 26	20 32		21 02		21 32		22 02		22 32	23 02			
Riddlesdown	d		19 06			19 36	19 49		20 06	20 14			20 36		21 06		21 36		22 06		22 36	23 06			
Sanderstead	d		19 09			19 39	19 52		20 09	20 17		20 30	20 39		21 09		21 39		22 09		22 39	23 09			
South Croydon 4	175 d																								
East Croydon	175, 177 a		19 13		19 19	19 43	19 57	20 06	20 13	20 22		20 36	20 43	20 54	21 13	21 30	21 43		22 13	22 33	22 43	23 13	23 28		
Norwood Junction 2	175, 177 a																								
London Bridge 4	⊖ 175, 177 a				19 35			20 21				20 51		21 11		21 49				22 49					
Clapham Junction 10	175, 177 a		19 25			19 55			20 25				20 55		21 25		21 55		22 25		22 55	23 25			
London Victoria 15	⊖ 175, 177 a		19 33			20 02			20 32				21 05		21 32		22 05		22 35		23 05	23 35			

For general notes see front of timetable
For details of catering facilities see Directory of Train Operators

b Arr. 1812

Table 184

Saturdays

Uckfield, East Grinstead and Oxted → London

Network Diagram - see first page of Table 184

Station		SN 1	SN 1	SN 1	SN 1	SN 1		SN 1	SN 1	SN 1
Uckfield	d		06 34			07 34				22 32
Buxted	d		06 39			07 39				22 37
Crowborough	d		06 46			07 46				22 44
Eridge	d		06 51			07 51				22 49
Ashurst	d		06 56			07 56				
Cowden	d		07 01			08 01				
Hever	d		07 05			08 05	and at			
Edenbridge Town	d		07 08			08 08	the same			23 01
East Grinstead	d	06 37		07 07	07 37		minutes	22 07	22 37	
Dormans	d	06 41		07 11	07 41			22 11	22 41	
Lingfield	d	06 44		07 14	07 44			22 14	22 44	
Hurst Green	d	06 51	07 15	07 21	07 51	08 15	past	22 21	22 51	23 08
Oxted 3	a	06 53	07 18	07 23	07 53	08 18		22 23	22 53	23 10
	d	06 53	07 19	07 23	07 53	08 19	each	22 23	22 53	23 11
Woldingham	d	06 59		07 29	07 59		hour until	22 29	22 59	
Upper Warlingham	d	07 02		07 32	08 02			22 32	23 02	
Riddlesdown	d	07 06		07 36	08 06			22 36	23 06	
Sanderstead	d	07 09		07 39	08 09			22 39	23 09	
South Croydon 4	175 d									
East Croydon	175, 177 a	07 13	07 33	07 43	08 13	08 32		22 43	23 13	23 26
Norwood Junction 2	175, 177 a									
London Bridge 4	⊖ 175, 177 a		07 52			08 49				
Clapham Junction 10	175, 177 a	07 25		07 55	08 25			22 55	23 25	
London Victoria 15	⊖ 175, 177 a	07 32		08 02	08 32			23 02	23 32	

Sundays

Station		SN 1	SN 1	SN 1	SN 1	SN 1		SN 1	SN 1	SN 1	SN 1
Uckfield	d				10 17			21 17		22 17	
Buxted	d				10 22			21 22		22 22	
Crowborough	d				10 29			21 29		22 29	
Eridge	d				10 34			21 34		22 34	
Ashurst	d				10 39			21 39		22 39	
Cowden	d				10 44			21 44		22 44	
Hever	d				10 48		and at	21 48		22 48	
Edenbridge Town	d				10 51		the same	21 51		22 51	
East Grinstead	d	07 52	08 52	09 52		10 52			21 52		22 52
Dormans	d	07 56	08 56	09 56		10 56	minutes		21 56		22 56
Lingfield	d	07 59	08 59	09 59		10 59			21 59		22 59
Hurst Green	d	08 06	09 06	10 06	10 58	11 06	past	21 58	22 06	22 58	23 06
Oxted 3	a	08 08	09 08	10 08	11 01	11 08		22 01	22 08	23 01	23 08
	d	08 08	09 08	10 08		11 08	each		22 08	23 02	23 08
Woldingham	d	08 14	09 14	10 14		11 14	hour until		22 14		23 14
Upper Warlingham	d	08 17	09 17	10 17		11 17			22 17		23 17
Riddlesdown	d	08 21	09 21	10 21		11 21			22 21		23 21
Sanderstead	d	08 24	09 24	10 24		11 24			22 24		23 24
South Croydon 4	175 d										
East Croydon	175, 177 a	08 28	09 28	10 28		11 28			22 28	23 14	23 28
Norwood Junction 2	175, 177 a										
London Bridge 4	⊖ 175, 177 a										
Clapham Junction 10	175, 177 a	08 41	09 41	10 41		11 41			22 41		23 41
London Victoria 15	⊖ 175, 177 a	08 48	09 48	10 48		11 48			22 50		23 51

For general notes see front of timetable
For details of catering facilities see Directory of Train Operators

Network Diagram for Tables 186, 188

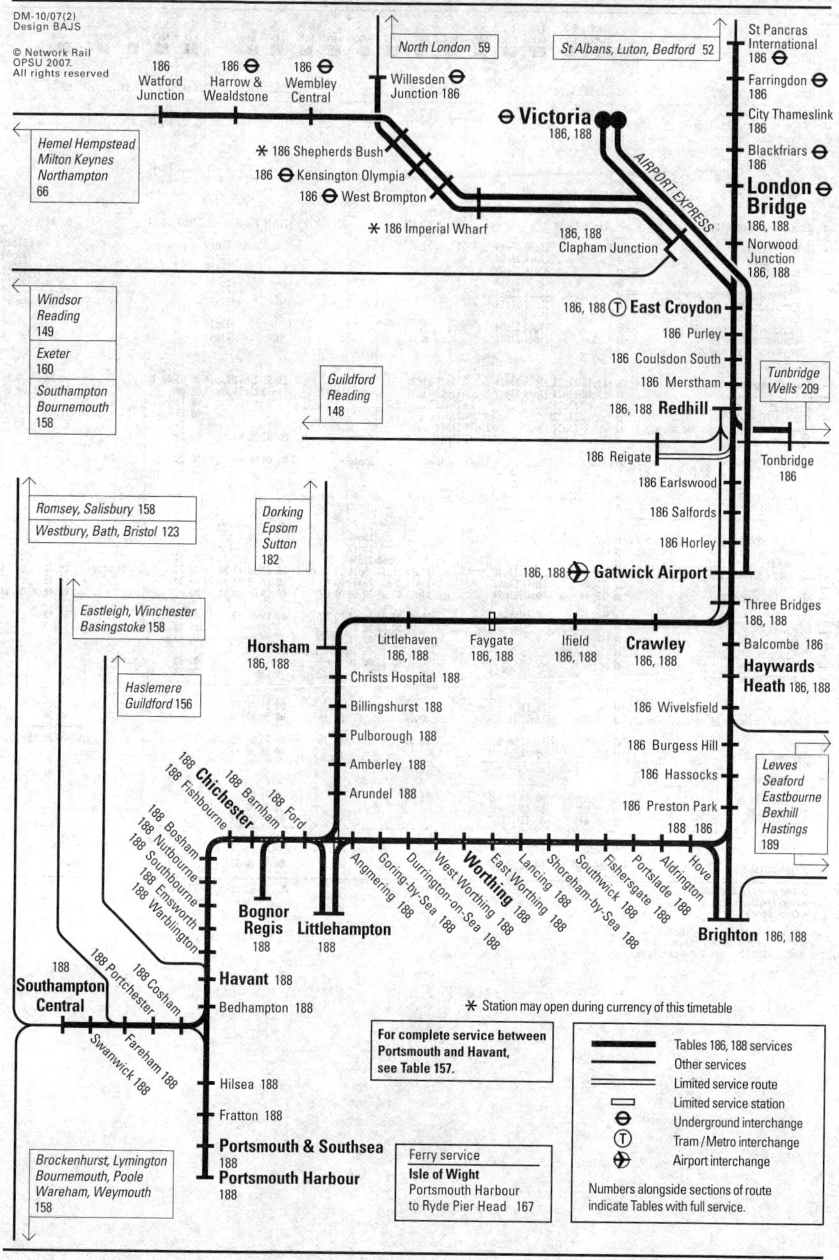
North London 59
St Albans, Luton, Bedford 52
186 Watford Junction
186 Harrow & Wealdstone
186 Wembley Central
Willesden Junction 186
Victoria 186, 188
St Pancras International 186
Farringdon 186
City Thameslink 186
Blackfriars 186
London Bridge 186, 188
Norwood Junction 186, 188
Hemel Hempstead
Milton Keynes
Northampton
66
* 186 Shepherds Bush
186 Kensington Olympia
186 West Brompton
* 186 Imperial Wharf
186, 188 Clapham Junction
AIRPORT EXPRESS
Windsor
Reading
149
Exeter
160
Southampton
Bournemouth
158
186, 188 East Croydon
186 Purley
186 Coulsdon South
186 Merstham
186, 188 Redhill
Tunbridge Wells 209
Guildford
Reading
148
186 Reigate
Tonbridge 186
186 Earlswood
186 Salfords
186 Horley
186, 188 Gatwick Airport
Romsey, Salisbury 158
Westbury, Bath, Bristol 123
Dorking
Epsom
Sutton
182
Eastleigh, Winchester
Basingstoke 158
Three Bridges 186, 188
Horsham 186, 188
Littlehaven 186, 188
Faygate 186, 188
Ifield 186, 188
Crawley 186, 188
Balcombe 186
Haywards Heath 186, 188
Haslemere
Guildford 156
Christs Hospital 188
Billingshurst 188
Pulborough 188
Amberley 188
Arundel 188
186 Wivelsfield
186 Burgess Hill
186 Hassocks
186 Preston Park
Lewes
Seaford
Eastbourne
Bexhill
Hastings
189
188 Chichester
188 Fishbourne
188 Barnham
188 Ford
188 Bosham
188 Nutbourne
188 Southbourne
188 Emsworth
188 Warblington
Angmering 188
Goring-by-Sea 188
Durrington-on-Sea 188
West Worthing 188
Worthing 188
East Worthing 188
Lancing 188
Shoreham-by-Sea 188
Southwick 188
Fishersgate 188
Portslade 188
Aldrington
Hove
188 186
Bognor Regis 188
Littlehampton 188
Brighton 186, 188
188 Southampton Central
188 Portchester
188 Cosham
Havant 188
Bedhampton 188
Swanwick 188
Fareham 188
* Station may open during currency of this timetable
For complete service between Portsmouth and Havant, see Table 157.
Hilsea 188
Fratton 188
Portsmouth & Southsea 188
Portsmouth Harbour 188
Brockenhurst, Lymington
Bournemouth, Poole
Wareham, Weymouth
158
Ferry service
Isle of Wight
Portsmouth Harbour to Ryde Pier Head 167
Tables 186, 188 services
Other services
Limited service route
Limited service station
Underground interchange
Tram/Metro interchange
Airport interchange
Numbers alongside sections of route indicate Tables with full service.

Watford Junction, Bedford and London → Brighton

Network Diagram - see first page of Table 186

Miles	Miles	Miles	Station		SN MX 1 ◇	SN MO 1	FC MX 1	FC MO 1	SN MO 1	SN MX 1	SN MX 1	SN MO 1	SN MX 1	SN MO 1	GW MX 1	SN MX 1	SN MO 1 ◇	FC	SN MX 1	SN MO 1	GX 1	GW MO 1	SN MX 1 ◇ A	FC MO
0	—	—	**London Victoria 15** ⊖	d	23p02	23p04				23p10	23p17			23p17		23p32	23p32		23p47		00 01		00 05	
—	0	—	Watford Junction	d																23p22				
—	6	—	Harrow & Wealdstone ⊖	d																23p28				
—	9½	—	Wembley Central	d																				
—	—	0	Willesden Jn. High Level	d																				
—	—	1½	Shepherds Bush § ⊖	d																				
—	15	2¾	Kensington Olympia ⊖	d																23p48				
—	16	3¾	West Brompton ⊖	d																23p50				
—	—	4¼	Imperial Wharf §	d																				
2¾	18½	6¼	Clapham Junction 10	d	23p08	23p10				23p16	23p23			23p23		23p38	23p38		23p53	00 02			00 11	
—	—	—	**Bedford 7**	d			21p50	21p40										22p10						22p40
—	—	—	Luton 10	d			22p14	22p04										22p34						23p04
—	—	—	Luton Airport Parkway 7 ✈	d			22p16	22p06										22p36						23p06
—	—	—	St Albans City	d			22p29	22p18										22p48						23p18
—	—	—	St Pancras International 15 ⊖	d			22p54	22p54										23p24						23p54
—	—	—	Farringdon 3 ⊖	d			22p59	22p59										23p29						23p59
—	—	—	City Thameslink 3	d			23p01																	
—	—	—	**London Blackfriars 3** ⊖	d			23p04	23p04										23p34						00 04
—	0	—	**London Bridge 4** ⊖	d			23p11	23p11										23p41						00 11
—	9	—	Norwood Junction 2	d																				
10½	10¼	—	**East Croydon**	a	23p18	23p23	23p24	23p26		23p28	23p33			23p36		23p51	23p52	23p56	00 05	00 20			00 24	00 26
—	—	—		d	23p18	23p23	23p24	23p27		23p28	23p33			23p37		23p52	23p53	23p57	00 06				00 25	00 27
13½	—	—	Purley 4	d		23p29				23p33									00 12					
15½	—	—	Coulsdon South	d		23p33			←	23p37									00 15					
19	—	—	Merstham	d		23p38			23p38	23p42									00 21					
21	0	0	**Redhill**	a	23p30	→			23p42	23p46			←			00 03	00 05		00 24					
—	—	—		d	23p31				23p42	23p46			23p46		00 03	00 05	00 05		00 25			00 34		
—	—	19¾	Tonbridge 4	a						→														
—	1¾	—	Reigate	a																				
21¾	—	—	Earlswood (Surrey)	d									23p49											
23¾	—	—	Salfords	d								←	23p52											
26	—	—	Horley 4	d					23p50			23p50	23p56						00 31					
26¾	—	—	**Gatwick Airport 10** ✈	a	23p38		23p41	23p48	→		23p50	23p54	23p58	00 01	00 11	00 13	00 13	00 16	00 33		00 35	00 41	00 42	00 46
—	—	—		d	23p39		23p41	23p50			23p51	23p55	23p59	00 02		00 14	00 14	00 17	00 34				00 43	00 47
29½	0	—	Three Bridges 15	a	23p44		23p47	23p54			23p55	00 01	00 04	00 07		00 18	00 18	00 24	00 39				00 48	00 54
—	—	—		d	23p44		23p47	23p54			23p56	00 01	00 04	00 07		00 19	00 19		00 39				00 48	
—	1½	—	Crawley	d								00 05	00 07						00 42					
—	2¾	—	Ifield	d								00 07	00 10						00 45					
—	5¼	—	Faygate	d																				
—	7½	—	Littlehaven	d								00 14	00 16						00 51					
—	8½	—	**Horsham 4**	a								00 17	00 19						00 54					
34	—	—	Balcombe	d			23p53									00 25	00 25							
38	—	—	**Haywards Heath 3**	a	23p52		23p58	00 03			00 04			00 16		00 30	00 30						01 00	
—	—	—		d	23p53		23p58	00 03			00 05			00 16		00 30	00 30						01 03 / 01 06	
41	0	—	Wivelsfield 4	d	23p57		00 02									00 34	00 34							
—	9¼	—	Lewes 4	a																			01 20	
41¾	—	—	Burgess Hill 4	d	23p59		00 04	00 08			00 10					00 36	00 36							
43¾	—	—	Hassocks 4	d	00 02		00 08									00 40	00 40							
49½	0	—	Preston Park	d	00 09		00 15									00 47	00 47							
—	1½	—	Hove 2	a							00 21			00 30									01s25	
51	—	—	**Brighton 10**	a	00 15		00 20	00 22								00 51	00 51						01s17	

For general notes see front of timetable
For details of catering facilities see Directory of Train Operators

§ It is unknown, at the time of going to press, when this station will open. For further details contact National Rail Enquiries 08457-484950 or see local publicity.

A To Eastbourne (Table 189)

Watford Junction, Bedford and London → Brighton

Network Diagram - see first page of Table 186

Station		FC MX	SN	GW MX	FC MX	GX	SN MO	SN MX	FC MO	FC MX	SN		FC	SN	FC	GX	FC	SN	FC	GX	FC	GX	SE	SN	GX
			1	1		1	1 ◇	1 ◇	1	1	1		1	1			1	1 ◇	1	1	1	1	88	1 ◇	
London Victoria 15	⊖ d		00 14			00 30	01 00	01 00			02 00			03 00		03 30		04 00		04 30		05 00		05 02	05 15
Watford Junction	d																								
Harrow & Wealdstone	⊖ d																								
Wembley Central	d																								
Willesden Jn. High Level	d																								
Shepherds Bush §	⊖ d																								
Kensington Olympia	⊖ d																								
West Brompton	⊖ d																								
Imperial Wharf §	d																								
Clapham Junction 10	d		00 20				01 08	01 08			02 08			03 08				04 08						05 08	
Bedford 7	d	22p40			23p10				23p40	23p40			00 40		01 40				02 40						
Luton 10	d	23p04			23p34				00 04	00 04			01 04		02 04				03 04						
Luton Airport Parkway 7	✈ d	23p06			23p36				00 06	00 06			01 06		02 06				03 06						
St Albans City	d	23p18			23p48				00 18	00 18			01 18		02 18				03 18						
St Pancras International 15	⊖ d	23p54			00 24				00 54	00 54			01 54		02 54		03 25		03 54		04 25				
Farringdon 3	⊖ d	23p59			00 29																				
City Thameslink 3	d																								
London Blackfriars 3	⊖ d	00 04			00 34				01 04	01 04			02 04		03 04		03 34		04 04		04 34				
London Bridge 4	⊖ d	00 11			00 41																				
Norwood Junction 2	d																								
East Croydon	a	00 26	00 32		00 56		01 21	01 21	01 30	01 32	02 21		02 30	03 21	03 30		04 00	04 21	04 30		05 00			05 21	
	d	00 27	00 33		00 57		01 22	01 22	01 32	01 32	02 22		02 32	03 22	03 32		04 02	04 22	04 32		05 02			05 22	
Purley 4	d		00 38				01 27	01 27			02 27			03 27				04 27						05 26	
Coulsdon South	d		00 41																					05 30	
Merstham	d		00 47																					05 35	
Redhill	a		00 50																					05 39	
	d		00 51	00 53																			05 35	05 40	
Tonbridge 4	a																								
Reigate	a																								
Earlswood (Surrey)	d																								
Salfords	d																								
Horley 4	d		00 57				01 43	01 43			02 42			03 42				04 43						05 46	
Gatwick Airport 10	✈ a	00 49	00 59	01 01	01 16	01 24	01 45	01 45	01 51	01 51	02 44		02 51	03 44	03 51	04 05	04 24	04 45	04 51	05 05	05 21	05 35	05 42	05 48	05 50
	d	00 50			01 17		01 47	01 47	01 52	01 52	02 46		02 52	03 46	03 52		04 24	04 47	04 52		05 22			05 49	
Three Bridges 15	a	00 54			01 24		01 51	01 51	01 58	01 58	02 50		02 58	03 50	03 58		04 30	04 51	04 58		05 26			05 54	
	d						01 52	01 52										04 52	04 58		05 26			05 54	
Crawley	d																								
Ifield	d																								
Faygate	d																								
Littlehaven	d																								
Horsham 4	a																								
Balcombe	d																							06 00	
Haywards Heath 3	a						02 03	02 04										05 00	05 08		05 36			06 05	
	d						02 03	02 04										05 01	05 08		05 36			06 06	
Wivelsfield 4	d																				05 40			06 10	
Lewes 4	a																								
Burgess Hill 4	d																				05 42			06 12	
Hassocks 4	d																				05 46			06 15	
Preston Park	d																				05 53			06 22	
Hove 2	a																								
Brighton 10	a						02 30	02 30										05 16	05 29		05 59			06 28	

For general notes see front of timetable
For details of catering facilities see Directory of Train Operators

§ It is unknown, at the time of going to press, when this station will open. For further details contact National Rail Enquiries 08457-484950 or see local publicity.

Watford Junction, Bedford and London → Brighton

Network Diagram - see first page of Table 186

	FC 1	GW 1	GW 1	SN 1 A	GX 1	SN 1 B	SN 1	FC 1	GX	SN 1 B	FC 1	GX 1	GW 1	GW 1	SN 1 C		GX 1	FC 1		SN 1 C	SN 1	GW 1	GX 1	SN 1
London Victoria 15 ⊖ d					05 30	05 32			05 45			06 00			06 02		06 15						06 30	
Watford Junction d																								
Harrow & Wealdstone ⊖ d																								
Wembley Central d																								
Willesden Jn. High Level d																								
Shepherds Bush § ⊖ d																								
Kensington Olympia ⊖ d																								
West Brompton ⊖ d																								
Imperial Wharf § d																								
Clapham Junction 10 d						05 38									06 08									
Bedford 7 d	03 40							04 10			04 20							04 50						
Luton 10 d	04 04							04 34			04 44							05 14						
Luton Airport Parkway 7 ✈ d	04 06							04 36			04 46							05 16						
St Albans City d	04 18							04 48			04 58							05 28						
St Pancras International 15 ⊖ d	04 54							05 14			05 34							06 04						
Farringdon 3 ⊖ d	04 59							05 19			05 39							06 09						
City Thameslink 3 d																		06 11						
London Blackfriars 3 ⊖ d	05 04							05 24			05 44							06 14						
London Bridge 4 ⊖ d								05 31			05 50							06 21						
Norwood Junction 2 d																								
East Croydon a	05 30					05 48		05 51			06 04				06 17			06 35						
d	05 32					05 49		05 52			06 04				06 18			06 36						
Purley 4 d						05 54									06 23									
Coulsdon South d						05 57									06 27									
Merstham d						06 03									06 33									
Redhill a						06 06				←					06 36					←				
d		05 44	05 44			06 07				06 07			06 14	06 24	06 40	06 42				06 40		06 46		
Tonbridge 4 a						→									→									
Reigate a			05 48										06 18	06 28		06 46								
Earlswood (Surrey) d										06 09										06 42				
Salfords d										06 13										06 46				
Horley 4 d										06 16										06 49				
Gatwick Airport 10 ✈ a	05 53	05 54			06 00			06 08	06 15	06 19	06 20	06 30					06 45	06 51		06 53		06 56	07 00	
d	05 54			05 59				06 08		06 20	06 20							06 52		06 54				
Three Bridges 15 a	05 59			06 03				06 14		06 24	06 26							06 56		06 59				
d	06 00			06 04				06 14		06 24	06 26							06 56		06 59	07 05			
Crawley d				06 07																07 03	07 08			
Ifield d				06 10																	07 11			
Faygate d																					07 15			
Littlehaven d				06 16																	07 19			
Horsham 4 a				06 19																07 11	07 22			
Balcombe d								06 20			06 32													
Haywards Heath 3 a	06 09							06 25		06 33	06 37							07 05						
d	06 10						06 13	06 25		06 34	06 38							07 06						07 12
Wivelsfield 4 d	06 14						06 17	06 29		06 38	06 42							07 10						07 16
Lewes 4 a							06 28			06 49														07 31
Burgess Hill 4 d	06 16							06 32			06 44							07 12						
Hassocks 4 d	06 19							06 35			06 47							07 15						
Preston Park d	06 26							06 42			06 54							07 22						
Hove 2 a																								
Brighton 10 a	06 32							06 46			06 59							07 27						

For general notes see front of timetable
For details of catering facilities see
Directory of Train Operators

§ It is unknown, at the time of going to press, when this station will open. For further details contact National Rail Enquiries 08457-484950 or see local publicity.

A To Southampton Central (Table 188)
B To Ore (Table 189)
C To Bognor Regis (Table 188)

Watford Junction, Bedford and London → Brighton

Network Diagram - see first page of Table 186

	SN 1 ◇	LO	SN 1 ◇ A	FC 1	GX 1	SN 1	SN 1 B	LO	SN 1 ◇ A		GX 1	GW 1	FC 1	SN 1	GW 1	SN 1	LO 1 C	GX 1	SN 1	FC 1	GW 1	SN 1 D	GX 1	LO
London Victoria 15 ⊖ d	06 21		06 32		06 45		06 47				07 00					07 06		07 15				07 17	07 30	
Watford Junction d						06 05																		
Harrow & Wealdstone ⊖ d						06 11																		
Wembley Central d																								
Willesden Jn. High Level d		06 08						06 38									06 54							07 08
Shepherds Bush § ⊖ d																								
Kensington Olympia ⊖ d		06 17				06 31		06 47									07 02							07 17
West Brompton ⊖ d		06 19				06 33		06 49									07 04							07 19
Imperial Wharf § d																								
Clapham Junction 10 d	06 27	06a28	06 38			06a42	06 53	06a59								07 12	07a13					07 23		07a28
Bedford 7 d				05 20									05 40							06 00				
Luton 10 d				05 44									06 04							06 24				
Luton Airport Parkway 7 ✈ d				05 46									06 06							06 26				
St Albans City d				05 58									06 18							06 38				
St Pancras International 15 ⊖ d				06 24									06 39							06 57				
Farringdon 3 ⊖ d				06 29									06 44							07 02				
City Thameslink 3 d				06 31									06 47							07 07				
London Blackfriars 3 ⊖ d				06 36									06 50							07 10				
London Bridge 4 ⊖ d				06 43									07 00							07 16				
Norwood Junction 2 d																								
East Croydon a	06 38		06 48	06 56			07 03						07 15			07 21				07 31		07 33		
d	06 39		06 49	06 56			07 03						07 16			07 22				07 32		07 34		
Purley 4 d	06 44		06 54													07 27								
Coulsdon South d			06 57													07 30								
Merstham d			07 03													07 36								
Redhill a	06 52		07 06													07 39						07 45		
d	06 53		07 07						← 07 07			07 11		07 17	07 28	07 40					07 43	07 46		
Tonbridge 4 a			→																					
Reigate a												07 15		07 22	07 32	07 45								
Earlswood (Surrey) d									07 09													07 48		
Salfords d									07 13													07 52		
Horley 4 d	06 59								07 16													07 55		
Gatwick Airport 10 ✈ a	07 03			07 11	07 15		07 18		07 19		07 30		07 31					07 45		07 48	07 54	07 58	08 00	
d	07 04			07 12			07 19		07 20				07 32							07 50		07 59		
Three Bridges 15 a	07 09			07 17			07 24		07 24				07 37							07 54		08 04		
d	07 09			07 18			07 24		07 28	07 30			07 38						07 52	07 54		08 05		
Crawley d										07 34									07 56			08 09		
Ifield d										07 36									07 58			08 11		
Faygate d																						08 15		
Littlehaven d										07 43									08 05			08 19		
Horsham 4 a										07 46									08 08			08 22		
Balcombe d	07 15								07 35											08 00				
Haywards Heath 3 a	07 20			07 27			07 32		07 40				07 47							08 06				
d	07 21			07 28			07 33		07 40				07 48							08 06				
Wivelsfield 4 d	07 25			07 32			07 37		07 44											08 10				
Lewes 4 a							07 52																	
Burgess Hill 4 d	07 27			07 34					07 46				07 54							08 12				
Hassocks 4 d	07 30			07 37					07 50											08 15				
Preston Park d	07 37			07 44					07 57											08 22				
Hove 2 a																								
Brighton 10 a	07 42			07 49					08 02				08 06							08 27				

For general notes see front of timetable
For details of catering facilities see
Directory of Train Operators

§ It is unknown, at the time of going to press, when this station will open. For further details contact National Rail Enquiries 08457-484950 or see local publicity.

A To Chichester (Table 188)
B To Ore (Table 189)
C Until 29 August and from 17 November
D To Southampton Central (Table 188)

Watford Junction, Bedford and London → Brighton

Network Diagram - see first page of Table 186

		SN	SN	SE	GW		SN	FC	GX	SN	SN	SN	SN	SN	SN	LO	GX	SN	GW	SN	SN	FC	GX	LO	SN
				43																					
		1	1		1		1	1	1	1	1	1	1	1	1		1	1	1	1	1 ◇	1	1	1	1
				A														B						C	
London Victoria 15	⊖ d						07 36		07 45	07 47			07 52				08 00	08 02			08 06		08 15		
Watford Junction	d											07 18													07 40
Harrow & Wealdstone	⊖ d											07 25													07 46
Wembley Central	d											07 29													07 51
Willesden Jn. High Level	d															07 38								07 53	
Shepherds Bush §	⊖ d																								
Kensington Olympia	⊖ d											07 43				07 47								08 02	08 07
West Brompton	⊖ d											07 45				07 49								08 04	08 10
Imperial Wharf §	d																								
Clapham Junction 10	d						07 42			07 53		07a52	07 58			07a58		08 08			08 12			08a13	08a16
Bedford 7	d							06 20														06 56			
Luton 10	d							06 44														07 16			
Luton Airport Parkway 7	✈ d							06 46																	
St Albans City	d							06 58														07 28			
St Pancras International 15	⊖ d							07 17														07 48			
Farringdon 3	⊖ d							07 22														07 52			
City Thameslink 3	d							07 27														07 55			
London Blackfriars 3	⊖ d							07 32														08 00			
London Bridge 4	⊖ d	07 28		07 34				07 40						07 54						08 03					
Norwood Junction 2	d	07 42												08 06						08 14					
East Croydon	🚋 a	07 45		07 48			07 52	07 55		08 03			08 08	08 11				08 18		08 19	08 22	08 25			
	d	07 46		07 49			07 52	07 56		08 03			08 08	08 11				08 18		08 20	08 22	08 26			
Purley 4	d						07 58													08 27					
Coulsdon South	d			07 56			08 01													08 31					
Merstham	d			08 01			08 07													08 36					
Redhill	a			08 05			08 10				←							08 31		08 40					
	d		07 59	08 05	08 09		08 11				08 11				08 15			08 32	08 33	08 41					
Tonbridge 4	a			08 35			→													→					
Reigate	a		08 03		08 13										08 19				08 37						
Earlswood (Surrey)	d										08 13														
Salfords	d										08 17														
Horley 4	d										08 21														
Gatwick Airport 10	✈ a	08 01						08 11	08 15	08 18	08 24		08 25	08 29			08 30	08 39				08 40	08 45		
	d	08 02						08 12		08 19	08 25		08 26	08 30				08 40				08 42			
Three Bridges 15	a	08 06						08 16			08 30							08 44			08 41	08 46			
	d	08 07						08 16			08 31							08 45			08 42	08 46			
Crawley	d										08 34							08 48							
Ifield	d										08 37														
Faygate	d										08 41														
Littlehaven	d										08 45														
Horsham 4	a										08 49							08 56							
Balcombe	d							08 22														08 52			
Haywards Heath 3	a	08 16						08 27		08 30			08 37	08 44							08 50	08 57			
	d	08 16						08 28		08 32			08 38	08 45							08 51	08 58			
Wivelsfield 4	d							08 32		08 36											08 55	09 02			
Lewes 4	a									08 51															
Burgess Hill 4	d	08 22						08 34													08 57	09 04			
Hassocks 4	d							08 37						08 51								09 07			
Preston Park	d							08 44						08 58								09 14			
Hove 2	a												08 53												
Brighton 10	a	08 33						08 49						09 03							09 08	09 20			

For general notes see front of timetable
For details of catering facilities see Directory of Train Operators

§ It is unknown, at the time of going to press, when this station will open. For further details contact National Rail Enquiries 08457-484950 or see local publicity.

A To Tunbridge Wells (Table 206)

B To Portsmouth Harbour (Table 188) and to Bognor Regis (Table 188)

C Until 29 August and from 17 November From Stratford Low Level (Table 59)

Watford Junction, Bedford and London → Brighton

Network Diagram - see first page of Table 186

	SN 1		FC 1	LO	SN 1	SN 1	SN 1	FC 1	SN 1	SN 1 ◇	GX 1	GW 1	SN 1	SN 1	SN 1	SN 1	LO	SN 1 ◇	SN 1 ◇	GX 1	SN 1		SN 1
														A ⊥		⊥	B				C ⊥		
London Victoria 15 ⊖ d	08 17						08 20			08 26	08 30			08 32		08 36			08 38	08 45	08 47		
Watford Junction d																							
Harrow & Wealdstone ⊖ d																							
Wembley Central d																							
Willesden Jn. High Level d				08 08																			
Shepherds Bush § ⊖ d																							
Kensington Olympia ⊖ d				08 17									08 25				08 31						
West Brompton ⊖ d				08 19									08 28				08 33						
Imperial Wharf § d																							
Clapham Junction 10 d	08 23			08a28			08 28			08 32			08a35	08 38		08 43	08a44		08 46		08 53		
Bedford 7 d			07 00																				
Luton 10 d			07 24																				
Luton Airport Parkway 7 ✈ d			07 26																				
St Albans City d			07 38																				
St Pancras International 15 ⊖ d			08 00																				
Farringdon 3 ⊖ d			08 04																				
City Thameslink 3 d			08 09																				
London Blackfriars 3 ⊖ d			08 12																				
London Bridge 4 ⊖ d			08 19		08 23										08 30								08 49
Norwood Junction 2 d															08 45								09 02
East Croydon ⇌ a	08 33		08 36		08 37		08 39							08 48	08 49	08 52			08 56		09 03		09 05
d	08 33		08 36		08 38		08 39							08 48	08 51	08 53			08 57		09 03		09 06
Purley 4 d															08 58								09 12
Coulsdon South d															09 02								09 15
Merstham d															09 07								→
Redhill a			08 47		08 52	←		←						08 59	09 11								
d			08 49		08 53	08 41		08 49				08 55		09 03	09 12								
Tonbridge 4 a			→												→								
Reigate a					08 57																		
Earlswood (Surrey) d						08 43																	
Salfords d						08 47																	
Horley 4 d						08 50																	
Gatwick Airport 10 ✈ a	08 48					08 53	08 54	08 56		08 57	09 00	09 02		09 10					09 12	09 15	09 18		
d	08 49					08 54	08 55	08 56		09 00				09 11					09 14		09 19		
Three Bridges 15 a						08 58		09 00		09 04				09 15					09 18				
d						08 58		09 00		09 05				09 16					09 19				
Crawley d						09 02								09 19									
Ifield d						09 04																	
Faygate d						09 08																	
Littlehaven d						09 12																	
Horsham 4 a						09 16								09 27									
Balcombe d																							
Haywards Heath 3 a	09 00						09 06	09 10	←	09 13									09 27		09 30		
d	09 13	09 04					09 06	09 10	09 13	09 17								←	09 28		09 34	09 37	
Wivelsfield 4 d	→								09 17	09 22								09 22	09 34				
Lewes 4 a									09 28	→											09 52		
Burgess Hill 4 d		09 09																09 24	09 36				
Hassocks 4 d																		09 27	09 39				
Preston Park d																		09 34					
Hove 2 a		09 21																				09 51	
Brighton 10 a							09 22	09 24								09 30		09 38	09 52				

For general notes see front of timetable
For details of catering facilities see Directory of Train Operators

§ It is unknown, at the time of going to press, when this station will open. For further details contact National Rail Enquiries 08457-484950 or see local publicity.

A To Southampton Central (Table 188) and to Bognor Regis (Table 188)

B 1 September to 14 November

C ⊥ to Lewes

Watford Junction, Bedford and London → Brighton

Network Diagram - see first page of Table 186

	FC	SN	SN	LO	GX	SN	SN	GW	SN	SN	SN	FC	GX	GW	SN	SE 13	SN	LO	SN			SE 88	LO	LO
	1	1	1		1	1	1	1	1	1	1 ◇	1	1	1	1		1		1			1		
									A 🍴		🍴							B	C 🍴			D	E	B
London Victoria 15 ⊖ d					09 00				09 02		09 06		09 15						09 17					
Watford Junction d																	08 42							
Harrow & Wealdstone ⊖ d																	08 48							
Wembley Central d																	08 53							
Willesden Jn. High Level d				08 38																			09⌇08	09⌇11
Shepherds Bush § ⊖ d																								
Kensington Olympia ⊖ d				08 47			08 58										09 08	09⌇08					09⌇17	09⌇20
West Brompton ⊖ d				08 49			09 00										09 11	09a11					09⌇19	09⌇22
Imperial Wharf § d																		⌇					⌇	⌇
Clapham Junction 10 d				08a58			09a07		09 08		09 12						09a18	09a22	09 23				09a30	09a32
Bedford 7 d	07 28											07 48												
Luton 10 d	07 48											08 12												
Luton Airport Parkway 7 ✈ d												08 14												
St Albans City d	08 00											08 27												
St Pancras International 15 ⊖ d	08 20											08 47												
Farringdon 3 ⊖ d	08 24											08 52												
City Thameslink 3 d	08 27											08 55												
London Blackfriars 3 ⊖ d	08 32											08 58												
London Bridge 4 ⊖ d		09 00										09 06				09 11								
Norwood Junction 2 d		09 11																						
East Croydon 🚋 a	09 06	09 15							09 18	←	09 22	09 23				09 25			09 33					
d	09 06	09 21 →							09 18	09 21	09 22	09 24				09 26			09 33					
Purley 4 d						←				09 27					←									
Coulsdon South d						09 15				09 30					09 30									
Merstham d						09 21				→					09 36									
Redhill a			←			09 24			09 30						09 39	09 43								
d			09 12			09 25		09 29	09 30					09 34	09 40	09 44						09 44		
Tonbridge 4 a																10 08								
Reigate a								09 33						09 38										
Earlswood (Surrey) d			09 14																					
Salfords d			09 18																					
Horley 4 d			09 21						09 36						09 46							09 50		
Gatwick Airport 10 ✈ a	09 22		09 24		09 30	09 32			09 39			09 40	09 45		09 48				09 48			09 54		
d	09 23		09 25						09 40			09 41			09 50				09 49			09 55		
Three Bridges 15 a	09 28		09 29						09 44			09 45			09 54							10 00		
d	09 28		09 30						09 45			09 45			09 55 →							10 00		
Crawley d			09 33						09 48													10 04		
Ifield d			09 36																			10 06		
Faygate d																								
Littlehaven d			09 42																			10 13		
Horsham 4 a			09 46						09 56													10 16		
Balcombe d												09 51												
Haywards Heath 3 a	09 36											09 56							10 00					
d	09 40											09 57							10 04	10 07				
Wivelsfield 4 d												10 01								10 11				
Lewes 4 a																				10 22				
Burgess Hill 4 d												10 03							10 09					
Hassocks 4 d												10 06												
Preston Park d												10 13												
Hove 2 a																			10 21					
Brighton 10 a	09 54										09 58	10 19												

For general notes see front of timetable
For details of catering facilities see Directory of Train Operators

§ It is unknown, at the time of going to press, when this station will open. For further details contact National Rail Enquiries 08457-484950 or see local publicity.

A To Portsmouth Harbour (Table 188) and to Bognor Regis (Table 188)
B 1 September to 14 November
C 🍴 to Lewes
D From Tonbridge (Table 209)
E Until 29 August and from 17 November From Stratford Low Level (Table 59)

Watford Junction, Bedford and London → Brighton

Network Diagram - see first page of Table 186

		FC	GW	GX	SN	SN	SN	SN	LO	SN	FC	GX	SN	SN	SN	LO	SN	FC	GW	SN	GX	SN	GW	SE 13
		1	1	1	1	1	1	1 ◇	1	1	1	1	1	1	1		1	1	1	1	1	1	1	
					A ☕				B					C ☕								D ☕		E
London Victoria 15	⊖ d			09 30	09 32			09 36				09 45		09 47							10 00	10 02		
Watford Junction	d												09 11											
Harrow & Wealdstone	⊖ d												09 17											
Wembley Central	d												09 22											
Willesden Jn. High Level	d								09 23							09 38								
Shepherds Bush §	⊖ d																							
Kensington Olympia	⊖ d						09 29		09 32				09 37			09 47								
West Brompton	⊖ d						09 31		09 34				09 40			09 49								
Imperial Wharf §	d														←									
Clapham Junction 10	d				09 38		09a38	09 42	09a43				09b54	09 53	09 54	09a58						10 08		
Bedford 7	d	08 04									08 20		→					08 40						
Luton 10	d	08 28									08 44							09 04						
Luton Airport Parkway 7	✈ d	08 30									08 46							09 06						
St Albans City	d	08 44									09 00							09 18						
St Pancras International 15	⊖ d	09 04									09 20							09 39						
Farringdon 3	⊖ d	09 08									09 24							09 44						
City Thameslink 3	d	09 13									09 27							09 46						
London Blackfriars 3	⊖ d	09 17									09 34							09 49						
London Bridge 4	⊖ d	09 25				09 33					09 42							09 56						10 03
Norwood Junction 2	d					09 46																		10 16
East Croydon	🚊 a	09 39			09 48	09 49		09 51			09 54			10 03	10 07			10 09				10 18		10 19
	d	09 39			09 48	09 51		09 52			09 54			10 03	10 07			10 09				10 18		10 21
Purley 4	d					09 57																		10 26
Coulsdon South	d					10 00																		10 30
Merstham	d					10 06																		10 35
Redhill	a				10 00	10 09																10 30		10 38
	d		09 48		10 00	10 10											← 10 10		10 14			10 30	10 34	10 39
Tonbridge 4	a					→																		11 08
Reigate	a																		10 18				10 38	
Earlswood (Surrey)	d																10 12							
Salfords	d																10 16							
Horley 4	d																10 19					10 36		
Gatwick Airport 10	✈ a	09 55	09 59	10 00	10 08						10 10	10 15		10 18	10 22		10 23	10 25		←	10 30	10 39		
	d	09 56			10 09						10 11			10 19	10 28		10 24	10 26		10 28		10 40		
Three Bridges 15	a	10 00			10 14						10 15				→		10 29			10 33		10 44		
	d	10 00			10 14					← 09 55	10 15						10 30			10 33		10 45		
Crawley	d				10 18												10 33					10 48		
Ifield	d																10 36							
Faygate	d																							
Littlehaven	d																10 42							
Horsham 4	a				10 26												10 47					10 56		
Balcombe	d										10 21													
Haywards Heath 3	a	10 08								10 08	10 26			10 30				10 36		10 42				
	d	10 10								10 18	10 27			10 34 10 37				10 38		10 46				
Wivelsfield 4	d									10 22	10 31									10 50				
Lewes 4	a													10 51										
Burgess Hill 4	d									10 24	10 33									10 52				
Hassocks 4	d									10 27	10 36									10 55				
Preston Park	d									10 34	10 43									11 02				
Hove 2	a													10 51						→				
Brighton 10	a	10 24						10 27		10 40	10 51							10 54						

For general notes see front of timetable
For details of catering facilities see Directory of Train Operators

§ It is unknown, at the time of going to press, when this station will open. For further details contact National Rail Enquiries 08457-484950 or see local publicity.

A To Southampton Central (Table 188) and to Bognor Regis (Table 188)
B Until 29 August and from 17 November
C ☕ to Lewes

D To Portsmouth Harbour (Table 188) and to Bognor Regis (Table 188)
E To Tunbridge Wells (Table 206)
b Arr. 0950

Watford Junction, Bedford and London → Brighton

Network Diagram - see first page of Table 186

	SN	SN	FC	GX	SN		GW	FC	LO	SE	GX	SN	SN	SN	FC	GX	SN	LO	SN		SN	SN	FC
	1 ◇	1	1	1	1		1	1		88 1	1	1	1	1 ◇	1	1	1		1		1	1	1
	🛒				A 🛒					B		C 🛒		🛒					A 🛒				
London Victoria 15 ⊖ d	10 06			10 15	10 17						10 30	10 32		10 36		10 45			10 47				
Watford Junction d																	10 11						
Harrow & Wealdstone ⊖ d																	10 17						
Wembley Central d																							
Willesden Jn. High Level d									10 08									10 38					
Shepherds Bush § ⊖ d																							
Kensington Olympia ⊖ d									10 17								10 37	10 47					
West Brompton ⊖ d									10 19								10 39	10 49			←		
Imperial Wharf § d																							
Clapham Junction 10 d	10 12				10 23				10a28			10 38		10 42			10b54	10a58	10 53		10 54		
Bedford 7 d			08 55					09 10							09 25		→						09 40
Luton 10 d			09 19					09 34							09 49								10 04
Luton Airport Parkway 7 ✈ d			09 21					09 36							09 51								10 06
St Albans City d			09 33					09 48							10 03								10 18
St Pancras International 15 ⊖ d			09 54					10 09							10 24								10 39
Farringdon 3 ⊖ d			09 59					10 14							10 29								10 44
City Thameslink 3 d			10 01					10 16							10 31								10 46
London Blackfriars 3 ⊖ d			10 05					10 20							10 35								10 50
London Bridge 4 ⊖ d			10 11					10 26					10 33		10 41								10 56
Norwood Junction 2 d													10 46										
East Croydon 🚋 a	10 22		10 24		10 33			10 39				10 48	10 49	10 52	10 54				11 03		11 07		11 09
d	10 22		10 24		10 33			10 39				10 48	10 51	10 52	10 54				11 03		11 07		11 09
Purley 4 d													10 57										
Coulsdon South d													11 00										
Merstham d													11 06										
Redhill a												11 00	11 09									←	
d							10 41			10 44		11 00	11 09									11 09	
Tonbridge 4 a													→										
Reigate a																							
Earlswood (Surrey) d																						11 12	
Salfords d																						11 15	
Horley 4 d										10 51												11 19	
Gatwick Airport 10 ✈ a			10 40	10 45	10 48		10 50	10 55		10 55	11 00	11 08			11 10	11 15			11 18		11 22	11 23	11 25
d			10 41		10 49			10 56		10 56		11 09			11 11				11 19		11 28	11 24	11 26
Three Bridges 15 a			10 45							11 00		11 14			11 15						→	11 29	
d			10 45							11 01		11 14			11 15							11 30	
Crawley d										11 04		11 18										11 33	
Ifield d										11 07												11 36	
Faygate d																							
Littlehaven d										11 13												11 42	
Horsham 4 a										11 16		11 26										11 47	
Balcombe d															11 21								
Haywards Heath 3 a			10 54		11 00			11 06							11 26				11 30				11 36
d			10 55		11 04	11 07		11 08							11 27				11 34	11 37			11 38
Wivelsfield 4 d			10 59			11 11									11 31								
Lewes 4 a						11 22													11 48				
Burgess Hill 4 d			11 01		11 09										11 33								
Hassocks 4 d		←	11 04												11 36								
Preston Park d		11 02	11 11												11 43								
Hove 2 a					11 21															11 51			
Brighton 10 a	10 58	11 07	11 17					11 24						11 27	11 49								11 54

For general notes see front of timetable
For details of catering facilities see Directory of Train Operators

§ It is unknown, at the time of going to press, when this station will open. For further details contact National Rail Enquiries 08457-484950 or see local publicity.

A 🛒 to Lewes
B To Tunbridge Wells (Table 206)
C To Southampton Central (Table 188) and to Bognor Regis (Table 188)
b Arr. 1050

Watford Junction, Bedford and London → Brighton

Network Diagram - see first page of Table 186

		GW	SN	GX	SN	GW	SE 13	SN	SN	FC	GX	SN		LO	GW		FC	SE 88	GX	SN	SN	SN	FC	GX	SN
		1	1	1	1	1	1	1 ◇	1	1	1	1			1		1	1	1	1	1	1 ◇	1	1	1
					A		B	[trolley]				C [trolley]						B		D		[trolley]			
London Victoria 15 ⊖	d			11 00	11 02			11 06			11 15	11 17							11 30	11 32		11 36		11 45	
Watford Junction	d																								
Harrow & Wealdstone ⊖	d																								11 11
Wembley Central	d																								11 17
Willesden Jn. High Level	d													11 08											
Shepherds Bush § ⊖	d																								
Kensington Olympia ⊖	d													11 17											11 37
West Brompton ⊖	d													11 19											11 39
Imperial Wharf §	d																								
Clapham Junction 10	d				11 08			11 12				11 23		11a28						11 38		11 42			11b54
Bedford 7	d									09 57							10 10						10 27		↪
Luton 10	d									10 19							10 34						10 49		
Luton Airport Parkway 7 ✈	d									10 21							10 36						10 51		
St Albans City	d									10 33							10 48						11 03		
St Pancras International 15 ⊖	d									10 54							11 09						11 24		
Farringdon 3 ⊖	d									10 59							11 14						11 29		
City Thameslink 3	d									11 01							11 16						11 31		
London Blackfriars 3 ⊖	d									11 05							11 20						11 35		
London Bridge 4 ⊖	d						11 03			11 11							11 26				11 33		11 41		
Norwood Junction 2	d						11 16														11 46				
East Croydon	a				11 18		11 19	11 22		11 24		11 33					11 39			11 48	11 49	11 52	11 54		
	d				11 18		11 21	11 22		11 24		11 33					11 39			11 48	11 51	11 52	11 54		
Purley 4	d						11 26														11 57				
Coulsdon South	d						11 30														12 00				
Merstham	d						11 35														12 06				
Redhill	a				11 30		11 38													12 00	12 09				
	d	11 14			11 30	11 34	11 39								11 41			11 44		12 00	12 10				
Tonbridge 4	a						12 08														↪				
Reigate	a	11 18				11 38																			
Earlswood (Surrey)	d																								
Salfords	d																								
Horley 4	d				11 36													11 51							
Gatwick Airport 10 ✈	a		←	11 30	11 39					11 40	11 45	11 48			11 50		11 55	11 55	12 00	12 08			12 10	12 15	
	d		11 28		11 40					11 41		11 49					11 56	11 56		12 09			12 11		
Three Bridges 15	a		11 33		11 44					11 45								12 00		12 14			12 15		
	d		11 33		11 45					11 45								12 01		12 14			12 15		
Crawley	d				11 48													12 04		12 18					
Ifield	d																	12 07							
Faygate	d																	12 11							
Littlehaven	d																	12 15							
Horsham 4	a				11 56													12 18		12 26					
Balcombe	d																						12 21		
Haywards Heath 3	a		11 42							11 54		12 00					12 06						12 26		
	d		11 46							11 55		12 04	12 07				12 08						12 27		
Wivelsfield 4	d		11 50							11 59			12 11										12 31		
Lewes 4	a												12 22												
Burgess Hill 4	d		11 52							12 01		12 09											12 33		
Hassocks 4	d		11 55						←	12 04													12 36		
Preston Park	d		12 02						12 02	12 11													12 43		
Hove 2	a		↪									12 21													
Brighton 10	a							11 58	12 07	12 17							12 24					12 27	12 49		

For general notes see front of timetable
For details of catering facilities see Directory of Train Operators

§ It is unknown, at the time of going to press, when this station will open. For further details contact National Rail Enquiries 08457-484950 or see local publicity.

A To Portsmouth Harbour (Table 188) and to Bognor Regis (Table 188)
B To Tunbridge Wells (Table 206)
C [trolley] to Lewes
D To Southampton Central (Table 188) and to Bognor Regis (Table 188)
b Arr. 1150

Watford Junction, Bedford and London → Brighton

Network Diagram - see first page of Table 186

	SN		SN	LO	SN	FC	GW	SN	GX	XC	SN	GW	SE 13	SN	SN	XC	FC	GX	SN		GW	FC		LO
	1		1		1	1	1	1	1	1 ◇	1	1		1 ◇	1	1 ◇	1	1	1		1	1		
	A										B		C						A					
	⊼									☕	⊼			⊼		☕			⊼					
London Victoria 15 ⊖ d	11 47								12 00		12 02			12 06				12 15	12 17					
Watford Junction d																								
Harrow & Wealdstone ⊖ d																								
Wembley Central d																								
Willesden Jn. High Level d				11 38																				12 08
Shepherds Bush § ⊖ d																								
Kensington Olympia ⊖ d				11 47						11 57														12 17
West Brompton ⊖ d				11 49																				12 19
Imperial Wharf § d			←																					
Clapham Junction 10 d	11 53		11 54	11a58							12 08			12 12					12 23					12a28
Bedford 7 d						10 40											10 55					11 10		
Luton 10 d						11 04											11 19					11 34		
Luton Airport Parkway 7 ✈ d						11 06											11 21					11 36		
St Albans City d						11 18											11 33					11 48		
St Pancras International 15 ⊖ d						11 39											11 54					12 09		
Farringdon 3 ⊖ d						11 44											11 59					12 14		
City Thameslink 3 d						11 46											12 01					12 16		
London Blackfriars 3 ⊖ d						11 50											12 05					12 20		
London Bridge 4 ⊖ d						11 56							12 03				12 11					12 26		
Norwood Junction 2 d													12 16											
East Croydon 🚊 a	12 03		12 07			12 09				12 16	12 18		12 19	12 22			12 24		12 33			12 39		
d	12 03		12 07			12 09				12 17	12 18		12 21	12 22			12 24		12 33			12 39		
Purley 4 d													12 26											
Coulsdon South d													12 30											
Merstham d													12 35											
Redhill a											12 30		12 38											
d					← 12 10		12 14				12 30	12 34	12 39								12 41			
Tonbridge 4 a													13 08											
Reigate a							12 18					12 38												
Earlswood (Surrey) d					12 12																			
Salfords d					12 16																			
Horley 4 d					12 19						12 36													
Gatwick Airport 10 ✈ a	12 18		12 22		12 23	12 25		←	12 30	12 33	12 39					←	12 40	12 45	12 48		12 50	12 55		
d	12 19		12 28		12 24	12 26		12 28		12 38	12 40					12 38	12 41		12 49			12 56		
Three Bridges 15 a			→		12 29			12 33		→	12 44						12 45							
d					12 30			12 33			12 45						12 45							
Crawley d					12 33						12 48													
Ifield d					12 36																			
Faygate d																								
Littlehaven d					12 42																			
Horsham 4 a					12 47						12 56													
Balcombe d																								
Haywards Heath 3 a	12 30					12 36		12 42								12 49	12 54		13 01			13 06		
d	12 34	12 37				12 38		12 46								12 50	12 55		13 04	13 07		13 08		
Wivelsfield 4 d								12 50									12 59			13 11				
Lewes 4 a	12 52																			13 22				
Burgess Hill 4 d								12 52									13 01		13 09					
Hassocks 4 d								12 55							←		13 04							
Preston Park d								13 02							13 02		13 11							
Hove 2 a		12 51						→											13 21					
Brighton 10 a						12 54								12 58	13 07	13 15	13 17					13 24		

For general notes see front of timetable
For details of catering facilities see Directory of Train Operators

§ It is unknown, at the time of going to press, when this station will open. For further details contact National Rail Enquiries 08457-484950 or see local publicity.

A ⊼ to Lewes

B To Portsmouth Harbour (Table 188) and to Bognor Regis (Table 188)

C To Tunbridge Wells (Table 206)

Watford Junction, Bedford and London → Brighton

Network Diagram - see first page of Table 186

		SE	GX	SN	SN	SN	FC	GX	SN	SN		SN	LO	SN	FC	GW	SN	GX	SN	GW	SE	SN	SN	FC	GX
		88																			13				
		1	1	1	1	1 ◇	1	1	1	1		1		1	1	1	1	1	1	1		1 ◇	1	1	1
		A		B						C									D		A				
						⚲				⚲									⚲			⚲			
London Victoria 15	⊖ d		12 30	12 32		12 36		12 45		12 47								13 00	13 02			13 06			13 15
Watford Junction	d								12 11																
Harrow & Wealdstone	⊖ d								12 17																
Wembley Central	d																								
Willesden Jn. High Level	d												12 38												
Shepherds Bush §	⊖ d																								
Kensington Olympia	⊖ d								12 37				12 47												
West Brompton	⊖ d								12 39				12 49												
Imperial Wharf §	d											←													
Clapham Junction 10	d			12 38		12 42			12b54	12 53		12 54	12a58						13 08			13 12			
Bedford 7	d						11 25		→						11 40									11 55	
Luton 10	d						11 49								12 04									12 19	
Luton Airport Parkway 7	✈ d						11 51								12 06									12 21	
St Albans City	d						12 03								12 18									12 33	
St Pancras International 15	⊖ d						12 24								12 39									12 54	
Farringdon 3	⊖ d						12 29								12 44									12 59	
City Thameslink 3	d						12 31								12 46									13 01	
London Blackfriars 3	⊖ d						12 35								12 50									13 05	
London Bridge 4	⊖ d				12 33		12 41								12 56						13 03			13 11	
Norwood Junction 2	d				12 46																13 16				
East Croydon	⇌ a			12 48	12 49	12 52	12 54			13 03		13 07			13 09				13 18		13 19	13 22		13 24	
	d			12 48	12 51	12 52	12 54			13 03		13 07			13 09				13 18		13 21	13 22		13 24	
Purley 4	d				12 57																13 26				
Coulsdon South	d				13 00																13 30				
Merstham	d				13 06																13 35				
Redhill	a			13 00	13 09														13 30		13 38				
	d	12 44		13 00	13 10									← 13 10		13 14			13 30	13 34	13 39				
Tonbridge 4	a				→																14 08				
Reigate	a															13 18				13 38					
Earlswood (Surrey)	d													13 12											
Salfords	d													13 16											
Horley 4	d	12 51												13 19					13 36						
Gatwick Airport 10	✈ a	12 55	13 00	13 08			13 10	13 15		13 18		13 22		13 23	13 25		←	13 30	13 39					13 40	13 45
	d	12 56		13 09			13 11			13 19		13 28		13 24	13 26		13 28		13 40					13 41	
Three Bridges 15	a	13 00		13 14			13 15					→		13 29			13 33		13 44					13 45	
	d	13 01		13 14			13 15							13 30			13 33		13 45					13 45	
Crawley	d	13 04		13 18										13 33					13 48						
Ifield	d	13 07												13 36											
Faygate	d																								
Littlehaven	d	13 13												13 42											
Horsham 4	a	13 16		13 26										13 47					13 56						
Balcombe	d						13 21																		
Haywards Heath 3	a						13 26			13 30					13 36		13 42							13 54	
	d						13 27			13 34	13 37				13 38		13 46							13 55	
Wivelsfield 4	d						13 31										13 50							13 59	
Lewes 4	a									13 48															
Burgess Hill 4	d						13 33										13 52							14 01	
Hassocks 4	d						13 36										13 55						←	14 04	
Preston Park	d						13 43										14 02						14 02	14 11	
Hove 2	a										13 51						→								
Brighton 10	a					13 27	13 49								13 54							13 58	14 07	14 17	

For general notes see front of timetable
For details of catering facilities see Directory of Train Operators

§ It is unknown, at the time of going to press, when this station will open. For further details contact National Rail Enquiries 08457-484950 or see local publicity.

A To Tunbridge Wells (Table 206)
B To Southampton Central (Table 188) and to Bognor Regis (Table 188)
C ⚲ to Lewes
D To Portsmouth Harbour (Table 188) and to Bognor Regis (Table 188)
b Arr. 1250

Watford Junction, Bedford and London → Brighton

Network Diagram - see first page of Table 186

	SN		LO	GW	FC	SE	GX		SN	SN	SN	FC	GX	SN	SN		SN	LO	SN	FC	GW	SN	GX	SN
	1			1	1	88 1	1		1	1	1 ◇	1	1	1	1		1		1	1	1	1	1	1
	A 🛒					B			C 🛒		🛒				A 🛒									D 🛒
London Victoria 15 ⊖ d	13 17						13 30		13 32		13 36		13 45		13 47								14 00	14 02
Watford Junction d														13 11										
Harrow & Wealdstone ⊖ d														13 17										
Wembley Central d																								
Willesden Jn. High Level d			13 08															13 38						
Shepherds Bush § ⊖ d																								
Kensington Olympia ⊖ d			13 17											13 37				13 47						
West Brompton ⊖ d			13 19											13 39			⟵	13 49						
Imperial Wharf § d																								
Clapham Junction 10 d	13 23		13a28						13 38		13 42			13b54	13 53		13 54	13a58						14 08
Bedford 7 d					12 10							12 25		⟶						12 40				
Luton 10 d					12 34							12 49								13 04				
Luton Airport Parkway 7 ✈ d					12 36							12 51								13 06				
St Albans City d					12 48							13 03								13 18				
St Pancras International 15 ⊖ d					13 09							13 24								13 39				
Farringdon 3 ⊖ d					13 14							13 29								13 44				
City Thameslink 3 d					13 16							13 31								13 46				
London Blackfriars 3 ⊖ d					13 20							13 35								13 50				
London Bridge 4 ⊖ d					13 26					13 33		13 41								13 56				
Norwood Junction 2 d										13 46														
East Croydon 🚊 a	13 33				13 39				13 48	13 49	13 52	13 54			14 03		14 07			14 09				14 18
d	13 33				13 39				13 48	13 51	13 52	13 54			14 03		14 07			14 09				14 18
Purley 4 d										13 57														
Coulsdon South d										14 00														
Merstham d										14 06														
Redhill a									14 00	14 09									⟵					14 30
d				13 41		13 44			14 00	14 10									14 10		14 14			14 30
Tonbridge 4 a										⟶														
Reigate a																					14 18			
Earlswood (Surrey) d																			14 12					
Salfords d																			14 16					
Horley 4 d						13 51													14 19					14 36
Gatwick Airport 10 ✈ a	13 48			13 50	13 55	13 55	14 00		14 08			14 10	14 15		14 18		14 22		14 23	14 25		⟵	14 30	14 39
d	13 49				13 56	13 56			14 09			14 11			14 19		14 28		14 24	14 26		14 28		14 40
Three Bridges 15 a						14 00			14 14			14 15					⟶		14 29			14 33		14 44
d						14 01			14 14			14 15							14 30			14 33		14 45
Crawley d						14 04			14 18										14 33					14 48
Ifield d						14 07													14 36					
Faygate d																								
Littlehaven d						14 13													14 42					
Horsham 4 a						14 16			14 26										14 47					14 56
Balcombe d												14 21												
Haywards Heath 3 a	14 00				14 06							14 26			14 30					14 36		14 42		
d	14 04	14 07			14 08							14 27			14 34	14 37				14 38		14 46		
Wivelsfield 4 d		14 11										14 31										14 50		
Lewes 4 a		14 22													14 48									
Burgess Hill 4 d	14 09											14 33										14 52		
Hassocks 4 d												14 36										14 55		
Preston Park d												14 43										15 02		
Hove 2 a	14 21															14 51						⟶		
Brighton 10 a					14 25						14 27	14 49								14 54				

For general notes see front of timetable
For details of catering facilities see Directory of Train Operators

§ It is unknown, at the time of going to press, when this station will open. For further details contact National Rail Enquiries 08457-484950 or see local publicity.

A 🛒 to Lewes
B To Tunbridge Wells (Table 206)
C To Southampton Central (Table 188) and to Bognor Regis (Table 188)
D To Portsmouth Harbour (Table 188) and to Bognor Regis (Table 188)
b Arr. 1350

Watford Junction, Bedford and London → Brighton

Network Diagram - see first page of Table 186

		GW	SE	SN	SN	FC	GX	SN		LO	GW	FC	SE	GX	SN	SN		SN	FC	GX	SN	SN		SN	LO
			13										88												
		1		1 ◇	1	1	1	1			1	1	1	1	1	1		1 ◇	1	1	1	1		1	
			A					B					A		C							B			
				⊤				⊤							⊤			⊤				⊤			
London Victoria 15	⊖ d			14 06			14 15	14 17						14 30	14 32			14 36		14 45		14 47			
Watford Junction	d																				14 11				
Harrow & Wealdstone	⊖ d																				14 17				
Wembley Central	d																								
Willesden Jn. High Level	d									14 08															14 38
Shepherds Bush §	⊖ d																								
Kensington Olympia	⊖ d									14 17											14 37				14 47
West Brompton	⊖ d									14 19											14 39				14 49
Imperial Wharf §	d																							←	
Clapham Junction 10	d			14 12				14 23		14a28					14 38			14 42			14b54	14 53		14 54	14a58
Bedford 7	d					12 55						13 10							13 25		→				
Luton 10	d					13 19						13 34							13 49						
Luton Airport Parkway 7	✈ d					13 21						13 36							13 51						
St Albans City	d					13 33						13 48							14 03						
St Pancras International 15	⊖ d					13 54						14 09							14 24						
Farringdon 3	⊖ d					13 59						14 14							14 29						
City Thameslink 3	d					14 01						14 16							14 31						
London Blackfriars 3	⊖ d					14 05						14 20							14 35						
London Bridge 4	⊖ d		14 03			14 11						14 26				14 33			14 41						
Norwood Junction 2	d		14 16													14 46									
East Croydon	a		14 19	14 22		14 24		14 33				14 39			14 48	14 49		14 52	14 54			15 03		15 07	
	d		14 21	14 22		14 24		14 33				14 39			14 48	14 51		14 52	14 54			15 03		15 07	
Purley 4	d		14 26													14 57									
Coulsdon South	d		14 30													15 00									
Merstham	d		14 35													15 06									
Redhill	a		14 38												15 00	15 09									
	d	14 34	14 39								14 41		14 44		15 00	15 10									
Tonbridge 4	a		15 08													→									
Reigate	a	14 38																							
Earlswood (Surrey)	d																								
Salfords	d																								
Horley 4	d												14 51												
Gatwick Airport 10	✈ a					14 40	14 45	14 48			14 50	14 55	14 55	15 00	15 08				15 10	15 15		15 18		15 22	
	d					14 41		14 49				14 56	14 56		15 09				15 11			15 19		15 28	
Three Bridges 15	a					14 45							15 00		15 14				15 15					→	
	d					14 45							15 01		15 14				15 15						
Crawley	d												15 04		15 18										
Ifield	d												15 07												
Faygate	d																								
Littlehaven	d												15 13												
Horsham 4	a												15 16		15 26										
Balcombe	d																		15 21						
Haywards Heath 3	a					14 54		15 00				15 06							15 26			15 30			
	d					14 55		15 04	15 07			15 08							15 27			15 34	15 37		
Wivelsfield 4	d					14 59			15 11										15 31			15 38			
Lewes 4	a								15 22													15 51			
Burgess Hill 4	d					15 01		15 09											15 33						
Hassocks 4	d				←	15 04													15 36						
Preston Park	d				15 02	15 11													15 43						
Hove 2	a							15 21															15 51		
Brighton 10	a			14 58	15 07	15 17						15 24						15 27	15 49						

For general notes see front of timetable
For details of catering facilities see Directory of Train Operators

§ It is unknown, at the time of going to press, when this station will open. For further details contact National Rail Enquiries 08457-484950 or see local publicity.

A To Tunbridge Wells (Table 206)
B ⊤ to Lewes
C To Southampton Central (Table 188) and to Bognor Regis (Table 188)
b Arr. 1450

Watford Junction, Bedford and London → Brighton

Network Diagram - see first page of Table 186

	SN	FC	GW	GW	SN	GX	SN	SE 13	SN	SN	FC	GX	SN	SN	LO	GW	FC	SE 88	GX	SN	SN	SN	FC	GX
	1	1	1	1	1	1	1	1	1 ◇	1	1	1	1			1	1	1	1	1	1	1 ◇	1	1
							A [catering]	B	[catering]				C [catering]					B		D		[catering]		
London Victoria 15 ⊖ d						15 00	15 02		15 06			15 15	15 17						15 30	15 32		15 36		15 45
Watford Junction d																								
Harrow & Wealdstone ⊖ d																								
Wembley Central d																								
Willesden Jn. High Level d															15 08									
Shepherds Bush § ⊖ d															15 17									
Kensington Olympia ⊖ d															15 19									
West Brompton ⊖ d																								
Imperial Wharf § d																								
Clapham Junction 10 d							15 08		15 12				15 23		15a28					15 38		15 42		
Bedford 7 d		13 40									13 55						14 10						14 25	
Luton 10 d		14 04									14 19						14 34						14 49	
Luton Airport Parkway 7 ✈ d		14 06									14 21						14 36						14 51	
St Albans City d		14 18									14 33						14 48						15 03	
St Pancras International 15 ⊖ d		14 39									14 54						15 09						15 24	
Farringdon 3 ⊖ d		14 44									14 59						15 14						15 29	
City Thameslink 3 d		14 46									15 01						15 16						15 31	
London Blackfriars 3 ⊖ d		14 50									15 05						15 20						15 35	
London Bridge 4 ⊖ d		14 56						15 03			15 11						15 26				15 33		15 41	
Norwood Junction 2 d								15 16													15 46			
East Croydon a		15 09					15 18	15 19	15 22		15 24		15 33				15 39			15 48	15 49	15 52	15 54	
East Croydon d		15 09					15 18	15 21	15 22		15 24		15 33				15 39			15 48	15 51	15 52	15 54	
Purley 4 d								15 26													15 57			
Coulsdon South d								15 30													16 00			
Merstham d								15 35													16 06			
Redhill a	←						15 30	15 39												16 00	16 09			
Redhill d	15 10		15 14	15 29			15 30	15 40								15 41		15 44		16 00	16 10			
Tonbridge 4 a								16 09													→			
Reigate a			15 18	15 33																				
Earlswood (Surrey) d	15 12																	15 46						
Salfords d	15 16																	15 50						
Horley 4 d	15 19						15 36											15 53						
Gatwick Airport 10 ✈ a	15 23	15 25			←	15 30	15 39				15 40	15 45	15 48			15 50	15 55	15 56	16 00	16 08			16 10	16 15
Gatwick Airport d	15 24	15 26			15 28		15 40				15 41		15 49				15 56	15 56		16 09			16 11	
Three Bridges 15 a	15 29				15 33		15 44				15 45						16 00	16 01		16 14			16 15	
Three Bridges d	15 30				15 33		15 45				15 45						16 00	16 01		16 14			16 15	
Crawley d	15 33						15 48											16 05		16 18				
Ifield d	15 36																	16 07						
Faygate d																		16 11						
Littlehaven d	15 42																	16 15						
Horsham 4 a	15 47						15 56											16 18		16 26				
Balcombe d																							16 21	
Haywards Heath 3 a		15 36			15 42						15 54		16 00				16 09						16 26	
Haywards Heath d		15 38			15 46						15 55		16 04	16 07			16 10						16 27	
Wivelsfield 4 d					15 50						15 59			16 11									16 31	
Lewes 4 a														16 22										
Burgess Hill 4 d					15 52						16 01		16 09										16 33	
Hassocks 4 d					15 55					←	16 04												16 36	
Preston Park d					16 02					16 02	16 11												16 43	
Hove 2 a					→								16 21											
Brighton 10 a		15 54							15 58	16 07	16 17						16 24					16 27	16 49	

For general notes see front of timetable
For details of catering facilities see Directory of Train Operators

§ It is unknown, at the time of going to press, when this station will open. For further details contact National Rail Enquiries 08457-484950 or see local publicity.

A To Portsmouth Harbour (Table 188) and to Bognor Regis (Table 188)
B To Tunbridge Wells (Table 206)
C [catering] to Lewes
D To Southampton Central (Table 188) and to Bognor Regis (Table 188)

Watford Junction, Bedford and London → Brighton

Network Diagram - see first page of Table 186

		SN		SN		SN	LO	SN	FC	GX	GW	SN	GW	SE	SN	SN	FC	GX	SE	SN	SN		LO	FC	SE
														13					88						88
		1		1		1		1	1	1	1	1	1		1	1	1	1	1	1	1			1	1
				A								B							C		A				C
				⊥											⊥						⊥				
London Victoria 15	⊖ d			15 47						16 00		16 02			16 06			16 15		16 10	16 17				
Watford Junction	d	15 11																							
Harrow & Wealdstone	⊖ d	15 17																							
Wembley Central	d																								
Willesden Jn. High Level	d						15 38																		
Shepherds Bush §	⊖ d																						16 08		
Kensington Olympia	⊖ d	15 39					15 47																16 17		
West Brompton	⊖ d	15 41					15 49																16 19		
Imperial Wharf §	d					←																			
Clapham Junction 10	d	15b54		15 53		15 54	15a58					16 08			16 12					16 16	16 23		16a28		
Bedford 7	d	↪							14 40								14 55							15 10	
Luton 10	d								15 04								15 19							15 34	
Luton Airport Parkway 7	✈ d								15 06								15 21							15 36	
St Albans City	d								15 18								15 33							15 48	
St Pancras International 15	⊖ d								15 39								15 54							16 09	
Farringdon 3	⊖ d								15 44								15 59							16 14	
City Thameslink 3	d								15 46								16 01							16 16	
London Blackfriars 3	⊖ d								15 50								16 05							16 20	
London Bridge 4	⊖ d								15 56					16 03			16 11							16 26	
Norwood Junction 2	d													16 16											
East Croydon	🚊 a			16 03		16 07			16 09			16 18		16 19	16 22		16 24			16 28	16 33			16 40	
	d			16 03		16 07			16 09			16 18		16 21	16 22		16 24			16 28	16 33			16 40	
Purley 4	d													16 26						16 34					
Coulsdon South	d													16 30						16 37					
Merstham	d													16 35						16 43					
Redhill	a							←				16 30		16 39						16 46					
	d							16 10			16 14	16 30	16 32	16 40					16 44	16 48					
Tonbridge 4	a													17 11											
Reigate	a										16 18		16 36							16 54					
Earlswood (Surrey)	d							16 12											16 46						
Salfords	d							16 16											16 50						
Horley 4	d							16 19				16 36							16 53 →						← 16 53
Gatwick Airport 10	✈ a			16 18		16 22		16 23	16 25	16 30		16 39					16 40	16 45			16 48			16 55	16 56
	d			16 19		16 23		16 24	16 26			16 40					16 41				16 49			16 56	16 57
Three Bridges 15	a					16 27		16 29	16 30			16 44					16 45							17 00	17 01
	d					16 27		16 30	16 30			16 45					16 45							17 00	17 02
Crawley	d							16 34				16 48													17 05
Ifield	d							16 36																	17 08
Faygate	d							16 40																	17 12
Littlehaven	d							16 44																	17 16
Horsham 4	a							16 47				16 56													17 19
Balcombe	d																								
Haywards Heath 3	a			16 30		16 39			16 40								16 54				17 00			17 10	
	d			16 33	16 37	16 46 →			16 40							← 16 46	16 55				17 04	17 06		17 10	
Wivelsfield 4	d			16 37												16 50	16 59					17 10			
Lewes 4	a			16 52																		17 21			
Burgess Hill 4	d															16 52	17 01				17 09				
Hassocks 4	d															16 55	17 04								
Preston Park	d															17 02	17 11								
Hove 2	a				16 51																17 20				
Brighton 10	a								16 54						17 00	17 07	17 17							17 26	

For general notes see front of timetable
For details of catering facilities see Directory of Train Operators

§ It is unknown, at the time of going to press, when this station will open. For further details contact National Rail Enquiries 08457-484950 or see local publicity.

A ⊥ to Lewes

B To Portsmouth Harbour (Table 188) and to Bognor Regis (Table 188)

C From Tonbridge (Table 209)

b Arr. 1547

Watford Junction, Bedford and London → Brighton

Network Diagram - see first page of Table 186

	GX	GW	SN	SN	SN	GW	SN		SN		FC	GX	SN	LO	SN	GX	SN	SE	SN	SN	FC	SN	FC
																		13					
	1	1	1	1	1	1	1		1		1	1	1		1	1	1		1	1	1	1	1
									A				B		C								
				⚲					⚲				⚲										
London Victoria 15 ⊖ d	16 30		16 32	16 36					16 38			16 45	16 47			17 00				17 02		17 07	
Watford Junction d																			16 29				
Harrow & Wealdstone ⊖ d																			16 35				
Wembley Central d																			16 40				
Willesden Jn. High Level d														16 38									
Shepherds Bush § ⊖ d																							
Kensington Olympia ⊖ d														16 47					16 53				
West Brompton ⊖ d														16 49					16 56				
Imperial Wharf § d																							
Clapham Junction 10 d			16 38	16 42					16 45				16 53	16a58					17a02	17 08		17 13	
Bedford 7 d											15 25												
Luton 10 d											15 49												
Luton Airport Parkway 7 ✈ d											15 51												
St Albans City d											16 03												
St Pancras International 15 ⊖ d											16 27												
Farringdon 3 ⊖ d											16 32												
City Thameslink 3 d											16 34												
London Blackfriars 3 ⊖ d											16 37												
London Bridge 4 ⊖ d							16 38				16 46				16 53			16 57			17 08		
Norwood Junction 2 d							16 51																
East Croydon a			16 48	16 52			16 54		16 55		16 59		17 03		17 07			17 11		17 18	17 20	17 23	
d			16 48	16 52			16 55		16 55		17 00		17 03		17 07			17 11		17 18	17 20	17 24	
Purley 4 d							17 01																
Coulsdon South d							17 07											17 18					
Merstham d							17 12											17 24					
Redhill a			17 00				17 16											17 27			17 32		
d		16 50	17 01			17 14	17 20	17 22									← 17 20	17 28			17 32		
Tonbridge 4 a							→											17 57					
Reigate a						17 18		17 28															
Earlswood (Surrey) d																	17 22						
Salfords d																	17 26						
Horley 4 d																	17 29					17 39	
Gatwick Airport 10 ✈ a	17 00	17 00	17 08		←				17 10		17 15	17 15	17 19			17 30	17 32			17 33	17 40		←
d			17 09		17 09				17 11		17 16		17 20				17 33			17 34	17 40		17 40
Three Bridges 15 a			→		17 14				17 16		17 20		17 25		17 28		17 38			17 38	→		17 45
d					17 14				17 20	17 23	17 20		17 25		17 29		17 38			17 39			17 46
Crawley d									17 23	17 27							17 41						
Ifield d										17 30							17 44						
Faygate d																							
Littlehaven d										17 36							17 50						
Horsham 4 a									17 31	17 39							17 55						
Balcombe d											17 26												17 52
Haywards Heath 3 a				17 15	17 23						17 31		17 34		17 37					17 47		17 51	17 57
d				17 16	17 24						17 32		17 35		17 38					17 48		17 52	17 58
Wivelsfield 4 d					17 28						17 36		17 39										18 02
Lewes 4 a													17 54										
Burgess Hill 4 d					17 30						17 39				17 43							17 57	18 05
Hassocks 4 d					17 34						17 43				17 47							18 01	18 09
Preston Park d					17 41						17 50				17 54							18 09	18 16
Hove 2 a															17 57								
Brighton 10 a				17 32	17 48						17 54									18 04		18 15	18 22

For general notes see front of timetable
For details of catering facilities see Directory of Train Operators

§ It is unknown, at the time of going to press, when this station will open. For further details contact National Rail Enquiries 08457-484950 or see local publicity.

A To Bognor Regis (Table 188)
B To Ore (Table 189)
C To Littlehampton (Table 188)

Watford Junction, Bedford and London → Brighton

Network Diagram - see first page of Table 186

		GX 1	GW 1	GW 1	LO 1 A	SN 1	SN 1		SN 1 B	LO	SN 1 C	SN 1	SN 1	GX 1	SN 1 D	SN 1	FC 1	SN 1	LO 1 E		GW 1	SN 1		GX 1	SN 1
London Victoria 15 ⊖	d	17 15				17 10			17 17		17 21	17 24		17 30				17 37				17 40		17 45	
Watford Junction	d																								
Harrow & Wealdstone ⊖	d																								
Wembley Central	d																								
Willesden Jn. High Level	d				16 53					17 08															
Shepherds Bush § ⊖	d																								
Kensington Olympia ⊖	d				17 02					17 17									17 33						
West Brompton ⊖	d				17 04					17 19									17 34						
Imperial Wharf §	d																								
Clapham Junction 10	d				17a13	17 16			17 23	17a28	17 27	17 30						17 43	17a44			17 46			
Bedford 7	d																16 10								
Luton 10	d																16 34								
Luton Airport Parkway 7 ✈	d																16 36								
St Albans City	d																16 48								
St Pancras International 15 ⊖	d																17 09								
Farringdon 3 ⊖	d																17 14								
City Thameslink 3	d																17 16								
London Blackfriars 3 ⊖	d																17 20								
London Bridge 4 ⊖	d						17 17								17 32		17 32								17 46
Norwood Junction 2	d																								
East Croydon	a					17 26	17 31		17 33		17 37	17 40			17 46		17 49	17 53				17 56			17 59
	d					17 26	17 32		17 33		17 37	17 40			17 46		17 50	17 54				17 57			18 00
Purley 4	d					17 33	17 37															18 03			
Coulsdon South	d					17 37	17 41															18 07			
Merstham	d					17 42	17 46															18 12			
Redhill	a					17 46	17 50										18 02					18 16			
	d		17 41	17 44		17 46	17 53	17 56					← 17 46			← 17 53	18 02				18 14	18 19	18 21		
Tonbridge 4	a					→	→															→			
Reigate	a			17 48				18 02													18 18		18 27		
Earlswood (Surrey)	d												17 49			17 56									
Salfords	d												17 52			18 00									
Horley 4	d												17 56		18 02	18 04		18 09							
Gatwick Airport 10 ✈	a	17 45	17 50									17 57	17 58	18 00		18 08	18 12							18 15	
	d											17 58	17 59			18 09	18 12								
Three Bridges 15	a								17 52		17 56		18 04			18 15	→								
	d								17 53		17 57		18 04			18 16									
Crawley	d										18 01		18 08			18 20									
Ifield	d												18 10			18 22									
Faygate	d												18 14												
Littlehaven	d										18 08		18 18			18 29									
Horsham 4	a										18 11		18 23			18 33									
Balcombe	d																								
Haywards Heath 3	a								18 02			18 09			18 14			18 20							18 23
	d								18 03			18 10			18 15			18 20							18 24
Wivelsfield 4	d								18 07																18 28
Lewes 4	a								18 18																18 44
Burgess Hill 4	d														18 20			18 26							
Hassocks 4	d														18 24			18 30							
Preston Park	d														18 32			18 37							
Hove 2	a											18 24			18 35										
Brighton 10	a																	18 44							

For general notes see front of timetable
For details of catering facilities see Directory of Train Operators

§ It is unknown, at the time of going to press, when this station will open. For further details contact National Rail Enquiries 08457-484950 or see local publicity.

A Until 29 August and from 17 November
B To Seaford (Table 189) and to Eastbourne (Table 189)
C To Bognor Regis (Table 188)
D To Littlehampton (Table 188)
E 1 September to 14 November

Watford Junction, Bedford and London → Brighton

Network Diagram - see first page of Table 186

	FC 1	SN 1 A	LO	SN 1 B	FC 1	SN 1 🛒	SN 1	GX 1	SN 1	SN 1	SN 1	FC 1	SN 1 🛒	SN 1	GW 1	LO 1 C	SN 1	GX 1	SN 1 D	SN 1 E 🛒		SN 1 G	LO	FC 1
London Victoria 15 ⊖ d		17 47				17 53		18 00					18 07				18 10	18 15		18 17		18 21		
Watford Junction d																								
Harrow & Wealdstone ⊖ d																								
Wembley Central d																								
Willesden Jn. High Level d			17 38													17 53							18 08	
Shepherds Bush § ⊖ d																								
Kensington Olympia ⊖ d			17 47													18 02							18 17	
West Brompton ⊖ d			17 49													18 04							18 19	
Imperial Wharf § d																								
Clapham Junction 10 d		17 53	17a58			17 59							18 13			18a14	18 16			18 23		18 27	18a28	
Bedford 7 d					16 36							17 00												17 10
Luton 10 d					17 00							17 18												17 34
Luton Airport Parkway 7 ✈ d					17 02																			17 36
St Albans City d					17 14							17 28												17 48
St Pancras International 15 ⊖ d					17 35							17 46												18 09
Farringdon 3 ⊖ d					17 40							17 50												18 14
City Thameslink 3 d					17 42							17 53												18 16
London Blackfriars 3 ⊖ d					17 46							17 57												18 20
London Bridge 4 ⊖ d				17 52	17 52		17 59		18 03										18 16					18 26
Norwood Junction 2 d																								
East Croydon a		18 03		18 06	18 08	18 10	18 12		18 16			18 20	18 23				18 26		18 29	18 33		18 37		18 40
d		18 03		18 06	18 08	18 10	18 13		18 16			18 20	18 24				18 26		18 30	18 33		18 37		18 40
Purley 4 d											←						18 33							
Coulsdon South d							18 20										18 37							
Merstham d							18 25				18 25						18 42							
Redhill a							→			←	18 29	18 32					18 46							
d										18 19	18 29	18 32			18 43		18 46							
Tonbridge 4 a																	→							
Reigate a															18 47									
Earlswood (Surrey) d										18 21														
Salfords d										18 25														
Horley 4 d										18 29	18 36		18 39											
Gatwick Airport 10 ✈ a	←				18 24	18 28		18 30		18 32		18 41						18 45	18 45	18 49				18 56
d	18 12				18 24	18 29				18 33		18 42							18 46	18 50				18 56
Three Bridges 15 a	18 18	18 22		18 25					18 35	18 38	18 41	18 51										18 57		19 01
d	18 18	18 23		18 26					18 36	18 38	18 44											18 57		19 02
Crawley d				18 30						18 42												19 01		
Ifield d				18 32						18 44														
Faygate d																								
Littlehaven d				18 39						18 51												19 09		
Horsham 4 a				18 42						18 56				←								19 12		
Balcombe d	18 24										18 50			18 50										19 08
Haywards Heath 3 a	18 29	18 32			18 36	18 41			18 44		→		18 49	18 55					18 58	19 01				19 12
d	18 30	18 32			18 36	18 41			18 45				18 50	18 55					18 58	19 05	19 08			19 12
Wivelsfield 4 d	18 34				18 42	18 46			18 49					18 59						19 09				
Lewes 4 a						19 01														19 24				
Burgess Hill 4 d	18 37	18 41			18 43				18 52				18 56	19 01					19 04					19 17
Hassocks 4 d	18 41	18 45			18 47				18 56				19 00						19 08					19 21
Preston Park d	18 48	18 53			18 56				19 02				19 07	19 10					19 16					
Hove 2 a		18 57																	19 19					
Brighton 10 a	18 54				19 02				19 09				19 13	19 19							19 25			19 32

For general notes see front of timetable
For details of catering facilities see Directory of Train Operators

§ It is unknown, at the time of going to press, when this station will open. For further details contact National Rail Enquiries 08457-484950 or see local publicity.

A To Littlehampton (Table 188)
B To Bognor Regis (Table 188)
C Until 29 August and from 17 November From Stratford Low Level (Table 59)
D To Southampton Central (Table 188) and to Littlehampton (Table 188)
E 🛒 to Lewes
G To Portsmouth & Southsea (Table 188) and to Bognor Regis (Table 188)

Watford Junction, Bedford and London → Brighton

Network Diagram - see first page of Table 186

		SN	GX	SN		SN	GW	SN	FC	SN	SN	GX	SN	SN		SN	SE 13	SN	LO	FC	SN	GX	GW	SN
		1	1	1		1	1	1	1	1	1	1	1	1		1		1		1	1	1	1	1
				A 🍴				B						C 🍴		B								D 🍴
London Victoria 15	⊖ d		18 30	18 32							18 40	18 45		18 47								19 00		19 02
Watford Junction	d												18 12											
Harrow & Wealdstone	⊖ d												18 18											
Wembley Central	d												18 23											
Willesden Jn. High Level	d																		18 38					
Shepherds Bush §	⊖ d																							
Kensington Olympia	⊖ d												18 39						18 47					
West Brompton	⊖ d												18 42						18 49					
Imperial Wharf §	d																	←						
Clapham Junction 10	d			18 38							18 46		18b55	18 53				18 55	18a58					19 08
Bedford 7	d												↦							17 36				
Luton 10	d																			18 00				
Luton Airport Parkway 7	✈ d																			18 02				
St Albans City	d																			18 14				
St Pancras International 15	⊖ d																			18 39				
Farringdon 3	⊖ d																			18 44				
City Thameslink 3	d																			18 46				
London Blackfriars 3	⊖ d																			18 49				
London Bridge 4	⊖ d							18 34	18 38								18 48			18 56				
Norwood Junction 2	d																							
East Croydon	🚋 a			18 48				18 48	18 52		18 56			19 03			19 03	19 07		19 10				19 18
	d			18 48				18 49	18 52		18 56			19 03			19 06	19 07		19 10				19 18
Purley 4	d							18 54			19 02													
Coulsdon South	d							18 58			19 05						19 14							
Merstham	d							19 03			19 11						19 20							
Redhill	a							19 07			19 14						19 23							19 30
	d	← 18 46				18 50	18 56	19 07		19 12	19 15					← 19 07	19 24				← 19 15		19 27	19 31
Tonbridge 4	a							↦			↦						19 56							
Reigate	a					18 54				19 16													19 31	
Earlswood (Surrey)	d	18 49														19 10					19 17			
Salfords	d	18 52														19 13					19 21			
Horley 4	d	18 56														19 17					19 24			
Gatwick Airport 10	✈ a	18 58	19 00	19 03			19 07		19 09			19 15		19 18		19 20		19 23		19 26	19 27	19 30		19 38
	d	18 59		19 04					19 10					19 19		19 21				19 26	19 28			19 39
Three Bridges 15	a	19 04														19 25				19 32	19 33			19 44
	d	19 07														19 26				19 32	19 34			19 44
Crawley	d	19 10														19 30					19 37			19 48
Ifield	d	19 13														19 32					19 40			
Faygate	d	19 17														19 36								
Littlehaven	d	19 21														19 40					19 46			
Horsham 4	a	19 26														19 43					19 51			19 56
Balcombe	d								19 18															
Haywards Heath 3	a			19 16					19 24					19 29						19 40				
	d			19 19	19 22				19 24					19 33	19 36					19 40				
Wivelsfield 4	d								19 28					19 37										
Lewes 4	a													19 52										
Burgess Hill 4	d								19 32											19 46				
Hassocks 4	d								19 36											19 50				
Preston Park	d								19 43															
Hove 2	a			19 34											19 51									
Brighton 10	a				19 39				19 48											20 00				

For general notes see front of timetable
For details of catering facilities see Directory of Train Operators

§ It is unknown, at the time of going to press, when this station will open. For further details contact National Rail Enquiries 08457-484950 or see local publicity.

A 🍴 to Brighton
B To Littlehampton (Table 188)
C 🍴 to Lewes
D To Portsmouth Harbour (Table 188) and to Bognor Regis (Table 188)
b Arr. 1848

Watford Junction, Bedford and London → Brighton

Network Diagram - see first page of Table 186

	SN	FC	SN	GX	SN	SN		GW	XC	LO	FC	SN	GX	SN	SN	XC	SN	FC	SN	GW	SN	GX	SN
	1	1	1	1	1	1		1	R 1		1	1	1	1	1	R 1	1	1	1	1	1	1	1
						A								B									
	🛒					🛒			☕					🛒	🛒	☕							
London Victoria 15 ⊖ d	19 06			19 15	19 10	19 17							19 30	19 32			19 36				19 40	19 45	
Watford Junction d																							19 11
Harrow & Wealdstone ⊖ d																							19 18
Wembley Central d																							19 23
Willesden Jn. High Level d										19 08													
Shepherds Bush § ⊖ d																							19 39
Kensington Olympia ⊖ d									19 02	19 17													19 41
West Brompton ⊖ d										19 19													
Imperial Wharf § d																							
Clapham Junction 10 d	19 12				19 16	19 23				19a28				19 38			19 42				19 46		19b54
																							→
Bedford 7 d		17 50									18 10							18 30					
Luton 10 d		18 14									18 34							18 52					
Luton Airport Parkway 7 ✈ d		18 16									18 36												
St Albans City d		18 28									18 48							19 03					
St Pancras International 15 ⊖ d		18 54									19 09							19 24					
Farringdon 3 ⊖ d		18 59									19 14							19 29					
City Thameslink 3 d		19 01									19 16							19 31					
London Blackfriars 3 ⊖ d		19 04									19 19							19 34					
London Bridge 4 ⊖ d		19 12									19 27							19 41					
Norwood Junction 2 d																							
East Croydon a	19 22	19 24			19 28	19 33			19 33		19 39			19 48			19 52	19 54			19 58		
d	19 22	19 24			19 28	19 33			19 36		19 39			19 48			19 52	19 54			19 58		
Purley 4 d					19 33																20 03		
Coulsdon South d					19 37																20 06		
Merstham d					19 42																20 12		
Redhill a					19 46									20 00							20 15		
												←											
d			19 31		19 46			19 41				19 46		20 00					20 05	20 14	20 16		
					→																→		
Tonbridge 4 a																			20 09	20 18			
Reigate a			19 35																				
Earlswood (Surrey) d												19 49											
Salfords d												19 52											
Horley 4 d												19 56											
Gatwick Airport 10 ✈ a		19 41		19 45		19 48		19 50	19 52		19 55	19 58	20 00	20 08				20 10				20 15	
d		19 41				19 49			19 53		19 55	19 59		20 09				20 11					
Three Bridges 15 a		19 45									20 00	20 04		20 14				20 15					
d		19 45									20 01	20 04		20 14				20 15					
Crawley d												20 08		20 18									
Ifield d												20 10											
Faygate d												20 14											
Littlehaven d												20 18											
Horsham 4 a												20 21		20 26									
Balcombe d		19 51															20 16	20 25					
Haywards Heath 3 a	19 45	19 57				20 00			20 04		20 09												
															←	←							
d	19 45	19 58				20 13 →	20 04		20 07 →		20 09				20 13	20 07	20 17	20 26					
Wivelsfield 4 d		20 02													20 17			20 30					
Lewes 4 a															20 28								
Burgess Hill 4 d		20 04					20 09				20 15							20 32					
Hassocks 4 d		20 07									20 19							20 35					
Preston Park d		20 14																20 42					
Hove 2 a							20 21																
Brighton 10 a	20 03	20 20									20 29					20 30	20 33	20 46					

For general notes see front of timetable
For details of catering facilities see Directory of Train Operators

§ It is unknown, at the time of going to press, when this station will open. For further details contact National Rail Enquiries 08457-484950 or see local publicity.

A 🛒 to Haywards Heath

B To Southampton Central (Table 188) and to Bognor Regis (Table 188)

b Arr. 1948

Watford Junction, Bedford and London → Brighton

Network Diagram - see first page of Table 186

	SN		SN	SN	LO	SN	GX	FC	SE	SN	SN	FC	SN	GX	SN		LO	GW	GW	SN		SN	GX	SN
									88															
	1 A ✂		1	1		1	1	1		1 B ✂	1 ◊	1	1		1			1	1	1		1	1	1
London Victoria 15 ⊖ d	19 47						20 00			20 02	20 06		20 10	20 15	20 17								20 30	
Watford Junction d																								
Harrow & Wealdstone ⊖ d																								
Wembley Central d																								
Willesden Jn. High Level d					19 38												20 08							
Shepherds Bush § ⊖ d																								
Kensington Olympia ⊖ d					19 47												20 17							
West Brompton ⊖ d					19 49												20 19							
Imperial Wharf § d				←																				
Clapham Junction 10 d	19 53			19 54	19a58					20 08	20 12		20 16		20 23		20a29							
Bedford 7 d								18 40				18 50												
Luton 10 d								19 04				19 14												
Luton Airport Parkway 7 ✈ d								19 06				19 16												
St Albans City d								19 18				19 28												
St Pancras International 15 ⊖ d								19 39				19 54												
Farringdon 3 ⊖ d								19 44				19 59												
City Thameslink 3 d								19 47				20 01												
London Blackfriars 3 ⊖ d								19 54				20 04												
London Bridge 4 ⊖ d			19 52					20 01				20 11								20 28				
Norwood Junction 2 d			20 03																					
East Croydon a	20 03		20 06	20 07				20 14		20 19	20 22	20 23	20 28		20 33					20 40				
d	20 03		20 07	20 07				20 14		20 19	20 22	20 23	20 29		20 33					20 41				
Purley 4 d			20 12										20 33											
Coulsdon South d			20 15										20 37											
Merstham d			20 21										20 42									←		
Redhill a			20 24							20 30			→									20 42		
						←																20 46		
d			20 25			20 16			20 28	20 31								20 34	20 41			20 46		20 54
Tonbridge 4 a																								
Reigate a			20 30															20 38						20 58
Earlswood (Surrey) d						20 18																20 49		
Salfords d						20 22																		
Horley 4 d						20 25																20 54		
Gatwick Airport 10 ✈ a	20 18			20 23		20 28	20 30	20 31	20 35	20 38		20 39		20 45	20 48				20 50	20 55		20 57	21 00	
d	20 19					20 29		20 31	20 36	20 39		20 40			20 49					20 56		20 58		
Three Bridges 15 a						20 34			20 40	20 44		20 43								21 01		21 02		
d						20 34				20 44		20 43								21 01		21 06		
Crawley d						20 38				20 48												21 09		
Ifield d						20 40																21 12		
Faygate d																								
Littlehaven d						20 47																21 18		
Horsham 4 a						20 50				20 56												21 21		
Balcombe d												20 49												
Haywards Heath 3 a	20 30							20 42			20 47	20 56			21 01					21 10				
d	20 34	20 36						20 42			20 47	20 58			21 05	21 07				21 11				
Wivelsfield 4 d		20 40										21 02				21 11								
Lewes 4 a		20 55														21 22								
Burgess Hill 4 d	20 39											21 04			21 10									
Hassocks 4 d	20 42											21 07												
Preston Park d	20 49											21 15												
Hove 2 a	20 53														21 21									
Brighton 10 a								20 58			21 01	21 20								21 26				

For general notes see front of timetable
For details of catering facilities see Directory of Train Operators

§ It is unknown, at the time of going to press, when this station will open. For further details contact National Rail Enquiries 08457-484950 or see local publicity.

A To Littlehampton (Table 188)
B To Portsmouth Harbour (Table 188) and to Bognor Regis (Table 188)

Watford Junction, Bedford and London → Brighton

Network Diagram - see first page of Table 186

Station		SN	SN	FC	GW	SN	GX	SN	SN		SN	LO	SN	XC	SN	GX	SN	SE	SN	SN	SN	FC	SN	GX	XC
		[1]	[1] ◇	[1]	[1]	[1]		[1]	[1]		[1]		[1]	R [1]	[1]	[1]	[1]	88	[1]	[1] ◇	[1]	[1]	[1]		R [1]
		A							B																
London Victoria [15]	⊖ d	20 32	20 36			20 40	20 45		20 47							21 00			21 02	21 06			21 10	21 15	
Watford Junction	d							20 11																	
Harrow & Wealdstone	⊖ d							20 17																	
Wembley Central	d																								
Willesden Jn. High Level	d											20 38													
Shepherds Bush §	⊖ d																								
Kensington Olympia	⊖ d							20 38				20 47		20 52											
West Brompton	⊖ d							20 41				20 49													
Imperial Wharf §	d										←														
Clapham Junction [10]	d	20 38	20 42			20 46		20b54	20 53		20 54	20a59							21 08	21 12			21 16		
Bedford [7]	d			19 20				→														19 50			
Luton [10]	d			19 44																		20 14			
Luton Airport Parkway [7]	✈ d			19 46																		20 16			
St Albans City	d			19 58																		20 28			
St Pancras International [15]	⊖ d			20 24																		20 54			
Farringdon [3]	⊖ d			20 29																		20 59			
City Thameslink [3]	d			20 31																		21 01			
London Blackfriars [3]	⊖ d			20 34																		21 04			
London Bridge [4]	⊖ d			20 41									20 58									21 11			
Norwood Junction [2]	d																								
East Croydon	a	20 48	20 52	20 54		20 58			21 03		21 07		21 10	21 15					21 18	21 22		21 24	21 28		
	d	20 48	20 52	20 54		20 58			21 03		21 07		21 11	21 16 →					21 18	21 22		21 24	21 28		
Purley [4]	d					21 03																	21 33		
Coulsdon South	d					21 06																	21 37		
Merstham	d					21 12																	21 42 →		
Redhill	a	21 00				21 15									←				21 30						←
	d	21 00			21 14	21 16									21 16		21 22	21 27	21 31						21 35
Tonbridge [4]	a					→																			
Reigate	a				21 18												21 26								
Earlswood (Surrey)	d														21 18										
Salfords	d														21 22										
Horley [4]	d														21 25										
Gatwick Airport [10]	✈ a	21 08		21 10			21 15		21 18		21 23		21 26		21 28	21 30		21 34	21 38		←	21 41		21 45	21 47
	d	21 09		21 11					21 19				21 27		21 29			21 35	21 39		21 39	21 41			
Three Bridges [15]	a	21 14		21 15									21 31		21 33			21 40	→		21 44	21 45			
	d	21 14		21 15									21 32		21 36						21 44	21 45			
Crawley	d	21 18													21 39										
Ifield	d														21 42										
Faygate	d																								
Littlehaven	d														21 48										
Horsham [4]	a	21 26													21 52										
Balcombe	d																					21 51			
Haywards Heath [3]	a		21 15	21 24					21 30				21 40							21 45	21 52	21 58			
	d		21 15	21 26					21 34	21 37			21 41							21 45	21 53	21 58			
Wivelsfield [4]	d			21 30						21 41											21 57	22 02			
Lewes [4]	a									21 54															
Burgess Hill [4]	d			21 32					21 39												21 59	22 04			
Hassocks [4]	d			21 35					21 42												22 02	22 08			
Preston Park	d			21 42					21 49												22 09	22 15			
Hove [2]	a								21 53																
Brighton [10]	a		21 30	21 48									21 54							22 00	22 15	22 20			

For general notes see front of timetable
For details of catering facilities see
Directory of Train Operators

§ It is unknown, at the time of going to press, when this station will open. For further details contact National Rail Enquiries 08457-484950 or see local publicity.

A To Southampton Central (Table 188) and to Bognor Regis (Table 188)

B To Littlehampton (Table 188)

b Arr. 2048

Watford Junction, Bedford and London → Brighton

Network Diagram - see first page of Table 186

	SN		LO	GW	XC	SN		GX	GW	SN	SN	SN	FC	SN	GX	SN	LO	SN		SN	SN	GX	SN	SE
	1			1	R 1	1		1	1	1	1	1 ◇	1	1		1		1		1	1	1	1	88
	A										B													
London Victoria 15 ⊖ d	21 17							21 30			21 32	21 36		21 40	21 45			21 47				22 00		
Watford Junction d																21 11								
Harrow & Wealdstone ⊖ d																21 17								
Wembley Central d																								
Willesden Jn. High Level d			21 08														21 38							
Shepherds Bush § ⊖ d																								
Kensington Olympia ⊖ d			21 17													21 36	21 47							
West Brompton ⊖ d			21 19													21 39	21 49							
Imperial Wharf § d																				←				
Clapham Junction 10 d	21 23		21a28								21 38	21 42		21 46		21b54	21a58	21 53		21 54				
Bedford 7 d													20 20			→								
Luton 10 d													20 44											
Luton Airport Parkway 7 ✈ d													20 46											
St Albans City d													20 58											
St Pancras International 15 ⊖ d													21 24											
Farringdon 3 ⊖ d													21 29											
City Thameslink 3 d													21 31											
London Blackfriars 3 ⊖ d													21 34											
London Bridge 4 ⊖ d													21 41											
Norwood Junction 2 d																								
East Croydon 🚋 a	21 33				←						21 48	21 52	21 54	21 58				22 03		22 07				
d	21 33				21 16						21 48	21 52	21 54	21 58				22 03		22 08				
Purley 4 d														22 03										
Coulsdon South d						←								22 06										
Merstham d						21 42								22 12										
Redhill a					21 34	21 46					21 59			22 15							←			
d				21 35	21 35	21 46			21 51	21 55	22 00			22 16							22 16		22 20	22 27
Tonbridge 4 a					→									→										
Reigate a				21 39						21 59													22 24	
Earlswood (Surrey) d						21 49															22 18			
Salfords d																					22 22			
Horley 4 d						21 54															22 25			
Gatwick Airport 10 ✈ a	21 48					21 57		22 00	22 04		22 08		22 10		22 15			22 18		22 23	22 28	22 30		22 35
d	21 49					21 58					22 09		22 11					22 19			22 29			22 35
Three Bridges 15 a	21 53					22 02					22 14		22 15								22 33			22 41
d	21 53					22 03					22 14		22 15								22 36			
Crawley d						22 06					22 18										22 39			
Ifield d						22 09															22 42			
Faygate d																								
Littlehaven d						22 15															22 48			
Horsham 4 a						22 18					22 26										22 52			
Balcombe d																								
Haywards Heath 3 a	22 02											22 15	22 24					22 30						
d	22 06	22 08										22 15	22 26					22 34	22 37					
Wivelsfield 4 d		22 12											22 30					22 38						
Lewes 4 a		22 23																22 51						
Burgess Hill 4 d	22 11												22 32											
Hassocks 4 d													22 35											
Preston Park d													22 42											
Hove 2 a	22 22																		22 51					
Brighton 10 a												22 30	22 48											

For general notes see front of timetable
For details of catering facilities see Directory of Train Operators

§ It is unknown, at the time of going to press, when this station will open. For further details contact National Rail Enquiries 08457-484950 or see local publicity.

A To Eastbourne (Table 189)
B To Portsmouth & Southsea (Table 188)
b Arr. 2147

Watford Junction, Bedford and London → Brighton

Network Diagram - see first page of Table 186

		XC	SN	SN	SN	FC	SN	GX	SN	LO	GW	SN	GX	GW	SN		SN	FC	SN	SN	GX	SN	SN		LO
		1◇	1◇	1◇	1◇	1	1		1		1	1	1	1	1		1	1	1	1		1	1		
															A										
		⚲																							
London Victoria 15	⊖ d		22 02	22 06			22 10	22 15	22 17				22 30		22 32		22 36			22 40	22 45		22 47		
Watford Junction	d																					22 12			
Harrow & Wealdstone	⊖ d																					22 18			
Wembley Central	d																								
Willesden Jn. High Level	d									22 08															22 38
Shepherds Bush §	⊖ d																								
Kensington Olympia	⊖ d									22 17												22 41			22 47
West Brompton	⊖ d									22 19												22 43			22 49
Imperial Wharf §	d																								
Clapham Junction 10	d		22 08	22 12			22 16		22 23	22a28					22 38		22 42			22 46		22a51	22 53		22a59
Bedford 7	d					20 50												21 20							
Luton 10	d					21 14												21 44							
Luton Airport Parkway 7	✈ d					21 16												21 46							
St Albans City	d					21 28												21 59							
St Pancras International 15	⊖ d					21 54												22 24							
Farringdon 3	⊖ d					21 59												22 29							
City Thameslink 3	d					22 01												22 31							
London Blackfriars 3	⊖ d					22 04												22 34							
London Bridge 4	⊖ d					22 11												22 41							
Norwood Junction 2	d																								
East Croydon	a		22 18	22 22		22 24	22 28		22 33						22 48		22 52	22 54		22 58			23 03		
	d		22 18	22 22		22 24	22 28		22 33						22 48		22 52	22 54		22 58			23 03		
Purley 4	d						22 33													23 03					
Coulsdon South	d						22 37					←								23 07					
Merstham	d						22 42 →					22 42								23 12					
Redhill	a	22 11	22 30									22 46			23 00					23 16					
	d	22 24	22 31								22 33	22 46		22 52	23 01				23 05	23 16					
Tonbridge 4	a																			↦					
Reigate	a										22 38								23 09						
Earlswood (Surrey)	d											22 49													
Salfords	d																								
Horley 4	d											22 54													
Gatwick Airport 10	✈ a	22 37	22 38		←	22 41		22 45	22 48			22 57	23 00	23 04	23 08			23 10			23 15		23 18		
	d		22 39		22 39	22 41			22 49			22 58			23 09			23 11					23 19		
Three Bridges 15	a		→		22 44	22 45			22 54			23 02			23 14			23 15							
	d				22 44	22 45			22 54			23 03			23 15			23 15							
Crawley	d											23 06			23 18										
Ifield	d											23 09													
Faygate	d																								
Littlehaven	d											23 15													
Horsham 4	a											23 18			23 26										
Balcombe	d					22 51																			
Haywards Heath 3	a			22 46	22 52	22 58			23 02								23 15	23 24					23 30		
	d			22 47	22 53	22 58			23 03								23 15	23 26					23 34	23 37	
Wivelsfield 4	d				22 57	23 02												23 30					23 38		
Lewes 4	a																						23 51		
Burgess Hill 4	d				22 59	23 04			23 08									23 32							
Hassocks 4	d				23 02	23 08												23 35							
Preston Park	d				23 09	23 15												23 42							
Hove 2	a								23 21															23 51	
Brighton 10	a			23 00	23 15	23 20											23 30	23 48							

For general notes see front of timetable
For details of catering facilities see Directory of Train Operators

§ It is unknown, at the time of going to press, when this station will open. For further details contact National Rail Enquiries 08457-484950 or see local publicity.

A To Chichester (Table 188)

Watford Junction, Bedford and London → Brighton

Network Diagram - see first page of Table 186

		SN 1	GX 1	GW 1	SN 1 ◇	SN 1 ◇	SN 1 ◇	FC 1	SN 1	GX	SN 1	LO	SN 1	GX 1	SN 1	FC 1	GX	SN 1	FC	FC	FC 1	SN 1
London Victoria 15 ⊖	d		23 00		23 02	23 06			23 10	23 15	23 17			23 30	23 32		23 45	23 47				
Watford Junction	d																					23 18
Harrow & Wealdstone ⊖	d																					23 24
Wembley Central	d																					
Willesden Jn. High Level	d											23 08										
Shepherds Bush § ⊖	d																					
Kensington Olympia ⊖	d											23 17										
West Brompton ⊖	d											23 19										23 44
Imperial Wharf §	d																					23 47
Clapham Junction 10	d				23 08	23 12			23 16		23 23	23a28			23 38			23 53				23a54
Bedford 7	d							21 50								22 10			22 40	23 10	23 40	
Luton 10	d							22 14								22 34			23 04	23 34	00 04	
Luton Airport Parkway 7 ✈	d							22 16								22 36			23 06	23 36	00 06	
St Albans City	d							22 29								22 48			23 18	23 48	00 18	
St Pancras International 15 ⊖	d							22 54								23 24			23 54	00 24	00 54	
Farringdon 3 ⊖	d							22 59								23 29			23 59	00 29		
City Thameslink 3	d							23 01														
London Blackfriars 3 ⊖	d							23 04								23 34			00 04	00 34	01 04	
London Bridge 4 ⊖	d							23 11								23 41			00 11	00 41		
Norwood Junction 2	d																					
East Croydon	a				23 18	23 22		23 24	23 28		23 33				23 51	23 56		00 05	00 26	00 56	01 32	
	d				23 18	23 22		23 24	23 28		23 33				23 52	23 57		00 06	00 27	00 57	01 32	
Purley 4	d								23 33									00 12				
Coulsdon South	d								23 37									00 15				
Merstham	d								23 42									00 21				
Redhill	a	←			23 30				23 46				←		00 03			00 24				
	d	23 16		23 29	23 31				23 46				23 46		00 05			00 25				
Tonbridge 4	a								↦													
Reigate	a			23 33																		
Earlswood (Surrey)	d	23 19											23 49									
Salfords	d	23 22											23 52									
Horley 4	d	23 26											23 56					00 31				
Gatwick Airport 10 ✈	a	23 28	23 30		23 38		←	23 41		23 45	23 50		23 58	00 05	00 13	00 16	00 20	00 33	00 49	01 16	01 51	
	d	23 29			23 39 ↦		23 39	23 41			23 51		23 59		00 14	00 17		00 34	00 50	01 17	01 52	
Three Bridges 15	a	23 34					23 44	23 47			23 55		00 04		00 18	00 24		00 39	00 54	01 24	01 58	
	d	23 38					23 44	23 47			23 56		00 04		00 19			00 39				
Crawley	d	23 41											00 07					00 42				
Ifield	d	23 44											00 10					00 45				
Faygate	d																					
Littlehaven	d	23 50											00 16					00 51				
Horsham 4	a	23 53											00 19					00 54				
Balcombe	d							23 53							00 25							
Haywards Heath 3	a					23 45	23 52	23 58			00 04				00 30							
	d					23 45	23 53	23 58			00 05				00 30							
Wivelsfield 4	d						23 57	00 02							00 34							
Lewes 4	a																					
Burgess Hill 4	d						23 59	00 04			00 10				00 36							
Hassocks 4	d						00 02	00 08							00 40							
Preston Park	d						00 09	00 15							00 47							
Hove 2	a										00 21											
Brighton 10	a					23 59	00 15	00 20							00 51							

For general notes see front of timetable
For details of catering facilities see
Directory of Train Operators

§ It is unknown, at the time of going to press, when this station will open. For further details contact National Rail Enquiries 08457-484950 or see local publicity.

Watford Junction, Bedford and London → Brighton

Network Diagram - see first page of Table 186

Station		SN 1◇	FC 1	SN 1	SN 1	SN 1	GW 1	SN 1	FC 1	SN 1	GX 1	SN 1◇ A	FC	SN 1	GW 1	FC	GX 1	SN 1◇	FC 1	SN 1	FC 1	SN 1	FC 1	GX
London Victoria 15 ⊖	d	23p02		23p10	23p17			23p32		23p47	00 01	00 05		00 14			00 30	01 00		02 00		03 00		03 30
Watford Junction	d																							
Harrow & Wealdstone ⊖	d																							
Wembley Central	d																							
Willesden Jn. High Level	d																							
Shepherds Bush § ⊖	d																							
Kensington Olympia ⊖	d																							
West Brompton ⊖	d																							
Imperial Wharf §	d																							
Clapham Junction 10	d	23p08		23p16	23p23			23p38		23p53		00 11		00 20				01 08		02 08		03 08		
Bedford 7	d		21p50						22p10				22p40			23p10			23p40		00 40		01 40	
Luton 10	d		22p14						22p34				23p04			23p34			00 04		01 04		02 04	
Luton Airport Parkway 7 ✈	d		22p16						22p36				23p06			23p36			00 06		01 06		02 06	
St Albans City	d		22p29						22p48				23p18			23p48			00 18		01 18		02 18	
St Pancras International 15 ⊖	d		22p54						23p24				23p54			00 24			00 54		01 54		02 54	
Farringdon 3 ⊖	d		22p59						23p29				23p59			00 29								
City Thameslink 3	d		23p01																					
London Blackfriars 3 ⊖	d		23p04						23p34				00 04			00 34			01 04		02 04		03 04	
London Bridge 4 ⊖	d		23p11						23p41				00 11			00 41								
Norwood Junction 2	d																							
East Croydon	a	23p18	23p24	23p28	23p33			23p51	23p56	00 05		00 24	00 26	00 32		00 56		01 21	01 32	02 21	02 30	03 21	03 30	
	d	23p18	23p24	23p28	23p33			23p52	23p57	00 06		00 25	00 27	00 33		00 57		01 22	01 32	02 22	02 32	03 22	03 32	
Purley 4	d			23p33						00 12				00 38				01 27		02 27		03 27		
Coulsdon South	d			23p37						00 15				00 41										
Merstham	d			23p42						00 21				00 47										
Redhill	a	23p30		23p46		←		00 03		00 24				00 50										
	d	23p31		23p46		23p46	00 03	00 05		00 25				00 51	00 53									
Tonbridge 4	a			→																				
Reigate	a																							
Earlswood (Surrey)	d					23p49																		
Salfords	d					23p52																		
Horley 4	d					23p56				00 31				00 57				01 43		02 42		03 42		
Gatwick Airport 10 ✈	a	23p38	23p41		23p50	23p58	00 11	00 13	00 16	00 33	00 35	00 42	00 49	00 59	01 01	01 16	01 20	01 45	01 51	02 44	02 51	03 44	03 51	04 05
	d	23p39	23p41		23p51	23p59		00 14	00 17	00 34		00 43	00 50			01 17		01 47	01 52	02 46	02 52	03 46	03 52	
Three Bridges 15	a	23p44	23p47		23p55	00 04		00 18	00 24	00 39		00 48	00 54			01 24		01 51	01 58	02 50	02 58	03 50	03 58	
	d	23p44	23p47		23p56	00 04		00 19		00 39		00 48						01 52						
Crawley	d					00 07				00 42														
Ifield	d					00 10				00 45														
Faygate	d																							
Littlehaven	d					00 16				00 51														
Horsham 4	a					00 19				00 54														
Balcombe	d		23p53					00 25																
Haywards Heath 3	a	23p52	23p58		00 04			00 30				01 00						02 06						
	d	23p53	23p58		00 05			00 30				01 03 / 01 06						02 06						
Wivelsfield 4	d	23p57	00 02					00 34																
Lewes 4	a											01 20												
Burgess Hill 4	d	23p59	00 04		00 10			00 36																
Hassocks 4	d	00 02	00 08					00 40																
Preston Park	d	00 09	00 15					00 47																
Hove 2	a				00 21							01s25												
Brighton 10	a	00 15	00 20					00 51				01s17						02 32						

For general notes see front of timetable
For details of catering facilities see
Directory of Train Operators

§ It is unknown, at the time of going to press, when this station will open. For further details contact National Rail Enquiries 08457-484950 or see local publicity.

A To Eastbourne (Table 189)

Watford Junction, Bedford and London → Brighton

Network Diagram - see first page of Table 186

		SN		FC	GX	FC	GX	SN	GX	GW	GW	FC	SN	GX	SN	SN	GX	FC	SN		GX	GW	SE	GW	LO
		1 ◇		1	1	1	1	1 ◇		1	1	1	1	1	1 ◇	1		1	1 ◇		1	1	88	1	
													A		B	C			B						
London Victoria 15 ⊖	d	04 00			04 30		05 00	05 02	05 15					05 30	05 32		05 45				06 00				
Watford Junction	d																								
Harrow & Wealdstone ⊖	d																								
Wembley Central	d																								
Willesden Jn. High Level	d																								
Shepherds Bush § ⊖	d																								06 08
Kensington Olympia ⊖	d																								
West Brompton ⊖	d																								06 17
Imperial Wharf §	d																								06 20
Clapham Junction 10	d	04 08						05 08							05 38										06a29
Bedford 7	d			02 40		03 10						03 40						04 20							
Luton 10	d			03 04		03 34						04 04						04 44							
Luton Airport Parkway 7 ✈	d			03 06		03 36						04 06						04 46							
St Albans City	d			03 18		03 48						04 18						04 58							
St Pancras International 15 ⊖	d			03 54		04 23						04 54						05 34							
Farringdon 3 ⊖	d											04 59						05 39							
City Thameslink 3	d																								
London Blackfriars 3 ⊖	d			04 04		04 34						05 04						05 44							
London Bridge 4 ⊖	d																	05 50							
Norwood Junction 2	d																								
East Croydon	a	04 21		04 30		05 00		05 21				05 32			05 48			06 04							
	d	04 22		04 32		05 02		05 22				05 32			05 48			06 05							
Purley 4	d	04 27						05 26							05 53										
Coulsdon South	d							05 30							05 57										
Merstham	d							05 35							06 03										
Redhill	a							05 39							06 06				←						
	d							05 39		05 43	05 44				06 07				06 07			06 14	06 27	06 34	
Tonbridge 4	a														→										
Reigate	a									05 47												06 18		06 38	
Earlswood (Surrey)	d																		06 11						
Salfords	d																		06 14						
Horley 4	d	04 43						05 45											06 18						
Gatwick Airport 10 ✈	a	04 45		04 51	05 05	05 21	05 35	05 48	05 50		05 53	05 54		06 00			06 15	06 20	06 20		06 30		06 34		
	d	04 47		04 52		05 22		05 50				05 54	05 58			06 11		06 20	06 21				06 36		
Three Bridges 15	a	04 51		04 58		05 27		05 54				06 00	06 02			06 15		06 25	06 25				06 40		
	d	04 52				05 28		05 54				06 00	06 03			06 16		06 26	06 30	06 34					
Crawley	d												06 06							06 37					
Ifield	d												06 09							06 40					
Faygate	d																								
Littlehaven	d												06 15							06 46					
Horsham 4	a												06 18							06 49					
Balcombe	d					05 35						06 06						06 32	06 36						
Haywards Heath 3	a	05 00				05 40		06 03				06 12				06 25		06 37	06 41						
	d	05 01				05 42		06 03				06 12				06 25		06 38	06 41						
Wivelsfield 4	d					05 46		06 07				06 16				06 29			06 45						
Lewes 4	a															06 40									
Burgess Hill 4	d					05 48		06 09				06 18							06 47						
Hassocks 4	d					05 52		06 13				06 22							06 51						
Preston Park	d					05 59		06 20				06 29							06 58						
Hove 2	a																								
Brighton 10	a	05 16				06 07		06 25				06 34						06 51	07 02						

For general notes see front of timetable
For details of catering facilities see Directory of Train Operators

§ It is unknown, at the time of going to press, when this station will open. For further details contact National Rail Enquiries 08457-484950 or see local publicity.

A To Southampton Central (Table 188) and to Bognor Regis (Table 188)

B To Portsmouth Harbour (Table 188)

C To Ore (Table 189)

Watford Junction, Bedford and London → Brighton

Network Diagram - see first page of Table 186

		GX	GW	SN		FC	SN	GX	FC	GW	SN	GX	SN	SN	SN	FC	LO	SN	SN	SN	GX	SE 55	FC	SN	GX
		1	1	1		1	1	1	1	1	1	1	1	1	1	1		1 ◇	1	1	1	1	1	1	1
				A			A				B									B					
London Victoria 15	⊖ d	06 15		06 10				06 30			06 40	06 45						07 06			07 00			07 10	07 15
Watford Junction	d												06 11												
Harrow & Wealdstone	⊖ d												06 17												
Wembley Central	d																								
Willesden Jn. High Level	d																06 38								
Shepherds Bush §	⊖ d																								
Kensington Olympia	⊖ d												06 42				06 47								
West Brompton	⊖ d												06 45				06 49								
Imperial Wharf §	d																								
Clapham Junction 10	d			06 16							06 46		06 54				06a59	07 12						07 16	
Bedford 7	d					04 50			05 20							05 40							05 50		
Luton 10	d					05 14			05 44							06 04							06 14		
Luton Airport Parkway 7	✈ d					05 16			05 46							06 06							06 16		
St Albans City	d					05 28			05 58							06 18							06 28		
St Pancras International 15	⊖ d					06 04			06 24							06 39							06 54		
Farringdon 3	⊖ d					06 09			06 29							06 44							06 59		
City Thameslink 3	d																								
London Blackfriars 3	⊖ d					06 20			06 35							06 50							07 05		
London Bridge 4	⊖ d					06 26			06 41							06 56							07 11		
Norwood Junction 2	d																								
East Croydon	🚋 a			06 27		06 39			06 54		06 57		07 07			07 09		07 22					07 24	07 28	
	d			06 28		06 39			06 54		06 58		07 07			07 09		07 22					07 24	07 30	
Purley 4	d			06 33							07 03													07 36	
Coulsdon South	d			06 36							07 06													07 39	
Merstham	d			06 42							07 12													07 45 ⟶	
Redhill	a			06 45			⟵				07 15									⟵					
	d		06 41	06 46			06 46			07 14	07 16									07 16		07 27			
Tonbridge 4	a			⟶							⟶														
Reigate	a									07 18															
Earlswood (Surrey)	d						06 48													07 18					
Salfords	d						06 52													07 22					
Horley 4	d						06 55													07 25					
Gatwick Airport 10	✈ a	06 45	06 50			06 55	06 58	07 00	07 10			07 15	07 22			07 25			⟵	07 28	07 30	07 34	07 40		07 45
	d					06 56	06 59		07 11				07 28 ⟶			07 26			07 28	07 29		07 35	07 41		
Three Bridges 15	a					07 00	07 03		07 15										07 33	07 33		07 39	07 45		
	d					07 00	07 04		07 15										07 33	07 34			07 45		
Crawley	d						07 07													07 37					
Ifield	d						07 10													07 40					
Faygate	d																								
Littlehaven	d						07 16													07 46					
Horsham 4	a						07 19													07 49					
Balcombe	d								07 21																
Haywards Heath 3	a					07 08			07 26							07 36			07 42				07 54		
	d					07 08			07 27					07 33	07 37	07 38			07 46				07 55		
Wivelsfield 4	d								07 31					07 37					07 50				07 59		
Lewes 4	a													07 48											
Burgess Hill 4	d								07 33										07 52				08 01		
Hassocks 4	d								07 36										07 55				08 04		
Preston Park	d								07 43										08 02				08 11		
Hove 2	a														07 51										
Brighton 10	a					07 24			07 49							07 54		07 58	08 08				08 17		

For general notes see front of timetable
For details of catering facilities see Directory of Train Operators

§ It is unknown, at the time of going to press, when this station will open. For further details contact National Rail Enquiries 08457-484950 or see local publicity.

A To Southampton Central (Table 188)
B To Portsmouth Harbour (Table 188)

Table 186

Saturdays

Watford Junction, Bedford and London → Brighton

Network Diagram - see first page of Table 186

		GW	GW	FC	SN	GX	LO	SN	SN	SN	FC	GX	SN		SN	SN	FC	GW	LO	SN	GX	SN	GW	SE
		1	1	1	1	1		1	1	1 ◇	1	1	1		1	1	1	1		1	1	1	1	13
								A														B		C
London Victoria 15	⊖ d					07 30		07 32		07 36		07 45	07 47								08 00	08 02		
Watford Junction	d																							
Harrow & Wealdstone	⊖ d														07 13									
Wembley Central	d														07 19									
Willesden Jn. High Level	d						07 08																	
Shepherds Bush §	⊖ d																		07 38					
Kensington Olympia	⊖ d						07 17								07 42				07 47					
West Brompton	⊖ d						07 19								07 45				07 49					
Imperial Wharf §	d																							
Clapham Junction 10	d						07a29	07 38		07 42			07 53		07 54				07a59			08 08		
Bedford 7	d			06 10							06 25						06 40							
Luton 10	d			06 34							06 49						07 04							
Luton Airport Parkway 7	✈ d			06 36							06 51						07 06							
St Albans City	d			06 48							07 03						07 18							
St Pancras International 15	⊖ d			07 09							07 24						07 39							
Farringdon 3	⊖ d			07 14							07 29						07 44							
City Thameslink 3	d																							
London Blackfriars 3	⊖ d			07 20							07 35						07 50							
London Bridge 4	⊖ d			07 26					07 33		07 41						07 56							08 03
Norwood Junction 2	d								07 46															08 16
East Croydon	🚋 a			07 39				07 48	07 49	07 52	07 54		08 03		08 07		08 09					08 18		08 19
	d			07 39				07 48	07 51	07 52	07 54		08 03		08 07		08 09					08 18		08 21
Purley 4	d								07 57															08 26
Coulsdon South	d				←				08 00															08 30
Merstham	d				07 45				08 06															08 35
Redhill	a				07 48			08 00	08 09							←						08 30		08 38
	d	07 34	07 41		07 49			08 00	08 10							08 10		08 14				08 30	08 34	08 39
Tonbridge 4	a								→															09 08
Reigate	a	07 38																08 18					08 38	
Earlswood (Surrey)	d															08 12								
Salfords	d															08 16								
Horley 4	d				07 55											08 19						08 36		
Gatwick Airport 10	✈ a		07 50	07 55	07 57	08 00		08 08			08 10	08 15	08 18		08 22	08 23	08 25			←	08 30	08 39		
	d			07 56	07 58			08 09			08 11		08 19		08 28	08 24	08 26			08 28		08 40		
Three Bridges 15	a				08 03			08 14			08 15				→	08 29				08 33		08 44		
	d				08 03			08 14			08 15					08 30				08 33		08 45		
Crawley	d				08 06			08 18								08 33						08 48		
Ifield	d				08 09											08 36								
Faygate	d																							
Littlehaven	d				08 15											08 42								
Horsham 4	a				08 19			08 26								08 47						08 56		
Balcombe	d										08 21													
Haywards Heath 3	a			08 06							08 26		08 30				08 36			08 42				
	d			08 08							08 27		08 34	08 37			08 38			08 46				
Wivelsfield 4	d										08 31									08 52				
Lewes 4	a												08 52											
Burgess Hill 4	d										08 33									08 54				
Hassocks 4	d										08 36									08 57				
Preston Park	d										08 43									09 04				
Hove 2	a													08 51						→				
Brighton 10	a			08 24						08 28	08 49						08 54							

For general notes see front of timetable
For details of catering facilities see Directory of Train Operators

§ It is unknown, at the time of going to press, when this station will open. For further details contact National Rail Enquiries 08457-484950 or see local publicity.

A To Southampton Central (Table 188) and to Bognor Regis (Table 188)

B To Portsmouth Harbour (Table 188) and to Bognor Regis (Table 188)

C To Tunbridge Wells (Table 206)

Table 186

Saturdays

Watford Junction, Bedford and London → Brighton

Network Diagram - see first page of Table 186

	SN	SN	FC	GX	SN		GW	FC	SE	GX	LO	SN	SN	SN	FC	GX	SN		SN	LO	SN	FC	GW
	1 ◇	1	1	1	1		1	1	88 1	1		1	1	1 ◇	1	1	1		1		1	1	1
									A			B					C 🚲						
London Victoria 15 ⊖ d	08 06			08 15	08 17					08 30		08 32		08 36		08 45	08 47						
Watford Junction d																			08 11				
Harrow & Wealdstone ⊖ d																			08 17				
Wembley Central d																							
Willesden Jn. High Level d											08 08									08 38			
Shepherds Bush § ⊖ d											08 17								08 42	08 47			
Kensington Olympia ⊖ d											08 19								08 45	08 49			
West Brompton ⊖ d																							
Imperial Wharf § d																							
Clapham Junction 10 d	08 12				08 23						08a29	08 38		08 42			08 53		08 54	08a59			
Bedford 7 d			06 55					07 10							07 25							07 40	
Luton 10 d			07 19					07 34							07 49							08 04	
Luton Airport Parkway 7 ✈ d			07 21					07 36							07 51							08 06	
St Albans City d			07 33					07 48							08 03							08 18	
St Pancras International 15 ⊖ d			07 54					08 10							08 24							08 39	
Farringdon 3 ⊖ d			07 59					08 14							08 29							08 44	
City Thameslink 3 d																							
London Blackfriars 3 ⊖ d			08 05					08 20							08 35							08 50	
London Bridge 4 ⊖ d			08 11					08 26					08 33		08 41							08 56	
Norwood Junction 2 d													08 46										
East Croydon 🚋 a	08 22		08 24		08 33			08 39				08 48	08 49	08 52	08 54		09 03		09 07			09 09	
d	08 22		08 24		08 33			08 39				08 48	08 51	08 52	08 54		09 03		09 07			09 09	
Purley 4 d													08 57										
Coulsdon South d													09 00										
Merstham d													09 06								←		
Redhill a												09 00	09 09								09 10		09 14
d							08 41		08 44			09 00	09 10										
Tonbridge 4 a													↦										09 18
Reigate a																							
Earlswood (Surrey) d																					09 12		
Salfords d																					09 16		
Horley 4 d									08 51												09 19		
Gatwick Airport 10 ✈ a			08 40	08 45	08 48		08 50	08 55	08 55	09 00		09 08			09 10	09 15	09 18		09 22		09 23	09 25	
d			08 41		08 49			08 56	08 56			09 09			09 11		09 19		09 28 ↦		09 24	09 26	
Three Bridges 15 a			08 45						09 00			09 14			09 15						09 29		
d			08 45						09 01			09 14			09 15						09 30		
Crawley d									09 04			09 18									09 33		
Ifield d									09 07												09 36		
Faygate d																							
Littlehaven d									09 13												09 42		
Horsham 4 a									09 16			09 26									09 47		
Balcombe d															09 21								
Haywards Heath 3 a			08 54		09 00			09 06							09 26		09 30					09 36	
d			08 55		09 04	09 07		09 08							09 27		09 34	09 37				09 38	
Wivelsfield 4 d			08 59			09 11									09 31								
Lewes 4 a						09 22											09 52						
Burgess Hill 4 d			09 01		09 09										09 33								
Hassocks 4 d		←	09 04												09 36								
Preston Park d		09 04	09 11												09 43								
Hove 2 a					09 21													09 51					
Brighton 10 a	08 58	09 09	09 18					09 24						09 27	09 49							09 54	

For general notes see front of timetable
For details of catering facilities see Directory of Train Operators

§ It is unknown, at the time of going to press, when this station will open. For further details contact National Rail Enquiries 08457-484950 or see local publicity.

A From Tonbridge (Table 209)
B To Southampton Central (Table 188) and to Bognor Regis (Table 188)

C 🚲 to Lewes

Table 186

Saturdays

Watford Junction, Bedford and London → Brighton

Network Diagram - see first page of Table 186

		SN [1]	GX [1]	SN [1] A	GW [1]	SE 13 B	SN [1] ◊ ⌶	SN [1]	FC [1]	GX [1]		SN [1] C ⌶		LO	GW [1]	SE 88 [1] D	FC [1]	GX [1]	SN [1] E	SN [1]	SN [1] ◊	FC [1]	GX [1]	SN [1] G ⌶	
London Victoria [15]	⊖ d		09 00	09 02			09 06			09 15		09 17						09 30	09 32		09 36		09 45	09 47	
Watford Junction	d																								
Harrow & Wealdstone	⊖ d																								
Wembley Central	d																								
Willesden Jn. High Level	d													09 08											
Shepherds Bush §	⊖ d																								
Kensington Olympia	⊖ d													09 17											
West Brompton	⊖ d													09 19											
Imperial Wharf §	d																								
Clapham Junction [10]	d			09 08			09 12					09 23		09a29					09 38		09 42			09 53	
Bedford [7]	d								07 55								08 10					08 25			
Luton [10]	d								08 19								08 34					08 49			
Luton Airport Parkway [7]	✈ d								08 21								08 36					08 51			
St Albans City	d								08 33								08 48					09 03			
St Pancras International [15]	⊖ d								08 54								09 09					09 24			
Farringdon [3]	⊖ d								08 59								09 14					09 29			
City Thameslink [3]	d								09 01								09 16					09 31			
London Blackfriars [3]	⊖ d								09 05								09 20					09 35			
London Bridge [4]	⊖ d					09 03			09 11								09 26			09 33		09 41			
Norwood Junction [2]	d					09 16														09 46					
East Croydon	🚋 a			09 18		09 19	09 22		09 24			09 33					09 39		09 48	09 49	09 52	09 54		10 03	
	d			09 18		09 21	09 22		09 24			09 33					09 39		09 48	09 51	09 52	09 54		10 03	
Purley [4]	d					09 26														09 57					
Coulsdon South	d					09 30														10 00					
Merstham	d					09 35														10 06					
Redhill	a			09 30		09 38													10 00	10 09					
	d			09 30	09 34	09 39									09 41	09 44			10 00	10 10					
Tonbridge [4]	a					10 08														↪					
Reigate	a				09 38																				
Earlswood (Surrey)	d																								
Salfords	d																								
Horley [4]	d			09 36												09 51									
Gatwick Airport [10]	✈ a	←	09 30	09 39					09 40	09 45		09 48			09 50	09 55	09 55	10 00	10 08			10 10	10 15	10 18	
	d	09 28		09 40					09 41			09 49				09 55	09 56		10 09			10 11		10 19	
Three Bridges [15]	a	09 33		09 44					09 45							10 00			10 14			10 15			
	d	09 33		09 45					09 45							10 01			10 14			10 15			
Crawley	d			09 48												10 04			10 18						
Ifield	d															10 07									
Faygate	d																								
Littlehaven	d															10 13									
Horsham [4]	a			09 56												10 16			10 26						
Balcombe	d																					10 21			
Haywards Heath [3]	a	09 42							09 54			10 00					10 06					10 26		10 30	
	d	09 46							09 55			10 04	10 07				10 08					10 27		10 34	10 37
Wivelsfield [4]	d	09 50							09 59				10 11									10 31			
Lewes [4]	a												10 22											10 52	
Burgess Hill [4]	d	09 52							10 01			10 09										10 33			
Hassocks [4]	d	09 55						←	10 04													10 36			
Preston Park	d	10 02						10 02	10 11													10 43			
Hove [2]	a	↪										10 21													10 51
Brighton [10]	a						09 58	10 07	10 17								10 24				10 27	10 49			

For general notes see front of timetable
For details of catering facilities see Directory of Train Operators

§ It is unknown, at the time of going to press, when this station will open. For further details contact National Rail Enquiries 08457-484950 or see local publicity.

A To Portsmouth Harbour (Table 188) and to Bognor Regis (Table 188)
B To Tunbridge Wells (Table 206)
C ⌶ to Haywards Heath
D From Tunbridge Wells (Table 209)
E To Southampton Central (Table 188) and to Bognor Regis (Table 188)
G ⌶ to Lewes

Table 186

Saturdays

Watford Junction, Bedford and London → Brighton

Network Diagram - see first page of Table 186

		SN	LO	SN	FC	GW	SN	GX	SN	GW	SE	SN	SN	FC	GX	SN		LO	GW	SE	FC	GX	SN	SN
											13									88				
		1		1	1	1	1	1	1	1	1	1 ◇	1	1	1	1			1	1	1	1	1	1
									A		B					C				D			E	
									🛒			🛒				🛒								
London Victoria 15	⊖ d							10 00	10 02			10 06			10 15	10 17						10 30	10 32	
Watford Junction	d	09 11																						
Harrow & Wealdstone	⊖ d	09 17																						
Wembley Central	d																							
Willesden Jn. High Level	d		09 38															10 08						
Shepherds Bush §	⊖ d																							
Kensington Olympia	⊖ d	09 42	09 47															10 17						
West Brompton	⊖ d	09 45	09 49															10 19						
Imperial Wharf §	d																							
Clapham Junction 10	d	09 54	09a59						10 08			10 12				10 23		10a29					10 38	
Bedford 7	d				08 40									08 55							09 10			
Luton 10	d				09 04									09 19							09 34			
Luton Airport Parkway 7	✈ d				09 06									09 21							09 36			
St Albans City	d				09 18									09 33							09 48			
St Pancras International 15	⊖ d				09 39									09 54							10 09			
Farringdon 3	⊖ d				09 44									09 59							10 14			
City Thameslink 3	d				09 46									10 01							10 16			
London Blackfriars 3	⊖ d				09 50									10 05							10 20			10 33
London Bridge 4	⊖ d				09 56						10 03			10 11							10 26			10 46
Norwood Junction 2	d										10 16													
East Croydon	🚋 a	10 07			10 09				10 18		10 19	10 22		10 24		10 33					10 39		10 48	10 49
	d	10 07			10 09				10 18		10 21	10 22		10 24		10 33					10 39		10 48	10 51
Purley 4	d										10 26													10 57
Coulsdon South	d										10 30													11 00
Merstham	d										10 35													11 06
Redhill	a			←					10 30		10 38												11 00	11 09
	d			10 10		10 14			10 30	10 34	10 39								10 41	10 44			11 00	11 10
Tonbridge 4	a										11 08													→
Reigate	a					10 18				10 38														
Earlswood (Surrey)	d			10 12																				
Salfords	d			10 16																				
Horley 4	d			10 19					10 36											10 51				
Gatwick Airport 10	✈ a	10 22		10 23	10 25		←	10 30	10 39					10 40	10 45	10 48			10 50	10 55	10 55	11 00	11 08	
	d	10 28		10 24	10 26		10 28		10 40					10 41		10 49				10 55	10 56		11 09	
Three Bridges 15	a	→		10 29			10 33		10 44					10 45						11 00			11 14	
	d			10 30			10 33		10 45					10 45						11 01			11 14	
Crawley	d			10 33					10 48											11 04			11 18	
Ifield	d			10 36																11 07				
Faygate	d																							
Littlehaven	d			10 42																11 13				
Horsham 4	a			10 47					10 56											11 16			11 26	
Balcombe	d																							
Haywards Heath 3	a				10 36		10 42							10 54		11 00					11 06			
	d				10 38		10 46							10 55		11 04	11 07				11 08			
Wivelsfield 4	d						10 50							10 59			11 11							
Lewes 4	a																11 22							
Burgess Hill 4	d						10 52							11 01		11 09								
Hassocks 4	d						10 55						←	11 04										
Preston Park	d						11 02						11 02	11 11										
Hove 2	a						→									11 21								
Brighton 10	a				10 54							10 58	11 07	11 17							11 24			

For general notes see front of timetable
For details of catering facilities see
Directory of Train Operators

§ It is unknown, at the time of going to press, when this station will open. For further details contact National Rail Enquiries 08457-484950 or see local publicity.

A To Portsmouth Harbour (Table 188) and to Bognor Regis (Table 188)
B To Tunbridge Wells (Table 206)
C 🛒 to Haywards Heath
D From Tunbridge Wells (Table 209)
E To Southampton Central (Table 188) and to Bognor Regis (Table 188)

Table 186

Saturdays

Watford Junction, Bedford and London → Brighton

Network Diagram - see first page of Table 186

		SN	FC	GX	SN		SN	LO	SN	FC	GW	SN	GX	SN	GW	SE	SN	SN	FC	GX	SN		LO	GW
		1 ◇	1	1	1		1		1	1	1	1	1	1	1	13	1 ◇	1	1	1	1			1
					A									B		C					D			
		🍴			🍴									🍴			🍴				🍴			
London Victoria 15	⊖ d	10 36		10 45	10 47								11 00	11 02			11 06			11 15	11 17			
Watford Junction	d						10 11																	
Harrow & Wealdstone	⊖ d						10 17																	
Wembley Central	d																							
Willesden Jn. High Level	d							10 38																
Shepherds Bush §	⊖ d																						11 08	
Kensington Olympia	⊖ d						10 42	10 47																
West Brompton	⊖ d						10 45	10 49															11 17	
Imperial Wharf §	d																						11 19	
Clapham Junction 10	d	10 42			10 53		10 54	10a59						11 08			11 12				11 23		11a29	
Bedford 7	d		09 25							09 40									09 55					
Luton 10	d		09 49							10 04									10 19					
Luton Airport Parkway 7	✈ d		09 51							10 06									10 21					
St Albans City	d		10 03							10 18									10 33					
St Pancras International 15	⊖ d		10 24							10 39									10 54					
Farringdon 3	⊖ d		10 29							10 44									10 59					
City Thameslink 3	d		10 31							10 46									11 01					
London Blackfriars 3	⊖ d		10 35							10 50									11 05					
London Bridge 4	⊖ d		10 41							10 56						11 03			11 11					
Norwood Junction 2	d															11 16								
East Croydon	a	10 52	10 54		11 03		11 07			11 09				11 18		11 19	11 22		11 24		11 33			
	d	10 52	10 54		11 03		11 07			11 09				11 18		11 21	11 22		11 24		11 33			
Purley 4	d															11 26								
Coulsdon South	d															11 30								
Merstham	d															11 35								
Redhill	a								←					11 30		11 38								
	d								11 10		11 14			11 30	11 34	11 39								11 41
Tonbridge 4	a															12 08								
Reigate	a										11 18				11 38									
Earlswood (Surrey)	d								11 12															
Salfords	d								11 16															
Horley 4	d								11 19					11 36										
Gatwick Airport 10	✈ a		11 10	11 15	11 18		11 22		11 23	11 25		←	11 30	11 39					11 40	11 45	11 48			11 50
	d		11 11		11 19		11 28		11 24	11 26		11 28		11 40					11 41		11 49			
Three Bridges 15	a		11 15				→		11 29			11 33		11 44					11 45					
	d		11 15						11 30			11 33		11 45					11 45					
Crawley	d								11 33					11 48										
Ifield	d								11 36															
Faygate	d																							
Littlehaven	d								11 42															
Horsham 4	a								11 47					11 56										
Balcombe	d		11 21																					
Haywards Heath 3	a		11 26		11 30					11 36		11 42							11 54		12 00			
	d		11 27		11 34	11 37				11 38		11 46							11 55		12 04	12 07		
Wivelsfield 4	d		11 31									11 50							11 59			12 11		
Lewes 4	a				11 52																	12 22		
Burgess Hill 4	d		11 33									11 52							12 01		12 09			
Hassocks 4	d		11 36									11 55						←	12 04					
Preston Park	d		11 43									12 02						12 02	12 11					
Hove 2	a					11 51						→									12 21			
Brighton 10	a	11 27	11 49							11 54							11 58	12 07	12 17					

For general notes see front of timetable
For details of catering facilities see Directory of Train Operators

§ It is unknown, at the time of going to press, when this station will open. For further details contact National Rail Enquiries 08457-484950 or see local publicity.

A 🍴 to Lewes
B To Portsmouth Harbour (Table 188) and to Bognor Regis (Table 188)
C To Tunbridge Wells (Table 206)
D 🍴 to Haywards Heath

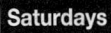

Watford Junction, Bedford and London → Brighton

Network Diagram - see first page of Table 186

		SE	FC	GX	LO	SN	SN	SN	FC	GX	SN		SN	SN	FC	GW		SN	GX	SN	LO	GW	SE	SN	SN
		88																					13		
		1	1	1		1	1	1 ◇	1	1	1		1	1	1	1		1	1	1		1		1 ◇	1
		A				B					C								D	E			G		
								⊥			⊥									⊥				⊥	
London Victoria 15 ⊖	d			11 30		11 32		11 36		11 45	11 47								12 00	12 02				12 06	
Watford Junction	d												11 11												
Harrow & Wealdstone ⊖	d												11 17												
Wembley Central	d																								
Willesden Jn. High Level	d				11 38																12 08				
Shepherds Bush § ⊖	d																								
Kensington Olympia ⊖	d				11 47								11 42								12 17				
West Brompton ⊖	d				11 49								11 45								12 19				
Imperial Wharf §	d																								
Clapham Junction 10	d				11a59	11 38		11 42			11 53		11 54							12 08	12a29			12 12	
Bedford 7	d		10 10						10 25						10 40										
Luton 10	d		10 34						10 49						11 04										
Luton Airport Parkway 7 ✈	d		10 36						10 51						11 06										
St Albans City	d		10 48						11 03						11 18										
St Pancras International 15 ⊖	d		11 09						11 24						11 39										
Farringdon 3 ⊖	d		11 14						11 29						11 44										
City Thameslink 3	d		11 16						11 31						11 46										
London Blackfriars 3 ⊖	d		11 20						11 35						11 50										
London Bridge 4 ⊖	d		11 26				11 33		11 41						11 56								12 03		
Norwood Junction 2	d						11 46																12 16		
East Croydon	a		11 39			11 48	11 49	11 52	11 54		12 03		12 07		12 09					12 18			12 19	12 22	
	d		11 39			11 48	11 51	11 52	11 54		12 03		12 07		12 09					12 18			12 21	12 22	
Purley 4	d						11 57																12 26		
Coulsdon South	d						12 00																12 30		
Merstham	d						12 06																12 35		
Redhill	a					12 00	12 09							←						12 30			12 38		
	d	11 44				12 00	12 10							12 10		12 14				12 30		12 34	12 39		
Tonbridge 4	a						→																13 08		
Reigate	a															12 18						12 38			
Earlswood (Surrey)	d													12 12											
Salfords	d													12 16											
Horley 4	d	11 51												12 19						12 36					
Gatwick Airport 10 ✈	a	11 55	11 55	12 00		12 08			12 10	12 15	12 18		12 22	12 23	12 25			←	12 30	12 39					
	d	11 55	11 56			12 09			12 11		12 19		12 28	12 24	12 26			12 28		12 40					
Three Bridges 15	a	12 00				12 14			12 15				→	12 29				12 33		12 44					
	d	12 01				12 14			12 15					12 30				12 33		12 45					
Crawley	d	12 04				12 18								12 33						12 48					
Ifield	d	12 07												12 36											
Faygate	d																								
Littlehaven	d	12 13												12 42											
Horsham 4	a	12 16				12 26								12 47						12 56					
Balcombe	d								12 21																
Haywards Heath 3	a		12 06						12 26		12 30				12 36			12 42							
	d		12 08						12 27		12 34	12 37			12 38			12 46							
Wivelsfield 4	d								12 31									12 50							
Lewes 4	a										12 52														
Burgess Hill 4	d								12 33									12 52							
Hassocks 4	d								12 36									12 55							←
Preston Park	d								12 43									13 02							13 02
Hove 2	a											12 51						→							
Brighton 10	a		12 24					12 27	12 49						12 54									12 58	13 07

For general notes see front of timetable
For details of catering facilities see Directory of Train Operators

§ It is unknown, at the time of going to press, when this station will open. For further details contact National Rail Enquiries 08457-484950 or see local publicity.

A From Tunbridge Wells (Table 209)
B To Southampton Central (Table 188) and to Bognor Regis (Table 188)
C ⊥ to Lewes
D Operating Company SN from 28 June
E To Portsmouth Harbour (Table 188) and to Bognor Regis (Table 188)
G To Tunbridge Wells (Table 206)

Table 186

Saturdays

Watford Junction, Bedford and London → Brighton

Network Diagram - see first page of Table 186

	FC	GX	SN	SN	GW	XC	SE	FC	GX	XC	LO	SN	SN	SN	XC	FC	GX		SN	SN	SN	SN	FC	GW
	1	1	1 A		1	1 ◇ B	88 1 C	1	1	1 ◇ D		1 E	1	1 ◇	1 ◇ D	1	1		1 G		1	1	1	1
London Victoria 15 ⊖ d		12 15	12 17						12 30			12 32		12 36			12 45		12 47					
Watford Junction d																								
Harrow & Wealdstone ⊖ d																					12 11			
Wembley Central d																					12 17			
Willesden Jn. High Level d											12 38													
Shepherds Bush § ⊖ d																								
Kensington Olympia ⊖ d						11 57					12 47										12 42			
West Brompton ⊖ d											12 49										12 45			
Imperial Wharf § d																								
Clapham Junction 10 d			12 23								12a59	12 38		12 42					12 53		12 54			
Bedford 7 d	10 55							11 10								11 25							11 40	
Luton 10 d	11 19							11 34								11 49							12 04	
Luton Airport Parkway 7 ✈ d	11 21							11 36								11 51							12 06	
St Albans City d	11 33							11 48								12 03							12 18	
St Pancras International 15 ⊖ d	11 54							12 09								12 24							12 39	
Farringdon 3 ⊖ d	11 59							12 14								12 29							12 44	
City Thameslink 3 d	12 01							12 16								12 31							12 46	
London Blackfriars 3 ⊖ d	12 05							12 20								12 35							12 50	
London Bridge 4 ⊖ d	12 11							12 26					12 33			12 41							12 56	
Norwood Junction 2 d													12 46											
East Croydon a	12 24		12 33			12 37		12 39				12 48	12 49	12 52		12 54			13 03		13 07		13 09	
d	12 24		12 33			12 37		12 39				12 48	12 51	12 52		12 54			13 03		13 07		13 09	
Purley 4 d													12 57											
Coulsdon South d													13 00											
Merstham d													13 06											
Redhill a												13 00	13 09									←		
d					12 41		12 44					13 00	13 10									13 10		13 14
Tonbridge 4 a													↳											
Reigate a																								13 18
Earlswood (Surrey) d																						13 12		
Salfords d																						13 16		
Horley 4 d							12 51															13 19		
Gatwick Airport 10 ✈ a	12 39	12 45	12 48		12 50	12 53	12 55	12 56	13 00	←		13 08				13 10	13 15		13 18		13 22	13 23	13 25	
d	12 40		12 49			13 01	12 55	12 56		13 01		13 09				13 11			13 19		13 28	13 24	13 26	
Three Bridges 15 a	12 45					→	13 00					13 14				13 15					→	13 29		
d	12 45						13 01					13 14				13 15						13 30		
Crawley d							13 04					13 18										13 33		
Ifield d							13 07															13 36		
Faygate d																								
Littlehaven d							13 13															13 42		
Horsham 4 a							13 16					13 26										13 47		
Balcombe d																13 21								
Haywards Heath 3 a	12 54		13 00					13 07		13 13					←	13 26			13 30				13 36	
d	12 55		13 04	13 07				13 08		13 18					13 18	13 27			13 34	13 37			13 38	
Wivelsfield 4 d	12 59			13 11						→						13 31								
Lewes 4 a				13 22															13 48					
Burgess Hill 4 d	13 01		13 09													13 33								
Hassocks 4 d	13 04															13 36								
Preston Park d	13 11															13 43								
Hove 2 a			13 21																	13 51				
Brighton 10 a	13 17							13 24						13 27	13 37	13 49							13 54	

For general notes see front of timetable
For details of catering facilities see Directory of Train Operators

§ It is unknown, at the time of going to press, when this station will open. For further details contact National Rail Enquiries 08457-484950 or see local publicity.

A to Haywards Heath
B From 13 September from Birmingham New Street
C From Tunbridge Wells (Table 209)
D from Birmingham New Street
E To Southampton Central (Table 188) and to Bognor Regis (Table 188)
G to Lewes

Table 186

Watford Junction, Bedford and London → Brighton

Network Diagram - see first page of Table 186

		SN 1	GX 1	SN 1 ◇ A ⚲	LO	GW 1	SE 13 B	SN 1 ◇ ⚲	SN 1	FC 1	GX 1	SN 1 C ⚲		GW 1	SE 88 1 D	FC 1	GX 1	SN 1 E	LO	SN 1	SN 1 ◇ ⚲	FC 1	GX 1
London Victoria 15	⊖ d		13 00	13 02				13 06			13 15	13 17					13 30	13 32			13 36		13 45
Watford Junction	d																						
Harrow & Wealdstone	⊖ d																						
Wembley Central	d																						
Willesden Jn. High Level	d				13 08														13 38				
Shepherds Bush §	⊖ d																						
Kensington Olympia	⊖ d				13 17														13 47				
West Brompton	⊖ d				13 19														13 49				
Imperial Wharf §	d																						
Clapham Junction 10	d			13 08	13a29			13 12				13 23						13 38	13a59		13 42		
Bedford 7	d									11 55						12 10						12 25	
Luton 10	d									12 19						12 34						12 49	
Luton Airport Parkway 7	✈ d									12 21						12 36						12 51	
St Albans City	d									12 33						12 48						13 03	
St Pancras International 15	⊖ d									12 54						13 09						13 24	
Farringdon 3	⊖ d									12 59						13 14						13 29	
City Thameslink 3	d									13 01						13 16						13 31	
London Blackfriars 3	⊖ d									13 05						13 20						13 35	
London Bridge 4	⊖ d						13 03			13 11						13 26				13 33		13 41	
Norwood Junction 2	d						13 16													13 46			
East Croydon	a			13 18			13 19	13 22		13 24		13 33				13 39		13 48		13 49	13 52	13 54	
	d			13 18			13 21	13 22		13 24		13 33				13 39		13 48		13 51	13 52	13 54	
Purley 4	d						13 26													13 57			
Coulsdon South	d						13 30													14 00			
Merstham	d						13 35													14 06			
Redhill	a			13 30			13 38											14 00		14 09			
	d			13 30		13 34	13 39							13 41	13 44			14 00		14 10			
Tonbridge 4	a						14 08													→			
Reigate	a					13 38																	
Earlswood (Surrey)	d																						
Salfords	d																						
Horley 4	d			13 36											13 51								
Gatwick Airport 10	✈ a	←	13 30	13 39						13 40	13 45	13 48		13 50	13 55	13 55	14 00	14 08				14 10	14 15
	d	13 28		13 40						13 41		13 49			13 55	13 56		14 09				14 11	
Three Bridges 15	a	13 33		13 44						13 45					14 00			14 14				14 15	
	d	13 33		13 45						13 45					14 01			14 14				14 15	
Crawley	d			13 48											14 04			14 18					
Ifield	d														14 07								
Faygate	d																						
Littlehaven	d														14 13								
Horsham 4	a			13 56											14 16			14 26					
Balcombe	d																					14 21	
Haywards Heath 3	a	13 42								13 54		14 00				14 06						14 26	
	d	13 46								13 55		14 04	14 07			14 08						14 27	
Wivelsfield 4	d	13 50								13 59			14 11									14 31	
Lewes 4	a												14 22										
Burgess Hill 4	d	13 52								14 01		14 09										14 33	
Hassocks 4	d	13 55							←	14 04												14 36	
Preston Park	d	14 02							14 02	14 11												14 43	
Hove 2	a	→										14 21											
Brighton 10	a							13 58	14 07	14 17						14 24					14 28	14 49	

For general notes see front of timetable
For details of catering facilities see Directory of Train Operators

§ It is unknown, at the time of going to press, when this station will open. For further details contact National Rail Enquiries 08457-484950 or see local publicity.

A To Portsmouth Harbour (Table 188) and to Bognor Regis (Table 188)
B To Tunbridge Wells (Table 206)
C ⚲ to Haywards Heath
D From Tunbridge Wells (Table 209)
E To Southampton Central (Table 188) and to Bognor Regis (Table 188)

Table 186

Saturdays

Watford Junction, Bedford and London → Brighton

Network Diagram - see first page of Table 186

		SN		SN	SN	FC	GW	SN	GX	SN	LO	GW	SE 13	SN	SN	FC	GX	SN		GW	SE 88	FC		GX	SN
		1		1	1	1	1	1	1	1		1		1 ◇	1	1	1	1		1	1	1		1	1
		A ⊥								B ⊥			C	⊥				D ⊥			E				G
London Victoria 15	⊖ d	13 47							14 00	14 02				14 06			14 15	14 17						14 30	14 32
Watford Junction	d			13 11																					
Harrow & Wealdstone	⊖ d			13 17																					
Wembley Central	d																								
Willesden Jn. High Level	d										14 08														
Shepherds Bush §	⊖ d																								
Kensington Olympia	⊖ d			13 42							14 17														
West Brompton	⊖ d			13 45							14 19														
Imperial Wharf §	d																								
Clapham Junction 10	d	13 53		13 54						14 08	14a29			14 12				14 23							14 38
Bedford 7	d					12 40										12 55						13 10			
Luton 10	d					13 04										13 19						13 34			
Luton Airport Parkway 7	✈ d					13 06										13 21						13 36			
St Albans City	d					13 18										13 33						13 48			
St Pancras International 15	⊖ d					13 39										13 54						14 09			
Farringdon 3	⊖ d					13 44										13 59						14 14			
City Thameslink 3	d					13 46										14 01						14 16			
London Blackfriars 3	⊖ d					13 50										14 05						14 20			
London Bridge 4	⊖ d					13 56							14 03			14 11						14 26			
Norwood Junction 2	d												14 16												
East Croydon	🚊 a	14 03		14 07		14 09				14 18			14 19	14 22		14 24		14 33				14 39			14 48
	d	14 03		14 07		14 09				14 18			14 21	14 22		14 24		14 33				14 39			14 48
Purley 4	d												14 26												
Coulsdon South	d												14 30												
Merstham	d												14 35												
Redhill	a				←					14 30			14 38												15 00
	d				14 10		14 14			14 30		14 34	14 39							14 41	14 44				15 00
Tonbridge 4	a												15 08												
Reigate	a						14 18					14 38													
Earlswood (Surrey)	d				14 12																				
Salfords	d				14 16																				
Horley 4	d				14 19					14 36											14 51				
Gatwick Airport 10	✈ a	14 18		14 22	14 23	14 25		←	14 30	14 39						14 40	14 45	14 48		14 50	14 55	14 55		15 00	15 08
	d	14 19		14 28	14 24	14 26		14 28		14 40						14 41		14 49			14 55	14 56			15 09
Three Bridges 15	a			→	14 29			14 33		14 44						14 45					15 00				15 14
	d				14 30			14 33		14 45						14 45					15 01				15 14
Crawley	d				14 33					14 48											15 04				15 18
Ifield	d				14 36																15 07				
Faygate	d																								
Littlehaven	d				14 42																15 13				
Horsham 4	a				14 47					14 56											15 16				15 26
Balcombe	d																								
Haywards Heath 3	a	14 30				14 36		14 42								14 54		15 00				15 06			
	d	14 34	14 37			14 38		14 46								14 55		15 04	15 07			15 08			
Wivelsfield 4	d							14 50								14 59			15 11						
Lewes 4	a	14 48																	15 22						
Burgess Hill 4	d							14 52								15 01		15 09							
Hassocks 4	d							14 55							←	15 04									
Preston Park	d							15 02							15 02	15 11									
Hove 2	a		14 51					→										15 21							
Brighton 10	a					14 54								14 58	15 07	15 17						15 24			

For general notes see front of timetable
For details of catering facilities see Directory of Train Operators

§ It is unknown, at the time of going to press, when this station will open. For further details contact National Rail Enquiries 08457-484950 or see local publicity.

A ⊥ to Lewes
B To Portsmouth Harbour (Table 188) and to Bognor Regis (Table 188)
C To Tunbridge Wells (Table 206)
D ⊥ to Haywards Heath
E From Tunbridge Wells (Table 209)
G To Southampton Central (Table 188) and to Bognor Regis (Table 188)

Table 186

Saturdays

Watford Junction, Bedford and London → Brighton

Network Diagram - see first page of Table 186

		LO	SN	SN	FC	GX	SN		SN	SN	FC	GW	SN	GX	SN	LO	GW	SE	SN	SN	FC	GX	SN		GW
			1	1 ◇	1	1	1		1	1	1	1	1	1	1		1	13	1 ◇	1	1	1	1		1
							A								B			C					D		
				🛒			🛒								🛒				🛒				🛒		
London Victoria 15	⊖ d			14 36		14 45	14 47							15 00	15 02				15 06			15 15	15 17		
Watford Junction	d								14 11																
Harrow & Wealdstone	⊖ d								14 17																
Wembley Central	d																								
Willesden Jn. High Level	d	14 38														15 08									
Shepherds Bush §	⊖ d																								
Kensington Olympia	⊖ d	14 47							14 42							15 17									
West Brompton	⊖ d	14 49							14 45							15 19									
Imperial Wharf §	d																								
Clapham Junction 10	d	14a59		14 42			14 53		14 54						15 08	15a29			15 12				15 23		
Bedford 7	d				13 25						13 40										13 55				
Luton 10	d				13 49						14 04										14 19				
Luton Airport Parkway 7	✈ d				13 51						14 06										14 21				
St Albans City	d				14 03						14 18										14 34				
St Pancras International 15	⊖ d				14 24						14 39										14 54				
Farringdon 3	⊖ d				14 29						14 44										14 59				
City Thameslink 3	d				14 31						14 46										15 01				
London Blackfriars 3	⊖ d				14 35						14 50										15 05				
London Bridge 4	⊖ d		14 33		14 41						14 56							15 03			15 11				
Norwood Junction 2	d		14 46															15 16							
East Croydon	🚋 a		14 49	14 52	14 54		15 03		15 07		15 09				15 18			15 19	15 22		15 24		15 33		
	d		14 51	14 52	14 54		15 03		15 07		15 09				15 18			15 21	15 22		15 24		15 33		
Purley 4	d		14 57															15 26							
Coulsdon South	d		15 00															15 30							
Merstham	d		15 06															15 35							
Redhill	a		15 09							⟵					15 30			15 38							15 41
	d		15 10							15 10		15 14			15 30		15 34	15 39							
Tonbridge 4	a		⟶															16 08							
Reigate	a											15 18					15 38								
Earlswood (Surrey)	d									15 12															
Salfords	d									15 16															
Horley 4	d									15 19					15 36										
Gatwick Airport 10	✈ a				15 10	15 15	15 18		15 22	15 23	15 25		⟵	15 30	15 39						15 40	15 45	15 48		15 50
	d				15 11		15 19		15 28	15 24	15 26		15 28		15 40						15 41		15 49		
Three Bridges 15	a				15 15				⟶	15 29			15 33		15 44						15 45				
	d				15 15					15 30			15 33		15 45						15 45				
Crawley	d									15 33					15 48										
Ifield	d									15 36															
Faygate	d																								
Littlehaven	d									15 42															
Horsham 4	a									15 47					15 56										
Balcombe	d				15 21																				
Haywards Heath 3	a				15 26		15 30				15 36		15 42								15 54		16 00		
	d				15 27		15 34	15 37			15 38		15 46								15 55		16 04	16 07	
Wivelsfield 4	d				15 31								15 50								15 59			16 11	
Lewes 4	a						15 48																	16 22	
Burgess Hill 4	d				15 33								15 52								16 01		16 09		
Hassocks 4	d				15 36								15 55							⟵	16 04				
Preston Park	d				15 43								16 02							16 02	16 11				
Hove 2	a							15 51					⟶										16 21		
Brighton 10	a			15 27	15 49						15 54								15 58	16 07	16 17				

For general notes see front of timetable
For details of catering facilities see Directory of Train Operators

§ It is unknown, at the time of going to press, when this station will open. For further details contact National Rail Enquiries 08457-484950 or see local publicity.

A 🛒 to Lewes
B To Portsmouth Harbour (Table 188) and to Bognor Regis (Table 188)
C To Tunbridge Wells (Table 206)
D 🛒 to Haywards Heath

Table 186

Watford Junction, Bedford and London → Brighton

Network Diagram - see first page of Table 186

		SE 88	FC	GX	SN	LO	SN	SN	FC	GX	SN	SN	SN	FC	GW	SN	GX	SN	GW	SE 13	SN	SN	FC
		1	1	1	1		1	1◇	1	1	1	1	1	1	1	1	1	1	1		1◇	1	1
		A			B			🛒			C 🛒							D 🛒		E	🛒		
London Victoria [15]	⊖ d			15 30	15 32			15 36		15 45	15 47						16 00	16 02			16 06		
Watford Junction	d											15 11											
Harrow & Wealdstone	⊖ d											15 17											
Wembley Central	d																						
Willesden Jn. High Level	d					15 38																	
Shepherds Bush §	⊖ d																						
Kensington Olympia	⊖ d					15 47						15 42											
West Brompton	⊖ d					15 49						15 45											
Imperial Wharf §	d																						
Clapham Junction [10]	d				15 38	15a59		15 42			15 53	15 54						16 08			16 12		
Bedford [7]	d		14 10						14 25					14 40									14 55
Luton [10]	d		14 34						14 49					15 04									15 19
Luton Airport Parkway [7]	✈ d		14 36						14 51					15 06									15 21
St Albans City	d		14 48						15 03					15 18									15 33
St Pancras International [15]	⊖ d		15 09						15 24					15 39									15 54
Farringdon [3]	⊖ d		15 14						15 29					15 44									15 59
City Thameslink [3]	d		15 16						15 31					15 46									16 01
London Blackfriars [3]	⊖ d		15 20						15 35					15 50									16 05
London Bridge [4]	⊖ d		15 26				15 33		15 41					15 56						16 03			16 11
Norwood Junction [2]	d						15 46													16 16			
East Croydon	⛴ a		15 39		15 48		15 49	15 52	15 54		16 03	16 07		16 09				16 18		16 19	16 22		16 24
	d		15 39		15 48		15 51	15 52	15 54		16 03	16 07		16 09				16 18		16 21	16 22		16 24
Purley [4]	d						15 57													16 26			
Coulsdon South	d						16 00													16 30			
Merstham	d						16 06													16 35			
Redhill	a				16 00		16 09						←					16 30		16 38			
	d	15 44			16 00		16 10						16 10		16 14			16 30	16 34	16 39			
Tonbridge [4]	a						→													17 08			
Reigate	a														16 18				16 38				
Earlswood (Surrey)	d												16 12										
Salfords	d												16 16										
Horley [4]	d	15 51											16 19					16 36					
Gatwick Airport [10]	✈ a	15 55	15 55	16 00	16 08				16 10	16 15	16 18	16 22	16 23	16 25		←	16 30	16 39					16 40
	d	15 55	15 56		16 09				16 11		16 19	16 28	16 24	16 26		16 28		16 40					16 41
Three Bridges [15]	a	16 00			16 14				16 15			→	16 29			16 33		16 44					16 45
	d	16 01			16 14				16 15				16 30			16 33		16 45					16 45
Crawley	d	16 04			16 18								16 33					16 48					
Ifield	d	16 07											16 36										
Faygate	d																						
Littlehaven	d	16 13											16 42										
Horsham [4]	a	16 16			16 26								16 47					16 56					
Balcombe	d								16 21														
Haywards Heath [3]	a		16 06						16 26		16 30			16 36		16 42							16 54
	d		16 08						16 27		16 34 / 16 37			16 38		16 46							16 55
Wivelsfield [4]	d								16 31							16 50							16 59
Lewes [4]	a										16 48												
Burgess Hill [4]	d								16 33							16 52							17 01
Hassocks [4]	d								16 36							16 55						←	17 04
Preston Park	d								16 43							17 02						17 02	17 11
Hove [2]	a										16 51					→							
Brighton [10]	a		16 24					16 27	16 49					16 54							16 58	17 07	17 17

For general notes see front of timetable
For details of catering facilities see Directory of Train Operators

§ It is unknown, at the time of going to press, when this station will open. For further details contact National Rail Enquiries 08457-484950 or see local publicity.

A From Tunbridge Wells (Table 209)
B To Southampton Central (Table 188) and to Bognor Regis (Table 188)
C 🛒 to Lewes
D To Portsmouth Harbour (Table 188) and to Bognor Regis (Table 188)
E To Tunbridge Wells (Table 206)

Watford Junction, Bedford and London → Brighton

Network Diagram - see first page of Table 186

Station		GX	SN	SN	GW	SE	FC	GX	LO	SN	SN	SN	FC	GX	SN	SN	SN	SN	FC	GW	SN	GX	LO	SN
		1	1 A 🛒		1	88 1 B	1	1		1 C	1	1 ◇ 🛒	1	1	1 D 🛒		1	1	1	1	1	1		1 E 🛒
London Victoria 15 ⊖	d	16 15	16 17					16 30		16 32		16 36		16 45	16 47							17 00		17 02
Watford Junction	d																16 11							
Harrow & Wealdstone ⊖	d																16 17							
Wembley Central	d																							
Willesden Jn. High Level	d								16 08														16 38	
Shepherds Bush § ⊖	d																							
Kensington Olympia ⊖	d								16 17								16 42						16 47	
West Brompton ⊖	d								16 19								16 45						16 49	
Imperial Wharf §	d																							
Clapham Junction 10	d		16 23						16a29	16 38		16 42			16 53		16 54						16a59	17 08
Bedford 7	d						15 10						15 25						15 40					
Luton 10	d						15 34						15 49						16 04					
Luton Airport Parkway 7 ✈	d						15 36						15 51						16 06					
St Albans City	d						15 48						16 03						16 18					
St Pancras International 15 ⊖	d						16 09						16 24						16 39					
Farringdon 3 ⊖	d						16 14						16 29						16 44					
City Thameslink 3	d						16 16						16 31						16 46					
London Blackfriars 3 ⊖	d						16 20						16 35						16 50					
London Bridge 4 ⊖	d						16 26				16 33		16 41						16 56					
Norwood Junction 2	d										16 46													
East Croydon 🚋	a		16 33				16 39			16 48	16 49	16 52	16 54		17 03		17 07		17 09					17 18
	d		16 33				16 39			16 48	16 51	16 52	16 54		17 03		17 07		17 09					17 18
Purley 4	d										16 57													
Coulsdon South	d										17 00													
Merstham	d										17 06													
Redhill	a									17 00	17 09							←						17 30
	d				16 41	16 44				17 00	17 10							17 10		17 14				17 30
Tonbridge 4	a										→									17 18				
Reigate	a																							
Earlswood (Surrey)	d																	17 12						
Salfords	d																	17 16						
Horley 4	d					16 51												17 19						17 36
Gatwick Airport 10 ✈	a	16 45	16 48		16 50	16 55	16 55	17 00		17 08			17 10	17 15	17 18		17 22	17 23	17 25		←	17 30		17 39
	d		16 49			16 55	16 56			17 09			17 11		17 19		17 28	17 24	17 26		17 28			17 40
Three Bridges 15	a					17 00				17 14			17 15				→	17 29			17 33			17 44
	d					17 01				17 14			17 15					17 30			17 33			17 45
Crawley	d					17 04				17 18								17 33						17 48
Ifield	d					17 07												17 36						
Faygate	d																							
Littlehaven	d					17 13												17 42						
Horsham 4	a					17 16				17 26								17 47						17 56
Balcombe	d												17 21											
Haywards Heath 3	a		17 00				17 06						17 26		17 30				17 36		17 42			
	d		17 04	17 07			17 08						17 27		17 34	17 37			17 38		17 46			
Wivelsfield 4	d			17 11									17 31								17 50			
Lewes 4	a			17 22											17 52									
Burgess Hill 4	d		17 09										17 33								17 52			
Hassocks 4	d												17 36								17 55			
Preston Park	d												17 43								18 02			
Hove 2	a		17 21													17 51					→			
Brighton 10	a						17 24					17 27	17 49						17 54					

For general notes see front of timetable
For details of catering facilities see Directory of Train Operators

§ It is unknown, at the time of going to press, when this station will open. For further details contact National Rail Enquiries 08457-484950 or see local publicity.

A 🛒 to Haywards Heath
B From Tunbridge Wells (Table 209)
C To Southampton Central (Table 188) and to Bognor Regis (Table 188)
D 🛒 to Lewes
E To Portsmouth Harbour (Table 188) and to Bognor Regis (Table 188)

Table 186

Saturdays

Watford Junction, Bedford and London → Brighton

Network Diagram - see first page of Table 186

		GW	SE 13	SN	SN	FC		GX	SN		GW	SE 88	FC	GX	LO	SN	SN	SN	FC	GX	SN		SN	LO	SN
		1	A	1 ◇ 🛒	1	1		1	1 B 🛒		1	1 C	1	1		1 D	1	1 ◇ 🛒	1	1	1 E 🛒		1		1
London Victoria 15 ⊖	d			17 06				17 15	17 17					17 30		17 32		17 36		17 45	17 47				
Watford Junction	d																								
Harrow & Wealdstone ⊖	d																						17 11		
Wembley Central	d																						17 17		
Willesden Jn. High Level	d																								
Shepherds Bush § ⊖	d														17 08									17 38	
Kensington Olympia ⊖	d																								
West Brompton ⊖	d														17 17								17 42	17 47	
Imperial Wharf §	d														17 19								17 45	17 49	
Clapham Junction 10	d			17 12					17 23						17a29	17 38		17 42			17 53		17 54	17a59	
Bedford 7	d					15 55							16 10						16 25						
Luton 10	d					16 19							16 34						16 49						
Luton Airport Parkway 7 ✈	d					16 21							16 36						16 51						
St Albans City	d					16 33							16 48						17 03						
St Pancras International 15 ⊖	d					16 54							17 09						17 24						
Farringdon 3 ⊖	d					16 59							17 14						17 29						
City Thameslink 3	d					17 01							17 16						17 31						
London Blackfriars 3 ⊖	d					17 05							17 20						17 35						
London Bridge 4 ⊖	d		17 03			17 11							17 26				17 33		17 41						
Norwood Junction 2	d		17 16														17 46								
East Croydon	a		17 19	17 22		17 24			17 33				17 39			17 48	17 49	17 52	17 54		18 03		18 07		
	d		17 21	17 22		17 24			17 33				17 39			17 48	17 51	17 52	17 54		18 03		18 07		
Purley 4	d		17 26														17 57								
Coulsdon South	d		17 30														18 00								
Merstham	d		17 35														18 06								
Redhill	a		17 38													18 00	18 09								←
	d	17 34	17 39								17 41	17 44				18 00	18 10								18 10
Tonbridge 4	a		18 08														→								
Reigate	a	17 38																							
Earlswood (Surrey)	d																								18 12
Salfords	d																								18 16
Horley 4	d											17 51													18 19
Gatwick Airport 10 ✈	a					17 40		17 45	17 48		17 50	17 55	17 55	18 00		18 08			18 10	18 15	18 18		18 22		18 23
	d					17 41			17 49			17 55	17 56			18 09			18 11		18 19		18 28		18 24
Three Bridges 15	a					17 45						18 00				18 14			18 15				→		18 29
	d					17 45						18 01				18 14			18 15						18 30
Crawley	d											18 04				18 18									18 33
Ifield	d											18 07													18 36
Faygate	d																								
Littlehaven	d											18 13													18 42
Horsham 4	a											18 16				18 26									18 47
Balcombe	d																		18 21						
Haywards Heath 3	a					17 54			18 00				18 06						18 26		18 30				
	d					17 55			18 04	18 07			18 08						18 27		18 34	18 37			
Wivelsfield 4	d					17 59				18 11									18 31						
Lewes 4	a									18 22											18 52				
Burgess Hill 4	d					18 01			18 09										18 33						
Hassocks 4	d				←	18 04													18 36						
Preston Park	d				18 02	18 11													18 43						
Hove 2	a								18 21													18 51			
Brighton 10	a			17 58	18 07	18 17							18 24					18 27	18 49						

For general notes see front of timetable
For details of catering facilities see Directory of Train Operators

§ It is unknown, at the time of going to press, when this station will open. For further details contact National Rail Enquiries 08457-484950 or see local publicity.

A To Tunbridge Wells (Table 206)
B 🛒 to Haywards Heath
C From Tunbridge Wells (Table 209)
D To Southampton Central (Table 188) and to Bognor Regis (Table 188)
E 🛒 to Lewes

Table 186

Watford Junction, Bedford and London → Brighton

Saturdays

Network Diagram - see first page of Table 186

Station		FC	GW	SN	GX	SE 88	SN	GW		SE 13	SN	SN	FC	GX	SN		GW	SE 88	FC	GX	LO	SN	SN	SN	FC
		1	1	1	1		1	1			1 ◇	1	1	1	1		1	1	1	1		1	1	1 ◇	1
							A 🛒			B	🛒				C 🛒			D				E		🛒	
London Victoria 15 ⊖	d				18 00		18 02				18 06			18 15	18 17					18 30		18 32		18 36	
Watford Junction	d																								
Harrow & Wealdstone ⊖	d																								
Wembley Central	d																								
Willesden Jn. High Level	d																				18 08				
Shepherds Bush § ⊖	d																								
Kensington Olympia ⊖	d																				18 17				
West Brompton ⊖	d																				18 19				
Imperial Wharf §	d																								
Clapham Junction 10	d						18 08				18 12				18 23						18a29	18 38		18 42	
Bedford 7	d	16 40											16 55						17 10						17 25
Luton 10	d	17 04											17 19						17 34						17 49
Luton Airport Parkway 7 ✈	d	17 06											17 21						17 36						17 51
St Albans City	d	17 18											17 33						17 48						18 03
St Pancras International 15 ⊖	d	17 39											17 54						18 09						18 24
Farringdon 3 ⊖	d	17 44											17 59						18 14						18 29
City Thameslink 3	d	17 46											18 01						18 16						18 31
London Blackfriars 3 ⊖	d	17 50											18 05						18 20						18 35
London Bridge 4 ⊖	d	17 56								18 03			18 11						18 26				18 33		18 41
Norwood Junction 2	d									18 16													18 46		
East Croydon 🚊	a	18 09					18 18			18 19	18 22		18 24		18 33				18 39			18 48	18 49	18 52	18 54
	d	18 09					18 18			18 21	18 22		18 24		18 33				18 39			18 48	18 51	18 52	18 54
Purley 4	d									18 26													18 57		
Coulsdon South	d									18 30													19 00		
Merstham	d									18 35													19 06		
Redhill	a						18 30			18 38												19 00	19 09		
	d		18 14			18 27	18 30	18 34		18 39							18 41	18 44				19 00	19 10		
Tonbridge 4	a									19 08													→		
Reigate	a		18 18					18 38																	
Earlswood (Surrey)	d																								
Salfords	d																								
Horley 4	d						18 36											18 51							
Gatwick Airport 10 ✈	a	18 25		←	18 30	18 34	18 39						18 40	18 45	18 48		18 50	18 55	18 55	19 00		19 08			19 10
	d	18 26		18 28		18 35	18 40						18 41		18 49			18 55	18 56			19 09			19 11
Three Bridges 15	a			18 33		18 40	18 44						18 45					19 00				19 14			19 15
	d			18 33			18 45						18 45					19 01				19 14			19 15
Crawley	d						18 48											19 04				19 18			
Ifield	d																	19 07							
Faygate	d																								
Littlehaven	d																	19 13							
Horsham 4	a						18 56											19 16				19 26			
Balcombe	d																								19 21
Haywards Heath 3	a	18 36		18 42									18 54		19 00				19 06						19 26
	d	18 38		18 46									18 55		19 04	19 07			19 08						19 27
Wivelsfield 4	d			18 50									18 59			19 11									19 31
Lewes 4	a															19 22									
Burgess Hill 4	d			18 52									19 01		19 09										19 33
Hassocks 4	d			18 55								←	19 04												19 36
Preston Park	d			19 02								19 02	19 11												19 43
Hove 2	a			→											19 21										
Brighton 10	a	18 54									18 58	19 07	19 17						19 24					19 27	19 49

For general notes see front of timetable
For details of catering facilities see Directory of Train Operators

§ It is unknown, at the time of going to press, when this station will open. For further details contact National Rail Enquiries 08457-484950 or see local publicity.

A To Portsmouth Harbour (Table 188) and to Bognor Regis (Table 188)
B To Tunbridge Wells (Table 206)
C 🛒 to Haywards Heath
D From Tunbridge Wells (Table 209)
E To Southampton Central (Table 188) and to Bognor Regis (Table 188)

Table 186

Saturdays

Watford Junction, Bedford and London → Brighton

Network Diagram - see first page of Table 186

		GX	SN		SN	LO	SN	FC	GW	SN	GX	SE 88	SN	GW	SE 13	SN	SN	FC	SN	GX	SN		LO	GW
		1	1 A (trolley)		1		1	1	1	1	1		1 B (trolley)	1		1 ◇ (trolley)	1	1	1	1	1 C (trolley)			1
London Victoria [15]	⊖ d	18 45	18 47								19 00		19 02			19 06			19 10	19 15	19 17			
Watford Junction	d				18 11																			
Harrow & Wealdstone	⊖ d				18 17																			
Wembley Central	d																							
Willesden Jn. High Level	d					18 38																		
Shepherds Bush §	⊖ d																						19 08	
Kensington Olympia	⊖ d				18 42	18 47																		
West Brompton	⊖ d				18 45	18 49																	19 17	
Imperial Wharf §	d																						19 19	
Clapham Junction [10]	d		18 53		18 54	18a59							19 08			19 12			19 16		19 23		19a29	
Bedford [7]	d							17 40										17 50						
Luton [10]	d							18 04										18 14						
Luton Airport Parkway [7]	✈ d							18 06										18 16						
St Albans City	d							18 18										18 28						
St Pancras International [15]	⊖ d							18 39										18 54						
Farringdon [3]	⊖ d							18 44										18 59						
City Thameslink [3]	d							18 46										19 01						
London Blackfriars [3]	⊖ d							18 50										19 04						
London Bridge [4]	⊖ d							18 56							19 03			19 11						
Norwood Junction [2]	d														19 16									
East Croydon	a		19 03		19 07			19 09					19 18		19 19	19 22		19 24	19 28		19 33			
	d		19 03		19 07			19 09					19 18		19 21	19 22		19 24	19 28		19 33			
Purley [4]	d														19 25				19 33					
Coulsdon South	d														19 29				19 37					
Merstham	d														19 34				19 42					
Redhill	a						←						19 30		19 38				→					
	d						19 10		19 14			19 27	19 30	19 34	19 39									19 41
Tonbridge [4]	a														20 08									
Reigate	a								19 18					19 38										
Earlswood (Surrey)	d						19 12																	
Salfords	d						19 16																	
Horley [4]	d						19 19						19 36											
Gatwick Airport [10]	✈ a	19 15	19 18		19 22		19 23	19 25		←	19 30	19 34	19 39					19 40		19 45	19 48			19 50
	d		19 19		19 28		19 24	19 26		19 28		19 35	19 40					19 41			19 49			
Three Bridges [15]	a				→		19 28			19 33		19 40	19 44					19 45						
	d						19 30			19 33			19 45					19 45						
Crawley	d						19 33						19 48											
Ifield	d						19 36																	
Faygate	d																							
Littlehaven	d						19 42																	
Horsham [4]	a						19 47						19 56											
Balcombe	d																							
Haywards Heath [3]	a		19 30					19 36		19 42								19 54			20 00			
	d		19 34	19 37				19 38		19 46								19 55			20 04	20 07		
Wivelsfield [4]	d									19 50								19 59				20 11		
Lewes [4]	a		19 52																			20 22		
Burgess Hill [4]	d									19 52								20 01			20 09			
Hassocks [4]	d									19 55							←	20 04						
Preston Park	d									20 02							20 02	20 11						
Hove [2]	a			19 51						→											20 21			
Brighton [10]	a							19 54								19 58	20 07	20 17						

For general notes see front of timetable
For details of catering facilities see Directory of Train Operators

§ It is unknown, at the time of going to press, when this station will open. For further details contact National Rail Enquiries 08457-484950 or see local publicity.

A (trolley) to Lewes

B To Portsmouth Harbour (Table 188) and to Bognor Regis (Table 188)

C (trolley) to Haywards Heath

Watford Junction, Bedford and London → Brighton

Network Diagram - see first page of Table 186

		XC	SN	FC	GX	LO	SN	SN	XC	SN	FC	GX	SN	SN	SN	SN	FC	GW	SN	GX	SE 88	SN	LO	SN
		1 ◇	1	1	1		1	1	1 ◇	1 ◇	1	1	1		1	1	1	1	1	1		1		1 ◇
		A					B		A				C	C								D		
London Victoria 15 ⊖	d				19 30		19 32			19 36		19 45	19 47							20 00		20 02		20 06
Watford Junction	d														19 11									
Harrow & Wealdstone ⊖	d														19 17									
Wembley Central	d																							
Willesden Jn. High Level	d					19 38																	20 08	
Shepherds Bush § ⊖	d																							
Kensington Olympia ⊖	d	19 02				19 47									19 42								20 17	
West Brompton ⊖	d					19 49									19 45								20 19	
Imperial Wharf §	d																							
Clapham Junction 10	d					19a59	19 38			19 42			19 53		19 54							20 08	20a29	20 12
Bedford 7	d			18 10							18 20						18 40							
Luton 10	d			18 34							18 44						19 04							
Luton Airport Parkway 7 ✈	d			18 36							18 46						19 06							
St Albans City	d			18 48							18 58						19 18							
St Pancras International 15 ⊖	d			19 09							19 24						19 39							
Farringdon 3 ⊖	d			19 14							19 29						19 44							
City Thameslink 3	d			19 16							19 30						19 46							
London Blackfriars 3 ⊖	d			19 20							19 35						19 50							
London Bridge 4 ⊖	d			19 26				19 33			19 41						19 56							
Norwood Junction 2	d							19 46																
East Croydon	a	19 36		19 39			19 48	19 50		19 52	19 54		20 03		20 07		20 09					20 19		20 22
	d	19 37		19 39			19 48	19 51		19 52	19 54		20 03		20 07		20 09					20 19		20 22
Purley 4	d							19 57																
Coulsdon South	d		←					20 00																
Merstham	d		19 42					20 06																
Redhill	a		19 46				20 00	20 09								←						20 30		
	d		19 46				20 00	20 10								20 10		20 14			20 27	20 31		
Tonbridge 4	a							→																
Reigate	a																	20 18						
Earlswood (Surrey)	d															20 12								
Salfords	d															20 16								
Horley 4	d		19 52													20 19								
Gatwick Airport 10 ✈	a	19 52	19 55	19 56	20 00		20 08				20 10	20 15	20 18		20 22	20 23	20 25		←	20 30	20 34	20 38		
	d	19 53	19 56	19 56			20 09				20 11		20 19		20 28	20 24	20 26		20 28		20 35	20 39		
Three Bridges 15	a		20 01				20 14				20 15				→	20 29			20 33		20 40	20 44		
	d		20 01				20 14				20 15					20 33			20 33			20 44		
Crawley	d		20 05				20 18									20 36						20 48		
Ifield	d		20 07													20 39								
Faygate	d																							
Littlehaven	d		20 14													20 45								
Horsham 4	a		20 17				20 26									20 49						20 56		
Balcombe	d										20 21													
Haywards Heath 3	a	20 04		20 10					←	20 15	20 26		20 30				20 36		20 42					
	d	20 09		20 11					20 09	20 15	20 27		20 34	20 37			20 38		20 46					
Wivelsfield 4	d	→									20 31			20 41					20 50					
Lewes 4	a													20 54										
Burgess Hill 4	d										20 33		20 39						20 52					
Hassocks 4	d										20 36		20 42						20 55					
Preston Park	d										20 43		20 49						21 02					
Hove 2	a												20 53						→					
Brighton 10	a			20 26					20 28	20 29	20 49						20 54							20 58

For general notes see front of timetable
For details of catering facilities see Directory of Train Operators

§ It is unknown, at the time of going to press, when this station will open. For further details contact National Rail Enquiries 08457-484950 or see local publicity.

A from Birmingham New Street
B To Southampton Central (Table 188) and to Bognor Regis (Table 188)
C To Littlehampton (Table 188)
D To Portsmouth Harbour (Table 188) and to Bognor Regis (Table 188)

Saturdays

Watford Junction, Bedford and London → Brighton

Network Diagram - see first page of Table 186

		GW	SN	FC	SN	GX	SN		GW	SN	GX	SN	LO	SN	FC	GW	SN	GX	SN		SN	SN	GX	SE 88
		1	1	1	1		1		1	1	1	1		1 ◇	1	1	1		1		1	1	1	
											A	B							C					
London Victoria 15 ⊖	d				20 10	20 15	20 17				20 30	20 32		20 36			20 40	20 45	20 47				21 00	
Watford Junction	d																				20 13			
Harrow & Wealdstone ⊖	d																				20 19			
Wembley Central	d																							
Willesden Jn. High Level	d												20 38											
Shepherds Bush § ⊖	d																							
Kensington Olympia ⊖	d												20 47								20 42			
West Brompton ⊖	d												20 49								20 45			
Imperial Wharf §	d																							
Clapham Junction 10	d				20 16		20 23					20 38	21a00	20 42			20 46		20 53		20 54			
Bedford 7	d			18 50											19 20									
Luton 10	d			19 14											19 44									
Luton Airport Parkway 7 ✈	d			19 16											19 46									
St Albans City	d			19 28											19 58									
St Pancras International 15 ⊖	d			19 54											20 24									
Farringdon 3 ⊖	d			19 59											20 29									
City Thameslink 3	d			20 01											20 31									
London Blackfriars 3 ⊖	d			20 04											20 34									
London Bridge 4 ⊖	d			20 11											20 41									
Norwood Junction 2	d																							
East Croydon	a			20 24	20 28		20 33					20 48		20 52	20 54		20 58		21 03		21 07			
	d			20 24	20 28		20 33					20 48		20 52	20 54		20 58		21 03		21 07			
Purley 4	d				20 33												21 03							
Coulsdon South	d				20 37					←							21 06							
Merstham	d				20 42					20 42							21 12							
Redhill	a				→					20 46		21 00					21 15					←		
	d	20 34							20 41	20 46		21 00				21 14	21 16					21 16		21 27
Tonbridge 4	a																→							
Reigate	a	20 38														21 18								
Earlswood (Surrey)	d																					21 18		
Salfords	d																					21 22		
Horley 4	d									20 52												21 25		
Gatwick Airport 10 ✈	a			20 41		20 45	20 48		20 50	20 56	21 00	21 08			21 10			21 15	21 18		21 22	21 28	21 30	21 34
	d			20 41			20 49			20 57		21 09			21 11				21 19			21 29		21 35
Three Bridges 15	a			20 45						21 02		21 14			21 15							21 33		21 40
	d			20 45						21 02		21 14			21 15							21 36		
Crawley	d									21 06		21 18										21 39		
Ifield	d									21 08												21 42		
Faygate	d																							
Littlehaven	d									21 15												21 48		
Horsham 4	a									21 18		21 26										21 52		
Balcombe	d			20 51																				
Haywards Heath 3	a			20 58			21 01							21 15	21 24				21 30					
	d			20 58			21 05	21 07						21 15	21 26				21 34	21 37				
Wivelsfield 4	d			21 02				21 11							21 30					21 41				
Lewes 4	a							21 22												21 54				
Burgess Hill 4	d			21 04			21 10								21 32				21 39					
Hassocks 4	d		←	21 08											21 35				21 42					
Preston Park	d		21 02	21 15											21 42				21 49					
Hove 2	a						21 21												21 53					
Brighton 10	a		21 07	21 20										21 30	21 48									

For general notes see front of timetable
For details of catering facilities see Directory of Train Operators

§ It is unknown, at the time of going to press, when this station will open. For further details contact National Rail Enquiries 08457-484950 or see local publicity.

A Operating Company SN from 28 June

B To Southampton Central (Table 188) and to Bognor Regis (Table 188)

C To Littlehampton (Table 188)

Table 186

Saturdays

Watford Junction, Bedford and London → Brighton

Network Diagram - see first page of Table 186

		XC	LO	SN	SN	SN	FC	SN	GX	XC	SN	SN	GW	SN	GW	GX	SN	LO	SN	FC	SN	GX	SN	SN
		1 ◇		1 ◇	1 ◇	1 ◇	1	1		1 ◇	1		1	1	1	1	1		1 ◇	1	1		1	
		A								A	B						C							
		⊡								⊡														
London Victoria 15	⊖ d			21 02	21 06			21 10	21 15		21 17					21 30	21 32		21 36		21 40	21 45	21 47	
Watford Junction	d																							
Harrow & Wealdstone	⊖ d																							
Wembley Central	d																							
Willesden Jn. High Level	d		21 08															21 38						
Shepherds Bush §	⊖ d																							
Kensington Olympia	⊖ d		21 17															21 47						
West Brompton	⊖ d		21 19															21 49						
Imperial Wharf §	d																							
Clapham Junction 10	d		21a29	21 08	21 12			21 16			21 23						21 38	21a59	21 42		21 46		21 53	
Bedford 7	d						19 50													20 20				
Luton 10	d						20 14													20 44				
Luton Airport Parkway 7	✈ d						20 16													20 46				
St Albans City	d						20 28													20 58				
St Pancras International 15	⊖ d						20 54													21 24				
Farringdon 3	⊖ d						20 59													21 29				
City Thameslink 3	d						21 01																	
London Blackfriars 3	⊖ d						21 04													21 34				
London Bridge 4	⊖ d						21 11													21 41				
Norwood Junction 2	d																							
East Croydon	⇌ a			21 18	21 22		21 24	21 28			21 33						21 48		21 52	21 54	21 58		22 03	
	d			21 18	21 22		21 24	21 28			21 33						21 48		21 52	21 54	21 58		22 03	
Purley 4	d							21 33													22 03			
Coulsdon South	d							21 37						←							22 06			
Merstham	d							21 42						21 42							22 12			
Redhill	a	21 28		21 30				→		←				21 46			21 59				22 15			
	d	21 34		21 31						21 34			21 36	21 46	21 49		22 00				22 16			
Tonbridge 4	a	→																			→			
Reigate	a												21 40											
Earlswood (Surrey)	d																							
Salfords	d																							
Horley 4	d													21 52										
Gatwick Airport 10	✈ a			21 38		←	21 40		21 45	21 47	21 48			21 55	21 59	22 00	22 08			22 10		22 15	22 18	
	d			21 39		21 39	21 41				21 49			21 56			22 09			22 11			22 19	
Three Bridges 15	a			→		21 44	21 45				21 53			22 00			22 14			22 15				
	d					21 44	21 45				21 53			22 01			22 14			22 15				
Crawley	d													22 05			22 18							
Ifield	d													22 07										
Faygate	d																							
Littlehaven	d													22 14										
Horsham 4	a													22 17			22 26							
Balcombe	d						21 51																	
Haywards Heath 3	a				21 45	21 52	21 58				22 02								22 15	22 24			22 30	
	d				21 45	21 53	21 58				22 06	22 08							22 15	22 26			22 34	22 37
Wivelsfield 4	d					21 57	22 02					22 12								22 30			22 38	
Lewes 4	a											22 23											22 51	
Burgess Hill 4	d					21 59	22 04				22 11									22 32				
Hassocks 4	d					22 02	22 08													22 35				
Preston Park	d					22 09	22 15													22 42				
Hove 2	a										22 22													22 51
Brighton 10	a				22 00	22 15	22 20												22 30	22 48				

For general notes see front of timetable
For details of catering facilities see
Directory of Train Operators

§ It is unknown, at the time of going to press, when this station will open. For further details contact National Rail Enquiries 08457-484950 or see local publicity.

A from Birmingham New Street
B To Eastbourne (Table 189)
C To Portsmouth & Southsea (Table 188)

Saturdays

Watford Junction, Bedford and London → Brighton

Network Diagram - see first page of Table 186

		SN	SN	GX	SE 88	SN	LO	SN	SN	FC	SN	GX	SN	GW	SN	GX	GW	SN	LO	SN	FC	SN	GX
		1	1	1		1 ◇		1 ◇	1 ◇	1	1		1	1	1	1	1	1		1 ◇	1	1	
																		A					
London Victoria 15	⊖ d			22 00		22 02		22 06			22 10	22 15	22 17			22 30		22 32		22 36		22 40	22 45
Watford Junction	d	21 13																					
Harrow & Wealdstone	⊖ d	21 19																					
Wembley Central	d																						
Willesden Jn. High Level	d						22 08												22 38				
Shepherds Bush §	⊖ d																						
Kensington Olympia	⊖ d	21 42					22 17												22 47				
West Brompton	⊖ d	21 45					22 19												22 49				
Imperial Wharf §	d																						
Clapham Junction 10	d	21 54				22 08	22a29	22 12			22 16		22 23					22 38	22a59	22 42		22 46	
Bedford 7	d									20 50											21 20		
Luton 10	d									21 14											21 44		
Luton Airport Parkway 7	✈ d									21 16											21 46		
St Albans City	d									21 28											21 58		
St Pancras International 15	⊖ d									21 54											22 24		
Farringdon 3	⊖ d									21 59											22 29		
City Thameslink 3	d																						
London Blackfriars 3	⊖ d									22 04											22 34		
London Bridge 4	⊖ d									22 11											22 41		
Norwood Junction 2	d																						
East Croydon	a	22 07				22 18		22 22		22 24	22 28		22 33					22 48		22 52	22 54	22 58	
	d	22 07				22 18		22 22		22 24	22 28		22 33					22 48		22 52	22 54	22 58	
Purley 4	d										22 33											23 03	
Coulsdon South	d										22 37				←							23 07	
Merstham	d										22 42				22 42							23 12	
Redhill	a		←			22 30					→				22 46			23 00				23 16	
	d		22 16		22 27	22 31								22 33	22 46		22 56	23 01				23 16	
Tonbridge 4	a																					→	
Reigate	a													22 38									
Earlswood (Surrey)	d		22 18																				
Salfords	d		22 22																				
Horley 4	d		22 25												22 52								
Gatwick Airport 10	✈ a	22 23	22 28	22 30	22 34	22 38			←	22 40		22 45	22 50		22 55	23 00	23 03	23 08			23 10		23 15
	d		22 29		22 35	22 39			22 39	22 41			22 51		22 56			23 09			23 11		
Three Bridges 15	a		22 33		22 41	→			22 44	22 45			22 55		23 00			23 14			23 15		
	d		22 36						22 44	22 45			22 55		23 01			23 15			23 15		
Crawley	d		22 39												23 04			23 18					
Ifield	d		22 42												23 07								
Faygate	d																						
Littlehaven	d		22 48												23 13								
Horsham 4	a		22 52												23 16			23 26					
Balcombe	d									22 51													
Haywards Heath 3	a							22 45	22 52	22 58			23 04							23 15	23 24		
	d							22 45	22 53	22 58			23 04							23 15	23 26		
Wivelsfield 4	d								22 57	23 02											23 30		
Lewes 4	a																						
Burgess Hill 4	d								22 59	23 04			23 10								23 32		
Hassocks 4	d								23 02	23 08											23 35		
Preston Park	d								23 09	23 15											23 42		
Hove 2	a												23 21										
Brighton 10	a							23 00	23 15	23 20										23 30	23 48		

For general notes see front of timetable
For details of catering facilities see
Directory of Train Operators

§ It is unknown, at the time of going to press, when this station will open. For further details contact National Rail Enquiries 08457-484950 or see local publicity.

A To Chichester (Table 188)

Table 186

Saturdays

Watford Junction, Bedford and London → Brighton

Network Diagram - see first page of Table 186

		SN 1		SN 1	GX 1	SN 1	GW 1	SN 1 ◇	LO	SN 1 ◇	SN 1 ◇	FC 1	SN 1	GX	SN 1	SN 1	GX 1	SN 1	FC	GX		SN 1	FC	FC 1	SN 1
London Victoria 15 ⊖	d	22 47			23 00			23 02		23 06			23 10	23 15	23 17		23 30	23 32		23 45		23 47			
Watford Junction	d					22 11																			23 13
Harrow & Wealdstone ⊖	d					22 17																			23 19
Wembley Central	d																								
Willesden Jn. High Level	d								23 08																
Shepherds Bush § ⊖	d																								
Kensington Olympia ⊖	d					22 42			23 17																23 42
West Brompton ⊖	d					22 45			23 19																23 45
Imperial Wharf §	d																								
Clapham Junction 10	d	22 53				22a52		23 08	23a29	23 12			23 16		23 23			23 38				23 53			23a53
Bedford 7	d											21 50							22 10				22 40	23 10	
Luton 10	d											22 14							22 34				23 04	23 34	
Luton Airport Parkway 7 ✈	d											22 16							22 36				23 06	23 36	
St Albans City	d											22 28							22 48				23 18	23 48	
St Pancras International 15 ⊖	d											22 54							23 24				23 54	00 24	
Farringdon 3 ⊖	d											22 59							23 29				23 59	00 29	
City Thameslink 3	d																								
London Blackfriars 3 ⊖	d											23 04							23 34				00 04	00 34	
London Bridge 4 ⊖	d											23 11							23 41				00 16	00 41	
Norwood Junction 2	d																								
East Croydon	a	23 03						23 18		23 22		23 24	23 28		23 33			23 52	23 56			00 06	00 29	00 56	
	d	23 03						23 18		23 22		23 24	23 28		23 33			23 52	23 57			00 06	00 29	00 57	
Purley 4	d												23 33									00 12			
Coulsdon South	d												23 37									00 15			
Merstham	d												23 42									00 21			
Redhill	a			←				23 30					23 46			←		00 03				00 24			
	d			23 16			23 29	23 31					23 46			23 46		00 05				00 25			
Tonbridge 4	a												→												
Reigate	a						23 33																		
Earlswood (Surrey)	d			23 19												23 49									
Salfords	d			23 22												23 52									
Horley 4	d			23 26												23 56						00 31			
Gatwick Airport 10 ✈	a	23 18		23 28	23 30			23 38			←	23 40		23 45	23 50	23 58	00 05	00 13	00 17	00 20		00 33	00 47	01 16	
	d	23 19		23 29				23 39			23 39	23 41			23 51	23 59		00 14	00 18			00 34	00 47	01 17	
Three Bridges 15	a			23 34				→			23 44	23 45			23 55	00 04		00 18	00 24			00 39	00 54	01 24	
	d			23 38							23 44	23 45			23 56	00 04		00 19				00 39			
Crawley	d			23 41												00 07						00 42			
Ifield	d			23 44												00 10						00 45			
Faygate	d																								
Littlehaven	d			23 50												00 16						00 51			
Horsham 4	a			23 53												00 19						00 54			
Balcombe	d											23 53						00 27							
Haywards Heath 3	a	23 30								23 45	23 52	23 58			00 04			00 34							
	d	23 34	23 37							23 45	23 53	23 58			00 05			00 34							
Wivelsfield 4	d	23 38									23 57	00 02						00 38							
Lewes 4	a	23 51																							
Burgess Hill 4	d										23 59	00 04			00 10			00 40							
Hassocks 4	d										00 02	00 08						00 44							
Preston Park	d										00 09	00 15						00 51							
Hove 2	a		23 51												00 21										
Brighton 10	a									23 59	00 15	00 20						00 55							

For general notes see front of timetable
For details of catering facilities see
Directory of Train Operators

§ It is unknown, at the time of going to press, when this station will open. For further details contact National Rail Enquiries 08457-484950 or see local publicity.

Table 186

Sundays

Watford Junction, Bedford and London → Brighton

Network Diagram - see first page of Table 186

Station		SN 1 ◇	FC 1	SN 1	SN 1	SN 1	GW 1	SN 1	FC	SN 1	GX 1	SN 1 A	FC	SN 1	GW 1	FC 1	GX 1	SN 1	SN 1	SN 1	GX	SN 1	GX 1	GX 1
London Victoria 15 ⊖	d	23p02		23p10	23p17			23p32		23p47	00 01	00 05		00 14			00 30	01 00	02 00	03 00	03 30	04 00	04 30	05 00
Watford Junction	d																							
Harrow & Wealdstone ⊖	d																							
Wembley Central	d																							
Willesden Jn. High Level	d																							
Shepherds Bush § ⊖	d																							
Kensington Olympia ⊖	d																							
West Brompton ⊖	d																							
Imperial Wharf §	d																							
Clapham Junction 10	d	23p08		23p16	23p23			23p38		23p53		00 11		00 20				01 08	02 08	03 08		04 08		
Bedford 7	d		21p50						22p10				22p40			23p10								
Luton 10	d		22p14						22p34				23p04			23p34								
Luton Airport Parkway 7 ✈	d		22p16						22p36				23p06			23p36								
St Albans City	d		22p28						22p48				23p18			23p48								
St Pancras International 15 ⊖	d		22p54						23p24				23p54			00 24								
Farringdon 3 ⊖	d		22p59						23p29				23p59			00 29								
City Thameslink 3	d																							
London Blackfriars 3 ⊖	d		23p04						23p34				00 04			00 34								
London Bridge 4 ⊖	d		23p11						23p41				00 16			00 41								
Norwood Junction 2	d																							
East Croydon	a	23p18	23p24	23p28	23p33			23p52	23p56	00 06		00 24	00 29	00 32		00 56		01 21	02 21	03 21		04 21		
	d	23p18	23p24	23p28	23p33			23p52	23p57	00 06		00 25	00 29	00 33		00 57		01 22	02 22	03 22		04 22		
Purley 4	d			23p33						00 12				00 38				01 27	02 27	03 27		04 27		
Coulsdon South	d			23p37						00 15				00 41										
Merstham	d			23p42						00 21				00 47										
Redhill	a	23p30		23p46		←		00 03		00 24				00 50										
	d	23p31		23p46		23p46	00 03	00 05		00 25				00 51	00 54									
Tonbridge 4	a			↳																				
Reigate	a																							
Earlswood (Surrey)	d					23p49																		
Salfords	d					23p52																		
Horley 4	d					23p56				00 31				00 57				01 43	02 42	03 42		04 43		
Gatwick Airport 10 ✈	a	23p38	23p40		23p50	23p58	00 10	00 13	00 17	00 33	00 35	00 42	00 47	00 59	01 02	01 16	01 20	01 45	02 44	03 44	04 05	04 45	05 05	05 35
	d	23p39	23p41		23p51	23p59		00 14	00 18	00 34		00 43	00 47	01 00		01 17		01 47	02 46	03 46		04 47		
Three Bridges 15	a	23p44	23p45		23p55	00 04		00 18	00 24	00 39		00 48	00 54	01 05		01 24		01 51	03 00	04 00		04 54		
	d	23p44	23p45		23p56	00 04		00 19		00 39		00 48						01 52				04 55		
Crawley	d					00 07				00 42														
Ifield	d					00 10				00 45														
Faygate	d																							
Littlehaven	d					00 16				00 51														
Horsham 4	a					00 19				00 54														
Balcombe	d		23p53					00 27																
Haywards Heath 3	a	23p52	23p58		00 04			00 34				01 00												
	d	23p53	23p58		00 05			00 34				01 03 / 01 06												
Wivelsfield 4	d	23p57	00 02					00 38																
Lewes 4	a											01 20												
Burgess Hill 4	d	23p59	00 04		00 10			00 40																
Hassocks 4	d	00 02	00 08					00 44																
Preston Park	d	00 09	00 15					00 51																
Hove 2	a				00 21							01s25												
Brighton 10	a	00 15	00 20					00 55				01s17						02 20				05 21		

For general notes see front of timetable
For details of catering facilities see Directory of Train Operators

§ It is unknown, at the time of going to press, when this station will open. For further details contact National Rail Enquiries 08457-484950 or see local publicity.

A To Eastbourne (Table 189)

Table 186

Sundays

Watford Junction, Bedford and London → Brighton

Network Diagram - see first page of Table 186

		SN	GX	GX		GX	SN	SN	GX	GX	GW	SN	GX	SN	GX	GW	GX	GW	SE	SN	FC	SN	GX	GX	SN
		1		1			1	1 ◇	1	1	1	1	1	1 ◇	1	1	1	1	88	1	1		1	1	1 ◇
												A								B		C			
London Victoria 15	⊖ d	05 02	05 15	05 30		05 45		05 47	06 00	06 15			06 30	06 32	06 45		07 00			07 02			07 15	07 30	07 32
Watford Junction	d																								
Harrow & Wealdstone	⊖ d																								
Wembley Central	d																								
Willesden Jn. High Level	d																								
Shepherds Bush §	⊖ d																								
Kensington Olympia	⊖ d																								
West Brompton	⊖ d																								
Imperial Wharf §	d																								
Clapham Junction 10	d	05 08						05 53						06 38						07 08					07 38
Bedford 7	d																				05 40				
Luton 10	d																				06 04				
Luton Airport Parkway 7	✈ d																				06 06				
St Albans City	d																				06 18				
St Pancras International 15	⊖ d																				06 54				
Farringdon 3	⊖ d																				06 59				
City Thameslink 3	d																								
London Blackfriars 3	⊖ d																				07 04				
London Bridge 4	⊖ d																				07 11	07 14			
Norwood Junction 2	d																					07 26			
East Croydon	⇌ a	05 22						06 05						06 51						07 23	07 26	07 30			07 50
	d	05 23						06 06						06 52						07 23	07 27	07 31			07 51
Purley 4	d	05 29												06 56						07 28		07 37			
Coulsdon South	d													07 00								07 40			
Merstham	d													07 05								07 46			
Redhill	a							06 18						07 09						07 36		07 50			08 03
	d							06 19			06 20			07 09		07 15		07 21	07 29	07 37					08 04
Tonbridge 4	a																								
Reigate	a										06 24							07 25							
Earlswood (Surrey)	d																								
Salfords	d																								
Horley 4	d							06 22						07 15						07 44					
Gatwick Airport 10	✈ a	05 45	05 50	06 05		06 20		06 31	06 35	06 50			07 05	07 18	07 20	07 27	07 35		07 38	07 46	07 48		07 50	08 05	08 11
	d	05 46					06 29	06 32				06 58		07 19					07 39	07 47	07 50				08 12
Three Bridges 15	a	05 50					06 33	06 36				07 02		07 23					07 43	07 52	07 54				08 16
	d	05 51					06 40	06 36				07 03		07 24						07 52	07 54				08 17
Crawley	d						06 43													07 55					
Ifield	d						06 46													07 58					
Faygate	d																								
Littlehaven	d						06 52													08 04					
Horsham 4	a						06 56													08 07					
Balcombe	d													07 30											08 23
Haywards Heath 3	a	05 59						06 46				07 11		07 35							08 03				08 28
	d	06 00						06 47				07 12		07 36							08 03				08 28
Wivelsfield 4	d							06 51						07 40											08 32
Lewes 4	a											07 27													
Burgess Hill 4	d							06 53						07 42							08 08				08 34
Hassocks 4	d							06 56						07 45											08 38
Preston Park	d							07 03						07 52											08 45
Hove 2	a																								
Brighton 10	a	06 18						07 08						07 58							08 22				08 50

For general notes see front of timetable
For details of catering facilities see
Directory of Train Operators

§ It is unknown, at the time of going to press, when this station will open. For further details contact National Rail Enquiries 08457-484950 or see local publicity.

A Until 7 September. To Eastbourne (Table 189)

B To Bognor Regis (Table 188)

C Until 7 September

Table 186

Sundays

Watford Junction, Bedford and London → Brighton

Network Diagram - see first page of Table 186

		SN	SN	FC	GX	SN	SN	SN		GW	GW	GX	SE	SN	FC	SN	GX	SN	GX	SN	SN	SN	SN	FC	GX
													55												
		1	1	1	1	1	1	1		1	1	1		1	1		1	1	1	1	1◇	1	1	1	1
		A	B			A	B						C	D		A						A	B		
London Victoria 15 ⊖	d	07 34	07 34		07 45							08 00		08 04			08 15	08 17	08 30		08 32	08 34	08 34		08 45
Watford Junction	d																								
Harrow & Wealdstone ⊖	d																								
Wembley Central	d																								
Willesden Jn. High Level	d																								
Shepherds Bush § ⊖	d																								
Kensington Olympia ⊖	d							07 47												08 18					
West Brompton ⊖	d							07 49												08 20					
Imperial Wharf §	d																								
Clapham Junction 10	d	07 40	07 40					08a00						08 10				08 23		08a30	08 38	08 40	08 40		
Bedford 7	d			06 10											06 40									07 10	
Luton 10	d			06 34											07 04									07 34	
Luton Airport Parkway 7 ✈	d			06 36											07 06									07 36	
St Albans City	d			06 48											07 18									07 48	
St Pancras International 15 ⊖	d			07 24											07 54									08 24	
Farringdon 3 ⊖	d			07 29											07 59									08 29	
City Thameslink 3	d																								
London Blackfriars 3 ⊖	d			07 34											08 04									08 34	
London Bridge 4 ⊖	d			07 41											08 11	08 14								08 41	
Norwood Junction 2	d															08 26									
East Croydon	a	07 53	07 53	07 56										08 23	08 26	08 30		08 36			08 50	08 53	08 53	08 56	
	d	07 54	07 54	07 57										08 23	08 27	08 31		08 37			08 51	08 54	08 54	08 57	
Purley 4	d	07 59	07 59											08 29		08 37						08 59	08 59		
Coulsdon South	d	08 03	08 03				←									08 40						09 03	09 03		
Merstham	d	08 08	08 08				08 08									08 46						09 08	09 08		
Redhill	a	08 12	→			←	08 12							08 37		08 50					09 03	09 12	→		
	d	08 12				08 12	08 12			08 19	08 21		08 29	08 38							09 04	09 12			
Tonbridge 4	a	→																				→			
Reigate	a									08 23															
Earlswood (Surrey)	d					08 15																			
Salfords	d					08 18																			
Horley 4	d					08 22	08 22							08 44											
Gatwick Airport 10 ✈	a			08 18	08 20	08 24	08 24				08 32	08 35	08 38	08 46	08 48		08 50	08 54	09 05		09 11			09 18	09 20
	d			08 20		08 25	08 25						08 39	08 47	08 50			08 56			09 12			09 20	
Three Bridges 15	a			08 24		08 30	08 30						08 43	08 52	08 54						09 16			09 24	
	d			08 24		08 33	08 33							08 52	08 54						09 17			09 24	
Crawley	d					08 36	08 36							08 55											
Ifield	d					08 39	08 39																		
Faygate	d																								
Littlehaven	d					08 45	08 45																		
Horsham 4	a					08 49	08 49							09 04											
Balcombe	d																				09 23				
Haywards Heath 3	a			08 33											09 03			09 06			09 28			09 33	
	d			08 33											09 03			09 07			09 28			09 33	
Wivelsfield 4	d																				09 32				
Lewes 4	a																								
Burgess Hill 4	d			08 38											09 08			09 12			09 34			09 38	
Hassocks 4	d			08 42																	09 38			09 42	
Preston Park	d																				09 45				
Hove 2	a																	09 24							
Brighton 10	a			08 52											09 22						09 50			09 52	

For general notes see front of timetable
For details of catering facilities see Directory of Train Operators

§ It is unknown, at the time of going to press, when this station will open. For further details contact National Rail Enquiries 08457-484950 or see local publicity.

A Until 7 September
B From 14 September
C From Gillingham (Kent) (Table 208)
D To Bognor Regis (Table 188)

Watford Junction, Bedford and London → Brighton

Network Diagram - see first page of Table 186

		SN	SN	SN	GW	GW	GX	SE	SN	SN	FC	SN	GX	SN	GX	SN	SN	SN	FC	LO	GX	SN	SN	SN
								55																
		1	1	1	1	1	1		1	1	1	1	1	1	1	1 ◊	1	1	1		1	1	1	1
		A	B					C		D		A					A	B				A	B	
				⊥												⊥								⊥
London Victoria [15]	⊖ d			08 47			09 00			09 04			09 15	09 17	09 30	09 32	09 34	09 34			09 45			09 47
Watford Junction	d																							
Harrow & Wealdstone	⊖ d																							
Wembley Central	d																							
Willesden Jn. High Level	d																			09 06				
Shepherds Bush §	⊖ d																							
Kensington Olympia	⊖ d								08 48											09 15				
West Brompton	⊖ d								08a50											09 17				
Imperial Wharf §	d																							
Clapham Junction [10]	d			08 53					09a00	09 10				09 23		09 38	09 40	09 40		09a26				09 53
Bedford [7]	d										07 50								08 20					
Luton [10]	d										08 14								08 44					
Luton Airport Parkway [7]	✈ d										08 16								08 46					
St Albans City	d										08 28								08 58					
St Pancras International [15]	⊖ d										08 54								09 24					
Farringdon [3]	⊖ d										08 59								09 29					
City Thameslink [3]	d																							
London Blackfriars [3]	⊖ d										09 04								09 34					
London Bridge [4]	⊖ d										09 11	09 14							09 41					
Norwood Junction [2]	d											09 26												
East Croydon	a			09 06						09 23	09 26	09 30		09 36		09 50	09 53	09 53	09 56					10 06
	d			09 07						09 23	09 27	09 31		09 37		09 51	09 54	09 54	09 57					10 07
Purley [4]	d									09 29		09 37					09 59	09 59						
Coulsdon South	d		←									09 40					10 03	10 03					←	
Merstham	d		09 08									09 46					10 08	10 08					10 08	
Redhill	a	←	09 12							09 37		09 50				10 03	10 12	→				←	10 12	
	d	09 12	09 12		09 20	09 23		09 29		09 38						10 04	10 12					10 12	10 12	
Tonbridge [4]	a																→							
Reigate	a				09 24																			
Earlswood (Surrey)	d	09 15																				10 15		
Salfords	d	09 18																				10 18		
Horley [4]	d	09 22	09 22							09 44												10 22	10 22	
Gatwick Airport [10]	✈ a	09 24	09 24	09 27		09 31	09 35	09 38		09 46	09 48		09 50	09 54	10 05	10 11			10 18		10 20	10 24	10 24	10 27
	d	09 25	09 25	09 29				09 39		09 47	09 50			09 56		10 12			10 20			10 25	10 25	10 29
Three Bridges [15]	a	09 30	09 30					09 43		09 52	09 54					10 16			10 24			10 30	10 30	
	d	09 33	09 33							09 52	09 54					10 17			10 24			10 33	10 33	
Crawley	d	09 36	09 36							09 55												10 36	10 36	
Ifield	d	09 39	09 39																			10 39	10 39	
Faygate	d																							
Littlehaven	d	09 45	09 45																			10 45	10 45	
Horsham [4]	a	09 49	09 49							10 04												10 49	10 49	
Balcombe	d															10 23								
Haywards Heath [3]	a			09 40							10 03			10 06		10 28			10 33					10 40
	d			09 41							10 03			10 07		10 28			10 33					10 41
Wivelsfield [4]	d			09 45												10 32								10 45
Lewes [4]	a			09 58																				10 58
Burgess Hill [4]	d										10 08			10 12		10 34			10 38					
Hassocks [4]	d															10 38			10 42					
Preston Park	d															10 45								
Hove [2]	a													10 24										
Brighton [10]	a										10 22					10 50			10 52					

For general notes see front of timetable
For details of catering facilities see
Directory of Train Operators

§ It is unknown, at the time of going to press, when this station will open. For further details contact National Rail Enquiries 08457-484950 or see local publicity.

A Until 7 September
B From 14 September
C From Maidstone West (Table 208)
D To Bognor Regis (Table 188)

Table 186

Sundays

Watford Junction, Bedford and London → Brighton

Network Diagram - see first page of Table 186

	SN	GW	GW	GX	SE	SN	SN	FC	SN	GX	SN	GX	SN	SN	SN	FC	LO	GX	SN	SN	SN	SN	GW
	1	1	1	1	55	1 ◇	1	1		1	1	1	1 ◇	1	1	1		1	1	1	1	1	1
					A	B	C		B					B	D				B	D			
London Victoria 15 ⊖ d				10 00		10 02	10 04			10 15	10 17	10 30	10 32	10 34	10 34			10 45			10 47		
Watford Junction d	09 22																						
Harrow & Wealdstone ⊖ d	09 28																					10 22	
Wembley Central d																						10 27	
Willesden Jn. High Level d																							
Shepherds Bush § ⊖ d																	10 06						
Kensington Olympia ⊖ d	09 47																						
West Brompton ⊖ d	09 49																10 15					10 47	
Imperial Wharf § d																	10 17					10 49	
Clapham Junction 10 d	10a00					10 07	10 10				10 23		10 38	10 40	10 40		10a26				10 53	11a00	
Bedford 7 d								08 50								09 20							
Luton 10 d								09 14								09 44							
Luton Airport Parkway 7 ✈ d								09 16								09 46							
St Albans City d								09 28								09 58							
St Pancras International 15 ⊖ d								09 54								10 24							
Farringdon 3 ⊖ d								09 59								10 29							
City Thameslink 3 d																							
London Blackfriars 3 ⊖ d								10 04								10 34							
London Bridge 4 ⊖ d								10 11	10 14							10 41							
Norwood Junction 2 d									10 26														
East Croydon a						10 20	10 23	10 26	10 30		10 36		10 50	10 53	10 53	10 56					11 06		
East Croydon d						10 20	10 23	10 27	10 31		10 37		10 51	10 54	10 54	10 57					11 07		
Purley 4 d							10 29		10 37					10 59	10 59								
Coulsdon South d									10 40					11 03	11 03					←			
Merstham d									10 46					11 08	11 08					11 08			
Redhill a							10 37		10 50				11 03	11 12	→				←	11 12			
Redhill d		10 19	10 21		10 29		10 38						11 04	11 12					11 12	11 12			11 20
Tonbridge 4 a														→									
Reigate a		10 23																					11 24
Earlswood (Surrey) d																			11 15				
Salfords d																			11 18				
Horley 4 d							10 44												11 22	11 22			
Gatwick Airport 10 ✈ a			10 30	10 35	10 38	10 41	10 46	10 48		10 50	10 54	11 05	11 11			11 18		11 20	11 24	11 24	11 27		
Gatwick Airport d					10 39	10 42	10 47	10 50			10 56		11 12			11 20			11 25	11 25	11 29		
Three Bridges 15 a					10 43		10 52	10 54					11 16			11 24			11 30	11 30			
Three Bridges d							10 52	10 54					11 17			11 24			11 33	11 33			
Crawley d							10 55												11 36	11 36			
Ifield d																			11 39	11 39			
Faygate d																							
Littlehaven d																			11 45	11 45			
Horsham 4 a							11 04												11 49	11 49			
Balcombe d													11 23										
Haywards Heath 3 a								11 03			11 06		11 28			11 33					11 40		
Haywards Heath d								11 03			11 07		11 28			11 33					11 41		
Wivelsfield 4 d													11 32								11 45		
Lewes 4 a																					11 58		
Burgess Hill 4 d								11 08			11 12		11 34			11 38							
Hassocks 4 d													11 38			11 42							
Preston Park d													11 45										
Hove 2 a											11 24												
Brighton 10 a						11 05		11 22					11 50			11 52							

For general notes see front of timetable
For details of catering facilities see Directory of Train Operators

§ It is unknown, at the time of going to press, when this station will open. For further details contact National Rail Enquiries 08457-484950 or see local publicity.

A From Maidstone West (Table 208)
B Until 7 September
C To Bognor Regis (Table 188)
D From 14 September

Table 186

Sundays

Watford Junction, Bedford and London → Brighton

Network Diagram - see first page of Table 186

Station		GW	GX	SE 55	SN	SN	FC	SN	GX	SN	GX	SN	SN	SN	FC	LO	GX	SN	SN	SN	SN	GW	GW	GX
		1	1		1 ◇	1	1		1	1	1	1 ◇	1	1	1		1	1	1	1	1	1	1	1
				A	B	C		B					B	D				B	D					
					⚲	⚲						⚲								⚲				
London Victoria 15	⊖ d		11 00		11 02	11 04			11 15	11 17	11 30	11 32	11 34	11 34			11 45			11 47				12 00
Watford Junction	d																				11 22			
Harrow & Wealdstone	⊖ d																				11 28			
Wembley Central	d																							
Willesden Jn. High Level	d															11 06								
Shepherds Bush §	⊖ d																							
Kensington Olympia	⊖ d															11 15					11 47			
West Brompton	⊖ d															11 17					11 49			
Imperial Wharf §	d																							
Clapham Junction 10	d				11 07	11 10				11 23		11 38	11 40	11 40		11a26				11 53	12a00			
Bedford 7	d						09 50								10 20									
Luton 10	d						10 14								10 44									
Luton Airport Parkway 7	✈ d						10 16								10 46									
St Albans City	d						10 28								10 58									
St Pancras International 15	⊖ d						10 54								11 24									
Farringdon 3	⊖ d						10 59								11 29									
City Thameslink 3	d																							
London Blackfriars 3	⊖ d						11 04								11 34									
London Bridge 4	⊖ d						11 11	11 14							11 41									
Norwood Junction 2	d							11 26																
East Croydon	a				11 20	11 23	11 26	11 30		11 36		11 50	11 53	11 53	11 56					12 06				
	d				11 20	11 23	11 27	11 31		11 37		11 51	11 54	11 54	11 57					12 07				
Purley 4	d					11 29		11 37					11 59	11 59					←					
Coulsdon South	d							11 40					12 03	12 03										
Merstham	d							11 46					12 08	12 08					12 08					
Redhill	a					11 37		11 50				12 03	12 12	→				←	12 12					
	d	11 22		11 29		11 38						12 04	12 12					12 12	12 12			12 19	12 21	
Tonbridge 4	a												→									12 23		
Reigate	a																							
Earlswood (Surrey)	d																	12 15						
Salfords	d																	12 18						
Horley 4	d					11 44												12 22	12 22					
Gatwick Airport 10	✈ a	11 31	11 35	11 38	11 41	11 46	11 48		11 50	11 54	12 05	12 11			12 18		12 20	12 24	12 24	12 27			12 30	12 35
	d			11 39	11 42	11 47	11 50			11 56		12 12			12 20			12 25	12 25	12 29				
Three Bridges 15	a			11 43		11 52	11 54					12 16			12 24			12 30	12 30					
	d					11 52	11 54					12 17			12 24			12 33	12 33					
Crawley	d					11 55												12 36	12 36					
Ifield	d																	12 39	12 39					
Faygate	d																							
Littlehaven	d																	12 45	12 45					
Horsham 4	a					12 04												12 49	12 49					
Balcombe	d											12 23												
Haywards Heath 3	a						12 03			12 06		12 28			12 33					12 40				
	d						12 03			12 07		12 28			12 33					12 41				
Wivelsfield 4	d											12 32								12 45				
Lewes 4	a																			12 58				
Burgess Hill 4	d						12 08			12 12		12 34			12 38									
Hassocks 4	d											12 38			12 42									
Preston Park	d											12 45												
Hove 2	a									12 24														
Brighton 10	a				12 05		12 22					12 49			12 52									

For general notes see front of timetable
For details of catering facilities see
Directory of Train Operators

§ It is unknown, at the time of going to press, when this station will open. For further details contact National Rail Enquiries 08457-484950 or see local publicity.

A From Maidstone West (Table 208)
B Until 7 September
C To Bognor Regis (Table 188)
D From 14 September

Sundays

Watford Junction, Bedford and London → Brighton

Network Diagram - see first page of Table 186

		SE 55	SN	SN	FC	SN	GX	SN	GX	SN	SN	SN	FC	LO	GX	SN	SN	SN	SN	GW	GW	GX	SE 55	SN	SN
			1 ◇	1	1		1	1	1	1 ◇	1	1	1		1	1	1	1	1	1	1	1		1	1
		A	B	C		B					B	D				B	D						A	B	C
				⊼						⊼								⊼							⊼
London Victoria 15	⊖ d		12 02	12 04			12 15	12 17	12 30	12 32	12 34	12 34			12 45			12 47				13 00		13 02	13 04
Watford Junction	d																		12 22						
Harrow & Wealdstone	⊖ d																		12 28						
Wembley Central	d																								
Willesden Jn. High Level	d													12 06											
Shepherds Bush §	⊖ d																								
Kensington Olympia	⊖ d													12 15					12 47						
West Brompton	⊖ d													12 17					12 49						
Imperial Wharf §	d																								
Clapham Junction 10	d		12 07	12 10				12 23		12 38	12 40	12 40		12a26				12 53	13a00					13 07	13 10
Bedford 7	d				10 50								11 20												
Luton 10	d				11 14								11 44												
Luton Airport Parkway 7	✈ d				11 16								11 46												
St Albans City	d				11 28								11 58												
St Pancras International 15	⊖ d				11 54								12 24												
Farringdon 3	⊖ d				11 59								12 29												
City Thameslink 3	d																								
London Blackfriars 3	⊖ d				12 04								12 34												
London Bridge 4	⊖ d				12 11	12 14							12 41												
Norwood Junction 2	d					12 26																			
East Croydon	⇌ a		12 20	12 23	12 26	12 30		12 36		12 50	12 53	12 53	12 56					13 06						13 20	13 23
	d		12 20	12 23	12 27	12 31		12 37		12 51	12 54	12 54	12 57					13 07						13 20	13 23
Purley 4	d			12 29		12 37					12 59	12 59													13 29
Coulsdon South	d					12 40					13 03	13 03					←								
Merstham	d					12 46					13 08	13 08					13 08								
Redhill	a			12 37		12 50				13 03	13 12	→				←	13 12								13 37
	d	12 29		12 38						13 04	13 12					13 12	13 12			13 20	13 22		13 29		13 38
Tonbridge 4	a										→														
Reigate	a																			13 24					
Earlswood (Surrey)	d															13 15									
Salfords	d															13 18									
Horley 4	d			12 44												13 22	13 22								13 44
Gatwick Airport 10	✈ a	12 38	12 41	12 46	12 48		12 50	12 54	13 05	13 11			13 18		13 20	13 24	13 24	13 27			13 31	13 35	13 38	13 41	13 46
	d	12 39	12 42	12 47	12 50			12 56		13 12			13 20			13 25	13 25	13 29					13 39	13 42	13 47
Three Bridges 15	a	12 43		12 52	12 54					13 16			13 24			13 30	13 30						13 43		13 52
	d			12 52	12 54					13 17			13 24			13 33	13 33								13 52
Crawley	d			12 55												13 36	13 36								13 55
Ifield	d															13 39	13 39								
Faygate	d																								
Littlehaven	d															13 45	13 45								
Horsham 4	a			13 04												13 49	13 49								14 04
Balcombe	d									13 23															
Haywards Heath 3	a				13 03			13 06		13 28			13 33					13 40							
	d				13 03			13 07		13 28			13 33					13 41							
Wivelsfield 4	d									13 32								13 45							
Lewes 4	a																	13 58							
Burgess Hill 4	d				13 08			13 12		13 34			13 38												
Hassocks 4	d									13 38			13 42												
Preston Park	d									13 45															
Hove 2	a							13 24																	
Brighton 10	a		13 05		13 22					13 50			13 52											14 05	

For general notes see front of timetable
For details of catering facilities see Directory of Train Operators

§ It is unknown, at the time of going to press, when this station will open. For further details contact National Rail Enquiries 08457-484950 or see local publicity.

A From Maidstone West (Table 208)
B Until 7 September
C To Bognor Regis (Table 188)
D From 14 September

Watford Junction, Bedford and London → Brighton

Network Diagram - see first page of Table 186

	FC		SN	GX	SN	GX	SN	SN	SN	FC	LO	GX	SN	SN	SN	SN	GW	GW	GX	SE 55	SN	SN	FC	SN
	1			1	1	1	1 ◇	1	1	1		1	1	1	1	1	1	1	1		1 ◇	1	1	
			A					A	B				A	B						C	A	D		A
							🛒								🛒							🛒		
London Victoria 15 ⊖ d				13 15	13 17	13 30	13 32	13 34	13 34			13 45			13 47				14 00		14 02	14 04		
Watford Junction d																13 22								
Harrow & Wealdstone ⊖ d																13 28								
Wembley Central d																								
Willesden Jn. High Level d											13 06													
Shepherds Bush § ⊖ d																								
Kensington Olympia ⊖ d											13 15					13 47								
West Brompton ⊖ d											13 17					13 48								
Imperial Wharf § d																								
Clapham Junction 10 d					13 23		13 38	13 40	13 40		13a26				13 53	14a00					14 07	14 10		
Bedford 7 d	11 50									12 20													12 50	
Luton 10 d	12 14									12 44													13 14	
Luton Airport Parkway 7 ✈ d	12 16									12 46													13 16	
St Albans City d	12 28									12 58													13 28	
St Pancras International 15 ⊖ d	12 54									13 24													13 54	
Farringdon 3 ⊖ d	12 59									13 29													13 59	
City Thameslink 3 d																								
London Blackfriars 3 ⊖ d	13 04									13 34													14 04	
London Bridge 4 ⊖ d	13 11		13 14							13 41													14 11	14 14
Norwood Junction 2 d			13 26																					14 26
East Croydon a	13 26		13 30		13 36		13 50	13 53	13 53	13 56					14 06						14 20	14 23	14 26	14 30
East Croydon d	13 27		13 31		13 37		13 51	13 54	13 54	13 57					14 07						14 20	14 23	14 27	14 31
Purley 4 d			13 37					13 59	13 59													14 29		14 37
Coulsdon South d			13 40					14 03	14 03					←										14 40
Merstham d			13 46					14 08	14 08					14 08										14 46
Redhill a			13 50				14 03	14 12	→				←	14 12								14 37		14 53
Redhill d							14 04	14 12					14 12	14 12			14 19	14 21		14 29		14 38		
Tonbridge 4 a								→																
Reigate a																	14 23							
Earlswood (Surrey) d													14 15											
Salfords d													14 18											
Horley 4 d													14 22	14 22								14 44		
Gatwick Airport 10 ✈ a	13 48			13 50	13 54	14 05	14 11			14 18		14 20	14 24	14 24	14 27			14 30	14 35	14 38	14 41	14 46	14 48	
Gatwick Airport d	13 50				13 56		14 12			14 20			14 25	14 25	14 29					14 39	14 42	14 47	14 50	
Three Bridges 15 a	13 54						14 16			14 24			14 30	14 30						14 43		14 52	14 54	
Three Bridges d	13 54						14 17			14 24			14 33	14 33								14 52	14 54	
Crawley d													14 36	14 36								14 55		
Ifield d													14 39	14 39										
Faygate d																								
Littlehaven d													14 45	14 45										
Horsham 4 a													14 49	14 49								15 04		
Balcombe d							14 23																	
Haywards Heath 3 a	14 03				14 06		14 28			14 33					14 40								15 03	
Haywards Heath d	14 03				14 07		14 28			14 33					14 41								15 03	
Wivelsfield 4 d							14 32								14 45									
Lewes 4 a															14 58									
Burgess Hill 4 d	14 08				14 12		14 34			14 38													15 08	
Hassocks 4 d							14 38			14 42														
Preston Park d							14 45																	
Hove 2 a					14 24																			
Brighton 10 a	14 22						14 50			14 52											15 05		15 22	

For general notes see front of timetable
For details of catering facilities see
Directory of Train Operators

§ It is unknown, at the time of going to press, when this station will open. For further details contact National Rail Enquiries 08457-484950 or see local publicity.

A Until 7 September
B From 14 September
C From Maidstone West (Table 208)
D To Bognor Regis (Table 188)

Table 186

Sundays

Watford Junction, Bedford and London → Brighton

Network Diagram - see first page of Table 186

Station		GX	SN	GX	SN	SN	SN	FC	LO	GX	SN	SN	SN	SN	LO	GW	GW	GX	SE	SN	SN	FC	SN	GX
		1	1	1	1 ◇	1	1	1		1	1	1	1	1		1	1	1	55	1 ◇	1	1		1
						A	B				A	B							C	A	D		A	
					(catering symbol)								(catering symbol)								(catering symbol)			
London Victoria 15	⊖ d	14 15	14 17	14 30	14 32	14 34	14 34			14 45			14 47					15 00		15 02	15 04			15 15
Watford Junction	d													14 22										
Harrow & Wealdstone	⊖ d													14 28										
Wembley Central	d																							
Willesden Jn. High Level	d								14 06						14 51									
Shepherds Bush §	⊖ d																							
Kensington Olympia	⊖ d								14 15					14 47	15 00									
West Brompton	⊖ d								14 17					14 49	15 02									
Imperial Wharf §	d																							
Clapham Junction 10	d		14 23		14 38	14 40	14 40		14a26				14 53	15a00	15a11					15 07	15 10			
Bedford 7	d							13 20														13 50		
Luton 10	d							13 44														14 14		
Luton Airport Parkway 7	✈ d							13 46														14 16		
St Albans City	d							13 58														14 28		
St Pancras International 15	⊖ d							14 24														14 54		
Farringdon 3	⊖ d							14 29														14 59		
City Thameslink 3	d																							
London Blackfriars 3	⊖ d							14 34														15 04		
London Bridge 4	⊖ d							14 41														15 11	15 14	
Norwood Junction 2	d																						15 26	
East Croydon	a		14 36		14 50	14 53	14 53	14 56					15 06							15 20	15 23	15 26	15 30	
	d		14 37		14 51	14 54	14 54	14 57					15 07							15 20	15 23	15 27	15 31	
Purley 4	d					14 59	14 59														15 29		15 37	
Coulsdon South	d					15 03	15 03					←											15 40	
Merstham	d					15 08	15 08					15 08											15 46	
Redhill	a				15 03	15 12	→				←	15 12									15 37		15 53	
	d				15 04	15 12					15 12	15 12				15 20	15 22		15 29		15 38			
Tonbridge 4	a					→																		
Reigate	a															15 24								
Earlswood (Surrey)	d										15 15													
Salfords	d										15 18													
Horley 4	d										15 22	15 22									15 44			
Gatwick Airport 10	✈ a	14 50	14 54	15 05	15 11			15 18		15 20	15 24	15 24	15 27				15 31	15 35	15 38	15 41	15 46	15 48		15 50
	d		14 56		15 12			15 20			15 25	15 25	15 29						15 39	15 42	15 47	15 50		
Three Bridges 15	a				15 16			15 24			15 30	15 30							15 43		15 52	15 54		
	d				15 17			15 24			15 33	15 33									15 52	15 54		
Crawley	d										15 36	15 36									15 55			
Ifield	d										15 39	15 39												
Faygate	d																							
Littlehaven	d										15 45	15 45												
Horsham 4	a										15 49	15 49									16 04			
Balcombe	d				15 23																			
Haywards Heath 3	a		15 06		15 28			15 33					15 40									16 03		
	d		15 07		15 28			15 33					15 41									16 03		
Wivelsfield 4	d				15 32								15 45											
Lewes 4	a												15 58											
Burgess Hill 4	d		15 12		15 34			15 38														16 08		
Hassocks 4	d				15 38			15 42																
Preston Park	d				15 45																			
Hove 2	a		15 24																					
Brighton 10	a				15 50			15 52												16 05		16 22		

For general notes see front of timetable
For details of catering facilities see
Directory of Train Operators

§ It is unknown, at the time of going to press, when this station will open. For further details contact National Rail Enquiries 08457-484950 or see local publicity.

A Until 7 September
B From 14 September
C From Maidstone West (Table 208)
D To Bognor Regis (Table 188)

Table 186

Sundays

Watford Junction, Bedford and London → Brighton

Network Diagram - see first page of Table 186

Station		SN	GX	SN	SN	SN	FC	LO	GX	SN		SN	SN	SN	LO	GW	GW	GX	SE	SN	SN	FC	SN	GX	SN
																			55						
		1	1	1 ◇	1	1	1		1	1		1	1	1		1	1	1		1 ◇	1	1		1	1
					A	B				A		B							C	A	D		A		
				🍴									🍴								🍴				
London Victoria 15	⊖ d	15 17	15 30	15 32	15 34	15 34			15 45				15 47					16 00		16 02	16 04			16 15	16 17
Watford Junction	d													15 22											
Harrow & Wealdstone	⊖ d													15 28											
Wembley Central	d																								
Willesden Jn. High Level	d							15 21							15 51										
Shepherds Bush §	⊖ d																								
Kensington Olympia	⊖ d							15 30						15 48	16 00										
West Brompton	⊖ d							15 32						15 50	16 02										
Imperial Wharf §	d																								
Clapham Junction 10	d	15 23		15 38	15 40	15 40		15a41					15 53	16a00	16a11					16 07	16 10				16 23
Bedford 7	d						14 20															14 50			
Luton 10	d						14 44															15 14			
Luton Airport Parkway 7	✈ d						14 46															15 16			
St Albans City	d						14 58															15 28			
St Pancras International 15	⊖ d						15 24															15 54			
Farringdon 3	⊖ d						15 29															15 59			
City Thameslink 3	d																					16 04			
London Blackfriars 3	⊖ d						15 34																		
London Bridge 4	⊖ d						15 41															16 11	16 14		
Norwood Junction 2	d																						16 26		
East Croydon	🚊 a	15 36		15 50	15 53	15 53	15 56						16 06							16 20	16 23	16 26	16 30		16 36
	d	15 37		15 51	15 54	15 54	15 57						16 07							16 20	16 23	16 27	16 31		16 37
Purley 4	d				15 59	15 59						←									16 29		16 37		
Coulsdon South	d				16 03	16 03																	16 40		
Merstham	d				16 08	16 08						16 08											16 46		
Redhill	a			16 03	16 12	→				←		16 12									16 37		16 50		
	d			16 04	16 12					16 12		16 12				16 19	16 21		16 29		16 38				
Tonbridge 4	a				→																				
Reigate	a															16 23									
Earlswood (Surrey)	d									16 15															
Salfords	d									16 18															
Horley 4	d									16 22		16 22									16 44				
Gatwick Airport 10	✈ a	15 54	16 05	16 11			16 18		16 20	16 24		16 24	16 27				16 30	16 35	16 38	16 41	16 46	16 48		16 50	16 54
	d	15 56		16 12			16 20			16 25		16 25	16 29						16 39	16 42	16 47	16 50			16 56
Three Bridges 15	a			16 16			16 24			16 30		16 30							16 43		16 52	16 54			
	d			16 17			16 24			16 33		16 33									16 52	16 54			
Crawley	d									16 36		16 36									16 55				
Ifield	d									16 39		16 39													
Faygate	d																								
Littlehaven	d									16 45		16 45													
Horsham 4	a									16 49		16 49									17 04				
Balcombe	d			16 23																					
Haywards Heath 3	a	16 06		16 28			16 33						16 40									17 03			17 06
	d	16 07		16 28			16 33						16 41									17 03			17 07
Wivelsfield 4	d			16 32									16 45												
Lewes 4	a												16 58												
Burgess Hill 4	d	16 12		16 34			16 38															17 08			17 12
Hassocks 4	d			16 38			16 42																		
Preston Park	d			16 45																					
Hove 2	a	16 24																							17 24
Brighton 10	a			16 50			16 52													17 05		17 22			

For general notes see front of timetable
For details of catering facilities see Directory of Train Operators

§ It is unknown, at the time of going to press, when this station will open. For further details contact National Rail Enquiries 08457-484950 or see local publicity.

A Until 7 September
B From 14 September
C From Maidstone West (Table 208)
D To Bognor Regis (Table 188)

Sundays

Watford Junction, Bedford and London → Brighton

Network Diagram - see first page of Table 186

		GX	SN	SN	SN	FC	LO	GX	SN	SN	SN	SN	LO	GW	GW	GX	SE 55	SN	SN	FC	SN	GX	SN	GX
		1	1 ◇	1	1	1		1	1	1	1	1		1	1	1		1 ◇	1	1		1	1	1
				A	B				A	B							C		D		A			
London Victoria 15	⊖ d	16 30	16 32	16 34	16 34			16 45			16 47					17 00		17 02	17 04			17 15	17 17	17 30
Watford Junction	d											16 22												
Harrow & Wealdstone	⊖ d											16 28												
Wembley Central	d																							
Willesden Jn. High Level	d						16 21						16 51											
Shepherds Bush §	⊖ d																							
Kensington Olympia	⊖ d						16 30					16 48	17 00											
West Brompton	⊖ d						16 32					16 50	17 02											
Imperial Wharf §	d																							
Clapham Junction 10	d		16 38	16 40	16 40		16a41				16 53	17a00	17a11					17 07	17 10				17 23	
Bedford 7	d					15 20														15 50				
Luton 10	d					15 44														16 14				
Luton Airport Parkway 7	✈ d					15 46														16 16				
St Albans City	d					15 58														16 28				
St Pancras International 15	⊖ d					16 24														16 54				
Farringdon 3	⊖ d					16 29														16 59				
City Thameslink 3	d																							
London Blackfriars 3	⊖ d					16 34														17 04				
London Bridge 4	⊖ d					16 41														17 11	17 14			
Norwood Junction 2	d																				17 26			
East Croydon	a		16 50	16 53	16 53	16 56					17 06							17 20	17 23	17 26	17 30		17 36	
	d		16 51	16 54	16 54	16 57					17 07							17 20	17 24	17 27	17 31		17 37	
Purley 4	d			16 59	16 59														17 29		17 37			
Coulsdon South	d			17 03	17 03					←											17 40			
Merstham	d			17 08	17 08					17 08											17 46			
Redhill	a		17 03	17 12	→				←	17 12									17 37		17 50			
	d		17 04	17 12					17 12	17 12				17 21	17 23		17 29		17 38					
Tonbridge 4	a			→																				
Reigate	a													17 25										
Earlswood (Surrey)	d								17 15															
Salfords	d								17 18															
Horley 4	d								17 22	17 22									17 44					
Gatwick Airport 10	✈ a	17 05	17 11			17 18		17 20	17 24	17 24	17 27				17 33	17 35	17 38	17 41	17 46	17 48		17 50	17 54	18 05
	d		17 12			17 20			17 25	17 25	17 29						17 39	17 42	17 47	17 50			17 56	
Three Bridges 15	a		17 16			17 24			17 30	17 30							17 43		17 52	17 54				
	d		17 17			17 24			17 33	17 33									17 52	17 54				
Crawley	d								17 36	17 36									17 55					
Ifield	d								17 39	17 39														
Faygate	d																							
Littlehaven	d								17 45	17 45														
Horsham 4	a								17 49	17 49									18 04					
Balcombe	d		17 23																					
Haywards Heath 3	a		17 28			17 33					17 40									18 03			18 06	
	d		17 28			17 33					17 41									18 03			18 07	
Wivelsfield 4	d		17 32								17 45													
Lewes 4	a										17 58													
Burgess Hill 4	d		17 34			17 38														18 08			18 12	
Hassocks 4	d		17 38			17 42																		
Preston Park	d		17 45																					
Hove 2	a																						18 24	
Brighton 10	a		17 50			17 52												18 05		18 22				

For general notes see front of timetable
For details of catering facilities see Directory of Train Operators

§ It is unknown, at the time of going to press, when this station will open. For further details contact National Rail Enquiries 08457-484950 or see local publicity.

A Until 7 September
B From 14 September
C From Maidstone West (Table 208)
D To Bognor Regis (Table 188)

Table 186

Watford Junction, Bedford and London → Brighton

Network Diagram - see first page of Table 186

		SN	SN	SN	FC	LO	GX	SN	SN	SN	SN	GW	GW	GX	SE	SN	SN	FC		SN	GX	SN	LO	GX	SN
															55										
		1 ◊	1	1	1		1	1	1	1	1	1	1	1		1 ◊	1	1			1	1		1	1 ◊
			A	B				A	B						C		D			A					
		ᴛ								ᴛ							ᴛ								ᴛ
London Victoria 15 ⊖	d	17 32	17{34	17{34			17 45			17 47				18 00		18 02	18 04				18 15	18 17		18 30	18 32
Watford Junction	d										17 22														
Harrow & Wealdstone ⊖	d										17 28														
Wembley Central	d																								
Willesden Jn. High Level	d					17 21																	17 51		
Shepherds Bush § ⊖	d																								
Kensington Olympia ⊖	d					17 30					17 48												18 00		
West Brompton ⊖	d					17 32					17 50												18 02		
Imperial Wharf §	d																								
Clapham Junction 10	d	17 38	17{40	17{40		17a41				17 53	18a00					18 07	18 10					18 23	18a11		18 38
Bedford 7	d				16 20													16 50							
Luton 10	d				16 44													17 14							
Luton Airport Parkway 7 ✈	d				16 46													17 16							
St Albans City	d				16 58													17 28							
St Pancras International 15 ⊖	d				17 24													17 54							
Farringdon 3 ⊖	d				17 29													17 59							
City Thameslink 3	d																								
London Blackfriars 3 ⊖	d				17 34													18 04							
London Bridge 4 ⊖	d				17 41													18 11		18{14					
Norwood Junction 2	d																			18{26					
East Croydon	a	17 50	17{53	17{53	17 56					18 06						18 20	18 23	18 26		18{30		18 36			18 50
	d	17 51	17{54	17{54	17 57					18 07						18 20	18 24	18 27		18{31		18 37			18 51
Purley 4	d		17{59	17{59													18 29			18{37					
Coulsdon South	d		18{03	18{03					←											18{40					
Merstham	d		18{08	18{08					18{08											18{46					
Redhill	a	18 03	18{12	→				←	18{12								18 37			18{50					19 03
	d	18 04	18{12					18{12	18{12			18 19	18 21		18 29		18 38								19 04
Tonbridge 4	a		→																						
Reigate	a											18 23													
Earlswood (Surrey)	d							18{15																	
Salfords	d							18{18																	
Horley 4	d							18{22	18{22								18 44								
Gatwick Airport 10 ✈	a	18 11			18 18		18 20	18{24	18{24	18 27			18 29	18 35	18 38	18 41	18 46	18 48			18 50	18 54		19 05	19 11
	d	18 12			18 20			18{25	18{25	18 29					18 39	18 42	18 47	18 50				18 56			19 12
Three Bridges 15	a	18 16			18 24			18{30	18{30						18 43		18 52	18 54							19 16
	d	18 17			18 24			18{33	18{33								18 52	18 54							19 17
Crawley	d							18{36	18{36								18 55								
Ifield	d							18{39	18{39																
Faygate	d																								
Littlehaven	d							18{45	18{45																
Horsham 4	a							18{49	18{49								19 04								
Balcombe	d	18 23																							19 23
Haywards Heath 3	a	18 28			18 33					18 40								19 03				19 06			19 28
	d	18 28			18 33					18 41								19 03				19 07			19 28
Wivelsfield 4	d	18 32								18 45															19 32
Lewes 4	a									18 58															
Burgess Hill 4	d	18 34			18 38													19 08				19 12			19 34
Hassocks 4	d	18 38			18 42																				19 38
Preston Park	d	18 45																							19 45
Hove 2	a																					19 24			
Brighton 10	a	18 50			18 52											19 05		19 22							19 50

For general notes see front of timetable
For details of catering facilities see
Directory of Train Operators

§ It is unknown, at the time of going to press, when this station will open. For further details contact National Rail Enquiries 08457-484950 or see local publicity.

A Until 7 September
B From 14 September
C From Maidstone West (Table 208)
D To Bognor Regis (Table 188)

Table 186

Sundays

Watford Junction, Bedford and London → Brighton

Network Diagram - see first page of Table 186

	SN	SN	FC	GX	LO	SN	SN	SN	SN	GW	GW	GX	SE 55	SN	SN	FC	SN	GX	SN	GX	SN		SN	LO
	1 A	1 B	1	1		1 A	1 B	1	1	1	1	1	C	1 ◇	1 D	1	A	1	1	1	1 ◇		1 A	
London Victoria 15 ⊖ d	18§34	18§34		18 45				18 47				19 00		19 02	19 04			19 15	19 17	19 30	19 32		19§34	
Watford Junction d									18 22															
Harrow & Wealdstone ⊖ d									18 28															
Wembley Central d																								
Willesden Jn. High Level d					18 21																			18 51
Shepherds Bush § ⊖ d																								
Kensington Olympia ⊖ d					18 30				18 48															19 00
West Brompton ⊖ d					18 32				18 50															19 02
Imperial Wharf § d																								
Clapham Junction 10 d	18§40	18§40			18a41			18 53	19a00					19 07	19 10				19 23		19 38		19§40	19a11
Bedford 7 d			17 20													17 50								
Luton 10 d			17 44													18 14								
Luton Airport Parkway 7 ✈ d			17 46													18 16								
St Albans City d			17 58													18 28								
St Pancras International 15 ⊖ d			18 24													18 54								
Farringdon 3 ⊖ d			18 29													18 59								
City Thameslink 3 d																								
London Blackfriars 3 ⊖ d			18 34													19 04								
London Bridge 4 ⊖ d			18 41													19 11	19§14							
Norwood Junction 2 d																	19§26							
East Croydon a	18§53	18§53	18 56					19 06						19 20	19 23	19 26	19§30		19 36		19 50		19§53	
d	18§54	18§54	18 57					19 07						19 20	19 24	19 27	19§31		19 37		19 51		19§54	
Purley 4 d	18§59	18§59													19 29		19§37						19§59	
Coulsdon South d	19§03	19§03					←										19§40						20§03	
Merstham d	19§08	19§08					19§08										19§46						20§08	
Redhill a	19§12	→				←	19§12								19 37		19§50				20 03		20§12	
d	19§12					19§12	19§12			19 21	19 23		19 29		19 38						20 04		20§12	
Tonbridge 4 a	→																						→	
Reigate a										19 25														
Earlswood (Surrey) d						19§15																		
Salfords d						19§18																		
Horley 4 d						19§22	19§22								19 44									
Gatwick Airport 10 ✈ a			19 18	19 20		19§24	19§24	19 27			19 33	19 35	19 38	19 41	19 46	19 48		19 50	19 54	20 05	20 11			
d			19 20			19§25	19§25	19 29					19 39	19 42	19 47	19 50			19 56		20 12			
Three Bridges 15 a			19 24			19§30	19§30						19 43		19 52	19 54					20 16			
d			19 24			19§33	19§33								19 52	19 54					20 17			
Crawley d						19§36	19§36								19 55									
Ifield d						19§39	19§39																	
Faygate d																								
Littlehaven d						19§45	19§45																	
Horsham 4 a						19§49	19§49								20 04									
Balcombe d																					20 23			
Haywards Heath 3 a			19 33					19 40								20 03			20 06		20 28			
d			19 33					19 41								20 03			20 07		20 28			
Wivelsfield 4 d								19 45													20 32			
Lewes 4 a								19 58																
Burgess Hill 4 d			19 38													20 08			20 12		20 34			
Hassocks 4 d			19 42																		20 38			
Preston Park d																					20 45			
Hove 2 a																			20 24					
Brighton 10 a			19 52											20 05		20 22					20 50			

For general notes see front of timetable
For details of catering facilities see
Directory of Train Operators

§ It is unknown, at the time of going to press, when this station will open. For further details contact National Rail Enquiries 08457-484950 or see local publicity.

A Until 7 September
B From 14 September
C From Maidstone West (Table 208)
D To Bognor Regis (Table 188)

Table 186

Sundays

Watford Junction, Bedford and London → Brighton

Network Diagram - see first page of Table 186

		SN	FC	GX	SN	SN	SN	LO	GW	GW	GX	SE 55	SN	SN	XC	SN	FC	SN	GX	SN	GX	SN	SN	SN	FC
		1	1	1	1	1	1		1	1	1		1	1 ◇	1 ◇	1	1			1	1	1 ◇	1	1	1
		A			B	A						C			D	E		B					B	A	
London Victoria 15	⊖ d	19 34		19 45			19 47				20 00			20 02		20 04			20 15	20 17	20 30	20 32	20 34	20 34	
Watford Junction	d												19 22												
Harrow & Wealdstone	⊖ d												19 28												
Wembley Central	d																								
Willesden Jn. High Level	d							19 21																	
Shepherds Bush §	⊖ d																								
Kensington Olympia	⊖ d							19 30					19 48												
West Brompton	⊖ d							19 32					19 50												
Imperial Wharf §	d																								
Clapham Junction 10	d	19 40					19 53	19a41					20a00	20 07		20 10				20 23		20 38	20 40	20 40	
Bedford 7	d		18 20														18 50								19 20
Luton 10	d		18 44														19 14								19 44
Luton Airport Parkway 7	✈ d		18 46														19 16								19 46
St Albans City	d		18 58														19 28								19 58
St Pancras International 15	⊖ d		19 24														19 54								20 24
Farringdon 3	⊖ d		19 29														19 59								20 29
City Thameslink 3	d																								
London Blackfriars 3	⊖ d		19 34														20 04								20 34
London Bridge 4	⊖ d		19 41														20 11	20 14							20 41
Norwood Junction 2	d																	20 26							
East Croydon	a	19 53	19 56				20 06							20 20		20 23	20 26	20 30		20 36		20 50	20 53	20 53	20 56
	d	19 54	19 57				20 07							20 20		20 23	20 27	20 31		20 37		20 51	20 54	20 54	20 57
Purley 4	d	19 59														20 29		20 37					20 59	20 59	
Coulsdon South	d	20 03																20 40					21 03	21 03	
Merstham	d	20 08				20 08												20 46					21 08	21 08	
Redhill	a					20 12									20 27	20 37		20 50				21 03	21 12		
	d				20 12	20 12			20 19	20 21		20 29			20 35	20 38						21 04	21 12		
Tonbridge 4	a																								
Reigate	a								20 23																
Earlswood (Surrey)	d				20 15																				
Salfords	d				20 18																				
Horley 4	d				20 22	20 22										20 44									
Gatwick Airport 10	✈ a		20 18	20 20	20 24	20 24	20 27			20 30	20 35	20 38		20 41	20 44	20 46	20 48		20 50	20 54	21 05	21 11			21 18
	d		20 20		20 25	20 25	20 29					20 39		20 42	20 45	20 47	20 50			20 56		21 12			21 20
Three Bridges 15	a		20 24		20 30	20 30						20 43				20 52	20 54					21 16			21 24
	d		20 24		20 33	20 33										20 52	20 54					21 17			21 24
Crawley	d				20 36	20 36										20 55									
Ifield	d				20 39	20 39																			
Faygate	d																								
Littlehaven	d				20 45	20 45																			
Horsham 4	a				20 49	20 49										21 04									
Balcombe	d																					21 23			
Haywards Heath 3	a		20 33				20 40								20 54		21 03			21 06		21 28			21 33
	d		20 33				20 41								20 54		21 03			21 07		21 28			21 33
Wivelsfield 4	d						20 45															21 32			
Lewes 4	a						20 58																		
Burgess Hill 4	d		20 38														21 08			21 12		21 34			21 38
Hassocks 4	d		20 42																			21 38			21 42
Preston Park	d																					21 45			
Hove 2	a																			21 24					
Brighton 10	a		20 52											21 05	21 13		21 22					21 50			21 52

For general notes see front of timetable
For details of catering facilities see Directory of Train Operators

§ It is unknown, at the time of going to press, when this station will open. For further details contact National Rail Enquiries 08457-484950 or see local publicity.

A From 14 September
B Until 7 September
C From Maidstone West (Table 208)
D Until 7 September. Until 13 July from Birmingham New Street (Table 116)
E To Bognor Regis (Table 188)

Table 186

Sundays

Watford Junction, Bedford and London → Brighton

Network Diagram - see first page of Table 186

		LO	GX	SN		SN	SN	LO	SN	GW	GW	GX	SE	XC	SN	XC	FC	SN	GX	SN	LO	GX	SN	SN	SN
													55												
				[1]		[1]	[1]		[1]	[1]	[1]	[1]		[1] ◇	[1]	[1] ◇	[1]			[1]		[1]	[1] ◇	[1]	[1]
				A		B							C	D	E	D		A						A	B
London Victoria [15]	⊖ d		20 45				20 47					21 00			21 04				21 15	21 17		21 30	21 32	21§34	21§34
Watford Junction	d								20 22																
Harrow & Wealdstone	⊖ d								20 28																
Wembley Central	d																								
Willesden Jn. High Level	d	19 51						20 21													20 51				
Shepherds Bush §	⊖ d																								
Kensington Olympia	⊖ d	20 00						20 30	20 48												21 00				
West Brompton	⊖ d	20 02						20 32	20 50												21 02				
Imperial Wharf §	d																								
Clapham Junction [10]	d	20a11					20 53	20a43	21a00						21 10					21 23	21a11		21 38	21§40	21§40
Bedford [7]	d																19 50								
Luton [10]	d																20 14								
Luton Airport Parkway [7]	✈ d																20 16								
St Albans City	d																20 28								
St Pancras International [15]	⊖ d																20 54								
Farringdon [3]	⊖ d																20 59								
City Thameslink [3]	d																								
London Blackfriars [3]	⊖ d																21 04								
London Bridge [4]	⊖ d																21 11	21§14							
Norwood Junction [2]	d																	21§26							
East Croydon	a						21 06								21 23		21 26	21§30		21 36			21 50	21§53	21§53
	d						21 07								21 23		21 27	21§31		21 37			21 51	21§54	21§54
Purley [4]	d														21 29			21§37						21§59	21§59
Coulsdon South	d					←												21§40						22§03	22§03
Merstham	d					21§08												21§46						22§08	22§08
Redhill	a			←		21§12								21§31	21 37	←		21§50					22 03	22§12	→
	d			21§12		21§12				21 20	21 22		21 29	21§35	21 38	21§35							22 04	22§12	
Tonbridge [4]	a													→										→	
Reigate	a									21 24															
Earlswood (Surrey)	d			21§15																					
Salfords	d			21§18																					
Horley [4]	d			21§22		21§22									21 44										
Gatwick Airport [10]	✈ a		21 20	21§24		21§24	21 27				21 31	21 36	21 38		21 46	21§47	21 48		21 50	21 54		22 05	22 11		
	d			21§25		21§25	21 29						21 39		21 47		21 50			21 56			22 12		
Three Bridges [15]	a			21§30		21§30							21 43		21 52		21 54						22 16		
	d			21§33		21§33									21 52		21 54						22 17		
Crawley	d			21§36		21§36									21 55										
Ifield	d			21§39		21§39																			
Faygate	d																								
Littlehaven	d			21§45		21§45																			
Horsham [4]	a			21§49		21§49									22 04										
Balcombe	d																						22 23		
Haywards Heath [3]	a						21 40										22 03			22 06			22 28		
	d						21 41										22 03			22 07			22 28		
Wivelsfield [4]	d						21 45																22 32		
Lewes [4]	a						21 58																		
Burgess Hill [4]	d																22 08			22 12			22 34		
Hassocks [4]	d																						22 38		
Preston Park	d																						22 45		
Hove [2]	a																			22 24					
Brighton [10]	a																22 22						22 50		

For general notes see front of timetable
For details of catering facilities see
Directory of Train Operators

§ It is unknown, at the time of going to press, when this station will open. For further details contact National Rail Enquiries 08457-484950 or see local publicity.

A Until 7 September
B From 14 September
C From Maidstone West (Table 208)
D From 20 July. From 14 September from Birmingham New Street
E To Bognor Regis (Table 188)

Table 186

Sundays

Watford Junction, Bedford and London → Brighton

Network Diagram - see first page of Table 186

Station		FC [1]	GX	LO	SN [1] A	SN [1] B	SN [1]	SN [1]		GW [1]	GW [1]	GX [1]	SN [1] C	FC [1]	SN A	GX	SN [1]	LO	GX [1]	SN [1] ◇	SN [1] A	SN [1] B	FC [1]	GX	LO
London Victoria [15]	⊖ d		21 45				21 47					22 00	22 04			22 15	22 17		22 30	22 32	22 34	22 34		22 45	
Watford Junction	d							21 22																	
Harrow & Wealdstone	⊖ d							21 28																	
Wembley Central	d																								
Willesden Jn. High Level	d			21 21														21 51							22 21
Shepherds Bush §	⊖ d																								
Kensington Olympia	⊖ d			21 30				21 48										22 00							22 30
West Brompton	⊖ d			21 32				21 50										22 02							22 32
Imperial Wharf §	d																								
Clapham Junction [10]	d			21a41			21 53	22a00					22 10				22 23	22a11		22 38	22 40	22 40			22a41
Bedford [7]	d	20 10												20 40									21 10		
Luton [10]	d	20 34												21 04									21 34		
Luton Airport Parkway [7]	✈ d	20 36												21 06									21 36		
St Albans City	d	20 48												21 18									21 48		
St Pancras International [15]	⊖ d	21 24												21 54									22 24		
Farringdon [3]	⊖ d	21 29												21 59									22 29		
City Thameslink [3]	d																								
London Blackfriars [3]	⊖ d	21 34												22 04									22 34		
London Bridge [4]	⊖ d	21 41												22 11	22 14								22 41		
Norwood Junction [2]	d														22 26										
East Croydon	🚋 a	21 56					22 06						22 23	22 26	22 30		22 36			22 50	22 53	22 53	22 56		
	d	21 57					22 07						22 23	22 27	22 31		22 37			22 51	22 54	22 54	22 57		
Purley [4]	d												22 29		22 37						22 59	22 59			
Coulsdon South	d					←									22 40						23 03	23 03			
Merstham	d					22 08									22 46						23 08	23 08			
Redhill	a				←	22 12							22 37		22 50					23 03	23 12	→			
	d				22 12	22 12				22 20	22 22		22 38							23 04	23 12				
Tonbridge [4]	a																				→				
Reigate	a									22 24															
Earlswood (Surrey)	d				22 15																				
Salfords	d				22 18																				
Horley [4]	d				22 22	22 22							22 44												
Gatwick Airport [10]	✈ a	22 18	22 20		22 24	22 24	22 27				22 30	22 35	22 46	22 48		22 50	22 54		23 05	23 11			23 18	23 20	
	d	22 20			22 25	22 25	22 29						22 47	22 50			22 56			23 12			23 20		
Three Bridges [15]	a	22 24			22 30	22 30							22 52	22 54						23 16			23 24		
	d	22 24			22 33	22 33							22 52	22 54						23 17			23 24		
Crawley	d				22 36	22 36							22 55												
Ifield	d				22 39	22 39																			
Faygate	d																								
Littlehaven	d				22 45	22 45																			
Horsham [4]	a				22 49	22 49							23 04												
Balcombe	d																			23 23					
Haywards Heath [3]	a	22 33					22 40							23 03			23 06			23 28			23 33		
	d	22 33					22 41							23 03			23 07			23 28			23 33		
Wivelsfield [4]	d						22 45													23 32					
Lewes [4]	a						22 58																		
Burgess Hill [4]	d	22 38												23 08			23 12			23 34			23 38		
Hassocks [4]	d	22 42																		23 38			23 42		
Preston Park	d																			23 45					
Hove [2]	a																23 24								
Brighton [10]	a	22 52												23 22						23 50			23 52		

For general notes see front of timetable
For details of catering facilities see
Directory of Train Operators

§ It is unknown, at the time of going to press, when this station will open. For further details contact National Rail Enquiries 08457-484950 or see local publicity.

A Until 7 September
B From 14 September
C To Bognor Regis (Table 188)

Watford Junction, Bedford and London → Brighton

Network Diagram - see first page of Table 186

Station		SN 1 A	SN 1 B	SN 1	SN 1	LO	GW 1	GW 1	GX 1	SN 1	FC 1	GX	SN 1	SN 1	GX 1	SN 1 ◇	FC	LO	SN 1	GX	FC	FC 1
London Victoria 15 ⊖	d			22 47					23 00	23 04		23 15		23 17	23 30	23 32				23 45		
Watford Junction	d				22 22														23 22			
Harrow & Wealdstone ⊖	d				22 28														23 28			
Wembley Central	d																					
Willesden Jn. High Level	d					22 51												23 21				
Shepherds Bush § ⊖	d																					
Kensington Olympia ⊖	d				22 48	23 00												23 30	23 48			
West Brompton ⊖	d				22 50	23 02												23 32	23 50			
Imperial Wharf §	d																					
Clapham Junction 10	d			22 53	23a00	23a11				23 10				23 23		23 38		23a41	00 02			
Bedford 7	d										21 40						22 10				22 40	23 40
Luton 10	d										22 04						22 34				23 04	00 04
Luton Airport Parkway 7 ✈	d										22 06						22 36				23 06	00 06
St Albans City	d										22 18						22 48				23 18	00 18
St Pancras International 15 ⊖	d										22 54						23 24				23 54	00 54
Farringdon 3 ⊖	d										22 59						23 29				23 59	
City Thameslink 3	d																					
London Blackfriars 3 ⊖	d										23 04						23 34				00 04	01 04
London Bridge 4 ⊖	d										23 11						23 41				00 11	
Norwood Junction 2	d																					
East Croydon	a			23 06						23 23	23 26			23 36		23 52	23 56		00 20		00 26	01 30
	d			23 07						23 23	23 27			23 37		23 53	23 57				00 27	01 32
Purley 4	d									23 29												
Coulsdon South	d		←							23 33			←									
Merstham	d		23 08							23 38			23 38									
Redhill	a	←	23 12							→			23 42			00 05						
	d	23 12	23 12				23 20	23 22					23 42			00 05						
Tonbridge 4	a																					
Reigate	a						23 24															
Earlswood (Surrey)	d	23 15																				
Salfords	d	23 18																				
Horley 4	d	23 22	23 22										23 50									
Gatwick Airport 10 ✈	a	23 24	23 24	23 27				23 31	23 35		23 48	23 50	23 54	00 01	00 05	00 13	00 16			00 20	00 46	01 51
	d	23 25	23 25	23 29							23 50		23 55	00 02		00 14	00 17				00 47	01 52
Three Bridges 15	a	23 30	23 30								23 54		00 01	00 07		00 18	00 24				00 54	01 58
	d	23 33	23 33								23 54		00 01	00 07		00 19						
Crawley	d	23 36	23 36										00 05									
Ifield	d	23 39	23 39										00 07									
Faygate	d																					
Littlehaven	d	23 45	23 45										00 14									
Horsham 4	a	23 49	23 49										00 17									
Balcombe	d															00 25						
Haywards Heath 3	a			23 40							00 03			00 16		00 30						
	d			23 41							00 03			00 16		00 30						
Wivelsfield 4	d			23 45												00 34						
Lewes 4	a			23 58																		
Burgess Hill 4	d										00 08					00 36						
Hassocks 4	d															00 40						
Preston Park	d															00 47						
Hove 2	a													00 30								
Brighton 10	a										00 22					00 51						

For general notes see front of timetable
For details of catering facilities see
Directory of Train Operators

A Until 7 September
B From 14 September

§ It is unknown, at the time of going to press, when this station will open. For further details contact National Rail Enquiries 08457-484950 or see local publicity.

Brighton → London, Bedford and Watford Junction

Network Diagram - see first page of Table 186

Miles	Miles	Miles			FC	FC	FC	FC	FC	FC	SN	SN	SN	SN	SN	SN	GX	FC	FC	GX	GW	GX	GW	GX	SN
					MX	MO	MX	MX	MO	MX	MX	MO	MX	MX	MO	MX		MX	MO		MO		MX		
					1	1	1	1	1	1	1	1	1	1 ◇	1 ◇	1 ◇		1	1	1	1		1	1	1
0	—	—	**Brighton** 10	d	22p07	22p16		22p33	22p44					23p02	23p02			23p37	23p44						
—	0	—	Hove 2	d																					
1½	1½	—	Preston Park	d	22p11			22p37						23p06	23p06			23p41							
7¼	—	—	Hassocks 4	d	22p17			22p43	22p52					23p12	23p12			23p47	23p52						
9¼	—	—	Burgess Hill 4	d	22p21	22p26		22p47	22p56					23p16	23p16			23p51	23p56						
—	0	—	Lewes 4	d																					
10	9¼	—	Wivelsfield 4	d	22p23			22p49						23p19	23p19			23p53							
13	—	—	**Haywards Heath** 3	a	22p28	22p30	←	22p54	23p00					23p23	23p23			23p58	00 01						
—	—	—		d	22p32 →	22p31	22p32	22p54	23p01					23p24	23p24			23p59	00 01						
17	—	—	Balcombe	d			22p37	23p00							23p29			00 04							
—	0	—	**Horsham** 4	d							23p02	23p04													
—	1	—	Littlehaven	d							23p05	23p07													
—	3¼	—	Faygate	d																					
—	5¾	—	Ifield	d							23p11	23p13													
—	7	—	Crawley	d							23p14	23p17													
21½	8½	—	Three Bridges 4	a		22p40	22p42	23p05	23p10	←	23p18	23p20		23p33	23p35	←		00 10	00 10						
—	—	—		d		22p40	22p42	23p12 →	23p10	23p12	23p18	23p22		23p47 →	23p42	23p47		00 10	00 10						
24¼	—	—	**Gatwick Airport** 10 ✈	a		22p44	22p46	→	23p14	23p16	23p22	23p26		→	23p46	23p52		00 14	00 14						
—	—	—		d		22p45	22p46		23p15	23p16	23p23	23p27			23p47	23p53	00 05	00 15	00 15	00 20		00 35		00 50	01 05
25	—	—	Horley 4	d							23p26	23p30			23b49	23b56									01 07
27¼	—	—	Salfords	d							23p29														
29¼	—	—	Earlswood (Surrey)	d							23p33														
—	0	—	Reigate	d																	00 26		00 45		
—	—	0	Tonbridge 4	d																					
30	1¾	19¾	**Redhill**	a							23p36	23p36			23p56	00 02		00 22	00 22		00 30		00 49		
—	—	—		d							23p37	23p37			00 02	00 03		00 22	00 22						
32	—	—	Merstham	d							23p41	23p41													
35½	—	—	Coulsdon South	d							23p46	23p46	←												
37½	—	—	Purley 4	d							23p49	23p50	23p49		00 11	00 11									01 22
40½	0	—	**East Croydon**	a		23p01	23p02		23p31	23p32	→	23p55	23p55		00 16	00 16		00 35	00 35						01 27
—	—	—		d		23p02	23p02		23p32	23p32		23p56	23p58		00 17	00 17		00 36	00 36						01 28
—	1¼	—	Norwood Junction 2	a																					
—	10¼	—	**London Bridge** 4 ⊖	a		23p15	23p15		23p45	23p45								00 52	00 52						
—	—	—	**London Blackfriars** 3 ⊖	a		23p23	23p22		23p53	23p52								00 59	00 59						
—	—	—	City Thameslink 3	a																					
—	—	—	Farringdon 3 ⊖	a		23p27	23p28		23p57	23p58															
—	—	—	St Pancras International 15 ⊖	a		23p31	23p32		00 02	00 02								01 07	01 07						
—	—	—	St Albans City	a		00 03	23p54		00 33	00 24								01 39	01 39						
—	—	—	Luton Airport Parkway 4 ✈	a		00 15	00 06		00 45	00 36								01 51	01 51						
—	—	—	Luton 7	a		00 19	00 10		00 49	00 40								01 55	01 55						
—	—	—	**Bedford** 10	a		00 45	00 35		01 15	01 05								02 20	02 20						
48¼	0	0	Clapham Junction 10	d								00 11	00 11		00 30	00 30									01 41
—	—	2	Imperial Wharf §	d																					
—	2½	2½	West Brompton ⊖	d																					
—	3½	3½	Kensington Olympia ⊖	d																					
—	—	4¾	Shepherds Bush § ⊖	d																					
—	—	6¼	Willesden Jn. High Level	a																					
—	9	—	Wembley Central	a																					
—	12½	—	Harrow & Wealdstone ⊖	a																					
—	18½	—	Watford Junction	a																					
51	—	—	**London Victoria** 15 ⊖	a								00 18	00 18		00 37	00 37	00 40			00 55		01 10		01 25	01 49

For general notes see front of timetable
For details of catering facilities see Directory of Train Operators

§ It is unknown, at the time of going to press, when this station will open. For further details contact National Rail Enquiries 08457-484950 or see local publicity.

b Previous night. Stops to set down only

Brighton → London, Bedford and Watford Junction

Network Diagram - see first page of Table 186

Station		GX 1	SN 1	FC 1	SN 1	FC 1	SN 1	SN 1	FC	GX	SN 1◇	SN	FC 1	SN 1◇	LO	SN	XC 1◇	GX 1	GW 1	GW 1	SN	XC 1◇ A	FC 1	GX 1	SN
Brighton 10	d										03 50												05 09		
Hove 2	d																								
Preston Park	d																						05 13		
Hassocks 4	d																						05 19		
Burgess Hill 4	d																						05 23		
Lewes 4	d																								
Wivelsfield 4	d																						05 26		
Haywards Heath 3	a										04 25												05 30		
	d										04 25												05 30		
Balcombe	d																								
Horsham 4	d																				05 17				
Littlehaven	d																				05 20				
Faygate	d																								
Ifield	d																				05 26				
Crawley	d																				05 29				
Three Bridges 4	a										04 45			←							05 33		05 40		
	d		01 59	02 25	02 55	03 25	03 55		04 25		04 54 →		04 55	04 54							05 33		05 40		
Gatwick Airport 10 ✈	a		02 03	02 29	02 59	03 29	03 59		04 29				04 59	05 02							05 37		05 45		
	d	01 35	02 05	02 30	03 05	03 30	04 00		04 30	04 35			05 00	05 03			05 15	05 20		05 31	05 38	05 45	05 46	05 50	
Horley 4	d		02 07		03 07		04 03							05 05							05 40				
Salfords	d																								
Earlswood (Surrey)	d																								
Reigate	d																		05 34						
Tonbridge 4	d																								
Redhill	a																05 22		05 39	05 41	05 47	05 51			
	d															05 28	05 33				05 48	06 04			←
Merstham	d																				05 52 →				05 52
Coulsdon South	d															05 36									05 57
Purley 4	d		02 22		03 22		04 22					05 07		05 23		05 39									06 00
East Croydon	a		02 27	02 47	03 27	03 47	04 27		04 47			05 12	05 17	05 28		05 48							06 01		06 06
	d		02 28	02 47	03 28	03 47	04 28		04 47			05 13	05 17	05 29		05 48							06 02		06 07
Norwood Junction 2	a											05 17													
London Bridge 4	⊖ a											05 41	05 34										06 15		
London Blackfriars 3	⊖ a			03 12		04 12			05 12				05 41										06 23		
City Thameslink 3	a																						06 25		
Farringdon 3	⊖ a								05 17				05 47										06 29		
St Pancras International 15	⊖ a			03 21		04 21			05 21				05 51										06 33		
St Albans City	a			03 53		04 53			05 53				06 23										06 54		
Luton Airport Parkway 4	✈ a			04 05		05 05			06 05				06 35										07 06		
Luton 7	a			04 09		05 09			06 09				06 39										07 09		
Bedford 10	a			04 35		05 35			06 35				07 07										07 37		
Clapham Junction 10	d		02 41		03 41		04 47	05 25						05 49	06 05	06 08									06 18
Imperial Wharf §	d																								
West Brompton	⊖ d							05 31							06 12										
Kensington Olympia	⊖ d							05 34							06 15										
Shepherds Bush §	⊖ d																								
Willesden Jn. High Level	a														06 27										
Wembley Central	a																								
Harrow & Wealdstone	⊖ a							05 51																	
Watford Junction	a							05 58																	
London Victoria 15	⊖ a	02 20	02 49		03 49		04 54			05 10				05 58		06 18		05 55						06 20	06 25

For general notes see front of timetable
For details of catering facilities see
Directory of Train Operators

§ It is unknown, at the time of going to press, when this station will open. For further details contact National Rail Enquiries 08457-484950 or see local publicity.

A To Birmingham New Street (Table 116)

Brighton → London, Bedford and Watford Junction

Network Diagram - see first page of Table 186

		SN	SE 88	GW	SN	SN	SN	GX	LO	SN	FC	GX	FC	SN	GW	GX	LO	FC	SE 13	SN	SN	SN	SE 13	FC
		1	A	1	1	1	1			1	1	1	1	1	1			1	B	1	1	1 C	B	1
Brighton 10	d	05 22									05 39		05 49								06 01			06 09
Hove 2	d													05 57										
Preston Park	d										05 43		05 53											06 13
Hassocks 4	d										05 49		05 59								06 09			06 19
Burgess Hill 4	d	05 31									05 53		06 03								06 12			06 23
Lewes 4	d				05 29																	06 05		
Wivelsfield 4	d										05 56		06 05								06 15			
Haywards Heath 3	a	05 36			05 46						06 00		06 09	06 12							06 19	06 22		06 29
	d	05 36			05 47						06 00		06 09	06 12							06 27			06 30
Balcombe	d	05 42									06 05													06 35
Horsham 4	d						05 41													06 15				
Littlehaven	d						05 44													06 18				
Faygate	d																							
Ifield	d						05 50													06 24				
Crawley	d						05 53													06 28				
Three Bridges 4	a	05 47					05 57				06 12		06 19	06 21						06 31	06 36			06 40
	d	05 48					05 57				06 12		06 20	06 21						06 32	06 37			06 40
Gatwick Airport 10 ✈	a	05 52			05 58		06 01				06 16		06 24	06 25						06 36	06 41			06 45
	d	05 53	05 54	05 57	05 59		06 02	06 05			06 16	06 20	06 24	06 26		06 35				06 37	06 42			06 46
Horley 4	d						06 05													06 40				
Salfords	d		05 58																	06 44				
Earlswood (Surrey)	d		06 02																	06 48				
Reigate	d														06 34									
Tonbridge 4	d																		06 14					
Redhill	a		06 05	06 08			06 12						06 32		06 38			←	06 45	06 51				
	d						06 13						06 33 →					06 33	06 46	06 51 →				
Merstham	d						06 17																	
Coulsdon South	d						06 22												06 53				←	
Purley 4	d						06 25												06 56				06 56	
East Croydon	a	06 10			06 14	←	06 30				06 32			06 41				06 43	→		06 58		07 01	07 01
	d	06 10 →			06 15	06 10	06 31				06 32			06 42				06 44			06 59		07 02	07 02
Norwood Junction 2	a																							
London Bridge 4	⊖ a										06 46							06 58			07 14		07 18	07 16
London Blackfriars 3	⊖ a										06 52							07 06						07 22
City Thameslink 3	a										06 55							07 09						07 25
Farringdon 3	⊖ a										06 59							07 12						07 28
St Pancras International 15	⊖ a										07 03							07 16						07 32
St Albans City	a										07 24							07 35						07 54
Luton Airport Parkway 4 ✈	a										07 35							07 49						08 05
Luton 7	a										07 38							07 52						08 08
Bedford 10	a										08 05							08 18						08 35
Clapham Junction 10	d				06 25	06b30	06 40		06 35	06 49				06 51			07 04							
Imperial Wharf §	d																							
West Brompton	⊖ d					06 35			06 42	06 54							07 11							
Kensington Olympia	⊖ d					06 39			06 45	06 57							07 14							
Shepherds Bush §	⊖ d																							
Willesden Jn. High Level	a								06 57								07 26							
Wembley Central	a					06 57				07 17														
Harrow & Wealdstone	⊖ a					07 02				07 22														
Watford Junction	a					07 09				07 30														
London Victoria 15	⊖ a				06 33		06 47	06 35				06 50		07 00		07 05								

For general notes see front of timetable
For details of catering facilities see Directory of Train Operators

§ It is unknown, at the time of going to press, when this station will open. For further details contact National Rail Enquiries 08457-484950 or see local publicity.

A To Tonbridge (Table 209)
B From Paddock Wood (Table 207)
C From Hastings (Table 189)

b Arr. 0625

Brighton → London, Bedford and Watford Junction

Network Diagram - see first page of Table 186

Station		GX 1	SN 1	LO 1 A	SN 1	LO	SN 1 B	SN 1	GW 1	FC 1	SN 1 B	GX 1	SN 1 C	SN 1	SN 1 B	GW 1	SN 1	GX 1	SN 1	SN 1 D	SN 1 E	GW 1	SN 1	SN 1	SN 1 G
																			⚒	⚒					
Brighton 10	d				06 20					06 24				06 41					06 47						
Hove 2	d												06 30												
Preston Park	d									06 28			06 34						06 51						
Hassocks 4	d				06 28					06 34			06 41						06 57						
Burgess Hill 4	d				06 31					06 38			06 45						07 01						
Lewes 4	d																								06 50
Wivelsfield 4	d									06 40			06 47						07 03						07 07
Haywards Heath 3	a				06 37					06 45			06 52	06 57					07 08						07 13
	d				06 37					06 45			07 00						07 08						07 13
Balcombe	d									06 51															07 19
Horsham 4	d						06 35													06 55	07 04				
Littlehaven	d						06 38													06 58					
Faygate	d						06 42																		
Ifield	d						06 46													07 05					
Crawley	d						06 49													07 08	07 13				
Three Bridges 4	a				06 46		06 52			06 56	←									07 12	07 17				07 24
	d				06 47		06 57			06 56	06 57						07 08			07 21					07 25
Gatwick Airport 10 ✈	a				06 51		→			07 01	07 02		07 11				07 12		07 21						07 29
	d	06 50			06 52				06 59	07 01	07 03	07 05	07 12				07 13	07 20	07 22						07 30
Horley 4	d				06 55						07 05						07 15			07 27					
Salfords	d										07 09				←		07 19								
Earlswood (Surrey)	d										07 13				07 13		07 23								
Reigate	d							06 58			→					07 18						07 34			
Tonbridge 4	d																								
Redhill	a		←		07 02			07 02	07 06	07 09					07 16	07 23	07 26					07 38		←	
	d		06 51		07 04					07 10					07 16		07 26 →							07 26	
Merstham	d		06 55												07 20									07 30	
Coulsdon South	d		07 00												07 25									07 35	
Purley 4	d		07 05																					07 39	
East Croydon	a		07 09		07 15					07 23			07 28		07 31				07 38	07 43				07 44	07 46
	d		07 10		07 16					07 24			07 29		07 32				07 38	07 44				07 45	07 47
Norwood Junction 2	a																								
London Bridge 4 ⊖	a												07 46		07 48										08 03
London Blackfriars 3 ⊖	a									07 50															
City Thameslink 3	a									07 55															
Farringdon 3 ⊖	a									07 58															
St Pancras International 15 ⊖	a									08 02															
St Albans City	a									08 23															
Luton Airport Parkway 4 ✈	a									08 36															
Luton 7	a									08 39															
Bedford 10	a									09 00															
Clapham Junction 10	d		07 20	07 17	07 25	07 35													07 48	07 54			07 57	07 57	
Imperial Wharf §	d																								
West Brompton ⊖	d			07 24		07 42																	08 02		
Kensington Olympia ⊖	d			07 27		07 45																	08 05		
Shepherds Bush § ⊖	d																								
Willesden Jn. High Level	a			07 38		07 57																			
Wembley Central	a																						08 21		
Harrow & Wealdstone ⊖	a																						08 26		
Watford Junction	a																						08 33		
London Victoria 15 ⊖	a	07 20	07 28		07 34							07 35						07 50	07 57	08 03				08 07	

For general notes see front of timetable
For details of catering facilities see Directory of Train Operators

§ It is unknown, at the time of going to press, when this station will open. For further details contact National Rail Enquiries 08457-484950 or see local publicity.

A Until 29 August and from 17 November. To Stratford Low Level (Table 59)
B From Havant (Table 188)
C From Littlehampton (Table 188)
D From Bognor Regis (Table 188)
E From Portsmouth Harbour (Table 188)
G From Eastbourne (Table 189)

Brighton → London, Bedford and Watford Junction

Network Diagram - see first page of Table 186

Station		SN 1	SN 1	GX 1	FC 1	SN 1 A	SN 1	SN 1	SN 1	SN 1 B ⚲	SN 1 ⚲	LO	SN 1	SN 1 A	LO 1 C	LO 1 D	SN 1	SN 1	SN 1	LO	SN 1 E ⚲	SN 1	GX 1	GW 1	FC 1
Brighton 10	d				07 00						07 16														07 26
Hove 2	d					07 11								07 20											
Preston Park	d				07 04						07 20														07 30
Hassocks 4	d				07 10	07 21								07 30											07 36
Burgess Hill 4	d				07 14						07 29														07 40
Lewes 4	d																				07 23				
Wivelsfield 4	d				07 18						07 32			07 35							07 39				
Haywards Heath 3	a				07 23	07 29					07 36			07 40							07 43				07 46
	d				07 23	07 30					07 37			07 40							07 44				07 47
Balcombe	d																								
Horsham 4	d		07 10				07 19			07 25															
Littlehaven	d		07 13				07 22			07 29															
Faygate	d		07 17																						
Ifield	d		07 21				07 28																		
Crawley	d		07 24				07 32			07 37															
Three Bridges 4	a		07 27		07 32		07 35			07 40															07 56
	d		07 28		07 32		07 36			07 41												07 44			07 56
Gatwick Airport 10 ✈	a		07 32		07 37		07 40															07 48			08 00
	d		07 33	07 35	07 37		07 41															07 49	07 50	07 58	08 01 →
Horley 4	d		07 36				07 43														07 59	07 52			
Salfords	d		07 40				07 47										←					07 56			
Earlswood (Surrey)	d		07 43				07 51										07 51					07 59			
Reigate	d	07 40					→											07 51							
Tonbridge 4	d																								
Redhill	a	07 44	07 47					←					←				07 54	07 55				08 02		08 05	
	d	07 45 →	07 48 →					07 45					07 48				07 54					08 03			
Merstham	d												07 52				07 59					08 07			
Coulsdon South	d												07 57				08 04					08 12			
Purley 4	d												08 01									08 16			
East Croydon	a				07 53	07 57		08 00		08 00	08 03		08 06	08 08			08 11				08 14	08 21			
	d				07 54	07 57		08 00	07 47	08 01	08 04		08 07	08 09			08 12				08 15	08 22			
Norwood Junction 2	a																								
London Bridge 4 ⊖	a							08 18					08 24	08 26								08 39			
London Blackfriars 3 ⊖	a				08 19																				
City Thameslink 3	a				08 25																				
Farringdon 3 ⊖	a				08 29																				
St Pancras International 15 ⊖	a				08 33																				
St Albans City	a				08 53																				
Luton Airport Parkway 4 ✈	a				09 05																				
Luton 7	a				09 08																				
Bedford 10	a				09 35																				
Clapham Junction 10	d					08 07			08 10	08 11	08 14	08 05			08⟆17	08⟆19	08 21		08 24	08 35	08 24				
Imperial Wharf §	d																								
West Brompton ⊖	d								08 16			08 12			08⟆24	08⟆26			08 29	08 42					
Kensington Olympia ⊖	d								08a19			08 15			08⟆27	08a29			08 32	08 45					
Shepherds Bush § ⊖	d																								
Willesden Jn. High Level	a											08 27			08⟆37					08 57					
Wembley Central	a																		08 48						
Harrow & Wealdstone ⊖	a																		08 53						
Watford Junction	a																		09 00						
London Victoria 15 ⊖	a			08 05		08 16				08 20	08 22						08 31				08 33		08 22		

For general notes see front of timetable
For details of catering facilities see Directory of Train Operators

§ It is unknown, at the time of going to press, when this station will open. For further details contact National Rail Enquiries 08457-484950 or see local publicity.

- **A** From Littlehampton (Table 188)
- **B** From Bognor Regis (Table 188)
- **C** Until 29 August and from 17 November. To Stratford Low Level (Table 59)
- **D** 1 September to 14 November
- **E** From Seaford (Table 189) and from Hastings (Table 189)

Brighton → London, Bedford and Watford Junction

Network Diagram - see first page of Table 186

		SN	SN	GX	SN	SN	FC	SN	SN	SN	SN	SN	LO	SN	GX	FC	GW	SN	SN	SN		GX	SN	SE	SN
		1	1	1	1	1	1	1	1	1	1	1		1	1	1	1	1	1	1		1	1	13	1
					A			B					C					D					E		
Brighton 10	d		07 33								07 47					07 50									
Hove 2	d							07 41																	
Preston Park	d		07 37								07 51					07 54									
Hassocks 4	d							07 51								08 00									
Burgess Hill 4	d		07 46								08 00														
Lewes 4	d								07 44														07 54		
Wivelsfield 4	d		07 49																				08 10		
Haywards Heath 3	a		07 53					07 58	08 02		08 05					08 08							08 14		
	d		07 54					07 59	08 03		08 06					08 09							08 15		
Balcombe	d		07 59													08 14							08 21		
Horsham 4	d	07 40			07 46									07 51				08 10							08 14
Littlehaven	d	07 43			07 50									07 54											08 17
Faygate	d													07 58											08 21
Ifield	d	07 50			07 57									08 02											08 25
Crawley	d	07 53			08 01									08 05				08 19							08 28
Three Bridges 4	a	07 57	08 05		08 05									08 08				08 23					08 27		08 31
	d	07 58	08 05		08 06									08 09				08 23					08 28		08 32
Gatwick Airport 10 ✈	a	08 02					←	08 12						08 13		08 22									08 36
	d	08 04		08 05			08 01	08 13						08 14	08 20	08 22						08 35			08 37
Horley 4	d	08 07												08 16				08 28							08 40
Salfords	d	08 11										←		08 20					←						08 44
Earlswood (Surrey)	d	08 14										08 14		08 24					08 24						08 47
Reigate	d	→				08 07								→			08 24			08 27					
Tonbridge 4	d																							07 56	
Redhill	a					08 11	08 12					08 17					08 29		08 27	08 31					08 50
	d						08 14					08 18							08 35						08 51 →
Merstham	d											08 22							08a39 →						
Coulsdon South	d											08 28												08 36	
Purley 4	d											08 32													
East Croydon	a		08 23		08 27		08 27	08 29	08 31		08 34	08 37				08 38		08 43					08 46	08 47	
	d		08 24		08 27		08 28	08 30	08 32		08 34	08 37				08 38		08 44					08 47	08 48	
Norwood Junction 2	a																								
London Bridge 4 ⊖	a		08 41		08 44				08 49															09 07	
London Blackfriars 3 ⊖	a						08 52									09 08									
City Thameslink 3	a						08 59									09 11									
Farringdon 3 ⊖	a						09 02									09 14									
St Pancras International 15 ⊖	a						09 06									09 18									
St Albans City	a						09 28									09 41									
Luton Airport Parkway 4 ✈	a						09 40									09 53									
Luton 7	a						09 43									09 55									
Bedford 10	a						10 08									10 20									
Clapham Junction 10	d							08 41		08 43	08 44	08 49	08 51					08 53					08 57		
Imperial Wharf §	d																								
West Brompton ⊖	d									08 49			08 59												
Kensington Olympia ⊖	d									08a52			09a02												
Shepherds Bush § ⊖	d																								
Willesden Jn. High Level	a																								
Wembley Central	a																								
Harrow & Wealdstone ⊖	a																								
Watford Junction	a																								
London Victoria 15 ⊖	a			08 35				08 49			08 52	08 58			08 52			09 02				09 05	09 07		

For general notes see front of timetable
For details of catering facilities see Directory of Train Operators

§ It is unknown, at the time of going to press, when this station will open. For further details contact National Rail Enquiries 08457-484950 or see local publicity.

A From Bognor Regis (Table 188) and from Southampton Central (Table 188)
B From Littlehampton (Table 188)
C 1 September to 14 November
D From Bognor Regis (Table 188) and from Portsmouth Harbour (Table 188)
E From Hastings (Table 189)

Brighton → London, Bedford and Watford Junction

Network Diagram - see first page of Table 186

Station		SN	GW	FC	SN	LO	GX	FC	SN	SN	LO	SN	SN	FC	GX	SN	SN	SN	SN	SN	LO	FC	SE 13	GW	GX
		1	1	1	1		1	1	1	1		1	1	1	1	1	1	1	1	1	1	1		1	1
					A								B 🚲				🚲	🚲			C		D		
Brighton 10	d			08 02				08 16						08 36				08 45							
Hove 2	d				08 11																				
Preston Park	d			08 06	08 15			08 20						08 40											
Hassocks 4	d			08 12	08 22			08 26						08 46											
Burgess Hill 4	d			08 16	08 26			08 30						08 50											
Lewes 4	d												08 23												
Wivelsfield 4	d			08 18				08 33					08 39												
Haywards Heath 3	a			08 23	08 31			08 37					08 44	08 55				08 57				←			
	d			08 23	08 31			08 38					08 44	09 00 →				08 58				09 00			
Balcombe	d																					09 06			
Horsham 4	d								08 35								08 49								
Littlehaven	d								08 38																
Faygate	d																								
Ifield	d								08 44																
Crawley	d								08 47								08 58								
Three Bridges 4	a			08 33	08 41			08 47	08 51								09 01					09 11			
	d			08 34	08 42			08 47	08 51								09 02					09 12			
Gatwick Airport 10 ✈	a			08 38				08 51	08 55				08 55				09 06	09 10				09 16			
	d			08 38			08 50	08 52	08 56				08 56		09 05		09 07	09 11				09 16		09 17	09 20
Horley 4	d								08 59				08 59												
Salfords	d								09 03											←					
Earlswood (Surrey)	d								09 06											09 06					
Reigate	d		08 42						→										09 03						
Tonbridge 4	d																						08 51		
Redhill	a		08 51																09 07	09 10			09 21	09 24	
	d	←										← 08 51							09 14				09 22		
Merstham	d	08 39										08 55							09 18						
Coulsdon South	d	08 44										09 00							09 23				09 29		
Purley 4	d	08 48										09 03											09 34 →		
East Croydon	a	08 53		08 54	09 01			09 08				09 08	09 14				09 22	09 26	09 29			09 32			
	d	08 53		08 54	09 01			09 08				09 09	09 14				09 22	09 26	09 29			09 32			
Norwood Junction 2	a																								
London Bridge 4 ⊖	a	09 15		09 10																		09 45			
London Blackfriars 3 ⊖	a			09 18				09 37														09 52			
City Thameslink 3	a			09 21				09 40														09 55			
Farringdon 3 ⊖	a			09 26				09 44														09 59			
St Pancras International 15 ⊖	a			09 33				09 48														10 03			
St Albans City	a			09 53				10 09														10 23			
Luton Airport Parkway 4 ✈	a			10 05				10 20														10 35			
Luton 7	a			10 08				10 24														10 38			
Bedford 10	a			10 35				10 50														11 05			
Clapham Junction 10	d				09 11	09 05				09 14	09 35	09 21	09 24			09 27	09 33	09 36	09 39		09 47				
Imperial Wharf §	d																								
West Brompton ⊖	d					09 12				09 22	09 42					09 32					09 54				
Kensington Olympia ⊖	d					09 15				09a25	09 45					09 35					09 57				
Shepherds Bush § ⊖	d																								
Willesden Jn. High Level	a					09 27					09 57										10 12				
Wembley Central	a															09 53									
Harrow & Wealdstone ⊖	a															09 58									
Watford Junction	a															10 05									
London Victoria 15 ⊖	a				09 19		09 20					09 29	09 33		09 35		09 42	09 44	09 48						09 50

For general notes see front of timetable
For details of catering facilities see Directory of Train Operators

§ It is unknown, at the time of going to press, when this station will open. For further details contact National Rail Enquiries 08457-484950 or see local publicity.

A From Littlehampton (Table 188)
B From Hastings (Table 189)
C Until 29 August and from 17 November
D From Strood (Table 208)

Brighton → London, Bedford and Watford Junction

Network Diagram - see first page of Table 186

		SN	SN	GW	SE 13	SN	FC	GX	SN	LO	SN	SN	GW	SN	FC	SN	XC	GX	SN	SN	SN	FC	SE 13	GW	GX
		[1]	[1]	[1]		[1]	[1]	[1]	[1]		[1]	[1] ◇	[1]	[1]	[1]	[1]	[1] ◇	[1]	[1]	[1]	[1]	[1]		[1]	[1]
			A (trolley)		B	C						(trolley)		D (trolley)		D (trolley)	E (trolley)		G	(trolley)					
Brighton [10]	d						09 00					09 17			09 04		09 21					09 34			
Hove [2]	d					08 52															09 22				
Preston Park	d														09 08										
Hassocks [4]	d					09 04	09 08								09 14										
Burgess Hill [4]	d					09 08	09 12								09 18						09 35				
Lewes [4]	d		08 47																	09 17					
Wivelsfield [4]	d		08 59												09 20					09 33					
Haywards Heath [3]	a		09 03			09 12	09 16					09 30			09 25		09 32			09 37 (joined)	09 40 (joined)	09 47			
	d		09 06			09 14	09 16					09 30			09 25		09 33			09 44		09 48			
Balcombe	d														09 31										
Horsham [4]	d	09 00												09 20					09 30						
Littlehaven	d	09 03																	09 33						
Faygate	d																		09 37						
Ifield	d	09 09																	09 41						
Crawley	d	09 13												09 29					09 44						
Three Bridges [4]	a	09 16	09 17				09 26							09 32	09 36				09 47						
	d	09 18	09 18				09 27							09 33	09 37				09 48						
Gatwick Airport [10]	a	09 22	09 22			09 26	09 31							09 37	09 41		09 44		09 52	09 55		10 00			
	d	09 23	09 23			09 27	09 31	09 35	09 37					09 38	09 41	←	09 46	09 50	09 52	09 56		10 01		10 03	10 05
Horley [4]	d	09 26												09 41 →		09 41			09 55						
Salfords	d	09 30									←														
Earlswood (Surrey)	d	09 33									09 33														
Reigate	d	→		09 24									09 37												
Tonbridge [4]	d																						09 34		
Redhill	a			09 29							09 36		09 41			09 47			10 02				10 04	10 10	
	d										09 37					09 48							10 05		
Merstham	d										09 41												10 09		
Coulsdon South	d				←						09 46												10 14		
Purley [4]	d				09 34						09 49												10 18		
East Croydon	a		09 39		09 40	09 42	09 47		09 52		09 54	09 55			09 57	09 59	10 03			10 11		10 16	10 23		
	d		09 39		09 40	09 43	09 47		09 52		09 55	09 56			09 57	10 00	10 08			10 12		10 17	10 24		
Norwood Junction [2]	a										09 59												10 28		
London Bridge [4]	a				09 55		10 00				10 12				10 15							10 30	10 40		
London Blackfriars [3]	a						10 07								10 22							10 37			
City Thameslink [3]	a						10 10								10 25							10 40			
Farringdon [3]	a						10 14								10 29							10 44			
St Pancras International [15]	a						10 18								10 33							10 48			
St Albans City	a						10 39								10 53							11 09			
Luton Airport Parkway [4]	a						10 50								11 05							11 20			
Luton [7]	a						10 54								11 08							11 24			
Bedford [10]	a						11 20								11 35							11 50			
Clapham Junction [10]	d		09 50			09 53			10 03	10 05		10 05				10 09				10 22					
Imperial Wharf §	d																								
West Brompton	d								10 09	10 12															
Kensington Olympia	d								10 12	10 15															
Shepherds Bush §	d																10 37								
Willesden Jn. High Level	a									10 27															
Wembley Central	a																								
Harrow & Wealdstone	a								10 29																
Watford Junction	a								10 45																
London Victoria [15]	a		09 58			10 00		10 05				10 13				10 16		10 20		10 28					10 35

For general notes see front of timetable
For details of catering facilities see Directory of Train Operators

§ It is unknown, at the time of going to press, when this station will open. For further details contact National Rail Enquiries 08457-484950 or see local publicity.

- **A** From Seaford (Table 189) and from Hastings (Table 189)
- **B** From Strood (Table 208)
- **C** From Littlehampton (Table 188)
- **D** From Bognor Regis (Table 188) and from Portsmouth Harbour (Table 188)
- **E** To Birmingham New Street (Table 116)
- **G** To Tunbridge Wells (Table 209)

Brighton → London, Bedford and Watford Junction

Network Diagram - see first page of Table 186

Station		SN	LO	SN	FC	GW	GX	SN	SN	SN	SN	FC	GW	GX	SN	LO	SN	SN		SN	FC	GX	SN	SN	SN
		1 ◇ ⛾		1 A	1	1	1	1	1 B ⛾	1 ⛾	1	1	1	1	1		1	1 ◇ ⛾		1 C	1	1	1 D	1 B ⛾	1 ⛾
Brighton [10]	d	09 49			09 37						09 55	10 04						10 19			10 07				
Hove [2]	d								09 51															10 21	
Preston Park	d				09 41						09 58										10 11				
Hassocks [4]	d				09 47						10 05										10 17				
Burgess Hill [4]	d				09 51				10 02		10 08										10 21				
Lewes [4]	d									09 49															10 20
Wivelsfield [4]	d				09 53						10 11										10 23				10 35
Haywards Heath [3]	a				09 58				10 06	10 09	10 15	10 18									10 28			10 35	10 40
	d				09 58				10 13		10 16	10 18									10 32			10 43	
Balcombe	d																				10 37				
Horsham [4]	d			09 52				10 00												10 20			10 32		
Littlehaven	d							10 03															10 35		
Faygate	d																								
Ifield	d							10 09															10 41		
Crawley	d			10 01				10 14												10 29			10 44		
Three Bridges [4]	a			10 04	10 07			10 18			10 25				←					10 32	10 42		10 48		
	d			10 05	10 10			10 18			10 31 →				10 31					10 33	10 42		10 48		
Gatwick Airport [10] ✈	a			10 09	10 15			10 22	10 24			10 30			10 35					10 37	10 46		10 52	10 54	
	d			10 10	10 16		10 20	10 23	10 25			10 31		10 35	10 37					10 38	10 46	10 50	10 53	10 55	
Horley [4]	d							10 26												10 41			10 55		
Salfords	d							10 30																	
Earlswood (Surrey)	d							10 33																	
Reigate	d					10 19							10 34												
Tonbridge [4]	d																								
Redhill	a			10 17		10 24		10 36					10 38							10 47			11 02		
	d			10 18				10 37 →									← 10 37			10 48					
Merstham	d																10 41								
Coulsdon South	d																10 46								
Purley [4]	d																10 49								
East Croydon 🚊	a	10 24		10 29	10 32				10 40			10 46			10 52		10 54	10 55		10 59	11 02			11 11	
	d	10 24		10 29	10 32				10 40			10 47			10 52		10 55	10 55		11 00	11 02			11 11	
Norwood Junction [2]	a																10 59								
London Bridge [4] ⊖	a				10 45							11 00					11 12				11 15				
London Blackfriars [3] ⊖	a				10 52							11 07									11 22				
City Thameslink [3]	a				10 55							11 10									11 25				
Farringdon [3] ⊖	a				10 59							11 14									11 29				
St Pancras International [15] ⊖	a				11 03							11 18									11 33				
St Albans City	a				11 23							11 39									11 53				
Luton Airport Parkway [4] ✈	a				11 35							11 50									12 05				
Luton [7]	a				11 38							11 54									12 08				
Bedford [10]	a				12 05							12 20									12 35				
Clapham Junction [10]	d	10 34	10 35	10 39					10 50						11 03	11 05		11 05		11 10				11 21	
Imperial Wharf §	d																								
West Brompton ⊖	d		10 42												11 09	11 12									
Kensington Olympia ⊖	d		10 45												11 12	11 15									
Shepherds Bush § ⊖	d																								
Willesden Jn. High Level	a		10 57													11 27									
Wembley Central	a																								
Harrow & Wealdstone ⊖	a														11 29										
Watford Junction	a														11 45										
London Victoria [15] ⊖	a	10 40		10 45			10 50		10 58					11 05				11 11		11 16		11 20		11 27	

For general notes see front of timetable
For details of catering facilities see Directory of Train Operators

§ It is unknown, at the time of going to press, when this station will open. For further details contact National Rail Enquiries 08457-484950 or see local publicity.

A From Bognor Regis (Table 188) and from Southampton Central (Table 188)

B ⛾ from Haywards Heath

C From Bognor Regis (Table 188) and from Portsmouth Harbour (Table 188)

D To Tunbridge Wells (Table 209)

Brighton → London, Bedford and Watford Junction

Network Diagram - see first page of Table 186

Station		FC	SE	GW	GX	SN	LO	SN	FC	GW	GX	SN	SN	SN	SN	FC	GW	GX	SN	LO	SN	SN	SN	FC	GX
			13																						
		1		1	1	1 ◇		1	1	1	1	1	1	1	1	1	1	1	1		1	1 ◇	1	1	1
			A					B															C		
						[trolley]		[trolley]					[trolley]									[trolley]			
Brighton 10	d	10 34				10 49			10 37						10 55	11 04						11 19		11 07	
Hove 2	d													10 51											
Preston Park	d								10 41						10 58									11 11	
Hassocks 4	d								10 47						11 05									11 17	
Burgess Hill 4	d								10 51					11 02	11 08									11 21	
Lewes 4	d												10 49												
Wivelsfield 4	d								10 53						11 11									11 23	
Haywards Heath 3	a	10 47							10 58				11 05	11 08	11 15	11 18								11 28	
	d	10 48							11 02				11 13		11 16	11 18								11 32	
Balcombe	d																							11 37	
Horsham 4	d							10 50				11 00											11 20		
Littlehaven	d											11 03													
Faygate	d																								
Ifield	d											11 09													
Crawley	d							10 59				11 14											11 29		
Three Bridges 4	a							11 02	11 11			11 18			11 25								11 32	11 42	
	d							11 03	11 12			11 18			11 31 →				← 11 31				11 33	11 42	
Gatwick Airport 10 ✈	a	11 00						11 07	11 16			11 22	11 24			11 30			11 35				11 37	11 46	
	d	11 01		11 03	11 05			11 08	11 16		11 20	11 23	11 25			11 31		11 35	11 37				11 38	11 46	11 50
Horley 4	d											11 26											11 41		
Salfords	d											11 30													
Earlswood (Surrey)	d											11 33													
Reigate	d									11 18							11 34								
Tonbridge 4	d		10 34																						
Redhill	a		11 04	11 10				11 15		11 24		11 36					11 38						11 48		
	d		11 05					11 16				11 37 →									← 11 37		11 49		
Merstham	d		11 09																		11 41				
Coulsdon South	d		11 14																		11 46				
Purley 4	d		11 18																		11 49				
East Croydon 🚋	a	11 16	11 23			11 23		11 27	11 32				11 40			11 46			11 52		11 54	11 55	12 00	12 02	
	d	11 17	11 24			11 24		11 28	11 32				11 40			11 47			11 52		11 55	11 55	12 00	12 02	
Norwood Junction 2	a		11 28																		11 59				
London Bridge 4 ⊖	a	11 30	11 40						11 45							12 00					12 12			12 15	
London Blackfriars 3 ⊖	a	11 37							11 52							12 07								12 22	
City Thameslink 3	a	11 40							11 55							12 10								12 25	
Farringdon 3 ⊖	a	11 44							11 59							12 14								12 29	
St Pancras International 15 ⊖	a	11 48							12 03							12 18								12 33	
St Albans City	a	12 09							12 23							12 39								12 53	
Luton Airport Parkway 4 ✈	a	12 20							12 35							12 50								13 05	
Luton 7	a	12 24							12 38							12 54								13 08	
Bedford 10	a	12 50							13 05							13 20								13 35	
Clapham Junction 10	d					11 33	11 35	11 37					11 50						12 03	12 05		12 05	12 11		
Imperial Wharf §	d																								
West Brompton ⊖	d						11 42												12 09	12 12					
Kensington Olympia ⊖	d						11 45												12 12	12 15					
Shepherds Bush § ⊖	d																								
Willesden Jn. High Level	a						11 57													12 27					
Wembley Central	a																								
Harrow & Wealdstone ⊖	a																		12 29						
Watford Junction	a																		12 45						
London Victoria 15 ⊖	a				11 35	11 40		11 44			11 50		11 58					12 05				12 11	12 18		12 20

For general notes see front of timetable
For details of catering facilities see Directory of Train Operators

§ It is unknown, at the time of going to press, when this station will open. For further details contact National Rail Enquiries 08457-484950 or see local publicity.

A From Tunbridge Wells (Table 206)
B From Bognor Regis (Table 188) and from Southampton Central (Table 188)
C From Bognor Regis (Table 188) and from Portsmouth Harbour (Table 188)

Brighton → London, Bedford and Watford Junction

Network Diagram - see first page of Table 186

		SN	SN	SN	FC	SE	GW	GX	SN	LO	SN	FC	GW	GX	SN	SN	SN	SN	FC	GW	GX	SN	LO	SN	SN
						13																			
		1	1	1	1		1	1	1 ◇		1	1	1	1	1	1	1	1	1	1	1	1		1	1 ◇
		A	B			C					D														
			🛒	🛒					🛒		🛒					🛒									🛒
Brighton [10]	d				11 34				11 49			11 37						11 55	12 04						12 19
Hove [2]	d		11 21														11 51								
Preston Park	d											11 41						11 58							
Hassocks [4]	d											11 47						12 05							
Burgess Hill [4]	d											11 51					12 02	12 08							
Lewes [4]	d			11 20												11 50									
Wivelsfield [4]	d			11 34								11 53						12 11							
Haywards Heath [3]	a		11 35	11 40	11 47							11 58				12 05	12 09	12 15	12 18						
	d		11 43		11 48							12 02				12 13		12 16	12 18						
Balcombe	d																								
Horsham [4]	d	11 32									11 50				12 00										
Littlehaven	d	11 35													12 03										
Faygate	d																								
Ifield	d	11 41													12 09										
Crawley	d	11 44									11 59				12 14										
Three Bridges [4]	a	11 48									12 02	12 11			12 18			12 25				←			
	d	11 48									12 03	12 12			12 18			12 31 →				12 31			
Gatwick Airport [10] ✈	a	11 52	11 54		12 00						12 07	12 16			12 22	12 24			12 30			12 35			
	d	11 53	11 55		12 01		12 03	12 05			12 08	12 16		12 20	12 23	12 25			12 31		12 35	12 37			
Horley [4]	d	11 55													12 26										
Salfords	d														12 30										
Earlswood (Surrey)	d														12 33										
Reigate	d												12 19							12 34					
Tonbridge [4]	d					11 34																			
Redhill	a	12 02				12 04	12 10				12 15		12 24		12 36					12 38				←	
	d					12 05					12 16				12 37 →									12 37	
Merstham	d					12 09																		12 41	
Coulsdon South	d					12 14																		12 46	
Purley [4]	d					12 18																		12 49	
East Croydon 🚋	a		12 10		12 16	12 23			12 23		12 27	12 32				12 40			12 46			12 52		12 54	12 55
	d		12 10		12 17	12 24			12 24		12 28	12 32				12 40			12 47			12 52		12 55	12 55
Norwood Junction [2]	a					12 28																		12 59	
London Bridge [4] ⊖	a				12 30	12 40						12 45							13 00					13 12	
London Blackfriars [3] ⊖	a				12 37							12 52							13 07						
City Thameslink [3]	a				12 40							12 55							13 10						
Farringdon [3] ⊖	a				12 44							12 59							13 14						
St Pancras International [15] ⊖	a				12 48							13 03							13 18						
St Albans City	a				13 09							13 23							13 39						
Luton Airport Parkway [4] ✈	a				13 20							13 35							13 50						
Luton [7]	a				13 24							13 38							13 54						
Bedford [10]	a				13 50							14 05							14 20						
Clapham Junction [10]	d		12 20						12 33	12 35	12 37					12 50						13 03	13 05		13 05
Imperial Wharf §	d																					13 09	13 12		
West Brompton ⊖	d									12 42												13 12	13 15		
Kensington Olympia ⊖	d									12 45															
Shepherds Bush § ⊖	d																								
Willesden Jn. High Level	a									12 57													13 27		
Wembley Central	a																					13 29			
Harrow & Wealdstone ⊖	a																					13 45			
Watford Junction	a																								
London Victoria [15] ⊖	a		12 29					12 35	12 40		12 44			12 50		12 57					13 05				13 11

For general notes see front of timetable
For details of catering facilities see Directory of Train Operators

§ It is unknown, at the time of going to press, when this station will open. For further details contact National Rail Enquiries 08457-484950 or see local publicity.

A To Tunbridge Wells (Table 209)
B 🛒 from Haywards Heath
C From Tunbridge Wells (Table 206)
D From Bognor Regis (Table 188) and from Southampton Central (Table 188)

Brighton → London, Bedford and Watford Junction

Network Diagram - see first page of Table 186

Station		SN	FC	GX	SN	SN	SN	FC	SE	GW	GX	SN	LO	SN	FC	GW		GX	SN	SN	SN	SN	FC	GW	GX
									13																
		[1]	[1]	[1]	[1]	[1]	[1]	[1]		[1]	[1]	[1] ◇		[1]	[1]	[1]		[1]	[1]	[1]	[1]	[1]	[1]	[1]	[1]
		A			B	C			D					E											
		🛒				🛒	🛒					🛒		🛒						🛒					
Brighton [10]	d		12 07					12 34				12 49			12 37							12 55	13 04		
Hove [2]	d					12 21															12 51				
Preston Park	d		12 11												12 41							12 58			
Hassocks [4]	d		12 17												12 47							13 05			
Burgess Hill [4]	d		12 21												12 51						13 02	13 08			
Lewes [4]	d						12 20													12 50					
Wivelsfield [4]	d		12 23				12 34								12 53							13 11			
Haywards Heath [3]	a		12 28			12 35	12 40	12 47							12 58					13 05	13 09	13 15	13 18		
	d		12 32			12 43		12 48							13 02					13 13		13 16	13 18		
Balcombe	d		12 37																						
Horsham [4]	d	12 20			12 30									12 50					13 00						
Littlehaven	d				12 33														13 03						
Faygate	d				12 37																				
Ifield	d				12 41														13 09						
Crawley	d	12 29			12 44									12 59					13 14						
Three Bridges [4]	a	12 32	12 42		12 47									13 02	13 11				13 18			13 25			
	d	12 33	12 42		12 48									13 03	13 12				13 18			13 31 →			
Gatwick Airport [10] ✈	a	12 37	12 46		12 52	12 54		13 00						13 07	13 16				13 22	13 24			13 30		
	d	12 38	12 46	12 50	12 52	12 55		13 01		13 03	13 05			13 08	13 16			13 20	13 23	13 25			13 31		13 35
Horley [4]	d	12 41			12 55														13 26						
Salfords	d																		13 30						
Earlswood (Surrey)	d																		13 33						
Reigate	d															13 18								13 34	
Tonbridge [4]	d								12 34																
Redhill	a	12 47			13 02				13 04	13 10				13 15		13 24			13 36					13 38	
	d	12 48							13 05					13 16					13 37 →						
Merstham	d								13 09																
Coulsdon South	d								13 14																
Purley [4]	d								13 18																
East Croydon	a	13 00	13 02			13 10		13 16	13 23			13 23		13 27	13 32					13 40			13 46		
	d	13 00	13 02			13 10		13 17	13 24			13 24		13 28	13 32					13 40			13 47		
Norwood Junction [2]	a								13 28																
London Bridge [4]	⊖ a		13 15					13 30	13 40						13 45								14 00		
London Blackfriars [3]	⊖ a		13 22					13 37							13 52								14 07		
City Thameslink [3]	a		13 25					13 40							13 55								14 10		
Farringdon [3]	⊖ a		13 29					13 44							13 59								14 14		
St Pancras International [15]	⊖ a		13 33					13 48							14 03								14 18		
St Albans City	a		13 53					14 09							14 23								14 39		
Luton Airport Parkway [4]	✈ a		14 05					14 20							14 35								14 50		
Luton [7]	a		14 08					14 24							14 38								14 54		
Bedford [10]	a		14 35					14 50							15 05								15 20		
Clapham Junction [10]	d	13 11				13 20						13 33	13 35	13 37						13 50					
Imperial Wharf §	d																								
West Brompton	⊖ d												13 42												
Kensington Olympia	⊖ d												13 45												
Shepherds Bush §	⊖ d																								
Willesden Jn. High Level	a												13 57												
Wembley Central	a																								
Harrow & Wealdstone	⊖ a																								
Watford Junction	a																								
London Victoria [15]	⊖ a	13 18		13 20		13 27					13 35	13 40		13 44				13 50		13 58					14 05

For general notes see front of timetable
For details of catering facilities see Directory of Train Operators

§ It is unknown, at the time of going to press, when this station will open. For further details contact National Rail Enquiries 08457-484950 or see local publicity.

A From Bognor Regis (Table 188) and from Portsmouth Harbour (Table 188)
B To Tunbridge Wells (Table 209)
C 🛒 from Haywards Heath
D From Tunbridge Wells (Table 206)
E From Bognor Regis (Table 188) and from Southampton Central (Table 188)

Brighton → London, Bedford and Watford Junction

Network Diagram - see first page of Table 186

		SN	LO	SN	SN	SN	FC	GX	SN	SN	SN	FC	SE 13	GW	GX	SN	LO	SN	FC	GW	GX	SN	SN	SN	SN
		1		1	1 ◇	1	1	1	1	1	1	1		1	1	1 ◇		1	1	1	1	1	1	1	1
						A			B	C			D					E							
					✠	✠				✠	✠					✠		✠					✠		
Brighton 10	d				13 19		13 07					13 34				13 49			13 37						13 55
Hove 2	d									13 21														13 51	
Preston Park	d						13 11												13 41						13 58
Hassocks 4	d						13 17												13 47						14 05
Burgess Hill 4	d						13 21												13 51					14 02	14 08
Lewes 4	d										13 20												13 50		
Wivelsfield 4	d						13 23				13 34								13 53						14 11
Haywards Heath 3	a						13 28			13 35	13 40	13 47							13 58				14 05	14 09	14 15
	d						13 32			13 43		13 48							14 02				14 13		14 16
Balcombe	d						13 37																		
Horsham 4	d					13 20			13 32									13 50				14 00			
Littlehaven	d								13 35													14 03			
Faygate	d																								
Ifield	d								13 41													14 09			
Crawley	d					13 29			13 44									13 59				14 14			
Three Bridges 4	a					13 32	13 42		13 48									14 02	14 11			14 18			14 25
	d	← 13 31				13 33	13 42		13 48									14 03	14 12			14 18			14 31 →
Gatwick Airport 10 ✈	a	13 35				13 37	13 46		13 52	13 54		14 00						14 07	14 16			14 22	14 24		
	d	13 37				13 38	13 46	13 50	13 53	13 55		14 01		14 03	14 05			14 08	14 16		14 20	14 23	14 25		
Horley 4	d					13 41			13 55													14 26			
Salfords	d																					14 30			
Earlswood (Surrey)	d																					14 33			
Reigate	d																			14 19					
Tonbridge 4	d												13 34												
Redhill	a					13 47			14 02				14 04	14 10				14 15		14 24		14 36			
	d			← 13 37		13 48							14 05					14 16				14 37 →			
Merstham	d			13 41									14 09												
Coulsdon South	d			13 46									14 14												
Purley 4	d			13 49									14 18												
East Croydon	a	13 52		13 54	13 55	14 00	14 02			14 10		14 16	14 23			14 23		14 27	14 32				14 40		
	d	13 52		13 55	13 55	14 00	14 02			14 10		14 17	14 24			14 24		14 28	14 32				14 40		
Norwood Junction 2	a			13 59									14 28												
London Bridge 4 ⊖	a			14 12			14 15					14 30	14 40						14 45						
London Blackfriars 3 ⊖	a						14 22					14 37							14 52						
City Thameslink 3	a						14 25					14 40							14 55						
Farringdon 3 ⊖	a						14 29					14 44							14 59						
St Pancras International 15 ⊖	a						14 33					14 48							15 03						
St Albans City	a						14 53					15 09							15 23						
Luton Airport Parkway 4 ✈	a						15 05					15 20							15 35						
Luton 7	a						15 08					15 24							15 38						
Bedford 10	a						15 35					15 50							16 05						
Clapham Junction 10	d	14 03	14 05		14 05	14 11				14 20						14 33	14 35	14 37					14 50		
Imperial Wharf §	d																								
West Brompton ⊖	d	14 09	14 12														14 42								
Kensington Olympia ⊖	d	14 12	14 15														14 45								
Shepherds Bush § ⊖	d																								
Willesden Jn. High Level	a		14 27														14 57								
Wembley Central	a																								
Harrow & Wealdstone ⊖	a	14 29																							
Watford Junction	a	14 45																							
London Victoria 15 ⊖	a				14 11	14 18		14 20		14 27					14 35	14 40		14 44			14 50		14 57		

For general notes see front of timetable
For details of catering facilities see Directory of Train Operators

§ It is unknown, at the time of going to press, when this station will open. For further details contact National Rail Enquiries 08457-484950 or see local publicity.

A From Bognor Regis (Table 188) and from Portsmouth Harbour (Table 188)
B To Tunbridge Wells (Table 209)
C ✠ from Haywards Heath
D From Tunbridge Wells (Table 206)
E From Bognor Regis (Table 188) and from Southampton Central (Table 188)

Brighton → London, Bedford and Watford Junction

Network Diagram - see first page of Table 186

		FC	GW	GX	SN	LO	SN	SN	SN	FC	GX	XC	SN	SN	SN	FC	SE	GW	GX	SN	LO	SN	FC	GW	GX
		1	1	1	1		1	1 ◇	1	1	1	R 1	1	1	1	1	13	1	1	1 ◇		1	1	1	1
									A				B	C			D					E			
								🛒				🍴		🛒	🛒					🛒					
Brighton 10	d	14 04						14 19		14 07		14 22				14 34				14 49			14 37		
Hove 2	d													14 21											
Preston Park	d									14 11													14 41		
Hassocks 4	d									14 17													14 47		
Burgess Hill 4	d									14 21													14 51		
Lewes 4	d														14 20										
Wivelsfield 4	d									14 23					14 34								14 53		
Haywards Heath 3	a	14 18								14 28				14 35	14 40	14 47							14 58		
	d	14 18								14 31				14 43		14 48							15 02		
Balcombe	d									14 37															
Horsham 4	d								14 20				14 32									14 50			
Littlehaven	d												14 35												
Faygate	d																								
Ifield	d												14 41												
Crawley	d								14 29				14 44									14 59			
Three Bridges 4	a								14 32	14 41			14 48									15 02	15 11		
	d				← 14 31				14 33	14 41			14 48									15 03	15 12		
Gatwick Airport 10 ✈	a	14 30			14 35				14 37	14 46		14 50	14 52	14 54		15 00						15 07	15 16		
	d	14 31		14 35	14 37				14 38	14 46	14 50	14 51	14 53	14 55		15 01		15 03	15 05			15 08	15 16		15 20
Horley 4	d								14 41				14 55												
Salfords	d																								
Earlswood (Surrey)	d																								
Reigate	d		14 34																					15 18	
Tonbridge 4	d																14 34								
Redhill	a		14 38						14 47				15 02				15 04	15 10				15 15		15 24	
	d						← 14 37		14 48								15 05					15 16			
Merstham	d						14 41										15 09								
Coulsdon South	d						14 46										15 14								
Purley 4	d						14 49										15 18								
East Croydon	a	14 46			14 52		14 54	14 55	15 00	15 01		15 08		15 09		15 16	15 23			15 23		15 27	15 32		
	d	14 47			14 52		14 55	14 55	15 00	15 01		15 09		15 10		15 17	15 24			15 24		15 28	15 32		
Norwood Junction 2	a						14 59										15 28								
London Bridge 4 ⊖	a	15 00					15 12			15 15						15 30	15 40						15 45		
London Blackfriars 3 ⊖	a	15 07								15 22						15 37							15 52		
City Thameslink 3	a	15 10								15 24						15 40							15 55		
Farringdon 3 ⊖	a	15 14								15 28						15 44							15 59		
St Pancras International 15 ⊖	a	15 18								15 33						15 48							16 03		
St Albans City	a	15 39								15 53						16 09							16 23		
Luton Airport Parkway 4 ✈	a	15 50								16 05						16 20							16 36		
Luton 7	a	15 54								16 08						16 24							16 40		
Bedford 10	a	16 20								16 35						16 50							17 05		
Clapham Junction 10	d				15 03	15 05		15 05	15 11					15 20						15 33	15 35	15 37			
Imperial Wharf §	d																								
West Brompton ⊖	d				15 09	15 12																			
Kensington Olympia ⊖	d				15 12	15 15						15 36									15 42				
Shepherds Bush § ⊖	d																				15 45				
Willesden Jn. High Level	a					15 27																			
Wembley Central	a																				15 57				
Harrow & Wealdstone ⊖	a				15 29																				
Watford Junction	a				15 45																				
London Victoria 15 ⊖	a			15 05				15 11	15 18		15 20			15 28					15 35	15 40		15 44			15 50

For general notes see front of timetable
For details of catering facilities see Directory of Train Operators

§ It is unknown, at the time of going to press, when this station will open. For further details contact National Rail Enquiries 08457-484950 or see local publicity.

A From Bognor Regis (Table 188) and from Portsmouth Harbour (Table 188)
B To Tonbridge (Table 209)
C 🛒 from Haywards Heath
D From Tunbridge Wells (Table 206)
E From Bognor Regis (Table 188) and from Southampton Central (Table 188)

Brighton → London, Bedford and Watford Junction

Network Diagram - see first page of Table 186

Station		SN	SN	SN	SN	FC	GW	GX	SN	SN	SN	LO	SN	FC	GX	SN	SN	SN	FC	SE 13	GW	GX	SN	LO
		1	1	1	1	1	1	1 A	1	1	1 ◇		1 B	1	1	1 C	1 D	1	1	E	1	1	1 ◇	
			⊼								⊼		⊼				⊼	⊼					⊼	
Brighton 10	d				14 55	15 04					15 19			15 07					15 34				15 49	
Hove 2	d			14 51													15 21							
Preston Park	d				14 58									15 11										
Hassocks 4	d				15 05									15 17										
Burgess Hill 4	d			15 02	15 08									15 21										
Lewes 4	d		14 50															15 19						
Wivelsfield 4	d				15 11									15 23				15 35						
Haywards Heath 3	a		15 05	15 09	15 15	15 18								15 28			15 35	15 39	15 48					
	d		15 13		15 16	15 18								15 32			15 44		15 48					
Balcombe	d													15 37										
Horsham 4	d	15 00											15 20			15 32								
Littlehaven	d	15 03														15 35								
Faygate	d																							
Ifield	d	15 09														15 41								
Crawley	d	15 14											15 29			15 44								
Three Bridges 4	a	15 18			15 25								15 32	15 42		15 48								
	d	15 18			15 31 →				← 15 31				15 33	15 42		15 48								
Gatwick Airport 10 ✈	a	15 22	15 24			15 30			15 35				15 37	15 46		15 52	15 55		16 00					
	d	15 23	15 25			15 31		15 35	15 37				15 38	15 46	15 50	15 53	15 56		16 01		16 03	16 05		
Horley 4	d	15 26											15 41			15 55								
Salfords	d	15 30																						
Earlswood (Surrey)	d	15 33																						
Reigate	d						15 34																	
Tonbridge 4	d																			15 34				
Redhill	a	15 36					15 38						15 47			16 02				16 04	16 10			
	d	15 37 →								← 15 37			15 48							16 05				
Merstham	d									15 41										16 09				
Coulsdon South	d									15 46										16 14				
Purley 4	d									15 49										16 18				
East Croydon	a		15 41			15 46			15 52	15 54	15 55		16 00	16 02			16 11		16 16	16 23			16 24	
	d		15 41			15 47			15 52	15 55	15 55		16 00	16 02			16 12		16 17	16 24			16 24	
Norwood Junction 2	a									15 59										16 28				
London Bridge 4 ⊖	a					16 00				16 12				16 15						16 41				
London Blackfriars 3 ⊖	a					16 07								16 24					16 48					
City Thameslink 3	a					16 10								16 28					16 52					
Farringdon 3 ⊖	a					16 14								16 31					16 56					
St Pancras International 15 ⊖	a					16 18								16 35					17 01					
St Albans City	a					16 39								16 56					17 21					
Luton Airport Parkway 4 ✈	a					16 51								17 09					17 34					
Luton 7	a					16 54								17 13					17 36					
Bedford 10	a					17 20								17 38					18 00					
Clapham Junction 10	d		15 52						16 03		16 05	16 05	16 11				16 21						16 34	16 35
Imperial Wharf §	d																							
West Brompton ⊖	d								16 09			16 12												16 42
Kensington Olympia ⊖	d								16 12			16 15												16 45
Shepherds Bush § ⊖	d																							16 57
Willesden Jn. High Level	a											16 27												
Wembley Central	a								16 26															
Harrow & Wealdstone ⊖	a								16 31															
Watford Junction	a								16 45															
London Victoria 15 ⊖	a		15 58					16 05			16 11		16 20		16 20		16 29					16 35	16 41	

For general notes see front of timetable
For details of catering facilities see Directory of Train Operators

§ It is unknown, at the time of going to press, when this station will open. For further details contact National Rail Enquiries 08457-484950 or see local publicity.

A Operating Company SN from 23 June
B From Bognor Regis (Table 188) and from Portsmouth Harbour (Table 188)
C To Tonbridge (Table 209)
D ⊼ from Haywards Heath
E From Tunbridge Wells (Table 206)

Brighton → London, Bedford and Watford Junction

Network Diagram - see first page of Table 186

		SN	FC	SN	GX	SN	GW	SN	SN	SN	SN	FC	GX	SN	SN	SN	LO	SN	GW	SN	FC	GX	SN	SN	LO
		1	1	1	1	1	1	1	1	1	1	1	1	1	1	1		1	1	1	1	1	1	1	1
		A		A	B													C						C	D
		🚲		🚲					🚲							🚲									
Brighton [10]	d		15 37								15 55	16 04				16 19					16 07				
Hove [2]	d									15 51															
Preston Park	d		15 41								15 58										16 11				
Hassocks [4]	d		15 47								16 05										16 17				
Burgess Hill [4]	d		15 51							16 02	16 08										16 21				
Lewes [4]	d								15 50																
Wivelsfield [4]	d		15 53								16 11														
Haywards Heath [3]	a		15 58						16 05	16 09	16 15	16 18									16 25				
	d		15 58						16 13		16 16	16 19									16 26				
Balcombe	d																				16 31				
Horsham [4]	d	15 50						16 02										16 20							
Littlehaven	d							16 05																	
Faygate	d																								
Ifield	d							16 11																	
Crawley	d	15 59						16 14										16 29							
Three Bridges [4]	a	16 02	16 07					16 18			16 25							16 32			16 37				
	d	16 03	16 07			16 17		16 18			16 31 →			← 16 31				16 33			16 37				
Gatwick Airport [10] ✈	a	16 07	16 11			16 21		16 22	16 26			16 30		16 35				16 37			16 41				
	d	16 08	16 11		16 20	16 23		16 23	16 27			16 31	16 35	16 37				16 38			16 41	16 50			
Horley [4]	d							16 26																	
Salfords	d							16 30																	
Earlswood (Surrey)	d							16 33																	
Reigate	d						16 21												16 40						
Tonbridge [4]	d																								
Redhill	a	16 17					16 26	16 36										16 47	16 47						
	d	16 18 →		← 16 18				16 37 →							← 16 37			16 48 →						← 16 48	
Merstham	d														16 41										
Coulsdon South	d														16 46										
Purley [4]	d														16 49										
East Croydon	a		16 27	16 30		16 38			16 42			16 46		16 52	16 54	16 55				←	16 57			17 01	
	d		16 27	16 30		16 38			16 42			16 47		16 52	16 55 →	16 55				16 55	16 57			17 01	
Norwood Junction [2]	a																								
London Bridge [4] ⊖	a		16 42									17 02													
London Blackfriars [3] ⊖	a		16 53																		17 25				
City Thameslink [3]	a		16 56																		17 28				
Farringdon [3] ⊖	a		17 01																		17 31				
St Pancras International [15] ⊖	a		17 05																		17 35				
St Albans City	a		17 26																		17 56				
Luton Airport Parkway [4] ✈	a		17 39																		18 09				
Luton [7]	a		17 42																		18 12				
Bedford [10]	a		18 08																		18 38				
Clapham Junction [10]	d			16 40		16 48			16 52					17 03		17 05	17 05			17 08			17 10	17 11	17 17
Imperial Wharf §	d																								
West Brompton ⊖	d													17 09			17 12						17 18		17 24
Kensington Olympia ⊖	d													17 12			17 15						17a21		17 27
Shepherds Bush § ⊖	d																								
Willesden Jn. High Level	a																17 27								17 38
Wembley Central	a													17 26											
Harrow & Wealdstone ⊖	a													17 31											
Watford Junction	a													17 45											
London Victoria [15] ⊖	a			16 46	16 50	16 56			16 58				17 05			17 11				17 14		17 20		17 20	

For general notes see front of timetable
For details of catering facilities see Directory of Train Operators

§ It is unknown, at the time of going to press, when this station will open. For further details contact National Rail Enquiries 08457-484950 or see local publicity.

A From Bognor Regis (Table 188) and from Southampton Central (Table 188)

B Operating Company SN from 23 June

C From Bognor Regis (Table 188) and from Portsmouth Harbour (Table 188)

D Until 29 August and from 17 November. To Stratford Low Level (Table 59)

Brighton → London, Bedford and Watford Junction

Network Diagram - see first page of Table 186

		LO [1] A	FC [1]	SN [1]	SN [1] B ⚮	SN [1] ⚮	GW [1]	GX [1]	SN [1]	SN [1] ⚮	LO	FC [1]	SN [1]	SN [1] C ⚮	GX [1]	SN [1]	GW [1]	SN	LO [1] D	SN [1] ⚮	SN [1]	SN [1]	FC [1]	GW [1]	GX [1]
Brighton [10]	d		16 14							16 49		16 29										16 55	17 03		
Hove [2]	d				16 21																16 51				
Preston Park	d											16 33										16 58			
Hassocks [4]	d											16 39										17 05			
Burgess Hill [4]	d		16 25									16 43									17 02	17 08	17 13		
Lewes [4]	d					16 19														16 51					
Wivelsfield [4]	d					16 35						16 46										17 11			
Haywards Heath [3]	a		16 30		16 35	16 39						16 50								17 05	17 09	17 15	17 18		
	d		16 38		16 44							16 50								17 13		17 21 →	17 18		
Balcombe	d											16 56													
Horsham [4]	d			16 30										16 52				17 00							
Littlehaven	d			16 33														17 03							
Faygate	d			16 37														17 07							
Ifield	d			16 41														17 11							
Crawley	d			16 44										17 01				17 14							
Three Bridges [4]	a		16 47	16 47								17 02		17 04				17 17					17 27		
	d		16 47	16 48								17 02		17 05				17 18					17 27		
Gatwick Airport [10] ✈	a		16 52	16 52	16 55							17 06		17 09				17 22		17 24			17 31		
	d		16 53	16 53	16 56		17 03	17 05				17 07		17 10	17 20			17 23		17 25			17 31		17 35
Horley [4]	d			16 56														17 26							
Salfords	d			17 00														17 30							
Earlswood (Surrey)	d			17 03														17 33							
Reigate	d															17 14	17 26							17 34	
Tonbridge [4]	d																								
Redhill	a			17 06			17 10		←					17 17		17 21	17 31	17 36						17 38	
	d			17 07 →					17 07					17 18		17 22		17 37 →							
Merstham	d								17 11							17 26									
Coulsdon South	d								17 16							17 31									
Purley [4]	d								17 19																
East Croydon	a		17 08		17 11				17 24	17 25		17 27	←	17 30		17 37				17 40			17 47		
	d		17 09		17 12				17 25 →	17 25		17 27	17 25	17 30		17 38				17 41			17 47		
Norwood Junction [2]	a																								
London Bridge [4]	⊖ a		17 29																				18 11		
London Blackfriars [3]	⊖ a		17 36									17 56											18 19		
City Thameslink [3]	a		17 38									18 08											18 28		
Farringdon [3]	⊖ a		17 41									18 11											18 31		
St Pancras International [15]	⊖ a		17 45									18 15											18 35		
St Albans City	a		18 06									18 36											18 56		
Luton Airport Parkway [4] ✈	a		18 19									18 50											19 09		
Luton [7]	a		18 22									18 53											19 12		
Bedford [10]	a		18 48									19 18											19 38		
Clapham Junction [10]	d	17{17			17 21					17 35	17 35		17 38	17 41		17 47			18{17	17 50					
Imperial Wharf §	d																								
West Brompton	⊖ d	17{24									17 42								18{24						
Kensington Olympia	⊖ d	17a27									17 45								18{27						
Shepherds Bush §	⊖ d																								
Willesden Jn. High Level	a										17 57								18{38						
Wembley Central	a																								
Harrow & Wealdstone	⊖ a																								
Watford Junction	a																								
London Victoria [15]	⊖ a				17 28			17 35		17 43			17 45	17 50	17 50	17 56				17 57					18 05

For general notes see front of timetable
For details of catering facilities see Directory of Train Operators

§ It is unknown, at the time of going to press, when this station will open. For further details contact National Rail Enquiries 08457-484950 or see local publicity.

A 1 September to 14 November

B ⚮ from Haywards Heath

C From Bognor Regis (Table 188) and from Southampton Central (Table 188)

D Until 29 August and from 17 November. To Stratford Low Level (Table 59)

Brighton → London, Bedford and Watford Junction

Network Diagram - see first page of Table 186

		SN	SN	LO	SN	SN	SN	SE 13	GX	SN	SN	SN		FC	GW	GX	SN	LO	SN	SN	SN	FC	GX	SN	GW
		1	1			1	1		1	1	1	1		1	1	1	1		1	1	1	1	1	1	1
						A					B										C				
			🛒			🛒					🛒	🛒					🛒				🛒				
Brighton [10]	d		17 19											17 23			17 49					17 37			
Hove [2]	d										17 21														
Preston Park	d													17 27								17 41			
Hassocks [4]	d													17 33								17 47			
Burgess Hill [4]	d													17 37								17 51			
Lewes [4]	d											17 19													
Wivelsfield [4]	d											17 35		17 40											
Haywards Heath [3]	a	←									17 35	17 39		17 45								17 56			
	d	17 21									17 43			17 46								17 56			
Balcombe	d	17 27																				18 02			
Horsham [4]	d					17 20				17 30											17 52				
Littlehaven	d									17 33															
Faygate	d									17 37															
Ifield	d									17 41															
Crawley	d					17 29				17 44											18 01				
Three Bridges [4]	a	17 32				17 32				17 47				17 56							18 04	18 08			
	d	17 32				17 33				17 48				17 56							18 05	18 12			
Gatwick Airport [10] ✈	a	17 36				17 37				17 52	17 55			18 00							18 09	18 16			
	d	17 37				17 38			17 50	17 53	17 56			18 01	18 03	18 05					18 10	18 16	18 20		
Horley [4]	d									17 56															
Salfords	d									18 00															
Earlswood (Surrey)	d									18 03															
Reigate	d						17 44												18 06						18 26
Tonbridge [4]	d							17 20																	
Redhill	a				←	17 46	17 50	17 51		18 06					18 10				18 10	←	18 17			←	18 31
	d				17 37	17 46	17 51	17 53		18 07 →									18 21 →	18 07	18 18			18 21	
Merstham	d				17 41															18 11				18 25	
Coulsdon South	d				17 46			18 00												18 16				18 30	
Purley [4]	d				17 49															18 19					
East Croydon 🚊	a	17 52	17 54		17 55	17 58	18 08	18 11			18 11			18 16			18 24			18 25	18 29	18 31		18 38	
	d	17 52	17 55		17 56	17 59	18 08	18 11			18 12			18 17			18 24			18 26	18 30	18 32		18 39	
Norwood Junction [2]	a																								
London Bridge [4]	⊖ a						18 24	18 26														18 45			
London Blackfriars [3]	⊖ a													18 49								18 55			
City Thameslink [3]	a													18 54								18 58			
Farringdon [3]	⊖ a													18 57								19 01			
St Pancras International [15]	⊖ a													19 01								19 05			
St Albans City	a													19 21								19 28			
Luton Airport Parkway [4]	✈ a																					19 40			
Luton [7]	a													19 34								19 43			
Bedford [10]	a													19 58								20 09			
Clapham Junction [10]	d	18 04	18 04	18 05	18 07	18 10					18 21						18 34	18 35		18 38	18 41			18 49	
Imperial Wharf §	d																								
West Brompton	⊖ d	18 09		18 12														18 42							
Kensington Olympia	⊖ d	18 12		18 15														18 45							
Shepherds Bush §	⊖ d																								
Willesden Jn. High Level	a			18 27														18 55							
Wembley Central	a	18 28																							
Harrow & Wealdstone	⊖ a	18 33																							
Watford Junction	a	18 45																							
London Victoria [15]	⊖ a		18 11		18 14	18 20			18 20		18 28					18 35	18 40			18 45	18 50		18 50	18 56	

For general notes see front of timetable
For details of catering facilities see Directory of Train Operators

§ It is unknown, at the time of going to press, when this station will open. For further details contact National Rail Enquiries 08457-484950 or see local publicity.

A From Bognor Regis (Table 188) and from Portsmouth Harbour (Table 188)

B 🛒 from Haywards Heath

C From Bognor Regis (Table 188) and from Southampton Central (Table 188)

Brighton → London, Bedford and Watford Junction

Network Diagram - see first page of Table 186

		SN	SN	SN	SN	FC	GX	SN	SN	SN	LO	SN	SN	GW	FC	GX	SN	SN	SN	SN	FC	GX	SN	LO	SN
		1	1	1	1	1	1	1	1	1		1	1	1	1	1	1	1	1	1	1	1	1 ◇		1
							A						B												
Brighton 10	d				17 55	18 03				18 19					18 07						18 34		18 49		
Hove 2	d			17 51																18 21					
Preston Park	d				17 58										18 11										
Hassocks 4	d				18 05										18 17										
Burgess Hill 4	d			18 02	18 08	18 13									18 21					18 33					
Lewes 4	d		17 50																18 18						
Wivelsfield 4	d				18 11										18 23				18 34						
Haywards Heath 3	a		18 05	18 09	18 15	18 18									18 28				18 38	18 41	18 47				
	d		18 13		18 22 →	18 18		← 18 22							18 32				18 45		18 48				
Balcombe	d														18 37										
Horsham 4	d	18 00											18 20					18 30							
Littlehaven	d	18 03																18 33							
Faygate	d	18 07																18 37							
Ifield	d	18 11																18 41							
Crawley	d	18 14											18 29					18 44							
Three Bridges 4	a	18 17						18 31					18 32		18 42			18 47							
	d	18 18						18 31					18 33		18 42			18 48							
Gatwick Airport 10 ✈	a	18 22	18 24			18 30		18 36					18 37		18 46			18 52	18 56		19 00				
	d	18 23	18 25			18 31	18 35	18 37					18 38		18 46	18 50		18 53	18 57		19 01	19 05			
Horley 4	d	18 26																18 56							
Salfords	d	18 30																19 00							
Earlswood (Surrey)	d	18 32																19 03							
Reigate	d											18 38		18 42			18 58								
Tonbridge 4	d																								
Redhill	a	18 36										18 42	18 47	18 52			19 02	19 06							
	d	18 37 →							← 18 37				18 47					19 07 →							← 19 07
Merstham	d								18 41																19 11
Coulsdon South	d								18 46																19 16
Purley 4	d								18 49																19 19
East Croydon	a		18 41			18 46		18 52	18 54	18 55			19 00		19 02				19 12		19 16		19 23		19 25
	d		18 42			18 47		18 52	18 55	18 55			19 00		19 02				19 12		19 17		19 24		19 26
Norwood Junction 2	a								18 59																
London Bridge 4 ⊖	a					19 00			19 12						19 15						19 30				
London Blackfriars 3 ⊖	a					19 07									19 22						19 37				
City Thameslink 3	a					19 12									19 25						19 40				
Farringdon 3 ⊖	a					19 15									19 29						19 44				
St Pancras International 15 ⊖	a					19 19									19 33						19 48				
St Albans City	a					19 40									19 54						20 09				
Luton Airport Parkway 4 ✈	a					19 53									20 06						20 20				
Luton 7	a					19 56									20 09						20 24				
Bedford 10	a					20 22									20 35						20 50				
Clapham Junction 10	d		18 52					19 03		19 05	19 05		19 11						19 22				19 33	19 35	19 37
Imperial Wharf §	d																								
West Brompton ⊖	d							19 08			19 12													19 42	
Kensington Olympia ⊖	d							19 11			19 15													19 45	
Shepherds Bush § ⊖	d																								
Willesden Jn. High Level	a										19 27													19 57	
Wembley Central	a							19 26																	
Harrow & Wealdstone ⊖	a							19 31																	
Watford Junction	a							19 45																	
London Victoria 15 ⊖	a		18 59				19 05			19 11			19 17			19 20			19 29			19 35	19 40		19 44

For general notes see front of timetable
For details of catering facilities see Directory of Train Operators

§ It is unknown, at the time of going to press, when this station will open. For further details contact National Rail Enquiries 08457-484950 or see local publicity.

A Operating Company SN from 23 June

B From Bognor Regis (Table 188) and from Portsmouth Harbour (Table 188)

Brighton → London, Bedford and Watford Junction

Network Diagram - see first page of Table 186

		SN 1 A	FC 1	GW 1	GX 1	SN 1	GW 1	SN 1	SN 1	SN 1	FC 1	GW 1	GX 1	SN 1	LO	SN 1 ◇	SN 1	SN 1 ◇	SN 1 B	FC 1	SN 1	GX 1	SN 1	SN 1	SN 1
Brighton 10	d		18 37													19 19		18 55		19 07					
Hove 2	d								18 52															19 22	
Preston Park	d		18 41															18 59		19 11					
Hassocks 4	d		18 47															19 05		19 17					
Burgess Hill 4	d		18 51															19 09		19 21				19 33	
Lewes 4	d									18 50													19 20		
Wivelsfield 4	d		18 53							19 05								19 11		19 23					
Haywards Heath 3	a		18 58						19 05	19 10								19 16		19 28			19 36	19 39	
	d		19 02						19 14									19 17		19 32			19 43		
Balcombe	d																			19 37					
Horsham 4	d	18 52						19 02											19 17						19 32
Littlehaven	d							19 05																	19 35
Faygate	d																								
Ifield	d							19 11																	19 41
Crawley	d	19 01						19 14											19 26						19 45
Three Bridges 4	a	19 04	19 12					19 18										19 28	19 30	19 42					19 48
	d	19 05	19 12					19 18			19 27							19 34		19 42					19 51
Gatwick Airport 10 ✈	a	19 09	19 16					19 22	19 25		19 31							19 38		19 46			19 54		19 55
	d	19 10	19 16	19 16	19 20			19 23	19 26		19 31		19 35	19 37				19 39		19 46		19 50	19 55		19 56
Horley 4	d							19 26																	19 59
Salfords	d							19 30																	
Earlswood (Surrey)	d							19 33																	
Reigate	d					19 21	19 30					19 34									19 47				
Tonbridge 4	d																								
Redhill	a	19 17		19 23		19 26	19 35	19 36				19 38						19 46			19 51				20 05
	d	19 18						19 37 →									← 19 37	19 47							20 08
Merstham	d																19 41								20 12 →
Coulsdon South	d																19 46								
Purley 4	d																19 49								
East Croydon	a	19 28	19 32						19 41		19 47			19 52		19 54	19 54	19 59		20 02			20 10		
	d	19 29	19 32						19 41		19 47			19 52		19 54	19 55	20 00		20 02			20 10		
Norwood Junction 2	a																								
London Bridge 4 ⊖	a		19 45								20 00									20 15					
London Blackfriars 3 ⊖	a		19 52								20 07									20 22					
City Thameslink 3	a		19 55								20 10									20 25					
Farringdon 3 ⊖	a		19 59								20 14									20 29					
St Pancras International 15 ⊖	a		20 03								20 18									20 33					
St Albans City	a		20 24								20 39									20 54					
Luton Airport Parkway 4 ✈	a		20 36								20 50									21 06					
Luton 7	a		20 39								20 54									21 09					
Bedford 10	a		21 05								21 20									21 35					
Clapham Junction 10	d	19 40							19 51					20 03	20 05	20 05	20 08	20 11					20 20		
Imperial Wharf §	d																								
West Brompton ⊖	d													20 09	20 12										
Kensington Olympia ⊖	d													20 12	20 15										
Shepherds Bush § ⊖	d																								
Willesden Jn. High Level	a														20 27										
Wembley Central	a																								
Harrow & Wealdstone ⊖	a													20 30											
Watford Junction	a													20 45											
London Victoria 15 ⊖	a	19 47			19 50				19 59				20 05			20 11	20 14	20 20				20 20	20 28		

For general notes see front of timetable
For details of catering facilities see Directory of Train Operators

§ It is unknown, at the time of going to press, when this station will open. For further details contact National Rail Enquiries 08457-484950 or see local publicity.

A From Bognor Regis (Table 188) and from Southampton Central (Table 188)

B From Portsmouth & Southsea (Table 188)

Brighton → London, Bedford and Watford Junction

Network Diagram - see first page of Table 186

		FC	GW	GX	SN	LO	SN	SN	SN	FC		GX	SN	SN	SN	SN	FC	GW	GX	SN	LO	SN	SN	SN	SN
		1	1	1	1 ◇		1	1	1	1		1	1	1	1	1 ◇	1	1	1	1		1 ◇	1	1 ◇	1
								A																	
Brighton 10	d	19 34			19 49					19 37						19 55	20 04					20 19			
Hove 2	d													19 52											
Preston Park	d									19 41						19 59									
Hassocks 4	d									19 47						20 05									
Burgess Hill 4	d									19 51						20 09									
Lewes 4	d														19 53										
Wivelsfield 4	d									19 53					20 05	20 11									
Haywards Heath 3	a	19 47								19 58				20 04	20 10	20 16	20 18							←	
	d	19 48								20 02				20 14		20 22 →	20 18							20 22	
Balcombe	d																								
Horsham 4	d							19 52					20 02												
Littlehaven	d												20 05												
Faygate	d																								
Ifield	d												20 11												
Crawley	d							20 01					20 14												
Three Bridges 4	a							20 05		20 11			20 18											20 32	
	d							20 05		20 12			20 18											20 32	
Gatwick Airport 10 ✈	a	20 00						20 10		20 16			20 22	20 25			20 31							20 37	
	d	20 01	20 03	20 05				20 11		20 16		20 20	20 23	20 26			20 31		20 35	20 37				20 38	
Horley 4	d												20 26												
Salfords	d												20 30												
Earlswood (Surrey)	d												20 33												
Reigate	d								20 14									20 34							20 46
Tonbridge 4	d																								
Redhill	a		20 10					20 18	20 18				20 36					20 38					←	20 46	20 50
	d						←	20 18					20 37 →										20 37	20 47	
Merstham	d						20 12																20 41		
Coulsdon South	d						20 17																20 46		
Purley 4	d						20 20																20 49		
East Croydon	a	20 16			20 23		20 25	20 30		20 32				20 41			20 47			20 52		20 55	20 57	20 59	
	d	20 17			20 24		20 26	20 30		20 32				20 42			20 47			20 52		20 55	20 57	21 00	
Norwood Junction 2	a																								
London Bridge 4 ⊖	a	20 30								20 45							21 00								
London Blackfriars 3 ⊖	a	20 37								20 52							21 07								
City Thameslink 3	a	20 40								20 55							21 10								
Farringdon 3 ⊖	a	20 44								20 59							21 14								
St Pancras International 15 ⊖	a	20 48								21 03							21 18								
St Albans City	a	21 09								21 24							21 39								
Luton Airport Parkway 4 ✈	a	21 20								21 36							21 50								
Luton 7	a	21 24								21 39							21 54								
Bedford 10	a	21 50								22 05							22 20								
Clapham Junction 10	d				20 33	20 35	20 38	20 41						20 51						21 03	21 05	21 05	21 08	21 11	
Imperial Wharf §	d																								
West Brompton ⊖	d					20 42														21 09	21 12				
Kensington Olympia ⊖	d					20 45														21 12	21 15				
Shepherds Bush § ⊖	d																								
Willesden Jn. High Level	a					20 57															21 27				
Wembley Central	a																								
Harrow & Wealdstone ⊖	a																			21 29					
Watford Junction	a																			21 45					
London Victoria 15 ⊖	a			20 35	20 40		20 46	20 50				20 50		20 59					21 05			21 11	21 14	21 20	

For general notes see front of timetable
For details of catering facilities see Directory of Train Operators

§ It is unknown, at the time of going to press, when this station will open. For further details contact National Rail Enquiries 08457-484950 or see local publicity.

A From Southampton Central (Table 188)

Brighton → London, Bedford and Watford Junction

Network Diagram - see first page of Table 186

		FC	GX	SN	SE 88	SN	FC	GW	GX	SN	LO	SN	SN	SN	FC	GX	GW	SN	SN	SN	SN	GX	SN	SN	SN
		1	1	1		1	1	1		1 ◊		1	1	1	1	1	1	1	1	1	1		1	1	1 ◊
														A											
Brighton 10	d	20 07					20 34			20 49					20 37										21 19
Hove 2	d			20 22															20 52						
Preston Park	d	20 11													20 41										
Hassocks 4	d	20 17													20 47										
Burgess Hill 4	d	20 21		20 33											20 51										
Lewes 4	d																			20 50					
Wivelsfield 4	d	20 23													20 53					21 06					
Haywards Heath 3	a	20 28		20 37			20 47								20 58				21 06	21 10					
	d	20 32		20 38			20 48								21 02				21 14						
Balcombe	d	20 37																							
Horsham 4	d					20 32								20 52				21 02							
Littlehaven	d					20 35												21 05							
Faygate	d																								
Ifield	d					20 41												21 11							
Crawley	d					20 45								21 01				21 14							
Three Bridges 4	a	20 42		20 47		20 48								21 05	21 11			21 18							
	d	20 42		20 47	20 48	20 51								21 05	21 12			21 18							
Gatwick Airport 10 ✈	a	20 46		20 51	20 52	20 56	21 00							21 10	21 16			21 22	21 25						
	d	20 46	20 50	20 53	20 53	20 57	21 01	21 03	21 05					21 11	21 16	21 20		21 23	21 26			21 35	21 37		
Horley 4	d					20 59												21 26							
Salfords	d																	21 30							
Earlswood (Surrey)	d																	21 33							
Reigate	d												21 13				21 24				21 34				
Tonbridge 4	d																								
Redhill	a				21 01	21 06		21 10					21 17	21 18			21 28	21 36			21 38				
	d					21 08						←		21 18				21 37 →						← 21 37	
Merstham	d					21 12 →						21 12												21 41	
Coulsdon South	d											21 17												21 46	
Purley 4	d											21 20												21 49	
East Croydon	a	21 02		21 09			21 16			21 23		21 25		21 30	21 32				21 41				21 52	21 54	21 55
	d	21 02		21 10			21 17			21 24		21 26		21 30	21 32				21 41				21 52	21 57 →	21 55
Norwood Junction 2	a																								
London Bridge 4	⊖ a	21 15					21 30								21 45										
London Blackfriars 3	⊖ a	21 22					21 37								21 52										
City Thameslink 3	a	21 25					21 40								21 55										
Farringdon 3	⊖ a	21 29					21 44								21 59										
St Pancras International 15	⊖ a	21 33					21 48								22 03										
St Albans City	a	21 54					22 08								22 24										
Luton Airport Parkway 4 ✈	a	22 06					22 20								22 36										
Luton 7	a	22 09					22 24								22 40										
Bedford 10	a	22 35					22 50								23 05										
Clapham Junction 10	d			21 19						21 33	21 35	21 38		21 41					21 51				22 03		22 05
Imperial Wharf §	d																								
West Brompton	⊖ d										21 42														
Kensington Olympia	⊖ d										21 45												22 09		
Shepherds Bush §	⊖ d																						22 12		
Willesden Jn. High Level	a										21 57														
Wembley Central	a																								
Harrow & Wealdstone	⊖ a																						22 29		
Watford Junction	a																						22 45		
London Victoria 15	⊖ a		21 20	21 29					21 35	21 40		21 47		21 48		21 50			21 58			22 05			22 11

For general notes see front of timetable
For details of catering facilities see Directory of Train Operators

§ It is unknown, at the time of going to press, when this station will open. For further details contact National Rail Enquiries 08457-484950 or see local publicity.

A From Southampton Central (Table 188)

Brighton → London, Bedford and Watford Junction

Network Diagram - see first page of Table 186

		LO	SN	SN	GW	FC	GX	SN	SE	SN	SN	GX	SN	LO	SN	SN	SN	FC	GX	GW	SN	SN	SN	SN	GX
			1	1 ◇	1	1	1	1	88	1	1		1 ◇		1	1	1 A	1	1	1	1	1	1	1	
Brighton 10	d			21 02		21 07					21 34		21 49					21 37							
Hove 2	d							21 22														21 52			
Preston Park	d			21 06		21 11												21 41							
Hassocks 4	d			21 12		21 17												21 47							
Burgess Hill 4	d			21 16		21 21		21 32										21 51				22 02			
Lewes 4	d																				21 50				
Wivelsfield 4	d			21 18		21 23												21 53			22 02				
Haywards Heath 3	a			21 23		21 28		21 37			21 46							21 58			22 06	22 09			
	d			21 23		21 32		21 38			21 46							22 02			22 13				
Balcombe	d					21 37																			
Horsham 4	d									21 32							21 52							22 02	
Littlehaven	d									21 35														22 05	
Faygate	d																								
Ifield	d									21 41														22 11	
Crawley	d									21 45							22 01							22 14	
Three Bridges 4	a			21 32		21 42		21 47		21 48	21 55						22 05	22 11						22 18	
	d			21 33		21 42		21 47	21 48	21 51	21 56						22 05	22 12						22 21	
Gatwick Airport 10 ✈	a			21 37		21 46		21 51	21 52	21 55	22 00						22 10	22 16			22 24			22 25	
	d			21 38		21 46	21 50	21 53	21 53	21 56	22 02	22 05					22 11	22 16	22 20	22 22	22 25			22 26	22 35
Horley 4	d									21 59														22 29	
Salfords	d																							22 33	
Earlswood (Surrey)	d																							22 36	
Reigate	d				21 44										22 11								22 32		
Tonbridge 4	d																								
Redhill	a			21 46	21 48				22 01	22 05					22 15		22 18			22 30			22 36	22 39	
	d			21 47						22 08						←	22 18							22 40 →	
Merstham	d									22 12 →						22 12									
Coulsdon South	d															22 17									
Purley 4	d															22 20									
East Croydon	a		←	21 59		22 02		22 09			22 17		22 23			22 25	22 30	22 32			22 40				
	d		21 57	22 00		22 02		22 10			22 17		22 24			22 26	22 30	22 32			22 41				
Norwood Junction 2	a																								
London Bridge 4 ⊖	a					22 15					22 32							22 45							
London Blackfriars 3 ⊖	a					22 22												22 52							
City Thameslink 3	a					22 25												22 55							
Farringdon 3 ⊖	a					22 29												22 59							
St Pancras International 15 ⊖	a					22 33												23 03							
St Albans City	a					22 54												23 24							
Luton Airport Parkway 4 ✈	a					23 06												23 36							
Luton 7	a					23 10												23 40							
Bedford 10	a					23 35												00 05							
Clapham Junction 10	d	22 05	22 08	22 11				22 19					22 33	22 35		22 38	22 41				22 51				
Imperial Wharf §	d																								
West Brompton ⊖	d	22 12												22 42											
Kensington Olympia ⊖	d	22 15												22 45											
Shepherds Bush § ⊖	d																								
Willesden Jn. High Level	a	22 27												22 57											
Wembley Central	a																								
Harrow & Wealdstone ⊖	a																								
Watford Junction	a																								
London Victoria 15 ⊖	a		22 14	22 20			22 20	22 27				22 35	22 40			22 44	22 50		22 50		22 58				23 05

For general notes see front of timetable
For details of catering facilities see Directory of Train Operators

§ It is unknown, at the time of going to press, when this station will open. For further details contact National Rail Enquiries 08457-484950 or see local publicity.

A From Southampton Central (Table 188)

Brighton → London, Bedford and Watford Junction

Network Diagram - see first page of Table 186

		SN	LO	SN	SN	GW	FC	GX	SE	SN	GX	FC	SN	FC	GW	GX	SN	GX	GX	GW	SN	SN	FC
									88														
		1		1	1 ◇	1	1	1		1		1	1	1	1	1	1		1	1	1 ◇	1	1
													A									B	
Brighton 10	d				22 00		22 07					22 33									23 02		23 37
Hove 2	d																						
Preston Park	d				22 04		22 11					22 37									23 06		23 41
Hassocks 4	d				22 10		22 17					22 43									23 12		23 47
Burgess Hill 4	d				22 14		22 21					22 47									23 16		23 51
Lewes 4	d												22 40										
Wivelsfield 4	d				22 16		22 23					22 49	22 54								23 19		23 53
Haywards Heath 3	a				22 21		22 28					22 54	22 58								23 23		23 58
	d				22 22		22 32					22 54	22 59								23 24		23 59
Balcombe	d						22 37					23 00											00 04
Horsham 4	d									22 49							23 02					23 25	
Littlehaven	d																23 05					23 28	
Faygate	d																						
Ifield	d																23 11					23 35	
Crawley	d									22 57							23 14					23 38	
Three Bridges 4	a				22 32		22 42			23 01		23 05	23 08	←			23 18				23 33	23 42	00 10
	d				22 32		22 42		22 48			23 12	23 08	23 12			23 18				23 47		00 10
Gatwick Airport 10 ✈	a				22 37		22 46		22 52			→	23 12	23 16			23 22				23 52		00 14
	d	22 37			22 38		22 46	22 50	22 53		23 05		23 13	23 16	23 18	23 20	23 23	23 35	23 50		23 53		00 15
Horley 4	d																23 26				23s56		
Salfords	d																23 29						
Earlswood (Surrey)	d																23 33						
Reigate	d					22 44														23 54			
Tonbridge 4	d																						
Redhill	a			←	22 46	22 48			23 01						23 25		23 36			23 58	00 02		00 22
	d			22 40	22 47												23 37				00 03		00 22
Merstham	d			22 44													23 41						
Coulsdon South	d			22 49													23 46						
Purley 4	d			22 52													23 49				00 11		
East Croydon	a	22 52		22 57	22 59		23 02						23 30	23 32			23 55				00 16		00 35
	d	22 52		22 58	23 00		23 02						23 30	23 32			23 58				00 17		00 36
Norwood Junction 2	a																						
London Bridge 4	⊖ a						23 15							23 45									00 52
London Blackfriars 3	⊖ a						23 22							23 52									00 59
City Thameslink 3	a																						
Farringdon 3	⊖ a						23 28							23 58									
St Pancras International 15	⊖ a						23 32							00 02									01 07
St Albans City	a						23 54							00 24									01 39
Luton Airport Parkway 4 ✈	a						00 06							00 36									01 51
Luton 7	a						00 10							00 40									01 55
Bedford 10	a						00 35							01 05									02 20
Clapham Junction 10	d	23 03	23 05	23 08	23 11								23 42				00 11				00 30		
Imperial Wharf §	d																						
West Brompton	⊖ d	23 09	23 12																				
Kensington Olympia	⊖ d	23 12	23 15																				
Shepherds Bush §	⊖ d																						
Willesden Jn. High Level	a		23 27																				
Wembley Central	a																						
Harrow & Wealdstone	⊖ a	23 28																					
Watford Junction	a	23 45																					
London Victoria 15	⊖ a			23 14	23 20			23 20			23 35		23 52			23 55	00 18	00 10	00 25		00 37		

For general notes see front of timetable
For details of catering facilities see Directory of Train Operators

§ It is unknown, at the time of going to press, when this station will open. For further details contact National Rail Enquiries 08457-484950 or see local publicity.

A From Ore (Table 189)
B From Southampton Central (Table 188)

Brighton → London, Bedford and Watford Junction

Network Diagram - see first page of Table 186

Station		FC 1	FC 1	SN 1	SN 1 ◇	GX	FC 1	GX 1	GX	GW 1	GX 1	SN 1	GX 1	SN 1	FC 1	SN 1	FC 1	SN 1	FC 1	GX	FC 1	SN 1 ◇ A	XC 1 ◇ B ☕	GX 1	GW 1
Brighton 10	d	22p07	22p33		23p02		23p37															03 50			
Hove 2	d																								
Preston Park	d	22p11	22p37		23p06		23p41																		
Hassocks 4	d	22p17	22p43		23p12		23p47																		
Burgess Hill 4	d	22p21	22p47		23p16		23p51																		
Lewes 4	d																								
Wivelsfield 4	d	22p23	22p49		23p19		23p53																		
Haywards Heath 3	a	22p28	22p54		23p23		23p58															04 24			
	d	22p32	22p54		23p24		23p59															04 25			
Balcombe	d	22p37	23p00				00 04																		
Horsham 4	d			23p02																					
Littlehaven	d			23p05																					
Faygate	d																								
Ifield	d			23p11																					
Crawley	d			23p14																					
Three Bridges 4	a	22p42	23p05	23p18	23p33		00 10															04 45			
	d	22p42	23p12	23p18	23p47		00 10							01 59	02 25	02 55	03 25	03 55	04 25		04 55	04 58			
Gatwick Airport 10 ✈	a	22p46	23p16	23p22	23p52		00 14							02 03	02 29	02 59	03 29	03 59	04 29		04 59	05 02			
	d	22p46	23p16	23p23	23p53	00 05	00 15	00 20	00 35		00 50	01 05	01 35	02 05	02 30	03 05	03 30	04 05	04 30	04 35	05 00	05 03	05 15	05 20	
Horley 4	d			23p26	23b56							01 07		02 07		03 07		04 07				05 05			
Salfords	d			23p29																					
Earlswood (Surrey)	d			23p33																					
Reigate	d									00 45															05 34
Tonbridge 4	d																								
Redhill	a			23p36	00 02		00 22			00 49													05 22		05 38
	d			23p37	00 03		00 22																05 33		
Merstham	d			23p41																					
Coulsdon South	d			23p46																					
Purley 4	d			23p49	00 11							01 22		02 22		03 22		04 22				05 24			
East Croydon	a	23p02	23p32	23p55	00 16		00 35					01 27		02 27	02 47	03 27	03 47	04 27	04 47		05 17	05 29			
	d	23p02	23p32	23p58	00 17		00 36					01 28		02 28	02 47	03 28	03 47	04 28	04 47		05 17	05 29			
Norwood Junction 2	a																								
London Bridge 4 ⊖	a	23p15	23p45				00 52																		
London Blackfriars 3 ⊖	a	23p22	23p52				00 59								03 12		04 12		05 12		05 42				
City Thameslink 3	a																								
Farringdon 3 ⊖	a	23p28	23p58																05 17		05 47				
St Pancras International 15 ⊖	a	23p32	00 02				01 07								03 21		04 21		05 21		05 51				
St Albans City	a	23p54	00 24				01 39								03 53		04 53		05 53		06 23				
Luton Airport Parkway 4 ✈	a	00 06	00 36				01 51								04 05		05 05		06 05		06 35				
Luton 7	a	00 10	00 40				01 55								04 09		05 09		06 09		06 39				
Bedford 10	a	00 35	01 05				02 20								04 35		05 35		06 35		07 05				
Clapham Junction 10	d			00 11	00 30							01 41		02 41		03 41		04 41				05 49			
Imperial Wharf §	d																								
West Brompton ⊖	d																								
Kensington Olympia ⊖	d																								
Shepherds Bush § ⊖	d																								
Willesden Jn. High Level	a																								
Wembley Central	a																								
Harrow & Wealdstone ⊖	a																								
Watford Junction	a																								
London Victoria 15 ⊖	a			00 18	00 37	00 40		00 55	01 10		01 25	01 49	02 20	02 49		03 49		04 49		05 10		05 58		05 55	

For general notes see front of timetable
For details of catering facilities see Directory of Train Operators

§ It is unknown, at the time of going to press, when this station will open. For further details contact National Rail Enquiries 08457-484950 or see local publicity.

A Also stops at Balham 0545
B Irom 13 September to Manchester Piccadilly

b Previous night. Stops to set down only

Table 186

Saturdays

Brighton → London, Bedford and Watford Junction

Network Diagram - see first page of Table 186

		FC	GW	SN	LO	XC	GX	SN	SN	SN	FC	GW	SN	GX	SN	GX	SN	SN	SN	SN	LO	GW	FC	GX	SN
		1	1	1		1 ◇	1	1	1	1	1	1	1		1	1	1	1 ◇	1	1		1	1		1
						A				B			B												
Brighton 10	d							05 21			05 24							05 50		05 56			06 04		
Hove 2	d																		05 54						
Preston Park	d										05 28									06 00					
Hassocks 4	d										05 34									06 06					
Burgess Hill 4	d										05 38												06 14		
Lewes 4	d									05 25															
Wivelsfield 4	d										05 40									06 11					
Haywards Heath 3	a							05 34		05 40	05 45		←					06 02	06 07	06 15			06 18		
	d							05 34		05 49 →	05 45		05 49					06 11		06 22 →			06 18		← 06 22
Balcombe	d										05 51														
Horsham 4	d								05 34								06 02								
Littlehaven	d								05 37								06 05								
Faygate	d																								
Ifield	d								05 43								06 11								
Crawley	d								05 47								06 14								
Three Bridges 4	a							05 43	05 50		05 56		05 59				06 18	06 20							06 32
	d	05 20		05 33				05 44	05 51		05 56		05 59				06 18	06 20							06 32
Gatwick Airport 10 ✈	a	05 24		05 37				05 48	05 55		06 00		06 03				06 22	06 24					06 30		06 36
	d	05 25	05 31	05 38		05 45	05 50	05 52	05 56		06 01	06 03		06 05		06 20	06 23	06 25					06 31	06 35	06 37
Horley 4	d			05 40					05 59								06 26								
Salfords	d																06 30								
Earlswood (Surrey)	d								06 04								06 33								
Reigate	d																					06 34			
Tonbridge 4	d																								
Redhill	a		05 39	05 47		05 52			06 07			06 12			←		06 36					06 38			
	d			05 48		05 52			06 08 →						06 08		06 37 →								
Merstham	d														06 12										
Coulsdon South	d														06 17										
Purley 4	d			05 58											06 20										
East Croydon	a	05 42		06 02		06 05		06 10			06 16				06 26			06 40					06 46		06 52
	d	05 42		06 07		06 07		06 10			06 17				06 27			06 41					06 47		06 53
Norwood Junction 2	a																								
London Bridge 4	⊖ a										06 31												07 01		
London Blackfriars 3	⊖ a	06 07									06 37												07 07		
City Thameslink 3	a																								
Farringdon 3	⊖ a	06 13									06 41												07 13		
St Pancras International 15	⊖ a	06 17									06 45												07 17		
St Albans City	a	06 41									07 09												07 41		
Luton Airport Parkway 4 ✈	a	06 52									07 20												07 52		
Luton 7	a	06 56									07 24												07 56		
Bedford 10	a	07 22									07 50												08 22		
Clapham Junction 10	d			06 18	06 05			06 23							06 37			06 50			06 35				07 03
Imperial Wharf §	d																								
West Brompton	⊖ d				06 12			06 29													06 42				07 09
Kensington Olympia	⊖ d				06 15	06 51		06 32													06 45				07 12
Shepherds Bush §	⊖ d																								
Willesden Jn. High Level	a				06 27																06 57				
Wembley Central	a																								
Harrow & Wealdstone	⊖ a							06 56																	07 29
Watford Junction	a							07 04																	07 36
London Victoria 15	⊖ a			06 26			06 20							06 35	06 44	06 50		06 58						07 05	

For general notes see front of timetable
For details of catering facilities see Directory of Train Operators

§ It is unknown, at the time of going to press, when this station will open. For further details contact National Rail Enquiries 08457-484950 or see local publicity.

A From Birmingham New Street (Table 116)
B From Eastbourne (Table 189)

Brighton → London, Bedford and Watford Junction

Network Diagram - see first page of Table 186

		GX	SN	LO	SN	SN	SN	FC	SE	GW	GX	SN	SN	GW	LO	FC	GX	SN	SN	SN	SN	GW	FC	GX
									13															
		1	1		1	1 ◇	1	1		1	1	1 ◇	1	1		1	1	1	1	1	1	1	1	1
			A								B		C											
Brighton 10	d					06 10		06 24				06 49				06 37					06 55		07 04	
Hove 2	d						06 21													06 51				
Preston Park	d					06 14		06 28								06 41					06 58			
Hassocks 4	d					06 20		06 34								06 47					07 05			
Burgess Hill 4	d					06 24		06 38								06 51				07 02	07 08			
Lewes 4	d																		06 50					
Wivelsfield 4	d					06 26		06 40								06 53					07 11			
Haywards Heath 3	a					06 31	06 35	06 45								06 58			07 05	07 08	07 15		07 18	
	d					06 39		06 45								07 02			07 13		07 16		07 18	
Balcombe	d							06 51																
Horsham 4	d		06 32										06 50					07 02						
Littlehaven	d		06 35															07 05						
Faygate	d																							
Ifield	d		06 41															07 11						
Crawley	d		06 44										06 59					07 14						
Three Bridges 4	a		06 48			06 48		06 56					07 02			07 11		07 18			07 25			
	d		06 48			06 48		06 56					07 03			07 12		07 18			07 31 →			
Gatwick Airport 10 ✈	a		06 52			06 52		07 00					07 07			07 16		07 22	07 24				07 30	
	d	06 50	06 53			06 54		07 01		07 03	07 05		07 08			07 16	07 20	07 23	07 25				07 31	07 35
Horley 4	d		06 55															07 26						
Salfords	d																	07 30						
Earlswood (Surrey)	d																	07 33						
Reigate	d													07 18								07 34		
Tonbridge 4	d																							
Redhill	a		07 02		←					07 10			07 15	07 23				07 36				07 38		
	d				06 37				07 05				07 16					07 37 →						
Merstham	d				06 41				07 09															
Coulsdon South	d				06 46				07 14															
Purley 4	d				06 49				07 18															
East Croydon	a				06 54	07 09		07 16	07 23			07 23	07 27			07 32			07 40				07 46	
	d				06 55	07 10		07 17	07 24			07 24	07 28			07 32			07 40				07 47	
Norwood Junction 2	a				06 59				07 28															
London Bridge 4 ⊖	a				07 12			07 31	07 40							07 45							08 01	
London Blackfriars 3 ⊖	a							07 37								07 52							08 07	
City Thameslink 3	a																							
Farringdon 3 ⊖	a							07 43								07 58							08 13	
St Pancras International 15 ⊖	a							07 47								08 02							08 17	
St Albans City	a							08 09								08 23							08 39	
Luton Airport Parkway 4 ✈	a							08 20								08 35							08 50	
Luton 7	a							08 24								08 38							08 54	
Bedford 10	a							08 50								09 05							09 20	
Clapham Junction 10	d			07 05		07 19						07 33	07 37		07 35				07 50					
Imperial Wharf §	d																							
West Brompton ⊖	d			07 12											07 42									
Kensington Olympia ⊖	d			07 15											07 45									
Shepherds Bush § ⊖	d																							
Willesden Jn. High Level	a			07 28											07 57									
Wembley Central	a																							
Harrow & Wealdstone ⊖	a																							
Watford Junction	a																							
London Victoria 15 ⊖	a	07 20				07 27					07 35	07 40	07 44				07 50		07 57					08 05

For general notes see front of timetable
For details of catering facilities see Directory of Train Operators

§ It is unknown, at the time of going to press, when this station will open. For further details contact National Rail Enquiries 08457-484950 or see local publicity.

A To Tonbridge (Table 209)
B Operating Company SN from 28 June
C From Havant (Table 188)

Table 186

Saturdays

Brighton → London, Bedford and Watford Junction

Network Diagram - see first page of Table 186

		SN	SN	SN	SN	LO	FC	GX	SN	SN	SN	FC	SE	GW	GX	SN	SN	GW	LO	FC	GX	SN	SN	SN	SN
													13												
		1	1	1 ◇	1		1	1	1	1	1	1		1	1	1 ◇	1	1		1	1	1	1	1	1
					A				B	C							D								
										🚲						🚲							🚲		
Brighton 10	d			07 19			07 07					07 34				07 49				07 37					07 55
Hove 2	d									07 22														07 51	
Preston Park	d						07 11													07 41					07 58
Hassocks 4	d						07 17													07 47					08 05
Burgess Hill 4	d						07 21													07 51				08 02	08 08
Lewes 4	d										07 20												07 50		
Wivelsfield 4	d						07 23				07 34									07 53					08 11
Haywards Heath 3	a						07 28			07 35	07 40	07 47								07 58			08 05	08 09	08 15
	d						07 32			07 43		07 48								08 02			08 13		08 16
Balcombe	d						07 37																		
Horsham 4	d				07 20				07 32								07 50					08 00			
Littlehaven	d								07 35													08 03			
Faygate	d																								
Ifield	d								07 41													08 09			
Crawley	d				07 29				07 44								07 59					08 14			
Three Bridges 4	a	←			07 32		07 42		07 48								08 02			08 11		08 18			
	d	07 31			07 33		07 42		07 48								08 03			08 12		08 18			08 25
Gatwick Airport 10 ✈	a	07 35			07 37		07 46		07 52	07 54		08 00					08 07			08 16		08 22	08 24		08 31 →
	d	07 37			07 38		07 46	07 50	07 53	07 55		08 01		08 03	08 05		08 08			08 16	08 20	08 23	08 25		
Horley 4	d				07 41				07 55													08 26			
Salfords	d																					08 30			
Earlswood (Surrey)	d																					08 33			
Reigate	d																	08 19							
Tonbridge 4	d												07 34												
Redhill	a		←		07 47				08 02				08 04	08 10			08 15	08 24				08 36			
	d		07 37		07 48								08 05				08 16					08 37 →			
Merstham	d		07 41										08 09												
Coulsdon South	d		07 46										08 14												
Purley 4	d		07 49										08 18												
East Croydon 🚊	a	07 52	07 54	07 55	07 59		08 02			08 10		08 16	08 23			08 23	08 27			08 32			08 40		
	d	07 52	07 55	07 55	08 00		08 02			08 10		08 17	08 24			08 24	08 28			08 32			08 40		
Norwood Junction 2	a		07 59										08 28												
London Bridge 4 ⊖	a		08 12				08 15					08 31	08 40							08 45					
London Blackfriars 3 ⊖	a						08 22					08 37								08 52					
City Thameslink 3	a																								
Farringdon 3 ⊖	a						08 28					08 43								08 58					
St Pancras International 15 ⊖	a						08 32					08 47								09 02					
St Albans City	a						08 54					09 09								09 23					
Luton Airport Parkway 4 ✈	a						09 05					09 20								09 35					
Luton 7	a						09 08					09 24								09 38					
Bedford 10	a						09 35					09 50								10 05					
Clapham Junction 10	d	08 03		08 05	08 11	08 05				08 20						08 33	08 37		08 35				08 50		
Imperial Wharf §	d																								
West Brompton ⊖	d	08 09				08 12													08 42						
Kensington Olympia ⊖	d	08 12				08 15													08 45						
Shepherds Bush § ⊖	d																								
Willesden Jn. High Level	a					08 28													08 57						
Wembley Central	a																								
Harrow & Wealdstone ⊖	a	08 29																							
Watford Junction	a	08 37																							
London Victoria 15 ⊖	a			08 11	08 18			08 20		08 27					08 35	08 40	08 44				08 50		08 57		

For general notes see front of timetable
For details of catering facilities see Directory of Train Operators

§ It is unknown, at the time of going to press, when this station will open. For further details contact National Rail Enquiries 08457-484950 or see local publicity.

A From Bognor Regis (Table 188) and from Portsmouth Harbour (Table 188)

B To Tunbridge Wells (Table 209)

C 🚲 from Haywards Heath

D From Bognor Regis (Table 188) and from Southampton Central (Table 188)

Table 186

Brighton → London, Bedford and Watford Junction

Network Diagram - see first page of Table 186

		GW	FC	GX	SN	SN	SN	SN	LO	FC	GX	SN	SN	SN	FC	SE	GW	GX	SN	SN	GW	LO	FC	GX	SN
		1	1	1	1	1	1 ◇	1		1	1	1	1	1	1	13	1	1	1 ◇	1	1		1	1	1
								A				B	C							D					
							[trolley]						[trolley]						[trolley]	[trolley]					
Brighton 10	d		08 04				08 19			08 07					08 34				08 49				08 37		
Hove 2	d												08 21												
Preston Park	d									08 11													08 41		
Hassocks 4	d									08 17													08 47		
Burgess Hill 4	d									08 21													08 51		
Lewes 4	d													08 20											
Wivelsfield 4	d									08 23				08 34									08 53		
Haywards Heath 3	a		08 18							08 28			08 35	08 40	08 47								08 58		
	d		08 18							08 32			08 43		08 49								09 02		
Balcombe	d									08 37															
Horsham 4	d							08 20				08 32								08 50					09 00
Littlehaven	d											08 35													09 03
Faygate	d																								
Ifield	d											08 41													09 09
Crawley	d							08 29				08 44								08 59					09 14
Three Bridges 4	a				←			08 32		08 42		08 48								09 02			09 11		09 18
	d				08 31			08 33		08 42		08 48								09 03			09 12		09 18
Gatwick Airport 10 ✈	a		08 30		08 35			08 37		08 46		08 52	08 54		09 00					09 07			09 16		09 22
	d		08 31	08 35	08 37			08 38		08 46	08 50	08 53	08 55		09 01		09 03	09 05		09 08			09 16	09 20	09 23
Horley 4	d							08 41				08 55													09 26
Salfords	d																								09 30
Earlswood (Surrey)	d																								09 33
Reigate	d	08 34																			09 18				
Tonbridge 4	d															08 34									
Redhill	a	08 38				←		08 47				09 02				09 04	09 10			09 15	09 23				09 36
	d					08 37		08 48								09 05				09 16					09 37 →
Merstham	d					08 41										09 09									
Coulsdon South	d					08 46										09 14									
Purley 4	d					08 49										09 18									
East Croydon	a		08 46		08 52	08 54	08 55	08 59		09 02			09 10		09 16	09 23			09 23	09 27			09 32		
	d		08 47		08 52	08 55	08 55	09 00		09 02			09 10		09 17	09 24			09 24	09 28			09 32		
Norwood Junction 2	a					08 59										09 28									
London Bridge 4 ⊖	a		09 01			09 12				09 15					09 30	09 40							09 45		
London Blackfriars 3 ⊖	a		09 08							09 22					09 37								09 52		
City Thameslink 3	a		09 10							09 25					09 40								09 55		
Farringdon 3 ⊖	a		09 14							09 29					09 44								09 59		
St Pancras International 15 ⊖	a		09 18							09 33					09 48								10 03		
St Albans City	a		09 39							09 53					10 09								10 23		
Luton Airport Parkway 4 ✈	a		09 50							10 05					10 20								10 35		
Luton 7	a		09 54							10 08					10 24								10 38		
Bedford 10	a		10 20							10 35					10 50								11 05		
Clapham Junction 10	d				09 03		09 05	09 11	09 05				09 20						09 33	09 37		09 35			
Imperial Wharf §	d																								
West Brompton ⊖	d				09 09				09 12													09 42			
Kensington Olympia ⊖	d				09 12				09 15													09 45			
Shepherds Bush § ⊖	d																								
Willesden Jn. High Level	a								09 27													09 57			
Wembley Central	a																								
Harrow & Wealdstone ⊖	a				09 29																				
Watford Junction	a				09 36																				
London Victoria 15 ⊖	a			09 05			09 11	09 18			09 20		09 27					09 35	09 40	09 44				09 50	

For general notes see front of timetable
For details of catering facilities see Directory of Train Operators

§ It is unknown, at the time of going to press, when this station will open. For further details contact National Rail Enquiries 08457-484950 or see local publicity.

A From Bognor Regis (Table 188) and from Portsmouth Harbour (Table 188)

B To Tunbridge Wells (Table 209)

C [trolley] from Haywards Heath

D From Bognor Regis (Table 188) and from Southampton Central (Table 188)

Brighton → London, Bedford and Watford Junction

Network Diagram - see first page of Table 186

		SN	SN	SN	GW	FC	GX	SN	SN	SN	SN	LO	FC	SN	XC	XC	GX		SN	SN	SN	FC	SE	GW	GX
		1	1	1	1	1	1	1	1	1 ◇	1		1	1	1 ◇	1 ◇	1		1	1	1	1	13	1	1
											A			A	B	C			D	E			G		
		⌶								⌶					⊏P	⊏P				⌶					
Brighton 10	d			08 55		09 04				09 19			09 07		09 15	09 15						09 34			
Hove 2	d		08 51																	09 21					
Preston Park	d			08 58									09 11												
Hassocks 4	d			09 05									09 17												
Burgess Hill 4	d			09 08									09 21												
Lewes 4	d	08 50																			09 20				
Wivelsfield 4	d			09 11																	09 34				
Haywards Heath 3	a	09 05	09 09	09 15		09 18							09 26		09 28	09 28				09 35	09 40	09 47			
	d	09 13		09 16		09 18							09 26		09 34	09 34				09 43		09 48			
Balcombe	d												09 32												
Horsham 4	d										09 20								09 32						
Littlehaven	d																		09 35						
Faygate	d																								
Ifield	d																		09 41						
Crawley	d										09 29								09 44						
Three Bridges 4	a			09 25				←			09 32		09 37						09 48						
	d			09 31 →				09 31			09 33		09 37						09 48						
Gatwick Airport 10 ✈	a	09 24				09 30		09 35			09 37		09 41		09 44	09 44			09 52	09 54		10 00			
	d	09 25				09 31	09 35	09 37			09 38		09 41	←	09 46	09 47	09 50		09 53	09 55		10 01		10 03	10 05
Horley 4	d										09 41 →			09 41					09 55						
Salfords	d																								
Earlswood (Surrey)	d																								
Reigate	d				09 34																				
Tonbridge 4	d																						09 34		
Redhill	a				09 38				←					09 47					10 02				10 04	10 10	
	d								09 37					09 48									10 05		
Merstham	d								09 41														10 09		
Coulsdon South	d								09 46														10 14		
Purley 4	d								09 49														10 18		
East Croydon 🚋	a	09 40				09 46		09 52	09 54	09 55			09 57	09 59	10 02	10 02				10 10		10 16	10 23		
	d	09 40				09 47		09 52	09 55	09 55			09 57	10 00	10 03	10 03				10 10		10 17	10 24		
Norwood Junction 2	a								09 59														10 28		
London Bridge 4 ⊖	a					10 00			10 12				10 15									10 30	10 40		
London Blackfriars 3 ⊖	a					10 07							10 22									10 37			
City Thameslink 3	a					10 10							10 25									10 40			
Farringdon 3 ⊖	a					10 14							10 29									10 44			
St Pancras International 15 ⊖	a					10 18							10 33									10 48			
St Albans City	a					10 39							10 53									11 09			
Luton Airport Parkway 4 ✈	a					10 50							11 05									11 20			
Luton 7	a					10 54							11 08									11 24			
Bedford 10	a					11 20							11 35									11 50			
Clapham Junction 10	d	09 50						10 03		10 05		10 05		10 11						10 20					
Imperial Wharf §	d																								
West Brompton ⊖	d							10 09				10 12													
Kensington Olympia ⊖	d							10 12				10 15			10 33	10 33									
Shepherds Bush § ⊖	d																								
Willesden Jn. High Level	a											10 27													
Wembley Central	a																								
Harrow & Wealdstone ⊖	a							10 29																	
Watford Junction	a							10 35																	
London Victoria 15 ⊖	a	09 57					10 05			10 11				10 18			10 20			10 27					10 35

For general notes see front of timetable
For details of catering facilities see Directory of Train Operators

§ It is unknown, at the time of going to press, when this station will open. For further details contact National Rail Enquiries 08457-484950 or see local publicity.

A From Bognor Regis (Table 188) and from Portsmouth Harbour (Table 188)
B Until 6 September. To Birmingham New Street (Table 116)
C From 13 September. To Birmingham New Street
D To Tunbridge Wells (Table 209)
E ⌶ from Haywards Heath
G From Tunbridge Wells (Table 206)

Table 186

Saturdays

Brighton → London, Bedford and Watford Junction

Network Diagram - see first page of Table 186

		SN 1 ◇	SN 1	GW 1	LO	FC 1	GX 1	SN 1	SN 1	SN 1	SN 1	GW 1	FC 1	GX 1	SN 1	SN 1	SN 1 ◇	SN 1	LO	FC 1	GX 1	SN 1	SN 1	SN 1	FC 1
			A															B				C	D		
		✠	✠					✠									✠						✠		
Brighton 10	d	09 49				09 37					09 55		10 04				10 19			10 07					10 34
Hove 2	d									09 51													10 21		
Preston Park	d					09 41					09 58									10 11					
Hassocks 4	d					09 47					10 05									10 17					
Burgess Hill 4	d					09 51				10 02	10 08									10 21					
Lewes 4	d							09 50																10 20	
Wivelsfield 4	d					09 53					10 11									10 23				10 34	
Haywards Heath 3	a					09 58		10 05		10 08	10 15		10 18							10 28			10 35	10 40	10 47
	d					10 02		10 09		10 12	10 16		10 18							10 32			10 43		10 48
Balcombe	d																			10 37					
Horsham 4	d		09 50						10 00									10 20				10 32			
Littlehaven	d								10 03													10 35			
Faygate	d																					10 41			
Ifield	d								10 09													10 44			
Crawley	d		09 59						10 14									10 29							
Three Bridges 4	a		10 02			10 11			10 18		10 25				←			10 32		10 42		10 48			
	d		10 03			10 12			10 18		10 31 →				10 31			10 33		10 42		10 48			
Gatwick Airport 10 ✈	a		10 07			10 16		10 21	10 22	10 25			10 30		10 35			10 37		10 46		10 52	10 54		11 00
	d		10 08			10 16	10 20	10 22	10 23	10 26			10 31	10 35	10 37			10 38		10 46	10 50	10 53	10 55		11 01
Horley 4	d								10 26									10 41				10 55			
Salfords	d								10 30																
Earlswood (Surrey)	d								10 33																
Reigate	d			10 19								10 34													
Tonbridge 4	d																								
Redhill	a		10 15	10 24					10 36			10 38				←		10 47				11 02			
	d		10 16						10 37 →							10 37		10 48							
Merstham	d															10 41									
Coulsdon South	d															10 46									
Purley 4	d															10 49									
East Croydon	a	10 23	10 27			10 32		10 38		10 42			10 46		10 52	10 54	10 55	11 00		11 02			11 10		11 16
	d	10 24	10 28			10 32		10 38		10 42			10 47		10 52	10 55	10 55	11 00		11 02			11 10		11 17
Norwood Junction 2	a															10 59									
London Bridge 4 ⊖	a					10 45							11 00			11 12				11 15					11 30
London Blackfriars 3 ⊖	a					10 52							11 07							11 22					11 37
City Thameslink 3	a					10 55							11 10							11 25					11 40
Farringdon 3 ⊖	a					10 59							11 14							11 29					11 44
St Pancras International 15 ⊖	a					11 03							11 18							11 33					11 48
St Albans City	a					11 23							11 39							11 53					12 09
Luton Airport Parkway 4 ✈	a					11 35							11 50							12 05					12 20
Luton 7	a					11 38							11 54							12 08					12 24
Bedford 10	a					12 05							12 20							12 35					12 50
Clapham Junction 10	d	10 33	10 37		10 35			10 48		10 52					11 03		11 05	11 11	11 05				11 20		
Imperial Wharf §	d																								
West Brompton ⊖	d				10 42										11 09				11 12						
Kensington Olympia ⊖	d				10 45										11 12				11 15						
Shepherds Bush § ⊖	d																								
Willesden Jn. High Level	a				10 57														11 27						
Wembley Central	a																								
Harrow & Wealdstone ⊖	a														11 29										
Watford Junction	a														11 36										
London Victoria 15 ⊖	a	10 40	10 44				10 50	10 56		10 59				11 05			11 11	11 18			11 20		11 27		

For general notes see front of timetable
For details of catering facilities see Directory of Train Operators

§ It is unknown, at the time of going to press, when this station will open. For further details contact National Rail Enquiries 08457-484950 or see local publicity.

A From Bognor Regis (Table 188) and from Southampton Central (Table 188)

B From Bognor Regis (Table 188) and from Portsmouth Harbour (Table 188)

C To Tunbridge Wells (Table 209)

D ✠ from Haywards Heath

Brighton → London, Bedford and Watford Junction

Network Diagram - see first page of Table 186

Station		SE 13 A	GW 1	GX 1	SN 1◇	SN 1 B	GW 1	LO	FC 1	GX 1	SN 1	SN 1	SN 1	SN 1	GW 1	FC 1	GX 1	SN 1	SN 1	SN 1◇	SN 1 C	LO	FC 1	GX 1	SN 1 D
Brighton 10	d				10 49				10 37					10 55		11 04				11 19			11 07		
Hove 2	d												10 51												
Preston Park	d								10 41					10 58									11 11		
Hassocks 4	d								10 47					11 05									11 17		
Burgess Hill 4	d								10 51				11 02	11 08									11 21		
Lewes 4	d											10 50													
Wivelsfield 4	d								10 53					11 11									11 23		
Haywards Heath 3	a								10 58			11 05	11 09	11 15		11 18							11 28		
	d								11 02			11 13		11 16		11 18							11 32		
Balcombe	d																						11 37		
Horsham 4	d					10 50					11 00										11 20				11 32
Littlehaven	d										11 03														11 35
Faygate	d																								
Ifield	d										11 09														11 41
Crawley	d					10 59					11 14										11 29				11 44
Three Bridges 4	a					11 02			11 11		11 18			11 25							11 32		11 42		11 48
	d					11 03			11 12		11 18			11 31 →				← 11 31			11 33		11 42		11 48
Gatwick Airport 10 ✈	a					11 07			11 16		11 22	11 24				11 30		11 35			11 37		11 46		11 52
	d		11 03	11 05		11 08			11 16	11 20	11 23	11 25				11 31	11 35	11 37			11 38		11 46	11 50	11 53
Horley 4	d										11 26										11 41				11 55
Salfords	d										11 30														
Earlswood (Surrey)	d										11 33														
Reigate	d						11 18								11 34										
Tonbridge 4	d	10 34																							
Redhill	a	11 04	11 10			11 15	11 24				11 36				11 38						11 47				12 02
	d	11 05				11 16					11 37 →								← 11 37		11 48				
Merstham	d	11 09																	11 41						
Coulsdon South	d	11 14																	11 46						
Purley 4	d	11 18																	11 49						
East Croydon	a	11 23			11 23	11 27			11 32			11 40				11 46		11 52	11 54	11 55	12 00		12 02		
	d	11 24			11 24	11 28			11 32			11 40				11 47		11 52	11 55	11 55	12 00		12 02		
Norwood Junction 2	a	11 28																	11 59						
London Bridge 4 ⊖	a	11 40							11 45							12 00			12 12				12 15		
London Blackfriars 3 ⊖	a								11 52							12 07							12 22		
City Thameslink 3	a								11 55							12 10							12 25		
Farringdon 3 ⊖	a								11 59							12 14							12 29		
St Pancras International 15 ⊖	a								12 03							12 18							12 33		
St Albans City	a								12 23							12 39							12 53		
Luton Airport Parkway 4 ✈	a								12 35							12 50							13 05		
Luton 7	a								12 38							12 54							13 08		
Bedford 10	a								13 05							13 20							13 35		
Clapham Junction 10	d				11 33	11 37		11 35				11 50						12 03		12 05	12 11	12 05			
Imperial Wharf §	d																								
West Brompton ⊖	d							11 42										12 09				12 12			
Kensington Olympia ⊖	d							11 45										12 12				12 15			
Shepherds Bush § ⊖	d																								
Willesden Jn. High Level	a							11 57														12 27			
Wembley Central	a																								
Harrow & Wealdstone ⊖	a																	12 29							
Watford Junction	a																	12 36							
London Victoria 15 ⊖	a			11 35	11 40	11 44				11 50		11 57					12 05			12 11	12 18			12 20	

For general notes see front of timetable
For details of catering facilities see Directory of Train Operators

§ It is unknown, at the time of going to press, when this station will open. For further details contact National Rail Enquiries 08457-484950 or see local publicity.

A From Tunbridge Wells (Table 206)
B From Bognor Regis (Table 188) and from Southampton Central (Table 188)
C From Bognor Regis (Table 188) and from Portsmouth Harbour (Table 188)
D To Tunbridge Wells (Table 209)

Table 186

Brighton → London, Bedford and Watford Junction

Network Diagram - see first page of Table 186

		SN	SN	FC	SE	GW	GX	SN	SN	GW	LO	FC	GX	SN		SN	SN	SN	GW	FC	GX	SN	SN	SN	SN
					13																				
		1	1	1		1	1	1 ◊	1	1		1	1	1		1	1	1	1	1	1	1	1	1 ◊	1
		A			B				C																D
		🛒						🛒	🛒							🛒								🛒	
Brighton [10]	d			11 34				11 49				11 37						11 55		12 04				12 19	
Hove [2]	d	11 21															11 51								
Preston Park	d											11 41						11 58							
Hassocks [4]	d											11 47						12 05							
Burgess Hill [4]	d											11 51					12 02	12 08							
Lewes [4]	d		11 20													11 50									
Wivelsfield [4]	d		11 34									11 53						12 11							
Haywards Heath [3]	a	11 35	11 40	11 47								11 58				12 05	12 09	12 15		12 18					
	d	11 43		11 48								12 02				12 13		12 16		12 18					
Balcombe	d																								
Horsham [4]	d								11 50					12 00											12 20
Littlehaven	d													12 03											
Faygate	d																								
Ifield	d													12 09											
Crawley	d								11 59					12 14											12 29
Three Bridges [4]	a								12 02			12 11		12 18				12 25				←			12 32
	d								12 03			12 12		12 18				12 31 →				12 31			12 33
Gatwick Airport [10] ✈	a	11 54		12 00					12 07			12 16		12 22		12 24				12 30		12 35			12 37
	d	11 55		12 01		12 03	12 05		12 08			12 16	12 20	12 23		12 25				12 31	12 35	12 37			12 38
Horley [4]	d													12 26											12 41
Salfords	d													12 30											
Earlswood (Surrey)	d													12 33											
Reigate	d									12 19									12 34						
Tonbridge [4]	d				11 34																				
Redhill	a				12 04	12 10			12 15	12 24				12 36					12 38				←		12 47
	d				12 05				12 16					12 37 →									12 37		12 48
Merstham	d				12 09																		12 41		
Coulsdon South	d				12 14																		12 46		
Purley [4]	d				12 18																		12 49		
East Croydon	a	12 10		12 16	12 23			12 23	12 27			12 32				12 40				12 46		12 52	12 54	12 55	13 00
	d	12 10		12 17	12 24			12 24	12 28			12 32				12 40				12 47		12 52	12 55	12 55	13 00
Norwood Junction [2]	a				12 28																		12 59		
London Bridge [4]	⊖ a			12 30	12 40							12 45								13 00			13 12		
London Blackfriars [3]	⊖ a			12 37								12 52								13 07					
City Thameslink [3]	a			12 40								12 55								13 10					
Farringdon [3]	⊖ a			12 44								12 59								13 14					
St Pancras International [15]	⊖ a			12 48								13 03								13 18					
St Albans City	a			13 09								13 23								13 39					
Luton Airport Parkway [4] ✈	a			13 20								13 35								13 50					
Luton [7]	a			13 24								13 38								13 54					
Bedford [10]	a			13 50								14 05								14 20					
Clapham Junction [10]	d	12 20						12 33	12 37		12 35					12 50						13 03		13 05	13 11
Imperial Wharf §	d																								
West Brompton	⊖ d										12 42											13 09			
Kensington Olympia	⊖ d										12 45											13 12			
Shepherds Bush §	⊖ d																								
Willesden Jn. High Level	a										12 57														
Wembley Central	a																					13 29			
Harrow & Wealdstone	⊖ a																					13 37			
Watford Junction	a																								
London Victoria [15]	⊖ a	12 27					12 35	12 40	12 44				12 50			12 57					13 05			13 11	13 18

For general notes see front of timetable
For details of catering facilities see Directory of Train Operators

§ It is unknown, at the time of going to press, when this station will open. For further details contact National Rail Enquiries 08457-484950 or see local publicity.

A 🛒 from Haywards Heath
B From Tunbridge Wells (Table 206)
C From Bognor Regis (Table 188) and from Southampton Central (Table 188)
D From Bognor Regis (Table 188) and from Portsmouth Harbour (Table 188)

Brighton → London, Bedford and Watford Junction

Network Diagram - see first page of Table 186

		LO	FC	GX	SN	SN	SN	FC	SE	GW	GX	SN	SN	GW	LO	FC	GX	SN	SN	SN	SN	GW	FC	GX	SN
									13																
			1	1	1	1	1	1		1	1	1 ◇	1	1		1	1	1	1	1	1	1	1	1	1
					A	B			C				D												
						🛒						🛒	🛒						🛒						
Brighton [10]	d		12 07					12 34				12 49				12 37					12 55		13 04		
Hove [2]	d					12 21														12 51					
Preston Park	d		12 11													12 41					12 58				
Hassocks [4]	d		12 17													12 47					13 05				
Burgess Hill [4]	d		12 21													12 51				13 02	13 08				
Lewes [4]	d						12 20												12 50						
Wivelsfield [4]	d		12 23				12 34									12 53					13 11				
Haywards Heath [3]	a		12 28			12 35	12 40	12 47								12 58			13 05	13 09	13 15		13 18		
	d		12 32			12 43		12 48								13 02			13 13		13 16		13 18		
Balcombe	d		12 37																						
Horsham [4]	d				12 32								12 50					13 00							
Littlehaven	d				12 35													13 03							
Faygate	d																								
Ifield	d				12 41													13 09							
Crawley	d				12 44								12 59					13 14							
Three Bridges [4]	a		12 42		12 48								13 02			13 11		13 18			13 25				←
	d		12 42		12 48								13 03			13 12		13 18			13 31				13 31
Gatwick Airport [10] ✈	a		12 46		12 52	12 54		13 00					13 07			13 16		13 22	13 24		→		13 30		13 35
	d		12 46	12 50	12 53	12 55		13 01		13 03	13 05		13 08			13 16	13 20	13 23	13 25				13 31	13 35	13 37
Horley [4]	d				12 55													13 26							
Salfords	d																	13 30							
Earlswood (Surrey)	d																	13 33							
Reigate	d													13 18								13 34			
Tonbridge [4]	d								12 34																
Redhill	a				13 02				13 04	13 10			13 15	13 23				13 36				13 38			
	d								13 05				13 16					13 37 →							
Merstham	d								13 09																
Coulsdon South	d								13 14																
Purley [4]	d								13 18																
East Croydon 🚊	a		13 02			13 10		13 16	13 23			13 23	13 27			13 32			13 40				13 46		13 52
	d		13 02			13 10		13 17	13 24			13 24	13 28			13 32			13 40				13 47		13 52
Norwood Junction [2]	a								13 28																
London Bridge [4] ⊖	a		13 15					13 30	13 40							13 45							14 00		
London Blackfriars [3] ⊖	a		13 22					13 37								13 52							14 07		
City Thameslink [3]	a		13 25					13 40								13 55							14 10		
Farringdon [3] ⊖	a		13 29					13 44								13 59							14 14		
St Pancras International [15] ⊖	a		13 33					13 48								14 03							14 18		
St Albans City	a		13 53					14 09								14 23							14 39		
Luton Airport Parkway [4] ✈	a		14 05					14 20								14 35							14 50		
Luton [7]	a		14 08					14 24								14 38							14 54		
Bedford [10]	a		14 35					14 50								15 05							15 20		
Clapham Junction [10]	d	13 05				13 20						13 33	13 37		13 35				13 50						14 03
Imperial Wharf §	d																								
West Brompton ⊖	d	13 12													13 42										14 09
Kensington Olympia ⊖	d	13 15													13 45										14 12
Shepherds Bush § ⊖	d																								
Willesden Jn. High Level	a	13 27													13 57										
Wembley Central	a																								
Harrow & Wealdstone ⊖	a																								14 29
Watford Junction	a																								14 37
London Victoria [15] ⊖	a			13 20		13 27					13 35	13 40	13 44				13 50		13 57					14 05	

For general notes see front of timetable
For details of catering facilities see Directory of Train Operators

§ It is unknown, at the time of going to press, when this station will open. For further details contact National Rail Enquiries 08457-484950 or see local publicity.

A To Tunbridge Wells (Table 209)
B 🛒 from Haywards Heath
C From Tunbridge Wells (Table 206)
D From Bognor Regis (Table 188) and from Southampton Central (Table 188)

Table 186

Saturdays

Brighton → London, Bedford and Watford Junction

Network Diagram - see first page of Table 186

		SN	SN	SN	LO	FC	GX	SN	SN	SN	FC	SE	GW	GX	SN	SN	GW	LO	FC	GX	SN	SN	SN	SN	GW
		1	1◇ ⌶	1 A		1	1	1 B	1 C ⌶	1	1	13 D	1	1	1◇ ⌶	1 E ⌶	1		1	1	1	1 ⌶	1	1	1
Brighton [10]	d		13 19			13 07					13 34				13 49				13 37					13 55	
Hove [2]	d								13 21														13 51		
Preston Park	d					13 11													13 41					13 58	
Hassocks [4]	d					13 17													13 47					14 05	
Burgess Hill [4]	d					13 21													13 51				14 02	14 08	
Lewes [4]	d									13 20												13 50			
Wivelsfield [4]	d					13 23				13 34									13 53					14 11	
Haywards Heath [3]	a					13 28			13 35	13 40	13 47								13 58			14 05	14 09	14 15	
	d					13 32			13 43		13 48								14 02			14 13		14 16	
Balcombe	d					13 37																			
Horsham [4]	d			13 20				13 32								13 50					14 00				
Littlehaven	d							13 35													14 03				
Faygate	d																								
Ifield	d							13 41													14 09				
Crawley	d			13 29				13 44								13 59					14 14				
Three Bridges [4]	a			13 32		13 42		13 48								14 02			14 11		14 18			14 25	
	d			13 33		13 42		13 48								14 03			14 12		14 18			14 31 →	
Gatwick Airport [10] ✈	a			13 37		13 46		13 52	13 54		14 00					14 07			14 16		14 22	14 24			
	d			13 38		13 46	13 50	13 53	13 55		14 01		14 03	14 05		14 08			14 16	14 20	14 23	14 25			
Horley [4]	d			13 41				13 55													14 26				
Salfords	d																				14 30				
Earlswood (Surrey)	d																				14 33				
Reigate	d																14 19								14 34
Tonbridge [4]	d											13 34													
Redhill	a	←		13 47				14 02				14 04	14 10			14 15	14 24				14 36				14 38
	d	13 37		13 48								14 05				14 16					14 37 →				
Merstham	d	13 41										14 09													
Coulsdon South	d	13 46										14 14													
Purley [4]	d	13 49										14 18													
East Croydon 🚊	a	13 54	13 55	14 00		14 02			14 10		14 16	14 23			14 23	14 27			14 32			14 40			
	d	13 55	13 55	14 00		14 02			14 10		14 17	14 24			14 24	14 28			14 32			14 40			
Norwood Junction [2]	a	13 59										14 28													
London Bridge [4] ⊖	a	14 12				14 15					14 30	14 40							14 45						
London Blackfriars [3] ⊖	a					14 22					14 37								14 52						
City Thameslink [3]	a					14 25					14 40								14 55						
Farringdon [3] ⊖	a					14 29					14 44								14 59						
St Pancras International [15] ⊖	a					14 33					14 48								15 03						
St Albans City	a					14 53					15 09								15 23						
Luton Airport Parkway [4] ✈	a					15 05					15 20								15 35						
Luton [7]	a					15 08					15 24								15 38						
Bedford [10]	a					15 35					15 50								16 05						
Clapham Junction [10]	d		14 05	14 11	14 05				14 20						14 33	14 37		14 35				14 50			
Imperial Wharf §	d																								
West Brompton ⊖	d				14 12													14 42							
Kensington Olympia ⊖	d				14 15													14 45							
Shepherds Bush § ⊖	d																								
Willesden Jn. High Level	a				14 27													14 57							
Wembley Central	a																								
Harrow & Wealdstone ⊖	a																								
Watford Junction	a																								
London Victoria [15] ⊖	a		14 11	14 18			14 20		14 27					14 35	14 40	14 44				14 50		14 57			

For general notes see front of timetable
For details of catering facilities see
Directory of Train Operators

§ It is unknown, at the time of going to press, when this station will open. For further details contact National Rail Enquiries 08457-484950 or see local publicity.

A From Bognor Regis (Table 188) and from Portsmouth Harbour (Table 188)

B To Tunbridge Wells (Table 209)

C ⌶ from Haywards Heath

D From Tunbridge Wells (Table 206)

E From Bognor Regis (Table 188) and from Southampton Central (Table 188)

Table 186

Brighton → London, Bedford and Watford Junction

Network Diagram - see first page of Table 186

		FC	GX	SN	SN	SN	SN	LO	FC	GX	XC	XC	SN	SN	SN	FC	SE	GW	GX	SN	SN	GW	LO	FC
		1	1	1	1	1 ◇	1		1	1	1 ◇	1 ◇	1	1	1	1	13	1	1	1 ◇	1	1		1
						🛒	A				B ☕	C ☕	D	E 🛒			G			🛒	H 🛒			
Brighton 10	d	14 04				14 19			14 07		14 22	14 22				14 34				14 49				14 37
Hove 2	d													14 21										
Preston Park	d								14 11															14 41
Hassocks 4	d								14 17															14 47
Burgess Hill 4	d								14 21															14 51
Lewes 4	d														14 20									
Wivelsfield 4	d								14 23						14 34									14 53
Haywards Heath 3	a	14 18							14 28					14 35	14 40	14 47								14 58
	d	14 18							14 32					14 43		14 48								15 02
Balcombe	d								14 37															
Horsham 4	d						14 20						14 32								14 50			
Littlehaven	d												14 35											
Faygate	d																							
Ifield	d												14 41											
Crawley	d						14 29						14 44								14 59			
Three Bridges 4	a			←			14 32		14 42				14 48								15 02			15 11
	d			14 31			14 33		14 42				14 48								15 03			15 12
Gatwick Airport 10 ✈	a	14 30		14 35			14 37		14 46		14 50	14 50	14 52	14 55		15 00					15 07			15 16
	d	14 31	14 35	14 37			14 38		14 46	14 50	14 52	14 52	14 53	14 56		15 01		15 03	15 05		15 08			15 16
Horley 4	d						14 41						14 55											
Salfords	d																							
Earlswood (Surrey)	d																							
Reigate	d																					15 18		
Tonbridge 4	d																14 34							
Redhill	a				←		14 47						15 02				15 04	15 10			15 15	15 23		
	d				14 37		14 48										15 05				15 16			
Merstham	d				14 41												15 09							
Coulsdon South	d				14 46												15 14							
Purley 4	d				14 49												15 18							
East Croydon	a	14 46		14 52	14 54	14 55	15 00		15 02		15 08	15 08		15 11		15 16	15 23			15 23	15 27			15 32
	d	14 47		14 52	14 55	14 55	15 00		15 02		15 08	15 09		15 11		15 17	15 24			15 24	15 28			15 32
Norwood Junction 2	a				14 59												15 28							
London Bridge 4	⊖ a	15 00			15 12				15 15							15 30	15 40							15 45
London Blackfriars 3	⊖ a	15 07							15 22							15 37								15 52
City Thameslink 3	a	15 10							15 25							15 40								15 55
Farringdon 3	⊖ a	15 14							15 29							15 44								15 59
St Pancras International 15	⊖ a	15 18							15 33							15 48								16 03
St Albans City	a	15 39							15 53							16 09								16 23
Luton Airport Parkway 4 ✈	a	15 50							16 05							16 20								16 35
Luton 7	a	15 54							16 08							16 24								16 38
Bedford 10	a	16 20							16 35							16 50								17 05
Clapham Junction 10	d			15 03		15 05	15 11	15 05						15 21						15 33	15 37		15 35	
Imperial Wharf §	d																							
West Brompton	⊖ d			15 09				15 12															15 42	
Kensington Olympia	⊖ d			15 12				15 15			15 40	15 40											15 45	
Shepherds Bush §	⊖ d																							
Willesden Jn. High Level	a							15 27															15 57	
Wembley Central	a																							
Harrow & Wealdstone	⊖ a			15 29																				
Watford Junction	a			15 37																				
London Victoria 15	⊖ a		15 05			15 11	15 18			15 20				15 27					15 35	15 40	15 44			

For general notes see front of timetable
For details of catering facilities see Directory of Train Operators

§ It is unknown, at the time of going to press, when this station will open. For further details contact National Rail Enquiries 08457-484950 or see local publicity.

A From Bognor Regis (Table 188) and from Portsmouth Harbour (Table 188)
B Until 6 September
C From 13 September. To Birmingham New Street
D To Tunbridge Wells (Table 209)
E 🛒 from Haywards Heath
G From Tunbridge Wells (Table 206)
H From Bognor Regis (Table 188) and from Southampton Central (Table 188)

Brighton → London, Bedford and Watford Junction

Network Diagram - see first page of Table 186

		GX	SN	SN	SN	SN	GW	FC	GX	SN	SN	SN	SN	LO	FC	GX	SN	SN	SN	FC	SE 13	GW	GX	SN	SN
		[1]	[1]	[1]	[1]	[1]	[1]	[1]	[1]	[1]	[1]	[1] ◇	[1]		[1]	[1]	[1]	[1]	[1]	[1]		[1]	[1]	[1] ◇	[1]
													A				B	C			D				E
				[trolley]								[trolley]						[trolley]						[trolley]	[trolley]
Brighton [10]	d					14 55		15 04				15 19			15 07					15 34				15 49	
Hove [2]	d				14 51													15 21							
Preston Park	d					14 58									15 11										
Hassocks [4]	d					15 05									15 17										
Burgess Hill [4]	d				15 02	15 08									15 21										
Lewes [4]	d			14 50															15 20						
Wivelsfield [4]	d					15 11									15 23				15 34						
Haywards Heath [3]	a			15 05	15 09	15 15		15 18							15 28			15 35	15 40	15 47					
	d			15 13		15 16		15 18							15 32			15 43		15 48					
Balcombe	d														15 37										
Horsham [4]	d		15 00										15 20				15 32								15 50
Littlehaven	d		15 03														15 35								
Faygate	d																								
Ifield	d		15 09														15 41								
Crawley	d		15 14										15 29				15 44								15 59
Three Bridges [4]	a		15 18			15 25				←			15 32		15 42		15 48								16 02
	d		15 18			15 31 →				15 31			15 33		15 42		15 48								16 03
Gatwick Airport [10] ✈	a		15 22	15 24				15 30		15 35			15 37		15 46		15 52	15 54		16 00					16 07
	d	15 20	15 23	15 25				15 31	15 35	15 37			15 38		15 46	15 50	15 53	15 55		16 01		16 03	16 05		16 08
Horley [4]	d		15 26										15 41				15 55								
Salfords	d		15 30																						
Earlswood (Surrey)	d		15 33																						
Reigate	d						15 34																		
Tonbridge [4]	d																				15 34				
Redhill	a		15 36				15 38				←		15 47				16 02				16 04	16 10			16 15
	d		15 37 →								15 37		15 48								16 05				16 16
Merstham	d										15 41										16 09				
Coulsdon South	d										15 46										16 14				
Purley [4]	d										15 49										16 18				
East Croydon	a			15 40				15 46		15 52	15 54	15 55	16 00		16 02			16 10		16 16	16 23			16 23	16 27
	d			15 40				15 47		15 52	15 55	15 55	16 00		16 02			16 10		16 17	16 24			16 24	16 28
Norwood Junction [2]	a										15 59										16 28				
London Bridge [4] ⊖	a							16 00			16 12				16 15					16 30	16 40				
London Blackfriars [3] ⊖	a							16 07							16 22					16 37					
City Thameslink [3]	a							16 10							16 25					16 40					
Farringdon [3] ⊖	a							16 14							16 29					16 44					
St Pancras International [15] ⊖	a							16 18							16 33					16 48					
St Albans City	a							16 39							16 53					17 09					
Luton Airport Parkway [4] ✈	a							16 50							17 05					17 20					
Luton [7]	a							16 54							17 08					17 24					
Bedford [10]	a							17 20							17 35					17 50					
Clapham Junction [10]	d			15 50						16 03		16 05	16 11	16 05				16 20						16 33	16 37
Imperial Wharf §	d																								
West Brompton ⊖	d									16 09				16 12											
Kensington Olympia ⊖	d									16 12				16 15											
Shepherds Bush § ⊖	d																								
Willesden Jn. High Level	a													16 27											
Wembley Central	a																								
Harrow & Wealdstone ⊖	a									16 29															
Watford Junction	a									16 37															
London Victoria [15] ⊖	a	15 50		15 57					16 05			16 11	16 18			16 20		16 27					16 35	16 40	16 44

For general notes see front of timetable
For details of catering facilities see Directory of Train Operators

§ It is unknown, at the time of going to press, when this station will open. For further details contact National Rail Enquiries 08457-484950 or see local publicity.

A From Bognor Regis (Table 188) and from Portsmouth Harbour (Table 188)
B To Tunbridge Wells (Table 209)
C [trolley] from Haywards Heath
D From Tunbridge Wells (Table 206)
E From Bognor Regis (Table 188) and from Southampton Central (Table 188)

Table 186

Saturdays

Brighton → London, Bedford and Watford Junction

Network Diagram - see first page of Table 186

		GW	LO	FC	GX	SN	SN	SN	SN	GW	FC	GX	SN	SN	SN	SN	LO	FC	GX	SN	SN	SN	FC	SE	GW
		1		1	1	1	1	1	1	1	1	1	1	1	1 ◇	1		1	1	1	1	1	1	13	1
																A				B	C			D	
							⊼								⊼						⊼				
Brighton 10	d			15 37					15 55		16 04				16 19			16 07					16 34		
Hove 2	d							15 51													16 21				
Preston Park	d			15 41					15 58									16 11							
Hassocks 4	d			15 47					16 05									16 17							
Burgess Hill 4	d			15 51				16 02	16 08									16 21							
Lewes 4	d						15 50															16 20			
Wivelsfield 4	d			15 53					16 11									16 23				16 34			
Haywards Heath 3	a			15 58			16 05	16 09	16 15		16 18							16 28			16 35	16 40	16 47		
	d			16 02			16 13		16 16		16 18							16 32			16 43		16 48		
Balcombe	d																	16 37							
Horsham 4	d					16 00										16 20				16 32					
Littlehaven	d					16 03														16 35					
Faygate	d																								
Ifield	d					16 09														16 41					
Crawley	d					16 14										16 29				16 44					
Three Bridges 4	a			16 11		16 18			16 25				←			16 32		16 42		16 48					
	d			16 12		16 18			16 31 →				16 31			16 33		16 42		16 48					
Gatwick Airport 10 ✈	a			16 16		16 22	16 24				16 30		16 35			16 37		16 46		16 52	16 54		17 00		
	d			16 16	16 20	16 23	16 25				16 31	16 35	16 37			16 38		16 46	16 50	16 53	16 55		17 01		17 03
Horley 4	d					16 26										16 41				16 55					
Salfords	d					16 30																			
Earlswood (Surrey)	d					16 33																			
Reigate	d	16 19								16 34															
Tonbridge 4	d																							16 34	
Redhill	a	16 24				16 36				16 38				←		16 47				17 02				17 04	17 10
	d					16 37 →								16 37		16 48								17 05	
Merstham	d													16 41										17 09	
Coulsdon South	d													16 46										17 14	
Purley 4	d													16 49										17 18	
East Croydon	a			16 32			16 40				16 46		16 52	16 54	16 55	17 00		17 02			17 10		17 16	17 23	
	d			16 32			16 40				16 47		16 52	16 55	16 55	17 00		17 02			17 10		17 17	17 24	
Norwood Junction 2	a													16 59										17 28	
London Bridge 4 ⊖	a			16 45							17 00			17 12				17 15					17 30	17 40	
London Blackfriars 3 ⊖	a			16 52							17 07							17 22					17 37		
City Thameslink 3	a			16 55							17 10							17 25					17 40		
Farringdon 3 ⊖	a			16 59							17 14							17 29					17 44		
St Pancras International 15 ⊖	a			17 03							17 18							17 33					17 48		
St Albans City	a			17 23							17 39							17 53					18 09		
Luton Airport Parkway 4 ✈	a			17 35							17 50							18 05					18 20		
Luton 7	a			17 38							17 54							18 08					18 24		
Bedford 10	a			18 05							18 20							18 35					18 50		
Clapham Junction 10	d		16 35				16 50						17 03		17 05	17 11	17 05				17 20				
Imperial Wharf §	d																								
West Brompton ⊖	d		16 42										17 09				17 12								
Kensington Olympia ⊖	d		16 45										17 12				17 15								
Shepherds Bush § ⊖	d																								
Willesden Jn. High Level	a		16 57														17 27								
Wembley Central	a																								
Harrow & Wealdstone ⊖	a												17 29												
Watford Junction	a												17 36												
London Victoria 15 ⊖	a				16 50		16 57					17 05			17 11	17 18			17 20		17 27				

For general notes see front of timetable
For details of catering facilities see Directory of Train Operators

§ It is unknown, at the time of going to press, when this station will open. For further details contact National Rail Enquiries 08457-484950 or see local publicity.

A From Bognor Regis (Table 188) and from Portsmouth Harbour (Table 188)

B To Tunbridge Wells (Table 209)

C ⊼ from Haywards Heath

D From Tunbridge Wells (Table 206)

Table 186

Saturdays

Brighton → London, Bedford and Watford Junction

Network Diagram - see first page of Table 186

	GX 1	SN 1 ◇	SN 1 A	GW 1	LO	FC 1	GX 1		SN 1	SN 1	SN 1	SN 1	GW 1	FC 1	GX 1	SN 1	SN 1	SN 1 ◇	SN 1 B	LO	FC 1	GX 1	SN 1 C	
Brighton 10 d		16 49				16 37						16 55		17 04				17 19			17 07			
Hove 2 d											16 51													
Preston Park d						16 41						16 58									17 11			
Hassocks 4 d						16 47						17 05									17 17			
Burgess Hill 4 d						16 51					17 02	17 08									17 21			
Lewes 4 d										16 50														
Wivelsfield 4 d						16 53						17 11									17 23			
Haywards Heath 3 a						16 58				17 05	17 09	17 15		17 18							17 28			
d						17 02				17 13		17 16		17 18							17 32			
Balcombe d																					17 37			
Horsham 4 d			16 50						17 00										17 20				17 32	
Littlehaven d									17 03														17 35	
Faygate d																								
Ifield d									17 09														17 41	
Crawley d			16 59						17 14										17 29				17 44	
Three Bridges 4 a			17 02			17 11			17 18			17 25							17 32		17 42		17 48	
d			17 03			17 12			17 18			17 31 →				← 17 31			17 33		17 42		17 48	
Gatwick Airport 10 ✈ a			17 07			17 16			17 22	17 24				17 30		17 35			17 37		17 46		17 52	
d	17 05		17 08			17 16	17 20		17 23	17 25				17 31	17 35	17 37			17 38		17 46	17 50	17 53	
Horley 4 d									17 26										17 41				17 55	
Salfords d									17 30															
Earlswood (Surrey) d									17 33															
Reigate d				17 18									17 34											
Tonbridge 4 d																								
Redhill a			17 15	17 23					17 36				17 38						17 47				18 02	
d			17 16						17 37 →								← 17 37		17 48					
Merstham d																	17 41							
Coulsdon South d																	17 46							
Purley 4 d																	17 49							
East Croydon a		17 23	17 27			17 32				17 40				17 46		17 52	17 54	17 55	18 00		18 02			
d		17 24	17 28			17 32				17 40				17 47		17 52	17 55	17 55	18 00		18 02			
Norwood Junction 2 a																	17 59							
London Bridge 4 ⊖ a						17 45								18 00			18 12				18 15			
London Blackfriars 3 ⊖ a						17 52								18 07							18 22			
City Thameslink 3 a						17 55								18 10							18 25			
Farringdon 3 ⊖ a						17 59								18 14							18 29			
St Pancras International 15 ⊖ a						18 03								18 18							18 33			
St Albans City a						18 23								18 39							18 53			
Luton Airport Parkway 4 ✈ a						18 35								18 50							19 05			
Luton 7 a						18 38								18 54							19 08			
Bedford 10 a						19 05								19 20							19 35			
Clapham Junction 10 d		17 33	17 37		17 35					17 50						18 03		18 05	18 11	18 05				
Imperial Wharf § d																								
West Brompton ⊖ d					17 42											18 09				18 12				
Kensington Olympia ⊖ d					17 45											18 12				18 15				
Shepherds Bush § ⊖ d																								
Willesden Jn. High Level a					17 57															18 27				
Wembley Central a																18 29								
Harrow & Wealdstone ⊖ a																18 37								
Watford Junction a																								
London Victoria 15 ⊖ a	17 35	17 40	17 44				17 50			17 57					18 05			18 11	18 18			18 20		

For general notes see front of timetable
For details of catering facilities see Directory of Train Operators

§ It is unknown, at the time of going to press, when this station will open. For further details contact National Rail Enquiries 08457-484950 or see local publicity.

A From Bognor Regis (Table 188) and from Southampton Central (Table 188)

B From Bognor Regis (Table 188) and from Portsmouth Harbour (Table 188)

C To Tunbridge Wells (Table 209)

Saturdays

Brighton → London, Bedford and Watford Junction

Network Diagram - see first page of Table 186

	SN	SN	FC	SE	GW	GX	SN	SN	GW	LO	FC	GX	SN	SN	SN	SN	GW	FC	GX	SN	SN	SN	SN	LO
				13																				
	1	1	1		1	1	1 ◇	1	1		1	1	1	1	1	1	1	1	1	1	1	1 ◇	1	
	A			B				C															D	
	🛒						🛒	🛒						🛒										
Brighton 10 d			17 34				17 49				17 37					17 55		18 04				18 19		
Hove 2 d	17 21														17 51									
Preston Park d											17 41					17 58								
Hassocks 4 d											17 47					18 05								
Burgess Hill 4 d											17 51				18 02	18 08								
Lewes 4 d		17 20												17 50										
Wivelsfield 4 d		17 34									17 53					18 11								
Haywards Heath 3 a	17 35	17 40	17 47								17 58			18 05	18 09	18 15		18 18						
d	17 43		17 48								18 02			18 13		18 16		18 18						
Balcombe d																								
Horsham 4 d								17 50					18 00										18 20	
Littlehaven d													18 03											
Faygate d																								
Ifield d													18 09											
Crawley d								17 59					18 14										18 29	
Three Bridges 4 a								18 02			18 11		18 18			18 25				←			18 32	
d								18 03			18 12		18 18			18 31 →				18 31			18 33	
Gatwick Airport 10 ✈ a	17 54		18 00					18 07			18 16		18 22	18 24				18 30		18 35			18 37	
d	17 55		18 01		18 03	18 05		18 08			18 16	18 20	18 23	18 25				18 31	18 35	18 37			18 38	
Horley 4 d													18 26										18 41	
Salfords d													18 30											
Earlswood (Surrey) d													18 33											
Reigate d									18 19								18 34							
Tonbridge 4 d				17 34																				
Redhill a				18 04	18 10			18 15	18 24				18 36				18 38				←		18 47	
d				18 05				18 16					18 37 →								18 37		18 48	
Merstham d				18 09																	18 41			
Coulsdon South d				18 14																	18 46			
Purley 4 d				18 18																	18 49			
East Croydon 🚊 a	18 10		18 16	18 23			18 23	18 27			18 32			18 40				18 46		18 52	18 54	18 55	19 00	
d	18 10		18 17	18 24			18 24	18 28			18 32			18 40				18 47		18 52	18 55	18 55	19 00	
Norwood Junction 2 a				18 28																	18 59			
London Bridge 4 ⊖ a			18 30	18 40							18 45							19 00			19 12			
London Blackfriars 3 ⊖ a			18 37								18 52							19 07						
City Thameslink 3 a			18 40								18 55							19 10						
Farringdon 3 ⊖ a			18 44								18 59							19 14						
St Pancras International 15 ⊖ a			18 48								19 03							19 18						
St Albans City a			19 09								19 24							19 39						
Luton Airport Parkway 4 ✈ a			19 20								19 36							19 50						
Luton 7 a			19 24								19 39							19 54						
Bedford 10 a			19 50								20 05							20 20						
Clapham Junction 10 d	18 20						18 33	18 37		18 35				18 50						19 03		19 05	19 11	19 05
Imperial Wharf § d																								
West Brompton ⊖ d										18 42										19 09				19 12
Kensington Olympia ⊖ d										18 45										19 12				19 15
Shepherds Bush § ⊖ d																								
Willesden Jn. High Level a										19 01														19 27
Wembley Central a																								
Harrow & Wealdstone ⊖ a																				19 29				
Watford Junction a																				19 37				
London Victoria 15 ⊖ a	18 27					18 35	18 40	18 44				18 50		18 57					19 05			19 11	19 18	

For general notes see front of timetable
For details of catering facilities see Directory of Train Operators

§ It is unknown, at the time of going to press, when this station will open. For further details contact National Rail Enquiries 08457-484950 or see local publicity.

A 🛒 from Haywards Heath
B From Tunbridge Wells (Table 206)
C From Bognor Regis (Table 188) and from Southampton Central (Table 188)
D From Bognor Regis (Table 188) and from Portsmouth Harbour (Table 188)

Saturdays

Brighton → London, Bedford and Watford Junction

Network Diagram - see first page of Table 186

Station		FC	GX	SE 88	SN	SN	SN	FC	GW	GX	SN	SN	SN	GW	LO	FC	GX	SN	SN	SN	SN	GW	FC	GX	SN
		1	1		1 A	1	1	1	1	1	1 ◇	1	1 B	1		1	1	1	1	1	1	1	1	1	1
Brighton 10	d	18 07						18 34			18 49					18 37					18 55		19 04		
Hove 2	d				18 21															18 51					
Preston Park	d	18 11														18 41					18 58				
Hassocks 4	d	18 17														18 47					19 05				
Burgess Hill 4	d	18 21														18 51				19 02	19 08				
Lewes 4	d					18 20													18 50						
Wivelsfield 4	d	18 23				18 34										18 53					19 11				
Haywards Heath 3	a	18 28			18 35	18 40		18 47								18 58			19 05	19 09	19 15		19 18		
	d	18 32			18 43			18 48								19 02			19 13		19 16		19 18		
Balcombe	d	18 37																							
Horsham 4	d						18 35						18 50					19 02							
Littlehaven	d						18 38											19 05							
Faygate	d																								
Ifield	d						18 44											19 11							
Crawley	d						18 47						18 59					19 14							
Three Bridges 4	a	18 42					18 51						19 02			19 12		19 18			19 25				←
	d	18 42		18 48			18 51						19 03			19 12		19 18			19 31 →				19 31
Gatwick Airport 10 ✈	a	18 46		18 52	18 54		18 55	19 00					19 07			19 16		19 22	19 24				19 31		19 35
	d	18 46	18 50	18 52	18 55		18 56	19 01	19 03	19 05			19 08			19 16	19 20	19 23	19 25				19 31	19 35	19 37
Horley 4	d						18 59											19 26							
Salfords	d																	19 30							
Earlswood (Surrey)	d																	19 33							
Reigate	d													19 18								19 34			
Tonbridge 4	d																								
Redhill	a			19 00			19 05		19 10				19 17	19 23				19 36				19 38			
	d						19 06					←	19 18					19 37 →							
Merstham	d						19 10 →					19 10													
Coulsdon South	d											19 15													
Purley 4	d											19 19													
East Croydon	a	19 02			19 10			19 16			19 23	19 24	19 28			19 32			19 40				19 47		19 52
	d	19 02			19 10			19 17			19 24	19 25	19 29			19 32			19 40				19 47		19 52
Norwood Junction 2	a																								
London Bridge 4 ⊖	a	19 15						19 30								19 45							20 00		
London Blackfriars 3 ⊖	a	19 22						19 37								19 52							20 07		
City Thameslink 3	a	19 25						19 40								19 55							20 10		
Farringdon 3 ⊖	a	19 29						19 44								19 59							20 14		
St Pancras International 15 ⊖	a	19 33						19 48								20 03							20 18		
St Albans City	a	19 54						20 09								20 24							20 39		
Luton Airport Parkway 4 ✈	a	20 06						20 20								20 36							20 50		
Luton 7	a	20 09						20 24								20 39							20 54		
Bedford 10	a	20 35						20 50								21 05							21 20		
Clapham Junction 10	d				19 20						19 33	19 37	19 40		19 35				19 50						20 03
Imperial Wharf §	d																								
West Brompton ⊖	d														19 42										20 09
Kensington Olympia ⊖	d														19 45										20 12
Shepherds Bush § ⊖	d																								
Willesden Jn. High Level	a														19 57										
Wembley Central	a																								
Harrow & Wealdstone ⊖	a																								20 29
Watford Junction	a																								20 37
London Victoria 15 ⊖	a		19 20		19 27					19 35	19 40	19 44	19 48				19 50		19 57					20 05	

For general notes see front of timetable
For details of catering facilities see Directory of Train Operators

§ It is unknown, at the time of going to press, when this station will open. For further details contact National Rail Enquiries 08457-484950 or see local publicity.

A catering from Haywards Heath
B From Bognor Regis (Table 188) and from Southampton Central (Table 188)

Table 186

Saturdays

Brighton → London, Bedford and Watford Junction

Network Diagram - see first page of Table 186

		SN	SN	LO	SN	SN	FC	GX	SE 55	SN	SN	SN	FC	GW	GX	SN	SN	SN	GW	LO	FC	GX	SN
		1	1 ◇		1	1	1	1		1	1	1	1	1	1	1 ◇	1	1	1		1	1	1
						A												B					
Brighton 10	d		19 19				19 07						19 34			19 49					19 37		
Hove 2	d									19 21													
Preston Park	d						19 11														19 41		
Hassocks 4	d						19 17														19 47		
Burgess Hill 4	d						19 21														19 51		
Lewes 4	d										19 20												
Wivelsfield 4	d						19 23				19 34										19 53		
Haywards Heath 3	a						19 28			19 35	19 40		19 47								19 58		
	d						19 32			19 43			19 48								20 02		
Balcombe	d						19 37																
Horsham 4	d					19 21						19 32						19 52					20 02
Littlehaven	d											19 35											20 05
Faygate	d																						
Ifield	d											19 41											20 11
Crawley	d					19 30						19 45						20 01					20 14
Three Bridges 4	a					19 33	19 42					19 48						20 05			20 12		20 18
	d					19 34	19 42		19 48			19 51						20 05			20 12		20 18
Gatwick Airport 10 ✈	a					19 38	19 46		19 52	19 54		19 55	20 00					20 10			20 16		20 22
	d					19 39	19 46	19 50	19 53	19 55		19 56	20 01	20 03	20 05			20 11			20 16	20 20	20 23
Horley 4	d											19 59											20 26
Salfords	d																						20 30
Earlswood (Surrey)	d																						20 33
Reigate	d																		20 19				
Tonbridge 4	d																						
Redhill	a	←				19 46			20 01			20 05		20 10				20 18	20 24				20 36
	d	19 37				19 47						20 08					←	20 18					20 37
Merstham	d	19 41										20 12					20 12						→
Coulsdon South	d	19 46										→					20 17						
Purley 4	d	19 49															20 20						
East Croydon	a	19 54	19 55		←	19 59	20 02			20 10			20 16			20 23	20 25	20 30			20 32		
	d	19 55	19 55		19 55	20 00	20 02			20 10			20 17			20 24	20 26	20 30			20 32		
Norwood Junction 2	a	→																					
London Bridge 4	⊖ a						20 15						20 30								20 45		
London Blackfriars 3	⊖ a						20 22						20 37								20 52		
City Thameslink 3	a						20 25						20 40								20 55		
Farringdon 3	⊖ a						20 29						20 44								20 59		
St Pancras International 15	⊖ a						20 33						20 48								21 03		
St Albans City	a						20 54						21 09								21 24		
Luton Airport Parkway 4 ✈	a						21 06						21 20								21 36		
Luton 7	a						21 09						21 24								21 40		
Bedford 10	a						21 35						21 50								22 05		
Clapham Junction 10	d		20 05	20 05	20 08	20 11				20 20						20 33	20 38	20 41		20 35			
Imperial Wharf §	d																						
West Brompton	⊖ d			20 12																20 42			
Kensington Olympia	⊖ d			20 15																20 45			
Shepherds Bush §	⊖ d																						
Willesden Jn. High Level	a			20 27																20 57			
Wembley Central	a																						
Harrow & Wealdstone	⊖ a																						
Watford Junction	a																						
London Victoria 15	⊖ a		20 11		20 14	20 17		20 20		20 27					20 35	20 40	20 44	20 50				20 50	

For general notes see front of timetable
For details of catering facilities see Directory of Train Operators

§ It is unknown, at the time of going to press, when this station will open. For further details contact National Rail Enquiries 08457-484950 or see local publicity.

A From Portsmouth & Southsea (Table 188)
B From Southampton Central (Table 188)

Table 186

Saturdays

Brighton → London, Bedford and Watford Junction

Network Diagram - see first page of Table 186

		SN	SN	SN	GW	FC	GX	SN	SN	SN	SN	LO	FC	GX	SN	SE	SN	FC	GW	GX	SN	SN	SN	GW	LO
		1	1	1 ◇	1	1	1	1	1 ◇	1	1 ◇		1	1	1	88	1	1	1		1	1	1 A	1	
Brighton 10	d			19 55		20 04			20 19				20 07					20 34			20 49				
Hove 2	d		19 52												20 22										
Preston Park	d			19 59									20 11												
Hassocks 4	d			20 05									20 17												
Burgess Hill 4	d		20 02	20 09									20 21												
Lewes 4	d	19 51																							
Wivelsfield 4	d	20 03		20 11									20 23												
Haywards Heath 3	a	20 07	20 09	20 16		20 18							20 28		20 36			20 47							
	d	20 13		20 22 →		20 18					← 20 22		20 32		20 38			20 48							
Balcombe	d												20 37												
Horsham 4	d																20 32						20 52		
Littlehaven	d																20 35								
Faygate	d																								
Ifield	d																20 41								
Crawley	d																20 45						21 01		
Three Bridges 4	a										20 32		20 42		20 47		20 48						21 05		
	d										20 32		20 42		20 48	20 48	20 51						21 05		
Gatwick Airport 10 ✈	a	20 24				20 30					20 37		20 46		20 52	20 52	20 55	21 00					21 10		
	d	20 25				20 31	20 35	20 37			20 38		20 46	20 50	20 53	20 53	20 56	21 01	21 03	21 05			21 11		
Horley 4	d																20 59								
Salfords	d																								
Earlswood (Surrey)	d																								
Reigate	d				20 34																			21 18	
Tonbridge 4	d																								
Redhill	a				20 38					←	20 46					21 02	21 05		21 10				21 18	21 23	
	d									20 37	20 47						21 08					←	21 18		
Merstham	d									20 41							21 12 →					21 12			
Coulsdon South	d									20 46												21 17			
Purley 4	d									20 51												21 20			
East Croydon	a	20 40				20 46		20 52	20 55	20 56	20 59		21 02		21 09			21 16			21 23	21 25	21 30		
	d	20 40				20 47		20 52	20 55	20 57	21 00		21 02		21 10			21 17			21 24	21 26	21 30		
Norwood Junction 2	a																								
London Bridge 4	⊖ a					21 00							21 15					21 30							
London Blackfriars 3	⊖ a					21 07							21 22					21 37							
City Thameslink 3	a																								
Farringdon 3	⊖ a					21 13							21 28					21 43							
St Pancras International 15	⊖ a					21 17							21 32					21 47							
St Albans City	a					21 39							21 54					22 09							
Luton Airport Parkway 4 ✈	a					21 50							22 06					22 20							
Luton 7	a					21 54							22 10					22 24							
Bedford 10	a					22 20							22 35					22 50							
Clapham Junction 10	d	20 50						21 03	21 05	21 08	21 11	21 05			21 20						21 33	21 38	21 41		21 35
Imperial Wharf §	d																								
West Brompton	⊖ d							21 09				21 12													21 42
Kensington Olympia	⊖ d							21 12				21 15													21 45
Shepherds Bush §	⊖ d																								
Willesden Jn. High Level	a											21 27													21 57
Wembley Central	a																								
Harrow & Wealdstone	⊖ a							21 29																	
Watford Junction	a							21 46																	
London Victoria 15	⊖ a	20 57					21 05		21 11	21 14	21 20			21 20	21 27					21 35	21 40	21 44	21 48		

For general notes see front of timetable
For details of catering facilities see Directory of Train Operators

§ It is unknown, at the time of going to press, when this station will open. For further details contact National Rail Enquiries 08457-484950 or see local publicity.

A From Southampton Central (Table 188)

Table 186

Saturdays

Brighton → London, Bedford and Watford Junction

Network Diagram - see first page of Table 186

Station		FC	GX	SN	SN	SN	GX	SN	SN	GW	SN	SN	LO	FC	GX	SN	SE	LO	SN	SN	GX	SN	FC	GX	GW
																	88								
		1	1	1	1	1		1	1 ◇	1	1	1 ◇		1	1	1			1 ◇	1		1	1	1	1
																						A			
Brighton 10	d	20 37							21 19			21 00		21 07					21 49				21 37		
Hove 2	d					20 52										21 22									
Preston Park	d	20 41										21 04		21 11									21 41		
Hassocks 4	d	20 47										21 10		21 17									21 47		
Burgess Hill 4	d	20 51				21 02						21 14		21 21									21 51		
Lewes 4	d				20 50																				
Wivelsfield 4	d	20 53			21 02							21 16		21 23									21 53		
Haywards Heath 3	a	20 58			21 06	21 08						21 21		21 28		21 36							21 58		
	d	21 02			21 13							21 22		21 32		21 38							22 02		
Balcombe	d													21 37											
Horsham 4	d			21 02																21 32		21 52			
Littlehaven	d			21 05																21 35					
Faygate	d																								
Ifield	d			21 11																21 41					
Crawley	d			21 14																21 45		22 01			
Three Bridges 4	a	21 11		21 18								21 32		21 42						21 48		22 05	22 11		
	d	21 12		21 19								21 32		21 42			21 48			21 51		22 05	22 12		
Gatwick Airport 10 ✈	a	21 16		21 23	21 24							21 37		21 46		21 51	21 52			21 55		22 10	22 16		
	d	21 16	21 20	21 24	21 25		21 35	21 37				21 38		21 46	21 50	21 53	21 53			21 56	22 05	22 11	22 16	22 20	22 22
Horley 4	d			21 27																21 59					
Salfords	d			21 31																					
Earlswood (Surrey)	d			21 34																					
Reigate	d									21 40															
Tonbridge 4	d																								
Redhill	a			21 38						21 44	←	21 46					22 01			22 05		22 18			22 30
	d			21 38 →							21 38	21 47								22 08		22 18			
Merstham	d										21 42									22 12					
Coulsdon South	d										21 47									22 17					
Purley 4	d										21 51									22 20					
East Croydon	a	21 32			21 40			21 52	21 55		21 56	21 59		22 02		22 09			22 23	22 25		22 30	22 32		
	d	21 32			21 40			21 52	21 55		21 57	22 00		22 02		22 10			22 24	22 26		22 30	22 32		
Norwood Junction 2	a																								
London Bridge 4 ⊖	a	21 45												22 15									22 45		
London Blackfriars 3 ⊖	a	21 52												22 22									22 52		
City Thameslink 3	a																								
Farringdon 3 ⊖	a	21 58												22 28									22 58		
St Pancras International 15 ⊖	a	22 02												22 32									23 02		
St Albans City	a	22 24												22 54									23 24		
Luton Airport Parkway 4 ✈	a	22 36												23 06									23 36		
Luton 7	a	22 40												23 10									23 40		
Bedford 10	a	23 05												23 35									00 05		
Clapham Junction 10	d				21 50			22 03	22 05		22 08	22 11	22 05			22 20		22 35	22 33	22 38		22 41			
Imperial Wharf §	d																								
West Brompton ⊖	d							22 09					22 12					22 42							
Kensington Olympia ⊖	d							22 12					22 15					22 45							
Shepherds Bush § ⊖	d																								
Willesden Jn. High Level	a												22 27					22 57							
Wembley Central	a																								
Harrow & Wealdstone ⊖	a							22 29																	
Watford Junction	a							22 46																	
London Victoria 15 ⊖	a		21 50		21 57		22 05		22 11		22 14	22 18			22 20	22 27			22 40	22 44	22 35	22 48		22 50	

For general notes see front of timetable
For details of catering facilities see Directory of Train Operators

§ It is unknown, at the time of going to press, when this station will open. For further details contact National Rail Enquiries 08457-484950 or see local publicity.

A From Southampton Central (Table 188)

Table 186 — **Saturdays**

Brighton → London, Bedford and Watford Junction

Network Diagram - see first page of Table 186

		SN	SN	LO	SN	GX	SN	FC	GW	GX	SE	SN	GX	FC	SN	FC	GW	GX	SN	GX	GX	GW	SN	SN	FC
											88														
		1	1		1		1 ◇	1	1	1		1		1	1	1	1	1	1		1	1	1 ◇	1	1
															A									B	
Brighton 10	d						22 00	22 07						22 33									23 02		23 37
Hove 2	d		21 52																						
Preston Park	d						22 04	22 11						22 37									23 06		23 41
Hassocks 4	d						22 10	22 17						22 43									23 12		23 47
Burgess Hill 4	d		22 02				22 14	22 21						22 47									23 16		23 51
Lewes 4	d	21 50													22 40										
Wivelsfield 4	d	22 02					22 16	22 23						22 49	22 54								23 19		23 53
Haywards Heath 3	a	22 06	22 08				22 21	22 28						22 54	22 58								23 23		23 58
	d		22 12				22 22	22 32						22 54	22 59								23 24		23 59
Balcombe	d							22 37						23 00											00 04
Horsham 4	d				22 02							22 49							23 02					23 25	
Littlehaven	d				22 05														23 05					23 28	
Faygate	d																								
Ifield	d				22 11														23 11					23 35	
Crawley	d				22 14							22 57							23 14					23 38	
Three Bridges 4	a				22 18		22 32	22 42				23 01		23 05	23 08	←			23 18				23 33	23 42	00 10
	d				22 21		22 32	22 42			22 48			23 12	23 08	23 12			23 18				23 47		00 10
Gatwick Airport 10 ✈	a		22 23		22 25		22 37	22 46			22 52			→	23 12	23 16			23 22				23 52		00 14
	d		22 25		22 26	22 35	22 38	22 46		22 50	22 53		23 05		23 13	23 16	23 18	23 20	23 23	23 35	23 50		23 53		00 15
Horley 4	d				22 29														23 26				23s56		
Salfords	d				22 33														23 30						
Earlswood (Surrey)	d				22 36														23 33						
Reigate	d								22 48													23 54			
Tonbridge 4	d																								
Redhill	a				22 39		22 46		22 52		23 01						23 25		23 36			23 58	00 02		00 22
	d				22 40		22 47												23 37				00 03		00 22
Merstham	d				22 44														23 41						
Coulsdon South	d				22 49														23 46						
Purley 4	d				22 52														23 49				00 11		
East Croydon	a		22 40		22 57		22 59	23 02							23 30	23 32			23 55				00 16		00 35
	d		22 40		22 58		23 00	23 02							23 30	23 32			23 56				00 17		00 36
Norwood Junction 2	a																								00 52
London Bridge 4 ⊖	a							23 15								23 45									00 59
London Blackfriars 3 ⊖	a							23 22								23 52									
City Thameslink 3	a																								
Farringdon 3 ⊖	a							23 28								23 58									
St Pancras International 15 ⊖	a							23 32								00 02									01 07
St Albans City	a							23 54								00 24									01 39
Luton Airport Parkway 4 ✈	a							00 06								00 36									01 51
Luton 7	a							00 10								00 40									01 55
Bedford 10	a							00 35								01 05									02 20
Clapham Junction 10	d		22 50	23 05	23 08		23 11								23 42				00 11				00 30		
Imperial Wharf §	d																								
West Brompton ⊖	d			23 12																					
Kensington Olympia ⊖	d			23 15																					
Shepherds Bush § ⊖	d																								
Willesden Jn. High Level	a			23 29																					
Wembley Central	a																								
Harrow & Wealdstone ⊖	a																								
Watford Junction	a																								
London Victoria 15 ⊖	a		22 57		23 14	23 05	23 17			23 20			23 35		23 52			23 55	00 18	00 10	00 25		00 37		

For general notes see front of timetable
For details of catering facilities see Directory of Train Operators

§ It is unknown, at the time of going to press, when this station will open. For further details contact National Rail Enquiries 08457-484950 or see local publicity.

A From Hastings (Table 189)
B From Southampton Central (Table 188)

Table 186

Sundays

Brighton → London, Bedford and Watford Junction

Network Diagram - see first page of Table 186

Station		FC	FC	SN	SN	GX	FC	GX	GX	GW	GX	SN	GX	SN	SN	SN	GX	SN	FC	GX	SN	GX	GX	GW	FC
		1	1	1	1 ◇		1	1		1	1	1	1	1	1	1		1 ◇	1	1	1	1		1	1
																		A							
Brighton 10	d	22p07	22p33		23p02		23p37											03 50							05 44
Hove 2	d																								
Preston Park	d	22p11	22p37		23p06		23p41																		
Hassocks 4	d	22p17	22p43		23p12		23p47																		05 52
Burgess Hill 4	d	22p21	22p47		23p16		23p51																		05 56
Lewes 4	d																								
Wivelsfield 4	d	22p23	22p49		23p19		23p53																		
Haywards Heath 3	a	22p28	22p54		23p23		23p58																		06 00
	d	22p32	22p54		23p24		23p59																		06 01
Balcombe	d	22p37	23p00				00 04																		
Horsham 4	d			23p02																					
Littlehaven	d			23p05																					
Faygate	d																								
Ifield	d			23p11																					
Crawley	d			23p14																					
Three Bridges 4	a	22p42	23p05	23p18	23p33		00 10											04 45							06 10
	d	22p42	23p12	23p18	23p47		00 10					01 10		02 10	03 10	04 10		04 58	05 10		05 30				06 10
Gatwick Airport 10 ✈	a	22p46	23p16	23p22	23p52		00 14					01 19		02 14	03 14	04 14		05 02	05 14		05 34				06 14
	d	22p46	23p16	23p23	23p53	00 05	00 15	00 20	00 35		00 50	01 20	01 35	02 15	03 15	04 15	04 35	05 03	05 15	05 20	05 36	05 50	06 05	06 09	06 15
Horley 4	d			23p26	23b56							01 22		02 18	03 18	04 18		05 05			05 38				
Salfords	d			23p30																					
Earlswood (Surrey)	d			23p33																					
Reigate	d									00 45															
Tonbridge 4	d																								
Redhill	a			23p36	00 02		00 22			00 49											05 46			06 17	
	d			23p37	00 03		00 22														05 46				
Merstham	d			23p41																					
Coulsdon South	d			23p46																					
Purley 4	d			23p49	00 11							01 37		02 33	03 33	04 33		05 22			05 56				
East Croydon 🚋	a	23p02	23p32	23p55	00 16		00 35					01 42		02 39	03 39	04 39		05 27	05 31		06 01				06 31
	d	23p02	23p32	23p56	00 17		00 36					01 43		02 40	03 40	04 40		05 28	05 32		06 02				06 32
Norwood Junction 2	a																								
London Bridge 4 ⊖	a	23p15	23p45				00 52																		
London Blackfriars 3 ⊖	a	23p22	23p52				00 59												05 54						06 54
City Thameslink 3	a																								
Farringdon 3 ⊖	a	23p28	23p58																						06 58
St Pancras International 15 ⊖	a	23p32	00 02				01 07												06 02						07 02
St Albans City	a	23p54	00 24				01 39												06 33						07 33
Luton Airport Parkway 4 ✈	a	00 06	00 36				01 51												06 45						07 45
Luton 7	a	00 10	00 40				01 55												06 49						07 49
Bedford 10	a	00 35	01 05				02 20												07 17						08 15
Clapham Junction 10	d			00 11	00 30							01 54		02 53	03 53	04 53		05 49			06 14				
Imperial Wharf §	d																								
West Brompton ⊖	d																								
Kensington Olympia ⊖	d																								
Shepherds Bush § ⊖	d																								
Willesden Jn. High Level	a																								
Wembley Central	a																								
Harrow & Wealdstone ⊖	a																								
Watford Junction	a																								
London Victoria 15 ⊖	a			00 18	00 37	00 40		00 55	01 10		01 25	02 05	02 20	03 05	04 05	05 05	05 10	05 58		05 55	06 22	06 25	06 40		

For general notes see front of timetable
For details of catering facilities see Directory of Train Operators

§ It is unknown, at the time of going to press, when this station will open. For further details contact National Rail Enquiries 08457-484950 or see local publicity.

A Also stops at Balham 0543

b Previous night. Stops to set down only

Table 186

Sundays

Brighton → London, Bedford and Watford Junction

Network Diagram - see first page of Table 186

Station		GX 1	SN 1	GX	FC 1	GX 1	SN 1	SN 1 ◇	SN 1	SN	SN 1	SN 1	GW 1	GX 1		GW 1	FC 1	GX 1	SN 1	SN 1	SN 1	GX 1	SN 1 ◇	FC 1	GX 1
							A	B	C	C										C	B				
Brighton 10	d				06 13		06 16	06 16									06 44						07 00	07 16	
Hove 2	d								06 24																
Preston Park	d						06 19	06 19															07 03		
Hassocks 4	d						06 26	06 26									06 52						07 10		
Burgess Hill 4	d				06 26		06 29	06 29									06 56						07 13	07 26	
Lewes 4	d						05 57																		
Wivelsfield 4	d						06 32	06 32															07 16		
Haywards Heath 3	a				06 30		06 36	06 36	06 39								07 00						07 20	07 30	
	d				06 31		06 37	06 40	06 40								07 01						07 21	07 31	
Balcombe	d																						07 26		
Horsham 4	d		06 04									06 34								07 04	07 04				
Littlehaven	d		06 07									06 37								07 07	07 07				
Faygate	d																								
Ifield	d		06 13									06 43								07 13	07 13				
Crawley	d		06 17									06 47								07 17	07 17				
Three Bridges 4	a		06 20		06 40		06 46	06 49				06 50					07 10			07 20	07 20		07 32	07 40	
	d		06 21		06 40		06 46	06 49				06 52					07 10			07 22	07 22		07 32	07 40	
Gatwick Airport 10 ✈	a		06 25		06 44		06 51	06 53	06 53			06 57					07 14			07 26	07 26		07 37	07 44	
	d	06 20		06 35	06 45	06 50		06 54	06 54			06 58		07 05		07 07	07 15	07 20		07 27	07 27	07 35	07 38	07 45	07 50
Horley 4	d											07 00								07 30	07 30				
Salfords	d																			07 34					
Earlswood (Surrey)	d																			07 37					
Reigate	d												07 03												
Tonbridge 4	d																								
Redhill	a											07 07	07 09			07 18				07 40	07 40		07 45		
	d									07 03		07 07								07 41	07 41		07 46		
Merstham	d									07 07		07 11								07 45	07 45				
Coulsdon South	d									07 12		07 16								07 50	07 50				
Purley 4	d									07 16		07 20								07 53	07 53				
East Croydon	a				07 01			07 09	07 09	07 21		07 26					07 31			07 58	07 58		07 58	08 01	
	d				07 02			07 10	07 10	07 22		07 27					07 32			07 59	07 59		07 59	08 02	
Norwood Junction 2	a									07 26															
London Bridge 4 ⊖	a				07 15					07 38							07 45							08 15	
London Blackfriars 3 ⊖	a				07 23												07 53							08 23	
City Thameslink 3	a																								
Farringdon 3 ⊖	a				07 27												07 57							08 27	
St Pancras International 15 ⊖	a				07 31												08 01							08 31	
St Albans City	a				08 03												08 33							09 03	
Luton Airport Parkway 4 ✈	a				08 15												08 45							09 15	
Luton 7	a				08 19												08 49							09 19	
Bedford 10	a				08 45												09 15							09 45	
Clapham Junction 10	d							07 24	07 24		07 35	07 40							08 05	08 09	08 09		08 12		
Imperial Wharf §	d																								
West Brompton ⊖	d										07 40								08 10						
Kensington Olympia ⊖	d										07a43								08a13						
Shepherds Bush § ⊖	d																								
Willesden Jn. High Level	a																								
Wembley Central	a																								
Harrow & Wealdstone ⊖	a																								
Watford Junction	a																								
London Victoria 15 ⊖	a	06 55		07 10		07 25		07 31	07 31			07 48		07 40				07 55		08 16	08 16	08 10	08 18		08 25

For general notes see front of timetable
For details of catering facilities see Directory of Train Operators

§ It is unknown, at the time of going to press, when this station will open. For further details contact National Rail Enquiries 08457-484950 or see local publicity.

A Until 7 September. From Eastbourne (Table 189)

B From 14 September

C Until 7 September

Sundays

Brighton → London, Bedford and Watford Junction

Network Diagram - see first page of Table 186

		SN	SN	SE	LO	SN	SN	GX	GW	GW	FC	GX	SN	SN	SN	GX	SN	FC	GX	SN	SN	SE	SN	GX	GW
				55																		55			
		1				1	1	1	1	1	1	1	1	1	1	1	1 ◇	1	1	1			1	1	1
			A	B	C		D								A						A	B	D		
		⊥															⊥			⊥			⊥		
Brighton 10	d										07 44						08 00	08 16							
Hove 2	d												07 54												
Preston Park	d																08 03								
Hassocks 4	d										07 52						08 10								
Burgess Hill 4	d										07 56		08 04				08 13	08 26							
Lewes 4	d	07 20																		08 16					
Wivelsfield 4	d	07 32															08 16			08 31					
Haywards Heath 3	a	07 36									08 00		08 09				08 20	08 30		08 36					
	d	07 39									08 01		08 10				08 21	08 31		08 39					
Balcombe	d																08 26								
Horsham 4	d						07 42								08 04								08 42		
Littlehaven	d														08 07										
Faygate	d																								
Ifield	d														08 13										
Crawley	d						07 51								08 17								08 51		
Three Bridges 4	a						07 54				08 10				08 20		08 32	08 40					08 54		
	d			07 50			07 54				08 10				08 22		08 32	08 40				08 50	08 54		
Gatwick Airport 10 ✈	a	07 51		07 54			07 58				08 14		08 21		08 26		08 37	08 44		08 51		08 54	08 58		
	d	07 53		07 55			07 59	08 05	08 07		08 15	08 20	08 23		08 27	08 35	08 38	08 45	08 50	08 53		08 55	08 59	09 05	09 07
Horley 4	d						08 02								08 30								09 02		
Salfords	d														08 34										
Earlswood (Surrey)	d														08 37										
Reigate	d									08 13															
Tonbridge 4	d																								
Redhill	a			08 03			08 08		08 15	08 17					08 40		08 45					09 03	09 08		09 15
	d		08 03				08 09								08 41		08 46				09 03		09 09		
Merstham	d		08 07												08 45						09 07				
Coulsdon South	d		08 12												08 50						09 12				
Purley 4	d		08 16				08 18								08 53						09 16		09 18		
East Croydon	a	08 09	08 21				08 24				08 31		08 39		08 58		08 58	09 01		09 09	09 21		09 24		
	d	08 10	08 22				08 25				08 32		08 40		08 59		08 59	09 02		09 10	09 22		09 25		
Norwood Junction 2	a		08 26																		09 26				
London Bridge 4	⊖ a		08 38								08 45							09 15			09 38				
London Blackfriars 3	⊖ a										08 53							09 23							
City Thameslink 3	a																								
Farringdon 3	⊖ a										08 57							09 27							
St Pancras International 15	⊖ a										09 01							09 31							
St Albans City	a										09 33							10 03							
Luton Airport Parkway 4 ✈	a										09 45							10 15							
Luton 7	a										09 49							10 19							
Bedford 10	a										10 15							10 45							
Clapham Junction 10	d	08 24			08 30	08 35	08 38						08 55	09 05	09 09		09 12			09 24			09 38		
Imperial Wharf §	d																								
West Brompton	⊖ d				08 37	08 40								09 10											
Kensington Olympia	⊖ d				08 40	08 43								09 13											
Shepherds Bush §	⊖ d																								
Willesden Jn. High Level	a				08 50																				
Wembley Central	a																								
Harrow & Wealdstone	⊖ a					09 06								09 32											
Watford Junction	a					09 14								09 42											
London Victoria 15	⊖ a	08 31					08 46	08 40				08 55	09 01		09 16	09 10	09 18		09 25	09 31			09 46	09 40	

For general notes see front of timetable
For details of catering facilities see Directory of Train Operators

§ It is unknown, at the time of going to press, when this station will open. For further details contact National Rail Enquiries 08457-484950 or see local publicity.

A Until 7 September
B To Maidstone West (Table 208)
C Until 31 August, 23, 30 November and 7 December to Stratford Low Level (Table 59)
D From Bognor Regis (Table 188)

Brighton → London, Bedford and Watford Junction

Network Diagram - see first page of Table 186

		GW	LO	FC	SN	GX		SN	SN	SN	SN	GX	SN	FC	GX	SN	SN	SE 55	SN	GX	GW	XC	GW	XC	LO
		1		1	1 ◇	1		1	1	1	1	1	1 ◇	1	1	1			1	1	1	1 ◇	1	1 ◇	
					A					A	B						A	C	D			E		G	
					[trolley]								[trolley]			[trolley]			[trolley]			[buffet]		[buffet]	
Brighton 10	d			08 44	08 51								09 00	09 16								09 40		09 40	
Hove 2	d							08 54																	
Preston Park	d												09 03												
Hassocks 4	d			08 52									09 10												
Burgess Hill 4	d			08 56				09 04					09 13	09 26											
Lewes 4	d															09 16									
Wivelsfield 4	d												09 16			09 31									
Haywards Heath 3	a			09 00				09 09					09 20	09 30		09 35						09 51		09 51	
	d			09 01				09 10					09 21	09 31		09 39						09 52		09 52	
Balcombe	d												09 26												
Horsham 4	d									09 04	09 04								09 42						
Littlehaven	d									09 07	09 07														
Faygate	d																								
Ifield	d									09 13	09 13														
Crawley	d									09 17	09 17								09 51						
Three Bridges 4	a			09 10						09 20	09 20		09 32	09 40					09 54						
	d			09 10						09 22	09 22		09 32	09 40				09 50	09 54						
Gatwick Airport 10 ✈	a			09 14	09 17			09 21		09 26	09 26		09 37	09 44		09 51		09 54	09 58			10 10		10 10	
	d			09 15	09 18	09 20		09 23		09 27	09 27	09 35	09 38	09 45	09 50	09 53		09 55	09 59	10 05	10 07	10 11 →		10 12	
Horley 4	d									09 30	09 30								10 02						
Salfords	d									09 34															
Earlswood (Surrey)	d									09 37															
Reigate	d	09 14																					10 13		
Tonbridge 4	d																								
Redhill	a	09 18								09 40	09 40		09 45					10 03	10 08		10 15		10 17	10 27	
	d									09 41	09 41		09 46				10 03		10 09					10 33	
Merstham	d									09 45	09 45						10 07								
Coulsdon South	d									09 50	09 50						10 12								
Purley 4	d									09 53	09 53						10 16		10 18						
East Croydon	a			09 31	09 34			09 39		09 58	09 58		09 58	10 01		10 09	10 21		10 24						
	d			09 32	09 35			09 40		09 59	09 59		09 59	10 02		10 10	10 22		10 25						
Norwood Junction 2	a																10 26								
London Bridge 4 ⊖	a			09 45										10 15			10 38								
London Blackfriars 3 ⊖	a			09 53										10 23											
City Thameslink 3	a																								
Farringdon 3 ⊖	a			09 57										10 27											
St Pancras International 15 ⊖	a			10 01										10 31											
St Albans City	a			10 33										11 03											
Luton Airport Parkway 4 ✈	a			10 45										11 15											
Luton 7	a			10 49										11 19											
Bedford 10	a			11 15										11 45											
Clapham Junction 10	d		09 30		09 47			09 55	10 05	10 09	10 09		10 12			10 24			10 38						10 30
Imperial Wharf §	d																								
West Brompton ⊖	d		09 37						10 10																10 37
Kensington Olympia ⊖	d		09 40						10 13																10 40
Shepherds Bush § ⊖	d																								10 50
Willesden Jn. High Level	a		09 50																						
Wembley Central	a																								
Harrow & Wealdstone ⊖	a								10 35																
Watford Junction	a								10 42																
London Victoria 15 ⊖	a				09 53	09 55		10 01		10 16	10 16	10 10	10 18		10 25	10 31			10 46	10 40					

For general notes see front of timetable
For details of catering facilities see Directory of Train Operators

§ It is unknown, at the time of going to press, when this station will open. For further details contact National Rail Enquiries 08457-484950 or see local publicity.

A Until 7 September
B From 14 September
C To Maidstone West (Table 208)
D From Bognor Regis (Table 188)
E From 14 September. To Birmingham New Street
G Until 7 September. To Birmingham New Street (Table 116)

Table 186

Sundays

Brighton → London, Bedford and Watford Junction

Network Diagram - see first page of Table 186

Station		FC	SN	GX	SN	XC	SN	SN	SN	GX	SN	FC	GX	SN	SN	SE 55	SN	GX	GW	GW	LO	FC	SN	GX
		1	1 ◇	1	1	1 ◇	1	1	1	1	1 ◇	1	1	1			1	1	1	1		1	1 ◇	1
			A			B		A	C						A	D	E						A	
			🛒			☕					🛒			🛒			🛒							
Brighton 10	d	09 44	09 51								10 00	10 16										10 44	10 51	
Hove 2	d				09 54																			
Preston Park	d										10 03													
Hassocks 4	d	09 52									10 10											10 52		
Burgess Hill 4	d	09 56			10 04						10 13	10 26										10 56		
Lewes 4	d													10 16										
Wivelsfield 4	d										10 16			10 31										
Haywards Heath 3	a	10 00			10 09						10 20	10 30		10 35								11 00		
	d	10 01			10 10						10 21	10 31		10 39								11 01		
Balcombe	d										10 26													
Horsham 4	d							10 04	10 04								10 42							
Littlehaven	d							10 07	10 07															
Faygate	d																							
Ifield	d							10 13	10 13															
Crawley	d							10 17	10 17								10 51							
Three Bridges 4	a	10 10						10 20	10 20		10 32	10 40					10 54					11 10		
	d	10 10						10 22	10 22		10 32	10 40				10 50	10 54					11 10		
Gatwick Airport 10 ✈	a	10 14	10 17		10 21	←		10 26	10 26		10 37	10 44		10 51		10 54	10 58					11 14	11 17	
	d	10 15	10 18	10 20	10 23	10 11		10 27	10 27	10 35	10 38	10 45	10 50	10 53		10 55	10 59	11 05	11 07			11 15	11 18	11 20
Horley 4	d							10 30	10 30								11 02							
Salfords	d							10 34																
Earlswood (Surrey)	d							10 37																
Reigate	d																			11 14				
Tonbridge 4	d																							
Redhill	a					10 28		10 40	10 40		10 45					11 03	11 08		11 15	11 18				
	d					10 33		10 41	10 41		10 46				11 03		11 09							
Merstham	d							10 45	10 45						11 07									
Coulsdon South	d							10 50	10 50						11 12									
Purley 4	d							10 53	10 53						11 16		11 18							
East Croydon	a	10 31	10 34		10 39			10 58	10 58		10 58	11 01		11 09	11 21		11 24					11 31	11 34	
	d	10 32	10 35		10 40			10 59	10 59		10 59	11 02		11 10	11 22		11 25					11 32	11 35	
Norwood Junction 2	a														11 26									
London Bridge 4 ⊖	a	10 45										11 15			11 38							11 45		
London Blackfriars 3 ⊖	a	10 53										11 23										11 53		
City Thameslink 3	a																							
Farringdon 3 ⊖	a	10 57										11 27										11 57		
St Pancras International 15 ⊖	a	11 01										11 31										12 01		
St Albans City	a	11 23										11 53										12 23		
Luton Airport Parkway 4 ✈	a	11 35										12 05										12 35		
Luton 7	a	11 39										12 09										12 39		
Bedford 10	a	12 05										12 35										13 05		
Clapham Junction 10	d		10 47		10 55		11 05	11 09	11 09		11 12			11 24			11 38				11 30		11 47	
Imperial Wharf §	d																							
West Brompton ⊖	d						11 10														11 37			
Kensington Olympia ⊖	d						11 13														11 40			
Shepherds Bush § ⊖	d																							
Willesden Jn. High Level	a																				11 50			
Wembley Central	a																							
Harrow & Wealdstone ⊖	a						11 32																	
Watford Junction	a						11 42																	
London Victoria 15 ⊖	a		10 53	10 55	11 01			11 16	11 16	11 10	11 18		11 25	11 31			11 46	11 40					11 53	11 55

For general notes see front of timetable
For details of catering facilities see Directory of Train Operators

§ It is unknown, at the time of going to press, when this station will open. For further details contact National Rail Enquiries 08457-484950 or see local publicity.

A Until 7 September
B From 14 September. To Birmingham New Street
C From 14 September
D To Maidstone West (Table 208)
E From Bognor Regis (Table 188)

Brighton → London, Bedford and Watford Junction

Network Diagram - see first page of Table 186

Station		SN	SN	SN	SN	GX	SN	FC	GX	SN	SN	SE	SN	GX	GW	GW	LO	FC	SN	GX	SN	SN	SN	SN	GX
												55													
		1	1	1	1	1	1 ◇	1	1	1			1	1	1	1		1	1 ◇	1	1	1	1	1	1
				A	B						A	C	D						A				A	B	
Brighton 10	d						11 00	11 16										11 44	11 51						
Hove 2	d	10 54																			11 54				
Preston Park	d						11 03																		
Hassocks 4	d						11 10											11 52							
Burgess Hill 4	d	11 04					11 13	11 26										11 56			12 04				
Lewes 4	d									11 16															
Wivelsfield 4	d						11 16			11 31															
Haywards Heath 3	a	11 09					11 20	11 30		11 35								12 00			12 09				
	d	11 10					11 21	11 31		11 39								12 01			12 10				
Balcombe	d						11 26																		
Horsham 4	d			11 04	11 04								11 42										12 04	12 04	
Littlehaven	d			11 07	11 07																		12 07	12 07	
Faygate	d																								
Ifield	d			11 13	11 13																		12 13	12 13	
Crawley	d			11 17	11 17								11 51										12 17	12 17	
Three Bridges 4	a			11 20	11 20		11 32	11 40					11 54					12 10					12 20	12 20	
	d			11 22	11 22		11 32	11 40				11 50	11 54					12 10					12 22	12 22	
Gatwick Airport 10	a	11 21		11 26	11 26		11 37	11 44		11 51		11 54	11 58					12 14	12 17		12 22		12 26	12 26	
	d	11 23		11 27	11 27	11 35	11 38	11 45	11 50	11 53		11 55	11 59	12 05	12 07			12 15	12 18	12 20	12 23		12 27	12 27	12 35
Horley 4	d			11 30	11 30								12 02										12 30	12 30	
Salfords	d			11 34																			12 34		
Earlswood (Surrey)	d			11 37																			12 37		
Reigate	d															12 13									
Tonbridge 4	d																								
Redhill	a			11 40	11 40		11 45					12 03	12 08		12 15	12 17							12 40	12 40	
	d			11 41	11 41		11 46				12 03		12 09										12 41	12 41	
Merstham	d			11 45	11 45						12 07												12 45	12 45	
Coulsdon South	d			11 50	11 50						12 12												12 50	12 50	
Purley 4	d			11 53	11 53						12 16		12 18										12 53	12 53	
East Croydon	a	11 39		11 58	11 58		11 58	12 01		12 09	12 21		12 24					12 31	12 34		12 39		12 58	12 58	
	d	11 40		11 59	11 59		11 59	12 02		12 10	12 22		12 25					12 32	12 35		12 40		12 59	12 59	
Norwood Junction 2	a										12 26														
London Bridge 4	⊖ a							12 15			12 38							12 45							
London Blackfriars 3	⊖ a							12 23										12 53							
City Thameslink 3	a																								
Farringdon 3	⊖ a							12 27										12 57							
St Pancras International 15	⊖ a							12 31										13 01							
St Albans City	a							12 53										13 23							
Luton Airport Parkway 4	✈ a							13 05										13 35							
Luton 7	a							13 09										13 39							
Bedford 10	a							13 35										14 05							
Clapham Junction 10	d	11 55	12 05	12 09	12 09		12 12			12 24			12 38				12 30		12 47		12 55	13 05	13 09	13 09	
Imperial Wharf §	d																								
West Brompton	⊖ d		12 10														12 37					13 10			
Kensington Olympia	⊖ d		12 13														12 40					13 13			
Shepherds Bush §	⊖ d																								
Willesden Jn. High Level	a																12 50								
Wembley Central	a																								
Harrow & Wealdstone	⊖ a		12 32																			13 32			
Watford Junction	a		12 41																			13 42			
London Victoria 15	⊖ a	12 01		12 16	12 16	12 10	12 18		12 25	12 31			12 46	12 40					12 53	12 55	13 01		13 16	13 16	13 10

For general notes see front of timetable
For details of catering facilities see Directory of Train Operators

§ It is unknown, at the time of going to press, when this station will open. For further details contact National Rail Enquiries 08457-484950 or see local publicity.

A Until 7 September
B From 14 September
C To Maidstone West (Table 208)
D From Bognor Regis (Table 188)

Table 186

Sundays

Brighton → London, Bedford and Watford Junction

Network Diagram - see first page of Table 186

Station		SN	FC	GX	SN	SN	SE	SN	GX	GW	GW	LO		FC	SN	GX	SN	SN	SN	SN	GX	SN	FC	GX	SN
							55																		
		1 ◊	1	1	1			1	1	1	1			1	1 ◊	1	1	1	1	1	1	1 ◊	1	1	1
						A	B	C							A				A	D					
		(trolley)			(trolley)			(trolley)														(trolley)			(trolley)
Brighton [10]	d	12 00	12 16											12 44	12 51							13 00	13 16		
Hove [2]	d																12 54								
Preston Park	d	12 03																				13 03			
Hassocks [4]	d	12 10												12 52								13 10			
Burgess Hill [4]	d	12 13	12 26											12 56			13 04					13 13	13 26		
Lewes [4]	d				12 16																				13 16
Wivelsfield [4]	d	12 16			12 31																	13 16			13 31
Haywards Heath [3]	a	12 20	12 30		12 35									13 00			13 09					13 20	13 30		13 35
	d	12 21	12 31		12 39									13 01			13 10					13 21	13 31		13 39
Balcombe	d	12 26																				13 26			
Horsham [4]	d							12 42											13 04	13 04					
Littlehaven	d																		13 07	13 07					
Faygate	d																								
Ifield	d																		13 13	13 13					
Crawley	d							12 51											13 17	13 17					
Three Bridges [4]	a	12 32	12 40					12 54						13 10					13 20	13 20		13 32	13 40		
	d	12 32	12 40				12 50	12 54						13 10					13 22	13 22		13 32	13 40		
Gatwick Airport [10] ✈	a	12 37	12 44		12 52		12 54	12 58						13 14	13 17		13 22		13 26	13 26		13 37	13 44		13 52
	d	12 38	12 45	12 50	12 53		12 55	12 59	13 05	13 07				13 15	13 18	13 20	13 23		13 27	13 27	13 35	13 38	13 45	13 50	13 53
Horley [4]	d							13 02											13 30	13 30					
Salfords	d																		13 34						
Earlswood (Surrey)	d																		13 37						
Reigate	d										13 14														
Tonbridge [4]	d																								
Redhill	a	12 45					13 03	13 08		13 15	13 18								13 40	13 40		13 45			
	d	12 46				13 03		13 09											13 41	13 41		13 46			
Merstham	d					13 07													13 45	13 45					
Coulsdon South	d					13 12													13 50	13 50					
Purley [4]	d					13 16		13 18											13 53	13 53					
East Croydon	a	12 58	13 01		13 09	13 21		13 24						13 31	13 34		13 39		13 58	13 58		13 58	14 01		14 09
	d	12 59	13 02		13 10	13 22		13 25						13 32	13 35		13 40		13 59	13 59		13 59	14 02		14 10
Norwood Junction [2]	a					13 26																			
London Bridge [4] ⊖	a		13 15			13 38								13 45									14 15		
London Blackfriars [3] ⊖	a		13 23											13 53									14 23		
City Thameslink [3]	a																								
Farringdon [3] ⊖	a		13 27											13 57									14 27		
St Pancras International [15] ⊖	a		13 31											14 01									14 31		
St Albans City	a		13 53											14 23									14 53		
Luton Airport Parkway [4] ✈	a		14 05											14 35									15 05		
Luton [7]	a		14 09											14 39									15 09		
Bedford [10]	a		14 35											15 05									15 35		
Clapham Junction [10]	d	13 12			13 24			13 38				13 30			13 47		13 55	14 05	14 09	14 09		14 12			14 24
Imperial Wharf §	d																								
West Brompton ⊖	d											13 37						14 10							
Kensington Olympia ⊖	d											13 40						14 13							
Shepherds Bush § ⊖	d																								
Willesden Jn. High Level	a											13 50													
Wembley Central	a																								
Harrow & Wealdstone ⊖	a																	14 32							
Watford Junction	a																	14 42							
London Victoria [15] ⊖	a	13 18		13 25	13 31			13 46	13 40						13 53	13 55	14 01		14 16	14 16	14 10	14 18		14 25	14 31

For general notes see front of timetable
For details of catering facilities see Directory of Train Operators

§ It is unknown, at the time of going to press, when this station will open. For further details contact National Rail Enquiries 08457-484950 or see local publicity.

A Until 7 September
B To Maidstone West (Table 208)
C From Bognor Regis (Table 188)
D From 14 September

Table 186 — Sundays

Brighton → London, Bedford and Watford Junction

Network Diagram - see first page of Table 186

		SN	SE 55	SN	GX	GW	GW	LO	FC	SN	GX	SN	SN	SN	SN	GX	SN	FC	GX	LO	SN	SN	SE 55	SN	GX
				1	1	1	1		1	1 ◇	1	1	1	1	1	1	1 ◇	1	1		1			1	1
		A	B	C						A				A	D							A	B	C	
Brighton 10	d								13 44	13 51							14 00	14 16							
Hove 2	d											13 54													
Preston Park	d																14 03								
Hassocks 4	d								13 52								14 10								
Burgess Hill 4	d								13 56			14 04					14 13	14 26							
Lewes 4	d																				14 16				
Wivelsfield 4	d																14 16				14 31				
Haywards Heath 3	a								14 00			14 09					14 20	14 30			14 35				
	d								14 01			14 10					14 21	14 31			14 39				
Balcombe	d																14 26								
Horsham 4	d			13 42										14 04	14 04									14 42	
Littlehaven	d													14 07	14 07										
Faygate	d																								
Ifield	d													14 13	14 13										
Crawley	d			13 51										14 17	14 17									14 51	
Three Bridges 4	a			13 54					14 10					14 20	14 20		14 32	14 40						14 54	
	d		13 50	13 54					14 10					14 22	14 22		14 32	14 40					14 50	14 54	
Gatwick Airport 10	a		13 54	13 58					14 14	14 17		14 22		14 26	14 26		14 37	14 44			14 52		14 54	14 58	
	d		13 55	13 59	14 05	14 07			14 15	14 18	14 20	14 23		14 27	14 27	14 35	14 38	14 45	14 50		14 53		14 55	14 59	15 05
Horley 4	d			14 02										14 30	14 30									15 02	
Salfords	d													14 34											
Earlswood (Surrey)	d													14 37											
Reigate	d						14 13																		
Tonbridge 4	d																								
Redhill	a		14 03	14 08		14 15	14 17							14 40	14 40		14 45						15 03	15 08	
	d	14 03		14 09										14 41	14 41		14 46					15 03		15 09	
Merstham	d	14 07												14 45	14 45							15 07			
Coulsdon South	d	14 12												14 50	14 50							15 12			
Purley 4	d	14 16		14 18										14 53	14 53							15 16		15 18	
East Croydon	a	14 21		14 24					14 31	14 34		14 39		14 58	14 58		14 58	15 01			15 09	15 21		15 24	
	d	14 22		14 25					14 32	14 35		14 40		14 59	14 59		14 59	15 02			15 10	15 22		15 25	
Norwood Junction 2	a	14 26																				15 26			
London Bridge 4	⊖ a	14 38							14 45									15 15				15 38			
London Blackfriars 3	⊖ a								14 53									15 23							
City Thameslink 3	a																								
Farringdon 3	⊖ a								14 57									15 27							
St Pancras International 15	⊖ a								15 01									15 31							
St Albans City	a								15 23									15 53							
Luton Airport Parkway 4	a								15 35									16 05							
Luton 7	a								15 39									16 09							
Bedford 10	a								16 05									16 36							
Clapham Junction 10	d			14 38				14 30		14 47		14 55	15 05	15 09	15 09		15 12			15 18	15 24			15 38	
Imperial Wharf §	d																								
West Brompton	⊖ d							14 37					15 10							15 25					
Kensington Olympia	⊖ d							14 40					15 13							15 28					
Shepherds Bush §	⊖ d																								
Willesden Jn. High Level	a							14 50												15 38					
Wembley Central	a																								
Harrow & Wealdstone	⊖ a												15 32												
Watford Junction	a												15 42												
London Victoria 15	⊖ a			14 46	14 40					14 53	14 55	15 01		15 16	15 16	15 10	15 18		15 25		15 31			15 46	15 40

For general notes see front of timetable
For details of catering facilities see Directory of Train Operators

§ It is unknown, at the time of going to press, when this station will open. For further details contact National Rail Enquiries 08457-484950 or see local publicity.

A Until 7 September
B To Maidstone West (Table 208)
C From Bognor Regis (Table 188)
D From 14 September

Brighton → London, Bedford and Watford Junction

Network Diagram - see first page of Table 186

		GW	GW	LO		FC	SN	GX	SN	SN	SN	SN	GX	SN	FC	GX	LO	SN	SN	SE	SN	GX	GW	GW	LO
		1	1			1	1 ◇	1	1	1	1	1	1	1 ◇	1	1		1		55	1	1	1	1	
							A				A	B							A	C	D				
														🍴				🍴			🍴				
Brighton 10	d					14 44	14 51							15 00	15 16										
Hove 2	d								14 54																
Preston Park	d													15 03											
Hassocks 4	d					14 52								15 10											
Burgess Hill 4	d					14 56			15 04					15 13	15 26										
Lewes 4	d																	15 16							
Wivelsfield 4	d													15 16				15 31							
Haywards Heath 3	a					15 00			15 09					15 20	15 30			15 35							
	d					15 01			15 10					15 21	15 31			15 39							
Balcombe	d													15 26											
Horsham 4	d										15 04	15 04									15 42				
Littlehaven	d										15 07	15 07													
Faygate	d																								
Ifield	d										15 13	15 13													
Crawley	d										15 17	15 17									15 51				
Three Bridges 4	a					15 10					15 20	15 20		15 32	15 40						15 54				
	d					15 10					15 22	15 22		15 32	15 40					15 50	15 54				
Gatwick Airport 10 ✈	a					15 14	15 17		15 22		15 26	15 26		15 37	15 44			15 52		15 54	15 58				
	d	15 07				15 15	15 18	15 20	15 23		15 27	15 27	15 35	15 38	15 45	15 50		15 53		15 55	15 59	16 05	16 07		
Horley 4	d										15 30	15 30									16 02				
Salfords	d										15 34														
Earlswood (Surrey)	d										15 37														
Reigate	d		15 14																						
Tonbridge 4	d																							16 13	
Redhill	a	15 15	15 18								15 40	15 40		15 45						16 03	16 08		16 15	16 17	
	d										15 41	15 41		15 46					16 03		16 09				
Merstham	d										15 45	15 45							16 07						
Coulsdon South	d										15 50	15 50							16 12						
Purley 4	d										15 53	15 53							16 16		16 18				
East Croydon 🚌	a					15 31	15 34		15 39		15 58	15 58		15 58	16 01			16 09	16 21		16 24				
	d					15 32	15 35		15 40		15 59	15 59		15 59	16 02			16 10	16 22		16 25				
Norwood Junction 2	a																		16 26						
London Bridge 4 ⊖	a					15 45									16 15				16 38						
London Blackfriars 3 ⊖	a					15 53									16 23										
City Thameslink 3	a																								
Farringdon 3 ⊖	a					15 57									16 27										
St Pancras International 15 ⊖	a					16 01									16 31										
St Albans City	a					16 23									16 53										
Luton Airport Parkway 4 ✈	a					16 37									17 05										
Luton 7	a					16 40									17 09										
Bedford 10	a					17 06									17 35										
Clapham Junction 10	d			15 48			15 47		15 55	16 05	16 09	16 09		16 12			16 18	16 24			16 38				16 48
Imperial Wharf §	d																								
West Brompton ⊖	d			15 55						16 10															
Kensington Olympia ⊖	d			15 58						16 13							16 25								16 55
Shepherds Bush § ⊖	d																16 28								16 58
Willesden Jn. High Level	a			16 08													16 38								17 08
Wembley Central	a																								
Harrow & Wealdstone ⊖	a									16 32															
Watford Junction	a									16 42															
London Victoria 15 ⊖	a						15 53	15 55	16 01		16 16	16 16	16 10	16 18		16 25		16 31			16 46	16 40			

For general notes see front of timetable
For details of catering facilities see Directory of Train Operators

§ It is unknown, at the time of going to press, when this station will open. For further details contact National Rail Enquiries 08457-484950 or see local publicity.

A Until 7 September
B From 14 September
C To Maidstone West (Table 208)
D From Bognor Regis (Table 188)

Brighton → London, Bedford and Watford Junction

Network Diagram - see first page of Table 186

Station		FC	SN	GX	SN	SN	SN	SN	GX	SN	FC	GX	LO	SN	SN	SE	SN	GX		GW	GW	LO	FC	SN	GX
																55									
		1	1 ◇	1	1	1	1	1	1	1 ◇	1	1		1			1	1		1	1		1	1 ◇	1
							A	B							A	C	D								
										🍴				🍴			🍴								
Brighton 10	d	15 44	15 51							16 00	16 16												16 44	16 51	
Hove 2	d				15 54																				
Preston Park	d									16 03															
Hassocks 4	d	15 52								16 10													16 52		
Burgess Hill 4	d	15 56			16 04					16 13	16 26												16 56		
Lewes 4	d													16 16											
Wivelsfield 4	d									16 16				16 31											
Haywards Heath 3	a	16 00			16 09					16 20	16 30			16 35									17 00		
	d	16 01			16 10					16 21	16 31			16 39									17 01		
Balcombe	d									16 26															
Horsham 4	d						16 04	16 04									16 42								
Littlehaven	d						16 07	16 07																	
Faygate	d																								
Ifield	d						16 13	16 13																	
Crawley	d						16 17	16 17									16 51								
Three Bridges 4	a	16 10					16 20	16 20		16 32	16 40						16 54						17 10		
	d	16 10					16 22	16 22		16 32	16 40					16 50	16 54						17 10		
Gatwick Airport 10 ✈	a	16 14	16 17		16 22		16 26	16 26		16 37	16 44			16 52		16 54	16 58						17 14	17 17	
	d	16 15	16 18	16 20	16 23		16 27	16 27	16 35	16 38	16 45	16 50		16 53		16 55	16 59	17 05		17 07			17 15	17 18	17 20
Horley 4	d						16 30	16 30									17 02								
Salfords	d						16 34																		
Earlswood (Surrey)	d						16 37																		
Reigate	d																				17 14				
Tonbridge 4	d																								
Redhill	a						16 40	16 40		16 45						17 03	17 08			17 15	17 20				
	d						16 41	16 41		16 46					17 03		17 09								
Merstham	d						16 45	16 45							17 07										
Coulsdon South	d						16 50	16 50							17 12										
Purley 4	d						16 53	16 53							17 16		17 18								
East Croydon	a	16 31	16 34		16 39		16 58	16 58		16 58	17 01			17 09	17 21		17 24						17 31	17 34	
	d	16 32	16 35		16 40		16 59	16 59		16 59	17 02			17 10	17 22		17 25						17 32	17 35	
Norwood Junction 2	a														17 26										
London Bridge 4 ⊖	a	16 45									17 15				17 38								17 45		
London Blackfriars 3 ⊖	a	16 53									17 23												17 53		
City Thameslink 3	a																								
Farringdon 3 ⊖	a	16 57									17 27												17 57		
St Pancras International 15 ⊖	a	17 01									17 31												18 01		
St Albans City	a	17 23									17 53												18 23		
Luton Airport Parkway 4 ✈	a	17 35									18 05												18 35		
Luton 7	a	17 39									18 09												18 39		
Bedford 10	a	18 05									18 35												19 05		
Clapham Junction 10	d		16 47		16 55	17 05	17 09	17 09		17 12			17 18	17 24			17 38					17 48		17 47	
Imperial Wharf §	d																								
West Brompton ⊖	d					17 10							17 25									17 55			
Kensington Olympia ⊖	d					17 13							17 28									17 58			
Shepherds Bush § ⊖	d																								
Willesden Jn. High Level	a												17 38									18 08			
Wembley Central	a																								
Harrow & Wealdstone ⊖	a					17 32																			
Watford Junction	a					17 42																			
London Victoria 15 ⊖	a		16 53	16 55	17 01		17 16	17 16	17 10	17 18		17 25		17 31			17 46	17 40						17 53	17 55

For general notes see front of timetable
For details of catering facilities see Directory of Train Operators

§ It is unknown, at the time of going to press, when this station will open. For further details contact National Rail Enquiries 08457-484950 or see local publicity.

A Until 7 September
B From 14 September
C To Maidstone West (Table 208)
D From Bognor Regis (Table 188)

Brighton → London, Bedford and Watford Junction

Network Diagram - see first page of Table 186

		SN	SN	SN	SN	GX	SN	FC	GX	SN	SN	SE	LO	SN	GX	GW	GW	LO	FC	SN	GX	SN	SN	SN	SN
												55													
		1	1	1	1	1	1 ◇	1	1	1				1	1	1	1		1	1 ◇	1	1	1	1	1
				A	B						A	C		D										A	B
							⊼			⊼				⊼											
Brighton 10	d						17 00	17 16											17 44	17 51					
Hove 2	d	16 54																				17 54			
Preston Park	d						17 03																		
Hassocks 4	d						17 10												17 52						
Burgess Hill 4	d	17 04					17 13	17 26											17 56			18 04			
Lewes 4	d									17 16															
Wivelsfield 4	d						17 16			17 31															
Haywards Heath 3	a	17 09					17 20	17 30		17 35									18 00			18 09			
	d	17 10					17 21	17 31		17 39									18 01			18 10			
Balcombe	d						17 26																		
Horsham 4	d			17 04	17 04									17 42										18 04	18 04
Littlehaven	d			17 07	17 07																			18 07	18 07
Faygate	d																								
Ifield	d			17 13	17 13																			18 13	18 13
Crawley	d			17 17	17 17									17 51										18 17	18 17
Three Bridges 4	a			17 20	17 20		17 32	17 40						17 54					18 10					18 20	18 20
	d			17 22	17 22		17 32	17 40				17 50		17 54					18 10					18 22	18 22
Gatwick Airport 10 ✈	a	17 22		17 26	17 26		17 37	17 44		17 52		17 54		17 58					18 14	18 17		18 22		18 26	18 26
	d	17 23		17 27	17 27	17 35	17 38	17 45	17 50	17 53		17 55		17 59	18 05	18 07			18 15	18 18	18 20	18 23		18 27	18 27
Horley 4	d			17 30	17 30									18 02										18 30	18 30
Salfords	d			17 34																				18 34	
Earlswood (Surrey)	d			17 37																				18 37	
Reigate	d																18 13								
Tonbridge 4	d																								
Redhill	a			17 40	17 40		17 45					18 03		18 08		18 15	18 17							18 40	18 40
	d			17 41	17 41		17 46				18 03			18 09										18 41	18 41
Merstham	d			17 45	17 45						18 07													18 45	18 45
Coulsdon South	d			17 50	17 50						18 12													18 50	18 50
Purley 4	d			17 53	17 53						18 16			18 18										18 53	18 53
East Croydon	a	17 39		17 58	17 58		17 58	18 01		18 09	18 21			18 24					18 31	18 34		18 39		18 58	18 58
	d	17 40		17 59	17 59		17 59	18 02		18 10	18 22			18 25					18 32	18 35		18 40		18 59	18 59
Norwood Junction 2	a										18 26														
London Bridge 4 ⊖	a							18 15			18 38								18 45						
London Blackfriars 3 ⊖	a							18 23											18 53						
City Thameslink 3	a																								
Farringdon 3 ⊖	a							18 27											18 57						
St Pancras International 15 ⊖	a							18 31											19 01						
St Albans City	a							18 53											19 24						
Luton Airport Parkway 4 ✈	a							19 05											19 35						
Luton 7	a							19 09											19 39						
Bedford 10	a							19 35											20 05						
Clapham Junction 10	d	17 55	18 05	18 09	18 09		18 12			18 24			18 18	18 38				18 48		18 47		18 55	19 05	19 09	19 09
Imperial Wharf §	d																								
West Brompton ⊖	d		18 10										18 25					18 55					19 10		
Kensington Olympia ⊖	d		18 13										18 28					18 58					19 13		
Shepherds Bush § ⊖	d																								
Willesden Jn. High Level	a												18 38					19 08							
Wembley Central	a																								
Harrow & Wealdstone ⊖	a		18 32																				19 32		
Watford Junction	a		18 42																				19 41		
London Victoria 15 ⊖	a	18 01		18 16	18 16	18 10	18 18		18 25	18 31				18 46	18 40					18 53	18 55	19 01		19 16	19 16

For general notes see front of timetable
For details of catering facilities see Directory of Train Operators

§ It is unknown, at the time of going to press, when this station will open. For further details contact National Rail Enquiries 08457-484950 or see local publicity.

A Until 7 September
B From 14 September
C To Maidstone West (Table 208)
D From Bognor Regis (Table 188)

Table 186

Sundays

Brighton → London, Bedford and Watford Junction

Network Diagram - see first page of Table 186

Station		GX	SN	FC	GX	LO	SN	SN	SE	SN		GX	GW	GW	LO	FC	SN	GX	SN	SN	SN	SN	GX	SN	LO
									55																
		1	1 ◇	1	1		1			1		1	1	1		1	1 ◇	1	1	1	1	1	1	1 ◇	
								A	B	C											A	D			
Brighton 10	d		18 00	18 16												18 44	18 51							19 00	
Hove 2	d																		18 54						
Preston Park	d		18 03																					19 03	
Hassocks 4	d		18 10													18 52								19 10	
Burgess Hill 4	d		18 13	18 26												18 56			19 04					19 13	
Lewes 4	d						18 16																		
Wivelsfield 4	d		18 16				18 31																	19 16	
Haywards Heath 3	a		18 20	18 30			18 35									19 00			19 09					19 20	
	d		18 21	18 31			18 39									19 01			19 10					19 21	
Balcombe	d		18 26																					19 26	
Horsham 4	d									18 42											19 04	19 04			
Littlehaven	d																				19 07	19 07			
Faygate	d																								
Ifield	d																				19 13	19 13			
Crawley	d									18 51											19 17	19 17			
Three Bridges 4	a		18 32	18 40						18 54						19 10					19 20	19 20		19 32	
	d		18 32	18 40					18 50	18 54						19 10					19 22	19 22		19 32	
Gatwick Airport 10 ✈	a		18 37	18 44			18 52		18 54	18 58						19 14	19 17		19 22		19 26	19 26		19 37	
	d	18 35	18 38	18 45	18 50		18 53		18 55	18 59		19 05	19 07			19 15	19 18	19 20	19 23		19 27	19 27	19 35	19 38	
Horley 4	d									19 02											19 30	19 30			
Salfords	d																				19 34				
Earlswood (Surrey)	d																				19 37				
Reigate	d													19 14											
Tonbridge 4	d																								
Redhill	a		18 45						19 03	19 08			19 15	19 20							19 40	19 40		19 45	
	d		18 46					19 03		19 09											19 41	19 41		19 46	
Merstham	d							19 07													19 45	19 45			
Coulsdon South	d							19 12													19 50	19 50			
Purley 4	d							19 16		19 18											19 53	19 53			
East Croydon	a		18 58	19 01			19 09	19 21		19 24						19 31	19 34		19 39		19 58	19 58		19 58	
	d		18 59	19 02			19 10	19 22		19 25						19 32	19 35		19 40		19 59	19 59		19 59	
Norwood Junction 2	a							19 26																	
London Bridge 4	⊖ a			19 15				19 38								19 45									
London Blackfriars 3	⊖ a			19 23												19 53									
City Thameslink 3	a																								
Farringdon 3	⊖ a			19 27												19 57									
St Pancras International 15	⊖ a			19 31												20 01									
St Albans City	a			19 54												20 24									
Luton Airport Parkway 4	✈ a			20 05												20 35									
Luton 7	a			20 09												20 39									
Bedford 10	a			20 35												21 05									
Clapham Junction 10	d		19 12			19 18	19 24			19 38					19 48		19 47		19 55	20 05	20 09	20 09		20 12	20 18
Imperial Wharf §	d																								
West Brompton	⊖ d					19 25									19 55					20 10					20 25
Kensington Olympia	⊖ d					19 28									19 58					20 13					20 28
Shepherds Bush §	⊖ d																								
Willesden Jn. High Level	a					19 38									20 08										20 40
Wembley Central	a																								
Harrow & Wealdstone	⊖ a																			20 32					
Watford Junction	a																			20 42					
London Victoria 15	⊖ a	19 10	19 18		19 25		19 31			19 46		19 40					19 53	19 55	20 01		20 16	20 16	20 10	20 18	

For general notes see front of timetable
For details of catering facilities see
Directory of Train Operators

§ It is unknown, at the time of going to press, when this station will open. For further details contact National Rail Enquiries 08457-484950 or see local publicity.

A Until 7 September
B To Maidstone West (Table 208)
C From Bognor Regis (Table 188)
D From 14 September

Table 186

Sundays

Brighton → London, Bedford and Watford Junction

Network Diagram - see first page of Table 186

		FC	GX	SN	SN	SE	SN	GX	GW	GW	LO	FC	SN	GX	SN	SN	SN	SN	GX	SN	FC	LO	GX	SN	SN
		1	1	1		55	1	1	1	1		1	1 ◇	1	1	1	1	1	1	1 ◇	1		1	1	
					A	B	C										A	D							A
Brighton 10	d	19 16										19 44	19 51							20 00	20 16				
Hove 2	d														19 54										
Preston Park	d																			20 03					
Hassocks 4	d											19 52								20 10					
Burgess Hill 4	d	19 26										19 56			20 04					20 13	20 26				
Lewes 4	d			19 16																				20 16	
Wivelsfield 4	d			19 31																20 16				20 31	
Haywards Heath 3	a	19 30		19 35								20 00			20 09					20 20	20 30			20 35	
	d	19 31		19 39								20 01			20 10					20 21	20 31			20 39	
Balcombe	d																			20 26					
Horsham 4	d						19 42										20 04	20 04							
Littlehaven	d																20 07	20 07							
Faygate	d																								
Ifield	d																20 13	20 13							
Crawley	d						19 51										20 17	20 17							
Three Bridges 4	a	19 40					19 54					20 10					20 20	20 20		20 32	20 40				
	d	19 40				19 50	19 54					20 10					20 22	20 22		20 32	20 40				
Gatwick Airport 10 ✈	a	19 44		19 52		19 54	19 58					20 14	20 17		20 22		20 26	20 26		20 37	20 44			20 52	
	d	19 45	19 50	19 53		19 55	19 59	20 05	20 07			20 15	20 18	20 20	20 23		20 27	20 27	20 35	20 38	20 45		20 50	20 53	
Horley 4	d						20 02										20 30	20 30							
Salfords	d																20 34								
Earlswood (Surrey)	d																20 37								
Reigate	d									20 13															
Tonbridge 4	d																								
Redhill	a					20 03	20 08		20 15	20 17							20 40	20 40		20 45					
	d				20 03		20 09										20 41	20 41		20 46					21 03
Merstham	d				20 07												20 45	20 45							21 07
Coulsdon South	d				20 12												20 50	20 50							21 12
Purley 4	d				20 16		20 18										20 53	20 53							21 16
East Croydon	a	20 01		20 09	20 21		20 24					20 31	20 34		20 39		20 58	20 58		20 58	21 01			21 09	21 21
	d	20 02		20 10	20 22		20 25					20 32	20 35		20 40		20 59	20 59		20 59	21 02			21 10	21 22
Norwood Junction 2	a				20 26																				21 26
London Bridge 4	⊖ a	20 15			20 38							20 45									21 15				21 39
London Blackfriars 3	⊖ a	20 23										20 53									21 23				
City Thameslink 3	a																								
Farringdon 3	⊖ a	20 27										20 57									21 27				
St Pancras International 15	⊖ a	20 31										21 01									21 31				
St Albans City	a	20 54										21 24									21 54				
Luton Airport Parkway 4 ✈	a	21 05										21 35									22 05				
Luton 7	a	21 09										21 39									22 09				
Bedford 10	a	21 35										22 05									22 35				
Clapham Junction 10	d			20 24			20 38				20 48		20 47		20 55	21 05	21 09	21 09		21 12		21 18		21 24	
Imperial Wharf §	d																								
West Brompton	⊖ d										20 55					21 10						21 25			
Kensington Olympia	⊖ d										20 58					21 13						21 28			
Shepherds Bush §	⊖ d																								
Willesden Jn. High Level	a										21 08											21 40			
Wembley Central	a																								
Harrow & Wealdstone	⊖ a															21 32									
Watford Junction	a															21 42									
London Victoria 15	⊖ a		20 25	20 31			20 46	20 40					20 53	20 55	21 01		21 16	21 16	21 10	21 18			21 25	21 31	

For general notes see front of timetable
For details of catering facilities see Directory of Train Operators

§ It is unknown, at the time of going to press, when this station will open. For further details contact National Rail Enquiries 08457-484950 or see local publicity.

A Until 7 September
B To Maidstone West (Table 208)
C From Bognor Regis (Table 188)
D From 14 September

Table 186

Sundays

Brighton → London, Bedford and Watford Junction

Network Diagram - see first page of Table 186

		SE 55		SN	GX	GW	GW	LO	FC	GX	SN	SN	SN	SN	GX	SN	LO	FC	GX	SN	SN	SE 55	SN	LO	GX
				1		1	1		1	1	1	1	1	1		1 ◇		1	1	1			1		
		A		B									C	D							C		B		
Brighton [10]	d								20 44							21 00		21 16							
Hove [2]	d										20 54														
Preston Park	d															21 03									
Hassocks [4]	d								20 52							21 10									
Burgess Hill [4]	d								20 56		21 04					21 13		21 26							
Lewes [4]	d																			21 16					
Wivelsfield [4]	d															21 16				21 31					
Haywards Heath [3]	a								21 00		21 09					21 20		21 30		21 35					
	d								21 01		21 10					21 21		21 31		21 39					
Balcombe	d															21 26									
Horsham [4]	d			20 42									21 04	21 04									21 42		
Littlehaven	d												21 07	21 07											
Faygate	d																								
Ifield	d												21 13	21 13											
Crawley	d			20 51									21 17	21 17									21 51		
Three Bridges [4]	a			20 54					21 10				21 20	21 20		21 32		21 40					21 54		
	d	20 50		20 54					21 10				21 22	21 22		21 32		21 40				21 50	21 54		
Gatwick Airport [10]	✈ a	20 54		20 58					21 14		21 22		21 26	21 26		21 37		21 44		21 52		21 54	21 58		
	d	20 55		20 59	21 05	21 07			21 15	21 20	21 23		21 27	21 27	21 35	21 38		21 45	21 50	21 53		21 55	21 59		22 05
Horley [4]	d			21 02									21 30	21 30									22 02		
Salfords	d												21 34												
Earlswood (Surrey)	d												21 37												
Reigate	d						21 14																		
Tonbridge [4]	d																								
Redhill	a	21 03		21 13		21 15	21 18						21 40	21 40		21 45						22 03	22 08		
	d			21 13									21 41	21 41		21 46					22 03		22 09		
Merstham	d												21 45	21 45							22 07				
Coulsdon South	d												21 50	21 50							22 12				
Purley [4]	d			21 23									21 53	21 53							22 16		22 18		
East Croydon	⛴ a			21 27					21 31		21 39		21 58	21 58		21 58		22 01		22 09	22 21		22 24		
	d			21 28					21 32		21 40		21 59	21 59		21 59		22 02		22 10	22 22		22 25		
Norwood Junction [2]	a																				22 26				
London Bridge [4]	⊖ a								21 45									22 15			22 38				
London Blackfriars [3]	⊖ a								21 53									22 23							
City Thameslink [3]	a																								
Farringdon [3]	⊖ a								21 57									22 27							
St Pancras International [15]	⊖ a								22 01									22 31							
St Albans City	a								22 24									23 03							
Luton Airport Parkway [4]	✈ a								22 35									23 15							
Luton [7]	a								22 39									23 19							
Bedford [10]	a								23 05									23 45							
Clapham Junction [10]	d			21 38				21 48			21 55	22 05	22 09	22 09		22 12	22 18			22 24			22 38	22 48	
Imperial Wharf §	d																								
West Brompton	⊖ d							21 55				22 10					22 25							22 55	
Kensington Olympia	⊖ d							21 58				22 13					22 28							22 58	
Shepherds Bush §	⊖ d																								
Willesden Jn. High Level	a							22 08									22 40							23 08	
Wembley Central	a																								
Harrow & Wealdstone	⊖ a											22 32													
Watford Junction	a											22 42													
London Victoria [15]	⊖ a			21 46	21 40					21 55	22 01		22 16	22 16	22 10	22 18			22 25	22 31			22 46		22 40

For general notes see front of timetable
For details of catering facilities see
Directory of Train Operators

§ It is unknown, at the time of going to press, when this station will open. For further details contact National Rail Enquiries 08457-484950 or see local publicity.

A To Gillingham (Kent) (Table 208)
B From Bognor Regis (Table 188)
C Until 7 September
D From 14 September

Sundays

Brighton → London, Bedford and Watford Junction

Network Diagram - see first page of Table 186

		GW 1	GW 1	FC 1	GX 1	SN 1 A	SN 1 B	GX	SN 1 ◇	FC 1	GX 1	SN 1 C	GX	GW 1	LO	GW 1	FC 1	GX 1	SN 1	GX	SN 1 ◇	GX 1	FC 1
Brighton 10	d			21 44					22 00	22 16							22 44				23 02		23 44
Hove 2	d																						
Preston Park	d								22 03												23 06		
Hassocks 4	d			21 52					22 10								22 52				23 12		23 52
Burgess Hill 4	d			21 56					22 13	22 26							22 56				23 16		23 56
Lewes 4	d																						
Wivelsfield 4	d								22 16												23 19		
Haywards Heath 3	a			22 00					22 20	22 30							23 00				23 23		00 01
	d			22 01					22 21	22 31							23 01				23 24		00 01
Balcombe	d								22 26												23 29		
Horsham 4	d					22 04	22 04					22 42							23 04				
Littlehaven	d					22 07	22 07												23 07				
Faygate	d																						
Ifield	d					22 13	22 13												23 13				
Crawley	d					22 17	22 17					22 51							23 17				
Three Bridges 4	a			22 10		22 20	22 20		22 32	22 40		22 54					23 10		23 20		23 35		00 10
	d			22 10		22 22	22 22		22 32	22 40		22 54					23 10		23 22		23 42		00 10
Gatwick Airport 10 ✈	a			22 14		22 26	22 26		22 37	22 44		22 58					23 14		23 26		23 46		00 14
	d	22 07		22 15	22 20	22 27	22 27	22 35	22 38	22 45	22 50	22 59	23 05	23 07			23 15	23 20	23 27	23 35	23 47	23 50	00 15
Horley 4	d					22 30	22 30					23 02							23 30		23s49		
Salfords	d					22 34																	
Earlswood (Surrey)	d					22 37																	
Reigate	d		22 13													23 14							
Tonbridge 4	d																						
Redhill	a	22 15	22 18			22 40	22 40		22 45			23 08		23 15		23 18			23 36		23 56		00 22
	d					22 41	22 41		22 46			23 09							23 37		00 02		00 22
Merstham	d					22 45	22 45												23 41				
Coulsdon South	d					22 50	22 50												23 46				
Purley 4	d					22 53	22 53					23 17							23 50		00 11		
East Croydon	a			22 31		22 58	22 58		22 58	23 01		23 24					23 31		23 55		00 16		00 35
	d			22 32		22 59	22 59		22 59	23 02		23 25					23 32		23 56		00 17		00 36
Norwood Junction 2	a																						
London Bridge 4 ⊖	a			22 45						23 15							23 45						00 52
London Blackfriars 3 ⊖	a			22 53						23 23							23 53						00 59
City Thameslink 3	a																						
Farringdon 3 ⊖	a			22 57						23 27							23 57						
St Pancras International 15 ⊖	a			23 01						23 31							00 02						01 07
St Albans City	a			23 34						00 03							00 33						01 39
Luton Airport Parkway 4 ✈	a			23 45						00 15							00 45						01 51
Luton 7	a			23 49						00 19							00 49						01 55
Bedford 10	a			00 15						00 45							01 15						02 20
Clapham Junction 10	d					23 10	23 10		23 13			23 38			23 18				00 11		00 30		
Imperial Wharf §	d																						
West Brompton ⊖	d																						
Kensington Olympia ⊖	d														23 25								
Shepherds Bush § ⊖	d														23 28								
Willesden Jn. High Level	a														23 38								
Wembley Central	a																						
Harrow & Wealdstone ⊖	a																						
Watford Junction	a																						
London Victoria 15 ⊖	a				22 55	23 16	23 16	23 10	23 20		23 25	23 46	23 40					23 55	00 18	00 10	00 37	00 25	

For general notes see front of timetable
For details of catering facilities see Directory of Train Operators

§ It is unknown, at the time of going to press, when this station will open. For further details contact National Rail Enquiries 08457-484950 or see local publicity.

A Until 7 September
B From 14 September
C From Bognor Regis (Table 188)

London, Gatwick Airport & Brighton → Sussex Coast, Portsmouth and Southampton

Network Diagram - see first page of Table 186

Miles	Miles	Miles			SN MX 1	SN MX 1	SN MX 1	SN MX 1	SN 1	SN MX 1	SN MO 1	SN MX 1 ◇	SN 1	SN 1	SN 1	SN 1	SN 1	SN 1	SN 1	SN 1	SN 1	SN 1	SN 1	SN 1	SN 1
0	—	0	**London Victoria** [15] ⊖	d	22p17	22p32		22p47	*23 06*	23p17	23p17	00 05									*04 00*				
2¾	—	—	Clapham Junction [10]	d	22p23	22p38		22p53	*23 12*	23p23	23p23	00 11									*04 08*				
—	0	—	London Bridge [4] ⊖	d					*23 00*	*23 11*	*23 00*	*23 53*													
10½	10¼	—	**East Croydon**	d	22p33	22p48		23p03	*23 22*	23p33	23p37	00 25									*04 22*	*04 32*			
26¾	—	—	**Gatwick Airport** [10] ✈	d	22p49	23p09		23p19	*23 19*	23p51	00 02	00 43									*04 47*	*04 52*			
29½	—	29½	**Three Bridges** [4]	a	22p54	23p14				23p55	00 07	00 48													
—	—	—		d	22p54	23p15			*23 15*	23p56	00 07	00 48									*04 52*	*04 58*			
—	—	31	Crawley	d		23p18																			
—	—	38	**Horsham** [4]	a		23p26																			
—	—	—		d		23p27																			
—	—	40½	Christs Hospital	d		23p30																			
—	—	45¼	Billingshurst	d		23p36																			
—	—	50¼	Pulborough	d		23p43																			
—	—	55	Amberley	d		23p49																			
—	—	58¾	Arundel	d		23p54																			
38	—	—	Haywards Heath [3]	d	23p03			23p37	*23 45*	00 05	00 16	01 03									*05 01*	*05 08*			
41¾	—	—	Burgess Hill	d	23p08				*23 32*	00 10															
—	0	—	**Brighton** [10]	d					00 10									05 15			05 30	05 44	05 53		
51	1½	—	Hove [2]	d	23p21			23p52	00a13	00 22	00 31	01s25						05 19			05 34	05a47	05 57		
—	2	—	Aldrington	d														05 21			05 36				
—	3	—	Portslade	d	23p24			23p55		00s25	00s34	01s28						05 23			05 38				
—	3½	—	Fishersgate	d														05 25			05 40				
—	4½	—	Southwick	d	23p27			23p58		00s28	00s37	01s31						05 27			05 42				
—	5½	—	Shoreham-by-Sea	d	23p30			00 01		00s31	00s40	01s34						05 30			05 45		06 03		
—	8¼	—	Lancing	d	23p34			00 05		00s35	00s44	01s38						05 34			05 49				
—	9¾	—	East Worthing	d														05 37			05 52				
—	10½	—	**Worthing** [4]	a	23p38			00 09		00 39	00 48	01 42						05 40			05 55		06 09		
—	—	—		d	23p39													05 40			05 55		06 09		
—	11½	—	West Worthing	d	23p41													05 42			05 57				
—	12¼	—	Durrington-on-Sea	d	23p43													05 45			06 00				
—	13	—	Goring-by-Sea	d	23p46													05 47			06 02				
0	15½	—	Angmering [3]	d	23p50													05 51			06 06				
6	—	—	**Littlehampton** [4]	a																					
—	—	—		d													05 35			06 04					06 39
8	19¾	61	Ford [4]	d	23p56	23p59											05 39	05 57		06 08	06 13				06 43
—	—	—	Bognor Regis [4]	d																					
—	22½	—	Barnham	a	00 01	00 04	⟵										05 43	06 02		06 12	06 17		06 24	⟵	06 47
0	—	—		d	00 09 ⟶	00 05	00 09						04 58	05 05	05 20	05 36	05 44	06 02	06 06	06 27 ⟶	06 18		06 24	06 27	06 48
3½	—	—	**Bognor Regis** [4]	a			00 15									05 42			06 12					06 35	06 54
—	28¾	—	**Chichester** [4]	a		00 12							05 05	05 12	05 27		05 51	06 10			06 25		06 32		
—	—	—		d									05 06	05 13	05 28		05 52	06 10			06 26		06 32		
—	30¼	—	Fishbourne (Sussex)	d													05 55						06 35		
—	31½	—	Bosham	d													05 58						06 38		
—	33¼	—	Nutbourne	d													06 01						06 42		
—	34¼	—	Southbourne	d													06 04				06 33		06 44		
—	35¾	—	Emsworth	d													06 07				06 36		06 47		
—	37	—	Warblington	d													06 10						06 50		
0	37½	—	**Havant**	d									05 17	05 24	05 39		06 13	06 21			06 40		06 53		
—	38¼	—	Bedhampton	a											*06 04*		06 15						06 56		
—	41¼	—	Hilsea	a											*06 10*		06 20						07 01		
—	44	—	Fratton	a										05 32	05 47		06 24						07 05		
—	44¾	—	Portsmouth & Southsea	a										05 36	05 51		06 28						07 08		
—	45½	—	**Portsmouth Harbour**	a										05 40	05 55		06 32						07 12		
4	—	—	Cosham	a									05 23					06 28			06 49				
6½	—	—	Portchester	a									05 28								06 54				
9¾	—	—	Fareham	a									05 33					06 37			06 59				
13½	—	—	Swanwick	a									05 40					06 44			07 06				
24¼	—	—	**Southampton Central**	a									05 59					07 02			07 26				

For general notes see front of timetable
For details of catering facilities see
Directory of Train Operators

For complete service between Three Bridges and Horsham see Table 186

London, Gatwick Airport & Brighton → Sussex Coast, Portsmouth and Southampton

Network Diagram - see first page of Table 186

		SN 1	SN 1	SN 1	SN 1	SN 1	SN 1	SN 1	SN 1	SN 1	SN 1	SN 1	SN 1	SN 1	SN 1	SN 1	SN 1	SN 1	SN 1	SN 1		SN 1	SN 1	SN 1	SN 1
London Victoria 15 ⊖	d			05 02				05 02					05b32	06 02						06b02		06 21	06 32		06b32
Clapham Junction 10	d			05 08				05 08					05b38	06 08						06b08		06 27	06 38		06b38
London Bridge 4 ⊖	d										05 31		05 50	05 55						06 21			06c43		06 43
East Croydon	d		05 02	05 32				05 32			05 52		06 04	06 18						06 36		06 39	06 49		06 56
Gatwick Airport 10 ✈	d		05 22	05 59				05 54			06 08		06 20	06 54						06 52		07 04	07 20		07 12
Three Bridges 4	a			06 03										06 59									07 24		
	d		05 26	06 04				06 00			06 14		06 26	06 59						06 56		07 09	07 30		07 18
Crawley	d			06 07										07 03									07 34		
Horsham 4	a			06 19										07 11									07 46		
	d			06 20										07 12									07 46		
Christs Hospital	d			06 23										07 15									07 50		
Billingshurst	d			06 29										07 21									07 56		
Pulborough	d			06 36										07 28									08 03		
Amberley	d			06 42										07 34									08 09		
Arundel	d			06 47										07 39									08 14		
Haywards Heath 3	d		05 36					06 10			06 25		06 38							07 06		07 21			07 28
Burgess Hill	d		05 42					06 16			06 32		06 44							07 12		07 27			07 34
Brighton 10	d	05 57	06 15		06 27			06 36			06 53		07 06		07 15			07 20	07 30	07 37		07 47		07 50	08 03
Hove 2	d	06 01	06 19		06 31			06 40			06 57		07 10		07 19			07 24	07 34	07 41		07 51		07 54	08 07
Aldrington	d	06 03	06 21								06 59							07 26						07 56	
Portslade	d	06 05	06 23					06 43			07 01				07 22			07 28	07 37	07 44		07 54		07 58	
Fishersgate	d	06 07	06 25								07 03							07 30						08 00	
Southwick	d	06 09	06 27					06 46			07 05				07 25			07 32	07 40	07 47		07 57		08 02	
Shoreham-by-Sea	d	06 12	06 30		06 37			06 49			07 09		07 16		07 28			07 35	07 43	07 50		08 00		08 06	08 13
Lancing	d	06 16	06 34					06 53			07 13				07 32			07 39	07 47	07 54		08 04		08 10	
East Worthing	d	06 19	06 37								07 16							07 42						08 13	
Worthing 4	a	06 22	06 40		06 43			06 57			07 18		07 22		07 36			07 45	07 51	07 58		08 08		08 15	08 19
	d	06 22	06 40		06 43			06 57			07 19		07 23		07 36			07 45	07 52	07 59		08 08		08 16	08 20
West Worthing	d	06 24	06a42		06 45			06 59			07 21		07 25					07 47	07 54	08 01				08 18	08 22
Durrington-on-Sea	d	06 27			06 48			07 02			07 23		07 27					07 50	07 56	08 03		08 12		08 20	08 24
Goring-by-Sea	d	06 29			06 50			07 04			07 26		07 30					07 52	07 59	08 06				08 23	08 27
Angmering 3	d	06 33			06 54			07 08			07 30		07 34					07 56	08 03	08 10		08 17		08 27	08 31
Littlehampton 4	a	06 42									07 38					⟵		08 05					08 21	08 38	
	d					07 00			07 18		07 49					07 49	07 58						08 26		
Ford 4	d			06 52		07 04		07 14	07 22		⟶		07 40	07 44		07 53	08 02		08 09	08 17			08 30		08 37
Bognor Regis 4	d																								
Barnham	a			06 56	07 04	07 08	⟵	07 19	07 26				07 45	07 49	07 52	07 57	08 06		08 13	08 21		08 27	08 34		08 41
	d			07 00 07 13	07 05	07 09	07 13	07 20	07 27	07 39		07 39	07 45	07 50	07 53	07 58	08 07		08 14	08 22		08 27	08 35		08 42
Bognor Regis 4	a			⟶			07 20			07 45		07 45		07 58			08 13					08 35			
Chichester 4	a			07 07	07 12	07 16		07 27	07 34				07 53		08 00	08 05			08 21	08 29			08 42		08 49
	d			07 08	07 13	07 17		07 28	07 35				07 53		08 01				08 22	08 30					08 50
Fishbourne (Sussex)	d					07 20			07 38						08 04										
Bosham	d				07 17				07 41						08 07										
Nutbourne	d					07 25			07 44						08 10										
Southbourne	d				07 22	07 27			07 47						08 13				08 29	08 37					
Emsworth	d				07 25	07 30			07 50						08 16				08 32	08 40					
Warblington	d				07 28				07 53						08 19										
Havant	d			07 19	07 31	07 35		07 41	07 57				08 04		08 22				08 37	08 44					09 01
Bedhampton	a			07 30		07 37		07 54	08 00						08 24										09 07
Hilsea	a			07 37		07 42		08 00	08 06						08 29										09 13
Fratton	a			07 41		07 46		07 49	08 10						08 33					08 53					09 11
Portsmouth & Southsea	a			07 46		07 50		07 53	08 15						08 37					08 56					09 16
Portsmouth Harbour	a							07 57	08 19						08 41					09 00					09 21
Cosham	a			07 25	07 38								08 15						08 44						
Portchester	a			07 30									08 19						08 48						
Fareham	a			07 35	07 46								08 24						08 53						
Swanwick	a			07 42	07 53								08 31						09 00						
Southampton Central	a			08 01	08 13								08 56						09 19						

For general notes see front of timetable
For details of catering facilities see Directory of Train Operators

b Change at East Croydon and Brighton
c Change at Gatwick Airport

For complete service between Three Bridges and Horsham see Table 186

London, Gatwick Airport & Brighton → Sussex Coast, Portsmouth and Southampton

Network Diagram - see first page of Table 186

Station		SN 1	SN 1	SN 1	SN 1	SN 1	SN 1	SN 1	SN 1	SN 1	SN 1	SN 1	SN 1		GW ◇	SN 1	SN 1	SN 1	SN 1		SN 1	SN 1	SN 1		SN 1	SN 1
															A								B 🚌			🚌
London Victoria 15	⊖ d			06b47	07 17			07b23		07 52			08 02					08 06			08 17		08 32			
Clapham Junction 10	d			06b53	07 23			07b29		07 58			08 08					08 12			08 23		08 38			
London Bridge 4	⊖ d			07 00	07c16			07 28		07 46	07 40		07 56					07b56			08 06		08 25			
East Croydon	d		07e03	07 16	07 34			07 46		08 08	07 56		08 18					08 22			08 33		08 48			
Gatwick Airport 10	✈ d		07 20	07 32	07 59			08 02		08 26	08 12		08 40					08 30			08 49		09 11			
Three Bridges 4	a				08 04								08 44										09 15			
	d		07 28	07 38	08 05			08 07		08 16	08 16		08 45					08 42			08 46		09 16			
Crawley	d				08 09								08 48										09 19			
Horsham 4	a				08 22								08 56			←							09 27			←
	d				08 23								09 00	09 04 →		09 04							09 31	09 35 →		09 35
Christs Hospital	d				08 26											09 07										09 38
Billingshurst	d				08 32											09 13										09 44
Pulborough	d				08 39											09 20										09 51
Amberley	d				08 45											09 26										09 57
Arundel	d				08 50											09 31										10 02
Haywards Heath 3	d		07 40	07 48				08 16		08 38	08 28							08 51			09 04					
Burgess Hill	d		07 46	07 54				08 22			08 34							08 57			09 09					
Brighton 10	d		08 07	08 23				08 39	08 44		08 53				09 00		09 03	09 14				09 23				
Hove 2	d		08 11	08 27				08 43	08a47	08 54	08 57				09 04		09 07	09a18			09 22	09 27				
Aldrington	d			08 29							08 59											09 29				
Portslade	d		08 14	08 31							09 01						09 10				09 25	09 31				
Fishersgate	d			08 33							09 03											09 33				
Southwick	d		08 17	08 35							09 05						09 13					09 35				
Shoreham-by-Sea	d		08 20	08 39				08 49		09 00	09 08				09 13		09 17				09 30	09 39				
Lancing	d		08 24	08 43						09 04	09 12						09 21					09 43				
East Worthing	d			08 46							09 15											09 46				
Worthing 4	a		08 28	08 48				08 55		09 08	09 18				09 21		09 25				09 36	09 48				
	d		08 28	08 49				08 56		09 08	09 18				09 22		09 26				09 37	09 49				
West Worthing	d		08 30	08a51						09 10	09a20						09 28				09 39	09a51				
Durrington-on-Sea	d		08 33					08 59		09 13											09 41					
Goring-by-Sea	d		08 35					09 02		09 15											09 44					
Angmering 3	d		08 39					09 06		09 19							09 33				09 48					
Littlehampton 4	a									09 28											09 58					
	d					08 58																			09 54	
Ford 4	d		08 45		08 55	09 02										09 36	09 40								09 58	10 07
Bognor Regis 4	d																									
Barnham	a		08 50		08 59	09 06		09 15					09 26		09 36	09 40	09 44						09 57		10 02	10 11
	d	08 45	08 52		09 00	09 07	09 08	09 16				09 24	09 27		09 38	09 41	09 45		09 52				09 58		10 03	10 12
Bognor Regis 4	a	08 52	08 58				09 14					09 30				09 47			09 58							10 18
Chichester 4	a				09 07	09 14		09 23					09 34		09 45		09 52						10 05		10 10	
	d				09 08	09 15		09 24					09 35		09 47		09 53						10 06		10 11	
Fishbourne (Sussex)	d					09 18																			10 14	
Bosham	d				09 12																		10 10		10 17	
Nutbourne	d				09 16																				10 20	
Southbourne	d					09 24		09 31															10 15		10 23	
Emsworth	d				09 20	09 27		09 34															10 18		10 26	
Warblington	d				09 23																				10 29	
Havant	d				09 26	09 31		09 38					09 46		09 59		10 04						10 22		10 33	
Bedhampton	a					09 34																	10 29		10 35	
Hilsea	a					09 41																	10 35		10 42	
Fratton	a					09 45							09 54				10 12						10 39		10 46	
Portsmouth & Southsea	a					09 49							09 58				10 16						10 43		10 49	
Portsmouth Harbour	a												10 02				10 20									
Cosham	a				09 33			09 45							10 05								10 29			
Portchester	a																						10 33			
Fareham	a				09 41			09 53							10 13								10 38			
Swanwick	a							10 00															10 45			
Southampton Central	a				10 03			10 19							10 38								11 02			

For general notes see front of timetable
For details of catering facilities see Directory of Train Operators

A To Great Malvern (Table 71)
B 🚌 to Horsham
b Change at East Croydon and Brighton
c Change at Gatwick Airport
e Change at Three Bridges and Brighton

For complete service between Three Bridges and Horsham see Table 186

London, Gatwick Airport & Brighton → Sussex Coast, Portsmouth and Southampton

Network Diagram - see first page of Table 186

		SN 1	SN 1	SN 1	SN 1	SN 1	SN 1		SN 1	SN 1	SN 1	SN 1	SN 1	SN 1		SN 1	SN 1		SN 1	SN 1	SN 1	SN 1	SN 1	SN 1		SN 1
											A			B										C		
							🛒				🛒			🛒			🛒							🛒		
London Victoria 15 ⊖	d	08 20	08 36		08 47		09 02		09 06		09 17			09 32					09 36			09 47		10 02		10 06
Clapham Junction 10	d	08 28	08 43		08 53		09 08		09 12		09 23			09 38					09 42			09 53		10 08		10 12
London Bridge 4 ⊖	d	08 19	08b27		08 41		08 49		09b00		09 11	09 06		09 25					09 25			09 42		09 56		09 56
East Croydon	d	08 39	08 53		09 03		09 18		09 22		09 33	09 24		09 48					09 52			10 03		10 18		10 22
Gatwick Airport 10 ✈	d	08 56	09 00		09 19		09 40		09 23		09 49	09 41		10 09					09 56			10 19		10 40		10 26
Three Bridges 4	a						09 44							10 14										10 44		
	d	09 00	09 05		09 19		09 45		09 28		09 45	09 45		10 14					10 00			10 15		10 45		10 15
Crawley	d						09 48							10 18										10 48		
Horsham 4	a						09 56							10 26										10 56		
	d						10 00	10 05						10 30	10 34 →		← 10 34							11 00	11 05	
Christs Hospital	d																10 37									
Billingshurst	d							10 13									10 43								11 13	
Pulborough	d							10 19									10 50								11 19	
Amberley	d																10 56									
Arundel	d							10 28									11 01								11 28	
Haywards Heath 3	d	09 10	09 17		09 37				09 40		10 04	09 57							10 10	10 18		10 37				10 38
Burgess Hill	d	09 04	09 24						09 36		10 09	10 03								10 24						10 33
Brighton 10	d	09 33	09 44			09 53			10 03	10 14		10 23							10 33	10 44			10 53			11 03
Hove 2	d	09 37	09a47		09 52	09 57			10 07	10a17	10 22	10 27							10 37	10a47		10 52	10 57			11 07
Aldrington	d					09 59						10 29											10 59			
Portslade	d	09 40				10 01			10 10		10 25	10 31							10 40				11 01			11 10
Fishersgate	d					10 03						10 33											11 03			
Southwick	d	09 43				10 05			10 13			10 35							10 43				11 05			11 13
Shoreham-by-Sea	d	09 46			09 58	10 09			10 16		10 30	10 39							10 46			10 58	11 09			11 16
Lancing	d	09 50			10 02	10 13			10 20			10 43							10 50			11 02	11 13			11 20
East Worthing	d					10 16						10 46											11 16			
Worthing 4	a	09 54			10 06	10 18			10 24		10 36	10 48							10 54			11 06	11 18			11 24
	d	09 55			10 07	10 19			10 25		10 37	10 49							10 55			11 07	11 19			11 25
West Worthing	d				10 09	10a21			10 27		10 39	10a51										11 09	11a21			11 27
Durrington-on-Sea	d	09 58			10 11						10 41								10 58			11 11				
Goring-by-Sea	d	10 01			10 14						10 44								11 01			11 14				
Angmering 3	d	10 05			10 18				10 33		10 48								11 05			11 18				11 33
Littlehampton 4	a				10 27						10 57											11 27				
	d			10 11												10 58					11 11					
Ford 4	d			10 15				10 33	10 40							11 02	11 06				11 15				11 33	11 40
Bognor Regis 4	d																									
Barnham	a	10 14		10 19			10 26	10 38	10 44					10 56		11 06	11 10		11 14		11 19			11 26	11 38	11 44
	d	10 15		10 22			10 27	10 38	10 45				10 52	10 57		11 07	11 11		11 15		11 22			11 27	11 38	11 45
Bognor Regis 4	a			10 28				10 45					10 58				11 17				11 28				11 45	
Chichester 4	a	10 22					10 34		10 52					11 04		11 14			11 22					11 34		11 52
	d	10 23					10 35		10 53					11 05		11 15			11 23					11 35		11 53
Fishbourne (Sussex)	d															11 18										
Bosham	d													11 09												
Nutbourne	d															11 23										
Southbourne	d	10 30												11 14		11 25			11 30							
Emsworth	d	10 33												11 17		11 28			11 33							
Warblington	d													11 20												
Havant	d	10 37					10 46		11 04					11 23		11 33			11 37					11 46		12 04
Bedhampton	a													11 29		11 35										
Hilsea	a													11 35		11 42										
Fratton	a						10 54		11 12					11 39		11 46								11 54		12 12
Portsmouth & Southsea	a						10 58		11 16					11 43		11 49								11 58		12 16
Portsmouth Harbour	a						11 02		11 20															12 02		12 20
Cosham	a	10 44												11 29					11 44							
Portchester	a													11 33												
Fareham	a	10 52												11 38					11 52							
Swanwick	a	10 59												11 45					11 59							
Southampton Central	a	11 18												12 02					12 18							

For general notes see front of timetable
For details of catering facilities see Directory of Train Operators

A 🛒 to Haywards Heath
B 🛒 to Horsham
C 🛒 to Bognor Regis

b Change at East Croydon and Brighton

For complete service between Three Bridges and Horsham see Table 186

London, Gatwick Airport & Brighton → Sussex Coast, Portsmouth and Southampton

Network Diagram - see first page of Table 186

		SN 1	SN 1 A ⌶	SN 1	SN 1	SN 1 B ⌶		SN 1	SN 1 ⌶	SN 1	SN 1	SN 1	SN 1	SN 1	SN 1			SN 1	SN 1	SN 1 A ⌶	SN 1	SN 1	SN 1		SN 1	SN 1
London Victoria 15 ⊖	d		10 17			10 32				*10 36*			10 47		11 02			*11 06*		11 17			11 32			
Clapham Junction 10	d		10 23			10 38				*10 42*			10 53		11 08			*11 12*		11 23			11 38			
London Bridge 4 ⊖	d		*10 11*	*10 11*		*10 26*				*10 26*			*10 41*	*10 41*	*10 56*			*10 56*		*11 11*	*11 11*		*11 26*			
East Croydon	d		10 33	*10 24*		10 48				*10 52*			11 03	*10 54*	11 18			*11 22*		11 33	*11 24*		11 48			
Gatwick Airport 10 ✈	d	*10 28*	10 49	*10 41*		11 09				*10 56*			11 19	*11 11*	11 40			*11 26*	*11 28*	11 49	*11 41*		12 09			
Three Bridges 4	a					11 14									11 44								12 14			
	d	*10 33*	*10 45*	*10 45*		11 14							*11 15*	*11 15*	11 45				*11 33*	*11 45*	*11 45*		12 14			
Crawley	d					11 18									11 48								12 18			
Horsham 4	a					11 26									11 56								12 26			
	d					11 30	11 34 →		← 11 34						12 00	12 05							12 30	12 34 →		← 12 34
Christs Hospital	d								11 37																	12 37
Billingshurst	d								11 43							12 13										12 43
Pulborough	d								11 50							12 19										12 50
Amberley	d								11 56																	12 56
Arundel	d								12 01							12 28										13 01
Haywards Heath 3	d	*10 46*	11 04	*10 55*						*11 08*			11 37	*11 27*				*11 38*	*11 46*	12 04	*11 55*					
Burgess Hill	d	*10 52*	11 09	*11 01*										*11 33*					*11 52*	12 09	*12 01*					
Brighton 10	d	11 14		11 23						11 33	11 44			11 53				12 03	12 14		12 23					
Hove 2	d	11a17	11 22	11 27						11 37	11a47		11 52	11 57				12 07	12a17	12 22	12 27					
Aldrington	d			11 29										11 59							12 29					
Portslade	d		11 25	11 31						11 40				12 01				12 10		12 25	12 31					
Fishersgate	d			11 33										12 03							12 33					
Southwick	d			11 35						11 43				12 05				12 13			12 35					
Shoreham-by-Sea	d		11 30	11 39						11 46			11 58	12 09				12 16		12 30	12 39					
Lancing	d			11 43						11 50			12 02	12 13				12 20			12 43					
East Worthing	d			11 46										12 16							12 46					
Worthing 4	a		11 36	11 48						11 54			12 06	12 18				12 24		12 36	12 48					
	d		11 37	11 49						11 55			12 07	12 19				12 25		12 37	12 49					
West Worthing	d		11 39	11a51									12 09	12a21				12 27		12 39	12a51					
Durrington-on-Sea	d		11 41							11 58			12 11							12 41						
Goring-by-Sea	d		11 44							12 01			12 14							12 44						
Angmering 3	d		11 48							12 05			12 18					12 33		12 48						
Littlehampton 4	a		11 57										12 27							12 57						
	d							11 58				12 11													12 58	
Ford 4	d							12 02	12 06			12 15				12 33		12 40							13 02	13 06
Bognor Regis 4	d																									
Barnham	a					11 56		12 06	12 10	12 14		12 19			12 26	12 38		12 44					12 56		13 06	13 10
	d				11 52	11 57		12 07	12 11	12 15		12 22			12 27	12 38		12 45				12 52	12 57		13 07	13 11
Bognor Regis 4	a				11 58				12 17			12 28				12 45						12 58				13 17
Chichester 4	a					12 04		12 14		12 22					12 34			12 52					13 04		13 14	
	d					12 05		12 15		12 23					12 35			12 53					13 05		13 15	
Fishbourne (Sussex)	d							12 18																	13 18	
Bosham	d					12 09																	13 09			
Nutbourne	d							12 23																	13 23	
Southbourne	d					12 14		12 25		12 30													13 14		13 25	
Emsworth	d					12 17		12 28		12 33													13 17		13 28	
Warblington	d					12 20																	13 20			
Havant	d					12 23		12 33		12 37					12 46			13 04					13 23		13 33	
Bedhampton	a					*12 29*		12 35															*13 29*		13 35	
Hilsea	a					*12 35*		12 41															*13 35*		13 42	
Fratton	a					*12 39*		12 45							12 54			13 12					*13 39*		13 46	
Portsmouth & Southsea	a					*12 43*		12 49							12 58			13 16					*13 43*		13 49	
Portsmouth Harbour	a														13 02			13 20								
Cosham	a					12 29				12 44													13 29			
Portchester	a					12 33																	13 33			
Fareham	a					12 38				12 52													13 38			
Swanwick	a					12 45				12 59													13 45			
Southampton Central	a					13 02				13 18													14 02			

For general notes see front of timetable
For details of catering facilities see Directory of Train Operators

A ⌶ to Haywards Heath
B ⌶ to Horsham

For complete service between Three Bridges and Horsham see Table 186

London, Gatwick Airport & Brighton → Sussex Coast, Portsmouth and Southampton

Network Diagram - see first page of Table 186

Station		SN 1	SN 1	SN 1	SN 1	SN 1	SN 1 A ✠		SN 1	SN 1	SN 1 B ✠	SN 1	SN 1	SN 1			SN 1	SN 1	SN 1	SN 1	SN 1	SN 1	SN 1	SN 1 A ✠		SN 1
London Victoria 15	⊖ d	11 36			11 47		12 02		12 06		12 17			12 32					12 36			12 47		13 02		13 06
Clapham Junction 10	d	11 42			11 53		12 08		12 12		12 23			12 38					12 42			12 53		13 08		13 12
London Bridge 4	⊖ d	11 26			11 41	11 41	11 56		11 56		12 11	12 11		12 26					12 26			12 41	12 41	12 56		12 56
East Croydon	d	11 52			12 03	11 54	12 18		12 22		12 33	12 24		12 48					12 52			13 03	12 54	13 18		13 22
Gatwick Airport 10	✈ d	11 56			12 19	12 11	12 40		12 26	12 28	12 49	12 41		13 09					12 56			13 19	13 11	13 40		13 26
Three Bridges 4	a						12 44							13 14										13 44		
	d				12 15	12 15	12 45			12 33	12 45	12 45		13 14								13 15	13 15	13 45		
Crawley	d						12 48							13 18										13 48		
Horsham 4	a						12 56							13 26										13 56		
	d						13 00	13 05						13 30	13 34 →			← 13 34						14 00	14 05	
Christs Hospital	d																	13 37								
Billingshurst	d							13 13										13 43							14 13	
Pulborough	d							13 19										13 50							14 19	
Amberley	d																	13 56								
Arundel	d							13 28										14 01							14 28	
Haywards Heath 3	d	12 08			12 37	12 27			12 38	12 46	13 04	12 55							13 08			13 37	13 27			13 38
Burgess Hill	d					12 33				12 52	13 09	13 01											13 33			
Brighton 10	d	12 33	12 44			12 53			13 03	13 14		13 23							13 33	13 44			13 53			14 03
Hove 2	d	12 37	12a47		12 52	12 57			13 07	13a17	13 22	13 27							13 37	13a47		13 52	13 57			14 07
Aldrington	d					12 59						13 29											13 59			
Portslade	d	12 40				13 01			13 10		13 25	13 31							13 40				14 01			14 10
Fishersgate	d					13 03						13 33											14 03			
Southwick	d	12 43				13 05			13 13			13 35							13 43				14 05			14 13
Shoreham-by-Sea	d	12 46			12 58	13 09			13 16		13 30	13 39							13 46			13 58	14 09			14 16
Lancing	d	12 50			13 02	13 13			13 20			13 43							13 50			14 02	14 13			14 20
East Worthing	d					13 16						13 46											14 16			
Worthing 4	a	12 54			13 06	13 18			13 24		13 36	13 48							13 54			14 06	14 18			14 24
	d	12 55			13 07	13 19			13 25		13 37	13 49							13 55			14 07	14 19			14 25
West Worthing	d				13 09	13a21			13 27		13 39	13a51										14 09	14a21			14 27
Durrington-on-Sea	d	12 58			13 11						13 41								13 58			14 11				
Goring-by-Sea	d	13 01			13 14						13 44								14 01			14 14				
Angmering 3	d	13 05			13 18				13 33		13 48								14 05			14 18				14 33
Littlehampton 4	a				13 27						13 57											14 27				
	d			13 11													13 58				14 11					
Ford 4	d			13 15				13 33	13 40								14 02	14 06			14 15				14 33	14 40
Bognor Regis 4	d																									
Barnham	a	13 14		13 19			13 26	13 38	13 44					13 56			14 06	14 10	14 14		14 19			14 26	14 38	14 44
	d	13 15		13 22			13 27	13 38	13 45				13 52	13 57			14 07	14 11	14 15		14 22			14 27	14 38	14 45
Bognor Regis 4	a			13 28				13 45					13 58					14 17			14 28				14 45	
Chichester 4	a	13 22					13 34		13 52					14 04			14 14		14 22					14 34		14 52
	d	13 23					13 35		13 53					14 05			14 15		14 23					14 35		14 53
Fishbourne (Sussex)	d																14 18									
Bosham	d													14 09												
Nutbourne	d																14 23									
Southbourne	d	13 30												14 14			14 25		14 30							
Emsworth	d	13 33												14 17			14 28		14 33							
Warblington	d													14 20												
Havant	d	13 37					13 46		14 04					14 23			14 33		14 37					14 46		15 04
Bedhampton	a													14 29			14 35									
Hilsea	a													14 35			14 42									
Fratton	a						13 54		14 12					14 39			14 46							14 54		15 12
Portsmouth & Southsea	a						13 58		14 16					14 43			14 49							14 58		15 16
Portsmouth Harbour	a						14 02		14 20															15 02		15 20
Cosham	a	13 44												14 29					14 44							
Portchester	a													14 33												
Fareham	a	13 52												14 38					14 52							
Swanwick	a	13 59												14 45					14 59							
Southampton Central	a	14 18												15 02					15 18							

For general notes see front of timetable
For details of catering facilities see Directory of Train Operators

A ✠ to Bognor Regis
B ✠ to Haywards Heath

For complete service between Three Bridges and Horsham see Table 186

London, Gatwick Airport & Brighton → Sussex Coast, Portsmouth and Southampton

Network Diagram - see first page of Table 186

Station		SN 1	SN 1	SN 1	SN 1	SN 1	SN 1	SN 1	SN 1	SN 1	SN 1	SN 1		SN 1	SN 1	SN 1	SN 1	SN 1	SN 1	SN 1	SN 1	SN 1	SN 1
				A ⚲		B ⚲		⚲							B ⚲		⚲				A ⚲	B ⚲	
London Victoria 15 ⊖	d			13 17		13 32			13 36			13 47			14 02			14 06			14 17	14 32	
Clapham Junction 10	d			13 23		13 38			13 42			13 53			14 08			14 12			14 23	14 38	
London Bridge 4 ⊖	d			13 11	13 11	13 26			13 26			13 41		13 41	13 56			13 56			14 11	14 26	
East Croydon	d			13 33	13 24	13 48			13 52			14 03		13 54	14 18			14 22			14 33	14 48	
Gatwick Airport 10	d	13 28		13 49	13 41	14 09			13 56			14 19		14 11	14 40			14 26	14 28		14 49	15 09	
Three Bridges 4	a					14 14									14 44							15 14	
	d	13 33		13 45	13 45	14 14						14 15		14 15	14 45				14 33		14 45	15 14	
Crawley	d					14 18									14 48							15 18	
Horsham 4	a					14 26									14 56							15 26	
	d					14 30 / 14 34 →		← 14 34							15 00 / 15 04 →		← 15 04					15 30 / 15 34 →	
Christs Hospital	d							14 37									15 07						
Billingshurst	d							14 43									15 13						
Pulborough	d							14 50									15 20						
Amberley	d							14 56															
Arundel	d							15 01									15 29						
Haywards Heath 3	d	13 46		14 04	13 55				14 08			14 37		14 27				14 38	14 46		15 04		
Burgess Hill	d	13 52		14 09	14 01									14 33					14 52		15 09		
Brighton 10	d	14 14			14 23				14 33	14 44				14 53				15 03	15 14				
Hove 2	d	14a17		14 22	14 27				14 37	14a47		14 52		14 57				15 07	15a17		15 22		
Aldrington	d				14 29									14 59									
Portslade	d			14 25	14 31				14 40					15 01				15 10			15 25		
Fishersgate	d				14 33									15 03									
Southwick	d				14 35				14 43					15 05				15 13					
Shoreham-by-Sea	d			14 30	14 39				14 46			14 58		15 09				15 16			15 30		
Lancing	d				14 43				14 50			15 02		15 13				15 20					
East Worthing	d				14 46									15 16									
Worthing 4	a			14 36	14 48				14 54			15 06		15 18				15 24			15 36		
	d			14 37	14 49				14 55			15 07		15 19				15 25			15 37		
West Worthing	d			14 39	14a51							15 09		15a21				15 27			15 39		
Durrington-on-Sea	d			14 41					14 58			15 11						15 29			15 41		
Goring-by-Sea	d			14 44					15 01			15 14						15 32			15 44		
Angmering 3	d			14 48					15 05			15 18						15 36			15 48		
Littlehampton 4	a			14 57								15 27									15 57		
	d						14 54									15 23							15 54
Ford 4	d						14 58	15 06								15 27	15 34	15 42					15 58
Bognor Regis 4	d																						
Barnham	a					14 56	15 02	15 10	15 14						15 26	15 31	15 38	15 46				15 56	16 02
	d		14 52			14 57	15 03	15 11	15 15		15 22				15 27	15 33	15 39	15 47		15 52		15 57	16 03
Bognor Regis 4	a		14 58					15 17			15 28						15 45			15 58			
Chichester 4	a					15 04	15 10		15 22						15 34	15 40		15 54				16 04	16 10
	d					15 05	15 11		15 23						15 35	15 41		15 55				16 05	16 11
Fishbourne (Sussex)	d						15 14									15 44							16 14
Bosham	d					15 09	15 17									15 47						16 09	16 17
Nutbourne	d						15 20									15 50							16 20
Southbourne	d					15 14	15 23		15 30							15 53						16 14	16 23
Emsworth	d					15 17	15 26		15 33							15 56						16 17	16 26
Warblington	d					15 20	15 29									15 59						16 20	16 29
Havant	d					15 23	15 32		15 37						15 46	16 02		16 06				16 23	16 32
Bedhampton	a					15 29	15 34									16 04						16 29	16 34
Hilsea	a					15 35	15 41															16 35	16 39
Fratton	a					15 39	15 45								15 54	16 12		16 15				16 35	16 43
Portsmouth & Southsea	a					15 43	15 49								15 58	16 15		16 19				16 43	16 49
Portsmouth Harbour	a														16 02	16 20		16 25					
Cosham	a					15 29			15 44													16 29	
Portchester	a					15 33																16 33	
Fareham	a					15 38			15 52													16 38	
Swanwick	a					15 45			15 59													16 45	
Southampton Central	a					16 02			16 18													17 02	

For general notes see front of timetable
For details of catering facilities see Directory of Train Operators

A ⚲ to Haywards Heath
B ⚲ to Horsham

For complete service between Three Bridges and Horsham see Table 186

London, Gatwick Airport & Brighton → Sussex Coast, Portsmouth and Southampton

Network Diagram - see first page of Table 186

		SN 1	SN 1	SN 1	SN 1	SN 1	SN 1	SN 1	SN 1		SN 1		SN 1	SN 1	SN 1	SN 1	SN 1	SN 1	SN 1		SN 1	SN 1	SN 1	SN 1	SN 1	SN 1
			⚲						A ⚲				⚲				B ⚲									
London Victoria 15 ⊖	d			*14 36*			14 47		15 02					*15 06*			15 17		15 32				*15 36*			15 47
Clapham Junction 10	d			*14 42*			14 53		15 08					*15 12*			15 23		15 38				*15 42*			15 53
London Bridge 4 ⊖	d	*14 11*		*14 26*			14 41	*14 41*	*14 56*					*14 56*			*15 11*	*15 11*	*15 26*				*15 26*			*15 41*
East Croydon	d	*14 24*		*14 52*			15 03	*14 54*	15 18					*15 22*			15 33	*15 24*	15 48				*15 52*			16 03
Gatwick Airport 10 ✈	d	*14 41*		*14 56*			15 19	*15 11*	15 40					*15 26*	*15 28*		15 49	*15 41*	16 09				*15 56*			16 19
Three Bridges 4	a								15 44										16 14							
	d	*14 45*					*15 15*	*15 15*	15 45						*15 33*		*15 45*	*15 45*	16 14				*16 00*			*16 15*
Crawley	d								15 48										16 18							
Horsham 4	a		←						15 56				←						16 26			←				
	d		15 34						16 00	16 04			16 04						16 30	16 34		16 34				
Christs Hospital	d		15 37							→			16 07							→		16 37				
Billingshurst	d		15 43										16 13									16 43				
Pulborough	d		15 50										16 20									16 50				
Amberley	d		15 56																			16 56				
Arundel	d		16 01										16 29									17 01				
Haywards Heath 3	d	*14 55*		*15 08*			15 37	*15 27*						*15 38*	*15 46*		16 04	*15 55*					*16 10*			16 37
Burgess Hill	d	*15 01*						*15 33*							*15 52*		16 09	*16 01*								
Brighton 10	d	15 23		15 33	15 44			15 53						16 03	16 14			16 23					16 33	16 44		
Hove 2	d	15 27		15 37	15a47		15 52	15 57						16 07	16a17		16 22	16 27					16 37	16a47		16 52
Aldrington	d	15 29						15 59										16 29								
Portslade	d	15 31		15 40				16 01						16 10			16 25	16 31					16 40			16 55
Fishersgate	d	15 33						16 03										16 33								
Southwick	d	15 35		15 43				16 05						16 13				16 35					16 43			
Shoreham-by-Sea	d	15 39		15 46			15 58	16 09						16 16			16 30	16 39					16 46			17 00
Lancing	d	15 43		15 50			16 02	16 13						16 20				16 43					16 50			17 04
East Worthing	d	15 46						16 16										16 46								
Worthing 4	a	15 48		15 54			16 06	16 18						16 24			16 36	16 48					16 54			17 08
	d	15 49		15 55			16 07	16 19						16 25			16 37	16 49					16 55			17 08
West Worthing	d	15 51					16 09	16a21						16 27			16 39	16a51								17 10
Durrington-on-Sea	d	15 53		15 58			16 11							16 29			16 41						16 58			17 13
Goring-by-Sea	d	15 56		16 01			16 14							16 32			16 44						17 01			17 15
Angmering 3	d	16 00		16 05			16 18							16 36			16 48						17 05			17 19
Littlehampton 4	a	16 10					16 27										16 57									17 28
	d										16 22										16 54				17 11	
Ford 4	d		16 06								16 26		16 34	16 42							16 58	17 06			17 15	
Bognor Regis 4	d																									
Barnham	a		16 10	16 14					16 26		16 30		16 38	16 46					16 56		17 02	17 10	17 14		17 19	
	d		16 11	16 15		16 24			16 27		16 31		16 39	16 47		16 52			16 57		17 03	17 11	17 15		17 22	
Bognor Regis 4	a		16 17			16 30							16 45			16 58						17 18			17 29	
Chichester 4	a			16 22					16 34		16 38			16 54					17 04		17 10		17 22			
	d			16 23					16 35		16 39			16 55					17 05		17 11		17 23			
Fishbourne (Sussex)	d										16 42										17 14					
Bosham	d										16 45										17 17					
Nutbourne	d										16 48										17 20					
Southbourne	d			16 30							16 51								17 12		17 23		17 30			
Emsworth	d			16 33							16 54								17 15		17 26		17 33			
Warblington	d										16 57										17 29					
Havant	d			16 37					16 46		17 00			17 08					17 19		17 32		17 37			
Bedhampton	a										17 02								*17 29*		17 34					
Hilsea	a										17 07								*17 35*		17 41					
Fratton	a								16 54		17 11			17 18					*17 39*		17 45		*17 58*			
Portsmouth & Southsea	a								16 58		17 15			17 22					*17 43*		17 49		*18 02*			
Portsmouth Harbour	a								17 02		17 19															
Cosham	a			16 44															17 25				17 44			
Portchester	a																		17 30							
Fareham	a			16 52															17 35				17 52			
Swanwick	a																		17 42				17 59			
Southampton Central	a			17 28															18 03				18 19			

For general notes see front of timetable
For details of catering facilities see Directory of Train Operators

A ⚲ to Horsham
B ⚲ to Haywards Heath

For complete service between Three Bridges and Horsham see Table 186

London, Gatwick Airport & Brighton → Sussex Coast, Portsmouth and Southampton

Network Diagram - see first page of Table 186

		SN 1	SN 1		GW ◇ A	SN 1	SN 1	SN 1	SN 1		SN 1 B ⚒	SN 1 ⚒		SN 1	SN 1	SN 1	SN 1	SN 1	SN 1 ⚒	SN 1	SN 1	SN 1	SN 1	SN 1 ⚒	SN 1	SN 1
London Victoria 15 ⊖	d		16 02		15b47		15b47	16 06			16 17	16 38					16b17	16 36			16c47	16b38		17 21	17 02	
Clapham Junction 10	d		16 08		15b53		15b53	16 12			16 23	16 45					16b23	16 42			16c53	16b45		17 27	17 08	
London Bridge 4 ⊖	d	15 41	15 56		15 56		15 56				16 11	16 33			16 11		16 26				16 53	16 46		17 17	16b57	
East Croydon	d	15 54	16 18		16 09		16 09	16 22			16 33	16 55			16 24		16 40	16 52			17 07	17 00		17 37	17 18	
Gatwick Airport 10 ✈	d	16 11	16 40		16 26		16 26				16 49	17 11			16 41		16 56				17 20	17 16		17 40	17 34	
Three Bridges 4	a		16 44									17 16									17 28			17 56		
	d	16 15	16 45		16 30		16 30				16 45	17 20	17 23		16 45		17 00		↤ 17 23		17 29	17 20		17 57	17 39	
Crawley	d		16 48									17 23	↦						17 27					18 01		
Horsham 4	a		16 56									17 31							17 39					18 11		
	d		17 00	17 04 ↦		↤ 17 04						17 32							17 40					18 12		
Christs Hospital	d					17 07													17 43					18 15		
Billingshurst	d					17 14													17 50					18 22		
Pulborough	d					17 21													17 56					18 29		
Amberley	d					17 27													18 02							
Arundel	d					17 32													18 07					18 38		
Haywards Heath 3	d	16 27			16 40		16 40	16 46			17 04				16 55		17 10	17 16			17 38	17 32			17 48	
Burgess Hill	d	16 33						16 52			17 09				17 01						17 43	17 39				
Brighton 10	d	16 53			17 00		17 03	17 14							17 23		17 33	17 44				17 58			18 08	18 14
Hove 2	d	16 57			17 04		17 07	17a17			17 21				17 27		17 37	17a47			17 58	18 02			18 12	18a17
Aldrington	d	16 59													17 29							18 04				
Portslade	d	17 01					17 10				17 24				17 31		17 40				18 01	18 06			18 15	
Fishersgate	d	17 03													17 33							18 08				
Southwick	d	17 05					17 13								17 35		17 43					18 10			18 18	
Shoreham-by-Sea	d	17 08			17 13		17 16				17 29				17 39		17 46				18 06	18 14			18 21	
Lancing	d	17 12					17 20				17 33				17 43		17 50				18 10	18 18			18 25	
East Worthing	d	17 15													17 46							18 21				
Worthing 4	a	17 18			17 21		17 24				17 37				17 48		17 54				18 14	18 23			18 29	
	d	17 18			17 22		17 25				17 38				17 49		17 55				18 14	18 24			18 30	
West Worthing	d	17 20					17 27				17 40				17 51		17 57				18 16	18 26			18 32	
Durrington-on-Sea	d						17 29				17 42				17 53		17 59				18 19	18 28			18 34	
Goring-by-Sea	d						17 32				17 45				17 56		18 02				18 21	18 31			18 37	
Angmering 3	d						17 36				17 49				18 00		18 06				18 25	18 35			18 41	
Littlehampton 4	a	17 34							↤		18 01				18 08						18 36	18 43				
	d	17 41							17 41					17 54						18 22						
Ford 4	d	↦				17 37	17 42		17 46					17 58			18 12		18 15	18 26					18 47	
Bognor Regis 4	d																									
Barnham	a		17 26		17 38	17 42	17 46		17 50			17 58		18 02			18 16		18 19	18 30				18 46	18 51	
	d		17 27		17 39	17 42	17 47		17 52			17 59		18 03		18 08	18 17		18 20	18 31			18 32	18 47	18 52	
Bognor Regis 4	a					17 51			17 58							18 14			18 28				18 38	18 55		
Chichester 4	a		17 34		17 46		17 54					18 06		18 10			18 24			18 38					18 59	
	d		17 35		17 47		17 55					18 07		18 11			18 25			18 39					19 00	
Fishbourne (Sussex)	d		17 38											18 14						18 42						
Bosham	d		17 41									18 11		18 17						18 45						
Nutbourne	d													18 20						18 48						
Southbourne	d		17 45				18 04					18 16		18 23						18 51						
Emsworth	d		17 48				18 07					18 19		18 26			18 33			18 54						
Warblington	d						18 10							18 29						18 57						
Havant	d		17 53		17 58		18 13					18 23		18 34			18 37			19 00					19 11	
Bedhampton	a		17 55		18 07							18 32		18 36						19 02						
Hilsea	a		18 00		18 12							18 38		18 41						19 07						
Fratton	a		18 04		18 16		18 22					18 42		18 45			18 59			19 12					19 19	
Portsmouth & Southsea	a		18 08		18 20		18 25					18 46		18 49			19 03			19 16					19 23	
Portsmouth Harbour	a		18 14				18 31													19 21					19 27	
Cosham	a				18 04							18 29					18 44									
Portchester	a											18 34														
Fareham	a				18 12							18 39					18 52									
Swanwick	a											18 46					18 59									
Southampton Central	a				18 38							19 05					19 19									

For general notes see front of timetable
For details of catering facilities see Directory of Train Operators

A To Worcester Shrub Hill (Table 57)
B ⚒ to Haywards Heath
b Change at East Croydon and Brighton
c Change at Three Bridges

For complete service between Three Bridges and Horsham see Table 186

London, Gatwick Airport & Brighton → Sussex Coast, Portsmouth and Southampton

Network Diagram - see first page of Table 186

		SN 1		SN 1	SN 1	SN 1	SN 1		SN 1	SN 1	SN 1	SN 1	SN 1		SN 1	SN 1	SN 1	SN 1		SN 1	SN 1	SN 1	SN 1	SN 1	SN 1	SN 1
																						A				
London Victoria 15 ⊖	d	17 24					17 07		17 37	17 47	17b47		18 21			17c53		18e07				18 32	18 17	18 32	18 47	18f32
Clapham Junction 10	d	17 30					17 13		17 43	17 53	17b53		18 27			17c59		18e13				18 38	18 23	18 38	18 53	18f38
London Bridge 4 ⊖	d				17 32		17 08		17c32	17g46	17 52		18 16			18 03		18 16				18 26	18c12	18 26	18 38	18 34
East Croydon	d	17 40			17 46		17 24		17 54	18 03	18 06		18 37		18h00	18 16		18 30				18 48	18 33	18 48	19 03	18 49
Gatwick Airport 10 ✈	d	17 58					17 40		17h58	18 12			18 42		18 12	18h29		18 46				19 04	18 50	19 04	19 19	19 21
Three Bridges 4	a									18 22	18 25		18 57													19 25
	d	17 53					17 46		17h53	18 23	18 26		18 57		18 18	18 36		18 44				19 02	18 44	19 02		19 26
Crawley	d										18 30		19 01													19 30
Horsham 4	a										18 42		19 12													19 43
	d										18 43		19 16	19 20 →						← 19 20						19 44
Christs Hospital	d										18 46									19 23						19 47
Billingshurst	d										18 53									19 30						19 53
Pulborough	d										19 00									19 37						20 00
Amberley	d										19 06									19 43						
Arundel	d										19 11									19 48						20 09
Haywards Heath 3	d	18 10			18 15		17 58		18 20	18 32					18 30	18 45		18 58				19 19	19 08	19 22	19 36	
Burgess Hill	d				18 20		18 05		18 26	18 41					18 37	18 52		19 04					19 01	19 17		
Brighton 10	d						18 35		18 49						19 03	19 14							19 34	19 44		
Hove 2	d	18 25			18 36		18 39		18a53	18 58					19 07	19a17		19 20				19 35	19 38	19a47	19 52	
Aldrington	d						18 41								19 09								19 40			
Portslade	d	18 28			18 39		18 43			19 01					19 11			19 23					19 42		19 55	
Fishersgate	d						18 45								19 13								19 44			
Southwick	d						18 47								19 15								19 46			
Shoreham-by-Sea	d	18 33			18 44		18 51			19 06					19 19			19 28				19 41	19 50		19 59	
Lancing	d	18 37			18 48		18 55			19 10					19 23			19 32					19 54		20 03	
East Worthing	d						18 58								19 26								19 57			
Worthing 4	a	18 41			18 52		19 00			19 14					19 28			19 36				19 47	19 59		20 07	
	d	18 44	18 47		18 52		19 01			19 14					19 29			19 40	19 42			19 48	20 00		20 08	
West Worthing	d		18 49		18 54					19 16					19 31				19 44			19 50	20 02		20 10	
Durrington-on-Sea	d		18 51		18 57					19 19					19 33				19 46			19 52			20 12	
Goring-by-Sea	d		18 54		18 59					19 21					19 36				19 49			19 55			20 15	
Angmering 3	d		18 58		19 03					19 25					19 40				19 53			19 59	20 07		20 19	
Littlehampton 4	a		19 08		19 14					19 37									20 04			20 11			20 29	20 20
	d			18 56								19 29									20 06					
Ford 4	d			19 00			19 12					19 33			19 46						20 10		20 13			
Bognor Regis 4	d																									
Barnham	a	18 59		19 04			19 16				19 19	19 37	19 42		19 50			19 55		19 58	20 14		20 18			
	d	18 59		19 05		19 07	19 17				19 20	19 38	19 43		19 52		19 52	19 56		19 59	20 22 →		20 18			
Bognor Regis 4	a					19 13					19 28	19 44					19 58			20 07						
Chichester 4	a	19 07		19 12			19 24						19 50		19 59			20 03					20 26			
	d	19 07		19 13			19 25						19 51		20 00			20 04					20 26			
Fishbourne (Sussex)	d			19 16														20 07								
Bosham	d			19 19														20 10								
Nutbourne	d			19 22														20 13								
Southbourne	d	19 14		19 25									19 58					20 16								
Emsworth	d	19 17		19 28			19 33						20 01					20 19								
Warblington	d			19 31														20 22								
Havant	d	19 22		19 35			19 38						20 05		20 11			20 25					20 37			
Bedhampton	a			19 37			19 44											20 31								
Hilsea	a			19 43			19 50											20 37								
Fratton	a			19 48			19 56						20 15		20 19			20 41					20 58			
Portsmouth & Southsea	a			19 53			20 03						20 20		20 23			20 44					21 02			
Portsmouth Harbour	a														20 27											
Cosham	a	19 30					19 44											20 33					20 44			
Portchester	a	19 34																					20 48			
Fareham	a	19 39					19 52											20 41					20 53			
Swanwick	a	19 46					19 59											20 48					21 00			
Southampton Central	a	20 05					20 18											21 07					21 18			

For general notes see front of timetable
For details of catering facilities see Directory of Train Operators

A ✠ to Haywards Heath
b Change at Three Bridges
c Change at East Croydon and Brighton
e Change at East Croydon
f Change at Gatwick Airport
g Change at Haywards Heath
h Change at Haywards Heath and Brighton

For complete service between Three Bridges and Horsham see Table 186

London, Gatwick Airport & Brighton → Sussex Coast, Portsmouth and Southampton

Network Diagram - see first page of Table 186

		SN 1	SN 1 A ⌶		SN 1		SN 1	SN 1	SN 1 B ⌶	SN 1	SN 1 A ⌶		SN 1	SN 1	SN 1	SN 1 C ⌶	SN 1	SN 1 A ⌶		SN 1	SN 1	SN 1	SN 1	SN 1		SN 1
London Victoria 15 ⊖	d		19 02					19 06	19 17		19 32				19 36	19 47		20 02		19b53	20 06	20 17		20 32		
Clapham Junction 10	d		19 08					19 12	19 23		19 38				19 42	19 53		20 08		19b59	20 12	20 23		20 38		
London Bridge 4 ⊖	d		18 56				18 38	18 56	19 12		19 27			19 12	19 27	19 41		20 01		20 01		20 11		20 28		
East Croydon	d		19 18				18 52	19 22	19 33		19 48			19 24	19 52	20 03		20 19		20 14	20 22	20 33		20 48		
Gatwick Airport 10 ✈	d		19 39				19 10	19 26	19 49		20 09			19 41	19 55	20 19		20 39		20 31		20 49		21 09		
Three Bridges 4	a		19 44								20 14							20 44						21 14		
	d		19 44					19 32	19 45		20 14			19 45	20 01	20 15		20 44		20 15		20 43		21 14		
Crawley	d		19 48								20 18							20 48						21 18		
Horsham 4	a		19 56								20 26							20 56						21 26		
	d		20 00	20 04							20 30	20 34						21 00	21 04					21 30	21 34	
Christs Hospital	d			20 07								20 37							21 07						21 37	
Billingshurst	d			20 13								20 43							21 13						21 43	
Pulborough	d			20 20								20 50							21 20						21 50	
Amberley	d			20 26								20 56							21 26						21 56	
Arundel	d			20 31								21 01							21 31						22 01	
Haywards Heath 3	d						19 24	19 45	20 04					19 58	20 17	20 34				20 42	20 47	21 05				
Burgess Hill	d						19 32	19 46	20 09					20 04	20 15	20 39				20 32		21 10				
Brighton 10	d						20 03	20 14						20 30	20 44					21 03	21 14					
Hove 2	d						20 07	20a17	20 22					20 34	20a47	20 54				21 07	21a17	21 22				
Aldrington	d						20 09							20 36						21 09						
Portslade	d						20 11		20 25					20 38		20 57				21 11		21 25				
Fishersgate	d						20 13							20 40						21 13						
Southwick	d						20 15							20 42						21 15						
Shoreham-by-Sea	d						20 19		20 30					20 46		21 01				21 19		21 30				
Lancing	d						20 23		20 34					20 50		21 05				21 23		21 34				
East Worthing	d						20 26							20 53						21 26						
Worthing 4	a						20 28		20 38					20 55		21 09				21 28		21 38				
	d						20 29		20 38					20 56		21 10				21 29		21 38				
West Worthing	d						20 31		20 40					20 58		21 12				21 31		21 40				
Durrington-on-Sea	d						20 33		20 43					21 00		21 14				21 33		21 43				
Goring-by-Sea	d						20 36		20 45					21 03		21 17				21 36		21 45				
Angmering 3	d						20 40		20 49					21 07		21 21				21 40		21 49				
Littlehampton 4	a								20 58							21 29						21 58				
	d				20 36								21 06													22 08
Ford 4	d			20 36	20 40		20 46					21 06	21 10	21 13					21 36	21 46					22 06	22 12
Bognor Regis 4	d																									
Barnham	a	⟵	20 26	20 40	20 44		20 50			⟵	20 56	21 10	21 14	21 17			⟵	21 26	21 40	21 50				21 56	22 10	22 16
	d	20 22	20 27	20 41	20 52		20 51			20 52	20 57	21 11	21 22	21 18			21 22	21 27	21 41	21 51			21 52	21 57	22 11	22 22
Bognor Regis 4	a	20 28		20 47	⟶					20 58		21 17	⟶				21 28		21 47				21 58		22 17	⟶
Chichester 4	a		20 34				20 58				21 04			21 25				21 34		21 58				22 04		
	d		20 35				20 59				21 05			21 26				21 35		21 59				22 05		
Fishbourne (Sussex)	d										21 08													22 08		
Bosham	d										21 11													22 11		
Nutbourne	d										21 14													22 14		
Southbourne	d		20 42								21 17							21 42						22 17		
Emsworth	d		20 45								21 20							21 45						22 20		
Warblington	d										21 23													22 23		
Havant	d		20 52				21 10				21 26			21 37				21 49		22 10				22 26		
Bedhampton	a										21 34							22 07						22 34		
Hilsea	a										21 40													22 39		
Fratton	a		21 01				21 18				21 44			21 55				21 58		22 18				22 43		
Portsmouth & Southsea	a		21 06				21 23				21 47			21 58				22 02		22 22				22 47		
Portsmouth Harbour	a						21 27											22 06		22 26						
Cosham	a										21 33			21 43										22 33		
Portchester	a										21 37															
Fareham	a										21 42			21 52										22 42		
Swanwick	a										21 49			21 59										22 49		
Southampton Central	a										22 07			22 17										23 06		

For general notes see front of timetable
For details of catering facilities see Directory of Train Operators

A ⌶ to Bognor Regis
B ⌶ to Haywards Heath
C ⌶ from Haywards Heath

b Change at East Croydon and Brighton

For complete service between Three Bridges and Horsham see Table 186

London, Gatwick Airport & Brighton → Sussex Coast, Portsmouth and Southampton

Network Diagram - see first page of Table 186

		SN 1	SN 1		SN 1	SN 1	SN 1	SN 1	SN 1	SN 1	SN 1	SN 1	SN 1	SN 1	SN 1	SN 1	SN 1	SN 1	SN 1	SN 1	SN 1	SN 1	SN 1	SN 1		
London Victoria 15 ⊖	d	20b17	20 36		20 47			20b47	21 06		21 17	21 32		21 36		21 47	22 06		22 17	22 36	22 32		22 47	23 17		
Clapham Junction 10	d	20b23	20 42		20 53			20b53	21 12		21 23	21 38		21 42		21 53	22 12		22 23	22 42	22 38		22 53	23 23		
London Bridge 4 ⊖	d	20 28			20 41			20 58			21 11	21 15		21b28		21 41	21b45		22 11	22b28	22 15		22 41	23 11		
East Croydon	d	20 41	20 52		21 03			21 11	21 22		21 33	21 48		21 52		22 03	22 22		22 33	22 52	22 48		23 03	23 33		
Gatwick Airport 10 ✈	d	20 56			21 19			21 27			21 49	22 09		21c49		22 19	22c19		22 49	22c49	23 09		23 19	23 51		
Three Bridges 4	a										21 53	22 14							22 54		23 14			23 55		
	d	21 01			21 15			21 32			21 53	22 14		21c53		22 15	22 15		22 54	22c54	23 15		23 15	23 56		
Crawley	d											22 18									23 18					
Horsham 4	a											22 26									23 26					
	d											22 27									23 27					
Christs Hospital	d											22 30									23 30					
Billingshurst	d											22 36									23 36					
Pulborough	d											22 43									23 43					
Amberley	d											22 49									23 49					
Arundel	d											22 54									23 54					
Haywards Heath 3	d	21 11	21 15		21 34			21 41	21 45		22 06			22 15		22 37	22 47		23 03	23 15			23 37	00 05		
Burgess Hill	d	21 04			21 39			21 32			22 11			22 04			22 32		23 08	23 04				00 10		
Brighton 10	d	21 33	21 44					22 03	22 14					22 34	22 44		23 14			23 44						
Hove 2	d	21 37	21a47		21 54			22 07	22a17		22 23			22 38	22a47	22 52	23a17		23 21	23a47			23 52	00 22		
Aldrington	d	21 39						22 09						22 40												
Portslade	d	21 41			21 57			22 11			22 26			22 42		22 55			23 24				23 55	00s25		
Fishersgate	d	21 43						22 13						22 44												
Southwick	d	21 45						22 15						22 46					23 27				23 58	00s28		
Shoreham-by-Sea	d	21 49			22 01			22 19			22 31			22 50		23 00			23 30				00 01	00s31		
Lancing	d	21 53			22 05			22 23			22 35			22 54		23 04			23 34				00 05	00s35		
East Worthing	d	21 56						22 26						22 57												
Worthing 4	a	21 58			22 09			22 28			22 39			22 59		23 08			23 38				00 09	00 39		
	d	21 59			22 10			22 29			22 39			23 00		23 08			23 39							
West Worthing	d	22 01			22 12			22 31			22 41			23 02		23 10			23 41							
Durrington-on-Sea	d	22 03			22 14			22 33			22 44			23 04		23 13			23 43							
Goring-by-Sea	d	22 06			22 17			22 36			22 46			23 07		23 15			23 46							
Angmering 3	d	22 10			22 21			22 40			22 50			23 11		23 19			23 50							
Littlehampton 4	a				22 31									23 19		23 28										
	d						22 38							23 24												
Ford 4	d	22 16					22 42	22 46			22 56	23 00		23 28					23 56		23 59					
Bognor Regis 4	d																									
Barnham	a	22 20				⟵	22 46	22 50		⟵	23 01	23 04	⟵	23 32					00 01		00 04	⟵				
	d	22 21				22 22	22 52	22 51		22 52	23 06	23 05	23 06	23 33				23 36	00 09		00 05	00 09				
Bognor Regis 4	a					22 28	⟶			22 58	⟶		23 12					23 42	⟶			00 15				
Chichester 4	a	22 28						22 58				23 12		23 40							00 12					
	d	22 29						22 59				23 13														
Fishbourne (Sussex)	d											23 16														
Bosham	d											23 19														
Nutbourne	d											23 22														
Southbourne	d	22 36										23 25														
Emsworth	d	22 39										23 28														
Warblington	d											23 31														
Havant	d	22 43						23 11				23 36														
Bedhampton	a	23 01						23 33				00 24														
Hilsea	a							23 39				00 30														
Fratton	a	22 53						23 20				23 49														
Portsmouth & Southsea	a	22 56						23 23				23 53														
Portsmouth Harbour	a	23 00						23 27																		
Cosham	a																									
Portchester	a																									
Fareham	a																									
Swanwick	a																									
Southampton Central	a																									

For general notes see front of timetable
For details of catering facilities see Directory of Train Operators

b Change at East Croydon and Brighton
c Change at Haywards Heath and Brighton

For complete service between Three Bridges and Horsham see Table 186

Table 188

Saturdays

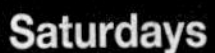

London, Gatwick Airport & Brighton → Sussex Coast, Portsmouth and Southampton

Network Diagram - see first page of Table 186

Station		SN 1	SN 1	SN 1	SN 1	SN 1	SN 1	SN 1 ◇	SN 1	SN 1	SN 1	SN 1		SN 1	SN 1	SN 1	SN 1	SN 1	SN 1	SN 1	SN 1	SN 1	SN 1	SN 1		SN 1
London Victoria 15 ⊖	d	22p17	22p32		22p47	23 06	23p17	00 05									04 00									
Clapham Junction 10	d	22p23	22p38		22p53	23 12	23p23	00 11									04 08									
London Bridge 4 ⊖	d					23b00	23 11	23 53																		
East Croydon	d	22p33	22p48		23p03	23 22	23p33	00 25									04 22						05 02			
Gatwick Airport 10 ✈	d	22p49	23p09		23p19	23c19	23p51	00 43									04 47						05 22			
Three Bridges 4	a	22p54	23p14				23p55	00 48																		
	d	22p54	23p15			23 15	23p56	00 48									04 52						05 28			
Crawley	d		23p18																							
Horsham 4	a		23p26																							
	d		23p27																							
Christs Hospital	d		23p30																							
Billingshurst	d		23p36																							
Pulborough	d		23p43																							
Amberley	d		23p49																							
Arundel	d		23p54																							
Haywards Heath 3	d	23p03			23p37	23 45	00 05	01 03									05 01						05 42			
Burgess Hill	d	23p08				23 32	00 10																05 48			
Brighton 10	d					00 10									05 15		05 27	05 44	05 53			06 01	06 14	06 23		
Hove 2	d	23p21			23p52	00a13	00 22	01s25							05 19		05 31	05a47	05 57			06 05	06a17	06 27		
Aldrington	d																05 33		05 59					06 29		
Portslade	d	23p24			23p55		00s25	01s28							05 22		05 35		06 01			06 08		06 31		
Fishersgate	d																05 37		06 03					06 33		
Southwick	d	23p27			23p58		00s28	01s31									05 39		06 05			06 11		06 35		
Shoreham-by-Sea	d	23p30			00 01		00s31	01s34							05 26		05 43		06 09			06 14		06 39		
Lancing	d	23p34			00 05		00s35	01s38							05 30		05 47		06 13			06 18		06 43		
East Worthing	d																05 50		06 16					06 46		
Worthing 4	a	23p38			00 09		00 39	01 42							05 34		05 52		06 18			06 22		06 48		
	d	23p39													05 35		05 53		06 19			06 23		06 49		
West Worthing	d	23p41													05 37		05 55		06a21			06 25		06a51		
Durrington-on-Sea	d	23p43													05 39		05 57					06 27				
Goring-by-Sea	d	23p46													05 42		06 00					06 30				
Angmering 3	d	23p50													05 46		06 04					06 34				
Littlehampton 4	a																									
	d															05 58					06 19					
Ford 4	d	23p56	23p59												05 52	06 02	06 10					06 40				
Bognor Regis 4	d																									
Barnham	a	00 01	00 04	⟵											05 57	06 06	06 14				06 26	06 44				
	d	00 09	00 05	00 09					04 55	05 15	05 20	05 30		05 38	05 57	06 07	06 15			06 22	06 27	06 45				06 52
Bognor Regis 4	a	⟶		00 15																06 28						06 58
Chichester 4	a		00 12						05 02	05 22	05 27	05 37		05 45	06 05	06 14	06 22				06 34	06 52				
	d								05 03	05 23	05 28	05 38		05 46	06 05	06 15	06 23				06 35	06 53				
Fishbourne (Sussex)	d															06 18										
Bosham	d														06 10											
Nutbourne	d															06 23										
Southbourne	d														06 14	06 25	06 30									
Emsworth	d														06 17	06 28	06 33									
Warblington	d														06 20											
Havant	d								05 14	05 34	05 39	05 49		05 57	06 23	06 33	06 37				06 46	07 04				
Bedhampton	a													06 03		06 35						07 21				
Hilsea	a													06 09		06 41						07 27				
Fratton	a									05 42		05 57		06 05		06 45					06 54	07 12				
Portsmouth & Southsea	a									05 46		06 01		06 09		06 49					06 58	07 17				
Portsmouth Harbour	a											06 05		06 16							07 02	07 21				
Cosham	a								05 22		05 49				06 30		06 44									
Portchester	a								05 27						06 34											
Fareham	a								05 32		05 57				06 39		06 52									
Swanwick	a								05 39		06 04				06 46		06 59									
Southampton Central	a								05 58		06 21				07 05		07 18									

For general notes see front of timetable
For details of catering facilities see Directory of Train Operators

b Change at East Croydon and Brighton
c Change at Haywards Heath and Brighton

For complete service between Three Bridges and Horsham see Table 186

Table 188

Saturdays

London, Gatwick Airport & Brighton → Sussex Coast, Portsmouth and Southampton

Network Diagram - see first page of Table 186

Station		SN 1	SN 1	SN 1	SN 1	SN 1	SN 1	SN 1	SN 1	SN 1	SN 1		SN 1	SN 1	SN 1	SN 1	SN 1	SN 1	SN 1	SN 1	SN 1	SN 1	SN 1		SN 1
London Victoria 15 ⊖	d	05 02			05 02					05 32	05b32					06 10		06b10			06c23	06b23	06 40		07 06
Clapham Junction 10	d	05 08			05 08					05 38	05b38					06 16		06b16			06c29	06b29	06 46		07 12
London Bridge 4 ⊖	d									05e50	05 50					06e26		06 26			06 41	06 41	06f41		06 56
East Croydon	d	05 22			05 22	05 32				05 48	06 05					06 28		06 39			06 54	06 54	06 58		07 22
Gatwick Airport 10 ✈	d	05 58			05 50	05 54				06 21	06 20		06 21			06 59		06 56			07 11	07 11	07 29		07 26
Three Bridges 4	a	06 02								06 25						07 03							07 33		
	d	06 03			05 54	06 00				06 34	06 26		06 30			07 04		07 00			07 15	07 15	07 34		
Crawley	d	06 06								06 37						07 07							07 37		
Horsham 4	a	06 18								06 49						07 19							07 49		
	d	06 19								06 50						07 20							07 50		
Christs Hospital	d	06 22								06 53						07 23							07 53		
Billingshurst	d	06 28								06 59						07 29							07 59		
Pulborough	d	06 35								07 06						07 36							08 06		
Amberley	d	06 41								07 12						07 42							08 12		
Arundel	d	06 46								07 17						07 47							08 17		
Haywards Heath 3	d				06 03	06 12					06 38		06 41					07 08			07 37	07 27			07 38
Burgess Hill	d				06 09	06 18							06 47									07 33			
Brighton 10	d				06 31	06 44		06 48	06 53		07 03		07 14	07 23				07 33	07 44			07 53			08 03
Hove 2	d				06 35	06a47		06 52	06 57		07 07		07a17	07 27				07 37	07a47		07 52	07 57			08 07
Aldrington	d								06 59					07 29								07 59			
Portslade	d				06 38			06 55	07 01		07 10			07 31				07 40				08 01			08 10
Fishersgate	d								07 03					07 33								08 03			
Southwick	d				06 41				07 05		07 13			07 35				07 43				08 05			08 13
Shoreham-by-Sea	d				06 44			06 59	07 09		07 16			07 39				07 46			07 58	08 09			08 16
Lancing	d				06 48			07 03	07 13		07 20			07 43				07 50			08 02	08 13			08 20
East Worthing	d								07 16					07 46								08 16			
Worthing 4	a				06 52			07 07	07 18		07 24			07 48				07 54			08 06	08 18			08 24
	d				06 53			07 08	07 19		07 25			07 49				07 55			08 07	08 19			08 25
West Worthing	d				06 55			07 10	07a21		07 27			07a51							08 09	08a21			08 27
Durrington-on-Sea	d				06 57			07 12										07 58			08 11				
Goring-by-Sea	d				07 00			07 15										08 01			08 14				
Angmering 3	d				07 04			07 19			07 33							08 05			08 18				08 33
Littlehampton 4	a							07 27													08 27				
	d		06 54				07 11										07 58			08 11					
Ford 4	d	06 51	06 58		07 10		07 15			07 22	07 40					07 52	08 02			08 15			08 22		08 40
Bognor Regis 4	d																								
Barnham	a	06 55	07 02		07 14		07 19			07 27	07 44					07 57	08 06	08 14		08 19			08 27		08 44
	d	07 05 → / 06 59	07 03	← 07 05	07 15		07 22			07 27	07 45				07 52	07 57	08 07	08 15		08 22			08 27		08 45
Bognor Regis 4	a			07 11			07 28								07 58					08 28					
Chichester 4	a	07 06	07 10		07 22					07 35	07 52					08 05	08 14	08 22					08 35		08 52
	d	07 07	07 11		07 23					07 35	07 53					08 05	08 15	08 23					08 35		08 53
Fishbourne (Sussex)	d		07 14														08 18								
Bosham	d		07 17													08 10									
Nutbourne	d		07 20														08 23								
Southbourne	d	07 14	07 23		07 30											08 14	08 25	08 30							
Emsworth	d	07 17	07 26		07 33											08 17	08 28	08 33							
Warblington	d		07 29													08 20									
Havant	d	07 23	07 33		07 37					07 46	08 04					08 23	08 33	08 37					08 46		09 04
Bedhampton	a		07 35								08 19						08 35								
Hilsea	a		07 41								08 25						08 41								
Fratton	a		07 45							07 55	08 13						08 45						08 55		09 12
Portsmouth & Southsea	a		07 49							07 58	08 18						08 49						08 58		09 16
Portsmouth Harbour	a									08 02	08 22												09 02		09 20
Cosham	a	07 29			07 44											08 29		08 44							
Portchester	a	07 33														08 34									
Fareham	a	07 38			07 52											08 39		08 52							
Swanwick	a	07 45			07 59											08 46		08 59							
Southampton Central	a	08 02			08 18											09 03		09 18							

For general notes see front of timetable
For details of catering facilities see
Directory of Train Operators

b Change at East Croydon and Brighton
c Change at East Croydon and Haywards Heath
e Change at Three Bridges
f Change at Gatwick Airport

For complete service between Three Bridges and Horsham see Table 186

Table 188

Saturdays

London, Gatwick Airport & Brighton → Sussex Coast, Portsmouth and Southampton

Network Diagram - see first page of Table 186

Station		SN	SN	SN	SN		SN	SN	SN	SN	SN	SN		SN	SN		GW	SN	SN	SN	SN	SN	SN			SN
		1	1	1	1		1	1	1	1	1	1		1	1		◇ A	1	1	1	1	1	1			1
London Victoria 15 ⊖	d				07 32				07 36			07 47			08 02		07b47	08 06		08 17			08 32			
Clapham Junction 10	d				07 38				07 42			07 53			08 08		07b53	08 12		08 23			08 38			
London Bridge 4 ⊖	d		07 11		07 26				07 26			07 41		07 41	07 56		07 56	07 56		08 11	08 11		08 26			
East Croydon	d		07 24		07 48				07 52			08 03		07 54	08 18		08 09	08 22		08 33	08 24		08 48			
Gatwick Airport 10 ✈	d	07 28	07 41		08 09				07 56			08 19		08 11	08 40		08 26	08 26	08 28	08 49	08 41		09 09			
Three Bridges 4	a				08 14										08 44								09 14			
	d	07 33	07 45		08 14							08 15		08 15	08 45				08 33	08 45	08 45		09 14			
Crawley	d				08 18										08 48								09 18			
Horsham 4	a				08 26										08 56								09 26			
	d				08 30	08 34 →		← 08 34							09 00	09 05							09 30	09 34 →		
Christs Hospital	d							08 37																		
Billingshurst	d							08 43								09 13										
Pulborough	d							08 50								09 19										
Amberley	d							08 56																		
Arundel	d							09 01								09 28										
Haywards Heath 3	d	07 46	07 55						08 08			08 37		08 27			08 38	08 38	08 46	09 04	08 55					
Burgess Hill	d	07 52	08 01											08 33					08 54	09 09	09 01					
Brighton 10	d	08 14	08 23						08 33	08 44				08 53			09 00	09 03	09 14		09 23					
Hove 2	d	08a17	08 27						08 37	08a47		08 52		08 57			09 04	09 07	09a17	09 22	09 27					
Aldrington	d		08 29											08 59							09 29					
Portslade	d		08 31						08 40					09 01				09 10		09 25	09 31					
Fishersgate	d		08 33											09 03							09 33					
Southwick	d		08 35						08 43					09 05				09 13			09 35					
Shoreham-by-Sea	d		08 39						08 46			08 58		09 09			09 13	09 17		09 30	09 39					
Lancing	d		08 43						08 50			09 02		09 13				09 21			09 43					
East Worthing	d		08 46											09 16							09 46					
Worthing 4	a		08 48						08 54			09 06		09 18			09 22	09 25		09 36	09 48					
	d		08 49						08 55			09 07		09 19			09 22	09 25		09 37	09 49					
West Worthing	d		08a51									09 09		09a21				09 28		09 39	09a51					
Durrington-on-Sea	d								08 58			09 11								09 41						
Goring-by-Sea	d								09 01			09 14								09 44						
Angmering 3	d								09 05			09 18						09 34		09 48						
Littlehampton 4	a											09 27								09 57						
	d						08 58				09 11															09 58
Ford 4	d						09 02	09 06			09 15					09 33		09 40								10 02
Bognor Regis 4	d																									
Barnham	a				08 56		09 06	09 10	09 14		09 19				09 26	09 38	09 40	09 44					09 56			10 06
	d			08 52	08 57		09 07	09 11	09 15		09 22				09 27	09 38	09 41	09 45				09 52	09 57			10 07
Bognor Regis 4	a			08 58				09 17			09 28					09 45						09 58				
Chichester 4	a				09 04		09 14		09 22						09 34		09 48	09 52					10 04			10 14
	d				09 05		09 15		09 23						09 35		09 49	09 53					10 05			10 15
Fishbourne (Sussex)	d						09 18																			10 18
Bosham	d				09 09																		10 09			
Nutbourne	d						09 23																			10 23
Southbourne	d				09 14		09 25		09 30														10 14			10 25
Emsworth	d				09 17		09 28		09 33														10 17			10 28
Warblington	d				09 20																		10 20			
Havant	d				09 23		09 33		09 37						09 46		10 00	10 04					10 23			10 33
Bedhampton	a				09 29		09 35																10 29			10 35
Hilsea	a				09 35		09 41																10 35			10 41
Fratton	a				09 39		09 45								09 54			10 12					10 39			10 45
Portsmouth & Southsea	a				09 43		09 49								09 58			10 16					10 43			10 49
Portsmouth Harbour	a														10 02			10 20								
Cosham	a				09 29				09 44								10 06						10 29			
Portchester	a				09 33																		10 33			
Fareham	a				09 38				09 52								10 14						10 38			
Swanwick	a				09 45				09 59														10 45			
Southampton Central	a				10 02				10 18								10 38						11 02			

For general notes see front of timetable
For details of catering facilities see Directory of Train Operators

A To Worcester Foregate Street (Table 71)
b Change at East Croydon and Brighton

For complete service between Three Bridges and Horsham see Table 186

Table 188

Saturdays

London, Gatwick Airport & Brighton → Sussex Coast, Portsmouth and Southampton

Network Diagram - see first page of Table 186

		SN 1	SN 1	SN 1	SN 1	SN 1	SN 1	SN 1		SN 1	SN 1	SN 1		SN 1	SN 1	SN 1		SN 1	SN 1	SN 1	SN 1	SN 1	SN 1	SN 1		
												A														
London Victoria 15 ⊖	d		08 36			08 47		09 02		09 06		09 17				09 32				09 36			09 47			
Clapham Junction 10	d		08 42			08 53		09 08		09 12		09 23				09 38				09 42			09 53			
London Bridge 4 ⊖	d		08 26			08 41	08 41	08 56		08 56		09 11		09 11		09 26				09 26			09 41	09 41		
East Croydon	d		08 52			09 03	08 54	09 18		09 22		09 33		09 24		09 48				09 52			10 03	09 54		
Gatwick Airport 10 ✈	d		08 56			09 19	09 11	09 40		09 26	09 28	09 49		09 41		10 09				09 56			10 19	10 11		
Three Bridges 4	a							09 44								10 14										
	d					09 15	09 15	09 45			09 33	09 45		09 45		10 14							10 15	10 15		
Crawley	d							09 48								10 18										
Horsham 4	a							09 56								10 26										
	d	← 09 34						10 00	10 05							10 30	10 34 →		← 10 34							
Christs Hospital	d	09 37																	10 37							
Billingshurst	d	09 43							10 13										10 43							
Pulborough	d	09 50							10 19										10 50							
Amberley	d	09 56																	10 56							
Arundel	d	10 01							10 28										11 01							
Haywards Heath 3	d		09 08			09 37	09 27			09 38	09 46	10 04		09 55						10 08			10 37	10 27		
Burgess Hill	d						09 33				09 52	10 09		10 01										10 33		
Brighton 10	d		09 33	09 44			09 53			10 03	10 14			10 23						10 33	10 44			10 53		
Hove 2	d		09 37	09a47		09 52	09 57			10 07	10a17	10 22		10 27						10 37	10a47		10 52	10 57		
Aldrington	d						09 59							10 29										10 59		
Portslade	d		09 40				10 01			10 10		10 25		10 31						10 40				11 01		
Fishersgate	d						10 03							10 33										11 03		
Southwick	d		09 43				10 05			10 13				10 35						10 43				11 05		
Shoreham-by-Sea	d		09 46			09 58	10 09			10 16		10 30		10 39						10 46			10 58	11 09		
Lancing	d		09 50			10 02	10 13			10 20				10 43						10 50			11 02	11 13		
East Worthing	d						10 16							10 46										11 16		
Worthing 4	a		09 54			10 06	10 18			10 24		10 36		10 48						10 54			11 06	11 18		
	d		09 55			10 07	10 19			10 25		10 37		10 49						10 55			11 07	11 19		
West Worthing	d					10 09	10a21			10 27		10 39		10a51									11 09	11a21		
Durrington-on-Sea	d		09 58			10 11						10 41								10 58			11 11			
Goring-by-Sea	d		10 01			10 14						10 44								11 01			11 14			
Angmering 3	d		10 05			10 18				10 33		10 48								11 05			11 18			
Littlehampton 4	a					10 27						10 57											11 27			
	d				10 11													10 58				11 11				
Ford 4	d	10 06			10 15				10 33	10 40								11 02	11 06			11 15				
Bognor Regis 4	d																									
Barnham	a	10 10	10 14		10 19			10 26	10 38	10 44						10 56		11 06	11 10	11 14		11 19				
	d	10 11	10 15		10 22			10 27	10 38	10 45					10 52	10 57		11 07	11 11	11 15		11 22				
Bognor Regis 4	a	10 17			10 28				10 45						10 58				11 17			11 28				
Chichester 4	a		10 22					10 34		10 52						11 04		11 14		11 22						
	d		10 23					10 35		10 53						11 05		11 15		11 23						
Fishbourne (Sussex)	d																	11 18								
Bosham	d															11 09										
Nutbourne	d																	11 23								
Southbourne	d		10 30													11 14		11 25		11 30						
Emsworth	d		10 33													11 17		11 28		11 33						
Warblington	d															11 20										
Havant	d		10 37					10 46		11 04						11 23		11 33		11 37						
Bedhampton	a															11 29		11 35								
Hilsea	a															11 35		11 41								
Fratton	a							10 54		11 12						11 39		11 45								
Portsmouth & Southsea	a							10 58		11 16						11 43		11 49								
Portsmouth Harbour	a							11 02		11 20																
Cosham	a		10 44													11 29				11 44						
Portchester	a															11 33										
Fareham	a		10 52													11 38				11 52						
Swanwick	a		10 59													11 45				11 59						
Southampton Central	a		11 18													12 02				12 18						

For general notes see front of timetable
For details of catering facilities see
Directory of Train Operators

A to Haywards Heath

For complete service between Three Bridges and Horsham see Table 186

Table 188

Saturdays

London, Gatwick Airport & Brighton → Sussex Coast, Portsmouth and Southampton

Network Diagram - see first page of Table 186

		SN		SN	SN	SN	SN	SN	SN		SN	SN		SN	SN	SN	SN	SN	SN		SN	SN	SN	SN		SN
		1		1	1	1	1	1	1		1	1		1	1	1	1	1	1		1	1	1	1		1
		A				B													A				B			
		⌶				⌶													⌶				⌶			
London Victoria 15 ⊖	d	10 02		10 06		10 17			10 32					10 36			10 47		11 02		11 06		11 17			
Clapham Junction 10	d	10 08		10 12		10 23			10 38					10 42			10 53		11 08		11 12		11 23			
London Bridge 4 ⊖	d	09 56		09 56		10 11	10 11		10 26					10 26			10 41	10 41	10 56		10 56		11 11	11 11		
East Croydon	d	10 18		10 22		10 33	10 24		10 48					10 52			11 03	10 54	11 18		11 22		11 33	11 24		
Gatwick Airport 10 ✈	d	10 40		10 26	10 28	10 49	10 41		11 09					10 56			11 19	11 11	11 40		11 26	11 28	11 49	11 41		
Three Bridges 4	a	10 44							11 14										11 44							
	d	10 45			10 33	10 45	10 45		11 14								11 15	11 15	11 45			11 33	11 45	11 45		
Crawley	d	10 48							11 18										11 48							
Horsham 4	a	10 56							11 26										11 56							
	d	11 00	11 05						11 30	11 34 →		← 11 34							12 00	12 05						
Christs Hospital	d											11 37														
Billingshurst	d		11 13									11 43								12 13						
Pulborough	d		11 19									11 50								12 19						
Amberley	d											11 56														
Arundel	d		11 28									12 01								12 28						
Haywards Heath 3	d			10 38	10 46	11 04	10 55							11 08			11 37	11 27			11 38	11 46	12 04	11 55		
Burgess Hill	d				10 52	11 09	11 01											11 33				11 52	12 09	12 01		
Brighton 10	d			11 03	11 14		11 23							11 33	11 44			11 53			12 03	12 14		12 23		
Hove 2	d			11 07	11a17	11 22	11 27							11 37	11a47		11 52	11 57			12 07	12a17	12 22	12 27		
Aldrington	d						11 29											11 59						12 29		
Portslade	d			11 10		11 25	11 31							11 40				12 01			12 10		12 25	12 31		
Fishersgate	d						11 33											12 03						12 33		
Southwick	d			11 13			11 35							11 43				12 05			12 13			12 35		
Shoreham-by-Sea	d			11 16		11 30	11 39							11 46			11 58	12 09			12 16		12 30	12 39		
Lancing	d			11 20			11 43							11 50			12 02	12 13			12 20			12 43		
East Worthing	d						11 46											12 16						12 46		
Worthing 4	a			11 24		11 36	11 48							11 54			12 06	12 18			12 24		12 36	12 48		
	d			11 25		11 37	11 49							11 55			12 07	12 19			12 25		12 37	12 49		
West Worthing	d			11 27		11 39	11a51										12 09	12a21			12 27		12 39	12a51		
Durrington-on-Sea	d					11 41								11 58			12 11						12 41			
Goring-by-Sea	d					11 44								12 01			12 14						12 44			
Angmering 3	d			11 33		11 48								12 05			12 18				12 33		12 48			
Littlehampton 4	a					11 57											12 27						12 57			
	d										11 58					12 11										
Ford 4	d		11 33	11 40							12 02	12 06				12 15				12 33	12 40					
Bognor Regis 4	d																									
Barnham	a	11 26	11 38	11 44					11 56		12 06	12 10		12 14		12 19			12 26	12 38	12 44					
	d	11 27	11 38	11 45				11 52	11 57		12 07	12 11		12 15		12 22			12 27	12 38	12 45					12 52
Bognor Regis 4	a		11 45					11 58				12 17				12 28				12 45						12 58
Chichester 4	a	11 34		11 52					12 04		12 14			12 22					12 34		12 52					
	d	11 35		11 53					12 05		12 15			12 23					12 35		12 53					
Fishbourne (Sussex)	d										12 18															
Bosham	d								12 09																	
Nutbourne	d										12 23															
Southbourne	d								12 14		12 25			12 30												
Emsworth	d								12 17		12 28			12 33												
Warblington	d								12 20																	
Havant	d	11 46		12 04					12 23		12 33			12 37					12 46		13 04					
Bedhampton	a								12 29		12 35															
Hilsea	a								12 35		12 41															
Fratton	a	11 54		12 12					12 39		12 45								12 54		13 12					
Portsmouth & Southsea	a	11 58		12 16					12 43		12 49								12 58		13 16					
Portsmouth Harbour	a	12 02		12 20															13 02		13 20					
Cosham	a								12 29					12 44												
Portchester	a								12 33																	
Fareham	a								12 38					12 52												
Swanwick	a								12 45					12 59												
Southampton Central	a								13 02					13 18												

For general notes see front of timetable
For details of catering facilities see Directory of Train Operators

A ⌶ to Bognor Regis
B ⌶ to Haywards Heath

For complete service between Three Bridges and Horsham see Table 186

Table 188

Saturdays

London, Gatwick Airport & Brighton → Sussex Coast, Portsmouth and Southampton

Network Diagram - see first page of Table 186

		SN 1		SN 1	SN 1	SN 1	SN 1	SN 1	SN 1	SN 1	SN 1 A ⚲			SN 1	SN 1	SN 1 B ⚲	SN 1	SN 1	SN 1		SN 1	SN 1	SN 1	SN 1		SN 1
London Victoria 15 ⊖	d	11 32				11 36			11 47		12 02			12 06		12 17			12 32				12 36			
Clapham Junction 10	d	11 38				11 42			11 53		12 08			12 12		12 23			12 38				12 42			
London Bridge 4 ⊖	d	11 26				11 26			11 41	11 41	11 56			11 56		12 11	12 11		12 26				12 26			
East Croydon	d	11 48				11 52			12 03	11 54	12 18			12 22		12 33	12 24		12 48				12 52			
Gatwick Airport 10 ✈	d	12 09				11 56			12 19	12 11	12 40			12 26	12 28	12 49	12 40		13 09				12 56	13 01		
Three Bridges 4	a	12 14									12 44								13 14							
	d	12 14							12 15	12 15	12 45				12 33	12 45	12 45		13 14							
Crawley	d	12 18									12 48								13 18							
Horsham 4	a	12 26									12 56								13 26							
	d	12 30	12 34 →		← 12 34						13 00	13 05							13 30	13 34 →		← 13 34				
Christs Hospital	d				12 37																	13 37				
Billingshurst	d				12 43							13 13										13 43				
Pulborough	d				12 50							13 19										13 50				
Amberley	d				12 56																	13 56				
Arundel	d				13 01							13 28										14 01				
Haywards Heath 3	d					12 08			12 37	12 27				12 38	12 46	13 04	12 55						13 08	13 18		
Burgess Hill	d									12 33					12 52	13 09	13 01									
Brighton 10	d					12 33	12 44			12 53				13 03	13 14		13 23						13 33	13 44		
Hove 2	d					12 37	12a47		12 52	12 57				13 07	13a17	13 22	13 27						13 37	13a47		
Aldrington	d									12 59							13 29									
Portslade	d					12 40				13 01				13 10		13 25	13 31						13 40			
Fishersgate	d									13 03							13 33									
Southwick	d					12 43				13 05				13 13			13 35						13 43			
Shoreham-by-Sea	d					12 46			12 58	13 09				13 16		13 30	13 39						13 46			
Lancing	d					12 50			13 02	13 13				13 20			13 43						13 50			
East Worthing	d									13 16							13 46									
Worthing 4	a					12 54			13 06	13 18				13 24		13 36	13 48						13 54			
	d					12 55			13 07	13 19				13 25		13 37	13 49						13 55			
West Worthing	d								13 09	13a21				13 27		13 39	13a51									
Durrington-on-Sea	d					12 58			13 11							13 41							13 58			
Goring-by-Sea	d					13 01			13 14							13 44							14 01			
Angmering 3	d					13 05			13 18					13 33		13 48							14 05			
Littlehampton 4	a								13 27							13 57										
	d			12 58				13 11													13 58					14 11
Ford 4	d			13 02	13 06			13 15				13 33		13 40							14 02	14 06				14 15
Bognor Regis 4	d																									
Barnham	a	12 56		13 06	13 10	13 14		13 19			13 26	13 38		13 44					13 56		14 06	14 10	14 14			14 19
	d	12 57		13 07	13 11	13 15		13 22			13 27	13 38		13 45				13 52	13 57		14 07	14 11	14 15			14 22
Bognor Regis 4	a				13 17			13 28				13 45						13 58				14 17				14 28
Chichester 4	a	13 04		13 14		13 22					13 34			13 52					14 04		14 14		14 22			
	d	13 05		13 15		13 23					13 35			13 53					14 05		14 15		14 23			
Fishbourne (Sussex)	d			13 18																	14 18					
Bosham	d	13 09																	14 09							
Nutbourne	d			13 23																	14 23					
Southbourne	d	13 14		13 25		13 30													14 14		14 25		14 30			
Emsworth	d	13 17		13 28		13 33													14 17		14 28		14 33			
Warblington	d	13 20																	14 20							
Havant	d	13 23		13 33		13 37					13 46			14 04					14 23		14 33		14 37			
Bedhampton	a	13 29		13 35															14 29		14 35					
Hilsea	a	13 35		13 41															14 35		14 41					
Fratton	a	13 39		13 45							13 54			14 12					14 39		14 45					
Portsmouth & Southsea	a	13 43		13 49							13 58			14 16					14 43		14 49					
Portsmouth Harbour	a										14 02			14 20												
Cosham	a	13 29				13 44													14 29				14 44			
Portchester	a	13 33																	14 33							
Fareham	a	13 38				13 52													14 38				14 52			
Swanwick	a	13 45				13 59													14 45				14 59			
Southampton Central	a	14 02				14 18													15 02				15 18			

For general notes see front of timetable
For details of catering facilities see Directory of Train Operators

A ⚲ to Bognor Regis
B ⚲ to Haywards Heath

For complete service between Three Bridges and Horsham see Table 186

Table 188

Saturdays

London, Gatwick Airport & Brighton → Sussex Coast, Portsmouth and Southampton

Network Diagram - see first page of Table 186

		SN 1	SN 1	SN 1 ◇ A ⌶		SN 1	SN 1	SN 1 B ⌶	SN 1	SN 1	SN 1			SN 1	SN 1	SN 1	SN 1	SN 1	SN 1	SN 1	SN 1 C ⌶		SN 1	SN 1		SN 1 B ⌶
London Victoria 15 ⊖	d	12 47		13 02		13 06		13 17			13 32					13 36			13 47		14 02		14 06			14 17
Clapham Junction 10	d	12 53		13 08		13 12		13 23			13 38					13 42			13 53		14 08		14 12			14 23
London Bridge 4 ⊖	d	12 41	12 41	12 56		12 56		13 11	13 11		13 26					13 26			13 41	13 41	13 56		13 56			14 11
East Croydon	d	13 03	12 54	13 18		13 22		13 33	13 24		13 48					13 52			14 03	13 54	14 18		14 22			14 33
Gatwick Airport 10 ✈	d	13 19	13 11	13 40		13 26	13 28	13 49	13 41		14 09					13 56			14 19	14 11	14 40		14 26	14 28		14 49
Three Bridges 4	a			13 44							14 14										14 44					
	d	13 15	13 15	13 45			13 33	13 45	13 45		14 14								14 15	14 15	14 45			14 33		14 45
Crawley	d			13 48							14 18										14 48					
Horsham 4	a			13 56							14 26										14 56					
	d			14 00	14 05						14 30	14 34 →			← 14 34						15 00	15 05				
Christs Hospital	d														14 37											
Billingshurst	d				14 13										14 43							15 13				
Pulborough	d				14 19										14 50							15 19				
Amberley	d														14 56											
Arundel	d				14 28										15 01							15 28				
Haywards Heath 3	d	13 37	13 27			13 38	13 46	14 04	13 55							14 08			14 37	14 27			14 38	14 46		15 04
Burgess Hill	d		13 33				13 52	14 09	14 01											14 33				14 52		15 09
Brighton 10	d		13 53			14 03	14 14		14 23							14 33	14 44			14 53			15 03	15 14		
Hove 2	d	13 52	13 57			14 07	14a17	14 22	14 27							14 37	14a47		14 52	14 57			15 07	15a17		15 22
Aldrington	d		13 59						14 29											14 59						
Portslade	d		14 01			14 10		14 25	14 31							14 40				15 01			15 10			15 25
Fishersgate	d		14 03						14 33											15 03						
Southwick	d		14 05			14 13			14 35							14 43				15 05			15 13			
Shoreham-by-Sea	d	13 58	14 09			14 16		14 30	14 39							14 46			14 58	15 09			15 16			15 30
Lancing	d	14 02	14 13			14 20			14 43							14 50			15 02	15 13			15 20			
East Worthing	d		14 16						14 46											15 16						
Worthing 4	a	14 06	14 18			14 24		14 36	14 48							14 54			15 06	15 18			15 24			15 36
	d	14 07	14 19			14 25		14 37	14 49							14 55			15 07	15 19			15 25			15 37
West Worthing	d	14 09	14a21			14 27		14 39	14a51										15 09	15a21			15 27			15 39
Durrington-on-Sea	d	14 11						14 41								14 58			15 11							15 41
Goring-by-Sea	d	14 14						14 44								15 01			15 14							15 44
Angmering 3	d	14 18				14 33		14 48								15 05			15 18				15 33			15 48
Littlehampton 4	a	14 27						14 57											15 27							15 57
	d													14 58				15 11								
Ford 4	d				14 33	14 40								15 02	15 06			15 15				15 33	15 40			
Bognor Regis 4	d																									
Barnham	a			14 26	14 38	14 44					14 56			15 06	15 10	15 14		15 19			15 26	15 38	15 44			
	d			14 27	14 38	14 45				14 52	14 57			15 07	15 11	15 15		15 22			15 27	15 38	15 45			
Bognor Regis 4	a				14 45					14 58					15 17			15 28				15 45				
Chichester 4	a			14 34		14 52					15 04			15 14		15 22					15 34		15 52			
	d			14 35		14 53					15 05			15 15		15 23					15 35		15 53			
Fishbourne (Sussex)	d													15 18												
Bosham	d										15 09															
Nutbourne	d													15 23												
Southbourne	d										15 14			15 25		15 30										
Emsworth	d										15 17			15 28		15 33										
Warblington	d										15 20															
Havant	d			14 46		15 04					15 23			15 33		15 37					15 46		16 04			
Bedhampton	a										15 29			15 35												
Hilsea	a										15 35			15 41												
Fratton	a			14 54		15 12					15 39			15 45							15 54		16 12			
Portsmouth & Southsea	a			14 58		15 16					15 43			15 49							15 58		16 16			
Portsmouth Harbour	a			15 02		15 20															16 02		16 20			
Cosham	a										15 29					15 44										
Portchester	a										15 33															
Fareham	a										15 38					15 52										
Swanwick	a										15 45					15 59										
Southampton Central	a										16 02					16 18										

For general notes see front of timetable
For details of catering facilities see Directory of Train Operators

A ⌶ to Bognor Regis
B ⌶ to Haywards Heath
C ⌶ to Horsham

For complete service between Three Bridges and Horsham see Table 186

Table 188

Saturdays

London, Gatwick Airport & Brighton → Sussex Coast, Portsmouth and Southampton

Network Diagram - see first page of Table 186

Station		SN 1	SN 1	SN 1		SN 1	SN 1	SN 1	SN 1	SN 1	SN 1	SN 1		SN 1 A		SN 1	SN 1	SN 1 B	SN 1	SN 1	SN 1		SN 1	SN 1		SN 1
London Victoria 15 ⊖	d			14 32				14 36			14 47			15 02		15 06		15 17			15 32					15 36
Clapham Junction 10	d			14 38				14 42			14 53			15 08		15 12		15 23			15 38					15 42
London Bridge 4 ⊖	d	14 11		14 26				14 26			14 41	14 41		14 56		14 56		15 11	15 11		15 26					15 26
East Croydon	d	14 24		14 48				14 52			15 03	14 54		15 18		15 22		15 33	15 24		15 48					15 52
Gatwick Airport 10 ✈	d	14 41		15 09				14 56			15 19	15 11		15 40		15 26	15 28	15 49	15 41		16 09					15 56
Three Bridges 4	a			15 14										15 44							16 14					
	d	14 45		15 14							15 15	15 15		15 45			15 33	15 45	15 45		16 14					
Crawley	d			15 18										15 48							16 18					
Horsham 4	a			15 26										15 56							16 26					
	d			15 30	15 34 →		← 15 34							16 00	16 05						16 30	16 34 →		← 16 34		
Christs Hospital	d						15 37																	16 37		
Billingshurst	d						15 43								16 13									16 43		
Pulborough	d						15 50								16 19									16 50		
Amberley	d						15 56																	16 56		
Arundel	d						16 01								16 28									17 01		
Haywards Heath 3	d	14 55						15 08			15 37	15 27				15 38	15 46	16 04	15 55							16 08
Burgess Hill	d	15 01										15 33					15 52	16 09	16 01							
Brighton 10	d	15 23						15 33	15 44			15 53				16 03	16 14		16 23							16 33
Hove 2	d	15 27						15 37	15a47		15 52	15 57				16 07	16a17	16 22	16 27							16 37
Aldrington	d	15 29										15 59							16 29							
Portslade	d	15 31						15 40				16 01				16 10		16 25	16 31							16 40
Fishersgate	d	15 33										16 03							16 33							
Southwick	d	15 35						15 43				16 05				16 13			16 35							16 43
Shoreham-by-Sea	d	15 39						15 46			15 58	16 09				16 16		16 30	16 39							16 46
Lancing	d	15 43						15 50			16 02	16 13				16 20			16 43							16 50
East Worthing	d	15 46										16 16							16 46							
Worthing 4	a	15 48						15 54			16 06	16 18				16 24		16 36	16 48							16 54
	d	15 49						15 55			16 07	16 19				16 25		16 37	16 49							16 55
West Worthing	d	15a51									16 09	16a21				16 27		16 39	16a51							
Durrington-on-Sea	d							15 58			16 11							16 41								16 58
Goring-by-Sea	d							16 01			16 14							16 44								17 01
Angmering 3	d							16 05			16 18					16 33		16 48								17 05
Littlehampton 4	a										16 27							16 57								
	d					15 58				16 11													16 58			
Ford 4	d					16 02	16 06			16 15					16 33	16 40							17 02	17 06		
Bognor Regis 4	d																									
Barnham	a			15 56		16 06	16 10	16 14		16 19				16 26	16 38	16 44					16 56		17 06	17 10		17 14
	d		15 52	15 57		16 07	16 11	16 15		16 22				16 27	16 38	16 45				16 52	16 57		17 07	17 11		17 15
Bognor Regis 4	a		15 58				16 17			16 28					16 45					16 58				17 17		
Chichester 4	a			16 04		16 14		16 22						16 34		16 52					17 04		17 14			17 22
	d			16 05		16 15		16 23						16 35		16 53					17 05		17 15			17 23
Fishbourne (Sussex)	d					16 18																	17 18			
Bosham	d			16 09																	17 09					
Nutbourne	d					16 23																	17 23			
Southbourne	d			16 14		16 25		16 30													17 14		17 25			17 30
Emsworth	d			16 17		16 28		16 33													17 17		17 28			17 33
Warblington	d			16 20																	17 20					
Havant	d			16 23		16 33		16 37						16 46		17 04					17 23		17 33			17 37
Bedhampton	a			16 29		16 35															17 29		17 35			
Hilsea	a			16 35		16 41															17 35		17 41			
Fratton	a			16 39		16 45								16 54		17 12					17 39		17 45			
Portsmouth & Southsea	a			16 43		16 49								16 58		17 16					17 43		17 49			
Portsmouth Harbour	a													17 02		17 20										
Cosham	a			16 29				16 44													17 29					17 44
Portchester	a			16 33																	17 33					
Fareham	a			16 38				16 52													17 38					17 52
Swanwick	a			16 45				16 59													17 45					17 59
Southampton Central	a			17 02				17 18													18 02					18 18

For general notes see front of timetable
For details of catering facilities see
Directory of Train Operators

A to Bognor Regis
B to Haywards Heath

For complete service between Three Bridges and Horsham see Table 186

Table 188

Saturdays

London, Gatwick Airport & Brighton → Sussex Coast, Portsmouth and Southampton

Network Diagram - see first page of Table 186

		SN 1	SN 1	SN 1	SN 1	SN 1		GW	SN 1	SN 1	SN 1	SN 1		SN 1	SN 1		SN 1	SN 1	SN 1	SN 1	SN 1	SN 1	SN 1	SN 1		SN 1
						A 🍴		B			C 🍴													A 🍴		
London Victoria 15 ⊖	d			15 47		16 02		15b47	16 06		16 17				16 32				16 36			16 47		17 02		17 06
Clapham Junction 10	d			15 53		16 08		15b53	16 12		16 23				16 38				16 42			16 53		17 08		17 12
London Bridge 4 ⊖	d			15 41	15 41	15 56		15 56	15 56		16 11	16 11			16 26				16 26			16 41	16 41	16 56		16 56
East Croydon	d			16 03	15 54	16 18		16 09	16 22		16 33	16 24			16 48				16 52			17 03	16 54	17 18		17 22
Gatwick Airport 10 ✈	d			16 19	16 11	16 40		16 26	16 26	16 28	16 49	16 41			17 09				16 56			17 19	17 11	17 40		17 26
Three Bridges 4	a					16 44									17 14									17 44		
	d			16 15	16 15	16 45				16 33	16 45	16 45			17 14							17 15	17 15	17 45		
Crawley	d					16 48									17 18									17 48		
Horsham 4	a					16 56									17 26									17 56		
	d					17 00	17 05								17 30	17 34 →		← 17 34						18 00	18 05	
Christs Hospital	d																	17 37								
Billingshurst	d						17 13											17 43							18 13	
Pulborough	d						17 19											17 50							18 19	
Amberley	d																	17 56								
Arundel	d						17 28											18 01							18 28	
Haywards Heath 3	d			16 37	16 27			16 38	16 38	16 46	17 04	16 55							17 08			17 37	17 27			17 38
Burgess Hill	d				16 33					16 52	17 09	17 01											17 33			
Brighton 10	d	16 44			16 53			17 00	17 03	17 14		17 23							17 33	17 44			17 53			18 03
Hove 2	d	16a47		16 52	16 57			17 04	17 07	17a17	17 22	17 27							17 37	17a47		17 52	17 57			18 07
Aldrington	d				16 59							17 29											17 59			
Portslade	d				17 01				17 10		17 25	17 31							17 40				18 01			18 10
Fishersgate	d				17 03							17 33											18 03			
Southwick	d				17 05				17 13			17 35							17 43				18 05			18 13
Shoreham-by-Sea	d			16 58	17 09			17 13	17 17		17 30	17 39							17 46			17 58	18 09			18 16
Lancing	d			17 02	17 13				17 21			17 43							17 50			18 02	18 13			18 20
East Worthing	d				17 16							17 46											18 16			
Worthing 4	a			17 06	17 18			17 22	17 25		17 36	17 48							17 54			18 06	18 18			18 24
	d			17 07	17 19			17 22	17 25		17 37	17 49							17 55			18 07	18 19			18 25
West Worthing	d			17 09	17a21				17 28		17 39	17a51										18 09	18a21			18 27
Durrington-on-Sea	d			17 11							17 41								17 58			18 11				
Goring-by-Sea	d			17 14							17 44								18 01			18 14				
Angmering 3	d			17 18					17 34		17 48								18 05			18 18				18 33
Littlehampton 4	a			17 27							17 57											18 27				
	d		17 11														17 58				18 11					
Ford 4	d		17 15				17 33		17 40								18 02	18 06			18 15				18 33	18 40
Bognor Regis 4	d																									
Barnham	a		17 19			17 26	17 38	17 40	17 44						17 56		18 06	18 10	18 14		18 19			18 26	18 38	18 44
	d		17 22			17 27	17 38	17 41	17 45					17 52	17 57		18 07	18 11	18 15		18 22			18 27	18 38	18 45
Bognor Regis 4	a		17 28				17 45							17 58				18 17			18 28				18 45	
Chichester 4	a					17 34		17 48	17 52						18 04		18 14		18 22					18 34		18 52
	d					17 35		17 49	17 53						18 05		18 15		18 23					18 35		18 53
Fishbourne (Sussex)	d																18 18									
Bosham	d														18 09											
Nutbourne	d																18 23									
Southbourne	d														18 14		18 25		18 30							
Emsworth	d														18 17		18 28		18 33							
Warblington	d														18 20											
Havant	d					17 46		18 00	18 04						18 23		18 33		18 37					18 46		19 04
Bedhampton	a														18 29		18 35									
Hilsea	a														18 35		18 41									
Fratton	a					17 54			18 12						18 39		18 45							18 54		19 12
Portsmouth & Southsea	a					17 58			18 16						18 43		18 49							18 58		19 16
Portsmouth Harbour	a					18 02			18 20															19 02		19 20
Cosham	a							18 06							18 29				18 44							
Portchester	a														18 33											
Fareham	a							18 14							18 38				18 52							
Swanwick	a														18 45				18 59							
Southampton Central	a							18 38							19 02				19 18							

For general notes see front of timetable
For details of catering facilities see Directory of Train Operators

A 🍴 to Bognor Regis
B To Cheltenham Spa (Table 57)
C 🍴 to Haywards Heath
b Change at East Croydon and Brighton

For complete service between Three Bridges and Horsham see Table 186

Table 188

Saturdays

London, Gatwick Airport & Brighton → Sussex Coast, Portsmouth and Southampton

Network Diagram - see first page of Table 186

Station		SN 1		SN 1 A ⚲	SN 1	SN 1		SN 1	SN 1	SN 1	SN 1	SN 1	SN 1	SN 1		SN 1 B ⚲		SN 1	SN 1	SN 1 A ⚲	SN 1	SN 1		SN 1	SN 1	SN 1
London Victoria 15 ⊖	d			17 17		17 32					17 36			17 47		18 02		18 06		18 17		18 32			18 36	
Clapham Junction 10	d			17 23		17 38					17 42			17 53		18 08		18 12		18 23		18 38			18 42	
London Bridge 4 ⊖	d			17 11		17 26			17 11		17 26			17 41		17 56		17 56		18 11		18 26		18 11	18 26	
East Croydon	d			17 33		17 48			17 24		17 52			18 03		18 18		18 22		18 33		18 48		18 24	18 52	
Gatwick Airport 10 ✈	d	17 28		17 49		18 09			17 41		17 56			18 19		18 40		18 26	18 28	18 49		19 09		18 41	18 56	
Three Bridges 4	a					18 14										18 44						19 14				
	d	17 33		17 45		18 14			17 45					18 15		18 45		18 15	18 33	18 45		19 14		18 45		
Crawley	d					18 18										18 48						19 18				
Horsham 4	a					18 26										18 56						19 26				
	d					18 30	18 34 →			← 18 34						19 00	19 05					19 30	19 34			
Christs Hospital	d									18 37													19 37			
Billingshurst	d									18 43							19 13						19 43			
Pulborough	d									18 50							19 19						19 50			
Amberley	d									18 56													19 56			
Arundel	d									19 01							19 28						20 01			
Haywards Heath 3	d	17 46		18 04					17 55		18 08			18 37				18 38	18 46	19 04				18 55	19 08	
Burgess Hill	d	17 52		18 09					18 01									18 33	18 52	19 09				19 01		
Brighton 10	d	18 14							18 23		18 33	18 44						19 03	19 14					19 27	19 44	
Hove 2	d	18a17		18 22					18 27		18 37	18a47		18 52				19 07	19a17	19 22				19 31	19a47	
Aldrington	d								18 29									19 09						19 33		
Portslade	d			18 25					18 31		18 40			18 55				19 11		19 25				19 35		
Fishersgate	d								18 33									19 13						19 37		
Southwick	d								18 35		18 43							19 15						19 39		
Shoreham-by-Sea	d			18 30					18 39		18 46			19 00				19 19		19 30				19 43		
Lancing	d								18 43		18 50			19 04				19 23		19 34				19 47		
East Worthing	d								18 46									19 26						19 50		
Worthing 4	a			18 36					18 48		18 54			19 08				19 28		19 38				19 52		
	d			18 37					18 49		18 55			19 08				19 29		19 38				19 53		
West Worthing	d			18 39					18 51					19 10				19 31		19 40				19 55		
Durrington-on-Sea	d			18 41					18 53		18 58			19 13				19 33		19 43				19 57		
Goring-by-Sea	d			18 44					18 56		19 01			19 15				19 36		19 45				20 00		
Angmering 3	d			18 48					19 00		19 05			19 19				19 40		19 49				20 04		
Littlehampton 4	a			18 57					19 10					19 28						19 58						
	d							18 58					19 11													20 11
Ford 4	d							19 02		19 06			19 15				19 33	19 46					20 06	20 10		20 15
Bognor Regis 4	d																									
Barnham	a					18 56		19 06		19 10	19 14		19 19			19 26	19 38	19 50				19 56	20 10	20 14		20 19
	d				18 52	18 57		19 07		19 11	19 15		19 22			19 27	19 38	19 51			19 52	19 57	20 11	20 15		20 22
Bognor Regis 4	a				18 58					19 17			19 28				19 45				19 58		20 17			20 28
Chichester 4	a					19 04		19 14			19 22					19 34		19 58				20 04		20 22		
	d					19 05		19 15			19 23					19 35		19 59				20 05		20 23		
Fishbourne (Sussex)	d							19 18														20 08				
Bosham	d					19 09																20 11				
Nutbourne	d							19 23														20 14				
Southbourne	d					19 14		19 25			19 30											20 17		20 30		
Emsworth	d					19 17		19 28			19 33											20 20		20 33		
Warblington	d					19 20																20 23				
Havant	d					19 23		19 33			19 37					19 46		20 10				20 26		20 37		
Bedhampton	a					19 29		19 35														20 32				
Hilsea	a					19 35		19 41														20 38				
Fratton	a					19 39		19 45								19 54		20 18				20 43				
Portsmouth & Southsea	a					19 43		19 49								19 58		20 22				20 48				
Portsmouth Harbour	a															20 02		20 26								
Cosham	a					19 29					19 44											20 32		20 44		
Portchester	a					19 33																20 36				
Fareham	a					19 38					19 52											20 41		20 52		
Swanwick	a					19 45					19 59											20 48		20 59		
Southampton Central	a					20 02					20 18											21 05		21 18		

For general notes see front of timetable
For details of catering facilities see Directory of Train Operators

A ⚲ to Haywards Heath
B ⚲ to Horsham

For complete service between Three Bridges and Horsham see Table 186

Table 188

Saturdays

London, Gatwick Airport & Brighton → Sussex Coast, Portsmouth and Southampton

Network Diagram - see first page of Table 186

Station																										
		SN 1	SN 1			SN 1	SN 1	SN 1	SN 1	SN 1		SN 1	SN 1	SN 1	SN 1	SN 1		SN 1		SN 1	SN 1	SN 1	SN 1	SN 1		SN 1
			A ⌶					B ⌶							B ⌶			A ⌶								
London Victoria 15 ⊖	d	18 47	19 02				19 06	19 17		19 32			19b17	19 36	19 47			20 02		20 06		20 17		20 32		
Clapham Junction 10	d	18 53	19 08				19 12	19 23		19 38			19b23	19 42	19 53			20 08		20 12		20 23		20 38		
London Bridge 4 ⊖	d	18 41	18 56			18 41	18 56	19 11		19 26			19 26		19 41			19 56		19 56		20 11		20 15		
East Croydon	d	19 03	19 18			18 54	19 22	19 33		19 48			19 39	19 52	20 03			20 19		20 22		20 33		20 48		
Gatwick Airport 10 ✈	d	19 19	19 40			19 11	19 28	19 49		20 09			19 56		20 19			20 39		20 26	20 28	20 49		21 09		
Three Bridges 4	a		19 44							20 14								20 44						21 14		
	d	19 15	19 45			19 15	19 33	19 45		20 14			19 45		20 15			20 44		20 15	20 33	20 45		21 14		
Crawley	d		19 48							20 18								20 48						21 18		
Horsham 4	a		19 56							20 26								20 56						21 26		
	d		20 00	20 05						20 30	20 34							21 00	21 04					21 30	21 34	
Christs Hospital	d										20 37								21 07						21 37	
Billingshurst	d			20 13							20 43								21 13						21 43	
Pulborough	d			20 19							20 50								21 20						21 50	
Amberley	d										20 56								21 26						21 56	
Arundel	d			20 28							21 01								21 31						22 01	
Haywards Heath 3	d	19 37				19 27	19 46	20 04					20 11	20 15	20 34					20 38	20 46	21 05				
Burgess Hill	d					19 33	19 52	20 09					20 01		20 39					20 33	20 52	21 10				
Brighton 10	d					19 56	20 14						20 30	20 44						21 03	21 14					
Hove 2	d	19 52				20 00	20a19	20 22					20 34	20a47	20 54					21 07	21a17	21 22				
Aldrington	d					20 02							20 36							21 09						
Portslade	d	19 55				20 04		20 25					20 38		20 57					21 11		21 25				
Fishersgate	d					20 06							20 40							21 13						
Southwick	d					20 08							20 42							21 15						
Shoreham-by-Sea	d	20 00				20 12		20 30					20 46		21 01					21 19		21 30				
Lancing	d	20 04				20 16		20 34					20 50		21 05					21 23		21 34				
East Worthing	d					20 19							20 53							21 26						
Worthing 4	a	20 08				20 21		20 38					20 55		21 09					21 28		21 38				
	d	20 08				20 22		20 38					20 56		21 10					21 29		21 38				
West Worthing	d	20 10				20 24		20 40					20 58		21 12					21 31		21 40				
Durrington-on-Sea	d	20 13				20 26		20 43					21 00		21 14					21 33		21 43				
Goring-by-Sea	d	20 15				20 29		20 45					21 03		21 17					21 36		21 45				
Angmering 3	d	20 19				20 33		20 49					21 07		21 21					21 40		21 49				
Littlehampton 4	a	20 28						20 58							21 29							21 58				
	d											21 06														22 08
Ford 4	d			20 33		20 39					21 06	21 10	21 13						21 36	21 46					22 06	22 12
Bognor Regis 4	d																									
Barnham	a		20 26	20 38		20 43				20 56	21 10	21 14	21 17					21 26	21 40	21 50				21 56	22 10	22 16
	d		20 27	20 38		20 44			20 52	20 57	21 11	21 22 →	21 18			← 21 22		21 27	21 41	21 51			21 52	21 57	22 11	22 22 →
Bognor Regis 4	a			20 45					20 58		21 17					21 28			21 47				21 58		22 17	
Chichester 4	a		20 34			20 51				21 04			21 25					21 34		21 58				22 04		
	d		20 35			20 52				21 05			21 26					21 35		21 59				22 05		
Fishbourne (Sussex)	d					20 55																		22 08		
Bosham	d									21 09														22 11		
Nutbourne	d					21 00																		22 14		
Southbourne	d					21 02				21 14								21 42						22 17		
Emsworth	d					21 05				21 17								21 45						22 20		
Warblington	d									21 20														22 23		
Havant	d		20 46			21 10				21 23			21 37					21 49		22 10				22 26		
Bedhampton	a									21 29														22 34		
Hilsea	a									21 35														22 39		
Fratton	a		20 54			21 18				21 39			21 54					21 59		22 18				22 43		
Portsmouth & Southsea	a		20 58			21 22				21 43			21 58					22 02		22 22				22 48		
Portsmouth Harbour	a		21 02			21 26												22 06		22 26						
Cosham	a									21 29			21 44											22 33		
Portchester	a									21 33																
Fareham	a									21 38			21 52											22 41		
Swanwick	a									21 45			21 59											22 48		
Southampton Central	a									22 02			22 18											23 05		

For general notes see front of timetable
For details of catering facilities see Directory of Train Operators

A ⌶ to Bognor Regis
B ⌶ to Haywards Heath
b Change at East Croydon and Brighton

For complete service between Three Bridges and Horsham see Table 186

Table 188

Saturdays

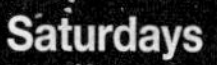

London, Gatwick Airport & Brighton → Sussex Coast, Portsmouth and Southampton

Network Diagram - see first page of Table 186

		SN 1	SN 1	SN 1	SN 1	SN 1	SN 1	SN 1	SN 1	SN 1	SN 1	SN 1	SN 1	SN 1	SN 1	SN 1	SN 1	SN 1	SN 1	SN 1	SN 1	SN 1	SN 1
London Victoria 15 ⊖	d		20 36	20 47				21 06		21 17	21 32		21 36		21 47	22 06		22 17	22 36	22 32		22 47	23 17
Clapham Junction 10	d		20 42	20 53				21 12		21 23	21 38		21 42		21 53	22 12		22 23	22 42	22 38		22 53	23 23
London Bridge 4 ⊖	d	20 11	20b15	20 41			20 41	20b45		21 11	21 15		21b15		21 41	21b45		22 11	22b15	22 15		22 41	23 11
East Croydon	d	20 24	20 52	21 03			20 54	21 22		21 33	21 48		21 52		22 03	22 22		22 33	22 52	22 48		23 03	23 33
Gatwick Airport 10 ✈	d	20 41	20c49	21 19			21 11	21c19		21 49	22 09		21c49		22 19	22c19		22 51	22c51	23 09		23 19	23 51
Three Bridges 4	a									21 53	22 14							22 55		23 14			23 55
	d	20 45		21 15			21 15			21 53	22 14		21c53		22 15	22 15		22 55	22c55	23 15		23 15	23 56
Crawley	d										22 18									23 18			
Horsham 4	a										22 26									23 26			
	d										22 27									23 27			
Christs Hospital	d										22 30									23 30			
Billingshurst	d										22 36									23 36			
Pulborough	d										22 43									23 43			
Amberley	d										22 49									23 49			
Arundel	d										22 54									23 54			
Haywards Heath 3	d	20 58	21 15	21 34			21 26	21 45		22 06			22 15		22 37	22 45		23 04	23 15			23 37	00 05
Burgess Hill	d	21 04		21 39			21 32			22 11			22 04			22 32		23 10	23 04				00 10
Brighton 10	d	21 33	21 44				22 03	22 14					22 34	22 44		23 14			23 44				
Hove 2	d	21 37	21a47	21 54			22 07	22a17		22 23			22 38	22a47	22 52	23a17		23 21	23a47			23 52	00 22
Aldrington	d	21 39					22 09						22 40										
Portslade	d	21 41		21 57			22 11			22 26			22 42		22 55			23 24				23 55	00s25
Fishersgate	d	21 43					22 13						22 44										
Southwick	d	21 45					22 15						22 46					23 27				23 58	00s28
Shoreham-by-Sea	d	21 49		22 01			22 19			22 31			22 50		23 00			23 30				00 01	00s31
Lancing	d	21 53		22 05			22 23			22 35			22 54		23 04			23 34				00 05	00s35
East Worthing	d	21 56					22 26						22 57										
Worthing 4	a	21 58		22 09			22 28			22 39			22 59		23 08			23 38				00 09	00s39
	d	21 59		22 10			22 29			22 39			23 00		23 08			23 39					
West Worthing	d	22 01		22 12			22 31			22 41			23 02		23 10			23 41					00s41
Durrington-on-Sea	d	22 03		22 14			22 33			22 44			23 04		23 13			23 43					00s44
Goring-by-Sea	d	22 06		22 17			22 36			22 46			23 07		23 15			23 46					00s46
Angmering 3	d	22 10		22 21			22 40			22 50			23 11		23 19			23 50					00s50
Littlehampton 4	a			22 31									23 19		23 28								
	d					22 38							23 24										
Ford 4	d	22 16				22 42	22 46			22 56	23 00		23 28					23 56		23 59			00s56
Bognor Regis 4	d																						
Barnham	a	22 20				22 46	22 50			23 01	23 04		23 32					00 01		00 04			01s01
	d	22 21			← 22 22	22 52 →	22 51		← 22 52	23 06 →	23 05	← 23 06	23 33				23 36	00 09 →		00 05	← 00 09		
Bognor Regis 4	a				22 28				22 58			23 12					23 42				00 15		
Chichester 4	a	22 28					22 58				23 12		23 40							00 12			01 09
	d	22 29					22 59				23 13												
Fishbourne (Sussex)	d										23 16												
Bosham	d										23 19												
Nutbourne	d										23 22												
Southbourne	d	22 36									23 25												
Emsworth	d	22 39									23 28												
Warblington	d										23 31												
Havant	d	22 43					23 10				23 36												
Bedhampton	a						23 33				00 24												
Hilsea	a						23 39				00 30												
Fratton	a	22 52					23 18				23 47												
Portsmouth & Southsea	a	22 55					23 22				23 51												
Portsmouth Harbour	a	22 59					23 26																
Cosham	a																						
Portchester	a																						
Fareham	a																						
Swanwick	a																						
Southampton Central	a																						

For general notes see front of timetable
For details of catering facilities see Directory of Train Operators

b Change at East Croydon and Brighton
c Change at Haywards Heath and Brighton

For complete service between Three Bridges and Horsham see Table 186

London, Gatwick Airport & Brighton → Sussex Coast, Portsmouth and Southampton

Network Diagram - see first page of Table 186

		SN 1	SN 1	SN 1	SN 1	SN 1	SN 1	SN 1	SN 1	SN 1	SN 1	SN 1	SN 1	SN 1		SN 1	SN 1	SN 1	SN 1	SN 1	SN 1	SN 1	SN 1	SN 1	SN 1	
London Victoria 15 ⊖	d	22p17	22p32		22p47	23 06	23p17	00 05				05 47					07 02	06 32				07 32		08 04	08 17	
Clapham Junction 10	d	22p23	22p38		22p53	23 12	23p23	00 11				05 53					07 08	06 38				07 38		08 10	08 23	
London Bridge 4 ⊖	d					23b00	23 00	23 53													07 11	07 41		07 44	08 14	
East Croydon	d	22p33	22p48		23p03	23 22	23p33	00 25				06 06					07 23	06 52			07 27	07 57		08 23	08 37	
Gatwick Airport 10 ✈	d	22p51	23p09		23p19	23c19	23p51	00 43				06 32					07 47	07 19			07 50	08 20		08 47	08 56	
Three Bridges 4	a	22p55	23p14				23p55	00 48									07 52							08 52		
	d	22p55	23p15			23 15	23p56	00 48				06 36					07 52	07 24			07 54	08 24		08 52	08 54	
Crawley	d		23p18														07 55							08 55		
Horsham 4	a		23p26														08 07							09 04		
	d		23p27														08 08							09 05		
Christs Hospital	d		23p30																					09 08		
Billingshurst	d		23p36														08 16							09 14		
Pulborough	d		23p43														08 24							09 21		
Amberley	d		23p49																					09 27		
Arundel	d		23p54														08 33							09 32		
Haywards Heath 3	d	23p04			23p37	23 45	00 05	01 03				06 47						07 36			08 03	08 33			09 07	
Burgess Hill	d	23p10				23 32	00 10					06 53						07 42			08 08	08 38			09 12	
Brighton 10	d					00 10						07 15		07 23				08 15		08 23	08 50	09 17				
Hove 2	d	23p21			23p52	00a13	00 22	01s25				07 18		07 26				08 18		08 26	08 53	09e26 →			09 24	
Aldrington	d													07 28						08 28	08 55					
Portslade	d	23p24			23p55		00s25	01s28						07 31						08 31	08 58					
Fishersgate	d													07 33						08 33	09 00					
Southwick	d	23p27			23p58		00s28	01s31						07 35						08 35	09 02					
Shoreham-by-Sea	d	23p30			00 01		00s31	01s34				07 24		07 38				08 24		08 38	09 05				09 30	
Lancing	d	23p34			00 05		00s35	01s38						07 42						08 42	09 09					
East Worthing	d													07 45						08 45	09 12					
Worthing 4	a	23p38			00 09		00s39	01 42				07 30		07 47				08 30		08 47	09 14				09 36	
	d	23p39										07 31		07 47				08 31		08 47	09 15				09 40	09 42
West Worthing	d	23p41					00s41							07 49						08 49	09 17					09 44
Durrington-on-Sea	d	23p43					00s44							07 52						08 52	09 19					09 46
Goring-by-Sea	d	23p46					00s46							07 54						08 54	09 22					09 49
Angmering 3	d	23p50					00s50					07 37		07 58				08 37		08 58	09 26					09 53
Littlehampton 4	a													08 07						09 07	09 35					10 02
	d									06 42	07 19		07 57	08 11					08 57	09 11						
Ford 4	d	23p56	23p59				00s56			06 46	07 23		08 01	08 15			08 38		09 01	09 15				09 39		
Bognor Regis 4	d																									
Barnham	a	00 01	00 04	←			01s01			06 50	07 27	07 47	08 08	08 19		←	08 42	08 47	09 08	09 19			←	09 43	09 54	
	d	00 09 →	00 05	00 09					06 45	06 51	07 28	07 47	08 26 →	08 20		08 26	08 43	08 47	09 26 →	09 20			09 26	09 44	09 55	
Bognor Regis 4	a			00 15					06 51		07 34					08 32	08 49						09 32	09 50		
Chichester 4	a		00 12				01 09			06 58		07 55		08 27				08 55		09 27					10 02	
	d									06 59		07 55		08 28				08 55		09 28					10 03	
Fishbourne (Sussex)	d													08 31						09 31						
Bosham	d													08 34						09 34						
Nutbourne	d													08 37						09 37						
Southbourne	d											08 02		08 40				09 02		09 40					10 10	
Emsworth	d											08 05		08 43				09 05		09 43					10 13	
Warblington	d													08 46						09 46						
Havant	d									07 10		08 10		08 49				09 10		09 49					10 17	
Bedhampton	a											08 47		08 51				09 47		09 51						
Hilsea	a																									
Fratton	a									07 18		08 18		08 59				09 18		09 59					10 26	
Portsmouth & Southsea	a									07 22		08 22		09 03				09 22		10 03					10 29	
Portsmouth Harbour	a									07 26		08 26		09 07				09 26		10 07					10 35	
Cosham	a																									
Portchester	a																									
Fareham	a																									
Swanwick	a																									
Southampton Central	a																									

For general notes see front of timetable
For details of catering facilities see
Directory of Train Operators

b Change at East Croydon and Brighton
c Change at Haywards Heath and Brighton
e Arr. 0920

For complete service between Three Bridges and Horsham see Table 186

Table 188

Sundays

London, Gatwick Airport & Brighton → Sussex Coast, Portsmouth and Southampton

Network Diagram - see first page of Table 186

		SN ■1	SN ■1	SN ■1	SN ■1		SN ■1	SN ■1	SN ■1		SN ■1	SN ■1	SN ■1	SN ■1	SN ■1 ⌶	GW ◇ A	SN ■1	SN ■1			SN ■1	SN ■1	SN ■1	SN ■1	SN ■1	SN ■1 ⌶
London Victoria 15 ⊖	d				07b34		08 32	09 04	09 17					08b47	10 04	10c02	10c02	10 17						10e02	11c02	11 04
Clapham Junction 10	d				07b40		08 38	09 10	09 23					08b53	10 10	10c07	10c07	10 23						10e07	11c07	11 10
London Bridge 4 ⊖	d				08 11		08 41	08 44	09 14					09 11	09 56	09e56	09e56	10 14						10 11	10e56	10 56
East Croydon	d				08 27		08 57	09 23	09 37					09 27	10 23	10g20	10g20	10 37						10 27	11g20	11 23
Gatwick Airport 10 ✈	d				08 50		09 20	09 47	09 56					09 50	10 47	10g42	10g42	10 56						10 50	11g42	11 47
Three Bridges 4	a							09 52							10 52											11 52
	d				08 54		09 24	09 52	09 54					09 54	10 52	10 24	10 24	10 54						10 54	11 24	11 52
Crawley	d							09 55							10 55											11 55
Horsham 4	a							10 04							11 04											12 04
	d							10 05							11 05											12 05
Christs Hospital	d							10 08							11 08											12 08
Billingshurst	d							10 14							11 14											12 14
Pulborough	d							10 21							11 21											12 21
Amberley	d							10 27							11 27											12 27
Arundel	d							10 32							11 32											12 32
Haywards Heath 3	d				09 03		09 33		10 07					10 03		10 33	10 33	11 07						11 03	11 33	
Burgess Hill	d				09 08		09 38		10 12					10 08		10 38	10 38	11 12						11 08	11 38	
Brighton 10	d		←		09 50		10 17					←		10 50		11 10	11 17					←		11 50	12 17	
Hove 2	d		09 26		09 53		10h26 →		10 24			10 26		10 53		11 14	11j26 →	11 24				11 26		11 53	12k26 →	
Aldrington	d		09 28		09 55							10 28		10 55								11 28		11 55		
Portslade	d		09 31		09 58							10 31		10 58								11 31		11 58		
Fishersgate	d		09 33		10 00							10 33		11 00								11 33		12 00		
Southwick	d		09 35		10 02							10 35		11 02								11 35		12 02		
Shoreham-by-Sea	d		09 38		10 05				10 30			10 38		11 05		11 20		11 30				11 38		12 05		
Lancing	d		09 42		10 09							10 42		11 09								11 42		12 09		
East Worthing	d		09 45		10 12							10 45		11 12								11 45		12 12		
Worthing 4	a		09 47		10 14				10 36			10 47		11 14		11 26		11 36				11 47		12 14		
	d		09 48		10 15				10 40	10 42		10 48		11 15		11 29		11 40	11 42			11 48		12 15		
West Worthing	d		09 50		10 17					10 44		10 50		11 17					11 44			11 50		12 17		
Durrington-on-Sea	d		09 52		10 19					10 46		10 52		11 19					11 46			11 52		12 19		
Goring-by-Sea	d		09 55		10 22					10 49		10 55		11 22					11 49			11 55		12 22		
Angmering 3	d		09 59		10 26					10 53		10 59		11 26					11 53			11 59		12 26		
Littlehampton 4	a				10 35					11 02				11 35					12 02					12 35		
	d	09 57									10 57										11 57					
Ford 4	d	10 01	10 05					10 38			11 01	11 05			11 38						12 01	12 05				12 38
Bognor Regis 4	d																									
Barnham	a	10 08	10 11	←				10 42	10 54		11 08	11 11	←		11 42	11 45		11 54			12 08	12 11	←			12 42
	d	10 15	10 12	10 15				10 43	10 55		11 15	11 12	11 15		11 43	11 46		11 55			12 15	12 12	12 15			12 43
Bognor Regis 4	a	→		10 21				10 49			→		11 21		11 49						→		12 21			12 49
Chichester 4	a		10 19						11 02			11 19				11 53		12 02				12 19				
	d		10 20						11 03			11 20				11 58		12 03				12 20				
Fishbourne (Sussex)	d		10 23									11 23										12 23				
Bosham	d		10 26									11 26										12 26				
Nutbourne	d		10 29									11 29										12 29				
Southbourne	d		10 32						11 10			11 32						12 10				12 32				
Emsworth	d		10 35						11 13			11 35						12 13				12 35				
Warblington	d		10 38									11 38										12 38				
Havant	d		10 41						11 17			11 41				12 10		12 17				12 41				
Bedhampton	a		10 43									11 43										12 43				
Hilsea	a																									
Fratton	a		10 51						11 26			11 52						12 26				12 51				
Portsmouth & Southsea	a		10 54						11 29			11 55						12 29				12 54				
Portsmouth Harbour	a		10 58						11 35			11 59						12 35				12 58				
Cosham	a															12 16										
Portchester	a																									
Fareham	a															12 31										
Swanwick	a																									
Southampton Central	a															12 53										

For general notes see front of timetable
For details of catering facilities see Directory of Train Operators

A Until 7 September to Bristol Parkway (Table 132)
b Change at East Croydon and Brighton
c From 14 September dep. 30 minutes earlier
e From 14 September dep. 15 minutes earlier
g From 14 September dep. 23 minutes earlier
h Arr. 1020
j Arr. 1120
k Arr. 1220

For complete service between Three Bridges and Horsham see Table 186

Table 188

Sundays

London, Gatwick Airport & Brighton → Sussex Coast, Portsmouth and Southampton

Network Diagram - see first page of Table 186

		SN 1		SN 1	SN 1	SN 1	SN 1	SN 1	SN 1 🚲	SN 1			SN 1	SN 1	SN 1	SN 1	SN 1	SN 1 🚲	SN 1		SN 1	SN 1	SN 1	SN 1	SN 1	SN 1 🚲
London Victoria 15 ⊖	d	11 17					11b02	12c02	12 04	12 17						12b02	13c02	13 04	13 17					13b02	14c02	14 04
Clapham Junction 10	d	11 23					11b07	12c07	12 10	12 23						12b07	13c07	13 10	13 23					13b07	14c07	14 10
London Bridge 4 ⊖	d	*11 14*					*11 11*	*11b56*	*11 56*	*12 14*						*12 11*	*12b56*	*12 56*	*13 14*					*13 11*	*13b56*	*13 56*
East Croydon	d	11 37					*11 27*	*12e20*	12 23	12 37						*12 27*	*13e20*	13 23	13 37					*13 27*	*14e20*	14 23
Gatwick Airport 10 ✈	d	11 56					*11 50*	*12e42*	12 47	12 56						*12 50*	*13e42*	13 47	13 56					*13 50*	*14e42*	14 47
Three Bridges 4	a								12 52									13 52								14 52
	d	*11 54*					*11 54*	*12 24*	12 52	*12 54*						*12 54*	*13 24*	13 52	*13 54*					*13 54*	*14 24*	14 52
Crawley	d								12 55									13 55								14 55
Horsham 4	a								13 04									14 04								15 04
	d								13 05									14 05								15 05
Christs Hospital	d								13 08									14 08								15 08
Billingshurst	d								13 14									14 14								15 14
Pulborough	d								13 21									14 21								15 21
Amberley	d								13 27									14 27								15 27
Arundel	d								13 32									14 32								15 32
Haywards Heath 3	d	12 07					*12 03*	*12 33*		13 07						*13 03*	*13 33*		14 07					*14 03*	*14 33*	
Burgess Hill	d	12 12					*12 08*	*12 38*		13 12						*13 08*	*13 38*		14 12					*14 08*	*14 38*	
Brighton 10	d				←		12 50	13 17						←		13 50	14 17					←		14 50	15 17	
Hove 2	d	12 24			12 26		12 53	13f26 →		13 24				13 26		13 53	14g26 →		14 24			14 26		14 53	15h26 →	
Aldrington	d				12 28		12 55							13 28		13 55						14 28		14 55		
Portslade	d				12 31		12 58							13 31		13 58						14 31		14 58		
Fishersgate	d				12 33		13 00							13 33		14 00						14 33		15 00		
Southwick	d				12 35		13 02							13 35		14 02						14 35		15 02		
Shoreham-by-Sea	d	12 30			12 38		13 05			13 30				13 38		14 05			14 30			14 38		15 05		
Lancing	d				12 42		13 09							13 42		14 09						14 42		15 09		
East Worthing	d				12 45		13 12							13 45		14 12						14 45		15 12		
Worthing 4	a	12 36			12 47		13 14			13 36				13 47		14 14			14 36			14 47		15 14		
	d	12 40	12 42		12 48		13 15			13 40	13 42			13 48		14 15			14 40	14 42		14 48		15 15		
West Worthing	d		12 44		12 50		13 17				13 44			13 50		14 17				14 44		14 50		15 17		
Durrington-on-Sea	d		12 46		12 52		13 19				13 46			13 52		14 19				14 46		14 52		15 19		
Goring-by-Sea	d		12 49		12 55		13 22				13 49			13 55		14 22				14 49		14 55		15 22		
Angmering 3	d		12 53		12 59		13 26				13 53			13 59		14 26				14 53		14 59		15 26		
Littlehampton 4	a		13 02				13 35				14 02					14 35				15 02				15 35		
	d			12 57									13 57								14 57					
Ford 4	d			13 01	13 05				13 38				14 01	14 05				14 38			15 01	15 05				15 38
Bognor Regis 4	d																									
Barnham	a	12 54		13 08	13 11	←			13 42	13 54			14 08	14 11	←			14 42	14 54		15 08	15 11	←			15 42
	d	12 55		13 15 →	13 12	13 15			13 43	13 55			14 15 →	14 12	14 15			14 43	14 55		15 15 →	15 12	15 15			15 43
Bognor Regis 4	a					13 21			13 49						14 21			14 49					15 21			15 49
Chichester 4	a	13 02			13 19					14 02				14 19					15 02			15 19				
	d	13 03			13 20					14 03				14 20					15 03			15 20				
Fishbourne (Sussex)	d				13 23									14 23								15 23				
Bosham	d				13 26									14 26								15 26				
Nutbourne	d				13 29									14 29								15 29				
Southbourne	d	13 10			13 32					14 10				14 32					15 10			15 32				
Emsworth	d	13 13			13 35					14 13				14 35					15 13			15 35				
Warblington	d				13 38									14 38								15 38				
Havant	d	13 17			13 41					14 17				14 41					15 17			15 41				
Bedhampton	a				13 43									14 43								15 43				
Hilsea	a																									
Fratton	a	13 26			13 51					14 26				14 51					15 26			15 51				
Portsmouth & Southsea	a	13 29			13 54					14 29				14 54					15 29			15 54				
Portsmouth Harbour	a	13 35			13 58					14 35				14 58					15 35			15 58				
Cosham	a																									
Portchester	a																									
Fareham	a																									
Swanwick	a																									
Southampton Central	a																									

For general notes see front of timetable
For details of catering facilities see Directory of Train Operators

b From 14 September dep. 15 minutes earlier
c From 14 September dep. 30 minutes earlier
e From 14 September dep. 23 minutes earlier
f Arr. 1320
g Arr. 1420
h Arr. 1520

For complete service between Three Bridges and Horsham see Table 186

Table 188

Sundays

London, Gatwick Airport & Brighton → Sussex Coast, Portsmouth and Southampton

Network Diagram - see first page of Table 186

		SN 1		SN 1		SN 1	SN 1	GW ◇	SN 1	SN 1	SN 1 🚲	SN 1		SN 1	SN 1	SN 1	SN 1	SN 1		SN 1 🚲	SN 1		SN 1	SN 1	SN 1	GW ◇
London Victoria 15 ⊖	d	14 17						14b02	14c02	15c02	15 04	15 17					15b02	16c02		16 04	16 17					16b02
Clapham Junction 10	d	14 23						14b07	14c07	15c07	15 10	15 23					15b07	16c07		16 10	16 23					16b07
London Bridge 4 ⊖	d	14 14						14 11	14 11	14b56	14 56	15 14					15 11	15b56		15 56	16 14					16 11
East Croydon	d	14 37						14 27	14 27	15e20	15 23	15 37					15 27	16e20		16 23	16 37					16 27
Gatwick Airport 10 ✈	d	14 56						14 50	14 50	15e42	15 47	15 56					15 50	16e42		16 47	16 56					16 50
Three Bridges 4	a										15 52									16 52						
	d	14 54						14 54	14 54	15 24	15 52	15 54					15 54	16 24		16 52	16 54					16 54
Crawley	d										15 55									16 55						
Horsham 4	a										16 04									17 04						
	d										16 05									17 05						
Christs Hospital	d										16 08									17 08						
Billingshurst	d										16 14									17 14						
Pulborough	d										16 21									17 21						
Amberley	d										16 27									17 27						
Arundel	d										16 32									17 32						
Haywards Heath 3	d	15 07						15 03	15 03	15 33		16 07					16 03	16 33			17 07					17 03
Burgess Hill	d	15 12						15 08	15 08	15 38		16 12					16 08	16 38			17 12					17 08
Brighton 10	d					←		15 47	15 50	16 17					←		16 50	17 17						←		17 47
Hove 2	d	15 24				15 26		15 51	15 53	16f26 →		16 24			16 26		16 53	17g26 →			17 24			17 26		17 51
Aldrington	d					15 28			15 55						16 28		16 55							17 28		
Portslade	d					15 31			15 58						16 31		16 58							17 31		
Fishersgate	d					15 33			16 00						16 33		17 00							17 33		
Southwick	d					15 35			16 02						16 35		17 02							17 35		
Shoreham-by-Sea	d	15 30				15 38		15 57	16 05			16 30			16 38		17 05				17 30			17 38		17 57
Lancing	d					15 42			16 09						16 42		17 09							17 42		
East Worthing	d					15 45			16 12						16 45		17 12							17 45		
Worthing 4	a	15 36				15 47		16 03	16 14			16 36			16 47		17 14				17 36			17 47		18 03
	d	15 40	15 42			15 48		16 08	16 15			16 40	16 42		16 48		17 15				17 40	17 42		17 48		18 08
West Worthing	d		15 44			15 50			16 17				16 44		16 50		17 17					17 44		17 50		
Durrington-on-Sea	d		15 46			15 52			16 19				16 46		16 52		17 19					17 46		17 52		
Goring-by-Sea	d		15 49			15 55			16 22				16 49		16 55		17 22					17 49		17 55		
Angmering 3	d		15 53			15 59			16 26				16 53		16 59		17 26					17 53		17 59		
Littlehampton 4	a		16 02						16 35				17 02				17 35					18 02				
	d			15 57										16 57									17 57			
Ford 4	d			16 01		16 05					16 38			17 01	17 05					17 38			18 01	18 05		
Bognor Regis 4	d																									
Barnham	a	15 54		16 08		16 11	←	16 25			16 42	16 54		17 08	17 11	←				17 42	17 54		18 08	18 11	←	18 25
	d	15 55		16 15 →		16 12	16 15	16 25			16 43	16 55		17 15 →	17 12	17 15				17 43	17 55		18 15 →	18 12	18 15	18 25
Bognor Regis 4	a						16 21				16 49					17 21				17 49					18 21	
Chichester 4	a	16 02				16 19		16 33				17 02			17 19						18 02			18 19		18 33
	d	16 03				16 20		16 34				17 03			17 20						18 03			18 20		18 34
Fishbourne (Sussex)	d					16 23									17 23									18 23		
Bosham	d					16 26									17 26									18 26		
Nutbourne	d					16 29									17 29									18 29		
Southbourne	d	16 10				16 32						17 10			17 32						18 10			18 32		
Emsworth	d	16 13				16 35						17 13			17 35						18 13			18 35		
Warblington	d					16 38									17 38									18 38		
Havant	d	16 17				16 41		16 48				17 17			17 41						18 17			18 41		18 48
Bedhampton	a					16 43									17 43									18 43		
Hilsea	a																									
Fratton	a	16 26				16 51						17 26			17 51						18 26			18 51		
Portsmouth & Southsea	a	16 29				16 54						17 29			17 54						18 29			18 54		
Portsmouth Harbour	a	16 35				16 58						17 35			17 58						18 35			18 58		
Cosham	a							16 54																		
Portchester	a																									
Fareham	a							17 02																		
Swanwick	a																									19 00
Southampton Central	a							17 24																		19 22

For general notes see front of timetable
For details of catering facilities see Directory of Train Operators

b From 14 September dep. 15 minutes earlier
c From 14 September dep. 30 minutes earlier
e From 14 September dep. 23 minutes earlier
f Arr. 1620
g Arr. 1720

For complete service between Three Bridges and Horsham see Table 186

Table 188

Sundays

London, Gatwick Airport & Brighton → Sussex Coast, Portsmouth and Southampton

Network Diagram - see first page of Table 186

		SN 1	SN 1	SN 1	SN 1		SN 1	SN 1	SN 1		SN 1	SN 1	SN 1	SN 1		SN 1	SN 1	SN 1	SN 1	SN 1	SN 1	SN 1			SN 1	SN 1
London Victoria 15 ⊖	d	16b02	17 02	17 04	17 17							18 02	18 04	18 17						19 02	19 04	19 17				
Clapham Junction 10	d	16b07	17 07	17 10	17 23							18 07	18 10	18 23						19 07	19 10	19 23				
London Bridge 4 ⊖	d	16 11	16c56	16 56	17 14						17 11	17c44	17 44	18 14					18 11	18c44	18 44	19 14				
East Croydon	d	16 27	17 20	17 24	17 37						17 27	18 20	18 24	18 37					18 27	19 20	19 24	19 37				
Gatwick Airport 10 ✈	d	16 50	17 42	17 47	17 56						17 50	18 42	18 47	18 56					18 50	19 42	19 47	19 56				
Three Bridges 4	a			17 52									18 52								19 52					
	d	16 54	17 24	17 52	17 54						17 54	18 24	18 52	18 54					18 54	19 24	19 52	19 54				
Crawley	d			17 55									18 55								19 55					
Horsham 4	a			18 04									19 04								20 04					
	d			18 05									19 05								20 05					
Christs Hospital	d			18 08									19 08								20 08					
Billingshurst	d			18 14									19 14								20 14					
Pulborough	d			18 21									19 21								20 21					
Amberley	d			18 27									19 27								20 27					
Arundel	d			18 32									19 32								20 32					
Haywards Heath 3	d	17 03	17 33		18 07						18 03	18 33		19 07					19 03	19 33		20 07				
Burgess Hill	d	17 08	17 38		18 12						18 08	18 38		19 12					19 08	19 38		20 12				
Brighton 10	d	17 50	18 17					←			18 50	19 17					←		19 50	20 17						←
Hove 2	d	17 53	18e26		18 24			18 26			18 53	19f26		19 24			19 26		19 53	20g26		20 24				20 26
Aldrington	d	17 55	→					18 28			18 55	→					19 28		19 55	→						20 31
Portslade	d	17 58						18 31			18 58						19 31		19 58							20 33
Fishersgate	d	18 00						18 33			19 00						19 33		20 00							20 35
Southwick	d	18 02						18 35			19 02						19 35		20 02							20 38
Shoreham-by-Sea	d	18 05			18 30			18 38			19 05			19 30			19 38		20 05			20 30				20 42
Lancing	d	18 09						18 42			19 09						19 42		20 09							20 45
East Worthing	d	18 12						18 45			19 12						19 45		20 12							20 47
Worthing 4	a	18 14			18 36			18 47			19 14			19 36			19 47		20 14			20 36				
	d	18 15			18 40	18 42		18 48			19 15			19 40	19 42		19 48		20 15			20 40	20 42			20 48
West Worthing	d	18 17				18 44		18 50			19 17				19 44		19 50		20 17				20 44			20 50
Durrington-on-Sea	d	18 19				18 46		18 52			19 19				19 46		19 52		20 19				20 46			20 52
Goring-by-Sea	d	18 22				18 49		18 55			19 22				19 49		19 55		20 22				20 49			20 55
Angmering 3	d	18 26				18 53		18 59			19 26				19 53		19 59		20 26				20 53			20 59
Littlehampton 4	a	18 35				19 02					19 35				20 02				20 35				21 02			
	d						18 57									19 57									20 57	
Ford 4	d			18 38			19 01	19 05					19 38			20 01	20 05				20 38				21 01	21 05
Bognor Regis 4	d																									
Barnham	a			18 42	18 54		19 08	19 11	←				19 42	19 54		20 08	20 11	←			20 42	20 54			21 08	21 11
	d			18 43	18 55		19 15 →	19 12	19 15				19 43	19 55		20 15 →	20 12	20 15			20 43	20 55			21 15 →	21 12
Bognor Regis 4	a			18 49					19 21				19 49					20 21			20 49					
Chichester 4	a				19 02			19 19						20 02			20 19					21 02				21 19
	d				19 03			19 20						20 03			20 20					21 03				21 20
Fishbourne (Sussex)	d							19 23									20 23									21 23
Bosham	d							19 26									20 26									21 26
Nutbourne	d							19 29									20 29									21 29
Southbourne	d				19 10			19 32						20 10			20 32					21 10				21 32
Emsworth	d				19 13			19 35						20 13			20 35					21 13				21 35
Warblington	d							19 38									20 38									21 38
Havant	d				19 17			19 41						20 17			20 41					21 17				21 41
Bedhampton	a							19 43									20 43									21 43
Hilsea	a																									
Fratton	a				19 26			19 51						20 26			20 51					21 26				21 51
Portsmouth & Southsea	a				19 29			19 54						20 29			20 54					21 29				21 54
Portsmouth Harbour	a				19 35			19 58						20 35			20 58					21 35				21 58
Cosham	a																									
Portchester	a																									
Fareham	a																									
Swanwick	a																									
Southampton Central	a																									

For general notes see front of timetable
For details of catering facilities see Directory of Train Operators

b From 14 September dep. 15 minutes earlier
c Change at East Croydon and Brighton
e Arr. 1820
f Arr. 1920
g Arr. 2020

For complete service between Three Bridges and Horsham see Table 186

Table 188

Sundays

London, Gatwick Airport & Brighton → Sussex Coast, Portsmouth and Southampton

Network Diagram - see first page of Table 186

		SN 1	SN 1	SN 1	SN 1	SN 1		SN 1	SN 1	SN 1	SN 1	SN 1	SN 1	SN 1		SN 1	SN 1	SN 1	SN 1	SN 1	SN 1	SN 1	SN 1
London Victoria 15 ⊖	d			20 02	20 04	20 17					20 32		21 04	21 17				20b47	21 32	22 04	22 17		23 17
Clapham Junction 10	d			20 07	20 10	20 23					20 38		21 10	21 23				20b53	21 38	22 10	22 23		23 23
London Bridge 4 ⊖	d		19 11	19b44	19 44	20 14				20 11	20 41		20 44	21 14				21 11	21 41	21 44	22 14		23c11
East Croydon	d		19 27	20 20	20 23	20 37				20 27	20 57		21 23	21 37				21 27	21 57	22 23	22 37		23 37
Gatwick Airport 10 ✈	d		19 50	20e45	20 47	20 56				20 50	21 20		21 47	21 56				21 50	22 20	22 47	22 56		00 02
Three Bridges 4	a				20 52								21 52							22 52			00 07
	d		19 54	20 24	20 52	20 54				20 54	21 24		21 52	21 54				21 54	22 24	22 52	22 54		00 07
Crawley	d				20 55								21 55							22 55			
Horsham 4	a				21 04								22 04							23 04			
	d				21 05								22 05							23 05			
Christs Hospital	d				21 08								22 08							23 08			
Billingshurst	d				21 14								22 14							23 14			
Pulborough	d				21 21								22 21							23 21			
Amberley	d				21 27								22 27							23 27			
Arundel	d				21 32								22 32							23 32			
Haywards Heath 3	d		20 03	20f54		21 07				21 03	21 33			22 07				22 03	22 33		23 07		00 16
Burgess Hill	d		20 08	20 38		21 12				21 08	21 38			22 12				22 08	22 38		23 12		
Brighton 10	d		20 50	21 17					←	21 50	22 10							22 40	23 15				
Hove 2	d		20 53	21g26		21 24			21 26	21 53	22a13			22 24				22 43	23a18		23 24		00 31
Aldrington	d		20 55	→					21 28	21 55								22 45					
Portslade	d		20 58						21 31	21 58								22 48			23 27		00s34
Fishersgate	d		21 00						21 33	22 00								22 50					
Southwick	d		21 02						21 35	22 02								22 52			23 30		00s37
Shoreham-by-Sea	d		21 05			21 30			21 38	22 05				22 30				22 55			23 33		00s40
Lancing	d		21 09						21 42	22 09								22 59			23 37		00s44
East Worthing	d		21 12						21 45	22 12								23 02					
Worthing 4	a		21 14			21 36			21 47	22 14				22 36				23 04			23 41		00 48
	d		21 15			21 40	21 42		21 48	22 15				22 40	22 42			23 04					
West Worthing	d		21 17				21 44		21 50	22 17					22 44			23 06					
Durrington-on-Sea	d		21 19				21 46		21 52	22 19					22 46			23 09					
Goring-by-Sea	d		21 22				21 49		21 55	22 22					22 49			23 11					
Angmering 3	d		21 26				21 53		21 59	22 26					22 53			23 15					
Littlehampton 4	a		21 35				22 02			22 35					23 02			23 24					
	d							21 57									23 06	23 29					
Ford 4	d				21 38			22 01	22 05				22 38				23 10	23 33		23 38			
Bognor Regis 4	d																						
Barnham	a	←			21 42	21 54		22 08	22 11			←	22 42	22 54			23 14	23 37		23 42		←	
	d	21 15			21 43	21 55		22 15	22 12			22 15	22 43	22 55		22 56	23 15	23 45		23 43		23 45	
Bognor Regis 4	a	21 21			21 49			→				22 21	22 49			23 02	23 21	→		23 49			
Chichester 4	a					22 02			22 19					23 02								23 52	
	d					22 03			22 20					23 03									
Fishbourne (Sussex)	d								22 23														
Bosham	d								22 26					23 07									
Nutbourne	d								22 29					23 11									
Southbourne	d					22 10			22 32					23 13									
Emsworth	d					22 13			22 35					23 16									
Warblington	d								22 38														
Havant	d					22 17			22 41					23 21									
Bedhampton	a								22 43					23 47									
Hilsea	a																						
Fratton	a					22 26			22 51					23 31									
Portsmouth & Southsea	a					22 29			22 54					23 34									
Portsmouth Harbour	a					22 35			22 58					23 38									
Cosham	a																						
Portchester	a																						
Fareham	a																						
Swanwick	a																						
Southampton Central	a																						

For general notes see front of timetable
For details of catering facilities see Directory of Train Operators

b Change at East Croydon and Brighton
c Until 30 November only
e From 14 September dep. 3 minutes earlier
f From 14 September dep. 23 minutes earlier
g Arr. 2120

For complete service between Three Bridges and Horsham see Table 186

Southampton, Portsmouth and Sussex Coast → Brighton, Gatwick Airport & London

Network Diagram - see first page of Table 186

Miles	Miles	Miles	Station		SN	SN	SN	SN	SN	SN	SN	SN	SN	SN	SN	SN	SN	SN	SN	SN	SN	SN	SN	SN	SN
					MX	MX	MX																		
					1	1	1	1	1	1	1	1	1	1	1	1	1	1	1	1	1	1	1	1	1
0	—	—	**Southampton Central**	d																					
10¾	—	—	Swanwick	d																					
14½	—	—	Fareham	d																					
17¾	—	—	Portchester	d																					
20¼	—	—	Cosham	d																					
—	0	—	**Portsmouth Harbour**	d	22p44		23p15														05 34		05 47		
—	¾	—	Portsmouth & Southsea	d	22p48		23p19			04b35											05 38		05 51		
—	1½	—	Fratton	d	22p52		23p23			04c39											05 42		05 55		
—	4¼	—	Hilsea	d	22p56		23p27			04e43											05 46		05 59		
—	7¼	—	Bedhampton	d	23p01		23p33			04f48											05 51		06 04		
24¼	8	—	**Havant**	d	23p05		23p36			05 01						05 32					05 54		06 07		
—	8½	—	Warblington	d			23p38														05 56				
—	9¾	—	Emsworth	d			23p41														05 59		06 11		
—	11¼	—	Southbourne	d			23p44														06 02		06 14		
—	12¼	—	Nutbourne	d			23p47														06 04				
—	14	—	Bosham	d			23p50														06 08		06 18		
—	15¼	—	Fishbourne (Sussex)	d			23p53														06 11		06 21		
—	16¾	—	**Chichester** 4	a	23p16		23p57			05 15						05 44					06 14		06 25		
—	—	—		d	23p17	23p52	23p57			05 16						05 51					06 15		06 26		
0	—	—	**Bognor Regis** 4	d					05 13				05 35	05 49				05 55	06 04	06 11					
3½	23	—	Barnham	a	23p24	23p59	00 05		05 19	05 23	←		05 41	05 55		05 58		06 01	06 10	06 17	06 22		06 34		
—	—	—		d	23p25	00 01	00 06	04 48	05 27 →	05 24	05 27		05 42			05 59		06 02	06 11	06 18	06 23		06 34		
—	—	—	Bognor Regis 4	a																					
0	25¾	0	Ford 4	d	23p29	00 05	00 10	04 52			05 31		05 46					06 06	06 15		06 27				
—	—	2	**Littlehampton** 4	a	23p34	00 10	00 15	04 57			05 36								06 20						
2	—	—		d	23p39	23g24		05 02					05g35		05 50				06g04					06 33	
8	30	—	Angmering 3	d	23p47			05 10		05 33			05 53		06 01			06 13			06 33			06 41	
—	32½	—	Goring-by-Sea	d	23p51			05 14					05 57		06 05			06 17			06 37			06 45	
—	33¼	—	Durrington-on-Sea	d	23p53			05 17					05 59		06 08			06 19			06 40			06 47	
—	34	—	West Worthing	d	23p55			05 19					06 01		06 10			06 21			06 42			06 50	
—	35	—	**Worthing** 4	a	23p58			05 21		05 40			06 04		06 12			06 24			06 44			06 52	
—	—	—		d	23p59			05 22		05 41			06 04		06 13			06 24			06 45			06 53	
—	35¾	—	East Worthing	d	00 01			05 24					06 07					06 27			06 47				
—	37¼	—	Lancing	d	00 04			05 27		05 45			06 10		06 17			06 30			06 50			06 57	
—	40	—	Shoreham-by-Sea	d	00 08			05 32		05 49			06 14		06 21			06 34			06 54			07 01	
—	41	—	Southwick	d	00 11			05 35					06 17					06 37			06 57				
—	42	—	Fishersgate	d	00 13			05 37					06 19					06 39			06 59				
—	42½	—	Portslade	d	00 15			05 39		05 53			06 21		06 26			06 41			07 01			07 06	
—	43½	—	Aldrington	d	00 18			05 41					06 23					06 43			07 04				
0	44	—	Hove 2	d	00 20			05 44		05 57		05 59	06 26		06 30		06 36	06 46			07 06			07 11	07 17
—	45½	—	**Brighton** 10	a	00 25			05 48				06 03	06 30				06 40	06 50			07 10				07 21
13	—	—	Haywards Heath 3	a				06 19		06 12		06 29	06 57		06 52		07 08	07 23			07 36			07 29	07 46
9¼	—	—	Burgess Hill	a											06 44										
—	—	2¼	Arundel	d												06 07				06 26					
—	—	6	Amberley	d																06 31					
—	—	10¾	Pulborough	d												06 16				06 37					
—	—	15¾	Billingshurst	d												06 23				06 44					
—	—	20½	Christs Hospital	d												06 29				06 50					
—	—	23	**Horsham** 4	a												06 34				06 54			07 03		
—	—	—		d												06 35				06 55		←	07 04		
—	—	30	Crawley	d												06 49				07 08		07 08	07 13		
21½	—	31½	**Three Bridges** 4	a				06 36		06 21		06 40			07h24	06 52	07j24	07 32		→		07 12	07 17		07 56
—	—	—		d						06 21						06 57						07 21			
24¼	—	—	**Gatwick Airport** 10 ✈	a				06 41		06 25		06 45	07 11		07 11	07 02	07 21	07 37				07 29			08 00
40½	0	—	**East Croydon**	a				06 58		06 41		07 01	07 28		07 28	07 31	07 38	07 53			08 03	07 43		07 57	08 23
—	10¼	—	London Bridge 4 ⊖	a				07 14		07 14		07 16	07 46		07 46	07 48	08k03	08k18			08k26	08m03		08 20	08 41
48¼	—	—	Clapham Junction 10	a						06 51		07k19			07n47	07q39	07 47	08k10			08 13	07 54		08 06	08k40
51	—	61	**London Victoria** 15 ⊖	a						07 00		07r20	07r50		07t50	07q48	07 57	08j16			08 22	08 03		08 16	08r35

For general notes see front of timetable
For details of catering facilities see Directory of Train Operators

b From 29 September dep. 0430
c From 29 September dep. 0434
e From 29 September dep. 0438
f From 29 September dep. 0443
g Change at Ford
h Change at Haywards Heath
j Change at Brighton and Haywards Heath
k Change at Brighton and East Croydon
m Change at Three Bridges
n Change at East Croydon
q Change at Three Bridges and East Croydon
r Change at Brighton and Gatwick Airport
t Change at Gatwick Airport

For complete service between Horsham and Three Bridges see Table 186

Southampton, Portsmouth and Sussex Coast → Brighton, Gatwick Airport & London

Network Diagram - see first page of Table 186

		SN 1	SN 1	SN 1	SN 1	SN 1	SN 1	SN 1	SN 1	SN 1		SN 1	SN 1	SN 1	SN 1	SN 1	SN 1	SN 1	SN 1	GW	SN 1	SN 1	SN 1	SN 1	SN 1	SN 1
					🚲										🚲									🚲		
Southampton Central	d									05 48				06 10											07 06	
Swanwick	d									06 06				06 27											07 24	
Fareham	d									06 13				06 34											07 31	
Portchester	d									06 18				06 40											07 36	
Cosham	d									06 23				06 44											07 40	
Portsmouth Harbour	d			06 04												06 46				07 01			07 20			
Portsmouth & Southsea	d			06 08										*06 20*		06 50				07 05			07 24			
Fratton	d			06 12										*06 24*		06 54				07 10			07 28			
Hilsea	d			*06 03*												06 58				*07 08*			*07 08*			
Bedhampton	d			*06 08*						06 34						07 03				*07 13*			*07 13*			
Havant	d			06 20						06 37				06 53		07 06				07 20			07 36		07 47	
Warblington	d									06 39						07 08									07 49	
Emsworth	d			06 24						06 42				06 57		07 11									07 52	
Southbourne	d			06 27						06 45				07 00		07 14									07 55	
Nutbourne	d									06 48						07 16									07 58	
Bosham	d									06 51						07 20									08 01	
Fishbourne (Sussex)	d									06 54						07 23									08 04	
Chichester 4	a			06 34						06 58				07 07		07 26				07 31			07 47		08 08	
	d			06 35						06 59				07 08		07 28				07 32			07 47		08 08	
Bognor Regis 4	d	06 31			06 41			06 50	06 57						07 17		07 27					07 38		07 55		
Barnham	a	06 37		06 42	06 47			06 56	07 03	07 07				07 15	07 23	07 35	07 33			07 39		07 44	07 55	08 01	08 16	
	d	06 38		06 43	06 48			06 57		07 11				07 16	07 24	07 36				07 40		07 45	07 55	08 02	08 16	
Bognor Regis 4	a																									
Ford 4	d	06 42		06 47	06 52			07 01						07 20								07 49	08 00	08 06		
Littlehampton 4	a	06 47						07 06														07 54				
	d		06 43	06b39								07 03		07b00				07 22	07 33		07 45	07b18	07b49	07b58		08 01
Angmering 3	d		06 51	06 56								07 11		07 26				07 33	07 41		07 53		08 06			08 10
Goring-by-Sea	d		06 55	07 00								07 15		07 30				07 37	07 45		07 57					08 14
Durrington-on-Sea	d		06 57	07 03								07 17		07 33				07 40	07 47		08 00		08 12			08 17
West Worthing	d		07 00	07 05		07 12						07 20		07 35				07 42	07 50		08 02					08 19
Worthing 4	a		07 02	07 07		07 14						07 22		07 37				07 44	07 52	07 56	08 04		08 16			08 21
	d		07 03	07 08		07 15						07 23		07 38				07 45	07 53	08 00	08 05		08 16			08 22
East Worthing	d					07 17												07 47			08 07					08 24
Lancing	d		07 07	07 12		07 20						07 27		07 42				07 50	07 57		08 10		08 20			08 27
Shoreham-by-Sea	d		07 11	07 16		07 25						07 31		07 46				07 55	08 01	08 06	08 15		08 24			08 32
Southwick	d			07 19		07 28								07 49				07 58			08 18		08 27			08 35
Fishersgate	d					07 30												08 00			08 20					08 37
Portslade	d		07 16	07 22		07 32						07 36		07 52				08 02	08 06		08 22		08 31			08 39
Aldrington	d					07 34												08 04			08 24					08 41
Hove 2	d		07 20	07 26		07 37						07 41	07 49	07 56				08 07	08 11	08 13	08 27		08 34			08 44
Brighton 10	a			07 30		07 41	←						07 53	08 00				08 11		08 19	08 31		08 38			08 48
Haywards Heath 3	a		07 40			*08 05*	07 40					07 58	*08 23*					*08 37*	08 31		*08 55*		*08 57*			*09 16*
Burgess Hill	a																		08 26							
Arundel	d				06 57					07 18					07 31									08 11		
Amberley	d														07 36									08 16		
Pulborough	d				07 06					07 28					07 42									08 22		
Billingshurst	d				07 13					07 35					07 49									08 29		
Christs Hospital	d				07 19					07 41					07 56									08 35		
Horsham 4	a				07 24					07 45					08 00	08 05								08 39	08 45	
	d				07 25					07 46					08 10									08 49		
Crawley	d				07 37					08 01					08 19									08 58		
Three Bridges 4	a		*07 56*		07 40	08c27				08 05		*08 27*	*08 33*		08 23			*08 47*	08 41				09c11	09 01		*09 26*
	d				07 41					08 06					08 23				08 42					09 02		
Gatwick Airport 10 ✈	a		*08 00* →		*07 48*	*08 22*						08 12	*08 38*					*08 51*	*08 51*				*09 10*	09 06		*09 31*
East Croydon	a				08 00	*08 34*	08 08			08 27		08 29	*08 54*		08 43			*09 08*	09 01				*09 26*	09 22		*09 47*
London Bridge 4 ⊖	a				*08 24*	08e59	08 26			08 44		08f49	*09 10*		*09 07*			09e42					09e45	*09 45*		*10 00*
Clapham Junction 10	a				08 10	*08 43*	08g24			08g43		08 40	09e10		08 53			09e23	09 10				*09 35*	09 32		10e03
London Victoria 15 ⊖	a				08 20	*08 52*	08g33			08g52		08 49	09e19		09 02			09e33	09 19				*09 44*	09 42		

For general notes see front of timetable
For details of catering facilities see Directory of Train Operators

- b Change at Ford
- c Change at Brighton and Haywards Heath
- e Change at Brighton and East Croydon
- f Change at Haywards Heath
- g Change at East Croydon

For complete service between Horsham and Three Bridges see Table 186

Southampton, Portsmouth and Sussex Coast → Brighton, Gatwick Airport & London

Network Diagram - see first page of Table 186

Station																										
		SN 1		SN 1	SN 1	SN 1	SN 1	SN 1	SN 1	SN 1	SN 1	SN 1	SN 1	SN 1	SN 1	SN 1	SN 1		SN 1	SN 1	SN 1	SN 1	SN 1	SN 1	SN 1	SN 1
																								A		
							🛒				🛒													🛒		
Southampton Central	d							07 36															08 10			
Swanwick	d							07 53															08 28			
Fareham	d							08 00															08 35			
Portchester	d																						08 40			
Cosham	d							08 08															08 44			
Portsmouth Harbour	d											08 10					08 26									
Portsmouth & Southsea	d							*07 50*		08 03		08 14					08 30									
Fratton	d							*07 54*		08 07		08 18					08 35									
Hilsea	d							*07 41*		08 11							*08 32*									
Bedhampton	d							*07 49*		08 16							*08 37*									
Havant	d							08 15		08 19		08 27					08 45						08 51			
Warblington	d									08 21													08 53			
Emsworth	d									08 24		08 31											08 56			
Southbourne	d									08 27													08 59			
Nutbourne	d									08 29																
Bosham	d							08 22															09 03			
Fishbourne (Sussex)	d							08 25																		
Chichester 4	a							08 29		08 35		08 40					08 55						09 08			
	d					08 18		08 30		08 36		08 41					08 56			09 03			09 13			
Bognor Regis 4	d				08 13		08 26		08 32					08 49					09 00		09 09					
Barnham	a				08 19	08 25	08 32	08 37	08 38	08 43		08 48		08 55			09 03		09 06	09 10	09 15		09 20			
	d				08 20	08 26	08 33	08 38		08 44		08 49					09 04		09 07	09 11			09 21			
Bognor Regis 4	a																									
Ford 4	d				08 24	08 30	08 37			08 48							09 08		09 11	09 15						
Littlehampton 4	a					08 35				08 53										09 20						
	d	08 15					*08b26*						08 45				*08b58*							09 15		
Angmering 3	d	08 23			08 30			08 47					08 53				09 14							09 23		
Goring-by-Sea	d	08 27			08 34								08 57				09 18							09 27		
Durrington-on-Sea	d	08 30			08 37			08 52					09 00				09 21							09 30		
West Worthing	d	08 32			08 39								09 02			09 09	09 23							09 32		09 39
Worthing 4	a	08 34			08 41			08 56					09 04			09 11	09 25							09 34		09 41
	d	08 35			08 42			08 57					09 05			09 12	09 26							09 36		09 42
East Worthing	d				08 44											09 14										09 44
Lancing	d	08 39			08 47			09 01					09 09			09 17	09 30									09 47
Shoreham-by-Sea	d	08 43			08 52			09 05					09 13			09 22	09 34							09 42		09 52
Southwick	d				08 55			09 08								09 25	09 37									09 55
Fishersgate	d				08 57											09 27										09 57
Portslade	d	08 48			08 59			09 11					09 18			09 29	09 40							09 47		09 59
Aldrington	d				09 01											09 31										10 01
Hove 2	d	08 52		08 54	09 04			09 15					09 22		09 24	09 34	09 44							09 51	09 54	10 04
Brighton 10	a			08 58	09 08			09 19							09 28	09 38	09 48								09 58	10 08
Haywards Heath 3	a	09 12		*09 25*	*09 32*								09 40		*09 47*		*10 15*							10 06	*10 18*	
Burgess Hill	a	09 07											09 35											10 02		
Arundel	d						08 42												09 16							
Amberley	d						08 47																			
Pulborough	d						08 53												09 25							
Billingshurst	d						09 00				←								09 31			←				
Christs Hospital	d						09 06 →				09 06								09 38 →			09 38				
Horsham 4	a										09 10	09 16										09 42	09 48			
	d										09 20											09 52				
Crawley	d										09 29											10 01				
Three Bridges 4	a	*09c26*		*09 36*							09 32		*10c07*		*10 07*		*10 25*					10 04		*10 25*	*10 42*	
	d										09 33											10 05				
Gatwick Airport 10 ✈	a	09 26		*09 41*	*09 44*						09 37		09 55		*10 00*							10 09		10 24	*10 30*	
East Croydon 🚃	a	09 42			*09 55*						09 59		10 11		*10 16*	*10 24*						10 29		10 40	*10 46*	*10 55*
London Bridge 4 ⊖	a	*10 00*		*10 15*	*10e22*						*10f15*		*10 30*		*10 30*	*10e45*						*10g45*		*11 00*	*11 00*	*11e15*
Clapham Junction 10	a	09 52			*10 05*						10 09		10 21			*10 33*						10 38		10 49	*11e03*	*11 04*
London Victoria 15 ⊖	a	10 00			*10 13*						10 16		10 28		*10h35*	*10 40*						10 45		10 58	*11h05*	*11 11*

For general notes see front of timetable
For details of catering facilities see Directory of Train Operators

A 🛒 from Haywards Heath
b Change at Ford
c Change at Haywards Heath
e Change at Brighton and East Croydon
f Change at Three Bridges
g Change at Gatwick Airport
h Change at Brighton and Gatwick Airport

For complete service between Horsham and Three Bridges see Table 186

Southampton, Portsmouth and Sussex Coast → Brighton, Gatwick Airport & London

Network Diagram - see first page of Table 186

		SN 1	SN 1	SN 1	SN 1	SN 1	SN 1	SN 1 A 🛒	SN 1	SN 1	SN 1	SN 1 🛒	SN 1	SN 1 🛒	SN 1	SN 1	SN 1	SN 1	SN 1	SN 1	SN 1	SN 1	SN 1	SN 1	SN 1 A 🛒
Southampton Central	d		08 36												09 11					09 36					
Swanwick	d		08 53												09 28					09 53					
Fareham	d		09 00												09 36					10 00					
Portchester	d														09 41										
Cosham	d		09 08												09 45					10 08					
Portsmouth Harbour	d			08 59			09 12				09 28													10 12	
Portsmouth & Southsea	d		*08 50*	09 03			09 16				09 32									*09 50*	10 03			10 16	
Fratton	d		*08 54*	09 07			09 20				09 36									*09 54*	10 07			10 20	
Hilsea	d			09 11							*09 32*										10 11				
Bedhampton	d			09 16							*09 37*										10 16				
Havant	d		09 15	09 19			09 30				09 45				09 52					10 15	10 19			10 30	
Warblington	d														09 54										
Emsworth	d		09 19	09 23											09 57					10 19	10 23				
Southbourne	d		09 22	09 26											10 00					10 22	10 26				
Nutbourne	d			09 28																	10 28				
Bosham	d														10 04										
Fishbourne (Sussex)	d			09 33																	10 33				
Chichester 4	a		09 29	09 36			09 40				09 55				10 09					10 29	10 36			10 40	
	d		09 30	09 37			09 41				09 56				10 11					10 30	10 37			10 41	
Bognor Regis 4	d	09 26			09 39							10 00	10 07						10 26			10 39			
Barnham	a	09 32	09 37	09 44	09 45		09 48				10 03	10 06	10 13		10 18				10 32	10 37	10 44	10 45		10 48	
	d	09 33	09 38	09 45			09 49				10 04	10 07	10 15		10 19				10 33	10 38	10 45			10 49	
Bognor Regis 4	a																								
Ford 4	d	09 37		09 49							10 08	10 11	10 19						10 37		10 49				
Littlehampton 4	a			09 54									10 24								10 54				
	d							09 45			*09b54*		*10b11*			10 15									10 45
Angmering 3	d		09 47					09 53			10 14					10 23				10 47					10 53
Goring-by-Sea	d							09 57			10 18					10 27									10 57
Durrington-on-Sea	d							10 00			10 21					10 30									11 00
West Worthing	d							10 02		10 09	10 23					10 32		10 39							11 02
Worthing 4	a		09 54					10 04		10 11	10 25					10 34		10 41		10 54					11 04
	d		09 56					10 06		10 12	10 26					10 36		10 42		10 56					11 06
East Worthing	d									10 14								10 44							
Lancing	d		10 00					10 10		10 17	10 30							10 47		11 00					11 10
Shoreham-by-Sea	d		10 04					10 14		10 22	10 34					10 42		10 52		11 04					11 14
Southwick	d		10 07							10 25	10 37							10 55		11 07					
Fishersgate	d									10 27								10 57							
Portslade	d		10 10							10 29	10 40					10 47		10 59		11 10					
Aldrington	d									10 31								11 01							
Hove 2	d		10 14					10 21	10 24	10 34	10 44					10 51	10 54	11 04		11 14					11 21
Brighton 10	a		10 18						10 28	10 38	10 48						10 58	11 08		11 18					
Haywards Heath 3	a							10 35	*10 47*		*11 15*					11 08	*11 18*								11 35
Burgess Hill	a															11 01									
Arundel	d	09 42										10 16							10 42						
Amberley	d	09 47																	10 47						
Pulborough	d	09 53										10 25		←					10 53						
Billingshurst	d	09 59				←						10 31		10 31					10 59				←		
Christs Hospital	d	10 06				10 06						→							11 06				11 06		
Horsham 4	a	→				10 10	10 16							10 40	10 46				→				11 10	11 16	
	d					10 20								10 50									11 20		
Crawley	d					10 29								10 59									11 29		
Three Bridges 4	a					10 32		*11 11*	*11 11*		*11 25*			11 02		*11c25*	*11 42*						11 32		*12 11*
	d					10 33								11 03									11 33		
Gatwick Airport 10 ✈	a					10 37		10 54	*11 00*					11 07		11 24	*11 30*						11 37		11 54
East Croydon 🚊	a					10 59		11 11	*11 16*	*11 23*				11 27		11 40	*11 46*	*11 55*					12 00		12 10
London Bridge 4 ⊖	a					*11e15*		*11 30*	*11 30*	*11f45*				*11 45*		*12 00*	*12 00*	*12f15*					*12e15*		*12 30*
Clapham Junction 10	a					11 09		11 20		*11 33*				11 37		11 49	*12f03*	*12 04*					12 11		12 20
London Victoria 15 ⊖	a					11 16		11 27	*11g35*	*11 40*				11 44		11 58	*12g05*	*12 11*					12 18		12 29

For general notes see front of timetable
For details of catering facilities see
Directory of Train Operators

- **A** 🛒 from Haywards Heath
- **b** Change at Ford
- **c** Change at Haywards Heath
- **e** Change at Gatwick Airport
- **f** Change at Brighton and East Croydon
- **g** Change at Brighton and Gatwick Airport

For complete service between Horsham and Three Bridges see Table 186

Southampton, Portsmouth and Sussex Coast → Brighton, Gatwick Airport & London

Network Diagram - see first page of Table 186

		SN 1		SN 1	SN 1	SN 1	SN 1	SN 1	SN 1	SN 1	SN 1	SN 1	SN 1	SN 1	SN 1	SN 1	SN 1	SN 1		SN 1	SN 1	SN 1	SN 1	SN 1	SN 1	
																				A						
						⌶		⌶					⌶				⌶			⌶				⌶		
Southampton Central	d								10 11					10 36												
Swanwick	d								10 28					10 53												
Fareham	d								10 35					11 00												
Portchester	d								10 40																	
Cosham	d								10 45					11 08												
Portsmouth Harbour	d				10 28													11 12					11 28			
Portsmouth & Southsea	d				10 32									*10 50*	11 03			11 16					11 32			
Fratton	d				10 36									*10 54*	11 07			11 20					11 36			
Hilsea	d				*10 32*										11 11								*11 32*			
Bedhampton	d				*10 37*										11 16								*11 37*			
Havant	d				10 45				10 51					11 15	11 19			11 30					11 45			
Warblington	d								10 53																	
Emsworth	d								10 56					11 19	11 23											
Southbourne	d								10 59					11 22	11 26											
Nutbourne	d														11 28											
Bosham	d								11 04																	
Fishbourne (Sussex)	d														11 33											
Chichester 4	a				10 55				11 08					11 29	11 36			11 40					11 55			
	d				10 56				11 11					11 30	11 37			11 41					11 56			
Bognor Regis 4	d					11 00	11 07						11 26			11 39								12 00	12 07	
Barnham	a				11 03	11 06	11 13		11 18				11 32	11 37	11 44	11 45		11 48					12 03	12 06	12 13	
	d				11 04	11 07	11 15		11 19				11 33	11 38	11 45			11 49					12 04	12 07	12 15	
Bognor Regis 4	a																									
Ford 4	d				11 08	11 11	11 19						11 37		11 49								12 08	12 11	12 19	
Littlehampton 4	a						11 24								11 54										12 24	
	d				*10b58*		*11b11*			11 15										11 45			*11 58*		*12 11*	
Angmering 3	d				11 14					11 23				11 47						11 53			12 14			
Goring-by-Sea	d				11 18					11 27										11 57			12 18			
Durrington-on-Sea	d				11 21					11 30										12 00			12 21			
West Worthing	d			11 09	11 23					11 32		11 39								12 02		12 09	12 23			
Worthing 4	a			11 11	11 25					11 34		11 41		11 54						12 04		12 11	12 25			
	d			11 12	11 26					11 36		11 42		11 56						12 06		12 12	12 26			
East Worthing	d			11 14								11 44										12 14				
Lancing	d			11 17	11 30							11 47		12 00						12 10		12 17	12 30			
Shoreham-by-Sea	d			11 22	11 34					11 42		11 52		12 04						12 14		12 22	12 34			
Southwick	d			11 25	11 37							11 55		12 07								12 25	12 37			
Fishersgate	d			11 27								11 57										12 27				
Portslade	d			11 29	11 40					11 47		11 59		12 10								12 29	12 40			
Aldrington	d			11 31								12 01										12 31				
Hove 2	d	11 24		11 34	11 44					11 51	11 54	12 04		12 14						12 21	12 24	12 34	12 44			
Brighton 10	a	11 28		11 38	11 48						11 58	12 08		12 18							12 28	12 38	12 48			
Haywards Heath 3	a	*11 47*			*12 15*					12 09	*12 18*									12 35	*12 47*		*13 15*			
Burgess Hill	a									12 01																
Arundel	d					11 16							11 42											12 16		
Amberley	d												11 47													
Pulborough	d					11 25		←					11 53				←							12 25		
Billingshurst	d					11 31 →		11 31					11 59											12 31 →		
Christs Hospital	d												12 06 →				12 06									
Horsham 4	a							11 40	11 46								12 10	12 16								
	d								11 50									12 20								
Crawley	d								11 59									12 29								
Three Bridges 4	a	*12 11*			*12 25*				12 02	*12c25*	*12 42*							12 32		*13 11*	*13 11*		*13 25*			
	d								12 03									12 33								
Gatwick Airport 10 ✈	a	*12 00*							12 07	12 24	*12 30*							12 37		12 54	*13 00*					
East Croydon	a	*12 16*		*12 23*					12 27	12 40	*12 46*	*12 55*						13 00		13 10	*13 16*	*13 23*				
London Bridge 4 ⊖	a	*12 30*		*12e45*					*12 45*	*13 00*	*13 00*	*13e15*						*13f15*		*13 30*	*13 30*	*13e45*				
Clapham Junction 10	a			*12 33*					12 37	12 49	*13e03*	*13 04*						13 11		13 19		*13 33*				
London Victoria 15 ⊖	a	*12g35*		*12 40*					12 44	12 57	*13g05*	*13 11*						13 18		13 27	*13g35*	*13 40*				

For general notes see front of timetable
For details of catering facilities see Directory of Train Operators

A ⌶ from Haywards Heath
b Change at Ford
c Change at Haywards Heath
e Change at Brighton and East Croydon
f Change at Gatwick Airport
g Change at Brighton and Gatwick Airport

For complete service between Horsham and Three Bridges see Table 186

Table 188

Mondays to Fridays

Southampton, Portsmouth and Sussex Coast → Brighton, Gatwick Airport & London

Network Diagram - see first page of Table 186

		SN 1	SN 1	SN 1	SN 1	SN 1	SN 1	SN 1	SN 1	SN 1	SN 1	SN 1	SN 1	SN 1	SN 1	SN 1	SN 1	SN 1	SN 1	SN 1	SN 1	SN 1	SN 1	SN 1	SN 1
													A												
		🛒					🛒				🛒		🛒				🛒		🛒						
Southampton Central	d		11 11					11 36												12 11					12 36
Swanwick	d		11 28					11 53												12 28					12 53
Fareham	d		11 35					12 00												12 35					13 00
Portchester	d		11 40																	12 40					
Cosham	d		11 45					12 09												12 44					13 08
Portsmouth Harbour	d											12 12				12 28									
Portsmouth & Southsea	d							11 50	12 03			12 16				12 32									12 50
Fratton	d							11 54	12 07			12 20				12 36									12 54
Hilsea	d								12 11							12 32									
Bedhampton	d								12 16							12 37									
Havant	d		11 51					12 15	12 19			12 30				12 45				12 51					13 15
Warblington	d		11 53																	12 53					
Emsworth	d		11 56					12 19	12 23											12 56					13 19
Southbourne	d		11 59					12 22	12 26											12 59					13 22
Nutbourne	d								12 29																
Bosham	d		12 04																	13 03					
Fishbourne (Sussex)	d								12 33																
Chichester 4	a		12 08					12 29	12 36			12 40				12 55				13 08					13 29
	d		12 11					12 30	12 37			12 41				12 56				13 11					13 30
Bognor Regis 4	d						12 26			12 39							13 00	13 07						13 26	
Barnham	a		12 18				12 32	12 37	12 44	12 45		12 48				13 03	13 06	13 13		13 18				13 32	13 37
	d		12 19				12 33	12 38	12 45			12 49				13 04	13 07	13 15		13 19				13 33	13 38
Bognor Regis 4	a																								
Ford 4	d						12 37		12 49							13 08	13 11	13 19						13 37	
Littlehampton 4	a								12 54									13 24							
	d			12 15									12 45			12b58		13b11			13 15				
Angmering 3	d			12 23				12 47					12 53			13 14					13 23				13 47
Goring-by-Sea	d			12 27									12 57			13 18					13 27				
Durrington-on-Sea	d			12 30									13 00			13 21					13 30				
West Worthing	d			12 32		12 39							13 02		13 09	13 23					13 32		13 39		
Worthing 4	a			12 34		12 41		12 54					13 04		13 11	13 25					13 34		13 41		13 54
	d			12 36		12 42		12 56					13 06		13 12	13 26					13 36		13 42		13 56
East Worthing	d					12 44									13 14								13 44		
Lancing	d					12 47		13 00					13 10		13 17	13 30							13 47		14 00
Shoreham-by-Sea	d			12 42		12 52		13 04					13 14		13 22	13 34					13 42		13 52		14 04
Southwick	d					12 55		13 07							13 25	13 37							13 55		14 07
Fishersgate	d					12 57									13 27								13 57		
Portslade	d			12 47		12 59		13 10							13 29	13 40					13 47		13 59		14 10
Aldrington	d					13 01									13 31								14 01		
Hove 2	d			12 51	12 54	13 04		13 14					13 21	13 24	13 34	13 44					13 51	13 54	14 04		14 14
Brighton 10	a				12 58	13 08		13 18						13 28	13 38	13 48						13 58	14 08		14 18
Haywards Heath 3	a			13 09	13 18								13 35	13 47		14 15					14 09	14 18			
Burgess Hill	a			13 01																	14 01				
Arundel	d						12 42										13 16							13 42	
Amberley	d						12 47																	13 47	
Pulborough	d	←					12 53										13 25		←					13 53	
Billingshurst	d	12 31					12 59				←						13 31 →		13 31					13 59	
Christs Hospital	d						13 06 →				13 06													14 06 →	
Horsham 4	a	12 40	12 46								13 10	13 16							13 40	13 46					
	d	12 50									13 20								13 50						
Crawley	d	12 59									13 29								13 59						
Three Bridges 4	a	13 02		13c25	13 42						13 32		14 11	14 11		14 25			14 02		14c25	14 41			
	d	13 03									13 33								14 03						
Gatwick Airport 10 ✈	a	13 07		13 24	13 30						13 37		13 54	14 00					14 07		14 24	14 30			14 50
East Croydon	a	13 27		13 40	13 46	13 55					14 00		14 10	14 16	14 23				14 27		14 40	14 46	14 55		15 08
London Bridge 4 ⊖	a	13 45		14 00	14 00	14e15					14f15		14 30	14 30	14e45				14 45		15 00	15 00	15e15		
Clapham Junction 10	a	13 37		13 49	14e03	14 04					14 11		14 19		14 33				14 37		14 49	15e03	15 04		15e25
London Victoria 15 ⊖	a	13 44		13 58	14g05	14 11					14 18		14 27	14g35	14 40				14 44		14 57	15g05	15 11		15g28

For general notes see front of timetable
For details of catering facilities see Directory of Train Operators

A 🛒 from Haywards Heath
b Change at Ford
c Change at Haywards Heath
e Change at Brighton and East Croydon
f Change at Gatwick Airport
g Change at Brighton and Gatwick Airport

For complete service between Horsham and Three Bridges see Table 186

Southampton, Portsmouth and Sussex Coast → Brighton, Gatwick Airport & London

Network Diagram - see first page of Table 186

Station		SN 1		SN 1	SN 1	SN 1	SN 1	SN 1	SN 1	SN 1	SN 1	SN 1	SN 1	SN 1	SN 1	SN 1	SN 1		SN 1	SN 1	SN 1	SN 1	SN 1	SN 1	SN 1	SN 1
							A ⚲												⚲				⚲		A ⚲	⚲
Southampton Central	d													13 11						13 36						
Swanwick	d													13 28						13 53						
Fareham	d													13 35						14 00						
Portchester	d													13 40												
Cosham	d													13 45						14 08						
Portsmouth Harbour	d					13 12				13 28														14 12		
Portsmouth & Southsea	d	13 03				13 16				13 32										*13 50*	14 03			14 16		
Fratton	d	13 07				13 20				13 36										*13 54*	14 07			14 20		
Hilsea	d	13 11								*13 32*											14 11					
Bedhampton	d	13 16								*13 37*											14 16					
Havant	d	13 19				13 30				13 45				13 51						14 15	14 19			14 30		
Warblington	d													13 53												
Emsworth	d	13 23												13 56						14 19	14 23					
Southbourne	d	13 26												13 59						14 22	14 26					
Nutbourne	d	13 28																			14 28					
Bosham	d													14 04												
Fishbourne (Sussex)	d	13 33																			14 33					
Chichester 4	a	13 36				13 40				13 55				14 08						14 29	14 36			14 40		
	d	13 37				13 41				13 56				14 11						14 30	14 37			14 41		
Bognor Regis 4	d			13 39							14 00	14 07							14 26			14 39				14 54
Barnham	a	13 44		13 45		13 48				14 03	14 06	14 13		14 18					14 32	14 37	14 44	14 45		14 48		15 00
	d	13 45				13 49				14 04	14 07	14 15		14 19					14 33	14 38	14 45			14 49		15 01
Bognor Regis 4	a																									
Ford 4	d	13 49								14 08	14 11	14 19							14 37		14 49					15 05
Littlehampton 4	a	13 54										14 24									14 54					
	d						13 45			*13b58*		*14b11*			14 15										14 45	*14b54*
Angmering 3	d						13 53			14 14					14 23					14 47					14 53	
Goring-by-Sea	d						13 57			14 18					14 27										14 57	
Durrington-on-Sea	d						14 00			14 21					14 30										15 00	
West Worthing	d						14 02		14 09	14 23					14 32		14 39								15 02	
Worthing 4	a						14 04		14 11	14 25					14 34		14 41			14 54					15 04	
	d						14 06		14 12	14 26					14 36		14 42			14 56					15 06	
East Worthing	d								14 14								14 44									
Lancing	d						14 10		14 17	14 30							14 47			15 00					15 10	
Shoreham-by-Sea	d						14 14		14 22	14 34					14 42		14 52			15 04					15 14	
Southwick	d								14 25	14 37							14 55			15 07						
Fishersgate	d								14 27								14 57									
Portslade	d								14 29	14 40					14 47		14 59			15 10						
Aldrington	d								14 31								15 01									
Hove 2	d						14 21	14 24	14 34	14 44					14 51	14 54	15 04			15 14					15 21	
Brighton 10	a							14 28	14 38	14 48						14 58	15 08			15 18						
Haywards Heath 3	a						14 35	*14 47*		*15 15*					15 09	*15 18*									15 35	
Burgess Hill	a														15 01											
Arundel	d										14 16								14 42							15c14
Amberley	d																		14 47							
Pulborough	d										14 25								14 53							15 23
Billingshurst	d										14 31 →		← 14 31						14 59							15 29
Christs Hospital	d				← 14 06														15 06 →				← 15 06			15 36 →
Horsham 4	a				14 10	14 16							14 40	14 46									15 10	15 16		
	d					14 20								14 50										15 20		
Crawley	d					14 29								14 59										15 29		
Three Bridges 4	a					14 32	*15 11*	*15 11*		*15 25*				15 02	*15e25*	15 42								15 32	*16 07*	
	d					14 33								15 03										15 33		
Gatwick Airport 10 ✈	a					14 37	14 54	*15 00*						15 07	15 24	*15 30*								15 37	15 55	
East Croydon	a					15 00	15 09	*15 16*	15 23					15 27	15 41	*15 46*	15 55							16 00	16 11	
London Bridge 4 ⊖	a					*15f15*	*15 30*	*15 30*	15g45					*15 45*	*16 00*	*16 00*	16g15							*16f15*	*16 41*	
Clapham Junction 10	a					15 11	15 19		*15 33*					15 37	15 51	16g03	*16 04*							16 11	16 21	
London Victoria 15 ⊖	a					15 18	15 28	15h35	*15 40*					15 44	15 58	16h05	*16 11*							16 20	16 29	

For general notes see front of timetable
For details of catering facilities see
Directory of Train Operators

A ⚲ from Haywards Heath
b Change at Ford
c Arr. 1510
e Change at Haywards Heath
f Change at Gatwick Airport
g Change at Brighton and East Croydon
h Change at Brighton and Gatwick Airport

For complete service between Horsham and Three Bridges see Table 186

Southampton, Portsmouth and Sussex Coast → Brighton, Gatwick Airport & London

Network Diagram - see first page of Table 186

		SN 1	SN 1	SN 1	SN 1	SN 1 🛒	SN 1	SN 1	SN 1	SN 1	GW ◇ A	SN 1	SN 1	SN 1	SN 1	SN 1	SN 1	SN 1 B 🛒	SN 1	SN 1	SN 1	SN 1 🛒	SN 1
Southampton Central	d						14 11				14 35		14 26										
Swanwick	d						14 28																
Fareham	d						14 35				14 56		15 02										
Portchester	d						14 40																
Cosham	d						14 45				15 04												
Portsmouth Harbour	d			14 28													15 12				15 28		
Portsmouth & Southsea	d			14 32							*14 50*		*14 50*	15 03			15 16				15 32		
Fratton	d			14 36							*14 54*		*14 54*	15 07			15 20				15 36		
Hilsea	d			*14 32*										15 11							*15 32*		
Bedhampton	d			*14 37*										15 16							*15 37*		
Havant	d			14 45			14 51				15 11		15 15	15 19			15 30				15 45		
Warblington	d						14 53																
Emsworth	d						14 56						15 19	15 23									
Southbourne	d						14 59						15 22	15 26									
Nutbourne	d													15 28									
Bosham	d						15 04																
Fishbourne (Sussex)	d													15 33									
Chichester 4	a			14 55			15 08				15 21		15 30	15 36			15 40				15 55		
	d			14 56			15 11				15 22		15 30	15 37			15 41				15 56		
Bognor Regis 4	d				15 09							15 26			15 39							16 00	16 09
Barnham	a			15 03	15 15		15 18				15 29	15 32	15 38	15 44	15 45		15 48				16 03	16 06	16 15
	d			15 04			15 19				15 30	15 33	15 38	15 45			15 49				16 04	16 07	
Bognor Regis 4	a																						
Ford 4	d			15 08								15 37		15 49							16 08	16 11	
Littlehampton 4	a													15 54									
	d							15 15				*15b23*						15 45		15 50	*15b54*		
Angmering 3	d			15 14				15 23					15 47					15 53		16 00	16 14		
Goring-by-Sea	d			15 18				15 27										15 57		16 04	16 18		
Durrington-on-Sea	d			15 21				15 30										16 00		16 07	16 21		
West Worthing	d		15 09	15 23				15 32		15 39								16 02		16 09	16 23		
Worthing 4	a		15 11	15 25				15 34		15 41	15 45		15 54					16 04		16 11	16 25		
	d		15 12	15 26				15 36		15 42	15 50		15 56					16 06		16 12	16 26		
East Worthing	d		15 14							15 44										16 14			
Lancing	d		15 17	15 30						15 47			16 00					16 10		16 17	16 30		
Shoreham-by-Sea	d		15 22	15 34				15 42		15 52	15 57		16 04					16 14		16 22	16 34		
Southwick	d		15 25	15 37						15 55			16 07							16 25	16 37		
Fishersgate	d		15 27							15 57										16 27			
Portslade	d		15 29	15 40				15 47		15 59			16 10							16 29	16 40		
Aldrington	d		15 31							16 01										16 31			
Hove 2	d	15 24	15 34	15 44				15 51	15 54	16 04	16 08		16 14					16 21	16 24	16 34	16 44		
Brighton 10	a	15 28	15 38	15 48					15 58	16 08	16 14		16 18						16 28	16 38	16 48		
Haywards Heath 3	a	*15 48*		*16 15*				16 09	*16 18*	*16 30*			*16 50*					16 35			*17 15*		
Burgess Hill	a							16 01															
Arundel	d											15 42										16 16	
Amberley	d											15 47											
Pulborough	d											15 53											
Billingshurst	d					←						15 59				←						16 25	
Christs Hospital	d					15 36						16 06 →				16 06						16 31	
Horsham 4	a					15 40	15 46									16 10	16 16					16 38 →	
	d					15 50										16 20							
Crawley	d					15 59										16 29							
Three Bridges 4	a	*16 07*		*16 25*		16 02		16c25	*16 37*	*16 47*			*17 02*			16 32		*16 47*					
	d					16 03										16 33							
Gatwick Airport 10 ✈	a	*16 00*				16 07		16 26	*16 30*	*16 52*			*17 06*			16 37		16 55					
East Croydon	a	*16 16*	*16 24*			16 30		16 42	*16 46*	*16 55*	*16 55*					17 01		17 11		*17 25*			
London Bridge 4 ⊖	a	16e41	16e56			16f42		17 02	*17 02*	17e26	17e26					*17 26*		17c29		17e54			
Clapham Junction 10	a		*16 33*			16 39		16 51	17e03	*17 04*	*17 04*					17 10		17 21		*17 34*			
London Victoria 15 ⊖	a	16g35	*16 41*			16 46		16 58	17g05	*17 11*	*17 11*					17 20		17 28		*17 43*			

For general notes see front of timetable
For details of catering facilities see Directory of Train Operators

A From Great Malvern (Table 71)
B 🛒 from Haywards Heath
b Change at Ford
c Change at Haywards Heath
e Change at Brighton and East Croydon
f Change at Three Bridges
g Change at Brighton and Gatwick Airport

For complete service between Horsham and Three Bridges see Table 186

Southampton, Portsmouth and Sussex Coast → Brighton, Gatwick Airport & London

Network Diagram - see first page of Table 186

		SN 1	SN 1	SN 1	SN 1	SN 1	SN 1	SN 1	SN 1	SN 1	SN 1	SN 1	SN 1	SN 1	SN 1	SN 1	SN 1	SN 1	SN 1	SN 1	SN 1	SN 1	SN 1	SN 1	SN 1
													A												
		🛒					🛒				🛒		🛒				🛒								
Southampton Central	d		15 11					15 36										16 11						16 36	
Swanwick	d		15 28					15 53										16 28						16 53	
Fareham	d		15 35					16 00										16 36						17 00	
Portchester	d		15 40															16 41							
Cosham	d		15 44					16 08										16 45						17 08	
Portsmouth Harbour	d											16 12				16 28						16 40			
Portsmouth & Southsea	d							*15 50*	16 03			16 16				16 32						16 46		*16 50*	17 03
Fratton	d							*15 54*	16 07			16 20				16 36						16 50		*16 54*	17 07
Hilsea	d								16 11							*16 32*						16 54			17 11
Bedhampton	d								16 16							*16 37*									17 16
Havant	d		15 51					16 15	16 19			16 30				16 45		16 52				17 00		17 15	17 19
Warblington	d		15 53															16 54				17 02			
Emsworth	d		15 56					16 19	16 23									16 57				17 05		17 19	17 23
Southbourne	d		15 59					16 22	16 26									17 00				17 08		17 22	17 26
Nutbourne	d								16 28													17 10			17 28
Bosham	d		16 03															17 04				17 14			
Fishbourne (Sussex)	d								16 33													17 17			17 33
Chichester 4	a		16 08					16 29	16 36			16 40				16 55		17 09				17 20		17 29	17 36
	d		16 13					16 30	16 37			16 41				16 56		17 11				17 21		17 30	17 37
Bognor Regis 4	d						16 26			16 39							17 00			17 15			17 26		
Barnham	a		16 20				16 32	16 37	16 44	16 45		16 48				17 03	17 06	17 18		17 21		17 28	17 32	17 37	17 44
	d		16 21				16 33	16 38	16 45			16 49				17 04	17 07	17 19		17 22		17 29	17 33	17 38	17 45
Bognor Regis 4	a																								
Ford 4	d						16 37		16 49							17 08	17 11			17 26			17 37		17 49
Littlehampton 4	a								16 54											17 31					17 54
	d			16 15			*16b22*						16 45			*16b54*			17 15	*17b11*					
Angmering 3	d			16 23				16 47					16 53			17 14			17 23					17 47	
Goring-by-Sea	d			16 27									16 57			17 18			17 27						
Durrington-on-Sea	d			16 30									17 00			17 21			17 30						
West Worthing	d			16 32		16 39							17 02		17 09	17 23			17 32						
Worthing 4	a			16 34		16 41		16 54					17 04		17 11	17 25			17 34			17 43		17 54	
	d			16 36		16 42		16 56					17 06		17 12	17 26			17 36			17 43		17 56	
East Worthing	d					16 44									17 14							17 46			
Lancing	d					16 47		17 00					17 10		17 17	17 30						17 49		18 00	
Shoreham-by-Sea	d			16 42		16 52		17 04					17 14		17 22	17 34			17 42			17 53		18 04	
Southwick	d					16 55		17 07							17 25	17 37						17 56		18 07	
Fishersgate	d					16 57									17 27							17 58			
Portslade	d			16 47		16 59		17 10							17 29	17 40			17 47			18 00		18 10	
Aldrington	d					17 01									17 31							18 02			
Hove 2	d			16 51	16 54	17 04		17 14					17 21	17 24	17 34	17 44			17 51		17 54	18 05		18 14	
Brighton 10	a				16 58	17 08		17 18						17 28	17 38	17 48					17 58	18 09		18 18	
Haywards Heath 3	a			17 09	*17 18*			*17 45*					17 35	*17 56*		*18 15*			18 09		*18 18*				
Burgess Hill	a			17 01															18 01						
Arundel	d						16 42										17 16						17 42		
Amberley	d						16 47																17 47		
Pulborough	d						16 53										17 25						17 53		
Billingshurst	d	←					16 59				←						17 31						17 59		
Christs Hospital	d	16 38					17 06 →				17 06						17 38						18 06 →		
Horsham 4	a	16 42	16 48								17 10	17 16					17 42	17 48							
	d	16 52									17 20						17 52								
Crawley	d	17 01									17 29						18 01								
Three Bridges 4	a	17 04		*17c27*	*17 27*			*17 56*			17 32		*17 56*	*18 08*			18 04		*18c31*		*18e31*				
	d	17 05									17 33						18 05								
Gatwick Airport 10 ✈	a	17 09		17 24	*17 31*			*18 00*			17 37		17 55	*18 16*			18 09		18 24		*18 30*				
East Croydon 🚌	a	17 30		17 40	*17 47*	*17 54*		*18 16*			17 58		18 11		*18 24*		18 29		18 41		*18 46*	*18 55*			
London Bridge 4 ⊖	a	*17 54*		*18 10*	*18f10*	*18f24*					*18 24*				*18f45*		*18g45*		*19 00*		*19 00*	*19f15*			
Clapham Junction 10	a	17 40		17 50	*18f02*	*18 04*					18 10		18 21		*18 33*		18 41		18 51		*19f02*	*19 04*			
London Victoria 15 ⊖	a	17 50		17 57		*18 11*		*18h35*			18 20		18 28		*18 40*		18 50		18 59		*19h05*	*19 11*			

For general notes see front of timetable
For details of catering facilities see Directory of Train Operators

A 🛒 from Haywards Heath
b Change at Ford
c Change at Haywards Heath
e Change at Brighton and Haywards Heath
f Change at Brighton and East Croydon
g Change at Gatwick Airport
h Change at Brighton and Gatwick Airport

For complete service between Horsham and Three Bridges see Table 186

Southampton, Portsmouth and Sussex Coast → Brighton, Gatwick Airport & London

Network Diagram - see first page of Table 186

		SN 1	SN 1	SN 1	SN 1	SN 1	SN 1	SN 1	SN 1	SN 1	SN 1	SN 1	SN 1	SN 1	SN 1	SN 1	SN 1	SN 1	SN 1	SN 1	SN 1	SN 1	SN 1	SN 1
Southampton Central	d								17 11					17 36									18 11	
Swanwick	d								17 28					17 53									18 28	
Fareham	d								17 35					18 00									18 35	
Portchester	d								17 40														18 40	
Cosham	d								17 44					18 08									18 44	
Portsmouth Harbour	d		17 12				17 28															18 28		
Portsmouth & Southsea	d		17 16				17 32					17 46		17 50		18 03						18 32		
Fratton	d		17 20				17 36					17 50		17 54		18 07						18 36		
Hilsea	d						17 32					17 54				18 11						18 32		
Bedhampton	d						17 37									18 16						18 37		
Havant	d		17 30				17 45		17 51			18 00		18 15		18 19						18 45	18 51	
Warblington	d								17 53			18 02												
Emsworth	d								17 56			18 05				18 23							18 55	
Southbourne	d								17 59			18 08				18 26							18 58	
Nutbourne	d											18 10				18 28								
Bosham	d								18 03			18 14												
Fishbourne (Sussex)	d											18 17				18 33								
Chichester [4]	a		17 41				17 55		18 08			18 20		18 25		18 36						18 55	19 05	
	d		17 41				17 56		18 13			18 21		18 26		18 37						18 56	19 07	
Bognor Regis [4]	d				17 50			18 00			18 19				18 33					18 41	18 54			
Barnham	a		17 49		17 56		18 03	18 06	18 20		18 25	18 28		18 33	18 39	18 44				18 47	19 00	19 03	19 14	
	d		17 49				18 04	18 07	18 21			18 29		18 34	18 40	18 45				18 48		19 04	19 15	
Bognor Regis [4]	a																							
Ford [4]	d						18 08	18 11				18 33			18 44					18 52			19 19	
Littlehampton [4]	a											18 38								18 57				
	d			17 45			17b54			18 15		18b22							18 52				18b56	19 15
Angmering [3]	d			17 53			18 14			18 23				18 43	18 53				19 00			19 13		19 23
Goring-by-Sea	d			17 57			18 18			18 27					18 57				19 04					19 27
Durrington-on-Sea	d			18 00			18 21			18 30				18 48	19 00				19 07			19 18		19 30
West Worthing	d			18 02			18 23			18 32					19 02				19 09					19 32
Worthing [4]	a			18 04			18 25			18 34				18 52	19 04		⟵		19 11			19 22		19 34
	d			18 06			18 26			18 35				18 53	19 05		19 05		19 12			19 23		19 35
East Worthing	d						18 28							18 55	⟶				19 14			19 25		
Lancing	d			18 10			18 31			18 39				18 58			19 09		19 17			19 28		19 39
Shoreham-by-Sea	d			18 14			18 35			18 43				19 02			19 13		19 22			19 32		19 43
Southwick	d						18 38							19 05					19 25			19 35		
Fishersgate	d						18 40							19 07					19 27			19 37		
Portslade	d						18 42			18 48				19 09			19 18		19 29			19 39		19 48
Aldrington	d						18 45							19 12					19 31			19 42		
Hove [2]	d			18 21		18 26	18 47			18 52			19 00	19 14			19 22	19 24	19 34			19 44		19 52
Brighton [10]	a					18 30	18 52						19 04	19 18				19 28	19 38			19 48		
Haywards Heath [3]	a			18 41		18 47	19 28			19 05							19 39	19 47				20 16		20 04
Burgess Hill	a			18 32													19 32							
Arundel	d							18 16								18 52							19 24	
Amberley	d																						19 29	
Pulborough	d							18 25								19 01							19 35	
Billingshurst	d	⟵						18 31								19 08							19 41	
Christs Hospital	d	18 06						18 38															19 48	
Horsham [4]	a	18 10	18 16					18 42	18 48							19 16							19 52	
	d	18 20						18 52								19 17							19 52	
Crawley	d	18 29						19 01								19 26							20 01	
Three Bridges [4]	a	18 32		19c12		19 12	19 42	19 04		19 28						19 30	20c11	20 11					20 05	20 32
	d	18 33						19 05								19 34							20 05	
Gatwick Airport [10] ✈	a	18 37		18 56		19 00	19 46	19 09		19 25						19 38	19 54	20 00					20 10	20 25
East Croydon 🚊	a	19 00		19 12		19 16		19 28		19 41			19 54			19 59	20 10	20 16	20 23				20 30	20 41
London Bridge [4] ⊖	a	19e15		19 30		19 30		19e45		20 00			20f15			20e15	20 30	20 30	20f45				20e45	21 00
Clapham Junction [10]	a	19 10		19 21		19 33		19 40		19 50			20 04			20 10	20 19		20 33				20 40	20 51
London Victoria [15] ⊖	a	19 17		19 29		19g35		19 47		19 59			20 11			20 20	20 28	20g35	20 40				20 50	20 59

For general notes see front of timetable
For details of catering facilities see Directory of Train Operators

b Change at Ford
c Change at Haywards Heath
e Change at Gatwick Airport
f Change at Brighton and East Croydon
g Change at Brighton and Gatwick Airport

For complete service between Horsham and Three Bridges see Table 186

Southampton, Portsmouth and Sussex Coast → Brighton, Gatwick Airport & London

Network Diagram - see first page of Table 186

Station		SN 1	SN 1	SN 1	SN 1	SN 1	SN 1	SN 1	SN 1	SN 1	SN 1	SN 1	SN 1	SN 1		SN 1	SN 1	SN 1	SN 1	SN 1	SN 1	SN 1	SN 1	SN 1	SN 1	SN 1
Southampton Central	d				18 27									19 11					19 36							20 11
Swanwick	d				18 47									19 28					19 53							20 28
Fareham	d				18 56									19 35					20 00							20 35
Portchester	d													19 40												20 40
Cosham	d				19 04									19 44					20 08							20 44
Portsmouth Harbour	d		18 36									19 28					19 40									
Portsmouth & Southsea	d		18 41		18 50						19 03	19 32					19 44		19 50				20 03	20 32		
Fratton	d		18 45		18 54						19 07	19 36					19 48		19 54				20 07	20 36		
Hilsea	d		18 49								19 11	19 32											20 11	20 32		
Bedhampton	d										19 16	19 37											20 16	20 37		
Havant	d		18 55		19 11						19 19	19 45		19 52			19 57		20 15				20 20	20 45		20 51
Warblington	d		18 57								19 21						19 59						20 22			
Emsworth	d		19 00								19 24			19 56			20 02						20 25			20 55
Southbourne	d		19 03								19 27			19 59			20 05						20 28			20 58
Nutbourne	d		19 05								19 29						20 07						20 30			
Bosham	d		19 09								19 33						20 11						20 34			
Fishbourne (Sussex)	d		19 12								19 36						20 14						20 37			
Chichester 4	a		19 15		19 21						19 39	19 55		20 06			20 17		20 25				20 40	20 55		21 05
	d		19 15		19 22						19 40	19 56		20 07			20 18		20 26				20 41	20 56		21 07
Bognor Regis 4	d	19 09					19 33	19 39					20 04							20 36					21 04	
Barnham	a	19 15	19 23		19 29		19 39	19 45			19 47	20 03	20 10	20 14			20 25		20 33	20 42			20 48	21 03	21 10	21 14
	d		19 23		19 30		19 40				19 49	20 04	20 11	20 15			20 27		20 34	20 43			20 50	21 04	21 11	21 15
Bognor Regis 4	a																									
Ford 4	d		19 28				19 44				19 54	20 08	20 15	20 19			20 31			20 47			20 54	21 08	21 15	21 19
Littlehampton 4	a		19 32								19 59		20 21				20 39						21 01		21 20	
	d						19b29			19 52			20b06			20 15				20b36		20 52			21b06	
Angmering 3	d				19 39		19 53			20 00		20 14				20 23			20 43	20 53		21 00		21 14		
Goring-by-Sea	d				19 43		19 57			20 04						20 27				20 57		21 04				
Durrington-on-Sea	d				19 46		20 00			20 07						20 30			20 48	21 00		21 07				
West Worthing	d				19 48		20 02			20 09						20 32				21 02		21 09				
Worthing 4	a				19 50		20 04			20 11		20 21				20 34			20 52	21 04		21 11		21 21		
	d				19 52		20 05			20 12		20 22				20 35			20 53	21 05		21 12		21 22		
East Worthing	d				19 55					20 14		20 25							20 55			21 14		21 25		
Lancing	d				19 58		20 09			20 17		20 28				20 39			20 58	21 09		21 17		21 28		
Shoreham-by-Sea	d				20 02		20 13			20 22		20 32				20 43			21 02	21 13		21 22		21 32		
Southwick	d				20 05					20 25		20 35							21 05			21 25		21 35		
Fishersgate	d				20 07					20 27		20 37							21 07			21 27		21 37		
Portslade	d				20 09		20 18			20 29		20 39				20 48			21 09	21 18		21 29		21 39		
Aldrington	d				20 11					20 31		20 41							21 12			21 31		21 41		
Hove 2	d			19 54	20 14		20 22		20 24	20 34		20 44				20 52		20 54	21 14	21 22	21 24	21 34		21 44		
Brighton 10	a			19 58	20 18				20 28	20 38		20 48						20 58	21 18		21 28	21 38		21 48		
Haywards Heath 3	a			20 18			20 37		20 47							21 06		21 23		21 37	21 46			22 21		
Burgess Hill	a						20 32													21 32						
Arundel	d													20 24												21 24
Amberley	d													20 29												21 29
Pulborough	d													20 35												21 35
Billingshurst	d													20 41												21 41
Christs Hospital	d													20 48												21 48
Horsham 4	a													20 52												21 52
	d					20 02								20 52												21 52
Crawley	d					20 14								21 01												22 01
Three Bridges 4	a			20c32		20 18	20 47		21 11					21 05		21 32		21 32		21 47	21 55			22 32		22 05
	d					20 18	20 47							21 05						21 47						22 05
Gatwick Airport 10 ✈	a			20 31		20 22	20 51		21 00					21 10		21 25		21 37		21 51	22 00			22 37		22 10
East Croydon	a			20 47		20 57	21 09		21 16	21 23				21 30		21 41		21 55		22 09	22 17	22 23		22 59		22 30
London Bridge 4 ⊖	a			21 00		21e00	21 30		21 30	21f45				21e45				22 15		22 32	22 32	22f45				22e45
Clapham Junction 10	a			21f03		21 07	21 19			21 33				21 40		21 50		22 04		22 19		22 33		23 10		22 40
London Victoria 15 ⊖	a			21 11		21 14	21 29		21g35	21 40				21 48		21 58		22 11		22 27	22g35	22 40		23 20		22 50

For general notes see front of timetable
For details of catering facilities see Directory of Train Operators

b Change at Ford
c Change at Brighton and Haywards Heath
e Change at Gatwick Airport
f Change at Brighton and East Croydon
g Change at Brighton and Gatwick Airport

For complete service between Horsham and Three Bridges see Table 186

Southampton, Portsmouth and Sussex Coast → Brighton, Gatwick Airport & London

Network Diagram - see first page of Table 186

		SN 1	SN 1	SN 1	SN 1	SN 1		SN 1	SN 1	SN 1	SN 1	SN 1	SN 1	SN 1	SN 1	SN 1	SN 1	SN 1	SN 1	SN 1	SN 1		SN 1	SN 1	SN 1	SN 1
Southampton Central	d				20 36							21 11				21 23			22 12					22 36		
Swanwick	d				20 53							21 28							22 29					22 53		
Fareham	d				21 00							21 39				21 56			22 36					23 00		
Portchester	d											21 44				22 01			22 41							
Cosham	d				21 08							21 48				22 06			22 45					23 08		
Portsmouth Harbour	d		20 40											21 40				22 15					22 44			23 15
Portsmouth & Southsea	d		20 44		*20 50*					21 15		*21 33*		21 44				22 19	*22 33*				22 48			23 19
Fratton	d		20 48		*20 54*					21 19		*21 37*		21 48				22 23	*22 37*				22 52			23 23
Hilsea	d									21 23		*21 41*		21 52				22 27	*22 41*				22 56			23 27
Bedhampton	d									21 28		*21 47*		21 57				22 32	*22 46*				23 01			23 33
Havant	d		20 57		21 15					21 31		21 55		22 00		22 14		22 35	22 58				23 05	23 15		23 36
Warblington	d		20 59							21 33						22 16										23 38
Emsworth	d		21 02							21 36						22 19		22 39	23 02							23 41
Southbourne	d		21 05							21 39						22 22		22 42	23 05							23 44
Nutbourne	d		21 07							21 41						22 24										23 47
Bosham	d		21 11							21 45						22 28										23 50
Fishbourne (Sussex)	d		21 14							21 48						22 31										23 53
Chichester 4	a		21 17		21 25					21 51		22 05		22 10		22 34		22 49	23 12				23 16	23 25		23 57
	d		21 18		21 26					21 52		22 06		22 11		22 40		22 52	23 12				23 17	23 26	23 52	23 57
Bognor Regis 4	d					21 39					22 00				22 30					23 15						
Barnham	a		21 25		21 33	21 45				21 59	22 06	22 13		22 18	22 36	22 47		22 59	23 20	23 21			23 24	23 33	23 59	00 05
	d		21 26		21 34					22 00	22 07	22 14		22 19	22 37	22 48		23 00	23 20				23 25	23 34	00 01	00 06
Bognor Regis 4	a																									
Ford 4	d		21 30		21 38					22 04	22 11			22 23	22 41	22 52		23 04					23 29		00 05	00 10
Littlehampton 4	a		21 35								22 16			22 28	22 46				23 31				23 34	23 42	00 10	00 15
	d	21 15							21 52					22 33		22b38							23 39		23b24	
Angmering 3	d	21 23			21 44				22 00	22 11				22 41				23 11					23 47			
Goring-by-Sea	d	21 27			21 48				22 04	22 15				22 45				23 15					23 51			
Durrington-on-Sea	d	21 30			21 51				22 07	22 17				22 47				23 17					23 53			
West Worthing	d	21 32			21 53				22 09	22 19				22 49				23 19					23 55			
Worthing 4	a	21 34			21 55				22 11	22 22				22 52				23 22					23 58			
	d	21 35			21 56				22 12	22 22				22 52				23 22					23 59			
East Worthing	d				21 58				22 14	22 25				22 55				23 25					00 01			
Lancing	d	21 39			22 01				22 17	22 28				22 58				23 28					00 04			
Shoreham-by-Sea	d	21 43			22 05				22 22	22 32				23 02				23 32					00 08			
Southwick	d				22 08				22 25	22 35				23 05				23 35					00 11			
Fishersgate	d				22 10				22 27	22 37				23 07				23 37					00 13			
Portslade	d	21 48			22 12				22 29	22 39				23 09				23 39					00 15			
Aldrington	d				22 15				22 31	22 41				23 11				23 41					00 18			
Hove 2	d	21 52		21 54	22 17			22 24	22 34	22 44			22 54	23 14			23 24	23 44			23 54		00 20			
Brighton 10	a			21 58	22 22			22 28	22 38	22 48			22 58	23 18			23 28	23 48			23 58		00 25			
Haywards Heath 3	a	22 09		*22 28*				*22 54*					*23 23*				*23 58*									
Burgess Hill	a	22 02																								
Arundel	d											22 22				22 57										
Amberley	d															23 02										
Pulborough	d											22 31				23 08										
Billingshurst	d											22 37				23 14										
Christs Hospital	d											22 44				23 21										
Horsham 4	a											22 48				23 25										
	d											22 49				23 25										
Crawley	d											22 57				23 38										
Three Bridges 4	a	*22c32*		*22 42*				*23 05*				23 01	*23 33*			23 42	*00 10*									
	d																									
Gatwick Airport 10 ✈	a	22 24		*22 46*				*23e12*				*23 12*	*23 52*			*23 52*	*00 14*									
East Croydon	a	22 40		*23 02*				*23e30*				*23 30*	*00 16*			*00 16*	*00 35*									
London Bridge 4 ⊖	a			*23 15*				*23 45*				*23 45*				*00 52*	*00 52*									
Clapham Junction 10	a	22 50		*23f25*				*00f11*				*23 42*	*00 29*			*00 29*	*01f02*									
London Victoria 15 ⊖	a	22 58		*23f35*				*23e52*				*23 52*	*00 37*			*00 37*	*00g55*									

For general notes see front of timetable
For details of catering facilities see Directory of Train Operators

b Change at Ford
c Change at Haywards Heath
e Change at Brighton and Haywards Heath
f Change at Brighton and East Croydon
g Change at Brighton and Gatwick Airport

For complete service between Horsham and Three Bridges see Table 186

Table 188

Southampton, Portsmouth and Sussex Coast → Brighton, Gatwick Airport & London

Network Diagram - see first page of Table 186

Station		SN 1	SN 1	SN 1	SN 1	SN 1	SN 1	SN 1	SN 1	SN 1	SN 1	SN 1	SN 1	SN 1	SN 1	SN 1		SN 1	SN 1	SN 1	SN 1	SN 1	SN 1	SN 1	SN 1	SN 1 A ⌶
Southampton Central	d																									
Swanwick	d																									
Fareham	d																									
Portchester	d																									
Cosham	d																									
Portsmouth Harbour	d	22p44		23p15																					06 12	
Portsmouth & Southsea	d	22p48		23p19			04 56							05b24								05 56			06 16	
Fratton	d	22p52		23p23			05 00							05c28								06 00			06 20	
Hilsea	d	22p56		23p27			04e56							05f32								06 04				
Bedhampton	d	23p01		23p33			05g01							05h37								06 09				
Havant	d	23p05		23p36			05 08							05 53								06 14			06 30	
Warblington	d			23p38																		06 16				
Emsworth	d			23p41										05 57								06 19				
Southbourne	d			23p44										06 00								06 22				
Nutbourne	d			23p47																		06 24				
Bosham	d			23p50																		06 28				
Fishbourne (Sussex)	d			23p53																		06 31				
Chichester 4	a	23p16		23p57			05 19							06 07								06 34			06 40	
	d	23p17	23p52	23p57			05 19							06 07							06 30	06 35			06 41	
Bognor Regis 4	d					05 13						05 43	06 04					06 26					06 39			
Barnham	a	23p24	23p59	00 05		05 19	05 27	←				05 49	06 10	06 15		←		06 32			06 37	06 42	06 45		06 48	
	d	23p25	00 01	00 06	04 48	05 31 →	05 27	05 31				05 50	06 20 →	06 15		06 20		06 33			06 38	06 43			06 49	
Bognor Regis 4	a																									
Ford 4	d	23p29	00 05	00 10	04 52			05 35				05 54		06 20		06 24		06 37				06 47				
Littlehampton 4	a	23p34	00 10	00 15	04 57			05 40								06 29						06 52				
	d	23p39	23j24		05 02					05 45				05j58	06 15											06 45
Angmering 3	d	23p47			05 10					05 53		06 00			06 23						06 47					06 55
Goring-by-Sea	d	23p51			05 14					05 57		06 04			06 27											06 59
Durrington-on-Sea	d	23p53			05 17					06 00		06 07			06 30											07 02
West Worthing	d	23p55			05 19					06 02		06 09			06 32					06 39						07 04
Worthing 4	a	23p58			05 21		05 41			06 04		06 11			06 34					06 41	06 54					07 06
	d	23p59			05 22		05 42			06 05		06 12			06 35					06 42	06 56					07 07
East Worthing	d	00 01			05 24							06 14								06 44						
Lancing	d	00 04			05 27					06 09		06 17			06 39					06 47	07 00					07 11
Shoreham-by-Sea	d	00 08			05 32		05 48			06 13		06 22			06 43					06 52	07 04					07 15
Southwick	d	00 11			05 35							06 25								06 55	07 07					
Fishersgate	d	00 13			05 37							06 27								06 57						
Portslade	d	00 15			05 39					06 17		06 29			06 47					06 59	07 10					
Aldrington	d	00 18			05 41							06 31								07 01						
Hove 2	d	00 20			05 44		05 54		05 56	06 21	06 24	06 34			06 51				06 54	07 04	07 14					07 22
Brighton 10	a	00 25			05 48				06 00		06 28	06 38							06 58	07 08	07 18					
Haywards Heath 3	a				06 15		06 07		06 18	06 35	06 58	07 15			07 08				07 18							07 35
Burgess Hill	a														07 01											
Arundel	d													06 24				06 42								
Amberley	d																	06 47								
Pulborough	d													06 33				06 53								
Billingshurst	d													06 40				06 59						←		
Christs Hospital	d																	07 06 →						07 06		
Horsham 4	a													06 48										07 10	07 16	
	d													06 50											07 20	
Crawley	d													06 59											07 29	
Three Bridges 4	a						06 20		06k32	06 48	07 11	07 25		07 02	07m25				07 42						07 32	08 11
	d						06 20			06 48				07 03											07 33	
Gatwick Airport 10 ✈	a						06 24		06 30	06 52	07 16			07 07	07 24				07 30						07 37	07 54
East Croydon	a						06 40		06 46	07 09		07 23		07 27	07 40				07 46	07 55					07 59	08 10
London Bridge 4 ⊖	a						07 01		07 01	07 31		07n45		07 45	08 01				08 01	08n15					08q15	08 31
Clapham Junction 10	a						06 50		07n03	07 19		07 33		07 37	07 49				08n03	08 04					08 11	08 19
London Victoria 15 ⊖	a						06 58		07r05	07 27		07 40		07 44	07 57				08r05	08 11					08 18	08 27

For general notes see front of timetable
For details of catering facilities see Directory of Train Operators

A ⌶ from Haywards Heath
b From 4 October dep. 0519
c From 4 October dep. 0523
e From 4 October dep. 0451
f From 4 October dep. 0527
g From 4 October dep. 0456
h From 4 October dep. 0532
j Change at Ford
k Change at Brighton and Haywards Heath
m Change at Haywards Heath
n Change at Brighton and East Croydon
q Change at Gatwick Airport
r Change at Brighton and Gatwick Airport

For complete service between Horsham and Three Bridges see Table 186

Saturdays

Southampton, Portsmouth and Sussex Coast → Brighton, Gatwick Airport & London

Network Diagram - see first page of Table 186

		SN 1	SN 1	SN 1	SN 1	SN 1	SN 1	SN 1	SN 1		SN 1	SN 1	GW	SN 1	SN 1	SN 1	SN 1	SN 1	SN 1	SN 1 A	SN 1	SN 1	SN 1	SN 1	SN 1
Southampton Central	d							06 11							06 36										
Swanwick	d							06 28							06 53										
Fareham	d							06 35							07 00										
Portchester	d							06 40																	
Cosham	d							06 44							07 08										
Portsmouth Harbour	d			06 28									06 48						07 12				07 28		
Portsmouth & Southsea	d			06 32									06 53		06 53	07 03			07 16				07 32		
Fratton	d			06 36									06 57		06 57	07 07			07 20				07 36		
Hilsea	d			06 32												07 11							07 32		
Bedhampton	d			06 37												07 16							07 37		
Havant	d			06 45				06 51					07 10		07 15	07 19			07 30				07 45		
Warblington	d							06 53																	
Emsworth	d							06 56							07 19	07 23									
Southbourne	d							06 59							07 22	07 26									
Nutbourne	d															07 28									
Bosham	d							07 03																	
Fishbourne (Sussex)	d															07 33									
Chichester 4	a			06 55				07 08					07 20		07 29	07 36			07 40				07 55		
	d			06 56				07 11					07 21		07 30	07 37			07 41				07 56		
Bognor Regis 4	d				07 00	07 07								07 26			07 39							08 00	08 07
Barnham	a			07 03	07 06	07 13		07 18					07 29	07 32	07 37	07 44	07 45		07 48				08 03	08 06	08 13
	d			07 04	07 07	07 15		07 19					07 29	07 33	07 38	07 45			07 49				08 04	08 07	08 15
Bognor Regis 4	a																								
Ford 4	d			07 08	07 11	07 19								07 37		07 49							08 08	08 11	08 19
Littlehampton 4	a					07 24										07 54									08 24
	d			06b54		07b11			07 15											07 45			07b58		08b11
Angmering 3	d			07 14					07 23						07 47					07 53			08 14		
Goring-by-Sea	d			07 18					07 27											07 57			08 18		
Durrington-on-Sea	d			07 21					07 30											08 00			08 21		
West Worthing	d		07 09	07 23					07 32			07 39								08 02		08 09	08 23		
Worthing 4	a		07 11	07 25					07 34			07 41	07 45		07 54					08 04		08 11	08 25		
	d		07 12	07 26					07 36			07 42	07 50		07 56					08 06		08 12	08 26		
East Worthing	d		07 14									07 44										08 14			
Lancing	d		07 17	07 30								07 47			08 00					08 10		08 17	08 30		
Shoreham-by-Sea	d		07 22	07 34					07 42			07 52	07 57		08 04					08 14		08 22	08 34		
Southwick	d		07 25	07 37								07 55			08 07							08 25	08 37		
Fishersgate	d		07 27									07 57										08 27			
Portslade	d		07 29	07 40					07 47			07 59			08 10							08 29	08 40		
Aldrington	d		07 31									08 01										08 31			
Hove 2	d	07 24	07 34	07 44					07 51		07 54	08 04	08 08		08 14					08 21	08 24	08 34	08 44		
Brighton 10	a	07 28	07 38	07 48							07 58	08 08	08 15		08 18						08 28	08 38	08 48		
Haywards Heath 3	a	07 47		08 15					08 09		08 18									08 35	08 47		09 15		
Burgess Hill	a								08 01																
Arundel	d				07 16									07 42										08 16	
Amberley	d													07 47											
Pulborough	d				07 25		←							07 53										08 25	
Billingshurst	d				07 31		07 31							07 59				←						08 31	
Christs Hospital	d				→									08 06 →				08 06						→	
Horsham 4	a						07 40	07 46										08 10	08 16						
	d						07 50											08 20							
Crawley	d						07 59											08 29							
Three Bridges 4	a	08 11		08 25			08 02		08c25		08 42							08 32		09 11	09 11		09 25		
	d						08 03											08 33							
Gatwick Airport 10 ✈	a	08 00					08 07		08 24		08 30							08 37		08 54	09 00				
East Croydon	a	08 16	08 23				08 27		08 40		08 46	08 55	08 55					08 59		09 10	09 16	09 23			
London Bridge 4 ⊖	a	08 31	08e45				08 45		09 01		09 01	09e15	09e15					09f15		09 30	09 30	09e45			
Clapham Junction 10	a		08 33				08 37		08 49		09e03	09 04	09 04					09 11		09 19		09 33			
London Victoria 15 ⊖	a	08g35	08 40				08 44		08 57		09g05	09 11	09 11					09 18		09 27	09g35	09 40			

For general notes see front of timetable
For details of catering facilities see Directory of Train Operators

A from Haywards Heath
b Change at Ford
c Change at Haywards Heath
e Change at Brighton and East Croydon
f Change at Gatwick Airport
g Change at Brighton and Gatwick Airport

For complete service between Horsham and Three Bridges see Table 186

Table 188

Saturdays

Southampton, Portsmouth and Sussex Coast → Brighton, Gatwick Airport & London

Network Diagram - see first page of Table 186

		SN 1	SN 1	SN 1		SN 1	SN 1	SN 1	SN 1	SN 1	SN 1	SN 1	SN 1	SN 1	SN 1	SN 1	SN 1	SN 1	SN 1	SN 1	SN 1		SN 1	SN 1	SN 1	SN 1
														A												
		🛒												🛒				🛒		🛒						
Southampton Central	d		07 11						07 36												08 11					
Swanwick	d		07 28						07 53												08 28					
Fareham	d		07 35						08 00												08 35					
Portchester	d		07 40																		08 40					
Cosham	d		07 44						08 09												08 44					
Portsmouth Harbour	d												08 12				08 28									
Portsmouth & Southsea	d								07 50	08 03			08 16				08 32									
Fratton	d								07 54	08 07			08 20				08 36									
Hilsea	d									08 11							08 32									
Bedhampton	d									08 16							08 37									
Havant	d		07 51						08 16	08 19			08 30				08 45				08 51					
Warblington	d		07 53																		08 53					
Emsworth	d		07 56						08 20	08 23											08 56					
Southbourne	d		07 59						08 23	08 26											08 59					
Nutbourne	d									08 29																
Bosham	d		08 03																		09 03					
Fishbourne (Sussex)	d									08 33																
Chichester 4	a		08 08						08 30	08 36			08 40				08 55				09 08					
	d		08 11						08 31	08 37			08 41				08 56				09 11					
Bognor Regis 4	d							08 26			08 39							09 00	09 07							09 26
Barnham	a		08 18					08 32	08 38	08 44	08 45		08 48				09 03	09 06	09 13		09 18					09 32
	d		08 19					08 33	08 39	08 45			08 49				09 04	09 07	09 15		09 19					09 33
Bognor Regis 4	a																									
Ford 4	d							08 37		08 49							09 08	09 11	09 19							09 37
Littlehampton 4	a									08 54									09 24							
	d			08 15										08 45			08b58		09b11				09 15			
Angmering 3	d			08 23					08 48					08 53			09 14						09 23			
Goring-by-Sea	d			08 27										08 57			09 18						09 27			
Durrington-on-Sea	d			08 30										09 00			09 21						09 30			
West Worthing	d			08 32			08 39							09 02		09 09	09 23						09 32		09 39	
Worthing 4	a			08 34			08 41		08 55					09 04		09 11	09 25						09 34		09 41	
	d			08 36			08 42		08 56					09 05		09 12	09 26						09 36		09 42	
East Worthing	d						08 44									09 14									09 44	
Lancing	d						08 47		09 00					09 09		09 17	09 30								09 47	
Shoreham-by-Sea	d			08 42			08 52		09 04					09 13		09 22	09 34						09 42		09 52	
Southwick	d						08 55		09 07							09 25	09 37								09 55	
Fishersgate	d						08 57									09 27									09 57	
Portslade	d			08 47			08 59		09 10							09 29	09 40						09 47		09 59	
Aldrington	d						09 01									09 31									10 01	
Hove 2	d			08 51		08 54	09 04		09 14					09 21	09 24	09 34	09 44						09 51	09 54	10 04	
Brighton 10	a					08 58	09 08		09 18						09 28	09 38	09 48							09 58	10 08	
Haywards Heath 3	a			09 09		09 18	09 28							09 35	09 47		10 15						10 08	10 18		
Burgess Hill	a																						10 01			
Arundel	d							08 42										09 16								09 42
Amberley	d							08 47																		09 47
Pulborough	d	←						08 53				←						09 25		←						09 53
Billingshurst	d	08 31						08 59										09 31 →		09 31						09 59
Christs Hospital	d							09 06 →				09 06														10 06 →
Horsham 4	a	08 40	08 46									09 10	09 16							09 40	09 46					
	d		08 50										09 20								09 50					
Crawley	d		08 59										09 29								09 59					
Three Bridges 4	a		09 02	09 25		09 37							09 32	10 11	10 11		10 25				10 02		10c25	10 42		
	d		09 03										09 33								10 03					
Gatwick Airport 10 ✈	a		09 07	09 24		09 30	09 44						09 37	09 54	10 00						10 07		10 25	10 30		
East Croydon	a		09 27	09 40		09 46	09 55						09 59	10 10	10 16	10 23					10 27		10 42	10 46	10 55	
London Bridge 4 ⊖	a		09 45	10 00		10 00	10e22						10f15	10 30	10 30	10e45					10 45		11 00	11 00	11e15	
Clapham Junction 10	a		09 37	09 49		10e03	10 04						10 11	10 19		10 33					10 37		10 51	11e03	11 04	
London Victoria 15 ⊖	a		09 44	09 57		10g05	10 11						10 18	10 27	10g35	10 40					10 44		10 59	11g05	11 11	

For general notes see front of timetable
For details of catering facilities see Directory of Train Operators

A 🛒 from Haywards Heath
b Change at Ford
c Change at Haywards Heath
e Change at Brighton and East Croydon
f Change at Three Bridges
g Change at Brighton and Gatwick Airport

For complete service between Horsham and Three Bridges see Table 186

Table 188

Saturdays

Southampton, Portsmouth and Sussex Coast → Brighton, Gatwick Airport & London

Network Diagram - see first page of Table 186

Station		SN 1	SN 1	SN 1	SN 1	SN 1	SN 1	SN 1	SN 1	SN 1	SN 1	SN 1	SN 1	SN 1		SN 1	SN 1	SN 1	SN 1	SN 1	SN 1	SN 1	SN 1	SN 1	SN 1	SN 1
							A 🛒				🛒		🛒												A 🛒	
Southampton Central	d	08 36												09 11						09 36						
Swanwick	d	08 53												09 28						09 53						
Fareham	d	09 00												09 35						10 00						
Portchester	d													09 40												
Cosham	d	09 08												09 44						10 08						
Portsmouth Harbour	d					09 12				09 28														10 12		
Portsmouth & Southsea	d	*08 50*	09 03			09 16				09 32										*09 50*	10 03			10 16		
Fratton	d	*08 54*	09 07			09 20				09 36										*09 54*	10 07			10 20		
Hilsea	d		09 11							*09 32*											10 11					
Bedhampton	d		09 16							*09 37*											10 16					
Havant	d	09 15	09 19			09 30				09 45				09 51						10 15	10 19			10 30		
Warblington	d													09 53												
Emsworth	d	09 19	09 23											09 56						10 19	10 23					
Southbourne	d	09 22	09 26											09 59						10 22	10 26					
Nutbourne	d		09 28																		10 28					
Bosham	d													10 03												
Fishbourne (Sussex)	d		09 33																		10 33					
Chichester 4	a	09 29	09 36			09 40				09 55				10 08						10 29	10 36			10 40		
	d	09 30	09 37			09 41				09 56				10 11						10 30	10 37			10 41		
Bognor Regis 4	d			09 39							10 00	10 07							10 26			10 39				
Barnham	a	09 37	09 44	09 45		09 48				10 03	10 06	10 13		10 18					10 32	10 37	10 44	10 45		10 48		
	d	09 38	09 45			09 49				10 04	10 07	10 15		10 19					10 33	10 38	10 45			10 49		
Bognor Regis 4	a																									
Ford 4	d		09 49							10 08	10 11	10 19							10 37		10 49					
Littlehampton 4	a		09 54									10 24									10 54					
	d						09 45			*09b58*		*10b11*				10 15									10 45	
Angmering 3	d	09 47					09 53			10 14						10 23				10 47					10 53	
Goring-by-Sea	d						09 57			10 18						10 27									10 57	
Durrington-on-Sea	d						10 00			10 21						10 30									11 00	
West Worthing	d						10 02		10 09	10 23						10 32		10 39							11 02	
Worthing 4	a	09 54					10 04		10 11	10 25						10 34		10 41		10 54					11 04	
	d	09 56					10 06		10 12	10 26						10 36		10 42		10 56					11 06	
East Worthing	d								10 14									10 44								
Lancing	d	10 00					10 10		10 17	10 30								10 47		11 00					11 10	
Shoreham-by-Sea	d	10 04					10 14		10 22	10 34						10 42		10 52		11 04					11 14	
Southwick	d	10 07							10 25	10 37								10 55		11 07						
Fishersgate	d								10 27									10 57								
Portslade	d	10 10							10 29	10 40						10 47		10 59		11 10						
Aldrington	d								10 31									11 01								
Hove 2	d	10 14					10 21	10 24	10 34	10 44						10 51	10 54	11 04		11 14					11 21	11 24
Brighton 10	a	10 18						10 28	10 38	10 48							10 58	11 08		11 18						11 28
Haywards Heath 3	a						10 35	*10 47*		*11 15*						11 09	*11 18*								11 35	*11 47*
Burgess Hill	a															11 01										
Arundel	d										10 16								10 42							
Amberley	d																		10 47							
Pulborough	d										10 25		←						10 53							
Billingshurst	d				←						10 31 →		10 31						10 59				←			
Christs Hospital	d				10 06														11 06 →				11 06			
Horsham 4	a				10 10	10 16							10 40	10 46									11 10	11 16		
	d				10 20								10 50										11 20			
Crawley	d				10 29								10 59										11 29			
Three Bridges 4	a				10 32		*11 11*	*11 11*		*11 25*			11 02			*11c25*	*11 42*						11 32		*12 11*	*12 11*
	d				10 33								11 03										11 33			
Gatwick Airport 10 ✈	a				10 37		10 54	*11 00*					11 07			11 24	*11 30*						11 37		11 54	*12 00*
East Croydon	a				11 00		11 10	*11 16*	*11 23*				11 27			11 40	*11 46*	*11 55*					12 00		12 10	*12 16*
London Bridge 4 ⊖	a				*11e15*		*11 30*	*11 30*	*11f45*				*11 45*			*12 00*	*12 00*	*12f15*					*12e15*		*12 30*	*12 30*
Clapham Junction 10	a				11 11		11 19		*11 33*				11 37			11 49	*12f03*	*12 04*					12 11		12 19	
London Victoria 15 ⊖	a				11 18		11 27	*11g35*	*11 40*				11 44			11 57	*12g05*	*12 11*					12 18		12 27	*12g35*

For general notes see front of timetable
For details of catering facilities see Directory of Train Operators

A 🛒 from Haywards Heath
b Change at Ford
c Change at Haywards Heath
e Change at Gatwick Airport
f Change at Brighton and East Croydon
g Change at Brighton and Gatwick Airport

For complete service between Horsham and Three Bridges see Table 186

Table 188

Saturdays

Southampton, Portsmouth and Sussex Coast → Brighton, Gatwick Airport & London

Network Diagram - see first page of Table 186

Station		SN 1	SN 1	SN 1	SN 1	SN 1	SN 1	SN 1	SN 1	SN 1	SN 1	SN 1	SN 1	SN 1	SN 1	SN 1	SN 1	SN 1	SN 1	SN 1	SN 1	SN 1	SN 1	SN 1
				🛒		🛒											A 🛒				🛒		🛒	
Southampton Central	d						10 11					10 36												11 11
Swanwick	d						10 28					10 53												11 28
Fareham	d						10 35					11 00												11 35
Portchester	d						10 40																	11 40
Cosham	d						10 44					11 08												11 44
Portsmouth Harbour	d		10 28													11 12				11 28				
Portsmouth & Southsea	d		10 32									*10 50*	11 03			11 16				11 32				
Fratton	d		10 36									*10 54*	11 07			11 20				11 36				
Hilsea	d		*10 32*										11 11							*11 32*				
Bedhampton	d		*10 37*										11 16							*11 37*				
Havant	d		10 45				10 51					11 15	11 19			11 30				11 45				11 51
Warblington	d						10 53																	11 53
Emsworth	d						10 56					11 19	11 23											11 56
Southbourne	d						10 59					11 22	11 26											11 59
Nutbourne	d												11 28											
Bosham	d						11 03																	12 03
Fishbourne (Sussex)	d												11 33											
Chichester 4	a		10 55				11 08					11 29	11 36			11 40				11 55				12 08
	d		10 56				11 11					11 30	11 37			11 41				11 56				12 11
Bognor Regis 4	d			11 00	11 07						11 26			11 39							12 00	12 07		
Barnham	a		11 03	11 06	11 13		11 18				11 32	11 37	11 44	11 45		11 48				12 03	12 06	12 13		12 18
	d		11 04	11 07	11 15		11 19				11 33	11 38	11 45			11 49				12 04	12 07	12 15		12 19
Bognor Regis 4	a																							
Ford 4	d		11 08	11 11	11 19						11 37		11 49							12 08	12 11	12 19		
Littlehampton 4	a				11 24								11 54									12 24		
	d		*10b58*		*11b11*			11 15									11 45			*11 58*		*12 11*		
Angmering 3	d		11 14					11 23				11 47					11 53			12 14				
Goring-by-Sea	d		11 18					11 27									11 57			12 18				
Durrington-on-Sea	d		11 21					11 30									12 00			12 21				
West Worthing	d	11 09	11 23					11 32		11 39							12 02		12 09	12 23				
Worthing 4	a	11 11	11 25					11 34		11 41		11 54					12 04		12 11	12 25				
	d	11 12	11 26					11 36		11 42		11 56					12 06		12 12	12 26				
East Worthing	d	11 14								11 44									12 14					
Lancing	d	11 17	11 30							11 47		12 00					12 10		12 17	12 30				
Shoreham-by-Sea	d	11 22	11 34					11 42		11 52		12 04					12 14		12 22	12 34				
Southwick	d	11 25	11 37							11 55		12 07							12 25	12 37				
Fishersgate	d	11 27								11 57									12 27					
Portslade	d	11 29	11 40					11 47		11 59		12 10							12 29	12 40				
Aldrington	d	11 31								12 01									12 31					
Hove 2	d	11 34	11 44					11 51	11 54	12 04		12 14					12 21	12 24	12 34	12 44				
Brighton 10	a	11 38	11 48						11 58	12 08		12 18						12 28	12 38	12 48				
Haywards Heath 3	a		*12 15*					12 09	*12 18*								12 35	*12 47*		*13 15*				
Burgess Hill	a							12 01																
Arundel	d			11 16							11 42										12 16			
Amberley	d										11 47													
Pulborough	d			11 25		←					11 53										12 25		←	
Billingshurst	d			11 31 →		11 31					11 59				←						12 31 →		12 31	
Christs Hospital	d										12 06 →				12 06									
Horsham 4	a					11 40	11 46								12 10	12 16							12 40	12 46
	d					11 50									12 20								12 50	
Crawley	d					11 59									12 29								12 59	
Three Bridges 4	a		*12 25*			12 02		*12c25*	*12 42*						12 32		*13 11*	*13 11*		*13 25*			13 02	
	d					12 03									12 33								13 03	
Gatwick Airport 10 ✈	a					12 07		12 24	*12 30*						12 37		12 54	*13 00*					13 07	
East Croydon 🚊	a	*12 23*				12 27		12 40	*12 46*	*12 55*					13 00		13 10	*13 16*	*13 23*				13 27	
London Bridge 4 ⊖	a	*12e45*				*12 45*		*13 00*	*13 00*	*13e15*					*13f15*		*13 30*	*13 30*	*13e45*				*13 45*	
Clapham Junction 10	a	*12 33*				12 37		12 49	*13e03*	*13 04*					13 11		13 19		*13 33*				13 37	
London Victoria 15 ⊖	a	*12 40*				12 44		12 57	*13g05*	*13 11*					13 18		13 27	*13g35*	*13 40*				13 44	

For general notes see front of timetable
For details of catering facilities see Directory of Train Operators

A 🛒 from Haywards Heath
b Change at Ford
c Change at Haywards Heath
e Change at Brighton and East Croydon
f Change at Gatwick Airport
g Change at Brighton and Gatwick Airport

For complete service between Horsham and Three Bridges see Table 186

Table 188

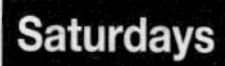

Southampton, Portsmouth and Sussex Coast → Brighton, Gatwick Airport & London

Network Diagram - see first page of Table 186

		SN 1	SN 1	SN 1	SN 1	SN 1	SN 1	SN 1	SN 1	SN 1	SN 1	SN 1	SN 1	SN 1	SN 1	SN 1		SN 1	SN 1	SN 1	SN 1	SN 1	SN 1	SN 1	SN 1	SN 1
											A 🛒				🛒			🛒								
Southampton Central	d					11 36													12 11					12 36		
Swanwick	d					11 53													12 28					12 53		
Fareham	d					12 00													12 35					13 00		
Portchester	d																		12 40							
Cosham	d					12 08													12 44					13 08		
Portsmouth Harbour	d									12 12				12 28												
Portsmouth & Southsea	d					11 50	12 03			12 16				12 32										12 50	13 03	
Fratton	d					11 54	12 07			12 20				12 36										12 54	13 07	
Hilsea	d						12 11							12 32											13 11	
Bedhampton	d						12 16							12 37											13 16	
Havant	d					12 15	12 19			12 30				12 45					12 51					13 15	13 19	
Warblington	d																		12 53							
Emsworth	d					12 19	12 23												12 56					13 19	13 23	
Southbourne	d					12 22	12 26												12 59					13 22	13 26	
Nutbourne	d						12 28																		13 28	
Bosham	d																		13 03							
Fishbourne (Sussex)	d						12 33																		13 33	
Chichester 4	a					12 29	12 36			12 40				12 55					13 08					13 29	13 36	
	d					12 30	12 37			12 41				12 56					13 11					13 30	13 37	
Bognor Regis 4	d				12 26			12 39							13 00	13 07							13 26			13 39
Barnham	a				12 32	12 37	12 44	12 45		12 48				13 03	13 06	13 13			13 18				13 32	13 37	13 44	13 45
	d				12 33	12 38	12 45			12 49				13 04	13 07	13 15			13 19				13 33	13 38	13 45	
Bognor Regis 4	a																									
Ford 4	d				12 37		12 49							13 08	13 11	13 19							13 37		13 49	
Littlehampton 4	a						12 54									13 24									13 54	
	d	12 15									12 45			12b58		13b11				13 15						
Angmering 3	d	12 23				12 47					12 53			13 14						13 23				13 47		
Goring-by-Sea	d	12 27									12 57			13 18						13 27						
Durrington-on-Sea	d	12 30									13 00			13 21						13 30						
West Worthing	d	12 32		12 39							13 02		13 09	13 23						13 32		13 39				
Worthing 4	a	12 34		12 41		12 54					13 04		13 11	13 25						13 34		13 41		13 54		
	d	12 36		12 42		12 56					13 06		13 12	13 26						13 36		13 42		13 56		
East Worthing	d			12 44									13 14									13 44				
Lancing	d			12 47		13 00					13 10		13 17	13 30								13 47		14 00		
Shoreham-by-Sea	d	12 42		12 52		13 04					13 14		13 22	13 34						13 42		13 52		14 04		
Southwick	d			12 55		13 07							13 25	13 37								13 55		14 07		
Fishersgate	d			12 57									13 27									13 57				
Portslade	d	12 47		12 59		13 10							13 29	13 40						13 47		13 59		14 10		
Aldrington	d			13 01									13 31									14 01				
Hove 2	d	12 51	12 54	13 04		13 14					13 21	13 24	13 34	13 44						13 51	13 54	14 04		14 14		
Brighton 10	a		12 58	13 08		13 18						13 28	13 38	13 48							13 58	14 08		14 18		
Haywards Heath 3	a	13 09	13 18								13 35	13 47		14 15						14 09	14 18					
Burgess Hill	a	13 01																		14 01						
Arundel	d				12 42										13 16								13 42			
Amberley	d				12 47																		13 47			
Pulborough	d				12 53										13 25								13 53			
Billingshurst	d				12 59				←						13 31 →			← 13 31					13 59			
Christs Hospital	d				13 06 →				13 06														14 06 →			
Horsham 4	a								13 10	13 16								13 40	13 46							
	d								13 20									13 50								
Crawley	d								13 29									13 59								
Three Bridges 4	a	13c25	13 42						13 32		14 11	14 11		14 25				14 02		14c25	14 42					
	d								13 33									14 03								
Gatwick Airport 10 ✈	a	13 24	13 30						13 37		13 54	14 00						14 07		14 24	14 30			14 50		
East Croydon	a	13 40	13 46	13 55					14 00		14 10	14 16	14 23					14 27		14 40	14 46	14 55		15 08		
London Bridge 4 ⊖	a	14 00	14 00	14e15					14f15		14 30	14 30	14e45					14 45		15 00	15 00	15e15				
Clapham Junction 10	a	13 49	14e03	14 04					14 11		14 19		14 33					14 37		14 49	15e03	15 04		15e25		
London Victoria 15 ⊖	a	13 57	14g05	14 11					14 18		14 27	14g35	14 40					14 44		14 57	15g05	15 11		15g27		

For general notes see front of timetable
For details of catering facilities see Directory of Train Operators

A 🛒 from Haywards Heath
b Change at Ford
c Change at Haywards Heath
e Change at Brighton and East Croydon
f Change at Gatwick Airport
g Change at Brighton and Gatwick Airport

For complete service between Horsham and Three Bridges see Table 186

Southampton, Portsmouth and Sussex Coast → Brighton, Gatwick Airport & London

Network Diagram - see first page of Table 186

		SN 1	SN 1	SN 1	SN 1	SN 1	SN 1	SN 1	SN 1		SN 1	SN 1	SN 1	SN 1	SN 1	SN 1	SN 1	SN 1	SN 1	SN 1	SN 1	SN 1	SN 1	SN 1	SN 1	SN 1
				A 🚲				🚲			🚲											A 🚲				🚲
Southampton Central	d											13 11					13 36									
Swanwick	d											13 28					13 53									
Fareham	d											13 35					14 00									
Portchester	d											13 40														
Cosham	d											13 44					14 08									
Portsmouth Harbour	d		13 12				13 28														14 12				14 28	
Portsmouth & Southsea	d		13 16				13 32										*13 50*	14 03			14 16				14 32	
Fratton	d		13 20				13 36										*13 54*	14 07			14 20				14 36	
Hilsea	d						*13 32*											14 11							*14 32*	
Bedhampton	d						*13 37*											14 16							*14 37*	
Havant	d		13 30				13 45					13 51					14 15	14 19			14 30				14 45	
Warblington	d											13 53														
Emsworth	d											13 56					14 19	14 23								
Southbourne	d											13 59					14 22	14 26								
Nutbourne	d																	14 28								
Bosham	d											14 03														
Fishbourne (Sussex)	d																	14 33								
Chichester 4	a		13 40				13 55					14 08					14 29	14 36			14 40				14 55	
	d		13 41				13 56					14 11					14 30	14 37			14 41				14 56	
Bognor Regis 4	d							14 00	14 07							14 26			14 39							15 00
Barnham	a		13 48				14 03	14 06	14 13			14 18				14 32	14 37	14 44	14 45		14 48				15 03	15 06
	d		13 49				14 04	14 07	14 15			14 19				14 33	14 38	14 45			14 49				15 04	15 07
Bognor Regis 4	a																									
Ford 4	d						14 08	14 11	14 19							14 37		14 49							15 08	15 11
Littlehampton 4	a								14 24									14 54								
	d			13 45			*13b58*		*14b11*				14 15									14 45			*14b58*	
Angmering 3	d			13 53			14 14						14 23				14 47					14 53			15 14	
Goring-by-Sea	d			13 57			14 18						14 27									14 57			15 18	
Durrington-on-Sea	d			14 00			14 21						14 30									15 00			15 21	
West Worthing	d			14 02		14 09	14 23						14 32		14 39							15 02		15 09	15 23	
Worthing 4	a			14 04		14 11	14 25						14 34		14 41		14 54					15 04		15 11	15 25	
	d			14 06		14 12	14 26						14 36		14 42		14 56					15 06		15 12	15 26	
East Worthing	d					14 14									14 44									15 14		
Lancing	d			14 10		14 17	14 30								14 47		15 00					15 10		15 17	15 30	
Shoreham-by-Sea	d			14 14		14 22	14 34						14 42		14 52		15 04					15 14		15 22	15 34	
Southwick	d					14 25	14 37								14 55		15 07							15 25	15 37	
Fishersgate	d					14 27									14 57									15 27		
Portslade	d					14 29	14 40						14 47		14 59		15 10							15 29	15 40	
Aldrington	d					14 31									15 01									15 31		
Hove 2	d			14 21	14 24	14 34	14 44						14 51	14 54	15 04		15 14					15 21	15 24	15 34	15 44	
Brighton 10	a				14 28	14 38	14 48							14 58	15 08		15 18						15 28	15 38	15 48	
Haywards Heath 3	a			14 35	*14 47*		*15 15*						15 09	*15 18*								15 35	*15 47*		*16 15*	
Burgess Hill	a												15 01													
Arundel	d							14 16								14 42										15 16
Amberley	d															14 47										
Pulborough	d							14 25			←					14 53										15 25
Billingshurst	d	←						14 31			14 31					14 59				←						15 31
Christs Hospital	d	14 06						→								15 06				15 06						→
Horsham 4	a	14 10	14 16								14 40	14 46				→				15 10	15 16					
	d		14 20									14 50									15 20					
Crawley	d		14 29									14 59									15 29					
Three Bridges 4	a		14 32	*15 11*	*15 11*		*15 25*					15 02	15c25	*15 42*							15 32	*16 11*	*16 11*		*16 25*	
	d		14 33									15 03									15 33					
Gatwick Airport 10 ✈	a		14 37	14 55	*15 00*							15 07	15 24	*15 30*							15 37	15 54	*16 00*			
East Croydon	a		15 00	15 11	*15 16*	*15 23*						15 27	15 40	*15 46*	*15 55*						16 00	16 10	*16 16*	*16 23*		
London Bridge 4 ⊖	a		*15e15*	*15 30*	*15 30*	*15f45*						*15 45*	*16 00*	*16 00*	*16f15*						*16e15*	*16 30*	*16 30*	*16f45*		
Clapham Junction 10	a		15 11	15 20		*15 33*						15 37	15 49	*16f03*	*16 04*						16 11	16 19		*16 33*		
London Victoria 15 ⊖	a		15 18	15 27	*15g35*	*15 40*						15 44	15 57	*16g05*	*16 11*						16 18	16 27	*16g35*	*16 40*		

For general notes see front of timetable
For details of catering facilities see Directory of Train Operators

A 🚲 from Haywards Heath
b Change at Ford
c Change at Haywards Heath
e Change at Gatwick Airport
f Change at Brighton and East Croydon
g Change at Brighton and Gatwick Airport

For complete service between Horsham and Three Bridges see Table 186

Southampton, Portsmouth and Sussex Coast → Brighton, Gatwick Airport & London

Network Diagram - see first page of Table 186

		SN 1		SN 1	SN 1	SN 1	SN 1	SN 1	GW	SN 1	SN 1	SN 1	SN 1	SN 1	SN 1	SN 1	SN 1	SN 1		SN 1	SN 1	SN 1	SN 1	SN 1	SN 1	SN 1
				🛒					◇ A							B 🛒					🛒		🛒			
Southampton Central	d				14 11				14 35		14 26													15 11		
Swanwick	d				14 28																			15 28		
Fareham	d				14 35				14 56		15 02													15 35		
Portchester	d				14 40																			15 40		
Cosham	d				14 44				15 04															15 44		
Portsmouth Harbour	d														15 12					15 28						
Portsmouth & Southsea	d								*14 50*		*14 50*	15 03			15 16					15 32						
Fratton	d								*14 54*		*14 54*	15 07			15 20					15 36						
Hilsea	d											15 11								*15 32*						
Bedhampton	d											15 16								*15 37*						
Havant	d				14 51				15 11		15 15	15 19			15 30					15 45				15 51		
Warblington	d				14 53																			15 53		
Emsworth	d				14 56						15 19	15 23												15 56		
Southbourne	d				14 59						15 22	15 26												15 59		
Nutbourne	d											15 28														
Bosham	d				15 03																			16 03		
Fishbourne (Sussex)	d											15 33														
Chichester 4	a				15 08				15 22		15 29	15 36			15 40					15 55				16 08		
	d				15 11				15 22		15 30	15 37			15 41					15 56				16 11		
Bognor Regis 4	d	15 07								15 26			15 39								16 00	16 07				
Barnham	a	15 13			15 18				15 30	15 32	15 37	15 44	15 45		15 48					16 03	16 06	16 13		16 18		
	d	15 15			15 19				15 30	15 33	15 38	15 45			15 49					16 04	16 07	16 15		16 19		
Bognor Regis 4	a																									
Ford 4	d	15 19								15 37		15 49								16 08	16 11	16 19				
Littlehampton 4	a	15 24										15 54										16 24				
	d	*15b11*				15 15										15 45				*15b58*		*16b11*			16 15	
Angmering 3	d					15 23					15 47					15 53				16 14					16 23	
Goring-by-Sea	d					15 27										15 57				16 18					16 27	
Durrington-on-Sea	d					15 30										16 00				16 21					16 30	
West Worthing	d					15 32		15 39								16 02		16 09		16 23					16 32	
Worthing 4	a					15 34		15 41	15 45		15 54					16 04		16 11		16 25					16 34	
	d					15 36		15 42	15 50		15 56					16 06		16 12		16 26					16 36	
East Worthing	d							15 44										16 14								
Lancing	d							15 47			16 00					16 10		16 17		16 30						
Shoreham-by-Sea	d					15 42		15 52	15 57		16 04					16 14		16 22		16 34					16 42	
Southwick	d							15 55			16 07							16 25		16 37						
Fishersgate	d							15 57										16 27								
Portslade	d					15 47		15 59			16 10							16 29		16 40					16 47	
Aldrington	d							16 01										16 31								
Hove 2	d					15 51	15 54	16 04	16 08		16 14					16 21	16 24	16 34		16 44					16 51	16 54
Brighton 10	a						15 58	16 08	16 14		16 18						16 28	16 38		16 48						16 58
Haywards Heath 3	a					16 09	*16 18*									16 35	*16 47*			*17 15*					17 09	*17 18*
Burgess Hill	a					16 01																			17 01	
Arundel	d									15 42											16 16					
Amberley	d									15 47																
Pulborough	d			←						15 53											16 25		←			
Billingshurst	d			15 31						15 59				←							16 31 →		16 31			
Christs Hospital	d									16 06 →				16 06												
Horsham 4	a			15 40	15 46									16 10	16 16								16 40	16 46		
	d			15 50										16 20									16 50			
Crawley	d			15 59										16 29									16 59			
Three Bridges 4	a			16 02		*16c25*	*16 42*							16 32		*17 11*	*17 11*			*17 25*			17 02		*17c25*	*17 42*
	d			16 03										16 33									17 03			
Gatwick Airport 10 ✈	a			16 07		16 24	*16 30*							16 37		16 54	*17 00*						17 07		17 24	*17 30*
East Croydon	a			16 27		16 40	*16 46*	*16 55*	*16 55*					17 00		17 10	*17 16*	*17 23*					17 27		17 40	*17 46*
London Bridge 4 ⊖	a			*16 45*		*17 00*	*17 00*	*17e15*	*17e15*					*17f15*		*17 30*	*17 30*	*17e45*					*17 45*		*18 00*	*18 00*
Clapham Junction 10	a			16 37		16 49	*17e03*	*17 04*	*17 04*					17 11		17 19		*17 33*					17 37		17 49	*18e03*
London Victoria 15 ⊖	a			16 44		16 57	*17g05*	*17 11*	*17 11*					17 18		17 27	*17g35*	*17 40*					17 44		17 57	*18g05*

For general notes see front of timetable
For details of catering facilities see Directory of Train Operators

- A From Great Malvern (Table 71)
- B 🛒 from Haywards Heath
- b Change at Ford
- c Change at Haywards Heath
- e Change at Brighton and East Croydon
- f Change at Gatwick Airport
- g Change at Brighton and Gatwick Airport

For complete service between Horsham and Three Bridges see Table 186

Southampton, Portsmouth and Sussex Coast → Brighton, Gatwick Airport & London

Network Diagram - see first page of Table 186

		SN 1	SN 1	SN 1	SN 1	SN 1	SN 1	SN 1	SN 1	SN 1	SN 1	SN 1	SN 1	SN 1	SN 1	SN 1	SN 1	SN 1	SN 1	SN 1	SN 1	SN 1	SN 1	SN 1	SN 1
									A 🚌				🚌		🚌										
Southampton Central	d			15 36												16 11					16 36				
Swanwick	d			15 53												16 28					16 53				
Fareham	d			16 00												16 35					17 00				
Portchester	d															16 40									
Cosham	d			16 08												16 44					17 08				
Portsmouth Harbour	d							16 12				16 28													17 12
Portsmouth & Southsea	d			*15 50*	16 03			16 16				16 32									*16 50*	17 03			17 16
Fratton	d			*15 54*	16 07			16 20				16 36									*16 54*	17 07			17 20
Hilsea	d				16 11							*16 32*										17 11			*17 18*
Bedhampton	d				16 16							*16 37*										17 16			
Havant	d			16 15	16 19			16 30				16 45				16 51					17 15	17 19			17 30
Warblington	d															16 53									
Emsworth	d			16 19	16 23											16 56					17 19	17 23			
Southbourne	d			16 22	16 26											16 59					17 22	17 26			
Nutbourne	d				16 28																	17 28			
Bosham	d															17 03									
Fishbourne (Sussex)	d				16 33																	17 33			
Chichester 4	a			16 29	16 36			16 40				16 55				17 08					17 29	17 36			17 40
	d			16 30	16 37			16 41				16 56				17 11					17 30	17 37			17 41
Bognor Regis 4	d		16 26			16 39							17 00	17 07						17 26			17 39		
Barnham	a		16 32	16 37	16 44	16 45		16 48				17 03	17 06	17 13		17 18				17 32	17 37	17 44	17 45		17 48
	d		16 33	16 38	16 45			16 49				17 04	17 07	17 15		17 19				17 33	17 38	17 45			17 49
Bognor Regis 4	a																								
Ford 4	d		16 37		16 49							17 08	17 11	17 19						17 37		17 49			
Littlehampton 4	a				16 54									17 24								17 54			
	d								16 45			*16b58*		*17b11*			17 15								
Angmering 3	d			16 47					16 53			17 14					17 23				17 47				
Goring-by-Sea	d								16 57			17 18					17 27								
Durrington-on-Sea	d								17 00			17 21					17 30								
West Worthing	d	16 39							17 02		17 09	17 23					17 32		17 39						
Worthing 4	a	16 41		16 54					17 04		17 11	17 25					17 34		17 41		17 54				
	d	16 42		16 56					17 06		17 12	17 26					17 36		17 42		17 56				
East Worthing	d	16 44									17 14								17 44						
Lancing	d	16 47		17 00					17 10		17 17	17 30							17 47		18 00				
Shoreham-by-Sea	d	16 52		17 04					17 14		17 22	17 34					17 42		17 52		18 04				
Southwick	d	16 55		17 07							17 25	17 37							17 55		18 07				
Fishersgate	d	16 57									17 27								17 57						
Portslade	d	16 59		17 10							17 29	17 40					17 47		17 59		18 10				
Aldrington	d	17 01									17 31								18 01						
Hove 2	d	17 04		17 14					17 21	17 24	17 34	17 44					17 51	17 54	18 04		18 14				
Brighton 10	a	17 08		17 18						17 28	17 38	17 48						17 58	18 08		18 18				
Haywards Heath 3	a								17 35	*17 47*		*18 15*					18 09	*18 18*							
Burgess Hill	a																18 01								
Arundel	d		16 42										17 16							17 42					
Amberley	d		16 47																	17 47					
Pulborough	d		16 53										17 25		←					17 53					
Billingshurst	d		16 59				←						17 31 →		17 31					17 59				←	
Christs Hospital	d		17 06 →				17 06													18 06 →				18 06	
Horsham 4	a						17 10	17 16							17 40	17 46								18 10	18 16
	d						17 20								17 50									18 20	
Crawley	d						17 29								17 59									18 29	
Three Bridges 4	a						17 32		*18 11*	*18 11*		*18 25*			18 02		*18c25*	*18 42*						18 32	
	d						17 33								18 03									18 33	
Gatwick Airport 10 ✈	a						17 37		17 54	*18 00*					18 07		18 24	*18 30*						18 37	
East Croydon 🚋	a	*17 55*					18 00		18 10	*18 16*	*18 23*				18 27		18 40	*18 46*	*18 55*					19 00	
London Bridge 4 ⊖	a	*18e15*					*18f15*		*18 30*	*18 30*	*18e45*				*18 45*		*19 00*	*19 00*	*19e15*					*19f15*	
Clapham Junction 10	a	*18 04*					18 11		18 19		*18 33*				18 37		18 49	*19e03*	*19 04*					19 11	
London Victoria 15 ⊖	a	*18 11*					18 18		18 27	*18g35*	*18 40*				18 44		18 57	*19g05*	*19 11*					19 18	

For general notes see front of timetable
For details of catering facilities see Directory of Train Operators

A 🚌 from Haywards Heath
b Change at Ford
c Change at Haywards Heath
e Change at Brighton and East Croydon
f Change at Gatwick Airport
g Change at Brighton and Gatwick Airport

For complete service between Horsham and Three Bridges see Table 186

Table 188

Saturdays

Southampton, Portsmouth and Sussex Coast → Brighton, Gatwick Airport & London

Network Diagram - see first page of Table 186

		SN 1 A 🛒	SN 1	SN 1		SN 1	SN 1	SN 1	SN 1	SN 1	SN 1	SN 1	SN 1	SN 1	SN 1	SN 1	SN 1	SN 1	SN 1	SN 1		SN 1	SN 1	SN 1	SN 1	SN 1
Southampton Central	d									17 11				17 36											18 11	
Swanwick	d									17 28				17 53											18 28	
Fareham	d									17 35				18 00											18 35	
Portchester	d									17 40															18 40	
Cosham	d									17 44				18 08											18 44	
Portsmouth Harbour	d					17 28																18 12	18 28			
Portsmouth & Southsea	d					17 32								*17 50*		18 03						18 16	18 32			
Fratton	d					17 36								*17 54*		18 07						18 20	18 36			
Hilsea	d					*17 32*										18 11							*18 32*			
Bedhampton	d					*17 37*										18 16							*18 37*			
Havant	d					17 45				17 51				18 15		18 19						18 28	18 45		18 51	
Warblington	d									17 53												18 30				
Emsworth	d									17 56				18 19		18 23						18 33			18 55	
Southbourne	d									17 59				18 22		18 26						18 36			18 58	
Nutbourne	d															18 28										
Bosham	d									18 03												18 41				
Fishbourne (Sussex)	d															18 33										
Chichester 4	a					17 55				18 08				18 29		18 36						18 45	18 55		19 05	
	d					17 56				18 11				18 30		18 37						18 46	18 56		19 07	
Bognor Regis 4	d						18 00	18 07							18 33		18 39							19 03		
Barnham	a					18 03	18 06	18 13		18 18				18 37	18 40	18 44	18 46					18 53	19 03	19 09	19 14	
	d					18 04	18 07	18 15		18 19				18 38	18 41	18 45						18 54	19 04	19 22 →	19 15	
Bognor Regis 4	a																									
Ford 4	d					18 08	18 11	18 19							18 45	18 49						18 58	19 08		19 19	
Littlehampton 4	a							18 24														19 03				
	d	17 45				*17*b*58*		*18*b*11*			18 15									18 52			*18*b*58*		*19*b*11*	19 15
Angmering 3	d	17 53				18 14					18 23			18 47	18 53					19 00			19 14			19 23
Goring-by-Sea	d	17 57				18 18					18 27				18 57					19 04			19 18			19 27
Durrington-on-Sea	d	18 00				18 21					18 30				19 00			←		19 07			19 21			19 30
West Worthing	d	18 02		18 09		18 23					18 32		18 39		19 02			19 02		19 09			19 23			19 32
Worthing 4	a	18 04		18 11		18 25					18 34		18 41	18 54	→			19 04		19 11			19 25			19 34
	d	18 06		18 12		18 26					18 36		18 42	18 56				19 06		19 12			19 26			19 35
East Worthing	d			18 14									18 44							19 14						
Lancing	d	18 10		18 17		18 30							18 47	19 00				19 10		19 17			19 30			19 39
Shoreham-by-Sea	d	18 14		18 22		18 34					18 42		18 52	19 04				19 14		19 22			19 34			19 43
Southwick	d			18 25		18 37							18 55	19 07						19 25			19 37			
Fishersgate	d			18 27									18 57							19 27						
Portslade	d			18 29		18 40					18 47		18 59	19 10						19 29			19 40			19 48
Aldrington	d			18 31									19 01							19 31						
Hove 2	d	18 21	18 24	18 34		18 44					18 51	18 54	19 04	19 14				19 21	19 24	19 34			19 44			19 52
Brighton 10	a		18 28	18 38		18 48						18 58	19 08	19 18					19 28	19 38			19 48			
Haywards Heath 3	a	18 35	*18 47*			*19 15*					19 09	*19 18*						19 35	*19 47*				*20 16*			20 09
Burgess Hill	a										19 01															20 02
Arundel	d						18 16									18 54									19 24	
Amberley	d															18 59									19 29	
Pulborough	d						18 25									19 05									19 35	
Billingshurst	d						18 31		←							19 11									19 41	
Christs Hospital	d						18 38 →		18 38																19 48	
Horsham 4	a								18 42	18 46						19 20									19 52	
	d								18 50							19 21									19 52	
Crawley	d								18 59							19 30									20 01	
Three Bridges 4	a		*19 12*			*19 25*			19 02		*19*c*25*	*19 42*				19 33		*20 12*	*20 12*						20 05	*20*c*32*
	d								19 03							19 34									20 05	
Gatwick Airport 10 ✈	a	18 54	*19 00*						19 07		19 24	*19 31*				19 38		19 54	*20 00*						20 10	20 24
East Croydon	a	19 10	*19 16*	*19 23*					19 28		19 40	*19 47*	*19 55*			19 59		20 10	*20 16*	*20 23*					20 30	20 40
London Bridge 4 ⊖	a		*19 30*	*19*e*45*					*19*f*45*		*20 00*	*20 00*	*20*e*15*			*20*f*15*		*20 30*	*20 30*	*20*e*45*					*20*f*45*	*21 00*
Clapham Junction 10	a	19 19		*19 33*					19 40		19 49	*20*e*03*	*20 04*			20 10		20 19		*20 33*					20 40	20 49
London Victoria 15 ⊖	a	19 27	*19*g*35*	*19 40*					19 48		19 57		*20 11*			20 17		20 27	*20*g*35*	*20 40*					20 50	20 57

For general notes see front of timetable
For details of catering facilities see Directory of Train Operators

A 🛒 from Haywards Heath
b Change at Ford
c Change at Haywards Heath
e Change at Brighton and East Croydon
f Change at Gatwick Airport
g Change at Brighton and Gatwick Airport

For complete service between Horsham and Three Bridges see Table 186

Table 188

Southampton, Portsmouth and Sussex Coast → Brighton, Gatwick Airport & London

Network Diagram - see first page of Table 186

Station		SN	SN	SN	SN	SN	SN	SN	SN	SN	SN	SN	SN		SN	SN	SN	SN	SN	SN	SN	SN	SN	SN	SN	SN
Southampton Central	d			18 36									19 11				19 36								20 11	
Swanwick	d			18 53									19 28				19 53								20 28	
Fareham	d			19 00									19 35				20 00								20 35	
Portchester	d												19 40												20 40	
Cosham	d			19 08									19 44				20 08								20 44	
Portsmouth Harbour	d									19 12	19 28												20 28			
Portsmouth & Southsea	d			18 50				19 03		19 16	19 32						19 50					20 03	20 32			
Fratton	d			18 54				19 07		19 20	19 36						19 54					20 07	20 36			
Hilsea	d							19 11			19 32											20 11	20 32			
Bedhampton	d							19 16			19 37											20 16	20 37			
Havant	d			19 15				19 19		19 28	19 45		19 52				20 15					20 19	20 45		20 51	
Warblington	d									19 30												20 21				
Emsworth	d			19 19				19 23		19 33			19 56									20 24			20 55	
Southbourne	d			19 22				19 26		19 36			19 59									20 27			20 58	
Nutbourne	d							19 28														20 29				
Bosham	d									19 41												20 33				
Fishbourne (Sussex)	d							19 33														20 36				
Chichester 4	a			19 29				19 36		19 45	19 55		20 06				20 25					20 39	20 55		21 05	
	d			19 30				19 37		19 46	19 56		20 07				20 26					20 40	20 56		21 07	
Bognor Regis 4	d				19 33				19 39			20 04						20 33	20 39					21 04		
Barnham	a	←		19 37	19 40			19 44	19 46	19 53	20 03	20 10	20 14				20 33	20 39	20 45			20 47	21 03	21 10	21 14	
	d	19 22		19 38	19 41			19 45		19 54	20 04	20 11	20 15				20 34	20 40				20 49	21 04	21 11	21 15	
Bognor Regis 4	a																									
Ford 4	d	19 26			19 45			19 49		19 58	20 08	20 15	20 19					20 44				20 53	21 08	21 15	21 19	
Littlehampton 4	a	19 32						19 54		20 03		20 20										21 01		21 20		
	d						19 52						20b11		20 15						20 52			21b06		21 15
Angmering 3	d			19 47	19 53		20 00				20 14				20 23		20 43	20 53			21 00		21 14			21 23
Goring-by-Sea	d				19 57		20 04								20 27			20 57			21 04					21 27
Durrington-on-Sea	d				20 00		20 07								20 30		20 48	21 00			21 07					21 30
West Worthing	d				20 02		20 09								20 32			21 02			21 09					21 32
Worthing 4	a			19 54	20 04		20 11				20 21				20 34		20 52	21 04			21 11		21 21			21 34
	d			19 54	20 05		20 12				20 22				20 35		20 53	21 05			21 12		21 22			21 35
East Worthing	d			19 57			20 14				20 25						20 55				21 14		21 25			
Lancing	d			20 00	20 09		20 17				20 28				20 39		20 58	21 09			21 17		21 28			21 39
Shoreham-by-Sea	d			20 04	20 13		20 22				20 32				20 43		21 02	21 13			21 22		21 32			21 43
Southwick	d			20 07			20 25				20 35						21 05				21 25		21 35			
Fishersgate	d			20 09			20 27				20 37						21 07				21 27		21 37			
Portslade	d			20 11	20 17		20 29				20 39				20 48		21 09	21 18			21 29		21 39			21 48
Aldrington	d			20 13			20 31				20 41						21 12				21 31		21 41			
Hove 2	d		19 54	20 16	20 22	20 24	20 34				20 44				20 52	20 54	21 14	21 22		21 24	21 34		21 44			21 52
Brighton 10	a		19 58	20 20		20 28	20 38				20 48					20 58	21 18			21 28	21 38		21 48			
Haywards Heath 3	a		20 18		20 36	20 47					21 21				21 08	21 28		21 36		21 58			22 21			22 08
Burgess Hill	a														21 02											22 02
Arundel	d												20 24												21 24	
Amberley	d												20 29												21 29	
Pulborough	d												20 35												21 35	
Billingshurst	d												20 41												21 41	
Christs Hospital	d												20 48												21 48	
Horsham 4	a												20 52												21 52	
	d												20 52												21 52	
Crawley	d												21 01												22 01	
Three Bridges 4	a		20c32		20 47	21 11					21 32		21 05		21e32	21 42		22 11		22 11			22 32		22 05	22e32
	d				20 48								21 05												22 05	
Gatwick Airport 10 ✈	a		20 30		20 52	21 00					21 37		21 10		21 24	21 46		21 51		22 16			22 37		22 10	22 23
East Croydon	a		20 46		21 09	21 16	21 23						21 30		21 40	21 55		22 09			22 23		22 59		22 30	22 40
London Bridge 4 ⊖	a		21 00		21 30	21 30	21f45						21g45			22 15					22f45				22g45	
Clapham Junction 10	a		21f03		21 19		21 33						21 40		21 49	22 04		22 19			22 33		23 10		22 40	22 49
London Victoria 15 ⊖	a		21h05		21 27	21h35	21 40						21 48		21 57	22 11		22 27			22 40		23 17		22 48	22 57

For general notes see front of timetable
For details of catering facilities see Directory of Train Operators

- b Change at Ford
- c Change at Brighton and Haywards Heath
- e Change at Haywards Heath
- f Change at Brighton and East Croydon
- g Change at Gatwick Airport
- h Change at Brighton and Gatwick Airport

For complete service between Horsham and Three Bridges see Table 186

Table 188

Saturdays

Southampton, Portsmouth and Sussex Coast → Brighton, Gatwick Airport & London

Network Diagram - see first page of Table 186

Station		SN 1	SN 1	SN 1	SN 1	SN 1		SN 1	SN 1	SN 1	SN 1	SN 1	SN 1	SN 1	SN 1	SN 1	SN 1	SN 1	SN 1	SN 1	SN 1	SN 1		SN 1	SN 1	
Southampton Central	d			20 36							21 11				21 23			22 11				22 36				
Swanwick	d			20 53							21 28				21 45			22 28				22 53				
Fareham	d			21 00							21 39				21 55			22 39				23 00				
Portchester	d										21 44				22 00			22 44								
Cosham	d			21 08							21 48				22 04			22 48				23 08				
Portsmouth Harbour	d	20 40							21 11				21 40				22 15				22 44				23 15	
Portsmouth & Southsea	d	20 44		20 50					21 15		21 24		21 44				22 19	22 24			22 48				23 19	
Fratton	d	20 48		20 54					21 19		21 28		21 48				22 23	22 28			22 52				23 23	
Hilsea	d								21 23		21 32		21 52				22 27	22 32			22 56				23 27	
Bedhampton	d								21 28		21 37		21 57				22 32	22 37			23 01				23 33	
Havant	d	20 57		21 15					21 31		21 55		22 00		22 14		22 35	22 55			23 04	23 15			23 36	
Warblington	d	20 59							21 33						22 16										23 38	
Emsworth	d	21 02							21 36						22 19		22 39	22 59							23 41	
Southbourne	d	21 05							21 39						22 22		22 42	23 02							23 44	
Nutbourne	d	21 07							21 41						22 24										23 47	
Bosham	d	21 11							21 45						22 28										23 50	
Fishbourne (Sussex)	d	21 14							21 48						22 31										23 53	
Chichester 4	a	21 17		21 25					21 51		22 05		22 10		22 34		22 49	23 09			23 16	23 25			23 57	
	d	21 18		21 26					21 52		22 06		22 11		22 40		22 52	23 09			23 17	23 26		23 52	23 57	
Bognor Regis 4	d				21 39					22 00				22 30					23 15							
Barnham	a	21 25		21 33	21 45				21 59	22 06	22 13		22 18	22 36	22 47		22 59	23 17	23 21		23 24	23 33		23 59	00 05	
	d	21 26		21 34					22 00	22 07	22 14		22 19	22 37	22 48		23 00	23 17			23 25	23 34		00 01	00 06	
Bognor Regis 4	a																									
Ford 4	d	21 30		21 38					22 04	22 11			22 23	22 41	22 52		23 04				23 29			00 05	00 10	
Littlehampton 4	a	21 35								22 16			22 28	22 46				23 25			23 34	23 42		00 10	00 15	
	d							21 52					22 33		22b38						23 39			23b24		
Angmering 3	d			21 44				22 00	22 11				22 41				23 11				23 47					
Goring-by-Sea	d			21 48				22 04	22 15				22 45				23 15				23 51					
Durrington-on-Sea	d			21 51				22 07	22 17				22 47				23 17				23 53					
West Worthing	d			21 53				22 09	22 19				22 49				23 19				23 55					
Worthing 4	a			21 55				22 11	22 22				22 52				23 22				23 58					
	d			21 56				22 12	22 22				22 52				23 22				23 59					
East Worthing	d			21 58				22 14	22 25				22 55				23 25				00 01					
Lancing	d			22 01				22 17	22 28				22 58				23 28				00 04					
Shoreham-by-Sea	d			22 05				22 22	22 32				23 02				23 32				00 08					
Southwick	d			22 08				22 25	22 35				23 05				23 35				00 11					
Fishersgate	d			22 10				22 27	22 37				23 07				23 37				00 13					
Portslade	d			22 12				22 29	22 39				23 09				23 39				00 15					
Aldrington	d			22 15				22 31	22 41				23 11				23 41				00 18					
Hove 2	d		21 54	22 17		22 24		22 34	22 44			22 54	23 14			23 24	23 44			23 54	00 20					
Brighton 10	a		21 58	22 22		22 28		22 38	22 48			22 58	23 18			23 28	23 48			23 58	00 25					
Haywards Heath 3	a		22 28			22 54						23 23				23 58										
Burgess Hill	a																									
Arundel	d										22 22				22 57											
Amberley	d														23 02											
Pulborough	d										22 31				23 08											
Billingshurst	d										22 37				23 14											
Christs Hospital	d										22 44				23 21											
Horsham 4	a										22 48				23 25											
	d										22 49				23 25											
Crawley	d										22 57				23 38											
Three Bridges 4	a		22 42			23 05					23 01	23 33			23 42	00 10										
	d																									
Gatwick Airport 10 ✈	a		22 46			23c12					23 12	23 52			23 52	00 14										
East Croydon	a		23 02			23 32					23 30	00 16			00 16	00 35										
London Bridge 4 ⊖	a		23 15			23 45					23 45				00 52	00 52										
Clapham Junction 10	a		23e25			00e11					23 42				01f02	01e02										
London Victoria 15 ⊖	a		23g52								23 52	00 37			00 37	00h55										

For general notes see front of timetable
For details of catering facilities see Directory of Train Operators

- b Change at Ford
- c Change at Brighton and Haywards Heath
- e Change at Brighton and East Croydon
- f Change at Three Bridges and East Croydon
- g Change at Brighton and Three Bridges
- h Change at Brighton and Gatwick Airport

For complete service between Horsham and Three Bridges see Table 186

Table 188

Sundays

Southampton, Portsmouth and Sussex Coast → Brighton, Gatwick Airport & London

Network Diagram - see first page of Table 186

Station		SN 1	SN 1	SN 1	SN 1	SN 1	SN 1	SN 1	SN 1	SN 1	SN 1	SN 1	SN 1	SN 1	SN 1	SN 1	SN 1	SN 1	SN 1	SN 1	SN 1	SN 1	SN 1	SN 1
					A																			
Southampton Central	d																							
Swanwick	d																							
Fareham	d																							
Portchester	d																							
Cosham	d																							
Portsmouth Harbour	d	22p44		23p15								07 14				07 43				08 14				08 43
Portsmouth & Southsea	d	22p48		23p19								07 18				07 47				08 18				08 47
Fratton	d	22p52		23p23								07 22				07 51				08 22				08 51
Hilsea	d	22p56		23p27																				
Bedhampton	d	23p01		23p33								07 30								08 30				
Havant	d	23p04		23p36								07 33				08 00				08 33				09 00
Warblington	d			23p38								07 35								08 35				
Emsworth	d			23p41								07 38				08 04				08 38				09 04
Southbourne	d			23p44								07 41				08 07				08 41				09 07
Nutbourne	d			23p47								07 43								08 43				
Bosham	d			23p50								07 47								08 47				
Fishbourne (Sussex)	d			23p53								07 50								08 50				
Chichester 4	a	23p16		23p57								07 53				08 14				08 53				09 14
	d	23p17	23p52	23p57	05⟨41							07 53				08 14				08 53				09 14
Bognor Regis 4	d						06 57				07 36		07 57						08 36		08 57			
Barnham	a	23p24	23p59	00 05	05⟨48		07 03				07 42	08 01	08 03	←		08 22			08 42	09 01	09 03	←		09 22
	d	23p25	00 01	00 06	05⟨49	06 06	07 05				07 43	08 08 →	08 05	08 08		08 22			08 43	09 08 →	09 05	09 08		09 22
Bognor Regis 4	a																							
Ford 4	d	23p29	00 05	00 10	⟨	06b46	07 09				07 47		08 09	08 12					08 47		09 09	09 12		
Littlehampton 4	a	23p34	00 10	00 15	⟨	06 13					07 52								08 52					
	d	23p39	23c24		⟨	06 20	06c42	07 14		07 41	07c19		07c57		08 14			08 41	08c11		08c57		09 14	
Angmering 3	d	23p47			⟨			07 22		07 49				08 18	08 22			08 49				09 18	09 22	
Goring-by-Sea	d	23p51			⟨			07 26		07 53				08 22	08 26			08 53				09 22	09 26	
Durrington-on-Sea	d	23p53			⟨			07 29		07 55				08 25	08 29			08 55				09 25	09 29	
West Worthing	d	23p55			⟨			07 31		07 57				08 27	08 31			08 57				09 27	09 31	
Worthing 4	a	23p58			06⟨03	06 33		07 33		08 00				08 29	08 33	08 37		09 00				09 29	09 33	09 37
	d	23p59			06⟨05	06 33		07 35		08 00				08 30	08 41			09 00				09 30	09 41	
East Worthing	d	00 01			⟨					08 02				08 32				09 02				09 32		
Lancing	d	00 04			06⟨09	06 37		07 39		08 05				08 35				09 05				09 35		
Shoreham-by-Sea	d	00 08			06⟨13	06 41		07 43		08 09				08 39	08 47			09 09				09 39	09 47	
Southwick	d	00 11			06⟨16	06 44		07 46		08 12				08 42				09 12				09 42		
Fishersgate	d	00 13			⟨					08 14				08 44				09 14				09 44		
Portslade	d	00 15			06⟨20	06 48		07 49		08 16				08 46				09 16				09 46		
Aldrington	d	00 18			⟨					08 19				08 49			←	09 19				09 49		
Hove 2	d	00 20			06⟨24	06 51		07 54	07 56	08 21				08e56 →	08 54		08 56	09 21				09f56 →	09 54	
Brighton 10	a	00 25			⟨	06 55			08 00	08 26							09 00	09 25						
Haywards Heath 3	a				06⟨39	07 20		08 09	08 30	09 00					09 09		09 30	09 51					10 09	
Burgess Hill	a				⟨			08 04							09 04								10 04	
Arundel	d				⟨		07 14						08 14								09 14			
Amberley	d				⟨		07 19						08 19								09 19			
Pulborough	d				⟨		07 25						08 25								09 25			
Billingshurst	d				⟨		07 31						08 31								09 31			
Christs Hospital	d				⟨		07 38						08 38								09 38			
Horsham 4	a				⟨		07 42						08 42								09 42			
	d				⟨		07 42						08 42								09 42			
Crawley	d				⟨		07 51						08 51								09 51			
Three Bridges 4	a				07⟨10	07 32	07 54	08g32	08 40	09 10			08 54		09g32		09 40	10 10			09 54		10g32	
	d				⟨		07 54						08 54								09 54			
Gatwick Airport 10 ✈	a				06⟨53	07 37	07 58	08 21	08 44	09 14			08 58		09 21		09 44	10 10			09 58		10 21	
East Croydon	a				07⟨09	07 58	08 24	08 39	09 01	09 31			09 24		09 39		10 01	10 31			10 24		10 39	
London Bridge 4 ⊖	a				07⟨38	08 15	08 45	09 12	09 15	09 45			09 45		10 12		10 15	10 45			10 45		11 12	
Clapham Junction 10	a				07⟨24	08 11	08 37	08 54	09h24	09j47			09 37		09 54		10h24	10j47			10 37		10 54	
London Victoria 15 ⊖	a				07⟨31	08 18	08 46	09 01	09k25	09 53			09 46		10 01		10k25	10 53			10 46		11 01	

For general notes see front of timetable
For details of catering facilities see Directory of Train Operators

A Until 7 September

b Change at Littlehampton
c Change at Ford
e Arr. 0851
f Arr. 0951
g Change at Haywards Heath

h Change at Brighton and East Croydon
j From 14 September arr. 7 minutes later change at Brighton and East Croydon
k Change at Brighton and Gatwick Airport

For complete service between Horsham and Three Bridges see Table 186

Table 188

Sundays

Southampton, Portsmouth and Sussex Coast → Brighton, Gatwick Airport & London

Network Diagram - see first page of Table 186

		SN	GW		SN	SN	SN	SN	SN	SN	SN		SN	SN	SN	SN	SN	SN	SN	SN		SN	SN	SN	SN	SN
		1	1		1	1	1	1	1	1	1		1	1	1	1	1	1	1	1		1	1	1	1	1
			A																							
			🍴					🍴									🍴									🍴
Southampton Central	d		08 31																							
Swanwick	d																									
Fareham	d		08 52																							
Portchester	d																									
Cosham	d		09 00																							
Portsmouth Harbour	d						09 14				09 43					10 14				10 43					11 14	
Portsmouth & Southsea	d						09 18				09 47					10 18				10 47					11 18	
Fratton	d						09 22				09 51					10 22				10 51					11 22	
Hilsea	d																									
Bedhampton	d						09 30									10 30									11 30	
Havant	d		09 11				09 33				10 00					10 33				11 00					11 33	
Warblington	d						09 35									10 35									11 35	
Emsworth	d						09 38				10 04					10 38				11 04					11 38	
Southbourne	d						09 41				10 07					10 41				11 07					11 41	
Nutbourne	d						09 43									10 43									11 43	
Bosham	d						09 47									10 47									11 47	
Fishbourne (Sussex)	d						09 50									10 50									11 50	
Chichester 4	a		09 22				09 53				10 14					10 53				11 14					11 53	
	d		09 22				09 53				10 14					10 53				11 14					11 53	
Bognor Regis 4	d					09 36		09 57							10 36		10 57							11 36		11 57
Barnham	a		09 30			09 42	10 01	10 03	←		10 22				10 42	11 01	11 03	←		11 22				11 42	12 01	12 03
	d		09 30			09 43	10 08 →	10 05	10 08		10 22				10 43	11 08 →	11 05	11 08		11 22				11 43	12 08 →	12 05
Bognor Regis 4	a																									
Ford 4	d					09 47		10 09	10 12						10 47		11 09	11 12						11 47		12 09
Littlehampton 4	a					09 52									10 52									11 52		
	d				09 41	09b11		09b57		10 14				10 41			10b57		11 14				11 41			11b57
Angmering 3	d				09 49				10 18	10 22				10 49				11 18	11 22				11 49			
Goring-by-Sea	d				09 53				10 22	10 26				10 53				11 22	11 26				11 53			
Durrington-on-Sea	d				09 55				10 25	10 29				10 55				11 25	11 29				11 55			
West Worthing	d				09 57				10 27	10 31				10 57				11 27	11 31				11 57			
Worthing 4	a		09 45		10 00				10 29	10 33	10 37			11 00				11 29	11 33	11 37			12 00			
	d		09 45		10 00				10 30	10 41				11 00				11 30	11 41				12 00			
East Worthing	d				10 02				10 32					11 02				11 32					12 02			
Lancing	d				10 05				10 35					11 05				11 35					12 05			
Shoreham-by-Sea	d		09 52		10 09				10 39	10 47				11 09				11 39	11 47				12 09			
Southwick	d				10 12				10 42					11 12				11 42					12 12			
Fishersgate	d				10 14				10 44					11 14				11 44					12 14			
Portslade	d				10 16				10 46					11 16				11 46					12 16			
Aldrington	d	←			10 19				10 49				←	11 19				11 49				←	12 19			
Hove 2	d	09 56	09 59		10 21				10c56 →	10 54			10 56	11 21				11e56 →	11 54			11 56	12 21			
Brighton 10	a	10 00	10 05		10 25								11 00	11 25								12 00	12 25			
Haywards Heath 3	a		10 30		11 00					11 09			11 30	12 00					12 09			12 30	13 00			
Burgess Hill	a									11 04									12 04							
Arundel	d							10 14									11 14									12 14
Amberley	d							10 19									11 19									12 19
Pulborough	d							10 25									11 25									12 25
Billingshurst	d							10 31									11 31									12 31
Christs Hospital	d							10 38									11 38									12 38
Horsham 4	a							10 42									11 42									12 42
	d							10 42									11 42									12 42
Crawley	d							10 51									11 51									12 51
Three Bridges 4	a		10 40		11 10			10 54		11f32			11 40	12 10			11 54		12f32			12 40	13 10			12 54
	d							10 54									11 54									12 54
Gatwick Airport 10 ✈	a		10 44		11 14			10 58		11 21			11 44	12 14			11 58		12 22			12 44	13 14			12 58
East Croydon 🚋	a		11 01		11 31			11 24		11 39			12 01	12 31			12 24		12 39			13 01	13 31			13 24
London Bridge 4 ⊖	a		11 15		11 45			11 45		12 12			12 15	12 45			12 45		13 12			13 15	13 45			13 45
Clapham Junction 10	a		11g24		11h47			11 37		11 54			12g24	12h47			12 37		12 54			13g24	13h47			13 37
London Victoria 15 ⊖	a		11j25		11 53			11 46		12 01			12j25	12 53			12 46		13 01			13j25	13 53			13 46

For general notes see front of timetable
For details of catering facilities see Directory of Train Operators

- A From Romsey
- b Change at Ford
- c Arr. 1051
- e Arr. 1151
- f Change at Haywards Heath
- g Change at Brighton and East Croydon
- h From 14 September arr. 7 minutes later change at Brighton and East Croydon
- j Change at Brighton and Gatwick Airport

For complete service between Horsham and Three Bridges see Table 186

Table 188

Sundays

Southampton, Portsmouth and Sussex Coast → Brighton, Gatwick Airport & London

Network Diagram - see first page of Table 186

Station		SN 1	SN 1	SN 1	SN 1		SN 1	SN 1	SN 1	SN 1 🚲	SN 1	SN 1	SN 1
Southampton Central	d												
Swanwick	d												
Fareham	d												
Portchester	d												
Cosham	d												
Portsmouth Harbour	d			11 43					12 14				12 43
Portsmouth & Southsea	d			11 47					12 18				12 47
Fratton	d			11 51					12 22				12 51
Hilsea	d												
Bedhampton	d								12 30				
Havant	d			12 00					12 33				13 00
Warblington	d								12 35				
Emsworth	d			12 04					12 38				13 04
Southbourne	d			12 07					12 41				13 07
Nutbourne	d								12 43				
Bosham	d								12 47				
Fishbourne (Sussex)	d								12 50				
Chichester 4	a			12 14					12 53				13 14
	d			12 14					12 53				13 14
Bognor Regis 4	d							12 36		12 57			
Barnham	a	←		12 22				12 42	13 01	13 03	←		13 22
	d	12 08		12 22				12 43	13 08 →	13 05	13 08		13 22
Bognor Regis 4	a												
Ford 4	d	12 12						12 47		13 09	13 12		
Littlehampton 4	a							12 52					
	d		12 14				12 41			12b57		13 14	
Angmering 3	d	12 18	12 22				12 49				13 18	13 22	
Goring-by-Sea	d	12 22	12 26				12 53				13 22	13 26	
Durrington-on-Sea	d	12 25	12 29				12 55				13 25	13 29	
West Worthing	d	12 27	12 31				12 57				13 27	13 31	
Worthing 4	a	12 29	12 33	12 37			13 00				13 29	13 33	13 37
	d	12 30	12 41				13 00				13 30	13 41	
East Worthing	d	12 32					13 02				13 32		
Lancing	d	12 35					13 05				13 35		
Shoreham-by-Sea	d	12 39	12 47				13 09				13 39	13 47	
Southwick	d	12 42					13 12				13 42		
Fishersgate	d	12 44					13 14				13 44		
Portslade	d	12 46					13 16				13 46		
Aldrington	d	12 49			←		13 19				13 49		
Hove 2	d	12c56 →	12 54		12 56		13 21				13e56 →	13 54	
Brighton 10	a				13 00		13 25						
Haywards Heath 3	a		13 09		13 30		14 00					14 09	
Burgess Hill	a		13 04									14 04	
Arundel	d									13 14			
Amberley	d									13 19			
Pulborough	d									13 25			
Billingshurst	d									13 31			
Christs Hospital	d									13 38			
Horsham 4	a									13 42			
	d									13 42			
Crawley	d									13 51			
Three Bridges 4	a		13g32		13 40		14 10			13 54		14g32	
	d									13 54			
Gatwick Airport 10 ✈	a		13 22		13 44		14 14			13 58		14 22	
East Croydon	a		13 39		14 01		14 31			14 24		14 39	
London Bridge 4 ⊖	a		14 12		14 15		14 45			14 45		15 12	
Clapham Junction 10	a		13 54		14h24		14j47			14 37		14 54	
London Victoria 15 ⊖	a		14 01		14k25		14 53			14 46		15 01	

Station			SN 1	SN 1	SN 1	SN 1	SN 1 🚲	SN 1	SN 1	SN 1		SN 1	GW ◇ A 🚲	SN 1
Southampton Central	d												13 08	
Swanwick	d													
Fareham	d												13 34	
Portchester	d													
Cosham	d												13 42	
Portsmouth Harbour	d					13 14				13 43				
Portsmouth & Southsea	d					13 18				13 47				
Fratton	d					13 22				13 51				
Hilsea	d													
Bedhampton	d					13 30								
Havant	d					13 33				14 00			14 04	
Warblington	d					13 35								
Emsworth	d					13 38				14 04				
Southbourne	d					13 41				14 07				
Nutbourne	d					13 43								
Bosham	d					13 47								
Fishbourne (Sussex)	d					13 50								
Chichester 4	a					13 53				14 14			14 19	
	d					13 53				14 14			14 19	
Bognor Regis 4	d				13 36		13 57							
Barnham	a				13 42	14 01	14 03	←		14 22			14 27	
	d				13 43	14 08 →	14 05	14 08		14 22			14 27	
Bognor Regis 4	a													
Ford 4	d				13 47		14 09	14 12						
Littlehampton 4	a				13 52									
	d			13 41			13b57		14 14					14 41
Angmering 3	d			13 49				14 18	14 22					14 49
Goring-by-Sea	d			13 53				14 22	14 26					14 53
Durrington-on-Sea	d			13 55				14 25	14 29					14 55
West Worthing	d			13 57				14 27	14 31					14 57
Worthing 4	a			14 00				14 29	14 33	14 37			14 44	15 00
	d			14 00				14 30	14 41				14 45	15 00
East Worthing	d			14 02				14 32						15 02
Lancing	d			14 05				14 35						15 05
Shoreham-by-Sea	d			14 09				14 39	14 47				14 51	15 09
Southwick	d			14 12				14 42						15 12
Fishersgate	d			14 14				14 44						15 14
Portslade	d			14 16				14 46						15 16
Aldrington	d		←	14 19				14 49				←		15 19
Hove 2	d		13 56	14 21				14f56 →	14 54			14 56	15 00	15 21
Brighton 10	a		14 00	14 25								15 00	15 06	15 25
Haywards Heath 3	a		14 30	15 00					15 09			15 30	15 30	16 00
Burgess Hill	a								15 04					
Arundel	d						14 14							
Amberley	d						14 19							
Pulborough	d						14 25							
Billingshurst	d						14 31							
Christs Hospital	d						14 38							
Horsham 4	a						14 42							
	d						14 42							
Crawley	d						14 51							
Three Bridges 4	a		14 40	15 10			14 54		15g32			15 40	15 40	16 10
	d						14 54							
Gatwick Airport 10 ✈	a		14 44	15 14			14 58		15 22			15 44	15 44	16 14
East Croydon	a		15 01	15 31			15 24		15 39			16 01	16 01	16 31
London Bridge 4 ⊖	a		15 15	15 45			15 45		16 12			16 15	16 15	16 45
Clapham Junction 10	a		15h24	15j47			15 37		15 54			16h24	16h24	16 47
London Victoria 15 ⊖	a		15k25	15 53			15 46		16 01			16k25	16k25	16 53

For general notes see front of timetable
For details of catering facilities see Directory of Train Operators

A Until 7 September from Bristol Parkway (Table 132)

b Change at Ford
c Arr. 1251
e Arr. 1351
f Arr. 1451
g Change at Haywards Heath
h Change at Brighton and East Croydon
j From 14 September arr. 7 minutes later change at Brighton and East Croydon
k Change at Brighton and Gatwick Airport

For complete service between Horsham and Three Bridges see Table 186

Table 188

Sundays

Southampton, Portsmouth and Sussex Coast → Brighton, Gatwick Airport & London

Network Diagram - see first page of Table 186

		SN 1	SN 1	SN 1	SN 1	SN 1	SN 1	SN 1	SN 1	SN 1	SN 1	SN 1	SN 1	SN 1	SN 1	SN 1	GW ◇	SN 1	SN 1	SN 1	SN 1	SN 1
																	A					
				🛒								🛒					🛒				🛒	
Southampton Central	d																15 22					
Swanwick	d																					
Fareham	d																15 51					
Portchester	d																					
Cosham	d																16 01					
Portsmouth Harbour	d		14 14				14 43				15 14				15 43					16 14		
Portsmouth & Southsea	d		14 18				14 47				15 18				15 47					16 18		
Fratton	d		14 22				14 51				15 22				15 51					16 22		
Hilsea	d																					
Bedhampton	d		14 30								15 30									16 30		
Havant	d		14 33				15 00				15 33				16 00		16 11			16 33		
Warblington	d		14 35								15 35									16 35		
Emsworth	d		14 38				15 04				15 38				16 04					16 38		
Southbourne	d		14 41				15 07				15 41				16 07					16 41		
Nutbourne	d		14 43								15 43									16 43		
Bosham	d		14 47								15 47									16 47		
Fishbourne (Sussex)	d		14 50								15 50									16 50		
Chichester 4	a		14 53				15 14				15 53				16 14		16 22			16 53		
	d		14 53				15 14				15 53				16 14		16 22			16 53		
Bognor Regis 4	d	14 36		14 57						15 36		15 57							16 36		16 57	
Barnham	a	14 42	15 01	15 03	←		15 22			15 42	16 01	16 03	←		16 22		16 30		16 42	17 01	17 03	←
	d	14 43	15 08 →	15 05	15 08		15 22			15 43	16 08 →	16 05	16 08		16 22		16 30		16 43	17 08 →	17 05	17 08
Bognor Regis 4	a																					
Ford 4	d	14 47		15 09	15 12					15 47		16 09	16 12						16 47		17 09	17 12
Littlehampton 4	a	14 52								15 52									16 52			
	d			14b57		15 14			15 41			15b57		16 14				16 41			16b57	
Angmering 3	d				15 18	15 22			15 49				16 18	16 22				16 49				17 18
Goring-by-Sea	d				15 22	15 26			15 53				16 22	16 26				16 53				17 22
Durrington-on-Sea	d				15 25	15 29			15 55				16 25	16 29				16 55				17 25
West Worthing	d				15 27	15 31			15 57				16 27	16 31				16 57				17 27
Worthing 4	a				15 29	15 33	15 37		16 00				16 29	16 33	16 37		16 45	17 00				17 29
	d				15 30	15 41			16 00				16 30	16 41			16 45	17 00				17 30
East Worthing	d				15 32				16 02				16 32					17 02				17 32
Lancing	d				15 35				16 05				16 35					17 05				17 35
Shoreham-by-Sea	d				15 39	15 47			16 09				16 39	16 47			16 52	17 09				17 39
Southwick	d				15 42				16 12				16 42					17 12				17 42
Fishersgate	d				15 44				16 14				16 44					17 14				17 44
Portslade	d				15 46				16 16				16 46					17 16				17 46
Aldrington	d				15 49			←	16 19				16 49			←		17 19				17 49
Hove 2	d				15c56	15 54		15 56	16 21				16e56	16 54		16 56	16 59	17 21				17f56
Brighton 10	a				→			16 00	16 25				→			17 00	17 05	17 25				→
Haywards Heath 3	a					16 09		*16 30*	*17 00*					17 09		*17 30*	*17 30*	*18 00*				
Burgess Hill	a					16 04								17 04								
Arundel	d			15 14								16 14									17 14	
Amberley	d			15 19								16 19									17 19	
Pulborough	d			15 25								16 25									17 25	
Billingshurst	d			15 31								16 31									17 31	
Christs Hospital	d			15 38								16 38									17 38	
Horsham 4	a			15 42								16 42									17 42	
	d			15 42								16 42									17 42	
Crawley	d			15 51								16 51									17 51	
Three Bridges 4	a			15 54		*16g32*		*16 40*	*17 10*			16 54		*17g32*		*17 40*	*17 40*	*18 10*			17 54	
	d			15 54								16 54									17 54	
Gatwick Airport 10 ✈	a			15 58		16 22		*16 44*	*17 14*			16 58		17 22		*17 44*	*17 44*	*18 14*			17 58	
East Croydon	a			16 24		16 39		*17 01*	*17 31*			17 24		17 39		*18 01*	*18 01*	*18 31*			18 24	
London Bridge 4 ⊖	a			*16 45*		*17 12*		*17 15*	*17 45*			*17 45*		*18 12*		*18 15*	*18 15*	*18 45*			*18 45*	
Clapham Junction 10	a			16 37		16 54		*17h24*	*17 47*			17 37		17 54		*18h24*	*18h24*	*18 47*			18 37	
London Victoria 15 ⊖	a			16 46		17 01		*17j25*	*17 53*			17 46		18 01		*18j25*	*18j25*	*18 53*			18 46	

For general notes see front of timetable
For details of catering facilities see Directory of Train Operators

A Until 7 September from Bristol Parkway (Table 132)
b Change at Ford
c Arr. 1551
e Arr. 1651
f Arr. 1751
g Change at Haywards Heath
h Change at Brighton and East Croydon
j Change at Brighton and Gatwick Airport

For complete service between Horsham and Three Bridges see Table 186

Southampton, Portsmouth and Sussex Coast → Brighton, Gatwick Airport & London

Network Diagram - see first page of Table 186

		SN 1	SN 1	SN 1	SN 1	SN 1	SN 1	SN 1		SN 1	SN 1	SN 1	SN 1	SN 1	SN 1	SN 1		SN 1	SN 1	SN 1	SN 1	SN 1	SN 1	SN 1		SN 1
Southampton Central	d																									
Swanwick	d																									
Fareham	d																									
Portchester	d																									
Cosham	d																									
Portsmouth Harbour	d		16 43				17 14					17 43				18 14					18 43					19 14
Portsmouth & Southsea	d		16 47				17 18					17 47				18 18					18 47					19 18
Fratton	d		16 51				17 22					17 51				18 22					18 51					19 22
Hilsea	d																									
Bedhampton	d						17 30									18 30										19 30
Havant	d		17 00				17 33					18 00				18 33					19 00					19 33
Warblington	d						17 35									18 35										19 35
Emsworth	d		17 04				17 38					18 04				18 38					19 04					19 38
Southbourne	d		17 07				17 41					18 07				18 41					19 07					19 41
Nutbourne	d						17 43									18 43										19 43
Bosham	d						17 47									18 47										19 47
Fishbourne (Sussex)	d						17 50									18 50										19 50
Chichester 4	a		17 14				17 53					18 14				18 53					19 14					19 53
	d		17 14				17 53					18 14				18 53					19 14					19 53
Bognor Regis 4	d					17 36		17 57							18 36			18 57						19 36		
Barnham	a		17 22			17 42	18 01	18 03		←		18 22			18 42	19 01		19 03	←		19 22			19 42		20 01
	d		17 22			17 43	18 08 →	18 05		18 08		18 22			18 43	19 08 →		19 05	19 08		19 22			19 43		20 08 →
Bognor Regis 4	a																									
Ford 4	d					17 47		18 09		18 12					18 47			19 09	19 12					19 47		
Littlehampton 4	a					17 52									18 52									19 52		
	d	17 14			17 41			17b57			18 14			18 41				18b57		19 14			19 41			
Angmering 3	d	17 22			17 49					18 18	18 22			18 49					19 18	19 22			19 49			
Goring-by-Sea	d	17 26			17 53					18 22	18 26			18 53					19 22	19 26			19 53			
Durrington-on-Sea	d	17 29			17 55					18 25	18 29			18 55					19 25	19 29			19 55			
West Worthing	d	17 31			17 57					18 27	18 31			18 57					19 27	19 31			19 57			
Worthing 4	a	17 33	17 37		18 00					18 29	18 33	18 37		19 00					19 29	19 33	19 37		20 00			
	d		17 41		18 00					18 30		18 41		19 00					19 30		19 41		20 00			
East Worthing	d				18 02					18 32				19 02					19 32				20 02			
Lancing	d				18 05					18 35				19 05					19 35				20 05			
Shoreham-by-Sea	d		17 47		18 09					18 39		18 47		19 09					19 39		19 47		20 09			
Southwick	d				18 12					18 42				19 12					19 42				20 12			
Fishersgate	d				18 14					18 44				19 14					19 44				20 14			
Portslade	d				18 16					18 46				19 16					19 46				20 16			
Aldrington	d			←	18 19					18 49			←	19 19					19 49			←	20 19			
Hove 2	d		17 54	17 56	18 21					18c56 →		18 54	18 56	19 21					19e56 →		19 54	19 56	20 21			
Brighton 10	a			18 00	18 25								19 00	19 25								20 00	20 25			
Haywards Heath 3	a		18 09	18 30	19 00							19 09	19 30	20 00							20 09	20 30	21 00			
Burgess Hill	a		18 04									19 04									20 04					
Arundel	d							18 14										19 14								
Amberley	d							18 19										19 19								
Pulborough	d							18 25										19 25								
Billingshurst	d							18 31										19 31								
Christs Hospital	d							18 38										19 38								
Horsham 4	a							18 42										19 42								
	d							18 42										19 42								
Crawley	d							18 51										19 51								
Three Bridges 4	a		18f32	18 40	19 10			18 54				19f32	19 40	20 10				19 54			20f32	20 40	21 10			
	d							18 54										19 54								
Gatwick Airport 10 ✈	a		18 22	18 44	19 14			18 58				19 22	19 44	20 14				19 58			20 22	20 44	21 14			
East Croydon	a		18 39	19 01	19 31			19 24				19 39	20 01	20 31				20 24			20 39	21 01	21 31			
London Bridge 4 ⊖	a		19 12	19 15	19 45			19 45				20 12	20 15	20 45				20 45			21 12	21 15	21 45			
Clapham Junction 10	a		18 54	19g24	19 47			19 37				19 54	20g24	20 47				20 37			20 54	21g24	21g54			
London Victoria 15 ⊖	a		19 01	19h25	19 53			19 46				20 01	20h25	20 53				20 46			21 01	21h25	21h55			

For general notes see front of timetable
For details of catering facilities see Directory of Train Operators

b Change at Ford
c Arr. 1851
e Arr. 1951
f Change at Haywards Heath
g Change at Brighton and East Croydon
h Change at Brighton and Gatwick Airport

For complete service between Horsham and Three Bridges see Table 186

Table 188

Sundays

Southampton, Portsmouth and Sussex Coast → Brighton, Gatwick Airport & London

Network Diagram - see first page of Table 186

		SN	SN	SN	SN	SN	SN	SN	SN	SN	SN	GW	SN	SN	SN	SN	SN	SN	SN	SN	SN	SN
		1	1	1	1	1	1	1	1	1	1	◇ A	1	1	1	1	1	1	1	1	1	1
Southampton Central	d											20 07										
Swanwick	d																					
Fareham	d											20 29										
Portchester	d																					
Cosham	d											20 44										
Portsmouth Harbour	d				19 43				20 14				20 43		21 14				21 43	22 14	22 43	
Portsmouth & Southsea	d				19 47				20 18				20 47		21 18				21 47	22 18	22 47	
Fratton	d				19 51				20 22				20 51		21 22				21 51	22 22	22 51	
Hilsea	d																					
Bedhampton	d								20 30						21 30					22 30		
Havant	d				20 00				20 33			20 53	21 00		21 33				22 00	22 33	23 00	
Warblington	d								20 35						21 35					22 35		
Emsworth	d				20 04				20 38				21 04		21 38				22 04	22 38	23 04	
Southbourne	d				20 07				20 41				21 07		21 41				22 07	22 41	23 07	
Nutbourne	d								20 43						21 43					22 43		
Bosham	d								20 47						21 47					22 47		
Fishbourne (Sussex)	d								20 50						21 50					22 50		
Chichester 4	a				20 14				20 53			21 03	21 14		21 53				22 14	22 53	23 14	
	d				20 14				20 53			21 04	21 14		21 53				22 14	22 53	23 14	
Bognor Regis 4	d	19 57						20 36		20 57				21 36		21 57		22 11				
Barnham	a	20 03	←		20 22			20 42	21 01	21 03	←	21 11	21 22	21 42	22 01	22 03	←	22 18	22 22	23 01	23 22	
	d	20 05	20 08		20 22			20 43	21 08 →	21 05	21 08	21 12	21 22	21 43	22 08 →	22 05	22 08		22 22	23 01	23 22	23 37
Bognor Regis 4	a																					
Ford 4	d	20 09	20 12					20 47		21 09	21 12		21 27	21 47		22 09	22 12		22 27	23 06	23 27	23 42
Littlehampton 4	a							20 52					21 31	21 52					22 31	23 10	23 32	23 46
	d	19b57		20 14			20 41			20b57			21 41			21b57			22 41		23b06	23b29
Angmering 3	d		20 18	20 22			20 49				21 18		21 49				22 18		22 49			
Goring-by-Sea	d		20 22	20 26			20 53				21 22		21 53				22 22		22 53			
Durrington-on-Sea	d		20 25	20 29			20 55				21 25		21 55				22 25		22 55			
West Worthing	d		20 27	20 31			20 57				21 27		21 57				22 27		22 57			
Worthing 4	a		20 29	20 33	20 37		21 00				21 29	21 34	22 00				22 29		23 00			
	d		20 30		20 41		21 00				21 30	21 34	22 00				22 30		23 00			
East Worthing	d		20 32				21 02				21 32		22 02				22 32		23 02			
Lancing	d		20 35				21 05				21 35		22 05				22 35		23 05			
Shoreham-by-Sea	d		20 39		20 47		21 09				21 39	21 45	22 09				22 39		23 09			
Southwick	d		20 42				21 12				21 42		22 12				22 42		23 12			
Fishersgate	d		20 44				21 14				21 44		22 14				22 44		23 14			
Portslade	d		20 46				21 16				21 46		22 16				22 46		23 16			
Aldrington	d		20 49			←	21 19				21 49		22 19				22 49		23 19			
Hove 2	d		20c56 →		20 54	20 56	21 21				21 51	21 55	22 21				22 51		23 21			
Brighton 10	a					21 00	21 25				21 55	22 01	22 26				22 56		23 25			
Haywards Heath 3	a				21 09	21 30	22 00				22 20	22 30	23 00				23 23		00 01			
Burgess Hill	a				21 04																	
Arundel	d	20 14								21 14						22 14						
Amberley	d	20 19								21 19						22 19						
Pulborough	d	20 25								21 25						22 25						
Billingshurst	d	20 31								21 31						22 31						
Christs Hospital	d	20 38								21 38						22 38						
Horsham 4	a	20 42								21 42						22 42						
	d	20 42								21 42						22 42						
Crawley	d	20 51								21 51						22 51						
Three Bridges 4	a	20 54			21e32	21 40	22 10			21 54	22 32	22 40	23 10			22 54	23 35		00 10			
	d	20 54								21 54						22 54						
Gatwick Airport 10 ✈	a	20 58			21 22	21 44	22 14			21 58	22 37	22 44	23 14			22 58	23 46		00 14			
East Croydon	a	21 27			21 39	22 01	22 31			22 24	22 58	23 01	23 31			23 24	00 16		00 35			
London Bridge 4 ⊖	a	21 45			22 12	22 15	22 45			22 45	23 15	23 15	23 45			23 45			00 52			
Clapham Junction 10	a	21 37			21 54	22f24	23f10			22 37	23 13	23f37	00f10			23 37			01f02			
London Victoria 15 ⊖	a	21 46			22 01	22g25	22g55			22 46	23 20	23 46	23g55			23 46	00 37		00g55			

For general notes see front of timetable
For details of catering facilities see Directory of Train Operators

A Until 7 September from Bristol Parkway (Table 132)
b Change at Ford
c Arr. 2051
e Change at Haywards Heath
f Change at Brighton and East Croydon
g Change at Brighton and Gatwick Airport

For complete service between Horsham and Three Bridges see Table 186

Table 189

London, Haywards Heath and Brighton → Lewes, Seaford, Eastbourne, Hastings and Ashford

Network Diagram - see first page of Table 184

Miles	Miles			SN	SN	SN	SN	SN	SN	SN	SN	SN	SN	SN	SN	SN		SN	SN	SN	SN	SE	SN	SN	SN
				MX	MX	MX	MO	MX														25			
				1	1	1	1	1	1	1	1	1	1	1	1	1		1	1	1	1	1	1	1	1
																						A			
—	—	**London Victoria 15**	⊖ d		22p47		22p47	00 05					04 00							05 02					05 02
—	—	Clapham Junction 10	d		22p53		22p53	00 11					04 08							05 08					05 08
—	—	**London Bridge 4**	⊖ d					23 53																	
—	—	East Croydon	d		23p03		23p07	00 25					04 22					04 32		05 32				05 02	05 22
—	—	**Gatwick Airport 10**	d		23p19		23p29	00 43					04 47					04 52		05 54				05 22	05 49
—	0	**Haywards Heath 3**	d		23p34		23p41	01 06					05 01					05 08		06 13				05 36	06 06
—	3	Wivelsfield 4	d		23p38		23p45													06 17				05 40	06 10
—	6¾	Plumpton	d		23p44		23p51																		
—	9½	Cooksbridge	d																						
0	—	**Brighton 10**	d	23p34									05 30					05 45	06 00					06 15	06 32
¾	—	London Road (Brighton)	d	23p37														05 48	06 03					06 18	
1¾	—	Moulsecoomb	d	23p39														05 50	06 05					06 20	
3½	—	Falmer	d	23p43														05 54	06 09					06 24	
8	12¼	**Lewes 4**	a	23p49	23p51	⟵	23p58	01 20					05 41					06 00	06 15	06 28				06 30	06 43
—	—		d	23p56	23p53	23p56	23p59	01 20					05 41					06 05		06 29				06 32	06 44
—	15¾	Southease	d	⟶																					
—	18¼	Newhaven Town	d			00 04												06 14		06 37					
—	18¾	Newhaven Harbour	d			00 06												06 15		06 39					
—	20¼	Bishopstone	d			00 09												06 18		06 42					
—	21¼	**Seaford**	a			00 12												06 22		06 45					
11	—	Glynde	d																					06 37	
15½	—	Berwick	d		00 02																			06 43	
19¾	—	Polegate	d		00 07		00 11	01s32					05 53											06 48	06 57
21¾	—	Hampden Park 4 §	d		00 11		00 15	01s36																06 52	
23¾	—	**Eastbourne 4**	a		00 16		00 20	01 41					06 00											07 01	07 04
—	—		d		00 22				05 00		05 24			06 04	06 15						06 34		06 51		07 08
25¾	—	Hampden Park 4 §	d												06 19								06 55		
28¾	—	Pevensey & Westham	d		00 29						05 31				06 24						06 41		07 00		
29½	—	Pevensey Bay	d																						
31½	—	Normans Bay	d																		06 46				
33¼	—	Cooden Beach	d		00 35										06 30								07 06		
34¾	—	Collington	d		00 38										06 33								07 09		
35½	—	**Bexhill 4**	d		00 40				05 14		05 40			06 18	06 35						06 52		07 11		07 22
39¼	—	**St Leonards Warrior Sq 4**	d		00 47				05 20		05 46			06 25	06 41						06 58	07 07	07 17		07 29
40	0	**Hastings 4**	a		00 50				05 24		05 50			06 29	06 45						07 02	07 11	07 22		07 32
—	—		d							05 30		05 55		06 30								07 15			07 34
—	1	Ore	d							05 32		05 57										07a18			
—	3¾	Three Oaks	d									06 03													
—	5	Doleham	d									06 06													
—	9¼	Winchelsea	d									06 12													
—	11¼	**Rye**	a							05 47		06 16		06 47											07 51
—	—		d							05 47		06 16		06 49		07 19									07 54
—	18	Appledore (Kent)	d							05 56		06 25		06 58		07 28									08 03
—	21	Ham Street	d							06 01		06 30		07 03		07 33									08 08
—	26½	**Ashford International**	a							06 15		06 39		07 11		07 41									08 16
—	—	London Bridge 4	⊖ a							07 54		08 14		08 34		09 22									09 39
—	—	London Cannon Street 4	⊖ a							08 00		08 20		08 41		09 28									09b57
—	—	London Waterloo (East) 4	⊖ a									08 04		08 41		09 01									09 45
—	—	London Charing Cross 4	⊖ a							08b07		08 09		08 47		09 07									09 50

For general notes see front of timetable
For details of catering facilities see Directory of Train Operators

§ For additional trains between Hampden Park and Eastbourne see Hastings to London pages

A From Tonbridge (Table 206)

b Change at Ashford International and London Bridge

London, Haywards Heath and Brighton → Lewes, Seaford, Eastbourne, Hastings and Ashford

Network Diagram - see first page of Table 184

		SN 1	SN 1	SN 1	SN 1	SN 1	SN 1	SN 1		SN 1	SN 1	SN 1	SN 1	SN 1	SN 1	SN 1	SN 1	SN 1	SN 1	SN 1	SN 1	SN 1		SN 1	SN 1
London Victoria 15 ⊖	d	05 32				05b32		06c02					06b02	06 47		06 21	06b32	06b47		07b06	07 47	07b23			
Clapham Junction 10	d	05 38				05b38		06c08					06b08	06 53		06 27	06b38	06b53		07b12	07 53	07b29			
London Bridge 4 ⊖	d	05e31		05 31		05 50		06 21					06 21				06 43	07 00		07 16	07 40	07 28			
East Croydon	d	05 49	05 32	05 52		06 04		06 36					06 36	07 03		06 39	06 56	07 16		07 32	08 03	07 46			
Gatwick Airport 10 ✈	d	06 20	05 54	06 08		06 20		06 52					06 52	07 19		07 04	07 12	07 32		07 50	08 19	08 02			
Haywards Heath 3	d	06 34	06 10	06 25		06 38		07 12					07 06	07 33		07 21	07 28	07 48		08 06	08 32	08 16			
Wivelsfield 4	d	06 38	06 14	06 29		06 42		07 16					07 10	07 37		07 25	07 32	07 44		08 10	08 36				
Plumpton	d							07 22						07 43							08 42				
Cooksbridge	d							07 26						07 47							08 47				
Brighton 10	d		06 39	06 52	07 00	07 13					07 22		07 32		07 40	07 52	08 03	08 13	08 22	08 32		08 38		08 45	08 52
London Road (Brighton)	d		06 42	06 55	07 03	07 16					07 25				07 43	07 55	08 06	08 16	08 25			08 41		08 48	08 55
Moulsecoomb	d		06 44	06 57	07 05	07 18					07 27				07 45	07 57	08 08	08 18	08 27			08 43		08 50	08 57
Falmer	d		06 48	07 01	07 09	07 22					07 31				07 49	08 01	08 12	08 22	08 31			08 47		08 54	09 01
Lewes 4	a	06 49	06 54	07 08	07 17	07 29		07 31		←	07 37		07 43	07 52	07 56	08 08	08 19	08 29	08 37	08 43	08 51	08 53		09 00	09 07
	d	06 51	06 55	07 10		07 36		07 33		07 36			07 44	07 53	07 58	08 09	08 23	08 30		08 44	08 52			09 02	09 08
Southease	d					→																			
Newhaven Town ⛴	d		07 03	07 18						07 44					08 06			08 38						09 10	
Newhaven Harbour	d		07 05	07f23						07 46					08 08			08 40						09 12	
Bishopstone	d		07 08	07 26						07 49					08 11			08 43						09 15	
Seaford	a		07 11	07 29						07 52					08 14			08 46						09 18	
Glynde	d	06 56						07 38								08 14	08 28								09 13
Berwick	d	07 02						07 44								08 20	08 34								09 19
Polegate	d	07 07						07 49					07 57	08 05		08 25	08 39			08 57	09 04				09 24
Hampden Park 4 §	d	07 11						07 53						08 09		08 29	08 43				09 08				09 28
Eastbourne 4	a	07 16						07 58					08 04	08 14		08 34	08 48			09 04	09 13				09 33
	d	07 21										07 38	08 08	08 21		08 40				09 08	09 20				09 37
Hampden Park 4 §	d	07 25										07 42		08 25		08 44					09 24				09 41
Pevensey & Westham	d	07 30										07 47	08 17	08 30		08 49					09 29				09 46
Pevensey Bay	d											07 49		08 32											
Normans Bay	d											07 53		08 36		08 53									09 51
Cooden Beach	d	07 36										07 56		08 39		08 57					09 35				09 54
Collington	d	07 39										07 59		08 42		09 00					09 38				09 57
Bexhill 4	d	07 41										08 01	08 25	08 45		09 02				09 22	09 41				10 00
St Leonards Warrior Sq 4	d	07 49										08 08	08 32	08 52		09 08				09 29	09 48				10 06
Hastings 4	a	07 52										08 13	08 35	08 56		09 12				09 32	09 51				10 10
	d	07 53										08 14	08 36	08 57		09 13				09 34	09 53				10 12
Ore	d	07a56										08a17		09a00		09a16					09a56				10a15
Three Oaks	d																								
Doleham	d																								
Winchelsea	d																								
Rye	a												08 53							09 51					
	d						08 23						08 54							09 54					
Appledore (Kent)	d						08 32						09 03							10 03					
Ham Street	d						08 37						09 08							10 08					
Ashford International	a						08 45						09 16							10 16					
London Bridge 4 ⊖	a												11 13							11 43					
London Cannon Street 4 ⊖	a												11g20							11g50					
London Waterloo (East) 4 ⊖	a												10 32							11 32					
London Charing Cross 4 ⊖	a												10 36							11 36					

For general notes see front of timetable
For details of catering facilities see Directory of Train Operators

§ For additional trains between Hampden Park and Eastbourne see Hastings to London pages

b Change at East Croydon and Brighton
c Change at East Croydon and Haywards Heath
e Change at Gatwick Airport
f Arr. 0720
g Change at Ashford International and London Bridge

London, Haywards Heath and Brighton → Lewes, Seaford, Eastbourne, Hastings and Ashford

Network Diagram - see first page of Table 184

Station		SN 1	SN 1	SN 1	SN 1	SN 1	SN 1 A	SN 1	SN 1	SN 1 A	SN 1	SN 1	SN 1	SN 1 A
London Victoria 15 ⊖	d	07b47	08 17		08 06	08 20	08 47	08 36		09 17	09 06		09 36	09 47
Clapham Junction 10	d	07b53	08 23		08 12	08 28	08 53	08 43		09 23	09 12		09 42	09 53
London Bridge 4 ⊖	d	07 54	08c19		07b56	08 19	08 41	08b27			09b00		09 25	09 42
East Croydon	d	08 11	08 33		08 22	08 39	09 03	08 53		09 33	09 22		09 52	10 03
Gatwick Airport 10	d	08 30	08 49			08 56	09 19		09 00	09 49	09 23		09 56	10 19
Haywards Heath 3	d	08 45	09 13		08 51	09 10	09 34		09 17	10 07	09 40		10 10	10 34
Wivelsfield 4	d	08 32	09 17		08 55	09 02			09 22	10 11	09 34		10 01	
Plumpton	d						09 43							10 43
Cooksbridge	d						09 48							
Brighton 10	d	09 10			09 22	09 32		09 40	09 52		10 10	10 22	10 32	
London Road (Brighton)	d	09 13			09 25			09 43	09 55		10 13	10 25		
Moulsecoomb	d	09 15			09 27			09 45	09 57		10 15	10 27		
Falmer	d	09 19			09 31			09 49	10 01		10 19	10 31		
Lewes 4	a	09 25	09 28	⟵	09 37	09 43	09 52	09 56	10 07	10 22	10 25	10 37	10 43	10 51
	d	09 32	09 29	09 32		09 44	09 53	09 58	10 09	10 23	10 28		10 44	10 53
Southease	d	⟶		09 38							10 34			
Newhaven Town ⛴	d			09 42				10 06			10 38			
Newhaven Harbour	d			09 44				10 08			10 40			
Bishopstone	d			09 47				10 11			10 43			
Seaford	a			09 50				10 14			10 46			
Glynde	d								10 14					
Berwick	d								10 20					
Polegate	d		09 41			09 57	10 05		10 25	10 35			10 57	11 05
Hampden Park 4 §	d		09 45						10 29	10 39				
Eastbourne 4	a		09 50			10 04	10 13		10 34	10 44			11 04	11 13
	d					10 08	10 19		10 40				11 08	11 19
Hampden Park 4 §	d						10 23		10 44					11 23
Pevensey & Westham	d						10 28		10 49					11 28
Pevensey Bay	d													
Normans Bay	d								10 53					
Cooden Beach	d						10 34		10 57					11 34
Collington	d						10 37		11 00					11 37
Bexhill 4	d					10 22	10 39		11 02				11 22	11 39
St Leonards Warrior Sq 4	d					10 29	10 45		11 08				11 29	11 45
Hastings 4	a					10 32	10 50		11 12				11 32	11 50
	d					10 34	10 51		11 13				11 34	11 51
Ore	d						10a54		11a16					11a54
Three Oaks	d													
Doleham	d													
Winchelsea	d													
Rye	a					10 51							11 51	
	d					10 54							11 54	
Appledore (Kent)	d					11 03							12 03	
Ham Street	d					11 08							12 08	
Ashford International	a					11 16							12 16	
London Bridge 4 ⊖	a					12 43							13 43	
London Cannon Street 4 ⊖	a					12e50							13e50	
London Waterloo (East) 4 ⊖	a					12 32							13 32	
London Charing Cross 4 ⊖	a					12 36							13 36	

Station			SN 1	SN 1	SN 1 A	SN 1	SN 1	SN 1	SN 1 A	SN 1	SN 1	SN 1 A
London Victoria 15 ⊖	d				10 17	10 06		10 36	10 47			11 17
Clapham Junction 10	d				10 23	10 12		10 42	10 53			11 23
London Bridge 4 ⊖	d					09 56	10 11	10 26				
East Croydon	d				10 33	10 22	10 24	10 52	11 03			11 33
Gatwick Airport 10	d				10 49	10 26	10 41	10 56	11 19			11 49
Haywards Heath 3	d			10 18	11 07	10 38	10 55	11 08	11 34			12 07
Wivelsfield 4	d			10 22	11 11	10 31	10 59					12 11
Plumpton	d											
Cooksbridge	d											
Brighton 10	d		10 40	10 52		11 10	11 22	11 32		11 40	11 52	
London Road (Brighton)	d		10 43	10 55		11 13	11 25			11 43	11 55	
Moulsecoomb	d		10 45	10 57		11 15	11 27			11 45	11 57	
Falmer	d		10 49	11 01		11 19	11 31			11 49	12 01	
Lewes 4	a		10 55	11 07	11 22	11 25	11 37	11 43	11 48	11 55	12 07	12 22
	d		10 58	11 09	11 23	11 28		11 44	11 53	11 58	12 09	12 23
Southease	d					11 34						
Newhaven Town ⛴	d		11 06			11 38				12 06		
Newhaven Harbour	d		11 08			11 40				12 08		
Bishopstone	d		11 11			11 43				12 11		
Seaford	a		11 14			11 46				12 14		
Glynde	d			11 14							12 14	
Berwick	d			11 20							12 20	
Polegate	d			11 25	11 35			11 57	12 05		12 25	12 35
Hampden Park 4 §	d			11 29	11 39						12 29	12 39
Eastbourne 4	a			11 34	11 44			12 04	12 13		12 34	12 44
	d			11 40				12 08	12 19		12 40	
Hampden Park 4 §	d			11 44					12 23		12 44	
Pevensey & Westham	d			11 49					12 28		12 49	
Pevensey Bay	d											
Normans Bay	d			11 53							12 53	
Cooden Beach	d			11 57					12 34		12 57	
Collington	d			12 00					12 37		13 00	
Bexhill 4	d			12 02				12 22	12 39		13 02	
St Leonards Warrior Sq 4	d			12 08				12 29	12 45		13 08	
Hastings 4	a			12 12				12 32	12 50		13 12	
	d			12 13				12 34	12 51		13 13	
Ore	d			12a16					12a54		13a16	
Three Oaks	d											
Doleham	d											
Winchelsea	d											
Rye	a							12 51				
	d							12 54				
Appledore (Kent)	d							13 03				
Ham Street	d							13 08				
Ashford International	a							13 16				
London Bridge 4 ⊖	a							14 43				
London Cannon Street 4 ⊖	a							14e50				
London Waterloo (East) 4 ⊖	a							14 32				
London Charing Cross 4 ⊖	a							14 36				

For general notes see front of timetable
For details of catering facilities see Directory of Train Operators

§ For additional trains between Hampden Park and Eastbourne see Hastings to London pages

A Trolley service to Lewes
b Change at East Croydon and Brighton
c Change at Haywards Heath
e Change at Ashford International and London Bridge

London, Haywards Heath and Brighton → Lewes, Seaford, Eastbourne, Hastings and Ashford

Network Diagram - see first page of Table 184

	SN 1	SN 1	SN 1	SN 1	SN 1		SN 1	SN 1	SN 1	SN 1	SN 1	SN 1	SN 1	SN 1	SN 1	SN 1	SN 1	SN 1	SN 1		SN 1	SN 1	SN 1	SN 1
				A				A				A			A				A				A	
London Victoria 15 ⊖ d	11 06		11 36	11 47				12 17	12 06		12 36	12 47			13 17	13 06		13 36	13 47				14 17	14 06
Clapham Junction 10 d	11 12		11 42	11 53				12 23	12 12		12 42	12 53			13 23	13 12		13 42	13 53				14 23	14 12
London Bridge 4 ⊖ d	10 56	11 11	11 26						11 56	12 11	12 26					12 56	13 11	13 26						13 56
East Croydon d	11 22	11 24	11 52	12 03				12 33	12 22	12 24	12 52	13 03			13 33	13 22	13 24	13 52	14 03				14 33	14 22
Gatwick Airport 10 ✈ d	11 26	11 41	11 56	12 19				12 49	12 26	12 41	12 56	13 19			13 49	13 26	13 41	13 56	14 19				14 49	14 26
Haywards Heath 3 d	11 38	11 55	12 08	12 34				13 07	12 38	12 55	13 08	13 34			14 07	13 38	13 55	14 08	14 34				15 07	14 38
Wivelsfield 4 d	11 31	11 59						13 11	12 31	12 59					14 11	13 31	13 59						15 11	14 31
Plumpton d				12 43																				
Cooksbridge d																								
Brighton 10 d	12 10	12 22	12 32		12 40		12 52		13 10	13 22	13 32		13 40	13 52		14 10	14 22	14 32			14 40	14 52		15 10
London Road (Brighton) d	12 13	12 25			12 43		12 55		13 13	13 25			13 43	13 55		14 13	14 25				14 43	14 55		15 13
Moulsecoomb d	12 15	12 27			12 45		12 57		13 15	13 27			13 45	13 57		14 15	14 27				14 45	14 57		15 15
Falmer d	12 19	12 31			12 49		13 01		13 19	13 31			13 49	14 01		14 19	14 31				14 49	15 01		15 19
Lewes 4 a	12 25	12 37	12 43	12 52	12 55		13 07	13 22	13 25	13 37	13 43	13 48	13 55	14 07	14 22	14 25	14 37	14 43	14 48		14 55	15 07	15 22	15 25
d	12 28		12 44	12 53	12 58		13 09	13 23	13 28		13 44	13 53	13 58	14 09	14 23	14 28		14 44	14 53		14 58	15 09	15 23	15 28
Southease d	12 34								13 34							14 34								15 34
Newhaven Town ⛴ d	12 38				13 06				13 38				14 06			14 38					15 06			15 38
Newhaven Harbour d	12 40				13 08				13 40				14 08			14 40					15 08			15 40
Bishopstone d	12 43				13 11				13 43				14 11			14 43					15 11			15 43
Seaford a	12 46				13 14				13 46				14 14			14 46					15 14			15 46
Glynde d							13 14							14 14								15 14		
Berwick d							13 20							14 20								15 20		
Polegate d			12 57	13 05			13 25	13 35			13 57	14 05		14 25	14 35			14 57	15 05			15 25	15 35	
Hampden Park 4 § d							13 29	13 39						14 29	14 39							15 29	15 39	
Eastbourne 4 a			13 04	13 13			13 34	13 44			14 04	14 13		14 34	14 44			15 04	15 13			15 34	15 44	
d			13 08	13 19			13 40				14 08	14 19		14 40				15 08	15 19			15 40		
Hampden Park 4 § d				13 23			13 44					14 23		14 44					15 23			15 44		
Pevensey & Westham d				13 28			13 49					14 28		14 49					15 28			15 49		
Pevensey Bay d																			15 30					
Normans Bay d							13 53							14 53					15 34			15 53		
Cooden Beach d				13 34			13 57					14 34		14 57					15 37			15 57		
Collington d				13 37			14 00					14 37		15 00					15 40			16 00		
Bexhill 4 d			13 22	13 39			14 02				14 22	14 39		15 02				15 22	15 42			16 02		
St Leonards Warrior Sq 4 d			13 29	13 45			14 08				14 29	14 45		15 08				15 29	15 49			16 08		
Hastings 4 a			13 32	13 50			14 12				14 32	14 50		15 12				15 32	15 52			16 12		
d			13 34	13 51			14 13				14 34	14 51		15 13				15 34	15 54			16 13		
Ore d				13a54			14a16					14a54		15a16					15a57			16a16		
Three Oaks d																								
Doleham d																								
Winchelsea d																								
Rye a			13 51								14 51							15 51						
d			13 54								14 54							15 54						
Appledore (Kent) d			14 03								15 03							16 03						
Ham Street d			14 08								15 08							16 08						
Ashford International a			14 16								15 16							16 16						
London Bridge 4 ⊖ a			15 43								16 29							17 31						
London Cannon Street 4 ⊖ a			15b50								16b36							17b39						
London Waterloo (East) 4 ⊖ a			15 32								16 34							17 36						
London Charing Cross 4 ⊖ a			15 36								16 38							17 41						

For general notes see front of timetable
For details of catering facilities see Directory of Train Operators

§ For additional trains between Hampden Park and Eastbourne see Hastings to London pages

A 🍴 to Lewes
b Change at Ashford International and London Bridge

London, Haywards Heath and Brighton → Lewes, Seaford, Eastbourne, Hastings and Ashford

Network Diagram - see first page of Table 184

Station		SN	SN	SN	SN	SN	SN	SN	SN	SN	SN	SN
		1	1	1	1	1	1	1	1	1	1	1
				A				A				A
				⚘				⚘				⚘
London Victoria 15 ⊖	d		14 36	14 47				15 17	15 06		15 36	15 47
Clapham Junction 10	d		14 42	14 53				15 23	15 12		15 42	15 53
London Bridge 4 ⊖	d	14 11	14 26						14 56	15 11	15 26	
East Croydon	d	14 24	14 52	15 03				15 33	15 22	15 24	15 52	16 03
Gatwick Airport 10 ✈	d	14 41	14 56	15 19				15 49	15 26	15 41	15 56	16 19
Haywards Heath 3	d	14 55	15 08	15 34				16 07	15 38	15 55	16 10	16 33
Wivelsfield 4	d	14 59		15 38				16 11	15 31	15 59		16 37
Plumpton	d			15 44								16 43
Cooksbridge	d											16 48
Brighton 10	d	15 22	15 32			15 40	15 52		16 10	16 22	16 32	
London Road (Brighton)	d	15 25				15 43	15 55		16 13	16 25		
Moulsecoomb	d	15 27				15 45	15 57		16 15	16 27		
Falmer	d	15 31				15 49	16 01		16 19	16 31		
Lewes 4	a	15 37	15 43	15 51		15 55	16 07	16 22	16 25	16 37	16 43	16 52
	d		15 44	15 53		15 58	16 09	16 23	16 28		16 44	16 53
Southease	d					16 04			16 34			
Newhaven Town ⛴	d					16 08			16 38			
Newhaven Harbour	d					16 10			16 40			
Bishopstone	d					16 13			16 43			
Seaford	a					16 16			16 46			
Glynde	d						16 14					
Berwick	d						16 20					17 02
Polegate	d		15 57	16 05			16 25	16 35			16 57	17 07
Hampden Park 4 §	d						16 29	16 39				
Eastbourne 4	a		16 04	16 13			16 34	16 44			17 04	17 14
	d		16 08	16 19			16 40				17 08	17 21
Hampden Park 4 §	d			16 23			16 44					17 25
Pevensey & Westham	d			16 28			16 49					17 30
Pevensey Bay	d											17 32
Normans Bay	d						16 53					17 36
Cooden Beach	d			16 34			16 57					17 39
Collington	d			16 37			17 00					17 42
Bexhill 4	d		16 22	16 39			17 02				17 22	17 44
St Leonards Warrior Sq 4	d		16 29	16 45			17 08				17 30	17 51
Hastings 4	a		16 32	16 49			17 12				17 33	17 54
	d		16 34	16 51	17 08		17 13				17 34	17 56
Ore	d			16a54	17 10		17a16					17a59
Three Oaks	d				17 16							
Doleham	d				17 19							
Winchelsea	d				17 25							
Rye	a		16 51		17 29						17 51	
	d		16 54		17 30						17 54	
Appledore (Kent)	d		17 03		17 39						18 03	
Ham Street	d		17 08		17 44						18 08	
Ashford International	a		17 16		17 52						18 16	
London Bridge 4 ⊖	a		18 28		19 25						20 08	
London Cannon Street 4 ⊖	a		18e37		19e37						20e27	
London Waterloo (East) 4 ⊖	a		18 33		19 31						19 46	
London Charing Cross 4 ⊖	a		18 37		19 35						19 50	

Station		SN	SN	SN	SN	SN	SN	SN	SE 22	SN	SN	SN	SN
		1	1	1	1	1	1	1	1	1	1	1	1
					A				B	A			
					⚘					⚘			
London Victoria 15 ⊖	d				16 17	16 06		16b17		16 47		16 36	
Clapham Junction 10	d				16 23	16 12		16b23		16 53		16 42	
London Bridge 4 ⊖	d				16 11	15 56		16 26		16c46			
East Croydon	d				16 33	16 22		16 40		17 03		16 52	
Gatwick Airport 10 ✈	d				16 49	16 26		16 56		17 20			17 09
Haywards Heath 3	d				17 06	16 40	16 46	17 10		17 35		17 16	17 24
Wivelsfield 4	d				17 10	16 31	16 50	16 59		17 39			17 28
Plumpton	d									17 45			
Cooksbridge	d									17 49			
Brighton 10	d		16 40	16 52		17 10	17 20	17 32				17 40	17 52
London Road (Brighton)	d		16 43	16 55		17 13	17 23					17 43	17 55
Moulsecoomb	d		16 45	16 57		17 15	17 25					17 45	17 57
Falmer	d		16 49	17 01		17 19	17 29					17 49	18 01
Lewes 4	a		16 55	17 07	17 21	17 25	17 35	17 43		17 54		17 55	18 07
	d		16 58	17 09	17 22	17 28	17 36	17 44		17 54		17 58	18 09
Southease	d					17 34							
Newhaven Town ⛴	d		17 06			17 38						18 06	
Newhaven Harbour	d		17 08			17 40						18 08	
Bishopstone	d		17 11			17 43						18 11	
Seaford	a		17 14			17 46						18 14	
Glynde	d			17 14									18 14
Berwick	d			17 20	17 31		17 45						18 20
Polegate	d			17 25	17 36		17 50	17 57		18 07			18 25
Hampden Park 4 §	d			17 29	17 40		17 55			18 11			18 31
Eastbourne 4	a			17 34	17 48		18 00	18 04		18 16			18 36
	d			17 40				18 08		18 23			18 50
Hampden Park 4 §	d			17 44						18 27			18 54
Pevensey & Westham	d			17 49						18 32			18 59
Pevensey Bay	d			17 51									
Normans Bay	d			17 55									19 03
Cooden Beach	d			17 58						18 38			19 07
Collington	d			18 01						18 41			19 10
Bexhill 4	d			18 03				18 23		18 43			19 12
St Leonards Warrior Sq 4	d			18 10				18 29	18 47	18 52			19 20
Hastings 4	a			18 13				18 33	18 51	18 56			19 24
	d			18 14				18 34	18 52	18 57			19 25
Ore	d			18a17					18a57	19a02			19a28
Three Oaks	d												
Doleham	d												
Winchelsea	d												
Rye	a							18 51					
	d	18 31						18 54			19 31		
Appledore (Kent)	d	18 40						19 03			19 40		
Ham Street	d	18 45						19 08			19 45		
Ashford International	a	18 53						19 17			19 53		
London Bridge 4 ⊖	a							20 38					
London Cannon Street 4 ⊖	a												
London Waterloo (East) 4 ⊖	a							20 43					
London Charing Cross 4 ⊖	a							20 48					

For general notes see front of timetable
For details of catering facilities see Directory of Train Operators

§ For additional trains between Hampden Park and Eastbourne see Hastings to London pages

A ⚘ to Lewes
B From London Charing Cross (Table 206)
b Change at East Croydon and Brighton
c Change at Gatwick Airport
e Change at Ashford International and London Bridge

London, Haywards Heath and Brighton → Lewes, Seaford, Eastbourne, Hastings and Ashford

Network Diagram - see first page of Table 184

		SN		SN		SN	SN	SN	SE 22	SN	SN	SN	SN	SN	SN	SN	SN	SN		SN	SN	SN	SN	SN	SN
		1		1		1	1	1	1	1	1	1	1	1	1	1	1	1		1	1	1	1	1	1
		A ⚻							B		A ⚻				A ⚻					A ⚻				A ⚻	
London Victoria 15 ⊖	d	17 17		16b38		17 02	17 07	17c37			17 53	17 37			18 17		18 07	18 17		18 47		18 32	19 06	19 17	
Clapham Junction 10	d	17 23		16b45		17 08	17 13	17c43			17 59	17 43			18 23		18 13	18 23		18 53		18 38	19 12	19 23	
London Bridge 4 ⊖	d	17 13		16 46		16b57	17 08	17 46			17e52	17b32			18e16		18 03	18b12			18f26	18 38	18 56	19g27	
East Croydon	d	17 33		17 00		17 18	17 24	18 00			18 10	17 54		18h00	18 33		18 24	18 33		19 03	18 40	18 52	19 22	19 33	
Gatwick Airport 10 ✈	d	17 40		17 16		17 34	17 40	17 58			18 29	17h58		18 12	18 50		18h29	18 50		19 19	18 56	19 10	19 26	19 49	
Haywards Heath 3	d	18 03		17 32		17 48	17 58	18 24			18 41	18 20		18 30	19 05		18 50	19 08		19 33	19 12	19 24	19 45	20 13	
Wivelsfield 4	d	18 07		17 36			18 02	18 28			18 46			18 34	19 09		18 49	18 59		19 37		19 28		20 17	
Plumpton	d							18 34			18 52				19 15					19 43					
Cooksbridge	d							18 39			18 56				19 20					19 47					
Brighton 10	d			18 05		18 17	18 30			18 36		18 50		19 05			19 22	19 32			19 40	19 52	20 10		
London Road (Brighton)	d			18 08		18 20				18 39		18 53		19 08			19 25				19 43	19 55	20 13		
Moulsecoomb	d			18 10		18 22				18 41		18 55		19 10			19 27				19 45	19 57	20 15		
Falmer	d			18 14		18 26				18 45		18 59		19 14			19 31				19 49	20 01	20 19		
Lewes 4	a	18 18		18 21		18 33	18 41	18 44		18 51	19 01	19 05		19 20	19 24		19 37	19 43		19 52	19 55	20 07	20 25	20 28	
	d	18 22	18 25			18 35	18 42	18 47		18 52	19 01	19 07	19 10	19 31	19 25	← 19 31		19 44		19 53	19 58	20 09	20 33	20 29	← 20 33
Southease	d					18 41				18 58			19 16	→							20 04		→		
Newhaven Town ⛴	d	18 30				18 45				19 02			19 20			19 39					20 08				20 41
Newhaven Harbour	d	18 32				18 47				19 05			19 22			19 41					20 10				20 43
Bishopstone	d	18 35				18 50				19 08			19 25			19 44					20 13				20 46
Seaford	a	18 40				18 53				19 11			19 28			19 47					20 16				20 49
Glynde	d		18 30					18 53				19 12										20 14		20 34	
Berwick	d		18 36					18 58				19 18			19 34							20 20		20 40	
Polegate	d		18 41				18 55	19 04			19 14	19 23			19 39			19 57		20 05		20 25		20 45	
Hampden Park 4 §	d		18 45					19 08			19 18	19 27			19 43							20 29		20 49	
Eastbourne 4	a		18 53				19 05	19 15			19 23	19 32			19 50			20 04		20 13		20 34		20 54	
	d						19 09				19 29	19 48						20 08		20 19					
Hampden Park 4 §	d										19 33	19 52								20 23					
Pevensey & Westham	d										19 38	19 57								20 28					
Pevensey Bay	d																								
Normans Bay	d																								
Cooden Beach	d										19 44	20 03								20 34					
Collington	d										19 47	20 06								20 37					
Bexhill 4	d						19 23				19 49	20 08						20 22		20 39					
St Leonards Warrior Sq 4	d						19 30		19 35		19 57	20 14						20 30		20 47					
Hastings 4	a						19 33		19 39		20 01	20 18						20 34		20 50					
	d						19 34		19 40		20 03	20 19						20 35		20 52					
Ore	d								19a45		20a08	20a22								20a57					
Three Oaks	d																								
Doleham	d																								
Winchelsea	d																								
Rye	a						19 51											20 52							
	d						19 54											20 54							
Appledore (Kent)	d						20 03											21 03							
Ham Street	d						20 08											21 08							
Ashford International	a						20 16											21 16							
London Bridge 4 ⊖	a						21 38											22 38							
London Cannon Street 4 ⊖	a																								
London Waterloo (East) 4 ⊖	a						21 43											22 43							
London Charing Cross 4 ⊖	a						21 48											22 48							

For general notes see front of timetable
For details of catering facilities see Directory of Train Operators

§ For additional trains between Hampden Park and Eastbourne see Hastings to London pages

A ⚻ to Lewes
B From London Charing Cross (Table 206)
b Change at East Croydon and Brighton
c Change at East Croydon
e Change at Gatwick Airport
f London Bridge
g Change at Haywards Heath
h Change at Haywards Heath and Brighton

London, Haywards Heath and Brighton → Lewes, Seaford, Eastbourne, Hastings and Ashford

Network Diagram - see first page of Table 184

		SN 1	SN 1	SN 1	SN 1	SN 1	SN 1	SN 1	SN 1	SN 1		SN 1	SN 1	SN 1	SN 1	SN 1	SN 1	SN 1	SN 1	SN 1	SN 1	SN 1	SN 1
			A ☕																				
London Victoria 15	⊖ d		19 47	19 36	19b53	20 17		20b17	20 47	20 36		21 06	21 17			21 36	21 47		22 06		22 36	22 47	
Clapham Junction 10	d		19 53	19 42	19b59	20 23		20b23	20 53	20 42		21 12	21 23			21 42	21 53		22 12		22 42	22 53	
London Bridge 4	⊖ d	19 12		19 27	20 01			20 28				20 58			21 11	21b28			21b45	22 11	22b28		
East Croydon	d	19 24	20 03	19 52	20 14	20 33		20 41	21 03	20 52		21 22	21 33		21 24	21 52	22 03		22 22	22 24	22 52	23 03	
Gatwick Airport 10	✈ d	19 41	20 19	19 55	20 31	20 49		20 56	21 19			21 27	21 49		21 41	21c49	22 19		22c19	22 41	22c49	23 19	
Haywards Heath 3	d	19 58	20 36	20 17	20 42	21 07		21 11	21 37	21 15		21 45	22 08		21 58	22 15	22 34		22 47	22 58	23 15	23 34	
Wivelsfield 4	d	20 02	20 40		20 30	21 11		21 02	21 41			21 30	22 12		22 02		22 38		22 30	23 02		23 38	
Plumpton	d		20 46						21 47								22 44					23 44	
Cooksbridge	d		20 50																				
Brighton 10	d	20 30		20 40	21 04			21 30		21 40		22 04			22 28	22 34			23 04	23 28	23 34		
London Road (Brighton)	d			20 43	21 07					21 43		22 07				22 37			23 07		23 37		
Moulsecoomb	d			20 45	21 09					21 45		22 09				22 39			23 09		23 39		
Falmer	d			20 49	21 13					21 49		22 13				22 43			23 13		23 43		
Lewes 4	a	20 43	20 55	20 55	21 19	21 22	←	21 43	21 54	21 55		22 19	22 23	←	22 39	22 49	22 51	←	23 19	23 39	23 49	23 51	←
	d	20 44	20 55	21 00	21 28	21 23	21 28	21 44	21 55	21 58		22 28	22 23	22 28	22 39	22 58	22 53	22 58	23 20	23 39	23 56	23 53	23 56
					→							→				→					→		
Southease	d									22 04								23 04					
Newhaven Town	⛴ d			21 08			21 36			22 08				22 36				23 08					00 04
Newhaven Harbour	d			21 10			21 38			22 10				22 38				23 10					00 06
Bishopstone	d			21 13			21 41			22 13				22 41				23 13					00 09
Seaford	a			21 16			21 44			22 16				22 44				23 16					00 12
Glynde	d					21 28							22 29						23 25				
Berwick	d					21 34							22 34						23 31			00 02	
Polegate	d	20 57	21 08			21 39		21 57	22 07				22 39		22 52		23 05		23 36	23 52		00 07	
Hampden Park 4 §	d					21 43							22 43				23 09		23 41			00 11	
Eastbourne 4	a	21 04	21 15			21 48		22 04	22 15				22 48		23 03		23 14		23 46	23 59		00 16	
	d	21 08	21 21					22 08	22 21								23 20					00 22	
Hampden Park 4 §	d		21 25						22 25								23 24						
Pevensey & Westham	d		21 30						22 30								23 29					00 29	
Pevensey Bay	d																						
Normans Bay	d																						
Cooden Beach	d		21 36						22 36								23 35					00 35	
Collington	d		21 39						22 39								23 38					00 38	
Bexhill 4	d	21 23	21 41					22 22	22 41								23 40					00 40	
St Leonards Warrior Sq 4	d	21 30	21 47					22 29	22 47								23 46					00 47	
Hastings 4	a	21 33	21 51					22 32	22 51								23 50					00 50	
	d	21 34	21 53																				
Ore	d	21 36	21a56																				
Three Oaks	d	21 42																					
Doleham	d	21 45																					
Winchelsea	d	21 51																					
Rye	a	21 55																					
	d	21 57																					
Appledore (Kent)	d	22 06																					
Ham Street	d	22 11																					
Ashford International	a	22 19																					
London Bridge 4	⊖ a	23 51																					
London Cannon Street 4	⊖ a																						
London Waterloo (East) 4	⊖ a	23 56																					
London Charing Cross 4	⊖ a	00 01																					

For general notes see front of timetable
For details of catering facilities see Directory of Train Operators

§ For additional trains between Hampden Park and Eastbourne see Hastings to London pages

A ☕ to Lewes
b Change at East Croydon and Brighton
c Change at Haywards Heath and Brighton

London, Haywards Heath and Brighton → Lewes, Seaford, Eastbourne, Hastings and Ashford

Network Diagram - see first page of Table 184

Station		SN 1	SN 1	SN 1	SN 1	SN 1	SN 1	SN 1	SN 1	SN 1		SN 1	SN 1	SN 1	SN 1	SN 1	SN 1	SN 1	SN 1	SN 1		SN 1	SN 1	SN 1	SN 1
London Victoria 15 ⊖	d		22p47		00 05			04 00							05 02	05 02				05 32			06b10	06c23	
Clapham Junction 10	d		22p53		00 11			04 08							05 08	05 08				05 38			06b16	06c29	
London Bridge 4 ⊖	d				23 53															05 50			06 26	06 41	
East Croydon	d		23p03		00 25										05 32	05 22		05 32					06 39	06 54	
Gatwick Airport 10 ✈	d		23p19		00 43										06 11	05 50		05 54					06 56	07 11	
Haywards Heath 3	d		23p34		01 06										06 25	06 03		06 12					07 08	07 33	
Wivelsfield 4	d		23p38												06 29	06 07		06 16						07 37	
Plumpton	d		23p44																						
Cooksbridge	d																								
Brighton 10	d	23p34						05 30				05 52		06 10		06 32		06 40	06 52	07 10		07 22	07 32		07 40
London Road (Brighton)	d	23p37										05 55		06 13				06 43	06 55	07 13		07 25			07 43
Moulsecoomb	d	23p39										05 57		06 15				06 45	06 57	07 15		07 27			07 45
Falmer	d	23p43										06 01		06 19				06 49	07 01	07 19		07 31			07 49
Lewes 4	a	23p49	23p51	←	01 20			05 41				06 07		06 25	06 40	06 43	←	06 55	07 07	07 25		07 37	07 43	07 48	07 55
	d	23p56	23p53	23p56	01 20			05 41				06 08		06 28	06 53	06 44	06 53	06 58	07 09	07 28			07 44	07 53	07 58
Southease	d	↪													↪										
Newhaven Town ⛴	d			00 04								06 16		06 36				07 06		07 36					08 06
Newhaven Harbour	d			00 06								06 18		06 38				07 08		07 38					08 08
Bishopstone	d			00 09										06 41				07 11		07 41					08 11
Seaford	a			00 12								06 23		06 44				07 14		07 44					08 14
Glynde	d																		07 14						
Berwick	d		00 02														07 02		07 20						
Polegate	d		00 07		01s32			05 53								06 57	07 07		07 25				07 57	08 05	
Hampden Park 4 §	d		00 11		01s36												07 11		07 29						
Eastbourne 4	a		00 16		01 41			06 00								07 04	07 16		07 34				08 04	08 13	
	d		00 22				05 45		06 05	06 18			06 45			07 08	07 21		07 40				08 08	08 19	
Hampden Park 4 §	d									06 22							07 25		07 44					08 23	
Pevensey & Westham	d		00 29							06 27							07 30		07 49					08 28	
Pevensey Bay	d																								
Normans Bay	d									06 31									07 53						
Cooden Beach	d		00 35							06 35							07 36		07 57					08 34	
Collington	d		00 38							06 38							07 39		08 00					08 37	
Bexhill 4	d		00 40				06 00		06 19	06 40			07 00			07 22	07 41		08 02				08 22	08 39	
St Leonards Warrior Sq 4	d		00 47				06 06		06 26	06 49			07 06			07 29	07 47		08 08				08 29	08 45	
Hastings 4	a		00 50				06 10		06 30	06 53			07 10			07 32	07 51		08 12				08 32	08 50	
	d					05 34	06 11		06 30	06 54			07 11			07 34	07 52		08 13				08 34	08 51	
Ore	d					05 37	06a14			06a57			07a14				07a55		08a16					08a54	
Three Oaks	d					05 43																			
Doleham	d					05 46																			
Winchelsea	d					05 52																			
Rye	a					05 55			06 47							07 51							08 51		
	d					05 56			06 50							07 54							08 54		
Appledore (Kent)	d					06 05			06 59							08 03							09 03		
Ham Street	d					06 10			07 04							08 08							09 08		
Ashford International	a					06 18			07 13							08 16							09 16		
London Bridge 4 ⊖	a					08 10			08 40							09 43							10 43		
London Cannon Street 4 ⊖	a					08e20			08e47							09e50							10e50		
London Waterloo (East) 4 ⊖	a					08 14			08 45							09 32							10 32		
London Charing Cross 4 ⊖	a					08 18			08 48							09 36							10 36		

For general notes see front of timetable
For details of catering facilities see Directory of Train Operators

§ For additional trains between Hampden Park and Eastbourne see Hastings to London pages

b Change at East Croydon and Brighton
c Change at East Croydon and Haywards Heath
e Change at Ashford International and London Bridge

London, Haywards Heath and Brighton → Lewes, Seaford, Eastbourne, Hastings and Ashford

Network Diagram - see first page of Table 184

		SN 1	SN 1	SN 1	SN 1	SN 1	SN 1	SN 1		SN 1	SN 1	SN 1	SN 1	SN 1	SN 1	SN 1	SN 1	SN 1		SN 1	SN 1	SN 1	SN 1	SN 1	SN 1
														A								A			
London Victoria 15 ⊖	d		07 06		07 36	07 47				08 17	08 06		08 36	08 47			09 17	09 06			09 36	09 47			10 17
Clapham Junction 10	d		07 12		07 42	07 53				08 23	08 12		08 42	08 53			09 23	09 12			09 42	09 53			10 23
London Bridge 4 ⊖	d		06 56	07 11	07 26						07 56	08 11	08 26					08 56		09 11	09 26	09 41			
East Croydon	d		07 22	07 24	07 52	08 03				08 33	08 22	08 24	08 52	09 03			09 33	09 22		09 24	09 52	10 03			10 33
Gatwick Airport 10 ✈	d		07 26	07 41	07 56	08 19				08 49	08 26	08 41	08 56	09 19			09 49	09 26		09 41	09 56	10 19			10 49
Haywards Heath 3	d		07 38	07 55	08 08	08 34				09 07	08 38	08 55	09 08	09 34			10 07	09 38		09 55	10 08	10 34			11 07
Wivelsfield 4	d		07 31	07 59						09 11	08 31	08 59					10 11	09 31		09 59					11 11
Plumpton	d													09 43								10 43			
Cooksbridge	d																								
Brighton 10	d	07 52	08 10	08 22	08 32		08 40	08 52			09 10	09 22	09 32		09 40	09 52		10 10		10 22	10 32		10 40	10 52	
London Road (Brighton)	d	07 55	08 13	08 25			08 43	08 55			09 13	09 25			09 43	09 55		10 13		10 25			10 43	10 55	
Moulsecoomb	d	07 57	08 15	08 27			08 45	08 57			09 15	09 27			09 45	09 57		10 15		10 27			10 45	10 57	
Falmer	d	08 01	08 19	08 31			08 49	09 01			09 19	09 31			09 49	10 01		10 19		10 31			10 49	11 01	
Lewes 4	a	08 07	08 25	08 37	08 43	08 52	08 55	09 07		09 22	09 25	09 37	09 43	09 52	09 55	10 07	10 22	10 25		10 37	10 43	10 52	10 55	11 07	11 22
	d	08 09	08 28		08 44	08 53	08 58	09 09		09 23	09 28		09 44	09 53	09 58	10 09	10 23	10 28			10 44	10 53	10 58	11 09	11 23
Southease	d										09 34							10 34							
Newhaven Town ⛴	d		08 36				09 06				09 38				10 06			10 38					11 06		
Newhaven Harbour	d		08 38				09 08				09 40				10 08			10 40					11 08		
Bishopstone	d		08 41				09 11				09 43				10 11			10 43					11 11		
Seaford	a		08 44				09 14				09 46				10 14			10 46					11 14		
Glynde	d	08 14						09 14								10 14								11 14	
Berwick	d	08 20						09 20								10 20								11 20	
Polegate	d	08 25			08 57	09 05		09 25		09 35			09 57	10 05		10 25	10 35				10 57	11 05		11 25	11 35
Hampden Park 4 §	d	08 29						09 29		09 39						10 29	10 39							11 29	11 39
Eastbourne 4	a	08 34			09 04	09 13		09 34		09 44			10 04	10 13		10 34	10 44				11 04	11 13		11 34	11 44
	d	08 40			09 08	09 19		09 40					10 08	10 19		10 40					11 08	11 19		11 40	
Hampden Park 4 §	d	08 44				09 23		09 44						10 23		10 44						11 23		11 44	
Pevensey & Westham	d	08 49				09 28		09 49						10 28		10 49						11 28		11 49	
Pevensey Bay	d																								
Normans Bay	d	08 53						09 53								10 53								11 53	
Cooden Beach	d	08 57				09 34		09 57						10 34		10 57						11 34		11 57	
Collington	d	09 00				09 37		10 00						10 37		11 00						11 37		12 00	
Bexhill 4	d	09 02			09 22	09 39		10 02					10 22	10 39		11 02					11 22	11 39		12 02	
St Leonards Warrior Sq 4	d	09 08			09 29	09 45		10 08					10 29	10 45		11 08					11 29	11 45		12 08	
Hastings 4	a	09 12			09 32	09 50		10 12					10 32	10 50		11 12					11 32	11 50		12 12	
	d	09 13			09 34	09 51		10 13					10 34	10 51		11 13					11 34	11 51		12 13	
Ore	d	09a16				09a54		10a16						10a54		11a16						11a54		12a16	
Three Oaks	d																								
Doleham	d																								
Winchelsea	d																								
Rye	a				09 51								10 51								11 51				
	d				09 54								10 54								11 54				
Appledore (Kent)	d				10 03								11 03								12 03				
Ham Street	d				10 08								11 08								12 08				
Ashford International	a				10 16								11 16								12 16				
London Bridge 4 ⊖	a				11 43								12 43								13 43				
London Cannon Street 4 ⊖	a				11b50								12b50								13b50				
London Waterloo (East) 4 ⊖	a				11 32								12 32								13 32				
London Charing Cross 4 ⊖	a				11 36								12 36								13 36				

For general notes see front of timetable
For details of catering facilities see Directory of Train Operators

§ For additional trains between Hampden Park and Eastbourne see Hastings to London pages

A to Lewes

b Change at Ashford International and London Bridge

Table 189

Saturdays

London, Haywards Heath and Brighton → Lewes, Seaford, Eastbourne, Hastings and Ashford

Network Diagram - see first page of Table 184

Station		SN 1	SN 1	SN 1	SN 1 A 🛒	SN 1	SN 1	SN 1	SN 1	SN 1	SN 1	SN 1 A 🛒	SN 1	SN 1	SN 1	SN 1	SN 1	SN 1	SN 1 A 🛒	SN 1	SN 1	SN 1	SN 1
London Victoria 15 ⊖	d	10 06		10 36	10 47			11 17	11 06		11 36	11 47			12 17	12 06		12 36	12 47			13 17	13 06
Clapham Junction 10	d	10 12		10 42	10 53			11 23	11 12		11 42	11 53			12 23	12 12		12 42	12 53			13 23	13 12
London Bridge 4 ⊖	d	09 56	10 11	10 26					10 56	11 11	11 26					11 56	12 11	12 26					12 56
East Croydon	d	10 22	10 24	10 52	11 03			11 33	11 22	11 24	11 52	12 03			12 33	12 22	12 24	12 52	13 03			13 33	13 22
Gatwick Airport 10 ✈	d	10 26	10 41	10 56	11 19			11 49	11 26	11 41	11 56	12 19			12 49	12 26	12 40	12 56	13 19		13 01	13 49	13 26
Haywards Heath 3	d	10 38	10 55	11 08	11 34			12 07	11 38	11 55	12 08	12 34			13 07	12 38	12 55	13 08	13 34		13 18	14 07	13 38
Wivelsfield 4	d	10 31	10 59					12 11	11 31	11 59					13 11	12 31	12 59					14 11	13 31
Plumpton	d				11 43							12 43											
Cooksbridge	d																						
Brighton 10	d	11 10	11 22	11 32		11 40	11 52		12 10	12 22	12 32		12 40	12 52		13 10	13 22	13 32		13 40	13 52		14 10
London Road (Brighton)	d	11 13	11 25			11 43	11 55		12 13	12 25			12 43	12 55		13 13	13 25			13 43	13 55		14 13
Moulsecoomb	d	11 15	11 27			11 45	11 57		12 15	12 27			12 45	12 57		13 15	13 27			13 45	13 57		14 15
Falmer	d	11 19	11 31			11 49	12 01		12 19	12 31			12 49	13 01		13 19	13 31			13 49	14 01		14 19
Lewes 4	a	11 25	11 37	11 43	11 52	11 55	12 07	12 22	12 25	12 37	12 43	12 52	12 55	13 07	13 22	13 25	13 37	13 43	13 48	13 55	14 07	14 22	14 25
	d	11 28		11 44	11 53	11 58	12 09	12 23	12 28		12 44	12 53	12 58	13 09	13 23	13 28		13 44	13 53	13 58	14 09	14 23	14 28
Southease	d	11 34							12 34							13 34							14 34
Newhaven Town ⛴	d	11 38				12 06			12 38				13 06			13 38				14 06			14 38
Newhaven Harbour	d	11 40				12 08			12 40				13 08			13 40				14 08			14 40
Bishopstone	d	11 43				12 11			12 43				13 11			13 43				14 11			14 43
Seaford	a	11 46				12 14			12 46				13 14			13 46				14 14			14 46
Glynde	d						12 14							13 14							14 14		
Berwick	d						12 20							13 20							14 20		
Polegate	d			11 57	12 05		12 25	12 35			12 57	13 05		13 25	13 35			13 57	14 05		14 25	14 35	
Hampden Park 4 §	d						12 29	12 39						13 29	13 39						14 29	14 39	
Eastbourne 4	a			12 04	12 13		12 34	12 44			13 04	13 13		13 34	13 44			14 04	14 13		14 34	14 44	
	d			12 08	12 19		12 40				13 08	13 19		13 40				14 08	14 19		14 40		
Hampden Park 4 §	d				12 23		12 44					13 23		13 44					14 23		14 44		
Pevensey & Westham	d				12 28		12 49					13 28		13 49					14 28		14 49		
Pevensey Bay	d																						
Normans Bay	d						12 53							13 53							14 53		
Cooden Beach	d				12 34		12 57					13 34		13 57					14 34		14 57		
Collington	d				12 37		13 00					13 37		14 00					14 37		15 00		
Bexhill 4	d			12 22	12 39		13 02				13 22	13 39		14 02				14 22	14 39		15 02		
St Leonards Warrior Sq 4	d			12 29	12 45		13 08				13 29	13 45		14 08				14 29	14 45		15 08		
Hastings 4	a			12 32	12 50		13 12				13 32	13 50		14 12				14 32	14 50		15 12		
	d			12 34	12 51		13 13				13 34	13 51		14 13				14 34	14 51		15 13		
Ore	d				12a54		13a16					13a54		14a16					14a54		15a16		
Three Oaks	d																						
Doleham	d																						
Winchelsea	d																						
Rye	a			12 51							13 51							14 51					
	d			12 54							13 54							14 54					
Appledore (Kent)	d			13 03							14 03							15 03					
Ham Street	d			13 08							14 08							15 08					
Ashford International	a			13 16							14 16							15 16					
London Bridge 4 ⊖	a			14 43							15 43							16 43					
London Cannon Street 4 ⊖	a			14b50							15b50							16b50					
London Waterloo (East) 4 ⊖	a			14 32							15 32							16 32					
London Charing Cross 4 ⊖	a			14 36							15 36							16 36					

For general notes see front of timetable
For details of catering facilities see
Directory of Train Operators

§ For additional trains between Hampden Park and Eastbourne see Hastings to London pages

A 🛒 to Lewes

b Change at Ashford International and London Bridge

Table 189

Saturdays

London, Haywards Heath and Brighton → Lewes, Seaford, Eastbourne, Hastings and Ashford

Network Diagram - see first page of Table 184

Station		SN 1	SN 1	SN 1	SN 1	SN 1	SN 1	SN 1	SN 1	SN 1	SN 1	SN 1	SN 1	SN 1	SN 1	SN 1	SN 1	SN 1	SN 1	SN 1	SN 1	SN 1	SN 1
				A ⚲							A ⚲							A ⚲					
London Victoria 15 ⊖	d		13 36	13 47			14 17	14 06		14 36	14 47			15 17	15 06		15 36	15 47			16 17	16 06	
Clapham Junction 10	d		13 42	13 53			14 23	14 12		14 42	14 53			15 23	15 12		15 42	15 53			16 23	16 12	
London Bridge 4 ⊖	d	13 11	13 26					13 56	14 11	14 26					14 56	15 11	15 26					15 56	16 11
East Croydon	d	13 24	13 52	14 03			14 33	14 22	14 24	14 52	15 03			15 33	15 22	15 24	15 52	16 03			16 33	16 22	16 24
Gatwick Airport 10 ✈	d	13 41	13 56	14 19			14 49	14 26	14 41	14 56	15 19			15 49	15 26	15 41	15 56	16 19			16 49	16 26	16 41
Haywards Heath 3	d	13 55	14 08	14 34			15 07	14 38	14 55	15 08	15 34			16 07	15 38	15 55	16 08	16 34			17 07	16 38	16 55
Wivelsfield 4	d	13 59					15 11	14 31	14 59					16 11	15 31	15 59					17 11	16 31	16 59
Plumpton	d																						
Cooksbridge	d																						
Brighton 10	d	14 22	14 32		14 40	14 52		15 10	15 22	15 32		15 40	15 52		16 10	16 22	16 32		16 40	16 52		17 10	17 22
London Road (Brighton)	d	14 25			14 43	14 55		15 13	15 25			15 43	15 55		16 13	16 25			16 43	16 55		17 13	17 25
Moulsecoomb	d	14 27			14 45	14 57		15 15	15 27			15 45	15 57		16 15	16 27			16 45	16 57		17 15	17 27
Falmer	d	14 31			14 49	15 01		15 19	15 31			15 49	16 01		16 19	16 31			16 49	17 01		17 19	17 31
Lewes 4	a	14 37	14 43	14 48	14 55	15 07	15 22	15 25	15 37	15 43	15 48	15 55	16 07	16 22	16 25	16 37	16 43	16 48	16 55	17 07	17 22	17 25	17 37
	d		14 44	14 53	14 58	15 09	15 23	15 28		15 44	15 53	15 58	16 09	16 23	16 28		16 44	16 53	16 58	17 09	17 23	17 28	
Southease	d							15 34							16 34							17 34	
Newhaven Town ⛴	d				15 06			15 38				16 06			16 38				17 06			17 38	
Newhaven Harbour	d				15 08			15 40				16 08			16 40				17 08			17 40	
Bishopstone	d				15 11			15 43				16 11			16 43				17 11			17 43	
Seaford	a				15 14			15 46				16 14			16 46				17 14			17 46	
Glynde	d					15 14							16 14							17 14			
Berwick	d					15 20							16 20							17 20			
Polegate	d		14 57	15 05		15 25	15 35			15 57	16 05		16 25	16 35			16 57	17 05		17 25	17 35		
Hampden Park 4 §	d					15 29	15 39						16 29	16 39						17 29	17 39		
Eastbourne 4	a		15 04	15 13		15 34	15 44			16 04	16 13		16 34	16 44			17 04	17 13		17 34	17 44		
	d		15 08	15 19		15 40				16 08	16 19		16 40				17 08	17 19		17 40			
Hampden Park 4 §	d			15 23		15 44					16 23		16 44					17 23		17 44			
Pevensey & Westham	d			15 28		15 49					16 28		16 49					17 28		17 49			
Pevensey Bay	d																						
Normans Bay	d					15 53							16 53							17 53			
Cooden Beach	d			15 34		15 57					16 34		16 57					17 34		17 57			
Collington	d			15 37		16 00					16 37		17 00					17 37		18 00			
Bexhill 4	d		15 22	15 39		16 02				16 22	16 39		17 02				17 22	17 39		18 02			
St Leonards Warrior Sq 4	d		15 29	15 45		16 08				16 29	16 45		17 08				17 29	17 46		18 08			
Hastings 4	a		15 32	15 50		16 12				16 32	16 50		17 12				17 32	17 50		18 12			
	d		15 34	15 51		16 13				16 34	16 51		17 13				17 34	17 52		18 13			
Ore	d			15a54		16a16					16a54		17a16					17a55		18a16			
Three Oaks	d																						
Doleham	d																						
Winchelsea	d																						
Rye	a		15 51							16 51							17 51						
	d		15 54							16 54							17 54						
Appledore (Kent)	d		16 03							17 03							18 03						
Ham Street	d		16 08							17 08							18 08						
Ashford International	a		16 16							17 16							18 16						
London Bridge 4 ⊖	a		17 43							19 08							19 38						
London Cannon Street 4 ⊖	a		17b50																				
London Waterloo (East) 4 ⊖	a		17 32							19 14							19 44						
London Charing Cross 4 ⊖	a		17 36							19 19							19 49						

For general notes see front of timetable
For details of catering facilities see Directory of Train Operators

§ For additional trains between Hampden Park and Eastbourne see Hastings to London pages

A ⚲ to Lewes

b Change at Ashford International and London Bridge

Table 189

Saturdays

London, Haywards Heath and Brighton → Lewes, Seaford, Eastbourne, Hastings and Ashford

Network Diagram - see first page of Table 184

Station		SN 1		SN 1 A	SN 1	SN 1	SN 1	SN 1	SN 1	SN 1	SN 1 A	SN 1		SN 1	SN 1	SN 1	SN 1	SN 1	SN 1 A	SN 1	SN 1	SN 1		SN 1	SN 1
London Victoria 15 ⊖	d	16 36		16 47			17 17	17 06		17 36	17 47				18 17	18 06		18 36	18 47			19 17		19 06	19b17
Clapham Junction 10	d	16 42		16 53			17 23	17 12		17 42	17 53				18 23	18 12		18 42	18 53			19 23		19 12	19b23
London Bridge 4 ⊖	d	16 26						16 56	17 11	17 26						17 56	18 11	18 26			18 41			18 56	19 26
East Croydon	d	16 52		17 03			17 33	17 22	17 24	17 52	18 03				18 33	18 22	18 24	18 52	19 03		18 54	19 33		19 22	19 39
Gatwick Airport 10	d	16 56		17 19			17 49	17 26	17 41	17 56	18 19				18 49	18 26	18 41	18 56	19 19		19 11	19 49		19 26	19 56
Haywards Heath 3	d	17 08		17 34			18 07	17 38	17 55	18 08	18 34				19 07	18 38	18 55	19 08	19 34		19 27	20 07		19 38	20 11
Wivelsfield 4	d						18 11	17 31	17 59						19 11	18 31	18 59				19 31	20 11			19 59
Plumpton	d			17 43							18 43								19 43						
Cooksbridge	d																								
Brighton 10	d	17 32			17 40	17 52		18 10	18 22	18 32		18 40		18 52		19 10	19 22	19 32		19 40	19 53			20 10	20 32
London Road (Brighton)	d				17 43	17 55		18 13	18 25			18 43		18 55		19 13	19 25			19 43	19 56			20 13	
Moulsecoomb	d				17 45	17 57		18 15	18 27			18 45		18 57		19 15	19 27			19 45	19 58			20 15	
Falmer	d				17 49	18 01		18 19	18 31			18 49		19 01		19 19	19 31			19 49	20 02			20 19	
Lewes 4	a	17 43		17 52	17 55	18 07	18 22	18 25	18 37	18 43	18 52	18 55		19 07	19 22	19 25	19 37	19 43	19 52	19 55	20 08	20 22		20 25	20 43
	d	17 44		17 53	17 58	18 09	18 23	18 28		18 44	18 53	18 58		19 09	19 23	19 28		19 44	19 53	19 58	20 09	20 23		20 28	20 44
Southease	d							18 34								19 34									
Newhaven Town	d				18 06			18 38				19 06				19 38				20 06				20 36	
Newhaven Harbour	d				18 08			18 40				19 08				19 40				20 08				20 38	
Bishopstone	d				18 11			18 43				19 11				19 43				20 11				20 41	
Seaford	a				18 14			18 46				19 14				19 46				20 14				20 44	
Glynde	d					18 14								19 14							20 14	20 28			
Berwick	d					18 20								19 20							20 20	20 34			
Polegate	d	17 57		18 05		18 25	18 35			18 57	19 05			19 25	19 35			19 57	20 05		20 25	20 39			20 57
Hampden Park 4 §	d					18 29	18 39							19 29	19 39						20 29	20 43			
Eastbourne 4	a	18 04		18 13		18 34	18 44			19 04	19 13			19 34	19 44			20 04	20 13		20 34	20 48			21 04
	d	18 08		18 19		18 40				19 08	19 19			19 40				20 08	20 19			20 54			21 08
Hampden Park 4 §	d			18 23		18 44					19 23			19 44					20 23						
Pevensey & Westham	d			18 28		18 49					19 28			19 49					20 28			21 01			
Pevensey Bay	d																								
Normans Bay	d					18 53								19 53											
Cooden Beach	d			18 34		18 57					19 34			19 57					20 34			21 07			
Collington	d			18 37		19 00					19 37			20 00					20 37						
Bexhill 4	d	18 22		18 39		19 02				19 22	19 39			20 02				20 22	20 39			21 11			21 24
St Leonards Warrior Sq 4	d	18 29		18 46		19 08				19 29	19 46			20 08				20 29	20 46			21 18			21 30
Hastings 4	a	18 32		18 50		19 12				19 32	19 50			20 12				20 32	20 50			21 21			21 34
	d	18 34		18 52		19 13				19 34	19 52			20 13				20 34	20 52						21 34
Ore	d			18a55		19a16					19a55			20a16					20a55						21 37
Three Oaks	d																								21 43
Doleham	d																								21 46
Winchelsea	d																								21 52
Rye	a	18 51								19 51								20 51							21 55
	d	18 54								19 54								20 54							21 57
Appledore (Kent)	d	19 03								20 03								21 03							22 06
Ham Street	d	19 08								20 08								21 08							22 11
Ashford International	a	19 16								20 16								21 16							22 19
London Bridge 4 ⊖	a	20 38								21 38								22 38							23 53
London Cannon Street 4 ⊖	a																								
London Waterloo (East) 4 ⊖	a	20 44								21 44								22 44							23 57
London Charing Cross 4 ⊖	a	20 49								21 49								22 49							00 01

For general notes see front of timetable
For details of catering facilities see Directory of Train Operators

§ For additional trains between Hampden Park and Eastbourne see Hastings to London pages

A 🍴 to Lewes

b Change at East Croydon and Brighton

Table 189

London, Haywards Heath and Brighton → Lewes, Seaford, Eastbourne, Hastings and Ashford

Network Diagram - see first page of Table 184

		SN 1	SN 1	SN 1	SN 1	SN 1	SN 1	SN 1	SN 1	SN 1		SN 1	SN 1	SN 1	SN 1	SN 1	SN 1	SN 1	SN 1	SN 1		SN 1	SN 1		
London Victoria 15 ⊖	d	19 47	19 36	20 06	20 17			20 47	20 36	21 06		21 17			21 36	21 47		22 06		22 36		22 47			
Clapham Junction 10	d	19 53	19 42	20 12	20 23			20 53	20 42	21 12		21 23			21 42	21 53		22 12		22 42		22 53			
London Bridge 4 ⊖	d			19 56			20 11		20b15	20b45				21 11	21b15			21b45	22 11	22b15					
East Croydon	d	20 03	19 52	20 22	20 33		20 24	21 03	20 52	21 22		21 33		21 24	21 52	22 03		22 22	22 24	22 52		23 03			
Gatwick Airport 10	d	20 19		20 26	20 49		20 41	21 19	20c49	21c19		21 49		21 41	21c49	22 19		22c19	22 41	22c51		23 19			
Haywards Heath 3	d	20 37	20 15	20 38	21 07		20 58	21 37	21 15	21 45		22 08		21 58	22 15	22 34		22 45	22 58	23 15		23 34			
Wivelsfield 4	d	20 41		20 31	21 11		21 02	21 41		21 30		22 12		22 02		22 38		22 30	23 02			23 38			
Plumpton	d	20 47						21 47								22 44						23 44			
Cooksbridge	d																								
Brighton 10	d		20 40	21 04			21 32		21 40	22 04				22 28	22 34			23 04	23 28	23 34					
London Road (Brighton)	d		20 43	21 07					21 43	22 07					22 37			23 07		23 37					
Moulsecoomb	d		20 45	21 09					21 45	22 09					22 39			23 09		23 39					
Falmer	d		20 49	21 13					21 49	22 13					22 43			23 13		23 43					
Lewes 4	a	20 54	20 55	21 19	21 22	←	21 43	21 54	21 55	22 19		22 23	←	22 39	22 49	22 51	←	23 19	23 39	23 49		23 51	←		
	d	20 55	20 58	21 28	21 23	21 28	21 44	21 55	21 58	22 28		22 23	22 28	22 39	22 58	22 53	22 58	23 20	23 39	23 56		23 53	23 56		
Southease	d			→						→					→					→					
Newhaven Town ⛴	d		21 06			21 36			22 06				22 36				23 06						00 04		
Newhaven Harbour	d		21 08			21 38			22 08				22 38				23 08						00 06		
Bishopstone	d		21 11			21 41			22 11				22 41				23 11						00 09		
Seaford	a		21 14			21 44			22 14				22 44				23 14						00 12		
Glynde	d				21 28							22 29						23 25							
Berwick	d				21 34							22 34						23 31				00 02			
Polegate	d	21 07			21 39		21 57	22 07				22 39		22 52		23 05		23 36	23 52			00 07			
Hampden Park 4 §	d				21 43							22 43				23 09		23 41				00 11			
Eastbourne 4	a	21 15			21 48		22 04	22 15				22 48		23 03		23 14		23 46	23 59			00 16			
	d	21 21					22 08	22 21						23 10		23 20						00 22			
Hampden Park 4 §	d	21 25						22 25								23 24									
Pevensey & Westham	d	21 30						22 30								23 29						00 29			
Pevensey Bay	d																								
Normans Bay	d																								
Cooden Beach	d	21 36						22 36								23 35						00 35			
Collington	d	21 39						22 39								23 38						00 38			
Bexhill 4	d	21 41					22 22	22 41						23 23		23 40						00 40			
St Leonards Warrior Sq 4	d	21 47					22 29	22 47						23 30		23 46						00 47			
Hastings 4	a	21 51					22 32	22 51						23 33		23 50						00 50			
	d	21 53																							
Ore	d	21a56																							
Three Oaks	d																								
Doleham	d																								
Winchelsea	d																								
Rye	a																								
	d																								
Appledore (Kent)	d																								
Ham Street	d																								
Ashford International	a																								
London Bridge 4 ⊖	a																								
London Cannon Street 4 ⊖	a																								
London Waterloo (East) 4 ⊖	a																								
London Charing Cross 4 ⊖	a																								

For general notes see front of timetable
For details of catering facilities see Directory of Train Operators

§ For additional trains between Hampden Park and Eastbourne see Hastings to London pages

b Change at East Croydon and Brighton
c Change at Haywards Heath and Brighton

Table 189

Sundays

London, Haywards Heath and Brighton → Lewes, Seaford, Eastbourne, Hastings and Ashford

Network Diagram - see first page of Table 184

		SN 1	SN 1	SN 1	SN 1	SN	SN 1	SN 1	SN 1	SN 1	SN 1	SN 1	SN 1	SN 1	SN 1	SN 1	SN 1	SN 1	SN 1	SN 1	SN 1	SN 1	SN 1	SN 1	SN 1
						A				A			A										B 𝌆		
London Victoria 15 ⊖	d		22p47		00 05	04 00			05 02	05 47	05 47					06 32				07 32		07b34	08 47		08 32
Clapham Junction 10	d		22p53		00 11	04 08			05 08	05 53	05 53					06 38				07 38		07b40	08 53		08 38
London Bridge 4 ⊖	d				23 53													07 11		07 41		08 11			08 41
East Croydon	d		23p03		00 25					06 06	06 06					06 52		07 27		07 57		08 27	09 07		08 57
Gatwick Airport 10 ✈	d		23p19		00 43					06 58	06 32					07 19		07 50		08 20		08 50	09 29		09 20
Haywards Heath 3	d		23p34		01 06					07 12	06 47					07 36		08 03		08 33		09 03	09 41		09 33
Wivelsfield 4	d		23p38								06 51					07 40				08 32			09 45		09 32
Plumpton	d		23p44																				09 51		
Cooksbridge	d																								
Brighton 10	d	23p34				06 20			07 09		07 15			07 43	07 50	08 09	08 20	08 43	08 50	09 09	09 20	09 39			10 09
London Road (Brighton)	d	23p37							07 12		07 18			07 46	07 53	08 12		08 46	08 53	09 12		09 42			10 12
Moulsecoomb	d	23p39							07 14		07 20			07 48	07 55	08 14		08 48	08 55	09 14		09 44			10 14
Falmer	d	23p43							07 18		07 24			07 52	07 59	08 18		08 52	08 59	09 18		09 48			10 18
Lewes 4	a	23p49	23p51	⟵	01 20	06 31			07 24	07 27	07 31		⟵	07 58	08 05	08 24	08 31	08 58	09 05	09 24	09 31	09 54	09 58	⟵	10 24
	d	23p56	23p53	23p56	01 20	06 31			07 25	07 37	07 32		07 37	07 59	08 06	08 25	08 32	08 59	09 06	09 25	09 32	10 03	09 59	10 03	10 25
Southease	d	⟶								⟶					08 12				09 12			⟶		10 09	
Newhaven Town ⛴	d			00 04		06 40					07 40				08 16	08 33			09 16	09 33				10 13	10 33
Newhaven Harbour	d			00 06		06 41					07 42				08 18	08 35			09 18	09 35				10 15	10 35
Bishopstone	d			00 09							07 45				08 21	08 38			09 21	09 38				10 18	10 38
Seaford	a			00 12		06 46					07 48				08 24	08 41			09 24	09 41				10 21	10 41
Glynde	d								07 30								08 37				09 37				
Berwick	d		00 02						07 36								08 43				09 43				
Polegate	d		00 07		01s32				07 41				07 49	08 11			08 49	09 11			09 49		10 11		
Hampden Park 4 §	d		00 11		01s36				07 45				07 53				08 53				09 53				
Eastbourne 4	a		00 16		01 41				07 50				08 01	08 19			08 58	09 19			09 58		10 19		
	d		00 22					07 26				07 58		08 26			09 03	09 26			10 03		10 26		
Hampden Park 4 §	d							07 30						08 30				09 30					10 30		
Pevensey & Westham	d		00 29					07 35						08 35				09 35					10 35		
Pevensey Bay	d																								
Normans Bay	d																								
Cooden Beach	d		00 35					07 41						08 41				09 41					10 41		
Collington	d		00 38					07 44						08 44				09 44					10 44		
Bexhill 4	d		00 40					07 46				08 11		08 46			09 16	09 46			10 16		10 46		
St Leonards Warrior Sq 4	d		00 47					07 53				08 18		08 53			09 23	09 53			10 23		10 53		
Hastings 4	a		00 50					07 56				08 22		08 56			09 26	09 56			10 26		10 56		
	d						07 22	07 57				08 22		08 57			09 27	09 57			10 27		10 57		
Ore	d						07 24	08a00						09a00				10a00					11a00		
Three Oaks	d						07 30																		
Doleham	d						07 33																		
Winchelsea	d						07 39																		
Rye	a						07 43					08 39					09 44				10 44				
	d						07 43					08 41					09 46				10 46				
Appledore (Kent)	d						07 52					08 50					09 55				10 55				
Ham Street	d						07 57					08 55					10 00				11 00				
Ashford International	a						08 06					09 03					10 08				11 08				
London Bridge 4 ⊖	a						09 39					10 39					11 39				12 39				
London Cannon Street 4 ⊖	a																								
London Waterloo (East) 4 ⊖	a						09 44					10 44					11 44				12 44				
London Charing Cross 4 ⊖	a						09 48					10 48					11 48				12 48				

For general notes see front of timetable
For details of catering facilities see Directory of Train Operators

§ For additional trains between Hampden Park and Eastbourne see Hastings to London pages

A Until 7 September
B 𝌆 to Lewes
b Change at East Croydon and Brighton

Table 189

Sundays

London, Haywards Heath and Brighton → Lewes, Seaford, Eastbourne, Hastings and Ashford

Network Diagram - see first page of Table 184

		SN 1		SN 1	SN 1	SN 1	SN 1	SN 1	SN 1	SN 1	SN 1	SN 1	SN 1	SN 1	SN 1	SN 1	SN 1	SN 1	SN 1	SN 1	SN 1	SN 1	SN 1	SN 1	SN 1
					A					A					A					A					A
London Victoria 15	⊖ d			08b47	09 47		10c02		10e02	10 47		11c02		11e02	11 47		12c02		12e02	12 47		13c02		13e02	13 47
Clapham Junction 10	d			08b53	09 53		10c07		10e07	10 53		11c07		11e07	11 53		12c07		12e07	12 53		13c07		13e07	13 53
London Bridge 4	⊖ d			09 11			09e56		10 11			10e56		11 11			11e56		12 11			12e56		13 11	
East Croydon	d			09 27	10 07		10f20		10 27	11 07		11f20		11 27	12 07		12f20		12 27	13 07		13f20		13 27	14 07
Gatwick Airport 10	✈ d			09 50	10 29		10f42		10 50	11 29		11f42		11 50	12 29		12f42		12 50	13 29		13f42		13 50	14 29
Haywards Heath 3	d			10 03	10 41		10 33		11 03	11 41		11 33		12 03	12 41		12 33		13 03	13 41		13 33		14 03	14 41
Wivelsfield 4	d				10 45		10 32			11 45		11 32			12 45		12 32			13 45		13 32			14 45
Plumpton	d				10 51					11 51															
Cooksbridge	d																								
Brighton 10	d	10 20		10 39			11 09	11 20	11 39			12 09	12 20	12 39			13 09	13 20	13 39			14 09	14 20	14 39	
London Road (Brighton)	d			10 42			11 12		11 42			12 12		12 42			13 12		13 42			14 12		14 42	
Moulsecoomb	d			10 44			11 14		11 44			12 14		12 44			13 14		13 44			14 14		14 44	
Falmer	d			10 48			11 18		11 48			12 18		12 48			13 18		13 48			14 18		14 48	
Lewes 4	a	10 31		10 54	10 58	←	11 24	11 31	11 54	11 58	←	12 24	12 31	12 54	12 58	←	13 24	13 31	13 54	13 58	←	14 24	14 31	14 54	14 58
	d	10 32		11 03	10 59	11 03	11 25	11 32	12 03	11 59	12 03	12 25	12 32	13 03	12 59	13 03	13 25	13 32	14 03	13 59	14 03	14 25	14 32	15 03	14 59
Southease	d			→		11 09			→		12 09			→		13 09			→		14 09			→	
Newhaven Town	⛴ d					11 13	11 33				12 13	12 33				13 13	13 33				14 13	14 33			
Newhaven Harbour	d					11 15	11 35				12 15	12 35				13 15	13 35				14 15	14 35			
Bishopstone	d					11 18	11 38				12 18	12 38				13 18	13 38				14 18	14 38			
Seaford	a					11 21	11 41				12 21	12 41				13 21	13 41				14 21	14 41			
Glynde	d	10 37						11 37					12 37					13 37					14 37		
Berwick	d	10 43						11 43					12 43					13 43					14 43		
Polegate	d	10 49			11 11			11 49		12 11			12 49		13 11			13 49		14 11			14 49		15 11
Hampden Park 4 §	d	10 53						11 53					12 53					13 53					14 53		
Eastbourne 4	a	10 58			11 19			11 58		12 19			12 58		13 19			13 58		14 19			14 58		15 19
	d	11 03			11 26			12 03		12 26			13 03		13 26			14 03		14 26			15 03		15 26
Hampden Park 4 §	d				11 30					12 30					13 30					14 30					15 30
Pevensey & Westham	d				11 35					12 35					13 35					14 35					15 35
Pevensey Bay	d																								
Normans Bay	d																								
Cooden Beach	d				11 41					12 41					13 41					14 41					15 41
Collington	d				11 44					12 44					13 44					14 44					15 44
Bexhill 4	d	11 16			11 46			12 16		12 46			13 16		13 46			14 16		14 46			15 16		15 46
St Leonards Warrior Sq 4	d	11 23			11 53			12 23		12 53			13 23		13 53			14 23		14 53			15 23		15 53
Hastings 4	a	11 26			11 56			12 26		12 56			13 26		13 56			14 26		14 56			15 26		15 56
	d	11 27			11 57			12 27		12 57			13 27		13 57			14 27		14 57			15 27		15 57
Ore	d				12a00					13a00					14a00					15a00					16a00
Three Oaks	d																								
Doleham	d																								
Winchelsea	d																								
Rye	a	11 44						12 44					13 44					14 44					15 44		
	d	11 46						12 46					13 46					14 46					15 46		
Appledore (Kent)	d	11 55						12 55					13 55					14 55					15 55		
Ham Street	d	12 00						13 00					14 00					15 00					16 00		
Ashford International	a	12 08						13 08					14 08					15 08					16 08		
London Bridge 4	⊖ a	13 39						14 39					15 39					16 39					17 39		
London Cannon Street 4	⊖ a																								
London Waterloo (East) 4	⊖ a	13 44						14 44					15 44					16 44					17 44		
London Charing Cross 4	⊖ a	13 48						14 48					15 48					16 48					17 48		

For general notes see front of timetable
For details of catering facilities see Directory of Train Operators

§ For additional trains between Hampden Park and Eastbourne see Hastings to London pages

A to Lewes
b Change at East Croydon and Brighton
c From 14 September dep. 30 minutes earlier
e From 14 September dep. 15 minutes earlier
f From 14 September dep. 23 minutes earlier

Table 189

Sundays

London, Haywards Heath and Brighton → Lewes, Seaford, Eastbourne, Hastings and Ashford

Network Diagram - see first page of Table 184

		SN 1	SN 1	SN 1		SN 1	SN 1 A ✠	SN 1	SN 1	SN 1	SN 1	SN 1 A ✠	SN 1	SN 1	SN 1	SN 1	SN 1 A ✠	SN 1	SN 1	SN 1	SN 1	SN 1 A ✠	SN 1	SN 1	SN 1
London Victoria 15	⊖ d		14b02			14c02	14 47		15b02		15c02	15 47		16b02		16c02	16 47		17 02			17 47		18 02	
Clapham Junction 10	d		14b07			14c07	14 53		15b07		15c07	15 53		16b07		16c07	16 53		17 07			17 53		18 07	
London Bridge 4	⊖ d		13c56			14 11			14c56		15 11			15c56		16 11			16e56		17 11			17e44	
East Croydon	d		14f20			14 27	15 07		15f20		15 27	16 07		16f20		16 27	17 07		17 20		17 27	18 07		18 20	
Gatwick Airport 10	✈ d		14f42			14 50	15 29		15f42		15 50	16 29		16f42		16 50	17 29		17 42		17 50	18 29		18 42	
Haywards Heath 3	d		14 33			15 03	15 41		15 33		16 03	16 41		16 33		17 03	17 41		17 33		18 03	18 41		18 33	
Wivelsfield 4	d		14 32				15 45		15 32			16 45		16 32			17 45		17 32			18 45		18 32	
Plumpton	d																17 51					18 51			
Cooksbridge	d																								
Brighton 10	d		15 09	15 20		15 39			16 09	16 20	16 39			17 09	17 20	17 39			18 09	18 20	18 39			19 09	19 20
London Road (Brighton)	d		15 12			15 42			16 12		16 42			17 12		17 42			18 12		18 42			19 12	
Moulsecoomb	d		15 14			15 44			16 14		16 44			17 14		17 44			18 14		18 44			19 14	
Falmer	d		15 18			15 48			16 18		16 48			17 18		17 48			18 18		18 48			19 18	
Lewes 4	a	←	15 24	15 31		15 54	15 58	←	16 24	16 31	16 54	16 58	←	17 24	17 31	17 54	17 58	←	18 24	18 31	18 54	18 58	←	19 24	19 31
	d	15 03	15 25	15 32		16 03	15 59	16 03	16 25	16 32	17 03	16 59	17 03	17 25	17 32	18 03	17 59	18 03	18 25	18 32	19 03	18 59	19 03	19 25	19 32
Southease	d	15 09				→		16 09			→		17 09			→		18 09			→		19 09		
Newhaven Town	⛴ d	15 13	15 33					16 13	16 33				17 13	17 33				18 13	18 33				19 13	19 33	
Newhaven Harbour	d	15 15	15 35					16 15	16 35				17 15	17 35				18 15	18 35				19 15	19 35	
Bishopstone	d	15 18	15 38					16 18	16 38				17 18	17 38				18 18	18 38				19 18	19 38	
Seaford	a	15 21	15 41					16 21	16 41				17 21	17 41				18 21	18 41				19 21	19 41	
Glynde	d			15 37						16 37					17 37					18 37					19 37
Berwick	d			15 43						16 43					17 43					18 43					19 43
Polegate	d			15 49			16 11			16 49		17 11			17 49		18 11			18 49		19 11			19 49
Hampden Park 4 §	d			15 53						16 53					17 53					18 53					19 53
Eastbourne 4	a			15 58			16 19			16 58		17 19			17 58		18 19			18 58		19 19			19 58
	d			16 03			16 26			17 03		17 26			18 03		18 26			19 03		19 26			20 03
Hampden Park 4 §	d						16 30					17 30					18 30					19 30			
Pevensey & Westham	d						16 35					17 35					18 35					19 35			
Pevensey Bay	d																								
Normans Bay	d																								
Cooden Beach	d						16 41					17 41					18 41					19 41			
Collington	d						16 44					17 44					18 44					19 44			
Bexhill 4	d			16 16			16 46			17 16		17 46			18 16		18 46			19 16		19 46			20 16
St Leonards Warrior Sq 4	d			16 23			16 53			17 23		17 53			18 23		18 53			19 23		19 53			20 23
Hastings 4	a			16 26			16 56			17 26		17 56			18 26		18 56			19 26		19 56			20 26
	d			16 27			16 57			17 27		17 57			18 27		18 57			19 27		19 57			20 27
Ore	d						17a00					18a00					19a00					20a00			
Three Oaks	d																								
Doleham	d																								
Winchelsea	d																								
Rye	a			16 44						17 44					18 44					19 44					20 44
	d			16 46						17 46					18 46					19 46					20 46
Appledore (Kent)	d			16 55						17 55					18 55					19 55					20 55
Ham Street	d			17 00						18 00					19 00					20 00					21 00
Ashford International	a			17 08						18 08					19 08					20 08					21 08
London Bridge 4	⊖ a			18 39						19 39					20 39					21 40					22 40
London Cannon Street 4	⊖ a																								
London Waterloo (East) 4	⊖ a			18 44						19 44					20 44					21 44					22 44
London Charing Cross 4	⊖ a			18 48						19 48					20 48					21 48					22 48

For general notes see front of timetable
For details of catering facilities see Directory of Train Operators

§ For additional trains between Hampden Park and Eastbourne see Hastings to London pages

A ✠ to Lewes
b From 14 September dep. 30 minutes earlier
c From 14 September dep. 15 minutes earlier
e Change at East Croydon and Brighton
f From 14 September dep. 23 minutes earlier

London, Haywards Heath and Brighton → Lewes, Seaford, Eastbourne, Hastings and Ashford

Network Diagram - see first page of Table 184

Station		SN 1	SN 1 A ⚲	SN 1	SN 1	SN 1	SN 1	SN 1 A ⚲	SN 1	SN 1	SN 1	SN 1	SN 1	SN 1	SN 1	SN 1	SN 1	SN 1	SN 1	SN 1	SN 1	SN 1	SN 1
London Victoria 15 ⊖	d		18 47		19 02			19 47		20 02			20 47		20 32		20b47	21 47		21 32		21b47	22 47
Clapham Junction 10	d		18 53		19 07			19 53		20 07			20 53		20 38		20b53	21 53		21 38		21b53	22 53
London Bridge 4 ⊖	d	18 11			18b44		19 11			19b44		20 11			20 41		21 11			21 41		22 11	
East Croydon	d	18 27	19 07		19 20		19 27	20 07		20 20		20 27	21 07		20 57		21 27	22 07		21 57		22 27	23 07
Gatwick Airport 10 ✈	d	18 50	19 29		19 42		19 50	20 29		20 42	20c45	20 50	21 29		21 20		21 50	22 29		22 20		22 50	23 29
Haywards Heath 3	d	19 03	19 41		19 33		20 03	20 41		20 33	20e54	21 03	21 41		21 33		22 03	22 41		22 33		23 03	23 41
Wivelsfield 4	d		19 45		19 32			20 45		20 32			21 45		21 32			22 45		22 32			23 45
Plumpton	d		19 51					20 51					21 51					22 51					23 51
Cooksbridge	d																						
Brighton 10	d	19 39			20 09	20 20	20 39			21 09	21 20	21 39			22 09	22 20	22 39			23 09	23 20	23 39	
London Road (Brighton)	d	19 42			20 12		20 42			21 12		21 42			22 12		22 42			23 12		23 42	
Moulsecoomb	d	19 44			20 14		20 44			21 14		21 44			22 14		22 44			23 14		23 44	
Falmer	d	19 48			20 18		20 48			21 18		21 48			22 18		22 48			23 18		23 48	
Lewes 4	a	19 54	19 58	←	20 24	20 31	20 54	20 58	←	21 24	21 31	21 54	21 58	←	22 24	22 31	22 54	22 58	←	23 24	23 31	23 54	23 58
	d	20 03	19 59	20 03	20 25	20 32	21 03	20 59	21 03	21 25	21 32	22 03	21 59	22 03	22 25	22 32	23 03	22 59	23 03		23 32		23 59
Southease	d	→		20 09			→					→					→						
Newhaven Town ⛴	d			20 13	20 33				21 11	21 33				22 11	22 33				23 11				
Newhaven Harbour	d			20 15	20 35				21 13	21 35				22 13	22 35				23 13				
Bishopstone	d			20 18	20 38				21 16	21 38				22 16	22 38				23 16				
Seaford	a			20 21	20 41				21 19	21 41				22 19	22 41				23 19				
Glynde	d					20 37					21 37					22 37					23 37		
Berwick	d					20 43					21 43					22 43					23 43		
Polegate	d		20 11			20 49		21 11			21 49		22 11			22 49		23 11			23 49		00 11
Hampden Park 4 §	d					20 53					21 53					22 53					23 53		00 15
Eastbourne 4	a		20 19			20 58		21 19			21 58		22 19			22 58		23 19			23 58		00 20
	d		20 26			21 03		21 26			22 03		22 26					23 26					
Hampden Park 4 §	d		20 30					21 30					22 30					23 30					
Pevensey & Westham	d		20 35					21 35					22 35					23 35					
Pevensey Bay	d																						
Normans Bay	d																						
Cooden Beach	d		20 41					21 41					22 41					23 41					
Collington	d		20 44					21 44					22 44					23 44					
Bexhill 4	d		20 46			21 16		21 46			22 16		22 46					23 46					
St Leonards Warrior Sq 4	d		20 55			21 23		21 52			22 23		22 56					23 52					
Hastings 4	a		20 59			21 26		21 56			22 26		23 00					23 56					
	d		21 00			21 27		21 57															
Ore	d		21a03					22a00															
Three Oaks	d																						
Doleham	d																						
Winchelsea	d																						
Rye	a					21 44																	
	d					21 46																	
Appledore (Kent)	d					21 55																	
Ham Street	d					22 00																	
Ashford International	a					22 08																	
London Bridge 4 ⊖	a																						
London Cannon Street 4 ⊖	a																						
London Waterloo (East) 4 ⊖	a																						
London Charing Cross 4 ⊖	a																						

For general notes see front of timetable
For details of catering facilities see Directory of Train Operators

§ For additional trains between Hampden Park and Eastbourne see Hastings to London pages

A ⚲ to Lewes
b Change at East Croydon and Brighton
c From 14 September dep. 2042
e From 14 September dep. 2033

Ashford, Hastings, Eastbourne, Seaford and Lewes → Brighton, Haywards Heath and London

Network Diagram - see first page of Table 184

Miles	Miles			SN	SN	SN	SN	SN	SN		SN	SN	SN	SN	SN	SN		SE	SE	SN	SN	SN	SN		SE
				MX														22	22						23
				1	1	1	1	1	1		1	1	1	1	1	1		1	1	1	1	1	1		1
																		A	B			C			D
																		🛒	🛒			🛒			🛒
—	—	London Charing Cross 4	⊖ d																						
—	—	London Waterloo (East) 4	⊖ d																						
—	—	London Cannon Street 4	⊖ d																						
—	—	London Bridge 4	⊖ d																						
—	0	**Ashford International**	d																						
—	5½	Ham Street	d																						
—	8½	Appledore (Kent)	d																						
—	15¼	Rye	a																						
—	—		d																						
—	17¼	Winchelsea	d																						
—	21½	Doleham	d																						
—	22¾	Three Oaks	d																						
—	25½	Ore	d															06 07	06 10						06 35
—	26½	**Hastings 4**	a															06 10	06 13						06 38
0	—		d	23p13							05 07					06 03		06 11	06 14				06 20		06 39
¾	—	**St Leonards Warrior Sq 4**	d	23p16							05 10					06 06		06a14	06a17				06 23		06a42
4½	—	**Bexhill 4**	d	23p22							05 16					06 12							06 29		
5¼	—	Collington	d	23p24							05 18												06 31		
6¾	—	Cooden Beach	d	23p27							05 21												06 34		
8½	—	Normans Bay	d																						
10½	—	Pevensey Bay	d																						
11¼	—	Pevensey & Westham	d	23p33							05 27												06 40		
14¼	—	Hampden Park 4 §	d	23p38							05 32					06 24							06 45		
16¼	—	**Eastbourne 4**	a	23p43							05 37					06 30							06 50		
—	—		d	23p48		05 08		05 32			05 42				06 24	06 38				06 47			06 57		
18¼	—	Hampden Park 4 §	d	23p52		05 12		05 36			05 46				06 28					06 51			07 01		
20¼	—	Polegate	d	23p56		05 16		05 41			05 50				06 32	06 45				06 55			07 05		
24½	—	Berwick	d								05 55				06 37					07 00					
29	—	Glynde	d												06 43					07 06					
—	0	**Seaford**	d		05 09				05 45					06 30								06 57			
—	1	Bishopstone	d		05 11				05 47					06 32								06 59			
—	2½	Newhaven Harbour	d		05 14				05 50					06 35								07 02			
—	2¾	Newhaven Town ⛴	d		05 16				05 52					06 37								07 04			
—	5½	Southease	d																			07 08			
32	9	**Lewes 4**	a	00 08	05 25	05 28	⟵	05 53	06 01		06 04	⟵		06 46	06 49	06 58				07 11		07 16	07 19		
—	—		d	00 08	05 32	05 29	05 32	05 54	06 09		06 05	06 09	06 26	06 47	06 50	07 00				07 12	07 23	07 23			
36½	—	Falmer	d	00 15	⟶		05 39	06 01	⟶			06 16	06 33	06 54		07 07				07 19	07 30				
38¼	—	Moulsecoomb	d	00 18			05 42	06 05				06 19	06 36	06 57		07 11				07 22	07 33				
39¼	—	London Road (Brighton)	d	00 21			05 43	06 07				06 21	06 38	06 59		07 13				07 24	07 35				
40	—	**Brighton 10**	a	00 24			05 48	06 11				06 25	06 42	07 03		07 17				07 28	07 39				
—	11¾	Cooksbridge	d												06 55							07 28			
—	14¼	Plumpton	d			05 37					06 13				07 00							07 33			
—	18¼	Wivelsfield 4	a				06 15	06 40					07 03	07 31	07 07					07 48		07 39			
—	21¼	**Haywards Heath 3**	a			05 46	06 19	06 37			06 22	06 57	07 08	07 36	07 13	07 46				07 53	08 05	07 43			
—	—	**Gatwick Airport 10** ✈	a			05 58	06 41	06 51			06 41	07 11	07 21		07 29	08 00				08b12	08 22	08 00			
—	—	East Croydon	a			06 14	06 58	07 15			06 58	07 28	07 38	08 03	07 46					08 23	08 34	08 14			
—	—	**London Bridge 4**	⊖ a			06 40	07 14	07c39			07 14	07 46	08c03	08c26	08 03					08 41	08c59	08 39			
—	—	Clapham Junction 10	a			06 25	07c19	07 25			07e19		07 47	08 13	08e02					08c40	08 43	08 24			
—	—	**London Victoria 15**	⊖ a			06 33	07c28	07 34			07e28		07 57	08 22	08e12					08c49	08 52	08 33			

For general notes see front of timetable
For details of catering facilities see Directory of Train Operators

§ For additional trains between Hampden Park and Eastbourne see London to Hastings pages

A From 13 October. To London Charing Cross (Table 206)

B Until 10 October. To London Charing Cross (Table 206)

C 🛒 from Lewes

D From 13 October. To London Cannon Street (Table 206)

b Change at Brighton and Haywards Heath

c Change at Brighton and East Croydon

e Change at East Croydon

Ashford, Hastings, Eastbourne, Seaford and Lewes → Brighton, Haywards Heath and London

Network Diagram - see first page of Table 184

		SE	SN	SN	SN	SN	SN	SN	SN	SN	SN	SN	SN	SN	SN	SE	SE	SN	SN	SN	SN	SN
		23														22	22					
		1	1	1	1	1	1	1	1	1	1	1	1	1	1	1	1	1	1	1	1	1
		A				B					B			B		C	D					B
		(trolley)				(trolley)					(trolley)			(trolley)								(trolley)
London Charing Cross 4	⊖ d																		*05 30*			
London Waterloo (East) 4	⊖ d																		*05 33*			
London Cannon Street 4	⊖ d																					
London Bridge 4	⊖ d																		*05 38*			
Ashford International	d							06 24	06 46										07 30	07 50		
Ham Street	d							06 33	06 55										07 39	07 59		
Appledore (Kent)	d							06 38	07 00										07 44	08 04		
Rye	a							06 47	07 09										07 53	08 13		
	d							06 49											07 54			
Winchelsea	d							06 52														
Doleham	d							06 59														
Three Oaks	d							07 02														
Ore	d	06 38						07 08								07 43	07 46					
Hastings 4	a	06 41						07 11								07 46	07 49		08 11			
	d	06 42				06 50		07 12			07 19				07 38	07 47	07 50		08 15			
St Leonards Warrior Sq 4	d	06a45				06 53		07 15			07 22				07 41	07a50	07a53		08 18			
Bexhill 4	d					07 00		07 22			07 31				07 47				08 25			
Collington	d					07 02					07 33				07 49							
Cooden Beach	d					07 05					07 36				07 52							
Normans Bay	d														07 55							
Pevensey Bay	d														07 59							
Pevensey & Westham	d					07 11					07 42				08 01							
Hampden Park 4 §	d					07 16					07 46				08 06							
Eastbourne 4	a					07 24		07 37			07 51				08 11				08 40			
	d			07 17		07 32		07 45			07 57	08 04			08 18				08 45			08 56
Hampden Park 4 §	d			07 21							08 01	08 08										09 00
Polegate	d			07 25		07 39		07 52			08 05	08 12			08 25				08 52			09 04
Berwick	d			07 30		07 44					08 11	08 18			08 30							
Glynde	d			07 36							08 16	08 23			08 36							
Seaford	d		07 16		07 33					07 58				08 21							08 57	
Bishopstone	d		07 18		07 35					08 00				08 23							08 59	
Newhaven Harbour	d		07 21		07 38					08 03				08 26							09 02	
Newhaven Town ⛴	d		07 23		07 40					08 05				08 28							09 04	
Southease	d		07 27		07 44					08 09				08 32								
Lewes 4	a		07 33	07 43	07 50	07 53		08 07		08 16	08 22	08 29		08 39	08 42				09 07		09 13	09 16
	d		07 34	07 44	07 51	07 54	07 58	08 07		08 16	08 23	08 30	08 46	08 47				08 58	09 07		09 14	09 17
Falmer	d		07 41		07 58		08 05			08 23		08 37	08 53					09 05			09 21	
Moulsecoomb	d		07 44		08 01		08 08			08 26		08 40	08 56					09 08			09 24	
London Road (Brighton)	d		07 46		08 03		08 10			08 29		08 42	08 58					09 10			09 27	
Brighton 10	a		07 50		08 07		08 14	08 20		08 35		08 46	09 02					09 14	09 20		09 30	
Cooksbridge	d			07 49		07 59					08 28											09 22
Plumpton	d			07 54		08 04					08 33											09 27
Wivelsfield 4	a		*08 18*		*08 33*	08 10					08 39	*09 20*		08 59							*09 53*	09 33
Haywards Heath 3	a		*08 23*	08 02	*08 37*	08 14		*08 55*		*08 57*	08 44	*09 16*		09 03				*09 32*			*09 47*	09 37
Gatwick Airport 10 ✈	a		*08 38*	08 22	*08 51*	08 38				*09 10*	08 55	*09 31*		09 22				*09 44*			*10 00*	09 55
East Croydon	a		*08 54*	08 31	*09 08*	08 46				*09 26*	09 14	*09 47*	*09 55*	09 39				*10 03*			*10 16*	10 11
London Bridge 4	⊖ a		*09 10*	08 49	*09b42*	*09 10*				*09b45*	09 42	*10 00*	*10b22*								*10 30*	10 30
Clapham Junction 10	a		*09b10*	08c43	*09b23*	08 56				*09 35*	09 23	*10b03*	*10 05*	09 49				*10b21*				10 21
London Victoria 15	⊖ a		*09b19*	08c52	*09b33*	09 07				*09 44*	09 33		*10 13*	09 58				*10b28*				10 28

For general notes see front of timetable
For details of catering facilities see Directory of Train Operators

§ For additional trains between Hampden Park and Eastbourne see London to Hastings pages

A Until 10 October. To London Cannon Street (Table 206)

B (trolley) from Lewes

C From 13 October. To London Charing Cross (Table 206)

D Until 10 October. To London Charing Cross (Table 206)

b Change at Brighton and East Croydon

c Change at Haywards Heath

Ashford, Hastings, Eastbourne, Seaford and Lewes → Brighton, Haywards Heath and London

Network Diagram - see first page of Table 184

		SN 1	SN 1	SN 1	SN 1	SN 1	SN 1	SN 1	SN 1	SN 1	SN 1	SN 1	SN 1	SN 1	SN 1	SN 1	SN 1	SN 1	SN 1	SN 1	SN 1	SN 1
				A				A			B	C	A				A			A		
London Charing Cross 4	⊖ d					*06 25*				*07 00*					*07 52*							*08 58*
London Waterloo (East) 4	⊖ d					*06 28*				*07 03*					*07 55*							*09 01*
London Cannon Street 4	⊖ d					*06b22*				*06b52*					*07b54*							*08b54*
London Bridge 4	⊖ d					*06 33*				*07 08*					*08 02*							*09 08*
Ashford International	d					08 30				08 50					09 30							10 30
Ham Street	d					08 39				08 59					09 39							10 39
Appledore (Kent)	d					08 44				09 04					09 44							10 44
Rye	a					08 53				09 13					09 53							10 53
	d					08 55				09 14					09 54							10 54
Winchelsea	d									09 17												
Doleham	d									09 24												
Three Oaks	d									09 27												
Ore	d	08 22		08 45					09 22	09 33			09 47					10 22		10 50		
Hastings 4	a	08 25		08 48		09 12			09 25	09 36			09 50		10 11			10 25		10 53		11 11
	d	08 26		08 52		09 13			09 26				09 52		10 12			10 26		10 55		11 12
St Leonards Warrior Sq 4	d	08 29		08 55		09 16			09 29				09 55		10 15			10 29		10 58		11 15
Bexhill 4	d	08 35		09 02		09 23			09 35				10 02		10 22			10 35		11 05		11 22
Collington	d	08 37		09 04					09 37				10 04					10 37		11 07		
Cooden Beach	d	08 40		09 07					09 40				10 07					10 40		11 10		
Normans Bay	d	08 43							09 43									10 43				
Pevensey Bay	d																					
Pevensey & Westham	d	08 48		09 13					09 48				10 13					10 48		11 16		
Hampden Park 4 §	d	08 52		09 17					09 52				10 17					10 52		11 20		
Eastbourne 4	a	08 57		09 22		09 38			09 57				10 22		10 37			10 57		11 25		11 37
	d	09 02		09 29		09 45		09 56	10 02				10 28		10 45		10 58	11 02		11 31		11 45
Hampden Park 4 §	d	09 06						10 00	10 06								11 02	11 06				
Polegate	d	09 11		09 36		09 52		10 04	10 11				10 34		10 52		11 06	11 11		11 37		11 52
Berwick	d	09 17						10 09	10 17									11 17				
Glynde	d	09 22							10 22									11 22				
Seaford	d		09 25				09 58				10 25	10 25				10 58			11 25			
Bishopstone	d		09 27				10 00				10 27	10 27				11 00			11 27			
Newhaven Harbour	d		09 30				10 03				10 30	10 30				11 03			11 30			
Newhaven Town	⛴ d		09 32				10 05				10 32	10 32				11 05			11 32			
Southease	d		09 36								10 36	10 36							11 36			
Lewes 4	a	09 28	09 44	09 48		10 07	10 14	10 19	10 28		10 44	10 44	10 48		11 08	11 14	11 18	11 28	11 44	11 49		12 07
	d	09 28	09 44	09 49	09 58	10 07	10 14	10 20	10 28		10 44	10 47	10 49	10 58	11 08	11 14	11 20	11 28	11 44	11 50	11 58	12 07
Falmer	d	09 35	09 51		10 05		10 21		10 35		10 51	10 54		11 05		11 21		11 35	11 51		12 05	
Moulsecoomb	d	09 38	09 54		10 08		10 24		10 38		10 54	10 57		11 08		11 24		11 38	11 54		12 08	
London Road (Brighton)	d	09 40	09 57		10 10		10 27		10 40		10 57	11 00		11 10		11 27		11 40	11 57		12 10	
Brighton 10	a	09 44	10 00		10 14	10 20	10 30		10 44		11 00	11 03		11 14	11 21	11 30		11 44	12 00		12 14	12 20
Cooksbridge	d			09 54									10 54									
Plumpton	d			09 59				10 28									11 28					
Wivelsfield 4	a	*10 11*	*10 23*				*10 53*	10 35	*11 11*		*11 23*	*11 23*				*11 53*	11 34	*12 11*	*12 23*			
Haywards Heath 3	a	*10 15*	*10 18*	10 09			*10 47*	10 40	*11 15*		*11 18*	*11 28*	11 05			*11 47*	11 40	*12 15*	*12 18*	12 05		
Gatwick Airport 10	✈ a		*10 30*	10 24			*11 00*	10 54	*11 30*		*11 30*	*11 46*	11 24			*12 00*	11 54		*12 30*	12 24		
East Croydon	a	*10 24*	*10 46*	10 40	*10 55*		*11 16*	11 11	*11 23*		*11 46*		11 40	*11 55*		*12 16*	12 10	*12 23*	*12 46*	12 40	*12 55*	
London Bridge 4	⊖ a	*10c45*	*11 00*	*11 00*	*11c15*		*11 30*	*11 30*	*11c45*		*12 00*		*12 00*	*12c15*		*12 30*	*12 30*	*12c45*	*13 00*	*13 00*	*13c15*	
Clapham Junction 10	a	*10 33*	*11c03*	10 49	*11 04*			11 20	*11 33*		*12c03*		11 49	*12 04*			12 20	*12 33*	*13c03*	12 49	*13 04*	
London Victoria 15	⊖ a	*10 40*		10 58	*11 11*			11 27	*11 40*				11 58	*12 11*			12 29	*12 40*		12 57	*13 11*	

For general notes see front of timetable
For details of catering facilities see Directory of Train Operators

§ For additional trains between Hampden Park and Eastbourne see London to Hastings pages

A from Lewes
B Until 26 September
C From 29 September
b Change at London Bridge and Ashford International
c Change at Brighton and East Croydon

Ashford, Hastings, Eastbourne, Seaford and Lewes → Brighton, Haywards Heath and London

Network Diagram - see first page of Table 184

		SN 1	SN 1	SN 1	SN 1	SN 1	SN 1	SN 1	SN 1	SN 1	SN 1	SN 1	SN 1	SN 1	SN 1	SN 1	SN 1	SN 1	SN 1	SN 1	SN 1	SN 1
			A			A				A			A				A			A		
London Charing Cross 4	⊖ d							09 53							10 53							11 53
London Waterloo (East) 4	⊖ d							09 56							10 56							11 56
London Cannon Street 4	⊖ d							09b30							10b30							11b30
London Bridge 4	⊖ d							09 38							10 38							11 38
Ashford International	d							11 30							12 30							13 30
Ham Street	d							11 39							12 39							13 39
Appledore (Kent)	d							11 44							12 44							13 44
Rye	a							11 53							12 53							13 53
	d							11 54							12 54							13 54
Winchelsea	d																					
Doleham	d																					
Three Oaks	d																					
Ore	d			11 22		11 50					12 22		12 50					13 22		13 50		
Hastings 4	a			11 25		11 53		12 11			12 25		12 53		13 11			13 25		13 53		14 11
	d			11 26		11 55		12 12			12 26		12 55		13 12			13 26		13 55		14 12
St Leonards Warrior Sq 4	d			11 29		11 58		12 15			12 29		12 58		13 15			13 29		13 58		14 15
Bexhill 4	d			11 35		12 05		12 22			12 35		13 05		13 22			13 35		14 05		14 22
Collington	d			11 37		12 07					12 37		13 07					13 37		14 07		
Cooden Beach	d			11 40		12 10					12 40		13 10					13 40		14 10		
Normans Bay	d			11 43							12 43							13 43				
Pevensey Bay	d																					
Pevensey & Westham	d			11 48		12 16					12 48		13 16					13 48		14 16		
Hampden Park 4 §	d			11 52		12 20					12 52		13 20					13 52		14 20		
Eastbourne 4	a			11 57		12 25		12 37			12 57		13 25		13 37			13 57		14 25		14 37
	d		11 58	12 02		12 31		12 45		12 58	13 02		13 31		13 45		13 58	14 02		14 31		14 45
Hampden Park 4 §	d		12 02	12 06						13 02	13 06						14 02	14 06				
Polegate	d		12 06	12 11		12 37		12 52		13 06	13 11		13 37		13 52		14 06	14 11		14 37		14 52
Berwick	d			12 17							13 17							14 17				
Glynde	d			12 22							13 22							14 22				
Seaford	d	11 58			12 25				12 58			13 25				13 58			14 25			
Bishopstone	d	12 00			12 27				13 00			13 27				14 00			14 27			
Newhaven Harbour	d	12 03			12 30				13 03			13 30				14 03			14 30			
Newhaven Town	⛴ d	12 05			12 32				13 05			13 32				14 05			14 32			
Southease	d				12 36							13 36							14 36			
Lewes 4	a	12 14	12 18	12 28	12 44	12 49		13 07	13 14	13 18	13 28	13 44	13 49		14 07	14 14	14 18	14 28	14 44	14 49		15 07
	d	12 14	12 20	12 28	12 44	12 50	12 58	13 07	13 14	13 20	13 28	13 44	13 50	13 58	14 07	14 14	14 20	14 28	14 44	14 50	14 58	15 07
Falmer	d	12 21		12 35	12 51		13 05		13 21		13 35	13 51		14 05		14 21		14 35	14 51		15 05	
Moulsecoomb	d	12 24		12 38	12 54		13 08		13 24		13 38	13 54		14 08		14 24		14 38	14 54		15 08	
London Road (Brighton)	d	12 27		12 40	12 57		13 10		13 27		13 40	13 57		14 10		14 27		14 40	14 57		15 10	
Brighton 10	a	12 30		12 44	13 00		13 14	13 20	13 30		13 44	14 00		14 14	14 20	14 30		14 44	15 00		15 14	15 20
Cooksbridge	d																					
Plumpton	d		12 28																			
Wivelsfield 4	a	*12 53*	12 34	*13 11*	*13 23*				*13 53*	13 34	*14 11*	*14 23*				*14 53*	14 34	*15 11*	*15 23*			
Haywards Heath 3	a	*12 47*	12 40	*13 15*	*13 18*	13 05			*13 47*	13 40	*14 15*	*14 18*	14 05			*14 47*	14 40	*15 15*	*15 18*	15 05		
Gatwick Airport 10	✈ a	*13 00*	12 54		*13 30*	13 24			*14 00*	13 54		*14 30*	14 24	*14 50*		*15 00*	14 54		*15 30*	15 24		
East Croydon	a	*13 16*	13 10	*13 23*	*13 46*	13 40	*13 55*		*14 16*	14 10	*14 23*	*14 46*	14 40	*14 55*		*15 16*	15 09	*15 23*	*15 46*	15 41	*15 55*	
London Bridge 4	⊖ a	*13 30*	*13 30*	*13c45*	*14 00*	*14 00*	*14c15*		*14 30*	*14 30*	*14c45*	*15 00*	*15 00*	*15c15*		*15 30*		*15c45*	*16 00*	*16 00*	*16c15*	
Clapham Junction 10	a		13 19	*13 33*	*14c03*	13 49	*14 04*			14 19	*14 33*	*15c03*	14 49	*15 04*			15 19	*15 33*	*16c03*	15 51	*16 04*	
London Victoria 15	⊖ a		13 27	*13 40*		13 58	*14 11*			14 27	*14 40*		14 57	*15 11*			15 28	*15 40*		15 58	*16 11*	

For general notes see front of timetable
For details of catering facilities see Directory of Train Operators

§ For additional trains between Hampden Park and Eastbourne see London to Hastings pages

A from Lewes
b Change at London Bridge and Ashford International
c Change at Brighton and East Croydon

Ashford, Hastings, Eastbourne, Seaford and Lewes → Brighton, Haywards Heath and London

Network Diagram - see first page of Table 184

Station		SN 1	SN 1	SN 1		SN 1	SN 1	SN 1	SN 1	SN 1	SN 1		SN 1	SN 1	SN 1	SN 1	SN 1	SN 1		SN 1	SN 1	SN 1	SN 1	SN 1	SN 1
			A				A				A				A					A			A		
London Charing Cross 4	⊖ d								12 53								13 53							14 53	
London Waterloo (East) 4	⊖ d								12 56								13 56							14 56	
London Cannon Street 4	⊖ d								12b30								13b30							14b30	
London Bridge 4	⊖ d								12 38								13 38							14 38	
Ashford International	d								14 30								15 30							16 30	
Ham Street	d								14 39								15 39							16 39	
Appledore (Kent)	d								14 44								15 44							16 44	
Rye	a								14 53								15 53							16 53	
	d								14 54								15 54							16 54	
Winchelsea	d																								
Doleham	d																								
Three Oaks	d																								
Ore	d			14 21			14 50						15 20		15 48						16 22		16 50		
Hastings 4	a			14 24			14 53		15 11				15 23		15 51		16 11				16 25		16 53	17 14	
	d			14 25			14 55		15 12				15 24		15 53		16 12				16 26		16 55	17 16	
St Leonards Warrior Sq 4	d			14 28			14 58		15 15				15 27		15 56		16 15				16 29		16 58	17 19	
Bexhill 4	d			14 35			15 05		15 22				15 33		16 03		16 23				16 35		17 05	17 26	
Collington	d			14 37			15 07						15 35		16 05						16 37		17 07		
Cooden Beach	d			14 40			15 10						15 38		16 08						16 40		17 10		
Normans Bay	d			14 43									15 41		16 11						16 43				
Pevensey Bay	d												15 45		16 14										
Pevensey & Westham	d			14 48			15 16						15 47		16 17						16 48		17 16		
Hampden Park 4 §	d			14 52			15 20						15 52		16 21						16 52		17 20		
Eastbourne 4	a			14 57			15 25		15 37				15 57		16 26		16 38				16 57		17 25	17 41	
	d		14 58	15 02			15 31		15 45		15 58		16 02		16 32		16 45			16 58	17 02		17 31	17 45	
Hampden Park 4 §	d		15 02	15 06							16 02		16 06				16 49			17 02	17 06				
Polegate	d		15 06	15 11			15 37		15 52		16 06		16 11		16 38		16 54			17 06	17 11		17 37	17 52	
Berwick	d			15 17									16 17								17 17				
Glynde	d			15 22									16 22								17 22				
Seaford	d	14 58				15 25				15 58				16 25				16 58				17 25			17 58
Bishopstone	d	15 00				15 27				16 00				16 27				17 00				17 27			18 00
Newhaven Harbour	d	15 03				15 30				16 03				16 30				17 03				17 30			18 03
Newhaven Town ⛴	d	15 05				15 32				16 05				16 32				17 05				17 32			18 05
Southease	d					15 36								16 36								17 36			
Lewes 4	a	15 14	15 18	15 28		15 44	15 49		16 07	16 14	16 18		16 28	16 44	16 50		17 07	17 14		17 18	17 28	17 44	17 49	18 05	18 14
	d	15 14	15 19	15 28		15 44	15 50	15 58	16 07	16 14	16 19		16 28	16 44	16 51	16 58	17 07	17 14		17 19	17 28	17 44	17 50	18 06	18 14
Falmer	d	15 21		15 35		15 51		16 05		16 21			16 35	16 51		17 05		17 21			17 35	17 51		18 13	18 21
Moulsecoomb	d	15 24		15 38		15 54		16 08		16 24			16 38	16 54		17 08		17 24			17 38	17 54		18 17	18 24
London Road (Brighton)	d	15 27		15 40		15 57		16 10		16 27			16 40	16 57		17 10		17 27			17 40	17 57		18 19	18 27
Brighton 10	a	15 30		15 44		16 00		16 14	16 20	16 30			16 44	17 00		17 14	17 20	17 30			17 44	18 00		18 23	18 30
Cooksbridge	d		15 24								16 24									17 24					
Plumpton	d		15 29								16 29									17 29					
Wivelsfield 4	a	*15 53*	15 35	*16 11*					*16 46*		16 35		*17 11*			*17 40*				17 35	*18 11*	*18 23*			*18 53*
Haywards Heath 3	a	*15 48*	15 39	*16 15*		*16 18*	16 05		*16 50*		16 39		*17 15*		17 05	*17 45*		*17 56*		17 39	*18 15*	*18 28*	18 05		*18 47*
Gatwick Airport 10 ✈	a	*16 00*	15 55			*16 30*	16 26		*17 06*		16 55		*17 31*		17 24	*18 00*		*18 16*		17 55	*18 30*	*18 46*	18 24		*19 00*
East Croydon	a	*16 16*	16 11	*16 24*		*16 46*	16 42	*16 55*			17 11		*17 25*		17 40	*17 54*				18 11	*18 24*	18 55	18 41		*19 16*
London Bridge 4	⊖ a	*16c41*	16 41	*16c56*		*17 02*	17 02	*17c26*			*17 54*		*17c54*		18 10	*18c24*				*18 45*	*18c45*	*19 15*	*19 00*		*19 30*
Clapham Junction 10	a		16 21	*16 33*		*17c03*	16 51	*17 04*			17 21		*17 34*		17 50	*18 04*				18 21	*18 33*	*19 04*	18 51		
London Victoria 15	⊖ a		16 29	*16 41*			16 58	*17 11*			17 28		*17 43*		17 57	*18 11*				18 28	*18 40*	*19 11*	18 59		

For general notes see front of timetable
For details of catering facilities see Directory of Train Operators

§ For additional trains between Hampden Park and Eastbourne see London to Hastings pages

A Trolley service from Lewes
b Change at London Bridge and Ashford International
c Change at Brighton and East Croydon

Ashford, Hastings, Eastbourne, Seaford and Lewes → Brighton, Haywards Heath and London

Network Diagram - see first page of Table 184

		SN 1 A ⚲	SN 1		SN 1	SN 1	SN 1	SN 1	SN 1	SN 1		SN 1	SN 1	SN 1	SN 1	SN 1	SN 1		SN 1	SN 1	SN 1	SN 1	SN 1	SN 1	SN 1
London Charing Cross 4	⊖ d							16 00	16 30										16 46	17 34					
London Waterloo (East) 4	⊖ d							16 03	16 33										16 49	17 37					
London Cannon Street 4	⊖ d							16b00	16b28										16b46	17 44					
London Bridge 4	⊖ d							16 08	16 39										16 54						
Ashford International	d							17 30	17 58										18 30	18 58					
Ham Street	d							17 39	18 07										18 39	19 07					
Appledore (Kent)	d							17 44	18 12										18 44	19 12					
Rye	a							17 53	18 21										18 53	19 21					
	d							17 54											18 54						
Winchelsea	d																								
Doleham	d																								
Three Oaks	d																								
Ore	d		17 22			17 50							18 22			18 50						19 24		19 50	
Hastings 4	a		17 25			17 53		18 11					18 25			18 53			19 11			19 27		19 53	
	d		17 26			17 55		18 12					18 26			18 55			19 12			19 27		19 55	
St Leonards Warrior Sq 4	d		17 29			17 58		18 15					18 29			18 58			19 15			19 30		19 58	
Bexhill 4	d		17 35			18 05		18 22					18 35			19 05			19 22			19 37		20 05	
Collington	d		17 37			18 07							18 37			19 07						19 39		20 07	
Cooden Beach	d		17 40			18 10							18 40			19 10						19 42		20 10	
Normans Bay	d		17 43										18 43												
Pevensey Bay	d																								
Pevensey & Westham	d		17 48			18 16							18 48			19 16						19 48		20 16	
Hampden Park 4 §	d		17 52			18 20							18 52			19 22						19 52		20 20	
Eastbourne 4	a		17 57			18 25		18 39					18 57			19 27			19 38			19 57		20 25	
	d	17 57	18 01			18 31		18 45				19 00	19 04			19 34			19 45			20 02		20 31	
Hampden Park 4 §	d	18 01	18 05										19 08									20 06			
Polegate	d	18 05	18 11			18 37		18 52				19 06	19 12			19 40			19 52			20 11		20 37	
Berwick	d		18 17										19 17									20 17			
Glynde	d		18 22										19 23									20 22			
Seaford	d				18 25		18 43			18 58				19 15	19 32						19 58		20 28		
Bishopstone	d				18 27					19 00				19 17	19 34						20 00		20 30		
Newhaven Harbour	d				18 30					19 03				19 20							20 03		20 33		
Newhaven Town ⛴	d				18 32		18 48			19 05				19 22	19 38						20 05		20 35		
Southease	d				18 36									19 26									20 39		
Lewes 4	a	18 17	18 29		18 44	18 49	18 57	19 07		19 14		19 19	19 28	19 33	19 47	19 52			20 07		20 14	20 28	20 46	20 49	←
	d	18 18	18 29		18 44	18 50	18 58	19 07		19 14		19 20	19 29	19 35	19 48	19 53	19 58		20 07		20 14	20 28	20 53 →	20 50	20 53
Falmer	d		18 36		18 51		19 05			19 21			19 36	19 42	19 55		20 05				20 21	20 35			21 00
Moulsecoomb	d		18 39		18 54		19 08			19 24			19 39	19 45	19 58		20 08				20 24	20 38			21 03
London Road (Brighton)	d		18 42		18 57		19 10			19 27			19 41	19 47	20 00		20 10				20 27	20 40			21 05
Brighton 10	a		18 45		19 00		19 14	19 20		19 31			19 45	19 51	20 04		20 14		20 20		20 33	20 44			21 09
Cooksbridge	d	18 23																							
Plumpton	d	18 28				18 58																		20 58	
Wivelsfield 4	a	18 34	*19 11*		*19 23*	19 05				*19 53*				*20 11*		20 05					*20 53*			21 06	
Haywards Heath 3	a	18 38	*19 16*		*19 28*	19 10		*19 47*		*19 58*		19 36		*20 16*		20 10			*20 47*		*20 58*			21 10	
Gatwick Airport 10 ✈	a	18 56	*19 38*		*19 46*	19 25		*20 00*		*20 16*		19 54		*20 31*		20 25			*21 00*		*21 16*			21 25	
East Croydon ⇌	a	19 12	*19 23*			19 41	*19 54*	*20 16*				20 10	*20 23*	*20 47*		20 41	*20 55*		*21 16*			*21 23*		21 41	*21 55*
London Bridge 4	⊖ a	*19 30*	*19c45*			*20 00*	*20c15*	*20 30*				*20 30*	*20c45*	*21 00*		*21 00*	*21c15*		*21 30*			*21c45*		*22 15*	*22c15*
Clapham Junction 10	a	19 21	*19 33*			19 50	*20 04*					20 19	*20 33*	*21c03*		20 51	*21 04*					*21 33*		21 50	*22 04*
London Victoria 15	⊖ a	19 29	*19 40*			19 59	*20 11*					20 28	*20 40*			20 59	*21 11*					*21 40*		21 58	*22 11*

For general notes see front of timetable
For details of catering facilities see Directory of Train Operators

§ For additional trains between Hampden Park and Eastbourne see London to Hastings pages

A ⚲ from Lewes
b Change at London Bridge and Ashford International
c Change at Brighton and East Croydon

Table 189

Ashford, Hastings, Eastbourne, Seaford and Lewes → Brighton, Haywards Heath and London

Network Diagram - see first page of Table 184

Station		SN 1		SN 1	SN 1	SN 1	SN 1	SN 1	SN 1		SN 1	SN 1	SN 1	SN 1	SN 1	SN 1		SN 1	SN 1	SN 1	SN 1	SN 1	SN 1		
London Charing Cross 4	⊖ d	17 56				18b23					19 00							20 00			21 00				
London Waterloo (East) 4	⊖ d	17 59				18 19					19 03							20 03			21 03				
London Cannon Street 4	⊖ d	18 04				18 30					18b50							20b00			21b00				
London Bridge 4	⊖ d	18 08				18 34					19 08							20 08			21 08				
Ashford International	d	19 30				19 58					20 30							21 30			22 24				
Ham Street	d	19 39				20 07					20 39							21 39			22 33				
Appledore (Kent)	d	19 44				20 12					20 44							21 44			22 38				
Rye	a	19 53				20 21					20 53							21 53			22 47				
	d	19 54				20 22					20 54							21 57			22 47				
Winchelsea	d																				22 51				
Doleham	d																				22 57				
Three Oaks	d																				23 01				
Ore	d				20 20			20 50							21 22					22 22	23 06				
Hastings 4	a	20 11			20 23	20 39		20 53			21 11				21 25			22 14		22 25	23 09				
	d	20 12			20 24			20 55			21 12				21 30			22 16		22 26			23 13		
St Leonards Warrior Sq 4	d	20 15			20 27			20 58			21 15				21 33			22 19		22 29			23 16		
Bexhill 4	d	20 22			20 35			21 05			21 22				21 39			22 26		22 38			23 22		
Collington	d				20 37			21 07							21 41					22 40			23 24		
Cooden Beach	d				20 40			21 10							21 44					22 43			23 27		
Normans Bay	d																			22 46					
Pevensey Bay	d																								
Pevensey & Westham	d				20 46			21 16							21 50					22 51			23 33		
Hampden Park 4 §	d				20 52			21 20							21 55					22 55			23 38		
Eastbourne 4	a	20 37			20 57			21 25			21 37				22 00			22 41		23 00			23 43		
	d	20 45			21 02			21 31			21 45		22 02		22 15			22 45		23 05			23 48		
Hampden Park 4 §	d				21 06								22 06		22 19					23 09			23 52		
Polegate	d	20 52			21 11			21 37			21 52		22 11		22 23			22 52		23 13			23 56		
Berwick	d				21 17								22 17		22 29					23 18					
Glynde	d				21 22								22 22							23 24					
Seaford	d			20 58			21 28					21 58		22 20					22 58			23 25			
Bishopstone	d			21 00			21 30					22 00		22 22					23 00			23 27			
Newhaven Harbour	d			21 03			21 33					22 03		22 25					23 03			23 30			
Newhaven Town ⛴	d			21 05			21 35					22 05		22 27					23 05			23 32			
Southease	d																								
Lewes 4	a	21 07		21 14	21 28		21 44	21 49			22 07	22 14	22 28	22 35	22 38			23 07	23 14	23 29		23 40	00 08		
	d	21 07		21 14	21 28		21 53 →	21 50	← 21 53		22 07	22 14	22 28	22 42 →	22 40	← 22 42		23 07	23 14	23 29		23 40	00 08		
Falmer	d			21 21	21 35				22 00			22 21	22 37			22 49			23 21	23 37		23 47	00 15		
Moulsecoomb	d			21 24	21 38				22 03			22 24	22 40			22 52			23 24	23 40		23 50	00 18		
London Road (Brighton)	d			21 27	21 40				22 05			22 27	22 42			22 54			23 27	23 42		23 53	00 21		
Brighton 10	a	21 20		21 33	21 44				22 09		22 20	22 31	22 46			22 58		23 20	23 31	23 46		23 56	00 24		
Cooksbridge	d																								
Plumpton	d														22 48										
Wivelsfield 4	a			21 53				22 02			22 49				22 54	23 19			23 53						
Haywards Heath 3	a	21 46		21 58				22 06			22 54				22 58	23 23			23 58						
Gatwick Airport 10 ✈	a	22 00		22 16				22 24			23c12				23 12	23 52			00 14						
East Croydon 🚋	a	22 17			22 23			22 40			23 30				23 30	00 16			00 35						
London Bridge 4	⊖ a	22 32			22e45						23 45				00 52	00 52			00 52						
Clapham Junction 10	a				22 33			22 50			00e11				23 42	00 29			01e02						
London Victoria 15	⊖ a				22 40			22 58			00e18				23 52	00 37			01e09						

For general notes see front of timetable
For details of catering facilities see
Directory of Train Operators

§ For additional trains between Hampden Park and Eastbourne see London to Hastings pages

b Change at London Bridge and Ashford International
c Change at Brighton and Haywards Heath
e Change at Brighton and East Croydon

Table 189

Saturdays

Ashford, Hastings, Eastbourne, Seaford and Lewes → Brighton, Haywards Heath and London

Network Diagram - see first page of Table 184

		SN 1	SN 1	SN 1	SN 1	SN 1	SN 1	SN 1	SN 1	SN 1 A	SN 1 B	SN 1	SN 1	SN 1	SN 1 C	SN 1	SN 1	SN 1	SN 1	SN 1	SN 1	SN 1 C
London Charing Cross 4	⊖ d																					
London Waterloo (East) 4	⊖ d																					
London Cannon Street 4	⊖ d																					
London Bridge 4	⊖ d																					
Ashford International	d																06 23					
Ham Street	d																06 32					
Appledore (Kent)	d																06 37					
Rye	a																06 46					
	d																06 48					
Winchelsea	d																06 51					
Doleham	d																06 58					
Three Oaks	d																07 01					
Ore	d												06 22		06 50		07 07			07 22		07 50
Hastings 4	a												06 25		06 53		07 10			07 25		07 53
	d	23p13											06 26		06 55		07 11			07 26		07 55
St Leonards Warrior Sq 4	d	23p16											06 29		06 58		07 14			07 29		07 58
Bexhill 4	d	23p22											06 35		07 05		07 22			07 35		08 05
Collington	d	23p24											06 37		07 07					07 37		08 07
Cooden Beach	d	23p27											06 40		07 10					07 40		08 10
Normans Bay	d												06 43							07 43		
Pevensey Bay	d																					
Pevensey & Westham	d	23p33											06 48		07 16					07 48		08 16
Hampden Park 4 §	d	23p38											06 52		07 20					07 52		08 20
Eastbourne 4	a	23p43											06 57		07 25		07 37			07 57		08 25
	d	23p48		05 03		05 50		06 24	06 37			06 58	07 02		07 31		07 45		07 58	08 02		08 31
Hampden Park 4 §	d	23p52		05 07				06 28				07 02	07 06						08 02	08 06		
Polegate	d	23p56		05 12		05 57		06 32	06 44			07 06	07 11		07 37		07 52		08 06	08 11		08 37
Berwick	d							06 38					07 17							08 17		
Glynde	d							06 43					07 22							08 22		
Seaford	d		05 05				06 28			06 58	06 58			07 28				07 58			08 25	
Bishopstone	d		05 07				06 30			07 00	07 00			07 30				08 00			08 27	
Newhaven Harbour	d		05 10				06 33			07 03	07 03			07 33				08 03			08 30	
Newhaven Town ⛴	d		05 12				06 35			07 05	07 05			07 35				08 05			08 32	
Southease	d																				08 36	
Lewes 4	a	00 08	05 21	05 24	←	06 10	06 44	06 49	06 57	07 14	07 14	07 18	07 28	07 44	07 49	....	08 07	08 14	08 18	08 28	08 44	08 49
	d	00 08	05 28	05 25	05 28	06 10	06 44	06 50	06 58	07 14	07 17	07 20	07 28	07 44	07 50	07 58	08 07	08 14	08 20	08 28	08 44	08 50
Falmer	d	00 15	→		05 35	06 18	06 51		07 05	07 21	07 24		07 35	07 51		08 05		08 21		08 35	08 51	
Moulsecoomb	d	00 18			05 38	06 21	06 54		07 09	07 24	07 27		07 38	07 54		08 08		08 24		08 38	08 54	
London Road (Brighton)	d	00 21			05 40	06 24	06 57		07 11	07 27	07 30		07 40	07 57		08 10		08 27		08 40	08 57	
Brighton 10	a	00 24			05 44	06 27	07 00		07 15	07 30	07 35		07 44	08 00		08 14	08 20	08 30		08 44	09 00	
Cooksbridge	d																					
Plumpton	d											07 28							08 28			
Wivelsfield 4	a				*06 11*	*06 53*	*07 23*		*07 53*	*07 53*		07 34	*08 11*	*08 23*				*08 53*	08 34	*09 11*		
Haywards Heath 3	a			05 40	*06 02*	*06 58*	*07 18*	07 05	*07 47*	*07 47*		07 40	*08 15*	*08 18*	08 05			*08 47*	08 40	*09 15*	*09 18*	09 05
Gatwick Airport 10 ✈	a			06 03	*06 24*	*07 16*	*07 30*	07 24	*08 00*	*08 00*		07 54	....	*08 30*	08 24			*09 00*	08 54	....	*09 30*	09 24
East Croydon	a			06b16	*06 40*	*07 23*	*07 46*	07 40	*07 55*	*08 16*		08 10	*08 23*	*08 46*	08 40	*08 55*		*09 16*	09 10	*09 23*	*09 46*	09 40
London Bridge 4	⊖ a			06b31	*07 01*	*07 45*	*08 01*	*08 01*	*08c15*	*08 31*		*08 31*	*08e45*	*09 01*	*09 01*	*09e15*		*09 30*	09 30	*09e45*	*10 00*	*10 00*
Clapham Junction 10	a			06f37	*06 50*	*07 33*	*08e03*	07 49	*08 04*			08 19	*08 33*	*09e03*	08 49	*09 04*			09 19	*09 33*	*10e03*	09 49
London Victoria 15	⊖ a			06f44	*06 58*	*07 40*	....	07 57	*08 11*			08 27	*08 40*	....	08 57	*09 11*			09 27	*09 40*	....	09 57

For general notes see front of timetable
For details of catering facilities see Directory of Train Operators

§ For additional trains between Hampden Park and Eastbourne see London to Hastings pages

A Until 27 September
B From 4 October
C from Lewes
b Change at Haywards Heath
c London Bridge. Change at Brighton and East Croydon
e Change at Brighton and East Croydon
f Change at Haywards Heath and East Croydon

Table 189

Saturdays

Ashford, Hastings, Eastbourne, Seaford and Lewes → Brighton, Haywards Heath and London

Network Diagram - see first page of Table 184

Station		SN 1	SN 1	SN 1	SN 1	SN 1	SN 1	SN 1 A ⚲	SN 1	SN 1	SN 1	SN 1
London Charing Cross 4	⊖ d									07 00		
London Waterloo (East) 4	⊖ d									07 03		
London Cannon Street 4	⊖ d											
London Bridge 4	⊖ d									07 08		
Ashford International	d		07 30							08 30		
Ham Street	d		07 39							08 39		
Appledore (Kent)	d		07 44							08 44		
Rye	a		07 53							08 53		
	d		07 54							08 54		
Winchelsea	d											
Doleham	d											
Three Oaks	d											
Ore	d					08 22		08 50				
Hastings 4	a		08 11			08 25		08 53		09 11		
	d		08 12			08 26		08 55		09 12		
St Leonards Warrior Sq 4	d		08 15			08 29		08 58		09 15		
Bexhill 4	d		08 22			08 35		09 05		09 22		
Collington	d					08 37		09 07				
Cooden Beach	d					08 40		09 10				
Normans Bay	d					08 43						
Pevensey Bay	d											
Pevensey & Westham	d					08 48		09 16				
Hampden Park 4 §	d					08 52		09 20				
Eastbourne 4	a		08 37			08 57		09 25		09 37		
	d		08 45		08 58	09 02		09 31		09 45		09 58
Hampden Park 4 §	d				09 02	09 06						10 02
Polegate	d		08 52		09 06	09 11		09 37		09 52		10 06
Berwick	d					09 17						
Glynde	d					09 22						
Seaford	d			08 58			09 25				09 58	
Bishopstone	d			09 00			09 27				10 00	
Newhaven Harbour	d			09 03			09 30				10 03	
Newhaven Town	⛴ d			09 05			09 32				10 05	
Southease	d						09 36					
Lewes 4	a		09 07	09 14	09 18	09 28	09 44	09 49		10 07	10 14	10 18
	d	08 58	09 07	09 14	09 20	09 28	09 44	09 50	09 58	10 07	10 14	10 20
Falmer	d	09 05		09 21		09 35	09 51		10 05		10 21	
Moulsecoomb	d	09 08		09 24		09 38	09 54		10 08		10 24	
London Road (Brighton)	d	09 10		09 27		09 40	09 57		10 10		10 27	
Brighton 10	a	09 14	09 20	09 30		09 44	10 00		10 14	10 20	10 30	
Cooksbridge	d											
Plumpton	d				09 28							10 28
Wivelsfield 4	a			09 53	09 34	10 11	10 23				10 53	10 34
Haywards Heath 3	a			09 47	09 40	10 15	10 18	10 05			10 47	10 40
Gatwick Airport 10	✈ a			10 00	09 54		10 30	10 21			11 00	10 54
East Croydon	a	09 55		10 16	10 10	10 23	10 46	10 38	10 55		11 16	11 10
London Bridge 4	⊖ a	10b22		10 30	10 30	10b45	11 00		11b15		11 30	11 30
Clapham Junction 10	a	10 04			10 19	10 33	11b03	10 47	11 04			11 19
London Victoria 15	⊖ a	10 11			10 27	10 40		10 56	11 11			11 27

Station		SN 1	SN 1	SN 1 A ⚲	SN 1	SN 1	SN 1	SN 1	SN 1	SN 1	SN 1 A ⚲
London Charing Cross 4	⊖ d					07 30					
London Waterloo (East) 4	⊖ d					07 33					
London Cannon Street 4	⊖ d										
London Bridge 4	⊖ d					07 38					
Ashford International	d					09 30					
Ham Street	d					09 39					
Appledore (Kent)	d					09 44					
Rye	a					09 53					
	d					09 54					
Winchelsea	d										
Doleham	d										
Three Oaks	d										
Ore	d	09 22		09 50					10 22		10 50
Hastings 4	a	09 25		09 53		10 11			10 25		10 53
	d	09 26		09 55		10 12			10 26		10 55
St Leonards Warrior Sq 4	d	09 29		09 58		10 15			10 29		10 58
Bexhill 4	d	09 35		10 05		10 22			10 35		11 05
Collington	d	09 37		10 07					10 37		11 07
Cooden Beach	d	09 40		10 10					10 40		11 10
Normans Bay	d	09 43							10 43		
Pevensey Bay	d										
Pevensey & Westham	d	09 48		10 16					10 48		11 16
Hampden Park 4 §	d	09 52		10 20					10 52		11 20
Eastbourne 4	a	09 57		10 25		10 37			10 57		11 25
	d	10 02		10 31		10 45		10 58	11 02		11 31
Hampden Park 4 §	d	10 06						11 02	11 06		
Polegate	d	10 11		10 37		10 52		11 06	11 11		11 37
Berwick	d	10 17							11 17		
Glynde	d	10 22							11 22		
Seaford	d		10 25				10 58			11 25	
Bishopstone	d		10 27				11 00			11 27	
Newhaven Harbour	d		10 30				11 03			11 30	
Newhaven Town	⛴ d		10 32				11 05			11 32	
Southease	d		10 36							11 36	
Lewes 4	a	10 28	10 44	10 49		11 07	11 14	11 18	11 28	11 44	11 49
	d	10 28	10 44	10 50	10 58	11 07	11 14	11 20	11 28	11 44	11 50
Falmer	d	10 35	10 51		11 05		11 21		11 35	11 51	
Moulsecoomb	d	10 38	10 54		11 08		11 24		11 38	11 54	
London Road (Brighton)	d	10 40	10 57		11 10		11 27		11 40	11 57	
Brighton 10	a	10 44	11 00		11 14	11 20	11 30		11 44	12 00	
Cooksbridge	d										
Plumpton	d										
Wivelsfield 4	a	11 11	11 23				11 53	11 34	12 11	12 23	
Haywards Heath 3	a	11 15	11 18	11 05			11 47	11 40	12 15	12 18	12 05
Gatwick Airport 10	✈ a		11 30	11 24			12 00	11 54		12 30	12 24
East Croydon	a	11 23	11 46	11 40	11 55		12 16	12 10	12 23	12 46	12 40
London Bridge 4	⊖ a	11b45	12 00	12 00	12b15		12 30	12 30	12b45	13 00	13 00
Clapham Junction 10	a	11 33	12b03	11 49	12 04			12 19	12 33	13b03	12 49
London Victoria 15	⊖ a	11 40		11 57	12 11			12 27	12 40		12 57

For general notes see front of timetable
For details of catering facilities see Directory of Train Operators

§ For additional trains between Hampden Park and Eastbourne see London to Hastings pages

A ⚲ from Lewes
b Change at Brighton and East Croydon

Table 189

Saturdays

Ashford, Hastings, Eastbourne, Seaford and Lewes → Brighton, Haywards Heath and London

Network Diagram - see first page of Table 184

Station		SN 1	SN 1	SN 1	SN 1	SN 1	SN 1	SN 1 A	SN 1	SN 1	SN 1	SN 1	SN 1	SN 1	SN 1 A	SN 1	SN 1	SN 1	SN 1	SN 1	SN 1	SN 1 A
London Charing Cross 4 ⊖	d		08 30							09 53							10 53					
London Waterloo (East) 4 ⊖	d		08 33							09 56							10 56					
London Cannon Street 4 ⊖	d		08b30							09b30							10b30					
London Bridge 4 ⊖	d		08 38							09 38							10 38					
Ashford International	d		10 30							11 30							12 30					
Ham Street	d		10 39							11 39							12 39					
Appledore (Kent)	d		10 44							11 44							12 44					
Rye	a		10 53							11 53							12 53					
	d		10 54							11 54							12 54					
Winchelsea	d																					
Doleham	d																					
Three Oaks	d																					
Ore	d					11 22		11 50					12 22		12 50					13 22		13 50
Hastings 4	a		11 11			11 25		11 53		12 11			12 25		12 53		13 11			13 25		13 53
	d		11 12			11 26		11 55		12 12			12 26		12 55		13 12			13 26		13 55
St Leonards Warrior Sq 4	d		11 15			11 29		11 58		12 15			12 29		12 58		13 15			13 29		13 58
Bexhill 4	d		11 22			11 35		12 05		12 22			12 35		13 05		13 22			13 35		14 05
Collington	d					11 37		12 07					12 37		13 07					13 37		14 07
Cooden Beach	d					11 40		12 10					12 40		13 10					13 40		14 10
Normans Bay	d					11 43							12 43							13 43		
Pevensey Bay	d																					
Pevensey & Westham	d					11 48		12 16					12 48		13 16					13 48		14 16
Hampden Park 4 §	d					11 52		12 20					12 52		13 20					13 52		14 20
Eastbourne 4	a		11 37			11 57		12 25		12 37			12 57		13 25		13 37			13 57		14 25
	d		11 45		11 58	12 02		12 31		12 45		12 58	13 02		13 31		13 45		13 58	14 02		14 31
Hampden Park 4 §	d				12 02	12 06						13 02	13 06						14 02	14 06		
Polegate	d		11 52		12 06	12 11		12 37		12 52		13 06	13 11		13 37		13 52		14 06	14 11		14 37
Berwick	d					12 17							13 17							14 17		
Glynde	d					12 22							13 22							14 22		
Seaford	d			11 58			12 25				12 58			13 25				13 58			14 25	
Bishopstone	d			12 00			12 27				13 00			13 27				14 00			14 27	
Newhaven Harbour	d			12 03			12 30				13 03			13 30				14 03			14 30	
Newhaven Town ⛴	d			12 05			12 32				13 05			13 32				14 05			14 32	
Southease	d						12 36							13 36							14 36	
Lewes 4	a		12 07	12 14	12 18	12 28	12 44	12 49		13 07	13 14	13 18	13 28	13 44	13 49		14 07	14 14	14 18	14 28	14 44	14 49
	d	11 58	12 07	12 14	12 20	12 28	12 44	12 50	12 58	13 07	13 14	13 20	13 28	13 44	13 50	13 58	14 07	14 14	14 20	14 28	14 44	14 50
Falmer	d	12 05		12 21		12 35	12 51		13 05		13 21		13 35	13 51		14 05		14 21		14 35	14 51	
Moulsecoomb	d	12 08		12 24		12 38	12 54		13 08		13 24		13 38	13 54		14 08		14 24		14 38	14 54	
London Road (Brighton)	d	12 10		12 27		12 40	12 57		13 10		13 27		13 40	13 57		14 10		14 27		14 40	14 57	
Brighton 10	a	12 14	12 20	12 30		12 44	13 00		13 14	13 20	13 30		13 44	14 00		14 14	14 20	14 30		14 44	15 00	
Cooksbridge	d																					
Plumpton	d				12 28																	
Wivelsfield 4	a			12 53	12 34	13 11	13 23				13 53	13 34	14 11	14 23				14 53	14 34	15 11	15 23	
Haywards Heath 3	a			12 47	12 40	13 15	13 18	13 05			13 47	13 40	14 15	14 18	14 05			14 47	14 40	15 15	15 18	15 05
Gatwick Airport 10 ✈	a			13 00	12 54		13 30	13 24			14 00	13 54		14 30	14 24	14 50		15 00	14 55		15 30	15 24
East Croydon	a	12 55		13 16	13 10	13 23	13 46	13 40	13 55		14 16	14 10	14 23	14 46	14 40	14 55		15 16	15 11	15 23	15 46	15 40
London Bridge 4 ⊖	a	13c15		13 30	13 30	13c45	14 00	14 00	14c15		14 30	14 30	14c45	15 00	15 00	15c15		15 30	15 30	15c45	16 00	16 00
Clapham Junction 10	a	13 04			13 19	13 33	14c03	13 49	14 04			14 19	14 33	15c03	14 49	15 04			15 20	15 33	16c03	15 49
London Victoria 15 ⊖	a	13 11			13 27	13 40		13 57	14 11			14 27	14 40		14 57	15 11			15 27	15 40		15 57

For general notes see front of timetable
For details of catering facilities see Directory of Train Operators

§ For additional trains between Hampden Park and Eastbourne see London to Hastings pages

A Trolley service from Lewes
b Change at London Bridge and Ashford International
c Change at Brighton and East Croydon

Table 189

Saturdays

Ashford, Hastings, Eastbourne, Seaford and Lewes → Brighton, Haywards Heath and London

Network Diagram - see first page of Table 184

		SN 1	SN 1	SN 1		SN 1	SN 1	SN 1	SN 1 A	SN 1	SN 1		SN 1	SN 1	SN 1	SN 1	SN 1 A	SN 1		SN 1	SN 1	SN 1	SN 1	SN 1	SN 1 A
London Charing Cross 4	⊖ d		*11 53*								*12 53*									*13 53*					
London Waterloo (East) 4	⊖ d		*11 56*								*12 56*									*13 56*					
London Cannon Street 4	⊖ d		*11b30*								*12b30*									*13b30*					
London Bridge 4	⊖ d		*11 38*								*12 38*									*13 38*					
Ashford International	d		13 30								14 30									15 30					
Ham Street	d		13 39								14 39									15 39					
Appledore (Kent)	d		13 44								14 44									15 44					
Rye	a		13 53								14 53									15 53					
	d		13 54								14 54									15 54					
Winchelsea	d																								
Doleham	d																								
Three Oaks	d																								
Ore	d						14 22		14 50						15 22		15 50						16 22		16 50
Hastings 4	a		14 11				14 25		14 53		15 11				15 25		15 53			16 11			16 25		16 53
	d		14 12				14 26		14 55		15 12				15 26		15 55			16 12			16 26		16 55
St Leonards Warrior Sq 4	d		14 15				14 29		14 58		15 15				15 29		15 58			16 15			16 29		16 58
Bexhill 4	d		14 22				14 35		15 05		15 22				15 35		16 05			16 22			16 35		17 05
Collington	d						14 37		15 07						15 37		16 07						16 37		17 07
Cooden Beach	d						14 40		15 10						15 40		16 10						16 40		17 10
Normans Bay	d						14 43								15 43								16 43		
Pevensey Bay	d																								
Pevensey & Westham	d						14 48		15 16						15 48		16 16						16 48		17 16
Hampden Park 4 §	d						14 52		15 20						15 52		16 20						16 52		17 20
Eastbourne 4	a		14 37				14 57		15 25		15 37				15 57		16 25			16 37			16 57		17 25
	d		14 45			14 58	15 02		15 31		15 45			15 58	16 02		16 31			16 45		16 58	17 02		17 31
Hampden Park 4 §	d					15 02	15 06							16 02	16 06							17 02	17 06		
Polegate	d		14 52			15 06	15 11		15 37		15 52			16 06	16 11		16 37			16 52		17 06	17 11		17 37
Berwick	d						15 17								16 17								17 17		
Glynde	d						15 22								16 22								17 22		
Seaford	d			14 58				15 25					15 58			16 25					16 58			17 25	
Bishopstone	d			15 00				15 27					16 00			16 27					17 00			17 27	
Newhaven Harbour	d			15 03				15 30					16 03			16 30					17 03			17 30	
Newhaven Town	⛴ d			15 05				15 32					16 05			16 32					17 05			17 32	
Southease	d							15 36								16 36								17 36	
Lewes 4	a		15 07	15 14		15 18	15 28	15 44	15 49		16 07		16 14	16 18	16 28	16 44	16 49			17 07	17 14	17 18	17 28	17 44	17 49
	d	14 58	15 07	15 14		15 20	15 28	15 44	15 50	15 58	16 07		16 14	16 20	16 28	16 44	16 50	16 58		17 07	17 14	17 20	17 28	17 44	17 50
Falmer	d	15 05		15 21			15 35	15 51		16 05			16 21		16 35	16 51		17 05			17 21		17 35	17 51	
Moulsecoomb	d	15 08		15 24			15 38	15 54		16 08			16 24		16 38	16 54		17 08			17 24		17 38	17 54	
London Road (Brighton)	d	15 10		15 27			15 40	15 57		16 10			16 27		16 40	16 57		17 10			17 27		17 40	17 57	
Brighton 10	a	15 14	15 20	15 30			15 44	16 00		16 14	16 20		16 30		16 44	17 00		17 14		17 20	17 30		17 44	18 00	
Cooksbridge	d																								
Plumpton	d													16 28								17 28			
Wivelsfield 4	a			*15 53*		15 34	*16 11*	*16 23*					*16 53*	16 34	*17 11*	*17 23*					*17 53*	17 34	*18 11*	*18 23*	
Haywards Heath 3	a			*15 47*		15 40	*16 15*	*16 18*	16 05				*16 47*	16 40	*17 15*	*17 18*	17 05				*17 47*	17 40	*18 15*	*18 18*	18 05
Gatwick Airport 10	✈ a			*16 00*		15 54		*16 30*	16 24				*17 00*	16 54		*17 30*	17 24				*18 00*	17 54		*18 30*	18 24
East Croydon	a	*15 55*		*16 16*		16 10	*16 23*	*16 46*	16 40	*16 55*			*17 16*	17 10	*17 23*	*17 46*	17 40	*17 55*			*18 16*	18 10	*18 23*	*18 46*	18 40
London Bridge 4	⊖ a	16c15		*16 30*		*16 30*	16c45	*17 00*	*17 00*	17c15			*17 30*	*17 30*	17c45	*18 00*	*18 00*	18c15			*18 30*	*18 30*	18c45	*19 00*	*19 00*
Clapham Junction 10	a	*16 04*				16 19	*16 33*	17c03	16 49	*17 04*				17 19	*17 33*	18c03	17 49	*18 04*				18 19	*18 33*	19c03	18 49
London Victoria 15	⊖ a	*16 11*				16 27	*16 40*		16 57	*17 11*				17 27	*17 40*		17 57	*18 11*				18 27	*18 40*		18 57

For general notes see front of timetable
For details of catering facilities see
Directory of Train Operators

§ For additional trains between Hampden Park and Eastbourne see London to Hastings pages

A from Lewes

b Change at London Bridge and Ashford International

c Change at Brighton and East Croydon

Table 189

Saturdays

Ashford, Hastings, Eastbourne, Seaford and Lewes → Brighton, Haywards Heath and London

Network Diagram - see first page of Table 184

Station		SN 1	SN 1		SN 1	SN 1	SN 1	SN 1	SN 1	SN 1		SN 1	SN 1	SN 1	SN 1	SN 1	SN 1		SN 1	SN 1	SN 1	SN 1	SN 1	SN 1	SN 1
London Charing Cross 4	⊖ d		14 53									15 53								16 53					
London Waterloo (East) 4	⊖ d		14 56									15 56								16 56					
London Cannon Street 4	⊖ d		14b30									15b30								16b30					
London Bridge 4	⊖ d		14 38									15 38								16 38					
Ashford International	d		16 30									17 30								18 30					
Ham Street	d		16 39									17 39								18 39					
Appledore (Kent)	d		16 44									17 44								18 44					
Rye	a		16 53									17 53								18 53					
	d		16 54									17 54								18 54					
Winchelsea	d																								
Doleham	d																								
Three Oaks	d																								
Ore	d						17 22		17 50						18 22		18 50					19 22		19 50	
Hastings 4	a		17 11				17 25		17 53			18 11			18 25		18 53			19 11		19 25		19 53	
	d		17 12				17 26		17 55			18 12			18 26		18 55			19 12		19 26		19 55	
St Leonards Warrior Sq 4	d		17 15				17 29		17 58			18 15			18 29		18 58			19 15		19 29		19 58	
Bexhill 4	d		17 22				17 35		18 05			18 22			18 35		19 05			19 22		19 35		20 05	
Collington	d						17 37		18 07						18 37		19 07					19 37		20 07	
Cooden Beach	d						17 40		18 10						18 40		19 10					19 40		20 10	
Normans Bay	d						17 43								18 43							19 43			
Pevensey Bay	d																								
Pevensey & Westham	d						17 48		18 16						18 48		19 16					19 48		20 16	
Hampden Park 4 §	d						17 52		18 20						18 52		19 21					19 52		20 20	
Eastbourne 4	a		17 37				17 57		18 25			18 37			18 57		19 26			19 37		19 57		20 25	
	d		17 45			17 58	18 02		18 31			18 45		18 58	19 02		19 32			19 45		20 02		20 31	
Hampden Park 4 §	d					18 02	18 06							19 02	19 06							20 06			
Polegate	d		17 52			18 06	18 11		18 37			18 52		19 06	19 11		19 38			19 52		20 11		20 37	
Berwick	d						18 17								19 17							20 17			
Glynde	d						18 22								19 22							20 22			
Seaford	d				17 58			18 25					18 58			19 25					19 58		20 28		
Bishopstone	d				18 00			18 27					19 00			19 27					20 00		20 30		
Newhaven Harbour	d				18 03			18 30					19 03			19 30					20 03		20 33		
Newhaven Town	⛴ d				18 05			18 32					19 05			19 32					20 05		20 35		
Southease	d							18 36								19 36									
Lewes 4	a		18 07		18 14	18 18	18 28	18 44	18 49			19 07	19 14	19 18	19 28	19 44	19 50			20 07	20 14	20 28	20 44	20 49	←
	d	17 58	18 07		18 14	18 20	18 28	18 44	18 50	18 58		19 07	19 14	19 20	19 28	19 44	19 51		19 58	20 07	20 14	20 30	20 53	20 50	20 53
Falmer	d	18 05			18 21		18 35	18 51		19 05			19 21		19 35	19 51			20 05		20 21	20 37	→		21 00
Moulsecoomb	d	18 08			18 24		18 38	18 54		19 08			19 24		19 38	19 54			20 08		20 24	20 40			21 03
London Road (Brighton)	d	18 10			18 27		18 40	18 57		19 10			19 27		19 40	19 57			20 10		20 27	20 42			21 05
Brighton 10	a	18 14	18 20		18 30		18 44	19 00		19 14		19 20	19 30		19 44	20 00			20 14	20 20	20 30	20 46			21 10
Cooksbridge	d																								
Plumpton	d					18 28								19 28											
Wivelsfield 4	a				18 53	18 34	19 11	19 23					19 53	19 34	20 11	20 23	20 03				20 53			21 02	
Haywards Heath 3	a				18 47	18 40	19 15	19 18	19 05				19 47	19 40	20 16	20 18	20 07				20 47			21 06	
Gatwick Airport 10	✈ a				19 00	18 54		19 31	19 24				20 00	19 54		20 30	20 24				21 00			21 24	
East Croydon	⇌ a	18 55			19 16	19 10	19 23	19 47	19 40	19 55			20 16	20 10	20 23	20 46	20 40		20 55		21 16			21 40	21 55
London Bridge 4	⊖ a	19c15			19 30	19 30	19c45	20 00	20 00	20c15			20 30	20 30	20c45	21 00	21 00		21c15		21 30			22 15	22c15
Clapham Junction 10	a	19 04				19 19	19 33	20c03	19 49	20 04				20 19	20 33	21c03	20 49		21 04		21 33			21 49	22 04
London Victoria 15	⊖ a	19 11				19 27	19 40		19 57	20 11				20 27	20 40		20 57		21 11		21 40			21 57	22 11

For general notes see front of timetable
For details of catering facilities see Directory of Train Operators

§ For additional trains between Hampden Park and Eastbourne see London to Hastings pages

b Change at London Bridge and Ashford International

c Change at Brighton and East Croydon

Table 189

Ashford, Hastings, Eastbourne, Seaford and Lewes → Brighton, Haywards Heath and London

Network Diagram - see first page of Table 184

		SN 1	SN 1	SN 1	SN 1	SN 1	SN 1	SN 1	SN 1	SN 1	SN 1	SN 1	SN 1	SN 1	SN 1	SN 1	SN 1	SN 1	SN 1
London Charing Cross 4	⊖ d	18 23						19 00						20 00			20 30		
London Waterloo (East) 4	⊖ d	18 26						19 03						20 03			20 33		
London Cannon Street 4	⊖ d	17b30						19b00						19b14					
London Bridge 4	⊖ d	17 38						19 08						20 08			20 38		
Ashford International	d	19 30						20 30						21 30			22 24		
Ham Street	d	19 39						20 39						21 39			22 33		
Appledore (Kent)	d	19 44						20 44						21 44			22 38		
Rye	a	19 53						20 53						21 53			22 47		
	d	19 54						20 54						21 57			22 47		
Winchelsea	d																22 51		
Doleham	d																22 57		
Three Oaks	d																23 01		
Ore	d			20 22		20 50				21 22						22 22	23 06		
Hastings 4	a	20 11		20 25		20 53		21 11		21 25				22 14		22 25	23 09		
	d	20 12		20 26		20 55		21 12		21 26		21 42		22 16		22 26			23 13
St Leonards Warrior Sq 4	d	20 15		20 29		20 58		21 15		21 29		21 45		22 19		22 29			23 16
Bexhill 4	d	20 22		20 35		21 05		21 22		21 35		21 51		22 25		22 38			23 22
Collington	d			20 37		21 07				21 37		21 53				22 40			23 24
Cooden Beach	d			20 40		21 10				21 40		21 56				22 43			23 27
Normans Bay	d			20 43												22 46			
Pevensey Bay	d																		
Pevensey & Westham	d			20 48		21 16				21 46		22 02				22 51			23 33
Hampden Park 4 §	d			20 52		21 20				21 51		22 07				22 55			23 38
Eastbourne 4	a	20 37		20 57		21 25		21 37		21 56		22 12		22 40		23 00			23 43
	d	20 45		21 02		21 31		21 45		22 02		22 18		22 45		23 05			23 48
Hampden Park 4 §	d			21 06						22 06						23 09			23 52
Polegate	d	20 52		21 11		21 37		21 52		22 11		22 24		22 52		23 13			23 56
Berwick	d			21 17						22 17						23 18			
Glynde	d			21 22						22 22						23 24			
Seaford	d		20 58		21 28				21 58		22 20				22 58			23 25	
Bishopstone	d		21 00		21 30				22 00		22 22				23 00			23 27	
Newhaven Harbour	d		21 03		21 33				22 03		22 25				23 03			23 30	
Newhaven Town ⛴	d		21 05		21 35				22 05		22 27				23 05			23 32	
Southease	d																		
Lewes 4	a	21 07	21 14	21 28	21 44	21 49	←	22 07	22 14	22 28	22 35	22 38	←	23 07	23 14	23 29		23 40	00 08
	d	21 07	21 14	21 28	21 53	21 50	21 53	22 07	22 14	22 28	22 42	22 40	22 42	23 07	23 14	23 29		23 40	00 08
Falmer	d		21 21	21 36	→		22 00		22 21	22 35	→		22 49		23 21	23 37		23 47	00 15
Moulsecoomb	d		21 24	21 39			22 03		22 24	22 38			22 52		23 24	23 40		23 50	00 18
London Road (Brighton)	d		21 27	21 41			22 05		22 27	22 40			22 54		23 27	23 42		23 53	00 21
Brighton 10	a	21 20	21 30	21 45			22 09	22 20	22 31	22 44			22 58	23 20	23 31	23 46		23 56	00 24
Cooksbridge	d																		
Plumpton	d											22 48							
Wivelsfield 4	a		21 53			22 02		22 49				22 54	23 19		23 53				
Haywards Heath 3	a		21 58			22 06		22 54				22 58	23 23		23 58				
Gatwick Airport 10 ✈	a		22 16			22 23		23c12				23 12	23 52		00 14				
East Croydon	a			22 23		22 40		23 32				23 30	00 16		00 35				
London Bridge 4	⊖ a			22e45				23 45				00f52	00e52						
Clapham Junction 10	a			22 33		22 49		00e11				23 42			01e02				
London Victoria 15	⊖ a			22 40		22 57		00e18				23 52			01e09				

For general notes see front of timetable
For details of catering facilities see Directory of Train Operators

§ For additional trains between Hampden Park and Eastbourne see London to Hastings pages

b Change at London Bridge and Ashford International
c Change at Brighton and Haywards Heath
e Change at Brighton and East Croydon
f Change at Gatwick Airport and East Croydon

Table 189

Sundays

Ashford, Hastings, Eastbourne, Seaford and Lewes → Brighton, Haywards Heath and London

Network Diagram - see first page of Table 184

Station		SN 1	SN 1 A	SN 1 A	SN 1 B	SN 1 C ⌶	SN 1	SN 1	SN 1 D ⌶	SN 1 E ⌶	SN 1	SN 1	SN 1	SN 1	SN 1 C ⌶	SN 1	SN 1	SN 1	SN 1	SN 1 C ⌶	SN 1	SN 1	SN 1
London Charing Cross 4	⊖ d																						
London Waterloo (East) 4	⊖ d																						
London Cannon Street 4	⊖ d																						
London Bridge 4	⊖ d																						
Ashford International	d																	08 15					09 21
Ham Street	d																	08 24					09 30
Appledore (Kent)	d																	08 29					09 35
Rye	a																	08 38					09 44
	d																	08 40					09 45
Winchelsea	d																	08 43					
Doleham	d																	08 50					
Three Oaks	d																	08 53					
Ore	d														08 14			08 59		09 14			
Hastings 4	a														08 17			09 02		09 17			10 02
	d	23p13							07 13						08 18			09 03		09 18			10 03
St Leonards Warrior Sq 4	d	23p16							07 16						08 21			09 06		09 21			10 06
Bexhill 4	d	23p22							07 22						08 27			09 13		09 27			10 13
Collington	d	23p24							07 24						08 29					09 29			
Cooden Beach	d	23p27							07 27						08 32					09 32			
Normans Bay	d																						
Pevensey Bay	d																						
Pevensey & Westham	d	23p33							07 33						08 38					09 38			
Hampden Park 4 §	d	23p38							07 38						08 43					09 43			
Eastbourne 4	a	23p43							07 43						08 48			09 29		09 48			10 29
	d	23p48	05 37			06 54	07 30		07 55	07 55			08 34		08 55			09 34		09 55			10 34
Hampden Park 4 §	d	23p52				06 58	07 34						08 38					09 38					10 38
Polegate	d	23p56	05 44			07 02	07 38		08 02	08 02			08 42		09 02			09 42		10 02			10 42
Berwick	d						07 44						08 48					09 48					10 48
Glynde	d						07 49						08 53					09 53					10 53
Seaford	d			06 54				07 53				08 28		08 53			09 28		09 53			10 28	
Bishopstone	d			06 56				07 55				08 30		08 55			09 30		09 55			10 30	
Newhaven Harbour	d			06 59				07 58				08 33		08 58			09 33		09 58			10 33	
Newhaven Town	⛴ d			07 01				08 00				08 35		09 00			09 35		10 00			10 35	
Southease	d			07 05				08 04						09 04					10 04				
Lewes 4	a	00 08	05 57	07 11		07 14	07 55	08 11	08 14	08 14	⟵	08 44	08 59	09 11	09 14	⟵	09 44	09 59	10 11	10 14	⟵	10 44	10 59
	d	00 08	05 57	07 18	07 18	07 20	07 56	08 18 ⟶	08 16	08 16	08 18	08 45	09 00	09 18 ⟶	09 16	09 18	09 45	10 00	10 18 ⟶	10 16	10 18	10 45	11 00
Falmer	d	00 15		07 25	07 25		08 03				08 25	08 52				09 25	09 52				10 25	10 52	
Moulsecoomb	d	00 18		07 28	07 28		08 07				08 28	08 55				09 28	09 55				10 28	10 55	
London Road (Brighton)	d	00 21		07 30	07 30		08 09				08 30	08 57				09 30	09 57				10 30	10 57	
Brighton 10	a	00 24	06 09	07 34	07 34		08 13				08 34	09 01	09 12			09 34	10 01	10 12			10 34	11 01	11 12
Cooksbridge	d																						
Plumpton	d								08 24	08 24					09 24					10 24			
Wivelsfield 4	a		06 32	08 16	08 16	07 32			08 31	08 31	09 16				09 31	10 16				10 31	11 16		
Haywards Heath 3	a		06 36	08 00	08 00	07 36			08 36	08 36	09 00		09 30		09 35	09 51		10 30		10 35	11 00		11 30
Gatwick Airport 10	✈ a		06 51	08 14	08 14	07 51			08 51	08 51	09 14		09 44		09 51	10 10		10 44		10 51	11 14		11 44
East Croydon	⛟ a		07b01	08 31	08 31	08 09			09 09	09 09	09 31		10 01		10 09	10 31		11 01		11 09	11 31		12 01
London Bridge 4	⊖ a		07b15	08 45	08 45	08c38			09 38	09 42	09 45		10 15		10c38	10 45		11 15		11c38	11 45		12 15
Clapham Junction 10	a		07e24	08f54	08f54	08 24			09 24	09 24	09g47		10f24		10 24	10g47		11f24		11 24	11g47		12f24
London Victoria 15	⊖ a		07e31	09f01	09f01	08 31			09 31	09 31	09g53		10f31		10 31	10g53		11f31		11 31	11g53		12f31

For general notes see front of timetable
For details of catering facilities see Directory of Train Operators

§ For additional trains between Hampden Park and Eastbourne see London to Hastings pages

A Until 7 September

B From 14 September

C ⌶ from Lewes

D Until 7 September. ⌶ from Lewes

E From 14 September. ⌶ from Lewes

b Change at Brighton

c Change at East Croydon from 14 September arr. 4 minutes later

e Change at Haywards Heath

f Change at Brighton and East Croydon

g From 14 September arr. 7 minutes later change at Brighton and East Croydon

Table 189

Sundays

Ashford, Hastings, Eastbourne, Seaford and Lewes → Brighton, Haywards Heath and London

Network Diagram - see first page of Table 184

		SN 1	SN 1	SN 1	SN 1		SN 1	SN 1	SN 1	SN 1	SN 1	SN 1	SN 1	SN 1		SN 1	SN 1	SN 1	SN 1	SN 1	SN 1	SN 1	SN 1		SN 1
			A 🛒						A 🛒					A 🛒						A 🛒					
London Charing Cross 4 ⊖	d						09 00					10 00						11 00					12 00		
London Waterloo (East) 4 ⊖	d						09 03					10 03						11 03					12 03		
London Cannon Street 4 ⊖	d																								
London Bridge 4 ⊖	d						09 08					10 08						11 08					12 08		
Ashford International	d						10 21					11 21						12 21					13 21		
Ham Street	d						10 30					11 30						12 30					13 30		
Appledore (Kent)	d						10 35					11 35						12 35					13 35		
Rye	a						10 44					11 44						12 44					13 44		
	d						10 45					11 45						12 45					13 45		
Winchelsea	d																								
Doleham	d																								
Three Oaks	d																								
Ore	d		10 14						11 14					12 14						13 14					
Hastings 4	a		10 17				11 02		11 17			12 02		12 17				13 02		13 17			14 02		
	d		10 18				11 03		11 18			12 03		12 18				13 03		13 18			14 03		
St Leonards Warrior Sq 4	d		10 21				11 06		11 21			12 06		12 21				13 06		13 21			14 06		
Bexhill 4	d		10 27				11 13		11 27			12 13		12 27				13 13		13 27			14 13		
Collington	d		10 29						11 29					12 29						13 29					
Cooden Beach	d		10 32						11 32					12 32						13 32					
Normans Bay	d																								
Pevensey Bay	d																								
Pevensey & Westham	d		10 38						11 38					12 38						13 38					
Hampden Park 4 §	d		10 43						11 43					12 43						13 43					
Eastbourne 4	a		10 48				11 29		11 48			12 29		12 48				13 29		13 48			14 29		
	d		10 55				11 34		11 55			12 34		12 55				13 34		13 55			14 34		
Hampden Park 4 §	d						11 38					12 38						13 38					14 38		
Polegate	d		11 02				11 42		12 02			12 42		13 02				13 42		14 02			14 42		
Berwick	d						11 48					12 48						13 48					14 48		
Glynde	d						11 53					12 53						13 53					14 53		
Seaford	d	10 53			11 28			11 53			12 28		12 53				13 28		13 53			14 28			14 53
Bishopstone	d	10 55			11 30			11 55			12 30		12 55				13 30		13 55			14 30			14 55
Newhaven Harbour	d	10 58			11 33			11 58			12 33		12 58				13 33		13 58			14 33			14 58
Newhaven Town ⛴	d	11 00			11 35			12 00			12 35		13 00				13 35		14 00			14 35			15 00
Southease	d	11 04						12 04					13 04						14 04						15 04
Lewes 4	a	11 11	11 14	←	11 44		11 59	12 11	12 14	←	12 44	12 59	13 11	13 14		←	13 44	13 59	14 11	14 14	←	14 44	14 59		15 11
	d	11 18	11 16	11 18	11 45		12 00	12 18	12 16	12 18	12 45	13 00	13 18	13 16		13 18	13 45	14 00	14 18	14 16	14 18	14 45	15 00		15 18
Falmer	d	→		11 25	11 52			→		12 25	12 52		→			13 25	13 52		→		14 25	14 52			→
Moulsecoomb	d			11 28	11 55					12 28	12 55					13 28	13 55				14 28	14 55			
London Road (Brighton)	d			11 30	11 57					12 30	12 57					13 30	13 57				14 30	14 57			
Brighton 10	a			11 34	12 01		12 12			12 34	13 01	13 12				13 34	14 01	14 12			14 34	15 01	15 12		
Cooksbridge	d																								
Plumpton	d		11 24																						
Wivelsfield 4	a		11 31	12 16					12 31	13 16				13 31		14 16				14 31	15 16				
Haywards Heath 3	a		11 35	12 00			12 30		12 35	13 00		13 30		13 35		14 00		14 30		14 35	15 00		15 30		
Gatwick Airport 10 ✈	a		11 51	12 14			12 44		12 52	13 14		13 44		13 52		14 14		14 44		14 52	15 14		15 44		
East Croydon	a		12 09	12 31			13 01		13 09	13 31		14 01		14 09		14 31		15 01		15 09	15 31		16 01		
London Bridge 4 ⊖	a		12b38	12 45			13 15		13b38	13 45		14 15		14b38		14 45		15 15		15b38	15 45		16 15		
Clapham Junction 10	a		12 24	12c47			13e24		13 24	13c47		14e24		14 24		14c47		15e24		15 24	15c47		16e24		
London Victoria 15 ⊖	a		12 31	12c53			13e31		13 31	13c53		14e31		14 31		14c53		15e31		15 31	15c53		16e31		

For general notes see front of timetable
For details of catering facilities see Directory of Train Operators

§ For additional trains between Hampden Park and Eastbourne see London to Hastings pages

A 🛒 from Lewes

b Change at East Croydon from 14 September arr. 4 minutes later

c From 14 September arr. 7 minutes later change at Brighton and East Croydon

e Change at Brighton and East Croydon

Table 189

Sundays

Ashford, Hastings, Eastbourne, Seaford and Lewes → Brighton, Haywards Heath and London

Network Diagram - see first page of Table 184

		SN	SN	SN	SN	SN	SN	SN	SN	SN	SN	SN	SN	SN	SN	SN	SN	SN	SN	SN	SN	SN	SN
		1	1	1	1	1	1	1	1	1	1	1	1	1	1	1	1	1	1	1	1	1	1
		A 🛒					A 🛒					A 🛒					A 🛒						
London Charing Cross 4	⊖ d				13 00					14 00					15 00					16 00			
London Waterloo (East) 4	⊖ d				13 03					14 03					15 03					16 03			
London Cannon Street 4	⊖ d																						
London Bridge 4	⊖ d				13 08					14 08					15 08					16 08			
Ashford International	d				14 21					15 21					16 21					17 21			
Ham Street	d				14 30					15 30					16 30					17 30			
Appledore (Kent)	d				14 35					15 35					16 35					17 35			
Rye	a				14 44					15 44					16 44					17 44			
	d				14 45					15 45					16 45					17 45			
Winchelsea	d																						
Doleham	d																						
Three Oaks	d																						
Ore	d	14 14					15 14					16 14					17 14					18 14	
Hastings 4	a	14 17			15 02		15 17			16 02		16 17			17 02		17 17			18 02		18 17	
	d	14 18			15 03		15 18			16 03		16 18			17 03		17 18			18 03		18 18	
St Leonards Warrior Sq 4	d	14 21			15 06		15 21			16 06		16 21			17 06		17 21			18 06		18 21	
Bexhill 4	d	14 27			15 13		15 27			16 13		16 27			17 13		17 27			18 13		18 27	
Collington	d	14 29					15 29					16 29					17 29					18 29	
Cooden Beach	d	14 32					15 32					16 32					17 32					18 32	
Normans Bay	d																						
Pevensey Bay	d																						
Pevensey & Westham	d	14 38					15 38					16 38					17 38					18 38	
Hampden Park 4 §	d	14 43					15 43					16 43					17 43					18 43	
Eastbourne 4	a	14 48			15 29		15 48			16 29		16 48			17 29		17 48			18 29		18 48	
	d	14 55			15 34		15 55			16 34		16 55			17 34		17 55			18 34		18 55	
Hampden Park 4 §	d				15 38					16 38					17 38					18 38			
Polegate	d	15 02			15 42		16 02			16 42		17 02			17 42		18 02			18 42		19 02	
Berwick	d				15 48					16 48					17 48					18 48			
Glynde	d				15 53					16 53					17 53					18 53			
Seaford	d			15 28		15 53			16 28		16 53			17 28		17 53			18 28		18 53		
Bishopstone	d			15 30		15 55			16 30		16 55			17 30		17 55			18 30		18 55		
Newhaven Harbour	d			15 33		15 58			16 33		16 58			17 33		17 58			18 33		18 58		
Newhaven Town	⛴ d			15 35		16 00			16 35		17 00			17 35		18 00			18 35		19 00		
Southease	d					16 04					17 04					18 04					19 04		
Lewes 4	a	15 14	←	15 44	15 59	16 11	16 14	←	16 44	16 59	17 11	17 14	←	17 44	17 59	18 11	18 14	←	18 44	18 59	19 11	19 14	←
	d	15 16	15 18	15 45	16 00	16 18 →	16 16	16 18	16 45	17 00	17 18 →	17 16	17 18	17 45	18 00	18 18 →	18 16	18 18	18 45	19 00	19 18 →	19 16	19 18
Falmer	d		15 25	15 52				16 25	16 52				17 25	17 52				18 25	18 52				19 25
Moulsecoomb	d		15 28	15 55				16 28	16 55				17 28	17 55				18 28	18 55				19 28
London Road (Brighton)	d		15 30	15 57				16 30	16 57				17 30	17 57				18 30	18 57				19 30
Brighton 10	a		15 34	16 01	16 12			16 34	17 01	17 12			17 34	18 01	18 12			18 34	19 01	19 12			19 34
Cooksbridge	d																						
Plumpton	d						16 24					17 24					18 24					19 24	
Wivelsfield 4	a	15 31	*16 16*				16 31	*17 16*				17 31	*18 16*				18 31	*19 16*				19 31	*20 16*
Haywards Heath 3	a	15 35	*16 00*		*16 30*		16 35	*17 00*		*17 30*		17 35	*18 00*		*18 30*		18 35	*19 00*		*19 30*		19 35	*20 00*
Gatwick Airport 10	✈ a	15 52	*16 14*		*16 44*		16 52	*17 14*		*17 44*		17 52	*18 14*		*18 44*		18 52	*19 14*		*19 44*		19 52	*20 14*
East Croydon	🚋 a	16 09	*16 31*		*17 01*		17 09	*17 31*		*18 01*		18 09	*18 31*		*19 01*		19 09	*19 31*		*20 01*		20 09	*20 31*
London Bridge 4	⊖ a	16b38	*16 45*		*17 15*		17b38	*17 45*		*18 15*		18b38	*18 45*		*19 15*		19b38	*19 45*		*20 15*		20b38	*20 45*
Clapham Junction 10	a	16 24	*16 47*		*17c24*		17 24	*17 47*		*18c24*		18 24	*18 47*		*19c24*		19 24	*19 47*		*20c24*		20 24	*20 47*
London Victoria 15	⊖ a	16 31	*16 53*		*17c31*		17 31	*17 53*		*18c31*		18 31	*18 53*		*19c31*		19 31	*19 53*		*20c31*		20 31	*20 53*

For general notes see front of timetable
For details of catering facilities see Directory of Train Operators

§ For additional trains between Hampden Park and Eastbourne see London to Hastings pages

A 🛒 from Lewes

b Change at East Croydon from 14 September arr. 4 minutes later

c Change at Brighton and East Croydon

Table 189

Sundays

Ashford, Hastings, Eastbourne, Seaford and Lewes → Brighton, Haywards Heath and London

Network Diagram - see first page of Table 184

Station		SN 1	SN 1	SN 1	SN 1		SN 1	SN 1	SN 1	SN 1	SN 1	SN 1	SN 1	SN 1		SN 1	SN 1	SN 1	SN 1	SN 1	SN 1	SN 1	SN 1		
London Charing Cross 4 ⊖	d		17 00						18 00					19 00					20 00			21 00			
London Waterloo (East) 4 ⊖	d		17 03						18 03					19 03					20 03			21 03			
London Cannon Street 4 ⊖	d																								
London Bridge 4 ⊖	d		17 08						18 08					19 08					20 08			21 08			
Ashford International	d		18 21						19 21					20 21					21 21			22 20			
Ham Street	d		18 30						19 30					20 30					21 30			22 29			
Appledore (Kent)	d		18 35						19 35					20 35					21 35			22 34			
Rye	a		18 44						19 44					20 44					21 44			22 43			
	d		18 45						19 45					20 45					21 45			22 43			
Winchelsea	d																					22 47			
Doleham	d																					22 53			
Three Oaks	d																					22 57			
Ore	d				19 14						20 14						21 14				22 14	23 02			
Hastings 4	a		19 02		19 17				20 02		20 17			21 02			21 17		22 02		22 17	23 05			
	d		19 03		19 18				20 03		20 18			21 03			21 18		22 03		22 18		23 18		
St Leonards Warrior Sq 4	d		19 06		19 21				20 06		20 21			21 06			21 21		22 06		22 21		23 21		
Bexhill 4	d		19 13		19 27				20 13		20 27			21 13			21 27		22 13		22 27		23 27		
Collington	d				19 29						20 29						21 29				22 29		23 29		
Cooden Beach	d				19 32						20 32						21 32				22 32		23 32		
Normans Bay	d																								
Pevensey Bay	d																								
Pevensey & Westham	d				19 38						20 38						21 38				22 38		23 38		
Hampden Park 4 §	d				19 43						20 43						21 43				22 43		23 43		
Eastbourne 4	a		19 29		19 48				20 29		20 48			21 29			21 48		22 29		22 48		23 48		
	d		19 34		19 55				20 34		20 55			21 34			21 55		22 34		22 55				
Hampden Park 4 §	d		19 38						20 38					21 38					22 38						
Polegate	d		19 42		20 02				20 42		21 02			21 42			22 02		22 42		23 02				
Berwick	d		19 48						20 48					21 48					22 48						
Glynde	d		19 53						20 53					21 53					22 53						
Seaford	d	19 28		19 53				20 28		20 53			21 28			21 53		22 28		22 53					
Bishopstone	d	19 30		19 55				20 30		20 55			21 30			21 55		22 30		22 55					
Newhaven Harbour	d	19 33		19 58				20 33		20 58			21 33			21 58		22 33		22 58					
Newhaven Town ⛴	d	19 35		20 00				20 35		21 00			21 35			22 00		22 35		23 00					
Southease	d			20 04																					
Lewes 4	a	19 44	19 59	20 11	20 14		←	20 44	20 59	21 09	21 14	←	21 44	21 59		22 09	22 14	22 44	22 59	23 09	23 14				
	d	19 45	20 00	20 18	20 16		20 18	20 45	21 00	21 18	21 16	21 18	21 45	22 00		22 10	22 18	22 45	23 00	23 10	23 18				
Falmer	d	19 52		→			20 25	20 52		→		21 25	21 52			22 17	22 25	22 52		23 17	23 25				
Moulsecoomb	d	19 55					20 28	20 55				21 28	21 55			22 20	22 28	22 55		23 20	23 28				
London Road (Brighton)	d	19 57					20 30	20 57				21 30	21 57			22 22	22 30	22 57		23 22	23 30				
Brighton 10	a	20 01	20 12				20 34	21 01	21 12			21 34	22 01	22 12		22 26	22 34	23 01	23 12	23 26	23 34				
Cooksbridge	d																								
Plumpton	d				20 24						21 24														
Wivelsfield 4	a				20 31		21 16				21 31	22 16													
Haywards Heath 3	a		20 30		20 35		21 00		21 30		21 35	22 00		22 30			23 00				00 01				
Gatwick Airport 10 ✈	a		20 44		20 52		21 14		21 44		21 52	22 14		22 44			23 14				00 14				
East Croydon 🚋	a		21 01		21 09		21 31		22 01		22 09	22 31		23 01			23 31				00 35				
London Bridge 4 ⊖	a		21 15		21b39		21 45		22 15		22b38	22 45		23 15			23 45								
Clapham Junction 10	a		21c24		21 24		21c54		22c24		22 24	23c10		23c37			00c10				01c02				
London Victoria 15 ⊖	a		21c31		21 31		22c01		22c31		22 31	23c16		23c46			00c18				01c09				

For general notes see front of timetable
For details of catering facilities see Directory of Train Operators

§ For additional trains between Hampden Park and Eastbourne see London to Hastings pages

b Change at East Croydon from 14 September arr. 4 minutes later

c Change at Brighton and East Croydon

Southeastern

These notes apply to Southeastern services on Tables 195 to 212. Southeastern services can be identified by the operator code SE at the head of the train column.

Spring Holiday

Monday 26 May	—	A service based on the normal Sunday timetable will operate

Late Summer Holiday

Monday 25 August	—	A service based on the normal Sunday timetable will operate

Network Diagram for Tables 195, 196

also 199 ★

DM-19/07
Design BAJS

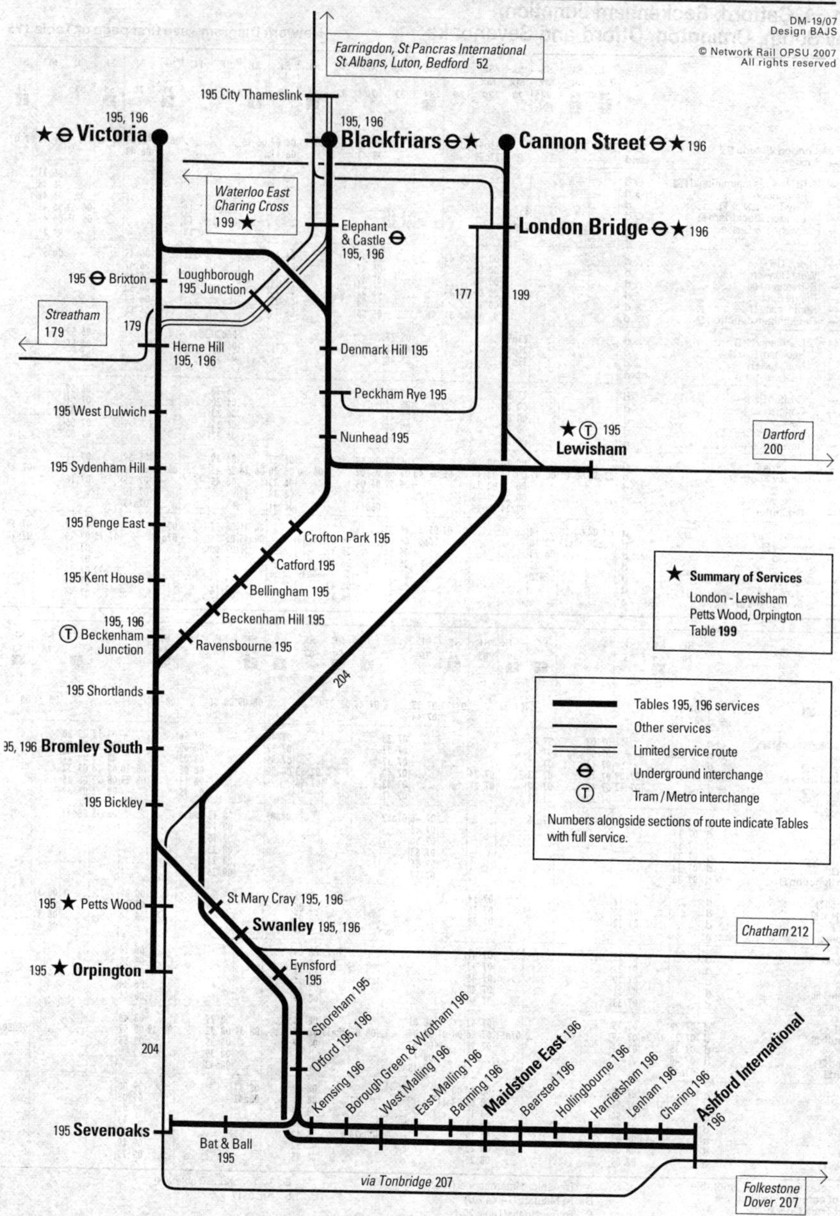

Farringdon, St Pancras International
St Albans, Luton, Bedford 52
195 City Thameslink
195, 196
★ ⊖ Victoria
195, 196
Blackfriars ⊖ ★
Cannon Street ⊖ ★ 196
Waterloo East
Charing Cross
199 ★
Elephant & Castle ⊖
195, 196
London Bridge ⊖ ★ 196
195 ⊖ Brixton
Loughborough
195 Junction
177
199
Streatham
179
179
Herne Hill
195, 196
Denmark Hill 195
Peckham Rye 195
195 West Dulwich
Nunhead 195
★ Ⓣ 195
Lewisham
Dartford
200
195 Sydenham Hill
195 Penge East
Crofton Park 195
Catford 195
195 Kent House
Bellingham 195
195, 196
Ⓣ Beckenham
Junction
Beckenham Hill 195
Ravensbourne 195
★ Summary of Services
London - Lewisham
Petts Wood, Orpington
Table 199
204
195 Shortlands
95, 196 Bromley South
195 Bickley
Tables 195, 196 services
Other services
Limited service route
Underground interchange
Tram / Metro interchange
Numbers alongside sections of route indicate Tables with full service.
195 ★ Petts Wood
St Mary Cray 195, 196
Swanley 195, 196
Chatham 212
195 ★ Orpington
Eynsford
195
Shoreham 195
Otford 195, 196
Kemsing 196
Borough Green & Wrotham 196
West Malling 196
East Malling 196
Barming 196
Maidstone East 196
Bearsted 196
Hollingbourne 196
Harrietsham 196
Lenham 196
Charing 196
Ashford International
196
204
195 Sevenoaks
Bat & Ball
195
via Tonbridge 207
Folkestone
Dover 207

For details of Bank Holiday service alterations please see first page of this table

London → Catford, Beckenham Junction, Bromley South, Orpington, Otford and Sevenoaks

Network Diagram - see first page of Table 195

Miles	Miles	Miles		SE MX 22 [1]	SE MO 54 [1]	SE MX 94 [1]	SE MX 73	SE MX 70	SE 60	SE 54 [1]	SE 83	SE 70	SE 83	SE 66 [1]	SE 70	SE 54 [1]	SE 83	FC	SE 37 [1]	SE 70	SE 64 [1]	SE 83	FC	SE 37 [1]
						A								B							C			
0	—	0	**London Victoria** 15 ⊖ d	23p39	23p42	23p51		23p53	00 35	05 32		05 36		06 10	06 04	06 16			06 39	06 36	06 47			07 07
3¼	—	—	Brixton ⊖ d					23p59				05 43			06 11					06 43				
—	—	—	St Pancras International 15 ⊖ d																				06 33	
—	—	—	Farringdon ⊖ d																				06 38	
—	—	—	City Thameslink 3 d																				06 41	
—	0	—	**London Blackfriars** 3 ⊖ d				23p43				05 27						06 08	06 11				06 42	06 46	
—	1¼	—	Elephant & Castle ⊖ d				23p46				05 30						06 12	06 14				06 45	06 49	
—	—	—	Loughborough Jn d															06 18					06 53	
4	—	—	Herne Hill 4 d					00 02	00 43			05 45			06 13			06a22		06 45			06a57	
5	—	—	West Dulwich d					00 04				05 47			06 15					06 47				
5¾	—	—	Sydenham Hill d					00 06				05 49			06 17					06 49				
7¼	—	—	Penge East d					00 09	00 48			05 52			06 20					06 52				
7¾	—	—	Kent House 4 d					00 11				05 54			06 22					06 54				
8¾	—	—	**Beckenham Junction** 4 d					00 13	00 51			05 56			06 24					06 56				
—	3¾	4¼	Denmark Hill 4 d				23p52				05 35						06b20					06 52		
—	4½	5	Peckham Rye 4 d				23p55				05 38						06 23					06 55		
—	5¼	5¾	Nunhead 4 d				23p57				05 40						06 25					06 57		
—	—	7½	Lewisham 4 a																					
—	6½	—	Crofton Park d				23p59				05 42						06 28					06 59		
—	7½	—	Catford d				00 01				05 44						06 30					07 01		
—	8¼	—	Bellingham d				00 04				05 47						06 33					07 04		
—	9	—	Beckenham Hill d				00 06				05 49						06 35					07 06		
—	9¾	—	Ravensbourne d				00 08				05 51						06 37					07 08		
10	10½	—	Shortlands 4 d				00 10	00 16			05 53	05 59			06 27		06 39			06 59		07 11		
11	11½	—	**Bromley South** 4 d	23p58	00 01	00 07	00 13	00 18	00 55	05 48	05 56	06 02		06 30	06 30	06 34	06 43		06 59	07 03	07 04	07 14		07 27
12	12½	—	Bickley 4 d				00 16	00 21			05 59	06 05			06 33		06 45			07 05		07 16		
13¾	—	—	Petts Wood 4 d				00 20	00 25				06 10			06 38					07 10				
15	—	—	**Orpington** 4 d				00a24	00a28				06a13			06a41					07a13				
—	14¾	—	St Mary Cray d	00 04	00 08	00 14			01 02	05 55	06 05					06 41	06 51		07 05			07 22		07 34
—	17½	—	**Swanley** 4 d	00a09	00a12	00 18			01a06	06a00	06 09		06 35	06 39		06a45	06 56		07a10		07 13	07 26		07a38
—	20½	—	Eynsford d			00 23					06 14		06 39				07 00					07 31		
—	22¾	—	Shoreham (Kent) d			00 27					06 17		06 43				07 04					07 34		
—	24	—	Otford 4 d			00a30					06 21		06 46	06a49			07 07				07a22	07 38		
—	25¾	—	Bat & Ball d								06 24		06 49				07 10					07 41		
—	27	—	**Sevenoaks** 4 a								06 27		06 52				07 13					07 44		

	SE 70	SE 64 [1]	SE 83	FC		FC [1]	SE 50 [1]	SE 83	SE 92 [1]	SE 70	FC	SE 96 [1]	SE 50 [1]	SE 83	FC [1]	SE 92 [1]	SE 70	FC	SE 64 [1]	SE 83	FC	FC [1]	SE 78	SE 50 [1]
		D						E																
London Victoria 15 ⊖ d	07 06	07 19					07 33		07 39	07 37		07 49	08 03			08 09	08 06		08 18				08 21	08 33
Brixton ⊖ d	07 13									07 44							08 13							
St Pancras International 15 ⊖ d				07 03		07 07					07 28				07 48			07 56			08 12	08 20		
Farringdon ⊖ d				07 08		07 12					07 32				07 52			08 00			08 16	08 24		
City Thameslink 3 d				07 11		07 17					07 37				07 55			08 03			08 19	08 27		
London Blackfriars 3 ⊖ d			07 09	07 16		07 23		07 24			07 40			07 53	08 00			08 08		08 20	08 24	08 32		
Elephant & Castle ⊖ d			07 12	07 19		07 27		07 27			07 43			07 56				08 11		08 23	08 27	08 35		
Loughborough Jn d				07 23		07 31					07 47							08 15			08 31	08 39		
Herne Hill 4 d	07 15			07a27		07a35				07 46	07a52				08a09		08 15	08a19			08a35	08a43		
West Dulwich d	07 17									07 48							08 17							
Sydenham Hill d	07 19									07 50							08 19							
Penge East d	07 22									07 53							08 22							
Kent House 4 d	07 24									07 55							08 24							
Beckenham Junction 4 d	07 26									07 57							08 26							
Denmark Hill 4 d			07 17					07 34						08 02						08 29			08 31	
Peckham Rye 4 d			07 20					07 36						08 05						08 32			08 35	
Nunhead 4 d			07 22					07 38						08 07						08 34			08 37	
Lewisham 4 a																							08 43	
Crofton Park d			07 25					07 41						08 09						08 36				
Catford d			07 27					07 43						08 12						08 39				
Bellingham d			07 29					07 46						08 15						08 42				
Beckenham Hill d			07 31					07 48						08 17						08 44				
Ravensbourne d			07 33					07 50						08 19						08 46				
Shortlands 4 d	07 29		07 35					07 52		08 01				08 21			08 29			08 48				
Bromley South 4 d	07 33	07 36	07 39				07a51	07 56	08 01	08 04		08 07	08a19	08 25		08 31	08 32		08 39	08 52				08a50
Bickley 4 d	07 35		07 41					07 58		08 07				08 27			08 35			08 55				
Petts Wood 4 d	07 40									08 12							08 39							
Orpington 4 d	07a43									08a15							08a42							
St Mary Cray d			07 47					08 04	08 07					08 33		08 37				09 00				
Swanley 4 d		07 45	07 51					08 08	08a11			08 17		08 37		08a42				09 05				
Eynsford d			07 56					08 13						08 42						09 09				
Shoreham (Kent) d			07 59					08 16						08 45						09 13				
Otford 4 d		07a54	08 03					08 19				08a26		08 49					08a57	09 16				
Bat & Ball d			08 06					08 22						08 52						09 19				
Sevenoaks 4 a			08 09					08 26						08 55						09 22				

For general notes see front of timetable
For details of catering facilities see Directory of Train Operators

A To Ashford International (Table 196)
B To Margate (Table 207)
C To Ramsgate (Table 207)
D To Canterbury West (Table 207)
E To Tonbridge (Table 204)
b Arr. 0617

For details of Bank Holiday service alterations please see first page of this table

London → Catford, Beckenham Junction, Bromley South, Orpington, Otford and Sevenoaks

Network Diagram - see first page of Table 195

Station		SE 92 [1]	SE 70	SE 94	SE 83	FC	FC		FC	SE 78	SE 50 [1]	SE 92 [1]	SE 70	FC	SE 92 [1] A	SE 92 [1] B	SE 64 [1]	SE 83	SE 70	FC	SE 78	SE 50 [1]	SE 92 [1]	SE 70	SE 94
London Victoria [15]	⊖ d	08 39	08 36	08 49						09 01	09 03	09 09	09 06			09 15	09 19		09 21		09 31	09 33	09 39	09 36	09 48
Brixton	⊖ d		08 43										09 13						09 28					09 43	
St Pancras International [15]	⊖ d					08 33	08 40		08 52					08 56						09 14					
Farringdon	⊖ d					08 37	08 44		08 56					09 00						09 18					
City Thameslink [3]	d					08 40	08 47		08 59					09 03						09 21					
London Blackfriars [3]	⊖ d				08 43	08 45	08 52		09 03					09 08				09 13		09 26					
Elephant & Castle	⊖ d				08 46		08 55		09 06					09 11	09 12			09 16		09 29					
Loughborough Jn	d						08 59		09 10					09 15						09 33					
Herne Hill [4]	d		08 46			08a54	09a03		09a13				09 17	09a19					09 32	09a39				09 46	
West Dulwich	d		08 48										09 19						09 34					09 48	
Sydenham Hill	d		08 50										09 21						09 36					09 50	
Penge East	d		08 53										09 24						09 39					09 53	
Kent House [4]	d		08 55										09 26						09 41					09 55	
Beckenham Junction [4]	d		08 57										09 28						09 43					09 57	
Denmark Hill [4]	d				08 52					09 12					09 20	09 25		09 22			09 42				
Peckham Rye [4]	d				08 55					09 14					09 22	09 28		09 25			09 44				
Nunhead [4]	d				08 57					09 16								09 27			09 46				
Lewisham [4]	a									09 25					09 31	09 34					09 52				
Crofton Park	d				08 59													09 29							
Catford	d				09 01													09 31							
Bellingham	d				09 04													09 34							
Beckenham Hill	d				09 06													09 36							
Ravensbourne	d				09 08													09 38							
Shortlands [4]	d		09 00		09 10								09 31					09 40	09 46					10 00	
Bromley South [4]	d	08 59	09 04	09 08	09 13						09a18	09 29	09 34				09 37	09 43	09 48			09a50	09 59	10 03	10 04
Bickley [4]	d		09 06		09 16								09 37					09 45	09 51					10 06	
Petts Wood [4]	d		09 12										09 42						09 55					10 10	
Orpington [4]	d		09a15										09a46						09a58					10a13	
St Mary Cray	d	09 05			09 21							09 35						09 51					10 05		
Swanley [4]	d	09a10		09 16	09 26							09a40						09 56					10a10		10 13
Eynsford	d				09 30													10 00							
Shoreham (Kent)	d				09 34													10 04							
Otford [4]	d			09a25	09 37												09a53	10 07							10a23
Bat & Ball	d				09 40													10 10							
Sevenoaks [4]	a				09 43													10 13							

Station		SE 83	FC	SE 70	FC		SE 78	SE 50 [1] ✕	SE 92 [1]	SE 70	SE 64 [1]	SE 83	FC	SE 70	FC	SE 78	SE 50 [1] ✕	SE 92 [1]	SE 70	SE 94	SE 83	FC	SE 70		
London Victoria [15]	⊖ d			09 51			10 01	10 03	10 09	10 06	10 18			10 21		10 31	10 33	10 39	10 36	10 48			10 51		
Brixton	⊖ d			09 58						10 13				10 28					10 43				10 58		
St Pancras International [15]	⊖ d		09 32		09 48								10 02		10 17							10 32			
Farringdon	⊖ d		09 36		09 52								10 07		10 22							10 37			
City Thameslink [3]	d		09 39		09 55								10 09		10 26							10 39			
London Blackfriars [3]	⊖ d	09 43	09 44		10 00							10 13	10 16		10 30						10 43	10 46			
Elephant & Castle	⊖ d	09 46	09 47		10 03							10 16	10 19		10 33						10 46	10 49			
Loughborough Jn	d		09 51		10 07								10 23		10 37							10 53			
Herne Hill [4]	d		09a55	10 00	10a11					10 15			10a27	10 30	10a41				10 45			10a57	11 00		
West Dulwich	d			10 03						10 18				10 33					10 48				11 03		
Sydenham Hill	d			10 05						10 20				10 35					10 50				11 05		
Penge East	d			10 08						10 23				10 38					10 53				11 08		
Kent House [4]	d			10 09						10 24				10 39					10 54				11 09		
Beckenham Junction [4]	d			10 11						10 26				10 41					10 56				11 11		
Denmark Hill [4]	d	09 52					10 12					10 22				10 42					10 52				
Peckham Rye [4]	d	09 55					10 14					10 25				10 44					10 55				
Nunhead [4]	d	09 57					10 16					10 27				10 46					10 57				
Lewisham [4]	a						10 22									10 52									
Crofton Park	d	10 00										10 30									11 00				
Catford	d	10 02										10 32									11 02				
Bellingham	d	10 04										10 34									11 04				
Beckenham Hill	d	10 06										10 36									11 06				
Ravensbourne	d	10 08										10 38									11 08				
Shortlands [4]	d	10 10		10 14						10 29		10 40		10 44					10 59		11 10		11 14		
Bromley South [4]	d	10 13		10 17				10a18	10 29	10 32	10 34	10 43		10 47			10a48	10 59	11 02	11 04	11 13		11 17		
Bickley [4]	d	10 16		10 20						10 35		10 46		10 50					11 05		11 16		11 20		
Petts Wood [4]	d			10 26						10 39				10 54					11 09				11 24		
Orpington [4]	d			10a29						10a42				10a57					11a12				11a27		
St Mary Cray	d	10 22							10 35			10 52						11 05			11 22				
Swanley [4]	d	10 26							10a40			10 56						11a10		11 13	11 26				
Eynsford	d	10 31										11 01									11 31				
Shoreham (Kent)	d	10 34										11 04									11 34				
Otford [4]	d	10 37									10a51	11 07								11a23	11 37				
Bat & Ball	d	10 40										11 10									11 40				
Sevenoaks [4]	a	10 43										11 13									11 43				

For general notes see front of timetable
For details of catering facilities see Directory of Train Operators

A 21 July to 29 August. To Ramsgate (Table 212)
B Until 18 July and from 1 September

For details of Bank Holiday service alterations please see first page of this table

London → Catford, Beckenham Junction, Bromley South, Orpington, Otford and Sevenoaks

Network Diagram - see first page of Table 195

Station		FC			SE 78	SE 50 [1] [trolley]	SE 92 [1]	SE 70	SE 94 [1]	SE 83	FC	SE 70	FC	SE 78	SE 50 [1] [trolley]	SE 92 [1]	SE 70	SE 94 [1]	SE 83	FC	SE 70	FC	SE 78	SE 50 [1] [trolley]
London Victoria [15]	⊖ d		and at the same minutes past each hour until		14 01	14 03	14 09	14 06	14 18			14 21		14 31	14 33	14 39	14 36	14 48			14 51		15 01	15 03
Brixton	⊖ d							14 13				14 28					14 43				14 58			
St Pancras International [15]	⊖ d	10 47									14 02		14 17							14 32		14 47		
Farringdon	⊖ d	10 52									14 07		14 22							14 37		14 52		
City Thameslink [3]	d	10 56									14 09		14 24							14 39		14 54		
London Blackfriars [3]	⊖ d	11 00								14 13	14 16		14 30						14 43	14 46		15 00		
Elephant & Castle	⊖ d	11 03								14 16	14 19		14 33						14 46	14 49		15 03		
Loughborough Jn	d	11 07									14 23		14 37							14 53		15 07		
Herne Hill [4]	d	11a11						14 15			14a27	14 30	14a41				14 45			14a57	15 00	15a11		
West Dulwich	d							14 18				14 33					14 48				15 03			
Sydenham Hill	d							14 20				14 35					14 50				15 05			
Penge East	d							14 23				14 38					14 53				15 08			
Kent House [4]	d							14 24				14 39					14 54				15 09			
Beckenham Junction [4]	d							14 26				14 41					14 56				15 11			
Denmark Hill [4]	d				14 12					14 22				14 42					14 52				15 12	
Peckham Rye [4]	d				14 14					14 25				14 44					14 55				15 14	
Nunhead [4]	d				14 16					14 27				14 46					14 57				15 16	
Lewisham [4]	a				14 22									14 52									15 22	
Crofton Park	d									14 30									15 00					
Catford	d									14 32									15 02					
Bellingham	d									14 34									15 04					
Beckenham Hill	d									14 36									15 06					
Ravensbourne	d									14 38									15 08					
Shortlands [4]	d							14 29		14 40		14 44					14 59		15 10		15 14			
Bromley South [4]	d					14a18	14 29	14 32	14 34	14 43		14 47			14a48	14 59	15 02	15 04	15 13		15 17			15a18
Bickley [4]	d							14 35		14 46		14 50					15 05		15 16		15 20			
Petts Wood [4]	d							14 39				14 54					15 09				15 24			
Orpington [4]	d							14a42				14a57					15a12				15a27			
St Mary Cray	d						14 35			14 52						15 05			15 22					
Swanley [4]	d						14a40			14 56						15a10		15 13	15 26					
Eynsford	d									15 01									15 31					
Shoreham (Kent)	d									15 04									15 34					
Otford [4]	d								14a51	15 07								15a23	15 37					
Bat & Ball	d									15 10									15 40					
Sevenoaks [4]	a									15 13									15 43					

Station		SE 92 [1]	SE 70	SE 94 [1]	SE 83	FC		SE 70	FC	SE 78	SE 50 [1] [trolley]	SE 92 [1]	SE 70	SE 94 [1]	SE 83	FC	SE 70	FC	SE 50 [1] [trolley]	SE 22	SE 70	SE 78	SE 50 [1]	SE 83	FC
London Victoria [15]	⊖ d	15 09	15 06	15 18				15 21		15 31	15 33	15 39	15 36	15 48			15 51		16 03	16 00	16 06	16 14	16 23		
Brixton	⊖ d		15 13					15 28					15 43				15 58				16 13				
St Pancras International [15]	⊖ d					15 02			15 17							15 32		15 47							16 02
Farringdon	⊖ d					15 07			15 22							15 37		15 52							16 07
City Thameslink [3]	d					15 09			15 24							15 39		15 54							16 09
London Blackfriars [3]	⊖ d				15 13	15 16			15 30						15 43	15 46		16 00						16 09	16 16
Elephant & Castle	⊖ d				15 16	15 19			15 33						15 46	15 49		16 03						16 13	16 19
Loughborough Jn	d					15 23			15 37							15 53		16 07							16 23
Herne Hill [4]	d		15 15			15a27		15 30	15a41				15 45			15a57	16 00	16a11			16 15				16a27
West Dulwich	d		15 18					15 33					15 48				16 03				16 18				
Sydenham Hill	d		15 20					15 35					15 50				16 05				16 20				
Penge East	d		15 23					15 38					15 53				16 08				16 23				
Kent House [4]	d		15 24					15 39					15 54				16 09				16 24				
Beckenham Junction [4]	d		15 26					15 41					15 56				16 11				16 26				
Denmark Hill [4]	d				15 22					15 42					15 52							16 27		16 18	
Peckham Rye [4]	d				15 25					15 44					15 55							16 29		16 21	
Nunhead [4]	d				15 27					15 46					15 57							16 31		16 24	
Lewisham [4]	a									15 52												16 40			
Crofton Park	d				15 30										16 00									16 26	
Catford	d				15 32										16 02									16 28	
Bellingham	d				15 34										16 04									16 31	
Beckenham Hill	d				15 36										16 06									16 33	
Ravensbourne	d				15 38										16 08									16 35	
Shortlands [4]	d		15 29		15 40			15 44					15 59		16 10		16 14				16 29			16 37	
Bromley South [4]	d	15 29	15 32	15 34	15 43			15 47			15a48	16 00	16 02	16 04	16 13		16 17		16a18	16 23	16 32		16a39	16 40	
Bickley [4]	d		15 35		15 46			15 50					16 05		16 16		16 20				16 35			16 43	
Petts Wood [4]	d		15 39					15 54					16 09				16 24				16 39				
Orpington [4]	d		15a42					15a57					16a12				16a27				16b44				
St Mary Cray	d	15 35			15 52							16 06			16 22					16 30				16 48	
Swanley [4]	d	15a40		15 43	15 56							16a11		16 13	16 26					16a34				16 53	
Eynsford	d				16 01										16 31									16 57	
Shoreham (Kent)	d				16 04										16 34									17 01	
Otford [4]	d			15a52	16 07									16a23	16 37									17 04	
Bat & Ball	d				16 10										16 40									17 07	
Sevenoaks [4]	a				16 13										16 43									17 12	

For general notes see front of timetable
For details of catering facilities see Directory of Train Operators

b Until 10 October arr 2 minutes earlier

For details of Bank Holiday service alterations please see first page of this table

London → Catford, Beckenham Junction, Bromley South, Orpington, Otford and Sevenoaks

Network Diagram - see first page of Table 195

	SE 22 [1]	SE 96 [1]	SE 70	FC	SE 30 [1]	SE 73	FC		SE 22	SE 83	FC [1]	SE 94 [1]	SE 70	SE 3	FC	SE 78	SE 40 [1] A	SE 70	SE 78	SE 94 [1]	SE 83	FC	SE 51 [1]	SE 21 B
London Victoria [15] ⊖ d	16 22	16 27	16 26		16 42				16 45			16 56	16 51			17 00	17 05	17 12	17 19	17 22			17 27	
Brixton ⊖ d			16 33										16 58					17 19						
St Pancras International [15] ⊖ d				16 15			16 32				16 36				16 45							17 01		
Farringdon ⊖ d				16 20			16 37				16 40				16 50							17 06		
City Thameslink [3] d				16 21			16 39				16 43				16 52						17 07	17 11		
London Blackfriars [3] ⊖ d				16 26		16 27	16 42			16 42	16 46			16 54	16 58						17 10	17 14		17 24
Elephant & Castle ⊖ d				16 30		16 31	16 45			16 46	16 50			16 58	17 02						17 14	17 17		17 28
Loughborough Jn d				16 34			16 49				16 54			17 01	17 06							17 21		
Herne Hill [4] d			16 35	16a38			16a53				16a57		17 00	17 05	17a10		17 13	17 21				17a25		17 36
West Dulwich d			16 37										17 02	17 08				17 23						
Sydenham Hill d			16 39										17 04	17 10				17 25						
Penge East d			16 42										17 07	17 13				17 28						
Kent House [4] d			16 44										17 09	17 15				17 30						
Beckenham Junction [4] d			16 47										17 12	17b19				17 33						
Denmark Hill [4] d						16 36				16 51						17 09			17 28		17 19			
Peckham Rye [4] d						16 40				16 55						17 13			17 31		17 23			
Nunhead [4] d						16 42				16 57						17 15			17 33		17 25			
Lewisham [4] a																17 23			17 43					
Crofton Park d						16 45				16 59											17 28			
Catford d						16 47				17 01											17 31			
Bellingham d						16 50				17 04											17 35			
Beckenham Hill d						16 52				17 06											17 37			
Ravensbourne d						16 54				17 08											17 39			
Shortlands [4] d			16 50			16 56				17 11			17 15					17 36			17 41			
Bromley South [4] d	16 44	16 48	16 53		16a58	17 00			17 03	17 15		17 15	17 18				17 24	17 39		17 40	17 46		17a44	17 48
Bickley [4] d			16 56			17 02				17 17			17 21					17 42			17 49			
Petts Wood [4] d			17 01			17 07							17 25					17 49						
Orpington [4] d			17b06			17a12							17c30					17a53						
St Mary Cray d	16 50								17 10	17 25							17 30			17 47	17 56			17 57
Swanley [4] d	16a55	16 57							17a14	17 30							17a35			17 52	18 01			18a01
Eynsford d										17 34											18 06			
Shoreham (Kent) d										17 38											18 09			
Otford [4] d		17a07								17 41		17a33								18a01	18 13			
Bat & Ball d										17 44											18 16			
Sevenoaks [4] a										17b49											18 19			

	FC	SE 96	SE 70	SE 83	FC	SE 78	SE 50 [1]	SE 22	SE 96 [1]		SE 70	SE 3	FC [1]	SE 97 [1]	SE 51 [1]	SE 70	FC	SE 83	SE 21 [1] B	SE 83	FC	SE 78	SE 94 [1]	SE 70
London Victoria [15] ⊖ d		17 32	17 35			17 41	17 49	17 48	17 58		17 52				18 04	18 02						18 08	18 18	18 21
Brixton ⊖ d			17 42								17 59					18 09								18 28
St Pancras International [15] ⊖ d	17 17				17 31								17 46				17 51				18 03			
Farringdon ⊖ d	17 22				17 36								17 50				17 56				18 08			
City Thameslink [3] d	17 24				17 38							17 47	17 53				17 58				18 10			
London Blackfriars [3] ⊖ d	17 30			17 36	17 42							17 52	17 57	18 00			18 02	18 05	18 11		18 14			
Elephant & Castle ⊖ d	17 34			17 39	17 45							17 56		18 04			18 06	18 08	18 15		18 18			
Loughborough Jn d	17 38				17 49							18 00					18 10				18 21			
Herne Hill [4] d	17a41		17 45		17a53						18 02	18 04	18a06			18 11	18a13		18 22		18a26			18 30
West Dulwich d			17 47								18 05	18 08												18 33
Sydenham Hill d			17 49								18 07	18 10												18 35
Penge East d			17 52								18 10	18 13												18 38
Kent House [4] d			17 54								18 11	18 14												18 40
Beckenham Junction [4] d		17 46	17 57								18 14	18a17				18 20								18 42
Denmark Hill [4] d				17 45		17 51												18 14				18 17		
Peckham Rye [4] d				17 48		17 54												18 17				18 20		
Nunhead [4] d				17 50		17 56												18 19				18 22		
Lewisham [4] a						18 05																18 28		
Crofton Park d				17 52														18 22		←				
Catford d				17 54														18 24 →		18 24				
Bellingham d				17 57																18 26				
Beckenham Hill d				17 59																18 28				
Ravensbourne d				18 01																18 30				
Shortlands [4] d			18 00	18 03							18 17					18 23				18 32				18 45
Bromley South [4] d		17 51	18 03	18 06			18a05	18 09	18 18		18 20			18 22	18a23	18 27			18 33	18 36			18 36	18 48
Bickley [4] d			18 05	18 09							18 23					18 30				18 38				18 51
Petts Wood [4] d			18 10								18 29					18 35								18 56
Orpington [4] d			18a15								18a33					18c41								19a01
St Mary Cray d		18 00		18 15				18 16						18 28					18 39	18 44			18 43	
Swanley [4] d		18 05		18 20				18a20						18 33					18a44	18e51			18 48	
Eynsford d				18 24																18 56				
Shoreham (Kent) d				18 28																18 59				
Otford [4] d		18a17		18 32					18a36					18a42						19 03			18a58	
Bat & Ball d				18 36																19 06				
Sevenoaks [4] a				18b42																19c11				

For general notes see front of timetable
For details of catering facilities see Directory of Train Operators

A To Canterbury East (Table 212)
B To Gillingham (Kent) (Table 212)
b Until 10 October arr 2 minutes earlier
c Until 10 October arr 1 minute earlier
e Arr. 1848

For details of Bank Holiday service alterations please see first page of this table

London → Catford, Beckenham Junction, Bromley South, Orpington, Otford and Sevenoaks

Network Diagram - see first page of Table 195

		SE 50 1	SE 83	FC	SE 92 1	SE 70	SE 94 1	SE 83	FC	SE 78	SE 70	FC		SE 50 1	SE 92 1	SE 70	FC	SE 78	SE 94 1	SE 83	SE 70	FC	SE 50 1	SE 92 1	SE 70
London Victoria 15	⊖ d	18 33			18 41	18 38	18 48			18 46	18 51			19 04	19 09	19 07		19 16	19 18		19 22		19 34	19 39	19 37
Brixton	⊖ d					18 45					18 58					19 14					19 29				19 44
St Pancras International 15	⊖ d			18 15					18 33			18 45					19 05					19 17			
Farringdon	⊖ d			18 20					18 38			18 50					19 10					19 22			
City Thameslink 3	d			18 22					18 40			18 52					19 12					19 24			
London Blackfriars 3	⊖ d		18 23	18 26				18 43	18 44			18 56					19 16			19 17		19 30			
Elephant & Castle	⊖ d		18 26	18 30				18 46	18 48			19 00					19 19			19 20		19 33			
Loughborough Jn	d			18 34					18 52			19 04					19 23					19 37			
Herne Hill 4	d			18a37		18 47			18a56		19 00	19a08				19 16	19a27				19 31	19a41			19 46
West Dulwich	d					18 49					19 03					19 18					19 33				19 48
Sydenham Hill	d					18 51					19 05					19 20					19 35				19 50
Penge East	d					18 54					19 08					19 23					19 38				19 53
Kent House 4	d					18 56					19 09					19 25					19 40				19 55
Beckenham Junction 4	d					18 58					19 11					19 27					19 42				19 57
Denmark Hill 4	d		18 32					18 52		18 57								19 27		19 25					
Peckham Rye 4	d		18 35					18 55		19 00								19 31		19 28					
Nunhead 4	d		18 37					18 57		19 02								19 33		19 30					
Lewisham 4	a									19 08								19 44							
Crofton Park	d		18 39					18 59												19 32					
Catford	d		18 42					19 01												19 34					
Bellingham	d		18 44					19 04												19 37					
Beckenham Hill	d		18 46					19 06												19 39					
Ravensbourne	d		18 48					19 08												19 41					
Shortlands 4	d		18 50			19 02		19 10			19 15					19 31				19 43	19 46				20 01
Bromley South 4	d	18a49	18 54		19 01	19 05	19 06	19 13			19 18			19a19	19 29	19 34			19 35	19 46	19 49		19a49	19 59	20 04
Bickley 4	d		18 56			19 07		19 16			19 21					19 37				19 48	19 52				20 07
Petts Wood 4	d					19 12					19 25					19 41					19 56				20 11
Orpington 4	d					19b17					19a31					19a44					19a59				20a14
St Mary Cray	d		19 03		19 10		19 12	19 21							19 35					19 54				20 05	
Swanley 4	d		19 07		19a15		19 16	19 26							19a40				19 44	19 58				20a10	
Eynsford	d		19 12					19 30												20 03					
Shoreham (Kent)	d		19 15					19 34												20 06					
Otford 4	d		19 18				19a26	19 37											19a53	20 10					
Bat & Ball	d		19 21					19 40												20 13					
Sevenoaks 4	a		19b26					19b45												20 16					

		FC	SE 78	SE 94 1	SE 83	SE 70	FC	SE 50 1	SE 92 1	SE 94 1	SE 83	FC	SE 70	FC		SE 50 1	SE 92 1	SE 94 1	SE 83	FC	SE 70	SE 50 1	SE 96 1	SE 83	FC
London Victoria 15	⊖ d		19 46	19 48		19 52		20 03	20 09	20 18			20 22			20 34	20 39	20 48			20 52	21 03	21 09		
Brixton	⊖ d					19 59							20 29								20 59				
St Pancras International 15	⊖ d	19 35					19 48					20 05		20 17						20 35					21 05
Farringdon	⊖ d	19 40					19 52					20 10		20 22						20 40					21 10
City Thameslink 3	d	19 42					19 55					20 12		20 24						20 42					21 12
London Blackfriars 3	⊖ d	19 46			19 47		20 00				20 13	20 16		20 30					20 43	20 46				21 13	21 16
Elephant & Castle	⊖ d	19 49			19 50		20 03				20 16	20 19		20 33					20 46	20 49				21 16	21 19
Loughborough Jn	d	19 53					20 07					20 23		20 37						20 53					21 23
Herne Hill 4	d	19a57				20 01	20a11					20a27	20 31	20a41						20a57	21 01				21a27
West Dulwich	d					20 03							20 33								21 03				
Sydenham Hill	d					20 05							20 35								21 05				
Penge East	d					20 08							20 38								21 08				
Kent House 4	d					20 10							20 40								21 10				
Beckenham Junction 4	d					20 12				20 32			20 42					21 02			21 12				
Denmark Hill 4	d		19 57		19 55						20 22								20 52					21 22	
Peckham Rye 4	d		20 01		19 58						20 25								20 55					21 25	
Nunhead 4	d		20 03		20 00						20 27								20 57					21 27	
Lewisham 4	a		20 14																						
Crofton Park	d				20 02						20 29								20 59					21 29	
Catford	d				20 04						20 31								21 01					21 31	
Bellingham	d				20 07						20 34								21 04					21 34	
Beckenham Hill	d				20 09						20 36								21 06					21 36	
Ravensbourne	d				20 11						20 38								21 08					21 38	
Shortlands 4	d				20 13	20 15					20 40		20 45						21 10		21 15			21 40	
Bromley South 4	d			20 07	20 16	20 19		20a18	20 29	20 37	20 43		20 48			20a49	20 59	21 07	21 13		21 17	21a18	21 29	21 43	
Bickley 4	d				20 18	20 22					20 46		20 51						21 16		21 20			21 46	
Petts Wood 4	d					20 26							20 55								21 24				
Orpington 4	d					20a29							20a58								21a27				
St Mary Cray	d				20 24				20 35		20 51						21 05		21 21				21 35	21 51	
Swanley 4	d				20 28				20a40	20 45	20 56						21a10		21 26				21 40	21 56	
Eynsford	d				20 33						21 00								21 30					22 00	
Shoreham (Kent)	d				20 36						21 04								21 34					22 04	
Otford 4	d			20a23	20 40					20a54	21 08							21a23	21 37				21a49	22 07	
Bat & Ball	d				20 43						21 11								21 40					22 10	
Sevenoaks 4	a				20 46						21 15								21 43					22 13	

For general notes see front of timetable
For details of catering facilities see Directory of Train Operators

b Until 10 October arr 2 minutes earlier

For details of Bank Holiday service alterations please see first page of this table

London → Catford, Beckenham Junction, Bromley South, Orpington, Otford and Sevenoaks

Network Diagram - see first page of Table 195

		SE 70	SE 37 1	SE 83	FC	SE 70	SE 50 1	SE 96 1	SE 83	FC	SE 70	SE 92 1	SE 73	FC	SE 70	SE 50 1		SE 66 1 A	SE 73	FC	SE 70	SE 22 1	SE 94 1 B	SE 73	SE 70
London Victoria 15	⊖ d	21 22	21 39			21 52	22 03	22 09			22 22	22 39			22 52	23 03		23 11			23 22	23 39	23 51		23 53
Brixton	⊖ d	21 29				21 59					22 29				22 59						23 29				23 59
St Pancras International 15	⊖ d				21 35					22 05				22 36						23 06					
Farringdon	⊖ d				21 40					22 10				22 40						23 10					
City Thameslink 3	d				21 42					22 12				22 42											
London Blackfriars 3	⊖ d			21 43	21 46				22 13	22 16			22 43	22 46					23 13	23 16				23 43	
Elephant & Castle	⊖ d			21 46	21 49				22 16	22 19			22 46	22 49					23 16	23 19				23 46	
Loughborough Jn	d				21 53					22 23				22 53						23s23					
Herne Hill 4	d	21 31			21a57	22 01				22a27	22 31			22a57	23 01					23a27	23 31				00 02
West Dulwich	d	21 33				22 03					22 33				23 03						23 33				00 04
Sydenham Hill	d	21 35				22 05					22 35				23 05						23 35				00 06
Penge East	d	21 38				22 08					22 38				23 08						23 38				00 09
Kent House 4	d	21 40				22 10					22 40				23 10						23 40				00 11
Beckenham Junction 4	🚋 d	21 42				22 12					22 42				23 12						23 42				00 13
Denmark Hill 4	d			21 52					22 22				22 52						23 22					23 52	
Peckham Rye 4	d			21 55					22 25				22 55						23 25					23 55	
Nunhead 4	d			21 57					22 27				22 57						23 27					23 57	
Lewisham 4	🚋 a																								
Crofton Park	d			21 59					22 29				22 59						23 29					23 59	
Catford	d			22 01					22 31				23 01						23 31					00 01	
Bellingham	d			22 04					22 34				23 04						23 34					00 04	
Beckenham Hill	d			22 06					22 36				23 06						23 36					00 06	
Ravensbourne	d			22 08					22 38				23 08						23 38					00 08	
Shortlands 4	d	21 45		22 10		22 15			22 40		22 45		23 10		23 15				23 40		23 45			00 10	00 16
Bromley South 4	d	21 48	21 59	22 13		22 18	22a18	22 29	22 43		22 48	22 59	23 13		23 18	23a18		23 30	23 43		23 48	23 58	00 07	00 13	00 18
Bickley 4	d	21 51		22 15		22 21			22 46		22 51		23 16		23 21				23 46		23 51			00 16	00 21
Petts Wood 4	d	21 55				22 25					22 55		23 20		23 26				23 50		23 55			00 20	00 25
Orpington 4	d	21a58				22a28					22a58		23a24		23a30				23a54		23a58			00a24	00a28
St Mary Cray	d		22 05	22 21				22 35	22 51			23 05						23 37				00 04	00 14		
Swanley 4	d		22a10	22 25				22 40	22 56			23a10						23 41				00a09	00 18		
Eynsford	d			22 29					23 00														00 23		
Shoreham (Kent)	d			22 33					23 04														00 27		
Otford 4	d			22 36				22a49	23 07									23a50					00a30		
Bat & Ball	d			22 39					23 10																
Sevenoaks 4	a			22 42					23 13																

Saturdays

		SE 22 1	SE 94 1 B	SE 73	SE 70	SE 60	SE 4 1	SE 55 1	SE 70	FC	SE 94 1 C	SE 82	SE 37 1	SE 83		FC	SE 70	SE 92	SE 64 1 C	SE 83	FC	SE 70	FC	SE 50 1	SE 92 1
London Victoria 15	⊖ d	23p39	23p51		23p53	00 35		05 39	05 51		06 18	06 13	06 39				06 51	07 09	07 18			07 21		07 33	07 39
Brixton	⊖ d				23p59				05 58								06 58					07 28			
St Pancras International 15	⊖ d															06 35					07 05				
Farringdon	⊖ d															06 40					07 10				
City Thameslink 3	d																								
London Blackfriars 3	⊖ d			23p43						06 16				06 43		06 46				07 13	07 16		07 30		
Elephant & Castle	⊖ d			23p46						06 19				06 46		06 49				07 16	07 19		07 33		
Loughborough Jn	d															06 53					07 23		07 37		
Herne Hill 4	d				00 02	00 43			06 00	06a26						06a57	07 00				07a27	07 30	07a41		
West Dulwich	d				00 04				06 03								07 03					07 33			
Sydenham Hill	d				00 06				06 05								07 05					07 35			
Penge East	d				00 09	00 48			06 08								07 08					07 38			
Kent House 4	d				00 11				06 09								07 09					07 39			
Beckenham Junction 4	🚋 d				00 13	00 51			06 11								07 11					07 41			
Denmark Hill 4	d			23p52								06 22		06 52						07 22					
Peckham Rye 4	d			23p55								06 25		06 55						07 25					
Nunhead 4	d			23p57								06 27		06 57						07 27					
Lewisham 4	🚋 a																								
Crofton Park	d			23p59								06 30		07 00						07 30					
Catford	d			00 01								06 32		07 02						07 32					
Bellingham	d			00 04								06 34		07 04						07 34					
Beckenham Hill	d			00 06								06 36		07 06						07 36					
Ravensbourne	d			00 08								06 38		07 08						07 38					
Shortlands 4	d			00 10	00 16				06 14			06 40		07 10			07 14			07 40		07 44			
Bromley South 4	d	23p58	00 07	00 13	00 18	00 55		05 59	06 17		06 34	06 43	06 59	07 13			07 17	07 29	07 34	07 43		07 47		07a48	07 59
Bickley 4	d			00 16	00 21				06 20			06 46		07 16			07 20			07 46		07 50			
Petts Wood 4	d			00 20	00 25				06 24								07 24					07 54			
Orpington 4	d			00a24	00a28		05 58		06a27								07a27					07a57			
St Mary Cray	d	00 04	00 14			01 02		06 05			06 41	06 52	07 05	07 22				07 35	07 41	07 52					08 05
Swanley 4	d	00a09	00 18			01a06		06a10			06 45	06 56	07a10	07 26				07a40	07 45	07 56					08a10
Eynsford	d		00 23									07 01		07 31						08 01					
Shoreham (Kent)	d		00 27									07 04		07 34						08 04					
Otford 4	d		00a30								06a54	07 07		07 37					07a54	08 07					
Bat & Ball	d											07 10		07 40						08 10					
Sevenoaks 4	a						06 07					07 13		07 43						08 13					

For general notes see front of timetable
For details of catering facilities see Directory of Train Operators

A To Canterbury West (Table 207)
B To Ashford International (Table 196)
C To Ramsgate (Table 207)

London → Catford, Beckenham Junction, Bromley South, Orpington, Otford and Sevenoaks

Network Diagram - see first page of Table 195

		SE 94 1	SE 83	FC	SE 70	FC		SE 78	SE 50 1	SE 92 1	SE 70	SE 64 1	SE 83	FC	SE 70	FC	SE 78	SE 50 1	SE 92 1	SE 70		SE 94	SE 83	FC	SE 70
London Victoria 15	⊖ d	07 48			07 51			08 01	08 03	08 09	08 06	08 18			08 21		08 31	08 33	08 39	08 36		08 48			08 51
Brixton	⊖ d				07 58						08 13				08 28					08 43					08 58
St Pancras International 15	⊖ d			07 32		07 47								08 02		08 17								08 32	
Farringdon	⊖ d			07 37		07 52								08 07		08 22								08 37	
City Thameslink 3	d																								
London Blackfriars 3	⊖ d		07 43	07b46		08 00							08 13	08c16		08 30							08 43	08e46	
Elephant & Castle	⊖ d		07 46	07 49		08 03							08 16	08 19		08 33							08 46	08 49	
Loughborough Jn	d			07 53		08 07								08 23		08 37								08 53	
Herne Hill 4	d			07a57	08 00	08a11					08 15			08a27	08 30	08a41				08 45				08a57	09 00
West Dulwich	d				08 03						08 18				08 33					08 48					09 03
Sydenham Hill	d				08 05						08 20				08 35					08 50					09 05
Penge East	d				08 08						08 23				08 38					08 53					09 08
Kent House 4	d				08 09						08 24				08 39					08 54					09 09
Beckenham Junction 4	🚊 d				08 11						08 26				08 41					08 56					09 11
Denmark Hill 4	d		07 52					08 12					08 22				08 42						08 52		
Peckham Rye 4	d		07 55					08 14					08 25				08 44						08 55		
Nunhead 4	d		07 57					08 16					08 27				08 46						08 57		
Lewisham 4	🚊 a							08 22									08 52								
Crofton Park	d		08 00										08 30										09 00		
Catford	d		08 02										08 32										09 02		
Bellingham	d		08 04										08 34										09 04		
Beckenham Hill	d		08 06										08 36										09 06		
Ravensbourne	d		08 08										08 38										09 08		
Shortlands 4	d		08 10		08 14						08 29		08 40		08 44					08 59			09 10		09 14
Bromley South 4	d	08 04	08 13		08 17				08a18	08 29	08 32	08 34	08 43		08 47			08a48	08 59	09 02		09 04	09 13		09 17
Bickley 4	d		08 16		08 20						08 35		08 46		08 50					09 05			09 16		09 20
Petts Wood 4	d				08 24						08 39				08 54					09 09					09 24
Orpington 4	d				08a27						08a42				08a57					09a12					09a27
St Mary Cray	d		08 22							08 35			08 52						09 05				09 22		
Swanley 4	d	08 13	08 26							08a40			08 56						09a10			09 13	09 26		
Eynsford	d		08 31										09 01										09 31		
Shoreham (Kent)	d		08 34										09 04										09 34		
Otford 4	d	08a23	08 37									08a51	09 07									09a23	09 37		
Bat & Ball	d		08 40										09 10										09 40		
Sevenoaks 4	a		08 43										09 13										09 43		

		FC	SE 78	SE 50 1	SE 92 1	SE 70	SE 64 1	SE 83	FC	SE 70	FC	SE 78		SE 50 1		SE 92 1	SE 70	SE 94	SE 83	FC	SE 70	FC	SE 78	SE 50 1	SE 92 1
London Victoria 15	⊖ d		09 01	09 03	09 09	09 06	09 18			09 21		09 31		09 33		09 39	09 36	09 48			09 51		10 01	10 03	10 09
Brixton	⊖ d					09 13				09 28							09 43				09 58				
St Pancras International 15	⊖ d	08 47							09 02		09 17									09 32		09 47			
Farringdon	⊖ d	08 52							09 07		09 22									09 37		09 52			
City Thameslink 3	d								09 09		09 24									09 39		09 54			
London Blackfriars 3	⊖ d	09 00						09 13	09 16		09 30								09 43	09 46		10 00			
Elephant & Castle	⊖ d	09 03						09 16	09 19		09 33								09 46	09 49		10 03			
Loughborough Jn	d	09 07							09 23		09 37									09 53		10 07			
Herne Hill 4	d	09a11				09 15			09a27	09 30	09a41						09 45			09a57	10 00	10a11			
West Dulwich	d					09 18				09 33							09 48				10 03				
Sydenham Hill	d					09 20				09 35							09 50				10 05				
Penge East	d					09 23				09 38							09 53				10 08				
Kent House 4	d					09 24				09 39							09 54				10 09				
Beckenham Junction 4	🚊 d					09 26				09 41							09 56				10 11				
Denmark Hill 4	d		09 12					09 22				09 42							09 52				10 12		
Peckham Rye 4	d		09 14					09 25				09 44							09 55				10 14		
Nunhead 4	d		09 16					09 27				09 46							09 57				10 16		
Lewisham 4	🚊 a		09 22									09 52											10 22		
Crofton Park	d							09 30											10 00						
Catford	d							09 32											10 02						
Bellingham	d							09 34											10 04						
Beckenham Hill	d							09 36											10 06						
Ravensbourne	d							09 38											10 08						
Shortlands 4	d					09 29		09 40		09 44							09 59		10 10		10 14				
Bromley South 4	d			09a18	09 29	09 32	09 34	09 43		09 47				09a48		09 59	10 02	10 04	10 13		10 17			10a18	10 29
Bickley 4	d					09 35		09 46		09 50							10 05		10 16		10 20				
Petts Wood 4	d					09 39				09 54							10 09				10 24				
Orpington 4	d					09a42				09a57							10a12				10a27				
St Mary Cray	d				09 35			09 52								10 05			10 22						10 35
Swanley 4	d				09a40			09 56								10a10		10 13	10 26						10a40
Eynsford	d							10 01											10 31						
Shoreham (Kent)	d							10 04											10 34						
Otford 4	d						09a51	10 07										10a23	10 37						
Bat & Ball	d							10 10											10 40						
Sevenoaks 4	a							10 13											10 43						

For general notes see front of timetable
For details of catering facilities see Directory of Train Operators

b Arr. 0743
c Arr. 0813
e Arr. 0843

London → Catford, Beckenham Junction, Bromley South, Orpington, Otford and Sevenoaks

Network Diagram - see first page of Table 195

	SE 70	SE 64 [1]	SE 83	FC	SE 70	FC	SE 78	SE 50 [1]			SE 92 [1]	SE 70	SE 94 [1]	SE 83	FC	SE 70	FC	SE 78	SE 50 [1]	SE 70	SE 96 [1]	SE 83	FC
London Victoria [15] ⊖ d	10 06	10 18			10 21		10 31	10 33	and at the same minutes past each hour until		18 39	18 36	18 48			18 51		19 01	19 03	19 06	19 18		
Brixton ⊖ d	10 13				10 28							18 43				18 58				19 13			
St Pancras International [15] ⊖ d				10 02		10 17									18 32		18 47						19 05
Farringdon ⊖ d				10 07		10 22									18 37		18 52						19 10
City Thameslink [3] d				10 09		10 24									18 39		18 54						19 12
London Blackfriars [3] ⊖ d			10 13	10 16		10 30								18 43	18 46		19 00					19 13	19 16
Elephant & Castle ⊖ d			10 16	10 19		10 33								18 46	18 49		19 03					19 16	19 19
Loughborough Jn d				10 23		10 37									18 53		19 07						19 23
Herne Hill [4] d	10 15			10a27	10 30	10a41						18 45			18a57	19 00	19a11			19 15			19a27
West Dulwich d	10 18				10 33							18 48				19 03				19 18			
Sydenham Hill d	10 20				10 35							18 50				19 05				19 20			
Penge East d	10 23				10 38							18 53				19 08				19 23			
Kent House [4] d	10 24				10 39							18 54				19 09				19 24			
Beckenham Junction [4] d	10 26				10 41							18 56				19 11				19 26			
Denmark Hill [4] d			10 22				10 42							18 52				19 12				19 22	
Peckham Rye [4] d			10 25				10 44							18 55				19 14				19 25	
Nunhead [4] d			10 27				10 46							18 57				19 16				19 27	
Lewisham [4] a							10 52											19 22					
Crofton Park d			10 30											19 00								19 30	
Catford d			10 32											19 02								19 32	
Bellingham d			10 34											19 04								19 34	
Beckenham Hill d			10 36											19 06								19 36	
Ravensbourne d			10 38											19 08								19 38	
Shortlands [4] d	10 29		10 40		10 44							18 59		19 10		19 14				19 29		19 40	
Bromley South [4] d	10 32	10 34	10 43		10 47			10a48			18 59	19 02	19 04	19 13		19 17			19a18	19 32	19 34	19 43	
Bickley [4] d	10 35		10 46		10 50							19 05		19 16		19 20				19 35		19 46	
Petts Wood [4] d	10 39				10 54							19 09				19 24				19 39			
Orpington [4] d	10a42				10a57							19a12				19a27				19a42			
St Mary Cray d			10 52								19 05			19 22							19 41	19 52	
Swanley [4] d			10 56								19a10		19 13	19 26							19 45	19 56	
Eynsford d			11 01											19 31								20 01	
Shoreham (Kent) d			11 04											19 34								20 04	
Otford [4] d		10a51	11 07										19a23	19 37							19a54	20 07	
Bat & Ball d			11 10											19 40								20 10	
Sevenoaks [4] a			11 13											19 43								20 13	

	SE 70	SE 78		SE 92 [1]	SE 70	SE 83	FC	SE 70	SE 50 [1]	SE 96 [1]	SE 83	FC	SE 70	SE 92 [1]	SE 83	FC		SE 70	SE 50 [1]	SE 96 [1]	SE 83	FC	SE 70	SE 92 [1]
London Victoria [15] ⊖ d	19 21	19 31		19 39	19 36			19 51	20 03	20 18			20 21	20 39				20 51	21 03	21 18			21 21	21 39
Brixton ⊖ d	19 28				19 43			19 58					20 28					20 58					21 28	
St Pancras International [15] ⊖ d							19 35					20 05				20 35						21 05		
Farringdon ⊖ d							19 40					20 10				20 40						21 10		
City Thameslink [3] d							19 42					20 12				20 42								
London Blackfriars [3] ⊖ d						19 43	19 46				20 13	20 16			20 43	20 46					21 13	21 16		
Elephant & Castle ⊖ d						19 46	19 49				20 16	20 19			20 46	20 49					21 16	21 19		
Loughborough Jn d							19 53					20 23				20 53						21 23		
Herne Hill [4] d	19 30				19 45		19a57	20 00				20a27	20 30			20a57		21 00				21a27	21 30	
West Dulwich d	19 33				19 48			20 03					20 33					21 03					21 33	
Sydenham Hill d	19 35				19 50			20 05					20 35					21 05					21 35	
Penge East d	19 38				19 53			20 08					20 38					21 08					21 38	
Kent House [4] d	19 39				19 54			20 09					20 39					21 09					21 39	
Beckenham Junction [4] d	19 41				19 56			20 11					20 41					21 11					21 41	
Denmark Hill [4] d		19 42				19 52					20 22				20 52						21 22			
Peckham Rye [4] d		19 44				19 55					20 25				20 55						21 25			
Nunhead [4] d		19 46				19 57					20 27				20 57						21 27			
Lewisham [4] a		19 53																						
Crofton Park d						20 00					20 30				21 00						21 30			
Catford d						20 02					20 32				21 02						21 32			
Bellingham d						20 04					20 34				21 04						21 34			
Beckenham Hill d						20 06					20 36				21 06						21 36			
Ravensbourne d						20 08					20 38				21 08						21 38			
Shortlands [4] d	19 44				19 59	20 10		20 14			20 40		20 44		21 10			21 14			21 40		21 44	
Bromley South [4] d	19 47			19 59	20 02	20 13		20 17	20a18	20 34	20 43		20 47	20 59	21 13			21 17	21a18	21 34	21 43		21 47	21 59
Bickley [4] d	19 50				20 05	20 16		20 20			20 46		20 50		21 16			21 20			21 46		21 50	
Petts Wood [4] d	19 54				20 09			20 24					20 54					21 24					21 54	
Orpington [4] d	19a57				20a12			20a27					20a57					21a27					21a57	
St Mary Cray d				20 05		20 22				20 41	20 52			21 05	21 22					21 41	21 52			22 05
Swanley [4] d				20a10		20 26				20 45	20 56			21a10	21 26					21 45	21 56			22a10
Eynsford d						20 31					21 01				21 31						22 01			
Shoreham (Kent) d						20 34					21 04				21 34						22 04			
Otford [4] d						20 37				20a54	21 07				21 37					21a54	22 07			
Bat & Ball d						20 40					21 10				21 40						22 10			
Sevenoaks [4] a						20 43					21 13				21 43						22 13			

For general notes see front of timetable
For details of catering facilities see Directory of Train Operators

Table 195

London → Catford, Beckenham Junction, Bromley South, Orpington, Otford and Sevenoaks

Network Diagram - see first page of Table 195

Saturdays

Station		SE 83	FC [1]	SE 70	SE 50 [1]	SE 96 [1]	SE 83	FC	SE 70		SE 75 [1]	SE 73	FC	SE 70	SE 50 [1]	SE 66 [1] A	SE 73	FC	SE 70	SE 22 [1]	SE 94 [1] B	SE 73	SE 70
London Victoria [15]	⊖ d			21 51	22 03	22 18			22 21		22 39			22 51	23 03	23 18			23 21	23 39	23 51		23 53
Brixton	⊖ d			21 58					22 28					22 58					23 28				23 59
St Pancras International [15]	⊖ d		21 35					22 05					22 36					23 06					
Farringdon	⊖ d		21 40					22 10					22 40					23 10					
City Thameslink [3]	d																						
London Blackfriars [3]	⊖ d	21 43	21 46				22 13	22 16				22 43	22 46				23 13	23 16				23 43	
Elephant & Castle	⊖ d	21 46	21 49				22 16	22 19				22 46	22 49				23 16	23 19				23 46	
Loughborough Jn	d		21 53					22 23					22 53					23s23					
Herne Hill [4]	d		21a57	22 00				22a27	22 30				22a57	23 00				23a27	23 30				00 02
West Dulwich	d			22 03					22 33					23 03					23 33				00 04
Sydenham Hill	d			22 05					22 35					23 05					23 35				00 06
Penge East	d			22 08					22 38					23 08					23 38				00 09
Kent House [4]	d			22 09					22 39					23 09					23 39				00 11
Beckenham Junction [4]	🚊 d			22 11					22 41					23 11					23 41				00 13
Denmark Hill [4]	d	21 52					22 22					22 52					23 22					23 52	
Peckham Rye [4]	d	21 55					22 25					22 55					23 25					23 55	
Nunhead [4]	d	21 57					22 27					22 57					23 27					23 57	
Lewisham [4]	🚊 a																						
Crofton Park	d	22 00					22 30					23 00					23 30					23 59	
Catford	d	22 02					22 32					23 02					23 32					00 01	
Bellingham	d	22 04					22 34					23 04					23 34					00 04	
Beckenham Hill	d	22 06					22 36					23 06					23 36					00 06	
Ravensbourne	d	22 08					22 38					23 08					23 38					00 08	
Shortlands [4]	d	22 10		22 14			22 40		22 44			23 10		23 14			23 40		23 44			00 10	00 16
Bromley South [4]	d	22 13		22 17	22a18	22 34	22 43		22 47		22 59	23 13		23 17	23a18	23 34	23 43		23 47	23 59	00 07	00 13	00 19
Bickley [4]	d	22 16		22 20			22 46		22 50			23 16		23 20			23 46		23 50			00 15	00 21
Petts Wood [4]	d			22 24					22 54			23 20		23 24			23 50		23 54			00 20	00 26
Orpington [4]	d			22a27					22a57			23a23		23a27			23a53		23a57			00a23	00a29
St Mary Cray	d	22 22				22 41	22 52				23 05					23 41				00 05	00 14		
Swanley [4]	d	22 26				22 45	22 56				23a10					23 45				00a10	00 18		
Eynsford	d	22 31					23 01														00 23		
Shoreham (Kent)	d	22 34					23 04														00 27		
Otford [4]	d	22 37				22a54	23 07									23a54					00a30		
Bat & Ball	d	22 40					23 10																
Sevenoaks [4]	a	22 43					23 13																

Sundays

Station		SE 22 [1]	SE 94 [1] B	SE 73	SE 70	SE 60	SE 54 [1]	SE 94 [1] A	SE 72	SE 70	SE 50 [1]	SE 72		SE 54 [1]	SE 70	SE 94 [1] A	SE 50 [1] C ⚮	SE 72	SE 70	SE 50 [1]	FC	SE 72	SE 54 [1]	SE 70	FC
London Victoria [15]	⊖ d	23p39	23p51		23p53	00 35	07 35	07 42	07 38	07 51	08 03	08 08		08 24	08 21	08 42	08 45	08 38	08 51	09 03		09 08	09 24	09 21	
Brixton	⊖ d				23p59					07 58					08 28				08 58					09 28	
St Pancras International [15]	⊖ d																				09 06				09 36
Farringdon	⊖ d																				09 10				09 40
City Thameslink [3]	d																								
London Blackfriars [3]	⊖ d			23p43																	09 16				09 46
Elephant & Castle	⊖ d			23p46																	09 19				09 49
Loughborough Jn	d																				09 23				09 53
Herne Hill [4]	d				00 02	00 43				08 00					08 30				09 00		09a27			09 30	09a57
West Dulwich	d				00 04					08 03					08 33				09 03					09 33	
Sydenham Hill	d				00 06					08 05					08 35				09 05					09 35	
Penge East	d				00 09	00 48				08 08					08 38				09 08					09 38	
Kent House [4]	d				00 11					08 09					08 39				09 09					09 39	
Beckenham Junction [4]	🚊 d				00 13	00 51				08 11					08 41				09 11					09 41	
Denmark Hill [4]	d			23p52					07 47			08 17						08 47				09 17			
Peckham Rye [4]	d			23p55					07 49			08 19						08 49				09 19			
Nunhead [4]	d			23p57					07 51			08 21						08 51				09 21			
Lewisham [4]	🚊 a																								
Crofton Park	d			23p59					07 54			08 24						08 54				09 24			
Catford	d			00 01					07 56			08 26						08 56				09 26			
Bellingham	d			00 04					07 58			08 28						08 58				09 28			
Beckenham Hill	d			00 06					08 00			08 30						09 00				09 30			
Ravensbourne	d			00 08					08 02			08 32						09 02				09 32			
Shortlands [4]	d			00 10	00 16				08 04	08 14		08 34			08 44			09 04	09 14			09 34		09 44	
Bromley South [4]	d	23p59	00 07	00 13	00 19	00 55	07 52	07 58	08 07	08 17	08a18	08 37		08 43	08 47	08 58	09a00	09 07	09 17	09a18		09 37	09 43	09 47	
Bickley [4]	d			00 15	00 21				08 10	08 20		08 40			08 50			09 10	09 20			09 40		09 50	
Petts Wood [4]	d			00 20	00 26					08 24					08 54				09 24					09 54	
Orpington [4]	d			00a23	00a29					08a27					08a57				09a27					09a57	
St Mary Cray	d	00 05	00 14			01 01	07 58	08 05	08 15			08 45		08 50		09 05		09 15				09 45	09 50		
Swanley [4]	d	00a10	00 18			01a05	08a03	08 10	08 20			08 50		08a54		09 10		09 20				09 50	09a54		
Eynsford	d		00 23						08 24			08 54						09 24				09 54			
Shoreham (Kent)	d		00 27						08 28			08 58						09 28				09 58			
Otford [4]	d		00a30					08a19	08 31			09 01				09a19		09 31				10 01			
Bat & Ball	d								08 34			09 04						09 34				10 04			
Sevenoaks [4]	a								08 37			09 07						09 37				10 07			

For general notes see front of timetable
For details of catering facilities see Directory of Train Operators

A To Canterbury West (Table 207)
B To Ashford International (Table 196)
C 20 July to 31 August

Table 195

Sundays

London → Catford, Beckenham Junction, Bromley South, Orpington, Otford and Sevenoaks

Network Diagram - see first page of Table 195

Station		SE 94 1 A	SE 50 1 B	SE 72	SE 70	SE 50 1	FC	SE 72	SE 54 1	SE 70	FC
London Victoria 15	⊖ d	09 42	09 45	09 38	09 51	10 03		10 08	10 24	10 21	
Brixton	⊖ d				09 58					10 28	
St Pancras International 15	⊖ d						10 06				10 36
Farringdon	⊖ d						10 10				10 40
City Thameslink 3	d										
London Blackfriars 3	⊖ d						10 16				10 46
Elephant & Castle	⊖ d						10 19				10 49
Loughborough Jn	d						10 23				10 53
Herne Hill 4	d				10 00		10a27			10 30	10a57
West Dulwich	d				10 03					10 33	
Sydenham Hill	d				10 05					10 35	
Penge East	d				10 08					10 38	
Kent House 4	d				10 09					10 39	
Beckenham Junction 4	d				10 11					10 41	
Denmark Hill 4	d			09 47				10 17			
Peckham Rye 4	d			09 49				10 19			
Nunhead 4	d			09 51				10 21			
Lewisham 4	a										
Crofton Park	d			09 54				10 24			
Catford	d			09 56				10 26			
Bellingham	d			09 58				10 28			
Beckenham Hill	d			10 00				10 30			
Ravensbourne	d			10 02				10 32			
Shortlands 4	d			10 04	10 14			10 34		10 44	
Bromley South 4	d	09 58	10a00	10 07	10 17	10a18		10 37	10 43	10 47	
Bickley 4	d			10 10	10 20			10 40		10 50	
Petts Wood 4	d				10 24					10 54	
Orpington 4	d				10a27					10a57	
St Mary Cray	d	10 05		10 15				10 45	10 50		
Swanley 4	d	10 10		10 20				10 50	10a54		
Eynsford	d			10 24				10 54			
Shoreham (Kent)	d			10 28				10 58			
Otford 4	d	10a19		10 31				11 01			
Bat & Ball	d			10 34				11 04			
Sevenoaks 4	a			10 37				11 07			

Station		SE 94 1 A	SE 72	SE 70	SE 50 1	FC		SE 72	SE 54 1	SE 70	FC
London Victoria 15	⊖ d	10 42	10 38	10 51	11 03		and at the same minutes past each hour until	20 08	20 24	20 21	
Brixton	⊖ d			10 58						20 28	
St Pancras International 15	⊖ d					11 06					20 36
Farringdon	⊖ d					11 10					20 40
City Thameslink 3	d										
London Blackfriars 3	⊖ d					11 16					20 46
Elephant & Castle	⊖ d					11 19					20 49
Loughborough Jn	d					11 23					20 53
Herne Hill 4	d			11 00		11a27				20 30	20a57
West Dulwich	d			11 03						20 33	
Sydenham Hill	d			11 05						20 35	
Penge East	d			11 08						20 38	
Kent House 4	d			11 09						20 39	
Beckenham Junction 4	d			11 11						20 41	
Denmark Hill 4	d		10 47					20 17			
Peckham Rye 4	d		10 49					20 19			
Nunhead 4	d		10 51					20 21			
Lewisham 4	a										
Crofton Park	d		10 54					20 24			
Catford	d		10 56					20 26			
Bellingham	d		10 58					20 28			
Beckenham Hill	d		11 00					20 30			
Ravensbourne	d		11 02					20 32			
Shortlands 4	d		11 04	11 14				20 34		20 44	
Bromley South 4	d	10 58	11 07	11 17	11a18			20 37	20 43	20 47	
Bickley 4	d		11 10	11 20				20 40		20 50	
Petts Wood 4	d			11 24						20 54	
Orpington 4	d			11a27						20a57	
St Mary Cray	d	11 05	11 15					20 45	20 50		
Swanley 4	d	11 10	11 20					20 50	20a54		
Eynsford	d		11 24					20 54			
Shoreham (Kent)	d		11 28					20 58			
Otford 4	d	11a19	11 31					21 01			
Bat & Ball	d		11 34					21 04			
Sevenoaks 4	a		11 37					21 07			

Station		SE 94 1	SE 72	SE 70	SE 50 1	SE 72	SE 54 1	SE 70	SE 94 1	SE 72	SE 70	SE 50 1
London Victoria 15	⊖ d	20 42	20 38	20 51	21 03	21 08	21 24	21 21	21 42	21 38	21 51	22 03
Brixton	⊖ d			20 58				21 28			21 58	
St Pancras International 15	⊖ d											
Farringdon	⊖ d											
City Thameslink 3	d											
London Blackfriars 3	⊖ d											
Elephant & Castle	⊖ d											
Loughborough Jn	d											
Herne Hill 4	d			21 00				21 30			22 00	
West Dulwich	d			21 03				21 33			22 03	
Sydenham Hill	d			21 05				21 35			22 05	
Penge East	d			21 08				21 38			22 08	
Kent House 4	d			21 09				21 39			22 09	
Beckenham Junction 4	d			21 11				21 41			22 11	
Denmark Hill 4	d		20 47			21 17				21 47		
Peckham Rye 4	d		20 49			21 19				21 49		
Nunhead 4	d		20 51			21 21				21 51		
Lewisham 4	a											
Crofton Park	d		20 54			21 24				21 54		
Catford	d		20 56			21 26				21 56		
Bellingham	d		20 58			21 28				21 58		
Beckenham Hill	d		21 00			21 30				22 00		
Ravensbourne	d		21 02			21 32				22 02		
Shortlands 4	d		21 04	21 14		21 34		21 44		22 04	22 14	
Bromley South 4	d	20 58	21 07	21 17	21a18	21 37	21 43	21 47	21 58	22 07	22 17	22a18
Bickley 4	d		21 10	21 20		21 40		21 50		22 10	22 20	
Petts Wood 4	d			21 24				21 54			22 24	
Orpington 4	d			21a27				21a57			22a27	
St Mary Cray	d	21 05	21 15			21 45	21 50		22 05	22 15		
Swanley 4	d	21 10	21 20			21 50	21a54		22 10	22 20		
Eynsford	d		21 24			21 54				22 24		
Shoreham (Kent)	d		21 28			21 58				22 28		
Otford 4	d	21a19	21 31			22 01			22a19	22 31		
Bat & Ball	d		21 34			22 04				22 34		
Sevenoaks 4	a		21 37			22 07				22 37		

Station		SE 72	SE 70	SE 94 1	SE 54 1	SE 72	SE 70	SE 50 1	SE 72	SE 70	SE 54 1
London Victoria 15	⊖ d	22 08	22 21	22 42	22 41	22 38	22 51	23 03	23 08	23 21	23 42
Brixton	⊖ d		22 28				22 58			23 28	
St Pancras International 15	⊖ d										
Farringdon	⊖ d										
City Thameslink 3	d										
London Blackfriars 3	⊖ d										
Elephant & Castle	⊖ d										
Loughborough Jn	d										
Herne Hill 4	d		22 30				23 00			23 30	
West Dulwich	d		22 33				23 03			23 33	
Sydenham Hill	d		22 35				23 05			23 35	
Penge East	d		22 38				23 08			23 38	
Kent House 4	d		22 39				23 09			23 39	
Beckenham Junction 4	d		22 41				23 11			23 41	
Denmark Hill 4	d	22 17				22 47			23 17		
Peckham Rye 4	d	22 19				22 49			23 19		
Nunhead 4	d	22 21				22 51			23 21		
Lewisham 4	a										
Crofton Park	d	22 24				22 54			23 24		
Catford	d	22 26				22 56			23 26		
Bellingham	d	22 28				22 58			23 28		
Beckenham Hill	d	22 30				23 00			23 30		
Ravensbourne	d	22 32				23 02			23 32		
Shortlands 4	d	22 34	22 44			23 04	23 14		23 34	23 44	
Bromley South 4	d	22 37	22 47	22 58	23 01	23 07	23 17	23a18	23 37	23 47	00 01
Bickley 4	d	22 40	22 50			23 10	23 20		23 40	23 50	
Petts Wood 4	d		22 54			23 14	23 24		23 44	23 54	
Orpington 4	d		22a57			23a17	23a27		23a47	23a57	
St Mary Cray	d	22 45		23 05	23 07						00 08
Swanley 4	d	22 50		23 10	23a12						00a12
Eynsford	d	22 54									
Shoreham (Kent)	d	22 58									
Otford 4	d	23 01		23a19							
Bat & Ball	d	23 04									
Sevenoaks 4	a	23 07									

For general notes see front of timetable
For details of catering facilities see Directory of Train Operators

A To Canterbury West (Table 207)
B 20 July to 31 August

For details of Bank Holiday service alterations please see first page of this table

Sevenoaks, Otford, Orpington, Bromley South, Beckenham Junction and Catford → London

Network Diagram - see first page of Table 195

Miles	Miles	Miles			SE 73	SE 60	SE 71	SE 70	FC	SE 73	FC	SE 70	SE 50	SE 83	FC	SE 70	SE 37	FC	SE 83	SE 94	SE 50	FC	SE 70	SE 97	FC
						1			A		A		1				1			1	1	A		1	
—	0	—	**Sevenoaks** 4	d										05 40					06 13						
—	1¼	—	Bat & Ball	d										05 43					06 16						
—	3	—	Otford 4	d										05 46					06 19	06 28				06 38	
—	4¼	—	Shoreham (Kent)	d										05 49					06 22						
—	6½	—	Eynsford	d										05 52					06 25						
—	9½	—	**Swanley** 4	d		04 33								05 57			06 30		06 31		06 41			06 49	
—	12¼	—	St Mary Cray	d		04 37								06 01			06 35		06 35		06 46				
0	—	—	**Orpington** 4	d	04 36		04 58	05 25		05 36		05 50				06 20							06 44		
1¼	—	—	Petts Wood 4	d	04 39		05 01	05 28		05 39		05 53				06 23							06 47		
3	14½	—	Bickley 4	d	04 43	04 43	05 05	05 32		05 43		05 57		06 06		06 27			06 41				06 51		
4	15½	—	**Bromley South** 4	d	04 46	04b51	05 08	05 36		05 46		06 01	06 14	06c15		06 31	06 42		06 44	06 48	06 52		06 54	06 58	
5	16½	—	Shortlands 4	d	04 48	04 53	05 10	05 38		05 48		06 03		06 17		06 33			06 46				06 56		
—	17¼	—	Ravensbourne	d	04 51					05 51				06 20					06 49						
—	18	—	Beckenham Hill	d	04 53					05 53				06 22					06 51						
—	18¾	—	Bellingham	d	04 55					05 55				06 24					06 53						
—	19½	—	Catford	d	04 57					05 57				06 26					06 55						
—	20½	—	Crofton Park	d	04 59					06 00				06 28					06 58						
—	—	0	Lewisham 4	d																					
—	21¾	1¾	Nunhead 4	d	05 02					06 02				06 31					07 00						
—	22½	2½	Peckham Rye 4	d	05 04					06 04				06 33					07 02						
—	23¼	3¼	Denmark Hill 4	d	05 06					06 07				06 35					07 05						
6½	—	—	**Beckenham Junction** 4	d		04 56	05 13	05 40				06 06				06 36							06 58		
7½	—	—	Kent House 4	d		04 58	05 15	05 42				06 08				06 38							07 00		
7¾	—	—	Penge East	d		05 00	05 17	05 44				06 10				06 40							07 02		
9¼	—	—	Sydenham Hill	d		05 03	05 20	05 47				06 13				06 43							07 05		
10	—	—	West Dulwich	d		05 05	05 22	05 49				06 15				06 45							07 07		
11	—	—	Herne Hill 4	d		05 07	05 25	05 52	05 54		06 14	06 18			06 45	06 48		06 59		06 58		07 04	07 10		07 24
—	—	—	Loughborough Jn	d							06 17				06 48			07 02				07 07			07 27
—	25¾	—	Elephant & Castle	⊖ d	05 12		05 30		06 02	06 13	06 22			06 41	06 53			07 07	07 11			07 12		07 15	07 32
—	27	—	**London Blackfriars** 3	⊖ d	05a16		05a34		06e08	06a18	06 28			06a45	06 58			07 12	07a15			07 18		07a18	07 38
—	—	—	City Thameslink 3	a					06 10		06 30				07 00			07 14				07 20			07 40
—	—	—	Farringdon	⊖ a					06 14		06 34				07 04			07 16				07 24			07 44
—	—	—	St Pancras International 15	⊖ a					06 18		06 38				07 08			07 21				07 28			07 48
11¾	—	—	Brixton	⊖ d		05 09		05 54				06 20				06 50							07 12		
15	—	7½	**London Victoria** 15	⊖ a		05f18		06f03				06f29	06f32			06f59	07f02			07 08	07 12		07 20		

		SE 71	SE 70		SE 83	SE 94	SE 31	SE 71	SE 22	SE 83	SE 70	SE 18	SE 97	SE 71	FC	SE 83	SE 50	SE 22	SE 3	SE 96	SE 4	SE 78	SE 73	SE 70	FC
						1	1 B						1				1			1 C					
Sevenoaks 4	d				06 43					07 07															
Bat & Ball	d				06 46					07 10															
Otford 4	d				06 49	07 09				07 13			07 19							07 32					
Shoreham (Kent)	d				06 52					07 16															
Eynsford	d				06 55					07 20															
Swanley 4	d				07 01	07 18			07 22	07 26			07 30			←		07 40		07 44					
St Mary Cray	d				07 06	07 23			07 27	07 31						07 31		07 45							
Orpington 4	d	07 02	07 06					07 23		→	07 27												07 44	07 50	
Petts Wood 4	d	07 05	07 09					07 26			07 30												07 47	07 53	
Bickley 4	d	07 09	07 13		07 11			07 30			07 34					07 37							07 53	07 57	
Bromley South 4	d	07 12	07 16		07 17	07 29	07 32	07 34	07 35		07 37		07 40			07 41	07 51	07 52		07 54			07 56	08 01	
Shortlands 4	d	07 14	07 18		07 19			07 36			07 39					07 43							07 58	08 03	
Ravensbourne	d				07 21											07 46									
Beckenham Hill	d				07 23											07 48									
Bellingham	d				07 25											07 50							08 04		
Catford	d				07 27											07 52							08 07		
Crofton Park	d				07 30											07 54							08 09		
Lewisham 4	d											07 44										08 04			
Nunhead 4	d				07 32							07 52				07 57						08 10	08 13		
Peckham Rye 4	d				07 34							07 55				07 59						08 12	08 15		
Denmark Hill 4	d				07 36							07 59				08 03				08 06		08 15	08 18		
Beckenham Junction 4	d	07 17	07 21					07 39			07 42								08 00					08 07	
Kent House 4	d	07 20	07 23					07 41			07 44			←					08 02		08 05				
Penge East	d	07 22	07 25					07 43			07 46			07 43					08 04		08 07				
Sydenham Hill	d	07 25	07 28					→			07 49			07 46					08 07		08 10				
West Dulwich	d	07 27	07 30								07 52			07 48					08 09		08 12			08 14	
Herne Hill 4	d	07 32	07 34				07 42				07 57			07 52	08 01				08 12		08 15			08 18	08 22
Loughborough Jn	d	07 34												07 55	08 03				08 14						08 25
Elephant & Castle	⊖ d	07 39			07 42								07 58	08 01	08 09	08 09			08 19				08 24		08 30
London Blackfriars 3	⊖ d	07a44			07a46								08a03	08a05	08g13	08a13			08a24				08a29		08 37
City Thameslink 3	a														08 15										08 39
Farringdon	⊖ a														08 19										08 42
St Pancras International 15	⊖ a														08 23										08 46
Brixton	⊖ d		07 37								07 59										08 17				
London Victoria 15	⊖ a		07h46			07 49	07 52		07 58		08h08	08h12					08 11	08 14		08 17	08 25	08h29		08h29	

For general notes see front of timetable
For details of catering facilities see Directory of Train Operators

- A From Selhurst (Table 177)
- B From Dover Priory (Table 212)
- C From Ashford International (Table 196)
- b Arr. 0446
- c Arr. 0608
- e Arr. 0605
- f Until 10 October arr 2 minutes earlier
- g Arr. 0807
- h Until 10 October arr 1 minute earlier

For details of Bank Holiday service alterations please see first page of this table

Sevenoaks, Otford, Orpington, Bromley South, Beckenham Junction and Catford → London

Network Diagram - see first page of Table 195

Station		SE 83	SE 23		SE 20 A	SE 94 [1]	SE 51 [1]	FC	SE 4	SE 78	SE 9	SE 70	FC [1]	SE 83	SE 96 [1]	SE 50 [1]	SE 22 [1]	FC	SE 3	FC [1]	SE 70	SE 18	SE 9	SE 83	SE 20 [1]
Sevenoaks [4]	d	07 39												07 52										08 19	
Bat & Ball	d	07 42												07 55										08 22	
Otford [4]	d	07 45				07 50								07 58	08 07									08 25	
Shoreham (Kent)	d	07 48												08 01										08 28	
Eynsford	d	07 51												08 04										08 32	
Swanley [4]	d	07 57	07 55		07 59	08 00								08 10			08 21							08 38	08 43
St Mary Cray	d	08 01	08 00		08 04									08 15			08 26							08 42	08 48
Orpington [4]	d											08 10									08 30				
Petts Wood [4]	d											08 13									08 33				
Bickley [4]	d											08 17		08 20							08 37			08 47	
Bromley South [4]	d	08 09	08 07		08 11		08 15				08 18	08 21		08b25	08 25	08 31	08 32				08 41		08 45	08 50	08 54
Shortlands [4]	d										08 20	08 23		08 28							08 43		08 47	08 52	
Ravensbourne	d	08 12									08 22												08 50		
Beckenham Hill	d	08 14									08 24												08 52		
Bellingham	d	08 16									08 26			08 32									08 54	08 56	
Catford	d	08 18									08 29			08 36									08 56	08 59	
Crofton Park	d													08 38									08 59		
Lewisham [4] 🚋	d									08 24												08 44			
Nunhead [4]	d									08 29				08 41								08 52	09 01		
Peckham Rye [4]	d									08 32	08 35			08 43								08 54	09 04	09 08	
Denmark Hill [4]	d	08 26			08 29					08 35	08 38			08 45								08 59	09 06	09 10	
Beckenham Junction [4] 🚋	d					08 13			08 22			08 27									08 46				
Kent House [4]	d								08 24			08 29							08 45		08 48				
Penge East	d								08 26										08 47		08 50				
Sydenham Hill	d								08 29										08 50		08 53				
West Dulwich	d								08 31			08 35							08 52		08 55				
Herne Hill [4]	d							08 31	08 35			08 39	08 43					08 53	08 56	09 00	08 58				
Loughborough Jn	d							08 34										08 56	09 00						
Elephant & Castle	⊖ d	08 34	08 31					08 39			08 44			08 51				09 00	09 04				09 12	09 16	
London Blackfriars [3]	⊖ d	08 39	08a37					08 43			08a49		08c57	08a56				09 05	09a09	09 09			09a17	09 22	
City Thameslink [3]	a	08 42						08 45					08 59					09 07		09 11				09 24	
Farringdon	⊖ a							08 50					09 02					09 10		09 14					
St Pancras International [15]	⊖ a							08 54					09 06					09 14		09 18					
Brixton	⊖ d								08 37												09 03				
London Victoria [15]	⊖ a				08 39	08 31	08 34		08 45	08e47		08e49			08 53	08 52	08 57				09 11	09e12			09 15

Station		SE 96 [1]	SE 50 [1]		SE 70	SE 78	FC	SE 73	SE 83	SE 34 [1]	SE 70	SE 66 [1]	SE 50 [1] 🍴	FC	SE 70	FC	SE 83	SE 94 [1]	SE 34 [1]	SE 78	SE 70	SE 30 [1] 🍴	FC	SE 70	SE 83
Sevenoaks [4]	d								08 46								09 12								09 34
Bat & Ball	d								08 49								09 15								09 37
Otford [4]	d	08 40							08 52			09 07					09 18	09 27							09 40
Shoreham (Kent)	d								08 55								09 21								09 43
Eynsford	d								08 58								09 24								09 47
Swanley [4]	d	08 50							09 04	09 07							09 30	09 36	09 36						09 52
St Mary Cray	d								09 08	09 12							09 35		09 41						09 56
Orpington [4]	d				08 53			08 57			09 08				09 23						09 38			09 53	
Petts Wood [4]	d				08 56			09 00			09 11				09 26						09 41			09 56	
Bickley [4]	d				09 00			09 04	09 12		09 15				09 30		09 39				09 45			10 00	10 01
Bromley South [4]	d	09 00	09 03		09 03			09 07	09 16	09 19	09 20	09 27	09 30		09 33		09 43	09 45	09 48		09 48	09 59		10 03	10 05
Shortlands [4]	d				09 05			09 09	09 18		09 22				09 35		09 45				09 50			10 05	10 07
Ravensbourne	d							09 11	09 20								09 47								10 09
Beckenham Hill	d							09 13	09 22								09 49								10 11
Bellingham	d							09 15	09 24								09 51								10 13
Catford	d							09 17	09 26								09 53								10 15
Crofton Park	d							09 20	09 29								09 56								10 18
Lewisham [4] 🚋	d					09 10														09 51					
Nunhead [4]	d					09 15		09 22	09 31								09 59			09 56					10 20
Peckham Rye [4]	d					09 18		09 25	09 34								10 01			09 58					10 22
Denmark Hill [4]	d					09 20		09 27	09 36								10 04			10 01					10 25
Beckenham Junction [4] 🚋	d				09 08						09 25				09 38						09 53			10 08	
Kent House [4]	d				09 10						09 27				09 40						09 55			10 10	
Penge East	d				09 12						09 29				09 42						09 57			10 12	
Sydenham Hill	d				09 15						09 32				09 45						10 00			10 15	
West Dulwich	d				09 17						09 33				09 47						10 02			10 17	
Herne Hill [4]	d				09 20		09 23				09 36			09 42	09 50	10 02					10 05		10 16	10 20	
Loughborough Jn	d						09 26							09 45		10 05							10 19		
Elephant & Castle	⊖ d						09 30	09 33	09 41					09 50		10 10	10 09						10 24		10 30
London Blackfriars [3]	⊖ d						09 34	09a37	09a46					09 58		10 14	10a12						10 28		10a33
City Thameslink [3]	a						09 36							10 00		10 16							10 30		
Farringdon	⊖ a						09 40							10 04		10 19							10 34		
St Pancras International [15]	⊖ a						09 44							10 08		10 23							10 38		
Brixton	⊖ d				09 22						09 38				09 52						10 07			10 22	
London Victoria [15]	⊖ a	09 18	09 26		09e31	09e33				09 38	09e46	09 50	09 49		10e01			10f04	10 06	10f14	10f16	10 17		10 29	

For general notes see front of timetable
For details of catering facilities see Directory of Train Operators

- A From Gillingham (Kent) (Table 212)
- b Arr. 0822
- c Arr. 0852
- e Until 10 October arr 1 minute earlier
- f Until 10 October arr 2 minutes earlier

For details of Bank Holiday service alterations please see first page of this table

Sevenoaks, Otford, Orpington, Bromley South, Beckenham Junction and Catford → London

Network Diagram - see first page of Table 195

	SE 64 1 A	FC		SE 78	SE 70	SE 30 1 🛒	FC	SE 70		SE 83	SE 94	SE 78	FC	SE 70	SE 92 1	SE 30 1 🛒	FC	SE 70	SE 83	SE 64 1	SE 78	FC	SE 70	SE 92 1
Sevenoaks 4 d										10 04									10 34					
Bat & Ball d										10 07									10 37					
Otford 4 d	09 56									10 10	10 27								10 40	10 57				
Shoreham (Kent) d										10 13									10 43					
Eynsford d										10 17									10 47					
Swanley 4 d	10 06									10 22	10 36				10 42				10 52					11 12
St Mary Cray d										10 26					10 47				10 56					11 17
Orpington 4 d					10 08			10 23						10 38				10 53					11 08	
Petts Wood 4 d					10 11			10 26						10 41				10 56					11 11	
Bickley 4 d					10 15			10 30		10 31				10 45				11 00	11 01				11 15	
Bromley South 4 d	10 15				10 18	10 30		10 33		10 35	10 45			10 48	10 54	11 00		11 03	11 05	11 15			11 18	11 24
Shortlands 4 d					10 20			10 35		10 37				10 50				11 05	11 07				11 20	
Ravensbourne d										10 39									11 09					
Beckenham Hill d										10 41									11 11					
Bellingham d										10 43									11 13					
Catford d										10 45									11 15					
Crofton Park d										10 48									11 18					
Lewisham 4 🚈 d				10 21								10 51									11 21			
Nunhead 4 d				10 26						10 50		10 56							11 20		11 26			
Peckham Rye 4 d				10 28						10 52		10 58							11 22		11 28			
Denmark Hill 4 d				10 31						10 55		11 01							11 25		11 31			
Beckenham Junction 4 🚈 d					10 23			10 38						10 53				11 08					11 23	
Kent House 4 d					10 25			10 40						10 55				11 10					11 25	
Penge East d					10 27			10 42						10 57				11 12					11 27	
Sydenham Hill d					10 30			10 45						11 00				11 15					11 30	
West Dulwich d					10 32			10 47						11 02				11 17					11 32	
Herne Hill 4 d		10 31			10 35		10 46	10 50					11 00	11 05			11 16	11 20				11 30	11 35	
Loughborough Jn d		10 34					10 49						11 04				11 19					11 34		
Elephant & Castle ⊖ d		10 39					10 54			11 00			11 09				11 24		11 30			11 39		
London Blackfriars 3 ⊖ d		10 43					10 58			11a03			11 13				11 28		11a33			11 43		
City Thameslink 3 a		10 45					11 00						11 15				11 30					11 45		
Farringdon ⊖ a		10 49					11 04						11 19				11 34					11 49		
St Pancras International 15 ⊖ a		10 53					11 08						11 23				11 38					11 53		
Brixton ⊖ d					10 37			10 52						11 07				11 22					11 37	
London Victoria 15 ⊖ a	10 32			10 42	10 44	10 47		10 59			11 02	11 12		11 14	11 17	11 17		11 29		11 32	11 42		11 44	11 47

	SE 30 1 🛒	FC	SE 70			SE 83	SE 94	SE 78	FC	SE 70	SE 92 1	SE 30 1 🛒	FC	SE 70	SE 83	SE 64 1	FC	SE 70	SE 92 1	SE 30 1 🛒	FC 1 B	FC	SE 78
Sevenoaks 4 d						15 04									15 34								
Bat & Ball d						15 07									15 37								
Otford 4 d						15 10	15 27								15 40	15 55							
Shoreham (Kent) d						15 13									15 43								
Eynsford d						15 17									15 46								
Swanley 4 d						15 22	15 36				15 42				15 52				16 12				
St Mary Cray d						15 26					15 47				15 56				16 17				
Orpington 4 d			11 23							15 38				15 53				16 08					
Petts Wood 4 d			11 26							15 41				15 56				16 11					
Bickley 4 d			11 30			15 31				15 45				16 00	16 01			16 15					
Bromley South 4 d	11 30		11 33	and at		15 35	15 45			15 48	15 53	16 00		16 03	16 05	16 14		16 19	16 23	16 30			
Shortlands 4 d			11 35	the same		15 37				15 50				16 05	16 07			16 21					
Ravensbourne d						15 39									16 09								
Beckenham Hill d				minutes		15 41									16 11								
Bellingham d						15 43									16 13								
Catford d				past		15 45									16 15								
Crofton Park d				each		15 48									16 18								
Lewisham 4 🚈 d								15 51															16 35
Nunhead 4 d				hour until		15 50		15 56							16 20								16 40
Peckham Rye 4 d						15 52		15 58							16 22								16 42
Denmark Hill 4 d						15 55		16 01							16 25								16 46
Beckenham Junction 4 🚈 d			11 38							15 53				16 08				16 25					
Kent House 4 d			11 40							15 55				16 10				16 27					
Penge East d			11 42							15 57				16 12				16 29					
Sydenham Hill d			11 45							16 00				16 15				16 32					
West Dulwich d			11 47							16 02				16 17				16 33					
Herne Hill 4 d		11 46	11 50						16 00	16 05			16 16	16 20			16 31	16 36			16 37	16 46	
Loughborough Jn d		11 49							16 04				16 19				16 34					16 49	
Elephant & Castle ⊖ d		11 54				16 00			16 09				16 24		16 30		16 40				16 43	16 54	
London Blackfriars 3 ⊖ d		11 58				16a03			16 14				16 30		16a33		16 44				16 50	17 00	
City Thameslink 3 a		12 00							16 16				16 32				16 46				16 52	17 02	
Farringdon ⊖ a		12 04							16 19				16 35				16 49				16 56	17 05	
St Pancras International 15 ⊖ a		12 08							16 24				16 39				16 53				17 01	17 09	
Brixton ⊖ d			11 52							16 07				16 22				16 38					
London Victoria 15 ⊖ a	11 47		11 59				16 02	16 12		16 14	16 18	16 17		16 30		16 33		16 45	16 49	16 50			17 03

For general notes see front of timetable
For details of catering facilities see Directory of Train Operators

A From Margate (Table 207)
B From Brighton (Table 52)

For details of Bank Holiday service alterations please see first page of this table

Sevenoaks, Otford, Orpington, Bromley South, Beckenham Junction and Catford → London

Network Diagram - see first page of Table 195

		SE	SE	SE	SE	SE		SE	FC	FC	SE	SE	SE	SE	FC	SE	SE	SE	FC	FC	SE	FC	SE	SE	SE
		83	70	96	92	83		30			78	83	70	64		70	92	31			83		70	96	78
					[1]			[1]						[1]			[1]	[1]		[1]				[1]	
														A											
								🚲										🚲							
Sevenoaks [4]	d	16 05				16 26						16 35									17 05				
Bat & Ball	d	16 08				16 29						16 38									17 08				
Otford [4]	d	16 11		16 27		16 32						16 41		16 54							17 12			17 28	
Shoreham (Kent)	d	16 14				16 35						16 44									17 15				
Eynsford	d	16 17				16 39						16 48									17 19				
Swanley [4]	d	16 22		16 38	16 42	16a45						16 54		17 05			17 13				17 24				
St Mary Cray	d	16 26			16 47							16 58					17 18				17 28				
Orpington [4]	d		16 36										17 04										17 36		
Petts Wood [4]	d		16 39										17 07										17 39		
Bickley [4]	d	16 31	16 44									17 03	17 11			←					17 33		17 44		
Bromley South [4]	d	16 35	16 47	16 47	16 53			17 00				17 06	17b17	17 14		17 17	17 25	17 33			17 36		17 47	17 47	
Shortlands [4]	d	16 37	16 49									17 08	→			17 19					17 38		17 49		
Ravensbourne	d	16 39										17 11									17 41				
Beckenham Hill	d	16 41										17 13									17 43				
Bellingham	d	16 43										17 15									17 45				
Catford	d	16 45										17 17									17 47				
Crofton Park	d	16 48										17 19									17 49				
Lewisham [4]	🚊 d										17 05														17 54
Nunhead [4]	d	16 50									17 13	17 22									17 52				17 59
Peckham Rye [4]	d	16 52									17 15	17 24									17 54				18 01
Denmark Hill [4]	d	16 55									17 18	17 27									17 57				18 04
Beckenham Junction [4]	🚊 d		16 52													17 22							17 52		
Kent House [4]	d		16 54													17 24							17 54		
Penge East	d		16 56													17 26							17 56		
Sydenham Hill	d		16 59													17 29							17 59		
West Dulwich	d		17 00													17 30							18 00		
Herne Hill [4]	d		17 03						17 06	17 14					17 31	17 33			17 37			17 57	18 03		
Loughborough Jn	d								17 10	17 17					17 34				17 40			18 01			
Elephant & Castle	⊖ d	17 00							17 04	17 22		17 32			17 39				17 44	17 52	18 02	18 06			
London Blackfriars [3]	⊖ d	17a05							17 18	17 32		17a39			17 44				17 48	18c06	18a08	18e14			
City Thameslink [3]	a								17 20	17 34					17 46				17 50	18 08		18 16			
Farringdon	⊖ a								17 24	17 38					17 49				17 53	18 11		18 23			
St Pancras International [15]	⊖ a								17 28	17 42					17 53				17 57	18 15		18 27			
Brixton	⊖ d		17 05													17 35							18 05		
London Victoria [15]	⊖ a		17 12	17 11	17 18			17 17			17 28			17 31		17 42	17 48	17 58					18 12	18 09	18 16

		SE	SE	FC	SE	SE		FC	SE	SE	SE	FC	FC	SE	SE	SE	SE	SE	SE	SE	FC	SE	SE	SE	FC
		92	50		83	94			70	92	30			78	83	83	94	70	92	30		78	83	94	
		[1]	[1]			[1]				[1]	[1]	[1]					[1]		[1]	[1]				[1]	
												B													
			🚲								🚲														
Sevenoaks [4]	d				17 35										17 57	18 16							18 37		
Bat & Ball	d				17 38										18 00	18 19							18 40		
Otford [4]	d				17 41	17 53									18 04	18 22	18 29						18 43	18 56	
Shoreham (Kent)	d				17 44										18 07	18 25							18 46		
Eynsford	d				17 47										18 10	18 29							18 49		
Swanley [4]	d	17 43			17 53	18 04				18 12					18f22	18a34			18 42				18g58	19 05	
St Mary Cray	d	17 47			17 57					18 16					18 26				18 47				19 02		
Orpington [4]	d								18 06									18 36							
Petts Wood [4]	d								18 09									18 39							
Bickley [4]	d				18 02				18 14						18 32			18 44					19 06		
Bromley South [4]	d	17 54	17 59		18 05	18 14			18 17	18 25	18 31				18 35		18 45	18 47	18 53	19 01			19 10	19 14	
Shortlands [4]	d				18 08				18 19						18 37			18 49					19 12		
Ravensbourne	d				18 10										18 39								19 14		
Beckenham Hill	d				18 12										18 41								19 16		
Bellingham	d				18 14										18 43								19 18		
Catford	d				18 16										18 45								19 20		
Crofton Park	d				18 19										18 48								19 23		
Lewisham [4]	🚊 d													18 41								19 06			
Nunhead [4]	d				18 21									18 45	18 50							19 10	19 25		
Peckham Rye [4]	d				18 23									18 47	18 52							19 12	19 28		
Denmark Hill [4]	d				18 26									18 50	18 55							19 15	19 31		
Beckenham Junction [4]	🚊 d								18 22									18 53							
Kent House [4]	d								18 24									18 55							
Penge East	d								18 26									18 57							
Sydenham Hill	d								18 29									19 00							
West Dulwich	d								18 30									19 01							
Herne Hill [4]	d			18 16				18 28	18 33			18 37	18 48					19 04			19 18				19 32
Loughborough Jn	d			18 19				18 31				18 40	18 51								19 21				19 35
Elephant & Castle	⊖ d			18 24	18 31			18 36				18 45	18 56		19 00						19 26		19 37		19 40
London Blackfriars [3]	⊖ d			18h32	18a35			18j46				18k52	19m02		19a03						19 30		19a40		19 44
City Thameslink [3]	a			18 34				18 48				18 54	19 04								19 32				19 46
Farringdon	⊖ a			18 37				18 51				18 57	19 07								19 36				19 49
St Pancras International [15]	⊖ a			18 41				18 55				19 01	19 11								19 40				19 53
Brixton	⊖ d								18 35									19 06							
London Victoria [15]	⊖ a	18 19	18 17			18 33			18 42	18 50	18 48			19 00			19 03	19 13	19 17	19 17		19 25		19 31	

For general notes see front of timetable
For details of catering facilities see Directory of Train Operators

A From Canterbury West (Table 207)
B From Brighton (Table 52)
b Arr. 1713
c Arr. 1756
e Arr. 1809
f Arr. 1815
g Arr. 1855
h Arr. 1829
j Arr. 1840
k Arr. 1849
m Arr. 1859

For details of Bank Holiday service alterations please see first page of this table

Sevenoaks, Otford, Orpington, Bromley South, Beckenham Junction and Catford → London

Network Diagram - see first page of Table 195

		SE 70	SE 92	SE 83	SE 30	FC		SE 70	SE 83	SE 94	SE 70	SE 83	SE 92	SE 30	FC	SE 70	SE 83	SE 94	SE 70	SE 50	FC	SE 83	SE 70	SE 92	FC
			1		1								1	1				1		1				1	
Sevenoaks 4	d			18 55					19 06			19 21					19 34					20 04			
Bat & Ball	d			18 58					19 09			19 24					19 37					20 07			
Otford 4	d			19 02					19 12	19 27		19 30					19 40	19 55				20 10			
Shoreham (Kent)	d			19 05					19 15			19 33					19 43					20 13			
Eynsford	d			19 08					19 18			19 36					19 46					20 16			
Swanley 4	d		19 12	19a13					19 24	19 36		19a41	19 42				19 52	20 04				20 22		20 42	
St Mary Cray	d		19 17						19 28				19 47				19 56	20 08				20 26		20 47	
Orpington 4	d	19 08						19 23			19 38					19 53			20 08				20 38		
Petts Wood 4	d	19 11						19 26			19 41					19 56			20 11				20 41		
Bickley 4	d	19 16						19 30	19 32		19 46					20 00	20 01		20 16			20 31	20 46		
Bromley South 4	d	19 19	19 23		19 30			19 33	19 35	19 45	19 49		19 53	19 58		20 03	20 05	20 15	20 19	20 32		20 35	20 49	20 53	
Shortlands 4	d	19 21						19 35	19 37		19 51					20 05	20 07		20 21			20 37	20 51		
Ravensbourne	d								19 40								20 09					20 39			
Beckenham Hill	d								19 42								20 11					20 41			
Bellingham	d								19 44								20 13					20 43			
Catford	d								19 46								20 15					20 45			
Crofton Park	d								19 48								20 18					20 48			
Lewisham 4	d																								
Nunhead 4	d								19 51								20 20					20 50			
Peckham Rye 4	d								19 53								20 22					20 52			
Denmark Hill 4	d								19 55								20 25					20 55			
Beckenham Junction 4	d	19 24						19 38			19 54					20 08			20 24				20 54		
Kent House 4	d	19 26						19 40			19 56					20 10			20 26				20 56		
Penge East	d	19 28						19 42			19 58					20 12			20 28				20 58		
Sydenham Hill	d	19 31						19 45			20 01					20 15			20 31				21 01		
West Dulwich	d	19 33						19 47			20 02					20 17			20 32				21 02		
Herne Hill 4	d	19 36				19 48		19 50			20 05				20 16	20 20			20 35		20 48		21 05		21 18
Loughborough Jn	d					19 51									20 19						20 51				21 21
Elephant & Castle	⊖ d					19 56			20 00						20 24		20 30				20 56	21 00			21 26
London Blackfriars 3	⊖ d					20 00			20a03						20 30		20a33				21 00	21a03			21 32
City Thameslink 3	a					20 02									20 32						21 02				21 34
Farringdon	⊖ a					20 06									20 36						21 06				21 39
St Pancras International 15	⊖ a					20 10									20 40						21 10				21 43
Brixton	⊖ d	19 38						19 52			20 07					20 22			20 37				21 07		
London Victoria 15	⊖ a	19 45	19 48		19 47			19 59		20 02	20 14		20 17	20 17		20 29		20 32	20 44	20 48			21 14	21 17	

		SE 83	SE 94	SE 70	SE 50	SE 83		FC	SE 70	SE 92	SE 83	SE 94	FC	SE 70	SE 50	SE 83	SE 70	SE 92	SE 83	SE 70	SE 94	SE 50	SE 55		
			1		1					1		1			1			1			1	1	1		
			A																						
Sevenoaks 4	d	20 34				21 04					21 35					22 04			22 37						
Bat & Ball	d	20 37				21 07					21 38					22 07			22 40						
Otford 4	d	20 40	20 53			21 10					21 41	21 54				22 10			22 43		23 04				
Shoreham (Kent)	d	20 43				21 13					21 44					22 13			22 46						
Eynsford	d	20 46				21 16					21 47					22 16			22 49						
Swanley 4	d	20 52	21 02			21 22				21 42	21 53	22 03				22 22		22 42	22 55		23 13		23 45		
St Mary Cray	d	20 56	21 07			21 26				21 47	21 57	22 07				22 26		22 47	22 59		23 17		23 49		
Orpington 4	d			21 08					21 38					22 08			22 38			23 08					
Petts Wood 4	d			21 11					21 41					22 11			22 41			23 11					
Bickley 4	d	21 01		21 16		21 31			21 46		22 01			22 16		22 31	22 46		23 03	23 16					
Bromley South 4	d	21 05	21 13	21 19	21 30	21 35			21 49	21 53	22 05	22 14		22 19	22 30	22 35	22 49	22 53	23 06	23 19	23 24	23 30	23 56		
Shortlands 4	d	21 07		21 21		21 37			21 51		22 07			22 21		22 37	22 51		23 08	23 21					
Ravensbourne	d	21 09				21 39					22 09					22 39			23 11						
Beckenham Hill	d	21 11				21 41					22 11					22 41			23 13						
Bellingham	d	21 13				21 43					22 13					22 43			23 15						
Catford	d	21 15				21 45					22 15					22 45			23 17						
Crofton Park	d	21 18				21 48					22 18					22 48			23 19						
Lewisham 4	d																								
Nunhead 4	d	21 20				21 50					22 20					22 50			23 22						
Peckham Rye 4	d	21 22				21 52					22 22					22 52			23 24						
Denmark Hill 4	d	21 25				21 55					22 25					22 55			23 26						
Beckenham Junction 4	d			21 24					21 54					22 24			22 54			23 24					
Kent House 4	d			21 26					21 56					22 26			22 56			23 26					
Penge East	d			21 28					21 58					22 28			22 58			23 28					
Sydenham Hill	d			21 31					22 01					22 31			23 01			23 31					
West Dulwich	d			21 32					22 02					22 32			23 02			23 32					
Herne Hill 4	d			21 35				21 56	22 05				22 26	22 35			23 05			23 35					
Loughborough Jn	d							21 59					22 30												
Elephant & Castle	⊖ d	21 30				22 00		22 04			22 30		22 35			23 00			23 31						
London Blackfriars 3	⊖ d	21a33				22a03		22 08			22a33		22 38			23a03			23a37						
City Thameslink 3	a							22 10					22 40												
Farringdon	⊖ a							22 14					22 44												
St Pancras International 15	⊖ a							22 18					22 48												
Brixton	⊖ d			21 37					22 07					22 37			23 07			23 37					
London Victoria 15	⊖ a		21 29	21 44	21 47				22 14	22 17		22 32		22 44	22 47		23 14	23 15		23 44	23 45	23 47	00 18		

For general notes see front of timetable
For details of catering facilities see Directory of Train Operators

A From Canterbury West (Table 207)

Sevenoaks, Otford, Orpington, Bromley South, Beckenham Junction and Catford → London

Network Diagram - see first page of Table 195

Station		FC A	SE 73	SE 54 [1]	FC A	SE 70	SE 83	FC A		SE 70	SE 92 [1]	SE 30 [1]	FC	SE 83	SE 64 [1]	SE 78		FC	SE 70	SE 92 [1]	SE 30 [1]	FC	SE 83	SE 78	FC
Sevenoaks [4]	d						06 04							06 34									07 04		
Bat & Ball	d						06 07							06 37									07 07		
Otford [4]	d						06 10							06 40	06 55								07 10		
Shoreham (Kent)	d						06 13							06 43									07 13		
Eynsford	d						06 17							06 47									07 17		
Swanley [4]	d			06 05			06 22				06 42			06 52	07 04					07 12			07 22		
St Mary Cray	d			06 10			06 26				06 47			06 56	07 08					07 17			07 26		
Orpington [4]	d		05 54			06 08				06 38									07 08						
Petts Wood [4]	d		05 57			06 11				06 41									07 11						
Bickley [4]	d		06 01			06 15	06 31			06 45				07 01					07 15				07 31		
Bromley South [4]	d		06 05	06 16		06 18	06 35			06 48	06 54	07 00		07 05	07 15				07 18	07 24	07 30		07 35		
Shortlands [4]	d		06 07			06 20	06 37			06 50				07 07					07 20				07 37		
Ravensbourne	d		06 09				06 39							07 09									07 39		
Beckenham Hill	d		06 11				06 41							07 11									07 41		
Bellingham	d		06 13				06 43							07 13									07 43		
Catford	d		06 15				06 45							07 15									07 45		
Crofton Park	d		06 18				06 48							07 18									07 48		
Lewisham [4]	d															07 20								07 50	
Nunhead [4]	d		06 20				06 50							07 20		07 25							07 50	07 55	
Peckham Rye [4]	d		06 22				06 52							07 22		07 28							07 52	07 58	
Denmark Hill [4]	d		06 25				06 55							07 25		07 31							07 55	08 01	
Beckenham Junction [4]	d					06 23				06 53									07 23						
Kent House [4]	d					06 25				06 55									07 25						
Penge East	d					06 27				06 57									07 27						
Sydenham Hill	d					06 30				07 00									07 30						
West Dulwich	d					06 32				07 02									07 32						
Herne Hill [4]	d	06 02			06 26	06 35		06 56		07 05			07 16					07 30	07 35			07 46			08 00
Loughborough Jn	d				06 30			07 00					07 19					07 34				07 49			08 04
Elephant & Castle	⊖ d	06 07	06 30		06 35		07 00	07 05					07 24	07 30				07 39				07 54	08 00		08 09
London Blackfriars [3]	⊖ d	06 13	06a33		06 43		07a03	07 13					07 28	07a33				07 43				07 58	08a03		08 13
City Thameslink [3]	a																								
Farringdon	⊖ a	06 18			06 48			07 18					07 33					07 48				08 03			08 18
St Pancras International [15]	⊖ a	06 22			06 52			07 22					07 38					07 53				08 08			08 23
Brixton	⊖ d					06 37				07 07									07 37						
London Victoria [15]	⊖ a			06 32		06 44				07 14	07 17	07 17			07 32	07 42			07 44	07 47	07 47			08 12	

Station		SE 70		SE 92 [1]	SE 30 [1]	FC	SE 83	SE 94 [1]	SE 78	FC		SE 70	SE 92 [1]	SE 30 [1]	FC	SE 70	SE 83	SE 94		SE 78	FC	SE 70	SE 92 [1]	SE 30 [1]	FC
Sevenoaks [4]	d						07 34										08 04								
Bat & Ball	d						07 37										08 07								
Otford [4]	d						07 40	07 55									08 10	08 26							
Shoreham (Kent)	d						07 43										08 13								
Eynsford	d						07 47										08 17								
Swanley [4]	d			07 42			07 52	08 04					08 12				08 22	08 35					08 42		
St Mary Cray	d			07 47			07 56	08 08					08 17				08 26						08 47		
Orpington [4]	d	07 38										08 08				08 23						08 38			
Petts Wood [4]	d	07 41										08 11				08 26						08 41			
Bickley [4]	d	07 45					08 01					08 15				08 30	08 31					08 45			
Bromley South [4]	d	07 48		07 54	08 00		08 05	08 15				08 18	08 24	08 30		08 33	08 35	08 45				08 48	08 54	09 00	
Shortlands [4]	d	07 50					08 07					08 20				08 35	08 37					08 50			
Ravensbourne	d						08 09										08 39								
Beckenham Hill	d						08 11										08 41								
Bellingham	d						08 13										08 43								
Catford	d						08 15										08 45								
Crofton Park	d						08 18										08 48								
Lewisham [4]	d								08 20											08 50					
Nunhead [4]	d						08 20		08 25								08 50			08 55					
Peckham Rye [4]	d						08 22		08 28								08 52			08 58					
Denmark Hill [4]	d						08 25		08 31								08 55			09 01					
Beckenham Junction [4]	d	07 53										08 23				08 38						08 53			
Kent House [4]	d	07 55										08 25				08 40						08 55			
Penge East	d	07 57										08 27				08 42						08 57			
Sydenham Hill	d	08 00										08 30				08 45						09 00			
West Dulwich	d	08 02										08 32				08 47						09 02			
Herne Hill [4]	d	08 05				08 16				08 31		08 35			08 46	08 50					09 00	09 05			09 16
Loughborough Jn	d					08 19				08 34					08 49						09 04				09 19
Elephant & Castle	⊖ d					08 24	08 30			08 39					08 54		09 00				09 09				09 24
London Blackfriars [3]	⊖ d					08 28	08a33			08 43					08 58		09a03				09 13				09 28
City Thameslink [3]	a														09 00						09 15				09 30
Farringdon	⊖ a					08 33				08 48					09 04						09 19				09 34
St Pancras International [15]	⊖ a					08 38				08 53					09 08						09 23				09 38
Brixton	⊖ d	08 07										08 37				08 52						09 07			
London Victoria [15]	⊖ a	08 14		08 17	08 17			08 32	08 42			08 44	08 47	08 47		08 59		09 02		09 12		09 14	09 17	09 17	

For general notes see front of timetable
For details of catering facilities see Directory of Train Operators

A From Selhurst (Table 177)

Table 195

Saturdays

Sevenoaks, Otford, Orpington, Bromley South, Beckenham Junction and Catford → London

Network Diagram - see first page of Table 195

Station		SE 70	SE 83	SE 94 [1]		SE 78	FC	SE 70	SE 92 [1]	SE 30 [1] ⚲	FC	SE 70		SE 83	SE 94	SE 78	FC	SE 70	SE 92 [1]	SE 30 [1] ⚲		FC	SE 70	SE 83	SE 94 [1]
Sevenoaks [4]	d		08 34											09 04										09 34	
Bat & Ball	d		08 37											09 07										09 37	
Otford [4]	d		08 40	08 57										09 10	09 26									09 40	09 57
Shoreham (Kent)	d		08 43											09 13										09 43	
Eynsford	d		08 47											09 17										09 47	
Swanley [4]	d		08 52						09 12					09 22	09 35				09 42					09 52	
St Mary Cray	d		08 56						09 17					09 26					09 47					09 56	
Orpington [4]	d	08 53						09 08				09 23						09 38					09 53		
Petts Wood [4]	d	08 56						09 11				09 26						09 41					09 56		
Bickley [4]	d	09 00	09 01					09 15				09 30		09 31				09 45					10 00	10 01	
Bromley South [4]	d	09 03	09 05	09 15				09 18	09 24	09 30		09 33		09 35	09 45			09 48	09 54	10 00			10 03	10 05	10 15
Shortlands [4]	d	09 05	09 07					09 20				09 35		09 37				09 50					10 05	10 07	
Ravensbourne	d		09 09											09 39										10 09	
Beckenham Hill	d		09 11											09 41										10 11	
Bellingham	d		09 13											09 43										10 13	
Catford	d		09 15											09 45										10 15	
Crofton Park	d		09 18											09 48										10 18	
Lewisham [4]	d					09 20										09 50									
Nunhead [4]	d		09 20			09 25								09 50		09 55								10 20	
Peckham Rye [4]	d		09 22			09 28								09 52		09 58								10 22	
Denmark Hill [4]	d		09 25			09 31								09 55		10 01								10 25	
Beckenham Junction [4]	d	09 08						09 23				09 38						09 53					10 08		
Kent House [4]	d	09 10						09 25				09 40						09 55					10 10		
Penge East	d	09 12						09 27				09 42						09 57					10 12		
Sydenham Hill	d	09 15						09 30				09 45						10 00					10 15		
West Dulwich	d	09 17						09 32				09 47						10 02					10 17		
Herne Hill [4]	d	09 20					09 30	09 35			09 46	09 50					10 00	10 05				10 16	10 20		
Loughborough Jn	d						09 34				09 49						10 04					10 19			
Elephant & Castle	⊖ d		09 30				09 39				09 54			10 00			10 09					10 24		10 30	
London Blackfriars [3]	⊖ d		09a33				09 43				09 58			10a03			10 13					10 28		10a33	
City Thameslink [3]	a						09 45				10 00						10 15					10 30			
Farringdon	⊖ a						09 49				10 04						10 19					10 34			
St Pancras International [15]	⊖ a						09 53				10 08						10 23					10 38			
Brixton	⊖ d	09 22						09 37				09 52						10 07					10 22		
London Victoria [15]	⊖ a	09 29		09 32		09 42		09 44	09 47	09 47		09 59			10 02	10 12		10 14	10 17	10 17			10 29		10 32

Station		SE 78	FC	SE 70		SE 92 [1]	SE 30 [1] ⚲	FC	SE 70	SE 83	SE 94	SE 78	FC	SE 70	SE 92 [1]	SE 30 [1] ⚲	FC	SE 70	SE 83	SE 64 [1]	SE 78	FC			
Sevenoaks [4]	d									10 04									10 34						
Bat & Ball	d									10 07									10 37						
Otford [4]	d									10 10	10 26								10 40	10 57					
Shoreham (Kent)	d									10 13									10 43						
Eynsford	d									10 17									10 47						
Swanley [4]	d					10 12				10 22	10 35				10 42				10 52						
St Mary Cray	d					10 17				10 26					10 47				10 56						
Orpington [4]	d			10 08					10 23					10 38				10 53							
Petts Wood [4]	d			10 11					10 26					10 41				10 56							
Bickley [4]	d			10 15					10 30	10 31				10 45				11 00	11 01						
Bromley South [4]	d			10 18		10 24	10 30		10 33	10 35	10 45			10 48	10 54	11 00		11 03	11 05	11 15					
Shortlands [4]	d			10 20					10 35	10 37				10 50				11 05	11 07						
Ravensbourne	d									10 39									11 09						
Beckenham Hill	d									10 41									11 11						
Bellingham	d									10 43									11 13						
Catford	d									10 45									11 15						
Crofton Park	d									10 48									11 18						
Lewisham [4]	d	10 20										10 50									11 20				
Nunhead [4]	d	10 25								10 50		10 55							11 20		11 25				
Peckham Rye [4]	d	10 28								10 52		10 58							11 22		11 28				
Denmark Hill [4]	d	10 31								10 55		11 01							11 25		11 31				
Beckenham Junction [4]	d			10 23					10 38					10 53				11 08							
Kent House [4]	d			10 25					10 40					10 55				11 10							
Penge East	d			10 27					10 42					10 57				11 12							
Sydenham Hill	d			10 30					10 45					11 00				11 15							
West Dulwich	d			10 32					10 47					11 02				11 17							
Herne Hill [4]	d		10 30	10 35				10 46	10 50				11 00	11 05			11 16	11 20				11 30			
Loughborough Jn	d		10 34					10 49					11 04				11 19					11 34			
Elephant & Castle	⊖ d		10 39					10 54		11 00			11 09				11 24		11 30			11 39			
London Blackfriars [3]	⊖ d		10 43					10 58		11a03			11 13				11 28		11a33			11 43			
City Thameslink [3]	a		10 45					11 00					11 15				11 30					11 45			
Farringdon	⊖ a		10 49					11 04					11 19				11 34					11 49			
St Pancras International [15]	⊖ a		10 53					11 08					11 23				11 38					11 53			
Brixton	⊖ d			10 37					10 52					11 07				11 22							
London Victoria [15]	⊖ a	10 42		10 44		10 47	10 47		10 59		11 02	11 12		11 14	11 17	11 17		11 29		11 32	11 42				

For general notes see front of timetable
For details of catering facilities see
Directory of Train Operators

Table 195

Saturdays

Sevenoaks, Otford, Orpington, Bromley South, Beckenham Junction and Catford → London

Network Diagram - see first page of Table 195

		SE 70			SE 92 [1]	SE 30 [1]	FC	SE 70	SE 83	SE 94	SE 78		FC	SE 70	SE 92 [1]	SE 30 [1]	FC	SE 70	SE 83		SE 64 [1] A	FC	SE 70	SE 92 [1]
Sevenoaks [4]	d								18 04										18 34					
Bat & Ball	d								18 07										18 37					
Otford [4]	d								18 10	18 26									18 40		18 55			
Shoreham (Kent)	d								18 13										18 43					
Eynsford	d								18 17										18 47					
Swanley [4]	d				18 12				18 22	18 35					18 42				18 52		19 04			19 12
St Mary Cray	d				18 17				18 26						18 47				18 56		19 08			19 17
Orpington [4]	d	11 08						18 23						18 38				18 53					19 08	
Petts Wood [4]	d	11 11						18 26						18 41				18 56					19 11	
Bickley [4]	d	11 15						18 30	18 31					18 45				19 00	19 01				19 15	
Bromley South [4]	d	11 18			18 24	18 30		18 33	18 35	18 45				18 48	18 54	19 00		19 03	19 05		19 15		19 18	19 24
Shortlands [4]	d	11 20	and at					18 35	18 37					18 50				19 05	19 07				19 20	
Ravensbourne	d		the same						18 39										19 09					
Beckenham Hill	d								18 41										19 11					
Bellingham	d		minutes						18 43										19 13					
Catford	d								18 45										19 15					
Crofton Park	d		past						18 48										19 18					
Lewisham [4]	d		each								18 50													
Nunhead [4]	d								18 50		18 55								19 20					
Peckham Rye [4]	d		hour until						18 52		18 58								19 22					
Denmark Hill [4]	d								18 55		19 01								19 25					
Beckenham Junction [4]	d	11 23						18 38						18 53				19 08					19 23	
Kent House [4]	d	11 25						18 40						18 55				19 10					19 25	
Penge East	d	11 27						18 42						18 57				19 12					19 27	
Sydenham Hill	d	11 30						18 45						19 00				19 15					19 30	
West Dulwich	d	11 32						18 47						19 02				19 17					19 32	
Herne Hill [4]	d	11 35					18 46	18 50					19 00	19 05			19 16	19 20				19 30	19 35	
Loughborough Jn	d						18 49						19 04				19 19					19 34		
Elephant & Castle	⊖ d						18 54		19 00				19 09				19 24		19 30			19 39		
London Blackfriars [3]	⊖ d						18 58		19a03				19 13				19 28		19a33			19 43		
City Thameslink [3]	a						19 00						19 15				19 30					19 45		
Farringdon	⊖ a						19 04						19 19				19 34					19 49		
St Pancras International [15]	⊖ a						19 08						19 23				19 38					19 53		
Brixton	⊖ d	11 37						18 52						19 07				19 22					19 37	
London Victoria [15]	⊖ a	11 44			18 47	18 47		18 59		19 02	19 12			19 14	19 17	19 17		19 29			19 32		19 44	19 47

		SE 30 [1]	FC	SE 70	SE 83	SE 70		SE 92 [1]	SE 30 [1]	FC	SE 70	SE 83	SE 94 [1]	SE 70		SE 92 [1]	SE 30 [1]	FC	SE 83	SE 70	SE 92 [1]	FC		SE 83	SE 94 [1]
Sevenoaks [4]	d				19 04							19 34							20 04					20 34	
Bat & Ball	d				19 07							19 37							20 07					20 37	
Otford [4]	d				19 10							19 40	19 55						20 10					20 40	20 55
Shoreham (Kent)	d				19 13							19 43							20 13					20 43	
Eynsford	d				19 17							19 47							20 17					20 47	
Swanley [4]	d				19 22			19 42				19 52	20 04			20 12			20 22		20 42			20 52	21 04
St Mary Cray	d				19 26			19 47				19 56	20 08			20 17			20 26		20 47			20 56	21 08
Orpington [4]	d			19 23		19 38					19 53			20 08						20 38					
Petts Wood [4]	d			19 26		19 41					19 56			20 11						20 41					
Bickley [4]	d			19 30	19 31	19 45					20 00	20 01		20 15					20 31	20 45				21 01	
Bromley South [4]	d	19 30		19 33	19 35	19 48		19 54	20 00		20 03	20 05	20 15	20 18		20 24	20 30		20 35	20 48	20 54			21 05	21 15
Shortlands [4]	d			19 35	19 37	19 50					20 05	20 07		20 20					20 37	20 50				21 07	
Ravensbourne	d				19 39							20 09							20 39					21 09	
Beckenham Hill	d				19 41							20 11							20 41					21 11	
Bellingham	d				19 43							20 13							20 43					21 13	
Catford	d				19 45							20 15							20 45					21 15	
Crofton Park	d				19 48							20 18							20 48					21 18	
Lewisham [4]	d																								
Nunhead [4]	d				19 50							20 20							20 50					21 20	
Peckham Rye [4]	d				19 52							20 22							20 52					21 22	
Denmark Hill [4]	d				19 55							20 25							20 55					21 25	
Beckenham Junction [4]	d			19 38		19 53					20 08			20 23						20 53					
Kent House [4]	d			19 40		19 55					20 10			20 25						20 55					
Penge East	d			19 42		19 57					20 12			20 27						20 57					
Sydenham Hill	d			19 45		20 00					20 15			20 30						21 00					
West Dulwich	d			19 47		20 02					20 17			20 32						21 02					
Herne Hill [4]	d		19 47	19 50		20 05				20 17	20 20			20 35				20 47		21 05		21 17			
Loughborough Jn	d		19 51							20 21								20 51				21 21			
Elephant & Castle	⊖ d		19 56		20 00					20 26		20 30						20 56	21 00			21 26		21 30	
London Blackfriars [3]	⊖ d		20 00		20a03					20 30		20a33						21 00	21a03			21 33		21a33	
City Thameslink [3]	a		20 02							20 32								21 02							
Farringdon	⊖ a		20 06							20 36								21 06				21 38			
St Pancras International [15]	⊖ a		20 10							20 40								21 10				21 42			
Brixton	⊖ d			19 52		20 07					20 22			20 37						21 07					
London Victoria [15]	⊖ a	19 47		19 59		20 14		20 17	20 17		20 29		20 32	20 44		20 47	20 47			21 14	21 17				21 32

For general notes see front of timetable
For details of catering facilities see
Directory of Train Operators

A From Canterbury West (Table 207)

Table 195

Saturdays

Sevenoaks, Otford, Orpington, Bromley South, Beckenham Junction and Catford → London

Network Diagram - see first page of Table 195

		SE 70	SE 30 1	SE 83	FC	SE 70	SE 92 1	SE 83		SE 94 1	FC	SE 70	SE 30 1	SE 83	FC	SE 70		SE 90 1	SE 83	SE 94 1	SE 70	SE 50 1	SE 90 1		
Sevenoaks 4	d			21 04				21 34						22 04					22 34						
Bat & Ball	d			21 07				21 37						22 07					22 37						
Otford 4	d			21 10				21 40		21 55				22 10					22 40	22 55					
Shoreham (Kent)	d			21 13				21 43						22 13					22 43						
Eynsford	d			21 17				21 47						22 17					22 47						
Swanley 4	d			21 22			21 42	21 52		22 04				22 22				22 42	22 52	23 04			23 42		
St Mary Cray	d			21 26			21 47	21 56		22 08				22 26				22 47	22 56	23 08			23 47		
Orpington 4	d	21 08				21 38						22 08				22 38					23 08				
Petts Wood 4	d	21 11				21 41						22 11				22 41					23 11				
Bickley 4	d	21 15		21 31		21 45		22 01				22 15		22 31		22 45			23 01		23 15				
Bromley South 4	d	21 18	21 30	21 35		21 48	21 54	22 05		22 15		22 18	22 30	22 35		22 48		22 54	23 05	23 15	23 18	23 30	23 54		
Shortlands 4	d	21 20		21 37		21 50		22 07				22 20		22 37		22 50			23 07		23 20				
Ravensbourne	d			21 39				22 09						22 39					23 09						
Beckenham Hill	d			21 41				22 11						22 41					23 11						
Bellingham	d			21 43				22 13						22 43					23 13						
Catford	d			21 45				22 15						22 45					23 15						
Crofton Park	d			21 48				22 18						22 48					23 18						
Lewisham 4	d																								
Nunhead 4	d			21 50				22 20						22 50					23 20						
Peckham Rye 4	d			21 52				22 22						22 52					23 22						
Denmark Hill 4	d			21 55				22 25						22 55					23 25						
Beckenham Junction 4	d	21 23				21 53						22 23				22 53					23 23				
Kent House 4	d	21 25				21 55						22 25				22 55					23 25				
Penge East	d	21 27				21 57						22 27				22 57					23 27				
Sydenham Hill	d	21 30				22 00						22 30				23 00					23 30				
West Dulwich	d	21 32				22 02						22 32				23 02					23 32				
Herne Hill 4	d	21 35			21 55	22 05					22 26	22 35			22 55	23 05					23 35				
Loughborough Jn	d				21 59						22 30														
Elephant & Castle	⊖ d			22 00	22 04			22 30			22 34			23 00	23 04				23 30						
London Blackfriars 3	⊖ d			22a03	22 07			22a33			22 37			23a03	23 09				23a33						
City Thameslink 3	a																								
Farringdon	⊖ a				22 13						22 43				23 13										
St Pancras International 15	⊖ a				22 17						22 47				23 17										
Brixton	⊖ d	21 37				22 07						22 37				23 07					23 37				
London Victoria 15	⊖ a	21 44	21 47			22 14	22 17			22 32		22 44	22 47			23 14		23 17		23 32	23 44	23 47	00 10		

Sundays

		SE 72	SE 70	SE 72	SE 55 1	SE 70	SE 72	SE 50 1	SE 94 1	SE 70	SE 72	SE 55 1	SE 70	SE 72	SE 30 1 🍴	SE 94 1		SE 70	SE 72	SE 92 1	SE 70	SE 72	SE 30 1 🍴	SE 94 1	SE 70
Sevenoaks 4	d										07 55			08 25					08 55			09 25			
Bat & Ball	d										07 58			08 28					08 58			09 28			
Otford 4	d								07 56		08 01			08 31		08 56			09 01			09 31		09 56	
Shoreham (Kent)	d										08 04			08 34					09 04			09 34			
Eynsford	d										08 07			08 37					09 07			09 37			
Swanley 4	d				07 29				08 05		08 12	08 29		08 42		09 05			09 12	09 29		09 42		10 05	
St Mary Cray	d				07 34				08 10		08 16	08 34		08 46		09 10			09 16	09 34		09 46		10 10	
Orpington 4	d	06 44	07 08	07 14		07 38	07 44			08 08			08 38					09 08			09 38				10 08
Petts Wood 4	d	06 47	07 11	07 17		07 41	07 47			08 11			08 41					09 11			09 41				10 11
Bickley 4	d	06 51	07 15	07 21		07 45	07 51			08 15	08 21		08 45	08 51				09 15	09 21		09 45	09 51			10 15
Bromley South 4	d	06 54	07 18	07 24	07 40	07 48	07 54	08 00	08 16	08 18	08 24	08 40	08 48	08 54	09 00	09 16		09 18	09 24	09 40	09 48	09 54	10 00	10 16	10 18
Shortlands 4	d	06 56	07 20	07 26		07 50	07 56			08 20	08 26		08 50	08 56				09 20	09 26		09 50	09 56			10 20
Ravensbourne	d	06 59		07 29			07 59				08 29			08 59					09 29			09 59			
Beckenham Hill	d	07 01		07 31			08 01				08 31			09 01					09 31			10 01			
Bellingham	d	07 03		07 33			08 03				08 33			09 03					09 33			10 03			
Catford	d	07 05		07 35			08 05				08 35			09 05					09 35			10 05			
Crofton Park	d	07 07		07 37			08 07				08 37			09 07					09 37			10 07			
Lewisham 4	d																								
Nunhead 4	d	07 10		07 40			08 10				08 40			09 10					09 40			10 10			
Peckham Rye 4	d	07 12		07 42			08 12				08 42			09 12					09 42			10 12			
Denmark Hill 4	d	07 14		07 44			08 14				08 44			09 14					09 44			10 14			
Beckenham Junction 4	d		07 23			07 53				08 23			08 53					09 23			09 53				10 23
Kent House 4	d		07 25			07 55				08 25			08 55					09 25			09 55				10 25
Penge East	d		07 27			07 57				08 27			08 57					09 27			09 57				10 27
Sydenham Hill	d		07 30			08 00				08 30			09 00					09 30			10 00				10 30
West Dulwich	d		07 31			08 01				08 32			09 01					09 31			10 01				10 31
Herne Hill 4	d		07 34			08 04				08 34			09 04					09 34			10 04				10 34
Loughborough Jn	d																								
Elephant & Castle	⊖ d																								
London Blackfriars 3	⊖ d																								
City Thameslink 3	a																								
Farringdon	⊖ a																								
St Pancras International 15	⊖ a																								
Brixton	⊖ d		07 36			08 06				08 36			09 06					09 36			10 06				10 36
London Victoria 15	⊖ a	07 23	07 43	07 53	08 01	08 13	08 23	08 16	08 32	08 43	08 53	09 01	09 13	09 23	09 16	09 32		09 43	09 53	10 01	10 13	10 23	10 16	10 32	10 43

For general notes see front of timetable
For details of catering facilities see
Directory of Train Operators

Table 195

Sundays

Sevenoaks, Otford, Orpington, Bromley South, Beckenham Junction and Catford → London

Network Diagram - see first page of Table 195

		SE 72	SE 92 [1]	FC	SE 70	SE 72	SE 30 [1]	FC	SE 94 [1] A	SE 70	and at the same minutes past each hour until	SE 72	SE 92 [1]	FC	SE 30 [1] B	SE 70	SE 72	SE 30 [1]	FC	SE 94 [1] A	SE 70	SE 72
Sevenoaks [4]	d	09 55				10 25						16 55					17 25					17 55
Bat & Ball	d	09 58				10 28						16 58					17 28					17 58
Otford [4]	d	10 01				10 31			10 56			17 01					17 31			17 56		18 01
Shoreham (Kent)	d	10 04				10 34						17 04					17 34					18 04
Eynsford	d	10 07				10 37						17 07					17 37					18 07
Swanley [4]	d	10 12	10 29			10 42			11 05			17 12	17 29				17 42			18 05		18 12
St Mary Cray	d	10 16	10 34			10 46			11 10			17 16	17 34				17 46			18 10		18 16
Orpington [4]	d				10 38					11 08						17 38					18 08	
Petts Wood [4]	d				10 41					11 11						17 41					18 11	
Bickley [4]	d	10 21			10 45	10 51				11 15		17 21				17 45	17 51				18 15	18 21
Bromley South [4]	d	10 24	10 40		10 48	10 54	11 00		11 16	11 18		17 24	17 40		17 42	17 48	17 54	18 00		18 16	18 18	18 24
Shortlands [4]	d	10 26			10 50	10 56				11 20		17 26				17 50	17 56				18 20	18 26
Ravensbourne	d	10 29				10 59						17 29					17 59					18 29
Beckenham Hill	d	10 31				11 01						17 31					18 01					18 31
Bellingham	d	10 33				11 03						17 33					18 03					18 33
Catford	d	10 35				11 05						17 35					18 05					18 35
Crofton Park	d	10 37				11 07						17 37					18 07					18 37
Lewisham [4]	d																					
Nunhead [4]	d	10 40				11 10						17 40					18 10					18 40
Peckham Rye [4]	d	10 42				11 12						17 42					18 12					18 42
Denmark Hill [4]	d	10 44				11 14						17 44					18 14					18 44
Beckenham Junction [4]	d				10 53					11 23						17 53					18 23	
Kent House [4]	d				10 55					11 25						17 55					18 25	
Penge East	d				10 57					11 27						17 57					18 27	
Sydenham Hill	d				11 00					11 30						18 00					18 30	
West Dulwich	d				11 01					11 31						18 01					18 31	
Herne Hill [4]	d			10 42	11 04			11 12		11 34				17 42		18 04			18 12		18 34	
Loughborough Jn	d			10 45				11 15						17 45					18 15			
Elephant & Castle	⊖ d			10 50				11 20						17 50					18 20			
London Blackfriars [3]	⊖ d			10 58				11 28						17 58					18 28			
City Thameslink [3]	a																					
Farringdon	⊖ a			11 02				11 32						18 02					18 32			
St Pancras International [15]	⊖ a			11 06				11 36						18 06					18 36			
Brixton	⊖ d				11 06					11 36						18 06					18 36	
London Victoria [15]	⊖ a	10 53	11 01		11 13	11 23	11 16		11 32	11 43		17 53	18 01		17 58	18 13	18 23	18 16		18 32	18 43	18 53

		SE 92 [1]	FC	SE 30 [1] B	SE 70	SE 72	SE 30 [1]		FC	SE 94 [1] A	SE 70	SE 72	SE 92 [1]	FC	SE 30 [1] B	SE 70	SE 72	SE 30 [1]	FC	SE 94 [1] A	SE 70	SE 72	SE 92 [1]		FC
Sevenoaks [4]	d					18 25						18 55					19 25					19 55			
Bat & Ball	d					18 28						18 58					19 28					19 58			
Otford [4]	d					18 31				18 56		19 01					19 31			19 56		20 01			
Shoreham (Kent)	d					18 34						19 04					19 34					20 04			
Eynsford	d					18 37						19 07					19 37					20 07			
Swanley [4]	d	18 29				18 42				19 05		19 12	19 29				19 42			20 05		20 12	20 29		
St Mary Cray	d	18 34				18 46				19 10		19 16	19 34				19 46			20 10		20 16	20 34		
Orpington [4]	d				18 38						19 08					19 38					20 08				
Petts Wood [4]	d				18 41						19 11					19 41					20 11				
Bickley [4]	d				18 45	18 51					19 15	19 21				19 45	19 51				20 15	20 21			
Bromley South [4]	d	18 40		18 42	18 48	18 54	19 00			19 16	19 18	19 24	19 40		19 42	19 48	19 54	20 00		20 16	20 18	20 24	20 40		
Shortlands [4]	d				18 50	18 56					19 20	19 26				19 50	19 56				20 20	20 26			
Ravensbourne	d					18 59						19 29					19 59					20 29			
Beckenham Hill	d					19 01						19 31					20 01					20 31			
Bellingham	d					19 03						19 33					20 03					20 33			
Catford	d					19 05						19 35					20 05					20 35			
Crofton Park	d					19 07						19 37					20 07					20 37			
Lewisham [4]	d																								
Nunhead [4]	d					19 10						19 40					20 10					20 40			
Peckham Rye [4]	d					19 12						19 42					20 12					20 42			
Denmark Hill [4]	d					19 14						19 44					20 14					20 44			
Beckenham Junction [4]	d				18 53						19 23					19 53					20 23				
Kent House [4]	d				18 55						19 25					19 55					20 25				
Penge East	d				18 57						19 27					19 57					20 27				
Sydenham Hill	d				19 00						19 30					20 00					20 30				
West Dulwich	d				19 01						19 31					20 01					20 31				
Herne Hill [4]	d		18 42		19 04				19 12		19 34			19 42		20 04			20 12		20 34				20 42
Loughborough Jn	d		18 44						19 14					19 44					20 14						20 44
Elephant & Castle	⊖ d		18 50						19 20					19 50					20 20						20 50
London Blackfriars [3]	⊖ d		18 58						19 28					19 58					20 28						20 58
City Thameslink [3]	a																								
Farringdon	⊖ a		19 02						19 32					20 02					20 32						21 02
St Pancras International [15]	⊖ a		19 06						19 36					20 06					20 36						21 06
Brixton	⊖ d				19 06						19 36					20 06					20 36				
London Victoria [15]	⊖ a	19 01		18 58	19 13	19 23	19 16			19 32	19 43	19 53	20 01		19 58	20 13	20 23	20 16		20 32	20 43	20 53	21 01		

For general notes see front of timetable
For details of catering facilities see Directory of Train Operators

A From Canterbury West (Table 207)
B 20 July to 31 August

Table 195

Sundays

Sevenoaks, Otford, Orpington, Bromley South, Beckenham Junction and Catford → London

Network Diagram - see first page of Table 195

		SE 70	SE 72	SE 30 1	FC	SE 94 1 A	SE 70	SE 72	SE 92 1	FC	SE 70	SE 72	SE 30 1	SE 94 1	SE 70	SE 72	SE 92 1	SE 70	SE 72	SE 30 1	SE 94 1	SE 72	SE 50 1
Sevenoaks 4	d		20 25					20 55				21 25				21 55			22 25				
Bat & Ball	d		20 28					20 58				21 28				21 58			22 28				
Otford 4	d		20 31			20 56		21 01				21 31		21 56		22 01			22 31		22 56		
Shoreham (Kent)	d		20 34					21 04				21 34				22 04			22 34				
Eynsford	d		20 37					21 07				21 37				22 07			22 37				
Swanley 4	d		20 42			21 05		21 12	21 29			21 42		22 05		22 12	22 29		22 42		23 05		23 32
St Mary Cray	d		20 46			21 10		21 16	21 34			21 46		22 10		22 16	22 34		22 46		23 10		23 36
Orpington 4	d	20 38					21 08				21 38				22 08			22 38				23 14	
Petts Wood 4	d	20 41					21 11				21 41				22 11			22 41				23 17	
Bickley 4	d	20 45	20 51				21 15	21 21			21 45	21 51			22 15	22 21		22 45	22 51			23 21	
Bromley South 4	d	20 48	20 54	21 00		21 16	21 18	21 24	21 40		21 48	21 54	22 00	22 16	22 18	22 24	22 40	22 48	22 54	23 00	23 16	23 24	23 42
Shortlands 4	d	20 50	20 56				21 20	21 26			21 50	21 56			22 20	22 26		22 50	22 56			23 26	
Ravensbourne	d		20 59					21 29				21 59				22 29			22 59			23 29	
Beckenham Hill	d		21 01					21 31				22 01				22 31			23 01			23 31	
Bellingham	d		21 03					21 33				22 03				22 33			23 03			23 33	
Catford	d		21 05					21 35				22 05				22 35			23 05			23 35	
Crofton Park	d		21 07					21 37				22 07				22 37			23 07			23 37	
Lewisham 4	d																						
Nunhead 4	d		21 10					21 40				22 10				22 40			23 10			23 40	
Peckham Rye 4	d		21 12					21 42				22 12				22 42			23 12			23 42	
Denmark Hill 4	d		21 14					21 44				22 14				22 44			23 14			23 44	
Beckenham Junction 4	d	20 53					21 23				21 53				22 23			22 53					
Kent House 4	d	20 55					21 25				21 55				22 25			22 55					
Penge East	d	20 57					21 27				21 57				22 27			22 57					
Sydenham Hill	d	21 00					21 30				22 00				22 30			23 00					
West Dulwich	d	21 01					21 31				22 01				22 31			23 01					
Herne Hill 4	d	21 04			21 12		21 34			21 42	22 04				22 34			23 04					
Loughborough Jn	d				21 14					21 44													
Elephant & Castle	⊖ d				21 20					21 50													
London Blackfriars 3	⊖ d				21 28					21 58													
City Thameslink 3	a																						
Farringdon	⊖ a				21 32					22 02													
St Pancras International 15	⊖ a				21 36					22 06													
Brixton	⊖ d	21 06					21 36				22 06				22 36			23 06					
London Victoria 15	⊖ a	21 13	21 23	21 16		21 32	21 43	21 53	22 01		22 13	22 23	22 16	22 32	22 43	22 53	23 01	23 13	23 24	23 16	23 32	23 53	23 59

For general notes see front of timetable
For details of catering facilities see Directory of Train Operators

A From Canterbury West (Table 207)

For details of Bank Holiday service alterations please see first page of Table 195

London → Maidstone East and Ashford International

Network Diagram - see first page of Table 195

Miles	Miles	Miles		SE MO 94 1	SE MX 66 1 A	SE MX 94 1	SE 64 1 B	SE 64 1 C	SE 66 1 C	SE 64 1 B	SE 64 1 A	SE 96 1	SE 64 1 A	SE 94	SE 09 1	SE 64 1 A	SE 94	SE 09 1	SE 64 1 A
0	—	—	**London Victoria 15** ⊖ 195 d	22p42	23p11	23p51			06 10	06 47	07 19	07 49	08 18	08 49		09 19	09 48		10 18
—	0	—	**London Blackfriars 3** ⊖ 195 d																
—	1¼	—	Elephant & Castle ⊖ 195 d																
4	—	—	Herne Hill 4 195 d																
8¾	—	—	Beckenham Junction 4 195 ⇌ d																
11	11½	—	Bromley South 4 195 d	22p58	23p30	00 07			06 30	07 04	07 36	08 07	08 39	09 08		09 37	10 04		10 34
—	—	—	London Charing Cross 4 ⊖ d																
—	—	—	London Waterloo (East) 4 ⊖ d																
—	—	0	**London Cannon Street 4** ⊖ d												09 13			10 14	
—	—	¾	London Bridge 4 ⊖ d												09 17			10 18	
14¾	—	—	St Mary Cray 195 d	23p05	23p37	00 14													
17½	—	—	Swanley 4 195 d	23p10	23p41	00 18			06 39	07 13	07 45	08 17		09 16			10 13		
24	—	—	Otford 4 195 d	23p19	23p50	00 30			06 49	07 22	07 54	08 26	08 57	09 25		09 53	10 23		10 51
27	—	—	Kemsing d						06 55	07 27	07 58	08 30		09 30			10 27		
29½	—	—	Borough Green & Wrotham d	23p26	23p57	00 37			06 59	07 31	08 03	08 35	09 04	09 34		10 00	10 32		10 58
34¾	—	—	West Malling d	23p32	00 03	00 43			07 05	07 37	08 09	08 41	09 10	09 40	09 57	10 06	10 38	10 57	11 04
35¾	—	—	East Malling d	23p35	00 06	00 46			07 08	07 40	08 11	08 43		09 43			10 41		
37½	—	—	Barming d	23p38	00 09	00 49			07 11	07 43	08 15	08 47		09 46			10 44		
40	—	37¾	**Maidstone East 4** a	23p43	00 14	00 54			07 16	07 48	08 19	08 51	09 17	09 51	10 05	10 13	10 49	11 05	11 11
—	—	—	d	23p43	00 14	00 54	05 56	06 33	07 23	07 49	08 21		09 17		10 05	10 14		11 05	11 13
42¾	—	—	Bearsted d	23p48	00 19	00 59	06 01	06 38	07 28	07 54	08 26		09 22		10 11	10 19		11 11	11 18
45	—	—	Hollingbourne d	23p52	00 23	01 03	06 05	06 42	07 32	07 58	08 30		09 26			10 23			11 22
47½	—	—	Harrietsham d	23p56	00 27	01 07	06 09	06 46	07 36	08 02	08 34		09 30			10 27			11 26
49¼	—	—	Lenham d	00 01	00 31	01 11	06 12	06 49	07 39	08 06	08 37		09 34			10 30			11 30
53¼	—	—	Charing d	00 05	00 36	01 16	06 17	06 54	07 44	08 11	08 42		09 39			10 35			11 35
59¼	—	57	**Ashford International** a	00 12	00 43	01 23	06 25	07 02	07 52	08 21	08 53		09 46		10 28	10 43		11 28	11 43

	SE 94	SE 09 1	SE 64 1 A	SE 94	SE 09 1	SE 64 1 A	SE 94	SE 09 1	SE 64 1 A	SE 94	SE 09 1	SE 94 1	SE 94 1	SE 09 1	SE 94 1	SE 94 1	SE 09 1	SE 96 1	SE 94 1
London Victoria 15 ⊖ 195 d	10 48		11 18	11 48		12 18	12 48		13 18	13 48		14 18	14 48		15 18	15 48		16 27	16 56
London Blackfriars 3 ⊖ 195 d																			
Elephant & Castle ⊖ 195 d																			
Herne Hill 4 195 d																			
Beckenham Junction 4 195 ⇌ d																			
Bromley South 4 195 d	11 04		11 34	12 04		12 34	13 04		13 34	14 04		14 34	15 04		15 34	16 04		16 48	17 15
London Charing Cross 4 ⊖ d																			
London Waterloo (East) 4 ⊖ d																			
London Cannon Street 4 ⊖ d		11 14			12 14			13 14			14 14			15 14			16 14		
London Bridge 4 ⊖ d		11 18			12 18			13 18			14 18			15 18			16 18		
St Mary Cray 195 d																			
Swanley 4 195 d	11 13			12 13			13 13			14 13			15 13		15 43	16 13		16 57	
Otford 4 195 d	11 23		11 51	12 23		12 51	13 23		13 51	14 23		14 51	15 23		15 52	16 23	16 48	17 07	17 33
Kemsing d	11 27			12 27			13 27			14 27			15 27		15 57			17 12	
Borough Green & Wrotham d	11 32		11 58	12 32		12 58	13 32		13 58	14 32		14 58	15 32		16 02	16 30		17 16	17 40
West Malling d	11 38	11 57	12 04	12 38	12 57	13 04	13 38	13 57	14 04	14 38	14 57	15 04	15 38	15 57	16 08	16 36	17 00	17 22	17 46
East Malling d	11 41			12 41			13 41			14 41			15 41		16 11			17 25	
Barming d	11 44			12 44			13 44			14 44			15 44		16 14			17 28	
Maidstone East 4 a	11 49	12 05	12 11	12 49	13 05	13 11	13 49	14 05	14 11	14 49	15 05	15 11	15 49	16 05	16 19	16 44	17 07	17 33	17 53
d		12 05	12 13		13 05	13 13		14 05	14 13		15 05	15 21	15 50	16 05	16 19	16 44	17 07	17 34	17 54
Bearsted d		12 11	12 18		13 11	13 18		14 11	14 18		15 11	15 26	15 55	16 11	16 24	16 49	17 13	17 39	17 59
Hollingbourne d			12 22			13 22			14 22			15 30			16 28	16 53	17 17	17 43	18 03
Harrietsham d			12 26			13 26			14 26			15 34			16 32	16 57	17 21	17 47	18 07
Lenham d			12 30			13 30			14 30			15 40	16 03		16 36	17 01	17 24	17 51	18 10
Charing d			12 35			13 35			14 35			15 45			16 41	17 06	17 29	17 56	18 15
Ashford International a		12 29	12 43		13 28	13 43		14 28	14 43		15 27	15 54	16 14	16 28	16 48	17 13	17b40	18 05	18b25

	SE 94 1	SE 96	SE 96 1	SE 97 1	SE 94 1	SE 94 1	SE 09 1	SE 94 1	SE 94 1	SE 94 1	SE 94 1	SE 96 1	SE 96 1	SE 66 1 A	SE 94 1
London Victoria 15 ⊖ 195 d	17 22	17 32	17 58		18 18	18 48		19 18	19 48	20 18	20 48	21 09	22 09	23 11	23 51
London Blackfriars 3 ⊖ 195 d				18 00											
Elephant & Castle ⊖ 195 d				18 04											
Herne Hill 4 195 d															
Beckenham Junction 4 195 ⇌ d		17 46								20 32	21 02				
Bromley South 4 195 d	17 40	17 51	18 18	18 22	18 36	19 06		19 35	20 07	20 37	21 07	21 29	22 29	23 30	00 07
London Charing Cross 4 ⊖ d															
London Waterloo (East) 4 ⊖ d															
London Cannon Street 4 ⊖ d							19 14								
London Bridge 4 ⊖ d							19 18								
St Mary Cray 195 d	17 47	18 00		18 28	18 43	19 12						21 35	22 35	23 37	00 14
Swanley 4 195 d	17 52	18 05		18 33	18 48	19 16		19 44		20 45		21 40	22 40	23 41	00 18
Otford 4 195 d	18 01	18 18	18 36	18 42	18 58	19 26	19 48	19 53	20 23	20 54	21 23	21 49	22 49	23 50	00 30
Kemsing d	18 06	18 22		18 46	19 02			19 58		20 59					
Borough Green & Wrotham d	18 11	18 27	18 43	18 51	19 07	19 33		20 02	20 30	21 03	21 30	21 56	22 56	23 57	00 37
West Malling d	18 17	18 33	18 49	18 57	19 13	19 39	20 00	20 08	20 36	21 09	21 36	22 02	23 02	00 03	00 43
East Malling d	18 19	18 35		18 59	19 15	19 41		20 11		21 12		22 04	23 04	00 06	00 46
Barming d	18 23	18 39		19 03	19 19	19 45		20 14		21 15		22 08	23 08	00 09	00 49
Maidstone East 4 a	18 27	18 44	18 56	19 07	19 23	19 49	20 07	20 19	20 43	21 20	21 43	22 12	23 12	00 14	00 54
d	18 29		18 56	19 08	19 25	19 50	20 08	20 20	20 44	21 21	21 44	22 13	23 13	00 14	00 54
Bearsted d	18 34		19 01	19 13	19 30	19 55	20 13	20 25	20 49	21 26	21 49	22 18	23 18	00 19	00 59
Hollingbourne d	18 38		19 05	19 17	19 34	19 59		20 29	20 53	21 30	21 53	22 22	23 22	00 23	01 03
Harrietsham d	18 42		19 09	19 21	19 38	20 03		20 33	20 57	21 34	21 57	22 26	23 26	00 27	01 07
Lenham d	18 45		19 13	19 24	19 41	20 07		20 36	21 01	21 37	22 01	22 30	23 30	00 31	01 11
Charing d	18 50		19 18	19 29	19 46	20 12		20 41	21 06	21 42	22 06	22 35	23 35	00 36	01 16
Ashford International a	18 58		19b28	19 37	19 55	20b21	20 32	20 49	21 14	21 50	22 15	22 42	23 42	00 43	01 23

For general notes see front of timetable
For details of catering facilities see Directory of Train Operators

A To Canterbury West (Table 207)
B To Ramsgate (Table 207)
C To Margate (Table 207)
b Until 10 October Arr. 2 minutes earlier

London → Maidstone East and Ashford International

Network Diagram - see first page of Table 195

		SE 66 1 A	SE 94 1	SE 64 1 B	SE 94 1 C	SE 64 1 C	SE 94 1	SE 64 1 A	SE 94	SE 09 1	SE 64 1 A	SE 94	SE 09 1	SE 64 1 A	SE 94	SE 09 1		SE 64 1 A	SE 94	SE 09 1	SE 64 1 A	SE 94	SE 09 1	SE 64 1 A	SE 94
London Victoria 15	⊖ 195 d	23p11	23p51		06 18	07 18	07 48	08 18	08 48		09 18	09 48		10 18	10 48			11 18	11 48		12 18	12 48		13 18	13 48
London Blackfriars 3	⊖ 195 d																								
Elephant & Castle	⊖ 195 d																								
Herne Hill 4	195 d																								
Beckenham Junction 4	195 d																								
Bromley South 4	195 d	23p30	00 07		06 34	07 34	08 04	08 34	09 04		09 34	10 04		10 34	11 04			11 34	12 04		12 34	13 04		13 34	14 04
London Charing Cross 4	⊖ d																								
London Waterloo (East) 4	⊖ d																								
London Cannon Street 4	⊖ d									09 14			10 14			11 14				12 14			13 14		
London Bridge 4	⊖ d									09 18			10 18			11 18				12 18			13 18		
St Mary Cray	195 d	23p37	00 14		06 41	07 41																			
Swanley 4	195 d	23p41	00 18		06 45	07 45	08 13		09 13			10 13			11 13				12 13			13 13			14 13
Otford 4	195 d	23p50	00 30		06 54	07 54	08 23	08 51	09 23		09 51	10 23		10 51	11 23			11 51	12 23		12 51	13 23		13 51	14 23
Kemsing	d						08 27		09 27			10 27			11 27				12 27			13 27			14 27
Borough Green & Wrotham	d	23p57	00 37		07 02	08 02	08 32	08 58	09 32		09 58	10 32		10 58	11 32			11 58	12 32		12 58	13 32		13 58	14 32
West Malling	d	00 03	00 43		07 08	08 08	08 38	09 04	09 38	09 57	10 04	10 38	10 57	11 04	11 38	11 57		12 04	12 38	12 57	13 04	13 38	13 57	14 04	14 38
East Malling	d	00 06	00 46		07 10	08 10	08 41		09 41			10 41			11 41				12 41			13 41			14 41
Barming	d	00 09	00 49		07 14	08 14	08 44		09 44			10 44			11 44				12 44			13 44			14 44
Maidstone East 4	a	00 14	00 54		07 18	08 18	08 49	09 11	09 49	10 05	10 11	10 49	11 05	11 11	11 49	12 05		12 11	12 49	13 05	13 11	13 49	14 05	14 11	14 49
	d	00 14	00 54	06 19	07 19	08 19	08 50	09 13		10 05	10 13		11 05	11 13		12 05		12 13		13 05	13 13		14 05	14 13	
Bearsted	d	00 19	00 59	06 24	07 24	08 24	08 55	09 18		10 11	10 18		11 11	11 18		12 11		12 18		13 11	13 18		14 11	14 18	
Hollingbourne	d	00 23	01 03	06 28	07 28	08 28		09 22			10 22			11 22				12 22			13 22			14 22	
Harrietsham	d	00 27	01 07	06 32	07 32	08 32		09 26			10 26			11 26				12 26			13 26			14 26	
Lenham	d	00 31	01 11	06 35	07 35	08 35		09 30			10 30			11 30				12 30			13 30			14 30	
Charing	d	00 36	01 16	06 40	07 40	08 40		09 35			10 35			11 35				12 35			13 35			14 35	
Ashford International	a	00 43	01 23	06 48	07 48	08 48	09 12	09 43		10 27	10 43		11 27	11 43		12 27		12 43		13 27	13 43		14 27	14 43	

		SE 09 1	SE 64 1 A	SE 94	SE 09 1	SE 64 1 A	SE 94	SE 09 1	SE 94 1	SE 94	SE 09 1	SE 94 1	SE 94	SE 09 1	SE 94 1	SE 94 1	SE 09 1	SE 96 1	SE 96 1	SE 96 1	SE 96 1	SE 66 1 A	SE 94 1
London Victoria 15	⊖ 195 d		14 18	14 48		15 18	15 48		16 18	16 48		17 18	17 48		18 18	18 48		19 18	20 18	21 18	22 18	23 18	23 51
London Blackfriars 3	⊖ 195 d																						
Elephant & Castle	⊖ 195 d																						
Herne Hill 4	195 d																						
Beckenham Junction 4	195 d																						
Bromley South 4	195 d		14 34	15 04		15 34	16 04		16 34	17 04		17 34	18 04		18 34	19 04		19 34	20 34	21 34	22 34	23 34	00 07
London Charing Cross 4	⊖ d																						
London Waterloo (East) 4	⊖ d																						
London Cannon Street 4	⊖ d	14 14			15 14			16 14			17 14			18 14			19 14						
London Bridge 4	⊖ d	14 18			15 18			16 18			17 18			18 18			19 18						
St Mary Cray	195 d																	19 41	20 41	21 41	22 41	23 41	00 14
Swanley 4	195 d			15 13			16 13			17 13			18 13			19 13		19 45	20 45	21 45	22 45	23 45	00 18
Otford 4	195 d		14 51	15 23		15 51	16 23		16 51	17 23		17 51	18 23		18 51	19 23		19 54	20 54	21 54	22 54	23 54	00 30
Kemsing	d			15 27			16 27			17 27			18 27			19 27							
Borough Green & Wrotham	d		14 58	15 32		15 58	16 32		16 58	17 32		17 58	18 32		18 58	19 32		20 02	21 02	22 02	23 02	00 02	00 37
West Malling	d	14 57	15 04	15 38	15 57	16 04	16 38	16 57	17 04	17 38	17 57	18 04	18 38	18 57	19 04	19 38	19 57	20 08	21 08	22 08	23 08	00 08	00 43
East Malling	d			15 41			16 41			17 41			18 41			19 41		20 10	21 10	22 10	23 10	00 10	00 46
Barming	d			15 44			16 44			17 44			18 44			19 44		20 14	21 14	22 14	23 14	00 14	00 49
Maidstone East 4	a	15 05	15 11	15 49	16 05	16 11	16 49	17 05	17 11	17 49	18 05	18 11	18 49	19 05	19 11	19 49	20 05	20 18	21 18	22 18	23 18	00 18	00 54
	d	15 05	15 13		16 05	16 13		17 05	17 13		18 05	18 13		19 05	19 13		20 05	20 19	21 19	22 19	23 19	00 19	00 54
Bearsted	d	15 11	15 18		16 11	16 18		17 11	17 18		18 11	18 18		19 11	19 18		20 11	20 24	21 24	22 24	23 24	00 24	00 59
Hollingbourne	d		15 22			16 22			17 22			18 22			19 22			20 28	21 28	22 28	23 28	00 28	01 03
Harrietsham	d		15 26			16 26			17 26			18 26			19 26			20 32	21 32	22 32	23 32	00 32	01 07
Lenham	d		15 30			16 30			17 29			18 29			19 29			20 35	21 35	22 35	23 35	00 35	01 11
Charing	d		15 35			16 35			17 34			18 34			19 34			20 40	21 40	22 40	23 40	00 40	01 16
Ashford International	a	15 27	15 43		16 27	16 43		17 27	17 43		18 27	18 42		19 27	19 42		20 27	20 48	21 48	22 48	23 48	00 48	01 23

For general notes see front of timetable
For details of catering facilities see Directory of Train Operators

A To Canterbury West (Table 207)
B To Margate (Table 207)
C To Ramsgate (Table 207)

Sundays

London → Maidstone East and Ashford International

Network Diagram - see first page of Table 195

	SE	SE	SE	SE	SE	SE	SE	SE	SE	SE	SE	SE	SE	SE	SE	SE	SE	SE
	66	94	94	94	94	94	94	94	94	94	94	94	94	94	94	94	94	94
	1	1	1	1	1	1	1	1	1	1	1	1	1	1	1	1	1	1
	A		A	A	A	A	A	A	A	A	A	A	A					
London Victoria 15 ⊖ 195 d	23p18	23p51	07 42	08 42	09 42	10 42	11 42	12 42	13 42	14 42	15 42	16 42	17 42	18 42	19 42	20 42	21 42	22 42
London Blackfriars 3 ⊖ 195 d																		
Elephant & Castle ⊖ 195 d																		
Herne Hill 4 195 d																		
Beckenham Junction 4 195 🚋 d																		
Bromley South 4 195 d	23p34	00 07	07 58	08 58	09 58	10 58	11 58	12 58	13 58	14 58	15 58	16 58	17 58	18 58	19 58	20 58	21 58	22 58
London Charing Cross 4 ⊖ d																		
London Waterloo (East) 4 ⊖ d																		
London Cannon Street 4 ⊖ d																		
London Bridge 4 ⊖ d																		
St Mary Cray 195 d	23p41	00 14	08 05	09 05	10 05	11 05	12 05	13 05	14 05	15 05	16 05	17 05	18 05	19 05	20 05	21 05	22 05	23 05
Swanley 4 195 d	23p45	00 18	08 10	09 10	10 10	11 10	12 10	13 10	14 10	15 10	16 10	17 10	18 10	19 10	20 10	21 10	22 10	23 10
Otford 4 195 d	23p54	00 30	08 19	09 19	10 19	11 19	12 19	13 19	14 19	15 19	16 19	17 19	18 19	19 19	20 19	21 19	22 19	23 19
Kemsing d																		
Borough Green & Wrotham d	00 02	00 37	08 26	09 26	10 26	11 26	12 26	13 26	14 26	15 26	16 26	17 26	18 26	19 26	20 26	21 26	22 26	23 26
West Malling d	00 08	00 43	08 32	09 32	10 32	11 32	12 32	13 32	14 32	15 32	16 32	17 32	18 32	19 32	20 32	21 32	22 32	23 32
East Malling d	00 10	00 46	08 35	09 35	10 35	11 35	12 35	13 35	14 35	15 35	16 35	17 35	18 35	19 35	20 35	21 35	22 35	23 35
Barming d	00 14	00 49	08 38	09 38	10 38	11 38	12 38	13 38	14 38	15 38	16 38	17 38	18 38	19 38	20 38	21 38	22 38	23 38
Maidstone East 4 a	00 18	00 54	08 43	09 43	10 43	11 43	12 43	13 43	14 43	15 43	16 43	17 43	18 43	19 43	20 43	21 43	22 43	23 43
d	00 19	00 54	08 43	09 43	10 43	11 43	12 43	13 43	14 43	15 43	16 43	17 43	18 43	19 43	20 43	21 43	22 43	23 43
Bearsted d	00 24	00 59	08 48	09 48	10 48	11 48	12 48	13 48	14 48	15 48	16 48	17 48	18 48	19 48	20 48	21 48	22 48	23 48
Hollingbourne d	00 28	01 03	08 52	09 52	10 52	11 52	12 52	13 52	14 52	15 52	16 52	17 52	18 52	19 52	20 52	21 52	22 52	23 52
Harrietsham d	00 32	01 07	08 56	09 56	10 56	11 56	12 56	13 56	14 56	15 56	16 56	17 56	18 56	19 56	20 56	21 56	22 56	23 56
Lenham d	00 35	01 11	09 00	10 00	11 00	12 00	13 00	14 00	15 00	16 00	17 00	18 00	19 00	20 00	21 00	22 00	23 00	00 01
Charing d	00 40	01 16	09 05	10 05	11 05	12 05	13 05	14 05	15 05	16 05	17 05	18 05	19 05	20 05	21 05	22 05	23 05	00 05
Ashford International a	00 48	01 23	09 12	10 12	11 12	12 12	13 12	14 12	15 12	16 12	17 12	18 12	19 12	20 12	21 12	22 12	23 12	00 12

For general notes see front of timetable
For details of catering facilities see Directory of Train Operators

A To Canterbury West (Table 207)

For details of Bank Holiday service alterations please see first page of Table 195

Ashford International and Maidstone East to London

Network Diagram - see first page of Table 195

Miles	Miles	Miles			SE 94 [1] A	SE 94 [1] B	SE 97 [1]	SE 94 [1]	SE 97 [1]	SE 96 [1] A	SE 96 [1] B	SE 94 [1]	SE 96 [1]	SE 96 [1]	SE 66 [1] C	SE 88 [1] D	SE 94 [1]	SE 64 [1] D	SE 09 [1]
0	—	0	**Ashford International**	d	05 30	05 33		06 12	06 23	06 33	06 36	06 54	07 13	07 43	08 14	08 32		09 04	09 34
6	—	—	Charing	d	05 38	05 41		06 20	06 31	06 41	06 44	07 02	07 21	07 51	08 22			09 12	
10	—	—	Lenham	d	05 43	05 46		06 25	06 36	06 46	06 49	07 07	07 26	07 56	08 27			09 17	
11¾	—	—	Harrietsham	d	05 46	05 49		06 28	06 39	06 49	06 52	07 10	07 29	07 59	08 30			09 20	
14¼	—	—	Hollingbourne	d	05 50	05 53		06 32	06 43	06 53	06 56	07 14	07 33	08 03	08 34			09 24	
16½	—	—	Bearsted	d	05 54	05 57	06 09	06 36	06 47	06 57	07 00	07 18	07 37	08 07	08 38	08 48		09 28	09 51
19¼	—	19¼	**Maidstone East [4]**	a	05 59	06 02	06 14	06 41	06 52	07 02	07 05	07 23	07 42	08 12	08 43	08 53		09 33	09 56
—	—	—		d	06 00	06 03	06 15	06 41	06 52	07 02	07 05	07 23	07 42	08 13	08 45	08 53	09 00	09 33	09 57
21¾	—	—	Barming	d	06 04	06 07		06 46	06 57	07 07	07 10	07 28	07 47	08 18			09 04		
23½	—	—	East Malling	d	06 08	06 11		06 49	07 00	07 10	07 13	07 31		08 21			09 08		
24½	—	—	West Malling	d	06 10	06 13	06 23	06 52	07 03	07 13	07 16	07 34	07 51	08 24	08 52	09 01	09 10	09 41	10 05
29¾	—	—	Borough Green & Wrotham	d	06 17	06 20	06 30	06 59	07 10	07 20	07 23	07 41	07 59	08 31	08 59		09 17	09 48	
32¼	—	—	Kemsing	d				07 04	07 14	07 24	07 27	07 45		08 35			09 22		
35¼	—	—	Otford [4]	195 a	06 28	06 28	06 38	07 09	07 19	07 32	07 32	07 50	08 07	08 40	09 07		09 27	09 56	
41¾	—	—	Swanley [4]	195 a			06 48	07 18	07 29	07 43	07 43	08 00		08 49			09 36	10 05	
44½	—	—	St Mary Cray	195 a				07 23											
—	—	56¼	London Bridge [4]	⊖ a												09 39			10 50
—	—	57	**London Cannon Street [4]**	⊖ a															10 54
—	—	—	London Waterloo (East) [4]	⊖ a												09 45			
—	—	—	London Charing Cross [4]	⊖ a												09b51			
48¼	0	—	Bromley South [4]	195 a	06 47	06 47	06 57	07 29	07 40	07 54	07 54		08 25	08 59	09 27		09 44	10 14	
50½	—	—	Beckenham Junction [4]	195 ⛴ a								08 13							
55¼	—	—	Herne Hill [4]	195 a	06 57	06 57													
—	10¼	—	Elephant & Castle	⊖ 195 a			07 15		07 57										
—	11½	—	**London Blackfriars [3]**	⊖ 195 a			07 18		08 03										
59¼	—	—	**London Victoria [15]**	⊖ 195 a	07 08	07 08		07 49		08 17	08 17	08 31	08 53	09 18	09 50		10c04	10 32	

		SE 94	SE 64 [1] C	SE 09 [1]	SE 94	SE 64 [1] C	SE 09 [1]	SE 94	SE 64 [1] C	SE 09 [1]	SE 94	SE 64 [1] C	SE 09 [1]	SE 94	SE 64 [1] C	SE 09 [1]	SE 94
Ashford International	d		10 05	10 36		11 05	11 36		12 05	12 36		13 05	13 36		14 05	14 36	
Charing	d		10 13			11 13			12 13			13 13			14 13		
Lenham	d		10 19			11 18			12 18			13 18			14 18		
Harrietsham	d		10 22			11 21			12 21			13 21			14 21		
Hollingbourne	d		10 26			11 25			12 25			13 25			14 25		
Bearsted	d		10 29	10 52		11 29	11 52		12 29	12 52		13 29	13 52		14 29	14 52	
Maidstone East [4]	a		10 34	10 57		11 34	11 57		12 34	12 57		13 34	13 57		14 34	14 57	
	d	10 00	10 35	10 57	11 00	11 34	11 57	12 00	12 34	12 57	13 00	13 34	13 57	14 00	14 34	14 57	15 00
Barming	d	10 04			11 04			12 04			13 04			14 04			15 04
East Malling	d	10 08			11 08			12 08			13 08			14 08			15 08
West Malling	d	10 10	10 42	11 05	11 10	11 42	12 05	12 10	12 42	13 05	13 10	13 42	14 05	14 10	14 42	15 05	15 10
Borough Green & Wrotham	d	10 17	10 50		11 17	11 49		12 17	12 49		13 17	13 49		14 17	14 49		15 17
Kemsing	d	10 22			11 22			12 22			13 22			14 22			15 22
Otford [4]	195 a	10 27	10 57		11 27	11 57		12 27	12 57		13 27	13 57		14 27	14 57		15 27
Swanley [4]	195 a	10 36			11 36			12 36			13 36			14 36			15 36
St Mary Cray	195 a																
London Bridge [4]	⊖ a			11 50			12 50			13 50			14 50			15 50	
London Cannon Street [4]	⊖ a			11 54			12 54			13 54			14 54			15 54	
London Waterloo (East) [4]	⊖ a																
London Charing Cross [4]	⊖ a																
Bromley South [4]	195 a	10 44	11 14		11 44	12 14		12 44	13 14		13 44	14 14		14 44	15 14		15 44
Beckenham Junction [4]	195 ⛴ a																
Herne Hill [4]	195 a																
Elephant & Castle	⊖ 195 a																
London Blackfriars [3]	⊖ 195 a																
London Victoria [15]	⊖ 195 a	11 02	11 32		12 02	12 32		13 02	13 32		14 02	14 32		15 02	15 32		16 02

		SE 64 [1] C	SE 88 [1]	SE 96	SE 64 [1] C	SE 88 [1]	SE 96 [1]	SE 94 [1]	SE 88 [1]	SE 94 [1]	SE 94 [1]	SE 94	SE 94 [1]	SE 94 [1] C	SE 94 [1]	SE 94 [1]
Ashford International	d	15 03	15 21	15 27	15 59	16 24	16 32	16 58	17 26	17 31	18 00		19 00	19 58	20 58	22 08
Charing	d	15 11		15 35	16 07		16 40	17 06		17 39	18 08		19 08	20 06	21 06	22 16
Lenham	d	15 16		15 40	16 12		16 45	17 11		17 44	18 13		19 13	20 11	21 11	22 21
Harrietsham	d	15 19		15 43	16 15		16 48	17 14		17 47	18 16		19 16	20 14	21 14	22 24
Hollingbourne	d	15 23		15 47	16 19		16 52	17 18		17 51	18 20		19 20	20 18	21 18	22 28
Bearsted	d	15 27	15 37	15 51	16 23	16 40	16 56	17 22	17 42	17 55	18 24		19 24	20 22	21 22	22 32
Maidstone East [4]	a	15 32	15 42	15 56	16 28	16 45	17 01	17 27	17 47	18 00	18 29		19 29	20 27	21 27	22 37
	d	15 32	15 43	16 00	16 28	16 48	17 01	17 28	17 48	18 02	18 30	19 00	19 29	20 28	21 28	22 38
Barming	d			16 05	16 33		17 06	17 32		18 07	18 35	19 04	19 34	20 32	21 33	22 42
East Malling	d			16 08	16 36		17 09	17 36		18 10	18 38	19 08	19 37	20 36	21 36	22 46
West Malling	d	15 40	15 50	16 11	16 39	16 55	17 12	17 38	17 55	18 13	18 41	19 10	19 40	20 38	21 39	22 48
Borough Green & Wrotham	d	15 47		16 18	16 46		17 19	17 45		18 20	18 48	19 17	19 47	20 45	21 46	22 55
Kemsing	d			16 22			17 23			18 24		19 22				
Otford [4]	195 a	15 55		16 27	16 54		17 28	17 53		18 29	18 56	19 27	19 55	20 53	21 54	23 04
Swanley [4]	195 a			16 38	17 05			18 04			19 05	19 36	20 04	21 02	22 03	23 13
St Mary Cray	195 a												20 08	21 07	22 07	23 17
London Bridge [4]	⊖ a		16 34			17 38			18 40							
London Cannon Street [4]	⊖ a															
London Waterloo (East) [4]	⊖ a		16 39			17 44			18 45							
London Charing Cross [4]	⊖ a		16 45			17 48			18 48							
Bromley South [4]	195 a	16 14		16 47	17 14		17 47	18 13		18 45	19 14	19 44	20 14	21 13	22 13	23 23
Beckenham Junction [4]	195 ⛴ a															
Herne Hill [4]	195 a															
Elephant & Castle	⊖ 195 a															
London Blackfriars [3]	⊖ 195 a															
London Victoria [15]	⊖ 195 a	16 33		17 11	17 31		18 09	18 33		19 03	19 31	20 02	20 32	21 29	22 32	23 45

For general notes see front of timetable
For details of catering facilities see Directory of Train Operators

- **A** From 13 October
- **B** Until 10 October
- **C** From Canterbury West (Table 207)
- **D** From Margate (Table 207)
- **b** Until 10 October arr 1 minute earlier
- **c** Until 10 October arr 2 minutes earlier

Table 196

Saturdays

Ashford International and Maidstone East to London

Network Diagram - see first page of Table 195

		SE 64 1	SE 94 1	SE 09 1	SE 94		SE 94 1	SE 09 1	SE 94	SE 94 1		SE 09 1	SE 94	SE 64 1 A	SE 09 1		SE 94	SE 64 1 A	SE 09 1	SE 94		SE 64 1 A	SE 09 1	SE 94	SE 64 1 A
Ashford International	d	06 00	07 00	07 36			08 05	08 36		09 05		09 36		10 05	10 36			11 05	11 36			12 05	12 36		13 05
Charing	d	06 08	07 08				08 13			09 13				10 13				11 13				12 13			13 13
Lenham	d	06 13	07 13				08 18			09 18				10 18				11 18				12 18			13 18
Harrietsham	d	06 16	07 16				08 21			09 21				10 21				11 21				12 21			13 21
Hollingbourne	d	06 20	07 20				08 25			09 25				10 25				11 25				12 25			13 25
Bearsted	d	06 24	07 24	07 52			08 29	08 52		09 29		09 52		10 29	10 52			11 29	11 52			12 29	12 52		13 29
Maidstone East 4	a	06 29	07 29	07 57			08 34	08 57		09 34		09 57		10 34	10 57			11 34	11 57			12 34	12 57		13 34
	d	06 30	07 30	07 57	08 00		08 34	08 57	09 00	09 34		09 57	10 00	10 34	10 57		11 00	11 34	11 57	12 00		12 34	12 57	13 00	13 34
Barming	d	06 34	07 34		08 04				09 04				10 04				11 04			12 04				13 04	
East Malling	d	06 38	07 38		08 08				09 08				10 08				11 08			12 08				13 08	
West Malling	d	06 40	07 40	08 05	08 10		08 42	09 05	09 10	09 42		10 05	10 10	10 42	11 05		11 10	11 42	12 05	12 10		12 42	13 05	13 10	13 42
Borough Green & Wrotham	d	06 47	07 47		08 17		08 49		09 17	09 49			10 17	10 49			11 17	11 49		12 17		12 49		13 17	13 49
Kemsing	d				08 22				09 22				10 22				11 22			12 22				13 22	
Otford 4	195 a	06 55	07 55		08 26		08 57		09 26	09 57			10 26	10 57			11 26	11 57		12 26		12 57		13 26	13 57
Swanley 4	195 a	07 04	08 04		08 35				09 35				10 35				11 35			12 35				13 35	
St Mary Cray	195 a	07 08	08 08																						
London Bridge 4	⊖ a			08 50				09 50				10 50			11 50				12 50				13 50		
London Cannon Street 4	⊖ a			08 54				09 54				10 54			11 54				12 54				13 54		
London Waterloo (East) 4	⊖ a																								
London Charing Cross 4	⊖ a																								
Bromley South 4	195 a	07 14	08 14		08 44		09 14		09 44	10 14			10 44	11 14			11 44	12 14		12 44		13 14		13 44	14 14
Beckenham Junction 4	195 🚋 a																								
Herne Hill 4	195 a																								
Elephant & Castle	⊖ 195 a																								
London Blackfriars 3	⊖ 195 a																								
London Victoria 15	⊖ 195 a	07 32	08 32		09 02		09 32		10 02	10 32			11 02	11 32			12 02	12 32		13 02		13 32		14 02	14 32

		SE 09 1	SE 94		SE 64 1 A	SE 09 1	SE 94	SE 64 1 A		SE 09 1	SE 94	SE 64 1 A	SE 09 1		SE 94	SE 64 1 A	SE 09 1	SE 94	SE 64 1 A	SE 94 1	SE 94 1	SE 94 1	SE 94 1		
Ashford International	d	13 36			14 05	14 36		15 05		15 36		16 05	16 36			17 05	17 36		18 00	19 00	20 00	21 00	22 00		
Charing	d				14 13			15 13				16 13				17 13			18 08	19 08	20 08	21 08	22 08		
Lenham	d				14 18			15 18				16 18				17 18			18 13	19 13	20 13	21 13	22 13		
Harrietsham	d				14 21			15 21				16 21				17 21			18 16	19 16	20 16	21 16	22 16		
Hollingbourne	d				14 25			15 25				16 25				17 25			18 20	19 20	20 20	21 20	22 20		
Bearsted	d	13 52			14 29	14 52		15 29		15 52		16 29	16 52			17 29	17 52		18 24	19 24	20 24	21 24	22 24		
Maidstone East 4	a	13 57			14 34	14 57		15 34		15 57		16 34	16 57			17 34	17 57		18 29	19 29	20 29	21 29	22 29		
	d	13 57	14 00		14 34	14 57	15 00	15 34		15 57	16 00	16 34	16 57		17 00	17 34	17 57	18 00	18 30	19 30	20 30	21 30	22 30		
Barming	d		14 04				15 04				16 04				17 04			18 04	18 34	19 34	20 34	21 34	22 34		
East Malling	d		14 08				15 08				16 08				17 08			18 08	18 38	19 38	20 38	21 38	22 38		
West Malling	d	14 05	14 10		14 42	15 05	15 10	15 42		16 05	16 10	16 42	17 05		17 10	17 42	18 05	18 10	18 40	19 40	20 40	21 40	22 40		
Borough Green & Wrotham	d		14 17		14 49		15 17	15 49			16 17	16 49			17 17	17 49		18 17	18 47	19 47	20 47	21 47	22 47		
Kemsing	d		14 22				15 22				16 22				17 22			18 22							
Otford 4	195 a		14 26		14 57		15 26	15 57			16 26	16 57			17 26	17 57		18 26	18 55	19 55	20 55	21 55	22 55		
Swanley 4	195 a		14 35				15 35				16 35				17 35			18 35	19 04	20 04	21 04	22 04	23 04		
St Mary Cray	195 a																		19 08	20 08	21 08	22 08	23 08		
London Bridge 4	⊖ a	14 50				15 50				16 50			17 50				18 50								
London Cannon Street 4	⊖ a	14 54				15 54				16 54			17 54				18 54								
London Waterloo (East) 4	⊖ a																								
London Charing Cross 4	⊖ a																								
Bromley South 4	195 a		14 44		15 14		15 44	16 14			16 44	17 14			17 44	18 14		18 44	19 14	20 14	21 14	22 14	23 14		
Beckenham Junction 4	195 🚋 a																								
Herne Hill 4	195 a																								
Elephant & Castle	⊖ 195 a																								
London Blackfriars 3	⊖ 195 a																								
London Victoria 15	⊖ 195 a		15 02		15 32		16 02	16 32			17 02	17 32			18 02	18 32		19 02	19 32	20 32	21 32	22 32	23 32		

For general notes see front of timetable
For details of catering facilities see
Directory of Train Operators

A From Canterbury West (Table 207)

Table 196

Sundays

Ashford International and Maidstone East to London

Network Diagram - see first page of Table 195

		SE	SE	SE	SE	SE	SE	SE	SE	SE	SE	SE	SE	SE	SE	SE	SE
		94	94	94	94	94	94	94	94	94	94	94	94	94	94	94	94
		[1]	[1]	[1]	[1]	[1]	[1]	[1]	[1]	[1]	[1]	[1]	[1]	[1]	[1]	[1]	[1]
					A	A	A	A	A	A	A	A	A	A	A		
Ashford International	d	07 01	08 01	09 01	10 01	11 01	12 01	13 01	14 01	15 01	16 01	17 01	18 01	19 01	20 01	21 01	22 01
Charing	d	07 09	08 09	09 09	10 09	11 09	12 09	13 09	14 09	15 09	16 09	17 09	18 09	19 09	20 09	21 09	22 09
Lenham	d	07 14	08 14	09 14	10 14	11 14	12 14	13 14	14 14	15 14	16 14	17 14	18 14	19 14	20 14	21 14	22 14
Harrietsham	d	07 17	08 17	09 17	10 17	11 17	12 17	13 17	14 17	15 17	16 17	17 17	18 17	19 17	20 17	21 17	22 17
Hollingbourne	d	07 21	08 21	09 21	10 21	11 21	12 21	13 21	14 21	15 21	16 21	17 21	18 21	19 21	20 21	21 21	22 21
Bearsted	d	07 25	08 25	09 25	10 25	11 25	12 25	13 25	14 25	15 25	16 25	17 25	18 25	19 25	20 25	21 25	22 25
Maidstone East [4]	a	07 30	08 30	09 30	10 30	11 30	12 30	13 30	14 30	15 30	16 30	17 30	18 30	19 30	20 30	21 30	22 30
	d	07 30	08 30	09 30	10 30	11 30	12 30	13 30	14 30	15 30	16 30	17 30	18 30	19 30	20 30	21 30	22 30
Barming	d	07 35	08 35	09 35	10 35	11 35	12 35	13 35	14 35	15 35	16 35	17 35	18 35	19 35	20 35	21 35	22 35
East Malling	d	07 38	08 38	09 38	10 38	11 38	12 38	13 38	14 38	15 38	16 38	17 38	18 38	19 38	20 38	21 38	22 38
West Malling	d	07 41	08 41	09 41	10 41	11 41	12 41	13 41	14 41	15 41	16 41	17 41	18 41	19 41	20 41	21 41	22 41
Borough Green & Wrotham	d	07 48	08 48	09 48	10 48	11 48	12 48	13 48	14 48	15 48	16 48	17 48	18 48	19 48	20 48	21 48	22 48
Kemsing	d																
Otford [4]	195 a	07 56	08 56	09 56	10 56	11 56	12 56	13 56	14 56	15 56	16 56	17 56	18 56	19 56	20 56	21 56	22 56
Swanley [4]	195 a	08 05	09 05	10 05	11 05	12 05	13 05	14 05	15 05	16 05	17 05	18 05	19 05	20 05	21 05	22 05	23 05
St Mary Cray	195 a	08 10	09 10	10 10	11 10	12 10	13 10	14 10	15 10	16 10	17 10	18 10	19 10	20 10	21 10	22 10	23 10
London Bridge [4]	⊖ a																
London Cannon Street [4]	⊖ a																
London Waterloo (East) [4]	⊖ a																
London Charing Cross [4]	⊖ a																
Bromley South [4]	195 a	08 16	09 16	10 16	11 16	12 16	13 16	14 16	15 16	16 16	17 16	18 16	19 16	20 16	21 16	22 16	23 16
Beckenham Junction [4]	195 🚋 a																
Herne Hill [4]	195 a																
Elephant & Castle	⊖ 195 a																
London Blackfriars [3]	⊖ 195 a																
London Victoria [15]	⊖ 195 a	08 32	09 32	10 32	11 32	12 32	13 32	14 32	15 32	16 32	17 32	18 32	19 32	20 32	21 32	22 32	23 32

For general notes see front of timetable
For details of catering facilities see
Directory of Train Operators

A From Canterbury West (Table 207)

London → Lewisham, Hither Green, Petts Wood and Orpington (Summary of Services)

For details of Bank Holiday service alterations please see first page of Table 195

		SE MX 12	SE MO 12	SE MX 73	SE MX 70	SE MX 70	SE MO 50	SE MX 24	SE MO 24	SE MO 12	FC	SE MX 50	SE MX 02	SN MX	SE 62	FC MX	SE 14	SE 50	SE 72	SE 84	SE 52	FC 1		SE 25	SE 70
London Charing Cross 4	⊖ d	23p26	23p26			23p47	23p47	23p52	23p53	23p56		00 04	00 10	00 12	00 14		00 48	04 50	04 56	05 04	05 18				05 26
London Waterloo (East) 4	⊖ d	23p29	23p29			23p50	23p50	23p55	23p56	23p59		00 07	00 13	00 15	00 17		00 51	04 53	04 59	05 07	05 21				05 29
London Cannon Street 4	⊖ d																								
London Blackfriars 3	⊖ d			23p43							00 04					00 34						05 24			
London Bridge 4	⊖ d	23p34	23p35			23p55	23p55	23p58	00 02	00 05	00a10	00 13	00 18	00a19	00 23	00a40	00 56	04 58	05 04	05a11	05b28	05a30			05 34
London Victoria 15	⊖ d				23p53																				
New Cross 4	⊖ d					00 01	00 01	00 04	00 07			00 18			00 28		01 01	05 03	05 09		05 33			05 37	05 39
St Johns	d							00 06	00 09																
Lewisham 4	a	23p42	23p44			00 04	00 04	00 08	00 11	00 14		00 22			00 32		01 05	05 07	05 13		05 37			05 41	05 43
Hither Green 4	a	23p47	23p48				00 09			00 19		00 27					01 09	05 11			05 41				
Petts Wood 4	a	00 01	00 01	00 20	00 25					00 31			00 39				01 23								
Orpington 4	a	00 03	00 03	00 24	00 28					00 34			00 42				01 26								

		SE 18 1	SE 70	SE 64	SE 14	FC 1	SE 54	SE 11	SE 24	SE 80	SE 70	SE 72	SE 11	SN	SE 65	FC 1	SE 16 1	SE 11	SE 52	SE 4 1	SE 84	SE 25		SE 70	SE 70
London Charing Cross 4	⊖ d	05 30		05 34	05 40		05 46		05 49	05 54		06 02		06 05			06 16		06 20	06 25		06 27			06 32
London Waterloo (East) 4	⊖ d	05 33		05 37	05 43		05 49		05 52	05 57		06 05		06 08			06 19		06 23	06 28		06 30			06 35
London Cannon Street 4	⊖ d							05 50					06 06		06 12			06 22			06 30				
London Blackfriars 3	⊖ d					05 44										06 14									
London Bridge 4	⊖ d	05 38		05 42	05 48	05a50	05 54	05a53	05 57	06a01		06 10	06a09	06a12	06 16	06a20	06 24	06a25	06 28	06 33	06a33	06 35			06 40
London Victoria 15	⊖ d		05 36								06 04													06 36	
New Cross 4	⊖ d				05 53		05 59					06 15							06 33			06 41			06 47
St Johns	d						06 01					06 17										06 43			
Lewisham 4	a			05 51	05 57		06 03		06 05			06 19			06 23				06 37			06 45			06 51
Hither Green 4	a				06 01		06 07										06 33		06 41						
Petts Wood 4	a		06 10		06 13						06 38						06 45							07 10	
Orpington 4	a	05 54	06 13		06 16						06 41						06 48			06 49				07 13	

		FC 1	SE 65	SE 54	SE 16	SE 11	FC 1	SE 24	SE 86	SE 70	SE 4 1	SE 60	SE 25	FC 1	SE 12	SE 30 1	SE 70	SE 73	SE 52	SE 34	SE 80	SE 12		SE 22 1	SE 71
London Charing Cross 4	⊖ d		06 40		06 47			06 51	06 54		07 00	07 03	07 06		07 10	07 16			07 20	07 22				07 28	07 30
London Waterloo (East) 4	⊖ d		06 43		06 50			06 54	06 57		07 03	07 06	07 09		07 13	07 19			07 23	07 25				07 31	07 33
London Cannon Street 4	⊖ d			06 48		06 52				07 04								07 22			07 32				
London Blackfriars 3	⊖ d	06 36					06 50							07 10											
London Bridge 4	⊖ d	06a42	06 48	06 52	06 56	06a55	06a56	06 59	07a02	07 08	07 08	07 11	07 14	07a16	07 19	07 24		07 26	07 28	07a29	07a35			07 36	07 38
London Victoria 15	⊖ d																07 06								
New Cross 4	⊖ d							07 05		07 13			07 20						07 33						07 43
St Johns	d							07 07		07 15			07 22												07 45
Lewisham 4	a		06 55	06 59				07 09		07 17		07 21	07 24					07 33	07 37			←			07 47
Hither Green 4	a			07 03	07 06										07 29 →				07 41			07 29			
Petts Wood 4	a				07 22												07 40					07 42			
Orpington 4	a				07 25						07 25					07 40	07 43					07 45		07 54	

		FC 1	SE 57	SE 12	SE 23 1	SE 40	SE 44	SE 25	SE 73	SE 12	SE 70	SE 4 1	SE 61	SE 14	SE 12	SE 70	SE 51	SE 84	SE 1	SE 71	FC 1	SE 61		SE 22 1 ⌶	SE 25
London Charing Cross 4	⊖ d			07 37		07 42		07 45				07 52		07 56			08 00	08 03	08 08					08 14	
London Waterloo (East) 4	⊖ d			07 40		07 45		07 48				07 55		07 59			08 03	08 06	08 11					08 17	
London Cannon Street 4	⊖ d		07 39		07 45		07 48		07 54				07 58		08 03					08 14		08 17			08 20
London Blackfriars 3	⊖ d	07 32																			08 12				
London Bridge 4	⊖ d	07a39	07 43	07 45	07 49	07 50	07a51	07 53	07 58			08 02	08 02	08 04	08 07		08 09	08a10	08 16	08 18	08a18	08 21		08a22	08 24
London Victoria 15	⊖ d										07 37					08 06									
New Cross 4	⊖ d		07 49					07 59	08 03				08 07		08 12					08 23		08 26			08 29
St Johns	d							08 01	08 05											08 25					08 31
Lewisham 4	a		07 53					08 04	08 07	←			08 11		08 16					08 27		08 31			08 33
Hither Green 4	a		07 57	07 53 →		08 01				07 53					08 20		08 18		08 27						
Petts Wood 4	a									08 09	08 12				08 33	08 39									
Orpington 4	a				08 08					08 12	08 15	08 19		08 23	08 36	08 42									

		SE 78	SE 12	SE 4 1	SE 42	SE 80	SE 34	SE 71	SE 16	SE 55	SE 36	SE 12	SE 25	SE 12	SE 23 1 ⌶	SE 80	SE 10	SE 63	SE 25	SE 34	SE 90 1	SE 12		SE 12	SE 70
London Charing Cross 4	⊖ d		08 20	08 22		08 24	08 26	08 28	08 29		08 36			08 38		08 41	08 44			08 52	08 54	08 56			
London Waterloo (East) 4	⊖ d		08 23	08 25		08 27	08 29	08 31	08 32		08 39			08 41		08 44	08 47			08 55	08 57	08 59			
London Cannon Street 4	⊖ d				08 26					08 34			08 40		08 45			08 50	08 54						
London Blackfriars 3	⊖ d																								
London Bridge 4	⊖ d		08 28	08 30	08 30	08a31	08a33	08 36	08 38	08 38	08a43		08 44	08 46	08 49	08a49	08 52	08 54	08 58	08a59	09a01	09 04 →			
London Victoria 15	⊖ d	08 21																							
New Cross 4	⊖ d							08 42		08 45			08 49						09 05						08 36
St Johns	d									08 47			08 51						09 07						
Lewisham 4	a	08 43						08 46		08 49		←	08 53					09 02	09 09					←	
Hither Green 4	a		08 37 →		08 41					08 53		08 37		08 55 →			09 02							08 55	
Petts Wood 4	a											08 50												09 09	09 12
Orpington 4	a			08 47					08 55			08 56			09 07									09 12	09 15

For general notes see front of timetable
For details of catering facilities see Directory of Train Operators

b Arr. 0525

For details of Bank Holiday service alterations please see first page of Table 195

London → Lewisham, Hither Green, Petts Wood and Orpington (Summary of Services)

		FC	SE	SE	SE	SE	SE	SE	SE	SE	SE	SE	SE	FC	SE	SE	SE	SE	SE	SE	SE	SE		SE	SE
			71	90	36	12	54	78	81	09	23	70	34		47	92	70	25	82	16	87	2		70	67
		1		1						1	1			1		1 A						1			
London Charing Cross 4	⊖ d			08 58	09 00		09 02						09 14				09 15		09 20	09 26		09 30			
London Waterloo (East) 4	⊖ d			09 01	09 04		09 06						09 17				09 20		09 23	09 29		09 33			
London Cannon Street 4	⊖ d		09 02			←			09 10	09 13	09 17				09 20			09 24			09 30				09 34
London Blackfriars 3	⊖ d	08 58												09 17											
London Bridge 4	⊖ d	09a05	09 06	09 08	09a09	09 04	09 12		09a13	09a16	09 21		09a21	09a23	09 24		09 26	09 28	09a29	09 34	09 34	09 38			09 38
London Victoria 15	⊖ d							09 01				09 06				09 15								09 21	
New Cross 4	⊖ d		09 11												09 29			09 35							09 44
St Johns	d														09 31			09 37							
Lewisham 4	a		09 15				09 19	09 25							09 33	09 34	09 35	09 39		09 42 →					09 47
Hither Green 4	a					09 15	09 23								09 37										
Petts Wood 4	a			09 23		09 30						09 42												09 55	
Orpington 4	a			09 26		09 33					09 39	09 46										09 54		09 58	

		SE	SE	SE	SE	FC	SE	SE	SE	SE	SE	FC	SE	SE	SE	SE	SE	SE	SE	SE	SE	SE		SE	FC
		16	54	78	70		34	81	23	47	22		70	25	82	12	87	8	70	67	12	54		78	
						1			1 B		1	1													1
London Charing Cross 4	⊖ d		09 32				09 36				09 45		09 49		09 52	09 56		10 00				10 02			
London Waterloo (East) 4	⊖ d		09 35				09 39				09 48		09 52		09 55	09 59		10 03				10 05			
London Cannon Street 4	⊖ d							09 42	09 45	09 48				09 54			10 00			10 04					
London Blackfriars 3	⊖ d					09 34						09 49													10 05
London Bridge 4	⊖ d		09 40			09a41	09a44	09a45	09 49	09 52	09a53	09a55	09 57	09 58	09a59	10 04	10 04	10 08		10 08		10 10			10a11
London Victoria 15	⊖ d			09 31	09 36														09 51					10 01	
New Cross 4	⊖ d									09 57				10 05						10 14					
St Johns	d	←								09 59				10 07							←				
Lewisham 4	a	09 42	09 49	09 52					09 56				10 05	10 09		10 12 →				10 17	10 12	10 19		10 22	
Hither Green 4	a	09 47	09 53							10 05											10 17	10 23			
Petts Wood 4	a	10 00			10 10													10 22	10 26		10 30				
Orpington 4	a	10 03			10 13													10 25	10 29		10 33				

		SE	SE	SE	SE	SE	SE	SE	FC	SE	SE	SE	SE	SE	SE	SE	SE	SE	SE	SE	FC	SE		SE	SN
		81	34	09	47	22	70	70		25	82	16	87	8	70	67	16	54	78	70		81		34	
				1		1			1					1							1				
London Charing Cross 4	⊖ d		10 06			10 15		10 17			10 20	10 26		10 30				10 32						10 36	10 40
London Waterloo (East) 4	⊖ d		10 09			10 18		10 20			10 23	10 29		10 33				10 35						10 39	10 43
London Cannon Street 4	⊖ d	10 10		10 14	10 18					10 24			10 30			10 34						10 40			
London Blackfriars 3	⊖ d								10 20												10 35				
London Bridge 4	⊖ d	10a13	10a14	10a17	10 22	10 23		10 25	10a26	10 28	10a28	10 34	10 34	10 38		10 38		10 40			10a41	10a43		10a44	10a47
London Victoria 15	⊖ d						10 06								10 21				10 31	10 36					
New Cross 4	⊖ d				10 27					10 33						10 44									
St Johns	d				10 29					10 35							←								
Lewisham 4	a							10 34		10 37		10 42 →				10 47	10 42	10 49	10 52						
Hither Green 4	a				10 35												10 47	10 53							
Petts Wood 4	a						10 39								10 54		11 00			11 09					
Orpington 4	a					10 39	10 42							10 53	10 57		11 03			11 12					

			SE	SE	SE	FC	SE	SE	SE	SE	SE	SE	SE	SE	SE	SE	FC	SE	SE	SN	SE	SE	SE	SE	SE
			47	22	70		25	82	12	87	8	70	67	12	54	78		81	34		09	47	22	70	70
				1		1					1						1				1		1		
London Charing Cross 4	⊖ d			10 45	10 47			10 50	10 56		11 00				11 02				11 06	11 10			11 15		11 17
London Waterloo (East) 4	⊖ d			10 48	10 50			10 53	10 59		11 03				11 05				11 09	11 13			11 18		11 20
London Cannon Street 4	⊖ d		10 48				10 54			11 00			11 04					11 10			11 14	11 18			
London Blackfriars 3	⊖ d					10 50											11 05								
London Bridge 4	⊖ d		10 52	10a52	10 55	10a56	10 58	10a58	11 04	11 04	11 08		11 08		11 10		11a11	11a13	11a14	11a17	11a17	11 22	11 23		11 25
London Victoria 15	⊖ d											10 51				11 01								11 06	
New Cross 4	⊖ d		10 57				11 03						11 14									11 27			
St Johns	d		10 59				11 05							←								11 29			
Lewisham 4	a				11 04		11 07		11 12 →				11 17	11 12	11 19	11 22									11 34
Hither Green 4	a		11 05											11 17	11 23							11 35			
Petts Wood 4	a										11 22	11 24		11 30										11 39	
Orpington 4	a										11 25	11 27		11 33									11 39	11 42	

		FC	SE	SE	SE	SE	SE	SE	SE	SE	SE	SE	SE	FC	SE	SE	SN			SE	SE	SE	FC	SE
			25	82	16	87	8	70	67	16	54	78	70		81	34				47	22	70		25
		1					1							1							1		1	
London Charing Cross 4	⊖ d			11 20	11 26		11 30				11 32					11 36	11 40	and at			15 45	15 47		
London Waterloo (East) 4	⊖ d			11 23	11 29		11 33				11 35					11 39	11 43	the same			15 48	15 50		
London Cannon Street 4	⊖ d		11 24			11 30			11 34						11 40			minutes		15 48				15 54
London Blackfriars 3	⊖ d	11 20												11 35				past					15 50	
London Bridge 4	⊖ d	11a26	11 28	11a28	11 34	11 34	11 38		11 38		11 40			11a41	11a43	11a44	11a47	each		15 52	15a52	15 55	15a56	15 58
London Victoria 15	⊖ d							11 21				11 31	11 36					hour until						
New Cross 4	⊖ d		11 33						11 44											15 57				16 03
St Johns	d		11 35							←										15 59				16 05
Lewisham 4	a		11 37		11 42 →				11 47	11 42	11 49	11 52										16 04		16 07
Hither Green 4	a									11 47	11 53									16 04				
Petts Wood 4	a							11 54		12 00			12 09											
Orpington 4	a						11 53	11 57		12 03			12 12											

For general notes see front of timetable
For details of catering facilities see Directory of Train Operators

A Until 18 July and from 1 September
B 21 July to 29 August

London → Lewisham, Hither Green, Petts Wood and Orpington (Summary of Services)

For details of Bank Holiday service alterations please see first page of Table 195

Station		SE 62	SE 70	SE 16	SE 81	SE 70	SE 8 [1]	SE 54	FC [1]	SE 24	SE 57	SN	SE 09 [1]	SE 74	SE 81	SE 22 [1]	SE 16	SE 16	FC [1]	SE 62	SE 78	SE 70	SE 4 [1]	SE 73
London Charing Cross 4	⊖ d	15 50		15 56			16 00	16 02		16 06		16 08		16 11		16 15	16 16			16 21			16 23	
London Waterloo (East) 4	⊖ d	15 53		15 59			16 03	16 05		16 09		16 11		16 14		16 18	16 19			16 24			16 26	
London Cannon Street 4	⊖ d				16 00						16 10		16 14		16 18			16 22						
London Blackfriars 3	⊖ d								16 05										16 20					
London Bridge 4	⊖ d	15 59		16 04	16a03		16a07	16 10	16a11	16 14	16 14	16a15	16a17	16 19	16a21	16a22	16 25	16 26	16a26	16 29			16a30	16 27
London Victoria 15	⊖ d		15 51			16 06															16 14	16 26		
New Cross 4	⊖ d							16 16			16 20			16 25										
St Johns	d										16 22													
Lewisham 4	a	16 09		16 12				16 19		16 22	16 26			16 28				16 34		16 37	16 40			
Hither Green 4	a			16 17				16 23			16 31							16 39						
Petts Wood 4	a		16 24	16 29		16 39											16 43	16 51				17 00		17 06
Orpington 4	a		16 27	16 32		16b44											16c49	16 55				17b06		17 12

Station		SE 81	SE 40	SE 24	SE 8 [1]	SE 76	SE 57	FC [1]	SE 65	SE 74	SE 07 [1]	SE 12	SE 25	SE 80	SE 4 [1]	SE 42	SE 77	SE 30 [1]	SE 34	SE 17	SE 70	SE 76	SE 23 [1]	SE 46
London Charing Cross 4	⊖ d		16 25	16 26	16 30	16 33				16 37		16 42		16 44	16 46	16 48		16 50	16 52			16 55		16 58
London Waterloo (East) 4	⊖ d		16 28	16 29	16 33	16 36				16 40		16 45		16 47	16 49	16 51		16 53	16 55			16 58		17 01
London Cannon Street 4	⊖ d	16 28					16 38		16 42		16 44		16 46				16 52			16 56			17 00	
London Blackfriars 3	⊖ d							16 37																
London Bridge 4	⊖ d	16a31	16 33	16 34	16a38	16 41	16 42	16a43	16 46	16e48	16a47	16 50	16 50	16a51	16a53	16a55	16 56	16a57	16a59	17 00		17 03	17a03	17 06
London Victoria 15	⊖ d																				16 51			
New Cross 4	⊖ d		16 39				16 49						16 56				17 02							
St Johns	d		16 41				16 51						16 58											
Lewisham 4	a			16 44		16 50	16 53		16 55	16 58			17 01				17 05					17 14		
Hither Green 4	a		16 46				16 57					17 02												
Petts Wood 4	a											17 15								17 21	17 25			17 16
Orpington 4	a											17 21								17 24	17c30			

Station		SE 85	SE 64	SE 25	SE 78	SE 87	SE 12	SE 80	SE 51	SE 17	SE 70	SE 77	SE 34	SE 76	SE 13	SE 30 [1]	SE 87	SE 46	SE 65	SE 78	FC [1]	SE 12	SE 25	SE 80
London Charing Cross 4	⊖ d		17 00				17 04	17 06					17 14	17 18		17 20		17 21				17 28		17 29
London Waterloo (East) 4	⊖ d		17 03				17 07	17 09					17 17	17 21		17 23		17 24				17 31		17 32
London Cannon Street 4	⊖ d	17 02		17 04		17 06			17 10	17 14		17 16			17 22		17 24		17 26				17 32	
London Blackfriars 3	⊖ d																				17 20			
London Bridge 4	⊖ d	17a05	17 08	17 08		17a09	17 12	17a13	17 14	17 18		17 20	17a21	17 26	17 26	17a27	17a27	17 30	17 30		17a31		17 36	17a38
London Victoria 15	⊖ d				17 00						17 12									17 19				
New Cross 4	⊖ d			17 16					17 20			17 26			17 32								17 42	
St Johns	d			17 18					17 22														17 44	
Lewisham 4	a		17 17	17 20	17 23				17 25			17 29		17 35					17 38	17 43			17 46	
Hither Green 4	a						17 22		17 30									17 40				17 46		
Petts Wood 4	a						17 35			17 43	17 49				17 51							17 58		
Orpington 4	a						17c42			17 46	17 53				17 57							18c05		

Station		SE 51	SE 17	SE 70	SE 76	SE 77	SE 30 [1]	SE 65	SE 78	SE 46	SE 87	FC [1]	SE 07 [1]	SE 25	SE 12	SE 51	SE 80	SE 17	SE 70	SE 70	SE 34	SE 77	SE 9 [1]	SE 70
London Charing Cross 4	⊖ d				17 37		17 41			17 43					17 49		17 54				17 58			18 01
London Waterloo (East) 4	⊖ d				17 40		17 44			17 46					17 52		17 57				18 01			18 04
London Cannon Street 4	⊖ d	17 36	17 40			17 42		17 46			17 48		17 50	17 52		17 56		18 00				18 02	18 04	
London Blackfriars 3	⊖ d											17 46												
London Bridge 4	⊖ d	17 40	17 44		17 45	17 46	17a48	17 50		17 51	17a51	17a52	17a53	17 56	17 57	18 00	18a01	18 04			18a05	18 06	18a07	18 10
London Victoria 15	⊖ d			17 35					17 41										17 52	18 02				
New Cross 4	⊖ d	17 47				17 52								18 02		18 06								
St Johns	d													18 04		18 08								
Lewisham 4	a	17 50			17 53	17 56		17 59	18 05					18 07		18 11								
Hither Green 4	a	17 55								18 00					18 07	18 16						18 14		18 19
Petts Wood 4	a		18 05	18 09											18 19			18 25	18 29	18 34				
Orpington 4	a		18 08	18 15											18c26			18 29	18 33	18c41				

Station		SE 30 [1]	SE 85	SE 64	SE 07 [1]	SE 46	SE 25	SE 78	SE 12	SE 15	SE 70	SE 80	SE 77	SE 51	FC [1]	SE 23 [1]	SE 24	SE 70	SE 3 [1]	SE 30 [1]	SE 62	SE 16	SE 57	SE 80
London Charing Cross 4	⊖ d	18 04		18 05		18 08			18 12			18 14					18 23	18 25		18 28	18 30	18 32		18 34
London Waterloo (East) 4	⊖ d	18 07		18 08		18 11			18 15			18 17					18 26	18 28		18 31	18 33	18 35		18 37
London Cannon Street 4	⊖ d		18 08		18 10		18 12			18 16			18 19	18 22		18 26			18 30				18 36	
London Blackfriars 3	⊖ d														18 20									
London Bridge 4	⊖ d	18a11	18a11	18 14	18a13	18 16	18 16			18 20		18a21	18 23	18 26	18a26	18a29	18 31	18 34	18a33	18a35	18 38	18 40	18 40	18a41
London Victoria 15	⊖ d							18 08			18 21													
New Cross 4	⊖ d						18 22			18 26				18 32									18 46	
St Johns	d						18 24																18 48	
Lewisham 4	a			18 23			18 26	18 28		18 30			18 32	18 35			18 40	18 43					18 51	
Hither Green 4	a					18 26			18 29					18 40							18 46		18 56	
Petts Wood 4	a								18 43	18 46	18 56											18 50 →		
Orpington 4	a								18b49	18 51	19 01													

For general notes see front of timetable
For details of catering facilities see Directory of Train Operators

b Until 10 October arr. 2 minutes earlier
c Until 10 October arr. 1 minute earlier
e Arr. 1645

London → Lewisham, Hither Green, Petts Wood and Orpington (Summary of Services)

For details of Bank Holiday service alterations please see first page of Table 195

		SE 8 [1]	SE 24	SE 07 [1]	SE 16	SE 70	SE 70	SE 78	SE 13	FC [1]	SE 16	SE 62	SE 80	SE 77	SE 4 [1] 🍴	SE 23 [1]	SE 70	SE 70	SE 54	FC [1]	SE 24	SE 87	SE 09 [1]	SE 80
London Charing Cross [4]	⊖ d	18 40	18 42				18 46				18 52	18 54	18 56		19 00				19 02		19 06			19 11
London Waterloo (East) [4]	⊖ d	18 43	18 45				18 49				18 55	18 57	18 59		19 03				19 05		19 09			19 14
London Cannon Street [4]	⊖ d			18 46					18 50					19 02		19 06						19 10	19 14	
London Blackfriars [3]	⊖ d									18 49										19 04				
London Bridge [4]	⊖ d	18 48	18 50	18a49			18 54		18 54	18a56	19 00	19 02	19a03	19 06	19a07	19 10			19 10	19a11	19 14	19a13	19a17	19a18
London Victoria [15]	⊖ d					18 38		18 46									18 51	19 07						
New Cross [4]	⊖ d						19 00							19 12							19 20			
St Johns	d													19 14							19 22			
Lewisham [4]	a		18 59		←		19 04	19 08				19 11		19 16					19 21		19 24			
Hither Green [4]	a				18 50						19 10								19 25					
Petts Wood [4]	a				19 04	19 12			19 17		19 23						19 25	19 41						
Orpington [4]	a	19 04			19 10	19b17			19c23		19 27					19 27	19 31	19 44						

		SE 13	SE 22 [1] 🍴	SE 70	SE 57	FC [1]	SE 62	SE 25	SE 4 [1]	SE 81	SE 16	SE 78	SE 07 [1]	SE 90	SE 70	SE 77	FC [1]	SE 16	SE 70	SE 54	SE 11	SN	SE 24	SE 80
London Charing Cross [4]	⊖ d		19 15	19 17			19 21		19 24		19 26			19 30						19 34		19 37	19 38	19 41
London Waterloo (East) [4]	⊖ d		19 18	19 20			19 24		19 27		19 29			19 33						19 37		19 40	19 41	19 44
London Cannon Street [4]	⊖ d	19 18			19 22			19 26		19 28			19 32			19 36					19 40			
London Blackfriars [3]	⊖ d					19 19											19 34							
London Bridge [4]	⊖ d	19 22	19a22	19 25	19 26	19a26	19 29	19 30	19a31	19a31	19 34		19a35	19 38		19 40	19a40			19 43	19a43	19a44	19 46	19a48
London Victoria [15]	⊖ d											19 16			19 22				19 37					
New Cross [4]	⊖ d				19 31			19 35								19 45				19 48			19 52	
St Johns	d				19 33			19 37								19 47		←					19 54	
Lewisham [4]	a	19 30		19 34			19 37	19 39			19 42 →	19 44				19 49		19 42		19 52			19 56	
Hither Green [4]	a	19 35			19 37													19 47		19 57				
Petts Wood [4]	a	19 48													19 56			19 59	20 11					
Orpington [4]	a	19 52												19 54	19 59			20 02	20 14					

		SE 13	SE 22 [1]	SE 70	SE 57	SE 62	SE 25	SE 4 [1]	FC [1]	SE 81	SE 70	SE 16	SE 78	SE 4 [1] 🍴	FC [1]	SE 50	SN	SE 80	SE 11	SE 22 [1]	SE 70	SE 62	SE 24	SE 12
London Charing Cross [4]	⊖ d		19 45	19 47		19 50		19 52				19 56		20 00		20 04	20 07	20 10		20 15	20 17	20 20	20 22	20 26
London Waterloo (East) [4]	⊖ d		19 48	19 50		19 53		19 55				19 59		20 03		20 07	20 10	20 13		20 18	20 20	20 23	20 25	20 29
London Cannon Street [4]	⊖ d	19 48			19 52		19 56			20 00									20 15					
London Blackfriars [3]	⊖ d								19 54						20 04									
London Bridge [4]	⊖ d	19 52	19a52	19 55	19 56	19 59	20 00	20a00	20a01	20a03		20 04		20a07	20a10	20 13	20a14	20a17	20a18	20 23	20 25	20 29	20 30	20 34
London Victoria [15]	⊖ d										19 52		19 46											
New Cross [4]	⊖ d				20 01		20 05									20 18					20 30		20 35	
St Johns	d				20 04		20 07																20 37	
Lewisham [4]	a	20 00		20 03		20 07	20 09					20 12	20 14			20 22					20 34	20 37	20 39	20 42 →
Hither Green [4]	a	20 05			20 09							20 17				20 27								
Petts Wood [4]	a	20 17									20 26	20 29												
Orpington [4]	a	20 20									20 29	20 32								20 40				

		SE 81	SE 90 [1] 🍴	SE 70	SE 12	SE 15	FC [1]	SE 50	SN	SE 80	SE 22 [1]	SE 70	SE 62	SE 24	SE 16	SE 81	SE 4 [1] 🍴	SE 70	FC [1]	SE 16	SE 50	SN	SE 80	SE 22 [1]
London Charing Cross [4]	⊖ d		20 30					20 34	20 37	20 40	20 45	20 47	20 50	20 52	20 56		21 00				21 04	21 07	21 10	21 15
London Waterloo (East) [4]	⊖ d		20 33					20 37	20 40	20 43	20 48	20 50	20 53	20 55	20 59		21 03				21 07	21 10	21 13	21 18
London Cannon Street [4]	⊖ d	20 30				20 35										21 00								
London Blackfriars [3]	⊖ d						20 34												21 04					
London Bridge [4]	⊖ d	20a33	20 38			20 39	20a40	20 43	20a44	20a47	20 53	20 55	20 59	21 00	21 04	21a03	21 08		21a10		21 13	21a14	21a17	21 23
London Victoria [15]	⊖ d			20 22														20 52						
New Cross [4]	⊖ d					20 44		20 48				21 00		21 05							21 18			
St Johns	d				←	20 46								21 07						←				
Lewisham [4]	a				20 42	20 48		20 52				21 04	21 07	21 09	21 12 →					21 12	21 22			
Hither Green [4]	a				20 47	20 53		20 57												21 17	21 27			
Petts Wood [4]	a			20 55	21 00	21 05												21 24		21 29				
Orpington [4]	a		20 54	20 58	21 03	21 10					21 10						21 24	21 27		21 32				21 40

		SE 70	SE 62	SE 24	SE 12	SE 90 [1]	SE 70	FC [1]	SE 12	SE 50	SN	SE 80	SE 22 [1]	SE 70	SE 62	SE 24	SE 12	SE 4 [1]	SE 70	FC [1]	SE 12	SE 50	SN	SE 80
London Charing Cross [4]	⊖ d	21 17	21 20	21 22	21 26	21 30				21 34	21 37	21 40	21 45	21 47	21 50	21 52	21 56	22 00				22 04	22 07	22 10
London Waterloo (East) [4]	⊖ d	21 20	21 23	21 25	21 29	21 33				21 37	21 40	21 43	21 48	21 50	21 53	21 55	21 59	22 03				22 07	22 10	22 13
London Cannon Street [4]	⊖ d																							
London Blackfriars [3]	⊖ d							21 34												22 04				
London Bridge [4]	⊖ d	21 25	21 29	21 30	21 34	21 38		21a40		21 43	21a44	21a47	21 53	21 55	21 59	22 00	22 04	22 08		22a10		22 13	22a14	22a17
London Victoria [15]	⊖ d						21 22												21 52					
New Cross [4]	⊖ d	21 30		21 35						21 48				22 00		22 05						22 18		
St Johns	d			21 37					←							22 07					←			
Lewisham [4]	a	21 34	21 37	21 39	21 42 →				21 42	21 52				22 04	22 07	22 09	22 12 →				22 12	22 22		
Hither Green [4]	a								21 47	21 57											22 17	22 27		
Petts Wood [4]	a						21 55		22 00										22 25		22 30			
Orpington [4]	a					21 54	21 58		22 03				22 10					22 24	22 28		22 33			

For general notes see front of timetable
For details of catering facilities see Directory of Train Operators

b Until 10 October arr. 2 minutes earlier
c Until 10 October arr. 1 minute earlier

London → Lewisham, Hither Green, Petts Wood and Orpington (Summary of Services)

For details of Bank Holiday service alterations please see first page of Table 195

Mondays to Fridays

		SE 22 ■1	SE 70	SE 62	SE 24	SE 12	SE 8 ■1	SE 70	FC ■1	SE 12	SE 50	SN	SE 80	SE 22 ■1	SE 73	SE 70	SE 62	SE 24	SE 12		SE 2 ■1	SE 70	FC ■1	SE 12	SE 50
London Charing Cross 4	⊖ d	22 15	22 17	22 20	22 22	22 26	22 30				22 34	22 37	22 40	22 45		22 47	22 50	22 52	22 56		23 00				23 04
London Waterloo (East) 4	⊖ d	22 18	22 20	22 23	22 25	22 29	22 33				22 37	22 40	22 43	22 48		22 50	22 53	22 55	22 59		23 03				23 07
London Cannon Street 4	⊖ d																								
London Blackfriars 3	⊖ d								22 34						22 43								23 04		
London Bridge 4	⊖ d	22 23	22 25	22 29	22 30	22 34	22 38		22a40		22 43	22a44	22a47	22 53		22 55	22 59	23 00	23 04		23 08		23a10		23 13
London Victoria 15	⊖ d							22 22														22 52			
New Cross 4	⊖ d		22 30		22 35						22 48					23 00		23 05							23 18
St Johns	d				22 37					←								23 07						←	
Lewisham 4	a		22 34	22 37	22 39	22 42 →				22 42	22 52					23 04	23 07	23 09	23 13 →					23 13	23 22
Hither Green 4	a									22 47	22 57													23 17	23 27
Petts Wood 4	a							22 55		23 00					23 20							23 26		23 31	
Orpington 4	a	22 40					22 54	22 58		23 03				23 10	23 24						23 24	23 30		23 34	

		SN	SE 73	SE 80	SE 22 ■1	SE 70	SE 62	SE 24	SE 12	SE 2 ■1	SE 70	FC ■1	SE 12	SE 50	SE 22 ■1	SE 73	SE 80	SN	SE 70		SE 70	SE 24
London Charing Cross 4	⊖ d	23 07		23 10	23 15	23 17	23 20	23 22	23 26	23 30				23 34	23 37		23 40	23 45			23 47	23 52
London Waterloo (East) 4	⊖ d	23 10		23 13	23 18	23 20	23 23	23 25	23 29	23 33				23 37	23 40		23 43	23 48			23 50	23 55
London Cannon Street 4	⊖ d																					
London Blackfriars 3	⊖ d		23 13									23 34				23 43						
London Bridge 4	⊖ d	23a14		23a17	23 23	23 25	23 29	23 30	23 34	23 38		23a40		23 43	23a44		23a47	23a52			23 55	23 58
London Victoria 15	⊖ d										23 22								23 53			
New Cross 4	⊖ d					23 30		23 35						23 48							00 01	00 04
St Johns	d							23 37					←									00 06
Lewisham 4	a					23 34	23 37	23 39	23 42 →				23 42	23 52							00 04	00 08
Hither Green 4	a												23 47	23 57								
Petts Wood 4	a		23 50								23 55		00 01			00 20			00 25			
Orpington 4	a		23 54		23 40					23 56	23 58		00 03			00 24			00 28			

Saturdays

		SE 12	SE 73	SE 70	SE 70	SE 24	FC	SE 50	SE 02 ■1	SN	SE 62	FC	SE 14	SE 52	SE 54	SE 80	FC ■1		SE 70	SE 62	SE 24	SE 12	SE 4 ■1	SE 70	SE 12
London Charing Cross 4	⊖ d	23p26			23p47	23p52		00 04	00 10	00 12	00 14		00 48	05 04	05 34	05 40			05 47	05 50	05 52	05 56	06 00		
London Waterloo (East) 4	⊖ d	23p29			23p50	23p55		00 07	00 13	00 15	00 17		00 51	05 07	05 37	05 43			05 50	05 53	05 55	05 59	06 03		
London Cannon Street 4	⊖ d																								
London Blackfriars 3	⊖ d		23p43				00 04					00 34					05 44								
London Bridge 4	⊖ d	23p34			23p55	23p58	00a10	00 13	00 18	00a19	00 23	00a40	00 56	05 13	05 43	05a47	05a49		05 55	05 59	06 01	06 04	06 08		
London Victoria 15	⊖ d			23p53																				05 51	
New Cross 4	⊖ d				00 01	00 04		00 18			00 28		01 01	05 18	05 48						06 06				
St Johns	d					00 06															06 08				←
Lewisham 4	a	23p42			00 04	00 08		00 22			00 32		01 05	05 22	05 52				06 04	06 06	06 10	06 12 →			06 12
Hither Green 4	a	23p47						00 27					01 09	05 27	05 57										06 17
Petts Wood 4	a	00 01	00 20	00 25					00 39				01 23											06 24	06 30
Orpington 4	a	00 03	00 24	00 28					00 42				01 26										06 26	06 27	06 33

		SE 54	SE 80	SE 70	FC ■1	SE 62	SE 24	SE 16	FC ■1	SE 54	SE 80	SE 70		FC ■1	SE 62	SE 24	SE 12	SE 4 ■1	SE 70	FC ■1	SE 12	SE 54	SE 80	SE 70	FC ■1
London Charing Cross 4	⊖ d	06 04	06 10	06 17		06 20	06 22	06 26		06 34	06 40	06 47			06 50	06 52	06 56	07 00				07 04	07 10	07 17	
London Waterloo (East) 4	⊖ d	06 07	06 13	06 20		06 23	06 25	06 29		06 37	06 43	06 50			06 53	06 55	06 59	07 03				07 07	07 13	07 20	
London Cannon Street 4	⊖ d																								
London Blackfriars 3	⊖ d				06 20				06 35					06 50						07 05					07 20
London Bridge 4	⊖ d	06 13	06a17	06 25	06a26	06 29	06 31	06 34	06a41	06 43	06a47	06 55		06a56	06 59	07 01	07 04	07 08		07a11		07 13	07a17	07 25	07a26
London Victoria 15	⊖ d																		06 51						
New Cross 4	⊖ d	06 18					06 36			06 48						07 06						07 18			
St Johns	d						06 38									07 08					←				
Lewisham 4	a	06 22		06 34		06 36	06 40	06 42		06 52		07 04			07 06	07 10	07 12 →				07 12	07 22		07 34	
Hither Green 4	a	06 27						06 47		06 57											07 17	07 27			
Petts Wood 4	a							07 00											07 24		07 30				
Orpington 4	a							07 03										07 26	07 27		07 33				

For general notes see front of timetable
For details of catering facilities see
Directory of Train Operators

Table 199

London → Lewisham, Hither Green, Petts Wood and Orpington (Summary of Services)

		SE 62	SE 24	SE 16	SE 4 [1]	SE 70	FC [1]		SE 16	SE 54	SN	SE 80	SE 22 [1]	SE 70	FC [1]	SE 62	SE 24	SE 12	SE 4 [1]	SE 70	SE 12	SE 54	SE 78	FC [1]	SE 81
London Charing Cross [4]	⊖ d	07 20	07 22	07 26	07 30					07 34	07 40	07 42	07 45	07 47		07 50	07 52	07 56	08 00			08 02			
London Waterloo (East) [4]	⊖ d	07 23	07 25	07 29	07 33					07 37	07 43	07 45	07 48	07 50		07 53	07 55	07 59	08 03			08 05			
London Cannon Street [4]	⊖ d																								08 10
London Blackfriars [3]	⊖ d						07 35								07 50									08 05	
London Bridge [4]	⊖ d	07 29	07 31	07 34	07 38		07a41			07 43	07a47	07a49	07 53	07 55	07a56	07 59	08 01	08 04	08 08			08 10		08a11	08a13
London Victoria [15]	⊖ d					07 21														07 51			08 01		
New Cross [4]	⊖ d		07 36							07 48							08 06					08 15			
St Johns	d		07 38						←								08 08				←				
Lewisham [4]	a	07 36	07 40	07 42 →					07 42	07 52				08 04		08 06	08 10	08 12 →			08 12	08 19	08 22		
Hither Green [4]	a								07 47	07 57											08 17	08 23			
Petts Wood [4]	a					07 54			08 00											08 24	08 30				
Orpington [4]	a				07 55	07 57			08 03				08 09						08 25	08 27	08 33				

		SN		SE 22 [1]	SE 70	SE 70	FC [1]	SE 62	SE 24	SE 16	SE 47	SE 4 [1]	SE 70	SE 16	SE 54	SE 78	SE 70	FC [1]	SE 81		SN	SE 47	SE 22 [1]	SE 70	FC [1]
London Charing Cross [4]	⊖ d	08 10		08 15		08 17		08 20	08 22	08 26		08 30			08 32						08 40		08 45	08 47	
London Waterloo (East) [4]	⊖ d	08 13		08 18		08 20		08 23	08 25	08 29		08 33			08 35						08 43		08 48	08 50	
London Cannon Street [4]	⊖ d										08 30								08 40			08 48			
London Blackfriars [3]	⊖ d						08 20											08 35							08 50
London Bridge [4]	⊖ d	08a17		08 23		08 25	08a26	08 29	08 31	08 34	08 34	08 38			08 40			08a41	08a43		08a47	08 52	08a52	08 55	08a56
London Victoria [15]	⊖ d				08 06								08 21			08 31	08 36								
New Cross [4]	⊖ d								08 36						08 45							08 57			
St Johns	d								08 38					←								08 59			
Lewisham [4]	a					08 33		08 36	08 40	08 42 →				08 42	08 49	08 52								09 04	
Hither Green [4]	a													08 47	08 53							09 04			
Petts Wood [4]	a				08 39								08 54	09 00			09 09								
Orpington [4]	a			08 39	08 42							08 55	08 57	09 03			09 12								

		SE 25	SE 82	SE 12	SE 47	SE 4 [1]	SE 70	SE 67	SE 12	SE 54	SE 78	FC [1]	SE 81	SE 24		SN	SE 09 [1]	SE 47	SE 22 [1]	SE 70	SE 70	FC [1]	SE 25	SE 82	SE 16
London Charing Cross [4]	⊖ d		08 50	08 56		09 00				09 02				09 06		09 10			09 15		09 17			09 20	09 26
London Waterloo (East) [4]	⊖ d		08 53	08 59		09 03				09 05				09 09		09 13			09 18		09 20			09 23	09 29
London Cannon Street [4]	⊖ d	08 54			09 00			09 04					09 10				09 14	09 18					09 24		
London Blackfriars [3]	⊖ d											09 05										09 20			
London Bridge [4]	⊖ d	08 58	08a58	09 04	09 04	09 08		09 08		09 10		09a11	09a13	09a14		09a17	09a17	09 22	09 23		09 25	09a26	09 28	09a28	09 34
London Victoria [15]	⊖ d						08 51				09 01									09 06					
New Cross [4]	⊖ d	09 03						09 14										09 27					09 33		
St Johns	d	09 05							←									09 29					09 35		
Lewisham [4]	a	09 07		09 12 →				09 17	09 12	09 19	09 22										09 34		09 37		09 42 →
Hither Green [4]	a								09 17	09 23								09 34							
Petts Wood [4]	a						09 24		09 30											09 39					
Orpington [4]	a					09 26	09 27		09 33										09 39	09 42					

		SE 47	SE 4 [1]	SE 70	SE 67	SE 16	SE 54	SE 78	SE 70		FC [1]	SE 81	SE 24	SN		SE 47	SE 22 [1]	SE 70	FC [1]	SE 25	SE 82	SE 12	SE 87	SE 8 [1]	SE 70
London Charing Cross [4]	⊖ d		09 30				09 32						09 36	09 40			09 45	09 47			09 50	09 56		10 00	
London Waterloo (East) [4]	⊖ d		09 33				09 35						09 39	09 43			09 48	09 50			09 53	09 59		10 03	
London Cannon Street [4]	⊖ d	09 30			09 34							09 40				09 48				09 54			10 00		
London Blackfriars [3]	⊖ d										09 35								09 50						
London Bridge [4]	⊖ d	09 34	09 38		09 38		09 40				09a41	09a43	09a44	09a47		09 52	09a52	09 55	09a56	09 58	09a58	10 04	10 04	10 08	
London Victoria [15]	⊖ d			09 21				09 31	09 36																09 51
New Cross [4]	⊖ d				09 44											09 57				10 03					
St Johns	d					←										09 59				10 05					
Lewisham [4]	a				09 47	09 42	09 49	09 52										10 04		10 07		10 12 →			
Hither Green [4]	a					09 47	09 53									10 04									
Petts Wood [4]	a			09 54		10 00			10 09															10 22	10 24
Orpington [4]	a		09 53	09 57		10 03			10 12															10 26	10 27

		SE 67	SE 12	SE 54	SE 78	FC [1]	SE 81	SE 34	SN	SE 09 [1]	SE 47	SE 22 [1]	SE 70	SE 70	FC [1]	SE 25	SE 82	SE 16	SE 87	SE 8 [1]	SE 70	SE 67	SE 16	SE 54	SE 78
London Charing Cross [4]	⊖ d			10 02				10 06	10 10			10 15		10 17			10 20	10 26		10 30				10 32	
London Waterloo (East) [4]	⊖ d			10 05				10 09	10 13			10 18		10 20			10 23	10 29		10 33				10 35	
London Cannon Street [4]	⊖ d	10 04					10 10			10 14	10 18					10 24			10 30			10 34			
London Blackfriars [3]	⊖ d					10 05									10 20										
London Bridge [4]	⊖ d	10 08		10 10		10a11	10a13	10a14	10a17	10a17	10 22	10 23		10 25	10a26	10 28	10a28	10 34	10 34	10 38		10 38		10 40	
London Victoria [15]	⊖ d				10 01								10 06								10 21				10 31
New Cross [4]	⊖ d	10 14									10 27					10 33						10 44			
St Johns	d		←								10 29					10 35							←		
Lewisham [4]	a	10 17	10 12	10 19	10 22									10 34		10 37		10 42 →				10 47	10 42	10 49	10 52
Hither Green [4]	a		10 17	10 23							10 34												10 47	10 53	
Petts Wood [4]	a		10 30										10 39								10 54		11 00		
Orpington [4]	a		10 33									10 39	10 42							10 53	10 57		11 03		

For general notes see front of timetable
For details of catering facilities see
Directory of Train Operators

London → Lewisham, Hither Green, Petts Wood and Orpington (Summary of Services)

	SE 70	FC 1	SE 81	SE 34	SN	and at the same minutes past each hour until		SE 47	SE 22 1 🍴	SE 70	FC 1	SE 25	SE 82	SE 12	SE 87	SE 8 1	SE 70	SE 67	SE 12	SE 54	SE 78	FC 1	SE 81
London Charing Cross 4 ⊖ d				10 36	10 40				17 45	17 47			17 50	17 56		18 00				18 02			
London Waterloo (East) 4 ⊖ d				10 39	10 43				17 48	17 50			17 53	17 59		18 03				18 05			
London Cannon Street 4 ⊖ d			10 40					17 48				17 54			18 00			18 04					18 10
London Blackfriars 3 ⊖ d		10 35									17 50											18 05	
London Bridge 4 ⊖ d		10a41	10a43	10a44	10a47			17 52	17a52	17 55	17a56	17 58	17a58	18 04	18a03	18 08		18 08		18 10		18a11	18a13
London Victoria 15 ⊖ d	10 36																17 51				18 01		
New Cross 4 ⊖ d								17 57				18 03						18 14					
St Johns d								17 59				18 05							←				
Lewisham 4 a										18 04		18 07		18 12 →				18 17	18 12	18 19	18 22		
Hither Green 4 a								18 04											18 17	18 23			
Petts Wood 4 a	11 09															18 22	18 24		18 30				
Orpington 4 a	11 12															18 26	18 27		18 33				

	SE 24	SN		SE 09 1	SE 47	SE 22 1 🍴	SE 70	SE 70	FC 1	SE 25	SE 62	SE 25	SE 16	SE 87	SE 90 1	SE 70	SE 16	SE 54	SE 78		SE 70	FC 1	SE 81	SE 24
London Charing Cross 4 ⊖ d	18 06	18 10				18 15		18 17			18 20		18 26		18 30			18 32						18 36
London Waterloo (East) 4 ⊖ d	18 09	18 13				18 18		18 20			18 23		18 29		18 33			18 35						18 39
London Cannon Street 4 ⊖ d				18 14	18 18					18 24				18 30									18 40	
London Blackfriars 3 ⊖ d									18 20													18 35		
London Bridge 4 ⊖ d	18a14	18a17		18a17	18 22	18 23		18 25	18a26	18 28	18 29		18 34	18a33	18 38			18 40				18a41	18a43	18a44
London Victoria 15 ⊖ d							18 06					←				18 21			18 31		18 36			
New Cross 4 ⊖ d					18 27					18 35 →		18 35												
St Johns d					18 29							18 37					←							
Lewisham 4 a								18 33			18 36	18 39	18 44 →				18 44	18 49	18 51					
Hither Green 4 a					18 34												18 48	18 53						
Petts Wood 4 a							18 39									18 54	19 00				19 09			
Orpington 4 a						18 40	18 42								18 54	18 57	19 03				19 12			

	SN	SE 47	SE 22 1 🍴	SE 70	FC 1	SE 62	SE 25	SE 12	SE 87	SE 4 1 🍴	SE 70	FC 1	SE 12	SE 54		SE 78	SN	SE 81	SE 09 1	SE 22 1 🍴	SE 70	SE 70	FC 1	SE 62
London Charing Cross 4 ⊖ d	18 40		18 45	18 47		18 50	18 52	18 56		19 00				19 04			19 07	19 10		19 15		19 17		19 20
London Waterloo (East) 4 ⊖ d	18 43		18 48	18 50		18 53	18 55	18 59		19 03				19 07			19 10	19 13		19 18		19 20		19 23
London Cannon Street 4 ⊖ d		18 48							19 00										19 14					
London Blackfriars 3 ⊖ d					18 50							19 04											19 20	
London Bridge 4 ⊖ d	18a47	18 52	18a52	18 55	18a56	18 59	19 01	19 04	19a03	19 08		19a10		19 13			19a14	19a17	19a17	19 23		19 25	19a26	19 29
London Victoria 15 ⊖ d											18 51					19 01					19 06			
New Cross 4 ⊖ d		18 57					19 06																	
St Johns d		18 59					19 08						←											
Lewisham 4 a				19 04		19 07	19 10	19 14 →					19 14	19 20		19 22						19 34		19 36
Hither Green 4 a		19 04											19 18	19 24										
Petts Wood 4 a											19 24		19 30								19 39			
Orpington 4 a										19 24	19 27		19 33							19 40	19 42			

	SE 24	SE 16	SE 90 1	SE 70	FC 1	SE 16	SE 50	SE 78	SN		SE 80	SE 22 1	SE 70	SE 70	FC 1	SE 62	SE 24	SE 12	SE 4 1 🍴	SE 70	FC 1	SE 12	SE 50	SN
London Charing Cross 4 ⊖ d	19 22	19 26	19 30				19 34		19 37		19 40	19 45		19 47		19 50	19 52	19 56	20 00				20 04	20 07
London Waterloo (East) 4 ⊖ d	19 25	19 29	19 33				19 37		19 39		19 43	19 48		19 50		19 53	19 55	19 59	20 03				20 07	20 10
London Cannon Street 4 ⊖ d																								
London Blackfriars 3 ⊖ d					19 35										19 50						20 04			
London Bridge 4 ⊖ d	19 31	19 34	19 38		19a41		19 43		19a44		19a47	19 53		19 55	19a56	19 59	20 01	20 04	20 08		20a10		20 13	20a14
London Victoria 15 ⊖ d				19 21				19 31					19 36							19 51				
New Cross 4 ⊖ d	19 36						19 48							20 00			20 06						20 18	
St Johns d	19 38					←											20 08					←		
Lewisham 4 a	19 40	19 42 →				19 42	19 52	19 53						20 04		20 06	20 10	20 12 →				20 12	20 22	
Hither Green 4 a						19 47	19 57															20 17	20 27	
Petts Wood 4 a				19 54		20 00							20 09							20 24		20 30		
Orpington 4 a			19 54	19 57		20 03						20 10	20 12						20 24	20 27		20 33		

	SE 80	SE 70	SE 62	SE 24		SE 12	SE 90 1	SE 70	FC 1	SE 12	SE 50	SN	SE 80	SE 22 1	SE 70	SE 62	SE 24	SE 16	SE 4 1	SE 70	FC 1		SE 16	SE 50
London Charing Cross 4 ⊖ d	20 10	20 17	20 20	20 22		20 26	20 30				20 34	20 37	20 40	20 45	20 47	20 50	20 52	20 56	21 00					21 04
London Waterloo (East) 4 ⊖ d	20 13	20 20	20 23	20 25		20 29	20 33				20 37	20 40	20 43	20 48	20 50	20 53	20 55	20 59	21 03					21 07
London Cannon Street 4 ⊖ d																								
London Blackfriars 3 ⊖ d									20 34												21 04			
London Bridge 4 ⊖ d	20a17	20 25	20 29	20 31		20 34	20 38		20a40		20 43	20a44	20a47	20 53	20 55	20 59	21 01	21 04	21 08		21a10			21 13
London Victoria 15 ⊖ d								20 21												20 51				
New Cross 4 ⊖ d		20 30		20 36							20 48				21 00		21 06							21 18
St Johns d				20 38						←							21 08						←	
Lewisham 4 a		20 34	20 36	20 40		20 42 →				20 42	20 52				21 04	21 06	21 10	21 12 →					21 12	21 22
Hither Green 4 a										20 47	20 57												21 17	21 27
Petts Wood 4 a								20 54		21 00										21 24			21 30	
Orpington 4 a							20 54	20 57		21 03				21 10					21 24	21 27			21 33	

For general notes see front of timetable
For details of catering facilities see Directory of Train Operators

Table 199

Saturdays

London → Lewisham, Hither Green, Petts Wood and Orpington (Summary of Services)

		SN	SE 80	SE 70	SE 62	SE 24	SE 12	SE 90 [1]	SE 70	FC [1]	SE 12	SE 50	SN	SE 80	SE 22 [1]	SE 70	SE 62		SE 24	SE 12	SE 4 [1]	SE 70	FC [1]	SE 12	SE 50
London Charing Cross 4	⊖ d	21 07	21 10	21 17	21 20	21 22	21 26	21 30				21 34	21 37	21 40	21 45	21 47	21 50		21 52	21 56	22 00				22 04
London Waterloo (East) 4	⊖ d	21 10	21 13	21 20	21 23	21 25	21 29	21 33				21 37	21 40	21 43	21 48	21 50	21 53		21 55	21 59	22 03				22 07
London Cannon Street 4	⊖ d																								
London Blackfriars 3	⊖ d									21 34													22 04		
London Bridge 4	⊖ d	21a14	21a17	21 25	21 29	21 31	21 34	21 38		21a40		21 43	21a44	21a47	21 53	21 55	21 59		22 01	22 04	22 08		22a10		22 13
London Victoria 15	⊖ d								21 21													21 51			
New Cross 4	⊖ d			21 30		21 36						21 48				22 00			22 06						22 18
St Johns	d					21 38					←								22 08					←	
Lewisham 4	a			21 34	21 36	21 40	21 42 →				21 42	21 52				22 04	22 06		22 10	22 12 →				22 12	22 22
Hither Green 4	a										21 47	21 57												22 17	22 27
Petts Wood 4	a								21 54		22 00											22 24		22 30	
Orpington 4	a							21 54	21 57		22 03				22 10						22 24	22 27		22 33	

		SN	SE 80	SE 70	SE 62	SE 24	SE 12	SE 90 [1]	SE 70	FC [1]	SE 12	SE 50		SN	SE 80	SE 22 [1]	SE 73	SE 70	SE 62	SE 24	SE 12	SE 8 [1]	SE 70	FC [1]	SE 12
London Charing Cross 4	⊖ d	22 07	22 10	22 17	22 20	22 22	22 26	22 30				22 34		22 37	22 40	22 45		22 47	22 50	22 52	22 56	23 00			
London Waterloo (East) 4	⊖ d	22 10	22 13	22 20	22 23	22 25	22 29	22 33				22 37		22 40	22 43	22 48		22 50	22 53	22 55	22 59	23 03			
London Cannon Street 4	⊖ d																								
London Blackfriars 3	⊖ d									22 34							22 43							23 04	
London Bridge 4	⊖ d	22a14	22a17	22 25	22 29	22 31	22 34	22 38		22a40		22 43		22a44	22a47	22 53		22 55	22 59	23 01	23 04	23 08		23a10	
London Victoria 15	⊖ d								22 21														22 51		
New Cross 4	⊖ d			22 30		22 36						22 48						23 00		23 06					
St Johns	d					22 38					←									23 08					←
Lewisham 4	a			22 34	22 36	22 40	22 42 →				22 42	22 52						23 04	23 06	23 10	23 12 →				23 12
Hither Green 4	a										22 47	22 57													23 17
Petts Wood 4	a								22 54		23 00						23 20						23 24		23 30
Orpington 4	a							22 54	22 57		23 03					23 10	23 23					23 24	23 27		23 33

		SE 50	SN	SE 73	SE 80	SE 70	SE 62		SE 24	SE 12	SE 8 [1]	SE 70	FC	SE 12	SE 50	SE 73	SN	SE 70	SE 70	SE 80	SE 24				
London Charing Cross 4	⊖ d	23 04	23 07		23 10	23 17	23 20		23 22	23 26	23 30				23 34		23 45		23 47	23 49	23 52				
London Waterloo (East) 4	⊖ d	23 07	23 10		23 13	23 20	23 23		23 25	23 29	23 33				23 37		23 48		23 50	23 52	23 55				
London Cannon Street 4	⊖ d																								
London Blackfriars 3	⊖ d			23 13									23 34			23 43									
London Bridge 4	⊖ d	23 13	23a14		23a17	23 25	23 29		23 31	23 34	23 38		23a40		23 43		23a52		23 55	23a56	23 58				
London Victoria 15	⊖ d											23 21						23 53							
New Cross 4	⊖ d	23 18				23 30			23 36						23 48				23 59		00 04				
St Johns	d								23 38					←							00 06				
Lewisham 4	a	23 22				23 34	23 36		23 40	23 42 →				23 42	23 52				00 04		00 08				
Hither Green 4	a	23 27												23 47	23 57										
Petts Wood 4	a			23 50								23 54		00 01		00 20		00 26							
Orpington 4	a			23 53							23 54	23 57		00 03		00 23		00 29							

Sundays

		SE 12	SE 73	SE 70	SE 70	SE 24	SE 50	FC	SE 02 [1]	SN	SE 62	FC [1]	SE 14	FC [1]	SE 12	FC [1]	SN	SE 72	SE 80	SE 70	SE 50	SE 24	SE 16	FC [1]	SN
London Charing Cross 4	⊖ d	23p26			23p47	23p52	00 04		00 10	00 12	00 14		00 48				07 34	07 37	07 40		07 47	07 53	07 56		08 04
London Waterloo (East) 4	⊖ d	23p29			23p50	23p55	00 07		00 13	00 15	00 17		00 51				07 37	07 40	07 43		07 50	07 56	07 59		08 07
London Cannon Street 4	⊖ d																								
London Blackfriars 3	⊖ d		23p43					00 04				00 34		07 04		07 34								08 04	
London Bridge 4	⊖ d	23p34			23p55	23p58	00 13	00a15	00 18	00a19	00 22	00a40	00 56	07a10	07 35	07a40	07a42	07 45	07a47		07 55	08 02	08 05	08a10	08a12
London Victoria 15	⊖ d			23p53																07 51					
New Cross 4	⊖ d				23p59	00 04	00 18				00 27		01 01					07 50			08 00	08 07			
St Johns	d					00 06																08 09			
Lewisham 4	a	23p42			00 04	00 08	00 22				00 31		01 05		07 44			07 54			08 04	08 11	08 14		
Hither Green 4	a	23p47					00 27						01 09		07 49						08 09		08 19		
Petts Wood 4	a	00 01	00 20	00 26					00 39				01 23		08 01					08 24			08 31		
Orpington 4	a	00 03	00 23	00 29					00 42				01 26		08 04					08 27			08 34		

		SE 70	SE 80	SE 22 [1]	SE 50	SE 62	SE 24	SE 12	SE 90 [1]	SE 70	FC [1]	SN	SE 82	SE 80	SE 12	SE 50	SE 62	SE 24	SE 16	SE 4 [1]	SE 70	FC [1]	SN	SE 70	SE 84
London Charing Cross 4	⊖ d	08 07	08 10	08 14	08 17	08 20	08 23	08 26	08 30			08 34	08 37	08 40		08 47	08 50	08 53	08 56	09 00			09 04	09 07	09 10
London Waterloo (East) 4	⊖ d	08 10	08 13	08 17	08 20	08 23	08 26	08 29	08 33			08 37	08 40	08 43		08 50	08 53	08 56	08 59	09 03			09 07	09 10	09 13
London Cannon Street 4	⊖ d																								
London Blackfriars 3	⊖ d										08 34											09 04			
London Bridge 4	⊖ d	08 15	08a17	08 22	08 25	08 29	08 32	08 35	08 38		08a40	08a42	08 45	08a47		08 55	08 59	09 02	09 05	09 08		09a10	09a12	09 15	09a17
London Victoria 15	⊖ d									08 21											08 51				
New Cross 4	⊖ d	08 20			08 30		08 37						08 50			09 00		09 07						09 20	
St Johns	d						08 39								←			09 09							
Lewisham 4	a	08 24			08 34	08 37	08 41	08 44 →					08 54		08 44	09 04	09 07	09 11	09 14					09 24	
Hither Green 4	a				08 39										08 49	09 09			09 19						
Petts Wood 4	a									08 54					09 01				09 31		09 24				
Orpington 4	a			08 38					08 54	08 57					09 04				09 34	09 24	09 27				

For general notes see front of timetable
For details of catering facilities see
Directory of Train Operators

Sundays

London → Lewisham, Hither Green, Petts Wood and Orpington (Summary of Services)

		SE 22 [1]	SE 50	FC	SE 62	SE 24	SE 12	SE 90 [1]	SE 70	FC [1]	SN	SE 70	SE 84	SE 12	SE 22 [1]	SE 50	FC [1]	SE 62	SE 24	SE 16	SE 4 [1]	SE 70		FC [1]	SN
London Charing Cross [4]	⊖ d	09 14	09 17		09 20	09 23	09 26	09 30			09 34	09 37	09 40		09 44	09 47		09 50	09 53	09 56	10 00				10 04
London Waterloo (East) [4]	⊖ d	09 17	09 20		09 23	09 26	09 29	09 33			09 37	09 40	09 43		09 47	09 50		09 53	09 56	09 59	10 03				10 07
London Cannon Street [4]	⊖ d																								
London Blackfriars [3]	⊖ d			09 19						09 34							09 49							10 04	
London Bridge [4]	⊖ d	09 22	09 25	09a25	09 29	09 32	09 35	09 38		09a40	09a42	09 45	09a47		09 52	09 55	09a55	09 59	10 02	10 05	10 08			10a10	10a12
London Victoria [15]	⊖ d								09 21													09 51			
New Cross [4]	⊖ d		09 30			09 37						09 50				10 00			10 07						
St Johns	d					09 39								←					10 09						
Lewisham [4]	a		09 34		09 37	09 41	09 44					09 54		09 44		10 04		10 07	10 11	10 15					
Hither Green [4]	a		09 39				→							09 49		10 09				10 19					
Petts Wood [4]	a								09 54					10 01						10 31		10 24			
Orpington [4]	a	09 38						09 54	09 57					10 04	10 08					10 34	10 24	10 27			

		SE 70	SE 84	SE 22 [1]	SE 50	FC [1]	SE 62		SE 24	SE 12	SE 90 [1]	SE 70	FC [1]	SN	SE 70	SE 84	SE 12	SE 22 [1]	SE 50	FC [1]	SE 62	SE 24	SE 16	SE 4 [1]	SE 70
London Charing Cross [4]	⊖ d	10 07	10 10	10 14	10 17		10 20		10 23	10 26	10 30			10 34	10 37	10 40		10 44	10 47		10 50	10 53	10 56	11 00	
London Waterloo (East) [4]	⊖ d	10 10	10 13	10 17	10 20		10 23		10 26	10 29	10 33			10 37	10 40	10 43		10 47	10 50		10 53	10 56	10 59	11 03	
London Cannon Street [4]	⊖ d																								
London Blackfriars [3]	⊖ d					10 19							10 34							10 49					
London Bridge [4]	⊖ d	10 15	10a17	10 22	10 25	10a25	10 29		10 32	10 35	10 38		10a40	10a42	10 45	10a47		10 52	10 55	10a55	10 59	11 02	11 05	11 08	
London Victoria [15]	⊖ d											10 21													10 51
New Cross [4]	⊖ d	10 20			10 30				10 37						10 50				11 00			11 07			
St Johns	d								10 39								←					11 09			
Lewisham [4]	a	10 24			10 34		10 37		10 41	10 44					10 54		10 44		11 04		11 07	11 11	11 14		
Hither Green [4]	a				10 39					→							10 49		11 09				→		
Petts Wood [4]	a											10 54					11 01								11 24
Orpington [4]	a			10 38							10 54	10 57					11 04	11 08						11 24	11 27

		FC [1]	SN	SE 16	SE 70	SE 84	SE 22 [1]	SE 50	FC [1]	SE 62	and at	SE 24	SE 12	SE 90 [1]	SE 70	FC [1]	SN	SE 72	SE 80	SE 12	SE 22 [1]	SE 50	SE 62	SE 24
London Charing Cross [4]	⊖ d		11 04		11 07	11 10	11 14	11 17		11 20	the same	17 23	17 26	17 30			17 34	17 37	17 40		17 44	17 47	17 50	17 53
London Waterloo (East) [4]	⊖ d		11 07		11 10	11 13	11 17	11 20		11 23		17 26	17 29	17 33			17 37	17 40	17 43		17 47	17 50	17 53	17 56
London Cannon Street [4]	⊖ d										minutes													
London Blackfriars [3]	⊖ d	11 04							11 19							17 34								
London Bridge [4]	⊖ d	11a10	11a12		11 15	11a17	11 22	11 25	11a25	11 29	past	17 32	17 35	17 38		17a40	17a42	17 45	17a47		17 52	17 55	17 59	18 02
London Victoria [15]	⊖ d														17 21									
New Cross [4]	⊖ d				11 20			11 30			each	17 37						17 50				18 00		18 07
St Johns	d			←								17 39								←				18 09
Lewisham [4]	a			11 14	11 24			11 34		11 37	hour until	17 41	17 44					17 54		17 44		18 04	18 07	18 11
Hither Green [4]	a			11 19				11 39					→							17 49		18 09		
Petts Wood [4]	a			11 31											17 54					18 01				
Orpington [4]	a			11 34			11 38							17 54	17 57					18 04	18 08			

		SE 16	SE 4 [1]	SE 70	FC [1]	SN	SE 16	SE 70	SE 80	SE 22 [1]	SE 50	SE 60	SE 24	SE 12	SE 90 [1]	SE 70	FC [1]	SN	SE 72	SE 80	SE 12	SE 22 [1]	SE 50	SE 62	SE 24
London Charing Cross [4]	⊖ d	17 56	18 00			18 04		18 07	18 10	18 14	18 17	18 20	18 23	18 26	18 30			18 34	18 37	18 40		18 44	18 47	18 50	18 53
London Waterloo (East) [4]	⊖ d	17 59	18 03			18 07		18 10	18 13	18 17	18 20	18 23	18 26	18 29	18 33			18 37	18 40	18 43		18 47	18 50	18 53	18 56
London Cannon Street [4]	⊖ d																								
London Blackfriars [3]	⊖ d				18 04												18 34								
London Bridge [4]	⊖ d	18 05	18 08		18a10	18a12		18 15	18a17	18 22	18 25	18 29	18 32	18 35	18 38		18a40	18a42	18 45	18a47		18 52	18 55	18 59	19 02
London Victoria [15]	⊖ d			17 51												18 21									
New Cross [4]	⊖ d							18 20			18 30		18 37						18 50				19 00		19 07
St Johns	d						←						18 39								←				19 09
Lewisham [4]	a	18 14					18 14	18 24			18 34	18 37	18 41	18 44					18 54		18 44		19 04	19 07	19 11
Hither Green [4]	a	→					18 19				18 39			→							18 49		19 09		
Petts Wood [4]	a			18 24			18 31									18 54					19 01				
Orpington [4]	a		18 24	18 27			18 34			18 38					18 54	18 57					19 04	19 08			

		SE 16	SE 4 [1]		SE 70	FC [1]	SN	SE 16	SE 70	SE 80	SE 22 [1]	SE 50	SE 62	SE 24	SE 12	SE 90 [1]	SE 70	FC [1]	SN	SE 72	SE 80	SE 12	SE 22 [1]	SE 50	SE 62
London Charing Cross [4]	⊖ d	18 56	19 00				19 04		19 07	19 10	19 14	19 17	19 20	19 23	19 26	19 30			19 34	19 37	19 40		19 44	19 47	19 50
London Waterloo (East) [4]	⊖ d	18 59	19 03				19 07		19 10	19 13	19 17	19 20	19 23	19 26	19 29	19 33			19 37	19 40	19 43		19 47	19 50	19 53
London Cannon Street [4]	⊖ d																								
London Blackfriars [3]	⊖ d					19 04												19 34							
London Bridge [4]	⊖ d	19 05	19 08			19a10	19a12		19 15	19a17	19 22	19 25	19 29	19 32	19 35	19 38		19a40	19a42	19 45	19a47		19 52	19 55	19 59
London Victoria [15]	⊖ d				18 51												19 21								
New Cross [4]	⊖ d								19 20			19 30		19 37						19 50				20 00	
St Johns	d							←						19 39								←			
Lewisham [4]	a	19 14						19 14	19 24			19 34	19 37	19 41	19 44					19 54		19 44		20 04	20 07
Hither Green [4]	a	→						19 19				19 39			→							19 49		20 09	
Petts Wood [4]	a				19 24			19 31									19 54					20 01			
Orpington [4]	a		19 24		19 27			19 34			19 38					19 54	19 57					20 04	20 08		

For general notes see front of timetable
For details of catering facilities see
Directory of Train Operators

Sundays

London → Lewisham, Hither Green, Petts Wood and Orpington (Summary of Services)

		SE 24	SE 12	SE 4 [1]	SE 70	FC [1]	SN	SE 70	SE 80	SE 12	SE 22 [1]	SE 50	SE 62	SE 24	SE 12	SE 90 [1]	SE 70	FC [1]	SN	SE 72	SE 80	SE 12	SE 50	SE 62	SE 24
London Charing Cross 4	⊖ d	19 53	19 56	20 00			20 04	20 07	20 10		20 14	20 17	20 20	20 23	20 26	20 30			20 34	20 37	20 40		20 47	20 50	20 53
London Waterloo (East) 4	⊖ d	19 56	19 59	20 03			20 07	20 10	20 13		20 17	20 20	20 23	20 26	20 29	20 33			20 37	20 40	20 43		20 50	20 53	20 56
London Cannon Street 4	⊖ d																								
London Blackfriars 3	⊖ d					20 04												20 34							
London Bridge 4	⊖ d	20 02	20 05	20 08		20a10	20a12	20 15	20a17		20 22	20 25	20 29	20 32	20 35	20 38		20a40	20a42	20 45	20a47		20 55	20 59	21 02
London Victoria 15	⊖ d				19 51												20 21								
New Cross 4	⊖ d	20 07						20 20				20 30		20 37						20 50			21 00		21 07
St Johns	d	20 09								←				20 39								←			21 09
Lewisham 4	a	20 11	20 14 →					20 24		20 14		20 34	20 37	20 41	20 44 →					20 54		20 44	21 04	21 07	21 11
Hither Green 4	a									20 19		20 39										20 49	21 09		
Petts Wood 4	a				20 24					20 31							20 54					21 01			
Orpington 4	a			20 24	20 27					20 34	20 38					20 54	20 57					21 04			

		SE 12	SE 4 [1]	SE 70	FC [1]	SN	SE 70	SE 80	SE 12	SE 22 [1]	SE 50	FC [1]	SE 62	SE 24	SE 12	SE 90 [1]	SE 70	FC [1]	SN	SE 72	SE 80	SE 12	SE 50	SE 62	SE 24
London Charing Cross 4	⊖ d	20 56	21 00			21 04	21 07	21 10		21 14	21 17		21 20	21 23	21 26	21 30			21 34	21 37	21 40		21 47	21 50	21 53
London Waterloo (East) 4	⊖ d	20 59	21 03			21 07	21 10	21 13		21 17	21 20		21 23	21 26	21 29	21 33			21 37	21 40	21 43		21 50	21 53	21 56
London Cannon Street 4	⊖ d																								
London Blackfriars 3	⊖ d				21 04							21 19						21 34							
London Bridge 4	⊖ d	21 05	21 08		21a10	21a12	21 15	21a17		21 22	21 25	21a25	21 29	21 32	21 35	21 38		21a40	21a42	21 45	21a47		21 55	21 59	22 02
London Victoria 15	⊖ d			20 51													21 21								
New Cross 4	⊖ d						21 20				21 30			21 37						21 50			22 00		22 07
St Johns	d								←					21 39								←			22 09
Lewisham 4	a	21 14 →					21 24		21 14		21 34		21 37	21 41	21 44 →					21 54		21 44	22 04	22 07	22 11
Hither Green 4	a								21 19		21 39											21 49	22 09		
Petts Wood 4	a			21 24					21 31								21 54					22 01			
Orpington 4	a		21 24	21 27					21 34	21 38						21 54	21 57					22 04			

		SE 12	SE 4 [1]	SE 70	FC [1]	SN	SE 70	SE 80	SE 12	SE 22 [1]	SE 50	SE 62	SE 24	SE 12	SE 2 [1]	SE 70	FC [1]	SN	SE 12	SE 72	SE 72	SE 80	SE 70	SE 50	SE 62
London Charing Cross 4	⊖ d	21 56	22 00			22 04	22 07	22 10		22 14	22 17	22 20	22 23	22 26	22 30			22 34			22 37	22 40		22 47	22 50
London Waterloo (East) 4	⊖ d	21 59	22 03			22 07	22 10	22 13		22 17	22 20	22 23	22 26	22 29	22 33			22 37			22 40	22 43		22 50	22 53
London Cannon Street 4	⊖ d																								
London Blackfriars 3	⊖ d				22 04												22 34								
London Bridge 4	⊖ d	22 05	22 08		22a10	22a12	22 15	22a17		22 22	22 25	22 29	22 32	22 35	22 38		22a40	22a42			22 45	22a47		22 55	22 59
London Victoria 15	⊖ d			21 51												22 21				22 38			22 51		
New Cross 4	⊖ d						22 20				22 30		22 37								22 50			23 00	
St Johns	d								←				22 39						←						
Lewisham 4	a	22 14 →					22 24		22 14		22 34	22 37	22 41	22 44 →					22 44		22 54			23 04	23 07
Hither Green 4	a								22 19		22 39								22 49					23 09	
Petts Wood 4	a			22 24					22 31							22 54			23 01	23 14			23 24		
Orpington 4	a		22 24	22 27					22 34	22 38					22 54	22 57			23 04	23 17			23 27		

		SE 24	SE 12	FC [1]	SN	SE 70	SE 80	SE 22 [1]	SE 72	SE 50	SE 62	SE 24	SE 12	SE 8 [1]	SE 70	FC	SN	SE 70	SE 80	SE 12	SE 50	SE 24	SE 12		
London Charing Cross 4	⊖ d	22 53	22 56		23 04	23 07	23 10	23 14		23 17	23 20	23 23	23 26	23 30			23 34	23 37	23 40		23 47	23 53	23 56		
London Waterloo (East) 4	⊖ d	22 56	22 59		23 07	23 10	23 13	23 17		23 20	23 23	23 26	23 29	23 33			23 37	23 40	23 43		23 50	23 56	23 59		
London Cannon Street 4	⊖ d																								
London Blackfriars 3	⊖ d			23 04												23 34									
London Bridge 4	⊖ d	23 02	23 05	23a10	23a12	23 15	23a17	23 22		23 25	23 29	23 32	23 35	23 38		23a40	23a42	23 45	23a47		23 55	00 02	00 05		
London Victoria 15	⊖ d								23 08						23 21										
New Cross 4	⊖ d	23 07				23 20				23 30		23 37						23 50			00 01	00 07			
St Johns	d	23 09										23 39								←		00 09			
Lewisham 4	a	23 11	23 14			23 24				23 34	23 37	23 41	23 44 →					23 54		23 44	00 04	00 11	00 14		
Hither Green 4	a		23 19							23 39										23 48	00 09		00 19		
Petts Wood 4	a		23 31						23 44						23 54					00 01			00 31		
Orpington 4	a		23 34					23 38	23 47					23 54	23 57					00 03			00 34		

For general notes see front of timetable
For details of catering facilities see
Directory of Train Operators

Orpington, Petts Wood, Hither Green and Lewisham → London (Summary of Services)

For details of Bank Holiday service alterations please see first page of Table 195

		FC	FC 1	SE 73	SE 52	SE 71	FC 1	SE 50	SN	SE 11	SE 02	SE 24	SE 80	SE 70	SE 11	SE 70	SE 73	SE 30 1	SE 50	SE 82	SE 11	FC 1	SE 24	SE 70	SE 70
Orpington 4	d			04 36		04 58					05 20					05 25	05 36	05 50							05 50
Petts Wood 4	d			04 39		05 01					05 23					05 28	05 39								05 53
Hither Green 4	d				05 08			05 23			05 34								05 55						
Lewisham 4	d				05 13			05 28				05 40		05 48					06 00				06 10	06 16	
St Johns	d											05 42											06 12		
New Cross 4	⊖ d				05 16			05 32			05 39	05 44		05 52					06 04				06 14	06 20	
London Victoria 15	⊖ a															06b03									06b29
London Bridge 4	⊖ d	00 20	00 52		05 22		05 34	05 38	05 41	05 42	05 46	05 50	05 53	05 58	05 58			06 06	06 10	06 13	06 14	06 15	06 20	06 26	
London Blackfriars 3	⊖ a	00 26	00 59	05 16		05 34	05 41										06 18					06 23			
London Cannon Street 4	⊖ a									05 45					06 01						06 17				
London Waterloo (East) 4	⊖ d				05 28			05 44	05 46		05 51	05 55	05 58	06 03				06 11	06 15	06 18			06 25	06 31	
London Charing Cross 4	⊖ a				05 31			05 47	05 49		05b56	06b00	06 02	06 06				06 14	06 18	06 21			06b30	06 34	

		SE 14	SE 11	SE 62	SE 07 1	SE 5 1	SE 2 1	SE 50	SE 84	SE 77	FC 1	SE 70	SE 14	SE 05	SE 24	SE 14	SE 22 1	FC 1	SE 62	SE 11		SE 4 1	SE 70	SE 03 1	SE 40
Orpington 4	d	06 00				06 17						06 20	06 24	06 31											
Petts Wood 4	d	06 03										06 23	06 27			←									
Hither Green 4	d	06 15						06 25					06 39			06 39									06 52
Lewisham 4	d	06 20		06 24				06 30		06 34			→		06 40	06 44			06 52				06 56		
St Johns	d							06 32							06 42										06 56
New Cross 4	⊖ d	06 24						06 34		06 38					06 44										06 58
London Victoria 15	⊖ a											06b59													
London Bridge 4	⊖ d	06 30	06 30	06 33	06 34	06 37	06 37	06 40	06 43	06 44	06 46			06 50	06 50	06 53	06 56	06 59	07 01	07 02		07 04	07 06	07 08	07 09
London Blackfriars 3	⊖ a										06 52							07 06							
London Cannon Street 4	⊖ a		06 33		06b40	06b43				06 47				06b55						07b07				07 13	
London Waterloo (East) 4	⊖ d	06 35		06 38			06 42	06 45	06 48						06 55	06 58	07 01		07 06			07 09	07 11		07 13
London Charing Cross 4	⊖ a	06 38		06 41			06b48	06 48	06 51						07b00	07b03	07c06		07c11			07c15	07c16		07c18

		SE 24	SE 80	SE 70	FC 1	SE 14	SE 13	SE 17	SE 55	SE 90 1	SE 87	SE 40	SE 13	SE 70	SE 07 1	SE 71	SE 70	SE 12	SE 23 1	SE 62	SE 46	SE 77	SE 12	SE 80	SE 51
Orpington 4	d			06 44		06 49	06 57	06 59								07 02	07 06	07 10	07 13						
Petts Wood 4	d			06 47		06 52	07 00						←			07 05	07 09	07 13					←		
Hither Green 4	d					07 06	07 14		07 02			07 10	07 14					→			07 22		07 13		
Lewisham 4	d	07 00					→		07 08			07 15		07 18						07 22		07 25	07 26		07 26
St Johns	d								07 10													07 27			07 32
New Cross 4	⊖ d	07 04							07 12				07 19									07 29			07 36
London Victoria 15	⊖ a			07 20													07c46								
London Bridge 4	⊖ d	07 11	07 14		07 16			07 16	07 19	07 22	07 23	07 25	07 26	07 28	07 28				07 31	07 31	07 34	07 36	07 37	07 41	07 42
London Blackfriars 3	⊖ a				07 22											07 44									
London Cannon Street 4	⊖ a							07c22	07c25		07b29		07c32		07c34				07c37			07c42			07 48
London Waterloo (East) 4	⊖ d	07 16	07 19			07 24				07 27		07 30		07 33						07 36	07 39		07 42	07 46	
London Charing Cross 4	⊖ a	07c21	07c25			07c29				07c33		07c35		07c38						07c41	07c44		07c47	07c52	

		SE 24	SE 66	SE 83	SE 30 1	SE 07 1	SE 77	SE 46	SE 5 1	SE 80	SE 71	SE 70	SE 17	SE 18	SE 25	SE 12	SE 87	SE 51		SE 74	SE 63	SE 07 1	SE 30 1	SE 77	SE 46
Orpington 4	d										07 23	07 27	07 30			07 36									
Petts Wood 4	d										07 26	07 30	07 33			07 39									
Hither Green 4	d							07 42					07 46					07 49							08 02
Lewisham 4	d	07 35	07 38				07 41							07 44	07 50			07 54		07 56				08 01	
St Johns	d						07 44								07 52									08 04	
New Cross 4	⊖ d						07 46								07 54			07 59						08 06	
London Victoria 15	⊖ a											08c08		08c12											
London Bridge 4	⊖ d	07 44		07 45	07 50	07 50	07 53	07 54	07 55	07 58			07 59		08 01	08 02	08 04	08 06		08 07	08 08	08 10	08 11	08 13	08 15
London Blackfriars 3	⊖ a										08 05														
London Cannon Street 4	⊖ a			07c52		07c56	07c58		08c01				08 04		08c07		08c10	08c12			08b15	08c16		08c19	
London Waterloo (East) 4	⊖ d	07 48	07 51		07 55			07 58		08 03						08 08				08 12			08 16		08 20
London Charing Cross 4	⊖ a	07 53	07c57		07 59			08 03		08c08						08c13				08c18			08 21		08c25

		SE 3 1	SE 73	SE 78	SE 70	SE 17	SE 86	SE 12	SE 25	SE 70	SE 23 1 ⚲	SE 81	SE 57	SE 12	SE 65	SE 30 1	SE 07 1	SE 77	SE 46	SE 91 1	SE 78	SE 70	SE 17	SE 86	SE 25
Orpington 4	d		07 44		07 50	07 53		07 56						08 00								08 10	08 13		
Petts Wood 4	d		07 47		07 53	07 56		07 59						08 03								08 13	08 16		
Hither Green 4	d												08 09	08 16					08 22						
Lewisham 4	d			08 04					08 10	08 12			08 14		08 18			08 21			08 24				08 30
St Johns	d								08 12									08 24							08 32
New Cross 4	⊖ d								08 14				08 18					08 26							08 34
London Victoria 15	⊖ a			08c29	08c29																08c49	08c49			
London Bridge 4	⊖ d	08 15				08 18	08 19		08 21	08 23	08 23	08 25	08 27	08 27	08 29	08 31	08 31	08 34	08 35	08 36			08 38	08 39	08 41
London Blackfriars 3	⊖ a		08 29																						
London Cannon Street 4	⊖ a	08c21				08c24			08c27		08c29	08c31	08c33		08c35		08c37	08 39		08c42			08b45		08c47
London Waterloo (East) 4	⊖ d						08 24	08 26		08 28				08 32		08 36			08 40					08 44	
London Charing Cross 4	⊖ a						08c29	08c31		08c33				08c37		08 41			08 45					08c49	

For general notes see front of timetable
For details of catering facilities see Directory of Train Operators

b Until 10 October arr 2 minutes earlier
c Until 10 October arr 1 minute earlier

For details of Bank Holiday service alterations please see first page of Table 195

Orpington, Petts Wood, Hither Green and Lewisham → London (Summary of Services)

Station		SE 40	SE 87	SE 57	SE 12	SE 74	SE 63	SE 30 [1]	SE 07 [1]	SE 77	SE 46	SE 3 [1]	SE 18	SE 70	SE 17	SE 86		SE 12	SE 25	SE 57	SE 70	SE 23 [1] trolley	SE 40	SE 81	FC [1]
Orpington [4]	d				08 20									08 30	08 33			08 38							
Petts Wood [4]	d				08 23									08 33	08 36			08 41							
Hither Green [4]	d			08 29	08 36						08 42									08 49			08 56		
Lewisham [4]	d			08 34		08 36				08 41			08 44						08 50	08 54	08 56				
St Johns	d									08 44									08 52						
New Cross [4]	⊖ d			08 38						08 46					08 52				08 54	08 58					
London Victoria [15]	⊖ a												09b12	09b12											
London Bridge [4]	⊖ d	08 43	08 43	08 46		08 47	08 49	08 51	08 51	08 54	08 55	08 56			08 58	08 59			09 01	09 04	09 05	09 06	09 08	09 09	09 11
London Blackfriars [3]	⊖ a																								09 18
London Cannon Street [4]	⊖ a		08c50	08b52			08b55		08b57	09b00		09b02			09b04				09b07	09b11		09b13		09b15	
London Waterloo (East) [4]	⊖ d	08 48			08 50	08 52		08 56			09 00					09 04		09 06			09 10		09 14		
London Charing Cross [4]	⊖ a	08b53			08b55	08b57		09 01			09b05					09b09		09c13			09b15		09c20		

Station		SE 07 [1]	SE 63	SE 34	SE 77	SE 30 [1]	SE 86	SE 5 [1]	SE 70	SE 78	SE 73	SE 12	SE 72	SE 47	SE 25	SE 22 [1]	SE 54	SE 25	SE 88 [1]	SE 81	SE 70	SE 17	SE 24	FC [1]	SE 70
Orpington [4]	d								08 53		08 57	09 00									09 08	09 12			
Petts Wood [4]	d								08 56		09 00	09 03									09 11	09 15			
Hither Green [4]	d											09 16		09 20			09 23					09 28			
Lewisham [4]	d				09 04					09 10			09 20		09 24		09 28	←				09 33			09 36
St Johns	d				09 06									09 24	09 28			09 28							09 38
New Cross [4]	⊖ d				09 08									09 26	→			09 30							09 40
London Victoria [15]	⊖ a								09b31	09b33											09b48				
London Bridge [4]	⊖ d	09 11	09 13	09 14	09 16	09 19	09 22	09 23				09 26	09 30	09 33		09 34	09 37	09 38	09 40	09 40		09 42	09 44	09 45	09 49
London Blackfriars [3]	⊖ a										09 37													09 52	
London Cannon Street [4]	⊖ a	09b17	09b19		09c23			09 28						09b39				09b44		09c47		09c49			
London Waterloo (East) [4]	⊖ d			09 20		09 24	09 27					09 31	09 35			09 39	09 42		09 45				09 49		09 55
London Charing Cross [4]	⊖ a			09b25		09 29	09b31					09b36	09b40			09 44	09b48		09b51				09c54		10b00

Station		SE 87	SE 70	SE 16	SE 22 [1] trolley	SE 62	SE 47	SE 4 [1] trolley	FC [1]	SE 25	SE 78	SE 16	SE 70	SE 70		SE 54	SE 34	SE 81	SE 70	SE 8 [1]	FC [1]	SE 25	SE 82	SE 47	SN
Orpington [4]	d		09 23	09 35	09 36								09 38	09 53						09 55					
Petts Wood [4]	d		09 26	09 38								←	09 41	09 56						09 59					
Hither Green [4]	d			09 50			09 44					09 50				09 54								10 10	
Lewisham [4]	d			→		09 46				09 48	09 51	09 55				09 59			10 02			10 06			
St Johns	d						09 48			09 52												10 08		10 14	
New Cross [4]	⊖ d						09 50			09 54												10 10		10 16	
London Victoria [15]	⊖ a		10b01								10c14		10c16	10 29											
London Bridge [4]	⊖ d	09 52			09 52	09 55	09 57	09 58	10 00	10 03		10 04					10 08	10 10	10 11	10 13	10 15	10 17	10 19	10 22	10 22
London Blackfriars [3]	⊖ a								10 07												10 22				
London Cannon Street [4]	⊖ a	09b58					10 01			10 06								10 13				10 20		10 27	
London Waterloo (East) [4]	⊖ d				09 57	10 00		10 03				10 09				10 11	10 14		10 16	10 19			10 24		10 27
London Charing Cross [4]	⊖ a				10 01	10 05		10c09				10 12				10 14	10 17		10 20	10 22			10 28		10 30

Station		SE 22 [1] trolley	SE 67	SE 34	FC [1]	SE 81	SE 78	SE 12	SE 54	SE 70	SE 70	SE 70		SE 8 [1]	SE 87	FC [1]	SE 25	SE 82	SE 09 [1]	SN	SE 47	SE 22 [1] trolley	SE 67	SE 34	FC [1]
Orpington [4]	d							10 05			10 08	10 23		10 25											
Petts Wood [4]	d							10 08			10 11	10 26		10 29											
Hither Green [4]	d							10 20	10 24												10 40				
Lewisham [4]	d		10 16				10 21	10 25	10 29	10 32							10 36						10 46		
St Johns	d																10 38				10 45				
New Cross [4]	⊖ d		10 20														10 40				10 47		10 50		
London Victoria [15]	⊖ a						10 42				10 44	10 59													
London Bridge [4]	⊖ d	10 25	10 27	10 29	10 30	10 30		10 35	10 38	10 41				10 43	10 44	10 45	10 47	10 49	10 51	10 52	10 54	10 55	10 57	10 59	11 00
London Blackfriars [3]	⊖ a				10 37											10 52									11 07
London Cannon Street [4]	⊖ a		10 30			10 33									10 47		10 50		10 54		10 57		11 00		
London Waterloo (East) [4]	⊖ d	10 30		10 35				10 40	10 43	10 46				10 48				10 54		10 57		11 00		11 05	
London Charing Cross [4]	⊖ a	10 33		10 39				10 44	10 47	10 50				10 51				10 58		11 00		11 03		11 09	

Station		SE 81	SE 78	SE 16	SE 54	SE 70	SE 70	SE 70	SE 8 [1]	SE 87	FC [1]	SE 25	SE 82	SN	SE 47	SE 22 [1] trolley	SE 67	SE 34	FC [1]	SE 81	SE 78	SE 12	SE 54	SE 70	SE 70
Orpington [4]	d			10 35			10 38	10 53	10 57							11 05						11 05			11 08
Petts Wood [4]	d			10 38			10 41	10 56														11 08			11 11
Hither Green [4]	d			10 50	10 54										11 10							11 20	11 24		
Lewisham [4]	d		10 51	10 55	10 59	11 02						11 06					11 16				11 21	11 25	11 29	11 32	
St Johns	d											11 08			11 15										
New Cross [4]	⊖ d											11 10			11 17		11 20								
London Victoria [15]	⊖ a		11 12				11 14	11 29													11 42				11 44
London Bridge [4]	⊖ d	11 00		11 05	11 08	11 11			11 13	11 14	11 15	11 17	11 19	11 22	11 24	11 25	11 27	11 29	11 30	11 30		11 35	11 38	11 41	
London Blackfriars [3]	⊖ a										11 22								11 37						
London Cannon Street [4]	⊖ a	11 03								11 17		11 20			11 27		11 30			11 33					
London Waterloo (East) [4]	⊖ d			11 10	11 13	11 16			11 18				11 24	11 27		11 30		11 35				11 40	11 43	11 46	
London Charing Cross [4]	⊖ a			11 14	11 17	11 20			11 21				11 28	11 30		11 33		11 39				11 44	11 47	11 50	

For general notes see front of timetable
For details of catering facilities see Directory of Train Operators

b Until 10 October arr 1 minute earlier
c Until 10 October arr 2 minutes earlier

Orpington, Petts Wood, Hither Green and Lewisham → London (Summary of Services)

For details of Bank Holiday service alterations please see first page of Table 195

		SE 70	and at the same minutes past each hour until	SE 8 [1]	SE 87	FC [1]	SE 25	SE 82	SE 09 [1]	SN	SE 47	SE 22 [1]	SE 67	SE 34	FC [1]	SE 81	SE 78	SE 16	SE 54	SE 70	SE 70	SE 70	SE 8 [1]
Orpington 4	d	11 23		15 25														15 35			15 38	15 53	15 57
Petts Wood 4	d	11 26		15 29														15 38			15 41	15 56	
Hither Green 4	d										15 40							15 50	15 54				
Lewisham 4	d						15 36						15 46				15 51	15 55	15 59	16 02			
St Johns	d						15 38				15 45												
New Cross 4	⊖ d						15 40				15 47		15 50										
London Victoria 15	⊖ a	11 59															16 12				16 14	16 30	
London Bridge 4	⊖ d			15 43	15 44	15 45	15 47	15 49	15 51	15 52	15 54	15 55	15 57	15 59	16 00	16 00		16 04	16 08	16 11			16 13
London Blackfriars 3	⊖ a					15 52									16 07								
London Cannon Street 4	⊖ a				15 47		15 50		15 54		15 57		16 00			16 03							
London Waterloo (East) 4	⊖ d			15 48				15 54		15 57		16 00		16 04				16 10	16 14	16 18			16 18
London Charing Cross 4	⊖ a			15 51				15 58		16 00		16 03		16 07				16 13	16 17	16 23			16 21

		SE 87	FC [1]	SE 25	SE 82	SE 47	SE 13	SE 23 [1]	SE 66	SE 2 [1]	SE 81	SE 34	SE 70	SE 88 [1]	SE 13	FC [1]	SE 55	SE 70	SE 12	SE 87	SE 12	SE 78	SE 24	SE 81	SE 22 [1]
Orpington 4	d						16 05	16 07										16 08	16 20		16 33				16 34
Petts Wood 4	d						16 08								←			16 11	16 23		16 36				
Hither Green 4	d					16 10	16 20								16 20		16 28		16 36						
Lewisham 4	d			16 08			→		16 16			16 21	16 24		16 28		16 33				→	16 35	16 38		
St Johns	d			16 10		16 15											16 35						16 40		
New Cross 4	⊖ d			16 12		16 17											16 37						16 42		
London Victoria 15	⊖ a																	16 45				17 03			
London Bridge 4	⊖ d	16 14	16 15	16 19	16 20	16 24		16 24	16 27	16 29	16 30	16 32	16 33	16 34	16 38	16 42	16 43		16 46	16 48			16 50	16 52	16 53
London Blackfriars 3	⊖ a		16 24													16 53									
London Cannon Street 4	⊖ a	16 17		16 22		16 27					16 33		16 36				16 46			16 52				16 55	
London Waterloo (East) 4	⊖ d				16 25			16 29	16 33	16 35		16 37		16 39	16 43				16 52				16 56		16 58
London Charing Cross 4	⊖ a				16 28			16 33	16 36	16 38		16 40		16 45	16 47				16 55				16 59		17 01

		SE 63		SE 47	SE 4 [1]	SE 71	SE 12	SE 57	SE 44	SE 87	SE 70	SE 23 [1]	SE 12	SE 81	SE 16	SE 25	SE 34	SE 81	SE 12	SE 78	SE 10	SE 51	SE 8 [1]	SE 63	FC [1]
Orpington 4	d						←				16 36	16 50	16 52		16 56				←				17 02		
Petts Wood 4	d						16 36				16 39		16 55						16 55						
Hither Green 4	d			16 42			16 52	16 50	16 56				→						17 09		17 13	17 06			
Lewisham 4	d	16 46				16 50		16 56								17 02				17 05		17 12		17 18	
St Johns	d			16 47												17 04						17 14			
New Cross 4	⊖ d			16 49		16 54										17 06						17 16			
London Victoria 15	⊖ a										17 12									17 28					
London Bridge 4	⊖ d	16 55		16 57	17 00	17 01	17 03	17 05	17 07	17 09		17 09		17 12	17 13	17 15	17 16	17 19	17 19		17 24	17 24	17 27	17 27	17 29
London Blackfriars 3	⊖ a																								17 36
London Cannon Street 4	⊖ a			17 00		17 05		17 08		17 13				17 15		17 18		17 23				17 29	17 31		
London Waterloo (East) 4	⊖ d	17 00			17 05		17 08		17 12			17 15			17 19		17 21		17 24		17 29			17 32	
London Charing Cross 4	⊖ a	17 03			17 10		17 13		17 15			17 19			17 24		17 25		17 28		17 32			17 35	

		SE 53	SE 70	SE 12	SE 2 [1]	SE 25	SE 12	SE 81	SE 88 [1]	SE 55	SE 12	SE 53	SE 22 [1]	SE 71	SE 87	SE 12	SE 16	SE 81	SE 34	SE 63	SE 70	SE 4 [1]		SE 63	SE 51
Orpington 4	d		17 04	17 07	17 13		←				17 21		17 26			←	17 34				17 36	17 40			
Petts Wood 4	d		17 07	17 10			17 10				17 24					17 24	17 37				17 39				
Hither Green 4	d	17 16		→			17 23			17 24	→	17 31				17 40									17 44
Lewisham 4	d					17 21				17 31				17 36					17 44	17 47					17 51
St Johns	d					17 23				17 33															17 55
New Cross 4	⊖ d					17 25				17 35				17 39											17 57
London Victoria 15	⊖ a		17 42																		18 12				
London Bridge 4	⊖ d	17 30			17 32	17 33	17 35	17 36	17 39	17 42		17 42	17 44	17 46	17 48	17 49	17 52	17 54	17 55	17 58				18 01	18 04
London Blackfriars 3	⊖ a																								
London Cannon Street 4	⊖ a	17 33				17 36		17 39		17 45				17 51	17 53			17 57		18 01					18 07
London Waterloo (East) 4	⊖ d				17 37		17 40		17 44			17 47	17 50			17 54	17 58		18 00			18 04		18 06	
London Charing Cross 4	⊖ a				17 41		17 46		17 48			17 50	17 55			17 57	18 01		18 03			18 07		18 09	

		SE 53	SE 10	SE 34	SE 12	FC [1]	SE 78	SE 85	SE 51	SE 25	SE 22 [1]	SE 77	SE 34	SE 74	SE 70	SE 12	SE 16	SE 4 [1]	SE 61	SE 53	SE 16	SE 34	SE 88 [1]	SE 81	SE 44
Orpington 4	d				17 51						18 00				18 06	18 08	18 11	18 12			←				
Petts Wood 4	d				17 54										18 09		18 14				18 14				
Hither Green 4	d	17 50	17 55		18 06				18 04								→			18 18	18 26				18 32
Lewisham 4	d						17 54			18 10				18 14					18 20	18 24		18 29			
St Johns	d													18 16						18 26					
New Cross 4	⊖ d													18 18						18 28					
London Victoria 15	⊖ a						18 16								18 42										
London Bridge 4	⊖ d	18 05	18 07	18 10		18 11		18 12	18 16		18 20	18 20	18 23	18 26		18 26		18 29	18 31	18 34	18 35	18 38	18 40	18 42	18 43
London Blackfriars 3	⊖ a					18 19																			
London Cannon Street 4	⊖ a							18 15				18 23		18 29						18 37				18 45	
London Waterloo (East) 4	⊖ d	18 10	18 12	18 16	18 20				18 22	18 24	18 27		18 28			18 32		18 34	18 37		18 40	18 44	18 45		18 49
London Charing Cross 4	⊖ a	18 13	18 15	18 19	18 23				18 25	18 27	18 30		18 33			18 37		18 37	18 40		18 45	18 49	18 48		18 53

For general notes see front of timetable
For details of catering facilities see Directory of Train Operators

Orpington, Petts Wood, Hither Green and Lewisham → London (Summary of Services)

For details of Bank Holiday service alterations please see first page of Table 195

Station		FC 1	SE 66	SE 22 1	SE 22 1	SE 78	SE 24	SE 70	SE 12	SE 90 1	FC 1	SE 87	SE 52	SE 25	SE 12	SE 74	SE 81	SE 22 1	FC 1	SE 78		SE 24	SE 50	SE 62	SE 16
Orpington 4	d			18 33	18 36			18 36	18 39	18 40					←			18 56							19 05
Petts Wood 4	d							18 39	18 42						18 42										19 08
Hither Green 4	d								→				18 44		18 54								19 07		19 20
Lewisham 4	d		18 36			18 41	18 45						18 49	18 56		19 01				19 06		19 09	19 12	19 15	→
St Johns	d		18 38										18 51	18 58								19 11			
New Cross 4	⊖ d		18 40										18 53	19 00								19 13			
London Victoria 15	⊖ a					19 00		19 13												19 25					
London Bridge 4	⊖ d	18 45	18 49	18 50	18 52		18 55			18 58	19 00	19 02	19 03	19 06	19 06	19 10	19 12	19 13	19 16			19 19	19 22	19 23	
London Blackfriars 3	⊖ a	18 55									19 07								19 22						
London Cannon Street 4	⊖ a			18 53								19 05		19 10			19 15						19 25		
London Waterloo (East) 4	⊖ d		18 54		18 57		19 00			19 03			19 08		19 11	19 16		19 18				19 25		19 29	
London Charing Cross 4	⊖ a		18 57		19 00		19 05			19 07			19 11		19 14	19 20		19 21				19 29		19 32	

Station		SE 90 1	SE 24	FC 1	SE 74	SE 81	SE 70	SE 22 1	SE 16	SE 74	SN	SE 50	FC 1	SE 80	SE 62	SE 70	SE 16	SE 57	SE 22 1	SE 24	FC 1	SE 70	SE 16	SE 81	SE 70
Orpington 4	d	19 08					19 08	19 14	←							19 23	19 35		19 38				←		19 38
Petts Wood 4	d						19 11									19 26	19 38								19 41
Hither Green 4	d								19 20			19 26					19 50						19 50		
Lewisham 4	d		19 17		19 26				19 28			19 31			19 45		→			19 47		19 52	19 57		
St Johns	d		19 19							←										19 49					
New Cross 4	⊖ d		19 21		19 30					19 30		19 34								19 51		19 56			
London Victoria 15	⊖ a				→		19 45									19 59									20 14
London Bridge 4	⊖ d	19 26	19 29	19 30		19 34		19 34	19 36	19 38	19 39	19 44	19 45	19 49	19 53			19 54	19 56	19 59	20 00	20 04	20 06	20 08	
London Blackfriars 3	⊖ a			19 37									19 52								20 07				
London Cannon Street 4	⊖ a					19 37				19 41								19 57						20 11	
London Waterloo (East) 4	⊖ d	19 32	19 34					19 39	19 42		19 45	19 50		19 55	19 58				20 01	20 04		20 09	20 11		
London Charing Cross 4	⊖ a	19 35	19 37					19 42	19 45		19 49	19 53		19 59	20 01				20 04	20 07		20 13	20 15		

Station		SE 90 1	SN	SE 54	FC 1	SE 80	SE 62	SE 70	SE 16	SE 57	SE 22 1	SE 24	FC 1	SE 70	SE 16	SE 81	SE 70	SE 18 1		SN	SE 54	FC 1	SE 80	SE 62	SE 16
Orpington 4	d	19 50						19 53	20 05		20 08				←		20 08	20 20							20 35
Petts Wood 4	d							19 56	20 08								20 11								20 38
Hither Green 4	d			19 56					20 20						20 20						20 26				20 50
Lewisham 4	d			20 02			20 15		→			20 17		20 22	20 27						20 31			20 44	→
St Johns	d											20 19													
New Cross 4	⊖ d			20 05								20 21		20 26							20 34				
London Victoria 15	⊖ a							20 29									20 44								
London Bridge 4	⊖ d	20 09	20 11	20 14	20 15	20 19	20 23			20 24	20 26	20 29	20 30	20 34	20 36	20 38		20 39		20 41	20 44	20 45	20 49	20 53	
London Blackfriars 3	⊖ a				20 22								20 37									20 52			
London Cannon Street 4	⊖ a									20 27						20 41									
London Waterloo (East) 4	⊖ d	20 14	20 17	20 19		20 25	20 28				20 31	20 34		20 39	20 41			20 44		20 47	20 49		20 55	20 58	
London Charing Cross 4	⊖ a	20 18	20 20	20 22		20 29	20 31				20 34	20 37		20 43	20 45			20 48		20 50	20 52		20 59	21 01	

Station		SE 22 1	SE 24	FC 1	SE 70	SE 16	SE 70	SE 90 1	SN	SE 54	FC 1	SE 80	SE 62	SE 12	SE 22 1	SE 24	FC 1	SE 70	SE 12	SE 70	SE 4 1	SN	SE 54	FC 1	SE 80
Orpington 4	d	20 38				←	20 38	20 50						21 05	21 08				←	21 08	21 20				
Petts Wood 4	d						20 41							21 08						21 11					
Hither Green 4	d					20 50				20 56				21 20					21 20				21 26		
Lewisham 4	d		20 47		20 52	20 57				21 01			21 14	→		21 17		21 22	21 27				21 31		
St Johns	d		20 49													21 19									
New Cross 4	⊖ d		20 51		20 56					21 04						21 21		21 26					21 34		
London Victoria 15	⊖ a						21 14													21 44					
London Bridge 4	⊖ d	20 56	20 59	21 00	21 04	21 06		21 09	21 11	21 14	21 15	21 19	21 23		21 26	21 29	21 30	21 34	21 36		21 39	21 41	21 44	21 45	21 49
London Blackfriars 3	⊖ a			21 07							21 22						21 37							21 52	
London Cannon Street 4	⊖ a																								
London Waterloo (East) 4	⊖ d	21 01	21 04		21 09	21 11		21 14	21 17	21 19		21 25	21 28		21 31	21 34		21 39	21 41		21 44	21 47	21 49		21 55
London Charing Cross 4	⊖ a	21 04	21 07		21 13	21 15		21 18	21 20	21 22		21 29	21 31		21 34	21 37		21 43	21 45		21 48	21 50	21 52		21 59

Station		SE 60	SE 16	SE 22 1	SE 24	SE 70	SE 16	SE 70	SE 90 1	SN	SE 52	FC 1	SE 80	SE 62	SE 12	SE 22 1		SE 24	SE 70	SE 12	SE 70	SE 4 1	SN	SE 50	FC 1
Orpington 4	d		21 35	21 38				21 38	21 50						22 05	22 08				←	22 08	22 20			
Petts Wood 4	d		21 38				←	21 41							22 08						22 11				
Hither Green 4	d		21 50				21 50				21 56				22 20					22 20				22 26	
Lewisham 4	d	21 44	→		21 47	21 52	21 57				22 01			22 14	→			22 17	22 22	22 27				22 31	
St Johns	d				21 49													22 19							
New Cross 4	⊖ d				21 51	21 56					22 04							22 21	22 26					22 34	
London Victoria 15	⊖ a							22 14													22 44				
London Bridge 4	⊖ d	21 53		21 56	21 59	22 04	22 06		22 09	22 11	22 14	22 15	22 19	22 23		22 26		22 29	22 34	22 36		22 39	22 41	22 44	22 45
London Blackfriars 3	⊖ a											22 22													22 52
London Cannon Street 4	⊖ a																								
London Waterloo (East) 4	⊖ d	21 58		22 01	22 04	22 09	22 11		22 14	22 17	22 19		22 25	22 28		22 31		22 34	22 39	22 41		22 44	22 47	22 49	
London Charing Cross 4	⊖ a	22 01		22 04	22 07	22 13	22 15		22 18	22 20	22 22		22 29	22 31		22 34		22 37	22 43	22 45		22 48	22 50	22 52	

For general notes see front of timetable
For details of catering facilities see Directory of Train Operators

Orpington, Petts Wood, Hither Green and Lewisham → London (Summary of Services)

For details of Bank Holiday service alterations please see first page of Table 195

	SE 80	SE 62	SE 16	SE 22 [1]	SE 24	SE 70	SE 16	SE 70	SE 90 [1]	SN	SE 80	FC [1]	SE 22 [1]	SE 50	SE 24	SE 12	SN	SE 82	SE 70	SE 70	FC [1]	SE 4 [1]		
Orpington [4] d			22 35	22 38				22 38	22 50				23 02			23 05			23 08			23 34		
Petts Wood [4] d			22 38				←	22 41								23 08			23 11					
Hither Green [4] d			22 50				22 50							23 06		23 20								
Lewisham [4] d		22 44	→		22 47	22 52	22 57							23 11	23 17	23 27				23 32				
St Johns d					22 49										23 19									
New Cross [4] ⊖ d					22 51	22 56								23 14	23 21					23 36				
London Victoria [15] ⊖ a								23 14											23 44					
London Bridge [4] ⊖ d	22 49	22 53		22 56	22 59	23 04	23 06		23 09	23 11	23 14	23 15	23 20	23 24	23 29	23 36	23 39	23 41		23 44	23 45	23 52		
London Blackfriars [3] ⊖ a												23 22									23 52			
London Cannon Street [4] ⊖ a																								
London Waterloo (East) [4] ⊖ d	22 55	22 58		23 01	23 04	23 09	23 11		23 14	23 17	23 19		23 25	23 29	23 34	23 41	23 44	23 47		23 50		23 57		
London Charing Cross [4] ⊖ a	22 59	23 01		23 04	23 07	23 13	23 15		23 18	23 20	23 22		23 28	23 32	23 37	23 44	23 48	23 50		23 53		00 01		

Saturdays

	FC	FC [1]	SE 80	SE 24	SE 12	SE 70	SE 52	SE 80	SE 73	SE 24	FC [1]	SE 12	SE 70	SE 70	SE 2 [1]	SE 52	SE 80	SE 62	SE 24	FC [1]	SE 12	SE 70	SE 70	SE 54
Orpington [4] d					05 35				05 54			06 05		06 08	06 21						06 35		06 38	
Petts Wood [4] d					05 38				05 57			06 08		06 11							06 38		06 41	
Hither Green [4] d					05 50		05 56					06 20				06 26					06 50			06 56
Lewisham [4] d				05 47	05 57	05 59	06 02			06 17		06 27	06 29			06 31		06 41	06 47		06 57	06 59		07 02
St Johns d				05 49						06 19									06 49					
New Cross [4] ⊖ d				05 51			06 05			06 21						06 34			06 51					07 05
London Victoria [15] ⊖ a														06 44									07 14	
London Bridge [4] ⊖ d	00 20	00 52	05 49	05 59	06 05	06 08	06 14	06 19		06 29	06 31	06 35	06 38		06 40	06 44	06 48	06 51	06 59	07 01	07 05	07 08		07 14
London Blackfriars [3] ⊖ a	00 26	00 59							06 33		06 37									07 07				
London Cannon Street [4] ⊖ a																								
London Waterloo (East) [4] ⊖ d			05 55	06 04	06 10	06 12	06 19	06 25		06 34		06 40	06 42		06 45	06 49	06 55	06 55	07 04		07 10	07 12		07 19
London Charing Cross [4] ⊖ a			05 59	06 07	06 13	06 15	06 23	06 29		06 37		06 43	06 45		06 48	06 52	06 59	06 58	07 07		07 13	07 15		07 22

	SE 80	SE 62	SN	SE 12	SE 22 [1]	SE 24	FC [1]	SE 78	SE 12	SE 70	SE 70	SE 2 [1]		SE 54	FC [1]	SE 81	SE 62	SN	SE 22 [1]	SE 24	SE 81	FC [1]	SE 78	SE 16
Orpington [4] d				07 05	07 08						07 08	07 20							07 35					07 35
Petts Wood [4] d				07 08					←		07 11													07 38
Hither Green [4] d				07 20					07 20					07 26										07 49
Lewisham [4] d		07 11		→		07 17		07 20	07 27	07 29				07 32			07 41			07 47			07 50	07 55
St Johns d						07 19														07 49				
New Cross [4] ⊖ d						07 21								07 35						07 51				
London Victoria [15] ⊖ a								07 42			07 44												08 12	
London Bridge [4] ⊖ d	07 19	07 22	07 24		07 27	07 29	07 31		07 35	07 38		07 40		07 44	07 45	07 46	07 50	07 52	07 55	07 59	08 00	08 01		08 05
London Blackfriars [3] ⊖ a							07 37								07 52							08 07		
London Cannon Street [4] ⊖ a																07 50					08 03			
London Waterloo (East) [4] ⊖ d	07 25	07 26	07 29		07 31	07 34			07 40	07 42		07 45		07 49			07 54	07 57	08 00	08 04				08 10
London Charing Cross [4] ⊖ a	07 29	07 29	07 32		07 34	07 37			07 43	07 45		07 48		07 52			07 58	08 00	08 05	08 07				08 14

	SE 70	SE 70	SE 90 [1]	SE 54	FC [1]	SE 25	SE 62	SN	SE 47	SE 22 [1] ⚲	SE 24	SE 81	FC [1]	SE 78	SE 12	SE 54	SE 70	SE 4 [1]	SE 70	SE 87	FC [1]	SE 25	SE 62	SE 09 [1]
Orpington [4] d		07 38	07 53							08 05					08 05		08 08	08 20						
Petts Wood [4] d		07 41													08 08		08 11							
Hither Green [4] d				07 56					08 10						08 19	08 24								
Lewisham [4] d	07 59			08 02		08 06	08 11							08 20	08 25	08 29			08 32			08 36	08 41	
St Johns d						08 08			08 14													08 38		
New Cross [4] ⊖ d				08 05		08 10			08 17							08 32						08 40		
London Victoria [15] ⊖ a		08 14												08 42			08 44							
London Bridge [4] ⊖ d	08 08		08 10	08 14	08 15	08 17	08 19	08 22	08 23	08 25	08 29	08 30	08 31		08 35	08 38		08 41	08 43	08 44	08 45	08 47	08 49	08 51
London Blackfriars [3] ⊖ a					08 22								08 37								08 52			
London Cannon Street [4] ⊖ a						08 20			08 27			08 33								08 47		08 50		08 54
London Waterloo (East) [4] ⊖ d	08 12		08 15	08 19			08 24	08 27		08 30	08 35				08 40	08 43		08 45	08 48				08 54	
London Charing Cross [4] ⊖ a	08 15		08 18	08 22			08 28	08 30		08 33	08 39				08 44	08 47		08 48	08 51				08 58	

	SN	SE 47	SE 70		SE 22 [1] ⚲	SE 24	SE 81	FC [1]	SE 78	SE 16	SE 54	SE 70	SE 90 [1]	SE 70	SE 87	FC [1]	SE 25	SE 82	SN	SE 47	SE 70	SE 22 [1] ⚲	SE 67	SE 34
Orpington [4] d			08 23		08 35					08 35		08 38	08 53								08 53	09 05		
Petts Wood [4] d			08 26							08 38		08 41									08 56			
Hither Green [4] d		08 40								08 49	08 54									09 10				
Lewisham [4] d									08 50	08 55	08 59			09 02			09 06						09 16	
St Johns d		08 45															09 08			09 14				
New Cross [4] ⊖ d		08 47									09 02						09 10			09 17			09 20	
London Victoria [15] ⊖ a			08 59						09 12			09 14									09 29			
London Bridge [4] ⊖ d	08 52	08 53			08 55	08 59	09 00	09 01		09 05	09 08		09 11	09 13	09 14	09 15	09 17	09 19	09 22	09 23		09 25	09 27	09 29
London Blackfriars [3] ⊖ a								09 08								09 22								
London Cannon Street [4] ⊖ a		08 57					09 03								09 17		09 20			09 27			09 30	
London Waterloo (East) [4] ⊖ d	08 57				09 00	09 05				09 10	09 13		09 15	09 18				09 24	09 27			09 30		09 35
London Charing Cross [4] ⊖ a	09 00				09 03	09 09				09 14	09 17		09 18	09 21				09 28	09 30			09 33		09 39

For general notes see front of timetable
For details of catering facilities see
Directory of Train Operators

Table 199

Saturdays

Orpington, Petts Wood, Hither Green and Lewisham → London (Summary of Services)

		FC	SE	SE	SE	SE	SE	SE	SE	SE	SE	FC	SE	SE	SE	SN	SE		SE		SE	SE	FC	SE	SE
			81	78	12	54	70	70	70	8	87		25	82	09		47		22		67	34		81	78
		[1]								[1]		[1]			[1]				[1]				[1]		
Orpington [4]	d				09 05			09 08	09 23	09 26									09 35						
Petts Wood [4]	d				09 08			09 11	09 26	09 29															
Hither Green [4]	d				09 19	09 24											09 40								
Lewisham [4]	d			09 20	09 25	09 29	09 32						09 36								09 46				09 50
St Johns	d												09 38				09 44								
New Cross [4]	⊖ d					09 32							09 40				09 47				09 50				
London Victoria [15]	⊖ a			09 42				09 44	09 59																10 12
London Bridge [4]	⊖ d	09 30	09 30		09 35	09 38	09 41			09 44	09 44	09 45	09 47	09 49	09 51	09 52	09 54		09 55		09 57	09 59	10 00	10 00	
London Blackfriars [3]	⊖ a	09 37										09 52											10 07		
London Cannon Street [4]	⊖ a		09 33								09 47		09 50		09 54		09 57				10 00			10 03	
London Waterloo (East) [4]	⊖ d				09 40	09 43	09 46			09 48				09 54		09 57			10 00			10 05			
London Charing Cross [4]	⊖ a				09 44	09 47	09 50			09 51				09 58		10 00			10 03			10 09			

		SE	SE	SE	SE	SE	SE	SE	FC	SE	SE	SN	SE	SE	SE	SE	FC	SE	SE	SE	SE	SE	SE	SE	SE
		16	54	70	70	70	8	87		25	82		47	22	67	34		81	78	12	54	70	70	70	8
							[1]		[1]					[1]			[1]								[1]
Orpington [4]	d	09 35			09 38	09 53	09 57							10 05						10 05			10 08	10 23	10 26
Petts Wood [4]	d	09 38			09 41	09 56														10 08			10 11	10 26	10 29
Hither Green [4]	d	09 50	09 54										10 10							10 19	10 24				
Lewisham [4]	d	09 55	09 59	10 02						10 06					10 16				10 20	10 25	10 29	10 32			
St Johns	d									10 08			10 14												
New Cross [4]	⊖ d									10 10			10 17		10 20										
London Victoria [15]	⊖ a				10 14	10 29													10 42				10 44	10 59	
London Bridge [4]	⊖ d	10 05	10 08	10 11			10 13	10 14	10 15	10 17	10 19	10 22	10 24	10 25	10 27	10 29	10 30	10 30		10 35	10 38	10 41			10 44
London Blackfriars [3]	⊖ a								10 22								10 37								
London Cannon Street [4]	⊖ a							10 17		10 20			10 27		10 30			10 34							
London Waterloo (East) [4]	⊖ d	10 10	10 13	10 16			10 18				10 24	10 27		10 30		10 35				10 40	10 43	10 46			10 48
London Charing Cross [4]	⊖ a	10 14	10 17	10 20			10 21				10 28	10 31		10 33		10 39				10 44	10 47	10 50			10 51

		SE	FC	SE	SE	SE	SN	SE	SE			SE	SE	FC	SE	SE	SE	SE	SE	SE	SE	SE	SE	FC
		87		25	82	09		47	22			67	24		81	78	16	54	70	70	70	8	87	
			[1]			[1]			[1]	and at the same minutes past each hour until				[1]								[1]		[1]
Orpington [4]	d																17 35			17 38	17 53	17 57		
Petts Wood [4]	d																17 38			17 41	17 56			
Hither Green [4]	d							10 40									17 50	17 54						
Lewisham [4]	d			10 36								17 46				17 50	17 55	17 59	18 02					
St Johns	d			10 38				10 44																
New Cross [4]	⊖ d			10 40				10 47				17 50												
London Victoria [15]	⊖ a															18 12				18 14	18 29			
London Bridge [4]	⊖ d	10 44	10 45	10 47	10 49	10 51	10 52	10 54	10 55			17 57	17 59	18 00	18 00		18 05	18 08	18 11			18 13	18 14	18 15
London Blackfriars [3]	⊖ a		10 52											18 07										18 22
London Cannon Street [4]	⊖ a	10 47		10 50		10 54		10 57				18 00			18 03								18 17	
London Waterloo (East) [4]	⊖ d				10 54		10 57		11 00				18 05				18 10	18 13	18 16			18 18		
London Charing Cross [4]	⊖ a				10 58		11 00		11 03				18 09				18 14	18 17	18 20			18 21		

		SE	SE	SN	SE	SE	SE	SE	SE	SE	SE	FC	SE	SE	SE	SE	SE	FC	SE	SE	SN	SE	SE	SE	FC
		25	82		47	12	22	67	78	70	4		81	24	12	54	70		62	09		70	22	24	
							[1]				[1]	[1]						[1]		[1]			[1]		[1]
Orpington [4]	d					18 05	18 05			18 08	18 11				←							18 23	18 35		
Petts Wood [4]	d					18 08				18 11												18 26			
Hither Green [4]	d				18 10	18 19 →									18 19	18 24									
Lewisham [4]	d	18 06						18 16	18 20					18 23	18 26	18 29	18 32		18 41					18 47	
St Johns	d	18 08			18 14											18 31								18 49	
New Cross [4]	⊖ d	18 10			18 17			18 20								18 32								18 51	
London Victoria [15]	⊖ a								18 42	18 44												18 59			
London Bridge [4]	⊖ d	18 17	18 19	18 22	18 24		18 25	18 27			18 28	18 30	18 30	18 34	18 36	18 38	18 41	18 45	18 50	18 51	18 52		18 55	18 59	19 00
London Blackfriars [3]	⊖ a											18 37						18 52							19 07
London Cannon Street [4]	⊖ a	18 20			18 27			18 30					18 33							18 54					
London Waterloo (East) [4]	⊖ d		18 24	18 27			18 30				18 33			18 38	18 42	18 44	18 46		18 54		18 57		19 01	19 04	
London Charing Cross [4]	⊖ a		18 28	18 30			18 33				18 36			18 41	18 45	18 48	18 50		18 58		19 00		19 06	19 07	

		SE		SE	SE	SE	SE	SE	SE	SE	FC	SE	SE	SE	SE	SN	SE	SE	FC	SE	SE	SE	SE	SN	SE
		80		78	16	70	4	54	70	54		80	62	70	12		22	24		70	12	70	90		54
							[1]				[1]						[1]		[1]				[1]		
Orpington [4]	d				18 35	18 38	18 51							18 53	19 05		19 08				←	19 08	19 20		
Petts Wood [4]	d				18 38	18 41								18 56	19 08							19 11			
Hither Green [4]	d				18 49			18 56							19 20 →						19 20				19 26
Lewisham [4]	d			18 50	18 55			19 01	19 02	←			19 11					19 17		19 22	19 27				19 31
St Johns	d																	19 19							
New Cross [4]	⊖ d							19 04 →		19 04								19 21		19 26					19 34
London Victoria [15]	⊖ a			19 12		19 14								19 29								19 44			
London Bridge [4]	⊖ d	19 04			19 06		19 09		19 11	19 14	19 15	19 19	19 21			19 24	19 26	19 29	19 30	19 34	19 36		19 39	19 41	19 44
London Blackfriars [3]	⊖ a										19 22								19 37						
London Cannon Street [4]	⊖ a																								
London Waterloo (East) [4]	⊖ d	19 10			19 12		19 15		19 16	19 19		19 23	19 26			19 28	19 31	19 34		19 39	19 41		19 45	19 47	19 49
London Charing Cross [4]	⊖ a	19 13			19 15		19 19		19 20	19 22		19 26	19 29			19 31	19 34	19 37		19 43	19 45		19 49	19 51	19 52

For general notes see front of timetable
For details of catering facilities see
Directory of Train Operators

Table 199

Saturdays

Orpington, Petts Wood, Hither Green and Lewisham → London (Summary of Services)

		FC ■1	SE 80	SE 62	SE 70	SE 24	FC ■1	SE 70	SE 16	SE 70	SE 4 ■1	SN	SE 54	FC ■1	SE 80		SE 62	SE 70	SE 12	SE 22 ■1	SE 24	FC ■1	SE 70	SE 12	SE 70
Orpington [4]	d				19 23				19 35	19 38	19 51							19 53	20 05	20 08					20 08
Petts Wood [4]	d				19 26				19 38	19 41								19 56	20 08					←	20 11
Hither Green [4]	d								19 50				19 56						20 20					20 20	
Lewisham [4]	d			19 44		19 47		19 52	19 57				20 01				20 14		→		20 17		20 22	20 27	
St Johns	d					19 49															20 19				
New Cross [4]	⊖ d					19 51		19 56					20 04								20 21		20 26		
London Victoria [15]	⊖ a				19 59					20 14								20 29							20 44
London Bridge [4]	⊖ d	19 45	19 49	19 53		19 59	20 00	20 04	20 06		20 09	20 11	20 14	20 15	20 19		20 23			20 26	20 29	20 30	20 34	20 36	
London Blackfriars [3]	⊖ a	19 52					20 07							20 22											
London Cannon Street [4]	⊖ a																					20 37			
London Waterloo (East) [4]	⊖ d		19 55	19 58		20 04		20 09	20 11		20 15	20 17	20 19		20 25		20 28			20 31	20 34		20 39	20 41	
London Charing Cross [4]	⊖ a		19 59	20 01		20 07		20 13	20 15		20 19	20 21	20 22		20 29		20 31			20 34	20 37		20 43	20 45	

		SE 90 ■1	SN	SE 54	FC ■1	SE 80	SE 62	SE 24	FC ■1	SE 70	SE 16	SE 70	SE 4 ■1	SN	SE 54	FC ■1	SE 80	SE 62	SE 12	SE 22 ■1	SE 24	FC ■1	SE 70	SE 12	SE 70
Orpington [4]	d	20 20									20 35	20 38	20 51						21 05	21 08					21 08
Petts Wood [4]	d										20 38	20 41							21 08					←	21 11
Hither Green [4]	d			20 26							20 50				20 56				21 20					21 20	
Lewisham [4]	d			20 31			20 44	20 47		20 52	20 57				21 01			21 14	→		21 17		21 22	21 27	
St Johns	d							20 49													21 19				
New Cross [4]	⊖ d			20 34				20 51		20 56					21 04						21 21		21 26		
London Victoria [15]	⊖ a											21 14													21 44
London Bridge [4]	⊖ d	20 39	20 41	20 44	20 45	20 49	20 53	20 59	21 00	21 04	21 06		21 09	21 11	21 14	21 15	21 19	21 23		21 26	21 29	21 30	21 34	21 36	
London Blackfriars [3]	⊖ a				20 52				21 07							21 22									
London Cannon Street [4]	⊖ a																					21 37			
London Waterloo (East) [4]	⊖ d	20 45	20 47	20 49		20 55	20 58	21 04		21 09	21 11		21 15	21 17	21 19		21 25	21 28		21 31	21 34		21 39	21 41	
London Charing Cross [4]	⊖ a	20 49	20 51	20 52		20 59	21 01	21 07		21 13	21 15		21 19	21 21	21 22		21 29	21 31		21 34	21 37		21 43	21 45	

		SE 90 ■1	SN	SE 50	FC ■1	SE 80		SE 62	SE 24	SE 70	SE 16	SE 70	SE 4 ■1	SN	SE 50	FC ■1	SE 80	SE 62	SE 16	SE 22 ■1	SE 24	SE 70	SE 16	SE 70	SE 90 ■1
Orpington [4]	d	21 20									21 35	21 38	21 51						22 05	22 08				22 08	22 20
Petts Wood [4]	d										21 38	21 41							22 08				←	22 11	
Hither Green [4]	d			21 26							21 50				21 56				22 20				22 20		
Lewisham [4]	d			21 31				21 44	21 47	21 52	21 57				22 01			22 14	→		22 17	22 22	22 27		
St Johns	d								21 49												22 19				
New Cross [4]	⊖ d			21 34					21 51	21 56					22 04						22 21	22 26			
London Victoria [15]	⊖ a											22 14												22 44	
London Bridge [4]	⊖ d	21 39	21 41	21 44	21 45	21 49		21 53	21 59	22 04	22 06		22 09	22 11	22 14	22 15	22 19	22 23		22 26	22 29	22 34	22 36		22 39
London Blackfriars [3]	⊖ a				21 52											22 22									
London Cannon Street [4]	⊖ a																								
London Waterloo (East) [4]	⊖ d	21 45	21 47	21 49		21 55		21 58	22 04	22 09	22 11		22 15	22 17	22 19		22 25	22 28		22 31	22 34	22 39	22 41		22 45
London Charing Cross [4]	⊖ a	21 49	21 51	21 52		21 59		22 01	22 07	22 13	22 15		22 19	22 21	22 22		22 29	22 31		22 34	22 37	22 43	22 45		22 49

		SN	SE 50	FC ■1	SE 80	SE 62	SE 24	SE 70	SE 12	SE 70	SE 90 ■1	SN	SE 80	FC ■1	SE 50	SE 24	SE 12	SN	SE 80	SE 70	SE 70	FC ■1	SE 4 ■1		
Orpington [4]	d								22 35	22 38	22 51						23 05			23 08			23 37		
Petts Wood [4]	d								22 38	22 41							23 08			23 11					
Hither Green [4]	d		22 26						22 50						23 06		23 20								
Lewisham [4]	d		22 31			22 44	22 47	22 52	22 57						23 11	23 17	23 27				23 32				
St Johns	d						22 49									23 19									
New Cross [4]	⊖ d		22 34				22 51	22 56							23 14	23 21					23 36				
London Victoria [15]	⊖ a									23 14										23 44					
London Bridge [4]	⊖ d	22 41	22 44	22 45	22 49	22 53	22 59	23 04	23 06		23 09	23 11	23 14	23 15	23 24	23 29	23 35	23 39	23 41		23 44	23 45	23 53		
London Blackfriars [3]	⊖ a			22 52										23 22								23 52			
London Cannon Street [4]	⊖ a																								
London Waterloo (East) [4]	⊖ d	22 47	22 49		22 55	22 58	23 04	23 09	23 11		23 14	23 17	23 19		23 29	23 34	23 40	23 44	23 47		23 50		23 58		
London Charing Cross [4]	⊖ a	22 51	22 52		22 59	23 01	23 07	23 13	23 15		23 18	23 20	23 22		23 32	23 37	23 43	23 48	23 50		23 53		00 01		

Sundays

		FC	FC ■1	SN	FC ■1	SE 72	SE 70	SE 14	SE 80	SE 50	SE 70	SE 72	SE 8 ■1		SN	FC ■1	SE 70	SE 62	SE 12	SE 70	SE 8 ■1	SE 12	SE 80	SE 50	SN
Orpington [4]	d					06 44		07 01			07 08	07 14	07 24						07 31	07 38	07 41				
Petts Wood [4]	d					06 47		07 04			07 11	07 17							07 34	07 41		←			
Hither Green [4]	d							07 15		07 21									07 45			07 45		07 51	
Lewisham [4]	d						07 16	07 20		07 26							07 36	07 45	→			07 50		07 56	
St Johns	d																								
New Cross [4]	⊖ d						07 20			07 30							07 40							08 00	
London Victoria [15]	⊖ a					07 23					07 43	07 53								08 13					
London Bridge [4]	⊖ d	00 20	00 52	07 12	07 15		07 27	07 30	07 34	07 37			07 40		07 42	07 45	07 48	07 54			07 57	07 59	08 04	08 07	08 12
London Blackfriars [3]	⊖ a	00 26	00 59		07 23											07 53									
London Cannon Street [4]	⊖ a																								
London Waterloo (East) [4]	⊖ d			07 17			07 31	07 34	07 39	07 42			07 45		07 47		07 53	07 59			08 02	08 04	08 09	08 12	08 17
London Charing Cross [4]	⊖ a			07 20			07 36	07 37	07 42	07 45			07 48		07 50		07 56	08 02			08 05	08 07	08 12	08 15	08 20

For general notes see front of timetable
For details of catering facilities see
Directory of Train Operators

Table 199

Sundays

Orpington, Petts Wood, Hither Green and Lewisham → London (Summary of Services)

Station		FC [1]	SE 72	SE 24		SE 72	SE 60	SE 12	SE 80	SE 50	SE 70	SE 8 [1]	SN	FC [1]	SE 70	SE 24	SE 62		SE 12	SE 70	SE 22 [1]	SE 12	SE 80	SE 50	SE 4 [1]
Orpington [4]	d					07 44		08 01			08 08	08 24							08 31	08 38	08 39	←			08 54
Petts Wood [4]	d					07 47		08 04			08 11								08 34	08 41					
Hither Green [4]	d							08 15		08 21									08 45			08 45		08 51	
Lewisham [4]	d		08 06	08 11			08 15	08 20		08 26					08 36	08 41	08 45		→			08 50		08 56	
St Johns	d			08 13												08 43									
New Cross [4]	⊖ d		08 10	08 15						08 30					08 40	08 45								09 00	
London Victoria [15]	⊖ a					08 23					08 43									09 13					
London Bridge [4]	⊖ d	08 15	08 18	08 21			08 24	08 29	08 34	08 37		08 40	08 42	08 45	08 48	08 51	08 54				08 56	08 59	09 04	09 07	09 10
London Blackfriars [3]	⊖ a	08 23												08 53											
London Cannon Street [4]	⊖ a																								
London Waterloo (East) [4]	⊖ d		08 23	08 26			08 29	08 34	08 39	08 42		08 45	08 47		08 53	08 56	08 59				09 02	09 04	09 09	09 12	09 15
London Charing Cross [4]	⊖ a		08 26	08 29			08 32	08 37	08 42	08 45		08 48	08 50		08 56	08 59	09 02				09 05	09 07	09 12	09 15	09 18

Station		SN	FC [1]	SE 72	SE 24	SE 62	SE 16	SE 70		SE 22 [1]	SE 16	SE 80	SE 50	SE 90 [1]	SN	FC [1]	SE 70	SE 24	SE 60	SE 12	SE 70		SE 22 [1]	SE 12	SE 80
Orpington [4]	d						09 01	09 08		09 09	←			09 24						09 31	09 38		09 39	←	
Petts Wood [4]	d						09 04	09 11												09 34	09 41				
Hither Green [4]	d						09 15				09 15		09 21							09 45				09 45	
Lewisham [4]	d			09 06	09 11	09 15	→				09 20		09 26				09 36	09 41	09 45	→				09 50	
St Johns	d				09 13													09 43							
New Cross [4]	⊖ d			09 10	09 15								09 30				09 40	09 45							
London Victoria [15]	⊖ a							09 43													10 13				
London Bridge [4]	⊖ d	09 12	09 15	09 18	09 21	09 24				09 26	09 29	09 34	09 37	09 40	09 42	09 45	09 48	09 51	09 54				09 56	09 59	10 04
London Blackfriars [3]	⊖ a		09 23													09 53									
London Cannon Street [4]	⊖ a																								
London Waterloo (East) [4]	⊖ d	09 17		09 23	09 26	09 29				09 32	09 34	09 39	09 42	09 45	09 47		09 53	09 56	09 59				10 02	10 04	10 09
London Charing Cross [4]	⊖ a	09 20		09 26	09 29	09 32				09 35	09 37	09 42	09 45	09 48	09 50		09 56	09 59	10 02				10 05	10 07	10 12

Station		SE 50	SE 4 [1]	SN	FC [1]	SE 72	SE 24	SE 60	SE 16	SE 70	SE 22 [1]	SE 16		FC [1]	SE 80	SE 50		SE 90 [1]	SN	FC [1]	SE 70	SE 24	SE 60	SE 12	SE 70
Orpington [4]	d		09 54						10 01	10 08	10 09	←						10 24						10 31	10 38
Petts Wood [4]	d								10 04	10 11														10 34	10 41
Hither Green [4]	d	09 51							10 15			10 15				10 21								10 45	
Lewisham [4]	d	09 56				10 06	10 11	10 15	→			10 20				10 26					10 36	10 41	10 45	→	
St Johns	d						10 13															10 43			
New Cross [4]	⊖ d	10 00				10 10	10 15									10 30					10 40	10 45			
London Victoria [15]	⊖ a									10 43															11 13
London Bridge [4]	⊖ d	10 07	10 10	10 12	10 15	10 18	10 21	10 24			10 26	10 29		10 30	10 34	10 37		10 40	10 42	10 45	10 48	10 51	10 54		
London Blackfriars [3]	⊖ a				10 23									10 37						10 53					
London Cannon Street [4]	⊖ a																								
London Waterloo (East) [4]	⊖ d	10 12	10 15	10 17		10 23	10 26	10 29			10 32	10 34			10 39	10 42		10 45	10 47		10 53	10 56	10 59		
London Charing Cross [4]	⊖ a	10 15	10 18	10 20		10 26	10 29	10 32			10 35	10 37			10 42	10 45		10 48	10 50		10 56	10 59	11 02		

Station		SE 22 [1]	SE 12	FC [1]	SE 84	SE 50	SE 4 [1]	SN	FC [1]	SE 70	SE 24	SE 60	SE 16	SE 70	SE 22 [1]	SE 16	FC [1]	SE 84	SE 50	and at the same minutes past each hour until		SE 90 [1]	SN	FC [1]
Orpington [4]	d	10 39	←				10 54						11 01	11 08	11 09	←						18 24		
Petts Wood [4]	d												11 04	11 11										
Hither Green [4]	d		10 45			10 51							11 15			11 15			11 21					
Lewisham [4]	d		10 50			10 56				11 06	11 11	11 15	→			11 20			11 26					
St Johns	d										11 13													
New Cross [4]	⊖ d					11 00				11 10	11 15								11 30					
London Victoria [15]	⊖ a													11 43										
London Bridge [4]	⊖ d	10 56	10 59	11 00	11 04	11 07	11 10	11 12	11 15	11 18	11 21	11 24			11 26	11 29	11 30	11 34	11 37			18 40	18 42	18 45
London Blackfriars [3]	⊖ a			11 07					11 23								11 37							18 53
London Cannon Street [4]	⊖ a																							
London Waterloo (East) [4]	⊖ d	11 02	11 04		11 09	11 12	11 15	11 17		11 23	11 26	11 29			11 32	11 34		11 39	11 42			18 45	18 47	
London Charing Cross [4]	⊖ a	11 06	11 07		11 12	11 15	11 18	11 20		11 26	11 29	11 32			11 35	11 37		11 42	11 45			18 48	18 50	

Station		SE 70	SE 24	SE 62	SE 12	SE 70	SE 22 [1]	SE 12	SE 84	SE 50	SE 4 [1]	SN		FC [1]	SE 72	SE 24	SE 62	SE 16	SE 70	SE 22 [1]	SE 16	SE 80	SE 50	SE 90 [1]	SN
Orpington [4]	d				18 31	18 38	18 39	←			18 54							19 01	19 08	19 09	←			19 24	
Petts Wood [4]	d				18 34	18 41												19 04	19 11						
Hither Green [4]	d				18 45			18 45		18 51								19 15			19 15		19 21		
Lewisham [4]	d	18 36	18 41	18 45	→			18 50		18 56					19 06	19 11	19 15	→			19 20		19 26		
St Johns	d		18 43													19 13									
New Cross [4]	⊖ d	18 40	18 45							19 00					19 10	19 15							19 30		
London Victoria [15]	⊖ a					19 13													19 43						
London Bridge [4]	⊖ d	18 48	18 51	18 54			18 56	18 59	19 04	19 07	19 10	19 12		19 15	19 18	19 21	19 24			19 26	19 29	19 34	19 37	19 40	19 42
London Blackfriars [3]	⊖ a													19 23											
London Cannon Street [4]	⊖ a																								
London Waterloo (East) [4]	⊖ d	18 53	18 56	18 59			19 02	19 04	19 09	19 12	19 15	19 17			19 23	19 26	19 29			19 32	19 34	19 39	19 42	19 45	19 47
London Charing Cross [4]	⊖ a	18 56	18 59	19 02			19 06	19 07	19 12	19 15	19 18	19 20			19 26	19 29	19 32			19 35	19 37	19 42	19 45	19 48	19 50

For general notes see front of timetable
For details of catering facilities see
Directory of Train Operators

Table 199

Sundays

Orpington, Petts Wood, Hither Green and Lewisham → London (Summary of Services)

		FC [1]	SE 70		SE 24	SE 62	SE 12	SE 70	SE 22 [1]	SE 12	SE 80	SE 50	SE 4 [1]	SN	FC [1]	SE 72		SE 24	SE 62	SE 16	SE 80	SE 50	SE 70	SE 90 [1]	SN
Orpington [4]	d						19 31	19 38	19 40				19 54							20 01			20 08	20 24	
Petts Wood [4]	d						19 34	19 41		⟵										20 04			20 11		
Hither Green [4]	d						19 45			19 45		19 51								20 15		20 21			
Lewisham [4]	d		19 36		19 41	19 45	⟶			19 50		19 56				20 06		20 11	20 15	20 20		20 26			
St Johns	d				19 43													20 13							
New Cross [4]	⊖ d		19 40		19 45							20 00				20 10		20 15				20 30			
London Victoria [15]	⊖ a							20 13															20 43		
London Bridge [4]	⊖ d	19 45	19 48		19 51	19 54			19 56	19 59	20 04	20 07	20 10	20 12	20 15	20 18		20 21	20 24	20 29	20 34	20 37		20 40	20 42
London Blackfriars [3]	⊖ a	19 53													20 23										
London Cannon Street [4]	⊖ a																								
London Waterloo (East) [4]	⊖ d		19 53		19 56	19 59			20 02	20 04	20 09	20 12	20 15	20 17		20 23		20 26	20 29	20 34	20 39	20 42		20 45	20 47
London Charing Cross [4]	⊖ a		19 56		19 59	20 02			20 05	20 07	20 12	20 15	20 18	20 20		20 26		20 29	20 32	20 37	20 42	20 45		20 48	20 50

		FC [1]	SE 70	SE 24	SE 62	SE 12	SE 70		SE 22 [1]	SE 12	SE 80	SE 50	SE 4 [1]	SN	FC [1]	SE 72	SE 24	SE 62	SE 12	SE 80		SE 50	SE 70	SE 90 [1]	SN
Orpington [4]	d					20 31	20 38		20 40				20 54						21 01				21 08	21 24	
Petts Wood [4]	d					20 34	20 41			⟵									21 04				21 11		
Hither Green [4]	d					20 45				20 45		20 51							21 15			21 21			
Lewisham [4]	d		20 36	20 41	20 45	⟶				20 50		20 56				21 06	21 11	21 15	21 20			21 26			
St Johns	d			20 43													21 13								
New Cross [4]	⊖ d		20 40	20 45								21 00				21 10	21 15					21 30			
London Victoria [15]	⊖ a						21 13																21 43		
London Bridge [4]	⊖ d	20 45	20 48	20 51	20 54				20 56	20 59	21 04	21 07	21 10	21 12	21 15	21 18	21 21	21 24	21 29	21 34		21 37		21 40	21 42
London Blackfriars [3]	⊖ a	20 53													21 23										
London Cannon Street [4]	⊖ a																								
London Waterloo (East) [4]	⊖ d		20 53	20 56	20 59				21 02	21 04	21 09	21 12	21 15	21 17		21 23	21 26	21 29	21 34	21 39		21 42		21 45	21 47
London Charing Cross [4]	⊖ a		20 56	20 59	21 02				21 05	21 07	21 12	21 15	21 18	21 20		21 26	21 29	21 32	21 37	21 42		21 45		21 48	21 50

		FC [1]	SE 70	SE 24	SE 62	SE 12	SE 70	SE 22 [1]	SE 12	SE 80	SE 50		SE 4 [1]	SN	FC [1]	SE 72	SE 24	SE 62	SE 12	SE 80	SE 50	SE 70	SE 90 [1]	SN	FC [1]
Orpington [4]	d					21 31	21 38	21 40					21 54						22 01			22 08	22 24		
Petts Wood [4]	d					21 34	21 41		⟵										22 04			22 11			
Hither Green [4]	d					21 45			21 45		21 51								22 15		22 21				
Lewisham [4]	d		21 36	21 41	21 45	⟶			21 50		21 56					22 06	22 11	22 15	22 20		22 26				
St Johns	d			21 43													22 13								
New Cross [4]	⊖ d		21 40	21 45							22 00					22 10	22 15				22 30				
London Victoria [15]	⊖ a						22 13															22 43			
London Bridge [4]	⊖ d	21 45	21 48	21 51	21 54			21 56	21 59	22 04	22 07		22 10	22 12	22 15	22 18	22 21	22 24	22 29	22 34	22 37		22 40	22 42	22 45
London Blackfriars [3]	⊖ a	21 53													22 23										22 53
London Cannon Street [4]	⊖ a																								
London Waterloo (East) [4]	⊖ d		21 53	21 56	21 59			22 02	22 04	22 09	22 12		22 15	22 17		22 23	22 26	22 29	22 34	22 39	22 42		22 45	22 47	
London Charing Cross [4]	⊖ a		21 56	21 59	22 02			22 05	22 07	22 12	22 15		22 18	22 20		22 26	22 29	22 32	22 37	22 42	22 45		22 48	22 50	

		SE 70		SE 24	SE 62	SE 12	SE 70	SE 22 [1]	SE 12	SE 80	SE 50	SE 4 [1]	SN	FC [1]	SE 72		SE 24	SE 12	SE 50	FC [1]	SE 24	SE 72			
Orpington [4]	d					22 31	22 38	22 40				22 54						23 01				23 14			
Petts Wood [4]	d					22 34	22 41		⟵									23 04				23 17			
Hither Green [4]	d					22 45			22 45		22 51							23 15	23 21						
Lewisham [4]	d	22 36		22 41	22 45	⟶			22 50		22 56				23 06		23 11	23 20	23 26		23 41				
St Johns	d			22 43													23 13				23 43				
New Cross [4]	⊖ d	22 40		22 45							23 00				23 10		23 15		23 30		23 45				
London Victoria [15]	⊖ a						23 13															23 53			
London Bridge [4]	⊖ d	22 48		22 51	22 54			22 56	22 59	23 04	23 07	23 10	23 12	23 15	23 18		23 21	23 29	23 37	23 45	23 51				
London Blackfriars [3]	⊖ a													23 23						23 53					
London Cannon Street [4]	⊖ a																								
London Waterloo (East) [4]	⊖ d	22 53		22 56	22 59			23 02	23 04	23 09	23 12	23 15	23 17		23 23		23 26	23 34	23 42		23 56				
London Charing Cross [4]	⊖ a	22 56		22 59	23 02			23 05	23 07	23 12	23 15	23 18	23 20		23 26		23 29	23 37	23 45		23 59				

For general notes see front of timetable
For details of catering facilities see
Directory of Train Operators

Network Diagram for Tables 200, 203, 204 | also 199★

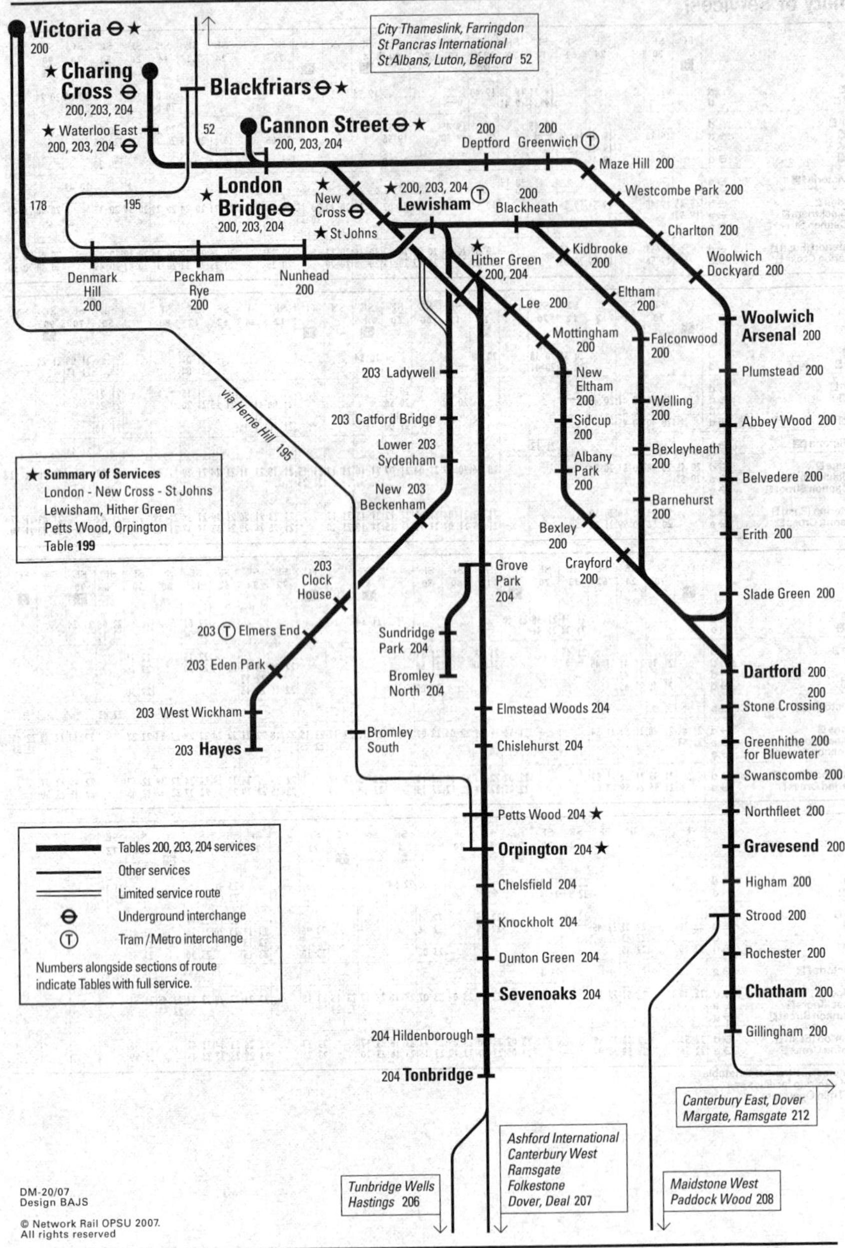

Victoria ⊖ ★ 200
★ Charing Cross ⊖ 200, 203, 204
★ Waterloo East 200, 203, 204 ⊖
Blackfriars ⊖ ★
52
City Thameslink, Farringdon
St Pancras International
St Albans, Luton, Bedford 52
Cannon Street ⊖ ★ 200, 203, 204
★ London Bridge ⊖ 200, 203, 204
178
195
★ New Cross ⊖
★ St Johns
★ 200, 203, 204 Lewisham Ⓣ
200 Deptford
200 Greenwich Ⓣ
Maze Hill 200
Westcombe Park 200
200 Blackheath
Charlton 200
Woolwich Dockyard 200
Woolwich Arsenal 200
Denmark Hill 200
Peckham Rye 200
Nunhead 200
★ Hither Green 200, 204
Kidbrooke 200
Eltham 200
Lee 200
Mottingham 200
Falconwood 200
Plumstead 200
203 Ladywell
203 Catford Bridge
Lower 203 Sydenham
New 203 Beckenham
New Eltham 200
Sidcup 200
Albany Park 200
Welling 200
Bexleyheath 200
Barnehurst 200
Abbey Wood 200
Belvedere 200
Erith 200
Bexley 200
Crayford 200
Slade Green 200
via Herne Hill 195
★ Summary of Services
London - New Cross - St Johns
Lewisham, Hither Green
Petts Wood, Orpington
Table 199
203 Clock House
203 Ⓣ Elmers End
203 Eden Park
203 West Wickham
203 Hayes
Grove Park 204
Sundridge Park 204
Bromley North 204
Bromley South
Elmstead Woods 204
Chislehurst 204
Petts Wood 204 ★
Orpington 204 ★
Chelsfield 204
Knockholt 204
Dunton Green 204
Sevenoaks 204
204 Hildenborough
204 Tonbridge
Dartford 200
200 Stone Crossing
Greenhithe 200 for Bluewater
Swanscombe 200
Northfleet 200
Gravesend 200
Higham 200
Strood 200
Rochester 200
Chatham 200
Gillingham 200
Tables 200, 203, 204 services
Other services
Limited service route
⊖ Underground interchange
Ⓣ Tram / Metro interchange
Numbers alongside sections of route indicate Tables with full service.
Canterbury East, Dover
Margate, Ramsgate 212
Tunbridge Wells
Hastings 206
Ashford International
Canterbury West
Ramsgate
Folkestone
Dover, Deal 207
Maidstone West
Paddock Wood 208

DM-20/07
Design BAJS

For details of Bank Holiday service alterations please see first page of Table 195

London → Dartford and Gillingham

Network Diagram - see first page of Table 200

Miles	Miles	Miles	Miles	Miles			SE MO 62	SE MX 62	SE MO 62	SE MX 62	SE MX 50	SE MO 70	SE MO 80	SE MX 80	SE MX 70	SE MO 50	SE MX 50	SE 62	SE 20 [1] A	SE 50	SE 72	SE 84	SE 52	SE 70	SE 64
0	—	0	0	—	**London Charing Cross** [4]	⊖ d	22p50	22p50	23p20	23p20	23p34	23p37	23p40	23p40	23p47	23p47	00 04	00 14		04 50	04 56	05 04	05 18	05 26	05 34
¾	—	¾	¾	—	**London Waterloo (East)** [4]	⊖ d	22p53	22p53	23p23	23p23	23p37	23p40	23p43	23p43	23p50	23p50	00 07	00 17		04 53	04 59	05 07	05 21	05 29	05 37
—	0	—	—	—	**London Cannon Street** [4]	⊖ d																			
1¾	¾	1¾	1¾	—	**London Bridge** [4]	⊖ d	22p59	22p59	23p29	23p29	23p43	23p45	23p48	23p48	23p55	23p55	00 13	00 23		04 58	05 04	05 12	05 28	05 34	05 42
—	3¾	—	—	—	Deptford	d							23p53	23p54								05 17			
—	4¼	—	—	—	Greenwich [4]	d							23p55	23p56								05 19			
—	5¼	—	—	—	Maze Hill	d							23p59	00 01								05 23			
—	5¾	—	—	—	Westcombe Park	d							00 01	00 02								05 25			
—	—	—	—	0	**London Victoria** [15]	⊖ d																			
—	—	—	—	4¼	Denmark Hill [4]	d																			
—	—	—	—	5	Peckham Rye [4]	d																			
—	—	—	—	5¾	Nunhead [4]	d																			
—	—	4¾	4¾	—	New Cross [4]	⊖ d					23p48	23p50			00 01	00 01	00 18	00 28		05 03	05 09		05 33	05 39	
—	—	5½	5½	—	St Johns	d																			
6	—	6	6	7½	Lewisham [4]	d	23p08	23p08	23p38	23p38	23p53	23p55			00 05	00 05	00 23	00 33		05 08	05 14		05 38	05 44	05 52
7	—	7	—	8½	Blackheath [4]	d	23p11	23p11	23p41	23p41		23p58			00 07			00 36			05 16			05 46	05 54
—	—	8	—	9½	Kidbrooke	d						00 01			00 10						05 19			05 49	
—	—	9	—	10½	Eltham	d						00 04			00 14						05 23			05 53	
—	—	10¼	—	11¾	Falconwood	d						00 07			00 16						05 25			05 55	
—	—	11¼	—	12¾	Welling	d						00 09			00 19						05 28			05 58	
—	—	12¾	—	14¼	Bexleyheath	d						00 12			00 21						05 30			06 00	
—	—	14	—	15½	Barnehurst [4]	d						00 15			00 24						05 33			06 03	
—	—	—	7¼	—	Hither Green [4]	d					23p57					00 09	00 27			05 11			05 41		
—	—	—	8	—	Lee	d					23p59					00 11	00 29			05 13			05 43		
—	—	—	9½	—	Mottingham	d					00 02					00 14	00 32			05 16			05 46		
—	—	—	10½	—	New Eltham	d					00 05					00 16	00 35			05 19			05 49		
—	—	—	12	—	Sidcup [4]	d					00 08					00 20	00 38			05 22			05 52		
—	—	—	13	—	Albany Park	d					00 10					00 22	00 40			05 24			05 54		
—	—	—	14	—	Bexley	d					00 12					00 24	00 42			05 26			05 56		
—	—	—	15½	—	Crayford	d					00 15					00 27	00 45			05 29			05 59		
9	6½	—	—	—	Charlton [4]	d	23p15	23p15	23p45	23p45			00 03	00 04				00 40				05 28			05 58
10	7½	—	—	—	Woolwich Dockyard	d							00 06	00 07											
10¾	8¼	—	—	—	**Woolwich Arsenal** [4]	d	23p20	23p20	23p50	23p50			00 09	00 10				00 45				05 33			06 03
11¼	8¾	—	—	—	Plumstead	d							00 11	00 12				00 47				05 35			
12¾	10¼	—	—	—	Abbey Wood	d	23p25	23p25	23p55	23p55			00 14	00 15				00 50				05 39			06 08
14¼	11¾	—	—	—	Belvedere	d							00 17	00 18				00 53				05 41			
15¼	13	—	—	—	Erith	d							00 20	00 21				00 56				05 44			
16¾	14¼	—	—	—	Slade Green [4]	d							00 23	00 24				00 58				05 48			06 13
18¾	16¼	17	17¼	18½	**Dartford** [4]	a	23p33	23p33	00 03	00 04	00 20	00 21	00 27	00 29	00 31	00 31	00 50	01 03		05 33	05 41	05 53	06 03	06 11	06 19
—	—	—	—	—		d	23p34	23p34	00 04	00 04								01 04	05 06		05 42	05 54		06 12	06 20
20¾	—	—	19¼	—	Stone Crossing	d	23p37	23p37		00 08											05 45	05 57		06 15	06 23
21½	—	—	20	—	Greenhithe for Bluewater	d	23p40	23p40	00 09	00 10								01 09	05 11		05 48	06 00		06 18	06 26
22¾	—	—	21¼	—	Swanscombe	d	23p42	23p42		00 12											05 50	06 02		06 20	06 28
23¼	—	—	22	—	Northfleet	d	23p44	23p44		00 14											05 52	06 04		06 22	06 30
25½	—	—	24	—	**Gravesend** [4]	d	23p48	23p50	00 16	00 20								01 16	05 18		05 56	06a08		06 26	06 34
30	—	—	28½	—	Higham	d	23p54	23p56	00 22	00 26								01 22	05 24		06 02			06 32	06 40
32¾	—	—	31¼	—	Strood [4]	d	23p58	00 02	00 27	00 32								01 28	05 29		06 08			06 38	06a45
—	—	—	—	—	Maidstone West [4]	a													*06 03*		*06 41*				
33¾	—	—	32¼	—	Rochester [4]	d	00 03	00 07	00 31	00 39								01 31	05 33		06 11			06 41	
34¼	—	—	32¾	—	**Chatham** [4]	d	00 06	00 09	00 34	00 42								01 34	05 36		06 14			06 44	
36	—	—	34½	—	**Gillingham (Kent)** [4]	a	00 09	00 13	00 37	00 45								01 37	05 39		06 21			06 47	

For general notes see front of timetable
For details of catering facilities see Directory of Train Operators

A To Dover Priory (Table 212)

For details of Bank Holiday service alterations please see first page of Table 195

London → Dartford and Gillingham

Network Diagram - see first page of Table 200

		SE 54	SE 80	SE 72	SE 65	SE 52	SE 84	SE 70	SE 65	SE 54	SE 86	SE 70	SE 60	SE 73	SE 52	SE 80	SE 71	SE 57	SE 86 A	SE 80	SE 40	SE 44	SE 73	SE 61	SE 51
London Charing Cross 4	⊖ d	05 46	05 54	06 02		06 20		06 32	06 40		06 54		07 03		07 20		07 30				07 42				08 00
London Waterloo (East) 4	⊖ d	05 49	05 57	06 05		06 23		06 35	06 43		06 57		07 06		07 23		07 33				07 45				08 03
London Cannon Street 4	⊖ d				06 12		06 30			06 48		07 04		07 22		07 32		07 39				07 48	07 54	07 58	
London Bridge 4	⊖ d	05 54	06 02	06 10	06 16	06 28	06 34	06 40	06 48	06 52	07 04	07 08	07 11	07 26	07 28	07 36	07 38	07 43			07 50	07 52	07 58	08 02	08 09
Deptford	d		06 07				06 39				07 09					07 41									
Greenwich 4	⛴ d		06 09				06 41				07 11					07 43						07 59			
Maze Hill	d		06 13				06 45				07 15					07 47									
Westcombe Park	d		06 15				06 47				07 17					07 49									
London Victoria 15	⊖ d																								
Denmark Hill 4	d																								
Peckham Rye 4	d																								
Nunhead 4	d																								
New Cross 4	⊖ d	05 59		06 15		06 33		06 47				07 13			07 33		07 43	07 49					08 03	08 07	
St Johns	d	06 01		06 17								07 15					07 45						08 05		
Lewisham 4	⛴ d	06 04		06 20	06 24	06 38		06 52	06 56	07 00		07 18	07 22	07 34	07 38		07 48	07 53					08 08	08 12	
Blackheath 4	d			06 22	06 26			06 54	06 58			07 20	07 24	07 36			07 50						08 10	08 14	
Kidbrooke	d			06 25				06 57				07 23		07 39			07 53						08 13		
Eltham	d			06 29				07 01				07 27		07 43			07 57						08 17		
Falconwood	d			06 31				07 03				07 29		07 45			07 59						08 19		
Welling	d			06 34				07 06				07 32		07 48			08 02						08 22		
Bexleyheath	d			06 36				07 08				07 34		07 50			08 04						08 24		
Barnehurst 4	d			06 39				07 11				07 37		07a53			08 07		07 56				08 27		
Hither Green 4	d	06 07				06 41				07 03					07 41			07 57			08 01				08 18
Lee	d	06 09				06 43				07 05					07 43						08 03				
Mottingham	d	06 12				06 46				07 08					07 46						08 06				
New Eltham	d	06 15				06 49				07 11					07 49						08 09				
Sidcup 4	d	06 18				06 52				07 14					07 52			08a05			08 12				08 26
Albany Park	d	06 20				06 54				07 16					07 54						08 14				08 28
Bexley	d	06 22				06 56				07 18					07 56						08 16				08 30
Crayford	d	06 25				06 59				07 21	07a46				07 59						08 19				08a33
Charlton 4	d		06 18		06 30		06 50		07 02		07 20		07 28			07 52				←		08 06		08 18	
Woolwich Dockyard	d		06 20				06 52				07 22					07 54				07 54					
Woolwich Arsenal 4	d		06 23		06 35		06 55		07 07		07 25		07 33			→				07 57		08 11		08 23	
Plumstead	d		06 25				06 57				07 27									07 59					
Abbey Wood	d		06 29		06 40		07 01		07 12		07 31		07 38							08 03		08 16		08 28	
Belvedere	d		06 31				07 03				07 33									08 05					
Erith	d		06 34				07 06				07 36									08 08					
Slade Green 4	d		06 38		06 45		07 09				07a39		07 43						08a00	08 11					
Dartford 4	a	06 30	06 43	06 45	06 51	07 04	07 15	07 16	07 22	07 25		07 46	07 49		08 04		08 13			08 16	08 24	08 26	08 33	08 36	
	d	06 30		06 46	06 52	07 05		07 16	07 28	07 30					08 05							08 28	08 34		
Stone Crossing	d				06 55	07 08				07 33					08 08							08 31			
Greenhithe for Bluewater	d				06 58	07 11		07 21	07 33	07 36					08 11							08 34	08 39		
Swanscombe	d				07 00	07 13				07 38					08 13							08 36			
Northfleet	d				07 02	07 15				07 40					08 15							08 38			
Gravesend 4	d	06a40		06 56	07 06	07 19		07 28	07 40	07a45					08 19							08a42	08 46		
Higham	d			07 02	07 12	07 25		07 34	07 46						08 25								08 52		
Strood 4	d			07 08	07a18	07 32		07a40	07 52						08 32								08 58		
Maidstone West 4	a			*07 35*		*07 57*			*08 19*						*08 57*								*09 24*		
Rochester 4	d			07b19		07a36			07 55						08a36								09 01		
Chatham 4	d			07 22					07 58														09 04		
Gillingham (Kent) 4	a			07 25					08 01														09 07		

For general notes see front of timetable
For details of catering facilities see Directory of Train Operators

A To London Charing Cross
b Arr. 0712

Table 200

Mondays to Fridays

For details of Bank Holiday service alterations please see first page of Table 195

London → Dartford and Gillingham

Network Diagram - see first page of Table 200

Station		SE 84	SE [1]	SE 84	SE 71	SE 61	SE 42	SE 78	SE 80	SE 71	SE 55	SE 71	SE 80	SE 10		SE 80	SE 63	SE 71	SE 54	SE 78	SE 92 [1] A	SE 81	SE 47 B	SE 92 [1] C	SE 81
London Charing Cross [4]	⊖ d	08 03	08 08						08 24	08 28			08 41	08 44					09 02						
London Waterloo (East) [4]	⊖ d	08 06	08 11						08 27	08 31			08 44	08 47					09 06						
London Cannon Street [4]	⊖ d				08 14	08 17	08 26				08 34						08 50	09 02				09 10	09 20		
London Bridge [4]	⊖ d	08 12	08 16		08 18	08 21	08 30		08 32	08 36	08 38		08 50	08 52			08 54	09 06	09 12			09 14	09 24		
Deptford	d	08 18							08 38				08 56									09 20			
Greenwich [4]	d	08 20							08 40				08 58									09 22			
Maze Hill	d	08 24							08 44				09 02									09 26			
Westcombe Park	d	08 26							08 46				09 04									09 28			
London Victoria [15]	⊖ d							08 21												09 01				09 15	
Denmark Hill [4]	d							08 31												09 12	09 20			09 25	
Peckham Rye [4]	d							08 35												09 14	09 22			09 28	
Nunhead [4]	d							08 37												09 16					
New Cross [4]	⊖ d				08 23	08 26				08 42	08 45							09 11					09 29		
St Johns	d				08 25						08 47												09 31		
Lewisham [4]	d				08 28	08 32		08 44		08 48	08 50						09 04	09 16	09 20	09 26	09 31		09 34	09 35	
Blackheath [4]	d				08 30	08 34		08 46		08 50							09 06	09 18		09 28					
Kidbrooke	d				08 33			08 49		08 53								09 21		09 31					
Eltham	d				08 37			08 53		08 57		←						09 25		09 35	09 39			09 42	
Falconwood	d				08 39			08 55		08 59		08 59						09 27		09 37	→				
Welling	d				08 42			08 58		→		09 02						09 30		09 40					
Bexleyheath	d				08 44			09 00				09 04						09 32		09 42					
Barnehurst [4]	d				08 47			09 03				09 08						09 35		09 45					
Hither Green [4]	d		08 27				08 41				08 53			09 03					09 23				09 37		
Lee	d		08 29				08 43				08 55			09 05					09 25				09 39		
Mottingham	d		08 32				08 46				08 58			09 08					09 28				09 42		
New Eltham	d		08 35				08 49				09 01			09 11					09 31				09 45		
Sidcup [4]	d		08 38				08 52				09 04			09 14					09 34				09 48		
Albany Park	d		08 40				08 54				09 06			09 16					09 36				09 50		
Bexley	d		08 42				08 56				09 08			09 18					09 38				09 52		
Crayford	d		08 45				08 59				09 11			09 21					09 41				09 58		
Charlton [4]	d	08 28		←		08 40			08 48				09 06			←	09 12					09 30			
Woolwich Dockyard	d	08 30		08 30					08 50				09 08			09 08						09 32			
Woolwich Arsenal [4]	d	→		08 33		08 45			08 53				→			09 11	09 17					09 35			
Plumstead	d			08 35					08 55							09 13						09 37			
Abbey Wood	d			08 39		08 50			08 59							09 17	09 22					09 41			
Belvedere	d			08 41					09 01							09 19						09 43			
Erith	d			08 44					09 04							09 22						09 46			←
Slade Green [4]	d			08 47					09 07							09 25						09 49	10a04		09 49
Dartford [4]	a		08 50	08 51	08 54	09 00	09 04	09 09	09 13		09 15	09 18		09 26		09 30	09 33	09 41	09 45	09 51		→		09 54	09 55
	d			08 52		09 02					09 16						09 34		09 46					09 54	
Stone Crossing	d			08 55							09 19								09 49						
Greenhithe for Bluewater	d			08 58		09 07					09 22						09 39		09 52						
Swanscombe	d			09 00							09 24								09 54						
Northfleet	d			09 02							09 26								09 56						
Gravesend [4]	d			09a06		09 14					09a30						09 46		10a00					10 04	
Higham	d					09 20											09 52								
Strood [4]	d					09 26											09 58								
Maidstone West [4]	a					*09 54*											*10 24*								
Rochester [4]	d					09 29											10 01								
Chatham [4]	d					09 32											10 04							10 19	
Gillingham (Kent) [4]	a					09 35											10 07							10 22	

For general notes see front of timetable
For details of catering facilities see Directory of Train Operators

A 21 July to 29 August. From Elephant & Castle (Table 195) to Ramsgate (Table 212)

B To London Cannon Street (Table 199)

C Until 18 July and from 1 September. To Ramsgate (Table 212)

For details of Bank Holiday service alterations please see first page of Table 195

London → Dartford and Gillingham

Network Diagram - see first page of Table 200

Station		SE 92	SE 70	SE 82	SE 87	SE 67	SE 54	SE 78	SE 81	SE 47	SE 70	SE 82	SE 87	SE 67	SE 54	SE 78	SE 81	SE 47	SE 70	SE 82	SE 87	SE 67	SE 54	SE 78
		1 A			B					B			B					B			B			
London Charing Cross 4	⊖ d		09 15	09 20			09 32				09 49	09 52			10 02				10 17	10 20			10 32	
London Waterloo (East) 4	⊖ d		09 20	09 23			09 35				09 52	09 55			10 05				10 20	10 23			10 35	
London Cannon Street 4	⊖ d				09 30	09 34			09 42	09 48			10 00	10 04			10 10	10 18			10 30	10 34		
London Bridge 4	⊖ d		09 26	09 29	09 34	09 38	09 40		09 46	09 52	09 57	10 00	10 04	10 08	10 10		10 14	10 22	10 25	10 29	10 34	10 38	10 40	
Deptford	d				09 40				09 52				10 10				10 20				10 40			
Greenwich 4	⛴ d			09 37	09 42				09 54			10 07	10 12				10 22			10 37	10 42			
Maze Hill	d				09 46				09 58				10 16				10 26				10 46			
Westcombe Park	d				09 48				10 00				10 18				10 28				10 48			
London Victoria 15	⊖ d							09 31								10 01								10 31
Denmark Hill 4	d							09 42								10 12								10 42
Peckham Rye 4	d							09 44								10 14								10 44
Nunhead 4	d							09 46								10 16								10 46
New Cross 4	⊖ d					09 44				09 57				10 14				10 27				10 44		
St Johns	d									09 59								10 29						
Lewisham 4	⛴ d		09 36			09 48	09 50	09 53			10 06			10 18	10 20	10 23			10 35			10 48	10 50	10 53
Blackheath 4	d		09 38			09 50		09 55			10 08			10 20		10 25			10 37			10 50		10 55
Kidbrooke	d	←	09 41					09 58			10 11					10 28			10 40					10 58
Eltham	d	09 39	09 45					10 02			10 15					10 32			10 44					11 02
Falconwood	d		09 47					10 04			10 17					10 34			10 46					11 04
Welling	d		09 50					10 07			10 20					10 37			10 49					11 07
Bexleyheath	d		09 52					10 09			10 22					10 39			10 51					11 09
Barnehurst 4	d		09 55					10 12			10 25					10 42			10 54					11 12
Hither Green 4	d						09 53			10 05					10 23			10 35					10 53	
Lee	d						09 55			10 07					10 25			10 37					10 55	
Mottingham	d						09 58			10 10					10 28			10 40					10 58	
New Eltham	d						10 01			10 13					10 31			10 43					11 01	
Sidcup 4	d						10 04			10 16					10 34			10 46					11 04	
Albany Park	d						10 06			10 18					10 36			10 48					11 06	
Bexley	d						10 08			10 20					10 38			10 50					11 08	
Crayford	d						10 11			10b28					10 41			10c58					11 11	
Charlton 4	d			09 44	09 50	09 57			10 02			10 14	10 20	10 25			10 30			10 44	10 50	10 55		
Woolwich Dockyard	d				09 52				10 04				10 22				10 32				10 52			
Woolwich Arsenal 4	d			09 49	09 55	10 02			10 07			10 19	10 25	10 30			10 35			10 49	10 55	11 00		
Plumstead	d				09 57	10a04			10 09				10 27	10a32			10 37				10 57	11a02		
Abbey Wood	d			09 53	10 01				10 13			10 23	10 31				10 41			10 53	11 01			
Belvedere	d				10 03				10 15				10 33				10 43				11 03			
Erith	d				10 06				10 18				10 36				10 46				11 06			
Slade Green 4	d				10a09				10 21	10a36			10a39				10 49	11a06			11a09			
Dartford 4	a	09 57	10 01	10 03			10 15	10 17	10 27		10 31	10 33			10 45	10 47	10 53		11 01	11 03			11 15	11 17
	d	09 58		10 04			10 16					10 34			10 46					11 04			11 16	
Stone Crossing	d						10 19								10 49								11 19	
Greenhithe for Bluewater	d			10 09			10 22					10 39			10 52					11 09			11 22	
Swanscombe	d						10 24								10 54								11 24	
Northfleet	d						10 26								10 56								11 26	
Gravesend 4	d	10 10		10 16			10a30					10 46			11a00					11 16			11a30	
Higham	d			10 22								10 52								11 22				
Strood 4	d			10 28								10 58								11 28				
Maidstone West 4	a			*10 54*								*11 24*								*11 54*				
Rochester 4	d			10 31								11 01								11 31				
Chatham 4	d	10 24		10 34								11 04								11 34				
Gillingham (Kent) 4	a	10 28		10 37								11 07								11 37				

For general notes see front of timetable
For details of catering facilities see Directory of Train Operators

A 21 July to 29 August. From Elephant & Castle (Table 195) to Ramsgate (Table 212)

B To London Cannon Street (Table 199)

b Arr. 1024

c Arr. 1054

For details of Bank Holiday service alterations please see first page of Table 195

London → Dartford and Gillingham

Network Diagram - see first page of Table 200

		SE 81	SE 47 A	SE 70	SE 82	SE 87 A	SE 67		SE 54	SE 78	SE 81	SE 47 A	SE 70	SE 82	SE 87 A	SE 67	SE 54	SE 78	SE 81	SE 47 A	SE 70	SE 82	SE 87 A	SE 67
London Charing Cross [4]	⊖ d			10 47	10 50				14 02				14 17	14 20			14 32				14 47	14 50		
London Waterloo (East) [4]	⊖ d			10 50	10 53				14 05				14 20	14 23			14 35				14 50	14 53		
London Cannon Street [4]	⊖ d	10 40	10 48			11 00	11 04				14 10	14 18			14 30	14 34			14 40	14 48			15 00	15 04
London Bridge [4]	⊖ d	10 44	10 52	10 55	10 59	11 04	11 08		14 10		14 14	14 22	14 25	14 29	14 34	14 38	14 40		14 44	14 52	14 55	14 59	15 04	15 08
Deptford	d	10 50				11 10					14 20				14 40				14 50				15 10	
Greenwich [4]	⛴ d	10 52			11 07	11 12					14 22			14 37	14 42				14 52			15 07	15 12	
Maze Hill	d	10 56				11 16					14 26				14 46				14 56				15 16	
Westcombe Park	d	10 58				11 18					14 28				14 48				14 58				15 18	
London Victoria [15]	⊖ d									14 01								14 31						
Denmark Hill [4]	d									14 12								14 42						
Peckham Rye [4]	d									14 14								14 44						
Nunhead [4]	d									14 16								14 46						
New Cross [4]	⊖ d		10 57				11 14					14 27				14 44				14 57				15 14
St Johns	d		10 59									14 29								14 59				
Lewisham [4]	⛴ d			11 05			11 18		14 20	14 23			14 35			14 48	14 50	14 53			15 05			15 18
Blackheath [4]	d			11 07			11 20			14 25			14 37			14 50		14 55			15 07			15 20
Kidbrooke	d			11 10						14 28			14 40					14 58			15 10			
Eltham	d			11 14				and at		14 32			14 44					15 02			15 14			
Falconwood	d			11 16						14 34			14 46					15 04			15 16			
Welling	d			11 19				the same		14 37			14 49					15 07			15 19			
Bexleyheath	d			11 21						14 39			14 51					15 09			15 21			
Barnehurst [4]	d			11 24				minutes		14 42			14 54					15 12			15 24			
Hither Green [4]	d		11 05					past	14 23			14 35					14 53			15 05				
Lee	d		11 07						14 25			14 37					14 55			15 07				
Mottingham	d		11 10					each	14 28			14 40					14 58			15 10				
New Eltham	d		11 13						14 31			14 43					15 01			15 13				
Sidcup [4]	d		11 16					hour until	14 34			14 46					15 04			15 16				
Albany Park	d		11 18						14 36			14 48					15 06			15 18				
Bexley	d		11 20						14 38			14 50					15 08			15 20				
Crayford	d		11b28						14 41			14c58					15 11			15e28				
Charlton [4]	d	11 00			11 14	11 20	11 25				14 30			14 44	14 50	14 55			15 00			15 14	15 20	15 25
Woolwich Dockyard	d	11 02				11 22					14 32				14 52				15 02				15 22	
Woolwich Arsenal [4]	d	11 05			11 19	11 25	11 30				14 35			14 49	14 55	15 00			15 05			15 19	15 25	15 30
Plumstead	d	11 07				11 27	11a32				14 37				14 57	15a02			15 07				15 27	15a32
Abbey Wood	d	11 11			11 23	11 31					14 41			14 53	15 01				15 11			15 23	15 31	
Belvedere	d	11 13				11 33					14 43				15 03				15 13				15 33	
Erith	d	11 16				11 36					14 46				15 06				15 16				15 36	
Slade Green [4]	d	11 19	11a36			11a39					14 49	15a05			15a09				15 19	15a34			15a39	
Dartford [4]	a	11 23		11 31	11 33				14 45	14 47	14 53		15 01	15 03			15 15	15 19	15 23		15 31	15 33		
	d				11 34				14 46					15 04			15 16					15 34		
Stone Crossing	d								14 49								15 19							
Greenhithe for Bluewater	d				11 39				14 52					15 09			15 22					15 39		
Swanscombe	d								14 54								15 24							
Northfleet	d								14 56								15 26							
Gravesend [4]	d				11 46				15a00					15 16			15a30					15 46		
Higham	d				11 52									15 22								15 52		
Strood [4]	d				11 58									15 28								15 58		
Maidstone West [4]	a				*12 24*									*15 54*								*16 35*		
Rochester [4]	d				12 01									15 31								16 01		
Chatham [4]	d				12 04									15 34								16 04		
Gillingham (Kent) [4]	a				12 07									15 37								16 07		

For general notes see front of timetable
For details of catering facilities see Directory of Train Operators

A To London Cannon Street (Table 199)
b Arr. 1124
c Arr. 1454
e Arr. 1524

For details of Bank Holiday service alterations please see first page of Table 195

London → Dartford and Gillingham

Network Diagram - see first page of Table 200

		SE 54	SE 78	SE 81		SE 47 A	SE 70	SE 82	SE 87 A	SE 67	SE 54	SE 78	SE 81	SE 47	SE 70	SE 62	SE 81	SE 54	SE 81	SE 57 A	SE 74	SE 81	SE 74	SE 62	SE 78
London Charing Cross 4	⊖ d	15 02					15 17	15 20			15 32				15 47	15 50		16 02			16 11			16 21	
London Waterloo (East) 4	⊖ d	15 05					15 20	15 23			15 35				15 50	15 53		16 05			16 14			16 24	
London Cannon Street 4	⊖ d			15 10		15 18			15 30	15 34			15 40	15 48			16 00			16 10		16 18			
London Bridge 4	⊖ d	15 10		15 14		15 22	15 25	15 29	15 34	15 38	15 40		15 44	15 52	15 55	15 59	16 04	16 10		16 14	16 19	16 22		16 29	
Deptford	d			15 20					15 40				15 50				16 10								
Greenwich 4	⛴ d			15 22				15 37	15 42				15 52				16 12					16 29			
Maze Hill	d			15 26					15 46				15 56				16 16								
Westcombe Park	d			15 28					15 48				15 58				16 18								
London Victoria 15	⊖ d		15 01									15 31													16 14
Denmark Hill 4	d		15 12									15 42													16 27
Peckham Rye 4	d		15 14									15 44													16 29
Nunhead 4	d		15 16									15 46													16 31
New Cross 4	⊖ d					15 27				15 44				15 57				16 16		16 20	16 25				
St Johns	d					15 29								15 59						16 22					
Lewisham 4	⛴ d	15 20	15 23				15 35			15 48	15 50	15 53			16 05	16 10		16 20		16 27	16 29			16 38	16 41
Blackheath 4	d		15 25				15 37			15 50		15 55			16 07	16 13					16 32			16 41	16 44
Kidbrooke	d		15 28				15 40					15 58			16 10						16 35		←		16 47
Eltham	d		15 32				15 44					16 02			16 14						16 39 →		16 39		16 51
Falconwood	d		15 34				15 46					16 04			16 16								16 41		16 53
Welling	d		15 37				15 49					16 07			16 19								16 44		16 56
Bexleyheath	d		15 39				15 51					16 09			16 21								16 47		16 59
Barnehurst 4	d		15 42				15 54					16 12			16 24								16 50		17 02
Hither Green 4	d	15 23				15 35					15 53			16 05				16 23		16 31					
Lee	d	15 25				15 37					15 55			16 07				16 25		16 33					
Mottingham	d	15 28				15 40					15 58			16 10				16 28		16 36					
New Eltham	d	15 31				15 43					16 01			16 13				16 31		16 39					
Sidcup 4	d	15 34				15 46					16 04			16a17				16 34		16 42					
Albany Park	d	15 36				15 48					16 06							16 36		16 44					
Bexley	d	15 38				15 50					16 08							16 38		16 46					
Crayford	d	15 41				15b58					16 11							16 41		16c58					
Charlton 4	d			15 30				15 44	15 50	15 55			16 00			16 17	16 22		←			16 35		16 45	
Woolwich Dockyard	d			15 32					15 52				16 02				16 25 →		16 25						
Woolwich Arsenal 4	d			15 35				15 49	15 55	16 00			16 05			16 23			16 28			16 41		16 51	
Plumstead	d			15 37					15 57	16a02			16 07						16 30						
Abbey Wood	d			15 41				15 53	16 01				16 11			16 28			16 34			16 46		16 56	
Belvedere	d			15 43					16 03				16 13						16 37						
Erith	d			15 46					16 06				16 16						16 40						
Slade Green 4	d			15 49		16a04			16a09				16 19						16 43	17a08		16 52			
Dartford 4	a	15 45	15 47	15 53			16 01	16 03			16 15	16 17	16 24		16 34	16 36		16 45	16e50			16e59	17 00	17 05	17 09
	d	15 46						16 04			16 16					16 36		16 46						17 06	
Stone Crossing	d	15 49									16 19							16 49							
Greenhithe for Bluewater	d	15 52						16 09			16 22					16 41		16 52						17 11	
Swanscombe	d	15 54									16 24							16 54							
Northfleet	d	15 56									16 26							16 56							
Gravesend 4	d	16a00						16 16			16a30					16 48		17a02						17 18	
Higham	d							16 22								16 54								17 24	
Strood 4	d							16 28								17f04								17 30	
Maidstone West 4	a															17 28								17 59	
Rochester 4	d							16 31								17 07								17 35	
Chatham 4	d							16 34								17 10								17 38	
Gillingham (Kent) 4	a							16 37								17 18								17g43	

For general notes see front of timetable
For details of catering facilities see Directory of Train Operators

A To London Cannon Street (Table 199)
b Arr. 1554
c Arr. 1650
e Until 10 October arr 2 minutes earlier
f Arr. 1701
g Until 10 October arr 1 minute earlier

For details of Bank Holiday service alterations please see first page of Table 195

London → Dartford and Gillingham

Network Diagram - see first page of Table 200

		SE 81	SE 40	SE 81	SE 76	SE 57	SE 65	SE 74	SE 80	SE 42	SE 74	SE 80	SE 77	SE 85 A	SE 76	SE 46	SE 85	SE 64	SE 42	SE 78	SE 87	SE 51	SE 80	SE 77	SE 76
London Charing Cross 4	⊖ d		16 25		16 33			16 37	16 44	16 48					16 55	16 58		17 00	17 10				17 06		17 18
London Waterloo (East) 4	⊖ d		16 28		16 36			16 40	16 47	16 51					16 58	17 01		17 03	17 13				17 09		17 21
London Cannon Street 4	⊖ d	16 28				16 38	16 42						16 52				17 02				17 06	17 10		17 16	
London Bridge 4	⊖ d	16 32	16 33		16 41	16 42	16 46	16 48	16 52	16 56			16 56		17 03	17 06	17 06	17 08			17 10	17 14	17 15	17 20	17 26
Deptford	d	16 38							16 58												17 16		17 22		
Greenwich 4	⛴ d	16 40							17 00								17 13				17 18		17 24		
Maze Hill	d	16 44							17 04												17 22		17 28		
Westcombe Park	d	16 46							17 06												17 24		17 30		
London Victoria 15	⊖ d																			17 00					
Denmark Hill 4	d																			17 09					
Peckham Rye 4	d																			17 13					
Nunhead 4	d																			17 15					
New Cross 4	⊖ d		16 39			16 49							17 02									17 20		17 26	
St Johns	d		16 41			16 51																17 22			
Lewisham 4	⛴ d				16 52	16 53	16 56	16 59					17 06		17 15			17 18		17 24		17 27		17 30	17 35
Blackheath 4	d				16 55		16 59	17 02					17 09		17 18			17 21		17 27				17 33	17 38
Kidbrooke	d				16 58			17 05			←		17 12		17 21					17 30				17 36	17 41
Eltham	d				17 02			17 09			17 09		17 16		17 25					17 34				17 40	17 45
Falconwood	d				17 04			→			17 12		17 18		17 27					17 36				17 42	17 47
Welling	d				17 07						17 14		17 21		17 30					17 39				17 45	17 50
Bexleyheath	d				17 10						17 17		17 24		17 33					17 42				17 48	17 53
Barnehurst 4	d				17 13						17 20		17a30	17 31	17 36					17 45				17a54	17 58
Hither Green 4	d		16 46			16 57										17 16						17 30			
Lee	d		16 48			16 59										17 18						17 32			
Mottingham	d		16 52			17 02										17 22						17 36			
New Eltham	d		16 55			17 05				17 11						17 25			17 31			17 39			
Sidcup 4	d		16 58			17a11				17 14						17a31			17 34			17 42			
Albany Park	d		17 00							17 16									17 36			17 44			
Bexley	d		17 02							17 18									17 38			17 46			
Crayford	d		17 05		17a30					17 21									17 41			17 49			
Charlton 4	d	16 48		←			17 03		17 08			←						17 25			17 28		17 34		
Woolwich Dockyard	d	16 51		16 51					17 11			17 11									17 31		17 37		
Woolwich Arsenal 4	d	→		16 54			17 09		→			17 14					17 24	17 31			17 34		17 40		
Plumstead	d			16 56								17 16									17 36		17 42		
Abbey Wood	d			17 00			17 14					17 20					17 29	17 36			17 40		17 46		
Belvedere	d			17 03								17 23									17 43		17 49		
Erith	d			17 06								17 26									17 46		17 52		
Slade Green 4	d			17 09								17 29		17a35	17a42		17 35				17a51		17 55		18a10
Dartford 4	a		17 09	17b15			17 22			17 25	17 29	17b35					17 39	17 45	17 48	17 52		17 54	18 00		
	d		17 10				17 22			17 26	17 30						17 40	17 46	17 50						
Stone Crossing	d		17 13								17 33								17 53						
Greenhithe for Bluewater	d		17 16				17 27			17 31	17 36						17 45	17 51	17 56						
Swanscombe	d		17 18								17 39								17 59						
Northfleet	d		17 20								17 41								18 01						
Gravesend 4	d		17a26				17 34			17 40	17a46						17 52	17 58	18b07						
Higham	d						17 40			17 49							17 58	18 04							
Strood 4	d						17c47			17 55							18b06	18 14							
Maidstone West 4	a																*18 31*								
Rochester 4	d									18 00								18 22							
Chatham 4	d									18 03								18 25							
Gillingham (Kent) 4	a									18b08								18 29							

For general notes see front of timetable
For details of catering facilities see Directory of Train Operators

A To London Cannon Street
b Until 10 October arr 1 minute earlier
c Until 10 October arr 2 minutes earlier

For details of Bank Holiday service alterations please see first page of Table 195

London → Dartford and Gillingham

Network Diagram - see first page of Table 200

		SE 87	SE 46	SE 65	SE 42	SE 74	SE 78	SE 80	SE 51	SE 80	SE 76	SE 77	SE 65	SE 46	SE 87	SE 42	SE 74	SE 78	SE 51	SE 80	SE 77	SE 70	SE 85	SE 64
London Charing Cross	⊖ d		17 21		17 32	17 25		17 29			17 37			17 43		17 52	17 46			17 54		18 01		18 05
London Waterloo (East)	⊖ d		17 24		17 35	17 28		17 32			17 40			17 46		17 55	17 49			17 57		18 04		18 08
London Cannon Street	⊖ d	17 24		17 26					17 36			17 42	17 46		17 48				17 56		18 02		18 08	
London Bridge	⊖ d	17 28	17 30	17 30				17 38	17 40		17 45	17 46	17 50	17 51	17 52				18 00	18 02	18 06	18 10	18 12	18 14
Deptford	d	17 34						17 44							17 58					18 08				
Greenwich	d	17 36						17 46							18 00					18 10			18 20	
Maze Hill	d	17 40						17 50							18 04					18 14				
Westcombe Park	d	17 42						17 52							18 06					18 16				
London Victoria	⊖ d						17 19											17 41						
Denmark Hill	d						17 28											17 51						
Peckham Rye	d						17 31											17 54						
Nunhead	d						17 33											17 56						
New Cross	⊖ d								17 47			17 52							18 06					
St Johns	d																		18 08					
Lewisham	d			17 38			17b46		17 52		17 54	17 57	18 00					18 06	18 12		18 15	18 20		18 24
Blackheath	d			17 41			17 49				17 57	18 00	18 02					18 09			18 18	18 23		18 27
Kidbrooke	d					17 48	17 52				18 00	18 04					18 08	18 12			18 21	18 26		
Eltham	d					17 52	17 56				18 04	18 08					18 12	18 16			18 25	18 30		
Falconwood	d					17 54	17 58				18 06	18 10					18 14	18 18			18 27	18 32		
Welling	d					17 57	18 01				18 09	18 13					18 17	18 21			18 30	→		
Bexleyheath	d					18 00	18 04				18 12	18 16					18 20	18 24			18 33			
Barnehurst	d					18 03	18 07				18 16	18 20		18a30			18 23	18 27			18 37			
Hither Green	d		17 40						17 55					18 00					18 16					
Lee	d		17 42						17 57					18 02					18 18					
Mottingham	d		17 46						18 01					18 06					18 22					
New Eltham	d		17 49		17 53				18 04					18 09		18 14			18 25					
Sidcup	d		17a55		17 57				18 07					18 12		18 17			18 28					
Albany Park	d				17 59				18 09					18 14		18 19			18 30					
Bexley	d				18 01				18 11					18 16		18 21			18 32					
Crayford	d				18 04				18 14					18a20		18 24			18 35					
Charlton	d	17 48		17 45				17 54		←			18 06		18 10					18 18				18 31
Woolwich Dockyard	d	17 51						17 57 →		17 57					18 13					18 21				
Woolwich Arsenal	d	17 54		17 51						18 00			18 12		18 16					18 24			18 31	18 37
Plumstead	d	17 56								18 02					18 18					18 26				
Abbey Wood	d	18 00		17 56						18 06			18 17		18 22					18 30			18 36	18 42
Belvedere	d	18 03								18 09					18 25					18 32				
Erith	d	18 06								18 12					18 28					18 36				
Slade Green	d	18a11								18 15	18a23	18a27			18a32					18 39	18a43		18 42	
Dartford	a			18 05	18 08	18 12	18 14		18c20	18e22			18 25			18 29	18 32	18 34	18 40	18e46			18 46	18 51
	d			18 06	18 10	18 14							18 26			18 30	18 34						18 48	18 52
Stone Crossing	d					18 17											18 37							18 55
Greenhithe for Bluewater	d			18 11	18 15	18 20							18 31			18c35	18 40						18 53	18 58
Swanscombe	d					18 23											18 43							19 01
Northfleet	d					18 25											18 45							19 03
Gravesend	d			18 18	18f25	18c31							18 38			18 42	18c51						19 00	19c09
Higham	d			18 24	18 33								18 44			18f52							19 06	
Strood	d			18c31	18 39								18c51			18 59							19g14	
Maidstone West	a				*19 02*																		*19 39*	
Rochester	d				18 43											19 02							19 19	
Chatham	d				18 46											19 05							19 22	
Gillingham (Kent)	a				18 50											19c10							19c27	

For general notes see front of timetable
For details of catering facilities see Directory of Train Operators

b Arr. 1743
c Until 10 October arr 1 minute earlier
e Until 10 October arr 2 minutes earlier
f Arr. 4 minutes earlier
g Arr. 1911

For details of Bank Holiday service alterations please see first page of Table 195

London → Dartford and Gillingham

Network Diagram - see first page of Table 200

		SE 46	SE 70	SE 78	SE 42	SE 80	SE 77	SE 51	SE 70	SE 62	SE 44	SE 57	SE 80	SE 70	SE 78	SE 62	SE 80	SE 77	SE 54	SE 80	SE 87	SE 80	SE 70	SE 57	SE 62
London Charing Cross 4	⊖ d	18 08			18 20	18 14			18 25	18 30	18 37		18 34	18 46		18 54	18 56		19 02			19 11	19 17		19 21
London Waterloo (East) 4	⊖ d	18 11			18 23	18 17			18 28	18 33	18 40		18 37	18 49		18 57	18 59		19 05			19 14	19 20		19 24
London Cannon Street 4	⊖ d						18 19	18 22				18 36						19 02			19 10			19 22	
London Bridge 4	⊖ d	18 16				18 22	18 23	18 26	18 34	18 38		18 40	18 42	18 54		19 02	19 04	19 06	19 10		19 14	19 20	19 25	19 26	19 29
Deptford	d					18 28							18 48				19 10				19 20	19 26			
Greenwich 4	d					18 30							18 50				19 12				19 22	19 28			
Maze Hill	d					18 34							18 54				19 16				19 26	19 32			
Westcombe Park	d					18 36							18 56				19 18				19 28	19 34			
London Victoria 15	⊖ d			18 08											18 46										
Denmark Hill 4	d			18 17											18 57										
Peckham Rye 4	d			18 20											19 00										
Nunhead 4	d			18 22											19 02										
New Cross 4	⊖ d							18 32				18 46		19 00				19 12						19 31	
St Johns	d											18 48						19 14						19 33	
Lewisham 4	d			18 29			18 33	18 36	18 44	18 48		18 52		19 04	19 08	19 12		19 17	19 22				19 35		19 38
Blackheath 4	d			18 33			18 37		18 47	18 51				19 07	19 11	19 15		19 19					19 37		19 41
Kidbrooke	d			18 36			18 40		18 50					19 10	19 14			19 22					19 40		
Eltham	d		←	18 40			18 44		18 54					19 14	19 18			19 26					19 44		
Falconwood	d		18 32	18 42			18 46		18 56					19 16	19 20			19 28					19 46		
Welling	d		18 35	18 45			18 49		18 59					19 19	19 23			19 31					19 49		
Bexleyheath	d		18 38	18 48			18 52		19 02					19 22	19 26			19 33					19 51		
Barnehurst 4	d		18 41	18 51			18b58		19 05					19 25	19 29			19a37					19 54		
Hither Green 4	d	18 26						18 40				18 56							19 25					19 37	
Lee	d	18 28			18 38			18 42			18 55	18 58							19 27					19 39	
Mottingham	d	18 32			18 42			18 46			18 58	19 02							19 30					19 42	
New Eltham	d	18 35			18 45			18 49			19 01	19 05							19 33					19 45	
Sidcup 4	d	18a41			18 48			18 52			19 05	19 08							19 36					19 49	
Albany Park	d				18 50			18 54			19 07	19 10							19 38					19 51	
Bexley	d				18 52			18 56			19 09	19 12							19 40					19 53	
Crayford	d				18 55			18 59			19 12	19 15							19 43					19 56	
Charlton 4	d					18 38				18 55			18 58			19 19	19 22			←	19 30	19 36			19 45
Woolwich Dockyard	d					18 41							19 01				19 25			19 25	19 33	19 39			
Woolwich Arsenal 4	d					18 44				19 01			19 04			19 25	→			19 28	19 36	19 42			19 50
Plumstead	d					18 46							19 06							19 30	19 38	19 44			
Abbey Wood	d					18 50				19 06			19 10			19 30				19 34	19 41	19 47			19 55
Belvedere	d					18 53							19 13							19 37	19 44	19 50			
Erith	d					18 56							19 16							19 40	19 47	19 53			
Slade Green 4	d					18 59							19 19							19 43	19a50	19 56		20a04	
Dartford 4	a		18b52	18 57	18 59	19b06		19b06	19b14	19 15	19 18	19 22	19b26	19b34	19 36	19 39			19 47	19 48		20 01	20 03		20 05
	d				19 00					19 16	19 20					19 40			19 48						20 06
Stone Crossing	d										19 23								19 51						
Greenhithe for Bluewater	d				19 05					19 21	19 26					19 45			19 54						20 11
Swanscombe	d										19 29								19 56						
Northfleet	d										19 31								19 58						
Gravesend 4	d				19 12					19 28	19c37					19 52			20a02						20 18
Higham	d				19 18					19 34						19 58									20 24
Strood 4	d				19e28					19f44						20 04									20 30
Maidstone West 4	a				*19 56*											*20 34*									*20 56*
Rochester 4	d				19 32					19 48						20 08									20 33
Chatham 4	d				19 35					19 51						20 11									20 36
Gillingham (Kent) 4	a				19 40					19 55						20c16									20 39

For general notes see front of timetable
For details of catering facilities see Directory of Train Operators

b Until 10 October arr 2 minutes earlier
c Until 10 October arr 1 minute earlier
e Arr. 1923
f Arr. 1939

For details of Bank Holiday service alterations please see first page of Table 195

London → Dartford and Gillingham

Network Diagram - see first page of Table 200

		SE 78	SE 81	SE 77	SE 54	SE 80	SE 70	SE 57	SE 62	SE 78	SE 81	SE 50	SE 80	SE 70	SE 62	SE 81	SE 50	SE 80	SE 70	SE 62	SE 81	SE 50	SE 80	SE 70	SE 62
London Charing Cross 4	⊖ d				19 34	19 41	19 47		19 50			20 04	20 10	20 17	20 20		20 34	20 40	20 47	20 50		21 04	21 10	21 17	21 20
London Waterloo (East) 4	⊖ d				19 37	19 44	19 50		19 53			20 07	20 13	20 20	20 23		20 37	20 43	20 50	20 53		21 07	21 13	21 20	21 23
London Cannon Street 4	⊖ d		19 28	19 36				19 52			20 00					20 30					21 00				
London Bridge 4	⊖ d		19 32	19 40	19 43	19 49	19 55	19 56	19 59		20 04	20 13	20 18	20 25	20 29	20 34	20 43	20 48	20 55	20 59	21 04	21 13	21 18	21 25	21 29
Deptford	d		19 38			19 54					20 10		20 24			20 40		20 54			21 10		21 24		
Greenwich 4	⛴ d		19 40			19 56					20 12		20 26			20 42		20 56			21 12		21 26		
Maze Hill	d		19 44			20 00					20 16		20 30			20 46		21 00			21 16		21 30		
Westcombe Park	d		19 46			20 02					20 18		20 32			20 48		21 02			21 18		21 32		
London Victoria 15	⊖ d	19 16								19 46															
Denmark Hill 4	d	19 27								19 57															
Peckham Rye 4	d	19 31								20 01															
Nunhead 4	d	19 33								20 03															
New Cross 4	⊖ d			19 45	19 48			20 01				20 18		20 30			20 48		21 00			21 18		21 30	
St Johns	d			19 47				20 04																	
Lewisham 4	⛴ d	19 45		19 50	19 53		20 05		20 08	20 15		20 23		20 35	20 38		20 53		21 05	21 08		21 23		21 35	21 38
Blackheath 4	d	19 47		19 52			20 07		20 11	20 17				20 37	20 41				21 07	21 11				21 37	21 41
Kidbrooke	d	19 50		19 55			20 10			20 20				20 40					21 10					21 40	
Eltham	d	19 54		19 59			20 14			20 24				20 44					21 14					21 44	
Falconwood	d	19 56		20 01			20 16			20 26				20 46					21 16					21 46	
Welling	d	19 59		20 04			20 19			20 29				20 49					21 19					21 49	
Bexleyheath	d	20 01		20 06			20 21			20 31				20 51					21 21					21 51	
Barnehurst 4	d	20 04		20a10			20 24			20 34				20 54					21 24					21 54	
Hither Green 4	d				19 57			20 09				20 27					20 57					21 27			
Lee	d				19 59			20 11				20 29					20 59					21 29			
Mottingham	d				20 02			20 14				20 32					21 02					21 32			
New Eltham	d				20 05			20 17				20 35					21 05					21 35			
Sidcup 4	d				20 08			20 20				20 38					21 08					21 38			
Albany Park	d				20 10			20 22				20 40					21 10					21 40			
Bexley	d				20 12			20 24				20 42					21 12					21 42			
Crayford	d				20 15			20 27				20 45					21 15					21 45			
Charlton 4	d		19 50			20 04			20 15		20 20		20 34		20 45	20 50		21 04		21 15	21 20		21 34		21 45
Woolwich Dockyard	d		19 53			20 07					20 23		20 37			20 53		21 07			21 23		21 37		
Woolwich Arsenal 4	d		19 56			20 10			20 20		20 26		20 40		20 50	20 56		21 10		21 20	21 26		21 40		21 50
Plumstead	d		19 58			20 12					20 28		20 42			20 58		21 12			21 28		21 42		
Abbey Wood	d		20 01			20 15			20 25		20 31		20 45		20 55	21 01		21 15		21 25	21 31		21 45		21 55
Belvedere	d		20 04			20 18					20 34		20 48			21 04		21 18			21 34		21 48		
Erith	d		20 07			20 21					20 37		20 51			21 07		21 21			21 37		21 51		
Slade Green 4	d		20 10			20 24		20a34			20 40		20 54			21 10		21 24			21 40		21 54		
Dartford 4	a	20 11	20 15		20 19	20 29	20 31		20 33	20 41	20 45	20 50	20 59	21 01	21 03	21 15	21 22	21 29	21 31	21 33	21 45	21 52	21 59	22 01	22 03
	d				20 20				20 34						21 04					21 34					22 04
Stone Crossing	d				20 23				20 37											21 37					
Greenhithe for Bluewater	d				20 26				20 40						21 09					21 40					22 09
Swanscombe	d				20 28				20 42											21 42					
Northfleet	d				20 30				20 44											21 44					
Gravesend 4	d				20a34				20 50						21 16					21 50					22 16
Higham	d								20 56						21 22					21 56					22 22
Strood 4	d								21b04						21 28					22 02					22 28
Maidstone West 4	a								*21 30*						*21 56*										*22 56*
Rochester 4	d								21 09						21 31					22 07					22 31
Chatham 4	d								21 12						21 34					22 09					22 34
Gillingham (Kent) 4	a								21 17						21 37					22 13					22 37

For general notes see front of timetable
For details of catering facilities see Directory of Train Operators

b Arr. 2101

For details of Bank Holiday service alterations please see first page of Table 195

London → Dartford and Gillingham

Network Diagram - see first page of Table 200

Station		SE 61 A	SE 81	SE 50	SE 80	SE 70	SE 62	SE 81	SE 50	SE 80	SE 70	SE 62	SE 50	SE 80	SE 70	SE 62	SE 50	SE 80	SE 70	SE 62	SE 50	SE 80	SE 70
London Charing Cross 4	⊖ d			21 34	21 40	21 47	21 50		22 04	22 10	22 17	22 20	22 34	22 40	22 47	22 50	23 04	23 10	23 17	23 20	23 34	23 40	23 47
London Waterloo (East) 4	⊖ d			21 37	21 43	21 50	21 53		22 07	22 13	22 20	22 23	22 37	22 43	22 50	22 53	23 07	23 13	23 20	23 23	23 37	23 43	23 50
London Cannon Street 4	⊖ d																						
London Bridge 4	⊖ d		21 34	21 43	21 48	21 55	21 59	22 04	22 13	22 18	22 25	22 29	22 43	22 48	22 55	22 59	23 13	23 18	23 25	23 29	23 43	23 48	23 55
Deptford	d		21 40		21 54			22 10		22 24				22 54				23 24				23 54	
Greenwich 4	d		21 42		21 56			22 12		22 26				22 56				23 26				23 56	
Maze Hill	d		21 46		22 00			22 16		22 30				23 00				23 30				00 01	
Westcombe Park	d		21 48		22 02			22 18		22 32				23 02				23 32				00 02	
London Victoria 15	⊖ d																						
Denmark Hill 4	d																						
Peckham Rye 4	d																						
Nunhead 4	d																						
New Cross 4	⊖ d			21 48		22 00			22 18		22 30		22 48		23 00		23 18		23 30		23 48		00 01
St Johns	d																						
Lewisham 4	d			21 53		22 05	22 08		22 23		22 35	22 38	22 53		23 05	23 08	23 23		23 35	23 38	23 53		00 05
Blackheath 4	d					22 07	22 11				22 37	22 41			23 07	23 11			23 37	23 41			00 07
Kidbrooke	d					22 10					22 40				23 10				23 40				00 10
Eltham	d					22 14					22 44				23 14				23 44				00 14
Falconwood	d					22 16					22 46				23 16				23 46				00 16
Welling	d					22 19					22 49				23 19				23 49				00 19
Bexleyheath	d					22 21					22 51				23 21				23 51				00 21
Barnehurst 4	d					22 24					22 54				23 24				23 54				00 24
Hither Green 4	d			21 57					22 27				22 57				23 27				23 57		
Lee	d			21 59					22 29				22 59				23 29				23 59		
Mottingham	d			22 02					22 32				23 02				23 32				00 02		
New Eltham	d			22 05					22 35				23 05				23 35				00 05		
Sidcup 4	d			22 08					22 38				23 08				23 38				00 08		
Albany Park	d			22 10					22 40				23 10				23 40				00 10		
Bexley	d			22 12					22 42				23 12				23 42				00 12		
Crayford	d			22 15					22 45				23 15				23 45				00 15		
Charlton 4	d		21 50		22 04		22 15	22 20		22 34		22 45		23 04		23 15		23 34		23 45		00 04	
Woolwich Dockyard	d		21 53		22 07			22 23		22 37				23 07				23 37				00 07	
Woolwich Arsenal 4	d		21 56		22 10		22 20	22 26		22 40		22 50		23 10		23 20		23 40		23 50		00 10	
Plumstead	d		21 58		22 12			22 28		22 42				23 12				23 42				00 12	
Abbey Wood	d		22 01		22 15		22 25	22 31		22 45		22 55		23 15		23 25		23 45		23 55		00 15	
Belvedere	d		22 04		22 18			22 34		22 48				23 18				23 48				00 18	
Erith	d		22 07		22 21			22 37		22 51				23 21				23 51				00 21	
Slade Green 4	d		22 10		22 24			22 40		22 54				23 24				23 54				00 24	
Dartford 4	a		22 15	22 22	22 29	22 31	22 33	22 45	22 50	22 59	23 01	23 03	23 20	23 29	23 31	23 33	23 50	23 59	00 01	00 04	00 20	00 29	00 31
	d						22 34					23 04				23 34				00 04			
Stone Crossing	d						22 37									23 37				00 08			
Greenhithe for Bluewater	d						22 40					23 09				23 40				00 10			
Swanscombe	d						22 42									23 42				00 12			
Northfleet	d						22 44									23 44				00 14			
Gravesend 4	d						22 50					23 16				23 50				00 20			
Higham	d						22 56					23 22				23 56				00 26			
Strood 4	d	22 46					23 02					23 28				00 02				00 32			
Maidstone West 4	a																						
Rochester 4	d	22 49					23 07					23 31				00 07				00 39			
Chatham 4	d	22 51					23 09					23 34				00 09				00 42			
Gillingham (Kent) 4	a	22 55					23 13					23 37				00 13				00 45			

For general notes see front of timetable
For details of catering facilities see Directory of Train Operators

A From Paddock Wood (Table 209)

Saturdays

For details of Bank Holiday service alterations please see first page of Table 195

London → Dartford and Gillingham

Network Diagram - see first page of Table 200

		SE	SE	SE	SE	SE	SE	SE	SE	SE	SE	SE	SE	SE	SE	SE	SE	SE	SE	SE	SE	SE	SE
		62	62	50	80	70	50	62	20	52	54	80	70	80	62	54	80	70	62	54	80	70	62
									1 A														
London Charing Cross 4	⊖ d	22p50	23p20	23p34	23p40	23p47	00 04	00 14		05 04	05 34	05 40	05 47		05 50	06 04	06 10	06 17	06 20	06 34	06 40	06 47	06 50
London Waterloo (East) 4	⊖ d	22p53	23p23	23p37	23p43	23p50	00 07	00 17		05 07	05 37	05 43	05 50		05 53	06 07	06 13	06 20	06 23	06 37	06 43	06 50	06 53
London Cannon Street 4	⊖ d																						
London Bridge 4	⊖ d	22p59	23p29	23p43	23p48	23p55	00 13	00 23		05 13	05 43	05 48	05 55		05 59	06 13	06 18	06 25	06 29	06 43	06 48	06 55	06 59
Deptford	d				23p54							05 54					06 24				06 54		
Greenwich 4	d				23p56							05 56					06 26				06 56		
Maze Hill	d				00 01							06 00					06 30				07 00		
Westcombe Park	d				00 02							06 02					06 32				07 02		
London Victoria 15	⊖ d																						
Denmark Hill 4	d																						
Peckham Rye 4	d																						
Nunhead 4	d																						
New Cross 4	⊖ d			23p48		00 01	00 18	00 28		05 18	05 48					06 18				06 48			
St Johns	d																						
Lewisham 4	d	23p08	23p38	23p53		00 05	00 23	00 33		05 23	05 53		06 05		06 07	06 23		06 35	06 37	06 53		07 05	07 07
Blackheath 4	d	23p11	23p41			00 07		00 36					06 07		06 09			06 38	06 40			07 08	07 10
Kidbrooke	d					00 10							06 10					06 41				07 11	
Eltham	d					00 14							06 14					06 44				07 14	
Falconwood	d					00 16							06 16					06 47				07 17	
Welling	d					00 19							06 19					06 49				07 19	
Bexleyheath	d					00 21							06 21					06 52				07 22	
Barnehurst 4	d					00 24							06 24					06 54				07 24	
Hither Green 4	d			23p57			00 27			05 27	05 57					06 27				06 57			
Lee	d			23p59			00 29			05 29	05 59					06 29				06 59			
Mottingham	d			00 02			00 32			05 32	06 02					06 32				07 02			
New Eltham	d			00 05			00 35			05 35	06 05					06 35				07 05			
Sidcup 4	d			00 08			00 38			05 38	06 08					06 38				07 08			
Albany Park	d			00 10			00 40			05 40	06 10					06 40				07 10			
Bexley	d			00 12			00 42			05 42	06 12					06 42				07 12			
Crayford	d			00 15			00 45			05 45	06 16					06 46				07 16			
Charlton 4	d	23p15	23p45		00 04			00 40				06 04		←	06 14		06 34		06 44		07 04		07 14
Woolwich Dockyard	d				00 07							06 07 →		06 07			06 37				07 07		
Woolwich Arsenal 4	d	23p20	23p50		00 10			00 45						06 10	06 19		06 40		06 49		07 10		07 19
Plumstead	d				00 12			00 47						06 12			06 42				07 12		
Abbey Wood	d	23p25	23p55		00 15			00 50						06 15	06 23		06 45		06 53		07 15		07 23
Belvedere	d				00 18			00 53						06 18			06 48				07 18		
Erith	d				00 21			00 56						06 21			06 51				07 21		
Slade Green 4	d				00 24			00 58						06 26			06 54				07 24		
Dartford 4	a	23p33	00 04	00 20	00 29	00 31	00 50	01 03		05 49	06 20		06 29	06 31	06 34	06 50	06 59	07 01	07 03	07 20	07 28	07 31	07 33
	d	23p34	00 04					01 04	05 17	05 49	06 21				06 34	06 51			07 04	07 21			07 34
Stone Crossing	d	23p37	00 08								06 24					06 54				07 24			
Greenhithe for Bluewater	d	23p40	00 10					01 09	05 22	05 54	06 27				06 39	06 57			07 09	07 27			07 39
Swanscombe	d	23p42	00 12								06 29					06 59				07 29			
Northfleet	d	23p44	00 14								06 31					07 01				07 31			
Gravesend 4	d	23p50	00 20					01 16	05 29	06 01	06a35				06 46	07a05			07 16	07a35			07 46
Higham	d	23p56	00 26					01 22	05 35	06 07					06 52				07 22				07 52
Strood 4	d	00 02	00 32					01 28	05 40	06 12					06 58				07 28				07 58
Maidstone West 4	a								*06 25*	*06 53*					*07 24*				*07 54*				*08 24*
Rochester 4	d	00 07	00 39					01 31	05 44	06 16					07 01				07 31				08 01
Chatham 4	d	00 09	00 42					01 34	05 46	06 19					07 04				07 34				08 04
Gillingham (Kent) 4	a	00 13	00 45					01 37	05 50	06 22					07 07				07 37				08 07

For general notes see front of timetable
For details of catering facilities see Directory of Train Operators

A To Dover Priory (Table 212)

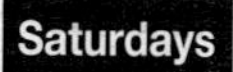

For details of Bank Holiday service alterations please see first page of Table 195

London → Dartford and Gillingham

Network Diagram - see first page of Table 200

Station		SE 54	SE 80	SE 70	SE 62	SE 54	SE 80	SE 70	SE 62	SE 54	SE 78	SE 81
London Charing Cross 4	⊖ d	07 04	07 10	07 17	07 20	07 34	07 42	07 47	07 50	08 02		
London Waterloo (East) 4	⊖ d	07 07	07 13	07 20	07 23	07 37	07 45	07 50	07 53	08 05		
London Cannon Street 4	⊖ d											08 10
London Bridge 4	⊖ d	07 13	07 18	07 25	07 29	07 43	07 50	07 55	07 59	08 10		08 14
Deptford	d		07 24				07 55					08 20
Greenwich 4	⛴ d		07 26				07 57					08 22
Maze Hill	d		07 30				08 01					08 26
Westcombe Park	d		07 32				08 03					08 28
London Victoria 15	⊖ d										08 01	
Denmark Hill 4	d										08 12	
Peckham Rye 4	d										08 14	
Nunhead 4	d										08 16	
New Cross 4	⊖ d	07 18				07 48				08 15		
St Johns	d											
Lewisham 4	⛴ d	07 23		07 35	07 37	07 53		08 05	08 07	08 20	08 23	
Blackheath 4	d			07 38	07 40			08 08	08 10		08 25	
Kidbrooke	d			07 41				08 11			08 28	
Eltham	d			07 44				08 14			08 32	
Falconwood	d			07 47				08 17			08 34	
Welling	d			07 49				08 19			08 37	
Bexleyheath	d			07 52				08 22			08 39	
Barnehurst 4	d			07 54				08 24			08 42	
Hither Green 4	d	07 27				07 57				08 23		
Lee	d	07 29				07 59				08 25		
Mottingham	d	07 32				08 02				08 28		
New Eltham	d	07 35				08 05				08 31		
Sidcup 4	d	07 38				08 08				08 34		
Albany Park	d	07 40				08 10				08 36		
Bexley	d	07 42				08 12				08 38		
Crayford	d	07 46				08 16				08 41		
Charlton 4	d		07 34		07 44		08 05		08 14			08 30
Woolwich Dockyard	d		07 37				08 08					08 32
Woolwich Arsenal 4	d		07 40		07 49		08 11		08 19			08 35
Plumstead	d		07 42				08 13					08 37
Abbey Wood	d		07 45		07 53		08 16		08 23			08 41
Belvedere	d		07 48				08 19					08 43
Erith	d		07 51				08 22					08 46
Slade Green 4	d		07 54				08 24					08 49
Dartford 4	a	07 50	07 59	08 00	08 03	08 20	08 28	08 30	08 33	08 45	08 47	08 53
	d	07 51			08 04	08 21			08 34	08 46		
Stone Crossing	d	07 54				08 24				08 49		
Greenhithe for Bluewater	d	07 57			08 09	08 27			08 39	08 52		
Swanscombe	d	07 59				08 29				08 54		
Northfleet	d	08 01				08 31				08 56		
Gravesend 4	d	08a05			08 16	08a35			08 46	09a00		
Higham	d				08 22				08 52			
Strood 4	d				08 28				08 58			
Maidstone West 4	a				*08 54*				*09 24*			
Rochester 4	d				08 31				09 01			
Chatham 4	d				08 34				09 04			
Gillingham (Kent) 4	a				08 37				09 07			

Station		SE 70	SE 62	SE 47 A	SE 54	SE 78	SE 81	SE 47 A	SE 70	SE 82	SE 47 A	SE 67
London Charing Cross 4	⊖ d	08 17	08 20		08 32				08 47	08 50		
London Waterloo (East) 4	⊖ d	08 20	08 23		08 35				08 50	08 53		
London Cannon Street 4	⊖ d			08 30			08 40	08 48			09 00	09 04
London Bridge 4	⊖ d	08 25	08 29	08 34	08 40		08 44	08 52	08 55	08 59	09 04	09 08
Deptford	d			08 40			08 50				09 10	
Greenwich 4	⛴ d			08 42			08 52			09 07	09 12	
Maze Hill	d			08 46			08 56				09 16	
Westcombe Park	d			08 48			08 58				09 18	
London Victoria 15	⊖ d					08 31						
Denmark Hill 4	d					08 42						
Peckham Rye 4	d					08 44						
Nunhead 4	d					08 46						
New Cross 4	⊖ d				08 45			08 57				09 14
St Johns	d							08 59				
Lewisham 4	⛴ d	08 33	08 37		08 50	08 53			09 06			09 18
Blackheath 4	d	08 38	08 40			08 55			09 08			09 20
Kidbrooke	d	08 41				08 58			09 11			
Eltham	d	08 45				09 02			09 15			
Falconwood	d	08 47				09 04			09 17			
Welling	d	08 50				09 07			09 20			
Bexleyheath	d	08 52				09 09			09 22			
Barnehurst 4	d	08 55				09 12			09 25			
Hither Green 4	d				08 53			09 05				
Lee	d				08 55			09 07				
Mottingham	d				08 58			09 10				
New Eltham	d				09 01			09 13				
Sidcup 4	d				09 04			09 16				
Albany Park	d				09 06			09 18				
Bexley	d				09 08			09 20				
Crayford	d				09 11			09b28				
Charlton 4	d		08 44	08 50			09 00			09 14	09 20	09 25
Woolwich Dockyard	d			08 52			09 02				09 22	
Woolwich Arsenal 4	d		08 49	08 55			09 05			09 19	09 25	09 30
Plumstead	d			08 57			09 07				09 27	09a32
Abbey Wood	d		08 53	09 01			09 11			09 23	09 31	
Belvedere	d			09 03			09 13				09 33	
Erith	d			09 06			09 16				09 36	
Slade Green 4	d			09a09			09 19	09a34			09a39	
Dartford 4	a	09 00	09 03		09 15	09 17	09 23		09 30	09 33		
	d		09 04		09 16					09 34		
Stone Crossing	d				09 19							
Greenhithe for Bluewater	d		09 09		09 22					09 39		
Swanscombe	d				09 24							
Northfleet	d				09 26							
Gravesend 4	d		09 16		09a30					09 46		
Higham	d		09 22							09 52		
Strood 4	d		09 28							09 58		
Maidstone West 4	a		*09 54*							*10 24*		
Rochester 4	d		09 31							10 01		
Chatham 4	d		09 34							10 04		
Gillingham (Kent) 4	a		09 37							10 07		

For general notes see front of timetable
For details of catering facilities see Directory of Train Operators

A To London Cannon Street (Table 199)
b Arr. 0924

For details of Bank Holiday service alterations please see first page of Table 195

London → Dartford and Gillingham

Network Diagram - see first page of Table 200

		SE 54	SE 78	SE 81	SE 47 A		SE 70	SE 82	SE 47 A	SE 67	SE 54	SE 78	SE 81	SE 47 A	SE 70	SE 82	SE 87 A	SE 67	SE 54	SE 78	SE 81	SE 47 A		SE 70
London Charing Cross 4	⊖ d	09 02					09 17	09 20			09 32				09 47	09 50			10 02					16 17
London Waterloo (East) 4	⊖ d	09 05					09 20	09 23			09 35				09 50	09 53			10 05					16 20
London Cannon Street 4	⊖ d			09 10	09 18				09 30	09 34			09 40	09 48			10 00	10 04			10 10	10 18		
London Bridge 4	⊖ d	09 10		09 14	09 22		09 25	09 29	09 34	09 38	09 40		09 44	09 52	09 55	09 59	10 04	10 08	10 10		10 14	10 22		16 25
Deptford	d			09 20					09 40				09 50				10 10				10 20			
Greenwich 4	🚈 d			09 22				09 37	09 42				09 52			10 07	10 12				10 22			
Maze Hill	d			09 26					09 46				09 56				10 16				10 26			
Westcombe Park	d			09 28					09 48				09 58				10 18				10 28			
London Victoria 15	⊖ d		09 01									09 31								10 01				
Denmark Hill 4	d		09 12									09 42								10 12				
Peckham Rye 4	d		09 14									09 44								10 14				
Nunhead 4	d		09 16									09 46								10 16				
New Cross 4	⊖ d				09 27					09 44				09 57				10 14				10 27		
St Johns	d				09 29									09 59								10 29		
Lewisham 4	🚈 d	09 20	09 23				09 36			09 48	09 50	09 53			10 06			10 18	10 20	10 23				16 36
Blackheath 4	d		09 25				09 38			09 50		09 55			10 08			10 20		10 25				16 38
Kidbrooke	d		09 28				09 41					09 58			10 11					10 28				16 41
Eltham	d		09 32				09 45					10 02			10 15					10 32			and at	16 45
Falconwood	d		09 34				09 47					10 04			10 17					10 34				16 47
Welling	d		09 37				09 50					10 07			10 20					10 37			the same	16 50
Bexleyheath	d		09 39				09 52					10 09			10 22					10 39				16 52
Barnehurst 4	d		09 42				09 55					10 12			10 25					10 42			minutes	16 55
Hither Green 4	d	09 23			09 35						09 53			10 05					10 23			10 35	past	
Lee	d	09 25			09 37						09 55			10 07					10 25			10 37		
Mottingham	d	09 28			09 40						09 58			10 10					10 28			10 40	each	
New Eltham	d	09 31			09 43						10 01			10 13					10 31			10 43		
Sidcup 4	d	09 34			09 46						10 04			10 16					10 34			10 46	hour until	
Albany Park	d	09 36			09 48						10 06			10 18					10 36			10 48		
Bexley	d	09 38			09 50						10 08			10 20					10 38			10 50		
Crayford	d	09 41			09b58						10 11			10c28					10 41			10e58		
Charlton 4	d			09 30				09 44	09 50	09 55			10 00			10 14	10 20	10 25			10 30			
Woolwich Dockyard	d			09 32					09 52				10 02				10 22				10 32			
Woolwich Arsenal 4	d			09 35				09 49	09 55	10 00			10 05			10 19	10 25	10 30			10 35			
Plumstead	d			09 37					09 57	10a02			10 07				10 27	10a32			10 37			
Abbey Wood	d			09 41				09 53	10 01				10 11			10 23	10 31				10 41			
Belvedere	d			09 43					10 03				10 13				10 33				10 43			
Erith	d			09 46					10 06				10 16				10 36				10 46			
Slade Green 4	d			09 49	10a04				10a09				10 19	10a34			10a39				10 49	11a04		
Dartford 4	a	09 45	09 47	09 53			10 00	10 03			10 15	10 17	10 23		10 30	10 33			10 45	10 47	10 53			17 00
	d	09 46						10 04			10 16					10 34			10 46					
Stone Crossing	d	09 49									10 19								10 49					
Greenhithe for Bluewater	d	09 52						10 09			10 22					10 39			10 52					
Swanscombe	d	09 54									10 24								10 54					
Northfleet	d	09 56									10 26								10 56					
Gravesend 4	d	10a00						10 16			10a30					10 46			11a00					
Higham	d							10 22								10 52								
Strood 4	d							10 28								10 58								
Maidstone West 4	a							*10 54*								*11 24*								
Rochester 4	d							10 31								11 01								
Chatham 4	d							10 34								11 04								
Gillingham (Kent) 4	a							10 37								11 07								

For general notes see front of timetable
For details of catering facilities see Directory of Train Operators

A To London Cannon Street (Table 199)
b Arr. 0954
c Arr. 1024
e Arr. 1054

Table 200

For details of Bank Holiday service alterations please see first page of Table 195

London → Dartford and Gillingham

Network Diagram - see first page of Table 200

Station		SE 82	SE 87 A	SE 67	SE 54	SE 78	SE 81	SE 47 A	SE 70	SE 82	SE 47 A	SE 67	SE 54	SE 78	SE 81	SE 47	SE 70	SE 82	SE 87	SE 67	SE 54	SE 78
London Charing Cross 4	⊖ d	16 20			16 32				16 47	16 50			17 02				17 17	17 20			17 32	
London Waterloo (East) 4	⊖ d	16 23			16 35				16 50	16 53			17 05				17 20	17 23			17 35	
London Cannon Street 4	⊖ d		16 30	16 34			16 40	16 48			17 00	17 04			17 10	17 18			17 30	17 34		
London Bridge 4	⊖ d	16 29	16 34	16 38	16 40		16 44	16 52	16 55	16 59	17 04	17 08	17 10		17 14	17 22	17 25	17 29	17 34	17 38	17 40	
Deptford	d		16 40				16 50				17 10				17 20				17 40			
Greenwich 4	d	16 37	16 42				16 52			17 07	17 12				17 22			17 37	17 42			
Maze Hill	d		16 46				16 56				17 16				17 26				17 46			
Westcombe Park	d		16 48				16 58				17 18				17 28				17 48			
London Victoria 15	⊖ d					16 31								17 01								17 31
Denmark Hill 4	d					16 42								17 12								17 42
Peckham Rye 4	d					16 44								17 14								17 44
Nunhead 4	d					16 46								17 16								17 46
New Cross 4	⊖ d			16 44				16 57				17 14				17 27				17 44		
St Johns	d							16 59								17 29						
Lewisham 4	d			16 48	16 50	16 53			17 06			17 18	17 20	17 23			17 36			17 48	17 50	17 53
Blackheath 4	d			16 50		16 55			17 08			17 20		17 25			17 38			17 50		17 55
Kidbrooke	d					16 58			17 11					17 28			17 41					17 58
Eltham	d					17 02			17 15					17 32			17 45					18 02
Falconwood	d					17 04			17 17					17 34			17 47					18 04
Welling	d					17 07			17 20					17 37			17 50					18 07
Bexleyheath	d					17 09			17 22					17 39			17 52					18 09
Barnehurst 4	d					17 12			17 25					17 42			17 55					18 12
Hither Green 4	d				16 53			17 05					17 23			17 35					17 53	
Lee	d				16 55			17 07					17 25			17 37					17 55	
Mottingham	d				16 58			17 10					17 28			17 40					17 58	
New Eltham	d				17 01			17 13					17 31			17 43					18 01	
Sidcup 4	d				17 04			17 16					17 34			17 46					18 04	
Albany Park	d				17 06			17 18					17 36			17 48					18 06	
Bexley	d				17 08			17 20					17 38			17 50					18 08	
Crayford	d				17 11			17b28					17 41			17a54					18 11	
Charlton 4	d	16 44	16 50	16 55			17 00			17 14	17 20	17 25			17 30			17 44	17 50	17 55		
Woolwich Dockyard	d		16 52				17 02				17 22				17 32				17 52			
Woolwich Arsenal 4	d	16 49	16 55	17 00			17 05			17 19	17 25	17 30			17 35			17 49	17 55	18 00		
Plumstead	d		16 57	17a02			17 07				17 27	17a32			17 37				17 57	18a02		
Abbey Wood	d	16 53	17 01				17 11			17 23	17 31				17 41			17 53	18 01			
Belvedere	d		17 03				17 13				17 33				17 43				18 03			
Erith	d		17 06				17 16				17 36				17 46				18 06			
Slade Green 4	d		17a09				17 19	17a34			17a39				17 49				18a09			
Dartford 4	a	17 03			17 15	17 17	17 23		17 30	17 33			17 45	17 47	17 53		18 00	18 03			18 15	18 17
	d	17 04			17 16					17 34			17 46					18 04			18 16	
Stone Crossing	d				17 19								17 49								18 19	
Greenhithe for Bluewater	d	17 09			17 22					17 39			17 52					18 09			18 22	
Swanscombe	d				17 24								17 54								18 24	
Northfleet	d				17 26								17 56								18 26	
Gravesend 4	d	17 16			17a30					17 46			18a00					18 16			18a30	
Higham	d	17 22								17 52								18 22				
Strood 4	d	17 28								17 58								18 28				
Maidstone West 4	a	*17 54*								*18 24*								*18 54*				
Rochester 4	d	17 31								18 01								18 31				
Chatham 4	d	17 34								18 04								18 34				
Gillingham (Kent) 4	a	17 37								18 07								18 37				

For general notes see front of timetable
For details of catering facilities see Directory of Train Operators

A To London Cannon Street (Table 199)
b Arr. 1724

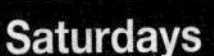

For details of Bank Holiday service alterations please see first page of Table 195

London → Dartford and Gillingham

Network Diagram - see first page of Table 200

		SE 81	SE 47	SE 70	SE 82	SE 87	SE 67	SE 54	SE 78	SE 81		SE 47	SE 70	SE 62	SE 87	SE 54	SE 78	SE 81	SE 47	SE 70		SE 62	SE 87	SE 54	SE 78
London Charing Cross 4	⊖ d			17 47	17 50			18 02					18 17	18 20		18 32				18 47		18 50		19 04	
London Waterloo (East) 4	⊖ d			17 50	17 53			18 05					18 20	18 23		18 35				18 50		18 53		19 07	
London Cannon Street 4	⊖ d	17 40	17 48			18 00	18 04			18 10		18 18			18 30			18 40	18 48				19 00		
London Bridge 4	⊖ d	17 44	17 52	17 55	17 59	18 04	18 08	18 10		18 14		18 22	18 25	18 29	18 34	18 40		18 44	18 52	18 55		18 59	19 04	19 13	
Deptford	d	17 50				18 10				18 20					18 40			18 50					19 10		
Greenwich 4	d	17 52			18 07	18 12				18 22					18 42			18 52					19 12		
Maze Hill	d	17 56				18 16				18 26					18 46			18 56					19 16		
Westcombe Park	d	17 58				18 18				18 28					18 48			18 58					19 18		
London Victoria 15	⊖ d								18 01								18 31								19 01
Denmark Hill 4	d								18 12								18 42								19 12
Peckham Rye 4	d								18 14								18 44								19 14
Nunhead 4	d								18 16								18 46								19 16
New Cross 4	⊖ d		17 57				18 14					18 27							18 57						
St Johns	d		17 59									18 29							18 59						
Lewisham 4	d			18 06			18 18	18 20	18 23				18 33	18 37		18 50	18 53			19 05		19 08		19 21	19 23
Blackheath 4	d			18 08			18 20		18 25				18 36	18 39			18 55			19 09		19 10			19 25
Kidbrooke	d			18 11					18 28				18 41				18 58			19 12					19 28
Eltham	d			18 15					18 32				18 45				19 02			19 15					19 32
Falconwood	d			18 17					18 34				18 47				19 04			19 17					19 34
Welling	d			18 20					18 37				18 50				19 07			19 20					19 37
Bexleyheath	d			18 22					18 39				18 52				19 09			19 22					19 39
Barnehurst 4	d			18 25					18 42				18 55				19 12			19 25					19 42
Hither Green 4	d		18 05					18 23				18 35				18 53			19 05					19 24	
Lee	d		18 07					18 25				18 37				18 55			19 07					19 26	
Mottingham	d		18 10					18 28				18 40				18 58			19 10					19 29	
New Eltham	d		18 13					18 31				18 43				19 01			19 13					19 32	
Sidcup 4	d		18 16					18 34				18 46				19 04			19 16					19 35	
Albany Park	d		18 18					18 36				18 48				19 06			19 18					19 37	
Bexley	d		18 20					18 38				18 50				19 08			19 20					19 39	
Crayford	d		18a24					18 41				18a54				19 11			19a24					19 42	
Charlton 4	d	18 00			18 14	18 20	18 25			18 30				18 44	18 50			19 00				19 14	19 20		
Woolwich Dockyard	d	18 02				18 22				18 32					18 52			19 02					19 22		
Woolwich Arsenal 4	d	18 05			18 19	18 25	18 30			18 35				18 49	18 55			19 05				19 19	19 25		
Plumstead	d	18 07				18 27	18a32			18 37					18 57			19 07					19 27		
Abbey Wood	d	18 11			18 23	18 31				18 41				18 53	19 01			19 11				19 23	19 31		
Belvedere	d	18 13				18 33				18 43					19 03			19 13					19 33		
Erith	d	18 16				18 36				18 46					19 06			19 16					19 36		
Slade Green 4	d	18 19				18a39				18 49					19a09			19 19					19a39		
Dartford 4	a	18 23		18 30	18 33			18 45	18 48	18 55			19 00	19 03		19 15	19 17	19 25		19 31		19 33		19 46	19 48
	d				18 34			18 46						19 04		19 16						19 34		19 47	
Stone Crossing	d							18 49								19 19								19 50	
Greenhithe for Bluewater	d				18 39			18 52						19 09		19 22						19 39		19 53	
Swanscombe	d							18 54								19 24								19 55	
Northfleet	d							18 56								19 26								19 57	
Gravesend 4	d				18 46			19a00						19 16		19a30						19 46		20a01	
Higham	d				18 52									19 22								19 52			
Strood 4	d				18 58									19 28								19 58			
Maidstone West 4	a				*19 24*									*19 54*								*20 24*			
Rochester 4	d				19 01									19 31								20 01			
Chatham 4	d				19 04									19 34								20 04			
Gillingham (Kent) 4	a				19 07									19 37								20 07			

For general notes see front of timetable
For details of catering facilities see Directory of Train Operators

Table 200

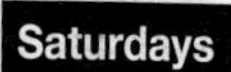

For details of Bank Holiday service alterations please see first page of Table 195

London → Dartford and Gillingham

Network Diagram - see first page of Table 200

		SE 81	SE 70	SE 62	SE 50	SE 78	SE 50	SE 80	SE 70	SE 62	SE 50	SE 80	SE 70	SE 62	SE 50	SE 80	SE 70	SE 62	SE 50	SE 80	SE 70	SE 62	SE 50
London Charing Cross 4	⊖ d	19 10	19 17	19 20	19 34			19 40	19 47	19 50	20 04	20 10	20 17	20 20	20 34	20 40	20 47	20 50	21 04	21 10	21 17	21 20	21 34
London Waterloo (East) 4	⊖ d	19 13	19 20	19 23	19 37			19 43	19 50	19 53	20 07	20 13	20 20	20 23	20 37	20 43	20 50	20 53	21 07	21 13	21 20	21 23	21 37
London Cannon Street 4	⊖ d																						
London Bridge 4	⊖ d	19 18	19 25	19 29	19 43			19 48	19 55	19 59	20 13	20 18	20 25	20 29	20 43	20 48	20 55	20 59	21 13	21 18	21 25	21 29	21 43
Deptford	d	19 24						19 54				20 24				20 54				21 24			
Greenwich 4	⛴ d	19 26						19 56				20 26				20 56				21 26			
Maze Hill	d	19 30						20 00				20 30				21 00				21 30			
Westcombe Park	d	19 32						20 02				20 32				21 02				21 32			
London Victoria 15	⊖ d					19 31																	
Denmark Hill 4	d					19 42																	
Peckham Rye 4	d					19 44																	
Nunhead 4	d					19 46																	
New Cross 4	⊖ d				19 48				20 00		20 18		20 30		20 48		21 00		21 18		21 30		21 48
St Johns	d																						
Lewisham 4	⛴ d		19 35	19 37	19 53	19 54			20 05	20 07	20 23		20 35	20 37	20 53		21 05	21 07	21 23		21 35	21 37	21 53
Blackheath 4	d		19 37	19 39		19 56			20 07	20 09			20 37	20 39			21 07	21 09			21 37	21 39	
Kidbrooke	d		19 40			19 59			20 10				20 40				21 10				21 40		
Eltham	d		19 44			20 03			20 14				20 44				21 14				21 44		
Falconwood	d		19 46			20 05			20 16				20 46				21 16				21 46		
Welling	d		19 49			20 08			20 19				20 49				21 19				21 49		
Bexleyheath	d		19 51			20 10			20 21				20 51				21 21				21 51		
Barnehurst 4	d		19 54			20 13			20 24				20 54				21 24				21 54		
Hither Green 4	d				19 57						20 27				20 57				21 27				21 57
Lee	d				19 59						20 29				20 59				21 29				21 59
Mottingham	d				20 02		←				20 32				21 02				21 32				22 02
New Eltham	d				20 05 →		20 05				20 35				21 05				21 35				22 05
Sidcup 4	d						20 08				20 38				21 08				21 38				22 08
Albany Park	d						20 10				20 40				21 10				21 40				22 10
Bexley	d						20 12				20 42				21 12				21 42				22 12
Crayford	d						20 15				20 45				21 15				21 45				22 15
Charlton 4	d	19 34		19 44				20 04		20 14		20 34		20 44		21 04		21 14		21 34		21 44	
Woolwich Dockyard	d	19 37						20 07				20 37				21 07				21 37			
Woolwich Arsenal 4	d	19 40		19 49				20 10		20 19		20 40		20 49		21 10		21 19		21 40		21 49	
Plumstead	d	19 42						20 12				20 42				21 12				21 42			
Abbey Wood	d	19 45		19 53				20 15		20 23		20 45		20 53		21 15		21 23		21 45		21 53	
Belvedere	d	19 48						20 18				20 48				21 18				21 48			
Erith	d	19 51						20 21				20 51				21 21				21 51			
Slade Green 4	d	19 54						20 24				20 54				21 24				21 54			
Dartford 4	a	19 59	20 01	20 03		20 18	20 20	20 29	20 31	20 33	20 50	20 59	21 01	21 03	21 20	21 29	21 31	21 33	21 50	21 59	22 01	22 03	22 20
	d			20 04						20 34				21 04				21 34				22 04	
Stone Crossing	d									20 37								21 37					
Greenhithe for Bluewater	d			20 09						20 40				21 09				21 40				22 09	
Swanscombe	d									20 42								21 42					
Northfleet	d									20 44								21 44					
Gravesend 4	d			20 16						20 48				21 16				21 50				22 16	
Higham	d			20 22						20 54				21 22				21 56				22 22	
Strood 4	d			20 28						21 01				21 28				22 02				22 28	
Maidstone West 4	a			*20 54*						*21 24*				*21 54*									
Rochester 4	d			20 31						21 05				21 31				22 06				22 31	
Chatham 4	d			20 34						21 08				21 34				22 09				22 34	
Gillingham (Kent) 4	a			20 37						21 13				21 37				22 13				22 37	

For general notes see front of timetable
For details of catering facilities see Directory of Train Operators

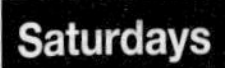

For details of Bank Holiday service alterations please see first page of Table 195

London → Dartford and Gillingham

Network Diagram - see first page of Table 200

		SE 80	SE 70	SE 62	SE 50	SE 80	SE 70	SE 62	SE 50	SE 80	SE 70	SE 62	SE 50	SE 80	SE 70	SE 62	SE 50	SE 70	SE 80
London Charing Cross 4	⊖ d	21 40	21 47	21 50	22 04	22 10	22 17	22 20	22 34	22 40	22 47	22 50	23 04	23 10	23 17	23 20	23 34	23 47	23 49
London Waterloo (East) 4	⊖ d	21 43	21 50	21 53	22 07	22 13	22 20	22 23	22 37	22 43	22 50	22 53	23 07	23 13	23 20	23 23	23 37	23 50	23 52
London Cannon Street 4	⊖ d																		
London Bridge 4	⊖ d	21 48	21 55	21 59	22 13	22 18	22 25	22 29	22 43	22 48	22 55	22 59	23 13	23 18	23 25	23 29	23 43	23 55	23 57
Deptford	d	21 54				22 24				22 54				23 24					00 03
Greenwich 4	d	21 56				22 26				22 56				23 26					00 05
Maze Hill	d	22 00				22 30				23 00				23 30					00 09
Westcombe Park	d	22 02				22 32				23 02				23 32					00 11
London Victoria 15	⊖ d																		
Denmark Hill 4	d																		
Peckham Rye 4	d																		
Nunhead 4	d																		
New Cross 4	⊖ d		22 00		22 18		22 30		22 48		23 00		23 18		23 30		23 48	23 59	
St Johns	d																		
Lewisham 4	d		22 05	22 07	22 23		22 35	22 37	22 53		23 05	23 07	23 23		23 35	23 37	23 53	00 05	
Blackheath 4	d		22 07	22 09			22 37	22 39			23 07	23 09			23 37	23 39		00 07	
Kidbrooke	d		22 10				22 40				23 10				23 40			00 10	
Eltham	d		22 14				22 44				23 14				23 44			00 14	
Falconwood	d		22 16				22 46				23 16				23 46			00 16	
Welling	d		22 19				22 49				23 19				23 49			00 19	
Bexleyheath	d		22 21				22 51				23 21				23 51			00 21	
Barnehurst 4	d		22 24				22 54				23 24				23 54			00 24	
Hither Green 4	d				22 27				22 57				23 27				23 57		
Lee	d				22 29				22 59				23 29				23 59		
Mottingham	d				22 32				23 02				23 32				00 02		
New Eltham	d				22 35				23 05				23 35				00 05		
Sidcup 4	d				22 38				23 08				23 38				00 08		
Albany Park	d				22 40				23 10				23 40				00 10		
Bexley	d				22 42				23 12				23 42				00 12		
Crayford	d				22 45				23 15				23 45				00 15		
Charlton 4	d	22 04		22 14		22 34		22 44		23 04		23 14		23 34		23 44			00 13
Woolwich Dockyard	d	22 07				22 37				23 07				23 37					00 16
Woolwich Arsenal 4	d	22 10		22 19		22 40		22 49		23 10		23 19		23 40		23 49			00 19
Plumstead	d	22 12				22 42				23 12				23 42					00 21
Abbey Wood	d	22 15		22 23		22 45		22 53		23 15		23 23		23 45		23 53			00 24
Belvedere	d	22 18				22 48				23 18				23 48					00 27
Erith	d	22 21				22 51				23 21				23 51					00 30
Slade Green 4	d	22 24				22 54				23 24				23 54					00 33
Dartford 4	a	22 28	22 30	22 33	22 50	22 59	23 01	23 03	23 20	23 29	23 31	23 33	23 50	23 59	00 01	00 03	00 20	00 31	00 38
	d			22 34				23 04				23 34				00 04			
Stone Crossing	d			22 37								23 37				00 07			
Greenhithe for Bluewater	d			22 40				23 09				23 40				00 09			
Swanscombe	d			22 42								23 42				00 12			
Northfleet	d			22 44								23 44				00 14			
Gravesend 4	d			22 50				23 16				23 50				00 17			
Higham	d			22 56				23 22				23 56				00 23			
Strood 4	d			23 02				23 28				00 02				00 28			
Maidstone West 4	a																		
Rochester 4	d			23 06				23 31				00 06				00 32			
Chatham 4	d			23 09				23 34				00 09				00 35			
Gillingham (Kent) 4	a			23 13				23 37				00 13				00 38			

For general notes see front of timetable
For details of catering facilities see Directory of Train Operators

Table 200

Sundays

London → Dartford and Gillingham

Network Diagram - see first page of Table 200

		SE 62	SE 62	SE 50	SE 70	SE 80	SE 55	SE 50	SE 62	SE 63	SE 72	SE 80	SE 50	SE 70	SE 80	SE 50	SE 62	SE 82	SE 80	SE 50	SE 62	SE 70
London Charing Cross 4	⊖ d	22p50	23p20	23p34	23p47	23p49		00 04	00 14		07 37	07 40	07 47	08 07	08 10	08 17	08 20	08 37	08 40	08 47	08 50	09 07
London Waterloo (East) 4	⊖ d	22p53	23p23	23p37	23p50	23p52		00 07	00 17		07 40	07 43	07 50	08 10	08 13	08 20	08 23	08 40	08 43	08 50	08 53	09 10
London Cannon Street 4	⊖ d																					
London Bridge 4	⊖ d	22p59	23p29	23p43	23p55	23p57		00 13	00 22		07 45	07 48	07 55	08 15	08 18	08 25	08 29	08 45	08 48	08 55	08 59	09 15
Deptford	d					00 03						07 53			08 23				08 53			
Greenwich 4	d					00 05						07 55			08 25				08 55			
Maze Hill	d					00 09						07 59			08 29				08 59			
Westcombe Park	d					00 11						08 01			08 31				09 01			
London Victoria 15	⊖ d																					
Denmark Hill 4	d																					
Peckham Rye 4	d																					
Nunhead 4	d																					
New Cross 4	⊖ d			23p48	23p59			00 18	00 27		07 50		08 00	08 20		08 30		08 50		09 00		09 20
St Johns	d																					
Lewisham 4	d	23p07	23p37	23p53	00 05			00 23	00 31		07 55		08 05	08 25		08 35	08 38	08 55		09 05	09 08	09 25
Blackheath 4	d	23p09	23p39		00 07				00 34		07 58			08 28			08 41	08 58			09 11	09 28
Kidbrooke	d				00 10						08 01			08 31				09 01				09 31
Eltham	d				00 14						08 04			08 34				09 04				09 34
Falconwood	d				00 16						08 07			08 37				09 07				09 37
Welling	d				00 19						08 09			08 39				09 09				09 39
Bexleyheath	d				00 21						08 12			08 42				09 12				09 42
Barnehurst 4	d				00 24						08 15			08 45				09 15				09 45
Hither Green 4	d			23p57				00 27					08 09			08 39				09 09		
Lee	d			23p59				00 29					08 11			08 41				09 11		
Mottingham	d			00 02				00 32					08 14			08 44				09 14		
New Eltham	d			00 05				00 35					08 16			08 46				09 16		
Sidcup 4	d			00 08				00 38					08 20			08 50				09 20		
Albany Park	d			00 10				00 40					08 22			08 52				09 22		
Bexley	d			00 12				00 42					08 24			08 54				09 24		
Crayford	d			00 15				00 45					08 27			08 57				09 27		
Charlton 4	d	23p14	23p44			00 13			00 38			08 03			08 33		08 45		09 03		09 15	
Woolwich Dockyard	d					00 16						08 06			08 36				09 06			
Woolwich Arsenal 4	d	23p19	23p49			00 19			00 42			08 09			08 39		08 50		09 09		09 20	
Plumstead	d					00 21			00 44			08 11			08 41				09 11			
Abbey Wood	d	23p23	23p53			00 24			00 47			08 14			08 44		08 55		09 14		09 25	
Belvedere	d					00 27			00 50			08 17			08 47				09 17			
Erith	d					00 30			00 53			08 20			08 50				09 20			
Slade Green 4	d					00 33			00 55	07 57		08 23			08 53				09 23			
Dartford 4	a	23p33	00 03	00 20	00 31	00 38		00 50	00 59	08 01	08 21	08 27	08 31	08 51	08 57	09 01	09 03	09 21	09 27	09 31	09 33	09 51
	d	23p34	00 04						01 00	08 02	08 22	08 28		08 52			09 04	09 22			09 34	09 52
Stone Crossing	d	23p37	00 07							08 05	08 25	08 31		08 55				09 25				09 55
Greenhithe for Bluewater	d	23p40	00 09						01 05	08 08	08 28	08 34		08 58			09 09	09 28			09 39	09 58
Swanscombe	d	23p42	00 12							08 10	08 30	08 36		09 00				09 30				10 00
Northfleet	d	23p44	00 14							08 12	08 32	08 38		09 02				09 32				10 02
Gravesend 4	d	23p50	00 17						01 12	08 16	08a36	08 42		09a06			09 16	09a36			09 46	10a06
Higham	d	23p56	00 23						01 18	08 22		08 48					09 22				09 52	
Strood 4	d	00 02	00 28				22 36		01 23	08 28		08 54					09 27				09 57	
Maidstone West 4	a									*08 56*							*09 56*					
Rochester 4	d	00 06	00 32				22 40		01 27	08 32		08 58					09 31				10 01	
Chatham 4	d	00 09	00 35				22 43		01 30	08 35		09 01					09 34				10 04	
Gillingham (Kent) 4	a	00 13	00 38				22 46		01 33	08 38		09 04					09 37				10 07	

For general notes see front of timetable
For details of catering facilities see
Directory of Train Operators

London → Dartford and Gillingham

Network Diagram - see first page of Table 200

Station		SE 84	SE 50	SE 62	SE 67	SE 70	SE 84	SE 50	SE 62	SE 67	SE 70	SE 84	SE 50	SE 62	SE 67	SE 70	SE 84	SE 50	SE 62	SE 67		SE 70
London Charing Cross [4]	⊖ d	09 10	09 17	09 20		09 37	09 40	09 47	09 50		10 07	10 10	10 17	10 20		10 37	10 40	10 47	10 50			19 07
London Waterloo (East) [4]	⊖ d	09 13	09 20	09 23		09 40	09 43	09 50	09 53		10 10	10 13	10 20	10 23		10 40	10 43	10 50	10 53			19 10
London Cannon Street [4]	⊖ d																					
London Bridge [4]	⊖ d	09 18	09 25	09 29	09 36	09 45	09 48	09 55	09 59	10 06	10 15	10 18	10 25	10 29	10 36	10 45	10 48	10 55	10 59	11 06		19 15
Deptford	d	09 23			09 41		09 53			10 11		10 23			10 41		10 53			11 11		
Greenwich [4]	⛴ d	09 25			09 43		09 55			10 13		10 25			10 43		10 55			11 13		
Maze Hill	d	09 29			09 47		09 59			10 17		10 29			10 47		10 59			11 17		
Westcombe Park	d	09 31			09 49		10 01			10 19		10 31			10 49		11 01			11 19		
London Victoria [15]	⊖ d																					
Denmark Hill [4]	d																					
Peckham Rye [4]	d																					
Nunhead [4]	d																					
New Cross [4]	⊖ d		09 30			09 50		10 00			10 20		10 30			10 50		11 00				19 20
St Johns	d																					
Lewisham [4]	⛴ d		09 35	09 38		09 55		10 05	10 08		10 25		10 35	10 38		10 55		11 05	11 08			19 25
Blackheath [4]	d			09 41		09 58			10 11		10 28			10 41		10 58			11 11			19 28
Kidbrooke	d					10 01					10 31					11 01					and at the same minutes past each hour until	19 31
Eltham	d					10 04					10 34					11 04						19 34
Falconwood	d					10 07					10 37					11 07						19 37
Welling	d					10 09					10 39					11 09						19 39
Bexleyheath	d					10 12					10 42					11 12						19 42
Barnehurst [4]	d					10 15					10 45					11 15						19 45
Hither Green [4]	d		09 39					10 09					10 39					11 09				
Lee	d		09 41					10 11					10 41					11 11				
Mottingham	d		09 44					10 14					10 44					11 14				
New Eltham	d		09 46					10 16					10 46					11 16				
Sidcup [4]	d		09 50					10 20					10 50					11 20				
Albany Park	d		09 52					10 22					10 52					11 22				
Bexley	d		09 54					10 24					10 54					11 24				
Crayford	d		09 57					10 27					10 57					11 27				
Charlton [4]	d	09 33		09 45	09 51		10 03		10 15	10 21		10 33		10 45	10 51		11 03		11 15	11 21		
Woolwich Dockyard	d	09 36			09 54		10 06			10 24		10 36			10 54		11 06			11 24		
Woolwich Arsenal [4]	d	09 39		09 50	09 57		10 09		10 20	10 27		10 39		10 50	10 57		11 09		11 20	11 27		
Plumstead	d	09 41			09a59		10 11			10a29		10 41			10a59		11 11			11a29		
Abbey Wood	d	09 44		09 55			10 14		10 25			10 44		10 55			11 14		11 25			
Belvedere	d	09 47					10 17					10 47					11 17					
Erith	d	09 50					10 20					10 50					11 20					
Slade Green [4]	d	09 53					10 23					10 53					11 23					
Dartford [4]	a	09 57	10 01	10 03		10 21	10 27	10 31	10 33		10 51	10 57	11 01	11 03		11 21	11 27	11 31	11 33			19 51
	d			10 04		10 22			10 34		10 52			11 04		11 22			11 34			
Stone Crossing	d					10 25					10 55					11 25						
Greenhithe for Bluewater	d			10 09		10 28			10 39		10 58			11 09		11 28			11 39			
Swanscombe	d					10 30					11 00					11 30						
Northfleet	d					10 32					11 02					11 32						
Gravesend [4]	d			10 16		10a36			10 46		11a06			11 16		11a36			11 46			
Higham	d			10 22					10 52					11 22					11 52			
Strood [4]	d			10 27					10 57					11 27					11 57			
Maidstone West [4]	a			*10 56*										*11 56*								
Rochester [4]	d			10 31					11 01					11 31					12 01			
Chatham [4]	d			10 34					11 04					11 34					12 04			
Gillingham (Kent) [4]	a			10 37					11 07					11 37					12 07			

For general notes see front of timetable
For details of catering facilities see Directory of Train Operators

Sundays

London → Dartford and Gillingham

Network Diagram - see first page of Table 200

		SE 80		SE 50	SE 62	SE 72	SE 80	SE 50	SE 62		SE 70	SE 80	SE 50	SE 62	SE 72	SE 80		SE 50	SE 62	SE 70	SE 80	SE 50	SE 62		SE 55
London Charing Cross 4	⊖ d	19 10		19 17	19 20	19 37	19 40	19 47	19 50		20 07	20 10	20 17	20 20	20 37	20 40		20 47	20 50	21 07	21 10	21 17	21 20		
London Waterloo (East) 4	⊖ d	19 13		19 20	19 23	19 40	19 43	19 50	19 53		20 10	20 13	20 20	20 23	20 40	20 43		20 50	20 53	21 10	21 13	21 20	21 23		
London Cannon Street 4	⊖ d																								
London Bridge 4	⊖ d	19 18		19 25	19 29	19 45	19 48	19 55	19 59		20 15	20 18	20 25	20 29	20 45	20 48		20 55	20 59	21 15	21 18	21 25	21 29		
Deptford	d	19 23					19 53					20 23				20 53					21 23				
Greenwich 4	d	19 25					19 55					20 25				20 55					21 25				
Maze Hill	d	19 29					19 59					20 29				20 59					21 29				
Westcombe Park	d	19 31					20 01					20 31				21 01					21 31				
London Victoria 15	⊖ d																								
Denmark Hill 4	d																								
Peckham Rye 4	d																								
Nunhead 4	d																								
New Cross 4	⊖ d			19 30		19 50		20 00			20 20		20 30		20 50			21 00		21 20		21 30			
St Johns	d																								
Lewisham 4	d			19 35	19 38	19 55		20 05	20 08		20 25		20 35	20 38	20 55			21 05	21 08	21 25		21 35	21 38		
Blackheath 4	d				19 41	19 58			20 11		20 28			20 41	20 58				21 11	21 28			21 41		
Kidbrooke	d					20 01					20 31				21 01					21 31					
Eltham	d					20 04					20 34				21 04					21 34					
Falconwood	d					20 07					20 37				21 07					21 37					
Welling	d					20 09					20 39				21 09					21 39					
Bexleyheath	d					20 12					20 42				21 12					21 42					
Barnehurst 4	d					20 15					20 45				21 15					21 45					
Hither Green 4	d			19 39				20 09					20 39					21 09				21 39			
Lee	d			19 41				20 11					20 41					21 11				21 41			
Mottingham	d			19 44				20 14					20 44					21 14				21 44			
New Eltham	d			19 46				20 16					20 46					21 16				21 46			
Sidcup 4	d			19 50				20 20					20 50					21 20				21 50			
Albany Park	d			19 52				20 22					20 52					21 22				21 52			
Bexley	d			19 54				20 24					20 54					21 24				21 54			
Crayford	d			19 57				20 27					20 57					21 27				21 57			
Charlton 4	d	19 33			19 45		20 03		20 15			20 33		20 45		21 03			21 15		21 33		21 45		
Woolwich Dockyard	d	19 36					20 06					20 36				21 06					21 36				
Woolwich Arsenal 4	d	19 39			19 50		20 09		20 20			20 39		20 50		21 09			21 20		21 39		21 50		
Plumstead	d	19 41					20 11					20 41				21 11					21 41				
Abbey Wood	d	19 44			19 55		20 14		20 25			20 44		20 55		21 14			21 25		21 44		21 55		
Belvedere	d	19 47					20 17					20 47				21 17					21 47				
Erith	d	19 50					20 20					20 50				21 20					21 50				
Slade Green 4	d	19 53					20 23					20 53				21 23					21 53				
Dartford 4	a	19 57		20 01	20 03	20 21	20 27	20 31	20 33		20 51	20 57	21 01	21 03	21 21	21 27		21 31	21 33	21 51	21 57	22 01	22 03		
	d				20 04				20 34					21 04					21 34				22 04		
Stone Crossing	d								20 37										21 37						
Greenhithe for Bluewater	d				20 09				20 40					21 09					21 40				22 09		
Swanscombe	d								20 42										21 42						
Northfleet	d								20 44										21 44						
Gravesend 4	d				20 16				20 48					21 16					21 48				22 16		
Higham	d				20 22				20 54					21 22					21 54				22 22		
Strood 4	d				20 27				21 00					21 27					22 00				22 27		22 36
Maidstone West 4	a				*20 56*									*21 56*											
Rochester 4	d				20 31				21 04					21 31					22 04				22 31		22 40
Chatham 4	d				20 34				21 07					21 34					22 07				22 34		22 43
Gillingham (Kent) 4	a				20 37				21 10					21 37					22 10				22 37		22 46

For general notes see front of timetable
For details of catering facilities see Directory of Train Operators

Table 200

Sundays

London → Dartford and Gillingham

Network Diagram - see first page of Table 200

		SE 72	SE 80	SE 50	SE 62	SE 70	SE 80		SE 50	SE 62	SE 72	SE 80	SE 50	SE 62		SE 70	SE 80	SE 50	SE 62	SE 70	SE 80		SE 50		
London Charing Cross 4	⊖ d	21 37	21 40	21 47	21 50	22 07	22 10		22 17	22 20	22 37	22 40	22 47	22 50		23 07	23 10	23 17	23 20	23 37	23 40		23 47		
London Waterloo (East) 4	⊖ d	21 40	21 43	21 50	21 53	22 10	22 13		22 20	22 23	22 40	22 43	22 50	22 53		23 10	23 13	23 20	23 23	23 40	23 43		23 50		
London Cannon Street 4	⊖ d																								
London Bridge 4	⊖ d	21 45	21 48	21 55	21 59	22 15	22 18		22 25	22 29	22 45	22 48	22 55	22 59		23 15	23 18	23 25	23 29	23 45	23 48		23 55		
Deptford	d		21 53				22 23					22 53					23 23				23 53				
Greenwich 4	⛴ d		21 55				22 25					22 55					23 25				23 55				
Maze Hill	d		21 59				22 29					22 59					23 29				23 59				
Westcombe Park	d		22 01				22 31					23 01					23 31				00 01				
London Victoria 15	⊖ d																								
Denmark Hill 4	d																								
Peckham Rye 4	d																								
Nunhead 4	d																								
New Cross 4	⊖ d	21 50		22 00		22 20			22 30		22 50		23 00			23 20		23 30		23 50			00 01		
St Johns	d																								
Lewisham 4	⛴ d	21 55		22 05	22 08	22 25			22 35	22 38	22 55		23 05	23 08		23 25		23 35	23 38	23 55			00 05		
Blackheath 4	d	21 58			22 11	22 28				22 41	22 58			23 11		23 28			23 41	23 58					
Kidbrooke	d	22 01				22 31					23 01					23 31				00 01					
Eltham	d	22 04				22 34					23 04					23 34				00 04					
Falconwood	d	22 07				22 37					23 07					23 37				00 07					
Welling	d	22 09				22 39					23 09					23 39				00 09					
Bexleyheath	d	22 12				22 42					23 12					23 42				00 12					
Barnehurst 4	d	22 15				22 45					23 15					23 45				00 15					
Hither Green 4	d			22 09					22 39				23 09					23 39					00 09		
Lee	d			22 11					22 41				23 11					23 41					00 11		
Mottingham	d			22 14					22 44				23 14					23 44					00 14		
New Eltham	d			22 16					22 46				23 16					23 46					00 16		
Sidcup 4	d			22 20					22 50				23 20					23 50					00 20		
Albany Park	d			22 22					22 52				23 22					23 52					00 22		
Bexley	d			22 24					22 54				23 24					23 54					00 24		
Crayford	d			22 27					22 57				23 27					23 57					00 27		
Charlton 4	d		22 03		22 15		22 33			22 45		23 03		23 15			23 33		23 45		00 03				
Woolwich Dockyard	d		22 06				22 36					23 06					23 36				00 06				
Woolwich Arsenal 4	d		22 09		22 20		22 39			22 50		23 09		23 20			23 39		23 50		00 09				
Plumstead	d		22 11				22 41					23 11					23 41				00 11				
Abbey Wood	d		22 14		22 25		22 44			22 55		23 14		23 25			23 44		23 55		00 14				
Belvedere	d		22 17				22 47					23 17					23 47				00 17				
Erith	d		22 20				22 50					23 20					23 50				00 20				
Slade Green 4	d		22 23				22 53					23 23					23 53				00 23				
Dartford 4	a	22 21	22 27	22 31	22 33	22 51	22 57		23 01	23 03	23 21	23 27	23 31	23 33		23 51	23 57	00 01	00 03	00 21	00 27		00 31		
	d				22 34					23 04				23 34					00 04						
Stone Crossing	d				22 37									23 37											
Greenhithe for Bluewater	d				22 40					23 09				23 40					00 09						
Swanscombe	d				22 42									23 42											
Northfleet	d				22 44									23 44											
Gravesend 4	d				22 48					23 16				23 48					00 16						
Higham	d				22 54					23 22				23 54					00 22						
Strood 4	d				23 00					23 27				23 58					00 27						
Maidstone West 4	a																								
Rochester 4	d				23 04					23 31				00 03					00 31						
Chatham 4	d				23 07					23 34				00 06					00 34						
Gillingham (Kent) 4	a				23 10					23 37				00 09					00 37						

For general notes see front of timetable
For details of catering facilities see Directory of Train Operators

For details of Bank Holiday service alterations please see first page of Table 195

Gillingham and Dartford → London

Network Diagram - see first page of Table 200

Miles	Miles	Miles	Miles	Miles			SE MX 58 A	SE 52	SE 50	SE 80	SE 70	SE 82	SE 55	SE 50	SE 82	SE 70	SE 62	SE 50	SE 84	SE 77	SE 70	SE 62	SE 61	SE 70
0	—	—	0	—	**Gillingham (Kent)** [4]	d	00 07	04 12				04 52	04 56				05 22					05 52	06 03	
1¾	—	—	1¾	—	**Chatham** [4]	d	00 11	04 16				04 56	04 59				05 26					05 56	06 07	
2¼	—	—	2¼	—	Rochester [4]	d	00 13	04 18				04 58	05 01				05 28					05 58	06 09	
—	—	—	—	—	Maidstone West [4]	d																		
3¼	—	—	3¼	—	Strood [4]	d	00 17	04 23				05 03	05a05				05 33					06 03	06a13	
6	—	—	6	—	Higham	d	00 22	04 28				05 08					05 38					06 08		
10½	—	—	10½	—	**Gravesend** [4]	d	00 28	04 35				05 15					05 45		05 48			06 15		
12½	—	—	12½	—	Northfleet	d						05 19							05 51					
13¼	—	—	13¼	—	Swanscombe	d						05 21							05 53					
14½	—	—	14½	—	Greenhithe for Bluewater	d	00 34					05 24					05 50		05 56			06 20		
15¼	—	—	15¼	—	Stone Crossing	d						05 27							05 58					
17¼	0	0	17¼	0	**Dartford** [4]	a	00 41	04 44				05 30					05 56		06 02			06 25		
—	—	—	—	—		d	00 42	04 46	05 02	05 12	05 18	05 32		05 34		05 48	05 58	06 00	06 02		06 22	06 26		
19¼	2	—	—	—	Slade Green [4]	d				05 16		05 36							06 06					
20½	3¼	—	—	—	Erith	d				05 18		05 38							06 08					
21¾	4½	—	—	—	Belvedere	d				05 21		05 41							06 11					
23¼	6	—	—	—	Abbey Wood	d				05 24		05 44					06 07		06 14			06 35		
24¾	7½	—	—	—	Plumstead	d				05 27		05 47			←				06 17					
25¼	8	—	—	—	**Woolwich Arsenal** [4]	d				05 30		05 50			05 50		06 12		06 20			06 40		
26	8¾	—	—	—	Woolwich Dockyard	d						→							06 22					
27	9¾	—	—	—	Charlton [4]	d				05 35					05 55				06 25					
—	—	—	19	—	Crayford	d		04 49	05 05					05 37				06 03						
—	—	—	20½	—	Bexley	d		04 52	05 08					05 40				06 06						
—	—	—	21½	—	Albany Park	d		04 54	05 10					05 42				06 08						
—	—	—	22½	—	Sidcup [4]	d		04 57	05 13					05 45				06 11						
—	—	—	24	—	New Eltham	d		05 00	05 16					05 48				06 14						
—	—	—	25	—	Mottingham	d		05 02	05 18					05 50				06 16						
—	—	—	26½	—	Lee	d		05 05	05 21					05 53				06 19						
—	—	—	27¼	—	Hither Green [4]	d		05 08	05 23					05 55				06b25						
—	—	3	—	3	Barnehurst [4]	d					05 24					05 54				06 12	06c32			
—	—	4¼	—	4¼	Bexleyheath	d					05 27					05 57				06 15	06 35			←
—	—	5¾	—	5¾	Welling	d					05 30					06 00				06 18	06 38			06 38
—	—	6¾	—	6¾	Falconwood	d					05 33					06 03				06 21	→			06 41
—	—	8	—	8	Eltham	d					05 36					06 06				06 24				06 44
—	—	9	—	9	Kidbrooke	d					05 39					06 09				06 27				06 47
29	—	10	—	10	Blackheath [4]	d					05 42					06 12	06 20			06 30		06 48		06 52
30	—	11	28½	11	Lewisham [4]	d		05 13	05 28		05e48			06 00		06 16	06 24	06 30		06 34		06 52		06 56
—	—	11½	29	—	St Johns	d												06 32						
—	—	12¼	29¾	—	New Cross [4]	⊖ d		05 16	05 32		05 52			06 04		06 20		06 34		06 38				
—	—	—	—	12¾	Nunhead [4]	d																		
—	—	—	—	13½	Peckham Rye [4]	d																		
—	—	—	—	14¼	Denmark Hill [4]	d																		
—	—	—	—	18½	**London Victoria** [15]	⊖ a	01 13																	
—	10½	—	—	—	Westcombe Park	d				05 37					05 57				06 27					
—	11	—	—	—	Maze Hill	d				05 39					05 59				06 29					
—	12	—	—	—	Greenwich [4]	d				05 43					06 03				06 33					
—	12½	—	—	—	Deptford	d				05 45					06 05				06 35					
34¼	15½	15¼	32¾	—	**London Bridge** [4]	⊖ a		05 22	05 38	05 53	05 58			06 10	06 13	06 26	06 33	06 40	06 43	06 43		07 01		07 06
—	16¼	—	—	—	**London Cannon Street** [4]	⊖ a														06 47				
35¼	—	16¼	33¾	—	**London Waterloo (East)** [4]	⊖ a		05 27	05 43	05 58	06 03			06 15	06 18	06 31	06 38	06 45	06 48			07 06		07 11
36	—	17	34½	—	**London Charing Cross** [4]	⊖ a		05 31	05 47	06 02	06 06			06 18	06 21	06 34	06 41	06 48	06 51			07 11		07 16

For general notes see front of timetable
For details of catering facilities see Directory of Train Operators

A From Faversham (Table 212)
b Arr. 0622
c Arr. 0628
e Arr. 0545

For details of Bank Holiday service alterations please see first page of Table 195

Gillingham and Dartford → London

Network Diagram - see first page of Table 200

		SE 40	SE 80	SE 55	SE 87	SE 40	SE 70	SE 62	SE 46	SE 77	SE 80	SE 51	SE 74	SE 66	SE 83	SE 77	SE 18	SE 46	SE 80	SE 87	SE 51	SE 74	SE 63
Gillingham (Kent) 4	d							06 22							06 37								06 53
Chatham 4	d							06 26							06 41								06 57
Rochester 4	d							06 28							06 43								06 59
Maidstone West 4	d														*06 19*								
Strood 4	d							06 33							06 48								07 06
Higham	d							06 38							06 53								07 10
Gravesend 4	d			06 20				06 45					06 48		07 00							07 11	07 18
Northfleet	d			06 24									06 52									07 15	
Swanscombe	d			06 26									06 54									07 17	
Greenhithe for Bluewater	d			06 29				06 50					06 57		07 06							07 20	07 24
Stone Crossing	d			06 31									06 59									07 22	
Dartford 4	a			06 36				06 55					07 03		07 11							07 26	07 29
	d	06 28	06 32	06 37		06 45	06 48	06 56			07 00	07 02	07 04		07 12				07 16		07 24	07 26	07 30
Slade Green 4	d		06 36		06 46						07 04			07 08					07 20	07 26			
Erith	d		06 38		06 48						07 06			07 10					07 22	07 28			
Belvedere	d		06 41		06 51						07 09			07 13					07 25	07 31			
Abbey Wood	d		06 44		06 54			07 05			07 12			07 16	07 21				07 28	07 34			07 39
Plumstead	d		06 47		06 57						07 15			07 19					07 31	07 37			
Woolwich Arsenal 4	d		06 50		07 00			07 10			07 18			07 22	07 26				07 34	07 40			07 44
Woolwich Dockyard	d		06 52		07 02						07 20			07 24					07 36	07 42			
Charlton 4	d		06 55		07 05						07 23			07 27					07 39	07 45			
Crayford	d	06 31		06 41		06 49			07 02			07 06						07 22			07 28		
Bexley	d	06 34		06 44		06 52			07 05			07 09						07 25			07 31		
Albany Park	d	06 36		06 47		06 55			07 08			07 12						07 28			07 34		
Sidcup 4	d	06 39		06 50		06 58			07 11			07 15						07 31			07 37		
New Eltham	d	06 42		06 53		07 01			07 14			07 18						07 34			07 40		
Mottingham	d	06 44		06 55		07 03			07 16			07 20						07 36			07 42		
Lee	d	06 47		06 58		07 06			07 19			07 23						07 39			07 45		
Hither Green 4	d	06 52		07 02		07 10			07 22			07 26						07 42			07 49		
Barnehurst 4	d						06 54			07 03			07 10			07 19	07 23					07 33	
Bexleyheath	d						06 57			07 06			07 13			07 22	07 26					07 36	
Welling	d						07 00			07 09			07 16			07 25	07 29					07 39	
Falconwood	d						07 03			07 11			07 19			07 27	07 31					07 41	
Eltham	d						07 06			07 14			07 22			07 30	07 34					07 44	
Kidbrooke	d						07 09			07 17			07 25			07 33	07 37					07 47	
Blackheath 4	d						07 12	07 18		07 21				07 32		07 38	07 41					07 51	07 54
Lewisham 4	d			07 08		07 15	07 18	07 22		07 25		07 32		07 38		07 41	07 44				07 54	07 56	
St Johns	d	06 56		07 10						07 27						07 44					07 59		
New Cross 4	⊖ d	06 58		07 12						07 29		07 36				07 46							
Nunhead 4	d																07 52						
Peckham Rye 4	d																07 55						
Denmark Hill 4	d																07 59						
London Victoria 15	⊖ a																08 12						
Westcombe Park	d		06 57		07 07						07 25								07 41	07 47			
Maze Hill	d		06 59		07 09						07 27								07 43	07 49			
Greenwich 4	d		07 03		07 13						07 31								07 47	07 53			
Deptford	d		07 05		07 15						07 33								07 49	07 55			
London Bridge 4	⊖ a	07 08	07 13	07 17	07 21	07 25	07 27	07 30	07 33	07 34	07 40	07 41			07 44	07 52		07 53	07 57	08 02	08 04	08 06	08 06
London Cannon Street 4	⊖ a			07 25	07 29					07 42		07 48			07 52	07 58				08 10	08 12		08 15
London Waterloo (East) 4	⊖ a	07 13	07 19			07 30	07 33	07 36	07 39		07 46		07 44	07 51				07 58	08 02			08 11	
London Charing Cross 4	⊖ a	07 18	07 25			07 35	07 38	07 41	07 44		07 52		07 50	07 57				08 03	08 08			08 18	

For general notes see front of timetable
For details of catering facilities see Directory of Train Operators

For details of Bank Holiday service alterations please see first page of Table 195

Gillingham and Dartford → London

Network Diagram - see first page of Table 200

Station		SE 77	SE 43	SE 86 A	SE 78	SE 76	SE 46	SE 86	SE 81		SE 70	SE 81	SE 57	SE 65	SE 77	SE 42	SE 20	SE 78	SE 74	SE 46	SE 86		SE 87	SE 74	SE 63
Gillingham (Kent) 4	d															07 13	07 28								07 33
Chatham 4	d															07 17	07 32								07 37
Rochester 4	d															07 19	07 34								07 39
Maidstone West 4	d															*06 53*									
Strood 4	d		07 10													07b28			07 36						07 46
Higham	d		07 14													07 32			07 40						07 50
Gravesend 4	d		07 22											07 34		07 40			07 48					07 52	07 58
Northfleet	d													07 38										07 56	
Swanscombe	d													07 40										07 58	
Greenhithe for Bluewater	d		07 28											07 43		07 46			07 54					08 00	08 04
Stone Crossing	d													07 45										08 02	
Dartford 4	a		07 33											07 49		07 51			07 59					08 06	08 09
	d		07 34		07 36				07 42		07 44			07 50		07 52		07 56	08 00				08 02	08 06	08 10
Slade Green 4	d			07 39				07 40	07 46					07 54							08 00		08 06		
Erith	d							07 42	07 48												08 02		08 08		
Belvedere	d							07 45	07 51												08 05		08 11		
Abbey Wood	d							07 48	07 54					08 01							08 08		08 14		08 19
Plumstead	d							07 51	07 57			←									08 11		08 17		
Woolwich Arsenal 4	d							07 54	08 00			08 00		08 06							08 14		08 20		08 24
Woolwich Dockyard	d							07 56	→			08 02									08 16		08 22		→
Charlton 4	d							07 59				08 05									08 19		08 25		
Crayford	d		07 38	07a46									07 48			07 56									
Bexley	d		07 41										07 51			07 59									
Albany Park	d		07 44										07 54			08 02									
Sidcup 4	d		07 47				07 51						07 57			08 05				08 11					
New Eltham	d		07 50				07 54						08 00			08 08				08 14					
Mottingham	d						07 56						08 02							08 16					
Lee	d						07 59						08 05							08 19					
Hither Green 4	d						08 02						08 09							08 22					
Barnehurst 4	d	07 39			07 43	07 47					07 50				07 59			08 03	08 07		07 56			08 13	
Bexleyheath	d	07 42			07 46	07 50					07 53				08 02			08 06	08 10					08 16	
Welling	d	07 45			07 49	07 53					07 56				08 05			08 09	08 13					08 19	
Falconwood	d	07 47			07 51	07 55					07 59				08 07			08 11	08 15					08 21	
Eltham	d	07 50			07 54	07 58					08 02				08 10			08 14	08 18					→	
Kidbrooke	d	07 53			07 57	08 01					08 05				08 13			08 17	08 21						
Blackheath 4	d	07 58			08 01	08 05					08 08			08 14	08 18			08 21							
Lewisham 4	d	08 01			08 04						08 12		08 14	08 18	08 21			08 24							
St Johns	d	08 04													08 24										
New Cross 4	⊖ d	08 06											08 18		08 26										
Nunhead 4	d				08 10													08 29							
Peckham Rye 4	d				08 12													08 32							
Denmark Hill 4	d				08 15												08 27	08 35							
London Victoria 15	⊖ a				08 29												08 38	08 47							
Westcombe Park	d							08 01				08 07									08 21		08 27		
Maze Hill	d							08 03				08 09									08 23		08 29		
Greenwich 4	d							08 07				08 13									08 27		08 33		
Deptford	d							08 09				08 15									08 29		08 35		
London Bridge 4	⊖ a	08 12					08 13	08 18			08 21	08 23	08 25	08 27	08 33					08 33	08 38		08 41		
London Cannon Street 4	⊖ a	08 19										08 31	08 33	08 35	08 39								08 50		
London Waterloo (East) 4	⊖ a		08 08			08 17	08 19	08 23			08 27					08 29			08 37	08 39	08 43				
London Charing Cross 4	⊖ a		08 14			08 24	08 25	08 29			08 33					08 35			08 43	08 45	08 49				

For general notes see front of timetable
For details of catering facilities see Directory of Train Operators

A From London Charing Cross
b Arr. 0724

For details of Bank Holiday service alterations please see first page of Table 195

Gillingham and Dartford → London

Network Diagram - see first page of Table 200

	SE 40	SE 57	SE 74	SE 63	SE 77	SE 18	SE 46	SE 86	SE 64	SE 57	SE 70	SE 81	SE 40	SE 63	SE 77	SE 86	SE 78	SE 72	SE 47	SE 81	SE 54	SE 81
Gillingham (Kent) 4 d																		08 15				
Chatham 4 d																		08 19				
Rochester 4 d														07 58				08 21				
Maidstone West 4 d									*07 26*									*08 01*				
Strood 4 d									07 56					08b08				08 28				
Higham d									08 00					08 12				08 32				
Gravesend 4 d									08 08					08 20				08 40				
Northfleet d														08 23								
Swanscombe d														08 25								
Greenhithe for Bluewater d									08 14					08 28				08 46				
Stone Crossing d														08 30								
Dartford 4 a									08 19					08 34				08 52				
d	08 12								08 20	08 24	08 26		08 32	08 35			08 43	08 53		08 57	09 01	
Slade Green 4 d						08 17		08 18	08 24			08 30		08 39		08 43				09 03		
Erith d								08 20				08 32				08 45				09 05		
Belvedere d								08 23				08 35				08 48				09 08		
Abbey Wood d								08 26	08 31			08 38		08 45		08 51				09 11		
Plumstead d				←				08 29				08 41				08 54				09 14		←
Woolwich Arsenal 4 d				08 24				08 32	08 36			08 44		08 50		08 57				09 17		09 17
Woolwich Dockyard d								08 34				08 46				08 59				→		09 19
Charlton 4 d								08 37				08 49				09 02						09 22
Crayford d	08 16	08 08								08 28			08 36		08 35				09 00		09 04	
Bexley d	08 19	08 11								08 31			08 39						09 02		09 07	
Albany Park d	08 22	08 14								08 34			08 42						09 05		09 09	
Sidcup 4 d	08 25	08 17					08 31			08 37			08 45						09 08		09 12	
New Eltham d	08 28	08 20					08 34			08 40			08 48						09 12		09 15	
Mottingham d		08 22					08 36			08 42			08 50						09 14		09 17	
Lee d		08 25					08 39			08 45			08 53						09 17		09 20	
Hither Green 4 d		08 29					08 42			08 49			08 56						09 20		09 23	
Barnehurst 4 d					08 19	08 23					08 33				08 43		08 49	08 59				
Bexleyheath d					08 22	08 26					08 36				08 46		08 52	09 02				
Welling d			←		08 25	08 29					08 39				08 49		08 55	09 05				
Falconwood d			08 21		08 27	08 31					08 41				08 51		08 57	09 07				
Eltham d			08 24		08 31	08 34					08 44				08 54		09 00	09 10				
Kidbrooke d			08 27		08 34	08 37					08 47				08 57		09 03	09 13				
Blackheath 4 d			08 31	08 34	08 38	08 41			08 44		08 51			08 58	09 01		09 07	09 17				
Lewisham 4 ⛴ d		08 34	08 36		08 41	08 44				08 54	08 56				09 04		09 10	09 20			09 28	
St Johns d					08 44										09 06				09 24			
New Cross 4 ⊖ d		08 38			08 46					08 58					09 08				09 26			
Nunhead 4 d						08 52											09 15					
Peckham Rye 4 d						08 54											09 18					
Denmark Hill 4 d						08 59											09 20					
London Victoria 15 ⊖ a						09 12											09 33					
Westcombe Park d								08 39				08 51				09 04						09 24
Maze Hill d								08 41				08 53				09 06						09 26
Greenwich 4 ⛴ d								08 45				08 57				09 10						09 30
Deptford d								08 47				08 59				09 12						09 32
London Bridge 4 ⊖ a	08 42	08 44	08 46	08 47	08 52		08 53	08 57		09 04	09 04	09 07	09 07	09 11	09 14	09 21		09 29	09 31		09 36	09 39
London Cannon Street 4 ⊖ a		08 52		08 55	09 00					09 11		09 15		09 19	09 23				09 39			09 47
London Waterloo (East) 4 ⊖ a	08 47		08 51				08 59	09 03	08 57		09 09		09 13			09 26		09 34			09 42	
London Charing Cross 4 ⊖ a	08 53		08 57				09 05	09 09	09 04		09 15		09 20			09 32		09 40			09 48	

For general notes see front of timetable
For details of catering facilities see Directory of Train Operators

b Arr. 0802

For details of Bank Holiday service alterations please see first page of Table 195

Gillingham and Dartford → London

Network Diagram - see first page of Table 200

		SE 70	SE 87	SE 62	SE 47	SE 78	SE 81	SE 54	SE 70	SE 47	SE 82	SE 47	SE 67	SE 81	SE 78	SE 54	SE 70	SE 87 A	SE 82	SE 47 A	SE 67	SE 81	SE 78	SE 54
Gillingham (Kent) 4	d										09 14								09 44					
Chatham 4	d										09 18								09 48					
Rochester 4	d			08 52							09 20								09 50					
Maidstone West 4	d			*08 29*							*09 01*								*09 28*					
Strood 4	d			08 57							09 25								09 55					
Higham	d			09 01							09 29								09 59					
Gravesend 4	d	08 50		09 08				09 14			09 36					09 42			10 06					10 12
Northfleet	d	08 54						09 18								09 46								10 16
Swanscombe	d	08 56						09 20								09 48								10 18
Greenhithe for Bluewater	d	08 59		09 13				09 23			09 41					09 51			10 11					10 21
Stone Crossing	d	09 01						09 25								09 53								10 23
Dartford 4	a	09 06		09 19				09 30			09 46					09 57			10 16					10 29
	d	09 07		09 21		09 24	09 27	09 31	09 35	09 43	09 47			09 49	09 54	10 01	10 05		10 17			10 19	10 24	10 31
Slade Green 4	d		09 15				09 33							09 53				10 07		10 10		10 23		
Erith	d		09 17				09 35							09 55				10 09				10 25		
Belvedere	d		09 20				09 38							09 58				10 12				10 28		
Abbey Wood	d		09 23	09 29			09 41				09 55			10 01				10 15	10 25			10 31		
Plumstead	d		09 26				09 44						10 01	10 04				10 18			10 31	10 34		
Woolwich Arsenal 4	d		09 29	09 33			09 47				09 59		10 03	10 07				10 21	10 29		10 33	10 37		
Woolwich Dockyard	d		09 31				09 49							10 09				10 23				10 39		
Charlton 4	d		09 34	09 38			09 52				10 04		10 08	10 12				10 26	10 34		10 38	10 42		
Crayford	d				09 24			09 35		09b50						10 05				10 20				10 35
Bexley	d				09 27			09 38		09 52						10 08				10 22				10 38
Albany Park	d				09 29			09 40		09 55						10 10				10 25				10 40
Sidcup 4	d				09 32			09 43		09 58		←				10 13				10 28				10 43
New Eltham	d				09 35			09 46		10 01 →		10 01				10 16				10 31				10 46
Mottingham	d				09 37			09 48				10 03				10 18				10 33				10 48
Lee	d				09 40			09 51				10 06				10 21				10 36				10 51
Hither Green 4	d				09 44			09 54				10 10				10 24				10 40				10 54
Barnehurst 4	d	09 13				09 29			09 41						10 00		10 11						10 30	
Bexleyheath	d	09 16				09 32			09 44						10 02		10 14						10 32	
Welling	d	09 19				09 35			09 47						10 05		10 17						10 35	
Falconwood	d	09 21				09 37			09 49						10 08		10 19						10 38	
Eltham	d	09 24				09 40			09 52						10 11		10 22						10 41	
Kidbrooke	d	09 27				09 43			09 55						10 14		10 25						10 44	
Blackheath 4	d	09 31		09 43		09 47			09 59				10 13		10 17		10 29				10 43		10 47	
Lewisham 4	d	09 36		09 46		09 51		09 59	10 02				10 16		10 21	10 29	10 32				10 46		10 51	10 59
St Johns	d	09 38			09 48							10 14								10 45				
New Cross 4	⊖ d	09 40			09 50							10 16	10 20							10 47	10 50			
Nunhead 4	d					09 56									10 26								10 56	
Peckham Rye 4	d					09 58									10 28								10 58	
Denmark Hill 4	d					10 01									10 31								11 01	
London Victoria 15	⊖ a					10 14									10 42								11 12	
Westcombe Park	d		09 36				09 54							10 14				10 28				10 44		
Maze Hill	d		09 38				09 56							10 16				10 30				10 46		
Greenwich 4	d		09 42				10 00				10 10			10 20				10 34	10 40			10 50		
Deptford	d		09 44				10 02							10 22				10 36				10 52		
London Bridge 4	⊖ a	09 49	09 50	09 54	09 56		10 09		10 10		10 19	10 21	10 26	10 29		10 37	10 40	10 43	10 49	10 53	10 56	10 59		11 07
London Cannon Street 4	⊖ a		09 58		10 01		10 13					10 27	10 30	10 33				10 47		10 57	11 00	11 03		
London Waterloo (East) 4	⊖ a	09 54		09 59				10 11	10 16		10 24					10 42	10 45		10 54					11 12
London Charing Cross 4	⊖ a	10 00		10 05				10 14	10 20		10 28					10 47	10 50		10 58					11 17

For general notes see front of timetable
For details of catering facilities see Directory of Train Operators

A From London Cannon Street (Table 199)
b Arr. 0947

Table 200

Mondays to Fridays

For details of Bank Holiday service alterations please see first page of Table 195

Gillingham and Dartford → London

Network Diagram - see first page of Table 200

	SE 70		SE 87 A	SE 82	SE 47 A	SE 67	SE 81	SE 78	SE 54	SE 70	SE 87 A		SE 82	SE 47 A	SE 67	SE 81	SE 78	SE 54	SE 70	SE 87 A	SE 82	SE 47 A	SE 67	SE 81
Gillingham (Kent) 4 d				10 14									10 44								11 14			
Chatham 4 d				10 18									10 48								11 18			
Rochester 4 d				10 20									10 50								11 20			
Maidstone West 4 d				*09 58*									*10 27*								*10 58*			
Strood 4 d				10 25									10 55								11 25			
Higham d				10 29									10 59								11 29			
Gravesend 4 d				10 36					10 42				11 06					11 12			11 36			
Northfleet d									10 46									11 16						
Swanscombe d									10 48									11 18						
Greenhithe for Bluewater d				10 41					10 51				11 11					11 21			11 41			
Stone Crossing d									10 53									11 23						
Dartford 4 a				10 46					10 57				11 16					11 27			11 46			
d	10 35			10 47			10 49	10 54	11 01	11 05			11 17			11 19	11 24	11 31	11 35		11 47			11 49
Slade Green 4 d			10 37		10 40		10 53				11 07			11 10		11 23				11 37		11 40		11 53
Erith d			10 39				10 55				11 09					11 25				11 39				11 55
Belvedere d			10 42				10 58				11 12					11 28				11 42				11 58
Abbey Wood d			10 45	10 55			11 01				11 15		11 25			11 31				11 45	11 55			12 01
Plumstead d			10 48			11 01	11 04				11 18				11 31	11 34				11 48			12 01	12 04
Woolwich Arsenal 4 d			10 51	10 59		11 03	11 07				11 21		11 29		11 33	11 37				11 51	11 59		12 03	12 07
Woolwich Dockyard d			10 53				11 09				11 23					11 39				11 53				12 09
Charlton 4 d			10 56	11 04		11 08	11 12				11 26		11 34		11 38	11 42				11 56	12 04		12 08	12 12
Crayford d					10 50				11 05					11 20				11 35				11 50		
Bexley d					10 52				11 08					11 22				11 38				11 52		
Albany Park d					10 55				11 10					11 25				11 40				11 55		
Sidcup 4 d					10 58				11 13					11 28				11 43				11 58		
New Eltham d					11 01				11 16					11 31				11 46				12 01		
Mottingham d					11 03				11 18					11 33				11 48				12 03		
Lee d					11 06				11 21					11 36				11 51				12 06		
Hither Green 4 d					11 10				11 24					11 40				11 54				12 10		
Barnehurst 4 d	10 41							11 00		11 11							11 30		11 41					
Bexleyheath d	10 44							11 02		11 14							11 32		11 44					
Welling d	10 47							11 05		11 17							11 35		11 47					
Falconwood d	10 49							11 08		11 19							11 38		11 49					
Eltham d	10 52							11 11		11 22							11 41		11 52					
Kidbrooke d	10 55							11 14		11 25							11 44		11 55					
Blackheath 4 d	10 59					11 13		11 17		11 29					11 43		11 47		11 59				12 13	
Lewisham 4 ⛴ d	11 02					11 16		11 21	11 29	11 32					11 46		11 51	11 59	12 02				12 16	
St Johns d					11 15									11 45								12 15		
New Cross 4 ⊖ d					11 17	11 20								11 47	11 50							12 17	12 20	
Nunhead 4 d								11 26									11 56							
Peckham Rye 4 d								11 28									11 58							
Denmark Hill 4 d								11 31									12 01							
London Victoria 15 ⊖ a								11 42									12 12							
Westcombe Park d			10 58				11 14				11 28					11 44				11 58				12 14
Maze Hill d			11 00				11 16				11 30					11 46				12 00				12 16
Greenwich 4 ⛴ d			11 04	11 10			11 20				11 34		11 40			11 50				12 04	12 10			12 20
Deptford d			11 06				11 22				11 36					11 52				12 06				12 22
London Bridge 4 ⊖ a	11 10		11 13	11 19	11 23	11 26	11 29		11 37	11 40	11 43		11 49	11 53	11 56	11 59		12 07	12 10	12 13	12 19	12 23	12 26	12 29
London Cannon Street 4 ⊖ a			11 17		11 27	11 30	11 33				11 47			11 57	12 00	12 03				12 17		12 27	12 30	12 33
London Waterloo (East) 4 ⊖ a	11 15			11 24					11 42	11 45			11 54					12 12	12 15		12 24			
London Charing Cross 4 ⊖ a	11 20			11 28					11 47	11 50			11 58					12 17	12 20		12 28			

For general notes see front of timetable
For details of catering facilities see Directory of Train Operators

A From London Cannon Street (Table 199)

Table 200

Mondays to Fridays

For details of Bank Holiday service alterations please see first page of Table 195

Gillingham and Dartford → London

Network Diagram - see first page of Table 200

Station		SE 78	SE 54	SE 70	SE 87 A		SE 82	SE 47 A	SE 67	SE 81	SE 78	SE 54	SE 70	SE 87 A	SE 82	SE 47 A	SE 66	SE 81	SE 70	SE 55	SE 78	SE 87 A
Gillingham (Kent) 4	d						14 44								15 14							
Chatham 4	d						14 48								15 18							
Rochester 4	d						14 50								15 20							
Maidstone West 4	d						*14 27*								*14 58*							
Strood 4	d						14 55								15 25							
Higham	d						14 59								15 29							
Gravesend 4	d		11 42				15 06					15 12			15 36				15 40			
Northfleet	d		11 46									15 16							15 44			
Swanscombe	d		11 48									15 18							15 46			
Greenhithe for Bluewater	d		11 51				15 11					15 21			15 41				15 49			
Stone Crossing	d		11 53									15 23							15 51			
Dartford 4	a		11 57				15 16					15 27			15 46				15 55			
	d	11 54	12 01	12 05			15 17			15 19	15 24	15 31	15 35		15 47			15 49	15 56	16 01	16 05	
Slade Green 4	d				12 07			15 10		15 23				15 37		15 40		15 53				16 09
Erith	d				12 09					15 25				15 39				15 55				16 11
Belvedere	d				12 12					15 28				15 42				15 58				16 14
Abbey Wood	d				12 15		15 25			15 31				15 45	15 55			16 01				16 17
Plumstead	d				12 18				15 31	15 34				15 48			16 01	16 04				16 20
Woolwich Arsenal 4	d				12 21		15 29		15 33	15 37				15 51	15 59		16 03	16 07				16 23
Woolwich Dockyard	d				12 23					15 39				15 53				16 09				16 25
Charlton 4	d				12 26	and at	15 34		15 38	15 42				15 56	16 04		16 08	16 12				16 28
Crayford	d		12 05			the same		15 20				15 35				15 50				16 05		
Bexley	d		12 08					15 22				15 38				15 52				16 08		
Albany Park	d		12 10			minutes		15 25				15 40				15 55				16 10		
Sidcup 4	d		12 13					15 28				15 43				15 58				16 13		
New Eltham	d		12 16			past		15 31				15 46				16 01				16 16		
Mottingham	d		12 18					15 33				15 48				16 03				16 18		
Lee	d		12 21			each		15 36				15 51				16 06				16 21		
Hither Green 4	d		12 24					15 40				15 54				16 10				16b28		
Barnehurst 4	d	12 00		12 11		hour until					15 30		15 41						16 02		16 11	
Bexleyheath	d	12 02		12 14							15 32		15 44						16 05		16 14	
Welling	d	12 05		12 17							15 35		15 47						16 08		16 17	
Falconwood	d	12 08		12 19							15 38		15 49						16 10		16 19	
Eltham	d	12 11		12 22							15 41		15 52						16 13		16 22	
Kidbrooke	d	12 14		12 25							15 44		15 55						16 16		16 25	
Blackheath 4	d	12 17		12 29					15 43		15 47		15 59				16 13		16 20		16 29	
Lewisham 4	d	12 21	12 29	12 32					15 46		15 51	15 59	16 02				16 16		16 24	16 33	16 35	
St Johns	d							15 45								16 15				16 35		
New Cross 4	⊖ d							15 47	15 50							16 17				16 37		
Nunhead 4	d	12 26									15 56										16 40	
Peckham Rye 4	d	12 28									15 58										16 42	
Denmark Hill 4	d	12 31									16 01										16 46	
London Victoria 15	⊖ a	12 42									16 12										17 03	
Westcombe Park	d				12 28					15 44				15 58				16 14				16 30
Maze Hill	d				12 30					15 46				16 00				16 16				16 32
Greenwich 4	d				12 34		15 40			15 50				16 04	16 10			16 20				16 36
Deptford	d				12 36					15 52				16 06				16 22				16 38
London Bridge 4	⊖ a		12 37	12 40	12 43		15 49	15 53	15 56	15 59		16 07	16 11	16 13	16 19	16 23	16 26	16 29	16 32	16 42		16 46
London Cannon Street 4	⊖ a				12 47			15 57	16 00	16 03				16 17		16 27		16 33	16 36	16 46		16 52
London Waterloo (East) 4	⊖ a		12 42	12 45			15 54					16 13	16 18		16 24		16 32					
London Charing Cross 4	⊖ a		12 47	12 50			15 58					16 17	16 23		16 28		16 36					

For general notes see front of timetable
For details of catering facilities see Directory of Train Operators

A From London Cannon Street (Table 199)
b Arr. 1624

For details of Bank Holiday service alterations please see first page of Table 195

Gillingham and Dartford → London

Network Diagram - see first page of Table 200

		SE 81	SE 63	SE 47 A	SE 71	SE 57	SE 81	SE 44	SE 87	SE 78	SE 81	SE 81	SE 51	SE 63	SE 53	SE 81	SE 55	SE 53	SE 71	SE 57 A	SE 81	SE 63	SE 51
Gillingham (Kent) 4	d		15 44											16 14								16 44	
Chatham 4	d		15 48											16 18								16 48	
Rochester 4	d		15 50											16 20								16 50	
Maidstone West 4	d													*15 44*								*16 27*	
Strood 4	d		15 55											16 25								16 55	
Higham	d		15 59											16 29								16 59	
Gravesend 4	d		16 08					16 12						16 36			16 42					17 06	
Northfleet	d							16 16									16 46						
Swanscombe	d							16 18									16 48						
Greenhithe for Bluewater	d		16 14					16 21						16 41			16 51					17 11	
Stone Crossing	d							16 23									16 53						
Dartford 4	a		16 20					16 29						16 46			16 57					17 17	
	d	16 15	16 21		16 23		16 29	16 31		16 37			16 43	16 49		16 51	17 01		17 05		17 11	17 19	17 21
Slade Green 4	d			16 10			16 35		16 29			16 42				16 55				17 09	17 15		
Erith	d						16 37		16 31							16 57				17 11	17 17		
Belvedere	d						16 40		16 34							17 00				17 14	17 20		
Abbey Wood	d	16 25	16 29				16 43		16 37			16 49		16 57		17 03				17 17	17 23	17 29	
Plumstead	d						16 46		16 40		⟵					17 06				17 20	17 26		
Woolwich Arsenal 4	d	16 29	16 33				16 49		16 43		16 49	16 53		17 02		17 09				17 23	17 29	17 34	
Woolwich Dockyard	d						⟶		16 45		16 51					17 11				17 25	17 31		
Charlton 4	d	16 34	16 38	15 50					16 48		16 54	16 58		17 07		17 14				17 28	17 34	17 39	
Crayford	d			16 20				16 35					16 47		16 57		17 05						17 25
Bexley	d			16 22				16 37					16 50		16 59		17 07						17 27
Albany Park	d			16 25				16 40					16 52		17 02		17 10						17 30
Sidcup 4	d			16 28		16 38		16 43					16 55		17 05		17 13	17 25					17 33
New Eltham	d			16 31		16 41		16 46					16 58		17 08		17 16						17 36
Mottingham	d			16 33		16 43		16 48					17 00		17 10		17 18						17 38 ⟶
Lee	d			16 36		16 46		16 51					17 03		17 13		17 21						
Hither Green 4	d			16b42		16 50		16c56					17 06		17 16		17 24	17 31					
Barnehurst 4	d				16 29					16 43									17 13				
Bexleyheath	d				16 32					16 46									17 16				
Welling	d				16 35					16 49									17 19				
Falconwood	d				16 37					16 51									17 21				
Eltham	d				16 40					16 54									17 24				
Kidbrooke	d				16 43					16 57									17 27				
Blackheath 4	d		16 42		16 47					17 01				17 12					17 31			17 43	
Lewisham 4	d		16 46		16 50	16 56				17 05			17 12	17e18			17 31		17 36			17 47	
St Johns	d			16 47									17 14				17 33						
New Cross 4	⊖ d			16 49	16 54								17 16				17 35		17 39	16 20			
Nunhead 4	d									17 13													
Peckham Rye 4	d									17 15													
Denmark Hill 4	d									17 18													
London Victoria 15	⊖ a									17 28													
Westcombe Park	d								16 50		16 56					17 16				17 30	17 36		
Maze Hill	d								16 52		16 58					17 18				17 32	17 38		
Greenwich 4	d	16 40							16 56		17 02	17 06				17 22				17 36	17 42		
Deptford	d			15 40					16 58		17 04					17 24				17 38	17 44		
London Bridge 4	⊖ a	16 50	16 55	16 56	16 59	17 04		17 06	17 07		17 11	17 17	17 23	17 26	17 29	17 35	17 41	17 41	17 45	17 48	17 53	17 56	
London Cannon Street 4	⊖ a	16 55		17 00	17 05	17 08			17 13		17 15	17 23	17 29		17 33	17 39	17 45		17 51	17 53	17 57	18 01	
London Waterloo (East) 4	⊖ a		17 00					17 11						17 31				17 46					
London Charing Cross 4	⊖ a		17 03					17 15						17 35				17 50					

For general notes see front of timetable
For details of catering facilities see Directory of Train Operators

A From London Cannon Street (Table 199)
b Arr. 1639
c Arr. 1653
e Arr. 1715

For details of Bank Holiday service alterations please see first page of Table 195

Gillingham and Dartford → London

Network Diagram - see first page of Table 200

Station		SE 63	SE 51	SE 53	SE 85	SE 78	SE 51	SE 66	SE 74	SE 61	SE 53	SE 81	SE 44	SE 66	SE 78	SE 46 A	SE 87	SE 52	SE 81	SE 74	SE 78	SE 81	SE 50
Gillingham (Kent) [4]	d									17 14								17 48					
Chatham [4]	d									17 18								17 52					
Rochester [4]	d									17 20								17 54					
Maidstone West [4]	d									*16 55*								*17 25*					
Strood [4]	d									17 25								17 59					
Higham	d									17 29								18 03					
Gravesend [4]	d	17 08							17 32	17 38			17 52					18 10		18 14			
Northfleet	d	17 12							17 36				17 56							18 18			
Swanscombe	d	17 14							17 38				17 58							18 20			
Greenhithe for Bluewater	d	17 17							17 41	17 45			18 01					18 15		18 23			
Stone Crossing	d	17 19							17 43				18 03							18 25			
Dartford [4]	a	17 23							17 47	17 50			18 07					18 20		18 30			
	d	17 25				17 27	17 41		17 47	17 53		18 01	18 09		18 11			18 21	18 31	18 33	18 39		18 43
Slade Green [4]	d	17 31			17 35			17 43			17 52	18 05		18 12			18 23		18 35				
Erith	d				17 37			17 45				18 07					18 25		18 37				
Belvedere	d				17 40			17 48				18 10					18 28		18 40				
Abbey Wood	d	17 37			17 43			17 51		18 01		18 13		18 19			18 31		18 43				
Plumstead	d				17 46			17 54				18 16					18 34		18 46			←	
Woolwich Arsenal [4]	d	17 41			17 49			17 57		18 06		18 19		18 23			18 37		18 49 →			18 49	
Woolwich Dockyard	d				17 51			17 59				18 21					18 39					18 51	
Charlton [4]	d	17 46			17 54			18 02		18 11		18 24		18 28			18 42					18 54	
Crayford	d			17 35			17 45				18 01		18 13			18 20		18 25					18 47
Bexley	d			17 37			17 47				18 03		18 15					18 27					18 50
Albany Park	d			17 40			17 50				18 06		18 18					18 30					18 52
Sidcup [4]	d			17 43			17 53				18 09		18 21					18 33					18 55
New Eltham	d		←				17 56				18 12		18 24					18 36					18 58
Mottingham	d		17 38				17 58						18 26					18 38					19 00
Lee	d		17 41				18 01						18 29					18 41					19 03
Hither Green [4]	d		17 44	17 50			18 04				18 18		18 32			18 00		18 44					19 07
Barnehurst [4]	d				17 31	17 33			17 53						18 17	18a30				18 39	18 45		
Bexleyheath	d					17 36			17 56						18 20					18 42	18 48		
Welling	d					17 39			17 59						18 23					18 45	18 51		
Falconwood	d					17 41			18 01						18 25					18 47	18 53		
Eltham	d					17 44			18 04						18 28					18 50	18 56		
Kidbrooke	d					17 47			18 07						18 31					18 53	18 59		
Blackheath [4]	d					17 51			18 11	18 15				18 32	18 36					18 57	19 02		
Lewisham [4]	d		17 51			17 54			18 14	18 20	18 24			18 36	18 41			18 49		19 01	19 06		19 12
St Johns	d		17 55						18 16		18 26			18 38				18 51					
New Cross [4]	⊖ d		17 57						18 18		18 28			18 40				18 53					
Nunhead [4]	d					17 59									18 45						19 10		
Peckham Rye [4]	d					18 01									18 47						19 12		
Denmark Hill [4]	d					18 04									18 50						19 15		
London Victoria [15]	⊖ a					18 16									19 00						19 25		
Westcombe Park	d				17 56			18 04				18 26					18 44					18 56	
Maze Hill	d				17 58			18 06				18 28					18 46					18 58	
Greenwich [4]	d	17 52			18 02			18 10				18 32					18 50					19 02	
Deptford	d				18 04			18 12				18 34					18 52					19 04	
London Bridge [4]	⊖ a	18 00	18 03	18 03	18 11		18 15	18 19	18 25	18 31	18 33	18 41	18 42	18 48			19 01	19 02		19 09		19 11	19 21
London Cannon Street [4]	⊖ a		18 07		18 15			18 23	18 29		18 37	18 45					19 05					19 15	19 25
London Waterloo (East) [4]	⊖ a	18 05		18 09			18 21			18 36			18 48	18 53				19 07		19 15			
London Charing Cross [4]	⊖ a	18 09		18 13			18 25			18 40			18 53	18 57				19 11		19 20			

For general notes see front of timetable
For details of catering facilities see
Directory of Train Operators

A From London Charing Cross (Table 199)

For details of Bank Holiday service alterations please see first page of Table 195

Gillingham and Dartford → London

Network Diagram - see first page of Table 200

		SE 62	SE 81	SE 74	SE 50	SE 80	SE 62	SE 70	SE 81	SE 54	SE 80	SE 62		SE 70	SE 81	SE 54	SE 80	SE 62	SE 70	SE 81	SE 54	SE 80	SE 62	SE 70	SE 81
Gillingham (Kent) 4	d	18 13					18 44					19 14						19 44					20 16		
Chatham 4	d	18 17					18 48					19 18						19 48					20 20		
Rochester 4	d	18 19					18 50					19 20						19 50					20 22		
Maidstone West 4	d						*18 12*					*18 47*						*19 27*					*20 00*		
Strood 4	d	18 24					18 55					19 25						19 55					20 27		
Higham	d	18 28					18 59					19 29						19 59					20 31		
Gravesend 4	d	18 35			18 44		19 06			19 16		19 36				19 46		20 06			20 12		20 38		
Northfleet	d				18 48					19 20						19 50					20 16				
Swanscombe	d				18 50					19 22						19 52					20 18				
Greenhithe for Bluewater	d	18 41			18 53		19 11			19 25		19 41				19 55		20 11			20 21		20 43		
Stone Crossing	d				18 55					19 27						19 57					20 23				
Dartford 4	a	18 46			18 59		19 17			19 31		19 46				20 00		20 16			20 27		20 48		
	d	18 49	18 53	18 59	19 03	19 07	19 19	19 23	19 27	19 33	19 37	19 49		19 53	19 57	20 03	20 07	20 19	20 23	20 27	20 33	20 37	20 49	20 53	20 57
Slade Green 4	d		18 57			19 11			19 31		19 41				20 01		20 11			20 31		20 42			21 01
Erith	d		18 59			19 13			19 33		19 43				20 03		20 13			20 33		20 44			21 03
Belvedere	d		19 02			19 16			19 36		19 46				20 06		20 16			20 36		20 47			21 06
Abbey Wood	d	18 57	19 05			19 19	19 27		19 39		19 49	19 57			20 09		20 19	20 27		20 39		20 50	20 57		21 09
Plumstead	d		19 08			19 22			19 42		19 52				20 12		20 22			20 42		20 53			21 12
Woolwich Arsenal 4	d	19 01	19 11			19 25	19 31		19 45		19 55	20 01			20 15		20 25	20 31		20 45		20 56	21 01		21 15
Woolwich Dockyard	d		19 13			19 27			19 47		19 57				20 17		20 27			20 47		20 58			21 17
Charlton 4	d	19 06	19 16			19 30	19 36		19 50		20 00	20 06			20 20		20 30	20 36		20 50		21 01	21 06		21 20
Crayford	d				19 07					19 37						20 07					20 37				
Bexley	d				19 10					19 39						20 10					20 40				
Albany Park	d				19 12					19 42						20 12					20 42				
Sidcup 4	d				19 15					19 45						20 15					20 45				
New Eltham	d				19 18					19 48						20 18					20 48				
Mottingham	d				19 20					19 50						20 20					20 50				
Lee	d				19 23					19 53						20 23					20 53				
Hither Green 4	d				19 26					19 56						20 26					20 56				
Barnehurst 4	d			19 05				19 31						20 01					20 31					21 01	
Bexleyheath	d			19 08				19 34						20 04					20 34					21 04	
Welling	d			19 11				19 37						20 07					20 37					21 07	
Falconwood	d			19 13				19 39						20 09					20 39					21 09	
Eltham	d			19 16				19 42						20 12					20 42					21 12	
Kidbrooke	d			19 19				19 45						20 15					20 45					21 15	
Blackheath 4	d	19 10		19 23			19 40	19 49				20 10		20 19				20 40	20 49				21 10	21 19	
Lewisham 4	d	19 15		19 26	19 31		19 45	19 52		20 02		20 15		20 22		20 31		20 44	20 52		21 01		21 14	21 22	
St Johns	d																								
New Cross 4	⊖ d			19 30	19 34			19 56		20 05				20 26		20 34			20 56		21 04			21 26	
Nunhead 4	d																								
Peckham Rye 4	d																								
Denmark Hill 4	d																								
London Victoria 15	⊖ a																								
Westcombe Park	d		19 18			19 32			19 52		20 02				20 22		20 32			20 52		21 03			21 22
Maze Hill	d		19 20			19 34			19 54		20 04				20 24		20 34			20 54		21 05			21 24
Greenwich 4	d		19 24			19 38			19 58		20 08				20 28		20 38			20 58		21 09			21 28
Deptford	d		19 26			19 40			20 00		20 10				20 30		20 40			21 00		21 11			21 30
London Bridge 4	⊖ a	19 23	19 33	19 36	19 43	19 49	19 53	20 03	20 07	20 13	20 19	20 23		20 33	20 37	20 43	20 49	20 53	21 03	21 07	21 13	21 19	21 23	21 33	21 37
London Cannon Street 4	⊖ a		19 37	19 41					20 11						20 41										
London Waterloo (East) 4	⊖ a	19 28			19 49	19 54	19 58	20 08		20 18	20 24	20 28		20 38		20 48	20 54	20 58	21 08		21 18	21 24	21 28	21 38	
London Charing Cross 4	⊖ a	19 32			19 53	19 59	20 01	20 13		20 22	20 29	20 31		20 43		20 52	20 59	21 01	21 13		21 22	21 29	21 31	21 43	

For general notes see front of timetable
For details of catering facilities see
Directory of Train Operators

For details of Bank Holiday service alterations please see first page of Table 195

Gillingham and Dartford → London

Network Diagram - see first page of Table 200

Station		SE 54		SE 80	SE 60	SE 70	SE 81	SE 52	SE 80	SE 62	SE 70	SE 81	SE 50	SE 80		SE 62	SE 70	SE 80	SE 50	SE 82	SE 70				
Gillingham (Kent) [4]	d				20 42					21 14						21 42				22 22					
Chatham [4]	d				20 46					21 18						21 46				22 26					
Rochester [4]	d				20 48					21 20						21 48				22 28					
Maidstone West [4]	d				*20 24*					*21 00*						*21 27*				*22 02*					
Strood [4]	d				20 53					21b27						21 53				22 33					
Higham	d				20 57					21 31						21 57				22 37					
Gravesend [4]	d	20 44			21 04					21 38						22 04				22 44					
Northfleet	d	20 48			21 07											22 07				22 47					
Swanscombe	d	20 50			21 09											22 09				22 49					
Greenhithe for Bluewater	d	20 53			21 12					21 43						22 12				22 52					
Stone Crossing	d	20 55			21 14											22 14				22 54					
Dartford [4]	a	20 59			21 18					21 48						22 18				22 58					
	d	21 03		21 07	21 19	21 23	21 27	21 33	21 37	21 49	21 53	21 57	22 03	22 07		22 19	22 23	22 31	22 43	23 01	23 03				
Slade Green [4]	d			21 11			21 31		21 41			22 01		22 11				22 35		23 05					
Erith	d			21 13			21 33		21 43			22 03		22 13				22 37		23 07					
Belvedere	d			21 16			21 36		21 46			22 06		22 16				22 40		23 10					
Abbey Wood	d			21 19	21 27		21 39		21 49	21 57		22 09		22 19		22 27		22 43		23 13					
Plumstead	d			21 22			21 42		21 52			22 12		22 22				22 46		23 16					
Woolwich Arsenal [4]	d			21 25	21 31		21 45		21 55	22 01		22 15		22 25		22 31		22 49		23 19					
Woolwich Dockyard	d			21 27			21 47		21 57			22 17		22 27				22 51		23 21					
Charlton [4]	d			21 30	21 36		21 50		22 00	22 06		22 20		22 30		22 36		22 54		23 24					
Crayford	d	21 07						21 37					22 07						22 47						
Bexley	d	21 10						21 40					22 10						22 49						
Albany Park	d	21 12						21 42					22 12						22 52						
Sidcup [4]	d	21 15						21 45					22 15						22 55						
New Eltham	d	21 18						21 48					22 18						22 58						
Mottingham	d	21 20						21 50					22 20						23 00						
Lee	d	21 23						21 53					22 23						23 03						
Hither Green [4]	d	21 26						21 56					22 26						23 06						
Barnehurst [4]	d					21 31					22 01						22 31				23 11				
Bexleyheath	d					21 34					22 04						22 34				23 14				
Welling	d					21 37					22 07						22 37				23 17				
Falconwood	d					21 39					22 09						22 39				23 19				
Eltham	d					21 42					22 12						22 42				23 22				
Kidbrooke	d					21 45					22 15						22 45				23 25				
Blackheath [4]	d				21 40	21 49				22 10	22 19					22 40	22 49				23 29				
Lewisham [4]	d	21 31			21 44	21 52		22 01		22 14	22 22		22 31			22 44	22 52		23 11		23 32				
St Johns	d																								
New Cross [4]	⊖ d	21 34				21 56		22 04			22 26		22 34				22 56		23 14		23 36				
Nunhead [4]	d																								
Peckham Rye [4]	d																								
Denmark Hill [4]	d																								
London Victoria [15]	⊖ a																								
Westcombe Park	d			21 32			21 52		22 02			22 22		22 32				22 56		23 26					
Maze Hill	d			21 34			21 54		22 04			22 24		22 34				22 58		23 28					
Greenwich [4]	d			21 38			21 58		22 08			22 28		22 38				23 02		23 32					
Deptford	d			21 40			22 00		22 10			22 30		22 40				23 04		23 34					
London Bridge [4]	⊖ a	21 43		21 49	21 53	22 03	22 07	22 13	22 19	22 23	22 33	22 37	22 43	22 49		22 53	23 03	23 13	23 22	23 41	23 43				
London Cannon Street [4]	⊖ a																								
London Waterloo (East) [4]	⊖ a	21 48		21 54	21 58	22 08		22 18	22 24	22 28	22 38		22 48	22 54		22 58	23 08	23 18	23 28	23 46	23 49				
London Charing Cross [4]	⊖ a	21 52		21 59	22 01	22 13		22 22	22 29	22 31	22 43		22 52	22 59		23 01	23 13	23 22	23 32	23 50	23 53				

For general notes see front of timetable
For details of catering facilities see Directory of Train Operators

b Arr. 2124

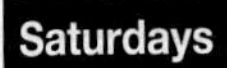

For details of Bank Holiday service alterations please see first page of Table 195

Gillingham and Dartford → London

Network Diagram - see first page of Table 200

		SE 58 A	SE 80	SE 70	SE 52	SE 80	SE 70	SE 52	SE 80	SE 62	SE 61 B	SE 54	SE 70	SE 54	SE 80	SE 62	SE 01	SE 78	SE 54	SE 70	SE 54	SE 81
Gillingham (Kent) 4	d	00 07			04 53			05 23		05 44	05 48					06 13	06 18					
Chatham 4	d	00 11			04 57			05 27		05 48	05 51					06 17	06 21					
Rochester 4	d	00 13			04 59			05 29		05 50	05 53					06 19	06 23					
Maidstone West 4	d																					
Strood 4	d	00 17			05 04			05 34		05 54	05a57					06 24	06a27					
Higham	d	00 22			05 09			05 39		05 59						06 29						
Gravesend 4	d	00 28			05 16			05 46		06 05		06 12				06 35			06 42			
Northfleet	d				05 19			05 49				06 16							06 46			
Swanscombe	d				05 21			05 51				06 18							06 48			
Greenhithe for Bluewater	d	00 34			05 24			05 54		06 10		06 21				06 40			06 51			
Stone Crossing	d				05 26			05 56				06 23							06 53			
Dartford 4	a	00 41			05 30			06 00		06 15		06 27				06 45			06 57			
	d	00 42	05 07	05 32	05 33	05 37	06 02	06 03	06 07	06 16		06 29	06 32		06 37	06 46		06 54	06 59	07 02		07 07
Slade Green 4	d		05 11			05 41			06 11						06 41							07 11
Erith	d		05 13			05 43			06 13						06 43							07 13
Belvedere	d		05 16			05 46			06 16						06 46							07 16
Abbey Wood	d		05 19			05 49			06 19	06 24					06 49	06 54						07 19
Plumstead	d		05 22			05 52			06 22						06 52							07 22
Woolwich Arsenal 4	d		05 25			05 55			06 25	06 28					06 55	06 58						07 25
Woolwich Dockyard	d		05 27			05 57			06 27						06 57							07 27
Charlton 4	d		05 30			06 00			06 30	06 33					07 00	07 03						07 30
Crayford	d				05 37			06 07				06 36							07 06			
Bexley	d				05 40			06 10				06 40							07 10			
Albany Park	d				05 42			06 12				06 42		←					07 12		←	
Sidcup 4	d				05 45			06 15				06 45 →		06 45					07 15 →		07 15	
New Eltham	d				05 48			06 18						06 48							07 18	
Mottingham	d				05 50			06 20						06 50							07 20	
Lee	d				05 53			06 23						06 53							07 23	
Hither Green 4	d				05 56			06 26						06 56							07 26	
Barnehurst 4	d			05 38			06 08						06 38					06 59		07 08		
Bexleyheath	d			05 41			06 11						06 41					07 02		07 11		
Welling	d			05 44			06 14						06 44					07 05		07 14		
Falconwood	d			05 46			06 16						06 46					07 07		07 16		
Eltham	d			05 49			06 19						06 49					07 10		07 19		
Kidbrooke	d			05 52			06 22						06 52					07 13		07 22		
Blackheath 4	d			05 56			06 26			06 38			06 56			07 08		07 17		07 26		
Lewisham 4	d			05 59	06 02		06 29	06 31		06 41			06 59	07 02		07 11		07 20		07 29	07 32	
St Johns	d																					
New Cross 4	⊖ d				06 05			06 34						07 05							07 35	
Nunhead 4	d																	07 25				
Peckham Rye 4	d																	07 28				
Denmark Hill 4	d																	07 31				
London Victoria 15	⊖ a	01 13																07 42				
Westcombe Park	d		05 32			06 02			06 32						07 02							07 32
Maze Hill	d		05 34			06 04			06 34						07 04							07 34
Greenwich 4	d		05 38			06 08			06 38						07 08							07 38
Deptford	d		05 40			06 10			06 40						07 10							07 40
London Bridge 4	⊖ a		05 49	06 07	06 13	06 19	06 37	06 43	06 48	06 50			07 07	07 13	07 19	07 21				07 37	07 43	07 46
London Cannon Street 4	⊖ a																					07 50
London Waterloo (East) 4	⊖ a		05 54	06 12	06 18	06 24	06 42	06 48	06 54	06 55			07 12	07 18	07 24	07 26				07 42	07 48	
London Charing Cross 4	⊖ a		05 59	06 15	06 23	06 29	06 45	06 52	06 59	06 58			07 15	07 22	07 29	07 29				07 45	07 52	

For general notes see front of timetable
For details of catering facilities see Directory of Train Operators

A From Faversham (Table 212)
B To Paddock Wood (Table 209)

Table 200

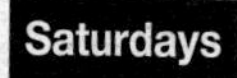

For details of Bank Holiday service alterations please see first page of Table 195

Gillingham and Dartford → London

Network Diagram - see first page of Table 200

Station		SE 62	SE 81	SE 78	SE 54	SE 70	SE 54	SE 62	SE 47	SE 81	SE 78	SE 54	SE 70	SE 87	SE 62	SE 47	SE 81	SE 78	SE 54	SE 70	SE 87	SE 82
Gillingham (Kent)	d	06 44						07 14							07 44							08 14
Chatham	d	06 48						07 18							07 48							08 18
Rochester	d	06 50						07 20							07 50							08 20
Maidstone West	d	*06 27*						*06 57*							*07 27*							*07 58*
Strood	d	06 54						07 24							07 54							08 25
Higham	d	06 59						07 29							07 59							08 29
Gravesend	d	07 05			07 12			07 35				07 42			08 05				08 12			08 36
Northfleet	d				07 16							07 46							08 16			
Swanscombe	d				07 18							07 48							08 18			
Greenhithe for Bluewater	d	07 10			07 21			07 40				07 51			08 10				08 21			08 41
Stone Crossing	d				07 23							07 53							08 23			
Dartford	a	07 15			07 27			07 45				07 57			08 15				08 27			08 46
	d	07 16	07 19	07 24	07 30	07 32		07 46		07 49	07 54	08 01	08 05		08 16		08 19	08 24	08 31	08 35		08 47
Slade Green	d		07 23							07 53				08 07			08 23				08 37	
Erith	d		07 26							07 56				08 09			08 26				08 39	
Belvedere	d		07 29							07 59				08 12			08 29				08 42	
Abbey Wood	d	07 24	07 31					07 54		08 01				08 15	08 24		08 31				08 45	08 55
Plumstead	d		07 34							08 04				08 18			08 34				08 48	
Woolwich Arsenal	d	07 28	07 37					07 58		08 07				08 21	08 28		08 37				08 51	08 59
Woolwich Dockyard	d		07 39							08 09				08 23			08 39				08 53	
Charlton	d	07 33	07 42					08 03		08 12				08 26	08 33		08 42				08 56	09 04
Crayford	d				07 36				07 51			08 05				08 21			08 35			
Bexley	d				07 40				07 53			08 08				08 23			08 38			
Albany Park	d				07 42		←		07 56			08 10				08 26			08 40			
Sidcup	d				07 45		07 45		07 59			08 13				08 29			08 43			
New Eltham	d				→		07 48		08 02			08 16				08 32			08 46			
Mottingham	d						07 50		08 04			08 18				08 34			08 48			
Lee	d						07 53		08 07			08 21				08 37			08 51			
Hither Green	d						07 56		08 10			08 24				08 40			08 54			
Barnehurst	d			07 29		07 38					07 59		08 11					08 29		08 41		
Bexleyheath	d			07 32		07 41					08 02		08 14					08 32		08 44		
Welling	d			07 35		07 44					08 05		08 17					08 35		08 47		
Falconwood	d			07 37		07 46					08 07		08 19					08 37		08 49		
Eltham	d			07 40		07 49					08 10		08 22					08 40		08 52		
Kidbrooke	d			07 43		07 52					08 13		08 25					08 43		08 55		
Blackheath	d	07 38		07 47		07 56		08 08			08 17		08 29		08 37			08 47		08 59		
Lewisham	d	07 41		07 50		07 59	08 02	08 11			08 20	08 29	08 32		08 41			08 50	08 59	09 02		
St Johns	d								08 14							08 45						
New Cross	⊖ d						08 05		08 17			08 32				08 47			09 02			
Nunhead	d			07 55							08 25							08 55				
Peckham Rye	d			07 58							08 28							08 58				
Denmark Hill	d			08 01							08 31							09 01				
London Victoria	⊖ a			08 12							08 42							09 12				
Westcombe Park	d		07 44							08 14				08 28			08 44				08 58	
Maze Hill	d		07 46							08 16				08 30			08 46				09 00	
Greenwich	d		07 50							08 20				08 34			08 50				09 04	09 10
Deptford	d		07 52							08 22				08 36			08 52				09 06	
London Bridge	⊖ a	07 49	07 59			08 07	08 13	08 19	08 23	08 29		08 38	08 43	08 43	08 49	08 53	08 59		09 08	09 13	09 13	09 19
London Cannon Street	⊖ a		08 03						08 27	08 33				08 47		08 57	09 03				09 17	
London Waterloo (East)	⊖ a	07 54				08 12	08 18	08 24				08 42	08 47		08 54				09 12	09 17		09 24
London Charing Cross	⊖ a	07 58				08 15	08 22	08 28				08 47	08 51		08 58				09 17	09 21		09 28

For general notes see front of timetable
For details of catering facilities see Directory of Train Operators

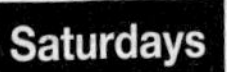

For details of Bank Holiday service alterations please see first page of Table 195

Gillingham and Dartford → London

Network Diagram - see first page of Table 200

Station		SE 47	SE 67	SE 81	SE 78	SE 54	SE 70	SE 87	SE 82	SE 47 A	SE 67	SE 81	SE 78	SE 54	SE 70	SE 87 A	SE 82	SE 47 A	SE 67	SE 81	SE 78	SE 54
Gillingham (Kent) 4	d								08 44								09 14					
Chatham 4	d								08 48								09 18					
Rochester 4	d								08 50								09 20					
Maidstone West 4	d								*08 27*								*08 58*					
Strood 4	d								08 55								09 25					
Higham	d								08 59								09 29					
Gravesend 4	d					08 42			09 06					09 12			09 36					09 42
Northfleet	d					08 45								09 16								09 46
Swanscombe	d					08 47								09 18								09 48
Greenhithe for Bluewater	d					08 50			09 11					09 21			09 41					09 51
Stone Crossing	d					08 52								09 23								09 53
Dartford 4	a					08 56			09 16					09 27			09 46					09 57
	d			08 49	08 54	09 01	09 05		09 17			09 19	09 24	09 31	09 35		09 47			09 49	09 54	10 01
Slade Green 4	d			08 53				09 07		09 10		09 23				09 37		09 40		09 53		
Erith	d			08 55				09 09				09 25				09 39				09 55		
Belvedere	d			08 58				09 12				09 28				09 42				09 58		
Abbey Wood	d			09 01				09 15	09 25			09 31				09 45	09 55			10 01		
Plumstead	d		09 01	09 04				09 18			09 31	09 34				09 48			10 01	10 04		
Woolwich Arsenal 4	d		09 03	09 07				09 21	09 29		09 33	09 37				09 51	09 59		10 03	10 07		
Woolwich Dockyard	d			09 09				09 23				09 39				09 53				10 09		
Charlton 4	d		09 08	09 12				09 26	09 34		09 38	09 42				09 56	10 04		10 08	10 12		
Crayford	d	08 51				09 05				09 20				09 35				09 50				10 05
Bexley	d	08 53				09 08				09 22				09 38				09 52				10 08
Albany Park	d	08 56				09 10				09 25				09 40				09 55				10 10
Sidcup 4	d	08 59				09 13				09 28				09 43				09 58				10 13
New Eltham	d	09 02				09 16				09 31				09 46				10 01				10 16
Mottingham	d	09 04				09 18				09 33				09 48				10 03				10 18
Lee	d	09 07				09 21				09 36				09 51				10 06				10 21
Hither Green 4	d	09 10				09 24				09 40				09 54				10 10				10 24
Barnehurst 4	d				08 59		09 11						09 29		09 41						09 59	
Bexleyheath	d				09 02		09 14						09 32		09 44						10 02	
Welling	d				09 05		09 17						09 35		09 47						10 05	
Falconwood	d				09 07		09 19						09 37		09 49						10 07	
Eltham	d				09 10		09 22						09 40		09 52						10 10	
Kidbrooke	d				09 13		09 25						09 43		09 55						10 13	
Blackheath 4	d		09 13		09 17		09 29				09 43		09 47		09 59				10 13		10 17	
Lewisham 4	d		09 16		09 20	09 29	09 32				09 46		09 50	09 59	10 02				10 16		10 20	10 29
St Johns	d	09 14								09 44								10 14				
New Cross 4	⊖ d	09 17	09 20			09 32				09 47	09 50							10 17	10 20			
Nunhead 4	d				09 25								09 55								10 25	
Peckham Rye 4	d				09 28								09 58								10 28	
Denmark Hill 4	d				09 31								10 01								10 31	
London Victoria 15	⊖ a				09 42								10 12								10 42	
Westcombe Park	d			09 14				09 28				09 44				09 58				10 14		
Maze Hill	d			09 16				09 30				09 46				10 00				10 16		
Greenwich 4	d			09 20				09 34	09 40			09 50				10 04	10 10			10 20		
Deptford	d			09 22				09 36				09 52				10 06				10 22		
London Bridge 4	⊖ a	09 23	09 26	09 29		09 38	09 40	09 43	09 49	09 53	09 56	09 59		10 07	10 10	10 13	10 19	10 23	10 26	10 29		10 37
London Cannon Street 4	⊖ a	09 27	09 30	09 33				09 47		09 57	10 00	10 03				10 17		10 27	10 30	10 34		
London Waterloo (East) 4	⊖ a					09 42	09 45		09 54					10 12	10 15		10 24					10 42
London Charing Cross 4	⊖ a					09 47	09 50		09 58					10 17	10 20		10 28					10 47

For general notes see front of timetable
For details of catering facilities see Directory of Train Operators

A From London Cannon Street (Table 199)

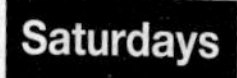

For details of Bank Holiday service alterations please see first page of Table 195

Gillingham and Dartford → London

Network Diagram - see first page of Table 200

Station		SE 70	SE 87 A	SE 82	SE 47 A	SE 67		SE 81	SE 78	SE 54	SE 70	SE 87 A	SE 82	SE 47 A	SE 67	SE 81	SE 78	SE 54	SE 70	SE 62	SE 80
Gillingham (Kent) 4	d			09 44									17 14							17 44	
Chatham 4	d			09 48									17 18							17 48	
Rochester 4	d			09 50									17 20							17 50	
Maidstone West 4	d			*09 27*									*16 58*							*17 27*	
Strood 4	d			09 55									17 25							17 55	
Higham	d			09 59									17 29							17 59	
Gravesend 4	d			10 06						17 12			17 36					17 42		18 06	
Northfleet	d									17 16								17 46			
Swanscombe	d									17 18								17 48			
Greenhithe for Bluewater	d			10 11						17 21			17 41					17 51		18 11	
Stone Crossing	d									17 23								17 53			
Dartford 4	a			10 16						17 27			17 46					17 57		18 16	
	d	10 05		10 17				17 19	17 24	17 31	17 35		17 47			17 49	17 54	18 01	18 05	18 17	18 19
Slade Green 4	d		10 07		10 10			17 23				17 37		17 40		17 53					18 23
Erith	d		10 09					17 25				17 39				17 55					18 25
Belvedere	d		10 12					17 28				17 42				17 58					18 28
Abbey Wood	d		10 15	10 25				17 31				17 45	17 55			18 01				18 25	18 31
Plumstead	d		10 18			10 31		17 34				17 48			18 01	18 04					18 34
Woolwich Arsenal 4	d		10 21	10 29		10 33		17 37				17 51	17 59		18 03	18 07				18 29	18 37
Woolwich Dockyard	d		10 23					17 39				17 53				18 09					18 39
Charlton 4	d		10 26	10 34		10 38	and at	17 42				17 56	18 04		18 08	18 12				18 34	18 42
Crayford	d				10 20		the same			17 35				17 50				18 05			
Bexley	d				10 22		minutes			17 38				17 52				18 08			
Albany Park	d				10 25		past			17 40				17 55				18 10			
Sidcup 4	d				10 28		each			17 43				17 58				18 13			
New Eltham	d				10 31		hour until			17 46				18 01				18 16			
Mottingham	d				10 33					17 48				18 03				18 18			
Lee	d				10 36					17 51				18 06				18 21			
Hither Green 4	d				10 40					17 54				18 10				18 24			
Barnehurst 4	d	10 11							17 29		17 41						17 59		18 11		
Bexleyheath	d	10 14							17 32		17 44						18 02		18 14		
Welling	d	10 17							17 35		17 47						18 05		18 17		
Falconwood	d	10 19							17 37		17 49						18 07		18 19		
Eltham	d	10 22							17 40		17 52						18 10		18 22		
Kidbrooke	d	10 25							17 43		17 55						18 13		18 25		
Blackheath 4	d	10 29				10 43			17 47		17 59				18 13		18 17		18 29		
Lewisham 4	d	10 32				10 46			17 50	17 59	18 02				18 16		18 20	18 29	18 32	18 38	
St Johns	d				10 44									18 14				18 31		18 41	
New Cross 4	⊖ d				10 47	10 50								18 17	18 20			18 32			
Nunhead 4	d								17 55								18 25				
Peckham Rye 4	d								17 58								18 28				
Denmark Hill 4	d								18 01								18 31				
London Victoria 15	⊖ a								18 12								18 42				
Westcombe Park	d		10 28					17 44				17 58				18 14					18 44
Maze Hill	d		10 30					17 46				18 00				18 16					18 46
Greenwich 4	d		10 34	10 40				17 50				18 04	18 10			18 20					18 50
Deptford	d		10 36					17 52				18 06				18 22					18 53
London Bridge 4	⊖ a	10 40	10 43	10 49	10 53	10 56		17 59		18 07	18 10	18 13	18 19	18 23	18 26	18 29		18 38	18 40	18 49	19 03
London Cannon Street 4	⊖ a		10 47		10 57	11 00		18 03				18 17		18 27	18 30	18 33					
London Waterloo (East) 4	⊖ a	10 45		10 54						18 12	18 15		18 24					18 43	18 45	18 54	19 09
London Charing Cross 4	⊖ a	10 50		10 58						18 17	18 20		18 28					18 48	18 50	18 58	19 13

For general notes see front of timetable
For details of catering facilities see Directory of Train Operators

A From London Cannon Street (Table 199)

Table 200

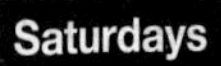

Saturdays

For details of Bank Holiday service alterations please see first page of Table 195

Gillingham and Dartford → London

Network Diagram - see first page of Table 200

		SE 78	SE 54	SE 70	SE 54	SE 80	SE 62	SE 70	SE 54	SE 80	SE 62	SE 70	SE 54	SE 80	SE 62	SE 70	SE 54	SE 80	SE 62	SE 70	SE 54	SE 80
Gillingham (Kent) 4	d						18 14				18 44				19 14				19 44			
Chatham 4	d						18 18				18 48				19 18				19 48			
Rochester 4	d						18 20				18 50				19 20				19 50			
Maidstone West 4	d						*17 58*				*18 27*				*18 58*				*19 27*			
Strood 4	d						18 25				18 55				19 25				19 55			
Higham	d						18 29				18 59				19 29				19 59			
Gravesend 4	d		18 12				18 36		18 42		19 06		19 12		19 36		19 42		20 06		20 12	
Northfleet	d		18 16						18 46				19 16				19 46				20 16	
Swanscombe	d		18 18						18 48				19 18				19 48				20 18	
Greenhithe for Bluewater	d		18 21				18 41		18 51		19 11		19 21		19 41		19 51		20 11		20 21	
Stone Crossing	d		18 23						18 53				19 23				19 53				20 23	
Dartford 4	a		18 27				18 46		18 57		19 16		19 27		19 46		19 57		20 16		20 27	
	d	18 24	18 31	18 35		18 37	18 47	18 53	19 03	19 07	19 19	19 23	19 33	19 37	19 49	19 53	20 03	20 07	20 19	20 23	20 33	20 37
Slade Green 4	d					18 41				19 11				19 41				20 11				20 41
Erith	d					18 43				19 13				19 43				20 13				20 43
Belvedere	d					18 46				19 16				19 46				20 16				20 46
Abbey Wood	d					18 49	18 55			19 19	19 27			19 49	19 57			20 19	20 27			20 49
Plumstead	d					18 52				19 22				19 52				20 22				20 52
Woolwich Arsenal 4	d					18 55	18 59			19 25	19 31			19 55	20 01			20 25	20 31			20 55
Woolwich Dockyard	d					18 57				19 27				19 57				20 27				20 57
Charlton 4	d					19 00	19 04			19 30	19 36			20 00	20 06			20 30	20 36			21 00
Crayford	d		18 37						19 07				19 37				20 07				20 37	
Bexley	d		18 40						19 10				19 40				20 10				20 40	
Albany Park	d		18 42						19 12				19 42				20 12				20 42	
Sidcup 4	d		18 45						19 15				19 45				20 15				20 45	
New Eltham	d		18 48						19 18				19 48				20 18				20 48	
Mottingham	d		18 50						19 20				19 50				20 20				20 50	
Lee	d		18 53						19 23				19 53				20 23				20 53	
Hither Green 4	d		18 56						19 26				19 56				20 26				20 56	
Barnehurst 4	d	18 29		18 41				19 01				19 31				20 01				20 31		
Bexleyheath	d	18 32		18 44				19 04				19 34				20 04				20 34		
Welling	d	18 35		18 47				19 07				19 37				20 07				20 37		
Falconwood	d	18 37		18 49				19 09				19 39				20 09				20 39		
Eltham	d	18 40		18 52				19 12				19 42				20 12				20 42		
Kidbrooke	d	18 43		18 55				19 15				19 45				20 15				20 45		
Blackheath 4	d	18 47		18 59			19 08	19 19			19 40	19 49			20 10	20 19			20 40	20 49		
Lewisham 4	d	18 50	19 01	19 02			19 11	19 22	19 31		19 44	19 52	20 01		20 14	20 22	20 31		20 44	20 52	21 01	
St Johns	d				←																	
New Cross 4	⊖ d		19 04		19 04			19 26	19 34			19 56	20 04			20 26	20 34			20 56	21 04	
Nunhead 4	d	18 55	→																			
Peckham Rye 4	d	18 58																				
Denmark Hill 4	d	19 01																				
London Victoria 15	⊖ a	19 12																				
Westcombe Park	d					19 02				19 32				20 02				20 32				21 02
Maze Hill	d					19 04				19 34				20 04				20 34				21 04
Greenwich 4	d					19 08				19 38				20 08				20 38				21 08
Deptford	d					19 10				19 40				20 10				20 40				21 10
London Bridge 4	⊖ a			19 11	19 13	19 18	19 21	19 33	19 43	19 49	19 53	20 03	20 13	20 19	20 23	20 33	20 43	20 49	20 53	21 03	21 13	21 19
London Cannon Street 4	⊖ a																					
London Waterloo (East) 4	⊖ a			19 15	19 18	19 23	19 25	19 38	19 48	19 54	19 58	20 08	20 18	20 24	20 28	20 38	20 48	20 54	20 58	21 08	21 18	21 24
London Charing Cross 4	⊖ a			19 20	19 22	19 26	19 29	19 43	19 52	19 59	20 01	20 13	20 22	20 29	20 31	20 43	20 52	20 59	21 01	21 13	21 22	21 29

For general notes see front of timetable
For details of catering facilities see Directory of Train Operators

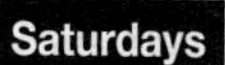

For details of Bank Holiday service alterations please see first page of Table 195

Gillingham and Dartford → London

Network Diagram - see first page of Table 200

		SE 62	SE 70	SE 50	SE 80	SE 62	SE 70	SE 50	SE 80	SE 62	SE 70	SE 50	SE 80	SE 62	SE 70	SE 80	SE 50	SE 80	SE 70
Gillingham (Kent) 4	d	20 14				20 42				21 14				21 42				22 22	
Chatham 4	d	20 18				20 46				21 18				21 46				22 26	
Rochester 4	d	20 20				20 48				21 20				21 48				22 28	
Maidstone West 4	d	*19 58*				*20 27*				*20 58*				*21 28*					
Strood 4	d	20 25				20 53				21 25				21 53				22 33	
Higham	d	20 29				20 57				21 29				21 57				22 37	
Gravesend 4	d	20 36				21 04				21 36				22 04				22 44	
Northfleet	d					21 07								22 07				22 47	
Swanscombe	d					21 09								22 09				22 49	
Greenhithe for Bluewater	d	20 41				21 12				21 41				22 12				22 52	
Stone Crossing	d					21 14								22 14				22 54	
Dartford 4	a	20 46				21 18				21 46				22 18				22 58	
	d	20 49	20 53	21 03	21 07	21 19	21 23	21 33	21 37	21 49	21 53	22 03	22 07	22 19	22 23	22 31	22 43	23 00	23 03
Slade Green 4	d				21 11				21 41				22 11			22 35		23 05	
Erith	d				21 13				21 43				22 13			22 37		23 07	
Belvedere	d				21 16				21 46				22 16			22 40		23 10	
Abbey Wood	d	20 57			21 19	21 27			21 49	21 57			22 19	22 27		22 43		23 13	
Plumstead	d				21 22				21 52				22 22			22 46		23 16	
Woolwich Arsenal 4	d	21 01			21 25	21 31			21 55	22 01			22 25	22 31		22 49		23 19	
Woolwich Dockyard	d				21 27				21 57				22 27			22 51		23 21	
Charlton 4	d	21 06			21 30	21 36			22 00	22 06			22 30	22 36		22 54		23 24	
Crayford	d			21 07				21 37				22 07					22 47		
Bexley	d			21 10				21 40				22 10					22 49		
Albany Park	d			21 12				21 42				22 12					22 52		
Sidcup 4	d			21 15				21 45				22 15					22 55		
New Eltham	d			21 18				21 48				22 18					22 58		
Mottingham	d			21 20				21 50				22 20					23 00		
Lee	d			21 23				21 53				22 23					23 03		
Hither Green 4	d			21 26				21 56				22 26					23 06		
Barnehurst 4	d		21 01				21 31				22 01				22 31				23 11
Bexleyheath	d		21 04				21 34				22 04				22 34				23 14
Welling	d		21 07				21 37				22 07				22 37				23 17
Falconwood	d		21 09				21 39				22 09				22 39				23 19
Eltham	d		21 12				21 42				22 12				22 42				23 22
Kidbrooke	d		21 15				21 45				22 15				22 45				23 25
Blackheath 4	d	21 10	21 19			21 40	21 49			22 10	22 19			22 40	22 49				23 29
Lewisham 4	⛴ d	21 14	21 22	21 31		21 44	21 52	22 01		22 14	22 22	22 31		22 44	22 52		23 11		23 32
St Johns	d																		
New Cross 4	⊖ d		21 26	21 34			21 56	22 04			22 26	22 34			22 56		23 14		23 36
Nunhead 4	d																		
Peckham Rye 4	d																		
Denmark Hill 4	d																		
London Victoria 15	⊖ a																		
Westcombe Park	d				21 32				22 02				22 32			22 56		23 26	
Maze Hill	d				21 34				22 04				22 34			22 58		23 28	
Greenwich 4	⛴ d				21 38				22 08				22 38			23 02		23 32	
Deptford	d				21 40				22 10				22 40			23 04		23 34	
London Bridge 4	⊖ a	21 23	21 33	21 43	21 49	21 53	22 03	22 13	22 19	22 23	22 33	22 43	22 49	22 53	23 03	23 13	23 22	23 41	23 43
London Cannon Street 4	⊖ a																		
London Waterloo (East) 4	⊖ a	21 28	21 38	21 48	21 54	21 58	22 08	22 18	22 24	22 28	22 38	22 48	22 54	22 58	23 08	23 18	23 28	23 46	23 49
London Charing Cross 4	⊖ a	21 31	21 43	21 52	21 59	22 01	22 13	22 22	22 29	22 31	22 43	22 52	22 59	23 01	23 13	23 22	23 32	23 50	23 53

For general notes see front of timetable
For details of catering facilities see Directory of Train Operators

Table 200

Sundays

Gillingham and Dartford → London

Network Diagram - see first page of Table 200

		SE 58 A	SE 70	SE 80	SE 50	SE 70	55 B	SE 62		SE 80	SE 50	SE 72	SE 60	SE 80	SE 50	SE 70		SE 62	SE 80	SE 50	SE 67	SE 72	SE 62	SE 80	SE 50
Gillingham (Kent) 4	d	00 05					06 30	06 40					07 15					07 40					08 15		
Chatham 4	d	00 09					06 34	06 44					07 19					07 44					08 19		
Rochester 4	d	00 11					06 37	06 47					07 22					07 47					08 22		
Maidstone West 4	d												*07 00*										*08 00*		
Strood 4	d	00 15					06a41	06 52					07 27					07 52					08 27		
Higham	d	00 20						06 56					07 32					07 56					08 32		
Gravesend 4	d	00 26						07 03					07 38					08 03					08 38		
Northfleet	d							07 07										08 07							
Swanscombe	d							07 09										08 09							
Greenhithe for Bluewater	d	00 32						07 12					07 44					08 12					08 44		
Stone Crossing	d							07 15										08 15							
Dartford 4	a	00 39						07 18					07 49					08 18					08 49		
	d	00 40	06 48	06 53	06 57	07 08		07 19		07 23	07 27	07 38	07 49	07 53	07 57	08 08		08 19	08 23	08 27		08 38	08 49	08 53	08 57
Slade Green 4	d			06 57						07 27				07 57					08 27					08 57	
Erith	d			07 00						07 30				08 00					08 30					09 00	
Belvedere	d			07 03						07 33				08 03					08 33					09 03	
Abbey Wood	d			07 06				07 28		07 36			07 58	08 06				08 28	08 36				08 58	09 06	
Plumstead	d			07 09						07 39				08 09					08 39		08 49			09 09	
Woolwich Arsenal 4	d			07 11				07 32		07 41			08 02	08 11				08 32	08 41		08 51		09 02	09 11	
Woolwich Dockyard	d			07 13						07 43				08 13					08 43		08 53			09 13	
Charlton 4	d			07 17				07 37		07 47			08 07	08 17				08 37	08 47		08 57		09 07	09 17	
Crayford	d				07 01						07 31				08 01					08 31					09 01
Bexley	d				07 04						07 34				08 04					08 34					09 04
Albany Park	d				07 06						07 36				08 06					08 36					09 06
Sidcup 4	d				07 09						07 39				08 09					08 39					09 09
New Eltham	d				07 12						07 42				08 12					08 42					09 12
Mottingham	d				07 14						07 44				08 14					08 44					09 14
Lee	d				07 17						07 47				08 17					08 47					09 17
Hither Green 4	d				07 21						07 51				08 21					08 51					09 21
Barnehurst 4	d		06 54			07 14						07 44				08 14						08 44			
Bexleyheath	d		06 56			07 16						07 46				08 16						08 46			
Welling	d		06 59			07 19						07 49				08 19						08 49			
Falconwood	d		07 02			07 22						07 52				08 22						08 52			
Eltham	d		07 05			07 25						07 55				08 25						08 55			
Kidbrooke	d		07 08			07 28						07 58				08 28						08 58			
Blackheath 4	d		07 11			07 31		07 41				08 01	08 11			08 31		08 41				09 01	09 11		
Lewisham 4	d		07 16		07 26	07 36		07 45			07 56	08 06	08 15		08 26	08 36		08 45		08 56		09 06	09 15		09 26
St Johns	d																								
New Cross 4	⊖ d		07 20		07 30	07 40					08 00	08 10			08 30	08 40				09 00		09 10			09 30
Nunhead 4	d																								
Peckham Rye 4	d																								
Denmark Hill 4	d																								
London Victoria 15	⊖ a	01 11																							
Westcombe Park	d			07 19						07 49				08 19					08 49		08 59			09 19	
Maze Hill	d			07 21						07 51				08 21					08 51		09 01			09 21	
Greenwich 4	d			07 25						07 55				08 25					08 55		09 05			09 25	
Deptford	d			07 27						07 57				08 27					08 57		09 07			09 27	
London Bridge 4	⊖ a		07 26	07 34	07 36	07 48		07 53		08 04	08 06	08 18	08 23	08 34	08 36	08 48		08 53	09 04	09 06	09 14	09 18	09 23	09 34	09 36
London Cannon Street 4	⊖ a																								
London Waterloo (East) 4	⊖ a		07 31	07 39	07 41	07 53		07 58		08 09	08 11	08 23	08 28	08 39	08 41	08 53		08 58	09 09	09 11		09 23	09 28	09 39	09 41
London Charing Cross 4	⊖ a		07 36	07 42	07 45	07 56		08 02		08 12	08 15	08 26	08 32	08 42	08 45	08 56		09 02	09 12	09 15		09 26	09 32	09 42	09 45

For general notes see front of timetable
For details of catering facilities see
Directory of Train Operators

A From Faversham (Table 212)
B To Three Bridges (Table 209)

Table 200

Sundays

Gillingham and Dartford → London

Network Diagram - see first page of Table 200

		SE 67	SE 70	SE 60	SE 80	SE 50	SE 67	SE 72	SE 60	SE 80	SE 50	SE 67	SE 70	SE 60	SE 84	SE 50	SE 67	SE 70	SE 60	SE 84	SE 50	SE 67
Gillingham (Kent) [4]	d			08 45					09 15					09 45					10 15			
Chatham [4]	d			08 49					09 19					09 49					10 19			
Rochester [4]	d			08 52					09 22					09 52					10 22			
Maidstone West [4]	d								*09 00*										*10 00*			
Strood [4]	d			08 57					09 27					09 57					10 27			
Higham	d			09 02					09 32					10 02					10 32			
Gravesend [4]	d		08 52	09 08				09 22	09 38				09 52	10 08				10 22	10 38			
Northfleet	d		08 56					09 26					09 56					10 26				
Swanscombe	d		08 58					09 28					09 58					10 28				
Greenhithe for Bluewater	d		09 01	09 14				09 31	09 44				10 01	10 14				10 31	10 44			
Stone Crossing	d		09 03					09 33					10 03					10 33				
Dartford [4]	a		09 07	09 19				09 37	09 49				10 07	10 19				10 37	10 49			
	d		09 08	09 19	09 23	09 27		09 38	09 49	09 53	09 57		10 08	10 19	10 23	10 27		10 38	10 49	10 53	10 57	
Slade Green [4]	d				09 27					09 57					10 27					10 57		
Erith	d				09 30					10 00					10 30					11 00		
Belvedere	d				09 33					10 03					10 33					11 03		
Abbey Wood	d			09 28	09 36				09 58	10 06				10 28	10 36				10 58	11 06		
Plumstead	d	09 19			09 39		09 49			10 09		10 19			10 39		10 49			11 09		11 19
Woolwich Arsenal [4]	d	09 21		09 32	09 41		09 51		10 02	10 11		10 21		10 32	10 41		10 51		11 02	11 11		11 21
Woolwich Dockyard	d	09 23			09 43		09 53			10 13		10 23			10 43		10 53			11 13		11 23
Charlton [4]	d	09 27		09 37	09 47		09 57		10 07	10 17		10 27		10 37	10 47		10 57		11 07	11 17		11 27
Crayford	d					09 31					10 01					10 31					11 01	
Bexley	d					09 34					10 04					10 34					11 04	
Albany Park	d					09 36					10 06					10 36					11 06	
Sidcup [4]	d					09 39					10 09					10 39					11 09	
New Eltham	d					09 42					10 12					10 42					11 12	
Mottingham	d					09 44					10 14					10 44					11 14	
Lee	d					09 47					10 17					10 47					11 17	
Hither Green [4]	d					09 51					10 21					10 51					11 21	
Barnehurst [4]	d		09 14					09 44					10 14					10 44				
Bexleyheath	d		09 16					09 46					10 16					10 46				
Welling	d		09 19					09 49					10 19					10 49				
Falconwood	d		09 22					09 52					10 22					10 52				
Eltham	d		09 25					09 55					10 25					10 55				
Kidbrooke	d		09 28					09 58					10 28					10 58				
Blackheath [4]	d		09 31	09 41				10 01	10 11				10 31	10 41				11 01	11 11			
Lewisham [4]	d		09 36	09 45		09 56		10 06	10 15		10 26		10 36	10 45		10 56		11 06	11 15		11 26	
St Johns	d																					
New Cross [4]	⊖ d		09 40			10 00		10 10			10 30		10 40			11 00		11 10			11 30	
Nunhead [4]	d																					
Peckham Rye [4]	d																					
Denmark Hill [4]	d																					
London Victoria [15]	⊖ a																					
Westcombe Park	d	09 29			09 49		09 59			10 19		10 29			10 49		10 59			11 19		11 29
Maze Hill	d	09 31			09 51		10 01			10 21		10 31			10 51		11 01			11 21		11 31
Greenwich [4]	d	09 35			09 55		10 05			10 25		10 35			10 55		11 05			11 25		11 35
Deptford	d	09 37			09 57		10 07			10 27		10 37			10 57		11 07			11 27		11 37
London Bridge [4]	⊖ a	09 44	09 48	09 53	10 04	10 06	10 14	10 18	10 23	10 34	10 36	10 44	10 48	10 53	11 04	11 06	11 14	11 18	11 23	11 34	11 36	11 44
London Cannon Street [4]	⊖ a																					
London Waterloo (East) [4]	⊖ a		09 53	09 58	10 09	10 11		10 23	10 28	10 39	10 41		10 53	10 58	11 09	11 11		11 23	11 28	11 39	11 41	
London Charing Cross [4]	⊖ a		09 56	10 02	10 12	10 15		10 26	10 32	10 42	10 45		10 56	11 02	11 12	11 15		11 26	11 32	11 42	11 45	

For general notes see front of timetable
For details of catering facilities see
Directory of Train Operators

Table 200

Sundays

Gillingham and Dartford → London

Network Diagram - see first page of Table 200

Station		SE 70		SE 62	SE 84	SE 50	SE 72	SE 62	SE 80	SE 50	SE 70	SE 62	SE 80	SE 50	SE 72	SE 62	SE 80	SE 50	SE 70	SE 62	SE 80
Gillingham (Kent) 4	d			17 45				18 15				18 45				19 15				19 43	
Chatham 4	d			17 49				18 19				18 49				19 19				19 47	
Rochester 4	d			17 52				18 22				18 52				19 22				19 49	
Maidstone West 4	d							*18 00*								*19 00*					
Strood 4	d			17 57				18 27				18 57				19 27				19 54	
Higham	d			18 02				18 32				19 02				19 32				19 59	
Gravesend 4	d	10 52		18 08			18 22	18 38			18 52	19 08			19 22	19 38				20 05	
Northfleet	d	10 56					18 26				18 56				19 26					20 09	
Swanscombe	d	10 58					18 28				18 58				19 28					20 11	
Greenhithe for Bluewater	d	11 01		18 14			18 31	18 44			19 01	19 14			19 31	19 44				20 14	
Stone Crossing	d	11 03					18 33				19 03				19 33					20 16	
Dartford 4	a	11 07		18 19			18 37	18 49			19 07	19 19			19 37	19 49				20 19	
	d	11 08		18 19	18 23	18 27	18 38	18 49	18 53	18 57	19 08	19 19	19 23	19 27	19 38	19 49	19 53	19 57	20 08	20 19	20 23
Slade Green 4	d				18 27				18 57				19 27				19 57				20 27
Erith	d				18 30				19 00				19 30				20 00				20 30
Belvedere	d				18 33				19 03				19 33				20 03				20 33
Abbey Wood	d			18 28	18 36			18 58	19 06			19 28	19 36			19 58	20 06			20 28	20 36
Plumstead	d				18 39				19 09				19 39				20 09				20 39
Woolwich Arsenal 4	d			18 32	18 41			19 02	19 11			19 32	19 41			20 02	20 11			20 32	20 41
Woolwich Dockyard	d				18 43				19 13				19 43				20 13				20 43
Charlton 4	d		and at the same minutes past each hour until	18 37	18 47			19 07	19 17			19 37	19 47			20 07	20 17			20 37	20 47
Crayford	d					18 31				19 01				19 31				20 01			
Bexley	d					18 34				19 04				19 34				20 04			
Albany Park	d					18 36				19 06				19 36				20 06			
Sidcup 4	d					18 39				19 09				19 39				20 09			
New Eltham	d					18 42				19 12				19 42				20 12			
Mottingham	d					18 44				19 14				19 44				20 14			
Lee	d					18 47				19 17				19 47				20 17			
Hither Green 4	d					18 51				19 21				19 51				20 21			
Barnehurst 4	d	11 14					18 44				19 14				19 44				20 14		
Bexleyheath	d	11 16					18 46				19 16				19 46				20 16		
Welling	d	11 19					18 49				19 19				19 49				20 19		
Falconwood	d	11 22					18 52				19 22				19 52				20 22		
Eltham	d	11 25					18 55				19 25				19 55				20 25		
Kidbrooke	d	11 28					18 58				19 28				19 58				20 28		
Blackheath 4	d	11 31		18 41			19 01	19 11			19 31	19 41			20 01	20 11			20 31	20 41	
Lewisham 4	d	11 36		18 45		18 56	19 06	19 15		19 26	19 36	19 45		19 56	20 06	20 15		20 26	20 36	20 45	
St Johns	d																				
New Cross 4	⊖ d	11 40				19 00	19 10			19 30	19 40			20 00	20 10			20 30	20 40		
Nunhead 4	d																				
Peckham Rye 4	d																				
Denmark Hill 4	d																				
London Victoria 15	⊖ a																				
Westcombe Park	d				18 49				19 19				19 49				20 19				20 49
Maze Hill	d				18 51				19 21				19 51				20 21				20 51
Greenwich 4	d				18 55				19 25				19 55				20 25				20 55
Deptford	d				18 57				19 27				19 57				20 27				20 57
London Bridge 4	⊖ a	11 48		18 53	19 04	19 06	19 18	19 23	19 34	19 36	19 48	19 53	20 04	20 06	20 18	20 23	20 34	20 36	20 48	20 53	21 04
London Cannon Street 4	⊖ a																				
London Waterloo (East) 4	⊖ a	11 53		18 58	19 09	19 11	19 23	19 28	19 39	19 41	19 53	19 58	20 09	20 11	20 23	20 28	20 39	20 41	20 53	20 58	21 09
London Charing Cross 4	⊖ a	11 56		19 02	19 12	19 15	19 26	19 32	19 42	19 45	19 56	20 02	20 12	20 15	20 26	20 32	20 42	20 45	20 56	21 02	21 12

For general notes see front of timetable
For details of catering facilities see Directory of Train Operators

Table 200

Sundays

Gillingham and Dartford → London

Network Diagram - see first page of Table 200

		SE 50	SE 72	SE 62	SE 80	SE 50	SE 70	SE 62	SE 80	SE 50	SE 72	SE 62	SE 80	SE 50	SE 70	SE 62	SE 80	SE 50	SE 72	SE 50
Gillingham (Kent) 4	d			20 15				20 40				21 15				21 40				22 15
Chatham 4	d			20 19				20 44				21 19				21 44				22 19
Rochester 4	d			20 22				20 47				21 22				21 47				22 22
Maidstone West 4	d											*21 00*								
Strood 4	d			20 27				20 52				21 27				21 52				22 27
Higham	d			20 32				20 56				21 32				21 56				22 32
Gravesend 4	d			20 38				21 03				21 38				22 03				22 39
Northfleet	d							21 07								22 07				22 43
Swanscombe	d							21 09								22 09				22 45
Greenhithe for Bluewater	d			20 44				21 12				21 44				22 12				22 48
Stone Crossing	d							21 15								22 15				22 50
Dartford 4	a			20 49				21 18				21 49				22 18				22 53
	d	20 27	20 38	20 49	20 53	20 57	21 08	21 19	21 23	21 27	21 38	21 49	21 53	21 57	22 08	22 19	22 23	22 27	22 38	22 57
Slade Green 4	d				20 57				21 27				21 57				22 27			
Erith	d				21 00				21 30				22 00				22 30			
Belvedere	d				21 03				21 33				22 03				22 33			
Abbey Wood	d			20 58	21 06			21 28	21 36			21 58	22 06			22 28	22 36			
Plumstead	d				21 09				21 39				22 09				22 39			
Woolwich Arsenal 4	d			21 02	21 11			21 32	21 41			22 02	22 11			22 32	22 41			
Woolwich Dockyard	d				21 13				21 43				22 13				22 43			
Charlton 4	d			21 07	21 17			21 37	21 47			22 07	22 17			22 37	22 47			
Crayford	d	20 31				21 01				21 31				22 01				22 31		23 01
Bexley	d	20 34				21 04				21 34				22 04				22 34		23 04
Albany Park	d	20 36				21 06				21 36				22 06				22 36		23 06
Sidcup 4	d	20 39				21 09				21 39				22 09				22 39		23 09
New Eltham	d	20 42				21 12				21 42				22 12				22 42		23 12
Mottingham	d	20 44				21 14				21 44				22 14				22 44		23 14
Lee	d	20 47				21 17				21 47				22 17				22 47		23 17
Hither Green 4	d	20 51				21 21				21 51				22 21				22 51		23 21
Barnehurst 4	d		20 44				21 14				21 44				22 14				22 44	
Bexleyheath	d		20 46				21 16				21 46				22 16				22 46	
Welling	d		20 49				21 19				21 49				22 19				22 49	
Falconwood	d		20 52				21 22				21 52				22 22				22 52	
Eltham	d		20 55				21 25				21 55				22 25				22 55	
Kidbrooke	d		20 58				21 28				21 58				22 28				22 58	
Blackheath 4	d		21 01	21 11			21 31	21 41			22 01	22 11			22 31	22 41			23 01	
Lewisham 4	d	20 56	21 06	21 15		21 26	21 36	21 45		21 56	22 06	22 15		22 26	22 36	22 45		22 56	23 06	23 26
St Johns	d																			
New Cross 4	⊖ d	21 00	21 10			21 30	21 40			22 00	22 10			22 30	22 40			23 00	23 10	23 30
Nunhead 4	d																			
Peckham Rye 4	d																			
Denmark Hill 4	d																			
London Victoria 15	⊖ a																			
Westcombe Park	d				21 19				21 49				22 19				22 49			
Maze Hill	d				21 21				21 51				22 21				22 51			
Greenwich 4	d				21 25				21 55				22 25				22 55			
Deptford	d				21 27				21 57				22 27				22 57			
London Bridge 4	⊖ a	21 06	21 18	21 23	21 34	21 36	21 48	21 53	22 04	22 06	22 18	22 23	22 34	22 36	22 48	22 53	23 04	23 06	23 18	23 36
London Cannon Street 4	⊖ a																			
London Waterloo (East) 4	⊖ a	21 11	21 23	21 28	21 39	21 41	21 53	21 58	22 09	22 11	22 23	22 28	22 39	22 41	22 53	22 58	23 09	23 11	23 23	23 41
London Charing Cross 4	⊖ a	21 15	21 26	21 32	21 42	21 45	21 56	22 02	22 12	22 15	22 26	22 32	22 42	22 45	22 56	23 02	23 12	23 15	23 26	23 45

For general notes see front of timetable
For details of catering facilities see Directory of Train Operators

For details of Bank Holiday service alterations please see first page of Table 195

London → Hayes (Kent) via Catford Bridge

Network Diagram - see first page of Table 200

Miles	Miles			SE MX 24	SE MO 24	SE MX 24	SE MO 24	SE 25	SE 24	SE 25	SE 24	SE 25	SE 34	SE 25	SE 25	SE 34	SE 36	SE 25	SE 25	SE 34	SE 25	SE 36 A
0	—	**London Charing Cross** 4	⊖ d	23p22	23p23	23p52	23p53		05 49	06 27	06 51	07 06	07 22	07 45		08 26	08 36			08 52		09 00
¾	—	**London Waterloo (East)** 4	⊖ d	23p25	23p26	23p55	23p56		05 52	06 30	06 54	07 09	07 25	07 48		08 29	08 39			08 55		09 04
—	0	**London Cannon Street** 4	⊖ d												08 20			08 40	08 54			
1¾	¾	**London Bridge** 4	⊖ d	23p30	23p32	23p58	00 02		05 57	06 35	06 59	07 14	07 30	07 53	08 24	08 34	08 44	08 44	08 58	09 00		09 10
4¾	—	New Cross 4	⊖ d	23p35	23p37	00 04	00 07	05 37		06 41	07 05	07 20		07 59	08 29			08 49	09 05		←	
5½	—	St Johns	d	23p37	23p39	00 06	00 09			06 43	07 07	07 22		08 01	08 31			08 51	09 07		09 07	
6	—	**Lewisham** 4	d	23p40	23p42	00 09	00 12	05 42	06 06	06 46	07 10	07b27		08 04	08 34			08 54	→		09c12	
6¾	—	Ladywell	d	23p42	23p44	00 11	00 14	05 44	06 08	06 48	07 12	07 29	07 39	08 07	08 37	08 43	08 53	08 57		09 09	09 14	09 18
7½	—	**Catford Bridge**	d	23p44	23p46	00 13	00 16	05 46	06 10	06 50	07 14	07 31	07 41	08 09	08 39	08 45	08 55	08 59		09 11	09 16	09 21
9	—	Lower Sydenham	d	23p47	23p49	00 16	00 19	05 49	06 13	06 53	07 17	07 34	07 44	08 12	08 42	08 48	08 58	09 02			09 19	09 23
9½	—	New Beckenham 4	d	23p49	23p51	00 18	00 21	05 51	06 15	06 55	07 19	07 36	07 46	08 14	08 44	08 50	09a00	09 06		09 16	09 22	09a26
10¼	—	Clock House	d	23p51	23p53	00 20	00 23	05 53	06 17	06 57	07 21	07 38	07 48	08 16	08 46	08 52		09 08		09 18	09 24	
11	—	Elmers End 4	d	23p54	23p56	00 23	00 26	05 56	06 20	07 00	07 24	07 41	07 51	08 19	08 49	08 55		09 11		09 21	09 27	
12½	—	Eden Park	d	23p58	00 01	00 27	00 30	06 00	06 24	07 04	07 28	07 45	07 55	08 23	08 53	08 59		09 15			09 31	
13¼	—	West Wickham	d	00 01	00 02	00 29	00 32	06 02	06 26	07 06	07 30	07 47	07 57	08 25	08 55	09 01		09 17			09 33	
14½	—	**Hayes (Kent)**	a	00 03	00 05	00 32	00 35	06 05	06 29	07 09	07 33	07 50	08 00	08 28	08 58	09 04		09 20		09 28	09 38	

		SE 34	SE 25 B	SE 34	SE 25	SE 34	SE 25	SE 34	SE 25		SE 34	SE 25	SE 34	SE 25	SE 24	SE 24	SE 25	SE 34	SE 25	SE 34
London Charing Cross 4	⊖ d	09 14		09 36		10 06		10 36		and at	15 06		15 36		16 06	16 26		16 52		17 14
London Waterloo (East) 4	⊖ d	09 17		09 39		10 09		10 39			15 09		15 39		16 09	16 29		16 55		17 17
London Cannon Street 4	⊖ d		09 24		09 54		10 24		10 54	the same		15 24		15 54			16 46		17 04	
London Bridge 4	⊖ d	09 22	09 28	09 45	09 58	10 15	10 28	10 45	10 58		15 15	15 28	15 45	15 58	16 14	16 34	16 50	17 00	17 08	17 22
New Cross 4	⊖ d		09 35		10 05		10 33		11 03	minutes		15 33		16 03			16 56		17 16	
St Johns	d		09 37		10 07		10 35		11 05			15 35		16 05			16 58		17 18	
Lewisham 4	d		09 40		10 10		10 38		11 08	past		15 38		16 08	16 24	16 44	17 02		17 22	
Ladywell	d	09 32	09 42	09 55	10 12	10 25	10 40	10 55	11 10		15 25	15 40	15 55	16 10	16 27	16 47	17 05	17 11	17 25	17 35
Catford Bridge	d	09 34	09 44	09 57	10 14	10 27	10 42	10 57	11 12	each	15 27	15 42	15 57	16 12	16 29	16 49	17 07	17 13	17 27	17 37
Lower Sydenham	d	09 37	09 47	10 00	10 17	10 30	10 45	11 00	11 15		15 30	15 45	16 00	16 15	16 32	16 52	17 10	17 16	17 30	17 40
New Beckenham 4	d	09 39	09a49	10 02	10 19	10 32	10 47	11 02	11 17	hour until	15 32	15 47	16 02	16 17	16 34	16 54	17 12	17 18	17 32	17 42
Clock House	d	09 41		10 04	10 21	10 34	10 49	11 04	11 19		15 34	15 49	16 04	16 19	16 37	16 57	17 15	17 21	17 35	17 45
Elmers End 4	d	09 44		10 07	10 24	10 37	10 52	11 07	11 22		15 37	15 52	16 07	16 22	16 40	17 00	17 18	17 24	17 38	17 48
Eden Park	d	09 48		10 11	10 28	10 41	10 56	11 11	11 26		15 41	15 56	16 11	16 26	16 43	17 03	17 21	17 27	17 41	17 51
West Wickham	d	09 50		10 13	10 30	10 43	10 58	11 13	11 28		15 43	15 58	16 13	16 28	16 45	17 05	17 23	17 29	17 43	17 53
Hayes (Kent)	a	09 53		10 16	10 33	10 46	11 01	11 16	11 31		15 46	16 01	16 16	16 31	16e51	17e11	17 28	17e35	17 48	17 58

		SE 25	SE 34	SE 25	SE 34	SE 25	SE 24	SE 24	SE 24	SE 25	SE 24	SE 25	SE 24	SE 24	SE 24	SE 24	SE 24	SE 24	SE 24	SE 24
London Charing Cross 4	⊖ d		17 38		17 58		18 23	18 42	19 06		19 38		20 22	20 52	21 22	21 52	22 22	22 52	23 22	23 52
London Waterloo (East) 4	⊖ d		17 41		18 01		18 26	18 45	19 09		19 41		20 25	20 55	21 25	21 55	22 25	22 55	23 25	23 55
London Cannon Street 4	⊖ d	17 32		17 52		18 12				19 26		19 56								
London Bridge 4	⊖ d	17 36		17 56	18 06	18 16	18 31	18 50	19 14	19 30	19 46	20 00	20 30	21 00	21 30	22 00	22 30	23 00	23 30	23 58
New Cross 4	⊖ d	17 42		18 02		18 22			19 20	19 35	19 52	20 05	20 35	21 05	21 35	22 05	22 35	23 05	23 35	00 04
St Johns	d	17 44		18 04		18 24			19 22	19 37	19 54	20 07	20 37	21 07	21 37	22 07	22 37	23 07	23 37	00 06
Lewisham 4	d	17 46		18 08		18 26	18 40	19 00	19 24	19 40	19 57	20 10	20 40	21 10	21 40	22 10	22 40	23 10	23 40	00 09
Ladywell	d	17 49	17 57	18 11	18 19	18 29	18 43	19 03	19 27	19 42	19 59	20 12	20 42	21 12	21 42	22 12	22 42	23 12	23 42	00 11
Catford Bridge	d	17 51	17 59	18 13	18 21	18 31	18 45	19 05	19 29	19 45	20 01	20 14	20 44	21 14	21 44	22 14	22 44	23 14	23 44	00 13
Lower Sydenham	d	17 54	18 02	18 16	18 24	18 34	18 48	19 08	19 32	19 47	20 04	20 17	20 47	21 17	21 47	22 17	22 47	23 17	23 47	00 16
New Beckenham 4	d	17 56	18 04	18 18	18 26	18 36	18 50	19 10	19 34	19 50	20 06	20 19	20 49	21 19	21 49	22 19	22 49	23 19	23 49	00 18
Clock House	d	17 59	18 07	18 21	18 29	18 39	18 53	19 13	19 37	19 52	20 08	20 21	20 51	21 21	21 51	22 21	22 51	23 21	23 51	00 20
Elmers End 4	d	18 02	18 10	18 24	18 32	18 42	18 56	19 16	19 40	19 55	20 11	20 24	20 54	21 24	21 54	22 24	22 54	23 24	23 54	00 23
Eden Park	d	18 05	18 13	18 27	18 35	18 45	18 59	19 19	19 43	19 58	20 15	20 28	20 58	21 28	21 58	22 28	22 58	23 28	23 58	00 27
West Wickham	d	18 07	18 15	18 29	18 37	18 47	19 01	19 21	19 45	20 00	20 17	20 30	21 00	21 30	22 00	22 30	23 00	23 30	00 01	00 29
Hayes (Kent)	a	18 12	18e21	18 34	18e43	18e53	19e07	19e27	19 50	20 05	20 20	20 33	21 03	21 33	22 03	22 33	23 03	23 33	00 03	00 32

Saturdays

		SE 24	SE 24	SE 24	SE 24	SE 24	SE 24	SE 24	SE 24	SE 25	SE 24	SE 25	SE 24	SE 25	SE 34	SE 25	SE 34
London Charing Cross 4	⊖ d	23p22	23p52	05 52	06 22	06 52	07 22	07 52	08 22		09 06		09 36		10 06		10 36
London Waterloo (East) 4	⊖ d	23p25	23p55	05 55	06 25	06 55	07 25	07 55	08 25		09 09		09 39		10 09		10 39
London Cannon Street 4	⊖ d									08 54		09 24		09 54		10 24	
London Bridge 4	⊖ d	23p30	23p58	06 01	06 31	07 01	07 31	08 01	08 31	08 58	09 15	09 28	09 45	09 58	10 15	10 28	10 45
New Cross 4	⊖ d	23p35	00 04	06 06	06 36	07 06	07 36	08 06	08 36	09 03		09 33		10 03		10 33	
St Johns	d	23p37	00 06	06 08	06 38	07 08	07 38	08 08	08 38	09 05		09 35		10 05		10 35	
Lewisham 4	d	23p40	00 09	06 10	06 40	07 10	07 40	08 10	08 40	09 08		09 38		10 08		10 38	
Ladywell	d	23p42	00 11	06 13	06 43	07 13	07 43	08 13	08 43	09 10	09 25	09 40	09 55	10 10	10 25	10 40	10 55
Catford Bridge	d	23p44	00 13	06 15	06 45	07 15	07 45	08 15	08 45	09 12	09 27	09 42	09 57	10 12	10 27	10 42	10 57
Lower Sydenham	d	23p47	00 16	06 18	06 48	07 18	07 48	08 18	08 48	09 15	09 30	09 45	10 00	10 15	10 30	10 45	11 00
New Beckenham 4	d	23p49	00 18	06 20	06 50	07 20	07 50	08 20	08 50	09 17	09 32	09 47	10 02	10 17	10 32	10 47	11 02
Clock House	d	23p51	00 20	06 22	06 52	07 22	07 52	08 22	08 52	09 19	09 34	09 49	10 04	10 19	10 34	10 49	11 04
Elmers End 4	d	23p54	00 23	06 25	06 55	07 25	07 55	08 25	08 55	09 22	09 35	09 52	10 05	10 22	10 37	10 52	11 07
Eden Park	d	23p58	00 27	06 29	06 59	07 29	07 59	08 29	08 59	09 26	09 39	09 56	10 09	10 26	10 41	10 56	11 11
West Wickham	d	00 01	00 29	06 31	07 01	07 31	08 01	08 31	09 01	09 28	09 41	09 58	10 11	10 28	10 43	10 58	11 13
Hayes (Kent)	a	00 03	00 32	06 34	07 04	07 34	08 04	08 34	09 04	09 31	09 46	10 01	10 16	10 31	10 46	11 01	11 16

For general notes see front of timetable
For details of catering facilities see Directory of Train Operators

- **A** To Beckenham Junction arr 0929
- **B** To Beckenham Junction arr 0952
- **b** Arr. 0724
- **c** Arr. 0909
- **e** Until 10 October arr 1 minute earlier

Table 203

London → Hayes (Kent) via Catford Bridge

Saturdays

Network Diagram - see first page of Table 200

		SE 25		SE 24	SE 25	SE 24	SE 25	SE 24	SE 24	SE 24	SE 24	SE 24	SE 24	SE 24	SE 24	SE 24	SE 24
London Charing Cross 4	⊖ d		and at	18 06		18 36	18 52	19 22	19 52	20 22	20 52	21 22	21 52	22 22	22 52	23 22	23 52
London Waterloo (East) 4	⊖ d		the same	18 09		18 39	18 55	19 25	19 55	20 25	20 55	21 25	21 55	22 25	22 55	23 25	23 55
London Cannon Street 4	⊖ d	10 54	minutes		18 24												
London Bridge 4	⊖ d	10 58	past	18 15	18 28	18 45	19 01	19 31	20 01	20 31	21 01	21 31	22 01	22 31	23 01	23 31	23 58
New Cross 4	⊖ d	11 03	each		18 35		19 06	19 36	20 06	20 36	21 06	21 36	22 06	22 36	23 06	23 36	00 04
St Johns	d	11 05	hour until		18 37		19 08	19 38	20 08	20 38	21 08	21 38	22 08	22 38	23 08	23 38	00 06
Lewisham 4	d	11 08			18 40		19 10	19 40	20 10	20 40	21 10	21 40	22 10	22 40	23 10	23 40	00 09
Ladywell	d	11 10		18 25	18 42	18 55	19 13	19 43	20 13	20 43	21 13	21 43	22 13	22 43	23 13	23 43	00 11
Catford Bridge	d	11 12		18 27	18 44	18 57	19 15	19 45	20 15	20 45	21 15	21 45	22 15	22 45	23 15	23 45	00 13
Lower Sydenham	d	11 15		18 30	18 47	19 00	19 18	19 48	20 18	20 48	21 18	21 48	22 18	22 48	23 18	23 48	00 16
New Beckenham 4	d	11 17		18 32	18 49	19 02	19 20	19 50	20 20	20 50	21 20	21 50	22 20	22 50	23 20	23 50	00 18
Clock House	d	11 19		18 34	18 51	19 04	19 22	19 52	20 22	20 52	21 22	21 52	22 22	22 52	23 22	23 52	00 20
Elmers End 4	d	11 22		18 35	18 53	19 07	19 25	19 55	20 25	20 55	21 25	21 55	22 25	22 55	23 25	23 55	00 23
Eden Park	d	11 26		18 39	18 57	19 11	19 29	19 59	20 29	20 59	21 29	21 59	22 29	22 59	23 29	23 59	00 27
West Wickham	d	11 28		18 41	18 59	19 13	19 31	20 01	20 31	21 01	21 31	22 01	22 31	23 01	23 31	00 01	00 29
Hayes (Kent)	a	11 31		18 46	19 02	19 16	19 34	20 04	20 34	21 04	21 34	22 04	22 34	23 04	23 34	00 04	00 32

Sundays

		SE 24	SE 24	SE 24	SE 24	SE 24	SE 24		SE 24	SE 24	SE 24
London Charing Cross 4	⊖ d	23p22	23p52	07 53	08 23	08 53	09 23		22 53	23 23	23 53
London Waterloo (East) 4	⊖ d	23p25	23p55	07 56	08 26	08 56	09 26		22 56	23 26	23 56
London Cannon Street 4	⊖ d							and			
London Bridge 4	⊖ d	23p31	23p58	08 02	08 32	09 02	09 32	every 30	23 02	23 32	00 02
New Cross 4	⊖ d	23p36	00 04	08 07	08 37	09 07	09 37	minutes	23 07	23 37	00 07
St Johns	d	23p38	00 06	08 09	08 39	09 09	09 39	until	23 09	23 39	00 09
Lewisham 4	d	23p40	00 09	08 12	08 42	09 12	09 42		23 12	23 42	00 12
Ladywell	d	23p43	00 11	08 14	08 44	09 14	09 44		23 14	23 44	00 14
Catford Bridge	d	23p45	00 13	08 16	08 46	09 16	09 46		23 16	23 46	00 16
Lower Sydenham	d	23p48	00 16	08 19	08 49	09 19	09 49		23 19	23 49	00 19
New Beckenham 4	d	23p50	00 18	08 21	08 51	09 21	09 51		23 21	23 51	00 21
Clock House	d	23p52	00 20	08 23	08 53	09 23	09 53		23 23	23 53	00 23
Elmers End 4	d	23p55	00 23	08 26	08 56	09 26	09 56		23 26	23 56	00 26
Eden Park	d	23p59	00 27	08 30	09 00	09 30	10 00		23 30	00 01	00 30
West Wickham	d	00 01	00 29	08 32	09 02	09 32	10 02		23 32	00 02	00 32
Hayes (Kent)	a	00 04	00 32	08 35	09 05	09 35	10 05		23 35	00 05	00 35

For general notes see front of timetable
For details of catering facilities see Directory of Train Operators

For details of Bank Holiday service alterations please see first page of Table 195

Hayes (Kent) → London via Catford Bridge

Network Diagram - see first page of Table 200

Mondays to Fridays

Miles	Miles	Station		SE 24 A	SE 24 B	SE 24 A	SE 24 B	SE 24 A	SE 24 B	SE 24	SE 24	SE 25	SE 34	SE 25	SE 24	SE 25	SE 34	SE 25	SE 34	SE 25	SE 24
0	—	Hayes (Kent)	d	05 13	05 16	05 43	05 46	06 13	06 16	06 36	07 10	07 25	07 37	07 45	07 57	08 05	08 17	08 25	08 40	09 00	09 15
1¼	—	West Wickham	d	05 16	05 19	05 46	05 49	06 16	06 19	06 39	07 13	07 28	07 40	07 48	08 00	08 08	08 20	08 28	08 43	09 03	09 18
2	—	Eden Park	d	05 18	05 21	05 48	05 51	06 18	06 21	06 41	07 15	07 30	07 42	07 50	08 02	08 10	08 22	08 30	08 45	09 05	09 20
3¼	—	Elmers End 4	d	05 22	05 25	05 52	05 55	06 22	06 25	06 45	07 19	07 34	07 46	07 54	08 06	08 14	08 26	08 34	08 49	09 09	09 24
4¼	—	Clock House	d	05 24	05 27	05 54	05 57	06 24	06 27	06 47	07 21	07 36	07 48	07 56	08 08	08 16	08 28	08 36	08 51	09 11	09 26
5	—	New Beckenham 4	d	05 26	05 29	05 56	05 59	06 26	06 29	06 49	07 24	07 39	07 51	07 59	08 11	08 19	08 31	08 39	08 54	09 14	09 28
5½	—	Lower Sydenham	d	05 28	05 31	05 58	06 01	06 28	06 31	06 51	07 25	07 40	07 52	08 00	08 12	08 20	08 32	08 40	08 55	09 15	09 30
7	—	Catford Bridge	d	05 31	05 34	06 01	06 04	06 31	06 34	06 54	07 29	07 44	07 56	08 04	08 16	08 24	08 36	08 44	08 59	09 19	09 33
7¾	—	Ladywell	d	05 36	05 36	06 06	06 06	06 36	06 36	06 56	07 31	07 46	07 58	08 06	08 18	08 26	08 38	08 46	09 01	09 21	09 35
8½	—	Lewisham 4	d	05 40	05 40	06 10	06 10	06 40	06 40	07 00	07 35	07 50		08 10		08 30		08 50		09 24	
9	—	St Johns	a	05 42	05 42	06 12	06 12	06 42	06 42			07 52		08 12		08 32		08 52		09 28	
9¾	—	New Cross 4	⊖ a	05 44	05 44	06 14	06 14	06 44	06 44	07 04		07 54		08 14		08 34		08 54		09 30	
12¼	0	London Bridge 4	⊖ a	05 50	05 50	06 20	06 20	06 50	06 50	07 11	07 43	08 00		08 20		08 40		09 00	09 13	09 37	09 43
—	¾	London Cannon Street 4	⊖ a									08b07		08b27		08b47		09b07		09b44	
13¾	—	London Waterloo (East) 4	⊖ a	05 55	05 55	06 25	06 25	06 55	06 55	07 16	07 48		08 13		08 33		08 53		09 19		09 48
14½	—	London Charing Cross 4	⊖ a	06 00	05 58	06 30	06 28	07 00	06 58	07b21	07 53		08b19		08b39		09b00		09b25		09b54

Station		SE 25	SE 34	SE 25	SE 34	SE 25	SE 34	SE 25	SE 34	SE 25		SE 34	SE 34 C	SE 25	SE 34	SE 24	SE 25	SE 34	SE 25	SE 34
Hayes (Kent)	d	09 25	09 35	09 42	09 57	10 12	10 27	10 42	10 57	11 12		15 27		15 42	15 57	16 12	16 37	16 47	16 57	17 17
West Wickham	d	09 28	09 38	09 45	10 00	10 15	10 30	10 45	11 00	11 15	and at	15 30		15 45	16 00	16 15	16 40		17 00	17 20
Eden Park	d	09 30	09 40	09 47	10 02	10 17	10 32	10 47	11 02	11 17		15 32		15 47	16 02	16 17	16 42		17 02	17 22
Elmers End 4	d	09 34	09 44	09 51	10 06	10 21	10 36	10 51	11 06	11 21	the same	15 36		15 51	16 06	16 21	16 46	16 54	17 06	17 26
Clock House	d	09 36	09 46	09 53	10 08	10 23	10 38	10 53	11 08	11 23		15 38		15 53	16 08	16 23	16 48	16 56	17 08	17 28
New Beckenham 4	d	09 38	09 48	09 55	10 10	10 25	10 40	10 55	11 10	11 25	minutes	15 40	15 48	15 55	16 10	16 25	16 50	16 58	17 10	17 30
Lower Sydenham	d	09 40	09 50	09 57	10 12	10 27	10 42	10 57	11 12	11 27		15 42	15 49	15 57	16 12	16 27	16 52		17 12	17 32
Catford Bridge	d	09 43	09 53	10 00	10 15	10 30	10 45	11 00	11 15	11 30	past	15 45	15 53	16 00	16 15	16 30	16 55	17 02	17 15	17 35
Ladywell	d	09 45	09 55	10 02	10 17	10 32	10 47	11 02	11 17	11 32		15 47	15 55	16 02	16 17	16 32	16 57	17 04	17 17	17 37
Lewisham 4	d	09 48		10 06		10 36		11 06		11 36	each			16 08	16 21	16c38	17 02		17 21	17e44
St Johns	a	09 52		10 08		10 38		11 08		11 38				16 10		16 40	17 04		17 23	
New Cross 4	⊖ a	09 54		10 10		10 40		11 10		11 40	hour until			16 12		16 42	17 06		17 25	
London Bridge 4	⊖ a	10 01	10 07	10 16	10 27	10 46	10 57	11 16	11 27	11 46		15 57		16 18	16 31	16 49	17 14	17 15	17 32	17 54
London Cannon Street 4	⊖ a	10 06		10 20		10 50		11 20		11 50				16 22			17 18		17 36	
London Waterloo (East) 4	⊖ a		10 14		10 34		11 04		11 34			16 03	16 11		16 36	16 55		17 20		17 59
London Charing Cross 4	⊖ a		10 17		10 39		11 09		11 39			16 07	16 15		16 40	16 59		17 25		18 03

Station		SE 34	SE 25	SE 34	SE 34	SE 24	SE 25	SE 24	SE 24	SE 24	SE 24	SE 24	SE 24	SE 24	SE 24	SE 24	SE 24
Hayes (Kent)	d	17 37	17 43	17 55	18 05	18 21	18 31	18 43	18 53	19 23	19 53	20 23	20 53	21 23	21 53	22 23	22 53
West Wickham	d	17 40	17 46		18 08	18 24	18 34	18 46	18 56	19 26	19 56	20 26	20 56	21 26	21 56	22 26	22 56
Eden Park	d	17 42	17 48		18 10	18 26	18 36	18 48	18 58	19 28	19 58	20 28	20 58	21 28	21 58	22 28	22 58
Elmers End 4	d	17 46	17 54	18 01	18 14	18 30	18 40	18 52	19 02	19 32	20 02	20 32	21 02	21 32	22 02	22 32	23 02
Clock House	d	17 48	17 56	18 03	18 16	18 32	18 42	18 54	19 04	19 34	20 04	20 34	21 04	21 34	22 04	22 34	23 04
New Beckenham 4	d	17 50	17 58	18 06	18 18	18 34	18 44	18 56	19 06	19 36	20 06	20 36	21 06	21 36	22 06	22 36	23 06
Lower Sydenham	d	17 52	18 00		18 20	18 36	18 46	18 58	19 08	19 38	20 08	20 38	21 08	21 38	22 08	22 38	23 08
Catford Bridge	d	17 55	18 03	18 10	18 23	18 39	18 49	19 01	19 11	19 41	20 11	20 41	21 11	21 41	22 11	22 41	23 11
Ladywell	d	17 57	18 05	18 12	18 25	18 41	18 51	19 03	19 13	19 43	20 13	20 43	21 13	21 43	22 13	22 43	23 13
Lewisham 4	d		18 10		18 29	18 45	18 56	19f09	19 17	19 47	20 17	20 47	21 17	21 47	22 17	22 47	23 17
St Johns	a						18 58	19 11	19 19	19 49	20 19	20 49	21 19	21 49	22 19	22 49	23 19
New Cross 4	⊖ a						19 00	19 13	19 21	19 51	20 21	20 51	21 21	21 51	22 21	22 51	23 21
London Bridge 4	⊖ a	18 09		18 22	18 37	18 54	19 05	19 19	19 28	19 58	20 28	20 58	21 28	21 58	22 28	22 58	23 28
London Cannon Street 4	⊖ a						19 10										
London Waterloo (East) 4	⊖ a	18 15	18 23	18 27	18 42	18 59		19 24	19 33	20 03	20 33	21 03	21 33	22 03	22 33	23 03	23 33
London Charing Cross 4	⊖ a	18 19	18 27	18 33	18 49	19 05		19 29	19 37	20 07	20 37	21 07	21 37	22 07	22 37	23 07	23 37

Saturdays

Station		SE 24	SE 24	SE 24	SE 24	SE 24	SE 25	SE 24	SE 25	SE 24	SE 25	SE 34	SE 25	SE 34	SE 25	SE 34		SE 25
Hayes (Kent)	d	05 23	05 53	06 23	06 53	07 23	07 42	07 57	08 12	08 27	08 42	08 57	09 12	09 27	09 42	09 57		17 12
West Wickham	d	05 26	05 56	06 26	06 56	07 26	07 45	08 00	08 15	08 30	08 45	09 00	09 15	09 30	09 45	10 00	and at	17 15
Eden Park	d	05 28	05 58	06 28	06 58	07 28	07 47	08 02	08 17	08 32	08 47	09 02	09 17	09 32	09 47	10 02		17 17
Elmers End 4	d	05 32	06 02	06 32	07 02	07 32	07 51	08 06	08 21	08 36	08 51	09 06	09 21	09 36	09 51	10 06	the same	17 21
Clock House	d	05 34	06 04	06 34	07 04	07 34	07 53	08 08	08 23	08 38	08 53	09 08	09 23	09 38	09 53	10 08		17 23
New Beckenham 4	d	05 36	06 06	06 36	07 06	07 36	07 55	08 10	08 25	08 40	08 55	09 10	09 25	09 40	09 55	10 10	minutes	17 25
Lower Sydenham	d	05 38	06 08	06 38	07 08	07 38	07 57	08 12	08 27	08 42	08 57	09 12	09 27	09 42	09 57	10 12		17 27
Catford Bridge	d	05 41	06 11	06 41	07 11	07 41	08 00	08 15	08 30	08 45	09 00	09 15	09 30	09 45	10 00	10 15	past	17 30
Ladywell	d	05 43	06 13	06 43	07 13	07 43	08 02	08 17	08 32	08 47	09 02	09 17	09 32	09 47	10 02	10 17		17 32
Lewisham 4	d	05 47	06 17	06 47	07 17	07 47	08 06		08 36		09 06		09 36		10 06		each	17 36
St Johns	a	05 49	06 19	06 49	07 19	07 49	08 08		08 38		09 08		09 38		10 08			17 38
New Cross 4	⊖ a	05 51	06 21	06 51	07 21	07 51	08 10		08 40		09 10		09 40		10 10		hour until	17 40
London Bridge 4	⊖ a	05 58	06 29	06 58	07 29	07 58	08 16	08 27	08 46	08 57	09 16	09 27	09 46	09 57	10 16	10 27		17 46
London Cannon Street 4	⊖ a						08 20		08 50		09 20		09 50		10 20			17 50
London Waterloo (East) 4	⊖ a	06 03	06 34	07 03	07 33	08 03		08 34		09 04		09 34		10 04		10 34		
London Charing Cross 4	⊖ a	06 07	06 37	07 07	07 37	08 07		08 39		09 09		09 39		10 09		10 39		

For general notes see front of timetable
For details of catering facilities see Directory of Train Operators

A From 13 October
B Until 10 October
C From Beckenham Junction dep 1542
b Unitl 10 October arr 1 minute earlier
c Arr. 1635
e Arr. 1740
f Arr. 1906

Table 203

Saturdays

Hayes (Kent) → London via Catford Bridge

Network Diagram - see first page of Table 200

		SE 24	SE 25	SE 24	SE 24	SE 24	SE 24	SE 24	SE 24	SE 24	SE 24	SE 24	SE 24	SE 24
Hayes (Kent)	d	17 27	17 42	17 57	18 23	18 53	19 23	19 53	20 23	20 53	21 23	21 53	22 23	22 53
West Wickham	d	17 30	17 45	18 00	18 26	18 56	19 26	19 56	20 26	20 56	21 26	21 56	22 26	22 56
Eden Park	d	17 32	17 47	18 02	18 28	18 58	19 28	19 58	20 28	20 58	21 28	21 58	22 28	22 58
Elmers End 4	d	17 36	17 51	18 06	18 32	19 02	19 32	20 02	20 32	21 02	21 32	22 02	22 32	23 02
Clock House	d	17 38	17 53	18 08	18 34	19 04	19 34	20 04	20 34	21 04	21 34	22 04	22 34	23 04
New Beckenham 4	d	17 40	17 55	18 10	18 36	19 06	19 36	20 06	20 36	21 06	21 36	22 06	22 36	23 06
Lower Sydenham	d	17 42	17 57	18 12	18 38	19 08	19 38	20 08	20 38	21 08	21 38	22 08	22 38	23 08
Catford Bridge	d	17 45	18 00	18 15	18 41	19 11	19 41	20 11	20 41	21 11	21 41	22 11	22 41	23 11
Ladywell	d	17 47	18 02	18 17	18 43	19 13	19 43	20 13	20 43	21 13	21 43	22 13	22 43	23 13
Lewisham 4	d	.	18 06	18 23	18 47	19 17	19 47	20 17	20 47	21 17	21 47	22 17	22 47	23 17
St Johns	a	.	18 08	.	18 49	19 19	19 49	20 19	20 49	21 19	21 49	22 19	22 49	23 19
New Cross 4	⊖ a	.	18 10	.	18 51	19 21	19 51	20 21	20 51	21 21	21 51	22 21	22 51	23 21
London Bridge 4	⊖ a	17 57	18 16	18 33	18 58	19 28	19 58	20 28	20 58	21 28	21 58	22 28	22 58	23 28
London Cannon Street 4	⊖ a	.	18 20	.	.	.	.	.	.	.	.	.	.	.
London Waterloo (East) 4	⊖ a	18 04	.	18 38	19 03	19 33	20 03	20 33	21 03	21 33	22 03	22 33	23 03	23 33
London Charing Cross 4	⊖ a	18 09	.	18 41	19 07	19 37	20 07	20 37	21 07	21 37	22 07	22 37	23 07	23 37

Sundays

		SE 24	SE 24	SE 24		SE 24	SE 24	SE 24
Hayes (Kent)	d	07 47	08 17	08 47	and every 30 minutes until	22 17	22 47	23 17
West Wickham	d	07 50	08 20	08 50		22 20	22 50	23 20
Eden Park	d	07 52	08 22	08 52		22 22	22 52	23 22
Elmers End 4	d	07 56	08 26	08 56		22 26	22 56	23 26
Clock House	d	07 58	08 28	08 58		22 28	22 58	23 28
New Beckenham 4	d	08 00	08 30	09 00		22 30	23 00	23 30
Lower Sydenham	d	08 02	08 32	09 02		22 32	23 02	23 32
Catford Bridge	d	08 05	08 35	09 05		22 35	23 05	23 35
Ladywell	d	08 07	08 37	09 07		22 37	23 07	23 37
Lewisham 4	d	08 11	08 41	09 11		22 41	23 11	23 41
St Johns	a	08 13	08 43	09 13		22 43	23 13	23 43
New Cross 4	⊖ a	08 15	08 45	09 15		22 45	23 15	23 45
London Bridge 4	⊖ a	08 21	08 51	09 21		22 51	23 21	23 51
London Cannon Street 4	⊖ a	.	.	.		.	.	.
London Waterloo (East) 4	⊖ a	08 26	08 56	09 26		22 56	23 26	23 56
London Charing Cross 4	⊖ a	08 29	08 59	09 29		22 59	23 29	23 59

For general notes see front of timetable
For details of catering facilities see Directory of Train Operators

For details of Bank Holiday service alterations please see first page of Table 195

London → Grove Park, Bromley North, Orpington, Sevenoaks and Tonbridge

Network Diagram - see first page of Table 200

Miles	Miles	Station		SE MX 12	SE MO 12	SE MO 8 [1]	SE MX 2 [1] A	SE MX 12	SE MO 12	SE MX 22 [1]	SE MX 70	SE MO 12	SE MX 02	SE MX 01	SE 14	SE 18 [1] B	SE 70	SE 14	SE 01	SE 70	SE 16 [1] C	SE 4 [1] B	SE 01	SE 16 [1] C
0	—	**London Charing Cross** [4]	⊖ d	23p26	23p26	23p30	23p30			23p37		23p56	00 10		00 48	05 30		05 40			06 16	06 25		
¾	—	**London Waterloo (East)** [4]	⊖ d	23p29	23p29	23p33	23p33			23p40		23p59	00 13		00 51	05 33		05 43			06 19	06 28		
—	—	**London Cannon Street** [4]	⊖ d																					
1¾	—	**London Bridge** [4]	⊖ d	23p34	23p35	23p38	23p38			23p45		00 05	00 18		00 56	05 38		05 48			06 24	06 33		
4¾	—	New Cross [4]	⊖ d												01 01			05 53						
5½	—	St Johns	d																					
6	—	**Lewisham** [4]	d	23p43	23p44							00 15			01 05			05 57						
7¼	—	Hither Green [4]	d	23p47	23p48			←	←			00 19			01 09			06 01			06 33			
9	0	**Grove Park** [4]	d	23p51 →	23p52 →			23p51	23p52			00 23	00 29	00 33	01 13			06 04	06 17		06 36		06 42	
—	1¼	Sundridge Park	d											00 36					06 20				06 45	
—	1¾	**Bromley North**	a											00 38					06 22				06 47	
10¼	—	Elmstead Woods	d					23p53	23p55			00 25	00 32		01 16			06 07			06 39			
11½	—	Chislehurst	d					23p56	23p57			00 28	00 35		01 19			06 09			06 41			
12¾	—	Petts Wood [4]	d					23p59	23p59		00 25	00 31	00 39		01 23		06 10	06 13		06 38	06 45			
13¾	—	**Orpington** [4]	a			23p54	23p56	00 03	00 03		00 28	00 34	00 42		01 26	05 54	06 13	06 16		06 41	06 48	06 49		←
—	—		d			23p54	23p56						00 42			05 54		06 22			06 54 →	06 50		06 54
15½	—	Chelsfield [3]	d										00 46			05 58		06 25						06 57
16½	—	Knockholt	d													06 01		06 27						06 59
20½	—	Dunton Green	d													06 07		06 32						07 04
22	—	**Sevenoaks** [4]	a			00 04	00 06			00 10			00 54			06 10		06 36				06 59		07 08
—	—		d			00 04	00 06			00 10			00 54			06 11						07 00		07 08
27	—	Hildenborough	d				00 12						01 00			06 17						07 06		07 14
29½	—	**Tonbridge** [4]	a			00 13	00 17			00 20			01 05			06 21						07 10		07 19

Station		SE 01	SE 16	SE 70	SE 4 [1]	SE 16	SE 01	SE 12	SE 30 [1] C	SE 70	SE 12	SE 22 [1] D	SE 01	SE 12	SE 23 [1] E	SE 83 G	SE 12	SE 70	SE 4 [1]	SE 01	SE 83 G	SE 14	SE 12
London Charing Cross [4]	⊖ d		06 47		07 00			07 10	07 16			07 28		07 37					07 52			07 56	
London Waterloo (East) [4]	⊖ d		06 50		07 03			07 13	07 19			07 31		07 40					07 55			07 59	
London Cannon Street [4]	⊖ d														07 45								08 03
London Bridge [4]	⊖ d		06 56		07 08			07 19	07 24			07 36		07 45	07 49				08 02			08 04	08 07
New Cross [4]	⊖ d																						08 12
St Johns	d																						
Lewisham [4]	d																						08 16
Hither Green [4]	d		07 06					07 29						07 53									08 20
Grove Park [4]	d	07 03	07 13				07 24	07 33					07 44	07 57						08 05			08 24
Sundridge Park	d	07 06					07 27						07 47							08 08			
Bromley North	a	07 08				←	07 29				←		07 49				←			08 10			
Elmstead Woods	d		07 16 →			07 16		07 35 →			07 35			08 02 →			08 02						08 27
Chislehurst	d					07 19					07 39						08 05						08 30
Petts Wood [4]	d			07 10		07 22				07 40	07 42						08 09	08 12					08 33
Orpington [4]	a			07 13	07 25	07 25			07 40	07 43	07 45	07 54			08 08		08 12	08 15	08 19			08 23	08 36
	d				07 26	07 28			07 41		07 46	07 55			08 09				08 20			08 24	
Chelsfield [3]	d					07 31					07 49				08 12							08 27	
Knockholt	d					07 33					07 51				08 15							08 29	
Dunton Green	d					07 38					07 56				08 20							08 34	
Sevenoaks [4]	a				07 35	07 42			07 50		08 01	08 04			08 24	08 26			08 29		←	08 38	
	d				07 36				07 51			08 05			08 24	08 34 →			08 30		08 34		
Hildenborough	d								07 57			08 11									08 40		
Tonbridge [4]	a				07 44				08 01			08 15			08 32				08 38		08 44		

Station		SE 22 [1] (catering)	SE 01	SE 70	SE 12	SE 4 [1]	SE 16	SE 12	SE 01	SE 12	SE 23 [1] H (catering)	SE 90 [1]	SE 12	SE 01	SE 70	SE 12	SE 90 [1] J	SE 12	SE 23 [1] (catering)	SE 01	SE 70	SE 16	SE 2 [1] A
London Charing Cross [4]	⊖ d	08 14			08 20	08 22	08 29			08 38		08 54				08 56	08 58					09 26	09 30
London Waterloo (East) [4]	⊖ d	08 17			08 23	08 25	08 32			08 41		08 57				08 59	09 01					09 29	09 33
London Cannon Street [4]	⊖ d										08 45								09 17				
London Bridge [4]	⊖ d	08 23			08 28	08 30	08 38			08 46	08 49	09 02				09 04	09 08		09 21			09 34	09 38
New Cross [4]	⊖ d																						
St Johns	d																						
Lewisham [4]	d																					09 43	
Hither Green [4]	d				08 37					08 56						09 17		←				09 47	
Grove Park [4]	d		08 25		08 41				08 45	09 00				09 05		09 21 →		09 21		09 26		09 51 →	
Sundridge Park	d		08 28						08 48					09 08						09 29			
Bromley North	a		08 30					←	08 50				←	09 10						09 31			
Elmstead Woods	d				08 44 →			08 44		09 03 →			09 03					09 23					
Chislehurst	d							08 47					09 06					09 26					
Petts Wood [4]	d			08 39				08 50					09 09		09 12		09 23	09 30			09 42		
Orpington [4]	a			08 42		08 47	08 55	08 56			09 07		09 12		09 15		09 26	09 33	09 39		09 46		09 54
	d					08 48	08 56				09 08						09 26	09 33	09 40				09 54
Chelsfield [3]	d						08 59											09 36					
Knockholt	d						09 01											09 39					
Dunton Green	d						09 06											09 44					
Sevenoaks [4]	a	08 46				08 57	09 10				09 17						09 36	09 47	09 50				10 04
	d	08 47				08 58					09 18						09 36		09 50				10 04
Hildenborough	d										09 24						09 42						10 10
Tonbridge [4]	a	08 55				09 06					09 28	09 35					09 47		09 59				10 15

For general notes see front of timetable
For details of catering facilities see Directory of Train Operators

- **A** To Dover Priory (Table 207)
- **B** To Ramsgate (Table 207)
- **C** To Tunbridge Wells (Table 206)
- **D** To Hastings (Table 206) and to Dover Priory (Table 207)
- **E** To Hastings (Table 206)
- **G** From London Blackfriars (Table 195)
- **H** To Hastings (Table 206) and to Hastings (Table 206)
- **J** To Margate (Table 207)

For details of Bank Holiday service alterations please see first page of Table 195

London → Grove Park, Bromley North, Orpington, Sevenoaks and Tonbridge

Network Diagram - see first page of Table 200

Station		SE 23 [1]		SE 22 [1]	SE 70	SE 16	SE 01	SE 4 [1]	SE 70	SE 12	SE 8 A	SE 70	SE 12			SE 22 [1]	SE 01	SE 90 [1]	SE 70	SE 16	SE 8 [1] A	SE 22 [1]	SE 70	SE 16	SE 01
London Charing Cross 4	⊖ d	09 45		09 45				09 53		09 56	10 00					10 15		10 23		10 26	10 30	10 45			
London Waterloo (East) 4	⊖ d			09 48				09 56		09 59	10 03					10 18		10 26		10 29	10 33	10 48			
London Cannon Street 4	⊖ d																								
London Bridge 4	⊖ d	09 49		09 53						10 04	10 08					10 23				10 34	10 38	10 53			
New Cross 4	⊖ d																								
St Johns	d																								
Lewisham 4	d	09 57								10 13										10 43					
Hither Green 4	d	10 01				←				10 17			←							10 47				←	
Grove Park 4	d	10 05				09 51	09 56			10 21			10 21				10 26			10 51				10 51	10 56
Sundridge Park	d						09 59			→							10 29			→					10 59
Bromley North	a						10 01										10 31								11 01
Elmstead Woods	d	10 08				09 53							10 23											10 53	
Chislehurst	d	10 11				09 56							10 26											10 56	
Petts Wood 4	d	10 16			09 55	10 00			10 10		10 22	10 26	10 30						10 39				10 54	11 00	
Orpington 4	a	10 19			09 58	10 03			10 13		10 25	10 29	10 33			10 39			10 42		10 53		10 57	11 03	
	d	10 20									10 26		10 33			10 40					10 54				
Chelsfield 3	d												10 36												
Knockholt	d												10 39												
Dunton Green	d												10 44												
Sevenoaks 4	a	10 29		10 16							10 36		10 47			10 50					11 04	11 15			
	d	10 30		10 16							10 36					10 50					11 04	11 16			
Hildenborough	d										10 42										11 10				
Tonbridge 4	a	10 38		10 24				10 31			10 47					10 59		11 02			11 15	11 24			

Station		SE 4 [1]	SE 70	SE 12	SE 8 [1] A	SE 70	SE 12			SE 22 [1]	SE 01	SE 90 [1]	SE 70	SE 16	SE 8 [1] A	SE 70	SE 16	SE 22 [1]	SE 01		SE 90 [1]	SE 70	SE 16	SE 8 [1] A
London Charing Cross 4	⊖ d	10 53		10 56	11 00			and at the same minutes past each hour until		15 15		15 23		15 26	15 30			15 45			15 53		15 56	16 00
London Waterloo (East) 4	⊖ d	10 56		10 59	11 03					15 18		15 26		15 29	15 33			15 48			15 56		15 59	16 03
London Cannon Street 4	⊖ d																							
London Bridge 4	⊖ d			11 04	11 08					15 23				15 34	15 38			15 53					16 04	16 08
New Cross 4	⊖ d																							
St Johns	d																							
Lewisham 4	d			11 13										15 43									16 13	
Hither Green 4	d			11 17			←							15 47			←						16 17	
Grove Park 4	d			11 21			11 21				15 26			15 51			15 51		15 56				16 21	
Sundridge Park	d			→							15 29			→					15 59					
Bromley North	a										15 31								16 01					
Elmstead Woods	d						11 23										15 53						16 23	
Chislehurst	d						11 26										15 56						16 26	
Petts Wood 4	d		11 09		11 22	11 24	11 30						15 39			15 54	15 59					16 09	→	
Orpington 4	a		11 12		11 25	11 27	11 33			15 39			15 42		15 53	15 57	16 02					16 12		
	d				11 26		11 33			15 40					15 54		16 02							
Chelsfield 3	d						11 36										16 05							
Knockholt	d						11 39										16 08							
Dunton Green	d						11 44										16 13							
Sevenoaks 4	a				11 36		11 47			15 50					16 04		16 16	16 19						16 32
	d				11 36					15 50					16 04			16 20						16 32
Hildenborough	d				11 42										16 10									16 38
Tonbridge 4	a	11 30			11 47					15 59		16 02			16 15			16 28			16 32			16 43

Station		SE 70	SE 16	SE 22 [1]	SE 01	SE 70	SE 16	SE 16	SE 4 [1]		SE 8 [1] A	SE 16	SE 01	SE 70	SE 12	SE 4 [1]	SE 30 [1] B	SE 17	SE 23 [1] C	SE 17		SE 01	SE 70	SE 12	SE 17
London Charing Cross 4	⊖ d			16 15			16 16		16 23		16 30				16 42	16 46	16 50							17 04	
London Waterloo (East) 4	⊖ d			16 18			16 19		16 26		16 33				16 45	16 49	16 53							17 07	
London Cannon Street 4	⊖ d							16 22										16 56	17 00						17 14
London Bridge 4	⊖ d			16 23			16 25	16 26	16 31		16 39				16 50	16 54	16 58	17 00	17 04					17 12	17 18
New Cross 4	⊖ d																								
St Johns	d																								
Lewisham 4	d							16 35																	
Hither Green 4	d							16 39							17 03									17 23	
Grove Park 4	d				16 26		16 38	16 43					16 47		17 07			17 12				17 16		17 27	17 33
Sundridge Park	d				16 29								16 50									17 19			
Bromley North	a				16 31								16 52									17 21			
Elmstead Woods	d		←					16 45				←			17 09			17 15						17 29	17 35
Chislehurst	d		16 26					16 48				16 48			17 12			17 18		←				17 32	17 38
Petts Wood 4	d	16 24	16 29			16 39	16 43	→				16 51		17 01	17 15			17 21		17 21			17 25	17 35	→
Orpington 4	a	16 27	16 32			16b44	16c49					16 55		17b06	17 21			→		17 24			17c30	17c42	
	d		16 33									16 56								17 24					
Chelsfield 3	d		16 36									17 00								17 27					
Knockholt	d		16 39									17 03								17 30					
Dunton Green	d		16 44									17 08								17 36					
Sevenoaks 4	a		16 47	16 49					16 55		17 02	17 13					17 21		17 27	17c42					
	d			16 50					16 56		17 02						17 22		17 28						
Hildenborough	d										17 08						17 28		17 34						
Tonbridge 4	a			16 58					17 04		17 13					17 24	17 32		17 38						

For general notes see front of timetable
For details of catering facilities see Directory of Train Operators

A To Ashford International (Table 207)
B To Tunbridge Wells (Table 206)
C To Hastings (Table 206)
b Until 10 October arr 2 minutes earlier
c Until 10 October arr 1 minute earlier

For details of Bank Holiday service alterations please see first page of Table 195

London → Grove Park, Bromley North, Orpington, Sevenoaks and Tonbridge

Network Diagram - see first page of Table 200

Station		SE 90 [1]	SE 9 [1]	SE 01	SE 4 [1]	SE 4 [1]	SE 17	SE 70	SE 13	SE 30 [1]	SE 12	SE 17	SE 17	SE 91 [1]	SE 30 [1]	SE 17	SE 01	SE 70	SE 12	SE 17	SE 9 [1]	SE 30 [1]	SE 17
			A		🛒	🛒				B					B						A	B	
London Charing Cross [4]	⊖ d	17 12			17 34	17 56				17 20	17 28				17 41				17 49			18 04	
London Waterloo (East) [4]	⊖ d	17 15			17 37	17 59				17 23	17 31				17 44				17 52			18 07	
London Cannon Street [4]	⊖ d		17 20						17 22				17 40	17 44						18 00	18 04		
London Bridge [4]	⊖ d								17 26	17 28			17 44		17 49				17 57	18 04	18 08	18 12	
New Cross [4]	⊖ d								17 32														
St Johns	d																						
Lewisham [4]	d																						
Hither Green [4]	d										17 46								18 07				
Grove Park [4]	d			17 36					17 41		17 50		17 57				18 00		18 11	18 17			
Sundridge Park	d			17 39													18 03						
Bromley North	a			17 41													18 05						
Elmstead Woods	d						←		17 43		17 53		17 59			←			18 13	18 19			←
Chislehurst	d						17 38		17 46		17 56		18 02			18 02			18 16	18 22			18 22
Petts Wood [4]	d						17 43	17 49	17 51		17 58		→			18 05		18 10	18 19	→			18 25
Orpington [4]	a						17 46	17 53	17 57		18b05					18 08		18 15	18b26				18 29
	d						17 46									18 08							18 30
Chelsfield [3]	d						17 49			17 47					18 07	18 11						18 31	18 33
Knockholt	d						17 52					←				18 14							18 36
Dunton Green	d						17 58					17 58				18 20							18 41
Sevenoaks [4]	a		17 51				→			17 55		18 03		18 11	18 16	18b26					18 33	18 39	18b47
	d		17 52							17 56				18 12	18 16						18 34	18 40	
Hildenborough	d		17 58							18 02					18 22						18 40	18 46	
Tonbridge [4]	a	17 50	18 02		18 15	18 34				18 06				18 20	18 27						18 44	18 51	

Station		SE 01	SE 70	SE 70	SE 12	SE 4 [1]	SE 15	SE 3 [1]	SE 30 [1]	SE 15	SE 01	SE 16	SE 70	SE 8 [1]	SE 22 [1]	SE 16	SE 01	SE 70	SE 13	SE 16	SE 4 [1]	SE 23 [1]	SE 16
						🛒			B						🛒						A 🛒	C	
London Charing Cross [4]	⊖ d				18 12	18 16			18 28			18 32		18 40	18 50					18 52	19 00		
London Waterloo (East) [4]	⊖ d				18 15	18 19			18 31			18 35		18 43	18 53					18 55	19 03		
London Cannon Street [4]	⊖ d						18 16	18 30											18 50			19 06	
London Bridge [4]	⊖ d						18 20	18 34	18 36			18 40		18 48					18 54	19 00	19 08	19 10	
New Cross [4]	⊖ d						18 26																
St Johns	d																						
Lewisham [4]	d						18 30																
Hither Green [4]	d				18 29							18 51								19 10			
Grove Park [4]	d	18 20			18 33		18 37				18 42	18 55					19 02		19 06	19 14			
Sundridge Park	d	18 23									18 45						19 05						
Bromley North	a	18 25								←	18 47					←	19 07						←
Elmstead Woods	d				18 35		18 39			18 39		18 57				18 57			19 08	19 16			19 16
Chislehurst	d				18 38		→			18 42		→				19 00			19 11	→			19 19
Petts Wood [4]	d		18 29	18 35	18 43					18 46			18 56			19 04		19 12	19 17				19 23
Orpington [4]	a		18 33	18b41	18c49					18 51			19 01	19 04		19 10		19c17	19b23			19 27	19 27
	d									18 56				19 05		19 16						19 28	19 30
Chelsfield [3]	d								18 56	18 59						19 19					19 26		19 33
Knockholt	d									19 02						19 22							19 36
Dunton Green	d									19 07						19 27							19 41
Sevenoaks [4]	a					18 48		18 58	19 04	19 12				19 14	19 20	19 32					19 34	19 37	19 46
	d					18 48		18 58	19 05					19 15	19 20						19 34	19 38	
Hildenborough	d								19 11												19 40	19 44	
Tonbridge [4]	a					18 57		19 07	19 15					19 23	19 29						19 45	19 48	

Station		SE 01	SE 70	SE 70	SE 13	SE 22 [1]	SE 4 [1]	SE 16	SE 90	SE 70	SE 16	SE 01	SE 70	SE 13	SE 22 [1]	SE 4 [1]	SE 16	SE 4 [1]	SE 70	SE 16	SE 22 [1]	SE 01	SE 12
						🛒			B									D 🛒					
London Charing Cross [4]	⊖ d					19 15	19 24	19 26	19 30						19 45	19 52	19 56	20 00			20 15		20 26
London Waterloo (East) [4]	⊖ d					19 18	19 27	19 29	19 33						19 48	19 55	19 59	20 03			20 18		20 29
London Cannon Street [4]	⊖ d				19 18									19 48									
London Bridge [4]	⊖ d				19 22	19 23	19 32	19 34	19 38					19 52	19 53	20 01	20 04	20 08			20 23		20 34
New Cross [4]	⊖ d																						
St Johns	d																						
Lewisham [4]	d				19 31			19 43						20 01			20 13						20 43
Hither Green [4]	d				19 35			19 47			←			20 05			20 17						20 47
Grove Park [4]	d	19 22			19 39			19 51			19 51	19 55		20 09			20 21					20 25	20 51
Sundridge Park	d	19 25						→				19 58										20 28	→
Bromley North	a	19 27										20 00								←		20 30	
Elmstead Woods	d				19 41						19 53			20 11			20 23						
Chislehurst	d				19 44						19 56			20 14			20 26			20 26			
Petts Wood [4]	d		19 25	19 41	19 48					19 56	19 59		20 11	20 17			→		20 26	20 29			
Orpington [4]	a		19 31	19 44	19 52				19 54	19 59	20 02		20 14	20 20					20 29	20 32	20 40		
	d								19 54		20 02									20 32	20 40		
Chelsfield [3]	d								19 58		20 05									20 35			
Knockholt	d										20 08									20 38			
Dunton Green	d										20 13									20 43			
Sevenoaks [4]	a					19 50			20 06		20 16				20 19			20 31		20 46	20 50		
	d					19 50			20 06						20 20			20 32			20 50		
Hildenborough	d								20 12									20 38					
Tonbridge [4]	a					19 59	20 02		20 17						20 28	20 32		20 42			20 58		

For general notes see front of timetable
For details of catering facilities see Directory of Train Operators

- **A** To Ashford International (Table 207)
- **B** To Tunbridge Wells (Table 206)
- **C** To Hastings (Table 206)
- **D** To Ramsgate (Table 207)
- **b** Until 10 October arr 1 minute earlier
- **c** Until 10 October arr 2 minutes earlier

For details of Bank Holiday service alterations please see first page of Table 195

London → Grove Park, Bromley North, Orpington, Sevenoaks and Tonbridge

Network Diagram - see first page of Table 200

Station		SE 90 1 A	SE 70	SE 12	SE 01	SE 15	SE 22 1	SE 16	SE 4 1 A	SE 70	SE 16	SE 22 1	SE 01	SE 12	SE 90 1 B	SE 70	SE 12	SE 22 1	SE 01	SE 12	SE 4 1 A	SE 70	SE 12
London Charing Cross 4	⊖ d	20 30					20 45	20 56	21 00			21 15		21 26	21 30			21 45		21 56	22 00		
London Waterloo (East) 4	⊖ d	20 33					20 48	20 59	21 03			21 18		21 29	21 33			21 48		21 59	22 03		
London Cannon Street 4	⊖ d					20 35																	
London Bridge 4	⊖ d	20 38				20 39	20 53	21 04	21 08			21 23		21 34	21 38			21 53		22 04	22 08		
New Cross 4	⊖ d					20 44																	
St Johns	d					20 46																	
Lewisham 4	d					20 49		21 13						21 43						22 13			
Hither Green 4	d			←		20 53		21 17			←			21 47			←			22 17			←
Grove Park 4	d			20 51	20 55	20 57		21 21			21 21		21 25	21 51			21 51		21 55	22 21			22 21
Sundridge Park	d				20 58			→					21 28	→					21 58	→			
Bromley North	a				21 00								21 30						22 00				
Elmstead Woods	d			20 53		20 59					21 23						21 53						22 23
Chislehurst	d			20 56		21 02					21 26						21 56						22 26
Petts Wood 4	d		20 55	21 00		21 05				21 24	21 29					21 55	22 00					22 25	22 30
Orpington 4	a	20 54	20 58	21 03		21 10	21 10		21 24	21 27	21 32	21 40			21 54	21 58	22 03	22 10			22 24	22 28	22 33
	d	20 55					21 10		21 24		21 32	21 40			21 54			22 10			22 24		
Chelsfield 3	d										21 35												
Knockholt	d										21 38												
Dunton Green	d										21 43												
Sevenoaks 4	a	21 04					21 20		21 34		21 46	21 50			22 04			22 20			22 34		
	d	21 05					21 20		21 34			21 50			22 04			22 20			22 34		
Hildenborough	d	21 11							21 40						22 10						22 40		
Tonbridge 4	a	21 15					21 28		21 45			21 58			22 15			22 28			22 45		

Station		SE 22 1 C	SE 01	SE 12	SE 8 1 D	SE 70	SE 12	SE 22 1	SE 01	SE 12	SE 2 1 E	SE 70	SE 12	SE 22 1 C	SE 01	SE 12	SE 2 1 E	SE 22 1	SE 70	SE 12	SE 01
London Charing Cross 4	⊖ d	22 15		22 26	22 30			22 45		22 56	23 00			23 15		23 26	23 30	23 37			
London Waterloo (East) 4	⊖ d	22 18		22 29	22 33			22 48		22 59	23 03			23 18		23 29	23 33	23 40			
London Cannon Street 4	⊖ d																				
London Bridge 4	⊖ d	22 23		22 34	22 38			22 53		23 04	23 08			23 23		23 34	23 38	23 45			
New Cross 4	⊖ d																				
St Johns	d																				
Lewisham 4	d			22 43						23 13						23 43					
Hither Green 4	d			22 47			←			23 17			←			23 47				←	
Grove Park 4	d		22 25	22 51			22 51		22 55	23 21			23 21		23 25	23 51				23 51	23 56
Sundridge Park	d		22 28	→					22 58	→					23 28	→					23 59
Bromley North	a		22 30						23 00						23 30						00 01
Elmstead Woods	d						22 53						23 24							23 53	
Chislehurst	d						22 56						23 26							23 56	
Petts Wood 4	d					22 55	23 00					23 26	23 31						23 55	23 59	
Orpington 4	a	22 40			22 54	22 58	23 03	23 10			23 24	23 30	23 34	23 40			23 56		23 58	00 03	
	d	22 40			22 54			23 10			23 24			23 40			23 56				
Chelsfield 3	d	22 44												23 44							
Knockholt	d																				
Dunton Green	d																				
Sevenoaks 4	a	22 52			23 04			23 20			23 34			23 52			00 06	00 10			
	d	22 52			23 04			23 20			23 34			23 52			00 06	00 10			
Hildenborough	d				23 10						23 40						00 12				
Tonbridge 4	a	23 00			23 14			23 28			23 45			00 01			00 17	00 20			

For general notes see front of timetable
For details of catering facilities see Directory of Train Operators

A To Ramsgate (Table 207)
B To Margate (Table 207)
C To Tunbridge Wells (Table 206)
D To Canterbury West (Table 207)
E To Dover Priory (Table 207)

London → Grove Park, Bromley North, Orpington, Sevenoaks and Tonbridge

Network Diagram - see first page of Table 200

Station		SE 12	SE 2 [1] A	SE 12	SE 22 [1]	SE 70	SE 02 [1]	SE 01	SE 14	SE 4 [1] B	SE 12	SE 4 [1] C	SE 70	SE 12	SE 01	SE 16	SE 01	SE 12	SE 4 [1] C	SE 70	SE 12	SE 01	SE 16	SE 4 [1]	SE 70
London Charing Cross [4]	⊖ d	23p26	23p30		23p37		00 10		00 48		05 56	06 00				06 26		06 56	07 00				07 26	07 30	
London Waterloo (East) [4]	⊖ d	23p29	23p33		23p40		00 13		00 51		05 59	06 03				06 29		06 59	07 03				07 29	07 33	
London Cannon Street [4]	⊖ d																								
London Bridge [4]	⊖ d	23p34	23p38		23p45		00 18		00 56		06 04	06 08				06 34		07 04	07 08				07 34	07 38	
New Cross [4]	⊖ d								01 01																
St Johns	d																								
Lewisham [4]	d	23p43							01 05		06 13					06 43		07 13					07 43		
Hither Green [4]	d	23p47		←					01 09		06 17			←		06 47		07 17			←		07 47		
Grove Park [4]	d	23p51		23p51			00 29	00 33	01 13		06 21			06 21	06 26	06 51	06 56	07 21			07 21	07 26	07 51		
Sundridge Park	d	→						00 36			→				06 29		06 59	→				07 29	→		
Bromley North	a							00 38							06 31		07 01					07 31			
Elmstead Woods	d			23p53			00 32		01 16					06 23		06 53					07 23				
Chislehurst	d			23p56			00 35		01 19					06 26		06 56					07 26				
Petts Wood [4]	d			00 01		00 25	00 39		01 23				06 24	06 30		07 00				07 24	07 30				07 54
Orpington [4]	a		23p56	00 03		00 28	00 42		01 26			06 26	06 27	06 33		07 03			07 26	07 27	07 33			07 55	07 57
	d		23p56				00 42			05 58		06 26		06 33					07 26		07 33			07 56	
Chelsfield [3]	d						00 46							06 36							07 36				
Knockholt	d													06 39							07 39				
Dunton Green	d													06 44							07 44				
Sevenoaks [4]	a		00 06		00 10		00 54			06 07		06 36		06 47					07 36		07 47			08 05	
	d		00 06		00 10		00 54			06 08		06 36							07 36					08 06	
Hildenborough	d		00 12				01 00			06 14		06 42							07 42						
Tonbridge [4]	a		00 17		00 20		01 05			06 18		06 47							07 47					08 14	

Station		SE 16	SE 22 [1]	SE 01	SE 12	SE 4 [1] D	SE 70	SE 12	SE 22 [1]	SE 01	SE 70	SE 16		SE 4 [1]	SE 22 [1]	SE 70	SE 16	SE 01	SE 70	SE 12	SE 4 [1] D	SE 70	SE 12	SE 22 [1]	SE 01
London Charing Cross [4]	⊖ d		07 45		07 56	08 00			08 15			08 26		08 30	08 45					08 56	09 00			09 15	
London Waterloo (East) [4]	⊖ d		07 48		07 59	08 03			08 18			08 29		08 33	08 48					08 59	09 03			09 18	
London Cannon Street [4]	⊖ d																								
London Bridge [4]	⊖ d		07 53		08 04	08 08			08 23			08 34		08 38	08 53					09 04	09 08			09 23	
New Cross [4]	⊖ d																								
St Johns	d																								
Lewisham [4]	d				08 13							08 43								09 13					
Hither Green [4]	d	←			08 17			←				08 47					←			09 17			←		
Grove Park [4]	d	07 51		07 56	08 21			08 21		08 26		08 51					08 51	08 56		09 21			09 21		09 26
Sundridge Park	d			07 59	→					08 29		→						08 59		→					09 29
Bromley North	a			08 01						08 31								09 01							09 31
Elmstead Woods	d	07 53						08 23									08 53						09 23		
Chislehurst	d	07 56						08 26									08 56						09 26		
Petts Wood [4]	d	08 00					08 24	08 30			08 39					08 54	09 00		09 09			09 24	09 30		
Orpington [4]	a	08 03	08 09			08 25	08 27	08 33	08 39		08 42			08 55		08 57	09 03		09 12		09 26	09 27	09 33	09 39	
	d		08 10			08 26		08 33	08 40					08 56							09 26		09 33	09 40	
Chelsfield [3]	d							08 36															09 36		
Knockholt	d							08 39															09 39		
Dunton Green	d							08 44															09 44		
Sevenoaks [4]	a		08 20			08 35		08 47	08 50					09 05	09 15						09 36		09 47	09 50	
	d		08 20			08 36			08 51					09 06	09 16						09 36			09 51	
Hildenborough	d					08 42															09 42				
Tonbridge [4]	a		08 28			08 46			08 59					09 14	09 24						09 47			09 59	

Station		SE 70	SE 16	SE 4 [1] E	SE 22 [1]	SE 70	SE 16	SE 01	SE 4 [1]	SE 70	SE 12	SE 8 [1] E	SE 70	SE 12	SE 22 [1]	SE 01	SE 90 [1]	SE 70	SE 16	SE 8 [1] E	SE 22 [1]	SE 70	SE 16	SE 01
London Charing Cross [4]	⊖ d		09 26	09 30	09 45				09 53		09 56	10 00			10 15		10 23		10 26	10 30	10 45			
London Waterloo (East) [4]	⊖ d		09 29	09 33	09 48				09 56		09 59	10 03			10 18		10 26		10 29	10 33	10 48			
London Cannon Street [4]	⊖ d																							
London Bridge [4]	⊖ d		09 34	09 38	09 53						10 04	10 08			10 23				10 34	10 38	10 53			
New Cross [4]	⊖ d																							
St Johns	d																							
Lewisham [4]	d		09 43								10 13								10 43					
Hither Green [4]	d		09 47				←				10 17			←					10 47				←	
Grove Park [4]	d		09 51				09 51	09 56			10 21			10 21		10 26			10 51				10 51	10 56
Sundridge Park	d		→					09 59			→					10 29			→					10 59
Bromley North	a							10 01								10 31								11 01
Elmstead Woods	d						09 53							10 23									10 53	
Chislehurst	d						09 56							10 26									10 56	
Petts Wood [4]	d	09 39				09 54	10 00			10 09		10 22	10 24	10 30				10 39				10 54	11 00	
Orpington [4]	a	09 42		09 53		09 57	10 03			10 12		10 26	10 27	10 33	10 39			10 42		10 53		10 57	11 03	
	d			09 54								10 26		10 33	10 40					10 54				
Chelsfield [3]	d													10 36										
Knockholt	d													10 39										
Dunton Green	d													10 44										
Sevenoaks [4]	a			10 04	10 15							10 36		10 47	10 50					11 04	11 15			
	d			10 04	10 16							10 36			10 51					11 04	11 16			
Hildenborough	d			10 11								10 43								11 11				
Tonbridge [4]	a			10 15	10 24				10 30			10 47			10 59		11 02			11 15	11 24			

For general notes see front of timetable
For details of catering facilities see Directory of Train Operators

- **A** To Dover Priory (Table 207)
- **B** To Ramsgate (Table 207)
- **C** To Margate (Table 207)
- **D** To Ramsgate (Table 207) and to Margate (Table 207)
- **E** To Ashford International (Table 207)

Table 204

Saturdays

London → Grove Park, Bromley North, Orpington, Sevenoaks and Tonbridge

Network Diagram - see first page of Table 200

Station		SE 4 [1] 🛒	SE 70	SE 12	SE 8 [1] A	SE 70	SE 12	SE 22 [1] 🛒	SE 01	SE 90 [1] 🛒	SE 70	SE 16	SE 8 [1] A	SE 22 [1] 🛒	SE 70	SE 16	SE 01		SE 4 [1] 🛒	SE 70	SE 12	SE 8 [1] A
London Charing Cross [4]	⊖ d	10 53		10 56	11 00			11 15		11 23		11 26	11 30	11 45					17 53		17 56	18 00
London Waterloo (East) [4]	⊖ d	10 56		10 59	11 03			11 18		11 26		11 29	11 33	11 48					17 56		17 59	18 03
London Cannon Street [4]	⊖ d																					
London Bridge [4]	⊖ d			11 04	11 08			11 23				11 34	11 38	11 53				and at			18 04	18 08
New Cross [4]	⊖ d																					
St Johns	d																	the same				
Lewisham [4]	d			11 13								11 43									18 13	
Hither Green [4]	d			11 17			←					11 47				←		minutes			18 17	
Grove Park [4]	d			11 21			11 21		11 26			11 51				11 51	11 56				18 21	
Sundridge Park	d			→					11 29			→					11 59	past			→	
Bromley North	a								11 31								12 01	each				
Elmstead Woods	d						11 23									11 53		hour until				
Chislehurst	d						11 26									11 56						
Petts Wood [4]	d		11 09		11 22	11 24	11 30				11 39				11 54	12 00				18 09		18 22
Orpington [4]	a		11 12		11 26	11 27	11 33	11 39			11 42		11 53		11 57	12 03				18 12		18 26
	d				11 26		11 33	11 40					11 54									18 26
Chelsfield [3]	d						11 36															
Knockholt	d						11 39															
Dunton Green	d						11 44															
Sevenoaks [4]	a				11 36		11 47	11 50					12 04	12 15								18 36
	d				11 36			11 51					12 04	12 16								18 36
Hildenborough	d				11 43								12 11									18 43
Tonbridge [4]	a	11 30			11 47			11 59		12 02			12 15	12 24					18 30			18 47

Station		SE 70	SE 12	SE 22 [1] 🛒	SE 01	SE 4 [1] 🛒	SE 70	SE 16	SE 90 [1]	SE 22 [1] 🛒	SE 70	SE 16	SE 01	SE 70	SE 12	SE 4 [1] B 🛒	SE 70	SE 12	SE 22 [1] 🛒	SE 01	SE 70	SE 16	SE 90 [1]	SE 70	SE 16
London Charing Cross [4]	⊖ d			18 15		18 23		18 26	18 30	18 45					18 56	19 00			19 15			19 26	19 30		
London Waterloo (East) [4]	⊖ d			18 18		18 26		18 29	18 33	18 48					18 59	19 03			19 18			19 29	19 33		
London Cannon Street [4]	⊖ d																								
London Bridge [4]	⊖ d			18 23				18 34	18 38	18 53					19 04	19 08			19 23			19 34	19 38		
New Cross [4]	⊖ d																								
St Johns	d																								
Lewisham [4]	d							18 44							19 14							19 43			
Hither Green [4]	d		←					18 48				←			19 18			←				19 47			←
Grove Park [4]	d		18 21		18 26			18 52				18 52	18 56		19 22			19 22		19 26		19 51			19 51
Sundridge Park	d				18 29			→					18 59		→					19 29		→			
Bromley North	a				18 31								19 01							19 31					
Elmstead Woods	d		18 23									18 55						19 24							19 53
Chislehurst	d		18 26									18 57						19 27							19 56
Petts Wood [4]	d	18 24	18 30				18 39				18 54	19 00		19 09			19 24	19 30			19 39			19 54	20 00
Orpington [4]	a	18 27	18 33	18 40			18 42		18 54		18 57	19 03		19 12		19 24	19 27	19 33	19 40		19 42		19 54	19 57	20 03
	d		18 33	18 40					18 54							19 24		19 33	19 40				19 54		
Chelsfield [3]	d		18 36															19 36							
Knockholt	d		18 39															19 39							
Dunton Green	d		18 44															19 44							
Sevenoaks [4]	a		18 47	18 50					19 04	19 16						19 34		19 47	19 51				20 04		
	d			18 51					19 04	19 17						19 34			19 51				20 04		
Hildenborough	d															19 40									
Tonbridge [4]	a			18 59		19 02			19 13	19 25						19 45			19 59				20 13		

Station		SE 22 [1]	SE 01	SE 70	SE 12	SE 4 [1] B 🛒	SE 70	SE 12	SE 01	SE 12		SE 90 [1]	SE 70	SE 12	SE 22 [1]	SE 01	SE 16	SE 4 [1] B	SE 70	SE 16	SE 01	SE 12	SE 90 [1]	SE 70	SE 12
London Charing Cross [4]	⊖ d	19 45			19 56	20 00				20 26		20 30			20 45		20 56	21 00				21 26	21 30		
London Waterloo (East) [4]	⊖ d	19 48			19 59	20 03				20 29		20 33			20 48		20 59	21 03				21 29	21 33		
London Cannon Street [4]	⊖ d																								
London Bridge [4]	⊖ d	19 53			20 04	20 08				20 34		20 38			20 53		21 04	21 08				21 34	21 38		
New Cross [4]	⊖ d																								
St Johns	d																								
Lewisham [4]	d				20 13					20 43							21 13					21 43			
Hither Green [4]	d				20 17			←		20 47				←			21 17			←		21 47			←
Grove Park [4]	d		19 56		20 21			20 21	20 26	20 51				20 51		20 56	21 21			21 21	21 26	21 51			21 51
Sundridge Park	d		19 59		→				20 29	→						20 59	→				21 29	→			
Bromley North	a		20 01						20 31							21 01					21 31				
Elmstead Woods	d							20 23						20 53						21 23					21 53
Chislehurst	d							20 26						20 56						21 26					21 56
Petts Wood [4]	d			20 09			20 24	20 30					20 54	21 00					21 24	21 30				21 54	22 00
Orpington [4]	a	20 10		20 12		20 24	20 27	20 33				20 54	20 57	21 03	21 10			21 24	21 27	21 33			21 54	21 57	22 03
	d	20 10				20 24		20 33				20 54			21 10			21 24		21 33			21 54		
Chelsfield [3]	d							20 36												21 36					
Knockholt	d							20 39												21 39					
Dunton Green	d							20 44												21 44					
Sevenoaks [4]	a	20 20				20 34		20 47				21 04			21 20			21 34		21 47			22 04		
	d	20 20				20 34						21 04			21 20			21 34					22 04		
Hildenborough	d					20 40												21 40							
Tonbridge [4]	a	20 28				20 45						21 13			21 28			21 45					22 13		

For general notes see front of timetable
For details of catering facilities see
Directory of Train Operators

A To Ashford International (Table 207)
B To Ramsgate (Table 207)

Table 204

London → Grove Park, Bromley North, Orpington, Sevenoaks and Tonbridge

Network Diagram - see first page of Table 200

		SE 22	SE 01	SE 12	SE 4	SE 70	SE 12	SE 01	SE 12	SE 90	SE 70	SE 12	SE 22	SE 01	SE 12	SE 8	SE 70	SE 12	SE 01	SE 12	SE 8	SE 70	SE 12	SE 01
		1			1					1			1			1					1			
					A											B					B			
London Charing Cross 4	⊖ d	21 45		21 56	22 00				22 26	22 30			22 45		22 56	23 00				23 26	23 30			
London Waterloo (East) 4	⊖ d	21 48		21 59	22 03				22 29	22 33			22 48		22 59	23 03				23 29	23 33			
London Cannon Street 4	⊖ d																							
London Bridge 4	⊖ d	21 53		22 04	22 08				22 34	22 38			22 53		23 04	23 08				23 34	23 38			
New Cross 4	⊖ d																							
St Johns	d																							
Lewisham 4	d			22 13					22 43						23 13					23 43				
Hither Green 4	d			22 17			←		22 47			←			23 17			←		23 47			←	
Grove Park 4	d		21 56	22 21			22 21	22 26	22 51			22 51		22 56	23 21			23 21	23 26	23 51			23 51	23 56
Sundridge Park	d		21 59	→				22 29	→					22 59	→				23 29	→				23 59
Bromley North	a		22 01					22 31						23 01					23 31					00 01
Elmstead Woods	d						22 23					22 53						23 23					23 53	
Chislehurst	d						22 26					22 56						23 26					23 56	
Petts Wood 4	d					22 24	22 30				22 54	23 00					23 24	23 30				23 54	00 01	
Orpington 4	a	22 10			22 24	22 27	22 33			22 54	22 57	23 03	23 10			23 24	23 27	23 33			23 54	23 57	00 03	
	d	22 10			22 24					22 54			23 10			23 24					23 54			
Chelsfield 3	d				22 28											23 28								
Knockholt	d																							
Dunton Green	d																							
Sevenoaks 4	a	22 20			22 36					23 04			23 20			23 36					00 04			
	d	22 20			22 36					23 04			23 20			23 36					00 04			
Hildenborough	d				22 43											23 42					00 10			
Tonbridge 4	a	22 28			22 47					23 13			23 28			23 46					00 15			

Sundays

		SE 12	SE 8	SE 12	SE 70		SE 02	SE 01	SE 14	SE 12		SE 70	SE 16	SE 22	SE 16		SE 12	SE 90	SE 70	SE 12		SE 16	SE 4	SE 70	SE 22
			1				1							1				1					1		1
			B															C							
London Charing Cross 4	⊖ d	23p26	23p30				00 10		00 48				07 56	08 14			08 26	08 30				08 56	09 00		09 14
London Waterloo (East) 4	⊖ d	23p29	23p33				00 13		00 51				07 59	08 17			08 29	08 33				08 59	09 03		09 17
London Cannon Street 4	⊖ d																								
London Bridge 4	⊖ d	23p34	23p38				00 18		00 56	07 35			08 05	08 22			08 35	08 38				09 05	09 08		09 22
New Cross 4	⊖ d								01 01																
St Johns	d																								
Lewisham 4	d	23p43							01 05	07 45			08 15				08 45					09 15			
Hither Green 4	d	23p47		←					01 09	07 49			08 19				08 49			←		09 19			
Grove Park 4	d	23p51		23p51			00 29	00 34	01 13	07 53			08 23				08 53			08 53		09 23			
Sundridge Park	d	→						00 37									→								
Bromley North	a							00 39																	
Elmstead Woods	d			23p53			00 32		01 16	07 55			08 25		←					08 55		09 25			
Chislehurst	d			23p56			00 35		01 19	07 58			08 28		08 28					08 58		09 28			
Petts Wood 4	d			00 01	00 26		00 39		01 23	08 01		08 24	→		08 31				08 54	09 01		→		09 24	
Orpington 4	a		23p54	00 03	00 29		00 42		01 26	08 04		08 27		08 38	08 34			08 54	08 57	09 04			09 24	09 27	09 38
	d		23p54				00 42							08 38	08 42			08 54					09 24		09 38
Chelsfield 3	d						00 46								08 45										
Knockholt	d														08 48										
Dunton Green	d														08 53										
Sevenoaks 4	a		00 04				00 54							08 48	08 56			09 04					09 34		09 48
	d		00 04				00 54							08 48				09 04					09 34		09 48
Hildenborough	d		00 10				01 00											09 10							
Tonbridge 4	a		00 15				01 05							08 56				09 15					09 43		09 56

		SE 16		SE 12	SE 90	SE 70	SE 12	SE 22	SE 16	SE 4	SE 70	SE 22	SE 16			SE 12	SE 90	SE 70	SE 12		SE 22	SE 12	SE 4	SE 70
					1			1		1		1					1				1		1	
					D												A							
London Charing Cross 4	⊖ d			09 26	09 30			09 44	09 56	10 00		10 14				19 26	19 30				19 44	19 56	20 00	
London Waterloo (East) 4	⊖ d			09 29	09 33			09 47	09 59	10 03		10 17				19 29	19 33				19 47	19 59	20 03	
London Cannon Street 4	⊖ d																							
London Bridge 4	⊖ d			09 35	09 38			09 52	10 05	10 08		10 22		and at		19 35	19 38				19 52	20 05	20 08	
New Cross 4	⊖ d																							
St Johns	d													the same										
Lewisham 4	d			09 45					10 15							19 45						20 15		
Hither Green 4	d			09 49			←		10 19					minutes		19 49			←			20 19		
Grove Park 4	d			09 53			09 53		10 23							19 53			19 53			20 23		
Sundridge Park	d			→										past		→						→		
Bromley North	a																							
Elmstead Woods	d	←					09 55		10 26				←	each					19 55					
Chislehurst	d	09 28					09 58		10 28				10 28						19 58					
Petts Wood 4	d	09 31				09 54	10 01		→		10 24		10 31	hour until				19 54	20 01					20 24
Orpington 4	a	09 34			09 54	09 57	10 04	10 08		10 24	10 27	10 38	10 34				19 54	19 57	20 04		20 08		20 24	20 27
	d	09 42			09 54			10 08		10 24		10 38	10 42				19 54				20 08		20 24	
Chelsfield 3	d	09 45											10 45											
Knockholt	d	09 48											10 48											
Dunton Green	d	09 53											10 53											
Sevenoaks 4	a	09 56			10 04			10 18		10 34		10 48	10 56				20 04				20 18		20 34	
	d				10 04			10 18		10 34		10 48					20 04				20 18		20 34	
Hildenborough	d				10 10												20 10							
Tonbridge 4	a				10 15			10 26		10 43		10 56					20 15				20 26		20 43	

For general notes see front of timetable
For details of catering facilities see Directory of Train Operators

A To Ramsgate (Table 207)
B To Dover Priory (Table 207)
C To Margate (Table 207) and to Ramsgate (Table 207)
D To Margate (Table 207)

Sundays

London → Grove Park, Bromley North, Orpington, Sevenoaks and Tonbridge

Network Diagram - see first page of Table 200

		SE 12	SE 22	SE 12	SE 90	SE 70	SE 12		SE 12	SE 4	SE 70	SE 12		SE 22	SE 12	SE 90	SE 70		SE 12	SE 12	SE 4	SE 70		SE 12
			1		1					1				1		1					1			
			A		B									A		B								
London Charing Cross 4	⊖ d		20 14	20 26	20 30				20 56	21 00				21 14	21 26	21 30				21 56	22 00			
London Waterloo (East) 4	⊖ d		20 17	20 29	20 33				20 59	21 03				21 17	21 29	21 33				21 59	22 03			
London Cannon Street 4	⊖ d																							
London Bridge 4	⊖ d		20 22	20 35	20 38				21 05	21 08				21 22	21 35	21 38				22 05	22 08			
New Cross 4	⊖ d																							
St Johns	d																							
Lewisham 4	d			20 45					21 15						21 45					22 15				
Hither Green 4	d	←		20 49			←		21 19			←			21 49				←	22 19				←
Grove Park 4	d	20 23		20 53			20 53		21 23			21 23			21 53				21 53	22 23				22 23
Sundridge Park	d			↳					↳						↳					↳				
Bromley North	a																							
Elmstead Woods	d	20 25					20 55					21 25							21 55					22 25
Chislehurst	d	20 28					20 58					21 28							21 58					22 28
Petts Wood 4	d	20 31				20 54	21 01				21 24	21 31					21 54		22 01			22 24		22 31
Orpington 4	a	20 34	20 38		20 54	20 57	21 04			21 24	21 27	21 34		21 38		21 54	21 57		22 04		22 24	22 27		22 34
	d		20 38		20 54					21 24				21 38		21 54					22 24			
Chelsfield 3	d		20 42											21 42										
Knockholt	d																							
Dunton Green	d																							
Sevenoaks 4	a		20 50		21 04					21 34				21 50		22 04					22 34			
	d		20 50		21 04					21 34				21 50		22 04					22 34			
Hildenborough	d				21 10											22 10								
Tonbridge 4	a		20 58		21 15					21 43				21 58		22 15					22 43			

		SE 22	SE 12	SE 2	SE 70		SE 12	SE 72	SE 70	SE 12		SE 22	SE 72	SE 12	SE 8		SE 70	SE 12	SE 12
		1		1								1			1				
		A		C								A							
London Charing Cross 4	⊖ d	22 14	22 26	22 30						22 56		23 14		23 26	23 30				23 56
London Waterloo (East) 4	⊖ d	22 17	22 29	22 33						22 59		23 17		23 29	23 33				23 59
London Cannon Street 4	⊖ d																		
London Bridge 4	⊖ d	22 22	22 35	22 38						23 05		23 22		23 35	23 38				00 05
New Cross 4	⊖ d																		
St Johns	d																		
Lewisham 4	d		22 45							23 15				23 44					00 15
Hither Green 4	d		22 49				←			23 19				23 48				←	00 19
Grove Park 4	d		22 53				22 53			23 23				23 52				23 52	00 23
Sundridge Park	d		↳											↳					
Bromley North	a																		
Elmstead Woods	d						22 55			23 25								23 55	00 25
Chislehurst	d						22 58			23 28								23 57	00 28
Petts Wood 4	d				22 54		23 01	23 14	23 24	23 31			23 44				23 54	23 59	00 31
Orpington 4	a	22 38		22 54	22 57		23 04	23 17	23 27	23 35		23 38	23 47		23 54		23 57	00 03	00 34
	d	22 38		22 54								23 38			23 54				
Chelsfield 3	d	22 42										23 42							
Knockholt	d																		
Dunton Green	d																		
Sevenoaks 4	a	22 50		23 04								23 50			00 04				
	d	22 50		23 04								23 50			00 04				
Hildenborough	d			23 10															
Tonbridge 4	a	22 58		23 15								23 58			00 13				

For general notes see front of timetable
For details of catering facilities see Directory of Train Operators

A To Hastings (Table 206)
B To Ramsgate (Table 207)
C To Dover Priory (Table 207)

Table 204

Mondays to Fridays

For details of Bank Holiday service alterations please see first page of Table 195

Tonbridge, Sevenoaks, Orpington Bromley North, Grove Park → London

Network Diagram - see first page of Table 200

Miles	Miles			SE MX 01	SE 02 A	SE 02 B	SE 70	SE 30 1 C	SE 70	SE 14	SE 5 1 D	SE 2 1	SE 70	SE 01	SE 14	SE 83	SE 05	SE 14	SE 22 1 E	SE 4 1	SE 70	SE 01	SE 14	SE 13	SE 17
0	—	**Tonbridge** 4	d		04 56	04 56		05 26			05 55	06 02					06 05		06 18	06 30					
2½	—	Hildenborough	d		05 00	05 00		05 31			06 00								06 22						
7½	—	**Sevenoaks** 4	a		05 07	05 08		05 38			06 07	06 12					06 15		06 30	06 39					
—	—		d		05 08	05 09		05 39			06 07	06 13				06 13	06 16		06 30	06 40					06 44
1½	—	Dunton Green	d														06 18								06 46
5½	—	Knockholt	d														06 24								06 52
6¾	—	Chelsfield 3	d		05 16	05 17		05 47									06 27								06 55
8¾	—	**Orpington** 4	a		05 20	05 20		05 50			06 16						06 30								06 58
—	—		d		05 20	05 20	05 25	05 50	05 50	06 00	06 17		06 20		06 24		06 31				06 44		06 49	06 57	06 59
9½	—	Petts Wood 4	d		05 23	05 23	05a28		05a53	06 03			06a23		06 27						06a47		06 52	07 00	
10¾	—	Chislehurst	d		05 26	05 26				06 06					06 30			←					06 57	07 04	
11¾	—	Elmstead Woods	d		05 28	05 28				06 08					06 32			06 32					06 59	07 06	
—	0	**Bromley North**	d	00 06										06 26	→							06 52		→	
—	½	Sundridge Park	d	00 08										06 28								06 54			
13	1¾	**Grove Park** 4	d	00a11	05 31	05 31				06 11				06a31				06 35				06a57	07 02		
14¾	—	Hither Green 4	d		05 34	05 35				06 15								06 39					07 06		
16	—	**Lewisham** 4	d							06 20								06 44							
16½	—	St Johns	a																						
17¼	—	New Cross 4	⊖ a		05 39	05 40				06 24															
20¼	—	**London Bridge** 4	⊖ a		05 45	05 46		06 06		06 30	06 35	06 36					06 48	06 53	06 55	07 03					07 15
—	—	**London Cannon Street** 4	⊖ a								06b43						06b55								07c22
21¼	—	**London Waterloo (East)** 4	⊖ a		05 50	05 51		06 11		06 35		06 41						06 58	07 00	07 08			07 24		
22	—	**London Charing Cross** 4	⊖ a		05 56	05 54		06 14		06 38		06b48						07b03	07c06	07c15			07c29		

		SE 90 1 G	SE 13	SE 70	SE 01	SE 12	SE 23 1	SE 12	SE 70	SE 01	SE 17	SE 30 1 C	SE 5 1 D	SE 17	SE 4 1	SE 12	SE 70	SE 17	SE 30 1 C	SE 3 1 H	SE 01	SE 17	SE 90 1	SE 12	SE 12
Tonbridge 4	d	06 45					06 53					07 06	07 16		07 25				07 31	07 36			07 42		
Hildenborough	d	06 49										07 10	07 20						07 36	07 40					
Sevenoaks 4	a	06 57					07 03					07 18	07 28		07 35				07 43	07 48			07 52		
	d	06 58					07 03				07 13	07 19	07 29		07 35			07 38	07 44	07 49			07 53		
Dunton Green	d										07 16							07 40							
Knockholt	d										07 22							07 46							
Chelsfield 3	d										07 25	07 28						07 49	07 53						
Orpington 4	a						07 12				07 28							07 52							
	d			07 06		07 10	07 13		07 27		07 30					07 36	07 50	07 53						07 56	08 00
Petts Wood 4	d			07a09		07 13			07a30		07 33			←		07 39	07a53	07 56				←		07 59	08 03
Chislehurst	d		←			07 17		←			07 37			07 37		07 43		07 59				07 59		08 03	08 07
Elmstead Woods	d		07 06			07 19		07 19			→			07 39		07 45		→				08 01		08 05	08 09
Bromley North	d				07 13	→				07 33											07 54				
Sundridge Park	d				07 15					07 35											07 56				
Grove Park 4	d		07 09		07a18			07 22		07a38				07 42		07 48					07a59	08 04		08 08	08 12
Hither Green 4	d		07 14					07 26						07 46											08 16
Lewisham 4	d																								
St Johns	a																								
New Cross 4	⊖ a		07 19																						
London Bridge 4	⊖ a	07 21	07 25				07 29	07 36				07 50	07 54	07 58		08 01			08 10	08 14		08 16			08 26
London Cannon Street 4	⊖ a		07c32				07c37						08c01	08 04						08c21		08c24			
London Waterloo (East) 4	⊖ a	07 27						07 42				07 55			08 04	08 07			08 15				08 21	08 25	08 31
London Charing Cross 4	⊖ a	07c33						07c47				07 59			08 09	08c13			08 21				08c27	08c31	08c37

		SE 70	SE 17	SE 30 1 C	SE 91 1	SE 4 1	SE 01	SE 17	SE 12	SE 70	SE 17	SE 01	SE 30 1 C	SE 3 1 H	SE 90 1	SE 17	SE 12	SE 01	SE 70	SE 30 1 C	SE 5 1	SE 12	SE 70	SE 17	SE 22 1
Tonbridge 4	d			07 51	07 58	08 02							08 11	08 17	08 25					08 36	08 46				09 00
Hildenborough	d			07 56									08 16	08 21						08 41					
Sevenoaks 4	a			08 03	08 08	08 12							08 23	08 29						08 48	08 56				09 09
	d		07 58	08 04	08 09	08 13					08 18		08 24	08 30						08 49	08 57			09 00	09 10
Dunton Green	d		08 00								08 20									08 52					
Knockholt	d		08 06								08 26									08 58					
Chelsfield 3	d		08 09	08 13							08 29		08 33							09 01				09 08	
Orpington 4	a		08 12								08 32													09 11	
	d	08 10	08 13						08 20	08 30	08 33						08 38		08 53			09 00	09 08	09 12	
Petts Wood 4	d	08a13	08 16					←	08 23	08a33	08 36					←	08 41		08a56			09 03	09a11	09 15	
Chislehurst	d		08 19					08 19	08 27		08 39					08 39	08 44					09 07		09 19	
Elmstead Woods	d		→					08 21	08 29		→					08 41	08 46					09 09		→	
Bromley North	d						08 15					08 35						08 55							
Sundridge Park	d						08 17					08 37						08 57							
Grove Park 4	d						08a20	08 24	08 32			08a40				08 44	08 50	09a00				09 12			
Hither Green 4	d								08 36													09 16			
Lewisham 4	d																								
St Johns	a																								
New Cross 4	⊖ a															08 52									
London Bridge 4	⊖ a			08 30	08 34			08 36					08 50	08 54		08 58				09 18	09 22	09 25			09 33
London Cannon Street 4	⊖ a				08c42			08c45						09c02		09c04					09 28				
London Waterloo (East) 4	⊖ a			08 35		08 41			08 49				08 55		09 01		09 06			09 23		09 31			09 38
London Charing Cross 4	⊖ a			08 41		08 47			08c55				09 01		09 07		09c13			09 29		09c36			09 44

For general notes see front of timetable
For details of catering facilities see Directory of Train Operators

A From 13 October
B Until 10 October
C From Tunbridge Wells (Table 206)
D From Ashford International (Table 207)
E From Hastings (Table 206)
G From Ramsgate (Table 207)
H From Dover Priory (Table 207)
b Until 10 October arr 2 minutes earlier
c Until 10 October arr 1 minute earlier

For details of Bank Holiday service alterations please see first page of Table 195

Tonbridge, Sevenoaks, Orpington Bromley North, Grove Park → London

Network Diagram - see first page of Table 200

		SE 01	SE 17	SE 70	SE 01	SE 16	SE 22	SE 4	SE 70	SE 16	SE 70	SE 8	SE 22	SE 4	SE 01	SE 12	SE 70	SE 70	SE 8	SE 16	SE 22	SE 90	SE 01	SE 16	SE 70
							1	1				1	1	1					1		1	1			
							A																		
							🛒	🛒					🛒	🛒							🛒	🛒			
Tonbridge [4]	d						09 14	09 24				09 28	09 46	09 58					10 04		10 18	10 28			
Hildenborough	d						09 18					09 32							10 08						
Sevenoaks [4]	a						09 26	09 34				09 39	09 55						10 15		10 27				
	d					09 18	09 26	09 34				09 40	09 56						10 16	10 18	10 28				
Dunton Green	d					09 20						09 43								10 20					
Knockholt	d					09 26						09 49								10 26					
Chelsfield [3]	d					09 29						09 52								10 29					
Orpington [4]	a					09 32	09 35					09 55							10 25	10 32					
	d			09 23		09 35	09 36		09 38		09 53	09 55				10 05	10 08	10 23	10 25	10 35				←	10 38
Petts Wood [4]	d		←	09a26		09 38			09a41		09a56	09 59				10 08	10a11	10a26	10 29	10 38				10 38	10a41
Chislehurst	d		09 19			09 41				←						10 11				→				10 41	
Elmstead Woods	d		09 21			09 43				09 43						10 13								10 43	
Bromley North	d	09 15			09 35	→									10 05								10 35		
Sundridge Park	d	09 17			09 37										10 07								10 37		
Grove Park [4]	d	09a20	09 24		09a40					09 46					10a10	10 16							10a40	10 46	
Hither Green [4]	d		09 28							09 50						10 20								10 50	
Lewisham [4] 🚊	d		09 33							09 55						10 25								10 55	
St Johns	a																								
New Cross [4]	⊖ a																								
London Bridge [4]	⊖ a		09 41				09 51	09 57		10 04		10 13	10 24			10 34			10 43		10 54			11 04	
London Cannon Street [4]	⊖ a		09b49																						
London Waterloo (East) [4]	⊖ a						09 57	10 03		10 09		10 18	10 29	10 32		10 39			10 48		10 59	11 02		11 09	
London Charing Cross [4]	⊖ a						10 01	10b09		10 12		10 22	10 33	10 36		10 44			10 51		11 03	11 06		11 14	

		SE 70	SE 01	SE 8	SE 22	SE 2	SE 12	SE 70	SE 70	SE 8	SE 14	SE 22	SE 90	SE 01	SE 14	SE 70	SE 70	SE 01		SE 8	SE 22	SE 2	SE 12
				1	1	1				1		1	1							1	1	1	
				B						B										B			
					🛒	🛒						🛒	🛒								🛒	🛒	
Tonbridge [4]	d			10 36	10 46	10 58				11 04		11 18	11 28							14 36	14 46	14 58	
Hildenborough	d			10 39						11 08										14 40			
Sevenoaks [4]	a			10 48	10 55					11 15		11 27							and at	14 47	14 55		
	d			10 48	10 56					11 16	11 18	11 28								14 48	14 56		
Dunton Green	d										11 20								the same				
Knockholt	d										11 26												
Chelsfield [3]	d										11 29								minutes				
Orpington [4]	a			10 57	11 05					11 25	11 32									14 57	15 05		
	d	10 53		10 57	11 05		11 05	11 08	11 23	11 25	11 35				←	11 38	11 53		past	14 57	15 05		15 05
Petts Wood [4]	d	10a56					11 08	11a11	11a26	11 29	11 38				11 38	11a41	11a56						15 08
Chislehurst	d						11 11				→				11 41				each				15 11
Elmstead Woods	d						11 13								11 43								15 13
Bromley North	d		11 05											11 35				12 05	hour until				
Sundridge Park	d		11 07											11 37				12 07					
Grove Park [4]	d		11a10				11 16							11a40	11 46			12a10					15 16
Hither Green [4]	d						11 20								11 50								15 20
Lewisham [4] 🚊	d						11 25								11 55								15 25
St Johns	a																						
New Cross [4]	⊖ a																						
London Bridge [4]	⊖ a			11 13	11 24		11 34			11 43		11 54			12 04					15 13	15 24		15 34
London Cannon Street [4]	⊖ a																						
London Waterloo (East) [4]	⊖ a			11 18	11 29	11 32	11 39			11 48		11 59	12 02		12 09					15 18	15 29	15 32	15 40
London Charing Cross [4]	⊖ a			11 21	11 33	11 36	11 44			11 51		12 03	12 06		12 14					15 21	15 33	15 36	15 44

		SE 70	SE 70	SE 8	SE 16	SE 22	SE 90	SE 01	SE 16	SE 70	SE 70	SE 01	SE 8	SE 13	SE 23	SE 2	SE 70	SE 13	SE 12	SE 12	SE 01	SE 22	SE 70	SE 83	SE 4
				1		1	1						1		1	1						1			1
				B									B		A							A			
						🛒										🛒									🛒
Tonbridge [4]	d			15 04		15 18	15 28						15 36		15 46	15 54						16 06			16 23
Hildenborough	d			15 08									15 40									16 10			
Sevenoaks [4]	a			15 15		15 27							15 48		15 55	16 03						16 18			16 32
	d			15 16	15 18	15 28							15 48		15 56	16 04						16 18		16 26	16 33
Dunton Green	d				15 20																	16 20			
Knockholt	d				15 26																	16 26			
Chelsfield [3]	d				15 29										16 04							16 29			
Orpington [4]	a			15 25	15 32								15 57		16 07							16 34			
	d	15 08	15 23	15 25	15 35				←	15 38	15 53		15 57	16 05	16 07		16 08		16 20	16 33		16 34	16 36		
Petts Wood [4]	d	15a11	15a26	15 29	15 38				15 38	15a41	15a56			16 08			16a11		16 23	16 36			16a39		
Chislehurst	d				→				15 41					16 11				←	16 26	16 39					
Elmstead Woods	d								15 43					16 13				16 13	16 28	16 41					
Bromley North	d							15 35				16 05		→						→	16 35				
Sundridge Park	d							15 37				16 07									16 37				
Grove Park [4]	d							15a40	15 46			16a10						16 16	16 31		16a40				
Hither Green [4]	d								15 50									16 20	16 36						
Lewisham [4] 🚊	d								15 55									16c28							
St Johns	a																								
New Cross [4]	⊖ a																								
London Bridge [4]	⊖ a			15 43		15 54			16 04				16 13		16 24	16 29		16 37	16 45			16 52			17 00
London Cannon Street [4]	⊖ a																								
London Waterloo (East) [4]	⊖ a			15 48		15 59	16 02		16 09				16 18		16 29	16 34		16 43	16 51			16 57			17 05
London Charing Cross [4]	⊖ a			15 51		16 03	16 06		16 13				16 21		16 33	16 38		16 47	16 55			17 01			17 10

For general notes see front of timetable
For details of catering facilities see Directory of Train Operators

A From Hastings (Table 206)
B From Ashford International (Table 207)
b Until 10 October arr 1 minute earlier
c Arr. 1624

For details of Bank Holiday service alterations please see first page of Table 195

Tonbridge, Sevenoaks, Orpington Bromley North, Grove Park → London

Network Diagram - see first page of Table 200

		SE 12	SE 01	SE 23 1 A 🛒	SE 12	SE 16	SE 12	SE 8 1 B	SE 70	SE 12	SE 2 1 C 🛒	SE 12	SE 01	SE 12	SE 22 1	SE 12	SE 16	SE 70	SE 4 1 D 🛒	SE 01	SE 12	SE 22 1	SE 70	SE 12	SE 01
Tonbridge 4	d			16 28				16 40			16 51				17 06				17 18			17 40			
Hildenborough	d							16 44			16 55								17 22						
Sevenoaks 4	a			16 37				16 52			17 03				17 15				17 30			17 50			
	d			16 38		16 42		16 52			17 03				17 16		17 20		17 30			17 50		17 54	
Dunton Green	d					16 44											17 22							17 56	
Knockholt	d					16 50											17 28							18 02	
Chelsfield 3	d			16 46		16 52											17 30							18 05	
Orpington 4	a			16 49		16 55		17 02			17 12				17 26		17 33		17 39			17 59		18 08	
	d			16 50	16 52	16 56		17 02	17 04	17 07	17 13			17 21	17 26		17 34	17 36	17 40		17 51	18 00	18 06	18 08	
Petts Wood 4	d				16 55				17a07	17 10				17 24			17 37	17a39			17 54		18a09		
Chislehurst	d	←			16 58		←			17 13		←		17 27		←					17 57				
Elmstead Woods	d	16 41			17 00 →		17 00			17 15 →		17 15		17 29 →		17 29					17 59				
Bromley North	d		16 56										17 25							17 45					18 10
Sundridge Park	d		16 58										17 27							17 47					18 12
Grove Park 4	d	16 44	17a01				17 03					17 18	17a30			17 32				17a50	18 02				18a15
Hither Green 4	d	16 52					17 09					17 23				17 40					18 06				
Lewisham 4	d																								
St Johns	a																								
New Cross 4	⊖ a																								
London Bridge 4	⊖ a	17 02		17 09		17 13	17 18	17 26			17 31	17 35			17 44	17 49	17 51					18 19		18 25	
London Cannon Street 4	⊖ a							17 31																	
London Waterloo (East) 4	⊖ a	17 07		17 14		17 17	17 23				17 36	17 40			17 50	17 54	17 57		18 03		18 19	18 26		18 30	
London Charing Cross 4	⊖ a	17 13		17 19		17 24	17 28				17 41	17 46			17 55	17 57	18 01		18 07		18 23	18 30		18 37	

		SE 16	SE 4 1 E 🛒	SE 16	SE 01	SE 22 1 G	SE 22 1 🛒	SE 70	SE 12	SE 90 1	SE 12	SE 01	SE 22 1	SE 16	SE 70	SE 90 1 H	SE 22 1	SE 16	SE 01	SE 70	SE 01	SE 18 1	SE 16	SE 22 1 A	SE 70
Tonbridge 4	d		17 50			18 06	18 16			18 20			18 36			18 46	18 54					19 11		19 16	
Hildenborough	d		17 54			18 10										18 50								19 20	
Sevenoaks 4	a		18 02			18 18	18 25			18 29			18 46			18 58	19 04							19 28	
	d		18 02			18 18	18 26			18 30			18 46	18 50		18 58	19 05						19 22	19 28	
Dunton Green	d					18 21								18 52											
Knockholt	d					18 26								18 58											
Chelsfield 3	d					18 29								19 01									19 30		
Orpington 4	a		18 11			18 32	18 35			18 39			18 55	19 04		19 07	19 14						19 33	19 37	
	d	18 11	18 12			18 33	18 36	18 36	18 39	18 40			18 56	19 05	19 08	19 08	19 14			19 23			19 35	19 38	19 38
Petts Wood 4	d	18 14						18a39	18 42					19 08	19a11					19a26			19 38		19a41
Chislehurst	d	18 17		←					18 45		←			19 11				←					19 41		
Elmstead Woods	d	18 19 →		18 19					18 47 →		18 47			19 13 →				19 13					19 43 →		
Bromley North	d				18 30							18 52							19 12		19 32				
Sundridge Park	d				18 32							18 54							19 14		19 34				
Grove Park 4	d			18 22	18a35						18 50	18a57						19 16	19a17		19a37				
Hither Green 4	d			18 26							18 54							19 20							
Lewisham 4	d																	19b28							
St Johns	a																								
New Cross 4	⊖ a																								
London Bridge 4	⊖ a		18 28	18 35		18 49	18 51			18 57	19 05		19 12			19 25	19 33	19 36						19 55	
London Cannon Street 4	⊖ a					18 53																			
London Waterloo (East) 4	⊖ a		18 33	18 40			18 56			19 02	19 10		19 17			19 31	19 38	19 41				19 46		20 00	
London Charing Cross 4	⊖ a		18 37	18 45			19 00			19 07	19 14		19 21			19 35	19 42	19 45				19 50		20 04	

		SE 16	SE 01	SE 90 1 🛒	SE 70	SE 16	SE 22 1	SE 70	SE 16	SE 01	SE 18 1 🛒	SE 16	SE 22 1 G	SE 70	SE 16	SE 01	SE 90 1	SE 12	SE 22 1	SE 70	SE 12	SE 01	SE 4 1	SE 16	SE 22 1 G
Tonbridge 4	d			19 30			19 48				20 00		20 16				20 31		20 48				21 00		21 16
Hildenborough	d												20 20												21 20
Sevenoaks 4	a			19 39			19 57				20 09		20 28				20 40		20 57				21 09		21 28
	d			19 40		19 50	19 58				20 10	20 22	20 28				20 40		20 58				21 10	21 22	21 28
Dunton Green	d					19 52																			
Knockholt	d					19 58																			
Chelsfield 3	d					20 01						20 30												21 30	
Orpington 4	a			19 49		20 04	20 07				20 19	20 33	20 37				20 49		21 07				21 19	21 33	21 37
	d			19 50	19 53	20 05	20 08	20 08			20 20	20 35	20 38	20 38			20 50	21 05	21 08	21 08			21 20	21 35	21 38
Petts Wood 4	d				19a56	20 08		20a11				20 38		20a41				21 08		21a11				21 38	
Chislehurst	d	←				20 11			←			20 41			←			21 11			←			21 41	
Elmstead Woods	d	19 43				20 13 →			20 13			20 43 →			20 43			21 13 →			21 13			21 43 →	
Bromley North	d		20 05							20 35						21 05						21 35			
Sundridge Park	d		20 07							20 37						21 07						21 37			
Grove Park 4	d	19 46	20a10						20 16	20a40					20 46	21a10					21 16	21a40			
Hither Green 4	d	19 50							20 20						20 50						21 20				
Lewisham 4	d	19c57							20e27						20f57						21g27				
St Johns	a																								
New Cross 4	⊖ a																								
London Bridge 4	⊖ a	20 06		20 08			20 25		20 36		20 38		20 55		21 06		21 08		21 25		21 36		21 38		21 55
London Cannon Street 4	⊖ a																								
London Waterloo (East) 4	⊖ a	20 11		20 13			20 30		20 41		20 43		21 00		21 11		21 13		21 30		21 41		21 43		22 00
London Charing Cross 4	⊖ a	20 15		20 18			20 34		20 45		20 48		21 04		21 15		21 18		21 34		21 45		21 48		22 04

For general notes see front of timetable
For details of catering facilities see Directory of Train Operators

- A From Hastings (Table 206)
- B From Ashford International (Table 207)
- C From Dover Priory (Table 207) and from Ramsgate (Table 207)
- D From Ramsgate (Table 207) and from Margate (Table 207)
- E From Ramsgate (Table 207) and from Ramsgate (Table 207)
- G From Tunbridge Wells (Table 206)
- H From Ramsgate (Table 207)
- b Arr. 1924
- c Arr. 1954
- e Arr. 2024
- f Arr. 2054
- g Arr. 2124

For details of Bank Holiday service alterations please see first page of Table 195

Tonbridge, Sevenoaks, Orpington Bromley North, Grove Park → London

Network Diagram - see first page of Table 200

		SE 70	SE 16	SE 01	SE 90 ■1	SE 12	SE 22 ■1	SE 70	SE 12	SE 01	SE 4 ■1	SE 16	SE 22 ■1 A	SE 70	SE 16	SE 01	SE 83	SE 90 ■1	SE 22 ■1	SE 12	SE 70	SE 4 ■1 B	SE 01	
Tonbridge ■4	d				21 30		21 48				22 00		22 16					22 30	22 42			23 10		
Hildenborough	d												22 20									23 14		
Sevenoaks ■4	a				21 39		21 57				22 09		22 28					22 39	22 51			23 22		
	d				21 40		21 58				22 10	22 22	22 28				22 37	22 40	22 52			23 22		
Dunton Green	d																							
Knockholt	d																							
Chelsfield ■3	d											22 30										23 30		
Orpington ■4	a				21 49		22 07				22 19	22 33	22 37					22 49	23 01			23 33		
	d	21 38			21 50	22 05	22 08	22 08			22 20	22 35	22 38	22 38				22 50	23 02	23 05	23 08	23 34		
Petts Wood ■4	d	21a41				22 08		22a11				22 38		22a41						23 08	23a11			
Chislehurst	d		←			22 11			←			22 41			←					23 11				
Elmstead Woods	d		21 43			22 13			22 13			22 43			22 43					23 13				
Bromley North	d			22 05		→				22 35		→				23 05							23 35	
Sundridge Park	d			22 07						22 37						23 07							23 37	
Grove Park ■4	d		21 46	22a10					22 16	22a40					22 46	23a10				23 16			23a40	
Hither Green ■4	d		21 50						22 20						22 50					23 20				
Lewisham ■4	d		21b57						22c27						22e57					23f27				
St Johns	a																							
New Cross ■4	⊖ a																							
London Bridge ■4	⊖ a		22 06		22 08		22 25		22 36		22 38		22 55		23 06			23 08	23 19	23 35		23 51		
London Cannon Street ■4	⊖ a																							
London Waterloo (East) ■4	⊖ a		22 11		22 13		22 30		22 41		22 43		23 00		23 11			23 13	23 24	23 40		23 56		
London Charing Cross ■4	⊖ a		22 15		22 18		22 34		22 45		22 48		23 04		23 15			23 18	23 28	23 44		00 01		

Saturdays

		SE 01	SE 12	SE 12	SE 70	SE 01	SE 2 ■1 C	SE 12	SE 70	SE 01	SE 12	SE 22 ■1	SE 70	SE 12	SE 01	SE 2 ■1 C	SE 16	SE 22 ■1	SE 70	SE 16	SE 01	SE 90 ■1 D	SE 22 ■1 🍴	SE 12	SE 70
Tonbridge ■4	d						06 00					06 46				06 59		07 16				07 31	07 46		
Hildenborough	d						06 04									07 03						07 36			
Sevenoaks ■4	a						06 12					06 56				07 11		07 26				07 43	07 55		
	d		05 22				06 12	06 22				06 57				07 11	07 18	07 26				07 44	07 56		
Dunton Green	d																07 20								
Knockholt	d																07 26								
Chelsfield ■3	d		05 29					06 29									07 29								
Orpington ■4	a		05 32				06 21	06 32				07 07				07 20	07 32	07 35				07 53	08 05		
	d		05 35	06 05	06 08		06 21	06 35	06 38		07 05	07 08	07 08			07 20	07 35	07 35	07 38			07 53	08 05	08 05	08 08
Petts Wood ■4	d		05 38	06 08	06a11			06 38	06a41		07 08		07a11				07 38		07a41					08 08	08a11
Chislehurst	d		05 41	06 11				06 41			07 11			←			07 41			←				08 11	
Elmstead Woods	d		05 43	06 13				06 43			07 13			07 13			07 43			07 43				08 13	
Bromley North	d	00 06				06 35				07 05	→				07 35		→				08 05				
Sundridge Park	d	00 08				06 37				07 07					07 37						08 07				
Grove Park ■4	d	00a11	05 46	06 16		06a40		06 46		07a10				07 16	07a40					07 46	08a10			08 16	
Hither Green ■4	d		05 50	06 20				06 50						07 20						07 49				08 19	
Lewisham ■4	d		05g57	06h27				06j57						07k27						07 55				08 25	
St Johns	a																								
New Cross ■4	⊖ a																								
London Bridge ■4	⊖ a		06 05	06 35			06 40	07 05				07 26		07 35		07 40		07 54		08 05		08 10	08 24	08 35	
London Cannon Street ■4	⊖ a																								
London Waterloo (East) ■4	⊖ a		06 10	06 40			06 44	07 10				07 31		07 40		07 44		07 59		08 09		08 14	08 29	08 39	
London Charing Cross ■4	⊖ a		06 13	06 43			06 48	07 13				07 34		07 43		07 48		08 05		08 14		08 18	08 33	08 44	

For general notes see front of timetable
For details of catering facilities see Directory of Train Operators

A From Tunbridge Wells (Table 206)
B From Ramsgate (Table 207)
C From Dover Priory (Table 207)
D From Ramsgate (Table 207) and from Ramsgate (Table 207)
b Arr. 2154
c Arr. 2224
e Arr. 2254
f Arr. 2324
g Arr. 0554
h Arr. 0624
j Arr. 0654
k Arr. 0724

Table 204

Saturdays

Tonbridge, Sevenoaks, Orpington Bromley North, Grove Park → London

Network Diagram - see first page of Table 200

Station		SE 01	SE 4 ■1	SE 70	SE 16	SE 22 ■1 🍴	SE 70	SE 16	SE 70	SE 01	SE 90 ■1 A	SE 22 ■1 🍴	SE 4 ■1 🍴	SE 12	SE 70	SE 70	SE 8 ■1 B	SE 16	SE 22 ■1 🍴	SE 90 ■1 🍴	SE 01	SE 70	SE 16	SE 70	SE 01
Tonbridge 4	d		08 00			08 16					08 31	08 46	08 58				09 04		09 16	09 28					
Hildenborough	d										08 36						09 08								
Sevenoaks 4	a		08 09			08 26					08 43	08 55					09 15		09 26						
	d		08 10		08 18	08 26					08 44	08 56					09 16	09 18	09 26						
Dunton Green	d				08 20													09 20							
Knockholt	d				08 26													09 26							
Chelsfield 3	d				08 29													09 29							
Orpington 4	a		08 19		08 32	08 35					08 53	09 05					09 25	09 32	09 35						
	d		08 20	08 23	08 35	08 35	08 38		08 53		08 53	09 05		09 05	09 08	09 23	09 26	09 35	09 35			09 38		09 53	
Petts Wood 4	d			08a26	08 38		08a41		08a56					09 08	09a11	09a26	09 29	09 38				09a41		09a56	
Chislehurst	d				08 41			←						09 11				09 41					←		
Elmstead Woods	d				08 43			08 43						09 13				09 43					09 43		
Bromley North	d	08 35			→					09 05								→			09 35				10 05
Sundridge Park	d	08 37								09 07											09 37				10 07
Grove Park 4	d	08a40						08 46		09a10				09 16							09a40		09 46		10a10
Hither Green 4	d							08 49						09 19									09 50		
Lewisham 4	🚊 d							08 55						09 25									09 55		
St Johns	a																								
New Cross 4	⊖ a																								
London Bridge 4	⊖ a		08 40			08 54		09 05			09 10	09 24		09 34			09 43		09 54				10 04		
London Cannon Street 4	⊖ a																								
London Waterloo (East) 4	⊖ a		08 45			08 59		09 09			09 15	09 29	09 32	09 39			09 48		09 59	10 02			10 09		
London Charing Cross 4	⊖ a		08 48			09 03		09 14			09 18	09 33	09 36	09 44			09 51		10 03	10 06			10 14		

Station		SE 8 ■1 B		SE 22 ■1 🍴	SE 4 ■1 🍴	SE 12	SE 70	SE 70	SE 8 ■1 B	SE 16	SE 22 ■1 🍴	SE 90 ■1 🍴	SE 01	SE 16	SE 70	SE 70	SE 01	SE 8 ■1 B	and at the same minutes past each hour until	SE 22 ■1 🍴	SE 4 ■1 🍴	SE 12	SE 70	SE 70
Tonbridge 4	d	09 36		09 46	09 58				10 04		10 18	10 28						10 36		16 46	16 58			
Hildenborough	d	09 40							10 08									10 40						
Sevenoaks 4	a	09 47		09 55					10 15		10 27							10 47		16 55				
	d	09 48		09 56					10 16	10 18	10 28							10 48		16 56				
Dunton Green	d									10 20														
Knockholt	d									10 26														
Chelsfield 3	d									10 29														
Orpington 4	a	09 57		10 05					10 25	10 32								10 57		17 05				
	d	09 57		10 05		10 05	10 08	10 23	10 26	10 35				←	10 38	10 53		10 57		17 05		17 05	17 08	17 23
Petts Wood 4	d					10 08	10a11	10a26	10 29	10 38				10 38	10a41	10a56						17 08	17a11	17a26
Chislehurst	d					10 11				→				10 41								17 11		
Elmstead Woods	d					10 13								10 43								17 13		
Bromley North	d												10 35				11 05							
Sundridge Park	d												10 37				11 07							
Grove Park 4	d					10 16							10a40	10 46			11a10					17 16		
Hither Green 4	d					10 19								10 50								17 19		
Lewisham 4	🚊 d					10 25								10 55								17 25		
St Johns	a																							
New Cross 4	⊖ a																							
London Bridge 4	⊖ a	10 13		10 24		10 34			10 43		10 54			11 04				11 13		17 24		17 34		
London Cannon Street 4	⊖ a																							
London Waterloo (East) 4	⊖ a	10 18		10 29	10 32	10 39			10 48		10 59	11 02		11 09				11 18		17 29	17 32	17 39		
London Charing Cross 4	⊖ a	10 21		10 33	10 36	10 44			10 51		11 03	11 06		11 14				11 21		17 33	17 36	17 44		

Station		SE 8 ■1 B	SE 16	SE 22 ■1 🍴	SE 90 ■1 🍴	SE 01	SE 16	SE 70	SE 70	SE 01	SE 8 ■1 B	SE 12	SE 22 ■1 🍴	SE 70	SE 4 ■1 A 🍴	SE 12	SE 70	SE 01	SE 16	SE 22 ■1 🍴	SE 70	SE 16	SE 01	SE 4 ■1 C 🍴	SE 70
Tonbridge 4	d	17 04		17 18	17 28						17 36		17 46		17 48					18 16				18 30	
Hildenborough	d	17 08									17 40				17 53									18 34	
Sevenoaks 4	a	17 15		17 27							17 47		17 55		18 00					18 26				18 42	
	d	17 16	17 18	17 28							17 48		17 56		18 01				18 18	18 26				18 42	
Dunton Green	d		17 20																18 20						
Knockholt	d		17 26																18 26						
Chelsfield 3	d		17 29																18 29						
Orpington 4	a	17 25	17 32								17 57		18 05		18 10				18 32	18 35				18 51	
	d	17 26	17 35				←	17 38	17 53		17 57	18 05	18 05	18 08	18 11		18 23		18 35	18 35	18 38			18 51	18 53
Petts Wood 4	d	17 29	17 38				17 38	17a41	17a56			18 08		18a11			18a26		18 38		18a41				18a56
Chislehurst	d		→				17 41					18 11				←			18 41			←			
Elmstead Woods	d						17 43					18 13				18 13			18 43			18 43			
Bromley North	d					17 35				18 05		→						18 35	→				19 05		
Sundridge Park	d					17 37				18 07								18 37					19 07		
Grove Park 4	d					17a40	17 46			18a10						18 16		18a40				18 46	19a10		
Hither Green 4	d						17 50									18 19						18 49			
Lewisham 4	🚊 d						17 55									18 26						18 55			
St Johns	a																								
New Cross 4	⊖ a																								
London Bridge 4	⊖ a	17 43		17 54			18 04				18 13		18 24		18 28	18 35				18 54		19 06		19 08	
London Cannon Street 4	⊖ a																								
London Waterloo (East) 4	⊖ a	17 48		17 59	18 02		18 09				18 18		18 29		18 32	18 41				19 00		19 11		19 14	
London Charing Cross 4	⊖ a	17 51		18 03	18 06		18 14				18 21		18 33		18 36	18 45				19 06		19 15		19 19	

For general notes see front of timetable
For details of catering facilities see Directory of Train Operators

A From Ramsgate (Table 207) and from Ramsgate (Table 207)

B From Ashford International (Table 207)

C From Ramsgate (Table 207)

Table 204

Saturdays

Tonbridge, Sevenoaks, Orpington Bromley North, Grove Park → London

Network Diagram - see first page of Table 200

		SE 12	SE 22 [1]	SE 70	SE 12	SE 01	SE 90 [1]	SE 70	SE 16	SE 70	SE 01	SE 4 [1] A	SE 70	SE 12	SE 22 [1]	SE 70	SE 12	SE 01	SE 90 [1]	SE 16	SE 70	SE 01	SE 4 [1] A	SE 12	SE 22 [1]
Tonbridge 4	d		18 46				19 00					19 30			19 46				20 00				20 30		20 46
Hildenborough	d											19 34											20 34		
Sevenoaks 4	a		18 56				19 09					19 42			19 56				20 09				20 42		20 56
	d		18 57				19 10		19 18			19 42			19 57				20 10	20 18			20 42		20 57
Dunton Green	d								19 20											20 20					
Knockholt	d								19 26											20 26					
Chelsfield 3	d								19 29											20 29					
Orpington 4	a		19 07				19 19		19 32			19 51			20 07				20 19	20 32			20 51		21 07
	d	19 05	19 08	19 08			19 20	19 23	19 35	19 38		19 51	19 53	20 05	20 08	20 08			20 20	20 35	20 38		20 51	21 05	21 08
Petts Wood 4	d	19 08		19a11				19a26	19 38	19a41			19a56	20 08		20a11				20 38	20a41			21 08	
Chislehurst	d	19 11			←				19 41					20 11			←			20 41				21 11	
Elmstead Woods	d	19 13			19 13				19 43					20 13			20 13			20 43				21 13	
Bromley North	d	→				19 35					20 05			→				20 35				21 05		→	
Sundridge Park	d					19 37					20 07							20 37				21 07			
Grove Park 4	d				19 16	19a40			19 46		20a10						20 16	20a40		20 46		21a10			
Hither Green 4	d				19 20				19 50								20 20			20 50					
Lewisham 4	d				19b27				19c57								20e27			20f57					
St Johns	a																								
New Cross 4	⊖ a																								
London Bridge 4	⊖ a		19 26		19 36		19 38		20 06			20 08			20 26		20 36		20 38	21 06			21 08		21 25
London Cannon Street 4	⊖ a																								
London Waterloo (East) 4	⊖ a		19 30		19 41		19 44		20 11			20 14			20 30		20 41		20 44	21 11			21 14		21 30
London Charing Cross 4	⊖ a		19 34		19 45		19 49		20 15			20 19			20 34		20 45		20 49	21 15			21 19		21 34

		SE 70	SE 12	SE 01	SE 90 [1]	SE 16	SE 70	SE 01	SE 4 [1] A	SE 16	SE 22 [1]	SE 70	SE 16	SE 01	SE 90 [1]	SE 12	SE 70	SE 01	SE 90 [1] B	SE 12	SE 70	SE 01	SE 4 [1] A
Tonbridge 4	d				21 00				21 30		21 46				22 00				22 30				23 13
Hildenborough	d								21 34										22 34				23 18
Sevenoaks 4	a				21 09				21 42		21 56				22 09				22 42				23 25
	d				21 10	21 22			21 42		21 57				22 10	22 22			22 42				23 26
Dunton Green	d																						
Knockholt	d																						
Chelsfield 3	d					21 29										22 29							23 34
Orpington 4	a				21 19	21 32			21 51		22 07				22 19	22 32			22 51				23 37
	d	21 08			21 20	21 35	21 38		21 51	22 05	22 08	22 08			22 20	22 35	22 38		22 51	23 05	23 08		23 37
Petts Wood 4	d	21a11				21 38	21a41			22 08		22a11				22 38	22a41			23 08	23a11		
Chislehurst	d		←			21 41				22 11			←			22 41				23 11			
Elmstead Woods	d		21 13			21 43				22 13			22 13			22 43				23 13			
Bromley North	d			21 35				22 05		→				22 35				23 05				23 35	
Sundridge Park	d			21 37				22 07						22 37				23 07				23 37	
Grove Park 4	d		21 16	21a40		21 46		22a10					22 16	22a40		22 46		23a10		23 16		23a40	
Hither Green 4	d		21 20			21 50							22 20			22 50				23 20			
Lewisham 4	d		21g27			21h57							22j27			22k57				23m27			
St Johns	a																						
New Cross 4	⊖ a																						
London Bridge 4	⊖ a		21 36		21 38	22 06			22 08		22 25		22 36		22 38	23 06			23 08	23 35			23 53
London Cannon Street 4	⊖ a																						
London Waterloo (East) 4	⊖ a		21 41		21 44	22 11			22 14		22 30		22 41		22 44	23 11			23 13	23 40			23 57
London Charing Cross 4	⊖ a		21 45		21 49	22 15			22 19		22 34		22 45		22 49	23 15			23 18	23 43			00 01

Sundays

		SE 01	SE 72	SE 14	SE 70	SE 72		SE 8 [1]	SE 12	SE 70	SE 8 [1] C	SE 12		SE 72	SE 12	SE 70	SE 8 [1] C	SE 12		SE 70	SE 22 [1]	SE 12	SE 4 [1]	SE 16	SE 70
Tonbridge 4	d							07 01			07 17						08 00				08 19		08 33		
Hildenborough	d							07 05			07 21						08 04								
Sevenoaks 4	a							07 13			07 29						08 12				08 28		08 43		
	d							07 14			07 29						08 12	08 17			08 29		08 44		
Dunton Green	d																	08 19							
Knockholt	d																	08 25							
Chelsfield 3	d										07 37						08 20	08 27							
Orpington 4	a							07 23			07 40						08 23	08 30			08 38		08 53		
	d		06 44	07 01	07 08	07 14		07 24	07 31	07 38	07 41			07 44	08 01	08 08	08 24	08 31		08 38	08 39		08 54	09 01	09 08
Petts Wood 4	d		06a47	07 04	07a11	07a17			07 34	07a41				07a47	08 04	08a11		08 34		08a41				09 04	09a11
Chislehurst	d			07 07					07 37			←			08 07			08 37				←		09 07	
Elmstead Woods	d			07 09					07 39			07 39			08 09			08 39				08 39		09 09	
Bromley North	d	00 05							→									→						→	
Sundridge Park	d	00 07																							
Grove Park 4	d	00a10		07 12								07 42			08 12							08 42			
Hither Green 4	d			07 15								07 45			08 15							08 45			
Lewisham 4	d			07 20								07 50			08 20							08 50			
St Johns	a																								
New Cross 4	⊖ a																								
London Bridge 4	⊖ a			07 29				07 39			07 56	07 58			08 28		08 39				08 56	08 58	09 09		
London Cannon Street 4	⊖ a																								
London Waterloo (East) 4	⊖ a			07 34				07 44			08 01	08 03			08 33		08 44				09 01	09 03	09 14		
London Charing Cross 4	⊖ a			07 37				07 48			08 05	08 07			08 37		08 48				09 05	09 07	09 18		

For general notes see front of timetable
For details of catering facilities see Directory of Train Operators

A From Ramsgate (Table 207)
B From Ramsgate (Table 207) and from Ramsgate (Table 207)
C From Ashford International (Table 207)
b Arr. 1924
c Arr. 1954
e Arr. 2024
f Arr. 2054
g Arr. 2124
h Arr. 2154
j Arr. 2224
k Arr. 2254
m Arr. 2324

Table 204

Sundays

Tonbridge, Sevenoaks, Orpington Bromley North, Grove Park → London

Network Diagram - see first page of Table 200

		SE 22 [1]	SE 16	SE 90 [1] A	SE 12	SE 70	SE 72	SE 22 [1]	SE 12	SE 4 [1]	SE 16	SE 70	SE 22 [1]	SE 16	SE 90 [1] B	SE 12	SE 70	SE 72	SE 22 [1]	SE 12	SE 4 [1]
Tonbridge [4]	d	08 49		09 01				09 19		09 33			09 49		10 01				10 20		10 33
Hildenborough	d			09 05											10 05						
Sevenoaks [4]	a	08 58		09 13				09 28		09 43			09 58		10 13				10 29		10 43
	d	08 59		09 14	09 17		09 25	09 29		09 44			09 59		10 14	10 17		10 25	10 30		10 44
Dunton Green	d				09 19											10 19					
Knockholt	d				09 25											10 25					
Chelsfield [3]	d				09 27											10 27					
Orpington [4]	a	09 08		09 23	09 30			09 38		09 53			10 08		10 23	10 30			10 39		10 53
	d	09 09		09 24	09 31	09 38		09 39		09 54	10 01	10 08	10 09		10 24	10 31	10 38		10 39		10 54
Petts Wood [4]	d				09 34	09a41					10 04	10a11				10 34	10a41				
Chislehurst	d		←		09 37				←		10 07			←		10 37				←	
Elmstead Woods	d		09 09		09 39				09 39		10 09			10 09		10 39				10 39	
Bromley North	d				→						→					→					
Sundridge Park	d																				
Grove Park [4]	d		09 12						09 42					10 12						10 42	
Hither Green [4]	d		09 15						09 45					10 15						10 45	
Lewisham [4]	d		09 20						09 50					10 20						10 50	
St Johns	a																				
New Cross [4]	⊖ a																				
London Bridge [4]	⊖ a	09 26	09 28	09 39				09 56	09 58	10 09			10 26	10 28	10 39				10 56	10 58	11 09
London Cannon Street [4]	⊖ a																				
London Waterloo (East) [4]	⊖ a	09 31	09 33	09 44				10 01	10 03	10 14			10 31	10 33	10 44				11 01	11 03	11 14
London Charing Cross [4]	⊖ a	09 35	09 37	09 48				10 05	10 07	10 18			10 35	10 37	10 48				11 06	11 07	11 18

		SE 16	SE 70	SE 72	SE 22 [1]	SE 16		SE 90 [1] B	SE 12	SE 70	SE 22 [1] C	SE 12	SE 4 [1]	SE 16	SE 70	SE 90 [1] B	SE 12	SE 70	SE 22 [1] C	SE 12	SE 4 [1]
Tonbridge [4]	d				10 49			19 01			19 19		19 33			20 01			20 19		20 33
Hildenborough	d							19 05								20 05					
Sevenoaks [4]	a				10 58			19 13			19 28		19 43			20 13			20 28		20 43
	d			10 55	10 59			19 14	19 17		19 29		19 44			20 14	20 20		20 29		20 44
Dunton Green	d						and at		19 19												
Knockholt	d								19 25												
Chelsfield [3]	d						the same		19 27		19 37						20 27		20 37		
Orpington [4]	a				11 08			19 23	19 30		19 40		19 53			20 23	20 30		20 40		20 53
	d	11 01	11 08		11 09		minutes	19 24	19 31	19 38	19 40		19 54	20 01	20 08	20 24	20 31	20 38	20 40		20 54
Petts Wood [4]	d	11 04	11a11						19 34	19a41				20 04	20a11		20 34	20a41			
Chislehurst	d	11 07				←	past		19 37			←		20 07			20 37			←	
Elmstead Woods	d	11 09				11 09			19 39			19 39		20 09			20 39			20 39	
Bromley North	d	→					each		→								→				
Sundridge Park	d						hour until														
Grove Park [4]	d					11 12						19 42		20 12						20 42	
Hither Green [4]	d					11 15						19 45		20 15						20 45	
Lewisham [4]	d					11 20						19 50		20 20						20 50	
St Johns	a																				
New Cross [4]	⊖ a																				
London Bridge [4]	⊖ a				11 26	11 28		19 39			19 56	19 58	20 09	20 28		20 39			20 56	20 58	21 09
London Cannon Street [4]	⊖ a																				
London Waterloo (East) [4]	⊖ a				11 31	11 33		19 44			20 01	20 03	20 14	20 33		20 44			21 01	21 03	21 14
London Charing Cross [4]	⊖ a				11 35	11 37		19 48			20 05	20 07	20 18	20 37		20 48			21 05	21 07	21 18

		SE 12	SE 70	SE 90 [1] B	SE 12	SE 70	SE 22 [1] C	SE 12	SE 4 [1]	SE 12	SE 70	SE 90 [1] B	SE 12	SE 70	SE 22 [1] C	SE 12	SE 4 [1] D	SE 12	SE 72
Tonbridge [4]	d			21 02			21 19		21 33			22 02			22 19		22 31		
Hildenborough	d			21 07								22 07					22 35		
Sevenoaks [4]	a			21 14			21 28		21 43			22 14			22 28		22 43		
	d			21 15			21 29		21 44			22 15			22 29		22 44		
Dunton Green	d																		
Knockholt	d																		
Chelsfield [3]	d						21 37								22 37				
Orpington [4]	a			21 24			21 40		21 53			22 24			22 40		22 53		
	d	21 01	21 08	21 24	21 31	21 38	21 40		21 54	22 01	22 08	22 24	22 31	22 38	22 40		22 54	23 01	23 14
Petts Wood [4]	d	21 04	21a11		21 34	21a41				22 04	22a11		22 34	22a41				23 04	23a17
Chislehurst	d	21 07			21 37			←		22 07			22 37			←		23 07	
Elmstead Woods	d	21 09			21 39			21 39		22 09			22 39			22 39		23 09	
Bromley North	d				→								→						
Sundridge Park	d																		
Grove Park [4]	d	21 12						21 42		22 12						22 42		23 12	
Hither Green [4]	d	21 15						21 45		22 15						22 45		23 15	
Lewisham [4]	d	21 20						21 50		22 20						22 50		23 20	
St Johns	a																		
New Cross [4]	⊖ a																		
London Bridge [4]	⊖ a	21 28		21 40			21 56	21 58	22 09	22 28		22 40			22 56	22 58	23 09	23 28	
London Cannon Street [4]	⊖ a																		
London Waterloo (East) [4]	⊖ a	21 33		21 44			22 01	22 03	22 14	22 33		22 44			23 01	23 03	23 14	23 33	
London Charing Cross [4]	⊖ a	21 37		21 48			22 05	22 07	22 18	22 37		22 48			23 05	23 07	23 18	23 37	

For general notes see front of timetable
For details of catering facilities see Directory of Train Operators

A From Ramsgate (Table 207)
B From Margate (Table 207)
C From Hastings (Table 206)
D From Ramsgate (Table 207) and from Ramsgate (Table 207)

Network Diagram for Tables 206, 207, 208, 209

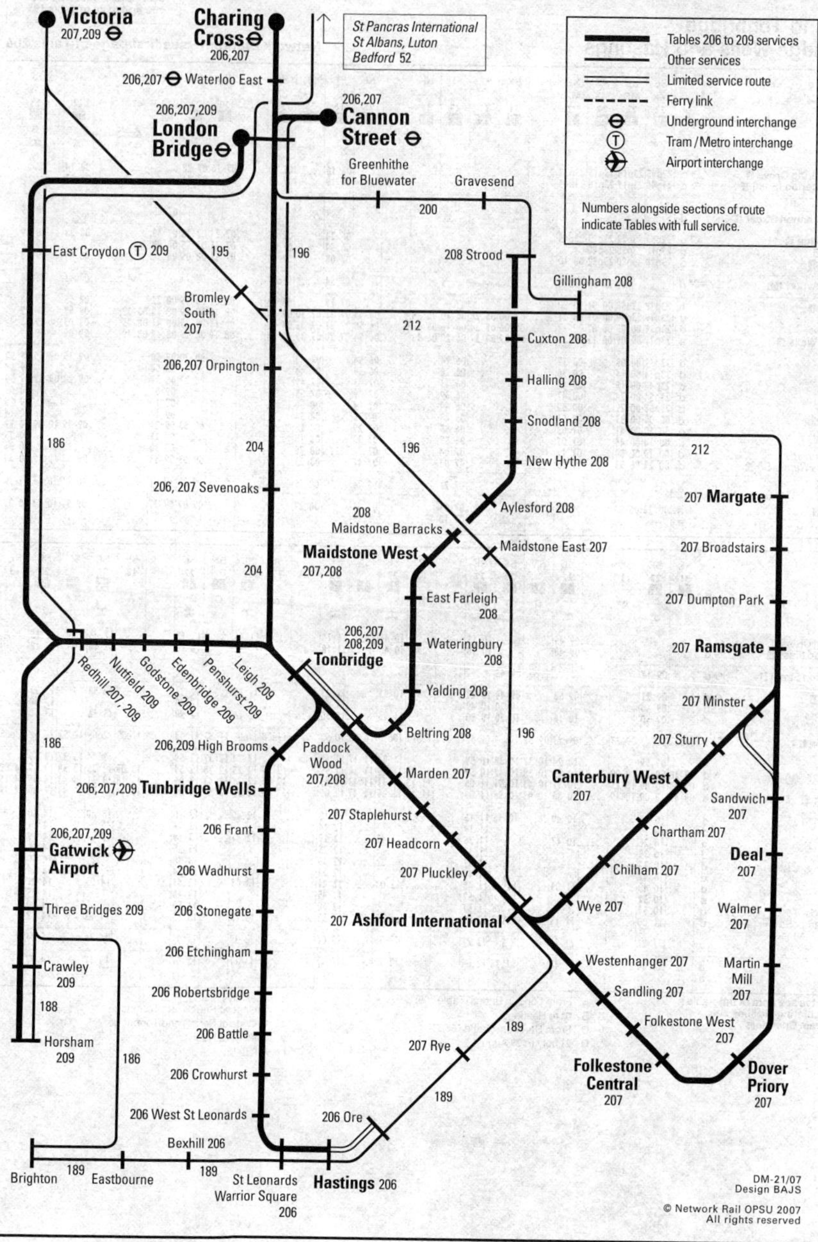

Victoria 207,209
Charing Cross 206,207
St Pancras International
St Albans, Luton
Bedford 52
Tables 206 to 209 services
Other services
Limited service route
Ferry link
Underground interchange
Tram / Metro interchange
Airport interchange
Numbers alongside sections of route indicate Tables with full service.
206,207 Waterloo East
206,207,209 London Bridge
206,207 Cannon Street
Greenhithe for Bluewater
Gravesend
200
East Croydon 209
195
196
208 Strood
Gillingham 208
Bromley South 207
212
Cuxton 208
206,207 Orpington
Halling 208
Snodland 208
186
204
196
New Hythe 208
212
206, 207 Sevenoaks
207 Margate
Aylesford 208
208 Maidstone Barracks
Maidstone East 207
Maidstone West 207,208
207 Broadstairs
204
East Farleigh 208
207 Dumpton Park
206,207 208,209 Tonbridge
Wateringbury 208
207 Ramsgate
Redhill 207, 209
Nutfield 209
Godstone 209
Edenbridge 209
Penshurst 209
Leigh 209
Yalding 208
207 Minster
186
206,209 High Brooms
Paddock Wood 207,208
Beltring 208
196
207 Sturry
Marden 207
Canterbury West 207
Sandwich 207
206,207,209 Tunbridge Wells
207 Staplehurst
Chartham 207
206 Frant
206,207,209 Gatwick Airport
207 Headcorn
Deal 207
206 Wadhurst
207 Pluckley
Chilham 207
Three Bridges 209
206 Stonegate
207 Ashford International
Wye 207
Walmer 207
206 Etchingham
Westenhanger 207
Crawley 209
Martin Mill 207
206 Robertsbridge
Sandling 207
188
189
Folkestone West 207
Horsham 209
206 Battle
207 Rye
186
Folkestone Central 207
Dover Priory 207
206 Crowhurst
189
206 West St Leonards
206 Ore
Bexhill 206
Brighton
189
Eastbourne
189
St Leonards Warrior Square 206
Hastings 206
DM-21/07
Design BAJS
© Network Rail OPSU 2007
All rights reserved

For details of Bank Holiday service alterations please see first page of Table 195

London and Tonbridge → Tunbridge Wells and Hastings

Network Diagram - see first page of Table 206

Miles			SE MX 22 [1]	SE MO 22 [1]	SE MX 22 [1]	SE MX 22 [1]		SE 31 [1]	SE 31 [1]	SE 25 [1]	SE 31 [1]		SE 25 [1]	SE 16 [1]	SE 25 [1]	SE 31 [1]		SE 30 [1]	SE 22 [1]	SE 23 [1]	SE 43 A		SE 22 [1] 🛒	SE 23 [1] B 🛒	
0	**London Charing Cross**	⊖ d	22p45	23p14	23p15	23p37								06 16		07 00		07 16	07 28				08 14		
¾	**London Waterloo (East)**	⊖ d	22p48	23p17	23p18	23p40								06 19		07 03		07 19	07 31				08 17		
—	**London Cannon Street**	⊖ d																		07 45				08 45	
1¾	**London Bridge**	⊖ d	22p53	23p22	23p23	23p45								06 24		07 08		07 24	07 36	07 49			08 23	08 49	
13¾	Orpington	d	23p10	23p38	23p40									06 54		07 26		07 41	07 55	08 09				09 08	
22	Sevenoaks	d	23p20	23p50	23p52	00 10								07 08		07 36		07 51	08 05	08 24			08 47	09 18	
—	Gatwick Airport 10	✈ d			*22 53*	*23b23*								*05 54*		*06c37*			*07c13*		*07e41*		*07c41*	*08c04*	
29½	**Tonbridge**	a	23p28	23p58	00 01	00 20								07 19		07 44		08 01	08 15	08 32			08 55	09 28	
—		d	23p29	23p59	00 01	00 21		05 00	05 28	06 10	06 24		06 44	07 21	07 30	07 54		08 10	08 19	08 33	08 39		08 57	09 29	
33	High Brooms	d	23p35	00 05	00 07	00 27		05 06	05 34	06 16	06 30		06 50	07 27	07 35	08 00		08 15	08 25	08 41	08 45		09 03	09 35	
34½	**Tunbridge Wells**	a	23p39	00 09	00 12	00 31		05 09	05 37	06 20	06 33		06 54	07 30	07 39	08 04		08 19	08 29	08 45	08 49		09 09	09 39	
—		d	23p39	00 09		00 32				06 24			06 54		07 40				08 30	08 50			09 15	09 45	09 50
36¾	Frant	d	23p44	00 14		00 36				06 28			06 59		07 44					08 54					09 54
39¼	Wadhurst	d	23p48	00 18		00 41				06 33			07 03		07 49				08 37	08 59			09 22	09 52	09 59
43¼	Stonegate	d	23p54	00 24		00 47				06 39			07 09		07 55					09 05					10 05
47½	Etchingham	d	23p58	00 29		00 52				06 44			07 14		08 00					09 10					10 10
49¼	Robertsbridge	d	00 03	00 33		00 56				06 48			07f22		08 04					09 14					10 14
55½	Battle	d	00 10	00 41		01 03				06 55			07 29		08 11				08 53	09 21			09 39	10 09	10 21
57½	Crowhurst	d	00 14	00 45		01 07				06 59			07 33		08 15					09 25					10 25
60¾	West St Leonards	d	00 19	00 50		01 12				07 04			07 38		08 20					09 30					10 31
61¾	St Leonards Warrior Sq	d	00 22	00 53		01 15				07 07			07 41		08 23				09 03	09 33			09 53	10 19	10 34
—	Bexhill	a								*07 21*			*08 24*		*08 35*				*09 22*	*10 01*			*10 21*	*10 35*	
62½	**Hastings**	a	00 26	00 56		01 19				07 11			07 45		08 27				09 07	09 37			09 57	10 23	10 37
63½	Ore	a								07 18															

		SE 31 [1]	SE 23 [1] 🛒	SE 13 A		SE 22 [1] 🛒	SN [1] C	SE 23 [1] D	SE 22 [1] 🛒		SE 13 A	SE 22 [1] 🛒	SN [1] C	SE 22 [1] 🛒		SE 13 A	SE 22 [1] 🛒	SN [1] C	SE 22 [1] 🛒		SE 13 A	SE 22 [1] 🛒	SN [1] C	SE 22 [1] 🛒	SE 13 A
London Charing Cross	⊖ d					09 45			10 15			10 45		11 15			11 45		12 15			12 45		13 15	
London Waterloo (East)	⊖ d					09 48			10 18			10 48		11 18			11 48		12 18			12 48		13 18	
London Cannon Street	⊖ d		09 17					09 45																	
London Bridge	⊖ d		09 21			09 53		09 49	10 23			10 53		11 23			11 53		12 23			12 53		13 23	
Orpington	d		09 40					10 20	10 40					11 40					12 40					13 40	
Sevenoaks	d		09 50			10 16		10 30	10 50			11 16		11 50			12 16		12 50			13 16		13 50	
Gatwick Airport 10	✈ d	*08c37*		*09e23*		*09c23*	09 52		*09 52*		*10e10*	*10c10*	10 53	*10 53*		*11e08*	*11c08*	11 53	*11 53*		*12e08*	*12c08*	12 52	*12 52*	*13e08*
Tonbridge	a		09 59			10 24	10 37	10 38	10 59			11 24	11 37	11 59			12 24	12 37	12 59			13 24	13 37	13 59	
	d	09 38	09 59	10 09		10 25	10 38	10 42	10 59		11 09	11 25	11 38	11 59		12 09	12 25	12 38	12 59		13 09	13 25	13 38	13 59	14 09
High Brooms	d	09 43	10 05	10 15		10 31	10 43	10 51	11 05		11 15	11 31	11 43	12 05		12 15	12 31	12 43	13 05		13 15	13 31	13 43	14 05	14 15
Tunbridge Wells	a	09 47	10 09	10 19		10 36	10 47	10 55	11 09		11 19	11 35	11 47	12 09		12 19	12 35	12 47	13 09		13 19	13 35	13 47	14 09	14 19
	d		10 15			10 40		10 56	11 15			11 40		12 10			12 40		13 10			13 40		14 10	
Frant	d		10 19						11 19					12 14					13 14					14 14	
Wadhurst	d		10 26			10 47			11 26			11 47		12 19			12 47		13 19			13 47		14 19	
Stonegate	d		10 32						11 32					12 25					13 25					14 25	
Etchingham	d		10 37						11 37					12 30					13 30					14 30	
Robertsbridge	d		10 41						11 41					12 34					13 34					14 34	
Battle	d		10 48			11 03		11 18	11 48			12 03		12 41			13 03		13 41			14 03		14 41	
Crowhurst	d		10 52						11 52					12 45					13 45					14 45	
West St Leonards	d		10 57					11 25	11 57					12 50					13 50					14 50	
St Leonards Warrior Sq	d		11 00			11 13		11 33	12 00			12 13		12 53			13 13		13 53			14 13		14 53	
Bexhill	a		*11 21*			*11 35*			*12 21*			*12 35*		*13 04*			*13 35*		*14 04*			*14 35*		*15 04*	
Hastings	a		11 04			11 17		11 36	12 04			12 17		12 57			13 17		13 57			14 17		14 57	
Ore	a																								

For general notes see front of timetable
For details of catering facilities see Directory of Train Operators

A From London Bridge (Table 209)
B 🛒 to Hastings
C From Horsham (Table 186)
D 21 July to 29 August
b Tuesdays to Fridays. Change at Redhill and Tonbridge
c Change at Redhill and Tonbridge
e Change at Redhill
f Arr. 0718

For details of Bank Holiday service alterations please see first page of Table 195

London and Tonbridge → Tunbridge Wells and Hastings

Network Diagram - see first page of Table 206

		SE 22 1 🛒	SN 1 A	SE 22 1 🛒	SE 13 B	SE 22 1 🛒	SE 31	SE 22 1 🛒	SE 13 B	SE 22 1 🛒	SE 22 1 🛒	SE 31	SE 30 1	SE 23 1	SE 22 1	SE 30 1	SE 23 1 C 🛒		SE 30 1	SE 22 1
London Charing Cross 4	⊖ d	13 45		14 15		14 45		15 15		15 45	16 15		16 50		17 16	17 20			17 41	18 00
London Waterloo (East) 4	⊖ d	13 48		14 18		14 48		15 18		15 48	16 18		16 53		17 19	17 23			17 44	18 03
London Cannon Street 4	⊖ d													17 00			17 38			
London Bridge 4	⊖ d	13 53		14 23		14 53		15 23		15 53	16 23		16 58	17 04		17 28			17 49	
Orpington 4	d			14 40				15 40												
Sevenoaks 4	d	14 16		14 50		15 16		15 50		16 20	16 50		17 22	17 28		17 56			18 16	
Gatwick Airport 10	✈ d	13b08	13 53	13 53	14c08	14b08	14 53	14 53	15c08	15b08	15 53		16b08			17b10				
Tonbridge 4	a	14 24	14 37	14 59		15 24		15 59		16 28	16 58		17 32	17 38		18 06			18 27	
	d	14 25	14 38	14 59	15 09	15 25	15 46	15 59	16 13	16 29	16 59	17 09	17 33	17 39		18 07			18 28	
High Brooms	d	14 31	14 43	15 05	15 15	15 31	15 52	16 05	16 19	16 35	17 05	17 15	17 39	17 45	17 59	18 13	18 19		18 34	18 43
Tunbridge Wells 4	a	14 35	14 47	15 09	15 19	15 35	15 56	16 09	16 23	16 39	17 09	17 19	17 44	17 49	18 03	18 18	18 23		18 40	18 47
	d	14 40		15 10		15 40		16 12		16 40	17 10			17 50	18 04		18 28	18 32		18 52
Frant	d			15 14				16 16		16 44	17 14			17 54	18 08			18 36		18 56
Wadhurst	d	14 47		15 19		15 47		16 21		16 49	17 19			17 59	18 13		18 35	18 41		19 01
Stonegate	d			15 25				16 27		16 55	17 25			18 05	18 19			18 47		19 07
Etchingham	d			15 30				16 32		17 00	17 30			18 10	18 24		18 44	18 52		19 12
Robertsbridge	d			15 34		15 57		16 36		17 04	17 34			18 14	18 28			18 56		19 16
Battle	d	15 03		15 41		16 05		16 43		17 11	17 41			18 21	18 35		18 54	19 03		19 23
Crowhurst	d			15 45				16 47		17 15	17 45			18 25	18 39			19 07		19 27
West St Leonards	d			15 50				16 52		17 20	17 52			18 32	18 44			19 12		19 32
St Leonards Warrior Sq 4	d	15 13		15 53		16 15		16 55		17 23	17 56			18 35	18 47		19 03	19 15		19 35
Bexhill 4	a	*15 33*		*16 22*		*16 35*		*17 25*		*17 35*	*18 21*				*19 04*		*19 21*			*20 04*
Hastings 4	a	15 17		15 57		16 19		16 59		17 27	18 01			18 41	18 51		19 09	19 21		19 39
Ore	a														18 57					19 45

		SE 30 1	SE 23 1	SE 30 1	SE 22 1 🛒	SE 23 1	SE 22 1 🛒	SE 90	SE 22 1	SE 22 1	SE 22 1	SE 22 1	SE 22 1	SE 22 1	SE 22 1	SE 22 1	SE 22 1
London Charing Cross 4	⊖ d	18 04		18 28	18 50		19 15	19 30	19 45	20 15	20 45	21 15	21 45	22 15	22 45	23 15	23 37
London Waterloo (East) 4	⊖ d	18 07		18 31	18 53		19 18	19 33	19 48	20 18	20 48	21 18	21 48	22 18	22 48	23 18	23 40
London Cannon Street 4	⊖ d		18 26			19 06											
London Bridge 4	⊖ d	18 12	18 30	18 36		19 10	19 23	19 38	19 53	20 23	20 53	21 23	21 53	22 23	22 53	23 23	23 45
Orpington 4	d					19 28		19 54		20 40	21 10	21 40	22 10	22 40	23 10	23 40	
Sevenoaks 4	d	18 40		19 05	19 20	19 38	19 50	20 06	20 20	20 50	21 20	21 50	22 20	22 52	23 20	23 52	00 10
Gatwick Airport 10	✈ d	17b38		18b10	18b38			19b10	19b10	19b39		20 53		21 53	21 53	22 53	23e23
Tonbridge 4	a	18 51		19 15	19 29	19 48	19 59	20 17	20 28	20 58	21 28	21 58	22 28	23 00	23 28	00 01	00 20
	d	18 52		19 16	19 31	19 49	19 59	20 17	20 29	20 59	21 29	21 59	22 29	23 05	23 29	00 01	00 21
High Brooms	d	18 58	19 06	19 22	19 37	19 55	20 06	20 23	20 35	21 05	21 35	22 05	22 35	23 11	23 35	00 07	00 27
Tunbridge Wells 4	a	19 04	19 10	19 28	19 41	19 59	20 10	20 28	20 42	21 09	21 39	22 10	22 39	23 15	23 39	00 12	00 31
	d		19 17		19 42	20 00	20 10		20 42	21 10	21 40		22 40		23 39		00 32
Frant	d		19 21		19 46	20 04	20 15			21 14	21 44		22 44		23 44		00 36
Wadhurst	d		19 26		19 51	20 09	20 19		20 50	21 19	21 49		22 49		23 48		00 41
Stonegate	d		19 32		19 57	20 15	20 25			21 25	21 55		22 55		23 54		00 47
Etchingham	d		19 37		20 02	20 20	20 30		20 59	21 30	22 00		23 00		23 58		00 52
Robertsbridge	d		19 41		20 06	20 24	20 34			21 34	22 04		23 04		00 03		00 56
Battle	d		19 48		20 13	20 31	20 42		21 08	21 41	22 11		23 11		00 10		01 03
Crowhurst	d		19 52		20 17		20 46			21 45	22 15		23 15		00 14		01 07
West St Leonards	d		19 59		20 22		20 51			21 50	22 20		23 20		00 19		01 12
St Leonards Warrior Sq 4	d		20 02		20 25	20 41	20 54		21 18	21 53	22 23		23 23		00 22		01 15
Bexhill 4	a		*20 21*			*21 04*	*21 21*		*21 39*	*22 25*	*22 38*						
Hastings 4	a		20 08		20 30	20 45	20 58		21 21	21 57	22 27		23 27		00 26		01 19
Ore	a																

For general notes see front of timetable
For details of catering facilities see Directory of Train Operators

A From Horsham (Table 186)
B From London Bridge (Table 209)
C 🛒 to Hastings
b Change at Redhill and Tonbridge
c Change at Redhill
e Tuesdays to Saturdays only. Change at Redhill and Tonbridge

For details of Bank Holiday service alterations please see first page of Table 195

London and Tonbridge → Tunbridge Wells and Hastings

Network Diagram - see first page of Table 206

		SE MX 22 [1]	SE MO 22 [1]	SE MX 22 [1]	SE MX 22 [1]	SE 31 [1]	SE 31 [1]	SE 25 [1]	SE 31 [1]	SE 25 [1]	SE 16 [1]	SE 25 [1]	SE 31 [1]	SE 30 [1]	SE 22 [1]	SE 23 [1]	SE 43 A	SE 22 [1] 🛒	SE 23 [1] B 🛒	
London Charing Cross [4]	⊖ d	22p45	23p14	23p15	23p37						06 16		07 00	07 16	07 28			08 14		
London Waterloo (East) [4]	⊖ d	22p48	23p17	23p18	23p40						06 19		07 03	07 19	07 31			08 17		
London Cannon Street [4]	⊖ d															07 45			08 45	
London Bridge [4]	⊖ d	22p53	23p22	23p23	23p45						06 24		07 08	07 24	07 36	07 49		08 23	08 49	
Orpington [4]	d	23p10	23p38	23p40							06 54		07 26	07 41	07 55	08 09			09 08	
Sevenoaks [4]	d	23p20	23p50	23p52	00 10						07 08		07 36	07 51	08 05	08 24		08 47	09 18	
Gatwick Airport [10]	✈ d			22 53	23b23						05 54		06c37		07c13		07e41	07c41	08c04	
Tonbridge [4]	a	23p28	23p58	00 01	00 20						07 19		07 44	08 01	08 15	08 32		08 55	09 28	
	d	23p29	23p59	00 01	00 21	05 00	05 28	06 10	06 24	06 44	07 21	07 30	07 54	08 10	08 19	08 33	08 39	08 57	09 29	
High Brooms	d	23p35	00 05	00 07	00 27	05 06	05 34	06 16	06 30	06 50	07 27	07 35	08 00	08 15	08 25	08 41	08 45	09 03	09 35	
Tunbridge Wells [4]	a	23p39	00 09	00 12	00 31	05 09	05 37	06 20	06 33	06 54	07 30	07 39	08 04	08 19	08 29	08 45	08 49	09 09	09 39	
	d	23p39	00 09		00 32			06 24		06 54		07 40			08 30	08 50		09 15	09 45	09 50
Frant	d	23p44	00 14		00 36			06 28		06 59		07 44				08 54				09 54
Wadhurst	d	23p48	00 18		00 41			06 33		07 03		07 49			08 37	08 59		09 22	09 52	09 59
Stonegate	d	23p54	00 24		00 47			06 39		07 09		07 55				09 05				10 05
Etchingham	d	23p58	00 29		00 52			06 44		07 14		08 00				09 10				10 10
Robertsbridge	d	00 03	00 33		00 56			06 48		07f22		08 04				09 14				10 14
Battle	d	00 10	00 41		01 03			06 55		07 29		08 11			08 53	09 21		09 39	10 09	10 21
Crowhurst	d	00 14	00 45		01 07			06 59		07 33		08 15				09 25				10 25
West St Leonards	d	00 19	00 50		01 12			07 04		07 38		08 20				09 30				10 31
St Leonards Warrior Sq [4]	d	00 22	00 53		01 15			07 07		07 41		08 23			09 03	09 33		09 53	10 19	10 34
Bexhill [4]	a							*07 21*		*08 24*		*08 35*			*09 22*	*10 01*		*10 21*	*10 35*	
Hastings [4]	a	00 26	00 56		01 19			07 11		07 45		08 27			09 07	09 37		09 57	10 23	10 37
Ore	a							07 18												

		SE 31 [1]	SE 23 [1] 🛒	SE 13 A	SE 22 [1] 🛒	SN [1] C	SE 22 [1] 🛒	SE 13 A	SE 22 [1] 🛒	SN [1] C	SE 22 [1] 🛒	SE 13 A	SE 22 [1] 🛒	SN [1] C	SE 22 [1] 🛒	SE 13 A	SE 22 [1] 🛒	SN [1] C	SE 22 [1] 🛒
London Charing Cross [4]	⊖ d				09 45		10 15		10 45		11 15		11 45		12 15		12 45		13 15
London Waterloo (East) [4]	⊖ d				09 48		10 18		10 48		11 18		11 48		12 18		12 48		13 18
London Cannon Street [4]	⊖ d		09 17																
London Bridge [4]	⊖ d		09 21		09 53		10 23		10 53		11 23		11 53		12 23		12 53		13 23
Orpington [4]	d		09 40				10 40				11 40				12 40				13 40
Sevenoaks [4]	d		09 50		10 16		10 50		11 16		11 50		12 16		12 50		13 16		13 50
Gatwick Airport [10]	✈ d	*08c37*		*09e23*	*09c23*	09 52	*09 52*	*10e10*	*10c10*	10 53	*10 53*	*11e08*	*11c08*	11 53	*11 53*	*12e08*	*12c08*	12 52	*12 52*
Tonbridge [4]	a		09 59		10 24	10 37	10 59		11 24	11 37	11 59		12 24	12 37	12 59		13 24	13 37	13 59
	d	09 38	09 59	10 09	10 25	10 38	10 59	11 09	11 25	11 38	11 59	12 09	12 25	12 38	12 59	13 09	13 25	13 38	13 59
High Brooms	d	09 43	10 05	10 15	10 31	10 43	11 05	11 15	11 31	11 43	12 05	12 15	12 31	12 43	13 05	13 15	13 31	13 43	14 05
Tunbridge Wells [4]	a	09 47	10 09	10 19	10 36	10 47	11 09	11 19	11 35	11 47	12 09	12 19	12 35	12 47	13 09	13 19	13 35	13 47	14 09
	d		10 15		10 40		11 15		11 40		12 10		12 40		13 10		13 40		14 10
Frant	d		10 19				11 19				12 14				13 14				14 14
Wadhurst	d		10 26		10 47		11 26		11 47		12 19		12 47		13 19		13 47		14 19
Stonegate	d		10 32				11 32				12 25				13 25				14 25
Etchingham	d		10 37				11 37				12 30				13 30				14 30
Robertsbridge	d		10 41				11 41				12 34				13 34				14 34
Battle	d		10 48		11 03		11 48		12 03		12 41		13 03		13 41		14 03		14 41
Crowhurst	d		10 52				11 52				12 45				13 45				14 45
West St Leonards	d		10 57				11 57				12 50				13 50				14 50
St Leonards Warrior Sq [4]	d		11 00		11 13		12 00		12 13		12 53		13 13		13 53		14 13		14 53
Bexhill [4]	a		*11 21*		*11 35*		*12 21*		*12 35*		*13 04*		*13 35*		*14 04*		*14 35*		*15 04*
Hastings [4]	a		11 04		11 17		12 04		12 17		12 57		13 17		13 57		14 17		14 57
Ore	a																		

For general notes see front of timetable
For details of catering facilities see Directory of Train Operators

A From London Bridge (Table 209)
B 🛒 to Hastings
C From Horsham (Table 186)

b Tuesdays to Fridays. Change at Redhill and Tonbridge
c Change at Redhill and Tonbridge
e Change at Redhill
f Arr. 0718

For details of Bank Holiday service alterations please see first page of Table 195

London and Tonbridge → Tunbridge Wells and Hastings

Network Diagram - see first page of Table 206

		SE 13 A	SE 22 ■1 🛒	SN ■1 B	SE 22 ■1 🛒	SE 13 A	SE 22 ■1 🛒	SE 31	SE 22 ■1 🛒	SE 13 A	SE 22 ■1 🛒	SE 22 ■1 🛒	SE 31	SE 30 ■1	SE 23 ■1	SE 22 ■1	SE 30 ■1	SE 23 ■1 C 🛒 (i)	SE 23 ■1 C 🛒 (ii)	SE 30 ■1
London Charing Cross ■4	⊖ d		13 45		14 15		14 45		15 15		15 45	16 15		16 50		17 16	17 20			17 41
London Waterloo (East) ■4	⊖ d		13 48		14 18		14 48		15 18		15 48	16 18		16 53		17 19	17 23			17 44
London Cannon Street ■4	⊖ d														17 00			17 38		
London Bridge ■4	⊖ d		13 53		14 23		14 53		15 23		15 53	16 23		16 58	17 04		17 28			17 49
Orpington ■4	d				14 40				15 40											
Sevenoaks ■4	d		14 16		14 50		15 16		15 50		16 20	16 50		17 22	17 28		17 56			18 16
Gatwick Airport ■10	✈ d	13b08	13c08	13 53	13 53	14b08	14c08	14 53	14 53	15b08	15c08	15 53		16c08			17c10			
Tonbridge ■4	a		14 24	14 37	14 59		15 24		15 59		16 28	16 58		17 32	17 38		18 06			18 27
	d	14 09	14 25	14 38	14 59	15 09	15 25	15 46	15 59	16 13	16 29	16 59	17 09	17 33	17 39		18 07			18 28
High Brooms	d	14 15	14 31	14 43	15 05	15 15	15 31	15 52	16 05	16 19	16 35	17 05	17 15	17 39	17 45	17 59	18 13	18 19		18 34
Tunbridge Wells ■4	a	14 19	14 35	14 47	15 09	15 19	15 35	15 56	16 09	16 23	16 39	17 09	17 19	17 45	17 49	18 03	18 19	18 23		18 40
	d		14 40		15 10		15 40		16 12		16 40	17 10			17 50	18 04		18 28	18 32	
Frant	d				15 14				16 16		16 44	17 14			17 54	18 08			18 36	
Wadhurst	d		14 47		15 19		15 47		16 21		16 49	17 19			17 59	18 13		18 35	18 41	
Stonegate	d				15 25				16 27		16 55	17 25			18 05	18 19			18 47	
Etchingham	d				15 30				16 32		17 00	17 30			18 10	18 24		18 44	18 52	
Robertsbridge	d				15 34		15 57		16 36		17 04	17 34			18 14	18 28			18 56	
Battle	d		15 03		15 41		16 05		16 43		17 11	17 41			18 21	18 35		18 54	19 03	
Crowhurst	d				15 45				16 47		17 15	17 45			18 25	18 39			19 07	
West St Leonards	d				15 50				16 52		17 20	17 52			18 32	18 44			19 12	
St Leonards Warrior Sq ■4	d		15 13		15 53		16 15		16 55		17 23	17 56			18 35	18 47		19 03	19 15	
Bexhill ■4	a		*15 33*		*16 22*		*16 35*		*17 25*		*17 35*	*18 21*				*19 04*		*19 21*		
Hastings ■4	a		15 17		15 57		16 19		16 59		17 27	18 02			18 41	18 51		19 09	19 21	
Ore	a															18 57				

		SE 22 ■1	SE 30 ■1	SE 23 ■1	SE 30 ■1	SE 22 ■1 🛒	SE 23 ■1	SE 22 ■1 🛒	SE 90	SE 22 ■1	SE 22 ■1	SE 22 ■1	SE 22 ■1	SE 22 ■1	SE 22 ■1	SE 22 ■1	SE 22 ■1	SE 22 ■1
London Charing Cross ■4	⊖ d	18 00	18 04		18 28	18 50		19 15	19 30	19 45	20 15	20 45	21 15	21 45	22 15	22 45	23 15	23 37
London Waterloo (East) ■4	⊖ d	18 03	18 07		18 31	18 53		19 18	19 33	19 48	20 18	20 48	21 18	21 48	22 18	22 48	23 18	23 40
London Cannon Street ■4	⊖ d			18 26			19 06											
London Bridge ■4	⊖ d		18 12	18 30	18 36		19 10	19 23	19 38	19 53	20 23	20 53	21 23	21 53	22 23	22 53	23 23	23 45
Orpington ■4	d						19 28		19 54		20 40	21 10	21 40	22 10	22 40	23 10	23 40	
Sevenoaks ■4	d		18 40		19 05	19 20	19 38	19 50	20 06	20 20	20 50	21 20	21 50	22 20	22 52	23 20	23 52	00 10
Gatwick Airport ■10	✈ d		17c38		18c10	18c38			19c10	19c10	19c39		20 53		21 53	21 53	22 53	23e23
Tonbridge ■4	a		18 51		19 15	19 29	19 48	19 59	20 17	20 28	20 58	21 28	21 58	22 28	23 00	23 28	00 01	00 20
	d		18 52		19 16	19 31	19 49	19 59	20 17	20 29	20 59	21 29	21 59	22 29	23 05	23 29	00 01	00 21
High Brooms	d	18 43	18 58	19 06	19 22	19 37	19 55	20 06	20 23	20 35	21 05	21 35	22 05	22 35	23 11	23 35	00 07	00 27
Tunbridge Wells ■4	a	18 47	19 04	19 10	19 28	19 41	19 59	20 10	20 28	20 42	21 09	21 39	22 10	22 39	23 15	23 39	00 12	00 31
	d	18 52		19 17		19 42	20 00	20 10		20 42	21 10	21 40		22 40		23 39		00 32
Frant	d	18 56		19 21		19 46	20 04	20 15			21 14	21 44		22 44		23 44		00 36
Wadhurst	d	19 01		19 26		19 51	20 09	20 19		20 50	21 19	21 49		22 49		23 48		00 41
Stonegate	d	19 07		19 32		19 57	20 15	20 25			21 25	21 55		22 55		23 54		00 47
Etchingham	d	19 12		19 37		20 02	20 20	20 30		20 59	21 30	22 00		23 00		23 58		00 52
Robertsbridge	d	19 16		19 41		20 06	20 24	20 34			21 34	22 04		23 04		00 03		00 56
Battle	d	19 23		19 48		20 13	20 31	20 42		21 08	21 41	22 11		23 11		00 10		01 03
Crowhurst	d	19 27		19 52		20 17		20 46			21 45	22 15		23 15		00 14		01 07
West St Leonards	d	19 32		19 59		20 22		20 51			21 50	22 20		23 20		00 19		01 12
St Leonards Warrior Sq ■4	d	19 35		20 02		20 25	20 41	20 54		21 18	21 53	22 23		23 23		00 22		01 15
Bexhill ■4	a	*20 04*		*20 21*			*21 04*	*21 21*		*21 39*	*22 25*	*22 38*						
Hastings ■4	a	19 39		20 08		20 31	20 45	20 58		21 21	21 57	22 27		23 27		00 26		01 19
Ore	a	19 45																

For general notes see front of timetable
For details of catering facilities see Directory of Train Operators

A From London Bridge (Table 209)
B From Horsham (Table 186)
C 🛒 to Hastings
b Change at Redhill
c Change at Redhill and Tonbridge
e Tuesdays to Saturdays only. Change at Redhill and Tonbridge

Table 206

London and Tonbridge → Tunbridge Wells and Hastings

Network Diagram - see first page of Table 206

		SE	SE	SE	SE	SE	SE	SN	SE	SE	SE	SN	SE
		22	22	22	25	25	22		22	13	22		22
		1	1	1	1	1	1	1	1		1	1	1
								A		B		A	
											☕		☕
London Charing Cross 4	⊖ d	22p45	23p15	23p37			07 45		08 15		08 45		09 15
London Waterloo (East) 4	⊖ d	22p48	23p18	23p40			07 48		08 18		08 48		09 18
London Cannon Street 4	⊖ d												
London Bridge 4	⊖ d	22p53	23p23	23p45			07 53		08 23		08 53		09 23
Orpington 4	d	23p10	23p40				08 10		08 40				09 40
Sevenoaks 4	d	23p20	23p52	00 10			08 20		08 51		09 16		09 51
Gatwick Airport 10	✈ d		*22 53*	*23b23*	*05c45*	*06 53*		07 53	*07 53*	*08e08*	*08c08*	08 53	*08 53*
Tonbridge 4	a	23p28	00 01	00 20			08 28	08 37	08 59		09 24	09 37	09 59
	d	23p29	00 01	00 21	07 00	08 00	08 30	08 38	09 00	09 09	09 26	09 38	10 00
High Brooms	d	23p35	00 07	00 27	07 06	08 06	08 36	08 43	09 06	09 15	09 33	09 43	10 06
Tunbridge Wells 4	a	23p39	00 12	00 31	07 10	08 10	08 40	08 47	09 10	09 19	09 37	09 47	10 10
	d	23p39		00 32	07 10	08 10	08 40		09 10		09 40		10 10
Frant	d	23p44		00 36	07 15	08 15	08 45		09 15				10 15
Wadhurst	d	23p48		00 41	07 19	08 19	08 49		09 19		09 47		10 19
Stonegate	d	23p54		00 47	07 25	08 25	08 55		09 25				10 25
Etchingham	d	23p58		00 52	07 30	08 30	09 00		09 30				10 30
Robertsbridge	d	00 03		00 56	07 34	08 34	09 04		09 34				10 34
Battle	d	00 10		01 03	07 42	08 42	09 17		09 42		10 03		10 42
Crowhurst	d	00 14		01 07	07 46	08 46	09 21		09 46				10 46
West St Leonards	d	00 19		01 12	07 51	08 51	09 26		09 51				10 51
St Leonards Warrior Sq 4	d	00 22		01 15	07 54	08 54	09 33		09 54		10 13		10 54
Bexhill 4	a				*08 21*	*09 21*	*10 04*		*10 21*		*10 35*		*11 21*
Hastings 4	a	00 26		01 19	07 58	08 58	09 36		09 57		10 17		10 57
Ore	a												

		SE		SE	SE	SE	SE	SE	SE	SE	SE	SE	SE	SE
		13		22	22	22	31	22	31	22	31	22	31	25
				1	1	1	1	1	1	1	1	1	1	1
		B												
				☕	☕									
London Charing Cross 4	⊖ d			18 45	19 15	19 45		20 45		21 45		22 45		23 30
London Waterloo (East) 4	⊖ d			18 48	19 18	19 48		20 48		21 48		22 48		23 33
London Cannon Street 4	⊖ d													
London Bridge 4	⊖ d		and at	18 53	19 23	19 53		20 53		21 53		22 53		23 37
Orpington 4	d				19 40	20 10		21 10		22 10		23 10		23 53
Sevenoaks 4	d		the same	19 17	19 51	20 20		21 20		22 20		23 20		00 04
Gatwick Airport 10	✈ d	*09e08*	minutes	*18c08*	*18 52*	*19c08*	*19 53*		*20 53*		*21 53*		*22 53*	*23c23*
Tonbridge 4	a			19 25	19 59	20 28		21 28		22 28		23 28		00 15
	d	10 09	past	19 26	20 00	20 30	20 50	21 30	21 50	22 30	22 55	23 30	23 50	00 21
High Brooms	d	10 15		19 33	20 06	20 36	20 55	21 36	21 56	22 36	23 00	23 36	23 55	00 27
Tunbridge Wells 4	a	10 19	each	19 37	20 10	20 40	20 59	21 40	21 59	22 40	23 04	23 40	23 59	00 31
	d			19 40	20 10	20 40		21 40		22 40		23 40		00 31
Frant	d		hour until		20 15	20 45		21 45		22 45		23 45		00 36
Wadhurst	d			19 47	20 19	20 49		21 49		22 49		23 49		00 40
Stonegate	d				20 25	20 55		21 55		22 55		23 55		00 46
Etchingham	d				20 30	21 00		22 00		23 00		00 01		00 51
Robertsbridge	d				20 34	21 04		22 04		23 04		00 04		00 55
Battle	d			20 03	20 42	21 12		22 12		23 12		00 12		01 03
Crowhurst	d				20 46	21 16		22 16		23 16		00 16		01 07
West St Leonards	d				20 51	21 21		22 21		23 21		00 21		01 12
St Leonards Warrior Sq 4	d			20 13	20 54	21 24		22 24		23 24		00 24		01 15
Bexhill 4	a			*20 35*	*21 21*	*21 35*		*22 38*						
Hastings 4	a			20 17	20 57	21 27		22 27		23 27		00 27		01 18
Ore	a													

For general notes see front of timetable
For details of catering facilities see Directory of Train Operators

A From Horsham (Table 186)
B From London Bridge (Table 209)
b Saturdays. Change at Redhill and Tonbridge
c Change at Redhill and Tonbridge
e Change at Redhill

Table 206

Sundays

London and Tonbridge
→ Tunbridge Wells and Hastings

Network Diagram - see first page of Table 206

		SE 22 1	SE 25 1	SE 22 1	SE 22 1	SE 22 1			SE 22 1	SE 22 1		SE 22 1	SE 22 1	SE 22 1		SE 22 1	SE 22 1	SE 22 1	SE 22 1	SE 22 1	SE 22 1	SE 22 1		
London Charing Cross 4	⊖ d	22p45	23p30		08 14				09 14	09 44		17 14	17 44	18 14		18 44	19 14	19 44	20 14	21 14	22 14	23 14		
London Waterloo (East) 4	⊖ d	22p48	23p33		08 17				09 17	09 47		17 17	17 47	18 17		18 47	19 17	19 47	20 17	21 17	22 17	23 17		
London Cannon Street 4	⊖ d																							
London Bridge 4	⊖ d	22p53	23p37		08 22				09 22	09 52		17 22	17 52	18 22		18 52	19 22	19 52	20 22	21 22	22 22	23 22		
Orpington 4	d	23p10	23p53		08 38				09 38	10 08		17 38	18 08	18 38		19 08	19 38	20 08	20 38	21 38	22 38	23 38		
Sevenoaks 4	d	23p20	00p04		08 48				09 48	10 18	and at	17 48	18 18	18 48		19 18	19 48	20 18	20 50	21 50	22 50	23 50		
Gatwick Airport 10	✈ d		*23b23*		*07 55*				*08 55*		the same	*16 55*		*17 55*			*18 55*		*19 55*	*20 55*	*21 55*			
Tonbridge 4	a	23p28	00 15		08 56				09 56	10 26	minutes	17 56	18 26	18 56		19 26	19 56	20 26	20 58	21 58	22 58	23 58		
	d	23p30	00 21	08 19	08 57	09 27			09 57	10 27		17 57	18 27	18 57		19 27	19 57	20 27	20 59	21 59	22 59	23 59		
High Brooms	d	23p36	00 27	08 25	09 03	09 33			10 03	10 33	past	18 03	18 33	19 03		19 33	20 03	20 33	21 05	22 05	23 05	00 05		
Tunbridge Wells 4	a	23p40	00 31	08 29	09 07	09 37			10 07	10 37		18 07	18 37	19 07		19 37	20 07	20 37	21 09	22 09	23 09	00 09		
	d	23p40	00 31		09 08	09 39			10 08	10 38	each	18 08	18 38	19 08		19 38	20 08		21 11	22 09	23 11	00 09		
Frant	d	23p45	00 36		09 13				10 13			18 13		19 13			20 13		21 16	22 14	23 16	00 14		
Wadhurst	d	23p49	00 40		09 17	09 46			10 17	10 46	hour until	18 17	18 46	19 17		19 46	20 17		21 20	22 18	23 20	00 18		
Stonegate	d	23p55	00 46		09 23				10 23			18 23		19 23			20 23		21 26	22 24	23 26	00 24		
Etchingham	d	00 01	00 51		09 29				10 28			18 28		19 28			20 28		21 32	22 29	23 32	00 29		
Robertsbridge	d	00 04	00 55		09 33	09 56				10 56			18 56			19 56			21 36	22 33	23 36	00 33		
Battle	d	00 12	01 03		09 41	10 04			10 38	11 03		18 38	19 03	19 38		20 03	20 38		21 44	22 41	23 44	00 41		
Crowhurst	d	00 16	01 07		09 45	10 08				11 07			19 07			20 07			21 48	22 45	23 48	00 45		
West St Leonards	d	00 21	01 12		09c54	10 13				11 12			19 12	19 45		20 12			21 54	22 50	23 54	00 50		
St Leonards Warrior Sq 4	d	00 24	01 15		09 58	10 16			10 47	11 15		18 47	19 15	19 48		20 15	20 47		21 58	22 53	23 57	00 53		
Bexhill 4	a				*10 12*	*10 27*			*11 12*	*11 27*		*19 12*	*19 27*	*20 12*		*20 27*	*21 12*		*22 12*	*23 27*				
Hastings 4	a	00 27	01 18		10 01	10 19			10 51	11 19		18 51	19 19	19 51		20 19	20 51		22 01	22 56	00 01	00 56		
Ore	a																							

For general notes see front of timetable
For details of catering facilities see
Directory of Train Operators

b Sundays.
Change at Redhill and Tonbridge

c Arr. 0950

Table 206

Mondays to Fridays
until 10 October

For details of Bank Holiday service alterations please see first page of Table 195

Hastings and Tunbridge Wells → Tonbridge and London

Network Diagram - see first page of Table 206

Miles	Station		SE 30 [1]	SE 31 [1]	SE 22 [1]	SE 23 [1]	SE 25 [1]	SE 30 [1]	SE 22 [1] Trolley	SE 22 [1]	SE 30 [1]	SE 23 [1] Trolley	SE 30 [1]	SE 22 [1] Trolley	SE 30 [1]	SE 23 [1] Trolley	SE 30 [1]	SE 22 [1]	SE 31	SE 22 [1] Trolley	SE 22 [1] Trolley	SE 88 [1] A	SE 22 [1] Trolley
0	Ore	d							06 10			06 38						07 46					
1	**Hastings [3]**	d			05 16	05 44	05 56		06 14	06 26		06 42		07 02		07 28		07 50		08 10	08 42		09 31
—	Bexhill [3]	d				*05 14*						*06 18*		*06 52*		*07 11*		*07 22*		*08 01*	*08 25*		*09 22*
1¾	St Leonards Warrior Sq [3]	d			05 19	05 47	05 59		06 17	06 29		06 45		07 05		07 31		07 53		08 13	08 45		09 34
2¾	West St Leonards	d			05 22	05 50			06 20			06 48		07 08		07 34		07 56		08 16	08 48		
6	Crowhurst	d			05 27	05 55			06 25			06 53		07 13		07 39		08 01		08 21	08 53		
8	Battle	d			05 31	05 59	06 09		06 29	06 39		06 57		07 17		07 43		08 05		08 25	08 57		09 44
14¼	Robertsbridge	d			05 39	06 07			06 37			07 05		07 25		07 51		08 13		08 33	09 05		
16	Etchingham	d			05 43	06 11	06 19		06 41	06 49		07 09		07 29		07 55		08 17		08 37	09 09		
19¾	Stonegate	d			05 48	06 16			06 46			07 14		07 34		08 00		08 23		08 43	09 14		
24¼	Wadhurst	d			05 55	06 23	06 29		06 53	06 59		07 21		07 41		08 07		08 29		08 49	09 21		10 00
26¼	Frant	d			05 59	06 27			06 57			07 25		07 45		08 11		08 34		08 54	09 25		
29	**Tunbridge Wells [3]**	a			06 05	06 33	06 37		07 03	07 07		07 31		07 51		08 17		08 38		08 58	09 30		10 07
—		d	05 16	05 44	06 06	06 42		06 56	07 12		07 20	07 36	07 40	07 56	08 00	08 22	08 26	08 40	08 56	09 02	09 36	09 52	10 08
30½	High Brooms	d	05 20	05 47	06 10	06 46		07 00	07 16		07 24	07 40	07 44	08 00	08 04	08 26	08 30	08 44	09 00	09 06	09 39	09 55	10 11
34	**Tonbridge [3]**	a	05 26	05 52	06 17	06 53		07 05			07 29		07 50		08 10		08 36	08 50	09 06	09 13	09 45	10 01	10 17
—		d	05 26		06 18	06 53		07 06			07 31		07 51		08 11		08 36	09 00		09 14	09 46	10 04	10 18
—	Gatwick Airport [10] ✈	a		*06b53*	*07b54*						*08b39*				*09b02*		*09b39*	09 54		*10b23*	10 55	10 55	*11b23*
41½	Sevenoaks [3]	a	05 38		06 30	07 03		07 18			07 43		08 03		08 23		08 48	09 09		09 26	09 55		10 27
49¾	Orpington [3]	a	05 50			07 12														09 35			
61¾	**London Bridge [3]**	⊖ a	06 06		06 55	07 29		07 50			08 10	08 21	08 30		08 50	09 05	09 18	09 33		09 51	10 24		10 54
—	**London Cannon Street [3]**	⊖ a				07 36						08 28				09 12							
62¾	**London Waterloo (East) [3]**	⊖ a	06 11		07 00			07 55	08 00		08 15		08 35	08 45	08 55		09 23	09 38		09 57	10 29		10 59
63½	**London Charing Cross [3]**	⊖ a	06 14		07 05			07 59	08 05		08 21		08 41	08 51	09 01		09 29	09 44		10 01	10 33		11 03

Station		SE 13	SE 22 [1] Trolley	SE 88 [1] A	SE 22 [1] Trolley	SE 13	SE 22 [1] Trolley	SE 88 [1] A	SE 22 [1] Trolley	SE 13	SE 22 [1] Trolley	SE 88 [1] A	SE 22 [1] Trolley	SE 13	SE 22 [1] Trolley	SE 88 [1] A	SE 22 [1] Trolley	SE 13	SE 22 [1] Trolley	SE 88 [1] A	SE 22 [1] Trolley	SE 13	SE 23 [1]
Ore	d																						
Hastings [4]	d		09 47		10 31		10 47		11 31		11 47		12 31		12 47		13 31		13 47		14 31		14 47
Bexhill [4]	d				*10 22*		*10 39*		*11 22*		*11 39*		*12 22*		*12 39*		*13 22*		*13 39*		*14 22*		*14 39*
St Leonards Warrior Sq [4]	d		09 50		10 34		10 50		11 34		11 50		12 34		12 50		13 34		13 50		14 34		14 50
West St Leonards	d		09 53				10 53				11 53				12 53				13 53				14 53
Crowhurst	d		09 58				10 58				11 58				12 58				13 58				14 58
Battle	d		10 02		10 44		11 02		11 44		12 02		12 44		13 02		13 44		14 02		14 44		15 02
Robertsbridge	d		10 10				11 10				12 10				13 10				14 10				15 10
Etchingham	d		10 14				11 14				12 14				13 14				14 14				15 14
Stonegate	d		10 19				11 19				12 19				13 19				14 19				15 19
Wadhurst	d		10 26		11 00		11 26		12 00		12 26		13 00		13 26		14 00		14 26		15 00		15 26
Frant	d		10 30				11 30				12 30				13 30				14 30				15 30
Tunbridge Wells [4]	a		10 35		11 07		11 35		12 07		12 35		13 07		13 35		14 07		14 35		15 07		15 35
	d	10 24	10 36	10 52	11 08	11 24	11 36	11 52	12 08	12 24	12 36	12 52	13 08	13 24	13 36	13 52	14 08	14 24	14 36	14 52	15 08	15 24	15 36
High Brooms	d	10 27	10 39	10 55	11 11	11 27	11 39	11 55	12 11	12 27	12 39	12 55	13 11	13 27	13 39	13 55	14 11	14 27	14 39	14 55	15 11	15 27	15 39
Tonbridge [4]	a	10 33	10 45	11 01	11 17	11 33	11 45	12 01	12 17	12 33	12 45	13 01	13 17	13 33	13 45	14 01	14 17	14 33	14 45	15 01	15 17	15 33	15 45
	d		10 46	11 04	11 18		11 46	12 04	12 18		12 46	13 04	13 18		13 46	14 04	14 18		14 46	15 04	15 18		15 46
Gatwick Airport [10] ✈	a	*11c23*	*11 55*	11 55	*12b23*	*12c23*	*12 55*	12 55	*13b23*	*13c23*	*13 55*	13 55	*14b23*	*14c23*	*14 55*	14 55	*15b23*	*15c23*	*15 56*	15 56	*16b23*	*16c23*	*16 56*
Sevenoaks [4]	a		10 55		11 27		11 55		12 27		12 55		13 27		13 55		14 27		14 55		15 27		15 55
Orpington [4]	a		11 05				12 05				13 05				14 05				15 05				16 07
London Bridge [4]	⊖ a		11 24		11 54		12 24		12 54		13 24		13 54		14 24		14 54		15 24		15 54		16 24
London Cannon Street [4]	⊖ a																						
London Waterloo (East) [4]	⊖ a		11 29		11 59		12 29		12 59		13 29		13 59		14 29		14 59		15 29		15 59		16 29
London Charing Cross [4]	⊖ a		11 33		12 03		12 33		13 03		13 33		14 03		14 33		15 03		15 33		16 03		16 33

Station		SE 22 [1]	SE 23 [1] Trolley	SE 31 [1]	SE 22 [1]	SE 22 [1]	SE 22 [1]	SE 22 [1] Trolley	SE 22 [1]	SE 22 [1]	SE 22 [1]	SE 22 [1]	SE 22 [1]	SE 22 [1]	SE 22 [1]	SE 22 [1]	SE 22 [1]	SE 22 [1]	SE 25 [1]	SE 31
Ore	d																			
Hastings [4]	d	15 07	15 35		16 07	16 35		17 11		17 47	18 17	18 47		19 47		20 47		21 35	22 05	
Bexhill [4]	d		*15 22*		*15 42*	*16 22*		*17 02*		*17 22*	*18 03*	*18 23*		*19 23*		*20 22*		*21 23*	*21 41*	
St Leonards Warrior Sq [4]	d	15 10	15 38		16 10	16 38		17 14		17 50	18 20	18 50		19 50		20 50		21 38	22 08	
West St Leonards	d	15 13			16 13	16 41		17 17		17 53	18 23	18 53		19 53		20 53		21 41	22 11	
Crowhurst	d	15 18			16 18	16 46		17 22		17 58	18 28	18 58		19 58		20 58		21 46	22 16	
Battle	d	15 22	15 48		16 22	16 50		17 26		18 02	18 32	19 02		20 02		21 02		21 50	22 20	
Robertsbridge	d	15 30			16 30	16 58		17 34		18 10	18 40	19 10		20 10		21 10		21 58	22 28	
Etchingham	d	15 34			16 34	17 02		17 38		18 14	18 44	19 14		20 14		21 14		22 02	22 32	
Stonegate	d	15 39			16 39	17 07		17 43		18 19	18 49	19 19		20 19		21 19		22 07	22 37	
Wadhurst	d	15 46	16 04		16 46	17 14		17 50		18 26	18 56	19 26		20 26		21 26		22 14	22 44	
Frant	d	15 50			16 50	17 18		17 54		18 30	19 00	19 30		20 30		21 30		22 18	22 48	
Tunbridge Wells [4]	a	15 55	16 11		16 55	17 24		17 59		18 39	19 05	19 35		20 35		21 35		22 23	22 53	
	d	15 56	16 16	16 36	16 56	17 30	17 54	18 04	18 26	18 40	19 06	19 38	20 06	20 36	21 06	21 36	22 06	22 26	22 56	23 30
High Brooms	d	15 59	16 19	16 39	16 59	17 33	17 57	18 07	18 29	18 43	19 09	19 41	20 09	20 39	21 09	21 39	22 09	22 29	22 59	23 33
Tonbridge [4]	a	16 06	16 26	16 46	17 06	17 40	18 03	18 14	18 36	18 50	19 15	19 47	20 15	20 46	21 15	21 46	22 15	22 36	23 05	23 39
	d	16 06	16 28		17 06	17 40	18 06	18 16	18 36	18 54	19 16	19 48	20 16	20 48	21 16	21 48	22 16	22 42		
Gatwick Airport [10] ✈	a	*17b32*			*18b12*			*19b07*		*19b58*		*20 35*		*21 34*		*22 35*			*00b11*	
Sevenoaks [4]	a	16 18	16 37		17 15	17 50	18 18	18 25	18 46	19 04	19 28	19 57	20 28	20 57	21 28	21 57	22 28	22 51		
Orpington [4]	a	16 34	16 49		17 26	17 59	18 32	18 35	18 55	19 14	19 37	20 07	20 37	21 07	21 37	22 07	22 37	23 01		
London Bridge [4]	⊖ a	16 52	17 09		17 44	18 19	18 49	18 51	19 12	19 33	19 55	20 25	20 55	21 25	21 55	22 25	22 55	23 19		
London Cannon Street [4]	⊖ a						18 53													
London Waterloo (East) [4]	⊖ a	16 57	17 14		17 50	18 26		18 56	19 17	19 38	20 00	20 30	21 00	21 30	22 00	22 30	23 00	23 24		
London Charing Cross [4]	⊖ a	17 01	17 19		17 55	18 30		19 00	19 21	19 42	20 04	20 34	21 04	21 34	22 04	22 34	23 04	23 28		

For general notes see front of timetable
For details of catering facilities see Directory of Train Operators

A To Horsham (Table 186)
b Change at Tonbridge and Redhill
c Change at Redhill

For details of Bank Holiday service alterations please see first page of Table 195

Hastings and Tunbridge Wells → Tonbridge and London

Network Diagram - see first page of Table 206

	SE	SE	SE	SE	SE	SE	SE	SE	SE	SE	SE	SE	SE	SE	SE	SE	SE	SE	SE	SE	SE	SE
	30	31	22	23	25	30	22	22	30	23	30	22	30	23	30	22	31	22	22	88	22	13
	1	1	1	1	1	1	1	1	1	1	1	1	1	1	1	1		1	1	1	1	
																				A		
							⊥			⊥		⊥		⊥				⊥	⊥		⊥	
Ore d							06 07			06 35						07 43						
Hastings 4 d			05 16	05 42	05 56		06 11	06 26		06 39		06 59		07 25		07 47		08 10	08 42		09 31	
Bexhill 4 d				*05 14*						*06 18*		*06 35*		*07 11*		*07 22*		*08 01*	*08 25*		*09 22*	
St Leonards Warrior Sq 4 d			05 19	05 45	05 59		06 14	06 29		06 42		07 02		07 28		07 50		08 13	08 45		09 34	
West St Leonards d			05 22	05 48			06 17			06 45		07 05		07 31		07 53		08 16	08 48			
Crowhurst d			05 27	05 53			06 22			06 50		07 10		07 36		07 58		08 21	08 53			
Battle d			05 31	05 57	06 09		06 26	06 39		06 54		07 14		07 40		08 02		08 25	08 57		09 44	
Robertsbridge d			05 39	06 05			06 34			07 02		07 22		07 48		08 13		08 33	09 05			
Etchingham d			05 43	06 09	06 19		06 38	06 49		07 06		07 26		07 52		08 17		08 37	09 09			
Stonegate d			05 48	06 14			06 43			07 11		07 31		07 57		08 23		08 43	09 14			
Wadhurst d			05 55	06 21	06 29		06 50	06 59		07 18		07 38		08 04		08 29		08 49	09 21		10 00	
Frant d			05 59	06 25			06 54			07 22		07 42		08 08		08 34		08 54	09 25			
Tunbridge Wells 4 a			06 05	06 32	06 37		07 03	07 07		07 28		07 51		08 14		08 38		08 58	09 30		10 07	
d	05 16	05 44	06 06	06 42		06 56	07 12		07 20	07 36	07 40	07 56	08 00	08 22	08 26	08 40	08 56	09 02	09 36	09 52	10 08	10 24
High Brooms d	05 20	05 47	06 10	06 46		07 00	07 16		07 24	07 40	07 44	08 00	08 04	08 26	08 30	08 44	09 00	09 06	09 39	09 55	10 11	10 27
Tonbridge 4 a	05 26	05 52	06 17	06 53		07 05			07 29		07 50		08 10		08 36	08 50	09 06	09 13	09 45	10 01	10 17	10 33
d	05 26		06 18	06 53		07 06			07 31		07 51		08 11		08 36	09 00		09 14	09 46	10 04	10 18	
Gatwick Airport 10 ✈ a		*06b53*	*07b54*						*08b39*				*09b02*		*09b39*	*09 54*		*10b23*	*10 55*	10 55	*11b23*	*11c23*
Sevenoaks 4 a	05 38		06 30	07 03		07 18			07 43		08 03		08 23		08 48	09 09		09 26	09 55		10 27	
Orpington 4 a	05 50			07 12														09 35				
London Bridge 4 ⊖ a	06 06		06 55	07 29		07 50			08 10	08 21	08 30		08 50	09 05	09 18	09 33		09 51	10 24		10 54	
London Cannon Street 4 ⊖ a				07 37						08 29				09 13								
London Waterloo (East) 4 ⊖ a	06 11		07 00			07 55	08 00		08 15		08 35	08 45	08 55		09 23	09 38		09 57	10 29		10 59	
London Charing Cross 4 ⊖ a	06 14		07 06			07 59	08 06		08 21		08 41	08 51	09 01		09 29	09 44		10 01	10 33		11 03	

	SE	SE	SE	SE	SE	SE	SE	SE	SE	SE	SE	SE	SE	SE	SE	SE	SE	SE	SE	SE	SE
	22	88	22	13	22	88	22	13	22	88	22	13	22	88	22	13	22	88	22	13	23
	1	1	1		1	1	1		1	1	1		1	1	1		1	1	1		1
		A				A				A				A				A			
	⊥		⊥		⊥		⊥		⊥		⊥		⊥		⊥		⊥		⊥		
Ore d																					
Hastings 4 d	09 47		10 31		10 47		11 31		11 47		12 31		12 47		13 31		13 47		14 31		14 47
Bexhill 4 d			*10 22*		*10 39*		*11 22*		*11 39*		*12 22*		*12 39*		*13 22*		*13 39*		*14 22*		*14 39*
St Leonards Warrior Sq 4 d	09 50		10 34		10 50		11 34		11 50		12 34		12 50		13 34		13 50		14 34		14 50
West St Leonards d	09 53				10 53				11 53				12 53				13 53				14 53
Crowhurst d	09 58				10 58				11 58				12 58				13 58				14 58
Battle d	10 02		10 44		11 02		11 44		12 02		12 44		13 02		13 44		14 02		14 44		15 02
Robertsbridge d	10 10				11 10				12 10				13 10				14 10				15 10
Etchingham d	10 14				11 14				12 14				13 14				14 14				15 14
Stonegate d	10 19				11 19				12 19				13 19				14 19				15 19
Wadhurst d	10 26		11 00		11 26		12 00		12 26		13 00		13 26		14 00		14 26		15 00		15 26
Frant d	10 30				11 30				12 30				13 30				14 30				15 30
Tunbridge Wells 4 a	10 35		11 07		11 35		12 07		12 35		13 07		13 35		14 07		14 35		15 07		15 35
d	10 36	10 52	11 08	11 24	11 36	11 52	12 08	12 24	12 36	12 52	13 08	13 24	13 36	13 52	14 08	14 24	14 36	14 52	15 08	15 24	15 36
High Brooms d	10 39	10 55	11 11	11 27	11 39	11 55	12 11	12 27	12 39	12 55	13 11	13 27	13 39	13 55	14 11	14 27	14 39	14 55	15 11	15 27	15 39
Tonbridge 4 a	10 45	11 01	11 17	11 33	11 45	12 01	12 17	12 33	12 45	13 01	13 17	13 33	13 45	14 01	14 17	14 33	14 45	15 01	15 17	15 33	15 45
d	10 46	11 04	11 18		11 46	12 04	12 18		12 46	13 04	13 18		13 46	14 04	14 18		14 46	15 04	15 18		15 46
Gatwick Airport 10 ✈ a	*11 55*	11 55	*12b23*	*12c23*	*12 55*	12 55	*13b23*	*13c23*	*13 55*	13 55	*14b23*	*14c23*	*14 55*	14 55	*15b23*	*15c23*	*15 56*	15 56	*16b23*	*16c23*	*16 56*
Sevenoaks 4 a	10 55		11 27		11 55		12 27		12 55		13 27		13 55		14 27		14 55		15 27		15 55
Orpington 4 a	11 05				12 05				13 05				14 05				15 05				16 07
London Bridge 4 ⊖ a	11 24		11 54		12 24		12 54		13 24		13 54		14 24		14 54		15 24		15 54		16 24
London Cannon Street 4 ⊖ a																					
London Waterloo (East) 4 ⊖ a	11 29		11 59		12 29		12 59		13 29		13 59		14 29		14 59		15 29		15 59		16 29
London Charing Cross 4 ⊖ a	11 33		12 03		12 33		13 03		13 33		14 03		14 33		15 03		15 33		16 03		16 33

For general notes see front of timetable
For details of catering facilities see Directory of Train Operators

- **A** To Horsham (Table 186)
- **b** Change at Tonbridge and Redhill
- **c** Change at Redhill

For details of Bank Holiday service alterations please see first page of Table 195

Hastings and Tunbridge Wells → Tonbridge and London

Network Diagram - see first page of Table 206

		SE 22 1	SE 23 1 🍴	SE 31 1	SE 22 1		SE 22 1	SE 22 1	SE 22 1 🍴	SE 22 1	SE 22 1		SE 22 1		SE 22 1	SE 22 1	SE 22 1	SE 22 1	SE 22 1	SE 22 1	SE 22 1	SE 25 1	SE 31		
Ore	d																								
Hastings 4	d	15 07	15 35		16 07		16 35		17 11		17 47		18 17		18 47		19 47		20 47		21 35	22 05			
Bexhill 4	d		*15 22*		*15 42*		*16 22*		*17 02*		*17 22*		*18 03*		*18 23*		*19 23*		*20 22*		*21 23*	*21 41*			
St Leonards Warrior Sq 4	d	15 10	15 38		16 10		16 38		17 14		17 50		18 20		18 50		19 50		20 50		21 38	22 08			
West St Leonards	d	15 13			16 13		16 41		17 17		17 53		18 23		18 53		19 53		20 53		21 41	22 11			
Crowhurst	d	15 18			16 18		16 46		17 22		17 58		18 28		18 58		19 58		20 58		21 46	22 16			
Battle	d	15 22	15 48		16 22		16 50		17 26		18 02		18 32		19 02		20 02		21 02		21 50	22 20			
Robertsbridge	d	15 30			16 30		16 58		17 34		18 10		18 40		19 10		20 10		21 10		21 58	22 28			
Etchingham	d	15 34			16 34		17 02		17 38		18 14		18 44		19 14		20 14		21 14		22 02	22 32			
Stonegate	d	15 39			16 39		17 07		17 43		18 19		18 49		19 19		20 19		21 19		22 07	22 37			
Wadhurst	d	15 46	16 04		16 46		17 14		17 50		18 26		18 56		19 26		20 26		21 26		22 14	22 44			
Frant	d	15 50			16 50		17 18		17 54		18 30		19 00		19 30		20 30		21 30		22 18	22 48			
Tunbridge Wells 4	a	15 55	16 11		16 55		17 24		17 59		18 39		19 05		19 35		20 35		21 35		22 23	22 53			
	d	15 56	16 16	16 36	16 56		17 30	17 54	18 04	18 26	18 40		19 06		19 38	20 06	20 36	21 06	21 36	22 06	22 26	22 56	23 30		
High Brooms	d	15 59	16 19	16 39	16 59		17 33	17 57	18 07	18 29	18 43		19 09		19 41	20 09	20 39	21 09	21 39	22 09	22 29	22 59	23 33		
Tonbridge 4	a	16 06	16 26	16 46	17 06		17 40	18 03	18 14	18 36	18 50		19 15		19 47	20 15	20 46	21 15	21 46	22 15	22 36	23 05	23 39		
	d	16 06	16 28		17 06		17 40	18 06	18 16	18 36	18 54		19 16		19 48	20 16	20 48	21 16	21 48	22 16	22 42				
Gatwick Airport 10 ✈	a	*17b32*			*18b12*				*19b07*		*19b58*				*20 35*		*21 34*		*22 35*			*00b11*			
Sevenoaks 4	a	16 18	16 37		17 15		17 50	18 18	18 25	18 46	19 04		19 28		19 57	20 28	20 57	21 28	21 57	22 28	22 51				
Orpington 4	a	16 34	16 49		17 26		17 59	18 32	18 35	18 55	19 14		19 37		20 07	20 37	21 07	21 37	22 07	22 37	23 01				
London Bridge 4	⊖ a	16 52	17 09		17 44		18 19	18 49	18 51	19 12	19 33		19 55		20 25	20 55	21 25	21 55	22 25	22 55	23 19				
London Cannon Street 4	⊖ a							18 53																	
London Waterloo (East) 4	⊖ a	16 57	17 14		17 50		18 26		18 56	19 17	19 38		20 00		20 30	21 00	21 30	22 00	22 30	23 00	23 24				
London Charing Cross 4	⊖ a	17 01	17 19		17 55		18 30		19 00	19 21	19 42		20 04		20 34	21 04	21 34	22 04	22 34	23 04	23 28				

Saturdays

		SE 88	SE 22 1		SE 22 1	SE 22 1 🍴		SE 22 1 🍴	SE 22 1 🍴		SE 88 1 A	SE 22 1 🍴		SE 13		SE 22 1 🍴	SE 88 1 A	SE 22 1 🍴	SE 13			SE 22 1 🍴	SE 88 1 A	SE 22 1 🍴
Ore	d																							
Hastings 4	d		05 47		06 16	06 47		07 18	07 47			08 18				08 47		09 31				16 47		17 19
Bexhill 4	d				*06 00*	*06 19*		*07 00*	*07 22*			*08 02*				*08 39*		*09 22*				*16 39*		*17 02*
St Leonards Warrior Sq 4	d		05 50		06 19	06 50		07 21	07 50			08 21				08 50		09 34		and at		16 50		17 22
West St Leonards	d		05 53		06 22	06 53			07 53							08 53						16 53		
Crowhurst	d		05 58		06 27	06 58			07 58							08 58				the same		16 58		
Battle	d		06 02		06 32	07 02		07 32	08 02			08 32				09 02		09 44				17 02		17 32
Robertsbridge	d		06 10		06 40	07 10		07 44	08 10			08 44				09 10				minutes		17 10		17 44
Etchingham	d		06 14		06 44	07 14		07 48	08 14			08 48				09 14						17 14		17 48
Stonegate	d		06 20		06 50	07 20			08 20							09 20				past		17 20		
Wadhurst	d		06 26		06 56	07 26		07 58	08 26			08 58				09 26		10 00				17 26		17 58
Frant	d		06 31		07 01	07 31			08 31							09 31				each		17 31		
Tunbridge Wells 4	a		06 35		07 05	07 35		08 05	08 35			09 05				09 35		10 07				17 35		18 05
	d	05 37	06 36		07 06	07 36		08 06	08 36		08 52	09 06		09 24		09 36	09 52	10 08	10 24	hour until		17 36	17 52	18 06
High Brooms	d	05 40	06 39		07 09	07 39		08 09	08 39		08 55	09 09		09 27		09 39	09 55	10 11	10 27			17 39	17 55	18 09
Tonbridge 4	a	05 46	06 45		07 16	07 45		08 16	08 45		09 01	09 16		09 33		09 45	10 01	10 17	10 33			17 45	18 01	18 16
	d	05 52	06 46		07 16	07 46		08 16	08 46		09 04	09 16				09 46	10 04	10 18				17 46	18 04	18 16
Gatwick Airport 10 ✈	a	06 34	*07 34*		*08b23*	*08 55*		*09b23*	*09 55*		09 55	*10b23*		*10c23*		*10 55*	10 55	*11b23*	*11c23*			*18 34*	18 55	
Sevenoaks 4	a		06 56		07 26	07 55		08 26	08 55			09 26				09 55		10 27				17 55		18 26
Orpington 4	a		07 07		07 35	08 05		08 35	09 05			09 35				10 05						18 05		18 35
London Bridge 4	⊖ a		07 26		07 54	08 24		08 54	09 24			09 54				10 24		10 54				18 24		18 54
London Cannon Street 4	⊖ a																							
London Waterloo (East) 4	⊖ a		07 31		07 59	08 29		08 59	09 29			09 59				10 29		10 59				18 29		19 00
London Charing Cross 4	⊖ a		07 34		08 05	08 33		09 03	09 33			10 03				10 33		11 03				18 33		19 06

For general notes see front of timetable
For details of catering facilities see Directory of Train Operators

A To Horsham (Table 186)
b Change at Tonbridge and Redhill
c Change at Redhill

Table 206

Hastings and Tunbridge Wells → Tonbridge and London

Saturdays

Network Diagram - see first page of Table 206

		SE 22 [1]	SE 31 [1]	SE 22 [1]	SE 31 [1]	SE 22 [1]	SE 31 [1]	SE 22 [1]	SE 31 [1]	SE 25 [1]	SE 31 [1]
Ore	d										
Hastings [4]	d	17 47		18 47		19 47		20 47		22 07	
Bexhill [4]	d	*17 22*		*18 22*		*19 22*		*20 22*		*21 41*	
St Leonards Warrior Sq [4]	d	17 50		18 50		19 50		20 50		22 10	
West St Leonards	d	17 53		18 53		19 53		20 53		22 13	
Crowhurst	d	17 58		18 58		19 58		20 58		22 18	
Battle	d	18 02		19 02		20 02		21 02		22 22	
Robertsbridge	d	18 10		19 10		20 10		21 10		22 30	
Etchingham	d	18 14		19 14		20 14		21 14		22 34	
Stonegate	d	18 20		19 20		20 20		21 20		22 39	
Wadhurst	d	18 26		19 26		20 26		21 26		22 46	
Frant	d	18 31		19 31		20 31		21 31		22 50	
Tunbridge Wells [4]	a	18 35		19 35		20 35		21 35		22 55	
	d	18 36	19 10	19 36	20 10	20 36	21 10	21 36	22 10	22 55	23 30
High Brooms	d	18 39	19 13	19 39	20 13	20 39	21 13	21 39	22 13	22 59	23 33
Tonbridge [4]	a	18 45	19 19	19 45	20 19	20 45	21 19	21 45	22 19	23 05	23 39
	d	18 46		19 46		20 46		21 46			
Gatwick Airport [10] ✈	a	*19 34*		*20 34*		*21 34*		*22 34*		*00b10*	
Sevenoaks [4]	a	18 56		19 56		20 56		21 56			
Orpington [4]	a	19 07		20 07		21 07		22 07			
London Bridge [4]	⊖ a	19 26		20 26		21 25		22 25			
London Cannon Street [4]	⊖ a										
London Waterloo (East) [4]	⊖ a	19 30		20 30		21 30		22 30			
London Charing Cross [4]	⊖ a	19 34		20 34		21 34		22 34			

Sundays

		SE 22 [1]	SE 22 [1]	SE 22 [1]	SE 22 [1]	SE 22 [1]	SE 22 [1]		SE 22 [1]	SE 22 [1]	SE 22 [1]	SE 22 [1]	SE 22 [1]	SE 22 [1]	SE 22 [1]	SE 22 [1]
Ore	d							and at the same minutes past each hour until								
Hastings [4]	d	07 18		08 13	08 54	09 28	09 54		17 28	17 54	18 12	19 12		20 12	21 12	22 12
Bexhill [4]	d			*07 46*	*08 11*	*09 16*			*17 16*		*17 46*	*18 46*		*19 46*	*20 46*	*21 46*
St Leonards Warrior Sq [4]	d	07 21		08 16	08 57	09 31	09 57		17 31	17 57	18 15	19 15		20 15	21 15	22 15
West St Leonards	d	07 24		08 20		09 34			17 34		18 19	19 19		20 19	21 18	22 18
Crowhurst	d	07 29		08 25		09 39			17 39		18 24	19 24		20 24	21 24	22 23
Battle	d	07 34		08 30	09 07	09 43	10 07		17 43	18 07	18 29	19 29		20 29	21 28	22 27
Robertsbridge	d	07 41		08 38		09 51			17 51		18 40	19 40		20 40	21 36	22 35
Etchingham	d	07 45		08 42	09 17		10 17			18 17	18 45	19 45		20 45	21 41	22 39
Stonegate	d	07 51		08 48	09 22		10 22			18 22	18 50	19 50		20 50	21 46	22 44
Wadhurst	d	07 57		08 54	09 29	10 01	10 29		18 01	18 29	18 57	19 57		20 57	21 53	22 51
Frant	d	08 02		08 59	09 33		10 33			18 33	19 01	20 01		21 01	21 57	22 55
Tunbridge Wells [4]	a	08 07		09 04	09 38	10 08	10 38		18 08	18 38	19 06	20 06		21 06	22 02	23 00
	d	08 08	08 38	09 08	09 39	10 10	10 39		18 10	18 39	19 08	20 08	20 48	21 08	22 08	23 00
High Brooms	d	08 12	08 42	09 12	09 42	10 13	10 42		18 13	18 42	19 12	20 12	20 51	21 12	22 12	23 04
Tonbridge [4]	a	08 18	08 48	09 18	09 48	10 19	10 48		18 19	18 48	19 18	20 18	20 57	21 18	22 18	23 10
	d	08 19	08 49	09 19	09 49	10 20	10 49		18 20	18 49	19 19	20 19		21 19	22 19	
Gatwick Airport [10] ✈	a		*09 38*		*10 38*		*11 38*			*19 38*	*20 38*	*21 38*				
Sevenoaks [4]	a	08 28	08 58	09 28	09 58	10 29	10 58		18 29	18 58	19 28	20 28		21 28	22 28	
Orpington [4]	a	08 38	09 08	09 38	10 08	10 39	11 08		18 39	19 08	19 40	20 40		21 40	22 40	
London Bridge [4]	⊖ a	08 56	09 26	09 56	10 26	10 56	11 26		18 56	19 26	19 56	20 56		21 56	22 56	
London Cannon Street [4]	⊖ a															
London Waterloo (East) [4]	⊖ a	09 01	09 31	10 01	10 31	11 01	11 31		19 01	19 31	20 01	21 01		22 01	23 01	
London Charing Cross [4]	⊖ a	09 05	09 35	10 05	10 35	11 06	11 35		19 06	19 35	20 05	21 05		22 05	23 05	

For general notes see front of timetable
For details of catering facilities see Directory of Train Operators

b Change at Tonbridge and Redhill

Table 207

Mondays to Fridays
until 10 October

For details of Bank Holiday service alterations please see first page of Table 195

London and Tonbridge → Ashford International, Folkestone, Dover, Canterbury West, Ramsgate and Margate

Network Diagram - see first page of Table 206

Miles	Miles	Miles			SE	SE	SE	SE	SE	SE	SE	SE	SE	SE	SE	SE	SE	SE	SE	SE	SE	SE	SE	SE
					MO	MX	MO	MX	MX	MO	MX	MX												
					4	4	2	8	2	8	66	2	8	61	64	61	61	18	64	61	18	61	4	66
					1	1	1	1	1	1	1	1	1	1	1		1	1	1		1		1	1
														A										
0	—	—	**London Charing Cross** 4 ⊖	d	22p00	22p00	22p30	22p30	23p00	23p30	.	23p30	.	.	.	.	.	05 30	.	.	.	.	06 25	.
¾	—	—	**London Waterloo (East)** 4 ⊖	d	22p03	22p03	22p33	22p33	23p03	23p33	.	23p33	.	.	.	.	.	05 33	.	.	.	.	06 28	.
—	—	—	**London Cannon Street** 4 ⊖	d	.	.	.	.	.	.	.	.	.	.	.	.	.	.	.	.	.	.	*06 22*	.
1¾	—	—	**London Bridge** 4 ⊖	d	22p08	22p08	22p38	22p38	23p08	23p38	.	23p38	.	.	.	.	.	05 38	.	.	.	.	06 33	.
13¾	—	—	Orpington 4	d	22p24	22p24	22p54	22p54	23p24	23p54	.	23p56	.	.	.	.	.	05 54	.	.	.	.	06 50	.
22	—	—	Sevenoaks 4	d	22p34	22p34	23p04	23p04	23p34	00 04	.	00 06	.	.	.	.	.	06 11	.	.	.	.	07 00	.
—	—	—	Gatwick Airport 10 ✈	d	.	.	.	.	.	*22 53*	.	*22 53*	.	.	.	.	.	.	.	.	.	.	*05 54*	.
—	—	—	Redhill	d	.	.	.	.	.	*23 10*	.	*23 10*	.	.	.	.	.	.	.	.	.	.	*06 09*	.
29½	—	—	**Tonbridge** 4	a	22p43	22p45	23p15	23p15	23p45	00 13	.	00 17	.	.	.	.	.	06 21	.	.	.	.	07 10	.
—	—	—		d	22p43	22p45	23p15	23p15	23p45	00 13	.	00 17	04 53	.	.	05 47	.	06 22	.	.	.	.	07 11	.
34¾	—	—	Paddock Wood 4	d	22p50	22p52	23p22	23p22	23p52	00 20	.	00 24	05 00	.	.	05 55	.	06 29	.	06 32	.	07 06	07 18	.
—	—	—	Maidstone West 4	a	.	.	.	.	.	.	.	.	*06 15*	.	.	06 15	.	*07 26*	.	06 52	.	07 26	.	.
39½	—	—	Marden	d	.	.	23p28	23p28	.	.	.	00 30	05 06	.	.	.	.	06 35	.	.	.	.	07 24	.
41¾	—	—	Staplehurst	d	22p59	23p01	23p33	23p32	00 01	00 29	.	00 35	05 10	.	.	.	.	06 39	.	.	.	.	07 28	.
45¼	—	—	Headcorn 4	d	.	23p06	23p38	23p37	00 06	.	.	00 40	05 15	.	.	.	.	06 44	.	.	.	.	07 33	.
50½	—	—	Pluckley	d	.	.	23p45	23p44	.	.	.	00 47	05 21	.	.	.	.	06 51	.	.	.	.	07 40	.
—	0	—	**London Victoria** 15 ⊖	d	.	.	.	.	*22 09*	.	23p11	*23 11*	.	.	.	.	.	.	.	.	.	.	.	06 10
—	11	—	Bromley South 4	d	.	.	.	.	*22 29*	.	23p30	*23 30*	.	.	.	.	.	.	.	.	.	.	.	06 30
—	40	—	Maidstone East 4	d	.	.	.	.	*23 13*	.	00 14	*00 14*	.	.	05 56	.	.	.	06 33	.	.	.	.	07 23
56	59¼	—	**Ashford International**	a	23p12	23p17	23p52	23p52	00 17	00 42	00 43	00 54	05 29	.	06 25	.	.	06 59	07 02	.	.	.	07 52	07 52
—	—	—		d	23p18	23p20	23p53	23p53	00 20	.	00 57	00 58	05 34	06 12	06 28	.	06 35	07 03	07 07	.	.	.	07 55	07 56
—	—	—	Rye	a	.	.	.	.	.	.	.	.	*06 47*	.	*07 09*	.	.	.	*07 53*	.	.	.	.	.
—	63½	—	Wye	d	.	.	.	23p58	.	.	01 03	.	.	.	06 34	.	.	.	07 13	.	.	.	.	08 02
—	68¾	—	Chilham	d	.	.	.	00 05	.	.	01 09	.	.	.	06 41	.	.	.	07 19	.	.	.	.	08 09
—	70¾	—	Chartham	d	.	.	.	00 09	.	.	01 13	.	.	.	06 44	.	.	.	07 23	.	.	.	.	08 12
—	73¾	—	**Canterbury West** 4	d	.	.	.	00a15	.	.	01a18	.	.	.	06 50	.	.	.	07 30	.	.	.	.	08b20
—	75¾	—	Sturry	d	.	.	.	.	.	.	.	.	.	.	06 55	.	.	.	07 34	.	.	.	.	08 24
64½	—	—	Westenhanger	d	23p27	23p30	00 02	.	00 30	.	.	01 07	05 43	06 21	.	.	06 44	07 12	.	.	.	.	08 05	.
65¾	—	—	Sandling	d	23p30	23p33	00 05	.	00 33	.	.	01 10	05 46	06 24	.	.	06 47	07 15	.	.	.	.	08 08	.
69¾	—	—	Folkestone West	d	23p35	23p38	00 10	.	00 38	.	.	01 15	05 51	06 29	.	.	06 52	07 20	.	.	.	.	08 13	.
70	—	—	**Folkestone Central**	d	23p38	23p41	00 13	.	00 41	.	.	01 18	05 54	06 33	.	.	06 55	07 23	.	.	←	.	08 15	.
77¼	—	—	**Dover Priory** 4 ⛴	a	23p50	23p52	00 25	.	00 52	.	.	01 30	06 05	06 44	.	.	07 06	07 35	.	.		.	08 27	.
—	—	—		d	23p50	23p54	.	.	.	.	.	.	06 06	.	.	.	07 12	07 53 →	.	.	07 53	.	08 28	.
82¼	—	—	Martin Mill	d	23p59	00 03	.	.	.	.	.	.	06 15	.	.	.	07 21		.	.	08 02	.	08 37	.
85	—	—	Walmer	d	00 04	00 07	.	.	.	.	.	.	06 19	.	.	.	07 25	.	.	.	08 06	.	08 41	.
86½	—	—	**Deal**	d	00 07	00 11	.	.	.	.	.	.	06 22	.	.	.	07 29	.	.	.	08 11	.	08 45	.
90¾	—	0	Sandwich	d	00 14	00 17	.	.	.	.	.	.	06c33	.	.	.	07 35	.	.	.	08 19	.	08 51	.
—	84¾	4½	Minster 4	d	.	.	.	.	.	.	.	.	.	.	07 06	.	.	.	07 45	.	08e31	.	.	08 36
99	88¾	—	**Ramsgate** 4 ✈	a	00 25	00 30	.	.	.	.	.	.	06 45	.	07 12	.	07 48	.	07 52	.	08 38	.	09 04	08 42
100	89¾	—	Dumpton Park	a	.	.	.	.	.	.	.	.	*06 52*	.	*07 24*	.	*07 54*	.	07 58	.	.	.	.	08 45
101½	91	—	Broadstairs	a	.	.	.	.	.	.	.	.	*06 55*	.	*07 27*	.	*07 57*	.	08 01	.	*08 48*	.	.	08 48
104½	94¼	—	**Margate** 4	a	.	.	.	.	.	.	.	.	*06 59*	.	*07 31*	.	*08 01*	.	08 06	.	*08 53*	.	.	08 53

For general notes see front of timetable
For details of catering facilities see Directory of Train Operators

A To Faversham (Table 212)
b Arr. 0817
c Arr. 4 minutes earlier
e Arr. 0826

London and Tonbridge → Ashford International, Folkestone, Dover, Canterbury West, Ramsgate and Margate

For details of Bank Holiday service alterations please see first page of Table 195

Network Diagram - see first page of Table 206

		SE 64 1	SE 4 1	SE 64 1	SE 64 1		SE 61	SE 2 1	SE 64 1		SE 4 1	SE 55 A	SE 4 1	SE 64 1	SE 90 1	SE 90 1	SE 64 1		SE 61	SE 2 1	SE 64 1		SE 4 1 B 🍴	SE 8	SE 61
London Charing Cross 4	⊖ d		07 00					07 28			07 52		08 22		08 54	08 58				09 30			09 53	10 00	
London Waterloo (East) 4	⊖ d		07 03					07 31			07 55		08 25		08 57	09 01				09 33			09 56	10 03	
London Cannon Street 4	⊖ d		*06 52*					*07 22*			*07 54*		*08 20*		*08 54*					*09 30*					
London Bridge 4	⊖ d		07 08					07 36			08 02		08 30		09 02	09 08				09 38				10 08	
Orpington 4	d		07 26					07 55			08 20		08 48			09 26				09 54				10 26	
Sevenoaks 4	d		07 36					08 05			08 30		08 58			09 36				10 04				10 36	
Gatwick Airport 10	✈ d		*06b37*					*07b13*			*07b41*		*08b04*		*08b37*					*09b23*					
Redhill	d		*06 58*					*07 35*			*08 05*	08 29	*08 29*		*08 59*					*09 44*					
Tonbridge 4	a		07 44					08 15			08 38	08 59	09 06		09 35	09 47				10 15			10 31	10 47	
	d		07 49					08 23			08 40	09 00	09 08		09 35	09 47				10 15			10 31	10 47	
Paddock Wood 4	d		07 56				08 09	08 30			08 47	09 08	09 15		09 42	09 54			10 03	10 22				10 54	11 01
Maidstone West 4	a		*08 29*				08 29				*09 28*	09 28				*10 23*			10 23	*11 21*					11 21
Marden	d		08 02								08 53		09 21			10 00								11 00	
Staplehurst	d		08 06					08 38			08 57		09 25		09 51	10 05				10 31				11 05	
Headcorn 4	d		08 11					08 43			09 02		09 30			10 10				10 36				11 10	
Pluckley	d		08 18								09 09		09 37			10 17								11 17	
London Victoria 15	⊖ d	06 47	*06 47*		07 19			*07 19*						08 18	*08 18*		09 19			*09 19*					
Bromley South 4	d	07 04	*07 04*		07 36			*07 36*						08 39	*08 39*		09 37			*09 37*					
Maidstone East 4	d	07 49	*07 49*		08 21			*08 21*						09 17			10 14			*10 14*					
Ashford International	a	08 21	08 27	←	08 53			08 55	←	09 17			09 45	09 46	10 05	10 25	10 43			10 48	←	10 54		11 26	
	d	08 32	08 28	08 32	09 03			09 02	09 03	09 20	09 24		09 50	09 51	10 09	10 27	10 50			10 48	10 50	10 58	11 01		
Rye	a	*08 53*	*09 13*		→						*09 53*					*10 53*	→						*11 53*		
Wye	d	→		08 39					09 09					09 57									11 08		
Chilham	d			08 45					09 15					10 03									11 14		
Chartham	d			08 49					09 19					10 07									11 18		
Canterbury West 4	d			08 55					09a24		09 42			10a12		10 46					11a06		11 24		
Sturry	d			08 59							09 47					10 50							11 29		
Westenhanger	d		08 37					09 11					09 59		10 18							11 08			
Sandling	d		08 40					09 14					10 02		10 21							11 11			
Folkestone West	d		08 45					09 19					10 07		10 26							11 16			
Folkestone Central	d		08 48					09 22		09 35			10 10		10 29					11 03		11 18			
Dover Priory 4	⛴ a		08 59					09 34		09 46			10 24		10 40					11 15		11 31			
	d		09 00							09 48			10 28									11 31			
Martin Mill	d		09 09							09 57			10 37									11 40			
Walmer	d		09 13							10 01			10 41									11 45			
Deal	d		09 17							10 05			10 45									11 48			
Sandwich	d		09 23							10 11			10 51									11 55			
Minster 4	d			09 10							09 58					11 01							11 40		
Ramsgate 4	✈ a		09 35	09 17						10 25	10 04		11 05			11 09						12 07	11 46		
Dumpton Park	a		09 40	*09 24*							10 08					11 13									
Broadstairs	a		09 43	*09 28*						*11 03*	10 11		*11 16*			11 16									
Margate 4	a		09 48	*09 32*						*11 08*	10 16		*11 22*			11 22									

For general notes see front of timetable
For details of catering facilities see Directory of Train Operators

A To Strood (Table 208)
B 🍴 to Ramsgate
b Change at Redhill and Tonbridge

For details of Bank Holiday service alterations please see first page of Table 195

London and Tonbridge → Ashford International, Folkestone, Dover, Canterbury West, Ramsgate and Margate

Network Diagram - see first page of Table 206

		SE		SE	SE	SE			SE	SE	SE		SE	SE	SE		SE	SE	SE			SE	SE	SE	
		90		64	8	4			8	61	90		64	8	4		8	61	90			64	8	4	
		1		1	1	1			1		1		1	1	1		1		1			1	1	1	
		A				A					A				A				B					A	
		⚮				⚮					⚮				⚮				⚮					⚮	
London Charing Cross 4	⊖ d	10 23			10 30	10 53			11 00		11 23			11 30	11 53		12 00		12 23				12 30	12 53	
London Waterloo (East) 4	⊖ d	10 26			10 33	10 56			11 03		11 26			11 33	11 56		12 03		12 26				12 33	12 56	
London Cannon Street 4	⊖ d				10 30									11 30									12 30		
London Bridge 4	⊖ d				10 38				11 08					11 38			12 08						12 38		
Orpington 4	d				10 54				11 26					11 54			12 26						12 54		
Sevenoaks 4	d				11 04				11 36					12 04			12 36						13 04		
Gatwick Airport 10	✈ d	09 52			10b10									11b08									12b08		
Redhill	d	10 07			10 39									11 39									12 39		
Tonbridge 4	a	11 02			11 15	11 30			11 47		12 02			12 15	12 30		12 47		13 02				13 15	13 30	
	d	11 03			11 15	11 31			11 47		12 03			12 15	12 31		12 47		13 03				13 15	13 31	
Paddock Wood 4	d	11 10			11 22				11 54	12 06	12 10			12 22			12 54	13 06	13 10				13 22		
Maidstone West 4	a									12 26								13 26							
Marden	d								12 00								13 00								
Staplehurst	d	11 18			11 31				12 05		12 18			12 31			13 05		13 18				13 31		
Headcorn 4	d				11 36				12 10					12 36			13 10						13 36		
Pluckley	d								12 17								13 17								
London Victoria 15	⊖ d	09c48		10 18		10 18					10c48		11 18		11 18				11c48			12 18		12 18	
Bromley South 4	d	10c04		10 34		10 34					11c04		11 34		11 34				12c04			12 34		12 34	
Maidstone East 4	d	11 05		11 13							12 05		12 13						13 05			13 13			
Ashford International	a	11 32		11 43	11 50	11 53			12 26		12 32		12 43	12 50	12 53		13 26		13 32			13 43	13 50	13 53	
	d	11 36	11 38	11 46		11 58	12 01				12 36	12 38	12 46		12 58	13 01			13 36	13 38		13 46		13 58	14 01
Rye	a						12 53									13 53									14 53
Wye	d			11 52									12 52									13 52			
Chilham	d			11 58									12 58									13 58			
Chartham	d			12 02									13 02									14 02			
Canterbury West 4	d	11 54		12a07			12 20				12 54		13a07			13 20			13 54			14a07			14 20
Sturry	d	11 59									12 59								13 59						
Westenhanger	d		11 47									12 47								13 47					
Sandling	d		11 50									12 50								13 50					
Folkestone West	d		11 55									12 55								13 55					
Folkestone Central	d		11 58			12 12						12 58			13 12					13 58				14 12	
Dover Priory 4	⛴ a		12 10			12 24						13 10			13 24					14 10				14 24	
	d					12 25									13 25									14 25	
Martin Mill	d					12 35									13 35									14 35	
Walmer	d					12 39									13 39									14 39	
Deal	d					12 43									13 43									14 43	
Sandwich	d					12 49									13 49									14 49	
Minster 4	d	12 10									13 10								14 10						
Ramsgate 4	✈ a	12 17				13 02	12 38				13 17				14 02	13 38			14 16					15 02	14 41
Dumpton Park	a	12 24					12 43				13 24					13 43			14 20						
Broadstairs	a	12 28					12 46				13 28				14 23	13 46			14 23					15 23	
Margate 4	a	12 32					12 51				13 32				14 28	13 51			14 28					15 28	

For general notes see front of timetable
For details of catering facilities see
Directory of Train Operators

A ⚮ to Ramsgate
B ⚮ to Margate
b Change at Redhill and Tonbridge
c Change at Maidstone East and Ashford International

Table 207

Mondays to Fridays
until 10 October

London and Tonbridge → Ashford International, Folkestone, Dover, Canterbury West, Ramsgate and Margate

For details of Bank Holiday service alterations please see first page of Table 195

Network Diagram - see first page of Table 206

		SE 8 [1]	SE 61	SE 90 [1] A ✠		SE 64 [1]	SE 8	SE 18 [1] B ✠		SE 8 [1]		SE 61	SE 18 [1] ✠	SE 90 [1] C ✠		SE 8 [1]	SE 90 [1] C ✠		SE 18 [1]	SE 8 [1]	SE 61	SE 90 [1]			SE 8 [1]
London Charing Cross [4]	⊖ d	13 00		13 23			13 30	13 53		14 00				14 23		14 30	14 53			15 00		15 23			15 30
London Waterloo (East) [4]	⊖ d	13 03		13 26			13 33	13 56		14 03				14 26		14 33	14 56			15 03		15 26			15 33
London Cannon Street [4]	⊖ d						13 30									14 30									15 30
London Bridge [4]	⊖ d	13 08					13 38			14 08						14 38				15 08					15 38
Orpington [4]	d	13 26					13 54			14 26						14 54				15 26					15 54
Sevenoaks [4]	d	13 36					14 04			14 36						15 04				15 36					16 04
Gatwick Airport [10]	✈ d						13b08	13b08								14b08				14 53					15b08
Redhill	d						13 39	13 39								14 39				15 07					15 40
Tonbridge [4]	a	13 47		14 02			14 15	14 30		14 47				15 02		15 15	15 30			15 47		16 02			16 15
	d	13 47		14 03			14 15	14 31		14 47				15 03		15 15	15 31			15 47		16 03			16 15
Paddock Wood [4]	d	13 54	14 06	14 10			14 22			14 54		15 06		15 10		15 22				15 54	16 06	16 10			16 22
Maidstone West [4]	a		14 26									15 26								16 26	16 26	16 45			
Marden	d	14 00								15 00										16 00					16 28
Staplehurst	d	14 05		14 18			14 31			15 05				15 18		15 31				16 05		16 18			16 33
Headcorn [4]	d	14 10					14 36			15 10						15 36				16 10					16 38
Pluckley	d	14 17								15 17										16 17					16 45
London Victoria [15]	⊖ d			12c48		13 18		13 18						13c48			14 18					14 48			
Bromley South [4]	d			13c04		13 34		13 34						14c04			14 34					15 04			
Maidstone East [4]	d			14 05		14 13								15 05			15 21					16 05			
Ashford International	a	14 26		14 32		14 43	14 50	14 53		15 26				15 32		15 50	15 53			16 26		16 32			16 54
	d			14 36	14 38	14 46		14 58	15 01					15 36	15 39		15 58	16 01				16 36	16 39		
Rye	a								15 53									16 53							
Wye	d					14 52								15 43			16 05					16 43			
Chilham	d					14 58								15 49			16 11					16 49			
Chartham	d					15 02								15 53			16 15					16 53			
Canterbury West [4]	d			14 54		15a07			15 20					15 59			16 21					16 59			
Sturry	d			14 59					15 24					16 04			16 26					17 04			
Westenhanger	d				14 47										15 48			16 10					16 48		
Sandling	d				14 50										15 51			16 13					16 51		
Folkestone West	d				14 55										15 56			16 18					16 56		
Folkestone Central	d				14 58			15 12							15 59			16 21					16 59		
Dover Priory [4]	⛴ a				15 10			15 24							16 11			16 34	←				17 11		
	d							15 27				←			16 12 →			16 35	16 12				17 12 →		
Martin Mill	d							15 36 →				15 36						16 44	16 21						
Walmer	d											15 41						16 48	16 25						
Deal	d											15 44						16 52	16 29						
Sandwich	d											15e54						16 58	16 35						
Minster [4]	d			15 10					15 35			16f06	16 15				16 37		16g47			17 15			
Ramsgate [4]	✈ a			15 16					15 43			16 12	16 23				16 44	17 10	16 54			17 22			
Dumpton Park	a			15 20								16 16					16 50					17 52			
Broadstairs	a			15 23								16 19					16 53		17 28			17 55			
Margate [4]	a			15 28								16 24					16 58					18 00			

For general notes see front of timetable
For details of catering facilities see Directory of Train Operators

A ✠ to Margate
B ✠ to Martin Mill
C ✠ to Ramsgate
b Change at Redhill and Tonbridge
c Change at Maidstone East and Ashford International
e Arr. 1551
f Arr. 1601
g Arr. 1643

Table 207

Mondays to Fridays

until 10 October

For details of Bank Holiday service alterations please see first page of Table 195

London and Tonbridge → Ashford International, Folkestone, Dover, Canterbury West, Ramsgate and Margate

Network Diagram - see first page of Table 206

Station		SE	SE		SE	SE	SE	SE		SE	SE			SE	SE	SE	SE	SE	SE		SE		SE	SE	SE
		61	90		18	8	61	4		8	4			61	90	9	4	61	91		4		9	61	4
			1		1	1		1		1	1				1	1	1		1		1		1		1
			A					A			B										A				
			🍴					🍴			🍴						🍴				🍴				🍴
London Charing Cross 4 ⊖	d		15 53			16 00		16 23		16 30	16 46				17 12	16b50	17 34		17b20		17 56				18 16
London Waterloo (East) 4 ⊖	d		15 56			16 03		16 26		16 33	16 49				17 15	16b53	17 37		17b23		17 59				18 19
London Cannon Street 4 ⊖	d					16 00		16 22								17 20			17 44				18 04		
London Bridge 4 ⊖	d					16 08		16 31		16 39	16 54					17 04			17 28				18 08		18 12
Orpington 4	d					16 02		16 33								17 24			17 46						
Sevenoaks 4	d					16 32		16 56		17 02						17 52			18 12				18 34		18 48
Gatwick Airport 10 ✈	d					15 53					16c08					17c10									18c10
Redhill	d					16 07					16 40				17 07	17 28									18 23
Tonbridge 4	a		16 32			16 43		17 04		17 13	17 24				17 50	18 02	18 15		18 20		18 34		18 44		18 57
	d		16 33			16 43		17 05		17 13	17 25				17 51	18 03	18 16		18 21		18 35		18 45		18 57
Paddock Wood 4	d	16 25				16 50	17 02	17 12		17 20	17 32			17 52	17 58	18 11	18 23	18 23	18 28		18 43		18 52	18 57	19 05
Maidstone West 4	a	16 45				17 22	17 22				18 12			18 12		18 43		18 43						19 17	
Marden	d					16 56				17 26					18 04	18 17					18 49		18 58		
Staplehurst	d					17 01		17 20		17 31	17 40				18 09	18 22	18 32				18 53		19 03		19 13
Headcorn 4	d					17 06				17 36	17 45				18 14	18 27	18 37				18 58		19 08		19 18
Pluckley	d					17 13				17 43					18 21		18 44				19 05		19 15		
London Victoria 15 ⊖	d		15 18					15 48							16 56										17 58
Bromley South 4	d		15 34					16 04							17 15										18 18
Maidstone East 4	d		16 19					16 44			17 07				17 54										18 56
Ashford International	a		16 57			17 24		17 35		17 52	17 57				18 29	18 41	18 51		18 53		19 14		19 24		19 30
	d		17 01	17 03				17 39	17 42		18 02	18 05			18 32		18 57		18 58	18 59	19 18	19 20			19 34
Rye	a					17 53				18 21		18 53								19 21			19 53		
Wye	d		17 08						17 49			18 12			18 39				19 04			19 27			
Chilham	d		17 14						17 55			18 18			18 45				19 11			19 33			
Chartham	d		17 18						17 59			18 22			18 49				19 14			19 37			
Canterbury West 4	d		17 24						18 05			18 29			18 55				19a19			19 44			
Sturry	d		17 29						18 10			18 33			19 00							19 48			
Westenhanger	d			17 12				17 48			18 11						19 07			19 09	19 27				19 43
Sandling	d			17 15				17 51			18 14						19 10			19 12	19 30				19 46
Folkestone West	d			17 20				17 56			18 19						19 15			19 18	19 35				19 51
Folkestone Central	d			17 23				17 59			18 22						19 18			19a20	19 38				19 54
Dover Priory 4 ⛴	a			17 35	←			18 11			18 34						19 29				19 50				20 06
	d			17 36	17 12			18 12			18 36						19 30				19 55				20 06
Martin Mill	d			17 45	17 21			18 21			18 45						19 39				20 04				20 15
Walmer	d			17 49	17 25			18 25			18 49						19 43				20 08				20 20
Deal	d			17 53	17 29			18 29			18 53						19 47				20 12				20 23
Sandwich	d			17 59	17 35			18 35			18 59						19 53				20 18				20 30
Minster 4	d		17 40		17e49				18 21			18 44			19 11							20 01			
Ramsgate 4 ✈	a		17 47	18 10	17 56			18 50	18 28		19 11	18 51			19 20		20 04				20 32	20 10			20 44
Dumpton Park	a			18 15	18 15				18 50		19 15	18 55			19 50		20 08								20 52
Broadstairs	a			18 18	18 18			19 18			19 18	18 58			19 53		20 11				20 44				20 55
Margate 4	a			18 23	18 23			19 26			19 26	19 05			19 58		20 17					20 51			20 59

For general notes see front of timetable
For details of catering facilities see Directory of Train Operators

A 🍴 to Ramsgate
B 🍴 to Margate
b Change at Sevenoaks
c Change at Redhill and Tonbridge
e Arr. 1743

London and Tonbridge → Ashford International, Folkestone, Dover, Canterbury West, Ramsgate and Margate

For details of Bank Holiday service alterations please see first page of Table 195

Network Diagram - see first page of Table 206

Station		SE 3 [1]		SE 8 [1]		SE 88 A	SE 4 [1]	SE 61	SE 4 [1]		SE 4 [1]	SE 4 [1]	SE 61	SE 90 [1]	SE 4 [1]	SE 61		SE 90 [1]	SE 4 [1]	SE 8 [1]	SE 2 [1]	SE 66 [1]	SE 2 [1]		
London Charing Cross [4]	⊖ d			18 40			19 00		19 24		19 52	20 00		20 30	21 00			21 30	22 00	22 30	23 00		23 30		
London Waterloo (East) [4]	⊖ d			18 43			19 03		19 27		19 55	20 03		20 33	21 03			21 33	22 03	22 33	23 03		23 33		
London Cannon Street [4]	⊖ d	18 30					*18 50*		*19 22*		*19 52*	*20 00*		*20 30*	*21 00*					*21b00*					
London Bridge [4]	⊖ d	18 34		18 48			19 08		19 32		20 01	20 08		20 38	21 08			21 38	22 08	22 38	23 08		23 38		
Orpington [4]	d	*18 30*		19 05								*20 02*		20 55	21 24			21 54	22 24	22 54	23 24		23 56		
Sevenoaks [4]	d	18 58		19 15			19 34					20 32		21 05	21 34			22 04	22 34	23 04	23 34		00 06		
Gatwick Airport [10]	✈ d						*18c38*		*19c10*			*19c39*			*20 53*				*21 53*		*22 53*		*22 53*		
Redhill	d					18 55	*18 55*		*19 24*			*20 08*			*21 07*				*22 07*		*23 10*		*23 10*		
Tonbridge [4]	a	19 07		19 23		19 24	19 45		20 02		20 32	20 42		21 15	21 45			22 15	22 45	23 15	23 45		00 17		
	d	19 07		19 24		19 28	19 45		20 03		20 33	20 43		21 16	21 45			22 15	22 45	23 15	23 45		00 17		
Paddock Wood [4]	d	19 14		19 31		19e38	19 52	20 03	20 10		20 40	20 50	21 01	21 23	21 52	21 57		22 22	22 52	23 22	23 52		00 24		
Maidstone West [4]	a					19 58	*20 23*	20 23				*21 21*	21 21		*22 17*	22 17									
Marden	d	19 20		19 37			19 58					20 56		21 29				22 28		23 28			00 30		
Staplehurst	d	19 25		19 41			20 03		20 19		20 49	21 01		21 33	22 01			22 33	23 01	23 32	00 01		00 35		
Headcorn [4]	d	19 30		19 46			20 08		20 24		20 54	21 06		21 38	22 06			22 38	23 06	23 37	00 06		00 40		
Pluckley	d	19 37		19 53			20 15					21 13		21 45				22 45		23 44			00 47		
London Victoria [15]	⊖ d								*18 48*		*19 18*	*19 48*			*20 48*			*21 09*		*22 09*	*22 09*	23 11	*23 11*		
Bromley South [4]	d	*18 22*							*19 06*		*19 35*	*20 07*			*21 07*			*21 29*		*22 29*	*22 29*	23 30	*23 30*		
Maidstone East [4]	d	*19 08*							*20 08*		*20 20*	*20 44*			*21 44*			*22 13*		*23 13*	*23 13*	00 14			
Ashford International	a	19 45		20 02			20 24		20 36		21 06	21 21		21 53	22 17			22 52	23 17	23 52	00 17	00 43	00 54		
	d	19 51	19 53	20 06					20 40	20 42	21 07	21 24		21 54	22 20			22 53	23 20	23 53	00 20	00 57	00 58		
Rye	a		*20 21*				*20 53*					*21 53*			*22 47*										
Wye	d		19 59	20 13						20 49	21 14			22 01				23 00		23 58		01 03			
Chilham	d		20 05	20 19						20 55	21 20			22 07				23 06		00 05		01 09			
Chartham	d		20 09	20 23						20 59	21 24			22 11				23 10		00 09		01 13			
Canterbury West [4]	d		20 15	20 30						21 05	21 30			22 17				23 16		00a15		01a18			
Sturry	d		20 20	20 34						21 10	21 35			22 21				23 21							
Westenhanger	d	20 00							20 49			21 33			22 30				23 30		00 30		01 07		
Sandling	d	20 03							20 52			21 36			22 33				23 33		00 33		01 10		
Folkestone West	d	20 09							20 58			21 41			22 38				23 38		00 38		01 15		
Folkestone Central	d	20 12							21 01			21 44			22 41				23 41		00 41		01 18		
Dover Priory [4]	⛴ a	20 26							21 12			21 56			22 52				23 52		00 52		01 30		
	d								21 14			22 00			22 54				23 54						
Martin Mill	d								21 23			22 09			23 03				00 03						
Walmer	d								21 27			22 13			23 07				00 07						
Deal	d								21 31			22 17			23 11				00 11						
Sandwich	d								21 37			22 23			23 17				00 17						
Minster [4]	d		20 31	20 45						21 21	21 46			22 32				23 32							
Ramsgate [4]	✈ a		20 37	20 52					21 48	21 27	21 53	22 36		22 41	23 30			23 39	00 30						
Dumpton Park	a		20 41						*21 57*	21 31				*22 55*				23 43							
Broadstairs	a		20 44	*21 34*					*22 00*	21 34	*22 15*			*22 58*	*23 46*			23 46							
Margate [4]	a		20 51						*22 04*	21 39	*22 19*			*23 03*	*23 51*			23 51							

For general notes see front of timetable
For details of catering facilities see Directory of Train Operators

A To Strood (Table 208)
b Change at London Bridge and Orpington
c Change at Redhill and Tonbridge
e Arr. 1935

Table 207

Mondays to Fridays
from 13 October

For details of Bank Holiday service alterations please see first page of Table 195

London and Tonbridge → Ashford International, Folkestone, Dover, Canterbury West, Ramsgate and Margate

Network Diagram - see first page of Table 206

		SE MO 4 1	SE MX 4 1	SE MO 2 1	SE MX 8 1	SE MX 2 1	SE MO 8 1	SE MX 66 1	SE MX 2 1	SE 8 1	SE 61 1 A	SE 64 1	SE 61	SE 61 1	SE 18 1	SE 64 1	SE 61	SE 18 1	SE 61	SE 4 1	SE 66 1	SE 64 1	SE 4 1
London Charing Cross 4	⊖ d	22p00	22p00	22p30	22p30	23p00	23p30		23p30						05 30					06 25			07 00
London Waterloo (East) 4	⊖ d	22p03	22p03	22p33	22p33	23p03	23p33		23p33						05 33					06 28			07 03
London Cannon Street 4	⊖ d																			06 22			06 52
London Bridge 4	⊖ d	22p08	22p08	22p38	22p38	23p08	23p38		23p38						05 38					06 33			07 08
Orpington 4	d	22p24	22p24	22p54	22p54	23p24	23p54		23p56						05 54					06 50			07 26
Sevenoaks 4	d	22p34	22p34	23p04	23p04	23p34	00 04		00 06						06 11					07 00			07 36
Gatwick Airport 10 ✈	d						22 53		22 53											05 54			06b37
Redhill	d						23 10		23 10											06 09			06 58
Tonbridge 4	a	22p43	22p45	23p15	23p15	23p45	00 13		00 17						06 21					07 10			07 44
	d	22p43	22p45	23p15	23p15	23p45	00 13		00 17	04 53			05 47		06 22					07 11			07 49
Paddock Wood 4	d	22p50	22p52	23p22	23p22	23p52	00 20		00 24	05 00			05 55		06 29		06 32		07 06	07 18			07 56
Maidstone West 4	a									06 15			06 15		07 26		06 52		07 26				08 29
Marden	d			23p28	23p28				00 30	05 06					06 35					07 24			08 02
Staplehurst	d	22p59	23p01	23p33	23p32	00 01	00 29		00 35	05 10					06 39					07 28			08 06
Headcorn 4	d		23p06	23p38	23p37	00 06			00 40	05 15					06 44					07 33			08 11
Pluckley	d			23p45	23p44				00 47	05 21					06 51					07 40			08 18
London Victoria 15	⊖ d					22 09		23p11	23 11												06 10	06 47	06 47
Bromley South 4	d					22 29		23p30	23 30												06 30	07 04	07 04
Maidstone East 4	d					23 13		00 14	00 14			05 56				06 33					07 23	07 49	07 49
Ashford International	a	23p12	23p17	23p52	23p52	00 17	00 42	00 43	00 54	05 29		06 25			06 59	07 02				07 52	07 52	08 21	08 27
	d	23p18	23p20	23p53	23p53	00 20		00 57	00 58	05 34	06 12	06 28		06 35	07 03	07 07				07 55	07 56	08 32	08 28
Rye	a									06 47		07 09				07 53						08 53	09 13
Wye	d				23p58			01 03				06 34				07 13					08 02 ⟶		
Chilham	d				00 05			01 09				06 41				07 19					08 09		
Chartham	d				00 09			01 13				06 44				07 23					08 12		
Canterbury West 4	d				00a15			01a18				06 50				07 30					08c20		
Sturry	d											06 55				07 34					08 24		
Westenhanger	d	23p27	23p30	00 02		00 30			01 07	05 43	06 21			06 44	07 12					08 05			08 37
Sandling	d	23p30	23p33	00 05		00 33			01 10	05 46	06 24			06 47	07 15					08 08			08 40
Folkestone West	d	23p35	23p38	00 10		00 38			01 15	05 51	06 29			06 52	07 20					08 13			08 45
Folkestone Central	d	23p38	23p41	00 13		00 41			01 18	05 54	06 33			06 55	07 23					08 15			08 48
Dover Priory 4	⛴ a	23p50	23p52	00 25		00 52			01 30	06 05	06 44			07 06	07 35			⟵		08 27			08 59
	d	23p50	23p54							06 06				07 12	07 53 ⟶			07 53		08 28			09 00
Martin Mill	d	23p59	00 03							06 15				07 21				08 02		08 37			09 09
Walmer	d	00 04	00 07							06 19				07 25				08 06		08 41			09 13
Deal	d	00 07	00 11							06 22				07 29				08 11		08 45			09 17
Sandwich	d	00 14	00 17							06e33				07 35				08 19		08 51			09 23
Minster 4	d											07 06				07 45		08f31			08 36		
Ramsgate 4	✈ a	00 25	00 30							06 45		07 12		07 48		07 52		08 38		09 04	08 42		09 35
Dumpton Park	a									06 49		07 24		07 54		07 58					08 45		09 40
Broadstairs	a									06 52		07 27		07 57		08 01		08 48			08 48		09 43
Margate 4	a									06 56		07 31		08 01		08 06		08 53			08 53		09 48

For general notes see front of timetable
For details of catering facilities see Directory of Train Operators

A To Faversham (Table 212)
b Change at Redhill and Tonbridge
c Arr. 0817
e Arr. 4 minutes earlier
f Arr. 0826

London and Tonbridge → Ashford International, Folkestone, Dover, Canterbury West, Ramsgate and Margate

For details of Bank Holiday service alterations please see first page of Table 195

Network Diagram - see first page of Table 206

		SE 64 [1]	SE 64 [1]	SE 61	SE 2 [1]	SE 64 [1]	SE 4 [1]			SE 55 A	SE 4 [1]	SE 64 [1]	SE 90 [1]	SE 90 [1]	SE 64 [1]	SE 61	SE 2 [1]	SE 64 [1]		SE 4 [1] B 🍴		SE 8	SE 61	SE 90 [1] B 🍴	
London Charing Cross [4]	⊖ d				07 28		07 52				08 22		08 54	08 58			09 30			09 53		10 00		10 23	
London Waterloo (East) [4]	⊖ d				07 31		07 55				08 25		08 57	09 01			09 33			09 56		10 03		10 26	
London Cannon Street [4]	⊖ d				*07 22*		*07 54*				*08 20*		*08 54*				*09 30*								
London Bridge [4]	⊖ d				07 36		08 02				08 30		09 02	09 08			09 38					10 08			
Orpington [4]	d				07 55		08 20				08 48			09 26			09 54					10 26			
Sevenoaks [4]	d				08 05		08 30				08 58			09 36			10 04					10 36			
Gatwick Airport [10]	✈ d				*07b13*		*07b41*				*08b04*		*08b37*				*09b23*							*09 52*	
Redhill	d				*07 35*		*08 05*			08 29	*08 29*		*08 59*				*09 44*							*10 07*	
Tonbridge [4]	a				08 15		08 38			08 59	09 06		09 35	09 47			10 15			10 31		10 47		11 02	
	d				08 23		08 40			09 00	09 08		09 35	09 47			10 15			10 31		10 47		11 03	
Paddock Wood [4]	d			08 09	08 30		08 47			09 08	09 15		09 42	09 54		10 03	10 22					10 54	11 01	11 10	
Maidstone West [4]	a			08 29			*09 28*			09 28				*10 23*		10 23	*11 21*						11 21		
Marden	d						08 53				09 21			10 00								11 00			
Staplehurst	d				08 38		08 57				09 25		09 51	10 05			10 31					11 05		11 18	
Headcorn [4]	d				08 43		09 02				09 30			10 10			10 36					11 10			
Pluckley	d						09 09				09 37			10 17								11 17			
London Victoria [15]	⊖ d		07 19		*07 19*							08 18	*08 18*		09 19		*09 19*							*09c48*	
Bromley South [4]	d		07 36		*07 36*							08 39	*08 39*		09 37		*09 37*							*10c04*	
Maidstone East [4]	d		08 21		*08 21*							09 17			10 14		*10 14*							*11 05*	
Ashford International	a	←	08 53		08 55	←	09 17				09 45	09 46	10 05	10 25	10 43		10 48	←		10 54		11 26		11 32	
	d	08 32	09 03		09 02	09 03	09 20	09 24			09 50	09 51	10 09	10 27	10 50		10 48	10 50		10 58	11 01			11 36	11 38
Rye	a		↪					*09 53*						*10 53*	→						*11 53*				
Wye	d	08 39				09 09						09 57									11 08				
Chilham	d	08 45				09 15						10 03									11 14				
Chartham	d	08 49				09 19						10 07									11 18				
Canterbury West [4]	d	08 55				09a24		09 42				10a12		10 46				11a06			11 24			11 54	
Sturry	d	08 59						09 47						10 50							11 29			11 59	
Westenhanger	d				09 11						09 59		10 18							11 08					11 47
Sandling	d				09 14						10 02		10 21							11 11					11 50
Folkestone West	d				09 19						10 07		10 26							11 16					11 55
Folkestone Central	d				09 22		09 35				10 10		10 29				11 03			11 18					11 58
Dover Priory [4]	⛴ a				09 34		09 46				10 24		10 40				11 15			11 31					12 10
	d						09 48				10 28									11 31					
Martin Mill	d						09 57				10 37									11 40					
Walmer	d						10 01				10 41									11 45					
Deal	d						10 05				10 45									11 48					
Sandwich	d						10 11				10 51									11 55					
Minster [4]	d	09 10						09 58						11 01							11 40			12 10	
Ramsgate [4]	✈ a	09 17					10 25	10 04			11 05			11 09						12 07	11 46			12 17	
Dumpton Park	a	*09 24*						10 08						11 13										*12 24*	
Broadstairs	a	*09 28*					*11 03*	10 11			*11 16*			11 16										*12 28*	
Margate [4]	a	*09 32*					*11 08*	10 16			*11 22*			11 22										*12 32*	

For general notes see front of timetable
For details of catering facilities see Directory of Train Operators

A To Strood (Table 208)
B 🍴 to Ramsgate
b Change at Redhill and Tonbridge
c Change at Maidstone East and Ashford International

For details of Bank Holiday service alterations please see first page of Table 195

London and Tonbridge → Ashford International, Folkestone, Dover, Canterbury West, Ramsgate and Margate

Network Diagram - see first page of Table 206

Station		SE 64 [1]	SE 8 [1]	SE 4 [1] A ⚒		SE 8 [1]	SE 61	SE 90 [1] A ⚒		SE 64 [1]	SE 8 [1]	SE 4 [1] A ⚒		SE 8 [1]	SE 61	SE 90 [1] B ⚒		SE 64 [1]	SE 8 [1]	SE 4 [1] A ⚒		SE 8 [1]	SE 61
London Charing Cross [4] ⊖	d		10 30	10 53		11 00		11 23			11 30	11 53		12 00		12 23			12 30	12 53		13 00	
London Waterloo (East) [4] ⊖	d		10 33	10 56		11 03		11 26			11 33	11 56		12 03		12 26			12 33	12 56		13 03	
London Cannon Street [4] ⊖	d		*10 30*								*11 30*								*12 30*				
London Bridge [4] ⊖	d		10 38			11 08					11 38			12 08					12 38			13 08	
Orpington [4]	d		10 54			11 26					11 54			12 26					12 54			13 26	
Sevenoaks [4]	d		11 04			11 36					12 04			12 36					13 04			13 36	
Gatwick Airport [10] ✈	d		*10b10*								*11b08*								*12b08*				
Redhill	d		*10 39*								*11 39*								*12 39*				
Tonbridge [4]	a		11 15	11 30		11 47		12 02			12 15	12 30		12 47		13 02			13 15	13 30		13 47	
	d		11 15	11 31		11 47		12 03			12 15	12 31		12 47		13 03			13 15	13 31		13 47	
Paddock Wood [4]	d		11 22			11 54	12 06	12 10			12 22			12 54	13 06	13 10			13 22			13 54	14 06
Maidstone West [4]	a						12 26								13 26								14 26
Marden	d					12 00								13 00								14 00	
Staplehurst	d		11 31			12 05		12 18			12 31			13 05		13 18			13 31			14 05	
Headcorn [4]	d		11 36			12 10					12 36			13 10					13 36			14 10	
Pluckley	d					12 17								13 17								14 17	
London Victoria [15] ⊖	d	10 18		*10 18*				*10c48*		11 18		*11 18*				*11c48*		12 18		*12 18*			
Bromley South [4]	d	10 34		*10 34*				*11c04*		11 34		*11 34*				*12c04*		12 34		*12 34*			
Maidstone East [4]	d	11 13						*12 05*		12 13						*13 05*		13 13					
Ashford International	a	11 43	11 50	11 53		12 26		12 32		12 43	12 50	12 53		13 26		13 32		13 43	13 50	13 53		14 26	
	d	11 46		11 58	12 01			12 36	12 38	12 46		12 58	13 01			13 36	13 38	13 46		13 58	14 01		
Rye	a				*12 53*								*13 53*								*14 53*		
Wye	d	11 52								12 52								13 52					
Chilham	d	11 58								12 58								13 58					
Chartham	d	12 02								13 02								14 02					
Canterbury West [4]	d	12a07			12 20			12 54		13a07			13 20			13 54		14a07			14 20		
Sturry	d							12 59								13 59							
Westenhanger	d								12 47								13 47						
Sandling	d								12 50								13 50						
Folkestone West	d								12 55								13 55						
Folkestone Central	d			12 12					12 58			13 12					13 58			14 12			
Dover Priory [4] ⛴	a			12 24					13 10			13 24					14 10			14 24			
	d			12 25								13 25								14 25			
Martin Mill	d			12 35								13 35								14 35			
Walmer	d			12 39								13 39								14 39			
Deal	d			12 43								13 43								14 43			
Sandwich	d			12 49								13 49								14 49			
Minster [4]	d							13 10								14 10							
Ramsgate [4] ✈	a			13 02	12 38			13 17				14 02	13 38			14 16				15 02	14 41		
Dumpton Park	a				12 43			*13 24*					13 43			14 20							
Broadstairs	a				12 46			*13 28*				*14 23*	13 46			14 23				*15 23*			
Margate [4]	a				12 51			*13 32*				*14 28*	13 51			14 28				*15 28*			

For general notes see front of timetable
For details of catering facilities see Directory of Train Operators

A ⚒ to Ramsgate
B ⚒ to Margate
b Change at Redhill and Tonbridge
c Change at Maidstone East and Ashford International

Mondays to Fridays
from 13 October

London and Tonbridge → Ashford International, Folkestone, Dover, Canterbury West, Ramsgate and Margate

For details of Bank Holiday service alterations please see first page of Table 195

Network Diagram - see first page of Table 206

		SE 90 1 A [trolley]		SE 64 1		SE 8	SE 18 1 B [trolley]		SE 8 1	SE 61	SE 18 1 [trolley]	SE 90 1 C [trolley]		SE 8 1		SE 90 1 C [trolley]		SE 18 1	SE 8 1	SE 61	SE 90 1		SE 8 1	SE 61	
London Charing Cross 4	⊖ d	13 23				13 30	13 53		14 00			14 23		14 30		14 53			15 00		15 23		15 30		
London Waterloo (East) 4	⊖ d	13 26				13 33	13 56		14 03			14 26		14 33		14 56			15 03		15 26		15 33		
London Cannon Street 4	⊖ d					*13 30*								*14 30*									*15 30*		
London Bridge 4	⊖ d					13 38			14 08					14 38					15 08				15 38		
Orpington 4	d					13 54			14 26					14 54					15 26				15 54		
Sevenoaks 4	d					14 04			14 36					15 04					15 36				16 04		
Gatwick Airport 10	✈ d					*13b08*	*13b08*							*14b08*					*14 53*				*15b08*		
Redhill	d					*13 39*	*13 39*							*14 39*					*15 07*				*15 40*		
Tonbridge 4	a	14 02				14 15	14 30		14 47			15 02		15 15		15 30			15 47		16 02		16 15		
	d	14 03				14 15	14 31		14 47			15 03		15 15		15 31			15 47		16 03		16 15		
Paddock Wood 4	d	14 10				14 22			14 54	15 06		15 10		15 22					15 54	16 06	16 10		16 22	16 25	
Maidstone West 4	a									15 26									*16 26*	16 26	*16 45*			16 45	
Marden	d								15 00										16 00				16 28		
Staplehurst	d	14 18				14 31			15 05			15 18		15 31					16 05		16 18		16 33		
Headcorn 4	d					14 36			15 10					15 36					16 10				16 38		
Pluckley	d								15 17										16 17				16 45		
London Victoria 15	⊖ d	*12c48*		13 18			*13 18*					*13c48*				*14 18*					*14 48*				
Bromley South 4	d	*13c04*		13 34			*13 34*					*14c04*				*14 34*					*15 04*				
Maidstone East 4	d	*14 05*		14 13								*15 05*				*15 21*					*16 05*				
Ashford International	a	14 32		14 43		14 50	14 53		15 26			15 32		15 50		15 53			16 26		16 32		16 54		
	d	14 36	14 38	14 46			14 58	15 01				15 36	15 39			15 58	16 01				16 36	16 39			
Rye	a							*15 53*									*16 53*								
Wye	d			14 52								15 43				16 05					16 43				
Chilham	d			14 58								15 49				16 11					16 49				
Chartham	d			15 02								15 53				16 15					16 53				
Canterbury West 4	d	14 54		15a07				15 20				15 59				16 21					16 59				
Sturry	d	14 59						15 24				16 04				16 26					17 04				
Westenhanger	d		14 47										15 48				16 10					16 48			
Sandling	d		14 50										15 51				16 13					16 51			
Folkestone West	d		14 55										15 56				16 18					16 56			
Folkestone Central	d		14 58				15 12						15 59				16 21					16 59			
Dover Priory 4	⛴ a		15 10				15 24						16 11				16 34	←				17 11			
	d						15 27				←		16 12 →				16 35	16 12				17 12 →			
Martin Mill	d						15 36 →				15 36						16 44	16 21							
Walmer	d										15 41						16 48	16 25							
Deal	d										15 44						16 52	16 29							
Sandwich	d										15e54						16 58	16 35							
Minster 4	d	15 10						15 35			16f06	16 15				16 37		16g47			17 15				
Ramsgate 4	✈ a	15 16						15 43			16 12	16 23				16 44	17 10	16 54			17 22				
Dumpton Park	a	15 20									16 16					*16 50*					*17 52*				
Broadstairs	a	15 23									16 19					*16 53*		*17 28*			*17 55*				
Margate 4	a	15 28									16 24					*16 58*					*18 00*				

For general notes see front of timetable
For details of catering facilities see Directory of Train Operators

A [trolley] to Margate
B [trolley] to Martin Mill
C [trolley] to Ramsgate
b Change at Redhill and Tonbridge
c Change at Maidstone East and Ashford International
e Arr. 1551
f Arr. 1601
g Arr. 1643

Table 207

Mondays to Fridays
from 13 October

For details of Bank Holiday service alterations please see first page of Table 195

London and Tonbridge → Ashford International, Folkestone, Dover, Canterbury West, Ramsgate and Margate

Network Diagram - see first page of Table 206

		SE		SE	SE	SE	SE		SE	SE		SE	SE	SE	SE	SE	SE		SE		SE	SE	SE
		90		18	8	61	4		8	4		61	90	9	4	61	91		4		9	61	4
		1		1	1		1		1	1			1	1	1		1		1		1		1
		A					A			B									A				
		[trolley]					[trolley]			[trolley]					[trolley]				[trolley]				[trolley]
London Charing Cross 4	⊖ d	15 53			16 00		16 23		16 30	16 46			17 12	16b50	17 34		17b20		17 56				18 16
London Waterloo (East) 4	⊖ d	15 56			16 03		16 26		16 33	16 49			17 15	16b53	17 37		17b23		17 59				18 19
London Cannon Street 4	⊖ d				16 00		16 22							17 20			17 44				18 04		
London Bridge 4	⊖ d				16 08		16 31		16 39	16 54				17 04			17 28				18 08		18 12
Orpington 4	d				16 02		16c02							17 24			17 46						
Sevenoaks 4	d				16 32		16 56		17 02					17 52			18 12				18 34		18 48
Gatwick Airport 10	✈ d				15 53					16e08				17e10									18e10
Redhill	d				16 07					16 40			17 07	17 28									18 23
Tonbridge 4	a	16 32			16 43		17 04		17 13	17 24			17 50	18 02	18 15		18 20		18 34		18 44		18 57
	d	16 33			16 43		17 05		17 13	17 25			17 51	18 03	18 15		18 21		18 35		18 45		18 57
Paddock Wood 4	d				16 50	17 02	17 12		17 20	17 32		17 52	17 58	18 11	18 23	18 23	18 28		18 43		18 52	18 57	19 05
Maidstone West 4	a				17 22	17 22				18 12		18 12		18 43		18 43						19 17	
Marden	d				16 56				17 26				18 04	18 17					18 49		18 58		
Staplehurst	d				17 01		17 20		17 31	17 40			18 09	18 22	18 31				18 53		19 03		19 13
Headcorn 4	d				17 06				17 36	17 45			18 14	18 27	18 36				18 58		19 08		19 18
Pluckley	d				17 13				17 43				18 21		18 43				19 05		19 15		
London Victoria 15	⊖ d	15 18					15 48						16 56										17 58
Bromley South 4	d	15 34					16 04						17 15										18 18
Maidstone East 4	d	16 19					16 44			17 07			17 54										18 56
Ashford International	a	16 57			17 25		17 35		17 53	17 57			18 29	18 42	18 51		18 53		19 14		19 24		19 30
	d	17 01	17 03				17 39	17 42		18 02	18 05		18 32		18 57		18 58	18 59	19 18	19 20			19 34
Rye	a				17 53				18 21		18 53							19 21			19 53		
Wye	d	17 08						17 49			18 12		18 39				19 04			19 27			
Chilham	d	17 14						17 55			18 18		18 45				19 11			19 33			
Chartham	d	17 18						17 59			18 22		18 49				19 14			19 37			
Canterbury West 4	d	17 24						18 05			18 29		18 55				19a21			19 44			
Sturry	d	17 29						18 10			18 33		19 00							19 48			
Westenhanger	d		17 12				17 48			18 11					19 06			19 09	19 27				19 43
Sandling	d		17 15				17 51			18 14					19 09			19 12	19 30				19 46
Folkestone West	d		17 20				17 56			18 19					19 14			19 18	19 35				19 51
Folkestone Central	d		17 23				17 59			18 22					19 17			19a20	19 38				19 54
Dover Priory 4	⛴ a		17 35	←			18 11			18 34					19 29				19 50				20 06
	d		17 36	17 12			18 12			18 36					19 29				19 55				20 06
Martin Mill	d		17 45	17 21			18 21			18 45					19 38				20 04				20 15
Walmer	d		17 49	17 25			18 25			18 49					19 43				20 08				20 20
Deal	d		17 53	17 29			18 29			18 53					19 46				20 12				20 23
Sandwich	d		17 59	17 35			18 35			18 59					19 53				20 18				20 30
Minster 4	d	17 40		17f49				18 21			18 44		19 11							20 01			
Ramsgate 4	✈ a	17 47	18 10	17 56			18 50	18 28		19 11	18 51		19 20		20 04				20 32	20 10			20 44
Dumpton Park	a		18 15	18 15				18 50		19 15	18 55		19 50		20 07								20 52
Broadstairs	a		18 18	18 18			19 18			19 18	18 58		19 53		20 10				20 44				20 55
Margate 4	a		18 23	18 23			19 26			19 26	19 05		19 58		20 18					20 51			20 59

For general notes see front of timetable
For details of catering facilities see Directory of Train Operators

A [trolley] to Ramsgate
B [trolley] to Margate
b Change at Sevenoaks
c Until 24 October dep. 1633
e Change at Redhill and Tonbridge
f Arr. 1743

London and Tonbridge → Ashford International, Folkestone, Dover, Canterbury West, Ramsgate and Margate

For details of Bank Holiday service alterations please see first page of Table 195

Network Diagram - see first page of Table 206

		SE		SE		SE	SE	SE	SE		SE	SE	SE	SE		SE	SE	SE	SE	SE	SE	SE	SE		
		3		8		88	4	61	4		4	4	61	90		4	61	90	4	8	2	66	2		
		1		1			1		1		1	1		1		1		1	1	1	1	1	1		
						A																			
							🛒					🛒		🛒		🛒									
London Charing Cross 4	⊖ d			18 40			19 00		19 24		19 52	20 00		20 30		21 00		21 30	22 00	22 30	23 00		23 30		
London Waterloo (East) 4	⊖ d			18 43			19 03		19 27		19 55	20 03		20 33		21 03		21 33	22 03	22 33	23 03		23 33		
London Cannon Street 4	⊖ d	18 30					18 50		19 22		19 52	20 00		20 30		21 00				21b00					
London Bridge 4	⊖ d	18 34		18 48			19 08		19 32		20 01	20 08		20 38		21 08		21 38	22 08	22 38	23 08		23 38		
Orpington 4	d	18 30		19 05								20 02		20 55		21 24		21 54	22 24	22 54	23 24		23 56		
Sevenoaks 4	d	18 58		19 15			19 34					20 32		21 05		21 34		22 04	22 34	23 04	23 34		00 06		
Gatwick Airport 10	✈ d						18c38		19c10			19c39				20 53			21 53		22 53		22 53		
Redhill	d					18 55	18 55		19 24			20 08				21 07			22 07		23 10		23 10		
Tonbridge 4	a	19 07		19 23		19 24	19 45		20 02		20 32	20 42		21 15		21 45		22 15	22 45	23 15	23 45		00 17		
	d	19 07		19 24		19 28	19 45		20 03		20 33	20 43		21 16		21 45		22 15	22 45	23 15	23 45		00 17		
Paddock Wood 4	d	19 14		19 31		19e38	19 52	20 03	20 10		20 40	20 50	21 01	21 23		21 52	21 57	22 22	22 52	23 22	23 52		00 24		
Maidstone West 4	a					19 58	20 23	20 23				21 21	21 21			22 17	22 17								
Marden	d	19 20		19 37			19 58					20 56		21 29				22 28		23 28			00 30		
Staplehurst	d	19 25		19 41			20 03		20 19		20 49	21 01		21 33		22 01		22 33	23 01	23 32	00 01		00 35		
Headcorn 4	d	19 30		19 46			20 08		20 24		20 54	21 06		21 38		22 06		22 38	23 06	23 37	00 06		00 40		
Pluckley	d	19 37		19 53			20 15					21 13		21 45				22 45		23 44			00 47		
London Victoria 15	⊖ d								18 48		19 18	19 48				20 48		21 09		22 09	22 09	23 11	23 11		
Bromley South 4	d	18 22							19 06		19 35	20 07				21 07		21 29		22 29	22 29	23 30	23 30		
Maidstone East 4	d	19 08							20 08		20 20	20 44				21 44		22 13		23 13	23 13	00 14			
Ashford International	a	19 45		20 02			20 24		20 36		21 06	21 21		21 53		22 17		22 52	23 17	23 52	00 17	00 43	00 54		
	d	19 51	19 53	20 06					20 40	20 42	21 07	21 24		21 54		22 20		22 53	23 20	23 53	00 20	00 57	00 58		
Rye	a		20 21				20 53					21 53				22 47									
Wye	d		19 59	20 13						20 49	21 14			22 01				23 00		23 58		01 03			
Chilham	d		20 05	20 19						20 55	21 20			22 07				23 06		00 05		01 09			
Chartham	d		20 09	20 23						20 59	21 24			22 11				23 10		00 09		01 13			
Canterbury West 4	d		20 15	20 30						21 05	21 30			22 17				23 16		00a15		01a18			
Sturry	d		20 20	20 34						21 10	21 35			22 21				23 21							
Westenhanger	d	20 00							20 49			21 33				22 30			23 30		00 30		01 07		
Sandling	d	20 03							20 52			21 36				22 33			23 33		00 33		01 10		
Folkestone West	d	20 09							20 58			21 41				22 38			23 38		00 38		01 15		
Folkestone Central	d	20 12							21 01			21 44				22 41			23 41		00 41		01 18		
Dover Priory 4	⛴ a	20 26							21 12			21 56				22 52			23 52		00 52		01 30		
	d								21 14			22 00				22 54			23 54						
Martin Mill	d								21 23			22 09				23 03			00 03						
Walmer	d								21 27			22 13				23 07			00 07						
Deal	d								21 31			22 17				23 11			00 11						
Sandwich	d								21 37			22 23				23 17			00 17						
Minster 4	d		20 31	20 45						21 21	21 46			22 32				23 32							
Ramsgate 4	✈ a		20 37	20 52					21 48	21 27	21 53	22 36		22 41		23 30		23 39	00 30						
Dumpton Park	a		20 41						21 57	21 31				22 55				23 43							
Broadstairs	a		20 44	21 34					22 00	21 34	22 15			22 58		23 46		23 46							
Margate 4	a		20 51						22 04	21 39	22 19			23 03		23 51		23 51							

For general notes see front of timetable
For details of catering facilities see Directory of Train Operators

A To Strood (Table 208)
b Change at London Bridge and Orpington
c Change at Redhill and Tonbridge
e Arr. 1935

Table 207

Saturdays

London and Tonbridge → Ashford International, Folkestone, Dover, Canterbury West, Ramsgate and Margate

Network Diagram - see first page of Table 206

Station		SE	SE	SE	SE	SE	SE	SE	SE	SE	SE	SE	SE	SE	SE	SE		SE	SE	SE	SE		SE
		4	8	2	66	2	64	4	4	94	61	4	64	61	4	4		64	61	4	4		64
		1	1	1	1	1	1	1	1	1		1	1		1	1		1		1	1		1
London Charing Cross [4] ⊖	d	22p00	22p30	23p00		23p30			06 00			07 00			07 30	08 00				08 30	09 00		
London Waterloo (East) [4] ⊖	d	22p03	22p33	23p03		23p33			06 03			07 03			07 33	08 03				08 33	09 03		
London Cannon Street [4] ⊖	d																			08 30	09 00		
London Bridge [4] ⊖	d	22p08	22p38	23p08		23p38			06 08			07 08			07 38	08 08				08 38	09 08		
Orpington [4]	d	22p24	22p54	23p24		23p56		05 58	06 26			07 26			07 56	08 26				08 56	09 26		
Sevenoaks [4]	d	22p34	23p04	23p34		00 06		06 08	06 36			07 36			08 06	08 36				09 06	09 36		
Gatwick Airport [10] ✈	d					22 53			05b45			06 53				07 53				08b08	08 53		
Redhill	d					23 07			06 11			07 07				08 07				08 39	09 07		
Tonbridge [4]	a	22p45	23p15	23p45		00 17		06 18	06 47			07 47			08 14	08 46				09 14	09 47		
	d	22p45	23p15	23p45		00 17		06 19	06 47			07 47			08 15	08 47				09 15	09 47		
Paddock Wood [4]	d	22p52	23p22	23p52		00 24		06 26	06 54		07 01	07 54		08 01	08 23	08 54			09 01	09 23	09 55		
Maidstone West [4]	a								07 21		07 21	08 21		08 21		09 21			09 21		10 21		
Marden	d		23p28			00 30			07 00			08 00				09 01					10 01		
Staplehurst	d	23p01	23p32	00 01		00 35		06 34	07 05			08 05			08 32	09 05				09 32	10 06		
Headcorn [4]	d	23p06	23p37	00 06		00 40		06 39	07 10			08 10			08 37	09 11				09 37	10 11		
Pluckley	d		23p44			00 47			07 17			08 17				09 18					10 18		
London Victoria [15] ⊖	d			22 09	23p11	23 18				06 18		06 18	07 18		07 18	07 48		08 18		08 18	08c48		09 18
Bromley South [4]	d			22 29	23p30	23 34				06 34		06 34	07 34		07 34	08 04		08 34		08 34	09c04		09 34
Maidstone East [4]	d			23 13	00 14	00 19	06 19			07 19			08 19			08 50		09 13			10 05		10 13
Ashford International	a	23p17	23p52	00 17	00 43	00 54	06 48	06 50	07 26	07 48		08 24	08 48		08 48	09 26		09 43		09 49	10 26		10 43
	d	23p20	23p53	00 20	00 57	00 58	06 53	06 57	07 28	07 51		08 25	08 51		08 57	09 31	09 36	09 46		09 57	10 32	10 36	10 46
Rye	a							07 53				08 53			09 53					10 53			
Wye	d		23p58		01 03		06 59			07 57			08 57					09 52					10 52
Chilham	d		00 05		01 09		07 05			08 03			09 03					09 58					10 58
Chartham	d		00 09		01 13		07 09			08 07			09 07					10 02					11 02
Canterbury West [4]	d		00a15		01a18		07 14			08 13			09 13				09 54	10a07				10 54	11a07
Sturry	d						07 19			08 18			09 18				09 58					10 58	
Westenhanger	d	23p30		00 30		01 07		07 06	07 37			08 34			09 07					10 06			
Sandling	d	23p33		00 33		01 10		07 09	07 40			08 37			09 10					10 09			
Folkestone West	d	23p38		00 38		01 15		07 14	07 45			08 42			09 15					10 14			
Folkestone Central	d	23p41		00 41		01 18		07 17	07 48			08 45			09 18	09 46				10 17	10 47		
Dover Priory [4] ⛴	a	23p52		00 52		01 30		07 28	07 59			08 56			09 29	09 58				10 28	10 58		
	d	23p54						07 29	08 00			08 59			09 30	09 58				10 29	10 59		
Martin Mill	d	00 03						07 38	08 09			09 08			09 39	10 07				10 38	11 08		
Walmer	d	00 07						07 42	08 13			09 12			09 43	10 12				10 42	11 12		
Deal	d	00 11						07 46	08 17			09 16			09 47	10 15				10 46	11 16		
Sandwich	d	00 17						07 52	08 23			09 22			09 53	10 22				10 52	11 22		
Minster [4]	d						07 31			08 31			09 31				10 09					11 09	
Ramsgate [4] ✈	a	00 30					07 37	08 03	08 34	08 38		09 33	09 38		10 04	10 33	10 16			11 03	11 33	11 16	
Dumpton Park	a						07 40	08 24	08 38	09 24		09 37					10 19					11 19	
Broadstairs	a						07 43	08 28	08 41	09 03		09 40	10 03		10 22	11 03	10 22			11 22	11 50	11 22	
Margate [4]	a						07 48	08 32	08 46	09 08		09 45	10 08		10 27	11 08	10 27			11 27	11 55	11 27	

Station		SE	SE	SE		SE	SE	SE		SE	SE	SE		SE	SE	SE		SE	SE	SE		SE
		61	4	4		8	61	90		64	8	4		8	61	90		64	8	4		8
			1	1		1		1		1	1	1		1		1		1	1	1		1
London Charing Cross [4] ⊖	d		09 30	09 53		10 00		10 23			10 30	10 53		11 00		11 23			11 30	11 53		12 00
London Waterloo (East) [4] ⊖	d		09 33	09 56		10 03		10 26			10 33	10 56		11 03		11 26			11 33	11 56		12 03
London Cannon Street [4] ⊖	d		09 30								10 30								11 30			
London Bridge [4] ⊖	d		09 38			10 08					10 38			11 08					11 38			12 08
Orpington [4]	d		09 54			10 26					10 54			11 26					11 54			12 26
Sevenoaks [4]	d		10 04			10 36					11 04			11 36					12 04			12 36
Gatwick Airport [10] ✈	d		09b08								10b08								11b08			
Redhill	d		09 39								10 39								11 39			
Tonbridge [4]	a		10 15	10 30		10 47		11 02			11 15	11 30		11 47		12 02			12 15	12 30		12 47
	d		10 15	10 31		10 47		11 03			11 15	11 31		11 47		12 03			12 15	12 31		12 47
Paddock Wood [4]	d	10 01	10 23			10 55	11 01	11 10			11 23			11 55	12 01	12 10			12 23			12 55
Maidstone West [4]	a	10 21					11 21								12 21							
Marden	d					11 01								12 01								13 01
Staplehurst	d		10 32			11 06		11 18			11 32			12 06		12 18			12 32			13 06
Headcorn [4]	d		10 37			11 11					11 37			12 11					12 37			13 11
Pluckley	d					11 18								12 18								13 18
London Victoria [15] ⊖	d			09 18				09c48		10 18		10 18				10c48		11 18		11 18		
Bromley South [4]	d			09 34				10c04		10 34		10 34				11c04		11 34		11 34		
Maidstone East [4]	d							11 05		11 13						12 05		12 13				
Ashford International	a		10 50	10 52		11 26		11 32		11 43	11 50	11 52		12 26		12 32		12 43	12 50	12 52		13 26
	d			11 01	11 04			11 36	11 38	11 46		11 57	12 01			12 36	12 38	12 46		12 57	13 00	
Rye	a				11 53								12 53								13 53	
Wye	d									11 52								12 52				
Chilham	d									11 58								12 58				
Chartham	d									12 02								13 02				
Canterbury West [4]	d				11 22			11 54		12a07			12 20			12 54		13a07			13e20	
Sturry	d							11 59								12 59						
Westenhanger	d			11 10					11 47								12 47					
Sandling	d			11 13					11 50								12 50					
Folkestone West	d			11 18					11 55								12 55					
Folkestone Central	d			11 21					11 58			12 11					12 58			13 11		
Dover Priory [4] ⛴	a			11 32					12 09			12 23					13 09			13 23		
	d			11 33					12 10			12 25					13 10			13 25		
Martin Mill	d			11 42					12 19			12 35					13 19			13 35		
Walmer	d			11 46					12 23			12 39					13 23			13 39		
Deal	d			11 50					12 27			12 43					13 27			13 43		
Sandwich	d			11 56					12 33			12 49					13 33			13 49		
Minster [4]	d							12 10								13 10						
Ramsgate [4] ✈	a			12 07	11 41			12 17	12 44			13 02	12 38			13 17	13 44			14 02	13 38	
Dumpton Park	a				11 44			12 24					12 43			13 24					13 43	
Broadstairs	a				11 47			12 28					12 46			13 28					13 46	
Margate [4]	a				11 52			12 32					12 51			13 32					13 51	

For general notes see front of timetable
For details of catering facilities see Directory of Train Operators

b Change at Redhill and Tonbridge
c Change at Maidstone East and Ashford International
e Arr. 1317

Table 207

London and Tonbridge → Ashford International, Folkestone, Dover, Canterbury West, Ramsgate and Margate

Network Diagram - see first page of Table 206

Station		SE 61	SE 90 1 🛒		SE 64 1	SE 8 1	SE 4 1 🛒		SE 8 1	SE 61	SE 90 1 🛒		SE 64 1	SE 8 1	SE 4 1 🛒		SE 8 1	SE 61	SE 90 1 🛒		SE 64 1	SE 8 1
London Charing Cross 4	⊖ d		12 23			12 30	12 53		13 00		13 23			13 30	13 53		14 00		14 23			14 30
London Waterloo (East) 4	⊖ d		12 26			12 33	12 56		13 03		13 26			13 33	13 56		14 03		14 26			14 33
London Cannon Street 4	⊖ d					12 30								13 30								14 30
London Bridge 4	⊖ d					12 38			13 08					13 38			14 08					14 38
Orpington 4	d					12 54			13 26					13 54			14 26					14 54
Sevenoaks 4	d					13 04			13 36					14 04			14 36					15 04
Gatwick Airport 10	✈ d					12b08								13b08								14b08
Redhill	d					12 39								13 39								14 39
Tonbridge 4	a		13 02			13 15	13 30		13 47		14 02			14 15	14 30		14 47		15 02			15 15
	d		13 03			13 15	13 31		13 47		14 03			14 15	14 31		14 47		15 03			15 15
Paddock Wood 4	d	13 01	13 10			13 23			13 55	14 01	14 10			14 23			14 55	15 01	15 10			15 23
Maidstone West 4	a	13 21								14 21								15 21				
Marden	d								14 01								15 01					
Staplehurst	d		13 18			13 32			14 06		14 18			14 32			15 06		15 18			15 32
Headcorn 4	d					13 37			14 11					14 37			15 11					15 37
Pluckley	d								14 18								15 18					
London Victoria 15	⊖ d		11c48		12 18		12 18				12c48		13 18		13 18				13c48		14 18	
Bromley South 4	d		12c04		12 34		12 34				13c04		13 34		13 34				14c04		14 34	
Maidstone East 4	d		13 05		13 13						14 05		14 13						15 05		15 13	
Ashford International	a		13 32		13 43	13 50	13 52		14 26		14 32		14 43	14 50	14 52		15 26		15 32		15 43	15 50
	d		13 36	13 38	13 46		13 57	14 00			14 36	14 38	14 46		14 57	15 00			15 36	15 39	15 46	
Rye	a							14 53								15 53						
Wye	d				13 52								14 52								15 52	
Chilham	d				13 58								14 58								15 58	
Chartham	d				14 02								15 02								16 02	
Canterbury West 4	d		13 54		14a07			14e20			14 54		15a07			15f20			15 54		16a07	
Sturry	d		13 59								14 59								15 59			
Westenhanger	d			13 47								14 47								15 48		
Sandling	d			13 50								14 50								15 51		
Folkestone West	d			13 55								14 55								15 56		
Folkestone Central	d			13 58			14 11					14 58			15 11					15 59		
Dover Priory 4	⛴ a			14 09			14 23					15 09			15 23					16 10		
	d			14 10			14 25					15 10			15 25					16 11		
Martin Mill	d			14 19			14 35					15 19			15 35					16 20		
Walmer	d			14 23			14 39					15 23			15 39					16 24		
Deal	d			14 27			14 43					15 27			15 43					16 28		
Sandwich	d			14 33			14 49					15 33			15 49					16 34		
Minster 4	d		14 10								15 10								16 10			
Ramsgate 4	✈ a		14 17	14 44			15 02	14 38			15 17	15 44			16 02	15 38			16 17	16 45		
Dumpton Park	a		14 24					14 43			15 24					15 43			16 24			
Broadstairs	a		14 28					14 46			15 28					15 46			16 28			
Margate 4	a		14 32					14 51			15 32					15 51			16 32			

Station		SE 4 1 🛒		SE 8 1	SE 61	SE 90 1 A 🛒		SE 64 1	SE 8 1	SE 4 1 🛒		SE 8 1	SE 61	SE 90 1 A 🛒		SE 8 1	SE 4 1 🛒		SE 8 1	SE 61	SE 90 1 B 🛒		SE 8 1
London Charing Cross 4	⊖ d	14 53		15 00		15 23			15 30	15 53		16 00		16 23		16 30	16 53		17 00		17 23		17 30
London Waterloo (East) 4	⊖ d	14 56		15 03		15 26			15 33	15 56		16 03		16 26		16 33	16 56		17 03		17 26		17 33
London Cannon Street 4	⊖ d								15 30														
London Bridge 4	⊖ d			15 08					15 38			16 08				16 38			17 08				17 38
Orpington 4	d			15 26					15 54			16 26				16 54			17 26				17 54
Sevenoaks 4	d			15 36					16 04			16 36				17 04			17 36				18 04
Gatwick Airport 10	✈ d								15b08														
Redhill	d								15 39														
Tonbridge 4	a	15 30		15 47		16 02			16 15	16 30		16 47		17 02		17 15	17 30		17 47		18 02		18 15
	d	15 31		15 47		16 03			16 15	16 31		16 47		17 03		17 15	17 31		17 47		18 03		18 15
Paddock Wood 4	d			15 55	16 01	16 10			16 23			16 55	17 01	17 10		17 23			17 55	18 01	18 10		18 23
Maidstone West 4	a				16 21								17 21							18 21			
Marden	d			16 01								17 01							18 01				
Staplehurst	d			16 06		16 18			16 32			17 06		17 18		17 32			18 06		18 18		18 32
Headcorn 4	d			16 11					16 37			17 11				17 37			18 11				18 37
Pluckley	d			16 18								17 18							18 18				
London Victoria 15	⊖ d	14 18				14c48		15 18		15 18				15c48			16 18				16c48		
Bromley South 4	d	14 34				15c04		15 34		15 34				16c04			16 34				17c04		
Maidstone East 4	d					16 05		16 13						17 05			17 13				18 05		
Ashford International	a	15 52		16 26		16 32		16 43	16 50	16 56		17 26		17 32		17 50	17 52		18 26		18 32		18 50
	d	15 57	16 01			16 36	16 38	16 46		16 57	17 00			17 36	17 38		17 57	18 00			18 36	18 38	
Rye	a		16 53								17 53							18 53					
Wye	d							16 52						17 43							18 43		
Chilham	d							16 58						17 49							18 49		
Chartham	d							17 02						17 53							18 53		
Canterbury West 4	d		16 20			16 54		17a07			17g20			17 59				18h20			18 59		
Sturry	d					16 59								18 04							19 04		
Westenhanger	d						16 47								17 47							18 47	
Sandling	d						16 50								17 50							18 50	
Folkestone West	d						16 55								17 55							18 55	
Folkestone Central	d	16 11					16 58			17 11					17 58		18 11					18 58	
Dover Priory 4	⛴ a	16 23					17 09			17 23					18 09		18 23					19 09	
	d	16 25					17 10			17 27					18 10		18 25					19 10	
Martin Mill	d	16 35					17 19			17 37					18 19		18 35					19 19	
Walmer	d	16 39					17 23			17 41					18 23		18 39					19 23	
Deal	d	16 43					17 27			17 45					18 27		18 43					19 27	
Sandwich	d	16 49					17 33			17 51					18 33		18 49					19 33	
Minster 4	d					17 10								18 15							19 15		
Ramsgate 4	✈ a	17 02	16 38			17 17	17 44			18 06	17 38			18 23	18 44		19 02	18 38			19 22	19 44	
Dumpton Park	a		16 43			17 24				18 24	17 43				18 54			18 43			19 27	19 54	
Broadstairs	a		16 46			17 28				18 28	17 46			18 46			19 30	18 46			19 30		
Margate 4	a		16 51			17 32				18 32	17 51			18 51			19 35	18 51			19 35		

For general notes see front of timetable
For details of catering facilities see Directory of Train Operators

A 🛒 to Ramsgate
B 🛒 to Margate
b Change at Redhill and Tonbridge
c Change at Maidstone East and Ashford International
e Arr. 1417
f Arr. 1517
g Arr. 1717
h Arr. 1817

Table 207

Saturdays

London and Tonbridge → Ashford International, Folkestone, Dover, Canterbury West, Ramsgate and Margate

Network Diagram - see first page of Table 206

		SE 4 1		SE 8 1		SE 4 1	SE 8 1	SE 61	SE 90 1	SE 4 1	SE 61	SE 90 1	SE 4 1		SE 01	SE 90 1	SE 4 1	SE 90 1	SE 4 1	SE 90 1	SE 8 1	SE 66 1	SE 8 1	SE 66 1	
London Charing Cross 4	⊖ d	17 53		18 00		18 23			18 30	19 00		19 30	20 00			20 30	21 00	21 30	22 00	22 30	23 00		23 30		
London Waterloo (East) 4	⊖ d	17 56		18 03		18 26			18 33	19 03		19 33	20 03			20 33	21 03	21 33	22 03	22 33	23 03		23 33		
London Cannon Street 4	⊖ d								*18 30*	*19 00*		*19 14*				*19b14*									
London Bridge 4	⊖ d			18 08					18 38	19 08		19 38	20 08			20 38	21 08	21 38	22 08	22 38	23 08		23 38		
Orpington 4	d			18 26					18 54	19 24		19 54	20 24			20 54	21 24	21 54	22 24	22 54	23 24		23 54		
Sevenoaks 4	d			18 36					19 04	19 34		20 04	20 34			21 04	21 34	22 04	22 36	23 04	23 36		00 04		
Gatwick Airport 10	✈ d								*18c08*	*18 52*		*19c08*	*19 53*				*20 53*		*21 53*		*22 53*		*22 53*		
Redhill	d								*18 39*	*19 06*		*19 39*	*20 07*				*21 07*		*22 07*		*23 07*		*23 07*		
Tonbridge 4	a	18 30		18 47		19 02			19 13	19 45		20 13	20 45			21 13	21 45	22 13	22 47	23 13	23 46		00 15		
	d	18 31		18 47		19 03			19 15	19 45		20 15	20 45			21 15	21 45	22 15	22 47	23 15	23 47		00 18		
Paddock Wood 4	d			18 55				19 01	19 22	19 52	20 01	20 22	20 52		21 01	21 22	21 52	22 22	22 55	23 22	23 54		00 25		
Maidstone West 4	a							19 21		*20 21*	20 21		*21 21*		21 21										
Marden	d			19 01			←			19 58			20 58				21 58		23 01		23 59		00 31		
Staplehurst	d			19 06			19 06		19 31	20 03		20 31	21 03			21 31	22 03	22 31	23 06	23 31	00 04		00 36		
Headcorn 4	d			→			19e18		19 36	20 08		20 36	21 08			21 36	22 08	22 36	23 11	23 36	00 09		00 41		
Pluckley	d						19 25			20 15			21 15				22 15		23 18		00 16		00 48		
London Victoria 15	⊖ d	*17 18*							*18 18*			*18f48*	*19 18*				*20 18*		*21 18*		*22 18*	23 18	*23 18*		
Bromley South 4	d	*17 34*							*18 34*			*19f04*	*19 34*				*20 34*		*21 34*		*22 34*	23 34	*23 34*		
Maidstone East 4	d	*18 13*							*19 13*			*20 05*	*20 19*				*21 19*		*22 19*		*23 19*	00 19	*00 19*		
Ashford International	a	18 52				19 24	19 32		19 48	20 23		20 48	21 23			21 48	22 23	22 48	23 26	23 48	00 24	00 48	00 55	←	
	d	18 57	19 00			19 27			19 49	20 23		20 49	21 23			21 49	22 24	22 49	23 27	23 51	00 27	00 58	00 56	00 58	
Rye	a					*19 53*				*20 53*			*21 53*			*22 47*						→			
Wye	d		19 07						19 56			20 56				21 56		22 56		23 58				01 04	
Chilham	d		19 13						20 02			21 02				22 02		23 02		00 04				01 10	
Chartham	d		19 17						20 06			21 06				22 06		23 06		00 08				01 14	
Canterbury West 4	d		19 24						20 12			21 12				22 12		23 12		00a13				01a19	
Sturry	d		19 28						20 17			21 17				22 17		23 17							
Westenhanger	d					19 36				20 33			21 33				22 33		23 37		00 37		01 05		
Sandling	d					19 39				20 36			21 36				22 36		23 40		00 40		01 08		
Folkestone West	d					19 44				20 41			21 41				22 41		23 45		00 45		01 13		
Folkestone Central	d	19 11				19 47				20 43			21 43				22 44		23 48		00 47		01 16		
Dover Priory 4	⛴ a	19 23				19 58				20 55			21 55				22 55		23 59		00 59		01 27		
	d	19 25				19 59				20 55			21 55				22 56		23 59						
Martin Mill	d	19 35				20 08				21 04			22 04				23 05		00 09						
Walmer	d	19 39				20 12				21 09			22 09				23 09		00 14						
Deal	d	19 43				20 16				21 12			22 12				23 13		00 17						
Sandwich	d	19 49				20 22				21 19			22 19				23 19		00 24						
Minster 4	d		19g42						20 28			21 28				22 28		23 28							
Ramsgate 4	✈ a	20 02	19 49			20 33			20 37	21 30		21 35	22 32			22 36	23 30	23 35	00 36						
Dumpton Park	a	20 15	*20 15*						*20 54*			21 41				22 41		23 41							
Broadstairs	a	20 18							*20 58*	*21 44*		21 44	*22 44*			22 44	*23 44*	23 44							
Margate 4	a	20 23							*21 02*	*21 49*		21 49	*22 49*			22 49	*23 49*	23 49							

For general notes see front of timetable
For details of catering facilities see Directory of Train Operators

b Change at London Bridge and Orpington
c Change at Redhill and Tonbridge
e Arr. 1911
f Change at Maidstone East and Ashford International
g Arr. 1939

Table 207

Sundays

London and Tonbridge → Ashford International, Folkestone, Dover, Canterbury West, Ramsgate and Margate

Network Diagram - see first page of Table 206

		SE	SE	SE	SE	SE	SE	SE	SE	SE		SE	SE	SE		SE	SE	SE	SE	SE		SE	SE	SE	SE
		4	90	8	66	8	66	61	4	90		94	55	90		94	55	4	90	94		55	4	90	94
		1	1	1	1	1	1		1	1		1		1		1		1	1	1			1	1	1
													A				A					A			
London Charing Cross [4]	⊖ d	22p00	22p30	23p00		23p30								08 30				09 00	09 30				10 00	10 30	
London Waterloo (East) [4]	⊖ d	22p03	22p33	23p03		23p33								08 33				09 03	09 33				10 03	10 33	
London Cannon Street [4]	⊖ d																								
London Bridge [4]	⊖ d	22p08	22p38	23p08		23p38								08 38				09 08	09 38				10 08	10 38	
Orpington [4]	d	22p24	22p54	23p24		23p54								08 54				09 24	09 54				10 24	10 54	
Sevenoaks [4]	d	22p36	23p04	23p36		00 04								09 04				09 34	10 04				10 34	11 04	
Gatwick Airport [10]	✈ d												07 55	*07 55*			08 55		*08 55*			09 55		*09 55*	
Redhill	d												08 10	*08 10*			09 10		*09 10*			10 10		*10 10*	
Tonbridge [4]	a	22p47	23p13	23p46		00 15							08 40	09 15			09 40	09 43	10 15			10 40	10 43	11 15	
	d	22p47	23p15	23p47		00 18		07 40	08 15				08 40	09 15			09 40	09 43	10 15			10 40	10 43	11 15	
Paddock Wood [4]	d	22p55	23p22	23p54		00 25		07 47	08 22				08 47	09 22			09 47	09 50	10 22			10 47	10 50	11 22	
Maidstone West [4]	a							08 07	*09 07*				09 07	*10 07*			10 07		*11 07*			11 07		*12 07*	
Marden	d	23p01		23p59		00 31			08 28					09 28					10 28					11 28	
Staplehurst	d	23p06	23p31	00 04		00 36			08 33					09 33				09 59	10 33				10 59	11 33	
Headcorn [4]	d	23p11	23p36	00 09		00 41			08 38					09 38					10 38					11 38	
Pluckley	d	23p18		00 16		00 48			08 45					09 45					10 45					11 45	
London Victoria [15]	⊖ d			*22 09*	23p18	*22 42*						07 42		*07 42*		08 42				09 42			*09 42*		10 42
Bromley South [4]	d			*22 29*	23p34	*22 58*						07 58		*07 58*		08 58		*08 58*		09 58			*09 58*		10 58
Maidstone East [4]	d			*23 13*	00 19	*23 43*						08 43				09 43				10 43					11 43
Ashford International	a	23p26	23p48	00 24	00 48	00 55	←		08 52			09 12		09 52		10 12		10 12	10 52	11 12			11 12	11 52	12 12
	d	23p27	23p51	00 27	00 58	00 56	00 58		08 56	08 58		09 16		09 56	09 58	10 17		10 17	10 53	11 16			11 17	11 53	12 16
Rye	a				→							*09 44*						*10 44*					*11 44*		
Wye	d		23p58				01 04		09 03					10 03					11 00					12 00	
Chilham	d		00 04				01 10		09 09					10 09					11 06					12 06	
Chartham	d		00 08				01 14		09 13					10 13					11 10					12 10	
Canterbury West [4]	d		00a13				01a19		09 19			09a32		10 19		10a33			11 16	11a32				12 16	12a32
Sturry	d								09 23					10 23					11 20					12 20	
Westenhanger	d	23p37		00 37		01 05				09 07					10 07			10 26					11 26		
Sandling	d	23p40		00 40		01 08				09 10					10 10			10 29					11 29		
Folkestone West	d	23p45		00 45		01 13				09 15					10 15			10 34					11 34		
Folkestone Central	d	23p48		00 47		01 16				09 18					10 18			10 37					11 37		
Dover Priory [4]	⛴ a	23p59		00 59		01 27				09 30					10 30			10 49					11 49		
	d	23p59								09 30					10 30			10 49					11 49		
Martin Mill	d	00 09								09 39					10 39			10 58					11 58		
Walmer	d	00 14								09 44					10 44			11 03					12 03		
Deal	d	00 17								09 47					10 47			11 06					12 06		
Sandwich	d	00 24								09 54					10 54			11 13					12 13		
Minster [4]	d								09 34					10 34					11 31					12 31	
Ramsgate [4]	✈ a	00 36							09 41	10 05				10 41	11 05			11 24	11 38				12 24	12 38	
Dumpton Park	a								09 46	*10 24*				10 46	*11 24*				11 43					12 43	
Broadstairs	a								09 49	*10 28*				10 49				*11 46*	11 46				*12 46*	12 46	
Margate [4]	a								09 54	*10 32*				10 54				*11 51*	11 51				*12 51*	12 51	

For general notes see front of timetable
For details of catering facilities see Directory of Train Operators

A From Three Bridges (Table 186)

Table 207

Sundays

London and Tonbridge → Ashford International, Folkestone, Dover, Canterbury West, Ramsgate and Margate

Network Diagram - see first page of Table 206

	SE 55	SE 4	SE 90	SE 94	SE 55	SE 4	SE 90	SE 94	SE 55	SE 4	SE 90	SE 94	SE 55	SE 4	SE 90	SE 94	SE 55	SE 4	SE 90	SE 94	SE 55	SE 4
		1	1	1		1	1	1		1	1	1		1	1	1		1	1	1		1
	A				A				A				A				A				A	
London Charing Cross 4 ⊖ d		11 00	11 30			12 00	12 30			13 00	13 30			14 00	14 30			15 00	15 30			16 00
London Waterloo (East) 4 ⊖ d		11 03	11 33			12 03	12 33			13 03	13 33			14 03	14 33			15 03	15 33			16 03
London Cannon Street 4 ⊖ d																						
London Bridge 4 ⊖ d		11 08	11 38			12 08	12 38			13 08	13 38			14 08	14 38			15 08	15 38			16 08
Orpington 4 d		11 24	11 54			12 24	12 54			13 24	13 54			14 24	14 54			15 24	15 54			16 24
Sevenoaks 4 d		11 34	12 04			12 34	13 04			13 34	14 04			14 34	15 04			15 34	16 04			16 34
Gatwick Airport 10 ✈ d	10 55		*10 55*		11 55		*11 55*		12 55		*12 55*		13 55		*13 55*		14 55		*14 55*		15 55	
Redhill d	11 10		*11 10*		12 10		*12 10*		13 10		*13 10*		14 10		*14 10*		15 10		*15 10*		16 10	
Tonbridge 4 a	11 40	11 43	12 15		12 40	12 43	13 15		13 40	13 43	14 15		14 40	14 43	15 15		15 40	15 43	16 15		16 40	16 43
d	11 40	11 43	12 15		12 40	12 43	13 15		13 40	13 43	14 15		14 40	14 43	15 15		15 40	15 43	16 15		16 40	16 43
Paddock Wood 4 d	11 47	11 50	12 22		12 47	12 50	13 22		13 47	13 50	14 22		14 47	14 50	15 22		15 47	15 50	16 22		16 47	16 50
Maidstone West 4 a	12 07		*13 07*		13 07		*14 07*		14 07		*15 07*		15 07		*16 07*		16 07		*17 07*		17 07	
Marden d			12 28				13 28				14 28				15 28				16 28			
Staplehurst d		11 59	12 33			12 59	13 33			13 59	14 33			14 59	15 33			15 59	16 33			16 59
Headcorn 4 d			12 38				13 38				14 38				15 38				16 38			
Pluckley d			12 45				13 45				14 45				15 45				16 45			
London Victoria 15 ⊖ d		*10 42*		11 42		*11 42*		12 42		*12 42*		13 42		*13 42*		14 42		*14 42*		15 42		*15 42*
Bromley South 4 d		*10 58*		11 58		*11 58*		12 58		*12 58*		13 58		*13 58*		14 58		*14 58*		15 58		*15 58*
Maidstone East 4 d				12 43				13 43				14 43				15 43				16 43		
Ashford International a		12 12	12 52	13 12		13 12	13 52	14 12		14 12	14 52	15 12		15 12	15 52	16 12		16 12	16 52	17 12		17 12
d		12 17	12 53	13 16		13 17	13 53	14 16		14 17	14 53	15 16		15 17	15 53	16 16		16 17	16 58	17 16		17 17
Rye a		*12 44*				*13 44*				*14 44*				*15 44*				*16 44*				*17 44*
Wye d			13 00				14 00				15 00				16 00				17 05			
Chilham d			13 06				14 06				15 06				16 06				17 11			
Chartham d			13 10				14 10				15 10				16 10				17 15			
Canterbury West 4 d			13 16	13a32			14 16	14a32			15 16	15a32			16 16	16a32			17 21	17a32		
Sturry d			13 20				14 20				15 20				16 20				17 25			
Westenhanger d		12 26				13 26				14 26				15 26				16 26				17 26
Sandling d		12 29				13 29				14 29				15 29				16 29				17 29
Folkestone West d		12 34				13 34				14 34				15 34				16 34				17 34
Folkestone Central d		12 37				13 37				14 37				15 37				16 37				17 37
Dover Priory 4 ⛴ a		12 49				13 49				14 49				15 49				16 49				17 49
d		12 49				13 49				14 49				15 49				16 49				17 49
Martin Mill d		12 58				13 58				14 58				15 58				16 58				17 58
Walmer d		13 03				14 03				15 03				16 03				17 03				18 03
Deal d		13 06				14 06				15 06				16 06				17 06				18 06
Sandwich d		13 13				14 13				15 13				16 13				17 13				18 13
Minster 4 d			13 31				14 31				15 31				16 31				17 36			
Ramsgate 4 ⛴ a		13 24	13 38			14 24	14 38			15 24	15 38			16 24	16 38			17 24	17 43			18 24
Dumpton Park a			13 43				14 43				15 43				16 43				17 48			
Broadstairs a		*13 46*	13 46			*14 46*	14 46			*15 46*	15 46			*16 46*	16 46			*17 51*	17 51			*18 46*
Margate 4 a		*13 51*	13 51			*14 51*	14 51			*15 51*	15 51			*16 51*	16 51			*17 56*	17 56			*18 51*

	SE 90	SE 94	SE 55	SE 4	SE 90	SE 94	SE 55	SE 4	SE 90	SE 55	SE 4	SE 90	SE 55	SE 4	SE 90	SE 55	SE 4	SE 90	SE 4	SE 2	SE 8
	1	1		1	1	1		1	1		1	1		1	1		1	1	1	1	1
			A				A			A			A			B					
London Charing Cross 4 ⊖ d	16 30			17 00	17 30			18 00	18 30		19 00	19 30		20 00	20 30		21 00	21 30	22 00	22 30	23 30
London Waterloo (East) 4 ⊖ d	16 33			17 03	17 33			18 03	18 33		19 03	19 33		20 03	20 33		21 03	21 33	22 03	22 33	23 33
London Cannon Street 4 ⊖ d																					
London Bridge 4 ⊖ d	16 38			17 08	17 38			18 08	18 38		19 08	19 38		20 08	20 38		21 08	21 38	22 08	22 38	23 38
Orpington 4 d	16 54			17 24	17 54			18 24	18 54		19 24	19 54		20 24	20 54		21 24	21 54	22 24	22 54	23 54
Sevenoaks 4 d	17 04			17 34	18 04			18 34	19 04		19 34	20 04		20 34	21 04		21 34	22 04	22 34	23 04	00 04
Gatwick Airport 10 ✈ d	*15 55*		16 55		*16 55*		17 55		*17 55*	18 55		*18 55*	19 55		*19 55*	20 55		*20 55*		*21 55*	
Redhill d	*16 10*		17 10		*17 10*		18 10		*18 10*	19 10		*19 10*	20 10		*20 10*	21 10		*21 10*		*22 10*	
Tonbridge 4 a	17 15		17 40	17 43	18 15		18 40	18 43	19 15	19 40	19 43	20 15	20 40	20 43	21 15	21 40	21 43	22 15	22 43	23 15	00 13
d	17 15		17 40	17 43	18 15		18 40	18 43	19 15	19 40	19 43	20 15	20 40	20 43	21 15	21 40	21 43	22 15	22 43	23 15	00 13
Paddock Wood 4 d	17 22		17 47	17 50	18 22		18 47	18 50	19 22	19 47	19 50	20 22	20 47	20 50	21 22	21 47	21 50	22 22	22 50	23 22	00 20
Maidstone West 4 a	*18 07*		18 07		*19 07*		19 07		*20 07*	20 07		*21 07*	21 07		*22 07*	22 07					
Marden d	17 28				18 28				19 28			20 28			21 28			22 28		23 28	
Staplehurst d	17 33			17 59	18 33			18 59	19 33		19 59	20 33		20 59	21 33		21 59	22 33	22 59	23 33	00 29
Headcorn 4 d	17 38				18 38				19 38			20 38			21 38			22 38		23 38	
Pluckley d	17 45				18 45				19 45			20 45			21 45			22 45		23 45	
London Victoria 15 ⊖ d		16 42		*16 42*		17 42		*17 42*			*18 42*			*19 42*			*20 42*		21b42	*21 42*	
Bromley South 4 d		16 58		*16 58*		17 58		*17 58*			*18 58*			*19 58*			*20 58*		21b58	*21 58*	
Maidstone East 4 d		17 43				18 43					*19 43*			*20 43*			*21 43*		22b43	*22 43*	
Ashford International a	17 52	18 12		18 12	18 52	19 12		19 12	19 52		20 12	20 52		21 12	21 52		22 12	22 52	23 12	23 52	00 42
d	17 53	18 16		18 17	18 53	19 16		19 17	19 53		20 17	20 53		21 17	21 53		22 17	22 53	23 18	23 53	
Rye a				*18 44*				*19 44*			*20 44*			*21 44*			*22 43*				
Wye d	18 00				19 00				20 00			21 00			22 00			23 00			
Chilham d	18 06				19 06				20 06			21 06			22 06			23 06			
Chartham d	18 10				19 10				20 10			21 10			22 10			23 10			
Canterbury West 4 d	18 16	18a32			19 16	19a32			20 16			21 16			22 16			23 16			
Sturry d	18 20				19 20				20 20			21 20			22 20			23 20			
Westenhanger d				18 26				19 26			20 26			21 26			22 26		23 27	00 02	
Sandling d				18 29				19 29			20 29			21 29			22 29		23 30	00 05	
Folkestone West d				18 34				19 34			20 34			21 34			22 34		23 35	00 10	
Folkestone Central d				18 37				19 37			20 37			21 37			22 37		23 38	00 13	
Dover Priory 4 ⛴ a				18 49				19 49			20 49			21 49			22 49		23 50	00 25	
d				18 49				19 49			20 49			21 49			22 49		23 50		
Martin Mill d				18 58				19 58			20 58			21 58			22 58		23 59		
Walmer d				19 03				20 03			21 03			22 03			23 03		00 04		
Deal d				19 06				20 06			21 06			22 06			23 06		00 07		
Sandwich d				19 13				20 13			21 13			22 13			23 13		00 14		
Minster 4 d	18 31				19 31				20 31			21 31			22 31			23 31			
Ramsgate 4 ⛴ a	18 38			19 24	19 38			20 24	20 38		21 24	21 38		22 24	22 38		23 24	23 38	00 25		
Dumpton Park a	18 43				19 43				20 43			*21 54*									
Broadstairs a	18 46			*19 46*	19 46			*20 46*	20 46			*21 57*									
Margate 4 a	18 51			*19 51*	19 51			*20 51*	20 51			*22 02*									

For general notes see front of timetable
For details of catering facilities see Directory of Train Operators

A From Three Bridges (Table 186)
B From Three Bridges (Table 186) to Gillingham (Kent) (Table 208)
b Until 30 November only

Margate, Ramsgate, Canterbury West, Dover, Folkestone, Ashford International, → Tonbridge and London

For details of Bank Holiday service alterations please see first page of Table 195

Network Diagram - see first page of Table 206

Miles	Miles	Miles			SE 5 1	SE 55	SE 2 1	SE 13	SE 4 1	SE 61	SE 90 1	SE 61	SE 5 1	SE 4 1	SE 3 1	SE 90 1	SE 91 1	SE 4 1	SE 61	SE 3 1	SE 90 1	SE 66 1	SE 5 1
						A		B										🛒					
0	0	—	**Margate 4**	d													*06 07*	06 07			06 41		*06 41*
3¼	3¼	—	Broadstairs	d													*06 12*	06 12			06 46		*06 46*
4½	4½	—	Dumpton Park	d													*06 15*	06 15			06 49		
5½	5½	—	**Ramsgate 4** ✈	d					04 49		05 18			05 39		06 12	06 32	06 19			06 53		06 59
—	9½	0	Minster 4	d							05 24					06 18	06 38				06 59		
13¾	—	4¾	Sandwich	d					05 01					05 51				06 31					07 11
18	—	—	**Deal**	d					05 07					05 57				06 37					07 17
19½	—	—	Walmer	d					05 10					06 00				06 40					07 20
22¼	—	—	Martin Mill	d					05 16					06 06				06 46					07 26
27¼	—	—	**Dover Priory 4** ⛴	a					05 24					06 14				06 54					07 34
—	—	—		d			04 51		05 25					06 15	06 25			06 55		07 05			07 35
34½	—	—	**Folkestone Central**	d			05 03		05 37					06 27	06 37			07 07		07 17			07 47
35¼	—	—	Folkestone West	d			05 05		05 39					06 29	06 39			07 09		07 19			07 49
39	—	—	Sandling	d			05 11		05 45					06 35	06 45			07 15		07 25			07 55
40¼	—	—	Westenhanger	d			05 14		05 48					06 38	06 48			07 18		07 28			07 58
—	18½	—	Sturry	d							05 36					06 30	06 50				07 10		
—	20¾	—	**Canterbury West 4**	d							05 42					06 36	06 56				07 16	07 47	
—	24	—	Chartham	d							05 47					06 41	07 01				07 22		
—	26	—	Chilham	d							05 51					06 45	07 05				07 26		
—	30¾	—	Wye	d							05 58					06 52	07 12				07 32	07 59	
—	—	—	Rye	d									*05 47*	*06 16*			*06 49*						*07 19*
48½	35	—	**Ashford International**	a			05 23		05 57		06 06			06 47	06 57	07 00	07 20	07 27		07 37	07 40	08 05	08 07
—	—	—		d	05 19		05 24		05 58		06 07		06 38	06 50	06 58	07 02	07 22	07 30		07 38	07 45	08 14	08 10
—	54¼	—	Maidstone East 4	a			*06 02*				*06 41*			*07 23*		*07 42*				*08 12*		→	*08 43*
—	83½	—	Bromley South 4	a			*06 47*				*07 29*					*08 25*				*08 59*			*09 27*
—	94¼	—	**London Victoria 15** ⊖	a			*07 08*				*07 49*			*08 31*		*08 53*				*09 18*			*09 50*
54	—	—	Pluckley	d			05 31				06 14			06 57	07 05	07 09	07 29			07 45	07 52		
59¼	—	—	Headcorn 4	d	05 30		05 37		06 08		06 20		06 51	07 03	07 11	07 15	07 35	07 40		07 51	07 58		08 20
62¾	—	—	Staplehurst	d	05 36		05 42		06 13		06 25		06 56	07 08	07 16	07 20	07 40	07 45		07 56	08 03		08 26
65	—	—	Marden	d	05 40		05 47				06 30		07 01		07 21	07 25				08 01	08 08		
—	—	—	Maidstone West 4	d		05 28	*05 28*			06 06	*06 06*	06 43	*06 43*						07 39	*07 39*			
69¾	—	—	Paddock Wood 4	d	05 46	05 49	05 53	06 06	06 21	06a26	06 36	07a02	07 07	07 16	07 27	07 31	07 48	07 53	07a59	08 07	08 14		08 34
75	—	—	**Tonbridge 4**	a	05 54	05 56	06 01	06 13	06 29		06 44		07 16	07 25	07 35	07 38	07 58	08 02		08 16	08 25		08 44
—	—	—		d	05 55	06 00	06 02	06 14	06 30		06 45		07 16	07 25	07 36	07 42	07 58	08 02		08 17	08 25		08 46
—	—	—	Redhill	a	*06 30*	06 30	*06 45*	06 45			*07 20*			*08 08*				*08 48*					*09 21*
—	—	—	Gatwick Airport 10 ✈	a	*06b53*	*06 53*	*07b03*	*07 03*			*07b54*			*08b39*				*09b02*					*09b39*
82¼	—	—	Sevenoaks 4	a	06 07		06 12		06 39		06 57		07 28	07 35	07 48	07 52	08 08	08 12		08 29			08 56
90¾	—	—	Orpington 4	a	06 16		*06 30*		*06 58*		*07 12*		*07 52*			*08 12*		*08 32*					*09 11*
102¾	—	—	**London Bridge 4** ⊖	a	06 35		06 36		07 03		07 21		07 54	*08 10*	08 14	*08 30*	08 34	*08 50*		08 54			09 22
—	—	—	**London Cannon Street 4** ⊖	a	06 41		*06 47*		*07 13*		*07 31*		08 00	*08 20*	08 20	*08c39*	08 41	*08c59*		09 01			09 28
103¾	—	—	**London Waterloo (East) 4** ⊖	a			06 41		07 08		07 27			08 04		08 21		08 41		*09e23*	09 01		
104½	—	—	**London Charing Cross 4** ⊖	a			06 46		07 14		07 32			08 09		08 26		08 47		*09e29*	09 07		

For general notes see front of timetable
For details of catering facilities see Directory of Train Operators

- **A** From Gillingham (Kent) (Table 208)
- **B** To London Bridge (Table 186)
- **b** Change at Tonbridge and Redhill
- **c** Change at Sevenoaks and London Bridge
- **e** Change at Sevenoaks

Margate, Ramsgate, Canterbury West, Dover, Folkestone, Ashford International, → Tonbridge and London

For details of Bank Holiday service alterations please see first page of Table 195

Network Diagram - see first page of Table 206

		SE	SE	SE	SE	SE	SE	SE	SE	SE		SE	SE	SE	SE	SE	SE	SE	SE	SE		SE	SE	SE	SE
		13	8	66	4	18	88	4	18	61		64	4	90	90	4	8	61	64	8		2	90	8	64
			1	1	1	1	1	1	1			1	1	1	1	1	1		1	1		1	1	1	1
		A																							
Margate 4	d				07 07	07 07	07 28					07 43	07 43	08 13	09 04	08 18							09 20		
Broadstairs	d				07 12	07 12	07 33					07 48	07 48	08 18	09 09	08 23									
Dumpton Park	d				07 15		07 36					07 50		08 21	09 12	08 26									
Ramsgate 4	d				07 19	07 27	07 42					07 55	08 05	08 29	09 17	08 50							09 43		
Minster 4	d					07b38	07 48					08 01	08c16	08 35									09 48		
Sandwich	d				07 31	07 45							08 24			09 02									
Deal	d				07 37	07 51							08 30			09 08									
Walmer	d				07 40	07 55							08 33			09 11									
Martin Mill	d				07 46	08 00							08 39			09 17									
Dover Priory 4	a				07 54	08 09			←				08 47			09 25									
	d				07 55	08 10			08 10				08 48			09 26						09 50			
Folkestone Central	d				08 07	→			08 21				09 00			09 38						10 01			
Folkestone West	d				08 09				08 24							09 40						10 04			
Sandling	d				08 15				08 29							09 46						10 09			
Westenhanger	d				08 18				08 32							09 49						10 12			
Sturry	d						07 59					08 12		08 47									10 00		
Canterbury West 4	d						08 06					08e20		08 53	09 37				09 43				10 06		10 24
Chartham	d						08 11					08 25		08 58					09 48						10 29
Chilham	d						08 15					08 28		09 02					09 52						10 33
Wye	d						08 22					08 34		09 09					09 58						10 39
Rye	d						07 54	←				08 23	08 54									09 54			
Ashford International	a			←	08 27		08 31	08 27	08 41			08 42	09 13	09 16	09 54	09 58			10 05			10 21	10 24		10 48
	d		08 14	08 14			08 32		08 46			09 04		09 21		10 01	09 56		10 05	10 20			10 28		11 05
Maidstone East 4	a			08 43			08 53					09 33		09 56					10 34				10 57		→
Bromley South 4	a			09 27	09f44		09 44		10 14			10 14		10f44					11 14						
London Victoria 15	⊖ a			09 50	10f02		10 02		10 32			10 32		11f02					11 32					←	
Pluckley	d		08 21			→			08 53					09 28			10 03			10 27 →				10 27	
Headcorn 4	d		08 27						08 59					09 34			10g13							10h40	
Staplehurst	d		08 32						09 04					09 39			10 18						10 41	10 45	
Marden	d		08 37						09 09					09 44			10 22							10 50	
Maidstone West 4	d	08 19	08 19							09 25				09 25				10 24					10 24		
Paddock Wood 4	d	08 40	08 43						09 15	09a45				09 50			10 28	10a44					10 49	10 56	
Tonbridge 4	a	08 49	08 53						09 23					09 57		10 25	10 35						10 57	11 03	
	d	08 51	09 00						09 24					09 58		10 28	10 36						10 58	11 04	
Redhill	a	09 21	09 39						10 04					10 40		11 04							11 40		
Gatwick Airport 10	✈ a	09 39	09 54						10j23					10 55		11j23							11 55		
Sevenoaks 4	a		09 09						09 34								10 48							11 15	
Orpington 4	a		09 32						09 55								10 57							11 25	
London Bridge 4	⊖ a		09 33				09 39		09 57								11 13							11 43	
London Cannon Street 4	⊖ a		09 43				09 57		10 06								11 20								
London Waterloo (East) 4	⊖ a		09 38				09 45		10 03					10 32		11 02	11 18						11 32	11 48	
London Charing Cross 4	⊖ a		09 44				09 50		10 07					10 36		11 06	11 21						11 36	11 51	

For general notes see front of timetable
For details of catering facilities see Directory of Train Operators

A From Strood (Table 208) to London Bridge (Table 186)
b Arr. 0733
c Arr. 0811
e Arr. 0817
f Change at Ashford International and Maidstone East
g Arr. 1009
h Arr. 1034
j Change at Tonbridge and Redhill

For details of Bank Holiday service alterations please see first page of Table 195

Margate, Ramsgate, Canterbury West, Dover, Folkestone, Ashford International, → Tonbridge and London

Network Diagram - see first page of Table 206

		SE 8	SE 90 1	SE 4 1	SE 8	SE 61	SE 64 1	SE 8 1		SE 2 1	SE 90 1	SE 8 1	SE 64 1	SE 8	SE 90 1	SE 4 1	SE 8	SE 61		SE 64 1	SE 8 1	SE 2 1	SE 90 1	SE 8 1	SE 64 1
Margate 4	d		10 04	*09 43*							*10 19*				11 04	*10 41*							*11b15*		
Broadstairs	d		10 09												11 09										
Dumpton Park	d		10 12												11 12										
Ramsgate 4	d		10 19	09 57							10 43				11 19	10 57							11 43		
Minster 4	d										10 48												11 48		
Sandwich	d			10 09												11 09									
Deal	d			10 15												11 15									
Walmer	d			10 18												11 18									
Martin Mill	d			10 24												11 24									
Dover Priory 4	a			10 32												11 32									
	d			10 33						10 50						11 33						11 50			
Folkestone Central	d			10 45						11 01						11 45						12 01			
Folkestone West	d									11 04												12 04			
Sandling	d									11 09												12 09			
Westenhanger	d									11 12												12 12			
Sturry	d										11 00												12 00		
Canterbury West 4	d		10 39								11 06		11 24		11 39								12 06		12 24
Chartham	d												11 29												12 29
Chilham	d												11 33												12 33
Wye	d												11 39												12 39
Rye	d									*10 54*												*11 54*			
Ashford International	a		10 56	10 59			←			11 21	11 24		11 46		11 56	11 59				←		12 21	12 24		12 46
	d	10 57	11 03				11 05	11 20		11 28			12 05	11 57	12 03					12 05	12 20	12 28			13 05
Maidstone East 4	a		*11 34*				11 34			*11 57*			→		*12 34*					12 34		*12 57*			→
Bromley South 4	a		*12 14*				12 14								*13 14*					13 14					
London Victoria 15	⊖ a		*12 32*				12 32					←			*13 32*					13 32				←	
Pluckley	d							11 27 →				11 27									12 27 →			12 27	
Headcorn 4	d	11c14			←							11e40		12f14			←							12g40	
Staplehurst	d	11 19			11 19					11 41		11 45		12 19			12 19					12 41		12 45	
Marden	d	→										11 50		→										12 50	
Maidstone West 4	d					11 24				*11 24*								12 24				*12 24*			
Paddock Wood 4	d				11 28	11a44				11 49		11 56					12 28	12a44				12 49		12 56	
Tonbridge 4	a		11 25		11 35					11 57		12 03			12 25		12 35					12 57		13 03	
	d		11 28		11 36					11 58		12 04			12 28		12 36					12 58		13 04	
Redhill	a		*12 04*							*12 39*					*13 04*							*13 39*			
Gatwick Airport 10	a		*12h23*							*12 55*					*13h23*							*13 55*			
Sevenoaks 4	a				11 47							12 15					12 47							13 15	
Orpington 4	a				11 56							12 25					12 57							13 25	
London Bridge 4	⊖ a				12 12							12 43					13 13							13 43	
London Cannon Street 4	⊖ a																								
London Waterloo (East) 4	⊖ a		12 02		12 17					12 32		12 48			13 02		13 18					13 32		13 48	
London Charing Cross 4	⊖ a		12 06		12 21					12 36		12 51			13 06		13 21					13 36		13 51	

For general notes see front of timetable
For details of catering facilities see Directory of Train Operators

b Until 18 July and from 1 September only
c Arr. 1108
e Arr. 1134
f Arr. 1208
g Arr. 1234
h Change at Tonbridge and Redhill

For details of Bank Holiday service alterations please see first page of Table 195

Margate, Ramsgate, Canterbury West, Dover, Folkestone, Ashford International, → Tonbridge and London

Network Diagram - see first page of Table 206

Station		SE 8 [1]	SE 90 [1]	SE 4 [1] ⚒	SE 8 [1]	SE 61	SE 64 [1]	SE 8 [1]	SE 2 [1] ⚒	SE 90 [1]	SE 8 [1]	SE 64 [1]	SE 8 [1]	SE 90 [1]	SE 4 [1] ⚒	SE 8 [1]	SE 61	SE 64 [1]	SE 8 [1]	SE 2 [1]	SE 90 [1] ⚒	SE 8 [1]
Margate [4]	d		12 04	*11 41*						*12 15*				13 04	*12 41*						*13 15*	
Broadstairs	d		12 09											13 09								
Dumpton Park	d		12 12											13 12								
Ramsgate [4]	d		12 19	11 57						12 43				13 19	12 57						13 42	
Minster [4]	d									12 48											13 48	
Sandwich	d			12 09											13 09							
Deal	d			12 15											13 15							
Walmer	d			12 18											13 18							
Martin Mill	d			12 24											13 24							
Dover Priory [4]	a			12 32											13 32							
	d			12 33					12 50						13 33					13 50		
Folkestone Central	d			12 45					13 01						13 45					14 02		
Folkestone West	d								13 04											14 04		
Sandling	d								13 09											14 10		
Westenhanger	d								13 12											14 13		
Sturry	d									13 00											14 00	
Canterbury West [4]	d		12 39							13 06		13 24		13 39							14 06	
Chartham	d											13 29										
Chilham	d											13 33										
Wye	d											13 39										
Rye	d								*12 54*											*13 54*		
Ashford International	a		12 56	12 59					13 21	13 24		13 46		13 56	13 59					14 21	14 24	
	d	12 57	13 03				← 13 05	13 20	13 28			14 05 →	13 57	14 03				← 14 05	14 20	14 28		
Maidstone East [4]	a		*13 34*				13 34		*13 57*					*14 34*				14 34		*14 57*		
Bromley South [4]	a		*14 14*				14 14							*15 14*				15 14		*16 14*		
London Victoria [15]	⊖ a		*14 32*				14 32							*15 32*				15 32		*16 33*		
Pluckley	d							13 27 →			← 13 27								14 27 →			← 14 27
Headcorn [4]	d	13b14									13c40		14e14									14f40
Staplehurst	d	13 19 →			← 13 19				13 41		13 45		14 19 →			← 14 19				14 41		14 45
Marden	d										13 50											14 50
Maidstone West [4]	d					13 24			*13 24*								14 24			*14 24*		
Paddock Wood [4]	d				13 28	13a44			13 49		13 56					14 28	14a44			14 49		14 56
Tonbridge [4]	a		13 25		13 35				13 57		14 03			14 25		14 35				14 57		15 03
	d		13 28		13 36				13 58		14 04			14 28		14 36				14 58		15 04
Redhill	a		*14 04*						*14 39*					*15 04*						*15 39*		
Gatwick Airport [10]	✈ a		*14g23*						*14 55*					*15g23*						*15 56*		
Sevenoaks [4]	a				13 47						14 15					14 47						15 15
Orpington [4]	a				13 57						14 25					14 57						15 25
London Bridge [4]	⊖ a				14 13						14 43					15 13						15 43
London Cannon Street [4]	⊖ a																					
London Waterloo (East) [4]	⊖ a		14 02		14 18				14 32		14 48			15 02		15 18				15 32		15 48
London Charing Cross [4]	⊖ a		14 06		14 21				14 36		14 51			15 06		15 21				15 36		15 51

Station		SE 90 [1]	SE 4 [1]	SE 8 [1]	SE 61	SE 64 [1]	SE 2 [1] ⚒	SE 90 [1]	SE 4 [1] ⚒	SE 90 [1]	SE 61	SE 64 [1]	SE 8 [1]	SE 2 [1] ⚒	SE 90 [1]	SE 61	SE 4 [1] ⚒	SE 90 [1]	SE 4 [1] ⚒	SE 90 [1]	SE 61	SE 90 [1]	SE 4 [1]
Margate [4]	d	14 04	*13 41*					*14 15*		14 50					*14 50*			15 36	*15 41*			16 36	*16 15*
Broadstairs	d	14 09	*13 46*						*14 20*	14 55							*15 20*	15 41	*15 46*			16 41	
Dumpton Park	d	14 12								14 58							*15 23*	15 44				16 44	
Ramsgate [4]	d	14 17	13 55					14 38	14 34	15 02					15 27		15 32	15 48	16 04	16 27		16 48	16 32
Minster [4]	d							14 44							15 33			15 54		16 33		16 54	
Sandwich	d		14 07						14 47								15 44		16 16				16 44
Deal	d		14 13						14 53								15 50		16 22				16 50
Walmer	d		14 16						14 56								15 53		16 25				16 53
Martin Mill	d		14 22						15 02								15 59		16 31				16 59
Dover Priory [4]	a		14 30						15 11								16 07		16 39				17 07
	d		14 31				14 46		15 12					15 40			16 08		16 40				17 08
Folkestone Central	d		14 43				14 58		15 24					15 52			16 20		16 52				17 20
Folkestone West	d						15 00							15 54					16 54				
Sandling	d						15 06							16 00					17 00				
Westenhanger	d						15 09							16 03					17 03				
Sturry	d							14 56							15 45			16 05		16 45		17 05	
Canterbury West [4]	d	14 37				14 24		15 02		15 22		15 32			15 51			16 11		16 51		17 11	
Chartham	d					14 29						15 37			15 56			16 17		16 56		17 17	
Chilham	d					14 33						15 41			16 00			16 21		17 00		17 21	
Wye	d					14 39						15 47			16 07			16 27		17 07		17 27	
Rye	d						*14 54*										*15 54*					*16 54*	
Ashford International	a	14 54	14 54			14 46	15 17	15 20	15 37	15 42		15 54		16 12	16 14		16 34	16 36	17 12	17 14		17 34	17 36
	d	15 02		14 52		15 03	15 24		15 46			15 59	16 06	16 19			16 41		17 19			17 41	
Maidstone East [4]	a					15 32	*15 56*					16 28		*16 45*			*17 27*		*17 47*			*18 29*	
Bromley South [4]	a					16 14	*16 47*					17 14		*17 47*			*18 13*		*18 45*			*19 14*	
London Victoria [15]	⊖ a					16 33	*17 11*		*17 31*			17 31		*18 09*			*18 33*		*19 03*			*19 31*	
Pluckley	d			14 59					15 53								16 48					17 48	
Headcorn [4]	d			15h13					15 59					16 29			16 54					17 54	
Staplehurst	d			15 18			15 37		16 04				16 20	16 34			16 59		17 32			17 59	
Marden	d			15 22					16 09								17 04					18 04	
Maidstone West [4]	d				15 24						15 55		*15 55*			16 38	*16 38*				17 28	*17 28*	
Paddock Wood [4]	d			15 28	15a44		15 45		16 15		16a15		16 28	16 42		16a58	17 10		17 40		17a48	18 10	
Tonbridge [4]	a	15 25		15 36			15 53		16 22				16 36	16 50			17 17		17 49			18 18	
	d	15 28		15 36			15 54		16 23				16 40	16 51			17 18		17 50			18 20	
Redhill	a	*16 04*					*16 39*		*16 59*					*17 51*			*18 13*		*18 51*				
Gatwick Airport [10]	✈ a	*16g23*					*16 56*		*17g32*					*18g12*			*18g32*		*19g07*				
Sevenoaks [4]	a			15 48			16 03		16 32				16 52	17 03			17 30		18 02			18 29	
Orpington [4]	a			15 57			*16 34*		*16 49*				17 02	17 12			17 39		18 11			18 39	
London Bridge [4]	⊖ a			16 13			16 29		17 00				17 26	17 31			*18 19*		18 28			18 57	
London Cannon Street [4]	⊖ a			*16 22*			*16 36*		*17 08*				17 31	*17 39*			*18j29*		*18 37*			*19 05*	
London Waterloo (East) [4]	⊖ a	16 02		16 18			16 34		17 05					17 36			18 03		18 33			19 02	
London Charing Cross [4]	⊖ a	16 06		16 21			16 38		17 10					17 41			18 07		18 37			19 07	

For general notes see front of timetable
For details of catering facilities see Directory of Train Operators

b Arr. 1308
c Arr. 1334
e Arr. 1408
f Arr. 1434
g Change at Tonbridge and Redhill
h Arr. 1507
j Change at Orpington and London Bridge

Mondays to Fridays

until 10 October

Margate, Ramsgate, Canterbury West, Dover, Folkestone, Ashford International, → Tonbridge and London

For details of Bank Holiday service alterations please see first page of Table 195

Network Diagram - see first page of Table 206

		SE	SE	SE	SE	SE	SE	SE	SE	SE	SE	SE	SE	SE	SE	SE	SE	SE	SE	SE	SE	SE
		18	61	90	61	18	90	18	90	18	61	90	94	4	61	90	4	61	90	4	01	4
		1 🍴		1		1 🍴	1 🍴	1 🍴	1	1 🍴		1	1	1		1	1		1	1	1	1
Margate 4	d						*17 45*		*18 13*			18 52		*18 52*		*19 40*			*20 47*		*21 43*	
Broadstairs	d	*16 52*					*17 51*		*18 19*			18 57		*18 57*		*19 46*			*20 52*		*21 48*	
Dumpton Park	d						*17 53*		*18 21*			19 00				*19 48*			*20 55*		*21 27*	
Ramsgate 4	d	17 10		17 27			18 04	18 09	18 36			19 04		19 14		20 04	20 20		21 04	21 20	22 22	22 32
Minster 4	d	17b20		17 33			18 10	18c20	18 42			19 10				20 10			21 10		22 27	
Sandwich	d	17 28						18 27						19 26			20 32			21 32		22 44
Deal	d	17 34						18 33						19 32			20 38			21 38		22 50
Walmer	d	17 37						18 37						19 35			20 41			21 41		22 53
Martin Mill	d	17 43						18 42						19 41			20 47			21 47		22 59
Dover Priory 4	a	17 51				←		18 51		←				19 49			20 55			21 55		23 08
	d	17 52				17 52		18 52		18 52				19 50			20 56			22 00		23 20
Folkestone Central	d	→				18 04		→		19 04				20 02			21 08			22 12		23 32
Folkestone West	d					18 06				19 06				20 04			21 11			22 14		23 34
Sandling	d					18 12				19 12				20 10			21 16			22 20		23 40
Westenhanger	d					18 15				19 15				20 13			21 19			22 23		23 43
Sturry	d			17 45			18 21		18 53			19 21				20 21			21 21		22 38	
Canterbury West 4	d			17 51			18 27		18 59			19 27	19 34			20 27			21 27		22 44	
Chartham	d			17 56			18 33		19 05			19 33	19 39			20 33			21 33		22 50	
Chilham	d			18 00			18 37		19 09			19 37	19 43			20 37			21 37		22 53	
Wye	d			18 07			18 43		19 15			19 43	19 49			20 43			21 43		23 00	
Rye	d					*17 54*			*18 54*				*19 31*	*19 54*			*20 54*			*21 57*		
Ashford International	a			18 14		18 23	18 50		19 22	19 24		19 50	19 57	20 22		20 50	21 28		21 50	22 32	23 06	23 51
	d			18 16		18 25	18 51		19 29			19 51	19 58	20 29		20 51	21 29		21 51	22 33		
Maidstone East 4	a						*19 29*						20 27			*21 27*			*22 37*			
Bromley South 4	a						*20 14*					*21 13*	21 13			*22 13*			*23 23*			
London Victoria 15	⊖ a						*20 32*					*21 29*	21 29			*22 32*			*23 45*			
Pluckley	d					18 32	18 58					19 58				20 58			21 58	22 40		
Headcorn 4	d					18 38	19 04					20 04				21 04			22 04	22 46		
Staplehurst	d			18 29		18 43	19 09		19 42			20 09		20 42		21 09	21 42		22 09	22 51		
Marden	d					18 48	19 14					20 14				21 14			22 14	22 56		
Maidstone West 4	d		17 59	*17 59*	18 31		*18 31*				19 39	*19 39*			20 35	*20 35*		21 32	*21 32*			
Paddock Wood 4	d		18a19	18 37	18a51	18 54	19 20		19 50		19a59	20 20		20 50	20a55	21 20	21 50	21a52	22 20	23 02		
Tonbridge 4	a			18 45		19 03	19 27		19 58			20 27		20 58		21 28	21 58		22 28	23 09		
	d			18 46		19 11	19 30		20 00			20 31		21 00		21 30	22 00		22 30	23 10		
Redhill	a			*19 39*			*20 24*					*21 24*				*22 23*				*23 48*		
Gatwick Airport 10	a			*19e58*			*20 35*					*21 34*				*22 35*				*00e11*		
Sevenoaks 4	a			18 58			19 39		20 09			20 40		21 09		21 39	22 09		22 39	23 22		
Orpington 4	a			19 07			19 49		20 19			20 49		21 19		21 49	22 19		22 49	23 33		
London Bridge 4	⊖ a			19 25			20 08		20 38			21 08		21 38		22 08	22 38		23 08	23 51		
London Cannon Street 4	⊖ a			*19 37*			*20 27*															
London Waterloo (East) 4	⊖ a			19 31		19 46	20 13		20 43			21 13		21 43		22 13	22 43		23 13	23 56		
London Charing Cross 4	⊖ a			19 35		19 50	20 18		20 48			21 18		21 48		22 18	22 48		23 18	00 01		

For general notes see front of timetable
For details of catering facilities see Directory of Train Operators

b Arr. 1716
c Arr. 1815
e Change at Tonbridge and Redhill

For details of Bank Holiday service alterations please see first page of Table 195

Margate, Ramsgate, Canterbury West, Dover, Folkestone, Ashford International, → Tonbridge and London

Network Diagram - see first page of Table 206

		SE 5 1	SE 55	SE 2 1	SE 13	SE 4 1	SE 61	SE 90 1	SE 61	SE 5 1	SE 4 1	SE 3 1	SE 90 1	SE 91 1	SE 4 1	SE 61	SE 3 1	SE 90 1	SE 66 1	SE 5 1	SE 13	SE 8 1	SE 66 1
			A		B										🍴						C		
Margate 4	d													*06 07*	06 07			06 41		*06 41*			
Broadstairs	d													*06 12*	06 12			06 46		*06 46*			
Dumpton Park	d													*06 15*	06 15			06 49					
Ramsgate 4 ✈	d					04 46		05 15			05 39		06 09	06 29	06 19			06 53		06 59			
Minster 4	d							05 21					06 15	06 35				06 59					
Sandwich	d					04 58					05 51				06 31					07 11			
Deal	d					05 04					05 57				06 37					07 17			
Walmer	d					05 07					06 00				06 40					07 20			
Martin Mill	d					05 13					06 06				06 46					07 26			
Dover Priory 4 ⛴	a					05 21					06 14				06 54					07 34			
	d			04 48		05 22					06 15	06 22			06 55		07 02			07 35			
Folkestone Central	d			05 00		05 34					06 27	06 34			07 07		07 14			07 47			
Folkestone West	d			05 02		05 36					06 29	06 36			07 09		07 16			07 49			
Sandling	d			05 08		05 42					06 35	06 42			07 15		07 22			07 55			
Westenhanger	d			05 11		05 45					06 38	06 45			07 18		07 25			07 58			
Sturry	d							05 33					06 27	06 47				07 10					
Canterbury West 4	d							05 39					06 33	06 53				07 16	07 47				
Chartham	d							05 44					06 38	06 58				07 22					
Chilham	d							05 48					06 42	07 02				07 26					
Wye	d							05 55					06 49	07 09				07 32	07 59				
Rye	d									*05 47*	*06 16*			*06 49*						*07 19*			
Ashford International	a			05 22		05 54		06 03			06 47	06 54	06 57	07 17	07 27		07 34	07 40	08 05	08 07			⟵
	d	05 19		05 23		05 55		06 04		06 38	06 50	06 58	07 02	07 19	07 30		07 35	07 45	08 14	08 10		08 14	08 14
Maidstone East 4	a			*05 59*				*06 41*			*07 23*		*07 42*				*08 12*		⟶	*08 43*			08 43
Bromley South 4	a			*06 47*				*07 29*					*08 25*				*08 59*			*09 27*			09 27
London Victoria 15 ⊖	a			*07 08*				*07 49*			*08 31*		*08 53*				*09 18*			*09 50*			09 50
Pluckley	d			05 30				06 11			06 57	07 05	07 09	07 26			07 42	07 52				08 21	
Headcorn 4	d	05 30		05 36		06 05		06 17		06 51	07 03	07 11	07 15	07 32	07 40		07 48	07 58		08 20		08 27	
Staplehurst	d	05 36		05 41		06 10		06 22		06 56	07 08	07 16	07 20	07 37	07 45		07 53	08 03		08 26		08 32	
Marden	d	05 40		05 46				06 27		07 01		07 21	07 25				07 58	08 08				08 37	
Maidstone West 4	d		05 28			*05 28*	06 06	*06 06*	06 43	*06 43*						07 39	*07 39*				08 19	*08 19*	
Paddock Wood 4	d	05 46	05 49	05 52	06 06	06 18	06a26	06 33	07a02	07 07	07 16	07 27	07 31	07 45	07 53	07a59	08 04	08 14		08 34	08 40	08 43	
Tonbridge 4	a	05 54	05 56	06 00	06 13	06 28		06 41		07 16	07 25	07 35	07 38	07 58	08 02		08 14	08 25		08 44	08 49	08 53	
	d	05 55	06 00	06 02	06 14	06 30		06 45		07 16	07 25	07 36	07 42	07 58	08 02		08 17	08 25		08 46	08 51	09 00	
Redhill	a	*06 30*	06 30	*06 45*	06 45			*07 20*			*08 08*						*08 48*			*09 21*	09 21	*09 39*	
Gatwick Airport 10 ✈	a	*06b53*	*06 53*	*07b03*	*07 03*			*07b54*			*08b39*						*09b02*			*09b39*	*09 39*	*09 54*	
Sevenoaks 4	a	06 07		06 12		06 39		06 57		07 28	07 35	07 48	07 52	08 08	08 12		08 29			08 56		09 09	
Orpington 4	a	06 16		*06 30*		*06 58*		*07 12*		*07 52*			*08 12*		*08 32*					*09 11*		*09 32*	
London Bridge 4 ⊖	a	06 35		06 36		07 03		07 21		07 54	*08 10*	08 14	*08 30*	08 34	*08 50*		08 54			09 22		09 33	
London Cannon Street 4 ⊖	a	06 43		*06 47*		*07 13*		*07 32*		08 01	*08 21*	08 21	*08c39*	08 42	*09c00*		09 02			09 28		*09 44*	
London Waterloo (East) 4 ⊖	a			06 41		07 08		07 27			08 04		08 21		08 41		*09e23*	09 01				09 38	
London Charing Cross 4 ⊖	a			06 48		07 15		07 33			08 09		08 27		08 47		*09e29*	09 07				09 44	

For general notes see front of timetable
For details of catering facilities see Directory of Train Operators

A From Gillingham (Kent) (Table 208)
B To London Bridge (Table 186)
C From Strood (Table 208) to London Bridge (Table 186)
b Change at Tonbridge and Redhill
c Change at Sevenoaks and London Bridge
e Change at Sevenoaks

Table 207

Mondays to Fridays

from 13 October

Margate, Ramsgate, Canterbury West, Dover, Folkestone, Ashford International, → Tonbridge and London

For details of Bank Holiday service alterations please see first page of Table 195

Network Diagram - see first page of Table 206

		SE 4 1		SE 18 1	SE 88 1	SE 4 1	SE 18 1	SE 61	SE 64 1	SE 4 1	SE 90 1		SE 90 1	SE 4 1	SE 8 1	SE 61	SE 64 1	SE 8 1	SE 2 1	SE 90 1		SE 8 1	SE 64 1	SE 8	
Margate 4	d	07 04		*07 04*	07 28				07 43	*07 43*	08 13		09 04	*08 18*						*09 20*					
Broadstairs	d	07 09		*07 09*	07 33				07 48	*07 48*	08 18		09 09	*08 23*											
Dumpton Park	d	07 12			07 36				07 50		08 21		09 12	*08 26*											
Ramsgate 4	d	07 19		07 27	07 42				07 55	08 05	08 29		09 17	08 50						09 43					
Minster 4	d			07b38	07 48				08 01	08c16	08 35									09 48					
Sandwich	d	07 31		07 45						08 24				09 02											
Deal	d	07 37		07 51						08 30				09 08											
Walmer	d	07 40		07 55						08 33				09 11											
Martin Mill	d	07 46		08 00						08 39				09 17											
Dover Priory 4	a	07 54		08 09			←			08 47				09 25											
	d	07 55		08 10			08 10			08 48				09 26					09 50						
Folkestone Central	d	08 07		→			08 21			09 00				09 38					10 01						
Folkestone West	d	08 09					08 24							09 40					10 04						
Sandling	d	08 15					08 29							09 46					10 09						
Westenhanger	d	08 18					08 32							09 49					10 12						
Sturry	d				07 59				08 12		08 47									10 00					
Canterbury West 4	d				08 06				08e20		08 53		09 37				09 43			10 06			10 24		
Chartham	d				08 11				08 25		08 58						09 48						10 29		
Chilham	d				08 15				08 28		09 02						09 52						10 33		
Wye	d				08 22				08 34		09 09						09 58						10 39		
Rye	d				*07 54*	←			*08 23*	*08 54*									*09 54*						
Ashford International	a	08 27			08 31	08 27	08 41		08 42	09 13	09 16		09 54	09 58			10 05		10 21	10 24			10 48		
	d				08 32	08 46			09 04	09 21			10 01		09 56		10 05	10 20	10 28				11 05	10 57	
Maidstone East 4	a				08 53				09 33	*09 56*							10 34		*10 57*				→		
Bromley South 4	a	*09f44*			*09 44*	*10 14*			10 14	*10f44*							11 14								
London Victoria 15	⊖ a	*10f04*			*10 04*	*10 32*			10 32	*11f02*							11 32					←			
Pluckley	d	→				08 53				09 28					10 03			10 27 →				10 27			
Headcorn 4	d					08 59				09 34					10g13							10h40		11j14	
Staplehurst	d					09 04				09 39					10 18				10 41			10 45		11 19	
Marden	d					09 09				09 44					10 22							10 50		→	
Maidstone West 4	d							09 25		*09 25*						10 24			*10 24*						
Paddock Wood 4	d					09 15		09a45		09 50					10 28	10a44			10 49			10 56			
Tonbridge 4	a					09 23				09 57			10 25		10 35				10 57			11 03			
	d					09 24				09 58			10 28		10 36				10 58			11 04			
Redhill	a					*10 04*				*10 40*			*11 04*						*11 40*						
Gatwick Airport 10	✈ a					*10k23*				*10 55*			*11m23*						*11 55*						
Sevenoaks 4	a					09 34									10 48							11 15			
Orpington 4	a					*09 55*									10 57							11 25			
London Bridge 4	⊖ a				09 39	09 57									11 13							11 43			
London Cannon Street 4	⊖ a				*09 58*	*10 06*									*11 20*										
London Waterloo (East) 4	⊖ a				09 45	10 03				10 32			11 02		11 18				11 32			11 48			
London Charing Cross 4	⊖ a				09 51	10 09				10 36			11 06		11 21				11 36			11 51			

For general notes see front of timetable
For details of catering facilities see Directory of Train Operators

b Arr. 0733
c Arr. 0811
e Arr. 0817
f Change at Ashford International and Maidstone East
g Arr. 1009
h Arr. 1034
j Arr. 1108
k Change at Tonbridge and Redhill
m Change at Redhill and Tonbridge

For details of Bank Holiday service alterations please see first page of Table 195

Margate, Ramsgate, Canterbury West, Dover, Folkestone, Ashford International, → Tonbridge and London

Network Diagram - see first page of Table 206

		SE	SE	SE	SE	SE		SE	SE	SE	SE	SE	SE	SE	SE		SE	SE	SE	SE	SE	SE	SE		SE
		90	4	8	61	64		8	2	90	8	64	8	90	4		8	61	64	8	2	90	8		64
		1	1			1		1	1	1	1	1		1	1				1	1	1	1	1		1
			🛒						🛒					🛒							🛒				
Margate [4]	d	10 04	*09 43*							*10 19*				11 04	*10 41*							*11 15*			
Broadstairs	d	10 09												11 09											
Dumpton Park	d	10 12												11 12											
Ramsgate [4] ✈	d	10 19	09 57							10 43				11 19	10 57							11 43			
Minster [4]	d									10 48												11 48			
Sandwich	d		10 09												11 09										
Deal	d		10 15												11 15										
Walmer	d		10 18												11 18										
Martin Mill	d		10 24												11 24										
Dover Priory [4] ⛴	a		10 32												11 32										
	d		10 33						10 50						11 33						11 50				
Folkestone Central	d		10 45						11 01						11 45						12 01				
Folkestone West	d								11 04												12 04				
Sandling	d								11 09												12 09				
Westenhanger	d								11 12												12 12				
Sturry	d									11 00												12 00			
Canterbury West [4]	d	10 39								11 06		11 24		11 39								12 06			12 24
Chartham	d											11 29													12 29
Chilham	d											11 33													12 33
Wye	d											11 39													12 39
Rye	d								*10 54*												*11 54*				
Ashford International	a	10 56	10 59						11 21	11 24		11 46		11 56	11 59						12 21	12 24			12 46
	d	11 03				← 11 05		11 20	11 28			12 05	11 57	12 03					← 12 05	12 20	12 28				13 05
Maidstone East [4]	a	*11 34*				11 34			*11 57*			→		*12 34*					12 34		*12 57*				→
Bromley South [4]	a	*12 14*				12 14								*13 14*					13 14						
London Victoria [15] ⊖	a	*12 32*				12 32					←			*13 32*					13 32				←		
Pluckley	d							11 27 →			11 27									12 27 →			12 27		
Headcorn [4]	d			←							11b40		12c14				←						12e40		
Staplehurst	d			11 19					11 41		11 45		12 19 →				12 19				12 41		12 45		
Marden	d										11 50												12 50		
Maidstone West [4]	d				11 24				*11 24*									12 24			*12 24*				
Paddock Wood [4]	d			11 28	11a44				11 49		11 56						12 28	12a44			12 49		12 56		
Tonbridge [4]	a	11 25		11 35					11 57		12 03			12 25			12 35				12 57		13 03		
	d	11 28		11 36					11 58		12 04			12 28			12 36				12 58		13 04		
Redhill	a	*12 04*							*12 39*					*13 04*							*13 39*				
Gatwick Airport [10] ✈	a	*12f23*							*12 55*					*13f23*							*13 55*				
Sevenoaks [4]	a			11 47							12 15						12 47						13 15		
Orpington [4]	a			11 56							12 25						12 57						13 25		
London Bridge [4] ⊖	a			12 12							12 43						13 13						13 43		
London Cannon Street [4] ⊖	a																								
London Waterloo (East) [4] ⊖	a	12 02		12 17					12 32		12 48			13 02			13 18				13 32		13 48		
London Charing Cross [4] ⊖	a	12 06		12 21					12 36		12 51			13 06			13 21				13 36		13 51		

For general notes see front of timetable
For details of catering facilities see Directory of Train Operators

b Arr. 1134
c Arr. 1208
e Arr. 1234
f Change at Tonbridge and Redhill

Mondays to Fridays
from 13 October

Margate, Ramsgate, Canterbury West, Dover, Folkestone, Ashford International, → Tonbridge and London

For details of Bank Holiday service alterations please see first page of Table 195

Network Diagram - see first page of Table 206

		SE	SE	SE	SE	SE	SE	SE		SE	SE	SE	SE	SE	SE	SE		SE	SE	SE	SE	SE	SE	SE	
		8	90	4	8	61	64	8		2	90	8	64	8	90	4		8	61	64	8	2	90	8	
		1	1	1	1		1	1		1	1	1	1	1	1	1		1		1	1	1	1	1	
Margate 4	d		12 04	11 41							12 15				13 04	12 41							13 15		
Broadstairs	d		12 09												13 09										
Dumpton Park	d		12 12												13 12										
Ramsgate 4	d		12 19	11 57							12 43				13 19	12 57							13 42		
Minster 4	d										12 48												13 48		
Sandwich	d			12 09												13 09									
Deal	d			12 15												13 15									
Walmer	d			12 18												13 18									
Martin Mill	d			12 24												13 24									
Dover Priory 4	a			12 32												13 32									
	d			12 33						12 50						13 33						13 50			
Folkestone Central	d			12 45						13 01						13 45						14 02			
Folkestone West	d									13 04												14 04			
Sandling	d									13 09												14 10			
Westenhanger	d									13 12												14 13			
Sturry	d										13 00												14 00		
Canterbury West 4	d		12 39								13 06		13 24		13 39								14 06		
Chartham	d												13 29												
Chilham	d												13 33												
Wye	d												13 39												
Rye	d									12 54												13 54			
Ashford International	a		12 56	12 59			←			13 21	13 24		13 46		13 56	13 59				←		14 21	14 24		
	d	12 57	13 03				13 05	13 20		13 28			14 05	13 57	14 03					14 05	14 20	14 28			
Maidstone East 4	a		13 34				13 34			13 57			→		14 34					14 34		14 57			
Bromley South 4	a		14 14				14 14								15 14					15 14		16 14			
London Victoria 15	⊖ a		14 32				14 32					←			15 32					15 32		16 33		←	
Pluckley	d							13 27 →				13 27									14 27 →			14 27	
Headcorn 4	d	13b14			←							13c40		14e14				←						14f40	
Staplehurst	d	13 19 →			13 19					13 41		13 45		14 19 →				14 19				14 41		14 45	
Marden	d											13 50												14 50	
Maidstone West 4	d					13 24				13 24									14 24			14 24			
Paddock Wood 4	d				13 28	13a44				13 49		13 56						14 28	14a44			14 49		14 56	
Tonbridge 4	a		13 25		13 35					13 57		14 03			14 25			14 35				14 57		15 03	
	d		13 28		13 36					13 58		14 04			14 28			14 36				14 58		15 04	
Redhill	a		14 04							14 39					15 04							15 39			
Gatwick Airport 10	a		14g23							14 55					15g23							15 56			
Sevenoaks 4	a				13 47							14 15						14 47						15 15	
Orpington 4	a				13 57							14 25						14 57						15 25	
London Bridge 4	⊖ a				14 13							14 43						15 13						15 43	
London Cannon Street 4	⊖ a																								
London Waterloo (East) 4	⊖ a		14 02		14 18					14 32		14 48			15 02			15 18				15 32		15 48	
London Charing Cross 4	⊖ a		14 06		14 21					14 36		14 51			15 06			15 21				15 36		15 51	

For general notes see front of timetable
For details of catering facilities see Directory of Train Operators

b Arr. 1308
c Arr. 1334
e Arr. 1408
f Arr. 1434
g Change at Tonbridge and Redhill

Margate, Ramsgate, Canterbury West, Dover, Folkestone, Ashford International, → Tonbridge and London

For details of Bank Holiday service alterations please see first page of Table 195

Network Diagram - see first page of Table 206

Station		SE 90	SE 4	SE 8		SE 61	SE 64	SE 2	SE 90	SE 4	SE 90	SE 61		SE 64	SE 8	SE 2	SE 90	SE 61	SE 4	SE 90		SE 4	SE 90	SE 61
		1	1	1			1	1	1	1	1			1	1	1	1		1	1		1	1	
								⚒		⚒						⚒			⚒			⚒		
Margate 4	d	14 04	13 41						14 15		14 50						14 50			15 36		15 41		
Broadstairs	d	14 09	13 46							14 20	14 55								15 20	15 41		15 46		
Dumpton Park	d	14 12									14 58								15 23	15 44				
Ramsgate 4	d	14 17	13 55						14 38	14 34	15 02						15 27		15 32	15 48		16 04	16 27	
Minster 4	d								14 44								15 33			15 54			16 33	
Sandwich	d		14 07							14 47									15 44			16 16		
Deal	d		14 13							14 53									15 50			16 22		
Walmer	d		14 16							14 56									15 53			16 25		
Martin Mill	d		14 22							15 02									15 59			16 31		
Dover Priory 4	a		14 30							15 11									16 07			16 39		
	d		14 31					14 46		15 12						15 40			16 08			16 40		
Folkestone Central	d		14 43					14 58		15 24						15 52			16 20			16 52		
Folkestone West	d							15 00								15 54						16 54		
Sandling	d							15 06								16 00						17 00		
Westenhanger	d							15 09								16 03						17 03		
Sturry	d								14 56								15 45			16 05			16 45	
Canterbury West 4	d	14 37					14 24		15 02		15 22			15 32			15 51			16 11			16 51	
Chartham	d						14 29							15 37			15 56			16 17			16 56	
Chilham	d						14 33							15 41			16 00			16 21			17 00	
Wye	d						14 39							15 47			16 07			16 27			17 07	
Rye	d							14 54											15 54					
Ashford International	a	14 54	14 57				14 46	15 17	15 20	15 37	15 42			15 54		16 12	16 14		16 34	16 36		17 12	17 14	
	d	15 02		14 52			15 03	15 24		15 46				15 59	16 06	16 19			16 41			17 19		
Maidstone East 4	a						15 32	15 56						16 28		16 45			17 27			17 47		
Bromley South 4	a						16 14	16 47						17 14		17 47			18 13			18 45		
London Victoria 15	⊖ a						16 33	17 11		17 31				17 31		18 09			18 33			19 03		
Pluckley	d			14 59						15 53									16 48					
Headcorn 4	d			15b13						15 59						16 29			16 54					
Staplehurst	d			15 18				15 37		16 04					16 20	16 34			16 59			17 32		
Marden	d			15 22						16 09									17 04					
Maidstone West 4	d					15 24						15 55			15 55			16 38	16 38					17 28
Paddock Wood 4	d			15 28		15a44		15 45		16 15		16a15			16 28	16 42		16a58	17 10			17 40		17a48
Tonbridge 4	a	15 25		15 36				15 53		16 22					16 36	16 50			17 17			17 49		
	d	15 28		15 36				15 54		16 23					16 40	16 51			17 18			17 50		
Redhill	a	16 04						16 39		16 59						17 51			18 13			18 51		
Gatwick Airport 10	✈ a	16c23						16 56		17e32						18e12			18e32			19e07		
Sevenoaks 4	a			15 48				16 03		16 32					16 52	17 03			17 30			18 02		
Orpington 4	a			15 57				16 34		16 49					17 02	17 12			17 39			18 11		
London Bridge 4	⊖ a			16 13				16 29		17 00					17 26	17 31			18 19			18 28		
London Cannon Street 4	⊖ a			16 22				16 36		17 08					17 31	17 39			18f29			18 37		
London Waterloo (East) 4	⊖ a	16 02		16 18				16 34		17 05						17 36			18 03			18 33		
London Charing Cross 4	⊖ a	16 06		16 21				16 38		17 10						17 41			18 07			18 37		

Station		SE 90	SE 4	SE 18	SE 61	SE 90		SE 61	SE 18	SE 90	SE 18	SE 90	SE 18	SE 61		SE 90	SE 94	SE 4	SE 61	SE 90	SE 4	SE 61	SE 90	SE 4	SE 01
		1	1	1		1			1	1	1	1	1			1	1	1		1	1		1	1	1
				⚒					⚒	⚒	⚒		⚒												
Margate 4	d	16 36	16 15							17 45		18 13				18 52		18 52		19 40			20 47		21 43
Broadstairs	d	16 41		16 52						17 51		18 19				18 57		18 57		19 46			20 52		21 48
Dumpton Park	d	16 44								17 53		18 21				19 00				19 48			20 55		21 27
Ramsgate 4	d	16 48	16 32	17 10		17 27				18 04	18 09	18 36				19 04		19 14		20 04	20 20		21 04	21 20	22 22
Minster 4	d	16 54		17g20		17 33				18 10	18h20	18 42				19 10				20 10			21 10		22 27
Sandwich	d		16 44	17 28							18 27							19 26			20 32			21 32	
Deal	d		16 50	17 34							18 33							19 32			20 38			21 38	
Walmer	d		16 53	17 37							18 37							19 35			20 41			21 41	
Martin Mill	d		16 59	17 43							18 42							19 41			20 47			21 47	
Dover Priory 4	a		17 07	17 51					←		18 51		←					19 49			20 55			21 55	
	d		17 08	17 52					17 52		18 52		18 52					19 50			20 56			22 00	
Folkestone Central	d		17 20	→					18 04		→		19 04					20 02			21 08			22 12	
Folkestone West	d								18 06				19 06					20 04			21 11			22 14	
Sandling	d								18 12				19 12					20 10			21 16			22 20	
Westenhanger	d								18 15				19 15					20 13			21 19			22 23	
Sturry	d	17 05				17 45				18 21		18 53				19 21				20 21			21 21		22 38
Canterbury West 4	d	17 11				17 51				18 27		18 59				19 27	19 34			20 27			21 27		22 44
Chartham	d	17 17				17 56				18 33		19 05				19 33	19 39			20 33			21 33		22 50
Chilham	d	17 21				18 00				18 37		19 09				19 37	19 43			20 37			21 37		22 53
Wye	d	17 27				18 07				18 43		19 15				19 43	19 49			20 43			21 43		23 00
Rye	d	16 54							17 54			18 54					19 31	19 54			20 54			21 57	
Ashford International	a	17 34	17 36			18 14			18 23	18 50		19 22	19 24			19 50	19 57	20 22		20 50	21 28		21 50	22 32	23 06
	d	17 41				18 16			18 25	18 51		19 29				19 51	19 58	20 29		20 51	21 29		21 51	22 33	
Maidstone East 4	a	18 29								19 29							20 27			21 27			22 37		
Bromley South 4	a	19 14								20 14						21 13	21 13			22 13			23 23		
London Victoria 15	⊖ a	19 31								20 32						21 29	21 29			22 32			23 45		
Pluckley	d	17 48							18 32	18 58						19 58				20 58			21 58	22 40	
Headcorn 4	d	17 54							18 38	19 04						20 04				21 04			22 04	22 46	
Staplehurst	d	17 59				18 29			18 43	19 09		19 42				20 09		20 42		21 09	21 42		22 09	22 51	
Marden	d	18 04							18 48	19 14						20 14				21 14			22 14	22 56	
Maidstone West 4	d	17 28			17 59	17 59		18 31		18 31				19 39		19 39			20 35	20 35		21 32	21 32		
Paddock Wood 4	d	18 10			18a19	18 37		18a51	18 54	19 20		19 50		19a59		20 20		20 50	20a55	21 20	21 50	21a52	22 20	23 02	
Tonbridge 4	a	18 18				18 45			19 03	19 27		19 58				20 27		20 58		21 28	21 58		22 28	23 09	
	d	18 20				18 46			19 11	19 30		20 00				20 31		21 00		21 30	22 00		22 30	23 10	
Redhill	a					19 39				20 24						21 24				22 23				23 48	
Gatwick Airport 10	✈ a					19e58				20 35						21 34				22 35				00e11	
Sevenoaks 4	a	18 29				18 58				19 39		20 09				20 40		21 09		21 39	22 09		22 39	23 22	
Orpington 4	a	18 39				19 07				19 49		20 19				20 49		21 19		21 49	22 19		22 49	23 33	
London Bridge 4	⊖ a	18 57				19 25				20 08		20 38				21 08		21 38		22 08	22 38		23 08	23 51	
London Cannon Street 4	⊖ a	19 05				19 37				20 27															
London Waterloo (East) 4	⊖ a	19 02				19 31			19 46	20 13		20 43				21 13		21 43		22 13	22 43		23 13	23 56	
London Charing Cross 4	⊖ a	19 07				19 35			19 50	20 18		20 48				21 18		21 48		22 18	22 48		23 18	00 01	

For general notes see front of timetable
For details of catering facilities see Directory of Train Operators

b Arr. 1507
c Change at Redhill and Tonbridge
e Change at Tonbridge and Redhill
f Change at Orpington and London Bridge
g Arr. 1716
h Arr. 1815

Table 207

Mondays to Fridays

from 13 October

Margate, Ramsgate, Canterbury West, Dover, Folkestone, Ashford International, → Tonbridge and London

For details of Bank Holiday service alterations please see first page of Table 195

Network Diagram - see first page of Table 206

		SE 4 1
Margate 4	d	
Broadstairs	d	
Dumpton Park	d	
Ramsgate 4	d	22 32
Minster 4	d	
Sandwich	d	22 44
Deal	d	22 50
Walmer	d	22 53
Martin Mill	d	22 59
Dover Priory 4	a	23 08
	d	23 20
Folkestone Central	d	23 32
Folkestone West	d	23 34
Sandling	d	23 40
Westenhanger	d	23 43
Sturry	d	
Canterbury West 4	d	
Chartham	d	
Chilham	d	
Wye	d	
Rye	d	
Ashford International	a	23 51
	d	
Maidstone East 4	a	
Bromley South 4	a	
London Victoria 15	⊖ a	
Pluckley	d	
Headcorn 4	d	
Staplehurst	d	
Marden	d	
Maidstone West 4	d	
Paddock Wood 4	d	
Tonbridge 4	a	
	d	
Redhill	a	
Gatwick Airport 10	a	
Sevenoaks 4	a	
Orpington 4	a	
London Bridge 4	⊖ a	
London Cannon Street 4	⊖ a	
London Waterloo (East) 4	⊖ a	
London Charing Cross 4	⊖ a	

For general notes see front of timetable
For details of catering facilities see Directory of Train Operators

Margate, Ramsgate, Canterbury West, Dover, Folkestone, Ashford International, → Tonbridge and London

Network Diagram - see first page of Table 206

		SE	SE	SE	SE	SE	SE	SE	SE	SE	SE	SE	SE	SE	SE	SE	SE	SE	SE	SE	SE	SE	SE
		2	61	2	90	4	61	4	90	4	61	8	4	90	8	8	90	4	8	8	61	4	90
		[1]		[1]	[1]	[1]		[1]	[1]	[1]		[1]	[1]	[1]	[1]	[1]	[1]	[1]	[1]	[1]		[1]	[1]
													🛒	🛒			🛒	🛒				🛒	
Margate [4]	d												06 49	07 26			08 04	07 26				07 46	
Broadstairs	d												06 54	07 31			08 09					07 51	
Dumpton Park	d												06 56	07 34			08 12					07 53	
Ramsgate [4] ✈	d				06 01	05 42		06 18	07 01	06 47			07 14	07 38			08 16	07 57				08 14	08 43
Minster [4]	d				06 07				07 07					07 44									08 49
Sandwich	d					05 54		06 30		06 59			07 26					08 09				08 26	
Deal	d					06 00		06 36		07 05			07 32					08 15				08 32	
Walmer	d					06 03		06 39		07 08			07 36					08 18				08 36	
Martin Mill	d					06 09		06 45		07 14			07 41					08 24				08 41	
Dover Priory [4] ⛴	a					06 17		06 53		07 22			07 50					08 32				08 50	
	d	04 44		05 43		06 18		06 54		07 23			07 50					08 33				08 50	
Folkestone Central	d	04 56		05 55		06 29		07 06		07 35			08 02					08 45				09 02	
Folkestone West	d	04 58		05 57		06 32		07 08					08 04									09 04	
Sandling	d	05 04		06 03		06 37		07 14					08 10									09 10	
Westenhanger	d	05 07		06 06		06 40		07 17					08 13									09 13	
Sturry	d				06 18				07 18					07 55									09 00
Canterbury West [4]	d				06 24				07 24					08 01			08 35						09 06
Chartham	d				06 29				07 29					08 07			08 40						
Chilham	d				06 33				07 33					08 11			08 44						
Wye	d				06 40				07 40					08 17			08 51						
Rye	d				*05 56*			*06 50*					*07 54*									*08 54*	
Ashford International	a	05 15		06 14	06 47	06 49		07 26	07 47	07 49			08 21	08 24			08 58	09 00				09 21	09 24
	d	05 21		06 20	06 52			07 26	07 52			08 20	08 28			08 57	09 04		09 20			09 28	
Maidstone East [4]	a	*06 29*			*07 29*			*07 57*	*08 34*				*08 57*				*09 34*					*09 57*	
Bromley South [4]	a	*07 14*			*08 14*				*09 14*								*10 14*						
London Victoria [15]	⊖ a	*07 32*			*08 32*				*09 32*						←		*10 32*						
Pluckley	d	05 28		06 27	06 59				07 59			08 27 →			08 27				09 27 →	←			
Headcorn [4]	d	05 34		06 33	07 06			07 37	08 06						08b40	09c14							
Staplehurst	d	05 39		06 38	07 11			07 42	08 11				08 41		08 45	09 19 →				09 19		09 41	
Marden	d	05 44		06 43	07 15				08 15						08 50								
Maidstone West [4]	d		06 26	*06 26*			07 24	*07 24*			08 24		*08 24*								09 24	*09 24*	
Paddock Wood [4]	d	05 50	06a45	06 49	07 21		07a44	07 50	08 21		08a44		08 49		08 56					09 28	09a44	09 49	
Tonbridge [4]	a	05 58		06 57	07 31			07 58	08 30				08 57		09 03		09 25			09 35		09 57	
	d	06 00		06 59	07 31			08 00	08 31				08 58		09 04		09 28			09 36		09 58	
Redhill	a	*07 23*		*08 04*				*08 39*	*09 04*				*09 39*				*10 04*					*10 39*	
Gatwick Airport [10] ✈	a	*07 34*		*08e23*				*08 55*	*09e23*				*09 55*				*10e23*					*10 55*	
Sevenoaks [4]	a	06 12		07 11	07 43			08 09	08 43						09 15					09 47			
Orpington [4]	a	06 21		07 20	07 53			08 19	08 53						09 25					09 57			
London Bridge [4]	⊖ a	06 40		07 40	08 10			08 40	09 10						09 43					10 13			
London Cannon Street [4]	⊖ a			*07 50*	*08 20*			*08 47*	*09 17*						*09 50*								
London Waterloo (East) [4]	⊖ a	06 44		07 44	08 14			08 45	09 15				09 32		09 48		10 02			10 18		10 32	
London Charing Cross [4]	⊖ a	06 48		07 48	08 18			08 48	09 18				09 36		09 51		10 06			10 21		10 36	

For general notes see front of timetable
For details of catering facilities see Directory of Train Operators

b Arr. 0834
c Arr. 0908
e Change at Tonbridge and Redhill

Table 207

Saturdays

Margate, Ramsgate, Canterbury West, Dover, Folkestone, Ashford International, → Tonbridge and London

Network Diagram - see first page of Table 206

		SE	SE	SE	SE	SE		SE	SE	SE	SE	SE	SE	SE	SE		SE	SE	SE	SE	SE	SE	SE	SE	SE
		8	64	8	90	4		8	61	64	8	4	90	8	64		8	90	4	8	61	64	8	4	90
		1	1	1	1	1		1		1	1	1	1	1	1		1	1	1	1		1	1	1	1
					⊼	⊼						⊼						⊼	⊼					⊼	
Margate 4	d				09 04							08 48						10 04	09 41						10 15
Broadstairs	d				09 09							08 53						10 09							
Dumpton Park	d				09 12							08 56						10 12							
Ramsgate 4 ✈	d				09 20	08 57						09 14	09 43					10 20	09 57					10 14	10 43
Minster 4	d												09 49												10 49
Sandwich	d					09 09						09 26							10 09					10 26	
Deal	d					09 15						09 32							10 15					10 32	
Walmer	d					09 18						09 36							10 18					10 36	
Martin Mill	d					09 24						09 41							10 24					10 41	
Dover Priory 4 ⛴	a					09 32						09 50							10 32					10 50	
	d					09 33						09 50							10 33					10 50	
Folkestone Central	d					09 45						10 02							10 45					11 02	
Folkestone West	d											10 04												11 04	
Sandling	d											10 10												11 10	
Westenhanger	d											10 13												11 13	
Sturry	d												10 00												11 00
Canterbury West 4	d		09 24		09 39								10 06		10 24			10 39							11 06
Chartham	d		09 29												10 29										
Chilham	d		09 33												10 33										
Wye	d		09 39												10 39										
Rye	d											09 54												10 54	
Ashford International	a		09 46		09 56	09 59						10 21	10 24		10 46			10 56	10 59					11 21	11 24
	d		10 05 →	09 57	10 03					← 10 05	10 20	10 28			11 05 →		10 57	11 03				← 11 05	11 20	11 28	
Maidstone East 4	a				10 34					10 34		10 57						11 34				11 34		11 57	
Bromley South 4	a				11 14					11 14								12 14				12 14			
London Victoria 15	⊖ a	←			11 32					11 32				←				12 32				12 32			
Pluckley	d	09 27									10 27 →			10 27									11 27 →		
Headcorn 4	d	09b40		10c14				←						10e40			11f14			←					
Staplehurst	d	09 45		10 19 →				10 19				10 41		10 45			11 19 →			11 19				11 41	
Marden	d	09 50												10 50											
Maidstone West 4	d								10 24			10 24									11 24			11 24	
Paddock Wood 4	d	09 56						10 28	10a44			10 49		10 56						11 28	11a44			11 49	
Tonbridge 4	a	10 03			10 25			10 35				10 57		11 03				11 25		11 35				11 57	
	d	10 04			10 28			10 36				10 58		11 04				11 28		11 36				11 58	
Redhill	a				11 04							11 39						12 04						12 39	
Gatwick Airport 10 ✈	a				11g23							11 55						12g23						12 55	
Sevenoaks 4	a	10 15						10 47						11 15						11 47					
Orpington 4	a	10 25						10 57						11 25						11 57					
London Bridge 4	⊖ a	10 43						11 13						11 43						12 13					
London Cannon Street 4	⊖ a	10 50						11 20						11 50											
London Waterloo (East) 4	⊖ a	10 48			11 02			11 18				11 32		11 48				12 02		12 18				12 32	
London Charing Cross 4	⊖ a	10 51			11 06			11 21				11 36		11 51				12 06		12 21				12 36	

		SE	SE		SE	SE	SE	SE	SE	SE	SE	SE	SE		SE	SE	SE	SE	SE	SE	SE	SE		SE	
		8	64		8	90	4	8	61	64	8	4	90		8	64	8	90	4	8	61	64		8	
		1	1		1	1	1	1		1	1	1	1		1	1	1	1	1	1		1		1	
						⊼	⊼					⊼						⊼	⊼						
Margate 4	d					11 04	10 41						11 15					12 04	11 41						
Broadstairs	d					11 09												12 09							
Dumpton Park	d					11 12												12 12							
Ramsgate 4 ✈	d					11 20	10 57					11 14	11 43					12 20	11 57						
Minster 4	d												11 49												
Sandwich	d						11 09					11 26							12 09						
Deal	d						11 15					11 32							12 15						
Walmer	d						11 18					11 36							12 18						
Martin Mill	d						11 24					11 41							12 24						
Dover Priory 4 ⛴	a						11 32					11 50							12 32						
	d						11 33					11 50							12 33						
Folkestone Central	d						11 45					12 02							12 45						
Folkestone West	d											12 04													
Sandling	d											12 10													
Westenhanger	d											12 13													
Sturry	d												12 00												
Canterbury West 4	d		11 24			11 39							12 06			12 24		12 39							
Chartham	d		11 29													12 29									
Chilham	d		11 33													12 33									
Wye	d		11 39													12 39									
Rye	d											11 54													
Ashford International	a		11 46			11 56	11 59					12 21	12 24			12 46		12 56	12 59						
	d		12 05 →		11 57	12 03				← 12 05	12 20	12 28				13 05 →	12 57	13 03				← 13 05		13 20	
Maidstone East 4	a					12 34				12 34		12 57						13 34				13 34			
Bromley South 4	a					13 14				13 14								14 14				14 14			
London Victoria 15	⊖ a	←				13 32				13 32					←			14 32				14 32			
Pluckley	d	11 27									12 27 →				12 27									13 27 →	
Headcorn 4	d	11h40			12j14			←							12k40		13m14			←					
Staplehurst	d	11 45			12 19 →			12 19				12 41			12 45		13 19 →			13 19					
Marden	d	11 50													12 50										
Maidstone West 4	d								12 24			12 24									13 24				
Paddock Wood 4	d	11 56						12 28	12a44			12 49			12 56					13 28	13a44				
Tonbridge 4	a	12 03				12 25		12 35				12 57			13 03			13 25		13 35					
	d	12 04				12 28		12 36				12 58			13 04			13 28		13 36					
Redhill	a					13 04						13 39						14 04							
Gatwick Airport 10 ✈	a					13g23						13 55						14g23							
Sevenoaks 4	a	12 15						12 47							13 15					13 47					
Orpington 4	a	12 25						12 57							13 25					13 57					
London Bridge 4	⊖ a	12 43						13 13							13 43					14 13					
London Cannon Street 4	⊖ a																								
London Waterloo (East) 4	⊖ a	12 48				13 02		13 18				13 32			13 48			14 02		14 18					
London Charing Cross 4	⊖ a	12 51				13 06		13 21				13 36			13 51			14 06		14 21					

For general notes see front of timetable
For details of catering facilities see Directory of Train Operators

b Arr. 0934
c Arr. 1008
e Arr. 1034
f Arr. 1108
g Change at Tonbridge and Redhill
h Arr. 1134
j Arr. 1208
k Arr. 1234
m Arr. 1308

Table 207

Saturdays

Margate, Ramsgate, Canterbury West, Dover, Folkestone, Ashford International, → Tonbridge and London

Network Diagram - see first page of Table 206

		SE	SE	SE	SE	SE	SE	SE	SE		SE	SE	SE	SE	SE	SE	SE	SE		SE	SE	SE	SE	SE	SE
		4	90	8	64	8	90	4	8		61	64	8	4	90	8	64	8		90	4	8	61	64	8
		1	1	1	1	1	1	1	1			1	1	1	1	1	1	1		1	1	1		1	1
		⊼					⊼	⊼						⊼						⊼	⊼				
Margate 4	d		12 15				13 04	12 41							13 15					14 04	13 41				
Broadstairs	d						13 09													14 09					
Dumpton Park	d						13 12													14 12					
Ramsgate 4 ✈	d	12 14	12 43				13 20	12 57						13 14	13 43					14 20	13 57				
Minster 4	d		12 49												13 49										
Sandwich	d	12 26						13 09						13 26							14 09				
Deal	d	12 32						13 15						13 32							14 15				
Walmer	d	12 36						13 18						13 36							14 18				
Martin Mill	d	12 41						13 24						13 41							14 24				
Dover Priory 4 ⛴	a	12 50						13 32						13 50							14 32				
	d	12 50						13 33						13 50							14 33				
Folkestone Central	d	13 02						13 45						14 02							14 45				
Folkestone West	d	13 04												14 04											
Sandling	d	13 10												14 10											
Westenhanger	d	13 13												14 13											
Sturry	d		13 00												14 00										
Canterbury West 4	d		13 06		13 24		13 39								14 06		14 24			14 39					
Chartham	d				13 29												14 29								
Chilham	d				13 33												14 33								
Wye	d				13 39												14 39								
Rye	d	12 54												13 54											
Ashford International	a	13 21	13 24		13 46		13 56	13 59				←		14 21	14 24		14 46			14 56	14 59			←	
	d	13 28			14 05 →	13 57	14 03					14 05	14 20	14 28			15 05 →	14 57		15 03				15 05	15 20
Maidstone East 4	a	13 57					14 34					14 34		14 57						15 34				15 34	
Bromley South 4	a						15 14					15 14								16 14				16 14	
London Victoria 15	⊖ a			←			15 32					15 32				←				16 32				16 32	
Pluckley	d			13 27									14 27 →			14 27									15 27 →
Headcorn 4	d			13b40		14c14			←							14e40		15f14				←			
Staplehurst	d	13 41		13 45		14 19 →			14 19					14 41		14 45		15 19 →				15 19			
Marden	d			13 50												14 50									
Maidstone West 4	d	13 24									14 24			14 24									15 24		
Paddock Wood 4	d	13 49		13 56					14 28		14a44			14 49		14 56						15 28	15a44		
Tonbridge 4	a	13 57		14 03			14 25		14 35					14 57		15 03				15 25		15 35			
	d	13 58		14 04			14 28		14 36					14 58		15 04				15 28		15 36			
Redhill	a	14 39					15 04							15 39						16 04					
Gatwick Airport 10 ✈	a	14 55					15g23							15 55						16g23					
Sevenoaks 4	a			14 15					14 47							15 15						15 47			
Orpington 4	a			14 25					14 57							15 25						15 57			
London Bridge 4	⊖ a			14 43					15 13							15 43						16 13			
London Cannon Street 4	⊖ a																								
London Waterloo (East) 4	⊖ a	14 32		14 48			15 02		15 18					15 32		15 48				16 02		16 18			
London Charing Cross 4	⊖ a	14 36		14 51			15 06		15 21					15 36		15 51				16 06		16 21			

		SE	SE	SE	SE		SE	SE	SE	SE	SE	SE	SE	SE	SE		SE	SE	SE	SE	SE	SE	SE	SE	SE
		4	90	8	64		8	90	4	8	61	64	8	4	90		8	64	8	90	4	8	64	4	90
		1	1	1	1		1	1	1	1		1	1	1	1		1	1	1	1	1	1	1	1	1
		⊼						⊼	⊼					⊼						⊼	⊼			⊼	
Margate 4	d		14 15					15 04	14 41						15 15					16 04				15 41	
Broadstairs	d							15 09												16 09				15 46	
Dumpton Park	d							15 12												16 12					
Ramsgate 4 ✈	d	14 14	14 43					15 20	14 57					15 14	15 43					16 20	15 50			16 01	16 25
Minster 4	d		14 49												15 49										16 31
Sandwich	d	14 26							15 09					15 26							16 02			16 13	
Deal	d	14 32							15 15					15 32							16 08			16 19	
Walmer	d	14 36							15 18					15 36							16 11			16 22	
Martin Mill	d	14 41							15 24					15 41							16 17			16 28	
Dover Priory 4 ⛴	a	14 50							15 32					15 50							16 25			16 36	
	d	14 50							15 33					15 50							16 28			16 37	
Folkestone Central	d	15 02							15 45					16 02							16 39			16 49	
Folkestone West	d	15 04												16 04							16 42				
Sandling	d	15 10												16 10							16 48				
Westenhanger	d	15 13												16 13							16 51				
Sturry	d		15 00												16 00										16 42
Canterbury West 4	d		15 06		15 24			15 39							16 06			16 24		16 39					16 48
Chartham	d				15 29													16 29							
Chilham	d				15 33													16 33							
Wye	d				15 39													16 39							
Rye	d	14 54												15 54											
Ashford International	a	15 21	15 24		15 46			15 56	15 59			←		16 21	16 24			16 46		16 56	16 59		←	17 02	17 05
	d	15 28			16 05 →		15 57	16 03				16 05	16 20	16 28				17 05 →	16 57	17 03			17 05	17 09	
Maidstone East 4	a	15 57						16 34				16 34		16 57						17 34			17 34	17 57	
Bromley South 4	a							17 14				17 14								18 14			18 14		
London Victoria 15	⊖ a			←				17 32				17 32					←			18 32			18 32		
Pluckley	d			15 27									16 27 →				16 27							17 16	
Headcorn 4	d			15h40			16j14			←							16k40		17m14			←		17 23	
Staplehurst	d	15 41		15 45			16 19 →			16 19				16 41			16 45		17 19 →			17 19		17 28	
Marden	d			15 50													16 50							17 32	
Maidstone West 4	d	15 24									16 24			16 24											
Paddock Wood 4	d	15 49		15 56						16 28	16a44			16 49			16 56					17 28		17 38	
Tonbridge 4	a	15 57		16 03				16 25		16 35				16 57			17 03			17 25		17 35		17 48	
	d	15 58		16 04				16 28		16 36				16 58			17 04			17 28		17 36		17 48	
Redhill	a	16 39						17 04						17 39						18 04				18 23	
Gatwick Airport 10 ✈	a	16 55						17g23						17 55						18g23				18 34	
Sevenoaks 4	a			16 15						16 47							17 15					17 47		18 00	
Orpington 4	a			16 25						16 57							17 25					17 57		18 10	
London Bridge 4	⊖ a			16 43						17 13							17 43					18 13		18 28	
London Cannon Street 4	⊖ a																					18 20		18 54	
London Waterloo (East) 4	⊖ a	16 32		16 48				17 02		17 18				17 32			17 48			18 02		18 18		18 32	
London Charing Cross 4	⊖ a	16 36		16 51				17 06		17 21				17 36			17 51			18 06		18 21		18 36	

For general notes see front of timetable
For details of catering facilities see Directory of Train Operators

- b Arr. 1334
- c Arr. 1408
- e Arr. 1434
- f Arr. 1508
- g Change at Tonbridge and Redhill
- h Arr. 1534
- j Arr. 1608
- k Arr. 1634
- m Arr. 1708

Table 207

Saturdays

Margate, Ramsgate, Canterbury West, Dover, Folkestone, Ashford International, → Tonbridge and London

Network Diagram - see first page of Table 206

	SE 61	SE 64 1		SE 4 1 (bus)	SE 61	SE 64 1	SE 90 1	SE 4 1	SE 61	SE 90 1	SE 4 1		SE 61	SE 90 1	SE 4 1	SE 90 1	SE 90 1	SE 4 1	SE 01 1	SE 4 1		SE 01 1	SE 61 1	
Margate 4 d				16 15			17 15			18 15				19 15		20 15		20 15	21 24			21 47	22 17	
Broadstairs d				16 20			17 20			18 20				19 20		20 20			21 29	20 52		21 52	22 22	
Dumpton Park d				16 23			17 23			18 23				19 23		20 23			21 32	20 54		21 54	22 25	
Ramsgate 4 d				16 43			17 39	17 43		18 39	18 43			19 39	19 43	20 39	21 00	20 35	21 36	21 29		22 20	22 32	
Minster 4 d							17 45			18 45				19 45		20 45	21 06		21 42			22 26		
Sandwich d				16 55				17 55			18 55				19 55			20 47		21 41			22 44	
Deal d				17 01				18 01			19 01				20 01			20 53		21 47			22 50	
Walmer d				17 04				18 04			19 04				20 04			20 56		21 50			22 53	
Martin Mill d				17 10				18 10			19 10				20 10			21 02		21 56			22 59	
Dover Priory 4 a				17 18				18 18			19 18				20 18			21 12		22 04			23 07	
d				17 19				18 19			19 19				20 19			21 15		22 05			23 08	
Folkestone Central d				17 31				18 31			19 31				20 31			21 27		22 16			23 19	
Folkestone West d				17 33				18 33			19 33				20 33			21 29		22 19			23 22	
Sandling d				17 39				18 39			19 39				20 39			21 35		22 24			23 27	
Westenhanger d				17 42				18 42			19 42				20 42			21 38		22 27			23 30	
Sturry d							17 56			18 56				19 56		20 56	21 17		21 53			22 37		
Canterbury West 4 d		17 24					18b04			19c04				20e04		21f04	21 23		21 59			22 43		
Chartham d		17 29					18 10			19 10				20 10		21 10	21 28		22 05			22 49		
Chilham d		17 33					18 14			19 14				20 14		21 14	21 32		22 09			22 53		
Wye d		17 39					18 20			19 20				20 20		21 20	21 39		22 15			22 59		
Rye d				16 54			17 54			18 54				19 54		20 54				21 57				
Ashford International a		17 46		17 50		←	18 28	18 50		19 28	19 50			20 28	20 50	21 28	21 46	21 48	22 22	22 36		23 06	23 39	
d		18 00		17 51		18 00	18 28	18 51		19 28	19 51			20 28	20 51	21 28	21 52			22 36				
Maidstone East 4 a		→		18 29		18 29		19 29			20 29				21 29		22 29							
Bromley South 4 a				19 14		19 14		20 14			21 14				22 14		23 14							
London Victoria 15 ⊖ a				19 32		19 32		20 32			21 32				22 32		23 32							
Pluckley d				17 58				18 58			19 58				20 58		21 59			22 43				
Headcorn 4 d				18 04			18 39	19 04		19 39	20 04			20 39	21 04	21 39	22 05			22 50				
Staplehurst d				18 09			18 44	19 09		19 44	20 09			20 44	21 09	21 44	22 10			22 55				
Marden d				18 14				19 14			20 14				21 14		22 15			22 59				
Maidstone West 4 d	17 24			17 24	18 24		18 24		19 24	19 24			20 24	20 24										
Paddock Wood 4 d	17a44			18 20	18a44		18 52	19 20	19a44	19 52	20 20		20a44	20 52	21 20	21 52	22 21			23 05				
Tonbridge 4 a				18 28			18 59	19 28		19 59	20 28			20 59	21 28	21 59	22 29			23 13				
d				18 30			19 00	19 30		20 00	20 30			21 00	21 30	22 00	22 30			23 13				
Redhill a				19 23				20 23			21 23				22 23		23 49							
Gatwick Airport 10 ✈ a				19 34				20 34			21 34				22 34		00g10							
Sevenoaks 4 a				18 42			19 09	19 42		20 09	20 42			21 09	21 42	22 09	22 42			23 25				
Orpington 4 a				18 51			19 19	19 51		20 19	20 51			21 19	21 51	22 19	22 51			23 37				
London Bridge 4 ⊖ a				19 08			19 38	20 08		20 38	21 08			21 38	22 08	22 38	23 08			23 53				
London Cannon Street 4 ⊖ a																								
London Waterloo (East) 4 ⊖ a				19 14			19 44	20 14		20 44	21 14			21 44	22 14	22 44	23 13			23 57				
London Charing Cross 4 ⊖ a				19 19			19 49	20 19		20 49	21 19			21 49	22 19	22 49	23 18			00 01				

For general notes see front of timetable
For details of catering facilities see Directory of Train Operators

b Arr. 1801
c Arr. 1901
e Arr. 2001
f Arr. 2101
g Change at Tonbridge and Redhill

Table 207

Sundays

Margate, Ramsgate, Canterbury West, Dover, Folkestone, Ashford International, → Tonbridge and London

Network Diagram - see first page of Table 206

		SE	SE	SE	SE	SE	SE	SE	SE	SE	SE	SE	SE	SE	SE	SE	SE	SE	SE	SE	SE	SE
		8	55	8	4	55	90	4	55	90	94	4	55	90	94	4	55	90	94	4	55	90
		[1]		[1]	[1]		[1]	[1]		[1]	[1]	[1]		[1]	[1]	[1]		[1]	[1]	[1]		[1]
			A			B			B				B				B				B	
Margate [4]	d									08 24		*08 24*		09 24		*09 24*		10 24		*10b24*		11 24
Broadstairs	d									08 29		*08 29*		09 29		*09 29*		10 29		*10c29*		11 29
Dumpton Park	d									08 32				09 32				10 32		*10e32*		11 32
Ramsgate [4] ✈	d				06 56		07 36	07 56		08 36		08 56		09 36		09 56		10 36		10 56		11 36
Minster [4]	d						07 42			08 42				09 42				10 42				11 42
Sandwich	d				07 08			08 08				09 08				10 08				11 08		
Deal	d				07 14			08 14				09 14				10 14				11 14		
Walmer	d				07 17			08 17				09 17				10 17				11 17		
Martin Mill	d				07 23			08 23				09 23				10 23				11 23		
Dover Priory [4] ⛴	a				07 31			08 31				09 31				10 31				11 31		
	d				07 32			08 32				09 32				10 32				11 32		
Folkestone Central	d				07 44			08 44				09 44				10 44				11 44		
Folkestone West	d				07 46			08 46				09 46				10 46				11 46		
Sandling	d				07 52			08 52				09 52				10 52				11 52		
Westenhanger	d				07 55			08 55				09 55				10 55				11 55		
Sturry	d						07 54			08 54				09 54				10 54				11 54
Canterbury West [4]	d						08 00			09 00	09 44			10 00	10 44			11 00	11 44			12 00
Chartham	d						08 05			09 05				10 05				11 05				12 05
Chilham	d						08 09			09 09				10 09				11 09				12 09
Wye	d						08 16			09 16				10 16				11 16				12 16
Rye	d						*07 43*			*08 41*				*09 46*				*10 46*				*11 46*
Ashford International	a				08 03		08 23	09 03		09 23	10 00	10 03		10 23	11 00	11 03		11 23	12 00	12 03		12 23
	d	06 40		07 23	08 04		08 24	09 04		09 24	10 01	10 04		10 24	11 01	11 04		11 24	12 01	12 04		12 24
Maidstone East [4]	a						*09 30*				10 30				11 30				12 30			
Bromley South [4]	a						*10 16*			*11 16*	11 16			*12 16*	12 16			*13 16*	13 16			*14 16*
London Victoria [15] ⊖	a						*10 32*			*11 32*	11 32			*12 32*	12 32			*13 32*	13 32			*14 32*
Pluckley	d	06 47		07 30			08 31			09 31				10 31				11 31				12 31
Headcorn [4]	d	06 53		07 36			08 37			09 37				10 37				11 37				12 37
Staplehurst	d	06 58		07 41	08 17		08 42	09 17		09 42		10 17		10 42		11 17		11 42		12 17		12 42
Marden	d	07 03		07 46			08 47			09 47				10 47				11 47				12 47
Maidstone West [4]	d		07 15	*07 15*		08 15	*08 15*		09 15	*09 15*			10 15	*10 15*			11 15	*11 15*			12 15	*12 15*
Paddock Wood [4]	d	07 09	07 35	07 52	08 25	08 35	08 53	09 25	09 35	09 53		10 25	10 35	10 53		11 25	11 35	11 53		12 25	12 35	12 53
Tonbridge [4]	a	07 16	07 43	07 59	08 32	08 43	09 00	09 32	09 43	10 00		10 32	10 43	11 00		11 32	11 43	12 00		12 32	12 43	13 00
	d	07 17	07 53	08 00	08 33	08 53	09 01	09 33	09 53	10 01		10 33	10 53	11 01		11 33	11 53	12 01		12 33	12 53	13 01
Redhill	a	*08 24*	08 24		*09 24*	09 24		*10 24*	10 24			*11 24*	11 24			*12 24*	12 24			*13 24*	13 24	
Gatwick Airport [10] ✈	a	*08 38*	08 38		*09 38*	09 38		*10 38*	10 38			*11 38*	11 38			*12 38*	12 38			*13 38*	13 38	
Sevenoaks [4]	a	07 29		08 12	08 43		09 13	09 43		10 13		10 43		11 13		11 43		12 13		12 43		13 13
Orpington [4]	a	07 40		08 23	08 53		09 23	09 53		10 23		10 53		11 23		11 53		12 23		12 53		13 23
London Bridge [4] ⊖	a	07 56		08 39	09 09		09 39	10 09		10 39		11 09		11 39		12 09		12 39		13 09		13 39
London Cannon Street [4] ⊖	a																					
London Waterloo (East) [4] ⊖	a	08 01		08 44	09 14		09 44	10 14		10 44		11 14		11 44		12 14		12 44		13 14		13 44
London Charing Cross [4] ⊖	a	08 05		08 48	09 18		09 48	10 18		10 48		11 18		11 48		12 18		12 48		13 18		13 48

For general notes see front of timetable
For details of catering facilities see Directory of Train Operators

A From Gillingham (Kent) (Table 208) to Three Bridges (Table 186)
B To Three Bridges (Table 186)
b 20 July to 31 August dep. 1029
c 20 July to 31 August dep. 1034
e 20 July to 31 August dep. 1037

Sundays

Margate, Ramsgate, Canterbury West, Dover, Folkestone, Ashford International, → Tonbridge and London

Network Diagram - see first page of Table 206

		SE	SE	SE	SE	SE	SE	SE	SE	SE	SE	SE	SE	SE	SE	SE	SE	SE	SE	SE	SE
		94	4	55	90	94	4	55	90	94	4	55	90	94	4	55	90	94	4	55	90
		1	1		1	1	1		1	1	1		1	1	1		1	1	1		1
				A				A				A				A				A	
Margate 4	d		*11b24*		12 24		*12 24*		13 24		*13 24*		14 24		*14 24*		15 24		*15 24*		16 24
Broadstairs	d		*11c29*		12 29		*12 29*		13 29		*13 29*		14 29		*14 29*		15 29		*15 29*		16 29
Dumpton Park	d		*11e32*		12 32				13 32				14 32				15 32				16 32
Ramsgate 4	d		11 56		12 36		12 56		13 36		13 56		14 36		14 56		15 36		15 56		16 36
Minster 4	d				12 42				13 42				14 42				15 42				16 42
Sandwich	d		12 08				13 08				14 08				15 08				16 08		
Deal	d		12 14				13 14				14 14				15 14				16 14		
Walmer	d		12 17				13 17				14 17				15 17				16 17		
Martin Mill	d		12 23				13 23				14 23				15 23				16 23		
Dover Priory 4	a		12 31				13 31				14 31				15 31				16 31		
	d		12 32				13 32				14 32				15 32				16 32		
Folkestone Central	d		12 44				13 44				14 44				15 44				16 44		
Folkestone West	d		12 46				13 46				14 46				15 46				16 46		
Sandling	d		12 52				13 52				14 52				15 52				16 52		
Westenhanger	d		12 55				13 55				14 55				15 55				16 55		
Sturry	d				12 54				13 54				14 54				15 54				16 54
Canterbury West 4	d	12 44			13 00	13 44			14 00	14 44			15 00	15 44			16 00	16 44			17 00
Chartham	d				13 05				14 05				15 05				16 05				17 05
Chilham	d				13 09				14 09				15 09				16 09				17 09
Wye	d				13 16				14 16				15 16				16 16				17 16
Rye	d				*12 46*				*13 46*				*14 46*				*15 46*				*16 46*
Ashford International	a	13 00	13 03		13 23	14 00	14 03		14 23	15 00	15 03		15 23	16 00	16 03		16 23	17 00	17 03		17 23
	d	13 01	13 04		13 24	14 01	14 04		14 24	15 01	15 04		15 24	16 01	16 04		16 24	17 01	17 04		17 24
Maidstone East 4	a	13 30				14 30				15 30				16 30				17 30			
Bromley South 4	a	14 16			*15 16*	15 16			*16 16*	16 16			*17 16*	17 16			*18 16*	18 16			*19 16*
London Victoria 15	⊖ a	14 32			*15 32*	15 32			*16 32*	16 32			*17 32*	17 32			*18 32*	18 32			*19 32*
Pluckley	d				13 31				14 31				15 31				16 31				17 31
Headcorn 4	d				13 37				14 37				15 37				16 37				17 37
Staplehurst	d		13 17		13 42		14 17		14 42		15 17		15 42		16 17		16 42		17 17		17 42
Marden	d				13 47				14 47				15 47				16 47				17 47
Maidstone West 4	d			13 15	*13 15*			14 15	*14 15*			15 15	*15 15*			16 15	*16 15*			17 15	*17 15*
Paddock Wood 4	d		13 25	13 35	13 53		14 25	14 35	14 53		15 25	15 35	15 53		16 25	16 35	16 53		17 25	17 35	17 53
Tonbridge 4	a		13 32	13 43	14 00		14 32	14 43	15 00		15 32	15 43	16 00		16 32	16 43	17 00		17 32	17 43	18 00
	d		13 33	13 53	14 01		14 33	14 53	15 01		15 33	15 53	16 01		16 33	16 53	17 01		17 33	17 53	18 01
Redhill	a		*14 24*	14 24			*15 24*	15 24			*16 24*	16 24			*17 24*	17 24			*18 24*	18 24	
Gatwick Airport 10	a		*14 38*	14 38			*15 38*	15 38			*16 38*	16 38			*17 38*	17 38			*18 38*	18 38	
Sevenoaks 4	a		13 43		14 13		14 43		15 13		15 43		16 13		16 43		17 13		17 43		18 13
Orpington 4	a		13 53		14 23		14 53		15 23		15 53		16 23		16 53		17 23		17 53		18 23
London Bridge 4	⊖ a		14 09		14 39		15 09		15 39		16 09		16 39		17 09		17 39		18 09		18 39
London Cannon Street 4	⊖ a																				
London Waterloo (East) 4	⊖ a		14 14		14 44		15 14		15 44		16 14		16 44		17 14		17 44		18 14		18 44
London Charing Cross 4	⊖ a		14 18		14 48		15 18		15 48		16 18		16 48		17 18		17 48		18 18		18 48

		SE	SE	SE	SE	SE	SE	SE	SE	SE	SE	SE	SE	SE	SE	SE	SE	SE	SE
		94	4	55	90	94	4	55	90	94	4	55	90	4	61	90	90	4	4
		1	1		1	1	1		1	1	1		1	1		1	1	1	1
				A				A				A							
Margate 4	d		*16 24*		17 24		*17 24*		18 24		*18 24*		19 24	*19 24*		20 24	*20 45*		21 24
Broadstairs	d		*16 29*		17 29		*17 29*		18 29		*18 29*		19 29	*19 29*		20 29	*20 50*		21 29
Dumpton Park	d				17 32				18 32				19 32			20 32	*20 53*		21 32
Ramsgate 4	d		16 56		17 36		17 56		18 36		18 56		19 36	19 56		20 36	21 00	20 43	21 36
Minster 4	d				17 42				18 42				19 42			20 42	21 06		
Sandwich	d		17 08				18 08				19 08			20 08				20 55	21 48
Deal	d		17 14				18 14				19 14			20 14				21 01	21 54
Walmer	d		17 17				18 17				19 17			20 17				21 04	21 57
Martin Mill	d		17 23				18 23				19 23			20 23				21 10	22 03
Dover Priory 4	a		17 31				18 31				19 31			20 31				21 18	22 11
	d		17 32				18 32				19 32			20 32				21 19	22 12
Folkestone Central	d		17 44				18 44				19 44			20 44				21 31	22 24
Folkestone West	d		17 46				18 46				19 46			20 46				21 33	22 26
Sandling	d		17 52				18 52				19 52			20 52				21 39	22 32
Westenhanger	d		17 55				18 55				19 55			20 55				21 42	22 35
Sturry	d				17 54				18 54				19 54			20 54	21 18		
Canterbury West 4	d	17 44			18 00	18 44			19 00	19 44			20 00			21 00	21 24		
Chartham	d				18 05				19 05				20 05			21 05	21 29		
Chilham	d				18 09				19 09				20 09			21 09	21 33		
Wye	d				18 16				19 16				20 16			21 16	21 40		
Rye	d				*17 46*				*18 46*				*19 46*			*20 46*			
Ashford International	a	18 00	18 03		18 23	19 00	19 03		19 23	20 00	20 03		20 23	21 03		21 23	21 47	21 50	22 43
	d	18 01	18 04		18 24	19 01	19 04		19 24	20 01	20 04		20 24	21 04		21 24	21 54		
Maidstone East 4	a	18 30				19 30				20 30			*21 30*				*22 30*		
Bromley South 4	a	19 16			*20 16*	20 16			*21 16*	21 16			*22 16*				*23 16*		
London Victoria 15	⊖ a	19 32			*20 32*	20 32			*21 32*	21 32			*22 32*				*23 32*		
Pluckley	d				18 31				19 31				20 31			21 31	22 01		
Headcorn 4	d				18 37				19 37				20 37			21 37	22 07		
Staplehurst	d		18 17		18 42		19 17		19 42		20 17		20 42	21 17		21 42	22 12		
Marden	d				18 47				19 47				20 47			21 47	22 17		
Maidstone West 4	d			18 15	*18 15*			19 15	*19 15*			20 15	*20 15*		21 15	*21 15*			
Paddock Wood 4	d		18 25	18 35	18 53		19 25	19 35	19 53		20 25	20 35	20 53	21 25	21 35	21 53	22 23		
Tonbridge 4	a		18 32	18 43	19 00		19 32	19 43	20 00		20 32	20 43	21 02	21 32	21 43	22 02	22 30		
	d		18 33	18 53	19 01		19 33	19 53	20 01		20 33	20 53	21 02	21 33		22 02	22 31		
Redhill	a		*19 24*	19 24			*20 24*	20 24			*21 24*	21 24							
Gatwick Airport 10	a		*19 38*	19 38			*20 38*	20 38			*21 38*	21 38							
Sevenoaks 4	a		18 43		19 13		19 43		20 13		20 43		21 14	21 43		22 14	22 43		
Orpington 4	a		18 53		19 23		19 53		20 23		20 53		21 24	21 53		22 24	22 53		
London Bridge 4	⊖ a		19 09		19 39		20 09		20 39		21 09		21 40	22 09		22 40	23 09		
London Cannon Street 4	⊖ a																		
London Waterloo (East) 4	⊖ a		19 14		19 44		20 14		20 44		21 14		21 44	22 14		22 44	23 14		
London Charing Cross 4	⊖ a		19 18		19 48		20 18		20 48		21 18		21 48	22 18		22 48	23 18		

For general notes see front of timetable
For details of catering facilities see Directory of Train Operators

A To Three Bridges (Table 186)
b 20 July to 31 August dep. 1129
c 20 July to 31 August dep. 1134
e 20 July to 31 August dep. 1137

For details of Bank Holiday service alterations please see first page of Table 195

Strood → Maidstone West and Paddock Wood

Network Diagram - see first page of Table 206

Miles			SE 55 A	SE 61	SE 61	SE 61	SE 01	SE 13 B	SE 01	SE 61	SE 01	SE 61	SE 01	SE 61	SE 01	SE 61	SE 01	SE 61
—	**London Charing Cross 3** ⊖	d			04b56	06 02	06 20	06 40	07 20				09 20	09 52	10 20	10 50	11 20	11 50
—	**London Waterloo (East) 3** ⊖	d			04b59	06 05	06 23	06 43	07 23				09 23	09 55	10 23	10 53	11 23	11 53
—	**London Cannon Street 3** ⊖	d				05c50	06 12	06c30	07c04	07 54	08 17	08 50	09c20	09c48	10c18	10c48	11c18	11c48
—	**London Bridge 3** ⊖	d																
—	Greenhithe for Bluewater	d		05 11	05b48	06 26	07 11	07 33	08 11	08 39	09 07	09 39	10 09	10 39	11 09	11 39	12 09	12 39
—	Gravesend 3	d		05 18	05b56	06 56	07 19	07 40	08 19	08 46	09 14	09 46	10 16	10 46	11 16	11 46	12 16	12 46
—	Gillingham (Kent) 3	d	04 56	05 22	06 03	06 53	07 13	07 33	08 15		09 14	09 44	10 14	10 44	11 14	11 44	12 14	12 44
0	**Strood 3**	d	05 09	05 40	06 18	07 12	07 34	07 55	08 34	09 01	09 31	10 01	10 31	11 01	11 31	12 01	12 31	13 01
2¼	Cuxton	d		05 44	06 23	07 16	07 38	07 59	08 38	09 05	09 35	10 05	10 35	11 05	11 35	12 05	12 35	13 05
4	Halling	d		05 48	06 26	07 20	07 42	08 03	08 42	09 09	09 39	10 09	10 39	11 09	11 39	12 09	12 39	13 09
5½	Snodland	d	05 16	05 51	06 29	07 23	07 45	08 06	08 45	09 12	09 42	10 12	10 42	11 12	11 42	12 12	12 42	13 12
7	New Hythe	d	05 18	05 53	06 32	07 25	07 47	08 09	08 47	09 14	09 44	10 14	10 44	11 14	11 44	12 14	12 44	13 14
7¾	Aylesford	d	05 21	05 56	06 34	07 28	07 50	08 12	08 50	09 17	09 47	10 17	10 47	11 17	11 47	12 17	12 47	13 17
11	Maidstone Barracks	d	05 26	06 01	06 39	07 33	07 55	08 17	08 55	09 22	09 52	10 22	10 52	11 22	11 52	12 22	12 52	13 22
11¼	**Maidstone West 3**	a	05 28	06 03	06 41	07 35	07 57	08 19	08 57	09 24	09 54	10 24	10 54	11 24	11 54	12 24	12 54	13 24
—		d	05 28	06 06	06 43	07 39		08 19		09 25		10 24		11 24		12 24		13 24
13	East Farleigh	d	05 32	06 10	06 46	07 43		08 23		09 29		10 28		11 28		12 28		13 28
16	Wateringbury	d	05 38	06 15	06 51	07 48		08 28		09 34		10 33		11 33		12 33		13 33
17¾	Yalding	d	05 41	06 18	06 55	07 51		08 31		09 37		10 36		11 36		12 36		13 36
19½	Beltring	d	05 44	06 22	06 58	07 55		08 35		09 41		10 40		11 40		12 40		13 40
21¼	**Paddock Wood 3**	a	05 49	06 26	07 02	07 59		08 39		09 45		10 44		11 44		12 44		13 44
26½	Tonbridge 3	a	05 56	06e44	07 16	08f16		08 49		09 57		10 57		11 57		12 57		13 57
—	**London Bridge 3** ⊖	a	06 36	07 21	07 54	08 54		09 33		11 13		11 43		12 43		13 43		14 43
—	**London Cannon Street 3** ⊖	a	06g47	07h31	08j00	09j01		09k43		11m27		11m54		12m54		13m54		14m54
—	**London Waterloo (East) 3** ⊖	a	06 41	07 27	08 04	09 01		09 38		10 32		11 32		12 32		13 32		14 32
—	**London Charing Cross 3** ⊖	a	06f46	07j32	08 09	09 07		09 44		10 36		11 36		12 36		13 36		14 36

		SE 01	SE 61	SE 01	SE 61	SE 61	SE 61	SE 61	SE 61	SE 61	SE 01	SE 61	SE 01	SE 61	SE 01	SE 61	SE 01	SE 01
London Charing Cross 4 ⊖	d	12 20	12 50	13 20	13 50	14 20	14 50	15 50	16 21	16 48	17 32	17 52	18 20	18 54	19 21	19 50	20 20	21 20
London Waterloo (East) 4 ⊖	d	12 23	12 53	13 23	13 53	14 23	14 53	15 53	16 24	16 51	17 35	17 55	18 23	18 57	19 24	19 53	20 23	21 23
London Cannon Street 4 ⊖	d	12c18	12c48	13c18	13c48	14c18	14c48	15c48	16c18	17 02	17 26	18 08		18c50	19c18	19c48	20c15	21c00
London Bridge 4 ⊖	d																	
Greenhithe for Bluewater	d	13 09	13 39	14 09	14 39	15 09	15 39	16 41	17 11	17 45	18 15	18 53	19 05	19 45	20 11	20 40	21 09	22 09
Gravesend 4	d	13 16	13 46	14 16	14 46	15 16	15 46	16 48	17 18	17 52	18 22	19 00	19 12	19 52	20 18	20 50	21 16	22 16
Gillingham (Kent) 4	d	13 14	13 44	14 14	14 44	15 14	15 44	16 44	17 14	17 48	18 12	18 44	19 14	19 44	20 16	20 42	21 14	21 42
Strood 4	d	13 31	14 01	14 31	15 01	15 31	16 12	17 05	17 36	18 08	18 42	19 16	19 34	20 11	20 33	21 07	21 33	22 33
Cuxton	d	13 35	14 05	14 35	15 05	15 35	16 16	17 09	17 40	18 12	18 46	19 20	19 38	20 15	20 37	21 11	21 37	22 37
Halling	d	13 39	14 09	14 39	15 09	15 39	16 20	17 13	17 44	18 16	18 50	19 24	19 41	20 19	20 41	21 15	21 41	22 41
Snodland	d	13 42	14 12	14 42	15 12	15 42	16 23	17 16	17 47	18 19	18 53	19 27	19 44	20 22	20 44	21 18	21 44	22 44
New Hythe	d	13 44	14 14	14 44	15 14	15 44	16 25	17 18	17 49	18 21	18 55	19 29	19 47	20 24	20 46	21 20	21 46	22 46
Aylesford	d	13 47	14 17	14 47	15 17	15 47	16 28	17 21	17 52	18 24	18 58	19 32	19 49	20 27	20 49	21 23	21 49	22 49
Maidstone Barracks	d	13 52	14 22	14 52	15 22	15 52	16 33	17 26	17 57	18 29	19 03	19 37	19 54	20 32	20 54	21 28	21 54	22 54
Maidstone West 4	a	13 54	14 24	14 54	15 24	15 54	16 35	17 28	17 59	18 31	19 05	19 39	19 56	20 34	20 56	21 30	21 56	22 56
	d		14 24		15 24	15 55	16 38	17 28	17 59	18 31		19 39		20 35		21 32		
East Farleigh	d		14 28		15 28	15 59	16 42	17 32	18 03	18 35		19 43		20 39		21 36		
Wateringbury	d		14 33		15 33	16 04	16 47	17 37	18 08	18 40		19 48		20 44		21 41		
Yalding	d		14 36		15 36	16 07	16 50	17 40	18 11	18 43		19 51		20 47		21 44		
Beltring	d		14 40		15 40	16 11	16 54	17 44	18 15	18 47		19 55		20 51		21 48		
Paddock Wood 4	a		14 44		15 44	16 15	16 58	17 48	18 19	18 51		19 59		20 55		21 52		
Tonbridge 4	a		14 57		16 21	16 36	17 17	18 18	18 45	19 27		20 27		21 28		22 28		
London Bridge 4 ⊖	a		15 43		17 00	17 26	18 28	18 57	19 25	20 08		21 08		22 08		23 08		
London Cannon Street 4 ⊖	a		15m54		17m08	17 31	18m37	19m05	19m37	20m27								
London Waterloo (East) 4 ⊖	a		15 32		17 05	17 36	18 03	19 02	19 31	20 13		21 13		22 13		23 13		
London Charing Cross 4 ⊖	a		15 36		17 10	17 41	18 07	19 07	19 35	20 18		21 18		22 18		23 18		

For general notes see front of timetable
For details of catering facilities see Directory of Train Operators

- **A** To Redhill (Table 209)
- **B** To London Bridge (Table 209)
- **b** Change at Strood
- **c** Change at London Bridge and Strood
- **e** From 13 October arr. 3 minutes earlier
- **f** From 13 October arr. 2 minutes earlier
- **g** Change at Tonbridge and London Bridge
- **h** Change at Paddock Wood and London Bridge. From 13 October arr. 1 minute earlier
- **j** From 13 October arr. 1 minute later
- **k** Change at Tonbridge and London Bridge. From 13 October arr. 1 minute earlier
- **m** Change at Paddock Wood and London Bridge

Table 208

Saturdays

Strood → Maidstone West and Paddock Wood

Network Diagram - see first page of Table 206

		SE 61	SE 01	SE 61	SE 01	SE 61	SE 01	SE 61	SE 01	SE 61	SE 01	SE 61	SE 01	SE 61	SE 01	SE 61	SE 01	SE 61
London Charing Cross	⊖ d		05b04	05 50	06 20	06 50	07 20	07 50	08 20	08 50	09 20	09 50	10 20	10 50	11 20	11 50	12 20	12 50
London Waterloo (East)	⊖ d		05b07	05 53	06 23	06 53	07 23	07 53	08 23	08 53	09 23	09 53	10 23	10 53	11 23	11 53	12 23	12 53
London Cannon Street	⊖ d								08c10	08c48	09c18	09c48	10c18	10c48	11c18	11c48	12c18	12c48
London Bridge	⊖ d																	
Greenhithe for Bluewater	d	05b22	05b54	06 39	07 09	07 39	08 09	08 39	09 09	09 39	10 09	10 39	11 09	11 39	12 09	12 39	13 09	13 39
Gravesend	d	05b29	06b01	06 46	07 16	07 46	08 16	08 46	09 16	09 46	10 16	10 46	11 16	11 46	12 16	12 46	13 16	13 46
Gillingham (Kent)	d	05 48	06 16	06 44	07 14	07 44	08 14	08 44	09 14	09 44	10 14	10 44	11 14	11 44	12 14	12 44	13 14	13 44
Strood	d	06 02	06 30	07 01	07 31	08 01	08 31	09 01	09 31	10 01	10 31	11 01	11 31	12 01	12 31	13 01	13 31	14 01
Cuxton	d	06 07	06 34	07 05	07 35	08 05	08 35	09 05	09 35	10 05	10 35	11 05	11 35	12 05	12 35	13 05	13 35	14 05
Halling	d	06 10	06 38	07 09	07 39	08 09	08 39	09 09	09 39	10 09	10 39	11 09	11 39	12 09	12 39	13 09	13 39	14 09
Snodland	d	06 13	06 41	07 12	07 42	08 12	08 42	09 12	09 42	10 12	10 42	11 12	11 42	12 12	12 42	13 12	13 42	14 12
New Hythe	d	06 16	06 43	07 14	07 44	08 14	08 44	09 14	09 44	10 14	10 44	11 14	11 44	12 14	12 44	13 14	13 44	14 14
Aylesford	d	06 18	06 46	07 17	07 47	08 17	08 47	09 17	09 47	10 17	10 47	11 17	11 47	12 17	12 47	13 17	13 47	14 17
Maidstone Barracks	d	06 23	06 51	07 22	07 52	08 22	08 52	09 22	09 52	10 22	10 52	11 22	11 52	12 22	12 52	13 22	13 52	14 22
Maidstone West	a	06 25	06 53	07 24	07 54	08 24	08 54	09 24	09 54	10 24	10 54	11 24	11 54	12 24	12 54	13 24	13 54	14 24
	d	06 26		07 24		08 24		09 24		10 24		11 24		12 24		13 24		14 24
East Farleigh	d	06 29		07 28		08 28		09 28		10 28		11 28		12 28		13 28		14 28
Wateringbury	d	06 34		07 33		08 33		09 33		10 33		11 33		12 33		13 33		14 33
Yalding	d	06 38		07 36		08 36		09 36		10 36		11 36		12 36		13 36		14 36
Beltring	d	06 41		07 40		08 40		09 40		10 40		11 40		12 40		13 40		14 40
Paddock Wood	a	06 45		07 44		08 44		09 44		10 44		11 44		12 44		13 44		14 44
Tonbridge	a	07 31		07 58		08 57		09 57		10 57		11 57		12 57		13 57		14 57
London Bridge	⊖ a	08 10		08 40		09 43		10 43		11 43		12 43		13 43		14 43		15 43
London Cannon Street	⊖ a	08e20		08e50		09e54		10e54		11e54		12e54		13e54		14e54		15e54
London Waterloo (East)	⊖ a	08 14		08 45		09 32		10 32		11 32		12 32		13 32		14 32		15 32
London Charing Cross	⊖ a	08 18		08 48		09 36		10 36		11 36		12 36		13 36		14 36		15 36

		SE 01	SE 61	SE 01	SE 61	SE 01	SE 61	SE 01	SE 61	SE 01	SE 61	SE 01	SE 61	SE 01	SE 01	SE 01
London Charing Cross	⊖ d	13 20	13 50	14 20	14 50	15 20	15 50	16 20	16 50	17 20	17 50	18 20	18 50	19 20	19 50	20 20
London Waterloo (East)	⊖ d	13 23	13 53	14 23	14 53	15 23	15 53	16 23	16 53	17 23	17 53	18 23	18 53	19 23	19 53	20 23
London Cannon Street	⊖ d	13c18	13c48	14c18	14c48	15c18	15c48	16c18	16c48	17c18	17c48	18c18	18c48	19c14		
London Bridge	⊖ d															
Greenhithe for Bluewater	d	14 09	14 39	15 09	15 39	16 09	16 39	17 09	17 39	18 09	18 39	19 09	19 39	20 09	20 40	21 09
Gravesend	d	14 16	14 46	15 16	15 46	16 16	16 46	17 16	17 46	18 16	18 46	19 16	19 46	20 16	20 48	21 16
Gillingham (Kent)	d	14 14	14 44	15 14	15 44	16 14	16 44	17 14	17 44	18 14	18 44	19 14	19 44	20 14	20 42	21 14
Strood	d	14 31	15 01	15 31	16 01	16 31	17 01	17 31	18 01	18 31	19 01	19 31	20 01	20 31	21 01	21 31
Cuxton	d	14 35	15 05	15 35	16 05	16 35	17 05	17 35	18 05	18 35	19 05	19 35	20 05	20 35	21 05	21 35
Halling	d	14 39	15 09	15 39	16 09	16 39	17 09	17 39	18 09	18 39	19 09	19 39	20 09	20 39	21 09	21 39
Snodland	d	14 42	15 12	15 42	16 12	16 42	17 12	17 42	18 12	18 42	19 12	19 42	20 12	20 42	21 12	21 42
New Hythe	d	14 44	15 14	15 44	16 14	16 44	17 14	17 44	18 14	18 44	19 14	19 44	20 14	20 44	21 14	21 44
Aylesford	d	14 47	15 17	15 47	16 17	16 47	17 17	17 47	18 17	18 47	19 17	19 47	20 17	20 47	21 17	21 47
Maidstone Barracks	d	14 52	15 22	15 52	16 22	16 52	17 22	17 52	18 22	18 52	19 22	19 52	20 22	20 52	21 22	21 52
Maidstone West	a	14 54	15 24	15 54	16 24	16 54	17 24	17 54	18 24	18 54	19 24	19 54	20 24	20 54	21 24	21 54
	d		15 24		16 24		17 24		18 24		19 24		20 24			
East Farleigh	d		15 28		16 28		17 28		18 28		19 28		20 28			
Wateringbury	d		15 33		16 33		17 33		18 33		19 33		20 33			
Yalding	d		15 36		16 36		17 36		18 36		19 36		20 36			
Beltring	d		15 40		16 40		17 40		18 40		19 40		20 40			
Paddock Wood	a		15 44		16 44		17 44		18 44		19 44		20 44			
Tonbridge	a		15 57		16 57		18 28		18 59		19 59		20 59			
London Bridge	⊖ a		16 43		17 43		19 08		19 38		20 38		21 38			
London Cannon Street	⊖ a		16e54		17e54											
London Waterloo (East)	⊖ a		16 32		17 32		19 14		19 44		20 44		21 44			
London Charing Cross	⊖ a		16 36		17 36		19 19		19 49		20 49		21 49			

For general notes see front of timetable
For details of catering facilities see Directory of Train Operators

b Change at Strood
c Change at London Bridge and Strood
e Change at Paddock Wood and London Bridge

Sundays

Strood → Maidstone West and Paddock Wood

Network Diagram - see first page of Table 206

		SE 55 A	SE 01	SE 55 A	SE 01	SE 55 A	SE 01	SE 55 A	SE 01	SE 55 A	SE 01	SE 55 A	SE 01	SE 55 A	SE 01	SE 55 A	SE 01	SE 55 A
London Charing Cross	⊖ d						08 20		09 20		10 20		11 20		12 20		13 20	
London Waterloo (East)	⊖ d						08 23		09 23		10 23		11 23		12 23		13 23	
London Cannon Street	⊖ d																	
London Bridge	⊖ d																	
Greenhithe for Bluewater	d				08 08		09 09		10 09		11 09		12 09		13 09		14 09	
Gravesend	d				08 16		09 16		10 16		11 16		12 16		13 16		14 16	
Gillingham (Kent)	d	06 30	07 15		08 15		09 15		10 15		11 15		12 15		13 15		14 15	
Strood	d	06 48	07 33		08 33		09 33		10 33		11 33		12 33		13 33		14 33	
Cuxton	d	06 52	07 37		08 37		09 37		10 37		11 37		12 37		13 37		14 37	
Halling	d	06 55	07 41		08 41		09 41		10 41		11 41		12 41		13 41		14 41	
Snodland	d	06 57	07 44		08 44		09 44		10 44		11 44		12 44		13 44		14 44	
New Hythe	d	06 59	07 46		08 46		09 46		10 46		11 46		12 46		13 46		14 46	
Aylesford	d	07 01	07 49		08 49		09 49		10 49		11 49		12 49		13 49		14 49	
Maidstone Barracks	d	07 06	07 54		08 54		09 54		10 54		11 54		12 54		13 54		14 54	
Maidstone West	a	07 08	07 56		08 56		09 56		10 56		11 56		12 56		13 56		14 56	
	d	07 15		08 15		09 15		10 15		11 15		12 15		13 15		14 15		15 15
East Farleigh	d	07 18		08 18		09 18		10 18		11 18		12 18		13 18		14 18		15 18
Wateringbury	d	07 23		08 23		09 23		10 23		11 23		12 23		13 23		14 23		15 23
Yalding	d	07 27		08 27		09 27		10 27		11 27		12 27		13 27		14 27		15 27
Beltring	d	07 30		08 30		09 30		10 30		11 30		12 30		13 30		14 30		15 30
Paddock Wood	a	07 34		08 34		09 34		10 34		11 34		12 34		13 34		14 34		15 34
Tonbridge	a	07 43		08 43		09 43		10 43		11 43		12 43		13 43		14 43		15 43
London Bridge	⊖ a	08 39		09 26		10 26		11 26		12 26		13 26		14 26		15 26		16 26
London Cannon Street	⊖ a																	
London Waterloo (East)	⊖ a	08 44		09 31		10 31		11 31		12 31		13 31		14 31		15 31		16 31
London Charing Cross	⊖ a	08 48		09 35		10 35		11 35		12 35		13 35		14 35		15 35		16 35

		SE 01	SE 55 A	SE 01	SE 55 A	SE 01	SE 55 A	SE 01	SE 55 A	SE 01	SE 55 A	SE 01	SE 61	SE 01
London Charing Cross	⊖ d	14 20		15 20		16 20		17 20		18 20		19 20		20 20
London Waterloo (East)	⊖ d	14 23		15 23		16 23		17 23		18 23		19 23		20 23
London Cannon Street	⊖ d													
London Bridge	⊖ d													
Greenhithe for Bluewater	d	15 09		16 09		17 09		18 09		19 09		20 09		21 09
Gravesend	d	15 16		16 16		17 16		18 16		19 16		20 16		21 16
Gillingham (Kent)	d	15 15		16 15		17 15		18 15		19 15		20 15		21 15
Strood	d	15 33		16 33		17 33		18 33		19 33		20 33		21 33
Cuxton	d	15 37		16 37		17 37		18 37		19 37		20 37		21 37
Halling	d	15 41		16 41		17 41		18 41		19 41		20 41		21 41
Snodland	d	15 44		16 44		17 44		18 44		19 44		20 44		21 44
New Hythe	d	15 46		16 46		17 46		18 46		19 46		20 46		21 46
Aylesford	d	15 49		16 49		17 49		18 49		19 49		20 49		21 49
Maidstone Barracks	d	15 54		16 54		17 54		18 54		19 54		20 54		21 54
Maidstone West	a	15 56		16 56		17 56		18 56		19 56		20 56		21 56
	d		16 15		17 15		18 15		19 15		20 15		21 15	
East Farleigh	d		16 18		17 18		18 18		19 18		20 18		21 18	
Wateringbury	d		16 23		17 23		18 23		19 23		20 23		21 23	
Yalding	d		16 27		17 27		18 27		19 27		20 27		21 27	
Beltring	d		16 30		17 30		18 30		19 30		20 30		21 30	
Paddock Wood	a		16 34		17 34		18 34		19 34		20 34		21 34	
Tonbridge	a		16 43		17 43		18 43		19 43		20 43		21 43	
London Bridge	⊖ a		17 26		18 26		19 26		20 39		21 40		22 40	
London Cannon Street	⊖ a													
London Waterloo (East)	⊖ a		17 31		18 31		19 31		20 44		21 44		22 44	
London Charing Cross	⊖ a		17 35		18 35		19 35		20 48		21 48		22 48	

For general notes see front of timetable
For details of catering facilities see Directory of Train Operators

A To Three Bridges (Table 209)

For details of Bank Holiday service alterations please see first page of Table 195

Paddock Wood and Maidstone West → Strood

Network Diagram - see first page of Table 206

Miles			SE 61	SE 61	SE 61	SE 01	SE 61	SE 01	SE 55 A	SE 01	SE 61	SE 01	SE 61	SE 01	SE 61	SE 01	SE 61	SE 01
—	**London Charing Cross** 4	⊖ d			05 30		07 00		08 14		08 58		10 00		11 00		12 00	
—	**London Waterloo (East)** 4	⊖ d			05 33		07 03		08 17		09 01		10 03		11 03		12 03	
—	**London Cannon Street** 4	⊖ d					06b52		08c14		08b54		10b00		11b00		12b00	
—	**London Bridge** 4	⊖ d																
0	Tonbridge 4	d	05 47						09 00									
5¼	**Paddock Wood** 4	d	05 55	06 32	07 06		08 09		09 08		10 03		11 01		12 06		13 06	
7	Beltring	d	05 59	06 36	07 10		08 13		09 12		10 07		11 05		12 10		13 10	
8¾	Yalding	d	06 03	06 40	07 14		08 17		09 16		10 11		11 09		12 14		13 14	
10½	Wateringbury	d	06 06	06 43	07 17		08 20		09 19		10 14		11 12		12 17		13 17	
13½	East Farleigh	d	06 11	06 48	07 22		08 25		09 24		10 19		11 17		12 22		13 22	
15¼	**Maidstone West** 4	a	06 15	06 52	07 26		08 29		09 28		10 23		11 21		12 26		13 26	
—		d	06 19	06 53	07 26	08 01	08 29	09 01	09 28	09 58	10 27	10 58	11 27	11 58	12 27	12 58	13 27	13 58
15½	Maidstone Barracks	d	06 21	06 55	07 28	08 03	08 31	09 03	09 30	10 00	10 29	11 00	11 29	12 00	12 29	13 00	13 29	13 59
18¾	Aylesford	d	06 26	07 00	07 33	08 08	08 36	09 08	09 35	10 05	10 34	11 05	11 34	12 05	12 34	13 05	13 34	14 04
19½	New Hythe	d	06 29	07 03	07 36	08 10	08 39	09 10	09 38	10 07	10 37	11 07	11 37	12 07	12 37	13 07	13 37	14 07
21	Snodland	d	06 31	07 05	07 38	08 13	08 41	09 13	09 40	10 10	10 39	11 10	11 39	12 10	12 39	13 10	13 39	14 09
22½	Halling	d	06 34	07 08	07 41	08 16	08 44	09 16	09 43	10 13	10 42	11 13	11 42	12 13	12 42	13 13	13 42	14 12
24¼	Cuxton	d	06 38	07 12	07 45	08 19	08 48	09 19	09 47	10 16	10 46	11 16	11 46	12 16	12 46	13 16	13 46	14 15
26½	**Strood** 4	a	06 42	07 16	07 49	08 24	08 52	09 24	09 51	10 21	10 50	11 21	11 50	12 21	12 50	13 21	13 50	14 20
—	Gillingham (Kent) 4	a	07 25		08 01		09 07	09 35	10 07	10 37	11 07	11 37	12 07	12 37	13 07	13 37	14 07	14 37
—	Gravesend 4	a	06 59	07 39	08 07	08 39	09 08		10 06	10 36	11 06	11 36	12 06	12 36	13 06	13 36	14 06	14 36
—	Greenhithe for Bluewater	a	07 06	07 46	08 14	08 46	09 13		10 11	10 41	11 11	11 41	12 11	12 41	13 11	13 41	14 11	14 41
—	**London Bridge** 4	⊖ a	07 44	08 47	09 11	09 29	09 54		10 49	11 19	11 49	12 19	12 49	13 19	13 49	14 19	14 49	15 19
—	London Cannon Street 4	⊖ a	07e51	08f54	09e18	09g43	10h06		10h57	11h27	12h00	12h27	12h57	13h27	13h57	14h27	14h57	15h27
—	London Waterloo (East) 4	⊖ a	08 08	08 29	08 57	09 34	09 59		10 54	11 24	11 54	12 24	12 54	13 24	13 54	14 24	14 54	15 24
—	London Charing Cross 4	⊖ a	08f13	08e34	09e03	09f39	10 05		10 58	11 28	11 58	12 28	12 58	13 28	13 58	14 28	14 58	15 28

		SE 61	SE 01	SE 61	SE 61	SE 61	SE 61	SE 61	SE 61	SE 01	SE 61	SE 88 A	SE 61	SE 01	SE 61	SE 01	SE 61
London Charing Cross 4	⊖ d	13 00		14 00	15 00	15 23	16 00	16 46	17 12		17 56	18 40	19 00		20 00		21 00
London Waterloo (East) 4	⊖ d	13 03		14 03	15 03	15 26	16 03	16 49	17 15		17 59	18 43	19 03		20 03		21 03
London Cannon Street 4	⊖ d	13b00		14b00	15b00		16b00	16b46	17 20		18 04	18c36	18b50		20b00		21b00
London Bridge 4	⊖ d																
Tonbridge 4	d											19 28					
Paddock Wood 4	d	14 06		15 06	16 06	16 25	17 02	17 52	18 23		18 57	19 38	20 03		21 01		21 57
Beltring	d	14 10		15 10	16 10	16 29	17 06	17 56	18 27		19 01	19 42	20 07		21 05		22 01
Yalding	d	14 14		15 14	16 14	16 33	17 10	18 00	18 31		19 05	19 45	20 11		21 08		22 05
Wateringbury	d	14 17		15 17	16 17	16 36	17 13	18 03	18 34		19 08	19 49	20 14		21 12		22 08
East Farleigh	d	14 22		15 22	16 22	16 41	17 18	18 08	18 39		19 13	19 54	20 19		21 17		22 13
Maidstone West 4	a	14 26		15 26	16 26	16 45	17 22	18 12	18 43		19 17	19 58	20 23		21 21		22 17
	d	14 27	14 58	15 44	16 27	16 55	17 25	18 12	18 47	19 09	19 27	20 00	20 24	21 00	21 27	22 02	22 19
Maidstone Barracks	d	14 29	15 00	15 46	16 29	16 57	17 27	18 14	18 49	19 11	19 29	20 01	20 26	21 02	21 28	22 04	22 21
Aylesford	d	14 34	15 05	15 51	16 34	17 02	17 32	18 19	18 54	19 16	19 34	20 06	20 31	21 07	21 33	22 09	22 26
New Hythe	d	14 37	15 07	15 54	16 37	17 05	17 35	18 22	18 57	19 18	19 37	20 09	20 34	21 09	21 36	22 11	22 29
Snodland	d	14 39	15 10	15 56	16 39	17 07	17 37	18 24	18 59	19 21	19 39	20 11	20 36	21 12	21 38	22 14	22 31
Halling	d	14 42	15 13	15 59	16 42	17 10	17 40	18 27	19 02	19 24	19 42	20 14	20 39	21 15	21 41	22 17	22 34
Cuxton	d	14 46	15 16	16 03	16 46	17 14	17 44	18 31	19 06	19 27	19 46	20 17	20 43	21 18	21 44	22 20	22 38
Strood 4	a	14 50	15 21	16 07	16 50	17 18	17 48	18 35	19 10	19 32	19 50	20 22	20 47	21 23	21 49	22 25	22 42
Gillingham (Kent) 4	a	15 07	15 37	16 37	17 18	17f42	18f06	19e07	19e26	19 55	20e15	20 39	21 17	21 37	22 13	22 37	22 55
Gravesend 4	a	15 06	15 36	16 36	17 06	17 36	18 10	19 06	19 36		20 06	20 38	21 04	21 38	22 04	22 44	00j28
Greenhithe for Bluewater	a	15 11	15 41	16 41	17 11	17 45	18 15	19 11	19 41		20 11	20 43	21 12	21 43	22 12	22 52	00j34
London Bridge 4	⊖ a	15 49	16 19	17 26	17 56	18 31	19 02	19 53	20 23		20 53	21 23	21 53	22 23	22 53	23 41	
London Cannon Street 4	⊖ a	15h57	16h27	17h36	18 01	18h45	19h15	20h11	20h41								
London Waterloo (East) 4	⊖ a	15 54	16 24	17 31		18 36	19 07	19 58	20 28		20 58	21 28	21 58	22 28	22 58	23 46	
London Charing Cross 4	⊖ a	15 58	16 28	17 35		18 40	19 11	20 01	20 31		21 01	21 31	22 01	22 31	23 01	23 50	

For general notes see front of timetable
For details of catering facilities see Directory of Train Operators

- **A** From Redhill (Table 209)
- **b** Change at London Bridge and Paddock Wood
- **c** Change at London Bridge and Tonbridge
- **e** From 13 October arr. 1 minute later
- **f** From 13 October arr. 1 minute earlier
- **g** Change at Strood and London Bridge. From 13 October arr. 1 minute later
- **h** Change at Strood and London Bridge
- **j** Change at Strood

Table 208

Paddock Wood and Maidstone West → Strood

Network Diagram - see first page of Table 206

		SE 01	SE 01	SE 61	SE 01	SE 61	SE 01	SE 61	SE 01	SE 61	SE 01	SE 61	SE 01	SE 61	SE 01	SE 61	SE 01	SE 61
London Charing Cross 4	⊖ d			06 00		07 00		08 00		09 00		10 00		11 00		12 00		13 00
London Waterloo (East) 4	⊖ d			06 03		07 03		08 03		09 03		10 03		11 03		12 03		13 03
London Cannon Street 4	⊖ d									09b00		10b00		11b00		12b00		13b00
London Bridge 4	⊖ d																	
Tonbridge 4	d																	
Paddock Wood 4	d			07 01		08 01		09 01		10 01		11 01		12 01		13 01		14 01
Beltring	d			07 05		08 05		09 05		10 05		11 05		12 05		13 05		14 05
Yalding	d			07 09		08 09		09 09		10 09		11 09		12 09		13 09		14 09
Wateringbury	d			07 12		08 12		09 12		10 12		11 12		12 12		13 12		14 12
East Farleigh	d			07 17		08 17		09 17		10 17		11 17		12 17		13 17		14 17
Maidstone West 4	a			07 21		08 21		09 21		10 21		11 21		12 21		13 21		14 21
	d	06 27	06 57	07 27	07 58	08 27	08 58	09 27	09 58	10 27	10 58	11 27	11 58	12 27	12 58	13 27	13 58	14 27
Maidstone Barracks	d	06 29	06 59	07 29	08 00	08 29	09 00	09 29	10 00	10 29	11 00	11 29	12 00	12 29	13 00	13 29	14 00	14 29
Aylesford	d	06 34	07 04	07 34	08 05	08 34	09 05	09 34	10 05	10 34	11 05	11 34	12 05	12 34	13 05	13 34	14 05	14 34
New Hythe	d	06 36	07 06	07 37	08 07	08 37	09 07	09 37	10 07	10 37	11 07	11 37	12 07	12 37	13 07	13 37	14 07	14 37
Snodland	d	06 39	07 09	07 39	08 10	08 39	09 10	09 39	10 10	10 39	11 10	11 39	12 10	12 39	13 10	13 39	14 10	14 39
Halling	d	06 42	07 12	07 42	08 13	08 42	09 13	09 42	10 13	10 42	11 13	11 42	12 13	12 42	13 13	13 42	14 13	14 42
Cuxton	d	06 45	07 15	07 46	08 16	08 46	09 16	09 46	10 16	10 46	11 16	11 46	12 16	12 46	13 16	13 46	14 16	14 46
Strood 4	a	06 50	07 20	07 50	08 21	08 50	09 21	09 50	10 21	10 50	11 21	11 50	12 21	12 50	13 21	13 50	14 21	14 50
Gillingham (Kent) 4	a	07 07	07 37	08 07	08 37	09 07	09 37	10 07	10 37	11 07	11 37	12 07	12 37	13 07	13 37	14 07	14 37	15 07
Gravesend 4	a	07 05	07 35	08 05	08 36	09 06	09 36	10 06	10 36	11 06	11 36	12 06	12 36	13 06	13 36	14 06	14 36	15 06
Greenhithe for Bluewater	a	07 10	07 40	08 10	08 41	09 11	09 41	10 11	10 41	11 11	11 41	12 11	12 41	13 11	13 41	14 11	14 41	15 11
London Bridge 4	⊖ a	07 49	08 19	08 49	09 19	09 49	10 19	10 49	11 19	11 49	12 19	12 49	13 19	13 49	14 19	14 49	15 19	15 49
London Cannon Street 4	⊖ a	08c03	08c33	09c03	09c30	09c57	10c27	10c57	11c27	11c57	12c27	12c57	13c27	13c57	14c27	14c57	15c27	15c57
London Waterloo (East) 4	⊖ a	07 54	08 24	08 54	09 24	09 54	10 24	10 54	11 24	11 54	12 24	12 54	13 24	13 54	14 24	14 54	15 24	15 54
London Charing Cross 4	⊖ a	07 58	08 28	08 58	09 28	09 58	10 28	10 58	11 28	11 58	12 28	12 58	13 28	13 58	14 28	14 58	15 28	15 58

		SE 01	SE 61	SE 01	SE 61	SE 01	SE 61	SE 01	SE 61	SE 01	SE 61	SE 01	SE 61	SE 01	SE 01	SE 01
London Charing Cross 4	⊖ d		14 00		15 00		16 00		17 00		18 00		19 00		20 00	
London Waterloo (East) 4	⊖ d		14 03		15 03		16 03		17 03		18 03		19 03		20 03	
London Cannon Street 4	⊖ d		14b00		15b00		16b00		17b00		18b00		19b00		19b14	
London Bridge 4	⊖ d															
Tonbridge 4	d															
Paddock Wood 4	d		15 01		16 01		17 01		18 01		19 01		20 01		21 01	
Beltring	d		15 05		16 05		17 05		18 05		19 05		20 05		21 05	
Yalding	d		15 09		16 09		17 09		18 09		19 09		20 09		21 09	
Wateringbury	d		15 12		16 12		17 12		18 12		19 12		20 12		21 12	
East Farleigh	d		15 17		16 17		17 17		18 17		19 17		20 17		21 17	
Maidstone West 4	a		15 21		16 21		17 21		18 21		19 21		20 21		21 21	
	d	14 58	15 27	15 58	16 27	16 58	17 27	17 58	18 27	18 58	19 27	19 58	20 27	20 58		21 28
Maidstone Barracks	d	15 00	15 29	16 00	16 29	17 00	17 29	18 00	18 29	19 00	19 29	20 00	20 29	21 00		21 30
Aylesford	d	15 05	15 34	16 05	16 34	17 05	17 34	18 05	18 34	19 05	19 34	20 05	20 34	21 05		21 35
New Hythe	d	15 07	15 37	16 07	16 37	17 07	17 37	18 07	18 37	19 07	19 37	20 07	20 37	21 07		21 37
Snodland	d	15 10	15 39	16 10	16 39	17 10	17 39	18 10	18 39	19 10	19 39	20 10	20 39	21 10		21 40
Halling	d	15 13	15 42	16 13	16 42	17 13	17 42	18 13	18 42	19 13	19 42	20 13	20 42	21 13		21 43
Cuxton	d	15 16	15 46	16 16	16 46	17 16	17 46	18 16	18 46	19 16	19 46	20 16	20 46	21 16		21 46
Strood 4	a	15 21	15 50	16 21	16 50	17 21	17 50	18 21	18 50	19 21	19 50	20 21	20 50	21 21		21 51
Gillingham (Kent) 4	a	15 37	16 07	16 37	17 07	17 37	18 07	18 37	19 07	19 37	20 07	20 37	21 13	21 37		22 13
Gravesend 4	a	15 36	16 06	16 36	17 06	17 36	18 06	18 36	19 06	19 36	20 06	20 36	21 04	21 36		22 04
Greenhithe for Bluewater	a	15 41	16 11	16 41	17 11	17 41	18 11	18 41	19 11	19 41	20 11	20 41	21 12	21 41		22 12
London Bridge 4	⊖ a	16 19	16 49	17 19	17 49	18 19	18 49	19 21	19 53	20 23	20 53	21 23	21 53	22 23		22 53
London Cannon Street 4	⊖ a	16c27	16c57	17c27	17c57	18c27										
London Waterloo (East) 4	⊖ a	16 24	16 54	17 24	17 54	18 24	18 54	19 25	19 58	20 28	20 58	21 28	21 58	22 28		22 58
London Charing Cross 4	⊖ a	16 28	16 58	17 28	17 58	18 28	18 58	19 29	20 01	20 31	21 01	21 31	22 01	22 31		23 01

For general notes see front of timetable
For details of catering facilities see Directory of Train Operators

b Change at London Bridge and Paddock Wood
c Change at Strood and London Bridge

Sundays

Paddock Wood and Maidstone West → Strood

Network Diagram - see first page of Table 206

		SE 01	SE 01	SE 61	SE 01	SE 55 A	SE 01	SE 55 A	SE 01	SE 55 A	SE 01	SE 55 A	SE 01	SE 55 A	SE 01	SE 55 A	SE 01	SE 55 A
London Charing Cross 4	⊖ d							08 30		09 44		10 44		11 44		12 44		13 44
London Waterloo (East) 4	⊖ d							08 33		09 47		10 47		11 47		12 47		13 47
London Cannon Street 4	⊖ d																	
London Bridge 4	⊖ d																	
Tonbridge 4	d			07 40		08 40		09 40		10 40		11 40		12 40		13 40		14 40
Paddock Wood 4	d			07 47		08 47		09 47		10 47		11 47		12 47		13 47		14 47
Beltring	d			07 51		08 51		09 51		10 51		11 51		12 51		13 51		14 51
Yalding	d			07 55		08 55		09 55		10 55		11 55		12 55		13 55		14 55
Wateringbury	d			07 59		08 59		09 59		10 59		11 59		12 59		13 59		14 59
East Farleigh	d			08 04		09 04		10 04		11 04		12 04		13 04		14 04		15 04
Maidstone West 4	a			08 07		09 07		10 07		11 07		12 07		13 07		14 07		15 07
	d	07 00	08 00		09 00		10 00		11 00		12 00		13 00		14 00		15 00	
Maidstone Barracks	d	07 02	08 02		09 02		10 02		11 02		12 02		13 02		14 02		15 02	
Aylesford	d	07 07	08 07		09 07		10 07		11 07		12 07		13 07		14 07		15 07	
New Hythe	d	07 09	08 09		09 09		10 09		11 09		12 09		13 09		14 09		15 09	
Snodland	d	07 12	08 12		09 12		10 12		11 12		12 12		13 12		14 12		15 12	
Halling	d	07 15	08 15		09 15		10 15		11 15		12 15		13 15		14 15		15 15	
Cuxton	d	07 18	08 18		09 18		10 18		11 18		12 18		13 18		14 18		15 18	
Strood 4	a	07 23	08 23		09 23		10 23		11 23		12 23		13 23		14 23		15 23	
Gillingham (Kent) 4	a		08 38		09 37		10 37		11 37		12 37		13 37		14 37		15 37	
Gravesend 4	a	07 38	08 38		09 38		10 38		11 38		12 38		13 38		14 38		15 38	
Greenhithe for Bluewater	a	07 44	08 44		09 44		10 44		11 44		12 44		13 44		14 44		15 44	
London Bridge 4	⊖ a	08 23	09 23		10 23		11 23		12 23		13 23		14 23		15 23		16 23	
London Cannon Street 4	⊖ a																	
London Waterloo (East) 4	⊖ a	08 28	09 28		10 28		11 28		12 28		13 28		14 28		15 28		16 28	
London Charing Cross 4	⊖ a	08 32	09 32		10 32		11 32		12 32		13 32		14 32		15 32		16 32	

		SE 01	SE 55 A	SE 01	SE 55 A	SE 01	SE 55 A	SE 01	SE 55 A	SE 01	SE 55 A	SE 01	SE 55 A	SE 55 A
London Charing Cross 4	⊖ d		14 44		15 44		16 44		17 44		18 44		19 44	20 30
London Waterloo (East) 4	⊖ d		14 47		15 47		16 47		17 47		18 47		19 47	20 33
London Cannon Street 4	⊖ d													
London Bridge 4	⊖ d													
Tonbridge 4	d		15 40		16 40		17 40		18 40		19 40		20 40	21 40
Paddock Wood 4	d		15 47		16 47		17 47		18 47		19 47		20 47	21 47
Beltring	d		15 51		16 51		17 51		18 51		19 51		20 51	21 51
Yalding	d		15 55		16 55		17 55		18 55		19 55		20 55	21 55
Wateringbury	d		15 59		16 59		17 59		18 59		19 59		20 59	21 59
East Farleigh	d		16 04		17 04		18 04		19 04		20 04		21 04	22 04
Maidstone West 4	a		16 07		17 07		18 07		19 07		20 07		21 07	22 07
	d	16 00		17 00		18 00		19 00		20 00		21 00		22 08
Maidstone Barracks	d	16 02		17 02		18 02		19 02		20 02		21 02		22 10
Aylesford	d	16 07		17 07		18 07		19 07		20 07		21 07		22 15
New Hythe	d	16 09		17 09		18 09		19 09		20 09		21 09		22 17
Snodland	d	16 12		17 12		18 12		19 12		20 12		21 12		22 20
Halling	d	16 15		17 15		18 15		19 15		20 15		21 15		22 23
Cuxton	d	16 18		17 18		18 18		19 18		20 18		21 18		22 26
Strood 4	a	16 23		17 23		18 23		19 23		20 23		21 23		22 31
Gillingham (Kent) 4	a	16 37		17 37		18 37		19 37		20 37		21 37		
Gravesend 4	a	16 38		17 38		18 38		19 38		20 38		21 38		22 46
Greenhithe for Bluewater	a	16 44		17 44		18 44		19 44		20 44		21 44		
London Bridge 4	⊖ a	17 23		18 23		19 23		20 23		21 23		22 23		
London Cannon Street 4	⊖ a													
London Waterloo (East) 4	⊖ a	17 28		18 28		19 28		20 28		21 28		22 28		
London Charing Cross 4	⊖ a	17 32		18 32		19 32		20 32		21 32		22 32		

For general notes see front of timetable
For details of catering facilities see Directory of Train Operators

A From Three Bridges (Table 209)

Table 209

Mondays to Fridays

For details of Bank Holiday service alterations please see first page of Table 195

Tunbridge Wells and Tonbridge → London, Gatwick Airport and Horsham via Redhill

Network Diagram - see first page of Table 206

Miles	Miles			SE 88	SE 55 A	SE 13 B	SE 88	SE 88	SE 13	SE 88	SE 13 C	SE 88 [1]	SE 13	SE 88 [1]	SE 13	SE 88 [1]	SE 13	SE 88 [1]	SE 13
—	—	**Tunbridge Wells [4]**	d		05 44		06 06	07 20	07 40	08 00	08 26	08 40	09 02	09 52	10 24	10 52	11 24	11 52	12 24
—	—	High Brooms	d		05 47		06 10	07 24	07 44	08 04	08 30	08 44	09 06	09 55	10 27	10 55	11 27	11 55	12 27
—	—	**Tonbridge [4]**	a											10 01	10 33	11 01	11 33	12 01	12 33
—	0		d	05 00	06 00	06 14	06 50	07 38	07 56	08 18	08 51	09 08	09 34	10 04	10 34	11 04	11 34	12 04	12 34
—	2½	Leigh (Kent)	d	05 04	06 04	06 18	06 54	07 42	08 00	08 22	08 55	09 12	09 38	10 08	10 38	11 08	11 38	12 08	12 38
—	4¼	Penshurst	d	05 07	06 07	06 21	06 57	07 45	08 04	08 25	08 58	09 16	09 41	10 12	10 41	11 12	11 41	12 12	12 41
—	9¼	Edenbridge	d	05 14	06 14	06 28	07 04	07 52	08 11	08 32	09 05	09 23	09 48	10 19	10 48	11 19	11 48	12 19	12 48
—	14	Godstone	d	05 20	06 20	06 34	07 10	07 58	08 17	08 38	09 11	09 29	09 54	10 25	10 54	11 25	11 54	12 25	12 54
—	17¾	Nutfield	d	05 26	06 26	06 40	07 16	08 04	08 23	08 44	09 17	09 35	10 00	10 31	11 00	11 31	12 00	12 31	13 00
—	19¾	**Redhill**	a	05 31	06 30	06 45	07 20	08 08		08 48	09 21	09 39	10 04	10 40	11 04	11 40	12 04	12 39	13 04
—	—	East Croydon	a	05 48	06 38	07 01	07 21	08 18	08 47	08 37	09 40	09 25	10 23	10 48	11 23	11 48	12 23	12 48	13 23
—	—	**London Bridge [4]**	⊖ a	06b15	06b40	07 18	07b43	08b41	09 07	09b05	09 55	09b45	10 40	11b12	11 40	12b12	12 40	13b12	13 40
—	—	**London Victoria [15]**	⊖ a	05b58	06b47	07b16	07b48	08b46	09c16	09b02	09b42	09b58	10c45	11b11	11c44	12b11	12c44	13b11	13c44
0	—	**Redhill**	d	05 35								09 44		10 44		11 44		12 44	
—	—	Reigate	a	05 48	06 46	07e15	07 32	08 19		08 57	09e33	10 18	10e18	11 18	11e18	12 18	12e18	13 18	13e18
5¾	—	**Gatwick Airport [10]** ✈	a	05 42	06 53	07e03	07 54	08 39		09 02	09e39	09 54	10e23	10 55	11e23	11 55	12e23	12 55	13e23
8½	—	Three Bridges [4]	a	05 54	06 59	07e09	08 04	08 44		09 15	09e44	10 00	10e29	11 00	11e29	12 00	12e29	13 00	13e29
10	—	Crawley	a									10 04		11 04		12 04		13 04	
17	—	**Horsham [4]**	a									10 16		11 16		12 18		13 16	

		SE 88 [1]	SE 13	SE 88 [1]	SE 13	SE 88 [1]	SE 13	SE 88 [1]	SE 88	SE 13	SE 88	SE 88	SE 88	SE 88	SE 88	SE 88	SE 88
Tunbridge Wells [4]	d	12 52	13 24	13 52	14 24	14 52	15 24	15 36	15 56	16 56		18 04	18 40	19 38	20 36	21 36	22 56
High Brooms	d	12 55	13 27	13 55	14 27	14 55	15 27	15 39	15 59	16 59		18 07	18 43	19 41	20 39	21 39	22 59
Tonbridge [4]	a	13 01	13 33	14 01	14 33	15 01	15 33										
	d	13 04	13 34	14 04	14 34	15 04	15 34	16 04	16 29	17 20	17 43	18 21	19 09	19 53	20 53	21 53	23 17
Leigh (Kent)	d	13 08	13 38	14 08	14 38	15 08	15 38	16 08	16 33	17 24	17 47	18 25	19 13	19 57	20 57	21 57	23 21
Penshurst	d	13 12	13 41	14 12	14 41	15 12	15 41	16 12	16 36	17 27	17 50	18 28	19 16	20 00	21 00	22 00	23 24
Edenbridge	d	13 19	13 48	14 19	14 48	15 19	15 48	16 19	16 43	17 34	17 57	18 35	19 23	20 07	21 07	22 07	23 31
Godstone	d	13 25	13 54	14 25	14 54	15 25	15 54	16 25	16 49	17 40	18 03	18 41	19 29	20 13	21 13	22 13	23 37
Nutfield	d	13 31	14 00	14 31	15 00	15 31	16 00	16 31	16 55	17 46	18 09	18 47	19 35	20 19	21 19	22 19	23 43
Redhill	a	13 39	14 04	14 39	15 04	15 39	16 04	16 39	16 59	17 51	18 13	18 51	19 39	20 24	21 24	22 23	23 48
East Croydon	a	13 48	14 23	14 48	15 23	15 48	16 23	16 28	16 54	18 11	17 56	18 48	19 28	20 19	21 15	22 18	00 05
London Bridge [4]	⊖ a	14b12	14 40	15b12	15 40	16b12	16 41	16b56	17b26	18 26	18b24	19b12	20b00	20b45	21b45	22b45	00b52
London Victoria [15]	⊖ a	14b11	14c44	15b11	15c44	16b11	16c46	16b56	17b20	18c40	18b28	19b11	19b59	20b40	21b40	22b40	00b18
Redhill	d	13 44		14 44		15 44		16 44						20 28	21 27	22 27	
Reigate	a	14 18	14e18	15 18	15e18	16 18	16e18	16 54	17 18	18e02	18 27	19 16	20 09	20 38	21 39	22 38	
Gatwick Airport [10] ✈	a	13 55	14e23	14 55	15e23	15 56	16e23	16 56	17 32	18e12	18 32	19 07	19 58	20 35	21 34	22 35	00 11
Three Bridges [4]	a	14 00	14e29	15 00	15e29	16 01	16e29	17 01	17 38	18e18	18 38	19 25	20 04	20 40	21 40	22 41	00 18
Crawley	a	14 04		15 04		16 05		17 05									
Horsham [4]	a	14 16		15 16		16 18		17 19									

Saturdays

		SE 88	SE 88	SE 55 [1]	SE 13	SE 88 [1]	SE 13	SE 88 [1]	SE 13	SE 88 [1]	SE 13	SE 88 [1]	SE 13	SE 88 [1]	SE 13	SE 88 [1]	SE 13	SE 88 [1]
Tunbridge Wells [4]	d		05 37	06 36	07 06	07 36	08 06	08 52	09 24	09 52	10 24	10 52	11 24	11 52	12 24	12 52	13 24	13 52
High Brooms	d		05 40	06 39	07 09	07 39	08 09	08 55	09 27	09 55	10 27	10 55	11 27	11 55	12 27	12 55	13 27	13 55
Tonbridge [4]	a		05 46					09 01	09 33	10 01	10 33	11 01	11 33	12 01	12 33	13 01	13 33	14 01
	d	05 37	05 52	06 52	07 34	08 04	08 34	09 04	09 34	10 04	10 34	11 04	11 34	12 04	12 34	13 04	13 34	14 04
Leigh (Kent)	d		05 56	06 56	07 38	08 08	08 38	09 08	09 38	10 08	10 38	11 08	11 38	12 08	12 38	13 08	13 38	14 08
Penshurst	d		06 00	07 00	07 41	08 12	08 41	09 12	09 41	10 12	10 41	11 12	11 41	12 12	12 41	13 12	13 41	14 12
Edenbridge	d	05 47	06 06	07 06	07 48	08 19	08 48	09 19	09 48	10 19	10 48	11 19	11 48	12 19	12 48	13 19	13 48	14 19
Godstone	d	05 54	06 13	07 13	07 54	08 25	08 54	09 25	09 54	10 25	10 54	11 25	11 54	12 25	12 54	13 25	13 54	14 25
Nutfield	d	05 59	06 18	07 18	08 00	08 31	09 00	09 31	10 00	10 31	11 00	11 31	12 00	12 31	13 00	13 31	14 00	14 31
Redhill	a	06 04	06 23	07 23	08 04	08 39	09 04	09 39	10 04	10 39	11 04	11 39	12 04	12 39	13 04	13 39	14 04	14 39
East Croydon	a		06 27	07 28	08 23	08 48	09 23	09 48	10 23	10 48	11 23	11 48	12 23	12 48	13 23	13 48	14 23	14 48
London Bridge [4]	⊖ a		07b01	07b52	08 40	09b12	09 40	10b12	10 40	11b12	11 40	12b12	12 40	13b12	13 40	14b12	14 40	15b12
London Victoria [15]	⊖ a		06b58	07b57	08c44	09b11	09c44	10b11	10c44	11b11	11c44	12b11	12c44	13b11	13c44	14b11	14c44	15b11
Redhill	d		06 27	07 27		08 44		09 44		10 44		11 44		12 44		13 44		14 44
Reigate	a	06 18	06 38	07 38	08e18	09 18	09e18	10 18	10e18	11 18	11e18	12 18	12e18	13 18	13e18	14 18	14e18	15 18
Gatwick Airport [10] ✈	a		06 34	07 34	08e23	08 55	09e23	09 55	10e23	10 55	11e23	11 55	12e23	12 55	13e23	13 55	14e23	14 55
Three Bridges [4]	a	06 40	06 40	07 39	08e29	09 00	09e29	10 00	10e29	11 00	11e29	12 00	12e29	13 00	13e29	14 00	14e29	15 00
Crawley	a					09 04		10 04		11 04		12 04		13 04		14 04		15 04
Horsham [4]	a					09 16		10 16		11 16		12 16		13 16		14 16		15 16

For general notes see front of timetable
For details of catering facilities see Directory of Train Operators

- **A** From Gillingham (Kent) (Table 208)
- **B** From Paddock Wood (Table 207)
- **C** From Strood (Table 208)
- **b** Change at Redhill and East Croydon
- **c** Change at East Croydon
- **e** Change at Redhill

Table 209

Saturdays

Tunbridge Wells and Tonbridge → London, Gatwick Airport and Horsham via Redhill

Network Diagram - see first page of Table 206

		SE 13	SE 88 ■1	SE 13	SE 88 ■1	SE 13	SE 88 ■1	SE 13	SE 88	SE 88 ■1	SE 88	SE 88	SE 88	SE 88	SE 88
Tunbridge Wells ■4	d	14 24	14 52	15 24	15 52	16 24	16 52	17 24	17 36	17 52	18 36	19 36	20 36	21 36	22 55
High Brooms	d	14 27	14 55	15 27	15 55	16 27	16 55	17 27	17 39	17 55	18 39	19 39	20 39	21 39	22 59
Tonbridge ■4	a	14 33	15 01	15 33	16 01	16 33	17 01	17 33		18 01					
	d	14 34	15 04	15 34	16 04	16 34	17 04	17 34	17 52	18 04	18 52	19 52	20 52	21 52	23 15
Leigh (Kent)	d	14 38	15 08	15 38	16 08	16 38	17 08	17 38	17 56	18 08	18 56	19 56	20 56	21 56	23 19
Penshurst	d	14 41	15 12	15 41	16 12	16 41	17 12	17 41	18 00	18 12	19 00	20 00	21 00	22 00	23 23
Edenbridge	d	14 48	15 19	15 48	16 19	16 48	17 19	17 48	18 06	18 19	19 06	20 06	21 06	22 06	23 29
Godstone	d	14 54	15 25	15 54	16 25	16 54	17 25	17 54	18 13	18 25	19 13	20 13	21 13	22 13	23 36
Nutfield	d	15 00	15 31	16 00	16 31	17 00	17 31	18 00	18 18	18 31	19 18	20 18	21 18	22 18	23 41
Redhill	a	15 04	15 39	16 04	16 39	17 04	17 39	18 04	18 23	18 39	19 23	20 23	21 23	22 23	23 49
East Croydon	a	15 23	15 48	16 23	16 48	17 23	17 48	18 23	18 18	18 48	19 18	20 19	21 18	22 18	00 06
London Bridge ■4	⊖ a	15 40	16b12	16 40	17b12	17 40	18b12	18 40	18b40	19b12	19b45	20b45	21b45	22b45	00b52
London Victoria ■15	⊖ a	15c44	16b11	16c44	17b11	17c44	18b11	18c44	18b40	19b11	19b40	20b40	21b40	22b40	00b18
Redhill	d		15 44		16 44		17 44		18 27	18 44	19 27	20 27	21 27	22 27	
Reigate	a	15e18	16 18	16e18	17 18	17e18	18 18	18e18	18 38	19 18	19 38	20 38	21 40	22 38	
Gatwick Airport ■10	✈ a	15e23	15 55	16e23	16 55	17e23	17 55	18e23	18 34	18 55	19 34	20 34	21 34	22 34	00 10
Three Bridges ■4	a	15e29	16 00	16e29	17 00	17e29	18 00	18e29	18 40	19 00	19 40	20 40	21 40	22 41	00 18
Crawley	a		16 04		17 04		18 04			19 04					
Horsham ■4	a		16 16		17 16		18 16			19 16					

Sundays

		SE 88	SE 55 A	SE 55 B	SE 55 B	SE 55 B	SE 55 B	SE 55 B	SE 55 B	SE 55 B	SE 55 B	SE 55 B	SE 55 B	SE 55 B	SE 55 B	SE 55 B
Tunbridge Wells ■4	d			08 38	09 39	10 39	11 39	12 39	13 39	14 39	15 39	16 39	17 39	18 39	19 08	20 08
High Brooms	d			08 42	09 42	10 42	11 42	12 42	13 42	14 42	15 42	16 42	17 42	18 42	19 12	20 12
Tonbridge ■4	a															
	d	06 57	07 53	08 53	09 53	10 53	11 53	12 53	13 53	14 53	15 53	16 53	17 53	18 53	19 53	20 53
Leigh (Kent)	d		07 57	08 57	09 57	10 57	11 57	12 57	13 57	14 57	15 57	16 57	17 57	18 57	19 57	20 57
Penshurst	d		08 01	09 01	10 01	11 01	12 01	13 01	14 01	15 01	16 01	17 01	18 01	19 01	20 01	21 01
Edenbridge	d	07 08	08 07	09 07	10 07	11 07	12 07	13 07	14 07	15 07	16 07	17 07	18 07	19 07	20 07	21 07
Godstone	d	07 14	08 14	09 14	10 14	11 14	12 14	13 14	14 14	15 14	16 14	17 14	18 14	19 14	20 14	21 14
Nutfield	d	07 20	08 19	09 19	10 19	11 19	12 19	13 19	14 19	15 19	16 19	17 19	18 19	19 19	20 19	21 19
Redhill	a	07 24	08 24	09 24	10 24	11 24	12 24	13 24	14 24	15 24	16 24	17 24	18 24	19 24	20 24	21 24
East Croydon	a	07 23	08 23	09 23	10 23	11 23	12 23	13 23	14 23	15 23	16 23	17 23	18 23	19 23	20 23	21 23
London Bridge ■4	⊖ a	07b45	08b45	09b45	10b45	11b45	12b45	13b45	14b45	15b45	16b45	17b45	18b45	19b45	20b45	21b45
London Victoria ■15	⊖ a	08b16	08b48	09b48	10b48	11b48	12b48	13b48	14b48	15b48	16b48	17b48	18b48	19b48	20b48	21b46
Redhill	d	07 29	08 29	09 29	10 29	11 29	12 29	13 29	14 29	15 29	16 29	17 29	18 29	19 29	20 29	21 29
Reigate	a	08 23	09 24	10 23	11 24	12 23	13 24	14 23	15 24	16 23	17 25	18 23	19 25	20 23	21 24	22 24
Gatwick Airport ■10	✈ a	07 38	08 38	09 38	10 38	11 38	12 38	13 38	14 38	15 38	16 38	17 38	18 38	19 38	20 38	21 38
Three Bridges ■4	a	07 43	08 43	09 43	10 43	11 43	12 43	13 43	14 43	15 43	16 43	17 43	18 43	19 43	20 43	21 43
Crawley	a															
Horsham ■4	a															

For general notes see front of timetable
For details of catering facilities see Directory of Train Operators

A From Gillingham (Kent) (Table 208)
B From Maidstone West (Table 208)
b Change at Redhill and East Croydon
c Change at East Croydon
e Change at Redhill

Table 209

For details of Bank Holiday service alterations please see first page of Table 195

Horsham, Gatwick Airport and London → Tonbridge and Tunbridge Wells via Redhill

Network Diagram - see first page of Table 206

Miles	Miles			SE MX 88	SE 88	SE 88	SE 88	SE 43	SE 55 A	SE 88	SE 13	SN 1	SE 13	SN 1	SE 13	SN 1	SE 13	SN 1	SE 13
0	—	**Horsham** 4	d									09 30		10 32		11 32		12 30	
7	—	Crawley	d									09 44		10 44		11 44		12 44	
8½	—	Three Bridges 4	d		05 40	06 32	07 08	07b36	07 58	08 32	09b18	09 48	10b05	10 48	11b03	11 48	12b03	12 48	13b03
11¼	—	**Gatwick Airport** 10 ✈	d		05 54	06 37	07 13	07b41	08 04	08 37	09b23	09 52	10b10	10 53	11b08	11 53	12b08	12 52	13b08
—	—	Reigate	d		05 34	06 34	07 18	07b51	08 07	08 42	09b24	09 37	10b19	10 34	11b18	11 34	12b19	12 34	13b18
17	—	**Redhill**	a		06 05							10 02		11 02		12 02		13 02	
—	—	**London Victoria** 15 ⊖	d		05 02	06 21	06 32	07c23	07 36	08e17	09c02	09 32	10b02	10 32	11b02	11 32	12b02	12 32	13b02
—	—	**London Bridge** 4 ⊖	d			05e55	06e21	07 34	07 34	08 23	09 11	09e25	10 03	10e26	11 03	11e26	12 03	12e26	13 03
—	—	East Croydon	d		05 22	06 39	06 49	07 49	07 52	08 38	09 26	09 48	10 21	10 48	11 21	11 48	12 21	12 48	13 21
—	0	**Redhill**	d	23p53	06 09	06 58	07 35	08 05	08 29	08 59	09 44	10 07	10 39	11 07	11 39	12 07	12 39	13 07	13 39
—	2	Nutfield	d		06 13	07 02	07 39	08 10	08 33	09 03		10 11	10 43	11 11	11 43	12 11	12 43	13 11	13 43
—	5¾	Godstone	d		06 19	07 08	07 45	08 15	08 39	09 09		10 17	10 49	11 17	11 49	12 17	12 49	13 17	13 49
—	10½	Edenbridge	d	00 04	06 24	07 13	07 50	08 21	08 44	09 14	09 57	10 22	10 54	11 22	11 54	12 22	12 54	13 22	13 54
—	15½	Penshurst	d		06 31	07 20	07 57	08 27	08 51	09 21		10 29	11 01	11 29	12 01	12 29	13 01	13 29	14 01
—	17¼	Leigh (Kent)	d		06 34	07 23	08 02	08 30	08 54	09 24		10 32	11 04	11 32	12 04	12 32	13 04	13 32	14 04
—	19¾	**Tonbridge** 4	a	00 15	06 42	07 27	08 06	08 35	08 59	09 28	10 08	10 37	11 08	11 37	12 08	12 37	13 08	13 37	14 08
—	—		d					08 39			10 09	10 38	11 09	11 38	12 09	12 38	13 09	13 38	14 09
—	—	High Brooms	a	00 27	07 27	08 00	08 15	08 45	09 35	09 43	10 15	10 43	11 15	11 43	12 15	12 43	13 15	13 43	14 15
—	—	**Tunbridge Wells** 4	a	00 31	07 30	08 04	08 19	08 49	09 39	09 47	10 19	10 47	11 19	11 47	12 19	12 47	13 19	13 47	14 19

		SN 1	SE 13	SN 1	SE 13	SN 1	SE 13	SE 88	SE 13	SE 88	SE 88	SE 88 A	SE 13	SE 88	SE 88	SE 88	SE 88	SE 88
Horsham 4	d	13 32		14 32		15 32												
Crawley	d	13 44		14 44		15 44												
Three Bridges 4	d	13 48	14b03	14 48	15b03	15 48	16b03	16 33	17b05	17 33	18 05	18 33	19b05	19 34	20 48	21 48	22 48	23 18
Gatwick Airport 10 ✈	d	13 53	14b08	14 53	15b08	15 53	16b08	16 38	17b10	17 38	18 10	18 38	19b10	19 39	20 53	21 53	22 53	23 23
Reigate	d	13 34	14b19	14 34	15b18	15 34	16b21	16 40	17b14	17 44	18 06	18 38	18b58	19 47	20 46	21 44	22 44	
Redhill	a	14 02		15 02		16 02									21 01	22 01	23 01	
London Victoria 15 ⊖	d	13 32	14b02	14 32	15b02	15 32	16b02	16 32	16c47	17e24	17 40	18 10	18c40	19 32	20 32	21 32	22 32	23 10
London Bridge 4 ⊖	d	13e26	14 03	14e26	15 03	15e26	16 03	16e26	16 57	17 32		18e03	18 48	19e27	20e28	21e15	22e15	23e00
East Croydon	d	13 48	14 21	14 48	15 21	15 48	16 21	16 48	17 11	17 50	17 57	18 26	19 06	19 48	20 48	21 48	22 48	23 28
Redhill	d	14 07	14 39	15 07	15 40	16 07	16 40	17 07	17 28	18 07	18 23	18 55	19 24	20 08	21 07	22 07	23 10	23 53
Nutfield	d	14 11	14 43	15 11	15 44	16 11	16 44	17 11	17 32	18 11	18 27	18 59	19 28	20 12	21 11	22 11	23 14	
Godstone	d	14 17	14 49	15 17	15 50	16 17	16 50	17 17	17 38	18 17	18 33	19 05	19 34	20 18	21 17	22 17	23 20	
Edenbridge	d	14 22	14 54	15 22	15 55	16 22	16 55	17 22	17 43	18 22	18 38	19 10	19 39	20 23	21 22	22 22	23 25	00 04
Penshurst	d	14 29	15 01	15 29	16 02	16 29	17 02	17 29	17 50	18 29	18 45	19 17	19 46	20 30	21 29	22 29	23 32	
Leigh (Kent)	d	14 32	15 04	15 32	16 05	16 32	17 05	17 32	17 53	18 32	18 48	19 20	19 49	20 33	21 32	22 32	23 35	
Tonbridge 4	a	14 37	15 08	15 39	16 09	16 36	17 11	17 36	17 57	18 36	18 52	19 24	19 56	20 37	21 37	22 37	23 39	00 15
	d	14 38	15 09		16 13													
High Brooms	a	14 43	15 15	15 52	16 19	17 05	17 39		18 13	18 58	19 22	19 37	20 23	21 05	22 05	23 35	00 27	00 27
Tunbridge Wells 4	a	14 47	15 19	15 56	16 23	17 09	17f44		18g18	19 04	19 28	19 41	20 28	21 09	22 10	23 39	00 31	00 31

Saturdays

		SE 88	SE 88	SN 1	SN 1	SE 13	SN 1	SE 13	SN 1	SE 13	SN 1	SE 13	SN 1	SE 13	SN 1	SE 13	SN 1	SE 13
Horsham 4	d			06 32	07 32		08 32		09 32		10 32		11 32		12 32		13 32	
Crawley	d			06 44	07 44		08 44		09 44		10 44		11 44		12 44		13 44	
Three Bridges 4	d		05 33	06 48	07 48	08b03	08 48	09b03	09 48	10b03	10 48	11b03	11 48	12b03	12 48	13b03	13 48	14b03
Gatwick Airport 10 ✈	d		05 45	06 53	07 53	08b08	08 53	09b08	09 53	10b08	10 53	11b08	11 53	12b08	12 53	13b08	13 53	14b08
Reigate	d		05 34	06 34	07 34	08b19	08 34	09b18	09 34	10b19	10 34	11b18	11 34	12b19	12 34	13b18	13 34	14b19
Redhill	a			07 02	08 02		09 02		10 02		11 02		12 02		13 02		14 02	
London Victoria 15 ⊖	d		05 32	06 10	07 32	08b02	08 32	09b02	09 32	10b02	10 32	11b02	11 32	12b02	12 32	13b02	13 32	14b02
London Bridge 4 ⊖	d			06e08	07e26	08 03	08e26	09 03	09e26	10 03	10e26	11 03	11e26	12 03	12e26	13 03	13e26	14 03
East Croydon	d		05 48	06 28	07 48	08 21	08 48	09 21	09 48	10 21	10 48	11 21	11 48	12 21	12 48	13 21	13 48	14 21
Redhill	d	23p53	06 11	07 07	08 07	08 39	09 07	09 39	10 07	10 39	11 07	11 39	12 07	12 39	13 07	13 39	14 07	14 39
Nutfield	d		06 15	07 11	08 11	08 43	09 11	09 43	10 11	10 43	11 11	11 43	12 11	12 43	13 11	13 43	14 11	14 43
Godstone	d		06 20	07 17	08 17	08 49	09 17	09 49	10 17	10 49	11 17	11 49	12 17	12 49	13 17	13 49	14 17	14 49
Edenbridge	d	00 04	06 26	07 22	08 22	08 54	09 22	09 54	10 22	10 54	11 22	11 54	12 22	12 54	13 22	13 54	14 22	14 54
Penshurst	d		06 32	07 29	08 29	09 01	09 29	10 01	10 29	11 01	11 29	12 01	12 29	13 01	13 29	14 01	14 29	15 01
Leigh (Kent)	d		06 36	07 32	08 32	09 04	09 32	10 04	10 32	11 04	11 32	12 04	12 32	13 04	13 32	14 04	14 32	15 04
Tonbridge 4	a	00 15	06 40	07 36	08 37	09 08	09 37	10 08	10 37	11 08	11 37	12 08	12 37	13 08	13 37	14 08	14 37	15 08
	d				08 38	09 09	09 38	10 09	10 38	11 09	11 38	12 09	12 38	13 09	13 38	14 09	14 38	15 09
High Brooms	a	00 27	07 06	08 06	08 43	09 15	09 43	10 15	10 43	11 15	11 43	12 15	12 43	13 15	13 43	14 15	14 43	15 15
Tunbridge Wells 4	a	00 31	07 10	08 10	08 47	09 19	09 47	10 19	10 47	11 19	11 47	12 19	12 47	13 19	13 47	14 19	14 47	15 19

For general notes see front of timetable
For details of catering facilities see Directory of Train Operators

- **A** To Strood (Table 208)
- **b** Change at Redhill
- **c** Change at East Croydon
- **e** Change at East Croydon and Redhill
- **f** From 13 October arr. 1745
- **g** From 13 October arr. 1819

Table 209

Saturdays

Horsham, Gatwick Airport and London → Tonbridge and Tunbridge Wells via Redhill

Network Diagram - see first page of Table 206

		SN 1	SE 13	SN 1	SE 13	SN 1	SE 13	SN 1	SE 13	SE 88	SE 13	SE 55	SE 88	SE 88	SE 88	SE 88
Horsham 4	d	14 32		15 32		16 32		17 32								
Crawley	d	14 44		15 44		16 44		17 44								
Three Bridges 4	d	14 48	15b03	15 48	16b03	16 48	17b03	17 48	18b03	18 48	19b03	19 48	20 48	21 48	22 48	23 18
Gatwick Airport 10 ✈	d	14 53	15b08	15 53	16b08	16 53	17b08	17 53	18b08	18 52	19b08	19 53	20 53	21 53	22 53	23 23
Reigate	d	14 34	15b18	15 34	16b19	16 34	17b18	17 34	18b19	18 34	19b18	19 34	20 34	21 40	22 48	
Redhill	a	15 02		16 02		17 02		18 02		19 00		20 01	21 02	22 01	23 01	
London Victoria 15 ⊖	d	14 32	15b02	15 32	16b02	16 32	17b02	17 32	18b02	18 32	19b02	19 32	20 32	21 32	22 32	23 10
London Bridge 4 ⊖	d	14c26	15 03	15c26	16 03	16c26	17 03	17c26	18 03	18c26	19 03	19c26	20c15	21c15	22c15	23c00
East Croydon	d	14 48	15 21	15 48	16 21	16 48	17 21	17 48	18 21	18 48	19 21	19 48	20 48	21 48	22 48	23 28
Redhill	d	15 07	15 39	16 07	16 39	17 07	17 39	18 07	18 39	19 06	19 39	20 07	21 07	22 07	23 07	23 54
Nutfield	d	15 11	15 43	16 11	16 43	17 11	17 43	18 11	18 43	19 10	19 43	20 11	21 11	22 11	23 11	
Godstone	d	15 16	15 49	16 17	16 49	17 17	17 49	18 17	18 49	19 16	19 49	20 17	21 17	22 17	23 17	
Edenbridge	d	15 22	15 54	16 22	16 54	17 22	17 54	18 22	18 54	19 21	19 54	20 22	21 22	22 22	23 22	00 06
Penshurst	d	15 28	16 01	16 29	17 01	17 29	18 01	18 29	19 01	19 28	20 01	20 29	21 29	22 29	23 29	
Leigh (Kent)	d	15 32	16 04	16 32	17 04	17 32	18 04	18 32	19 04	19 31	20 04	20 32	21 32	22 32	23 32	
Tonbridge 4	a	15 37	16 08	16 37	17 08	17 37	18 08	18 37	19 08	19 37	20 08	20 37	21 37	22 37	23 37	00 16
	d	15 38	16 09	16 38	17 09	17 38	18 09	18 38	19 09							
High Brooms	a	15 43	16 15	16 43	17 15	17 43	18 15	18 43	19 15	20 06	20 36	20 55	21 56	23 00	23 55	00 27
Tunbridge Wells 4	a	15 47	16 19	16 47	17 19	17 47	18 19	18 47	19 19	20 10	20 40	20 59	21 59	23 04	23 59	00 31

Sundays

		SE 88	SE 55 A	SE 55 A	SE 55 A	SE 55 A	SE 55 A	SE 55 A	SE 55 A	SE 55 A	SE 55 A	SE 55 A	SE 55 A	SE 55 A	SE 55 A	SE 55 B	SE 55
Horsham 4	d																
Crawley	d																
Three Bridges 4	d		07 50	08 50	09 50	10 50	11 50	12 50	13 50	14 50	15 50	16 50	17 50	18 50	19 50	20 50	21 50
Gatwick Airport 10 ✈	d		07 55	08 55	09 55	10 55	11 55	12 55	13 55	14 55	15 55	16 55	17 55	18 55	19 55	20 55	21 55
Reigate	d			08 13	09 14	10 13	11 14	12 13	13 14	14 13	15 14	16 13	17 14	18 13	19 14	20 13	21 14
Redhill	a		08 03	09 03	10 03	11 03	12 03	13 03	14 03	15 03	16 03	17 03	18 03	19 03	20 03	21 03	22 03
London Victoria 15 ⊖	d		07 32	08 32	09 32	10 32	11 32	12 32	13 32	14 32	15 32	16 32	17 32	18 32	19 32	20 32	21 32
London Bridge 4 ⊖	d		07e14	08f14	09c26	10c26	11c26	12c26	13c26	14c26	15c26	16c26	17c26	18f14	19f14	20f14	21f14
East Croydon	d		07 51	08 51	09 51	10 51	11 51	12 51	13 51	14 51	15 51	16 51	17 51	18 51	19 51	20 51	21 51
Redhill	d	23p54	08 10	09 10	10 10	11 10	12 10	13 10	14 10	15 10	16 10	17 10	18 10	19 10	20 10	21 10	22 10
Nutfield	d		08 14	09 14	10 14	11 14	12 14	13 14	14 14	15 14	16 14	17 14	18 14	19 14	20 14	21 14	22 14
Godstone	d		08 20	09 20	10 20	11 20	12 20	13 20	14 20	15 20	16 20	17 20	18 20	19 20	20 20	21 20	22 20
Edenbridge	d	00 06	08 25	09 25	10 25	11 25	12 25	13 25	14 25	15 25	16 25	17 25	18 25	19 25	20 25	21 25	22 25
Penshurst	d		08 32	09 32	10 32	11 32	12 32	13 32	14 32	15 32	16 32	17 32	18 32	19 32	20 32	21 32	22 32
Leigh (Kent)	d		08 35	09 35	10 35	11 35	12 35	13 35	14 35	15 35	16 35	17 35	18 35	19 35	20 35	21 35	22 35
Tonbridge 4	a	00 16	08 40	09 40	10 40	11 40	12 40	13 40	14 40	15 40	16 40	17 40	18 40	19 40	20 40	21 40	22 40
	d																
High Brooms	a	00 27	09 03	10 03	11 03	12 03	13 03	14 03	15 03	16 03	17 03	18 03	19 03	20 03	21 05	22 05	23 05
Tunbridge Wells 4	a	00 31	09 07	10 07	11 07	12 07	13 07	14 07	15 07	16 07	17 07	18 07	19 07	20 07	21 09	22 09	23 09

For general notes see front of timetable
For details of catering facilities see Directory of Train Operators

A To Maidstone West (Table 208)
B To Gillingham (Kent) (Table 208)
b Change at Redhill
c Change at East Croydon and Redhill
e Until 7 September change at Redhill. From 14 September dep. 0711, change at East Croydon and Redhill
f Until 7 September change at Redhill. From 14 September change at East Croydon and Redhill

Network Diagram for Table 212

DM-22/07
Design BAJS

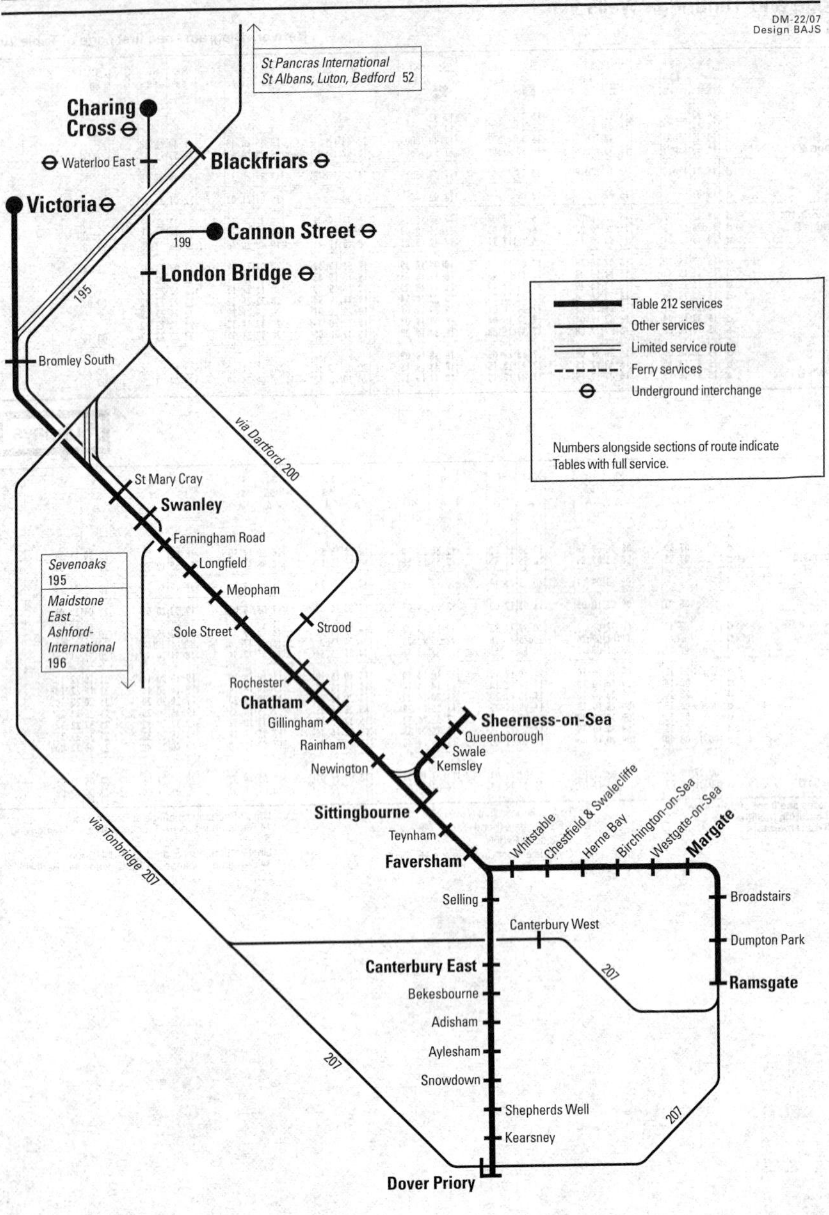

St Pancras International
St Albans, Luton, Bedford 52
Charing Cross
Waterloo East
Blackfriars
Victoria
Cannon Street
199
London Bridge
195
Bromley South
via Dartford 200
St Mary Cray
Swanley
Farningham Road
Longfield
Meopham
Sole Street
Sevenoaks
195
Maidstone East
Ashford-International
196
Strood
Rochester
Chatham
Gillingham
Rainham
Newington
Sheerness-on-Sea
Queenborough
Swale
Kemsley
Sittingbourne
Teynham
Faversham
Whitstable
Chestfield & Swalecliffe
Herne Bay
Birchington-on-Sea
Westgate-on-Sea
Margate
Broadstairs
Dumpton Park
Ramsgate
Selling
Canterbury West
207
Canterbury East
Bekesbourne
Adisham
Aylesham
Snowdown
Shepherds Well
Kearsney
Dover Priory
via Tonbridge 207
207
207
Table 212 services
Other services
Limited service route
Ferry services
Underground interchange
Numbers alongside sections of route indicate Tables with full service.

For details of Bank Holiday service alterations please see first page of Table 195

London → Medway, Sheerness-on-Sea, Dover and Ramsgate

Network Diagram - see first page of Table 212

Miles	Miles	Miles			SE MX 92 [1]	SE MO 54 [1]	SE MX 50 [1]	SE MO 50 [1]	SE MX 01	SE MX 22 [1]	SE MO 54 [1]	SE MX 50 [1]	SE 80 [1]	SE 97	SE 01	SE 4 [1]	SE 20 [1]	SE 01	SE 90 [1]	SE 81 [1]	SE 01	SE 4 [1]		SE 88 [1]	SE 54 [1]
0	0	—	**London Victoria [15]**	⊖ d	22p39	22p41	23p03	23p03		23p39	23p42	00 03													05 32
—	—	—	**London Blackfriars [3]**	⊖ d																					
—	—	—	Elephant & Castle	⊖ d																					
11	11	—	Bromley South [4]	d	22p59	23p01	23p19	23p19		23p58	00 01														05 48
14¾	14¾	—	St Mary Cray	d	23p05	23p07				00 04	00 08														05 55
17½	17½	—	Swanley [4]	d	23p10	23p12				00 09	00 12														06 00
20½	20½	—	Farningham Road	d	23p14	23p16				00 13	00 17														06 05
23½	23½	—	Longfield	d	23p19	23p21				00 18	00 21														06 10
26	26	—	Meopham	d	23p23	23p25				00 23	00 26														06 15
27	27	—	Sole Street	d	23p26	23p28				00 26	00 28														06 17
—	—	—	**London Charing Cross [4]**	⊖ d						22 50	23 20	23 20													04 56
—	—	—	**London Waterloo (East) [4]**	⊖ d						22 53	23 23	23 23													04 59
—	—	0	**London Cannon Street [4]**	⊖ d																					
—	—	—	**London Bridge [4]**	⊖ d						22 59	23 29	23 29													05 04
—	—	—	Dartford [4]	d						23 34	23 34						05 06								05 42
—	—	—	Greenhithe for Bluewater	d						23 40	23 40						05 11								05 48
—	—	—	Gravesend [4]	d						23 50	23 48						05 18								05 56
—	—	—	Strood [4]	d						00 02	23 58	00 32					05 29								06 08
33¾	33¾	32	Rochester [4]	d	23p36	23p37	23p43	23p43		00 35	00 38	00 43					05 33								06 26
34¼	34¼	—	**Chatham [4]**	d	23p39	23p39	23p46	23p46		00 38	00 40	00 46					05 36								06 29
36	36	—	**Gillingham (Kent) [4]**	d	23p43	23p43	23p49	23p50		00a41	00a44	00 50		05 00			05 40								06 33
39	39	—	Rainham (Kent)	d	23p48	23p48	23p54	23p55				00 55		05 04			05 45								06 38
41½	41½	—	Newington	d	23p52	23p52						00 58		05 08			05 49								06 42
44¾	44¾	0	**Sittingbourne [4]**	a	23p57	23p57	00 01	00 02				01 03					05 54								06 47
—	—	—		d	23p57	23p57	00 01	00 02	00 08			01 03			05 37		05 54	06 12			06 23				06 48
—	—	2	Kemsley	d					00 12					05 14	05 41			06 16			06 27				
—	—	4	Swale	d					00 15					05 17	05 45			06 19			06 30				
—	—	6	Queenborough	d					00 20					05 22	05 49			06 24			06b40				
—	—	8	**Sheerness-on-Sea**	a					00 26					05 28	05 55			06 30			06 46				
47½	47½	—	Teynham	d	00 01	00 01						01 07					05 58								06 52
52	52	—	**Faversham [2]**	a	00 07	00 07	00 11					01 12					06 04								07 01
—	—	—		d			00 12					01 13	04 50				06 05			06 13					07 02
—	55¼	—	Selling	d													06 10								
—	61¾	—	**Canterbury East [4]**	d									05 02				06 19								
—	64¾	—	Bekesbourne	d													06 23								
—	67¾	—	Adisham	d									05 10				06 28								
—	68¾	—	Aylesham	d									05 12				06 30								
—	69¾	—	Snowdown	d									05 15				06 33								
—	71¾	—	Shepherds Well	d									05 19				06 37								
—	75	—	Kearsney	d									05 23				06 41								
—	77¼	—	**Dover Priory [4]**	a									05 28				06 48								
59	—	—	Whitstable	d			00 20	00 22				01 21								06 21					07 10
60½	—	—	Chestfield & Swalecliffe	d			00 23	00 25				01 24								06 24					07 13
62¾	—	—	**Herne Bay**	d			00 27	00 29				01 27								06 28					07 17
70¾	—	—	Birchington-on-Sea	d			00 36	00 38				01 36								06 37					07 26
72½	—	—	Westgate-on-Sea	d			00 39	00 41				01 39								06 41					07 30
73¾	—	—	**Margate [4]**	d			00 43	00 45				01 43				06 07			06 41	06 45		07 07		07 28	07 34
77	—	—	Broadstairs	d			00 48	00 50				01 48				06 12			06 46	06 50		07 12		07 33	07 39
78¼	—	—	Dumpton Park	d			00 51	00 53				01 51				06 15			06 49	06 52		07 15		07 36	07 41
79¼	—	—	**Ramsgate [4]**	a			00 54	00 56				01 54				06 18			06 52	06 56		07 18		07 39	07 45

For general notes see front of timetable
For details of catering facilities see Directory of Train Operators

For services from London to Ramsgate, Dover and Canterbury via Ashford see Table 207

b Arr. 0635

Table 212

Mondays to Fridays

until 10 October

For details of Bank Holiday service alterations please see first page of Table 195

London → Medway, Sheerness-on-Sea, Dover and Ramsgate

Network Diagram - see first page of Table 212

		SE 01	SE 80 1	SE 01	SE 64 1 A	SE 81 1	SE 90 1	SE 54 1	SE 80 1	SE 01	SE 37 1	SE 81 1	SE 01	SE 37 1	SE 01	SE 90 1	SE 50 1	SE 37 1	SE 92 1		SE 50 1		SE 01	SE 92 1	SE 90 1
London Victoria 15	⊖ d							06 16			06 39			07 07			07 33		07 39		08 03			08 09	
London Blackfriars 3	⊖ d							05 27			06 08			06 42			07 09		07 24					07 53	
Elephant & Castle	⊖ d							05 30			06 12			06 45			07 12		07 27					07 56	
Bromley South 4	d							06 34			06 59			07 27			07 52		08 01		08 20			08 31	
St Mary Cray	d							06 41			07 05			07 34					08 07					08 37	
Swanley 4	d							06 46			07 10			07 39					08 12					08 42	
Farningham Road	d							06 51			07 14			07 44					08 16					08 47	
Longfield	d							06 56			07 19			07 48					08 21					08 51	
Meopham	d							07 01			07 23			07 53					08 25					08 56	
Sole Street	d							07 03			07 26			07 56					08 28					08 58	
London Charing Cross 4	⊖ d							05 26			06 02			06 40			06 40				07 20			07b45	
London Waterloo (East) 4	⊖ d							05 29			06 05			06 43			06 43				07 23			07b48	
London Cannon Street 4	⊖ d										05b50			06b30			06c30				07b04			07 54	
London Bridge 4	⊖ d							05 34			06 10			06 48			06 48				07 28			07 58	
Dartford 4	d							06 12			06 46			07 28			07 28				08 05			08 34	
Greenhithe for Bluewater	d							06 18			06e26			07 33			07 33				08 11			08 39	
Gravesend 4	d							06 26			06 56			07 40			07 40				08 19			08 46	
Strood 4	d							06 38			07 08			07 52			07 52				08 32			08 58	
Rochester 4	d							07 15			07 39			08 06					08 38		08 45			09 09	
Chatham 4	d							07 17			07 42			08 08			08 19		08 41		08 48			09 11	
Gillingham (Kent) 4	d							07 21			07 45			08 12			08 23		08 45		08 51			09 15	
Rainham (Kent)	d							07 26			07 50			08 17			08 28		08 50		08 56			09 20	
Newington	d							07 30			07 54			08 21					08 54					09 24	
Sittingbourne 4	a							07 35			07 59			08 26			08 36		08 59		09 03			09 29	
	d	06 58		07 19				07 35		07 46	08 04		08 15	08 27	08 28		08 37		08 59		09 04		09 05	09 29	
Kemsley	d	07 04		07f26						07 50			08 19		08 32								09 09		
Swale	d	07 08		07 32						07 55			08 22		08 36								09 12		
Queenborough	d	07 12		07 36						07 59			08 27		08 41								09 17		
Sheerness-on-Sea	a	07 18		07 41						08 04			08 32		08 47								09 23		
Teynham	d							07 39			08 09			08 31					09 03					09 33	
Faversham 2	a							07 45			08 15			08 37			08 45	←	09 09		09 12			09 39	
	d		07 04			07 20		07 46	07 53		08 17	08 19		08 49			08 47	08 49			09 15	09 18			
Selling	d		07 09						07 58		08 22			→				08 54							
Canterbury East 4	d		07 18						08 08		08 32							09 04				09 32			
Bekesbourne	d		07 22						08 12		08 36							09 08							
Adisham	d		07 27						08 17		08 41							09 13							
Aylesham	d		07 29						08 19		08 43							09 15							
Snowdown	d		07 32						08 22		08 46							09 18							
Shepherds Well	d		07 36						08 26		08 50							09 22							
Kearsney	d		07 40						08 30		08 54							09 26							
Dover Priory 4	⛴ a		07 45						08 36		09 00							09 32				09 52			
Whitstable	d					07 28		07 54				08 28					08 56				09 23				
Chestfield & Swalecliffe	d					07 31		07 57				08 31					08 59								
Herne Bay	d					07 35		08 01				08 35					09 03				09 28				
Birchington-on-Sea	d					07 44		08 10				08 44					09 12				09 37				
Westgate-on-Sea	d					07 48		08 14				08 47					09 16								
Margate 4	d				07 43	07 52	08 13	08 18				08 52				09 04	09 20				09 43				10 04
Broadstairs	d				07 48	07 57	08 18	08 23				08 57				09 09	09 25				09 48				10 09
Dumpton Park	d				07 50	07 59	08 21	08 26				09 00				09 12	09 27								10 12
Ramsgate 4	✈ a				07 53	08 03	08 24	08 29				09 03				09 15	09 30				09 52				10 15

For general notes see front of timetable
For details of catering facilities see Directory of Train Operators

For services from London to Ramsgate, Dover and Canterbury via Ashford see Table 207

A To London Victoria (Table 196)
b Change at London Bridge and Rochester
c Change at London Bridge and Chatham
e Change at Gravesend and Rochester
f Arr. 0723

For details of Bank Holiday service alterations please see first page of Table 195

London → Medway, Sheerness-on-Sea, Dover and Ramsgate

Network Diagram - see first page of Table 212

		SE 50 **1**	SE 01	SE 92 **1**	SE 50 **1**	SE 01	SE 92 **1**	SE 90 **1**	SE 50 **1**	SE 92 **1**	SE 92 **1**	SE 01	SE 92 **1**	SE 50 **1**	SE 01	SE 92 **1**	SE 90 **1**	SE 50 **1**	SE 01
								⌶		A	B			C ⌶				C ⌶	
London Victoria 15	⊖ d	08 33		08 39	09 03		09 09		09 33	09 15			09 39	10 03		10 09		10 33	
London Blackfriars 3	⊖ d			08 20	08 43				09 13		09 03			09 43				10 13	
Elephant & Castle	⊖ d			08 23	08 46				09 16		09 12			09 46				10 16	
Bromley South 4	d	08 51		08 59	09 19		09 29		09 50				09 59	10 19		10 29		10 49	
St Mary Cray	d			09 05			09 35						10 05			10 35			
Swanley 4	d			09 10			09 40						10 10			10 40			
Farningham Road	d			09 14			09 44						10 14			10 44			
Longfield	d			09 19			09 49						10 19			10 49			
Meopham	d			09 24			09 53						10 23			10 53			
Sole Street	d			09 26			09 56						10 26			10 56			
London Charing Cross 4	⊖ d			08b08			08b41			09 02	09 02		09 20			09 52			
London Waterloo (East) 4	⊖ d			08b11			08b44			09 06	09 06		09 23			09 55			
London Cannon Street 4	⊖ d			08 17			08 50			09 02	09 02		09b20			09b48			
London Bridge 4	⊖ d			08 21			08 54			09 12	09 12		09 29			10 00			
Dartford 4	d			09 02			09 34			09 54	09 58		10 04			10 34			
Greenhithe for Bluewater	d			09 07			09 39			09 52	09 52		10 09			10 39			
Gravesend 4	d			09 14			09 46			10 04	10 10		10 16			10 46			
Strood 4	d			09 26			09 58			09 58	09 58		10 28			10 58			
Rochester 4	d	09 16		09 36	09 43		10 05		10 15				10 35	10 44		11 05		11 13	
Chatham 4	d	09 18		09 39	09 47		10 08		10 17	10 19	10 24		10 38	10 47		11 08		11 17	
Gillingham (Kent) 4	d	09 22		09 43	09 50		10 12		10 21	10 22	10 28		10 41	10 50		11 11		11 20	
Rainham (Kent)	d	09 26		09 48	09 55		10 17		10 26				10 46	10 55		11 16		11 25	
Newington	d			09 52			10 21						10 50			11 20			
Sittingbourne 4	a	09 34		09 57	10 02		10 26		10 33				10 55	11 02		11 25		11 32	
	d	09 34	09 36	09 57	10 02	10 05	10 26		10 33			10 35	10 55	11 02	11 05	11 25		11 32	11 35
Kemsley	d		09 40			10 09						10 39			11 09				11 39
Swale	d		09 43			10 12						10 42			11 12				11 42
Queenborough	d		09 47			10 17						10 47			11 17				11 47
Sheerness-on-Sea	a		09 53			10 23						10 53			11 23				11 53
Teynham	d			10 01			10 30						10 59			11 29			
Faversham 2	a	09 42		10 07	10 10		10 36		10 41				11 05	11 10		11 35		11 40	
	d	09 46 / 09 48			10 14 / 10 16				10 44 / 10 47					11 14 / 11 16				11 44 / 11 46	
Selling	d	09 53							10 52									11 51	
Canterbury East 4	d	10c08			10 28				11 01					11 28				12 00	
Bekesbourne	d	10 13							11 05									12 05	
Adisham	d	10 17							11 10									12 09	
Aylesham	d	10 20							11 12									12 12	
Snowdown	d	10 22							11 15									12 14	
Shepherds Well	d	10 26							11 19									12 18	
Kearsney	d	10 31							11 23									12 23	
Dover Priory 4	⛴ a	10 35			10 45				11 27					11 44				12 28	
Whitstable	d	09 55			10 22				10 53	10 46	10 59			11 22				11 52	
Chestfield & Swalecliffe	d	09 58							10 56									11 55	
Herne Bay	d	10 02			10 27				11 00	10 52	11 05			11 27				11 59	
Birchington-on-Sea	d	10 11			10 35				11 08	11 01	11 14			11 35				12 08	
Westgate-on-Sea	d	10 15							11 11	11 05	11 18							12 11	
Margate 4	d	10 19			10 41			11 04	11 15	11 09	11 22			11 41			12 04	12 15	
Broadstairs	d	10 24			10 46			11 09	11 21	11 15	11 27			11 46			12 09	12 20	
Dumpton Park	d	10 27						11 12	11 23								12 12	12 23	
Ramsgate 4	⛴ a	10 30			10 51			11 15	11 27	11 20	11 32			11 51			12 15	12 26	

For general notes see front of timetable
For details of catering facilities see Directory of Train Operators

For services from London to Ramsgate, Dover and Canterbury via Ashford see Table 207

A Until 18 July and from 1 September
B 21 July to 29 August
C ⌶ to Ramsgate

b Change at London Bridge and Rochester
c Arr. 1002

For details of Bank Holiday service alterations please see first page of Table 195

London → Medway, Sheerness-on-Sea, Dover and Ramsgate

Network Diagram - see first page of Table 212

		SE 92 1	SE 50 1 A ⛟		SE 01	SE 92 1	SE 90 1	SE 50 1 A ⛟		SE 01	SE 92 1	SE 50 1 A ⛟		SE 01	SE 92 1	SE 90 1	SE 50 1 A ⛟		SE 01	SE 92 1	SE 50 1 A ⛟		SE 01	SE 92 1
London Victoria 15	⊖ d	10 39	11 03			11 09		11 33			11 39	12 03			12 09		12 33			12 39	13 03			13 09
London Blackfriars 3	⊖ d		*10 43*					*11 13*				*11 43*					*12 13*				*12 43*			
Elephant & Castle	⊖ d		*10 46*					*11 16*				*11 46*					*12 16*				*12 46*			
Bromley South 4	d	10 59	11 19			11 29		11 49			11 59	12 19			12 29		12 49			12 59	13 19			13 29
St Mary Cray	d	11 05				11 35					12 05				12 35					13 05				13 35
Swanley 4	d	11 10				11 40					12 10				12 40					13 10				13 40
Farningham Road	d	11 14				11 44					12 14				12 44					13 14				13 44
Longfield	d	11 19				11 49					12 19				12 49					13 19				13 49
Meopham	d	11 23				11 53					12 23				12 53					13 23				13 53
Sole Street	d	11 26				11 56					12 26				12 56					13 26				13 56
London Charing Cross 4	⊖ d	*10 20*				*10 50*					*11 20*				*11 50*					*12 20*				*12 50*
London Waterloo (East) 4	⊖ d	*10 23*				*10 53*					*11 23*				*11 53*					*12 23*				*12 53*
London Cannon Street 4	⊖ d	*10b18*				*10b48*					*11b18*				*11b48*					*12b18*				*12b48*
London Bridge 4	⊖ d	*10 29*				*10 59*					*11 29*				*11 59*					*12 29*				*12 59*
Dartford 4	d	*11 04*				*11 34*					*12 04*				*12 34*					*13 04*				*13 34*
Greenhithe for Bluewater	d	*11 09*				*11 39*					*12 09*				*12 39*					*13 09*				*13 39*
Gravesend 4	d	*11 16*				*11 46*					*12 16*				*12 46*					*13 16*				*13 46*
Strood 4	d	*11 28*				*11 58*					*12 28*				*12 58*					*13 28*				*13 58*
Rochester 4	d	11 35	11 43			12 05		12 13			12 35	12 43			13 05		13 13			13 35	13 43			14 05
Chatham 4	d	11 38	11 47			12 08		12 17			12 38	12 47			13 08		13 17			13 38	13 47			14 08
Gillingham (Kent) 4	d	11 41	11 50			12 11		12 20			12 41	12 50			13 11		13 20			13 41	13 50			14 11
Rainham (Kent)	d	11 46	11 55			12 16		12 25			12 46	12 55			13 16		13 25			13 46	13 55			14 16
Newington	d	11 50				12 20					12 50				13 20					13 50				14 20
Sittingbourne 4	a	11 55	12 02			12 25		12 32			12 55	13 02			13 25		13 32			13 55	14 02			14 25
	d	11 55	12 02		12 05	12 25		12 32		12 35	12 55	13 02		13 05	13 25		13 32		13 35	13 55	14 02		14 05	14 25
Kemsley	d				12 09					12 39				13 09					13 39				14 09	
Swale	d				12 12					12 42				13 12					13 42				14 12	
Queenborough	d				12 17					12 47				13 17					13 47				14 17	
Sheerness-on-Sea	a				12 23					12 53				13 23					13 53				14 23	
Teynham	d	11 59				12 29					12 59				13 29					13 59				14 29
Faversham 2	a	12 05	12 10			12 35		12 40			13 05	13 10			13 35		13 40			14 05	14 10			14 35
	d		12 14	12 16				12 44	12 46			13 14	13 16				13 44	13 46			14 14	14 16		
Selling	d								12 51									13 51						
Canterbury East 4	d			12 28					13 00				13 28					14 00				14 28		
Bekesbourne	d								13 05									14 05						
Adisham	d								13 09									14 09						
Aylesham	d								13 12									14 12						
Snowdown	d								13 14									14 14						
Shepherds Well	d								13 18									14 18						
Kearsney	d								13 23									14 23						
Dover Priory 4	⛴ a			12 44					13 28				13 44					14 28				14 44		
Whitstable	d		12 22					12 52				13 22					13 52				14 22			
Chestfield & Swalecliffe	d							12 55									13 55							
Herne Bay	d		12 27					12 59				13 27					13 59				14 27			
Birchington-on-Sea	d		12 35					13 08				13 35					14 08				14 35			
Westgate-on-Sea	d							13 11									14 11							
Margate 4	d		12 41				13 04	13 15				13 41				14 04	14 15				14 41			
Broadstairs	d		12 46				13 09	13 20				13 46				14 09	14 20				14 46			
Dumpton Park	d						13 12	13 23								14 12	14 23							
Ramsgate 4	⛴ a		12 51				13 15	13 26				13 51				14 15	14 26				14 51			

For general notes see front of timetable
For details of catering facilities see Directory of Train Operators

For services from London to Ramsgate, Dover and Canterbury via Ashford see Table 207

A ⛟ to Ramsgate
b Change at London Bridge and Rochester

For details of Bank Holiday service alterations please see first page of Table 195

London → Medway, Sheerness-on-Sea, Dover and Ramsgate

Network Diagram - see first page of Table 212

	SE 90 [1]	SE 50 [1] A 🛒		SE 01	SE 92 [1]	SE 90 [1]	SE 50 [1] A 🛒		SE 01		SE 92 [1]	SE 50 [1] A 🛒		SE 01	SE 92 [1]	SE 90 [1]	SE 50 [1] A 🛒		SE 01	SE 92 [1]	SE 50 [1] A 🛒		SE 01	SE 92 [1]
London Victoria [15] ⊖ d		13 33			13 39		14 03				14 09	14 33			14 39		15 03			15 09	15 33			15 39
London Blackfriars [3] ⊖ d		*13 13*					*13 43*					*14 13*					*14 43*				*15 13*			
Elephant & Castle ⊖ d		*13 16*					*13 46*					*14 16*					*14 46*				*15 16*			
Bromley South [4] d		13 49			13 59		14 19				14 29	14 49			14 59		15 19			15 29	15 49			16 00
St Mary Cray d					14 05						14 35				15 05					15 35				16 06
Swanley [4] d					14 10						14 40				15 10					15 40				16 11
Farningham Road d					14 14						14 44				15 14					15 44				16 15
Longfield d					14 19						14 49				15 19					15 49				16 20
Meopham d					14 23						14 53				15 23					15 53				16 24
Sole Street d					14 26						14 56				15 26					15 56				16 27
London Charing Cross [4] ⊖ d					*13 20*						*13 50*				*14 20*					*14 50*				*15 20*
London Waterloo (East) [4] ⊖ d					*13 23*						*13 53*				*14 23*					*14 53*				*15 23*
London Cannon Street [4] ⊖ d					*13b18*						*13b48*				*14b18*					*14b48*				*15b18*
London Bridge [4] ⊖ d					*13 29*						*13 59*				*14 29*					*14 59*				*15 29*
Dartford [4] d					*14 04*						*14 34*				*15 04*					*15 34*				*16 04*
Greenhithe for Bluewater d					*14 09*						*14 39*				*15 09*					*15 39*				*16 09*
Gravesend [4] d					*14 16*						*14 46*				*15 16*					*15 46*				*16 16*
Strood [4] d					*14 28*						*14 58*				*15 28*					*15 58*				*16 28*
Rochester [4] d		14 13			14 35		14 43				15 05	15 13			15 35		15 43			16 05	16 13			16 36
Chatham [4] d		14 17			14 38		14 47				15 08	15 17			15 38		15 47			16 08	16 16			16 39
Gillingham (Kent) [4] d		14 21			14 41		14 50				15 11	15 20			15 41		15 51			16 12	16 20			16 43
Rainham (Kent) d		14 26			14 46		14 55				15 16	15 25			15 46		15 56			16 17	16 25			16 48
Newington d					14 50						15 20				15 50					16 21				16 52
Sittingbourne [4] a		14 33			14 55		15 02				15 25	15 32			15 55		16 03			16 26	16 32			16 57
d		14 33		14 35	14 55		15 02		15 05		15 25	15 32		15 35	15 55		16 03		16 05	16 26	16 32		16 35	16 57
Kemsley d				14 39					15 09					15 39					16 09				16 39	
Swale d				14 43					15 13					15 43					16 13				16 43	
Queenborough d				14 47					15 17					15 47					16 17				16 47	
Sheerness-on-Sea a				14 53					15 23					15 53					16 23				16 53	
Teynham d					14 59						15 29				15 59					16 30				17 01
Faversham [2] a		14 41			15 05		15 10				15 35	15 40			16 05		16 11			16 36	16 40			17 07
d		14 44	14 47				15 14	15 16				15 44	15 46				16 15	16 17			16 44	16 47		
Selling d			14 52										15 51					16 22				16 52		
Canterbury East [4] d			15 02					15 28					16 00					16 32				17 01		
Bekesbourne d			15 06										16 05					16 36				17 06		
Adisham d			15 11										16 09					16 41				17 10		
Aylesham d			15 13										16 12					16 43				17 13		
Snowdown d			15 16										16 14					16 46				17 15		
Shepherds Well d			15 20										16 18					16 50				17 19		
Kearsney d			15 24										16 23					16 54				17 24		
Dover Priory [4] ⛴ a			15 30					15 44					16 27					16 59				17 28		
Whitstable d		14 52					15 22					15 52					16 23				16 52			
Chestfield & Swalecliffe d		14 55										15 55					16 26				16 55			
Herne Bay d		14 59					15 27					15 59					16 30				16 59			
Birchington-on-Sea d		15 08					15 35					16 08					16 39				17 08			
Westgate-on-Sea d		15 11										16 11					16 42				17 11			
Margate [4] d	14 50	15 15				15 36	15 41					16 15				16 36	16 47				17 16			
Broadstairs d	14 55	15 20				15 41	15 46					16 20				16 41	16 52				17 21			
Dumpton Park d	14 58	15 23				15 44						16 23				16 44	16 55				17 24			
Ramsgate [4] ✈ a	15 01	15 26				15 47	15 51					16 26				16 47	16 58				17 27			

For general notes see front of timetable
For details of catering facilities see Directory of Train Operators

For services from London to Ramsgate, Dover and Canterbury via Ashford see Table 207

A 🛒 to Ramsgate
b Change at London Bridge and Rochester

Table 212

Mondays to Fridays
until 10 October

For details of Bank Holiday service alterations please see first page of Table 195

London → Medway, Sheerness-on-Sea, Dover and Ramsgate

Network Diagram - see first page of Table 212

		SE 50 [1] A ⊼		SE 22	SE 01	SE 50 [1]			SE 01	SE 22 [1]	SE 30 [1]	SE 07 [1]	SE 22	SE 30 [1]	SE 01	SE 07 [1]	SE 40 [1]	SE 90 [1]	SE 51 [1] A ⊼		SE 51 [1] ⊼	SE 07 [1]	SE 40 [1]	SE 21	SE 01
London Victoria [15]	⊖ d	16 03		16 00		16 23				16 22	16 42		16 45				17 05		17 09		17 27				
London Blackfriars [3]	⊖ d	*15 43*								*16 09*			*16 27*				*16 42*							17 24	
Elephant & Castle	⊖ d	*15 46*								*16 13*			*16 31*				*16 46*							17 28	
Bromley South [4]	d	16 19		16 23		16 40				16 44	16 58		17 03				17 23				17 44			17 48	
St Mary Cray	d			16 30						16 50			17 10				17 30							17 57	
Swanley [4]	d			16 35						16 55			17 15				17 37							18 01	
Farningham Road	d			16 39						17 00			17 19				17 41						←	18 06	
Longfield	d			16 44						17 04			17 24				17 46						17 46	18 11	
Meopham	d			16 48						17 09			17 28				→						17 51	18 16	
Sole Street	d			16 51						17 11			17 31										17 54	18 18	
London Charing Cross [4]	⊖ d					*15 20*					*15 50*	*16b33*				*16c21*			*16 21*		*16 48*		*16 48*	*17 00*	
London Waterloo (East) [4]	⊖ d					*15 23*					*15 53*	*16b36*				*16c24*			*16 24*		*16 51*		*16 51*	*17 03*	
London Cannon Street [4]	⊖ d					*15e18*					*15e48*	16 44				17 08			*16f22*		*16e46*	17 30	*16f46*	*17f00*	
London Bridge [4]	⊖ d					*15 29*					*15 59*	16 48				*16 29*			*16 29*		*16 56*		*16 56*	*17 08*	
Dartford [4]	d					*16 04*					*16 36*					*17 06*			*17 06*		*17 26*		*17 26*	*17 46*	
Greenhithe for Bluewater	d					*16 09*					*16 41*					*17 11*			*17 11*		*17 31*		*17 31*	*17 51*	
Gravesend [4]	d					*16 16*					*16 48*					*17 18*			*17 18*		*17 38*		*17 38*	*17 58*	
Strood [4]	d					*16 28*					*17 04*					*17 30*			*17 30*		*17 54*		*17 54*	*18 14*	
Rochester [4]	d	16 43		17a03						17a23	*17 07*		17a43			*17 35*			17 53		*17 59*		18g18	18 28	
Chatham [4]	d	16 47				17 08					17 28	17 32				17 49			17 56		18 10	18 14	18 21	18 30	
Gillingham (Kent) [4]	d	16 50				17 12					17 32	17 36				17 54			18 00		18 15	18 19	18 25	18a35	
Rainham (Kent)	d	16 55				17 17					17 37	17 41				17 59			18 05		18 20	18 24	18 30		
Newington	d					17 21										18 03			18 09				18 34		
Sittingbourne [4]	a	17 02				17 26					17 45	17 50				18 08			18 14		18 27	18 31	18 39		
	d	17 03			17 07	17 27			17 29		17 45	17 50			17 58	18 08			18 15		18 27	18 31	18 39		18 41
Kemsley	d				17 11				17 33						18 02										18 45
Swale	d				17 14				17 36						18 06										18 48
Queenborough	d				17 19				17 41						18 10										18 53
Sheerness-on-Sea	a				17 25				17 47						18 16										18 59
Teynham	d					17 31										18 13			18 19				18 44		
Faversham [2]	a	17 11				17 37					17 54	17 59				18 19			18 25		18 35	18 40	18 50		
	d	17 15	17 18			17 41	17 45				18 03	18 00		← 18 03		18 19			18 29	18 34	18 40	18 44	18 50		
Selling	d		17 23				17 50				→			18 08						18 39			18 55		
Canterbury East [4]	d		17 33				18 00							18 18						18 49			19a04		
Bekesbourne	d		17 37				18 04							18 22						18 53					
Adisham	d		17 42				18 09							18 27						18 58					
Aylesham	d		17 44				18 11							18 29						19 00					
Snowdown	d		17 47				18 14							18 32						19 03					
Shepherds Well	d		17 51				18 18							18 36						19 07					
Kearsney	d		17 55				18 22							18 40						19 11					
Dover Priory [4]	⛴ a		18 03				18 30							18 48						19 17					
Whitstable	d	17 23				17 49						18 08				18 27			18 38		18 48	18 52			
Chestfield & Swalecliffe	d	17 26				17 52						18 11							18 41		18 51	18 55			
Herne Bay	d	17 30				17 57						18 16				18 33			18 45		18 56	19 00			
Birchington-on-Sea	d	17 38				18 06						18 25				18 42			18 55		19 05	19 09			
Westgate-on-Sea	d	17 41				18 09						18 28							18 58		19 08	19 12			
Margate [4]	d	17 45				18 13						18 32				18 48		18 52	19 03		19 12	19 16			
Broadstairs	d	17 51				18 19						18 37				18 54		18 57	19 08		19 18	19 22			
Dumpton Park	d	17 53				18 21						18 40						19 00	19 11		19 21				
Ramsgate [4]	✈ a	17 56				18 26						18 46				19 00		19 03	19 17		19 25	19 28			

For general notes see front of timetable
For details of catering facilities see Directory of Train Operators
For services from London to Ramsgate, Dover and Canterbury via Ashford see Table 207

A ⊼ to Ramsgate
b Change at London Bridge
c Change at Chatham
e Change at London Bridge and Chatham
f Change at London Bridge and Rochester
g Arr. 1803

For details of Bank Holiday service alterations please see first page of Table 195

London → Medway, Sheerness-on-Sea, Dover and Ramsgate

Network Diagram - see first page of Table 212

	SE 30 [1]		SE 07 [1]		SE 22	SE 30 [1]	SE 01	SE 31 [1]		SE 07 [1]	SE 21 [1]	SE 31 [1]	SE 01	SE 50 [1]		SE 01	SE 07 [1]	SE 92 [1]	SE 50 [1]		SE 01	SE 92 [1]		SE 07 [1]
								A 🚌						B 🚌					B 🚌					
London Victoria 15 ⊖ d	17 49				17 48			18 04						18 33				18 41	19 04			19 09		
London Blackfriars 3 ⊖ d	17 24				17 36			17 36			18 11			18 11				18 23	18 43					
Elephant & Castle ⊖ d	17 28				17 39			17 39			18 15							18 26	18 46					
Bromley South 4 d	18 05				18 09			18 24			18 33			18 49				19 01	19 20			19 29		
St Mary Cray d					18 16						18 39							19 10				19 35		
Swanley 4 d					18 21						18 44							19 15				19 40		
Farningham Road d					18 25						18 49							19 19				19 44		
Longfield d					18 30						18 53							19 24				19 49		
Meopham d					18 34						18 58							19 28				19 53		
Sole Street d					18 37						19 00							19 31				19 56		
London Charing Cross 4 ⊖ d	17 00		17b43							18b01	17 00						18b34	17c58	17e58			18 30		19b24
London Waterloo (East) 4 ⊖ d	17 03		17b46							18b04	17 03						18b37	18c01	18e01			18 33		19b27
London Cannon Street 4 ⊖ d	17e00		17 50							18 10	17c00						18 46	18 08	18 08			18c30		19 32
London Bridge 4 ⊖ d	17 08		17 54					17f30		18 14	17g50			17f50			18 50	18g14	18f14			18 38		19 36
Dartford 4 d	17 46							18 10			18 30			18 30			18 48	19 00	19 00			19 16		19 40
Greenhithe for Bluewater d	17 51							18 15			18 35			18 35			18 53	19 05	19 05			19 21		19 45
Gravesend 4 d	17 58							18 22			18 42			18 42			19 00	19 12	19 12			19 28		19 52
Strood 4 d	18 14							18 36			18 54			18 54			19 14	19 28	19 28			19 44		20 04
Rochester 4 d	18 22				18a51			18 41			19 11						19 19	19 40				20 05		20 12
Chatham 4 d	18 34		18 38					18 55		18 59	19 13			19 17			19 28	19 43	19 48			20 07		20 15
Gillingham (Kent) 4 d	18 38		18 42					18 59		19 03	19a19			19 21			19 32	19 47	19 52			20 11		20 20
Rainham (Kent) d	18 44		18 47					19 04		19 08				19 27			19 37	19 52	19 57			20 16		20 25
Newington d										19 12							19 41	19 56				20 20		20 35
Sittingbourne 4 a	18 51		18 55					19 12		19 17				19 34			19 46	20 01	20 04			20 27		→
d	18 52		18 55				18 58	19 12		19 18			19 27	19 35		19 42	19 47	20 01	20 05		20 13	20 27		
Kemsley d							19 02						19 31			19 46					20 17			
Swale d							19 05						19 35			19 50					20 21			
Queenborough d							19 10						19 39			19 55					20 25			
Sheerness-on-Sea a							19 16						19 45			20 01					20 30			
Teynham d										19 22							19 51	20 05				20 31		
Faversham 2 a	19 00		19 04					19 21		19 28				19 43			19 57	20 12	20 15			20 37		
d	19 11	19 04	19 08			← 19 11		19 32	19 24	19 29		← 19 32		19 47	19 49		19 58		20 19	20 21				
Selling d	→					19 16		→				19 37			19 54					20 26				
Canterbury East 4 d						19 26						19 47			20h06					20 36				
Bekesbourne d						19 30						19 51			20 10					20 40				
Adisham d						19 35						19 56			20 15					20 45				
Aylesham d						19 37						19 58			20 17					20 47				
Snowdown d						19 40						20 01			20 20					20 50				
Shepherds Well d						19 44						20 05			20 24					20 54				
Kearsney d						19 48						20 09			20 28					20 58				
Dover Priory 4 ⛴ a						19 55						20 15			20 33					21 03				
Whitstable d		19 12	19 16						19 33	19 38				19 56			20 06		20 27					
Chestfield & Swalecliffe d			19 19						19 36	19 41				19 59			20 09							
Herne Bay d		19 19	19 24						19 40	19 45				20 03			20 13		20 32					
Birchington-on-Sea d		19 28	19 33						19 49	19 54				20 12			20 22		20 41					
Westgate-on-Sea d			19 36						19 53	19 58				20 16			20 26							
Margate 4 d		19 33	19 40						19 57	20 03				20 20			20 30		20 47					
Broadstairs d		19a39	19 46						20a02	20 09				20 26			20a36		20 52					
Dumpton Park d			19 48							20 12				20 28					20 55					
Ramsgate 4 ⛴ a			19 54							20 18				20 32					20 59					

For general notes see front of timetable
For details of catering facilities see Directory of Train Operators

For services from London to Ramsgate, Dover and Canterbury via Ashford see Table 207

A 🚌 to Broadstairs
B 🚌 to Ramsgate
b Change at London Bridge
c Change at London Bridge and Rochester
e Change at London Bridge and Chatham
f Change at Dartford and Chatham
g Change at Dartford and Rochester
h Arr. 2002

For details of Bank Holiday service alterations please see first page of Table 195

London → Medway, Sheerness-on-Sea, Dover and Ramsgate

Network Diagram - see first page of Table 212

		SE 50 [1]		SE 01	SE 07 [1]	SE 92 [1]	SE 50 [1]		SE 01	SE 92 [1]	SE 50 [1]		SE 92 [1]	SE 50 [1]		SE 01	SE 37 [1]	SE 50 [1]	SE 37 [1]	SE 01	SE 92 [1]	SE 50 [1]	SE 22 [1]
London Victoria 15	⊖ d	19 34				19 39	20 03			20 09	20 34		20 39	21 03			21 39	22 03			22 39	23 03	23 39
London Blackfriars 3	⊖ d	*19 17*					*19 47*				*20 13*			*20 43*			*21 13*	*21 43*			*22 13*	*22 43*	*23 13*
Elephant & Castle	⊖ d	*19 20*					*19 50*				*20 16*			*20 46*			*21 16*	*21 46*			*22 16*	*22 46*	*23 16*
Bromley South 4	d	19 50				19 59	20 19			20 29	20 50		20 59	21 19			21 59	22 19			22 59	23 19	23 58
St Mary Cray	d					20 05				20 35			21 05				22 05				23 05		00 04
Swanley 4	d					20 10				20 40			21 10				22 10				23 10		00 09
Farningham Road	d					20 14				20 44			21 14				22 14				23 14		00 13
Longfield	d					20 19				20 49			21 19	21 33			22 19				23 19		00 18
Meopham	d					20 23				20 53			21 23				22 23				23 23		00 23
Sole Street	d					20 26				20 56			21 26				22 26				23 26		00 26
London Charing Cross 4	⊖ d	*18 54*				*19 21*					*19 50*		*20 20*				*21 20*				*22 20*		*22 50*
London Waterloo (East) 4	⊖ d	*18 57*				*19 24*					*19 53*		*20 23*				*21 23*				*22 23*		*22 53*
London Cannon Street 4	⊖ d	*18*b*50*				*19*b*22*					*19*b*52*		*20*b*15*				*21*b*00*						
London Bridge 4	⊖ d					*19 29*					*19 59*		*20 29*				*21 29*				*22 29*		*22 59*
Dartford 4	d					*20 06*					*20 34*		*21 04*				*22 04*				*23 04*		*23 34*
Greenhithe for Bluewater	d					*20 11*					*20 40*		*21 09*				*22 09*				*23 09*		*23 40*
Gravesend 4	d					*20 18*					*20 50*		*21 16*				*22 16*				*23 16*		*23 50*
Strood 4	d					*20 30*					*21 04*		*21 28*				*22 28*				*23 28*		*00 02*
Rochester 4	d	20 16				20 37	20 43			21 05	21 14		21 35	21 47			22 35	22 43			23 36	23 43	00 35
Chatham 4	d	20 19				20 40	20 47			21 07	21 18		21 38	21 50			22 38	22 46			23 39	23 46	00 38
Gillingham (Kent) 4	d	20 24				20 43	20 50			21 11	21 22		21 41	21 53			22 41	22 49			23 43	23 49	00a41
Rainham (Kent)	d	20 29			←	20 48	20 55			21 16	21 27		21 46	21 58			22 46	22 54			23 48	23 54	
Newington	d				20 35	20 52				21 20			21 50				22 50				23 52		
Sittingbourne 4	a	20 36			20 42	20 57	21 02			21 25	21 34		21 55	22 05			22 55	23 01			23 57	00 01	
	d	20 36		20 39	20 43	20 57	21 02		21 05	21 25	21 34		21 55	22 05		22 09	22 55	23 01		23 07	23 57	00 01	
Kemsley	d			20 43					21 09							22 13				23 11			
Swale	d			20 47					21 13							22 17				23 14			
Queenborough	d			20 51					21 17							22 21				23 19			
Sheerness-on-Sea	a			20 57					21 23							22 26				23 25			
Teynham	d				20 47	21 02				21 29			22 00				23 00				00 01		
Faversham 2	a	20 44			20 54	21 08	21 12			21 35	21 42		22 06	22 13			23 06	23 10	←		00 07	00 11	
	d	20 48	20 52				21 16	21 18			21 46	21 48		22 17	22 20		23 13	23 11	23 13			00 12	
Selling	d		20 57					21 23				21 53			22 25		→		23 18				
Canterbury East 4	d		21 06					21 32				22a03			22 34				23 27				
Bekesbourne	d		21 11					21 36							22 38								
Adisham	d		21 15					21 41							22 43								
Aylesham	d		21 17					21 43							22 45				23 36				
Snowdown	d		21 19					21 46							22 48								
Shepherds Well	d		21 23					21 50							22 52								
Kearsney	d		21 27					21 54							22 56								
Dover Priory 4	⛴ a		21 33					21 59							23 01				23 47				
Whitstable	d	20 56					21 24				21 54			22 25				23 19				00 20	
Chestfield & Swalecliffe	d	20 59									21 57			22 28				23 22				00 23	
Herne Bay	d	21 03					21 29				22 01			22 32				23 26				00 27	
Birchington-on-Sea	d	21 11					21 37				22 10			22 41				23 35				00 36	
Westgate-on-Sea	d	21 14									22 13			22 44				23 38				00 39	
Margate 4	d	21 19					21 43				22 18			22 48				23 42				00 43	
Broadstairs	d	21 24					21 48				22 23			22 53				23 47				00 48	
Dumpton Park	d	21 27									22 26			22 56				23 50				00 51	
Ramsgate 4	✈ a	21 30					21 53				22 29			22 59				23 53				00 54	

For general notes see front of timetable
For details of catering facilities see Directory of Train Operators

For services from London to Ramsgate, Dover and Canterbury via Ashford see Table 207

b Change at London Bridge and Rochester

Table 212

Mondays to Fridays

from 13 October

For details of Bank Holiday service alterations please see first page of Table 195

London → Medway, Sheerness-on-Sea, Dover and Ramsgate

Network Diagram - see first page of Table 212

		SE	SE	SE	SE	SE	SE	SE	SE	SE	SE	SE	SE	SE		SE	SE	SE	SE	SE	SE	SE	SE	SE	SE
		MX	MO	MX	MO	MX	MX	MO	MX																
		92 [1]	54 [1]	50 [1]	50 [1]	01	22 [1]	54 [1]	50 [1]	80 [1]	97	01	4 [1]	20 [1]		01	90 [1]	81 [1]	01	4 [1]	88 [1]	54 [1]	01	80 [1]	01
London Victoria [15]	⊖ d	22p39	22p41	23p03	23p03		23p39	23p42	00 03													05 32			
London Blackfriars [3]	⊖ d																								
Elephant & Castle	⊖ d																								
Bromley South [4]	d	22p59	23p01	23p19	23p19		23p58	00 01														05 48			
St Mary Cray	d	23p05	23p07				00 04	00 08														05 55			
Swanley [4]	d	23p10	23p12				00 09	00 12														06 00			
Farningham Road	d	23p14	23p16				00 13	00 17														06 05			
Longfield	d	23p19	23p21				00 18	00 21														06 10			
Meopham	d	23p23	23p25				00 23	00 26														06 15			
Sole Street	d	23p26	23p28				00 26	00 28														06 17			
London Charing Cross [4]	⊖ d						22 50	23 20	23 20													04 56			
London Waterloo (East) [4]	⊖ d						22 53	23 23	23 23													04 59			
London Cannon Street [4]	⊖ d																								
London Bridge [4]	⊖ d						22 59	23 29	23 29													05 04			
Dartford [4]	d						23 34	23 34						05 06								05 42			
Greenhithe for Bluewater	d						23 40	23 40						05 11								05 48			
Gravesend [4]	d						23 50	23 48						05 18								05 56			
Strood [4]	d						00 02	23 58	00 32					05 29								06 08			
Rochester [4]	d	23p36	23p37	23p43	23p43		00 35	00 38	00 43					05 33								06 26			
Chatham [4]	d	23p39	23p39	23p46	23p46		00 38	00 40	00 46					05 36								06 29			
Gillingham (Kent) [4]	d	23p43	23p43	23p49	23p50		00a41	00a44	00 50		05 00			05 40								06 33			
Rainham (Kent)	d	23p48	23p48	23p54	23p55				00 55		05 04			05 45								06 38			
Newington	d	23p52	23p52						00 58		05 08			05 49								06 42			
Sittingbourne [4]	a	23p57	23p57	00 01	00 02				01 03					05 54								06 47			
	d	23p57	23p57	00 01	00 02	00 08			01 03			05 37		05 54		06 12			06 23			06 48	06 58		07 19
Kemsley	d					00 12					05 14	05 41				06 16			06 27				07 04		07b26
Swale	d					00 15					05 17	05 45				06 19			06 30				07 08		07 32
Queenborough	d					00 20					05 22	05 49				06 24			06c40				07 12		07 36
Sheerness-on-Sea	a					00 26					05 28	05 55				06 30			06 46				07 18		07 41
Teynham	d	00 01	00 01						01 07					05 58								06 52			
Faversham [2]	a	00 07	00 07	00 11					01 12					06 04								07 01			
	d			00 12					01 13	04 50				06 05				06 13				07 02		07 04	
Selling	d													06 10										07 09	
Canterbury East [4]	d									05 02				06 19										07 18	
Bekesbourne	d													06 23										07 22	
Adisham	d									05 10				06 28										07 27	
Aylesham	d									05 12				06 30										07 29	
Snowdown	d									05 15				06 33										07 32	
Shepherds Well	d									05 19				06 37										07 36	
Kearsney	d									05 23				06 41										07 40	
Dover Priory [4]	a									05 28				06 48										07 45	
Whitstable	d			00 20	00 22				01 21									06 21				07 10			
Chestfield & Swalecliffe	d			00 23	00 25				01 24									06 24				07 13			
Herne Bay	d			00 27	00 29				01 27									06 28				07 17			
Birchington-on-Sea	d			00 36	00 38				01 36									06 37				07 26			
Westgate-on-Sea	d			00 39	00 41				01 39									06 41				07 30			
Margate [4]	d			00 43	00 45				01 43				06 07				06 41	06 45		07 04	07 28	07 34			
Broadstairs	d			00 48	00 50				01 48				06 12				06 46	06 50		07 09	07 33	07 39			
Dumpton Park	d			00 51	00 53				01 51				06 15				06 49	06 52		07 12	07 36	07 41			
Ramsgate [4]	a			00 54	00 56				01 54				06 18				06 52	06 56		07 15	07 39	07 45			

For general notes see front of timetable
For details of catering facilities see Directory of Train Operators

For services from London to Ramsgate, Dover and Canterbury via Ashford see Table 207

b Arr. 0723
c Arr. 0635

Table 212

Mondays to Fridays

from 13 October

For details of Bank Holiday service alterations please see first page of Table 195

London → Medway, Sheerness-on-Sea, Dover and Ramsgate

Network Diagram - see first page of Table 212

	SE 64 [1] A	SE 81 [1]	SE 90 [1]	SE 54 [1]	SE 80 [1]		SE 01	SE 37 [1]	SE 81 [1]	SE 01	SE 37 [1]	SE 01	SE 90 [1]	SE 50 [1]	SE 37 [1]	SE 92 [1]	SE 50 [1]		SE 01		SE 92 [1]	SE 90 [1]	SE 50 [1]	
London Victoria 15 ⊖ d				06 16				06 39			07 07			07 33		07 39	08 03				08 09		08 33	
London Blackfriars 3 ⊖ d				*05 27*				*06 08*			*06 42*			*07 09*		*07 24*					*07 53*			
Elephant & Castle ⊖ d				*05 30*				*06 12*			*06 45*			*07 12*		*07 27*					*07 56*			
Bromley South 4 d				06 34				06 59			07 27			07 52		08 01	08 20				08 31		08 51	
St Mary Cray d				06 41				07 05			07 34					08 07					08 37			
Swanley 4 d				06 46				07 10			07 39					08 12					08 42			
Farningham Road d				06 51				07 14			07 44					08 16					08 47			
Longfield d				06 56				07 19			07 48					08 21					08 51			
Meopham d				07 01				07 23			07 53					08 25					08 56			
Sole Street d				07 03				07 26			07 56					08 28					08 58			
London Charing Cross 4 ⊖ d				*05 26*				*06 02*			*06 40*			*06 40*			*07 20*				*07b45*			
London Waterloo (East) 4 ⊖ d				*05 29*				*06 05*			*06 43*			*06 43*			*07 23*				*07b48*			
London Cannon Street 4 ⊖ d								*05b50*			*06b30*			*06c30*			*07b04*				*07 54*			
London Bridge 4 ⊖ d				*05 34*				*06 10*			*06 48*			*06 48*			*07 28*				*07 58*			
Dartford 4 d				*06 12*				*06 46*			*07 28*			*07 28*			*08 05*				*08 34*			
Greenhithe for Bluewater d				*06 18*				*06e26*			*07 33*			*07 33*			*08 11*				*08 39*			
Gravesend 4 d				*06 26*				*06 56*			*07 40*			*07 40*			*08 19*				*08 46*			
Strood 4 d				*06 38*				*07 08*			*07 52*			*07 52*			*08 32*				*08 58*			
Rochester 4 d				07 15				07 39			08 06					08 38	08 45				09 09		09 16	
Chatham 4 d				07 17				07 42			08 08			08 19		08 41	08 48				09 11		09 18	
Gillingham (Kent) 4 d				07 21				07 45			08 12			08 23		08 45	08 51				09 15		09 22	
Rainham (Kent) d				07 26				07 50			08 17			08 28		08 50	08 56				09 20		09 26	
Newington d				07 30				07 54			08 21					08 54					09 24			
Sittingbourne 4 a				07 35				07 59			08 26			08 36		08 59	09 03				09 29		09 34	
d				07 35			07 46	08 04		08 15	08 27	08 28		08 37		08 59	09 04		09 05		09 29		09 34	
Kemsley d							07 50			08 19		08 32							09 09					
Swale d							07 55			08 22		08 36							09 12					
Queenborough d							07 59			08 27		08 41							09 17					
Sheerness-on-Sea a							08 04			08 32		08 47							09 23					
Teynham d				07 39				08 09			08 31					09 03					09 33			
Faversham 2 a				07 45				08 15			08 37			08 45	←	09 09	09 12				09 39		09 42	
d		07 20		07 46	07 53			08 17	08 19		08 49			08 47	08 49		09 15	09 18					09 46	09 48
Selling d					07 58			08 22			→				08 54									09 53
Canterbury East 4 d					08 08			08 32							09 04			09 32						10f08
Bekesbourne d					08 12			08 36							09 08									10 13
Adisham d					08 17			08 41							09 13									10 17
Aylesham d					08 19			08 43							09 15									10 20
Snowdown d					08 22			08 46							09 18									10 22
Shepherds Well d					08 26			08 50							09 22									10 26
Kearsney d					08 30			08 54							09 26									10 31
Dover Priory 4 ⛴ a					08 36			09 00							09 32			09 52						10 35
Whitstable d		07 28		07 54					08 28					08 56			09 23						09 55	
Chestfield & Swalecliffe d		07 31		07 57					08 31					08 59									09 58	
Herne Bay d		07 35		08 01					08 35					09 03			09 28						10 02	
Birchington-on-Sea d		07 44		08 10					08 44					09 12			09 37						10 11	
Westgate-on-Sea d		07 48		08 14					08 47					09 16									10 15	
Margate 4 d	07 43	07 52	08 13	08 18					08 52				09 04	09 20			09 43					10 04	10 19	
Broadstairs d	07 48	07 57	08 18	08 23					08 57				09 09	09 25			09 48					10 09	10 24	
Dumpton Park d	07 50	07 59	08 21	08 26					09 00				09 12	09 27								10 12	10 27	
Ramsgate 4 ✈ a	07 53	08 03	08 24	08 29					09 03				09 15	09 30			09 52					10 15	10 30	

For general notes see front of timetable
For details of catering facilities see Directory of Train Operators

For services from London to Ramsgate, Dover and Canterbury via Ashford see Table 207

A To London Victoria (Table 196)
b Change at London Bridge and Rochester
c Change at London Bridge and Chatham
e Change at Gravesend and Rochester
f Arr. 1002

Mondays to Fridays
from 13 October

For details of Bank Holiday service alterations please see first page of Table 195

London → Medway, Sheerness-on-Sea, Dover and Ramsgate

Network Diagram - see first page of Table 212

	SE 01	SE 92	SE 50		SE 01	SE 92	SE 90	SE 50		SE 92	SE 01	SE 92	SE 50		SE 01	SE 92	SE 90	SE 50		SE 01	SE 92	SE 50	
		1	1			1	1	1		1		1	1			1	1	1			1	1	
							[trolley]						A [trolley]					A [trolley]				A [trolley]	
London Victoria [15] ⊖ d		08 39	09 03			09 09		09 33		09 15		09 39	10 03			10 09		10 33			10 39	11 03	
London Blackfriars [3] ⊖ d		08 20	08 43					09 13					09 43					10 13				10 43	
Elephant & Castle ⊖ d		08 23	08 46					09 16					09 46					10 16				10 46	
Bromley South [4] d		08 59	09 19			09 29		09 50				09 59	10 19			10 29		10 49			10 59	11 19	
St Mary Cray d		09 05				09 35						10 05				10 35					11 05		
Swanley [4] d		09 10				09 40						10 10				10 40					11 10		
Farningham Road d		09 14				09 44						10 14				10 44					11 14		
Longfield d		09 19				09 49						10 19				10 49					11 19		
Meopham d		09 24				09 53						10 23				10 53					11 23		
Sole Street d		09 26				09 56						10 26				10 56					11 26		
London Charing Cross [4] ⊖ d		08b08				08b41				09 02		09 20				09 52					10 20		
London Waterloo (East) [4] ⊖ d		08b11				08b44				09 06		09 23				09 55					10 23		
London Cannon Street [4] ⊖ d		08 17				08 50				09 02		09b20				09b48					10b18		
London Bridge [4] ⊖ d		08 21				08 54				09 12		09 29				10 00					10 29		
Dartford [4] d		09 02				09 34				09 54		10 04				10 34					11 04		
Greenhithe for Bluewater d		09 07				09 39				09 52		10 09				10 39					11 09		
Gravesend [4] d		09 14				09 46				10 04		10 16				10 46					11 16		
Strood [4] d		09 26				09 58				09 58		10 28				10 58					11 28		
Rochester [4] d		09 36	09 43			10 05		10 15				10 35	10 44			11 05		11 13			11 35	11 43	
Chatham [4] d		09 39	09 47			10 08		10 17		10 19		10 38	10 47			11 08		11 17			11 38	11 47	
Gillingham (Kent) [4] d		09 43	09 50			10 12		10 21		10 22		10 41	10 50			11 11		11 20			11 41	11 50	
Rainham (Kent) d		09 48	09 55			10 17		10 26				10 46	10 55			11 16		11 25			11 46	11 55	
Newington d		09 52				10 21						10 50				11 20					11 50		
Sittingbourne [4] a		09 57	10 02			10 26		10 33				10 55	11 02			11 25		11 32			11 55	12 02	
d	09 36	09 57	10 02		10 05	10 26		10 33			10 35	10 55	11 02		11 05	11 25		11 32		11 35	11 55	12 02	
Kemsley d	09 40				10 09						10 39				11 09					11 39			
Swale d	09 43				10 12						10 42				11 12					11 42			
Queenborough d	09 47				10 17						10 47				11 17					11 47			
Sheerness-on-Sea a	09 53				10 23						10 53				11 23					11 53			
Teynham d		10 01				10 30						10 59				11 29					11 59		
Faversham [2] a		10 07	10 10			10 36		10 41				11 05	11 10			11 35		11 40			12 05	12 10	
d			10 14	10 16				10 44	10 47				11 14	11 16				11 44	11 46			12 14	12 16
Selling d									10 52										11 51				
Canterbury East [4] d				10 28					11 01					11 28					12 00				12 28
Bekesbourne d									11 05										12 05				
Adisham d									11 10										12 09				
Aylesham d									11 12										12 12				
Snowdown d									11 15										12 14				
Shepherds Well d									11 19										12 18				
Kearsney d									11 23										12 23				
Dover Priory [4] ⛴ a				10 45					11 27					11 44					12 28				12 44
Whitstable d			10 22					10 53		10 46			11 22					11 52				12 22	
Chestfield & Swalecliffe d								10 56										11 55					
Herne Bay d			10 27					11 00		10 52			11 27					11 59				12 27	
Birchington-on-Sea d			10 35					11 08		11 01			11 35					12 08				12 35	
Westgate-on-Sea d								11 11		11 05								12 11					
Margate [4] d			10 41				11 04	11 15		11 09			11 41				12 04	12 15				12 41	
Broadstairs d			10 46				11 09	11 21		11 15			11 46				12 09	12 20				12 46	
Dumpton Park d							11 12	11 23									12 12	12 23					
Ramsgate [4] ✈ a			10 51				11 15	11 27		11 20			11 51				12 15	12 26				12 51	

For general notes see front of timetable
For details of catering facilities see Directory of Train Operators

For services from London to Ramsgate, Dover and Canterbury via Ashford see Table 207

A [trolley] to Ramsgate
b Change at London Bridge and Rochester

Table 212

Mondays to Fridays

from 13 October

For details of Bank Holiday service alterations please see first page of Table 195

London → Medway, Sheerness-on-Sea, Dover and Ramsgate

Network Diagram - see first page of Table 212

		SE 01	SE 92 1	SE 90 1		SE 50 1 A ⊼		SE 01	SE 92 1	SE 50 1 A ⊼		SE 01	SE 92 1	SE 90 1	SE 50 1 A ⊼		SE 01	SE 92 1		SE 50 1 A ⊼		SE 01	SE 92 1	SE 90 1
London Victoria 15	⊖ d		11 09			11 33			11 39	12 03			12 09		12 33			12 39		13 03			13 09	
London Blackfriars 3	⊖ d					*11 13*				*11 43*					*12 13*					*12 43*				
Elephant & Castle	⊖ d					*11 16*				*11 46*					*12 16*					*12 46*				
Bromley South 4	d		11 29			11 49			11 59	12 19			12 29		12 49			12 59		13 19			13 29	
St Mary Cray	d		11 35						12 05				12 35					13 05					13 35	
Swanley 4	d		11 40						12 10				12 40					13 10					13 40	
Farningham Road	d		11 44						12 14				12 44					13 14					13 44	
Longfield	d		11 49						12 19				12 49					13 19					13 49	
Meopham	d		11 53						12 23				12 53					13 23					13 53	
Sole Street	d		11 56						12 26				12 56					13 26					13 56	
London Charing Cross 4	⊖ d		*10 50*						*11 20*				*11 50*					*12 20*					*12 50*	
London Waterloo (East) 4	⊖ d		*10 53*						*11 23*				*11 53*					*12 23*					*12 53*	
London Cannon Street 4	⊖ d		*10b48*						*11b18*				*11b48*					*12b18*					*12b48*	
London Bridge 4	⊖ d		*10 59*						*11 29*				*11 59*					*12 29*					*12 59*	
Dartford 4	d		*11 34*						*12 04*				*12 34*					*13 04*					*13 34*	
Greenhithe for Bluewater	d		*11 39*						*12 09*				*12 39*					*13 09*					*13 39*	
Gravesend 4	d		*11 46*						*12 16*				*12 46*					*13 16*					*13 46*	
Strood 4	d		*11 58*						*12 28*				*12 58*					*13 28*					*13 58*	
Rochester 4	d		12 05			12 13			12 35	12 43			13 05		13 13			13 35		13 43			14 05	
Chatham 4	d		12 08			12 17			12 38	12 47			13 08		13 17			13 38		13 47			14 08	
Gillingham (Kent) 4	d		12 11			12 20			12 41	12 50			13 11		13 20			13 41		13 50			14 11	
Rainham (Kent)	d		12 16			12 25			12 46	12 55			13 16		13 25			13 46		13 55			14 16	
Newington	d		12 20						12 50				13 20					13 50					14 20	
Sittingbourne 4	a		12 25			12 32			12 55	13 02			13 25		13 32			13 55		14 02			14 25	
	d	12 05	12 25			12 32		12 35	12 55	13 02		13 05	13 25		13 32		13 35	13 55		14 02		14 05	14 25	
Kemsley	d	12 09						12 39				13 09					13 39					14 09		
Swale	d	12 12						12 42				13 12					13 42					14 12		
Queenborough	d	12 17						12 47				13 17					13 47					14 17		
Sheerness-on-Sea	a	12 23						12 53				13 23					13 53					14 23		
Teynham	d		12 29						12 59				13 29					13 59					14 29	
Faversham 2	a		12 35			12 40			13 05	13 10			13 35		13 40			14 05		14 10			14 35	
	d					12 44	12 46			13 14	13 16				13 44	13 46				14 14	14 16			
Selling	d						12 51									13 51								
Canterbury East 4	d						13 00				13 28					14 00					14 28			
Bekesbourne	d						13 05									14 05								
Adisham	d						13 09									14 09								
Aylesham	d						13 12									14 12								
Snowdown	d						13 14									14 14								
Shepherds Well	d						13 18									14 18								
Kearsney	d						13 23									14 23								
Dover Priory 4	⛴ a						13 28				13 44					14 28					14 44			
Whitstable	d					12 52				13 22					13 52					14 22				
Chestfield & Swalecliffe	d					12 55									13 55									
Herne Bay	d					12 59				13 27					13 59					14 27				
Birchington-on-Sea	d					13 08				13 35					14 08					14 35				
Westgate-on-Sea	d					13 11									14 11									
Margate 4	d			13 04		13 15				13 41				14 04	14 15					14 41				14 50
Broadstairs	d			13 09		13 20				13 46				14 09	14 20					14 46				14 55
Dumpton Park	d			13 12		13 23								14 12	14 23									14 58
Ramsgate 4	⛴ a			13 15		13 26				13 51				14 15	14 26					14 51				15 01

For general notes see front of timetable
For details of catering facilities see Directory of Train Operators

For services from London to Ramsgate, Dover and Canterbury via Ashford see Table 207

A ⊼ to Ramsgate
b Change at London Bridge and Rochester

For details of Bank Holiday service alterations please see first page of Table 195

London → Medway, Sheerness-on-Sea, Dover and Ramsgate

Network Diagram - see first page of Table 212

		SE 50 [1] A trolley		SE 01	SE 92 [1]	SE 90 [1]	SE 50 [1] A trolley		SE 01	SE 92 [1]		SE 50 [1] A trolley		SE 01	SE 92 [1]	SE 90 [1]	SE 50 [1] A trolley		SE 01	SE 92 [1]	SE 50 [1] A trolley		SE 01	SE 92 [1]	
London Victoria [15]	⊖ d	13 33			13 39		14 03			14 09		14 33			14 39		15 03			15 09	15 33			15 39	
London Blackfriars [3]	⊖ d	13 13					13 43					14 13					14 43				15 13				
Elephant & Castle	⊖ d	13 16					13 46					14 16					14 46				15 16				
Bromley South [4]	d	13 49			13 59		14 19			14 29		14 49			14 59		15 19			15 29	15 49			16 00	
St Mary Cray	d				14 05					14 35					15 05					15 35				16 06	
Swanley [4]	d				14 10					14 40					15 10					15 40				16 11	
Farningham Road	d				14 14					14 44					15 14					15 44				16 15	
Longfield	d				14 19					14 49					15 19					15 49				16 20	
Meopham	d				14 23					14 53					15 23					15 53				16 24	
Sole Street	d				14 26					14 56					15 26					15 56				16 27	
London Charing Cross [4]	⊖ d				13 20					13 50					14 20					14 50				15 20	
London Waterloo (East) [4]	⊖ d				13 23					13 53					14 23					14 53				15 23	
London Cannon Street [4]	⊖ d				13b18					13b48					14b18					14b48				15b18	
London Bridge [4]	⊖ d				13 29					13 59					14 29					14 59				15 29	
Dartford [4]	d				14 04					14 34					15 04					15 34				16 04	
Greenhithe for Bluewater	d				14 09					14 39					15 09					15 39				16 09	
Gravesend [4]	d				14 16					14 46					15 16					15 46				16 16	
Strood [4]	d				14 28					14 58					15 28					15 58				16 28	
Rochester [4]	d	14 13			14 35		14 43			15 05		15 13			15 35		15 43			16 05	16 13			16 36	
Chatham [4]	d	14 17			14 38		14 47			15 08		15 17			15 38		15 47			16 08	16 16			16 39	
Gillingham (Kent) [4]	d	14 21			14 41		14 50			15 11		15 20			15 41		15 51			16 12	16 20			16 43	
Rainham (Kent)	d	14 26			14 46		14 55			15 16		15 25			15 46		15 56			16 17	16 25			16 48	
Newington	d				14 50					15 20					15 50					16 21				16 52	
Sittingbourne [4]	a	14 33			14 55		15 02			15 25		15 32			15 55		16 03			16 26	16 32			16 57	
	d	14 33		14 35	14 55		15 02		15 05	15 25		15 32		15 35	15 55		16 03		16 05	16 26	16 32		16 35	16 57	
Kemsley	d			14 39					15 09					15 39					16 09				16 39		
Swale	d			14 43					15 13					15 43					16 13				16 43		
Queenborough	d			14 47					15 17					15 47					16 17				16 47		
Sheerness-on-Sea	a			14 53					15 23					15 53					16 23				16 53		
Teynham	d				14 59					15 29					15 59					16 30				17 01	
Faversham [2]	a	14 41			15 05		15 10			15 35		15 40			16 05		16 11			16 36	16 40			17 07	
	d	14 44	14 47				15 14	15 16				15 44	15 46				16 15	16 17			16 44	16 47			
Selling	d		14 52										15 51					16 22				16 52			
Canterbury East [4]	d		15 02					15 28					16 00					16 32				17 01			
Bekesbourne	d		15 06										16 05					16 36				17 06			
Adisham	d		15 11										16 09					16 41				17 10			
Aylesham	d		15 13										16 12					16 43				17 13			
Snowdown	d		15 16										16 14					16 46				17 15			
Shepherds Well	d		15 20										16 18					16 50				17 19			
Kearsney	d		15 24										16 23					16 54				17 24			
Dover Priory [4]	a		15 30					15 44					16 27					16 59				17 28			
Whitstable	d	14 52					15 22					15 52					16 23				16 52				
Chestfield & Swalecliffe	d	14 55										15 55					16 26				16 55				
Herne Bay	d	14 59					15 27					15 59					16 30				16 59				
Birchington-on-Sea	d	15 08					15 35					16 08					16 39				17 08				
Westgate-on-Sea	d	15 11										16 11					16 42				17 11				
Margate [4]	d	15 15				15 36	15 41					16 15				16 36	16 47				17 16				
Broadstairs	d	15 20				15 41	15 46					16 20				16 41	16 52				17 21				
Dumpton Park	d	15 23				15 44						16 23				16 44	16 55				17 24				
Ramsgate [4]	a	15 26				15 47	15 51					16 26				16 47	16 58				17 27				

For general notes see front of timetable
For details of catering facilities see Directory of Train Operators

For services from London to Ramsgate, Dover and Canterbury via Ashford see Table 207

A trolley to Ramsgate
b Change at London Bridge and Rochester

For details of Bank Holiday service alterations please see first page of Table 195

London → Medway, Sheerness-on-Sea, Dover and Ramsgate

Network Diagram - see first page of Table 212

Station		SE 50 1 A [trolley]		SE 22	SE 01	SE 50 1		SE 01	SE 22 1	SE 30 1	SE 07 1	SE 22	SE 30 1	SE 01	SE 07 1	SE 40 1	SE 90 1	SE 51 1 A [trolley]		SE 51 1 [trolley]	SE 07 1	SE 40 1	SE 21
London Victoria [15]	⊖ d	16 03		16 00		16 23			16 22	16 42		16 45				17 05		17 09		17 27			
London Blackfriars [3]	⊖ d	15 43							16 09			16 27				16 42							17 24
Elephant & Castle	⊖ d	15 46							16 13			16 31				16 46							17 28
Bromley South [4]	d	16 19		16 23		16 40			16 44	16 58		17 03				17 23				17 44			17 48
St Mary Cray	d			16 30					16 50			17 10				17 30							17 57
Swanley [4]	d			16 35					16 55			17 15				17 37							18 01
Farningham Road	d			16 39					17 00			17 19				17 41						←	18 06
Longfield	d			16 44					17 04			17 24				17 46						17 46	18 11
Meopham	d			16 48					17 09			17 28				→						17 51	18 16
Sole Street	d			16 51					17 11			17 31										17 54	18 18
London Charing Cross [4]	⊖ d					15 20				15 50	16b33				16c21			16 21		16 48		16 48	17 00
London Waterloo (East) [4]	⊖ d					15 23				15 53	16b36				16c24			16 24		16 51		16 51	17 03
London Cannon Street [4]	⊖ d					15e18				15e48	16 44				17 08			16f22		16e46	17 30	16f46	17f00
London Bridge [4]	⊖ d					15 29				15 59	16 48				16 29			16 29		16 56		16 56	17 08
Dartford [4]	d					16 04				16 36					17 06			17 06		17 26		17 26	17 46
Greenhithe for Bluewater	d					16 09				16 41					17 11			17 11		17 31		17 31	17 51
Gravesend [4]	d					16 16				16 48					17 18			17 18		17 38		17 38	17 58
Strood [4]	d					16 28				17 04					17 30			17 30		17 54		17 54	18 14
Rochester [4]	d	16 43		17a03					17a24	17 07		17a43			17 35			17 53		17 59		18g18	18 28
Chatham [4]	d	16 47				17 08				17 28	17 32				17 49			17 56		18 10	18 14	18 21	18 30
Gillingham (Kent) [4]	d	16 50				17 12				17 32	17 36				17 54			18 00		18 15	18 19	18 25	18a35
Rainham (Kent)	d	16 55				17 17				17 37	17 41				17 59			18 05		18 20	18 24	18 30	
Newington	d					17 21									18 03			18 09				18 34	
Sittingbourne [4]	a	17 02				17 26				17 45	17 50				18 08			18 14		18 27	18 31	18 39	
	d	17 03			17 07	17 27		17 29		17 45	17 50			17 58	18 08			18 15		18 27	18 31	18 39	
Kemsley	d				17 11			17 33						18 02									
Swale	d				17 14			17 36						18 06									
Queenborough	d				17 19			17 41						18 10									
Sheerness-on-Sea	a				17 25			17 47						18 16									
Teynham	d					17 31									18 13			18 19				18 44	
Faversham [2]	a	17 11				17 37				17 54	17 59		←		18 19			18 25		18 35	18 40	18 50	
	d	17 15	17 18			17 41	17 45			18 03	18 00		18 03		18 19			18 29	18 34	18 40	18 44	18 50	
Selling	d		17 23				17 50			→			18 08						18 39			18 55	
Canterbury East [4]	d		17 33				18 00						18 18						18 49			19a06	
Bekesbourne	d		17 37				18 04						18 22						18 53				
Adisham	d		17 42				18 09						18 27						18 58				
Aylesham	d		17 44				18 11						18 29						19 00				
Snowdown	d		17 47				18 14						18 32						19 03				
Shepherds Well	d		17 51				18 18						18 36						19 07				
Kearsney	d		17 55				18 22						18 40						19 11				
Dover Priory [4]	⛴ a		18 03				18 30						18 48						19 17				
Whitstable	d	17 23				17 49					18 08				18 27			18 38		18 48	18 52		
Chestfield & Swalecliffe	d	17 26				17 52					18 11							18 41		18 51	18 55		
Herne Bay	d	17 30				17 57					18 16				18 33			18 45		18 56	19 00		
Birchington-on-Sea	d	17 38				18 06					18 25				18 42			18 55		19 05	19 09		
Westgate-on-Sea	d	17 41				18 09					18 28							18 58		19 08	19 12		
Margate [4]	d	17 45				18 13					18 32				18 48		18 52	19 03		19 12	19 16		
Broadstairs	d	17 51				18 19					18 37				18 54		18 57	19 08		19 18	19 22		
Dumpton Park	d	17 53				18 21					18 40						19 00	19 11		19 21			
Ramsgate [4]	✈ a	17 58				18 28					18 46				19 02		19 03	19 17		19 26	19 29		

For general notes see front of timetable
For details of catering facilities see Directory of Train Operators
For services from London to Ramsgate, Dover and Canterbury via Ashford see Table 207

A [trolley] to Ramsgate
b Change at London Bridge
c Change at Chatham
e Change at London Bridge and Chatham
f Change at London Bridge and Rochester
g Arr. 1803

Mondays to Fridays
from 13 October

For details of Bank Holiday service alterations please see first page of Table 195

London → Medway, Sheerness-on-Sea, Dover and Ramsgate

Network Diagram - see first page of Table 212

		SE 01	SE 30 [1]		SE 07 [1]	SE 22	SE 30 [1]	SE 01	SE 31 [1] A ⚲		SE 07 [1]	SE 21 [1]	SE 31 [1]	SE 01	SE 50 [1] B ⚲		SE 01	SE 07 [1]	SE 92 [1]	SE 50 [1] B ⚲		SE 01	SE 92 [1]	SE 07 [1]
London Victoria [15]	⊖ d		17 49			17 48			18 04						18 33				18 41	19 04			19 09	
London Blackfriars [3]	⊖ d		17 24			17 36			17 36			18 11			18 11				18 23	18 43				
Elephant & Castle	⊖ d		17 28			17 39			17 39			18 15							18 26	18 46				
Bromley South [4]	d		18 05			18 09			18 24			18 33			18 49				19 01	19 20			19 29	
St Mary Cray	d					18 16						18 39							19 10				19 35	
Swanley [4]	d					18 21						18 44							19 15				19 40	
Farningham Road	d					18 25						18 49							19 19				19 44	
Longfield	d					18 30						18 53							19 24				19 49	
Meopham	d					18 34						18 58							19 28				19 53	
Sole Street	d					18 37						19 00							19 31				19 56	
London Charing Cross [4]	⊖ d		17 00		17b43						18b01	17 00						18b34	17c58	17e58			18 30	19b24
London Waterloo (East) [4]	⊖ d		17 03		17b46						18b04	17 03						18b37	18c01	18e01			18 33	19b27
London Cannon Street [4]	⊖ d		17e00		17 50						18 10	17c00						18 46	18 08	18 08			18c30	19 32
London Bridge [4]	⊖ d		17 08		17 54				17f30		18 14	17g50			17f50			18 50	18g14	18f14			18 38	19 36
Dartford [4]	d		17 46						18 10			18 30			18 30			18 48	19 00	19 00			19 16	19 40
Greenhithe for Bluewater	d		17 51						18 15			18 35			18 35			18 53	19 05	19 05			19 21	19 45
Gravesend [4]	d		17 58						18 22			18 42			18 42			19 00	19 12	19 12			19 28	19 52
Strood [4]	d		18 14						18 36			18 54			18 54			19 14	19 28	19 28			19 44	20 04
Rochester [4]	d		18 22			18a51			18 41			19 11						19 19	19 40				20 05	20 12
Chatham [4]	d		18 34		18 38				18 55		18 59	19 13			19 17			19 28	19 43	19 48			20 07	20 15
Gillingham (Kent) [4]	d		18 38		18 42				18 59		19 03	19a19			19 21			19 32	19 47	19 52			20 11	20 20
Rainham (Kent)	d		18 44		18 47				19 04		19 08				19 27			19 37	19 52	19 57			20 16	20 25
Newington	d										19 12							19 41	19 56				20 20	20 35
Sittingbourne [4]	a		18 51		18 55				19 12		19 17				19 34			19 46	20 01	20 04			20 27	→
	d	18 41	18 52		18 55			18 58	19 12		19 18			19 27	19 35		19 42	19 47	20 01	20 05		20 13	20 27	
Kemsley	d	18 45						19 02						19 31			19 46					20 17		
Swale	d	18 48						19 05						19 35			19 50					20 21		
Queenborough	d	18 53						19 10						19 39			19 55					20 25		
Sheerness-on-Sea	a	18 59						19 16						19 45			20 01					20 30		
Teynham	d										19 22							19 51	20 05				20 31	
Faversham [2]	a		19 00		19 04		←		19 21		19 28		←		19 43			19 57	20 14	20 15			20 37	
	d		19 11	19 04	19 08		19 11		19 32	19 24	19 29		19 32		19 47	19 49		19 58		20 19	20 21			
Selling	d		→				19 16		→				19 37			19 54					20 26			
Canterbury East [4]	d						19 26						19 47			20h06					20 36			
Bekesbourne	d						19 30						19 51			20 10					20 40			
Adisham	d						19 35						19 56			20 15					20 45			
Aylesham	d						19 37						19 58			20 17					20 47			
Snowdown	d						19 40						20 01			20 20					20 50			
Shepherds Well	d						19 44						20 05			20 24					20 54			
Kearsney	d						19 48						20 09			20 28					20 58			
Dover Priory [4]	⛴ a						19 55						20 15			20 33					21 03			
Whitstable	d			19 12	19 16					19 33	19 38				19 56			20 06		20 27				
Chestfield & Swalecliffe	d				19 19					19 36	19 41				19 59			20 09						
Herne Bay	d			19 19	19 24					19 40	19 45				20 03			20 13		20 32				
Birchington-on-Sea	d			19 28	19 33					19 49	19 54				20 12			20 22		20 41				
Westgate-on-Sea	d				19 36					19 53	19 58				20 16			20 26						
Margate [4]	d			19 33	19 40					19 57	20 03				20 20			20 30		20 47				
Broadstairs	d			19a41	19 46					20a04	20 09				20 26			20a38		20 52				
Dumpton Park	d				19 48						20 12				20 28					20 55				
Ramsgate [4]	✈ a				19 54						20 18				20 34					20 59				

For general notes see front of timetable
For details of catering facilities see Directory of Train Operators

For services from London to Ramsgate, Dover and Canterbury via Ashford see Table 207

- A ⚲ to Broadstairs
- B ⚲ to Ramsgate
- b Change at London Bridge
- c Change at London Bridge and Rochester
- e Change at London Bridge and Chatham
- f Change at Dartford and Chatham
- g Change at Dartford and Rochester
- h Arr. 2002

For details of Bank Holiday service alterations please see first page of Table 195

London → Medway, Sheerness-on-Sea, Dover and Ramsgate

Network Diagram - see first page of Table 212

Station		SE 50 1		SE 01	SE 07 1	SE 92 1	SE 50 1		SE 01	SE 92 1	SE 50 1		SE 92 1	SE 50 1		SE 01	SE 37 1	SE 50 1	SE 37 1	SE 01	SE 92 1	SE 50 1	SE 22 1
London Victoria 15 ⊖	d	19 34				19 39	20 03			20 09	20 34		20 39	21 03			21 39	22 03			22 39	23 03	23 39
London Blackfriars 3 ⊖	d	19 17					19 47				20 13			20 43			21 13	21 43			22 13	22 43	23 13
Elephant & Castle ⊖	d	19 20					19 50				20 16			20 46			21 16	21 46			22 16	22 46	23 16
Bromley South 4	d	19 50				19 59	20 19			20 29	20 50		20 59	21 19			21 59	22 19			22 59	23 19	23 58
St Mary Cray	d					20 05				20 35			21 05				22 05				23 05		00 04
Swanley 4	d					20 10				20 40			21 10				22 10				23 10		00 09
Farningham Road	d					20 14				20 44			21 14				22 14				23 14		00 13
Longfield	d					20 19				20 49			21 19	21 33			22 19				23 19		00 18
Meopham	d					20 23				20 53			21 23				22 23				23 23		00 23
Sole Street	d					20 26				20 56			21 26				22 26				23 26		00 26
London Charing Cross 4 ⊖	d	18 54				19 21					19 50		20 20				21 20				22 20		22 50
London Waterloo (East) 4 ⊖	d	18 57				19 24					19 53		20 23				21 23				22 23		22 53
London Cannon Street 4 ⊖	d	18b50				19b22					19b52		20b15				21b00						
London Bridge 4 ⊖	d					19 29					19 59		20 29				21 29				22 29		22 59
Dartford 4	d					20 06					20 34		21 04				22 04				23 04		23 34
Greenhithe for Bluewater	d					20 11					20 40		21 09				22 09				23 09		23 40
Gravesend 4	d					20 18					20 50		21 16				22 16				23 16		23 50
Strood 4	d					20 30					21 04		21 28				22 28				23 28		00 02
Rochester 4	d	20 16				20 37	20 43			21 05	21 14		21 35	21 47			22 35	22 43			23 36	23 43	00 35
Chatham 4	d	20 19				20 40	20 47			21 07	21 18		21 38	21 50			22 38	22 46			23 39	23 46	00 38
Gillingham (Kent) 4	d	20 24				20 43	20 50			21 11	21 22		21 41	21 53			22 41	22 49			23 43	23 49	00a41
Rainham (Kent)	d	20 29			⟵	20 48	20 55			21 16	21 27		21 46	21 58			22 46	22 54			23 48	23 54	
Newington	d				20 35	20 52				21 20			21 50				22 50				23 52		
Sittingbourne 4	a	20 36			20 42	20 57	21 02			21 25	21 34		21 55	22 05			22 55	23 01			23 57	00 01	
	d	20 36		20 39	20 43	20 57	21 02		21 05	21 25	21 34		21 55	22 05		22 09	22 55	23 01		23 07	23 57	00 01	
Kemsley	d			20 43					21 09							22 13				23 11			
Swale	d			20 47					21 13							22 17				23 14			
Queenborough	d			20 51					21 17							22 21				23 19			
Sheerness-on-Sea	a			20 57					21 23							22 26				23 25			
Teynham	d				20 47	21 02				21 29			22 00				23 00				00 01		
Faversham 2	a	20 44			20 54	21 08	21 12			21 35	21 42		22 06	22 13			23 06	23 10	⟵		00 07	00 11	
	d	20 48	20 52				21 16	21 18			21 46	21 48		22 17	22 20		23 13	23 11	23 13			00 12	
Selling	d		20 57					21 23				21 53			22 25		⟶		23 18				
Canterbury East 4	d		21 06					21 32				22a03			22 34				23 27				
Bekesbourne	d		21 11					21 36							22 38								
Adisham	d		21 15					21 41							22 43								
Aylesham	d		21 17					21 43							22 45				23 36				
Snowdown	d		21 19					21 46							22 48								
Shepherds Well	d		21 23					21 50							22 52								
Kearsney	d		21 27					21 54							22 56				23 47				
Dover Priory 4 ⛴	a		21 33					21 59							23 01								
Whitstable	d	20 56					21 24				21 54			22 25				23 19				00 20	
Chestfield & Swalecliffe	d	20 59									21 57			22 28				23 22				00 23	
Herne Bay	d	21 03					21 29				22 01			22 32				23 26				00 27	
Birchington-on-Sea	d	21 11					21 37				22 10			22 41				23 35				00 36	
Westgate-on-Sea	d	21 14									22 13			22 44				23 38				00 39	
Margate 4	d	21 19					21 43				22 18			22 48				23 42				00 43	
Broadstairs	d	21 24					21 48				22 23			22 53				23 47				00 48	
Dumpton Park	d	21 27									22 26			22 56				23 50				00 51	
Ramsgate 4 ⛴	a	21 30					21 53				22 29			22 59				23 53				00 54	

For general notes see front of timetable
For details of catering facilities see Directory of Train Operators

For services from London to Ramsgate, Dover and Canterbury via Ashford see Table 207

b Change at London Bridge and Rochester

Table 212

Saturdays

London → Medway, Sheerness-on-Sea, Dover and Ramsgate

Network Diagram - see first page of Table 212

		SE 92 [1]	SE 50 [1]	SE 01	SE 22 [1]	SE 50 [1]	SE 20 [1]	SE 81 [1]	SE 01	SE 90 [1] (trolley)	SE 55 [1]	SE 80 [1]	SE 01	SE 90 [1] (trolley)	SE 37 [1]		SE 01	SE 92	SE 90 [1] (trolley)	SE 50 [1]		SE 01	SE 92 [1]
London Victoria [15]	⊖ d	22p39	23p03		23p39	00 03					05 39				06 39			07 09		07 33			07 39
London Blackfriars [3]	⊖ d																	*06 43*		*07 13*			
Elephant & Castle	⊖ d																	*06 46*		*07 16*			
Bromley South [4]	d	22p59	23p19		23p58						05 59				06 59			07 29		07 49			07 59
St Mary Cray	d	23p05			00 04						06 05				07 05			07 35					08 05
Swanley [4]	d	23p10			00 09						06 10				07 10			07 40					08 10
Farningham Road	d	23p14			00 13						06 14				07 14			07 44					08 14
Longfield	d	23p19			00 18						06 19				07 19			07 49					08 19
Meopham	d	23p23			00 23						06 23				07 23			07 53					08 23
Sole Street	d	23p26			00 26						06 26				07 26			07 56					08 26
London Charing Cross [4]	⊖ d				*22 50*	*23 20*					*05 04*				*06 20*			*06 50*		*06 50*			*07 20*
London Waterloo (East) [4]	⊖ d				*22 53*	*23 23*					*05 07*				*06 23*			*06 53*		*06 53*			*07 23*
London Cannon Street [4]	⊖ d																						
London Bridge [4]	⊖ d				*22 59*	*23 29*					*05 13*				*06 29*			*06 59*		*06 59*			*07 29*
Dartford [4]	d				*23 34*		05 17				*05 49*				*07 04*			*07 34*		*07 34*			*08 04*
Greenhithe for Bluewater	d				*23 40*		05 22				*05 54*				*07 09*			*07 39*		*07 39*			*08 09*
Gravesend [4]	d				*23 50*		05 29				*06 01*				*07 16*			*07 46*		*07 46*			*08 16*
Strood [4]	d				*00 02*	*00 32*	05 40				*06 12*				*07 28*			*07 58*		*07 58*			*08 28*
Rochester [4]	d	23p36	23p43		00 35	00 43	05 44				06 36				07 36			08 06		08 13			08 36
Chatham [4]	d	23p39	23p46		00 38	00 46	05 46				06 38				07 38			08 08		08 17			08 38
Gillingham (Kent) [4]	d	23p43	23p49		00a41	00 50	05 50				06 41				07 41			08 11		08 20			08 41
Rainham (Kent)	d	23p48	23p54			00 55	05 54				06 46				07 46			08 16		08 25			08 46
Newington	d	23p52				00 58	05 58				06 50				07 50			08 20					08 50
Sittingbourne [4]	a	23p57	00 01			01 03	06 03				06 55				07 55			08 25		08 32			08 55
	d	23p57	00 01	00 08		01 03	06 03		06 05		06 55		07 05		07 55		08 05	08 25		08 32		08 35	08 55
Kemsley	d			00 12					06 09				07 09				08 09					08 39	
Swale	d			00 15					06 12				07 12				08 12					08 42	
Queenborough	d			00 20					06 17				07 17				08 17					08 47	
Sheerness-on-Sea	a			00 26					06 22				07 22				08 22					08 52	
Teynham	d	00 01				01 07	06 08				06 59				07 59			08 29					08 59
Faversham [2]	a	00 07	00 11			01 12	06 14				07 05				08 05			08 35		08 40			09 05
	d		00 12			01 13	06 15	06 17			07 14	07 16			08 14	08 16				08 44	08 46		
Selling	d						06 20					07 21			08 19						08 51		
Canterbury East [4]	d						06 29					07 30			08b30						09 00		
Bekesbourne	d						06 33					07 35			08 35						09 05		
Adisham	d						06 38					07 39			08 39						09 09		
Aylesham	d						06 40					07 42			08 42						09 12		
Snowdown	d						06 43					07 44			08 44						09 14		
Shepherds Well	d						06 47					07 48			08 48						09 18		
Kearsney	d						06 51					07 53			08 53						09 23		
Dover Priory [4]	a						06 56					07 57			08 57						09 28		
Whitstable	d		00 20			01 21		06 25			07 22					08 25				08 52			
Chestfield & Swalecliffe	d		00 23			01 24		06 28			07 25					08 28				08 55			
Herne Bay	d		00 27			01 27		06 32			07 29					08 32				08 59			
Birchington-on-Sea	d		00 36			01 36		06 41			07 38					08 41				09 08			
Westgate-on-Sea	d		00 39			01 39		06 45			07 42					08 44				09 11			
Margate [4]	d		00 43			01 43		06 49		07 26	07 46			08 04		08 48			09 04	09 15			
Broadstairs	d		00 48			01 48		06 54		07 31	07 51			08 09		08 53			09 09	09 20			
Dumpton Park	d		00 51			01 51		06 56		07 34	07 53			08 12		08 56			09 12	09 23			
Ramsgate [4]	a		00 54			01 54		06 59		07 37	07 58			08 15		08 59			09 15	09 26			

For general notes see front of timetable
For details of catering facilities see Directory of Train Operators

For services from London to Ramsgate, Dover and Canterbury via Ashford see Table 207

b Arr. 0827

Table 212

Saturdays

London → Medway, Sheerness-on-Sea, Dover and Ramsgate

Network Diagram - see first page of Table 212

	SE		SE	SE	SE	SE		SE	SE	SE		SE	SE	SE	SE		SE	SE	SE		SE	SE	SE
	50		01	92	90	50		01	92	50		01	92	90	50		01	92	50		01	92	90
	1			1	1	1			1	1			1	1	1			1	1			1	1
																			A				
					trolley									trolley					trolley				trolley
London Victoria 15 ⊖ d	08 03			08 09		08 33			08 39	09 03			09 09		09 33			09 39	10 03			10 09	
London Blackfriars 3 ⊖ d	07 43					08 13				08 43					09 13				09 43				
Elephant & Castle ⊖ d	07 46					08 16				08 46					09 16				09 46				
Bromley South 4 d	08 19			08 29		08 49			08 59	09 19			09 29		09 49			09 59	10 19			10 29	
St Mary Cray d				08 35					09 05				09 35					10 05				10 35	
Swanley 4 d				08 40					09 10				09 40					10 10				10 40	
Farningham Road d				08 44					09 14				09 44					10 14				10 44	
Longfield d				08 49					09 19				09 49					10 19				10 49	
Meopham d				08 53					09 23				09 53					10 23				10 53	
Sole Street d				08 56					09 26				09 56					10 26				10 56	
London Charing Cross 4 ⊖ d				07 50					08 20				08 50					09 20				09 50	
London Waterloo (East) 4 ⊖ d				07 53					08 23				08 53					09 23				09 53	
London Cannon Street 4 ⊖ d									08b10				08b48					09b18				09b48	
London Bridge 4 ⊖ d				07 59					08 29				08 59					09 29				09 59	
Dartford 4 d				08 34					09 04				09 34					10 04				10 34	
Greenhithe for Bluewater d				08 39					09 09				09 39					10 09				10 39	
Gravesend 4 d				08 46					09 16				09 46					10 16				10 46	
Strood 4 d				08 58					09 28				09 58					10 28				10 58	
Rochester 4 d	08 43			09 06		09 13			09 36	09 43			10 06		10 13			10 36	10 43			11 06	
Chatham 4 d	08 47			09 08		09 17			09 38	09 47			10 08		10 17			10 38	10 47			11 08	
Gillingham (Kent) 4 d	08 50			09 11		09 20			09 41	09 50			10 11		10 20			10 41	10 50			11 11	
Rainham (Kent) d	08 55			09 16		09 25			09 46	09 55			10 16		10 25			10 46	10 55			11 16	
Newington d				09 20					09 50				10 20					10 50				11 20	
Sittingbourne 4 a	09 02			09 25		09 32			09 55	10 02			10 25		10 32			10 55	11 02			11 25	
d	09 02		09 05	09 25		09 32		09 35	09 55	10 02		10 05	10 25		10 32		10 35	10 55	11 02		11 05	11 25	
Kemsley d			09 09					09 39				10 09					10 39				11 09		
Swale d			09 12					09 42				10 12					10 42				11 12		
Queenborough d			09 17					09 47				10 17					10 47				11 17		
Sheerness-on-Sea a			09 22					09 52				10 22					10 52				11 22		
Teynham d				09 29					09 59				10 29					10 59				11 29	
Faversham 2 a	09 10			09 35		09 40			10 05	10 10			10 35		10 40			11 05	11 10			11 35	
d	09 14	09 16				09 44	09 46			10 14	10 16				10 44	10 46			11 14	11 16			
Selling d							09 51									10 51							
Canterbury East 4 d		09c31					10 00				10e31					11 00				11f31			
Bekesbourne d							10 05									11 05							
Adisham d							10 09									11 09							
Aylesham d							10 12									11 12							
Snowdown d							10 14									11 14							
Shepherds Well d							10 18									11 18							
Kearsney d							10 23									11 23							
Dover Priory 4 ⛴ a		09 46					10 28				10 46					11 28				11 46			
Whitstable d	09 22					09 52				10 22					10 52				11 22				
Chestfield & Swalecliffe d						09 55									10 55								
Herne Bay d	09 27					09 59				10 27					10 59				11 27				
Birchington-on-Sea d	09 35					10 08				10 35					11 08				11 35				
Westgate-on-Sea d						10 11									11 11								
Margate 4 d	09 41				10 04	10 15				10 41				11 04	11 15				11 41				12 04
Broadstairs d	09 46				10 09	10 20				10 46				11 09	11 20				11 46				12 09
Dumpton Park d					10 12	10 23								11 12	11 23								12 12
Ramsgate 4 ⛴ a	09 51				10 15	10 26				10 51				11 15	11 26				11 51				12 15

For general notes see front of timetable
For details of catering facilities see Directory of Train Operators
For services from London to Ramsgate, Dover and Canterbury via Ashford see Table 207

A trolley to Ramsgate
b Change at London Bridge and Rochester
c Arr. 0928
e Arr. 1028
f Arr. 1128

Table 212

London → Medway, Sheerness-on-Sea, Dover and Ramsgate

Network Diagram - see first page of Table 212

		SE 50 1 A		SE 01		SE 92 1	SE 50 1 A		SE 01	SE 92 1	SE 90 1	SE 50 1 A		SE 01	SE 92 1	SE 50 1 A		SE 01	SE 92 1	SE 90 1		SE 50 1 A		SE 01	SE 92 1
London Victoria 15	⊖ d	10 33				10 39	11 03			11 09		11 33			11 39	12 03			12 09			12 33			12 39
London Blackfriars 3	⊖ d	*10 13*					*10 43*					*11 13*				*11 43*						*12 13*			
Elephant & Castle	⊖ d	*10 16*					*10 46*					*11 16*				*11 46*						*12 16*			
Bromley South 4	d	10 49				10 59	11 19			11 29		11 49			11 59	12 19			12 29			12 49			12 59
St Mary Cray	d					11 05				11 35					12 05				12 35						13 05
Swanley 4	d					11 10				11 40					12 10				12 40						13 10
Farningham Road	d					11 14				11 44					12 14				12 44						13 14
Longfield	d					11 19				11 49					12 19				12 49						13 19
Meopham	d					11 23				11 53					12 23				12 53						13 23
Sole Street	d					11 26				11 56					12 26				12 56						13 26
London Charing Cross 4	⊖ d					*10 20*				*10 50*					*11 20*				*11 50*						*12 20*
London Waterloo (East) 4	⊖ d					*10 23*				*10 53*					*11 23*				*11 53*						*12 23*
London Cannon Street 4	⊖ d					*10b18*				*10b48*					*11b18*				*11b48*						*12b18*
London Bridge 4	⊖ d					*10 29*				*10 59*					*11 29*				*11 59*						*12 29*
Dartford 4	d					*11 04*				*11 34*					*12 04*				*12 34*						*13 04*
Greenhithe for Bluewater	d					*11 09*				*11 39*					*12 09*				*12 39*						*13 09*
Gravesend 4	d					*11 16*				*11 46*					*12 16*				*12 46*						*13 16*
Strood 4	d					*11 28*				*11 58*					*12 28*				*12 58*						*13 28*
Rochester 4	d	11 13				11 36	11 43			12 06		12 13			12 36	12 43			13 06			13 13			13 36
Chatham 4	d	11 17				11 38	11 47			12 08		12 17			12 38	12 47			13 08			13 17			13 38
Gillingham (Kent) 4	d	11 20				11 41	11 50			12 11		12 20			12 41	12 50			13 11			13 20			13 41
Rainham (Kent)	d	11 25				11 46	11 55			12 16		12 25			12 46	12 55			13 16			13 25			13 46
Newington	d					11 50				12 20					12 50				13 20						13 50
Sittingbourne 4	a	11 32				11 55	12 02			12 25		12 32			12 55	13 02			13 25			13 32			13 55
	d	11 32		11 35		11 55	12 02		12 05	12 25		12 32		12 35	12 55	13 02		13 05	13 25			13 32		13 35	13 55
Kemsley	d			11 39					12 09					12 39				13 09						13 39	
Swale	d			11 42					12 12					12 42				13 12						13 42	
Queenborough	d			11 47					12 17					12 47				13 17						13 47	
Sheerness-on-Sea	a			11 52					12 22					12 52				13 22						13 52	
Teynham	d					11 59				12 29					12 59				13 29						13 59
Faversham 2	a	11 40				12 05	12 10			12 35		12 40			13 05	13 10			13 35			13 40			14 05
	d	11 44	11 46				12 14	12 16				12 44	12 46			13 14	13 16					13 44	13 46		
Selling	d		11 51										12 51										13 51		
Canterbury East 4	d		12 00					12c31					13 00				13e31						14 00		
Bekesbourne	d		12 05										13 05										14 05		
Adisham	d		12 09										13 09										14 09		
Aylesham	d		12 12										13 12										14 12		
Snowdown	d		12 14										13 14										14 14		
Shepherds Well	d		12 18										13 18										14 18		
Kearsney	d		12 23										13 23										14 23		
Dover Priory 4	a		12 28					12 46					13 28				13 46						14 28		
Whitstable	d	11 52					12 22					12 52				13 22						13 52			
Chestfield & Swalecliffe	d	11 55										12 55										13 55			
Herne Bay	d	11 59					12 27					12 59				13 27						13 59			
Birchington-on-Sea	d	12 08					12 35					13 08				13 35						14 08			
Westgate-on-Sea	d	12 11										13 11										14 11			
Margate 4	d	12 15					12 41				13 04	13 15				13 41				14 04		14 15			
Broadstairs	d	12 20					12 46				13 09	13 20				13 46				14 09		14 20			
Dumpton Park	d	12 23									13 12	13 23								14 12		14 23			
Ramsgate 4	a	12 26					12 51				13 15	13 26				13 51				14 15		14 26			

For general notes see front of timetable
For details of catering facilities see Directory of Train Operators

For services from London to Ramsgate, Dover and Canterbury via Ashford see Table 207

A to Ramsgate
b Change at London Bridge and Rochester
c Arr. 1228
e Arr. 1328

London → Medway, Sheerness-on-Sea, Dover and Ramsgate

Network Diagram - see first page of Table 212

Station		SE 50 1 A		SE 01	SE 92 1	SE 90 1	SE 50 1 A		SE 01	SE 92 1	SE 50 1 A		SE 01	SE 92 1	SE 90 1	SE 50 1 A		SE 01	SE 92 1	SE 50 1 A		SE 01	SE 92 1
London Victoria 15	⊖ d	13 03			13 09		13 33			13 39	14 03			14 09		14 33			14 39	15 03			15 09
London Blackfriars 3	⊖ d	12 43					13 13				13 43					14 13				14 43			
Elephant & Castle	⊖ d	12 46					13 16				13 46					14 16				14 46			
Bromley South 4	d	13 19			13 29		13 49			13 59	14 19			14 29		14 49			14 59	15 19			15 29
St Mary Cray	d				13 35					14 05				14 35					15 05				15 35
Swanley 4	d				13 40					14 10				14 40					15 10				15 40
Farningham Road	d				13 44					14 14				14 44					15 14				15 44
Longfield	d				13 49					14 19				14 49					15 19				15 49
Meopham	d				13 53					14 23				14 53					15 23				15 53
Sole Street	d				13 56					14 26				14 56					15 26				15 56
London Charing Cross 4	⊖ d				12 50					13 20				13 50					14 20				14 50
London Waterloo (East) 4	⊖ d				12 53					13 23				13 53					14 23				14 53
London Cannon Street 4	⊖ d				12b48					13b18				13b48					14b18				14b48
London Bridge 4	⊖ d				12 59					13 29				13 59					14 29				14 59
Dartford 4	d				13 34					14 04				14 34					15 04				15 34
Greenhithe for Bluewater	d				13 39					14 09				14 39					15 09				15 39
Gravesend 4	d				13 46					14 16				14 46					15 16				15 46
Strood 4	d				13 58					14 28				14 58					15 28				15 58
Rochester 4	d	13 43			14 06		14 13			14 36	14 43			15 06		15 13			15 36	15 43			16 06
Chatham 4	d	13 47			14 08		14 17			14 38	14 47			15 08		15 17			15 38	15 47			16 08
Gillingham (Kent) 4	d	13 50			14 11		14 20			14 41	14 50			15 11		15 20			15 41	15 50			16 11
Rainham (Kent)	d	13 55			14 16		14 25			14 46	14 55			15 16		15 25			15 46	15 55			16 16
Newington	d				14 20					14 50				15 20					15 50				16 20
Sittingbourne 4	a	14 02			14 25		14 32			14 55	15 02			15 25		15 32			15 55	16 02			16 25
	d	14 02		14 05	14 25		14 32		14 35	14 55	15 02		15 05	15 25		15 32		15 35	15 55	16 02		16 05	16 25
Kemsley	d			14 09					14 39				15 09					15 39				16 09	
Swale	d			14 12					14 42				15 12					15 43				16 12	
Queenborough	d			14 17					14 47				15 17					15 47				16 17	
Sheerness-on-Sea	a			14 22					14 52				15 22					15 52				16 22	
Teynham	d				14 29					14 59				15 29					15 59				16 29
Faversham 2	a	14 10			14 35		14 40			15 05	15 10			15 35		15 40			16 05	16 10			16 35
	d	14 14	14 16				14 44	14 46			15 14	15 16				15 44	15 46			16 14	16 16		
Selling	d							14 51									15 51						
Canterbury East 4	d		14c31					15 00				15e31					16 00				16f31		
Bekesbourne	d							15 05									16 05						
Adisham	d							15 09									16 09						
Aylesham	d							15 12									16 12						
Snowdown	d							15 14									16 14						
Shepherds Well	d							15 18									16 18						
Kearsney	d							15 23									16 23						
Dover Priory 4	a		14 46					15 28				15 46					16 28				16 46		
Whitstable	d	14 22					14 52				15 22					15 52				16 22			
Chestfield & Swalecliffe	d						14 55									15 55							
Herne Bay	d	14 27					14 59				15 27					15 59				16 27			
Birchington-on-Sea	d	14 35					15 08				15 35					16 08				16 35			
Westgate-on-Sea	d						15 11									16 11							
Margate 4	d	14 41				15 04	15 15				15 41				16 04	16 15				16 41			
Broadstairs	d	14 46				15 09	15 20				15 46				16 09	16 20				16 46			
Dumpton Park	d					15 12	15 23								16 12	16 23							
Ramsgate 4	a	14 51				15 15	15 26				15 51				16 15	16 26				16 51			

For general notes see front of timetable
For details of catering facilities see Directory of Train Operators

For services from London to Ramsgate, Dover and Canterbury via Ashford see Table 207

A to Ramsgate
b Change at London Bridge and Rochester
c Arr. 1428
e Arr. 1528
f Arr. 1628

Table 212

Saturdays

London → Medway, Sheerness-on-Sea, Dover and Ramsgate

Network Diagram - see first page of Table 212

		SE		SE	SE	SE		SE	SE	SE		SE	SE	SE		SE	SE	SE		SE	SE		SE	SE
		50		01	92	50		01	92	50		01	92	50		01	92	50		92	50		01	92
		1			1	1			1	1			1	1			1	1		1	1			1
		A				A				A				A				A			A			
		⚲				⚲				⚲				⚲				⚲			⚲			
London Victoria 15 ⊖	d	15 33			15 39	16 03			16 09	16 33			16 39	17 03			17 09	17 33		17 39	18 03			18 09
London Blackfriars 3 ⊖	d	15 13				15 43				16 13				16 43				17 13			17 43			
Elephant & Castle ⊖	d	15 16				15 46				16 16				16 46				17 16			17 46			
Bromley South 4	d	15 49			15 59	16 19			16 29	16 49			16 59	17 19			17 29	17 49		17 59	18 19			18 29
St Mary Cray	d				16 05				16 35				17 05				17 35			18 05				18 35
Swanley 4	d				16 10				16 40				17 10				17 40			18 10				18 40
Farningham Road	d				16 14				16 44				17 14				17 44			18 14				18 44
Longfield	d				16 19				16 49				17 19				17 49			18 19				18 49
Meopham	d				16 23				16 53				17 23				17 53			18 23				18 53
Sole Street	d				16 26				16 56				17 26				17 56			18 26				18 56
London Charing Cross 4 ⊖	d				15 20				15 50				16 20				16 50			17 20				17 50
London Waterloo (East) 4 ⊖	d				15 23				15 53				16 23				16 53			17 23				17 53
London Cannon Street 4 ⊖	d				15b18				15b48				16b18				16b48			17b18				17b48
London Bridge 4 ⊖	d				15 29				15 59				16 29				16 59			17 29				17 59
Dartford 4	d				16 04				16 34				17 04				17 34			18 04				18 34
Greenhithe for Bluewater	d				16 09				16 39				17 09				17 39			18 09				18 39
Gravesend 4	d				16 16				16 46				17 16				17 46			18 16				18 46
Strood 4	d				16 28				16 58				17 28				17 58			18 28				18 58
Rochester 4	d	16 13			16 36	16 43			17 06	17 13			17 36	17 43			18 06	18 13		18 36	18 43			19 06
Chatham 4	d	16 17			16 38	16 47			17 08	17 17			17 38	17 47			18 08	18 17		18 38	18 47			19 08
Gillingham (Kent) 4	d	16 20			16 41	16 50			17 11	17 20			17 41	17 50			18 11	18 20		18 41	18 50			19 11
Rainham (Kent)	d	16 25			16 46	16 55			17 16	17 25			17 46	17 55			18 16	18 25		18 46	18 55			19 16
Newington	d				16 50				17 20				17 50				18 20			18 50				19 20
Sittingbourne 4	a	16 32			16 55	17 02			17 25	17 32			17 55	18 02			18 25	18 32		18 55	19 02			19 25
	d	16 32		16 35	16 55	17 02		17 05	17 25	17 32		17 35	17 55	18 02		18 05	18 25	18 32		18 55	19 02		19 05	19 25
Kemsley	d			16 39				17 09				17 39				18 09							19 09	
Swale	d			16 42				17 12				17 42				18 12							19 12	
Queenborough	d			16 47				17 17				17 47				18 17							19 17	
Sheerness-on-Sea	a			16 52				17 22				17 52				18 22							19 22	
Teynham	d				16 59				17 29				17 59				18 29			18 59				19 29
Faversham 2	a	16 40			17 05	17 10			17 35	17 40			18 05	18 10			18 35	18 40		19 05	19 10			19 35
	d	16 44	16 46			17 14	17 16			17 44	17 46			18 14	18 16			18 44	18 46		19 14	19 16		
Selling	d		16 51								17 51								18 51					
Canterbury East 4	d		17 00				17c31				18 00				18e31				19 00			19f31		
Bekesbourne	d		17 05								18 05								19 05					
Adisham	d		17 09								18 09								19 09					
Aylesham	d		17 12								18 12								19 12					
Snowdown	d		17 14								18 14								19 14					
Shepherds Well	d		17 18								18 18								19 18					
Kearsney	d		17 23								18 23								19 23					
Dover Priory 4 ⛴	a		17 28				17 46				18 28				18 46				19 28			19 46		
Whitstable	d	16 52				17 22				17 52				18 22				18 52			19 22			
Chestfield & Swalecliffe	d	16 55								17 55								18 55						
Herne Bay	d	16 59				17 27				17 59				18 27				18 59			19 27			
Birchington-on-Sea	d	17 08				17 35				18 08				18 35				19 08			19 35			
Westgate-on-Sea	d	17 11								18 11								19 11						
Margate 4	d	17 15				17 41				18 15				18 41				19 15			19 41			
Broadstairs	d	17 20				17 46				18 20				18 46				19 20			19 46			
Dumpton Park	d	17 23								18 23								19 23						
Ramsgate 4 ✈	a	17 26				17 51				18 26				18 51				19 26			19 51			

For general notes see front of timetable
For details of catering facilities see Directory of Train Operators

For services from London to Ramsgate, Dover and Canterbury via Ashford see Table 207

A ⚲ to Ramsgate
b Change at London Bridge and Rochester
c Arr. 1728
e Arr. 1828
f Arr. 1928

London → Medway, Sheerness-on-Sea, Dover and Ramsgate

Network Diagram - see first page of Table 212

	SE 50 1 A		SE 92 1		SE 50 1		SE 01	SE 92 1	SE 01 1	SE 50 1		SE 01	SE 92 1	SE 61 1	SE 50 1		SE 01	SE 92 1	SE 50 1		SE 01	SE 75 1	SE 50 1	SE 22 1
London Victoria 15 ⊖ d	18 33		18 39		19 03			19 39		20 03			20 39		21 03			21 39	22 03			22 39	23 03	23 39
London Blackfriars 3 ⊖ d	*18 13*				*18 43*			*19 13*		*19 43*			*20 13*		*20 43*			*21 13*	*21 43*			*22 13*	*22 43*	*23 13*
Elephant & Castle ⊖ d	*18 16*				*18 46*			*19 16*		*19 46*			*20 16*		*20 46*			*21 16*	*21 46*			*22 16*	*22 46*	*23 16*
Bromley South 4 d	18 49		18 59		19 19			19 59		20 19			20 59		21 19			21 59	22 19			22 59	23 19	23 59
St Mary Cray d			19 05					20 05					21 05					22 05				23 05		00 05
Swanley 4 d			19 10					20 10					21 10					22 10				23 10		00 10
Farningham Road d			19 14					20 14					21 14					22 14				23 14		00 14
Longfield d			19 19		19 33			20 19		20 33			21 19		21 33			22 19				23 19		00 19
Meopham d			19 23					20 23					21 23					22 23				23 23		00 23
Sole Street d			19 26					20 26					21 26					22 26				23 26		00 26
London Charing Cross 4 ⊖ d			*18 20*					*19 20*					*20 20*					*21 20*				*22 20*		*23 20*
London Waterloo (East) 4 ⊖ d			*18 23*					*19 23*					*20 23*					*21 23*				*22 23*		*23 23*
London Cannon Street 4 ⊖ d			*18b18*					*19b14*																
London Bridge 4 ⊖ d			*18 29*					*19 29*					*20 29*					*21 29*				*22 29*		*23 29*
Dartford 4 d			*19 04*					*20 04*					*21 04*					*22 04*				*23 04*		*23 34*
Greenhithe for Bluewater d			*19 09*					*20 09*					*21 09*					*22 09*				*23 09*		*23 40*
Gravesend 4 d			*19 16*					*20 16*					*21 16*					*22 16*				*23 16*		*23 50*
Strood 4 d			*19 28*					*20 28*					*21 28*					*22 28*				*23 28*		*00 28*
Rochester 4 d	19 13		19 36		19 47			20 36		20 47			21 36		21 47			22 36	22 47			23 36	23 47	00 36
Chatham 4 d	19 17		19 38		19 49			20 38		20 49			21 38		21 49			22 38	22 49			23 38	23 49	00 38
Gillingham (Kent) 4 d	19 20		19 41		19 53			20 41		20 53			21 41		21 53			22 41	22 53			23 41	23 53	00a41
Rainham (Kent) d	19 25		19 46		19 58			20 46		20 58			21 46		21 58			22 46	22 58			23 46	23 58	
Newington d			19 50					20 50					21 50					22 50				23 50		
Sittingbourne 4 a	19 32		19 55		20 05			20 55		21 05			21 55		22 05			22 55	23 05			23 55	00 05	
d	19 32		19 55		20 05		20 07	20 55		21 05		21 07	21 55		22 05		22 07	22 55	23 05		23 07	23 55	00 05	
Kemsley d							20 11					21 11					22 11				23 11			
Swale d							20 14					21 14					22 14				23 14			
Queenborough d							20 19					21 19					22 19				23 19			
Sheerness-on-Sea a							20 24					21 24					22 24				23 24			
Teynham d			19 59					20 59					21 59					22 59				23 59		
Faversham 2 a	19 40		20 05		20 13			21 05		21 13			22 05		22 13			23 05	23 13			00 05	00 13	
d	19 44	19 46			20 16	20 18				21 16	21 18				22 16	22 18			23 16	23 18			00 16	
Selling d		19 51				20 23					21 23					22 23								
Canterbury East 4 d		20 00				20 33					21 33					22 33				23 32				
Bekesbourne d		20 05				20 37					21 37					22 37								
Adisham d		20 09				20 42					21 42					22 42								
Aylesham d		20 12				20 44					21 44					22 44								
Snowdown d		20 14				20 47					21 47					22 47								
Shepherds Well d		20 18				20 51					21 51					22 51								
Kearsney d		20 23				20 55					21 55					22 55								
Dover Priory 4 ⛴ a		20 28				21 01					22 01					23 01				23 47				
Whitstable d	19 52				20 24					21 24					22 24				23 24				00 24	
Chestfield & Swalecliffe d	19 55				20 27					21 27					22 27				23 27				00 27	
Herne Bay d	19 59				20 31					21 31					22 31				23 31				00 31	
Birchington-on-Sea d	20 08				20 40					21 40					22 40				23 40				00 40	
Westgate-on-Sea d	20 11				20 43					21 43					22 43				23 43				00 43	
Margate 4 d	20 15				20 47				21 24	21 47				22 17	22 47				23 47				00 47	
Broadstairs d	20 20				20 52				21 29	21 52				22 22	22 52				23 52				00 52	
Dumpton Park d	20 23				20 54				21 32	21 54				22 25	22 54				23 54				00 55	
Ramsgate 4 ⛴ a	20 26				20 57				21 35	21 57				22 28	22 57				23 57				00 58	

For general notes see front of timetable
For details of catering facilities see Directory of Train Operators

For services from London to Ramsgate, Dover and Canterbury via Ashford see Table 207

A 🚌 to Ramsgate
b Change at London Bridge and Rochester

Table 212

Sundays

London → Medway, Sheerness-on-Sea, Dover and Ramsgate

Network Diagram - see first page of Table 212

		SE 50 1	SE 01	SE 22 1	SE 50 1	SE 01	SE 90 1	SE 01	SE 54 1	SE 90 1	SE 50 1		SE 54 1	SE 90 1	SE 50 1 A	SE 01	SE 50 1		SE 54 1	SE 90 1	SE 50 1 A	SE 01
London Victoria 15 ⊖	d	23p03		23p39	00 03				07 35		08 03		08 24		08 45		09 03		09 24		09 45	
London Blackfriars 3 ⊖	d																					
Elephant & Castle ⊖	d																					
Bromley South 4	d	23p19		23p59					07 52		08 19		08 43		09 01		09 19		09 43		10 01	
St Mary Cray	d			00 05					07 58				08 50						09 50			
Swanley 4	d			00 10					08 03				08 54						09 54			
Farningham Road	d			00 14					08 07				08 59						09 59			
Longfield	d			00 19					08 12				09 03						10 03			
Meopham	d			00 23					08 16				09 08						10 08			
Sole Street	d			00 26					08 19				09 10						10 10			
London Charing Cross 4 ⊖	d			23 20									07 40				08 20		08 50			
London Waterloo (East) 4 ⊖	d			23 23									07 43				08 23		08 53			
London Cannon Street 4 ⊖	d																					
London Bridge 4 ⊖	d			23 29									07 48				08 29		08 59			
Dartford 4	d			23 34							08 02		08 28				09 04		09 34			
Greenhithe for Bluewater	d			23 40							08 08		08 34				09 09		09 39			
Gravesend 4	d			23 50							08 16		08 42				09 16		09 46			
Strood 4	d			00 28							08 28		08 54				09 27		09 57			
Rochester 4	d	23p47		00 36	00 47				08 28		08 43		09 20		09 25		09 43		10 20		10 25	
Chatham 4	d	23p49		00 38	00 49				08 31		08 46		09 22		09 28		09 46		10 22		10 28	
Gillingham (Kent) 4	d	23p53		00a41	00 53				08 35		08 50		09 26		09 32		09 50		10 26		10 32	
Rainham (Kent)	d	23p58			00 58				08 40		08 55		09 31		09 37		09 55		10 31		10 37	
Newington	d				01 01				08 44				09 35						10 35			
Sittingbourne 4	a	00 05			01 06				08 49		09 02		09 40		09 44		10 02		10 40		10 44	
	d	00 05	00 07		01 06	07 48		08 48	08 49		09 02		09 41		09 45	09 48	10 02		10 41		10 45	10 48
Kemsley	d		00 11			07 52		08 52								09 52						10 52
Swale	d		00 14			07 55		08 55								09 55						10 55
Queenborough	d		00 19			08 00		09 00								10 00						11 00
Sheerness-on-Sea	a		00 24			08 05		09 05								10 05						11 05
Teynham	d				01 10				08 54				09 45						10 45			
Faversham 2	a	00 13			01 15				09 00		09 10		09 52		09 55		10 10		10 52		10 55	
	d	00 16			01 16						09 14	09 16	09 52		09 56		10 14	10 16	10 52		10 56	
Selling	d											09 21						10 21				
Canterbury East 4	d											09 30	10a04					10 30	11a04			
Bekesbourne	d											09 35						10 35				
Adisham	d											09 39						10 39				
Aylesham	d											09 42						10 42				
Snowdown	d											09 44						10 44				
Shepherds Well	d											09 48						10 48				
Kearsney	d											09 53						10 53				
Dover Priory 4 ⛴	a											09 58						10 58				
Whitstable	d	00 24			01 24						09 22				10 04		10 22				11 04	
Chestfield & Swalecliffe	d	00 27			01 27						09 25				10 07		10 25				11 07	
Herne Bay	d	00 31			01 31						09 29				10 11		10 29				11 11	
Birchington-on-Sea	d	00 40			01 40						09 38				10 20		10 38				11 20	
Westgate-on-Sea	d	00 43			01 43						09 41				10 24		10 41				11 24	
Margate 4	d	00 47			01 47		08 24			09 24	09 45			10 24	10 29		10 45			11 24	11 29	
Broadstairs	d	00 52			01 52		08 29			09 29	09 50			10 29	10 34		10 50			11 29	11 34	
Dumpton Park	d	00 55			01 55		08 32			09 32	09 53			10 32	10 37		10 53			11 32	11 37	
Ramsgate 4 ✈	a	00 58			01 58		08 35			09 35	09 56			10 35	10 40		10 56			11 35	11 40	

For general notes see front of timetable
For details of catering facilities see Directory of Train Operators

For services from London to Ramsgate, Dover and Canterbury via Ashford see Table 207

A 20 July to 31 August

Table 212

Sundays

London → Medway, Sheerness-on-Sea, Dover and Ramsgate

Network Diagram - see first page of Table 212

	SE		SE	SE	SE	SE		SE	SE	SE	SE		SE	SE	SE	SE		SE	SE	SE
	50		54	01	90	50		54	01	90	50		54	01	90	50		54	01	90
	[1] ⊤		[1]		[1]	[1] ⊤		[1]		[1]	[1] ⊤		[1]		[1]	[1] ⊤		[1]		[1]
London Victoria [15] ⊖ d	10 03		10 24			11 03		11 24			12 03		12 24			13 03		13 24		
London Blackfriars [3] ⊖ d																				
Elephant & Castle ⊖ d																				
Bromley South [4] d	10 19		10 43			11 19		11 43			12 19		12 43			13 19		13 43		
St Mary Cray d			10 50					11 50					12 50					13 50		
Swanley [4] d			10 54					11 54					12 54					13 54		
Farningham Road d			10 59					11 59					12 59					13 59		
Longfield d			11 03					12 03					13 03					14 03		
Meopham d			11 08					12 08					13 08					14 08		
Sole Street d			11 10					12 10					13 10					14 10		
London Charing Cross [4] ⊖ d	*09 20*		*09 50*			*10 20*		*10 50*			*11 20*		*11 50*			*12 20*		*12 50*		
London Waterloo (East) [4] ⊖ d	*09 23*		*09 53*			*10 23*		*10 53*			*11 23*		*11 53*			*12 23*		*12 53*		
London Cannon Street [4] ⊖ d																				
London Bridge [4] ⊖ d	*09 29*		*09 59*			*10 29*		*10 59*			*11 29*		*11 59*			*12 29*		*12 59*		
Dartford [4] d	*10 04*		*10 34*			*11 04*		*11 34*			*12 04*		*12 34*			*13 04*		*13 34*		
Greenhithe for Bluewater d	*10 09*		*10 39*			*11 09*		*11 39*			*12 09*		*12 39*			*13 09*		*13 39*		
Gravesend [4] d	*10 16*		*10 46*			*11 16*		*11 46*			*12 16*		*12 46*			*13 16*		*13 46*		
Strood [4] d	*10 27*		*10 57*			*11 27*		*11 57*			*12 27*		*12 57*			*13 27*		*13 57*		
Rochester [4] d	10 43		11 20			11 43		12 20			12 43		13 20			13 43		14 20		
Chatham [4] d	10 46		11 22			11 46		12 22			12 46		13 22			13 46		14 22		
Gillingham (Kent) [4] d	10 50		11 26			11 50		12 26			12 50		13 26			13 50		14 26		
Rainham (Kent) d	10 55		11 31			11 55		12 31			12 55		13 31			13 55		14 31		
Newington d			11 35					12 35					13 35					14 35		
Sittingbourne [4] a	11 02		11 40			12 02		12 40			13 02		13 40			14 02		14 40		
d	11 02		11 41	11 48		12 02		12 41	12 48		13 02		13 41	13 48		14 02		14 41	14 48	
Kemsley d				11 52					12 52					13 52					14 52	
Swale d				11 55					12 55					13 55					14 55	
Queenborough d				12 00					13 00					14 00					15 00	
Sheerness-on-Sea a				12 05					13 05					14 05					15 05	
Teynham d			11 45					12 45					13 45					14 45		
Faversham [2] a	11 10		11 52			12 10		12 52			13 10		13 52			14 10		14 52		
d	11 14	11 16	11 52			12 14	12 16	12 52			13 14	13 16	13 52			14 14	14 16	14 52		
Selling d		11 21					12 21					13 21					14 21			
Canterbury East [4] d		11 30	12a04				12 30	13a04				13 30	14a04				14 30	15a04		
Bekesbourne d		11 35					12 35					13 35					14 35			
Adisham d		11 39					12 39					13 39					14 39			
Aylesham d		11 42					12 42					13 42					14 42			
Snowdown d		11 44					12 44					13 44					14 44			
Shepherds Well d		11 48					12 48					13 48					14 48			
Kearsney d		11 53					12 53					13 53					14 53			
Dover Priory [4] ⛴ a		11 58					12 58					13 58					14 58			
Whitstable d	11 22					12 22					13 22					14 22				
Chestfield & Swalecliffe d	11 25					12 25					13 25					14 25				
Herne Bay d	11 29					12 29					13 29					14 29				
Birchington-on-Sea d	11 38					12 38					13 38					14 38				
Westgate-on-Sea d	11 41					12 41					13 41					14 41				
Margate [4] d	11 45				12 24	12 45				13 24	13 45				14 24	14 45				15 24
Broadstairs d	11 50				12 29	12 50				13 29	13 50				14 29	14 50				15 29
Dumpton Park d	11 53				12 32	12 53				13 32	13 53				14 32	14 53				15 32
Ramsgate [4] ✈ a	11 56				12 35	12 56				13 35	13 56				14 35	14 56				15 35

For general notes see front of timetable
For details of catering facilities see Directory of Train Operators

For services from London to Ramsgate, Dover and Canterbury via Ashford see Table 207

Table 212

Sundays

London → Medway, Sheerness-on-Sea, Dover and Ramsgate

Network Diagram - see first page of Table 212

	SE 50 1 🚲		SE 54 1	SE 01	SE 90 1	SE 50 1 🚲		SE 54 1	SE 01	SE 90 1	SE 50 1 🚲		SE 54 1	SE 01	SE 90 1	SE 50 1 🚲		SE 54 1	SE 01	SE 90 1
London Victoria 15 ⊖ d	14 03		14 24			15 03		15 24			16 03		16 24			17 03		17 24		
London Blackfriars 3 ⊖ d																				
Elephant & Castle ⊖ d																				
Bromley South 4 d	14 19		14 43			15 19		15 43			16 19		16 43			17 19		17 43		
St Mary Cray d			14 50					15 50					16 50					17 50		
Swanley 4 d			14 54					15 54					16 54					17 54		
Farningham Road d			14 59					15 59					16 59					17 59		
Longfield d			15 03					16 03					17 03					18 03		
Meopham d			15 08					16 08					17 08					18 08		
Sole Street d			15 10					16 10					17 10					18 10		
London Charing Cross 4 ⊖ d	13 20		13 50			14 20		14 50			15 20		15 50			16 20		16 50		
London Waterloo (East) 4 ⊖ d	13 23		13 53			14 23		14 53			15 23		15 53			16 23		16 53		
London Cannon Street 4 ⊖ d																				
London Bridge 4 ⊖ d	13 29		13 59			14 29		14 59			15 29		15 59			16 29		16 59		
Dartford 4 d	14 04		14 34			15 04		15 34			16 04		16 34			17 04		17 34		
Greenhithe for Bluewater d	14 09		14 39			15 09		15 39			16 09		16 39			17 09		17 39		
Gravesend 4 d	14 16		14 46			15 16		15 46			16 16		16 46			17 16		17 46		
Strood 4 d	14 27		14 57			15 27		15 57			16 27		16 57			17 27		17 57		
Rochester 4 d	14 43		15 20			15 43		16 20			16 43		17 20			17 43		18 20		
Chatham 4 d	14 46		15 22			15 46		16 22			16 46		17 22			17 46		18 22		
Gillingham (Kent) 4 d	14 50		15 26			15 50		16 26			16 50		17 26			17 50		18 26		
Rainham (Kent) d	14 55		15 31			15 55		16 31			16 55		17 31			17 55		18 31		
Newington d			15 35					16 35					17 35					18 35		
Sittingbourne 4 a	15 02		15 40			16 02		16 40			17 02		17 40			18 02		18 40		
d	15 02		15 41	15 48		16 02		16 41	16 48		17 02		17 41	17 48		18 02		18 41	18 48	
Kemsley d				15 52					16 52					17 52					18 52	
Swale d				15 55					16 55					17 55					18 55	
Queenborough d				16 00					17 00					18 00					19 00	
Sheerness-on-Sea a				16 05					17 05					18 05					19 05	
Teynham d			15 45					16 45					17 45					18 45		
Faversham 2 a	15 10		15 52			16 10		16 52			17 10		17 52			18 10		18 52		
d	15 14	15 16	15 52			16 14	16 16	16 52			17 14	17 16	17 52			18 14	18 16	18 52		
Selling d		15 21					16 21					17 21					18 21			
Canterbury East 4 d		15 30	16a04				16 30	17a04				17 30	18a04				18 30	19a04		
Bekesbourne d		15 35					16 35					17 35					18 35			
Adisham d		15 39					16 39					17 39					18 39			
Aylesham d		15 42					16 42					17 42					18 42			
Snowdown d		15 44					16 44					17 44					18 44			
Shepherds Well d		15 48					16 48					17 48					18 48			
Kearsney d		15 53					16 53					17 53					18 53			
Dover Priory 4 ⛴ a		15 58					16 58					17 58					18 58			
Whitstable d	15 22					16 22					17 22					18 22				
Chestfield & Swalecliffe d	15 25					16 25					17 25					18 25				
Herne Bay d	15 29					16 29					17 29					18 29				
Birchington-on-Sea d	15 38					16 38					17 38					18 38				
Westgate-on-Sea d	15 41					16 41					17 41					18 41				
Margate 4 d	15 45				16 24	16 45				17 24	17 45				18 24	18 45				19 24
Broadstairs d	15 50				16 29	16 50				17 29	17 50				18 29	18 50				19 29
Dumpton Park d	15 53				16 32	16 53				17 32	17 53				18 32	18 53				19 32
Ramsgate 4 ⇄ a	15 56				16 35	16 56				17 35	17 56				18 35	18 56				19 35

For general notes see front of timetable
For details of catering facilities see Directory of Train Operators

For services from London to Ramsgate, Dover and Canterbury via Ashford see Table 207

Table 212

Sundays

London → Medway, Sheerness-on-Sea, Dover and Ramsgate

Network Diagram - see first page of Table 212

		SE 50 1	SE 54 1	SE 01	SE 90 1	SE 50 1	SE 54 1	SE 01	SE 4 1	SE 50 1	SE 54 1	SE 01	SE 50 1	SE 54 1	SE 01	SE 50 1	SE 54 1	SE 50 1
London Victoria 15	⊖ d	18 03	18 24			19 03	19 24			20 03	20 24		21 03	21 24		22 03	22 41	23 03
London Blackfriars 3	⊖ d																	
Elephant & Castle	⊖ d																	
Bromley South 4	d	18 19	18 43			19 19	19 43			20 19	20 43		21 19	21 43		22 19	23 01	23 19
St Mary Cray	d		18 50				19 50				20 50			21 50			23 07	
Swanley 4	d		18 54				19 54				20 54			21 54			23 12	
Farningham Road	d		18 59				19 59				20 59			21 59			23 16	
Longfield	d		19 03				20 03				21 03			22 03			23 21	
Meopham	d		19 08				20 08				21 08			22 08			23 25	
Sole Street	d		19 10				20 10				21 10			22 10			23 28	
London Charing Cross 4	⊖ d	17 20	17 50			18 20	18 50			19 20	19 50		20 20	20 50		21 20	22 20	
London Waterloo (East) 4	⊖ d	17 23	17 53			18 23	18 53			19 23	19 53		20 23	20 53		21 23	22 23	
London Cannon Street 4	⊖ d																	
London Bridge 4	⊖ d	17 29	17 59			18 29	18 59			19 29	19 59		20 29	20 59		21 29	22 29	
Dartford 4	d	18 04	18 34			19 04	19 34			20 04	20 34		21 04	21 34		22 04	23 04	
Greenhithe for Bluewater	d	18 09	18 39			19 09	19 40			20 09	20 40		21 09	21 40		22 09	23 09	
Gravesend 4	d	18 16	18 46			19 16	19 48			20 16	20 48		21 16	21 48		22 16	23 16	
Strood 4	d	18 27	18 57			19 27	20 00			20 27	21 00		21 27	22 00		22 27	23 27	
Rochester 4	d	18 43	19 20			19 43	20 20			20 43	21 20		21 43	22 20		22 43	23 37	23 43
Chatham 4	d	18 46	19 22			19 46	20 22			20 46	21 22		21 46	22 22		22 46	23 39	23 46
Gillingham (Kent) 4	d	18 50	19 26			19 50	20 26			20 50	21 26		21 50	22 26		22 50	23 43	23 50
Rainham (Kent)	d	18 55	19 31			19 55	20 31			20 55	21 31		21 55	22 31		22 55	23 48	23 55
Newington	d		19 35				20 35				21 35			22 35			23 52	
Sittingbourne 4	a	19 02	19 40			20 02	20 40			21 02	21 40		22 02	22 40		23 02	23 57	00 02
	d	19 02	19 41	19 48		20 02	20 41	20 48		21 02	21 41	21 48	22 02	22 41	22 48	23 02	23 57	00 02
Kemsley	d			19 52				20 52				21 52			22 52			
Swale	d			19 55				20 55				21 55			22 55			
Queenborough	d			20 00				21 00				22 00			23 00			
Sheerness-on-Sea	a			20 05				21 05				22 05			23 05			
Teynham	d		19 45				20 45				21 45			22 45			00 01	
Faversham 2	a	19 10	19 51			20 10	20 51			21 10	21 51		22 10	22 51		23 10	00 07	
	d	19 14 / 19 16				20 14 / 20 16				21 14 / 21 16			22 14 / 22 16			23 14 / 23 16		
Selling	d	19 21				20 21				21 21			22 21					
Canterbury East 4	d	19 30				20 30				21 30			22 30			23 30		
Bekesbourne	d	19 35				20 35				21 35			22 35					
Adisham	d	19 39				20 39				21 39			22 39					
Aylesham	d	19 42				20 42				21 42			22 42					
Snowdown	d	19 44				20 44				21 44			22 44					
Shepherds Well	d	19 48				20 48				21 48			22 48					
Kearsney	d	19 53				20 53				21 53			22 53					
Dover Priory 4	a	19 58				20 58				21 58			22 58			23 46		
Whitstable	d	19 22				20 22				21 22			22 22			23 22		00 22
Chestfield & Swalecliffe	d	19 25				20 25				21 25			22 25			23 25		00 25
Herne Bay	d	19 29				20 29				21 29			22 29			23 29		00 29
Birchington-on-Sea	d	19 38				20 38				21 38			22 38			23 38		00 38
Westgate-on-Sea	d	19 41				20 41				21 41			22 41			23 41		00 41
Margate 4	d	19 45			20 24	20 45			21 24	21 45			22 45			23 45		00 45
Broadstairs	d	19 50			20 29	20 50			21 29	21 50			22 50			23 50		00 50
Dumpton Park	d	19 53			20 32	20 53			21 32	21 53			22 53			23 53		00 53
Ramsgate 4	a	19 56			20 35	20 56			21 35	21 56			22 56			23 56		00 56

For general notes see front of timetable
For details of catering facilities see Directory of Train Operators

For services from London to Ramsgate, Dover and Canterbury via Ashford see Table 207

Table 212

Sundays

London → Medway, Sheerness-on-Sea, Dover and Ramsgate

Network Diagram - see first page of Table 212

		SE 54 [1]
London Victoria [15]	⊖ d	23 42
London Blackfriars [3]	⊖ d	
Elephant & Castle	⊖ d	
Bromley South [4]	d	00 01
St Mary Cray	d	00 08
Swanley [4]	d	00 12
Farningham Road	d	00 17
Longfield	d	00 21
Meopham	d	00 26
Sole Street	d	00 28
London Charing Cross [4]	⊖ d	*23 20*
London Waterloo (East) [4]	⊖ d	*23 23*
London Cannon Street [4]	⊖ d	
London Bridge [4]	⊖ d	*23 29*
Dartford [4]	d	*23 34*
Greenhithe for Bluewater	d	*23 40*
Gravesend [4]	d	*23 48*
Strood [4]	d	*23 58*
Rochester [4]	d	00 38
Chatham [4]	d	00 40
Gillingham (Kent) [4]	d	00a44
Rainham (Kent)	d	
Newington	d	
Sittingbourne [4]	a	
	d	
Kemsley	d	
Swale	d	
Queenborough	d	
Sheerness-on-Sea	a	
Teynham	d	
Faversham [2]	a	
	d	
Selling	d	
Canterbury East [4]	d	
Bekesbourne	d	
Adisham	d	
Aylesham	d	
Snowdown	d	
Shepherds Well	d	
Kearsney	d	
Dover Priory [4]	⛴ a	
Whitstable	d	
Chestfield & Swalecliffe	d	
Herne Bay	d	
Birchington-on-Sea	d	
Westgate-on-Sea	d	
Margate [4]	d	
Broadstairs	d	
Dumpton Park	d	
Ramsgate [4]	✈ a	

For general notes see front of timetable
For details of catering facilities see Directory of Train Operators

For services from London to Ramsgate, Dover and Canterbury via Ashford see Table 207

Table 212

Mondays to Fridays
until 10 October

For details of Bank Holiday service alterations please see first page of Table 195

Ramsgate, Dover, Sheerness-on-Sea and Medway → London

Network Diagram - see first page of Table 212

Miles	Miles	Miles			SE MX 58	SE 50 [1]	SE 07 [1]	SE 37 [1]	SE 01	SE 50 [1]	SE 03 [1]	SE 01	SE 51 [1]	SE 07 [1]	SE 07 [1]	SE 22	SE 31 [1]	SE 22	SE 07 [1]	SE 01	SE 22	SE 50 [1]	SE 07 [1]
0	—	—	**Ramsgate [4]** ✈	d		04 38				05 04			05 28		05 46							06 11	
1	—	—	Dumpton Park	d		04 40							05 30		05 49							06 14	
2¼	—	—	Broadstairs	d		04 43				05 09			05 33		05 52							06 17	06 24
5½	—	—	**Margate [4]**	d		04 48				05 14			05 38		05 57							06 22	06 29
6¾	—	—	Westgate-on-Sea	d		04 51							05 41		06 01							06 25	
8½	—	—	Birchington-on-Sea	d		04 54				05 19			05 44		06 04							06 29	06 34
16½	—	—	**Herne Bay**	d		05 03				05 28			05 53		06 13							06 37	06 43
18½	—	—	Chestfield & Swalecliffe	d		05 07							05 56		06 17							06 40	
20½	—	—	Whitstable	d		05 10				05 33			06 00		06 20							06 44	06 49
—	0	—	**Dover Priory [4]** ⛴	d				04 50			05 12						05 49						
—	2¼	—	Kearsney	d				04 54			05 16						05 53						
—	5½	—	Shepherds Well	d				04 59			05 22						05 58						
—	7½	—	Snowdown	d				05 02			05 26						06 01						
—	8½	—	Aylesham	d				05 05			05 28						06 04						
—	9½	—	Adisham	d				05 07			05 31						06 06						
—	12½	—	Bekesbourne	d				05 12			05 35						06 11						
—	15½	—	**Canterbury East [4]**	d				05 17			05 41						06 17						
—	22	—	Selling	d				05 26			05 51						06 26						
27¼	25¼	—	**Faversham [2]**	a		05 18		05 30		05 41	05 55		06 09		06 29		06 30		←			06 52	06 57
—	—	—		d	23p42	05 19	05 22	05 31		05 43	05 56		06 10	06 16	06 36 →		06 32		06 36			06 53	06 58
31¾	29¾	—	Teynham	d	23p47		05 27	05 36		05 48				06 21			06 37		06 41				
—	—	0	**Sheerness-on-Sea**	d					05 31			05 58								06 36			
—	—	2	Queenborough	d					05 36			06 03								06 41			
—	—	4	Swale	d					05 40			06 08								06 46			
—	—	6	Kemsley	d					05 43			06 11								06 49			
34½	32½	8	**Sittingbourne [4]**	a	23p52	05 27	05 32	05 41	05 48	05 53	06 04	06 16	06 18	06 26			06 42		06 46	06 54		07 01	07 06
—	—	—		d	23p52	05 28	05 32	05 41		05 54	06 04		06 18	06 27			06 43		06 46			07 02	07 06
37¾	35¾	—	Newington	d	23p57		05 37	05 46		05 59				06 32			06 48		06 52				
40¼	38¼	—	Rainham (Kent)	d	00 01	05 36	05 42	05 50		06 04	06 12		06 26	06 37			06 53		06 56			07 10	07 14
43¼	41¼	—	**Gillingham (Kent) [4]**	d	00 07	05 42	05 48	05 56		06 09	06 18		06 32	06 42		06 49	06 58		07 02		07 06	07 16	07 20
45	43	—	**Chatham [4]**	d	00 11	05 46	05 52	06 01		06 13	06 22		06 36	06 46		06 53	07 02		07 06		07 10	07 20	07 24
45½	43½	0	Rochester [4]	d	00 13		05 54	06 03		06 15	06 28		06 43	06 48		06 55			07 19		07 13		07 34
—	—	—	Strood [4]	a	00 17	06 03	06 03			06 33	06 33		06 48	07 04		07 04			07 24		07 24		07 44
—	—	—	Gravesend [4]	a	00 28	06 14	06 14			06 44	06 44		06 59	07 17		07 17			07 39		07 39		07 57
—	—	—	Greenhithe for Bluewater	a	00 34	06 20	06 20			06 50	06 50		07 06	07 24		07 24			07 46		07 46		08 04
—	—	—	Dartford [4]	a	00 41	06 25	06 25			06 55	06 55		07 11	07 29		07 29			07 51		07 51		08 09
—	—	—	**London Bridge [4]** ⊖	a		07 01	06 33			07 30	07 07		07 44	07 26		08 06			07 49		08b41		08 08
—	—	30	**London Cannon Street [4]** ⊖	a		07c13	06 38			07e41	07 13		07 51	07 33		08 13			07 55			08 54	08 15
—	—	—	**London Waterloo (East) [4]** ⊖	a		07 06	06f41			07 36	07f16		07c55	07f36		08e15			07f58			08c55	08f19
—	—	—	**London Charing Cross [4]** ⊖	a		07 10	06f46			07 40	07f20		07c59	07f40		08e21			08f03			09c01	08f24
52¼	50¼	—	Sole Street	d				06 14		06 24						07 06		←			07 24		
53¼	51¼	—	Meopham	d				06 16		06 26						07 08 →		07 08			07 26 →		
55¾	53¾	—	Longfield	d				06 20		06 30								07 13					
58¾	56¾	—	Farningham Road	d				06 24		06 34								07 17					
61¾	59¾	—	Swanley [4]	a				06 29		06 40								07 22					
64¼	62¼	—	St Mary Cray	a				06 35		06 45								07 27					
68¼	66¼	—	Bromley South [4]	a		06 13		06 42		06 51							07 32	07 35				07 50	
—	—	—	Elephant & Castle ⊖	a		07 10				07 15							07 57	07 57				08 24	
—	—	—	**London Blackfriars [3]** ⊖	a		07 15				07 18							08 03	08 03				08 29	
79¼	77¼	—	**London Victoria [15]** ⊖	a	01 13	06 30		07 00		07 12			07 24				07 52	07 58				08 11	

For general notes see front of timetable
For details of catering facilities see Directory of Train Operators

For services from Ramsgate, Dover and Canterbury to London via Ashford see Table 207

b Change at Rochester and Dartford
c Change at Chatham and London Bridge
e Change at Rochester and London Bridge
f Change at London Bridge

For details of Bank Holiday service alterations please see first page of Table 195

Ramsgate, Dover, Sheerness-on-Sea and Medway → London

Network Diagram - see first page of Table 212

		SE 01	SE 80 1	SE 22	SE 23		SE 20	SE 51 1	SE 07 1	SE 01	SE 61 1 A	SE 22 1	SE 50 1		SE 07 1	SE 01	SE 34 1	SE 22 1	SE 07 1	SE 20 1	SE 50 1		SE 34 1	SE 34 1	SE 01
Ramsgate 4	d							06 30					06 50						07 11		07 22				
Dumpton Park	d							06 32					06 52						07 14		07 24				
Broadstairs	d							06 35	06 47				06 55		07 06				07 17		07 27				
Margate 4	d							06 40	06 52				07 00		07 11				07 22		07 32				
Westgate-on-Sea	d							06 43					07 03		07 15				07 26		07 35				
Birchington-on-Sea	d							06 47	06 57				07 06		07 18				07 29		07 38				
Herne Bay	d							06 57	07 06				07 16		07 27				07 38		07 48				
Chestfield & Swalecliffe	d							07 00					07 19		07 31				07 42		07 51				
Whitstable	d							07 04	07 12				07 23		07 35				07 45		07 55				
Dover Priory 4	d		06 24								06 45						07 09							07 50	
Kearsney	d		06 28								06 49						07 13							07 54	
Shepherds Well	d		06 33								06 54						07 18							07 59	
Snowdown	d		06 36								06 57						07 21							08 02	
Aylesham	d		06 39								07 00						07 24							08 05	
Adisham	d		06 41								07 02						07 26							08 07	
Bekesbourne	d		06 46								07 07						07 31							08 12	
Canterbury East 4	d		06 51								07 13						07 37							08 18	
Selling	d		07 00								07 22						07 46							08 27	
Faversham 2	a		07 06					07 12	07 20		07 28		07 31		07 43		07 50		07 54		08 03		←	08 31	
	d							07 13	07 21				07 32		07 44		08 07 →		07 55		08 04		08 07	08 38	
Teynham	d							07 18					07 37						08 00				08 12	→	
Sheerness-on-Sea	d	06 57								07 21						07 44									08 07
Queenborough	d	07 02								07 25						07 48									08 12
Swale	d	07 05								07 29						07 52									08 16
Kemsley	d	07 09								07 33						07 56									08 19
Sittingbourne 4	a	07 15						07 23	07 29	07 38			07 42		07 52	08 02			08 05		08 12		08 17		08 23
	d							07 24	07 29				07 43		07 52				08 05		08 12		08 18		
Newington	d							07 29					07 48						08 11				08 23		
Rainham (Kent)	d							07 34	07 37				07 53		08 00				08 15		08 20		08 28		
Gillingham (Kent) 4	d						07 28	07 39	07 43			07 47	07 58		08 06				08 21		08 25		08 33		
Chatham 4	d						07 32	07 43	07 47			07 51	08 02		08 10				08 25		08 29		08 37		
Rochester 4	d				07 29		07 34					07 53			*08 21*					08 16	08 31		08 39		
Strood 4	a						*07 44*					*08 02*			*08 26*								*08 56*		
Gravesend 4	a						*07 57*					*08 19*			*08 39*								*09 08*		
Greenhithe for Bluewater	a						*08 04*					*08 28*			*08 46*								*09 13*		
Dartford 4	a						*08 09*					*08 34*			*08 52*								*09 19*		
London Bridge 4	⊖ a						*08 47*		08 29			*09 11*			08 49				09 09				*09 54*		
London Cannon Street 4	⊖ a						*08 54*		08 36			*09 18*	*09b38*		08 56				09 16				*10c06*		
London Waterloo (East) 4	⊖ a						*08c55*		*08e39*			*09c23*	*09 34*		*08e59*				*09e19*				*09 59*		
London Charing Cross 4	⊖ a						*09c01*		*08e44*			*09c29*	*09 39*		*09e04*				*09e24*				*10 05*		
Sole Street	d			←	07 40							08 04						←		08 27			08 50		
Meopham	d			07 26	07 42		07 46					08 07						08 07		08 29			08 53		
Longfield	d			07 30	07 46		07 51					→						08 11		08 33			08 58		
Farningham Road	d			07 34	07 50													08 15		08 37			09 02		
Swanley 4	a			07 39	07 55		07 58											08 20		08 42			09 07		
St Mary Cray	a			07 44	08 00		08 03											08 25		08 47			09 12		
Bromley South 4	a			07 51	08 07		08 11	08 15					08 30					08 32		08 54	09 03		09 18		
Elephant & Castle	⊖ a			*08 24*	08 31		*08 43*	*08 50*										*09 11*			*09 32*				
London Blackfriars 3	⊖ a			*08 29*	08 37		*08 49*	*08 56*										*09 17*			*09 37*				
London Victoria 15	⊖ a			08 14			08 38	08 34					08 52					08 57		09 15	09 26		09 38		

For general notes see front of timetable
For details of catering facilities see Directory of Train Operators

For services from Ramsgate, Dover and Canterbury to London via Ashford see Table 207

A From Ashford International (Table 207)
b Change at Chatham and London Bridge
c Change at Rochester and London Bridge
e Change at London Bridge

For details of Bank Holiday service alterations please see first page of Table 195

Ramsgate, Dover, Sheerness-on-Sea and Medway → London

Network Diagram - see first page of Table 212

		SE	SE	SE	SE	SE	SE	SE	SE	SE	SE	SE	SE	SE	SE	SE	SE	SE	SE	SE	SE	SE	SE
		50	64	34	01	01	30	50	66	01	30	50	92	01	30	50	4	92	01	30	50	90	92
		1	1	1			1	1	1		1	1	1		1	1	1	1		1	1	1	1
									A														
		🍴						🍴				🍴				🍴					🍴		
Ramsgate 4	d	07 52	07 56					08 17	08 43			08 50				09 22	09 37				09 59	10 05	
Dumpton Park	d	07 54	07 58					08 19	08 45			08 52				09 24	09 40					10 08	
Broadstairs	d	07 57	08 01					08 22	08 48			08 56				09 28	09 43				10 03	10 11	
Margate 4	d	08 02	08a06					08 28	08a53			09 02				09 34	09a48				10 08	10a16	
Westgate-on-Sea	d	08 05						08 31				09 05				09 37							
Birchington-on-Sea	d	08 08						08 34				09 09				09 40					10 13		
Herne Bay	d	08 17						08 44				09 18				09 49					10 21		
Chestfield & Swalecliffe	d	08 21						08 47				09 22				09 52							
Whitstable	d	08 24						08 50				09 26				09 56					10 26		
Dover Priory 4	d						08 17				09 04				09 22					10 04			
Kearsney	d						08 21								09 26								
Shepherds Well	d						08 26								09 31								
Snowdown	d						08 29								09 35								
Aylesham	d						08 32								09 37								
Adisham	d						08 34								09 39								
Bekesbourne	d						08 39								09 43								
Canterbury East 4	d						08 44				09 21				09 49					10 21			
Selling	d						08 53								09 58								
Faversham 2	a	08 32		←			08 57	08 59			09 32	09 35			10 02	10 05				10 32	10 35		
	d	08 34		08 38			09 03				09 38		09 45		10 08			10 15		10 38			10 45
Teynham	d			08 43			09 08						09 50					10 20					10 50
Sheerness-on-Sea	d				08 36	08 50				09 26				09 56					10 26				
Queenborough	d				08 42	08 55				09 31				10 01					10 31				
Swale	d				08 47	08 59				09 36				10 06					10 36				
Kemsley	d				08 50	09 03				09 39				10 09					10 39				
Sittingbourne 4	a	08 42		08 48	08 55	09 08	09 13			09 44	09 46		09 55	10 14	10 16			10 25	10 44	10 46			10 55
	d	08 43		08 49			09 13				09 47		09 55		10 17			10 25		10 47			10 55
Newington	d			08 54									10 00					10 30					11 00
Rainham (Kent)	d	08 51		08 58			09 21				09 54		10 05		10 24			10 35		10 54			11 05
Gillingham (Kent) 4	d	08 56		09 03			09 26				09 59		10 10		10 29			10 40		10 59			11 10
Chatham 4	d	09 00		09 07			09 30				10 03		10 14		10 33			10 44		11 03			11 14
Rochester 4	d			09 09			09 32				10 06		10 16		10 36			10 46		11 06			11 16
Strood 4	a	09 24		09 24			09 54						10 24					10 54					11 24
Gravesend 4	a	09 36		09 36			10 06						10 36					11 06					11 36
Greenhithe for Bluewater	a	09 41		09 41			10 11						10 41					11 11					11 41
Dartford 4	a	09 46		09 46			10 16						10 46					11 16					11 46
London Bridge 4	⊖ a	10 19		10 19			10 49						11 19					11 49					12 19
London Cannon Street 4	⊖ a	10b30		10c30			10c57						11c27					11c57					12c27
London Waterloo (East) 4	⊖ a	10 24		10 24			10 54						11 24					11 54					12 24
London Charing Cross 4	⊖ a	10 28		10 28			10 58						11 28					11 58					12 28
Sole Street	d			09 20									10 27					10 57					11 27
Meopham	d			09 23			09 42						10 29					10 59					11 29
Longfield	d			09 27			09 46						10 33					11 03					11 33
Farningham Road	d			09 31									10 37					11 07					11 37
Swanley 4	a			09 36									10 42					11 12					11 42
St Mary Cray	a			09 41									10 47					11 17					11 47
Bromley South 4	a	09 29		09 47			09 59				10 29		10 54		10 59			11 24		11 29			11 54
Elephant & Castle	⊖ a	10 09					10 30				11 00				11 30					12 00			
London Blackfriars 3	⊖ a	10 12					10 33				11 03				11 33					12 03			
London Victoria 15	⊖ a	09 49		10 06			10 17				10 47		11 17		11 17			11 47		11 47			12 17

For general notes see front of timetable
For details of catering facilities see Directory of Train Operators
For services from Ramsgate, Dover and Canterbury to London via Ashford see Table 207

A From London Victoria (Table 196)
b Change at Chatham and London Bridge
c Change at Rochester and London Bridge

Table 212

Mondays to Fridays
until 10 October

For details of Bank Holiday service alterations please see first page of Table 195

Ramsgate, Dover, Sheerness-on-Sea and Medway → London

Network Diagram - see first page of Table 212

Station		SE 01	SE 30	SE 50	SE 92	SE 01	SE 30	SE 50	SE 90	SE 92	SE 01	SE 30	SE 50	SE 92	SE 01	SE 30	SE 50	SE 92	SE 01	SE 30	SE 50	SE 90
			1	1	1		1	1	1	1		1	1	1		1	1	1		1	1	1
				✕				✕					✕				✕				✕	
Ramsgate 4	d			10 22				10 59	11 10				11 22				11 59				12 22	12 40
Dumpton Park	d			10 24					11 13				11 24								12 24	12 43
Broadstairs	d			10 28				11 03	11 16				11 28				12 03				12 28	12 46
Margate 4	d			10 34				11 08	11a22				11 34				12 08				12 34	12a51
Westgate-on-Sea	d			10 37									11 37								12 37	
Birchington-on-Sea	d			10 40				11 13					11 40				12 13				12 40	
Herne Bay	d			10 49				11 21					11 49				12 21				12 49	
Chestfield & Swalecliffe	d			10 52									11 52								12 52	
Whitstable	d			10 56				11 26					11 56				12 26				12 56	
Dover Priory 4	d		10 22				11 04					11 22				12 04				12 22		
Kearsney	d		10 26									11 26								12 26		
Shepherds Well	d		10 31									11 31								12 31		
Snowdown	d		10 35									11 35								12 35		
Aylesham	d		10 37									11 37								12 37		
Adisham	d		10 39									11 39								12 39		
Bekesbourne	d		10 43									11 43								12 43		
Canterbury East 4	d		10 49				11 21					11 49				12 21				12 49		
Selling	d		10 58									11 58								12 58		
Faversham 2	a		11 02	11 05			11 32	11 35				12 02	12 05			12 32	12 35			13 02	13 05	
	d		11 08		11 15		11 38			11 45		12 08		12 15		12 38		12 45		13 08		
Teynham	d				11 20					11 50				12 20				12 50				
Sheerness-on-Sea	d	10 56				11 26					11 56				12 26				12 56			
Queenborough	d	11 01				11 31					12 01				12 31				13 01			
Swale	d	11 06				11 36					12 06				12 36				13 06			
Kemsley	d	11 09				11 39					12 09				12 39				13 09			
Sittingbourne 4	a	11 14	11 16		11 25	11 44	11 46			11 55	12 14	12 16		12 25	12 44	12 46		12 55	13 14	13 16		
	d		11 17		11 25		11 47			11 55		12 17		12 25		12 47		12 55		13 17		
Newington	d				11 30					12 00				12 30				13 00				
Rainham (Kent)	d		11 24		11 35		11 54			12 05		12 24		12 35		12 54		13 05		13 24		
Gillingham (Kent) 4	d		11 29		11 40		11 59			12 10		12 29		12 40		12 59		13 10		13 29		
Chatham 4	d		11 33		11 44		12 03			12 14		12 33		12 44		13 03		13 14		13 33		
Rochester 4	d		11 36		11 46		12 06			12 16		12 36		12 46		13 06		13 16		13 36		
Strood 4	a				11 54					12 24				12 54				13 24				
Gravesend 4	a				12 06					12 36				13 06				13 36				
Greenhithe for Bluewater	a				12 11					12 41				13 11				13 41				
Dartford 4	a				12 16					12 46				13 16				13 46				
London Bridge 4	⊖ a				12 49					13 19				13 49				14 19				
London Cannon Street 4	⊖ a				12b57					13b27				13b57				14b27				
London Waterloo (East) 4	⊖ a				12 54					13 24				13 54				14 24				
London Charing Cross 4	⊖ a				12 58					13 28				13 58				14 28				
Sole Street	d				11 57					12 27				12 57				13 27				
Meopham	d				11 59					12 29				12 59				13 29				
Longfield	d				12 03					12 33				13 03				13 33				
Farningham Road	d				12 07					12 37				13 07				13 37				
Swanley 4	a				12 12					12 42				13 12				13 42				
St Mary Cray	a				12 17					12 47				13 17				13 47				
Bromley South 4	a		11 59		12 24		12 29			12 54		12 59		13 24		13 29		13 54		13 59		
Elephant & Castle	⊖ a		12 30				13 00					13 30				14 00				14 30		
London Blackfriars 3	⊖ a		12 33				13 03					13 33				14 03				14 33		
London Victoria 15	⊖ a		12 17		12 47		12 47			13 17		13 17		13 47		13 47		14 17		14 17		

For general notes see front of timetable
For details of catering facilities see Directory of Train Operators

For services from Ramsgate, Dover and Canterbury to London via Ashford see Table 207

b Change at Rochester and London Bridge

For details of Bank Holiday service alterations please see first page of Table 195

Ramsgate, Dover, Sheerness-on-Sea and Medway → London

Network Diagram - see first page of Table 212

		SE 92	SE 01	SE 30	SE 50	SE 92	SE 01	SE 30	SE 50	SE 90	SE 92	SE 30	SE 50	SE 90	SE 01	SE 92	SE 30	SE 50	SE 01	SE 92	SE 30	SE 50
		1		1	1	1		1	1	1	1	1	1	1		1	1	1		1	1	1
					🍴				🍴				🍴	🍴				🍴				🍴
Ramsgate 4 ⇌	d				12 59				13 22	13 40			13 59	14 17				14 21				14 57
Dumpton Park	d								13 24	13 43				14 20				14 23				
Broadstairs	d				13 03				13 28	13 46			14 03	14 23				14 27				15 01
Margate 4	d				13 08				13 34	13a51			14 08	14a28				14 32				15 06
Westgate-on-Sea	d								13 37									14 35				
Birchington-on-Sea	d				13 13				13 40				14 13					14 38				15 11
Herne Bay	d				13 21				13 49				14 21					14 47				15 19
Chestfield & Swalecliffe	d								13 52									14 50				
Whitstable	d				13 26				13 56				14 26					14 54				15 24
Dover Priory 4 ⛴	d			13 04				13 22				14 04					14 20				15 02	
Kearsney	d							13 26									14 24					
Shepherds Well	d							13 31									14 29					
Snowdown	d							13 35									14 33					
Aylesham	d							13 37									14 35					
Adisham	d							13 39									14 37					
Bekesbourne	d							13 43									14 41					
Canterbury East 4	d			13 21				13 49				14 21					14 47				15 19	
Selling	d							13 58									14 56					
Faversham 2	a			13 32	13 35			14 02	14 05			14 32	14 35				15 00	15 03			15 30	15 33
	d	13 15		13 38		13 45		14 08			14 15	14 38				14 45	15 06			15 15	15 36	
Teynham	d	13 20				13 50					14 20					14 50				15 20		
Sheerness-on-Sea	d		13 26				13 56								14 30				15 00			
Queenborough	d		13 31				14 01								14 35				15 05			
Swale	d		13 36				14 06								14 39				15 09			
Kemsley	d		13 39				14 09								14 43				15 13			
Sittingbourne 4	a	13 25	13 44	13 46		13 55	14 14	14 16			14 25	14 46			14 48	14 55	15 14		15 18	15 25	15 44	
	d	13 25		13 47		13 55		14 17			14 25	14 47				14 55	15 15			15 25	15 45	
Newington	d	13 30				14 00					14 30					15 00				15 30		
Rainham (Kent)	d	13 35		13 54		14 05		14 24			14 35	14 54				15 05	15 22			15 35	15 52	
Gillingham (Kent) 4	d	13 40		13 59		14 10		14 29			14 40	14 59				15 10	15 27			15 40	15 57	
Chatham 4	d	13 44		14 03		14 14		14 33			14 44	15 03				15 14	15 31			15 44	16 01	
Rochester 4	d	13 46		14 06		14 16		14 36			14 46	15 06				15 16	15 34			15 46	16 03	
Strood 4	a	*13 54*				*14 24*					*14 54*					*15 24*				*15 54*		
Gravesend 4	a	*14 06*				*14 36*					*15 06*					*15 36*				*16 08*		
Greenhithe for Bluewater	a	*14 11*				*14 41*					*15 11*					*15 41*				*16 14*		
Dartford 4	a	*14 16*				*14 46*					*15 16*					*15 46*				*16 20*		
London Bridge 4 ⊖	a	*14 49*				*15 19*					*15 49*					*16 19*				*16 55*		
London Cannon Street 4 ⊖	a	*14b57*				*15b27*					*15b57*					*16b27*				*17b05*		
London Waterloo (East) 4 ⊖	a	*14 54*				*15 24*					*15 54*					*16 24*				*17 00*		
London Charing Cross 4 ⊖	a	*14 58*				*15 28*					*15 58*					*16 28*				*17 03*		
Sole Street	d	13 57				14 27					14 57					15 27				15 57		
Meopham	d	13 59				14 29					14 59					15 29				15 59		
Longfield	d	14 03				14 33					15 03					15 33				16 03		
Farningham Road	d	14 07				14 37					15 07					15 37				16 07		
Swanley 4	a	14 12				14 42					15 12					15 42				16 12		
St Mary Cray	a	14 17				14 47					15 17					15 47				16 17		
Bromley South 4	a	14 24		14 29		14 54		14 59			15 24	15 29				15 53	15 59			16 23	16 30	
Elephant & Castle ⊖	a			*15 00*				*15 30*				*16 00*					*16 30*				*17 00*	
London Blackfriars 3 ⊖	a			*15 03*				*15 33*				*16 03*					*16 33*				*17 05*	
London Victoria 15 ⊖	a	14 47		14 47		15 17		15 17			15 47	15 47				16 18	16 17			16 49	16 50	

For general notes see front of timetable
For details of catering facilities see Directory of Train Operators

For services from Ramsgate, Dover and Canterbury to London via Ashford see Table 207

b Change at Rochester and London Bridge

Mondays to Fridays

until 10 October

For details of Bank Holiday service alterations please see first page of Table 195

Ramsgate, Dover, Sheerness-on-Sea and Medway → London

Network Diagram - see first page of Table 212

	SE 90 1 ⚲	SE 01	SE 92 1	SE 30 1	SE 50 1 ⚲	SE 01	SE 92 1	SE 31 1	SE 51 1 ⚲	SE 18 1 ⚲	SE 01	SE 92 1	SE 30 1	SE 50 1 ⚲	SE 01	SE 92 1	SE 30 1	SE 50 1 ⚲	SE 01	SE 92 1	SE 01
Ramsgate 4 d	15 17				15 21				15 52	16 13				16 20				16 48			
Dumpton Park d	15 20				15 23				15 54	16 16				16 22				16 50			
Broadstairs d	15 23				15 27				15 58	16 19				16 26				16 53			
Margate 4 d	15a28				15 32				16 04	16a24				16 32				16 59			
Westgate-on-Sea d					15 35				16 07					16 35				17 02			
Birchington-on-Sea d					15 38				16 10					16 38				17 06			
Herne Bay d					15 47				16 19					16 47				17 15			
Chestfield & Swalecliffe d					15 50				16 22					16 50				17 19			
Whitstable d					15 54				16 26					16 54				17 22			
Dover Priory 4 d				15 20				15 52					16 20				16 48				
Kearsney d				15 24				15 56					16 24				16 52				
Shepherds Well d				15 29				16 01					16 29				16 57				
Snowdown d				15 33				16 05					16 33				17 00				
Aylesham d				15 35				16 07					16 35				17 03				
Adisham d				15 37				16 09					16 37				17 05				
Bekesbourne d				15 41				16 13					16 41				17 10				
Canterbury East 4 d				15 47				16 19					16 47				17 16				
Selling d				15 56				16 28					16 56				17 25				
Faversham 2 a				16 00	16 03			16 32	16 35				17 00	17 03			17 29	17 31			
d			15 44	16 06			16 14	16 38				16 44	17 06			17 14	17 35			17 44	
Teynham d			15 49				16 19					16 49				17 19				17 49	
Sheerness-on-Sea d		15 30				16 00					16 30				17 00				17 36		17 53
Queenborough d		15 35				16 05					16 35				17 05				17 41		17 58
Swale d		15 39				16 09					16 39				17 10				17 45		18 02
Kemsley d		15 43				16 13					16 43				17 13				17 49		18 06
Sittingbourne 4 a		15 49	15 54	16 14		16 18	16 24	16 46			16 48	16 54	17 14		17 18	17 24	17 43		17 53	17 54	18 11
d			15 54	16 15			16 24	16 47				16 54	17 15			17 24	17 43			17 54	
Newington d			15 59				16 29					16 59				17 29				17 59	
Rainham (Kent) d			16 04	16 22			16 34	16 54				17 04	17 22			17 34	17 51			18 04	
Gillingham (Kent) 4 d			16 09	16 27			16 39	16 59				17 09	17 27			17 39	17 56			18 09	
Chatham 4 d			16 13	16 31			16 43	17 03				17 13	17 31			17 43	18 00			18 13	
Rochester 4 d			16 15	16 33			16 45	17 06				17 15	17 33			17 45	18 02			18 15	
Strood 4 a			16 24				16 54					17 24				17 58	18 22			18b22	
Gravesend 4 a			16 36				17 06					17 36				18 10	18 34			18b34	
Greenhithe for Bluewater a			16 41				17 11					17 45				18 15	18 40			18b40	
Dartford 4 a			16 46				17 17					17 50				18 20	18 46			18b46	
London Bridge 4 ⊖ a			17 26				17 56					18 31				19 02	19 23			19b23	
London Cannon Street 4 ⊖ a			17c33				18 01					18c45				19c10	19c37			19e37	
London Waterloo (East) 4 ⊖ a			17 31				18c05					18 36				19 07	19 28			19b28	
London Charing Cross 4 ⊖ a			17 35				18c09					18 40				19 11	19 32			19b32	
Sole Street d			16 26				16 56					17 26				17 56				18 26	
Meopham d			16 29				16 59					17 29				17 59				18 29	
Longfield d			16 33				17 03					17 33				18 03				18 33	
Farningham Road d			16 37				17 08					17 37				18 07				18 37	
Swanley 4 a			16 42				17 13					17 43				18 12				18 42	
St Mary Cray a			16 47				17 18					17 47				18 16				18 47	
Bromley South 4 a			16 53	16 59			17 25	17 33				17 53	17 59			18 23	18 31			18 53	
Elephant & Castle ⊖ a				17 32			18 02						18 31				19 00				
London Blackfriars 3 ⊖ a				17 39			18 08						18 35				19 03				
London Victoria 15 ⊖ a			17 18	17 17			17 48	17 58				18 19	18 17			18 50	18 48			19 17	

For general notes see front of timetable
For details of catering facilities see Directory of Train Operators

For services from Ramsgate, Dover and Canterbury to London via Ashford see Table 207

b Change at Chatham
c Change at Rochester and London Bridge
e Change at Chatham and London Bridge

For details of Bank Holiday service alterations please see first page of Table 195

Ramsgate, Dover, Sheerness-on-Sea and Medway → London

Network Diagram - see first page of Table 212

Station		SE 30	SE 50	SE 92	SE 30	SE 50	SE 4	SE 01	SE 92	SE 30	SE 50	SE 01	SE 01	SE 50	SE 30	SE 90	SE 4	SE 92	SE 01	SE 01	SE 50	SE 30
Ramsgate	d		17 22			17 50	18 12				18 21			18 48		18 52	19 12				19 48	
Dumpton Park	d		17 24			17 52	18 15				18 23			18 50		18 55	19 15				19 50	
Broadstairs	d		17 28			17 55	18 18				18 26			18 53		18 58	19 18				19 53	
Margate	d		17 34			18 01	18a23				18 32			18 59		19a05	19a26				19 59	
Westgate-on-Sea	d		17 37			18 04					18 35			19 02							20 02	
Birchington-on-Sea	d		17 40			18 08					18 39			19 06							20 06	
Herne Bay	d		17 49			18 17					18 48			19 15							20 15	
Chestfield & Swalecliffe	d		17 52			18 21					18 52			19 19							20 19	
Whitstable	d		17 56			18 24					18 55			19 22							20 22	
Dover Priory	d	17 22			17 50					18 21					18 54							19 52
Kearsney	d	17 26			17 54					18 25					18 58							19 56
Shepherds Well	d	17 31			17 59					18 30					19 03							20 01
Snowdown	d	17 35			18 02					18 33					19 06							20 04
Aylesham	d	17 37			18 05					18 36					19 09							20 07
Adisham	d	17 39			18 07					18 38					19 11							20 09
Bekesbourne	d	17 43			18 12					18 43					19 16							20 14
Canterbury East	d	17 49			18 18					18 49					19 22							20 19
Selling	d	17 58			18 27					18 58					19 31							20 28
Faversham	a	18 02	18 06		18 31	18 33				19 02	19 04			19 31	19 35						20 31	20 33
	d	18 09		18 14	18 37				18 44	19 08				19 39				19 45			20 37	
Teynham	d			18 19					18 49									19 50				
Sheerness-on-Sea	d							18 28				19 02	19 20						19 50	20 05		
Queenborough	d							18 33				19b11	19 25						19 56	20 10		
Swale	d							18 38				19 15	19 29						20 01	20 15		
Kemsley	d							18 41				19 19	19 33						20 04	20 18		
Sittingbourne	a	18 17		18 24	18 45			18 46	18 54	19 16		19 23	19 38	19 47				19 55	20 09	20 23	20 45	
	d	18 17		18 24	18 45				18 54	19 17				19 47				19 55			20 45	
Newington	d			18 29					18 59									20 00				
Rainham (Kent)	d	18 25		18 34	18 53				19 04	19 24				19 55				20 05			20 53	
Gillingham (Kent)	d	18 31		18 40	18 58				19 10	19 29				20 00				20 10			20 58	
Chatham	d	18 35		18 44	19 02				19 14	19 33				20 04				20 14			21 02	
Rochester	d	18 37		18 46	19 04				19 16	19 50				20 06				20 16			21 04	
Strood	a			18 54					19 24	19 54								20 26				
Gravesend	a			19 06					19 36	20 06								20 38				
Greenhithe for Bluewater	a			19 11					19 41	20 11								20 43				
Dartford	a			19 17					19 46	20 16								20 48				
London Bridge	⊖ a			19 53					20 23	20 53								21 23				
London Cannon Street	⊖ a			20c11					20c41													
London Waterloo (East)	⊖ a			19 58					20 28	20 58								21 28				
London Charing Cross	⊖ a			20 01					20 31	21 01								21 31				
Sole Street	d			18 57					19 27									20 27				
Meopham	d			19 00					19 30									20 30				
Longfield	d			19 04					19 34									20 34				
Farningham Road	d			19 08					19 38									20 38				
Swanley	a			19 12					19 42									20 42				
St Mary Cray	a			19 17					19 47									20 47				
Bromley South	a	19 00		19 23	19 30				19 53	19 58				20 32				20 53			21 29	
Elephant & Castle	⊖ a	19 36			20 00					20 30								21 30			22 00	
London Blackfriars	⊖ a	19 40			20 03					20 33								21 33			22 03	
London Victoria	⊖ a	19 17		19 48	19 47				20 17	20 17				20 48				21 17			21 47	

For general notes see front of timetable
For details of catering facilities see Directory of Train Operators

For services from Ramsgate, Dover and Canterbury to London via Ashford see Table 207

b Arr. 1907
c Change at Rochester and London Bridge

Mondays to Fridays

until 10 October

For details of Bank Holiday service alterations please see first page of Table 195

Ramsgate, Dover, Sheerness-on-Sea and Medway → London

Network Diagram - see first page of Table 212

Station		SE 4 1 ⚯	SE 01	SE 92 1	SE 91 1	SE 97		SE 01	SE 50 1	SE 30 1	SE 90 1	SE 92 1	SE 01	SE 80 1		SE 50 1	SE 55 1	SE 01	SE 80 1	SE 81 1	SE 58	SE 90 1
Ramsgate 4 ✈	d	20 05			20 39				20 50		21 28					21 55	22 10			22 53		23 40
Dumpton Park	d	20 08			20 41				20 52		21 31					21 57				22 55		23 43
Broadstairs	d	20 11			20 44				20 55		21 34					22 00	22 15			22 58		23 46
Margate 4	d	20a17			20a51				21 01		21a39					22 06	22 20			23 04		23a51
Westgate-on-Sea	d								21 04							22 09				23 07		
Birchington-on-Sea	d								21 07							22 12	22 25			23 11		
Herne Bay	d								21 17							22 22	22 34			23 20		
Chestfield & Swalecliffe	d								21 20							22 25				23 24		
Whitstable	d								21 24							22 29	22 39			23 27		
Dover Priory 4 ⛴	d									20 52				21 55					23 01			
Kearsney	d									20 56				21 59								
Shepherds Well	d									21 01				22 04								
Snowdown	d									21 04				22 07								
Aylesham	d									21 07				22 10								
Adisham	d									21 09				22 12								
Bekesbourne	d									21 14				22 17								
Canterbury East 4	d									21 20				22 22					23 18			
Selling	d									21 29				22 31								
Faversham 2	a								21 32	21 34				22 35		22 37	22 47		23 30	23 36		
	d			20 45					21 38			21 45				22 38	22 48				23 42	
Teynham	d			20 50								21 50					22 53				23 47	
Sheerness-on-Sea	d		20 34			21 01		21 26					22 30					23 28				
Queenborough	d		20 39			21 06		21 31					22 35					23 33				
Swale	d		20 43			21 10		21 36					22 39					23 38				
Kemsley	d		20 47			21 14		21 39					22 42					23 41				
Sittingbourne 4	a		20 52	20 55				21 44	21 46			21 55	22 46			22 47	22 58	23 46			23 52	
	d			20 55					21 47			21 55				22 47	22 58				23 52	
Newington	d			21 00		21 21						22 00					23 03				23 57	
Rainham (Kent)	d			21 05		21 25			21 54			22 05				22 54	23 08				00 01	
Gillingham (Kent) 4	d			21 10		21a30			21 59			22 10				22 59	23 13				00 07	
Chatham 4	d			21 14					22 03			22 14				23 03	23 17				00 11	
Rochester 4	d			21 16								22 16					23 19				00 13	
Strood 4	a			*21 24*					*22 32*			*22 32*					*00 17*				00 17	
Gravesend 4	a			*21 38*					*22 44*			*22 44*					*00 28*				00 28	
Greenhithe for Bluewater	a			*21 43*					*22 52*			*22 52*					*00 34*				00 34	
Dartford 4	a			*21 48*					*22 58*			*22 58*					*00 41*				00 41	
London Bridge 4 ⊖	a			*22 23*					*23 41*			*23 41*										
London Cannon Street 4 ⊖	a																					
London Waterloo (East) 4 ⊖	a			*22 28*					*23 46*			*23 46*										
London Charing Cross 4 ⊖	a			*22 31*					*23 50*			*23 50*										
Sole Street	d			21 27								22 27					23 30					
Meopham	d			21 30								22 30					23 32					
Longfield	d			21 34								22 34					23 36					
Farningham Road	d			21 38								22 38					23 40					
Swanley 4	a			21 42								22 42					23 45					
St Mary Cray	a			21 47								22 47					23 49					
Bromley South 4	a			21 53					22 30			22 53				23 30	23 55					
Elephant & Castle ⊖	a			*22 30*					*23 00*			*23 31*										
London Blackfriars 3 ⊖	a			*22 33*					*23 03*			*23 37*										
London Victoria 15 ⊖	a			22 17					22 47			23 15				23 47	00 18				01 13	

For general notes see front of timetable
For details of catering facilities see Directory of Train Operators

For services from Ramsgate, Dover and Canterbury to London via Ashford see Table 207

Table 212

Ramsgate, Dover, Sheerness-on-Sea and Medway → London

Mondays to Fridays
from 13 October

Network Diagram - see first page of Table 212

		SE	SE	SE	SE	SE	SE	SE	SE	SE	SE	SE	SE	SE	SE	SE	SE	SE	SE	SE	SE	SE	SE	SE	SE
		MX																							
		58	50	07	37	01	50	03	01	51	07	07	22	31	22	07	01	22	50	07	01	80	22	23	20
			1	1	1		1	1		1	1	1		1		1			1	1		1			
Ramsgate 4 ✈	d		04 35				05 01			05 25		05 44							06 08						
Dumpton Park	d		04 37							05 27		05 47							06 11						
Broadstairs	d		04 40				05 06			05 30		05 50							06 14	06 21					
Margate 4	d		04 45				05 11			05 35		05 55							06 19	06 26					
Westgate-on-Sea	d		04 48							05 38		05 59							06 22						
Birchington-on-Sea	d		04 51				05 16			05 41		06 02							06 26	06 31					
Herne Bay	d		05 00				05 25			05 50		06 11							06 34	06 40					
Chestfield & Swalecliffe	d		05 04							05 53		06 15							06 37						
Whitstable	d		05 07				05 30			05 57		06 18							06 41	06 46					
Dover Priory 4 ⛴	d				04 47			05 09						05 49								06 24			
Kearsney	d				04 51			05 13						05 53								06 28			
Shepherds Well	d				04 56			05 19						05 58								06 33			
Snowdown	d				04 59			05 23						06 01								06 36			
Aylesham	d				05 02			05 25						06 04								06 39			
Adisham	d				05 04			05 28						06 06								06 41			
Bekesbourne	d				05 09			05 32						06 11								06 46			
Canterbury East 4	d				05 14			05 38						06 17								06 51			
Selling	d				05 23			05 48						06 26								07 00			
Faversham 2	a		05 15		05 27		05 38	05 52		06 09		06 27		06 30		←			06 49	06 56		07 06			
	d	23p42	05 19	05 22	05 31		05 43	05 56		06 10	06 16	06 36		06 32		06 36			06 53	06 58					
Teynham	d	23p47		05 27	05 36		05 48				06 21	→		06 37		06 41									
Sheerness-on-Sea	d					05 31			05 58								06 36				06 57				
Queenborough	d					05 36			06 03								06 41				07 02				
Swale	d					05 40			06 08								06 46				07 05				
Kemsley	d					05 43			06 11								06 49				07 09				
Sittingbourne 4	a	23p52	05 27	05 32	05 41	05 48	05 53	06 04	06 16	06 18	06 26			06 42		06 46	06 54		07 01	07 06	07 15				
	d	23p52	05 28	05 32	05 41		05 54	06 04		06 18	06 27			06 43		06 46			07 02	07 06					
Newington	d	23p57		05 37	05 46		05 59				06 32			06 48		06 52									
Rainham (Kent)	d	00 01	05 36	05 42	05 50		06 04	06 12		06 26	06 37			06 53		06 56			07 10	07 14					
Gillingham (Kent) 4	d	00 07	05 42	05 48	05 56		06 09	06 18		06 32	06 42		06 49	06 58		07 02		07 06	07 16	07 20					07 28
Chatham 4	d	00 11	05 46	05 52	06 01		06 13	06 22		06 36	06 46		06 53	07 02		07 06		07 10	07 20	07 24					07 32
Rochester 4	d	00 13		05 54	06 03		06 15	*06 28*		*06 43*	06 48		06 55			*07 19*		07 13		*07 34*				07 29	07 34
Strood 4	a	00 17	*06 03*	*06 03*			*06 33*	*06 33*		*06 48*	*07 04*		*07 04*			*07 24*		*07 24*		*07 44*					*07 44*
Gravesend 4	a	00 28	*06 14*	*06 14*			*06 44*	*06 44*		*06 59*	*07 17*		*07 17*			*07 39*		*07 39*		*07 57*					*07 57*
Greenhithe for Bluewater	a	00 34	*06 20*	*06 20*			*06 50*	*06 50*		*07 06*	*07 24*		*07 24*			*07 46*		*07 46*		*08 04*					*08 04*
Dartford 4	a	00 41	*06 25*	*06 25*			*06 55*	*06 55*		*07 11*	*07 29*		*07 29*			*07 51*		*07 51*		*08 09*					*08 09*
London Bridge 4 ⊖	a		*07 01*	06 33			*07 30*	07 07		*07 44*	07 26		*08 06*			07 49		*08b41*		08 08					*08 47*
London Cannon Street 4 ⊖	a		*07c13*	06 40			*07e42*	07 13		*07 52*	07 34		*08 15*			07 56			*08 55*	08 16					*08 55*
London Waterloo (East) 4 ⊖	a		*07 06*	*06f41*			*07 36*	*07f16*		*07c55*	*07f36*		*08e15*			*07f58*			*08c55*	*08f19*					*08e55*
London Charing Cross 4 ⊖	a		*07 11*	*06f48*			*07 41*	*07f21*		*07c59*	*07f41*		*08e21*			*08f03*			*09c01*	*08f25*					*09e01*
Sole Street	d				06 14		06 24						07 06		←			07 24					←	07 40	
Meopham	d				06 16		06 26						07 08 →		07 08			07 26 →					07 26	07 42	07 46
Longfield	d				06 20		06 30								07 13								07 30	07 46	07 51
Farningham Road	d				06 24		06 34								07 17								07 34	07 50	
Swanley 4	a				06 29		06 40								07 22								07 39	07 55	07 58
St Mary Cray	a				06 35		06 45								07 27								07 44	08 00	08 03
Bromley South 4	a		06 13		06 42		06 51							07 32	07 35				07 50				07 51	08 07	08 11
Elephant & Castle ⊖	a		*07 10*				*07 15*							*07 57*	*07 57*				*08 24*				*08 24*	08 31	*08 43*
London Blackfriars 3 ⊖	a		*07 15*				*07 18*							*08 03*	*08 03*				*08 29*				*08 29*	08 37	*08 49*
London Victoria 15 ⊖	a	01 13	06 32		07 02		07 12			07 24				07 52	07 58				08 11				08 14		08 38

For general notes see front of timetable
For details of catering facilities see Directory of Train Operators
For services from Ramsgate, Dover and Canterbury to London via Ashford see Table 207

b Change at Rochester and Dartford
c Change at Chatham and London Bridge
e Change at Rochester and London Bridge
f Change at London Bridge

Ramsgate, Dover, Sheerness-on-Sea and Medway → London

Mondays to Fridays
from 13 October

Network Diagram - see first page of Table 212

		SE 51	SE 07	SE 01	SE 61	SE 22	SE 50	SE 07	SE 01	SE 34	SE 22	SE 07	SE 20	SE 50	SE 34	SE 34	SE 01	SE 50	SE 64	SE 34	SE 01	SE 01	SE 30	SE 50	SE 66
		1	1		1	1	1	1		1	1	1	1	1	1	1		1	1	1			1	1	1
					A																				B
Ramsgate 4	d	06 30					06 47					07 11		07 22				07 52	07 56					08 17	08 43
Dumpton Park	d	06 32					06 49					07 14		07 24				07 54	07 58					08 19	08 45
Broadstairs	d	06 35	06 44				06 52	07 03				07 17		07 27				07 57	08 01					08 22	08 48
Margate 4	d	06 40	06 49				06 57	07 08				07 22		07 32				08 02	08a06					08 28	08a53
Westgate-on-Sea	d	06 43					07 00	07 12				07 26		07 35				08 05						08 31	
Birchington-on-Sea	d	06 47	06 54				07 03	07 15				07 29		07 38				08 08						08 34	
Herne Bay	d	06 57	07 03				07 13	07 24				07 38		07 48				08 17						08 44	
Chestfield & Swalecliffe	d	07 00					07 16	07 28				07 42		07 51				08 21						08 47	
Whitstable	d	07 04	07 09				07 20	07 32				07 45		07 55				08 24						08 50	
Dover Priory 4	d				06 45					07 09						07 50							08 17		
Kearsney	d				06 49					07 13						07 54							08 21		
Shepherds Well	d				06 54					07 18						07 59							08 26		
Snowdown	d				06 57					07 21						08 02							08 29		
Aylesham	d				07 00					07 24						08 05							08 32		
Adisham	d				07 02					07 26						08 07							08 34		
Bekesbourne	d				07 07					07 31						08 12							08 39		
Canterbury East 4	d				07 13					07 37						08 18							08 44		
Selling	d				07 22					07 46						08 27							08 53		
Faversham 2	a	07 12	07 17		07 28		07 28	07 40		07 50		07 54		08 03	←	08 31		08 32		←			08 57	08 59	
	d	07 13	07 21				07 32	07 44		08 07 →		07 55		08 04	08 07	08 38 →		08 34		08 38			09 03		
Teynham	d	07 18					07 37					08 00			08 12					08 43			09 08		
Sheerness-on-Sea	d			07 21					07 44								08 07				08 36	08 50			
Queenborough	d			07 25					07 48								08 12				08 42	08 55			
Swale	d			07 29					07 52								08 16				08 47	08 59			
Kemsley	d			07 33					07 56								08 19				08 50	09 03			
Sittingbourne 4	a	07 23	07 29	07 38			07 42	07 52	08 02			08 05		08 12	08 17		08 23	08 42		08 48	08 55	09 08	09 13		
	d	07 24	07 29				07 43	07 52				08 05		08 12	08 18			08 43		08 49			09 13		
Newington	d	07 29					07 48					08 11			08 23					08 54					
Rainham (Kent)	d	07 34	07 37				07 53	08 00				08 15		08 20	08 28			08 51		08 58			09 21		
Gillingham (Kent) 4	d	07 39	07 43			07 47	07 58	08 06				08 21		08 25	08 33			08 56		09 03			09 26		
Chatham 4	d	07 43	07 47			07 51	08 02	08 10				08 25		08 29	08 37			09 00		09 07			09 30		
Rochester 4	d					07 53		*08 21*					08 16	08 31	08 39					09 09			09 32		
Strood 4	a					*08 02*		*08 26*							*08 56*			*09 24*		*09 24*			*09 54*		
Gravesend 4	a					*08 19*		*08 39*							*09 08*			*09 36*		*09 36*			*10 06*		
Greenhithe for Bluewater	a					*08 28*		*08 46*							*09 13*			*09 41*		*09 41*			*10 11*		
Dartford 4	a					*08 34*		*08 52*							*09 19*			*09 46*		*09 46*			*10 16*		
London Bridge 4	⊖ a		08 29			*09 11*		08 49				09 09			*09 54*			*10 19*		*10 19*			*10 49*		
London Cannon Street 4	⊖ a		08 37			*09 19*	09b39	08 57				09 17			*10c06*			*10b30*		*10c30*			*10c57*		
London Waterloo (East) 4	⊖ a		08e39			*09c23*	09 34	08e59				09e19			*09 59*			*10 24*		*10 24*			*10 54*		
London Charing Cross 4	⊖ a		08e45			*09c29*	09 40	09e05				09e25			*10 05*			*10 28*		*10 28*			*10 58*		
Sole Street	d					08 04					←		08 27		08 50					09 20					
Meopham	d					08 07 →					08 07		08 29		08 53					09 23			09 42		
Longfield	d										08 11		08 33		08 58					09 27			09 46		
Farningham Road	d										08 15		08 37		09 02					09 31					
Swanley 4	a										08 20		08 42		09 07					09 36					
St Mary Cray	a										08 25		08 47		09 12					09 41					
Bromley South 4	a	08 15					08 30				08 32		08 54	09 03	09 18			09 29		09 47			09 59		
Elephant & Castle	⊖ a	*08 50*									*09 11*			*09 32*				*10 09*					*10 30*		
London Blackfriars 3	⊖ a	*08 56*									*09 17*			*09 37*				*10 12*					*10 33*		
London Victoria 15	⊖ a	08 34					08 52				08 57		09 15	09 26	09 38			09 51		10 05			10 17		

For general notes see front of timetable
For details of catering facilities see Directory of Train Operators

For services from Ramsgate, Dover and Canterbury to London via Ashford see Table 207

A From Ashford International (Table 207)
B From London Victoria (Table 196)
b Change at Chatham and London Bridge
c Change at Rochester and London Bridge
e Change at London Bridge

from 13 October

Ramsgate, Dover, Sheerness-on-Sea and Medway → London

Network Diagram - see first page of Table 212

		SE 01	SE 30	SE 50	SE 92	SE 01	SE 30	SE 50	SE 4	SE 92	SE 01	SE 30	SE 50	SE 90	SE 92	SE 01	SE 30	SE 50	SE 92	SE 01	SE 30	SE 50	SE 90	SE 92
			1	1	1		1	1	1	1		1	1	1	1		1	1	1		1	1	1	1
				🍴				🍴					🍴					🍴				🍴		
Ramsgate 4	d			08 50				09 22	09 37				09 59	10 05				10 22				10 59	11 10	
Dumpton Park	d			08 52				09 24	09 40					10 08				10 24					11 13	
Broadstairs	d			08 56				09 28	09 43				10 03	10 11				10 28				11 03	11 16	
Margate 4	d			09 02				09 34	09a48				10 08	10a16				10 34				11 08	11a22	
Westgate-on-Sea	d			09 05				09 37										10 37						
Birchington-on-Sea	d			09 09				09 40					10 13					10 40				11 13		
Herne Bay	d			09 18				09 49					10 21					10 49				11 21		
Chestfield & Swalecliffe	d			09 22				09 52										10 52						
Whitstable	d			09 26				09 56					10 26					10 56				11 26		
Dover Priory 4 ⛴	d		09 04				09 22					10 04					10 22				11 04			
Kearsney	d						09 26										10 26							
Shepherds Well	d						09 31										10 31							
Snowdown	d						09 35										10 35							
Aylesham	d						09 37										10 37							
Adisham	d						09 39										10 39							
Bekesbourne	d						09 43										10 43							
Canterbury East 4	d		09 21				09 49					10 21					10 49				11 21			
Selling	d						09 58										10 58							
Faversham 2	a		09 32	09 35			10 02	10 05				10 32	10 35				11 02	11 05			11 32	11 35		
	d			09 38	09 45			10 08		10 15			10 38		10 45			11 08	11 15			11 38		11 45
Teynham	d				09 50					10 20					10 50				11 20					11 50
Sheerness-on-Sea	d	09 26				09 56					10 26					10 56				11 26				
Queenborough	d	09 31				10 01					10 31					11 01				11 31				
Swale	d	09 36				10 06					10 36					11 06				11 36				
Kemsley	d	09 39				10 09					10 39					11 09				11 39				
Sittingbourne 4	a	09 44		09 46	09 55	10 14		10 16		10 25	10 44		10 46		10 55	11 14		11 16	11 25	11 44		11 46		11 55
	d			09 47	09 55			10 17		10 25			10 47		10 55			11 17	11 25			11 47		11 55
Newington	d				10 00					10 30					11 00				11 30					12 00
Rainham (Kent)	d			09 54	10 05			10 24		10 35			10 54		11 05			11 24	11 35			11 54		12 05
Gillingham (Kent) 4	d			09 59	10 10			10 29		10 40			10 59		11 10			11 29	11 40			11 59		12 10
Chatham 4	d			10 03	10 14			10 33		10 44			11 03		11 14			11 33	11 44			12 03		12 14
Rochester 4	d			10 06	10 16			10 36		10 46			11 06		11 16			11 36	11 46			12 06		12 16
Strood 4	a				*10 24*					*10 54*					*11 24*				*11 54*					*12 24*
Gravesend 4	a				*10 36*					*11 06*					*11 36*				*12 06*					*12 36*
Greenhithe for Bluewater	a				*10 41*					*11 11*					*11 41*				*12 11*					*12 41*
Dartford 4	a				*10 46*					*11 16*					*11 46*				*12 16*					*12 46*
London Bridge 4 ⊖	a				*11 19*					*11 49*					*12 19*				*12 49*					*13 19*
London Cannon Street 4 ⊖	a				*11b27*					*11b57*					*12b27*				*12b57*					*13b27*
London Waterloo (East) 4 ⊖	a				*11 24*					*11 54*					*12 24*				*12 54*					*13 24*
London Charing Cross 4 ⊖	a				*11 28*					*11 58*					*12 28*				*12 58*					*13 28*
Sole Street	d				10 27					10 57					11 27				11 57					12 27
Meopham	d				10 29					10 59					11 29				11 59					12 29
Longfield	d				10 33					11 03					11 33				12 03					12 33
Farningham Road	d				10 37					11 07					11 37				12 07					12 37
Swanley 4	a				10 42					11 12					11 42				12 12					12 42
St Mary Cray	a				10 47					11 17					11 47				12 17					12 47
Bromley South 4	a			10 29	10 54			10 59		11 24			11 29		11 54			11 59	12 24			12 29		12 54
Elephant & Castle ⊖	a			*11 00*				*11 30*					*12 00*					*12 30*				*13 00*		
London Blackfriars 3 ⊖	a			*11 03*				*11 33*					*12 03*					*12 33*				*13 03*		
London Victoria 15 ⊖	a			10 47	11 17			11 17		11 47			11 47		12 17			12 17	12 47			12 47		13 17

For general notes see front of timetable
For details of catering facilities see Directory of Train Operators
For services from Ramsgate, Dover and Canterbury to London via Ashford see Table 207

b Change at Rochester and London Bridge

Table 212

Ramsgate, Dover, Sheerness-on-Sea and Medway → London

Mondays to Fridays

from 13 October

Network Diagram - see first page of Table 212

		SE	SE	SE	SE	SE	SE	SE	SE	SE	SE	SE	SE
		01	30	50	92	01	30	50	92	01	30	50	90
			1	1	1		1	1	1		1	1	1
				⚲				⚲				⚲	
Ramsgate 4 ✈	d			11 22				11 59				12 22	12 40
Dumpton Park	d			11 24								12 24	12 43
Broadstairs	d			11 28				12 03				12 28	12 46
Margate 4	d			11 34				12 08				12 34	12a51
Westgate-on-Sea	d			11 37								12 37	
Birchington-on-Sea	d			11 40				12 13				12 40	
Herne Bay	d			11 49				12 21				12 49	
Chestfield & Swalecliffe	d			11 52								12 52	
Whitstable	d			11 56				12 26				12 56	
Dover Priory 4 ⛴	d		11 22				12 04				12 22		
Kearsney	d		11 26								12 26		
Shepherds Well	d		11 31								12 31		
Snowdown	d		11 35								12 35		
Aylesham	d		11 37								12 37		
Adisham	d		11 39								12 39		
Bekesbourne	d		11 43								12 43		
Canterbury East 4	d		11 49				12 21				12 49		
Selling	d		11 58								12 58		
Faversham 2	a		12 02	12 05			12 32	12 35			13 02	13 05	
	d		12 08		12 15		12 38		12 45		13 08		
Teynham	d				12 20				12 50				
Sheerness-on-Sea	d	11 56				12 26				12 56			
Queenborough	d	12 01				12 31				13 01			
Swale	d	12 06				12 36				13 06			
Kemsley	d	12 09				12 39				13 09			
Sittingbourne 4	a	12 14	12 16		12 25	12 44	12 46		12 55	13 14	13 16		
	d		12 17		12 25		12 47		12 55		13 17		
Newington	d				12 30				13 00				
Rainham (Kent)	d		12 24		12 35		12 54		13 05		13 24		
Gillingham (Kent) 4	d		12 29		12 40		12 59		13 10		13 29		
Chatham 4	d		12 33		12 44		13 03		13 14		13 33		
Rochester 4	d		12 36		12 46		13 06		13 16		13 36		
Strood 4	a				12 54				13 24				
Gravesend 4	a				13 06				13 36				
Greenhithe for Bluewater	a				13 11				13 41				
Dartford 4	a				13 16				13 46				
London Bridge 4 ⊖	a				13 49				14 19				
London Cannon Street 4 ⊖	a				13b57				14b27				
London Waterloo (East) 4 ⊖	a				13 54				14 24				
London Charing Cross 4 ⊖	a				13 58				14 28				
Sole Street	d				12 57				13 27				
Meopham	d				12 59				13 29				
Longfield	d				13 03				13 33				
Farningham Road	d				13 07				13 37				
Swanley 4	a				13 12				13 42				
St Mary Cray	a				13 17				13 47				
Bromley South 4	a		12 59		13 24		13 29		13 54		13 59		
Elephant & Castle ⊖	a		13 30				14 00				14 30		
London Blackfriars 3 ⊖	a		13 33				14 03				14 33		
London Victoria 15 ⊖	a		13 17		13 47		13 47		14 17		14 17		

		SE	SE	SE	SE	SE	SE	SE	SE	SE	SE	SE	SE
		92	01	30	50	92	01	30	50	90	92	30	50
		1		1	1	1		1	1	1	1	1	1
					⚲				⚲				⚲
Ramsgate 4 ✈	d				12 59				13 22	13 40			13 59
Dumpton Park	d								13 24	13 43			
Broadstairs	d				13 03				13 28	13 46			14 03
Margate 4	d				13 08				13 34	13a51			14 08
Westgate-on-Sea	d								13 37				
Birchington-on-Sea	d				13 13				13 40				14 13
Herne Bay	d				13 21				13 49				14 21
Chestfield & Swalecliffe	d								13 52				
Whitstable	d				13 26				13 56				14 26
Dover Priory 4 ⛴	d			13 04				13 22				14 04	
Kearsney	d							13 26					
Shepherds Well	d							13 31					
Snowdown	d							13 35					
Aylesham	d							13 37					
Adisham	d							13 39					
Bekesbourne	d							13 43					
Canterbury East 4	d			13 21				13 49				14 21	
Selling	d							13 58					
Faversham 2	a			13 32	13 35			14 02	14 05			14 32	14 35
	d	13 15		13 38		13 45		14 08			14 15	14 38	
Teynham	d	13 20				13 50					14 20		
Sheerness-on-Sea	d		13 26				13 56						
Queenborough	d		13 31				14 01						
Swale	d		13 36				14 06						
Kemsley	d		13 39				14 09						
Sittingbourne 4	a	13 25	13 44	13 46		13 55	14 14	14 16			14 25	14 46	
	d	13 25		13 47		13 55		14 17			14 25	14 47	
Newington	d	13 30				14 00					14 30		
Rainham (Kent)	d	13 35		13 54		14 05		14 24			14 35	14 54	
Gillingham (Kent) 4	d	13 40		13 59		14 10		14 29			14 40	14 59	
Chatham 4	d	13 44		14 03		14 14		14 33			14 44	15 03	
Rochester 4	d	13 46		14 06		14 16		14 36			14 46	15 06	
Strood 4	a	13 54				14 24					14 54		
Gravesend 4	a	14 06				14 36					15 06		
Greenhithe for Bluewater	a	14 11				14 41					15 11		
Dartford 4	a	14 16				14 46					15 16		
London Bridge 4 ⊖	a	14 49				15 19					15 49		
London Cannon Street 4 ⊖	a	14b57				15b27					15b57		
London Waterloo (East) 4 ⊖	a	14 54				15 24					15 54		
London Charing Cross 4 ⊖	a	14 58				15 28					15 58		
Sole Street	d	13 57				14 27					14 57		
Meopham	d	13 59				14 29					14 59		
Longfield	d	14 03				14 33					15 03		
Farningham Road	d	14 07				14 37					15 07		
Swanley 4	a	14 12				14 42					15 12		
St Mary Cray	a	14 17				14 47					15 17		
Bromley South 4	a	14 24		14 29		14 54		14 59			15 24	15 29	
Elephant & Castle ⊖	a			15 00				15 30				16 00	
London Blackfriars 3 ⊖	a			15 03				15 33				16 03	
London Victoria 15 ⊖	a	14 47		14 47		15 17		15 17			15 47	15 47	

For general notes see front of timetable
For details of catering facilities see Directory of Train Operators

For services from Ramsgate, Dover and Canterbury to London via Ashford see Table 207

b Change at Rochester and London Bridge

Table 212

Mondays to Fridays

from 13 October

Ramsgate, Dover, Sheerness-on-Sea and Medway → London

Network Diagram - see first page of Table 212

		SE 90	SE 01	SE 92	SE 30	SE 50	SE 01	SE 92	SE 30	SE 50	SE 90	SE 01	SE 92	SE 30	SE 50	SE 01	SE 92	SE 31	SE 51	SE 18	SE 01	SE 92	SE 30	SE 50	SE 01
		1		1	1	1		1	1	1	1		1	1	1		1	1	1	1		1	1	1	
		⊼				⊼				⊼	⊼				⊼				⊼	⊼				⊼	
Ramsgate 4 ✈	d	14 17				14 21				14 57	15 17				15 21				15 52	16 13				16 20	
Dumpton Park	d	14 20				14 23					15 20				15 23				15 54	16 16				16 22	
Broadstairs	d	14 23				14 27				15 01	15 23				15 27				15 58	16 19				16 26	
Margate 4	d	14a28				14 32				15 06	15a28				15 32				16 04	16a24				16 32	
Westgate-on-Sea	d					14 35									15 35				16 07					16 35	
Birchington-on-Sea	d					14 38				15 11					15 38				16 10					16 38	
Herne Bay	d					14 47				15 19					15 47				16 19					16 47	
Chestfield & Swalecliffe	d					14 50									15 50				16 22					16 50	
Whitstable	d					14 54				15 24					15 54				16 26					16 54	
Dover Priory 4 ⛴	d				14 20				15 02					15 20				15 52					16 20		
Kearsney	d				14 24									15 24				15 56					16 24		
Shepherds Well	d				14 29									15 29				16 01					16 29		
Snowdown	d				14 33									15 33				16 05					16 33		
Aylesham	d				14 35									15 35				16 07					16 35		
Adisham	d				14 37									15 37				16 09					16 37		
Bekesbourne	d				14 41									15 41				16 13					16 41		
Canterbury East 4	d				14 47				15 19					15 47				16 19					16 47		
Selling	d				14 56									15 56				16 28					16 56		
Faversham 2	a				15 00	15 03			15 30	15 33				16 00	16 03			16 32	16 35				17 00	17 03	
	d			14 45	15 06			15 15	15 36				15 44	16 06			16 14	16 38				16 44	17 06		
Teynham	d			14 50				15 20					15 49				16 19					16 49			
Sheerness-on-Sea	d		14 30				15 00					15 30				16 00					16 30				17 00
Queenborough	d		14 35				15 05					15 35				16 05					16 35				17 05
Swale	d		14 39				15 09					15 39				16 09					16 39				17 10
Kemsley	d		14 43				15 13					15 43				16 13					16 43				17 13
Sittingbourne 4	a		14 48	14 55	15 14		15 18	15 25	15 44			15 49	15 54	16 14		16 18	16 24	16 46			16 48	16 54	17 14		17 18
	d			14 55	15 15			15 25	15 45				15 54	16 15			16 24	16 47				16 54	17 15		
Newington	d			15 00				15 30					15 59				16 29					16 59			
Rainham (Kent)	d			15 05	15 22			15 35	15 52				16 04	16 22			16 34	16 54				17 04	17 22		
Gillingham (Kent) 4	d			15 10	15 27			15 40	15 57				16 09	16 27			16 39	16 59				17 09	17 27		
Chatham 4	d			15 14	15 31			15 44	16 01				16 13	16 31			16 43	17 03				17 13	17 31		
Rochester 4	d			15 16	15 34			15 46	16 03				16 15	16 33			16 45	17 06				17 15	17 33		
Strood 4	a			15 24				15 54					16 24				16 54					17 24			
Gravesend 4	a			15 36				16 08					16 36				17 06					17 36			
Greenhithe for Bluewater	a			15 41				16 14					16 41				17 11					17 45			
Dartford 4	a			15 46				16 20					16 46				17 17					17 50			
London Bridge 4 ⊖	a			16 19				16 55					17 26				17 56					18 31			
London Cannon Street 4 ⊖	a			16b27				17b05					17b33				18 01					18b45			
London Waterloo (East) 4 ⊖	a			16 24				17 00					17 31				18b05					18 36			
London Charing Cross 4 ⊖	a			16 28				17 03					17 35				18b09					18 40			
Sole Street	d			15 27				15 57					16 26				16 56					17 26			
Meopham	d			15 29				15 59					16 29				16 59					17 29			
Longfield	d			15 33				16 03					16 33				17 03					17 33			
Farningham Road	d			15 37				16 07					16 37				17 08					17 37			
Swanley 4	a			15 42				16 12					16 42				17 13					17 43			
St Mary Cray	a			15 47				16 17					16 47				17 18					17 47			
Bromley South 4	a			15 53	15 59			16 23	16 30				16 53	16 59			17 25	17 33				17 53	17 59		
Elephant & Castle ⊖	a				16 30				17 00					17 32			18 02						18 31		
London Blackfriars 3 ⊖	a				16 33				17 05					17 39			18 08						18 35		
London Victoria 15 ⊖	a			16 18	16 17			16 49	16 50				17 18	17 17			17 48	17 58				18 19	18 17		

For general notes see front of timetable
For details of catering facilities see Directory of Train Operators

For services from Ramsgate, Dover and Canterbury to London via Ashford see Table 207

b Change at Rochester and London Bridge

Table 212

Ramsgate, Dover, Sheerness-on-Sea and Medway → London

Mondays to Fridays

from 13 October

Network Diagram - see first page of Table 212

	SE 92 1	SE 30 1	SE 50 1 ♂	SE 01	SE 92 1	SE 01	SE 30 1	SE 50 1	SE 92 1	SE 30 1	SE 50 1	SE 4 1	SE 01	SE 92 1	SE 30 1	SE 50 1	SE 01	SE 01	SE 50 1	SE 30 1	SE 90 1	SE 4 1 ♂	SE 92 1	SE 01
Ramsgate 4 ✈ d			16 48					17 22			17 50	18 12				18 21			18 48		18 52	19 12		
Dumpton Park d			16 50					17 24			17 52	18 15				18 23			18 50		18 55	19 15		
Broadstairs d			16 53					17 28			17 55	18 18				18 26			18 53		18 58	19 18		
Margate 4 d			16 59					17 34			18 01	18a23				18 32			18 59		19a05	19a26		
Westgate-on-Sea d			17 02					17 37			18 04					18 35			19 02					
Birchington-on-Sea d			17 06					17 40			18 08					18 39			19 06					
Herne Bay d			17 15					17 49			18 17					18 48			19 15					
Chestfield & Swalecliffe d			17 19					17 52			18 21					18 52			19 19					
Whitstable d			17 22					17 56			18 24					18 55			19 22					
Dover Priory 4 ⛴ d		16 48					17 22			17 50					18 21					18 54				
Kearsney d		16 52					17 26			17 54					18 25					18 58				
Shepherds Well d		16 57					17 31			17 59					18 30					19 03				
Snowdown d		17 00					17 35			18 02					18 33					19 06				
Aylesham d		17 03					17 37			18 05					18 36					19 09				
Adisham d		17 05					17 39			18 07					18 38					19 11				
Bekesbourne d		17 10					17 43			18 12					18 43					19 16				
Canterbury East 4 d		17 16					17 49			18 18					18 49					19 22				
Selling d		17 25					17 58			18 27					18 58					19 31				
Faversham 2 a		17 29	17 31				18 02	18 06		18 31	18 33				19 02	19 04			19 31	19 35				
d	17 14	17 35			17 44		18 09		18 14	18 37				18 44	19 08				19 39				19 45	
Teynham d	17 19				17 49				18 19					18 49									19 50	
Sheerness-on-Sea d				17 36		17 53							18 28				19 02	19 20						19 50
Queenborough d				17 41		17 58							18 33				19b11	19 25						19 56
Swale d				17 45		18 02							18 38				19 15	19 29						20 01
Kemsley d				17 49		18 06							18 41				19 19	19 33						20 04
Sittingbourne 4 a	17 24	17 43		17 53	17 54	18 11	18 17		18 24	18 45			18 46	18 54	19 16		19 23	19 38	19 47				19 55	20 09
d	17 24	17 43			17 54		18 17		18 24	18 45				18 54	19 17				19 47				19 55	
Newington d	17 29				17 59				18 29					18 59									20 00	
Rainham (Kent) d	17 34	17 51			18 04		18 25		18 34	18 53				19 04	19 24				19 55				20 05	
Gillingham (Kent) 4 d	17 39	17 56			18 09		18 31		18 40	18 58				19 10	19 29				20 00				20 10	
Chatham 4 d	17 43	18 00			18 13		18 35		18 44	19 02				19 14	19 33				20 04				20 14	
Rochester 4 d	17 45	18 02			18 15		18 37		18 46	19 04				19 16	19 50				20 06				20 16	
Strood 4 a	17 58	18 22			18c22				18 54					19 24	19 54								20 26	
Gravesend 4 a	18 10	18 34			18c34				19 06					19 36	20 06								20 38	
Greenhithe for Bluewater a	18 15	18 40			18c40				19 11					19 41	20 11								20 43	
Dartford 4 a	18 20	18 46			18c46				19 17					19 46	20 16								20 48	
London Bridge 4 ⊖ a	19 02	19 23			19c23				19 53					20 23	20 53								21 23	
London Cannon Street 4 ⊖ a	19e10	19e37			19f37				20e11					20e41										
London Waterloo (East) 4 ⊖ a	19 07	19 28			19c28				19 58					20 28	20 58								21 28	
London Charing Cross 4 ⊖ a	19 11	19 32			19c32				20 01					20 31	21 01								21 31	
Sole Street d	17 56				18 26				18 57					19 27									20 27	
Meopham d	17 59				18 29				19 00					19 30									20 30	
Longfield d	18 03				18 33				19 04					19 34									20 34	
Farningham Road d	18 07				18 37				19 08					19 38									20 38	
Swanley 4 a	18 12				18 42				19 12					19 42									20 42	
St Mary Cray a	18 16				18 47				19 17					19 47									20 47	
Bromley South 4 a	18 23	18 31			18 53		19 00		19 23	19 30				19 53	19 58				20 32				20 53	
Elephant & Castle ⊖ a		19 00					19 36			20 00					20 30								21 30	
London Blackfriars 3 ⊖ a		19 03					19 40			20 03					20 33								21 33	
London Victoria 15 ⊖ a	18 50	18 48			19 17		19 17		19 48	19 47				20 17	20 17				20 48				21 17	

For general notes see front of timetable
For details of catering facilities see Directory of Train Operators

For services from Ramsgate, Dover and Canterbury to London via Ashford see Table 207

b Arr. 1907
c Change at Chatham
e Change at Rochester and London Bridge
f Change at Chatham and London Bridge

Ramsgate, Dover, Sheerness-on-Sea and Medway → London

Network Diagram - see first page of Table 212

		SE 01	SE 50 1	SE 30 1	SE 4 1	SE 01	SE 92 1	SE 91 1	SE 97	SE 01	SE 50 1	SE 30 1	SE 90 1	SE 92 1	SE 01	SE 80 1	SE 50 1	SE 55 1	SE 01	SE 80 1	SE 81 1	SE 58	SE 90 1
Ramsgate 4	d		19 48		20 04			20 39			20 50		21 28				21 55	22 10			22 53		23 40
Dumpton Park	d		19 50		20 07			20 41			20 52		21 31				21 57				22 55		23 43
Broadstairs	d		19 53		20 10			20 44			20 55		21 34				22 00	22 15			22 58		23 46
Margate 4	d		19 59		20a18			20a51			21 01		21a39				22 06	22 20			23 04		23a51
Westgate-on-Sea	d		20 02								21 04						22 09				23 07		
Birchington-on-Sea	d		20 06								21 07						22 12	22 25			23 11		
Herne Bay	d		20 15								21 17						22 22	22 34			23 20		
Chestfield & Swalecliffe	d		20 19								21 20						22 25				23 24		
Whitstable	d		20 22								21 24						22 29	22 39			23 27		
Dover Priory 4	d			19 52								20 52				21 55				23 01			
Kearsney	d			19 56								20 56				21 59							
Shepherds Well	d			20 01								21 01				22 04							
Snowdown	d			20 04								21 04				22 07							
Aylesham	d			20 07								21 07				22 10							
Adisham	d			20 09								21 09				22 12							
Bekesbourne	d			20 14								21 14				22 17							
Canterbury East 4	d			20 19								21 20				22 22				23 18			
Selling	d			20 28								21 29				22 31							
Faversham 2	a		20 31	20 33							21 32	21 34				22 35	22 37	22 47		23 30	23 36		
	d		20 37				20 45				21 38			21 45			22 38	22 48				23 42	
Teynham	d						20 50							21 50				22 53				23 47	
Sheerness-on-Sea	d	20 05				20 34			21 01	21 26					22 30				23 28				
Queenborough	d	20 10				20 39			21 06	21 31					22 35				23 33				
Swale	d	20 15				20 43			21 10	21 36					22 39				23 38				
Kemsley	d	20 18				20 47			21 14	21 39					22 42				23 41				
Sittingbourne 4	a	20 23	20 45			20 52	20 55			21 44	21 46			21 55	22 46		22 47	22 58	23 46			23 52	
	d		20 45				20 55				21 47			21 55			22 47	22 58				23 52	
Newington	d						21 00		21 21					22 00				23 03				23 57	
Rainham (Kent)	d		20 53				21 05		21 25		21 54			22 05			22 54	23 08				00 01	
Gillingham (Kent) 4	d		20 58				21 10		21a30		21 59			22 10			22 59	23 13				00 07	
Chatham 4	d		21 02				21 14				22 03			22 14			23 03	23 17				00 11	
Rochester 4	d		21 04				21 16							22 16				23 19				00 13	
Strood 4	a						21 24				22 32			22 32				00 17				00 17	
Gravesend 4	a						21 38				22 44			22 44				00 28				00 28	
Greenhithe for Bluewater	a						21 43				22 52			22 52				00 34				00 34	
Dartford 4	a						21 48				22 58			22 58				00 41				00 41	
London Bridge 4	⊖ a						22 23				23 41			23 41									
London Cannon Street 4	⊖ a																						
London Waterloo (East) 4	⊖ a						22 28				23 46			23 46									
London Charing Cross 4	⊖ a						22 31				23 50			23 50									
Sole Street	d						21 27							22 27				23 30					
Meopham	d						21 30							22 30				23 32					
Longfield	d						21 34							22 34				23 36					
Farningham Road	d						21 38							22 38				23 40					
Swanley 4	a						21 42							22 42				23 45					
St Mary Cray	a						21 47							22 47				23 49					
Bromley South 4	a		21 29				21 53				22 30			22 53			23 30	23 55					
Elephant & Castle	⊖ a		22 00				22 30				23 00			23 31									
London Blackfriars 3	⊖ a		22 03				22 33				23 03			23 37									
London Victoria 15	⊖ a		21 47				22 17				22 47			23 15			23 47	00 18				01 13	

For general notes see front of timetable
For details of catering facilities see Directory of Train Operators

For services from Ramsgate, Dover and Canterbury to London via Ashford see Table 207

Ramsgate, Dover, Sheerness-on-Sea and Medway → London

Network Diagram - see first page of Table 212

		SE 58	SE 54 [1]	SE 92 [1]	SE 30 [1]	SE 50 [1]	SE 92 [1]		SE 01	SE 30 [1]	SE 50 [1]	SE 92 [1]	SE 30 [1]	SE 50 [1]		SE 92 [1]	SE 01	SE 30 [1]	SE 50 [1]	SE 92 [1]	SE 30 [1]	SE 50 [1]		SE 64 [1]	SE 92 [1]
Ramsgate [4] ⇋	d		04 38			05 22					05 59			06 22					06 59			07 22		07 38	
Dumpton Park	d					05 24								06 24								07 24		07 40	
Broadstairs	d					05 28					06 03			06 28					07 03			07 28		07 43	
Margate [4]	d		04 46			05 34					06 08			06 34					07 08			07 34		07a48	
Westgate-on-Sea	d					05 37								06 37								07 37			
Birchington-on-Sea	d					05 40					06 13			06 40					07 13			07 40			
Herne Bay	d		04 58			05 49					06 21			06 49					07 21			07 49			
Chestfield & Swalecliffe	d					05 52								06 52								07 52			
Whitstable	d		05 03			05 56					06 26			06 56					07 26			07 56			
Dover Priory [4] ⛴	d				05 22					06 04			06 22					07 04			07 22				
Kearsney	d				05 26								06 26								07 26				
Shepherds Well	d				05 31								06 31								07 31				
Snowdown	d				05 35								06 35								07 35				
Aylesham	d				05 37								06 37								07 37				
Adisham	d				05 39								06 39								07 39				
Bekesbourne	d				05 43								06 43								07 43				
Canterbury East [4]	d				05 49					06 21			06 49					07 21			07 49				
Selling	d				05 58								06 58								07 58				
Faversham [2]	a		05 11		06 02	06 05				06 32	06 35		07 02	07 05				07 32	07 35		08 02	08 05			
	d	23p42	05 12	05 45	06 08		06 15			06 38		06 45	07 08			07 15		07 38		07 45	08 08				08 15
Teynham	d	23p47		05 50			06 20					06 50				07 20				07 50					08 20
Sheerness-on-Sea	d								06 26								07 26								
Queenborough	d								06 31								07 31								
Swale	d								06 36								07 36								
Kemsley	d								06 39								07 39								
Sittingbourne [4]	a	23p52	05 20	05 55	06 16		06 25		06 44	06 46		06 55	07 16			07 25	07 44	07 46		07 55	08 16				08 25
	d	23p52	05 20	05 55	06 17		06 25			06 47		06 55	07 17			07 25		07 47		07 55	08 17				08 25
Newington	d	23p57		06 00			06 30					07 00				07 30				08 00					08 30
Rainham (Kent)	d	00 01	05 28	06 05	06 24		06 35			06 54		07 05	07 24			07 35		07 54		08 05	08 24				08 35
Gillingham (Kent) [4]	d	00 07	05 33	06 10	06 29		06 40			06 59		07 10	07 29			07 40		07 59		08 10	08 29				08 40
Chatham [4]	d	00 11	05 37	06 14	06 33		06 44			07 03		07 14	07 33			07 44		08 03		08 14	08 33				08 44
Rochester [4]	d	00 13	05 39	06 16	06 36		06 46			07 06		07 16	07 36			07 46		08 06		08 16	08 36				08 46
Strood [4]	a	00 17	*05 54*	*06b23*			*06 54*					*07 24*				*07 54*				*08 24*					*08 54*
Gravesend [4]	a	00 28	*06 05*	*06b35*			*07 05*					*07 35*				*08 05*				*08 36*					*09 06*
Greenhithe for Bluewater	a	00 34	*06 10*	*06b40*			*07 10*					*07 40*				*08 10*				*08 41*					*09 11*
Dartford [4]	a	00 41	*06 15*	*06b45*			*07 15*					*07 45*				*08 15*				*08 46*					*09 16*
London Bridge [4] ⊖	a		*06 50*	*07b21*			*07 49*					*08 19*				*08 49*				*09 19*					*09 49*
London Cannon Street [4] ⊖	a			*07c50*			*08e03*					*08e27*				*08e57*				*09e27*					*09e57*
London Waterloo (East) [4] ⊖	a		*06 55*	*07b26*			*07 54*					*08 24*				*08 54*				*09 24*					*09 54*
London Charing Cross [4] ⊖	a		*06 58*	*07b29*			*07 58*					*08 28*				*08 58*				*09 28*					*09 58*
Sole Street	d		05 50	06 27			06 57					07 27				07 57				08 27					08 57
Meopham	d		05 52	06 29			06 59					07 29				07 59				08 29					08 59
Longfield	d		05 56	06 33			07 03					07 33				08 03				08 33					09 03
Farningham Road	d		06 00	06 37			07 07					07 37				08 07				08 37					09 07
Swanley [4]	a		06 05	06 42			07 12					07 42				08 12				08 42					09 12
St Mary Cray	a		06 10	06 47			07 17					07 47				08 17				08 47					09 17
Bromley South [4]	a		06 16	06 54	06 59		07 24			07 29		07 54	07 59			08 24		08 29		08 54	08 59				09 24
Elephant & Castle ⊖	a		*07 00*		*07 30*					*08 00*			*08 30*					*09 00*			*09 30*				
London Blackfriars [3] ⊖	a		*07 03*		*07 33*					*08 03*			*08 33*					*09 03*			*09 33*				
London Victoria [15] ⊖	a	01 13	06 32	07 17	07 17		07 47			07 47		08 17	08 17			08 47		08 47		09 17	09 17				09 47

For general notes see front of timetable
For details of catering facilities see Directory of Train Operators

For services from Ramsgate, Dover and Canterbury to London via Ashford see Table 207

b Change at Chatham
c Change at Chatham and London Bridge
e Change at Rochester and London Bridge

Table 212

Saturdays

Ramsgate, Dover, Sheerness-on-Sea and Medway → London

Network Diagram - see first page of Table 212

Station		SE 01	SE 30	SE 50	SE 92	SE 01	SE 30	SE 50	SE 4	SE 92	SE 01	SE 30	SE 50	SE 92	SE 01	SE 30	SE 50	SE 4	SE 92	SE 01	SE 30	SE 50
Ramsgate 4	d			07 59				08 22	08 35				08 59				09 22	09 34				09 59
Dumpton Park	d							08 24	08 38								09 24	09 37				
Broadstairs	d			08 03				08 28	08 41				09 03				09 28	09 40				10 03
Margate 4	d			08 08				08 34	08a46				09 08				09 34	09a45				10 08
Westgate-on-Sea	d							08 37									09 37					
Birchington-on-Sea	d			08 13				08 40					09 13				09 40					10 13
Herne Bay	d			08 21				08 49					09 21				09 49					10 21
Chestfield & Swalecliffe	d							08 52									09 52					
Whitstable	d			08 26				08 56					09 26				09 56					10 26
Dover Priory 4	d		08 04				08 22					09 04				09 22					10 04	
Kearsney	d						08 26									09 26						
Shepherds Well	d						08 31									09 31						
Snowdown	d						08 35									09 35						
Aylesham	d						08 37									09 37						
Adisham	d						08 39									09 39						
Bekesbourne	d						08 43									09 43						
Canterbury East 4	d		08 21				08 49					09 21				09 49					10 21	
Selling	d						08 58									09 58						
Faversham 2	a		08 32	08 35			09 02	09 05				09 32	09 35			10 02	10 05				10 32	10 35
	d			08 38	08 45			09 08		09 15			09 38	09 45			10 08		10 15			10 38
Teynham	d				08 50					09 20				09 50					10 20			
Sheerness-on-Sea	d	08 26				08 56					09 26				09 56					10 26		
Queenborough	d	08 31				09 01					09 31				10 01					10 31		
Swale	d	08 36				09 06					09 36				10 06					10 36		
Kemsley	d	08 39				09 09					09 39				10 09					10 39		
Sittingbourne 4	a	08 44		08 46	08 55	09 14		09 16		09 25	09 44		09 46	09 55	10 14		10 16		10 25	10 44		10 46
	d			08 47	08 55			09 17		09 25			09 47	09 55			10 17		10 25			10 47
Newington	d				09 00					09 30				10 00					10 30			
Rainham (Kent)	d			08 54	09 05			09 24		09 35			09 54	10 05			10 24		10 35			10 54
Gillingham (Kent) 4	d			08 59	09 10			09 29		09 40			09 59	10 10			10 29		10 40			10 59
Chatham 4	d			09 03	09 14			09 33		09 44			10 03	10 14			10 33		10 44			11 03
Rochester 4	d			09 06	09 16			09 36		09 46			10 06	10 16			10 36		10 46			11 06
Strood 4	a				09 24					09 54				10 24					10 54			
Gravesend 4	a				09 36					10 06				10 36					11 06			
Greenhithe for Bluewater	a				09 41					10 11				10 41					11 11			
Dartford 4	a				09 46					10 16				10 46					11 16			
London Bridge 4	⊖ a				10 19					10 49				11 19					11 49			
London Cannon Street 4	⊖ a				10b27					10b57				11b27					11b57			
London Waterloo (East) 4	⊖ a				10 24					10 54				11 24					11 54			
London Charing Cross 4	⊖ a				10 28					10 58				11 28					11 58			
Sole Street	d				09 27					09 57				10 27					10 57			
Meopham	d				09 29					09 59				10 29					10 59			
Longfield	d				09 33					10 03				10 33					11 03			
Farningham Road	d				09 37					10 07				10 37					11 07			
Swanley 4	a				09 42					10 12				10 42					11 12			
St Mary Cray	a				09 47					10 17				10 47					11 17			
Bromley South 4	a			09 29	09 54			09 59		10 24			10 29	10 54			10 59		11 24			11 29
Elephant & Castle	⊖ a			10 00				10 30					11 00				11 30					12 00
London Blackfriars 3	⊖ a			10 03				10 33					11 03				11 33					12 03
London Victoria 15	⊖ a			09 47	10 17			10 17		10 47			10 47	11 17			11 17		11 47			11 47

For general notes see front of timetable
For details of catering facilities see Directory of Train Operators

For services from Ramsgate, Dover and Canterbury to London via Ashford see Table 207

b Change at Rochester and London Bridge

Table 212

Saturdays

Ramsgate, Dover, Sheerness-on-Sea and Medway → London

Network Diagram - see first page of Table 212

		SE 90 [1]	SE 92 [1]	SE 01	SE 30 [1] 🚲	SE 50 [1] 🚲	SE 92 [1]	SE 01	SE 30 [1] 🚲	SE 50 [1] 🚲	SE 90 [1]	SE 92 [1]	SE 01	SE 30 [1] 🚲	SE 50 [1] 🚲	SE 90 [1] 🚲	SE 92 [1]	SE 01	SE 30 [1] 🚲	SE 50 [1] 🚲	SE 92 [1]	SE 01
Ramsgate [4] ✈	d	10 16				10 22				10 59	11 16				11 22	11 41				11 59		
Dumpton Park	d	10 19				10 24					11 19				11 24	11 44						
Broadstairs	d	10 22				10 28				11 03	11 22				11 28	11 47				12 03		
Margate [4]	d	10a27				10 34				11 08	11a27				11 34	11a52				12 08		
Westgate-on-Sea	d					10 37									11 37							
Birchington-on-Sea	d					10 40				11 13					11 40					12 13		
Herne Bay	d					10 49				11 21					11 49					12 21		
Chestfield & Swalecliffe	d					10 52									11 52							
Whitstable	d					10 56				11 26					11 56					12 26		
Dover Priory [4] ⛴	d				10 22				11 04					11 22					12 04			
Kearsney	d				10 26									11 26								
Shepherds Well	d				10 31									11 31								
Snowdown	d				10 35									11 35								
Aylesham	d				10 37									11 37								
Adisham	d				10 39									11 39								
Bekesbourne	d				10 43									11 43								
Canterbury East [4]	d				10 49				11 21					11 49					12 21			
Selling	d				10 58									11 58								
Faversham [2]	a				11 02	11 05			11 32	11 35				12 02	12 05				12 32	12 35		
	d		10 45		11 08		11 15		11 38			11 45		12 08			12 15		12 38		12 45	
Teynham	d		10 50				11 20					11 50					12 20				12 50	
Sheerness-on-Sea	d			10 56				11 26					11 56					12 26				12 56
Queenborough	d			11 01				11 31					12 01					12 31				13 01
Swale	d			11 06				11 36					12 06					12 36				13 06
Kemsley	d			11 09				11 39					12 09					12 39				13 09
Sittingbourne [4]	a		10 55	11 14	11 16		11 25	11 44	11 46			11 55	12 14	12 16			12 25	12 44	12 46		12 55	13 14
	d		10 55		11 17		11 25		11 47			11 55		12 17			12 25		12 47		12 55	
Newington	d		11 00				11 30					12 00					12 30				13 00	
Rainham (Kent)	d		11 05		11 24		11 35		11 54			12 05		12 24			12 35		12 54		13 05	
Gillingham (Kent) [4]	d		11 10		11 29		11 40		11 59			12 10		12 29			12 40		12 59		13 10	
Chatham [4]	d		11 14		11 33		11 44		12 03			12 14		12 33			12 44		13 03		13 14	
Rochester [4]	d		11 16		11 36		11 46		12 06			12 16		12 36			12 46		13 06		13 16	
Strood [4]	a		11 24				11 54					12 24					12 54				13 24	
Gravesend [4]	a		11 36				12 06					12 36					13 06				13 36	
Greenhithe for Bluewater	a		11 41				12 11					12 41					13 11				13 41	
Dartford [4]	a		11 46				12 16					12 46					13 16				13 46	
London Bridge [4] ⊖	a		12 19				12 49					13 19					13 49				14 19	
London Cannon Street [4] ⊖	a		12b27				12b57					13b27					13b57				14b27	
London Waterloo (East) [4] ⊖	a		12 24				12 54					13 24					13 54				14 24	
London Charing Cross [4] ⊖	a		12 28				12 58					13 28					13 58				14 28	
Sole Street	d		11 27				11 57					12 27					12 57				13 27	
Meopham	d		11 29				11 59					12 29					12 59				13 29	
Longfield	d		11 33				12 03					12 33					13 03				13 33	
Farningham Road	d		11 37				12 07					12 37					13 07				13 37	
Swanley [4]	a		11 42				12 12					12 42					13 12				13 42	
St Mary Cray	a		11 47				12 17					12 47					13 17				13 47	
Bromley South [4]	a		11 54		11 59		12 24		12 29			12 54		12 59			13 24		13 29		13 54	
Elephant & Castle ⊖	a				12 30				13 00					13 30					14 00			
London Blackfriars [3] ⊖	a				12 33				13 03					13 33					14 03			
London Victoria [15] ⊖	a		12 17		12 17		12 47		12 47			13 17		13 17			13 47		13 47		14 17	

For general notes see front of timetable
For details of catering facilities see Directory of Train Operators

For services from Ramsgate, Dover and Canterbury to London via Ashford see Table 207

b Change at Rochester and London Bridge

Table 212

Saturdays

Ramsgate, Dover, Sheerness-on-Sea and Medway → London

Network Diagram - see first page of Table 212

		SE	SE	SE	SE	SE	SE	SE		SE	SE	SE	SE	SE	SE		SE	SE	SE	SE	SE	SE	SE		SE
		30	50	90	92	01	30	50		92	01	30	50	90	92		01	30	50	92	01	30	50		90
		1	1	1	1		1	1		1		1	1	1	1			1	1	1		1	1		1
		🛒	🛒	🛒			🛒	🛒				🛒	🛒	🛒				🛒	🛒			🛒	🛒		🛒
Ramsgate 4 ✈	d		12 22	12 40				12 59					13 22	13 40					13 59				14 22		14 40
Dumpton Park	d		12 24	12 43									13 24	13 43									14 24		14 43
Broadstairs	d		12 28	12 46				13 03					13 28	13 46					14 03				14 28		14 46
Margate 4	d		12 34	12a51				13 08					13 34	13a51					14 08				14 34		14a51
Westgate-on-Sea	d		12 37										13 37										14 37		
Birchington-on-Sea	d		12 40					13 13					13 40						14 13				14 40		
Herne Bay	d		12 49					13 21					13 49						14 21				14 49		
Chestfield & Swalecliffe	d		12 52										13 52										14 52		
Whitstable	d		12 56					13 26					13 56						14 26				14 56		
Dover Priory 4 ⛴	d	12 22					13 04					13 22						14 04				14 22			
Kearsney	d	12 26										13 26										14 26			
Shepherds Well	d	12 31										13 31										14 31			
Snowdown	d	12 35										13 35										14 35			
Aylesham	d	12 37										13 37										14 37			
Adisham	d	12 39										13 39										14 39			
Bekesbourne	d	12 43										13 43										14 43			
Canterbury East 4	d	12 49					13 21					13 49						14 21				14 49			
Selling	d	12 58										13 58										14 58			
Faversham 2	a	13 02	13 05				13 32	13 35				14 02	14 05					14 32	14 35			15 02	15 05		
	d	13 08			13 15		13 38			13 45		14 08			14 15			14 38		14 45		15 08			
Teynham	d				13 20					13 50					14 20					14 50					
Sheerness-on-Sea	d					13 26					13 56						14 26				14 56				
Queenborough	d					13 31					14 01						14 31				15 01				
Swale	d					13 36					14 06						14 36				15 06				
Kemsley	d					13 39					14 09						14 39				15 09				
Sittingbourne 4	a	13 16			13 25	13 44	13 46			13 55	14 14	14 16			14 25		14 44	14 46		14 55	15 14	15 16			
	d	13 17			13 25		13 47			13 55		14 17			14 25			14 47		14 55		15 17			
Newington	d				13 30					14 00					14 30					15 00					
Rainham (Kent)	d	13 24			13 35		13 54			14 05		14 24			14 35			14 54		15 05		15 24			
Gillingham (Kent) 4	d	13 29			13 40		13 59			14 10		14 29			14 40			14 59		15 10		15 29			
Chatham 4	d	13 33			13 44		14 03			14 14		14 33			14 44			15 03		15 14		15 33			
Rochester 4	d	13 36			13 46		14 06			14 16		14 36			14 46			15 06		15 16		15 36			
Strood 4	a				*13 54*					*14 24*					*14 54*					*15 24*					
Gravesend 4	a				*14 06*					*14 36*					*15 06*					*15 36*					
Greenhithe for Bluewater	a				*14 11*					*14 41*					*15 11*					*15 41*					
Dartford 4	a				*14 16*					*14 46*					*15 16*					*15 46*					
London Bridge 4 ⊖	a				*14 49*					*15 19*					*15 49*					*16 19*					
London Cannon Street 4 ⊖	a				*14*b*57*					*15*b*27*					*15*b*57*					*16*b*27*					
London Waterloo (East) 4 ⊖	a				*14 54*					*15 24*					*15 54*					*16 24*					
London Charing Cross 4 ⊖	a				*14 58*					*15 28*					*15 58*					*16 28*					
Sole Street	d				13 57					14 27					14 57					15 27					
Meopham	d				13 59					14 29					14 59					15 29					
Longfield	d				14 03					14 33					15 03					15 33					
Farningham Road	d				14 07					14 37					15 07					15 37					
Swanley 4	a				14 12					14 42					15 12					15 42					
St Mary Cray	a				14 17					14 47					15 17					15 47					
Bromley South 4	a	13 59			14 24		14 29			14 54		14 59			15 24			15 29		15 54		15 59			
Elephant & Castle ⊖	a	*14 30*					*15 00*					*15 30*						*16 00*				*16 30*			
London Blackfriars 3 ⊖	a	*14 33*					*15 03*					*15 33*						*16 03*				*16 33*			
London Victoria 15 ⊖	a	14 17			14 47		14 47			15 17		15 17			15 47			15 47		16 17		16 17			

For general notes see front of timetable
For details of catering facilities see Directory of Train Operators

For services from Ramsgate, Dover and Canterbury to London via Ashford see Table 207

b Change at Rochester and London Bridge

Table 212

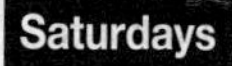

Saturdays

Ramsgate, Dover, Sheerness-on-Sea and Medway → London

Network Diagram - see first page of Table 212

		SE 92 1	SE 01	SE 30 1 ⊼	SE 50 1 ⊼	SE 92 1	SE 01	SE 30 1 ⊼	SE 50 1 ⊼	SE 90 1 ⊼	SE 92 1	SE 01	SE 30 1 ⊼	SE 50 1 ⊼	SE 92 1	SE 01	SE 30 1 ⊼	SE 50 1 ⊼	SE 90 1 ⊼	SE 92 1	SE 01
Ramsgate 4	d				14 59				15 22	15 40				15 59				16 22	16 40		
Dumpton Park	d								15 24	15 43								16 24	16 43		
Broadstairs	d				15 03				15 28	15 46				16 03				16 28	16 46		
Margate 4	d				15 08				15 34	15a51				16 08				16 34	16a51		
Westgate-on-Sea	d								15 37									16 37			
Birchington-on-Sea	d				15 13				15 40					16 13				16 40			
Herne Bay	d				15 21				15 49					16 21				16 49			
Chestfield & Swalecliffe	d								15 52									16 52			
Whitstable	d				15 26				15 56					16 26				16 56			
Dover Priory 4	d			15 04				15 22					16 04				16 22				
Kearsney	d							15 26									16 26				
Shepherds Well	d							15 31									16 31				
Snowdown	d							15 35									16 35				
Aylesham	d							15 37									16 37				
Adisham	d							15 39									16 39				
Bekesbourne	d							15 43									16 43				
Canterbury East 4	d			15 21				15 49					16 21				16 49				
Selling	d							15 58									16 58				
Faversham 2	a			15 32	15 35			16 02	16 05				16 32	16 35			17 02	17 05			
	d	15 15		15 38		15 45		16 08			16 15		16 38		16 45		17 08			17 15	
Teynham	d	15 20				15 50					16 20				16 50					17 20	
Sheerness-on-Sea	d		15 26				15 56					16 26				16 56					17 26
Queenborough	d		15 31				16 01					16 31				17 01					17 31
Swale	d		15 36				16 06					16 36				17 06					17 36
Kemsley	d		15 39				16 09					16 39				17 09					17 39
Sittingbourne 4	a	15 25	15 44	15 46		15 55	16 14	16 16			16 25	16 44	16 46		16 55	17 14	17 16			17 25	17 44
	d	15 25		15 47		15 55		16 17			16 25		16 47		16 55		17 17			17 25	
Newington	d	15 30				16 00					16 30				17 00					17 30	
Rainham (Kent)	d	15 35		15 54		16 05		16 24			16 35		16 54		17 05		17 24			17 35	
Gillingham (Kent) 4	d	15 40		15 59		16 10		16 29			16 40		16 59		17 10		17 29			17 40	
Chatham 4	d	15 44		16 03		16 14		16 33			16 44		17 03		17 14		17 33			17 44	
Rochester 4	d	15 46		16 06		16 16		16 36			16 46		17 06		17 16		17 36			17 46	
Strood 4	a	15 54				16 24					16 54				17 24					17 54	
Gravesend 4	a	16 06				16 36					17 06				17 36					18 06	
Greenhithe for Bluewater	a	16 11				16 41					17 11				17 41					18 11	
Dartford 4	a	16 16				16 46					17 16				17 46					18 16	
London Bridge 4	⊖ a	16 49				17 19					17 49				18 19					18 49	
London Cannon Street 4	⊖ a	16b57				17b27					17b57				18b27						
London Waterloo (East) 4	⊖ a	16 54				17 24					17 54				18 24					18 54	
London Charing Cross 4	⊖ a	16 58				17 28					17 58				18 28					18 58	
Sole Street	d	15 57				16 27					16 57				17 27					17 57	
Meopham	d	15 59				16 29					16 59				17 29					17 59	
Longfield	d	16 03				16 33					17 03				17 33					18 03	
Farningham Road	d	16 07				16 37					17 07				17 37					18 07	
Swanley 4	a	16 12				16 42					17 12				17 42					18 12	
St Mary Cray	a	16 17				16 47					17 17				17 47					18 17	
Bromley South 4	a	16 24		16 29		16 54		16 59			17 24		17 29		17 54		17 59			18 24	
Elephant & Castle	⊖ a			17 00				17 30					18 00				18 30				
London Blackfriars 3	⊖ a			17 03				17 33					18 03				18 33				
London Victoria 15	⊖ a	16 47		16 47		17 17		17 17			17 47		17 47		18 17		18 17			18 47	

For general notes see front of timetable
For details of catering facilities see Directory of Train Operators

For services from Ramsgate, Dover and Canterbury to London via Ashford see Table 207

b Change at Rochester and London Bridge

Table 212

Ramsgate, Dover, Sheerness-on-Sea and Medway → London

Network Diagram - see first page of Table 212

Station		SE 30 1	SE 50 1	SE 92 1	SE 01	SE 30 1	SE 50 1	SE 90 1	SE 92 1	SE 01	SE 30 1	SE 50 1	SE 92 1	SE 30 1	SE 50 1	SE 90 1	SE 92 1	SE 01	SE 30 1	SE 50 1	SE 90 1	SE 92 1
Ramsgate 4	d		16 59				17 22	17 40				17 59			18 22	18 40				18 52	19 24	
Dumpton Park	d						17 24	17 43							18 24	18 43				18 54	19 27	
Broadstairs	d		17 03				17 28	17 46				18 03			18 28	18 46				18 58	19 30	
Margate 4	d		17 08				17 34	17a51				18 08			18 34	18a51				19 04	19a35	
Westgate-on-Sea	d						17 37								18 37					19 07		
Birchington-on-Sea	d		17 13				17 40					18 13			18 40					19 10		
Herne Bay	d		17 21				17 49					18 21			18 49					19 19		
Chestfield & Swalecliffe	d						17 52								18 52					19 22		
Whitstable	d		17 26				17 56					18 26			18 56					19 26		
Dover Priory 4	d	17 04				17 22					18 04			18 22					18 52			
Kearsney	d					17 26								18 26					18 56			
Shepherds Well	d					17 31								18 31					19 01			
Snowdown	d					17 35								18 35					19 05			
Aylesham	d					17 37								18 37					19 07			
Adisham	d					17 39								18 39					19 09			
Bekesbourne	d					17 43								18 43					19 13			
Canterbury East 4	d	17 21				17 49					18 21			18 49					19 19			
Selling	d					17 58								18 58					19 28			
Faversham 2	a	17 32	17 35			18 02	18 05				18 32	18 35		19 02	19 05				19 32	19 35		
	d	17 38		17 45		18 08			18 15		18 38		18 45	19 08			19 15		19 38			19 45
Teynham	d			17 50					18 20				18 50				19 20					19 50
Sheerness-on-Sea	d				17 56					18 26								19 26				
Queenborough	d				18 01					18 31								19 31				
Swale	d				18 06					18 36								19 36				
Kemsley	d				18 09					18 39								19 39				
Sittingbourne 4	a	17 46		17 55	18 14	18 16			18 25	18 44	18 46		18 55	19 16			19 25	19 44	19 46			19 55
	d	17 47		17 55		18 17			18 25		18 47		18 55	19 17			19 25		19 47			19 55
Newington	d			18 00					18 30				19 00				19 30					20 00
Rainham (Kent)	d	17 54		18 05		18 24			18 35		18 54		19 05	19 24			19 35		19 54			20 05
Gillingham (Kent) 4	d	17 59		18 10		18 29			18 40		18 59		19 10	19 29			19 40		19 59			20 10
Chatham 4	d	18 03		18 14		18 33			18 44		19 03		19 14	19 33			19 44		20 03			20 14
Rochester 4	d	18 06		18 16		18 36			18 46		19 06		19 16	19 36			19 46		20 06			20 16
Strood 4	a			18 24					18 54				19 24				19 54					20 24
Gravesend 4	a			18 36					19 06				19 36				20 06					20 36
Greenhithe for Bluewater	a			18 41					19 11				19 41				20 11					20 41
Dartford 4	a			18 46					19 16				19 46				20 16					20 46
London Bridge 4	⊖ a			19 21					19 53				20 23				20 53					21 23
London Cannon Street 4	⊖ a																					
London Waterloo (East) 4	⊖ a			19 25					19 58				20 28				20 58					21 28
London Charing Cross 4	⊖ a			19 29					20 01				20 31				21 01					21 31
Sole Street	d			18 27					18 57				19 27				19 57					20 27
Meopham	d			18 29					18 59				19 29				19 59					20 29
Longfield	d			18 33					19 03				19 33				20 03					20 33
Farningham Road	d			18 37					19 07				19 37				20 07					20 37
Swanley 4	a			18 42					19 12				19 42				20 12					20 42
St Mary Cray	a			18 47					19 17				19 47				20 17					20 47
Bromley South 4	a	18 29		18 54		18 59			19 24		19 29		19 54	19 59			20 24		20 29			20 54
Elephant & Castle	⊖ a	19 00				19 30					20 00			20 30					21 00			21 30
London Blackfriars 3	⊖ a	19 03				19 33					20 03			20 33					21 03			21 33
London Victoria 15	⊖ a	18 47		19 17		19 17			19 47		19 47		20 17	20 17			20 47		20 47			21 17

For general notes see front of timetable
For details of catering facilities see Directory of Train Operators

For services from Ramsgate, Dover and Canterbury to London via Ashford see Table 207

Table 212

Saturdays

Ramsgate, Dover, Sheerness-on-Sea and Medway → London

Network Diagram - see first page of Table 212

Station		SE 30 1	SE 50 1	SE 4 1	SE 01	SE 92 1	SE 30 1	SE 50 1	SE 01	SE 90 1	SE 90 1	SE 50 1	SE 50 1	SE 01	SE 90 1	SE 90 1	SE 01	SE 81 1	SE 58 1	SE 58	SE 90 1
Ramsgate 4 ✈	d		19 52	20 12				20 52			21 38		21 52			22 38			22 55		23 38
Dumpton Park	d		19 54	20 15				20 54			21 41		21 54			22 41			22 57		23 41
Broadstairs	d		19 58	20 18				20 58			21 44		21 58			22 44			23 00		23 44
Margate 4	d		20 04	20a23				21 04			21a49		22 04			22a49			23 06		23a49
Westgate-on-Sea	d		20 07					21 07					22 07						23 09		
Birchington-on-Sea	d		20 10					21 10					22 10						23 13		
Herne Bay	d		20 19					21 19					22 19						23 22		
Chestfield & Swalecliffe	d		20 22					21 22					22 22						23 26		
Whitstable	d		20 26					21 26					22 26						23 29		
Dover Priory 4 ⛴	d	19 52					20 52					21 52						23 04			
Kearsney	d	19 56					20 56					21 56									
Shepherds Well	d	20 01					21 01					22 01									
Snowdown	d	20 05					21 05					22 05									
Aylesham	d	20 07					21 07					22 07									
Adisham	d	20 09					21 09					22 09									
Bekesbourne	d	20 13					21 13					22 13									
Canterbury East 4	d	20 19					21 19					22 19						23 22			
Selling	d	20 28					21 28					22 28									
Faversham 2	a	20 32	20 35				21 32	21 35				22 32	22 35					23 34	23 38		
	d	20 38				20 45	21 38			21 45		22 38			22 45					23 42	
Teynham	d					20 50				21 50					22 50					23 47	
Sheerness-on-Sea	d				20 30				21 30					22 30			23 30				
Queenborough	d				20 35				21 35					22 35			23 35				
Swale	d				20 40				21 40					22 40			23 40				
Kemsley	d				20 43				21 43					22 43			23 43				
Sittingbourne 4	a	20 46			20 48	20 55	21 46		21 48	21 55		22 46		22 48	22 55		23 48			23 52	
	d	20 47				20 55	21 47			21 55		22 47			22 55					23 52	
Newington	d					21 00				22 00					23 00						
Rainham (Kent)	d	20 54				21 05	21 54			22 05		22 54			23 05					23 59	
Gillingham (Kent) 4	d	20 59				21 10	21 59			22 10		22 59			23 10					00 05	
Chatham 4	d	21 03				21 14	22 03			22 14		23 03			23 14					00 09	
Rochester 4	d	21 06				21 16	22 06			22 16		23 06			23 16					00 11	
Strood 4	a					21 24				22 32					00 15					00 15	
Gravesend 4	a					21 36				22 44					00 26					00 26	
Greenhithe for Bluewater	a					21 41				22 52					00 32					00 32	
Dartford 4	a					21 46				22 58					00 39					00 39	
London Bridge 4	⊖ a					22 23				23 41											
London Cannon Street 4	⊖ a																				
London Waterloo (East) 4	⊖ a					22 28				23 46											
London Charing Cross 4	⊖ a					22 31				23 50											
Sole Street	d					21 27				22 27					23 27						
Meopham	d					21 29				22 29					23 29						
Longfield	d					21 33				22 33					23 33						
Farningham Road	d					21 37				22 37					23 37						
Swanley 4	a					21 42				22 42					23 42						
St Mary Cray	a					21 47				22 47					23 47						
Bromley South 4	a	21 29				21 54	22 29			22 54		23 29			23 54						
Elephant & Castle	⊖ a	22 00				22 30	23 00			23 30											
London Blackfriars 3	⊖ a	22 03				22 33	23 03			23 33											
London Victoria 15	⊖ a	21 47				22 17	22 47			23 17		23 47			00 10					01 11	

For general notes see front of timetable
For details of catering facilities see Directory of Train Operators

For services from Ramsgate, Dover and Canterbury to London via Ashford see Table 207

Ramsgate, Dover, Sheerness-on-Sea and Medway → London

Network Diagram - see first page of Table 212

		SE	SE	SE	SE	SE	SE	SE	SE	SE	SE	SE	SE	SE	SE	SE	SE	SE	SE	SE	SE	SE
		58	55	50	55	30	50	01	92	30	50	01	92	30	50	4	01	92	30	50	90	01
			1	1	1	1	1		1	1	1		1	1	1	1		1	1	1	1	
Ramsgate 4	d			06 22			07 22				08 22				09 22	09 43				10 22	10 43	
Dumpton Park	d			06 24			07 24				08 24				09 24	09 46				10 24	10 46	
Broadstairs	d			06 28			07 28				08 28				09 28	09 49				10 28	10 49	
Margate 4	d			06 34			07 34				08 34				09 34	09a54				10 34	10a54	
Westgate-on-Sea	d			06 37			07 37				08 37				09 37					10 37		
Birchington-on-Sea	d			06 40			07 40				08 40				09 40					10 40		
Herne Bay	d			06 49			07 49				08 49				09 49					10 49		
Chestfield & Swalecliffe	d			06 52			07 52				08 52				09 52					10 52		
Whitstable	d			06 56			07 56				08 56				09 56					10 56		
Dover Priory 4	d					07 22				08 22				09 22					10 22			
Kearsney	d					07 26				08 26				09 26					10 26			
Shepherds Well	d					07 31				08 31				09 31					10 31			
Snowdown	d					07 35				08 35				09 35					10 35			
Aylesham	d					07 37				08 37				09 37					10 37			
Adisham	d					07 39				08 39				09 39					10 39			
Bekesbourne	d					07 43				08 43				09 43					10 43			
Canterbury East 4	d					07 49				08 49				09 49				10 19	10 49			
Selling	d					07 57				08 57				09 57					10 57			
Faversham 2	a			07 05		08 02	08 05			09 02	09 05			10 02	10 05			10 31	11 02	11 05		
	d	23p42	06 32	07 08	07 32		08 08		08 32		09 08		09 32		10 08			10 32		11 08		
Teynham	d	23p47	06 37		07 37				08 37				09 37					10 37				
Sheerness-on-Sea	d							08 18				09 18					10 18					11 18
Queenborough	d							08 23				09 23					10 23					11 23
Swale	d							08 27				09 27					10 27					11 27
Kemsley	d							08 31				09 31					10 31					11 31
Sittingbourne 4	a	23p52	06 42	07 16	07 42		08 16	08 35	08 42		09 16	09 35	09 42		10 16		10 35	10 42		11 16		11 35
	d	23p52	06 42	07 17	07 42		08 17		08 42		09 17		09 42		10 17			10 42		11 17		
Newington	d		06 47		07 47				08 47				09 47					10 47				
Rainham (Kent)	d	23p59	06 52	07 24	07 52		08 24		08 52		09 24		09 52		10 24			10 52		11 24		
Gillingham (Kent) 4	d	00 05	06 57	07 30	07 57		08 29		08 57		09 29		09 57		10 29			10 57		11 29		
Chatham 4	d	00 09	07 01	07 33	08 01		08 33		09 01		09 33		10 01		10 33			11 01		11 33		
Rochester 4	d	00 11	07 03	07 35	08 03		08 36		09 03		09 36		10 03		10 36			11 03		11 36		
Strood 4	a	00 15	07 26	07 51	08 26		08 56		09 26		09 56		10 26		10 56			11 26		11 56		
Gravesend 4	a	00 26	07 38	08 03	08 38		09 08		09 38		10 08		10 38		11 08			11 38		12 08		
Greenhithe for Bluewater	a	00 32	07 44	08 12	08 44		09 14		09 44		10 14		10 44		11 14			11 44		12 14		
Dartford 4	a	00 39	07 49	08 18	08 49		09 19		09 49		10 19		10 49		11 19			11 49		12 19		
London Bridge 4	⊖ a		08 23	08 53	09 23		09 53		10 23		10 53		11 23		11 53			12 23		12 53		
London Cannon Street 4	⊖ a																					
London Waterloo (East) 4	⊖ a		08 28	08 58	09 28		09 58		10 28		10 58		11 28		11 58			12 28		12 58		
London Charing Cross 4	⊖ a		08 32	09 02	09 32		10 02		10 32		11 02		11 32		12 02			12 32		13 02		
Sole Street	d		07 14		08 14				09 14				10 14					11 14				
Meopham	d		07 16		08 16				09 16				10 16					11 16				
Longfield	d		07 20		08 20				09 20				10 20					11 20				
Farningham Road	d		07 24		08 24				09 24				10 24					11 24				
Swanley 4	a		07 29		08 29				09 29				10 29					11 29				
St Mary Cray	a		07 34		08 34				09 34				10 34					11 34				
Bromley South 4	a		07 40	08 00	08 40		09 00		09 40		10 00		10 40		11 00			11 40		12 00		
Elephant & Castle	⊖ a																					
London Blackfriars 3	⊖ a																					
London Victoria 15	⊖ a	01 11	08 01	08 16	09 01		09 16		10 01		10 16		11 01		11 16			12 01		12 16		

For general notes see front of timetable
For details of catering facilities see
Directory of Train Operators

For services from Ramsgate, Dover and Canterbury to
London via Ashford see Table 207

Table 212

Sundays

Ramsgate, Dover, Sheerness-on-Sea and Medway → London

Network Diagram - see first page of Table 212

Station		SE 92 [1]	SE 30 [1]	SE 50 [1] 🚲	SE 90 [1]	SE 01	SE 92 [1]	SE 30 [1]	SE 50 [1] 🚲	SE 90 [1]	SE 01	SE 92 [1]	SE 30 [1]	SE 50 [1] 🚲	SE 90 [1]	SE 01	SE 92 [1]	SE 30 [1]	SE 50 [1] 🚲	SE 90 [1]	SE 01
Ramsgate [4]	d			11 22	11 40				12 22	12 40				13 22	13 40				14 22	14 40	
Dumpton Park	d			11 24	11 43				12 24	12 43				13 24	13 43				14 24	14 43	
Broadstairs	d			11 28	11 46				12 28	12 46				13 28	13 46				14 28	14 46	
Margate [4]	d			11 34	11a51				12 34	12a51				13 34	13a51				14 34	14a51	
Westgate-on-Sea	d			11 37					12 37					13 37					14 37		
Birchington-on-Sea	d			11 40					12 40					13 40					14 40		
Herne Bay	d			11 49					12 49					13 49					14 49		
Chestfield & Swalecliffe	d			11 52					12 52					13 52					14 52		
Whitstable	d			11 56					12 56					13 56					14 56		
Dover Priory [4]	d		11 22					12 22					13 22					14 22			
Kearsney	d		11 26					12 26					13 26					14 26			
Shepherds Well	d		11 31					12 31					13 31					14 31			
Snowdown	d		11 35					12 35					13 35					14 35			
Aylesham	d		11 37					12 37					13 37					14 37			
Adisham	d		11 39					12 39					13 39					14 39			
Bekesbourne	d		11 43					12 43					13 43					14 43			
Canterbury East [4]	d	11 19	11 49				12 19	12 49				13 19	13 49				14 19	14 49			
Selling	d		11 57					12 57					13 57					14 57			
Faversham [2]	a	11 31	12 02	12 05			12 31	13 02	13 05			13 31	14 02	14 05			14 31	15 02	15 05		
	d	11 32	12 08				12 32	13 08				13 32	14 08				14 32	15 08			
Teynham	d	11 37					12 37					13 37					14 37				
Sheerness-on-Sea	d					12 18					13 18					14 18					15 18
Queenborough	d					12 23					13 23					14 23					15 23
Swale	d					12 27					13 27					14 27					15 27
Kemsley	d					12 31					13 31					14 31					15 31
Sittingbourne [4]	a	11 42	12 16			12 35	12 42	13 16			13 35	13 42	14 16			14 35	14 42	15 16			15 35
	d	11 42	12 17				12 42	13 17				13 42	14 17				14 42	15 17			
Newington	d	11 47					12 47					13 47					14 47				
Rainham (Kent)	d	11 52	12 24				12 52	13 24				13 52	14 24				14 52	15 24			
Gillingham (Kent) [4]	d	11 57	12 29				12 57	13 29				13 57	14 29				14 57	15 29			
Chatham [4]	d	12 01	12 33				13 01	13 33				14 01	14 33				15 01	15 33			
Rochester [4]	d	12 03	12 36				13 03	13 36				14 03	14 36				15 03	15 36			
Strood [4]	a	*12 26*	*12 56*				*13 26*	*13 56*				*14 26*	*14 56*				*15 26*	*15 56*			
Gravesend [4]	a	*12 38*	*13 08*				*13 38*	*14 08*				*14 38*	*15 08*				*15 38*	*16 08*			
Greenhithe for Bluewater	a	*12 44*	*13 14*				*13 44*	*14 14*				*14 44*	*15 14*				*15 44*	*16 14*			
Dartford [4]	a	*12 49*	*13 19*				*13 49*	*14 19*				*14 49*	*15 19*				*15 49*	*16 19*			
London Bridge [4]	⊖ a	*13 23*	*13 53*				*14 23*	*14 53*				*15 23*	*15 53*				*16 23*	*16 53*			
London Cannon Street [4]	⊖ a																				
London Waterloo (East) [4]	⊖ a	*13 28*	*13 58*				*14 28*	*14 58*				*15 28*	*15 58*				*16 28*	*16 58*			
London Charing Cross [4]	⊖ a	*13 32*	*14 02*				*14 32*	*15 02*				*15 32*	*16 02*				*16 32*	*17 02*			
Sole Street	d	12 14					13 14					14 14					15 14				
Meopham	d	12 16					13 16					14 16					15 16				
Longfield	d	12 20					13 20					14 20					15 20				
Farningham Road	d	12 24					13 24					14 24					15 24				
Swanley [4]	a	12 29					13 29					14 29					15 29				
St Mary Cray	a	12 34					13 34					14 34					15 34				
Bromley South [4]	a	12 40	13 00				13 40	14 00				14 40	15 00				15 40	16 00			
Elephant & Castle	⊖ a																				
London Blackfriars [3]	⊖ a																				
London Victoria [15]	⊖ a	13 01	13 16				14 01	14 16				15 01	15 16				16 01	16 16			

For general notes see front of timetable
For details of catering facilities see Directory of Train Operators

For services from Ramsgate, Dover and Canterbury to London via Ashford see Table 207

Table 212

Sundays

Ramsgate, Dover, Sheerness-on-Sea and Medway → London

Network Diagram - see first page of Table 212

Station		SE 92 1	SE 30 1	SE 50 1	SE 90 1	SE 01	SE 92 1	SE 30 1 A	SE 30 1	SE 50 1	SE 90 1	SE 01	SE 92 1	SE 30 1 A	SE 30 1	SE 50 1	SE 90 1	SE 01	SE 92 1	SE 30 1 A	SE 30 1	SE 50 1
Ramsgate 4	d			15 22	15 40			16 08		16 22	16 40			17 08		17 22	17 45			18 08		18 22
Dumpton Park	d			15 24	15 43			16 10		16 24	16 43			17 10		17 24	17 48			18 10		18 24
Broadstairs	d			15 28	15 46			16 14		16 28	16 46			17 14		17 28	17 51			18 14		18 28
Margate 4	d			15 34	15a51			16 19		16 34	16a51			17 19		17 34	17a56			18 19		18 34
Westgate-on-Sea	d			15 37				16 22		16 37				17 22		17 37				18 22		18 37
Birchington-on-Sea	d			15 40				16 26		16 40				17 26		17 40				18 26		18 40
Herne Bay	d			15 49				16 34		16 49				17 34		17 49				18 34		18 49
Chestfield & Swalecliffe	d			15 52				16 38		16 52				17 38		17 52				18 38		18 52
Whitstable	d			15 56				16 42		16 56				17 42		17 56				18 42		18 56
Dover Priory 4	d		15 22						16 22						17 22						18 22	
Kearsney	d		15 26						16 26						17 26						18 26	
Shepherds Well	d		15 31						16 31						17 31						18 31	
Snowdown	d		15 35						16 35						17 35						18 35	
Aylesham	d		15 37						16 37						17 37						18 37	
Adisham	d		15 39						16 39						17 39						18 39	
Bekesbourne	d		15 43						16 43						17 43						18 43	
Canterbury East 4	d	15 19	15 49				16 19		16 49				17 19		17 49				18 19		18 49	
Selling	d		15 57						16 57						17 57						18 57	
Faversham 2	a	15 31	16 02	16 05			16 31	16 50	17 02	17 05			17 31	17 50	18 02	18 05			18 31	18 50	19 02	19 05
	d	15 32	16 08				16 32	16 50	17 08				17 32	17 50	18 08				18 32	18 50	19 08	
Teynham	d	15 37					16 37						17 37						18 37			
Sheerness-on-Sea	d					16 18						17 18						18 18				
Queenborough	d					16 23						17 23						18 23				
Swale	d					16 27						17 27						18 27				
Kemsley	d					16 31						17 31						18 31				
Sittingbourne 4	a	15 42	16 16			16 35	16 42	16 58	17 16			17 35	17 42	17 58	18 16			18 35	18 42	18 58	19 16	
	d	15 42	16 17				16 42	16 59	17 17				17 42	17 59	18 17				18 42	18 59	19 17	
Newington	d	15 47					16 47						17 47						18 47			
Rainham (Kent)	d	15 52	16 24				16 52	17 06	17 24				17 52	18 06	18 24				18 52	19 06	19 24	
Gillingham (Kent) 4	d	15 57	16 29				16 57	17 11	17 29				17 57	18 11	18 29				18 57	19 11	19 29	
Chatham 4	d	16 01	16 33				17 01	17 15	17 33				18 01	18 15	18 33				19 01	19 15	19 33	
Rochester 4	d	16 03	16 36				17 03	17 17	17 36				18 03	18 17	18 36				19 03	19 17	19 36	
Strood 4	a	16 26	16 56				17 26	17 26	17 56				18 26	18 26	18 56				19 26	19 26	19 54	
Gravesend 4	a	16 38	17 08				17 38	17 38	18 08				18 38	18 38	19 08				19 38	19 38	20 05	
Greenhithe for Bluewater	a	16 44	17 14				17 44	17 44	18 14				18 44	18 44	19 14				19 44	19 44	20 14	
Dartford 4	a	16 49	17 19				17 49	17 49	18 19				18 49	18 49	19 19				19 49	19 49	20 19	
London Bridge 4	⊖ a	17 23	17 53				18 23	18 23	18 53				19 23	19 23	19 53				20 23	20 23	20 53	
London Cannon Street 4	⊖ a																					
London Waterloo (East) 4	⊖ a	17 28	17 58				18 28	18 28	18 58				19 28	19 28	19 58				20 28	20 28	20 58	
London Charing Cross 4	⊖ a	17 32	18 02				18 32	18 32	19 02				19 32	19 32	20 02				20 32	20 32	21 02	
Sole Street	d	16 14					17 14						18 14						19 14			
Meopham	d	16 16					17 16						18 16						19 16			
Longfield	d	16 20					17 20						18 20						19 20			
Farningham Road	d	16 24					17 24						18 24						19 24			
Swanley 4	a	16 29					17 29						18 29						19 29			
St Mary Cray	a	16 34					17 34						18 34						19 34			
Bromley South 4	a	16 40	17 00				17 40	17 42	18 00				18 40	18 42	19 00				19 40	19 42	20 00	
Elephant & Castle	⊖ a																					
London Blackfriars 3	⊖ a																					
London Victoria 15	⊖ a	17 01	17 16				18 01	17 58	18 16				19 01	18 58	19 16				20 01	19 58	20 16	

For general notes see front of timetable
For details of catering facilities see Directory of Train Operators

For services from Ramsgate, Dover and Canterbury to London via Ashford see Table 207

A 20 July to 31 August

Sundays

Ramsgate, Dover, Sheerness-on-Sea and Medway → London

Network Diagram - see first page of Table 212

		SE 90 [1]	SE 01	SE 92 [1]	SE 30 [1]	SE 50 [1]	SE 90 [1]	SE 01	SE 92 [1]	SE 30 [1]	SE 50 [1]	SE 90 [1]	SE 01	SE 92 [1]	SE 30 [1]	SE 50 [1]	SE 01	SE 80 [1]	SE 50 [1]
Ramsgate [4] ✈	d	18 40				19 22	19 40				20 22	20 40				21 22			21 52
Dumpton Park	d	18 43				19 24	19 43				20 24	20 43				21 24			21 54
Broadstairs	d	18 46				19 28	19 46				20 28	20 46				21 28			21 57
Margate [4]	d	18a51				19 34	19a51				20 34	20a51				21 34			22 04
Westgate-on-Sea	d					19 37					20 37					21 37			22 07
Birchington-on-Sea	d					19 40					20 40					21 40			22 10
Herne Bay	d					19 49					20 49					21 49			22 18
Chestfield & Swalecliffe	d					19 52					20 52					21 52			22 22
Whitstable	d					19 56					20 56					21 56			22 25
Dover Priory [4] ⛴	d				19 22					20 22					21 22			21 52	
Kearsney	d				19 26					20 26					21 26			21 56	
Shepherds Well	d				19 31					20 31					21 31			22 01	
Snowdown	d				19 35					20 35					21 35			22 05	
Aylesham	d				19 37					20 37					21 37			22 07	
Adisham	d				19 39					20 39					21 39			22 09	
Bekesbourne	d				19 43					20 43					21 43			22 13	
Canterbury East [4]	d			19 19	19 49					20 49					21 49			22 19	
Selling	d				19 57					20 57					21 57			22 27	
Faversham [2]	a			19 31	20 02	20 05				21 02	21 05				22 02	22 05		22 32	22 34
	d			19 32	20 08				20 32	21 08				21 32	22 08				22 35
Teynham	d			19 37					20 37					21 37					22 40
Sheerness-on-Sea	d		19 18					20 18					21 18				22 18		
Queenborough	d		19 23					20 23					21 23				22 23		
Swale	d		19 27					20 27					21 27				22 27		
Kemsley	d		19 31					20 31					21 31				22 31		
Sittingbourne [4]	a		19 35	19 42	20 16			20 35	20 42	21 16			21 35	21 42	22 16		22 35		22 44
	d			19 42	20 17				20 42	21 17				21 42	22 17				22 45
Newington	d			19 47					20 47					21 47					22 50
Rainham (Kent)	d			19 52	20 24				20 52	21 24				21 52	22 24				22 54
Gillingham (Kent) [4]	d			19 57	20 29				20 57	21 29				21 57	22 29				22 59
Chatham [4]	d			20 01	20 33				21 01	21 33				22 01	22 33				23 03
Rochester [4]	d			20 03	20 36				21 03	21 36				22 03	22 36				23 05
Strood [4]	a			20 26	20 51				21 26	21 51				22 26					
Gravesend [4]	a			20 38	21 03				21 38	22 03				22 39					
Greenhithe for Bluewater	a			20 44	21 12				21 44	22 12				22 48					
Dartford [4]	a			20 49	21 18				21 49	22 18				22 53					
London Bridge [4]	⊖ a			21 23	21 53				22 23	22 53				23 36					
London Cannon Street [4]	⊖ a																		
London Waterloo (East) [4]	⊖ a			21 28	21 58				22 28	22 58				23 41					
London Charing Cross [4]	⊖ a			21 32	22 02				22 32	23 02				23 45					
Sole Street	d			20 14					21 14					22 14					23 15
Meopham	d			20 16					21 16					22 16					23 17
Longfield	d			20 20					21 20					22 20					23 21
Farningham Road	d			20 24					21 24					22 24					23 26
Swanley [4]	a			20 29					21 29					22 29					23 32
St Mary Cray	a			20 34					21 34					22 34					23 36
Bromley South [4]	a			20 40	21 00				21 40	22 00				22 40	23 00				23 42
Elephant & Castle	⊖ a																		
London Blackfriars [3]	⊖ a																		
London Victoria [15]	⊖ a			21 01	21 16				22 01	22 16				23 01	23 16				23 59

For general notes see front of timetable
For details of catering facilities see Directory of Train Operators

For services from Ramsgate, Dover and Canterbury to London via Ashford see Table 207

Network Diagram for Tables 216, 217, 218, 219, 221, 222

DM-49/04
Design BAJS

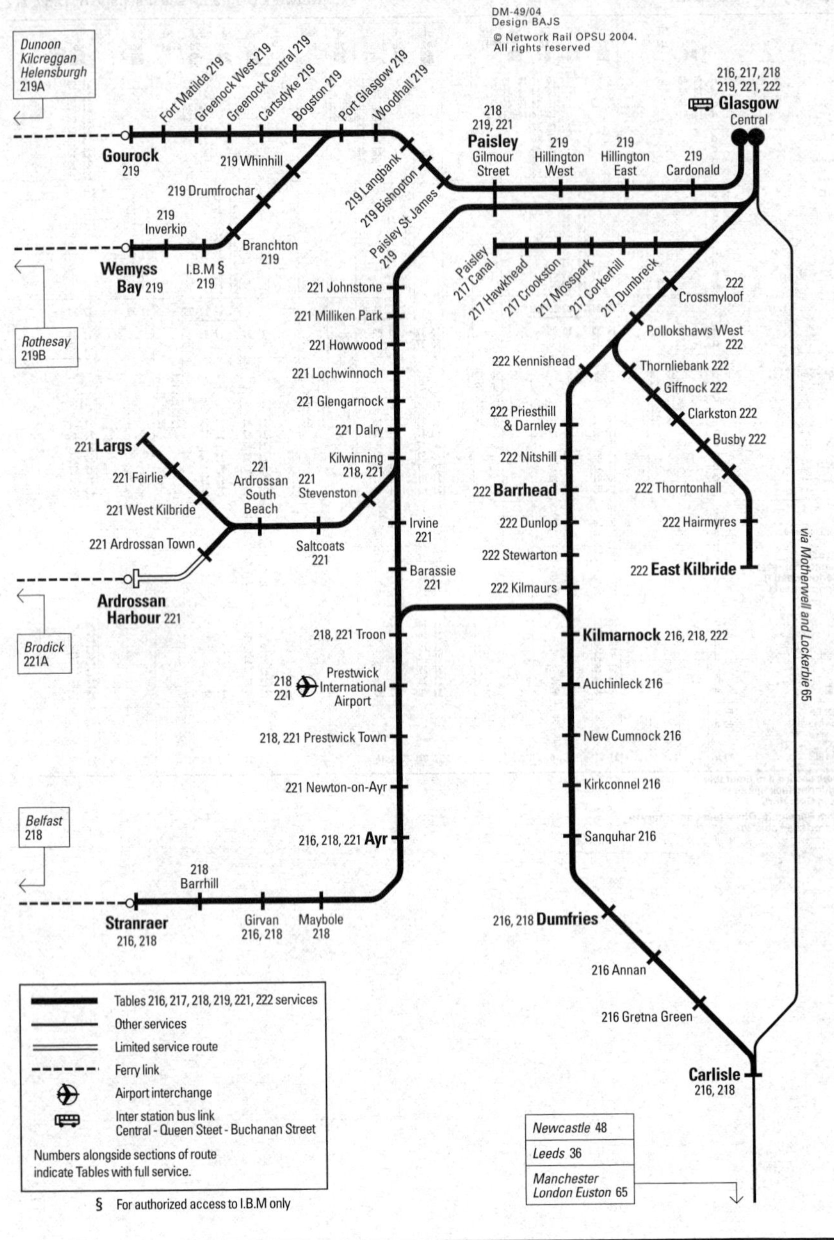

Dunoon
Kilcreggan
Helensburgh
219A
Fort Matilda 219
Greenock West 219
Greenock Central 219
Cartsdyke 219
Bogston 219
Port Glasgow 219
Woodhall 219
Gourock
219
219 Whinhill
219 Drumfrochar
219
Inverkip
Branchton
219
Wemyss
Bay 219
I.B.M §
219
Rothesay
219B
219 Langbank
219 Bishopton
Paisley St James
219
218
219, 221
Paisley
Gilmour
Street
219
Hillington
West
219
Hillington
East
219
Cardonald
216, 217, 218
219, 221, 222
Glasgow
Central
Paisley
217 Canal
217 Hawkhead
217 Crookston
217 Mosspark
217 Corkerhill
217 Dumbreck
222
Crossmyloof
Pollokshaws West
222
222 Kennishead
Thornliebank 222
Giffnock 222
Clarkston 222
Busby 222
222 Thorntonhall
222 Hairmyres
222 East Kilbride
222 Priesthill
& Darnley
222 Nitshill
222 Barrhead
222 Dunlop
222 Stewarton
222 Kilmaurs
Kilmarnock 216, 218, 222
Auchinleck 216
New Cumnock 216
Kirkconnel 216
Sanquhar 216
216, 218 Dumfries
216 Annan
216 Gretna Green
Carlisle
216, 218
via Motherwell and Lockerbie 65
221 Johnstone
221 Milliken Park
221 Howwood
221 Lochwinnoch
221 Glengarnock
221 Dalry
Kilwinning
218, 221
221 Largs
221 Fairlie
221 West Kilbride
221 Ardrossan Town
221
Ardrossan
South
Beach
221
Stevenston
Saltcoats
221
Irvine
221
Barassie
221
Ardrossan
Harbour 221
Brodick
221A
218, 221 Troon
218
221
Prestwick
International
Airport
218, 221 Prestwick Town
221 Newton-on-Ayr
216, 218, 221 Ayr
Belfast
218
218
Barrhill
Stranraer
216, 218
Girvan
216, 218
Maybole
218
Tables 216, 217, 218, 219, 221, 222 services
Other services
Limited service route
Ferry link
Airport interchange
Inter station bus link
Central - Queen Steet - Buchanan Street
Numbers alongside sections of route
indicate Tables with full service.
§ For authorized access to I.B.M only
Newcastle 48
Leeds 36
Manchester
London Euston 65

Glasgow Central, Stranraer and Kilmarnock → Dumfries and Carlisle

Network Diagram - see first page of Table 216

Mondays to Fridays

Miles	Miles		SR	SR	SR	SR	SR	SR ◇	SR	SR	SR	SR	SR	SR	SR
0	—	**Glasgow Central** 15 65, 222 d			06b42	08 28	09 53	11b03	12 03	13 03		15 48	17 30	20 03	22 03
—	0	**Stranraer** 218 d				07 09		10 00		11 48					
—	38¼	Girvan 218 d			06 40	08 01		10 52	11 40	12 40		14 40		18 42	
—	59¼	Ayr 218 d			07 10	08 36		11 22	12 09	13 09		15 17		19 09	
24¼	74½	**Kilmarnock** 3 218, 222 a			07 40	09 06	10 38	11 49	12 41	13 42		16 25	18 06	20 39	22 39
—	—	d			07 41	09 13	10 39	11 50	12 41	13 42		16 27	18 09	20 40	22 43
38	89¼	Auchinleck d			07 57	09 29	10 56	12 09	12 57	13 59		16 44	18 28	20 57	22 59
45½	96¾	New Cumnock d			08 06	09 38	11 04	12 17	13 06	14 07		16 52	18 36	21 07	23 08
52¾	104½	Kirkconnel d			08 14	09 46	11 13	12 26	13 14	14 16		17 01	18 45	21 16	23 16
56	107¾	Sanquhar d			08 19	09 51	11 18	12 31	13 19	14 21		17 06	18 50	21 21	23 21
82¼	135	**Dumfries** d	06 28	07 31	08 49	10 17	11 47	12 57	13 48	14 47	17 01	17 31	19 18	21 47	23c53
97¾	150½	Annan d	06 43	07 46	09 06	10 32	12 02	13 12	14 03	15 04	17 16	17 47	19 33	22 02	00 08
105½	158	Gretna Green d	06 52	07 55	09 15	10 43	12 11	13 21	14 12	15 11	17 25	17 55	19 42	22 11	00 17
115½	168	**Carlisle** 8 65 a	07 06	08 08	09 28	10 56	12 26	13 35	14 26	15 28	17 38	18 16	19 55	22 24	00 34
—	—	Newcastle 8 48 ⛴ a	08 57	09 59	10 55	12 57		14 57	15 58	18e08		19 47	22 59		

Saturdays

	SR	SR	SR	SR	SR	SR	SR ◇	SR	SR	SR	SR	SR	SR	SR	SR	SR	SR	SR
Glasgow Central 15 65, 222 d			06b42	08 28		09 53	11b03	12 03		13 03			15 48		17 30	20 03		22 03
Stranraer 218 d				07 09			10 00			11 48								
Girvan 218 d			06 40	08 01			10 52	11 40		12 40			14 40			18 42		
Ayr 218 d			07 10	08 36			11 22	12 09		13 09			15 17			19 09		
Kilmarnock 3 218, 222 a			07 40	09 06		10 38	11 45	12 41		13 42			16 25		18 06	20 39		22 39
d			07 41	09 09		10 39	11 46	12 41		13 42			16 27		18 15	20 40		22 43
Auchinleck d			07 57	09 25		10 56	12 03	12 57		13 59			16 44		18 33	20 57		22 59
New Cumnock d			08 06	09 34		11 04	12 11	13 06		14 07			16 52		18 42	21 07		23 08
Kirkconnel d			08 14	09 42		11 13	12 20	13 14		14 16			17 01		18 50	21 16		23 16
Sanquhar d			08 19	09 47		11 18	12 25	13 19		14 21			17 06		18 55	21 21		23 21
Dumfries d	06 28	07 28	08 49	10 15	10 39	11 47	12 53	13 48	14 26	14 47	16 15	17 01	17 31	18 20	19 24	21 47	22 10	23c53
Annan d	06 43	07 43	09 06	10 30	10 54	12 02	13 08	14 03	14 43	15 04	16 30	17 16	17 47	18 35	19 39	22 02	22 25	00 08
Gretna Green d	06 52	07 52	09 15	10 39	11 03	12 11	13 17	14 12	14 52	15 11	16 39	17 25	17 55	18 41	19 48	22 11	22 34	00 17
Carlisle 8 65 a	07 06	08 05	09 28	10 53	11 14	12 26	13 31	14 26	15 07	15 28	16 52	17 38	18 10	18 59	20 01	22 24	22 47	00 34
Newcastle 8 48 ⛴ a	08 57	10 01	10 55		12 57		14 59	16 00	16 50	17 59	18 55		19 46	21 01	22 59			

Sundays

	SR	SR	SR	SR	SR
Glasgow Central 15 65, 222 d			14 48		22 28
Stranraer 218 d					
Girvan 218 d					
Ayr 218 d					
Kilmarnock 3 218, 222 a			15 27		23 04
d			15 28		23 05
Auchinleck d			15 45		23 22
New Cumnock d			15 53		23 30
Kirkconnel d			16 02		23 39
Sanquhar d			16 07		23 44
Dumfries d	13 00	14 37	16 35	22 14	00 12
Annan d	13 15	14 52	16 50	22 29	00 27
Gretna Green d	13 24	15 01	16 59	22 38	00 36
Carlisle 8 65 a	13 37	15 19	17 18	22 51	00 49
Newcastle 8 48 ⛴ a	15 40	17 40	19 40		

For general notes see front of timetable
For details of catering facilities see Directory of Train Operators

- **b** Change at Kilmarnock
- **c** Arr. 2345
- **e** From 8 September arr. 1807

For connections to London Euston, please refer to Table 65

Carlisle and Dumfries → Kilmarnock, Stranraer and Glasgow Central

Network Diagram - see first page of Table 216

Mondays to Fridays

Miles	Miles	Station		SR	SR	NT	SR	SR	NT ◇	SR	SR	SR	NT ◇	SR	SR
—	—	Newcastle 8	48 d			06b49	*09 24*	*11 24*	12 39	*13c24*	*14 24*	*15 24*	17 13	*19 10*	*21e06*
0	0	**Carlisle 8**	65 d	05 40	06 09	08 19	11 07	13 09	14 22	15 00	16 11	17 51	18 51	21 08	22 53
9¾	9¾	Gretna Green	d	05 51	06 20	08 30	11 18	13 23	14 33	15 16	16 22	18 04	19 02	21 19	23 04
17½	17½	Annan	d	06 00	06 31	08 38	11 26	13 32	14 42	15 25	16 31	18 12	19 10	21 28	23 13
33	33	**Dumfries**	d	06a18	06 50	08 55	11 43	13 49	14 59	15 41	16a48	18 29	19 29	21 44	23a30
59¼	59¼	Sanquhar	d		07 16	09 21	12 09	14 15	15 25	16 07		18 55	19 55	22 10	
62½	62½	Kirkconnel	d		07 21	09 26	12 14	14 20	15 30	16 12		19 00	20 00	22 15	
69¾	69¾	New Cumnock	d		07 30	09 35	12 23	14 29	15 39	16 21		19 09	20 09	22 24	
77¼	77¼	Auchinleck	d		07 38	09 43	12 31	14 37	15 48	16 29		19 17	20 17	22 32	
91	91	**Kilmarnock 3**	218, 222 a		07 57	10 02	12 48	14 55	16 07	16 46		19 36	20 36	22 49	
—	—		d		07 58	10 04	12 50	14 55	16 09	16 47		19 50	20 37	22 50	
—	106¼	Ayr	218 a		*09 38*		*13 36*		16 32	*18 38*			20 59		
—	127¼	Girvan	218 a		*10 08*		*14 05*		16 59				21 26		
—	168	**Stranraer**	218 a		*11 11*				17 55				22 24		
115¼	—	**Glasgow Central 15**	65, 222 a		08 37	10 41	13 29	15 33		17 31		20 27	*21f27*	23 28	

Saturdays

Station		SR	SR	NT	SR	SR	SR	SR	NT ◇	SR	SR	SR	SR	SR	NT ◇	SR	SR	SR
Newcastle 8	48 d			06 34		*09 24*	*10 24*	*11 22*	12 39	*13 24*		*14 24*	*15 24*		17 11	*18 24*	*19 10*	*21g10*
Carlisle 8	65 d	05 40	06 09	08 19	09 52	11 07	12 18	13 09	14 22	15 00	15 22	16 13	17 24	17 51	18 51	20 08	21 08	22 56
Gretna Green	d	05 51	06 20	08 30	10 03	11 18	12 29	13 23	14 33	15 16	15 34	16 24	17 35	18 03	19 02	20 19	21 19	23 07
Annan	d	06 00	06 31	08 38	10 12	11 26	12 38	13 32	14 42	15 25	15 43	16 33	17 44	18 12	19 10	20 28	21 28	23 16
Dumfries	d	06a18	06 50	08 55	10a29	11 43	12a55	13 49	14 59	15 41	16a00	16a50	18a01	18 29	19 29	20 44	21a45	23a33
Sanquhar	d		07 16	09 21		12 09		14 15	15 25	16 07				18 55	19 55	21 10		
Kirkconnel	d		07 21	09 26		12 14		14 20	15 30	16 12				19 00	20 00	21 15		
New Cumnock	d		07 30	09 35		12 23		14 29	15 39	16 21				19 09	20 09	21 24		
Auchinleck	d		07 38	09 43		12 31		14 37	15 48	16 29				19 17	20 17	21 32		
Kilmarnock 3	218, 222 a		07 57	10 02		12 48		14 55	16 07	16 46				19 36	20 36	21 49		
	d		07 58	10 04		12 50		14 55	16 09	16 47				19 50	20 37	21 50		
Ayr	218 a		*09 38*			*13 36*			16 32	*18 45*					20 59	*23 10*		
Girvan	218 a		*10 08*			*14 05*			16 59						21 26	*23 36*		
Stranraer	218 a		*11 11*						17 55						22 24	*00 37*		
Glasgow Central 15	65, 222 a		08 37	10 41		13 29		15 33		17 31				20 27	*21f27*	22 27		

Sundays

Station		SR ◇	SR	SR	SR
Newcastle 8	48 d	*11 10*		*17 10*	*18 10*
Carlisle 8	65 d	12 52	13 47	19 35	21 12
Gretna Green	d	13 03	13 58	19 46	21 23
Annan	d	13 11	14 07	19 54	21 32
Dumfries	d	13 28	14a24	20 11	21a49
Sanquhar	d	13 54		20 37	
Kirkconnel	d	13 59		20 42	
New Cumnock	d	14 08		20 51	
Auchinleck	d	14 16		20 59	
Kilmarnock 3	218, 222 a	14 34		21 16	
	d	14 35		21 18	
Ayr	218 a				
Girvan	218 a				
Stranraer	218 a				
Glasgow Central 15	65, 222 a	15 14		21 55	

For general notes see front of timetable
For details of catering facilities see Directory of Train Operators

b Until 5 September dep. 0654
c Until 5 September only
e From 8 September only
f Change at Kilmarnock
g Until 6 September only

For connections from London Euston, please refer to Table 65

Table 217

Mondays to Saturdays

Glasgow Central — Paisley Canal

Network Diagram - see first page of Table 216

Miles			SR SO	SR	SR		SR	SR
0	**Glasgow Central** 15	d	00 07	06 07	06 37	and every 30 minutes until	22 37	23 07
1¾	Dumbreck	d	00 13	06 13	06 43		22 43	23 13
3¼	Corkerhill	d	00 15	06 15	06 45		22 45	23 15
3¾	Mosspark	d	00 17	06 17	06 47		22 47	23 17
4½	Crookston	d	00 19	06 19	06 49		22 49	23 19
6½	Hawkhead	d	00 22	06 22	06 52		22 52	23 22
7	**Paisley Canal**	a	00 25	06 25	06 55		22 55	23 25

Sundays

from 30 November

		SR	SR		SR
Glasgow Central 15	d	09 37	10 37	and every hour until	17 37
Dumbreck	d	09 43	10 43		17 43
Corkerhill	d	09 45	10 45		17 45
Mosspark	d	09 47	10 47		17 47
Crookston	d	09 49	10 49		17 49
Hawkhead	d	09 52	10 52		17 52
Paisley Canal	a	09 55	10 55		17 55

Mondays to Saturdays

Miles			SR	SR	SR	SR	SR	SR	SR A		SR	SR	SR	SR
0	**Paisley Canal**	d	06 30	07 00	07 30	08 00	08 30	09 00	09 30	and every 30 minutes until	21 30	22 00	22 30	23 00
½	Hawkhead	d	06 33	07 03	07 33	08 03	08 33	09 03	09 33		21 33	22 03	22 33	23 03
2½	Crookston	d	06 36	07 06	07 36	08 06	08 36	09 06	09 36		21 36	22 06	22 36	23 06
3¼	Mosspark	d	06 38	07 08	07 38	08 08	08 38	09 08	09 38		21 38	22 08	22 38	23 08
3¾	Corkerhill	d	06 40	07 10	07 40	08 10	08 40	09 10	09 40		21 40	22 10	22 40	23 10
5¼	Dumbreck	d	06 43	07 13	07 43	08 13	08 43	09 13	09 43		21 43	22 13	22 43	23 13
7	**Glasgow Central** 15	a	06 49	07 19	07 52	08 21	08 52	09 19	09 49		21 49	22 20	22 50	23 20

Sundays

from 30 November

		SR	SR		SR
Paisley Canal	d	09 00	10 00	and every hour until	17 00
Hawkhead	d	09 03	10 03		17 03
Crookston	d	09 06	10 06		17 06
Mosspark	d	09 08	10 08		17 08
Corkerhill	d	09 10	10 10		17 10
Dumbreck	d	09 13	10 13		17 13
Glasgow Central 15	a	09 19	10 19		17 19

For general notes see front of timetable
For details of catering facilities see Directory of Train Operators

A 1730 from Paisley Canal arr. Glasgow Central 1753

No Sunday service until 23 November

Glasgow Central and Kilmarnock → Girvan, Stranraer and Belfast

Network Diagram - see first page of Table 216

Miles	Miles			SR	SR ◇	SR ◇ A	SR	SR		SR ◇	SR	SR ◇ A	SR ◇	SR		SR	SR SX	SR SO	SR ◇ A	SR	SR ◇	SR		
0	—	**Glasgow Central** 15	219, 221, 222 d		07 13		08b30	09 03		11 42	12b30		15b30	16b00		17c13				18 30	20b00	22b00		
7¼	—	Paisley Gilmour Street	219, 221 ⇄ d		07 24		08b41	09b11		11 53	12b41		15b41	16b11		17c24				18 41	20b11	22b11		
26¾	—	Kilwinning	221 d		07 41		09e03	09f32		12 10	12b59		15b59	16b29		17c42				19 01	20b29	22b29		
—	—	Newcastle 8	48 d								09g24		12 39				13h24	13j24			17k13	18m24		
—	—	Carlisle 8	216 d				06 09				11 07		14 22				15 00	15 00			18 51	20n08		
—	—	Dumfries	216 d				06 50				11 43		14 59				15 41	15 41			19 29	20n44		
—	0	**Kilmarnock** 3	222 a					09 48					16 07								20 36			
—	—		d				09 10	09 55			13 10		16 09	16 31			18 11	18 19			20 37	22 44		
35	10¾	Troon	221 d				09 24	10 07			13 22		16 19	16 44			18 24	18 31			20 50	22 56		
37¾	11¾	Prestwick Int. Airport	221 ⇄ d		07q45		09 29	10 12		12 15	13 27		16 15	16 49		17r56	18 29	18 36		19 17	20 43	23 01		
38¼	12½	Prestwick Town	221 d		07q47		09 31	10 14		12 17	13 29		16 17	16 51		17r58	18 31	18 38		19 19	20 45	23 03		
41½	15½	**Ayr**	221 a		07 59		09 38	10 21		12 29	13 36		16 32	16 58			18 38	18 45			20 59	23 10		
—	—		d	06 00	08 00		09 43	10 22		12 30	13 38		16 34	17 00		18 10				19 31	21 01	23 11		
50½	24½	Maybole	d	06 11	08 11		09 54	10 34		12 41	13 49		16 45	17 11		18 21				19 42	21 12	23 22		
62¾	36½	**Girvan**	d	06a27	08 26		10 09	10a51		13 01	14a05		17 00	17a27		18a37				19 57	21 27	23 37		
75	51¼	Barrhill	d		08 45		10t35			13 20			17 19							20 16	21 46	00 01		
101	77¼	**Stranraer**	a		09 21		11 11			13 56			17 55							20 52	22 24	00 37		
—	—	Stranraer Harbour §	⛴ d			09 55						14 45							19 50					
—	—	Belfast Port §	⛴ a			11 40						16 30							21 20					

Sundays

		SR ◇ A	SR ◇ B	SR ◇ C	SR ◇ A	SR ◇	SR ◇ A
Glasgow Central 15	219, 221, 222 d		11 37	11 42		16 25	
Paisley Gilmour Street	219, 221 ⇄ d		11 48	11 53		16 39	
Kilwinning	221 d		12 05	12 10		16 56	
Newcastle 8	48 d						
Carlisle 8	216 d						
Dumfries	216 d						
Kilmarnock 3	222 a						
	d						
Troon	221 d						
Prestwick Int. Airport	221 ⇄ d		12v13	12 13		16 45	
Prestwick Town	221 d		12v15	12 15		16 47	
Ayr	221 a		12 29	12 34		17 17	
	d		12 30	12 35		17 19	
Maybole	d		12 41	12 46		17 30	
Girvan	d		12 56	13 01		17 47	
Barrhill	d		13 14	13 19		18 06	
Stranraer	a		13 51	13 56		18 42	
Stranraer Harbour §	⛴ d	09 55			14 45		19 50
Belfast Port §	⛴ a	11 40			16 30		21 20

For general notes see front of timetable
For details of catering facilities see Directory of Train Operators

§ Stena HSS and shipping services operated by Stena Line
A Ship service
B Until 23 November
C From 30 November
b Change at Ayr
c Saturdays dep. Glasgow Central 1700, Paisley Gilmour Street 1711, Kilwinning 1735
e Change at Ayr. Saturdays dep. 0905
f Change at Ayr. Saturdays dep. 0929
g Change at Carlisle and Kilmarnock
h Change at Carlisle and Kilmarnock. From 8 September dep. 1239
j Until 6 September only. Change at Carlisle and Kilmarnock
k Saturdays dep. 2 minutes earlier
m Saturdays only.Until 6 September only. Change at Carlisle and Kilmarnock
n Saturdays only
q Saturdays dep. Prestwick Int. Airport 0743, Prestwick Town 0745
r Saturdays dep. 5 minutes earlier
t Arr. 1030
v 5 October to 23 November dep. Prestwick Int. Airport 1145, Prestwick Town 1147

Belfast, Stranraer and Girvan → Kilmarnock and Glasgow Central

Network Diagram - see first page of Table 216

Miles	Miles			SR	SR ◇	SR ◇ A	SR SO ◇	SR SX ◇	SR	SR SX ◇	SR SO ◇	SR ◇ A	SR	SR ◇	SR	SR	SR ◇ A	SR ◇	SR ◇	SR SX ◇
—	—	Belfast Port §	d			07 35						12 20					17 10			
—	—	Stranraer Harbour §	a			09 10						14 05					18 55			
0	—	**Stranraer**	d		07 09		10 00	10 00		11 48	11 48			14 37				19 40	21 10	23 25
26	—	Barrhill	d		07 43		10 34	10 34		12 22	12 22			15 11				20 19	21 50	23 59
38¼	—	**Girvan**	d	06 40	08 01		10 52	10 52	11 40	12 40	12 40		14 40	15 29	17 32	18 42		20 37	22 08	00 19
50½	—	Maybole	d	06 56	08 25		11 08	11 08	11 56	12 56	12 56		14 56	15 45	17 48	18 58		20 53	22 24	00 35
59¼	—	**Ayr**	a	07 08	08 35		11 20	11 20	12 08	13 08	13 08		15 08	15 58	18 00	19 08		21 05	22 37	00 47
—	—		d	07 10	08 36		11 22	11 22	12 09	13 09	13 09		15 17	15 58		19 09		21 06	22 38	
62½	—	Prestwick Town 221	a	07 19	08 41		11 48	11 48	12 14	13 14	13 14		15b22	16 19	18 19	19 14		21 19	23 06	
63	—	Prestwick Int. Airport 221 ✈	a	07 21	08 43		11 50	11 50	12 16	13 16	13 16		15c24	16 21	18 21	19 16		21 21	23 08	
63¾	0	Troon 221	a	07 18	08 48		11 30	11 30	12 21	13 21	13 21		15 29			19 21				
—	10¾	**Kilmarnock** 3	a	07 40	09 03		11 45	11 49	12 37	13 37	13 38		15 42			19 40				
—	—		d	07 41	09 12		11 46	11 50		13 50	13 50		15 48							
—	—	Dumfries 216	a	08 49	10e17		12 52	12 56	13 47	14 47	14 46		17 31			21 46				
—	—	Carlisle 8 216	a	09 28	10e56		13 31	13 35	14 26	15 28	15 28		18f16			22 24				
—	—	Newcastle 8 48	a	10 55	12g57		14 59	14 57	15h58	18j08	17g59		19k47							
74¼	—	Kilwinning 221	a	07m36	09m04		12m04	12m04	12m36	13m36	13m36		15m36	16 13	18 36	19m37		21 21	22 54	
93¾	—	Paisley Gilmour Street 219, 221 ✈	a	07n57	09m24		12m22	12m22	12m55	13m55	13m55		15m57	16 33	18 57	19m55		21 44	23 14	
101	—	**Glasgow Central** 15 219, 221, 222	a	08n09	09q50		12r27	12m34	13m07	14t27	14t27		16v32	16 45	19 09	20m07		21 55	23 26	

Sundays

		SR ◇ A	SR ◇	SR ◇ A	SR ◇	SR ◇ A	SR ◇
Belfast Port §	d	07 35		12 20		17 10	
Stranraer Harbour §	a	09 10		14 05		18 55	
Stranraer	d		10 40		14 40		19 40
Barrhill	d		11 14		15 14		20 15
Girvan	d		11 32		15 32		20 33
Maybole	d		11 48		15 48		20 49
Ayr	a		12 01		16 01		21 01
	d		12 01		16 01		21 02
Prestwick Town 221	a		12w18		16y18		21 48
Prestwick Int. Airport 221 ✈	a		12w20		16y20		21 50
Troon 221	a						
Kilmarnock 3	a						
	d						
Dumfries 216	a						
Carlisle 8 216	a						
Newcastle 8 48	a						
Kilwinning 221	a		12 16		16 16		21 17
Paisley Gilmour Street 219, 221 ✈	a		12 36		16 37		21 36
Glasgow Central 15 219, 221, 222	a		12 51		16 49		21 48

For general notes see front of timetable
For details of catering facilities see Directory of Train Operators

- § Stena HSS and shipping services operated by Stena Line
- A Ship service
- b By changing at Ayr, passengers may arrive at 1519
- c By changing at Ayr, passengers may arrive at 1521
- e Saturdays arr. 3 minutes earlier
- f Saturdays arr. 1810
- g Change at Kilmarnock and Carlisle
- h Change at Kilmarnock and Carlisle. Saturdays arr. 1600
- j Change at Kilmarnock and Carlisle. From 8 September arr. 1807
- k Saturdays arr. 1946
- m Change at Ayr
- n Change at Ayr. Saturdays arr. Paisley Gilmour Street 0804, Glasgow Central 0816
- q By changing at Ayr, passengers may arrive at 0936
- r Change at Kilmarnock
- t By changing at Ayr, passengers may arrive at 1407
- v By changing at Ayr, passengers may arrive at 1609
- w 5 October to 23 November arr. Prestwick Town 1248, Prestwick Int. Airport 1250
- y 5 October to 23 November arr. Prestwick Town 1648, Prestwick Int. Airport 1650

Glasgow Central → Wemyss Bay and Gourock

Network Diagram - see first page of Table 216

Miles	Miles	Station		SR	SR	SR	SR	SR	SR	SR	SR	SR	SR	SR	SR	SR	SR	SR	SR	SR
0	0	**Glasgow Central** 15 221	d	05 55	06 05	06 25	06 32	06 55	07 05	07 25	07 35	07 50	08 05	08 25	08b36	08 50	09 05	09 25	09 35	09 50
3¾	3¾	Cardonald	d				06 39		07 12	07 32	07 42		08 12		08 42		09 12		09 42	
4½	4½	Hillington East	d		06 14		06 41		07 14	07 34	07 44		08 14		08 44		09 14		09 44	
5	5	Hillington West	d	06 03	06 16		06 43	07 03	07 16	07 36	07 46	07 58	08 16		08 46		09 16		09 46	
7¼	7¼	Paisley Gilmour Street 221 ⇐	d	06 07	06 20	06 36	06 47	07 07	07 20	07 40	07 50	08 02	08 20	08 36	08 50	09 01	09 20	09 36	09 50	10 01
8	8	Paisley St James	d			06 38			07 22		07 52		08 22		08 52		09 22		09 52	
12¼	12¼	Bishopton	d	06 13	06 26	06 44	06 53	07 13	07 28	07 46	07 58	08 08	08 28	08 42	08 58	09 07	09 28	09 42	09 58	10 07
16¼	16¼	Langbank	d			06 49			07 34		08 04		08 34		09 04		09 34		10 04	
19	19	Woodhall	d		06 34	06 53	07 01		07 38	07 54	08 08		08 38		09 08		09 38		10 08	
20¼	20¼	Port Glasgow	d	06 23	06 37	06 56	07 04	07 23	07 41	07 57	08 11	08 18	08 41	08 51	09 11	09 16	09 41	09 51	10 11	10 16
—	22½	Whinhill	d		06 41		07 08					08 22				09 21				10 21
—	23	Drumfrochar	d		06 44		07 11					08 25				09 23				10 23
—	24¾	Branchton	d		06 47		07 14					08 28				09 26				10 26
—	25½	I.B.M. §	d		06 49		07 16					08 30				09 29				10 29
—	28¾	Inverkip	d		06 54		07 25					08 35				09 34				10 34
—	31	**Wemyss Bay**	a		07 00		07 30					08 40				09 40				10 40
21¼	—	Bogston	d			06 58		07 25	07 43	07 59	08 13		08 43		09 13		09 43		10 13	
22	—	Cartsdyke	d	06 26		07 01		07 27	07 45	08 01	08 15		08 45		09 15		09 45		10 15	
23	—	Greenock Central	d	06 28		07 03		07 29	07 47	08 03	08 17		08 47	08 56	09 17		09 47	09 56	10 17	
23¾	—	Greenock West	d	06 31		07 05		07 32	07 50	08 06	08 20		08 50	08 59	09 20		09 50	09 59	10 20	
25	—	Fort Matilda	d			07 08		07 35	07 53	08 09	08 23		08 53	09 02	09 23		09 53	10 02	10 23	
26¼	—	**Gourock**	a	06 36		07 13		07 39	07 57	08 13	08 27		08 57	09 07	09 27		09 58	10 06	10 27	

Station		SR		SR	SR	SR	SR	SR	SR	SR	SR	SR	SR	SR	SR	SR	SR	SR	SR
Glasgow Central 15 221	d	10 05		15 05	15 25	15 35	15 50	16 05	16 23	16 33	16 55	17 05	17 15	17 25	17 40	17 50	18 05	18 25	18 35
Cardonald	d	10 12		15 12		15 42		16 12	16 30	16 40		17 12	17 22		17 47		18 12		18 42
Hillington East	d	10 14		15 14		15 44		16 14	16 32	16 42		17 14	17 24		17 49		18 14		18 44
Hillington West	d	10 16		15 16		15 46	15 58	16 16	16 34	16 44	17 03	17 16			17 51		18 16		18 46
Paisley Gilmour Street 221 ⇐	d	10 20		15 20	15 36	15 50	16 02	16 20	16 38	16 48	17 07	17 20	17 29	17 36	17 55	18 01	18 20	18 36	18 50
Paisley St James	d	10 22	and at	15 22		15 52		16 22	16 40			17 22			17 57		18 22		18 52
Bishopton	d	10 28	the same	15 28	15 42	15 58	16 08	16 28	16 46	16 54	17 13	17 28	17 35		18 03	18 07	18 28	18 42	18 58
Langbank	d	10 34		15 34		16 04		16 34	16 52			17 34			18 09		18 34		19 04
Woodhall	d	10 38		15 38		16 08		16 38	16 56			17 38			18 12		18 38		19 08
Port Glasgow	d	10 41	minutes	15 41	15 51	16 11	16 18	16 41	16 59	17 04	17 23	17 41	17 45	17 50	18 14	18 18	18 41	18 51	19 11
Whinhill	d		past				16 22			17 08			17 49			18 22			
Drumfrochar	d						16 25			17 11			17 52			18 25			
Branchton	d		each				16 28			17 14			17 55			18 28			
I.B.M. §	d						16 30						17 57			18 30			
Inverkip	d		hour until				16 35			17 19			18 02			18 35			
Wemyss Bay	a						16 40			17 25			18 08			18 41			
Bogston	d	10 43		15 43		16 13		16 43	17 01		17 25	17 43			18 18		18 43		19 13
Cartsdyke	d	10 45		15 45		16 15		16 45	17 03		17 27	17 45			18 20		18 45		19 15
Greenock Central	d	10 47		15 47	15 56	16 17		16 47	17 05		17 29	17 47		17 55	18 22		18 47	18 56	19 17
Greenock West	d	10 50		15 50	15 59	16 20		16 50	17 08		17 32	17 50		17 57	18 25		18 50	18 59	19 20
Fort Matilda	d	10 53		15 53	16 02	16 23		16 53	17 11		17 35	17 53		18 00	18 28		18 53	19 02	19 23
Gourock	a	10 57		15 57	16 06	16 27		16 57	17 15		17 39	17 57		18 05	18 32		18 57	19 06	19 27

Station		SR	SR	SR	SR	SR	SR	SR	SR	SR	SR	SR	SR	SR	SR	SR	SR
Glasgow Central 15 221	d	18 50	19 05	19 25	19 35	19 50	20 05	20 35	20 50	21 05	21 35	21 50	22 05	22 35	22 50	23 20	23 50
Cardonald	d		19 12		19 42		20 12	20 42		21 12	21 42		22 12	22 42		23 27	23 57
Hillington East	d		19 14		19 44		20 14	20 44		21 14	21 44		22 14	22 44		23 29	23 59
Hillington West	d		19 16		19 46		20 16	20 46		21 16	21 46		22 16	22 46		23 31	00 01
Paisley Gilmour Street 221 ⇐	d	19 01	19 20	19 36	19 50	20 01	20 20	20 50	21 01	21 20	21 50	22 01	22 20	22 50	23 01	23 35	00 05
Paisley St James	d		19 22		19 52		20 22	20 52		21 22	21 52		22 22	22 52		23 37	00 07
Bishopton	d	19 07	19 28	19 42	19 58	20 07	20 28	20 58	21 07	21 28	21 58	22 07	22 28	22 58	23 07	23 43	00 13
Langbank	d		19 34		20 04		20 34	21 04		21 34	22 04		22 34	23 04		23 49	00 19
Woodhall	d		19 38		20 08		20 38	21 08		21 38	22 08		22 38	23 08		23 53	00 23
Port Glasgow	d	19 16	19 41	19 51	20 11	20 16	20 41	21 11	21 16	21 41	22 11	22 16	22 41	23 11	23 16	23 56	00 26
Whinhill	d	19 21			20 15			21 15			22 15			23 15			
Drumfrochar	d	19 23			20 18			21 18			22 18			23 18			
Branchton	d	19 26			20 21			21 21			22 21			23 21			
I.B.M. §	d	19 29			20 23			21 23			22 23			23 23			
Inverkip	d	19 34			20 28			21 28			22 28			23 28			
Wemyss Bay	a	19 40			20 34			21 34			22 34			23 34			
Bogston	d		19 43				20 43			21 43			22 43			23 58	00 28
Cartsdyke	d		19 45			20 20	20 45		21 20	21 45		22 20	22 45		23 20	23 59	00 30
Greenock Central	d		19 47	19 56		20 22	20 47		21 22	21 47		22 22	22 47		23 22	00 02	00 32
Greenock West	d		19 50	19 59		20 24	20 50		21 24	21 50		22 24	22 50		23 24	00 05	00 35
Fort Matilda	d		19 53	20 02		20 27	20 53		21 27	21 53		22 29	22 53		23 29	00 08	00 38
Gourock	a		19 57	20 06		20 32	20 57		21 32	21 57		22 33	22 57		23 33	00 12	00 42

For general notes see front of timetable
For details of catering facilities see
Directory of Train Operators

§ For authorised access to and from I.B.M. only

b Saturdays dep. 1 minute earlier

Sundays

until 23 November

Glasgow Central → Wemyss Bay and Gourock

Network Diagram - see first page of Table 216

		SR	SR	SR	SR	SR	SR	SR	SR A	SR		SR	SR	SR	SR	SR	SR
Glasgow Central 15	221 d	07 20	07 50	08 20	08 50	09 20	09 50	10 20	10 50	11 20	and at the same minutes past each hour until	19 20	19 50	20 20	21 20	22 20	23 20
Cardonald	d	07 27		08 27		09 27		10 27		11 27		19 27		20 27	21 27	22 27	23 27
Hillington East	d	07 29	07 58	08 29	08 58	09 29	09 58	10 29	10 58	11 29		19 29	19 58	20 29	21 29	22 29	23 29
Hillington West	d	07 31		08 31		09 31		10 31		11 31		19 31		20 31	21 31	22 31	23 31
Paisley Gilmour Street	221 ✈ d	07 35	08 03	08 35	09 03	09 35	10 03	10 35	11 03	11 35		19 35	20 03	20 35	21 35	22 35	23 35
Paisley St James	d			08 37		09 37		10 37		11 37		19 37		20 37	21 37	22 37	23 37
Bishopton	d	07 41	08 09	08 43	09 09	09 43	10 09	10 43	11 09	11 43		19 43	20 09	20 43	21 43	22 43	23 43
Langbank	d			08 49		09 49		10 49		11 49		19 49		20 49	21 49	22 49	23 49
Woodhall	d	07 49		08 53		09 53		10 53		11 53		19 53		20 53	21 53	22 53	23 53
Port Glasgow	d	07 52	08 19	08 56	09 19	09 56	10 19	10 56	11 19	11 56		19 56	20 19	20 56	21 56	22 56	23 56
Whinhill	d		08 23		09 23		10 23		11 23				20 23				
Drumfrochar	d		08 26		09 26		10 26		11 26				20 26				
Branchton	d		08 29		09 29		10 29		11 29				20 29				
I.B.M. §	d		08 31		09 31		10 31		11 31				20 31				
Inverkip	d		08 36		09 36		10 36		11 36				20 36				
Wemyss Bay	a		08 42		09 42		10 42		11 42				20 42				
Bogston	d	07 54		08 58		09 58		10 58		11 58		19 58		20 58	21 58	22 58	23 58
Cartsdyke	d	07 56		09 00		10 00		11 00		12 00		20 00		21 00	22 00	23 00	23 59
Greenock Central	d	07 58		09 02		10 02		11 02		12 02		20 02		21 02	22 02	23 02	00 02
Greenock West	d	08 01		09 05		10 05		11 05		12 05		20 05		21 05	22 05	23 05	00 05
Fort Matilda	d			09 08		10 08		11 08		12 08		20 08		21 08	22 08	23 08	00 08
Gourock	a	08 06		09 12		10 12		11 12		12 12		20 12		21 12	22 12	23 12	00 12

Sundays

from 30 November

		SR	SR	SR	SR	SR	SR	SR	SR	SR	SR A	SR	SR		SR	SR	SR	SR	SR	SR	SR	SR	SR	SR
Glasgow Central 15	221 d	07 20	07 50	08 20	08 50	09 20	09 35	09 50	10 20	10 35	10 50	11 20	11 35	and at the same minutes past each hour until	17 35	17 50	18 20	18 50	19 20	19 50	20 20	21 20	22 20	23 20
Cardonald	d	07 27		08 27		09 27	09 42		10 27	10 42		11 27	11 42		17 42		18 27		19 27		20 27	21 27	22 27	23 27
Hillington East	d	07 29	07 58	08 29	08 58	09 29	09 44	09 58	10 29	10 44	10 58	11 29	11 44		17 44	17 58	18 29	18 58	19 29	19 58	20 29	21 29	22 29	23 29
Hillington West	d	07 31		08 31		09 31	09 46		10 31	10 46		11 31	11 46		17 46		18 31		19 31		20 31	21 31	22 31	23 31
Paisley Gilmour Street	221 ✈ d	07 35	08 03	08 35	09 03	09 35	09 50	10 03	10 35	10 50	11 03	11 35	11 50		17 50	18 03	18 35	19 03	19 35	20 03	20 35	21 35	22 35	23 35
Paisley St James	d			08 37		09 37	09 52		10 37	10 52		11 37	11 52		17 52		18 37		19 37		20 37	21 37	22 37	23 37
Bishopton	d	07 41	08 09	08 43	09 09	09 43	09 58	10 09	10 43	10 58	11 09	11 43	11 58		17 58	18 09	18 43	19 09	19 43	20 09	20 43	21 43	22 43	23 43
Langbank	d			08 49		09 49	10 04		10 49	11 04		11 49	12 04		18 04		18 49		19 49		20 49	21 49	22 49	23 49
Woodhall	d	07 49		08 53		09 53	10 08		10 53	11 08		11 53	12 08		18 08		18 53		19 53		20 53	21 53	22 53	23 53
Port Glasgow	d	07 52	08 19	08 56	09 19	09 56	10 11	10 19	10 56	11 11	11 19	11 56	12 11		18 11	18 19	18 56	19 19	19 56	20 19	20 56	21 56	22 56	23 56
Whinhill	d		08 23		09 23			10 23			11 23					18 23		19 23		20 23				
Drumfrochar	d		08 26		09 26			10 26			11 26					18 26		19 26		20 26				
Branchton	d		08 29		09 29			10 29			11 29					18 29		19 29		20 29				
I.B.M. §	d		08 31		09 31			10 31			11 31					18 31		19 31		20 31				
Inverkip	d		08 36		09 36			10 36			11 36					18 36		19 36		20 36				
Wemyss Bay	a		08 42		09 42			10 42			11 42					18 42		19 42		20 42				
Bogston	d	07 54		08 58		09 58	10 13		10 58	11 13		11 58	12 13		18 13		18 58		19 58		20 58	21 58	22 58	23 58
Cartsdyke	d	07 56		09 00		10 00	10 15		11 00	11 15		12 00	12 15		18 15		19 00		20 00		21 00	22 00	23 00	23 59
Greenock Central	d	07 58		09 02		10 02	10 17		11 02	11 17		12 02	12 17		18 17		19 02		20 02		21 02	22 02	23 02	00 02
Greenock West	d	08 01		09 05		10 05	10 20		11 05	11 20		12 05	12 20		18 20		19 05		20 05		21 05	22 05	23 05	00 05
Fort Matilda	d			09 08		10 08	10 23		11 08	11 23		12 08	12 23		18 23		19 08		20 08		21 08	22 08	23 08	00 08
Gourock	a	08 06		09 12		10 12	10 27		11 12	11 27		12 12	12 27		18 27		19 12		20 12		21 12	22 12	23 12	00 12

For general notes see front of timetable
For details of catering facilities see
Directory of Train Operators

§ For authorised access to and from I.B.M. only

A 1150 from Glasgow Central arr. Wemyss Bay 1243. 1250 from Glasgow Central stops additionally at Hillington West 1300

Gourock and Wemyss Bay → Glasgow Central

Network Diagram - see first page of Table 216

Miles	Miles			SR	SR SX	SR SO	SR SX	SR A	SR SX	SR SO	SR	SR SX	SR SO	SR SX	SR	SR	SR SX	SR	SR	SR B	SR
0	—	**Gourock**	d	06 05	06 22	06 36	06 44		07 06	07 06		07 22	07 36	07 47	07 52		08 08	08 24	08 36		09 06
1¼	—	Fort Matilda	d	06 08	06 25	06 39	06 47		07 09	07 09		07 25	07 39		07 55		08 11	08 27	08 39		09 09
2¼	—	Greenock West	d	06 11	06 28	06 42	06 50		07 12	07 12		07 28	07 42	07 52	07 58		08 14	08 30	08 42		09 12
3¼	—	Greenock Central	d	06 14	06 31	06 45	06 53		07 15	07 15		07 31	07 45	07 55	08 01		08 17	08 33	08 45		09 15
4¼	—	Cartsdyke	d	06 16	06 33	06 47	06 55		07 17	07 17		07 33	07 47		08 03			08 35	08 47		09 17
5	—	Bogston	d		06 35	06 49	06 57		07 19	07 19		07 35	07 49		08 05			08 37	08 49		09 19
—	0	**Wemyss Bay**	d								07 13					07 50				08 50	
—	2¼	Inverkip	d								07 18					07 54				08 54	
—	4¾	I.B.M. §	d								07 23					07 59				08 59	
—	6¼	Branchton	d								07 25					08 02				09 02	
—	8	Drumfrochar	d								07 28					08 04				09 04	
—	8½	Whinhill	d								07 30					08 07				09 07	
6	10¾	Port Glasgow	d	06 19	06 38	06 52	07 00		07 22	07 22	07 35	07 38	07 52	07 59	08 08	08 11	08 21	08 40	08 52	09 11	09 22
7¼	12	Woodhall	d		06 40	06 54	07 02			07 24	07 37	07 40	07 54		08 10	08 14		08 42	08 54		09 24
10	14¾	Langbank	d		06 45	06 59	07 07			07 29		07 45	07 59			08 18		08 47	08 59		09 29
14	18	Bishopton	d	06 28	06 50	07 04	07 12		07 31	07 34	07 45	07 50	08 04	08 08	08 18	08 24	08 30	08 52	09 04	09 20	09 34
18¾	22¼	Paisley St James	d	06 34	06 56	07 10	07 18			07 40		07 56	08 10			08 29		08 58	09 10		09 40
19	23	Paisley Gilmour Street 221 ⇄	d	06 37	06 59	07 13	07 21	07 34	07 38	07 43	07 52	07 59	08 13	08 15	08 25	08 32	08 37	09 01	09 13	09 27	09 43
21¼	25¼	Hillington West	d	06 40	07 02	07 16	07 24	07 38	07 41	07 46	07 55	08 02	08 16	08 18	08 28			09 04	09 16		09 46
21¾	25¾	Hillington East	d	06 42	07 04	07 18	07 26		07 43	07 48	07 57	08 04	08 18	08 20	08 30			09 06	09 18		09 48
22½	26½	Cardonald	d	06 44	07 06	07 20	07 28		07 45	07 50	07 59	08 06	08 20	08 22	08 32			09 08	09 20		09 50
26½	31	**Glasgow Central** 15	221 a	06 52	07 14	07 28	07 36	07 47	07 54	07 58	08 07	08 14	08 28	08 30	08 40	08 44	08 48	09 16	09 28	09 38	09 58

		SR		SR	SR	SR	SR	SR	SR	SR	SR	SR	SR	SR	SR	SR	SR	SR	SR
Gourock	d	09 23		14 23	14 36		15 06	15 23	15 36		16 06	16 23	16 36		17 06	17 23	17 45		18 06	18 23
Fort Matilda	d	09 26		14 26	14 39		15 09	15 26	15 39		16 09	16 26	16 39		17 09	17 26	17 48		18 09	18 26
Greenock West	d	09 29		14 29	14 42		15 12	15 29	15 42		16 12	16 29	16 42		17 12	17 29	17 51		18 12	18 29
Greenock Central	d	09 32		14 32	14 45		15 15	15 32	15 45		16 15	16 32	16 45		17 15	17 32	17 54		18 15	18 32
Cartsdyke	d				14 47		15 17		15 47		16 17		16 47		17 17		17 56		18 17	
Bogston	d		and at		14 49		15 19		15 49		16 19		16 49		17 19		17 58		18 19	
Wemyss Bay	d		the same			14 50				15 55				16 45				17 49		
Inverkip	d		minutes			14 54				15 59				16 49				17 53		
I.B.M. §	d		past			14 59				16 04				16 54				18 02		
Branchton	d		each			15 02				16 07				16 57				18 04		
Drumfrochar	d		hour until			15 04				16 09				16 59				18 07		
Whinhill	d					15 07				16 12				17 02				18 09		
Port Glasgow	d	09 36		14 36	14 52	15 11	15 22	15 36	15 52	16 16	16 22	16 36	16 52	17 06	17 22	17 36	18 01	18 14	18 22	18 36
Woodhall	d				14 54		15 24		15 54		16 24		16 54		17 24		18 03		18 24	
Langbank	d				14 59		15 29		15 59		16 29		16 59		17 29		18 08		18 29	
Bishopton	d	09 45		14 45	15 04	15 20	15 34	15 45	16 04	16 25	16 34	16 45	17 04	17 15	17 34	17 45	18 13	18 23	18 34	18 45
Paisley St James	d				15 10		15 40		16 10		16 40		17 10		17 40		18 19		18 40	
Paisley Gilmour Street 221 ⇄	d	09 52		14 52	15 13	15 27	15 43	15 52	16 13	16 32	16 43	16 52	17 13	17 22	17 43	17 52	18 22	18 31	18 43	18 52
Hillington West	d				15 16		15 46	15 55	16 16		16 46	16 55	17 16		17 46		18 25		18 46	
Hillington East	d				15 18		15 48		16 18		16 48		17 18		17 48		18 27		18 48	
Cardonald	d				15 20		15 50		16 20		16 50		17 20		17 50		18 29		18 50	
Glasgow Central 15	221 a	10 03		15 03	15 28	15 38	15 58	16 05	16 28	16 43	16 58	17 05	17 28	17 33	17 58	18 03	18 39	18 43	18 58	19 03

		SR	SR	SR	SR	SR	SR	SR	SR	SR	SR	SR	SR	SR SX	SR SO	SR	SR	SR	SR	SR SO
Gourock	d		18 40		19 06	19 20	19 45		20 20	20 45		21 20	21 45			22 20	22 45		23 20	
Fort Matilda	d		18 43		19 09	19 23	19 48		20 23	20 48		21 23	21 48			22 23	22 48		23 23	
Greenock West	d		18 46		19 12	19 26	19 51		20 26	20 51		21 26	21 51			22 26	22 51		23 26	
Greenock Central	d		18 49		19 15	19 29	19 54		20 29	20 54		21 29	21 54			22 29	22 54		23 29	
Cartsdyke	d		18 51		19 17	19 31	19 56		20 31	20 56		21 31	21 56			22 31	22 56		23 31	
Bogston	d		18 53		19 19	19 33			20 33			21 33				22 33			23 33	
Wemyss Bay	d	18 23		18 55				19 45			20 44			21 44	21 50			22 44		23 40
Inverkip	d	18 27		18 59				19 48			20 48			21 48	21 54			22 48		23 44
I.B.M. §	d	18 36		19 04				19 53			20 53			21 53	21 59			22 53		23 49
Branchton	d	18 38		19 07				19 56			20 56			21 56	22 02			22 56		23 52
Drumfrochar	d	18 41		19 09				19 58			20 58			21 58	22 04			22 58		23 54
Whinhill	d	18 43		19 12				20 01			21 01			22 01	22 07			23 01		23 57
Port Glasgow	d	18 48	18 56	19 16	19 22	19 36	19 59	20 06	20 36	20 59	21 06	21 36	21 59	22 06	22 11	22 36	22 59	23 06	23 36	00 01
Woodhall	d		18 58		19 24	19 38		20 08	20 38		21 08	21 38		22 08	22 14	22 38		23 08	23 38	
Langbank	d		19 03		19 29	19 43		20 13	20 43		21 13	21 43		22 13	22 18	22 43		23 13	23 43	
Bishopton	d	18 57	19 08	19 25	19 34	19 48	20 08	20 18	20 48	21 08	21 18	21 48	22 08	22 18	22 24	22 48	23 08	23 18	23 48	00 10
Paisley St James	d		19 14		19 40	19 54		20 24	20 54		21 24	21 54		22 24	22 29	22 54		23 24	23 54	
Paisley Gilmour Street 221 ⇄	d	19 03	19 17	19 32	19 43	19 57	20 15	20 27	20 57	21 15	21 27	21 57	22 15	22 27	22 32	22 57	23 17	23 27	23 57	00 17
Hillington West	d		19 20		19 46	20 00		20 30	21 00		21 30	22 00		22 30	22 35	23 00		23 30	00 01	
Hillington East	d		19 22		19 48	20 02		20 32	21 02		21 32	22 02		22 32	22 37	23 02		23 32	00 02	
Cardonald	d		19 24		19 50	20 04		20 34	21 04		21 34	22 04		22 34	22 39	23 04		23 34	00 04	
Glasgow Central 15	221 a	19 15	19 32	19 43	19 58	20 12	20 26	20 43	21 12	21 26	21 42	22b15	22 26	22 42	22 46	23 14	23c30	23 42	00 12	00 28

For general notes see front of timetable
For details of catering facilities see Directory of Train Operators

§ For authorised access to and from I.B.M. only

A From Largs (Table 221)

B 1050 from Wemyss Bay departs 1055 and runs 5 minutes later throughout arr. Glasgow Central 1143

b Saturdays arr. 2214

c Saturdays arr. 2328

Table 219

Sundays

until 23 November

Gourock and Wemyss Bay → Glasgow Central

Network Diagram - see first page of Table 216

		SR	SR	SR	SR	SR	SR	SR	SR	SR	SR	SR	SR	SR
Gourock	d	08 20		09 20		10 20		11 20		12 20		13 20		14 20
Fort Matilda	d	08 23		09 23		10 23		11 23		12 23		13 23		14 23
Greenock West	d	08 26		09 26		10 26		11 26		12 26		13 26		14 26
Greenock Central	d	08 29		09 29		10 29		11 29		12 29		13 29		14 29
Cartsdyke	d	08 31		09 31		10 31		11 31		12 31		13 31		14 31
Bogston	d	08 33		09 33		10 33		11 33		12 33		13 33		14 33
Wemyss Bay	d		08 50		09 50		10 55		11 50		12 50		13 50	
Inverkip	d		08 54		09 54		10 59		11 54		12 54		13 54	
I.B.M. §	d		08 59		09 59		11 04		11 59		12 59		13 59	
Branchton	d		09 02		10 02		11 07		12 02		13 02		14 02	
Drumfrochar	d		09 04		10 04		11 09		12 04		13 04		14 04	
Whinhill	d		09 07		10 07		11 12		12 07		13 07		14 07	
Port Glasgow	d	08 36	09 11	09 36	10 11	10 36	11 16	11 36	12 11	12 36	13 11	13 36	14 11	14 36
Woodhall	d	08 38		09 38		10 38		11 38		12 38		13 38		14 38
Langbank	d	08 43		09 43		10 43		11 43		12 43		13 43		14 43
Bishopton	d	08 48	09 20	09 48	10 20	10 48	11 25	11 48	12 20	12 48	13 20	13 48	14 20	14 48
Paisley St James	d	08 54		09 54		10 54		11 53		12 54		13 54		14 54
Paisley Gilmour Street 221 ✈	d	08 57	09 28	09 57	10 28	10 57	11 32	11 57	12 28	12 57	13 27	13 57	14 27	14 57
Hillington West	d	09 00		10 00		11 00		12 00		13 00		14 00		15 00
Hillington East	d	09 02	09 32	10 02	10 32	11 02	11 36	12 02	12 32	13 02	13 31	14 02	14 31	15 02
Cardonald	d	09 04		10 04		11 04		12 04		13 04		14 04		15 04
Glasgow Central 15 221	a	09 12	09 40	10 12	10 40	11 12	11 46	12 12	12 40	13 12	13 40	14 12	14 40	15 12

		SR	SR	SR	SR	SR	SR	SR	SR	SR	SR	SR	SR	SR	SR	SR
Gourock	d		15 20		16 20		17 20		18 20		19 20		20 20		21 20	22 20
Fort Matilda	d		15 23		16 23		17 23		18 23		19 23		20 23		21 23	22 23
Greenock West	d		15 26		16 26		17 26		18 26		19 26		20 26		21 26	22 26
Greenock Central	d		15 29		16 29		17 29		18 29		19 29		20 29		21 29	22 29
Cartsdyke	d		15 31		16 31		17 31		18 31		19 31		20 31		21 31	22 31
Bogston	d		15 33		16 33		17 33		18 33		19 33		20 33		21 33	22 33
Wemyss Bay	d	14 50		15 55		16 50		17 50		18 55		19 50		20 50		
Inverkip	d	14 54		15 59		16 54		17 54		18 59		19 54		20 54		
I.B.M. §	d	14 59		16 04		16 59		17 59		19 04		19 59		20 59		
Branchton	d	15 02		16 07		17 02		18 02		19 07		20 02		21 02		
Drumfrochar	d	15 04		16 09		17 04		18 04		19 09		20 04		21 04		
Whinhill	d	15 07		16 12		17 07		18 07		19 12		20 07		21 07		
Port Glasgow	d	15 11	15 36	16 16	16 36	17 11	17 36	18 11	18 36	19 16	19 36	20 11	20 36	21 11	21 36	22 36
Woodhall	d		15 38		16 38		17 38		18 38		19 38		20 38		21 38	22 38
Langbank	d		15 43		16 43		17 43		18 43		19 43		20 43		21 43	22 43
Bishopton	d	15 20	15 48	16 25	16 48	17 20	17 48	18 20	18 48	19 25	19 48	20 20	20 48	21 20	21 48	22 48
Paisley St James	d		15 54		16 54		17 54		18 54		19 54		20 54		21 54	22 54
Paisley Gilmour Street 221 ✈	d	15 27	15 57	16 32	16 57	17 27	17 57	18 27	18 57	19 32	19 57	20 27	20 57	21 27	21 57	22 57
Hillington West	d		16 00		17 00		18 00		19 00		20 00		21 00		22 00	23 00
Hillington East	d	15 31	16 02	16 36	17 02	17 31	18 02	18 31	19 02	19 36	20 02	20 31	21 02	21 31	22 02	23 02
Cardonald	d		16 04		17 04		18 04		19 04		20 04		21 04		22 04	23 04
Glasgow Central 15 221	a	15 40	16 12	16 45	17 12	17 40	18 12	18 40	19 12	19 44	20 12	20 40	21 12	21 40	22 12	23 12

Sundays

from 30 November

		SR	SR	SR	SR	SR	SR	SR	SR	SR	SR	SR	SR	SR	SR	SR	SR	SR	SR	SR
Gourock	d	08 20		09 20	09 36		10 20	10 36		11 20	11 36		12 20	12 36		13 20	13 36		14 20	14 36
Fort Matilda	d	08 23		09 23	09 39		10 23	10 39		11 23	11 39		12 23	12 39		13 23	13 39		14 23	14 39
Greenock West	d	08 26		09 26	09 42		10 26	10 42		11 26	11 42		12 26	12 42		13 26	13 42		14 26	14 42
Greenock Central	d	08 29		09 29	09 45		10 29	10 45		11 29	11 45		12 29	12 45		13 29	13 45		14 29	14 45
Cartsdyke	d	08 31		09 31	09 47		10 31	10 47		11 31	11 47		12 31	12 47		13 31	13 47		14 31	14 47
Bogston	d	08 33		09 33	09 49		10 33	10 49		11 33	11 49		12 33	12 49		13 33	13 49		14 33	14 49
Wemyss Bay	d		08 50			09 50			10 55			11 50			12 50			13 50		
Inverkip	d		08 54			09 54			10 59			11 54			12 54			13 54		
I.B.M. §	d		08 59			09 59			11 04			11 59			12 59			13 59		
Branchton	d		09 02			10 02			11 07			12 02			13 02			14 02		
Drumfrochar	d		09 04			10 04			11 09			12 04			13 04			14 04		
Whinhill	d		09 07			10 07			11 12			12 07			13 07			14 07		
Port Glasgow	d	08 36	09 11	09 36	09 52	10 11	10 36	10 52	11 16	11 36	11 52	12 11	12 36	12 52	13 11	13 36	13 52	14 11	14 36	14 52
Woodhall	d	08 38		09 38	09 54		10 38	10 54		11 38	11 54		12 38	12 54		13 38	13 54		14 38	14 54
Langbank	d	08 43		09 43	09 59		10 43	10 59		11 43	11 59		12 43	12 59		13 43	13 59		14 43	14 59
Bishopton	d	08 48	09 20	09 48	10 04	10 20	10 48	11 04	11 25	11 48	12 04	12 20	12 48	13 04	13 20	13 48	14 04	14 20	14 48	15 04
Paisley St James	d	08 54		09 54	10 10		10 54	11 10		11 53	12 10		12 54	13 10		13 54	14 10		14 54	15 10
Paisley Gilmour Street 221 ✈	d	08 57	09 28	09 57	10 13	10 28	10 57	11 13	11 32	11 57	12 13	12 28	12 57	13 13	13 27	13 57	14 13	14 27	14 57	15 13
Hillington West	d	09 00		10 00	10 16		11 00	11 16		12 00	12 16		13 00	13 18		14 00	14 16		15 00	15 16
Hillington East	d	09 02	09 32	10 02	10 18	10 32	11 02	11 18	11 36	12 02	12 18	12 32	13 02	13 20	13 31	14 02	14 18	14 31	15 02	15 18
Cardonald	d	09 04		10 04	10 20		11 04	11 20		12 04	12 20		13 04	13 22		14 04	14 20		15 04	15 20
Glasgow Central 15 221	a	09 12	09 41	10 12	10 29	10 41	11 12	11 29	11 46	12 12	12 28	12 41	13 12	13 29	13 41	14 12	14 28	14 41	15 12	15 28

For general notes see front of timetable
For details of catering facilities see
Directory of Train Operators

§ For authorised access to and from I.B.M. only

Table 219

Sundays

from 30 November

Gourock and Wemyss Bay → Glasgow Central

Network Diagram - see first page of Table 216

		SR	SR	SR		SR	SR	SR		SR	SR	SR		SR	SR	SR		SR	SR	SR		SR	SR	SR		
Gourock	d		15 20	15 36			16 20	16 36			17 20	17 36			18 20			19 20		20 20			21 20	22 20		
Fort Matilda	d		15 23	15 39			16 23	16 39			17 23	17 39			18 23			19 23		20 23			21 23	22 23		
Greenock West	d		15 26	15 42			16 26	16 42			17 26	17 42			18 26			19 26		20 26			21 26	22 26		
Greenock Central	d		15 29	15 45			16 29	16 45			17 29	17 45			18 29			19 29		20 29			21 29	22 29		
Cartsdyke	d		15 31	15 47			16 31	16 47			17 31	17 47			18 31			19 31		20 31			21 31	22 31		
Bogston	d		15 33	15 49			16 33	16 49			17 33	17 49			18 33			19 33		20 33			21 33	22 33		
Wemyss Bay	d	14 50				15 55				16 50				17 50		18 55			19 50			20 50				
Inverkip	d	14 54				15 59				16 54				17 54		18 59			19 54			20 54				
I.B.M. §	d	14 59				16 04				16 59				17 59		19 04			19 59			20 59				
Branchton	d	15 02				16 07				17 02				18 02		19 07			20 02			21 02				
Drumfrochar	d	15 04				16 09				17 04				18 04		19 09			20 04			21 04				
Whinhill	d	15 07				16 12				17 07				18 07		19 12			20 07			21 07				
Port Glasgow	d	15 11	15 36	15 52		16 16	16 36	16 52		17 11	17 36	17 52		18 11	18 36	19 16		19 36	20 11	20 36		21 11	21 36	22 36		
Woodhall	d		15 38	15 54			16 38	16 54			17 38	17 54			18 38			19 38		20 38			21 38	22 38		
Langbank	d		15 43	15 59			16 43	16 59			17 43	17 59			18 43			19 43		20 43			21 43	22 43		
Bishopton	d	15 20	15 48	16 04		16 25	16 48	17 04		17 20	17 48	18 04		18 20	18 48	19 25		19 48	20 20	20 48		21 20	21 48	22 48		
Paisley St James	d		15 54	16 10			16 54	17 10			17 54	18 10			18 54			19 54		20 54			21 54	22 54		
Paisley Gilmour Street 221 ⇌	d	15 27	15 57	16 13		16 32	16 57	17 13		17 27	17 57	18 13		18 27	18 57	19 32		19 57	20 27	20 57		21 27	21 57	22 57		
Hillington West	d		16 00	16 16			17 00	17 16			18 00	18 16			19 00			20 00		21 00			22 00	23 00		
Hillington East	d	15 31	16 02	16 18		16 36	17 02	17 18		17 31	18 02	18 18		18 31	19 02	19 36		20 02	20 31	21 02		21 31	22 02	23 02		
Cardonald	d		16 04	16 20			17 04	17 20			18 04	18 20			19 04			20 04		21 04			22 04	23 04		
Glasgow Central 15 221	a	15 41	16 12	16 28		16 45	17 12	17 28		17 41	18 12	18 28		18 40	19 12	19 44		20 12	20 40	21 12		21 40	22 12	23 12		

For general notes see front of timetable
For details of catering facilities see
Directory of Train Operators

§ For authorised access to and from I.B.M. only

until 18 October

Glasgow and Gourock → Dunoon, Kilcreggan and Helensburgh Pier

Cowal Ferries Ltd in association with First ScotRail Limited

All Kilcreggan and Helensburgh Pier sailings operated by Clyde Marine Motoring Ltd. Tel 01475 721281

			SX		SX	SX		SX																		
Glasgow Central 15	219 d	05 55	05 55		06 25	06 25		06 55	07 05		07 25	07 35		08 25	09 05		09 25	10 25		10 35	11 25		11 25	12 25		13 25
Paisley Gilmour Street	219 d	06 07	06 07		06 36	06 36		07 07	07 20		07 40	07 50		08 36	09 20		09 36	10 36		10 50	11 36		11 36	12 36		13 36
Gourock	219 a	06 36	06 36		07 13	07 13		07 39	07 57		08 13	08 27		09 07	09 58		10 06	11 06		11 27	12 06		12 06	13 06		14 06
Gourock	d	**06 50**	**07 00**		**07 20**	**07 30**		**07 50**	**08 05**		**08 20**	**08 35**		**09 20**	**10 05**		**10 20**	**11 20**		**11 35**	**12 20**		**12 25**	**13 20**		**14 15**
Dunoon	a	**07 13**			**07 43**			**08 13**			**08 43**			**09 43**			**10 43**	**11 43**			**12 43**			**13 43**		
Kilcreggan	d		**07 12**			**07 42**			**08 17**						**10 20**					**11 47**			**12 37**			**14 30**
Helensburgh Pier	a											**09 05**			**10 45**											**14 55**

														SX												
Glasgow Central 15	219 d	13 25	14 25		14 35	15 25		15 25	15 35		16 05	16 23		16 23	17 25		17 25	18 25		19 25						
Paisley Gilmour Street	219 d	13 36	14 36		14 50	15 36		15 36	15 50		16 20	16 38		16 38	17 36		17 36	18 36		19 36						
Gourock	219 a	14 06	15 06		15 27	16 06		16 06	16 27		16 57	17 15		17 15	18 05		18 05	19 06		20 06						
Gourock	d	**14 20**	**15 20**		**15 45**	**16 15**		**16 20**	**16 50**		**17 20**	**17 25**		**17 45**	**18 10**		**18 20**	**19 20**		**20 18**						
Dunoon	a	**14 43**	**15 43**					**16 43**			**17 43**			**18 08**			**18 43**	**19 43**		**20 41**						
Kilcreggan	d				**15 57**	**16 27**			**17 03**			**17 37**			**18 25**											
Helensburgh Pier	a														**18 50**											

Sundays

until 12 October

Glasgow Central 15	219 d	07 20	08 20	09 20		09 20	10 20	10 20		11 20	11 20	12 20		13 20	13 20	14 20		14 20	15 20	16 20		17 20	18 20	19 20		
Paisley Gilmour Street	219 d	07 35	08 35	09 35		09 35	10 35	10 35		11 35	11 35	12 35		13 35	13 35	14 35		14 35	15 35	16 35		17 35	18 35	19 35		
Gourock	219 a	08 06	09 12	09 12		10 12	11 12	11 12		12 12	12 12	13 12		14 12	14 12	15 12		15 12	16 12	17 12		18 12	19 12	20 12		
Gourock	d	**08 20**	**09 20**	**10 20**		**11 15**	**11 20**	**11 45**		**12 20**	**13 15**	**13 20**		**14 20**	**14 25**	**15 20**		**16 15**	**16 20**	**17 20**		**18 20**	**19 20**	**20 18**		
Dunoon	a	**08 43**	**09 43**	**10 43**			**11 43**			**12 43**		**13 43**		**14 43**		**15 43**			**16 43**	**17 43**		**18 43**	**19 43**	**20 41**		
Kilcreggan	d					**11 27**									**14 40**			**16 27**								
Helensburgh Pier	a							**12 15**			**13 45**				**15 10**											

For general notes see front of timetable
For details of catering facilities see
Directory of Train Operators

For details of sailings from 19 October 2008 telephone Cowal Ferries on 08000 66 5000.

until 18 October

Helensburgh Pier, Kilcreggan and Dunoon → Gourock and Glasgow

Cowal Ferries Ltd in association with First ScotRail Limited

All Helensburgh Pier and Kilcreggan sailings operated by Clyde Marine Motoring Ltd. Tel 01475 721281

		SX	SX			SX		SX			SX															
Helensburgh Pier	⛴ d													09 10				10 50								
Kilcreggan	⛴ d		07 15			07 50			08 20					09 40				11 15		11 50			12 45			
Dunoon	⛴ d	06 50			07 20			07 50			08 20	08 50			09 50		10 50				11 50			12 50		13 50
Gourock	⛴ a	07 13	07 27		07 43	08 02		08 13	08 32		08 43	09 13		09 52	10 13		11 13	11 27		12 02	12 13		12 57	13 13		14 13
Gourock	219 d	07 22	07 47		07 52	08 08		08 24	09 06		09 06	09 23		10 06	10 23		11 23	11 36		12 23	12 23		13 06	13 23		14 23
Paisley Gilmour Street	219 a	07 58	08 14		08 24	08 36		09 00	09 42		09 42	09 51		10 42	10 51		11 51	12 12		12 51	12 51		13 42	13 51		14 51
Glasgow Central [15]	219 a	08 14	08 30		08 40	08 48		09 16	09 58		09 58	10 03		10 58	11 03		12 03	12 28		13 03	13 03		13 58	14 03		15 03

															SX											
Helensburgh Pier	⛴ d		15 00															18 55								
Kilcreggan	⛴ d		15 30			16 00		16 30			17 05	17 40						19 20								
Dunoon	⛴ d	14 50			15 50				16 50					17 50	18 15		18 50			19 50	20 45					
Gourock	⛴ a	15 13	15 42		16 13	16 12		16 42	17 13		17 17	17 52		18 13	18 38		19 13	19 32		20 13	21 08					
Gourock	219 d	15 23	16 06		16 23	16 23		17 06	17 23		17 23	18 06		18 23	19 06		19 20	19 45		20 20	21 20					
Paisley Gilmour Street	219 a	15 51	16 42		16 51	16 51		17 42	17 51		17 51	18 42		18 51	19 42		19 56	20 14		20 56	21 56					
Glasgow Central [15]	219 a	16 05	16 58		17 05	17 05		17 58	18 03		18 03	18 58		19 03	19 58		20 12	20 26		21 12	22 15					

Sundays

until 12 October

Helensburgh Pier	⛴ d							12 20				13 50			15 15											
Kilcreggan	⛴ d					11 30									15 45			16 30								
Dunoon	⛴ d	08 50	09 50	10 50			11 50			12 50	13 50			14 50		15 50			16 50	17 50		18 50	19 50	20 45		
Gourock	⛴ a	09 13	10 13	11 13		11 42	12 13	12 50		13 13	14 13	14 20		15 13	15 57	16 13		16 42	17 13	18 13		19 13	20 13	21 08		
Gourock	219 d	09 20	10 20	11 20		12 20	12 20	13 20		13 20	14 20	15 20		15 20	16 20	16 20		17 20	17 20	18 20		19 20	20 20	21 20		
Paisley Gilmour Street	219 a	09 56	10 56	11 56		12 56	12 56	13 56		13 56	14 56	15 56		15 56	16 56	16 56		17 56	17 56	18 56		19 56	20 56	21 56		
Glasgow Central [15]	219 a	10 12	11 12	12 12		13 12	13 12	14 12		14 12	15 12	16 12		16 12	17 12	17 12		18 12	18 12	19 12		20 12	21 12	22 12		

For general notes see front of timetable
For details of catering facilities see
Directory of Train Operators

For details of sailings from 19 October 2008 telephone Cowal Ferries on 08000 66 5000

until 18 October

Glasgow and Wemyss Bay — Rothesay (Bute)

Caledonian MacBrayne Ltd in association with First ScotRail Limited

		SX																				FSO	SO A		
Glasgow Central 15	219 d	06 05	06 32	.....	07 50	08 50	.....	09 50	10 50	.....	11 50	12 50	.....	13 50	14 50	.....	15 50	16 33	.....	17 15	17 50	18 50	19 35	20 35	.....	.....
Paisley Gilmour Street	219 d	06 20	06 47	.	08 02	09 01	.	10 01	11 01	.	12 01	13 01	.	14 01	15 01	.	16 02	16 48	.	17 29	18 01	19 01	19 50	20 50	.	.
Wemyss Bay	219 a	07 00	07 30	.....	08 40	09 40	.....	10 40	11 40	.....	12 40	13 40	.....	14 40	15 40	.....	16 40	17 25	.....	18 08	18 41	19 40	20 34	21 34	.....	.....
Wemyss Bay	⛴ d	**07 15**	**08 00**	.	**08 45**	**10 15**	.	**11 00**	**12 15**	.	**13 00**	**13 45**	.	**15 15**	**16 00**	.	**16 45**	**17 30**	.	**18 15**	**19 00**	**19 45**	**20 40**	**22 00**	.	.
Rothesay	⛴ a	**07 50**	**08 35**	.....	**09 20**	**10 50**	.....	**11 35**	**12 50**	.....	**13 35**	**14 20**	.....	**15 50**	**16 35**	.....	**17 20**	**18 05**	.....	**18 50**	**19 35**	**20 20**	**21 15**	**22 35**	.....	.....

Sundays

until 12 October

Glasgow Central 15	219 d	07 50	.....	08 50	.....	09 50	.....	10 50	.....	11 50	.....	12 50	.....	14 50	.....	15 50	.....	16 50	.....	17 50	.....	18 50	.....	.....	.....	.....
Paisley Gilmour Street	219 d	08 03	.	09 03	.	10 03	.	11 03	.	12 03	.	13 03	.	15 03	.	16 03	.	17 03	.	18 03	.	19 03	.	.	.	.
Wemyss Bay	219 a	08 42	.....	09 42	.....	10 42	.....	11 42	.....	12 43	.....	13 42	.....	15 42	.....	16 42	.....	17 42	.....	18 42	.....	19 42	.....	.....	.....	.....
Wemyss Bay	⛴ d	**08 45**	.	**10 15**	.	**11 00**	.	**12 15**	.	**13 00**	.	**14 30**	.	**16 00**	.	**17 30**	.	**18 15**	.	**19 00**	.	**19 45**	.	.	.	.
Rothesay	⛴ a	**09 20**	.....	**10 50**	.....	**11 35**	.....	**12 50**	.....	**13 35**	.....	**15 05**	.....	**16 35**	.....	**18 05**	.....	**18 50**	.....	**19 35**	.....	**20 20**	.....	.....	.....	.....

Mondays to Saturdays

until 18 October

		SX																				FSO	SO A		
Rothesay	⛴ d	**06 30**	**07 00**	.....	**08 00**	**08 45**	.....	**10 10**	**11 00**	.....	**11 45**	**13 00**	.....	**13 45**	**15 15**	.....	**16 00**	**16 45**	.....	**17 30**	**18 15**	**19 00**	**19 45**	**21 10**	.....	.....
Wemyss Bay	⛴ a	**07 05**	**07 35**	.	**08 35**	**09 20**	.	**10 45**	**11 35**	.	**12 20**	**13 35**	.	**14 20**	**15 50**	.	**16 35**	**17 20**	.	**18 05**	**18 50**	**19 35**	**20 20**	**21 45**	.	.
Wemyss Bay	219 d	07 13	07 50	.....	08 50	09 50	.....	10 55	11 50	.....	12 50	13 50	.....	14 50	15 55	.....	16 45	17 49	.....	18 23	18 55	19 45	20 44	21 50	.....	.....
Paisley Gilmour Street	219 a	07 51	08 32	.	09 26	10 26	.	11 31	12 26	.	13 26	14 26	.	15 26	16 31	.	17 21	18 31	.	19 03	19 31	20 26	21 26	22 32	.	.
Glasgow Central 15	219 a	08 07	08 44	.....	09 38	10 38	.....	11 43	12 38	.....	13 38	14 38	.....	15 38	16 43	.....	17 33	18 43	.....	19 15	19 43	20 43	21 42	22 46	.....	.....

Sundays

until 12 October

Rothesay	⛴ d	**08 00**	.....	**10 10**	.....	**11 00**	.....	**11 45**	.....	**13 00**	.....	**13 45**	.....	**15 15**	.....	**16 00**	.....	**16 45**	.....	**18 15**	.....	**19 00**	.....	**19 45**	.....	.....
Wemyss Bay	⛴ a	**08 35**	.	**10 45**	.	**11 35**	.	**12 20**	.	**13 35**	.	**14 20**	.	**15 50**	.	**16 35**	.	**17 20**	.	**18 50**	.	**19 35**	.	**20 20**	.	.
Wemyss Bay	219 d	08 50	.....	10 55	.....	11 50	.....	12 50	.....	13 50	.....	14 50	.....	15 55	.....	16 50	.....	17 50	.....	18 55	.....	19 50	.....	20 50	.....	.....
Paisley Gilmour Street	219 a	09 27	.	11 31	.	12 27	.	13 26	.	14 26	.	15 26	.	16 31	.	17 26	.	18 26	.	19 31	.	20 26	.	21 26	.	.
Glasgow Central 15	219 a	09 40	.....	11 46	.....	12 40	.....	13 40	.....	14 40	.....	15 40	.....	16 45	.....	17 40	.....	18 40	.....	19 44	.....	20 40	.....	21 40	.....	.....

For general notes see front of timetable
For details of catering facilities see
Directory of Train Operators

A 31 May to 23 August

For details of sailings from 19 October 2008 telephone Caledonian MacBrayne on 08000 66 5000

Network Diagram for Tables 220, 223, 224, 226, 232

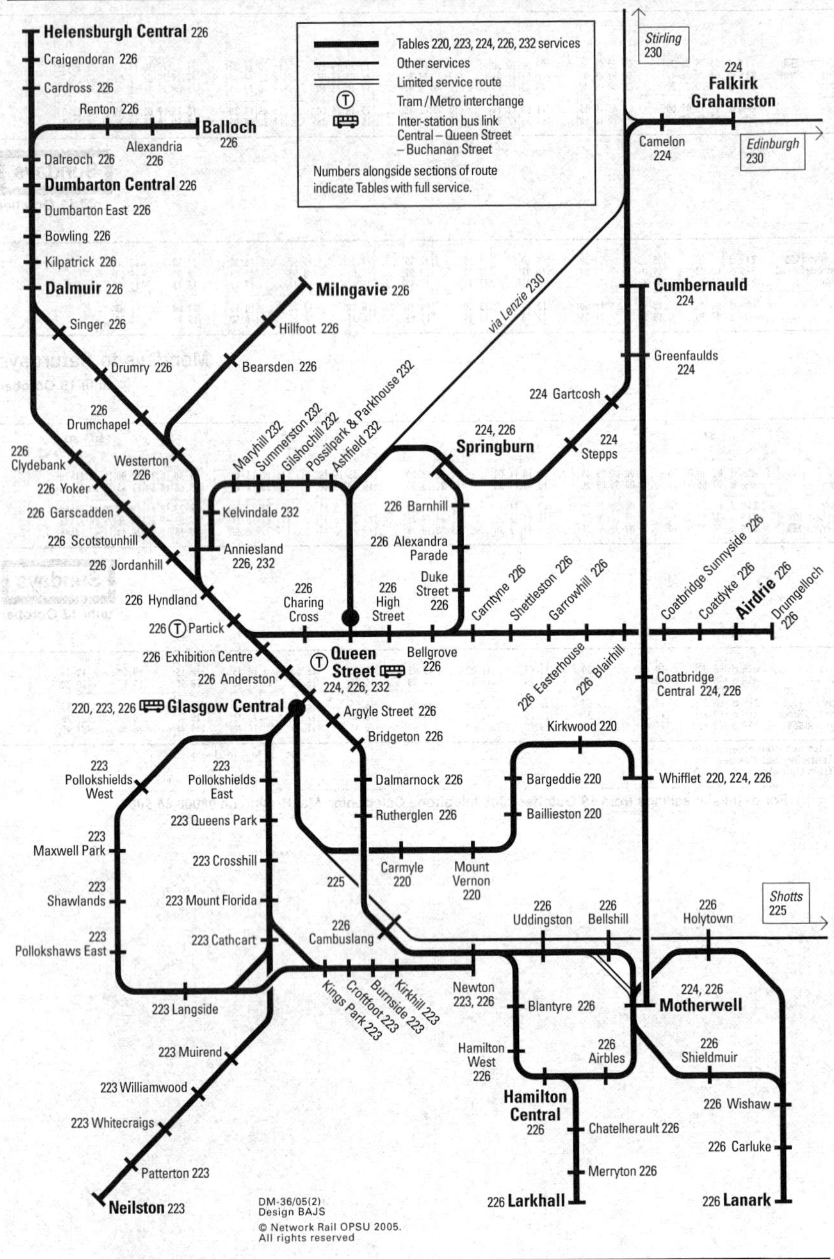

Glasgow Central — Whifflet

Network Diagram - see first page of Table 220

Miles			SR SO	SR	SR	SR	SR	SR A		SR
0	**Glasgow Central** 15	d	00 13	06 13	06 43	07 13	07 43	08 13	and every 30 minutes until	23 13
5½	Carmyle	d	00 23	06 23	06 53	07 23	07 53	08 23		23 23
6¾	Mount Vernon	d	00 26	06 26	06 56	07 26	07 56	08 26		23 26
8	Baillieston	d	00 29	06 29	06 59	07 29	07 59	08 29		23 29
9¼	Bargeddie	d	00 32	06 32	07 02	07 32	08 02	08 32		23 32
10	Kirkwood	d	00 35	06 35	07 05	07 35	08 05	08 35		23 35
12½	**Whifflet**	a	00 42	06 45	07 12	07 46	08 12	08 42		23 42

Sundays

from 30 November

		SR	SR	SR		SR
Glasgow Central 15	d	09 22	09 52	10 22	and every 30 minutes until	18 22
Carmyle	d	09 33	10 03	10 33		18 33
Mount Vernon	d	09 36	10 06	10 36		18 36
Baillieston	d	09 39	10 09	10 39		18 39
Bargeddie	d	09 42	10 12	10 42		18 42
Kirkwood	d	09 45	10 15	10 45		18 45
Whifflet	a	09 50	10 21	10 50		18 50
	d	09 50		10 50		18 50
Holytown	d	09 59		10 59		18 59
Carfin	d	10 01		11 01		19 01
Cleland	d	10 05		11 05		19 05
Hartwood	d	10 11		11 11		19 11
Shotts	a	10 17		11 17		19 17

Mondays to Saturdays

Miles			SR	SR		SR	SR
0	**Whifflet**	d	06 07	06 37	and every 30 minutes until	22 37	23 07
2½	Kirkwood	d	06 10	06 40		22 40	23 10
3¼	Bargeddie	d	06 13	06 43		22 43	23 13
4½	Baillieston	d	06 16	06 46		22 46	23 16
5¾	Mount Vernon	d	06 19	06 49		22 49	23 19
7	Carmyle	d	06 23	06 53		22 53	23 23
12½	**Glasgow Central** 15	a	06 36	07 06		23 06	23 36

Sundays

from 30 November

		SR	SR	SR	SR	SR	SR	SR	SR	SR	SR	SR	SR	SR	SR	SR	SR	SR	SR	SR
Shotts	d	08 45		09 45		10 45		11 45		12 45		13 45		14 45		15 45		16 45		17 45
Hartwood	d	08 48		09 48		10 48		11 48		12 48		13 48		14 48		15 48		16 48		17 48
Cleland	d	08 52		09 52		10 52		11 52		12 52		13 52		14 52		15 52		16 52		17 52
Carfin	d	08 56		09 56		10 56		11 56		12 56		13 56		14 56		15 56		16 56		17 56
Holytown	d	08 58		09 58		10 58		11 58		12 58		13 58		14 58		15 58		16 58		17 58
Whifflet	a	09 07		10 07		11 07		12 07		13 07		14 07		15 07		16 07		17 07		18 07
	d	09 07	09 37	10 07	10 37	11 07	11 37	12 07	12 37	13 07	13 37	14 07	14 37	15 07	15 37	16 07	16 37	17 07	17 37	18 07
Kirkwood	d	09 10	09 40	10 10	10 40	11 10	11 40	12 10	12 40	13 10	13 40	14 10	14 40	15 10	15 40	16 10	16 40	17 10	17 40	18 10
Bargeddie	d	09 13	09 43	10 13	10 43	11 13	11 43	12 13	12 43	13 13	13 43	14 13	14 43	15 13	15 43	16 13	16 43	17 13	17 43	18 13
Baillieston	d	09 16	09 46	10 16	10 46	11 16	11 46	12 16	12 46	13 16	13 46	14 16	14 46	15 16	15 46	16 16	16 46	17 16	17 46	18 16
Mount Vernon	d	09 19	09 49	10 19	10 49	11 19	11 49	12 19	12 49	13 19	13 49	14 19	14 49	15 19	15 49	16 19	16 49	17 19	17 49	18 19
Carmyle	d	09 23	09 53	10 23	10 53	11 23	11 53	12 23	12 53	13 23	13 53	14 23	14 53	15 23	15 53	16 23	16 53	17 23	17 53	18 23
Glasgow Central 15	a	09 38	10 06	10 36	11 07	11 36	12 08	12 36	13 07	13 38	14 06	14 38	15 06	15 40	16 07	16 36	17 08	17 36	18 10	18 40

For general notes see front of timetable
For details of catering facilities see
Directory of Train Operators

A 1813 from Glasgow Central arr. Whifflet 1845

No Sunday service until 23 November

Glasgow Central → Ardrossan, Largs and Ayr

Network Diagram - see first page of Table 216

Miles	Miles	Miles			SR MX	SR	SR	SR	SR SX	SR SO	SR SO	SR SX	SR ◇ A	SR SX	SR SO	SR	SR	SR SX	SR SX	SR SO	SR B	SR	SR	SR SO	SR SX	SR C
0	0	—	**Glasgow Central** 15 219	d	00 15	06 00	06 15	06 30	06 45	06 45	07 00	07 00	07 13	07 15	07 15	07 30	08 00	08 15	08 30	08 30		08 33	08 45	09 00	09 00	09 03
7¼	7¼	—	Paisley Gilmour Street 219 ✈	d	00 26	06 11	06 26	06 41	06 56	06 56	07 11	07 11	07 24	07 26	07 26	07 41	08 11	08 26	08 41	08 41		08 44	08 56	09 11	09 11	
10¾	10¾	—	Johnstone	d	00 30	06 15	06 30	06 45	07 00	07 00	07 15	07 15		07 30	07 30	07 45	08 15	08 30	08 45	08 45		08 48	09 00	09 15	09 15	
11½	11½	—	Milliken Park	d			06 33		07 03	07 03				07 33	07 33			08 33				08 51	09 03			
13	13	—	Howwood	d			06 36			07 06		07 19			07 36			08 36		08 49						
16½	16½	—	Lochwinnoch	d			06 40							07 38	07 40			08 40				08 56				
20½	20½	—	Glengarnock	d			06 45		07 11	07 13				07 43	07 45		08 24	08 45	08 54	08 56		09 01	09 11			
23¼	23¼	—	Dalry	d			06 49		07 15	07 17				07 47	07 49		08 28	08 49	08 58	09 00		09 05				
26¾	26¾	—	Kilwinning	d	00 42	06 29	06 54	06 59	07 20	07 22	07 29	07 31	07 41	07 52	07 54	07 59	08 33	08 54	09 03	09 05		09 10	09 18	09 29	09 32	
—	29	—	Stevenston	d			06 57		07 23	07 25				07 55	07 57			08 57				09 13	09 21			
—	30½	—	Saltcoats	d			07 00		07 26	07 28				08 00	08 02			09 00				09 16	09 24			
—	31¼	—	Ardrossan South Beach	d			07 02		07 28	07 30				08 02	08 04			09a02				09 18	09 26			
—	—	31¾	Ardrossan Town	d					07a34	07a34												09 22				
—	—	32¼	**Ardrossan Harbour**	a																		09 25				
—	35¾	—	West Kilbride	d			07 08							08 08	08 10								09 32			
—	39¾	—	Fairlie	d			07 13							08 14	08 16								09 37			
—	42¾	—	**Largs**	a			07 20							08 20	08 22								09 44			
30	—	—	Irvine	d	00 46	06 33		07 03			07 33	07 35				08 03	08 37		09 07	09 09				09 33	09 36	
33¾	—	—	Barassie	d	00 51			07 08								08 08	08 42		09 12	09 14						
35	—	—	Troon	d	00 54	06 39		07 11			07 39	07 41				08 11	08 45		09 15	09 17	09 24			09 39	09 42	10 07
37¾	—	—	Prestwick Int. Airport ✈	d	00 58	06 43		07 15			07 43	07 45				08 15	08 49		09 19	09 21	09 29			09 43	09 46	10 12
38¾	—	—	Prestwick Town	d	01 00	06 45		07 17			07 45	07 47				08 17	08 51		09 21	09 23	09 31			09 45	09 48	10 14
40¼	—	—	Newton-on-Ayr	d	01 03			07 20								08 20	08 54		09 24	09 26						
41½	—	—	**Ayr**	a	01 10	06 52		07 24			07 52	07 54	07 59			08 25	08 58		09 28	09 30	09 38			09 52	09 53	10 21

		SR	SR	SR	SR	SR	SR	SR	SR SO	SR SX	SR	SR	SR ◇ A	SR	SR	SR	SR	SR D	SR	SR	SR	SR	SR	SR	SR	SR
Glasgow Central 15 219	d	09 15	09 30	09 45	10 00	10 15	10 30	10 45	11 00	11 00	11 15	11 30	11 42	11 45	12 00	12 15	12 30		12 45	13 00	13 15	13 30	13 45	14 00	14 15	14 30
Paisley Gilmour Street 219 ✈	d	09 26	09 41	09 56	10 11	10 26	10 41	10 56	11 11	11 11	11 26	11 41	11 53	11 56	12 11	12 26	12 41		12 56	13 11	13 26	13 41	13 56	14 11	14 26	14 41
Johnstone	d	09 30	09 45	10 00	10 15	10 30	10 45	11 00	11 15	11 15	11 30	11 45		12 00	12 15	12 30	12 45		13 00	13 15	13 30	13 45	14 00	14 15	14 30	14 45
Milliken Park	d	09 33		10 03		10 33		11 03			11 33			12 03		12 33			13 03		13 33		14 03		14 33	
Howwood	d	09 36				10 36					11 36					12 36					13 36				14 36	
Lochwinnoch	d	09 40				10 40					11 40					12 40					13 40				14 40	
Glengarnock	d	09 45	09 54	10 11		10 45	10 54	11 11			11 45			12 11		12 45			13 11		13 45		14 11		14 45	
Dalry	d	09 49		10 15	10 26	10 49					11 49					12 49			13 15		13 49			14 26	14 49	
Kilwinning	d	09 54	10 01	10 20	10 31	10 54	11 01	11 18	11 29	11 29	11 54	11 59	12 10	12 18	12 29	12 54	12 59		13 20	13 29	13 54	13 59	14 18	14 31	14 54	14 59
Stevenston	d	09 57		10 23		10 57		11 21			11 57			12 21		12 57			13 23		13 57		14 21		14 57	
Saltcoats	d	10 00		10 26		11 00		11 24			12 00			12 24		13 00			13 26		14 00		14 24		15 00	
Ardrossan South Beach	d	10 02		10 28		11 02		11 26			12 02			12 26		13 02			13 28		14 02		14 26		15 01	
Ardrossan Town	d	10a06				11a06					12 06					13a06					14a06				15 06	
Ardrossan Harbour	a										12 09														15 09	
West Kilbride	d			10 34				11 32						12 32					13 34				14 32			
Fairlie	d			10 39				11 37						12 37					13 39				14 37			
Largs	a			10 47				11 44						12 44					13 46				14 44			
Irvine	d		10 05		10 35		11 05		11 33	11 33		12 03			12 33		13 03			13 33		14 03		14 35		15 03
Barassie	d		10 10				11 10					12 08					13 08					14 08				15 08
Troon	d		10 13		10 41		11 13		11 39	11 43		12 11			12 39		13 11	13 22		13 39		14 11		14 41		15 11
Prestwick Int. Airport ✈	d		10 17		10 45		11 17		11 43	11 47		12 15			12 43		13 15	13 27		13 43		14 15		14 45		15 15
Prestwick Town	d		10 19		10 47		11 19		11 45	11 49		12 17			12 45		13 17	13 29		13 45		14 17		14 47		15 17
Newton-on-Ayr	d		10 22				11 22					12 20					13 20					14 20				15 20
Ayr	a		10 26		10 54		11 26		11 52	11 54		12 24	12 29		12 52		13 24	13 36		13 52		14 24		14 54		15 24

		SR	SR	SR	SR	SR ◇ E	SR	SR	SR D	SR	SR	SR	SR	SR SX	SR	SR SX	SR SO	SR SX G	SR	SR SO G	SR	SR	SR	SR	SR	SR
Glasgow Central 15 219	d	14 45	15 00	15 15	15 30		15 45	16 00		16 18	16 30	16 50	17 00	17 13	17 20	17 30	17 30		17 35		17 45	18 00	18 15	18 30	18 45	19 00
Paisley Gilmour Street 219 ✈	d	14 56	15 11	15 26	15 41		15 56	16 11		16 29	16 41	17 01	17 11	17u24	17 32	17u41	17 41		17 46		17 56	18 11	18 26	18 41	18 56	19 11
Johnstone	d	15 00	15 15	15 30	15 45		16 00	16 15		16 33	16 45	17 05	17 15		17 36		17 45		17 50		18 00	18 15	18 30	18 45	19 00	19 15
Milliken Park	d	15 03		15 33			16 03			16 36		17 08			17 39				17 53		18 03		18 33		19 03	
Howwood	d			15 36						16 39		17 11							17 56				18 36			
Lochwinnoch	d			15 40						16 43			17 21						18 00				18 40			
Glengarnock	d	15 11		15 45			16 11			16 48		17 18	17 26	17 35					18 05		18 11		18 45		19 11	
Dalry	d			15 49						16 52		17 22	17 30		17 49				18 09		18 15	18 26	18 49	18 56		
Kilwinning	d	15 18	15 29	15 54	15 59		16 18	16 29		16 57	16 59	17 27	17 35	17 42	17 54		17 59		18 14		18 20	18 31	18 54	19 01	19 18	19 29
Stevenston	d	15 21		15 57			16 21			17 01		17 30			17 57				18 17		18 23		18 57		19 21	
Saltcoats	d	15 23		16 00			16 24			17b09		17 33			18 01				18 20		18 26		19 00		19 24	
Ardrossan South Beach	d	15 26		16 02			16 26			17 11					18 03				18 22		18 28		19 02		19 26	
Ardrossan Town	d			16a06								17 40							18a26				19a06			
Ardrossan Harbour	a											17 44														
West Kilbride	d	15 32					16 32			17 17					18 09						18 34				19 32	
Fairlie	d	15 37					16 37			17 22					18 14						18 39				19 37	
Largs	a	15 44					16 44			17 28					18 20						18 48				19 44	
Irvine	d		15 33		16 03			16 33			17 03		17 39	17 46		17 59	18 03					18 35		19 05		19 33
Barassie	d				16 08						17 08		17 44			18 04	18 08					18 40		19 10		
Troon	d		15 39		16 11	16 19		16 39	16 44		17 11		17 47	17 52		18 07	18 11	18 24		18 31		18 43		19 13		19 39
Prestwick Int. Airport ✈	d		15 43		16 15			16 43	16 49		17 15		17 51	17 56		18 11	18 15	18 29		18 36		18 47		19 17		19 43
Prestwick Town	d		15 45		16 17			16 45	16 51		17 17		17 53	17 58		18 13	18 17	18 31		18 38		18 49		19 19		19 45
Newton-on-Ayr	d				16 20						17 20		17 56			18 16	18 20					18 52		19 22		
Ayr	a		15 52		16 24	16 32		16 52	16 58		17 25		18 00	18 05		18 20	18 24	18 38		18 45		18 56		19 26		19 52

For general notes see front of timetable
For details of catering facilities see Directory of Train Operators

- **A** To Stranraer (Table 218)
- **B** From Kilmarnock to Stranraer (Table 218)
- **C** To Girvan (Table 218)
- **D** From Kilmarnock to Girvan (Table 218)
- **E** From Newcastle (Table 48) to Stranraer (Table 218)
- **G** From Kilmarnock (Table 218)
- **b** Arr. 1704

Glasgow Central → Ardrossan, Largs and Ayr

Network Diagram - see first page of Table 216

		SR	SR	SR	SR	SR	SR	SR	SR	SR	SR	SR	SR	SR	SR	SR	SR	SR	SR	SR	SR	SR	SR	SR
																				FO	FX		FSX	FO
						◇ A									B									
Glasgow Central 15	219 d	19 15	19 30	19 45	20 00		20 15	20 30	20 45	21 00	21 15	21 30	21 45	22 00		22 15	22 30	22 45	23 00	23 15	23 15	23 30	23 45	23 45
Paisley Gilmour Street	219 ✈ d	19 26	19 41	19 56	20 11		20 26	20 41	20 56	21 11	21 26	21 41	21 56	22 11		22 26	22 41	22 56	23 11	23 26	23 26	23 41	23 56	23 56
Johnstone	d	19 30	19 45	20 00	20 15		20 30	20 45	21 00	21 15	21 30	21 45	22 00	22 15		22 30	22 45	23 00	23 15	23 30	23 30	23 45	23 59	23 59
Milliken Park	d	19 33		20 03			20 33		21 03		21 33		22 03			22 33		23 03		23 33	23 33		00 03	00 03
Howwood	d	19 36					20 36				21 36					22 36				23 36	23 36		00 06	00 06
Lochwinnoch	d	19 40					20 40				21 40					22 40				23 40	23 40		00 10	00 10
Glengarnock	d	19 45		20 11			20 45		21 11		21 45		22 11			22 45		23 11		23 45	23 45		00 15	00 15
Dalry	d	19 49					20 49				21 49					22 49				23 49	23 49		00 19	00 19
Kilwinning	d	19 54	19 59	20 18	20 29		20 54	20 59	21 18	21 29	21 54	21 59	22 18	22 29		22 54	22 59	23 18	23 29	23 54	23 54	23 59	00 24	00 24
Stevenston	d	19 57		20 21			20 57		21 21		21 57		22 21			22 57		23 21		23 57	23 57		00 27	00 27
Saltcoats	d	20 00		20 24			21 00		21 24		22 00		22 24			23 00		23 24		23 59	00 01		00 30	00 30
Ardrossan South Beach	d	20 02		20 26			21 02		21 26		22 02		22 26			23 02		23 26		00 02	00 02		00a32	00 32
Ardrossan Town	d	20 06					21a06				22a06					23a06				00a06				
Ardrossan Harbour	a	20 09																						
West Kilbride	d			20 32					21 32				22 32					23 32			00 08			00 38
Fairlie	d			20 37					21 37				22 37					23 37			00 14			00 43
Largs	a			20 44					21 44				22 44					23 44			00 19			00 49
Irvine	d		20 03		20 33			21 03		21 33		22 03		22 33			23 03		23 33			00 03		
Barassie	d		20 08					21 08				22 08					23 08					00 08		
Troon	d		20 11		20 39	20 50		21 11		21 39		22 11		22 39	22 56		23 11		23 39			00 11		
Prestwick Int. Airport	✈ d		20 15		20 43			21 15		21 43		22 15		22 43	23 01		23 15		23 43			00 15		
Prestwick Town	d		20 17		20 45			21 17		21 45		22 17		22 45	23 03		23 17		23 45			00 17		
Newton-on-Ayr	d		20 20					21 20				22 20					23 20					00 20		
Ayr	a		20 24		20 52	20 59		21 24		21 52		22 24		22 52	23 10		23 24		23 52			00 25		

Sundays

until 28 September

		SR	SR	SR	SR	SR	SR	SR	SR	SR	SR	SR	SR	SR	SR	SR	SR	SR	SR	SR	SR	SR	SR	SR
												◇ C												
Glasgow Central 15	219 d	08 40	09 00	09 30	09 40	10 00	10 30	10 40	11 00	11 15	11 30	11 37	11 40	12 00	12 30	12 40	13 00	13 30	13 40	14 00	14 05	14 30	14 40	15 00
Paisley Gilmour Street	219 ✈ d	08 51	09 11	09 41	09 51	10 11	10 41	10 51	11 11	11 26	11 41	11 48	11 51	12 11	12 41	12 51	13 11	13 41	13 51	14 11	14 16	14 41	14 51	15 11
Johnstone	d	08 55	09 15	09 45	09 55	10 15	10 45	10 55	11 15	11 30	11 45		11 55	12 15	12 45	12 55	13 15	13 45	13 55	14 15	14 20	14 45	14 55	15 15
Milliken Park	d	08 58			09 58			10 58		11 33			11 58			12 58			13 58		14 23		14 58	
Howwood	d				10 01			11 01					12 01			13 01			14 01				15 01	
Lochwinnoch	d				10 05			11 05					12 05			13 05			14 05				15 05	
Glengarnock	d	09 06			10 10			11 10					12 10			13 10			14 10				15 10	
Dalry	d	09 10			10 14			11 14					12 14			13 14			14 14				15 14	
Kilwinning	d	09 15	09 29	09 59	10 19	10 29	10 59	11 19	11 29	11 46	11 59	12 05	12 19	12 29	12 59	13 19	13 29	13 59	14 19	14 29	14 39	14 59	15 19	15 29
Stevenston	d	09 18			10 22			11 22		11 49			12 22			13 22			14 22		14 42		15 22	
Saltcoats	d	09 21			10 25			11 25		11 52			12 25			13 25			14 25		14 45		15 25	
Ardrossan South Beach	d	09 23			10 27			11 27		11 54			12 27			13 27			14 27		14 47		15 27	
Ardrossan Town	d																							
Ardrossan Harbour	a	09 37								12 02											14 59			
West Kilbride	d				10 33			11 33					12 33			13 33			14 33				15 33	
Fairlie	d				10 39			11 39					12 39			13 39			14 39				15 39	
Largs	a				10 45			11 45					12 45			13 45			14 45				15 45	
Irvine	d		09 33	10 03		10 33	11 03		11 33		12 03			12 33	13 03		13 33	14 03		14 33		15 03		15 33
Barassie	d		09 38			10 38			11 38					12 38			13 38			14 38				15 38
Troon	d		09 41	10 09		10 41	11 09		11 41		12 09			12 41	13 09		13 41	14 09		14 41		15 09		15 41
Prestwick Int. Airport	✈ d		09 45	10 13		10 45	11 13		11 45		12 13			12 45	13 13		13 45	14 13		14 45		15 13		15 45
Prestwick Town	d		09 47	10 15		10 47	11 15		11 47		12 15			12 47	13 15		13 47	14 15		14 47		15 15		15 47
Newton-on-Ayr	d																							
Ayr	a		09 54	10 22		10 54	11 22		11 54		12 22	12 29		12 54	13 22		13 54	14 22		14 54		15 22		15 54

		SR	SR	SR	SR	SR	SR	SR	SR	SR	SR	SR	SR	SR	SR	SR	SR	SR	SR	SR	SR	SR	SR
					◇ C																		
Glasgow Central 15	219 d	15 30	15 40	16 00	16 25	16 30	16 40	16 55	17 00	17 30	17 40	18 00	18 30	18 40	19 00	19 40	20 00	20 40	21 00	21 40	22 00	22 40	23 00
Paisley Gilmour Street	219 ✈ d	15 41	15 51	16 11	16 39	16 41	16 51	17 07	17 11	17 41	17 51	18 11	18 41	18 51	19 11	19 51	20 11	20 51	21 11	21 51	22 11	22 51	23 11
Johnstone	d	15 45	15 55	16 15		16 45	16 55	17 11	17 15	17 45	17 55	18 15	18 45	18 55	19 15	19 55	20 15	20 55	21 15	21 55	22 15	22 55	23 15
Milliken Park	d		15 58				16 58	17 14			17 58			18 58		19 58		20 58		21 58		22 58	
Howwood	d		16 01				17 01				18 01			19 01		20 01		21 01		22 01		23 01	
Lochwinnoch	d		16 05				17 05				18 05			19 05		20 05		21 05		22 05		23 05	
Glengarnock	d		16 10				17 10				18 10			19 10		20 10		21 10		22 10		23 10	
Dalry	d		16 14				17 14				18 14			19 14		20 14		21 14		22 14		23 14	
Kilwinning	d	15 59	16 19	16 29	16 56	17 03	17 19	17 27	17 29	17 59	18 19	18 29	18 59	19 19	19 29	20 19	20 29	21 19	21 29	22 19	22 29	23 18	23 29
Stevenston	d		16 22				17 22	17 30			18 22			19 22		20 22		21 22		22 22		23 22	
Saltcoats	d		16 25				17 25	17 33			18 25			19 25		20 25		21 25		22 25		23 24	
Ardrossan South Beach	d		16 27				17 27	17 35			18 27			19 27		20 27		21 27		22 27		23 26	
Ardrossan Town	d																						
Ardrossan Harbour	a							17 43															
West Kilbride	d		16 33				17 33				18 33			19 33		20 33		21 33		22 33		23 32	
Fairlie	d		16 39				17 39				18 39			19 39		20 39		21 39		22 39		23 38	
Largs	a		16 47				17 45				18 45			19 45		20 45		21 45		22 44		23 44	
Irvine	d	16 03		16 33		17 05				17 33	18 03		18 33	19 03		19 33		20 33		21 33		22 33		23 33
Barassie	d			16 38					17 38			18 38			19 38		20 38		21 38		22 38		23 38
Troon	d	16 09		16 41		17 09			17 41	18 09		18 41	19 09		19 41		20 41		21 41		22 41		23 41
Prestwick Int. Airport	✈ d	16 13		16 45		17 13			17 45	18 13		18 45	19 13		19 45		20 45		21 45		22 45		23 45
Prestwick Town	d	16 15		16 47		17 15			17 47	18 15		18 47	19 15		19 47		20 47		21 47		22 47		23 47
Newton-on-Ayr	d																						
Ayr	a	16 22		16 54	17 17	17 24			17 54	18 22		18 54	19 22		19 54		20 54		21 54		22 54		23 54

For general notes see front of timetable
For details of catering facilities see Directory of Train Operators

A From Newcastle (Table 48) to Stranraer (Table 218)
B From Kilmarnock to Stranraer (Table 218)
C To Stranraer (Table 218)

Table 221

Sundays

5 October to 23 November

Glasgow Central → Ardrossan, Largs and Ayr

Network Diagram - see first page of Table 216

	SR	SR	SR	SR	SR	SR	SR	SR	SR	SR	SR	SR	SR	SR	SR	SR	SR
								◇ A									
Glasgow Central 15 .... 219 d	08 40	09 00	09 40	10 00	10 40	11 00	11 15	11 37	11 40	12 00	12 40	13 00	13 40	14 00	14 05	14 40	15 00
Paisley Gilmour Street 219 ✈ d	08 51	09 11	09 51	10 11	10 51	11 11	11 26	11 48	11 51	12 11	12 51	13 11	13 51	14 11	14 16	14 51	15 11
Johnstone d	08 55	09 15	09 55	10 15	10 55	11 15	11 30		11 55	12 15	12 55	13 15	13 55	14 15	14 20	14 55	15 15
Milliken Park d	08 58		09 58		10 58		11 33		11 58		12 58		13 58		14 23	14 58	
Howwood d			10 01		11 01				12 01		13 01		14 01			15 01	
Lochwinnoch d			10 05		11 05				12 05		13 05		14 05			15 05	
Glengarnock d	09 06		10 10		11 10				12 10		13 10		14 10			15 10	
Dalry d	09 10		10 14		11 14				12 14		13 14		14 14			15 14	
Kilwinning d	09 15	09 29	10 19	10 29	11 19	11 29	11 46	12 05	12 19	12 29	13 19	13 29	14 19	14 29	14 39	15 19	15 29
Stevenston d	09 18		10 22		11 22		11 49		12 22		13 22		14 22		14 42	15 22	
Saltcoats d	09 21		10 25		11 25		11 52		12 25		13 25		14 25		14 45	15 25	
Ardrossan South Beach d	09 23		10 27		11 27		11 54		12 27		13 27		14 27		14 47	15 27	
Ardrossan Town d																	
Ardrossan Harbour a	09 37						12 09								14 59		
West Kilbride d			10 33		11 33				12 33		13 33		14 33			15 33	
Fairlie d			10 39		11 39				12 38		13 39		14 39			15 39	
Largs a			10 52		11 52				12 53		13 52		14 52			15 52	
Irvine d		09 33		10 33		11 33				12 33		13 33		14 33			15 33
Barassie d		09 38		10 38		11 38				12 38		13 38		14 38			15 38
Troon d		09 41		10 41		11 41				12 41		13 41		14 41			15 41
Prestwick Int. Airport ✈ d		09 45		10 45		11 45				12 45		13 45		14 45			15 45
Prestwick Town d		09 47		10 47		11 47				12 47		13 47		14 47			15 47
Newton-on-Ayr d																	
Ayr a		10 01		11 01		12 01		12 29		13 01		14 01		15 01			16 01

	SR	SR	SR	SR	SR	SR	SR	SR	SR	SR	SR	SR	SR	SR	SR	SR	SR	SR
			◇ A															
Glasgow Central 15 .... 219 d	15 40	16 00	16 25	16 40	16 55	17 00	17 40	18 00	18 40	19 00	19 40	20 00	20 40	21 00	21 40	22 00	22 40	23 00
Paisley Gilmour Street 219 ✈ d	15 51	16 11	16 39	16 51	17 07	17 11	17 51	18 11	18 51	19 11	19 51	20 11	20 51	21 11	21 51	22 11	22 51	23 11
Johnstone d	15 55	16 15		16 55	17 11	17 15	17 55	18 15	18 55	19 15	19 55	20 15	20 55	21 15	21 55	22 15	22 55	23 15
Milliken Park d	15 58			16 58	17 14		17 58		18 58		19 58		20 58		21 58		22 58	
Howwood d	16 01			17 01			18 01		19 01		20 01		21 01		22 01		23 01	
Lochwinnoch d	16 05			17 05			18 05		19 05		20 05		21 05		22 05		23 05	
Glengarnock d	16 10			17 10			18 10		19 10		20 10		21 10		22 10		23 10	
Dalry d	16 14			17 14			18 14		19 14		20 14		21 14		22 14		23 14	
Kilwinning d	16 19	16 29	16 56	17 19	17 27	17 29	18 19	18 29	19 19	19 29	20 19	20 29	21 19	21 29	22 19	22 29	23 18	23 29
Stevenston d	16 22			17 22	17 30		18 22		19 22		20 22		21 22		22 22		23 22	
Saltcoats d	16 25			17 25	17 33		18 25		19 25		20 25		21 25		22 25		23 24	
Ardrossan South Beach d	16 27			17 27	17 35		18 27		19 27		20 27		21 27		22 27		23 26	
Ardrossan Town d																		
Ardrossan Harbour a					17 43													
West Kilbride d	16 33			17 33			18 33		19 33		20 33		21 33		22 33		23 32	
Fairlie d	16 39			17 39			18 39		19 39		20 39		21 39		22 39		23 38	
Largs a	16 53			17 45			18 45		19 45		20 45		21 45		22 44		23 44	
Irvine d		16 33				17 33		18 33		19 33		20 33		21 33		22 33		23 33
Barassie d		16 38				17 38		18 38		19 38		20 38		21 38		22 38		23 38
Troon d		16 41				17 41		18 41		19 41		20 41		21 41		22 41		23 41
Prestwick Int. Airport ✈ d		16 45				17 45		18 45		19 45		20 45		21 45		22 45		23 45
Prestwick Town d		16 47				17 47		18 47		19 47		20 47		21 47		22 47		23 47
Newton-on-Ayr d																		
Ayr a		16 54	17 17			17 54		18 54		19 54		20 54		21 54		22 55		23 54

Sundays

from 30 November

	SR	SR	SR	SR	SR	SR	SR	SR	SR	SR	SR	SR	SR	SR	SR	SR	SR	SR	SR	SR	SR	SR
											◇ A											
Glasgow Central 15 .... 219 d	08 40	09 00	09 30	09 45	10 00	10 30	10 45	11 00	11 15	11 30	11 42	11 45	12 00	12 30	12 45	13 00	13 30	13 45	14 00	14 05	14 30	14 45
Paisley Gilmour Street 219 ✈ d	08 51	09 11	09 41	09 53	10 11	10 41	10 56	11 11	11 26	11 41	11 53	11 57	12 11	12 41	12 56	13 11	13 41	13 56	14 11	14 16	14 41	14 56
Johnstone d	08 55	09 15	09 45	09 56	10 15	10 45	11 00	11 15	11 30	11 45		12 01	12 15	12 45	13 00	13 15	13 45	14 00	14 15	14 20	14 45	15 00
Milliken Park d	08 58			10 00			11 03		11 33			12 04			13 03			14 03		14 23		15 03
Howwood d				10 03			11 06					12 07			13 06			14 06				15 06
Lochwinnoch d				10 07			11 10					12 11			13 10			14 10				15 10
Glengarnock d	09 06			10 12			11 15					12 16			13 15			14 15				15 15
Dalry d	09 10			10 16			11 19					12 20			13 19			14 19				15 19
Kilwinning d	09 15	09 29	09 59	10 21	10 29	10 59	11 24	11 29	11 46	11 59	12 10	12 25	12 29	12 59	13 24	13 29	13 59	14 24	14 29	14 39	14 59	15 24
Stevenston d	09 18			10 23			11 27		11 49			12 28			13 27			14 27		14 42		15 27
Saltcoats d	09 21			10 27			11 30		11 52			12 31			13 30			14 30		14 45		15 30
Ardrossan South Beach d	09 23			10 28			11 32		11 54			12 34			13 32			14 32		14 47		15 32
Ardrossan Town d																						
Ardrossan Harbour a	09 37								12 09											14 59		
West Kilbride d				10 34			11 38					12 40			13 38			14 38				15 38
Fairlie d				10 41			11 44					12 45			13 44			14 44				15 44
Largs a				10 52			11 52					12 52			13 52			14 56				15 52
Irvine d		09 33	10 03		10 33	11 03		11 33		12 03			12 33	13 03		13 33	14 03		14 33		15 03	
Barassie d		09 38			10 38			11 38					12 38			13 38			14 38			
Troon d		09 41	10 09		10 41	11 09		11 41		12 09			12 41	13 09		13 41	14 09		14 41		15 09	
Prestwick Int. Airport ✈ d		09 45	10 13		10 45	11 13		11 45		12 13			12 45	13 13		13 45	14 13		14 45		15 13	
Prestwick Town d		09 47	10 15		10 47	11 15		11 47		12 15			12 47	13 15		13 47	14 15		14 47		15 15	
Newton-on-Ayr d																						
Ayr a		10 01	10 22		11 01	11 22		12 01		12 22	12 34		13 01	13 22		14 01	14 22		15 01		15 22	

For general notes see front of timetable
For details of catering facilities see
Directory of Train Operators

A To Stranraer (Table 218)

Sundays

from 30 November

Glasgow Central → Ardrossan, Largs and Ayr

Network Diagram - see first page of Table 216

		SR	SR	SR	SR	SR ◇ A	SR	SR		SR	SR	SR	SR
Glasgow Central 15 219	d	15 00	15 30	15 45	16 00	16 25	16 30	16 45		16 55	17 00	17 30	17 45
Paisley Gilmour Street 219 ✈	d	15 11	15 41	15 56	16 11	16 39	16 43	16 56		17 07	17 11	17 41	17 56
Johnstone	d	15 15	15 45	16 00	16 15		16 47	17 00		17 11	17 15	17 45	18 00
Milliken Park	d			16 03				17 03		17 14			18 03
Howwood	d			16 06				17 06					18 06
Lochwinnoch	d			16 10				17 10					18 10
Glengarnock	d			16 15				17 15					18 15
Dalry	d			16 19				17 19					18 19
Kilwinning	d	15 29	15 56	16 22	16 29	16 56	17 01	17 24		17 27	17 29	17 59	18 24
Stevenston	d			16 25				17 27		17 30			18 27
Saltcoats	d			16 28				17 30		17 33			18 30
Ardrossan South Beach	d			16 30				17 32		17 35			18 32
Ardrossan Town	d												
Ardrossan Harbour	a									17 43			
West Kilbride	d			16 36				17 38					18 38
Fairlie	d			16 42				17 44					18 44
Largs	a			16 52				17 50					18 50
Irvine	d	15 33	16 06		16 33		17 05				17 33	18 03	
Barassie	d	15 38			16 38						17 38		
Troon	d	15 41	16 13		16 41		17 11				17 41	18 09	
Prestwick Int. Airport ✈	d	15 45	16 17		16 45		17 15				17 45	18 13	
Prestwick Town	d	15 47	16 19		16 47		17 17				17 47	18 15	
Newton-on-Ayr	d												
Ayr	a	16 01	16 26		16 54	17 17	17 24				17 54	18 22	

		SR	SR	SR	SR	SR	SR	SR	SR	SR	SR	SR		
Glasgow Central 15 219	d	18 00	18 40	19 00	19 40	20 00	20 40	21 00	21 40	22 00	22 40	23 00		
Paisley Gilmour Street 219 ✈	d	18 11	18 51	19 11	19 51	20 11	20 51	21 11	21 51	22 11	22 51	23 11		
Johnstone	d	18 15	18 55	19 15	19 55	20 15	20 55	21 15	21 55	22 15	22 55	23 15		
Milliken Park	d		18 58		19 58		20 58		21 58		22 58			
Howwood	d		19 01		20 01		21 01		22 01		23 01			
Lochwinnoch	d		19 05		20 05		21 05		22 05		23 05			
Glengarnock	d		19 10		20 10		21 10		22 10		23 10			
Dalry	d		19 14		20 14		21 14		22 14		23 14			
Kilwinning	d	18 29	19 19	19 29	20 19	20 29	21 19	21 29	22 19	22 29	23 18	23 29		
Stevenston	d		19 22		20 22		21 22		22 22		23 22			
Saltcoats	d		19 25		20 25		21 25		22 25		23 24			
Ardrossan South Beach	d		19 27		20 27		21 27		22 27		23 26			
Ardrossan Town	d													
Ardrossan Harbour	a													
West Kilbride	d		19 33		20 33		21 33		22 33		23 32			
Fairlie	d		19 39		20 39		21 39		22 39		23 38			
Largs	a		19 45		20 45		21 45		22 44		23 44			
Irvine	d	18 33		19 33		20 33		21 33		22 33		23 33		
Barassie	d	18 38		19 38		20 38		21 38		22 38		23 38		
Troon	d	18 41		19 41		20 41		21 41		22 41		23 41		
Prestwick Int. Airport ✈	d	18 45		19 45		20 45		21 45		22 45		23 45		
Prestwick Town	d	18 47		19 47		20 47		21 47		22 47		23 47		
Newton-on-Ayr	d													
Ayr	a	18 54		19 54		20 54		21 54		22 55		23 54		

For general notes see front of timetable
For details of catering facilities see
Directory of Train Operators

A To Stranraer (Table 218)

Ayr, Largs and Ardrossan → Glasgow Central

Network Diagram - see first page of Table 216

Miles	Miles	Miles		SR	SR	SR	SR	SR	SR SX	SR	SR SX	SR SO		SR SX	SR SX	SR	SR	SR SX	SR SX	SR SX	SR SO	SR SX		SR	SR
										A															◇ B
0	—	—	**Ayr** d	05 40	06 13		06 43		06 57	07 10	07 13	07 13		07 25		07 43		07 58		08 13				08 43	08 36
1¼	—	—	Newton-on-Ayr d	05 43	06 16		06 46				07 16	07 16						08 01		08 16					
3¼	—	—	Prestwick Town d	05 46	06 19		06 49		07 02		07 19	07 19		07 30		07 48		08 04		08 19				08 48	08 41
3¾	—	—	Prestwick Int. Airport ✈ d	05 48	06 21		06 51		07 04		07 21	07 21		07 32		07 50		08 06		08 21				08 50	08 43
6½	—	—	Troon d	05 52	06 25		06 55		07 08	07a18	07 25	07 25		07 36		07 54		08 10		08 25				08 54	08 48
7¾	—	—	Barassie d	05 54	06 27		06 57		07 10		07 27	07 27		07 38				08 12		08 27					
11½	—	—	Irvine d	05 59	06 32		07 02		07 15		07 32	07 32		07 43		07 59		08 17		08 32				08 59	
—	0	—	**Largs** d					06 41							07 23		07 42					08 28			
—	3	—	Fairlie d					06 46							07 28		07 47					08 33			
—	7	—	West Kilbride d					06 51							07 33		07 52					08 38			
—	—	0	**Ardrossan Harbour** d																						
—	—	½	Ardrossan Town d			06 31													08 14		08 31				
—	11½	1	Ardrossan South Beach d			06 34		06 57							07 39		07 58		08 17		08 34	08 44			
—	12¾	2	Saltcoats d			06 36		07 02							07 41		08 00		08 19		08 36	08 46			
—	13¾	3¼	Stevenston d			06 39		07 05							07 44		08 03		08 22		08 39	08 49			
14¾	16	5¼	Kilwinning d	06 04	06 37	06 43	07 07	07 10	07 20		07 37	07 37			07 49	08 04	08 08	08 22	08 25	08 37	08 42	08 53		09 04	
18½	19¾	9¼	Dalry d	06 08		06 47		07 14	07 24		07 41	07 41			07 53		08 12		08 30		08 47	08 58			
21	22¼	11¾	Glengarnock d	06 12		06 51		07 18	07 28			07 45		07 52			08 16		08 34		08 51	09 02			
25	26¼	15¾	Lochwinnoch d	06 17		06 56			07 33			07 50			08 00		08 21		08 39		08 56				
28½	29¾	19¼	Howwood d	06 21		07 00			07 37			07 54		07 59					08 43		09 00				
30	31¼	20¾	Milliken Park d	06 24		07 03		07 26	07 40			07 57			08 05		08 26		08 46		09 03	09 10			
30¾	32	21½	Johnstone d	06 27	06 50	07 06	07 20	07 29	07 43		07 52	08 00		08 03	08 08	08 18	08 29	08 35	08 48	08 50	09 05	09 12		09 18	
34¼	35½	25	Paisley Gilmour Street 219 ✈ d	06 32	06 55	07 11	07 26	07 34	07 48		07 57	08 05		08 08	08 13	08 23	08 34	08 41	08 53	08 56	09 11	09 17		09 24	
41½	42¾	32¼	**Glasgow Central** 15 219 a	06 43	07 07	07 22	07 38	07 47	07 59		08 09	08 16		08 18	08 24	08 34	08 46	08 54	09 04	09 07	09 22	09 30		09 36	09 50

	SR SX	SR SO	SR	SR	SR	SR	SR	SR	SR		SR	SR	SR	SR	SR	SR	SR	SR	SR		SR	SR	SR	SR	SR
													◇ C				D								◇ B
Ayr d			09 13		09 43		10 13		10 43			11 13	11 22		11 43		12 09	12 13			12 43		13 13		13 09
Newton-on-Ayr d			09 16				10 16					11 16						12 16					13 16		
Prestwick Town d			09 19		09 48		10 19		10 48			11 19			11 48		12 14	12 19			12 48		13 19		13 14
Prestwick Int. Airport ✈ d			09 21		09 50		10 21		10 50			11 21			11 50		12 16	12 21			12 50		13 22		13 16
Troon d			09 25		09 54		10 25		10 54			11 25	11a30		11 54		12a21	12 25			12 54		13 25		13 21
Barassie d			09 27				10 27					11 27						12 27					13 27		
Irvine d			09 32		09 59		10 32		10 59			11 32			11 59			12 32			12 59		13 32		
Largs d		08 51				09 53					10 53					11 53						12 53			
Fairlie d		08 56				09 58					10 58					11 58						12 58			
West Kilbride d		09 01				10 03					11 03					12 03						13 03			
Ardrossan Harbour d				09 30															12 28						
Ardrossan Town d				09 33				10 31						11 31					12 31					13 31	
Ardrossan South Beach d	09 07	09 07		09 36		10 09		10 34			11 09			11 34		12 09			12 34			13 09		13 34	
Saltcoats d	09 09	09 09		09 38		10 11		10 36			11 11			11 36		12 11			12 36			13 11		13 36	
Stevenston d	09 12	09 12		09 41		10 14		10 39			11 14			11 39		12 14			12 39			13 14		13 39	
Kilwinning d	09 16	09 16	09 37	09 45	10 04	10 18	10 37	10 43	11 04		11 18	11 37		11 43	12 04	12 18		12 37	12 43		13 04	13 18	13 37	13 43	
Dalry d			09 41	09 49				10 47						11 47					12 47					13 47	
Glengarnock d	09 22	09 22		09 53		10 25		10 51			11 25			11 51		12 25			12 51			13 25		13 51	
Lochwinnoch d	09 27	09 27		09 58				10 56						11 56					12 56					13 56	
Howwood d	09 31	09 31			10 16			11 00						12 00					13 00					14 00	
Milliken Park d	09 32	09 32		10 03		10 33		11 03			11 33			12 03		12 33			13 03			13 33		14 03	
Johnstone d	09 35	09 35	09 52	10 06	10 20	10 35	10 50	11 06	11 18		11 35	11 50		12 06	12 18	12 35		12 50	13 06		13 18	13 35	13 50	14 06	
Paisley Gilmour Street 219 ✈ d	09 40	09 40	09 57	10 11	10 25	10 40	10 55	11 11	11 23		11 40	11 55		12 11	12 23	12 40		12 55	13 11		13 23	13 40	13 55	14 11	
Glasgow Central 15 219 a	09 53	09 53	10 09	10 22	10 36	10 52	11 07	11 22	11 34		11 52	12 07		12 22	12 34	12 52		13 07	13 22		13 34	13 52	14 07	14 22	14 27

	SR	SR	SR	SR	SR	SR		SR	SR	SR	SR	SR	SR	SR	SR	SR		SR	SR	SR	SR	SR	SR	SR	SR
										E		◇ B													
Ayr d	13 43		14 13		14 43			15 13		15 17	15 43	15 58		16 13		16 43			17 13			17 43		18 13	
Newton-on-Ayr d			14 16					15 16						16 16		16 46			17 16					18 16	
Prestwick Town d	13 48		14 19		14 48			15 19		15 22	15 48			16 19		16 49			17 19			17 48		18 19	
Prestwick Int. Airport ✈ d	13 50		14 21		14 50			15 21		15 24	15 50			16 21		16 51			17 21			17 50		18 21	
Troon d	13 54		14 25		14 54			15 25		15 29	15 54			16 25		16 55			17 25			17 54		18 25	
Barassie d			14 27					15 27						16 27					17 27					18 27	
Irvine d	13 59		14 32		14 59			15 32			15 59			16 32		17 00			17 32			17 59		18 32	
Largs d		13 53				14 53							15 53					16 50			17 35				
Fairlie d		13 58				14 58							15 58					16 55			17 40				
West Kilbride d		14 03				15 03							16 03					17 00			17 45				
Ardrossan Harbour d									15 28														18 00		
Ardrossan Town d				14 31					15 31						16 31								18 03		18 31
Ardrossan South Beach d		14 09		14 34		15 09			15 34				16 09		16 34			17 06		17 40	17 51		18 06		18 34
Saltcoats d		14 11		14 36		15 11			15 36				16 11		16 36			17 08		17 42	17 53		18 09		18 36
Stevenston d		14 14		14 39		15 14			15 39				16 14		16 39			17 11		17 45	17 56		18 12		18 39
Kilwinning d	14 04	14 18	14 37	14 43	15 04	15 18		15 37	15 43		16 04	16 13	16 18	16 37	16 43	17 05		17 15	17 37	17 48	18 00	18 04	18 16	18 37	18 43
Dalry d				14 47					15 47						16 47			17 20	17 41	17 53	18 05	18 09		18 41	18 47
Glengarnock d		14 25		14 51		15 25		15 43	15 51				16 25	16 43	16 51			17 24		17 57		18 13	18 23		18 51
Lochwinnoch d				14 56					15 56						16 56			17 29				18 18			18 56
Howwood d				15 00					16 00						17 00						18 14		18 30		19 00
Milliken Park d		14 33		15 03		15 33			16 03				16 33		17 03			17 34		18 05			18 33		19 03
Johnstone d	14 18	14 35	14 50	15 06	15 18	15 35		15 52	16 06		16 18		16 35	16 52	17 06	17 19		17 36	17 52	18 07	18 18	18 24	18 35	18 52	19 06
Paisley Gilmour Street 219 ✈ d	14 23	14 40	14 55	15 11	15 23	15 40		15 57	16 11		16 23	16 34	16 40	16 57	17 11	17 24		17 41	17 57	18 12	18 23	18 29	18 40	18 57	19 11
Glasgow Central 15 219 a	14 34	14 52	15 07	15 22	15 34	15 52		16 09	16 22	16 32	16 34	16 45	16 52	17 09	17 22	17 35		17 55	18 09	18 23	18 34	18 41	18 52	19 09	19 22

For general notes see front of timetable
For details of catering facilities see Directory of Train Operators

A From Girvan (Table 218) to Newcastle (Table 48)
B From Stranraer (Table 218)
C From Stranraer (Table 218) to Newcastle (Table 48)
D From Girvan to Kilmarnock (Table 218)
E From Girvan (Table 218)

Ayr, Largs and Ardrossan → Glasgow Central

Network Diagram - see first page of Table 216

	SR	SR	SR A	SR	SR	SR	SR	SR	SR	SR	SR	SR ◇ B
Ayr d	18 43		19 09	19 13		19 43		20 13		20 43		21 06
Newton-on-Ayr d				19 16				20 16				
Prestwick Town d	18 48		19 14	19 19		19 48		20 19		20 48		
Prestwick Int. Airport ✈ d	18 50		19 16	19 21		19 50		20 21		20 50		
Troon d	18 54		19a21	19 25		19 54		20 25		20 54		
Barassie d				19 27				20 27				
Irvine d	18 59			19 32		19 59		20 32		20 59		
Largs d		18 53					19 53				20 53	
Fairlie d		18 58					19 58				20 58	
West Kilbride d		19 03					20 03				21 03	
Ardrossan Harbour d									20 28			
Ardrossan Town d					19 31				20 31			
Ardrossan South Beach d		19 09			19 34		20 09		20 34		21 09	
Saltcoats d		19 11			19 36		20 11		20 36		21 11	
Stevenston d		19 14			19 39		20 14		20 39		21 14	
Kilwinning d	19 04	19 18		19 37	19 43	20 04	20 18	20 37	20 43	21 04	21 18	21 21
Dalry d					19 47				20 47			
Glengarnock d		19 25			19 51		20 25		20 51		21 25	
Lochwinnoch d					19 56				20 56			
Howwood d					20 00				21 00			
Milliken Park d		19 33			20 03		20 33		21 03		21 33	
Johnstone d	19 18	19 35		19 50	20 06	20 18	20 35	20 50	21 06	21 18	21 35	
Paisley Gilmour Street 219 ✈ d	19 23	19 40		19 55	20 11	20 23	20 40	20 55	21 11	21 23	21 40	21 44
Glasgow Central 15 219 a	19 34	19 52		20 07	20 22	20 34	20 52	21 07	21 22	21 34	21 52	21 55

	SR	SR	SR	SR	SR	SR	SR ◇ B	SR	SR
Ayr d	21 13		21 43		22 13		22 38		23 00
Newton-on-Ayr d	21 16				22 16				23 03
Prestwick Town d	21 19		21 48		22 19				23 06
Prestwick Int. Airport ✈ d	21 21		21 50		22b21				23 08
Troon d	21 25		21 54		22 25				23 12
Barassie d	21 27				22 27				23 14
Irvine d	21 32		21 59		22 32				23 19
Largs d				21 53				22 53	
Fairlie d				21 58				22 58	
West Kilbride d				22 03				23 03	
Ardrossan Harbour d									
Ardrossan Town d		21 31				22 31			
Ardrossan South Beach d		21 34		22 09		22 34		23 09	
Saltcoats d		21 36		22 11		22 36		23 11	
Stevenston d		21 39		22 14		22 39		23 14	
Kilwinning d	21 37	21 43	22 04	22 18	22 37	22 43	22 54	23 18	23 24
Dalry d	21 41	21 47	22 09	22 23	22 41	22 47			23 28
Glengarnock d		21 51		22 27		22 51		23 25	23 32
Lochwinnoch d		21 56				22 56			
Howwood d		22 00				23 00		23 32	
Milliken Park d		22 03		22 35		23 03		23 35	
Johnstone d	21 52	22 06	22 20	22 37	22 52	23 06		23 37	23 41
Paisley Gilmour Street 219 ✈ d	21 57	22 11	22 25	22 42	22 57	23 11	23 15	23 42	23 46
Glasgow Central 15 219 a	22 09	22 22	22 36	22 54	23 10	23 22	23 26	23 54	23 58

Sundays

until 28 September

	SR	SR	SR	SR	SR	SR	SR	SR	SR	SR	SR ◇ B	SR	SR
Ayr d	08 43		09 13	09 43		10 13	10 43		11 13	11 43	12 01		12 13
Newton-on-Ayr d													
Prestwick Town d	08 48		09 18	09 48		10 18	10 48		11 18	11 48			12 18
Prestwick Int. Airport ✈ d	08 50		09 20	09 50		10 20	10 50		11 20	11 50			12 20
Troon d	08 54		09 24	09 54		10 24	10 54		11 24	11 54			12 24
Barassie d	08 56			09 56			10 56			11 56			
Irvine d	09 01		09 29	10 01		10 29	11 01		11 29	12 01			12 29
Largs d		08 53			09 53			10 53				11 53	
Fairlie d		08 58			09 58			10 58				11 58	
West Kilbride d		09 03			10 03			11 03				12 03	
Ardrossan Harbour d													
Ardrossan Town d													
Ardrossan South Beach d		09 09			10 09			11 09				12 09	
Saltcoats d		09 11			10 11			11 11				12 11	
Stevenston d		09 14			10 14			11 14				12 14	
Kilwinning d	09 06	09 18	09 34	10 06	10 18	10 34	11 06	11 18	11 34	12 06	12 16	12 20	12 34
Dalry d		09 23			10 23			11 23				12 18	
Glengarnock d		09 27			10 27			11 27				12 23	
Lochwinnoch d		09 32			10 32			11 32				12 27	
Howwood d		09 36			10 36			11 36				12 32	
Milliken Park d		09 39			10 39			11 39				12 36	
Johnstone d	09 19	09 41	09 48	10 19	10 41	10 48	11 19	11 41	11 48	12 19		12 39	12 48
Paisley Gilmour Street 219 ✈ d	09 24	09 47	09 53	10 24	10 47	10 53	11 24	11 47	11 53	12 24	12 37	12 41	12 53
Glasgow Central 15 219 a	09 36	09 58	10 04	10 36	10 58	11 07	11 36	11 58	12 04	12 36	12 51	12 47	13 04

	SR	SR	SR	SR	SR	SR	SR	SR	SR	SR	SR	SR
Ayr d		12 43		13 13	13 43		14 13	14 43			15 13	15 43
Newton-on-Ayr d												
Prestwick Town d		12 48		13 18	13 48		14 18	14 48			15 18	15 48
Prestwick Int. Airport ✈ d		12 50		13 20	13 50		14 20	14 50			15 20	15 50
Troon d		12 54		13 24	13 54		14 24	14 54			15 24	15 54
Barassie d		12 56			13 56			14 56				15 56
Irvine d		13 01		13 29	14 01		14 29	15 01			15 29	16 01
Largs d			12 53			13 53				14 53		
Fairlie d			12 58			13 58				14 58		
West Kilbride d			13 03			14 03				15 03		
Ardrossan Harbour d	12 35								15 04			
Ardrossan Town d												
Ardrossan South Beach d	12 40		13 09			14 09			15 09	15 14		
Saltcoats d	12 42		13 11			14 11			15 11	15 16		
Stevenston d	12 45		13 14			14 14			15 14	15 19		
Kilwinning d	12 49	13 06	13 18	13 34	14 06	14 18	14 34	15 06	15 18	15 23	15 34	16 06
Dalry d			13 23			14 23				15 27		
Glengarnock d			13 27			14 27				15 31		
Lochwinnoch d			13 32			14 32				15 36		
Howwood d			13 36			14 36				15 40		
Milliken Park d	13 02		13 39			14 39			15 31	15 43		
Johnstone d	13 04	13 19	13 41	13 48	14 19	14 41	14 48	15 19	15 33	15 46	15 48	16 19
Paisley Gilmour Street 219 ✈ d	13 10	13 24	13 47	13 53	14 24	14 47	14 53	15 24	15 39	15 51	15 53	16 24
Glasgow Central 15 219 a	13 28	13 36	13 58	14 04	14 36	14 58	15 07	15 36	15 50	16 01	16 06	16 36

	SR ◇ B	SR	SR	SR	SR	SR	SR	SR	SR	SR	SR	SR
Ayr d	16 01		16 13	16 43		17 13	17 43			18 13	18 43	
Newton-on-Ayr d												
Prestwick Town d			16 18	16 48		17 18	17 48			18 18	18 48	
Prestwick Int. Airport ✈ d			16 20	16 50		17 20	17 50			18 20	18 50	
Troon d			16 24	16 54		17 24	17 54			18 24	18 54	
Barassie d				16 56			17 56				18 56	
Irvine d			16 29	17 01		17 29	18 01			18 29	19 01	
Largs d		15 53			16 53				17 53			18 53
Fairlie d		15 58			16 58				17 58			18 58
West Kilbride d		16 03			17 03				18 03			19 03
Ardrossan Harbour d								18 00				
Ardrossan Town d												
Ardrossan South Beach d		16 09			17 09			18 05	18 09			19 09
Saltcoats d		16 11			17 11			18 07	18 11			19 11
Stevenston d		16 14			17 14			18 10	18 14			19 14
Kilwinning d	16 17	16 21	16 34	17 06	17 18	17 34	18 06	18 14	18 18	18 34	19 06	19 18
Dalry d		16 25			17 23				18 23			19 23
Glengarnock d		16 29			17 27				18 27			19 27
Lochwinnoch d		16 34			17 32				18 32			19 32
Howwood d		16 38			17 36				18 36			19 36
Milliken Park d		16 41			17 39			18 27	18 39			19 39
Johnstone d		16 44	16 48	17 19	17 41	17 51	18 19	18 29	18 41	18 48	19 19	19 41
Paisley Gilmour Street 219 ✈ d	16 38	16 49	16 53	17 24	17 47	17 56	18 24	18 39	18 47	18 53	19 24	19 47
Glasgow Central 15 219 a	16 49	16 59	17 04	17 36	17 58	18 07	18 36	18 49	18 58	19 04	19 36	19 58

	SR	SR	SR	SR	SR	SR ◇ B	SR	SR	SR	SR	SR
Ayr d	19 13	19 43			20 43	21 02		21 43		23 00	
Newton-on-Ayr d											
Prestwick Town d	19 18	19 48			20 48			21 48		23 05	
Prestwick Int. Airport ✈ d	19 20	19 50			20 50			21 50		23 07	
Troon d	19 24	19 54			20 54			21 54		23 11	
Barassie d		19 56			20 56			21 56		23 13	
Irvine d	19 29	20 01			21 01			22 01		23 18	
Largs d			19 53				20 53		21 53		22 58
Fairlie d			19 58				20 58		21 58		23 03
West Kilbride d			20 03				21 03		22 03		23 08
Ardrossan Harbour d				20 31							
Ardrossan Town d											
Ardrossan South Beach d			20 09	20 36			21 09		22 09		23 14
Saltcoats d			20 11	20 38			21 11		22 11		23 16
Stevenston d			20 14	20 41			21 14		22 14		23 19
Kilwinning d	19 34	20 06	20 18	20 45	21 06	21 17	21 18	22 06	22 18	23 23	23 27
Dalry d			20 23				21 23		22 23		23 31
Glengarnock d			20 27				21 27		22 27		23 35
Lochwinnoch d			20 32				21 32		22 32		23 40
Howwood d			20 36				21 36		22 36		23 44
Milliken Park d			20 39	20 58			21 39		22 39		23 47
Johnstone d	19 48	20 19	20 41	21 00	21 19		21 41	22 19	22 41	23 36	23 50
Paisley Gilmour Street 219 ✈ d	19 53	20 24	20 47	21 06	21 24	21 36	21 47	22 24	22 47	23 41	23 55
Glasgow Central 15 219 a	20 04	20 36	20 58	21 17	21 36	21 48	21 59	22 36	22 58	23 53	00 05

For general notes see front of timetable
For details of catering facilities see Directory of Train Operators

A From Girvan to Kilmarnock (Table 218)
B From Stranraer (Table 218)
b Saturdays arr.2309

Table 221

Sundays

5 October to 23 November

Ayr, Largs and Ardrossan → Glasgow Central

Network Diagram - see first page of Table 216

	SR	SR	SR	SR	SR	SR ◇ A	SR	SR	SR	SR	SR	SR	SR	SR	SR	SR	SR ◇ A
Ayr d	09 43		10 43		11 43	12 01			12 43		13 43		14 43			15 43	16 01
Newton-on-Ayr d																	
Prestwick Town d	09 48		10 48		11 48				12 48		13 48		14 48			15 48	
Prestwick Int. Airport ✈ d	09 50		10 50		11 50				12 50		13 50		14 50			15 50	
Troon d	09 54		10 54		11 54				12 54		13 54		14 54			15 54	
Barassie d	09 56		10 56		11 56				12 56		13 56		14 56			15 56	
Irvine d	10 01		11 01		12 01				13 01		14 01		15 01			16 01	
Largs d		09 58		10 58			11 58			12 58		13 58			14 58		
Fairlie d		10 03		11 03			12 03			13 03		14 03			15 03		
West Kilbride d		10 08		11 08			12 08			13 08		14 08			15 08		
Ardrossan Harbour d								12 35						15 04			
Ardrossan Town d																	
Ardrossan South Beach d		10 14		11 14			12 14	12 40		13 14		14 14		15 09	15 14		
Saltcoats d		10 16		11 16			12 16	12 42		13 16		14 16		15 11	15 16		
Stevenston d		10 19		11 19			12 19	12 45		13 19		14 19		15 14	15 19		
Kilwinning d	10 06	10 23	11 06	11 23	12 06	12 16	12 23	12 49	13 06	13 23	14 06	14 23	15 06	15 18	15 23	16 06	16 17
Dalry d		10 28		11 28			12 28			13 28		14 28			15 28		
Glengarnock d		10 32		11 32			12 32			13 32		14 32			15 32		
Lochwinnoch d		10 37		11 37			12 37			13 37		14 37			15 37		
Howwood d		10 41		11 41			12 41			13 41		14 41			15 41		
Milliken Park d		10 44		11 44			12 44	13 02		13 44		14 44		15 31	15 44		
Johnstone d	10 19	10 46	11 19	11 46	12 19		12 46	13 04	13 19	13 46	14 19	14 46	15 19	15 33	15 46	16 19	
Paisley Gilmour Street 219 ✈ d	10 31	10 52	11 31	11 52	12 31	12 37	12 52	13 10	13 31	13 52	14 31	14 52	15 31	15 39	15 52	16 24	16 38
Glasgow Central 15 219 a	10 43	11 10	11 43	12 10	12 43	12 51	13 10	13 28	13 43	14 10	14 43	15 10	15 43	15 57	16 10	16 43	16 49

	SR	SR	SR	SR	SR	SR	SR	SR	SR	SR	SR	SR	SR ◇ A	SR	SR	SR	SR	SR
Ayr d		16 43		17 43			18 43		19 43			20 43	21 02		21 43		23 00	
Newton-on-Ayr d																		
Prestwick Town d		16 48		17 48			18 48		19 48			20 48			21 48		23 05	
Prestwick Int. Airport ✈ d		16 50		17 50			18 50		19 50			20 50			21 50		23 07	
Troon d		16 54		17 54			18 54		19 54			20 54			21 54		23 11	
Barassie d		16 56		17 56			18 56		19 56			20 56			21 56		23 13	
Irvine d		17 01		18 01			19 01		20 01			21 01			22 01		23 18	
Largs d	15 58		16 58			17 58		18 58		19 58				20 58		21 58		22 58
Fairlie d	16 03		17 03			18 03		19 03		20 03				21 03		22 03		23 03
West Kilbride d	16 08		17 08			18 08		19 08		20 08				21 08		22 08		23 08
Ardrossan Harbour d					18 00						20 31							
Ardrossan Town d																		
Ardrossan South Beach d	16 14		17 14		18 05	18 14		19 14		20 14	20 36			21 14		22 14		23 14
Saltcoats d	16 16		17 16		18 07	18 16		19 16		20 16	20 38			21 16		22 16		23 16
Stevenston d	16 19		17 19		18 10	18 19		19 19		20 19	20 41			21 19		22 19		23 19
Kilwinning d	16 23	17 06	17 23	18 06	18 14	18 23	19 06	19 23	20 06	20 23	20 45	21 06	21 17	21 23	22 06	22 23	23 23	23 27
Dalry d	16 28		17 28			18 28		19 28		20 28				21 28		22 28		23 31
Glengarnock d	16 32		17 32			18 32		19 32		20 32				21 32		22 32		23 35
Lochwinnoch d	16 37		17 37			18 37		19 37		20 37				21 37		22 37		23 40
Howwood d	16 41		17 41			18 41		19 41		20 41				21 41		22 41		23 44
Milliken Park d	16 44		17 44		18 27	18 44		19 44		20 44	20 58			21 44		22 44		23 47
Johnstone d	16 46	17 19	17 46	18 19	18 29	18 46	19 19	19 46	20 19	20 46	21 00	21 19		21 46	22 19	22 46	23 36	23 50
Paisley Gilmour Street 219 ✈ d	16 52	17 24	17 52	18 24	18 39	18 52	19 24	19 52	20 24	20 52	21 06	21 24	21 36	21 52	22 24	22 52	23 41	23 55
Glasgow Central 15 219 a	17 03	17 36	18 03	18 36	18 49	19 03	19 36	20 03	20 36	21 03	21 17	21 36	21 48	22 03	22 36	23 03	23 53	00 05

Sundays

from 30 November

	SR	SR	SR	SR	SR	SR	SR	SR	SR ◇ A	SR	SR	SR	SR	SR	SR	SR	SR	SR	SR	SR	SR	SR
Ayr d	09 13	09 43		10 13	10 43		11 13	11 43	12 01		12 13		12 43		13 13	13 43		14 13	14 43			15 13
Newton-on-Ayr d																						
Prestwick Town d	09 18	09 48		10 18	10 48		11 18	11 48			12 18		12 48		13 18	13 48		14 18	14 48			15 18
Prestwick Int. Airport ✈ d	09 20	09 50		10 20	10 50		11 20	11 50			12 20		12 50		13 20	13 50		14 20	14 50			15 20
Troon d	09 24	09 54		10 24	10 54		11 24	11 54			12 24		12 54		13 24	13 54		14 24	14 54			15 24
Barassie d		09 56			10 56			11 56					12 56			13 56			14 56			
Irvine d	09 29	10 01		10 29	11 01		11 29	12 01			12 29		13 01		13 29	14 01		14 29	15 01			15 29
Largs d			09 58			10 58				11 58				12 58			13 58				14 58	
Fairlie d			10 03			11 03				12 03				13 03			14 03				15 03	
West Kilbride d			10 08			11 08				12 08				13 08			14 08				15 08	
Ardrossan Harbour d												12 35								15 04		
Ardrossan Town d																						
Ardrossan South Beach d			10 14			11 14				12 14		12 40		13 14			14 14			15 09	15 14	
Saltcoats d			10 16			11 16				12 16		12 42		13 16			14 16			15 11	15 16	
Stevenston d			10 19			11 19				12 19		12 45		13 19			14 19			15 14	15 19	
Kilwinning d	09 34	10 06	10 23	10 34	11 06	11 23	11 34	12 06	12 16	12 23	12 34	12 49	13 06	13 23	13 34	14 06	14 23	14 34	15 06	15 18	15 23	15 34
Dalry d			10 28			11 28				12 28				13 28			14 28				15 28	
Glengarnock d			10 32			11 32				12 32				13 32			14 32				15 32	
Lochwinnoch d			10 37			11 37				12 37				13 37			14 37				15 37	
Howwood d			10 41			11 41				12 41				13 41			14 41				15 41	
Milliken Park d			10 44			11 44				12 44		13 02		13 44			14 44			15 31	15 44	
Johnstone d	09 48	10 19	10 46	10 51	11 19	11 46	11 51	12 19		12 46	12 51	13 04	13 19	13 46	13 51	14 19	14 46	14 51	15 19	15 33	15 46	15 51
Paisley Gilmour Street 219 ✈ d	09 53	10 31	10 52	10 56	11 31	11 52	11 56	12 31	12 37	12 52	12 56	13 10	13 31	13 52	13 56	14 31	14 52	14 56	15 31	15 39	15 52	15 56
Glasgow Central 15 219 a	10 04	10 43	11 04	11 07	11 43	12 04	12 07	12 43	12 51	13 04	13 07	13 27	13 43	14 04	14 09	14 43	15 04	15 07	15 43	15 57	16 04	16 07

For general notes see front of timetable
For details of catering facilities see
Directory of Train Operators

A From Stranraer (Table 218)

Table 221

from 30 November

Ayr, Largs and Ardrossan → Glasgow Central

Network Diagram - see first page of Table 216

		SR	SR	SR	SR	SR	SR	SR		SR	SR	SR	SR	SR	SR	SR	SR	SR	SR	SR	SR	SR	SR	SR		
			◇ A																◇ A							
Ayr	d	15 43	16 01		16 13	16 43		17 13		17 43			18 43		19 43			20 43	21 02		21 43		23 00			
Newton-on-Ayr	d																									
Prestwick Town	d	15 48			16 18	16 48		17 18		17 48			18 48		19 48			20 48			21 48		23 05			
Prestwick Int. Airport ✈	d	15 50			16 20	16 50		17 20		17 50			18 50		19 50			20 50			21 50		23 07			
Troon	d	15 54			16 24	16 54		17 24		17 54			18 54		19 54			20 54			21 54		23 11			
Barassie	d	15 56				16 56				17 56			18 56		19 56			20 56			21 56		23 13			
Irvine	d	16 01			16 29	17 01		17 29		18 01			19 01		20 01			21 01			22 01		23 18			
Largs	d			15 58			16 58					17 58		18 58		19 58				20 58		21 58		22 58		
Fairlie	d			16 03			17 03					18 03		19 03		20 03				21 03		22 03		23 03		
West Kilbride	d			16 08			17 08					18 08		19 08		20 08				21 08		22 08		23 08		
Ardrossan Harbour	d										18 00						20 31									
Ardrossan Town	d																									
Ardrossan South Beach	d			16 14			17 14				18 05	18 14		19 14		20 14	20 36			21 14		22 14		23 14		
Saltcoats	d			16 16			17 16				18 07	18 16		19 16		20 16	20 38			21 16		22 16		23 16		
Stevenston	d			16 19			17 19				18 10	18 19		19 19		20 19	20 41			21 19		22 19		23 19		
Kilwinning	d	16 06	16 17	16 23	16 34	17 06	17 23	17 34		18 06	18 14	18 23	19 06	19 23	20 06	20 23	20 45	21 06	21 17	21 23	22 06	22 23	23 23	23 27		
Dalry	d			16 28			17 28					18 28		19 28		20 28				21 28		22 28		23 31		
Glengarnock	d			16 32			17 32					18 32		19 32		20 32				21 32		22 32		23 35		
Lochwinnoch	d			16 37			17 37					18 37		19 37		20 37				21 37		22 37		23 40		
Howwood	d			16 41			17 41					18 41		19 41		20 41				21 41		22 41		23 44		
Milliken Park	d			16 44			17 44				18 27	18 44		19 44		20 44	20 58			21 44		22 44		23 47		
Johnstone	d	16 19		16 46	16 51	17 19	17 46	17 51		18 19	18 29	18 46	19 19	19 46	20 19	20 46	21 00	21 19		21 46	22 19	22 46	23 36	23 50		
Paisley Gilmour Street 219 ✈	d	16 24	16 38	16 52	16 56	17 24	17 52	17 56		18 24	18 39	18 52	19 24	19 52	20 24	20 52	21 06	21 24	21 36	21 52	22 24	22 52	23 41	23 55		
Glasgow Central 15 219	a	16 41	16 49	17 04	17 07	17 36	18 04	18 07		18 36	18 49	19 04	19 36	20 03	20 36	21 03	21 17	21 36	21 48	22 03	22 36	23 03	23 53	00 05		

For general notes see front of timetable
For details of catering facilities see
Directory of Train Operators

A From Stranraer (Table 218)

Table 221A **SHIPPING SERVICES** **Mondays to Saturdays**

until 18 October

Glasgow and Ardrossan — Brodick (Arran)

Caledonian MacBrayne Ltd in association with First ScotRail Limited

						FO
Glasgow Central 15	221 d	08 33	11 15	14 15	16 50	19 15
Paisley Gilmour Street	221 d	08 44	11 26	14 26	17 01	19 26
Ardrossan Harbour	221 a	09 25	12 09	15 09	17 44	20 09
Ardrossan Harbour	⛴ d	**09 45**	**12 30**	**15 15**	**18 00**	**20 30**
Brodick	⛴ a	**10 40**	**13 25**	**16 10**	**18 55**	**21 25**

Sundays

until 12 October

Glasgow Central 15	221 d	08 40	11 15	14 05	16 55
Paisley Gilmour Street	221 d	08 51	11 26	14 16	17 07
Ardrossan Harbour	221 a	09 37	12b02	14 59	17 43
Ardrossan Harbour	⛴ d	**09 45**	**12 30**	**15 15**	**18 00**
Brodick	⛴ a	**10 40**	**13 25**	**16 10**	**18 55**

Mondays to Saturdays

until 18 October

Brodick	⛴ d	**08 20**	**11 05**	**13 50**	**16 40**	**19 20**
Ardrossan Harbour	⛴ a	**09 15**	**12 00**	**14 45**	**17 35**	**20 15**
Ardrossan Harbour	221 d	09 30	12 28	15 28	18 00	20 28
Paisley Gilmour Street	221 a	10 10	13 10	16 10	18 39	21 10
Glasgow Central 15	221 a	10 22	13 22	16 22	18 52	21 22

Sundays

until 12 October

Brodick	⛴ d	**11 05**	**13 50**	**16 40**	**19 20**
Ardrossan Harbour	⛴ a	**12 00**	**14 45**	**17 35**	**20 15**
Ardrossan Harbour	221 d	12 35	15 04	18 00	20 31
Paisley Gilmour Street	221 a	13 09	15 38	18 38	21 05
Glasgow Central 15	221 a	13 28	15c50	18 49	21 17

For general notes see front of timetable
For details of catering facilities see Directory of Train Operators

b Arr. 1209 from 5 October
c Arr. 1557 from 5 October

For details of sailings from 19 October telephone Caledonian MacBrayne on 08000 66 5000

Table 222

Glasgow Central → East Kilbride, Barrhead and Kilmarnock

Network Diagram - see first page of Table 216

Miles	Miles			SR SO 1	SR SO	SR	SR	SR	SR	SR SX	SR SX	SR SO	SR SX	SR	SR SO	SR SX	SR A	SR SX	SR	SR B	SR	SR	SR	SR	SR A
0	0	**Glasgow Central 15**	d	00 03	00 12	06 12	06 42	06 53	07 07	07 33	07 37	07 42	07 52	08 07	08 12	08 17	08 28	08 33	08 42	09 03	09 07	09 12	09 37	09 42	09 53
2¼	2¼	Crossmyloof	d	00 09	00 18	06 18		06 59	07 13	07 39	07 43	07 48	07 58	08 13	08 18	08 23		08 39	08 48		09 13	09 18	09 43	09 48	
3¼	3¼	Pollokshaws West	d	00 12	00 21	06 21		07 02	07 16	07 42	07 46	07 51	08 01	08 16	08 21	08 26		08 42	08 51		09 16	09 21	09 46	09 51	
—	4½	Thornliebank	d		00 24	06 24		07 05		07 45		07 54	08 04		08 24	08 29			08 54			09 24		09 54	
—	5¼	Giffnock	d		00 27	06 27		07 08		07 48		07 57	08 07		08 27	08 32			08 57			09 27		09 57	
—	6¼	Clarkston	d		00 30	06 30		07 11		07 51		08 00	08 10		08 30	08 35			09 00			09 30		10 00	
—	7¼	Busby	d		00 33	06 33		07 15		07 56		08 03	08 15		08 33	08 40			09 03			09 33		10 03	
—	8½	Thorntonhall	d			06 36						08 06				08 42			09 06					10 06	
—	10	Hairmyres	d		00 39	06 40		07 21		08 02		08 10	08 21		08 39	08 46			09 10			09 39		10 10	
—	11½	**East Kilbride**	a		00 42	06 43		07 24		08 09		08 13	08 24		08 42	08 50			09 15			09 43		10 13	
4½	—	Kennishead	d	00 15			06 50		07 19		07 49			08 19				08 45			09 19		09 49		
5	—	Priesthill & Darnley	d	00 17			06 52		07 21		07 51			08 21				08 47			09 21		09 51		
5¾	—	Nitshill	d	00 20			06 55		07 24		07 54			08 24				08 50			09 24		09 54		
7¼	—	**Barrhead**	d	00 23			06 59		07a27		07a59			08a27			08 40	08a55		09 15	09a29		09a57		10 05
16¼	—	Dunlop	d	00 35			07 11										08 51			09 34					10 26
18¾	—	Stewarton	d	00 39			07 15										08 55			09 38					10 30
22	—	Kilmaurs	d	00 44			07 20										09 00			09 43					10 35
24¼	—	**Kilmarnock 3**	a	00 49			07 25										09 06			09 48					10 38

		SR	SR	SR	SR	SR	SR	SR	SR	SR	SR A	SR	SR	SR	SR	SR A	SR	SR	SR	SR	SR	SR	SR	SR	SR
Glasgow Central 15	d	10 07	10 12	10 37	10 42	11 03	11 07	11 12	11 37	11 42	12 03	12 07	12 12	12 37	12 42	13 03	13 07	13 12	13 37	13 42	14 03	14 07	14 12	14 37	14 42
Crossmyloof	d	10 13	10 18	10 43	10 48		11 13	11 18	11 43	11 48		12 13	12 18	12 43	12 48		13 13	13 18	13 43	13 48		14 13	14 18	14 43	14 48
Pollokshaws West	d	10 16	10 21	10 46	10 51		11 16	11 21	11 46	11 51		12 16	12 21	12 46	12 51		13 16	13 21	13 46	13 51		14 16	14 21	14 46	14 51
Thornliebank	d		10 24		10 54			11 24		11 54			12 24		12 54			13 24		13 54			14 24		14 54
Giffnock	d		10 27		10 57			11 27		11 57			12 27		12 57			13 27		13 57			14 27		14 57
Clarkston	d		10 30		11 00			11 30		12 00			12 30		13 00			13 30		14 00			14 30		15 00
Busby	d		10 33		11 03			11 33		12 03			12 33		13 03			13 33		14 03			14 33		15 03
Thorntonhall	d				11 06					12 06					13 06					14 06					15 06
Hairmyres	d		10 39		11 10			11 39		12 10			12 39		13 10			13 39		14 10			14 39		15 10
East Kilbride	a		10 42		11 13			11 42		12 13			12 42		13 13			13 42		14 13			14 42		15 13
Kennishead	d	10 19		10 49			11 19		11 49			12 19		12 49			13 19		13 49			14 19		14 49	
Priesthill & Darnley	d	10 21		10 51			11 21		11 51			12 21		12 51			13 21		13 51			14 21		14 51	
Nitshill	d	10 24		10 54			11 24		11 54			12 24		12 54			13 24		13 54			14 24		14 54	
Barrhead	d	10a29		10a57		11 15	11a27		11a57		12 15	12a27		12a57		13 15	13a27		13a57		14 15	14a27		14a57	
Dunlop	d					11 27					12 27					13 27					14 27				
Stewarton	d					11 31					12 31					13 31					14 31				
Kilmaurs	d					11 36					12 36					13 36					14 36				
Kilmarnock 3	a					11 41					12 41					13 42					14 41				

		SR	SR	SR	SR	SR SX	SR SO	SR C	SR	SR	SR	SR	SR	SR SX	SR SO	SR SX	SR SO	SR SX	SR SX	SR A	SR	SR	SR SX	SR
Glasgow Central 15	d	15 03	15 07	15 12	15 37	15 41	15 42	15 48	16 07	16 12	16 33	16 42	16 48	16 52	17 07	17 10	17 12	17 14	17 23	17 30	17 37	17 42	17 57	18 03
Crossmyloof	d		15 13	15 18	15 43	15 48	15 48		16 13	16 18	16 39	16 48		16 58	17 13	17 16	17 18		17 29		17 43	17 48	18 03	
Pollokshaws West	d		15 16	15 21	15 46	15 51	15 51		16 16	16 21	16 42	16 51		17 01	17 16	17 19	17 21		17 32		17 45	17 51	18 06	
Thornliebank	d			15 24		15 54	15 54			16 24		16 54		17 04			17 24		17 35			17 54	18 09	
Giffnock	d			15 27		15 57	15 57			16 27		16 57		17 07			17 27		17 38			17 57	18 12	
Clarkston	d			15 30		16 01	16 00			16 30		17 00		17 10			17 30	17 29	17 41			18 00	18 15	
Busby	d			15 33		16 04	16 03			16 33		17 03		17a14			17 33		17 44			18 03	18 18	
Thorntonhall	d					16 07	16 06			16 36		17 06					17 36		17 47			18 06		
Hairmyres	d			15 39		16 11	16 10			16 40		17 10					17 40	17 36	17 51			18 10	18 24	
East Kilbride	a			15 42		16 14	16 13			16 43		17 13					17 43	17 40	17 54			18 13	18 27	
Kennishead	d		15 19		15 49				16 19		16 45				17 19	17 22					17 48			
Priesthill & Darnley	d		15 21		15 51				16 21		16 47				17 21	17 24					17 50			
Nitshill	d		15 24		15 54				16 24		16 50				17 24	17 27					17 53			
Barrhead	d	15 16	15a27		15a57			16 00	16a27		16a53		17 00		17a27	17a30				17 42	17a59			18 15
Dunlop	d	15 28						16 12					17 12							17 54				18 27
Stewarton	d	15 32						16 16					17 16							17 58				18 31
Kilmaurs	d	15 37						16 20					17 20							18 02				18 36
Kilmarnock 3	a	15 46						16 25					17 25							18 06				18 43

		SR	SR SO	SR SX	SR	SR	SR	SR	SR	SR	SR A	SR	SR	SR	SR	SR	SR	SR	SR A	SR	SR	SR	SR	SR
Glasgow Central 15	d	18 07	18 12	18 23	18 37	18 42	19 03	19 12	19 22	19 42	20 03	20 12	20 22	20 42	21 03	21 12	21 22	21 42	22 03	22 12	22 22	22 42	23 03	23 12
Crossmyloof	d	18 13	18 18	18 29	18 43	18 48		19 18	19 28	19 48		20 18	20 28	20 48		21 18	21 28	21 48		22 18	22 28	22 48	23 09	23 18
Pollokshaws West	d	18 16	18 21	18 32	18 46	18 51		19 21	19 31	19 51		20 21	20 31	20 51		21 21	21 31	21 51		22 21	22 31	22 51	23 12	23 21
Thornliebank	d		18 24	18 35		18 54		19 24		19 54		20 24		20 54		21 24		21 54		22 24		22 54		23 24
Giffnock	d		18 27	18 38		18 57		19 27		19 57		20 27		20 57		21 27		21 57		22 27		22 57		23 27
Clarkston	d		18 30	18 41		19 00		19 30		20 00		20 30		21 00		21 30		22 00		22 30		23 00		23 30
Busby	d		18 33	18 44		19 03		19 33		20 03		20 33		21 03		21 33		22 03		22 33		23 03		23 33
Thorntonhall	d					19 06				20 06				21 06				22 06				23 06		23 36
Hairmyres	d		18 39	18 50		19 10		19 39		20 10		20 39		21 10		21 39		22 10		22 39		23 10		23 40
East Kilbride	a		18 42	18 53		19 13		19 42		20 13		20 42		21 13		21 42		22 13		22 42		23 13		23b43
Kennishead	d	18 19			18 49				19 34				20 34				21 34				22 34		23 15	
Priesthill & Darnley	d	18 21			18 51				19 36				20 36				21 36				22 36		23 17	
Nitshill	d	18 24			18 54				19 39				20 39				21 39				22 39		23 20	
Barrhead	d	18a28			18a57		19 15		19a42		20 15		20a42		21 15		21a42		22 15		22a43		23 23	
Dunlop	d						19 27				20 27				21 27				22 27				23 35	
Stewarton	d						19 31				20 31				21 31				22 31				23 39	
Kilmaurs	d						19 36				20 36				21 36				22 36				23 44	
Kilmarnock 3	a						19 41				20 39				21 41				22 39				23 49	

For general notes see front of timetable
For details of catering facilities see Directory of Train Operators

A To Carlisle (Table 216)
B To Girvan (Table 218)
C To Newcastle (Table 48)

b Saturdays arr. 2341

Glasgow Central → East Kilbride, Barrhead and Kilmarnock

Network Diagram - see first page of Table 216

		SR	SR A	SR	and at the same minutes past each hour until	SR	SR	SR	SR	SR	SR	SR	SR B	SR	SR
Glasgow Central 15	d	08 42	08 48	09 12		19 12	19 42	20 12	20 42	21 12	21 42	22 12	22 28	22 42	23 12
Crossmyloof	d	08 48	.	09 18		19 18	19 48	20 18	20 48	21 18	21 48	22 18	.	22 48	23 18
Pollokshaws West	d	08 51	08 56	09 21		19 21	19 51	20 21	20 51	21 21	21 51	22 21	.	22 51	23 21
Thornliebank	d	08 54	.	09 24		19 24	19 54	20 24	20 54	21 24	21 54	22 24	.	22 54	23 24
Giffnock	d	08 57	.	09 27		19 27	19 57	20 27	20 57	21 27	21 57	22 27	.	22 57	23 27
Clarkston	d	09 00	.	09 30		19 30	20 00	20 30	21 00	21 30	22 00	22 30	.	23 00	23 30
Busby	d	09 03	.	09 33		19 33	20 03	20 33	21 03	21 33	22 03	22 33	.	23 03	23 33
Thorntonhall	d	09 06	.	.		.	20 06	.	21 06	.	22 06	.	.	23 06	23 36
Hairmyres	d	09 10	.	09 39		19 39	20 10	20 39	21 10	21 39	22 10	22 39	.	23 10	23 40
East Kilbride	a	09 13	.	09 42		19 42	20 13	20 42	21 13	21 42	22 13	22 42	.	23 13	23 43
Kennishead	d	.	.	.		.	.	.	.	.	.	.	.	.	.
Priesthill & Darnley	d	.	.	.		.	.	.	.	.	.	.	.	.	.
Nitshill	d	.	.	.		.	.	.	.	.	.	.	.	.	.
Barrhead	d	.	09 02	.		.	.	.	.	.	.	.	22 40	.	.
Dunlop	d	.	09 15	.		.	.	.	.	.	.	.	22 52	.	.
Stewarton	d	.	09 19	.		.	.	.	.	.	.	.	22 56	.	.
Kilmaurs	d	.	09 24	.		.	.	.	.	.	.	.	23 01	.	.
Kilmarnock 3	a	.	09 29	.		.	.	.	.	.	.	.	23 04	.	.

For general notes see front of timetable
For details of catering facilities see Directory of Train Operators

A 1448 from Glasgow Central to Kilmarnock arr. Kilmarnock 1527 and is to Carlisle (Table 216)

B To Carlisle (Table 216)

Kilmarnock, Barrhead and East Kilbride → Glasgow Central

Network Diagram - see first page of Table 216

Miles	Miles			SR SX	SR	SR	SR	SR SX	SR SX	SR SX	SR SO	SR SO	SR SX	SR SX	SR	SR SX	SR SO	SR SX	SR	SR SX	SR SO	SR SX	SR SX	SR	SR ◇
															A										B
0	—	**Kilmarnock** 3	d		06 32				07 32			07 32			07 58										09 12
2¼	—	Kilmaurs	d		06 36				07 36			07 36			08 02										09 16
5½	—	Stewarton	d		06 41				07 41			07 41			08 08										09 21
7¾	—	Dunlop	d		06 46				07 46			07 46			08 13										09 26
16¾	—	**Barrhead**	d		06 56		07 35		07 56			07 56	08 05		08 24				08 35				09 10		09 37
18½	—	Nitshill	d		06 59		07 38					07 59	08 08						08 38				09 13		
19½	—	Priesthill & Darnley	d		07 01		07 40					08 01	08 10						08 40				09 15		
20	—	Kennishead	d		07 03		07 42					08 03	08 12						08 42				09 17		
—	0	**East Kilbride**	d	06 18		07 05		07 29		07 47	07 46			08 03			08 18	08 17		08 30	08 48	08 55		09 20	
—	1½	Hairmyres	d	06 21		07 08		07 32		07 51	07 49			08 07			08 21	08 24		08 33	08 51	08 58		09 23	
—	3	Thorntonhall	d	06 25		07 12		07 36			07 53			08 10			08 25	08 27		08 37	08 55	09 02			
—	4¼	Busby	d	06 28		07 15		07 39			07 56			08 14		08 23	08 28	08 30		08 40	08 58	09 05		09 28	
—	5	Clarkston	d	06 30		07 18		07 42		07 59	07 58			08 17		08 26	08 30	08 33		08 42	09 00	09 07		09 31	
—	6¼	Giffnock	d	06 33		07 21		07 46			08 01			08 20		08 29	08 32	08 36		08 45	09 03	09 10		09 33	
—	7¼	Thornliebank	d	06 36		07 23		07 49			08 04			08 23		08 31	08 35	08 38		08 48	09 06	09 13		09 36	
21¼	8¼	Pollokshaws West	d	06 39	07 07	07 26	07 45	07 52			08 06	08 11	08 15	08 26		08 34	08 38	08 42	08 45		09 09	09 16	09 20	09 39	
22¼	9¼	Crossmyloof	d	06 42	07 10	07 29	07 48	07 54			08 09	08 13	08 18	08 29		08 37	08 42	08 45	08 48		09 12	09 19	09 23	09 42	
24¼	11½	**Glasgow Central** 15	a	06 48	07 18	07 35	07 55	08 01	08 09	08 13	08 15	08 21	08 25	08 35	08 37	08 43	08 48	08 51	08 55	08 57	09 18	09 25	09 30	09 48	09 50

		SR	SR	SR	SR	SR	SR	SR	SR	SR	SR	SR	SR	SR	SR	SR	SR	SR	SR	SR	SR	SR	SR	SR
					C															A				
Kilmarnock 3	d				10 04					10 50					11 50					12 50				
Kilmaurs	d				10 08					10 54					11 54					12 54				
Stewarton	d				10 13					10 59					11 59					12 59				
Dunlop	d				10 18					11 04					12 04					13 04				
Barrhead	d	09 40		10 05	10 28		10 35		11 05	11 14		11 35		12 05	12 14		12 35		13 05	13 14		13 35		14 05
Nitshill	d	09 43		10 08			10 38		11 08			11 38		12 08			12 38		13 08			13 38		14 08
Priesthill & Darnley	d	09 45		10 10			10 40		11 10			11 40		12 10			12 40		13 10			13 40		14 10
Kennishead	d	09 47		10 12			10 42		11 12			11 42		12 12			12 42		13 12			13 42		14 12
East Kilbride	d		09 48			10 20		10 48			11 20		11 48			12 20		12 48			13 20		13 48	
Hairmyres	d		09 51			10 23		10 51			11 23		11 51			12 23		12 51			13 23		13 51	
Thorntonhall	d		09 55					10 55					11 55					12 55					13 55	
Busby	d		09 58			10 28		10 58			11 28		11 58			12 28		12 58			13 28		13 58	
Clarkston	d		10 00			10 31		11 00			11 31		12 00			12 31		13 00			13 31		14 00	
Giffnock	d		10 03			10 33		11 03			11 33		12 03			12 33		13 03			13 33		14 03	
Thornliebank	d		10 06			10 36		11 06			11 36		12 06			12 36		13 06			13 36		14 06	
Pollokshaws West	d	09 50	10 09	10 15		10 39	10 45	11 09	11 15		11 39	11 45	12 09	12 15		12 39	12 45	13 09	13 15		13 39	13 45	14 09	14 15
Crossmyloof	d	09 53	10 12	10 18		10 42	10 48	11 12	11 18		11 42	11 48	12 12	12 18		12 42	12 48	13 12	13 18		13 42	13 48	14 12	14 18
Glasgow Central 15	a	10 01	10 18	10 25	10 41	10 48	10 55	11 18	11 25	11 27	11 48	11 55	12 18	12 25	12 27	12 48	12 55	13 18	13 25	13 29	13 48	13 55	14 18	14 25

		SR ◇	SR	SR	SR	SR	SR	SR	SR	SR	SR	SR	SR	SR	SR	SR	SR	SR	SR	SR	SR	SR	SR	SR
		B					A					D					A							
Kilmarnock 3	d	13 50					14 55					15 48					16 47			17 28				
Kilmaurs	d	13 54					14 59					15 52					16 51			17 32				
Stewarton	d	13 59					15 04					15 57					16 57			17 37				
Dunlop	d	14 04					15 09					16 02					17 01			17 42				
Barrhead	d	14 14		14 35		15 05	15 19		15 35		16 05	16 17		16 35		17 05	17 18		17 35	17 59		18 05		18 35
Nitshill	d			14 38		15 08			15 38		16 08			16 38		17 08			17 38			18 08		18 38
Priesthill & Darnley	d			14 40		15 10			15 40		16 10			16 40		17 10			17 40			18 10		18 40
Kennishead	d			14 42		15 12			15 42		16 12			16 42		17 12			17 42			18 12		18 42
East Kilbride	d		14 20		14 48			15 20		15 48			16 20		16 48			17 20			17b47		18 20	
Hairmyres	d		14 23		14 51			15 23		15 51			16 23		16 51			17 23			17 51		18 23	
Thorntonhall	d				14 55					15 55					16 55						17 55			
Busby	d		14 28		14 58			15 28		15 58			16 28		16 58			17 28			17 58		18 28	
Clarkston	d		14 31		15 00			15 31		16 00			16 31		17 00			17 31			18 00		18 31	
Giffnock	d		14 33		15 03			15 33		16 03			16 33		17 03			17 33			18 03		18 33	
Thornliebank	d		14 36		15 06			15 36		16 06			16 36		17 06			17 36			18 06		18 36	
Pollokshaws West	d		14 39	14 45	15 09	15 15		15 39	15 45	16 09	16 15		16 39	16 45	17 09	17 15		17 39	17 45		18 09	18 15	18 39	18 45
Crossmyloof	d		14 42	14 48	15 12	15 18		15 42	15 48	16 12	16 18		16 42	16 48	17 12	17 18		17 42	17 48		18 12	18 18	18 42	18 48
Glasgow Central 15	a	14 27	14 48	14 55	15 18	15 25	15 33	15 48	15 55	16 18	16 25	16 32	16 48	16 55	17 18	17 27	17 31	17 51	17 55	18 12	18 20	18 25	18 51	18 55

		SR	SR	SR	SR	SR	SR	SR	SR	SR	SR	SR	SR	SR	SR	SR	SR	SR	SR	SR	SR	SR
								A								E				G		
Kilmarnock 3	d			18 50				19 50				20 50				21 50				22 50		
Kilmaurs	d			18 54				19 54				20 54				21 54				22 54		
Stewarton	d			18 59				19 59				20 59				21 59				22 59		
Dunlop	d			19 04				20 04				21 04				22 04				23 04		
Barrhead	d		19 05	19 14		19 50		20 14		20 50		21 14		21 50		22 14		22 50		23 14		
Nitshill	d		19 08			19 53				20 53				21 53				22 53				
Priesthill & Darnley	d		19 10			19 55				20 55				21 55				22 55				
Kennishead	d		19 12			19 57				20 57				21 57				22 57				
East Kilbride	d	18c46			19 20		19 48		20 20		20 48		21 20		21 48		22 20		22 48		23 20	23 48
Hairmyres	d	18 51			19 23		19 51		20 23		20 51		21 23		21 51		22 23		22 51		23 23	23 51
Thorntonhall	d	18 55					19 55				20 55				21 55				22 55			23 55
Busby	d	18 58			19 28		19 58		20 28		20 58		21 28		21 58		22 28		22 58		23 28	23 58
Clarkston	d	19 00			19 31		20 00		20 31		21 00		21 31		22 00		22 31		23 00		23 31	00 01
Giffnock	d	19 03			19 33		20 03		20 33		21 03		21 33		22 03		22 33		23 03		23 33	00 03
Thornliebank	d	19 06			19 36		20 06		20 36		21 06		21 36		22 06		22 36		23 06		23 36	00 06
Pollokshaws West	d	19 09	19 15		19 39	20 00	20 09		20 39	21 00	21 09		21 39	22 00	22 09		22 39	23 00	23 09		23 39	00 09
Crossmyloof	d	19 12	19 18		19 42	20 03	20 12		20 42	21 03	21 12		21 42	22 03	22 12		22 42	23 03	23 12		23 42	00 12
Glasgow Central 15	a	19 19	19 25	19 27	19 48	20 10	20 18	20 27	20 48	21 10	21 18	21 27	21 48	22 10	22 18	22e29	22 48	23 12	23 18	23f28	23 48	00 18

For general notes see front of timetable
For details of catering facilities see Directory of Train Operators

A From Carlisle (Table 216)
B From Stranraer (Table 218)
C From Newcastle (Table 48)
D From Girvan (Table 218)
E Saturdays from Carlisle (Table 216)
G Mondays to Fridays from Carlisle (Table 216)
b Saturdays dep. 1748
c Saturdays dep. 1848
e Saturdays arr. 2227
f Saturdays arr. 2327

Table 222

Sundays

Kilmarnock, Barrhead and East Kilbride → Glasgow Central

Network Diagram - see first page of Table 216

		SR	SR	SR A		SR	SR	SR	SR	SR	SR B	SR	SR	SR	SR	SR
Kilmarnock 3	d			09 35		19 35					21 18					
Kilmaurs	d			09 39		19 39					21 22					
Stewarton	d			09 44	and at	19 44					21 27					
Dunlop	d			09 49		19 49					21 32					
Barrhead	d			09 59	the same	19 59					21 42					
Nitshill	d															
Priesthill & Darnley	d				minutes											
Kennishead	d															
East Kilbride	d	08 48	09 20		past		19 48	20 20	20 48	21 20		21 48	22 20	22 48	23 20	23 48
Hairmyres	d	08 51	09 23		each		19 51	20 23	20 51	21 23		21 51	22 23	22 51	23 23	23 51
Thorntonhall	d	08 55					19 55		20 55			21 55		22 55		23 55
Busby	d	08 58	09 28		hour until		19 58	20 28	20 58	21 28		21 58	22 28	22 58	23 28	23 58
Clarkston	d	09 00	09 31				20 00	20 31	21 00	21 31		22 00	22 31	23 00	23 31	00 01
Giffnock	d	09 03	09 34				20 03	20 33	21 03	21 33		22 03	22 33	23 03	23 33	00 03
Thornliebank	d	09 06	09 36				20 06	20 36	21 06	21 36		22 06	22 36	23 06	23 36	00 06
Pollokshaws West	d	09 09	09 39	10 05		20 05	20 09	20 39	21 09	21 39		22 09	22 39	23 09	23 39	00 09
Crossmyloof	d	09 12	09 42				20 12	20 42	21 12	21 42		22 12	22 42	23 12	23 42	00 12
Glasgow Central 15	a	09 18	09 48	10 14		20 14	20 18	20 48	21 18	21 48	21 55	22 18	22 48	23 18	23 48	00 18

For general notes see front of timetable
For details of catering facilities see Directory of Train Operators

A 1435 from Kilmarnock is ◇ and from Carlisle (Table 216)
B From Carlisle (Table 216)

Glasgow Central, Cathcart Circle, Neilston and Newton

Network Diagram - see first page of Table 220

Miles	Miles	Miles		SR	SR	SR	SR	SR	SR	SR	SR	SR	SR	SR	SR	SR	SR	SR	SR	SR	SR	SR	SR
								SX		SX	SX	SX	SO	SX	SO	SX		SX	SX		SX	SX	SX
						A		B				A							B		A		
0	0	0	**Glasgow Central** 15 .... 226 d	06 10	06 20	06 27	06 35	06 40	06 50	06 58	07 03	07 05	07 10	07 20	07 20	07 25	07 35	07 39	07 44	07 50	07 55	07 59	08 05
2¼	—	—	Pollokshields West d			06 32	06 40					07 10					07 40				08 00		
2¾	—	—	Maxwell Park d			06 34	06 42					07 12					07 42				08 02		
3½	—	—	Shawlands d			06 36	06 44					07 14					07 44				08 04		
3¾	—	—	Pollokshaws East d			06 37	06 45					07 15					07 45				08 05		
4¼	—	—	Langside d			06 39	06 47					07 17					07 47				08 07		
—	1¾	1¾	Pollokshields East d	06 14	06 24			06 44	06 54	07 02	07 07		07 14	07 24	07 24	07 29			07 48	07 54		08 03	08 09
—	2¼	2¼	Queens Park d	06 16	06 26			06 46	06 56	07 04	07 09		07 16	07 26	07 26	07 31			07 50	07 56		08 05	08 11
—	2½	2½	Crosshill d	06 17	06 27			06 47	06 57	07 05	07 10		07 17	07 27	07 27	07 32			07 51	07 57		08 06	08 12
—	3¼	3¼	Mount Florida d	06 19	06 29			06 49	06 59	07 07	07 12		07 19	07 29	07 29	07 34			07 53	07 59		08 08	08 14
5¼	—	4	Cathcart d		06 31	06a41		06a51	07 01		07 14	07a19			07 31	07 36			07a55	08 01	08a09		08 16
—	—	4¾	Muirend d		06 33				07 03		07 16				07 33	07 38		07 48		08 03			08 18
—	—	6	Williamwood d		06 36				07 06		07 19				07 36	07 41		07 51		08 06			08 21
—	—	6¾	Whitecraigs d		06 38				07 08		07 21				07 38	07 43		07 53		08 08			08 23
—	—	7¾	Patterton d		06 41				07 11		07 24				07 41	07 46		07 55		08 11			08 26
—	—	11¾	**Neilston** a		06 47				07 17		07 30				07 47	07 52		08 01		08 17			08 32
5¾	4½	—	Kings Park d	06 21			06 51			07 09			07 21	07 31			07 50					08 10	
6	4¾	—	Croftfoot d	06 23			06 53			07 11			07 23	07 33			07 52					08 12	
7	5¾	—	Burnside d	06 26			06 55			07 14			07 26	07 36			07 56					08 15	
8½	7¼	—	Kirkhill a	06 29			06 58			07 17			07 29	07 39			07 59					08 18	
10	8¾	—	**Newton** 226 a	06 32			07 01			07 20			07 32	07 43			08 02					08 21	

	SR	SR	SR	SR	SR	SR	SR	SR	SR	SR	SR	SR	SR	SR	SR	SR	SR	SR		SR
	SX	SO	SX	SO	SX	SX	SX	SX			SX	SX								
	B		A			B		A			B	A				B		A		A
Glasgow Central 15 .... 226 d	08 10	08 10	08 19	08 20	08 21	08 23	08 26	08 30	08 35	08 50	08 57	09 05	09 10	09 20	09 35	09 40	09 50	10 05	and at the same minutes past each hour until	15 05
Pollokshields West d			08 24					08 36	08 40			09 10			09 40			10 10		15 10
Maxwell Park d			08 26					08 38	08 42			09 12			09 42			10 12		15 12
Shawlands d			08 28					08 40	08 44			09 14			09 44			10 14		15 14
Pollokshaws East d			08 29					08 41	08 45			09 15			09 45			10 15		15 15
Langside d			08 31					08 43	08 47			09 17			09 47			10 17		15 17
Pollokshields East d	08 14	08 14		08 24	08 25	08 27	08 30			08 54	09 01		09 14	09 24		09 44	09 54			
Queens Park d	08 16	08 16		08 26	08 27	08 29	08 32			08 56	09 03		09 16	09 26		09 46	09 56			
Crosshill d	08 17	08 17		08 27	08 28	08 30	08 33			08 57	09 04		09 17	09 27		09 47	09 57			
Mount Florida d	08 19	08 19		08 29	08 30	08 32	08 35			08 59	09 06		09 19	09 29		09 49	09 59			
Cathcart d	08a21		08a33	08 31	08 32	08a34		08a46		09 01	09a08	09a20		09 31		09a51	10 01	10a20		15a20
Muirend d				08 33	08 34					09 03				09 33			10 03			
Williamwood d				08 36	08 37					09 06				09 36			10 06			
Whitecraigs d				08 38	08 39					09 08				09 38			10 08			
Patterton d				08 41	08 43					09 11				09 41			10 11			
Neilston a				08 47	08 48					09 17				09 47			10 17			
Kings Park d		08 21					08 37		08 51				09 21		09 51					
Croftfoot d		08 23					08 39		08 53				09 23		09 53					
Burnside d		08 26					08 42		08 55				09 26		09 55					
Kirkhill a		08 29					08 45		08 58				09 29		09 58					
Newton 226 a		08 32					08 48		09 03				09 32		10 01					

	SR	SR	SR	SR	SR	SR	SR	SR	SR	SR	SR	SR	SR	SR	SR	SR	SR	SR	SR	SR	SR	SR
		SO	SX	SX		SO	SO	SX	SX							SX		SX	SO	SX	SX	SX
				B		B			B	A				B			A				A	
Glasgow Central 15 .... 226 d	15 10	15 20	15 20	15 33	15 35	15 40	15 50	15 56	16 00	16 05	16 10	16 20	16 35	16 40	16 50	17 03	17 05	17 08	17 10	17 12	17 16	17 20
Pollokshields West d					15 40					16 10			16 40				17 10				17 21	
Maxwell Park d					15 42					16 12			16 42				17 12				17 23	
Shawlands d					15 44					16 14			16 44				17 14				17 25	
Pollokshaws East d					15 45					16 15			16 45				17 15				17 26	
Langside d					15 47					16 17			16 47				17 17				17 28	
Pollokshields East d	15 14	15 24	15 24	15 37		15 44	15 54	16 00	16 04		16 14	16 24		16 44	16 54	17 07			17 14	17 16		17 24
Queens Park d	15 16	15 26	15 26	15 39		15 46	15 56	16 02	16 06		16 16	16 26		16 46	16 56	17 09			17 16	17 18		17 26
Crosshill d	15 17	15 27	15 27	15b47		15 47	15 57	16 03	16 07		16 17	16 27		16 47	16 57	17 10			17 17	17 19		17 27
Mount Florida d	15 19	15 29	15 29	15 49		15 49	15 59	16 05	16 09		16 19	16 29		16 49	16 59	17 12			17 19	17 21		17 29
Cathcart d		15 31	15 31	15a51		15a51	16 01	16 07	16a11	16a19		16 31		16a51	17 01		17a20			17 24	17a30	
Muirend d		15 33	15 33				16 03	16 09				16 33			17 03			17 17		17 27		
Williamwood d		15 36	15 36				16 06	16 12				16 36			17 06			17 20		17 30		
Whitecraigs d		15 38	15 38				16 08	16 14				16 38			17 08			17 22		17 32		
Patterton d		15 41	15c45				16 11	16 17				16 41			17 11			17 24		17 34		
Neilston a		15 47	15 50				16 17	16 23				16 47			17 17			17 30		17 41		
Kings Park d	15 21				15 51						16 21		16 51			17 14			17 21			17 31
Croftfoot d	15 23				15 53						16 23		16 53			17 16			17 23			17 33
Burnside d	15 26				15 55						16 26		16 55			17 19			17 26			17 36
Kirkhill a	15 29				15 58						16 29		16 58			17 22			17 29			17 39
Newton 226 a	15 32				16 01						16 32		17 01			17 25			17 32			17 42

For general notes see front of timetable
For details of catering facilities see Directory of Train Operators

A Cathcart Circle service. To Glasgow Central via Queens Park

B Cathcart Circle service. To Glasgow Central via Maxwell Park

b Arr. 1540

c Arr. 1541

Glasgow Central, Cathcart Circle, Neilston and Newton

Network Diagram - see first page of Table 220

Mondays to Saturdays

	SR SO	SR SX	SR	SR SO A	SR SX A	SR	SR B	SR	SR	SR	SR A	SR	SR B	SR		SR	SR	SR FO
Glasgow Central 15 .... 226 d	17 20	17 28	17 35	17 40	17 44	17 50	18 05	18 10	18 20	18 35	18 40	18 50	19 05	19 10	and at the same minutes past each hour until	23 10	23 20	23 50
Pollokshields West d			17 40				18 10			18 40			19 10					
Maxwell Park d			17 42				18 12			18 42			19 12					
Shawlands d			17 44				18 14			18 44			19 14					
Pollokshaws East d			17 45				18 15			18 45			19 15					
Langside d			17 47				18 17			18 47			19 17					
Pollokshields East d	17 24	17 32		17 44	17 48	17 54		18 14	18 24		18 44	18 54		19 14		23 14	23 24	23 54
Queens Park d	17 26	17 34		17 46	17 50	17 56		18 16	18 26		18 46	18 56		19 16		23 16	23 26	23 56
Crosshill d	17 27	17 35		17 47	17 51	17 57		18 17	18 27		18 47	18 57		19 17		23 17	23 27	23 57
Mount Florida d	17 29	17 37		17 49	17 53	17 59		18 19	18 29		18 49	18 59		19 19		23 19	23 29	23 59
Cathcart d	17 31	17 39		17a51	17a55	18 01	18a19		18 31		18a51	19 01	19a20				23 31	00 01
Muirend d	17 33	17 41				18 03			18 33			19 03					23 33	00 03
Williamwood d	17 36	17 44				18 06			18 36			19 06					23 36	00 06
Whitecraigs d	17 38	17 46				18 08			18 38			19 08					23 38	00 08
Patterton d	17 41	17 49				18 11			18 41			19 11					23 41	00 11
Neilston a	17 47	17 55				18 17			18 47			19 17					23 47	00 17
Kings Park d			17 51					18 21		18 51				19 21		23 21		
Croftfoot d			17 53					18 23		18 53				19 23		23 23		
Burnside d			17 55					18 26		18 55				19 26		23 26		
Kirkhill a			17 58					18 29		18 58				19 29		23 29		
Newton 226 a			18 02					18 32		19 00				19 32		23b32		

Sundays

	SR	SR	SR	SR		SR	SR	SR	SR	SR
Glasgow Central 15 .... 226 d	08 20	08 35	08 50	09 10	and at the same minutes past each hour until	22 10	22 20	22 35	22 50	23 10
Pollokshields West d		08 40						22 40		
Maxwell Park d		08 42						22 42		
Shawlands d		08 44						22 44		
Pollokshaws East d		08 45						22 45		
Langside d		08 47						22 47		
Pollokshields East d	08 24		08 54	09 14		22 14	22 24		22 54	23 14
Queens Park d	08 26		08 56	09 16		22 16	22 26		22 56	23 16
Crosshill d	08 27		08 57	09 17		22 17	22 27		22 57	23 17
Mount Florida d	08 29		08 59	09 19		22 19	22 29		22 59	23 19
Cathcart d	08 31		09 01				22 31		23 01	
Muirend d	08 33		09 03				22 33		23 03	
Williamwood d	08 36		09 06				22 36		23 06	
Whitecraigs d	08 38		09 08				22 38		23 08	
Patterton d	08 41		09 11				22 41		23 11	
Neilston a	08 47		09 17				22 47		23 17	
Kings Park d		08 51		09 21		22 21		22 51		23 21
Croftfoot d		08 53		09 23		22 23		22 53		23 23
Burnside d		08 55		09 26		22 26		22 55		23 26
Kirkhill a		08 58		09 29		22 29		22 58		23 29
Newton 226 a		09 01		09 32		22 32		23 03		23 32

For general notes see front of timetable
For details of catering facilities see Directory of Train Operators

A Cathcart Circle service. To Glasgow Central via Queens Park

B Cathcart Circle service. To Glasgow Central via Maxwell Park

b Saturdays arr. 2332

Newton, Neilston, Cathcart Circle and Glasgow Central

Network Diagram - see first page of Table 220

Miles	Miles	Miles		SR	SR A	SR	SR SX B	SR	SR SX A	SR	SR	SR SX	SR SO	SR SX	SR SX B	SR SX	SR SX A	SR SO	SR SX	SR SX	SR SX B	SR SO		SR SX	SR SX A
0	0	—	**Newton** 226 d	06 11		06 41				07 11		07 34	07 41			07 48						08 11		08 17	
1½	1½	—	Kirkhill d	06 14		06 44				07 14		07 38	07 44			07 51						08 14		08 20	
2¾	2¾	—	Burnside d	06 17		06 47				07 17		07 41	07 47			07 54						08 17		08 23	
3¾	3¾	—	Croftfoot d	06 19		06 49				07 19		07 43	07 49			07 56						08 19		08 25	
4¼	4¼	—	Kings Park d	06 21		06 51				07 21		07 45	07 51			07 58						08 21		08 27	
—	—	0	**Neilston** d					06 56			07 26			07 39				07 56	08 03	08 10					
—	—	3¾	Patterton d					07 01			07 31			07 44				08 01	08 08	08 15					
—	—	4¾	Whitecraigs d					07 03			07 33			07 46				08 03	08 10	08 17					
—	—	5½	Williamwood d					07 06			07 36			07 49				08 06	08 13	08 20					
—	—	7	Muirend d					07 09			07 39			07 51				08 09	08 15	08 22					
4¾	—	7¾	Cathcart d		06 41		06 52	07 11	07 21		07 41			07 53	07 55		08 09	08 11	08 17		08 21				08 34
—	5½	8½	Mount Florida d		06 43	06 53		07 13	07 23		07 43	07 47	07 53	07 55			08 11	08 13	08 19					08 29	08 36
—	6	9	Crosshill d		06 45	06 55		07 15	07 25		07 45	07 49	07 55	07 57			08 13	08 15	08 21					08 31	08 38
—	6½	9½	Queens Park d		06 47	06 57		07 17	07 27		07 47	07 51	07 57	07 59			08 15	08 17	08 23					08 35	08 40
—	6¾	9¾	Pollokshields East d		06 48	06 58		07 18	07 28		07 48	07 52	07 58	08 00			08 16	08 18	08 24					08 36	08 41
5¾	—	—	Langside d	06 24			06 54			07 24					07 57	08 01					08 24	08 24			
6¼	—	—	Pollokshaws East d	06 26			06 56			07 26					07 59	08 03					08 26	08 26			
6¾	—	—	Shawlands d	06 28			06 58			07 28					08 01	08 05					08 28	08 28			
7½	—	—	Maxwell Park d	06 29			06 59			07 29					08 02	08 06					08 29	08 29			
8	—	—	Pollokshields West d	06 31			07 01			07 31					08 04	08 08					08 31	08 31			
10	8¾	11¾	**Glasgow Central 15** 226 a	06 37	06 53	07 03	07 07	07 23	07 33	07 38	07 53	07 57	08 03	08 05	08 11	08 15	08 21	08 23	08 30	08 32	08 39	08 39		08 41	08 47

	SR SX B	SR	SR SX A	SR SX	SR SO	SR SX	SR SX	SR SX B	SR SO	SR SX	SR SX A	SR	SR	SR		SR B	SR	SR A	SR	SR	SR	and at the same minutes past each hour until		SR
Newton 226 d				08 34	08 41		08 58					09 11		09 41					10 11		10 41			15 41
Kirkhill d				08 38	08 44		09 01					09 14		09 44					10 14		10 44			15 44
Burnside d				08 41	08 47		09 04					09 17		09 47					10 17		10 47			15 47
Croftfoot d				08 43	08 49		09 06					09 19		09 49					10 19		10 49			15 49
Kings Park d				08 45	08 51		09 08					09 21		09 51					10 21		10 51			15 51
Neilston d		08 26				08 41			08 56	09 02			09 26				09 56			10 26				
Patterton d		08 31				08 46			09 01	09 07			09 31				10 01			10 31				
Whitecraigs d		08 33				08 48			09 03	09 09			09 33				10 03			10 33				
Williamwood d		08 36				08 51			09 06	09 12			09 36				10 06			10 36				
Muirend d		08 39				08 53			09 09	09 14			09 39				10 09			10 39				
Cathcart d	08 34	08 41	08 46			08 55		09 08	09 11	09 16	09 21		09 41			09 52	10 11	10 21		10 41				
Mount Florida d		08 43	08 48		08 53	08 57	09 10		09 13	09 18	09 23		09 43	09 53			10 13	10 23		10 43	10 53			15 53
Crosshill d		08 45	08 50		08 55	08 59	09 12		09 15	09 20	09 25		09 45	09 55			10 15	10 25		10 45	10 55			15 55
Queens Park d		08 47	08 52		08 57	09 01	09 14		09 17	09 22	09 27		09 47	09 57			10 17	10 27		10 47	10 57			15 57
Pollokshields East d		08 48	08 53		08 58	09 02	09 15		09 18	09 23	09 28		09 48	09 58			10 18	10 28		10 48	10 58			15 58
Langside d	08 36			08 48				09 10				09 24				09 54			10 24					
Pollokshaws East d	08 38			08 50				09 12				09 26				09 56			10 26					
Shawlands d	08 40			08 52				09 14				09 28				09 58			10 28					
Maxwell Park d	08 41			08 53				09 15				09 29				09 59			10 29					
Pollokshields West d	08 43			08 55				09 17				09 31				10 01			10 31					
Glasgow Central 15 226 a	08 49	08 53	08 59	09 01	09 03	09 07	09 20	09 23	09 23	09 28	09 33	09 38	09 53	10 03		10 07	10 23	10 33	10 38	10 53	11 03			16 03

	SR B	SR	SR SX B	SR A	SR	SR SO	SR SX	SR	SR B	SR SO	SR SX	SR A	SR	SR SX A	SR	SR SX	SR SO	SR SO B	SR SX		SR SX B	SR	SR A	SR	SR SX
Newton 226 d					16 11			16 41					17 11			17 41	17 41							18 11	
Kirkhill d					16 14			16 44					17 14			17 44	17 44							18 14	
Burnside d					16 17			16 47					17 17			17 47	17 47							18 17	
Croftfoot d					16 19			16 49					17 19			17 49	17 49							18 19	
Kings Park d					16 21			16 51					17 21			17 51	17 51							18 21	
Neilston d		15 56				16 26	16 33			16 56	17 02				17 26				17 42			17 56			18 13
Patterton d		16 01				16 31	16 38			17 01	17 07				17 31							18 01			18 18
Whitecraigs d		16 03				16 33	16 40			17 03	17 09				17 33							18 03			18 20
Williamwood d		16 06				16 36	16 43			17 06	17 12				17 36							18 06			18 23
Muirend d		16 09				16 39	16 45			17 09	17 14				17 39							18 09			18 26
Cathcart d	15 52	16 11	16 13	16 21		16 41	16 47		16 52	17 11	17 16	17 21		17 32	17 41			17 52	17 54		17 55	18 11	18 21		18 28
Mount Florida d		16 13		16 23		16 43	16 49	16 53		17 13	17 18	17 23		17 34	17 43	17 53	17 53		17 56			18 13	18 23		18 30
Crosshill d		16 15		16 25		16 45	16 51	16 55		17 15	17 20	17 25		17 36	17 45		17 55		17 58			18 15	18 25		18 32
Queens Park d		16 17		16 27		16 47	16 53	16 57		17 17	17 22	17 27		17 37	17 47		17 57		18 00			18 17	18 27		18 34
Pollokshields East d		16 18		16 28		16 48	16 54	16 58		17 18	17 23	17 28		17 39	17 48		17 58		18 01			18 18	18 28		18 35
Langside d	15 54		16 15		16 24				16 54				17 24					17 54			17 57			18 24	
Pollokshaws East d	15 56		16 17		16 26				16 56				17 26					17 56			17 59			18 26	
Shawlands d	15 58		16 19		16 28				16 58				17 28					17 58			18 01			18 28	
Maxwell Park d	15 59		16 20		16 29				16 59				17 29					17 59			18 02			18 29	
Pollokshields West d	16 01		16 22		16 31				17 01				17 31					18 01			18 04			18 31	
Glasgow Central 15 226 a	16 07	16 23	16 28	16 33	16 38	16 53	16 59	17 03	17 07	17 23	17 29	17 33	17 38	17 44	17 53	18 03	18 03	18 07	18 07		18 10	18 23	18 33	18 38	18 40

For general notes see front of timetable
For details of catering facilities see
Directory of Train Operators

A Cathcart Circle service.
From Glasgow Central via Maxwell Park

B Cathcart Circle service.
From Glasgow Central via Queens Park

Newton, Neilston, Cathcart Circle and Glasgow Central

Network Diagram - see first page of Table 220

Mondays to Saturdays

	SR	SR		SR A	SR	SR B	SR	SR	SR		SR	SR A	SR	SR B	SR	SR	SR	SR A	SR	SR B	SR	SR
Newton 226 d		18 41					19 11		19 41		21 41				22 11		22 41				23 11	
Kirkhill d		18 44					19 14		19 44		21 44				22 14		22 44				23 14	
Burnside d		18 47					19 17		19 47		21 47				22 17		22 47				23 17	
Croftfoot d		18 49					19 19		19 49		21 49				22 19		22 49				23 19	
Kings Park d		18 51					19 21		19 51	and at	21 51				22 21		22 51				23 21	
Neilston d	18 26				18 56			19 26					21 56			22 26			22 56			23 26
Patterton d	18 31				19 01			19 31		the same			22 01			22 31			23 01			23 31
Whitecraigs d	18 33				19 03			19 33					22 03			22 33			23 03			23 33
Williamwood d	18 36				19 06			19 36		minutes			22 06			22 36			23 06			23 36
Muirend d	18 39				19 09			19 39					22 09			22 39			23 09			23 39
Cathcart d	18 41			18 52	19 11	19 21		19 41		past		21 52	22 11	22 21		22 41		22 52	23 11	23 21		23 41
Mount Florida d	18 43	18 53			19 13	19 23		19 43	19 53	each	21 53		22 13	22 23		22 43	22 53		23 13	23 23		23 43
Crosshill d	18 45	18 55			19 15	19 25		19 45	19 55		21 55		22 15	22 25		22 45	22 55		23 15	23 25		23 45
Queens Park d	18 47	18 57			19 17	19 27		19 47	19 57	hour until	21 57		22 17	22 27		22 47	22 57		23 17	23 27		23 47
Pollokshields East d	18 48	18 58			19 18	19 28		19 48	19 58		21 58		22 18	22 28		22 48	22 58		23 18	23 28		23 48
Langside d				18 54			19 24					21 54			22 24			22 54			23 24	
Pollokshaws East d				18 56			19 26					21 56			22 26			22 56			23 26	
Shawlands d				18 58			19 28					21 58			22 28			22 58			23 28	
Maxwell Park d				18 59			19 29					21 59			22 29			22 59			23 29	
Pollokshields West d				19 01			19 31					22 01			22 31			23 01			23 31	
Glasgow Central 15 226 a	18 53	19 05		19 07	19 23	19 33	19 38	19 53	20 03		22 03	22 08	22 23	22 33	22 41	22b56	23 03	23 08	23 24	23 33	23 38	23 53

Sundays

		SR	SR	SR	SR			SR		SR		SR		SR
Newton 226 d			09 11		09 41			22 41				23 11		
Kirkhill d			09 14		09 44			22 44				23 14		
Burnside d			09 17		09 47			22 47				23 17		
Croftfoot d			09 19		09 49			22 49				23 19		
Kings Park d			09 21		09 51			22 51				23 21		
Neilston d		08 56		09 26		and at				22 56				23 26
Patterton d		09 01		09 31		the same				23 01				23 31
Whitecraigs d		09 03		09 33						23 03				23 33
Williamwood d		09 06		09 36		minutes				23 06				23 36
Muirend d		09 09		09 39						23 09				23 39
Cathcart d		09 11		09 41		past				23 11				23 41
Mount Florida d		09 13		09 43	09 53	each		22 53		23 13				23 43
Crosshill d		09 15		09 45	09 55			22 55		23 15				23 45
Queens Park d		09 17		09 47	09 57	hour until		22 57		23 17				23 47
Pollokshields East d		09 18		09 48	09 58			22 58		23 18				23 48
Langside d			09 24									23 24		
Pollokshaws East d			09 26									23 26		
Shawlands d			09 28									23 28		
Maxwell Park d			09 29									23 29		
Pollokshields West d			09 31									23 31		
Glasgow Central 15 226 a		09 23	09 38	09 53	10 03			23 03		23 23		23 38		23 53

For general notes see front of timetable
For details of catering facilities see Directory of Train Operators

A Cathcart Circle service. From Glasgow Central via Queens Park

B Cathcart Circle service. From Glasgow Central via Maxwell Park

b Saturdays arr. 2253

Motherwell and Glasgow Queen Street → Cumbernauld and Falkirk Grahamston

Network Diagram - see first page of Table 220

Miles	Miles			SR	SR	SR	SR	SR	SR	SR SX A	SR	SR	SR	SR	SR	SR		SR	SR	SR		SR SX	SR SO	SR	SR
—	0	**Motherwell** 226	d			06 12				07 12	07 34			08 37				09 37			and at			16 37	
—	4½	Whifflet	d			06 20				07 19	07 42			08 45				09 45						16 45	
—	5¼	**Coatbridge Central**	d			06a23	06 45			07a23	07 45			08 48				09 48			the same			16 48	
0	—	**Glasgow Queen Street** 10	d	05 52	06 22			06 52	07 22			07 52	08 22		08 54	09 22			09 52	10 22	minutes	16 22	16 22		16 52
1¼	—	Springburn	d	05 56	06 26			06 56	07 26			07 56	08 26		08 56	09 26			09 56	10 26		16 26	16 26		16 56
5¼	—	Stepps	d	06 03	06 33			07 03	07 33			08 03	08 33		09 03	09 33			10 03	10 33	past	16 33	16 33		17 03
7¾	—	Gartcosh	d	06 07	06 37			07 07	07 37			08 07	08 37		09 07	09 37			10 07	10 37		16 37	16 37		17 07
13¼	11	Greenfaulds	d	06 15	06 45		06 54	07 15	07 45		07 53	08 15	08 45	08 56	09 15	09 45		09 57	10 15	10 45	each	16 45	16 45	16 57	17 15
14	11¾	**Cumbernauld**	d	06a20	06 47		06a57	07a19	07 47		07a57	08a19	08 47	09a01	09a21	09 47		10a00	10a19	10 47	hour until	16 47	16 47	17a00	17a19
22½	—	Camelon	d		07 01				08 01				09 01			10 01				11 01		17 01	17 06		
24	—	**Falkirk Grahamston**	a		07 07				08 09				09 07			10 07				11 07		17 04	17 12		
—	—	Edinburgh 10	a		*08 14*				*09 02*				*10 02*			*11 01*				*12 01*		*18 02*	*18 02*		
—	—	Stirling	a		*07 50*				*08 53*				*09 53*			*10 53*				*11 53*		*17 52*	*17 52*		

		SR SX B	SR	SR SX B	SR	SR	SR SX C	SR	SR	SR	SR	SR	SR	SR	SR	SR	SR	SR	SR	SR	SR	SR B	SR	SR		
Motherwell 226	d	16 42		17 12	17 37		17 56		18 37			19 37			20 37			21 37				22 41				
Whifflet	d	16 48		17 18	17 45		18 02		18 45			19 45			20 45			21 45				22 48				
Coatbridge Central	d	16a53		17a22	17 48		18a06		18 48			19 48			20 48			21 48				22a52				
Glasgow Queen Street 10	d		17 22			17 52		18 24		18 52	19 22		19 52	20 23		20 52	21 24		21 52	22 22	22 52		23 24	23 53		
Springburn	d		17 26			17 56		18 26		18 56	19 27		19 56	20 26		20 56	21 26		21 56	22 26	22 56		23 26	23 57		
Stepps	d		17 33			18 03		18 33		19 03	19 34		20 03	20 33		21 03	21 33		22 03	22 33	23 03		23 33	00 04		
Gartcosh	d		17 37			18 07		18 37		19 07	19 37		20 07	20 37		21 07	21 37		22 07	22 37	23 07		23 37	00 07		
Greenfaulds	d		17 45		17 57	18 15		18 45	18 57	19 15	19 45	19 57	20 15	20 45	20 59	21 15	21 45	21 59	22 15	22 45	23 15		23 45	00 15		
Cumbernauld	d		17 47		18a00	18a19		18 47	19a00	19a19	19a50	20a00	20 17	20a50	21a02	21 17	21a51	22a03	22 17	22a49	23 17		23a51	00a21		
Camelon	d		18 01					19 01					20 31			21 31			22 31		23 33					
Falkirk Grahamston	a		18 07					19 07					20 36			21 36			22 36		23 39					
Edinburgh 10	a		*19 01*					*20 04*					*21 31*			*23 01*			*00 07*							
Stirling	a		*18 52*					*19 53*					*21 23*			*22b24*			*23c23*		*00 24*					

Sundays

until 23 November

		SR	SR		SR	SR		SR	SR		SR	SR		SR	SR		SR	SR		SR	SR		SR			
Glasgow Queen Street	d	08 22	09 24		10 22	11 22		12 23	13 22		14 22	15 22		16 23	17 22		18 23	19 22		20 22	21 26		22 23			
Springburn	d	08 27	09 29		10 27	11 27		12 28	13 27		14 27	15 27		16 27	17 27		18 27	19 27		20 27	21 31		22 27			
Stepps	d	08 34	09 34		10 34	11 34		12 34	13 34		14 34	15 34		16 34	17 34		18 34	19 34		20 34	21 38		22 34			
Gartcosh	d	08 38	09 38		10 38	11 38		12 38	13 38		14 38	15 38		16 38	17 38		18 38	19 38		20 38	21 42		22 38			
Greenfaulds	d	08 46	09 46		10 46	11 46		12 46	13 46		14 46	15 46		16 46	17 46		18 46	19 46		20 46	21 50		22 46			
Cumbernauld	a	08 49	09 51		10 49	11 49		12 50	13 49		14 49	15 49		16 51	17 49		18 50	19 49		20 49	21 53		22 50			

Sundays

from 30 November

		SR	SR	SR	SR	SR	SR	SR	SR	SR	SR	SR	SR	SR	SR	SR	SR	SR	SR	SR	SR	SR	SR	SR	SR	SR
Glasgow Queen Street	d	08 22	08 42	09 24	09 50	10 22	10 50	11 22	11 52	12 23	12 52	13 22	13 52	14 22	14 52	15 22	15 55	16 23	16 52	17 22	17 52	18 23	19 22	20 22	21 26	22 23
Springburn	d	08 27	08 47	09 29	09 55	10 27	10 55	11 27	11 59	12 28	12 59	13 27	13 57	14 27	14 57	15 27	16 01	16 27	16 57	17 27	17 57	18 27	19 27	20 27	21 31	22 28
Stepps	d	08 34	08 54	09 34	10 02	10 34	11 02	11 34	12 06	12 34	13 06	13 34	14 04	14 34	15 04	15 34	16 08	16 34	17 04	17 34	18 04	18 34	19 34	20 34	21 38	22 35
Gartcosh	d	08 38	08 58	09 38	10 06	10 38	11 06	11 38	12 10	12 38	13 10	13 38	14 08	14 38	15 08	15 38	16 11	16 38	17 08	17 38	18 08	18 38	19 38	20 38	21 42	22 39
Greenfaulds	d	08 46	09 06	09 46	10 14	10 46	11 14	11 46	12 18	12 46	13 18	13 46	14 16	14 46	15 17	15 46	16 19	16 46	17 16	17 46	18 16	18 46	19 46	20 46	21 50	22 47
Cumbernauld	a	08 49	09 09	09 51	10 17	10 49	11 17	11 49	12 21	12 50	13 21	13 49	14 19	14 49	15 20	15 49	16 23	16 51	17 19	17 49	18 19	18 50	19 49	20 49	21 53	22 50

For general notes see front of timetable
For details of catering facilities see
Directory of Train Operators

A From Garscadden (Table 226)
B From Milngavie (Table 226)
C From Dalmuir (Table 226)

b Saturdays arr. 2226
c Saturdays arr. 2324

Table 224

Mondays to Saturdays

Falkirk Grahamston and Cumbernauld → Glasgow Queen Street and Motherwell

Network Diagram - see first page of Table 220

Miles	Miles			SR	SR	SR	SR	SR	SR	SR	SR	SR	SR	SR	SR	SR	SR	SR	SR	SR	SR	SR	SR
									SX		SO	SX											
					A				A														
—	—	Stirling	d				05 30				07 16	07 16			08 06			09 06			10 06		
—	—	Edinburgh 10	d				05 18				07 03	07 03			08 03			09 03			10 03		
0	—	**Falkirk Grahamston**	d	05 42			06 42				07 43	07 40			08 42			09 42			10 42		
1½	—	Camelon	d	05 45			06 45				07 46	07 43			08 45			09 45			10 45		
10	0	**Cumbernauld**	d	05 58		06 29	06 59	07 08		07 29	07 59	07b59	08 10	08 29	08 59	09 10	09 29	09 58	10 10	10 29	10 58	11 10	11 29
10¾	¾	Greenfaulds	d	06 00		06 31	07 00	07 10		07 31	08 00	08 00	08 12	08 31	09 00	09 12	09 31	10 00	10 12	10 31	11 00	11 12	11 31
16¼	—	Gartcosh	d	06 07		06 37	07 07			07 37	08 07	08 07		08 37	09 07		09 37	10 07		10 37	11 07		11 37
18¾	—	Stepps	d	06 11		06 41	07 11			07 41	08 11	08 11		08 41	09 11		09 41	10 11		10 41	11 11		11 41
22¾	—	Springburn	d	06 17		06 47	07 17			07 47	08 17	08 17		08 47	09 17		09 47	10 17		10 47	11 17		11 47
24	—	**Glasgow Queen Street 10**	a	06 26		06 56	07 29			07 56	08 28	08 28		08 58	09 26		09 56	10 26		10 56	11 25		11 56
—	6¼	**Coatbridge Central**	d		06 40			07 18	07 40				08 20			09 20			10 20			11 20	
—	7¼	Whifflet	d		06 42			07 20	07 42				08 22			09 22			10 22			11 22	
—	11¾	**Motherwell** 226	a		06 49			07 30	07 49				08 32			09 32			10 32			11 32	

		SR		SR	SR	SR	SR	SR	SR	SR	SR	SR	SR	SR	SR	SR	SR	SR	SR	SR	SR	SR	SR	SR	SR
						SX	SX				SX														
						B	B				A														
Stirling	d	11 06	and at the same minutes past each hour until	16 06					17 06				18 06			19 06					20 36			21 06	
Edinburgh 10	d	11 03		16 03					17 03				18 03			19 03					20 33			21c33	
Falkirk Grahamston	d	11 42		16 42					17 42				18 43			19 43					21 13			22 13	
Camelon	d	11 45		16 45					17 45				18 45			19 45					21 15			22 15	
Cumbernauld	d	11 58		16 59	17 10			17 29	17 59	18 10		18 29	18 59	19 10	19 29	19 59	20 10	20 29	20 59	21 10	21 29	21 59	22 10	22 29	22 59
Greenfaulds	d	12 00		17 00	17 12			17 31	18 00	18 12		18 31	19 00	19 12	19 31	20 00	20 12	20 31	21 01	21 12	21 30	22 01	22 12	22 30	23 01
Gartcosh	d	12 07		17 07				17 37	18 07			18 37	19 07		19 37	20 07		20 37	21 07		21 37	22 07		22 37	23 07
Stepps	d	12 11		17 11				17 41	18 11			18 41	19 11		19 41	20 11		20 41	21 11		21 41	22 11		22 41	23 11
Springburn	d	12 17		17 17				17 47	18 17			18 47	19 17		19 47	20 17		20 47	21 17		21 47	22 17		22 47	23 17
Glasgow Queen Street 10	a	12 27		17 26				17 56	18 26			18 56	19 27		19 56	20 27		20 56	21 26		21 56	22 26		22 56	23 28
Coatbridge Central	d				17 20	17 30	17 56			18 20	18 39			19 20			20 20			21 20			22 20		
Whifflet	d				17 22	17 32	17 58			18 22	18 41			19 22			20 22			21 22			22 22		
Motherwell 226	a				17 32	17 39	18 07			18 32	18 49			19 32			20 32			21 32			22 32		

		SR
Stirling	d	22 06
Edinburgh 10	d	22 33
Falkirk Grahamston	d	23 13
Camelon	d	23 15
Cumbernauld	d	23 29
Greenfaulds	d	23 30
Gartcosh	d	23 37
Stepps	d	23 41
Springburn	d	23 47
Glasgow Queen Street 10	a	23 58
Coatbridge Central	d	
Whifflet	d	
Motherwell 226	a	

Sundays

until 23 November

		SR	SR		SR	SR	SR	SR
Cumbernauld	d	09 01	09 59	and at the same minutes past each hour until	19 59	21 01	22 00	22 59
Greenfaulds	d	09 03	10 01		20 01	21 03	22 01	23 01
Gartcosh	d	09 08	10 08		20 08	21 08	22 08	23 08
Stepps	d	09 12	10 12		20 12	21 12	22 12	23 12
Springburn	d	09 18	10 18		20 18	21 16	22 18	23 18
Glasgow Queen Street	a	09 28	10 26		20 26	21 28	22 27	23 26

Sundays

from 30 November

		SR	SR	SR	SR	SR	SR		SR	SR	SR	SR	SR
Cumbernauld	d	09 01	09 27	09 59	10 27	10 59	11 29	and at the same minutes past each hour until	18 59	19 59	21 01	22 00	22 59
Greenfaulds	d	09 03	09 29	10 01	10 29	11 01	11 31		19 01	20 01	21 03	22 02	23 01
Gartcosh	d	09 10	09 36	10 08	10 36	11 08	11 38		19 08	20 08	21 10	22 09	23 08
Stepps	d	09 14	09 40	10 12	10 40	11 12	11 42		19 12	20 12	21 14	22 13	23 12
Springburn	d	09 20	09 46	10 18	10 46	11 18	11 48		19 18	20 16	21 18	22 19	23 18
Glasgow Queen Street	a	09 28	09 54	10 26	10 54	11 26	11 59		19 26	20 26	21 28	22 27	23 26

For general notes see front of timetable
For details of catering facilities see Directory of Train Operators

A To Milngavie (Table 226)
B To Dalmuir (Table 226)
b Arr. 0753
c Saturdays dep. 2136

Network Diagram for Tables 225, 228, 229, 230, 238, 240, 242

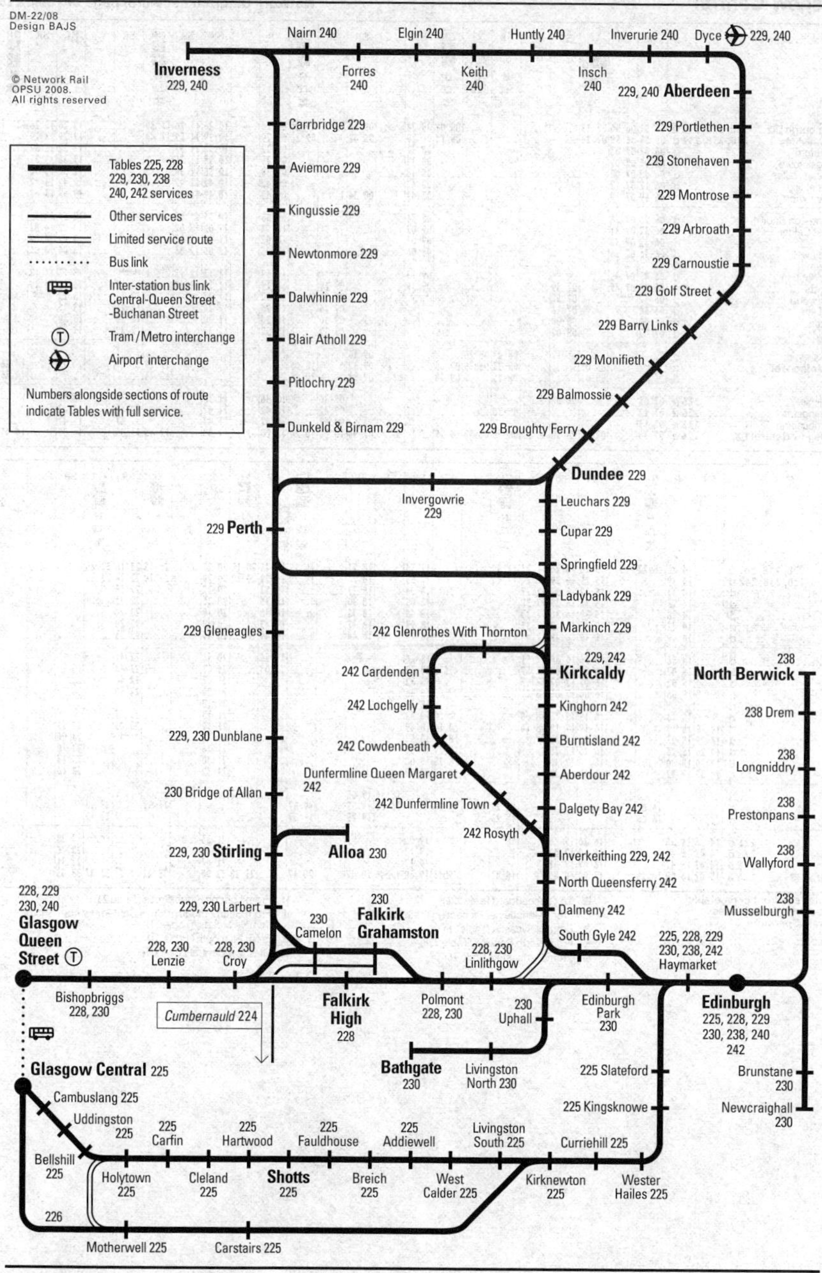
DM-22/08
Design BAJS
© Network Rail
OPSU 2008.
All rights reserved
Tables 225, 228 229, 230, 238 240, 242 services
Other services
Limited service route
Bus link
Inter-station bus link Central-Queen Street -Buchanan Street
Tram / Metro interchange
Airport interchange
Numbers alongside sections of route indicate Tables with full service.
Inverness 229, 240
Nairn 240
Forres 240
Elgin 240
Keith 240
Huntly 240
Insch 240
Inverurie 240
Dyce 229, 240
229, 240 Aberdeen
229 Portlethen
229 Stonehaven
229 Montrose
229 Arbroath
229 Carnoustie
229 Golf Street
229 Barry Links
229 Monifieth
229 Balmossie
229 Broughty Ferry
Dundee 229
Carrbridge 229
Aviemore 229
Kingussie 229
Newtonmore 229
Dalwhinnie 229
Blair Atholl 229
Pitlochry 229
Dunkeld & Birnam 229
Invergowrie 229
229 Perth
Leuchars 229
Cupar 229
Springfield 229
Ladybank 229
Markinch 229
229 Gleneagles
242 Glenrothes With Thornton
229, 242 Kirkcaldy
242 Cardenden
242 Lochgelly
Kinghorn 242
242 Cowdenbeath
Burntisland 242
229, 230 Dunblane
Dunfermline Queen Margaret 242
Aberdour 242
230 Bridge of Allan
242 Dunfermline Town
Dalgety Bay 242
242 Rosyth
229, 230 Stirling
Alloa 230
Inverkeithing 229, 242
North Queensferry 242
Dalmeny 242
229, 230 Larbert
230 Camelon
230 Falkirk Grahamston
South Gyle 242
228, 229 230, 240 Glasgow Queen Street
228, 230 Lenzie
228, 230 Croy
228, 230 Linlithgow
225, 228, 229 230, 238, 242 Haymarket
238 North Berwick
238 Drem
238 Longniddry
238 Prestonpans
238 Wallyford
238 Musselburgh
Bishopbriggs 228, 230
Cumbernauld 224
Falkirk High 228
Polmont 228, 230
230 Uphall
Edinburgh Park 230
Edinburgh 225, 228, 229 230, 238, 240 242
Bathgate 230
Livingston North 230
225 Slateford
225 Kingsknowe
Brunstane 230
Newcraighall 230
Glasgow Central 225
Cambuslang 225
Uddingston 225
Bellshill 225
225 Carfin
225 Hartwood
225 Fauldhouse
225 Addiewell
Livingston South 225
Curriehill 225
Holytown 225
Cleland 225
Shotts 225
Breich 225
West Calder 225
Kirknewton 225
Wester Hailes 225
226
Motherwell 225
Carstairs 225

Edinburgh → Shotts, Carstairs, Motherwell and Glasgow Central

Network Diagram - see first page of Table 225

Miles	Miles		SR	SR	XC	SR		SR	VT	GR	SR		SR	SR	GR	SR		SR	SR	GR	SR		SR	SR	GR
					1 ◇				1 ◇	R 1					R 1					R 1					R 1
					A			B	C	D			E		G					H					H
0	0	**Edinburgh** 10 230, 238, 242 d	05 51	06 56	07 25					08 09	08 24		08 38		09 21	09 26		10 26	11 26	11 39			12 26	13 26	13 41
1¼	1¼	Haymarket 230, 238, 242 d	05 55	06 59	07 29					08 14	08 29		08 42		09 26	09 29		10 29	11 29	11 44			12 29	13 29	
3	3	Slateford d	06 02	07 02							08 32					09 32		10 32	11 32				12 32	13 32	
3¾	3¾	Kingsknowe d	06 05	07 05							08 35					09 35		10 35	11 35				12 35	13 35	
4¾	4¾	Wester Hailes d	06 08	07 08							08 38					09 38		10 38	11 38				12 38	13 38	
7½	7½	Curriehill d	06 12	07 12							08 42					09 42		10 42	11 42				12 42	13 42	
11	11	Kirknewton d	06 19	07 19							08 49		08 54			09 49		10 49	11 49				12 49	13 49	
14	—	Livingston South d	06 26	07 26							08 56					09 56		10 56	11 56				12 56	13 56	
16¾	—	West Calder a	06 32	07 31							09 02					10 02		11 02	12 02				13 02	14 02	
—	—	d	06 32	07 32							09 02					10 02		11 02	12 02				13 02	14 02	
18½	—	Addiewell d	06 36	07 36							09 06					10 06		11 06	12 06				13 06	14 06	
21	—	Breich d																							
23½	—	Fauldhouse d	06 43	07 43		←					09 13			←		10 13		11 13	12 13		←		13 13	14 13	
26¾	—	**Shotts** d	06 49	07 49		07 49					09 19			09 19		10 19		11 19	12 19		12 19		13 19	14 19	
28¼	—	Hartwood d	06 52	→		07 52					→			09 22		10 22		11 22	→		12 22		13 22	→	
31½	—	Cleland d	06 56			07 56								09 26		10 26		11 26			12 26		13 26		
33¼	—	Carfin d	07 00			08 00								09 30		10 30		11 30			12 30		13 30		
34¼	—	Holytown d	07 02			08 02								09 32		10 32		11 32			12 32		13 32		
—	28½	Carstairs d						08 03	08 18				09 16												
—	44½	**Motherwell** a			08 06			08 23	08s35	09 06			09 33		10 05					12 25					14 26
—	—	d			08 07			08 25		09 08			09 33		10 05					12 25					14 26
36	—	Bellshill 226 d	07 06			08 06								09 36		10 36		11 36			12 36		13 36		
38¾	—	Uddingston 226 d	07 12					08 30						09 42		10 42		11 42			12 42		13 42		
42	—	Cambuslang 226 d	07 17											09 47		10 47		11 47			12 47		13 47		
47¼	57¼	**Glasgow Central** 15 226 a	07 30		08 28	08 30		08b48	08 58	09 25			09 55	10 00	10 24	11 00		12 00		12 45	13 00		14 00		14 45

	SR	SR	GR		SR	SR	SR	GR		SR	SR	SR	SR		GR	SR	XC	SR		XC	SR	GR	SR		
			R 1					R 1							R 1		R 1			R 1		R 1			
			H					H					E		H		J			K		H			
Edinburgh 10 230, 238, 242 d		14 26	15 22		15 26	16 26	17 21	17 39			17 56		18 21		19 15	19 25	20 15	20 25		21 15	22 10	22 25			
Haymarket 230, 238, 242 d		14 29			15 29	16 29	17 24	17 44			17 59		18 24		19 20	19 29	20 19	20 29		21 19	22 14	22 30			
Slateford d		14 32			15 32	16 32	17 27				18 02		18 27			19 32		20 32			22 18				
Kingsknowe d		14 35			15 35	16 35	17 30				18 05		18 30			19 35		20 35			22 21				
Wester Hailes d		14 38			15 38	16 38	17 33				18 08		18 33			19 38		20 38			22 24				
Curriehill d		14 42			15 42	16 42	17 37				18 12		18 37			19 42		20 42			22 28				
Kirknewton d		14 49			15 49	16 49	17 44				18 19		18 44			19 49		20 49			22 35				
Livingston South d		14 56			15 56	16 56	17 51				18 26					19 56		20 56			22 41				
West Calder a		15 02			16 02	17 02	17 57				18 32					20 03		21 02			22 46				
d		15 02			16 02	17 02	17 57				18 32							21 02			22 46				
Addiewell d		15 06			16 06	17 06	18 01				18 36							21 06			22 50				
Breich d											18 39							21x10							
Fauldhouse d	←	15 13			16 13	17 13	18 08			←	18 43							21 13			22 57		←		
Shotts d	14 19	15 19			16 19	17 19	18 14			18 14	18 49							21 19			23 03		23 03		
Hartwood d	14 22	15 22			16 22	17 22	→			18 17	18 52							21 22			→		23 06		
Cleland d	14 26	15 26			16 26	17 26				18 21	18 56							21 26					23 10		
Carfin d	14 30	15 30			16 30	17 30				18 25	19 00							21 30					23 14		
Holytown d	14 32	15 32			16 32	17 32				18 27	19 02							21 32					23 16		
Carstairs d												18 36	19 05				20s46								
Motherwell a			16 06					18 23		18 36		18 59	19 25		19 57					21s59		23 13			
d			16 06					18 23					19 25		19 57							23 13			
Bellshill 226 d	14 36	15 36			16 36	17 36					19 06							21 36					23 20		
Uddingston 226 d	14 42	15 42			16 42	17 42					19 12							21 42					23 26		
Cambuslang 226 d	14 47	15 47			16 47	17 47					19 17							21 47					23 31		
Glasgow Central 15 226 a	15 02	16 00	16 25		17 00	18 00		18 41		19b16	19 30	19b46	19 47		20 17		21 28	22 00		22 42		23 33	23 43		

For general notes see front of timetable
For details of catering facilities see Directory of Train Operators

A From Dunbar (Table 26)
B To Garscadden (Table 226)
C From Manchester Piccadilly (Table 65)
D From Newcastle (Table 26)
E From North Berwick (Table 238)
G From Doncaster (Table 26)
H From London Kings Cross (Table 26)
J From Bournemouth (from 8 September from Bristol Temple Meads) (Table 51)
K From Plymouth (Table 51)
b Glasgow Central Low Level

Table 225

Saturdays

Edinburgh → Shotts, Carstairs, Motherwell and Glasgow Central

Network Diagram - see first page of Table 225

	SR	SR	XC	VT		VT	SR	GR	SR		SR	SR	GR	SR		SR	SR	GR	SR		SR	SR	GR	SR	SR
			1 ◊	1 ◊		1 ◊		R 1					R 1					R 1					R 1		
			A	B		C		D			E		G					H					H		
Edinburgh 10 230, 238, 242 d	05 51	06 56	07 15				07 54	08 12	08 24		08 58	09 26	09 38			10 26	11 26	11 39			12 26	13 26	13 39		14 26
Haymarket 230, 238, 242 d	05 55	06 59					07 59		08 29		09 00	09 29	09 43			10 29	11 29	11 44			12 29	13 29	13 44		14 29
Slateford d	06 02	07 02					08 02		08 32		09 02	09 32				10 32	11 32				12 32	13 32			14 32
Kingsknowe d	06 05	07 05					08 05		08 35		09 05	09 35				10 35	11 35				12 35	13 35			14 35
Wester Hailes d	06 08	07 08					08 08		08 38		09 08	09 38				10 38	11 38				12 38	13 38			14 38
Curriehill d	06 12	07 12					08 12		08 42		09 12	09 42				10 42	11 42				12 42	13 42			14 42
Kirknewton d	06 19	07 19					08 19		08 49		09 19	09 49				10 49	11 49				12 49	13 49			14 49
Livingston South d	06 26	07 26					08 25		08 56			09 56				10 56	11 56				12 56	13 56			14 56
West Calder a	06 32	07 31					08 32		09 02			10 02				11 02	12 02				13 02	14 02			15 02
d	06 32	07 32							09 02			10 02				11 02	12 02				13 02	14 02			15 02
Addiewell d	06 36	07 36							09 06			10 06				11 06	12 06				13 06	14 06			15 06
Breich d																									
Fauldhouse d	06 43	07 43							09 13			10 13		←		11 13	12 13		←		13 13	14 13		←	15 13
Shotts d	06 49	07 49							09 19			10 19		10 19		11 19	12 19		12 19		13 19	14 19		14 19	15 19
Hartwood d	06 52	07 52							09 22			→		10 22		11 22	→		12 22		13 22	→		14 22	15 22
Cleland d	06 56	07 56							09 26					10 26		11 26			12 26		13 26			14 26	15 26
Carfin d	07 00	08 00							09 30					10 30		11 30			12 30		13 30			14 30	15 30
Holytown d	07 02	08 02							09 32					10 32		11 32			12 32		13 32			14 32	15 32
Carstairs d				08 16		08 16					09 40														
Motherwell a			08 13	08s27		08s30		08 55			09 56		10 27					12 28					14 27		
d			08 14					08 55			09 57		10 27					12 28					14 27		
Bellshill 226 d	07 06	08 06							09 36					10 36		11 36			12 36		13 36			14 36	15 36
Uddingston 226 d	07 12	08 12							09 42					10 42		11 42			12 42		13 42			14 42	15 42
Cambuslang 226 d	07 17	08 17							09 47					10 47		11 47			12 47		13 47			14 47	15 47
Glasgow Central 15 226 a	07 30	08 30	08 38	09 00		09 00		09 15	10 00		10 14		10 48	11 00		12 00		12 50	13 00		14 00		14 47	15 02	16 00

	SR		GR	SR	SR	SR		SR	SR	GR	SR		SR	GR	XC	SR		XC	XC	SR	GR		SR		
			R 1							R 1				R 1	R 1			R 1	R 1		R 1				
			H		J	K				H				H	L			N	L		H				
Edinburgh 10 230, 238, 242 d	15 26		15 37		15 56	15 56		16 26	17 26	17 40			18 23	19 38	20 22	20 25		21 15	21 15	21 23	21 39		22 40		
Haymarket 230, 238, 242 d	15 29		15 42		15 59	15 59		16 29	17 29				18 27	19 43	20 26	20 29		21s18	21 19	21 27	21 44		22 44		
Slateford d	15 32				16 02	16 02		16 32	17 32				18 32			20 32				21 31			22 48		
Kingsknowe d	15 35				16 05	16 05		16 35	17 35				18 35			20 35				21 34			22 51		
Wester Hailes d	15 38				16 08	16 08		16 38	17 38				18 38			20 38				21 37			22 54		
Curriehill d	15 42				16 12	16 12		16 42	17 42				18 42			20 42				21 41			22 58		
Kirknewton d	15 49				16 19	16 19		16 49	17 49				18 49			20 49				21 48			23 05		
Livingston South d	15 56							16 56	17 56				18 56			20 56				21 54			23 11		
West Calder a	16 02							17 02	18 02				19 02			21 02				22 01			23 16		
d	16 02							17 02	18 02				19 02			21 02							23 16		
Addiewell d	16 06							17 06	18 06				19 06			21 06							23 20		
Breich d													19 09			21x10									
Fauldhouse d	16 13			←				17 13	18 13		←		19 13			21 13							23 27		
Shotts d	16 19			16 19				17 19	18 19		18 19		19 19			21 19							23 34		
Hartwood d	→			16 22				17 22	→		18 22		19 22			21 22							23 37		
Cleland d				16 26				17 26			18 26		19 26			21 26							23 41		
Carfin d				16 30				17 30			18 30		19 30			21 30							23 45		
Holytown d				16 32				17 32			18 32		19 32			21 32							23 48		
Carstairs d					16 44	16 44									20s50										
Motherwell a			16 27		17 01	17 04				18 28	18 40			20 20					21s59		22 26				
d			16 27		17 02	17 04				18 28				20 20							22 26				
Bellshill 226 d				16 36				17 36					19 36			21 36							23 52		
Uddingston 226 d				16 42				17 42					19 42			21 42							23 58		
Cambuslang 226 d				16 47				17 47					19 47			21 47							00 03		
Glasgow Central 15 226 a			16 50	17 00	17 23	17 23		18 00		18 50			20 00	20 44	21 32	22 00		22 23	22 42		22 46		00 15		

For general notes see front of timetable
For details of catering facilities see Directory of Train Operators

- **A** Until 6 September
- **B** From 13 September. From Manchester Piccadilly (Table 65)
- **C** Until 6 September. From Manchester Piccadilly (Table 65)
- **D** From Newcastle (Table 26)
- **E** From North Berwick (Table 238)
- **G** From Doncaster (Table 26)
- **H** From London Kings Cross (Table 26)
- **J** From 13 September. From North Berwick (Table 238)
- **K** Until 6 September. From North Berwick (Table 238)
- **L** From 13 September. From Bristol Temple Meads (Table 51)
- **N** Until 6 September. From Paignton (Table 51)

Table 225

Sundays

Edinburgh → West Calder, Motherwell andGlasgow Central

Network Diagram - see first page of Table 225

		GR	SR	GR	XC		XC	SR	GR	SR		GR	SR	GR	XC		XC	XC	SR	SR	XC	XC	XC	XC	GR		
		R 1		R 1	1 ◇		1 ◇		R 1			R 1		R 1	R 1		R 1	R 1			R 1	R 1	R 1	R 1	R 1		
		A			B		C		D			D		D	E		G	H	J	K	L	N	Q	U	D		
Edinburgh 10	230, 242 d	12 03	12 23	12 43	14§14		14§14	14 23	15 13	16 23		17 41	18 24	19 37	20§14		20§14	20§24	20§23	20§28	21§14	21§14	21§21	21§25	21 41		
Haymarket	230, 242 d	12 08	12 27	12 48	14§19		14§18	14 27	15 18	16 27		17 46	18 27	19 42	20§18		20§19	§	20§27	20§32	21§17	21§19	21§25	21§30	21 46		
Slateford	d		12 31		§		§	14 31		16 31			18 31		§		§	§	20§31	20§36	§	§	§	§			
Kingsknowe	d		12 34		§		§	14 34		16 34			18 34		§		§	§	20§34	20§39	§	§	§	§			
Wester Hailes	d		12 37		§		§	14 37		16 37			18 37		§		§	§	20§37	20§42	§	§	§	§			
Curriehill	d		12 41		§		§	14 41		16 41			18 41		§		§	§	20§41	20§46	§	§	§	§			
Kirknewton	d		12 48		§		§	14 48		16 48			18 48		§		§	§	20§48	20§53	§	§	§	§			
Livingston South	d		12 54		§		§	14 54		16 54			18 54		§		§	§	20§54	20§59	§	§	§	§			
West Calder	a		13 01		§		§	15 00		17 00			19 01		§		§	§	21§00	21§05	§	§	§	§			
Motherwell	a	12 47		13 33	14s52		14s58		15 56			18 24		20 19	20s53		20s57	21s09			21s59	22s00	22s05	22s11	22 23		
	d	12 47		13 33	§		§		15 56			18 24		20 19	§		§	§			§	§	§	§	22 23		
Glasgow Central	a	13 05		13 53	15§16		15§25		16 14			18 44		20 37	21§19		21§34	21§51			22§23	22§30	22§29	22§40	22 44		

For general notes see front of timetable
For details of catering facilities see Directory of Train Operators

A From York (Table 26)
B From 14 September. From Leeds (Table 26)
C Until 7 September. From Leeds (Table 26)
D From London Kings Cross (Table 26)
E From 14 September. From Plymouth (Table 51)
G Until 13 July. From Plymouth (Table 51)
H 20 July to 7 September. From Bournemouth (Table 51)
J Until 13 July
K From 20 July
L 14 September to 2 November. From Bournemouth (Table 158). to Edinburgh
N Until 13 July. From Bournemouth (Table 51)
Q From 9 November. From Bournemouth (Table 51)
U 20 July to 7 September. From Penzance (Table 135)

On Sundays from 30 November, there is an hourly service between Shotts and Glasgow Central via Whifflet. Please refer to Table 220 for details.

Glasgow Central, Motherwell, Carstairs and Shotts → Edinburgh

Network Diagram - see first page of Table 225

Miles	Miles			XC	SR	SR		GR	SR	SR		SR	GR	VT		XC	SR	SR		GR	SR	SR		GR	SR	SR
				[R] [1] A ⊡				[R] [1] B ✕ 🛒		C			[R] [1] B ✕ 🛒	[1] ◇		[R] [1] D ⊡				[R] [1] B ⊡ 🛒				[R] [1] B E ⊡ 🛒		
0	0	**Glasgow Central** [15]	226 d	06 00	06 16			06 50		07 05		07 13	07 50			09 00		09 15		09 50	10 15	11 15		11 50	12 15	13 15
5¼	—	Cambuslang	226 d		06 23							07 23						09 23			10 23	11 23			12 23	13 23
8½	—	Uddingston	226 d		06 28							07 28						09 28			10 28	11 28			12 28	13 28
11¼	—	Bellshill	226 d		06 34							07 34						09 34			10 34	11 34			12 34	13 34
—	12¼	**Motherwell**	a					07 04		07 27			08 07							10 04				12 04		
—	—		d			06 59		07 04		07 28			08 07			09u14				10 04				12 04		
—	28½	Carstairs	d			07a21				07 43				08 40												
13¼	—	Holytown	d		06 38							07 38						09 38			10 38	11 38			12 38	13 38
14	—	Carfin	d		06 40							07 40						09 40			10 40	11 40			12 40	13 40
15¾	—	Cleland	d		06 44							07 44						09 44			10 44	11 44			12 44	13 44
19	—	Hartwood	d		06 50							07 50						09 50			10 50	11 50			12 50	13 50
20½	—	**Shotts**	d		06 54							07 54						09 54			10 54	11 54			12 54	13 54
24	—	Fauldhouse	d		07 00							08 00						10 00			11 00	12 00			13 00	14 00
26¼	—	Breich	d									08 03														
28¾	—	Addiewell	d		07 07							08 07						10 07			11 07	12 07			13 07	14 07
30½	—	West Calder	d		07 10				07 38			08 10					09 40	10 10			11 10	12 10			13 10	14 10
33¼	—	Livingston South	d		07 15				07 43			08 15					09 45	10 15			11 15	12 15			13 15	14 15
36¼	46¼	Kirknewton	d		07 20				07 48	08 05		08 20					09 50	10 20			11 20	12 20			13 20	14 20
40¾	49¾	Curriehill	d		07 25				07 53	08 10		08 25					09 55	10 25			11 25	12 25			13 25	14 25
42½	52½	Wester Hailes	d		07 29					08 13		08 29					09 59	10 29			11 29	12 29			13 29	14 29
43½	53½	Kingsknowe	d		07 31					08 16		08 31					10 01	10 31			11 31	12 31			13 31	14 31
44¼	54¼	Slateford	d		07 34					08 18		08 34					10 04	10 34			11 34	12 34			13 34	14 34
46	56	Haymarket	230, 238, 242 d	06 52	07 39			07 50	08 04	08 28		08 39	08 50	09s05		09 54	10 11	10 39		10 50	11 39	12 39		12 50	13 39	14 39
47¼	57¼	**Edinburgh** [10]	230, 238, 242 a	06 56	07 49			07 55	08 09	08 34		08 48	08 55	09 11		09 59	10 17	10 47		10 56	11 47	12 47		12 56	13 47	14 47

		GR	SR		SR	SR	SR		GR	SR	SR		SR	GR	SR		SR	GR	SR		XC	SR				
		[R] [1] B ⊡ 🛒				C			[R] [1] B ⊡ 🛒				G	[R] [1] B ⊡ 🛒				[R] [1] H ⊡ 🛒			[1] ◇ J					
Glasgow Central [15]	226 d	13 50	14 15		15 15	15 19			15 50	16 15	17 19			17 50	18 15			19 50	20 15		21 55	23 06				
Cambuslang	226 d		14 23		15 23					16 23			17 42		18 23				20 23			23 15				
Uddingston	226 d		14 28		15 28					16 28			17 47		18 28				20 28			23 20				
Bellshill	226 d		14 34		15 34					16 34	17 34		17 51		18 34				20 34			23 26				
Motherwell	a	14 04				15 35			16 04				17 57	18 04				20 04			22 24					
	d	14 04				15 38			16 04				17 58	18 04				20 04			22 25					
Carstairs	d					15 56							18a26													
Holytown	d		14 38		15 38					16 38	17 38				18 38				20 38			23 30				
Carfin	d		14 40		15 40					16 40	17 40				18 40				20 40			23 32				
Cleland	d		14 44		15 44					16 44	17 44				18 44				20 44			23 36				
Hartwood	d		14 50		15 50		←			16 50	17 50				18 50				20 50			23 42				
Shotts	d		14 54		15 54		15 54			16 54	17 54				18 54				20 54			23 46				
Fauldhouse	d		15 00		→		16 00			17 00	18 00				19 00				21 00			23 52				
Breich	d																									
Addiewell	d		15 07				16 07			17 07	18 07				19 07				21 07			23 58				
West Calder	d		15 10				16 10			17 10	18 10				19 10		20 10		21 10			00 02				
Livingston South	d		15 15				16 15			17 15	18 15				19 15		20 15		21 15			00 06				
Kirknewton	d		15 20				16 20			17 20	18 20				19 20		20 20		21 20			00 11				
Curriehill	d		15 25				16 25			17 25	18 25				19 25		20 26		21 25			00 17				
Wester Hailes	d		15 29				16 29			17 29	18 29				19 29		20 29		21 29			00 21				
Kingsknowe	d		15 31				16 31			17 31	18 31				19 31		20 32		21 31			00 23				
Slateford	d		15 34				16 34			17 34	18 34				19 34		20 34		21 34			00 26				
Haymarket	230, 238, 242 d	14 50	15 39			16 30	16 39		16 50	17 39	18 39			18 49	19 43		20 41	20 50	21 41		23 10	00 31				
Edinburgh [10]	230, 238, 242 a	14 56	15 47			16 36	16 48		16 55	17 47	18 47			18 57	19 50		20 47	20 55	21 47		23 19	00 38				

For general notes see front of timetable
For details of catering facilities see Directory of Train Operators

- **A** To Bournemouth (from 8 September to Bristol Temple Meads) (Table 51)
- **B** To London Kings Cross (Table 26)
- **C** To North Berwick (Table 238)
- **D** Until 5 September to Penzance (Table 135). From 8 September to Plymouth (Table 51)
- **E** **The Flying Scotsman**
- **G** From Dalmuir (Table 226)
- **H** To York (Table 26)
- **J** Fridays to Dunbar (Table 26)

Table 225

Saturdays

Glasgow Central, Motherwell, Carstairs and Shotts → Edinburgh

Network Diagram - see first page of Table 225

Station		SR	XC	XC	SR	GR	SR	GR	SR	SR	GR	XC	SR	GR	SR	SR	GR	SR
			1 ◇	1 ◇		R 1		R 1			R 1	1 ◇		R 1			R 1	
			A	B		C	D	C			C	E		C			C G	
Glasgow Central 15	226 d	00 06	05 50	06 00	06 16	06 50	07 05	07 50		08 15	08 50	09 00	09 15	09 50	10 15	11 15	11 50	12 15
Cambuslang	226 d	00 15			06 23					08 23			09 23		10 23	11 23		12 23
Uddingston	226 d	00 20			06 28					08 28			09 28		10 28	11 28		12 28
Bellshill	226 d	00 26			06 34					08 34			09 34		10 34	11 34		12 34
Motherwell	a					07 06	07 20	08 04			09 04			10 04			12 04	
	d		06u09			07 06	07 20	08 04			09 04	09u14		10 04			12 04	
Carstairs	d						07 43											
Holytown	d	00 30			06 38					08 38			09 38		10 38	11 38		12 38
Carfin	d	00 32			06 40					08 40			09 40		10 40	11 40		12 40
Cleland	d	00 36			06 44					08 44			09 44		10 44	11 44		12 44
Hartwood	d	00 42			06 50					08 50			09 50		10 50	11 50		12 50
Shotts	d	00 46			06 54					08 54			09 54		10 54	11 54		12 54
Fauldhouse	d	00 52			07 00					09 00			10 00		11 00	12 00		13 00
Breich	d									09 03								
Addiewell	d	00 58			07 07					09 07			10 07		11 07	12 07		13 07
West Calder	d	01 02			07 10				08 40	09 10			10 10		11 10	12 10		13 10
Livingston South	d	01a08			07 15				08 45	09 15			10 15		11 15	12 15		13 15
Kirknewton	d				07 20		08 05		08 50	09 20			10 20		11 20	12 20		13 20
Curriehill	d				07 25		08 10		08 55	09 25			10 25		11 25	12 25		13 25
Wester Hailes	d				07 29		08 13		08 59	09 29			10 29		11 29	12 29		13 29
Kingsknowe	d				07 31		08 16		09 01	09 31			10 31		11 31	12 31		13 31
Slateford	d				07 34		08 18		09 04	09 34			10 34		11 34	12 34		13 34
Haymarket	230, 238, 242 d		06 51	06 52	07 39	07 47	08 28	08 49	09 09	09 39		09 54	10 39	10 50	11 39	12 39	12 50	13 39
Edinburgh 10	230, 238, 242 a		06 57	06 57	07 49	07 51	08 34	08 55	09 15	09 48	09 55	09 59	10 47	10 55	11 47	12 47	12 55	13 47

Station		SR	GR	SR	SR	SR	SR	GR	SR	SR	GR	SR	SR	SR	SR
			R 1					R 1			R 1				
			C			D		C			H				
Glasgow Central 15	226 d	13 15	13 50	14 15	15 15	15 19		15 50	16 15	17 15	17 50	18 15	20 15		23 06
Cambuslang	226 d	13 23		14 23	15 23				16 23	17 23		18 23	20 23		23 15
Uddingston	226 d	13 28		14 28	15 28				16 28	17 28		18 28	20 28		23 20
Bellshill	226 d	13 34		14 34	15 34				16 34	17 34		18 34	20 34		23 26
Motherwell	a		14 06			15 38		16 04			18 04				
	d		14 06			15 39		16 04			18 04				
Carstairs	d					15 57									
Holytown	d	13 38		14 38	15 38				16 38	17 38		18 38	20 38		23 30
Carfin	d	13 40		14 40	15 40				16 40	17 40		18 40	20 40		23 32
Cleland	d	13 44		14 44	15 44				16 44	17 44		18 44	20 44		23 36
Hartwood	d	13 50		14 50	15 50		←		16 50	17 50		18 50	20 50		23 42
Shotts	d	13 54		14 54	15 54		15 54		16 54	17 54		18 54	20 54		23 46
Fauldhouse	d	14 00		15 00	→		16 00		17 00	18 00		19 00	21 00		23 52
Breich	d														
Addiewell	d	14 07		15 07			16 07		17 07	18 07		19 07	21 07		23 58
West Calder	d	14 10		15 10			16 10		17 10	18 10		19 10	21 10	22 40	00 02
Livingston South	d	14 15		15 15			16 15		17 15	18 15		19 15	21 15	22 45	00 06
Kirknewton	d	14 20		15 20			16 20		17 20	18 20		19 20	21 20	22 50	00 11
Curriehill	d	14 25		15 25			16 25		17 25	18 25		19 25	21 25	22 55	00 17
Wester Hailes	d	14 29		15 29			16 29		17 29	18 29		19 29	21 29	22 59	00 21
Kingsknowe	d	14 31		15 31			16 31		17 31	18 31		19 31	21 31	23 01	00 23
Slateford	d	14 34		15 34			16 34		17 34	18 34		19 34	21 34	23 04	00 26
Haymarket	230, 238, 242 d	14 39	14 50	15 39		16 30	16 39	16 50	17 39	18 39	18 50	19 39	21 41	23 11	00 31
Edinburgh 10	230, 238, 242 a	14 47	14 55	15 47		16 36	16 48	16 56	17 47	18 47	18 55	19 48	21 49	23 16	00 38

For general notes see front of timetable
For details of catering facilities see Directory of Train Operators

A Until 6 September. To Bournemouth (Table 51)
B From 13 September. To Bristol Temple Meads (Table 51)
C To London Kings Cross (Table 26)
D To North Berwick (Table 238)
E To Paignton (from 13 September to Bristol Temple Meads) (Table 51)
G **The Flying Scotsman**
H To Leeds (Table 26)

Sundays

Glasgow Central, Motherwell and West Calder → Edinburgh

Network Diagram - see first page of Table 225

		XC R 1 A	XC R 1 B	XC R 1 C	GR R 1 D	XC R 1 E	XC R 1 G	SR	GR R 1 D	SR	GR R 1 D	XC 1 ◊ H	XC 1 ◊ J	GR R 1 D	SR	GR R 1 D	SR	GR R 1 K	SR
Glasgow Central	d	10ʃ04	10ʃ27	10ʃ30	10 50	11ʃ18	11ʃ30		12 50		14 50	15ʃ44	15ʃ45	15 50		17 50		19 50	
Motherwell	a	⌇	⌇	⌇	11 05	⌇	⌇		13 05		15 05	⌇	⌇	16 05		18 05		20 04	
	d	10u29	10u57	10u56	11 05	11u38	11u56		13 05		15 05	16u00	15u59	16 05		18 05		20 04	
West Calder	d	⌇	⌇	⌇		⌇	⌇	13 12		15 16		⌇	⌇		17 14		19 12		21 14
Livingston South	d	⌇	⌇	⌇		⌇	⌇	13 17		15 21		⌇	⌇		17 19		19 17		21 18
Kirknewton	d	⌇	⌇	⌇		⌇	⌇	13 22		15 26		⌇	⌇		17 24		19 22		21 23
Curriehill	d	⌇	⌇	⌇		⌇	⌇	13 27		15 31		⌇	⌇		17 29		19 27		21 29
Wester Hailes	d	⌇	⌇	⌇		⌇	⌇	13 31		15 35		⌇	⌇		17 33		19 31		21 32
Kingsknowe	d	⌇	⌇	⌇		⌇	⌇	13 33		15 37		⌇	⌇		17 35		19 33		21 35
Slateford	d	⌇	⌇	⌇		⌇	⌇	13 36		15 40		⌇	⌇		17 38		19 36		21 37
Haymarket 230, 242	d	11ʃ16	11ʃ36	11ʃ37	11 49	⌇	12ʃ37	13 42	13 50	15 46	15 49	16ʃ38	16ʃ39	16 46	17 44	18 46	19 43	20 45	21 43
Edinburgh 10 230, 242	a	11ʃ21	11ʃ41	11ʃ42	11 54	12ʃ27	12ʃ42	13 46	13 56	15 50	15 55	16ʃ44	16ʃ44	16 52	17 48	18 53	19 47	20 51	21 48

For general notes see front of timetable
For details of catering facilities see Directory of Train Operators

- **A** 20 July to 7 September. To Plymouth (Table 51)
- **B** Until 13 July. To Bournemouth (Table 51)
- **C** From 14 September. To Bournemouth (Table 51)
- **D** To London Kings Cross (Table 26)
- **E** 20 July to 7 September. To Bournemouth (Table 51)
- **G** Until 13 July and from 14 September. To Plymouth (Table 51)
- **H** Until 7 September. To Birmingham New Street (Table 51)
- **J** From 14 September. To Birmingham New Street (Table 51)
- **K** To Newcastle (Table 26)

On Sundays from 30 November, there is an hourly service between Glasgow Central and Shotts via Whifflet. Please refer to Table 220 for details.

Lanark, Coatbridge, Motherwell, Larkhall, Hamilton, Drumgelloch, Airdrie and Springburn → Glasgow → Milngavie, Dalmuir, Balloch and Helensburgh

Network Diagram - see first page of Table 220

Miles	Miles	Miles	Miles	Miles	Station		SR	SR	SR	SR	SR	SR	SR	SR	SR	SR	SR	SR	SR	SR	SR	SR	SR	SR	SR
								A								SO	SX		SX					SO	SX
0	—	—	—	—	**Lanark**	d																	06 23		
8½	—	—	—	—	Carluke	d																	06 33		
13	—	—	—	—	Wishaw	d																	06 38		
16½	—	—	—	—	Holytown	d																			
15	—	—	—	—	Shieldmuir	d																	06 42		
—	—	—	—	0	**Coatbridge Central**	d																			
—	—	—	—	1	Whifflet	d																			
16¾	0	0	—	5½	**Motherwell**	a																	06 45		
—	—	—	—	—		d									06 16			06 20					06 46		
—	3	—	—	—	Bellshill	d									06 22								06 52		
20½	5½	—	—	—	Uddingston	d									06 26								06 56		
—	—	¾	—	—	Airbles	d												06 22							
—	—	—	—	0	**Larkhall**	d						06 07								06 37					
—	—	—	—	1¼	Merryton	d						06 09								06 39					
—	—	—	—	2¾	Chatelherault	d						06 12								06 42					
—	—	3	—	5¼	**Hamilton Central**	d						06 15						06 27		06 45					
—	—	3¾	—	0	Hamilton West	d						06 18						06 30		06 48					
—	—	5¾	—	—	Blantyre	d						06 21						06 33		06 51					
22½	—	8¼	—	—	Newton	d												06 37							
24	9	—	—	—	Cambuslang	d									06 31			06 41					07 01		
25¾	10¾	—	—	—	Rutherglen	d						06 29			06 34			06 45		06 59			07 04		
26½	11½	—	—	—	Dalmarnock	d									06 36			06 47					07 06		
27	12	—	—	—	Bridgeton	d									06 38			06 49					07 08		
—	—	—	0	—	**Drumgelloch**	d			05 27				06 08								06 38				
—	—	—	1½	—	**Airdrie**	a			05 30				06 11								06 41				
—	—	—	—	—		d			05 31		05 57		06 12				06 27				06 42				06 57
—	—	—	2½	—	Coatdyke	d			05 33		05 59		06 14				06 29				06 44				06 59
—	—	—	3½	—	Coatbridge Sunnyside	d			05 35		06 01		06 16				06 31				06 46				07 01
—	—	—	4	—	Blairhill	d			05 38		06 04		06 19				06 34				06 49				07 04
—	—	—	6¾	—	Easterhouse	d			05 42		06 08		06 23				06 38				06 53				07 08
—	—	—	7¾	—	Garrowhill	d			05 44		06 10		06 25				06 40				06 55				07 10
—	—	—	9	—	Shettleston	d			05 47		06 13		06 28				06 43				06 58				07 13
—	—	—	9¾	—	Carntyne	d			05 49		06 15		06 30				06 45				07 00				07 15
—	—	—	—	0	**Springburn**	d										06 39			06 49					07 09	
—	—	—	—	¼	Barnhill	d										06 40			06 50					07 10	
—	—	—	—	1¼	Alexandra Parade	d										06 43			06 53					07 13	
—	—	—	—	1¾	Duke Street	d										06 44			06 54					07 14	
—	—	—	11½	2¼	Bellgrove	d			05 52		06 18		06 33			06 46	06 48		06 56		07 03			07 16	07 18
—	—	—	12	2¾	High Street	d			05 54		06 20		06 35			06 48	06 50		06 58		07 05			07 18	07 20
—	—	—	12½	3¼	**Glasgow Queen Street** 10 §	a			05 56		06 22		06 37			06 51	06 52		07 01		07 07			07 21	07 22
—	—	—	—	—		d	05b30		05 57		06 23		06 40			06 53	06 53		07 02		07 10			07 23	07 23
—	—	—	13¼	4	Charing Cross	d			06 00		06 25		06 42			06 55	06 55		07 04		07 12			07 25	07 25
28½	13½	—	—	—	Argyle Street	d						06 34			06 42			06 53		07 04			07 12		
28¾	13¾	—	—	—	**Glasgow Central** 15 §	a						06 37			06 46			06 56		07 07			07 16		
—	—	—	—	—		d						06 37			06 46			06 58		07 07			07 16		
29¼	14¼	—	—	—	Anderston	d						06 39			06 48			06 59		07 09			07 18		
29¾	14¾	—	—	—	Exhibition Centre	d						06 41			06 50			07 01		07 11			07 20		
31	16	—	15¼	6	Partick	d			06 04		06 30	06 45	06 47		06 54	07 00	07 00	07 05	07 09	07 15	07 17		07 24	07 30	07 30
31½	16½	0	15¾	6½	Hyndland	d			06 06		06 32	06 47	06 50		06 56	07 02	07 02	07 08	07 11	07 17	07 20		07 26	07 32	07 32
—	—	½	—	—	Jordanhill	d			06 08						06 58				07 13				07 28		
—	—	1½	—	—	Scotstounhill	d			06 11						07 00				07 15				07 30		
—	—	2	—	—	Garscadden	d			06 13				06 54		07 02				07 17				07 32		
—	—	3	—	—	Yoker	d			06 15						07 05				07 20				07 35		
—	—	4	—	—	Clydebank	d			06 17						07 07				07 22				07 37		
32½	17½	—	16¾	7½	Anniesland	d					06 35	06 50				07 05	07 05	07 11		07 20				07 35	07 35
33¾	18¾	—	18	8¾	Westerton	d	05a43	05 56			06 38	06 53				07 08	07 08	07 14		07 23				07 38	07 38
35	—	—	—	—	Bearsden	d												07 16							
35¾	—	—	—	—	Hillfoot	d												07 18							
37¼	—	—	—	—	**Milngavie**	a								←				07 22				←			
—	20	—	19¼	10	Drumchapel	d					06 40	06 55		06 55		07 10	07 10			07 25		07 25		07 40	07 40
—	20¾	—	20	10¾	Drumry	d					06 42	→		06 57		07 12	07 12			→		07 27		07 42	07 42
—	21¾	—	21	11¾	Singer	d					06 45			07 00		07 15	07 15					07 30		07 45	07 45
—	22½	5¼	21¾	12½	**Dalmuir**	a		06 03	06 21		06 47		06 58	07 02	07 11	07 17	07 17		07 26		07 28	07 32	07 41	07 47	07 47
—	—	—	—	—		d		06 04	06 21	06 32	06 48		06 59			07 18	07 18				07 29			07 48	07 48
—	—	—	23	13¾	Kilpatrick	d				06 34	06 51					07 21	07 21							07 51	07 51
—	—	—	24¾	15½	Bowling	d				06 37	06 54					07 24	07 24							07 54	07 54
—	—	—	27¼	18¼	Dumbarton East	d			06 29	06 42	06 58		07 06			07 28	07 28				07 36			07 58	07 58
—	—	—	28¼	19	Dumbarton Central	d			06 30	06 44	07 00		07 08			07 30	07 30				07 38			08 00	08 00
—	—	—	28½	19½	Dalreoch	d			06 32	06 46	07 02		07 10			07 32	07 32				07 40			08 02	08 02
—	—	—	—	20¾	Renton	d			06 35		07 05					07 35	07 35							08 05	08 05
—	—	—	—	22	Alexandria	d			06 37		07 07					07 37	07 37							08 07	08 07
—	—	—	—	23	**Balloch**	a			06 40		07 10					07 40	07 40							08 10	08 10
—	—	—	31¾	—	Cardross	d				06 51			07 15								07 45				
—	—	—	35½	—	Craigendoran	d				06 56			07 20								07 50				
—	—	—	36½	—	**Helensburgh Central**	a		06c26		06 59			07 23								07 53				

For general notes see front of timetable
For details of catering facilities see Directory of Train Operators

§ Low Level

A Limited seating accommodation. Also conveys overnight Sleeping Car accommodation from London Euston to Fort William (Tables 65 and 404)

b Glasgow Queen Street High Level

c Helensburgh Upper

Lanark, Coatbridge, Motherwell, Larkhall, Hamilton, Drumgelloch, Airdrie and Springburn → Glasgow → Milngavie, Dalmuir, Balloch and Helensburgh

Network Diagram - see first page of Table 220

		SR	SR	SR	SR	SR	SR	SR	SR	SR	SR	SR	SR	SR	SR	SR	SR	SR	SR	SR	SR	SR	SR	SR	SR
				SX		SX	SO		SX	SX	SO	SO	SX	SO	SX	SX	SX	SO			SX		SO	SX	SO
			A																			◇ B 🍴			
Lanark	d									06 53							07 23						07 23		
Carluke	d									07 03							07 33						07 33		
Wishaw	d									07 08							07 38						07 38		
Holytown	d		07 02																						
Shieldmuir	d									07 12							07 42						07 42		
Coatbridge Central	d	06 40																							
Whifflet	d	06 42																							
Motherwell	a	06 49								07 16							07 45						07 45		
	d	06 50								07 16	07 16			07 20	07 20		07 46						07 46		
Bellshill	d		07 06							07 22	07 22												07 52		
Uddingston	d		07 12							07 26	07 26												07 56		
Airbles	d	06 52												07 22	07 22										
Larkhall	d				07 07													07 37						07 37	
Merryton	d				07 09													07 39						07 39	
Chatelherault	d				07 12													07 42						07 42	
Hamilton Central	d	06 57			07 15									07 27	07 27			07 45						07 45	
Hamilton West	d	07 00			07 18									07 30	07 30			07 48						07 48	
Blantyre	d	07 03			07 21									07 33	07 33			07 51						07 51	
Newton	d	07 07												07 37	07 37									07 55	
Cambuslang	d	07 11	07 17							07 31	07 31			07 41	07 41								08 01	08 00	
Rutherglen	d	07 15			07 29					07 34	07 34			07 45	07 45		07 56	07 59					08 04	08 04	
Dalmarnock	d	07 17								07 36	07 36			07 47	07 47								08 06	08 06	
Bridgeton	d	07 19								07 38	07 38			07 49	07 49								08 08	08 08	
Drumgelloch	d					07 08	07 08												07 38						
Airdrie	a					07 11	07 11												07 41						
	d					07 12	07 12		07 22				07 27						07 42		07 52				
Coatdyke	d					07 14	07 14		07 24				07 29						07 44		07 54				
Coatbridge Sunnyside	d					07 16	07 16		07 26				07 31						07 46		07 56				
Blairhill	d					07 19	07 19		07 29				07 34						07 49		07 59				
Easterhouse	d					07 23	07 23						07 38						07 53						
Garrowhill	d					07 25	07 25						07 40						07 55						
Shettleston	d					07 28	07 28						07 43						07 58						
Carntyne	d					07 30	07 30						07 45						08 00						
Springburn	d			07 19								07 39				07 49									08 09
Barnhill	d			07 20								07 40				07 50									08 10
Alexandra Parade	d			07 23								07 43				07 53									08 13
Duke Street	d			07 24								07 44				07 54									08 14
Bellgrove	d			07 26		07 33	07 33					07 46	07 48			07 56			08 03						08 16
High Street	d			07 28		07 35	07 35		07 40			07 48	07 50			07 58			08 05		08 10				08 18
Glasgow Queen Street 10 § ⛴	a			07 31		07 37	07 37		07 42			07 51	07 52			08 01			08 07		08 12				08 21
	d			07 32		07 40	07 40		07 43			07 53	07 53			08 02			08 10		08 13	08b21			08 23
Charing Cross	d			07 34		07 42	07 42		07 45			07 55	07 55			08 04			08 12		08 15				08 25
Argyle Street	d	07 23			07 34					07 42	07 42			07 53	07 53		08 02	08 04					08 12	08 12	
Glasgow Central 15 §	a	07 26	07c30		07 37					07 46	07 46			07 56	07 56		08 06	08 07					08 16	08 16	
	d	07 28			07 37					07 46	07 46			07 58	07 58		08 07	08 07					08 16	08 16	
Anderston	d	07 29			07 39					07 48	07 48			07 59	07 59		08 09	08 09					08 18	08 18	
Exhibition Centre	d	07 31			07 41					07 50	07 50			08 01	08 01		08 11	08 11					08 20	08 20	
Partick ⛴	d	07 35		07 39	07 45	07 46	07 47		07 50	07 54	07 54	08 00	08 00	08 05	08 05	08 09	08 15	08 15	08 17		08 20		08 24	08 24	08 30
Hyndland	d	07 38		07 41	07 47	07 49	07 50		07 53	07 56	07 56	08 02	08 02	08 08	08 08	08 11	08 17	08 17	08 20		08 23		08 26	08 26	08 32
Jordanhill	d			07 43						07 58	07 58					08 13							08 28	08 28	
Scotstounhill	d			07 45						08 00	08 00					08 15							08 30	08 30	
Garscadden	d			07 47						08 02	08 02					08 17							08 32	08 32	
Yoker	d			07 50						08 05	08 05					08 20							08 35	08 36	
Clydebank	d			07 52						08 07	08 07					08 22							08 37	08 38	
Anniesland	d	07 41			07 50				07 56			08 05	08 05	08 11	08 11		08 20	08 20			08 26				08 35
Westerton	d	07 44			07 53				07 59			08 08	08 08	08 14	08 14		08 23	08 23			08 29				08 38
Bearsden	d	07 46							08 01					08 16	08 16						08 31				
Hillfoot	d	07 48							08 03					08 18	08 18						08 33				
Milngavie	a	07 52						←	08 07					08 22	08 27					←	08 37				
Drumchapel	d				07 55			07 55				08 10	08 10				08 25	08 25		08 25					08 40
Drumry	d				→			07 57				08 12	08 12				→	→		08 27					08 42
Singer	d							08 00				08 15	08 15							08 30					08 45
Dalmuir	a			07 56		07 59	07 59	08 02		08 11	08 11	08 17	08 17			08 28			08 29	08 32		08 38	08 41	08 42	08 47
	d					07 59	07 59					08 18	08 18						08 29			08 39			08 48
Kilpatrick	d											08 21	08 21												08 51
Bowling	d											08 24	08 24												08 54
Dumbarton East	d					08 06	08 06					08 28	08 28						08 36						08 58
Dumbarton Central	d					08 08	08 08					08 30	08 30						08 38			08 48			09 00
Dalreoch	d					08 10	08 10					08 32	08 32						08 40						09 02
Renton	d											08 35	08 35												09 05
Alexandria	d											08 37	08 37												09 07
Balloch	a											08 40	08 40												09 10
Cardross	d					08 20	08 15												08 45						
Craigendoran	d					08 25	08 20												08 50						
Helensburgh Central	a					08 28	08 23												08 55			09e03			

For general notes see front of timetable
For details of catering facilities see Directory of Train Operators

§ Low Level

A From Edinburgh (Table 225)

B To Oban (Table 227). All Saturdays and Mondays to Fridays from 29 September also conveys portion to Mallaig

b Glasgow Queen Street High Level

c Glasgow Central High Level

e Helensburgh Upper

Lanark, Coatbridge, Motherwell, Larkhall, Hamilton, Drumgelloch, Airdrie and Springburn → Glasgow → Milngavie, Dalmuir, Balloch and Helensburgh

Network Diagram - see first page of Table 220

		SR SX	SR SX	SR SX	SR SO	SR SX A	SR SX	SR SO A	SR SX		SR SO	SR SX	SR	SR SX	SR	SR SX ◇ B 🍴	SR	SR SO	SR SX	SR SX C	SR SO	SR SX	SR SX	SR SO	SR SX
Lanark	d								07 45									07 53							
Carluke	d								07 55									08 03		08 14					
Wishaw	d								08 03									08 08		08 18					
Holytown	d					08 02		08 02										08 13							
Shieldmuir	d								08 07											08 21					
Coatbridge Central	d			07 40																					
Whifflet	d			07 42																					
Motherwell	a			07 49					08 10									08 20		08 23					
	d		07 50	07 50	07 50				08 10								08 16	08 20	08 20	08 25					
Bellshill	d		07 56			08 06		08 06									08 22								
Uddingston	d		08 00					08 12	08 18								08 26			08 30					
Airbles	d			07 52	07 52													08 22	08 22						
Larkhall	d										08 07	08 07													
Merryton	d										08 09	08 09													
Chatelherault	d										08 12	08 12													
Hamilton Central	d			07 57	07 57						08 15	08 15						08 27	08 27						
Hamilton West	d			08 00	08 00						08 18	08 18						08 30	08 30						
Blantyre	d			08 03	08 03						08 21	08 21						08 33	08 33				←	←	
Newton	d			08 07	08 07													08 37	08 37				08 37	08 37	
Cambuslang	d		08 05	08 11	08 11			08 17				08 27					08 31	→	→				08 41	08 41	
Rutherglen	d		08 10	08 15	08 15						08 29						08 34						08 45	08 45	
Dalmarnock	d		08 12	08 17	08 17												08 36						08 47	08 47	
Bridgeton	d		08 14	08 19	08 19												08 38						08 49	08 49	
Drumgelloch	d												08 08												
Airdrie	a												08 11												
	d	07 57											08 12	08 22								08 27			
Coatdyke	d	07 59											08 14	08 24								08 29			
Coatbridge Sunnyside	d	08 01											08 16	08 26								08 31			
Blairhill	d	08 04											08 19	08 29								08 34			
Easterhouse	d	08 08											08 23									08 38			
Garrowhill	d	08 10											08 25									08 40			
Shettleston	d	08 13											08 28									08 43			
Carntyne	d	08 15											08 30									08 45			
Springburn	d						08 19														08 39				08 49
Barnhill	d						08 20														08 40				08 50
Alexandra Parade	d						08 23														08 43				08 53
Duke Street	d						08 24														08 44				08 54
Bellgrove	d	08 18					08 26						08 33								08 46	08 48			08 56
High Street	d	08 20					08 28						08 35	08 40							08 48	08 50			08 58
Glasgow Queen Street [10] §	a	08 22					08 31						08 37	08 42							08 51	08 52			09 01
	d	08 23					08 32						08 40	08 43		08b51					08 53	08 53			09 02
Charing Cross	d	08 25					08 34						08 42	08 45							08 55	08 55			09 04
Argyle Street	d		08 18	08 23	08 23				08 31		08 34	08 34					08 42			08 47			08 53	08 55	
Glasgow Central [15] §	a		08 19	08 26	08 26	08c30		08c30	08 32		08 37	08 37					08 46			08 48			08 56	08 57	
	d		08 19	08 28	08 28				08 33		08 37	08 37					08 46			08 49			08 58	08 58	
Anderston	d		08a23	08 29	08 29				08 35		08 39	08 39					08 48			08 50			08 59	09 00	
Exhibition Centre	d			08 31	08 31				08 38		08 41	08 41					08 50			08 53			09 01	09 02	
Partick	d	08 30		08 35	08 35		08 39		08 42		08 45	08 45	08 47	08 50			08 54			08 57	09 00	09 00	09 05	09 05	09 09
Hyndland	d	08 32		08 38	08 38		08 41		08 44		08 47	08 47	08 50	08 53			08 56			08 59	09 02	09 02	09 08	09 08	09 11
Jordanhill	d						08 43		08 46								08 58			09 01					09 13
Scotstounhill	d						08 45		08 48								09 00			09 03					09 15
Garscadden	d						08 47		08a51								09 02			09a06					09 17
Yoker	d						08 50										09 05								09 20
Clydebank	d						08 52										09 07								09 22
Anniesland	d	08 35		08 41	08 41						08 50	08 50		08 56							09 05	09 05	09 11	09 11	
Westerton	d	08 38		08 44	08 44						08 53	08 53		08 59							09 08	09 08	09 14	09 14	
Bearsden	d			08 46	08 46									09 01									09 16	09 16	
Hillfoot	d			08 48	08 48									09 03									09 18	09 18	
Milngavie	a			08 52	08 52									09 07	←								09 22	09 22	
Drumchapel	d	08 40									08 55 →	08 55 →			08 55						09 10	09 10			
Drumry	d	08 42													08 57						09 12	09 12			
Singer	d	08 45													09 00						09 15	09 15			
Dalmuir	a	08 47					08 56						08 59		09 02	09 07	09 11				09 17	09 17			09 26
	d	08 48											08 59			09 07					09 18	09 18			
Kilpatrick	d	08 51																			09 21	09 21			
Bowling	d	08 54																			09 24	09 24			
Dumbarton East	d	08 58											09 06								09 28	09 28			
Dumbarton Central	d	09 00											09 08			09 16					09 30	09 30			
Dalreoch	d	09 02											09 10								09 32	09 32			
Renton	d	09 05																			09 35	09 35			
Alexandria	d	09 07																			09 37	09 37			
Balloch	a	09 10																			09 40	09 40			
Cardross	d												09 15												
Craigendoran	d												09 20												
Helensburgh Central	a												09 25			09e32									

For general notes see front of timetable
For details of catering facilities see Directory of Train Operators

§ Low Level

A From Edinburgh (Table 225)
B Until 26 September. To Mallaig (Table 227)
C From Carstairs (Table 225)

b Glasgow Queen Street High Level
c Glasgow Central High Level
e Helensburgh Upper

Table 226

Mondays to Saturdays

Lanark, Coatbridge, Motherwell, Larkhall, Hamilton, Drumgelloch, Airdrie and Springburn → Glasgow → Milngavie, Dalmuir, Balloch and Helensburgh

Network Diagram - see first page of Table 220

		SR SX	SR	SR	SR	SR SX	SR SO	SR SX	SR SO	SR SX	SR	SR	SR	SR	SR	SR	SR	SR	SR SX	SR SO	SR SX A	SR B	SR	SR	SR
Lanark	d	08 23					08 23													08 53					
Carluke	d	08 33					08 33													09 03	09 26				
Wishaw	d	08 38					08 38													09 08					
Holytown	d																			09 13		09 32			
Shieldmuir	d	08 42					08 42																		
Coatbridge Central	d																								
Whifflet	d																								
Motherwell	a	08 45					08 46													09 20	09 33				
	d	08 46					08 46	08 46			08 50						09 16		09 20	09 20	09 33				
Bellshill	d						08 52	08 52									09 22					09 36			
Uddingston	d						08 56	08 56									09 26					09 40			
Airbles	d										08 52								09 22	09 22					
Larkhall	d		08 37										09 07											09 37	
Merryton	d		08 39										09 09											09 39	
Chatelherault	d		08 42										09 12											09 42	
Hamilton Central	d		08 45								08 57		09 15						09 27	09 27				09 45	
Hamilton West	d		08 48								09 00		09 18						09 30	09 30				09 48	
Blantyre	d		08 51								09 03		09 21						09 33	09 33				09 51	
Newton	d										09 07								09 37	09 37					
Cambuslang	d						09 01	09 01			09 11						09 31		09 41	09 43		09 45			
Rutherglen	d	08 56	08 59				09 04	09 04			09 15		09 29				09 34		09 45	09 45				09 59	
Dalmarnock	d						09 06	09 06			09 17						09 36		09 47	09 47					
Bridgeton	d						09 08	09 08			09 19						09 38		09 49	09 49					
Drumgelloch	d			08 38										09 08											09 38
Airdrie	a			08 41										09 11											09 41
	d			08 42						08 57				09 12				09 27							09 42
Coatdyke	d			08 44						08 59				09 14				09 29							09 44
Coatbridge Sunnyside	d			08 46						09 01				09 16				09 31							09 46
Blairhill	d			08 49						09 04				09 19				09 34							09 49
Easterhouse	d			08 53						09 08				09 23				09 38							09 53
Garrowhill	d			08 55						09 10				09 25				09 40							09 55
Shettleston	d			08 58						09 13				09 28				09 43							09 58
Carntyne	d			09 00						09 15				09 30				09 45							10 00
Springburn	d								09 09			09 19											09 49		
Barnhill	d								09 10			09 20											09 50		
Alexandra Parade	d								09 13			09 23											09 53		
Duke Street	d								09 14			09 24											09 54		
Bellgrove	d			09 03		09 08			09 16	09 18		09 26		09 33	09 38			09 48					09 56		10 03
High Street	d			09 05		09 10			09 18	09 20		09 28		09 35	09 40			09 50					09 58		10 05
Glasgow Queen Street 10 §	a			09 07		09 12			09 21	09 22		09 31		09 37	09 42			09 52					10 01		10 07
	d			09 10		09 13			09 23	09 23		09 32		09 40	09 43			09 53					10 02		10 10
Charing Cross	d			09 12		09 15			09 25	09 25		09 34		09 42	09 45			09 55					10 04		10 12
Argyle Street	d	09 01	09 04				09 12	09 12			09 23		09 34				09 42		09 53	09 53				10 04	
Glasgow Central 15 §	a	09 03	09 07				09 16	09 16			09 26		09 37				09 46		09 56	09 58	09b55	10b00		10 07	
	d	09 03	09 07				09 16	09 16			09 28		09 37				09 46		09 58	09 58				10 07	
Anderston	d	09 05	09 09				09 18	09 18			09 29		09 39				09 48		09 59	09 59				10 09	
Exhibition Centre	d	09 08	09 11				09 20	09 20			09 31		09 41				09 50		10 01	10 01				10 11	
Partick	d	09 12	09 15	09 17		09 20	09 24	09 24	09 30	09 30	09 35	09 39	09 45	09 47	09 50		09 54	10 00	10 05	10 05			10 09	10 15	10 17
Hyndland	d	09 14	09 17	09 20		09 23	09 26	09 26	09 32	09 32	09 38	09 41	09 47	09 50	09 53		09 56	10 02	10 08	10 08			10 11	10 17	10 20
Jordanhill	d	09 16					09 28	09 28				09 43					09 58						10 13		
Scotstounhill	d	09 19					09 30	09 30				09 45					10 00						10 15		
Garscadden	d	09a21					09 32	09 32				09 47					10 02						10 17		
Yoker	d						09 35	09 35				09 50					10 05						10 20		
Clydebank	d						09 37	09 37				09 52					10 07						10 22		
Anniesland	d		09 20			09 26			09 35	09 35	09 41		09 50		09 56			10 05	10 11	10 11				10 20	
Westerton	d		09 23			09 29			09 38	09 38	09 44		09 53		09 59			10 08	10 14	10 14				10 23	
Bearsden	d					09 31					09 46				10 01				10 16	10 16					
Hillfoot	d					09 33					09 48				10 03				10 18	10 18					
Milngavie	a				←	09 37					09 52				10 07	←			10 22	10 22					
Drumchapel	d		09 25 →		09 25				09 40	09 40			09 55 →			09 55		10 10						10 25 →	
Drumry	d				09 27				09 42	09 42						09 57		10 12							
Singer	d				09 30				09 45	09 45						10 00		10 15							
Dalmuir	a			09 29	09 32		09 41	09 43	09 47	09 47		09 56		09 59		10 02	10 11	10 17					10 26		10 29
	d			09 29					09 48	09 48				09 59				10 18							10 29
Kilpatrick	d								09 51	09 51								10 21							
Bowling	d								09 54	09 54								10 24							
Dumbarton East	d			09 36					09 58	09 58				10 06				10 28							10 36
Dumbarton Central	d			09 38					10 00	10 00				10 08				10 30							10 38
Dalreoch	d			09 40					10 02	10 02				10 10				10 32							10 40
Renton	d								10 05	10 05								10 35							
Alexandria	d								10 07	10 07								10 37							
Balloch	a								10 10	10 10								10 40							
Cardross	d			09 45										10 15											10 45
Craigendoran	d			09 50										10 20											10 50
Helensburgh Central	a			09 55										10 23											10 56

For general notes see front of timetable
For details of catering facilities see Directory of Train Operators

§ Low Level

A From North Berwick (Table 238)
B From Edinburgh (Table 225)
b Glasgow Central High Level

Lanark, Coatbridge, Motherwell, Larkhall, Hamilton, Drumgelloch, Airdrie and Springburn → Glasgow → Milngavie, Dalmuir, Balloch and Helensburgh

Network Diagram - see first page of Table 220

		SR	SR	SR	SR	SR	SR	SR	SR	SR	SR	SR	SR		SR	SR	SR	SR	SR	SR	SR	SR	SR	SR	SR
							SO	SO ◇																	
							A	B										C							
Lanark	d			09 23													09 53							10 23	
Carluke	d			09 33			09 49										10 02							10 33	
Wishaw	d			09 38													10 08							10 38	
Holytown	d																10 13	10 32							
Shieldmuir	d			09 42																				10 42	
Coatbridge Central	d																								
Whifflet	d																								
Motherwell	a			09 46			09 56										10 20							10 46	
	d			09 46		09 50	09 57								10 16		10 20							10 46	
Bellshill	d			09 52											10 22			10 36						10 52	
Uddingston	d			09 56											10 26			10 40						10 56	
Airbles	d					09 52											10 22								
Larkhall	d									10 07										10 37					
Merryton	d									10 09										10 39					
Chatelherault	d									10 12										10 42					
Hamilton Central	d					09 57				10 15							10 27			10 45					
Hamilton West	d					10 00				10 18							10 30			10 48					
Blantyre	d					10 03				10 21							10 33			10 51					
Newton	d					10 07											10 37								
Cambuslang	d			10 01		10 11									10 31		10 41	10 45						11 01	
Rutherglen	d			10 04		10 15				10 29					10 34		10 45			10 59				11 04	
Dalmarnock	d			10 06		10 17									10 36		10 47							11 06	
Bridgeton	d			10 08		10 19									10 38		10 49							11 08	
Drumgelloch	d										10 08										10 38				
Airdrie	a										10 11										10 41				
	d				09 57						10 12					10 27					10 42				10 57
Coatdyke	d				09 59						10 14					10 29					10 44				10 59
Coatbridge Sunnyside	d				10 01						10 16					10 31					10 46				11 01
Blairhill	d				10 04						10 19					10 34					10 49				11 04
Easterhouse	d				10 08						10 23					10 38					10 53				11 08
Garrowhill	d				10 10						10 25					10 40					10 55				11 10
Shettleston	d				10 13						10 28					10 43					10 58				11 13
Carntyne	d				10 15						10 30					10 45					11 00				11 15
Springburn	d								10 19										10 49						
Barnhill	d								10 20										10 50						
Alexandra Parade	d								10 23										10 53						
Duke Street	d								10 24										10 54						
Bellgrove	d		10 08		10 18				10 26		10 33		10 38			10 48			10 56		11 03		11 08		11 18
High Street	d		10 10		10 20				10 28		10 35		10 40			10 50			10 58		11 05		11 10		11 20
Glasgow Queen Street 10 §	a		10 12		10 22				10 31		10 37		10 42			10 52			11 01		11 07		11 12		11 22
	d		10 13		10 23			10b37	10 32		10 40		10 43			10 53			11 02		11 10		11 13		11 23
Charing Cross	d		10 15		10 25				10 34		10 42		10 45			10 55			11 04		11 12		11 15		11 25
Argyle Street	d			10 12		10 23				10 34					10 42		10 53			11 04				11 12	
Glasgow Central 15 §	a			10 16		10 26	10c14			10 37					10 46		10 56	11c00		11 07				11 16	
	d			10 16		10 28				10 37					10 46		10 58			11 07				11 16	
Anderston	d			10 18		10 29				10 39					10 48		10 59			11 09				11 18	
Exhibition Centre	d			10 20		10 31				10 41					10 50		11 01			11 11				11 20	
Partick	d		10 20	10 24	10 30	10 35			10 39	10 45	10 47		10 50		10 54	11 00	11 05		11 09	11 15	11 17		11 20	11 24	11 30
Hyndland	d		10 23	10 26	10 32	10 38			10 41	10 47	10 50		10 53		10 56	11 02	11 08		11 11	11 17	11 20		11 23	11 26	11 32
Jordanhill	d			10 28					10 43						10 58				11 13					11 28	
Scotstounhill	d			10 30					10 45						11 00				11 15					11 30	
Garscadden	d			10 32					10 47						11 02				11 17					11 32	
Yoker	d			10 35					10 50						11 05				11 20					11 35	
Clydebank	d			10 37					10 52						11 07				11 22					11 37	
Anniesland	d		10 26		10 35	10 41				10 50			10 56			11 05	11 11			11 20			11 26		11 35
Westerton	d		10 29		10 38	10 44				10 53			10 59			11 08	11 14			11 23			11 29		11 38
Bearsden	d		10 31			10 46							11 01				11 16						11 31		
Hillfoot	d		10 33			10 48							11 03				11 18						11 33		
Milngavie	a	←	10 37			10 52						←	11 07				11 24					←	11 37		
Drumchapel	d	10 25			10 40					10 55 →		10 55				11 10				11 25 →		11 25			11 40
Drumry	d	10 27			10 42							10 57				11 12						11 27			11 42
Singer	d	10 30			10 45							11 00				11 15						11 30			11 45
Dalmuir	a	10 32		10 41	10 47			10 50	10 56		10 59	11 02			11 11	11 17			11 26		11 29	11 32		11 42	11 47
	d				10 48			10 50			10 59					11 18					11 29				11 48
Kilpatrick	d				10 51											11 21									11 51
Bowling	d				10 54											11 24									11 54
Dumbarton East	d				10 58						11 06					11 28					11 36				11 58
Dumbarton Central	d				11 00			11 04			11 08					11 30					11 38				12 00
Dalreoch	d				11 02						11 10					11 32					11 40				12 02
Renton	d				11 05											11 35									12 05
Alexandria	d				11 07											11 37									12 07
Balloch	a				11 10											11 40									12 10
Cardross	d										11 15										11 45				
Craigendoran	d										11 20										11 50				
Helensburgh Central	a							11e20			11 25										11 53				

For general notes see front of timetable
For details of catering facilities see Directory of Train Operators

§ Low Level

A From North Berwick (Table 238)
B Until 25 October. To Oban (Table 227)
C From Edinburgh (Table 225)

b Glasgow Queen Street High Level
c Glasgow Central High Level
e Helensburgh Upper

Lanark, Coatbridge, Motherwell, Larkhall, Hamilton, Drumgelloch, Airdrie and Springburn → Glasgow → Milngavie, Dalmuir, Balloch and Helensburgh

Network Diagram - see first page of Table 220

		SR	SR	SR	SR	SR	SR	SR	SR	SR	SR	SR	SR	SR	SR	SR	SR	SR	SR	SR	SR	SR	SR	SR	SR
											A						◇ B								
Lanark	d									10 53								11 23							
Carluke	d									11 03								11 33							
Wishaw	d									11 08								11 38							
Holytown	d									11 13	11 32														
Shieldmuir	d																	11 42							
Coatbridge Central	d																								
Whifflet	d																								
Motherwell	a									11 19								11 46							
	d	10 50						11 16		11 20								11 46		11 50					
Bellshill	d							11 22			11 36							11 52							
Uddingston	d							11 26			11 40							11 56							
Airbles	d	10 52								11 22										11 52					
Larkhall	d			11 07									11 37									12 07			
Merryton	d			11 09									11 39									12 09			
Chatelherault	d			11 12									11 42									12 12			
Hamilton Central	d	10 57		11 15						11 27			11 45							11 57		12 15			
Hamilton West	d	11 00		11 18						11 30			11 48							12 00		12 18			
Blantyre	d	11 03		11 21						11 33			11 51							12 03		12 21			
Newton	d	11 07								11 37										12 07					
Cambuslang	d	11 11						11 31		11 41	11 45							12 01		12 11					
Rutherglen	d	11 15		11 29				11 34		11 45			11 59					12 04		12 15		12 29			
Dalmarnock	d	11 17						11 36		11 47								12 06		12 17					
Bridgeton	d	11 19						11 38		11 49								12 08		12 19					
Drumgelloch	d				11 08									11 38									12 08		
Airdrie	a				11 11									11 41									12 11		
	d				11 12				11 27					11 42					11 57				12 12		
Coatdyke	d				11 14				11 29					11 44					11 59				12 14		
Coatbridge Sunnyside	d				11 16				11 31					11 46					12 01				12 16		
Blairhill	d				11 19				11 34					11 49					12 04				12 19		
Easterhouse	d				11 23				11 38					11 53					12 08				12 23		
Garrowhill	d				11 25				11 40					11 55					12 10				12 25		
Shettleston	d				11 28				11 43					11 58					12 13				12 28		
Carntyne	d				11 30				11 45					12 00					12 15				12 30		
Springburn	d		11 19									11 49									12 19				
Barnhill	d		11 20									11 50									12 20				
Alexandra Parade	d		11 23									11 53									12 23				
Duke Street	d		11 24									11 54									12 24				
Bellgrove	d		11 26		11 33		11 38		11 48			11 56		12 03		12 08			12 18		12 26		12 33		12 38
High Street	d		11 28		11 35		11 40		11 50			11 58		12 05		12 10			12 20		12 28		12 35		12 40
Glasgow Queen Street 10 §	a		11 31		11 37		11 42		11 52			12 01		12 07		12 12			12 22		12 31		12 37		12 42
	d		11 32		11 40		11 43		11 53			12 02		12 10		12 13	12b21		12 23		12 32		12 40		12 43
Charing Cross	d		11 34		11 42		11 45		11 55			12 04		12 12		12 15			12 25		12 34		12 42		12 45
Argyle Street	d	11 23		11 34				11 42		11 53			12 04					12 12		12 23		12 34			
Glasgow Central 15 §	a	11 26		11 37				11 46		11 56	12c00		12 07					12 16		12 26		12 37			
	d	11 28		11 37				11 46		11 58			12 07					12 16		12 28		12 37			
Anderston	d	11 29		11 39				11 48		11 59			12 09					12 18		12 29		12 39			
Exhibition Centre	d	11 31		11 41				11 50		12 01			12 11					12 20		12 31		12 41			
Partick	d	11 35	11 39	11 45	11 47		11 50	11 54	12 00	12 05		12 09	12 15	12 17		12 20		12 24	12 30	12 35	12 39	12 45	12 48		12 50
Hyndland	d	11 38	11 41	11 47	11 50		11 53	11 56	12 02	12 08		12 11	12 17	12 20		12 23		12 26	12 32	12 38	12 41	12 47	12 51		12 53
Jordanhill	d		11 43					11 58				12 13						12 28			12 43				
Scotstounhill	d		11 45					12 00				12 15						12 30			12 45				
Garscadden	d		11 47					12 02				12 17						12 32			12 47				
Yoker	d		11 50					12 05				12 20						12 35			12 50				
Clydebank	d		11 52					12 07				12 22						12 37			12 52				
Anniesland	d	11 41		11 50			11 56		12 05	12 11			12 20			12 26			12 35	12 41		12 50			12 56
Westerton	d	11 44		11 53			11 59		12 08	12 14			12 23			12 29			12 38	12 44		12 53			12 59
Bearsden	d	11 46					12 01			12 16						12 31				12 46					13 01
Hillfoot	d	11 48					12 03			12 18						12 33				12 48					13 03
Milngavie	a	11 52				←	12 07			12 22					←	12 37				12 52				←	13 07
Drumchapel	d			11 55 →		11 55			12 10				12 25 →		12 25				12 40			12 55 →		12 55	
Drumry	d					11 57			12 12						12 27				12 42					12 57	
Singer	d					12 00			12 15						12 30				12 45					13 00	
Dalmuir	a		11 56		11 59	12 02		12 11	12 17			12 26		12 29	12 32		12 38	12 41	12 47		12 56		12 59	13 02	
	d				11 59				12 18					12 29			12 42		12 48				12 59		
Kilpatrick	d								12 21										12 51						
Bowling	d								12 24										12 54						
Dumbarton East	d				12 06				12 28					12 36					12 58				13 06		
Dumbarton Central	d				12 08				12 30					12 38			12 48		13 00				13 08		
Dalreoch	d				12 10				12 32					12 40					13 02				13 10		
Renton	d								12 35										13 05						
Alexandria	d								12 37										13 07						
Balloch	a								12 40										13 10						
Cardross	d				12 15									12 45									13 15		
Craigendoran	d				12 20									12 50									13 20		
Helensburgh Central	a				12 23									12 53			13e03						13 26		

For general notes see front of timetable
For details of catering facilities see Directory of Train Operators

§ Low Level

A From Edinburgh (Table 225)
B To Oban and to Mallaig (Table 227)
b Glasgow Queen Street High Level
c Glasgow Central High Level
e Helensburgh Upper

Lanark, Coatbridge, Motherwell, Larkhall, Hamilton, Drumgelloch, Airdrie and Springburn → Glasgow → Milngavie, Dalmuir, Balloch and Helensburgh

Network Diagram - see first page of Table 220

		SR	SR	SR	SR A	SR	SR	SR	SR	SR	SR	SR	SR	SR	SR	SR	SR		SR	SR	SR	SR	SR A	SR	SR
Lanark	d			11 53							12 23											12 53			
Carluke	d			12 03							12 33											13 03			
Wishaw	d			12 08							12 38											13 08			
Holytown	d			12 13	12 32																	13 13	13 32		
Shieldmuir	d										12 42														
Coatbridge Central	d																								
Whifflet	d																								
Motherwell	a			12 20							12 46											13 19			
	d	12 16		12 20							12 46		12 50							13 16		13 20			
Bellshill	d	12 22			12 36						12 52									13 22			13 36		
Uddingston	d	12 26			12 40						12 56									13 26			13 40		
Airbles	d			12 22									12 52									13 22			
Larkhall	d						12 37								13 07										13 37
Merryton	d						12 39								13 09										13 39
Chatelherault	d						12 42								13 12										13 42
Hamilton Central	d			12 27			12 45						12 57		13 15							13 27			13 45
Hamilton West	d			12 30			12 48						13 00		13 18							13 30			13 48
Blantyre	d			12 33			12 51						13 03		13 21							13 33			13 51
Newton	d			12 37									13 07									13 37			
Cambuslang	d	12 31		12 41	12 45						13 01		13 11							13 31		13 41	13 45		
Rutherglen	d	12 34		12 45			12 59				13 04		13 15		13 29					13 34		13 45			13 59
Dalmarnock	d	12 36		12 47							13 06		13 17							13 36		13 47			
Bridgeton	d	12 38		12 49							13 08		13 19							13 38		13 49			
Drumgelloch	d							12 38								13 08									
Airdrie	a							12 41								13 11									
	d		12 27					12 42				12 57				13 12					13 27				
Coatdyke	d		12 29					12 44				12 59				13 14					13 29				
Coatbridge Sunnyside	d		12 31					12 46				13 01				13 16					13 31				
Blairhill	d		12 34					12 49				13 04				13 19					13 34				
Easterhouse	d		12 38					12 53				13 08				13 23					13 38				
Garrowhill	d		12 40					12 55				13 10				13 25					13 40				
Shettleston	d		12 43					12 58				13 13				13 28					13 43				
Carntyne	d		12 45					13 00				13 15				13 30					13 45				
Springburn	d					12 49								13 19										13 49	
Barnhill	d					12 50								13 20										13 50	
Alexandra Parade	d					12 53								13 23										13 53	
Duke Street	d					12 54								13 24										13 54	
Bellgrove	d		12 48			12 56		13 03		13 08		13 18		13 26		13 33			13 38		13 48			13 56	
High Street	d		12 50			12 58		13 05		13 10		13 20		13 28		13 35			13 40		13 50			13 58	
Glasgow Queen Street 10 §	a		12 52			13 01		13 07		13 12		13 22		13 31		13 37			13 42		13 52			14 01	
	d		12 53			13 02		13 10		13 13		13 23		13 32		13 40			13 43		13 53			14 02	
Charing Cross	d		12 55			13 04		13 12		13 15		13 25		13 34		13 42			13 45		13 55			14 04	
Argyle Street	d	12 42		12 53			13 04				13 12		13 23		13 34					13 42		13 53			14 04
Glasgow Central 15 §	a	12 46		12 56	13b00		13 07				13 16		13 26		13 37					13 46		13 56	14b00		14 07
	d	12 46		12 58			13 07				13 16		13 28		13 37					13 46		13 58			14 07
Anderston	d	12 48		12 59			13 09				13 18		13 29		13 39					13 48		13 59			14 09
Exhibition Centre	d	12 50		13 01			13 11				13 20		13 31		13 41					13 50		14 01			14 11
Partick	d	12 54	13 00	13 05		13 09	13 15	13 17		13 20	13 24	13 30	13 35	13 39	13 45	13 47			13 50	13 54	14 00	14 05		14 09	14 15
Hyndland	d	12 56	13 02	13 08		13 11	13 17	13 20		13 23	13 26	13 32	13 38	13 41	13 47	13 50			13 53	13 56	14 02	14 08		14 11	14 17
Jordanhill	d	12 58				13 13					13 28			13 43						13 58				14 13	
Scotstounhill	d	13 00				13 15					13 30			13 45						14 00				14 15	
Garscadden	d	13 02				13 17					13 32			13 47						14 02				14 17	
Yoker	d	13 05				13 20					13 35			13 50						14 05				14 20	
Clydebank	d	13 07				13 22					13 37			13 52						14 07				14 22	
Anniesland	d		13 05	13 11			13 20			13 26		13 35	13 41		13 50				13 56		14 05	14 11			14 20
Westerton	d		13 08	13 14			13 23			13 29		13 38	13 44		13 53				13 59		14 08	14 14			14 23
Bearsden	d			13 16						13 31			13 46						14 01			14 16			
Hillfoot	d			13 18						13 33			13 48						14 03			14 18			
Milngavie	a			13 22					←	13 37			13 52				←		14 07			14 22			
Drumchapel	d		13 10				13 25 →		13 25			13 40			13 55 →		13 55				14 10				14 25 →
Drumry	d		13 12						13 27			13 42					13 57				14 12				
Singer	d		13 15						13 30			13 45					14 00				14 15				
Dalmuir	a	13 11	13 17			13 26		13 29	13 32		13 41	13 47		13 56		13 59	14 02			14 11	14 17			14 26	
	d		13 18					13 29				13 48				13 59					14 18				
Kilpatrick	d		13 21									13 51									14 21				
Bowling	d		13 24									13 54									14 24				
Dumbarton East	d		13 28					13 36				13 58				14 06					14 28				
Dumbarton Central	d		13 30					13 38				14 00				14 08					14 30				
Dalreoch	d		13 32					13 40				14 02				14 10					14 32				
Renton	d		13 35									14 05									14 35				
Alexandria	d		13 37									14 07									14 37				
Balloch	a		13 40									14 10									14 40				
Cardross	d							13 45								14 15									
Craigendoran	d							13 50								14 20									
Helensburgh Central	a							13 53								14 23									

For general notes see front of timetable
For details of catering facilities see Directory of Train Operators

§ Low Level

A From Edinburgh (Table 225)

b Glasgow Central High Level

Lanark, Coatbridge, Motherwell, Larkhall, Hamilton, Drumgelloch, Airdrie and Springburn → Glasgow → Milngavie, Dalmuir, Balloch and Helensburgh

Network Diagram - see first page of Table 220

		SR	SR	SR	SR	SR	SR	SR	SR	SR	SR	SR	SR	SR	SR	SR A	SR	SR	SR SO	SR SX	SR	SR	SR	SR	SR
Lanark	d				13 23										13 53								14 23		
Carluke	d				13 33										14 03								14 33		
Wishaw	d				13 38										14 08								14 38		
Holytown	d														14 13	14 32									
Shieldmuir	d				13 42																		14 42		
Coatbridge Central	d																								
Whifflet	d																								
Motherwell	a				13 46										14 20								14 46		
	d				13 46		13 50						14 16		14 20								14 46		14 50
Bellshill	d				13 52								14 22			14 36							14 52		
Uddingston	d				13 56								14 26			14 40							14 56		
Airbles	d						13 52								14 22										14 52
Larkhall	d								14 07									14 37							
Merryton	d								14 09									14 39							
Chatelherault	d								14 12									14 42							
Hamilton Central	d						13 57		14 15						14 27			14 45							14 57
Hamilton West	d						14 00		14 18						14 30			14 48							15 00
Blantyre	d						14 03		14 21						14 33			14 51							15 03
Newton	d						14 07								14 37										15 07
Cambuslang	d				14 01		14 11						14 31		14 41	14 45							15 01		15 11
Rutherglen	d				14 04		14 15		14 29				14 34		14 45			14 59					15 04		15 15
Dalmarnock	d				14 06		14 17						14 36		14 47								15 06		15 17
Bridgeton	d				14 08		14 19						14 38		14 49								15 08		15 19
Drumgelloch	d	13 38								14 08									14 38	14 38					
Airdrie	a	13 41								14 11									14 41	14 41					
	d	13 42				13 57				14 12				14 27					14 42	14 42				14 57	
Coatdyke	d	13 44				13 59				14 14				14 29					14 44	14 44				14 59	
Coatbridge Sunnyside	d	13 46				14 01				14 16				14 31					14 46	14 46				15 01	
Blairhill	d	13 49				14 04				14 19				14 34					14 49	14 49				15 04	
Easterhouse	d	13 53				14 08				14 23				14 38					14 53	14 53				15 08	
Garrowhill	d	13 55				14 10				14 25				14 40					14 55	14 55				15 10	
Shettleston	d	13 58				14 13				14 28				14 43					14 58	14 58				15 13	
Carntyne	d	14 00				14 15				14 30				14 45					15 00	15 00				15 15	
Springburn	d							14 19									14 49								
Barnhill	d							14 20									14 50								
Alexandra Parade	d							14 23									14 53								
Duke Street	d							14 24									14 54								
Bellgrove	d	14 03		14 08		14 18		14 26		14 33		14 38		14 48			14 56		15 03	15 03		15 08		15 18	
High Street	d	14 05		14 10		14 20		14 28		14 35		14 40		14 50			14 58		15 05	15 05		15 10		15 20	
Glasgow Queen Street 10 § ⛴	a	14 07		14 12		14 22		14 31		14 37		14 42		14 52			15 01		15 07	15 07		15 12		15 22	
	d	14 10		14 13		14 23		14 32		14 40		14 43		14 53			15 02		15 10	15 10		15 13		15 23	
Charing Cross	d	14 12		14 15		14 25		14 34		14 42		14 45		14 55			15 04		15 12	15 12		15 15		15 25	
Argyle Street	d				14 12		14 23		14 34				14 42		14 53			15 04					15 12		15 23
Glasgow Central 15 §	a				14 16		14 26		14 37				14 46		14 56	15b02		15 07					15 16		15 26
	d				14 16		14 28		14 37				14 46		14 58			15 07					15 16		15 28
Anderston	d				14 18		14 29		14 39				14 48		14 59			15 09					15 18		15 29
Exhibition Centre	d				14 20		14 31		14 41				14 50		15 01			15 11					15 20		15 31
Partick ⛴	d	14 17		14 20	14 24	14 30	14 35	14 39	14 45	14 47		14 50	14 54	15 00	15 05		15 09	15 15	15 17	15 17		15 20	15 24	15 30	15 35
Hyndland	d	14 20		14 23	14 26	14 32	14 38	14 41	14 47	14 50		14 53	14 56	15 02	15 08		15 11	15 17	15 20	15 20		15 23	15 26	15 32	15 38
Jordanhill	d				14 28			14 43					14 58				15 13						15 28		
Scotstounhill	d				14 30			14 45					15 00				15 15						15 30		
Garscadden	d				14 32			14 47					15 02				15 17						15 32		
Yoker	d				14 35			14 50					15 05				15 20						15 35		
Clydebank	d				14 37			14 52					15 07				15 22						15 37		
Anniesland	d			14 26		14 35	14 41		14 50			14 56		15 05	15 11			15 20				15 26		15 35	15 41
Westerton	d			14 29		14 38	14 44		14 53			14 59		15 08	15 14			15 23				15 29		15 38	15 44
Bearsden	d			14 31			14 46					15 01			15 16							15 31			15 46
Hillfoot	d			14 33			14 48					15 03			15 18							15 33			15 48
Milngavie	a		←	14 37			14 52				←	15 07			15 24						←	15 37			15 54
Drumchapel	d		14 25			14 40			14 55 →		14 55			15 10				15 25 →			15 25			15 40	
Drumry	d		14 27			14 42					14 57			15 12							15 27			15 42	
Singer	d		14 30			14 45					15 00			15 15							15 30			15 45	
Dalmuir	a	14 29	14 32		14 41	14 47		14 56		14 59	15 02		15 11	15 17			15 26		15 28	15 29	15 32		15 41	15 47	
	d	14 29				14 48				14 59				15 18					15 29	15 29				15 48	
Kilpatrick	d					14 51								15 21										15 51	
Bowling	d					14 54								15 24										15 54	
Dumbarton East	d	14 36				14 58				15 06				15 28					15 36	15 36				15 58	
Dumbarton Central	d	14 38				15 00				15 08				15 30					15 38	15 38				16 00	
Dalreoch	d	14 40				15 02				15 10				15 32					15 40	15c45				16 02	
Renton	d					15 05								15 35										16 05	
Alexandria	d					15 07								15 37										16 07	
Balloch	a					15 10								15 40										16 10	
Cardross	d	14 45								15 15									15 45	15 50					
Craigendoran	d	14 50								15 20									15 50	15 55					
Helensburgh Central	a	14 54								15 26									15 53	15 58					

For general notes see front of timetable
For details of catering facilities see Directory of Train Operators

§ Low Level

A From Edinburgh (Table 225)
b Glasgow Central High Level
c Arr. 1540

Lanark, Coatbridge, Motherwell, Larkhall, Hamilton, Drumgelloch, Airdrie and Springburn → Glasgow → Milngavie, Dalmuir, Balloch and Helensburgh

Network Diagram - see first page of Table 220

		SR	SR	SR	SR	SR	SR	SR	SR	SR	SR	SR	SR	SR	SR	SR	SR	SR	SR SO	SR SX	SR		SR	SR	SR
										A															
Lanark	d								14 53							15 23									
Carluke	d								15 03							15 33									
Wishaw	d								15 08							15 38									
Holytown	d								15 13	15 32															
Shieldmuir	d															15 42									
Coatbridge Central	d																								
Whifflet	d																								
Motherwell	a								15 19							15 46									
	d						15 16		15 20							15 46		15 50							
Bellshill	d						15 22			15 36						15 52									
Uddingston	d						15 26			15 40						15 56									
Airbles	d								15 22									15 52							
Larkhall	d		15 07									15 37									16 07				
Merryton	d		15 09									15 39									16 09				
Chatelherault	d		15 12									15 42									16 12				
Hamilton Central	d		15 15						15 27			15 45						15 57			16 15				
Hamilton West	d		15 18						15 30			15 48						16 00			16 18				
Blantyre	d		15 21						15 33			15 51						16 03			16 21				
Newton	d								15 37									16 07							
Cambuslang	d						15 31		15 41	15 45						16 01		16 11							
Rutherglen	d		15 29				15 34		15 45			15 59				16 04		16 15			16 29				
Dalmarnock	d						15 36		15 47							16 06		16 17							
Bridgeton	d						15 38		15 49							16 08		16 19							
Drumgelloch	d			15 08									15 38										16 08		
Airdrie	a			15 11									15 41										16 11		
	d			15 12				15 27					15 42				15 57						16 12		
Coatdyke	d			15 14				15 29					15 44				15 59						16 14		
Coatbridge Sunnyside	d			15 16				15 31					15 46				16 01						16 16		
Blairhill	d			15 19				15 34					15 49				16 04						16 19		
Easterhouse	d			15 23				15 38					15 53				16 08						16 23		
Garrowhill	d			15 25				15 40					15 55				16 10						16 25		
Shettleston	d			15 28				15 43					15 58				16 13						16 28		
Carntyne	d			15 30				15 45					16 00				16 15						16 30		
Springburn	d	15 19									15 49								16 19	16 22					
Barnhill	d	15 20									15 50								16 20	16 23					
Alexandra Parade	d	15 23									15 53								16 23	16 26					
Duke Street	d	15 24									15 54								16 24	16 27					
Bellgrove	d	15 26		15 33	15 38			15 48			15 56		16 03		16 08		16 18		16 26	16 29			16 33		16 38
High Street	d	15 28		15 35	15 40			15 50			15 58		16 05		16 10		16 20		16 28	16 31			16 35		16 40
Glasgow Queen Street 10 § ⛴	a	15 31		15 37	15 42			15 52			16 01		16 07		16 12		16 22		16 31	16 34			16 37		16 42
	d	15 32		15 40	15 43			15 53			16 02		16 10		16 13		16 23		16 32	16 35			16 40		16 43
Charing Cross	d	15 34		15 42	15 45			15 55			16 04		16 12		16 15		16 25		16 34	16 37			16 42		16 45
Argyle Street	d		15 34				15 42		15 53			16 04				16 12		16 23			16 34				
Glasgow Central 15 §	a		15 37				15 46		15 56	16b00		16 07				16 16		16 26			16 37				
	d		15 37				15 46		15 58			16 07				16 16		16 28			16 37				
Anderston	d		15 39				15 48		15 59			16 09				16 18		16 29			16 39				
Exhibition Centre	d		15 41				15 50		16 01			16 11				16 20		16 31			16 41				
Partick ⛴	d	15 39	15 45	15 47	15 50		15 54	16 00	16 05		16 09	16 15	16 17		16 20	16 24	16 30	16 35	16 39	16 42	16 45		16 47		16 50
Hyndland	d	15 41	15 47	15 50	15 53		15 56	16 02	16 08		16 11	16 17	16 20		16 23	16 26	16 32	16 38	16 41	16 44	16 47		16 50		16 53
Jordanhill	d	15 43					15 58				16 13					16 28			16 43	16 46					
Scotstounhill	d	15 45					16 00				16 15					16 30			16 45	16 48					
Garscadden	d	15 47					16 02				16 17					16 32			16 47	16 50					
Yoker	d	15 50					16 05				16 20					16 35			16 50	16 53					
Clydebank	d	15 52					16 07				16 22					16 37			16 52	16 55					
Anniesland	d		15 50		15 56			16 05	16 11			16 20			16 26		16 35	16 41			16 50				16 56
Westerton	d		15 53		15 59			16 08	16 14			16 23			16 29		16 38	16 44			16 53				16 59
Bearsden	d				16 01				16 16						16 31			16 46							17 01
Hillfoot	d				16 03				16 18						16 33			16 48							17 03
Milngavie	a				16 07	←			16 22					←	16 37			16 52						←	17 07
Drumchapel	d		15 55 →			15 55		16 10				16 25 →		16 25			16 40				16 55 →			16 55	
Drumry	d					15 57		16 12						16 27			16 42							16 57	
Singer	d					16 00		16 15						16 30			16 45							17 00	
Dalmuir	a	15 56		15 59		16 02	16 11	16 17			16 25		16 29	16 32		16 41	16 47		16 56	16 59			16 59	17 02	
	d			15 59				16 18					16 29				16 48						16 59		
Kilpatrick	d							16 21									16 51								
Bowling	d							16 24									16 54								
Dumbarton East	d			16 06				16 28					16 36				16 58						17 06		
Dumbarton Central	d			16 08				16 30					16 38				17 00						17 08		
Dalreoch	d			16 10				16 32					16 40				17 02						17 10		
Renton	d							16 35									17 05								
Alexandria	d							16 37									17 07								
Balloch	a							16 40									17 10								
Cardross	d			16 15									16 45										17 15		
Craigendoran	d			16 20									16 50										17 20		
Helensburgh Central	a			16 23									16 53										17 26		

For general notes see front of timetable
For details of catering facilities see Directory of Train Operators

§ Low Level

A From Edinburgh (Table 225)
b Glasgow Central High Level

Lanark, Coatbridge, Motherwell, Larkhall, Hamilton, Drumgelloch, Airdrie and Springburn → Glasgow → Milngavie, Dalmuir, Balloch and Helensburgh

Network Diagram - see first page of Table 220

Station		SR	SR	SR	SR A	SR SO	SR SX	SR	SR	SR SX	SR	SR	SR	SR SX	SR	SR	SR SO B	SR SO C	SR	SR SX	SR SO	SR SX	SR SO	SR SX	SR
Lanark	d			15 53									16 23												
Carluke	d			16 03									16 33				16 52	16 55							
Wishaw	d			16 08									16 38				16 58	17 00							
Holytown	d			16 13	16 32																				
Shieldmuir	d												16 42												
Coatbridge Central	d																								
Whifflet	d																								
Motherwell	a			16 20									16 46				17 01	17 04							
	d	16 16		16 20									16 46			16 50	17 02	17 04							
Bellshill	d	16 22			16 36								16 52												
Uddingston	d	16 26			16 40								16 56						←						
Airbles	d			16 22												16 52			16 52						
Larkhall	d							16 37								→									17 07
Merryton	d							16 39																	17 09
Chatelherault	d							16 42																	17 12
Hamilton Central	d			16 27				16 45											16 57						17 15
Hamilton West	d			16 30				16 48											17 00						17 18
Blantyre	d			16 33				16 51											17 03						17 21
Newton	d			16 37															17 07						
Cambuslang	d	16 31		16 41	16 45								17 01						17 11						
Rutherglen	d	16 34		16 45				16 59					17 04						17 15						17 29
Dalmarnock	d	16 36		16 47									17 06						17 17						
Bridgeton	d	16 38		16 49									17 08						17 19						
Drumgelloch	d								16 38																
Airdrie	a								16 41																
	d		16 27						16 42						16 57										
Coatdyke	d		16 29						16 44						16 59										
Coatbridge Sunnyside	d		16 31						16 46						17 01										
Blairhill	d		16 34						16 49						17 04										
Easterhouse	d		16 38						16 53						17 08										
Garrowhill	d		16 40						16 55						17 10										
Shettleston	d		16 43						16 58						17 13										
Carntyne	d		16 45						17 00						17 15										
Springburn	d					16 49	16 52																17 19	17 22	
Barnhill	d					16 50	16 53																17 20	17 23	
Alexandra Parade	d					16 53	16 56																17 23	17 26	
Duke Street	d					16 54	16 57																17 24	17 27	
Bellgrove	d		16 48			16 56	16 59		17 03		17 08			17 15	17 18					17 27			17 26	17 29	
High Street	d		16 50			16 58	17 01		17 05		17 10			17 17	17 20					17 29			17 28	17 31	
Glasgow Queen Street 10 §	a		16 52			17 01	17 04		17 07		17 12			17 19	17 22					17 31			17 31	17 34	
	d		16 53			17 02	17 05		17 10		17 13			17 20	17 23					17 31			17 32	17 35	
Charing Cross	d		16 55			17 04	17 07		17 12		17 15			17 22	17 25					17 34			17 34	17 37	
Argyle Street	d	16 42		16 53				17 04					17 12						17 23						17 34
Glasgow Central 15 §	a	16 46		16 56	17b00			17 07					17 16				17b23	17b23	17 26						17 37
	d	16 46		16 58				17 07					17 16						17 28						17 37
Anderston	d	16 48		16 59				17 09					17 18						17 29						17 39
Exhibition Centre	d	16 50		17 01				17 11					17 20						17 31						17 41
Partick	d	16 54	17 00	17 05		17 09	17 12	17 15	17 17		17 20		17 24	17 27	17 30				17 35	17 39			17 39	17 42	17 45
Hyndland	d	16 56	17 02	17 08		17 11	17 14	17 17	17 20		17 23		17 26		17 32				17 38				17 41	17 44	17 47
Jordanhill	d	16 58				17 13	17 16						17 28										17 43	17 46	
Scotstounhill	d	17 00				17 15	17 18			←			17 30										17 45	17 48	
Garscadden	d	17 02				17 17	17 20			17 20			17 32										17 47	17 50	
Yoker	d	17 05				17 20	→			17 23			17 35										17 50	→	
Clydebank	d	17 07				17 22				17 25			17 37										17 52		
Anniesland	d		17 05	17 11				17 20			17 26				17 35				17 41						17 50
Westerton	d		17 08	17 14				17 23			17 29				17 38				17 44						17 53
Bearsden	d			17 16							17 31								17 46						
Hillfoot	d			17 18							17 33								17 48						
Milngavie	a			17 22							17 37	←							17 52						
Drumchapel	d		17 10					17 25				17 25			17 40						←	←			17 55
Drumry	d		17 12					→				17 27			17 42						17 42	17 42			→
Singer	d		17 15									17 30			→						17 45	17 45			
Dalmuir	a	17 11	17 17			17 26			17 28	17 29		17 32	17 41								17 47	17 47	17 56		
	d		17 18						17 29												17 48	17 50			
Kilpatrick	d		17 21																		17 51	17 52			
Bowling	d		17 24																		17 54	17 55			
Dumbarton East	d		17 28						17 36												17 58	18 00			
Dumbarton Central	d		17 30						17 38					17 46						17c59	18 00	18 02			
Dalreoch	d		17 32						17 40					17 48						18 00	18 02	18 03			
Renton	d		17 35																	18 03	18 05				
Alexandria	d		17 37																	18 06	18 07				
Balloch	a		17 41																	18 08	18 10				
Cardross	d								17 45					17 53								18 08			
Craigendoran	d								17 50					17 58								18 17			
Helensburgh Central	a								17 56					18 01								18 20			

For general notes see front of timetable
For details of catering facilities see Directory of Train Operators

§ Low Level

A From Edinburgh (Table 225)
B From 13 September. From North Berwick (Table 238)
C Until 6 September. From North Berwick (Table 238)
b Glasgow Central High Level
c Arr. 1755

Lanark, Coatbridge, Motherwell, Larkhall, Hamilton, Drumgelloch, Airdrie and Springburn → Glasgow → Milngavie, Dalmuir, Balloch and Helensburgh

Network Diagram - see first page of Table 220

		SR	SR SX	SR	SR	SR SX	SR SO	SR	SR SX	SR SO	SR	SR	SR SO	SR SX	SR	SR	SR	SR	SR	SR	SR SX	SR SO	SR	SR SX	SR SO
											A							◇ B ✠							
Lanark	d					16 53				16 53									17 23						
Carluke	d					17 03				17 03									17 33						
Wishaw	d					17 08				17 08									17 38						
Holytown	d									17 13	17 32														
Shieldmuir	d					17 12													17 42						
Coatbridge Central	d													17 30										17 56	
Whifflet	d													17 32										17 58	
Motherwell	a					17 16				17 19				17 39					17 45					18 07	
	d					17 16	17 16		17 20	17 20				17 39					17 46			17 50		18 10	
Bellshill	d					17 22	17 22				17 36								17 52					18 16	
Uddingston	d					17 26	17 26				17 40								17 56					18 20	
Airbles	d								17 22	17 22				17 42								17 52			
Larkhall	d												17 37								17 49				18 07
Merryton	d												17 39								17 51				18 09
Chatelherault	d												17 42								17 54				18 12
Hamilton Central	d								17 27	17 27			17 45	17 47							17 57	17 57			18 15
Hamilton West	d								17 30	17 30			17 48	17 49							18 00	18 00			18 18
Blantyre	d								17 33	17 33			17 51	17 53							18 03	18 03			18 21
Newton	d								17 37	17 37											18 07	18 07			
Cambuslang	d					17 31	17 31		17 41	17 41	17 45								18 01		18 11	18 11			
Rutherglen	d					17 34	17 34		17 45	17 45			17 59	18 00					18 04		18 15	18 15		18 29	18 29
Dalmarnock	d					17 36	17 36		17 47	17 47									18 06		18 17	18 17			
Bridgeton	d					17 38	17 38		17 49	17 49									18 08		18 19	18 19			
Drumgelloch	d	17 08													17 38										
Airdrie	a	17 11													17 41										
	d	17 12						17 27							17 42					17 57					
Coatdyke	d	17 14						17 29							17 44					17 59					
Coatbridge Sunnyside	d	17 16						17 31							17 46					18 01					
Blairhill	d	17 19						17 34							17 49					18 04					
Easterhouse	d	17 23						17 38							17 53					18 08					
Garrowhill	d	17 25						17 40							17 55					18 10					
Shettleston	d	17 28						17 43							17 58					18 13					
Carntyne	d	17 30						17 45							18 00					18 15					
Springburn	d											17 49											18 19		
Barnhill	d											17 50											18 20		
Alexandra Parade	d											17 53											18 23		
Duke Street	d											17 54											18 24		
Bellgrove	d	17 33			17 38			17 48				17 56			18 03		18 08			18 18			18 26		
High Street	d	17 35			17 40			17 50				17 58			18 05		18 10			18 20			18 28		
Glasgow Queen Street 10 §	⛴ a	17 37			17 42			17 52				18 01			18 07		18 12			18 22			18 31		
	d	17 40			17 43			17 53				18 02			18 10		18 13	18b21		18 23			18 32		
Charing Cross	d	17 42			17 45			17 55				18 04			18 12		18 15			18 25			18 34		
Argyle Street	d					17 42	17 42		17 53	17 53			18 04	18 05					18 12		18 23	18 23		18 34	18 34
Glasgow Central 15 §	a					17 46	17 46		17 56	17 56	18c00		18 07	18 07					18 16		18 26	18 26		18 37	18 37
	d					17 46	17 46		17 58	17 58			18 07	18 07					18 16		18 28	18 28		18 37	18 37
Anderston	d					17 48	17 48		17 59	17 59			18 09	18 09					18 18		18 29	18 29		18 39	18 39
Exhibition Centre	d					17 50	17 50		18 01	18 01			18 11	18 11					18 20		18 31	18 31		18 41	18 41
Partick	⛴ d	17 47			17 50	17 54	17 54	18 00	18 05	18 05		18 09	18 15	18 15	18 17		18 20		18 24	18 30	18 35	18 35	18 39	18 45	18 45
Hyndland	d	17 50			17 53	17 56	17 56	18 02	18 08	18 08		18 11	18 17	18 17	18 20		18 23		18 26	18 32	18 38	18 38	18 41	18 47	18 47
Jordanhill	d					17 58	17 58					18 13							18 28				18 43		
Scotstounhill	d		←			18 00	18 00					18 15							18 30				18 45		
Garscadden	d		17 50			18 02	18 02					18 17							18 32				18a47		
Yoker	d		17 53			18 05	18 05					18 20							18 35						
Clydebank	d		17 55			18 07	18 07					18 22							18 37						
Anniesland	d				17 56			18 05	18 11	18 11			18 20	18 20			18 26			18 35	18 41	18 41		18 50	18 50
Westerton	d				17 59			18 08	18 14	18 14			18 23	18 23			18 29			18 38	18 44	18 44		18 53	18 53
Bearsden	d				18 01				18 16	18 16							18 31				18 46	18 46			
Hillfoot	d				18 03				18 18	18 18							18 33				18 48	18 48			
Milngavie	a			←	18 08				18 22	18 22						←	18 37				18 52	18 52			
Drumchapel	d			17 55				18 10					18 25 →	18 25 →		18 25				18 40				18 55	18 55
Drumry	d			17 57				18 12								18 27				18 42				18 57	18 57
Singer	d			18 00				18 15								18 30				18 45				19 00	19 00
Dalmuir	a	17 58	17 59	18 04		18 11	18 13	18 17				18 26			18 29	18 32		18 35	18 41	18 47				19 02	19 02
	d	17 59						18 18							18 29			18 37		18 48					
Kilpatrick	d							18 21												18 51					
Bowling	d							18 24												18 54					
Dumbarton East	d	18 06						18 28							18 36					18 58					
Dumbarton Central	d	18 08						18 30							18 38			18 46		19 00					
Dalreoch	d	18 10						18 32							18 40					19 02					
Renton	d							18 35												19 05					
Alexandria	d							18 37												19 07					
Balloch	a							18 40												19 10					
Cardross	d	18 15													18 45										
Craigendoran	d	18 20													18 50										
Helensburgh Central	a	18 26													18 53			19e02							

For general notes see front of timetable
For details of catering facilities see Directory of Train Operators

§ Low Level

A From Edinburgh (Table 225)
B To Oban and to Mallaig (Table 227)
b Glasgow Queen Street High Level
c Glasgow Central High Level
e Helensburgh Upper

Table 226

Mondays to Saturdays

Lanark, Coatbridge, Motherwell, Larkhall, Hamilton, Drumgelloch, Airdrie and Springburn → Glasgow → Milngavie, Dalmuir, Balloch and Helensburgh

Network Diagram - see first page of Table 220

		SR	SR SX		SR SO	SR	SR SX	SR SO	SR SX A	SR	SR	SR	SR SO A	SR	SR	SR SX	SR SO	SR SX B	SR SX A	SR	SR	SR	SR	SR	SR SX C
Lanark	d							17 53						18 23										18 53	
Carluke	d							18 03						18 33				18 44						19 03	19 14
Wishaw	d							18 08						18 38				18 53						19 08	19 20
Holytown	d							18 13	18 27				18 32						19 02					19 13	
Shieldmuir	d													18 42				18 56							
Coatbridge Central	d															18 39									
Whifflet	d															18 41									
Motherwell	a							18 20	18 36				18 40	18 45		18 49		18 59						19 19	19 25
	d				18 16		18 20	18 20						18 46		18 50	18 50					19 16		19 20	19 25
Bellshill	d				18 22									18 52					19 06			19 22			
Uddingston	d				18 26									18 56					19 10			19 26			
Airbles	d						18 22	18 22								18 52	18 52							19 22	
Larkhall	d		18 06								18 37									19 07				↳	
Merryton	d		18 08								18 39									19 09					
Chatelherault	d		18 15								18 42									19 12					
Hamilton Central	d		18 19				18 27	18 27			18 45					18 57	18 57			19 15					
Hamilton West	d		18 21				18 30	18 30			18 48					19 00	19 00			19 18					
Blantyre	d		18 25				18 33	18 33			18 51					19 03	19 03			19 21					
Newton	d						18 37	18 37								19 07	19 07								
Cambuslang	d		18 31		18 31		18 41	18 41						19 01		19 11	19 11		19 15			19 31			
Rutherglen	d		18 34		18 34		18 45	18 45			18 59			19 04		19 15	19 15			19 29		19 34			
Dalmarnock	d		18 36		18 36		18 47	18 47						19 06		19 17	19 17					19 36			
Bridgeton	d		18 38		18 38		18 49	18 49						19 08		19 19	19 19					19 38			
Drumgelloch	d	18 08										18 38									19 08				
Airdrie	a	18 11										18 41									19 11				
	d	18 12				18 27						18 42									19 12				
Coatdyke	d	18 14				18 29						18 44									19 14				
Coatbridge Sunnyside	d	18 16				18 31						18 46									19 16				
Blairhill	d	18 19				18 34						18 49									19 19				
Easterhouse	d	18 23				18 38						18 53									19 23				
Garrowhill	d	18 25				18 40						18 55									19 25				
Shettleston	d	18 28				18 43						18 58									19 28				
Carntyne	d	18 30				18 45						19 00									19 30				
Springburn	d									18 49					19 09								19 39		
Barnhill	d									18 50					19 10								19 40		
Alexandra Parade	d									18 53					19 13								19 43		
Duke Street	d									18 54					19 14								19 44		
Bellgrove	d	18 33				18 48				18 56		19 03			19 16						19 33		19 46		
High Street	d	18 35				18 50				18 58		19 05			19 18						19 35		19 48		
Glasgow Queen Street 10 §	a	18 37				18 52				19 01		19 07			19 21						19 37		19 51		
	d	18 40				18 53				19 02		19 10			19 23						19 40		19 53		
Charing Cross	d	18 42				18 55				19 04		19 12			19 25						19 42		19 55		
Argyle Street	d		18 42		18 42		18 53	18 53			19 04			19 12		19 23	19 23			19 34		19 42			
Glasgow Central 15 §	a		18 46		18 46		18 56	18 56			19 07			19 16		19 26	19 26		19b30	19 37		19 46			19b47
	d		18 46		18 46		18 58	18 58			19 07			19 16		19 28	19 28			19 37		19 46			
Anderston	d		18 48		18 48		18 59	18 59			19 09			19 18		19 29	19 29			19 39		19 48			
Exhibition Centre	d		18 50		18 50		19 01	19 01			19 11			19 20		19 31	19 31			19 41		19 50			
Partick	d	18 47	18a53		18a53	19 00	19 05	19 05		19 09	19 15	19 17		19a23	19 30	19 35	19 35			19 45	19 47	19a53	20 00		
Hyndland	d	18 50				19 02	19 08	19 08		19 11	19 17	19 20			19 32	19 38	19 38			19 47	19 50		20 02		
Jordanhill	d	18 52								19 13		19 22									19 52				
Scotstounhill	d	18 54								19 15		19 24									19 54				
Garscadden	d	18 56								19a17		19 26									19 56				
Yoker	d	18 59										19 29									19 59				
Clydebank	d	19 01										19 31									20 01				
Anniesland	d					19 05	19 11	19 11			19 20				19 35	19 41	19 41			19 50			20 05		
Westerton	d					19 08	19 14	19 14			19 23				19 38	19 44	19 44			19 53			20 08		
Bearsden	d						19 16	19 16								19 46	19 46								
Hillfoot	d						19 18	19 18								19 48	19 48								
Milngavie	a						19 22	19 22								19 52	19 52								
Drumchapel	d					19 10					19 25				19 40					19 55			20 10		
Drumry	d					19 12					19 27				19 42					19 57			20 12		
Singer	d					19 15					19 30				19 45					20 00			20 15		
Dalmuir	a	19 04				19 17					19 32	19 34			19 47					20 02	20 04		20 17		
	d	19 05				19 18						19 35			19 48						20 05		20 18		
Kilpatrick	d					19 21									19 51								20 21		
Bowling	d					19 24									19 54								20 24		
Dumbarton East	d	19 12				19 28						19 42			19 58						20 12		20 28		
Dumbarton Central	d	19 14				19 30						19 44			20 00						20 14		20 30		
Dalreoch	d	19 16				19 32						19 46			20 02						20 16		20 32		
Renton	d					19 35									20 05								20 35		
Alexandria	d					19 37									20 07								20 37		
Balloch	a					19 40									20 10								20 40		
Cardross	d	19 21										19 51									20 21				
Craigendoran	d	19 26										19 56									20 26				
Helensburgh Central	a	19 29										19 59									20 29				

For general notes see front of timetable
For details of catering facilities see Directory of Train Operators

§ Low Level

A From Edinburgh (Table 225)
B From Carstairs (Table 225)
C From North Berwick (Table 238)

b Glasgow Central High Level

Lanark, Coatbridge, Motherwell, Larkhall, Hamilton, Drumgelloch, Airdrie and Springburn → Glasgow → Milngavie, Dalmuir, Balloch and Helensburgh

Network Diagram - see first page of Table 220

Station		SR	SR SO A	SR	SR	SR	SR	SR	SR	SR	SR	SR	SR	SR	SR	SR	SR	SR	SR	SR	SR	SR	SR	SR A	SR
Lanark	d					19 23							19 53			20 23							20 53		
Carluke	d					19 33							20 03			20 33							21 03		
Wishaw	d					19 38							20 08			20 38							21 08		
Holytown	d		19 32										20 13										21 13	21 32	
Shieldmuir	d					19 42										20 42									
Coatbridge Central	d																								
Whifflet	d																								
Motherwell	a					19 46							20 20			20 46							21 19		
	d					19 46		19 50			20 16		20 20			20 46		20 50			21 16		21 20		
Bellshill	d		19 36			19 52					20 22					20 52					21 22			21 36	
Uddingston	d	⟵	19 40			19 56					20 26					20 56					21 26			21 40	
Airbles	d	19 22						19 52					20 22					20 52					21 22		
Larkhall	d			19 37					20 07					20 37					21 07						21 37
Merryton	d			19 39					20 09					20 39					21 09						21 39
Chatelherault	d			19 42					20 12					20 42					21 12						21 42
Hamilton Central	d	19 27		19 45				19 57	20 15				20 27	20 45				20 57	21 15				21 27		21 45
Hamilton West	d	19 30		19 48				20 00	20 18				20 30	20 48				21 00	21 18				21 30		21 48
Blantyre	d	19 33		19 51				20 03	20 21				20 33	20 51				21 03	21 21				21 33		21 51
Newton	d	19 37						20 07					20 37					21 07					21 37		
Cambuslang	d	19 41	19 45			20 01		20 11			20 31		20 41			21 01		21 11			21 31		21 41	21 45	
Rutherglen	d	19 45		19 59		20 04		20 15	20 29		20 34		20 45	20 59		21 04		21 15	21 29		21 34		21 45		21 59
Dalmarnock	d	19 47				20 06		20 17			20 36		20 47			21 06		21 17			21 36		21 47		
Bridgeton	d	19 49				20 08		20 19			20 38		20 49			21 08		21 19			21 38		21 49		
Drumgelloch	d				19 38					20 08					20 38					21 08					
Airdrie	a				19 41					20 11					20 41					21 11					
	d				19 42					20 12					20 42					21 12					
Coatdyke	d				19 44					20 14					20 44					21 14					
Coatbridge Sunnyside	d				19 46					20 16					20 46					21 16					
Blairhill	d				19 49					20 19					20 49					21 19					
Easterhouse	d				19 53					20 23					20 53					21 23					
Garrowhill	d				19 55					20 25					20 55					21 25					
Shettleston	d				19 58					20 28					20 58					21 28					
Carntyne	d				20 00					20 30					21 00					21 30					
Springburn	d						20 09					20 39					21 09					21 39			
Barnhill	d						20 10					20 40					21 10					21 40			
Alexandra Parade	d						20 13					20 43					21 13					21 43			
Duke Street	d						20 14					20 44					21 14					21 44			
Bellgrove	d				20 03		20 16			20 33		20 46			21 03		21 16			21 33		21 46			
High Street	d				20 05		20 18			20 35		20 48			21 05		21 18			21 35		21 48			
Glasgow Queen Street 10 § ⛴	a				20 07		20 21			20 37		20 51			21 07		21 21			21 37		21 51			
	d				20 10		20 23			20 40		20 53			21 10		21 23			21 40		21 53			
Charing Cross	d				20 12		20 25			20 42		20 55			21 12		21 25			21 42		21 55			
Argyle Street	d	19 53		20 04		20 12		20 23	20 34		20 42		20 53	21 04		21 12		21 23	21 34		21 42		21 53		22 04
Glasgow Central 15 §	a	19 56	20b00	20 07		20 16		20 26	20 37		20 46		20 56	21 07		21 16		21 26	21 37		21 46		21 56	22b00	22 07
	d	19 58		20 07		20 16		20 28	20 37		20 46		20 58	21 07		21 16		21 28	21 37		21 46		21 58		22 07
Anderston	d	19 59		20 09		20 18		20 29	20 39		20 48		20 59	21 09		21 18		21 29	21 39		21 48		21 59		22 09
Exhibition Centre	d	20 01		20 11		20 20		20 31	20 41		20 50		21 01	21 11		21 20		21 31	21 41		21 50		22 01		22 11
Partick ⛴	d	20 05		20 15	20 17	20a23	20 30	20 35	20 45	20 47	20a53	21 00	21 05	21 15	21 17	21a23	21 30	21 35	21 45	21 47	21a53	22 00	22 05		22 15
Hyndland	d	20 08		20 17	20 20		20 32	20 38	20 47	20 50		21 02	21 08	21 17	21 20		21 32	21 38	21 47	21 50		22 02	22 08		22 17
Jordanhill	d				20 22					20 52					21 22					21 52					
Scotstounhill	d				20 24					20 54					21 24					21 54					
Garscadden	d				20 26					20 56					21 26					21 56					
Yoker	d				20 29					20 59					21 29					21 59					
Clydebank	d				20 31					21 01					21 31					22 01					
Anniesland	d	20 11		20 20			20 35	20 41	20 50			21 05	21 11	21 20			21 35	21 41	21 50			22 05	22 11		22 20
Westerton	d	20 14		20 23			20 38	20 44	20 53			21 08	21 14	21 23			21 38	21 44	21 53			22 08	22 14		22 23
Bearsden	d	20 16						20 46					21 16					21 46					22 16		
Hillfoot	d	20 18						20 48					21 18					21 48					22 18		
Milngavie	a	20 22						20 52					21 24					21 52					22 22		
Drumchapel	d			20 25			20 40		20 55			21 10		21 25			21 40		21 55			22 10			22 25
Drumry	d			20 27			20 42		20 57			21 12		21 27			21 42		21 57			22 12			22 27
Singer	d			20 30			20 45		21 00			21 15		21 30			21 45		22 00			22 15			22 30
Dalmuir	a			20 32	20 34		20 47		21 02	21 04		21 17		21 32	21 34		21 47		22 02	22 04		22 17			22 32
	d				20 35		20 48			21 05		21 18			21 35		21 48			22 05		22 18			
Kilpatrick	d						20 51					21 21					21 51					22 21			
Bowling	d						20 54					21 24					21 54					22 24			
Dumbarton East	d				20 42		20 58			21 12		21 28			21 42		21 58			22 12		22 28			
Dumbarton Central	d				20 44		21 00			21 14		21 30			21 44		22 00			22 14		22 30			
Dalreoch	d				20 46		21 02			21 16		21 32			21 46		22 02			22 16		22 32			
Renton	d						21 05					21 35					22 05					22 35			
Alexandria	d						21 07					21 37					22 07					22 37			
Balloch	a						21 10					21 40					22 10					22 40			
Cardross	d				20 51					21 21					21 51					22 21					
Craigendoran	d				20 56					21 26					21 56					22 26					
Helensburgh Central	a				20 59					21 29					21 59					22 29					

For general notes see front of timetable
For details of catering facilities see Directory of Train Operators

§ Low Level

A From Edinburgh (Table 225)
b Glasgow Central High Level

Lanark, Coatbridge, Motherwell, Larkhall, Hamilton, Drumgelloch, Airdrie and Springburn → Glasgow → Milngavie, Dalmuir, Balloch and Helensburgh

Network Diagram - see first page of Table 220

		SR	SR	SR	SR	SR	SR	SR	SR	SR	SR	SR	SR	SR	SR	SR	SR	SR SX A	SR FO	SR FX	SR FO	SR FO	SR SO A
Lanark	d		21 23							21 53			22 23										
Carluke	d		21 33							22 03			22 33										
Wishaw	d		21 38							22 08			22 38										
Holytown	d									22 13								23 16					23 48
Shieldmuir	d		21 42										22 42										
Coatbridge Central	d																						
Whifflet	d																						
Motherwell	a		21 46							22 19			22 46										
	d		21 46		21 50			22 16		22 20			22 46		22 50						23 20		
Bellshill	d		21 52					22 22					22 52					23 20					23 52
Uddingston	d		21 56					22 26					22 56					23 26					23 58
Airbles	d				21 52					22 22					22 52						23 22		
Larkhall	d					22 07					22 37					23 07						23 37	
Merryton	d					22 09					22 39					23 09						23 39	
Chatelherault	d					22 12					22 42					23 12						23 42	
Hamilton Central	d				21 57	22 15				22 27	22 45				22 57	23 15					23 27	23 45	
Hamilton West	d				22 00	22 18				22 30	22 48				23 00	23 18					23 30	23 48	
Blantyre	d				22 03	22 21				22 33	22 51				23 03	23 21					23 33	23 51	
Newton	d				22 07					22 37					23 07						23 37		
Cambuslang	d		22 01		22 11			22 31		22 41			23 01		23 11			23 31			23 41		00 03
Rutherglen	d		22 04		22 15	22 29		22 34		22 45	22 59		23 04		23 15	23 29					23 45	23 59	
Dalmarnock	d		22 06		22 17			22 36		22 47			23 06		23 17						23 47		
Bridgeton	d		22 08		22 19			22 38		22 49			23 08		23 19						23 49		
Drumgelloch	d	21 38					22 08					22 38					23 08						
Airdrie	a	21 41					22 11					22 41					23 11						
	d	21 42					22 12					22 42					23 12						
Coatdyke	d	21 44					22 14					22 44					23 14						
Coatbridge Sunnyside	d	21 46					22 16					22 46					23 16						
Blairhill	d	21 49					22 19					22 49					23 19						
Easterhouse	d	21 53					22 23					22 53					23 23						
Garrowhill	d	21 55					22 25					22 55					23 25						
Shettleston	d	21 58					22 28					22 58					23 28						
Carntyne	d	22 00					22 30					23 00					23 30						
Springburn	d			22 09					22 39					23 09					23 39	23 39			
Barnhill	d			22 10					22 40					23 10					23 40	23 40			
Alexandra Parade	d			22 13					22 43					23 13					23 43	23 43			
Duke Street	d			22 14					22 44					23 14					23 44	23 44			
Bellgrove	d	22 03		22 16			22 33		22 46			23 03		23 16			23 33		23 46	23 46			
High Street	d	22 05		22 18			22 35		22 48			23 05		23 18			23 35		23 48	23 48			
Glasgow Queen Street 10 § ⛴	a	22 07		22 21			22 37		22 51			23 07		23 21			23 37		23 51	23 51			
	d	22 10		22 23			22 40		22 53			23 10		23 23			23 45		23 53	23 53			
Charing Cross	d	22 12		22 25			22 42		22 55			23 12		23 25			23 47		23 55	23 55			
Argyle Street	d		22 12		22 23	22 34		22 42		22 53	23 04		23 12		23 23	23 34					23 53	00 04	
Glasgow Central 15 §	a		22 16		22 26	22 37		22 46		22 56	23 07		23 16		23 26	23 37		23b43			23 56	00 07	00b15
	d		22 16		22 28	22 37		22 46		22 58	23 07		23 16		23 28	23 37					23 58	00 07	
Anderston	d		22 18		22 29	22 39		22 48		22 59	23 09		23 18		23 29	23 39					23 59	00 09	
Exhibition Centre	d		22 20		22 31	22 41		22 50		23 01	23 11		23 20		23 31	23 41					00 01	00 11	
Partick ⛴	d	22 17	22a23	22 30	22 35	22 45	22 47	22a53	23 00	23 05	23 15	23 17	23 24	23 30	23 35	23 45	23 52		23 59	23 59	00 05	00 15	
Hyndland	d	22 20		22 32	22 38	22 47	22 50		23 02	23 08	23 17	23 20	23 26	23 32	23 38	23 47	23 55		00 02	00 01	00 08	00 17	
Jordanhill	d	22 22					22 52					23 22	23 28			23 49	23 57			00 03			
Scotstounhill	d	22 24					22 54					23 24	23 30			23 51	23 59			00 05			
Garscadden	d	22 26					22 56					23 26	23a33			23a53	00 01			00a07			
Yoker	d	22 29					22 59					23 29					00 04						
Clydebank	d	22 31					23 01					23 31					00 06						
Anniesland	d			22 35	22 41	22 50			23 05	23 11	23 20			23 35	23 41				00 05		00 11	00 20	
Westerton	d			22 38	22 44	22 53			23 08	23 14	23 23			23 38	23 44				00 08		00 14	00 23	
Bearsden	d				22 46					23 16					23 46						00 16		
Hillfoot	d				22 48					23 18					23 48						00 18		
Milngavie	a				22 52					23 22					23 52						00 22		
Drumchapel	d			22 40		22 55			23 10		23 25			23 40					00 10			00 25	
Drumry	d			22 42		22 57			23 12		23 27			23 42					00 12			00 27	
Singer	d			22 45		23 00			23 15		23 30			23 45					00 15			00 30	
Dalmuir	a	22 34		22 47		23 02	23 04		23 17		23 33	23 34		23 47			00 09		00 17			00 32	
	d	22 35		22 48			23 05		23 18			23 35		23 48			00 10		00 18				
Kilpatrick	d			22 51					23 21					23 51					00 21				
Bowling	d			22 54					23 24					23 54					00 24				
Dumbarton East	d	22 42		22 58			23 12		23 28			23 42		23 58			00 17		00 28				
Dumbarton Central	d	22 44		23 00			23 14		23 30			23 44		23 59			00 19		00 30				
Dalreoch	d	22 46		23 02			23 16		23 32			23 46		00 02			00 21		00 32				
Renton	d			23 05					23 35					00 05					00 35				
Alexandria	d			23 07					23 37					00 07					00 37				
Balloch	a			23 10					23 40					00 10					00 40				
Cardross	d	22 51					23 21					23 51					00 26						
Craigendoran	d	22 56					23 26					23 56					00 31						
Helensburgh Central	a	22 59					23 29					23 59					00 34						

For general notes see front of timetable
For details of catering facilities see Directory of Train Operators

§ Low Level

A From Edinburgh (Table 225)
b Glasgow Central High Level

Table 226

Sundays

until 23 November

Lanark, Coatbridge, Motherwell, Larkhall, Hamilton, Drumgelloch, Airdrie and Springburn → Glasgow → Milngavie, Dalmuir, Balloch and Helensburgh

Network Diagram - see first page of Table 220

		SR	SR	SR	SR	SR	SR	SR	SR	SR ◇ A	SR	SR	SR	SR	SR	SR	SR	SR	SR	SR	SR	SR	SR
Lanark	d																			10 12			
Carluke	d																			10 22			
Wishaw	d																			10 27			
Holytown	d																						
Shieldmuir	d																			10 31			
Coatbridge Central	d																						
Whifflet	d																						
Motherwell	a																			10 35			
	d					08 36	08 40		09 10				09 36	09 40		10 06	10 10			10 36	10 40		11 06
Bellshill	d					08 42							09 42			10 12				10 42			11 12
Uddingston	d					08 46							09 46			10 16				10 46			11 16
Airbles	d						08 42		09 12					09 42			10 12				10 42		
Larkhall	d											09 25							10 25				
Merryton	d											09 27							10 27				
Chatelherault	d											09 30							10 30				
Hamilton Central	d						08 47		09 17			09 33		09 47			10 17		10 33		10 47		
Hamilton West	d						08 50		09 20			09 36		09 50			10 20		10 36		10 50		
Blantyre	d						08 53		09 23			09 39		09 53			10 23		10 39		10 53		
Newton	d						08 57		09 27					09 57			10 27				10 57		
Cambuslang	d					08 51	09 01		09 31				09 51	10 01		10 21	10 31			10 51	11 01		11 21
Rutherglen	d					08 54	09 04		09 34			09 49	09 54	10 04		10 24	10 34		10 49	10 54	11 04		11 24
Dalmarnock	d																						
Bridgeton	d					08 57	09 07		09 37				09 57	10 07		10 27	10 37			10 57	11 07		11 27
Drumgelloch	d		07 54		08 24			08 54			09 24				09 54			10 24				10 54	
Airdrie	a		07 57		08 27			08 57			09 27				09 57			10 27				10 57	
	d		07 58		08 28			08 58			09 28				09 58			10 28				10 58	
Coatdyke	d		08 00		08 30			09 00			09 30				10 00			10 30				11 00	
Coatbridge Sunnyside	d		08 02		08 32			09 02			09 32				10 02			10 32				11 02	
Blairhill	d		08 05		08 35			09 05			09 35				10 05			10 35				11 05	
Easterhouse	d		08 09		08 39			09 09			09 39				10 09			10 39				11 09	
Garrowhill	d		08 11		08 41			09 11			09 41				10 11			10 41				11 11	
Shettleston	d		08 14		08 44			09 14			09 44				10 14			10 44				11 14	
Carntyne	d		08 16		08 46			09 16			09 46				10 16			10 46				11 16	
Springburn	d																						
Barnhill	d																						
Alexandra Parade	d																						
Duke Street	d																						
Bellgrove	d		08 19		08 49			09 19			09 49				10 19			10 49				11 19	
High Street	d		08 21		08 51			09 21			09 51				10 21			10 51				11 21	
Glasgow Queen Street 10 §	a		08 23		08 53			09 23			09 53				10 23			10 53				11 23	
	d		08 24		08 54			09 24		09b55	09 54				10 24			10 54				11 24	
Charing Cross	d		08 27		08 57			09 27			09 57				10 27			10 57				11 27	
Argyle Street	d												10 01	10 11		10 31	10 41		10 54	11 01	11 11		11 31
Glasgow Central 15 §	a					09 04	09 14		09 44			09 57	10 04	10 14		10 34	10 44		10 57	11 04	11 14		11 34
	d					09 04	09 14		09 44			09 57	10 04	10 14		10 34	10 44		10 57	11 04	11 14		11 34
Anderston	d																						
Exhibition Centre	d					09 08	09 18		09 48			10 01	10 08	10 18		10 38	10 48		11 01	11 08	11 18		11 38
Partick	d		08 32		09 02	09 12	09 22	09 32	09 52		10 02	10a04	10 12	10 22	10 32	10 42	10 52	11 02	11a04	11 12	11 22	11 32	11 42
Hyndland	d		08 34		09 04	09 16	09 24	09 34	09 54		10 04		10 16	10 24	10 34	10 46	10 54	11 04		11 16	11 24	11 34	11 46
Jordanhill	d						09 26		09 56					10 26			10 56				11 26		
Scotstounhill	d						09 28		09 58					10 28			10 58				11 28		
Garscadden	d						09 30		10 00					10 30			11 00				11 30		
Yoker	d	08 33		09 03			09 33		10 03					10 33			11 03				11 33		
Clydebank	d	08 35		09 05			09 35		10 05					10 35			11 05				11 35		
Anniesland	d		08 37		09 07	09 19		09 37			10 07		10 19		10 37	10 49		11 07		11 19		11 37	11 49
Westerton	d		08 40		09 10	09 22		09 40			10 10		10 22		10 40	10 52		11 10		11 22		11 40	11 52
Bearsden	d					09 25							10 25			10 55				11 25			11 55
Hillfoot	d					09 27							10 27			10 57				11 27			11 57
Milngavie	a					09 30							10 30			11 00				11 30			12 00
Drumchapel	d		08 42		09 12			09 42			10 12				10 42			11 12				11 42	
Drumry	d		08 44		09 14			09 44			10 14				10 44			11 14				11 44	
Singer	d		08 47		09 17			09 47			10 17				10 47			11 17				11 47	
Dalmuir	a	08 38	08 49	09 08	09 19		09 39	09 49	10 09	10 10	10 19			10 39	10 49		11 09	11 19			11 39	11 49	
	d	08 39	08 50	09 09	09 20		09 39	09 50	10 09	10 11	10 20			10 39	10 50		11 09	11 20			11 39	11 50	
Kilpatrick	d	08 41		09 11			09 41		10 11					10 41			11 11				11 41		
Bowling	d	08 44		09 14			09 44		10 14					10 44			11 14				11 44		
Dumbarton East	d	08 49	08 58	09 19	09 28		09 49	09 58	10 19		10 28			10 49	10 58		11 19	11 28			11 49	11 58	
Dumbarton Central	d	08 51	09 00	09 21	09 30		09 51	10 00	10 21	10 22	10 30			10 51	11 00		11 21	11 30			11 51	12 00	
Dalreoch	d	08 52	09 01	09 22	09 31		09 52	10 01	10 22		10 31			10 52	11 01		11 22	11 31			11 52	12 01	
Renton	d	08 55		09 25			09 55		10 25					10 55			11 25				11 55		
Alexandria	d	08 58		09 28			09 58		10 28					10 58			11 28				11 58		
Balloch	a	09 00		09 30			10 00		10 30					11 00			11 30				12 00		
Cardross	d		09 06		09 36			10 06			10 36				11 06			11 36				12 06	
Craigendoran	d		09 11		09 41			10 11			10 41				11 11			11 41				12 11	
Helensburgh Central	a		09 14		09 44			10 14		10c37	10 44				11 14			11 44				12 14	

For general notes see front of timetable
For details of catering facilities see Directory of Train Operators

§ Low Level

A Until 28 September. To Oban (Table 227)

b Glasgow Queen Street High Level

c Helensburgh Upper

Table 226

Sundays

until 23 November

Lanark, Coatbridge, Motherwell, Larkhall, Hamilton, Drumgelloch, Airdrie and Springburn → Glasgow → Milngavie, Dalmuir, Balloch and Helensburgh

Network Diagram - see first page of Table 220

Station		SR	SR	SR	SR	SR ◇ A	SR	SR	SR	SR	SR	SR	SR	SR	SR	SR	SR	SR	SR	SR	SR	SR	SR
Lanark	d				11 12							12 12							13 12				
Carluke	d				11 22							12 22							13 22				
Wishaw	d				11 27							12 27							13 27				
Holytown	d																						
Shieldmuir	d				11 31							12 31							13 31				
Coatbridge Central	d																						
Whifflet	d																						
Motherwell	a				11 35							12 35							13 35				
	d	11 10			11 36		11 40		12 10			12 36	12 40		13 06	13 10			13 36	13 40		14 06	14 10
Bellshill	d				11 42							12 42			13 12				13 42			14 12	
Uddingston	d				11 46							12 46			13 16				13 46			14 16	
Airbles	d	11 12					11 42		12 12				12 42			13 12				13 42			14 12
Larkhall	d			11 25							12 25							13 25					
Merryton	d			11 27							12 27							13 27					
Chatelherault	d			11 30							12 30							13 30					
Hamilton Central	d	11 17		11 33			11 47		12 17		12 33		12 47			13 17		13 33		13 47			14 17
Hamilton West	d	11 20		11 36			11 50		12 20		12 36		12 50			13 20		13 36		13 50			14 20
Blantyre	d	11 23		11 39			11 53		12 23		12 39		12 53			13 23		13 39		13 53			14 23
Newton	d	11 27					11 57		12 27				12 57			13 27				13 57			14 27
Cambuslang	d	11 31			11 51		12 01		12 31			12 51	13 01		13 21	13 31			13 51	14 01		14 21	14 31
Rutherglen	d	11 34		11 49	11 54		12 04		12 34		12 49	12 54	13 04		13 24	13 34		13 49	13 54	14 04		14 24	14 34
Dalmarnock	d																						
Bridgeton	d	11 37			11 57		12 07		12 37			12 57	13 07		13 27	13 37			13 57	14 07		14 27	14 37
Drumgelloch	d		11 24					11 54		12 24				12 54			13 24				13 54		
Airdrie	a		11 27					11 57		12 27				12 57			13 27				13 57		
	d		11 28					11 58		12 28				12 58			13 28				13 58		
Coatdyke	d		11 30					12 00		12 30				13 00			13 30				14 00		
Coatbridge Sunnyside	d		11 32					12 02		12 32				13 02			13 32				14 02		
Blairhill	d		11 35					12 05		12 35				13 05			13 35				14 05		
Easterhouse	d		11 39					12 09		12 39				13 09			13 39				14 09		
Garrowhill	d		11 41					12 11		12 41				13 11			13 41				14 11		
Shettleston	d		11 44					12 14		12 44				13 14			13 44				14 14		
Carntyne	d		11 46					12 16		12 46				13 16			13 46				14 16		
Springburn	d																						
Barnhill	d																						
Alexandra Parade	d																						
Duke Street	d																						
Bellgrove	d		11 49					12 19		12 49				13 19			13 49				14 19		
High Street	d		11 51					12 21		12 51				13 21			13 51				14 21		
Glasgow Queen Street 10 §	a		11 53					12 23		12 53				13 23			13 53				14 23		
	d		11 54			12b20		12 24		12 54				13 24			13 54				14 24		
Charing Cross	d		11 57					12 27		12 57				13 27			13 57				14 27		
Argyle Street	d	11 41		11 54	12 01		12 11		12 41		12 54	13 01	13 11		13 31	13 41		13 54	14 01	14 11		14 31	14 41
Glasgow Central 15 §	a	11 44		11 57	12 04		12 14		12 44		12 57	13 04	13 14		13 34	13 44		13 57	14 04	14 14		14 34	14 44
	d	11 44		11 57	12 04		12 14		12 44		12 57	13 04	13 14		13 34	13 44		13 57	14 04	14 14		14 34	14 44
Anderston	d																						
Exhibition Centre	d	11 48		12 01	12 08		12 18		12 48		13 01	13 08	13 18		13 38	13 48		14 01	14 08	14 18		14 38	14 48
Partick	d	11 52	12 02	12a04	12 12		12 22	12 32	12 52	13 02	13a04	13 12	13 22	13 32	13 42	13 52	14 02	14a04	14 12	14 22	14 32	14 42	14 52
Hyndland	d	11 54	12 04		12 16		12 24	12 34	12 54	13 04		13 16	13 24	13 34	13 46	13 54	14 04		14 16	14 24	14 34	14 46	14 54
Jordanhill	d	11 56					12 26		12 56				13 26			13 56				14 26			14 56
Scotstounhill	d	11 58					12 28		12 58				13 28			13 58				14 28			14 58
Garscadden	d	12 00					12 30		13 00				13 30			14 00				14 30			15 00
Yoker	d	12 03					12 33		13 03				13 33			14 03				14 33			15 03
Clydebank	d	12 05					12 35		13 05				13 35			14 05				14 35			15 05
Anniesland	d		12 07		12 19			12 37		13 07		13 19		13 37	13 49		14 07		14 19		14 37	14 49	
Westerton	d		12 10		12 22			12 40		13 10		13 22		13 40	13 52		14 10		14 22		14 40	14 52	
Bearsden	d				12 25							13 25			13 55				14 25			14 55	
Hillfoot	d				12 27							13 27			13 57				14 27			14 57	
Milngavie	a				12 30							13 30			14 00				14 30			15 00	
Drumchapel	d		12 12					12 42		13 12				13 42			14 12				14 42		
Drumry	d		12 14					12 44		13 14				13 44			14 14				14 44		
Singer	d		12 17					12 47		13 17				13 47			14 17				14 47		
Dalmuir	a	12 09	12 19			12 35	12 39	12 49	13 09	13 19			13 39	13 49		14 09	14 19			14 39	14 49		15 09
	d	12 09	12 20			12 35	12 39	12 50	13 09	13 20			13 39	13 50		14 09	14 20			14 39	14 50		15 09
Kilpatrick	d	12 11					12 41		13 11				13 41			14 11				14 41			15 11
Bowling	d	12 14					12 44		13 14				13 44			14 14				14 44			15 14
Dumbarton East	d	12 19	12 28				12 49	12 58	13 19	13 28			13 49	13 58		14 19	14 28			14 49	14 58		15 19
Dumbarton Central	d	12 21	12 30			12 43	12 51	13 00	13 21	13 30			13 51	14 00		14 21	14 30			14 51	15 00		15 21
Dalreoch	d	12 22	12 31				12 52	13 01	13 22	13 31			13 52	14 01		14 22	14 31			14 52	15 01		15 22
Renton	d	12 25					12 55		13 25				13 55			14 25				14 55			15 25
Alexandria	d	12 28					12 58		13 28				13 58			14 28				14 58			15 28
Balloch	a	12 30					13 00		13 30				14 00			14 30				15 00			15 30
Cardross	d		12 36					13 06		13 36				14 06			14 36				15 06		
Craigendoran	d		12 41					13 11		13 41				14 11			14 41				15 11		
Helensburgh Central	a		12 44			12c58		13 14		13 44				14 14			14 44				15 14		

For general notes see front of timetable
For details of catering facilities see Directory of Train Operators

§ Low Level

A Until 26 October. To Oban (Table 227). Until 28 September also conveys portion to Mallaig

b Glasgow Queen Street High Level

c Helensburgh Upper

Table 226

Sundays

until 23 November

Lanark, Coatbridge, Motherwell, Larkhall, Hamilton, Drumgelloch, Airdrie and Springburn → Glasgow → Milngavie, Dalmuir, Balloch and Helensburgh

Network Diagram - see first page of Table 220

		SR	SR	SR	SR	SR	SR	SR	SR	SR	SR	SR	SR	SR	SR	SR	SR	SR	SR	SR	SR	SR	SR
Lanark	d			14 12							15 12							16 12					
Carluke	d			14 22							15 22							16 22					
Wishaw	d			14 27							15 27							16 27					
Holytown	d																						
Shieldmuir	d			14 31							15 31							16 31					
Coatbridge Central	d																						
Whifflet	d																						
Motherwell	a			14 35							15 35							16 35					
	d			14 36	14 40		15 06	15 10			15 36	15 40		16 06	16 10			16 36	16 40		17 06	17 10	
Bellshill	d			14 42			15 12				15 42			16 12				16 42			17 12		
Uddingston	d			14 46			15 16				15 46			16 16				16 46			17 16		
Airbles	d				14 42			15 12				15 42			16 12				16 42			17 12	
Larkhall	d		14 25							15 25							16 25						
Merryton	d		14 27							15 27							16 27						
Chatelherault	d		14 30							15 30							16 30						
Hamilton Central	d		14 33		14 47			15 17		15 33		15 47			16 17		16 33		16 47			17 17	
Hamilton West	d		14 36		14 50			15 20		15 36		15 50			16 20		16 36		16 50			17 20	
Blantyre	d		14 39		14 53			15 23		15 39		15 53			16 23		16 39		16 53			17 23	
Newton	d				14 57			15 27				15 57			16 27				16 57			17 27	
Cambuslang	d			14 51	15 01		15 21	15 31			15 51	16 01		16 21	16 31			16 51	17 01		17 21	17 31	
Rutherglen	d		14 49	14 54	15 04		15 24	15 34		15 49	15 54	16 04		16 24	16 34		16 49	16 54	17 04		17 24	17 34	
Dalmarnock	d																						
Bridgeton	d			14 57	15 07		15 27	15 37			15 57	16 07		16 27	16 37			16 57	17 07		17 27	17 37	
Drumgelloch	d	14 24				14 54			15 24				15 54			16 24				16 54			17 24
Airdrie	a	14 27				14 57			15 27				15 57			16 27				16 57			17 27
	d	14 28				14 58			15 28				15 58			16 28				16 58			17 28
Coatdyke	d	14 30				15 00			15 30				16 00			16 30				17 00			17 30
Coatbridge Sunnyside	d	14 32				15 02			15 32				16 02			16 32				17 02			17 32
Blairhill	d	14 35				15 05			15 35				16 05			16 35				17 05			17 35
Easterhouse	d	14 39				15 09			15 39				16 09			16 39				17 09			17 39
Garrowhill	d	14 41				15 11			15 41				16 11			16 41				17 11			17 41
Shettleston	d	14 44				15 14			15 44				16 14			16 44				17 14			17 44
Carntyne	d	14 46				15 16			15 46				16 16			16 46				17 16			17 46
Springburn	d																						
Barnhill	d																						
Alexandra Parade	d																						
Duke Street	d																						
Bellgrove	d	14 49				15 19			15 49				16 19			16 49				17 19			17 49
High Street	d	14 51				15 21			15 51				16 21			16 51				17 21			17 51
Glasgow Queen Street 10 §	a	14 53				15 23			15 53				16 23			16 53				17 23			17 53
	d	14 54				15 24			15 54				16 24			16 54				17 24			17 54
Charing Cross	d	14 57				15 27			15 57				16 27			16 57				17 27			17 57
Argyle Street	d		14 54	15 01	15 11		15 31	15 41		15 54	16 01	16 11		16 31	16 41		16 54	17 01	17 11		17 31	17 41	
Glasgow Central 15 §	a		14 57	15 04	15 14		15 34	15 44		15 57	16 04	16 14		16 34	16 44		16 57	17 04	17 14		17 34	17 44	
	d		14 57	15 04	15 14		15 34	15 44		15 57	16 04	16 14		16 34	16 44		16 57	17 04	17 14		17 34	17 44	
Anderston	d																						
Exhibition Centre	d		15 01	15 08	15 18		15 38	15 48		16 01	16 08	16 18		16 38	16 48		17 01	17 08	17 18		17 38	17 48	
Partick	d	15 02	15a04	15 12	15 22	15 32	15 42	15 52	16 02	16a04	16 12	16 22	16 32	16 42	16 52	17 02	17a04	17 12	17 22	17 32	17 42	17 52	18 02
Hyndland	d	15 04		15 16	15 24	15 34	15 46	15 54	16 04		16 16	16 24	16 34	16 46	16 54	17 04		17 16	17 24	17 34	17 46	17 54	18 04
Jordanhill	d				15 26			15 56				16 26			16 56				17 26			17 56	
Scotstounhill	d				15 28			15 58				16 28			16 58				17 28			17 58	
Garscadden	d				15 30			16 00				16 30			17 00				17 30			18 00	
Yoker	d				15 33			16 03				16 33			17 03				17 33			18 03	
Clydebank	d				15 35			16 05				16 35			17 05				17 35			18 05	
Anniesland	d	15 07		15 19		15 37	15 49		16 07		16 19		16 37	16 49		17 07		17 19		17 37	17 49		18 07
Westerton	d	15 10		15 22		15 40	15 52		16 10		16 22		16 40	16 52		17 10		17 22		17 40	17 52		18 10
Bearsden	d			15 25			15 55				16 25			16 55				17 25			17 55		
Hillfoot	d			15 27			15 57				16 27			16 57				17 27			17 57		
Milngavie	a			15 30			16 00				16 30			17 00				17 30			18 00		
Drumchapel	d	15 12				15 42			16 12				16 42			17 12				17 42			18 12
Drumry	d	15 14				15 44			16 14				16 44			17 14				17 44			18 14
Singer	d	15 17				15 47			16 17				16 47			17 17				17 47			18 17
Dalmuir	a	15 19			15 39	15 49		16 09	16 19			16 39	16 49		17 09	17 19			17 39	17 49		18 09	18 19
	d	15 20			15 39	15 50		16 09	16 20			16 39	16 50		17 09	17 20			17 39	17 50		18 09	18 20
Kilpatrick	d				15 41			16 11				16 41			17 11				17 41			18 11	
Bowling	d				15 44			16 14				16 44			17 14				17 44			18 14	
Dumbarton East	d	15 28			15 49	15 58		16 19	16 28			16 49	16 58		17 19	17 28			17 49	17 58		18 19	18 28
Dumbarton Central	d	15 30			15 51	16 00		16 21	16 30			16 51	17 00		17 21	17 30			17 51	18 00		18 21	18 30
Dalreoch	d	15 31			15 52	16 01		16 22	16 31			16 52	17 01		17 22	17 31			17 52	18 01		18 22	18 31
Renton	d				15 55			16 25				16 55			17 25				17 55			18 25	
Alexandria	d				15 58			16 28				16 58			17 28				17 58			18 28	
Balloch	a				16 00			16 30				17 00			17 30				18 00			18 30	
Cardross	d	15 36				16 06			16 36				17 06			17 36				18 06			18 36
Craigendoran	d	15 41				16 11			16 41				17 11			17 41				18 11			18 41
Helensburgh Central	a	15 44				16 14			16 44				17 14			17 44				18 14			18 44

For general notes see front of timetable
For details of catering facilities see Directory of Train Operators

§ Low Level

Table 226

Sundays

until 23 November

Lanark, Coatbridge, Motherwell, Larkhall, Hamilton, Drumgelloch, Airdrie and Springburn → Glasgow → Milngavie, Dalmuir, Balloch and Helensburgh

Network Diagram - see first page of Table 220

Station		SR	SR	SR ◇ A	SR	SR	SR	SR	SR	SR	SR	SR	SR	SR	SR	SR	SR	SR	SR	SR	SR	SR	SR
Lanark	d		17 12								18 12							19 12					
Carluke	d		17 22								18 22							19 22					
Wishaw	d		17 27								18 27							19 27					
Holytown	d																						
Shieldmuir	d		17 31								18 31							19 31					
Coatbridge Central	d																						
Whifflet	d																						
Motherwell	a		17 35								18 35							19 35					
	d		17 36		17 40		18 06	18 10			18 36	18 40		19 06	19 10			19 36	19 40		20 06	20 10	
Bellshill	d		17 42				18 12				18 42			19 12				19 42			20 12		
Uddingston	d		17 46				18 16				18 46			19 16				19 46			20 16		
Airbles	d				17 42			18 12				18 42			19 12				19 42			20 12	
Larkhall	d	17 25								18 25							19 25						
Merryton	d	17 27								18 27							19 27						
Chatelherault	d	17 30								18 30							19 30						
Hamilton Central	d	17 33			17 47			18 17		18 33		18 47			19 17		19 33		19 47			20 17	
Hamilton West	d	17 36			17 50			18 20		18 36		18 50			19 20		19 36		19 50			20 20	
Blantyre	d	17 39			17 53			18 23		18 39		18 53			19 23		19 39		19 53			20 23	
Newton	d				17 57			18 27				18 57			19 27				19 57			20 27	
Cambuslang	d		17 51		18 01		18 21	18 31			18 51	19 01		19 21	19 31			19 51	20 01		20 21	20 31	
Rutherglen	d	17 49	17 54		18 04		18 24	18 34		18 49	18 54	19 04		19 24	19 34		19 49	19 54	20 04		20 24	20 34	
Dalmarnock	d																						
Bridgeton	d		17 57		18 07		18 27	18 37			18 57	19 07		19 27	19 37			19 57	20 07		20 27	20 37	
Drumgelloch	d					17 54			18 24				18 54			19 24				19 54			20 24
Airdrie	a					17 57			18 27				18 57			19 27				19 57			20 27
	d					17 58			18 28				18 58			19 28				19 58			20 28
Coatdyke	d					18 00			18 30				19 00			19 30				20 00			20 30
Coatbridge Sunnyside	d					18 02			18 32				19 02			19 32				20 02			20 32
Blairhill	d					18 05			18 35				19 05			19 35				20 05			20 35
Easterhouse	d					18 09			18 39				19 09			19 39				20 09			20 39
Garrowhill	d					18 11			18 41				19 11			19 41				20 11			20 41
Shettleston	d					18 14			18 44				19 14			19 44				20 14			20 44
Carntyne	d					18 16			18 46				19 16			19 46				20 16			20 46
Springburn	d																						
Barnhill	d																						
Alexandra Parade	d																						
Duke Street	d																						
Bellgrove	d					18 19			18 49				19 19			19 49				20 19			20 49
High Street	d					18 21			18 51				19 21			19 51				20 21			20 51
Glasgow Queen Street 10 §	a					18 23			18 53				19 23			19 53				20 23			20 53
	d			18b20		18 24			18 54				19 24			19 54				20 24			20 54
Charing Cross	d					18 27			18 57				19 27			19 57				20 27			20 57
Argyle Street	d	17 54	18 01		18 11																		
Glasgow Central 15 §	a	17 57	18 04		18 14		18 34	18 44		18 57	19 04	19 14		19 34	19 44		19 57	20 04	20 14		20 34	20 44	
	d	17 57	18 04		18 14		18 34	18 44		18 57	19 04	19 14		19 34	19 44		19 57	20 04	20 14		20 34	20 44	
Anderston	d																						
Exhibition Centre	d	18 01	18 08		18 18		18 38	18 48		19 01	19 08	19 18		19 38	19 48		20 01	20 08	20 18		20 38	20 48	
Partick	d	18a04	18 12		18 22	18 32	18 42	18 52	19 02	19a04	19 12	19 22	19 32	19 42	19 52	20 02	20a04	20 12	20 22	20 32	20 42	20 52	21 02
Hyndland	d		18 16		18 24	18 34	18 46	18 54	19 04		19 16	19 24	19 34	19 46	19 54	20 04		20 16	20 24	20 34	20 46	20 54	21 04
Jordanhill	d				18 26			18 56				19 26			19 56				20 26			20 56	
Scotstounhill	d				18 28			18 58				19 28			19 58				20 28			20 58	
Garscadden	d				18 30			19 00				19 30			20 00				20 30			21 00	
Yoker	d				18 33			19 03				19 33			20 03				20 33			21 03	
Clydebank	d				18 35			19 05				19 35			20 05				20 35			21 05	
Anniesland	d		18 19			18 37	18 49		19 07		19 19		19 37	19 49		20 07		20 19		20 37	20 49		21 07
Westerton	d		18 22			18 40	18 52		19 10		19 22		19 40	19 52		20 10		20 22		20 40	20 52		21 10
Bearsden	d		18 25				18 55				19 25			19 55				20 25			20 55		
Hillfoot	d		18 27				18 57				19 27			19 57				20 27			20 57		
Milngavie	a		18 30				19 00				19 30			20 00				20 30			21 00		
Drumchapel	d					18 42			19 12				19 42			20 12				20 42			21 12
Drumry	d					18 44			19 14				19 44			20 14				20 44			21 14
Singer	d					18 47			19 17				19 47			20 17				20 47			21 17
Dalmuir	a			18 35	18 39	18 49		19 09	19 19			19 39	19 49		20 09	20 19			20 39	20 49		21 09	21 19
	d			18 35	18 39	18 50		19 09	19 20			19 39	19 50		20 09	20 20			20 39	20 50		21 09	21 20
Kilpatrick	d				18 41			19 11				19 41			20 11				20 41			21 11	
Bowling	d				18 44			19 14				19 44			20 14				20 44			21 14	
Dumbarton East	d				18 49	18 58		19 19	19 28			19 49	19 58		20 19	20 28			20 49	20 58		21 19	21 28
Dumbarton Central	d			18c44	18 51	19 00		19 21	19 30			19 51	20 00		20 21	20 30			20 51	21 00		21 21	21 30
Dalreoch	d				18 52	19 01		19 22	19 31			19 52	20 01		20 22	20 31			20 52	21 01		21 22	21 31
Renton	d				18 55			19 25				19 55			20 25				20 55			21 25	
Alexandria	d				18 58			19 28				19 58			20 28				20 58			21 28	
Balloch	a				19 00			19 30				20 00			20 30				21 00			21 30	
Cardross	d					19 06			19 36				20 06			20 36				21 06			21 36
Craigendoran	d					19 11			19 41				20 11			20 41				21 11			21 41
Helensburgh Central	a			19e00		19 14			19 44				20 14			20 44				21 14			21 44

For general notes see front of timetable
For details of catering facilities see Directory of Train Operators

§ Low Level

A To Oban and to Mallaig (Table 227)
b Glasgow Queen Street High Level
c Arr. 1840
e Helensburgh Upper

Table 226

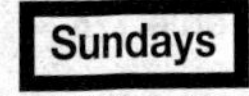

Sundays

until 23 November

Lanark, Coatbridge, Motherwell, Larkhall, Hamilton, Drumgelloch, Airdrie and Springburn → Glasgow → Milngavie, Dalmuir, Balloch and Helensburgh

Network Diagram - see first page of Table 220

		SR	SR	SR	SR	SR	SR	SR	SR	SR	SR	SR	SR	SR	SR	SR	SR	SR	SR	SR	SR	SR
Lanark	d		20 12							21 12							22 12					
Carluke	d		20 22							21 22							22 22					
Wishaw	d		20 27							21 27							22 27					
Holytown	d																					
Shieldmuir	d		20 31							21 31							22 31					
Coatbridge Central	d																					
Whifflet	d																					
Motherwell	a		20 35							21 35							22 35					
	d		20 36	20 40		21 06	21 10			21 36	21 40		22 06	22 10			22 36	22 40		23 06	23 10	
Bellshill	d		20 42			21 12				21 42			22 12				22 42			23 12		
Uddingston	d		20 46			21 16				21 46			22 16				22 46			23 16		
Airbles	d			20 42			21 12				21 42			22 12				22 42			23 12	
Larkhall	d	20 25							21 25							22 25						
Merryton	d	20 27							21 27							22 27						
Chatelherault	d	20 30							21 30							22 30						
Hamilton Central	d	20 33		20 47			21 17		21 33		21 47			22 17		22 33		22 47			23 17	
Hamilton West	d	20 36		20 50			21 20		21 36		21 50			22 20		22 36		22 50			23 20	
Blantyre	d	20 39		20 53			21 23		21 39		21 53			22 23		22 39		22 53			23 23	
Newton	d			20 57			21 27				21 57			22 27				22 57			23 27	
Cambuslang	d		20 51	21 01		21 21	21 31			21 51	22 01		22 21	22 31			22 51	23 01		23 21	23 31	
Rutherglen	d	20 49	20 54	21 04		21 24	21 34		21 49	21 54	22 04		22 24	22 34		22 49	22 54	23 04		23 24	23 34	
Dalmarnock	d																					
Bridgeton	d		20 57	21 07		21 27	21 37			21 57	22 07		22 27	22 37			22 57	23 07		23 27	23 37	
Drumgelloch	d				20 54			21 24				21 54			22 24				22 54			23 24
Airdrie	a				20 57			21 27				21 57			22 27				22 57			23 27
	d				20 58			21 28				21 58			22 28				22 58			23 28
Coatdyke	d				21 00			21 30				22 00			22 30				23 00			23 30
Coatbridge Sunnyside	d				21 02			21 32				22 02			22 32				23 02			23 32
Blairhill	d				21 05			21 35				22 05			22 35				23 05			23 35
Easterhouse	d				21 09			21 39				22 09			22 39				23 09			23 39
Garrowhill	d				21 11			21 41				22 11			22 41				23 11			23 41
Shettleston	d				21 14			21 44				22 14			22 44				23 14			23 44
Carntyne	d				21 16			21 46				22 16			22 46				23 16			23 46
Springburn	d																					
Barnhill	d																					
Alexandra Parade	d																					
Duke Street	d																					
Bellgrove	d				21 19			21 49				22 19			22 49				23 19			23 49
High Street	d				21 21			21 51				22 21			22 51				23 21			23 51
Glasgow Queen Street 10 §	a				21 23			21 53				22 23			22 53				23 23			23 53
	d				21 24			21 54				22 24			22 54				23 24			23 54
Charing Cross	d				21 27			21 57				22 27			22 57				23 27			23 57
Argyle Street	d																					
Glasgow Central 15 §	a	20 57	21 04	21 14		21 34	21 44		21 57	22 04	22 14		22 34	22 44		22 57	23 04	23 14		23 34	23 44	
	d	20 57	21 04	21 14		21 34	21 44		21 57	22 04	22 14		22 34	22 44		22 57	23 04	23 14		23 34	23 44	
Anderston	d																					
Exhibition Centre	d	21 01	21 08	21 18		21 38	21 48		22 01	22 08	22 18		22 38	22 48		23 01	23 08	23 18		23 38	23 48	
Partick	d	21a04	21 12	21 22	21 32	21 42	21 52	22 02	22a04	22 12	22 22	22 32	22 42	22 52	23 02	23a04	23 12	23 22	23 32	23 42	23 52	00 02
Hyndland	d		21 16	21 24	21 34	21 46	21 54	22 04		22 16	22 24	22 34	22 46	22 54	23 04		23 16	23 24	23 34	23 44	23 54	00 04
Jordanhill	d			21 26			21 56				22 26			22 56				23 26		23 46	23 56	00 06
Scotstounhill	d			21 28			21 58				22 28			22 58				23 28		23 48	23 58	00 08
Garscadden	d			21 30			22 00				22 30			23 00				23 30		23a50	00a01	00a10
Yoker	d			21 33			22 03				22 33			23 03				23 33				
Clydebank	d			21 35			22 05				22 35			23 05				23 35				
Anniesland	d		21 19		21 37	21 49		22 07		22 19		22 37	22 49		23 07		23 19		23 37			
Westerton	d		21 22		21 40	21 52		22 10		22 22		22 40	22 52		23 10		23 22		23 40			
Bearsden	d		21 25			21 55				22 25			22 55				23 25					
Hillfoot	d		21 27			21 57				22 27			22 57				23 27					
Milngavie	a		21 30			22 00				22 30			23 00				23 30					
Drumchapel	d				21 42			22 12				22 42			23 12				23 42			
Drumry	d				21 44			22 14				22 44			23 14				23 44			
Singer	d				21 47			22 17				22 47			23 17				23 47			
Dalmuir	a			21 39	21 49		22 09	22 19			22 39	22 49		23 09	23 19			23 39	23 49			
	d			21 39	21 50		22 09	22 20			22 39	22 50		23 09	23 20			23 39	23 50			
Kilpatrick	d			21 41			22 11				22 41			23 11				23 41				
Bowling	d			21 44			22 14				22 44			23 14				23 44				
Dumbarton East	d			21 49	21 58		22 19	22 28			22 49	22 58		23 19	23 28			23 49	23 58			
Dumbarton Central	d			21 51	22 00		22 21	22 30			22 51	23 00		23 21	23 30			23 51	23 59			
Dalreoch	d			21 52	22 01		22 22	22 31			22 52	23 01		23 22	23 31			23 52	00 01			
Renton	d			21 55			22 25				22 55			23 25				23 55				
Alexandria	d			21 58			22 28				22 58			23 28				23 58				
Balloch	a			22 00			22 30				23 00			23 30				00 01				
Cardross	d				22 06			22 36				23 06			23 36				00 06			
Craigendoran	d				22 11			22 41				23 11			23 41				00 11			
Helensburgh Central	a				22 14			22 44				23 14			23 44				00 14			

For general notes see front of timetable
For details of catering facilities see Directory of Train Operators

§ Low Level

Table 226

Sundays

from 30 November

Lanark, Coatbridge, Motherwell, Larkhall, Hamilton, Drumgelloch, Airdrie and Springburn → Glasgow → Milngavie, Dalmuir, Balloch and Helensburgh

Network Diagram - see first page of Table 220

		SR	SR	SR	SR	SR	SR	SR	SR	SR	SR	SR	SR	SR	SR	SR	SR	SR	SR	SR	SR	SR
Lanark	d																					
Carluke	d																					
Wishaw	d																					
Holytown	d																					
Shieldmuir	d																					
Coatbridge Central	d																					
Whifflet	d																					
Motherwell	a																					
	d					08 36	08 40				09 10				09 36		09 40			10 06		10 10
Bellshill	d					08 42									09 42					10 12		
Uddingston	d					08 46									09 46					10 16		
Airbles	d						08 42				09 12						09 42					10 12
Larkhall	d												09 25									
Merryton	d												09 27									
Chatelherault	d												09 30									
Hamilton Central	d						08 47				09 17		09 33				09 47					10 17
Hamilton West	d						08 50				09 20		09 36				09 50					10 20
Blantyre	d						08 53				09 23		09 39				09 53					10 23
Newton	d						08 57				09 27						09 57					10 27
Cambuslang	d					08 51	09 01				09 31				09 51		10 01			10 21		10 31
Rutherglen	d					08 54	09 04				09 34		09 49		09 54		10 04			10 24		10 34
Dalmarnock	d																					
Bridgeton	d					08 57	09 07				09 37				09 57		10 07			10 27		10 37
Drumgelloch	d		07 54		08 24			08 54				09 24						09 54				
Airdrie	a		07 57		08 27			08 57				09 27						09 57				
	d		07 58		08 28			08 58		09 13		09 28				09 43		09 58			10 13	
Coatdyke	d		08 00		08 30			09 00		09 15		09 30				09 45		10 00			10 15	
Coatbridge Sunnyside	d		08 02		08 32			09 02		09 17		09 32				09 47		10 02			10 17	
Blairhill	d		08 05		08 35			09 05		09 20		09 35				09 50		10 05			10 20	
Easterhouse	d		08 09		08 39			09 09		09 24		09 39				09 54		10 09			10 24	
Garrowhill	d		08 11		08 41			09 11		09 26		09 41				09 56		10 11			10 26	
Shettleston	d		08 14		08 44			09 14		09 29		09 44				09 59		10 14			10 29	
Carntyne	d		08 16		08 46			09 16		09 31		09 46				10 01		10 16			10 31	
Springburn	d								09 19					09 49					10 19			
Barnhill	d								09 20					09 50					10 20			
Alexandra Parade	d								09 23					09 53					10 23			
Duke Street	d								09 25					09 55					10 25			
Bellgrove	d		08 19		08 49			09 19	09 27	09 34		09 49		09 57		10 04		10 19	10 27		10 34	
High Street	d		08 21		08 51			09 21	09 29	09 36		09 51		09 59		10 06		10 21	10 29		10 36	
Glasgow Queen Street 10 §	a		08 23		08 53			09 23	09 31	09 39		09 53		10 01		10 09		10 23	10 31		10 39	
	d		08 24		08 54			09 24	09 31	09 39		09 54		10 01		10 09		10 24	10 31		10 39	
Charing Cross	d		08 27		08 57			09 27	09 33	09 42		09 57		10 03		10 12		10 27	10 33		10 42	
Argyle Street	d														10 01		10 11			10 31		10 41
Glasgow Central 15 §	a					09 04	09 14				09 44		09 57		10 04		10 14			10 34		10 44
	d					09 04	09 14				09 44		09 57		10 04		10 14			10 34		10 44
Anderston	d																					
Exhibition Centre	d					09 08	09 18				09 48		10 01		10 08		10 18			10 38		10 48
Partick	d		08 32		09 02	09 12	09 22	09 32	09 37	09 47	09 52	10 02	10a04	10 07	10 12	10 17	10 22	10 32	10 37	10 42	10 47	10 52
Hyndland	d		08 34		09 04	09 16	09 24	09 34	09 39	09 49	09 54	10 04		10 09	10 16	10 19	10 24	10 34	10 39	10 46	10 49	10 54
Jordanhill	d						09 26		09 41		09 56			10 11			10 26		10 41			10 56
Scotstounhill	d						09 28		09 43		09 58			10 13			10 28		10 43			10 58
Garscadden	d						09 30		09 46		10 00			10 16			10 30		10 46			11 00
Yoker	d	08 33		09 03			09 33		09 48		10 03			10 18			10 33		10 48			11 03
Clydebank	d	08 35		09 05			09 35		09 50		10 05			10 20			10 35		10 50			11 05
Anniesland	d		08 37		09 07	09 19		09 37		09 52		10 07			10 19	10 22		10 37		10 49	10 52	
Westerton	d		08 40		09 10	09 22		09 40		09 55		10 10			10 22	10 25		10 40		10 52	10 55	
Bearsden	d					09 25									10 25					10 55		
Hillfoot	d					09 27									10 27					10 57		
Milngavie	a					09 30									10 30					11 00		
Drumchapel	d		08 42		09 12			09 42		09 57		10 12				10 27		10 42			10 57	
Drumry	d		08 44		09 14			09 44		09 59		10 14				10 29		10 44			10 59	
Singer	d		08 47		09 17			09 47		10 02		10 17				10 32		10 47			11 02	
Dalmuir	a	08 38	08 49	09 08	09 19		09 39	09 49	09 53	10 04	10 09	10 19		10 23		10 34	10 39	10 49	10 53		11 04	11 09
	d	08 39	08 50	09 09	09 20		09 39	09 50			10 09	10 20					10 39	10 50				11 09
Kilpatrick	d	08 41		09 11			09 41				10 11						10 41					11 11
Bowling	d	08 44		09 14			09 44				10 14						10 44					11 14
Dumbarton East	d	08 49	08 58	09 19	09 28		09 49	09 58			10 19	10 28					10 49	10 58				11 19
Dumbarton Central	d	08 51	09 00	09 21	09 30		09 51	10 00			10 21	10 30					10 51	11 00				11 21
Dalreoch	d	08 52	09 01	09 22	09 31		09 52	10 01			10 22	10 31					10 52	11 01				11 22
Renton	d	08 55		09 25			09 55				10 25						10 55					11 25
Alexandria	d	08 58		09 28			09 58				10 28						10 58					11 28
Balloch	a	09 00		09 30			10 00				10 30						11 00					11 30
Cardross	d		09 06		09 36			10 06				10 36						11 06				
Craigendoran	d		09 11		09 41			10 11				10 41						11 11				
Helensburgh Central	a		09 14		09 44			10 14				10 44						11 14				

For general notes see front of timetable
For details of catering facilities see Directory of Train Operators

§ Low Level

Table 226

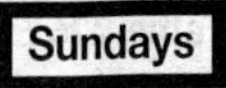

Sundays

from 30 November

Lanark, Coatbridge, Motherwell, Larkhall, Hamilton, Drumgelloch, Airdrie and Springburn → Glasgow → Milngavie, Dalmuir, Balloch and Helensburgh

Network Diagram - see first page of Table 220

		SR	SR	SR	SR	SR		SR	SR	SR	SR	SR	SR		SR	SR	SR	SR	SR	SR		SR	SR	SR	SR
Lanark	d				10 12													11 12							
Carluke	d				10 22													11 22							
Wishaw	d				10 27													11 27							
Holytown	d																								
Shieldmuir	d				10 31													11 31							
Coatbridge Central	d																								
Whifflet	d																								
Motherwell	a				10 35													11 35							
	d				10 36			10 40			11 06		11 10					11 36		11 40				12 06	
Bellshill	d				10 42						11 12							11 42						12 12	
Uddingston	d				10 46						11 16							11 46						12 16	
Airbles	d							10 42					11 12							11 42					
Larkhall	d		10 25													11 25									
Merryton	d		10 27													11 27									
Chatelherault	d		10 30													11 30									
Hamilton Central	d		10 33					10 47					11 17			11 33				11 47					
Hamilton West	d		10 36					10 50					11 20			11 36				11 50					
Blantyre	d		10 39					10 53					11 23			11 39				11 53					
Newton	d							10 57					11 27							11 57					
Cambuslang	d				10 51			11 01			11 21		11 31					11 51		12 01				12 21	
Rutherglen	d		10 49		10 54			11 04			11 24		11 34			11 49		11 54		12 04				12 24	
Dalmarnock	d																								
Bridgeton	d				10 57			11 07			11 27		11 37					11 57		12 07				12 27	
Drumgelloch	d	10 24							10 54						11 24							11 54			
Airdrie	a	10 27							10 57						11 27							11 57			
	d	10 28				10 43			10 58			11 13			11 28				11 43			11 58			12 13
Coatdyke	d	10 30				10 45			11 00			11 15			11 30				11 45			12 00			12 15
Coatbridge Sunnyside	d	10 32				10 47			11 02			11 17			11 32				11 47			12 02			12 17
Blairhill	d	10 35				10 50			11 05			11 20			11 35				11 50			12 05			12 20
Easterhouse	d	10 39				10 54			11 09			11 24			11 39				11 54			12 09			12 24
Garrowhill	d	10 41				10 56			11 11			11 26			11 41				11 56			12 11			12 26
Shettleston	d	10 44				10 59			11 14			11 29			11 44				11 59			12 14			12 29
Carntyne	d	10 46				11 01			11 16			11 31			11 46				12 01			12 16			12 31
Springburn	d			10 49						11 19							11 49						12 19		
Barnhill	d			10 50						11 20							11 50						12 20		
Alexandra Parade	d			10 53						11 23							11 53						12 23		
Duke Street	d			10 55						11 25							11 55						12 25		
Bellgrove	d	10 49		10 57		11 04			11 19	11 27		11 34			11 49		11 57		12 04			12 19	12 27		12 34
High Street	d	10 51		10 59		11 06			11 21	11 29		11 36			11 51		11 59		12 06			12 21	12 29		12 36
Glasgow Queen Street 10 §	a	10 53		11 01		11 09			11 23	11 31		11 39			11 53		12 01		12 09			12 23	12 31		12 39
	d	10 54		11 01		11 09			11 24	11 31		11 39			11 54		12 01		12 09			12 24	12 31		12 39
Charing Cross	d	10 57		11 03		11 12			11 27	11 33		11 42			11 57		12 03		12 12			12 27	12 33		12 42
Argyle Street	d		10 54		11 01			11 11			11 31		11 41			11 54		12 01		12 11				12 31	
Glasgow Central 15 §	a		10 57		11 04			11 14			11 34		11 44			11 57		12 04		12 14				12 34	
	d		10 57		11 04			11 14			11 34		11 44			11 57		12 04		12 14				12 34	
Anderston	d																								
Exhibition Centre	d		11 01		11 08			11 18			11 38		11 48			12 01		12 08		12 18				12 38	
Partick	d	11 02	11a04	11 07	11 12	11 17		11 22	11 32	11 37	11 42	11 47	11 52		12 02	12a04	12 07	12 12	12 17	12 22		12 32	12 37	12 42	12 47
Hyndland	d	11 04		11 09	11 16	11 19		11 24	11 34	11 39	11 46	11 49	11 54		12 04		12 09	12 16	12 19	12 24		12 34	12 39	12 46	12 49
Jordanhill	d			11 11				11 26		11 41			11 56				12 11			12 26			12 41		
Scotstounhill	d			11 13				11 28		11 43			11 58				12 13			12 28			12 43		
Garscadden	d			11 16				11 30		11 46			12 00				12 16			12 30			12 46		
Yoker	d			11 18				11 33		11 48			12 03				12 18			12 33			12 48		
Clydebank	d			11 20				11 35		11 50			12 05				12 20			12 35			12 50		
Anniesland	d	11 07			11 19	11 22			11 37		11 49	11 52			12 07			12 19	12 22			12 37		12 49	12 52
Westerton	d	11 10			11 22	11 25			11 40		11 52	11 55			12 10			12 22	12 25			12 40		12 52	12 55
Bearsden	d				11 25						11 55							12 25						12 55	
Hillfoot	d				11 27						11 57							12 27						12 57	
Milngavie	a				11 30						12 00							12 30						13 00	
Drumchapel	d	11 12				11 27			11 42			11 57			12 12				12 27			12 42			12 57
Drumry	d	11 14				11 29			11 44			11 59			12 14				12 29			12 44			12 59
Singer	d	11 17				11 32			11 47			12 02			12 17				12 32			12 47			13 02
Dalmuir	a	11 19		11 23		11 34		11 39	11 49	11 53		12 04	12 09		12 19		12 23		12 34	12 39		12 49	12 53		13 04
	d	11 20						11 39	11 50				12 09		12 20					12 39		12 50			
Kilpatrick	d							11 41					12 11							12 41					
Bowling	d							11 44					12 14							12 44					
Dumbarton East	d	11 28						11 49	11 58				12 19		12 28					12 49		12 58			
Dumbarton Central	d	11 30						11 51	12 00				12 21		12 30					12 51		13 00			
Dalreoch	d	11 31						11 52	12 01				12 22		12 31					12 52		13 01			
Renton	d							11 55					12 25							12 55					
Alexandria	d							11 58					12 28							12 58					
Balloch	a							12 00					12 30							13 00					
Cardross	d	11 36							12 06						12 36							13 06			
Craigendoran	d	11 41							12 11						12 41							13 11			
Helensburgh Central	a	11 44							12 14						12 44							13 14			

For general notes see front of timetable
For details of catering facilities see Directory of Train Operators

§ Low Level

Table 226

from 30 November

Lanark, Coatbridge, Motherwell, Larkhall, Hamilton, Drumgelloch, Airdrie and Springburn → Glasgow → Milngavie, Dalmuir, Balloch and Helensburgh

Network Diagram - see first page of Table 220

Station		SR	SR	SR	SR	SR	SR	SR	SR	SR	SR	SR	SR	SR	SR	SR	SR	SR	SR	SR	SR	SR
Lanark	d					12 12											13 12					
Carluke	d					12 22											13 22					
Wishaw	d					12 27											13 27					
Holytown	d																					
Shieldmuir	d					12 31											13 31					
Coatbridge Central	d																					
Whifflet	d																					
Motherwell	a					12 35											13 35					
	d	12 10				12 36		12 40			13 06		13 10				13 36		13 40			14 06
Bellshill	d					12 42					13 12						13 42					14 12
Uddingston	d					12 46					13 16						13 46					14 16
Airbles	d	12 12						12 42					13 12						13 42			
Larkhall	d			12 25											13 25							
Merryton	d			12 27											13 27							
Chatelherault	d			12 30											13 30							
Hamilton Central	d	12 17		12 33				12 47					13 17		13 33				13 47			
Hamilton West	d	12 20		12 36				12 50					13 20		13 36				13 50			
Blantyre	d	12 23		12 39				12 53					13 23		13 39				13 53			
Newton	d	12 27						12 57					13 27						13 57			
Cambuslang	d	12 31				12 51		13 01			13 21		13 31				13 51		14 01			14 21
Rutherglen	d	12 34		12 49		12 54		13 04			13 24		13 34		13 49		13 54		14 04			14 24
Dalmarnock	d																					
Bridgeton	d	12 37				12 57		13 07			13 27		13 37				13 57		14 07			14 27
Drumgelloch	d		12 24						12 54					13 24						13 54		
Airdrie	a		12 27						12 57					13 27						13 57		
	d		12 28				12 43		12 58			13 13		13 28				13 43		13 58		
Coatdyke	d		12 30				12 45		13 00			13 15		13 30				13 45		14 00		
Coatbridge Sunnyside	d		12 32				12 47		13 02			13 17		13 32				13 47		14 02		
Blairhill	d		12 35				12 50		13 05			13 20		13 35				13 50		14 05		
Easterhouse	d		12 39				12 54		13 09			13 24		13 39				13 54		14 09		
Garrowhill	d		12 41				12 56		13 11			13 26		13 41				13 56		14 11		
Shettleston	d		12 44				12 59		13 14			13 29		13 44				13 59		14 14		
Carntyne	d		12 46				13 01		13 16			13 31		13 46				14 01		14 16		
Springburn	d				12 49					13 19						13 49					14 19	
Barnhill	d				12 50					13 20						13 50					14 20	
Alexandra Parade	d				12 53					13 23						13 53					14 23	
Duke Street	d				12 55					13 25						13 55					14 25	
Bellgrove	d		12 49		12 57		13 04		13 19	13 27		13 34		13 49		13 57		14 04		14 19	14 27	
High Street	d		12 51		12 59		13 06		13 21	13 29		13 36		13 51		13 59		14 06		14 21	14 29	
Glasgow Queen Street [10] § ⛴	a		12 53		13 01		13 09		13 23	13 31		13 39		13 53		14 01		14 09		14 23	14 31	
	d		12 54		13 01		13 09		13 24	13 31		13 39		13 54		14 01		14 09		14 24	14 31	
Charing Cross	d		12 57		13 03		13 12		13 27	13 33		13 42		13 57		14 03		14 12		14 27	14 33	
Argyle Street	d			12 54		13 01		13 11			13 31		13 41		13 54		14 01		14 11			14 31
Glasgow Central [15] §	a	12 44		12 57		13 04		13 14			13 34		13 44		13 57		14 04		14 14			14 34
	d	12 44		12 57		13 04		13 14			13 34		13 44		13 57		14 04		14 14			14 34
Anderston	d																					
Exhibition Centre	d	12 48		13 01		13 08		13 18			13 38		13 48		14 01		14 08		14 18			14 38
Partick ⛴	d	12 52	13 02	13a04	13 07	13 12	13 17	13 22	13 32	13 37	13 42	13 47	13 52	14 02	14a04	14 07	14 12	14 17	14 22	14 32	14 37	14 42
Hyndland	d	12 54	13 04		13 09	13 16	13 19	13 24	13 34	13 39	13 46	13 49	13 54	14 04		14 09	14 16	14 19	14 24	14 34	14 39	14 46
Jordanhill	d	12 56			13 11			13 26		13 41			13 56			14 11			14 26		14 41	
Scotstounhill	d	12 58			13 13			13 28		13 43			13 58			14 13			14 28		14 43	
Garscadden	d	13 00			13 16			13 30		13 46			14 00			14 16			14 30		14 46	
Yoker	d	13 03			13 18			13 33		13 48			14 03			14 18			14 33		14 48	
Clydebank	d	13 05			13 20			13 35		13 50			14 05			14 20			14 35		14 50	
Anniesland	d		13 07			13 19	13 22		13 37		13 49	13 52		14 07			14 19	14 22		14 37		14 49
Westerton	d		13 10			13 22	13 25		13 40		13 52	13 55		14 10			14 22	14 25		14 40		14 52
Bearsden	d					13 25					13 55						14 25					14 55
Hillfoot	d					13 27					13 57						14 27					14 57
Milngavie	a					13 30					14 00						14 30					15 00
Drumchapel	d		13 12				13 27		13 42			13 57		14 12				14 27		14 42		
Drumry	d		13 14				13 29		13 44			13 59		14 14				14 29		14 44		
Singer	d		13 17				13 32		13 47			14 02		14 17				14 32		14 47		
Dalmuir	a	13 09	13 19		13 23		13 34	13 39	13 49	13 53		14 04	14 09	14 19		14 23		14 34	14 39	14 49	14 53	
	d	13 09	13 20					13 39	13 50				14 09	14 20					14 39	14 50		
Kilpatrick	d	13 11						13 41					14 11						14 41			
Bowling	d	13 14						13 44					14 14						14 44			
Dumbarton East	d	13 19	13 28					13 49	13 58				14 19	14 28					14 49	14 58		
Dumbarton Central	d	13 21	13 30					13 51	14 00				14 21	14 30					14 51	15 00		
Dalreoch	d	13 22	13 31					13 52	14 01				14 22	14 31					14 52	15 01		
Renton	d	13 25						13 55					14 25						14 55			
Alexandria	d	13 28						13 58					14 28						14 58			
Balloch	a	13 30						14 00					14 30						15 00			
Cardross	d		13 36						14 06					14 36						15 06		
Craigendoran	d		13 41						14 11					14 41						15 11		
Helensburgh Central	a		13 44						14 14					14 44						15 14		

For general notes see front of timetable
For details of catering facilities see
Directory of Train Operators

§ Low Level

Table 226

Sundays

from 30 November

Lanark, Coatbridge, Motherwell, Larkhall, Hamilton, Drumgelloch, Airdrie and Springburn → Glasgow → Milngavie, Dalmuir, Balloch and Helensburgh

Network Diagram - see first page of Table 220

Station		SR	SR	SR		SR	SR	SR	SR	SR	SR		SR	SR	SR	SR	SR	SR		SR	SR	SR	SR	SR	SR
Lanark	d							14 12													15 12				
Carluke	d							14 22													15 22				
Wishaw	d							14 27													15 27				
Holytown	d																								
Shieldmuir	d							14 31													15 31				
Coatbridge Central	d																								
Whifflet	d																								
Motherwell	a							14 35													15 35				
	d		14 10					14 36		14 40				15 06		15 10					15 36		15 40		
Bellshill	d							14 42						15 12							15 42				
Uddingston	d							14 46						15 16							15 46				
Airbles	d		14 12							14 42						15 12							15 42		
Larkhall	d					14 25												15 25							
Merryton	d					14 27												15 27							
Chatelherault	d					14 30												15 30							
Hamilton Central	d		14 17			14 33				14 47						15 17		15 33					15 47		
Hamilton West	d		14 20			14 36				14 50						15 20		15 36					15 50		
Blantyre	d		14 23			14 39				14 53						15 23		15 39					15 53		
Newton	d		14 27							14 57						15 27							15 57		
Cambuslang	d		14 31					14 51		15 01				15 21		15 31					15 51		16 01		
Rutherglen	d		14 34			14 49		14 54		15 04				15 24		15 34		15 49			15 54		16 04		
Dalmarnock	d																								
Bridgeton	d		14 37					14 57		15 07				15 27		15 37					15 57		16 07		
Drumgelloch	d			14 24							14 54						15 24							15 54	
Airdrie	a			14 27							14 57						15 27							15 57	
	d	14 13		14 28					14 43		14 58				15 13		15 28					15 43		15 58	
Coatdyke	d	14 15		14 30					14 45		15 00				15 15		15 30					15 45		16 00	
Coatbridge Sunnyside	d	14 17		14 32					14 47		15 02				15 17		15 32					15 47		16 02	
Blairhill	d	14 20		14 35					14 50		15 05				15 20		15 35					15 50		16 05	
Easterhouse	d	14 24		14 39					14 54		15 09				15 24		15 39					15 54		16 09	
Garrowhill	d	14 26		14 41					14 56		15 11				15 26		15 41					15 56		16 11	
Shettleston	d	14 29		14 44					14 59		15 14				15 29		15 44					15 59		16 14	
Carntyne	d	14 31		14 46					15 01		15 16				15 31		15 46					16 01		16 16	
Springburn	d						14 49						15 19							15 49					16 19
Barnhill	d						14 50						15 20							15 50					16 20
Alexandra Parade	d						14 53						15 23							15 53					16 23
Duke Street	d						14 55						15 25							15 55					16 25
Bellgrove	d	14 34		14 49			14 57		15 04		15 19		15 27		15 34		15 49			15 57		16 04		16 19	16 27
High Street	d	14 36		14 51			14 59		15 06		15 21		15 29		15 36		15 51			15 59		16 06		16 21	16 29
Glasgow Queen Street 10 §	a	14 39		14 53			15 01		15 09		15 23		15 31		15 39		15 53			16 01		16 09		16 23	16 31
	d	14 39		14 54			15 01		15 09		15 24		15 31		15 39		15 54			16 01		16 09		16 24	16 31
Charing Cross	d	14 42		14 57			15 03		15 12		15 27		15 33		15 42		15 57			16 03		16 12		16 27	16 33
Argyle Street	d		14 41			14 54		15 01		15 11				15 31		15 41		15 54			16 01		16 11		
Glasgow Central 15 §	a		14 44			14 57		15 04		15 14				15 34		15 44		15 57			16 04		16 14		
	d		14 44			14 57		15 04		15 14				15 34		15 44		15 57			16 04		16 14		
Anderston	d																								
Exhibition Centre	d		14 48			15 01		15 08		15 18				15 38		15 48		16 01			16 08		16 18		
Partick	d	14 47	14 52	15 02		15a04	15 07	15 12	15 17	15 22	15 32		15 37	15 42	15 47	15 52	16 02	16a04		16 07	16 12	16 17	16 22	16 32	16 37
Hyndland	d	14 49	14 54	15 04			15 09	15 16	15 19	15 24	15 34		15 39	15 46	15 49	15 54	16 04			16 09	16 16	16 19	16 24	16 34	16 39
Jordanhill	d		14 56				15 11			15 26			15 41			15 56				16 11			16 26		16 41
Scotstounhill	d		14 58				15 13			15 28			15 43			15 58				16 13			16 28		16 43
Garscadden	d		15 00				15 16			15 30			15 46			16 00				16 16			16 30		16 46
Yoker	d		15 03				15 18			15 33			15 48			16 03				16 18			16 33		16 48
Clydebank	d		15 05				15 20			15 35			15 50			16 05				16 20			16 35		16 50
Anniesland	d	14 52		15 07				15 19	15 22		15 37			15 49	15 52		16 07				16 19	16 22		16 37	
Westerton	d	14 55		15 10				15 22	15 25		15 40			15 52	15 55		16 10				16 22	16 25		16 40	
Bearsden	d							15 25						15 55							16 25				
Hillfoot	d							15 27						15 57							16 27				
Milngavie	a							15 30						16 00							16 30				
Drumchapel	d	14 57		15 12					15 27		15 42				15 57		16 12					16 27		16 42	
Drumry	d	14 59		15 14					15 29		15 44				15 59		16 14					16 29		16 44	
Singer	d	15 02		15 17					15 32		15 47				16 02		16 17					16 32		16 47	
Dalmuir	a	15 04	15 09	15 19			15 23		15 34	15 39	15 49		15 53		16 04	16 09	16 19			16 23		16 34	16 39	16 49	16 53
	d		15 09	15 20						15 39	15 50					16 09	16 20						16 39	16 50	
Kilpatrick	d		15 11							15 41						16 11							16 41		
Bowling	d		15 14							15 44						16 14							16 44		
Dumbarton East	d		15 19	15 28						15 49	15 58					16 19	16 28						16 49	16 58	
Dumbarton Central	d		15 21	15 30						15 51	16 00					16 21	16 30						16 51	17 00	
Dalreoch	d		15 22	15 31						15 52	16 01					16 22	16 31						16 52	17 01	
Renton	d		15 25							15 55						16 25							16 55		
Alexandria	d		15 28							15 58						16 28							16 58		
Balloch	a		15 30							16 00						16 30							17 00		
Cardross	d			15 36							16 06						16 36							17 06	
Craigendoran	d			15 41							16 11						16 41							17 11	
Helensburgh Central	a			15 44							16 14						16 44							17 14	

For general notes see front of timetable
For details of catering facilities see Directory of Train Operators

§ Low Level

Table 226

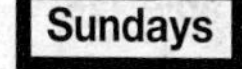

Sundays

from 30 November

Lanark, Coatbridge, Motherwell, Larkhall, Hamilton, Drumgelloch, Airdrie and Springburn → Glasgow → Milngavie, Dalmuir, Balloch and Helensburgh

Network Diagram - see first page of Table 220

		SR	SR	SR	SR	SR	SR	SR	SR	SR	SR	SR	SR	SR	SR	SR	SR	SR	SR	SR	SR ◇ A	SR
Lanark	d							16 12												17 12		
Carluke	d							16 22												17 22		
Wishaw	d							16 27												17 27		
Holytown	d																					
Shieldmuir	d							16 31												17 31		
Coatbridge Central	d																					
Whifflet	d																					
Motherwell	a							16 35												17 35		
	d	16 06		16 10				16 36		16 40			17 06		17 10					17 36		17 40
Bellshill	d	16 12						16 42					17 12							17 42		
Uddingston	d	16 16						16 46					17 16							17 46		
Airbles	d			16 12						16 42					17 12							17 42
Larkhall	d					16 25											17 25					
Merryton	d					16 27											17 27					
Chatelherault	d					16 30											17 30					
Hamilton Central	d			16 17		16 33				16 47					17 17		17 33					17 47
Hamilton West	d			16 20		16 36				16 50					17 20		17 36					17 50
Blantyre	d			16 23		16 39				16 53					17 23		17 39					17 53
Newton	d			16 27						16 57					17 27							17 57
Cambuslang	d	16 21		16 31				16 51		17 01			17 21		17 31					17 51		18 01
Rutherglen	d	16 24		16 34		16 49		16 54		17 04			17 24		17 34		17 49			17 54		18 04
Dalmarnock	d																					
Bridgeton	d	16 27		16 37				16 57		17 07			17 27		17 37					17 57		18 07
Drumgelloch	d				16 24						16 54					17 24						
Airdrie	a				16 27						16 57					17 27						
	d		16 13		16 28				16 43		16 58			17 13		17 28			17 38			
Coatdyke	d		16 15		16 30				16 45		17 00			17 15		17 30			17 40			
Coatbridge Sunnyside	d		16 17		16 32				16 47		17 02			17 17		17 32			17 42			
Blairhill	d		16 20		16 35				16 50		17 05			17 20		17 35			17 45			
Easterhouse	d		16 24		16 39				16 54		17 09			17 24		17 39			17 49			
Garrowhill	d		16 26		16 41				16 56		17 11			17 26		17 41			17 51			
Shettleston	d		16 29		16 44				16 59		17 14			17 29		17 44			17 54			
Carntyne	d		16 31		16 46				17 01		17 16			17 31		17 46			17 56			
Springburn	d						16 49					17 19						17 49				
Barnhill	d						16 50					17 20						17 50				
Alexandra Parade	d						16 53					17 23						17 53				
Duke Street	d						16 55					17 25						17 55				
Bellgrove	d		16 34		16 49		16 57		17 04		17 19	17 27		17 34		17 49		17 57	17 59			
High Street	d		16 36		16 51		16 59		17 06		17 21	17 29		17 36		17 51		17 59	18 01			
Glasgow Queen Street 10 § ⛴	a		16 39		16 53		17 01		17 09		17 23	17 31		17 39		17 53		18 01	18 04			
	d		16 39		16 54		17 01		17 09		17 24	17 31		17 39		17 54		18 01	18 04		18b20	
Charing Cross	d		16 42		16 57		17 03		17 12		17 27	17 33		17 42		17 57		18 03	18 07			
Argyle Street	d	16 31		16 41		16 54		17 01		17 11			17 31		17 41		17 54			18 01		18 11
Glasgow Central 15 §	a	16 34		16 44		16 57		17 04		17 14			17 34		17 44		17 57			18 04		18 14
	d	16 34		16 44		16 57		17 04		17 14			17 34		17 44		17 57			18 04		18 14
Anderston	d																					
Exhibition Centre	d	16 38		16 48		17 01		17 08		17 18			17 38		17 48		18 01			18 08		18 18
Partick ⛴	d	16 42	16 47	16 52	17 02	17a04	17 07	17 12	17 17	17 22	17 32	17 37	17 42	17 47	17 52	18 02	18a04	18 07	18 12	18 12		18 22
Hyndland	d	16 46	16 49	16 54	17 04		17 09	17 16	17 19	17 24	17 34	17 39	17 46	17 49	17 54	18 04		18 09	18 16	18 16		18 24
Jordanhill	d			16 56			17 11			17 26		17 41			17 56			18 11				18 26
Scotstounhill	d			16 58			17 13			17 28		17 43			17 58			18 13				18 28
Garscadden	d			17 00			17 16			17 30		17 46			18 00			18 16				18 30
Yoker	d			17 03			17 18			17 33		17 48			18 03			18 18				18 33
Clydebank	d			17 05			17 20			17 35		17 50			18 05			18 20				18 35
Anniesland	d	16 49	16 52		17 07			17 19	17 22		17 37		17 49	17 52		18 07			18 19	18 19		
Westerton	d	16 52	16 55		17 10			17 22	17 25		17 40		17 52	17 55		18 10			18 22	18 22		
Bearsden	d	16 55						17 25					17 55							18 25		
Hillfoot	d	16 57						17 27					17 57							18 27		
Milngavie	a	17 00						17 30					18 00							18 33		
Drumchapel	d		16 57		17 12				17 27		17 42			17 57		18 12			18 24			
Drumry	d		16 59		17 14				17 29		17 44			17 59		18 14			18 26			
Singer	d		17 02		17 17				17 32		17 47			18 02		18 17			18 29			
Dalmuir	a		17 04	17 09	17 19		17 23		17 34	17 39	17 49	17 53		18 04	18 09	18 19		18 23	18 31		18 35	18 39
	d			17 09	17 20					17 39	17 50				18 09	18 20					18 35	18 39
Kilpatrick	d			17 11						17 41					18 11							18 41
Bowling	d			17 14						17 44					18 14							18 44
Dumbarton East	d			17 19	17 28					17 49	17 58				18 19	18 28						18 49
Dumbarton Central	d			17 21	17 30					17 51	18 00				18 21	18 30					18c44	18 51
Dalreoch	d			17 22	17 31					17 52	18 01				18 22	18 31						18 52
Renton	d			17 25						17 55					18 25							18 55
Alexandria	d			17 28						17 58					18 28							18 58
Balloch	a			17 30						18 00					18 30							19 00
Cardross	d				17 36						18 06					18 36						
Craigendoran	d				17 41						18 11					18 41						
Helensburgh Central	a				17 44						18 14					18 44					19e00	

For general notes see front of timetable
For details of catering facilities see Directory of Train Operators

§ Low Level

A To Oban and to Mallaig (Table 227)
b Glasgow Queen Street High Level
c Arr. 1840
e Helensburgh Upper

Table 226

from 30 November

Lanark, Coatbridge, Motherwell, Larkhall, Hamilton, Drumgelloch, Airdrie and Springburn → Glasgow → Milngavie, Dalmuir, Balloch and Helensburgh

Network Diagram - see first page of Table 220

		SR		SR	SR	SR	SR	SR	SR		SR	SR	SR	SR	SR	SR		SR	SR	SR	SR	SR	SR		SR
Lanark	d							18 12								19 12									20 12
Carluke	d							18 22								19 22									20 22
Wishaw	d							18 27								19 27									20 27
Holytown	d																								
Shieldmuir	d							18 31								19 31									20 31
Coatbridge Central	d																								
Whifflet	d																								
Motherwell	a							18 35								19 35									20 35
	d			18 06	18 10			18 36	18 40			19 06	19 10			19 36		19 40		20 06	20 10				20 36
Bellshill	d			18 12				18 42				19 12				19 42				20 12					20 42
Uddingston	d			18 16				18 46				19 16				19 46				20 16					20 46
Airbles	d				18 12				18 42				19 12					19 42			20 12				
Larkhall	d						18 25								19 25								20 25		
Merryton	d						18 27								19 27								20 27		
Chatelherault	d						18 30								19 30								20 30		
Hamilton Central	d				18 17		18 33		18 47				19 17		19 33			19 47			20 17		20 33		
Hamilton West	d				18 20		18 36		18 50				19 20		19 36			19 50			20 20		20 36		
Blantyre	d				18 23		18 39		18 53				19 23		19 39			19 53			20 23		20 39		
Newton	d				18 27				18 57				19 27					19 57			20 27				
Cambuslang	d			18 21	18 31			18 51	19 01			19 21	19 31			19 51		20 01		20 21	20 31				20 51
Rutherglen	d			18 24	18 34		18 49	18 54	19 04			19 24	19 34		19 49	19 54		20 04		20 24	20 34		20 49		20 54
Dalmarnock	d																								
Bridgeton	d			18 27	18 37			18 57	19 07			19 27	19 37			19 57		20 07		20 27	20 37				20 57
Drumgelloch	d	17 54				18 24					18 54			19 24					19 54			20 24			
Airdrie	a	17 57				18 27					18 57			19 27					19 57			20 27			
	d	17 58				18 28					18 58			19 28					19 58			20 28			
Coatdyke	d	18 00				18 30					19 00			19 30					20 00			20 30			
Coatbridge Sunnyside	d	18 02				18 32					19 02			19 32					20 02			20 32			
Blairhill	d	18 05				18 35					19 05			19 35					20 05			20 35			
Easterhouse	d	18 09				18 39					19 09			19 39					20 09			20 39			
Garrowhill	d	18 11				18 41					19 11			19 41					20 11			20 41			
Shettleston	d	18 14				18 44					19 14			19 44					20 14			20 44			
Carntyne	d	18 16				18 46					19 16			19 46					20 16			20 46			
Springburn	d																								
Barnhill	d																								
Alexandra Parade	d																								
Duke Street	d																								
Bellgrove	d	18 19				18 49					19 19			19 49					20 19			20 49			
High Street	d	18 21				18 51					19 21			19 51					20 21			20 51			
Glasgow Queen Street 10 §	a	18 23				18 53					19 23			19 53					20 23			20 53			
	d	18 24				18 54					19 24			19 54					20 24			20 54			
Charing Cross	d	18 27				18 57					19 27			19 57					20 27			20 57			
Argyle Street	d																								
Glasgow Central 15 §	a			18 34	18 44		18 57	19 04	19 14			19 34	19 44		19 57	20 04		20 14		20 34	20 44		20 57		21 04
	d			18 34	18 44		18 57	19 04	19 14			19 34	19 44		19 57	20 04		20 14		20 34	20 44		20 57		21 04
Anderston	d																								
Exhibition Centre	d			18 38	18 48		19 01	19 08	19 18			19 38	19 48		20 01	20 08		20 18		20 38	20 48		21 01		21 08
Partick	d	18 32		18 42	18 52	19 02	19a04	19 12	19 22		19 32	19 42	19 52	20 02	20a04	20 12		20 22	20 32	20 42	20 52	21 02	21a04		21 12
Hyndland	d	18 34		18 46	18 54	19 04		19 16	19 24		19 34	19 46	19 54	20 04		20 16		20 24	20 34	20 46	20 54	21 04			21 16
Jordanhill	d				18 56				19 26				19 56					20 26			20 56				
Scotstounhill	d				18 58				19 28				19 58					20 28			20 58				
Garscadden	d				19 00				19 30				20 00					20 30			21 00				
Yoker	d				19 03				19 33				20 03					20 33			21 03				
Clydebank	d				19 05				19 35				20 05					20 35			21 05				
Anniesland	d	18 37		18 49		19 07		19 19			19 37	19 49		20 07		20 19			20 37	20 49		21 07			21 19
Westerton	d	18 40		18 52		19 10		19 22			19 40	19 52		20 10		20 22			20 40	20 52		21 10			21 22
Bearsden	d			18 55				19 25				19 55				20 25				20 55					21 25
Hillfoot	d			18 57				19 27				19 57				20 27				20 57					21 27
Milngavie	a			19 00				19 30				20 00				20 30				21 00					21 30
Drumchapel	d	18 42				19 12					19 42			20 12					20 42			21 12			
Drumry	d	18 44				19 14					19 44			20 14					20 44			21 14			
Singer	d	18 47				19 17					19 47			20 17					20 47			21 17			
Dalmuir	a	18 49			19 09	19 19			19 39		19 49		20 09	20 19				20 39	20 49		21 09	21 19			
	d	18 50			19 09	19 20			19 39		19 50		20 09	20 20				20 39	20 50		21 09	21 20			
Kilpatrick	d				19 11				19 41				20 11					20 41			21 11				
Bowling	d				19 14				19 44				20 14					20 44			21 14				
Dumbarton East	d	18 58			19 19	19 28			19 49		19 58		20 19	20 28				20 49	20 58		21 19	21 28			
Dumbarton Central	d	19 00			19 21	19 30			19 51		20 00		20 21	20 30				20 51	21 00		21 21	21 30			
Dalreoch	d	19 01			19 22	19 31			19 52		20 01		20 22	20 31				20 52	21 01		21 22	21 31			
Renton	d				19 25				19 55				20 25					20 55			21 25				
Alexandria	d				19 28				19 58				20 28					20 58			21 28				
Balloch	a				19 30				20 00				20 30					21 01			21 30				
Cardross	d	19 06				19 36					20 06			20 36					21 06			21 36			
Craigendoran	d	19 11				19 41					20 11			20 41					21 11			21 41			
Helensburgh Central	a	19 14				19 44					20 14			20 44					21 14			21 44			

For general notes see front of timetable
For details of catering facilities see
Directory of Train Operators

§ Low Level

Table 226

Sundays

from 30 November

Lanark, Coatbridge, Motherwell, Larkhall, Hamilton, Drumgelloch, Airdrie and Springburn → Glasgow → Milngavie, Dalmuir, Balloch and Helensburgh

Network Diagram - see first page of Table 220

		SR	SR	SR	SR	SR	SR	SR	SR	SR	SR	SR	SR	SR	SR	SR	SR	SR	SR	SR
Lanark	d							21 12							22 12					
Carluke	d							21 22							22 22					
Wishaw	d							21 27							22 27					
Holytown	d																			
Shieldmuir	d							21 31							22 31					
Coatbridge Central	d																			
Whifflet	d																			
Motherwell	a							21 35							22 35					
	d	20 40		21 06	21 10			21 36	21 40		22 06	22 10			22 36	22 40		23 06	23 10	
Bellshill	d			21 12				21 42			22 12				22 42			23 12		
Uddingston	d			21 16				21 46			22 16				22 46			23 16		
Airbles	d	20 42			21 12				21 42			22 12				22 42			23 12	
Larkhall	d						21 25							22 25						
Merryton	d						21 27							22 27						
Chatelherault	d						21 30							22 30						
Hamilton Central	d	20 47			21 17		21 33		21 47			22 17		22 33		22 47			23 17	
Hamilton West	d	20 50			21 20		21 36		21 50			22 20		22 36		22 50			23 20	
Blantyre	d	20 53			21 23		21 39		21 53			22 23		22 39		22 53			23 23	
Newton	d	20 57			21 27				21 57			22 27				22 57			23 27	
Cambuslang	d	21 01		21 21	21 31			21 51	22 01		22 21	22 31			22 51	23 01		23 21	23 31	
Rutherglen	d	21 04		21 24	21 34		21 49	21 54	22 04		22 24	22 34		22 49	22 54	23 04		23 24	23 34	
Dalmarnock	d																			
Bridgeton	d	21 07		21 27	21 37			21 57	22 07		22 27	22 37			22 57	23 07		23 27	23 37	
Drumgelloch	d		20 54			21 24				21 54			22 24				22 54			23 24
Airdrie	a		20 57			21 27				21 57			22 27				22 57			23 27
	d		20 58			21 28				21 58			22 28				22 58			23 28
Coatdyke	d		21 00			21 30				22 00			22 30				23 00			23 30
Coatbridge Sunnyside	d		21 02			21 32				22 02			22 32				23 02			23 32
Blairhill	d		21 05			21 35				22 05			22 35				23 05			23 35
Easterhouse	d		21 09			21 39				22 09			22 39				23 09			23 39
Garrowhill	d		21 11			21 41				22 11			22 41				23 11			23 41
Shettleston	d		21 14			21 44				22 14			22 44				23 14			23 44
Carntyne	d		21 16			21 46				22 16			22 46				23 16			23 46
Springburn	d																			
Barnhill	d																			
Alexandra Parade	d																			
Duke Street	d																			
Bellgrove	d		21 19			21 49				22 19			22 49				23 19			23 49
High Street	d		21 21			21 51				22 21			22 51				23 21			23 51
Glasgow Queen Street 10 §	a		21 23			21 53				22 23			22 53				23 23			23 53
	d		21 24			21 54				22 24			22 54				23 24			23 54
Charing Cross	d		21 27			21 57				22 27			22 57				23 27			23 57
Argyle Street	d																			
Glasgow Central 15 §	a	21 14		21 34	21 44		21 57	22 04	22 14		22 34	22 44		22 57	23 04	23 14		23 34	23 44	
	d	21 14		21 34	21 44		21 57	22 04	22 14		22 34	22 44		22 57	23 04	23 14		23 34	23 44	
Anderston	d																			
Exhibition Centre	d	21 18		21 38	21 48		22 01	22 08	22 18		22 38	22 48		23 01	23 08	23 18		23 38	23 48	
Partick	d	21 22	21 32	21 42	21 52	22 02	22a04	22 12	22 22	22 32	22 42	22 52	23 02	23a04	23 12	23 22	23 32	23 42	23 52	00 02
Hyndland	d	21 24	21 34	21 46	21 54	22 04		22 16	22 24	22 34	22 46	22 54	23 04		23 16	23 24	23 34	23 44	23 54	00 04
Jordanhill	d	21 26			21 56				22 26			22 56				23 26		23 46	23 56	00 06
Scotstounhill	d	21 28			21 58				22 28			22 58				23 28		23 48	23 58	00 08
Garscadden	d	21 30			22 00				22 30			23 00				23 30		23a50	00a01	00a10
Yoker	d	21 33			22 03				22 33			23 03				23 33				
Clydebank	d	21 35			22 05				22 35			23 05				23 35				
Anniesland	d		21 37	21 49		22 07		22 19		22 37	22 49		23 07		23 19		23 37			
Westerton	d		21 40	21 52		22 10		22 22		22 40	22 52		23 10		23 22		23 40			
Bearsden	d			21 55				22 25			22 55				23 25					
Hillfoot	d			21 57				22 27			22 57				23 27					
Milngavie	a			22 00				22 30			23 00				23 30					
Drumchapel	d		21 42			22 12				22 42			23 12				23 42			
Drumry	d		21 44			22 14				22 44			23 14				23 44			
Singer	d		21 47			22 17				22 47			23 17				23 47			
Dalmuir	a	21 39	21 49		22 09	22 19			22 39	22 49		23 09	23 19			23 39	23 49			
	d	21 39	21 50		22 09	22 20			22 39	22 50		23 09	23 20			23 39	23 50			
Kilpatrick	d	21 41			22 11				22 41			23 11				23 41				
Bowling	d	21 44			22 14				22 44			23 14				23 44				
Dumbarton East	d	21 49	21 58		22 19	22 28			22 49	22 58		23 19	23 28			23 49	23 58			
Dumbarton Central	d	21 51	22 00		22 21	22 30			22 51	23 00		23 21	23 30			23 51	23 59			
Dalreoch	d	21 52	22 01		22 22	22 31			22 52	23 01		23 22	23 31			23 52	00 01			
Renton	d	21 55			22 25				22 55			23 25				23 55				
Alexandria	d	21 58			22 28				22 58			23 28				23 58				
Balloch	a	22 00			22 30				23 00			23 30				00 01				
Cardross	d		22 06			22 36				23 06			23 36				00 06			
Craigendoran	d		22 11			22 41				23 11			23 41				00 11			
Helensburgh Central	a		22 14			22 44				23 14			23 44				00 14			

For general notes see front of timetable
For details of catering facilities see Directory of Train Operators

§ Low Level

Helensburgh, Balloch, Dalmuir and Milngavie → Glasgow → Springburn, Airdrie, Drumgelloch, Hamilton, Larkhall, Motherwell, Coatbridge and Lanark

Network Diagram - see first page of Table 220

Miles	Miles	Miles	Miles	Miles	Station		SR SO A	SR MX	SR	SR SX	SR SX	SR SO	SR B	SR SX	SR	SR	SR	SR SX	SR SX C	SR SO	SR SX	SR SO	SR SX	SR SO	SR
0	—	—	—	—	**Helensburgh Central**	d																			
1¼	—	—	—	—	Craigendoran	d																			
4¼	—	—	—	—	Cardross	d																			
—	0	—	—	—	**Balloch**	d																			
—	1	—	—	—	Alexandria	d																			
—	2¼	—	—	—	Renton	d																			
8	3¾	—	—	—	Dalreoch	d																			
8¼	4	—	—	—	Dumbarton Central	d																			
9	4¾	—	—	—	Dumbarton East	d																			
11¾	7½	—	—	—	Bowling	d																			
13½	9¼	—	—	—	Kilpatrick	d																			
14¾	10½	0	0	—	**Dalmuir**	a																			
—	—	—	—	—		d					05 48	05 48					06 01						06 16	06 16	06 23
15½	11¼	—	¾	—	Singer	d											06 03						06 18	06 18	
16½	12¼	—	1¾	—	Drumry	d											06 05						06 20	06 20	
17¼	13	—	2½	—	Drumchapel	d											06 08						06 23	06 23	
—	—	—	—	0	**Milngavie**	d																			
—	—	—	—	1½	Hillfoot	d																			
—	—	—	—	2¼	Bearsden	d																			
18½	14¼	—	3¾	3½	Westerton	d		00 05									06 10						06 25	06 25	
19¾	15½	—	5	4¾	Anniesland	d											06 14						06 28	06 28	
—	—	1¼	—	—	Clydebank	d					05 50	05 50													06 25
—	—	2¼	—	—	Yoker	d					05 52	05 52													06 27
—	—	3¼	—	—	Garscadden	d					05 55	05 55			06 00	06 08		06 16			06 20	06 20			06 31
—	—	3¾	—	—	Scotstounhill	d					05 57	05 57			06 02	06 10		06 18			06 22	06 22			06 33
—	—	4¾	—	—	Jordanhill	d					05 59	05 59			06 05	06 12		06 20			06 24	06 24			06 35
20¾	16½	5¼	6	5¾	Hyndland	d					06 01	06 01			06 07	06 14	06 17	06 22			06 26	06 26	06 31	06 31	06 37
21¼	17	—	6½	6¼	Partick	d					06 04	06 04			06 10	06 17	06 20	06 25			06 29	06 29	06 34	06 34	06 40
—	—	—	8¼	7½	Exhibition Centre	d									06 13		06 23				06 32	06 32			06 43
—	—	—	8½	8	Anderston	d									06 15		06 25				06 34	06 34			06 45
—	—	—	8¾	8½	**Glasgow Central** 15 §	a									06 17		06 26				06 35	06 35			06 47
—	—	—	—	—		d	00b06						06b16		06 17		06 27				06 37	06 37			06 47
—	—	—	9¼	9	Argyle Street	d									06 19		06 29				06 39	06 39			06 49
23¼	19	—	—	—	Charing Cross	d					06 08	06 08				06 22		06 29					06 38	06 38	
24	19¾	—	—	—	**Glasgow Queen Street** 10 §	a		00c19			06 10	06 10				06 24		06 31					06 40	06 40	
—	—	—	—	—		d					06 12	06 14				06 27		06 32					06 42	06 44	
24½	20¼	—	—	—	High Street	d					06 14	06 16				06 29		06 34					06 44	06 46	
25	20¾	—	—	—	Bellgrove	d					06 16	06 18				06 31		06 36					06 46	06 48	
—	21¼	—	—	—	Duke Street	d						06 20						06 38						06 50	
—	21½	—	—	—	Alexandra Parade	d						06 21						06 39						06 51	
—	22¾	—	—	—	Barnhill	d						06 24						06 42						06 54	
—	23	—	—	—	**Springburn**	a						06 26						06 44						06 56	
26¾	—	—	—	—	Carntyne	d					06 19					06 34							06 49		
27½	—	—	—	—	Shettleston	d					06 22					06 37							06 52		
28¾	—	—	—	—	Garrowhill	d					06 24					06 39							06 54		
29¾	—	—	—	—	Easterhouse	d					06 27					06 42							06 57		
32½	—	—	—	—	Blairhill	d					06 31					06 46							07 01		
33	—	—	—	—	Coatbridge Sunnyside	d					06 33					06 48							07 03		
34	—	—	—	—	Coatdyke	d					06 36					06 51							07 06		
35	—	—	—	—	**Airdrie**	a					06 39					06 53							07 09		
—	—	—	—	—		d										06 54									
36½	—	—	—	—	**Drumgelloch**	a										06 58									
—	—	—	10½	10¼	Bridgeton	d									06 22						06 42	06 42			06 52
—	—	—	11	10¾	Dalmarnock	d									06 24						06 44	06 44			06 54
—	—	—	11¾	11½	Rutherglen	d									06 26		06 34				06 46	06 46			06 56
—	—	—	13½	13¼	Cambuslang	d	00 15						06 23		06 31						06 50	06 50			07 01
—	—	0	—	14¼	Newton	d															06 54	06 54			
—	—	2½	—	—	Blantyre	d											06 44				06 58	06 58			
—	—	4½	—	—	Hamilton West	d											06 47				07 01	07 01			
0	—	5¼	—	—	**Hamilton Central**	d											06 50				07 03	07 03			
2¼	—	—	—	—	Chatelherault	d											06 54								
3¾	—	—	—	—	Merryton	d											06 58								
5¼	—	—	—	—	**Larkhall**	a											07 00								
0	—	7½	—	—	Airbles	d															07 08	07 08			
—	—	—	17	16¾	Uddingston	d	00 20						06 28		06 35										07 05
—	—	—	19½	—	Bellshill	d	00 26						06 34		06 40										07 10
—	—	8¼	22½	21	**Motherwell**	a									06 45						07 11	07 11			07 17
—	0	—	—	—		d			05 52	06 16				06 37	06 46				06 59	07 11	07 12				
—	4½	—	—	—	Whifflet	a															07 19				
—	5¼	—	—	—	**Coatbridge Central**	a															07 23				
—	—	—	—	22½	Shieldmuir	d			05 56	06 20					06 50				07 02	07 14					
—	—	—	—	21¼	Holytown	d	00a30						06a38	06 43											
—	—	—	—	24¼	Wishaw	d			05 59	06 23				06 48	06 53				07 06	07 18					
—	—	—	—	28¾	Carluke	d			06 06	06 30				06 55	07 00				07a10	07 26					
—	—	—	—	37¼	**Lanark**	a			06 16	06 42				07 07	07e13					07 36					

For general notes see front of timetable
For details of catering facilities see Directory of Train Operators

§ Low Level

A To Livingston South (Table 225)
B To Edinburgh (Table 225)
C To Carstairs (Table 225)
b Glasgow Central High Level
c Glasgow Queen Street High Level
e Saturdays arr. 1 minute earlier

Helensburgh, Balloch, Dalmuir and Milngavie → Glasgow → Springburn, Airdrie, Drumgelloch, Hamilton, Larkhall, Motherwell, Coatbridge and Lanark

Network Diagram - see first page of Table 220

		SR	SR	SR	SR SX	SR SO A	SR SX A	SR SX	SR SO	SR SX	SR SO	SR SX B	SR SO	SR SX	SR	SR	SR	SR SX	SR	SR SX	SR SO	SR SO	SR SX	SR SX	SR
Helensburgh Central	d		06 10													06 40									
Craigendoran	d		06 13													06 43									
Cardross	d		06 18													06 48									
Balloch	d									06 23	06 23									06 53	06 53				
Alexandria	d									06 25	06 25									06 55	06 55				
Renton	d									06 28	06 28									06 58	06 58				
Dalreoch	d		06 23							06 31	06 31					06 53				07 01	07 01				
Dumbarton Central	d		06 25							06 32	06 32					06 55				07 02	07 02				
Dumbarton East	d		06 27							06 34	06 34					06 57				07 04	07 04				
Bowling	d									06 39	06 39									07 09	07 09				
Kilpatrick	d									06 42	06 42									07 12	07 12				
Dalmuir	a		06 35							06 45	06 45					07 05				07 15	07 15				
	d	06 31	06 36							06 46	06 46		06 53	06 53	07 01	07 06				07 16	07 16	07 23	07 23		07 31
Singer	d	06 33		←						06 48	06 48				07 03		←			07 18	07 18				07 33
Drumry	d	06 35								06 50	06 50				07 05					07 20	07 20				07 35
Drumchapel	d	06 38		06 38						06 53	06 53				07 08		07 08			07 23	07 23				07 38
Milngavie	d	→						06 42	06 42						→				07 12					07 27	→
Hillfoot	d							06 45	06 45										07 15					07 30	
Bearsden	d							06 47	06 47										07 17					07 32	
Westerton	d			06 40				06 50	06 50	06 55	06 55						07 10		07 20	07 25	07 25			07 35	
Anniesland	d			06 44				06 53	06 53	06 58	06 58						07 14		07 23	07 28	07 28			07 38	
Clydebank	d												06 55	06 55								07 25	07 25		
Yoker	d												06 57	06 57								07 27	07 27		
Garscadden	d				06 46								07 01	07 01				07 16				07 31	07 31		
Scotstounhill	d				06 48								07 03	07 03				07 18				07 33	07 33		
Jordanhill	d				06 50								07 05	07 05				07 20				07 35	07 35		
Hyndland	d		06 44	06 47	06 52			06 56	06 56	07 01	07 01		07 07	07 07		07 14	07 17	07 22	07 26	07 31	07 31	07 37	07 37	07 41	
Partick	d		06 47	06 50	06 55			06 59	06 59	07 04	07 04		07 10	07 10		07 17	07 20	07 25	07 29	07 34	07 34	07 40	07 40	07 44	
Exhibition Centre	d			06 53				07 02	07 02				07 13	07 13			07 23		07 32			07 43	07 43		
Anderston	d			06 55				07 04	07 04				07 15	07 15			07 25		07 34			07 45	07 45		
Glasgow Central 15 §	a			06 56				07 05	07 05				07 17	07 17			07 26		07 35			07 47	07 47		
	d			06 57		07b05	07b05	07 07	07 07			07b13	07 17	07 17			07 27		07 37			07 47	07 47		
Argyle Street	d			06 59				07 09	07 09				07 19	07 19			07 29		07 39			07 49	07 49		
Charing Cross	d		06 52		06 59					07 08	07 08					07 22		07 29		07 38	07 38			07 49	
Glasgow Queen Street 10 §	a		06 54		07 01					07 10	07 10					07 24		07 31		07 40	07 40			07 51	
	d		06 57		07 02					07 12	07 14					07 27		07 32		07 42	07 44			07 51	
High Street	d		06 59		07 04					07 14	07 16					07 29		07 34		07 44	07 46			07a53	
Bellgrove	d		07 01		07 06					07 16	07 18					07 31		07 36		07 46	07 48				
Duke Street	d				07 08						07 20							07 38			07 50				
Alexandra Parade	d				07 09						07 21							07 39			07 51				
Barnhill	d				07 12						07 24							07 42			07 54				
Springburn	a				07 14						07 26							07 44			07 56				
Carntyne	d		07 04							07 19						07 34				07 49					
Shettleston	d		07 07							07 22						07 37				07 52					
Garrowhill	d		07 09							07 24						07 39				07 54					
Easterhouse	d		07 12							07 27						07 42				07 57					
Blairhill	d		07 16							07 31						07 46				08 01					
Coatbridge Sunnyside	d		07 18							07 33						07 48				08 03					
Coatdyke	d		07 21							07 36						07 51				08 06					
Airdrie	a		07 24							07 39						07 54				08 09					
	d		07 24													07 54									
Drumgelloch	a		07 28													07 58									
Bridgeton	d							07 12	07 12				07 22	07 22					07 42			07 52	07 52		
Dalmarnock	d							07 14	07 14				07 24	07 24					07 44			07 54	07 54		
Rutherglen	d			07 04				07 16	07 16				07 26	07 26			07 34		07 46			07 56	07 56		
Cambuslang	d							07 20	07 20			07 23	07 31	07 31					07 50			08 01	08 01		
Newton	d							07 24	07 24										07 54						
Blantyre	d			07 14				07 28	07 28								07 44		07 58						
Hamilton West	d			07 17				07 31	07 31								07 47		08 01						
Hamilton Central	d			07 20				07 33	07 33								07 50		08 03						
Chatelherault	d			07 24													07 54								
Merryton	d			07 28													07 58								
Larkhall	a			07 30													08 00								
Airbles	d							07 38	07 38										08 08						
Uddingston	d											07 28	07 35	07 35								08 05	08 05		
Bellshill	d											07 34	07 40	07 40								08 10	08 10		
Motherwell	a					07 20	07 27	07 41	07 41				07 46	07 46					08 11			08 16	08 17		
	d					07 20	07 28		07 42					07 46								08 16			
Whifflet	a																								
Coatbridge Central	a																								
Shieldmuir	d													07 50								08 20			
Holytown	d								07 47			07a38													
Wishaw	d					07 26	07 33		07 53					07 53								08 23			
Carluke	d					07a33	07a37		07 59					08 00								08 30			
Lanark	a								08 12					08 12								08 46			

For general notes see front of timetable
For details of catering facilities see Directory of Train Operators

§ Low Level

A To North Berwick (Table 238)
B To Edinburgh (Table 225)
b Glasgow Central High Level

Helensburgh, Balloch, Dalmuir and Milngavie → Glasgow → Springburn, Airdrie, Drumgelloch, Hamilton, Larkhall, Motherwell, Coatbridge and Lanark

Network Diagram - see first page of Table 220

		SR	SR	SR SX	SR SX	SR SO	SR SX	SR SO	SR SO A	SR	SR SX	SR	SR SX	SR SO	SR SX B	SR	SR SX	SR SO	SR SX	SR SO	SR SX	SR SX	SR SX	SR SO	SR SX
Helensburgh Central	d	07 10											07 35	07 40	07b42										
Craigendoran	d	07 13											07 38	07 43											
Cardross	d	07 18											07 43	07 48	07 51										
Balloch	d						07 23	07 23												07 53	07 53				
Alexandria	d						07 25	07 25												07 55	07 55				
Renton	d						07 28	07 28												07 58	07 58				
Dalreoch	d	07 23					07 31	07 31					07 48	07 53						08 01	08 01				
Dumbarton Central	d	07 25					07 32	07 32					07 50	07 55	07 57					08 02	08 03				
Dumbarton East	d	07 27					07 34	07 34					07 52	07 57						08 04					
Bowling	d						07 39	07 39					07 57							08 09					
Kilpatrick	d						07 42	07 42					08 00							08 12					
Dalmuir	a	07 35					07 45	07 45					08 03	08 05						08 15					
	d	07 36		07 38			07 46	07 46		07 53		08 01	08 04	08 06					08 08	08 16					
Singer	d						07 48	07 48				08 03			08 06					08 18					
Drumry	d		←				07 50	07 50				08 05				←				→					
Drumchapel	d		07 38				07 53	07 53				08 08				08 08									
Milngavie	d				07 42	07 42					07 57	→											08 10	08 12	08 18
Hillfoot	d				07 45	07 45					08 00												08 13	08 15	08 21
Bearsden	d				07 47	07 47					08 02												08 16	08 17	08 24
Westerton	d		07 40		07 50	07 50	07 55	07 55			08 05					08 10							08 19	08 20	
Anniesland	d		07 44		07 53	07 53	07 58	07 58			08 08					08 14							08 23	08 23	
Clydebank	d			07 40						07 55			08 06						08 10						
Yoker	d			07 42						07 57									08 12						
Garscadden	d			07 46						08 01									08 16						
Scotstounhill	d			07 48						08 03									08 18			←			
Jordanhill	d			07 50						08 05									08 21						
Hyndland	d	07 44	07 47	07 52	07 56	07 56	08 01	08 01		08 07	08 11		08 14	08 14		08 17			08 23			08 23	08 26	08 26	
Partick	d	07 47	07 50	07 55	07 59	07 59	08 04	08 04		08 10	08 14		08 17	08 17		08 20			→		08 22	08 26	08 29	08 29	
Exhibition Centre	d		07 53		08 02	08 02				08 13	08 17					08 23							08 32	08 32	
Anderston	d		07 55		08 04	08 04				08 15	08 19					08 25							08 34	08 34	
Glasgow Central 15 §	a		07 56		08 05	08 05				08 17	08 20					08 26							08 35	08 35	
	d		07 57		08 07	08 07			08c15	08 17	08 21					08 27							08 37	08 37	
Argyle Street	d		07 59		08 09	08 09				08 19	08 23					08 29							08 39	08 39	
Charing Cross	d	07 52		07 59			08 08	08 08					08 22	08 22							08 27	08 31			08 36
Glasgow Queen Street 10 §	a	07 54		08 01			08 10	08 10					08 24	08 24	08e37						08 29	08 33			08 37
	d	07 57		08 02			08 12	08 14					08 27	08 27							08 30	08 33			08 38
High Street	d	07 59		08 04			08 14	08 16					08 29	08 29							08 32	08a35			08 40
Bellgrove	d	08 01		08 06			08 16	08 18					08 31	08 31							08 34				08 42
Duke Street	d			08 08				08 20													08 36				08 44
Alexandra Parade	d			08 09				08 21													08 37				08 45
Barnhill	d			08 12				08 24													08 40				08 48
Springburn	a			08 14				08 26													08 42				08 53
Carntyne	d	08 04					08 19						08 34	08 34											
Shettleston	d	08 07					08 22						08 37	08 37											
Garrowhill	d	08 09					08 24						08 39	08 39											
Easterhouse	d	08 12					08 27						08 42	08 42											
Blairhill	d	08 16					08 31						08 46	08 46											
Coatbridge Sunnyside	d	08 18					08 33						08 48	08 48											
Coatdyke	d	08 21					08 36						08 51	08 51											
Airdrie	a	08 24					08 39						08 53	08 53											
	d	08 24											08 54	08 54											
Drumgelloch	a	08 28											08 58	08 58											
Bridgeton	d				08 12	08 12				08 22	08 26												08 42	08 42	
Dalmarnock	d				08 14	08 14				08 24	08 28												08 44	08 44	
Rutherglen	d		08 04		08 16	08 16				08 26	08 30					08 34							08 46	08 46	
Cambuslang	d				08 20	08 20			08 23	08 31													08 50	08 50	
Newton	d				08 24	08 24																	08 54	08 54	
Blantyre	d		08 14		08 28	08 28										08 44							08 58	08 58	
Hamilton West	d		08 17		08 31	08 31										08 47							09 01	09 01	
Hamilton Central	d		08 20		08 33	08 33										08 50							→	→	
Chatelherault	d		08 24													08 54									
Merryton	d		08 28													08 58									
Larkhall	a		08 30													09 00									
Airbles	d				08 38	08 38											←	←							
Uddingston	d								08 28	08 35							08 35	08 35							
Bellshill	d								08 34	→							08 40	08 40							
Motherwell	a				08 41	08 41					08 44						08 46	08 46							
	d					08 42											08 46								
Whifflet	a																								
Coatbridge Central	a																								
Shieldmuir	d																08 50								
Holytown	d					08 47			08a38																
Wishaw	d					08 53											08 53								
Carluke	d					08 59											09 00								
Lanark	a					09 12											09 12								

For general notes see front of timetable
For details of catering facilities see Directory of Train Operators

§ Low Level

A To Edinburgh (Table 225)
B From Arrochar & Tarbet (Table 227)
b Helensburgh Upper
c Glasgow Central High Level
e Glasgow Queen Street High Level

Helensburgh, Balloch, Dalmuir and Milngavie → Glasgow → Springburn, Airdrie, Drumgelloch, Hamilton, Larkhall, Motherwell, Coatbridge and Lanark

Network Diagram - see first page of Table 220

		SR	SR	SR	SR	SR	SR	SR	SR	SR	SR	SR	SR	SR	SR	SR	SR	SR	SR	SR	SR	SR	SR		SR
		SO	SX	SX	SX	SX			SX		SX	SO		SX	SO					SX					
																		A							
Helensburgh Central	d		07 54	08 01							08 08	08 10										08 40			
Craigendoran	d		07 57	08 04							08 11	08 13										08 43			
Cardross	d		08 02	08 09							08 16	08 18										08 48			
Balloch	d																08 23								
Alexandria	d																08 25								
Renton	d																08 28								
Dalreoch	d		08 07								08 21	08 23					08 31					08 53			
Dumbarton Central	d		08 09	08 15							08 23	08 25					08 32					08 55			
Dumbarton East	d		08 11								08 25	08 27					08 34					08 57			
Bowling	d										08 30						08 39								
Kilpatrick	d										08 33						08 42								
Dalmuir	a		08 19								08 35	08 35					08 45					09 05			
	d	←	08 20					08 23		08 31	08 36	08 36		08 38			08 46		08 53		09 01	09 06			09 08
Singer	d	08 18	08 22			←				08 33							08 48				09 03				
Drumry	d	08 20	08 24			08 24				08 35			←				08 50				09 05		←		
Drumchapel	d	08 23	→			08 27				08 38			08 38				08 53				09 08		09 08		
Milngavie	d								08 27	→						08 42				08 57	→				
Hillfoot	d								08 30							08 45				09 00					
Bearsden	d								08 32							08 47				09 02					
Westerton	d	08 25				08 29			08 35				08 40			08 50	08 55			09 05			09 10		
Anniesland	d	08 28				08 32			08 38				08 44			08 53	08 58			09 08			09 14		
Clydebank	d							08 25						08 40					08 55						09 10
Yoker	d							08 27						08 42					08 57						09 12
Garscadden	d							08 31						08 46	08 46				09 01						09 16
Scotstounhill	d			08 28				08 33						08 48	08 48				09 03						09 18
Jordanhill	d							08 35						08 50	08 50				09 05						09 20
Hyndland	d	08 31		08 33		08 35		08 37	08 41		08 44	08 44	08 47	08 52	08 52	08 56	09 01		09 07	09 11		09 14	09 17		09 22
Partick	d	08 34		08 35		08 38		08 40	08 44		08 47	08 47	08 50	08 55	08 55	08 59	09 04		09 10	09 14		09 17	09 20		09 25
Exhibition Centre	d							08 43					08 53			09 02			09 13				09 23		
Anderston	d				08 38			08 45					08 55			09 04			09 15				09 25		
Glasgow Central 15 §	a				08 39			08 47					08 56			09 05			09 17				09 26		
	d				08 40			08 47					08 57			09 07		09b15	09 17				09 27		
Argyle Street	d				08 42			08 49					08 59			09 09			09 19				09 29		
Charing Cross	d	08 38		08 40		08 42			08 49		08 52	08 52		08 59	08 59		09 08			09 19		09 22			09 29
Glasgow Queen Street 10 §	a	08 40		08 42		08 44			08 51		08 54	08 54		09 01	09 01		09 10			09 21		09 24			09 31
	d	08 44		08 42		08 45			08 51		08 57	08 57		09 02	09 02		09 12			09 21		09 27			09 32
High Street	d	08 46		08 44		08a47			08a53		08 59	08 59		09 04	09 04		09 14			09a23		09 29			09 34
Bellgrove	d	08 48		08 46							09 01	09 01		09 06	09 06		09 16					09 31			09 36
Duke Street	d	08 50												09 08	09 08										09 38
Alexandra Parade	d	08 51												09 09	09 09										09 39
Barnhill	d	08 54												09 12	09 12										09 42
Springburn	a	08 56												09 14	09 14										09 44
Carntyne	d			08 49							09 04	09 04					09 19					09 34			
Shettleston	d			08 52							09 07	09 07					09 22					09 37			
Garrowhill	d			08 54							09 09	09 09					09 24					09 39			
Easterhouse	d			08 57							09 12	09 12					09 27					09 42			
Blairhill	d			09 01							09 16	09 16					09 31					09 46			
Coatbridge Sunnyside	d			09 04							09 18	09 18					09 33					09 48			
Coatdyke	d			09 06							09 21	09 21					09 36					09 51			
Airdrie	a			09 09							09 23	09 23					09c39					09 53			
	d										09 24	09 24										09 54			
Drumgelloch	a										09 28	09 28										09 58			
Bridgeton	d				08 45			08 52								09 12			09 22						
Dalmarnock	d				08 47			08 54								09 14			09 24						
Rutherglen	d				08 49			08 56					09 04			09 16			09 26				09 34		
Cambuslang	d				08 55			09 01								09 20		09 23	09 31						
Newton	d															09 24									
Blantyre	d						←						09 14			09 28							09 44		
Hamilton West	d						09 01						09 17			09 31							09 47		
Hamilton Central	d						09 03						09 20			09 33							09 50		
Chatelherault	d												09 24										09 54		
Merryton	d												09 28										09 58		
Larkhall	a												09 30										10 00		
Airbles	d						09 08									09 38									
Uddingston	d				09 02			09 05										09 28	09 35						
Bellshill	d							09 10										09 34	09 40						
Motherwell	a				09 08		09 11	09 16								09 41			09 46						
	d							09 16								09 42									
Whifflet	a																								
Coatbridge Central	a																								
Shieldmuir	d							09 20																	
Holytown	d															09 47		09a38							
Wishaw	d							09 23								09 53									
Carluke	d							09 30								10 00									
Lanark	a							09 42								10 12									

For general notes see front of timetable
For details of catering facilities see Directory of Train Operators

§ Low Level

A To Edinburgh (Table 225)
b Glasgow Central High Level
c Saturdays arr. 0941

Helensburgh, Balloch, Dalmuir and Milngavie → Glasgow → Springburn, Airdrie, Drumgelloch, Hamilton, Larkhall, Motherwell, Coatbridge and Lanark

Network Diagram - see first page of Table 220

		SR	SR	SR	SR	SR	SR	SR	SR	SR	SR	SR	SR	SR	SR	SR	SR	SR	SR	SR	SR	SR	SR	SR	SR
												A													
Helensburgh Central	d						09 10									09 40								10 10	
Craigendoran	d						09 13									09 43								10 13	
Cardross	d						09 18									09 48								10 18	
Balloch	d		08 53								09 23									09 53					
Alexandria	d		08 55								09 25									09 55					
Renton	d		08 58								09 28									09 58					
Dalreoch	d		09 01				09 23				09 31					09 53				10 01				10 23	
Dumbarton Central	d		09 02				09 25				09 32					09 55				10 02				10 25	
Dumbarton East	d		09 04				09 27				09 34					09 57				10 04				10 27	
Bowling	d		09 09								09 39									10 09					
Kilpatrick	d		09 12								09 42									10 12					
Dalmuir	a		09 15				09 35				09 45					10 05				10 15				10 35	
	d		09 16	09 23		09 31	09 36		09 38		09 46		09 53		10 01	10 06		10 08		10 16	10 23		10 31	10 36	
Singer	d		09 18			09 33					09 48				10 03					10 18			10 33		
Drumry	d		09 20			09 35		←			09 50				10 05		←			10 20			10 35		←
Drumchapel	d		09 23			09 38		09 38			09 53				10 08		10 08			10 23			10 38		10 38
Milngavie	d	09 12			09 27	→				09 42				09 57	→				10 12			10 27	→		
Hillfoot	d	09 15			09 30					09 45				10 00					10 15			10 30			
Bearsden	d	09 17			09 32					09 47				10 02					10 17			10 32			
Westerton	d	09 20	09 25		09 35			09 40		09 50	09 55			10 05			10 10		10 20	10 25		10 35			10 40
Anniesland	d	09 23	09 28		09 38			09 44		09 53	09 58			10 08			10 14		10 23	10 28		10 38			10 44
Clydebank	d			09 25					09 40				09 55					10 10			10 25				
Yoker	d			09 27					09 42				09 57					10 12			10 27				
Garscadden	d			09 31					09 46				10 01					10 16			10 31				
Scotstounhill	d			09 33					09 48				10 03					10 18			10 33				
Jordanhill	d			09 35					09 50				10 05					10 20			10 35				
Hyndland	d	09 26	09 31	09 37	09 41		09 44	09 47	09 52	09 56	10 01		10 07	10 11		10 14	10 17	10 22	10 26	10 31	10 37	10 41		10 44	10 47
Partick	d	09 29	09 34	09 40	09 44		09 47	09 50	09 55	09 59	10 04		10 10	10 14		10 17	10 20	10 25	10 29	10 34	10 40	10 44		10 47	10 50
Exhibition Centre	d	09 32		09 43				09 53		10 02			10 13				10 23		10 32		10 43				10 53
Anderston	d	09 34		09 45				09 55		10 04			10 15				10 25		10 34		10 45				10 55
Glasgow Central 15 §	a	09 35		09 47				09 56		10 05			10 17				10 26		10 35		10 47				10 56
	d	09 37		09 47				09 57		10 07		10b15	10 17				10 27		10 37		10 47				10 57
Argyle Street	d	09 39		09 49				09 59		10 09			10 19				10 29		10 39		10 49				10 59
Charing Cross	d		09 38		09 49		09 52		09 59		10 08			10 19		10 22		10 29		10 38		10 49		10 52	
Glasgow Queen Street 10 §	a		09 40		09 51		09 54		10 01		10 10			10 21		10 24		10 31		10 40		10 51		10 54	
	d		09 42		09 51		09 57		10 02		10 12			10 21		10 27		10 32		10 42		10 51		10 57	
High Street	d		09 44		09a53		09 59		10 04		10 14			10a23		10 29		10 34		10 44		10a53		10 59	
Bellgrove	d		09 46				10 01		10 06		10 16					10 31		10 36		10 46				11 01	
Duke Street	d								10 08									10 38							
Alexandra Parade	d								10 09									10 39							
Barnhill	d								10 12									10 42							
Springburn	a								10 14									10 44							
Carntyne	d		09 49				10 04				10 19					10 34				10 49				11 04	
Shettleston	d		09 52				10 07				10 22					10 37				10 52				11 07	
Garrowhill	d		09 54				10 09				10 24					10 39				10 54				11 09	
Easterhouse	d		09 57				10 12				10 27					10 42				10 57				11 12	
Blairhill	d		10 01				10 16				10 31					10 46				11 01				11 16	
Coatbridge Sunnyside	d		10 03				10 18				10 33					10 48				11 03				11 18	
Coatdyke	d		10 06				10 21				10 36					10 51				11 06				11 21	
Airdrie	a		10 09				10 23				10 39					10 53				11 09				11 23	
	d						10 24									10 54								11 24	
Drumgelloch	a						10 28									10 58								11 28	
Bridgeton	d	09 42		09 52						10 12			10 22						10 42		10 52				
Dalmarnock	d	09 44		09 54						10 14			10 24						10 44		10 54				
Rutherglen	d	09 46		09 56				10 04		10 16			10 26				10 34		10 46		10 56				11 04
Cambuslang	d	09 50		10 01						10 20		10 23	10 31						10 50		11 01				
Newton	d	09 54								10 24									10 54						
Blantyre	d	09 58						10 14		10 28							10 44		10 58						11 14
Hamilton West	d	10 01						10 17		10 31							10 47		11 01						11 17
Hamilton Central	d	10 03						10 20		10 33							10 50		11 03						11 20
Chatelherault	d							10 24									10 54								11 24
Merryton	d							10 28									10 58								11 28
Larkhall	a							10 30									11 00								11 30
Airbles	d	10 08								10 38									11 08						
Uddingston	d			10 05								10 28	10 35								11 05				
Bellshill	d			10 10								10 34	10 40								11 10				
Motherwell	a	10 11		10 16						10 41			10 46						11 11		11 16				
	d			10 16						10 42											11 16				
Whifflet	a																								
Coatbridge Central	a																								
Shieldmuir	d			10 20																	11 20				
Holytown	d									10 47		10a38													
Wishaw	d			10 23						10 53											11 23				
Carluke	d			10 30						11 00											11 30				
Lanark	a			10c43						11 12											11 42				

For general notes see front of timetable
For details of catering facilities see Directory of Train Operators

§ Low Level

A To Edinburgh (Table 225)
b Glasgow Central High Level
c Saturdays arr. 1 minute earlier

Helensburgh, Balloch, Dalmuir and Milngavie → Glasgow → Springburn, Airdrie, Drumgelloch, Hamilton, Larkhall, Motherwell, Coatbridge and Lanark

Network Diagram - see first page of Table 220

		SR	SR	SR	SR	SR	SR	SR	SR	SR	SR	SR	SR	SR	SR	SR	SR	SR	SR	SR	SR	SR	SR	SR	SR
					A					◇ B ✕													A		
Helensburgh Central	d								10 40	10b41								11 10							
Craigendoran	d								10 43									11 13							
Cardross	d								10 48									11 18							
Balloch	d			10 23										10 53								11 23			
Alexandria	d			10 25										10 55								11 25			
Renton	d			10 28										10 58								11 28			
Dalreoch	d			10 31					10 53					11 01				11 23				11 31			
Dumbarton Central	d			10 32					10 55	10 58				11 02				11 25				11 32			
Dumbarton East	d			10 34					10 57					11 04				11 27				11 34			
Bowling	d			10 39										11 09								11 39			
Kilpatrick	d			10 42										11 12								11 42			
Dalmuir	a			10 45					11 05	11 08				11 15				11 35				11 45			
	d	10 38		10 46		10 53		11 01	11 06	11 08		11 08		11 16	11 23		11 31	11 36		11 38		11 46		11 53	
Singer	d			10 48				11 03						11 18			11 33					11 48			
Drumry	d			10 50				11 05			←			11 20			11 35		←			11 50			
Drumchapel	d			10 53				11 08			11 08			11 23			11 38		11 38			11 53			
Milngavie	d		10 42				10 57	→					11 12			11 27	→				11 42				11 57
Hillfoot	d		10 45				11 00						11 15			11 30					11 45				12 00
Bearsden	d		10 47				11 02						11 17			11 32					11 47				12 02
Westerton	d		10 50	10 55			11 05				11 10		11 20	11 25		11 35			11 40		11 50	11 55			12 05
Anniesland	d		10 53	10 58			11 08				11 14		11 23	11 28		11 38			11 44		11 53	11 58			12 08
Clydebank	d	10 40				10 55						11 10			11 25					11 40				11 55	
Yoker	d	10 42				10 57						11 12			11 27					11 42				11 57	
Garscadden	d	10 46				11 01						11 16			11 31					11 46				12 01	
Scotstounhill	d	10 48				11 03						11 18			11 33					11 48				12 03	
Jordanhill	d	10 50				11 05						11 20			11 35					11 50				12 05	
Hyndland	d	10 52	10 56	11 01		11 07	11 11		11 14		11 17	11 22	11 26	11 31	11 37	11 41		11 44	11 47	11 52	11 56	12 01		12 07	12 11
Partick	d	10 55	10 59	11 04		11 10	11 14		11 17		11 20	11 25	11 29	11 34	11 40	11 44		11 47	11 50	11 55	11 59	12 04		12 10	12 14
Exhibition Centre	d		11 02			11 13					11 23		11 32		11 43				11 53		12 02			12 13	
Anderston	d		11 04			11 15					11 25		11 34		11 45				11 55		12 04			12 15	
Glasgow Central 15 §	a		11 05			11 17					11 26		11 37		11 47				11 56		12 05			12 17	
	d		11 07		11c15	11 17					11 27		11 37		11 47				11 57		12 07		12c15	12 17	
Argyle Street	d		11 09			11 19					11 29		11 39		11 49				11 59		12 09			12 19	
Charing Cross	d	10 59		11 08			11 19		11 22			11 29		11 38		11 49		11 52		11 59		12 08			12 19
Glasgow Queen Street 10 §	a	11 01		11 10			11 21		11 24	11e28		11 31		11 40		11 51		11 54		12 01		12 10			12 21
	d	11 02		11 12			11 21		11 27			11 32		11 42		11 51		11 57		12 02		12 12			12 21
High Street	d	11 04		11 14			11a23		11 29			11 34		11 44		11a53		11 59		12 04		12 14			12a23
Bellgrove	d	11 06		11 16					11 31			11 36		11 46				12 01		12 06		12 16			
Duke Street	d	11 08										11 38								12 08					
Alexandra Parade	d	11 09										11 39								12 09					
Barnhill	d	11 12										11 42								12 12					
Springburn	a	11 14										11 44								12 14					
Carntyne	d			11 19					11 34					11 49				12 04				12 19			
Shettleston	d			11 22					11 37					11 52				12 07				12 22			
Garrowhill	d			11 24					11 39					11 54				12 09				12 24			
Easterhouse	d			11 27					11 42					11 57				12 12				12 27			
Blairhill	d			11 31					11 46					12 01				12 16				12 31			
Coatbridge Sunnyside	d			11 33					11 48					12 03				12 18				12 33			
Coatdyke	d			11 36					11 51					12 06				12 21				12 36			
Airdrie	a			11 39					11 53					12 09				12 23				12 39			
	d								11 54									12 24							
Drumgelloch	a								11 58									12 28							
Bridgeton	d		11 12			11 22							11 42		11 52						12 12			12 22	
Dalmarnock	d		11 14			11 24							11 44		11 54						12 14			12 24	
Rutherglen	d		11 16			11 26							11 46		11 56						12 16			12 26	
Cambuslang	d		11 20		11 23	11 31					11 34		11 50		12 01				12 04		12 20		12 23	12 31	
Newton	d		11 24										11 54								12 24				
Blantyre	d		11 28								11 44		11 58						12 14		12 28				
Hamilton West	d		11 31								11 47		12 01						12 17		12 31				
Hamilton Central	d		11 33								11 50		12 03						12 20		12 33				
Chatelherault	d										11 54								12 24						
Merryton	d										11 58								12 28						
Larkhall	a										12 00								12 30						
Airbles	d		11 38										12 08								12 38				
Uddingston	d				11 28	11 35									12 05								12 28	12 35	
Bellshill	d				11 34	11 40									12 10								12 34	12 40	
Motherwell	a		11 41			11 46							12 11		12 16						12 41			12 46	
	d		11 42												12 16						12 42				
Whifflet	a																								
Coatbridge Central	a																								
Shieldmuir	d														12 20										
Holytown	d		11 47		11a38																12 47		12a38		
Wishaw	d		11 53												12 23						12 53				
Carluke	d		12 00												12 30						13 00				
Lanark	a		12 12												12f46						13 12				

For general notes see front of timetable
For details of catering facilities see Directory of Train Operators

§ Low Level

A To Edinburgh (Table 225)
B From Oban and from Mallaig (Table 227)
b Helensburgh Upper
c Glasgow Central High Level
e Glasgow Queen Street High Level
f Saturdays arr. 1243

Table 226

Mondays to Saturdays

Helensburgh, Balloch, Dalmuir and Milngavie → Glasgow → Springburn, Airdrie, Drumgelloch, Hamilton, Larkhall, Motherwell, Coatbridge and Lanark

Network Diagram - see first page of Table 220

Station		SR	SR	SR	SR	SR	SR	SR	SR	SR	SR	SR	SR	SR	SR	SR	SR	SR	SR	SR	SR	SR	SR	SR	SR
																A									
Helensburgh Central	d		11 40								12 10									12 40					
Craigendoran	d		11 43								12 13									12 43					
Cardross	d		11 48								12 18									12 48					
Balloch	d						11 53								12 23									12 53	
Alexandria	d						11 55								12 25									12 55	
Renton	d						11 58								12 28									12 58	
Dalreoch	d		11 53				12 01				12 23				12 31					12 53				13 01	
Dumbarton Central	d		11 55				12 02				12 25				12 32					12 55				13 02	
Dumbarton East	d		11 57				12 04				12 27				12 34					12 57				13 04	
Bowling	d						12 09								12 39									13 09	
Kilpatrick	d						12 12								12 42									13 12	
Dalmuir	a		12 05				12 15				12 35				12 46					13 05				13 15	
	d	12 01	12 06		12 08		12 16	12 23		12 31	12 36		12 38		12 46		12 53		13 01	13 06		13 08		13 16	13 23
Singer	d	12 03					12 18			12 33					12 48				13 03					13 18	
Drumry	d	12 05		←			12 20			12 35		←			12 50				13 05		←			13 20	
Drumchapel	d	12 08		12 08			12 23			12 38		12 38			12 53				13 08		13 08			13 23	
Milngavie	d	→				12 12			12 27	→				12 42				12 57	→				13 12		
Hillfoot	d					12 15			12 30					12 45				13 00					13 15		
Bearsden	d					12 17			12 32					12 47				13 02					13 17		
Westerton	d			12 10		12 20	12 25		12 35			12 40		12 50	12 55			13 05			13 10		13 20	13 25	
Anniesland	d			12 14		12 23	12 28		12 38			12 44		12 53	12 58			13 08			13 14		13 23	13 28	
Clydebank	d				12 10			12 25					12 40				12 55					13 10			13 25
Yoker	d				12 12			12 27					12 42				12 57					13 12			13 27
Garscadden	d				12 16			12 31					12 46				13 01					13 16			13 31
Scotstounhill	d				12 18			12 33					12 48				13 03					13 18			13 33
Jordanhill	d				12 20			12 35					12 50				13 05					13 20			13 35
Hyndland	d		12 14	12 17	12 22	12 26	12 31	12 37	12 41		12 44	12 47	12 52	12 56	13 01		13 07	13 11		13 14	13 17	13 22	13 26	13 31	13 37
Partick	d		12 17	12 20	12 25	12 29	12 34	12 40	12 44		12 47	12 50	12 55	12 59	13 04		13 10	13 14		13 17	13 20	13 25	13 29	13 34	13 40
Exhibition Centre	d			12 23		12 32		12 43				12 53		13 02			13 13				13 23		13 32		13 43
Anderston	d			12 25		12 34		12 45				12 55		13 04			13 15				13 25		13 34		13 45
Glasgow Central 15 §	a			12 26		12 35		12 47				12 56		13 05			13 17				13 26		13 35		13 47
	d			12 27		12 37		12 47				12 57		13 07		13b15	13 17				13 27		13 37		13 47
Argyle Street	d			12 29		12 39		12 49				12 59		13 09			13 19				13 29		13 39		13 49
Charing Cross	d		12 22		12 29		12 38		12 49		12 52		12 59		13 08			13 19		13 22		13 29		13 38	
Glasgow Queen Street 10 §	a		12 24		12 31		12 40		12 51		12 54		13 01		13 10			13 21		13 24		13 31		13 40	
	d		12 27		12 32		12 42		12 51		12 57		13 02		13 12			13 21		13 27		13 32		13 42	
High Street	d		12 29		12 34		12 44		12a53		12 59		13 04		13 14			13a23		13 29		13 34		13 44	
Bellgrove	d		12 31		12 36		12 46				13 01		13 06		13 16					13 31		13 36		13 46	
Duke Street	d				12 38								13 08									13 38			
Alexandra Parade	d				12 39								13 09									13 39			
Barnhill	d				12 42								13 12									13 42			
Springburn	a				12 44								13 14									13 44			
Carntyne	d		12 34				12 49				13 04				13 19					13 34				13 49	
Shettleston	d		12 37				12 52				13 07				13 22					13 37				13 52	
Garrowhill	d		12 39				12 54				13 09				13 24					13 39				13 54	
Easterhouse	d		12 42				12 57				13 12				13 27					13 42				13 57	
Blairhill	d		12 46				13 01				13 16				13 31					13 46				14 01	
Coatbridge Sunnyside	d		12 48				13 03				13 18				13 33					13 48				14 03	
Coatdyke	d		12 51				13 06				13 21				13 36					13 51				14 06	
Airdrie	a		12 53				13 09				13 23				13 39					13 53				14 09	
	d		12 54								13 24									13 54					
Drumgelloch	a		12 58								13 28									13 58					
Bridgeton	d					12 42		12 52						13 12			13 22						13 42		13 52
Dalmarnock	d					12 44		12 54						13 14			13 24						13 44		13 54
Rutherglen	d			12 34		12 46		12 56				13 04		13 16			13 26				13 34		13 46		13 56
Cambuslang	d					12 50		13 01						13 20		13 23	13 31						13 50		14 01
Newton	d					12 54								13 24									13 54		
Blantyre	d			12 44		12 58						13 14		13 28							13 44		13 58		
Hamilton West	d			12 47		13 01						13 17		13 31							13 47		14 01		
Hamilton Central	d			12 50		13 03						13 20		13 33							13 50		14 03		
Chatelherault	d			12 54								13 24									13 54				
Merryton	d			12 58								13 28									13 58				
Larkhall	a			13 00								13 30									14 00				
Airbles	d					13 08								13 38									14 08		
Uddingston	d							13 05								13 28	13 35								14 05
Bellshill	d							13 10								13 34	13 40								14 10
Motherwell	a					13 11		13 16						13 41			13 46						14 11		14 16
	d							13 16						13 42											14 16
Whifflet	a																								
Coatbridge Central	a																								
Shieldmuir	d							13 20																	14 20
Holytown	d													13 47		13a38									
Wishaw	d							13 23						13 53											14 23
Carluke	d							13 30						14 00											14 30
Lanark	a							13 42						14 12											14c43

For general notes see front of timetable
For details of catering facilities see Directory of Train Operators

§ Low Level

A To Edinburgh (Table 225)
b Glasgow Central High Level
c Saturdays arr. 1 minute earlier

Helensburgh, Balloch, Dalmuir and Milngavie → Glasgow → Springburn, Airdrie, Drumgelloch, Hamilton, Larkhall, Motherwell, Coatbridge and Lanark

Network Diagram - see first page of Table 220

		SR	SR	SR	SR	SR	SR	SR	SR	SR	SR	SR	SR	SR	SR	SR	SR	SR	SR	SR	SR	SR	SR	SR
									A															
Helensburgh Central	d			13 10									13 40								14 10			
Craigendoran	d			13 13									13 43								14 13			
Cardross	d			13 18									13 48								14 18			
Balloch	d							13 23									13 53							
Alexandria	d							13 25									13 55							
Renton	d							13 28									13 58							
Dalreoch	d			13 23				13 31					13 53				14 01				14 23			
Dumbarton Central	d			13 25				13 32					13 55				14 02				14 25			
Dumbarton East	d			13 27				13 34					13 57				14 04				14 27			
Bowling	d							13 39									14 09							
Kilpatrick	d							13 42									14 12							
Dalmuir	a			13 35				13 45					14 05				14 15				14 35			
	d		13 31	13 36		13 38		13 46		13 53		14 01	14 06		14 08		14 16	14 23		14 31	14 36		14 38	
Singer	d		13 33					13 48				14 03					14 18			14 33				
Drumry	d		13 35		←			13 50				14 05		←			14 20			14 35		←		
Drumchapel	d		13 38		13 38			13 53				14 08		14 08			14 23			14 38		14 38		
Milngavie	d	13 27	→				13 42				13 57	→				14 12			14 27	→				14 42
Hillfoot	d	13 30					13 45				14 00					14 15			14 30					14 45
Bearsden	d	13 32					13 47				14 02					14 17			14 32					14 47
Westerton	d	13 35			13 40		13 50	13 55			14 05			14 10		14 20	14 25		14 35			14 40		14 50
Anniesland	d	13 38			13 44		13 53	13 58			14 08			14 14		14 23	14 28		14 38			14 44		14 53
Clydebank	d					13 40				13 55					14 10			14 25					14 40	
Yoker	d					13 42				13 57					14 12			14 27					14 42	
Garscadden	d					13 46				14 01					14 16			14 31					14 46	
Scotstounhill	d					13 48				14 03					14 18			14 33					14 48	
Jordanhill	d					13 50				14 05					14 20			14 35					14 50	
Hyndland	d	13 41		13 44	13 47	13 52	13 56	14 01		14 07	14 11		14 14	14 17	14 22	14 26	14 31	14 37	14 41		14 44	14 47	14 52	14 56
Partick	d	13 44		13 47	13 50	13 55	13 59	14 04		14 10	14 14		14 17	14 20	14 25	14 29	14 34	14 40	14 44		14 47	14 50	14 55	14 59
Exhibition Centre	d				13 53		14 02			14 13				14 23		14 32		14 43				14 53		15 02
Anderston	d				13 55		14 04			14 15				14 25		14 34		14 45				14 55		15 04
Glasgow Central 15 §	a				13 56		14 05			14 17				14 26		14 35		14 47				14 56		15 05
	d				13 57		14 07		14b15	14 17				14 27		14 37		14 47				14 57		15 07
Argyle Street	d				13 59		14 09			14 19				14 29		14 39		14 49				14 59		15 09
Charing Cross	d	13 49		13 52		13 59		14 08			14 19		14 22		14 29		14 38		14 49		14 52		14 59	
Glasgow Queen Street 10 §	a	13 51		13 54		14 01		14 10			14 21		14 24		14 31		14 40		14 51		14 54		15 01	
	d	13 51		13 57		14 02		14 12			14 21		14 27		14 32		14 42		14 51		14 57		15 02	
High Street	d	13a53		13 59		14 04		14 14			14a23		14 29		14 34		14 44		14a53		14 59		15 04	
Bellgrove	d			14 01		14 06		14 16					14 31		14 36		14 46				15 01		15 06	
Duke Street	d					14 08									14 38								15 08	
Alexandra Parade	d					14 09									14 39								15 09	
Barnhill	d					14 12									14 42								15 12	
Springburn	a					14 14									14 44								15 14	
Carntyne	d			14 04				14 19					14 34				14 49				15 04			
Shettleston	d			14 07				14 22					14 37				14 52				15 07			
Garrowhill	d			14 09				14 24					14 39				14 54				15 09			
Easterhouse	d			14 12				14 27					14 42				14 57				15 12			
Blairhill	d			14 16				14 31					14 46				15 01				15 16			
Coatbridge Sunnyside	d			14 18				14 33					14 48				15 03				15 18			
Coatdyke	d			14 21				14 36					14 51				15 06				15 21			
Airdrie	a			14 23				14 39					14 53				15 09				15 23			
	d			14 24									14 54								15 24			
Drumgelloch	a			14 28									14 58								15 28			
Bridgeton	d						14 12			14 22						14 42		14 52						15 12
Dalmarnock	d						14 14			14 24						14 44		14 54						15 14
Rutherglen	d				14 04		14 16			14 26				14 34		14 46		14 56				15 04		15 16
Cambuslang	d						14 20		14 23	14 31						14 50		15 01						15 20
Newton	d						14 24									14 54								15 24
Blantyre	d				14 14		14 28							14 44		14 58						15 14		15 28
Hamilton West	d				14 17		14 31							14 47		15 01						15 17		15 31
Hamilton Central	d				14 20		14 33							14 50		15 03						15 20		15 33
Chatelherault	d				14 24									14 54								15 24		
Merryton	d				14 28									14 58								15 28		
Larkhall	a				14 30									15 00								15 30		
Airbles	d						14 38									15 08								15 38
Uddingston	d								14 28	14 35								15 05						→
Bellshill	d								14 34	14 40								15 10						
Motherwell	a						14 41			14c48						15 11		15 16						
	d						14 42											15 16						
Whifflet	a																							
Coatbridge Central	a																							
Shieldmuir	d																	15 20						
Holytown	d						14 47		14a38															
Wishaw	d						14 53											15 23						
Carluke	d						15 00											15 30						
Lanark	a						15 12											15 42						

For general notes see front of timetable
For details of catering facilities see Directory of Train Operators

§ Low Level

A To Edinburgh (Table 225)
b Glasgow Central High Level
c Saturdays arr. 1446

Helensburgh, Balloch, Dalmuir and Milngavie → Glasgow → Springburn, Airdrie, Drumgelloch, Hamilton, Larkhall, Motherwell, Coatbridge and Lanark

Network Diagram - see first page of Table 220

		SR	SR A	SR	SR SX B	SR SO B	SR	SR	SR	SR	SR ◇ C	SR	SR	SR	SR	SR	SR	SR	SR	SR	SR SX ◇ D	SR	SR	SR SX	SR SO
Helensburgh Central	d										14b39	14 40								15 10	15b15				
Craigendoran	d											14 43								15 13					
Cardross	d											14 48								15 18					
Balloch	d	14 23														14 53									
Alexandria	d	14 25														14 55									
Renton	d	14 28														14 58									
Dalreoch	d	14 31										14 53				15 01				15 23					
Dumbarton Central	d	14 32									14 52	14 55				15 02				15 25	15 29				
Dumbarton East	d	14 34										14 57				15 04				15 27					
Bowling	d	14 39														15 09									
Kilpatrick	d	14 42														15 12									
Dalmuir	a	14 45									15 04	15 06				15 15				15 35	15 38				
	d	14 46		14 53						15 01	15 04	15 06		15 08		15 16	15 23		15 31	15 36	15 38		15 38		
Singer	d	14 48								15 03						15 18			15 33						
Drumry	d	14 50								15 05			←			15 20			15 35			←			
Drumchapel	d	14 53								15 08			15 08			15 23			15 38			15 38			
Milngavie	d								14 57	→					15 12			15 27	→					15 42	15 42
Hillfoot	d								15 00						15 15			15 30						15 45	15 45
Bearsden	d								15 02						15 17			15 32						15 47	15 47
Westerton	d	14 55							15 05				15 10		15 20	15 25		15 35				15 40		15 50	15 50
Anniesland	d	14 58							15 08				15 14		15 23	15 28		15 38				15 44		15 53	15 53
Clydebank	d			14 55										15 10			15 25						15 40		
Yoker	d			14 57										15 12			15 27						15 42		
Garscadden	d			15 01										15 16			15 31						15 46		
Scotstounhill	d			15 03										15 18			15 33						15 48		
Jordanhill	d			15 05										15 20			15 35						15 50		
Hyndland	d	15 01		15 07					15 11			15 14	15 17	15 22	15 27	15 31	15 37	15 41		15 44		15 47	15 52	15 56	15 56
Partick	d	15 04		15 10					15 14			15 17	15 20	15 25	15 29	15 34	15 40	15 44		15 47		15 50	15 55	15 59	15 59
Exhibition Centre	d			15 13									15 23		15 32		15 43					15 53		16 02	16 02
Anderston	d			15 15									15 25		15 34		15 45					15 55		16 04	16 04
Glasgow Central [15] §	a			15 17									15 26		15 35		15 47					15 56		16 05	16 05
	d		15c15	15 17	15c19	15c19							15 27		15 37		15 47					15 57		16 07	16 07
Argyle Street	d			15 19									15 29		15 39		15 49					15 59		16 09	16 09
Charing Cross	d	15 08							15 19			15 22		15 29		15 38		15 49		15 52			15 59		
Glasgow Queen Street [10] §	a	15 10							15 21		15e29	15 24		15 31		15 41		15 51		15 54	15e58		16 01		
	d	15 12							15 21			15 27		15 32		15 42		15 51		15 57			16 02		
High Street	d	15 14							15a23			15 29		15 34		15 44		15a53		15 59			16 04		
Bellgrove	d	15 16										15 31		15 36		15 46				16 01			16 06		
Duke Street	d													15 38									16 08		
Alexandra Parade	d													15 39									16 09		
Barnhill	d													15 42									16 12		
Springburn	a													15 44									16 14		
Carntyne	d	15 19										15 34				15 49				16 04					
Shettleston	d	15 22										15 37				15 52				16 07					
Garrowhill	d	15 24										15 39				15 54				16 09					
Easterhouse	d	15 27										15 42				15 57				16 12					
Blairhill	d	15 31										15 46				16 01				16 16					
Coatbridge Sunnyside	d	15 33										15 48				16 03				16 18					
Coatdyke	d	15 36										15 51				16 06				16 21					
Airdrie	a	15 39										15 53				16 09				16 23					
	d											15 54								16 24					
Drumgelloch	a											15 58								16 28					
Bridgeton	d			15 22											15 42		15 52							16 12	16 12
Dalmarnock	d			15 24											15 44		15 54							16 14	16 14
Rutherglen	d			15 26				←					15 34		15 46		15 56					16 04		16 16	16 16
Cambuslang	d		15 23	15 31				15 31							15 50		16 01							16 20	16 20
Newton	d			→											15 54									16 24	16 24
Blantyre	d												15 44		15 58							16 14		16 28	16 28
Hamilton West	d												15 47		16 01							16 17		16 31	16 31
Hamilton Central	d												15 50		16 03							16 20		16 33	16 33
Chatelherault	d												15 54									16 24			
Merryton	d												15 58									16 28			
Larkhall	a						←						16 00									16 30			
Airbles	d						15 38								16 08									16 38	16 38
Uddingston	d		15 28					15 35									16 05								
Bellshill	d		15 34					15 40									16 10								
Motherwell	a				15 35	15 38	15 41	15 46							16 11		16 16							16 41	16 41
	d				15 38	15 39	15 42										16 16							16 42	16 42
Whifflet	a																							16 48	
Coatbridge Central	a																							16 53	
Shieldmuir	d																16 20								
Holytown	d		15a38				15 47																		16 47
Wishaw	d						15 53										16 23								16 53
Carluke	d				15a47	15a48	16 00										16 30								17 00
Lanark	a						16 12										16f44								17 12

For general notes see front of timetable
For details of catering facilities see Directory of Train Operators

§ Low Level
A To Edinburgh (Table 225)
B To North Berwick (Table 238)
C From Mallaig (Table 227). All Saturdays and Mondays to Fridays from 29 September also conveys portion from Oban
D Until 26 September. From Oban (Table 227)
b Helensburgh Upper
c Glasgow Central High Level
e Glasgow Queen Street High Level
f Saturdays arr. 2 minutes earlier

Helensburgh, Balloch, Dalmuir and Milngavie → Glasgow → Springburn, Airdrie, Drumgelloch, Hamilton, Larkhall, Motherwell, Coatbridge and Lanark

Network Diagram - see first page of Table 220

Station		SR	SR A	SR	SR SX	SR SO	SR	SR	SR SX	SR	SR	SR	SR SO	SR SX	SR	SR SX	SR SO	SR SO	SR SX	SR	SR	SR	SR	SR SX	SR SO
Helensburgh Central	d							15 40													16 10				
Craigendoran	d							15 43													16 13				
Cardross	d							15 48													16 18				
Balloch	d	15 23													15 53										
Alexandria	d	15 25													15 55										
Renton	d	15 28													15 58										
Dalreoch	d	15 31						15 53							16 01						16 23				
Dumbarton Central	d	15 32						15 55							16 02						16 25				
Dumbarton East	d	15 34						15 57							16 04						16 27				
Bowling	d	15 39													16 09										
Kilpatrick	d	15 42													16 12										
Dalmuir	a	15 45						16 05							16 15						16 35				
	d	15 46		15 53			16 01	16 06				16 08			16 16	16 23	16 23			16 31	16 36		16 38		
Singer	d	15 48					16 03								16 18					16 33					
Drumry	d	15 50					16 05				←				16 20					16 35		←			
Drumchapel	d	15 53					16 08				16 08				16 23					16 38		16 38			
Milngavie	d				15 57	15 57	→						16 12	16 12				16 27	16 27	→					16 42
Hillfoot	d				16 00	16 00							16 15	16 15				16 30	16 30						16 45
Bearsden	d				16 02	16 02							16 17	16 17				16 32	16 32						16 47
Westerton	d	15 55			16 05	16 05					16 10		16 20	16 20	16 25			16 35	16 35			16 40			16 50
Anniesland	d	15 58			16 08	16 08					16 14		16 23	16 23	16 28			16 38	16 38			16 44			16 53
Clydebank	d			15 55								16 10				16 25	16 25						16 40		
Yoker	d			15 57								16 12				16 27	16 27						16 42		
Garscadden	d			16 01								16 15				16 31	16 31						16 46		
Scotstounhill	d			16 03								16 18				16 33	16 33						16 48		
Jordanhill	d			16 05								16 20				16 35	16 35						16 50		
Hyndland	d	16 01		16 07	16 11	16 11		16 14			16 17	16 22	16 26	16 26	16 31	16 37	16 37	16 41	16 41		16 44	16 47	16 52		16 56
Partick	d	16 04		16 10	16 14	16 14		16 17			16 20	16 25	16 29	16 29	16 34	16 40	16 40	16 44	16 44		16 47	16 50	16 55		16 59
Exhibition Centre	d			16 13							16 23		16 32	16 32		16 43	16 43					16 53			17 02
Anderston	d			16 15					16 23		16 25		16 34	16 34		16 45	16 45					16 55		17 04	17 04
Glasgow Central 15 §	a			16 17					16 24		16 26		16 35	16 35		16 47	16 47					16 56		17 05	17 05
	d		16b15	16 17					16 25		16 27		16 37	16 37		16 47	16 47					16 57		17 07	17 07
Argyle Street	d			16 19					16 27		16 29		16 39	16 39		16 49	16 49					16 59		17 09	17 09
Charing Cross	d	16 08			16 19	16 19		16 22				16 29			16 38			16 49	16 49		16 52		16 59		
Glasgow Queen Street 10 §	a	16 11			16 21	16 21		16 24				16 31			16 40			16 51	16 51		16 54		17 01		
	d	16 12			16 21	16 21		16 27				16 32			16 42			16 51	16 51		16 57		17 02		
High Street	d	16 14			16 23	16a23		16 29				16 34			16 44			16a53	16 54		16 59		17 04		
Bellgrove	d	16 16						16 31				16 36			16 46						17 01		17 06		
Duke Street	d											16 38											17 08		
Alexandra Parade	d											16 39											17 09		
Barnhill	d											16 42											17 12		
Springburn	a											16 44											17 14		
Carntyne	d	16 19						16 34							16 49						17 04				
Shettleston	d	16 22						16 37							16 52						17 07				
Garrowhill	d	16 24						16 39							16 54						17 09				
Easterhouse	d	16 27						16 42							16 57						17 12				
Blairhill	d	16 31			16 35			16 46							17 01				17 05		17 16				
Coatbridge Sunnyside	d	16 33			16 38			16 48							17 03				17 08		17 18				
Coatdyke	d	16 36			16 40			16 51							17 06				17 10		17 21				
Airdrie	a	16 39			16 45			16 53							17 09				17 15		17 23				
	d							16 54													17 24				
Drumgelloch	a							16 58													17 28				
Bridgeton	d			16 22									16 42	16 42		16 52	16 52							17 12	17 12
Dalmarnock	d			16 24									16 44	16 44		16 54	16 54								17 14
Rutherglen	d			16 26					16 32		16 34		16 46	16 46		16 56	16 56					17 04			17 16
Cambuslang	d		16 23	16 31									16 50	16 50		17 01	17 01					17 08			17 20
Newton	d												16 54	16 54											17 24
Blantyre	d										16 44		16 58	16 58								17 14			17 28
Hamilton West	d										16 47		17 01	17 01								17 17			17 31
Hamilton Central	d										16 50		17 03	17 03								17 20			17 33
Chatelherault	d										16 54											17 24			
Merryton	d										16 58											17 28			
Larkhall	a										17 00											17 30			
Airbles	d									←			17 08	17 08											17 38
Uddingston	d		16 28	16 35						16 35						17 05	17 05							17 20	
Bellshill	d		16 34	→						16 40						17 10	17 10								
Motherwell	a								16 44	16c47			17 11	17 11		17 16	17 16							17 28	17 41
	d								16 47					17 12			17 16							17 29	17 42
Whifflet	a													17 18											
Coatbridge Central	a													17 22											
Shieldmuir	d								16 50								17 20							17 32	
Holytown	d		16a38																						17 47
Wishaw	d								16 53								17 23							17 36	17 53
Carluke	d								17 00								17 30							17 43	18 00
Lanark	a								17 12								17 42							17 54	18 12

For general notes see front of timetable
For details of catering facilities see Directory of Train Operators

§ Low Level

A To Edinburgh (Table 225)
b Glasgow Central High Level
c Saturdays arr. 1 minute earlier

Helensburgh, Balloch, Dalmuir and Milngavie → Glasgow → Springburn, Airdrie, Drumgelloch, Hamilton, Larkhall, Motherwell, Coatbridge and Lanark

Network Diagram - see first page of Table 220

		SR	SR	SR	SR	SR	SR	SR	SR	SR	SR	SR	SR	SR	SR	SR	SR	SR	SR	SR	SR	SR	SR	SR	SR
		SX		SO	SX	SO	SX	SO	SX			SO	SX		SX	SX	SX	SO	SX		SO	SX			
				A	A					B			C				C								
Helensburgh Central	d										16 40														17 10
Craigendoran	d										16 43														17 13
Cardross	d										16 48														17 18
Balloch	d		16 23																	16 53					
Alexandria	d		16 25																	16 55					
Renton	d		16 28																	16 58					
Dalreoch	d		16 31								16 53									17 01					17 23
Dumbarton Central	d		16 32								16 55									17 02					17 25
Dumbarton East	d		16 34								16 57									17 04					17 27
Bowling	d		16 39																	17 09					
Kilpatrick	d		16 42																	17 12					
Dalmuir	a		16 45								17 05									17 15					17 35
	d		16 46			16 53	16 53			17 01	17 06			17 08						17 16	17 23	17 23		17 31	17 36
Singer	d		16 48							17 03		←	←							17 18				17 33	
Drumry	d		16 50							17 05										17 20				17 35	
Drumchapel	d		16 53							17 08		17 08	17 08							17 23				17 38	
Milngavie	d	16 42						16 57	16 57	→								17 12	17 12				17 27	→	
Hillfoot	d	16 45						17 00	17 00									17 15	17 15				17 30		
Bearsden	d	16 47						17 02	17 02									17 17	17 17				17 32		
Westerton	d	16 50	16 55					17 05	17 05			17 10	17 10					17 20	17 20	17 25			17 35		
Anniesland	d	16 53	16 58					17 08	17 08			17 14	17 14					17 23	17 23	17 28			17 38		
Clydebank	d					16 55	16 55							17 10							17 25	17 25			
Yoker	d					16 57	16 57							17 12							17 27	17 27			
Garscadden	d					17 01	17 01							17 16							17 31	17 31			
Scotstounhill	d					17 03	17 03							17 18							17 33	17 33			
Jordanhill	d					17 05	17 05							17 20							17 35	17 35			
Hyndland	d	16 56	17 01			17 07	17 07	17 11	17 11		17 14	17 17	17 17	17 22				17 26	17 26	17 31	17 37	17 37	17 41		17 44
Partick	d	16 59	17 04			17 10	17 10	17 14	17 14		17 17	17 20	17 20	17 25				17 29	17 29	17 34	17 40	17 40	17 44		17 47
Exhibition Centre	d	17b04				17 13	17 13					17 23	17 23					17 32	17c34		17 43	17 43			
Anderston	d	17 06				17 15	17 15					17 25	17 25		17 34			17 34	17 36		17 45	17 45			
Glasgow Central 15 §	a	17 08				17 17	17 17					17 26	17 26		17 35			17 35	17 38		17 47	17 47			
	d	17 09		17e15	17e19	17 17	17 21					17 27	17 27		17 37			17 37	17 39		17 47	17 47			
Argyle Street	d	17 11				17 19	17 23					17 29	17 29		17 39			17 39	17 41		17 49	17 49			
Charing Cross	d		17 08					17 19	17 19		17 22			17 29						17 38			17 49		17 52
Glasgow Queen Street 10 §	a		17 10					17 21	17 21		17 24			17 31						17 40			17 51		17 54
	d		17 12					17 21	17 21		17 27			17 32						17 42			17 51		17 57
High Street	d		17 14					17a23	17 23		17 29			17 34						17 44			17a53		17 59
Bellgrove	d		17 16								17 31			17 36						17 46					18 01
Duke Street	d													17 38											
Alexandra Parade	d													17 39											
Barnhill	d													17 42											
Springburn	a													17 44											
Carntyne	d		17 19								17 34									17 49					18 04
Shettleston	d		17 22								17 37									17 52					18 07
Garrowhill	d		17 24								17 39									17 54					18 09
Easterhouse	d		17 27								17 42									17 57					18 12
Blairhill	d		17 31						17 35		17 46									18 01					18 16
Coatbridge Sunnyside	d		17 33						17 38		17 48									18 03					18 18
Coatdyke	d		17 36						17 40		17 51									18 06					18 21
Airdrie	a		17 39						17 45		17 53									18 09					18 23
	d										17 54														18 24
Drumgelloch	a										17 58														18 28
Bridgeton	d	17 15				17 22	17 26						17 32					17 42	17 45		17 52	17 52			
Dalmarnock	d	17 17				17 24	17 28						17 34					17 44	17 47		17 54	17 54			
Rutherglen	d	17 19				17 26	17 31					17 34	17 36		17 44			17 46	17 49		17 56	17 56			
Cambuslang	d	17 23		17 23		17 31	17 35						17 42					17 50	17 53		18 01	18 01			
Newton	d	17 27					17 38									←		17 54	17 57						
Blantyre	d	17 33					17 42					17 44				17 42		17 58	18 01						
Hamilton West	d	17 36					→					17 47				17 45		18 01	18 04						
Hamilton Central	d	17 38										17 50				17 48		18 03	18 06						
Chatelherault	d	17 43										17 54							18 11						
Merryton	d	17 46										17 58							18 14						
Larkhall	a	17 48										18 00							18 16						
Airbles	d															17 53	←	18 08							
Uddingston	d			17 28		17 35							17 47				17 47				18 05	18 05			
Bellshill	d			17 34	17 34	17 40							→				17 51				18 10	18 10			
Motherwell	a					17 46									17 53	17 56	17 57	18 11			18 16	18 17			
	d														17 54	17 56	17 58				18 16				
Whifflet	a															18 02									
Coatbridge Central	a															18 06									
Shieldmuir	d														17 59		18 03				18 20				
Holytown	d			17a38	17a38																				
Wishaw	d														18 02		18 07				18 23				
Carluke	d														18 09		18a16				18 30				
Lanark	a														18 22						18 42				

For general notes see front of timetable
For details of catering facilities see Directory of Train Operators

§ Low Level

A To Edinburgh (Table 225)
B Mondays to Fridays to Carstairs (Table 225)
C To Carstairs (Table 225)
b Arr. 1701
c Arr. 1731
e Glasgow Central High Level

Helensburgh, Balloch, Dalmuir and Milngavie → Glasgow → Springburn, Airdrie, Drumgelloch, Hamilton, Larkhall, Motherwell, Coatbridge and Lanark

Network Diagram - see first page of Table 220

		SR	SR	SR	SR	SR	SR	SR	SR	SR	SR	SR	SR	SR	SR	SR	SR	SR	SR	SR	SR	SR	SR	SR	SR
						A											SO ◇ B								
Helensburgh Central	d								17 40					18 10			18b34			18 40					19 10
Craigendoran	d								17 43					18 13						18 43					19 13
Cardross	d								17 48					18 18						18 48					19 18
Balloch	d				17 23						17 53					18 23						18 53			
Alexandria	d				17 25						17 55					18 25						18 55			
Renton	d				17 28						17 58					18 28						18 58			
Dalreoch	d				17 31				17 53		18 01			18 23		18 31	18 47			18 53		19 01			19 23
Dumbarton Central	d				17 32				17 55		18 02			18 25		18 32				18 55		19 02			19 25
Dumbarton East	d				17 34				17 57		18 04			18 27		18 34				18 57		19 04			19 27
Bowling	d				17 39						18 09					18 39						19 09			
Kilpatrick	d				17 42						18 12					18 42						19 12			
Dalmuir	a				17 45				18 05		18 15			18 35		18 45	18 56			19 05		19 15			19 35
	d		17 38		17 46		17 53	18 01	18 05		18 16	18 23	18 31	18 35		18 46	18 56		19 01	19 05		19 16		19 31	19 35
Singer	d				17 48			18 03			18 18		18 33			18 48			19 03			19 18		19 33	
Drumry	d	←			17 50			18 05			18 20		18 35			18 50			19 05			19 20		19 35	
Drumchapel	d	17 38			17 53			18 08			18 23		18 38			18 53			19 08			19 23		19 38	
Milngavie	d			17 42						18 12					18 42						19 12				
Hillfoot	d			17 45						18 15					18 45						19 15				
Bearsden	d			17 47						18 17					18 47						19 17				
Westerton	d	17 40		17 50	17 55			18 10		18 20	18 25		18 40		18 50	18 55			19 10		19 20	19 25		19 40	
Anniesland	d	17 44		17 53	17 58			18 14		18 23	18 28		18 44		18 53	18 58			19 14		19 23	19 28		19 44	
Clydebank	d		17 40				17 55		18 07			18 25		18 37						19 07					19 37
Yoker	d		17 42				17 57		18 09			18 27		18 39						19 09					19 39
Garscadden	d		17 46				18 01		18 13			18 31		18 43						19 13					19 43
Scotstounhill	d		17 48				18 03		18 15			18 33		18 45						19 15					19 45
Jordanhill	d		17 50				18 05		18 17			18 35		18 47						19 17					19 47
Hyndland	d	17 47	17 52	17 56	18 01		18 07	18 17	18 21	18 26	18 31	18 37	18 47	18 51	18 55	19 01			19 17	19 21	19 26	19 31		19 47	19 51
Partick	d	17 50	17 55	17 59	18 04		18 10	18 20	18 24	18 29	18 34	18 40	18 50	18 54	18 59	19 04		19 10	19 20	19 24	19 29	19 34	19 40	19 50	19 54
Exhibition Centre	d	17 53		18 02			18 13	18 23		18 32		18 43	18 53		19 02			19 13	19 23		19 32		19 43	19 53	
Anderston	d	17 55		18 04			18 15	18 25		18 34		18 45	18 55		19 04			19 15	19 25		19 34		19 45	19 55	
Glasgow Central 15 §	a	17 56		18 05			18 17	18 26		18 35		18 47	18 56		19 05			19 16	19 26		19 35		19 46	19 56	
	d	17 57		18 07		18c15	18 17	18 27		18 37		18 47	18 57		19 07			19 17	19 27		19 37		19 47	19 57	
Argyle Street	d	17 59		18 09			18 19	18 29		18 39		18 49	18 59		19 09			19 19	19 29		19 39		19 49	19 59	
Charing Cross	d		17 59		18 08				18 29		18 38			18 59		19 08				19 29		19 38			19 59
Glasgow Queen Street 10 §	a		18 01		18 10				18 31		18 40			19 01		19 10	19e18			19 31		19 40			20 01
	d		18 02		18 12				18 32		18 44			19 02		19 14				19 32		19 44			20 02
High Street	d		18 04		18 14				18 34		18 46			19 04		19 16				19 34		19 46			20 04
Bellgrove	d		18 06		18 16				18 36		18 48			19 06		19 18				19 36		19 48			20 06
Duke Street	d		18 08								18 50					19 20						19 50			
Alexandra Parade	d		18 09								18 51					19 21						19 51			
Barnhill	d		18 12								18 54					19 24						19 54			
Springburn	a		18 15								18 56					19 26						19 56			
Carntyne	d				18 19				18 39					19 09						19 39					20 09
Shettleston	d				18 22				18 42					19 12						19 42					20 12
Garrowhill	d				18 24				18 44					19 14						19 44					20 14
Easterhouse	d				18 27				18 47					19 17						19 47					20 17
Blairhill	d				18 31				18 51					19 21						19 51					20 21
Coatbridge Sunnyside	d				18 33				18 53					19 23						19 53					20 23
Coatdyke	d				18 36				18 56					19 26						19 56					20 26
Airdrie	a				18 39				18 58					19 28						19 58					20 28
	d								18 59					19 29						19 59					20 29
Drumgelloch	a								19 03					19 33						20 03					20 33
Bridgeton	d			18 12			18 22			18 42		18 52			19 12			19 22			19 42		19 52		
Dalmarnock	d			18 14			18 24			18 44		18 54			19 14			19 24			19 44		19 54		
Rutherglen	d	18 04		18 16			18 26	18 34		18 46		18 56	19 04		19 16			19 26	19 34		19 46		19 56	20 04	
Cambuslang	d			18 20		18 23	18 31			18 50		19 01			19 20			19 31			19 50		20 01		
Newton	d			18 24						18 54					19 24						19 54				
Blantyre	d	18 14		18 28				18 44		18 58			19 14		19 28				19 44		19 58			20 14	
Hamilton West	d	18 17		18 31				18 47		19 01			19 17		19 31				19 47		20 01			20 17	
Hamilton Central	d	18 20		18 33				18 50		19 03			19 20		19 33				19 50		20 03			20 20	
Chatelherault	d	18 24						18 54					19 24						19 54					20 24	
Merryton	d	18 28						18 58					19 28						19 58					20 28	
Larkhall	a	18 30						19 00					19 30						20 00					20 30	
Airbles	d			18 38						19 08					19 38						20 08				
Uddingston	d					18 28	18 35					19 05						19 35					20 05		
Bellshill	d					18 34	18 40					19 10						19 40					20 10		
Motherwell	a			18 41			18 46			19 11		19 16			19 41			19 46			20 11		20 16		
	d			18 42								19 16			19 42								20 16		
Whifflet	a																								
Coatbridge Central	a																								
Shieldmuir	d											19 20											20 20		
Holytown	d			18 47		18a38									19 47										
Wishaw	d			18 53								19 23			19 53								20 23		
Carluke	d			19 00								19 30			20 00								20 30		
Lanark	a			19 12								19f43			20 12								20 42		

For general notes see front of timetable
For details of catering facilities see Directory of Train Operators

§ Low Level

A To Edinburgh (Table 225)
B Until 25 October. From Oban (Table 227)
b Helensburgh Upper
c Glasgow Central High Level
e Glasgow Queen Street High Level
f Saturdays arr. 1 minute earlier

Table 226 — Mondays to Saturdays

Helensburgh, Balloch, Dalmuir and Milngavie → Glasgow → Springburn, Airdrie, Drumgelloch, Hamilton, Larkhall, Motherwell, Coatbridge and Lanark

Network Diagram - see first page of Table 220

		SR	SR	SR	SR	SR	SR	SR	SR	SR	SR	SR	SR	SR	SR	SR	SR	SR	SR	SR	SR	SR	SR	SR	SR
				A													◇ B 🚲								
Helensburgh Central	d						19 40					20 10					20b40	20 40					21 10		
Craigendoran	d						19 43					20 13						20 43					21 13		
Cardross	d						19 48					20 18						20 48					21 18		
Balloch	d		19 23						19 53					20 23						20 53					21 23
Alexandria	d		19 25						19 55					20 25						20 55					21 25
Renton	d		19 28						19 58					20 28						20 58					21 28
Dalreoch	d		19 31				19 53		20 01			20 23		20 31				20 53		21 01			21 23		21 31
Dumbarton Central	d		19 32				19 55		20 02			20 25		20 32			20 53	20 55		21 02			21 25		21 32
Dumbarton East	d		19 34				19 57		20 04			20 27		20 34				20 57		21 04			21 27		21 34
Bowling	d		19 39						20 09					20 39						21 09					21 39
Kilpatrick	d		19 42						20 12					20 42						21 12					21 42
Dalmuir	a		19 45				20 05		20 15			20 35		20 45			21 04	21 05		21 15			21 35		21 45
	d		19 46			20 01	20 05		20 16		20 31	20 35		20 46		21 01	21 04	21 05		21 16		21 31	21 35		21 46
Singer	d		19 48			20 03			20 18		20 33			20 48		21 03				21 18		21 33			21 48
Drumry	d		19 50			20 05			20 20		20 35			20 50		21 05				21 20		21 35			21 50
Drumchapel	d		19 53			20 08			20 23		20 38			20 53		21 08				21 23		21 38			21 53
Milngavie	d	19 42						20 12					20 42						21 12					21 42	
Hillfoot	d	19 45						20 15					20 45						21 15					21 45	
Bearsden	d	19 47						20 17					20 47						21 17					21 47	
Westerton	d	19 50	19 55			20 10		20 20	20 25		20 40		20 50	20 55		21 10			21 20	21 25		21 40		21 50	21 55
Anniesland	d	19 53	19 58			20 14		20 23	20 28		20 44		20 53	20 58		21 14			21 23	21 28		21 44		21 53	21 58
Clydebank	d						20 07					20 37						21 07					21 37		
Yoker	d						20 09					20 39						21 09					21 39		
Garscadden	d						20 13					20 43						21 13					21 43		
Scotstounhill	d						20 15					20 45						21 15					21 45		
Jordanhill	d						20 17					20 47						21 17					21 47		
Hyndland	d	19 56	20 01			20 17	20 21	20 26	20 31		20 47	20 51	20 56	21 01		21 17		21 21	21 26	21 31		21 47	21 51	21 56	22 01
Partick	d	19 59	20 04		20 10	20 20	20 24	20 29	20 34	20 40	20 50	20 54	20 59	21 04	21 10	21 20		21 24	21 29	21 34	21 40	21 50	21 54	21 59	22 04
Exhibition Centre	d	20 02			20 13	20 23		20 32		20 43	20 53		21 02		21 13	21 23			21 32		21 43	21 53		22 02	
Anderston	d	20 04			20 15	20 25		20 34		20 45	20 55		21 04		21 15	21 25			21 34		21 45	21 55		22 04	
Glasgow Central 15 §	a	20 05			20 16	20 26		20 35		20 46	20 56		21 05		21 16	21 26			21 35		21 46	21 56		22 05	
	d	20 07		20c15	20 17	20 27		20 37		20 47	20 57		21 07		21 17	21 27			21 37		21 47	21 57		22 07	
Argyle Street	d	20 09			20 19	20 29		20 39		20 49	20 59		21 09		21 19	21 29			21 39		21 49	21 59		22 09	
Charing Cross	d		20 08				20 29		20 38			20 59		21 08				21 29		21 38			21 59		22 08
Glasgow Queen Street 10 §	a		20 10				20 31		20 40			21 01		21 10			21e29	21 31		21 40			22 01		22 10
	d		20 14				20 32		20 44			21 02		21 14				21 32		21 44			22 02		22 14
High Street	d		20 16				20 34		20 46			21 04		21 16				21 34		21 46			22 04		22 16
Bellgrove	d		20 18				20 36		20 48			21 06		21 18				21 36		21 48			22 06		22 18
Duke Street	d		20 20						20 50					21 20						21 50					22 20
Alexandra Parade	d		20 21						20 51					21 21						21 51					22 21
Barnhill	d		20 24						20 54					21 24						21 54					22 24
Springburn	a		20 26						20 56					21 26						21 56					22 26
Carntyne	d						20 39					21 09						21 39					22 09		
Shettleston	d						20 42					21 12						21 42					22 12		
Garrowhill	d						20 44					21 14						21 44					22 14		
Easterhouse	d						20 47					21 17						21 47					22 17		
Blairhill	d						20 51					21 21						21 51					22 21		
Coatbridge Sunnyside	d						20 53					21 23						21 53					22 23		
Coatdyke	d						20 56					21 26						21 56					22 26		
Airdrie	a						20 58					21 28						21 58					22 28		
	d						20 59					21 29						21 59					22 29		
Drumgelloch	a						21 03					21 33						22 03					22 33		
Bridgeton	d	20 12			20 22			20 42		20 52			21 12		21 22				21 42		21 52			22 12	
Dalmarnock	d	20 14			20 24			20 44		20 54			21 14		21 24				21 44		21 54			22 14	
Rutherglen	d	20 16			20 26	20 34		20 46		20 56	21 04		21 16		21 26	21 34			21 46		21 56	22 04		22 16	
Cambuslang	d	20 20		20 23	20 31			20 50		21 01			21 20		21 31				21 50		22 01			22 20	
Newton	d	20 24						20 54					21 24						21 54					22 24	
Blantyre	d	20 28				20 44		20 58			21 14		21 28			21 44			21 58			22 14		22 28	
Hamilton West	d	20 31				20 47		21 01			21 17		21 31			21 47			22 01			22 17		22 31	
Hamilton Central	d	20 33				20 50		21 03			21 20		21 33			21 50			22 03			22 20		22 33	
Chatelherault	d					20 54					21 24					21 54						22 24			
Merryton	d					20 58					21 28					21 58						22 28			
Larkhall	a					21 00					21 30					22 00						22 30			
Airbles	d	20 38						21 08					21 38						22 08					22 38	
Uddingston	d			20 28	20 35					21 05					21 35						22 05				
Bellshill	d			20 34	20 40					21 10					21 40						22 10				
Motherwell	a	20 41			20 46			21 11		21 16			21 41		21 46				22 11		22 16			22 41	
	d	20 42								21 16			21 42								22 16			22 41	
Whifflet	a																							22 48	
Coatbridge Central	a																							22 52	
Shieldmuir	d									21 20											22 20				
Holytown	d	20 47		20a38									21 47												
Wishaw	d	20 53								21 23			21 53								22 23				
Carluke	d	21 00								21 30			22 00								22 30				
Lanark	a	21 12								21 42			22 12								22 42				

For general notes see front of timetable
For details of catering facilities see Directory of Train Operators

§ Low Level

A To Edinburgh (Table 225)
B From Oban and from Mallaig (Table 227)
b Helensburgh Upper
c Glasgow Central High Level
e Glasgow Queen Street High Level

Helensburgh, Balloch, Dalmuir and Milngavie → Glasgow → Springburn, Airdrie, Drumgelloch, Hamilton, Larkhall, Motherwell, Coatbridge and Lanark

Network Diagram - see first page of Table 220

Station		SR	SR	SR	SR	SR	SR	SR	SR	SR	SR	SR	SR	SR	SR	SR	SR	SR	SR	SR	SR	SR	SR
										A					FO	FX	FO	FO	FO		FO		SX R B ⊡
Helensburgh Central	d			21 40					22 10						22 40					23 10			23b24
Craigendoran	d			21 43					22 13						22 43					23 13			
Cardross	d			21 48					22 18						22 48					23 18			
Balloch	d					21 53						22 23				22 53	22 53					23 23	
Alexandria	d					21 55						22 25				22 55	22 55					23 25	
Renton	d					21 58						22 28				22 58	22 58					23 28	
Dalreoch	d			21 53		22 01			22 23			22 31			22 53	23 01	23 01			23 23		23 31	
Dumbarton Central	d			21 55		22 02			22 25			22 32			22 55	23 02	23 02			23 25		23 32	
Dumbarton East	d			21 57		22 04			22 27			22 34			22 57	23 04	23 04			23 27		23 34	
Bowling	d					22 09						22 39				23 09	23 09					23 39	
Kilpatrick	d					22 12						22 42				23 12	23 12					23 42	
Dalmuir	a			22 05		22 15			22 35			22 45			23 05	23 15	23 15			23 35		23 45	23 49
	d		22 01	22 05		22 16		22 31	22 35			22 46		23 01	23 05	23 16	23 16		23 31	23 35			23 51
Singer	d		22 03			22 18		22 33				22 48		23 03		23 18	23 18		23 33				
Drumry	d		22 05			22 20		22 35				22 50		23 05		23 20	23 20		23 35				
Drumchapel	d		22 08			22 23		22 38				22 53		23 08		23 23	23 23		23 38				
Milngavie	d				22 12						22 42										23 42		
Hillfoot	d				22 15						22 45										23 45		
Bearsden	d				22 17						22 47										23 47		
Westerton	d		22 10		22 20	22 25		22 40			22 50	22 55		23 10		23 25	23 25		23 40		23 50		23a56
Anniesland	d		22 14		22 23	22 28		22 44			22 53	22 58		23 14		23 28	23 28		23 44		23 53		
Clydebank	d			22 07					22 37						23 07					23 37			
Yoker	d			22 09					22 39						23 09					23 39			
Garscadden	d			22 13					22 43						23 13					23 43			
Scotstounhill	d			22 15					22 45						23 15					23 45			
Jordanhill	d			22 17					22 47						23 17					23 47			
Hyndland	d		22 17	22 21	22 26	22 31		22 47	22 51		22 56	23 01		23 17	23 21	23 31	23 31		23 47	23 51	23 56		
Partick	d	22 10	22 20	22 24	22 29	22 34	22 40	22 50	22 54		22 59	23 04	23 10	23 20	23 24	23 34	23 34	23 40	23 50	23 54	23 59		
Exhibition Centre	d	22 13	22 23		22 32		22 43	22 53			23 02		23 13	23 23				23 43	23 53		00 02		
Anderston	d	22 15	22 25		22 34		22 45	22 55			23 04		23 15	23 25				23 45	23 55		00 04		
Glasgow Central 15 §	a	22 16	22 26		22 35		22 46	22 56			23 05		23 16	23 26				23 46	23 56		00 05		
	d	22 17	22 27		22 37		22 47	22 57		23c06	23 07		23 17	23 27				23 47	23 57		00 07		
Argyle Street	d	22 19	22 29		22 39		22 49	22 59			23 09		23 19	23 29				23 49	23 59		00 09		
Charing Cross	d			22 29		22 38			22 59			23 08			23 29	23 38	23 38			23 59			
Glasgow Queen Street 10 §	a			22 31		22 40			23 01			23 10			23 31	23 40	23 40			00 01			00e19
	d			22 32		22 44			23 02			23 14			23 32	23 44	23 44			00 02			
High Street	d			22 34		22 46			23 04			23 16			23 34	23 46	23 46			00 04			
Bellgrove	d			22 36		22 48			23 06			23 18			23 36	23 48	23 48			00 06			
Duke Street	d					22 50						23 20					23 50						
Alexandra Parade	d					22 51						23 21					23 51						
Barnhill	d					22 54						23 24					23 54						
Springburn	a					22 56						23 26					23 56						
Carntyne	d			22 39					23 09						23 39	23 51				00 09			
Shettleston	d			22 42					23 12						23 42	23 54				00 12			
Garrowhill	d			22 44					23 14						23 44	23 56				00 14			
Easterhouse	d			22 47					23 17						23 47	23 59				00 17			
Blairhill	d			22 51					23 21						23 51	00 03				00 21			
Coatbridge Sunnyside	d			22 53					23 23						23 53	00 05				00 23			
Coatdyke	d			22 56					23 26						23 56	00 08				00 26			
Airdrie	a			22 58					23 28						23 59	00 10				00 28			
	d			22 59					23 29						23 59	00 10				00 29			
Drumgelloch	a			23 03					23 33						00 03	00 14				00 33			
Bridgeton	d	22 22			22 42		22 52				23 12		23 22					23 52			00 12		
Dalmarnock	d	22 24			22 44		22 54				23 14		23 24					23 54			00 14		
Rutherglen	d	22 26	22 34		22 46		22 56	23 04			23 16		23 26	23 34				23 57	00 04		00 16		
Cambuslang	d	22 31			22 50		23 01			23 15	23 20		23 31					00 01			00 20		
Newton	d				22 54						23 24										00 24		
Blantyre	d		22 44		22 58			23 14			23 28			23 44					00 14		00 28		
Hamilton West	d		22 47		23 01			23 17			23 31			23 47					00 17		00 31		
Hamilton Central	d		22 50		23 03			23 20			23 33			23 50					00 20		00 33		
Chatelherault	d		22 54					23 24						23 54					00 24				
Merryton	d		22 58					23 28						23 58					00 28				
Larkhall	a		23 00					23 30						00 01					00 30				
Airbles	d				23 08						23 38										00 38		
Uddingston	d	22 35					23 05			23 20			23 35					00 05					
Bellshill	d	22 40					23 10			23 26			23 40					00 10					
Motherwell	a	22 46			23 11		23 16				23 41		23 46					00 16			00 41		
	d						23 16											00 16					
Whifflet	a																						
Coatbridge Central	a																						
Shieldmuir	d						23 20											00 20					
Holytown	d									23a30													
Wishaw	d						23 23											00 23					
Carluke	d						23 30											00 30					
Lanark	a						23 42											00 42					

For general notes see front of timetable
For details of catering facilities see Directory of Train Operators

§ Low Level

A To Edinburgh (Table 225)
B Limited seating accommodation. Also conveys overnight Sleeping Car accommodation from Fort William to London Euston (Tables 65 and 404)

b Helensburgh Upper
c Glasgow Central High Level
e Glasgow Queen Street High Level

Table 226

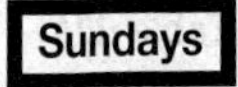

Sundays

until 23 November

Helensburgh, Balloch, Dalmuir and Milngavie → Glasgow → Springburn, Airdrie, Drumgelloch, Hamilton, Larkhall, Motherwell, Coatbridge and Lanark

Network Diagram - see first page of Table 220

		SR	SR	SR	SR	SR	SR	SR	SR	SR	SR	SR	SR	SR	SR	SR	SR	SR	SR	SR	SR	SR	SR	SR
Helensburgh Central	d			07 55			08 25				08 55			09 25				09 55			10 25			
Craigendoran	d			07 58			08 28				08 58			09 28				09 58			10 28			
Cardross	d			08 03			08 33				09 03			09 33				10 03			10 33			
Balloch	d				08 09			08 39				09 09			09 39				10 09			10 39		
Alexandria	d				08 11			08 41				09 11			09 41				10 11			10 41		
Renton	d				08 14			08 44				09 14			09 44				10 14			10 44		
Dalreoch	d			08 08	08 17		08 38	08 47			09 08	09 17		09 38	09 47			10 08	10 17		10 38	10 47		
Dumbarton Central	d			08 10	08 18		08 40	08 48			09 10	09 18		09 40	09 48			10 10	10 18		10 40	10 48		
Dumbarton East	d			08 12	08 20		08 42	08 50			09 12	09 20		09 42	09 50			10 12	10 20		10 42	10 50		
Bowling	d				08 24			08 54				09 24			09 54				10 24			10 54		
Kilpatrick	d				08 28			08 58				09 28			09 58				10 28			10 58		
Dalmuir	a			08 19	08 30		08 49	09 00			09 19	09 30		09 49	10 00			10 19	10 30		10 49	11 00		
	d	07 50	08 01	08 20	08 31		08 50	09 01			09 20	09 31		09 50	10 01			10 20	10 31		10 50	11 01		
Singer	d	07 52		08 22			08 52				09 22			09 52				10 22			10 52			
Drumry	d	07 55		08 25			08 55				09 25			09 55				10 25			10 55			
Drumchapel	d	07 57		08 27			08 57				09 27			09 57				10 27			10 57			
Milngavie	d								09 11				09 41			10 11				10 41			11 11	
Hillfoot	d								09 14				09 44			10 14				10 44			11 14	
Bearsden	d								09 16				09 46			10 16				10 46			11 16	
Westerton	d	08 00		08 30			09 00		09 19		09 30		09 49	10 00		10 19		10 30		10 49	11 00		11 19	
Anniesland	d	08 03		08 33			09 03		09 22		09 33		09 52	10 03		10 22		10 33		10 52	11 03		11 22	
Clydebank	d		08 03		08 33			09 03				09 33			10 03				10 33			11 03		
Yoker	d		08 05		08 35			09 05				09 35			10 05				10 35			11 05		
Garscadden	d		08 09		08 39			09 09				09 39			10 09				10 39			11 09		
Scotstounhill	d		08 11		08 41			09 11				09 41			10 11				10 41			11 11		
Jordanhill	d		08 13		08 43			09 13				09 43			10 13				10 43			11 13		
Hyndland	d	08 05	08 15	08 35	08 45	08 55	09 05	09 15	09 25		09 35	09 45	09 55	10 05	10 15	10 25		10 35	10 45	10 55	11 05	11 15	11 25	
Partick	d	08 08	08 18	08 38	08 48	08 58	09 08	09 18	09 28	09 34	09 38	09 48	09 58	10 08	10 18	10 28	10 34	10 38	10 48	10 58	11 08	11 18	11 28	11 34
Exhibition Centre	d		08 21		08 51	09 01		09 21	09 31	09 37		09 51	10 01		10 21	10 31	10 37		10 51	11 01		11 21	11 31	11 37
Anderston	d																							
Glasgow Central 15 §	a		08 23		08 53	09 03		09 23	09 33	09 39		09 53	10 03		10 23	10 33	10 39		10 53	11 03		11 23	11 33	11 39
	d		08 24		08 54	09 04		09 24	09 34	09 40		09 54	10 04		10 24	10 34	10 40		10 54	11 04		11 24	11 34	11 40
Argyle Street	d											09 56	10 06		10 26	10 36	10 42		10 56	11 06		11 26	11 36	11 42
Charing Cross	d	08 13		08 43			09 13				09 43			10 13				10 43			11 13			
Glasgow Queen Street 10 §	a	08 15		08 45			09 15				09 45			10 15				10 45			11 15			
	d	08 17		08 47			09 17				09 47			10 17				10 47			11 17			
High Street	d	08 19		08 49			09 19				09 49			10 19				10 49			11 19			
Bellgrove	d	08 21		08 51			09 21				09 51			10 21				10 51			11 21			
Duke Street	d																							
Alexandra Parade	d																							
Barnhill	d																							
Springburn	a																							
Carntyne	d	08 24		08 54			09 24				09 54			10 24				10 54			11 24			
Shettleston	d	08 27		08 57			09 27				09 57			10 27				10 57			11 27			
Garrowhill	d	08 29		08 59			09 29				09 59			10 29				10 59			11 29			
Easterhouse	d	08 32		09 02			09 32				10 02			10 32				11 02			11 32			
Blairhill	d	08 36		09 06			09 36				10 06			10 36				11 06			11 36			
Coatbridge Sunnyside	d	08 38		09 08			09 38				10 08			10 38				11 08			11 38			
Coatdyke	d	08 41		09 11			09 41				10 11			10 41				11 11			11 41			
Airdrie	a	08 44		09 14			09 44				10 14			10 44				11 14			11 44			
	d	08 45		09 15			09 45				10 15			10 45				11 15			11 45			
Drumgelloch	a	08 48		09 18			09 48				10 18			10 48				11 18			11 48			
Bridgeton	d		08 29		08 59	09 09		09 29	09 39			09 59	10 09		10 29	10 39			10 59	11 07		11 29	11 39	
Dalmarnock	d																							
Rutherglen	d		08 32		09 02	09 12		09 32	09 42	09 47		10 02	10 12		10 32	10 42	10 47		11 02	11 12		11 32	11 42	11 47
Cambuslang	d		08 36		09 06	09 16		09 36	09 46			10 06	10 16		10 36	10 46			11 06	11 16		11 36	11 46	
Newton	d				09 09			09 39				10 09			10 39				11 09			11 39		
Blantyre	d				09 13			09 43		09 55		10 13			10 43		10 55		11 13			11 43		11 55
Hamilton West	d				09 16			09 46		09 58		10 16			10 46		10 58		11 16			11 46		11 58
Hamilton Central	d				09 20			09 50		10 01		10 20			10 50		11 01		11 20			11 50		12 01
Chatelherault	d									10 06							11 06							12 06
Merryton	d									10 09							11 09							12 09
Larkhall	a									10 11							11 15							12 12
Airbles	d				09 25			09 55				10 25			10 55				11 25			11 55		
Uddingston	d		08 40			09 20			09 50				10 20			10 50				11 20			11 50	
Bellshill	d		08 45			09 25			09 55				10 25			10 55				11 25			11 55	
Motherwell	a		08 53		09 27	09 33		09 57	10 03			10 27	10 33		10 57	11 03			11 27	11 33		11 57	12 03	
	d					09 33							10 33							11 33				
Whifflet	a																							
Coatbridge Central	a																							
Shieldmuir	d					09 37							10 37							11 37				
Holytown	d																							
Wishaw	d					09 40							10 40							11 40				
Carluke	d					09 47							10 47							11 49				
Lanark	a					09 59							10 59							11 59				

For general notes see front of timetable
For details of catering facilities see Directory of Train Operators

§ Low Level

Table 226

Sundays

Helensburgh, Balloch, Dalmuir and Milngavie → Glasgow → Springburn, Airdrie, Drumgelloch, Hamilton, Larkhall, Motherwell, Coatbridge and Lanark

until 23 November

Network Diagram - see first page of Table 220

		SR	SR	SR		SR	SR	SR	SR	SR	SR	SR	SR	SR	SR	SR	SR		SR	SR	SR	SR	SR	SR	SR
Helensburgh Central	d	10 55				11 25				11 55			12 25				12 55				13 25				13 55
Craigendoran	d	10 58				11 28				11 58			12 28				12 58				13 28				13 58
Cardross	d	11 03				11 33				12 03			12 33				13 03				13 33				14 03
Balloch	d		11 09				11 39				12 09			12 39					13 09			13 39			
Alexandria	d		11 11				11 41				12 11			12 41					13 11			13 41			
Renton	d		11 14				11 44				12 14			12 44					13 14			13 44			
Dalreoch	d	11 08	11 17			11 38	11 47			12 08	12 17		12 38	12 47			13 08		13 17		13 38	13 47			14 08
Dumbarton Central	d	11 10	11 18			11 40	11 48			12 10	12 18		12 40	12 48			13 10		13 18		13 40	13 48			14 10
Dumbarton East	d	11 12	11 20			11 42	11 50			12 12	12 20		12 42	12 50			13 12		13 20		13 42	13 50			14 12
Bowling	d		11 24				11 54				12 24			12 54					13 24			13 54			
Kilpatrick	d		11 28				11 58				12 28			12 58					13 28			13 58			
Dalmuir	a	11 19	11 30			11 49	12 00			12 19	12 30		12 49	13 00			13 19		13 30		13 49	14 00			14 19
	d	11 20	11 31			11 50	12 01			12 20	12 31		12 50	13 01			13 20		13 31		13 50	14 01			14 20
Singer	d	11 22				11 52				12 22			12 52				13 22				13 52				14 22
Drumry	d	11 25				11 55				12 25			12 55				13 25				13 55				14 25
Drumchapel	d	11 27				11 57				12 27			12 57				13 27				13 57				14 27
Milngavie	d			11 41				12 11				12 41			13 11					13 41			14 11		
Hillfoot	d			11 44				12 14				12 44			13 14					13 44			14 14		
Bearsden	d			11 46				12 16				12 46			13 16					13 46			14 16		
Westerton	d	11 30		11 49		12 00		12 19		12 30		12 49	13 00		13 19		13 30			13 49	14 00		14 19		14 30
Anniesland	d	11 33		11 52		12 03		12 22		12 33		12 52	13 03		13 22		13 33			13 52	14 03		14 22		14 33
Clydebank	d		11 33				12 03				12 33			13 03					13 33			14 03			
Yoker	d		11 35				12 05				12 35			13 05					13 35			14 05			
Garscadden	d		11 39				12 09				12 39			13 09					13 39			14 09			
Scotstounhill	d		11 41				12 11				12 41			13 11					13 41			14 11			
Jordanhill	d		11 43				12 13				12 43			13 13					13 43			14 13			
Hyndland	d	11 35	11 45	11 55		12 05	12 15	12 25		12 35	12 45	12 55	13 05	13 15	13 25		13 35		13 45	13 55	14 05	14 15	14 25		14 35
Partick	d	11 38	11 48	11 58		12 08	12 18	12 28	12 34	12 38	12 48	12 58	13 08	13 18	13 28	13 34	13 38		13 48	13 58	14 08	14 18	14 28	14 34	14 38
Exhibition Centre	d		11 51	12 01			12 21	12 31	12 37		12 51	13 01		13 21	13 31	13 37			13 51	14 01		14 21	14 31	14 37	
Anderston	d																								
Glasgow Central 15 §	a		11 53	12 03			12 23	12 33	12 39		12 53	13 03		13 23	13 33	13 39			13 53	14 03		14 23	14 33	14 39	
	d		11 54	12 04			12 24	12 34	12 40		12 54	13 04		13 24	13 34	13 40			13 54	14 04		14 24	14 34	14 40	
Argyle Street	d		11 56	12 06			12 26	12 36	12 42		12 56	13 06		13 26	13 36	13 42			13 56	14 06		14 26	14 36	14 42	
Charing Cross	d	11 43				12 13				12 43			13 13				13 43				14 13				14 43
Glasgow Queen Street 10 §	a	11 45				12 15				12 45			13 15				13 45				14 15				14 45
	d	11 47				12 17				12 47			13 17				13 47				14 17				14 47
High Street	d	11 49				12 19				12 49			13 19				13 49				14 19				14 49
Bellgrove	d	11 51				12 21				12 51			13 21				13 51				14 21				14 51
Duke Street	d																								
Alexandra Parade	d																								
Barnhill	d																								
Springburn	a																								
Carntyne	d	11 54				12 24				12 54			13 24				13 54				14 24				14 54
Shettleston	d	11 57				12 27				12 57			13 27				13 57				14 27				14 57
Garrowhill	d	11 59				12 29				12 59			13 29				13 59				14 29				14 59
Easterhouse	d	12 02				12 32				13 02			13 32				14 02				14 32				15 02
Blairhill	d	12 06				12 36				13 06			13 36				14 06				14 36				15 06
Coatbridge Sunnyside	d	12 08				12 38				13 08			13 38				14 08				14 38				15 08
Coatdyke	d	12 11				12 41				13 11			13 41				14 11				14 41				15 11
Airdrie	a	12 14				12 44				13 14			13 44				14 14				14 44				15 14
	d	12 15				12 45				13 15			13 45				14 15				14 45				15 15
Drumgelloch	a	12 18				12 48				13 18			13 48				14 18				14 48				15 18
Bridgeton	d		11 59	12 09			12 29	12 39			12 59	13 09		13 29	13 39				13 59	14 09		14 29	14 39		
Dalmarnock	d																								
Rutherglen	d		12 02	12 12			12 32	12 42	12 47		13 02	13 12		13 32	13 42	13 47			14 02	14 12		14 32	14 42	14 47	
Cambuslang	d		12 06	12 16			12 36	12 46			13 06	13 16		13 36	13 46				14 06	14 16		14 36	14 46		
Newton	d		12 09				12 39				13 09			13 39					14 09			14 39			
Blantyre	d		12 13				12 43		12 55		13 13			13 43		13 55			14 13			14 43		14 55	
Hamilton West	d		12 16				12 46		12 58		13 16			13 46		13 58			14 16			14 46		14 58	
Hamilton Central	d		12 20				12 50		13 01		13 20			13 50		14 01			14 20			14 50		15 01	
Chatelherault	d								13 06							14 06								15 06	
Merryton	d								13 09							14 09								15 09	
Larkhall	a								13 15							14 13								15 11	
Airbles	d		12 25				12 55				13 25			13 55					14 25			14 55			
Uddingston	d			12 20				12 50				13 20			13 50					14 20			14 50		
Bellshill	d			12 25				12 55				13 25			13 55					14 25			14 55		
Motherwell	a		12 27	12 33			12 57	13 03			13 27	13 33		13 57	14 03				14 27	14 33		14 57	15 03		
	d			12 33								13 33								14 33					
Whifflet	a																								
Coatbridge Central	a																								
Shieldmuir	d			12 37								13 37								14 37					
Holytown	d																								
Wishaw	d			12 40								13 40								14 40					
Carluke	d			12 47								13 47								14 47					
Lanark	a			12 59								13 59								14 59					

For general notes see front of timetable
For details of catering facilities see Directory of Train Operators

§ Low Level

Table 226

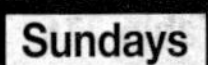

until 23 November

Helensburgh, Balloch, Dalmuir and Milngavie → Glasgow → Springburn, Airdrie, Drumgelloch, Hamilton, Larkhall, Motherwell, Coatbridge and Lanark

Network Diagram - see first page of Table 220

		SR	SR	SR	SR	SR ◇ A	SR	SR	SR	SR	SR	SR	SR	SR	SR	SR	SR	SR	SR	SR	SR	SR	SR
Helensburgh Central	d			14 25		14b39			14 55			15 25				15 55			16 25				16 55
Craigendoran	d			14 28					14 58			15 28				15 58			16 28				16 58
Cardross	d			14 33					15 03			15 33				16 03			16 33				17 03
Balloch	d	14 09			14 39					15 09			15 39				16 09			16 39			
Alexandria	d	14 11			14 41					15 11			15 41				16 11			16 41			
Renton	d	14 14			14 44					15 14			15 44				16 14			16 44			
Dalreoch	d	14 17		14 38	14 47				15 08	15 17		15 38	15 47			16 08	16 17		16 38	16 47			17 08
Dumbarton Central	d	14 18		14 40	14 48	14 53			15 10	15 18		15 40	15 48			16 10	16 18		16 40	16 48			17 10
Dumbarton East	d	14 20		14 42	14 50				15 12	15 20		15 42	15 50			16 12	16 20		16 42	16 50			17 12
Bowling	d	14 24			14 54					15 24			15 54				16 24			16 54			
Kilpatrick	d	14 28			14 58					15 28			15 58				16 28			16 58			
Dalmuir	a	14 30		14 49	15 00	15 05			15 19	15 30		15 49	16 00			16 19	16 30		16 49	17 00			17 19
	d	14 31		14 50	15 01	15 05			15 20	15 31		15 50	16 01			16 20	16 31		16 50	17 01			17 20
Singer	d			14 52					15 22			15 52				16 22			16 52				17 22
Drumry	d			14 55					15 25			15 55				16 25			16 55				17 25
Drumchapel	d			14 57					15 27			15 57				16 27			16 57				17 27
Milngavie	d		14 41				15 11				15 41			16 11				16 41			17 11		
Hillfoot	d		14 44				15 14				15 44			16 14				16 44			17 14		
Bearsden	d		14 46				15 16				15 46			16 16				16 46			17 16		
Westerton	d		14 49	15 00			15 19		15 30		15 49	16 00		16 19		16 30		16 49	17 00		17 19		17 30
Anniesland	d		14 52	15 03			15 22		15 33		15 52	16 03		16 22		16 33		16 52	17 03		17 22		17 33
Clydebank	d	14 33			15 03					15 33			16 03				16 33			17 03			
Yoker	d	14 35			15 05					15 35			16 05				16 35			17 05			
Garscadden	d	14 39			15 09					15 39			16 09				16 39			17 09			
Scotstounhill	d	14 41			15 11					15 41			16 11				16 41			17 11			
Jordanhill	d	14 43			15 13					15 43			16 13				16 43			17 13			
Hyndland	d	14 45	14 55	15 05	15 15		15 25		15 35	15 45	15 55	16 05	16 15	16 25		16 35	16 45	16 55	17 05	17 15	17 25		17 35
Partick	d	14 48	14 58	15 08	15 18		15 28	15 34	15 38	15 48	15 58	16 08	16 18	16 28	16 34	16 38	16 48	16 58	17 08	17 18	17 28	17 34	17 38
Exhibition Centre	d	14 51	15 01		15 21		15 31	15 37		15 51	16 01		16 21	16 31	16 37		16 51	17 01		17 21	17 31	17 37	
Anderston	d																						
Glasgow Central 15 §	a	14 53	15 03		15 23		15 33	15 39		15 53	16 03		16 23	16 33	16 39		16 53	17 03		17 23	17 33	17 39	
	d	14 54	15 04		15 24		15 34	15 40		15 54	16 04		16 24	16 34	16 40		16 54	17 04		17 24	17 34	17 40	
Argyle Street	d	14 56	15 06		15 26		15 36	15 42		15 56	16 06		16 26	16 36	16 42		16 56	17 06		17 26	17 36	17 42	
Charing Cross	d			15 13					15 43			16 13				16 43			17 13				17 43
Glasgow Queen Street 10 §	a			15 15		15c32			15 45			16 15				16 45			17 15				17 45
	d			15 17					15 47			16 17				16 47			17 17				17 47
High Street	d			15 19					15 49			16 19				16 49			17 19				17 49
Bellgrove	d			15 21					15 51			16 21				16 51			17 21				17 51
Duke Street	d																						
Alexandra Parade	d																						
Barnhill	d																						
Springburn	a																						
Carntyne	d			15 24					15 54			16 24				16 54			17 24				17 54
Shettleston	d			15 27					15 57			16 27				16 57			17 27				17 57
Garrowhill	d			15 29					15 59			16 29				16 59			17 29				17 59
Easterhouse	d			15 32					16 02			16 32				17 02			17 32				18 02
Blairhill	d			15 36					16 06			16 36				17 06			17 36				18 06
Coatbridge Sunnyside	d			15 38					16 08			16 38				17 08			17 38				18 08
Coatdyke	d			15 41					16 11			16 41				17 11			17 41				18 11
Airdrie	a			15 44					16 14			16 44				17 14			17 44				18 14
	d			15 45					16 15			16 45				17 15			17 45				18 15
Drumgelloch	a			15 48					16 18			16 48				17 18			17 48				18 18
Bridgeton	d	14 59	15 09		15 29		15 39			15 59	16 09		16 29	16 39			16 59	17 09		17 29	17 39		
Dalmarnock	d																						
Rutherglen	d	15 02	15 12		15 32		15 42	15 47		16 02	16 12		16 32	16 42	16 47		17 02	17 12		17 32	17 42	17 47	
Cambuslang	d	15 06	15 16		15 36		15 46			16 06	16 16		16 36	16 46			17 06	17 16		17 36	17 46		
Newton	d	15 09			15 39					16 09			16 39				17 09			17 39			
Blantyre	d	15 13			15 43			15 55		16 13			16 43		16 55		17 13			17 43		17 55	
Hamilton West	d	15 16			15 46			15 58		16 16			16 46		16 58		17 16			17 46		17 58	
Hamilton Central	d	15 20			15 50			16 01		16 20			16 50		17 01		17 20			17 50		18 01	
Chatelherault	d							16 06							17 06							18 06	
Merryton	d							16 09							17 09							18 09	
Larkhall	a							16 15							17 11							18 11	
Airbles	d	15 25			15 55					16 25			16 55				17 25			17 55			
Uddingston	d		15 20				15 50				16 20			16 50				17 20			17 50		
Bellshill	d		15 25				15 55				16 25			16 55				17 25			17 55		
Motherwell	a	15 27	15 33		15 57		16 02			16 27	16 33		16 57	17 03			17 27	17 33		17 57	18 03		
	d		15 33								16 33							17 33					
Whifflet	a																						
Coatbridge Central	a																						
Shieldmuir	d		15 37								16 37							17 37					
Holytown	d																						
Wishaw	d		15 40								16 40							17 40					
Carluke	d		15 47								16 47							17 47					
Lanark	a		15 59								16 59							17 59					

For general notes see front of timetable
For details of catering facilities see Directory of Train Operators

§ Low Level

A Until 26 October. From Oban (Table 227). Until 28 September also conveys portion from Mallaig

b Helensburgh Upper

c Glasgow Queen Street High Level

Table 226

Helensburgh, Balloch, Dalmuir and Milngavie → Glasgow → Springburn, Airdrie, Drumgelloch, Hamilton, Larkhall, Motherwell, Coatbridge and Lanark

until 23 November

Network Diagram - see first page of Table 220

		SR	SR	SR	SR	SR	SR	SR	SR	SR	SR	SR ◇ A		SR	SR	SR	SR	SR	SR	SR	SR	SR	SR	SR	SR
Helensburgh Central	d			17 25				17 55			18 25	18b34					18 55			19 25				19 55	
Craigendoran	d			17 28				17 58			18 28						18 58			19 28				19 58	
Cardross	d			17 33				18 03			18 33						19 03			19 33				20 03	
Balloch	d	17 09			17 39				18 09					18 39				19 09			19 39				20 09
Alexandria	d	17 11			17 41				18 11					18 41				19 11			19 41				20 11
Renton	d	17 14			17 44				18 14					18 44				19 14			19 44				20 14
Dalreoch	d	17 17		17 38	17 47			18 08	18 17		18 38			18 47			19 08	19 17		19 38	19 47			20 08	20 17
Dumbarton Central	d	17 18		17 40	17 48			18 10	18 18		18 40	18 47		18 48			19 10	19 18		19 40	19 48			20 10	20 18
Dumbarton East	d	17 20		17 42	17 50			18 12	18 20		18 42			18 50			19 12	19 20		19 42	19 50			20 12	20 20
Bowling	d	17 24			17 54				18 24					18 54				19 24			19 54				20 24
Kilpatrick	d	17 28			17 58				18 28					18 58				19 28			19 58				20 28
Dalmuir	a	17 30		17 49	18 00			18 19	18 30		18 49	18 56		19 00			19 19	19 30		19 49	20 00			20 19	20 30
	d	17 31		17 50	18 01			18 20	18 31		18 50	18 56		19 01			19 20	19 31		19 50	20 01			20 20	20 31
Singer	d			17 52				18 22			18 52						19 22			19 52				20 22	
Drumry	d			17 55				18 25			18 55						19 25			19 55				20 25	
Drumchapel	d			17 57				18 27			18 57						19 27			19 57				20 27	
Milngavie	d		17 41			18 11				18 41					19 11				19 41			20 11			
Hillfoot	d		17 44			18 14				18 44					19 14				19 44			20 14			
Bearsden	d		17 46			18 16				18 46					19 16				19 46			20 16			
Westerton	d		17 49	18 00		18 19		18 30		18 49	19 00				19 19		19 30		19 49	20 00		20 19		20 30	
Anniesland	d		17 52	18 03		18 22		18 33		18 52	19 03				19 22		19 33		19 52	20 03		20 22		20 33	
Clydebank	d	17 33			18 03				18 33					19 03				19 33			20 03				20 33
Yoker	d	17 35			18 05				18 35					19 05				19 35			20 05				20 35
Garscadden	d	17 39			18 09				18 39					19 09				19 39			20 09				20 39
Scotstounhill	d	17 41			18 11				18 41					19 11				19 41			20 11				20 41
Jordanhill	d	17 43			18 13				18 43					19 13				19 43			20 13				20 43
Hyndland	d	17 45	17 55	18 05	18 15	18 25		18 35	18 45	18 55	19 05			19 15	19 25		19 35	19 45	19 55	20 05	20 15	20 25		20 35	20 45
Partick	d	17 48	17 58	18 08	18 18	18 28	18 34	18 38	18 48	18 58	19 08			19 18	19 28	19 34	19 38	19 48	19 58	20 08	20 18	20 28	20 34	20 38	20 48
Exhibition Centre	d	17 51	18 01		18 21	18 31	18 37		18 51	19 01				19 21	19 31	19 37		19 51	20 01		20 21	20 31	20 37		20 51
Anderston	d																								
Glasgow Central 15 §	a	17 53	18 03		18 23	18 33	18 39		18 53	19 03				19 23	19 33	19 39		19 53	20 03		20 23	20 33	20 39		20 53
	d	17 54	18 04		18 24	18 34	18 40		18 54	19 04				19 24	19 34	19 40		19 54	20 04		20 24	20 34	20 40		20 54
Argyle Street	d	17 56	18 06																						
Charing Cross	d			18 13				18 43			19 13						19 43			20 13				20 43	
Glasgow Queen Street 10 §	a			18 15				18 45			19 15	19c18					19 45			20 15				20 45	
	d			18 17				18 47			19 17						19 47			20 17				20 47	
High Street	d			18 19				18 49			19 19						19 49			20 19				20 49	
Bellgrove	d			18 21				18 51			19 21						19 51			20 21				20 51	
Duke Street	d																								
Alexandra Parade	d																								
Barnhill	d																								
Springburn	a																								
Carntyne	d			18 24				18 54			19 24						19 54			20 24				20 54	
Shettleston	d			18 27				18 57			19 27						19 57			20 27				20 57	
Garrowhill	d			18 29				18 59			19 29						19 59			20 29				20 59	
Easterhouse	d			18 32				19 02			19 32						20 02			20 32				21 02	
Blairhill	d			18 36				19 06			19 36						20 06			20 36				21 06	
Coatbridge Sunnyside	d			18 38				19 08			19 38						20 08			20 38				21 08	
Coatdyke	d			18 41				19 11			19 41						20 11			20 41				21 11	
Airdrie	a			18 44				19 14			19 44						20 14			20 44				21 14	
	d			18 45				19 15			19 45						20 15			20 45				21 15	
Drumgelloch	a			18 48				19 18			19 48						20 18			20 48				21 18	
Bridgeton	d	17 59	18 09		18 29	18 39			18 59	19 09				19 29	19 39			19 59	20 09		20 29	20 39			20 59
Dalmarnock	d																								
Rutherglen	d	18 02	18 12		18 32	18 42	18 47		19 02	19 12				19 32	19 42	19 47		20 02	20 12		20 32	20 42	20 47		21 02
Cambuslang	d	18 06	18 16		18 36	18 46			19 06	19 16				19 36	19 46			20 06	20 16		20 36	20 46			21 06
Newton	d	18 09			18 39				19 09					19 39				20 09			20 39				21 09
Blantyre	d	18 13			18 43		18 55		19 13					19 43		19 55		20 13			20 43		20 55		21 13
Hamilton West	d	18 16			18 46		18 58		19 16					19 46		19 58		20 16			20 46		20 58		21 16
Hamilton Central	d	18 20			18 50		19 01		19 20					19 50		20 01		20 20			20 50		21 01		21 20
Chatelherault	d						19 06									20 06							21 06		
Merryton	d						19 09									20 09							21 09		
Larkhall	a						19 12									20 11							21e11		
Airbles	d	18 25			18 55				19 25					19 55				20 25			20 55				21 25
Uddingston	d		18 20			18 50				19 20					19 50				20 20			20 50			
Bellshill	d		18 25			18 55				19 25					19 55				20 25			20 55			
Motherwell	a	18 27	18 33		18 57	19 03			19 27	19 33				19 57	20 03			20 27	20 33		20 57	21 04			21 27
	d		18 33							19 33									20 33						
Whifflet	a																								
Coatbridge Central	a																								
Shieldmuir	d		18 37							19 37									20 37						
Holytown	d																								
Wishaw	d		18 40							19 40									20 40						
Carluke	d		18 47							19 47									20 47						
Lanark	a		18 59							19 59									20 59						

For general notes see front of timetable
For details of catering facilities see Directory of Train Operators

§ Low Level

A Until 28 September. From Oban (Table 227)

b Helensburgh Upper

c Glasgow Queen Street High Level

e 20 July to 7 September arr. 2113

Table 226

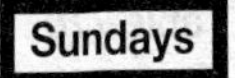

Sundays

until 23 November

Helensburgh, Balloch, Dalmuir and Milngavie → Glasgow → Springburn, Airdrie, Drumgelloch, Hamilton, Larkhall, Motherwell, Coatbridge and Lanark

Network Diagram - see first page of Table 220

		SR	SR	SR	SR ◇ A	SR	SR	SR	SR	SR	SR	SR	SR	SR	SR	SR	SR	SR	SR	SR R B	SR	SR
Helensburgh Central	d		20 25		20b40			20 55			21 25				21 55			22 25		22b37	22 55	
Craigendoran	d		20 28					20 58			21 28				21 58			22 28			22 58	
Cardross	d		20 33					21 03			21 33				22 03			22 33			23 03	
Balloch	d			20 39					21 09			21 39				22 09			22 39			23 09
Alexandria	d			20 41					21 11			21 41				22 11			22 41			23 11
Renton	d			20 44					21 14			21 44				22 14			22 44			23 14
Dalreoch	d		20 38	20 47				21 08	21 17		21 38	21 47			22 08	22 17		22 38	22 47		23 08	23 17
Dumbarton Central	d		20 40	20 48	20 53			21 10	21 18		21 40	21 48			22 10	22 18		22 40	22 48		23 10	23 18
Dumbarton East	d		20 42	20 50				21 12	21 20		21 42	21 50			22 12	22 20		22 42	22 50		23 12	23 20
Bowling	d			20 54					21 24			21 54				22 24			22 55			23 25
Kilpatrick	d			20 58					21 28			21 58				22 28			22 58			23 28
Dalmuir	a		20 49	21 00	21 05			21 19	21 30		21 49	22 00			22 19	22 30		22 49	23 01	23 02	23 19	23 31
	d		20 50	21 01	21 05			21 20	21 31		21 50	22 01			22 20	22 31		22 50	23 01	23 04		23 31
Singer	d		20 52					21 22			21 52				22 22			22 52				
Drumry	d		20 55					21 25			21 55				22 25			22 55				
Drumchapel	d		20 57					21 27			21 57				22 27			22 57				
Milngavie	d	20 41				21 11				21 41			22 11				22 41					
Hillfoot	d	20 44				21 14				21 44			22 14				22 44					
Bearsden	d	20 46				21 16				21 46			22 16				22 46					
Westerton	d	20 49	21 00			21 19		21 30		21 49	22 00		22 19		22 30		22 49	23 00		23a11		
Anniesland	d	20 52	21 03			21 22		21 33		21 52	22 03		22 22		22 33		22 52	23 03				
Clydebank	d			21 03					21 33			22 03				22 33			23 03			23 33
Yoker	d			21 05					21 35			22 05				22 35			23a05			23a35
Garscadden	d			21 09					21 39			22 09				22 39						
Scotstounhill	d			21 11					21 41			22 11				22 41						
Jordanhill	d			21 13					21 43			22 13				22 43						
Hyndland	d	20 55	21 05	21 15		21 25		21 35	21 45	21 55	22 05	22 15	22 25		22 35	22 45	22 55	23 05				
Partick	d	20 58	21 08	21 18		21 28	21 34	21 38	21 48	21 58	22 08	22 18	22 28	22 34	22 38	22 48	22 58	23 08				
Exhibition Centre	d	21 01		21 21		21 31	21 37		21 51	22 01		22 21	22 31	22 37		22 51	23 01					
Anderston	d																					
Glasgow Central 15 §	a	21 03		21 23		21 33	21 39		21 53	22 03		22 23	22 33	22 39		22 53	23 03					
	d	21 04		21 24		21 34	21 40		21 54	22 04		22 24	22 34	22 40		22 54	23 04					
Argyle Street	d																					
Charing Cross	d		21 13					21 43			22 13				22 43			23 13				
Glasgow Queen Street 10 §	a		21 15		21c27			21 45			22 15				22 45			23 15				
	d		21 17					21 47			22 17				22 47			23 17				
High Street	d		21 19					21 49			22 19				22 49			23 19				
Bellgrove	d		21 21					21 51			22 21				22 51			23 21				
Duke Street	d																					
Alexandra Parade	d																					
Barnhill	d																					
Springburn	a																					
Carntyne	d		21 24					21 54			22 24				22 54			23 24				
Shettleston	d		21 27					21 57			22 27				22 57			23 27				
Garrowhill	d		21 29					21 59			22 29				22 59			23 29				
Easterhouse	d		21 32					22 02			22 32				23 02			23 32				
Blairhill	d		21 36					22 06			22 36				23 06			23 36				
Coatbridge Sunnyside	d		21 38					22 08			22 38				23 08			23 38				
Coatdyke	d		21 41					22 11			22 41				23 11			23 41				
Airdrie	a		21 44					22 14			22 44				23 14			23 44				
	d		21 45					22 15			22 45				23 15			23 45				
Drumgelloch	a		21 48					22 18			22 48				23 18			23 48				
Bridgeton	d	21 09		21 29		21 39			21 59	22 09		22 29	22 39			22 59	23 09					
Dalmarnock	d																					
Rutherglen	d	21 12		21 32		21 42	21 47		22 02	22 12		22 32	22 42	22 47		23 02	23 12					
Cambuslang	d	21 16		21 36		21 46			22 06	22 16		22 36	22 46			23 06	23 16					
Newton	d			21 39					22 09			22 39				23 09						
Blantyre	d			21 43			21 55		22 13			22 43		22 55		23 13						
Hamilton West	d			21 46			21 58		22 16			22 46		22 58		23 16						
Hamilton Central	d			21 50			22 01		22 20			22 50		23 01		23 20						
Chatelherault	d						22 06							23 06								
Merryton	d						22 09							23 09								
Larkhall	a						22 13							23 11								
Airbles	d			21 55					22 25			22 55				23 25						
Uddingston	d	21 20				21 50				22 20			22 50				23 20					
Bellshill	d	21 25				21 55				22 25			22 55				23 25					
Motherwell	a	21 33		21 57		22 03			22 27	22 33		22 57	23 06			23 27	23 33					
	d	21 33								22 33												
Whifflet	a																					
Coatbridge Central	a																					
Shieldmuir	d	21 37								22 37												
Holytown	d																					
Wishaw	d	21 40								22 40												
Carluke	d	21 47								22 47												
Lanark	a	21 59								22 59												

For general notes see front of timetable
For details of catering facilities see Directory of Train Operators

§ Low Level

A From Oban and from Mallaig (Table 227)

B Limited seating accommodation. Also conveys overnight Sleeping Car accommodation from Fort William to London Euston (Tables 65 and 404)

b Helensburgh Upper

c Glasgow Queen Street High Level

Table 226

Sundays

from 30 November

Helensburgh, Balloch, Dalmuir and Milngavie → Glasgow → Springburn, Airdrie, Drumgelloch, Hamilton, Larkhall, Motherwell, Coatbridge and Lanark

Network Diagram - see first page of Table 220

		SR	SR	SR	SR	SR	SR	SR	SR	SR	SR	SR	SR	SR	SR	SR	SR	SR	SR	SR	SR	SR
Helensburgh Central	d			07 55			08 25						08 55					09 25				
Craigendoran	d			07 58			08 28						08 58					09 28				
Cardross	d			08 03			08 33						09 03					09 33				
Balloch	d				08 09			08 39						09 09					09 39			
Alexandria	d				08 11			08 41						09 11					09 41			
Renton	d				08 14			08 44						09 14					09 44			
Dalreoch	d			08 08	08 17		08 38	08 47					09 08	09 17				09 38	09 47			
Dumbarton Central	d			08 10	08 18		08 40	08 48					09 10	09 18				09 40	09 48			
Dumbarton East	d			08 12	08 20		08 42	08 50					09 12	09 20				09 42	09 50			
Bowling	d				08 24			08 54						09 24					09 54			
Kilpatrick	d				08 28			08 58						09 28					09 58			
Dalmuir	a			08 19	08 30		08 49	09 00					09 19	09 30				09 49	10 00			
	d	07 50	08 01	08 20	08 31		08 50	09 01	09 05		09 15		09 20	09 31	09 35		09 45	09 50	10 01	10 05		10 15
Singer	d	07 52		08 22			08 52		09 07				09 22		09 37			09 52		10 07		
Drumry	d	07 55		08 25			08 55		09 09				09 25		09 39			09 55		10 09		
Drumchapel	d	07 57		08 27			08 57		09 12				09 27		09 42			09 57		10 12		
Milngavie	d									09 11						09 41					10 11	
Hillfoot	d									09 14						09 44					10 14	
Bearsden	d									09 16						09 46					10 16	
Westerton	d	08 00		08 30			09 00		09 14	09 19			09 30		09 44	09 49		10 00		10 14	10 19	
Anniesland	d	08 03		08 33			09 03		09 17	09 22			09 33		09 47	09 52		10 03		10 17	10 22	
Clydebank	d		08 03		08 33			09 03			09 17			09 33			09 47		10 03			10 17
Yoker	d		08 05		08 35			09 05			09 19			09 35			09 49		10 05			10 19
Garscadden	d		08 09		08 39			09 09			09 22			09 39			09 52		10 09			10 22
Scotstounhill	d		08 11		08 41			09 11			09 24			09 41			09 54		10 11			10 24
Jordanhill	d		08 13		08 43			09 13			09 26			09 43			09 56		10 13			10 26
Hyndland	d	08 05	08 15	08 35	08 45	08 55	09 05	09 15	09 20	09 25	09 28		09 35	09 45	09 50	09 55	09 58	10 05	10 15	10 20	10 25	10 28
Partick	d	08 08	08 18	08 38	08 48	08 58	09 08	09 18	09 22	09 28	09 30	09 34	09 38	09 48	09 52	09 58	10 00	10 08	10 18	10 22	10 28	10 30
Exhibition Centre	d		08 21		08 51	09 01		09 21		09 31		09 37		09 51		10 01			10 21		10 31	
Anderston	d																					
Glasgow Central 15 §	a		08 23		08 53	09 03		09 23		09 33		09 39		09 53		10 03			10 23		10 33	
	d		08 24		08 54	09 04		09 24		09 34		09 40		09 54		10 04			10 24		10 34	
Argyle Street	d													09 56		10 06			10 26		10 36	
Charing Cross	d	08 13		08 43			09 13		09 26		09 34		09 43		09 56		10 04	10 13		10 26		10 34
Glasgow Queen Street 10 §	a	08 15		08 45			09 15		09 28		09 36		09 45		09 58		10 06	10 15		10 28		10 36
	d	08 17		08 47			09 17		09 29		09 37		09 47		09 59		10 07	10 17		10 29		10 37
High Street	d	08 19		08 49			09 19		09 31		09 39		09 49		10 01		10 09	10 19		10 31		10 39
Bellgrove	d	08 21		08 51			09 21		09 33		09 41		09 51		10 03		10 11	10 21		10 33		10 41
Duke Street	d								09 35						10 05					10 35		
Alexandra Parade	d								09 36						10 06					10 36		
Barnhill	d								09 39						10 09					10 39		
Springburn	a								09 41						10 11					10 41		
Carntyne	d	08 24		08 54			09 24				09 44		09 54				10 14	10 24				10 44
Shettleston	d	08 27		08 57			09 27				09 47		09 57				10 17	10 27				10 47
Garrowhill	d	08 29		08 59			09 29				09 49		09 59				10 19	10 29				10 49
Easterhouse	d	08 32		09 02			09 32				09 52		10 02				10 22	10 32				10 52
Blairhill	d	08 36		09 06			09 36				09 56		10 06				10 26	10 36				10 56
Coatbridge Sunnyside	d	08 38		09 08			09 38				09 58		10 08				10 28	10 38				10 58
Coatdyke	d	08 41		09 11			09 41				10 01		10 11				10 31	10 41				11 01
Airdrie	a	08 44		09 14			09 44				10 04		10 14				10 34	10 44				11 04
	d	08 45		09 15			09 45						10 15					10 45				
Drumgelloch	a	08 48		09 18			09 48						10 18					10 48				
Bridgeton	d		08 29		08 59	09 09		09 29		09 39				09 59		10 09			10 29		10 39	
Dalmarnock	d																					
Rutherglen	d		08 32		09 02	09 12		09 32		09 42		09 47		10 02		10 12			10 32		10 42	
Cambuslang	d		08 36		09 06	09 16		09 36		09 46				10 06		10 16			10 36		10 46	
Newton	d				09 09			09 39						10 09					10 39			
Blantyre	d				09 13			09 43				09 55		10 13					10 43			
Hamilton West	d				09 16			09 46				09 58		10 16					10 46			
Hamilton Central	d				09 20			09 50				10 01		10 20					10 50			
Chatelherault	d											10 06										
Merryton	d											10 09										
Larkhall	a											10 11										
Airbles	d				09 25			09 55						10 25					10 55			
Uddingston	d		08 40			09 20				09 50						10 20					10 50	
Bellshill	d		08 45			09 25				09 55						10 25					10 55	
Motherwell	a		08 53		09 27	09 33		09 57		10 03				10 27		10 33			10 57		11 03	
	d					09 33										10 33						
Whifflet	a																					
Coatbridge Central	a																					
Shieldmuir	d					09 37										10 37						
Holytown	d																					
Wishaw	d					09 40										10 40						
Carluke	d					09 47										10 47						
Lanark	a					09 59										10 59						

For general notes see front of timetable
For details of catering facilities see Directory of Train Operators

§ Low Level

Table 226

Sundays from 30 November

Helensburgh, Balloch, Dalmuir and Milngavie → Glasgow → Springburn, Airdrie, Drumgelloch, Hamilton, Larkhall, Motherwell, Coatbridge and Lanark

Network Diagram - see first page of Table 220

		SR	SR	SR	SR	SR	SR	SR	SR	SR	SR	SR	SR	SR	SR	SR	SR	SR	SR	SR	SR	SR
Helensburgh Central	d		09 55					10 25						10 55					11 25			
Craigendoran	d		09 58					10 28						10 58					11 28			
Cardross	d		10 03					10 33						11 03					11 33			
Balloch	d			10 09					10 39						11 09					11 39		
Alexandria	d			10 11					10 41						11 11					11 41		
Renton	d			10 14					10 44						11 14					11 44		
Dalreoch	d		10 08	10 17				10 38	10 47					11 08	11 17				11 38	11 47		
Dumbarton Central	d		10 10	10 18				10 40	10 48					11 10	11 18				11 40	11 48		
Dumbarton East	d		10 12	10 20				10 42	10 50					11 12	11 20				11 42	11 50		
Bowling	d			10 24					10 54						11 24					11 54		
Kilpatrick	d			10 28					10 58						11 28					11 58		
Dalmuir	a		10 19	10 30				10 49	11 00					11 19	11 30				11 49	12 00		
	d		10 20	10 31	10 35		10 45	10 50	11 01	11 05		11 15		11 20	11 31	11 35		11 45	11 50	12 01	12 05	
Singer	d		10 22		10 37			10 52		11 07				11 22		11 37			11 52		12 07	
Drumry	d		10 25		10 39			10 55		11 09				11 25		11 39			11 55		12 09	
Drumchapel	d		10 27		10 42			10 57		11 12				11 27		11 42			11 57		12 12	
Milngavie	d					10 41					11 11						11 41					12 11
Hillfoot	d					10 44					11 14						11 44					12 14
Bearsden	d					10 46					11 16						11 46					12 16
Westerton	d		10 30		10 44	10 49		11 00		11 14	11 19			11 30		11 44	11 49		12 00		12 14	12 19
Anniesland	d		10 33		10 47	10 52		11 03		11 17	11 22			11 33		11 47	11 52		12 03		12 17	12 22
Clydebank	d			10 33			10 47		11 03			11 17			11 33			11 47		12 03		
Yoker	d			10 35			10 49		11 05			11 19			11 35			11 49		12 05		
Garscadden	d			10 39			10 52		11 09			11 22			11 39			11 52		12 09		
Scotstounhill	d			10 41			10 54		11 11			11 24			11 41			11 54		12 11		
Jordanhill	d			10 43			10 56		11 13			11 26			11 43			11 56		12 13		
Hyndland	d		10 35	10 45	10 50	10 55	10 58	11 05	11 15	11 20	11 25	11 28		11 35	11 45	11 50	11 55	11 58	12 05	12 15	12 20	12 25
Partick	d	10 34	10 38	10 48	10 52	10 58	11 00	11 08	11 18	11 22	11 28	11 30	11 34	11 38	11 48	11 52	11 58	12 00	12 08	12 18	12 22	12 28
Exhibition Centre	d	10 37		10 51		11 01			11 21		11 31		11 37		11 51		12 01			12 21		12 31
Anderston	d																					
Glasgow Central 15 §	a	10 39		10 53		11 03			11 23		11 33		11 39		11 53		12 03			12 23		12 33
	d	10 40		10 54		11 04			11 24		11 34		11 40		11 54		12 04			12 24		12 34
Argyle Street	d	10 42		10 56		11 06			11 26		11 36		11 42		11 56		12 06			12 26		12 36
Charing Cross	d		10 43		10 56		11 04	11 13		11 26		11 34		11 43		11 56		12 04	12 13		12 26	
Glasgow Queen Street 10 §	a		10 45		10 58		11 06	11 15		11 28		11 36		11 45		11 58		12 06	12 15		12 28	
	d		10 47		10 59		11 07	11 17		11 29		11 37		11 47		11 59		12 07	12 17		12 29	
High Street	d		10 49		11 01		11 09	11 19		11 31		11 39		11 49		12 01		12 09	12 19		12 31	
Bellgrove	d		10 51		11 03		11 11	11 21		11 33		11 41		11 51		12 03		12 11	12 21		12 33	
Duke Street	d				11 05					11 35						12 05					12 35	
Alexandra Parade	d				11 06					11 36						12 06					12 36	
Barnhill	d				11 09					11 39						12 09					12 39	
Springburn	a				11 11					11 41						12 11					12 41	
Carntyne	d		10 54				11 14	11 24				11 44		11 54				12 14	12 24			
Shettleston	d		10 57				11 17	11 27				11 47		11 57				12 17	12 27			
Garrowhill	d		10 59				11 19	11 29				11 49		11 59				12 19	12 29			
Easterhouse	d		11 02				11 22	11 32				11 52		12 02				12 22	12 32			
Blairhill	d		11 06				11 26	11 36				11 56		12 06				12 26	12 36			
Coatbridge Sunnyside	d		11 08				11 28	11 38				11 58		12 08				12 28	12 38			
Coatdyke	d		11 11				11 31	11 41				12 01		12 11				12 31	12 41			
Airdrie	a		11 14				11 34	11 44				12 04		12 14				12 34	12 44			
	d		11 15					11 45						12 15					12 45			
Drumgelloch	a		11 18					11 48						12 18					12 48			
Bridgeton	d			10 59		11 07			11 29		11 39				11 59		12 09			12 29		12 39
Dalmarnock	d																					
Rutherglen	d	10 47		11 02		11 12			11 32		11 42		11 47		12 02		12 12			12 32		12 42
Cambuslang	d			11 06		11 16			11 36		11 46				12 06		12 16			12 36		12 46
Newton	d			11 09					11 39						12 09					12 39		
Blantyre	d	10 55		11 13					11 43				11 55		12 13					12 43		
Hamilton West	d	10 58		11 16					11 46				11 58		12 16					12 46		
Hamilton Central	d	11 01		11 20					11 50				12 01		12 20					12 50		
Chatelherault	d	11 06											12 06									
Merryton	d	11 09											12 09									
Larkhall	a	11 15											12 12									
Airbles	d			11 25					11 55						12 25					12 55		
Uddingston	d					11 20					11 50						12 20					12 50
Bellshill	d					11 25					11 55						12 25					12 55
Motherwell	a			11 27		11 33			11 57		12 03				12 27		12 33			12 57		13 03
	d					11 33											12 33					
Whifflet	a																					
Coatbridge Central	a																					
Shieldmuir	d					11 37											12 37					
Holytown	d																					
Wishaw	d					11 40											12 40					
Carluke	d					11 49											12 47					
Lanark	a					11 59											12 59					

For general notes see front of timetable
For details of catering facilities see Directory of Train Operators

§ Low Level

Table 226

Sundays

Helensburgh, Balloch, Dalmuir and Milngavie → Glasgow → Springburn, Airdrie, Drumgelloch, Hamilton, Larkhall, Motherwell, Coatbridge and Lanark

from 30 November

Network Diagram - see first page of Table 220

		SR	SR	SR	SR	SR	SR	SR	SR	SR	SR	SR	SR	SR	SR	SR	SR	SR	SR	SR	SR	SR
Helensburgh Central	d			11 55					12 25						12 55					13 25		
Craigendoran	d			11 58					12 28						12 58					13 28		
Cardross	d			12 03					12 33						13 03					13 33		
Balloch	d				12 09					12 39						13 09					13 39	
Alexandria	d				12 11					12 41						13 11					13 41	
Renton	d				12 14					12 44						13 14					13 44	
Dalreoch	d			12 08	12 17				12 38	12 47					13 08	13 17				13 38	13 47	
Dumbarton Central	d			12 10	12 18				12 40	12 48					13 10	13 18				13 40	13 48	
Dumbarton East	d			12 12	12 20				12 42	12 50					13 12	13 20				13 42	13 50	
Bowling	d				12 24					12 54						13 24					13 54	
Kilpatrick	d				12 28					12 58						13 28					13 58	
Dalmuir	a			12 19	12 30				12 49	13 00					13 19	13 30				13 49	14 00	
	d	12 15		12 20	12 31	12 35		12 45	12 50	13 01	13 05		13 15		13 20	13 31	13 35		13 45	13 50	14 01	14 05
Singer	d			12 22		12 37			12 52		13 07				13 22		13 37			13 52		14 07
Drumry	d			12 25		12 39			12 55		13 09				13 25		13 39			13 55		14 09
Drumchapel	d			12 27		12 42			12 57		13 12				13 27		13 42			13 57		14 12
Milngavie	d						12 41					13 11						13 41				
Hillfoot	d						12 44					13 14						13 44				
Bearsden	d						12 46					13 16						13 46				
Westerton	d			12 30		12 44	12 49		13 00		13 14	13 19			13 30		13 44	13 49		14 00		14 14
Anniesland	d			12 33		12 47	12 52		13 03		13 17	13 22			13 33		13 47	13 52		14 03		14 17
Clydebank	d	12 17			12 33			12 47		13 03			13 17			13 33			13 47		14 03	
Yoker	d	12 19			12 35			12 49		13 05			13 19			13 35			13 49		14 05	
Garscadden	d	12 22			12 39			12 52		13 09			13 22			13 39			13 52		14 09	
Scotstounhill	d	12 24			12 41			12 54		13 11			13 24			13 41			13 54		14 11	
Jordanhill	d	12 26			12 43			12 56		13 13			13 26			13 43			13 56		14 13	
Hyndland	d	12 28		12 35	12 45	12 50	12 55	12 58	13 05	13 15	13 20	13 25	13 28		13 35	13 45	13 50	13 55	13 58	14 05	14 15	14 20
Partick	d	12 30	12 34	12 38	12 48	12 52	12 58	13 00	13 08	13 18	13 22	13 28	13 30	13 34	13 38	13 48	13 52	13 58	14 00	14 08	14 18	14 22
Exhibition Centre	d		12 37		12 51		13 01			13 21		13 31		13 37		13 51		14 01			14 21	
Anderston	d																					
Glasgow Central 15 §	a		12 39		12 53		13 03			13 23		13 33		13 39		13 53		14 03			14 23	
	d		12 40		12 54		13 04			13 24		13 34		13 40		13 54		14 04			14 24	
Argyle Street	d		12 42		12 56		13 06			13 26		13 36		13 42		13 56		14 06			14 26	
Charing Cross	d	12 34		12 43		12 56		13 04	13 13		13 26		13 34		13 43		13 56		14 04	14 13		14 26
Glasgow Queen Street 10 §	a	12 36		12 45		12 58		13 06	13 15		13 28		13 36		13 45		13 58		14 06	14 15		14 28
	d	12 37		12 47		12 59		13 07	13 17		13 29		13 37		13 47		13 59		14 07	14 17		14 29
High Street	d	12 39		12 49		13 01		13 09	13 19		13 31		13 39		13 49		14 01		14 09	14 19		14 31
Bellgrove	d	12 41		12 51		13 03		13 11	13 21		13 33		13 41		13 51		14 03		14 11	14 21		14 33
Duke Street	d					13 05					13 35						14 05					14 35
Alexandra Parade	d					13 06					13 36						14 06					14 36
Barnhill	d					13 09					13 39						14 09					14 39
Springburn	a					13 11					13 41						14 11					14 41
Carntyne	d	12 44		12 54				13 14	13 24				13 44		13 54				14 14	14 24		
Shettleston	d	12 47		12 57				13 17	13 27				13 47		13 57				14 17	14 27		
Garrowhill	d	12 49		12 59				13 19	13 29				13 49		13 59				14 19	14 29		
Easterhouse	d	12 52		13 02				13 22	13 32				13 52		14 02				14 22	14 32		
Blairhill	d	12 56		13 06				13 26	13 36				13 56		14 06				14 26	14 36		
Coatbridge Sunnyside	d	12 58		13 08				13 28	13 38				13 58		14 08				14 28	14 38		
Coatdyke	d	13 01		13 11				13 31	13 41				14 01		14 11				14 31	14 41		
Airdrie	a	13 04		13 14				13 34	13 44				14 04		14 14				14 34	14 44		
	d			13 15					13 45						14 15					14 45		
Drumgelloch	a			13 18					13 48						14 18					14 48		
Bridgeton	d				12 59		13 09			13 29		13 39				13 59		14 09			14 29	
Dalmarnock	d																					
Rutherglen	d		12 47		13 02		13 12			13 32		13 42		13 47		14 02		14 12			14 32	
Cambuslang	d				13 06		13 16			13 36		13 46				14 06		14 16			14 36	
Newton	d				13 09					13 39						14 09					14 39	
Blantyre	d		12 55		13 13					13 43				13 55		14 13					14 43	
Hamilton West	d		12 58		13 16					13 46				13 58		14 16					14 46	
Hamilton Central	d		13 01		13 20					13 50				14 01		14 20					14 50	
Chatelherault	d		13 06											14 06								
Merryton	d		13 09											14 09								
Larkhall	a		13 15											14 13								
Airbles	d				13 25					13 55						14 25					14 55	
Uddingston	d						13 20					13 50						14 20				
Bellshill	d						13 25					13 55						14 25				
Motherwell	a				13 27		13 33			13 57		14 03				14 27		14 33			14 57	
	d						13 33											14 33				
Whifflet	a																					
Coatbridge Central	a																					
Shieldmuir	d						13 37											14 37				
Holytown	d																					
Wishaw	d						13 40											14 40				
Carluke	d						13 47											14 47				
Lanark	a						13 59											14 59				

For general notes see front of timetable
For details of catering facilities see Directory of Train Operators

§ Low Level

Table 226

Sundays

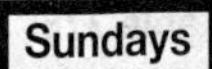

from 30 November

Helensburgh, Balloch, Dalmuir and Milngavie → Glasgow → Springburn, Airdrie, Drumgelloch, Hamilton, Larkhall, Motherwell, Coatbridge and Lanark

Network Diagram - see first page of Table 220

		SR	SR	SR	SR	SR	SR	SR	SR	SR	SR	SR	SR	SR	SR	SR	SR	SR	SR	SR	SR	SR
Helensburgh Central	d				13 55					14 25						14 55					15 25	
Craigendoran	d				13 58					14 28						14 58					15 28	
Cardross	d				14 03					14 33						15 03					15 33	
Balloch	d					14 09					14 39						15 09					15 39
Alexandria	d					14 11					14 41						15 11					15 41
Renton	d					14 14					14 44						15 14					15 44
Dalreoch	d				14 08	14 17				14 38	14 47					15 08	15 17				15 38	15 47
Dumbarton Central	d				14 10	14 18				14 40	14 48					15 10	15 18				15 40	15 48
Dumbarton East	d				14 12	14 20				14 42	14 50					15 12	15 20				15 42	15 50
Bowling	d					14 24					14 54						15 24					15 54
Kilpatrick	d					14 28					14 58						15 28					15 58
Dalmuir	a				14 19	14 30				14 49	15 00					15 19	15 30				15 49	16 00
	d		14 15		14 20	14 31	14 35		14 45	14 50	15 01	15 05		15 15		15 20	15 31	15 35		15 45	15 50	16 01
Singer	d				14 22		14 37			14 52		15 07				15 22		15 37			15 52	
Drumry	d				14 25		14 39			14 55		15 09				15 25		15 39			15 55	
Drumchapel	d				14 27		14 42			14 57		15 12				15 27		15 42			15 57	
Milngavie	d	14 11						14 41					15 11						15 41			
Hillfoot	d	14 14						14 44					15 14						15 44			
Bearsden	d	14 16						14 46					15 16						15 46			
Westerton	d	14 19			14 30		14 44	14 49		15 00		15 14	15 19			15 30		15 44	15 49		16 00	
Anniesland	d	14 22			14 33		14 47	14 52		15 03		15 17	15 22			15 33		15 47	15 52		16 03	
Clydebank	d		14 17			14 33			14 47		15 03			15 17			15 33			15 47		16 03
Yoker	d		14 19			14 35			14 49		15 05			15 19			15 35			15 49		16 05
Garscadden	d		14 22			14 39			14 52		15 09			15 22			15 39			15 52		16 09
Scotstounhill	d		14 24			14 41			14 54		15 11			15 24			15 41			15 54		16 11
Jordanhill	d		14 26			14 43			14 56		15 13			15 26			15 43			15 56		16 13
Hyndland	d	14 25	14 28		14 35	14 45	14 50	14 55	14 58	15 05	15 15	15 20	15 25	15 28		15 35	15 45	15 50	15 55	15 58	16 05	16 15
Partick	d	14 28	14 30	14 34	14 38	14 48	14 52	14 58	15 00	15 08	15 18	15 22	15 28	15 30	15 34	15 38	15 48	15 52	15 58	16 00	16 08	16 18
Exhibition Centre	d	14 31		14 37		14 51		15 01			15 21		15 31		15 37		15 51		16 01			16 21
Anderston	d																					
Glasgow Central 15 §	a	14 33		14 39		14 53		15 03			15 23		15 33		15 39		15 53		16 03			16 23
	d	14 34		14 40		14 54		15 04			15 24		15 34		15 40		15 54		16 04			16 24
Argyle Street	d	14 36		14 42		14 56		15 06			15 26		15 36		15 42		15 56		16 06			16 26
Charing Cross	d		14 34		14 43		14 56		15 04	15 13		15 26		15 34		15 43		15 56		16 04	16 13	
Glasgow Queen Street 10 §	a		14 36		14 45		14 58		15 06	15 15		15 28		15 36		15 45		15 58		16 06	16 15	
	d		14 37		14 47		14 59		15 07	15 17		15 29		15 37		15 47		15 59		16 07	16 17	
High Street	d		14 39		14 49		15 01		15 09	15 19		15 31		15 39		15 49		16 01		16 09	16 19	
Bellgrove	d		14 41		14 51		15 03		15 11	15 21		15 33		15 41		15 51		16 03		16 11	16 21	
Duke Street	d						15 05					15 35						16 05				
Alexandra Parade	d						15 06					15 36						16 06				
Barnhill	d						15 09					15 39						16 09				
Springburn	a						15 11					15 41						16 11				
Carntyne	d		14 44		14 54				15 14	15 24				15 44		15 54				16 14	16 24	
Shettleston	d		14 47		14 57				15 17	15 27				15 47		15 57				16 17	16 27	
Garrowhill	d		14 49		14 59				15 19	15 29				15 49		15 59				16 19	16 29	
Easterhouse	d		14 52		15 02				15 22	15 32				15 52		16 02				16 22	16 32	
Blairhill	d		14 56		15 06				15 26	15 36				15 56		16 06				16 26	16 36	
Coatbridge Sunnyside	d		14 58		15 08				15 28	15 38				15 58		16 08				16 28	16 38	
Coatdyke	d		15 01		15 11				15 31	15 41				16 01		16 11				16 31	16 41	
Airdrie	a		15 04		15 14				15 34	15 44				16 04		16 14				16 34	16 44	
	d				15 15					15 45						16 15					16 45	
Drumgelloch	a				15 18					15 48						16 18					16 48	
Bridgeton	d	14 39				14 59		15 09			15 29		15 39				15 59		16 09			16 29
Dalmarnock	d																					
Rutherglen	d	14 42		14 47		15 02		15 12			15 32		15 42		15 47		16 02		16 12			16 32
Cambuslang	d	14 46				15 06		15 16			15 36		15 46				16 06		16 16			16 36
Newton	d					15 09					15 39						16 09					16 39
Blantyre	d			14 55		15 13					15 43				15 55		16 13					16 43
Hamilton West	d			14 58		15 16					15 46				15 58		16 16					16 46
Hamilton Central	d			15 01		15 20					15 50				16 01		16 20					16 50
Chatelherault	d			15 06											16 06							
Merryton	d			15 09											16 09							
Larkhall	a			15 11											16 15							
Airbles	d					15 25					15 55						16 25					16 55
Uddingston	d	14 50						15 20					15 50						16 20			
Bellshill	d	14 55						15 25					15 55						16 25			
Motherwell	a	15 03				15 27		15 33			15 57		16 02				16 27		16 33			16 57
	d							15 33											16 33			
Whifflet	a																					
Coatbridge Central	a																					
Shieldmuir	d							15 37											16 37			
Holytown	d																					
Wishaw	d							15 40											16 40			
Carluke	d							15 47											16 47			
Lanark	a							15 59											16 59			

For general notes see front of timetable
For details of catering facilities see Directory of Train Operators

§ Low Level

Table 226

Helensburgh, Balloch, Dalmuir and Milngavie → Glasgow → Springburn, Airdrie, Drumgelloch, Hamilton, Larkhall, Motherwell, Coatbridge and Lanark

Sundays from 30 November

Network Diagram - see first page of Table 220

		SR	SR		SR	SR	SR	SR	SR	SR		SR	SR	SR	SR	SR	SR		SR	SR	SR	SR	SR	SR	SR
Helensburgh Central	d						15 55						16 25							16 55					17 25
Craigendoran	d						15 58						16 28							16 58					17 28
Cardross	d						16 03						16 33							17 03					17 33
Balloch	d							16 09						16 39							17 09				
Alexandria	d							16 11						16 41							17 11				
Renton	d							16 14						16 44							17 14				
Dalreoch	d						16 08	16 17					16 38	16 47						17 08	17 17				17 38
Dumbarton Central	d						16 10	16 18					16 40	16 48						17 10	17 18				17 40
Dumbarton East	d						16 12	16 20					16 42	16 50						17 12	17 20				17 42
Bowling	d							16 24						16 54							17 24				
Kilpatrick	d							16 28						16 58							17 28				
Dalmuir	a						16 19	16 30					16 49	17 00						17 19	17 30				17 49
	d	16 05			16 15		16 20	16 31	16 35			16 45	16 50	17 01	17 05		17 15			17 20	17 31	17 35		17 45	17 50
Singer	d	16 07					16 22		16 37				16 52		17 07					17 22		17 37			17 52
Drumry	d	16 09					16 25		16 39				16 55		17 09					17 25		17 39			17 55
Drumchapel	d	16 12					16 27		16 42				16 57		17 12					17 27		17 42			17 57
Milngavie	d		16 11							16 41						17 11							17 41		
Hillfoot	d		16 14							16 44						17 14							17 44		
Bearsden	d		16 16							16 46						17 16							17 46		
Westerton	d	16 14	16 19				16 30		16 44	16 49			17 00		17 14	17 19				17 30		17 44	17 49		18 00
Anniesland	d	16 17	16 22				16 33		16 47	16 52			17 03		17 17	17 22				17 33		17 47	17 52		18 03
Clydebank	d				16 17			16 33				16 47		17 03			17 17				17 33			17 47	
Yoker	d				16 19			16 35				16 49		17 05			17 19				17 35			17 49	
Garscadden	d				16 22			16 39				16 52		17 09			17 22				17 39			17 52	
Scotstounhill	d				16 24			16 41				16 54		17 11			17 24				17 41			17 54	
Jordanhill	d				16 26			16 43				16 56		17 13			17 26				17 43			17 56	
Hyndland	d	16 20	16 25		16 28		16 35	16 45	16 50	16 55		16 58	17 05	17 15	17 20	17 25	17 28			17 35	17 45	17 50	17 55	17 58	18 05
Partick	d	16 22	16 28		16 30	16 34	16 38	16 48	16 52	16 58		17 00	17 08	17 18	17 22	17 28	17 30		17 34	17 38	17 48	17 52	17 58	18 00	18 08
Exhibition Centre	d		16 31			16 37		16 51		17 01				17 21		17 31			17 37		17 51		18 01		
Anderston	d																								
Glasgow Central 15 §	a		16 33			16 39		16 53		17 03				17 23		17 33			17 39		17 53		18 03		
	d		16 34			16 40		16 54		17 04				17 24		17 34			17 40		17 54		18 04		
Argyle Street	d		16 36			16 42		16 56		17 06				17 26		17 36			17 42		17 56		18 06		
Charing Cross	d	16 26			16 34		16 43		16 56			17 04	17 13		17 26		17 34			17 43		17 56		18 04	18 13
Glasgow Queen Street 10 §	a	16 28			16 36		16 45		16 58			17 06	17 15		17 28		17 36			17 45		17 58		18 06	18 15
	d	16 29			16 37		16 47		16 59			17 07	17 17		17 29		17 37			17 47		17 59		18 07	18 17
High Street	d	16 31			16 39		16 49		17 01			17 09	17 19		17 31		17 39			17 49		18 01		18 09	18 19
Bellgrove	d	16 33			16 41		16 51		17 03			17 11	17 21		17 33		17 41			17 51		18 03		18 11	18 21
Duke Street	d	16 35							17 05						17 35							18 05			
Alexandra Parade	d	16 36							17 06						17 36							18 06			
Barnhill	d	16 39							17 09						17 39							18 09			
Springburn	a	16 41							17 11						17 41							18 11			
Carntyne	d				16 44		16 54					17 14	17 24				17 44			17 54				18 14	18 24
Shettleston	d				16 47		16 57					17 17	17 27				17 47			17 57				18 17	18 27
Garrowhill	d				16 49		16 59					17 19	17 29				17 49			17 59				18 19	18 29
Easterhouse	d				16 52		17 02					17 22	17 32				17 52			18 02				18 22	18 32
Blairhill	d				16 56		17 06					17 26	17 36				17 56			18 06				18 26	18 36
Coatbridge Sunnyside	d				16 58		17 08					17 28	17 38				17 58			18 08				18 28	18 38
Coatdyke	d				17 01		17 11					17 31	17 41				18 01			18 11				18 31	18 41
Airdrie	a				17 04		17 14					17 34	17 44				18 04			18 14				18 34	18 44
	d						17 15						17 45							18 15					18 45
Drumgelloch	a						17 18						17 48							18 18					18 48
Bridgeton	d		16 39					16 59		17 09				17 29		17 39					17 59		18 09		
Dalmarnock	d																								
Rutherglen	d		16 42			16 47		17 02		17 12				17 32		17 42			17 47		18 02		18 12		
Cambuslang	d		16 46					17 06		17 16				17 36		17 46					18 06		18 16		
Newton	d							17 09						17 39							18 09				
Blantyre	d					16 55		17 13						17 43					17 55		18 13				
Hamilton West	d					16 58		17 16						17 46					17 58		18 16				
Hamilton Central	d					17 01		17 20						17 50					18 01		18 20				
Chatelherault	d					17 06													18 06						
Merryton	d					17 09													18 09						
Larkhall	a					17 11													18 11						
Airbles	d							17 25						17 55							18 25				
Uddingston	d		16 50							17 20						17 50							18 20		
Bellshill	d		16 55							17 25						17 55							18 25		
Motherwell	a		17 03					17 27		17 33				17 57		18 03					18 27		18 33		
	d									17 33													18 33		
Whifflet	a																								
Coatbridge Central	a																								
Shieldmuir	d									17 37													18 37		
Holytown	d																								
Wishaw	d									17 40													18 40		
Carluke	d									17 47													18 47		
Lanark	a									17 59													18 59		

For general notes see front of timetable
For details of catering facilities see Directory of Train Operators

§ Low Level

Table 226

Sundays

from 30 November

Helensburgh, Balloch, Dalmuir and Milngavie → Glasgow → Springburn, Airdrie, Drumgelloch, Hamilton, Larkhall, Motherwell, Coatbridge and Lanark

Network Diagram - see first page of Table 220

		SR		SR	SR	SR	SR	SR	SR		SR	SR	SR	SR	SR	SR		SR	SR	SR	SR	SR	SR		SR
Helensburgh Central	d					17 55			18 25					18 55				19 25				19 55			
Craigendoran	d					17 58			18 28					18 58				19 28				19 58			
Cardross	d					18 03			18 33					19 03				19 33				20 03			
Balloch	d	17 39					18 09				18 39				19 09				19 39				20 09		
Alexandria	d	17 41					18 11				18 41				19 11				19 41				20 11		
Renton	d	17 44					18 14				18 44				19 14				19 44				20 14		
Dalreoch	d	17 47				18 08	18 17		18 38		18 47			19 08	19 17			19 38	19 47			20 08	20 17		
Dumbarton Central	d	17 48				18 10	18 18		18 40		18 48			19 10	19 18			19 40	19 48			20 10	20 18		
Dumbarton East	d	17 50				18 12	18 20		18 42		18 50			19 12	19 20			19 42	19 50			20 12	20 20		
Bowling	d	17 54					18 24				18 54				19 24				19 54				20 24		
Kilpatrick	d	17 58					18 28				18 58				19 28				19 58				20 28		
Dalmuir	a	18 00				18 19	18 30		18 49		19 00			19 19	19 30			19 49	20 00			20 19	20 30		
	d	18 01				18 20	18 31		18 50		19 01			19 20	19 31			19 50	20 01			20 20	20 31		
Singer	d					18 22			18 52					19 22				19 52				20 22			
Drumry	d					18 25			18 55					19 25				19 55				20 25			
Drumchapel	d					18 27			18 57					19 27				19 57				20 27			
Milngavie	d			18 11				18 41				19 11				19 41				20 11					20 41
Hillfoot	d			18 14				18 44				19 14				19 44				20 14					20 44
Bearsden	d			18 16				18 46				19 16				19 46				20 16					20 46
Westerton	d			18 19		18 30		18 49	19 00			19 19		19 30		19 49		20 00		20 19		20 30			20 49
Anniesland	d			18 22		18 33		18 52	19 03			19 22		19 33		19 52		20 03		20 22		20 33			20 52
Clydebank	d	18 03					18 33				19 03				19 33				20 03				20 33		
Yoker	d	18 05					18 35				19 05				19 35				20 05				20 35		
Garscadden	d	18 09					18 39				19 09				19 39				20 09				20 39		
Scotstounhill	d	18 11					18 41				19 11				19 41				20 11				20 41		
Jordanhill	d	18 13					18 43				19 13				19 43				20 13				20 43		
Hyndland	d	18 15		18 25		18 35	18 45	18 55	19 05		19 15	19 25		19 35	19 45	19 55		20 05	20 15	20 25		20 35	20 45		20 55
Partick	d	18 18		18 28	18 34	18 38	18 48	18 58	19 08		19 18	19 28	19 34	19 38	19 48	19 58		20 08	20 18	20 28	20 34	20 38	20 48		20 58
Exhibition Centre	d	18 21		18 31	18 37		18 51	19 01			19 21	19 31	19 37		19 51	20 01			20 21	20 31	20 37		20 51		21 01
Anderston	d																								
Glasgow Central 15 §	a	18 23		18 33	18 39		18 53	19 03			19 23	19 33	19 39		19 53	20 03			20 23	20 33	20 39		20 53		21 03
	d	18 24		18 34	18 40		18 54	19 04			19 24	19 34	19 40		19 54	20 04			20 24	20 34	20 40		20 54		21 04
Argyle Street	d																								
Charing Cross	d					18 43			19 13					19 43				20 13				20 43			
Glasgow Queen Street 10 §	a					18 45			19 15					19 45				20 15				20 45			
	d					18 47			19 17					19 47				20 17				20 47			
High Street	d					18 49			19 19					19 49				20 19				20 49			
Bellgrove	d					18 51			19 21					19 51				20 21				20 51			
Duke Street	d																								
Alexandra Parade	d																								
Barnhill	d																								
Springburn	a																								
Carntyne	d					18 54			19 24					19 54				20 24				20 54			
Shettleston	d					18 57			19 27					19 57				20 27				20 57			
Garrowhill	d					18 59			19 29					19 59				20 29				20 59			
Easterhouse	d					19 02			19 32					20 02				20 32				21 02			
Blairhill	d					19 06			19 36					20 06				20 36				21 06			
Coatbridge Sunnyside	d					19 08			19 38					20 08				20 38				21 08			
Coatdyke	d					19 11			19 41					20 11				20 41				21 11			
Airdrie	a					19 14			19 44					20 14				20 44				21 14			
	d					19 15			19 45					20 15				20 45				21 15			
Drumgelloch	a					19 18			19 48					20 18				20 48				21 18			
Bridgeton	d	18 29		18 39			18 59	19 09			19 29	19 39			19 59	20 09			20 29	20 39			20 59		21 09
Dalmarnock	d																								
Rutherglen	d	18 32		18 42	18 47		19 02	19 12			19 32	19 42	19 47		20 02	20 12			20 32	20 42	20 47		21 02		21 12
Cambuslang	d	18 36		18 46			19 06	19 16			19 36	19 46			20 06	20 16			20 36	20 46			21 06		21 16
Newton	d	18 39					19 09				19 39				20 09				20 39				21 09		
Blantyre	d	18 43			18 55		19 13				19 43		19 55		20 13				20 43		20 55		21 13		
Hamilton West	d	18 46			18 58		19 16				19 46		19 58		20 16				20 46		20 58		21 16		
Hamilton Central	d	18 50			19 01		19 20				19 50		20 01		20 20				20 50		21 01		21 20		
Chatelherault	d				19 06								20 06								21 06				
Merryton	d				19 09								20 09								21 09				
Larkhall	a				19 12								20 11								21 11				
Airbles	d	18 55					19 25				19 55				20 25				20 55				21 25		
Uddingston	d			18 50				19 20				19 50				20 20				20 50					21 20
Bellshill	d			18 55				19 25				19 55				20 25				20 55					21 25
Motherwell	a	18 57		19 03			19 27	19 33			19 57	20 03			20 27	20 33			20 57	21 04			21 27		21 33
	d							19 33								20 33									21 33
Whifflet	a																								
Coatbridge Central	a																								
Shieldmuir	d							19 37								20 37									21 37
Holytown	d																								
Wishaw	d							19 40								20 40									21 40
Carluke	d							19 47								20 47									21 47
Lanark	a							19 59								20 59									21 59

For general notes see front of timetable
For details of catering facilities see
Directory of Train Operators

§ Low Level

Table 226

from 30 November

Helensburgh, Balloch, Dalmuir and Milngavie → Glasgow → Springburn, Airdrie, Drumgelloch, Hamilton, Larkhall, Motherwell, Coatbridge and Lanark

Network Diagram - see first page of Table 220

		SR	SR	SR	SR	SR	SR	SR	SR	SR	SR	SR	SR	SR	SR	SR	SR	SR	SR	SR	SR
				◇ A															R B		
Helensburgh Central	d	20 25		20b40			20 55			21 25				21 55			22 25		22b37	22 55	
Craigendoran	d	20 28					20 58			21 28				21 58			22 28			22 58	
Cardross	d	20 33					21 03			21 33				22 03			22 33			23 03	
Balloch	d		20 39					21 09			21 39				22 09			22 39			23 09
Alexandria	d		20 41					21 11			21 41				22 11			22 41			23 11
Renton	d		20 44					21 14			21 44				22 14			22 44			23 14
Dalreoch	d	20 38	20 47				21 08	21 17		21 38	21 47			22 08	22 17		22 38	22 47		23 08	23 17
Dumbarton Central	d	20 40	20 48	20 53			21 10	21 18		21 40	21 48			22 10	22 18		22 40	22 48		23 10	23 18
Dumbarton East	d	20 42	20 50				21 12	21 20		21 42	21 50			22 12	22 20		22 42	22 50		23 12	23 20
Bowling	d		20 54					21 24			21 54				22 24			22 55			23 25
Kilpatrick	d		20 58					21 28			21 58				22 28			22 58			23 28
Dalmuir	a	20 49	21 00	21 05			21 19	21 30		21 49	22 00			22 19	22 30		22 49	23 01	23 02	23 19	23 31
	d	20 50	21 01	21 05			21 20	21 31		21 50	22 01			22 20	22 31		22 50	23 01	23 04		23 31
Singer	d	20 52					21 22			21 52				22 22			22 52				
Drumry	d	20 55					21 25			21 55				22 25			22 55				
Drumchapel	d	20 57					21 27			21 57				22 27			22 57				
Milngavie	d				21 11				21 41			22 11				22 41					
Hillfoot	d				21 14				21 44			22 14				22 44					
Bearsden	d				21 16				21 46			22 16				22 46					
Westerton	d	21 00			21 19		21 30		21 49	22 00		22 19		22 30		22 49	23 00		23a11		
Anniesland	d	21 03			21 22		21 33		21 52	22 03		22 22		22 33		22 52	23 03				
Clydebank	d		21 03					21 33			22 03				22 33			23 03			23 33
Yoker	d		21 05					21 35			22 05				22 35			23a05			23a35
Garscadden	d		21 09					21 39			22 09				22 39						
Scotstounhill	d		21 11					21 41			22 11				22 41						
Jordanhill	d		21 13					21 43			22 13				22 43						
Hyndland	d	21 05	21 15		21 25		21 35	21 45	21 55	22 05	22 15	22 25		22 35	22 45	22 55	23 05				
Partick	d	21 08	21 18		21 28	21 34	21 38	21 48	21 58	22 08	22 18	22 28	22 34	22 38	22 48	22 58	23 08				
Exhibition Centre	d		21 21		21 31	21 37		21 51	22 01		22 21	22 31	22 37		22 51	23 01					
Anderston	d																				
Glasgow Central 15 §	a		21 23		21 33	21 39		21 53	22 03		22 23	22 33	22 39		22 53	23 03					
	d		21 24		21 34	21 40		21 54	22 04		22 24	22 34	22 40		22 54	23 04					
Argyle Street	d																				
Charing Cross	d	21 13					21 43			22 13				22 43			23 13				
Glasgow Queen Street 10 §	a	21 15		21c27			21 45			22 15				22 45			23 15				
	d	21 17					21 47			22 17				22 47			23 17				
High Street	d	21 19					21 49			22 19				22 49			23 19				
Bellgrove	d	21 21					21 51			22 21				22 51			23 21				
Duke Street	d																				
Alexandra Parade	d																				
Barnhill	d																				
Springburn	a																				
Carntyne	d	21 24					21 54			22 24				22 54			23 24				
Shettleston	d	21 27					21 57			22 27				22 57			23 27				
Garrowhill	d	21 29					21 59			22 29				22 59			23 29				
Easterhouse	d	21 32					22 02			22 32				23 02			23 32				
Blairhill	d	21 36					22 06			22 36				23 06			23 36				
Coatbridge Sunnyside	d	21 38					22 08			22 38				23 08			23 38				
Coatdyke	d	21 41					22 11			22 41				23 11			23 41				
Airdrie	a	21 44					22 14			22 44				23 14			23 44				
	d	21 45					22 15			22 45				23 15			23 45				
Drumgelloch	a	21 48					22 18			22 48				23 18			23 48				
Bridgeton	d		21 29		21 39			21 59	22 09		22 29	22 39			22 59	23 09					
Dalmarnock	d																				
Rutherglen	d		21 32		21 42	21 47		22 02	22 12		22 32	22 42	22 47		23 02	23 12					
Cambuslang	d		21 36		21 46			22 06	22 16		22 36	22 46			23 06	23 16					
Newton	d		21 39					22 09			22 39				23 09						
Blantyre	d		21 43			21 55		22 13			22 43		22 55		23 13						
Hamilton West	d		21 46			21 58		22 16			22 46		22 58		23 16						
Hamilton Central	d		21 50			22 01		22 20			22 50		23 01		23 20						
Chatelherault	d					22 06							23 06								
Merryton	d					22 09							23 09								
Larkhall	a					22 13							23 11								
Airbles	d		21 55					22 25			22 55				23 25						
Uddingston	d				21 50				22 20			22 50				23 20					
Bellshill	d				21 55				22 25			22 55				23 25					
Motherwell	a		21 57		22 03			22 27	22 33		22 57	23 06			23 27	23 33					
	d								22 33												
Whifflet	a																				
Coatbridge Central	a																				
Shieldmuir	d								22 37												
Holytown	d																				
Wishaw	d								22 40												
Carluke	d								22 47												
Lanark	a								22 59												

For general notes see front of timetable
For details of catering facilities see Directory of Train Operators

§ Low Level

A From Oban and from Mallaig (Table 227)

B Limited seating accommodation. Also conveys overnight Sleeping Car accommodation from Fort William to London Euston (Tables 65 and 404)

b Helensburgh Upper

c Glasgow Queen Street High Level

Network Diagram for Tables 227, 239

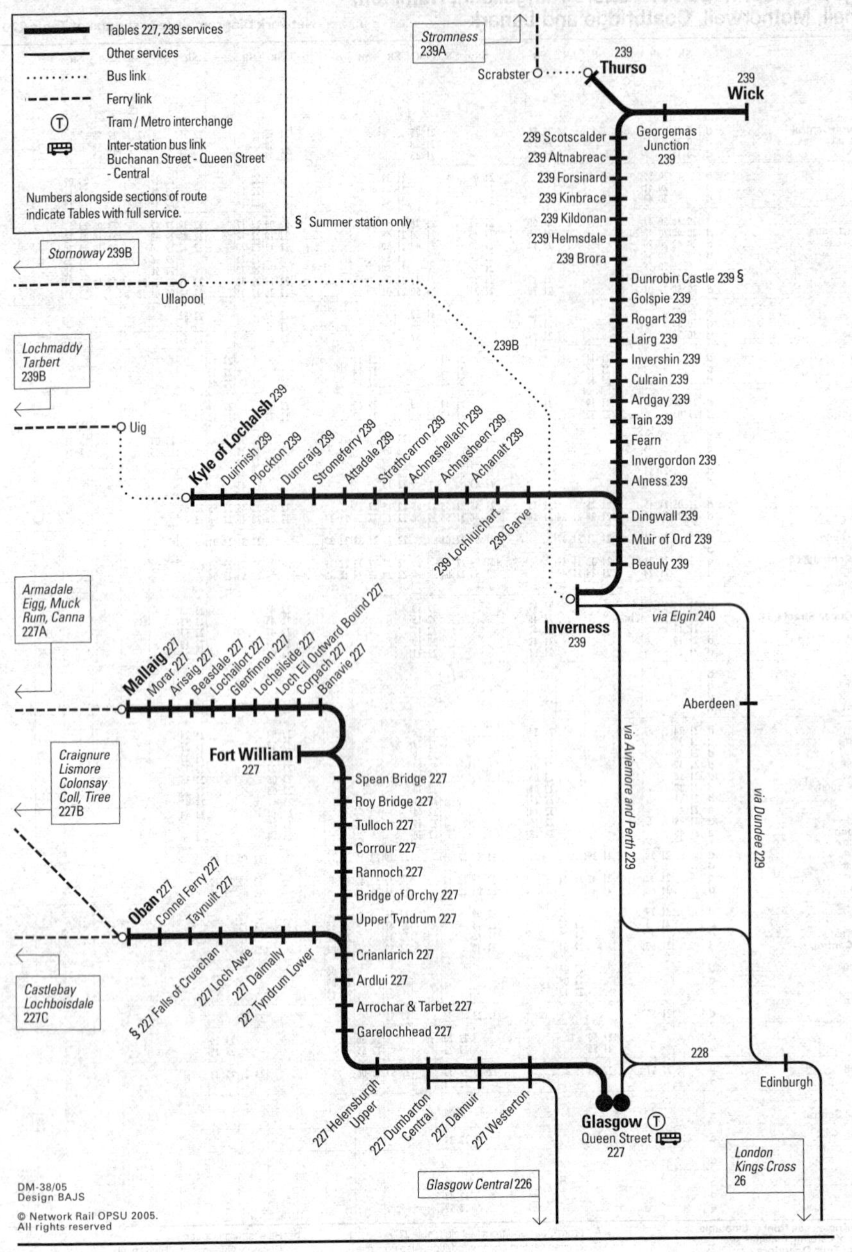

Tables 227, 239 services
Other services
Bus link
Ferry link
Tram / Metro interchange
Inter-station bus link Buchanan Street - Queen Street - Central
Numbers alongside sections of route indicate Tables with full service.
§ Summer station only
Stromness 239A
Scrabster
239 Thurso
239 Wick
Georgemas Junction 239
239 Scotscalder
239 Altnabreac
239 Forsinard
239 Kinbrace
239 Kildonan
239 Helmsdale
239 Brora
Dunrobin Castle 239 §
Golspie 239
Rogart 239
Lairg 239
Invershin 239
Culrain 239
Ardgay 239
Tain 239
Fearn
Invergordon 239
Alness 239
Dingwall 239
Muir of Ord 239
Beauly 239
Inverness 239
Stornoway 239B
Ullapool
239B
Lochmaddy Tarbert 239B
Uig
Kyle of Lochalsh 239
Duirinish 239
Plockton 239
Duncraig 239
Stromeferry 239
Attadale 239
Strathcarron 239
Achnashellach 239
Achnasheen 239
Achanalt 239
239 Lochluichart
239 Garve
via Elgin 240
Aberdeen
via Aviemore and Perth 229
via Dundee 229
Armadale Eigg, Muck Rum, Canna 227A
Mallaig 227
Morar 227
Arisaig 227
Beasdale 227
Lochailort 227
Glenfinnan 227
Locheilside 227
Loch Eil Outward Bound 227
Corpach 227
Banavie 227
Fort William 227
Craignure Lismore Colonsay Coll, Tiree 227B
Spean Bridge 227
Roy Bridge 227
Tulloch 227
Corrour 227
Rannoch 227
Bridge of Orchy 227
Upper Tyndrum 227
Oban 227
Connel Ferry 227
Taynuilt 227
§ 227 Falls of Cruachan
227 Loch Awe
227 Dalmally
227 Tyndrum Lower
Castlebay Lochboisdale 227C
Crianlarich 227
Ardlui 227
Arrochar & Tarbet 227
Garelochhead 227
228
Edinburgh
227 Helensburgh Upper
227 Dumbarton Central
227 Dalmuir
227 Westerton
Glasgow
Queen Street 227
Glasgow Central 226
London Kings Cross 26
DM-38/05
Design BAJS

Glasgow Queen Street → Oban, Fort William and Mallaig

Network Diagram - see first page of Table 227

Miles	Miles			SR	SR	WR	WR	SR	SR		SR	SR	SR		SR	
						SX	SO	SX	SO		SX	SO				
					R	R 1	R 1									
				◇				◇	◇		◇	◇	◇		◇	
					A	B	B C									
—	—	Edinburgh 228	d		04 50			07 15	07 15		07 45	09 30	11 15		17 15	
0	0	**Glasgow Queen Street** 10 226 ⛴	d		05 30			08 21	08 21		08 51	10 37	12 21		18 21	
5½	5½	Westerton 226	d		05 56			08 23	08 23		08 53	10 23	12 23		18 23	
10	10	Dalmuir 226	d		06 04			08 39	08 39		09 07	10 50	12 42		18 37	
16½	16½	Dumbarton Central 226	d					08 48	08 48		09 16	11 04	12 48		18 46	
25½	25½	Helensburgh Upper	a		06 26			09 03	09 03		09 32	11 20	13 03		19 02	
—	—		d		06 28			09 06	09 06		09 34	11 23	13 06		19 04	
32¼	32¼	Garelochhead	d		06 41			09 17	09 17		09 46	11 34	13 17		19 16	
43	43	Arrochar & Tarbet	d		07 07			09 37	09 37		10 08	11 54	13 37		19 36	
51	51	Ardlui	d		07x21			09 53	09 53		10 22	12 08	13 53		19 51	
59¾	59¾	**Crianlarich**	a		07 42			10 09	10 09		10 38	12 24	14 09		20 08	
—	—		d		07 43			10 15	10 15	10 21	10 53	12 27	14 15	14 21	20 14	20 17
64¾	—	Tyndrum Lower	d					10 24	10 24			12 36	14 24		20 23	
76¾	—	Dalmally	d					10 42	10 42			12 57	14 42		20 41	
79½	—	Loch Awe	d					10 47	10 47			13 02	14 47		20 46	
83½	—	Falls of Cruachan §	d					10x52	10x52			13x07	14x52		20x51	
88½	—	Taynuilt	d					11 03	11 03			13 18	15 03		21 02	
95¼	—	Connel Ferry	d					11 14	11 14			13 29	15 14		21 13	
101½	—	**Oban**	a					11 27	11 27			13 42	15 27		21 26	
—	64½	Upper Tyndrum	d		07 56					10 32	11 05			14 32		20 28
—	72¼	Bridge of Orchy	d		08 13					10 46	11 19			14 46		20 42
—	87¾	Rannoch	d		08 45					11 08	11 40			15 08		21 07
—	95	Corrour	d		08x58					11 20	11 52			15 20		21 19
—	105	Tulloch	d		09 18					11 36	12 12			15 36		21 35
—	110¾	Roy Bridge	d		09x29					11 46	12 22			15 46		21 45
—	114	Spean Bridge	d		09 37					11 54	12 29			15 53		21 52
—	122¾	**Fort William**	a		09 54					12 07	12 42			16 06		22 05
—	—		d	08 30		10 10	10 10			12 12	12 47			16 19		22 10
—	125	Banavie	d	08 36						12 18	12 53			16 25		22 16
—	126	Corpach	d	08 41						12 23	12 58			16 30		22 21
—	129	Loch Eil Outward Bound	d	08 47						12 29	13 04			16 36		22 27
—	132¾	Locheilside	d	08x52						12x34	13x09			16x41		22x32
—	139¼	Glenfinnan	d	09 03						12 46	13 20			16 54		22 43
—	148½	Lochailort	d	09x19						13x01	13x36			17x10		22x59
—	153¼	Beasdale	d	09x28						13x10	13x45			17x19		23x08
—	156¾	Arisaig	d	09 36						13 18	13 53			17 27		23 16
—	161¼	Morar	d	09 44						13 26	14 01			17 35		23 24
—	164¼	**Mallaig**	a	09 52		12 16	12 24			13 34	14 09			17 43		23 31

For general notes see front of timetable
For details of catering facilities see Directory of Train Operators

§ Summer Station Only

A Limited seating accommodation. Also conveys overnight Sleeping Car accommodation from London Euston (Tables 65 and 404)

B **The Jacobite.** Steam hauled service

C 28 June to 23 August

Glasgow Queen Street → Oban, Fort William and Mallaig

Network Diagram - see first page of Table 227

		SR	SR	WR	SR		SR	SR		SR	
				SX			SO				
			Ⓡ	R 1							
		◇			◇		◇	◇		◇	
			A	B	C		D	C		C	
			☕	☕	🛒		🛒	🛒		🛒	
Edinburgh	228 d		04 50		*07 15*		*09 30*	*11 15*		*17 15*	
Glasgow Queen Street 10	226 ⛴ d		*05 30*		08 21		10 37	12 21		18 21	
Westerton	226 d		05 56		*08 23*		*10 23*	*12 23*		*18 23*	
Dalmuir	226 d		06 04		08 39		10 50	12 42		18 37	
Dumbarton Central	226 d				08 48		11 04	12 48		18 46	
Helensburgh Upper	a		06 26		09 03		11 20	13 03		19 02	
	d		06 28		09 06		11 23	13 06		19 04	
Garelochhead	d		06 41		09 17		11 34	13 17		19 16	
Arrochar & Tarbet	d		07 07		09 37		11 54	13 37		19 36	
Ardlui	d		07x21		09 53		12 08	13 53		19 51	
Crianlarich	a		07 42		10 09		12 24	14 09		20 08	
	d		07 43		10 15	10 21	12 27	14 15	14 21	20 14	20 17
Tyndrum Lower	d				10 24		12 36	14 24		20 23	
Dalmally	d				10 42		12 57	14 42		20 41	
Loch Awe	d				10 47		13 02	14 47		20 46	
Falls of Cruachan §	d										
Taynuilt	d				11 03		13 18	15 03		21 02	
Connel Ferry	d				11 14		13 29	15 14		21 13	
Oban	a				11 27		13 42	15 27		21 26	
Upper Tyndrum	d		07 56			10 32			14 32		20 28
Bridge of Orchy	d		08 13			10 46			14 46		20 42
Rannoch	d		08 45			11 08			15 08		21 07
Corrour	d		08x58			11 20			15 20		21 19
Tulloch	d		09 18			11 36			15 36		21 35
Roy Bridge	d		09x29			11 46			15 46		21 45
Spean Bridge	d		09 37			11 54			15 53		21 52
Fort William	a		09 54			12 07			16 06		22 05
	d	08 30		10 10		12 12			16 19		22 10
Banavie	d	08 36				12 18			16 25		22 16
Corpach	d	08 41				12 23			16 30		22 21
Loch Eil Outward Bound	d	08 47				12 29			16 36		22 27
Locheilside	d	08x52				12x34			16x41		22x32
Glenfinnan	d	09 03				12 46			16 54		22 43
Lochailort	d	09x19				13x01			17x10		22x59
Beasdale	d	09x28				13x10			17x19		23x08
Arisaig	d	09 36				13 18			17 27		23 16
Morar	d	09 44				13 26			17 35		23 24
Mallaig	a	09 52		12 16		13 34			17 43		23 31

For general notes see front of timetable
For details of catering facilities see Directory of Train Operators

§ Summer Station Only

A Limited seating accommodation. Also conveys overnight Sleeping Car accommodation from London Euston (Tables 65 and 404)

B **The Jacobite.** Steam hauled service

C 🛒 to Oban and Fort William

D Until 25 October

Sundays

until 28 September

Glasgow Queen Street → Oban, Fort William and Mallaig

Network Diagram - see first page of Table 227

	WR	SR	SR	SR	SR	SR	SR
	R 1 A	◇	◇	◇		◇	
Edinburgh 228 d			*08 00*	*11 00*		*17 00*	
Glasgow Queen Street 10 226 d			09 55	12 20		18 20	
Westerton 226 d			*09 40*	*12 10*		*18 10*	
Dalmuir 226 d			10 11	12 35		18 35	
Dumbarton Central 226 d			10 22	12 43		18 44	
Helensburgh Upper a			10 37	12 58		19 00	
d			10 40	13 03		19 03	
Garelochhead d			10 51	13 14		19 14	
Arrochar & Tarbet d			11 11	13 34		19 34	
Ardlui d			11 25	13 51		19 52	
Crianlarich a			11 41	14 09		20 08	
d			11 44	14 15	14 21	20 14	20 17
Tyndrum Lower d			11 53	14 24		20 23	
Dalmally d			12 11	14 42		20 41	
Loch Awe d			12 16	14 47		20 46	
Falls of Cruachan § d			12x21	14x52		20x51	
Taynuilt d			12 36	15 03		21 02	
Connel Ferry d			12 47	15 14		21 13	
Oban a			13 00	15 27		21 26	
Upper Tyndrum d					14 32		20 28
Bridge of Orchy d					14 46		20 42
Rannoch d					15 08		21 07
Corrour d					15 20		21 19
Tulloch d					15 36		21 35
Roy Bridge d					15 46		21 45
Spean Bridge d					15 53		21 52
Fort William a					16 06		22 05
d	10 10	12 12			16 19		22 10
Banavie d		12 18			16 25		22 16
Corpach d		12 23			16 30		22 21
Loch Eil Outward Bound d		12 29			16 36		22 27
Locheilside d		12x34			16x41		22x32
Glenfinnan d		12 45			16 54		22 43
Lochailort d		13x01			17x10		22x59
Beasdale d		13x10			17x19		23x08
Arisaig d		13 18			17 27		23 16
Morar d		13 26			17 35		23 24
Mallaig a	12 18	13 34			17 43		23 31

For general notes see front of timetable
For details of catering facilities see Directory of Train Operators

§ Summer Station Only

A **The Jacobite.** Steam hauled service

from 5 October

Glasgow Queen Street → Oban, Fort William and Mallaig

Network Diagram - see first page of Table 227

		SR ◇ A 🍴	SR ◇ B 🍴	
Edinburgh 228	d	*11 00*	*17 00*	
Glasgow Queen Street 10 226 ⛴	d	12 20	18 20	
Westerton 226	d	*12 10*	*18 10*	
Dalmuir 226	d	12 35	18 35	
Dumbarton Central 226	d	12 43	18 44	
Helensburgh Upper	a	12 58	19 00	
	d	13 03	19 03	
Garelochhead	d	13 14	19 14	
Arrochar & Tarbet	d	13 34	19 34	
Ardlui	d	13 51	19 52	
Crianlarich	a	14 09	20 08	
	d	14 15	20 14	20 17
Tyndrum Lower	d	14 24	20 23	
Dalmally	d	14 42	20 41	
Loch Awe	d	14 47	20 46	
Falls of Cruachan §	d			
Taynuilt	d	15 03	21 02	
Connel Ferry	d	15 14	21 13	
Oban	a	15 27	21 26	
Upper Tyndrum	d			20 28
Bridge of Orchy	d			20 42
Rannoch	d			21 07
Corrour	d			21 19
Tulloch	d			21 35
Roy Bridge	d			21 45
Spean Bridge	d			21 52
Fort William	a			22 05
	d			22 10
Banavie	d			22 16
Corpach	d			22 21
Loch Eil Outward Bound	d			22 27
Locheilside	d			22x32
Glenfinnan	d			22 43
Lochailort	d			22x59
Beasdale	d			23x08
Arisaig	d			23 16
Morar	d			23 24
Mallaig	a			23 31

For general notes see front of timetable
For details of catering facilities see Directory of Train Operators

§ Summer Station Only

A Until 26 October
B 🍴 to Oban and Fort William

Mondays to Saturdays
until 27 September

Mallaig, Fort William and Oban → Glasgow Queen Street

Network Diagram - see first page Table 227

Miles	Miles			SR SX	SR ◇	SR ◇	SR SO ◇	SR SO ◇	SR SX ◇	SR SX ◇	WR R 1 A B	SR SO ◇	SR ◇	SR ◇	SR ◇	SR SX R C
—	0	**Mallaig**	d			06 03		10 10	10 10		14 10		16 05		18 15	
—	3	Morar	d			06 09		10 16	10 16				16 11		18 21	
—	7½	Arisaig	d			06 19		10 26	10 26				16 21		18 31	
—	11	Beasdale	d			06x25		10x32	10x32				16x27		18x37	
—	15¾	Lochailort	d			06x34		10x41	10x41				16x36		18x46	
—	25	Glenfinnan	d			06 51		10 58	10 58				16 51		19 03	
—	31½	Locheilside	d			07x01		11x08	11x08				17x01		19x11	
—	35¼	Loch Eil Outward Bound	d			07 07		11 14	11 14				17 07		19 17	
—	38¼	Corpach	d			07 13		11 20	11 20				17 13		19 23	
—	39¼	Banavie	d			07 17		11 24	11 24				17 17		19 27	
—	41½	**Fort William**	a			07 25		11 32	11 32		16 02		17 27		19 37	
—	—		d			07 42		11 40	11 40				17 37			19 50
—	50¼	Spean Bridge	d			07 55		11 53	11 53				17 50			20 10
—	53½	Roy Bridge	d			08 02		12 00	12 00				17 57			20x17
—	59¼	Tulloch	d			08 13		12 11	12 11				18 08			20 30
—	69¼	Corrour	d			08 30		12 28	12 28				18 25			20x51
—	76½	Rannoch	d			08 43		12 43	12 43				18 36			21 06
—	92	Bridge of Orchy	d			09 03		13 02	13 02				18 56			21 34
—	99¾	Upper Tyndrum	d			09 19		13 18	13 18				19 12			21 52
0	—	**Oban**	d		08 11		12 11			12 56		16 11		18 11		
6¼	—	Connel Ferry	d		08 23		12 23			13 08		16 27		18 23		
13	—	Taynuilt	d		08 35		12 35			13 20		16 39		18 35		
18½	—	Falls of Cruachan §	d		08x43		12x43			13x28		16x47		18x43		
22	—	Loch Awe	d		08 50		12 50			13 35		16 53		18 50		
24¾	—	Dalmally	d		08 56		12 56			13 41		17 00		18 56		
36¾	—	Tyndrum Lower	d		09 15		13 15			14 00		17 19		19 15		
42	104½	**Crianlarich**	a		09 29	09 30	13 29	13 30	13 30	14 09		17 28	19 26	19 27		22 04
—	—		d			09 36		13 36	13 36	14 11		17 31		19 33		22 05
50¾	113¼	Ardlui	d			09 52		13 52	13 52	14 28		17 47		19 53		22x26
58¾	121¼	Arrochar & Tarbet	d	07 08		10 07		14 07	14 07	14 42		18 02		20 08		22 44
69½	132	Garelochhead	d	07 30		10 29		14 27	14 27	15 03		18 22		20 28		23 10
76¼	138¾	Helensburgh Upper	a	07 41		10 39		14 38	14 38	15 13		18 33		20 39		23 23
—	—		d	07 42		10 41		14 39	14 39	15 15		18 34		20 40		23 24
85¼	147¾	Dumbarton Central 226	a	07 57		10 58		14 52	14 52	15 29		18 47		20 53		
92½	154¼	Dalmuir 226	a			11 08		15 04	15 04	15 38		18 56		21 04		23 49
96	157¾	Westerton 226	a			*11 25*		*15 25*	*15 25*	*15 55*		*19 10*		*21 25*		23 56
101½	164¼	**Glasgow Queen Street** 10 226 ⛴	a	08 37		11 28		15 28	15 28	15 58		19 18		21 29		*00 19*
—	—	Edinburgh 228	a	*09 48*		*12b35*		*16 38*	*16 39*	*17 06*		*20 20*		*22b50*		00 50

For general notes see front of timetable
For details of catering facilities see Directory of Train Operators

§ Summer Station Only

A All Mondays to Fridays, also Saturdays 28 June to 23 August

B **The Jacobite.** Steam hauled service

C Limiting seating accommodation. Also conveys overnight Sleeping Car accommodation to London Euston (Tables 65 and 404)

b Saturdays arr. 1 minute later

Mallaig, Fort William and Oban → Glasgow Queen Street

Network Diagram - see first page Table 227

		SR SX	SR	SR	SR	SR	WR SX	SR SO	SR	SR	SR	SR SX
							R 1					R
			◇	◇ A	◇	◇ A	B	◇ C	◇ A	◇	◇	D
			trolley	trolley	trolley	trolley	[icon]	trolley	trolley	trolley		[icon]
Mallaig	d			06 03		10 10	14 10		16 05		18 15	
Morar	d			06 09		10 16			16 11		18 21	
Arisaig	d			06 19		10 26			16 21		18 31	
Beasdale	d			06x25		10x32			16x27		18x37	
Lochailort	d			06x34		10x41			16x36		18x46	
Glenfinnan	d			06 51		10 58			16 51		19 03	
Locheilside	d			07x01		11x08			17x01		19x11	
Loch Eil Outward Bound	d			07 07		11 14			17 07		19 17	
Corpach	d			07 13		11 20			17 13		19 23	
Banavie	d			07 17		11 24			17 17		19 27	
Fort William	a			07 25		11 32	16 02		17 27		19 37	
	d			07 42		11 40			17 37			19 50
Spean Bridge	d			07 55		11 53			17 50			20 10
Roy Bridge	d			08 02		12 00			17 57			20x17
Tulloch	d			08 13		12 11			18 08			20 30
Corrour	d			08 30		12 28			18 25			20x51
Rannoch	d			08 43		12 43			18 36			21 06
Bridge of Orchy	d			09 03		13 02			18 56			21 34
Upper Tyndrum	d			09 19		13 18			19 12			21 52
Oban	d		08 11		12 11			16 11		18 11		
Connel Ferry	d		08 23		12 23			16 27		18 23		
Taynuilt	d		08 35		12 35			16 39		18 35		
Falls of Cruachan §	d											
Loch Awe	d		08 50		12 50			16 53		18 50		
Dalmally	d		08 56		12 56			17 00		18 56		
Tyndrum Lower	d		09 15		13 15			17 19		19 15		
Crianlarich	a		09 29	09 30	13 29	13 30		17 28	19 26	19 27		22 04
	d			09 36		13 36		17 31		19 33		22 05
Ardlui	d			09 52		13 52		17 47		19 53		22x26
Arrochar & Tarbet	d	07 08		10 07		14 07		18 02		20 08		22 44
Garelochhead	d	07 30		10 29		14 27		18 22		20 28		23 10
Helensburgh Upper	a	07 41		10 39		14 38		18 33		20 39		23 23
	d	07 42		10 41		14 39		18 34		20 40		23 24
Dumbarton Central 226	a	07 57		10 58		14 52		18 47		20 53		
Dalmuir 226	a			11 08		15 04		18 56		21 04		23 49
Westerton 226	a			*11 25*		*15 25*		*19 10*		*21 25*		23 56
Glasgow Queen Street 10 226	a	08 37		11 28		15 28		19 18		21 29		*00 19*
Edinburgh 228	a	*09 48*		*12b35*		*16c39*		*20 20*		*22b50*		00 50

For general notes see front of timetable
For details of catering facilities see Directory of Train Operators

§ Summer Station Only

A [trolley] from Fort William
B **The Jacobite.** Steam hauled service
C Until 25 October
D Limiting seating accommodation. Also conveys overnight Sleeping Car accommodation to London Euston (Tables 65 and 404)
b Saturdays arr. 1 minute later
c Saturdays arr. 1638

until 28 September

Mallaig, Fort William and Oban → Glasgow Queen Street

Network Diagram - see first page Table 227

		SR	SR	WR	SR	SR	SR	SR	SR
		◇	◇	R 1 A	◇	◇	◇	R B	◇
Mallaig	d		10 18	14 10		16 05			18 15
Morar	d		10 24			16 11			18 21
Arisaig	d		10 34			16 21			18 31
Beasdale	d		10x40			16x27			18x37
Lochailort	d		10x49			16x36			18x46
Glenfinnan	d		11 06			16 53			19 03
Locheilside	d		11x15			17x03			19x11
Loch Eil Outward Bound	d		11 22			17 09			19 17
Corpach	d		11 28			17 15			19 23
Banavie	d		11 32			17 19			19 27
Fort William	a		11 40	16 02		17 27			19 37
	d		11 44			17 37		19 00	
Spean Bridge	d		11 56			17 50		19 20	
Roy Bridge	d		12 02			17 57		19x27	
Tulloch	d		12 14			18 08		19 40	
Corrour	d		12 30			18 25		20x01	
Rannoch	d		12 44			18 36		20 15	
Bridge of Orchy	d		13 03			18 56		20b47	
Upper Tyndrum	d		13 19			19 12		21 05	
Oban	d	12 11			16 11		18 11		
Connel Ferry	d	12 23			16 27		18 23		
Taynuilt	d	12 35			16 39		18 35		
Falls of Cruachan §	d	12x43			16x47		18x43		
Loch Awe	d	12 50			16 53		18 50		
Dalmally	d	12 56			17 00		18 56		
Tyndrum Lower	d	13 15			17 19		19 15		
Crianlarich	a	13 29	13 30		17 28	19 26	19 27	21 16	
	d	13 36			17 31	19 33		21 18	
Ardlui	d	13 52			17 47	19 53		21x39	
Arrochar & Tarbet	d	14 07			18 02	20 08		21 57	
Garelochhead	d	14 27			18 22	20 28		22 23	
Helensburgh Upper	a	14 38			18 33	20 39		22 35	
	d	14 39			18 34	20 40		22 37	
Dumbarton Central 226	a	14 53			18 47	20 53			
Dalmuir 226	a	15 05			18 56	21 05		23 02	
Westerton 226	a	*15 30*			*19 30*	*21 30*		23 11	
Glasgow Queen Street 10 226	a	15 32			19 18	21 27			
Edinburgh 228	a	*16 55*			*20 21*	*23 24*		00 15	

For general notes see front of timetable
For details of catering facilities see Directory of Train Operators

§ Summer Station Only

A **The Jacobite.** Steam hauled service

B Limiting seating accommodation. Also conveys overnight Sleeping Car accommodation to London Euston (Tables 65 and 404)

b Arr. 2041

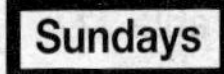

Sundays

from 5 October

Mallaig, Fort William and Oban → Glasgow Queen Street

Network Diagram - see first page of Table 227

		SR	SR	SR	SR
		◇	◇	◇	[R]
		A	B		C
		[trolley]	[trolley]	[trolley]	[sleeper]
Mallaig	d		16 05		
Morar	d		16 11		
Arisaig	d		16 21		
Beasdale	d		16x27		
Lochailort	d		16x36		
Glenfinnan	d		16 53		
Locheilside	d		17x03		
Loch Eil Outward Bound	d		17 09		
Corpach	d		17 15		
Banavie	d		17 19		
Fort William	a		17 27		
	d		17 37		19 00
Spean Bridge	d		17 50		19 20
Roy Bridge	d		17 57		19x27
Tulloch	d		18 08		19 40
Corrour	d		18 25		20x01
Rannoch	d		18 36		20 15
Bridge of Orchy	d		18 56		20b47
Upper Tyndrum	d		19 12		21 05
Oban	d	12 11		18 11	
Connel Ferry	d	12 23		18 23	
Taynuilt	d	12 35		18 35	
Falls of Cruachan §	d				
Loch Awe	d	12 50		18 50	
Dalmally	d	12 56		18 56	
Tyndrum Lower	d	13 15		19 15	
Crianlarich	a	13 29	19 26	19 27	21 16
	d	13 36	19 33		21 18
Ardlui	d	13 52	19 53		21x39
Arrochar & Tarbet	d	14 07	20 08		21 57
Garelochhead	d	14 27	20 28		22 23
Helensburgh Upper	a	14 38	20 39		22 35
	d	14 39	20 40		22 37
Dumbarton Central	226 a	14 53	20 53		
Dalmuir	226 a	15 05	21 05		23 02
Westerton	226 a	*15 30*	*21 30*		23 11
Glasgow Queen Street [10]	226 a	15 32	21 27		
Edinburgh	228 a	*16 55*	*23 24*		00 15

For general notes see front of timetable
For details of catering facilities see Directory of Train Operators

§ Summer Station Only

A Until 26 October

B [trolley] from Fort William

C Limiting seating accommodation. Also conveys overnight Sleeping Car accommodation to London Euston (Tables 65 and 404)

b Arr. 2041

Table 227A

Mallaig — Armadale (Skye) and Small Isles

Operated By Caledonian MacBrayne Ltd.

Mondays to Saturdays
until 18 October

		MO	TO A	WO	SR ThO		FO	SO B	SX C	SO	SX D	
Glasgow Queen Street 10	227 ⛴ d							08 21	08 21	08 21	08 51	12 21
Fort William	227 d	08 30	08 30	08 30	08 30	08 30	08 30	12 12	12 12	12 12	12 47	16 19
Mallaig	227 a	09 52	09 52	09 52	09 52	09 52	09 52	13 34	13 34	13 34	14 09	17 43
Mallaig	⛴ d	10 15	10 15	10 15	10 15	10 55	12 40	14 25	15 05	15 05	15 05	18 00
Armadale	⛴ a					11 25			15 35	15 35	15 35	18 30
Eigg	⛴ a	11 30	12 45		11 30			15 40				
Muck	⛴ a		11 55		12 20			16 25				
Rum	⛴ a	12 45		11 35			14 00	19 25				
Canna	⛴ a	13 55		12 45			15 10	18 15				

Sundays
until 12 October

		E	G
Glasgow Queen Street 10	227 ⛴ d		12 20
Fort William	227 d	12 12	16 19
Mallaig	227 a	13 34	17 34
Mallaig	⛴ d	14 40	18 00
Armadale	⛴ a	15 10	18 30
Eigg	⛴ a		
Muck	⛴ a		
Rum	⛴ a		
Canna	⛴ a		

Mondays to Saturdays
until 18 October

			FO	SO H	ThO		TO J	WO		MO	FO
Canna	⛴ d			10 15				14 35		14 10	15 25
Rum	⛴ d			09 05				15 45		15 20	16 35
Muck	⛴ d		10 20	12 00	12 35		13 50				
Eigg	⛴ d		11 10	12 50	13 20		13 00			16 35	
Armadale	⛴ d	08 50				14 25			17 05		
Mallaig	⛴ a	09 20	12 25	14 05	14 35	14 55	15 30	17 05	17 35	17 50	17 55
Mallaig	227 d	10 10	16 05	16 05	16 05	16 05	16 05	18 15	18 15	18 15	18 15
Fort William	227 a	11 32	17 27	17 27	17 27	17 27	17 27	19 37	19 37	19 37	19 37
Glasgow Queen Street 10	227 ⛴ a	15 29	21 29	21 29	21 29	21 29	21 29	00b19	00c19	00b19	00b19

Sundays
until 12 October

		K	L
Canna	⛴ d		
Rum	⛴ d		
Muck	⛴ d		
Eigg	⛴ d		
Armadale	⛴ d	15 20	16 50
Mallaig	⛴ a	15 50	17 20
Mallaig	227 d	16 05	18 15
Fort William	227 a	17 27	19 37
Glasgow Queen Street 10	227 ⛴ a	21 27	

For general notes see front of timetable
For details of catering facilities see Directory of Train Operators

- **A** Sails via Muck
- **B** Sails via Canna
- **C** From 29 September
- **D** Until 26 September
- **E** 1 June to 31 August
- **G** Until 28 September
- **H** Sails from Rum
- **J** Sails from Eigg
- **K** 1 June to 31 August
- **L** Until 28 September
- **b** Following day. Change at Fort William and Westerton. Reservations compulsory from Fort William
- **c** Tuesday to Saturday mornings only. Change at Fort William and Westerton. Reservations compulsory from Fort William

For details of sailings from 19 October telephone Caledonian MacBrayne on 08000 66 5000

Table 227B SHIPPING SERVICES Mondays to Saturdays until 18 October

Oban — Craignure (Mull), Lismore, Colonsay, Coll and Tiree

Operated by Caledonian MacBrayne Ltd.

		FO A	WO		SO	MO		ThO B	SO		SX	SO		SX	SO		TO	WO		TFO	MFO	FO		
Glasgow Queen Street 10	227 d	18b21	18b21		18b21	18 20		18b21	08 21		08 21	10 37		08 21	10 37		08 21	08 21	12 21	12 21	12 21	18 21		
Oban	227 a	21b26	21b26		21b26	21 26		21b26	11 27		11 27	13 42		11 27	13 42		11 27	11 27	15 27	15 27	15 27	21 26		
Oban	d	06 00	06 00		07 00	08 00		08 30	11 45		11 55	14 00		14 45	14 45		15 00	15 30	16 00	16 45	17 00	22 30		
Craignure	a								12 31		12 41	14 46							16 46			23 16		
Lismore	a													15 35	15 35					17 35				
Colonsay	a																	17 45			19 20			
Coll	a	10 30	08 40		09 40	10 55		11 10									17 40							
Tiree	a	09 20	09 40		10 45	12 05		12 15									18 40							

Sundays until 12 October

							C																	
Glasgow Queen Street 10	227 d	18b21					09 55					12 20					12 20							
Oban	227 a	21b26					13 00					15 27					15 27							
Oban	d	08 45					14 00					16 00					17 30							
Craignure	a						14 46					16 46												
Lismore	a																							
Colonsay	a																19 50							
Coll	a	11 40																						
Tiree	a	12 50																						

Mondays to Saturdays until 18 October

		ThO	SO	TO D	TO E	SX G	SO	SX H	SO	SX G	SX H	TThO J	SO	FO	WO K	WO	ThO	SO	SO	MO				
Tiree	d													09 35	09 55			11 15		12 25				
Coll	d													10 35	08 45			12 20		13 35				
Colonsay	d			07 50	07 50											11 45	11 55							
Lismore	d					09 45	09 45	09 45				11 45	11 45								15 45			
Craignure	d	06 45	07 00						10 30	10 55	10 55								15 00			17 00		
Oban	a	07 31	07 46	10 10	10 10	10 35	10 35	10 35	11 16	11 41	11 41	12 35	12 35	13 15	13 15	14 10	14 15	15 00	15 46	16 30	16 35	17 46		
Oban	227 d	08 11	08 11	12 11	12 56	12 11	12 11	12 56	12 11	12 11	12 56	12 56	16 11	18 11	18 11	18 11	18 11	16 11	16 11	18 11	18 11	18 11		
Glasgow Queen Street 10	227 a	11 28	11 28	15 29	16 00	15 29	15 29	16 00	15 29	15 29	16 00	16 00	19 18	21 29	21 29	21 29	21 29	19 18	19 18	21 29	21 29	21 29		

Sundays until 12 October

							L																	
Tiree	d											13 10												
Coll	d											14 20												
Colonsay	d																							
Lismore	d																							
Craignure	d	10 55					15 00										17 00							
Oban	a	11 41					15 46					17 15					17 46							
Oban	227 d	12 11					16 11					18 11					18 11							
Glasgow Queen Street 10	227 a	15 32					19 18					21 27					21 27							

For general notes see front of timetable
For details of catering facilities see Directory of Train Operators

- A Sails via Tiree
- B Sails to Barra arrive 1515
- C Until 28 September
- D From 30 September
- E Until 23 September
- G From 29 September
- H Until 26 September
- J Until 25 September
- K Sails from Coll
- L Until 28 September
- b Previous night

For details of sailings from 19 October telephone Caledonian MacBrayne on 08000 66 5000

Table 227C — SHIPPING SERVICES

Oban — Castlebay (Barra) and Lochboisdale (South Uist)

Operated by Caledonian MacBrayne Ltd

Mondays to Saturdays
until 18 October

		WFO	MO	TThO A	SO
Glasgow Queen Street [10]	227 d	08 21	08 21	08 21	10 37
Oban	227 a	11 27	11 27	11 27	13 42
Oban	d	13 40	15 10	15 30	15 30
Castlebay	a	18 30	20 00	22 50	20 20
Lochboisdale	a			20 50	

Sundays
until 12 October

		B
Glasgow Queen Street [10]	227 d	09 55
Oban	227 a	13 00
Oban	d	15 10
Castlebay	a	20 00
Lochboisdale	a	21 40

Mondays to Saturdays
until 18 October

		MO	TO	WFO C
Lochboisdale	d	07 30		09 00
Castlebay	d	09 20	09 20	07 00
Oban	a	14 10	14 10	14 20
Oban	227 d	18 11	18 11	18 11
Glasgow Queen Street [10]	227 a	21 29	21 29	21 29

Sundays
until 12 October

		D	E
Lochboisdale	d		
Castlebay	d	09 20	09 20
Oban	a	14 10	14 10
Oban	227 d	16 11	18 11
Glasgow Queen Street [10]	227 a	19 18	21 27

For general notes see front of timetable
For details of catering facilities see Directory of Train Operators

A Sails via Lochboisdale
B Until 28 September
C Sails from Castlebay
D Until 28 September
E 5 and 12 October

For details of sailings from 19 October telephone Caledonian MacBrayne on 08000 66 5000

Edinburgh → Falkirk High → Glasgow Queen Street

Network Diagram - see first page of Table 225

Mondays to Fridays

Miles			SR	SR	SR	SR	SR	SR	SR	SR	SR		SR	SR	SR	SR	SR	SR	SR	SR	SR		SR	SR	SR
			1	1	1	1	1	1		1			1	1	1	1	1	1	1	1	1		1	1	1
									A		A														
				🛒	🛒	🛒	🛒	🛒		🛒			🛒	🛒	🛒	🛒	🛒	🛒	🛒	🛒	🛒		🛒	🛒	🛒
0	**Edinburgh** 10	225, 230, 242 d	05 55	06 30	06 45	07 00	07 15	07 30		07 45			08 00	08 15	08 30	08 45	09 00	09 15	09 30	09 45	10 00		10 15	10 30	10 45
1¼	Haymarket	225, 230, 242 d	05 59	06 34	06 48	07 04	07 19	07 34		07 49			08 04	08 18	08 33	08 48	09 03	09 18	09 33	09 48	10 03		10 18	10 33	10 48
17½	Linlithgow	230 d	06 13	06 48	07 03		07 33	07 48	07 58	08 03				08 33		09 03		09 33		10 03			10 33		11 03
22¾	Polmont 3	230 d	06 19	06 55		07 19		07 54			←		08 21	08 39		09 09		09 39		10 09			10 39		11 09
25¼	**Falkirk High**	d	06 24	07 00	07 12	07 24	07 42	07 59	08b09	08 12	08b09		08 26	08 44	08 54	09 14	09 24	09 44	09 54	10 14	10 24		10 44	10 54	11 14
35¾	Croy 3	230 a	06 34	07 09	07 22		07 52	08 09	→				08 36		09 04		09 34		10 03		10 34			11 03	
41	Lenzie 3	230 a	*06 50*	*07 21*			*08 06*			08 24	08 29		*08 48*		*09 19*		*09 49*		*10 19*		*10 49*			*11 19*	
44	Bishopbriggs	230 a	*06 54*	*07 26*			*08 11*			08 29	08 34		*08 52*		*09 23*		*09 53*		*10 23*		*10 53*			*11 23*	
47¼	**Glasgow Queen Street** 10	230 ⛴ a	06 49	07 24	07 38	07 51	08 07	08 25		08 40	08 48		08 55	09 07	09 21	09 36	09 51	10 06	10 20	10 36	10 50		11 06	11 20	11 36

		SR	SR	SR	SR	SR	SR	SR	SR		SR	SR	SR	SR	SR	SR	SR	SR	SR		SR	SR	SR	SR	SR
		1	1	1	1	1	1	1	1		1	1	1	1	1	1	1	1	1		1	1	1	1	1
		🛒	🛒	🛒	🛒	🛒	🛒	🛒	🛒		🛒	🛒	🛒	🛒	🛒	🛒	🛒	🛒	🛒		🛒	🛒	🛒	🛒	🛒
Edinburgh 10	225, 230, 242 d	11 00	11 15	11 30	11 45	12 00	12 15	12 30	12 45		13 00	13 15	13 30	13 45	14 00	14 15	14 30	14 45	15 00		15 15	15 30	15 45	16 00	16 15
Haymarket	225, 230, 242 d	11 03	11 18	11 33	11 48	12 03	12 18	12 33	12 48		13 03	13 18	13 33	13 48	14 03	14 18	14 33	14 48	15 03		15 18	15 33	15 48	16 03	16 18
Linlithgow	230 d		11 33		12 03		12 33		13 03			13 33		14 03		14 33		15 03			15 33		16 03		16 33
Polmont 3	230 d		11 39		12 09		12 39		13 09			13 39		14 09		14 39		15 09			15 39		16 09		16 39
Falkirk High	d	11 24	11 44	11 54	12 14	12 24	12 44	12 54	13 14		13 24	13 44	13 54	14 14	14 24	14 44	14 54	15 14	15 24		15 44	15 54	16 14	16 24	16 44
Croy 3	230 a	11 33		12 03		12 33		13 03			13 33		14 03		14 33		15 03		15 34			16 03		16 33	
Lenzie 3	230 a	*11 49*		*12 19*		*12 49*		*13 19*			*13 49*		*14 19*		*14 49*		*15 19*		*15 49*			*16 19*		*16 49*	
Bishopbriggs	230 a	*11 53*		*12 23*		*12 53*		*13 23*			*13 53*		*14 23*		*14 53*		*15 23*		*15 53*			*16 23*		*16 53*	
Glasgow Queen Street 10	230 ⛴ a	11 50	12 06	12 20	12 37	12 50	13 06	13 20	13 36		13 50	14 06	14 20	14 36	14 50	15 06	15 21	15 37	15 51		16 07	16 20	16 36	16 51	17 06

		SR	SR	SR	SR	SR	SR		SR	SR	SR	SR	SR	SR	SR	SR	SR	SR	SR	SR	SR	SR	SR		
		1	1	1	1	1	1		1	1	1	1	1	1	1	1	1	1	1	1	1	1	1		
		🛒	🛒	🛒	🛒	🛒	🛒		🛒	🛒	🛒	🛒	🛒	🛒	🛒	🛒	🛒								
Edinburgh 10	225, 230, 242 d	16 30	16 45	17 00	17 15	17 30	17 45		18 00	18 15	18 30	18 45	19 00	19 15	19 30	20 00	20 30	21 00	21 30	22 00	22 30	23 00	23 30		
Haymarket	225, 230, 242 d	16 33	16 48	17 03	17 18	17 33	17 48		18 03	18 18	18 33	18 48	19 03	19 18	19 33	20 03	20 33	21 03	21 33	22 03	22 33	23 03	23 33		
Linlithgow	230 d		17 03		17 33		18 03			18 33		19 03		19 33	19 48	20 18	20 48	21 18	21 48	22 18	22 48	23 18	23 48		
Polmont 3	230 d		17 09		17 39		18 09			18 39		19 09		19 39		20 24		21 24		22 24		23 24	23 54		
Falkirk High	d	16 54	17 14	17 24	17 44	17 54	18 14		18 24	18 44	18 54	19 14	19 24	19 44	19 57	20 29	20 57	21 29	21 57	22 29	22 57	23 29	23 59		
Croy 3	230 a	17 03		17 33		18 03			18 33		19 03		19 33		20 07		21 07		22 07		23 06	23 39	00 08		
Lenzie 3	230 a	*17 19*		*17 49*		18 08			*18 49*		*19 19*				*20 19*		*21 19*		*22 19*		23 11	23 44	00 14		
Bishopbriggs	230 a	*17 23*		*17 53*		*18 24*			*18 53*		*19 23*				*20 23*		*21 22*		*22 23*		*23 22*	*23 52*			
Glasgow Queen Street 10	230 ⛴ a	17 21	17 36	17 51	18 06	18 22	18 37		18 50	19 06	19 21	19 36	19 49	20 06	20 21	20 50	21 21	21 50	22 21	22 50	23 24	00 03	00 27		

Saturdays

		SR	SR	SR	SR	SR	SR		SR	SR	SR	SR	SR	SR		SR	SR	SR	SR	SR	SR		SR	SR	SR
		1	1	1	1	1	1		1	1	1	1	1	1		1	1	1	1	1	1		1	1	1
				🛒	🛒	🛒	🛒		🛒	🛒	🛒	🛒	🛒	🛒		🛒	🛒	🛒	🛒	🛒	🛒		🛒	🛒	🛒
Edinburgh 10	225, 230, 242 d	05 55	06 30	07 00	07 15	07 30	07 45		08 00	08 15	08 30	08 45	09 00	09 15		09 30	09 45	10 00	10 15	10 30	10 45		11 00	11 15	11 30
Haymarket	225, 230, 242 d	05 59	06 34	07 04	07 19	07 34	07 49		08 04	08 18	08 33	08 48	09 03	09 18		09 33	09 48	10 03	10 18	10 33	10 48		11 03	11 18	11 33
Linlithgow	230 d	06 13	06 48		07 33	07 48	08 03			08 33		09 03		09 33			10 03		10 33		11 03			11 33	
Polmont 3	230 d	06 19	06 55	07 19		07 54			08 21	08 39		09 09		09 39			10 09		10 39		11 09			11 39	
Falkirk High	d	06 24	07 00	07 24	07 42	07 59	08 12		08 26	08 44	08 54	09 14	09 24	09 44		09 54	10 14	10 24	10 44	10 54	11 14		11 24	11 44	11 54
Croy 3	230 a	06 34	07 09		07 52	08 09			08 36		09 04		09 34			10 03		10 34		11 03			11 33		12 03
Lenzie 3	230 a	*06 50*	*07 21*		*08 04*		08 24		*08 48*		*09 19*		*09 49*			*10 19*		*10 49*		*11 19*			*11 49*		*12 19*
Bishopbriggs	230 a	*06 54*	*07 26*		*08 10*		08 29		*08 52*		*09 23*		*09 53*			*10 23*		*10 53*		*11 23*			*11 53*		*12 23*
Glasgow Queen Street 10	230 ⛴ a	06 49	07 24	07 48	08 07	08 25	08 38		08 55	09 07	09 22	09 36	09 51	10 06		10 20	10 36	10 50	11 06	11 20	11 36		11 50	12 06	12 20

		SR	SR	SR	SR	SR		SR	SR	SR	SR	SR	SR		SR	SR	SR	SR	SR	SR		SR	SR	SR	SR
		1	1	1	1	1		1	1	1	1	1	1		1	1	1	1	1	1		1	1	1	1
		🛒	🛒	🛒	🛒	🛒		🛒	🛒	🛒	🛒	🛒	🛒		🛒	🛒	🛒	🛒	🛒	🛒		🛒	🛒	🛒	🛒
Edinburgh 10	225, 230, 242 d	11 45	12 00	12 15	12 30	12 45		13 00	13 15	13 30	13 45	14 00	14 15		14 30	14 45	15 00	15 15	15 30	15 45		16 00	16 15	16 30	16 45
Haymarket	225, 230, 242 d	11 48	12 03	12 18	12 33	12 48		13 03	13 18	13 33	13 48	14 03	14 18		14 33	14 48	15 03	15 18	15 33	15 48		16 03	16 18	16 33	16 48
Linlithgow	230 d	12 03		12 33		13 03			13 33		14 03		14 33			15 03		15 33		16 03			16 33		17 03
Polmont 3	230 d	12 09		12 39		13 09			13 39		14 09		14 39			15 09		15 39		16 09			16 39		17 09
Falkirk High	d	12 14	12 24	12 44	12 54	13 14		13 24	13 44	13 54	14 14	14 24	14 44		14 54	15 14	15 24	15 44	15 54	16 14		16 24	16 44	16 54	17 14
Croy 3	230 a		12 33		13 03			13 33		14 03		14 33			15 03		15 34		16 03			16 33		17 03	
Lenzie 3	230 a		*12 49*		*13 19*			*13 49*		*14 19*		*14 49*			*15 19*		*15 49*		*16 19*			*16 49*		*17 19*	
Bishopbriggs	230 a		*12 53*		*13 23*			*13 53*		*14 23*		*14 53*			*15 23*		*15 53*		*16 23*			*16 53*		*17 23*	
Glasgow Queen Street 10	230 ⛴ a	12 37	12 50	13 06	13 20	13 36		13 50	14 06	14 20	14 36	14 50	15 06		15 21	15 37	15 51	16 07	16 20	16 36		16 51	17 06	17 21	17 36

		SR	SR	SR	SR		SR	SR	SR	SR	SR	SR		SR	SR	SR	SR	SR	SR		SR	SR	SR		
		1	1	1	1		1	1	1	1	1	1		1	1	1	1	1	1		1	1	1		
		🛒	🛒	🛒	🛒		🛒	🛒	🛒	🛒	🛒	🛒		🛒	🛒	🛒									
Edinburgh 10	225, 230, 242 d	17 00	17 15	17 30	17 45		18 00	18 15	18 30	18 45	19 00	19 15		19 30	20 00	20 30	21 00	21 30	22 00		22 30	23 00	23 30		
Haymarket	225, 230, 242 d	17 03	17 18	17 33	17 48		18 03	18 18	18 33	18 48	19 03	19 18		19 33	20 03	20 33	21 03	21 33	22 03		22 34	23 03	23 33		
Linlithgow	230 d		17 33		18 03			18 33		19 03		19 33		19 48	20 18	20 48	21 18	21 48	22 18		22 48	23 18	23 48		
Polmont 3	230 d		17 39		18 09			18 39		19 09		19 39			20 24		21 24		22 24			23 24	23 54		
Falkirk High	d	17 24	17 44	17 54	18 14		18 24	18 44	18 54	19 14	19 24	19 44		19 57	20 29	20 57	21 29	21 57	22 29		22 57	23 29	23 59		
Croy 3	230 a	17 33		18 03			18 33		19 03		19 33			20 07		21 07		22 07			23 07	23 40	00 08		
Lenzie 3	230 a	*17 49*		18 08			*18 49*		*19 19*					*20 19*		*21 19*		*22 19*			23 12	23 46	00 14		
Bishopbriggs	230 a	*17 53*		*18 24*			*18 53*		*19 23*					*20 23*		*21 22*		*22 23*			*23 22*	23 52			
Glasgow Queen Street 10	230 ⛴ a	17 51	18 06	18 22	18 37		18 50	19 06	19 21	19 36	19 49	20 06		20 21	20 50	21 21	21 50	22 21	22 50		23 24	00 03	00 28		

For general notes see front of timetable
For details of catering facilities see Directory of Train Operators

A From Kirkcaldy (Table 242). Also stops at Camelon 0812
b Falkirk Grahamston

Sundays

Edinburgh → Falkirk High → Glasgow Queen Street

Network Diagram - see first page of Table 225

		SR 1 ⚲	SR 1	SR 1 ⚲	SR 1 ⚲	SR 1 ⚲	SR 1 ⚲	SR 1 ⚲	SR 1 ⚲	SR 1 ⚲	SR 1	SR 1 ⚲	SR 1 ⚲	SR 1 ⚲
Edinburgh 10	225, 230, 242 d	08 00	09 00	10 00	11 00	12 00	12 30	13 00	13 30	14 00	14 30	15 00	15 30	16 00
Haymarket	225, 230, 242 d	08 04	09 04	10 04	11 04	12 04	12 34	13 04	13 34	14 04	14 34	15 04	15 34	16 04
Linlithgow	230 d	08 20	09 20	10 20	11 18	12 18	12 48	13 18	13 48	14 18	14 48	15 18	15 48	16 18
Polmont 3	230 d	08 27	09 27	10 27	11 25	12 25	.	13 25	.	14 25	.	15 25	.	16 25
Falkirk High	d	08 32	09 32	10 32	11 30	12 30	12 57	13 30	13 57	14 30	14 57	15 30	15 57	16 30
Croy 3	230 a	08 41	09 41	10 41	11 39	12 39	13 08	.	14 08	.	15 07	.	16 07	.
Lenzie 3	230 a	*09b55*	*09 55*	*10 55*	*11 52*	*12 52*	*13c52*		*14e52*		*15f54*		*16g52*	
Bishopbriggs	230 a	*09b59*	*09 59*	*10 59*	*11 56*	*12 56*	*13c56*	.	*14e56*	.	*15f58*	.	*16g56*	.
Glasgow Queen Street 10	230 ⛴ a	08 59	10 00	11 00	11 55	12 55	13 23	13 51	14 23	14 51	15 22	15 51	16 24	16 51

		SR 1 ⚲	SR 1 ⚲	SR 1 ⚲	SR 1 ⚲	SR 1 ⚲	SR 1 ⚲	SR 1 ⚲	SR 1 ⚲	SR 1 ⚲	SR 1 ⚲	SR 1	SR 1	SR 1
Edinburgh 10	225, 230, 242 d	16 30	17 00	17 30	18 00	18 30	19 00	19 30	20 00	20 30	21 00	22 00	23 00	23 30
Haymarket	225, 230, 242 d	16 34	17 04	17 34	18 04	18 34	19 04	19 34	20 04	20 34	21 04	22 04	23 04	23 34
Linlithgow	230 d	16 48	17 18	17 48	18 18	18 48	19 18	19 48	20 18	20 48	21 18	22 18	23 18	23 48
Polmont 3	230 d	.	17 25	.	18 25	.	19 25	.	20 25	.	21 25	22 25	23 25	23 55
Falkirk High	d	16 57	17 29	17 57	18 30	18 57	19 30	19 57	20 30	20 57	21 30	22 29	23 29	00 01
Croy 3	230 a	17 07	.	18 07	.	19 07	.	20 07	.	21 07	21 39	22 39	23 39	00 09
Lenzie 3	230 a	*17h52*		*18j53*		*19k52*		*20 52*			*21 52*			
Bishopbriggs	230 a	*17h56*	.	*18j57*	.	*19 56*	.	*20 56*	.	.	*21 56*	.	.	.
Glasgow Queen Street 10	230 ⛴ a	17 22	17 52	18 22	18 51	19 22	19 51	20 22	20 51	21 22	21 55	22 55	23 55	00 25

For general notes see front of timetable
For details of catering facilities see Directory of Train Operators

b 30 November and 7 December arr. Lenzie 0856, Bishopbriggs 0900

c 30 November and 7 December arr. Lenzie 1321, Bishopbriggs 1326

e 30 November and 7 December arr. Lenzie 1421, Bishopbriggs 1426

f 30 November and 7 December arr. Lenzie 1521, Bishopbriggs 1526

g 30 November and 7 December arr. Lenzie 1621, Bishopbriggs 1626

h 30 November and 7 December arr. Lenzie 1721, Bishopbriggs 1726

j 30 November and 7 December arr. Lenzie 1821, Bishopbriggs 1826

k 30 November and 7 December arr. Lenzie 1919, Bishopbriggs 1924

Glasgow Queen Street → Falkirk High → Edinburgh

Network Diagram - see first page of Table 225

Mondays to Fridays

Miles		SR	SR	SR	SR	SR	SR	SR	SR	SR		SR	SR	SR	SR	SR	SR	SR	SR	SR		SR	SR	SR
		1	1	1	1	1	1	1	1	1		1	1	1	1	1	1	1	1	1		1	1	1
			T	T	T	T	T	T	T	T		T	T	T	T	T	T	T	T	T		T	T	T
0	**Glasgow Queen Street** 10 230 ⛴ d	06 00	06 30	06 45	07 00	07 15	07 30	07 45	08 00	08 15		08 30	08 45	09 00	09 15	09 30	09 45	10 00	10 15	10 30		10 45	11 00	11 15
3¼	Bishopbriggs 230 d		06 19		06 54		07 23		07 53			08 23		08 53		09 23		09 53		10 23			10 53	
6¼	Lenzie 3 230 d		06 38		07 09		07 29		07 59			08 29		08 59		09 29		09 59		10 29			10 59	
11½	Croy 3 230 d		06 44	06 57			07 41		08 11			08 41		09 11		09 41		10 11		10 41			11 11	
21¾	**Falkirk High** d	06 19	06 51	07 07	07 22	07 34	07 51	08 03	08 21	08 33		08 51	09 03	09 21	09 33	09 51	10 03	10 21	10 33	10 51		11 03	11 21	11 33
25	Polmont 3 230 a	06 23	06 56		07 26	07 38		08 07	08 26				09 07		09 37		10 07		10 37			11 07		11 37
29¾	Linlithgow 230 a	06 30	07 02	07 15	07 33	07 45	07 58	08 14		08 41			09 14		09 44		10 14		10 44			11 14		11 44
46	Haymarket 225, 230, 242 a	06s46	07s18	07s31	07s50	08s01	08s16	08s31	08s46	09s00		09s13	09s30	09s43	10s01	10s15	10s30	10s45	11s00	11s14		11s30	11s45	12s00
47¼	**Edinburgh** 10 225, 230, 242 a	06 51	07 23	07 36	07 55	08 06	08 21	08 36	08 51	09 05		09 19	09 35	09 48	10 06	10 22	10 35	10 50	11 05	11 19		11 35	11 50	12 05

	SR	SR	SR	SR	SR	SR	SR	SR		SR	SR	SR	SR	SR	SR	SR	SR	SR		SR	SR	SR	SR	SR
	1	1	1	1	1	1	1	1		1	1	1	1	1	1	1	1	1		1	1	1	1	1
	T	T	T	T	T	T	T	T		T	T	T	T	T	T	T	T	T		T	T	T	T	T
Glasgow Queen Street 10 230 ⛴ d	11 30	11 45	12 00	12 15	12 30	12 45	13 00	13 15		13 30	13 45	14 00	14 15	14 30	14 45	15 00	15 15	15 30		15 45	16 00	16 15	16 30	16 45
Bishopbriggs 230 d	11 24		11 53		12 23		12 53			13 23		13 53		14 23		14 53		15 24			15 53		16 23	
Lenzie 3 230 d	11 30		11 59		12 29		12 59			13 29		13 59		14 29		14 59		15 30			15 59		16 29	
Croy 3 230 d	11 41		12 11		12 41		13 11			13 41		14 11		14 41		15 11		15 41			16 11		16 41	
Falkirk High d	11 51	12 03	12 21	12 33	12 51	13 03	13 21	13 33		13 51	14 03	14 21	14 33	14 51	15 03	15 21	15 33	15 51		16 03	16 21	16 33	16 51	17 03
Polmont 3 230 a		12 07		12 37		13 07		13 37			14 07		14 37		15 07		15 37			16 07		16 37		17 07
Linlithgow 230 a		12 14		12 44		13 14		13 44			14 14		14 44		15 14		15 44			16 14		16 44		17 14
Haymarket 225, 230, 242 a	12s13	12s30	12s45	13s00	13s12	13s30	13s45	14s00		14s14	14s30	14s45	15s00	15s12	15s30	15s45	16s00	16s13		16s33	16s46	17s01	17s13	17s34
Edinburgh 10 225, 230, 242 a	12 19	12 35	12 50	13 05	13 19	13 35	13 50	14 05		14 19	14 35	14 50	15 05	15 17	15 35	15 50	16 05	16 18		16 39	16 52	17 06	17 22	17 39

	SR	SR	SR	SR	SR	SR		SR	SR	SR	SR	SR	SR	SR	SR	SR	SR	SR	SR	SR	SR	SR		
	1	1	1		1			1	1	1	1	1	1	1	1	1	1	1	1	1	1	1		
				A		A																		
	T	T	T		T			T	T	T	T	T	T	T	T	T								
Glasgow Queen Street 10 230 ⛴ d	17 00	17 15	17 30	17 33	17 45			18 00	18 15	18 30	18 45	19 00	19 15	19 30	20 00	20 30	21 00	21 30	22 00	22 30	23 00	23 30		
Bishopbriggs 230 d	16 53		17 23	17 39				17 54		18 23		18 53			19 53		20 53		21 53		22 54	23 24		
Lenzie 3 230 d	16 59		17 29	17 44				18 00		18 29		18 59			19 59		20 59		21 59		22 59	23 28		
Croy 3 230 d	17 11		17 42			←		18 11		18 41		19 11			20 11		21 11		22 12		23 12	23 42		
Falkirk High d	17 21	17 35	17 52	18b01	18 03	18b01		18 21	18 33	18 51	19 03	19 21	19 33	19 48	20 21	20 48	21 21	21 48	22 22	22 48	23 22	23 52		
Polmont 3 230 a	17 27		17 57	→	18 07	18 11			18 37		19 07		19 37	19 52		20 52		21 53		22 52	23 27	23 57		
Linlithgow 230 a		17 42	18 03		18 14	18 18			18 44		19 14		19 44	19 59	20 29	20 59	21 29	21 59	22 29	22 59	23 33	00 03		
Haymarket 225, 230, 242 a	17s45	18s00	18s22		18s32			18s45	19s00	19s13	19s31	19s42	20s03	20s15	20s46	21s15	21s46	22s18	22s45	23s15	23s49	00s20		
Edinburgh 10 225, 230, 242 a	17 50	18 05	18 27		18 38			18 50	19 05	19 19	19 36	19 47	20 08	20 20	20 51	21 20	21 51	22 23	22 50	23 20	23 54	00 25		

Saturdays

	SR	SR	SR	SR	SR	SR		SR	SR	SR	SR	SR	SR		SR	SR	SR	SR	SR	SR		SR	SR	SR
	1	1	1	1	1	1		1	1	1	1	1	1		1	1	1	1	1	1		1	1	1
			T	T	T	T		T	T	T	T	T	T		T	T	T	T	T	T		T	T	T
Glasgow Queen Street 10 230 ⛴ d	06 00	06 30	07 00	07 15	07 30	07 45		08 00	08 15	08 30	08 45	09 00	09 15		09 30	09 45	10 00	10 15	10 30	10 45		11 00	11 15	11 30
Bishopbriggs 230 d		06 19	06 54		07 23			07 53		08 23		08 53			09 23		09 53		10 23			10 53		11 24
Lenzie 3 230 d		06 38	07 09		07 29			07 59		08 29		08 59			09 29		09 59		10 29			10 59		11 30
Croy 3 230 d		06 44			07 41			08 11		08 41		09 11			09 41		10 11		10 41			11 11		11 41
Falkirk High d	06 19	06 54	07 22	07 34	07 51	08 03		08 21	08 33	08 51	09 03	09 21	09 33		09 51	10 03	10 21	10 33	10 51	11 03		11 21	11 33	11 51
Polmont 3 230 a	06 23	06 58	07 26	07 38		08 07		08 26			09 07		09 37			10 07		10 37		11 07			11 37	
Linlithgow 230 a	06 30	07 05	07 33	07 45	07 58	08 14			08 41		09 14		09 44			10 14		10 44		11 14			11 44	
Haymarket 225, 230, 242 a	06s46	07s21	07s50	08s01	08s16	08s32		08s45	09s00	09s13	09s31	09s46	10s01		10s15	10s30	10s45	11s00	11s14	11s30		11s45	12s00	12s14
Edinburgh 10 225, 230, 242 a	06 51	07 26	07 55	08 06	08 23	08 37		08 50	09 05	09 19	09 36	09 52	10 06		10 22	10 35	10 50	11 06	11 22	11 35		11 52	12 05	12 22

	SR	SR	SR	SR	SR		SR	SR	SR	SR	SR	SR		SR	SR	SR	SR	SR	SR		SR	SR	SR	SR
	1	1	1	1	1		1	1	1	1	1	1		1	1	1	1	1	1		1	1	1	1
	T	T	T	T	T		T	T	T	T	T	T		T	T	T	T	T	T		T	T	T	T
Glasgow Queen Street 10 230 ⛴ d	11 45	12 00	12 15	12 30	12 45		13 00	13 15	13 30	13 45	14 00	14 15		14 30	14 45	15 00	15 15	15 30	15 45		16 00	16 15	16 30	16 45
Bishopbriggs 230 d		11 53		12 23			12 53		13 23		13 53			14 23		14 53		15 24			15 53		16 23	
Lenzie 3 230 d		11 59		12 29			12 59		13 29		13 59			14 29		14 59		15 30			15 59		16 29	
Croy 3 230 d		12 11		12 41			13 11		13 41		14 11			14 41		15 11		15 41			16 11		16 41	
Falkirk High d	12 03	12 21	12 33	12 51	13 03		13 21	13 33	13 51	14 03	14 21	14 33		14 51	15 03	15 21	15 33	15 51	16 03		16 21	16 33	16 51	17 03
Polmont 3 230 a	12 07		12 37		13 07			13 37		14 07		14 37			15 07		15 37		16 07			16 37		17 07
Linlithgow 230 a	12 14		12 44		13 14			13 44		14 14		14 44			15 14		15 44		16 14			16 44		17 14
Haymarket 225, 230, 242 a	12s30	12s45	13s00	13s12	13s30		13s45	14s00	14s12	14s30	14s45	15s00		15s12	15s30	15s45	16s00	16s13	16s33		16s46	17s01	17s13	17s34
Edinburgh 10 225, 230, 242 a	12 36	12 52	13 05	13 22	13 35		13 52	14 05	14 22	14 35	14 50	15 06		15 17	15 35	15 50	16 05	16 22	16 38		16 51	17 06	17 22	17 39

	SR	SR	SR	SR		SR	SR	SR	SR	SR	SR		SR	SR	SR	SR	SR	SR		SR	SR	SR		
	1	1	1	1		1	1	1	1	1	1		1	1	1	1	1	1		1	1	1		
	T	T	T	T		T	T	T	T	T	T		T	T	T									
Glasgow Queen Street 10 230 ⛴ d	17 00	17 15	17 30	17 45		18 00	18 15	18 30	18 45	19 00	19 15		19 30	20 00	20 30	21 00	21 30	22 00		22 30	23 00	23 30		
Bishopbriggs 230 d	16 53		17 23			17 54		18 23		18 53				19 53		20 53		21 53			22 54	23 24		
Lenzie 3 230 d	16 59		17 29			18 00		18 29		18 59				19 59		20 59		21 59			22 59	23 28		
Croy 3 230 d	17 11		17 42			18 11		18 41		19 11				20 11		21 11		22 12			23 12	23 42		
Falkirk High d	17 21	17 35	17 52	18 03		18 21	18 33	18 51	19 03	19 21	19 33		19 48	20 21	20 48	21 21	21 48	22 22		22 48	23 22	23 52		
Polmont 3 230 a	17 27		17 57	18 07			18 37		19 07		19 37		19 52		20 52		21 53			22 52	23 27	23 57		
Linlithgow 230 a		17 42	18 03	18 14			18 44		19 14		19 44		19 59	20 29	20 59	21 29	21 59	22 29		22 59	23 33	00 03		
Haymarket 225, 230, 242 a	17s45	18s00	18s22	18s32		18s45	19s00	19s13	19s31	19s42	20s03		20s15	20s46	21s15	21s46	22s18	22s46		23s15	23s49	00s20		
Edinburgh 10 225, 230, 242 a	17 50	18 06	18 27	18 38		18 50	19 05	19 19	19 36	19 47	20 08		20 20	20 51	21 22	21 53	22 23	22 51		23 22	23 54	00 25		

For general notes see front of timetable
For details of catering facilities see Directory of Train Operators

A To Kirkcaldy (Table 242). Also stops at Camelon 1758
b Falkirk Grahamston

Sundays

Glasgow Queen Street → Falkirk High → Edinburgh

Network Diagram - see first page of Table 225

		SR 1	SR 1	SR 1	SR 1	SR 1	SR 1	SR 1	SR 1	SR 1	SR 1	SR 1	SR 1	SR 1
			[trolley]	[trolley]	[trolley]	[trolley]	[trolley]	[trolley]		[trolley]	[trolley]	[trolley]		[trolley]
Glasgow Queen Street 10	230 d	07 50	08 30	09 30	10 30	11 30	12 30	13 00	13 30	14 00	14 30	15 00	15 30	16 00
Bishopbriggs	230 d	.	*08b21*	*09b20*	*10 21*	*11 21*	*12 21*	*12c21*	.	*13e21*	.	*14f21*	.	*15g21*
Lenzie 3	230 d	.	*08b27*	*09b26*	*10 27*	*11 27*	*12 27*	*12c27*	.	*13e27*	.	*14f27*	.	*15g27*
Croy 3	230 d	08 01	08 41	09 41	10 41	11 41	12 41	13 11	.	14 11	.	15 11	.	16 11
Falkirk High	d	08 11	08 51	09 51	10 51	11 51	12 51	13 21	13 48	14 21	14 48	15 21	15 48	16 21
Polmont 3	230 a	08 17	08 57	09 57	10 57	11 57	12 57	.	13 53	.	14 53	.	15 53	.
Linlithgow	230 a	08 23	09 03	10 03	11 03	12 03	13 03	13 29	14 00	14 30	15 00	15 30	16 00	16 30
Haymarket	225, 230, 242 a	08s44	09s23	10s23	11s19	12s19	13s21	13s46	14s16	14s47	15s16	15s46	16s16	16s50
Edinburgh 10	225, 230, 242 a	08 49	09 28	10 28	11 24	12 24	13 26	13 51	14 21	14 52	15 21	15 51	16 22	16 55

		SR 1	SR 1	SR 1	SR 1	SR 1	SR 1	SR 1	SR 1	SR 1	SR 1	SR 1	SR 1	SR 1
		[trolley]	[trolley]	[trolley]	[trolley]	[trolley]	[trolley]	[trolley]	[trolley]		[trolley]			
Glasgow Queen Street 10	230 d	16 30	17 00	17 30	18 00	18 30	19 00	19 30	20 00	20 30	21 00	21 30	22 30	23 30
Bishopbriggs	230 d	.	*16h21*	.	*17j21*	.	*18 21*	.	*19 21*	.	*20 21*	*21 21*	*22 21*	.
Lenzie 3	230 d	.	*16h27*	.	*17j27*	.	*18 27*	.	*19 27*	.	*20 27*	*21 27*	*22 27*	.
Croy 3	230 d	.	17 11	.	18 11	.	19 11	.	20 11	.	21 11	21 41	22 42	23 41
Falkirk High	d	16 48	17 21	17 48	18 21	18 48	19 21	19 48	20 21	20 48	21 21	21 51	22 52	23 51
Polmont 3	230 a	16 53	.	17 53	.	18 53	.	19 53	.	20 53	.	21 57	22 57	23 57
Linlithgow	230 a	17 00	17 30	18 00	18 30	19 00	19 29	20 00	20 30	21 00	21 30	22 03	23 03	00 03
Haymarket	225, 230, 242 a	17s16	17s47	18s16	18s50	19s16	19s47	20s16	20s46	21s17	21s45	22s20	23s19	00s19
Edinburgh 10	225, 230, 242 a	17 21	17 52	18 21	18 55	19 21	19 52	20 21	20 54	21 22	21 53	22 25	23 24	00 24

For general notes see front of timetable
For details of catering facilities see Directory of Train Operators

b 30 November and 7 December only

c 30 November and 7 December dep. Bishopbriggs 1253, Lenzie 1259

e 30 November and 7 December dep. Bishopbriggs 1354, Lenzie 1400

f 30 November and 7 December dep. Bishopbriggs 1453, Lenzie 1459

g 30 November and 7 December dep. Bishopbriggs 1554, Lenzie 1600

h 30 November and 7 December dep. Bishopbriggs 1653, Lenzie 1659

j 30 November and 7 December dep. Bishopbriggs 1754, Lenzie 1800

Table 229

Edinburgh and Glasgow Queen Street → Perth, Inverness, Dundee, Aberdeen and Dyce

Network Diagram - see first page of Table 225

Miles	Miles	Miles	Miles	Miles			SR SX	XC	SR	XC	SR	SR	SR	SR	SR	SR	SR	SR	SR	SR	SR	SR
								1 ◇	1	1 ◇	1	1 ◇	1	1 ◇	1 ◇	1 ◇	1 ◇	1 ◇	1 ◇	1 ◇	1 ◇	1
												A			A							
								🍽		🍽		🛒			🛒	🛒	🛒	🛒	🛒	🛒	🛒	
—	0	—	0	0	**Edinburgh** [10]	242 d				05 34		05b18	06 40	06c32	07 08	07b03	08 07	08b03	08 37	09 10	09b03	09 36
—	1¼	—	1¼	1¼	Haymarket	242 d						05b22	06 44	06b36	07 13	07b06	08 11	08b06	08 41	09 14	09e07	09 40
—	13¼	—	13¼	—	Inverkeithing	242 d				06 07			06 57		07 27				08 53	09 27		09 56
—	26	—	26	—	Kirkcaldy	242 d							07 15		07 43		08 39		09 09	09 43		10 12
—	33¼	—	33¼	—	Markinch	242 d				06 36			07 24		07 52		08 48		09 18			10 22
—	39¼	—	39¼	—	Ladybank	d							07 31		08 00							10 30
—	42¼	—	—	—	Springfield	d											08 59					
—	44½	—	—	—	Cupar	d				06 48					08 06		09 03			10 02		
—	51	—	—	—	Leuchars [3] §	d				06 55					08 13		09 10			10 09		
0	—	0	—	—	**Glasgow Queen Street** [10]	230 ⛴ d						05 55		07 05		07 41		08 41			09 41	
21	—	21	—	28¼	Larbert	230 d						06 16										
29	—	29	—	36½	Stirling	230 d						06 25		07 31		08 07		09 07			10 07	
34½	—	34½	—	42	Dunblane	230 d						06 31		07 37		08 14						
46½	—	46½	—	54½	Gleneagles	d						06 43										
62½	—	62½	57	70¾	**Perth**	a						06 59	07 54	08 04		08 40		09 37	09 54		10 37	10 56
—	—	—	—	—		d			06 32			07 01	07 55	08 05		08 41		09 38	09 55		10 38	
79¾	—	—	—	—	Invergowrie	d							08 13									
83¼	59¼	—	—	—	**Dundee**	a			06 52	07 16		07 22	08 21		08 25	09 03	09 22	10 00		10 21	11 00	
—	—	—	—	—		d		06 35	06 56			07 24			08 27	09 04	09 23	10 00		10 22	11 00	
87¼	63¼	—	—	—	Broughty Ferry	d																
94	70	—	—	—	Carnoustie	d			07 08			07 36					09 35				11 12	
100¼	76¼	—	—	—	Arbroath	d		06 51	07 15			07 43			08 43	09 20	09 42	10 16		10 38	11 19	
114	90	—	—	—	Montrose	d	06 30	07 05	07 29			07 57			08 58	09 37		10 30		10 53	11 32	
138¼	114¼	—	—	—	Stonehaven	d	06 52	07 25	07 51			08 19			09 19		10 16	10 52		11 14		
146½	122½	—	—	—	Portlethen	d	07 02		08 00			08 27						11 01				
154½	130½	—	—	—	**Aberdeen**	a	07 15	07 49	08 13			08 40			09 40	10 18	10 35	11 15		11 34	12 18	
—	—	—	—	—		240 d	07 18					08 46			09 47							
160¾	136¾	—	—	—	**Dyce**	240 ⇌ a	07 27	*08f31*				08 56			09 55		*11 09*	*11 49*			*12 47*	
—	—	78	72½	86¼	Dunkeld & Birnam	d								08g24								
—	—	91	85½	99¼	Pitlochry	d								08 41					10 24			
—	—	97¾	92¼	106	Blair Atholl	d								08 51								
—	—	121	116½	130¼	Dalwhinnie	d								09 17								
—	—	131¼	126¾	140½	Newtonmore	d								09 27								
—	—	134	129½	143¼	Kingussie	d					07 06			09 30					11 07			
—	—	145¾	141¼	155	Aviemore	d					07 24			09 43					11 19			
—	—	152¾	148¼	162	Carrbridge	d					07 32			09 52								
—	—	180	175	188¾	**Inverness**	a					08 05			10 26					11 59			

		SR	SR	GR	SR	SR	SR	SR	SR	SR	SR	SR	SR	SR	SR	GR	SR	SR	SR SO	SR SX	XC	SR SO
		1 ◇	1 ◇	R 1	1 ◇	1 ◇	1 ◇	1 ◇	1 ◇	1 ◇	1 ◇	1 ◇	R 1	1 ◇	1 ◇	R 1	1 ◇	1 ◇	1 ◇	1 ◇	R 1	1 ◇
				B					A					A		C D			A	A	E	
		🛒	🛒	🍽 🛒	🛒	🛒	🛒	🛒	🛒	🛒	🛒	🛒	🛒	🛒	🛒	🍽 🛒	🛒	🛒	🛒	🛒	🍽	🛒
Edinburgh [10]	242 d	*09b33*	10 10	10 26	*10b03*	11 10	*11b03*	11 36	12 10	*12b03*	13 10	*13b03*	13 36	14 10	*14b03*	15 00	*15b03*	*15b33*	16 05	16 05	16 30	*16b03*
Haymarket	242 d	*09b36*	10 14	10 31	*10b06*	11 14	*11b06*	11u40	12 14	*12b06*	13 14	*13b06*	13u40	14 14	*14b06*	15 04	*15b06*	*15b36*	16u09	16u09	16 35	*16b07*
Inverkeithing	242 d			10 47		11 27		11u56			13 27		13u54			15 19			16u25	16u25	16 48	
Kirkcaldy	242 d		10 42	11 04		11 43		12u12	12 42		13 43		14u10	14 42		15 36			16 41	16 41	17 03	
Markinch	242 d		10 51			11 52		12 21	12 51		13 52			14 51					16 50	16 50	17 12	
Ladybank	d		10 59						12 59				14 24	14 59					16 57	16 57		
Springfield	d																					
Cupar	d		11 05			12 02			13 05		14 02			15 05					17 04	17 04	17 25	
Leuchars [3] §	d		11 12	11 30		12 09			13 12		14 09			15 09		16 00			17 11	17 11	17 32	
Glasgow Queen Street [10]	230 ⛴ d	10 11			10 41		11 41			12 41		13 41			14 41		15 41	16 11				16 41
Larbert	230 d																					
Stirling	230 d	10 41			11 07		12 07			13 07		14 07			15 07		16 07	16 39				17 07
Dunblane	230 d	10 48																16 49				
Gleneagles	d	11 00																17 01				
Perth	a	11 17			11 37		12 37	12 56		13 37		14 37	14 54		15 37		16 37	17 20				17 37
	d	11 20			11 38		12 38	12 57		13 38		14 38	14 55		15 38		16 38	17 21				17 38
Invergowrie	d																					
Dundee	a		11 24	11 44	12 00	12 21	13 00		13 24	14 00	14 21	15 00		15 21	16 00	16 17	17 00		17 26	17 26	17 44	18 00
	d		11 25	11 44	12 00	12 22	13 00		13 25	14 00	14 22	15 01		15 22	16 00	16 18	17 00		17 27	17 29	17 46	18 00
Broughty Ferry	d																		17 34	17 36		
Carnoustie	d				12 12		13 12					15 12					17 12		17 42	17 43		18 12
Arbroath	d		11 42	12 02	12 19	12 38	13 19		13 42	14 18	14 38	15 19		15 44	16 17	16 35	17 19		17 49	17 50	18 02	18 19
Montrose	d			12 18	12 32	12 53	13 32			14 33	14 53	15 43			16 31	16 51	17 32		18 03	18 03	18 16	18 32
Stonehaven	d		12 15	12 41		13 14			14 17	14 52	15 14			16 17		17 14	17 53		18 25	18 25	18 36	18 54
Portlethen	d																					
Aberdeen	a		12 40	13 03	13 14	13 36	14 14		14 36	15 14	15 36	16 21		16 37	17 10	17 37	18 15		18 44	18 44	19 00	19 14
	240 d								14 42					16 41					18 46	18 46		
Dyce	240 ⇌ a		*13 21*			*14 20*			14 51	*15 32*				16 50	*17 51*	*18 30*			18 54	18 56		
Dunkeld & Birnam	d	11 38						13 15					15 12					17 39				
Pitlochry	d	11 51						13 28					15 25					17 52				
Blair Atholl	d	12 00						13 37					15 35					18 02				
Dalwhinnie	d	12 25											16 03									
Newtonmore	d							14 10										18 34				
Kingussie	d	12 38						14 15					16 16					18 39				
Aviemore	d	12 50						14 24					16 29					18 52				
Carrbridge	d	12 59																18 57				
Inverness	a	13 35						15 18					17 07					19 34				

For general notes see front of timetable
For details of catering facilities see Directory of Train Operators

§ For St Andrews
A 🛒 to Aberdeen
B From Leeds (Table 26)
C From London Kings Cross (Table 26)
D **The Northern Lights**
E From Bournemouth (Mondays to Fridays from 8 September from Plymouth, Saturdays from 13 September from Bristol Temple Meads) (Table 51)
b Change at Stirling
c Change at Stirling. Saturdays dep. 0633
e Change at Stirling. Saturdays dep. 0906
f Mondays to Fridays only
g Arr. 0819

Table 229

Mondays to Saturdays

Edinburgh and Glasgow Queen Street → Perth, Inverness, Dundee, Aberdeen and Dyce

Network Diagram - see first page of Table 225

		SR SX 1◇ ⊼	GR R 1 A B ✕ ⊡	SR SX	SR 1◇ C ⊼	SR SX D	SR SO D	SR SO 1◇ ⊼	SR SX 1◇ ⊼	SR	SR 1◇ ⊼	SR	SR	SR SO 1◇ ⊼	SR SX 1◇ E ⊼	GR R 1 G ⊡ ⊼	SR 1◇ ⊼	XC SX R 1 H ⊡	SR 1◇ ⊼	SR 1◇ ⊼	SR 1◇ ⊼
Edinburgh 10	242 d		16 33		17 04	17 14	17 16	17b03	17b26	17 28	17 40		17b33	18 10	18 10	18 32	18b03	19 01	19 10	19b03	19 36
Haymarket	242 d		16 38		17 08	17 18	17 20	17b06	17b30	17 32	17u44		17b36	18 14	18 14	18 37	18c06	19 06	19 14	19b06	19 40
Inverkeithing	242 d					17 39	17 39			17 52	17 58			18 27	18 27	18 54		19 20	19 27		19 54
Kirkcaldy	242 d				17 37	18 01	18 01				18 15			18 43	18 43	19 11		19 35	19 43		20 10
Markinch	242 d				17 46	18 11	18 11			18 33		←		18 52	18 52			19 44	19 52		20 20
Ladybank	d					18 18	18 18			18 40 →		18 40		19 00	19 00			19 51	20 00		
Springfield	d					18 23	18 23														
Cupar	d				17 58	18 27	18 27							19 06	19 06			19 58	20 06		
Leuchars 3 §	d				18 05	18 34	18 34							19 13	19 13	19 36		20 05	20 13		
Glasgow Queen Street 10	230 ⛴ d	16 41		17 12				17 41	17 42				18 11				18 41			19 41	
Larbert	230 d			17 33									18 31								
Stirling	230 d		17 19	17 45				18 07	18 14				18 41				19 07			20 07	
Dunblane	230 d			17 54				18 15	18 21				18 50				19 15				
Gleneagles	d		17 37	18 06				18 27	18 34				19 02				19 27				
Perth	a	17 37	17 55	18 23				18 41	18 48		18 54	19 07	19 19				19 43			20 37	20 53
	d	17 38	17 57					18 42	18 51		18 55						19 44			20 37	20 54
Invergowrie	d																20 01				
Dundee	a	18 00			18 22	18 49	18 49	19 06	19 13					19 27	19 27	19 50	20 08	20 25	20 26	21 00	
	d	18 00			18 24	18 52	18 52	19 08	19 14					19 29	19 29	19 50	20 09		20 27	21 00	
Broughty Ferry	d					18 59	18 59														
Carnoustie	d	18 12				19a15	19a15	19 24	19 26												
Arbroath	d	18 19			18 40			19 31	19 33					19 45	19 45	20 09	20 26		20 43	21 18	
Montrose	d				18 55			19 45	19 48							20 24	20 38		20 58	21 32	
Stonehaven	d	18 55			19 16			20 07	20 09					20 19	20 19	20 47			21 19	21 52	
Portlethen	d													20 27	20 27						
Aberdeen	a	19 14			19e38			20 27	20 31					20 41	20 44	21 09	21 19		21 39	22 14	
	240 d				19 39										20 55						
Dyce	240 ✈ a				19 48									*21 03*	21 04				*22 04*	*22 59*	
Dunkeld & Birnam	d										19 13										21 12
Pitlochry	d		18f33								19 26										21 25
Blair Atholl	d																				21 34
Dalwhinnie	d																				21 57
Newtonmore	d																				22 08
Kingussie	d		19 17								20 08										22 16
Aviemore	d		19 29								20 20										22 29
Carrbridge	d																				22 37
Inverness	a		20 08								20 58										23 10

		XC SO 1◇ J	XC SO 1◇ K	SR	GR SX R 1 G ⊡ ⊼	SR ◇ ⊼	SR SO 1◇ ⊼	SR SX	SR SO	SR 1◇	SR SX	SR SO	SR	SR SX	SR SO	SR SO	SR SX	SR
Edinburgh 10	242 d	19 39	19 39	20 11	20 31	20b03	21 10	21 24	21 24	20b33	21 33	21 36	22b33	22 33	22 35	23b33		23 10
Haymarket	242 d	19 44	19 44	20 15	20 36	20b06	21 14	21 28	21 28	20b36	21 38	21 40	22b38	22 37	22 39	23b38		23 14
Inverkeithing	242 d	19 59	19 59	20 35	20 51		21 27	21 47	21 47					22 57	22 58			23 29
Kirkcaldy	242 d	20 15	20 15	20 57	21 08		21 43	22 09	22 09					23 19	23 20			23 51
Markinch	242 d	20 24	20 27	21 06			21 52	22 18	22 18					23 28	23 29			00 01
Ladybank	d	20 31	20 34	21 13			22 00	22 26	22 26					23 35	23 36			00 08
Springfield	d													23 40	23 41			
Cupar	d	20 38	20 41	21 21			22 06	22 33	22 33					23 44	23 45			00 14
Leuchars 3 §	d	20 45	20 48	21 28	21 39		22 13	22 40	22 40					23 51	23 52			00 22
Glasgow Queen Street 10	230 ⛴ d					20 41				21 41			22 48			23 48	23 48	
Larbert	230 d										22 15	22 17	23 19			00 18	00 18	
Stirling	230 d					21 07				22 07	22 24	22 26	23g33			00 31	00h30	
Dunblane	230 d					21 14					22 34	22 36	23 42			00 41	00 42	
Gleneagles	d					21 26					22 46	22 48	23 56			00 55	00 56	
Perth	a					21 42				22 37	23 02	23 05	00 15			01 19	01 20	
	d					21 44				22 38								
Invergowrie	d					22 01												
Dundee	a	21 12	21 12	21 41	21 53	22 08	22 26	22 54	22 55	23 00				00 05	00 07			00 36
	d				21 53	22 09	22 28			23 00								
Broughty Ferry	d																	
Carnoustie	d									23 12								
Arbroath	d				22 11	22 25	22 44			23 19								
Montrose	d				22 27	22 40	22 59			23 32								
Stonehaven	d				22 50	23 01	23 20			23 53								
Portlethen	d									00 04								
Aberdeen	a				23 12	23 21	23 40			00 16								
	240 d																	
Dyce	240 ✈ a																	
Dunkeld & Birnam	d																	
Pitlochry	d																	
Blair Atholl	d																	
Dalwhinnie	d																	
Newtonmore	d																	
Kingussie	d																	
Aviemore	d																	
Carrbridge	d																	
Inverness	a																	

For general notes see front of timetable
For details of catering facilities see Directory of Train Operators

§ For St Andrews

A From London Kings Cross (Table 26). ✕ and ⊼ Mondays to Fridays. ⊡ and ⊼ Saturdays

B **The Highland Chieftain** Also stops at Falkirk Grahamston 1703

C ⊼ to Aberdeen

D Also stops at Balmossie 1902, Monifieth 1905, Barry Links 1909 and Golf Street 1910

E To Inverurie (Table 240)

G From London Kings Cross (Table 26)

H From Penzance (Table 135) (from 8 September from Paignton) (Table 51)

J Until 6 September. From Bristol Temple Meads (Table 51)

K From 13 September. From Paignton (Table 51)

b Change at Stirling

c Change at Stirling. Saturdays dep. 1807

e Saturdays arr. 1936

f Arr. 1827

g Arr. 2328

h Arr. 0027

Table 229

Sundays

Edinburgh and Glasgow Queen Street → Perth, Inverness, Dundee, Aberdeen and Dyce

Network Diagram - see first page of Table 225

	XC	GR	SR	SR	SR	SR	SR	SR	SR	SR	SR	SR	SR	SR	SR	GR	XC
	[1] ◇	[R] [1]		[1] ◇	[1] ◇	[1] ◇		[1] ◇	[1] ◇		[1] ◇	[1] ◇	[1] ◇		[1] ◇	[R] [1]	[1] ◇
													A			B C	D
	🍴	🍴 🛒		🛒	🛒	🛒		🛒	🛒		🛒	🛒	🛒		🛒	🍴 🛒	🍴
Edinburgh [10] 242 d	08 04	09 10	09 15		09 25	10 55	11 15	*10b33*	12 40	13 15	*12b34*	13 50	*13b38*	15 15	*14b34*	16 00	16 33
Haymarket 242 d	08 08	09 14	09 19		09 29	10 59	11 19	*10b37*	12 44	13 19	*12b38*	13 54	*13b42*	15 19	*14b38*	16 04	16 38
Inverkeithing 242 d	08 24	09 32	09 41		09 48	11 15	11 41		13 00	13 41		14 13		15 41		16 24	16 54
Kirkcaldy 242 d	08 39	09 49	10 03		10 10	11 31	12 03		13 16	14 03		14 31		16 03		16 41	17 09
Markinch 242 d	08 49		10 12				12 12			14 12				16 12			17 18
Ladybank d			10 19				12 19			14 19				16 19			
Springfield d																	
Cupar d	09 01		10 26				12 26			14 26				16 26			17 30
Leuchars [3] § d	09 08	10 13	10 33			11 55	12 33		13 40	14 33				16 33		17 10	17 37
Glasgow Queen Street [10] 230 d				09 38				11 45			13 45		14 40		15 45		
Larbert 230 d				10 01									15 00				
Stirling 230 d				10 10				12 12			14 12		15 09		16 12		
Dunblane 230 d				10 17				12 18			14 17		15 16		16 18		
Gleneagles d				10 29				12 29			14 29		15 28		16 29		
Perth a				10 45	10 51			12 46			14 46	15 12	15 45		16 45		
d				10 48	10 52			12 47			14 48	15 13	15 46		16 47		
Invergowrie d																	
Dundee a	09 20	10 27	10 49	11 09		12 07	12 48	13 10	13 52	14 48	15 09			16 48	17 09	17 24	17 49
d	09 21	10 28		11 11		12 08		13 11	13 53		15 11				17 11	17 24	17 51
Broughty Ferry d																	
Carnoustie d				11 23													
Arbroath d	09 37	10 45		11 27		12 25		13 27	14 10		15 27				17 27	17 42	18 07
Montrose d	09 51	11 01		11 42		12 37		13 42	14 24		15 42				17 42	18 00	18 21
Stonehaven d	10 12	11 24		12 03		12 59		14 03	14 46		16 03				18 03	18 23	18 41
Portlethen d						13 07											
Aberdeen a	10 39	11 47		12 27		13 23		14 23	15 05		16 23				18 23	18 46	19 05
240 d																	
Dyce 240 ⇄ a				*13 21*					*15 32*		*17 24*						
Dunkeld & Birnam d					11 09							15 31					
Pitlochry d					11 22							15 44	16 16				
Blair Atholl d					11 33							15 54					
Dalwhinnie d					12 00							16 19					
Newtonmore d					12 10							16 29					
Kingussie d					12 16							16 34	16 59				
Aviemore d					12 28							16c53	17 12				
Carrbridge d					12 37							17 03					
Inverness a					13 09							17 38	17 50				

	SR	GR	SR	SR	SR	SR	GR	SR	XC	SR	SR	SR	SR	SR	SR
	[1] ◇	[R] [1]		[1] ◇	[1] ◇	[1]	[R] [1]		[R] [1]	[1] ◇	[1] ◇	[1] ◇			[1]
		B			A		B		E						
	🛒	🍴 🛒		🛒	🛒		🍴 🛒			🛒		🛒			
Edinburgh [10] 242 d	17 05	17 12	17 15	*17b12*	*17b34*	17 50	18 43	19 15	19 25	*18b34*	21 00	*20e34*	22 25	22 36	*22b36*
Haymarket 242 d	17 09	17 16	17 19	*17b16*	*17b38*	17 54	18 47	19 19	19 30	*18b38*	21 04	*20e38*	22 29	22 40	*22b40*
Inverkeithing 242 d	17 22		17 38			18 07	19 05	19 38	19 44		21 17		22 48		
Kirkcaldy 242 d	17 38		18 00			18 23	19 22	20 00	20 06		21 33		23 10		
Markinch 242 d			18 09					20 09	20 15		21 44		23 19		
Ladybank d			18 16					20 16	20 22		21 51		23 26		
Springfield d															
Cupar d			18 23					20 23	20 37		21 58		23 33		
Leuchars [3] § d	18 02		18 30				19 47	20 30	20 44		22 05		23 40		
Glasgow Queen Street [10] 230 d				17 45	18 10					19 45		21 45			23 35
Larbert 230 d					18 30									23 18	00 05
Stirling 230 d		17 52		18 12	18 39					20 12		22 12		23 27	00 14
Dunblane 230 d					18 46					20 17		22 18		23 36	00 23
Gleneagles d		18 09			18 58					20 29		22 29		23 49	00 37
Perth a		18 27		18 44	19 15	19 02				20 46		22 46		00 06	00 56
d		18 29		18 45	19 16					20 47		22 47			
Invergowrie d															
Dundee a	18 14		18 46	19 08			20 01	20 46	21 05	21 10	22 17	23 09	23 56		
d	18 15			19 09			20 01			21 11	22 18	23 10			
Broughty Ferry d															
Carnoustie d				19 21								23 22			
Arbroath d	18 32			19 27			20 19			21 27	22 35	23 27			
Montrose d	18 46			19 42			20 35			21 42	22 49	23 42			
Stonehaven d	19 08			20 03			20 58			22 03	23 11	00 03			
Portlethen d	19 16										23 20				
Aberdeen a	19 30			20 26			21 21			22 24	23 33	00 25			
240 d															
Dyce 240 ⇄ a				*21 09*											
Dunkeld & Birnam d					19 34										
Pitlochry d		18 59			19 47										
Blair Atholl d					19 56										
Dalwhinnie d					20 21										
Newtonmore d					20 30										
Kingussie d		19 52			20 35										
Aviemore d		20 04			20 50										
Carrbridge d					20f59										
Inverness a		20 44			21 34										

For general notes see front of timetable
For details of catering facilities see Directory of Train Operators

§ For St Andrews
A To Elgin (Table 240)
B From London Kings Cross (Table 26)
C **The Northern Lights**
D From Birmingham New Street (Table 51)
E From Bournemouth (20 July to 7 September from Plymouth) (Table 51)
b Change at Stirling
c Arr. 1642
e Until 30 November only. Change at Stirling
f Arr. 2055

Dyce, Aberdeen, Dundee, Inverness and Perth → Glasgow Queen Street and Edinburgh

Network Diagram - see first page of Table 225

Miles	Miles	Miles	Miles	Miles			SR	SR	SR	SR	XC	SR	SR	SR	SR	SR	SR	SR	SR	XC	SR	SR
								SX		SX	SX		SX	SO	SX							
											[R] [1]			[1]	[1]	[1] ◇		[1] ◇		[R] [1]	[1] ◇	
									A		B ⊡					C ⊥	D		D	E ⊡	⊥	
—	—	0	0	0	**Inverness**	d																
—	—	28	28	28	Carrbridge	d																
—	—	34¾	34¾	34¾	Aviemore	d																
—	—	46½	46½	46½	Kingussie	d																
—	—	49¼	49¼	49¼	Newtonmore	d																
—	—	59½	59½	59½	Dalwhinnie	d																
—	—	82¾	82¾	82¾	Blair Atholl	d																
—	—	89½	89½	89½	Pitlochry	d																
—	—	102½	102½	102½	Dunkeld & Birnam	d																
0	0	—	—	—	**Dyce** 240 ⇌	d																
6¼	6¼	—	—	—	**Aberdeen** 240	a																
—	—	—	—	—		d										05 27		06 00			06 34	
14¼	14¼	—	—	—	Portlethen	d															06 44	
22½	22½	—	—	—	Stonehaven	d										05 44		06 16			06 53	
46¾	46¾	—	—	—	Montrose	d										06 05		06 38			07 15	
60½	60½	—	—	—	Arbroath	d										06 20		06 52			07 29	
66¾	66¾	—	—	—	Carnoustie	d										06 27	06 37	06 59			07 36	
73¼	73¼	—	—	—	Broughty Ferry	d										06 36	06 51					
77½	77½	—	—	—	**Dundee**	a										06 46	06 57	07 10	←		07 50	
—	—	—	—	—		d			06 16		06 38					06 48	07 16	07 11	07 16	07 35	07 52	07 59
81	—	—	—	—	Invergowrie	d											→					
98¼	—	118	118	118	**Perth**	a										07 13					08 12	
—	—	—	—	—		d	05 15	06 09		06 14		06 40	06 58	07 03	07 03	07 14					08 13	
114	—	133¾	—	133¾	Gleneagles	d	05 32	06 26				06 55	07 15			07 30					08 27	
121¼	—	146	—	146	Dunblane 230	d	05 45	06 40				07 07	07 29			07 42						
131¾	—	151½	—	151½	Stirling 230	d	05 53	06 49				07 16	07 38			07 52					08 44	
139¾	—	159½	—	159½	Larbert 230	d	06 02	06 59				07 25	07 47			08 02						
160¾	—	180½	—	—	**Glasgow Queen Street** [10] 230 ⛴	a	06 33	07 35					08 20			08 34					09 15	
—	85¾	—	—	—	Leuchars [3] §	d			06 28		06 51							07 23	07 29	07 48		08 11
—	92¼	—	—	—	Cupar	d			06 36		06 58							07 30	07 37	07 56		08 19
—	94½	—	—	—	Springfield	d													07 41			
—	97½	—	135¾	—	Ladybank	d			06 43	06 37	07 05			07 26	07 26				07 46	08 03		08 26
—	103½	—	141	—	Markinch 242	d			06 51	06 45	07 13			07 34	07 34				07 53	08 11		08 34
—	110¾	—	149	—	Kirkcaldy 242	d			07 01		07b25			07 44	07 44			07 50	08 04	08 20		08 43
—	123½	—	161¾	—	Inverkeithing 242	d			07 25	07 31	07 43			08 00	08 00				08 27	08 36		08 59
—	135½	—	173¾	186½	Haymarket 242	a	*07c25*		07 45	07 54	07 59	08 09	*08e39*	08 16	08 18	*08e57*		08 20	08 47	08 55	*09e57*	09 15
—	136¾	—	175	187¾	**Edinburgh** [10] 242	a	*07c33*		07 50	07 59	08 06	08 14	*08e45*	08 22	08 23	*09e02*		08 26	08 53	09 02	*10e02*	09 20

		SR	SR	SR	SR	SR	SR	GR	XC	GR	SR	SR	SR	SR	GR	SR	SR	SR	SR	SR
		SX	SO																	
		[1] ◇	[1] ◇	[1] ◇	[1]	[1] ◇	[1]	[R] [1]	[R] [1]	[R] [1]	[1] ◇	[1] ◇	[1]	[1] ◇	[R] [1]	[1]	[1] ◇	[1] ◇	[1] ◇	[1] ◇
		G ⊥	G ⊥	H ⊥		⊥		J ⊡ ⊥	E ⊡	K L ✕ ⊥	⊥	⊥		G ⊥	J N ✕ ⊡		G ⊥	⊥	⊥	⊥
Inverness	d			05 00	06 07	06 45				07 55								09 19		
Carrbridge	d				06 39													09 50		
Aviemore	d				06 47	07 22				08 29								10 01		
Kingussie	d				07a01	07 36				08 42								10 14		
Newtonmore	d																	10 18		
Dalwhinnie	d																	10 30		
Blair Atholl	d																	10 51		
Pitlochry	d					08 15				09 23								11 01		
Dunkeld & Birnam	d					08 27												11 13		
Dyce 240 ⇌	d	06 50	06 50	07 03					*07f45*		*08 03*			09 08			10 08			*10 42*
Aberdeen 240	a	07 00	07 00	07 14										09 18			10 18			
	d	07 07	07 07	07 20				07 52	08 20		08 39	08 51		09 32	09 50		10 22		10 42	11 22
Portlethen	d																			
Stonehaven	d	07 23	07 23	07 36				08 09	08 37			09 06		09 49	10 07		10 38			11 38
Montrose	d	07 45	07 45	07 58				08 32	08 59		09 15			10 10	10 30		11 00		11 16	12 00
Arbroath	d	07 59	07 59	08 12				08 48	09 15		09 29	09 42		10 28	10 47		11 14		11 30	12 14
Carnoustie	d	08 06	08 06	08 19							09 36			10 35					11 37	
Broughty Ferry	d													10 43						
Dundee	a	08 19	08 19	08 30				09 05	09 31		09 50	09 57		10 51	11 04		11 29		11 51	12 29
	d	08 21	08 21	08 31			08 47	09 06	09 32		09 52	09 59		10 52	11 04		11 30		11 52	12 30
Invergowrie	d						08 52													
Perth	a	08 43	08 43			08 46	09 06			09 54	10 12			11 13				11 35	12 13	
	d	08 43	08 43			08 47	09 08			09 55	10 13		11 08	11 14				11 38	12 14	
Gleneagles	d						09 23			10 12								11 53		
Dunblane 230	d						09 34											12 05		
Stirling 230	d		09 10				09 41			10 29	10 41			11 43				12 12	12 43	
Larbert 230	d																			
Glasgow Queen Street [10] 230 ⛴	a	09 44	09 44				10 15				11 14			12 15				12 44	13 15	
Leuchars [3] §	d			08 42				09 20	09 45			10 11			11 18		11 42			12 42
Cupar	d			08 50					09 52			10 19					11 50			12 50
Springfield	d															←				
Ladybank	d			08 58								10 26	11 35 →			11 35				12 57
Markinch 242	d			09 06					10 04			10 34				11 42	12 02			13 04
Kirkcaldy 242	d			09 15		09 25		09 44	10 12			10 43			11 42	11 52	12 12			13 14
Inverkeithing 242	d							10 00	10 27			10 59			11 59	12 08				13 30
Haymarket 242	a		*10e26*	09 46		09 55	*10e56*	10 18	10 46	11 09	*11e56*	11 16		*12e56*	12 17	12 23	12 45	*13e26*	*13e56*	13 45
Edinburgh [10] 242	a		*10e32*	09 50		10 01	*11e01*	10 26	10g54	11 16	*12e01*	11 20		*13e01*	12 23	12 28	12 50	*13e32*	*14e01*	13 50

For general notes see front of timetable
For details of catering facilities see Directory of Train Operators

- § For St Andrews
- **A** Mondays to Fridays to Newcraighall (Table 230)
- **B** To Plymouth (Table 51)
- **C** Also stops at Monifieth 0632
- **D** Also stops at Golf Street 0638, Barry Links 0641, Monifieth 0645 and Balmossie 0647
- **E** To Bournemouth (from 8 September to Bristol Temple Meads) (Table 51)
- **G** ⊥ from Aberdeen
- **H** Via Elgin (Table 240). ⊥ from Aberdeen
- **J** To London Kings Cross (Table 26)
- **K** To London Kings Cross (Table 26) ✕ and ⊥ Mondays to Fridays, ⊡ and ⊥ Saturdays
- **L** **The Highland Chieftain** Also stops at Falkirk Grahamston 1045
- **N** **The Northern Lights**
- **b** Arr. 0720
- **c** Change at Stirling. Saturdays arr. Haymarket 0726, Edinburgh 0734
- **e** Change at Stirling
- **f** Mondays to Fridays only
- **g** Saturdays arr. 1051

Dyce, Aberdeen, Dundee, Inverness and Perth → Glasgow Queen Street and Edinburgh

Network Diagram - see first page of Table 225

	SR	SR	SR	SR	SR	SR	SR	SR	SR	GR	SR	SR	SR	SR	SR	SR	SR	SR	SR	GR
																				SX
	1◇	1◇	1◇	1◇	1◇	1◇	1◇	1◇	1◇	R 1	1◇	1◇	1◇	1◇	1◇	1◇	R 1	1	1◇	R 1
										A	B					B				
	🛒	🛒	🛒	🛒	🛒	🛒	🛒	🛒	🛒	🍴 🅿	🛒	🛒	🛒	🛒	🛒	🛒	🛒		🛒	🅿 🛒
Inverness d	10 53					12 40						14 41					16 56			
Carrbridge d	11 26																			
Aviemore d	11 38					13 24						15 18					17 34			
Kingussie d	11 50					13 37						15 31					17 47			
Newtonmore d												15 35					17 51			
Dalwhinnie d																	18 03			
Blair Atholl d												16 05					18 24			
Pitlochry d	12 31					14 17						16 15					18 33			
Dunkeld & Birnam d	12 44					14 29						16 27					18 45			
Dyce 240 ✈ d			*11 50*		*12 48*			*13 23*		*14 20*	15 08			*16 00*		17 00			*17 26*	*17 56*
Aberdeen 240 a											15 18					17 10				
d		11 42	12 24	12 42	13 21		13 42	14 25	14 38	14 48	15 20		15 33	16 21	16 41	17 21			17 52	18 18
Portlethen d			12 34													17 32			18 03	
Stonehaven d			12 42	12 56	13 37			14 41		15 06	15 36			16 37	16 57	17 40			18 11	18 35
Montrose d		12 16		13 16	13 59		14 16		15 14	15 28	16 00		16 13		17 16	18b04			18 33	18 58
Arbroath d		12 30	13 16	13 30	14 13		14 30	15 15	15 28	15 45	16 14		16 27	17 11	17 30	18 18			18 47	19 14
Carnoustie d		12 37					14 37		15 35					17 18					18 54	
Broughty Ferry d																				
Dundee a		12 52	13 32	13 51	14 28		14 51	15 31	15 51	16 02	16 29		16 46	17 30	17 51	18 34			19 09	19 31
d		12 52	13 33	13 52	14 30		14 52	15 32	15 52	16 02	16 31		16 47	17 31	17 52	18 35			19 11	19 32
Invergowrie d													16 52							
Perth a	13 03	13 13		14 13		14 48	15 13		16 13			16 46	17 09		18 13		19 06		19 31	
d	13 04	13 14		14 14		14 49	15 14		16 14			16 48	17 10		18 14		19 08	19 13	19 33	
Gleneagles d													17 25				19 23			
Dunblane 230 d													17 36		18 38		19 35			
Stirling 230 d		13 43		14 43			15 43		16 43				17 41		18 43		19 41		20 00	
Larbert 230 d																				
Glasgow Queen Street 10 230 ⛴ a		14 14		15 14			16 15		17 18				18 17		19 14		20 17		20 36	
Leuchars 3 § d			13 45		14 42			15 44		16 16	16 43			17 43		18 47				19 46
Cupar d			13 52		14 49			15 52			16 50			17 50		18 54				
Springfield d											16 55									
Ladybank d	13 28				14 57						17 00	17 14		17 58				19 37		
Markinch 242 d			14 05		15 04	15 19		16 04			17 07	17 22		18 05		19 07		19 45		
Kirkcaldy 242 d	13 44		14 14		15 14	15 28		16 14		16 40	17 17	17 31		18 15		19 16		19 54		20 10
Inverkeithing 242 d	14 00				15 30	15 44		16 30		16 57	17 34	17 47				19 32		20 10		20 26
Haymarket 242 a	14 13	*14c56*	14 45	*15c56*	15 45	16 00	*16c56*	16 45	*17e55*	17 16	17 50	18 00	*18c56*	18 45	*19c56*	19 54		20 26	*20c56*	20s44
Edinburgh 10 242 a	14 21	*15c01*	14f50	*16c01*	15 50	16 05	*17c02*	16g50	*18c02*	17 24	17 55	18 11	*19c01*	18 50	*20c04*	19 58		20 32	*21c05*	20 50

	SR	SR	SR	SR	SR	SR	SR	SR	SR	XC	XC	SR	SR	SR	SR	SR
	SO		SO	SX		SO		SX	SO	SX	SO				FSX	FO
	1◇	1◇	1◇	1◇	1◇		1◇			1◇	1◇	1◇	1◇	1◇	1	1
			B	B					B		C					
	🛒	🛒	🛒	🛒	🛒		🛒		🛒							
Inverness d					18 27									20 10		
Carrbridge d					18 57											
Aviemore d					19 13									20 55		
Kingussie d					19 32									21 07		
Newtonmore d					19 36									21 12		
Dalwhinnie d					19 48									21 23		
Blair Atholl d					20 09									21 45		
Pitlochry d					20 19									21 55		
Dunkeld & Birnam d					20 31									22 07		
Dyce 240 ✈ d	*17 56*		19 05	19 05			*19 19*		19 55	*19 55*		*20 18*			*21 40*	*21 40*
Aberdeen 240 a			19 17	19 17					20 05							
d	18 25	18 40	19 25	19 25			19 41		20 20	20 26	20 30	20 42	21 22		22 30	23 29
Portlethen d							19 51								22 41	23 40
Stonehaven d	18 42		19 41	19 41			20 00		20 36	20 43	20 48	20 58	21 38		22 49	23 49
Montrose d	19 04	19 16					20 23		20 58	21 04	21 09	21 16	22 00		23 11	00 10
Arbroath d	19 19	19 30	20 15	20 17			20 37		21 12	21 20	21 25	21 30	22 15		23 25	00 25
Carnoustie d		19 38													23 32	00 32
Broughty Ferry d																
Dundee a	19 34	19 51	20 31	20 33			20 56		21 27	21 36	21 41	21 51	22 31		23 47	00 46
d	19 35	19 52	20 32	20 34		20 54	20 57	21 28	21 28	21 37	21 43	21 52	22 32		23 49	00 47
Invergowrie d															23 55	00 53
Perth a		20 14			20 50		21 13					22 13		22 27	00 13	01 11
d		20 14			20 51		21 14					22 14		22 28		
Gleneagles d		20 29												22 45		
Dunblane 230 d														22 57		
Stirling 230 d		20 43					21 43					22 43		23 03		
Larbert 230 d																
Glasgow Queen Street 10 230 ⛴ a		21 14					22 16					23 15		23 39		
Leuchars 3 § d	19 47		20 44	20 46		21 06		21 40	21 40	21 51	21 56		22 44			
Cupar d			20 51	20 53		21 14		21 48	21 48	21 58	22 03		22 52			
Springfield d																
Ladybank d			20 59	21 01	21 14	21 22		21 55	21 55		22 10		22 59			
Markinch 242 d			21 06	21 08		21 30		22 03	22 03	22 12	22 18		23 07			
Kirkcaldy 242 d	20 13		21 16	21 18	21 32	21 40		22 13	22 12				23 16			
Inverkeithing 242 d	20 29		21 32	21 34	21 48	22 02		22 36	22 35	22 46	22 51		23 39			
Haymarket 242 a	20 45	*21c56*	21 47	21 51	22 01	22 25	*22c56*	23 00	22 55				00 04	*00c02*		
Edinburgh 10 242 a	20 50	*22c01*	21 52	21 56	22 09	22 32	*23c01*	23 08	23 03	23 32	23 28		00 09	*00c07*		

For general notes see front of timetable
For details of catering facilities see Directory of Train Operators

§ For St Andrews

A To London Kings Cross (Table 26)
B 🛒 from Aberdeen
C Until 6 September
b Arr. 1801
c Change at Stirling
e Change at Stirling. Saturdays arr. 1756
f Saturdays arr. 1451
g Saturdays arr. 1652

Table 229

Sundays

Dyce, Aberdeen, Dundee, Inverness and Perth → Glasgow Queen Street and Edinburgh

Network Diagram - see first page of Table 225

	SR	SR	SR	SR	SR	GR	SR	GR	SR	GR	XC	SR	SR	SR	GR	SR	SR
		1			1◇ ⊼	R 1 A B ⊏⊐ ⊼		R 1 A ⊏⊐ ⊼	1◇ ⊼	R 1 A ⊏⊐ ⊼	R 1 C ⊏⊐		1◇ ⊼	1◇ ⊼	R 1 A ⊏⊐ ⊼	1◇	
Inverness d								09 38					12 30			13 25	
Carrbridge d								10 08					13 08				
Aviemore d								10 17					13 17			14 02	
Kingussie d								10 30					13 30			14 15	
Newtonmore d								10 35					13 35				
Dalwhinnie d													13 46				
Blair Atholl d								11 07					14 08				
Pitlochry d								11b22					14 17			14 54	
Dunkeld & Birnam d								11 35					14 30				
Dyce 240 ✈ d														*11 59*			
Aberdeen 240 a																	
d					09 30	09 48			11 28	11 42	11 58			13 30	13 50		
Portlethen d																	
Stonehaven d					09 46	10 05			11 44	11 59	12 16			13 46	14 07		
Montrose d					10 08	10 28			12 06	12 22	12 39			14 08	14 30		
Arbroath d					10 22	10 45			12 20	12 38	12 55			14 22	14 46		
Carnoustie d					10 29												
Broughty Ferry d																	
Dundee a					10 43	11 01			12 39	12 58	13 11			14 41	15 03		
d	07 25	08 43		09 25	10 43	11 02	11 25		12 43	12 59	13 12	13 25		14 43	15 04		15 25
Invergowrie d																	
Perth a		09 03			11 05			11 55	13 03				14 49	15 03		15 23	
d		09 05	09 27		11 05			11 55	13 05				14 50	15 05		15 25	
Gleneagles d		09 20	09 42		11 20			12 12	13 20				15 05	15 20			
Dunblane 230 d		09 31	09 54		11 31			12 26	13 31				15 16	15 30			
Stirling 230 d		09 38	10 02		11 38			12 32	13 38				15 22	15 38			
Larbert 230 d		09 47	10 11										15 31				
Glasgow Queen Street 10 230 ⛴ a		10 15			12 11				14 11				15 56	16 12			
Leuchars 3 § d	07 37			09 37		11 16	11 37			13 13	13 25	13 37			15 18		15 37
Cupar d	07 44			09 44			11 44				13 32	13 44					15 44
Springfield d																	
Ladybank d	07 52			09 52			11 52				13 39	13 52					15 52
Markinch 242 d	07 59			09 59			11 59				13 47	13 59					15 59
Kirkcaldy 242 d	08 09			10 09		11 40	12 09			13 37	13 55	14 08			15 42	16 02	16 08
Inverkeithing 242 d	08 30			10 32		11 56	12 32			13 56	14 10	14 32			16c02	16 18	16 32
Haymarket 242 a	08 55	*10e51*	10 51	10 59	*12e56*	12 17	12 59	13 12	*14e57*	14 18	14 28	14 59		*16e57*	16 20	16 34	16 54
Edinburgh 10 242 a	09 00	*10e58*	10 58	11 04	*13e01*	12 24	13 04	13 18	*15e02*	14 24	14 33	15 04		*17e02*	16 26	16 41	16 59

	SR	SR	SR	SR	SR	SR	SR	SR	SR	SR	SR	XC	SR
	1◇ ⊼	1◇ ⊼		1◇ ⊼	1◇ ⊼	1◇ ⊼		1◇ ⊼	1◇ ⊼	1◇ ⊼	1◇	1◇	1
Inverness d					16 15				18 30				
Carrbridge d					16 46				19 01				
Aviemore d					16 55				19 09				
Kingussie d					17 14				19 22				
Newtonmore d									19 26				
Dalwhinnie d									19 39				
Blair Atholl d					17 47				20 02				
Pitlochry d					17 56				20 11				
Dunkeld & Birnam d					18 09				20 24				
Dyce 240 ✈ d	*14 20*					*17 26*					*19 17*		
Aberdeen 240 a													
d	15 10	15 30		17 10		17 50		19 10		19 35	20 10	20 51	22 29
Portlethen d	15 20										20 20		
Stonehaven d	15 26	15 46		17 26		18 06		19 26		19 51	20 26	21 08	22 48
Montrose d	15 48	16 08		17 48		18 28		19 48		20 13	20 48	21 29	23 11
Arbroath d	16 02	16 22		18 02		18 42		20 02		20 27	21 01	21 44	23 25
Carnoustie d	16 09							20 09					23 32
Broughty Ferry d													
Dundee a	16 23	16 41		18 17		19 00		20 18		20 45	21 19	22 00	23 46
d	16 25	16 43	17 25	18 19		19 02	19 25	20 20		20 46	21 21	22 01	23 47
Invergowrie d													
Perth a		17 03			18 26	19 22			20 42	21 07			00 09
d		17 05			18 27	19 24			20 46	21 08			
Gleneagles d		17 20			18 44					21 23			
Dunblane 230 d		17 31			18 55					21 34			
Stirling 230 d		17 38			19 02	19f54				21 40			
Larbert 230 d					19 09								
Glasgow Queen Street 10 230 ⛴ a		18 12			19 36	20 32				22 11			
Leuchars 3 § d	16 37		17 37	18 31			19 37	20 32			21 33	22 14	
Cupar d			17 44				19 44				21 39	22 21	
Springfield d													
Ladybank d			17 52				19 52				21 48	22 28	
Markinch 242 d			17 59				19 59				21 54	22 36	
Kirkcaldy 242 d	17 02		18 08	18 56			20 08	20 59	21 25		22 05	22 44	
Inverkeithing 242 d	17 18		18 30	19 12			20 29	21 15	21 41		22 21	23 00	
Haymarket 242 a	17 34	*18e57*	18 52	19 27	*20e00*	*20e56*	20 52	21 31	22 00	*22e56*	22 37	23s16	
Edinburgh 10 242 a	17 41	*19e02*	19 00	19 35	*20e05*	*21e01*	20 59	21 36	22 06	*23e01*	22 44	23 26	

For general notes see front of timetable
For details of catering facilities see Directory of Train Operators

§ For St Andrews

A To London Kings Cross (Table 26)
B **The Northern Lights**
C To Bristol Temple Meads (20 July to 7 September to Southampton Central) (Table 51)

b Arr. 1118
c Arr. 1558
e Change at Stirling
f Arr. 1951

Edinburgh, Glasgow Queen Street and Falkirk Grahamston → Stirling, Alloa and Dunblane
Newcraighall → Edinburgh → Bathgate

Network Diagram - see first page of Table 225

Miles	Miles	Miles	Miles			SR	SR 1◇ A	SR	SR 1 B	SR 1 C	SR	SR 1 B	SR	SR	SR 1 C	SR 1 B	SR 1◇ D	SR	SR 1 B		SR	SR	SR 1 C	SR	SR 1
0	—	—	—	**Newcraighall**	d								06 18								06 48				
¾	—	—	—	Brunstane	d								06 20								06 50				
4¾	0	—	—	**Edinburgh 10**	a								06 31								06 58				
225	242	—	—		d	05 18			05 55		06 03	06 30	06 32			06 45		06 35	07 00		07 03			07 05	07 15
6	1¼	—	—	Haymarket	d	05 22			05 59		06 07	06 34	06 36			06 48		06 39	07 04		07 06			07 09	07 19
8½	3¾	—	—	Edinburgh Park	d	05 27					06 12		06 41					06 46			07 11			07 16	
17¼	—	—	—	Uphall	d						06 24							06 58						07 28	
20¼	—	—	—	Livingston North	d						06 29							07 03						07 33	
23¼	—	—	—	**Bathgate**	a						06 34							07 08						07 38	
—	17½	—	—	Linlithgow	d	05 39			06 13			06 48	06 53			07a03					07 23				07a33
—	22¼	—	—	Polmont 3	d	05 44			06a19			06a55	06 59						07a19		07 29				
—	—	0	0	**Glasgow Queen Street 10**	d		05 55	06 13		06 30				06 48	07 00		07 06					07 18	07 30		
—	—	3¼	3¼	Bishopbriggs	d			06 19						06 54								07 23			
—	—	6¼	6¼	Lenzie 3	d			06 24		06a38				07 00	07a08							07 29			
—	—	11½	11½	Croy 3	d			06 31						07 05								07 35	07a41		
—	25½	—	—	**Falkirk Grahamston**	d	05 50							07 04								07 34				
—	27	—	—	Camelon	d	05 53							07 07								07 37				
—	28¼	21	21	Larbert	d	05 59	06 16	06 42					07 14	07 18							07 41	07 48			
—	36½	29	29	**Stirling**	d	06 08	06 25	06 51					07 23	07b39			07 31				07 50	08c05			
—	—	—	35¾	**Alloa**	a			07 06														08 17			
—	40	32½	—	Bridge of Allan	d	06 13							07 27	07 43							07 54				
—	42	34½	—	**Dunblane**	a	06 20	06 31						07 35	07 50			07 37				08 03				

		SR 1◇ E	SR 1 B	SR	SR	SR 1 C	SR 1 B	SR	SR 1 B	SR	SR	SR 1 C		SR 1 B	SR 1◇ E	SR	SR	SR	SR 1 C	SR 1 B	SR	SR	SR	SR 1 C	SR 1 B
Newcraighall	d			07 18						07 48							08 18					08 48			
Brunstane	d			07 20						07 50							08 20					08 50			
Edinburgh 10	a			07 28						07 59							08 28					09 00			
	d		07 30	07 33			07 45	07 48	08 00	08 03				08 15		08 18	08 33			08 45	08 48	09 03			09 15
Haymarket	d		07 34	07 36			07 49	07 51	08 04	08 06				08 18		08 22	08 36			08 48	08 51	09 06			09 18
Edinburgh Park	d			07 41				07 56		08 11						08 26	08 41				08 56	09 11			
Uphall	d							08 08								08 38					09 08				
Livingston North	d							08 13								08 43					09 13				
Bathgate	a							08 20								08 50					09 20				
Linlithgow	d		07 48	07 53			08a03			08 23				08 33			08 53			09 03		09 23			09 33
Polmont 3	d		07a54	07 59					08a21	08 29				08a39			08 59			09a09		09 29			09a39
Glasgow Queen Street 10	d	07 41			07 48	08 00					08 18	08 30			08 41			08 48	09 00				09 18	09 30	
Bishopbriggs	d				07 53						08 23							08 53					09 23		
Lenzie 3	d				07 59						08 29							08 59					09 29		
Croy 3	d				08 05	08a11			08a36		08 35	08a41						09 05	09a11				09 35	09a41	
Falkirk Grahamston	d			08 04						08 34							09 04					09 34			
Camelon	d			08 07						08 37							09 07					09 37			
Larbert	d			08 14	08 18					08 44	08 48						09 14	09 18				09 44	09 48		
Stirling	d	08 07		08 23	08 31					08 53	09 01				09a06		09 23	09 31				09 53	10 01		
Alloa	a										09 13												10 13		
Bridge of Allan	d			08 27	08 36					08 57							09 27	09 36				09 57			
Dunblane	a	08 14		08 36	08 43					09 06							09 37	09 44				10 07			

		SR 1◇ E	SR	SR	SR		SR 1 C	SR 1 B	SR 1◇ D	SR	SR	SR	SR 1 C	SR 1 B	SR 1◇ E	SR	SR	SR	SR 1 C	SR 1 B		SR	SR	SR	SR 1 C
Newcraighall	d			09 18							09 48						10 18						10 48		
Brunstane	d			09 20							09 50						10 20						10 50		
Edinburgh 10	a			09 29							09 58						10 28						11 01		
	d		09 18	09 33				09 45		09 48	10 03			10 15		10 18	10 33			10 45		10 48	11 03		
Haymarket	d		09 21	09 36				09 48		09 51	10 06			10 18		10 21	10 36			10 48		10 51	11 06		
Edinburgh Park	d		09 26	09 41						09 56	10 11					10 26	10 41					10 56	11 11		
Uphall	d		09 38							10 08						10 38						11 08			
Livingston North	d		09 43							10 13						10 43						11 13			
Bathgate	a		09 50							10 20						10 50						11 20			
Linlithgow	d			09 53				10 03			10 23			10 33			10 53			11 03			11 23		
Polmont 3	d			09 59				10a09			10 29			10a39			10 59			11a09			11 29		
Glasgow Queen Street 10	d	09 41			09 48		10 00		10 11			10 18	10 30		10 41			10 48	11 00					11 18	11 30
Bishopbriggs	d				09 53							10 23						10 53						11 23	
Lenzie 3	d				09 59							10 29						10 59						11 29	
Croy 3	d				10 05		10a11					10 35	10a41					11 05	11a11					11 35	11a41
Falkirk Grahamston	d			10 04							10 34						11 04						11 34		
Camelon	d			10 07							10 37						11 07						11 37		
Larbert	d			10 14	10 18						10 44	10 48					11 14	11 18					11 44	11 48	
Stirling	d	10a07		10 23	10 31				10 41		10 53	11 01			11a07		11 23	11 31					11 53	12 01	
Alloa	a											11 13												12 13	
Bridge of Allan	d			10 27	10 36						10 57						11 27	11 36					11 57		
Dunblane	a			10 36	10 43				10 48		11 06						11 36	11 43					12 06		

For general notes see front of timetable
For details of catering facilities see Directory of Train Operators

- **A** To Dyce (Table 229)
- **B** To Glasgow Queen Street (Table 228)
- **C** To Edinburgh (Table 228)
- **D** To Inverness (Table 229)
- **E** To Aberdeen (Table 229)
- **b** Arr. 0728
- **c** Arr. 0759

Edinburgh, Glasgow Queen Street and Falkirk Grahamston → Stirling, Alloa and Dunblane
Newcraighall → Edinburgh → Bathgate

Network Diagram - see first page of Table 225

		SR	SR	SR	SR	SR	SR	SR	SR	SR	SR	SR	SR		SR	SR	SR	SR	SR	SR	SR	SR	SR	SR	SR
		1	1 ◇				1	1				1	1		1 ◇				1	1				1	1
		A	B				C	A				C	A		B				C	A				C	A
		🛒	🛒				🛒	🛒				🛒	🛒		🛒				🛒	🛒				🛒	🛒
Newcraighall	d				11 18					11 48							12 18					12 48			
Brunstane	d				11 20					11 50							12 20					12 50			
Edinburgh 10	a				11 28					11 58							12 32					12 59			
	d	11 15		11 18	11 33			11 45	11 48	12 03			12 15			12 18	12 33			12 45	12 48	13 03			13 15
Haymarket	d	11 18		11 21	11 36			11 48	11 51	12 06			12 18			12 21	12 36			12 48	12 51	13 06			13 18
Edinburgh Park	d			11 26	11 41				11 56	12 11						12 26	12 41				12 56	13 11			
Uphall	d			11 38					12 08							12 38					13 08				
Livingston North	d			11 43					12 13							12 43					13 13				
Bathgate	a			11 50					12 20							12 50					13 20				
Linlithgow	d	11 33			11 53			12 03		12 23			12 33				12 53			13 03		13 23			13 33
Polmont 3	d	11a39			11 59			12a09		12 29			12a39				12 59			13a09		13 29			13a39
Glasgow Queen Street 10	d		11 41			11 48	12 00				12 18	12 30			12 41			12 48	13 00				13 18	13 30	
Bishopbriggs	d					11 53					12 23							12 53					13 23		
Lenzie 3	d					11 59					12 29							12 59					13 29		
Croy 3	d					12 05	12a11				12 35	12a41						13 05	13a11				13 35	13a41	
Falkirk Grahamston	d				12 04					12 34							13 04					13 34			
Camelon	d				12 07					12 37							13 07					13 37			
Larbert	d				12 14	12 18				12 44	12 48						13 14	13 18				13 44	13 48		
Stirling	d		12a07		12 23	12 31				12 53	13 01				13a07		13 23	13 31				13 53	14 01		
Alloa	a										13 13												14 13		
Bridge of Allan	d				12 27	12 36				12 57							13 27	13 36				13 57			
Dunblane	a				12 36	12 42				13 06							13 36	13 43				14 06			

		SR	SR	SR	SR	SR		SR	SR	SR	SR	SR	SR	SR	SR	SR	SR	SR	SR	SR	SR		SR	SR	SR
		1 ◇				1		1				1	1	1 ◇				1	1					1	1
		B				C		A				C	A	B				C	A					C	A
		🛒				🛒		🛒				🛒	🛒	🛒				🛒	🛒					🛒	🛒
Newcraighall	d			13 18						13 48						14 18					14 48				
Brunstane	d			13 20						13 50						14 20					14 50				
Edinburgh 10	a			13 28						13 58						14 30					14 58				
	d		13 18	13 33				13 45	13 48	14 03			14 15		14 18	14 33			14 45	14 48	15 03				15 15
Haymarket	d		13 21	13 36				13 48	13 51	14 06			14 18		14 21	14 36			14 48	14 51	15 06				15 18
Edinburgh Park	d		13 26	13 41					13 56	14 11					14 26	14 41				14 56	15 11				
Uphall	d		13 38						14 08						14 38					15 08					
Livingston North	d		13 43						14 13						14 43					15 13					
Bathgate	a		13 50						14 20						14 50					15 20					
Linlithgow	d			13 53				14 03		14 23			14 33			14 53			15 03		15 23				15 33
Polmont 3	d			13 59				14a09		14 29			14a39			14 59			15a09		15 29				15a39
Glasgow Queen Street 10	d	13 41			13 48	14 00					14 18	14 30		14 41			14 48	15 00					15 18	15 30	
Bishopbriggs	d				13 53						14 23						14 53						15 24		
Lenzie 3	d				13 59						14 29						14 59						15 30		
Croy 3	d				14 05	14a11					14 35	14a41					15 05	15a11					15 37	15a41	
Falkirk Grahamston	d			14 04						14 34						15 04					15 34				
Camelon	d			14 07						14 37						15 09					15 37				
Larbert	d			14 14	14 18					14 44	14 48					15 14	15 18				15 44		15 48		
Stirling	d	14a07		14 23	14 31					14 53	15 01			15a06		15 23	15 31				15 53		16 01		
Alloa	a										15 13												16 13		
Bridge of Allan	d			14 27	14 36					14 57						15 27	15 36				15 57				
Dunblane	a			14 36	14 43					15 06						15 36	15 43				16 06				

		SR	SR	SR	SR	SR	SR	SR	SR	SR	SR	SR	SR	SR		SR	SR	GR	SR	SR	SR	SR	SR	SR	SR
		1 ◇					1	1	1 ◇				1			1		R 1			1		1		
		B					C	A	D				C			A		E G			C		A	H	
		🛒					🛒	🛒	🛒				🛒			🛒		✕ 🛒			🛒		🛒		
Newcraighall	d			15 18							15 48								16 18						
Brunstane	d			15 20							15 50								16 20						
Edinburgh 10	a			15 28							15 59								16 30						
	d		15 18	15 33				15 45		15 48	16 03					16 15	16 18	16 33	16 33				16 45		16 48
Haymarket	d		15 21	15 36				15 48		15 51	16 06					16 18	16 21	16 38	16 36				16 48		16 51
Edinburgh Park	d		15 26	15 41						15 56	16 11						16 26		16 45						16 56
Uphall	d		15 38							16 08							16 38								17 08
Livingston North	d		15 43							16 13							16 43								17 13
Bathgate	a		15 50							16 20							16 50								17 20
Linlithgow	d			15 53				16 03			16 23					16 33			16 57				17 03		
Polmont 3	d			15 59				16a09			16 29					16a39			17 03				17a09		
Glasgow Queen Street 10	d	15 41			15 48	15 51	16 00		16 11			16 18	16 30	16 33						16 48	17 00	17 03		17 12	
Bishopbriggs	d				15 53	15 55						16 23		16 39						16 53		17 09			
Lenzie 3	d				15 59	16 08						16 29		16a44						16 59		17a13			
Croy 3	d				16 05	16 15	16a11					16 35	16a41							17 05	17a11				
Falkirk Grahamston	d			16 04		16a34					16 34							17 03	17 08						
Camelon	d			16 07		16a28					16 37								17 11						
Larbert	d			16 14	16 18						16 44	16 48							17 18	17 25				17 33	
Stirling	d	16a07		16 23	16 31				16 39		16 53	17b05						17a19	17 27	17 35				17 45	
Alloa	a											17 17													
Bridge of Allan	d			16 27	16 36						16 57								17 31	17 41				17 50	
Dunblane	a			16 37	16 44				16 48		17 06								17 41	17 48				17 54	

For general notes see front of timetable
For details of catering facilities see Directory of Train Operators

- **A** To Glasgow Queen Street (Table 228)
- **B** To Aberdeen (Table 229)
- **C** To Edinburgh (Table 228)
- **D** To Inverness (Table 229)
- **E** From London Kings Cross (Table 26) to Inverness (Table 229)
- **G** **The Highland Chieftain**
- **H** To Perth (Table 229)
- **b** Arr. 1700

Edinburgh, Glasgow Queen Street and Falkirk Grahamston → Stirling, Alloa and Dunblane
Newcraighall → Edinburgh → Bathgate

Network Diagram - see first page of Table 225

		SR	SR	SR [1] A	SR [1] B	SR C	SR		SR	SR [1] ◇ D	SR	SR	SR [1] A	SR [1] B	SR E	SR	SR	SR	SR [1] A	SR [1] B	SR [1] ◇ D	SR		SR	SR
Newcraighall	d	16 48									17 18						17 48							18 18	
Brunstane	d	16 50									17 20						17 50							18 20	
Edinburgh [10]	a	16 59									17 28						17 58							18 29	
	d	17 03			17 15		17 18		17 26		17 33			17 45		17 48	18 03			18 15		18 18		18 33	
Haymarket	d	17 06			17 18		17 21		17 30		17 36			17 48		17 51	18 06			18 18		18 21		18 36	
Edinburgh Park	d	17 11					17 26				17 41					17 56	18 11					18 26		18 45	
Uphall	d						17 38									18 08						18 38			
Livingston North	d						17 43									18 13						18 43			
Bathgate	a						17 50									18 20						18 50			
Linlithgow	d	17 23			17 33						17 53			18 03			18 23			18 33				18 57	
Polmont [3]	d	17 29			17a39						17 59			18a09			18 29			18a39				19 03	
Glasgow Queen Street [10]	d		17 18	17 30		17 33				17 41		17 48	18 00		18 11			18 18	18 30		18 41				18 48
Bishopbriggs	d		17 23			17 39						17 53						18 23							18 53
Lenzie [3]	d		17 29			17 44						17 59						18 29							18 59
Croy [3]	d		17 35	17a42								18 05	18a11					18 35	18a41						19 05
Falkirk Grahamston	d	17 34				18a00					18 04						18 34							19 08	
Camelon	d	17 37				17a58					18 07						18 37							19 11	
Larbert	d	17 44	17 48						17 57		18 14	18 18			18 30		18 44	18 48						19 18	19 18
Stirling	d	17 53	18 01						18 05	18 15	18 23	18 31			18 41		18 53	19 01			19 07			19 27	19 31
Alloa	a		18 13															19 15							
Bridge of Allan	d	17 57							18 13		18 27	18 36			18 46		18 57							19 31	19 36
Dunblane	a	18 06							18 17	18 22	18 36	18 42			18 50		19 06				19 13			19 39	19 47

		SR [1] A	SR [1] B	SR	SR	SR	SR [1] ◇ D	SR [1] B	SR	SR [1] B	SR	SR	SR [1] A	SR [1] B	SR		SR	SR ◇ D	SR	SR [1] B	SR	SR	SR [1] A	SR	SR [1] B
Newcraighall	d				18 48						19 18				19 48						20 18				
Brunstane	d				18 50						19 20				19 50						20 20				
Edinburgh [10]	a				19 00						19 29				19 59						20 32				
	d		18 45	18 48	19 03			19 15	19 20	19 30	19 33			20 00	20 03				20 18	20 30	20 33				21 00
Haymarket	d		18 48	18 51	19 06			19 18	19 21	19 33	19 36			20 03	20 06				20 21	20 33	20 36				21 03
Edinburgh Park	d			18 56	19 11				19 26		19 41				20 11				20 26		20 41				
Uphall	d			19 08					19 38										20 38						
Livingston North	d			19 13					19 43										20 43						
Bathgate	a			19 20					19 52										20 50						
Linlithgow	d		19 03		19 23			19 32		19a48	19 53			20 18	20 23					20a48	20 53				21 18
Polmont [3]	d		19a09		19 29			19a38			19 59			20a24	20 29						20 59				21a24
Glasgow Queen Street [10]	d	19 00				19 18	19 41					19 48	20 00				20 18	20 41				20 48	21 00	21 18	
Bishopbriggs	d					19 23						19 53					20 23					20 53		21 23	
Lenzie [3]	d					19 29						19 59					20 29					20 59		21 29	
Croy [3]	d	19a11				19 35						20 05	20a11				20 35					21 05	21a11	21 35	
Falkirk Grahamston	d				19 34						20 04				20 34						21 04				
Camelon	d				19 37						20 07				20 37						21 07				
Larbert	d				19 44	19 48					20 14	20 18			20 44		20 48				21 14	21 18		21 48	
Stirling	d				19 53	20 01	20a07				20 23	20 31			20 53		21 01	21 08			21 23	21 31		22 01	
Alloa	a					20 13											21 13							22 13	
Bridge of Allan	d				19 57						20 27	20 36			20 57						21 27	21 36			
Dunblane	a				20 06						20 36	20 43			21 06			21 14			21 36	21 43			

		SR [1] ◇ D	SR	SR [1] B	SR E	SR	SR [1] A	SR		SR [1] B	SR	SR [1] B	SR	SR E	SR [1] A	SR	SR [1] B	SR [1] A	SR	SR [1] B	SR	SR E	SR		
Newcraighall	d		21 04								22 04								23 04				23 53		
Brunstane	d		21 06								22 06								23 06				23 56		
Edinburgh [10]	a		21 14								22 16								23 14				00 04		
	d		21 18	21 30	21 33					22 00	22 18	22 30	22 33				23 00		23 18	23 30	23 33		00 04		
Haymarket	d		21 21	21 33	21 36					22 03	22 21	22 33	22 36				23 03		23 21	23 33	23 36		00a08		
Edinburgh Park	d		21 26		21 41						22 26		22 41						23 26		23 41				
Uphall	d		21 38								22 38								23 38						
Livingston North	d		21 43								22 43								23 43						
Bathgate	a		21 50								22 49								23 49						
Linlithgow	d			21a48	21 53					22 18		22a47	22 53				23 18			23 47	23 53				
Polmont [3]	d				21 59					22a24			22 59				23 25			23a54	23 59				
Glasgow Queen Street [10]	d	21 41				21 48	22 00	22 18						22 48	23 00	23 18		23 30				23 48			
Bishopbriggs	d					21 53		22 23						22 53		23 23	23a50					23 54			
Lenzie [3]	d					21 59		22 29						22 59		23 29						23 59			
Croy [3]	d					22 05	22a12	22 35						23 05	23a12	23 35	23a39	23a42				00 06			
Falkirk Grahamston	d				22 04								23 04								00 04				
Camelon	d				22 07								23 07								00 07				
Larbert	d				22 14	22 18		22 48					23 14	23 18		23 48					00 14	00 18			
Stirling	d	22a07			22 23	22 30		23 01					23 23	23b33		00a01					00 23	00 30			
Alloa	a							23 13																	
Bridge of Allan	d				22 29	22 36							23 28	23 38							00 28	00 36			
Dunblane	a				22 33	22 43							23 36	23 42							00 36	00 41			

For general notes see front of timetable
For details of catering facilities see Directory of Train Operators

A To Edinburgh (Table 228)
B To Glasgow Queen Street (Table 228)
C To Kirkcaldy (Table 242)
D To Aberdeen (Table 229)
E To Perth (Table 229)
b Arr. 2328

Table 230

Saturdays

Edinburgh, Glasgow Queen Street and Falkirk Grahamston → Stirling, Alloa and Dunblane
Newcraighall → Edinburgh → Bathgate

Network Diagram - see first page of Table 225

		SR	SR 1◇ A	SR	SR 1 B	SR 1 C	SR	SR	SR 1 B	SR		SR	SR 1 C	SR 1◇ D	SR	SR 1 B	SR	SR	SR 1 C	SR		SR 1 B	SR 1◇ E	SR 1 B	SR
Newcraighall	d									06 18							06 48								07 18
Brunstane	d									06 20							06 50								07 20
Edinburgh 10	a									06 31							06 58								07 28
	d	05 18			05 55		06 03		06 30	06 32					06 35	07 00	07 03			07 05		07 15		07 30	07 33
Haymarket	d	05 22			05 59		06 07		06 34	06 36					06 39	07 04	07 06			07 09		07 19		07 34	07 36
Edinburgh Park	d	05 27					06 12			06 41					06 46		07 11			07 16					07 41
Uphall	d						06 24								06 58					07 28					
Livingston North	d						06 29								07 03					07 33					
Bathgate	a						06 34								07 08					07 38					
Linlithgow	d	05 39			06 13				06 48	06 53							07 23					07a33		07 48	07 53
Polmont 3	d	05 44			06a19				06a55	06 59						07a19	07 29							07a54	07 59
Glasgow Queen Street 10	d		05 55	06 13		06 30						06 48	07 00	07 06				07 18	07 30				07 41		
Bishopbriggs	d			06 19								06 54						07 23							
Lenzie 3	d			06 24		06 38						07 00	07a08					07 29							
Croy 3	d			06 31		06a44						07 05						07 35	07a41						
Falkirk Grahamston	d	05 50								07 04							07 34								08 04
Camelon	d	05 53								07 07							07 37								08 07
Larbert	d	05 59	06 16	06 42						07 14		07 18					07 41	07 48							08 14
Stirling	d	06 08	06 25	06 51				06 59		07 23		07b39		07 31			07 51	08c05					08 07		08 23
Alloa	a			07 06														08 17							
Bridge of Allan	d	06 13						07 03		07 27		07 43					07 54								08 27
Dunblane	a	06 20	06 31					07 10		07 35		07 50		07 37			08 03						08 14		08 36

		SR	SR 1 C	SR 1 B	SR	SR 1 B	SR	SR		SR 1 C	SR 1 B	SR 1◇ E	SR	SR	SR	SR 1 C	SR 1 B	SR		SR	SR	SR 1 C	SR 1 B	SR 1◇ E	SR
Newcraighall	d						07 48							08 18						08 48					
Brunstane	d						07 50							08 20						08 50					
Edinburgh 10	a						07 59							08 28						09 00					
	d			07 45	07 48	08 00	08 03				08 15		08 18	08 33			08 45	08 48		09 03			09 15		09 18
Haymarket	d			07 49	07 51	08 04	08 06				08 18		08 21	08 36			08 48	08 51		09 06			09 18		09 21
Edinburgh Park	d				07 56		08 11						08 26	08 41				08 56		09 11					09 26
Uphall	d				08 08								08 38					09 08							09 38
Livingston North	d				08 13								08 43					09 13							09 43
Bathgate	a				08 20								08 51					09 20							09 50
Linlithgow	d			08a03			08 23				08 33			08 53			09 03			09 23			09 33		
Polmont 3	d					08a21	08 29				08a39			08 59			09a09			09 29			09a39		
Glasgow Queen Street 10	d	07 48	08 00					08 18		08 30		08 41			08 48	09 00					09 18	09 30		09 41	
Bishopbriggs	d	07 53						08 23							08 53						09 23				
Lenzie 3	d	07 59						08 29							08 59						09 29				
Croy 3	d	08 05	08a11					08 35		08a41					09 05	09a11					09 35	09a41			
Falkirk Grahamston	d						08 34							09 04						09 34					
Camelon	d						08 37							09 07						09 37					
Larbert	d	08 18					08 44	08 48						09 14	09 18					09 44	09 48				
Stirling	d	08 31					08 53	09 01				09a06		09 23	09 31					09 53	10 01			10a07	
Alloa	a							09 13													10 13				
Bridge of Allan	d	08 36					08 57							09 27	09 36					09 57					
Dunblane	a	08 43					09 06							09 37	09 44					10 07					

		SR	SR	SR 1 C	SR 1 B	SR 1◇ D		SR	SR	SR	SR 1 C	SR 1 B	SR 1◇ E	SR	SR	SR		SR 1 C	SR 1 B	SR	SR	SR	SR 1 C	SR 1 B	SR 1◇ E
Newcraighall	d	09 18							09 48						10 18						10 48				
Brunstane	d	09 20							09 50						10 20						10 50				
Edinburgh 10	a	09 29							09 58						10 28						11 01				
	d	09 33			09 45			09 48	10 03			10 15		10 18	10 33				10 45	10 48	11 03			11 15	
Haymarket	d	09 36			09 48			09 50	10 06			10 18		10 21	10 36				10 48	10 51	11 06			11 18	
Edinburgh Park	d	09 41						09 55	10 11					10 26	10 41					10 56	11 11				
Uphall	d							10 05						10 38						11 08					
Livingston North	d							10 13						10 43						11 13					
Bathgate	a							10 20						10 50						11 20					
Linlithgow	d	09 53			10 03				10 23			10 33			10 53				11 03		11 23			11 33	
Polmont 3	d	09 59			10a09				10 29			10a39			10 59				11a08		11 29			11a39	
Glasgow Queen Street 10	d		09 48	10 00		10 11				10 18	10 30		10 41			10 48		11 00				11 18	11 30		11 41
Bishopbriggs	d		09 51							10 23						10 53						11 23			
Lenzie 3	d		09 56							10 29						10 59						11 29			
Croy 3	d		10 08	10a11						10 35	10a41					11 05		11a11				11 35	11a41		
Falkirk Grahamston	d	10 04							10 34						11 04						11 34				
Camelon	d	10 07							10 37						11 07						11 37				
Larbert	d	10 14	10 18						10 44	10 48					11 14	11 18					11 44	11 48			
Stirling	d	10 23	10 31			10 41			10 53	11 01			11a07		11 23	11 31					11 53	12 01			12a07
Alloa	a									11 13												12 13			
Bridge of Allan	d	10 27	10 36						10 57						11 27	11 36					11 57				
Dunblane	a	10 36	10 43			10 48			11 06						11 36	11 43					12 06				

For general notes see front of timetable
For details of catering facilities see Directory of Train Operators

- **A** To Dyce (Table 229)
- **B** To Glasgow Queen Street (Table 228)
- **C** To Edinburgh (Table 228)
- **D** To Inverness (Table 229)
- **E** To Aberdeen (Table 229)
- **b** Arr. 0728
- **c** Arr. 0759

Table 230

Saturdays

Edinburgh, Glasgow Queen Street and Falkirk Grahamston → Stirling, Alloa and Dunblane Newcraighall → Edinburgh → Bathgate

Network Diagram - see first page of Table 225

		SR	SR	SR		SR 1 A	SR 1 B	SR	SR	SR	SR 1 A	SR 1 B	SR 1 ◇ C	SR		SR	SR	SR 1 A	SR 1 B	SR	SR	SR	SR 1 A	SR 1 B	SR 1 ◇ C
Newcraighall	d		11 18						11 48							12 18					12 48				
Brunstane	d		11 20						11 50							12 20					12 50				
Edinburgh 10	a		11 28						11 58							12 32					12 59				
	d	11 18	11 33				11 45	11 48	12 03			12 15		12 18		12 33			12 45	12 48	13 03			13 15	
Haymarket	d	11 21	11 36				11 48	11 51	12 06			12 18		12 21		12 36			12 48	12 51	13 06			13 18	
Edinburgh Park	d	11 26	11 41					11 56	12 11					12 26		12 41				12 56	13 11				
Uphall	d	11 38						12 08						12 38						13 08					
Livingston North	d	11 43						12 13						12 43						13 13					
Bathgate	a	11 50						12 20						12 50						13 20					
Linlithgow	d		11 53				12 03		12 23			12 33				12 53			13 03		13 23			13 33	
Polmont 3	d		11 59				12a08		12 29			12a39				12 59			13a09		13 29			13a39	
Glasgow Queen Street 10	d			11 48		12 00				12 18	12 30		12 41				12 48	13 00				13 18	13 30		13 41
Bishopbriggs	d			11 53						12 23							12 53					13 23			
Lenzie 3	d			11 59						12 29							12 59					13 29			
Croy 3	d			12 05		12a11				12 35	12a41						13 05	13a11				13 35	13a41		
Falkirk Grahamston	d		12 04						12 34							13 04					13 34				
Camelon	d		12 07						12 37							13 07					13 37				
Larbert	d		12 14	12 18					12 44	12 48						13 14	13 18				13 44	13 48			
Stirling	d		12 23	12 31					12 53	13 01			13a07			13 23	13 31				13 53	14 01			14a07
Alloa	a									13 13												14 13			
Bridge of Allan	d		12 27	12 36					12 57							13 27	13 36				13 57				
Dunblane	a		12 36	12 42					13 06							13 36	13 43				14 06				

		SR		SR	SR	SR 1 A	SR 1 B	SR	SR	SR	SR 1 A	SR 1 B		SR 1 ◇ C	SR	SR	SR	SR 1 A	SR 1 B	SR	SR	SR		SR 1 A	SR 1 B
Newcraighall	d			13 18					13 48							14 18					14 48				
Brunstane	d			13 20					13 50							14 20					14 50				
Edinburgh 10	a			13 28					13 58							14 30					14 58				
	d	13 18		13 33			13 45	13 48	14 03			14 15			14 18	14 33			14 45	14 48	15 03				15 15
Haymarket	d	13 21		13 36			13 48	13 51	14 06			14 18			14 21	14 36			14 48	14 51	15 06				15 18
Edinburgh Park	d	13 26		13 41				13 56	14 11						14 26	14 41				14 56	15 11				
Uphall	d	13 38						14 08							14 38					15 08					
Livingston North	d	13 43						14 13							14 43					15 13					
Bathgate	a	13 50						14 20							14 50					15 20					
Linlithgow	d			13 53			14 03		14 23			14 33				14 53			15 03		15 23				15 33
Polmont 3	d			13 59			14a09		14 29			14a39				14 59			15a09		15 29				15a39
Glasgow Queen Street 10	d				13 48	14 00				14 18	14 30			14 41			14 48	15 00				15 18		15 30	
Bishopbriggs	d				13 53					14 23							14 53					15 24			
Lenzie 3	d				13 59					14 29							14 59					15 30			
Croy 3	d				14 05	14a11				14 35	14a41						15 05	15a11				15 37		15a41	
Falkirk Grahamston	d			14 04					14 34							15 04					15 34				
Camelon	d			14 07					14 37							15 07					15 37				
Larbert	d			14 14	14 18				14 44	14 48						15 14	15 18				15 44	15 48			
Stirling	d			14 23	14 31				14 53	15 01				15a06		15 23	15 31				15 53	16 01			
Alloa	a									15 13												16 13			
Bridge of Allan	d			14 27	14 36				14 57							15 27	15 36				15 57				
Dunblane	a			14 36	14 43				15 06							15 36	15 43				16 06				

		SR 1 ◇ C	SR	SR	SR	SR 1 A	SR 1 B	SR 1 ◇ D	SR	SR		SR	SR 1 A	SR 1 B	SR 1 ◇ C	SR	GR R 1 E G	SR	SR	SR 1 A		SR	SR 1 B	SR	SR
Newcraighall	d			15 18						15 48								16 18							16 48
Brunstane	d			15 20						15 50								16 20							16 50
Edinburgh 10	a			15 28						15 59								16 30							16 59
	d		15 18	15 33			15 45		15 48	16 03				16 15		16 18	16 33	16 33					16 45	16 48	17 03
Haymarket	d		15 21	15 36			15 48		15 51	16 06				16 18		16 21	16 38	16 36					16 48	16 51	17 06
Edinburgh Park	d		15 26	15 41					15 56	16 11						16 26		16 45						16 56	17 11
Uphall	d		15 38						16 08							16 38								17 08	
Livingston North	d		15 43						16 13							16 43								17 13	
Bathgate	a		15 50						16 20							16 50								17 20	
Linlithgow	d			15 53			16 03			16 23				16 33				16 57					17 03		17 23
Polmont 3	d			15 59			16a09			16 29				16a39				17 03					17a09		17 29
Glasgow Queen Street 10	d	15 41			15 48	16 00		16 11				16 18	16 30		16 41				16 48	17 00		17 03			
Bishopbriggs	d				15 53							16 23							16 53			17 09			
Lenzie 3	d				15 59							16 29							16 59			17 14			
Croy 3	d				16 05	16a11						16 35	16a41						17 05	17a11		17 21			
Falkirk Grahamston	d			16 04						16 34							17 03	17 08							17 34
Camelon	d			16 07						16 37								17 11							17 37
Larbert	d			16 14	16 18					16 44		16 48						17 18	17 25			17 33			17 44
Stirling	d	16a07		16 23	16 31			16 39		16 53		17b05			17a07		17a19	17 27	17 35			17 44			17 53
Alloa	a											17 17													
Bridge of Allan	d			16 27	16 36					16 57								17 31	17 41			17 49			17 57
Dunblane	a			16 37	16 44			16 48		17 06								17 41	17 48			17 53			18 06

For general notes see front of timetable
For details of catering facilities see
Directory of Train Operators

- **A** To Edinburgh (Table 228)
- **B** To Glasgow Queen Street (Table 228)
- **C** To Aberdeen (Table 229)
- **D** To Inverness (Table 229)
- **E** From London Kings Cross (Table 26) to Inverness (Table 229)
- **G** **The Highland Chieftain**
- **b** Arr. 1700

Table 230

Saturdays

Edinburgh, Glasgow Queen Street and Falkirk Grahamston → Stirling, Alloa and Dunblane
Newcraighall → Edinburgh → Bathgate

Network Diagram - see first page of Table 225

		SR	SR 1 A	SR 1 B	SR 1 ◇ C	SR	SR	SR		SR 1 A	SR 1 B	SR D	SR	SR	SR	SR 1 A	SR 1 B	SR 1 ◇ C		SR	SR	SR	SR 1 A	SR 1 B	SR
Newcraighall	d						17 18							17 48							18 18				
Brunstane	d						17 20							17 50							18 20				
Edinburgh 10	a						17 28							17 58							18 29				
	d			17 15		17 18	17 33				17 45		17 48	18 03			18 15			18 18	18 33			18 45	18 48
Haymarket	d			17 18		17 21	17 36				17 48		17 51	18 06			18 18			18 21	18 36			18 48	18 51
Edinburgh Park	d					17 26	17 41						17 56	18 11						18 26	18 45				18 56
Uphall	d					17 38							18 08							18 38					19 08
Livingston North	d					17 43							18 13							18 43					19 13
Bathgate	a					17 50							18 20							18 50					19 20
Linlithgow	d			17 33			17 53				18 03			18 23			18 33				18 57			19 03	
Polmont 3	d			17a39			17 59				18a09			18 29			18a39				19 03			19a09	
Glasgow Queen Street 10	d	17 18	17 30		17 41			17 48		18 00		18 11			18 18	18 30		18 41				18 48	19 00		
Bishopbriggs	d	17 23						17 53							18 23							18 53			
Lenzie 3	d	17 29						17 59							18 29							18 59			
Croy 3	d	17 35	17a42					18 05		18a11					18 35	18a41						19 05	19a11		
Falkirk Grahamston	d						18 04							18 34							19 08				
Camelon	d						18 07							18 37							19 11				
Larbert	d	17 48					18 14	18 18				18 30		18 44	18 48						19 18	19 18			
Stirling	d	18 01			18 07		18 23	18 31				18 41		18 53	19 01			19 07			19 27	19 31			
Alloa	a	18 13													19 15										
Bridge of Allan	d						18 27	18 36				18 46		18 57							19 31	19 36			
Dunblane	a				18 14		18 36	18 42				18 50		19 06				19 13			19 39	19 47			

		SR	SR	SR 1 B	SR 1 ◇ C	SR		SR 1 B	SR	SR	SR 1 A	SR 1 B	SR	SR	SR ◇ C	SR		SR 1 B	SR	SR	SR 1 A	SR	SR 1 B	SR 1 ◇ C	SR
Newcraighall	d	18 48							19 18				19 48						20 18						21 04
Brunstane	d	18 50							19 20				19 50						20 20						21 06
Edinburgh 10	a	19 00							19 29				19 59						20 32						21 14
	d	19 03		19 15		19 20		19 30	19 33			20 00	20 03			20 18		20 30	20 33				21 00		21 18
Haymarket	d	19 06		19 18		19 21		19 33	19 36			20 03	20 06			20 21		20 33	20 36				21 03		21 21
Edinburgh Park	d	19 11				19 26			19 41				20 11			20 26			20 41						21 26
Uphall	d					19 38										20 38									21 38
Livingston North	d					19 43										20 43									21 43
Bathgate	a					19 52										20 49									21 50
Linlithgow	d	19 23		19 32				19a48	19 53			20 18	20 23					20a48	20 53				21 18		
Polmont 3	d	19 29		19a38					19 59			20a24	20 29						20 59				21a24		
Glasgow Queen Street 10	d		19 18		19 41					19 48	20 00			20 18	20 41					20 48	21 00	21 18		21 41	
Bishopbriggs	d		19 23							19 53				20 23						20 53		21 23			
Lenzie 3	d		19 29							19 59				20 29						20 59		21 29			
Croy 3	d		19 35							20 05	20a11			20 35						21 05	21a11	21 35			
Falkirk Grahamston	d	19 34							20 04				20 34						21 04						
Camelon	d	19 37							20 07				20 37						21 07						
Larbert	d	19 44	19 48						20 14	20 18			20 44	20 48					21 14	21 18		21 48			
Stirling	d	19 53	20 01		20a07				20 23	20 31			20 53	21 01	21 08				21 23	21 31		22 01		22a07	
Alloa	a		20 13											21 13								22 13			
Bridge of Allan	d	19 57							20 27	20 36			20 57						21 27	21 36					
Dunblane	a	20 06							20 36	20 43			21 06		21 14				21 36	21 43					

		SR 1 B	SR D	SR		SR 1 A	SR	SR 1 B	SR	SR 1 B	SR	SR D	SR 1 A	SR		SR 1 B	SR 1 A	SR	SR 1 B	SR	SR D	SR			
Newcraighall	d								22 04									23 04				23 53			
Brunstane	d								22 06									23 06				23 56			
Edinburgh 10	a								22 15									23 14				00 04			
	d	21 30	21 33					22 00	22 18	22 30	22 33					23 00		23 18	23 30	23 33		00 04			
Haymarket	d	21 33	21 36					22 03	22 21	22 34	22 36					23 04		23 21	23 33	23 36		00a08			
Edinburgh Park	d		21 41						22 26		22 41							23 26		23 41					
Uphall	d								22 38									23 38							
Livingston North	d								22 43									23 43							
Bathgate	a								22 49									23 49							
Linlithgow	d	21a48	21 53					22 18		22a48	22 53					23 19			23 47	23 53					
Polmont 3	d		21 59					22a24			22 59					23a26			23a54	23 59					
Glasgow Queen Street 10	d			21 48		22 00	22 18					22 48	23 00	23 18			23 30				23 48				
Bishopbriggs	d			21 53			22 23					22 53		23 23							23 53				
Lenzie 3	d			21 59			22 29					22 59		23 29							23 59				
Croy 3	d			22 05		22a12	22 35					23 05	23a12	23 35			23a42				00 06				
Falkirk Grahamston	d		22 04								23 04									00 04					
Camelon	d		22 07								23 07									00 07					
Larbert	d		22 14	22 18			22 48				23 14	23 18		23 48						00 14	00 18				
Stirling	d		22 23	22 30			23 01				23 23	23b33		00a01						00 23	00 31				
Alloa	a						23 13																		
Bridge of Allan	d		22 29	22 36							23 28	23 38								00 28	00 36				
Dunblane	a		22 33	22 45							23 36	23 42								00 36	00 41				

For general notes see front of timetable
For details of catering facilities see Directory of Train Operators

A To Edinburgh (Table 228)
B To Glasgow Queen Street (Table 228)
C To Aberdeen (Table 229)
D To Perth (Table 229)
b Arr. 2328

Table 230

Sundays

Edinburgh, Glasgow Queen Street and Falkirk Grahamston → Stirling, Alloa and Dunblane
Edinburgh → Bathgate

Network Diagram - see first page of Table 225

	SR	SR	SR	SR	SR	SR	SR	SR	SR	SR	SR	SR	SR	SR	SR	SR	SR	SR	SR	SR	SR	SR
	[1]		[1]	[1]			[1]	[1]	[1] ◇					[1]	[1]					[1]	[1]	[1] ◇
	A	B	C	A	B	B	C	A	D		B			C	A	B				C	A	D
			🛒	🛒				🛒	🛒					🛒	🛒					🛒	🛒	🛒
Edinburgh [10] 225, 242 d			08 00				09 00			09 03		09 33		10 00			10 18	10 33		11 00		
Haymarket 225, 242 d			08 04				09 04			09 08		09 37		10 04			10 22	10 37		11 04		
Edinburgh Park d										09 13		09 42					10 27	10 42				
Uphall d										09 30							10 44					
Livingston North d										09 34							10 49					
Bathgate a										09 40							10 55					
Linlithgow d			08 20				09 20					09 59		10 20				10 54		11 18		
Polmont [3] d			08a27				09a27					10 04		10a27				10 59		11a25		
Glasgow Queen Street [10] d	07 50	08 15		08 30	08 48	09 14		09 30	09 38		09 47		10 15		10 30	10 47			11 15		11 30	11 45
Bishopbriggs d		08 21			08 54	09 20					09 53		10 21			10 53			11 21			
Lenzie [3] d		08 27			09 00	09 26			09 47		09 59		10 27			10 59			11 27			
Croy [3] d	08a02	08a33		08a42	09a06	09a32		09a42			10a05		10 33		10a42	11a05			11 33		11a42	
Falkirk Grahamston d												10 10						11 05				
Camelon d												10 13						11 08				
Larbert d									10 01			10 19	10 45					11 14	11 45			
Stirling d									10 10			10 28	10 55					11 23	11 55			12 12
Alloa a													11 07						12 07			
Bridge of Allan d												10 33						11 28				
Dunblane a									10 16			10 40						11 35				12 17

	SR	SR	SR	SR	SR	SR	SR	SR	SR	SR	SR	SR	SR	SR	SR	SR	SR	SR	SR	SR	SR	SR
					[1]	[1]			[1]	[1]			[1]	[1] ◇			[1]	[1]			[1]	[1] ◇
	B				C	A	B		C	A			C	D	B		C	A			C	E
					🛒	🛒			🛒	🛒			🛒	🛒			🛒	🛒				🛒
Edinburgh [10] 225, 242 d		11 18	11 34		12 00			12 18	12 30		12 34		13 00			13 18	13 30		13 38		14 00	
Haymarket 225, 242 d		11 22	11 38		12 04			12 22	12 34		12 38		13 04			13 22	13 34		13 42		14 04	
Edinburgh Park d		11 27	11 43					12 28			12 43					13 27			13 47			
Uphall d		11 39						12 39								13 39						
Livingston North d		11 44						12 44								13 44						
Bathgate a		11 49						12 50								13 49						
Linlithgow d			11 55		12 18				12a49		12 55		13 18				13a49		13 59		14 18	
Polmont [3] d			12 00		12a25						13 00		13a24						14 04		14a24	
Glasgow Queen Street [10] d	11 48			12 15		12 30	12 47			13 00		13 15		13 45	13 48			14 00		14 15		14 40
Bishopbriggs d	11 54			12 21			12 53					13 21			13 54					14 21		
Lenzie [3] d	12 00			12 27			12 59					13 27			14 00					14 27		
Croy [3] d	12a06			12 33		12a42	13a05			13a11		13 33			14a06			14a12		14 33		
Falkirk Grahamston d			12 06								13 06								14 10			
Camelon d			12 09								13 09								14 13			
Larbert d			12 15	12 45							13 15	13 45							14 19	14 45		15 00
Stirling d			12 24	12 55							13 24	13 55		14 12					14 28	14 55		15 09
Alloa a				13 07								14 07								15 07		
Bridge of Allan d			12 29								13 29								14 33			
Dunblane a			12 37								13 37			14 17					14 40			15 15

	SR	SR	SR	SR	SR	SR	SR	SR	SR	SR	SR	SR	SR	SR	SR	SR	SR	SR	SR	SR	SR	GR
																						[R]
			[1]	[1]			[1]	[1] ◇			[1]	[1]			[1]			[1]	[1]		[1]	[1]
	B		C	A			C	D	B		C	A			C	B		C	A		C	G H
			🛒	🛒			🛒	🛒			🛒	🛒			🛒			🛒	🛒		🛒	🍴 🛒
Edinburgh [10] 225, 242 d		14 18	14 30		14 34		15 00			15 18	15 30		15 34		16 00		16 18	16 30		16 34	17 00	17 12
Haymarket 225, 242 d		14 22	14 34		14 38		15 04			15 22	15 34		15 38		16 04		16 22	16 34		16 38	17 04	17 16
Edinburgh Park d		14 27			14 43					15 27			15 43				16 27			16 43		
Uphall d		14 39								15 39							16 37					
Livingston North d		14 44								15 44							16 42					
Bathgate a		14 49								15 49							16 49					
Linlithgow d			14a48		14 55		15 18				15a48		15 55		16 18			16a48		16 55	17 18	
Polmont [3] d					15 00		15a24						16 00		16a24					17 00	17a24	
Glasgow Queen Street [10] d	14 47			15 00		15 15		15 45	15 48			16 00		16 15		16 47			17 00			
Bishopbriggs d	14 53					15 21			15 54					16 21		16 53						
Lenzie [3] d	14 59					15 27			16 00					16 27		16 59						
Croy [3] d	15a05			15a12		15 33			16a06			16a12		16 33		17a05			17a12			
Falkirk Grahamston d					15 06								16 06							17 06		17 37
Camelon d					15 09								16 09							17 09		
Larbert d					15 15	15 45							16 15	16 45						17 15		
Stirling d					15 24	15 55		16 12					16 24	16 55						17 24		17a51
Alloa a						16 07								17 07								
Bridge of Allan d					15 29								16 29							17 29		
Dunblane a					15 36			16 17					16 36							17 36		

For general notes see front of timetable
For details of catering facilities see Directory of Train Operators

- **A** To Edinburgh (Table 228)
- **B** 30 November and 7 December
- **C** To Glasgow Queen Street (Table 228)
- **D** To Aberdeen (Table 229)
- **E** To Elgin (Table 240)
- **G** From London Kings Cross (Table 26) to Inverness (Table 229)
- **H** **The Highland Chieftain**

Sundays

Edinburgh, Glasgow Queen Street and Falkirk Grahamston → Stirling, Alloa and Dunblane Edinburgh → Bathgate

Network Diagram - see first page of Table 225

Station			SR	SR	SR	SR	SR	SR	SR	SR	SR	SR		SR	SR	SR	SR	SR	SR	SR	SR	SR	SR		SR	SR
				1 ◇ A ✕	B		1 C ✕	1 D ✕		1 ◇ E ✕		1 C ✕			1 C ✕	1 D ✕			1 C ✕	1 ◇ A ✕		1 C ✕			1 D ✕	
Edinburgh 10	225, 242	d				17 18	17 30		17 34			18 00		18 18	18 30		18 34		19 00		19 18	19 30	19 34			
Haymarket	225, 242	d				17 22	17 34		17 38			18 04		18 22	18 34		18 38		19 04		19 22	19 34	19 38			
Edinburgh Park		d				17 27			17 44					18 27			18 43				19 27		19 43			
Uphall		d				17 37								18 39							19 39					
Livingston North		d				17 41								18 44							19 44					
Bathgate		a				17 49								18 49							19 49					
Linlithgow		d					17a48		17 56			18 18			18a48		18 55		19 18			19a48	19 55			
Polmont 3		d							18 02			18a24					19 00		19a24				20 00			
Glasgow Queen Street 10		d	17 15	17 45	17 48			18 00		18 10	18 15					19 00		19 15		19 45					20 00	20 15
Bishopbriggs		d	17 21		17 54						18 21							19 21								20 21
Lenzie 3		d	17 27		18 00						18 27							19 27								20 27
Croy 3		d	17 33		18a06			18a12			18 33					19a12		19 33							20a12	20 33
Falkirk Grahamston		d							18 07								19 06						20 06			
Camelon		d							18 10								19 09						20 09			
Larbert		d	17 49						18 17	18 30	18 45						19 18	19 45					20 15			20 45
Stirling		d	17 59	18a12					18 26	18 39	18 55						19 27	19 55		20 12			20 24			20 55
Alloa		a	18 11								19 07							20 07								21 07
Bridge of Allan		d							18 30								19 32						20 29			
Dunblane		a							18 37	18 45							19 39			20 17			20 37			

Station			SR	SR	SR	SR	SR	SR	SR	SR	SR	SR		SR	SR	SR	SR	SR	SR	SR	SR	SR	SR	SR		
			1 C ✕		1 C ✕	1 D ✕			1 C ✕	1 D	1 ◇ A ✕					1 C	1 D		G	1 C	1 D	1 G		1 C		
Edinburgh 10	225, 242	d	20 00	20 18	20 30		20 34		21 00			21 18		21 34		22 00		22 18	22 36	23 00			23 18	23 30		
Haymarket	225, 242	d	20 04	20 22	20 34		20 38		21 04			21 22		21 38		22 04		22 22	22 40	23 04			23 22	23 34		
Edinburgh Park		d		20 27			20 43					21 27		21 43				22 27	22 46				23 27			
Uphall		d		20 39								21 39						22 39					23 39			
Livingston North		d		20 44								21 44						22 44					23 44			
Bathgate		a		20 49								21 49						22 49					23 49			
Linlithgow		d	20 18		20a48		20 55		21 18					21 55		22 18			22 58	23 18				23 48		
Polmont 3		d	20a24				21 00		21a25					22 00		22a25			23 03	23a25				23a55		
Glasgow Queen Street 10		d				21 00		21 15		21 30	21 45				22 15		22 30				23 30	23 35				
Bishopbriggs		d						21 21							22 21							23 41				
Lenzie 3		d						21 27							22 27							23 47				
Croy 3		d				21a12		21 33		21a42					22 33		22a42				23a42	23 53				
Falkirk Grahamston		d					21 06							22 06					23 09							
Camelon		d					21 09							22 09					23 12							
Larbert		d					21 15	21 45						22 15	22 45				23 18			00 05				
Stirling		d					21 24	21 55			22 12			22 24	22 55				23 27			00 14				
Alloa		a						22 07							23 07											
Bridge of Allan		d					21 29							22 29					23 32			00 18				
Dunblane		a					21 37				22 18			22 36					23 36			00 22				

For general notes see front of timetable
For details of catering facilities see Directory of Train Operators

A To Aberdeen (Table 229)
B 30 November and 7 December
C To Glasgow Queen Street (Table 228)
D To Edinburgh (Table 228)
E To Elgin (Table 240)
G To Perth (Table 229)

Dunblane, Alloa and Stirling → Falkirk Grahamston, Glasgow Queen Street and Edinburgh
Bathgate → Edinburgh → Newcraighall

Network Diagram - see first page of Table 225

Miles	Miles	Miles	Miles	Station		SR MO 1 A	SR MX 1 A	SR	SR 1 B	SR C	SR 1 A	SR	SR	SR	SR 1 B 🚲	SR	SR 1 B 🚲	SR	SR 1 A 🚲	SR D	SR 1 B 🚲	SR C	SR 1 B 🚲	SR	SR C
0	0	—	—	**Dunblane**	d					05 45												06 40			07 07
2	2	—	—	Bridge of Allan	d					05 48												06 43			07 10
—	—	—	0	**Alloa**	d									06 11											
5½	5½	—	6¾	**Stirling**	d			05 30		05 53				06 23		06 36						06 49			07 16
13½	13½	—	14¾	Larbert	d			05 38		06 02				06 32		06 45						06 59			07 25
—	15	—	—	Camelon	d			05 44								06 48									07 29
—	16½	—	—	**Falkirk Grahamston**	d			05 47								06 52									07 33
24	—	—	25¼	Croy 3	d	00 09	00 09			06 13	06 34			06 43					07 10			07 14		07 25	
29¼	—	—	30½	Lenzie 3	d		00 14			06 20				06 50								07 21		07 34	
32¼	—	—	33½	Bishopbriggs	d					06 24				06 54								07 25		07 38	
34½	—	—	35¾	**Glasgow Queen Street 10**	a	00 25	00 27			06 33	06 49			07 03					07 24			07 34		07 48	
—	19½	—	—	Polmont 3	d			05 53	06 24						06 59	06 58					07 27		07 39		07 43
—	24½	—	—	Linlithgow	d			06 00	06 30						07 05	07 05	07 15				07 34		07 45		07 50
—	—	0	—	**Bathgate**	d								06 39					07 13							
—	—	3	—	Livingston North	d								06 44					07 19							
—	—	6	—	Uphall	d								06 48					07 23							
—	38	14½	—	Edinburgh Park	d			06 13					06 58			07 18		07 32							08 03
—	40½	17¼	—	Haymarket	d			06 20	06s46			06 50	07 05		07s20	07 25	07s31	07 39		07 45	07s50		08s01		08 10
—	41¾	18½	—	**Edinburgh 10** 225, 242	a			06 24	06 51			06 54	07 11		07 25	07 32	07 36	07 44		07 50	07 55		08 06		08 14
—	—	—	—		d			06 25				06 55				07 34				07 54					
—	—	22½	—	Brunstane	d			06 32				07 02				07 41				08 00					
—	—	23¼	—	**Newcraighall**	a			06 37				07 07				07 46				08 09					

Station		SR	SR	SR 1 B 🚲	SR	SR 1 B 🚲	SR 1 A 🚲	SR C	SR	SR 1 A 🚲	SR 1 B 🚲	SR	SR 1 ◇ E	SR 1 A 🚲	SR G	SR	SR 1 B 🚲	SR GHX	SR 1 A 🚲	SR	SR	SR	SR 1 B 🚲	SR 1 ◇ E 🚲
Dunblane	d		07 22					07 29					07 42			07 57				08 14		08 27		
Bridge of Allan	d		07 25					07 33					07 46			08 00				08 17		08 30		
Alloa	d	07 10																07 54						
Stirling	d	07 21	07 30					07 38	07 48				07 52			08 06		08b10		08 23		08 36		08 44
Larbert	d	07 30	07 39					07 47	07 55				08 02			08 15		08 20		08 31		08 45		
Camelon	d								07 59						08 13	08 19						08 48		
Falkirk Grahamston	d								08 03						08 09	08 22						08 52		
Croy 3	d	07 42					07 52	07 59		08 09								08 31	08 36	08 41				
Lenzie 3	d	07 49						08 06					08 17	08 25	08 30			08 38		08 48				
Bishopbriggs	d	07 54						08 11						08 30	08 35			08 42		08 52				
Glasgow Queen Street 10	a	08 04					08 07	08 20		08 25			08 34	08 40	08 46			08 52	08 55	09 04				09 15
Polmont 3	d					08 07			08 13		08 26					08 31						08 59	09 07	
Linlithgow	d			07 59		08 14			08 20							08 38	08 42					09 06	09 14	
Bathgate	d				07 54							08 25									08 55			
Livingston North	d				08 00							08 30									08 59			
Uphall	d				08 05							08 34									09 03			
Edinburgh Park	d				08 18				08 33			08 45				08 50					09 12	09 19		
Haymarket	d		08 13	08s16	08 25	08s31			08 40		08s46	08 52				08 58	09s00				09 20	09 26	09s30	
Edinburgh 10 225, 242	a		08 18	08 21	08 30	08 36			08 45		08 51	08 59				09 02	09 05				09 25	09 31	09 35	
	d				08 34							09 03									09 26			
Brunstane	d				08 41							09 10									09 32			
Newcraighall	a				08 46							09 16									09 39			

Station		SR 1 A 🚲	SR	SR	SR	SR 1 B 🚲	SR 1 A 🚲	SR	SR	SR	SR 1 B 🚲	SR 1 D	SR 1 A 🚲	SR	SR	SR	SR 1 B 🚲	SR 1 A 🚲	SR	GR R 1 H J ✕ 🚲	SR	SR	SR 1 B 🚲	SR 1 ◇ E 🚲
Dunblane	d				08 57				09 14	09 28		09 34				09 58			10 14			10 28		
Bridge of Allan	d				09 00				09 17	09 31						10 01			10 17			10 31		
Alloa	d			08 41											09 41									
Stirling	d			08 53	09 06				09 23	09 36		09 41			09 53	10 06			10 23	10 29		10 36		10 41
Larbert	d			09 01	09 15				09 31	09 45					10 01	10 15			10 31			10 45		
Camelon	d				09 18					09 48						10 18						10 48		
Falkirk Grahamston	d				09 22					09 52						10 22				10 45		10 52		
Croy 3	d	09 04		09 13			09 34		09 43				10 03		10 13			10 34	10 43					
Lenzie 3	d			09 19					09 49						10 19				10 49					
Bishopbriggs	d			09 23					09 53						10 23				10 53					
Glasgow Queen Street 10	a	09 21		09 33			09 51		10 03			10 15	10 20		10 33			10 50	11 03					11 15
Polmont 3	d				09 29	09 37				09 59	10 07					10 29	10 37					10 59	11 07	
Linlithgow	d				09 36	09 44				10 06	10 14					10 36	10 44					11 06	11 14	
Bathgate	d		09 25					09 55						10 25							10 55			
Livingston North	d		09 29					09 59						10 29							10 59			
Uphall	d		09 33					10 03						10 33							11 03			
Edinburgh Park	d		09 42		09 49			10 12		10 19				10 42		10 49					11 12	11 19		
Haymarket	d		09 50		09 56	10s01		10 20		10 26	10s30			10 50		10 56	11s00			11 10	11 20	11 26	11s30	
Edinburgh 10 225, 242	a		09 55		10 02	10 06		10 25		10 32	10 35			10 55		11 01	11 05			11 16	11 25	11 32	11 35	
	d		09 56					10 26						10 56							11 26			
Brunstane	d		10 02					10 32						11 02							11 32			
Newcraighall	a		10 09					10 38						11 09							11 39			

For general notes see front of timetable
For details of catering facilities see Directory of Train Operators

A From Edinburgh (Table 228)
B From Glasgow Queen Street (Table 228)
C From Perth (Table 229)
D From Dundee (Table 229)
E From Aberdeen (Table 229)
G From Kirkcaldy (Table 242)
H From Inverness (Table 229) to London Kings Cross (Table 26)
J **The Highland Chieftain**
b Arr. 0804

Dunblane, Alloa and Stirling → Falkirk Grahamston, Glasgow Queen Street and Edinburgh Bathgate → Edinburgh → Newcraighall

Network Diagram - see first page of Table 225

		SR 1 A	SR	SR		SR	SR 1 B	SR 1 A	SR	SR	SR	SR 1 B	SR 1◇ C	SR 1 A	SR	SR	SR	SR 1 B	SR 1◇ D	SR 1 A	SR	SR	SR	SR 1 B	SR 1◇ E
Dunblane	d					10 58				11 14	11 28						11 58		12 05			12 14	12 28		
Bridge of Allan	d					11 01				11 17	11 31						12 01					12 17	12 31		
Alloa	d			10 41												11 41									
Stirling	d			10 53		11 06				11 23	11 36		11 41			11 53	12 06		12 12			12 23	12 36		12 41
Larbert	d			11 01		11 15				11 31	11 45					12 01	12 15					12 31	12 45		
Camelon	d					11 18					11 48						12 18						12 48		
Falkirk Grahamston	d					11 22					11 52						12 22						12 52		
Croy 3	d	11 03		11 13				11 33		11 43				12 03		12 13				12 33		12 43			
Lenzie 3	d			11 19						11 49						12 19						12 49			
Bishopbriggs	d			11 23						11 53						12 23						12 53			
Glasgow Queen Street 10	a	11 20		11 33				11 50		12 03			12 15	12 20		12 34			12 44	12 50		13 03			13 14
Polmont 3	d					11 29	11 37				11 59	12 07					12 29	12 37					12 59	13 07	
Linlithgow	d					11 36	11 44				12 06	12 14					12 36	12 44					13 06	13 14	
Bathgate	d		11 25						11 55						12 25						12 55				
Livingston North	d		11 29						11 59						12 29						12 59				
Uphall	d		11 33						12 03						12 33						13 03				
Edinburgh Park	d		11 42			11 49			12 12		12 19				12 42		12 49				13 12		13 19		
Haymarket	d		11 50			11 56	12s00		12 20		12 26	12s30			12 50		12 56	13s00			13 20		13 26	13s30	
Edinburgh 10 225, 242	a		11 55			12 01	12 05		12 25		12 32	12 35			12 55		13 01	13 05			13 25		13 32	13 35	
	d		11 56						12 26						12 56						13 26				
Brunstane	d		12 02						12 32						13 02						13 32				
Newcraighall	a		12 08						12 38						13 09						13 38				

		SR 1 A	SR	SR		SR	SR 1 B	SR 1 A	SR	SR	SR	SR 1 B	SR 1◇ E	SR 1 A	SR	SR	SR	SR 1 B	SR 1 A	SR	SR	SR	SR 1 B	SR 1◇ E	SR 1 A
Dunblane	d					12 58				13 14	13 28						13 58				14 14	14 28			
Bridge of Allan	d					13 01				13 17	13 31						14 01				14 17	14 31			
Alloa	d			12 41												13 41									
Stirling	d			12 53		13 06				13 23	13 36		13 41			13 53	14 06				14 23	14 36		14 41	
Larbert	d			13 01		13 15				13 31	13 45					14 01	14 15				14 31	14 45			
Camelon	d					13 18					13 48						14 18					14 48			
Falkirk Grahamston	d					13 22					13 52						14 22					14 52			
Croy 3	d	13 03		13 13				13 33		13 43				14 03		14 13			14 33		14 43				15 03
Lenzie 3	d			13 19						13 49						14 19					14 49				
Bishopbriggs	d			13 23						13 53						14 23					14 53				
Glasgow Queen Street 10	a	13 20		13 33				13 50		14 03			14 14	14 20		14 33			14 50		15 03			15 14	15 21
Polmont 3	d					13 29	13 37				13 59	14 07					14 29	14 37				14 59	15 07		
Linlithgow	d					13 36	13 44				14 06	14 14					14 36	14 44				15 06	15 14		
Bathgate	d		13 25						13 55						14 25					14 55					
Livingston North	d		13 29						13 59						14 29					14 59					
Uphall	d		13 33						14 03						14 33					15 03					
Edinburgh Park	d		13 42			13 49			14 12		14 19				14 42		14 49			15 12		15 19			
Haymarket	d		13 50			13 56	14s00		14 20		14 26	14s30			14 50		14 56	15s00		15 20		15 26	15s30		
Edinburgh 10 225, 242	a		13 55			14 01	14 05		14 25		14 32	14 35			14 55		15 01	15 05		15 25		15 32	15 35		
	d		13 56						14 26						14 56					15 25					
Brunstane	d		14 02						14 32						15 02					15 32					
Newcraighall	a		14 08						14 38						15 09					15 38					

		SR	SR	SR		SR 1 B	SR 1 A	SR	SR	SR	SR 1 B	SR 1◇ E	SR 1 A	SR	SR	SR	SR 1 B	SR 1 A	SR	SR	SR	SR 1 B	SR 1◇ E	SR 1 A	SR 1 B
Dunblane	d			14 58					15 14	15 28						15 58				16 14	16 28				
Bridge of Allan	d			15 01					15 17	15 31						16 01				16 17	16 31				
Alloa	d		14 41												15 41										
Stirling	d		14 53	15 06					15 23	15 36		15 41			15 53	16 06				16 23	16 36		16 41		
Larbert	d		15 01	15 15					15 31	15 45					16 01	16 15				16 31	16 45				
Camelon	d			15 18						15 48						16 18					16 48				
Falkirk Grahamston	d			15 22						15 52						16 22					16 52				
Croy 3	d		15 12				15 34		15 43				16 03		16 13			16 33		16 43				17 03	
Lenzie 3	d		15 19						15 49						16 19					16 49					
Bishopbriggs	d		15 23						15 53						16 23					16 53					
Glasgow Queen Street 10	a		15 34				15 51		16 04			16 15	16 20		16 33			16 51		17 03			17 18	17 21	
Polmont 3	d			15 29		15 37				15 59	16 07					16 29	16 37				16 59	17 07			17 27
Linlithgow	d			15 36		15 44				16 06	16 14					16 36	16 44				17 06	17 14			
Bathgate	d	15 25						15 55						16 25					16 55						
Livingston North	d	15 29						15 59						16 29					16 59						
Uphall	d	15 33						16 03						16 33					17 03						
Edinburgh Park	d	15 42		15 49				16 12		16 19				16 42		16 49			17 12		17 19				
Haymarket	d	15 50		15 56		16s00		16 20		16 26	16s33			16 50		16 56	17s01		17 20		17 26	17s34			17s45
Edinburgh 10 225, 242	a	15 55		16 01		16 05		16 25		16 34	16 39			16 55		17 02	17 06		17 25		17 32	17 39			17 50
	d	15 56						16 26						16 56					17 26						
Brunstane	d	16 02						16 32						17 02					17 32						
Newcraighall	a	16 08						16 39						17 09					17 39						

For general notes see front of timetable
For details of catering facilities see Directory of Train Operators

A From Edinburgh (Table 228)
B From Glasgow Queen Street (Table 228)
C From Dyce (Table 229)
D From Inverness (Table 229)
E From Aberdeen (Table 229)

Dunblane, Alloa and Stirling → Falkirk Grahamston, Glasgow Queen Street and Edinburgh Bathgate → Edinburgh → Newcraighall

Network Diagram - see first page of Table 225

		SR	SR	SR		SR	SR	SR	SR	SR	SR	SR	SR	SR	SR	SR	SR	SR	SR	SR	SR	SR	SR	SR	SR
						1	1		1			1		1 ◇	1				1	1				1	1 ◇
						A	B		A			A	C	D	B				A	B				A	D
						🛒	🛒		🛒			🛒		🛒	🛒				🛒	🛒				🛒	🛒
Dunblane	d			16 58							17 28			17 36				17 58				18 14	18 28		18 37
Bridge of Allan	d			17 01							17 31							18 01				18 17	18 31		
Alloa	d		16 41														17 41								
Stirling	d		16 53	17 06						17 23	17 36			17 41			17 53	18 06				18 22	18 36		18 41
Larbert	d		17 01	17 15						17 31	17 45						18 01	18 15				18 31	18 45		
Camelon	d			17 18							17 48		17 58					18 18					18 48		
Falkirk Grahamston	d			17 22							17 52		18 01					18 22					18 52		
Croy 3	d		17 13				17 33			17 43					18 03		18 13			18 33		18 43			
Lenzie 3	d		17 19							17 49					18 08		18 19					18 49			
Bishopbriggs	d		17 23							17 53			17 39				18 24					18 53			
Glasgow Queen Street 10	a		17 33				17 51			18 03				18 18	18 22		18 34			18 50		19 03			19 14
Polmont 3	d			17 29					17 57		17 59	18 07	18 12					18 29	18 37				18 59	19 07	
Linlithgow	d			17 36		17 42			18 04		18 06	18 14	18a18					18 36	18 44				19 06	19 14	
Bathgate	d	17 25						17 54								18 25					18 55				
Livingston North	d	17 29						17 59								18 29					18 59				
Uphall	d	17 33						18 03								18 33					19 03				
Edinburgh Park	d	17 42		17 49				18 12			18 19					18 42		18 49			19 12		19 19		
Haymarket	d	17 50		17 56		18s00		18 19	18s22		18 26	18s32				18 49		18 56	19s00		19 19		19 26	19s31	
Edinburgh 10 225, 242	a	17 55		18 02		18 05		18 25	18 27		18 32	18 38				18 55		19 01	19 05		19 25		19 32	19 36	
	d	17 56						18 26								18 56					19 26				
Brunstane	d	18 02						18 34								19 04					19 34				
Newcraighall	a	18 11						18 40								19 10					19 39				

		SR	SR	SR		SR	SR	SR	SR	SR	SR	SR	SR	SR	SR	SR	SR	SR	SR	SR	SR	SR	SR	SR	SR
		1					1	1				R 1	1	1		1 ◇		1				1 ◇	1	1	
		B					A	A				E	B	A		D		A				D	B	A	
		🛒					🛒	🛒				🛒	🛒	🛒		🛒		🛒				🛒	🛒		
Dunblane	d					18 58			19 14	19 28		19 35					20 02		20 14	20 28					
Bridge of Allan	d					19 01			19 17	19 31							20 04		20 17	20 31					
Alloa	d			18 37											19 41										20 41
Stirling	d			18 52		19 06			19 21	19 36		19 41			19 53	19 58	20 06		20 23	20 36		20 41			20 53
Larbert	d			19 01		19 15			19 32	19 45					20 01		20 15		20 31	20 45					21 01
Camelon	d					19 18				19 48							20 18			20 48					
Falkirk Grahamston	d					19 22				19 52							20 22			20 52					
Croy 3	d	19 03		19 13					19 43				20 07		20 13				20 43				21 07		21 13
Lenzie 3	d			19 19					19 50						20 19				20 49						21 19
Bishopbriggs	d			19 23					19 54						20 23				20 53						21 23
Glasgow Queen Street 10	a	19 21		19 33					20 03			20 17	20 21		20 33	20 38			21 04			21 15	21 21		21 34
Polmont 3	d					19 29	19 37	19 53		19 59							20 29	20 53		20 59					
Linlithgow	d					19 36	19 44	19 59		20 06				20 29			20 36	20 59		21 06				21 29	
Bathgate	d		19 27								20 03										21 03				
Livingston North	d		19 32								20 08										21 08				
Uphall	d		19 36								20 12										21 12				
Edinburgh Park	d		19 48			19 49				20 19	20 22						20 49			21 19	21 22				
Haymarket	d		19 54			19 56	20s03	20s15		20 26	20 29			20s46			20 56	21s15		21 26	21 29			21s46	
Edinburgh 10 225, 242	a		19 59			20 04	20 08	20 20		20 31	20 34			20 51			21 05	21 20		21 31	21 34			21 51	
	d		19 59								20 34										21 34				
Brunstane	d		20 07								20 42										21 42				
Newcraighall	a		20 12								20 47										21 47				

		SR	SR	SR		SR	SR	SR	SR	SR	SR	SR	SR	SR	SR	SR	SR	SR	SR	SR	SR	SR	SR		
			1				1 ◇	1		1		1			1 ◇	1		1	1 ◇			1	1		
			A				D	B		A		A			D	B		A	E			B	A		
							🛒																		
Dunblane	d	20 58				21 14					21 58			22 14					22 57	23 04					
Bridge of Allan	d	21 01				21 17					22 01			22 17					23 00	23 07					
Alloa	d								21 41								22 41								
Stirling	d	21 06				21 23	21 46		21 53		22 06			22 23	22 44		22 53		23 03	23 12					
Larbert	d	21 15				21 31			22 01		22 15			22 31			23 01			23 21					
Camelon	d	21 18									22 18									23 27					
Falkirk Grahamston	d	21 22									22 22									23 30					
Croy 3	d					21 43		22 07	22 12					22 43		23 06	23 13					23 40			
Lenzie 3	d					21 49			22 19					22 49		23 12	23 19					23 46			
Bishopbriggs	d					21 53			22 23					22 53			23 23					23 51			
Glasgow Queen Street 10	a					22 03	22 17	22 21	22 33					23 04	23 18	23 24	23 33		23 39			00 03			
Polmont 3	d	21 29	21 53								22 29	22 53						23 27		23 36			23 57		
Linlithgow	d	21 36	21 59							22 30	22 36	22 59						23 34		23 43			00 04		
Bathgate	d			22 03									23 03								23 52				
Livingston North	d			22 08									23 08								23 57				
Uphall	d			22 12									23 12								23 59				
Edinburgh Park	d	21 49		22 22							22 49		23 22							23 56	00 11				
Haymarket	d	21 56	22s18	22 29						22s45	22 56	23s15	23 29					23s49		00 03	00 17		00s20		
Edinburgh 10 225, 242	a	22 01	22 23	22 34						22 50	23 01	23 20	23 34					23 54		00 07	00 22		00 25		
	d			22 34									23 34												
Brunstane	d			22 42									23 42												
Newcraighall	a			22 47									23 47												

For general notes see front of timetable
For details of catering facilities see Directory of Train Operators

A From Glasgow Queen Street (Table 228)
B From Edinburgh (Table 228)
C From Glasgow Queen Street to Kirkcaldy (Table 242)
D From Aberdeen (Table 229)
E From Inverness (Table 229)

Table 230

Saturdays

Dunblane, Alloa and Stirling → Falkirk Grahamston, Glasgow Queen Street and Edinburgh
Bathgate → Edinburgh → Newcraighall

Network Diagram - see first page of Table 225

		SR [1] A	SR	SR [1] B	SR C	SR [1] A	SR	SR	SR	SR [1] B		SR	SR	SR [1] B 🛒	SR [1] A	SR	SR [1] B 🛒	SR C	SR [1] B 🛒	SR		SR	SR [1] B 🛒	SR [1] A 🛒	SR
Dunblane	d				05 45							06 27				06 45		07 07							07 22
Bridge of Allan	d				05 48							06 30				06 48		07 10							07 25
Alloa	d								06 11													07 10			
Stirling	d		05 30		05 53				06 23			06 36				06 54		07 16				07 21			07 30
Larbert	d		05 38		06 02				06 32			06 45				07 03		07 25				07 30			07 39
Camelon	d		05 44									06 48						07 29							
Falkirk Grahamston	d		05 47									06 52						07 33							
Croy [3]	d	00 09			06 13	06 34			06 43						07 10	07 14						07 42		07 52	07 58
Lenzie [3]	d	00 14			06 20				06 50					07 09		07 21						07 49			08 05
Bishopbriggs	d				06 24				06 54							07 25						07 54			08 10
Glasgow Queen Street [10]	a	00 27			06 33	06 49			07 03						07 24	07 34						08 04		08 07	08 19
Polmont [3]	d		05 53	06 24						06 59		06 59		07 27			07 39	07 43					08 07		
Linlithgow	d		06 00	06 30						07 05		07 06		07 34			07 45	07 50	07 59				08 14		
Bathgate	d							06 40					07 13							07 54					
Livingston North	d							06 44					07 19							08 00					
Uphall	d							06 48					07 23							08 05					
Edinburgh Park	d		06 13					06 58				07 19	07 32					08 03		08 18					
Haymarket	d		06 20	06s46			06 50	07 05		07s21		07 26	07 39	07s50			08s01	08 10	08s16	08 25			08s32		
Edinburgh [10] 225, 242	a		06 24	06 51			06 54	07 10		07 26		07 34	07 45	07 55			08 06	08 14	08 23	08 31			08 37		
	d		06 25				06 55					07 34	07 55							08 31					
Brunstane	d		06 32				07 02					07 42	08 04							08 39					
Newcraighall	a		06 37				07 07					07 46	08 08							08 44					

		SR [1] A 🛒	SR [1] B 🛒	SR	SR [1] ◇ D	SR	SR [1] A 🛒	SR [1] B 🛒		SR	SR [1] A 🛒	SR	SR	SR	SR [1] B 🛒	SR [1] ◇ D 🛒	SR [1] A 🛒	SR		SR	SR	SR [1] B 🛒	SR [1] ◇ E 🛒	SR [1] A 🛒	SR
Dunblane	d				07 42	07 57						08 14		08 27							08 57				
Bridge of Allan	d				07 46	08 00						08 17		08 30							09 00				
Alloa	d									07 54										08 41					
Stirling	d				07 52	08 06				08b10		08 23		08 36		08 44				08 53	09 06		09 10		
Larbert	d				08 02	08 15				08 20		08 31		08 45						09 01	09 15				
Camelon	d					08 19								08 48							09 18				
Falkirk Grahamston	d					08 22								08 52							09 22				
Croy [3]	d	08 09								08 31	08 36	08 41					09 04			09 13				09 34	
Lenzie [3]	d				08 17		08 25					08 48								09 19					
Bishopbriggs	d						08 30			08 42		08 52								09 23					
Glasgow Queen Street [10]	a	08 25			08 34		08 38			08 52	08 55	09 04				09 15	09 22			09 33			09 44	09 51	
Polmont [3]	d		08 26			08 31								08 59	09 07						09 29	09 37			
Linlithgow	d					08 38		08 42						09 06	09 14						09 36	09 44			
Bathgate	d			08 25									08 55					09 25							09 55
Livingston North	d			08 30									08 59					09 29							09 59
Uphall	d			08 34									09 03					09 33							10 03
Edinburgh Park	d			08 45		08 50							09 12	09 19				09 42			09 49				10 12
Haymarket	d		08s45	08 52		08 58		09s00					09 20	09 26	09s31			09 50			09 56	10s01			10 20
Edinburgh [10] 225, 242	a		08 50	08 56		09 02		09 05					09 25	09 32	09 36			09 55			10 02	10 06			10 25
	d			08 56									09 26					09 56							10 26
Brunstane	d			09 02									09 32					10 02							10 32
Newcraighall	a			09 09									09 39					10 09							10 38

		SR	SR	SR [1] B 🛒	SR [1] G	SR [1] A 🛒		SR	SR	SR	SR [1] B 🛒	SR [1] A 🛒	SR	GR [R] [1] H J 🍽 🛒	SR	SR		SR [1] B 🛒	SR [1] ◇ D 🛒	SR [1] A 🛒	SR	SR	SR	SR [1] B 🛒	SR [1] A 🛒
Dunblane	d	09 14	09 28		09 34					09 58			10 14			10 28							10 58		
Bridge of Allan	d	09 17	09 31							10 01			10 17			10 31							11 01		
Alloa	d								09 41													10 41			
Stirling	d	09 23	09 36		09 41				09 53	10 06			10 23	10 29		10 36			10 41			10 53	11 06		
Larbert	d	09 31	09 45						10 01	10 15			10 31			10 45						11 01	11 15		
Camelon	d		09 48							10 18						10 48							11 18		
Falkirk Grahamston	d		09 52							10 22				10 45		10 52							11 22		
Croy [3]	d	09 43				10 03			10 13			10 34	10 43							11 03		11 13			11 33
Lenzie [3]	d	09 49							10 19				10 49									11 19			
Bishopbriggs	d	09 53							10 23				10 53									11 23			
Glasgow Queen Street [10]	a	10 03			10 15	10 20			10 33			10 50	11 03						11 15	11 20		11 33			11 50
Polmont [3]	d		09 59	10 07						10 29	10 37					10 59		11 07					11 29	11 37	
Linlithgow	d		10 06	10 14						10 36	10 44					11 06		11 14					11 36	11 44	
Bathgate	d							10 25							10 55						11 25				
Livingston North	d							10 29							10 59						11 29				
Uphall	d							10 33							11 03						11 33				
Edinburgh Park	d		10 19					10 42		10 49					11 12	11 19					11 42		11 49		
Haymarket	d		10 26	10s30				10 50		10 56	11s00			11 09	11 20	11 26		11s30			11 50		11 56	12s00	
Edinburgh [10] 225, 242	a		10 32	10 35				10 55		11 01	11 06			11 16	11 25	11 32		11 35			11 55		12 01	12 05	
	d							10 56							11 26						11 56				
Brunstane	d							11 02							11 32						12 02				
Newcraighall	a							11 09							11 39						12 08				

For general notes see front of timetable
For details of catering facilities see Directory of Train Operators

A From Edinburgh (Table 228)
B From Glasgow Queen Street (Table 228)
C From Perth (Table 229)
D From Aberdeen (Table 229)
E From Dyce (Table 229)
G From Dundee (Table 229)
H From Inverness (Table 229) to London Kings Cross (Table 26)
J **The Highland Chieftain**
b Arr. 0804

Table 230

Saturdays

Dunblane, Alloa and Stirling → Falkirk Grahamston, Glasgow Queen Street and Edinburgh
Bathgate → Edinburgh → Newcraighall

Network Diagram - see first page of Table 225

		SR	SR	SR		SR 1 A	SR 1 ◇ B	SR 1 C	SR	SR	SR	SR 1 A	SR 1 ◇ D	SR 1 C		SR	SR	SR	SR 1 A	SR 1 ◇ E	SR 1 C	SR	SR	SR	SR 1 A
Dunblane	d		11 14	11 28							11 58		12 05				12 14	12 28						12 58	
Bridge of Allan	d		11 17	11 31							12 01						12 17	12 31						13 01	
Alloa	d									11 41													12 41		
Stirling	d		11 23	11 36			11 41			11 53	12 06		12 12				12 23	12 36		12 41			12 53	13 06	
Larbert	d		11 31	11 45						12 01	12 15						12 31	12 45					13 01	13 15	
Camelon	d			11 48							12 18							12 48						13 18	
Falkirk Grahamston	d			11 52							12 22							12 52						13 22	
Croy 3	d		11 43					12 03		12 13				12 33			12 43				13 03		13 13		
Lenzie 3	d		11 49							12 19							12 49						13 19		
Bishopbriggs	d		11 53							12 23							12 53						13 23		
Glasgow Queen Street 10	a		12 03				12 15	12 20		12 34			12 44	12 50			13 03			13 14	13 20		13 33		
Polmont 3	d			11 59		12 07					12 29	12 37						12 59	13 07					13 29	13 37
Linlithgow	d			12 06		12 14					12 36	12 44						13 06	13 14					13 36	13 44
Bathgate	d	11 55							12 25							12 55						13 25			
Livingston North	d	11 59							12 29							12 59						13 29			
Uphall	d	12 03							12 33							13 03						13 33			
Edinburgh Park	d	12 12		12 19					12 42		12 49					13 12		13 19				13 42		13 49	
Haymarket	d	12 20		12 26		12s30			12 50		12 56	13s00				13 20		13 26	13s30			13 50		13 56	14s00
Edinburgh 10 225, 242	a	12 25		12 32		12 36			12 55		13 01	13 05				13 25		13 32	13 35			13 55		14 01	14 05
	d	12 26							12 56							13 26						13 56			
Brunstane	d	12 32							13 02							13 32						14 02			
Newcraighall	a	12 38							13 09							13 38						14 08			

		SR 1 C		SR	SR	SR	SR 1 A	SR 1 ◇ E	SR 1 C	SR	SR	SR		SR 1 A	SR 1 C	SR	SR	SR	SR 1 A	SR 1 ◇ E	SR 1 C	SR		SR	SR
Dunblane	d				13 14	13 28						13 58					14 14	14 28							14 58
Bridge of Allan	d				13 17	13 31						14 01					14 17	14 31							15 01
Alloa	d										13 41													14 41	
Stirling	d				13 23	13 36		13 41			13 53	14 06					14 23	14 36		14 41				14 53	15 06
Larbert	d				13 31	13 45					14 01	14 15					14 31	14 45						15 01	15 15
Camelon	d					13 48						14 18						14 48							15 18
Falkirk Grahamston	d					13 52						14 22						14 52							15 22
Croy 3	d	13 33			13 43				14 03		14 13				14 33		14 43				15 03			15 13	
Lenzie 3	d				13 49						14 19						14 49							15 19	
Bishopbriggs	d				13 53						14 23						14 53							15 23	
Glasgow Queen Street 10	a	13 50			14 03			14 14	14 20		14 33				14 50		15 03			15 14	15 21			15 34	
Polmont 3	d					13 59	14 07					14 29		14 37				14 59	15 07						15 29
Linlithgow	d					14 06	14 14					14 36		14 44				15 06	15 14						15 36
Bathgate	d			13 55						14 25						14 55						15 25			
Livingston North	d			13 59						14 29						14 59						15 29			
Uphall	d			14 03						14 33						15 03						15 33			
Edinburgh Park	d			14 12		14 19				14 42		14 49				15 12		15 19				15 42			15 49
Haymarket	d			14 20		14 26	14s30			14 50		14 56		15s00		15 20		15 26	15s30			15 50			15 56
Edinburgh 10 225, 242	a			14 25		14 32	14 35			14 55		15 01		15 06		15 25		15 32	15 35			15 55			16 01
	d			14 26						14 56						15 26						15 56			
Brunstane	d			14 33						15 02						15 32						16 02			
Newcraighall	a			14 38						15 09						15 38						16 08			

		SR 1 A	SR 1 C	SR	SR	SR	SR 1 A	SR 1 ◇ E	SR 1 C	SR		SR	SR	SR 1 A	SR 1 C	SR	SR	SR	SR 1 A	SR 1 ◇ E		SR 1 C	SR 1 A	SR	SR
Dunblane	d				15 14	15 28							15 58				16 14	16 28							
Bridge of Allan	d				15 17	15 31							16 01				16 17	16 31							
Alloa	d											15 41													16 41
Stirling	d				15 23	15 36		15 41				15 53	16 06				16 23	16 36		16 41					16 53
Larbert	d				15 31	15 45						16 01	16 15				16 31	16 45							17 01
Camelon	d					15 48							16 18					16 48							
Falkirk Grahamston	d					15 52							16 22					16 52							
Croy 3	d		15 34		15 43				16 03			16 13			16 33		16 43					17 03			17 13
Lenzie 3	d				15 49							16 19					16 49								17 19
Bishopbriggs	d				15 53							16 23					16 53								17 23
Glasgow Queen Street 10	a		15 51		16 04			16 15	16 20			16 33			16 51		17 03			17 18		17 21			17 33
Polmont 3	d	15 37				15 59	16 07						16 29	16 37				16 59	17 07				17 27		
Linlithgow	d	15 44				16 06	16 14						16 36	16 44				17 06	17 14						
Bathgate	d			15 55						16 25						16 55								17 25	
Livingston North	d			15 59						16 29						16 59								17 29	
Uphall	d			16 03						16 33						17 03								17 33	
Edinburgh Park	d			16 12		16 19				16 42			16 49			17 12		17 19						17 42	
Haymarket	d	16s00		16 20		16 26	16s33			16 50			16 56	17s01		17 20		17 26	17s34				17s45	17 50	
Edinburgh 10 225, 242	a	16 05		16 26		16 34	16 38			16 55			17 02	17 06		17 25		17 32	17 39				17 50	17 55	
	d			16 29						16 56						17 26								17 56	
Brunstane	d			16 35						17 02						17 32								18 04	
Newcraighall	a			16 42						17 09						17 39								18 12	

For general notes see front of timetable
For details of catering facilities see Directory of Train Operators

A From Glasgow Queen Street (Table 228)
B From Dyce (Table 229)
C From Edinburgh (Table 228)
D From Inverness (Table 229)
E From Aberdeen (Table 229)

Table 230

Saturdays

Dunblane, Alloa and Stirling → Falkirk Grahamston, Glasgow Queen Street and Edinburgh
Bathgate → Edinburgh → Newcraighall

Network Diagram - see first page of Table 225

		SR	SR 1 A ⊼	SR 1 B ⊼	SR	SR	SR 1 A ⊼	SR		SR 1 A ⊼	SR 1◇ C ⊼	SR 1 B ⊼	SR	SR	SR	SR 1 A ⊼	SR 1 B ⊼	SR		SR	SR	SR 1 A ⊼	SR 1◇ C ⊼	SR 1 B ⊼	SR
Dunblane	d	16 58				17 14		17 28			17 36				17 58					18 14	18 28		18 37		
Bridge of Allan	d	17 01				17 17		17 31							18 01					18 17	18 31				
Alloa	d													17 41											
Stirling	d	17 06				17 23		17 36			17 41			17 53	18 06					18 22	18 36		18 41		
Larbert	d	17 15				17 31		17 45						18 01	18 15					18 31	18 45				
Camelon	d	17 18						17 48							18 18						18 48				
Falkirk Grahamston	d	17 22						17 52							18 22						18 52				
Croy 3	d			17 33		17 43						18 03		18 13			18 33			18 43				19 03	
Lenzie 3	d					17 49						18 08		18 19						18 49					
Bishopbriggs	d					17 53								18 24						18 53					
Glasgow Queen Street 10 ⛴	a			17 51		18 03					18 18	18 22		18 34			18 50			19 03			19 14	19 21	
Polmont 3	d	17 29					17 57	17 59		18 07					18 29	18 37					18 59	19 07			
Linlithgow	d	17 36	17 42				18 04	18 06		18 14					18 36	18 44					19 06	19 14			
Bathgate	d				17 54								18 25					18 55							19 27
Livingston North	d				17 59								18 29					18 59							19 32
Uphall	d				18 03								18 33					19 03							19 36
Edinburgh Park	d	17 49			18 12			18 19					18 42		18 49			19 12			19 19				19 48
Haymarket	d	17 56	18s00		18 19		18s22	18 26		18s32			18 49		18 56	19s00		19 19			19 26	19s31			19 54
Edinburgh 10 225, 242	a	18 02	18 06		18 25		18 27	18 32		18 38			18 55		19 01	19 05		19 25			19 32	19 36			19 59
	d				18 26								18 56					19 26							19 59
Brunstane	d				18 34								19 04					19 34							20 11
Newcraighall	a				18 40								19 10					19 40							20 16

		SR	SR	SR 1 A ⊼	SR 1 A ⊼	SR		SR	SR	SR R 1 D ⊼	SR 1 B ⊼	SR 1 A ⊼	SR	SR 1◇ C ⊼	SR	SR 1 A ⊼		SR	SR	SR	SR 1◇ C ⊼	SR 1 B ⊼	SR 1 A	SR	SR
Dunblane	d		18 58			19 14		19 28		19 35					20 02			20 14	20 28						20 58
Bridge of Allan	d		19 01			19 17		19 31							20 04			20 17	20 31						21 01
Alloa	d	18 37											19 41											20 41	
Stirling	d	18 52	19 06			19 21		19 36		19 41			19 53	19 58	20 06			20 23	20 36		20 41			20 53	21 06
Larbert	d	19 01	19 15			19 32		19 45					20 01		20 15			20 31	20 45					21 01	21 15
Camelon	d		19 18					19 48							20 18				20 48						21 18
Falkirk Grahamston	d		19 22					19 52							20 22				20 52						21 22
Croy 3	d	19 13				19 43					20 07		20 13					20 43				21 07		21 13	
Lenzie 3	d	19 19				19 50							20 19					20 49						21 19	
Bishopbriggs	d	19 23				19 54							20 23					20 53						21 23	
Glasgow Queen Street 10 ⛴	a	19 33				20 03				20 17	20 21		20 33	20 38				21 04			21 15	21 21		21 34	
Polmont 3	d		19 29	19 37	19 53			19 59							20 29	20 53			20 59						21 29
Linlithgow	d		19 36	19 44	19 59			20 06				20 29			20 36	20 59			21 06				21 29		21 36
Bathgate	d								20 03											21 03					
Livingston North	d								20 08											21 08					
Uphall	d								20 12											21 12					
Edinburgh Park	d		19 49					20 19	20 22						20 49				21 19	21 22					21 49
Haymarket	d		19 56	20s03	20s15			20 26	20 29			20s46			20 56	21s15			21 26	21 29			21s46		21 56
Edinburgh 10 225, 242	a		20 04	20 08	20 20			20 31	20 34			20 51			21 05	21 22			21 31	21 34			21 53		22 01
	d								20 34											21 34					
Brunstane	d								20 42											21 42					
Newcraighall	a								20 47											21 47					

		SR 1 A	SR	SR		SR 1◇ C ⊼	SR 1 B	SR	SR 1 A	SR	SR 1 A	SR	SR	SR 1◇ C		SR 1 B	SR	SR 1 A	SR 1◇ D	SR	SR	SR 1 B	SR 1 A		
Dunblane	d			21 14						21 58			22 14						22 57	23 04					
Bridge of Allan	d			21 17						22 01			22 17						23 00	23 07					
Alloa	d							21 41									22 41								
Stirling	d			21 23		21 46		21 53		22 06			22 23	22 44			22 53		23 03	23 12					
Larbert	d			21 31				22 01		22 15			22 31				23 01			23 21					
Camelon	d									22 18										23 27					
Falkirk Grahamston	d									22 22										23 30					
Croy 3	d			21 43			22 07	22 12					22 43			23 07	23 13					23 41			
Lenzie 3	d			21 49				22 19					22 49			23 13	23 19					23 48			
Bishopbriggs	d			21 53				22 23					22 53				23 23					23 52			
Glasgow Queen Street 10 ⛴	a			22 03		22 17	22 21	22 33					23 04	23 18		23 24	23 33		23 39			00 03			
Polmont 3	d	21 53								22 29	22 53							23 27		23 36			23 57		
Linlithgow	d	21 59							22 30	22 36	22 59							23 34		23 43			00 04		
Bathgate	d		22 03									23 03									23 52				
Livingston North	d		22 08									23 08									23 57				
Uphall	d		22 12									23 12									23 59				
Edinburgh Park	d		22 22							22 49		23 22								23 56	00 11				
Haymarket	d	22s18	22 28						22s46	22 56	23s15	23 29						23s49		00 03	00 17		00s20		
Edinburgh 10 225, 242	a	22 23	22 33						22 51	23 01	23 22	23 34						23 54		00 07	00 22		00 25		
	d		22 34									23 34													
Brunstane	d		22 41									23 42													
Newcraighall	a		22 47									23 47													

For general notes see front of timetable
For details of catering facilities see Directory of Train Operators

A From Glasgow Queen Street (Table 228)
B From Edinburgh (Table 228)
C From Aberdeen (Table 229)
D From Inverness (Table 229)

Table 230

Sundays

Dunblane, Alloa and Stirling → Falkirk Grahamston, Glasgow Queen Street and Edinburgh
Bathgate → Edinburgh

Network Diagram - see first page of Table 225

	SR	SR	SR	SR	SR	SR	SR	SR	SR		SR	SR	SR	SR	SR	SR	SR	SR	SR		SR	SR	SR	SR
	1	1	1	1					1		1		1			1	1						1	1
	A	B	A	B	C	C			A		B		D	C	E	A	B				C		A	B
			🛒	🛒							🛒					🛒	🛒						🛒	🛒
Dunblane d													09 30		09 54							10 58		
Bridge of Allan d															09 58							11 01		
Alloa d												09 13							10 13					
Stirling d							09 05					09 25	09 38		10 02				10 25			11 06		
Larbert d							09 13					09 34	09 47		10 11				10 34			11 16		
Camelon d							09 17								10 16							11 21		
Falkirk Grahamston d							09 20								10 19							11 24		
Croy 3 d	00 09		08 41		08 49	09 15			09 42			09 45		10 15		10 42			10 45		11 15		11 40	
Lenzie 3 d	00 14				08 56	09 22						09 52	10 02	10 22					10 52		11 22			
Bishopbriggs d					09 00	09 26						09 56		10 26					10 56		11 26			
Glasgow Queen Street 10 ⛴ a	00 28		08 59		09 10	09 35			10 00			10 08	10 15	10 35		11 00			11 08		11 35		11 55	
Polmont 3 d		08 17		08 57			09 28				09 57				10 25		10 57					11 30		11 57
Linlithgow d		08 24		09 04			09 35				10 04				10 32		11 04					11 37		12 04
Bathgate d								09 49										11 01						
Livingston North d								09 54										11 06						
Uphall d								09 58										11 10						
Edinburgh Park d							09 48	10 08							10 45			11 19				11 50		
Haymarket 225, 242 d		08s44		09s23			09s59	10s19			10s23				10 52		11s19	11 26				11 57		12s19
Edinburgh 10 225, 242 a		08 49		09 28			10 04	10 24			10 28				10 58		11 24	11 30				12 01		12 24

	SR	SR	SR	SR	SR	SR	GR		SR	SR	SR	SR	SR	SR	SR	SR	SR		SR	SR	SR	SR	SR	SR
			1 ◇			1	R 1		1			1	1			1				1 ◇	1	1		
			G	C		A	H J		B			A	B	C		B				G	A	B	C	
			🛒			🛒	🍴 🛒		🛒			🛒	🛒							🛒	🛒	🛒		
Dunblane d			11 30		11 58		12 26								12 58					13 30				13 58
Bridge of Allan d					12 01										13 01									14 01
Alloa d		11 13									12 13								13 13					
Stirling d		11 25	11 38		12 07		12 32				12 25				13 07				13 25	13 38				14 07
Larbert d		11 34			12 16						12 34				13 16				13 34					14 16
Camelon d					12 21										13 21									14 21
Falkirk Grahamston d					12 24		12 48								13 24									14 24
Croy 3 d		11 45		12 15		12 40					12 45	13 08		13 15					13 45		14 08		14 15	
Lenzie 3 d		11 52		12 22							12 52			13 22					13 52				14 22	
Bishopbriggs d		11 56		12 26							12 56			13 26					13 56				14 26	
Glasgow Queen Street 10 ⛴ a		12 05	12 12	12 35		12 55					13 05	13 23		13 35					14 06	14 12	14 23		14 35	
Polmont 3 d					12 30				12 57						13 31	13 54								14 31
Linlithgow d					12 37				13 04				13 30		13 38	14 00						14 30		14 38
Bathgate d	12 01									13 03							13 59							
Livingston North d	12 06									13 08							14 04							
Uphall d	12 10									13 12							14 08							
Edinburgh Park d	12 19				12 50					13 21					13 50		14 18							14 51
Haymarket 225, 242 d	12 26				12 57		13 12		13s21	13 29			13s46		13 58	14s16	14 24					14s47		14 58
Edinburgh 10 225, 242 a	12 30				13 01		13 18		13 26	13 33			13 51		14 02	14 21	14 29					14 52		15 02

	SR	SR	SR	SR	SR		SR	SR	SR	SR	SR	SR	SR	SR	SR		SR	SR	SR	SR	SR	SR	SR	SR
	1			1	1				1	1 ◇			1 ◇	1	1				1			1	1	
	B			A	B		C		B	K			G	A	B		C		B			A	B	C
	🛒			🛒	🛒					🛒			🛒	🛒	🛒				🛒			🛒	🛒	
Dunblane d								14 58		15 16			15 30					15 58						
Bridge of Allan d								15 01										16 01						
Alloa d			14 13									15 13									16 13			
Stirling d			14 25					15 07		15 22		15 25	15 38					16 07			16 25			
Larbert d			14 34					15 16		15 31		15 34						16 16			16 34			
Camelon d								15 21										16 21						
Falkirk Grahamston d								15 24										16 24						
Croy 3 d			14 45	15 07	15 12		15 15					15 45		16 07			16 15				16 45	17 07		17 15
Lenzie 3 d			14 52				15 22					15 52					16 22				16 52			17 22
Bishopbriggs d			14 56				15 26					15 56					16 26				16 56			17 26
Glasgow Queen Street 10 ⛴ a			15 06	15 22			15 35			15 56		16 09	16 12	16 24			16 35				17 06	17 22		17 35
Polmont 3 d	14 54							15 30	15 54									16 31	16 54					
Linlithgow d	15 00				15 30			15 37	16 00						16 30			16 38	17 00				17 30	
Bathgate d		14 59									15 59									16 59				
Livingston North d		15 04									16 04									17 04				
Uphall d		15 08									16 08									17 08				
Edinburgh Park d		15 17						15 50			16 17							16 51		17 17				
Haymarket 225, 242 d	15s16	15 24			15s46			15 57	16s16		16 24				16s50			16 58	17s16	17 24			17s47	
Edinburgh 10 225, 242 a	15 21	15 29			15 51			16 01	16 22		16 29				16 55			17 02	17 21	17 29			17 52	

For general notes see front of timetable
For details of catering facilities see Directory of Train Operators

- **A** From Edinburgh (Table 228)
- **B** From Glasgow Queen Street (Table 228)
- **C** 30 November and 7 December
- **D** From Dundee (Table 229)
- **E** From Perth (Table 229)
- **G** From Aberdeen (Table 229)
- **H** From Inverness (Table 229) to London Kings Cross (Table 26)
- **J** **The Highland Chieftain**
- **K** From Inverness (Table 229)

Table 230

Sundays

Dunblane, Alloa and Stirling → Falkirk Grahamston, Glasgow Queen Street and Edinburgh
Bathgate → Edinburgh

Network Diagram - see first page of Table 225

		SR	SR 1 A	SR		SR	SR 1◇ B	SR 1 C	SR 1 A	SR D	SR	SR 1 A	SR	SR		SR 1 C	SR 1 A	SR D	SR 1◇ E	SR	SR 1 A	SR	SR	SR 1 C	SR 1 A
Dunblane	d	16 58					17 30				17 58								18 55	19 02					
Bridge of Allan	d	17 01									18 01									19 05					
Alloa	d					17 13								18 15									19 13		
Stirling	d	17 07				17 25	17 38				18 07			18 25					19 02	19 11			19 25		
Larbert	d	17 16				17 34					18 16			18 34					19 09	19 20			19 34		
Camelon	d	17 21									18 21									19 25					
Falkirk Grahamston	d	17 24									18 24									19 28					
Croy 3	d					17 45		18 07		18 15				18 45		19 07		19 13					19 45	20 07	
Lenzie 3	d					17 52				18 22				18 52				19 20					19 52		
Bishopbriggs	d					17 56				18 26				18 56				19 24					19 56		
Glasgow Queen Street 10	a					18 06	18 12	18 22		18 35				19 07		19 22		19 33	19 36				20 06	20 22	
Polmont 3	d	17 30	17 54								18 31	18 54								19 34	19 54				
Linlithgow	d	17 37	18 00						18 30		18 38	19 00					19 30			19 41	20 00				20 30
Bathgate	d			17 59									18 59									19 59			
Livingston North	d			18 04									19 04									20 04			
Uphall	d			18 08									19 08									20 08			
Edinburgh Park	d	17 50		18 17							18 51		19 18							19 54		20 18			
Haymarket 225, 242	d	17 57	18s16	18 24					18s50		18 58	19s16	19 25				19s47			20 01	20s16	20 24			20s46
Edinburgh 10 225, 242	a	18 01	18 21	18 30					18 55		19 02	19 21	19 29				19 52			20 05	20 21	20 30			20 54

		SR 1◇ B		SR	SR 1 A	SR	SR	SR 1 C	SR 1 A	SR	SR 1 C	SR 1 A		SR	SR	SR 1◇ B	SR	SR 1 C	SR 1 A	SR	SR 1 C	SR 1 A	SR		
Dunblane	d			19 58						20 58						21 34	21 58								
Bridge of Allan	d			20 01						21 01							22 01								
Alloa	d						20 13								21 13										
Stirling	d	19 54		20 07			20 25			21 07					21 25	21 40	22 07								
Larbert	d			20 16			20 34			21 16					21 34		22 16								
Camelon	d			20 21						21 21							22 21								
Falkirk Grahamston	d			20 24						21 24							22 24								
Croy 3	d						20 45	21 07			21 40				21 45			22 39			23 39				
Lenzie 3	d						20 52								21 52										
Bishopbriggs	d						20 56								21 56										
Glasgow Queen Street 10	a	20 32					21 05	21 22			21 55				22 06	22 11		22 55			23 55				
Polmont 3	d			20 30	20 54					21 30		21 57					22 30		22 57			23 57			
Linlithgow	d			20 37	21 00				21 30	21 37		22 04					22 37		23 04			00 04			
Bathgate	d					20 59								22 02						23 02			23 59		
Livingston North	d					21 04								22 07						23 07			00 04		
Uphall	d					21 08								22 11						23 11			00 08		
Edinburgh Park	d			20 50		21 18				21 50				22 21			22 50			23 20			00 20		
Haymarket 225, 242	d			20 57	21s17	21 22			21s45	21 57		22s20		22 27			22 57		23s19	23 27		00s19	00 26		
Edinburgh 10 225, 242	a			21 01	21 22	21 29			21 53	22 01		22 25		22 32			23 01		23 24	23 31		00 24	00 31		

For general notes see front of timetable
For details of catering facilities see Directory of Train Operators

A From Glasgow Queen Street (Table 228)
B From Aberdeen (Table 229)
C From Edinburgh (Table 228)
D 30 November and 7 December
E From Inverness (Table 229)

Table 232

Mondays to Saturdays

Glasgow Queen Street — Maryhill and Anniesland

Network Diagram - see first page of Table 220

Miles			SR	SR		SR	SR
							FO
			A	B			
0	**Glasgow Queen Street** 10	d	06 26	06 56	and every 30 minutes until	23 26	23 56
2½	Ashfield	d	06 30	07 00		23 30	23 59
3	Possilpark & Parkhouse	d	06 32	07 02		23 32	00 02
3¼	Gilshochill	d	06 34	07 04		23 34	00 04
4¼	Summerston	d	06 36	07 06		23 36	00 06
4¾	**Maryhill**	d	06 38	07 08		23 38	00 08
5½	Kelvindale	d	06 40	07 10		23 40	00 10
6¼	**Anniesland**	226 a	06 44	07 14		23 44	00 14

Sundays

from 30 November

		SR	SR	SR	SR	SR	SR	SR	SR	SR	SR
Glasgow Queen Street 10	d	08 45	09 55	10 55	11 55	12 55	13 55	14 55	16 03	16 55	17 55
Ashfield	d	08 50	10 00	11 00	12 01	13 02	14 00	15 00	16 08	17 00	18 00
Possilpark & Parkhouse	d	08 52	10 02	11 02	12 03	13 04	14 02	15 02	16 10	17 02	18 02
Gilshochill	d	08 54	10 04	11 04	12 05	13 06	14 04	15 04	16 12	17 04	18 04
Summerston	d	08 56	10 06	11 06	12 07	13 08	14 06	15 06	16 14	17 06	18 06
Maryhill	d	08 58	10 08	11 08	12 09	13 10	14 08	15 08	16 16	17 08	18 08
Kelvindale	d	09 00	10 10	11 10	12 11	13 12	14 10	15 10	16 18	17 10	18 10
Anniesland	226 a	09 03	10 13	11 14	12 15	13 15	14 14	15 13	16 21	17 14	18 14

Mondays to Saturdays

Miles			SR	SR	SR	SR	SR	SR	SR	SR		SR	SR	SR
							SX							
							C							
0	**Anniesland**	226 d	06 23	06 53	07 23	07 53		08 25	08 53	09 23	and every 30 minutes until	14 53	15 26	15 53
¾	Kelvindale	d	06 25	06 55	07 25	07 55		08 26	08 55	09 25		14 55	15 28	15 55
1½	**Maryhill**	d	06 27	06 57	07 27	07 57	08 16	08 27	08 57	09 27		14 57	15 30	15 57
2	Summerston	d	06 28	06 58	07 28	07 58		08 28	08 58	09 28		14 58	15 31	15 58
3	Gilshochill	d	06 30	07 00	07 30	08 00		08 30	09 00	09 30		15 00	15 33	16 00
3¼	Possilpark & Parkhouse	d	06 32	07 02	07 32	08 02	08 21	08 32	09 02	09 32		15 02	15 35	16 02
4	Ashfield	d	06 34	07 04	07 34	08 04		08 34	09 04	09 34		15 04	15 38	16 04
6¼	**Glasgow Queen Street** 10	a	06 41	07 11	07 41	08 11	08 37	08 43	09 11	09 41		15 11	15 44	16 12

		SR	SR	SR	SR	SR	SR		SR
Anniesland	226 d	16 25	16 56	17 27	17 53	18 23	18 53	and every 30 minutes until	23 23
Kelvindale	d	16 27	16 57	17 28	17 55	18 25	18 55		23 25
Maryhill	d	16 29	16 59	17 29	17 57	18 27	18 57		23 27
Summerston	d	16 30	17 00	17 30	17 58	18 28	18 58		23 28
Gilshochill	d	16 32	17 02	17 32	18 00	18 30	19 00		23 30
Possilpark & Parkhouse	d	16 34	17 07	17 34	18 02	18 32	19 02		23 32
Ashfield	d	16 37	17 07	17 37	18 04	18 34	19 04		23 34
Glasgow Queen Street 10	a	16 45	17 15	17 45	18 11	18 41	19 11		23 41

Sundays

from 30 November

		SR		SR
Anniesland	226 d	09 23	and every hour until	18 23
Kelvindale	d	09 25		18 25
Maryhill	d	09 27		18 27
Summerston	d	09 28		18 28
Gilshochill	d	09 30		18 30
Possilpark & Parkhouse	d	09 32		18 32
Ashfield	d	09 35		18 35
Glasgow Queen Street 10	a	09 41		18 41

For general notes see front of timetable
For details of catering facilities see Directory of Train Operators

A 1226 from Glasgow Queen Street dep. 1227, Anniesland arr. 1245.
2126 from Glasgow Queen Street dep. 2127, Anniesland arr. 2145.
2156 from Glasgow Queen Street dep. 2157, Anniesland arr. 2215

B 1556 from Glasgow Queen Street dep. 1557, Anniesland arr. 1615

C From Arrochar & Tarbet (Table 227)

No Sunday service until 23 November

Table 238

Haymarket and Edinburgh → North Berwick

Network Diagram - see first page of Table 225

Miles			SR	SR	SR A	SR	SR	SR	SR	SR	SR	SR	SR A	SR	SR	SR	SR	SR	SR	SR	SR
0	**Haymarket**	225, 230, 242 d	06b52	07 39	08 28	09 35	10 19	11 19	12 19	13 19	14 18	15 35	16 30	17 05	17 31	18 06	18 19	19 20	19 56	20 58	22 29
1¼	**Edinburgh 10**	225, 230, 242 a	.	.	08 34	09 37	.	.	.	.	.	15 39	16 36	17 10	17 35	18 09	.	.	.	.	.
—		d	07 15	08 04	08 40	09 40	10 37	11 37	12 37	13 37	14 38	15 40	16 39	17 10	17 39	18 11	18 39	19 37	20 40	21 40	23 07
6½	Musselburgh	d	07 21	08 10	08 43	09 43	10 43	11 43	12 43	13 43	14 43	15 43	16 43	17 16	17 43	18 16	18 43	19 43	20 43	21 43	23 13
8¾	Wallyford	d	07 25	.	08 47	09 47	10 47	11 47	12 47	13 47	14 47	15 47	16 47	17 20	17 47	18 20	18 47	19 47	20 47	21 47	23 17
11	Prestonpans	d	07 28	.	08 50	09 50	10 50	11 50	12 50	13 50	14 50	15 50	16 50	17 23	17 50	18 23	18 50	19 50	20 50	21 50	23 20
14½	Longniddry	d	07 33	.	08 55	09 55	10 55	11 55	12 55	13 55	14 55	15 55	16 55	17 29	17 55	18 29	18 55	19 55	20 55	21 55	23 25
19	Drem	d	07 38	.	09 00	10 00	11 00	12 00	13 00	14 00	15 00	16 00	17 00	17 35	18 00	18 35	19 00	20 00	21 00	22 00	23 30
23½	**North Berwick**	a	07 48	08 29	09 13	10 13	11 10	12 10	13 10	14 10	15 11	16 13	17 14	17 45	18 14	18 46	19 12	20 10	21 13	22 13	23 50

Saturdays

		SR	SR A	SR	SR	SR	SR	SR	SR	SR	SR	SR	SR	SR
Haymarket	225, 230, 242 d	07 05	08 28	08 52	09 18	09 49	10 19	10 50	11 19	11 48	12 19	12 50	13 19	13 49
Edinburgh 10	225, 230, 242 a	.	08 34	.	.	.	.	.	.	.	.	.	.	.
	d	07 39	08 39	09 09	09 37	10 08	10 38	11 08	11 37	12 08	12 37	13 08	13 37	14 08
Musselburgh	d	07 43	08 43	09 13	09 43	10 13	10 43	11 13	11 43	12 13	12 43	13 13	13 43	14 13
Wallyford	d	07 47	08 47	09 17	09 47	10 17	10 47	11 17	11 47	12 17	12 47	13 17	13 47	14 17
Prestonpans	d	07 50	08 50	09 20	09 50	10 20	10 50	11 20	11 50	12 20	12 50	13 20	13 50	14 20
Longniddry	d	07 55	08 55	09 25	09 55	10 25	10 55	11 25	11 55	12 25	12 55	13 25	13 55	14 25
Drem	d	08 00	09 00	09 30	10 00	10 30	11 00	11 30	12 00	12 30	13 00	13 30	14 00	14 30
North Berwick	a	08 12	09 12	09 42	10 10	10 41	11 11	11 41	12 10	12 41	13 11	13 41	14 11	14 41

		SR	SR	SR	SR	SR A	SR	SR	SR	SR	SR	SR	SR	SR
Haymarket	225, 230, 242 d	14 18	14 50	15 18	15 49	16 30	16 50	17 19	17 49	18 19	19 18	19 56	20 58	22 28
Edinburgh 10	225, 230, 242 a	.	.	.	.	16 36	.	.	.	.	.	.	.	.
	d	14 37	15 09	15 37	16 08	16 39	17 08	17 37	18 08	18 37	19 37	20 40	21 40	23 07
Musselburgh	d	14 43	15 13	15 43	16 13	16 43	17 13	17 43	18 13	18 43	19 43	20 43	21 43	23 13
Wallyford	d	14 47	15 17	15 47	16 17	16 47	17 17	17 47	18 17	18 47	19 47	20 47	21 47	23 17
Prestonpans	d	14 50	15 24	15 50	16 20	16 50	17 20	17 50	18 20	18 50	19 50	20 50	21 50	23 20
Longniddry	d	14 55	15 30	15 55	16 25	16 55	17 25	17 55	18 25	18 55	19 55	20 55	21 55	23 25
Drem	d	15 00	15 37	16 00	16 30	17 00	17 30	18 00	18 30	19 00	20 00	21 00	22 00	23 30
North Berwick	a	15 10	15 44	16 10	16 41	17 12	17 41	18 10	18 41	19 10	20 10	21 13	22 13	23 50

Sundays

		SR	SR	SR	SR	SR	SR	SR	SR	SR	SR	SR	SR
Haymarket	225, 230, 242 d	08 56	11c00	11 57	13 12	13 58	15 00	15 57	16 58	17 57	18 58	20 01	20 57
Edinburgh 10	225, 230, 242 a	.	.	.	.	.	.	.	.	.	.	.	.
	d	10 33	11 33	12 33	13 33	14 33	15 33	16 33	17 33	18 33	19 33	20 33	21 33
Musselburgh	d	10 39	11 39	12 39	13 39	14 39	15 39	16 39	17 39	18 39	19 39	20 39	21 39
Wallyford	d	10 43	11 43	12 43	13 43	14 43	15 43	16 43	17 43	18 43	19 43	20 43	21 43
Prestonpans	d	10 46	11 46	12 46	13 46	14 46	15 46	16 46	17 46	18 46	19 46	20 46	21 46
Longniddry	d	10 51	11 51	12 51	13 51	14 51	15 51	16 51	17 51	18 51	19 51	20 51	21 51
Drem	d	10 57	11 57	12 57	13 57	14 57	15 57	16 57	17 57	18 57	19 57	20 57	21 57
North Berwick	a	11 06	12 06	13 06	14 06	15 06	16 06	17 06	18 06	19 06	20 06	21 06	22 06

For general notes see front of timetable
For details of catering facilities see Directory of Train Operators

A From Glasgow Central (Table 225)
b From 8 September dep. 0650
c 20 July to 7 September dep. 1116

North Berwick → Edinburgh and Haymarket

Network Diagram - see first page of Table 225

Mondays to Fridays

Miles			SR	SR	SR	SR A	SR	SR	SR	SR	SR	SR	SR	SR	SR	SR	SR A	SR	SR	SR	SR	SR	SR
0	North Berwick	d	06 47	07 20	.	07 56	08 34	09 20	10 20	11 20	12 20	13 20	14 15	15 20	16 20	17 20	17 50	18 20	18 51	19 20	20 20	21 20	22 20
4½	Drem	d	06 54	07 28	.	08 04	08 41	09 27	10 27	11 27	12 27	13 27	14 22	15 27	16 27	17 27	.	18 27	18 57	19 27	20 27	21 27	22 27
9	Longniddry	d	07 00	07 34	.	08 10	08 47	09 33	10 33	11 33	12 33	13 33	14 28	15 33	16 33	17 33	.	18 33	19 03	19 33	20 33	21 33	22 33
12¼	Prestonpans	d	07 05	07 39	08 08	08 15	08 52	09 38	10 38	11 38	12 38	13 38	14 33	15 38	16 38	17 38	.	18 38	19 08	19 38	20 38	21 38	22 38
14¾	Wallyford	d	07 08	07 43	08 11	08 19	08 55	09 41	10 41	11 41	12 41	13 41	14 36	15 41	16 41	17 41	.	18 41	19 11	19 41	20 41	21 41	22 41
17	Musselburgh	d	07 12	07 47	08 16	08 26	08 59	09 45	10 45	11 45	12 45	13 45	14 40	15 45	16 45	17 45	18 13	18 45	19 15	19 45	20 45	21 45	22 45
22¼	Edinburgh 10	225, 230, 242 a	07 20	07 53	08 22	08 34	09 10	09 53	10 53	11 53	12 53	13 53	14 48	15 53	16 53	17 53	18 21	18 53	19 24	19 53	20 53	21 53	22 53
—		d	07 21	.	.	08 38	09 12	.	.	.	.	.	15 07	15 55	16 54	.	18 21	.	.	.	.	.	.
23½	Haymarket	225, 230, 242 a	07 24	08 06	08 36	08 42	09 15	10 06	11 05	12 06	13 06	14 06	15b10	15 59	17 01	18 06	18 24	19 06	19 40	20 06	21 18	22 14	23 14

Saturdays

		SR	SR A	SR	SR	SR	SR	SR	SR	SR	SR	SR	SR	SR
North Berwick	d	07 27	08 20	09 20	09 48	10 20	10 50	11 20	11 50	12 20	12 50	13 20	13 53	14 15
Drem	d	07 35	08 27	09 27	09 55	10 27	10 57	11 27	11 57	12 27	12 57	13 27	13 57	14 22
Longniddry	d	07 41	08 33	09 33	10 01	10 33	11 03	11 33	12 03	12 33	13 03	13 33	14 03	14 28
Prestonpans	d	07 46	08 38	09 38	10 06	10 38	11 08	11 38	12 08	12 38	13 08	13 38	14 08	14 33
Wallyford	d	07 50	08 41	09 41	10 09	10 41	11 11	11 41	12 11	12 41	13 11	13 41	14 11	14 36
Musselburgh	d	07 54	08 45	09 45	10 13	10 45	11 15	11 45	12 15	12 45	13 15	13 45	14 15	14 40
Edinburgh 10	225, 230, 242 a	08 02	08 53	09 53	10 21	10 53	11 23	11 53	12 23	12 53	13 26	13 53	14 26	14 50
	d	.	08 58	.	.	.	.	.	.	.	.	.	.	.
Haymarket	225, 230, 242 a	08 18	09 01	10 06	10 36	11 05	11 36	12 06	12 36	13 06	13 43	14 06	14 45	15 03

		SR	SR A	SR	SR	SR	SR	SR	SR	SR	SR	SR	SR	SR
North Berwick	d	14 50	15 20	15 50	16 20	16 52	17 20	17 52	18 20	18 50	19 20	20 20	21 20	22 20
Drem	d	14 57	15 27	15 59	16 27	16 57	17 27	17 57	18 27	18 57	19 27	20 27	21 27	22 27
Longniddry	d	15 03	15 33	16 05	16 33	17 03	17 33	18 03	18 33	19 03	19 33	20 33	21 33	22 33
Prestonpans	d	15 08	15 38	16 10	16 38	17 08	17 38	18 08	18 38	19 08	19 38	20 38	21 38	22 38
Wallyford	d	15 11	15 41	16 13	16 41	17 11	17 41	18 11	18 41	19 11	19 41	20 41	21 41	22 41
Musselburgh	d	15 15	15 45	16 17	16 45	17 15	17 45	18 15	18 45	19 15	19 45	20 45	21 45	22 45
Edinburgh 10	225, 230, 242 a	15 23	15 53	16 27	16 53	17 23	17 53	18 25	18 53	19 23	19 53	20 53	21 53	22 53
	d	.	15 56	.	.	.	.	.	.	.	.	.	.	.
Haymarket	225, 230, 242 a	15 36	15 59	16 44	17 06	17 36	18 06	18 36	19 06	19 36	20 06	21 14	22 22	23 14

Sundays

		SR	SR	SR	SR	SR	SR	SR	SR	SR	SR	SR	SR
North Berwick	d	11 20	12 20	13 23	14 23	15 20	16 20	17 20	18 20	19 20	20 20	21 20	22 20
Drem	d	11 27	12 27	13 30	14 30	15 27	16 28	17 27	18 27	19 27	20 27	21 27	22 29
Longniddry	d	11 33	12 33	13 36	14 36	15 33	16 33	17 33	18 33	19 33	20 33	21 33	22 34
Prestonpans	d	11 38	12 38	13 41	14 41	15 38	16 38	17 38	18 38	19 38	20 38	21 38	22 39
Wallyford	d	11 41	12 41	13 44	14 44	15 41	16 41	17 41	18 41	19 41	20 41	21 41	22 42
Musselburgh	d	11 45	12 45	13 48	14 48	15 45	16 45	17 45	18 45	19 45	20 45	21 45	22 46
Edinburgh 10	225, 230, 242 a	11 53	12 53	13 56	14 56	15 53	16 53	17 53	18 53	19 53	20 53	21 53	22 53
	d	.	.	.	.	.	.	.	.	.	.	.	.
Haymarket	225, 230, 242 a	12 08	13 19	14c17	15 17	16 19	17 09	18 19	19 19	20e18	21f19	22 22	23 22

For general notes see front of timetable
For details of catering facilities see Directory of Train Operators

A To Glasgow Central (Table 225)
b By changing at Edinburgh, passengers may arrive at 1503
c 20 July to 7 September arr. 1418
e Until 7 September arr. 2019
f Until 13 July arr. 2118. 14 September to 2 November arr. 2117

Inverness → Kyle of Lochalsh, Thurso and Wick

Network Diagram - see first page of Table 227

Miles	Miles			SR	SR	SR	SR	SR	SR	SR	SR	SR	SR	SR	SR	SR
														SX	SO	
													[R]			
				◇	◇		◇	◇		◇				◇	◇	
					A			A		C				B		
				⚲	⚲		⚲	⚲		⚲			⚲	⚲		
—	—	Glasgow Queen Street [10] 229 ⛴	d				07 06		08b41		10 11		13b41			16c41
—	—	Edinburgh [10] 229	d				06b40		08 37		09b36		13 36			16 33
—	—	Aberdeen 240	d		06 25		07 28		09 27		11 40	13 12		15 23	15 23	17 15
0	0	**Inverness**	d	07 14	08 53	09 15	10 39	10 52	12 17	12⌇41	14 33	17 03	17 52	18 15	18 15	20 39
10	10	Beauly	d	07 28	09 08	09 30	10 56	11 09	12 32	12⌇56	14 48	17 18	18 07	18 29	18 29	20 53
13	13	Muir of Ord	d	07 34	09 14	09 37	11 02	11 16	12 38	13⌇02	14 55	17e26	18 13	18 36	18 36	20 59
18¾	18¾	Dingwall	d	07 45	09 24	10f04	11 12	11 26	12 48	13g14	15 05	17 36	18 23	18g49	18g49	21 09
—	30½	Garve	d		09 45			11 48		13⌇36				19 10	19 10	
—	36	Lochluichart	d		09x53			11x57		13x44				19x18	19x18	
—	40¼	Achanalt	d		09x59			12x03		13x50				19x24	19x24	
—	46½	Achnasheen	d		10 10			12 13		14⌇01				19 35	19 35	
—	59¼	Achnashellach	d		10x28			12x30		14x19				19x52	19x53	
—	64½	Strathcarron	d		10 38			12 42		14⌇29				20 03	20 03	
—	67	Attadale	d		10x43			12x47		14x34				20x08	20x08	
—	72	Stromeferry	d		10 56			13 00		14⌇47				20 21	20 21	
—	75¾	Duncraig	d		11x04			13x08		14x55				20x29	20x29	
—	77	Plockton	d		11 08			13 12		14⌇58				20 32	20 32	
—	78½	Duirinish	d		11x11			13x15		15x01				20x35	20x35	
—	82¼	**Kyle of Lochalsh**	a		11 20			13 25		15⌇12				20 47	20 47	
28½	—	Alness	d	07 57		10 16	11 24		13 00		15 17	17 48	18 35			21 21
31½	—	Invergordon	d	08 02		10a23	11e31		13a04		15a21	17 53	18 40			21 26
40¾	—	Fearn	d	08 13			11 42					18 04	18 51			21 38
44¼	—	Tain	d	08 19			11 48					18 10	18 57			21a43
57¾	—	Ardgay	d	08 35			12 04					18a25	19 13			
61	—	Culrain	d	08 41			12 10						19 19			
61½	—	Invershin	d	08x42			12x11						19 21			
67	—	Lairg	d	08 53			12 21						19 32			
77	—	Rogart	d	09x07			12x35						19 47			
84½	—	Golspie	d	09 18			12 45						19 57			
87	—	Dunrobin Castle §	d	09h22			12h49						20h02			
90½	—	Brora	d	09 29			12 56						20 08			
101½	—	Helmsdale	d	09g48			13 11						20 23			
111	—	Kildonan	d	10x01			13x23						20x36			
118½	—	Kinbrace	d	10x10			13x33						20x45			
125¾	—	Forsinard	d	10 23			13e46						20 56			
134	—	Altnabreac	d	10x33			13x56						21x06			
143	—	Scotscalder	d	10x42			14x04						21x15			
147¼	—	Georgemas Junction	a	10 51			14 15						21 24			
—	—		d	10 53			14 18						21 26			
154	—	**Thurso**	a	11 05			14 27						21 36			
—	—		d	11 07			14 30						21 38			
160¾	—	Georgemas Junction	d	11 17			14 40						21 48			
175	—	**Wick**	a	11 34			14 57						22 06			

For general notes see front of timetable
For details of catering facilities see Directory of Train Operators

§ Summer Station only
A ⚲ until 27 September
B First Class accommodation and ⚲ available to Inverness
C Until 27 September
b Change at Perth and Inverness
c Mondays to Fridays change at Perth and Inverness. Saturdays change at Stirling and Inverness
e Arr. 3 minutes earlier
f Arr. 0945
g Arr. 4 minutes earlier
h Until 27 September only. Stops on request

Table 239

Sundays

Inverness → Kyle of Lochalsh, Thurso and Wick

Network Diagram - see first page of Table 227

			SR ◇ A (trolley)	SR ◇ B (trolley)	SR ◇ (trolley)	SR ◇ A
Glasgow Queen Street 10	229 ⛴	d			*14 40*	
Edinburgh 10	229	d			*13 50*	
Aberdeen	240	d			*15 23*	
Inverness		d	10 56	11 18	18 00	18 15
Beauly		d	11 13	11 32	18 17	18 32
Muir of Ord		d	11 19	11 38	18 23	18 38
Dingwall		d	11 29	11 48	18 34	18 48
Garve		d		12 09		19 09
Lochluichart		d		12x17		19x17
Achanalt		d		12x23		19x23
Achnasheen		d		12 34		19 34
Achnashellach		d		12x52		19x52
Strathcarron		d		13 04		20 02
Attadale		d		13x09		20x07
Stromeferry		d		13 22		20 20
Duncraig		d		13x30		20x28
Plockton		d		13 34		20 31
Duirinish		d		13x37		20x34
Kyle of Lochalsh		a		13 46		20 45
Alness		d	11 41		18 46	
Invergordon		d	11 46		18 51	
Fearn		d	11 57		19 02	
Tain		d	12 04		19 09	
Ardgay		d	12 19		19 24	
Culrain		d	12 25		19 30	
Invershin		d	12x26		19x31	
Lairg		d	12 37		19 43	
Rogart		d	12x51		19x56	
Golspie		d	13 01		20 07	
Dunrobin Castle §		d	13x05		20b10	
Brora		d	13 12		20 18	
Helmsdale		d	13 28		20 33	
Kildonan		d	13x40		20x46	
Kinbrace		d	13x50		20x55	
Forsinard		d	14 01		21 06	
Altnabreac		d	14x11		21x16	
Scotscalder		d	14x19		21x25	
Georgemas Junction		a	14 29		21 34	
		d	14 32		21 36	
Thurso		a	14 41		21 46	
		d	14 44		21 48	
Georgemas Junction		d	14 53		21 58	
Wick		a	15 10		22 15	

For general notes see front of timetable
For details of catering facilities see Directory of Train Operators

§ Summer Station only

A Until 28 September
B (trolley) until 28 September

b Until 28 September only. Stops on request

Wick, Thurso and Kyle of Lochalsh → Inverness

Network Diagram - see first page of Table 227

Miles	Miles	Station		SR	SR ◇	SR ◇ 🍴	SR	SR ◇ 🍴	SR	SR ◇ A 🍴	SR	SR ◇ 🍴	SR ◇ B 🍴	SR ◇ A 🍴	SR ◇ 🍴	SR	SR
0	—	**Wick**	d			06 22		08 13				12 37			15 51		
14¼	—	Georgemas Junction	d			06 39		08 30				12 54			16 08		
21	—	**Thurso**	a			06 48		08 39				13 03			16 17		
—	—		d			06 52		08 42				13 06			16 20		
27¾	—	Georgemas Junction	a			07 01		08 51				13 15			16 29		
—	—		d			07 04		08 54				13 18			16 32		
32	—	Scotscalder	d			07x10						13x24			16x38		
41	—	Altnabreac	d			07x19						13x33			16x47		
49¼	—	Forsinard	d			07 30		09 16				13b47			16 58		
56¾	—	Kinbrace	d			07x40						13x57			17x08		
64	—	Kildonan	d			07x49						14x06			17x17		
73½	—	Helmsdale	d			08 03		09 48				14 20			17 31		
84½	—	Brora	d			08 18		10 03				14 35			17 46		
88	—	Dunrobin Castle §	d			08c25						14c42			17c53		
90½	—	Golspie	d			08 29		10 13				14 45			17 56		
98	—	Rogart	d			08 38		10x22				14x54			18x05		
108	—	Lairg	d	06 33		08e55		10 38				15 09			18 22		
113½	—	Invershin	d	06 42		09x03						15x19			18x31		
114	—	Culrain	d	06 44		09 05						15 21			18 33		
117¼	—	Ardgay	d	06 50		09 11		10 52				15 26			18 39	19 14	
130¾	—	Tain	d	07 05		09 26		11 08				15 42			18 55	19 29	21 48
134¼	—	Fearn	d	07 11		09 32						15 48			19 01	19x34	21 54
143½	—	Invergordon	d	07 23		09 44	10 33	11 26	13 11		15 30	15 59			19 12	19 45	22 05
146½	—	Alness	d			09 49	10 38		13 16		15 35	16 05			19 18	19x50	22 11
—	0	**Kyle of Lochalsh**	d		07 25					12 00			15 13	16 48			
—	3¾	Duirinish	d		07x34					12x09			15x26	16x57			
—	5¼	Plockton	d		07 38					12 13			15 30	17 01			
—	6½	Duncraig	d		07x41					12x16			15x33	17x04			
—	10¼	Stromeferry	d		07 50					12 25			15 42	17 13			
—	15¼	Attadale	d		08x01					12x36			15x53	17x24			
—	17¾	Strathcarron	d		08 07					12 42			16 01	17 30			
—	23	Achnashellach	d		08x15					12x50			16x09	17x38			
—	35¾	Achnasheen	d		08 34					13 09			16 27	17 57			
—	42	Achanalt	d		08x44					13x19			16x36	18x07			
—	46¼	Lochluichart	d		08x50					13x25			16x42	18x13			
—	51¾	Garve	d		09 00					13 36			16 53	18 22			
156¼	63½	Dingwall	d	07 42	09 24	10 05	10 50	11 44	13 29	13 58	15 49	16 20	17 15	18b48	19 34	20 04	22 24
162	69¼	Muir of Ord	d	07 52	09 35	10 14	11f13	11 53	13e41	14 07	15 58	16 29	17 24	18 57	19 43	20 13	22 33
164¾	72¼	Beauly	d	07 58	09 41	10 20	11 19		13 47	14 13	16 04	16 35	17 30	19 03	19 49	20 19	22 39
175	82¼	**Inverness**	a	08 14	09 57	10 37	11 37	12 13	14 03	14 29	16 20	16 51	17 45	19 19	20 05	20 35	22 55
—	—	Aberdeen 240	a	*10 53*	*12 59*		*14 31*			*17 37*		*19 30*	*20 29*			*23 38*	
—	—	Edinburgh [10] 229	a	*13g32*		*14 21*		*16 04*		*18 11*	*20h32*	*22 09*	*22 09*	*00g07*			
—	—	Glasgow Queen Street [10] 229	a	*12 44*		*14h14*		*16h15*		*18h18*	*20 17*	*22h17*	*22h17*	*23 39*			

For general notes see front of timetable
For details of catering facilities see Directory of Train Operators

§ Summer Station only

A 🍴 until 27 September
B Until 27 September
b Arr. 4 minutes earlier
c Until 27 September only. Stops on request
e Arr. 3 minutes earlier
f Arr. 1100
g Change at Inverness and Stirling
h Change at Inverness and Perth

Table 239

Sundays

Wick, Thurso and Kyle of Lochalsh → Inverness

Network Diagram - see first page of Table 227

		SR ◇ A	SR ◇ A 🛒	SR ◇ B 🛒	SR ◇ C 🛒	SR ◇ A 🛒
Wick	d		11 46	11 56		16 05
Georgemas Junction	d		12 03	12 13		16 22
Thurso	a		12 12	12 22		16 31
	d		12 15	12 25		16 34
Georgemas Junction	a		12 24	12 34		16 43
	d		12 27	12 37		16 46
Scotscalder	d		12x33	12x43		16x52
Altnabreac	d		12x42	12x52		17x01
Forsinard	d		12 53	13 03		17 12
Kinbrace	d		13x03	13x13		17x22
Kildonan	d		13x12	13x22		17x31
Helmsdale	d		13b29	13c38		17 45
Brora	d		13 44	13 53		18 00
Dunrobin Castle §	d		13x50			18x06
Golspie	d		13 53	14 02		18 09
Rogart	d		14x02	14x11		18x18
Lairg	d		14 17	14 26		18 34
Invershin	d		14x26	14x34		18x44
Culrain	d		14 28	14 36		18 45
Ardgay	d		14 33	14 42		18 50
Tain	d		14 49	14 57		19c08
Fearn	d		14 55	15 03		19 14
Invergordon	d		15 06	15 15		19 25
Alness	d		15 12	15 21		19 30
Kyle of Lochalsh	d	10 34			15 17	
Duirinish	d	10x43			15x26	
Plockton	d	10 47			15 30	
Duncraig	d	10x50			15x33	
Stromeferry	d	10 59			15 42	
Attadale	d	11x10			15x53	
Strathcarron	d	11 16			15 59	
Achnashellach	d	11x24			16x07	
Achnasheen	d	11 43			16 26	
Achanalt	d	11x53			16x36	
Lochluichart	d	11x59			16x42	
Garve	d	12 09			16 51	
Dingwall	d	12 33	15 27	15 36	17 14	19 46
Muir of Ord	d	12 41	15 37	15 45	17 23	19 55
Beauly	d	12 48	15 43	15 51	17 29	20 01
Inverness	a	13 02	15 59	16 08	17 44	20 17
Aberdeen 240	a		19 28	19 28		
Edinburgh 10 229	a		20e05		22 06	
Glasgow Queen Street 10 229 🚌	a		19 36		22f11	

For general notes see front of timetable
For details of catering facilities see Directory of Train Operators

§ Summer Station only

A Until 28 September
B From 5 October
C 🛒 until 28 September
b Arr. 4 minutes earlier
c Arr. 3 minutes earlier
e Change at Inverness and Stirling
f Change at Inverness and Perth

Scrabster — Stromness (Orkney Isles)

Operated by NorthLink Orkney & Shetland Ferries Ltd

Mondays to Saturdays

		SO	SX	
Inverness	239 d	07 14	07 14	10 39
Thurso §	239 a	11b05	11b05	14c27
Scrabster	⛴ d	12 00	13 15	19 00
Stromness	⛴ a	13 30	14 45	20 30

Sundays

		A
Inverness	239 d	10§56
Thurso §	239 a	14c41
Scrabster	⛴ d	19§00
Stromness	⛴ a	20§30

Mondays to Saturdays

		SX	SO B	SO C	SX	SO B
Stromness	⛴ d	06 30	06§30	09§00	11 00	11§00
Scrabster	⛴ a	08e00	08e00	10e30	12e30	12e30
Thurso §	239 d	08 42	08§42	13§06	13 06	13§06
Inverness	239 a	12 13	12§13	16§51	16 51	16§51

Sundays

		D	E
Stromness	⛴ d	09§00	09§00
Scrabster	⛴ a	10f30	10e30
Thurso §	239 d	12§15	12§25
Inverness	239 a	15§59	16§08

For general notes see front of timetable
For details of catering facilities see Directory of Train Operators

§ Highland Country Buses (01847 893123) and Scottish Citylink Coaches (08705 505050) operate a connecting Bus Service between Thurso-Scrabster-Thurso from whom details of bus times should be obtained

A Until 28 September

B 14 June to 16 August

C Until 7 June and from 23 August

D Until 28 September

E From 5 October

b Highland Country Bus connection. Departs Thurso Railway Station

c Scottish Citylink Coaches connection. Departs St. George's Street Post Office

e Highland Country Bus connection. Arrives Thurso Railway Station

f Scottish Citylink Coaches connection. Arrives St. George's Street church

Ullapool - Stornoway (Lewis), Uig (Skye), Tarbert (Harris) and Lochmaddy (North Uist)

Operated by Caledonian MacBrayne Ltd.

		TTh SX	TTh SO	WFO A	WFX	WFO B	TThO	SO C	SO D	TTh SX	WFO A
Edinburgh 10	229 d			08 37	09b36	09b36	06b40	06b40	06b40	06b40	13 36
Glasgow Queen Street 10	229 d			08b41	10 11	10 11	07 05	07 05	07 05	07 05	13b41
Inverness	229 a			11c59	13c35	13c35	10 26	10 26	10 26	10 26	17c07
Inverness	239 d	08 53	08 53				10 52	10 52	10 52	10 52	
Kyle of Lochalsh §	239 a	11e20	11e20				13f25	13f25	13f25	13f25	
Inverness ‡	d			13 30	14 35	14 35					19 50
Ullapool	a			14 50	15 55	15 55					21 10
Ullapool	d			15 50	17 15	17 15					22 00
Stornoway	a			18 35	20 00	20 00					00 45
Uig §	d	14 00	14 00				18 00	18 00	18 00	18 00	
Tarbert	a	15 40					19 40	19 40	19 40		
Lochmaddy	a		15 45					21 20		19 45	

Mondays to Saturdays
until 18 October

		MO E	MO G	WFO H	WFO J	WFX	WFO K	TTh SO	TTh SO	TTh SX	WFO J	WFX	WFO K
Lochmaddy	d	05 30						07 30		11 50			
Tarbert	d	07 30	07 30	07 30					11 50				
Uig §	a	09g10	09g10	09g10				09g15	13h30	13h35			
Stornoway	d				06 15	07 15	07 15				12 40	13 45	13 45
Ullapool	a				09 00	10 00	10 00				15 25	16 30	16 30
Ullapool	d				09 05	10 05	10 05				15 30	16 35	16 35
Inverness ‡	a				10j25	11j25	11j25				16 50	17j55	17j55
Kyle of Lochalsh §	239 d	12 00	12 00	12 00				12 00	16 48	16 48			
Inverness	239 a	14 29	14 29	14 29				14 29	19 19	19 19			
Inverness	229 d	14 41	14 41	14 41	10 53	12 40	12 40	14 41	20 10	20 10	18 27	18 27	18 27
Glasgow Queen Street 10	229 a	18k17	18k17	18k17	14k14	16k15	16k15	18k17	23 39	20 39	22k17	22k17	22k17
Edinburgh 10	229 a	18 11	18 11	18 11	14 21	16 05	16 05	18 11	00m07	00m07	22 09	22 09	22 09

For general notes see front of timetable
For details of catering facilities see Directory of Train Operators

§ Connecting bus service between Uig-Kyle of Lochalsh operated by Scottish Citylink Coaches (08705 505050)

‡ Bus Station. Connecting bus service between Inverness Bus Station-Ullapool operated by Scottish Citylink coaches (08705 505050)

- A 25 June to 29 August
- B Until 20 June and from 3 September
- C From 13 September
- D Until 6 September
- E From 15 September
- G Until 8 September
- H Until 27 September
- J 25 June to 29 August
- K Until 20 June and from 3 September
- b Change at Perth
- c Passengers make their own way between Bus Station and Rail Station
- e Bus connection dep. Kyle of Lochalsh 1215, Uig arr. 1350
- f Bus connection dep. Kyle of Lochalsh 1540, Uig arr. 1720
- g Bus connection dep. Uig 0930, Kyle of Lochalsh arr. 1114
- h Bus connection dep. Uig 1445, Kyle of Lochalsh arr. 1619
- j Passengers make their own way between Bus Station and Rail Station
- k Change at Perth
- m Change at Stirling

No Sunday Service

For confirmation of Scottish Citylink Coach connections from 6 October please telephone 08705 50 50 50

Aberdeen and Elgin — Inverness

Network Diagram - please see first page of Table 225

Miles			SR 1◇	SR 1◇	SR SX A	SR 1◇	SR SO	SR SX 1	SR 1◇ B	SR 1◇ trolley	SR 1◇ C	SR	SR 1◇ trolley	SR	SR 1◇ trolley
0	Aberdeen	d		06 25	07 18	07 28	07 52	08 22	08 46	09 27	09 47	11 00	11 40	12 38	13 12
6¼	Dyce ✈	a		06 34	07 27	07 37	08 01	08 31	08 56	09 36	09 55	11 09	11 49	12 47	13 21
—		d		06 37		07 39	08 04	08 31		09 36		11 10	11 49	12 49	13 21
17	Inverurie	d		06 50		07 51	08a18	08 43		09 48		11a21	12 01	13a03	13 33
27½	Insch	d		07 03		08 03		08 55		10 03			12 13		13 45
40¾	Huntly	d		07 20		08 19		09 11		10 24			12 29		14 02
53¼	Keith	d		07 34		08 33		09a27		10 37			12 43		14 16
71¼	Elgin	d	07 00	07 56		08 55				10 58			13 04		14b39
83½	Forres	d	07 14	08 10		09 15				11 17			13 19		14 54
93¼	Nairn	d	07 25	08 21		09 26				11 28			13 30		15 05
108¼	Inverness	a	07 43	08 41		09 44				11 46			13 48		15 23

Miles			SR	SR 1◇ C	SR 1◇ D trolley	SR 1◇ C	SR 1◇ trolley	SR	SR ◇ trolley	SR 1◇ C	SR 1◇ C	SR 1◇ trolley	SR ◇ E	SR 1◇	SR
0	Aberdeen	d	14 11	14 42	15 23	16 41	17 15	17 42	18 21	18 46	19 39	20 07	20 54	21 55	22 50
6¼	Dyce ✈	a	14 20	14 51	15 32	16 50	17 24	17 51	18 30	18 56	19 48	20 16	21 03	22 04	22 59
—		d	14 23		15 32		17 27		18 30			20 19	21 03	22 04	22 59
17	Inverurie	d	14a37		15 46		17 39		18 42			20 31	21a16	22 16	23a13
27½	Insch	d			15 58		17 51		18 54			20 43		22 28	
40¾	Huntly	d			16 14		18 08		19 09			21 00		22 46	
53¼	Keith	d			16 35		18 23		19 24			21 14		23 00	
71¼	Elgin	d			16 57		18 47		19 45			21 36		23 20	
83½	Forres	d			17 11		19 01		20 00			21 56		23 35	
93¼	Nairn	d			17c29		19 12		20 13			22 07		23 46	
108¼	Inverness	a			17 47		19 34		20 31			22 25		00 05	

Sundays

		SR 1◇ trolley	SR 1◇ trolley	SR 1◇ trolley	SR 1◇ trolley	SR 1◇ trolley
Aberdeen	d	10 00	13 12	15 23	17 15	21 00
Dyce ✈	a	10 09	13 21	15 32	17 24	21 09
	d	10 09	13 21	15 32	17 27	21 09
Inverurie	d	10 22	13 33	15 47	17 40	21 21
Insch	d	10 34	13 45	15 59	17 52	21 33
Huntly	d	10 50	14 02	16 15	18 08	21 49
Keith	d	11 05	14 16	16 34	18 22	22 03
Elgin	d	11 27	14 38	16 57	18 44	22e29
Forres	d	11 41	14 53	17 11	18 58	22 43
Nairn	d	11 53	15 04	17c29	19 11	22 55
Inverness	a	12 12	15 23	17 47	19 34	23 14

Mondays to Saturdays

Miles			SR 1◇ G	SR 1◇ H	SR SX	SR 1◇ trolley	SR SO	SR 1◇ G	SR 1◇ H	SR SX	SR R 1 trolley	SR	SR 1◇ trolley	SR	SR 1◇ trolley
0	Inverness	d		05 00		05 57					08 42		10 44		12 19
15	Nairn	d		05 17		06 14					08 59		11 01		12 36
24¾	Forres	d		05 28		06 25					09 10		11 12		12 47
37	Elgin	d		05 44		06 41					09 27		11 32		13f04
55	Keith	d		06 05		07 02				09 32	09 46		11 53		13 26
67½	Huntly	d		06 19		07g21				09 46	10 02		12 08		13 40
80¾	Insch	d		06 35		07 38				10 02	10 18		12 24		13 56
91¼	Inverurie	d		06h51		07 51	08 40			10 14	10 30	11 35	12 36	13 08	14 08
102	Dyce ✈	a		07 03		08 02	08 51			10 26	10 42	11 46	12 48	13 19	14 20
—		d	06 50	07 03	07 45	08 03	08 56	09 08	10 08	10 26	10 42	11 50	12 48	13 23	14 20
108¼	Aberdeen	a	07 00	07 14	07 56	08 15	09 07	09 18	10 18	10 37	10 53	12 01	12 59	13 34	14 31

Miles			SR	SR 1◇ H	SR 1◇ trolley	SR 1◇ H	SR 1◇ trolley	SR	SR 1◇ H	SR 1◇ trolley	SR J	SR 1◇	SR 1	SR	SR 1◇
0	Inverness	d			13 57		15 25			17 12		18 08	19 53		21 20
15	Nairn	d			14 14		15 42			17 28		18 25	20f14		21 39
24¾	Forres	d			14 25		15 53			17 39		18 36	20 25		21 50
37	Elgin	d			14g42		16 08			17 55		18g54	20a41		22 08
55	Keith	d			15 03		16 30			18 17		19 16			22 29
67½	Huntly	d			15 17		16 44			18 36		19 37			22f46
80¾	Insch	d			15 33		17 00			18 55		19 53			23 02
91¼	Inverurie	d	14 42		15 48		17 12			19 07		20 05		21 28	23 17
102	Dyce ✈	a	14 53		16 00		17 25			19 19		20 17		21 39	23 29
—		d	14 54	15 08	16 00	17 00	17 26	17 56	19 05	19 19	19 55	20 18		21 40	23 29
108¼	Aberdeen	a	15 05	15 18	16 11	17 10	17 37	18 06	19 17	19 30	20 05	20 29		21 51	23 40

Sundays

		SR 1◇ trolley	SR 1◇ trolley	SR 1◇ trolley	SR 1◇ trolley	SR 1◇ B trolley	SR 1◇ trolley	SR 1◇ B trolley
Inverness	d	09 55	12 19	15 25	17 10	18 00	20 52	21 42
Nairn	d	10 12	12 36	15 42	17 28	18 17	21 10	21 59
Forres	d	10 23	12 47	15 53	17 39	18 28	21 21	22 10
Elgin	d	10 38	13f04	16 08	17 55	18a44	21 37	22a26
Keith	d	10 59	13 26	16 30	18 17		21 58	
Huntly	d	11 18	13 40	16 44	18 36		22 17	
Insch	d	11 34	13 56	17 00	18 53		22 34	
Inverurie	d	11 47	14 08	17 12	19 05		22 47	
Dyce ✈	a	11 59	14 20	17 25	19 17		22 58	
	d	11 59	14 20	17 26	19 17		22 59	
Aberdeen	a	12 10	14 31	17 37	19 28		23 10	

For general notes see front of timetable
For details of catering facilities see Directory of Train Operators

A From Montrose (Table 229)
B From Glasgow Queen Street (Table 229)
C From Edinburgh (Table 229)
D To Kyle of Lochalsh (Table 239)
E Mondays to Fridays from Edinburgh (Table 229)
G To Glasgow Queen Street (Table 229)
H To Edinburgh (Table 229)
J Saturdays to Edinburgh (Table 229)

b Arr. 4 minutes earlier
c Arr. 7 minutes earlier
e Arr. 6 minutes earlier
f Arr. 4 minutes earlier
g Arr. 3 minutes earlier
h Arr. 6 minutes earlier

Edinburgh → Dunfermline, Kirkcaldy and Markinch

Network Diagram - see first page of Table 225

Miles	Miles	Miles			XC	SR	SR	SR	SR	SR	SR	SR	SR	SR	SR	SR	SR	SR	SR	SR	SR	SR	SR	SR
					1 ◇			1		1 ◇				1 ◇		1 ◇			1 ◇			1		
					A	B		A	C	D	C	B	C	E	B	G	C	B	E			H	C	B
					⊡					⌶				⌶		⌶			⌶					
0	0	0	**Edinburgh** 10	d	05 34	06 16	06 22	06 40		07 08	07 12	07 17	07 40	08 07	08 10	08 37	08 41	08 48	09 10	09 13	09 18	09 36	09 41	09 48
1¼	1¼	1¼	Haymarket	d		06 20	06 26	06 44		07 13	07 16	07 21	07 44	08 11	08 15	08 41	08 45	08 52	09 14	09 18	09 22	09 40	09 45	09 52
4½	4½	4½	South Gyle	d		06 25	06 31				07 21	07 27	07 50		08 20		08 50	08 57		09 22	09 27		09 50	09 57
9½	9½	9½	Dalmeny	d		06 32	06 38				07 28	07 34	07 56		08 26		08 56	09 03		09 28	09 34		09 56	10 03
11¼	11¼	11¼	North Queensferry	d		06 35	06 42				07 31	07 38	08 00		08 30		09 00	09 07		09 32	09 37		10 00	10 07
13¼	13¼	13¼	Inverkeithing	d	06 07	06 39	06 46	06 57		07 27	07 35	07 42	08 04		08 34	08 54	09 04	09 11	09 27	09 35	09 41	09 56	10 04	10 11
—	—	14¾	Rosyth	d		06 43						07 45			08 42			09 14			09 45			10 14
—	—	17	**Dunfermline Town**	d		06 48						07 50			08 47			09 19			09 50			10 19
—	—	18½	Dunfermline Queen Margaret	d		06 51						07 54			08 50			09 23			09 53			10 23
—	—	22½	Cowdenbeath	d		06 58						08 00			08 57			09 29			10a02			10 29
—	—	24¾	Lochgelly	d		07 03						08 06			09 02			09 35						10 35
—	—	27	Cardenden	d		07 07						08 10			09 06			09 39						10 39
14¾	14¾	—	Dalgety Bay	d			06 49				07 38		08 07				09 07			09 38			10 07	
17½	17½	—	Aberdour	d			06 54				07 43		08 12				09 12			09 43			10 12	
20¼	20¼	—	Burntisland	d			06 58				07 47		08 16				09 16			09 47			10 16	
22¾	22¾	—	Kinghorn	d			07 03				07 52		08 21				09 21			09 52			10 21	
26	26	—	Kirkcaldy	d			07a09	07 15	07 28	07 43	07 57		08 26	08 39		09 10	09 26		09a43	09 57		10 12	10 26	
—	35	31¾	Glenrothes With Thornton	a		07 14			07 36		08 05	08 20	08 34		09 13		09 34	09 45					10 34	10 45
33¼	—	—	**Markinch**	a	06 35			07 23		07 52				08 48		09 19				10 10		10 22		

		SR	SR	SR	GR	SR	SR	SR	SR	SR	SR	SR	SR	SR	SR	SR	SR	SR	SR	SR	SR	SR	SR
					R																		
		1 ◇			1			1 ◇			1 ◇			1 ◇					1 ◇				
		E			J	C	B	E			G	C	B	D			C	B	E			C	B
		⌶			⊡ ⌶			⌶			⌶			⌶					⌶				
Edinburgh 10	d	10 10	10 13	10 18	10 26	10 42	10 48	11 10	11 13	11 18	11 36	11 42	11 48	12 10	12 13	12 18	12 41	12 48	13 10	13 13	13 18	13 42	13 48
Haymarket	d	10 14	10 18	10 22	10 31	10 45	10 52	11 14	11 18	11 22	11u40	11 45	11 52	12 14	12 18	12 22	12 45	12 52	13 14	13 18	13 22	13 45	13 52
South Gyle	d		10 22	10 27		10 50	10 57		11 22	11 27		11 50	11 57		12 22	12 27	12 50	12 57		13 22	13 27	13 50	13 57
Dalmeny	d		10 28	10 34		10 56	11 03		11 28	11 34		11 56	12 03		12 28	12 33	12 56	13 03		13 28	13 33	13 56	14 03
North Queensferry	d			10 37		11 00	11 07		11 32	11 37		12 00	12 07		12 32	12 37	13 00	13 07		13 32	13 37	14 00	14 07
Inverkeithing	d		10 35	10 41	10 47	11 04	11 11	11 27	11 35	11 41	11u56	12 04	12 11		12 35	12 41	13 04	13 11	13 27	13 35	13 41	14 04	14 11
Rosyth	d			10 45			11 14			11 45			12 14			12 44		13 14			13 44		14 14
Dunfermline Town	d			10 50			11 19			11 50			12 19			12 49		13 19			13 49		14 19
Dunfermline Queen Margaret	d			10 53			11 23			11 53			12 23			12 53		13 23			13 53		14 23
Cowdenbeath	d			11a03			11 29			12a03			12 29			13a02		13 29			14a02		14 29
Lochgelly	d						11 35						12 35					13 35					14 35
Cardenden	d						11 39						12 39					13 39					14 39
Dalgety Bay	d		10 38			11 07			11 38			12 07			12 38		13 07			13 38		14 07	
Aberdour	d		10 43			11 12			11 43			12 12			12 43		13 12			13 43		14 12	
Burntisland	d		10 47			11 16			11 47			12 16			12 47		13 16			13 47		14 16	
Kinghorn	d		10 52			11 21			11 52			12 21			12 52		13 21			13 52		14 21	
Kirkcaldy	d	10 42	10 57		11a04	11 26		11 43	11 57		12u12	12 26		12 42	12 57		13 26		13 43	13 57		14 26	
Glenrothes With Thornton	a					11 34	11 45					12 34	12 45				13 34	13 45				14 34	14 45
Markinch	a	10 51	11 09					11 52	12 10		12 21			12 51	13 10				13 52	14 10			

		SR	SR	SR	SR	SR	GR	SR	SR	SR	SR	SR	SR	SR	XC	SR	SR	SR	SR	SR	SR	SR	SR
							R																
		1 ◇					1					1 ◇			1 ◇			1 ◇				1 ◇	
		D			C	B	K L			C	B	D	C		N	C		D	B	Q	H	G	C
		⌶					⊡ ⌶					⌶			⊡			⌶				⌶	
Edinburgh 10	d	14 10	14 13	14 18	14 41	14 48	15 00	15 13	15 18	15 42	15 49	16 05	16 08	16 18	16 30	16 40	16 46	17 04	17 10	17 14	17 28	17 40	17 49
Haymarket	d	14 14	14 18	14 22	14 45	14 52	15 04	15 16	15 22	15 45	15 52	16u09	16 13	16 22	16 35	16 45	16 51	17 08	17 14	17 18	17 32	17u44	17 53
South Gyle	d		14 22	14 27	14 50	14 57		15 22	15 27	15 50	15 57		16 18	16 27		16 50	16 56			17 23	17 37		17 58
Dalmeny	d		14 28	14 33	14 57	15 03		15 28	15 33	15 56	16 03		16 24	16 34		16 56	17 02			17 30	17 44		18 04
North Queensferry	d		14 32	14 37	15 00	15 07		15 32	15 37	16 00	16 07		16 28	16 37		17 00				17 34	17 48		18 08
Inverkeithing	d		14 35	14 41	15 04	15 11	15 19	15 35	15 41	16 04	16 11	16u25	16 32	16 41	16 48	17 04	17 09		17 28	17 38	17 52	17 58	18 12
Rosyth	d			14 44		15 14			15 44		16 14			16 45			17 13		17 31		17 55		
Dunfermline Town	d			14 49		15 19			15 49		16 19			16 50			17 18		17 36		18 00		
Dunfermline Queen Margaret	d			14 53		15 23			15 53		16 23			16 53			17 22		17 40		18 04		
Cowdenbeath	d			15a02		15 29			16a02		16 29			17a04			17a31		17 46		18 10		
Lochgelly	d					15 35					16 35								17 52		18 16		
Cardenden	d					15 39					16 45								17 56		18 20		
Dalgety Bay	d		14 38		15 07			15 38		16 07			16 35			17 07				17 42			18 15
Aberdour	d		14 43		15 12			15 43		16 12			16 40			17 12				17 47			18 20
Burntisland	d		14 47		15 16			15 47		16 16			16 44			17 16				17 51			18 24
Kinghorn	d		14 52		15 21			15 52		16 21			16 49			17 21				17 56			18 29
Kirkcaldy	d	14 42	14 57		15 26		15a35	15 57		16 26		16 41	16 54		17 03	17 26		17 37		18 01		18a14	18 34
Glenrothes With Thornton	a				15 34	15 45				16 34	16 45		17 02			17 34			18 02		18 26		18 43
Markinch	a	14 51	15 10					16 10				16 49			17 11			17 46		18 10	18 32		

For general notes see front of timetable
For details of catering facilities see Directory of Train Operators

- **A** To Dundee (Table 229)
- **B** To Edinburgh via Kirkcaldy
- **C** To Edinburgh via Cowdenbeath
- **D** To Dyce (Table 229)
- **E** To Aberdeen (Table 229)
- **G** To Inverness (Table 229)
- **H** To Perth (Table 229)
- **J** From Leeds (Table 26) to Aberdeen (Table 229)
- **K** From London Kings Cross (Table 26) to Aberdeen (Table 229)
- **L** **The Northern Lights**
- **N** From Bournemouth (from 8 September from Plymouth) (Table 51) to Aberdeen (Table 229)
- **Q** To Carnoustie (Table 229)

Edinburgh → Dunfermline, Kirkcaldy and Markinch

Network Diagram - see first page of Table 225

Mondays to Fridays

		SR A	SR 1◇ B	SR C	SR D	SR A	GR R 1 E	SR	XC R 1 G	SR 1◇ H	SR	SR 1◇ J	SR	SR K	GR R 1 E	SR	SR K	SR	SR K	SR K	SR
Edinburgh 10	d	17 53	18 10	18 13		18 25	18 32	18 50	19 01	19 10	19 18	19 36	19 48	20 11	20 31	20 50	21 24	21 52	22 33	23 10	23 21
Haymarket	d	17 58	18 14	18 18		18 29	18 37	18 54	19 06	19 14	19 22	19 40	19 52	20 15	20 36	20 54	21 28	21 56	22 37	23 14	23 25
South Gyle	d	18 03		18 23		18 35		18 59			19 27		19 57	20 20		20 59	21 33	22 01	22 42		23 30
Dalmeny	d	18 11		18 30	18 36	18 41		19 05			19 33		20 03	20 26		21 05	21 39	22 07	22 49	23 23	23 37
North Queensferry	d	18 14		18 33		18 45		19 09			19 37		20 07	20 30		21 09	21 43	22 11	22 52		23 40
Inverkeithing	d	18 18	18 27	18 37	18 43	18 49	18 54	19 13	19 20	19 27	19 41	19 53	20 11	20 35	20 51	21 13	21 47	22 15	22 57	23 29	23 44
Rosyth	d	18 23				18 54		19 16					20 14			21 16		22 18			23 48
Dunfermline Town	d	18 28				18 59		19 21					20 19			21 21		22 23			23 53
Dunfermline Queen Margaret	d	18 32				19 02		19 25					20 23			21 25		22 27			23 56
Cowdenbeath	d	18 38				19 09		19 31					20 29			21 31		22 33			00 03
Lochgelly	d	18 44				19 14		19 37					20 35			21 37		22 39			00 08
Cardenden	d	18 48				19 18		19 41					20 39			21 41		22 43			00 13
Dalgety Bay	d			18 40	18 46						19 44			20 38			21 50		23 00	23 32	
Aberdour	d			18 45	18 51						19 49			20 43			21 55		23 05	23 37	
Burntisland	d			18 49	18 56						19 53			20 47			21 59		23 09	23 41	
Kinghorn	d			18 54	19 01						19 58			20 52			22 04		23 14	23 46	
Kirkcaldy	d		18 43	18 59	19a05		19a11		19 35	19 43	20 03	20 09		20 57	21a08		22 09		23 19	23 51	
Glenrothes With Thornton	a	18 54		19 07		19 25		19 50					20 48			21 50		22 52			00 21
Markinch	a		18 52						19 43	19 52	20 15	20 18		21 06			22 18		23 28	23 59	

Saturdays

		XC 1◇ K	SR A	SR 1 K	SR C	SR 1◇ L	SR A	SR C	SR 1◇ H	SR A	SR 1◇ J	SR C	SR A	SR 1◇ H	SR	SR	SR 1 N	SR C	SR A	SR 1◇ H	SR	SR
Edinburgh 10	d	05 34	06 08	06 40	06 45	07 08	07 17	07 41	08 07	08 10	08 37	08 41	08 48	09 10	09 13	09 18	09 36	09 41	09 48	10 10	10 13	10 18
Haymarket	d		06 12	06 44	06 49	07 13	07 21	07 45	08 11	08 15	08 41	08 45	08 52	09 14	09 18	09 22	09 40	09 45	09 52	10 14	10 17	10 22
South Gyle	d		06 17		06 54		07 27	07 50		08 20		08 50	08 57		09 22	09 27		09 50	09 57		10 22	10 27
Dalmeny	d		06 23		07 01		07 34	07 56		08 26		08 57	09 03		09 28	09 34		09 56	10 03		10 28	10 34
North Queensferry	d		06 27		07 04		07 38	08 00		08 30		09 00	09 07		09 32	09 37		10 00	10 07			10 37
Inverkeithing	d	06 07	06 31	06 57	07 08	07 27	07 42	08 04		08 34	08 54	09 04	09 11	09 27	09 35	09 41	09 56	10 04	10 11		10 35	10 41
Rosyth	d		06 34				07 45			08 42			09 14			09 45			10 14			10 45
Dunfermline Town	d		06 39				07 50			08 47			09 19			09 50			10 19			10 50
Dunfermline Queen Margaret	d		06 43				07 54			08 50			09 23			09 53			10 23			10 53
Cowdenbeath	d		06 49				08 00			08 57			09 29			10a02			10 29			11a03
Lochgelly	d		06 55				08 06			09 02			09 35						10 35			
Cardenden	d		06 59				08 10			09 06			09 39						10 39			
Dalgety Bay	d				07 11			08 07				09 07			09 38			10 07			10 38	
Aberdour	d				07 16			08 12				09 12			09 43			10 12			10 43	
Burntisland	d				07 20			08 16				09 16			09 47			10 16			10 47	
Kinghorn	d				07 25			08 21				09 21			09 52			10 21			10 52	
Kirkcaldy	d			07 15	07 30	07 43		08 26	08 39		09 10	09 26		09a43	09 57		10 12	10 26		10 42	10 57	
Glenrothes With Thornton	a		07 08		07 38		08 20	08 34		09 13		09 36	09 45					10 34	10 45			
Markinch	a	06 35		07 23		07 52			08 48		09 19				10 10		10 22			10 51	11 09	

		GR R 1 Q	SR C	SR A	SR 1◇ H	SR	SR	SR 1◇ J	SR C	SR A	SR 1◇ L	SR	SR	SR C	SR A	SR 1◇ H	SR	SR	SR C	SR A	SR 1◇ L
Edinburgh 10	d	10 26	10 41	10 48	11 10	11 13	11 18	11 36	11 42	11 48	12 10	12 13	12 18	12 41	12 48	13 10	13 13	13 18	13 42	13 48	14 10
Haymarket	d	10 31	10 45	10 52	11 14	11 18	11 22	11u40	11 45	11 52	12 14	12 18	12 22	12 45	12 52	13 14	13 18	13 22	13 45	13 52	14 14
South Gyle	d		10 50	10 57		11 22	11 27		11 50	11 57		12 22	12 27	12 50	12 57		13 22	13 27	13 50	13 57	
Dalmeny	d		10 56	11 03		11 28	11 34		11 56	12 03		12 28	12 33	12 56	13 03		13 28	13 33	13 56	14 03	
North Queensferry	d		11 00	11 07		11 32	11 37		12 00	12 07		12 32	12 37	13 00	13 07		13 32	13 37	14 00	14 07	
Inverkeithing	d	10 47	11 04	11 11	11 27	11 35	11 41	11u56	12 04	12 11		12 35	12 41	13 04	13 11	13 27	13 35	13 41	14 04	14 11	
Rosyth	d			11 14			11 45			12 14			12 44		13 14			13 44		14 14	
Dunfermline Town	d			11 19			11 50			12 19			12 49		13 19			13 49		14 19	
Dunfermline Queen Margaret	d			11 23			11 53			12 23			12 53		13 23			13 53		14 23	
Cowdenbeath	d			11 29			12a03			12 29			13a02		13 29			14a02		14 29	
Lochgelly	d			11 35						12 35					13 35					14 35	
Cardenden	d			11 39						12 39					13 39					14 39	
Dalgety Bay	d		11 07			11 38			12 07			12 38		13 07			13 38		14 07		
Aberdour	d		11 12			11 43			12 12			12 43		13 12			13 43		14 12		
Burntisland	d		11 16			11 47			12 16			12 47		13 16			13 47		14 16		
Kinghorn	d		11 21			11 52			12 21			12 52		13 21			13 52		14 21		
Kirkcaldy	d	11a04	11 26		11 43	11 57		12u12	12 26		12 42	12 57		13 26		13 43	13 57		14 26		14 42
Glenrothes With Thornton	a		11 34	11 45					12 36	12 45				13 34	13 45				14 34	14 45	
Markinch	a				11 52	12 10		12 21			12 51	13 10				13 52	14 10				14 51

For general notes see front of timetable
For details of catering facilities see Directory of Train Operators

- **A** To Edinburgh via Kirkcaldy
- **B** To Inverurie (Table 240)
- **C** To Edinburgh via Cowdenbeath
- **D** From Glasgow Queen Street (Table 230)
- **E** From London Kings Cross (Table 26) to Aberdeen (Table 229)
- **G** From Penzance (Table 135) (From 8 September from Paignton) (Table 51) to Dundee (Table 229)
- **H** To Aberdeen (Table 229)
- **J** To Inverness (Table 229)
- **K** To Dundee (Table 229)
- **L** To Dyce (Table 229)
- **N** To Perth (Table 229)
- **Q** From Leeds (Table 26) to Aberdeen (Table 229)

Saturdays

Edinburgh → Dunfermline, Kirkcaldy and Markinch

Network Diagram - see first page of Table 225

		SR	SR	SR		SR	GR	SR	SR	SR		SR	SR	SR	SR	XC		SR	SR	SR	SR	SR		SR	SR
							R 1						1 ◇			R 1				1 ◇					1 ◇
				A		B	C D			A		B	E	A		G		A		E	B	H		J	K
Edinburgh 10	d	14 13	14 18	14 41		14 47	15 00	15 12	15 18	15 42		15 48	16 05	16 08	16 18	16 30		16 40	16 46	17 04	17 10	17 16		17 28	17 40
Haymarket	d	14 18	14 22	14 45		14 51	15 04	15 16	15 22	15 45		15 52	16u09	16 13	16 22	16 35		16 45	16 51	17 08	17 14	17 19		17 32	17u44
South Gyle	d	14 22	14 27	14 50		14 57		15 22	15 27	15 50		15 57		16 18	16 27			16 50	16 56			17 25		17 37	
Dalmeny	d	14 28	14 33	14 56		15 03		15 28	15 34	15 56		16 03		16 24	16 34			16 56	17 02			17 31		17 44	
North Queensferry	d	14 32	14 37	15 00		15 07		15 32	15 37	16 00		16 07		16 28	16 37			17 00				17 35		17 48	
Inverkeithing	d	14 35	14 41	15 04		15 11	15 19	15 35	15 41	16 04		16 11	16u25	16 32	16 41	16 48		17 04	17 09		17 28	17 38		17 52	17 59
Rosyth	d		14 44			15 14			15 45			16 14			16 45				17 13		17 31			17 55	
Dunfermline Town	d		14 49			15 19			15 50			16 19			16 50				17 18		17 36			18 00	
Dunfermline Queen Margaret	d		14 53			15 23			15 53			16 23			16 53				17 22		17 40			18 04	
Cowdenbeath	d		15a02			15 30			16a04			16 29			17a04				17a31		17 46			18 10	
Lochgelly	d					15 35						16 35									17 52			18 16	
Cardenden	d					15 39						16 39									17 56			18 20	
Dalgety Bay	d	14 38		15 07				15 38		16 07				16 35				17 07				17 42			
Aberdour	d	14 43		15 12				15 43		16 12				16 40				17 12				17 47			
Burntisland	d	14 47		15 16				15 47		16 16				16 44				17 16				17 51			
Kinghorn	d	14 52		15 21				15 52		16 21				16 49				17 21				17 56			
Kirkcaldy	d	14 57		15 26			15a35	15 57		16 26			16 41	16 54		17 03		17 26		17 37		18 01			18a14
Glenrothes With Thornton	a			15 34		15 45				16 34		16 45		17 02				17 34			18 02			18 26	
Markinch	a	15 10						16 10					16 49			17 11				17 46		18 10		18 32	

		SR	SR	SR	SR	GR		SR	SR	SR	SR	XC		SR	SR	SR	SR	SR		SR	SR	SR	SR		
			1 ◇			R 1			1 ◇		1 ◇	1 ◇					1 ◇								
		A	L	A	B	C			L		K	N			Q		L	Q			Q	Q			
Edinburgh 10	d	17 49	18 10	18 13	18 25	18 32		18 50	19 10	19 18	19 36	19 39		19 52	20 11	20 50	21 10	21 24		21 52	22 35	23 10	23 21		
Haymarket	d	17 53	18 14	18 18	18 29	18 37		18 54	19 14	19 22	19 40	19 44		19 56	20 15	20 54	21 14	21 28		21 56	22 39	23 14	23 25		
South Gyle	d	17 58		18 23	18 35			18 59		19 27				20 01	20 20	20 59		21 33		22 01	22 44		23 30		
Dalmeny	d	18 04		18 30	18 41			19 05		19 33				20 07	20 26	21 05		21 39		22 07	22 50	23 23	23 37		
North Queensferry	d	18 08		18 33	18 45			19 09		19 37				20 11	20 30	21 09		21 43		22 11	22 54		23 40		
Inverkeithing	d	18 12	18 27	18 37	18 49	18 54		19 13	19 27	19 41	19 54	19 59		20 15	20 35	21 13	21 27	21 47		22 15	22 58	23 29	23 44		
Rosyth	d				18 54			19 16						20 18		21 16				22 18			23 48		
Dunfermline Town	d				18 59			19 21						20 23		21 21				22 23			23 53		
Dunfermline Queen Margaret	d				19 02			19 25						20 27		21 25				22 27			23 56		
Cowdenbeath	d				19 09			19 31						20 33		21 31				22 33			00 03		
Lochgelly	d				19 14			19 37						20 39		21 37				22 39			00 08		
Cardenden	d				19 18			19 41						20 43		21 41				22 43			00 13		
Dalgety Bay	d	18 15		18 40						19 44					20 38			21 50			23 01	23 32			
Aberdour	d	18 20		18 45						19 49					20 43			21 55			23 06	23 37			
Burntisland	d	18 24		18 49						19 53					20 47			21 59			23 10	23 41			
Kinghorn	d	18 29		18 54						19 58					20 52			22 04			23 15	23 46			
Kirkcaldy	d	18 34	18 43	18 59		19a11			19 43	20 03	20 10	20 15			20 57		21 43	22 09			23 20	23 51			
Glenrothes With Thornton	a	18 43		19 07	19 25			19 50						20 52		21 50				22 52			00 21		
Markinch	a		18 52						19 52	20 15	20 18	20 26			21 06		21 52	22 18			23 29	23 59			

Sundays

		XC	GR	SR		SR	SR	SR		SR	SR	SR		SR	SR	SR		SR	SR	SR		SR	SR	GR	SR
		1 ◇	R 1			1 ◇	1			1 ◇					1 ◇			1 ◇						R 1	
		L	L	Q		K	B	A		L	Q	B		A	L	Q		K	B	A		Q	B	C D	A
Edinburgh 10	d	08 04	09 10	09 15		09 25	09 55	10 15		10 55	11 15	11 55		12 15	12 40	13 15		13 50	14 00	14 15		15 15	15 55	16 00	16 15
Haymarket	d	08 08	09 14	09 19		09 29	09 59	10 19		10 59	11 19	11 59		12 19	12 44	13 19		13 54	14 04	14 19		15 19	15 59	16 04	16 19
South Gyle	d			09 24			10 04	10 24			11 24	12 04		12 24		13 24			14 10	14 24		15 24	16 04		16 24
Dalmeny	d			09 30			10 11	10 30			11 30	12 10		12 30		13 30			14 19	14 30		15 30	16 10		16 30
North Queensferry	d			09 35			10 17	10 37			11 37	12 17		12 37		13 37			14 26	14 37		15 37	16 14		16 34
Inverkeithing	d	08 24	09 32	09 41		09 48	10 21	10 41		11 15	11 41	12 21		12 41	13 00	13 41		14 13	14 30	14 41		15 41	16 18	16 24	16 38
Rosyth	d						10 24					12 24							14 34				16 21		
Dunfermline Town	d						10 29					12 29							14 39				16 26		
Dunfermline Queen Margaret	d						10 33					12 33							14 42				16 30		
Cowdenbeath	d						10 39					12 39							14 49				16 36		
Lochgelly	d						10 45					12 45							14 54				16 42		
Cardenden	d						10 49					12 49							14 58				16 46		
Dalgety Bay	d			09 44				10 44			11 44			12 44		13 44				14 44		15 44			16 41
Aberdour	d			09 49				10 49			11 49			12 49		13 49				14 49		15 49			16 46
Burntisland	d			09 53				10 53			11 53			12 53		13 53				14 53		15 53			16 50
Kinghorn	d			09 58				10 58			11 58			12 58		13 58				14 58		15 58			16 55
Kirkcaldy	d	08 39	09a48	10 03		10a10		11 03		11a31	12 03			13 03	13a16	14 03		14a29		15 03		16 03		16a41	17 00
Glenrothes With Thornton	a						10 56	11 11				12 55		13 11					15 05	15 14			16 52		17 08
Markinch	a	08 48		10 12							12 12					14 12						16 12			

For general notes see front of timetable
For details of catering facilities see Directory of Train Operators

- **A** To Edinburgh via Cowdenbeath
- **B** To Edinburgh via Kirkcaldy
- **C** From London Kings Cross (Table 26) to Aberdeen (Table 229)
- **D** **The Northern Lights**
- **E** To Dyce (Table 229)
- **G** From Bournemouth to Aberdeen (from 13 September from Bristol Temple Meads (Table 51) to Aberdeen (Table 229)
- **H** To Carnoustie (Table 229)
- **J** To Perth (Table 229)
- **K** To Inverness (Table 229)
- **L** To Aberdeen (Table 229)
- **N** From Bristol Temple Meads (from 13 September from Paignton) (Table 51) to Dundee (Table 229)
- **Q** To Dundee (Table 229)

Edinburgh → Dunfermline, Kirkcaldy and Markinch

Network Diagram - see first page of Table 225

		XC	SR	SR	SR	SR	SR	GR	SR	XC	SR	SR	SR	SR	SR	SR	SR
		1 ◊	1 ◊		1			R 1		1 ◊			1 ◊				
		A	B	C	D	E	G	H	C	J	E	G	B		E	C	
Edinburgh 10	d	16 33	17 05	17 15	17 50	17 55	18 15	18 43	19 15	19 25	19 55	20 15	21 00	21 15	21 55	22 25	23 36
Haymarket	d	16 38	17 09	17 19	17 54	17 59	18 19	18 47	19 19	19 30	19 59	20 19	21 04	21 19	21 59	22 29	23 40
South Gyle	d			17 24		18 04	18 24		19 24		20 04	20 24		21 24	22 04	22 34	23 45
Dalmeny	d			17 30		18 10	18 30		19 29		20 10	20 30		21 30	22 10	22 40	23 51
North Queensferry	d			17 34		18 14	18 34		19 34		20 14	20 34		21 34	22 14	22 44	23 55
Inverkeithing	d	16 54	17 22	17 38	18 07	18 18	18 38	19 05	19 38	19 44	20 18	20 38	21 17	21 38	22 18	22 48	23a58
Rosyth	d					18 21					20 21				22 21		
Dunfermline Town	d					18 26					20 26				22 26		
Dunfermline Queen Margaret	d					18 30					20 30				22 30		
Cowdenbeath	d					18 36					20 36				22 36		
Lochgelly	d					18 42					20 42				22 42		
Cardenden	d					18 46					20 46				22 46		
Dalgety Bay	d			17 41			18 41		19 41			20 41		21 41		22 51	
Aberdour	d			17 46			18 46		19 46			20 46		21 46		22 56	
Burntisland	d			17 50			18 50		19 50			20 50		21 50		23 00	
Kinghorn	d			17 55			18 55		19 55			20 55		21 55		23 05	
Kirkcaldy	d	17 09	17a38	18 00	18a23		19 00	19a22	20 00	20 06		21 00	21 33	22a02		23 10	
Glenrothes With Thornton	a					18 52	19 09				20 52	21 09			22 54		
Markinch	a	17 17		18 09					20 09	20 14			21 43			23 19	

For general notes see front of timetable
For details of catering facilities see Directory of Train Operators

A From Birmingham New Street (Table 51) to Aberdeen (Table 229)
B To Aberdeen (Table 229)
C To Dundee (Table 229)
D To Perth (Table 228)
E To Edinburgh via Kirkcaldy
G To Edinburgh via Cowdenbeath
H From London Kings Cross (Table 26) to Aberdeen (Table 229)
J From Bournemouth (20 July to 7 September from Plymouth) (Table 51) to Dundee (Table 229)

Markinch, Kirkcaldy and Dunfermline → Edinburgh

Network Diagram - see first page of Table 225

Miles	Miles	Miles			SR	SR	SR	SR	SR	SR	XC	SR	SR	SR	SR	SR	SR	SR	XC	SR	SR	SR	SR	SR	SR
											R								R						
											1		1	1 ◇					1						1 ◇
								A	B	C	D	E	A	G				H	J	K	E	L	K		N
											☕								☕						🍴
0	—	—	Markinch	d	....	06 19	....	06 45	06 51	....	07 13	....	07 34	....	....	....	....	07 54	08 11	....	....	08 34	....	....	09 06
—	0	0	Glenrothes With Thornton	d	.	06 24	.	06 51	.	.	.	07 14	.	.	07 31	07 36	.	.	.	08 05	08 20	.	08 34	.	.
7¼	7¼	—	**Kirkcaldy**	d	05 53	....	....	....	07 01	07 15	07 25	07 30	07 44	07 50	....	....	07 57	08 05	08 20	....	08 28	08 43	....	09 03	09 15
10½	10	—	Kinghorn	d	05 58	....	....	....	07 07	07 20	.	07 35	.	.	.	.	08 02	08 10	.	.	08 33	.	.	09 07	.
13	12¾	—	Burntisland	d	06 03	....	....	....	07 11	07 24	....	07 39	....	....	....	....	08 06	08 15	....	....	08 37	....	....	09 12	....
15¾	17¼	—	Aberdour	d	06 08	.	.	.	07 16	07 29	.	07 44	.	.	.	.	08 11	08 19	.	.	08 42	.	.	09 16	.
18½	20¼	—	Dalgety Bay	d	06 13	....	....	....	07 21	07 34	....	07 49	....	....	....	....	08 16	08 24	....	....	08 47	....	....	09 21	....
—	—	4¾	Cardenden	d	.	06 32	.	06 58	.	.	.	.	.	.	07 38	07 43	.	.	.	08 13	.	.	08 42	.	.
—	—	7	Lochgelly	d	....	06 36	....	07 03	....	....	....	....	....	....	07 42	07 47	....	....	....	08 17	....	....	08 46	....	....
—	—	9½	Cowdenbeath	d	.	06 45	.	07 12	.	.	.	.	.	.	07 51	07 56	.	.	.	08 26	.	.	08 55	.	.
—	—	13¼	Dunfermline Queen Margaret	d	....	06 50	07 04	07 17	....	....	....	....	....	....	07 57	08 02	....	....	....	08 31	....	....	09 00	....	....
—	—	14¾	**Dunfermline Town**	d	.	06 54	07 07	07 21	.	.	.	.	.	.	08 00	08 06	.	.	.	08 35	.	.	09 04	.	.
—	—	17	Rosyth	d	....	06 58	07 11	07 25	....	....	....	....	....	....	08 04	08 10	....	....	....	08 38	....	....	09 08	....	....
19¾	21¾	18½	Inverkeithing	d	06 18	07 02	07 15	07 31	07 25	07 38	07 43	07 52	08 00	.	08 09	08 14	08 19	08 28	08 36	08 43	08 50	08 59	09 12	09 24	.
21¾	23¾	20½	North Queensferry	d	06 22	07 06	....	07 35	....	....	....	07 56	....	....	....	....	08 24	....	....	08 47	08 54	....	09 16	....	....
23½	25½	22¼	Dalmeny	d	06 26	07 10	.	07 39	.	07a44	.	08 00	.	.	08 16	08 21	08 28	.	.	08 51	08 58	.	09 20	.	.
28½	30½	27¼	South Gyle	d	06 33	07 16	....	07 46	07 37	....	....	08 06	....	....	08 22	08 27	08 34	08 39	....	08 57	09 04	....	09 26	....	....
31¾	33¾	30½	Haymarket	d	06 41	07 25	07 32	07 55	07 45	.	08 00	08 15	08 18	08 21	08 31	08 36	08 43	08 48	08 56	09 06	09 13	09 16	09 35	09 42	09 45
33½	35	31¾	**Edinburgh** 10	a	06 46	07 29	07 36	07 59	07 50	....	08 06	08 19	08 23	08 26	08 36	08 40	08 47	08 52	09 02	09 10	09 17	09 20	09 40	09 47	09 50

		SR	SR	GR	SR		SR	XC	SR	SR	SR	SR	SR	SR	SR	GR	SR	SR	SR	SR	SR	SR	SR	SR	SR
				R				R								R									
		1 ◇		1				1	1		1 ◇			1		1	1			1 ◇	1				1 ◇
		N	E	Q	K		E	U			G	K	E			Q V	A	K	E	X			K	E	G
		🍴		☕ 🍴				☕			🍴					☕ 🍴				🍴					🍴
Markinch	d	....	....	....	....	....	....	10 04	....	10 19	10 34	....	....	....	11 19	....	11 42	....	....	12 02	....	12 19	....	....	13 04
Glenrothes With Thornton	d	.	09 13	.	09 34	.	09 45	.	.	.	.	10 34	10 45	.	.	.	.	11 34	11 45	.	.	.	12 34	12 45	.
Kirkcaldy	d	09 25	09 30	09 44	....	....	09 57	10 12	....	10 28	10 43	....	10 57	....	11 28	11 42	11 52	....	11 57	12 12	....	12 29	....	12 57	13 14
Kinghorn	d	.	09 34	.	.	.	10 01	.	.	10 33	.	.	11 01	.	11 33	.	.	.	12 01	.	.	12 33	.	13 01	.
Burntisland	d	....	09 39	....	....	....	10 06	....	....	10 37	....	....	11 06	....	11 37	....	....	....	12 06	....	....	12 38	....	13 06	....
Aberdour	d	.	09 43	.	.	.	10 10	.	.	10 42	.	.	11 10	.	11 42	.	.	.	12 10	.	.	12 42	.	13 10	.
Dalgety Bay	d	....	09 48	....	....	....	10 15	....	....	10 47	....	....	11 15	....	11 47	....	....	....	12 15	....	....	12 47	....	13 15	....
Cardenden	d	.	.	.	09 42	.	.	.	.	.	.	10 42	.	.	.	.	.	11 42	.	.	.	.	12 42	.	.
Lochgelly	d	....	....	....	09 46	....	....	....	....	....	....	10 46	....	....	....	....	....	11 46	....	....	....	....	12 46	....	....
Cowdenbeath	d	.	.	.	09 55	.	.	.	10 22	.	.	10 55	.	11 26	.	.	.	11 55	.	.	12 26	.	12 55	.	.
Dunfermline Queen Margaret	d	....	....	....	10 00	....	....	....	10 27	....	....	11 00	....	11 30	....	....	....	12 00	....	....	12 30	....	13 00	....	....
Dunfermline Town	d	.	.	.	10 04	.	.	.	10 31	.	.	11 04	.	11 34	.	.	.	12 04	.	.	12 34	.	13 04	.	.
Rosyth	d	....	....	....	10 08	....	....	....	10 35	....	....	11 07	....	11 38	....	....	....	12 08	....	....	12 38	....	13 08	....	....
Inverkeithing	d	.	09 51	10 00	10 12	.	10 18	10 27	10 39	10 50	10 59	11 12	11 18	11 42	11 50	11 59	12 08	12 12	12 18	.	12 42	12 50	13 12	13 18	13 30
North Queensferry	d	....	09 56	....	10 16	....	10 22	....	10 43	10 54	....	11 16	11 22	11 46	11 54	....	....	12 16	12 22	....	12 46	12 54	13 16	13 22	....
Dalmeny	d	.	10 00	.	10 20	.	10 26	.	10 47	10 58	.	11 20	11 26	11 50	11 58	.	.	12 20	12 26	.	12 50	12 58	13 20	13 26	.
South Gyle	d	....	10 06	....	10 26	....	10 32	....	10 53	11 04	....	11 26	11 32	11 56	12 04	....	....	12 27	12 32	....	12 56	13 04	13 26	13 32	....
Haymarket	d	09 55	10 15	10 19	10 34	.	10 42	10 47	11 06	11 12	11 15	11 34	11 42	12 05	12 12	12 17	12 24	12 35	12 42	12 46	13 05	13 13	13 34	13 42	13 46
Edinburgh 10	a	10 01	10 19	10 26	10 40	....	10 47	10 54	11 10	11 17	11 20	11 39	11 47	12 11	12 17	12 23	12 28	12 40	12 47	12 50	13 10	13 19	13 40	13 47	13 50

		SR	SR	SR	SR	SR	SR		SR	SR	SR	SR	SR	SR	SR	SR	SR	SR	SR	SR	SR	GR	SR	SR	SR
																						R			
		1		1 ◇			1 ◇						1 ◇	1 ◇	1				1 ◇	1		1			1 ◇
				N	K	E	G				K	E	G	N			K	E	G			Q	K	E	X
				🍴			🍴						🍴	🍴					🍴			☕ 🍴			🍴
Markinch	d	....	13 19	....	....	....	14 05	....	....	14 19	....	....	15 04	15 18	....	15 24	....	....	16 04	....	16 17	....	....	....	17 07
Glenrothes With Thornton	d	.	.	.	13 34	13 45	.	.	.	.	14 34	14 45	.	.	.	.	15 34	15 45	.	.	.	.	16 34	16 45	.
Kirkcaldy	d	....	13 28	13 44	....	13 57	14 14	....	....	14 28	....	14 57	15 14	15 28	....	15 33	....	15 57	16 14	....	16 26	16 40	....	16 57	17 17
Kinghorn	d	.	13 33	.	.	14 01	.	.	.	14 33	.	15 01	.	.	.	15 38	.	16 01	.	.	16 31	.	.	17 01	.
Burntisland	d	....	13 37	....	....	14 06	....	....	....	14 37	....	15 06	....	....	....	15 42	....	16 06	....	....	16 35	....	....	17 06	....
Aberdour	d	.	13 42	.	.	14 10	.	.	.	14 42	.	15 10	.	.	.	15 47	.	16 10	.	.	16 40	.	.	17 10	.
Dalgety Bay	d	....	13 47	....	....	14 15	....	....	....	14 47	....	15 15	....	....	....	15 52	....	16 15	....	....	16 45	....	....	17 15	....
Cardenden	d	.	.	.	13 42	.	.	.	.	.	14 42	.	.	.	.	.	15 42	.	.	.	.	.	16 42	.	.
Lochgelly	d	....	....	....	13 46	....	....	....	....	....	14 46	....	....	....	....	....	15 46	....	....	....	....	....	16 46	....	....
Cowdenbeath	d	13 26	.	.	13 55	.	.	.	14 26	.	14 55	.	.	.	15 29	.	15 55	.	.	16 25	.	.	16 55	.	.
Dunfermline Queen Margaret	d	13 30	....	....	14 00	....	....	....	14 30	....	15 00	....	....	....	15 34	....	16 00	....	....	16 30	....	....	17 00	....	....
Dunfermline Town	d	13 34	.	.	14 04	.	.	.	14 34	.	15 04	.	.	.	15 38	.	16 04	.	.	16 34	.	.	17 04	.	.
Rosyth	d	13 38	....	....	14 08	....	....	....	14 38	....	15 08	....	....	....	15 42	....	16 08	....	....	16 38	....	....	17 08	....	....
Inverkeithing	d	13 42	13 50	14 00	14 12	14 18	.	.	14 42	14 50	15 12	15 18	15 30	15 44	15 49	15 55	16 12	16 18	16 30	16 42	16 48	16 57	17 12	17 18	17 33
North Queensferry	d	13 46	13 54	....	14 16	14 22	....	....	14 46	14 54	15 16	15 22	....	....	15 53	15 59	16 16	16 22	....	16 46	16 52	....	17 16	....	....
Dalmeny	d	13 50	13 58	.	14 20	14 26	.	.	14 50	14 58	15 20	15 26	.	.	15 57	16 03	16 20	16 26	.	16 50	16 56	.	17 20	.	.
South Gyle	d	13 56	14 04	....	14 26	14 32	....	....	14 56	15 04	15 26	15 32	....	....	16 03	16 09	16 26	16 32	....	16 56	17 02	....	17 26	....	....
Haymarket	d	14 05	14 12	14 13	14 34	14 42	14 45	.	15 05	15 12	15 34	15 42	15 46	15 59	16 11	16 18	16 34	16 42	16 46	17 05	17 11	17 16	17 34	17 39	17 48
Edinburgh 10	a	14 10	14 17	14 21	14 39	14 47	14 50	....	15 10	15 17	15 40	15 47	15 50	16 04	16 16	16 22	16 39	16 46	16 50	17 09	17 15	17 24	17 42	17 45	17 53

For general notes see front of timetable
For details of catering facilities see Directory of Train Operators

A From Perth (Table 229)
B From Dundee (Table 229) to Newcraighall (Table 230)
C To Glasgow Queen Street (Table 230)
D From Dundee (Table 229) to Plymouth (Table 51)
E From Edinburgh via Cowdenbeath
G From Aberdeen (Table 229)
H From Carnoustie (Table 229)
J From Dundee (Table 229) to Bournemouth (from 8 September to Bristol Temple Meads) (Table 51)
K From Edinburgh via Kirkcaldy
L From Dundee (Table 229)
N From Inverness (Table 229)
Q From Aberdeen (Table 229) to London Kings Cross (Table 26)
U From Aberdeen (Table 229) to Bournemouth (from 8 September to Bristol Temple Meads) (Table 51)
V **The Northern Lights**
X From Dyce (Table 229)

Markinch, Kirkcaldy and Dunfermline → Edinburgh

Network Diagram - see first page of Table 225

Mondays to Fridays

		SR A	SR 1◇ B 🍴	SR A	SR 1◇ C 🍴	SR D	SR A	SR D	SR 1◇ E 🍴	SR A	SR D	SR 1 G	GR R 1 C 🍽 🍴	SR	SR	SR 1◇ E 🍴	SR	SR 1◇ B 🍴	SR	SR H	XC 1◇ C	SR	SR 1◇ C
Markinch	d		17 22		18 05				19 07			19 45			20 32	21 08				22 03	22 12		23 07
Glenrothes With Thornton	d	17 02		17 34		18 09	18 43	18 54		19 07	19 25			19 58			21 00		21 58			23 00	
Kirkcaldy	d		17 31		18 15	18 21		19 06	19 16		19 36	19 54	20 10		20 42	21 18		21 32		22 13			23 16
Kinghorn	d					18 25		19 10			19 41				20 46					22 19			23 21
Burntisland	d					18 30		19 15			19 45				20 51					22 24			23 26
Aberdour	d					18 34		19 19			19 50				20 55					22 29			23 31
Dalgety Bay	d					18 39		19 24			19 55				21 00					22 34			23 36
Cardenden	d	17 09		17 42			18 50			19 15				20 05			21 07		22 05			23 07	
Lochgelly	d	17 13		17 46			18 54			19 19				20 09			21 11		22 09			23 11	
Cowdenbeath	d	17 22		17 55			19 03			19 28				20 18			21 20		22 18			23 17	
Dunfermline Queen Margaret	d	17 28		18 00			19 09			19 33				20 24			21 26		22 24			23 23	
Dunfermline Town	d	17 31		18 04			19 12			19 37				20 27			21 30		22 27			23 27	
Rosyth	d	17 35		18 08			19 16			19 40				20 31			21 33		22 31			23 30	
Inverkeithing	d	17 39	17 47	18 12		18 42	19 20	19 27	19 32	19 44	19 58	20 10	20 26	20 35	21 03	21 34	21 37	21 48	22 35	22 36	22 46	23 34	23 39
North Queensferry	d	17 43		18 16		18 46	19 24	19 31		19 48	20 02			20 39	21 07		21 41		22 39	22 44		23 38	23 44
Dalmeny	d	17 47		18 20		18 50	19 28	19 35		19 52	20 06			20 43	21 11		21 45		22 43	22 48		23 42	23 48
South Gyle	d	17 53		18 26		18 56	19 34	19 41		19 58	20 12			20 49	21 17		21 51		22 49	22 55		23 48	23 54
Haymarket	d	18 03	18 01	18 34	18 46	19 05	19 43	19 50	19 53	20 07	20 21	20 27	20s44	20 58	21 26	21 51	22 00	22 02	22 58	23 01		23 57	00 05
Edinburgh 10	a	18 07	18 11	18 38	18 50	19 09	19 47	19 54	19 57	20 11	20 25	20 32	20 50	21 02	21 31	21 56	22 06	22 09	23 02	23 05	23 32	00 01	00 09

Saturdays

		SR	SR	SR H	SR D	SR 1 G	SR 1◇ C	SR A	SR J	XC R 1 K 🍽	SR D	SR H	SR A	SR	SR 1◇ L 🍴	SR 1◇ B 🍴	SR D	GR R 1 N 🍽 🍴	SR A	SR D	XC 1◇ Q 🍽	SR 1
Markinch	d		06 33	06 51		07 34			07 54	08 11		08 34			09 06						10 04	
Glenrothes With Thornton	d		06 39		07 08			07 38			08 20		08 34				09 13		09 34	09 45		
Kirkcaldy	d	06 16		07 01	07 17	07 44	07 50		08 05	08 20	08 28	08 43		09 03	09 15	09 25	09 30	09 44		09 57	10 12	
Kinghorn	d	06 21		07 07	07 21				08 10		08 33			09 07			09 34			10 01		
Burntisland	d	06 26		07 11	07 26				08 15		08 37			09 12			09 39			10 06		
Aberdour	d	06 31		07 16	07 30				08 19		08 42			09 16			09 43			10 10		
Dalgety Bay	d	06 36		07 21	07 35				08 24		08 47			09 21			09 48			10 15		
Cardenden	d		06 47					07 46					08 42						09 42			
Lochgelly	d		06 51					07 50					08 46						09 46			
Cowdenbeath	d		06 57					07 59					08 55						09 55			10 22
Dunfermline Queen Margaret	d		07 02					08 04					09 00						10 00			10 27
Dunfermline Town	d		07 06					08 08					09 04						10 04			10 31
Rosyth	d		07 09					08 11					09 08						10 08			10 35
Inverkeithing	d	06 40	07 13	07 25	07 38	08 00		08 15	08 28	08 36	08 50	08 59	09 12	09 24			09 51	10 00	10 12	10 18	10 27	10 39
North Queensferry	d	06 44	07 17		07 42			08 19			08 54		09 16				09 56		10 16	10 22		10 43
Dalmeny	d	06 48	07 21		07 46			08 23			08 58		09 20				10 00		10 20	10 26		10 47
South Gyle	d	06 54	07 27	07 37	07 52			08 29	08 39		09 04		09 26				10 06		10 26	10 32		10 53
Haymarket	d	07 03	07 36	07 45	08 01	08 16	08 21	08 38	08 48	08 56	09 13	09 16	09 35	09 42	09 45	09 55	10 15	10 19	10 34	10 42	10 47	11 05
Edinburgh 10	a	07 07	07 40	07 50	08 06	08 21	08 26	08 42	08 52	09 01	09 17	09 20	09 40	09 47	09 50	10 01	10 19	10 26	10 41	10 47	10 51	11 10

		SR	SR 1◇ C 🍴	SR A	SR D	SR 1	SR	GR R 1 N U 🍽 🍴	SR 1 G	SR A	SR D	SR 1◇ E 🍴	SR 1	SR	SR A	SR D	SR 1◇ C 🍴	SR 1	SR	SR 1◇ B 🍴	SR A	SR D
Markinch	d	10 19	10 34				11 19		11 42			12 02		12 19			13 04		13 19			
Glenrothes With Thornton	d			10 34	10 45					11 34	11 45				12 34	12 45					13 34	13 45
Kirkcaldy	d	10 28	10 43		10 57		11 28	11 42	11 52		11 57	12 12		12 29		12 57	13 14		13 28	13 44		13 57
Kinghorn	d	10 33			11 01		11 33				12 01			12 33		13 01			13 33			14 01
Burntisland	d	10 37			11 06		11 37				12 06			12 38		13 06			13 37			14 06
Aberdour	d	10 42			11 10		11 42				12 10			12 42		13 10			13 42			14 10
Dalgety Bay	d	10 47			11 15		11 47				12 15			12 47		13 15			13 47			14 15
Cardenden	d			10 42						11 42					12 42						13 42	
Lochgelly	d			10 46						11 46					12 46						13 46	
Cowdenbeath	d			10 55		11 26				11 55			12 26		12 55			13 26			13 55	
Dunfermline Queen Margaret	d			11 00		11 30				12 00			12 30		13 00			13 30			14 00	
Dunfermline Town	d			11 04		11 34				12 04			12 34		13 04			13 34			14 04	
Rosyth	d			11 08		11 38				12 08			12 38		13 08			13 38			14 08	
Inverkeithing	d	10 50	10 59	11 12	11 18	11 42	11 50	11 59	12 08	12 12	12 18		12 42	12 50	13 12	13 18	13 30	13 42	13 50	14 00	14 12	14 18
North Queensferry	d	10 54		11 16	11 22	11 46	11 54			12 16	12 22		12 46	12 54	13 16	13 22		13 46	13 54		14 16	14 22
Dalmeny	d	10 58		11 20	11 26	11 50	11 58			12 20	12 26		12 50	12 58	13 20	13 26		13 50	13 58		14 20	14 26
South Gyle	d	11 04		11 26	11 32	11 56	12 04			12 26	12 32		12 56	13 04	13 26	13 32		13 56	14 04		14 26	14 32
Haymarket	d	11 12	11 15	11 34	11 42	12 05	12 12	12 17	12 24	12 34	12 42	12 46	13 05	13 13	13 34	13 42	13 46	14 05	14 12	14 13	14 34	14 42
Edinburgh 10	a	11 17	11 20	11 39	11 47	12 11	12 17	12 23	12 28	12 39	12 47	12 50	13 10	13 19	13 40	13 47	13 50	14 10	14 17	14 21	14 39	14 46

For general notes see front of timetable
For details of catering facilities see Directory of Train Operators

- **A** From Edinburgh via Kirkcaldy
- **B** From Inverness (Table 229)
- **C** From Aberdeen (Table 229)
- **D** From Edinburgh via Cowdenbeath
- **E** From Dyce (Table 229)
- **G** From Perth (Table 229)
- **H** From Dundee (Table 229)
- **J** From Carnoustie (Table 229)
- **K** From Dundee (Table 229) to Bournemouth (from 13 September to Bristol Temple Meads) (Table 51)
- **L** From Inverness (Table 229). 🍴 from Aberdeen
- **N** From Aberdeen (Table 229) to London Kings Cross (Table 26)
- **Q** From Aberdeen (Table 229) to Bournemouth (from 13 September to Bristol Temple Meads) (Table 51)
- **U** **The Northern Lights**

Table 242

Saturdays

Markinch, Kirkcaldy and Dunfermline → Edinburgh

Network Diagram - see first page of Table 225

		SR	SR	SR	SR	SR	SR	SR	SR	SR	SR	SR	SR	SR	SR	GR	SR	SR	SR	SR	SR	SR
		1◇ A ⚲			B	C	1◇ A ⚲	1◇ D ⚲	1		B	C	1◇ A ⚲	1		R 1 E ⚲	B	C	1◇ G ⚲	B	1◇ D ⚲	B
Markinch	d	14 05		14 19			15 04	15 18		15 24			16 04		16 17				17 07		17 22	
Glenrothes With Thornton	d				14 34	14 45					15 34	15 45					16 34	16 45		17 02		17 34
Kirkcaldy	d	14 14		14 28		14 57	15 14	15 28		15 33		15 57	16 14		16 26	16 40		16 57	17 17		17 31	
Kinghorn	d			14 33		15 01				15 38		16 01			16 31			17 01				
Burntisland	d			14 37		15 06				15 42		16 06			16 35			17 06				
Aberdour	d			14 42		15 10				15 47		16 10			16 40			17 10				
Dalgety Bay	d			14 47		15 15				15 52		16 15			16 45			17 15				
Cardenden	d				14 42						15 42						16 41			17 09		17 42
Lochgelly	d				14 46						15 46						16 46			17 13		17 46
Cowdenbeath	d		14 26		14 55				15 29		15 55			16 25			16 55			17 22		17 55
Dunfermline Queen Margaret	d		14 30		15 00				15 34		16 00			16 30			17 00			17 28		18 00
Dunfermline Town	d		14 34		15 04				15 38		16 04			16 34			17 04			17 31		18 04
Rosyth	d		14 38		15 08				15 42		16 08			16 38			17 08			17 35		18 08
Inverkeithing	d		14 42	14 50	15 12	15 18	15 30	15 44	15 49	15 55	16 12	16 18	16 30	16 42	16 48	16 57	17 12	17 18	17 33	17 39	17 47	18 12
North Queensferry	d		14 46	14 54	15 16	15 22			15 53	15 59	16 16	16 22		16 46	16 52		17 16			17 43		18 16
Dalmeny	d		14 50	14 58	15 20	15 26			15 57	16 03	16 20	16 26		16 50	16 56		17 20			17 47		18 20
South Gyle	d		14 56	15 04	15 26	15 32			16 03	16 09	16 26	16 32		16 56	17 02		17 26			17 53		18 26
Haymarket	d	14 45	15 05	15 12	15 34	15 41	15 46	15 59	16 11	16 18	16 34	16 42	16 46	17 05	17 11	17 16	17 34	17 39	17 48	18 03	18 01	18 34
Edinburgh 10	a	14 50	15 10	15 19	15 40	15 47	15 50	16 04	16 16	16 22	16 39	16 46	16 50	17 10	17 15	17 24	17 39	17 45	17 53	18 07	18 11	18 38

		SR	SR	SR	SR	SR	SR	SR	SR	SR	SR	SR	SR	SR	SR	SR	XC	SR	SR
		1◇ A ⚲	C	B	1◇ G ⚲	B	C	1 H	1◇ A ⚲			1◇ G ⚲		1◇ D ⚲	J	G ⚲		1◇ A	1◇ A
Markinch	d	18 05			19 07			19 45			20 32	21 06			21 30	22 03		22 18		23 07
Glenrothes With Thornton	d		18 04	18 43		19 07	19 25			19 58			21 00				22 04		23 00	
Kirkcaldy	d	18 15	18 21		19 16		19 36	19 54	20 13		20 42	21 16		21 32	21 40	22 12				23 16
Kinghorn	d		18 25				19 41				20 46				21 45	22 17				23 21
Burntisland	d		18 30				19 45				20 51				21 49	22 22				23 26
Aberdour	d		18 34				19 50				20 55				21 54	22 27				23 31
Dalgety Bay	d		18 39				19 55				21 00				21 59	22 32				23 36
Cardenden	d			18 50		19 15				20 05			21 07				22 11		23 07	
Lochgelly	d			18 54		19 19				20 09			21 11				22 15		23 11	
Cowdenbeath	d			19 03		19 28				20 18			21 20				22 24		23 17	
Dunfermline Queen Margaret	d			19 09		19 33				20 24			21 26				22 30		23 23	
Dunfermline Town	d			19 12		19 37				20 27			21 30				22 33		23 27	
Rosyth	d			19 16		19 40				20 31			21 33				22 37		23 30	
Inverkeithing	d		18 42	19 20	19 32	19 44	19 58	20 10	20 29	20 35	21 03	21 32	21 37	21 48	22 02	22 35	22 41	22 51	23 34	23 39
North Queensferry	d		18 46	19 24		19 48	20 02			20 39	21 07		21 41		22 07	22 40	22 45		23 38	23 44
Dalmeny	d		18 50	19 28		19 52	20 06			20 43	21 11		21 45		22 11	22 44	22 49		23 42	23 48
South Gyle	d		18 56	19 34		19 58	20 12			20 49	21 17		21 51		22 17	22 50	22 55		23 48	23 54
Haymarket	d	18 46	19 05	19 43	19 53	20 07	20 21	20 27	20 46	20 58	21 26	21 48	22 00	22 02	22 26	22 56	23 04		23 57	00 05
Edinburgh 10	a	18 50	19 09	19 47	19 57	20 11	20 25	20 32	20 50	21 02	21 31	21 52	22 06	22 09	22 32	23 03	23 08	23 28	00 01	00 09

Sundays

		SR	SR	SR	SR	GR	SR	SR	SR	GR	XC	SR	SR	SR	GR	SR	SR	SR
		J	J	1 C	B	R 1 E K ⚲	J	C	B	R 1 E ⚲	R 1 L	J	C	B	R 1 E ⚲	1◇ D	J	1◇ A ⚲
Markinch	d	07 59	09 59				11 59				13 47	13 59					15 59	
Glenrothes With Thornton	d			10 56	11 11			12 56	13 11				15 05	15 14				
Kirkcaldy	d	08 08	10 08	11 08		11 40	12 08	13 08		13 37	13 55	14 08	15 17		15 42	16 02	16 08	17 01
Kinghorn	d	08 13	10 13	11 13			12 13	13 13				14 15	15 22				16 15	
Burntisland	d	08 17	10 17	11 17			12 17	13 17				14 20	15 26				16 20	
Aberdour	d	08 22	10 22	11 22			12 22	13 22				14 24	15 31				16 24	
Dalgety Bay	d	08 27	10 27	11 27			12 27	13 27				14 29	15 36				16 29	
Cardenden	d				11 19				13 19					15 21				
Lochgelly	d				11 23				13 23					15 25				
Cowdenbeath	d				11 32				13 32					15 34				
Dunfermline Queen Margaret	d				11 37				13 37					15 40				
Dunfermline Town	d				11 41				13 41					15 43				
Rosyth	d				11 44				13 44					15 47				
Inverkeithing	d	08 30	10 32	11 32	11 48	11 56	12 32	13 33	13 48	13 56	14 10	14 32	15 39	15 51	16 02	16 18	16 32	17 17
North Queensferry	d	08 34	10 38	11 38	11 52		12 38	13 38	13 52			14 38	15 43	15 55			16 36	
Dalmeny	d	08 41	10 45	11 45	11 59		12 45	13 45	13 59			14 45	15 50	16 02			16 40	
South Gyle	d	08 47	10 51	11 51	12 05		12 51	13 51	14 05			14 51	15 56	16 08			16 46	
Haymarket	d	08 56	10 59	11 59	12 14	12 18	12 59	13 59	14 14	14 19	14 28	15 00	16 04	16 16	16 21	16 34	16 55	17 34
Edinburgh 10	a	09 00	11 04	12 05	12 18	12 24	13 04	14 04	14 18	14 24	14 33	15 04	16 09	19 01	16 26	16 43	16 59	17 41

For general notes see front of timetable
For details of catering facilities see Directory of Train Operators

- **A** From Aberdeen (Table 229)
- **B** From Edinburgh via Kirkcaldy
- **C** From Edinburgh via Cowdenbeath
- **D** From Inverness (Table 229)
- **E** From Aberdeen (Table 229) to London Kings Cross (Table 26)
- **G** From Dyce (Table 229)
- **H** From Perth (Table 229)
- **J** From Dundee (Table 229)
- **K** **The Northern Lights**
- **L** From Aberdeen (Table 229) to Bristol Temple Meads (20 July to 7 September to Southampton Central) (Table 51)

Table 242

Sundays

Markinch, Kirkcaldy and Dunfermline → Edinburgh

Network Diagram - see first page of Table 225

		SR A	SR B	SR C	SR 1◇ D (sleeper)	SR A	SR B	SR C	SR 1◇ D (sleeper)	SR A	SR 1◇ E (sleeper)	SR B	SR 1◇ D	SR	XC 1◇ D	SR
Markinch	d			17 59				19 59					21 54		22 36	
Glenrothes With Thornton	d	16 53	17 09			18 53	19 09			20 54		21 09				22 54
Kirkcaldy	d	17 07		18 08	18 56	19 07		20 08	20 59	21 09	21 25		22 05	22 13	22 44	23 06
Kinghorn	d	17 12		18 12		19 12		20 13		21 13				22 17		23 10
Burntisland	d	17 20		18 16		19 16		20 18		21 18				22 22		23 15
Aberdour	d	17 24		18 21		19 21		20 22		21 22				22 26		23 19
Dalgety Bay	d	17 29		18 26		19 26		20 27		21 27				22 31		23 24
Cardenden	d		17 16				19 16					21 16				
Lochgelly	d		17 20				19 20					21 20				
Cowdenbeath	d		17 29				19 29					21 29				
Dunfermline Queen Margaret	d		17 35				19 35					21 35				
Dunfermline Town	d		17 38				19 38					21 38				
Rosyth	d		17 42				19 42					21 42				
Inverkeithing	d	17 32	17 46	18 29	19 12	19 29	19 46	20 29	21 15	21 30	21 41	21 46	22 21	22 34	23 00	23 27
North Queensferry	d	17 36	17 50	18 33		19 33	19 50	20 34		21 34		21 50		22 38		23 31
Dalmeny	d	17 40	17 54	18 37		19 37	19 54	20 38		21 38		21 54		22 42		23 35
South Gyle	d	17 46	18 00	18 43		19 43	20 00	20 44		21 42		22 00		22 48		23 41
Haymarket	d	17 55	18 09	18 52	19 27	19 52	20 09	20 53	21 31	21 55	22 00	22 09	22 38	22 57	23s16	23 50
Edinburgh 10	a	18 01	18 14	19 00	19 35	19 56	20 15	20 59	21 38	21 59	22 06	22 13	22 44	23 01	23 26	23 56

For general notes see front of timetable
For details of catering facilities see Directory of Train Operators

A From Edinburgh via Cowdenbeath
B From Edinburgh via Kirkcaldy
C From Dundee (Table 229)
D From Aberdeen (Table 229)
E From Inverness (Table 229)

Sleeper Services

Sleepers enable you to make long distance journeys while having a relaxing night's sleep. You arrive early at your destination, saving a day's travel — or the early morning dash to the airport. Five Sleeper routes link London Euston direct with over 40 stations in Scotland including most principal business and holiday locations. Direct Sleeper services also link Southwest England with London. Customers joining at the starting point of the train may occupy cabins well before departure. At terminating stations customers may vacate cabins up to approximately 0800 on trains which arrive at an earlier time.

Full details of all Sleeper services are given in Tables 400–406 in this book.

Room Service

Sleepers have full air-conditioning and fingertip temperature control. Each cabin has wall-to-wall carpet, mirror, shaver sockets, drinking water — as well as hot water for the washbasin, and a comfortable bed.

Steward(ess) service is available at the touch of a button throughout the journey. **On First Great Western Sleepers,** additional benefits include a welcome toiletry pack, tea or coffee and biscuits, and a wake-up call. Showers and the First Class lounge are available on arrival at Paddington station, plus a free taxi transfer for Eurostar customers. The First Class package also includes complimentary orange juice, Croissant, preserve, tea and coffee and a morning newspaper (subject to availability).

On First ScotRail's Caledonian Sleepers First Class customers receive a toiletry pack and will be woken with a light breakfast accompanied by tea or coffee and a complimentary newspaper. Standard Class customers are served a light morning snack with tea or coffee. Customer lounges are available at the following locations - London Euston, Inverness, Carlisle (Lakes Court Hotel) and Edinburgh Waverley. At Glasgow Central customers may use the on-train Lounge Car which is available prior to departure.

Full details of the Caledonian Sleeper on-train and station facilities can be found inside the Caledonian Sleeper Guide which is available from principal sleeper departure points.

Sleeper Supplements

Holders of First Class tickets enjoy a single berth cabin on payment of the First Class reservation supplement. Holders of Standard travel tickets travel in either a single or 2 berth cabin on payment of the relevant Standard supplement. The number of berths available to holders of discounted tickets may be restricted at any time.

On First ScotRail's Caledonian Sleepers there are a number of berth inclusive fares available that include travel and accommodation at one all inclusive price. First Class travel is in single berth cabins while Standard Class is in twin berth cabins.

On First Great Western's Night Riviera there are a number of berth inclusive fares available that combine travel and accommodation on one ticket. First Class travel is available in single berth cabins, while Standard offers a choice of single berth or twin berth cabins.

Lounge Cars

The Lounge Car offers a pleasant relaxing atmosphere in which to unwind before a night's rest. **On First Great Western Sleepers,** a full range of drinks, snacks and meals are available. Hot and continental breakfasts are served in the morning. **On First ScotRail's Caledonian Sleepers** customers can choose from a wide selection of food and drinks including sandwiches, baguettes, snacks and a well stocked bar. At busy times, use of the Lounge Car may be restricted to First Class ticket holders.

Sleeper Reservations

To book rail tickets and reserve Sleepers, simply visit any main rail station or rail appointed travel agent. Alternatively you can book by phone using most credit/debit cards.

First ScotRail Telesales 08457 55 00 33
First Great Western Telesales 0845 700 0125

Enquiries by Telephone

For further information about rail tickets or services, call National Rail Enquiries on 08457 48 49 50 (calls may be recorded for training purposes).

Animals

Dogs and pets are not normally allowed in Sleeper cabins. There are special arrangements for guide dogs. **On First Great Western Sleepers,** animals may be conveyed if properly labelled and muzzled, and in suitable containers, in the parcels accommodation on payment of the appropriate charge.

On First ScotRail's Caledonian Sleepers accompanying dogs are only permitted in Sleeper Cabins providing the owner(s) has exclusive use of the cabin and pays the appropriate charge. There are special arrangements for guide dogs. Dogs and pets cannot be conveyed in the parcels accommodation.

First ScotRail's Caledonian Sleepers

Please note that as a result of on-going engineering work some Sleeping Car services may be subject to diversion causing an extension in journey times between Scotland and London. For full details log on to www.firstscotrail.com or telephone National Rail Enquiries on 08457 48 49 50 (calls may be recorded for training purposes).

Sleeper Services

First ScotRail Sleeper Services – The Caledonian Sleepers

Operated by First ScotRail

Table 400 London and Edinburgh

		Mon–Thu R	Fri F R	Fri D R	Fri E R	Sun B R	Sun A R	Sun C R
Cabins available from		*2300*	*2230*	*2230*	*2300*	*2200*	*2230*	*2300*
London Euston . . .	d	**2345**	**2300**	**2320**	**2345**	**2240**	**2300**	**2330**
Watford Junction	d	**0004***	**2319**	**2339**	**0004***	**—**	**2323**	**2351**
Carlisle . . .	a	**0503**	**0427***	**0436***	**0436**	**—**	**0458***	**0458***
Carstairs . . .	a	**0624**	**0534**	**0543**	**0543**	**—**	**0628**	**0628**
Edinburgh . . .	a	**0716**	**0640**	**0640**	**0640**	**0627***	**0716**	**0716**
Vacate cabins by		*0755*	*0755*	*0755*	*0755*	*0755*	*0755*	*0755*

		Mon–Thu R	Fri D R	Fri E R	Fri F R	Sun A R	Sun C R	Sun B R
Cabins available from		*2300*	*2300*	*2300*	*2300*	*2230*	*2230*	*2245*
Edinburgh . . .	d	**2340**	**2340**	**2340**	**2340**	**2315**	**2315**	**2315**
Carstairs . . .	d	**0016***	**0016***	**0016***	**0016***	**2350**	**2350**	**—**
Carlisle . . .	d	**0139**	**0139**	**0139**	**0139**	**0124***	**0124***	**—**
Watford Junction	a	**0634**	**0628**	**0632**	**0650**	**0603**	**0628**	**—**
London Euston . . .	a	**0700**	**0700**	**0700**	**0715**	**0628**	**0654**	**0720***
Vacate cabins by		*0800*	*0800*	*0800*	*0800*	*0800*	*0800*	*0800*

R Reservations Compulsory
* Following morning
Services in this table do not run on Saturday nights.
For details of overnight seated services, please refer to Table 65
A until 13 July 2008
B from 20 July until 07 September 2008
C from 14 September 2008
D until 11 July 2008
E from 18 July until 05 September 2008
F from 12 September 2008

Table 401 London and Glasgow

		Mon–Thu R	Fri F R	Fri D R	Fri E R	Sun B R	Sun A R	Sun C R
Cabins available from		*2300*	*2230*	*2230*	*2300*	*2200*	*2230*	*2300*
London Euston . . .	d	**2345**	**2300**	**2320**	**2345**	**2240**	**2300**	**2330**
Watford Junction	d	**0004***	**2319**	**2339**	**0004***	**—**	**2323**	**2351**
Carlisle . . .	a	**0503**	**0427***	**0436***	**0436**	**—**	**0458***	**0458***
Carstairs . . .	a	**0624**	**0534**	**0543**	**0543**	**0713***	**0628**	**0628**
Motherwell . . .	a	**0658**	**0610**	**0624**	**0624**	**0739**	**0658**	**0658**
Glasgow Central	a	**0717**	**0630**	**0643**	**0643**	**0758**	**0717**	**0717**
Vacate cabins by		*0800*	*0800*	*0800*	*0800*	*0800*	*0800*	*0800*

		Mon–Thu R	Fri D R	Fri E R	Fri F R	Sun B R	Sun A R	Sun C R
Cabins available from		*2200*	*2200*	*2200*	*2200*	*2100*	*2200*	*2200*
Glasgow Central . . .	d	**2341**	**2341**	**2341**	**2341**	**2142**	**2315**	**2315**
Motherwell . . .	d	**2356**	**2356**	**2356**	**2356**	**2201**	**2330**	**2330**
Carstairs . . .	d	**0016***	**0016***	**0016***	**0016***	**2222**	**2350**	**2350**
Carlisle . . .	d	**0139**	**0139**	**0139**	**0139**	**—**	**0124***	**0124***
Watford Junction . . .	a	**0634**	**0628**	**0632**	**0650**	**—**	**0603**	**0628**
London Euston . . .	a	**0700**	**0700**	**0700**	**0715**	**0720***	**0628**	**0654**
Vacate cabins by		*0800*	*0800*	*0800*	*0800*	*0800*	*0800*	*0800*

R Reservations Compulsory
* Following morning
Services in this table do not run on Saturday nights.
For details of overnight seated services, please refer to Table 65
A until 13 July 2008
B from 20 July until 07 September 2008
C from 14 September 2008
D until 11 July 2008
E from 18 July until 05 September 2008
F from 12 September 2008

Sleeper Services

First ScotRail Sleeper Services – The Caledonian Sleepers

Operated by First ScotRail

Table 402 London and Aberdeen

		Mon-Fri R	Sun C R	Sun D R	Sun B R
Cabins available from		*2030*	*1930*	*1930*	*1930*
London Euston	dep	**2115**	**2000**	**2000**	**2008**
Watford Junction	dep	**2133**	**2025**	**2021**	—
Crewe	dep	**2345**	**2319**	**2320**	—
Preston	dep	**0044***	**0053***	**0037***	—
Inverkeithing•	arr	**0458**	**0458**	**0458**	**0458***
Kirkcaldy•	arr	**0517**	**0517**	**0517**	**0517**
Leuchars for St Andrews•	arr	**0546**	**0546**	**0546**	**0546**
Dundee	arr	**0608**	**0608**	**0608**	**0608**
Carnoustie	arr	**0622**	**0622**	**0622**	**0622**
Arbroath	arr	**0631**	**0631**	**0631**	**0631**
Montrose	arr	**0650**	**0650**	**0650**	**0650**
Stonehaven	arr	**0716**	**0716**	**0716**	**0716**
Aberdeen	arr	**0737**	**0737**	**0737**	**0737**
Vacate cabins by		*0800*	*0800*	*0800*	*0800*

		Mon–Thu R	Fri R	Sun A R	Sun B R
Cabins available from		*2045*	*2045*	*2045*	*2045*
Aberdeen	dep	**2140**	**2140**	**2140**	**2140**
Stonehaven	dep	**2158**	**2158**	**2158**	**2158**
Montrose	dep	**2227**	**2227**	**2225**	**2225**
Arbroath	dep	**2245**	**2245**	**2243**	**2243**
Carnoustie	dep	**2252**	**2252**	**2250**	**2250**
Dundee	dep	**2306**	**2306**	**2304**	**2304**
Leuchars for St Andrews•	dep	**2324**	**2324**	**2322**	**2322**
Kirkcaldy•	dep	**2353**	**2353**	**2351**	**2351**
Inverkeithing•	dep	**0011***	**0011***	**0010***	**0010***
Preston	arr	**0429**	**0405**	**0422**	—
Crewe	arr	**0530**	**0502**	**0529**	—
London Euston	arr	**0743**	**0756c**	**0743**	**0928**
Vacate cabins by		*0800*	*0806*	*0800*	*0930*

R Reservations Compulsory
* Following morning
• Customers may depart from London or Watford later, and vacate cabins later, by travelling on the London Euston to Edinburgh Sleeper; then by local connecting service from Edinburgh
Services in this table do not run on Saturday nights
For details of overnight seated services, please refer to Table 65

A until 13 July and from 14 September 2008
B from 20 July until 7 September 2008
C from 14 September 2008
D until 13 July 2008
c arrives 0803 from 13 September 2008

Table 403 London and Inverness

		Mon-Fri R	Sun C R	Sun D R	Sun B R
Cabins available from		*2030*	*1930*	*1930*	*1930*
London Euston	dep	**2115**	**2000**	**2000**	**2008**
Watford Junction	dep	**2133**	**2025**	**2021**	—
Crewe	dep	**2345**	**2319**	**2320**	—
Preston	dep	**0044***	**0053***	**0037***	—
Stirling•	arr	**0457**	**0457**	**0457**	**0457***
Dunblane	arr	**0506**	**0506**	**0506**	**0506**
Gleneagles	arr	**0521**	**0521**	**0521**	**0521**
Perth•	arr	**0544**	**0544**	**0544**	**0544**
Dunkeld & Birnam	arr	**0605**	**0605**	**0605**	**0605**
Pitlochry	arr	**0619**	**0619**	**0619**	**0619**
Blair Atholl	arr	**0630**	**0630**	**0630**	**0630**
Dalwhinnie	arr	**0701**	**0701**	**0701**	**0701**
Newtonmore	arr	**0713**	**0713**	**0713**	**0713**
Kingussie	arr	**0718**	**0718**	**0718**	**0718**
Aviemore	arr	**0740**	**0740**	**0740**	**0740**
Inverness	arr	**0830**	**0830**	**0830**	**0830**
Vacate cabins by		*0830*	*0830*	*0830*	*0830*

		Mon–Thu R	Fri R	Sun A R	Sun B R
Cabins available from		*2000*	*2000*	*1945*	*1945*
Inverness	dep	**2038**	**2038**	**2025**	**2025**
Aviemore	dep	**2123**	**2123**	**2108**	**2108**
Kingussie	dep	**2137**	**2137**	**2122**	**2122**
Newtonmore	dep	**2143**	**2143**	**2129**	**2129**
Dalwhinnie	dep	**2159**	**2159**	**2143**	**2143**
Blair Atholl	dep	**2224**	**2224**	**2209**	**2209**
Pitlochry	dep	**2237**	**2237**	**2221**	**2221**
Dunkeld & Birnam	dep	**2251**	**2251**	**2236**	**2236**
Perth	dep	**2314**	**2314**	**2259**	**2259**
Gleneagles	dep	**2332**	**2332**	**2317**	**2317**
Dunblane	dep	**2349**	**2349**	**2333**	**2333**
Stirling•	dep	**2359**	**2359**	**2344**	**2344**
Falkirk Grahamston	dep	**0016***	**0016***	**0001***	**0001***
Preston	arr	**0429**	**0405**	**0422**	—
Crewe	arr	**0530**	**0502**	**0529**	—
London Euston	arr	**0743**	**0756c**	**0743**	**0928**
Vacate cabins by		*0800*	*0806*	*0800*	*0930*

R Reservations Compulsory
* Following morning
• Customers may depart from London or Watford later, and vacate cabins later, by travelling on the London Euston to Edinburgh Sleeper; then by local connecting service from Edinburgh.
Services in this table do not run on Saturday nights.
For details of overnight seated services, please refer to Table 65

A until 13 July and from 14 September 2008
B from 20 July until 7 September 2008
C from 14 September 2008
D until 13 July 2008
c arrives 0803 from 13 September 2008

Sleeper Services

First ScotRail Sleeper Services – The Caledonian Sleepers

Operated by First ScotRail

Table 404 London and Fort William

		Mon-Fri R	Sun C R	Sun D R	Sun B R
Cabins available from		*2030*	*1930*	*1930*	*1930*
London Euston	dep	**2115**	**2000**	**2000**	**2008**
Watford Junction	dep	**2133**	**2025**	**2021**	—
Crewe	dep	**2345**	**2319**	**2320**	—
Preston	dep	**0044***	**0053***	**0037***	—
Westerton	arr	**0555**	**0555**	**0555**	**0555***
Dalmuir	arr	**0603**	**0603**	**0603**	**0603**
Helensburgh Upper	arr	**0626**	**0626**	**0626**	**0626**
Garelochhead	arr	**0640**	**0640**	**0640**	**0640**
Arrochar & Tarbet	arr	**0706**	**0706**	**0706**	**0706**
Ardlui	arr	**0721x**	**0721x**	**0721x**	**0721x**
Crianlarich	arr	**0742**	**0742**	**0742**	**0742**
Upper Tyndrum	arr	**0754**	**0754**	**0754**	**0754**
Bridge of Orchy	arr	**0812**	**0812**	**0812**	**0812**
Rannoch	arr	**0840**	**0840**	**0840**	**0840**
Corrour	arr	**0858x**	**0858x**	**0858x**	**0858x**
Tulloch	arr	**0917**	**0917**	**0917**	**0917**
Roy Bridge	arr	**0929x**	**0929x**	**0929x**	**0929x**
Spean Bridge	arr	**0936**	**0936**	**0936**	**0936**
Fort William	arr	**0954**	**0954**	**0954**	**0954**
Vacate cabins by		*0956*	*0956*	*0956*	*0956*

		Mon–Thu R	Fri R	Sun A R	Sun B R
Cabins available from		*1915*	*1915*	*1830*	*1830*
Fort William	dep	**1950**	**1950**	**1900**	**1900**
Spean Bridge	dep	**2010**	**2010**	**1920**	**1920**
Roy Bridge	dep	**2017x**	**2017x**	**1927x**	**1927x**
Tulloch	dep	**2030**	**2030**	**1940**	**1940**
Corrour	dep	**2051x**	**2051x**	**2001x**	**2001x**
Rannoch	dep	**2106**	**2106**	**2015**	**2015**
Bridge of Orchy	dep	**2134**	**2134**	**2047**	**2047**
Upper Tyndrum	dep	**2152**	**2152**	**2105**	**2105**
Crianlarich	dep	**2205**	**2205**	**2118**	**2118**
Ardlui	dep	**2226x**	**2226x**	**2139x**	**2139x**
Arrochar & Tarbet	dep	**2244**	**2244**	**2157**	**2157**
Garelochhead	dep	**2310**	**2310**	**2223**	**2223**
Helensburgh Upper	dep	**2324**	**2324**	**2237**	**2237**
Dalmuir	dep	**2351**	**2351**	**2304**	**2304**
Westerton	dep	**2356**	**2356**	**2313**	**2313**
Preston	arr	**0429***	**0405***	**0422***	—
Crewe	arr	**0530**	**0502**	**0529**	—
London Euston	arr	**0743**	**0756c**	**0743**	**0928***
Vacate cabins by		*0800*	*0806*	*0800*	*0930*

R Reservations Compulsory
* Following morning

Services in this table do not run on Saturday nights.

For details of overnight seated services, please refer to Tables 65 and 227.

A until 13 July and from 14 September 2008
B from 20 July until 7 September 2008
C from 14 September 2008
D until 13 July 2008
c arrives 0803 from 13 September 2008

Sleeper Services

Table 406 London and Penzance

Operated by First Great Western

		Mon–Fri Ⓛ	Sun Ⓛ
Occupy cabins at Paddington:		*2230*	*2230*
London Paddington	dep	2345	2350
Reading ...	dep	0037*	0037*
Exeter St Davids	arr	0445	0403
Newton Abbot	arr	0507	0455
Plymouth ...	arr	0547	0535
Liskeard ...	arr	0614	0654
Bodmin Parkway	arr	0628	0714
Lostwithiel ...	arr	0635	0721
Par ...	arr	0642	0728
St Austell ...	arr	0650	0736
Truro ...	arr	0709	0755
Redruth ...	arr	0722	0810
Camborne ...	arr	0730	0817
Hayle ...	arr	0739	0827
St Erth ...	arr	0743	0838
Penzance ...	arr	0800	0859
Vacate cabins at Penzance by		*0830*	*0900*

		Mon–Thur Ⓛ	Fri Ⓛ	Sun Ⓛ Until 7 Sep	Sun Ⓛ From 14 Sep
Occupy cabins at Penzance:		*2130*	*2045*	*2045*	*2045*
Penzance	dep	2200	2200	2115	2115
St Erth	dep	2210	2210	2125	2125
Hayle	dep	2214	2214	....	....
Camborne	dep	2224	2224	2137	2137
Redruth	dep	2232	2232	2144	2144
Truro	dep	2244	2244	2157	2157
St Austell ...	dep	2302	2302	2215	2215
Par	dep	2311	2311	....	....
Lostwithiel	dep	2319	2319	....	....
Bodmin Parkway ...	dep	2326	2326	2232	2232
Liskeard	dep	2341	2341	2247	2247
Plymouth	dep	0020*	0020*	2320	2320
Totnes	dep	0048	0048	2348	2348
Newton Abbot ...	dep	0101	0101	0001*	0001*
Exeter St Davids ...	dep	0127	0127	0127	0127
Reading	arr	0450	0453	0354	0419
London Paddington ...	arr	0540	0541	0540	0540
Vacate cabins at Paddington by		*0730*	*0730*	*0730*	*0730*

Ⓛ Sleeper Lounge Car
* Following morning
Services in this table do not run on Saturday nights.
For details of overnight seated services, please refer to Table 135.

Excursion Trains

A journey by train for leisure is a unique form of enjoyment which can be made all the more special and self indulgent if the train is tailored exclusively to your own needs or those of your party. Whether for business travel, leisure travel or as a promotional vehicle, the excursion train is in a class of it's own conveying you effortlessly to sporting event, leisure resorts and conferences or simply cruising through the landscape exploring lines not normally open to passenger trains or experiencing the thrill of haulage by a steam locomotive from a bygone age.

Excursion trains are operated by a number of train operating companies on behalf of independent excursion train promoters and passenger rolling stock owners. Covering the length and breadth of Britain's rail network and operating thoughout the year they provide a diverse, enjoyable and altogether more flexible alternative to scheduled services with an exciting range of on board catering options available to make your journey even more enjoyable and relaxing.

For the corporate client the flexibility of the excursion train can be further enhanced by the inclusion of exhibition vehicles or the provision of a complete exhibition train for that unique "product launch" opportunity.

Advertised Excursion Trains

A varied range of advertised excursion trains operate from many parts of the country catering for both individual and group bookings. Examples of such excursions regularly include scenic day trips, wine and dine land cruises, special rail enthusiast tours and steam hauled operations that recall the halcyon days of rail travel.

How to hire an Excursion Train

Excursion trains normally require between fourteen and ten weeks notice from the booking date through to the train running, although it is possible to arrange less complicated itineraries at shorter notice. Once a destination has been decided upon, please contact one of the independant rolling stock providers listed below for a price quotation. They will normally require the following information:

- Point of origin (and other calling points if required)
- Destination
- Your preferred point of origin departure time OR destination arrival time – whichever is most important
- Number of passengers and preferred type of rolling stock
- Type of catering required
- Number of days duration

You will be offered a quotation as quickly as possible but complex itineraries may take a little longer.

Alternatively some passenger train operating companies have trains available for private hire, subject to availability. Contact details for train operating companies are given in the blue pages at the front of the timetable.

Independent Excursion train rolling stock providers

Atlantic & North Western Ltd
1 Manor Gardens, St Erth, Hayle, Cornwall, TR27 6JH
Tel/Fax: 01736 756927 Mobile 07768 637229 Email: atlanticnwtrains@aol.com
Rolling stock available – Luxury vintage Pullman dining car train
Other services – A la Carte railway catering providers

Mid Hants Railway PLC
The Railway Station, Alresford, Hampshire SO24 9JG. Tel: 01962 733810. Fax: 01962 735448
Rolling stock available – First Class and Standard seating train with dining option.

Northern Belle
The Old Bookstall, Victoria Station, Station Approach, Todd Street, Manchester M3 1PB
Tel: 020 7805 5100. email: NorthernBelle@orient-express.com
Rolling stock available – Pullman style dining cars.

Alliance Charter Trains (EWS Railway Ltd and Riviera Trains Ltd)
116 Ladbroke Grove, London W10 5NE. Tel: 020 7727 4036. Fax: 020 7727 2083.
email: charles.paget@riviera-trains.co.uk
Rolling stock available – First Class Luxury dining Train, Premier Class and Standard seating train with dining option.

Excursion Trains

The Great Scottish & Western Railway Company Limited
Stationmaster's House, Windsor Central Station, Thames Street, Windsor SL4 1PJ. Tel: 0131 555 1021.
Rolling Stock available – Limited seating capacity Luxury vintage dining and Sleeper train.

The Scottish Highland Railway Company Limited
Bedford House, 62 London Road, Maidstone, Kent ME16 8QL. Tel: 01622 688899. Fax: 01622 688855.
email: control@resco.co.uk
Rolling Stock available – Limited seating capacity Luxury vintage dining train.

The Scottish Railway Preservation Society
SRPS Railtours, Marchwell, 7 Dalmahoy Road, Ratho, Midlothian EH28 8RE.
Tel: 0131 333 1281 (weekday evenings only). email: railtours@srps.org.uk
Rolling Stock available – First Class and Standard seating train with dining option.

Venice Simplon-Orient Express Limited
Sea Containers House, 20 Upper Ground, London DE1 9PF. Tel: 020 7805 5100.
Rolling Stock available – Luxury vintage Pullman dining train.

Vintage Trains Limited
Birmingham Railway Museum, 670 Warwick Road, Tyseley, Birmingham B11 2HL.
Tel: 0121 707 4696. Fax: 0121 764 4645. website: www.vintagetrains.co.uk. email: office@vintagetrains.co.uk

Wessex Trains Limited
P.O. Box 34067, Haslemere GU27 3WE. Tel: 01428 654072 Fax: 01428 654144 email: wessextrains@marleyhill.com
Rolling Stock available – Luxury Premier Class and Standard seating trains with high class meal service available.

West Coast Railway Company Limited
Jesson Way, Carnforth, Lancashire LA5 9UR. Tel: 01524 732100. Fax: 01524 735518.
Rolling Stock available – Pullman style dining train, First Class and Standard seating trains with dining option.

Heritage and Tourist Railways

Information has been provided by the Operators shown below and all enquiries should be made to the appropriate Operator.

Romney Hythe and Dymchurch Light Railway — Hythe, New Romney and Dungeness

Operated by Steam and Diesel Traction

This service is operated exclusively by the Romney, Hythe and Dymchurch Light Railway Company to whom all enquiries and communications should be addressed at New Romney, Kent TN28 8PL. Telephone: 01797 362353. www.rhdr.org.uk

Since it opened over 80 years ago, the Romney, Hythe and Dymchurch Railway has become one of the most popular family attractions in Southern England. The railway, which runs for nearly 14 miles across Kent's historic Romney Marsh, links the important holiday centres of Hythe, Dymchurch and New Romney to the fishermen's cottages and lighthouse at Dungeness. It is also the world's only 15" gauge 'MAIN LINE IN MINIATURE'.

The railway is probably best known for its superb fleet of one third full size steam locomotives, altogether there are 11, most of them based on the high-speed express locomotives of the 1920s, and with names like Green Goddess, Northern Chief, Hercules, Hurricane and Black Prince they all evoke nostalgia for the golden age of steam. Two diesel locomotives add a modern touch.

Nearest National Rail stations Folkestone Central (then by bus from Folkestone (Bouverie Square) to Hythe), Sandling (then by bus to Hythe) and Rye (then by bus to New Romney).

East Kent Railway — Shepherdswell, Dover, Kent

The East Kent Railway operates heritage trains between Sheperdswell and Eythorne. Services run on Sundays from Easter to 21 September, bank holidays and Saturdays in August. Special events are held throughout the year, including Halloween and Santa Trains.Further details on 01304 832042, www.eastkentrailway.com or write to East Kent Railway, Station Road, Shepherdswell, Kent CT15 7PD.

Kent and East Sussex Railway — Tenterden Town, Northiam and Bodiam

Operated by Steam and Diesel Traction

This service is operated exclusively by the Kent and East Sussex Railway Co. Ltd. to whom all enquiries should be addressed at Tenterden Town Station, Station Road, Tenterden, Kent TN30 6HE, www.kesr.org.uk. Seasonal service – please telephone for free colour leaflet – 01580 765155.

Savour the characteristic sights, sounds and smells of steam as you travel through 10½ miles of attractive countryside on this charming, rural railway. Locomotives and carriages dating from Victorian times to the 1960s have been restored as a living reminder of rail travel from more elegant times.

Bus connections to Tenterden are available from Ashford, Hastings, Headcorn, Maidstone, Rye and Tunbridge Wells (and Paddock Wood on Sundays).
Bus connections to Northiam are available from Hastings and Rye.

Sittingbourne & Kemsley Light Railway — Sittingbourne Viaduct — Milton Regis Halt — Kemsley Down

"A Truly Industrial Railway"

Operated by Steam & occasional Diesel Traction

This service is operated by the Sittingbourne & Kemsley Light Railway Limited to whom all enquiries should be addressed at PO Box 300, Sittingbourne, Kent ME10 2DZ. For Customer Information, Trains Times, Fares, Footplate Experience details and Special Event Information, call the 0871 222 1568. Information and advance bookings 0871 222 1569/01622 755313 (evenings only). Website: www.sklr.net. The railway opens from April (or Easter if earlier) - September including every Sunday, Bank Holidays and most Wednesdays during school holidays. Santa Specials run during December. Travel behind original locomotives, some of which have plied their trade along these tracks for 100 years! The Sittingbourne & Kemsley Light Railway is the preserved southern half of the former Edward Lloyd Paper Mill/Bowater's Industrial Railway, which, until 1969, was used to convey both raw materials and finished paper products between the mills at Sittingbourne and Kemsley, and the docks at Ridham. The railway was a 24-hour a day operation, and an integral part of the production process. Today things move at a more leisurely pace and the SKLR is the perfect place to unwind and relax - with or without the kids! Facilities include: Café, Museum, Souvenir Shop, Model Railways, Children's play area and Wildlife Gardens. Full timetable available at www.sklr.net or send an SAE to the address above for a copy of the printed timetable. Trains depart from Sittingbourne Viaduct Station - a ten minute walk from the National Rail Services nearest main-line station (Sittingbourne) see Table 212. Access to Kemsley Down is from "Saxon Shore Way" coastal footpath or by train only.

Heritage and Tourist Railways

Information has been provided by the Operators shown below and all enquiries should be made to the appropriate Operator.

Bluebell Railway — Sheffield Park, Horsted Keynes and Kingscote

Operated by 100% steam

Vintage steam trains run between Sheffield Park, Horsted Keynes and Kingscote. A connecting bus links East Grinstead station at weekends and during school holidays. Trains operate weekends throughout the year, daily 17 March – October plus school holidays. Also "Santa Specials" in December and special events.

Pullman dining service Saturdays Evenings & Sunday lunchtimes. Address: Sheffield Park Station, near Uckfield, East Sussex TN22 3QL. Tel: 01825 720825 (24 hr talking timetable) 01825 720800 Customer Services 01825 720801 (Pullman reservations & charters)

Southern trains connect at East Grinstead with the Bluebell service 473 bus service weekends and school holidays to Kingscote. Through tickets available from all National Rail Stations all weekends (except Santa dates) and school holidays.

The Watercress Line — Alton and Alresford

Normally Operated by Steam Traction/Heritage Diesel

This service is operated exclusively by the Mid-Hants Railway Ltd, to whom all enquiries and communications should be addressed at The Railway Station, Alresford, Hants SO24 9JG. Telephone Alresford (01962) 733810. www.watercressline.co.uk.

The Watercress Line is the affectionate name given to the Mid-Hants Railway which reopened in 1977. It runs over 10 miles through unspoilt Hampshire countryside. At Alton the Watercress Line and National Rail share the station where simple interchange can be made. South West Trains services are half hourly to and from London Waterloo (see Table 158). Alternatively travel to Winchester (see Table 158) and take a bus to Alresford. At Ropley a variety of steam locomotives may be seen in various stages of restoration.

Stagecoach 64/X64, weekdays and 64A Sundays and Bank Holidays (Alton-Winchester) pass close to both the Ropley and Alresford stations, also stops at Alton station. At Winchester buses stop in City Road, approximately 5 minutes from the National Rail station.

Swanage Railway — Swanage — Corfe \Castle — Norden

Operated by Steam Traction

This service is operated exclusively by the Swanage Railway Company Limited to whom all enquiries and communications should be addressed at Station House, Swanage, Dorset BH19 1HB, telephone 01929 425800. www.swanagerailway.co.uk

The Swanage Railway now operates from Swanage to Norden via the historic village of Corfe Castle a distance of nearly six miles. Park and ride facilities are available at Norden. Coach parking at Norden.

Isle of Wight Steam Railway

Smallbrook Junction — Ashey — Havenstreet — Wootton

This service is operated by the Isle of Wight Railway Co Ltd., The Railway Station, Havenstreet, Ryde, Isle of Wight.
Tel: (01983) 882204.

Primarily a tourist attraction, the Railway runs steam hauled trains of vintage rolling-stock over a five mile line and has direct interchange with 'Island Line' at Smallbrook Junction.

Bargain 'Island Liner' tickets, available at any Island station or on the train, allow a whole day's unlimited travel on the steam and electric lines. Available on all Steam Railway operating days (except Santa Specials and Day out with Thomas).

Trains run on selected days March to November and December (daily from late May until mid September).

Bodmin & Wenford Railway — Bodmin Parkway — Bodmin General — Boscarne Junction

This service is operated exclusively by the Bodmin and Wenford Railway plc to whom all enquiries and communications should be addressed to Bodmin General Station, Bodmin, Cornwall PL31 1AQ. Telephone: Bodmin (01208) 73666.

Bodmin & Wenford trains run into a platform immediately adjacent to the main line platforms at Bodmin Parkway. For connecting National Rail services see tables 135 and 51.

Trains are usually steam-hauled (diesel on some Saturdays), and give an opportunity to sample steam train travel through the beautiful Cornish countryside. The line is 6½ miles long, and forms a convenient link from the National Rail station to Bodmin town centre, and on to Boscarne Junction (for the Camel Trail). Through tickets available from main line stations.

Services operate —

May 18, 20, 21, 24-31; June daily; July daily; August daily; September daily; October 1, 5, 8, 11, 12, 15, 19-26, 29, 31; November 2, 5; December 6, 7, 13, 14, 20, 21, 23, 24 (Santa Specials), 26-28, 31; January 1 2009.

Heritage and Tourist Railways

Information has been provided by the Operators shown below and all enquiries should be made to the appropriate Operator.

Paignton and Dartmouth Steam Railway

This service is operated exclusively by the Dart Valley Railway PLC to whom all enquiries and communications should be addressed at Queens Park Station, Torbay Road, Paignton, Devon TQ4 6AF. Telephone: 01803 555872.

Paignton & Dartmouth Steam Railway from Paignton is the holiday line with steam trains running for seven miles in Great Western tradition along the spectacular Torbay coast to Churston and through the wooded slopes bordering the Dart estuary to Kingswear. The scenery is superb, with seascapes right across Lyme Bay to Portland Bill on clear days. Approaching Kingswear is the beautiful River Dart, with its fascinating craft, and on the far side, the olde worlde town of Dartmouth and the famous Britannia Royal Naval College, Butterwalk, Bayards Cave and Dartmouth Castle. Combined River Excursions available.

East Somerset Railway

This service is operated by the East Somerset Railway Company Ltd, Cranmore Railway Station, Shepton Mallet, Somerset BA4 4QP. Tel: 01749 880417, web: www.eastsomersetrailway.com, email: info@eastsomersetrailway.com. Located 3 miles east of Shepton Mallet on A361 between Shepton Mallet and Frome. Standard gauge steam railway recreating an ex-GWR branchline of the 1950's. Open when trains are running - Saturdays in March and November, Saturdays and Sundays April to October, plus some Wednesdays and Thursdays in Summer. Refer to brochure or to the ESR's website for details.

Station, Shop, Art Gallery, Small Museum, Engine Sheds and Workshops (except Christmas and Boxing Day). Childrens play area. Picnic sites. Restaurant open on Steam Days.

West Somerset Railway — Minehead and Bishops Lydeard with connecting bus service to Taunton

This service is operated exclusively by the West Somerset Railway plc to whom all enquiries and communications should be addressed at The Railway Station, Minehead, Somerset TA24 5BG, telephone 0643 704996 www.West-Somerset-Railway.co.uk

The West Somerset is Britain's longest heritage railway. From Minehead it runs along the coast to Dunster and Blue Anchor, inland to Washford, back to the coast at Watchet from where it turns inland to serve Williton, Stogumber, Crowcombe Heathfield before finishing at Bishops Lydeard.

Connections to Taunton mainline railway station and bus station are operated by First Group on a half hourly basis.

Severn Valley Railway — Bridgnorth and Kidderminster Town

This service is operated exclusively by the Severn Valley Railway Company Ltd. to whom all enquiries and communications should be addressed. The Railway Station, Bewdley, Worcestershire DY12 1BG. Tel. 01299 403816. www.svr.co.uk.

Severn Valley Railway is a standard gauge steam railway running from Kidderminster Town, SVR's splendid station immediately adjacent to the National Rail station, to Bridgnorth, a distance of 16 miles. The journey provides extremely fine views of the Severn Valley and visitors have the opportunity of alighting at any of the four intermediate stations before arriving at Bridgnorth, the main locomotive depot of the SVR. Refreshment facilities are available at most stations, and on most trains. Call the above number for dates of operation.

NATIONAL RAIL — SEVERN VALLEY LINK — Kidderminster Town Station is adjacent to National Rail Station (see Table 71). Through tickets available from any manned station on the national railway network – please ask for tickets "To Bridgnorth" (not "Severn Valley Railway"). All passengers are carried in accordance with the Company's terms and conditions.

Rheilffordd Llyn Tegid: Bala Lake Railway

This service is operated exclusively by the Bala Lake Railway, to whom all train service enquiries should be addressed at Llanuwchllyn, Gwynedd LL23 7DD. Telephone Llanuwchllyn (01678) 540666. www.bala-lake-railway.co.uk.

A delightful 4½ mile journey alongside Wales's largest natural lake through some of the most beautiful scenery in the Snowdonia National Park.

Aberystwyth — Devil's Bridge
Vale of Rheidol Narrow Gauge Steam Railway

Narrow gauge line running through the magnificent scenery of the Rheidol Valley.

OPERATED BY STEAM TRACTION.

Vale of Rheidol Railway Locomotive Shed, Park Avenue, Aberystwyth, Ceredigion SY23 1PG.

For further details please telephone Aberystwyth (01970) 625819. Fax (01970) 623769. www.rheidolrailway.co.uk.

Brecon Mountain Railway: Merthyr Tydfil

Narrow gauge line running into the Brecon Beacons National Park.

This service is operated exclusively by Brecon Mountain Railway, Pant Station, Merthyr Tydfil CF48 2UP.

OPERATED BY STEAM TRACTION.

For further details please telephone Merthyr Tydfil (01685) 722988. Fax. (01685) 384854 or visit www.breconmountainrailway.co.uk.

Heritage and Tourist Railways

Information has been provided by the Operators shown below and all enquiries should be made to the appropriate Operator.

Dean Forest Railway

This service, operated largely by steam but with occasional diesel, runs between Lydney Junction (5 minutes walk from Lydney (NRT - table 57), Lydney Town, Norchard and Parkend. For train times etc. phone 01594 845840 (or 24 hour recorded information line 01594 843423), check web site: www.deanforestrailway.co.uk or write: Dean Forest Railway, Forest Road, Lydney GL15 4ET.

Talyllyn Railway — Tywyn, Abergynolwyn and Nant Gwernol

Operated by Steam Traction

This service is operated exclusively by the Talyllyn Railway Company to whom all enquiries and communications should be addressed at Wharf station, Tywyn, Gwynedd LL36 9EY. Telephone: Tywyn (01654) 710472. Fax (01654) 711755. www.talyllyn.co.uk For connecting National Rail services see Table 75.

Tywyn Wharf station is 300 yards from Tywyn station. Now with new cafe, shop and narrow gauge railway museum.

This, the World's First Preserved Railway, operates steam trains into The Snowdonia National Park to Dolgoch Falls and Nant Gwernol for splendid forest walks and waterfalls.

The Fairbourne Railway

Fairbourne — Penrhyn Point

This service is operated by the Fairbourne Railways Ltd to whom enquiries and communications should be addressed at Beach Road, Fairbourne, Gwynedd LL38 2EX. Tel (01341) 250362, Fax (01341) 250240, e-mail: fairbourne.rail@btconnect.com

Half-sized narrow gauge steam railway runs from Fairbourne to Barmouth Ferry Station where it meets the pedestrian ferry to Barmouth. Free Rowen Centre and model railway at Fairbourne Station.

Welsh Highland Railway — Porthmadog and Traeth Mawr

This service is operated by the Welsh Highland Railway Ltd (Porthmadog) to whom all train service enquiries and communications should be addressed - at Tremadog Road, Porthmadog, Gwynedd LL49 9DY. Telephone for general enquiries – (01766) 513402.

For connecting mainline service to nearest station (Porthmadog) see Table 75. The Welsh Highland station is immediately adjacent to the mainline station.

The narrow gauge Welsh Highland offers a short but nostalgic train journey, combined with a fascinating visit to the sheds. The half mile extension to Traeth Mawr is now open, doubling the length of the railway. Please apply for full details to:- Tel. (01766) 513402 or email info@whr.co.uk, or visit www.whr.co.uk.

Snowdon Mountain Railway — Llanberis and Snowdon Summit

This service is operated by the Snowdon Mountain Railway. All train service enquiries should be addressed to Snowdon Mountain Railway, Llanberis Gwynedd LL55 4TY. Telephone: 0870 720 0033 Fax: 01286 872518 E-mail: info@snowdonrailway.co.uk. Website: www.snowdonrailway.co.uk. Trains run every day from Mid March to early November subject to weather conditions.

For National Rail service to nearest station (Bangor) see Table 83. There is a direct local bus service, Bangor – Llanberis and more frequent services Bangor – Caernarfon, and Caernarfon – Llanberis.

Opened 1896, Britain's only public rack and pinion railway climbs more than 3,000 feet in just five miles. On fine days spectacular views are unrivalled of the Isle of Man and the Wicklow Mountains in Ireland.

Avon Valley Railway

This service is operated exclusively by the Avon Valley Railway Company to whom all enquiries should be addressed at Bitton Station, Bath Road, Bitton, Bristol BS30 6HD. Telephone 0117 932 7296 (24 hour talking timetable), 0117 932 5538 (General enquiries).

The Avon Valley Railway is situated at Bitton Station, between Bristol and Bath on the A431 road, one mile from Keynsham (Tables 123 and 132). Trains run between Bitton, Oldland Common, and Avon Riverside Stations on most Sundays and Bank Holidays and some Saturdays between Easter and October, also Tuesdays, Wednesdays and Thursdays during school holidays. Santa Specials operate during December. Most trains are steam hauled.

Heritage and Tourist Railways

Information has been provided by the Operators shown below and all enquiries should be made to the appropriate Operator.

Llanberis to Penllyn Direct / Penllyn – Cei Llydan – Padarn Park – Llanberis } Llanberis Lake Railway / Rheilffordd Llyn Padarn

Operated by Steam Traction

This service is operated exclusively by Rheilffordd Llyn Padarn Cyf. to whom all train service enquiries and communications should be addressed at Llanberis, Gwynedd LL55 4TY. Tel. Llanberis (01286) 870549. www.lake-railway.co.uk.

The steam trains of the Lake Railway provide an enjoyable excursion away from the bustle of roads and traffic. Travelling from Llanberis Village to Penllyn along the length of Llyn Padarn, they pass rivers, woods and heathland. Across the lake are fine views of Llanberis and the mountains dominated by Snowdon. On the return journey the train stops at Cei Llydan, where there are lakeside and tree-shaded picnic sites, and at Padarn Park for the Welsh Slate Museum, Quarry Hospital, nature trails and craft workshops. Passengers may disembark here and return by a later train. For National Rail services to nearest station (Bangor) see Table 81. For bus connections from Bangor, Betws-y-Coed or Porthmadog stations visit www.gwynedd.gov.uk and follow transport links.

Dates of operation: Daily, 18 May to 5 Sep; Suns to Fris, 7 to 26 Sept; Suns to Thurs, 28 Sept to 2 Nov; Weds only, 5 Nov to 10 Dec. Also Santa trains 6/7, 13/14 & 20/21 Dec.

Llangollen Railway — Llangollen and Carrog

This service is operated exclusively by the Llangollen Railway plc to whom all enquiries and communications should be addressed at Llangollen Station, Abbey Road, Llangollen, Denbighshire LL20 8SN. Telephone: Llangollen (01978) 860979, Talking Timetable: Llangollen (01978) 860951. e-mail: llangollen.railway@btinternet.com. Full information website: www.llangollen-railway.co.uk.

The Llangollen Railway has been opened to Carrog, in stages since 1981, along the route of the former Great Western Railway Ruabon to Barmouth line. Currently the Railway extends nearly 8 miles from near the centre of Llangollen along the highly scenic Dee Valley, via Berwyn for the Horseshoe Falls, and Glyndyfrdwy, to the village of Carrog.

Steam and vintage diesel trains run at regular intervals daily from early April to early October, and most other weekends throughout the year.

Nearest National Rail connection is Ruabon on the Chester/Wrexham/Shrewsbury line (see Table 75). 20 minute interval bus service from Ruabon to Llangollen (two hourly on Sundays).

Further information on connecting bus and train services from Llangollen Tourist Information Centre on 01978-860828. For local bus service enquiries: phone 0870 6082608. A through-ticket is available from most National Rail ticket offices.

Ffestiniog Railway

The Ffestiniog Railway is the oldest independent railway company in the world, founded by Act of Parliament in 1832. It was the very first narrow gauge railway in the world to introduce steam engines - in 1863. We operate the unique Double Fairlie articulated locomotives, which were pioneered on the line. The railway climbs from sea level at Porthmadog, over 700 feet up into the mountains through spectacular scenery, to the slate mining town of Blaenau Ffestiniog. There are connections with the main network at Minffordd, for the Cambrian Coast, and at Blaenau Ffestiniog, for the Conwy Valley Line.

Timetable details available by phone – 01766 516000, by email – enquiries@festrail.co.uk or visit our website – www.festrail.co.uk

Ffestiniog Railway, Harbour Station, Porthmadog, Gwynedd, LL49 9NF.

Welsh Highland Railway (Caernarfon)

The Rheilffordd Eryri/Welsh Highland Railway is an exciting Millennium funded project, which is rebuilding the lost line back to Porthmadog, where it will join with the Ffestiniog Railway, so creating a 40 mile long narrow gauge railway. The main motive power comes from huge South African Garratts, the largest 2' gauge locomotives in the world. The railway starts close to the famous castle in Caernarfon and runs for nearly 13 miles into the heart of the Snowdonia National Park, revealing ever changing panoramas of the magnificent scenery on its way, to the village of Rhyd Ddu on the slopes of Snowdon.

Timetable details available by phone – 01766 516000, by email – enquiries@festrail.co.uk or visit our website – www.festrail.co.uk

Welsh Highland Railway, St Helens Road, Caernarfon, Gwynedd LL5S 2YD (see Ffestiniog Railway for postal address)

Heritage and Tourist Railways

Information has been provided by the Operators shown below and all enquiries should be made to the appropriate Operator.

East Lancashire Railway

Runs between Heywood – Bury – Ramsbottom – Rawtenstall

The service is operated by the East Lancashire Light Railway Company Limited. Bolton Street Station, Bolton Street, Bury, Lancashire BL9 0EY. Telephone number for information office 0161 764 7790. email: admin@east-lancs-rly.co.uk. website: www.east-lancs.rly.co.uk.

The East Lancashire Railway operates every weekend and bank holidays throughout the year (except Christmas Day). Passenger trains also operate from May to September on Wednesdays, Thursdays and Fridays. The Railway is 12 miles long (24 mile round trip) and passengers can enjoy the lovely scenic Irwell Valley, travelling across viaducts and through tunnels. We run steam footplate experiences throughout the year - please contact the information office.

Isle of Man Railways

These services are operated by the Isle of Man Dept. of Tourism and Leisure to whom all train service enquiries and communications should be addressed at Transport Headquarters, Banks Circus, Douglas, Isle of Man IM1 5PT. Telephone: (01624) 663366. website: www.iombusandrail.info.

Isle of Man Steam Railway – Douglas – Castletown – Port Erin

Built in 1874 to cater for the island's visiting tourists and to provide local transport to and from Douglas, this 3ft gauge steam worked line continues to fulfil that function today, still using the locomotives and rolling stock originally supplied. The trains pass through areas of outstanding scenic and varied beauty all the way along this 15 mile railway. Operates daily during the Summer months.

Manx Electric Railway – Douglas – Laxey – Ramsey

A unique example of Victorian technology, the 3ft. gauge 17¾ miles long M.E.R. continues to operate using much of its original rolling stock and equipment. Cars 1 & 2 of 1893 are the oldest electric vehicles in the world still in regular commercial service. The line passes through spectacular coastal and mountain scenery on its route to Ramsey.
Operates daily during the Summer months.

Snaefell Mountain Railway – Laxey and Snaefell Summit

The first Mountain Railway in Britain (opened 1895) and still the only one using electric traction, the 4¾ mile double track line of 3ft. 6in. gauge is adhesion worked on a gradient of 1 in 12. On fine days the view from the Summit encompasses five kingdoms. Regular departures from LAXEY STATION between 1015 and 1545 (subject to weather).
Operates daily during the Summer months.

Great Central Railway — Loughborough, Quorn & Woodhouse, Rothley and Leicester North

Operated by Steam Traction

This service is operated exclusively by the Great Central Railway PLC to whom all communications and train service enquiries should be addressed at Great Central Station, Great Central Road, Loughborough, Leics LE11 1RW. Telephone (01509) 230726. www.gcrailway.co.uk

The present Great Central Railway operates a preserved stretch of the former G.C.R. main line from London to the North. The line runs through beautiful Leicestershire countryside with a spectacular viaduct which takes it across the middle of Swithland reservoir.

Bo'ness and Kinneil Railway – Bo'ness and Birkhill

Operated by Steam and Diesel Traction

This service is operated by the Scottish Railway Preservation Society to whom all enquiries and communications should be addressed at Bo'ness Station, Union Street, Bo'ness, West Lothian, EH51 9AQ, telephone Bo'ness (01506) 825855, fax 01506 828766, website: www.srps.org.uk.

The Bo'ness and Kinneil Railway is a Registered Museum and is a standard gauge line running for 3½ miles from the station in the town centre beside the former dock in Bo'ness. The line runs along the foreshore of the Firth of Forth then climbs through woods with views across the Firth towards Fife, to the rural station at Birkhill. The Scottish Railway Exhibition, telling the story of Scotland's railways, is located at Bo'ness Station.

Services run at weekends from the end of March until the end of October and daily in July and August. Special events throughout the year, Santa trains in December.

Nearest National Rail station is at Linlithgow (services operated by First ScotRail), 4 miles from Bo'ness.

Heritage and Tourist Railways

Information has been provided by the Operators shown below and all enquiries should be made to the appropriate Operator.

Gloucestershire Warwickshire Railway

The all volunteer operated heritage railway offers a 20 mile round trip between Cheltenham Race Course Station and its operational base at Toddington.

The railway runs mainly on embankments, travelling through some of the most spectacular scenery the Cotswolds have to offer on both sides of the line.

It passes hamlets, villages, with splendid views over the Vale of Evesham to the distant Malverns, through the second longest tunnel in preservation to Winchombe Station, where we have a picnic area with lovely views, offers walks in the countryside.

Toddington is the present terminus where our Steam and Diesel fleet are maintained and restored. Souvenirs can be bought in the railway shop and refreshments from the Flag and Whistle Tea Room.

Voted Ian Allan Independent Railway of the Year and Heritage Railway Association's annual award for 2003.

Nearest mainline station is at Cheltenham Spa, then Stagecoach Bus to Race Course Park and Ride, then its a three quarters of a mile walk.

More information can be obtained from: GWR, The Railway Station, Toddington, Gloucestershire GL54 5DT. Telephone number: 01242-621405. Website: www.gwsr.com Email: enquiries@gwsr.com

Nene Valley Railway — Yarwell, Wansford, Ferry Meadows (Nene Park), Orton Mere and Peterborough (Nene Valley)

Operated by Steam and Diesel Traction

This service is operated exclusively by Nene Valley Railway to whom all train service enquiries and communications should be addressed at Wansford Station, Stibbington, Peterborough PE8 6LR. Telephone: Stamford (01780) 784444, Fax: 01780 784440 or Talking Timetable: Stamford (01780) 784404.

The Nene Valley Railway is a preserved steam railway running on some 7½ miles of track and features a unique collection of locomotives, carriages and wagons from Europe including Britain. Wansford Station Yard and Loco Sheds are open all year. Services operate on Sundays from January; weekends from Easter to end of October; Wednesdays from May; plus other mid-week services in Summer. Special events throughout the year.
Santa Specials in December.

Peterborough Nene Valley station, the eastern end of the Nene Valley Railway is approximately 20 minutes walk from the main line station (clearly signposted).

North Norfolk Poppy Line. Sheringham - Weybourne - Holt

Steam and heritage diesel services operated by the North Norfolk Railway plc to whom all communications should be addressed at Sheringham Station, Sheringham, Norfolk NR26 8RA. Telephone: Sheringham 01263 820 800. Fax: 01263 820 801. Website: www.nnr.co.uk.

The scenic Poppy Line runs on former M&GN Joint Railway tracks from Sheringham along the coast to Weybourne and up through heathland to Holt. Steam trains most days 1 April-end of October. 10% fare reduction on presentation of current mainline ticket to Sheringham.

For Railway connecting services see table 16.

The Poppy Line Sheringham station is adjacent to National Rail station.

Embsay & Bolton Abbey Steam Railway

This service is operated exclusively by the Yorkshire Dales Railway Museum Trust to whom all train service enquiries and communications should be addressed at Bolton Abbey Station, Bolton Abbey, Skipton, North Yorkshire BD23 6AF. Telephone Skipton (01756) 710614 or Talking Timetable, Skipton (01756) 795189. Website: embsayboltonabbeyrailway.org.uk. The Embsay & Bolton Abbey Steam Railway runs 4 miles between the new award winning station at Bolton Abbey and Embsay Station built in 1888. Services operate every Sunday throughout the year, weekends between Easter and the end of October and daily in the Summer season. The nearest railway network connection is at Skipton, 2 miles from Embsay or Ilkley, 3 miles from Bolton Abbey Station.

Strathspey Railway — Aviemore, Boat of Garten and Broomhill

Operated by Steam Traction

This service is operated exclusively by the Strathspey Railway Company Limited to whom all enquiries and communications should be addressed at Aviemore Station, Dalfaber Road, Aviemore, Inverness-shire PH22 1PY. Telephone: (01479) 810725. Steam trains operate from Aviemore Station and run for the 10 miles to Boat of Garten and Broomhill through scenery that has seen only minor changes since the line was built 140 years ago. Please send s.a.e. for timetable leaflet. Website: www.strathspeyrailway.co.uk, email address for enquiries – strathtrains@strathspeyrailway.co.uk.

Heritage and Tourist Railways

Information has been provided by the Operators shown below and all enquiries should be made to the appropriate Operator.

Chasewater Railway — Brownhills West and Chasetown

This service is operated by the Chasewater Light Railway & Museum Company, to whom all communications should be addressed at Chasewater Country Park, Pool Road, Nr. Brownhills, Staffs WS8 7NL, telephone 01543 452 623. Operating as "The Colliery Line", this standard gauge railway is located in Chasewater Country Park, off A5, Brownhills West, near Walsall, in the heart of the former Cannock Chase Coalfield.

Industrial steam and diesel services run every Sunday and Bank Holiday Monday throughout the year, together with Summer Saturdays, Tuesdays and Thursdays (for details visit our website www.chaserail.com). Santa Specials operate during December.

The Railway is a Charitable Trust, operated entirely by volunteers.

Peak Rail

Peak Rail operates a steam hauled heritage railway between Matlock Riverside, Darley Dale and Rowsley offering an 8 mile round trip through the Derwent Valley. The Railway also operates dedicated dining services on its Palatine Restaurant Car in addition to regular special events throughout the year.

The railway is served by good public transport services operated by East Midlands Trains and Trent Buses between Derby and Matlock for which tickets by either operator are valid on bus and train services between these designated points.

For further information about Peak Rail please write to us at Matlock Station, Matlock, Derbyshire DE4 3NA or telephone 01629 580381, fax 01629-760645, www.peakrail.co.uk or email peakrail@peakrail.co.uk.

Midland Railway - Butterley

Trains operate from Butterley Station along the 3.5 mile railway to Swanwick Junction where the visitor is encouraged to alight to see this unique attraction. A large railway museum with exhibits dating as far back as 1866 together with the Princess Royal Class Locomotive Trust Depot, a country park, a farm park, a narrow gauge railway, a miniature railway, a demonstration signal box, a Victorian railwaymans church, model railways and much more make the Midland Railway Butterley a day out to remember.

Trains run every Saturday and Sunday from mid January through to the end of December and daily during most school holidays.

Further information is available from the Midland Railway Butterley, Butterley Station, Ripley, Derbyshire DE5 3QZ or by telephoning 01773 570140. Website: www.midlandrailwaycentre.co.uk. Email mrc@rapidial.co.uk.

Spa Valley Railway — Tunbridge Wells West and Groombridge

This service is operated by Tunbridge Wells and Eridge Railway Preservation Society to whom all enquiries should be addressed at West Station, Tunbridge Wells, Kent, TN2 5QY. Telephone 01892-537715.

This standard gauge railway reopened in 1996 and has its headquarters in the historic 1891 locomotive shed at Tunbridge Wells West. It runs for 3 miles from the spa town of Tunbridge Wells through pleasant countryside of the Weald to the village of Groombridge.

Please telephone for further details or visit our web site www.spavalleyrailway.co.uk.
Most services are operated by steam traction but sometimes diesel traction may be used.
Nearest National Rail station — Tunbridge Wells then 15 minute walk, or by frequent local bus.

South Devon Railway

The South Devon Railway traverses some of Devon's most glorious scenery. The River Dart is a fast flowing Salmon River, which has its origins high up on Dartmoor and becomes tidal just outside Totnes. Wildlife abounds in and around both the river and railway. Combine a nostalgic trip behind a steam locomotive, along a branch of the legendary Great Western Railway with a chance to view at leisure an almost inaccessible part of the countryside. Our station at Totnes is 464 yards from the mainline station and is within easy walking distance of the council car parks. Beside our station at Totnes is the Totnes Rare Breeds Centre, where there are many wild animals and birds to see. At Buckfastleigh there is ample free parking. As well as our preserved Great Western engines and coaches at Buckfastleigh, there is also a small museum, model railway, children's play area, shop, cafe and picnic area. Sharing our site at Buckfastleigh is the Buckfast Butterfly and Dartmoor Otter Sanctuary. Through tickets are available from any station in the country. On many days there is a free vintage bus service from our Buckfastleigh station to Buckfast, with it's famous Abbey and woollen mills and Buckfastleigh town, with the 'Valiant Soldier', a preserved pub. Whether you start at Totnes or Buckfastleigh enjoy a whole day out with us on the South Devon Railway. Check for dates and times of operation.

For further information contact South Devon Railway, The Station, Buckfastleigh, Devon TQ11 0DZ, tel: 0845-345-1466, www.southdevonrailway.org.

Heritage and Tourist Railways

Information has been provided by the Operators shown below and all enquiries should be made to the appropriate Operator.

Keighley & Worth Valley Railway — Keighley, Haworth and Oxenhope

This service is operated by the Keighley and Worth Valley Light Railway Ltd.; all enquiries to them at Haworth Station, Keighley, West Yorkshire BD22 8NJ. www.kwvr.co.uk. 24hr Talking Timetable 01535 647777. Other Enquiries 01535 645214. Fax 01535 647317.

Britain's last remaining complete branch line railway runs from Keighley to Oxenhope, along a rich seam of West Yorkshire's rail and cultural heritage. Travel via Ingrow, with its award winning Museum of Rail Travel and workshops, and Damems, the country's smallest complete station ("Ormston" in BBC TV's Born and Bred series), to Oakworth where the Railway Children was filmed. This is a superp example of an Edwardian Station, complete with authentic advertising signs, gas lighting and coal fires. From here, ride on to Haworth, home to another famous family - the Brontes. The line terminates 660 feet above sea level at Oxenhope, where a collection of historic locomotives and coaches can be inspected in the Exhibition Shed. There is a small buffet and a picnic site at the station, and why not take the Railway Children Walk which links Oakworth, Haworth and Oxenhope.

OPENING TIMES:

All year: weekends and public holidays; Tue-Thu mid June to early July, then daily until beginning of September.

North Yorkshire Moors Railway — Pickering — Levisham — Newton Dale Halt — Goathland — Grosmont — Whitby

Operated mainly by Steam Traction

This service is operated exclusively by the North Yorkshire Moors Railway to whom all enquiries and communications should be addressed at Customer Services, Pickering Station, Pickering, North Yorkshire, YO18 7AJ. Telephone 01751 472508. Fax 01751 476048. E-mail info@nymr.co.uk, website www.nymr.co.uk

For NYMR Whitby Endeavour Steam Services and National Rail Connection at Grosmont, see table 45, for Middlesbrough-Whitby (Esk Valley Line) through to Whitby on most days.

North Yorkshire Moors Railway is a standard Gauge steam railway running 18 miles from Pickering to Grosmont with services on many days now running a further 6 miles through to the quaint fishing port of Whitby. The journey takes the visitor through spectacular National Park scenery, moorland, forestry and scenic esk valley. Goathland station is better known as 'Aidensfield' in the YTV's 'Heartbeat' series. Dining and Special Events throughout the year.

A seasonal service of Heritage Trains (normally steam hauled) will run between Whitby, Grosmont and Goathland/Pickering.

All passengers carried in accordance with the company's terms and conditions.

Middleton Railway, Leeds

Operating in every year since 1758, the line runs from the station into Middleton Park at the edge of Yorkshire's biggest ancient woodland. Nature trails, playgrounds and picnic facilities.

A collection of 16 industrial steam and 8 diesel engines is on display. Many of the engines are over 100 years old.
The railway is proud to be:

1) The world's first railway to be enabled by an Act of Parliament - in 1758.

2) The place where the world's first commercially succesful steam engine operated. The first engine was called Salamanca and was built in 1812, 17 years before George Stephenson's Rocket.

3) The first preserved standard gauge railway in the UK in 1960.

Today the railway is run solely by volunteers and our new educational resource facility is supported by the heritage Lottery Fund.

Trains run on Saturdays (industrial diesel) from 1300; and Sundays and Bank Holiday Mondays (industrial steam) from 1100, Easter 2008 until end of November. Santa Specials in Christmas. Normal fare: Adults £4.50; children (3-15 years) £2.50; Family (2 Adults + 3 children) £12.00. Different prices apply at special events.

Location: Moor Road, Hunslet, Leeds LS10 2JQ. Adjacent M621 junction 5. Signposted also from A653 Dewsbury Road and A61 Hunslet Road. Ordinance Survey Grid Reference SE304310

Nearest mainline railway station Leeds City (2 miles) (Cross Country, East Midlands Trains, NXEC, Northern, WYPTE). Bus service from City Centre to Tunstall Road, off Dewsbury Road.

Address: The Station, Moor Road, Hunslet, Leeds LS10 2JQ **telephone** 0113 271 0320

Website: www.middletonrailway.org.uk **Email:** info@middletonrailway.org.uk

Heritage and Tourist Railways

Information has been provided by the Operators shown below and all enquiries should be made to the appropriate Operator.

Mid-Norfolk Railway

This service is operated by Mid-Norfolk Railway Preservation Trust to whom all enquiries should be addressed at The Railway Station, Station Road, Dereham, Norfolk NR19 1DF, www.mnr.org.uk, telephone 01362 690633. Seasonal service in operation – colour leaflet available on request.

The railway runs through 11 miles of attractive rural Norfolk, linking the ancient market towns of Dereham and Wymondham. It passes through river valleys and pretty villages and hamlets, providing both a great day out for visitors and a useful transport link for local people. Both Dereham and Wymondham are easily accessible by public transport.

Ravenglass and Eskdale Railway — Ravenglass and Dalegarth for Boot

This service is operated exclusively by the Ravenglass and Eskdale Railway Company Limited to whom all enquiries should be addressed at Ravenglass, Cumbria CA18 1SW Tel: 01229 717171 or email steam@ravenglass-railway.co.uk.

The Ravenglass and Eskdale is England's oldest narrow gauge railway and runs through seven miles of magnificent scenery totally within the Lake District National Park from coastal marshlands to the foot of England's highest mountains. Trains hauled by steam and diesel locomotives run daily from mid March until November with services varying from a minimum of seven return journeys a day to sixteen in high season. Restricted services do operate in the winter. Full timetable and other details can be found at www.ravenglass-railway.co.uk or by contacting the R&ER direct.

National Rail and R&ER stations adjoin at Ravenglass and money saving through tickets are available from main line stations and trains to Dalegarth for Boot. For connecting Northern services please see table 100.

Bure Valley Railway – Aylsham, Norfolk

Operated by Steam and Diesel Traction

This service is operated exclusively by the Bure Valley Railway Company to whom all enquiries and communications should be addressed at Aylsham Station, Norwich Road, Aylsham, Norwich, Norfolk NR11 6BW - www.bvrw.co.uk. Seasonal service – please telephone 01263 733858 or visit website for colour leaflet.

Opened in 1990, the BVR runs over the old Great Eastern Wroxham – Aylsham line and is paralleled throughout the entire 9 miles by the Bure Valley Walk and cycle path which offers excellent photographic opportunities.

Our steam and diesel trains pass through scenery which is as varied, interesting and beautiful as any to be found on a railway journey in England.

Combined train and boat tickets are available. These include a return train journey and a 1½ hours cruise on the Norfolk Broads. (Tickets must be booked in advance).

Trains run from March to October with services varying depending on the time of the year. Full timetable and other details can be found at www.bvrw.co.uk or by contacting the BVR direct.

National Rail and BVR stations adjoin at Wroxham and money saving through tickets are available from main line stations and trains to Wroxham.

For connecting services see table 16.

Passenger Representation

Passenger Focus

What is Passenger Focus?

Passenger Focus is the independent national rail consumer watchdog. Our mission is to get the best deal for Britain's rail passengers.

With a strong emphasis on evidence-based campaigning and research, we ensure that we know what is happening on the ground. We use our knowledge to influence decisions on behalf of rail passengers and we work with the rail industry, other passenger groups and government to secure journey improvements.

What can the Passenger Focus do for me?

We're here to put the interests of rail passengers first. We do this by:

Campaigning for improvements

- we gather research and information, like the National Passenger Survey, where 50,000 passengers give us their views about their rail journeys, so we understand the issues that matter to you
- we work with government and the rail industry to ensure that the passenger voice is heard when making decisions about the future of the railways
- we focus on a number of key issues:

- fares and tickets
- quality and level of services
- investment in the railway

Providing practical advice

- we provide passengers with advice on how to get the best from the national rail network, explain their rights and help them when things go wrong
- we work with other passenger groups to support them in their work

Resolving complaints

- if you make a complaint and you are unhappy with the response we can take up your complaint with the company involved

Making a complaint

If you have a complaint or comment about any aspect of your rail service, either on the train or at the station, please contact the railway company managing director concerned (contact details are shown on the TOC pages of this timetable).

What should you include in your complaint?

Depending on the nature of your complaint you should include:

- the reason for your complaint
- a description of the inconvenience caused
- which train and which day you travelled on, or which station you used and when
- how many people travelled with you
- your ticket(s) as evidence
- an explanation of the action you would like the company to take to rectify the problem

What next?

If you are not satisfied with the company's response you can contact Passenger Focus or, in the London area, London TravelWatch.

How to get in touch:

Telephone: 08453 022 022

8am - 8pm Monday - Friday
8am - 4pm at weekends

Address: Passenger Focus
FREEPOST
(RRRE-ETTC-LEET)
PO BOX 4257
MANCHESTER
M60 3AR

Fax: 0845 850 1392

E-mail: info@passengerfocus.org.uk

Website: www.passengerfocus.org.uk

London TravelWatch

London TravelWatch was set up under the Greater London Authority Act 1999 and represents the users of transport provided, procured or licensed by Transport for London and represents the users of rail services in and around London. London TravelWatch is independent of the transport industry and, like Passenger Focus, will consider representations from passengers who remain dissatisfied with the way that transport operators have dealt with their concerns.

If your journey began in London, please contact:

Telephone: 020 7505 9000

9.30am to 5pm Monday - Friday

Address: London TravelWatch
6 Middle Street
London
EC1A 7JA

Fax: 020 7505 9003

Website: www.londontravelwatch.org.uk

Compensation

Compensation may be payable under each rail company's Passenger's Charter scheme for poor performance (delays or cancellations). For daily tickets and weekly season tickets a fixed rate usually applies depending on the level of delay which you experience. Compensation is made in National Rail vouchers, as a rule, with a minimum of 20% of the fare for the affected journey leg.

Monthly or longer season tickets compensation can differ between companies. On some it is triggered if performance falls below agreed levels and is paid as discount on renewal. Others offer compensation on a journey-by journey basis like for daily tickets. Always check with the train company which issued your ticket or on which you travel for details of the relevant scheme.

Notes

Notes

Notes

Notes

Notes

Notes

Notes

Notes

Notes

Notes

Notes